GB Rail Timetable

Sunday 17 May to Saturday 12 Decemb

Britain's national railway network and stations are owned by Network Rail. Pass included in this timetable, who work together closely to provide a co-ordina opportunities. Details and identification codes are shown on the Train Operat

This timetable contains rail services operated over the National Rail netwo Ireland, the Isle of Man, the Isle of Wight and the Channel Islands. Network R operated on their behalf by the Train Operating Companies. Details are show shows the number of the individual table for each route.

CW00572780

Contents

Bank Holiday Services

Bank Holiday services can sometimes operate on an amended timetable. Visit nationalrail.co.uk to check the day you wish to travel, particularly as engineering work may take place on Bank Holidays.

Engineering Works

At times it is necessary to carry out essential maintenance work on railway lines. Services may be changed, particularly at weekends, to allow Engineering work to take place.

Engineering work is usually planned many weeks in advance. Details of planned engineering work can be found at nationalrail.co.uk/engineering.

National Rail Conditions of Carriage

A booklet containing the conditions on which all National Rail tickets are issued including the conditions which apply to passengers' luggage can be obtained, from the National Rail website – nationalrail.co.uk/nrcc.

What's New

Welcome to the GB Rail Timetable valid from Sunday 17 May 2009 to Saturday 12 December 2009.

East Midlands Trains the St Pancras International service to York at 0637 will run through to Scarborough on summer Saturdays (23 May to 5 September inclusive).

The return service from York at 1749 will start from Scarborough at 1703.

First Great Western additional Friday evening High Speed Train service (Friday only, 1836 from London Paddington) extended beyond Exeter to Plymouth.

Three additional Saturday trains in each direction between Oxford and Bicester Town, with a new Sunday service with nine trains in each direction.

Earlier start on Sunday trains on Exmouth branch during winter.

Improved service on Truro - Falmouth branch, with two trains per hour Monday to Saturday.

London Overground Imperial Wharf station (between Clapham Junction and West Brompton) will open during the currency of this timetable.

National Express East Anglia has introduced a new at-seat service for First Class customers on selected trains on the Norwich to London Intercity services, replacing the former restaurant service which was used by less than 1% of customers. A range of attractive new catering options can be ordered by First Class cutomers with both breakfast and evening offers available from the comfort of their seat, with choices served by a dedicated host along with any other items the customer wishes to buy from the Café Bar. The new service is designed to appeal to more customers and reflect their desire for a more contemporary catering offer. Standard ticket holders will still be able to purchase a range of drinks and snacks from the Café Bar or at seat trolley.

National Express East Coast the timetable and service pattern are broadly similar to December 2008 with the following notable differences.

<u>Monday to Friday</u> - Selected services between 1720 and 2030 will depart King's Cross slightly earlier. The newly timed 1819 service from King's Cross to Newcastle will no longer call at Stevenage, the 1830* departure from King's Cross will now call there. The 1950 service from Glasgow Central to York will call additionally at Northallerton to set down only.

* runs to Newcastle Monday-Thursday and to Edinburgh on Fridays only.

<u>Saturday</u> - The 0642 Skipton to King's Cross service will depart 13 minutes later.

<u>Sunday</u> - Selected morning services from Newcastle, Aberdeen and Leeds will depart slightly later.

The 0930 service from Newcastle to King's Cross will no longer call at Stevenage, the 0900 departure from Newcastle will now call there.

In response to customer feedback, we are pleased to announce that there are now two ways to enjoy First Class dining. The First Class Restaurant will be available during peak hours and will continue to offer the best in British cuisine. We are also delighted to introduce a new At Seat Dining Menu which offers a selection of mouth watering and affordable meals to enjoy from the comfort of your seat. All meals are freshly prepared on-board by our team of talented chefs. In Standard accommodation, our cafe bar and trolley service offers a wide range of hot and cold sandwiches, snacks and drinks.

North Yorkshire Moors Railway train times have been slightly changed to reflect the season demand for train services.

Southern Summer Sunday London Victoria to Brighton trains will run 2 per hour and faster. Trains from London Victoria will run faster to other main line destinations. Trains from London Bridge to Redhill, and Redhill to Tonbridge will be combined as direct London Bridge to Tonbridge trains.

ScotRail services to Ardrossan Harbour will be increased with most trains that currently terminate at Ardrossan Town being extended to Ardrossan Harbour. There will be improved connections at Ardrossan Harbour with the additional summer only shipping Services between Ardrossan and Brodick now being served by a through train service. Laurencekirk will open from the start of the May timetable and will be served by some trains on the Glasgow Queen Street/Edinburgh to Aberdeen route.

West Coast Railway can now provide on-line booking for all its services and 'The Cambrian' steam service is extended to Pwllheli.

How to use this Timetable

Some tables are self-contained (such as Table 1 London–Shoeburyness) showing every train running between any two stations on the route. Train journey-lengths vary from the under-three-quarters-of-a-mile Stourbridge Town – Stourbridge Junction shuttle to the 703 mile Penzance–Dundee service. To show details of longer-distance services in a single table, short-distance services are omitted, these appearing in separate 'composite' tables.

WHICH TABLE?

General Layout of the Timetable

There are several ways of finding the correct table(s) for a journey. Tables start with the north bank of the Thames and radiate anti-clockwise around London as far as the south bank (Table 212, London-Faversham-Margate) with non-London tables (like the Cardiff Valleys) placed close to the appropriate London route. Internal Scottish routes follow from Table 216. Tables numbered 400-406 cover domestic Sleeper services. Once used to this geographic layout, required tables can usually be found with relative ease, but there are more precise methods:

Using the Index

Look up your destination. If it appears in up to five tables, those tables are listed (for example Hilsea appears in Tables 156, 157, 158, 165 and 188). If it appears in six or more then there may be sub-divisions. If your destination is sub-divided in this way and your origin is NOT shown (for example Shipley is not shown under Lancaster) then look up the origin instead as it probably has fewer tables. Alongside the station name is shown a two character code indicating which operator is responsible for operating the facilities at that station (see also Train Operator pages).

Using the Timetable Network map

If your journey is more complicated and involves several changes between tables, the Timetable Network map will be very useful. For example, to plan a journey from North Berwick to Pontypridd one would not expect to find both in the same table. The map makes it clear that one has to change at Edinburgh and Cardiff and, as there is no through service between North Berwick and Pontypridd, allows one to look up possible routes, for example, via Crewe and Shrewsbury (Tables 65 and 131), Crewe and Birmingham (Tables 57 and 65) or York and Birmingham (Tables 51 and 57).

Using Route/Network Diagrams

For many tables a Route or Network Diagram is also provided. Route Diagrams are generally used for longer distance tables (for example Table 26) and show the route and stations served in diagrammatic form as well as the principal connecting links. Network Diagrams (for example Tables 152–154) are generally used where there is a dense network of shorter distance routes and show *all* stations and routes in the area concerned in diagrammatic form.

Using the Table

Having found the table you require make sure you look at the correct set of pages: Mondays to Fridays, Mondays to Saturdays, Saturdays, Sundays plus any relevant dates. Look for the station from which you will leave, read across until you find a suitable train, then read down to see when you will arrive at your destination.

↪ indicates the train is continued in a later column.

↩ indicates the train is continued from an earlier column.

When services in a table follow a particular pattern throughout a day or part of a day, the pattern is identified by thick downward lines at the start and end of the pattern and by a note within the lines stating "and at the same minutes past each hour until".

Bold times denote through trains whilst light, *italic*, times are connections (PLEASE READ CAREFULLY THE SECTION ON THE CONNECTIONS PAGE). Check if there is a column-heading and if there is, refer to the foot of the table for an explanation.

Because of the large number of services that 'cross' midnight, a railway timetable needs to be precise in the meaning of 'a day'. Trains starting their journeys before midnight are shown towards the end of a table – but if you are looking for the 'last' train don't stop there, as there may be later ones at the start of the table!

A train crossing midnight will be shown in full at the END of a table and any column heading denoting the day of the week applies to the day the train STARTS. For example a 2350 train headed 'SO' (see the general notes on inside front cover) commences 2350 Saturday and runs into Sunday. The train will also be shown at the front of the Sunday table with the times prior to midnight shown with note 'p', e.g. 23p50, to indicate that they refer to the previous night.

Don't worry about the ambiguity as to which day midnight itself belongs, for, to avoid this problem, all times skip from 2359 to 0001 and neither 0000 nor 2400 is ever used!

A two character code is shown at the head of each train column indicating which operator is providing the train service (see also Train Operator pages).

How to use this Timetable

Mileages between stations served (but not those shown for connecting purposes) are shown on the first page of each timetable.

Unique Timetable Number (as shown on the Insert Map and in the Index to Stations).

Stations served.

Catering Information.

Indicates the Operating Company of the train concerned

Indicates the days of the week (and in some cases dates) on which the timetable operates

Principal stations on the route are shown in **bold**.

For non-connecting stations only - indicates that additional services between these stations are included on other timetables (see also below under Route Diagrams).

Indicates the minimum interchange time (in minutes) that should be allowed when connecting between trains. Where no figure is shown, a minimum of 5 minutes should be allowed.

Train runs on Saturdays Only

Seat Reservations symbols.

Train time in ***italics*** indicate connecting times. The letter **'a'** alongside a connecting station indicates the arrival time at that station. Conversely, the letter **'d'** indicates the departure time.

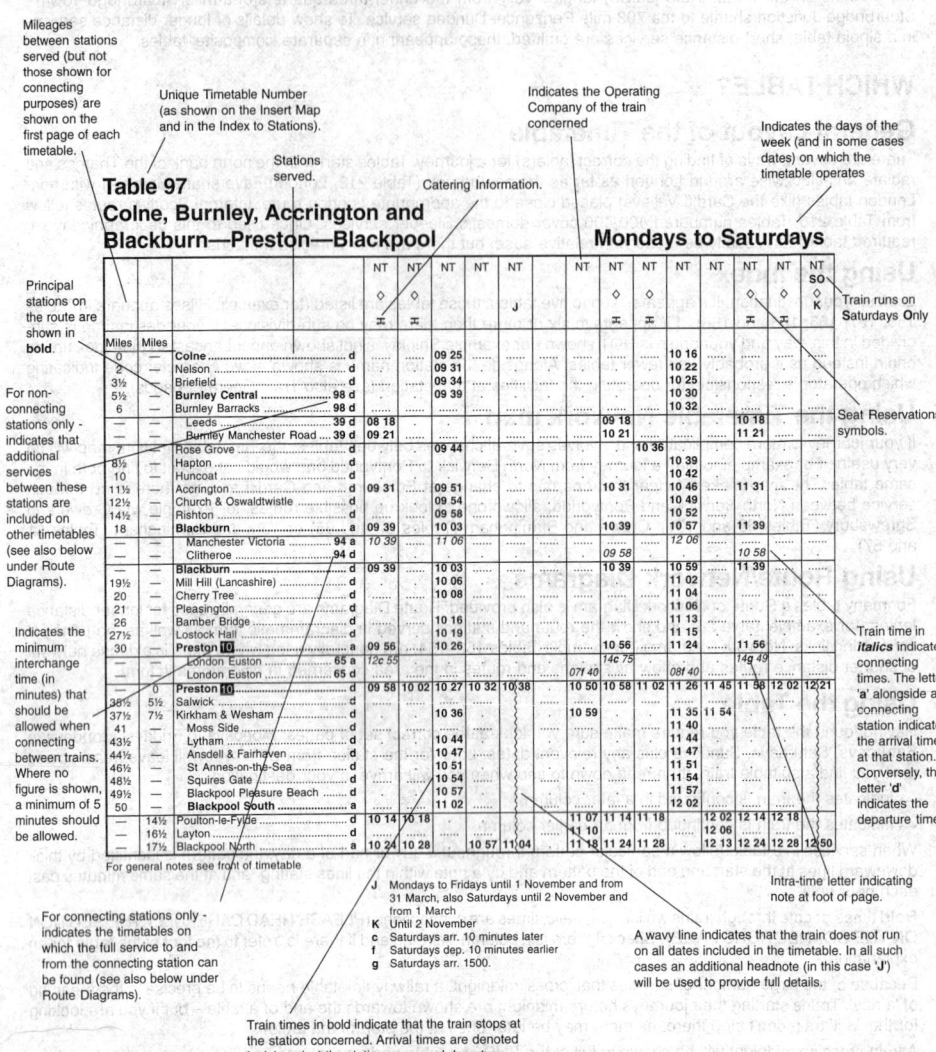

Table 97
Colne, Burnley, Accrington and Blackburn—Preston—Blackpool

Mondays to Saturdays

Miles	Miles		NT	NT	NT	NT	NT		NT	NT	NT	NT	NT	NT	NT	NT
																SO
			◇	◇						◇	◇			◇	◇	◇
							J									K
			🍴	🍴						🍴	🍴			🍴	🍴	
0	—	**Colne** d			**09 25**							**10 16**				
2	—	Nelson d			**09 31**							**10 22**				
3½	—	Briefield d			**09 34**							**10 25**				
5½	—	**Burnley Central** 98 d			**09 39**							**10 30**				
6	—	Burnley Barracks 98 d										**10 32**				
—	—	Leeds 39 d	**08 18**							**09 18**				**10 18**		
—	—	Burnley Manchester Road 39 d	**09 21**							**10 21**				**11 21**		
7	—	Rose Grove d			**09 44**						**10 36**					
8½	—	Hapton d										**10 39**				
10	—	Huncoat d										**10 42**				
11½	—	Accrington d	**09 31**		**09 51**					**10 31**		**10 46**		**11 31**		
12½	—	Church & Oswaldtwistle d			**09 54**							**10 49**				
14½	—	Rishton d			**09 58**							**10 52**				
18	—	**Blackburn** a	**09 39**		**10 03**					**10 39**		**10 57**		**11 39**		
—	—	Manchester Victoria 94 a	*10 39*		*11 06*							*12 06*				
—	—	Clitheroe 94 d								*09 58*				*10 58*		
—	—	**Blackburn** d	**09 39**		**10 03**					**10 39**		**10 59**		**11 39**		
19½	—	Mill Hill (Lancashire) d			**10 06**							**11 02**				
20	—	Cherry Tree d			**10 08**							**11 04**				
21	—	Pleasington d										**11 06**				
26	—	Bamber Bridge d			**10 16**							**11 13**				
27½	—	Lostock Hall d			**10 19**							**11 15**				
30	—	**Preston 10** a	**09 56**		**10 26**					**10 56**		**11 24**		**11 56**		
—	—	London Euston 65 a	*12c 55*							*14c 75*				*14g 49*		
—	—	London Euston 65 d							*07f 40*			*08f 40*				
—	0	**Preston 10** d	**09 58**	**10 02**	**10 27**	**10 32**	**10 38**		**10 50**	**10 58**	**11 02**	**11 26**	**11 45**	**11 58**	**12 02**	**12 21**
35½	5½	Salwick d														
37½	7½	Kirkham & Wesham d			**10 36**				**10 59**			**11 35**	**11 54**			
41	—	Moss Side d										**11 40**				
43½	—	Lytham d			**10 44**							**11 44**				
44½	—	Ansdell & Fairhaven d			**10 47**							**11 47**				
46½	—	St Annes-on-the-Sea d			**10 51**							**11 51**				
48½	—	Squires Gate d			**10 54**							**11 54**				
49½	—	Blackpool Pleasure Beach d			**10 57**							**11 57**				
50	—	**Blackpool South** a			**11 02**							**12 02**				
—	14½	Poulton-le-Fylde d	**10 14**	**10 18**					**11 07**	**11 14**	**11 18**		**12 02**	**12 14**	**12 18**	
—	16½	Layton d							**11 10**				**12 06**			
—	17½	Blackpool North a	**10 24**	**10 28**		**10 57**	**11 04**		**11 18**	**11 24**	**11 28**		**12 13**	**12 24**	**12 28**	**12 50**

For general notes see front of timetable

J Mondays to Fridays until 1 November and from 31 March, also Saturdays until 2 November and from 1 March
K Until 2 November
c Saturdays arr. 10 minutes later
f Saturdays dep. 10 minutes earlier
g Saturdays arr. 1500.

Intra-time letter indicating note at foot of page.

A wavy line indicates that the train does not run on all dates included in the timetable. In all such cases an additional headnote (in this case **'J'**) will be used to provide full details.

For connecting stations only - indicates the timetables on which the full service to and from the connecting station can be found (see also below under Route Diagrams).

Train times in bold indicate that the train stops at the station concerned. Arrival times are denoted by **'a'** against the station name and departure times by **'d'**. Where there is no time shown against a station then the train concerned does not serve that station.

Route/Network Diagrams (see previous page): For many tables a Route/Network Diagram is also provided to show the routes and stations served in diagrammatic form. Where this is the case, a reference to the Route/Network Diagram will be provided at the top of each page of the timetable concerned. Timetable numbers for connecting or alternative services will not be included within the Table itself but will instead be indicated on the accompanying Route/Network Diagram.

General Information

Smoking Policy

Smoking is not permitted on any National Rail service or in any station. In England and Wales, this includes all covered and uncovered concourses, ticket halls, platforms, footbridges and subways at station premises.

Left Luggage Facilities

Details of Left Luggage facilities at individual stations are available at nationalrail.co.uk/stations.

Penalty Fares

Penalty Fares are charged by Train Companies at some stations and on some trains. Where this is the case, warning notices will be displayed. Those stations at which Penalty Fares are in operation are indicated in the Station Index and Table numbers section (see also Train Operator pages). Please be aware that at some stations where Penalty Fare Schemes are in place not all Train Operator services calling at that station are included in the scheme.

If you can not produce a valid ticket for your entire journey when asked to do so you may be charged a Penalty Fare. This will be either twice the full single fare to the next station at which the train is due to stop, or £20 (£50 on Transport for London services and stations, reducing to £25 if paid within 21 days), whichever is the greater. Any travel beyond the next station will be charged at the full single fare.

To avoid paying a Penalty Fare, you must purchase a valid ticket to your destination, before starting your journey. If the ticket office is closed and you can not buy the ticket you want from a self service ticket machine, you must buy a Permit to Travel paying as much of your fare as possible. This permit must be exchanged for a valid ticket at the first opportunity. More information is available at nationalrail.co.uk/penaltyfares.

Timetable Accuracy, Contents, Presentation

Every effort is made to ensure that the information contained in the timetable is correct, but errors can still occur. If you have any questions or queries about the train services shown in this timetable, please write to the appropriate operator shown in the Directory of Train Operators.

General comments about this publication should be addressed to:–

TSO
PO Box 29
Norwich
NR3 1GN

Additional Amendments

A facility is available whereby details of any train service alterations introduced subsequent to the production of the GB Rail Timetable, may be accessed through the Network Rail website (see http://www.networkrail.co.uk). Follow the link to the "Electronic National Rail Timetable" in the "For Passengers" section. Additional amendments can be found under "Supporting Documentation".
From time to time, further alterations may apply at short notice and details of these may be found at nationalrail.co.uk/engineering.

Other National Rail Timetables

Regional and route specific timetables are available from individual train companies. Please contact the relevant train company to request the latest version of the timetable you require.

National Rail Enquiries offers an online 'Pocket Timetable' service which gives you the flexibility to create a customised timetable based around your origin and destination, your own time requirements and the days of the week that you intend to travel. Visit www.nationalrail.co.uk/pockettimetables for more details.

Connections

Bold type times in vertical columns in the timetable show direct trains. In a few cases, where one train overtakes another, the times appear in more than one column and arrow symbols indicate where the train continues in the timetable.

Many more journey opportunities are possible by changing trains. To help plan such journeys, times in light italic type are shown in many of the timetables for departures (if the time is earlier than the bold type times for the station below in the column at which you should change trains) or arrivals (if they are later than the bold type times for the station above in the column at which you should change trains).

Where light type italic times are not shown you may have to refer to other tables in the book to work out your connecting services. In order to find the right table to reference, first look at the Route/Network Diagram that covers the table you are working from. This will show the principal connecting links and their table references, which may include the destination you are searching for. If your journey is not covered, follow the advice given on page 3 'How to use this Timetable' under the headings 'Using the loose-leaf map' and 'Using the Index'.

Connections between trains cannot be guaranteed. The nature of the integrated operation of railway passenger services means that to delay one train to await customers from a late running train arriving at a station may cause significant disruption to many other customers when they make connections at other stations along the route. Every endeavour is made to minimise the total disruption and particular attention is given to services operating infrequently and the last train services each day.

The aim of all Train Operating Companies is to run punctually, but inevitably some disruption occurs from time to time. When planning a journey you may wish to consider the effects which any disruption could have and to allow some contingency margin when planning connections.

Minimum Interchange Times at Stations

Unless a connection is shown by times printed in light type, you should generally allow a minimum of five minutes between arrival and departure.

The exceptions to this rule are indicated by minimum interchange times (e.g. **15**) alongside the station name in the tables. In certain cases the minimum interchange time is different according to the Train Operators involved.

These are detailed below:-

STATION AND 'STANDARD' MINIMUM CONNECTIONAL ALLOWANCE (Minutes)		EXCEPTIONS *Showing the Train Operator(s) and minimum connectional allowance applicable*	
Barnham	5	*SN*	2
Bournemouth	5	*SW*	3
Brighton	10	*SN*	4
Cardiff Central	7	*AW*	3*
Clapham Junction	10	*SN*	5
Gatwick Airport	10	*SE, SN*	5
Guildford	5	*GW*	4
Leatherhead	5	*SN*	4
London Blackfriars	3	SE	5
London Victoria	15	*SE, SN*	10
Luton	10	*FC*	4
Luton Airport Parkway	7	*FC*	4
Redhill	5	*SN*	3
St. Denys	5	*SW*	3
Southampton Central	5	*SN, SW*	4
Tulse Hill	3	FC	4
Wimbledon	6	*SN, FC*	5

Example

At Barnham a different minimum connectional allowance applies for Train Operator SN. This means that if your journey involves changing between two trains *both of which* are operated by SN, you need only allow 2 minutes. If, however, one or both trains are provided by any other Operator then the minimum of 5 minutes (as shown after the station name) applies.

* Applicable to Valley Lines services only (table 130).

Train Information

National Rail Enquiries

Timetable and fares available at: www.nationalrail.co.uk

National Rail Enquiries provides up-to-the-minute advice on all aspects of journey planning, fares and buying tickets, live train running updates and other useful information.

08457 48 49 50 — 24 Hours Daily

(calls may be recorded for training purposes)

0845 60 40 500 — Welsh Language

0845 60 50 600 — Textphone – 06.00 - 21.00 Daily

For live train times for today and train timetables for the next three months call TrainTracker™ on:

0871 200 49 50

Average calls to TrainTracker cost 20p a minute from a BT fixed phone. Charges from other operators may vary. Calls may be recorded for training purposes.

For live departure and arrival times direct to your mobile text station name to TrainTracker™ on:

8 49 50

TrainTracker texts cost 25p for each successful response (plus usual text costs)

Train company numbers for disabled passengers requiring assistance:–

Company	Telephone	Textphone
Arriva Trains Wales	08453 003 005	Not available
c2c	01702 357640	08457 125 988
Chiltern Railways	08456 005 165	08457 078051
CrossCountry	0844 811 0125	0844 811 0126
East Midlands Trains	08457 125 678	18001 08457 125678
Eurostar	08705 186 186	Not available
First Capital Connect	0800 058 2844	0800 975 1052
First Great Western	0800 197 1329/0845 600 5604	0800 294 9209
First Hull Trains	08450 710 222	08456 786 967
First TransPennine Express	0800 107 2149	0800 107 2061
Gatwick Express	0845 850 15 30	Not available
Grand Central	0844 811 0071	Not available
Heathrow Connect	0800 197 1329	0800 294 9209
Heathrow Express	0845 600 1515	Not available
Island Line	0845 6000 650	0800 692 0792
London Midland	0800 0924260	0845 707 8051
London Overground	0845 601 4867	Not available
Merseyrail	0151 702 2071	0870 0552 681
National Express East Anglia	0800 028 28 78	0845 606 7245
National Express East Coast	08457 225 225	08451 202 067
Northern	0808 1561606	08456 045 608
ScotRail	0800 912 2 901	18001 0800 912 2 901
South West Trains	0800 52 82 100	0800 692 0792
Southeastern	0800 783 4524	0800 783 4548
Southern	0800 138 1016	0800 138 1018
Virgin Trains	08457 443366	08457 443367
Wrexham & Shropshire	0845 260 5200	Not available

Train Information

London Travel Information

020 7222 1234 | 24 hours (Daily) | www.tfl.gov.uk

Services to Europe on Eurostar via the Channel Tunnel

08705 186 186 | 0800-2100 (Daily) | www.eurostar.com

Ireland

NI Railways 028 90 66 6630 | 0700-2000 (Daily) | www.translink.co.uk.
Iarnrod Eireann (IE) (Irish Rail) 1850 366 222 | www.irishrail.ie

Transport Direct

Plan journeys by car, bus, train, tube, coach, plane at www.transportdirect.info. Transport Direct is the first door-to-door on-line journey planner for Great Britain.

It's free to use; simply enter your departure point, destination and time of travel and Transport Direct will offer a number of options by different modes of transport - both public and private. Journey plans are presented as step-by-step instructions supported by detailed maps including bus stops and other points of interest to travellers. Tickets for rail and coach journeys can be booked via retail web sites without the need to re-enter journey details. Transport Direct includes live travel news for rail and car users. The car journey planner gives route information that takes account of historical traffic level data, offering the user the choice to travel at a different time, or choose public transport. When travelling by public transport, users can adjust their expected walking speed to plan rail, coach and bus connections more efficiently. You can also access Transport Direct via mobile phone and PDA to find out when your next train is due or to check road conditions.

Bus Information in Great Britain

For details of buses within Greater London ring the Transport for London line: 020 7222 1234 (24-hours).

Bus information for the rest of Great Britain is available nationally from 'Traveline' which is run by local authorities and bus operators. There are regional call centres all of which share the same telephone number and any centre will switch calls pertaining to another part of the country through to the relevant centre. Alternatively codes for reaching the appropriate centre direct can be obtained from www.traveline.info/powercodes.htm.

The number is 0871 200 22 33 (calls from landlines cost 10p per minute) and centres are open at least between the hours of 0800 and 2000 daily (except Christmas Day and Boxing Day). Website: www.traveline.info.

PlusBus

PlusBus is an easy-to-use add-on to your train ticket which gives unlimited bus travel on most bus services around the whole urban area of your origin or destination town or city. ***PlusBus*** is available to over 240 towns and cities across Great Britain with season tickets also available for most ***PlusBus*** destinations. For more information visit www.plusbus.info.

Traintaxi

Taxi symbols on the Station index pages

Where appears against any station that has sub-entries, there will be a taxi rank outside the station from which taxis should usually be available. This also applies to Basingstoke, Bournemouth, Chelmsford, Cheltenham, Colchester, Lincoln, Middlesbrough, Milton Keynes, Northampton, Sunderland and Swindon.

Where appears against any other station, there will be a taxi rank or a cab office within 100 metres of the station. However, you are advised to check availability before travelling, and to pre-book if necessary. Indication of a rank or office is no guarantee of cabs being available.

Visit **www.traintaxi.co.uk** for information on cab firms serving **all** train, tram, metro and underground stations in Great Britain, and all bus and ferry destinations listed in this *GB Rail Timetable*.

Rail Travel for Disabled Passengers

All train operators are able to carry disabled passengers and can provide additional assistance for boarding and alighting rail services and during train journeys.

If using a wheelchair, it is recommended that passengers book assistance in advance as space on trains for wheelchair users is limited.

National Rail produce a booklet called 'Rail Travel Made Easy' which details the provisions Train Companies make for disabled people. The booklet is available from major stations or can be obtained by writing to: Disability & Inclusion Section, ATOC, 3rd Floor, 40 Bernard Street, London WC1N 1BY.

For more information visit www.nationalrail.co.uk/disabled

Seat Reservations, Luggage, Cycles and Pets

Seat Reservations

You can reserve seats on any train marked 🅁, 🆁, ◇ or ✕ at the top of the column in the timetable pages. Further detailed information is shown in the Directory of Train Operators.

Reservations can normally be made from about 2 months in advance of the day of travel, up to about 2 hours before the train departs from its start point, or, for early morning trains, up to 1600 hours the previous evening.

Where and How to reserve

You can reserve either by visiting a station identified in the Index pages by ◇, or a rail appointed travel agent or by calling one of the telephone booking facilities listed on each Train Operator's page. Telephone reservations are only available when made in conjunction with purchasing a ticket. When reserving you will need to tell your station or agent:

1. Starting and finishing point of your journey.
2. Date of travel (Take care if your departure is soon after midnight – see How to use this Timetable).
3. Departure time of train.
4. Number of seats required.
5. You may be able to specify other preferences such as facing or back to direction of travel*, window seat, seat in Restaurant Car where available, seats round a table or airline style with fold down table where available.
   *Customers should note that some trains reverse their direction of travel during the journey.
6. First Class or Standard accommodation (if you do not specify class of travel it will be assumed that you require Standard accommodation).

Names on seats

Your name can be included in your seat reservation label or on the electronic display above your seat, if you wish, when travelling First Class on some East Midlands Trains, National Express East Anglia and National Express East Coast services or First and Standard Class on CrossCountry, First Great Western, First TransPennine Express, ScotRail, South West Trains and Virgin Trains services.

Connecting reservations

If your journey involves changing between trains on which seats are reservable (including journeys crossing London or other major cities), through reservations on both services are available.

Children

Seats may be reserved for children, but for a child under 5 years of age a seat may be reserved only if an appropriate child rail ticket is held.

Reservations Recommended

Trains shown 🆁 at the head of a column in the timetable pages are expected to be very busy. Seat reservations are therefore recommended for a comfortable journey and will consequently be provided free of charge to holders of valid travel tickets.

Seat Reservations, Luggage, Cycles and Pets

Reservations Compulsory

On trains shown Ⓡ at the head of a column, seat reservations are compulsory and are available free of charge. Passengers may not be able to board the train if they do not have a reservation.

Trains For Weekends Away

Most long distance services after 1400 on Fridays and on Saturday mornings, also trains arriving in London on Sunday evenings and Monday mornings can be extremely busy.

Customers are advised to reserve seats in advance if planning to travel at these times.

Travelling at Peak Holiday Periods

Trains are usually extremely busy immediately before and after Bank Holidays and in some cases access to trains is only by reservation and/or boarding pass. Customers are advised to reserve seats as early as possible.

Cycles by Train

You can take your cycle on many National Rail services, however reservations may be required and restrictions may apply for peak services. Folded cycles can be carried on most train services. More information is shown in the Directory of Train Operators, the National Rail 'Cycling by Train' leaflet and online at www.nationalrail.co.uk/cycling. Cycle storage is also available at many stations.

Weekend First

Weekend First is available on many CrossCountry, East Midlands Trains, First Great Western, First TransPennine Express*, National Express East Anglia, National Express East Coast*, ScotRail*, South West Trains*, Virgin Trains and Wrexham & Shropshire* services on Saturdays, Sundays and Bank Holidays. If you hold a ticket for travel in Standard Class, you may be able to upgrade to the added comfort of First Class accommodation on payment of an additional fare. On some services a 'Weekend First' ticket allows you to upgrade to First Class at weekends and Bank Holidays. Holders of Annual Gold Cards may also be able to upgrade on off peak services for a small amount. Costs vary depending on the journey you are making.

*may only be purchased on trains at time of travel

More information can be found at nationalrail.co.uk/firstclass.

Customers' Luggage and Pets

Customers may take up to 3 items of personal luggage free of charge, this includes 2 large items (such as suitcases or rucksacks) and 1 item of smaller hand luggage (such as a briefcase). Folded prams, non-folding prams and carrycots are also able to be carried. Full details of the free allowances are available at stations. Excess luggage and certain more bulky items (such as skis) may be carried, subject to available space, at an extra charge. On Gatwick Express services, bulky items such as skis are conveyed free in the luggage van. There is plenty of space on board for other luggage.

Passengers may take dogs, cats and other small animals (maximum two per passenger), free of charge and subject to certain conditions, provided they do not endanger or inconvenience other passengers or staff.

ScotRail allows dogs to accompany able-bodied passengers in Sleeper services subject to a charge for cleaning of the compartment. The booking must be First Class, Standard Class with two people travelling together, or a Solo supplement is payable for exclusive use of a twin-berth cabin. First Great Western do not allow animals (except Guide Dogs) to travel in Sleeper accommodation. There is no charge for guide dogs.

More information can be found at nationalrail.co.uk/luggageandanimals

Directory of Train Operators

The following pages contain details of the Train Operating Companies who operate trains included in this timetable and indicate the services they provide.

Each operator is identified by a two character code listed below. The codes are displayed in the index alongside the station name indicating which operator is responsible for operating the facilities at that station. The code is also shown at the head of each train column in the timetable pages indicating which operator is providing the train service.

18 stations are the operating responsibility of Network Rail and are shown in the index by the code NR and information about Network Rail is shown at the end of the Train Operating Company pages.

AW Arriva Trains Wales AW

ADDRESS

St Marys House, 47 Penarth Road, Cardiff CF10 5DJ
Telephone: 08456 061 660
Website: www.arrivatrainswales.co.uk
Email: customer.relations@arrivatrainswales.co.uk

MANAGING DIRECTOR

Tim Bell

RESERVATIONS AND TICKETS BY TELEPHONE AND ONLINE

Tickets may be booked in advance and seats reserved, by telephone, from the following numbers (0800–2000 daily):
0870 9000 773 for Great Britain, tickets and reservations. 0870 9000 767 for Group and 0845 300 3005 for Disabled travel arrangements. Textphone 0845 300 6105
Please allow 5 days for delivery.

RESERVATION DETAILS

All seat reservations are free to ticket holders.

CATERING ON TRAINS

At-seat catering service of cold snacks, sandwiches and hot and cold drinks on all services marked ᴫ, for all or part of the journey.

Complimentary meal service for first class and a counter service of hot and cold snacks for standard class on trains with ⊠.

Train catering on Arriva Trains Wales services is provided by:

At Seat Catering (2003) Ltd,
Arriva Trains Wales
1st Floor
St Mary's House
47 Penarth Road
Cardiff
CF10 5DJ

CYCLES

See Cycling by Train leaflet, a guide to Arriva Trains Wales services for full details.

LOST PROPERTY

Contact Arriva Trains Wales Customer Relations on 0845 6061 660.

TRAIN SERVICE UPDATE

Please consult our website at www.arrivatrainswales.co.uk for real time service updates.

PENALTY FARES

Penalty Fares are not in force on Arriva Trains Wales services. Customers are reminded that they must have a valid ticket when boarding at a staffed station, if not it will be necessary to charge you the full single/return fare for the journey.

DISABLED PERSON'S PROTECTION POLICY

Address as above.

CODE OF PRACTICE FOR COMMENTS, COMPLAINTS AND SUGGESTIONS

Address as above.

ALCOHOL POLICY

Arriva Trains Wales have prohibited the consumption of alcohol on all services and stations between Caerphilly and Rhymney, Pontypridd and Treherbert & Pontypridd and Merthyr Tydfil.

c2c

A member of the National Express Group plc

ADDRESS	207 Old Street, London EC1V 9NR Telephone: 0845 601 4873 Fax: 01603 214517 Website: www.c2c-online.co.uk
MANAGING DIRECTOR	Julian Drury
RESERVATIONS AND TICKETS BY TELEPHONE AND ONLINE	Tickets may be booked in advance by telephoning 08457 44 44 22 - 0800 to 2000 daily.
RESERVATION DETAILS	Reservations are not available.
CATERING ON TRAINS	Not available.
CYCLES	Cycles can be taken on off-peak trains free-of-charge when accompanied by a fare-paying passenger, subject to space availability. Bicycles are not permitted, Mondays to Fridays on services that arrive in London between 0715 and 0945, or those which leave London between 1630 and 1840. To comply with safety regulations, all cycles, with the exception of folding cycles which are completely enclosed in a container or case throughout the journey, must be conveyed in the designated area on trains. During engineering work, cycles cannot be accommodated on replacement bus services.
LOST PROPERTY	Telephone: 01702 357 699
TRAIN SERVICE UPDATE	Up to date train running information is available on the c2c website www.c2c-online.co.uk, the National Rail Enquiries website or on ceefax page 433.
PENALTY FARES	If you travel without a valid ticket you may be charged a penalty fare of £20 or twice the full single fare, whichever is the greater.
DISABLED PERSON'S PROTECTION POLICY	Available from:- Customer Relations, c2c, FREEPOST ADM3968, Southend SS1 1ZS Telephone: 0845 601 4873 - 0830 to 1700 Monday to Friday
CODE OF PRACTICE FOR COMMENTS, COMPLAINTS AND SUGGESTIONS	Available from Customer Relations at above address or telephone 0845 601 4873.

CrossCountry

XC

ADDRESS	CrossCountry 5th Floor, Cannon House, 18 Priory Queensway, Birmingham B4 6BS Telephone: 0870 010 0084 Textphone: 0121 200 6420 Fax: 0121 200 6005 Website: www.crosscountrytrains.co.uk Email: customer.relations@crosscountrytrains.co.uk
MANAGING DIRECTOR	Andy Cooper
RESERVATIONS AND TICKETS BY TELEPHONE AND ONLINE	On-line at crosscountrytrains.co.uk is the easiest way to purchase your tickets. If you prefer, you can also make telephone bookings on 0844 811 0124 between 0800 and 2200 daily. Parties of 10 or more should contact Group Travel on 0871 244 2388 between 0800 and 1800 weekdays
RESERVATION DETAILS	You are strongly advised to make a seat reservation in advance; especially when travelling on trains shown ▣ in timetables. Seat reservations are free of charge.
CATERING ON TRAINS	Catering is available on most CrossCountry trains. In First Class, on weekdays between 0630 and 1830 customers can enjoy complimentary light refreshments including hot and soft drinks, served at seat. In Standard Class we offer a range of quality snacks, sandwiches and hot drinks plus soft and alcoholic beverages between 0600 and 2000. For more information on the Nottingham - Cardiff and Birmingham - Stansted Airport routes please refer to our timetables.
CYCLES	We do not charge to carry your cycle. However, as space is very limited you will need to reserve in advance on nearly all our services. Please enquire before travelling. We are unable to accept powered cycles, tricycles, tandems or trailers on any of our services.
LOST PROPERTY	Contact Customer Relations on 0870 010 0084 between 0800 and 2000 Monday to Saturday; or email lost.property@crosscountrytrains.co.uk
TRAIN SERVICE UPDATE	Details of major disruption to services and weekend engineering work are summarised on BBC Ceefax and BBCi on digital TV. Live travel updates are available on-line at crosscountrytrains.co.uk and details of all service disruptions can be found at nationalrail.co.uk/service_bulletins/
PENALTY FARES	A Penalty Fares scheme is not currently in operation on CrossCountry trains. Visit crosscountrytrains.co.uk for the most up to date information. Should you board one of our trains without a valid ticket you will be charged the full Single or Return fare for your journey unless the ticket office is closed and a self-service ticket machine is not available.
DISABLED PERSON'S PROTECTION POLICY	We provide a Journey Care service for the disabled, elderly and infirm. By phoning our team on 0844 811 0125, textphone 0844 811 0126, beforehand we will, where possible, arrange help for your journey. Our Disabled Persons Protection Policy is available on-line at crosscountrytrains.co.uk
CODE OF PRACTICE FOR COMMENTS, COMPLAINTS AND SUGGESTIONS	Copies of our Complaints Handling Procedure and Passenger's Charter are available on-line at crosscountrytrains.co.uk

Chiltern Railways

CH

ADDRESS

Customer Services, Banbury ICC, Merton Street
Banbury, Oxfordshire OX16 4RN
Telephone: 08456 005 165 (Mondays to Fridays 0830-1730)
Fax: 01926 729 914
Website: www.chilternrailways.co.uk

MANAGING DIRECTOR

Adrian Shooter (Acting)

RESERVATIONS AND TICKETS BY TELEPHONE AND ONLINE

Telephone 08456 005 165 (0700-2000, 7 days a week)

RESERVATION DETAILS

Reservations are not required on Chiltern Railways services.

CATERING ON TRAINS

An at-seat trolley catering service is provided on the busiest morning trains between the West Midlands and London. These are shown in timetables.

CYCLES

On Mondays to Fridays we're unable to convey cycles on our busiest trains. These are trains arriving at London Marylebone or Birmingham Snow Hill between 0745 and 1000 and trains departing London Marylebone or Birmingham Snow Hill between 1630 and 1930. These restrictions apply even if you're only travelling for part of the journey. Tandems are not carried at any time on Chiltern Railways. There are no restrictions on folding bikes. Bikes are not allowed on rail replacement buses.

LOST PROPERTY

If we find any item of lost property, we'll always do our best to contact the owner if they can be identified. Items can be collected from London Marylebone up to 3 months after they've been handed in - we charge a collection fee to cover our administration costs.

If you lose something on one of our trains or stations you can report it by:

* Using the online form on our website

* Using a Lost Property form available at any Chiltern Railways ticket office, and returning it to a member of Chiltern Railways Staff.

* By phone, fax or post using the contact details below

Phone: 08456 005 165
Fax: 020 7333 3002
Write to: Chiltern Railways Lost Property, Marylebone Station, London NW1 6JJ.

Lost Property Office Operating Hours: Mondays to Fridays 1200 to 2000. Please allow up to 2 weeks for processing lost items. If you do not hear from us in that period, you should assume the item has not been found.

TRAIN SERVICE UPDATE

Visit our website www.chilternrailways.co.uk for current train running information and details of changes to train times because of engineering work or other special events.

PENALTY FARES

If you do not have a valid rail ticket for the journey you are making, you will have to pay a Penalty Fare of £20 or twice the single fare, whichever is the greater, for the journey you are making on Chiltern Railways services. For full details write to the above address, or see our website.

DISABLED PERSON'S PROTECTION POLICY

Copies of the Disabled Person's Protection Policy can be obtained from the above address, or from our website.

CODE OF PRACTICE FOR COMMENTS, COMPLAINTS AND SUGGESTIONS

If you have any comments, complaints or suggestions regarding Chiltern Railways services, please write to the address shown above or telephone 08456 005 165 (0830-1730 Mondays to Fridays), Fax 01926 729 914. Alternatively you can use the 'Contact Us' option on our website.

East Midlands Trains

EM

ADDRESS	Customer Relations East Midlands Trains FREEPOST DY940 Derby DE1 2BR Telephone: 08457 125 678 Website: eastmidlandstrains.co.uk Email: getintouch@eastmidlandstrains.co.uk
MANAGING DIRECTOR	Tim Shoveller
RESERVATIONS AND TICKETS BY TELEPHONE AND ONLINE	Buy your tickets online at eastmidlandstrains.co.uk. You can buy tickets for all rail journeys (within Great Britain) with us. Alternatively call 08457 125 678 between 0800-2000 (7 days a week).
RESERVATION DETAILS	Seat reservations on East Midlands Trains services are free. Just book in advance when you buy your ticket. We advise that you always make a reservation, as seats cannot be guaranteed without one. On our Local services reservations are available on the Liverpool to Norwich services.
CATERING ON TRAINS	On our East Midlands London services (to/from St Pancras International), we offer a range of delicious healthy food options, plus snacks and hot and cold drinks. A trolley service is available on selected East Midlands Local services (denoted by a symbol within the timetable).
CYCLES	Two bicycles per train are accepted for free on all East Midlands Trains services; however reservations must be made in advance on reservable services subject to availability.
LOST PROPERTY	Please allow a minimum of 24 hours for the items to be received at a lost property office. If your item is located you will be charged for the return of it and will be advised of this cost. To enquire about lost property, please call Customer Relations on 08457 125 678.
TRAIN SERVICE UPDATE	Details of services and real time running information, including travel alerts by email are available through our website. Visit eastmidlandstrains.co.uk. Alternatively, call National Rail Enquiries on 08457 48 49 50 (calls may be recorded for training purposes).
PENALTY FARES	You should always buy a ticket in advance of boarding your train. Penalty fares may be in operation on your service.
DISABLED PERSON'S PROTECTION POLICY	We aim to make travelling with us accessible to all our customers. If you require assistance in travelling, have special needs or mobility problems please call our team on 08457 125 678 to arrange help for your journey. A text direct service is also available on 18001 08457 125 678 (for people with hearing problems).
CODE OF PRACTICE FOR COMMENTS, COMPLAINTS AND SUGGESTIONS	Our Customer Relations team is available to receive your comments, complaints or suggestions. Please write to Customer Relations at the above address, or email getintouch@eastmidlandstrains.co.uk

FC

First Capital Connect

FC

A member of the First Rail Division

ADDRESS	Freepost, RRBR-REEJ-KTKY, First Capital Connect, Customer Relations Department, PO Box 443, Plymouth PL4 6WP Telephone: 0845 026 4700 (open 7 days a week 0700-2200 with the exception of Christmas Day) Fax: 0845 676 9904 Website: www.firstcapitalconnect.co.uk Email: customer.relations.fcc@firstgroup.com
CHIEF EXECUTIVE	Moir Lockhead
MANAGING DIRECTOR	Elaine Holt
RESERVATIONS AND TICKETS BY TELEPHONE AND ONLINE	It is not necessary to pre-book on First Capital Connect services. There is no telesales.
RESERVATION DETAILS	First Capital Connect does not operate a reservation system.
CATERING ON TRAINS	None.
CYCLES	We welcome passengers with bicycles on services where they can be safely accommodated, however restrictions apply, bicycles cannot be carried on: • trains that are scheduled to arrive at a London terminal between 07:00 and 10:00; • trains that are scheduled to depart from a London terminal between 16:00 and 19:00; • trains running between Drayton Park and Moorgate; • services between Royston and Ely that depart or arrive at Cambridge between 07:45 and 08:45, with the exception of the 07:15 and 07:45 departures from King's Cross; • replacement bus services unless stated otherwise in any associated publicity; and • any train where a member of our staff asks you to remove your bicycle. • Bicycles cannot be conveyed within Travelcard zone 1 in any direction between the hours of 0700-1000 and 1600-1900 Monday to Friday Fold up bicycles can be carried on any service at any time.
LOST PROPERTY	In order to trace lost property please contact our Customer Relations department on 0845 026 4700, between 07:00 - 22:00 Monday to Sunday.
TRAIN SERVICE UPDATE	For current train information call First Capital Connect Travel Check on 0845 330 3660, National Rail enquiries on 08457 48 49 50 (calls may be recorded for training purposes) or check our website at: www.firstcapitalconnect.co.uk/live-info
PENALTY FARES	First Capital Connect operates a Penalty Fares System. If you do not have a valid ticket or permit to travel, you will be liable to pay a penalty fare. This is £20 or twice the appropriate single fare to the next station stop, whichever is greater. This does not apply for travel from Crews Hill. If you do not buy a ticket, you could also be prosecuted and this can lead to a criminal conviction.
DISABLED PERSON'S PROTECTION POLICY	Our Disabled Person's Protection Policy is available from Customer Relations, and is also available on our website and available at all staffed sations. First Capital Connect operates a dedicated telephone and textphone service for disabled or mobility impaired customers, the contact details are: Telephone: 0800 058 2844 Textphone: 0800 975 1052 These are available 07:00 - 22:00, Monday to Sunday, with the exception of Christmas Day.
CODE OF PRACTICE FOR COMMENTS, COMPLAINTS AND SUGGESTIONS	Our Passenger's Charter details our code of practice and is available from all staffed stations and from our Customer Relations department. The Customer Relations department will be happy to assist with any comments, complaints or suggestions and can be contacted using the contact details above.

First Great Western

GW

A member of the First Rail Division

ADDRESS	Milford House, 1 Milford Street, Swindon SN1 1HL Telephone: 01793 499400 Fax: 01793 499460 Website: www.firstgreatwestern.co.uk where customers can buy tickets, check train times, obtain current information on train services, download timetables, check latest alterations to services, view promotions and offers and contact us with your comments.
CHIEF OPERATING OFFICER	Andrew Haines
RESERVATIONS AND TICKETS BY TELEPHONE AND ONLINE	Tickets may be booked in advance using credit and debit cards and seats reserved by ringing **08457 000 125** (open 0700-2200 Mondays to Fridays and 0700-2100 Saturdays and Sundays). Allow at least 3 working days for postal delivery. A next day delivery can be arranged at £5 per transaction. Arrangements can be made for tickets to be collected from Fast Ticket machines (the credit or debit card used for purchase will be needed at many stations). For Group Travel call **08457 000 125**.
RESERVATION DETAILS	One complimentary seat reservation per single journey when purchasing a ticket, additional reservations, including those made by season ticket holders, will be subject to a £5 fee.
CATERING ON TRAINS	Most First Great Western high speed services offer a buffet or trolley service with a selection of hot and cold drinks and snacks, beers, wines, sandwiches, crisps and confectionery. First Class customers also enjoy additional complimentary services: • An at-seat trolley service offering light refreshments available on Monday to Friday services between 0700-1900 including hot and cold drinks and light snacks appropriate to the time of day. • A complimentary daily newspaper (available up to 09.00) and evening paper (after 15.00) on services out of London. • At the weekend and on weekdays after 1900 complimentary refreshments are available from the buffet on production of valid travel tickets. • Friday night wine offers first class customers a complimentary glass of wine between 1500 and 1900. Some weekday high speed services offer a Pullman Restaurant service and some offer hot food which is freshly prepared on board by one of our chefs. These services are available for both First and Standard Class Customers, subject to availability, on 35 services each weekday.
CYCLES	First Great Western welcomes customers with bicycles on services where they can be safely accommodated. However it is not possible to carry bicycles on some services particularly during peak periods. For full details of when bicycles cannot be carried or when reservations are required, please visit our website or pick up a leaflet at any of our staffed stations.
LOST PROPERTY	Customers who have left property on First Great Western services should contact our Customer Services team on **08457 000 125**.
TRAIN SERVICE UPDATE	For current train information including details of engineering work please visit our website: www.firstgreatwestern.co.uk
PENALTY FARES	These operate on most of our services. A penalty fare of £20 or twice the appropriate single fare to the next station stop (whichever is the greater) will be charged to anybody who is unable to produce a valid ticket or other authority when required to do so. For further information, pick up a leaflet about penalty fares from any staffed station.
DISABLED PERSON'S PROTECTION POLICY	Available from Customer Services Team First Great Western PO Box 313 Plymouth PL4 6YD Tel: 08457 000 125 Email: fgwfeedback@firstgroup.com Opening hours 0700-2200, daily. Customers requiring assistance should contact 0800 197 1329/0845 600 5604 (0800 294 9209 textphone service) giving 24 hours notice of travel plans, if possible.
CODE OF PRACTICE FOR COMMENTS, COMPLAINTS AND SUGGESTIONS	Your views leaflets and copies of the Passenger's Charter are available to download from our website www.firstgreatwestern.co.uk, at all staffed First Great Western stations or alternatively from the Customer Services Team at the address above.

First Hull Trains

A joint venture between First Rail Division and Renaissance Railways Ltd.

ADDRESS
First Hull Trains Customer Services, Freepost RLYY-XSTG-YXCK, 4th Floor, Europa House, 184 Ferensway, Hull HU1 3UT.
Telephone: 08456 76 99 05
Website: www.hulltrains.co.uk
Email: customer.services@hulltrains.co.uk

MANAGING DIRECTOR
Mark Leving

RESERVATIONS AND TICKETS BY TELEPHONE AND ONLINE
First Hull Trains tickets can be booked in advance and seats reserved by ringing 08450 710 222 (0700 to 2200 Monday to Friday and 0800 to 1900 Saturday and Sunday). Please allow five working days for delivery. Tickets on departure are available.

RESERVATION DETAILS
Seat reservations are free for First and Standard Class ticket holders. Season Ticket holders may reserve seats at a cost of £2 for First class and £1 for Standard class.

CATERING ON TRAINS
First Hull Trains provides a buffet on all services, and a comprehensive catering package for First Class passengers. Catering is subject to availability and may be limited when services are disrupted by engineering works or Bank Holidays.

CYCLES
Cycles and tandems are carried free of charge, however, a reservation is compulsory. Please telephone 08450 710 222

LOST PROPERTY
Please contact Customer Services.

TRAIN SERVICE UPDATE
Available at www.hulltrains.co.uk, or by telephone on 08450 710222.

PENALTY FARES
Penalty fares are not in force on any Hull Trains Service

DISABLED PERSON'S PROTECTION POLICY
Available at: www.hulltrains.co.uk. Alternatively, a copy can be requested from Customer Services.

CODE OF PRACTICE FOR COMMENTS, COMPLAINTS AND SUGGESTIONS
First Hull Trains' Passenger's Charter is available at www.hulltrains.co.uk. Alternatively, any comments, complaints or suggestions can be sent to Customer Services

First TransPennine Express

TP

A joint venture between First and Keolis

ADDRESS	7th Floor, Bridgewater House, 60 Whitworth Street, Manchester M1 6LT Telephone: 08700 005151 Website: www.tpexpress.co.uk
MANAGING DIRECTOR	Vernon Barker
RESERVATIONS AND TICKETS BY TELEPHONE AND ONLINE	Reservations and tickets are available from all local staffed stations.
RESERVATION DETAILS	Seat reservations are available at staffed stations. Seat reservations for travel on First TransPennine Express services can be booked up until the day before travel. There is no charge for making a seat reservation if you have a rail ticket, or buy one at the same time.
CATERING ON TRAINS	Catering trolley services are available between 0700 and 1900 Monday to Friday on First TransPennine Express trains between Manchester Piccadilly and York, Manchester Piccadilly and Doncaster and Manchester Piccadilly and Preston. In addition to the above, all services between Manchester Airport, Manchester Piccadilly, Carlisle, Glasgow Central and Edinburgh convey a trolley service for the whole journey. This facility is also provided at weekends.
CYCLES	Customers may take their bicycle with them on First TransPennine Express trains at no extra cost. As space is limited reservations for cycle space should be made at least 24 hours before the journey.
LOST PROPERTY	Customers who have left their property on First TransPennine Express trains or stations should contact 0845 600 1672.
TRAIN SERVICE UPDATE	Call TrainTracker on 0871 200 4950 for updated information on train departures and arrivals.
PENALTY FARES	Penalty Fares are not applicable on First TransPennine Express services. Customers are reminded that they must have a valid ticket when they travel. If not it will be necessary to charge the full Open Single or Return fare for the journey.
DISABLED PERSON'S PROTECTION POLICY	Available from: Customer Relations, First TransPennine Express, ADMAIL 3878, Freepost, Manchester M1 9YB Customers who have special needs and require customer assistance should contact us on 0800 107 2149. A textphone service is available on 0800 107 2061.
CODE OF PRACTICE FOR COMMENTS, COMPLAINTS AND SUGGESTIONS	Feedback leaflets and copies of the Passenger's Charter are available from all stations served by First TransPennine Express services or alternatively contact: Customer Relations, First TransPennine Express, ADMAIL 3878, Freepost, Manchester M1 9YB. Telephone: 0845 600 1671 Email: tpecustomer.relations@firstgroup.com

Gatwick Express

GX

ADDRESS	P.O. Box 227, Tonbridge, Kent TN9 2ZP Telephone: 0845 850 1530 (Overseas: +44 1214 105015) Fax: 020 8929 8687 (Overseas: +44 208 9298687) Website: www.gatwickexpress.com Email: queries.gex@airexp.co.uk
MANAGING DIRECTOR	Chris Burchell
RESERVATIONS AND TICKETS BY TELEPHONE AND ONLINE	Reservations are not necessary on Gatwick Express services. For information and telesales please call 0845 850 1530. Tickets can also be purchased through our website at www.gatwickexpress.com
RESERVATION DETAILS	Gatwick Express is a high frequency service therefore reservations are not required.
CATERING ON TRAINS	An at-seat trolley service of drinks and light refreshments is available throughout the day.
CYCLES	Cycles and other bulky items such as skis are conveyed free in the luggage van. There is plenty of space on board for other luggage – for further information call 0845 850 15 30.
LOST PROPERTY	Please call our Lost Property Office on 0845 850 15 30, select option 3.
TRAIN SERVICE UPDATE	Journey time is 30 minutes (35 minutes on Sundays). First Class and Express Class accommodation is available. From London Victoria at 0330, 0430, 0500 then every 15 minutes (xx15, xx30, xx45, xx00) until 0001, 0030. From Gatwick Airport at 0435, 0520, 0550 then every 15 minutes (xx05, xx20, xx35, xx50) until 0050, 0135. For current train information call 0845 850 15 30.
PENALTY FARES	Penalty Fares will be applied for passengers without the correct ticket between Brighton and Gatwick Airport. The only passengers permitted to buy a ticket on the train are those travelling between Gatwick Airport and London Victoria in either direction.
DISABLED PERSON'S PROTECTION POLICY	Customers requiring assistance can book this prior to travel. Arrangements can be made by calling 0845 850 15 30, textphone available. It is advisable to give 24 hours notice of travel plans, although customers will be given assistance if they arrive at the stations without notice but please allow a little extra time.
CODE OF PRACTICE FOR COMMENTS, COMPLAINTS AND SUGGESTIONS	Initially comments or issues requiring immediate attention should be addressed to any member of Gatwick Express staff on the train or platforms. Additionally Customer Comments forms and our Passenger's Charter are available at Gatwick Express ticket offices. Alternatively you may write to the Listening Company, P.O. Box 277, Tonbridge, Kent TN9 2ZP.

Grand Central

GC

ADDRESS	Grand Central Railway Company Ltd River House 17 Museum Street York YO1 7DJ Telephone: 01904 633307 Fax: 01904 466066 Website: www.grandcentralrail.com Email: info@grandcentralrail.com
MANAGING DIRECTOR	Tom Clift
RESERVATIONS AND TICKETS BY TELEPHONE AND ONLINE	Minimum transaction value: £10. Full details on the website.
RESERVATION DETAILS	All seats are reservable. No charge for reservations.
CATERING ON TRAINS	Full catering services are available. Full details on the website.
CYCLES	Normal cycles conveyed at no charge.
LOST PROPERTY	Contact the above address.
TRAIN SERVICE UPDATE	Please phone: 01904 633307 or check our website: www.grandcentralrail.com
PENALTY FARES	No penalty fares are applicable.
DISABLED PERSON'S PROTECTION POLICY	Available from the above address.
CODE OF PRACTICE FOR COMMENTS, COMPLAINTS AND SUGGESTIONS	Available from the above address.

HC **Heathrow Connect** HC

A joint venture between First Rail Division and BAA (Heathrow Express)

ADDRESS	Full postal address for customer correspondence Freepost RLRZ-TZXE-BYKY Heathrow Connect 6th Floor 50 Eastbourne Terrace London W2 6LX Telephone: 0845 678 6975 Fax: 020 8745 6615 Website: www.heathrowconnect.com Email: queries@heathrowconnect.com
MANAGING DIRECTORS	*Heathrow Connect is a joint venture between First Great Western and BAA (Heathrow Express).* Andrew Haines (First Great Western) Brian Raven (Heathrow Express)
RESERVATIONS AND TICKETS BY TELEPHONE AND ONLINE	Reservations are not necessary. Tickets can be booked by telephone on 0845 700 0125. Open 0700-2200 (0800-1900 Saturdays and Sundays). Allow 3 working days for delivery. A next day delivery can be arranged at £5 per transaction. Tickets may also be purchased through our website www.heathrowconnect.com
RESERVATION DETAILS	Heathrow Connect services are not reservable.
CATERING ON TRAINS	Catering on trains is not available.
CYCLES	Cycles are carried free of charge, but are not allowed on trains timed to arrive at London Paddington between 0745-0945, or depart London Paddington between 1630-1830 Mondays to Fridays. In the interest of safety and customer comfort, we reserve the right to limit the number of cycles at other times.
LOST PROPERTY	For property lost on a Heathrow Connect train or at London Paddington, call the Lost Property Office at Paddington on 0207 313 1514. For property left at Heathrow call the BAA Lost Property Office at Heathrow Central Station on 0208 745 7727. For property left at one of the intermediate stations contact the FGW Lost Property helpline on 0845 602 4304.
TRAIN SERVICE UPDATE	For current train information call 0845 678 6975. Website: www.heathrowconnect.com
PENALTY FARES	Penalty Fares apply at stations between Hayes & Harlington and Paddington (incl). Customers are liable to a Penalty Fare of £20 to the next station stop.
DISABLED PERSON'S PROTECTION POLICY	This is available from Customer Relations at the above address and telephone number.
CODE OF PRACTICE FOR COMMENTS, COMPLAINTS AND SUGGESTIONS	This is available from Customer Relations at the above address and telephone number.

Heathrow Express

HX

ADDRESS

Customer contact:
Freepost RLXY-ETJG-XKZS
London W2 6LG
Telephone: 0845 600 1515
(call centre)

Corporate contact:
Heathrow Express,
6th Floor, 50 Eastbourne Terrace,
London W2 6LX or
FREEPOST LON 16331, Hounslow TW6 2BR
Telephone: 020 8750 6600 (Overseas +44 845 600 1515)
Fax: 020 8750 6615
Website: www.heathrowexpress.com
Email: queries.hex@airexpress.co.uk

MANAGING DIRECTOR

Brian Raven

RESERVATIONS AND TICKETS BY TELEPHONE AND ONLINE

Reservations are not necessary on Heathrow Express services. Tickets may be purchased in advance from Heathrow Express sales desks, ticket machines and from a range of other appointed outlets as well as through our website www.heathrowexpress.com. For details call the Customer Care Line on 0845 600 15 15 or visit our website. (24-hour service – local rate call)

RESERVATION DETAILS

Heathrow Express operates a 'turn up and go' service and reservations are not necessary.

CATERING ON TRAINS

As the overall journey time is only 15 minutes, or 21 minutes to Terminal 5, there is currently no catering on Heathrow Express services. Terminal 4 is served by a connecting 'shuttle' service at Heathrow Terminals 1, 2 & 3, taking a minimum 8 minutes extra.

CYCLES

Limited accommodation is available for cycles on Heathrow Express services, for passengers flying with their cycles from the airport. Heathrow Express reserve the right to limit the number of cycles conveyed on each train to no more than three at busy times. Cyclists not travelling onwards by air may use the service to and from Heathrow Terminals, subject to space being available for airline passengers.

LOST PROPERTY

Property lost at Paddington station is collected by Network Rail, who can be contacted on 020 7313 1514. For items lost at Heathrow Airport call 020 8745 7727. For items lost on Heathrow Express trains, please ask our Customer Service Representatives, or alternatively write to: Excess Baggage Co., Heathrow Airport, Middlesex UB3 5AP or Email to heathrow.lostproperty@excess-baggage.com.

TRAIN SERVICE UPDATE

For current information on train services please contact our customer care line on 0845 600 15 15, or through our website www.heathrowexpress.com.

PENALTY FARES

Penalty Fares do not apply on Heathrow Express services, therefore customers may join the train without having first purchased a ticket or authority to travel. Customer Service Representatives on every train will accept cash, debit and credit cards, for ticket purchase. Please note however for tickets purchased on board there is a £3.00 premium to pay. Only full fare tickets are available to purchase on board the train. (However Disabled Railcard is accepted on board).

DISABLED PERSON'S PROTECTION POLICY

Heathrow Express trains have been specially designed with the needs of the disabled in mind. Platforms at all our stations give level access into the trains and there is space for wheelchairs on all trains.

For further information on facilities for the disabled, call the Customer Care Line on 0845 600 15 15, or write to the Managing Director at the address at the top of this page.

CODE OF PRACTICE FOR COMMENTS, COMPLAINTS AND SUGGESTIONS

It is our aim to try and resolve any issues or grievances on the spot. All our Customer Service Representatives have a supply of comment forms and our Customer Care Line on 0845 600 15 15 can deal with any issues over the telephone or submit any comments at queries.hex@airexp.co.uk. If you wish to write with a suggestion or complaint, please write to the Managing Director at the address at the top of this page, or through our website www.heathrowexpress.com.

Island Line

IL

ADDRESS	Friars Bridge Court, 41–45 Blackfriars Road, London SE1 8NZ Telephone: 08700 005151 Fax: 020 7620 5177 Website: www.southwesttrains.co.uk Email: customerrelations@swtrains.co.uk
MANAGING DIRECTOR	Stewart Palmer
RESERVATIONS AND TICKETS BY TELEPHONE AND ONLINE	Reservations are not required on Island Line Trains services. Group travel information can be obtained by calling 023 8072 8162.
RESERVATION DETAILS	Reservations are not required.
CATERING ON TRAINS	There are no catering facilities on trains.
CYCLES	A maximum of 4 cycles may be carried in the Shanklin end of all trains at no extra charge. For the safety and comfort of our passengers, the guard may refuse to carry any further cycles on the train.
LOST PROPERTY	All items of lost property are retained at Ryde Esplanade Ticket Office. If you have lost an item please telephone the Ticket Office on 01983 562492 (0900-1700 Daily). A charge may be applicable on collection.
TRAIN SERVICE UPDATE	For current train information, please call our helpline on 0845 6000 650 or visit www.island-line.com. For details of Bank Holiday services see also the boxed note on the page immediately preceding Table 149.
PENALTY FARES	Penalty Fares are not in force on any Island Line Trains services.
DISABLED PERSON'S PROTECTION POLICY	Island Line Trains is committed to making travel easier for customers with disabilities including wheelchair users. For travel on the mainland, please call our Assisted Travel line on 0800 5282 100 (textphone 0800 692 0792), giving 24 hours notice before travelling. For journeys wholly within Island Line Trains, please telephone 01983 812591 giving 24 hours notice if assistance is required.
CODE OF PRACTICE FOR COMMENTS, COMPLAINTS AND SUGGESTIONS	Feedback leaflets are available at Ryde Esplanade or Shanklin Ticket Offices. Copies of Island Line Trains' and South West Trains' Passenger's Charters are available from any staffed station or by writing to: Customer Service Centre, South West Trains, Overline House, Southampton SO15 1GW Telephone 0845 6000 650. Fax 023 8072 8187 Email: customerrelations@swtrains.co.uk The Passenger's Charter is also featured on the website www.island-line.com and www.southwesttrains.co.uk.

London Midland

ADDRESS	PO Box 4323 Birmingham B2 4JB Telephone: 0844 811 0133 Website: www.londonmidland.com Email: comments@londonmidland.com
MANAGING DIRECTOR	Stephen Banaghan
RESERVATIONS AND TICKETS BY TELEPHONE AND ONLINE	Tickets can be booked in advance on-line at www.londonmidland.com or by ringing 0844 811 0133, 0800-2000 Monday to Sunday, please allow 5 days for delivery.
RESERVATION DETAILS	Group travel enquiries and bookings can also be made on 0844 811 0133. Seat reservations are available on our Birmingham–Liverpool and Crewe–London trains, but free of charge with a valid rail ticket.
CATERING ON TRAINS	A trolley service of drinks and light refreshments is available on a number of our Birmingham–Liverpool and Crewe–London trains, as indicated by a trolley symbol in the timetable pages.
CYCLES	Cycles are carried free of charge on most off-peak services, however, advance reservations are required for our Birmingham–Liverpool and Crewe–London services. Cycles cannot be conveyed on trains arriving into London Euston between 0700 and 0959 and departing London Euston between 1600 and 1859 on Mondays to Fridays (excluding Bank Holidays). Folding cycles, completely folded down, are regarded as accompanied luggage and carried free.
LOST PROPERTY	Enquiries can be made at your nearest staffed station or by ringing Customer Relations on 0844 811 0133.
TRAIN SERVICE UPDATE	Available from National Rail Enquiries on 08457 48 49 50 (calls may be recorded for training purposes).
PENALTY FARES	A Penalty Fares system is in place across most of the London Midland network. If you board a service from a staffed station without a valid ticket or permit to travel, you will be liable to a £20 penalty fare or twice the standard single fare to the next station whichever is the greater. You can only purchase a ticket on-train when travelling from an unstaffed station. Details of the scheme are available at www.londonmidland.com or by writing to Customer Relations at the address below.
DISABLED PERSON'S PROTECTION POLICY	Available from Customer Relations, London Midland PO Box 4323 Birmingham B2 4JB Telephone: 0844 811 0133
CODE OF PRACTICE FOR COMMENTS, COMPLAINTS AND SUGGESTIONS	Available from Customer Relations at the above address.

London Overground

Operated by London Overground Rail Operations Ltd. (LOROL)
on behalf of Rail for London Ltd., a subsidiary of TfL

ADDRESS	125 Finchley Road London NW3 6HY Telephone: 0845 601 4867 Website: www.tfl.gov/overground Email: overgroundinfo@tfl.gov.uk
MANAGING DIRECTOR	Steve Murphy
RESERVATIONS AND TICKETS BY TELEPHONE AND ONLINE	Tickets may be booked in advance and seats reserved on many long distance national rail services from most London Overground ticket offices. Oyster tickets may be purchased online from https://oyster.tfl.gov.uk
RESERVATION DETAILS	Seat reservations cannot be made for journeys on London Overground services.
CATERING ON TRAINS	Catering is not provided on London Overground services.
CYCLES	London Overground allows cycles on its trains and conveys them free of charge provided it is safe to do so. Due to space constraints, cycles are not permitted on services between Willesden Junction High Level and Gospel Oak and between Gospel Oak and Blackhorse Road in either direction between 0800–1000 and 1630–1830. On the Euston to Watford Junction Line cycles are not permitted on London Overground services timed to arrive at London Euston between 0700–1000 or depart London Euston between 1630 and 1900. These restrictions apply on Mondays to Fridays only. There are no restrictions on Saturdays, Sundays and Bank Holidays. Folding bicycles can be carried on any London Overground Service at any time. Only one cycle is allowed per customer and this must be folded and within a limit of one cycle per vestibule area. Tandems and three-wheeled vehicles cannot be accommodated on any London Overground service. Cycles are not carried on buses that replace trains due to engineering work.
LOST PROPERTY	Please contact the TfL Lost Property Office at Baker Street on 0845 330 9882 or our Customer Services Team on 0845 601 4867.
TRAIN SERVICE UPDATE	Information about London Overground services and fares can be obtained by telephoning either: • London Travel Information on 020 7222 1234 (Textphone 020 7918 3015) • National Rail Enquiries 08457 48 49 50 (calls may be recorded for training purposes). (Textphone 08456 050 600, 0800-2000 daily) A wide range of information about London Overground is also available from our website: www.tfl.gov/overground
PENALTY FARES	London Overground operates a Penalty Fares scheme. If you cannot produce, on request, a valid ticket for your entire journey or, when using Oyster to Pay as You Go, your Oyster card containing a record of the start of your Pay as You Go journey, you will be liable to pay a Penalty Fare.
DISABLED PERSON'S PROTECTION POLICY	This can be obtained from our Customer Services Team at the above address.
CODE OF PRACTICE FOR COMMENTS, COMPLAINTS AND SUGGESTIONS	For a copy of the London Overground Passenger Charter leaflet please contact our Customer Services Team at the above address or ask for a copy at any London Overground station.

Merseyrail

A Serco/NedRailways company

ADDRESS	Rail House, Lord Nelson Street, Liverpool L1 1JF Telephone: 0151 702 2534 Fax: 0151 702 3074
MANAGING DIRECTOR	Bart Schmeink
RESERVATIONS AND TICKETS BY TELEPHONE AND ONLINE	Tickets may be booked in advance and seats reserved from most Merseyrail stations for National Rail Services.
RESERVATION DETAILS	Not available.
CATERING ON TRAINS	Not available.
CYCLES	Cycles carried free of charge at any time, subject to sufficient space being available.
LOST PROPERTY	Please contact:- Station Supervisor James Street Station James Street Liverpool L2 7PQ Phone: 0151 702 2951
TRAIN SERVICE UPDATE	For current train information please call 08457 48 49 50 (calls may be recorded for training purposes). ***For details of Bank Holiday services see also the boxed note immediately preceding Table 103.***
PENALTY FARES	Please refer to notices displayed at stations for details of the penalty fare scheme in operation.
DISABLED PERSON'S PROTECTION POLICY	Available from:– Customer Relations Merseyrail Rail House, Lord Nelson Street, Liverpool L1 1JF Phone : 0151 702 2071 (Textphone 0870 0552 681) Fax : 0151 702 2413
CODE OF PRACTICE FOR COMMENTS, COMPLAINTS AND SUGGESTIONS	Available from above address

National Express East Anglia (NXEA)

LE

ADDRESS

Customer Services Centre, National Express East Anglia, Grosvenor House, 112-114 Prince of Wales Road, Norwich, NR1 1NS
Telephone: 0845 600 7245
Fax: 01603 214567
Website: www.nationalexpresseastanglia.com
Email: nxea.customerrelations@nationalexpress.com

MANAGING DIRECTOR

Andrew Chivers

RESERVATIONS AND TICKETS BY TELEPHONE AND ONLINE

Tickets may be booked in advance by telephoning 0845 600 7245 between 0800 and 2200 (Mondays to Fridays) and 0900 and 1800 (weekends and Bank Holidays). For Business Travel, please telephone 0845 850 9080

RESERVATION DETAILS

NXEA offers seat reservations free of charge (except for season ticket holders) on main line services between London Liverpool Street and Norwich, and on direct services between London Liverpool Street and Lowestoft/Peterborough (via Ipswich).

CATERING ON TRAINS

Hot and cold drinks, sandwiches and light snacks are generally available on main line services between Norwich and London Liverpool Street and on Stansted Express services. In addition, full restaurant facilities are provided on some mainline services between Norwich and London.

CYCLES

Accompanied bicycles are conveyed free of charge on most NXEA services, but are not permitted on Stansted Express services at any time or on weekday peak services to and from London. A similar restriction also applies at Cambridge. On main line and rural services, the number of bicycles per train is limited, so a free reservation is recommended. For further details, please call NXEA customer services on 0845 600 7245.

LOST PROPERTY

If you have lost an item of property on one of our trains or stations, please contact NXEA customer services on 0845 600 7245 or email us at nxea.lostproperty@nationalexpress.com

TRAIN SERVICE UPDATE

For current train service information, please contact NXEA customer services on 0845 600 7245 or call our recorded information line on 020 7247 5488.

PENALTY FARES

NXEA operates a Penalty Fares System on most of its network, except from certain specified stations and on designated 'paytrain routes'
Stations within the Penalty Fares area are identified by warning notices at each entrance: when travelling from these stations, you must have a valid ticket for your journey. For journeys where Oyster Pay as you Go (PAYG) is accepted, you must touch in your Oyster card at the start of your journey. If travelling beyond the area where PAYG is accepted, you must have a valid ticket for the portion of the journey not covered by your Oyster card. If you cannot present a valid ticket for the journey you are making, you may be liable for a Penalty Fare (minimum £20).

DISABLED PERSON'S PROTECTION POLICY

Available from: Customer Services Centre, National Express East Anglia, Grosvenor House, 112-114 Prince of Wales Road, Norwich NR1 1NS.
Customers who require assistance are recommended to book at least 24 hours in advance through our Customer Services Centre on 0800 028 28 78 or Textphone 0845 606 7245.

CODE OF PRACTICE FOR COMMENTS, COMPLAINTS AND SUGGESTIONS

Available from: Customer Services Centre, National Express East Anglia, Grosvenor House, 112-114 Prince of Wales Road, Norwich NR1 1NS. The NXEA Passenger's Charter is also available from the same address.

GR National Express East Coast (NXEC) GR

ADDRESS	Freepost RRZG-ZZZX-LKXK, Newcastle upon Tyne NE1 5DN Telephone: 08457 225 333 Open 0830-1700 Monday-Friday Fax: 0191 227 5986 Website: www.nationalexpress.com Email: c.relations@nationalexpress.com
MANAGING DIRECTOR	Susan Goldsmith
RESERVATIONS AND TICKETS BY TELEPHONE AND ONLINE	Internet — Purchase tickets via the internet 24 hours a day at www.nationalexpress.com. Self service ticket machines are available at all National Express East Coast stations. Purchase tickets for today or collect pre-booked tickets. Telephone — 08457 225 225 Telesales — Open 0800-2000 Monday-Saturday, 1000-2000 Sunday Business Travel — Open 0800-1800 Monday-Friday For corporate credit card and account holder bookings. Group Travel — Open 0900-1800 Monday-Friday Discounts may be available for groups of 10 or more people. Assisted Travel — Open 0800-2000 Monday-Saturday, 1000-2000 Sunday The minimum transaction is £10. Please allow 7 days from the time of booking for tickets to reach you through the post.
RESERVATION DETAILS	Seat reservations can usually be made on any National Express East Coast train up to ten weeks in advance. They are available to any ticket holder upon request, and are compulsory with some ticket types. Only one reservation can be made per single journey.
CATERING ON TRAINS	We aim to offer excellent food with plenty of choice. Through our talented team of top chefs, we bring you the best of British cuisine in our Restaurant*, Café Bar and from our At Seat Dining*. * Available on selected services. Further details are available on our website.
CYCLES	Bicycles are welcome on National Express East Coast trains. A reservation must be made and bookings are subject to space being available. Reservations can be made by calling 08457 225 225 or at any National Express East Coast ticket office.
LOST PROPERTY	If you lose something on a National Express East Coast train or at a station please speak to a member of staf or contact us on 08457 225 333. Please note that charges are normally made for returning items of lost property and that we are unable to forward items of lost property on train services.
TRAIN SERVICE UPDATE	Visit www.nationalexpress.com or call National Rail Enquiries on 08457 48 49 50 (calls may be recorded for training purposes).
PENALTY FARES	National Express East Coast does not operate Penalty Fares scheme. However, you should always purchase a ticket valid for travel before you board any National Express East Coast service as only full fare tickets are sold on our trains. The only exception being Disabled Railcard holders who will be sold appropriate discounted tickets on-board.
DISABLED PERSON'S PROTECTION POLICY	A copy of our DPPP can be obtained free of charge from the address at the top of this page. Our Assisted Travel team can help you plan your journey and organise tickets, assistance and seat reservations. To ensure the best possible levels of assistance we recommend that you contact us no later than 1800 the day before you intend to travel. Telephone 08457 225 225 or textphone 08457 202 067* (open 0800-2000 Monday-Saturday, 1000-2000 Sunday). * Please note that this number should only be used to contact the Assisted Travel team. For all other enquiries please telephone 08457 225 225.
CODE OF PRACTICE FOR COMMENTS, COMPLAINTS AND SUGGESTIONS	Our Passenger's Charter is available from all National Express East Coast stations or from our website www.nationalexpress.com. All correspondence should be sent using the address at the top of this page.

NY North Yorkshire Moors Railway NY

(Operators of the steam and heritage services between Whitby, Grosmont, Goathland and Pickering)

ADDRESS	Pickering Station, Pickering, North Yorkshire, YO18 7AJ Telephone: 01751-472508 (Customer Services and Information) Fax: 01751-476048 Website: www.nymr.co.uk Email: info@nymr.co.uk
GENERAL MANAGER	Philip Benham
RESERVATIONS AND TICKETS BY TELEPHONE AND ONLINE	Telephone: 01751-472508 Hours of operation: 28 March to 1 November and other operating dates: 09:30-16:30 (Monday - Friday), 10:00-14:30 (Saturday and Sunday); All other times: 10:00-14:30 (Monday - Friday). At least 7 days should be allowed for receipt of tickets purchased by telephone. National Rail tickets can be booked in advance from our office in Whitby – telephone 01947 605872.
RESERVATION DETAILS	Reservations are not required on normal services. They can be made for groups of 20 or more passengers and are required on North Yorkshire Moors Railways dining train services (between Pickering and Grosmont).
CATERING ON TRAINS	An at seat trolley service of drinks and snacks is provided on most trains.
CYCLES	Cycles and dogs are carried for a charge of £2 (subject to space being available).
LOST PROPERTY	Enquiries about lost property should be made to Pickering Station at the above, or by telephone (01751-472508).
TRAIN SERVICE UPDATE	Updated train service information on all North Yorkshire Moors Railway is available on the website (see address above). A 'talking timetable' is also available giving current details of all North Yorkshire Moors Railway services by telephoning 01751-473535.
PENALTY FARES	Penalty fares are not in force on any North Yorkshire Moors Railway service.
DISABLED PERSON'S PROTECTION POLICY	Available from the address above, or Pickering and Grosmont Stations.
CODE OF PRACTICE FOR COMMENTS, COMPLAINTS AND SUGGESTIONS	North Yorkshire Moors Railway welcomes comments from passengers. Comments/suggestion cards are available from stations and on-board staff, or alternatively please write to the General Manager. Details of the company's policy are available from the above address, or Pickering and Grosmont Stations.

Northern

A Serco-NedRailways company

ADDRESS	Northern Rail Ltd., Northern House 9 Rougier Street York YO1 6HZ Telephone: 08700 005151 Website: www.northernrail.org
MANAGING DIRECTOR	Heidi Mottram
RESERVATIONS AND TICKETS BY TELEPHONE AND ONLINE	Reservations and tickets are available from all local staffed stations.
RESERVATION DETAILS	Reservations are not required on Northern services. For groups of 10 or more travelling together, telephone 01132 479 659. For groups of 10 or more travelling on the Leeds-Settle-Carlisle line, blocks of seats will be reserved wherever possible. Telephone 0800 9800 766, between 0900 and 1700 on Mondays to Fridays to make a booking. All accommodation on Northern trains is standard class.
CATERING ON TRAINS	On most Leeds-Settle-Carlisle services, food and drink can be purchased from the trolley which will pass through the train.
CYCLES	Up to two cycles can be carried on each service. This is subject to space being available, however, and cannot be booked in advance. For further details telephone 0845 000 0125.
LOST PROPERTY	Call 0870 602 3322, contact your nearest staffed station or write to Northern at the address below.
TRAIN SERVICE UPDATE	Information about Northern services and fares can be obtained by telephoning: **08457 48 49 50** (calls may be recorded for training purposes) or access the website on www.nationalrail.co.uk. For more information on our services, please visit our website on www.northernrail.org The latest information on train running is available by phoning TrainTracker™ from National Rail Enquiries on 0871 200 4915 or by texting TrainTracker™. Text to 84950.
PENALTY FARES	Penalty fares are not in force on any Northern service.
DISABLED PERSON'S PROTECTION POLICY	If you would like a copy of Northern's Policy or wish to arrange assistance for your journey, please phone: 0808 1561606. (Textphone 0845 604 5608) or by writing to Customer Relations, Northern, PO Box 208, Leeds LS1 2BU, or email: assistance@northernrail.org.
CODE OF PRACTICE FOR COMMENTS, COMPLAINTS AND SUGGESTIONS	Please contact our Customer Helpline on 0845 000 0125, a textphone is available on 0845 604 5608. Alternatively you can write to us at: Customer Relations, Northern, PO Box 208, Leeds LS1 2BU. If you would like a copy of the Northern Passenger's Charter, or Northern's Guide for Customers with Disabilities please contact our Customer Relations team.

ScotRail

A member of the First Rail Division

ADDRESS	1st Floor, Atrium Court, 50 Waterloo Street, Glasgow G2 6HQ Telephone: 08700 00 51 51 Fax: 0141 335 4592 Website: www.scotrail.co.uk Email: scotrailcustomerrelations@firstgroup.com
MANAGING DIRECTOR	Mary Grant
RESERVATIONS AND TICKETS BY TELEPHONE AND ONLINE	Tickets may be purchased in advance and Sleepers or seats reserved, by telephone, using a debit/credit card from the following number: 08457 550033 (opening hours 0700-2200) Please allow 3 days for tickets by post, tickets on departure arrangements available at selected stations. Tickets can also be purchased through the website - scotrail.co.uk ScotRail customers can buy selected Caledonian Sleeper tickets online - and have the ticket confirmation sent to their mobile phone. Passengers simply turn up for their train, show the text message to train staff and hop on board. A confirmatory email is sent as a back-up. This free SMS service is available for 'Bargain Berth' tickets on the Caledonian Sleeper, which connects Scottish cities to Central London. Tickets can be booked up to 12 weeks in advance of travel - and right up until midday on the day of travel, subject to availability. The berths start from just £19.
RESERVATION DETAILS	Seat Reservations are free and can be made from 12 weeks in advance up to 1800 hours one day prior to the date of departure. Caledonian Sleeper reservations can be made up to 12 weeks in advance.
CATERING ON TRAINS	A Lounge Car is provided on all Caledonian Sleeper services offering a wide range of drinks, snacks and hot meals. A trolley service is available on many longer distance services as indicated in the timetable. Any comments about our daytime catering services should be made to Garry Clark, Hospitality and Sleeper Manager tel: 0141 335 2685.
CYCLES	Cycles are carried free on all ScotRail services subject to availability. Reservations are required on Caledonian Sleeper services and on longer distance routes. Tandems, tricycles, cycle trailers, motorcycles, mopeds or motorised cycles are not carried on any ScotRail service.
LOST PROPERTY	Please phone 0141 335 3276 (0700-1900 Mon-Sat)
TRAIN SERVICE UPDATE	Register with JourneyCheck/JourneyAlert on our website: www.scotrail.co.uk
PENALTY FARES	Penalty Fares are not in force on any ScotRail services.
DISABLED PERSON'S PROTECTION POLICY	Available from the Customer Relations Manager, ScotRail, Disabled Assistance, PO Box 7034, Fort William PH33 6WS. Tel: 0800 912 2 901 or Typetalk 18001 0800 912 2 901 Fax: 0141 335 4611 Travel arrangements may be made for disabled people by calling 0800 912 2 901*. One lightweight travel scooter, length 104cm, width 56cm with a turning radius of 99cm and combined weight of 300kg can be conveyed per train. Customers who are unable to hear or speak on the phone can contact us through the BT TextDirect system, Typetalk on 18001 0800 912 2 901. This advanced technology provides a text-to-voice translation at no additional cost to your phone providers standard rate. Details of station facilities for disabled customers are also available on our website www.scotrail.co.uk *For assisted travel, an advance notice of up to 24 hours notice is appreciated.
CODE OF PRACTICE FOR COMMENTS, COMPLAINTS AND SUGGESTIONS	ScotRail welcomes comments on the services we provide. A leaflet is available at all staffed ScotRail stations explaining the procedures and is also available from the Customer Relations Manager at the address above. Tel: 0845 601 5929

South West Trains

ADDRESS	Friars Bridge Court, 41–45 Blackfriars Road, London SE1 8NZ Telephone: 08700 005151 Fax: 020 7620 5177 Website: www.southwesttrains.co.uk Email: customerrelations@swtrains.co.uk
CHAIRMAN	Ian Dobbs
MANAGING DIRECTOR	Stewart Palmer
RESERVATIONS AND TICKETS BY TELEPHONE AND ONLINE	Tickets may be booked in advance and seats reserved by telephone, on the following number: 0845 6000 650. Tickets may also be purchased via the South West Trains' website (see above). When ordering, please allow 5 working days for ticket delivery.
RESERVATION DETAILS	On many South West Trains' main line services (excluding peak time commuter services) seats can be reserved free of charge in First and Standard Class.
CATERING ON TRAINS	Catering on South West Trains is provided on those services marked with the symbol ⊡ for all or part of the journey. Catering may be provided from a buffet area, at seat trolley service or a combination of both according to the route and time of day. Comments on the service should be sent to the Customer Service Centre at the address below.
CYCLES	A limited number of cycles can be carried on most of our services except during the Monday to Friday peak periods. Restrictions apply on certain routes into and out of London Waterloo between 0715 and 1000 and between 1645 and 1900. At all times some services require advance reservations, as space is limited. To obtain full details of South West Trains Cycling Policy and full details of routes and times when cycles are not carried visit www.southwesttrains.co.uk, pick up a leaflet from stations served by South West Trains or contact our Customer Service Centre at the address shown. Cycles that can be folded to a size which allows them to be carried safely in the luggage racks on our services may be carried folded at all times. For reasons of safety and comfort of our passengers, if the available identified cycle spaces on the train are already taken, the guard has the right to refuse to carry any further cycles on that train.
LOST PROPERTY	A lost property helpline is available between 0730-1900 Mondays to Fridays by calling 020 7401 7861
TRAIN SERVICE UPDATE	For current train information, please call our helpline on 0845 6000 650 or visit www.southwesttrains.co.uk For details of Bank Holiday services see also the boxed note on the page immediately preceding Table 149.
PENALTY FARES	South West Trains has a duty to its fare paying passengers to ensure no-one travels for free. To this end South West Trains operates a penalty fares scheme across its network, with the only exceptions being stations west of Salisbury and Dean, Mottisfont & Dunbridge, Romsey and Chandlers Ford. Passengers travelling to and from stations within the penalty fares area without a valid ticket may be liable to a penalty of £20 or twice the single fare to the next station at which their train stops (whichever is the greater).
DISABLED PERSON'S PROTECTION POLICY	For a copy of this publication, please contact the Customer Service Centre at the address below. Assistance for mobility impaired passengers can be arranged by telephoning 0800 5282 100 between 0600 - 2200 daily. Please give at least 24 hours notice A textphone facility is available on 0800 6920 792 (calls are charged at local rates).
CODE OF PRACTICE FOR COMMENTS, COMPLAINTS AND SUGGESTIONS	Copies of South West Trains' Passenger's Charter are available from any staffed station or by writing to: Customer Service Centre, South West Trains, Overline House, Blechynden Terrace, Southampton SO15 1GW Telephone 0845 6000 650. Fax 023 8072 8187 Email: customerrelations@swtrains.co.uk The Passenger's Charter is also available on our website www.southwesttrains.co.uk

SE **Southeastern** SE

Southeastern

ADDRESS

Southeastern Customer Services, PO Box 63428, London SE1P 5FD
Telephone: 0845 000 2222
Assisted Travel: 0800 783 4524
Fax: 0845 678 6976
Textphone: 0800 783 4548

Website: www.southeasternrailway.co.uk

This customer service centre is staffed 24 hours a day, seven days a week (closed Christmas Day). Comments and complaints are dealt with here by post, fax, and web as well as on the telephone.

MANAGING DIRECTOR

Charles Horton

RESERVATIONS AND TICKETS BY TELEPHONE AND ONLINE

Group travel (parties of 10 persons or more) on Southeastern services must be booked at least seven days in advance so that space can be allocated. To order, go to www.southeasternrailway.co.uk, select tickets, then group tickets then complete the online form.

Customers can renew six monthly and annual season tickets online at www.southeasternrailway.co.uk or at local stations. Payment may be made by debit card and by most major credit and charge cards (NB customers must hold a rail photocard).

For new monthly season ticket purchases, please complete an application form available at local stations or online at www.southeasternrailway.co.uk.

A business and continental travel and reservations account service is available from Network Business Travel Service at First Floor Offices, Cannon Street Station, London EC4N 6AP.

To open an account telephone 020 7904 0500 or visit www.nbts.co.uk

RESERVATIONS

Reservations are only needed on Southeastern services for Group Travel and mobility impaired customers who require assistance.

CATERING ON TRAINS

A light refreshment trolley is available on trains marked with ⊼.

CYCLES

Cycles are not permitted on peak time services, which are those timed to arrive in London terminals between 0700 and 0959, and those timed to leave between 1600 and 1859. Folding cycles are permitted provided they are folded.

LOST PROPERTY

Customers who have lost property on a train or at a station should contact Southeastern Customer Services on 0845 000 2222.

TRAIN SERVICE UPDATE

For current train running information contact Southeastern Customer Services on 0845 000 2222

Information is also available from national and local radio station travel updates on Ceefax page 433, and from our website: www.southeasternrailway.co.uk, select plan my journey.

PENALTY FARES

Please check notices displayed at stations for details of any penalty fares or other revenue protection systems in operation on Southeastern services.

DISABLED PERSON'S PROTECTION POLICY

Copies of the Disabled Person's Protection Policy are available from Southeastern Customer Services.

If you have any special needs and would like help with planning your journey anywhere in Great Britain please call 0800 783 4524 or use the Textphone 0800 783 4548 - open 24 hours a day.

The Southeastern Assisted Travel team will offer advice and make any special arrangements you need. If at least 24 hours' notice can be given, this will be very much appreciated.

CODE OF PRACTICE FOR COMMENTS, COMPLAINTS AND SUGGESTIONS

Southeastern Passengers' Charter leaflets are available at any Southeastern sales point or Southeastern Customer Services at the address shown above.

Southern

ADDRESS

Southern Customer Services, PO Box 277, Tonbridge TN9 2ZP
Telephone: 08451 27 29 20 (Customer Services)
Fax: 08451 27 29 30 (Customer Services)
Website: www.southernrailway.com

MANAGING DIRECTOR

Chris Burchell

RESERVATIONS AND TICKETS BY TELEPHONE AND ONLINE

It is not necessary to pre-book on Southern services.

RESERVATION DETAILS

Reservations are not required, as Southern offer a high frequency train service.

CATERING ON TRAINS

A light refreshment of food and drinks is available on trains marked with ☕.

CYCLES

A limited number of cycles are carried on all services except on trains due to arrive into London and Brighton on Mondays to Fridays between 0700 and 1000, or due to depart from London Stations and Brighton between 1600 and 1900 Mondays to Fridays.

LOST PROPERTY

Please call Southern Customer Services on 08451 27 29 20.

TRAIN SERVICE UPDATE

For current train information call Customer Services on 08451 27 29 20 or check our website at www.southernrailway.com

PENALTY FARES

Southern operate a Penalty Fares Scheme on all routes. You must buy a valid ticket (or permit to travel) for your journey before boarding a train. If you do not have a valid ticket or permit to travel, you may have to pay a Penalty Fare of £20.00 or twice the single fare, whichever is the greater. Please pick up a Penalty Fare leaflet from a staffed station for your information.

DISABLED PERSON'S PROTECTION POLICY

Available from Southern Customer Services at P.O. Box 277, Tonbridge TN9 2ZP. Disabled and Special needs assistance on 0800 138 1016; minicom/textphone - 0800 138 1018; Fax - 0800 138 1017.

CODE OF PRACTICE FOR COMMENTS, COMPLAINTS AND SUGGESTIONS

Write to Southern Customer Services at the above address.
Copies of Southern Passenger's charter are available from any staffed stations. You can also obtain a copy by contacting Customer Services or from Southern's website.

Virgin Trains

The trading name of West Coast Trains Ltd

ADDRESS	Virgin Trains, 85 Smallbrook Queensway, Birmingham B5 4HA Telephone: 0845 000 8000 Textphone: 0121 654 7528 Website: www.virgintrains.com Email: customer.relations@virgintrains.co.uk
CHIEF EXECUTIVE	Tony Collins
MANAGING DIRECTOR	Chris Gibb
RESERVATIONS AND TICKETS BY TELEPHONE AND ONLINE	Buy tickets for Virgin Trains and any other train company in Great Britain on the internet at www.virgintrains.com or by calling 08457 222 333 - between 0800 and 2200 7 days a week. If you have a disability or have specific needs and wish to arrange assistance on your journey call the Virgin Trains JourneyCare service on 08457 44 33 66 (Textphone 08457 44 33 67) between 0800 and 2200 every day except Christmas Day or Boxing Day.
RESERVATION DETAILS	You are strongly advised to make a seat reservation in advance. Reservations can be made for the Quiet Zone carriage, where customers should refrain from using mobile phones or creating unnecessary noise. On routes to and from London, Standard Class Quiet Zone is in coach A and in coach H for First Class. On other routes, Quiet Zone is located in Standard Class, coach F. Seat reservations are free of charge.
CATERING ON TRAINS	In First Class on a Pendolino from Monday to Friday customers can enjoy a selection of snacks throughout the day, including a cooked breakfast on many morning peak services. In addition, Fairtrade tea, Fairtrade coffee, soft drinks and alcoholic drinks (alcohol is not offered with breakfast services) are served at seat throughout the day. A complimentary newspaper is also available. In First Class on Super Voyager from Monday to Friday customers can enjoy complimentary light refreshments, including Fairtrade tea, Fairtrade coffee, soft drinks and a newspaper with an at-seat service available, on most services. In Standard Class, we have a wide range of snacks and sandwiches, Fairtrade teas, fresh ground Fairtrade coffee, soft and alcoholic drinks and a selection of non-food items available at our onboard shop. The shop is generally open throughout. Pendolinos offer an at-seat trolley service to standard class customers on Mondays to Fridays. For more information about our onboard service pick up a copy of Travelling with Virgin Trains.
CYCLES	Subject to availability of space cycles can be carried on all trains. Most trains can carry 3 cycles, and on journeys to and from London Euston, Pendolinos can carry tandems (however, tandems are not carried on Voyager services). An advance reservation is required for all journeys.
LOST PROPERTY	Call Customer Relations on 0845 000 8000 – 0830 to 2015 Mondays to Fridays, 0900 to 1600 Saturdays, answerphone available at all other times.
TRAIN SERVICE UPDATE	Details of any disruption to services or weekend engineering work are summarised on BBC Ceefax and on BBCi on digital TV. Details of Engineering work can also be found at www.virgintrains.com.
PENALTY FARES	Penalty Fares are not applicable on any Virgin Trains service.
DISABLED PERSON'S PROTECTION POLICY	Our Customer Relations Manager (at the address above) will be pleased to supply a free copy of the Disabled Person's Protection Policy. It can also be downloaded at www.virgintrains.com. For information on station accessibility and to arrange special help please contact Virgin Trains JourneyCare (details above).
CODE OF PRACTICE FOR COMMENTS, COMPLAINTS AND SUGGESTIONS	We want you to tell us what you think of our service, good or bad. A copy of our Code of Practice for handling comments, complaints and suggestions together with Virgin Trains Passenger's Charter is available free on request from our Customer Relations Manager at the above address.

WR West Coast Railway Company WR

(Operators of the 'Jacobite' and 'Cambrian' Steam Services)

ADDRESS
Jesson Way, Carnforth, Lancashire LA5 9UR
Telephone: 01524 737751/737753
Fax: 01524 735518
Website: www.westcoastrailways.co.uk
Email: jacobite@wcrc.co.uk

GENERAL MANAGER
Mrs Pat Marshall

COMMERCIAL MANAGER
James Shuttleworth

RESERVATIONS AND TICKETS BY TELEPHONE AND ONLINE
Advance bookings are recommended and can be made on line, at www.westcoastrailways.co.uk, by post (enclose SAE) to the Carnforth Office (address above) or by telephone, on 01524 737751/737753, during normal office hours. Credit cards accepted. Tickets can also be purchased from the WCR Guard/Train Manager, on the train, on the day of travel (subject to availablility).

RESERVATION DETAILS
Phone 01524 737751/737753

CATERING ON TRAINS
A buffet service, serving hot and cold drinks and cold snacks, is available on all trains.

CYCLES
Cycles carried free-of-charge, subject to space.

LOST PROPERTY
Telephone: 01524 737751/737753

PENALTY FARES
Penalty fares are not in force on any West Coast Railway Co. service.

TRAIN SERVICE UPDATE
For current train information please phone 08457 48 49 50 (calls may be recorded for training purposes).

DISABLED PERSON'S PROTECTION POLICY
Available from the above address.

CODE OF PRACTICE FOR COMMENTS, COMPLAINTS AND SUGGESTIONS
West Coast Railway Co. welcomes comments on services provided. Write to Carnforth office (address above).

Wrexham & Shropshire

WS

ADDRESS	The Pump House, Coton Hill, Shrewsbury SY1 2DP Telephone: 0845 260 5233 Website: www.wrexhamandshropshire.co.uk Email: info@wrexhamandshropshire.co.uk
MANAGING DIRECTOR	Andy Hamilton
RESERVATIONS AND TICKETS BY TELEPHONE AND ONLINE	Wrexham & Shropshire tickets can be bought in advance and seats reserved by calling 0845 260 5900.
RESERVATION DETAILS	All First and Standard Class seats are reservable at no charge.
CATERING ON TRAINS	Wrexham & Shropshire provides a comprehensive range of catering on all services, seven days a week.
CYCLES	Cycles are carried free of charge.
LOST PROPERTY	Please contact the above address, or call 0845 260 5200.
TRAIN SERVICE UPDATE	Available at www.wrexhamandshropshire.co.uk
PENALTY FARES	Wrexham & Shropshire does not operate a penalty fares policy.
DISABLED PERSON'S PROTECTION POLICY	Please call Customer Services on 0845 260 5200.
CODE OF PRACTICE FOR COMMENTS, COMPLAINTS AND SUGGESTIONS	Please call Customer Services on 0845 260 5200.

Network Rail

NR

ADDRESS King's Place, Yorkway, London N1 9AG
Telephone: 020 7557 8000
Fax: 020 7557 9000
Website: www.networkrail.co.uk

CHIEF EXECUTIVE Iain Coucher

Network Rail is responsible for operating 18 managed stations, indicated in the index by the code **NR**. Details of facilities provided, including the Disabled Peoples Protection Policy, are obtainable from the Network Rail Station Manager at the following station addresses:–

London Bridge	Network Rail Offices, Platform 14, London Bridge Station, Station Approach, London SE1 9SP.
London Cannon Street	Cannon Street Station, Cannon Street, London EC4N 6AP.
London Charing Cross	Network Rail Offices, Charing Cross Station, The Strand, London WC2 5HS.
London Euston	Room 430, Stephenson Room, East Colonnade, Euston, London NW1 2RT.
London Fenchurch Street	Network Rail Office, Fenchurch Place, London EC3M 4AJ.
London Kings Cross	Room 304, West Side Offices, Kings Cross Station, London N1 9AP.
London Liverpool Street	Network Rail Station Reception, Platform 10, Liverpool Street Station, London EC2M 7PY.
London Paddington	Room B115, Tournament House, Paddington Station, London W2 1FT.
London Victoria	3rd Floor, Kent Side Offices, Victoria Station, London SW1V 1JU.
London Waterloo	CP2-4-G General Offices, Waterloo Station, London SE1 8SW.
Birmingham New Street	Reception, Network Rail Offices, Station Forecourt, Birmingham New Street Station, Birmingham B2 4ND.
Edinburgh Waverley	Room 255, North Block, Waverley Station, Edinburgh EH1 1BB.
Gatwick Airport	Gatwick Airport Station, Gatwick Airport, Sussex RH6 0RD.
Glasgow Central	Glasgow Central Station, Gordon Street, Glasgow G1 3SL.
Leeds City	Room 405, Administration Block, Leeds City Station, Leeds LS1 4DY.
Manchester Piccadilly	9th Floor, Piccadilly Tower, Piccadilly Station, Manchester M60 7RA.
Liverpool Lime Street	Station Manager, The Barrier Line Building, Liverpool Lime Street Station, Liverpool L1 1JF.
St Pancras	Station Reception, St Pancras International Station, Pancras Road, London NW1 2QP.

Staffed Left Luggage facilities, offering maximum security, are available at all Network Rail Stations.

If you wish to raise any issue concerning the rail infrastructure or the 18 managed stations operated by Network Rail (excluding matters concerning the running of trains or ticket purchase) please call the national 24 hour Helpline:- **08457 11 41 41**

Other Addresses

Department for Transport

Great Minster House, 76 Marsham Street, London SW1P 4DR

Telephone: 020 7944 8300

Email: rail@dft.gsi.gov.uk

Office of Rail Regulation

One Kemble Street, London WC2B 4AN
Telephone: 020 7282 2000 Fax: 020 7282 2040

Chairman: Chris Bolt

The main areas of the Regulator's statutory functions are:

- the issue, modification and enforcement of licences to operate trains, networks, stations and light maintenance depots;
- the approval of agreements for access by operators of railway assets to track, stations and light maintenance depots;
- the enforcement of domestic competition law; and consumer protection including a duty under the Railways Act 1993 in relation to the protection of the interests of users of railway services, including the disabled.

Publications are available from:

Sue MacSwan, The Library, ORR, 1 Waterhouse Square, 138–142 Holborn, London EC1N 2TQ (Telephone: 020 7282 2001). Email: rail.library@orr.gsi.gov.uk

Association of Train Operating Companies (ATOC)

3rd Floor, 40 Bernard Street, London WC1N 1BY. Telephone: 020 7841 8000

Director General: George Muir

ATOC represents the interests of most of the national and international passenger Train Operating Companies whose services are shown in this timetable. It manages a range of network services, products and responsibilities on behalf of these train operators including:

- the National Rail Conditions of Carriage (the passenger's contract with the train operators)
- the National Rail Enquiry Service
- the licensing of rail appointed travel agents
- national Railcards, the London Travelcard and Network Railcard.

London Underground Limited

55 Broadway, London SW1H 0BD Telephone: 020 7222 5600
Responsible for the operation of stations indicated in the index by the code **LT**

How to Cross London

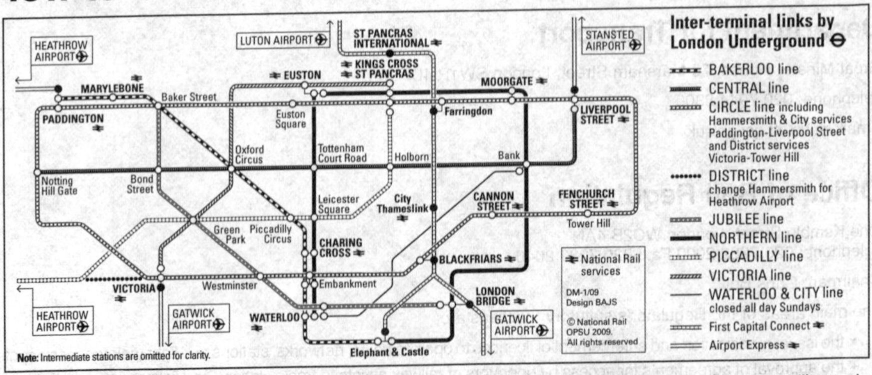

Introduction

The time taken to travel between London's stations will vary from journey to journey dependent on distance, mode of transport, time of day and the need to change en route. The quickest way to cross London is usually by the Underground network with frequent services operating between the following hours*:

- 0530 to 0015 on Monday to Friday
- 0630 to 0115 on Saturday
- 0700 to 0001 on Sunday

(* Times shown are approximate)

Buses also link many of London's main terminal stations including an extensive network of Night Bus services.

Ticket & Fares

Rail tickets for journeys routed via London are valid for transfer by London Underground or First Capital Connect services between London terminal stations, and other designated interchange stations* appropriate to the route of the through journey being made, at no extra cost. For example a Brighton to Leeds ticket is valid on London Underground services from Victoria to Kings Cross (Victoria Line), or alternatively on First Capital Connect services to St Pancras International. A Chelmsford to Southampton ticket is valid on London Underground services to Waterloo via either Liverpool Street (Circle Line) or Stratford (Jubilee Line).

(*NB. check which cross London routes your ticket is valid before you travel. A break of journey is permitted at an intermediate Underground station, but a further ticket must be purchased in order to continue the journey)

London's Fare Zones – National Rail, Underground and Docklands Light Railway (DLR) stations within the Greater London area are in one of nine Fare Zones. Single and return tickets are available for through journeys to and from all Underground and DLR stations with prices determined by the number of zones crossed or travelled through.

A range of day and longer period Travelcards are also available and provide unlimited travel on National Rail, London Underground, Docklands Light Railway and Croydon Tramlink services within the Fare Zones for which they are valid. All Travelcards, irrespective of the zones for which they are issued, can also be used on any London bus displaying this sign ⊖.

For information on ticket prices and availability contact your local staffed station, call National Rail Enquiries anytime on **08457 48 49 50*** (Textphone **0845 60 50 600**), or visit www.nationalrail.co.uk. * Calls may be recorded for training purposes.

More detailed information about London's Underground and Bus services, also Docklands Light Railway and Croydon Tramlink is available anytime from London Travel Information on **020 7222 1234** (textphone **020 7918 3015**) or visit **www.tfl.gov.uk**.

First Capital Connect and Southeastern

First Capital Connect operates fast, direct services from Bedford, Luton and St Albans via Central London to East Croydon, Gatwick Airport and Brighton and stopping trains between Luton, St Albans, North London, the City, Streatham, Wimbledon and Sutton. There are nine Central London First Capital Connect stations with Underground connections. First Capital Connect connects with East Midlands Trains at Luton, Luton Airport Parkway and Bedford – see Tables 52 and 53.

Southeastern, in partnership with First Capital Connect also operate trains between Kentish Town, the City and Sevenoaks and at peak times between Bedford, Luton, the City and various destinations in Kent.

London Overground

Trains run daily between Willesden Junction, Shepherd's Bush, Kensington (Olympia), West Brompton and Clapham Junction on Mondays to Sundays – see Table 186.

Southern Services

Direct trains are provided between East Croydon, South London, Clapham Junction and stations to Watford Junction and Milton Keynes Central. These trains also stop at West Brompton, Kensington Olympia and Shepherd's Bush.

These trains provide connections to most of the Southern network at Clapham Junction.

Passengers requiring step free interchange for Southern main line trains to Gatwick Airport and the Sussex Coast should change at East Croydon, and step free interchange for Southern Metro trains is usually available at Balham.

Interchange for the West Midlands and North West is available at either Watford Junction or Milton Keynes.

Cross London Transfer Times (in minutes)

	Blackfriars	Cannon Street	Charing Cross	Euston	Farringdon	Fenchurch Street*	Kings Cross	Liverpool Street	London Bridge	Marylebone	Paddington	St. Pancras International †	Victoria	Waterloo
Blackfriars	–	23	23	49	(b)	27	(b)	40	(b)	45	49	(b)	29	40
Cannon Street	23	–	34	60	44	30	55	43	(a)	56	60	58	40	51
Charing Cross	23	34	–	44	n/a	38	50	51	(a)	38	43	52	32	(a)
Euston	49	60	44	–	n/a	57	35	43	52	51	43	38	39	53
Farringdon	(b)	44	n/a	n/a	–	40	n/a	29	(b)	45	39	n/a	n/a	n/a
Fenchurch Street*	27	30	38	57	40	–	52	26	47	68	60	52	53	56
Kings Cross	(b)	55	50	35	n/a	52	–	41	50	50	45	30	41	55
Liverpool Street	40	43	51	43	29	26	41	–	49	56	55	41	57	62
London Bridge	(b)	(a)	(a)	52	(b)	47	50	49	–	58	62	60	n/a	(a)
Marylebone	45	56	38	51	45	68	50	56	58	–	32	53	43	47
Paddington	49	60	43	43	39	60	45	55	62	32	–	45	47	51
St. Pancras International †	(b)	58	52	38	n/a	52	30	41	60	53	45	–	41	61
Victoria	29	40	32	39	n/a	53	41	57	n/a	43	47	41	–	47
Waterloo	40	51	(a)	53	n/a	56	55	62	(a)	47	51	61	47	–

All times are based on use of London Underground services and are shown as a guide only – extra time should be allowed during the early morning/late evening and on Sundays.

* Tower Hill Underground station
† An additional 35 minutes should be allowed for Eurostar Connections
(a) Direct train services available (operated by Southeastern)
(b) Direct train services available (operated by First Capital Connect)
n/a Transfer not likely to be required as part of a through rail journey.

Some other useful transfers

If your journey requires a transfer between any of the following pairs of stations, you should allow a margin of at least the number of minutes shown when planning connections. All transfers are assumed to be by foot unless otherwise stated.

Ash Vale – North Camp	19
Bicester North – Town	30
Burnley Central – Manchester Rd	25
Burscough Bridge – Junction	20
Canterbury East – West	25
Catford – Bridge	10
Clock House – Kent House	15
Dorchester South – West	15
Dorking – Deepdene	9
Edenbridge – Town	20
Enfield Chase – Town	29
Falkirk High – Grahamston	44
Farnborough Main – North	24
Forest Gate – Wanstead Park	13
Gainsborough Central – Lea Rd	33
Hackney Central – Downs	14
Harringay – Green Lanes	14
Heath High Level – Low Level	10
Hertford North – East	34
Maidstone Barracks – East	16
New Mills Central – Newtown	25
Penge East – West	19
Seven Sisters – South Tottenham	14
Southend Central – Victoria	17
Upper Warlingham – Whyteleafe	10
Walthamstow Central – Queen's Rd	14
West Hampstead – Thameslink	11
Windsor & Eton Central – Riverside	14
Yeovil Junction – Pen Mill	60*

* There are no direct links by public transport between Yeovil Junction and Yeovil Pen Mill stations. Passengers are advised to seek alternative arrangements and should allow 60 minutes to make this connection.

M METRO Tyne and Wear Metro

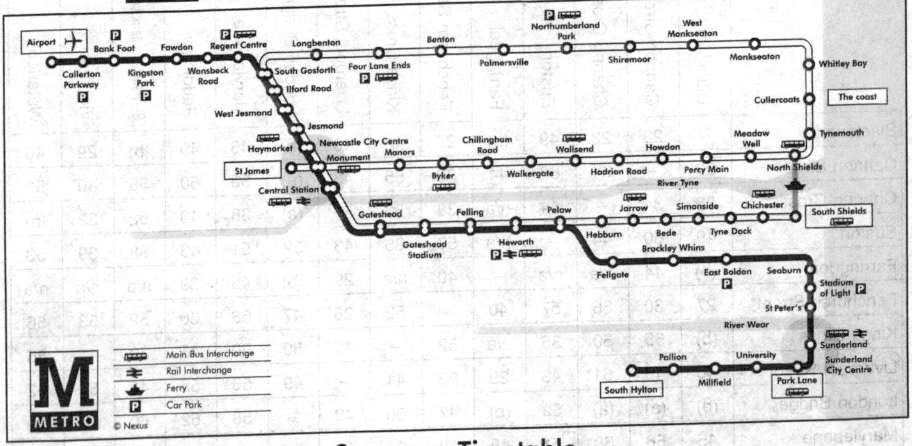

Summary Timetable

Route	Service Frequencies				
	Mon-Fri Peak	Mon-Fri Daytime	Saturday Daytime	Sunday Daytime	Evenings Daily
Airport - Monument - Pelaw - Sunderland - South Hylton	12 mins	12 mins	12 mins	15 mins	15 mins
St.James - Whitley Bay - Monument - Pelaw - South Shields	12 mins	12 mins	12 mins	15 mins	15 mins

First and last Metro trains to and from Newcastle Central Station

From Central Station to:	First Train Mon-Fri	First Train Saturday	First Train Sunday	Last Train Daily
South Hylton	0523	0524	0620	2305
Sunderland	0519	0519	0620	2320
Pelaw	0519	0519	0617	2343
South Shields	0514	0522	0635	2328
Tynemouth (via Benton)	0548	0557	0656	2337
Whitley Bay (via North Shields)	0548 ❑	0557 ❑	0656 ❑	2322 ❑
Airport	0551	0619	0641	2329

❑ Change at Monument

To Central Station from:	First Train Mon-Fri	First Train Saturday	First Train Sunday	Last Train Daily
South Hylton	0604	0605	0704	2346
Sunderland	0552	0552	0714	2356
Pelaw	0538	0547	0633	0015
South Shields	0549	0552	0703	2356
Tynemouth (via Benton)	0533	0538	0633	2311
Whitley Bay (via North Shields)	0542 ❑	0552 ❑	0639 ❑	2304 ❑
Airport	0538	0543	0627	2312

❑ Change at Monument

Ticketing

- Interchangeable tickets for both Rail and Metro are available between Sunderland and Newcastle Central Station.
- Tyne and Wear Metro operates a Penalty Fare policy.

Information

For all travel information call

traveline public transport info
0871 200 22 33
north east

For timetable information visit **www.nexus.org.uk**

Tramlink - serving Wimbledon, Croydon, New Addington, Elmers End and Beckenham

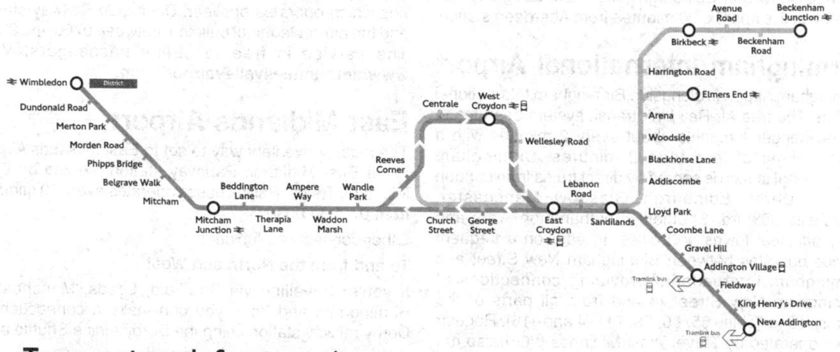

Tram network frequencies

From	To	Approximate journey time	Peak periods Frequency Mon - Fri: 0730 hrs - 1850 hrs Saturday: 0900 hrs - 1750 hrs	Off-peak periods Frequency Mon - Fri: after 1850 hrs Saturday: before 0900 and after 1750 hrs Sunday: all day	First tram Mon – Sat	First tram Sunday	Last tram (everyday) Depart	Last tram (everyday) Arrive
Elmers End	West Croydon	15 mins	12 mins	15 mins	0451	0721	0021T	0039
West Croydon	Elmers End	16 mins	12 mins	15 mins	0429	0659	0044	0059
Beckenham Junction	West Croydon	22 mins	12 mins	15 mins	0535	0720	0020T	0044
West Croydon	Beckenham Junction	24 mins	12 mins	15 mins	0509	0654	0039	0101
New Addington	Wimbledon	43 mins	7/8 mins	15 mins♦	0450	0638*	2353†	0035
Wimbledon	New Addington	45 mins	7/8 mins	15 mins♦	0539*	0719*	0019†	0103

Times shown above are a guide only. Please see timetable leaflet or departure times posters at each stop for full details.
♦New Addington to Wimbledon and Wimbledon to New Addington is 20 minutes before **06**00 Monday - Saturday.
T Later trams run to Therapia Lane and do not serve Centrale and West Croydon.
*Earlier trams start from Therapia Lane. †Later trams run to Therapia Lane only.

Website **www.tfl.gov.uk**

24 hour travel information **020 7222 1234**

MAYOR OF LONDON

Transport for London TRAMLINK

Airport Links

Aberdeen Airport

Dyce station is situated close to Aberdeen Airport and is served by trains between Aberdeen and Inverness (see Table 240). A new shuttle bus service has been introduced between Dyce station and the airport - these run approx. 0645 and 1940 Monday to Friday. Taxis are also available. In addition, there are several through trains daily to and from Glasgow and Edinburgh (see Table 229). Journey time by taxi is approx. 20 minutes from Aberdeen station.

Birmingham International Airport

Birmingham Airport is alongside Birmingham International station. The free Air-Rail Link transit system operates to the passenger terminals about every 2 minutes with a journey time of less than 2 minutes. Birmingham International station is served by direct trains from London Euston, Derby, Edinburgh, Glasgow, Manchester, Newcastle, Oxford, Sheffield, Southampton, York and other principal towns and cities. In addition a frequent service operates between Birmingham New Street and Birmingham International providing connections at Birmingham New Street to and from all parts of the country. (See Tables 65, 66, 68, 71, 74 and 116). Regular buses operated by Travel West Midlands (966) also run from Solihull station (see Tables 71 and 115). The journey time is approximately 20 minutes and through ticketing is available. Solihull is served by Chiltern Railways services from London Marylebone, Gerrards Cross, Beaconsfield, High Wycombe, Princes Risborough, Haddenham & Thame Parkway, Bicester North, Banbury, Leamington Spa and Warwick and by London Midland local services.

Bristol International Airport

First runs a frequent coach service from directly outside Bristol Temple Meads station. It departs every 15 minutes between 0600-1930 and at a reduced frequency between 0300-0600 and 1930-midnight. The journey time is approximately 25 minutes depending on traffic and further information is available from Traveline on **0871 200 22 33** or visit **www.traveline.info.**

Cardiff International Airport

The airport is served by bus service X45 and is operated by Veolia Transport Cymru on Mon-Sat and First on Sundays. This operates on an hourly daytime frequency to/from Barry station, Monday to Saturday. Journey time is 7 minutes. Cardiff bus service (X91) provides an hourly daytime service from Cardiff Central Bus Station (stop E1) direct to Cardiff International Airport. Services run every hour Monday to Saturday daytimes and every 2 hours on Sundays. Journey time is 30 minutes and through ticketing is available from any rail station.

The airport is served by a free bus link from Rhoose Cardiff International Rail Station to/from the airport operated by Veolia Transport Cymru. Full details of the timetable and further information can be obtained from Traveline on **0871 200 22 33** or visit **www.traveline.info.**

Coventry Airport

Coventry Airport is accessible from Coventry rail station by a scheduled bus service (No. 737). A combined discounted bus and rail ticket can be purchased for travel to the airport.

For bus times call **0871 200 22 33** or visit **www.traveline.info.**

Durham Tees Valley Airport

Darlington Railway station is situated just 5 miles away. Sky Express Tees Valley is a frequent dedicated shuttle bus which operates between Darlington Railway station and the airport terminal building, between 0700 and 2000. The service is free to airline passengers. Visit **www.durhamteesvalleyairport.com**.

East Midlands Airport

The most convenient way to get to East Midlands Airport is via East Midlands Parkway station, served by East Midlands Trains. Railink buses operates every 30 minutes from 0700 to 0030.

Other connections include:

To and from the North and West

If you're travelling via Sheffield, Leeds, Manchester, Birmingham and York, you can make a connection at Derby railway station using the Derby Airline Shuttle bus.

To and from the South

If you travel via Kettering, Luton and London for destinations in the south, you can make a connection at Loughborough railway station using the Loughborough Airline Shuttle bus.

To and from the East

If you're travelling to or from easterly destinations you can connect via Grantham, Lincoln, Newark, Peterborough and Mansfield to Nottingham railway station where you'll find the Nottingham Skyling bus.

For details of bus times call **Traveline on 0871 200 22 33**

Edinburgh Airport

A frequent bus service (No. 100) links Edinburgh Waverley and Haymarket stations with Edinburgh Airport. Journey time is approx. 25 minutes. Stagecoach operate a 747 service half hourly during the day, hourly evenings and Sundays between Inverkeithing and Edinburgh Airport. Through ticketing is available. For further information telephone **0131 555 6363**.

Exeter International Airport

Stagecoach operates an hourly daytime service (56 Monday - Saturday, 379 Sundays) from Exeter St. Davids station forecourt direct to Exeter Airport. For more information call Traveline on **0871 200 22 33** or visit **www.traveline.info.**

Airport Links

Glasgow Airport

Regular direct bus services are available to and from Glasgow Airport from the city centre (Central/Queen Street), Paisley Gilmour Street and Partick stations from early morning to late evening daily. Through bus/rail tickets are available between any station and Glasgow Airport via the Paisley Gilmour Street bus link, city centre bus link and First Glasgow bus service via Partick.

For further information on these services please contact the Strathclyde Passenger Transport Travel Centre at Glasgow Airport, on **0141 887 1111** or **0141 848 4330.**

Leeds Bradford International Airport

Leeds Bradford International Airport is located to the north of the cities of Bradford and Leeds, to the south of the spa town of Harrogate and to the west of the historic city of York. For more information on Leeds Bradford International Airport visit **www.lbia.co.uk**

From Leeds a direct bus service, MetroConnect 757, operates half hourly throughout the day Mondays to Saturdays (hourly early mornings, evenings and Sundays) every day from Stand S8 from outside Leeds Rail Station (Leeds Station Interchange). The journey time is approximately 40 minutes. Through ticketing is available.

From Bradford a half hourly direct bus service, MetroConnect 747, operates throughout the day Mondays to Saturdays (hourly evenings and Sundays) from Bradford Interchange and Forster Square rail stations. The journey time from Bradford is approximately 40 minutes. Through ticketing is available with a PlusBus ticket.

From Harrogate a direct bus service, Bus2Jet 767, operates daily from Harrogate, from Stand 11 in the Bus Station, to the airport. The journey time from Harrogate is approximately 35 minutes. Through ticketing is available with a PlusBus ticket.

From York an hourly direct express coach service operates daily from outside York Rail Station to the airport. The journey time from York is approximately 55 minutes. For more information telephone **01904 883 000** or visit **www.yorkaircoach.com**

For further information on the above services please telephone MetroLine **0113 245 7676** or visit **www.wymetro.com**.

Liverpool John Lennon Airport

The airport is located to the south of the city centre. A direct bus service operates between Lime Street, Moorfields and James Street stations to the airport seven days a week. Buses run every 30 minutes between 0600 & 0100 hours from the Liverpool City Centre Stations to the Airport, and between 0515 and 0015 from the Airport to the Liverpool City Centre Stations. Journey time is approximately 45 minutes. In addition regular bus services operate between Liverpool John Lennon Airport and the new Liverpool South Parkway station; journey time is 15 minutes. Liverpool South Parkway is served by direct services from North, South and East Liverpool, Manchester, Warrington, Southport, Crewe, Stafford, Wolverhampton and Birmingham. For further information please contact **0871 200 22 33,** or visit **www.traveline.info**.

London City Airport

London City Airport is located in London's Docklands. There are no National Rail services direct to the airport. However the Docklands Light Railway (DLR) airport link operates from Canning Town station on the Jubilee Line of London Underground. It takes you directly to the terminal building. Journey time is just 6 minutes from Canning Town to the airport, and the DLR trains run every 7-10 minutes.

If you are travelling to or from Central London the Jubilee Line has direct connections with National Rail at London Waterloo, London Bridge, West Ham and Stratford (east London). DLR operates from Bank and Tower Gateway stations.

For further information on London City Airport telephone **020 7646 0088** or visit **www.londoncityairport.com**.

London Gatwick Airport

Gatwick has its own railway station underneath the South Terminal. Access to the North Terminal is via a free transit. Direct train services also serve many parts of the country.

Airport to/from London

Gatwick Express operate a dedicated non-stop service every 15 minutes throughout the day to/from London (Victoria) and Gatwick Airport (See Table 186).

Southern provides frequent trains throughout the day and hourly throughout the night between London Victoria and Gatwick Airport (See Table 186). Frequent train services also run between Gatwick Airport and stations throughout Sussex, Surrey and parts of Hampshire and Kent.

First Capital Connect operate direct services throughout the day between St Pancras International, Farringdon, City Thameslink, London Blackfriars, London Bridge and Gatwick Airport (generally every 15 mins, See Table 52).

A reduced frequency between London and Gatwick operates through the night.

Airport to/from Reading

First Great Western operate a direct rail service between Reading and Gatwick – (See Table 148). Customers using this route should allow at least 7 minutes at Reading to make a connection.

Other direct services to/from Airport

Southern also operates direct services to/from Hastings, Southampton, Portsmouth and intermediate stations on the South Coast (See Tables 186, 187, 188, 189) Clapham Jn and East Croydon (SeeTable 186).

First Great Western operate services from Wokingham, North Camp and Guildford (See Table 148).

First Capital Connect operate direct services to Brighton and through St Pancras International to St Albans, Luton and Bedford. Connections with East Midlands Trans services to the East Midlands and South Yorkshire and Eurostar services to Continental Europe are available at St Pancras International.

First Capital Connect provide regular direct services from Gatwick Airport to St. Albans, Luton, Bedford, East Croydon, Haywards Heath and Brighton (See Table 52). At Luton Airport Parkway, Luton and Bedford, they also offer convenient connections with East Midlands Trains to Leicester, Derby, Nottingham and Sheffield (See Table 53).

Airport Links

London Heathrow Airport

Express dedicated coaches link Reading and Woking with all four terminals at Heathrow Airport. Other services link Watford, Luton, Stevenage, Feltham and Central London with the airport. For full details see the individual route information below.

Airport to/from Central London

Heathrow Express operates a direct rail service from the airport to London Paddington. Stations are located at Terminal 4, Terminal 5 and in the Central Terminal Area, serving Terminals 1, 2 and 3. Minimum journey time is 15 minutes between Paddington and Terminals 1, 2 and 3, 23 minutes to Terminal 5. Trains run every 15 minutes. (Terminal 4 is served by a connecting 'shuttle' service to/from Heathrow Terminals 1, 2 and 3, taking a minimum of 8 minutes extra.)

- 0510 to 2325 from Paddington
- 0507 to 2342 from Heathrow Terminal 5 (0503 to 2348 on Sundays)
- 0512 to 2348 from Heathrow Terminal 1, 2 and 3 (0508 to 2353 on Sundays)

For further details see Table 118.

Through tickets can be purchased from any National Rail or London Underground Station to the airport via Heathrow Express. For further information visit **www.heathrowexpress.com**.

Heathrow Connect operates a local rail service every 30 minutes between Heathrow Terminals 1,2,3 and London Paddington, calling at Hayes & Harlington, Southall, Hanwell, West Ealing and Ealing Broadway. For details see Table 117. Through tickets are available from most stations.

The London Underground Piccadilly Line connects central London with all five terminals (Terminal 1/2/3, Terminal 4 and Terminal 5). Through single and return tickets can be issued to customers travelling via a Rail terminus in Zone 1.

Sample journey time from Piccadilly Circus to the Airport is approximately one hour.

Airport to/from Reading

RailAir coaches leave from Reading railway station every 20 minutes during the daytime on Mondays to Fridays (every 30 minutes early weekday mornings and evenings, on weekends and public holidays). The luxury, air-conditioned coaches run non-stop to Terminals 1, 2 and 3 in 40-50 minutes. On the return journey from Heathrow Airport they only pick up passengers at Heathrow Central Bus Station (stands one and two) and not the terminals. Customers travelling to/from Terminal 4 should use Heathrow Express from Terminal 1.

Follow the RailAir signs from your platform at Reading station. You can buy your ticket in the RailAir lounge, or combined rail and coach tickets are also available from many stations. You should allow 15 minutes at Reading to transfer between train and coach.

For further information telephone **0118 957 9425** or visit **www.RailAir.com.**

Airport to/from Woking

Coaches leave at half-hourly intervals throughout most of the day to/from Terminal 5 and Heathrow Central Bus Station (for Terminals 1, 2 and 3) (see Table 158A).

Customers travelling to Heathrow should exit on platform 5 and the coach leaves from outside the station.

On arrival at Woking customers should allow at least 10 minutes to transfer to your train after the arrival of the coach at the station. Combined rail and coach tickets are available from most National Rail stations and from the Railair sales points at the airport. Tickets may also be booked at **www.nationalexpress.com** or by calling **08705 757 747**. For through trains and coach times, telephone **08457 48 49 50.** (calls may be recorded for training purposes)

Airport to/from Feltham

London Buses operates frequent bus services from Feltham Station to Heathrow Airport. Route 285 operates to Hatton Cross and Heathrow Central Bus Station for Terminals 1, 2 and 3. Buses operate every 10 minutes during the day, 15 minutes in the evenings and on Sundays and 30 minutes throughout the night.

Route 490 operates to Hatton Cross and Terminals 4 and 5. Buses operate every 12 minutes during the day, 20 minutes in the evenings and on Sundays.

Customers should allow 10 minutes at Feltham to transfer between train and bus from the station forecourt adjoining platform 1.

Other direct services to/from Airport

A coach service, Green Line 724, runs throughout the day between Heathrow, West Drayton, Uxbridge, Rickmansworth, Watford, St. Albans, Hatfield, Welwyn Garden City, Hertford and Harlow. Tickets can only be purchased on the coach. A frequent bus service (route 140) runs 24 hours between Hayes & Harlington and Heathrow Airport (Central Bus Station).

For further information telephone **0870 608 7261** (Green Line Travel Information)

London Luton Airport

A frequent dedicated shuttle bus links Luton Airport with Luton Airport Parkway station – journey time 5 minutes. Luton Airport Parkway is served by frequent First Capital Connect services direct to Bedford, Central London, South London, Gatwick Airport and Brighton – see Table 52 for details. East Midlands Trains services link Luton Airport Parkway with St Pancras International and Leicester, Derby, Nottingham and Sheffield – see Table 53 for details.

In addition a dedicated coach link operates between the Airport, Luton railway station and town centre and Milton Keynes Central railway station and town centre (see Table 65B for details).

Airport Links

London Stansted Airport

Stansted Airport has its own railway station right in the heart of the airport terminal building.

The Stansted Express is a dedicated rail service operating between London Liverpool Street and Stansted Airport station (See Table 22). Trains run every 15 minutes throughout the day, seven days per week.

Typical journey time is 46 minutes including an intermediate stop at Tottenham Hale to enable transfer onto the Victoria Line (London Underground) for the West End. Occasionally services may be diverted via Seven Sisters at weekends.

CrossCountry operates an hourly express service seven days a week between Birmingham and Stansted Airport calling at Leicester, Peterborough and Cambridge – see Table 49 – offering connections with services to Yorkshire and the North East. Customers should be advised to arrive at the airport 1 hour 45 minutes prior to their latest check-in time.

For further information telephone **08457 48 49 50**. (calls may be recorded for training purposes)

The airport is also served by the Stansted Coachlink (Service X22) – a limited stop coach service from Colchester station – which also calls intermediately at Braintree station. Coaches run hourly throughout the day, seven days per week.

For further information telephone **0871 200 22 33** or visit **www.traveline.info**

Manchester Airport

The airport railway station is right in the heart of the airport complex, linked by covered travellators. The station is served by up to 8 trains per hour from Manchester Piccadilly and direct services operate between Middlesbrough, Newcastle, York, Leeds, Huddersfield, Cleethorpes, Doncaster, Sheffield, Edinburgh, Glasgow, Carlisle, Barrow-in-Furness, Windermere, Lancaster, Preston, Liverpool and the Airport. Additional regular services operate during the day, to/from many stations which can be found under the entry for Manchester Airport in the index in this timetable.

Newcastle Airport

A frequent Tyne and Wear Metro service runs between Newcastle Central Station and Newcastle Airport providing links with Northern, National Express East Coast, First TransPennine Express and CrossCountry services. Inclusive 'Train and Metro' tickets are available at discount prices.

Metro journey time approximately 20 minutes.

Metro frequency up to 6 trains each way each hour. Service operates between approx. 0600 and 2300.

Prestwick International Airport

Prestwick International Airport Station is situated directly opposite the main airport terminal buildings. A covered walkway links the station with the airport terminal. The station is served by direct trains from Glasgow Central and Ayr, with a half hourly frequency operating between the hours of 0600 and 0015 approximately. (See Table 221). Journey time is approx. 45 minutes. Dyce station is situated close to Aberdeen Airport and is served by trains between Aberdeen and Inverness (Table 240). A new shuttle bus service has been introduced between Dyce station and the airport - these run between approx. 0645 and 1940 Monday to Friday. Taxis are also available. In addition, there are several through trains daily to and from Glasgow and Edinburgh (see Table 229). Journey time by taxi is 20 minutes approx. from Aberdeen Station. Discounts are available for airline users. For further information telephone **01292 678000**.

Robin Hood Airport

Robin Hood Airport, the UK's newest purpose built international airport, is built on the site of the former RAF Finningley airbase. It is situated 7 miles south of Doncaster. For more information on Robin Hood Airport visit **www.robinhoodairport.com**

From Doncaster a dedicated bus service, The Airport Arrow 707, operates hourly throughout the day from the Frenchgate Interchange (Stand A1) adjacent to Doncaster Rail Station from 0535 to 2235. The journey takes under 25 minutes.

The Airport Arrow 707 service runs alongside other local bus services which link to Robin Hood Airport, including service X19 from Barnsley.

For further information on the above services please telephone Travel South Yorkshire **01709 515151** or visit **www.travelsouthyorkshire.com**

Southampton Airport

Southampton Airport (Parkway) station is adjacent to Southampton Airport.

South West Trains operate up to 3 trains per hour between London Waterloo, Winchester and Southampton Airport with up to 2 direct services to Bournemouth, Poole, Wareham and Weymouth and most intermediate stations (See Table 158).

CrossCountry services link Southampton Airport (Parkway) with Reading, Oxford, the Midlands, North West and North East England and Scotland. (See Table 51).

Station index and table numbers

【10】 Connection time
Ⓟ Station Car Park
🚲 Bicycle storage facility
◇ Seat reservations can be made at this station
⚠ Penalty Fare Schemes in operation on some or all services from this station
🚕 Taxi rank or cab office at station, or signposted and within 100 metres
Ⓤ Unstaffed station
[ ] Station Operator Code

A

Station index and table numbers

- ▪10 Connection time
- Ⓟ Station Car Park
- 🚲 Bicycle storage facility
- ◇ Seat reservations can be made at this station
- ⚠ Penalty Fare Schemes in operation on some or all services from this station
- 🚕 Taxi rank or cab office at station, or signposted and within 100 metres
- Ⓤ Unstaffed station
- [ ] Station Operator Code

Attenborough [EM] Ⓤ 56, 57
Attleborough [LE] Ⓟ Ⓤ 17
Auchinleck [SR] Ⓟ 🚲 Ⓤ 216
Audley End [LE] Ⓟ 🚲 ⚠ 🚕 22, 49
Aughton Park [ME] ⚠ 103
Aviemore [SR] Ⓟ 🚲 ◇ 🚕 229, *Sleepers* 403
Avoncliff [GW] Ⓤ 123
Avonmouth [GW] ▪2 Ⓟ 🚲 Ⓤ 133
Axminster [SW] Ⓟ 🚲 ◇ 🚕 160
Aylesbury [CH] Ⓟ 🚲 ◇ ⚠ 🚕 114, 115
Aylesbury Vale Parkway [CH] Ⓟ 🚲 ◇ ⚠ 114
Aylesford [SE] Ⓤ 208
Aylesham [SE] Ⓟ 212
Ayr [SR] Ⓟ 🚲 ◇ 🚕 216, 218, 221

B

Bache [ME] Ⓤ 106
Backwell [GW] (see Nailsea)
Baglan [AW] Ⓟ 🚲 Ⓤ 128
Bagshot [SW] Ⓟ 🚲 ◇ ⚠ 149
Baildon [NT] Ⓟ Ⓤ 38
Baillieston [SR] 🚲 Ⓤ 220
Balcombe [SN] ◇ ⚠ 52, 186
Baldock [FC] Ⓟ ⚠ 25
Balham [SN] ▪4 ◇ ⚠ 🚕 176, 177, 178, 182
Balloch [SR] 🚲 🚕 226
Balmossie [SR] 🚲 Ⓤ 229
Bamber Bridge [NT] Ⓟ Ⓤ 97
Bamford [NT] Ⓟ Ⓤ 78
Banavie [SR] Ⓟ 🚲 Ⓤ 227
Banbury [CH] Ⓟ 🚲 ◇ ⚠ 🚕 51, 71, 75, 115, 116
Bangor (Gwynedd) [AW] Ⓟ ◇ 🚕 65, 81, 102, 131
Bank Hall [ME] ⚠ 103
Banstead [SN] ⚠ Ⓤ 182
Barassie [SR] Ⓟ 🚲 Ⓤ 221
Bardon Mill [NT] Ⓟ Ⓤ 48
Bare Lane [NT] Ⓟ Ⓤ 36, 98
Bargeddie [SR] Ⓟ 🚲 Ⓤ 220
Bargoed [AW] 🚕 130
Barking [CC] ◇ ⚠ 🚕 1, 62
Barlaston Orchard Place *Bus* 67
Barming [SE] Ⓟ ⚠ 196
Barmouth [AW] 🚲 75
Barnehurst [SE] ▪4 Ⓟ ⚠ 🚕 200
Barnes [SW] 🚲 ◇ ⚠ 149
Barnes Bridge [SW] 🚲 ◇ ⚠ Ⓤ 149
Barnetby [TP] Ⓟ Ⓤ 27, 29, 30
Barnham [SN] Ⓟ 🚲 ⚠ 🚕 123, 188
Barnhill [SR] 🚲 Ⓤ 226
Barnsbury [LO] (see Caledonian Road)
Barnsley [NT] Ⓟ 🚲 ◇ 🚕 30, 34
Barnstaple [GW] Ⓟ 🚲 ◇ 🚕 135, 136
Barnt Green [LM] Ⓟ ⚠ Ⓤ 69, 71
Barrhead [SR] Ⓟ 🚲 🚕 222
Barrhill [SR] Ⓟ 🚲 218
Barrow Haven [NT] Ⓤ 29
Barrow-in-Furness [TP] Ⓟ ◇ 🚕 65, 82, 100
Barrow Upon Soar [EM] Ⓤ 53
Barry [AW] ▪3 Ⓟ ◇ 🚕 130
Barry Docks [AW] Ⓤ 130
Barry Island [AW] Ⓤ 130
Barry Links [SR] 🚲 Ⓤ 229
Barton-on-Humber [NT] Ⓟ Ⓤ 29
Basildon [CC] 🚲 ◇ ⚠ 🚕 1
Basingstoke [SW] Ⓟ 🚲 ◇ ⚠ 🚕
  Aberdeen 51
  Bath 160
  Birmingham 51
  Bournemouth 158
  Bristol 160
  Brockenhurst 158
  Clapham Junction 155
  Coventry 51
  Crewe 51
  Derby 51
  Dorchester 158
  Dundee 51
  Eastleigh 158
  Edinburgh 51
  Exeter 160
  Fareham 158
  Farnborough 158
  Glasgow 51
  Leeds 51
  London 155
  Lymington 158
  Manchester 51
  Newcastle 51
  Oxford 51
  Plymouth 160
  Poole 158
  Portsmouth 158
  Preston 51
  Reading 122
  Salisbury 160
  Sheffield 51
  Southampton 158
  Southampton Airport 158
  Stoke-on-Trent 51
  Surbiton 155
  Torquay 160
  Weymouth 158
  Weybridge 155
  Wimbledon 155
  Winchester 158
  Woking 155
  Wolverhampton 51
  Yeovil 160
  York 51
Bat & Ball [SE] Ⓟ ⚠ Ⓤ 52, 195
Bath Spa [GW] ▪7 Ⓟ 🚲 ◇ ⚠ 🚕
  Bournemouth 123
  Brighton 123
  Bristol 132
  Cardiff 132
  Crewe 131
  Gatwick Airport 125
  Heathrow Airport 125
  London 125, 160
  Manchester 131
  Newport 132
  Oxford 125
  Portsmouth 123
  Reading 125
  Salisbury 123
  Shrewsbury 131
  Slough 125
  Southampton Central 123
  Swindon 125
  Taunton 134
  Westbury 123
  Weston-super-Mare 134
  Weymouth 123
  Yeovil 123
Bathgate [SR] Ⓟ 🚲 🚕 Ⓤ 230
Batley [NT] Ⓟ 🚲 Ⓤ 39
Battersby [NT] Ⓤ 45
Battersea Park [SN] ▪4 ◇ ⚠ 177, 178
Battle [SE] Ⓟ ◇ 🚕 206
Battlesbridge [LE] Ⓟ 🚲 Ⓤ 5
Bayford [FC] Ⓟ ⚠ Ⓤ 24
Beaconsfield [CH] Ⓟ 🚲 ◇ ⚠ 🚕 115
Bearley [LM] Ⓟ ⚠ Ⓤ 115
Bearsden [SR] Ⓟ 🚲 🚕 226
Bearsted [SE] Ⓟ 🚲 ◇ ⚠ 196
Beasdale [SR] 🚲 Ⓤ 227
Beaulieu Road [SW] 🚲 ⚠ Ⓤ 158
Beauly [SR] Ⓟ 🚲 Ⓤ 239
Bebington [ME] Ⓟ ⚠ 106
Beccles [LE] Ⓟ 🚲 Ⓤ 13
Beckenham Hill [SE] 🚲 ⚠ 52, 195
Beckenham Junction [SE] ▪4 Ⓟ 🚲 ◇ ⚠ 🚕 177, 195, 196
Bedford [FC] ▪7 Ⓟ 🚲 ◇ ⚠ 🚕
  Barnsley 53
  Bletchley 64
  Brighton 52, 186
  Chesterfield 53
  Derby 53
  Doncaster 53
  East Croydon 52
  Gatwick Airport 52, 186
  Haywards Heath 52, 186
  Herne Hill 52
  Hove 186
  Kettering 53
  Leeds 53
  Leicester 53
  London 52
  Luton 52
  Luton Airport Parkway 52
  Meadowhall 53
  Milton Keynes Central 64

Station index and table numbers

[10] Connection time
Ⓟ Station Car Park
🚲 Bicycle storage facility
◇ Seat reservations can be made at this station
⚠ Penalty Fare Schemes in operation on some or all services from this station
🚕 Taxi rank or cab office at station, or signposted and within 100 metres
Ⓤ Unstaffed station
[ ] Station Operator Code

Nottingham 53
Redhill 52, 186
St Albans 52
Sheffield 53
Sutton (Surrey) 52
Wakefield 53
Wellingborough 53
Wimbledon 52
York 53
Bedford Bus Station 🚕 *Bus* 65C
Bedford St Johns [LM] Ⓤ 64
Bedhampton [SW] 🚲 ◇ ⚠ 156, 157, 188
Bedminster [GW] Ⓤ 134
Bedworth [LM] Ⓟ Ⓤ 67
Bedwyn [GW] Ⓟ 🚲 Ⓤ 116
Beeston [EM] Ⓟ 🚲 ◇ 53, 56, 57
Bekesbourne [SE] Ⓟ Ⓤ 212
Belfast
Port *Catamaran/Ship* (via Stranraer Harbour) 218
Belle Vue [NT] Ⓤ 78
Bellgrove [SR] 🚲 Ⓤ 226
Bellingham [SE] 🚲 ⚠ 52, 195
Bellshill [SR] Ⓟ 🚲 225, 226
Belmont [SN] ⚠ Ⓤ 182
Belper [EM] Ⓤ 56
Beltring [SE] Ⓤ 208
Belvedere [SE] ⚠ 200
Bempton [NT] Ⓤ 43
Ben Rhydding [NT] Ⓟ Ⓤ 38
Benfleet [CC] Ⓟ 🚲 ◇ ⚠ 🚕 1
Bentham [NT] Ⓟ Ⓤ 36
Bentley [SW] Ⓟ 🚲 ◇ ⚠ 155
Bentley (S. Yorks.) [NT] Ⓟ 🚲 Ⓤ 29, 31
Bere Alston [GW] Ⓟ Ⓤ 139
Bere Ferrers [GW] Ⓟ 🚲 Ⓤ 139
Berkhamsted [LM] Ⓟ 🚲 ◇ 🚕 66, 176
Berkswell [LM] Ⓟ 🚲 ⚠ 68
Berney Arms [LE] 🚲 Ⓤ 15
Berry Brow [NT] Ⓤ 34
Berrylands [SW] Ⓟ 🚲 ◇ ⚠ 152
Berwick [SN] Ⓟ 🚲 ⚠ 189
Berwick-upon-Tweed [GR] Ⓟ 🚲 ◇ 🚕 26, 26K, 51
Bescar Lane [NT] Ⓤ 82
Bescot Stadium [LM] Ⓟ ◇ ⚠ 70
Betchworth [GW] Ⓤ 148
Bethnal Green [LE] 🚲 ⚠ Ⓤ 20, 21, 22
Betws-y-Coed [AW] Ⓤ 102
Beverley [NT] Ⓟ ◇ 🚕 43
Bexhill [SN] **[4]** ⚠ 🚕 189, 206
Bexley [SE] Ⓟ ⚠ 🚕 200
Bexleyheath [SE] Ⓟ 🚲 ⚠ 🚕 200
Bicester (Bure Place) *Bus* 65A
Bicester North [CH] **[3]** Ⓟ 🚲 ◇ ⚠ 🚕 115
Bicester Town [GW] Ⓟ 🚲 Ⓤ 116
Bickley [SE] **[4]** Ⓟ ⚠ 52, 195
Bidston [ME] Ⓟ ⚠ 101, 106
Biggleswade [FC] Ⓟ 🚲 ⚠ 25
Bilbrook [LM] Ⓤ 74
Billericay [LE] Ⓟ 🚲 ⚠ 🚕 5
Billingham [NT] 🚲 🚕 Ⓤ 44
Billingshurst [SN] Ⓟ 🚲 ⚠ 🚕 188
Bingham [EM] Ⓟ Ⓤ 19
Bingley [NT] Ⓟ 🚲 ◇ 36
Birchgrove [AW] Ⓤ 130
Birchington-on-Sea [SE] Ⓟ 🚲 🚕 212
Birchwood [TP] Ⓟ 🚲 🚕 39, 89
Birkbeck [SN] ⚠ Ⓤ 177
Birkdale [ME] Ⓟ ⚠ 103
Birkenhead Central [ME] ⚠ 106
Birkenhead North [ME] ⚠ 106
Birkenhead Park [ME] ⚠ 106
Birmingham International [VT] (for National Exhibition Centre and Airport) Ⓟ 🚲 ◇ ⚠ 🚕
Aberdeen 65
Aberystwyth 75
Banbury 71
Bangor (Gwynedd) 65, 81
Basingstoke 51
Birmingham 68
Blackpool 65
Bournemouth 51
Carlisle 65
Chester 65, 75, 81
Clapham Junction 66
Coventry 68
Crewe 65, 81
Derby 51
Dundee 65
East Croydon 66
Edinburgh 51, 65
Glasgow 51, 65
Holyhead 65, 75, 81
Inverness 65
Leamington Spa 71
Leeds 51
Liverpool 65
London 66, 116
Manchester 65
Manchester Airport 65
Milton Keynes Central 66
Newcastle 51
Northampton 66
Nottingham 51
Oxenholme Lake District 65
Oxford 51
Preston 65
Pwllheli 75
Reading 51
Rugby 66
Sheffield 51
Shrewsbury 75
Southampton 51
Stafford 68
Stoke-on-Trent 65
Watford 66
Wolverhampton 68
Wrexham 75
York 51
Birmingham
Moor Street [CH] ◇ ⚠ 🚕
New Street [NR] **[12]** 🚲 ◇ ⚠ 🚕
Snow Hill [LM] Ⓟ ◇ ⚠
Aberdeen 51, 65
Aberystwyth 75
Banbury 71
Bangor (Gwynedd) 65, 81
Barmouth 75
Barrow-in-Furness 65
Basingstoke 51
Birmingham International 68
Blackpool 65
Bournemouth 51
Bristol 57
Bromsgrove 71
Burton-on-Trent 57
Cambridge 49
Cardiff 57
Carlisle 65
Cheltenham Spa 57
Chester 75, 81
Clapham Junction 66
Coventry 68
Crewe 65
Darlington 51
Derby 57
Douglas (IOM) 98A
Dundee 51, 65
East Croydon 66
Edinburgh 51, 65
Ely 49
Exeter 51
Glasgow 51, 65
Gloucester 57
Hereford 71
Holyhead 65, 81
Inverness 65
Kidderminster 71
Leamington Spa 71
Leeds 51
Leicester 57
Lichfield 69
Liverpool 65, 91
Llandudno 81
London 66, 115, 116
Longbridge 69
Manchester 65, 84
Manchester Airport 65, 84
Milton Keynes Central 66
Newcastle 51
Newport (South Wales) 57
Northampton 66
Norwich 49
Nottingham 57
Nuneaton 57
Oxenholme Lake District 65
Oxford 116
Paignton 135
Penzance 135
Peterborough 49
Plymouth 135
Preston 65

Station index and table numbers

[10] Connection time
Ⓟ Station Car Park
🚲 Bicycle storage facility
◇ Seat reservations can be made at this station
⚠ Penalty Fare Schemes in operation on some or all services from this station
🚕 Taxi rank or cab office at station, or signposted and within 100 metres
Ⓤ Unstaffed station
[ ] Station Operator Code

Reading 116
Redditch 69
Rugby 66
Rugeley 70
Sheffield 51
Shrewsbury 74
Solihull 71
Southampton 51
Stafford 68, 70
Stansted Airport 49
Stockport 65
Stoke-on-Trent 65
Stourbridge 71
Stratford-upon-Avon 71
Swindon 125
Telford 74
Torquay 135
Walsall 70
Warrington 65
Warwick 71
Watford 66
Wigan 65
Wolverhampton 68
Worcester 71
Wrexham 75
York 51

Birnam [SR] (see Dunkeld)
Bishop Auckland [NT] Ⓟ 🚕 Ⓤ 44
Bishopbriggs [SR] 🚲 228, 230
Bishops Stortford [LE] Ⓟ 🚲 ◇ ⚠ 🚕 22
Bishopstone [SN] Ⓤ 189
Bishopton [SR] Ⓟ 🚲 219
Bitterne [SW] Ⓟ 🚲 ⚠ Ⓤ 165
Blackburn [NT] Ⓟ ◇ 🚕 41, 94, 97
Blackfriars [FC] (see London)
Blackheath [SE] [4] ⚠ 200
Blackhorse Road [LT] ⚠ 62
Blackpool
North [NT] Ⓟ ◇ 🚕
Pleasure Beach [NT] Ⓤ
South [NT] 🚕 Ⓤ
Aberdeen 65
Birmingham 65
Birmingham International 65
Blackburn 97
Bolton 82
Bradford 41
Burnley 97
Carlisle 36, 65
Colne 97
Coventry 65
Crewe 65
Dundee 65
Edinburgh 65
Glasgow 65
Inverness 65
Lancaster 65
Leeds 41
Liverpool 65, 90
London 65
Manchester 82
Manchester Airport 82
Milton Keynes Central 65
Oxenholme Lake District 65
Preston 97
Rugby 65
St Helens 90
Stafford 65
Stockport 82
Warrington 65
Watford 65
Wigan 65
Windermere 65
Wolverhampton 65
York 41

Blackrod [NT] Ⓤ 82
Blackwater [GW] Ⓟ Ⓤ 148
Blaenau Ffestiniog [AW] Ⓤ 102
Blair Atholl [SR] Ⓟ 🚲 229, *Sleepers* 403
Blairhill [SR] Ⓟ 🚲 🚕 226
Blake Street [LM] Ⓟ ⚠ 69
Blakedown [LM] Ⓟ ⚠ Ⓤ 71
Blantyre [SR] Ⓟ 🚲 226
Blaydon [NT] Ⓤ 48
Bleasby [EM] Ⓤ 27
Bledlow, Village Hall *Bus* 115A
Bletchley [LM] Ⓟ 🚲 ◇ 🚕 64, 66, 176
Bloxwich [LM] ⚠ Ⓤ 70
Bloxwich North [LM] ⚠ Ⓤ 70
Bluewater [SE] (see Greenhithe for Bluewater)
Blundellsands & Crosby [ME] Ⓟ ⚠ 103
Blythe Bridge [EM] Ⓟ Ⓤ 50
Bodmin Mount Folly *Bus* 135C
Bodmin Parkway [GW] Ⓟ 🚲 ◇ 🚕 51, 135, *Bus* 135C, *Sleepers* 406
Bodorgan [AW] Ⓟ Ⓤ 81
Bognor Regis [SN] [4] Ⓟ 🚲 ◇ ⚠ 🚕 188
Bogston [SR] 🚲 Ⓤ 219
Bolton [NT] 🚲 ◇ 🚕 65, 82, 94, 95
Bolton-upon-Dearne [NT] Ⓟ Ⓤ 31
Bookham [SW] Ⓟ 🚲 ◇ ⚠ 🚕 152, 182
Bootle [NT] Ⓤ 100
Bootle New Strand [ME] ⚠ 🚕 103
Bootle Oriel Road [ME] Ⓟ ⚠ 103
Bordesley [LM] ⚠ Ⓤ 71
Borehamwood [FC] (see Elstree)
Borough Green & Wrotham [SE] Ⓟ ⚠ 🚕 196
Borth [AW] Ⓟ Ⓤ 75
Bosham [SN] 🚲 ⚠ 188
Boston [EM] Ⓟ 🚲 ◇ 🚕 19
Botley [SW] Ⓟ 🚲 ⚠ Ⓤ 158
Bottesford [EM] Ⓟ Ⓤ 19
Bourne End [GW] [3] Ⓟ 🚲 ⚠ 120
Bournemouth [SW] Ⓟ 🚲 ◇ ⚠ 🚕 51, 123, 158
Bournville [LM] ⚠ 69
Bow Brickhill [LM] Ⓤ 64
Bowes Park [FC] ⚠ 24
Bowling [SR] Ⓟ 🚲 Ⓤ 226
Boxhill & Westhumble [SN] Ⓟ ⚠ Ⓤ 152, 182
Bracknell [SW] Ⓟ 🚲 ◇ ⚠ 🚕 149
Bradford
Forster Square [NT] Ⓟ 🚲 ◇ 🚕
Interchange [NT] 🚲 ◇ 🚕
Blackpool 41
Blackburn 41
Brighouse 41
Cambridge 26
Carlisle 36
Grantham 26
Halifax 41
Huddersfield 41
Ilkley 38
Lancaster 36
Leeds 37
Liverpool 41
London 26
Manchester 41
Morecambe 36
Newark 26
Norwich 26
Peterborough 26
Preston 41
Retford 26
Rochdale 41
Selby 40
Settle 36
Shipley 37
Skipton 36
York 40

Bradford-on-Avon [GW] Ⓟ 🚲 ◇ 🚕 123, 160
Brading [IL] Ⓟ Ⓤ 167
Braintree [LE] Ⓟ 🚲 ⚠ 🚕 11
Braintree Freeport [LE] 🚲 ⚠ Ⓤ 11
Bramhall [NT] 84
Bramley (Hants) [GW] ⚠ 122
Bramley [NT] Ⓟ Ⓤ 37, 41
Brampton (Cumbria) [NT] Ⓟ Ⓤ 48
Brampton (Suffolk) [LE] Ⓤ 13
Branchton [SR] Ⓟ 🚲 Ⓤ 219
Brandon [LE] Ⓟ Ⓤ 17
Branksome [SW] Ⓟ 🚲 ◇ ⚠ 158
Braystones [NT] Ⓤ 100
Bredbury [NT] Ⓟ 🚲 78
Breich [SR] 🚲 Ⓤ 225
Brentford [SW] Ⓟ 🚲 ◇ 🚕 149
Brentwood [LE] Ⓟ 🚲 ⚠ 🚕 5
Bricket Wood [LM] Ⓤ 61
Bridge of Allan [SR] Ⓟ 🚲 Ⓤ 230
Bridge of Orchy [SR] Ⓟ 🚲 Ⓤ 227, *Sleepers* 404
Bridgend [AW] Ⓟ 🚲 ◇ 🚕 125, 128, 130
Bridgeton [SR] 🚲 🚕 226

■10 Connection time
Ⓟ Station Car Park
🚲 Bicycle storage facility
◇ Seat reservations can be made at this station
⚠ Penalty Fare Schemes in operation on some or all services from this station
🚕 Taxi rank or cab office at station, or signposted and within 100 metres
Ⓤ Unstaffed station
[ ] Station Operator Code

Station index and table numbers

Station index and table numbers

■10 Connection time
Ⓟ Station Car Park
🚲 Bicycle storage facility
◇ Seat reservations can be made at this station
⚠ Penalty Fare Schemes in operation on some or all services from this station
🚕 Taxi rank or cab office at station, or signposted and within 100 metres
ⓤ Unstaffed station
[ ] Station Operator Code

Station index and table numbers

10 Connection time
Ⓟ Station Car Park
🚲 Bicycle storage facility
◇ Seat reservations can be made at this station
⚠ Penalty Fare Schemes in operation on some or all services from this station
🚕 Taxi rank or cab office at station, or signposted and within 100 metres
Ⓤ Unstaffed station
[ ] Station Operator Code

Station index and table numbers

10 Connection time
Ⓟ Station Car Park
🚲 Bicycle storage facility
◇ Seat reservations can be made at this station
⚠ Penalty Fare Schemes in operation on some or all services from this station
🚕 Taxi rank or cab office at station, or signposted and within 100 metres
👤 Unstaffed station
[ ] Station Operator Code

Station index and table numbers

[10] Connection time
Ⓟ Station Car Park
🚲 Bicycle storage facility
◇ Seat reservations can be made at this station
⚠ Penalty Fare Schemes in operation on some or all services from this station
🚕 Taxi rank or cab office at station, or signposted and within 100 metres
Ⓤ Unstaffed station
[ ] Station Operator Code

London 65, 67
Manchester 84
Manchester Airport 84
Milton Keynes Central 65, 67
Newport (South Wales) 131
Northampton 67
Nottingham 50
Oxenholme Lake District 65
Oxford 51
Paignton 51
Penzance 51
Perth 65, *Sleepers* 403
Plymouth 51
Preston 65
Reading 51
Rugby 65, 67
Runcorn 91
Shrewsbury 131
Southampton 51
Stafford 65, 67
Stirling *Sleepers* 403
Stockport 84
Stoke-on-Trent 50
Torquay 51
Watford 65
Wilmslow 84
Wolverhampton 65
Crewkerne [SW] Ⓟ 🚲 ◇ 160
Crews Hill [FC] ⚠ Ⓤ 24
Crianlarich [SR] Ⓟ 🚲 Ⓤ 227, *Sleepers* 404
Criccieth [AW] Ⓟ 🚲 Ⓤ 75
Cricklewood [FC] 🚲 ◇ ⚠ 52
Croftfoot [SR] 🚲 223
Crofton Park [SE] ⚠ 52, 195
Cromer [LE] Ⓟ 🚲 Ⓤ 16
Cromford [EM] Ⓟ Ⓤ 54, 56
Crompton [NT] (see Shaw)
Crookston [SR] 🚲 Ⓤ 217
Crosby [ME] (see Blundellsands)
Crossflatts [NT] Ⓟ 🚲 Ⓤ 36
Cross Gates [NT] Ⓟ 40
Cross Keys [AW] Ⓤ 127
Crosshill [SR] 223
Crossmyloof [SR] 🚲 Ⓤ 222
Croston [NT] Ⓟ Ⓤ 99
Crouch Hill [LO] ⚠ 62
Crowborough [SN] Ⓟ ⚠ 184
Crowhurst [SE] Ⓟ 206
Crowle [NT] Ⓤ 29
Crowthorne [GW] Ⓟ 🚲 148
Croy [SR] [3] Ⓟ 🚲 228, 230
Croydon
see East Croydon
see South Croydon
see West Croydon
Crystal Palace [SN] [4] Ⓟ ⚠ 🚕 177, 178
Cuddington [NT] Ⓟ Ⓤ 88
Cuffley [FC] Ⓟ 🚲 ⚠ 🚕 24
Culdrose (R.N.A.S.) *Bus* 135A
Culham [GW] Ⓟ 🚲 Ⓤ 116
Culrain [SR] 🚲 Ⓤ 239
Cumbernauld [SR] Ⓟ 🚲 🚕 224
Cupar [SR] Ⓟ 🚲 ◇ 51, 229
Curriehill [SR] Ⓟ 🚲 Ⓤ 225
Cuxton [SE] Ⓟ Ⓤ 208
Cwmbach [AW] Ⓟ Ⓤ 130
Cwmbran [AW] Ⓟ 🚲 ◇ 🚕 131
Cynghordy [AW] Ⓤ 129

D

Dagenham Dock [CC] Ⓟ 🚲 ◇ ⚠ 1
Daisy Hill [NT] Ⓟ 🚲 82
Dalgety Bay [SR] Ⓟ 🚲 🚕 Ⓤ 242
Dalmally [SR] Ⓟ 🚲 Ⓤ 227
Dalmarnock [SR] 226
Dalmeny [SR] Ⓟ 🚲 242
Dalmuir [SR] Ⓟ 🚲 226, 227, *Sleepers* 404
Dalreoch [SR] Ⓟ 🚲 226
Dalry [SR] Ⓟ 🚲 Ⓤ 221
Dalston [NT] Ⓟ Ⓤ 100
Dalston Kingsland [LO] ⚠ 59
Dalton [NT] Ⓟ Ⓤ 82
Dalwhinnie [SR] Ⓟ 🚲 Ⓤ 229, *Sleepers* 403
Danby [NT] Ⓟ Ⓤ 45
Danescourt [AW] Ⓤ 130
Danzey [LM] Ⓟ ⚠ Ⓤ 71
Darlington [GR] [7] Ⓟ 🚲 ◇ 🚕
Aberdeen 26
Birmingham 51
Bishop Auckland 44
Bournemouth 51
Bristol 51
Cambridge 26
Cardiff 51
Catterick Garrison *Bus* 26H
Derby 51
Doncaster 26
Durham 26
Dundee 26
Edinburgh 26
Exeter 51
Glasgow 26
Grantham 26
Huddersfield 39
Leeds 26
Liverpool 39
London 26
Manchester 39
Manchester Airport 39
Middlesbrough 44
Newark 26
Newcastle 26
Newport (South Wales) 51
Norwich 26
Northallerton 26
Oxford 51
Paignton 51
Penzance 51
Peterborough 26
Plymouth 51
Reading 51
Redcar 44
Retford 26
Richmond *Bus* 26H
Saltburn 44
Sheffield 26
Southampton 51
Stansted Airport 26
Sunderland 26, 44
Torquay 51
Whitby 45
York 26
Darnall [NT] Ⓤ 30
Darnley [SR] (see Priesthill)
Darsham [LE] Ⓟ 🚲 Ⓤ 13
Dartford [SE] [4] Ⓟ ◇ ⚠ 🚕 200, 212
Darton [NT] Ⓟ Ⓤ 34
Darwen [NT] Ⓤ 94
Datchet [SW] 🚲 ◇ ⚠ 149
Davenport [NT] Ⓟ 86
Dawlish [GW] Ⓟ ◇ 🚕 51, 135, 160
Dawlish Warren [GW] Ⓟ 🚲 Ⓤ 135, 160
Deal [SE] Ⓟ 🚲 ◇ 🚕 207
Dean [GW] 🚲 Ⓤ 158
Dean Lane [NT] Ⓤ 95
Deansgate [NT] 82, 84, 85, 86, 89
Deganwy [AW] Ⓤ 81, 102
Deighton [NT] Ⓤ 39
Delamere [NT] Ⓟ Ⓤ 88
Denby Dale [NT] Ⓟ Ⓤ 34
Denham [CH] Ⓟ 🚲 ◇ ⚠ 🚕 115
Denham Golf Club [CH] ⚠ Ⓤ 115
Denmark Hill [SE] [4] ⚠ 52, 178, 195, 200
Dent [NT] Ⓟ Ⓤ 36
Denton [NT] Ⓤ 78
Deptford [SE] ⚠ 200
Derby [EM] [10] Ⓟ 🚲 ◇ 🚕
Barnsley 53
Bedford 53
Belper 53, 56
Birmingham 57
Birmingham International 51
Bournemouth 51
Bristol 57
Burton-on-Trent 57
Cardiff 57
Chesterfield 53
Coventry 51
Crewe 50
Doncaster 53
Edinburgh 51
Exeter 51
Gatwick Airport 53
Gloucester 57
Kettering 53
Leeds 53
Leicester 53
London 53
Long Eaton 57
Loughborough 53

Station index and table numbers

[10] Connection time
Ⓟ Station Car Park
🚲 Bicycle storage facility
◇ Seat reservations can be made at this station
⚠ Penalty Fare Schemes in operation on some or all services from this station
🚕 Taxi rank or cab office at station, or signposted and within 100 metres
ⓤ Unstaffed station
[ ] Station Operator Code

Luton 53
Market Harborough 53
Matlock 56
Meadowhall 53
Newcastle 51
Newport (South Wales) 57
Nottingham 57
Oxford 51
Paignton 51
Penzance 51
Plymouth 51
Reading 51
Sheffield 53
Southampton 51
Stoke-on-Trent 50
Wakefield 53
Wellingborough 53
York 53

Derby Road [LE] 🚲 ⓤ 13
Dereham 🚕 *Bus* 26A
Derker [NT] ⓤ 95
Devonport [GW] Ⓟ 🚲 ⓤ 135, 139
Dewsbury [TP] Ⓟ 🚲 ◇ 🚕 39, 41
Didcot Parkway [GW] Ⓟ 🚲 ◇ ⚠ 🚕 116, 125
Digby & Sowton [GW] Ⓟ ⓤ 136
Dilton Marsh [GW] ⓤ 123
Dinas Powys [AW] ⓤ 130
Dinas Rhondda [AW] Ⓟ ⓤ 130
Dingle Road [AW] ⓤ 130
Dingwall [SR] Ⓟ 🚲 ◇ 🚕 239
Dinsdale [NT] ⓤ 44
Dinting [NT] [3] Ⓟ 🚲 79
Disley [NT] Ⓟ 86
Diss [LE] Ⓟ 🚲 ◇ 🚕 11
Dockyard [GW] ⓤ 135, 139
Dodworth [NT] Ⓟ ⓤ 34
Dolau [AW] 🚲 ⓤ 129
Doleham [SN] ⓤ 189
Dolgarrog [AW] ⓤ 102
Dolwyddelan [AW] Ⓟ ⓤ 102
Doncaster [GR] [7] Ⓟ 🚲 ◇ 🚕
Aberdeen 26
Bedford 53
Birmingham 51
Bournemouth 51
Bristol 51
Cambridge 26
Cleethorpes 29
Darlington 26
Derby 53
Dundee 26
Durham 26
Edinburgh 26
Exeter 51
Gainsborough 18
Glasgow 26
Goole 29
Grantham 26
Grimsby 29
Hull 29
Leeds 31
Leicester 53
Lincoln 18
London 26
Luton 53
Manchester 29
Manchester Airport 29
Middlesbrough 26
Newark 26
Newcastle 26
Norwich 26
Nottingham 53
Oxford 51
Paignton 51
Penzance 51
Peterborough 18, 26
Plymouth 51
Reading 51
Retford 26
Robin Hood Airport *Bus* 26F
Rotherham 29
Scunthorpe 29
Selby 29
Sheffield 29
Sleaford 18
Southampton 51
Spalding 18
Stansted Airport 26
Stevenage 26
Stockport 29
Sunderland 26
Torquay 51
Wakefield 31
York 26

Doncaster Interchange *Bus* 26F
Dorchester South [SW] Ⓟ 🚲 ◇ ⚠ 🚕 158
Dorchester West [GW] ⓤ 123, 158
Dore & Totley [NT] Ⓟ ⓤ 78
Dorking [SN] [4] Ⓟ 🚲 ◇ ⚠ 🚕 152, 182
Dorking Deepdene [GW] ⓤ 148
Dorking West [GW] ⓤ 148
Dormans [SN] ⚠ 184
Dorridge [LM] Ⓟ 🚲 ◇ ⚠ 71, 115
Douglas (IOM) *Ship* 98A
Dove Holes [NT] Ⓟ ⓤ 86
Dovercourt [LE] Ⓟ 🚲 11
Dover Priory [SE] [4] Ⓟ 🚲 ◇ 🚕 207, 212
Dovey Junction [AW] [4] ⓤ 75
Downham Market [FC] Ⓟ 🚲 ⚠ 🚕 17
Drayton Green [GW] ⓤ 117
Drayton Park [FC] 🚲 ⚠ 24
Drem [SR] Ⓟ 🚲 ⓤ 238
Driffield [NT] Ⓟ 🚲 🚕 43
Drigg [NT] ⓤ 100
Droitwich Spa [LM] Ⓟ ◇ ⚠ 71
Dronfield [NT] Ⓟ ⓤ 34
Drumchapel [SR] Ⓟ 🚲 🚕 226
Drumfrochar [SR] 🚲 ⓤ 219
Drumgelloch [SR] 🚲 ⓤ 226
Drumry [SR] Ⓟ 🚲 226
Dublin Ferryport *Ship* 81A
Duddeston [LM] ⚠ 69, 70
Dudley Port [LM] Ⓟ ⚠ 68
Duffield [EM] Ⓟ ⓤ 56
Duirinish [SR] Ⓟ 🚲 ⓤ 239
Duke Street [SR] 🚲 ⓤ 226
Dullingham [LE] Ⓟ 🚲 ⓤ 14
Dumbarton Central [SR] 🚲 ◇ 🚕 226, 227
Dumbarton East [SR] 🚲 ⓤ 226
Dumbreck [SR] 🚲 ⓤ 217
Dumfries [SR] Ⓟ 🚲 ◇ 🚕 216, 218
Dumpton Park [SE] ⓤ 207, 212
Dun Laoghaire *Ship* 81A
Dunbar [GR] Ⓟ 🚲 ◇ 26, 51
Dunblane [SR] Ⓟ 🚲 ◇ 229, 230, *Sleepers* 403
Duncraig [SR] 🚲 ⓤ 239
Dundee [SR] Ⓟ 🚲 ◇ 🚕 26, 51, 65, 229, *Sleepers* 402
Dunfermline Queen Margaret [SR] Ⓟ 🚲 ⓤ 242
Dunfermline Town [SR] Ⓟ 🚲 ◇ 🚕 242
Dunkeld & Birnam [SR] Ⓟ 🚲 ⓤ 229, *Sleepers* 403
Dunlop [SR] 🚲 ⓤ 222
Dunoon *Ship* 219A
Dunrobin Castle [SR] ⓤ *Summer only* 239
Duns *Bus* 26K
Dunstable *Bus* 52A
Dunster Steep *Bus* 135E
Dunston [NT] ⓤ 48
Dunton Green [SE] Ⓟ ⚠ ⓤ 204
Durham [GR] Ⓟ 🚲 ◇ 🚕 26, 39, 44, 51
Durrington-on-Sea [SN] 🚲 ⚠ 188
Dursley [GW] (see Cam & Dursley)
Dyce [SR] Ⓟ 🚲 🚕 ⓤ 229, 240
Dyffryn Ardudwy [AW] ⓤ 75

E

Eaglescliffe [NT] Ⓟ 🚲 🚕 ⓤ 26, 44
Ealing Broadway [GW] [3] ◇ ⚠ 🚕 116, 117
Earlestown [NT] [8] 81, 90
Earley [SW] Ⓟ 🚲 ⚠ 149
Earlsfield [SW] 🚲 ◇ ⚠ 152, 155
Earlston *Bus* 26K
Earlswood (Surrey) [SN] 🚲 ◇ ⚠ 186
Earlswood (West Midlands) [LM] Ⓟ ⚠ ⓤ 71
East Croydon [SN] 🚲 ◇ ⚠ 🚕
Bedford 52
Bexhill 189
Birmingham 66
Birmingham International 66

Station index and table numbers

[10] Connection time
Ⓟ Station Car Park
🚲 Bicycle storage facility
◇ Seat reservations can be made at this station
⚠ Penalty Fare Schemes in operation on some or all services from this station
🚕 Taxi rank or cab office at station, or signposted and within 100 metres
Ⓤ Unstaffed station
[ ] Station Operator Code

Station index and table numbers

⟦10⟧ Connection time
Ⓟ Station Car Park
🚲 Bicycle storage facility
◇ Seat reservations can be made at this station
⚠ Penalty Fare Schemes in operation on some or all services from this station
🚕 Taxi rank or cab office at station, or signposted and within 100 metres
ⓤ Unstaffed station
[ ] Station Operator Code

Ely [LE] ⟦6⟧ Ⓟ 🚲 ◇ ⚠ 🚕 14, 17, 49
Emerson Park [LE] 🚲 ⚠ ⓤ 4
Emsworth [SN] Ⓟ 🚲 ⚠ 188
Enfield Chase [FC] Ⓟ 🚲 ⚠ 24
Enfield Lock [LE] 🚲 ⚠ 22
Enfield Town [LE] ⚠ 21
Entwistle [NT] ⓤ 94
Epsom [SN] ⟦3⟧ Ⓟ 🚲 ◇ ⚠ 🚕 152, 182
Epsom Downs [SN] ⚠ ⓤ 182
Erdington [LM] ⚠ 69
Eridge [SN] ⚠ 184
Erith [SE] ⚠ 🚕 200
Esher [SW] Ⓟ 🚲 ◇ ⚠ 🚕 155
Eskdale [NT] (see Ravenglass)
Essex Road [FC] 🚲 ⚠ 24
Etchingham [SE] Ⓟ 🚲 206
Eton (see Windsor)
Euston [NR] (see London)
Euxton Balshaw Lane [NT] Ⓟ ⓤ 90
Evesham [GW] Ⓟ 🚲 🚕 126
Ewell East [SN] Ⓟ ◇ ⚠ 182
Ewell West [SW] Ⓟ 🚲 ◇ ⚠ 152
Exeter
- **Central [GW]** Ⓟ 🚲 ◇
- **St Davids [GW]** ⟦6⟧ Ⓟ 🚲 ◇ ⚠ 🚕
- **St Thomas [GW]** ⓤ

Aberdeen 51
Andover 160
Barnstaple 136
Basingstoke 160
Birmingham 51
Bristol 135
Bude Strand *Bus* 135D
Cardiff 135
Carlisle 51
Clapham Junction 160
Crewe 51
Derby 51
Dundee 51
Edinburgh 51
Exmouth 136
Gatwick Airport 135
Glasgow 51
Heathrow Airport 135, 160
Holsworthy Library *Bus* 135D
Leeds 51
London 135, 160, *Sleepers* 406
Manchester 51
Newcastle 51
Newport (South Wales) 135
Newquay 135
Newton Abbot 135
Nottingham 51
Okehampton *Summer only* 136
Okehampton West Street *Bus* 135D
Oxford 135
Paignton 135
Penzance 135
Plymouth 135
Portsmouth 160
Preston 51
Reading 135, *Sleepers* 406
Salisbury 160
Sheffield 51
Southampton Central 160
Taunton 135
Torquay 135
Truro 135
Weston-super-Mare 135
Wolverhampton 51
York 51

Exhibition Centre [SR] 🚲 226
Exmouth [GW] Ⓟ 🚲 ◇ 135, 136
Exton [GW] Ⓟ 🚲 ⓤ 136
Eynsford [SE] Ⓟ ⚠ 52, 195
Eynsham Church *Bus* 116C

F

Failsworth [NT] ⓤ 95
Fairbourne [AW] Ⓟ ⓤ 75
Fairfield [NT] ⓤ 78
Fairhaven [NT] (see Ansdell)
Fairlie [SR] Ⓟ 🚲 ⓤ 221
Fairwater [AW] ⓤ 130
Falconwood [SE] ⚠ 🚕 200
Falkirk Grahamston [SR] Ⓟ 🚲 ◇ 🚕 224, 230, *Sleepers* 403
Falkirk High [SR] Ⓟ 🚲 ◇ 🚕 228
Falls of Cruachan [SR] ⓤ *Summer only* 227
Falmer [SN] Ⓟ 🚲 ⚠ 189
Falmouth Docks [GW] Ⓟ ⓤ 135, 143
Falmouth Town [GW] ⓤ 143
Fambridge [LE] (North Fambridge)
Fareham [SW] Ⓟ 🚲 ◇ ⚠ 🚕 123, 158, 165, 188
Farnborough (Main) [SW] Ⓟ 🚲 ◇ ⚠ 🚕 155,158
Farnborough North [GW] Ⓟ ⓤ 148
Farncombe [SW] Ⓟ 🚲 ◇ ⚠ 156
Farnham [SW] Ⓟ 🚲 ◇ ⚠ 🚕 155
Farningham Road [SE] Ⓟ ⚠ 212
Farnworth [NT] 82
Farringdon [LT] (see London)
Fauldhouse [SR] Ⓟ 🚲 ⓤ 225
Faversham [SE] ⟦2⟧ Ⓟ 🚲 ◇ ⚠ 🚕 212
Faygate [SN] ⚠ ⓤ 186
Fazakerley [ME] ⚠ 103
Fearn [SR] Ⓟ 🚲 ⓤ 239
Featherstone [NT] ⓤ 32
Felixstowe [LE] 🚲 🚕 ⓤ 13
Feltham [SW] Ⓟ 🚲 ◇ ⚠ 149
Fenchurch Street [NR] (see London)
Feniton [SW] Ⓟ 🚲 ◇ 160
Fenny Stratford [LM] ⓤ 64
Fernhill [AW] ⓤ 130
Ferriby [NT] Ⓟ 🚲 ⓤ 29
Ferryside [AW] ⓤ 128
Ffairfach [AW] ⓤ 129
Filey [NT] Ⓟ 🚕 ⓤ 43
Filton Abbey Wood [GW] Ⓟ 🚲 123, 132, 134, 135
Finchley Road & Frognal [LO] ⚠ 59
Finsbury Park [FC] ⚠ 🚕 24, 25
Finstock [GW] ⓤ 126
Fishbourne (Sussex) [SN] ⚠ ⓤ 188
Fishersgate [SN] ⚠ ⓤ 188
Fishguard Harbour [AW] ⓤ 128
Fiskerton [EM] Ⓟ ⓤ 27
Fitzwilliam [NT] Ⓟ ⓤ 31
Five Ways [LM] ⚠ 69
Flamingo Land *Bus* 26G
Fleet [SW] Ⓟ 🚲 ◇ ⚠ 🚕 155, 158
Flimby [NT] ⓤ 100
Flint [AW] Ⓟ ◇ 81
Flitwick [FC] Ⓟ 🚲 ◇ ⚠ 🚕 52
Flixton [NT] 🚲 89
Flowery Field [NT] ⓤ 79
Folkestone Central [SE] Ⓟ 🚲 ◇ 🚕 207
Folkestone West [SE] Ⓟ 207
Ford [SN] ⟦4⟧ 🚲 ⚠ 188
Forest Gate [LE] 🚲 ⚠ 5
Forest Hill [SN] ⟦4⟧ Ⓟ ◇ ⚠ 178
Formby [ME] Ⓟ 🚲 ⚠ 103
Forres [SR] Ⓟ 🚲 ◇ 🚕 240
Forsinard [SR] Ⓟ 🚲 ⓤ 239
Fort Matilda [SR] Ⓟ 🚲 ⓤ 219
Fort William [SR] Ⓟ 🚲 ◇ 🚕 227, *Ship* 227A, *Sleepers* 404
Four Oaks [LM] Ⓟ ⚠ 69
Foxfield [NT] ⓤ 100
Foxton [FC] ⚠ ⓤ 25
Frant [SE] Ⓟ 206
Fratton [SW] Ⓟ 🚲 ◇ ⚠ 🚕 123, 156, 157, 158, 165, 188
Freshfield [ME] Ⓟ 🚲 ⚠ 103
Freshford [GW] Ⓟ ⓤ 123
Frimley [SW] Ⓟ 🚲 ◇ ⚠ 149
Frinton-on-Sea [LE] Ⓟ 🚲 ⚠ 11
Frizinghall [NT] Ⓟ ⓤ 36, 37, 38
Frodsham [AW] Ⓟ ⓤ 81
Frognal [LO] (see Finchley Road)
Frome [GW] Ⓟ 🚲 🚕 123
Fulwell [SW] 🚲 ◇ ⚠ 149, 152
Furness Vale [NT] ⓤ 86
Furze Platt [GW] 120

G

Gainsborough Central [NT] Ⓟ ⓤ 30

Station index and table numbers

10 Connection time
Ⓟ Station Car Park
🚲 Bicycle storage facility
◇ Seat reservations can be made at this station
⚠ Penalty Fare Schemes in operation on some or all services from this station
🚕 Taxi rank or cab office at station, or signposted and within 100 metres
Ⓤ Unstaffed station
[ ] Station Operator Code

Station index and table numbers

[10] Connection time
Ⓟ Station Car Park
🚲 Bicycle storage facility
◇ Seat reservations can be made at this station
⚠ Penalty Fare Schemes in operation on some or all services from this station
🚕 Taxi rank or cab office at station, or signposted and within 100 metres
🚶 Unstaffed station
[ ] Station Operator Code

H

Station index and table numbers

■10 Connection time
Ⓟ Station Car Park
🚲 Bicycle storage facility
◇ Seat reservations can be made at this station
⚠ Penalty Fare Schemes in operation on some or all services from this station
🚕 Taxi rank or cab office at station, or signposted and within 100 metres
Ⓤ Unstaffed station
[ ] Station Operator Code

Station index and table numbers

[10] Connection time
Ⓟ Station Car Park
🚲 Bicycle storage facility
◇ Seat reservations can be made at this station
⚠ Penalty Fare Schemes in operation on some or all services from this station
🚕 Taxi rank or cab office at station, or signposted and within 100 metres
Ⓤ Unstaffed station
[ ] Station Operator Code

Hillington West [SR] 🚲 219
Hillside [ME] ⚠ 103
Hilsea [SW] ⚠ 156, 157, 158, 165, 188
Hinchley Wood [SW] 🚲 ◇ ⚠ 152
Hinckley [EM] Ⓟ ◇ 🚕 57
Hindley [NT] Ⓟ 82
Hinton Admiral [SW] Ⓟ 🚲 ◇ ⚠ 158
Hitchin [FC] **[4]** Ⓟ 🚲 ◇ ⚠ 🚕 24, 25
Hither Green [SE] **[4]** ⚠ 199, 200, 204
Hockley [LE] Ⓟ 🚲 ⚠ 🚕 5
Hollingbourne [SE] Ⓟ ⚠ Ⓤ 196
Hollinwood [NT] Ⓤ 95
Holmes Chapel [NT] Ⓟ 🚲 84
Holmwood [SN] ⚠ Ⓤ 182
Holsworthy Library *Bus* 135D
Holton Heath [SW] Ⓟ 🚲 ⚠ Ⓤ 158
Holyhead [AW] ◇ 🚕 65, 81, 81A, 131
Holytown [SR] Ⓟ 🚲 Ⓤ 225, 226
Homerton [LO] 🚲 ⚠ 59
Honeybourne [GW] Ⓟ Ⓤ 126
Honiton [SW] Ⓟ 🚲 ◇ 🚕 160
Honley [NT] Ⓤ 34
Honor Oak Park [SN] ⚠ 178
Hook [SW] Ⓟ 🚲 🚕 155
Hooton [ME] Ⓟ 🚲 ⚠ 106, 109
Hope (Derbyshire) [NT] Ⓟ Ⓤ 78
Hope (Flintshire) [AW] Ⓤ 101
Hopton Heath [AW] Ⓤ 129
Horley [SN] **[4]** 🚲 ◇ ⚠ 186, 188
Hornbeam Park [NT] Ⓟ Ⓤ 35
Horndean Precinct *Bus* 156B
Hornsey [FC] 🚲 ⚠ 24
Horsforth [NT] Ⓟ 🚲 ◇ 35
Horsham [SN] **[4]** Ⓟ 🚲 ◇ ⚠ 🚕 182, 186, 188
Horsley [SW] Ⓟ 🚲 ◇ ⚠ 🚕 152
Horton-in-Ribblesdale [NT] Ⓟ Ⓤ 36
Horwich Parkway [NT] Ⓟ 🚲 82
Hoscar [NT] Ⓤ 82
Hough Green [NT] Ⓟ 89
Hounslow [SW] Ⓟ 🚲 ◇ ⚠ 🚕 149
Hove [SN] **[2]** Ⓟ 🚲 ◇ ⚠ 🚕 123, 186, 188
Hoveton & Wroxham [LE] Ⓟ 🚲 🚕 Ⓤ 16
Howden [NT] Ⓟ 🚲 Ⓤ 29, 39
How Wood (Herts) **[LM]** Ⓤ 61
Howwood (Renfrewshire) **[SR]** Ⓟ 🚲 Ⓤ 221
Hoylake [ME] Ⓟ 🚲 ⚠ 106
Hubberts Bridge [EM] Ⓤ 19
Hucknall [EM] Ⓟ Ⓤ 55
Huddersfield [TP] Ⓟ 🚲 ◇ 🚕
Barnsley 34
Bradford 41
Brighouse 41
Darlington 39
Durham 39
Halifax 41
Hull 39
Leeds 39
Lincoln 30
Liverpool 39
London 26
Manchester 39
Manchester Airport 39
Meadowhall 34
Middlesbrough 39
Newcastle 39
Peterborough 26
Retford 26, 30
Scarborough 39
Selby 39, 41
Sheffield 34
Wakefield 39
Worksop 30
York 39
Hull [TP] Ⓟ 🚲 ◇ 🚕
Aberdeen 26
Beverley 43
Bridlington 43
Cambridge 26
Darlington 26
Doncaster 29
Durham 26
Edinburgh 26
Filey 43
Glasgow 26
Goole 29
Grantham 26
Huddersfield 39
Leeds 39
Liverpool 39
London 26, 29
Manchester 29, 39
Manchester Airport 29, 39
Newark 26
Newcastle 26
Norwich 26
Peterborough 26
Retford 26
Scarborough 43
Selby 29
Sheffield 29
Stockport 29
York 33
Hull Paragon Interchange 🚕 *Bus* 29
Humphrey Park [NT] Ⓤ 89
Huncoat [NT] Ⓤ 97
Hungerford [GW] Ⓟ 🚲 Ⓤ 116, 135
Hunmanby [NT] Ⓤ 43
Hunstanton Bus Station *Bus* 17A
Hunts Cross [ME] ⚠ 89, 103
Huntingdon [FC] Ⓟ 🚲 ◇ ⚠ 🚕 25
Huntly [SR] Ⓟ 🚲 ◇ 240
Hurst Green [SN] Ⓟ ⚠ 184
Hutton Cranswick [NT] Ⓟ Ⓤ 43
Huyton [NT] Ⓟ 90
Hyde [NT] (see Newton for Hyde)
Hyde Central [NT] Ⓟ Ⓤ 78
Hyde North [NT] Ⓟ Ⓤ 78
Hykeham [EM] Ⓟ Ⓤ 27
Hyndland [SR] 🚲 226
Hythe (Essex) **[LE]** 🚲 ⚠ Ⓤ 11

I

IBM [SR] 🚲 Ⓤ 219
Ifield [SN] 🚲 ◇ ⚠ 186
Ilford [LE] **[2]** 🚲 ◇ ⚠ 5
Ilkley [NT] Ⓟ 🚲 ◇ 38
Imperial Wharf [LO] 66, 176
Ince [NT] Ⓤ 82
Ince & Elton [NT] Ⓟ Ⓤ 109
Ingatestone [LE] Ⓟ 🚲 ⚠ 11
Insch [SR] Ⓟ 🚲 Ⓤ 240
Invergordon [SR] Ⓟ 🚲 Ⓤ 239
Invergowrie [SR] 🚲 Ⓤ 229
Inverkeithing [SR] Ⓟ 🚲 ◇ 🚕
Aberdeen 229
Birmingham 51
Bournemouth 51
Bristol 51
Carlisle 51
Crewe *Sleepers* 402
Derby 51
Dundee 229
Edinburgh 242
Inverness 229
London 26, *Sleepers* 402
Newcastle 26
Oxford 51
Penzance 51
Perth 229
Plymouth 51
Preston 51, *Sleepers* 402
Reading 51
Sheffield 51
Southampton 51
York 26
Inverkip [SR] Ⓟ 🚲 Ⓤ 219
Inverness [SR] Ⓟ 🚲 ◇ 🚕
Aberdeen 240
Birmingham 65
Cambridge 26
Carlisle 65
Crewe 65, *Sleepers* 403
Dingwall 239
Edinburgh 229
Elgin 240
Glasgow 229
Inverkeithing 229
Kingussie 229
Kirkcaldy 229
Kyle of Lochalsh 239
Leeds 26
Liverpool 65
London 26, 65, *Sleepers* 403
Manchester 65
Newcastle 26

Station index and table numbers

[10] Connection time
Ⓟ Station Car Park
🚲 Bicycle storage facility
◇ Seat reservations can be made at this station
⚠ Penalty Fare Schemes in operation on some or all services from this station
🚕 Taxi rank or cab office at station, or signposted and within 100 metres
Ⓤ Unstaffed station
[ ] Station Operator Code

J

K

L

Station index and table numbers

[10] Connection time
Ⓟ Station Car Park
🚲 Bicycle storage facility
◇ Seat reservations can be made at this station
⚠ Penalty Fare Schemes in operation on some or all services from this station
🚕 Taxi rank or cab office at station, or signposted and within 100 metres
Ⓤ Unstaffed station
[ ] Station Operator Code

Station index and table numbers

■10 Connection time
Ⓟ Station Car Park
🚲 Bicycle storage facility
◇ Seat reservations can be made at this station
⚠ Penalty Fare Schemes in operation on some or all services from this station
🚕 Taxi rank or cab office at station, or signposted and within 100 metres
Ⓤ Unstaffed station
[ ] Station Operator Code

Liskeard [GW] ■6 Ⓟ 🚲 ◇ 51, 135, 140, *Sleepers* 406
Lismore *Ship* 227B
Liss [SW] Ⓟ 🚲 ◇ ⚠ 156
Lisvane & Thornhill [AW] Ⓟ Ⓤ 130
Litherland [ME] (see Seaforth & Litherland)
Little Kimble [CH] ⚠ Ⓤ 115
Little Sutton [ME] Ⓤ 106
Littleborough [NT] Ⓟ 41
Littlehampton [SN] ■4 Ⓟ 🚲 ⚠ 🚕 188
Littlehaven [SN] ◇ ⚠ 186
Littleport [FC] 🚲 ⚠ Ⓤ 17
Liverpool
- **Central [ME]** ■10 ⚠ 🚕
- **James Street [ME]** ◇ ⚠
- **Lime Street** (Main Line) **[NR]** ■10 Ⓟ 🚲 ◇ 🚕
- **Lime Street** (Low Level) **[ME]** ■10 ◇ ⚠ 🚕
- **Moorfields [ME]** ■10 ⚠

Aberdeen 65
Bangor (Gwynedd) 81
Barrow-in-Furness 65
Birkenhead 106
Birmingham 65
Birmingham International 65
Blackpool 65, 90
Bolton 82
Bradford 41
Cambridge 49
Cardiff 131
Carlisle 65
Chester 106
Coventry 65
Crewe 91
Darlington 39
Douglas (IOM) 98A
Dundee 65
Durham 39
Edinburgh 65
Ellesmere Port 106
Ely 49
Gatwick Airport 65
Glasgow 65
Hartford 91
Holyhead 81
Hooton 106
Huddersfield 39
Hull 39
Hunts Cross 89, 103
Inverness 65
Ipswich 49
Kirkby 103
Lancaster 65
Leeds 39, 41
Liverpool South Parkway 91
Llandudno 81
London 65
Manchester 89, 90
Manchester Airport 89
Middlesbrough 39
Milton Keynes Central 65
Mossley Hill 91
Motherwell 65
New Brighton 106
Newcastle 39
Newport (South Wales) 131
Norwich 49
Nottingham 49
Nuneaton 65
Ormskirk 103
Oxenholme Lake District 65
Peterborough 49
Preston 90, 99
Rhyl 81
Rochdale 95
Rock Ferry 106
Rugby 65
Runcorn 91
St Helens 90
Scarborough 39
Sheffield 89
Shrewsbury 131
Southport 103
Stafford 65
Stansted Airport 49
Stockport 89
Wakefield 39
Warrington 89, 90
Watford 65
West Kirby 106
Wigan 82, 90
Windermere 65
Wolverhampton 65
Wrexham 101
York 39

Liverpool Landing Stage *Ship* 98A
Liverpool South Parkway [ME] ■7 Ⓟ 🚲 ⚠ 🚕 49, 65, 89, 91, 103
Liverpool Street [NR] (see London)
Livingston North [SR] Ⓟ 🚲 Ⓤ 230
Livingston South [SR] Ⓟ 🚲 Ⓤ 225
Llanaber [AW] Ⓤ 75
Llanbedr [AW] Ⓤ 75
Llanbister Road [AW] Ⓤ 129
Llanbradach [AW] Ⓟ Ⓤ 130
Llandaf [AW] Ⓟ 130
Llandanwg [AW] Ⓤ 75
Llandecwyn [AW] Ⓤ 75
Llandeilo [AW] Ⓟ Ⓤ 129
Llandovery [AW] Ⓟ Ⓤ 129
Llandrindod [AW] Ⓟ ◇ 129
Llandudno [AW] ◇ 🚕 65, 81, 102
Llandudno Junction [AW] Ⓟ ◇ 🚕 65, 81, 102, 131
Llandybie [AW] Ⓟ Ⓤ 129
Llanelli [AW] ◇ 128, 129
Llanfairfechan [AW] Ⓟ Ⓤ 81
Llanfairpwll [AW] Ⓟ Ⓤ 81
Llangadog [AW] Ⓤ 129
Llangammarch [AW] Ⓤ 129
Llangennech [AW] Ⓤ 129
Llangynllo [AW] Ⓤ 129
Llanharan [AW] Ⓟ Ⓤ 128
Llanhilleth [AW] Ⓟ Ⓤ 127
Llanishen [AW] Ⓟ Ⓤ 130
Llanrwst [AW] Ⓤ 102
Llansamlet [AW] Ⓟ Ⓤ 128
Llantwit Major [AW] Ⓟ 🚲 Ⓤ 130
Llanwrda [AW] Ⓤ 129
Llanwrtyd [AW] Ⓟ Ⓤ 129
Llwyngwril [AW] Ⓤ 75
Llwynypia [AW] Ⓟ Ⓤ 130
Loch Awe [SR] Ⓟ 🚲 Ⓤ 227
Loch Eil Outward Bound [SR] 🚲 Ⓤ 227
Lochailort [SR] Ⓟ 🚲 Ⓤ 227
Lochboisdale *Ship* 227C
Locheilside [SR] Ⓟ 🚲 Ⓤ 227
Lochgelly [SR] Ⓟ 🚲 Ⓤ 242
Lochluichart [SR] Ⓟ Ⓤ 239
Lochmaddy *Ship* 239B
Lochwinnoch [SR] Ⓟ 🚲 Ⓤ 221
Lockerbie [SR] Ⓟ 🚲 ◇ 🚕 51, 65
Lockwood [NT] Ⓟ Ⓤ 34
London
- **Blackfriars [FC]** ■3 ◇ ⚠ 🚕
- **Cannon Street [NR]** ■4 ◇ ⚠ 🚕
- **Charing Cross [NR]** ■4 ◇ ⚠ 🚕
- **City Thameslink [FC]** ■3 ◇ ⚠ 🚕
- **Euston [NR]** ■15 Ⓟ 🚲 ◇ ⚠ 🚕
- **Farringdon [LT]** ■3 ⚠
- **Fenchurch Street [NR]** ■7 ◇ ⚠ 🚕
- **Kings Cross [NR]** ■15 Ⓟ 🚲 ◇ ⚠ 🚕
- **Liverpool Street [NR]** ■15 🚲 ◇ ⚠ 🚕
- **London Bridge [NR]** ■4 🚲 ◇ ⚠ 🚕
- **Marylebone [CH]** ■10 🚲 ◇ ⚠ 🚕
- **Moorgate [LT]** ⚠
- **Paddington [NR]** ■15 Ⓟ 🚲 ◇ ⚠ 🚕
- **St Pancras International [NR]** ■15 Ⓟ ◇ ⚠ 🚕
- **Victoria [NR]** ■15 Ⓟ 🚲 ◇ ⚠ 🚕
- **Waterloo [NR]** ■15 Ⓟ 🚲 ◇ ⚠ 🚕
- **Waterloo East [SE]** ■4 ⚠

Aberdeen 26, *Sleepers* 402
Aberystwyth 75
Aldershot 149, 155
Alexandra Palace 24
Alnmouth 26
Alton 155
Amersham 114
Arbroath 26, *Sleepers* 402
Ascot 149

Station index and table numbers

10	Connection time
℗	Station Car Park
🚲	Bicycle storage facility
◇	Seat reservations can be made at this station
⚠	Penalty Fare Schemes in operation on some or all services from this station
🚕	Taxi rank or cab office at station, or signposted and within 100 metres
ⓤ	Unstaffed station
[ ]	Station Operator Code

Station index and table numbers

10 Connection time
Ⓟ Station Car Park
🚲 Bicycle storage facility
◇ Seat reservations can be made at this station
⚠ Penalty Fare Schemes in operation on some or all services from this station
🚕 Taxi rank or cab office at station, or signposted and within 100 metres
Ⓤ Unstaffed station
[ ] Station Operator Code

M

Station index and table numbers

[10] Connection time
Ⓟ Station Car Park
🚲 Bicycle storage facility
◇ Seat reservations can be made at this station
⚠ Penalty Fare Schemes in operation on some or all services from this station
🚕 Taxi rank or cab office at station, or signposted and within 100 metres
Ⓤ Unstaffed station
[ ] Station Operator Code

Station index and table numbers

10 Connection time
Ⓟ Station Car Park
🚲 Bicycle storage facility
◇ Seat reservations can be made at this station
⚠ Penalty Fare Schemes in operation on some or all services from this station
🚕 Taxi rank or cab office at station, or signposted and within 100 metres
Ⓤ Unstaffed station
[ ] Station Operator Code

Station index and table numbers

■10 Connection time
Ⓟ Station Car Park
🚲 Bicycle storage facility
◇ Seat reservations can be made at this station
⚠ Penalty Fare Schemes in operation on some or all services from this station
🚕 Taxi rank or cab office at station, or signposted and within 100 metres
ⓤ Unstaffed station
[ ] Station Operator Code

N

Nafferton [NT] ⓤ 43
Nailsea & Backwell [GW] Ⓟ 🚲 134
Nairn [SR] Ⓟ 🚲 ◇ 🚕 240
Nantwich [AW] ⓤ 131
Narberth [AW] ⓤ 128
Narborough [EM] Ⓟ 57
National Exhibition Centre [VT] (see Birmingham International)
Navigation Road [NT] ⓤ 88
Neath [AW] Ⓟ 🚲 ◇ 🚕 125, 128
Needham Market [LE] ⓤ 11, 14
Neilston [SR] Ⓟ 🚲 🚕 223
Nelson [NT] Ⓟ ⓤ 97
Neston [AW] Ⓟ ⓤ 101
Netherfield [EM] ⓤ 19
Nethertown [NT] Ⓟ ⓤ 100
Netley [SW] Ⓟ 🚲 ◇ 165
New Barnet [FC] Ⓟ 🚲 ⚠ 24
New Beckenham [SE] ■4 Ⓟ 🚲 ⚠ 203
New Brighton [ME] ⚠ 106
New Clee [NT] ⓤ 29
New Cross [SE] ■4 🚲 ⚠ 199, 200, 203, 204
New Cross Gate [SN] ■4 ⚠ 178, 181, 182
New Cumnock [SR] Ⓟ 🚲 ⓤ 216
New Eltham [SE] Ⓟ ⚠ 200
New Haw [SW] (see Byfleet & New Haw)
New Hey [NT] ⓤ 95
New Holland [NT] 🚲 ⓤ 29
New Hythe [SE] ⓤ 208
New Inn [AW] (see Pontypool and New Inn)
New Lane [NT] ⓤ 82
New Malden [SW] ■6 Ⓟ 🚲 ◇ ⚠ 🚕 152
New Mills Central [NT] 78
New Mills Newtown [NT] Ⓟ 🚲 86
New Milton [SW] Ⓟ 🚲 ◇ ⚠ 🚕 158
New Pudsey [NT] Ⓟ 🚲 ◇ 37, 41
New Southgate [FC] Ⓟ ⚠ 24
Newark Castle [EM] Ⓟ 🚲 ⓤ 27
Newark North Gate [GR] ■7 Ⓟ 🚲 ◇ 🚕 26, 27
Newbridge [AW] Ⓟ ⓤ 127
Newbury [GW] Ⓟ 🚲 ◇ 🚕 116, 135
Newbury Racecourse [GW] ⓤ 116
Newcastle [GR] ■8 Ⓟ 🚲 ◇ 🚕
Aberdeen 26
Alnmouth 26
Arbroath 26
Belfast *Catamaran/Ship* 218
Berwick-upon-Tweed 26
Birmingham 51
Birmingham International 51
Bournemouth 51
Bradford 39
Bristol 51
Cambridge 26
Cardiff 51
Carlisle 48
Chathill 48
Darlington 26
Derby 51
Doncaster 26
Dundee 26
Edinburgh 26
Exeter 51
Glasgow 26, 216
Grantham 26
Haltwhistle 48
Hartlepool 44
Hexham 48
Huddersfield 39
Hull 26
Leeds 26
Liverpool 39
London 26
Manchester 39
Manchester Airport 39
MetroCentre 48
Middlesbrough 44
Morpeth 48
Newark 26
Newport (South Wales) 51
Northallerton 26
Norwich 26
Oxford 51
Paignton 51
Penzance 51
Peterborough 26
Plymouth 51
Preston 39
Reading 51
Retford 26
Sheffield 26
Southampton 51
Stansted Airport 26
Stockton 44
Stranraer 218
Sunderland 44
Torquay 51
Whitby 45
York 26
Newcraighall [SR] Ⓟ 🚲 ⓤ 242
Newhaven Harbour [SN] ⓤ 189
Newhaven Town [SN] 🚲 ⚠ 189
Newington [SE] Ⓟ ⚠ 212
Newmarket [LE] Ⓟ 🚲 ⓤ 14
Newport (Essex) [LE] Ⓟ 🚲 ⚠ 22
Newport (S. Wales) [AW] Ⓟ 🚲 ◇ 🚕
Aberdeen 51
Bangor (Gwynedd) 131
Bath Spa 132
Birmingham 57
Bournemouth 123
Bristol 132
Cardiff 132
Cheltenham Spa 57
Chester 131
Crewe 131
Darlington 51
Derby 57
Dundee 51
Durham 51
Edinburgh 51
Exeter 135
Gatwick Airport 125
Gloucester 132
Heathrow Airport 125
Hereford 131
Holyhead 131
Leeds 51
Liverpool 131
Llandudno Junction 131
London 125
Maesteg 128
Manchester 131
Milford Haven 128
Newcastle 51
Nottingham 57
Oxford 125
Paignton 135
Penzance 135
Plymouth 135
Portsmouth 123
Reading 125
Sheffield 51
Shrewsbury 131
Slough 125
Swansea 128
Swindon 125
Torquay 135
Weymouth 123
Worcester 57
York 51
Newquay [GW] Ⓟ 🚲 🚕 ⓤ 51, 135, 142
Newstead [EM] Ⓟ ⓤ 55
Newton (Lanarks.) **[SR]** 🚲 223, 226
Newton Abbot [GW] Ⓟ 🚲 ◇ ⚠ 🚕 51, 135, 160, *Sleepers* 406
Newton Aycliffe [NT] Ⓟ ⓤ 44
Newton for Hyde [NT] Ⓟ 79
Newton St Cyres [GW] ⓤ 136
Newton-le-Willows [NT] Ⓟ 81, 90
Newtonmore [SR] Ⓟ 🚲 ⓤ 229, *Sleepers* 403
Newton-on-Ayr [SR] 🚲 ⓤ 221
Newtown (Powys) [AW] 🚕 75
Ninian Park [AW] ⓤ 130
Nitshill [SR] 🚲 ⓤ 222
Norbiton [SW] Ⓟ 🚲 ◇ ⚠ 152
Norbury [SN] Ⓟ 🚲 ◇ ⚠ 176, 177
Normans Bay [SN] ⓤ 189
Normanton [NT] Ⓟ ⓤ 34
North Berwick [SR] Ⓟ 🚲 ⓤ 238
North Camp [GW] Ⓟ 🚲 148
North Dulwich [SN] 🚲 ⚠ 177, 179
North Fambridge [LE] Ⓟ 🚲 ⓤ 5
North Llanrwst [AW] Ⓟ ⓤ 102

Station index and table numbers

10 Connection time
Ⓟ Station Car Park
🚲 Bicycle storage facility
◇ Seat reservations can be made at this station
⚠ Penalty Fare Schemes in operation on some or all services from this station
🚕 Taxi rank or cab office at station, or signposted and within 100 metres
Ⓤ Unstaffed station
[ ] Station Operator Code

North Queensferry [SR] Ⓟ 🚲 Ⓤ 242
North Road [NT] 🚲 Ⓤ 44
North Sheen [SW] ◇ ⚠ 149
North Walsham [LE] Ⓟ 🚲 🚕 16
North Wembley [LT] 60
Northallerton [TP] Ⓟ 🚲 ◇ 🚕 26, 39
Northampton [LM] Ⓟ 🚲 ◇ 🚕 65, 66, 67, 68
Northfield [LM] Ⓟ ◇ ⚠ 69
Northfleet [SE] ⚠ 200
Northolt Park [CH] ⚠ 115
Northumberland Park [LE] ⚠ 22
Northwich [NT] Ⓟ ◇ 88
Norton Bridge Station Drive *Bus* 67A
Norwich [LE] Ⓟ 🚲 ◇ 🚕
Birmingham 49
Cambridge 17
Colchester 11
Cromer 16
Darlington 26
Doncaster 26
Edinburgh 26
Ely 17
Great Yarmouth 15
Harwich 11
Ipswich 11
Leeds 26
Leicester 49
Liverpool 49
London 11
Lowestoft 15
Manchester 49
Newcastle 26
Nottingham 49
Peterborough 17
Retford 26
Sheffield 49
Sheringham 16
Stockport 49
Stratford 11
York 26
Norwood Junction [SN] **2** 🚲 ⚠ 🚕
Balham 177
Brighton 186
Caterham 181
Clapham Junction 177
Crystal Palace 177
Dorking 182
East Croydon 177
East Grinstead 184
Epsom 182
Gatwick Airport 186
Guildford 182
Haywards Heath 186
Horsham 182, 186
Leatherhead 182
London 175
New Cross Gate 178
Oxted 184
Peckham Rye 177
Penge West 178
Purley 175
Redhill 186
Sutton (Surrey) 182
Tattenham Corner 181
Tonbridge 186
Tulse Hill 177
Uckfield 184
Wandsworth Common 177
West Croydon 177
Nottingham [EM] **8** Ⓟ 🚲 ◇ 🚕
Barnsley 34
Bedford 53
Birmingham 57
Birmingham International 51
Bournemouth 51
Bristol 57
Cambridge 49
Cardiff 57
Cheltenham Spa 57
Cleethorpes 27
Coventry 51
Crewe 50
Derby 57
Doncaster 53
Exeter 51
Gatwick Airport 53
Gloucester 57
Grantham 19
Grimsby Town 27
Ipswich 49
Kettering 53
Leeds 34, 53
Leicester 53
Lincoln 27
Liverpool 49
London 53
Loughborough 53
Luton 53
Manchester 49
Mansfield 55
Market Harborough 53
Matlock 56
Meadowhall 34, 53
Newark 27
Newport (South Wales) 57
Nuneaton 57
Oxford 51
Paignton 51
Penzance 51
Peterborough 49
Plymouth 51
Reading 51
Sheffield 34, 53
Skegness 19
Southampton 51
Stockport 49
Stoke-on-Trent 50
Wakefield 34, 53
Wellingborough 53
Worksop 55
York 53
Nuneaton [LM] Ⓟ ◇ 🚕 49, 57, 65, 66, 67
Nunhead [SE] **4** ⚠ 52, 195, 200
Nunthorpe [NT] Ⓟ 🚲 Ⓤ 45
Nutbourne [SN] ⚠ Ⓤ 188
Nutfield [SN] ⚠ Ⓤ 186

O

Oakengates [LM] Ⓟ Ⓤ 74
Oakham [EM] Ⓟ ◇ 🚕 49
Oakleigh Park [FC] ⚠ 24
Oban [SR] Ⓟ 🚲 ◇ 🚕 227, *Ship* 227B, 227C
Ockendon [CC] Ⓟ 🚲 ◇ ⚠ 🚕 1
Ockley [SN] Ⓟ ⚠ Ⓤ 182
Okehampton 136
Okehampton West Street *Bus* 135D
Old Hill [LM] Ⓟ ⚠ 71
Old Roan [ME] ⚠ 103
Old Street [LT] ⚠ 24
Oldfield Park [GW] 🚲 123, 132
Oldham Mumps [NT] Ⓟ 🚕 95
Oldham Werneth [NT] Ⓤ 95
Olton [LM] Ⓟ ⚠ 71
Ore [SN] Ⓤ 189, 206
Ormskirk [ME] Ⓟ 🚲 ◇ ⚠ 🚕 99, 103
Orpington [SE] **4** Ⓟ ◇ ⚠ 🚕 195, 199, 204, 206, 207
Orrell [NT] Ⓤ 82
Orrell Park [ME] ⚠ 103
Orston [EM] (see Elton & Orston)
Oswaldtwistle [NT] (see Church & Oswaldtwistle)
Otford [SE] **4** Ⓟ ⚠ 52, 195, 196
Oulton Broad North [LE] Ⓟ 🚲 Ⓤ 15
Oulton Broad South [LE] Ⓟ 🚲 Ⓤ 13
Oundle (Market Place) *Bus* 26B
Outwood [NT] Ⓟ 🚲 Ⓤ 31
Overpool [ME] Ⓤ 106
Overton [SW] Ⓟ 🚲 ◇ ⚠ 160
Oxenholme Lake District [VT] Ⓟ 🚲 ◇ 🚕 51, 65, 82, 83
Oxford [GW] Ⓟ 🚲 ◇ 🚕
Aberdeen 51
Abingdon High Street *Bus* 116B
Banbury 116
Bath Spa 125
Bicester Town 116
Birmingham 116
Bristol 125
Cardiff 125
Carlisle 51
Crewe 51
Derby 51
Dundee 51
Edinburgh 51
Exeter 135
Eynsham Church *Bus* 116C
Glasgow 51
Hereford 126

Station index and table numbers

■10 Connection time
Ⓟ Station Car Park
🚲 Bicycle storage facility
◇ Seat reservations can be made at this station
⚠ Penalty Fare Schemes in operation on some or all services from this station
🚕 Taxi rank or cab office at station, or signposted and within 100 metres
Ⓤ Unstaffed station
[ ] Station Operator Code

Station index and table numbers

- **10** Connection time
- Ⓟ Station Car Park
- 🚲 Bicycle storage facility
- ◇ Seat reservations can be made at this station
- ⚠ Penalty Fare Schemes in operation on some or all services from this station
- 🚕 Taxi rank or cab office at station, or signposted and within 100 metres
- Ⓤ Unstaffed station
- [ ] Station Operator Code

Newcastle 51
Newton Abbot 135
Nottingham 51
Paignton 135
Penzance 135
Preston 51
Reading 135, *Sleepers* 406
Salisbury 160
Sheffield 51
Taunton 135
Torquay 135
Wolverhampton 51
York 51
Pokesdown [SW] 🚲 ◇ ⚠ 158
Polegate [SN] Ⓟ 🚲 ⚠ 🚕 189
Polesworth [LM] Ⓟ Ⓤ 67
Pollokshaws East [SR] 🚲 Ⓤ 223
Pollokshaws West [SR] 🚲 Ⓤ 222
Pollokshields East [SR] 🚲 223
Pollokshields West [SR] 🚲 Ⓤ 223
Polmont [SR] **3** Ⓟ 🚲 ◇ 🚕 228, 230
Polsloe Bridge [GW] Ⓤ 136
Ponders End [LE] ⚠ 22
Pontarddulais [AW] Ⓟ Ⓤ 129
Pontefract Baghill [NT] Ⓟ Ⓤ 33
Pontefract Monkhill [NT] Ⓟ Ⓤ 32
Pontefract Tanshelf [NT] Ⓟ Ⓤ 32
Pontlottyn [AW] Ⓟ Ⓤ 130
Pont-y-Pant [AW] Ⓤ 102
Pontyclun [AW] Ⓟ Ⓤ 128
Pontypool & New Inn [AW] Ⓟ Ⓤ 131
Pontypridd [AW] **3** 🚲 ◇ 🚕 130
Poole [SW] **4** Ⓟ 🚲 ◇ ⚠ 🚕 158
Poppleton [NT] Ⓟ 🚲 Ⓤ 35
Portchester [SW] 🚲 ⚠ 158, 165, 188
Port Glasgow [SR] 🚲 🚕 219
Porth [AW] Ⓟ ◇ 130
Porthmadog [AW] Ⓤ 75
Portlethen [SR] Ⓟ 🚲 Ⓤ 229
Portslade [SN] Ⓟ 🚲 ⚠ 188
Portsmouth Arms [GW] Ⓟ Ⓤ 136
Portsmouth
Harbour [SW] 🚲 ◇ ⚠ 🚕
& Southsea [SW] Ⓟ 🚲 ◇ ⚠ 🚕
Bognor Regis 188
Brighton 188
Bristol 123
Cardiff 123
Chichester 188
Crawley 188
East Croydon 188
Exeter 160
Fareham 165
Gatwick Airport 188
Guildford 156
Haslemere 156
Havant 157
Horsham 188
Littlehampton 188
London 156, 158, 188
Reading
via Eastleigh 158
via Guildford 156
Redhill 188
Ryde 167
Salisbury 123
Sandown 167
Shanklin 167
Southampton Central 165
Winchester 158
Worthing 188
Port Sunlight [ME] 🚲 ⚠ 106
Port Talbot Parkway [AW] Ⓟ 🚲 ◇ 🚕 125, 128
Possilpark & Parkhouse [SR] 🚲 Ⓤ 232
Potters Bar [FC] Ⓟ ◇ ⚠ 🚕 24, 25
Poulton-le-Fylde [NT] Ⓟ ◇ 🚕 41, 82, 97
Poynton [NT] Ⓟ 84
Prees [AW] Ⓤ 131
Prescot [NT] Ⓟ 90
Prestatyn [AW] ◇ 🚕 Ⓤ 81
Prestbury [NT] Ⓟ Ⓤ 84
Preston [VT] **8** Ⓟ 🚲 ◇ 🚕
Aberdeen 65, *Sleepers* 402
Barrow-in-Furness 82
Birmingham 65
Birmingham International 65
Blackburn 97
Blackpool 97
Bolton 82
Bournemouth 51
Bradford 41
Bristol 51
Burnley 97
Carlisle 65
Chorley 82
Clitheroe 94, 97
Colne 97
Coventry 65
Crewe 65
Douglas (IOM) 98A
Dundee 65, *Sleepers* 402
Edinburgh 65
Exeter 51
Fort William *Sleepers* 404
Glasgow 65
Inverkeithing *Sleepers* 402
Inverness 65, *Sleepers* 403
Kirkcaldy *Sleepers* 402
Lancaster 65
Leeds 41
Liverpool 90, 99
London 65
Manchester 82
Manchester Airport 82
Milton Keynes Central 65
Ormskirk 99
Oxenholme Lake District 652
Oxford 51
Paignton 51
Penzance 51
Perth 65, *Sleepers* 403
Plymouth 51
Reading 51
Rugby 65
Southampton 51
Stafford 65
Stirling *Sleepers* 403
Stockport 82
Torquay 51
Warrington 65
Watford 65
Wigan 65
Windermere 653
Wolverhampton 65
York 41
Preston Park [SN] ⚠ 52, 186
Preston (Fishergate) *Bus* 65E
Prestonpans [SR] Ⓟ 🚲 Ⓤ 238
Prestwick International Airport Ⓤ 218, 221
Prestwick Town [SR] Ⓟ 🚲 🚕 218, 221
Priesthill & Darnley [SR] 🚲 Ⓤ 222
Princes Risborough [CH] **2** Ⓟ 🚲 ◇ ⚠ 🚕 115, 115A
Prittlewell [LE] Ⓟ 🚲 ⚠ 5
Prudhoe [NT] Ⓟ 🚲 Ⓤ 48
Pulborough [SN] Ⓟ 🚲 ⚠ 🚕 188
Purfleet [CC] Ⓟ 🚲 ◇ ⚠ 1
Purley [SN] **4** Ⓟ ⚠ 🚕 175, 181, 186
Purley Oaks [SN] Ⓟ ⚠ 175, 181
Putney [SW] 🚲 ◇ ⚠ 149
Pwllheli [AW] 🚲 🚕 75
Pyle [AW] Ⓟ 🚲 Ⓤ 128

Q

Quakers Yard [AW] Ⓤ 130
Queenborough [SE] Ⓟ 212
Queens Park (Glasgow) **[SR]** 🚲 223
Queen's Park (London) **[LT]** 60
Queens Road, Peckham [SN] 🚲 ◇ ⚠ 177, 178, 179
Queen's Road, Walthamstow [LO] (see Walthamstow Queen's Road)
Queenstown Road (Battersea) [SW] ⚠ Ⓤ 149
Quintrell Downs [GW] Ⓤ 142

R

Radcliffe (Notts.) **[EM]** Ⓟ Ⓤ 19
Radlett [FC] Ⓟ 🚲 ◇ ⚠ 🚕 52

Station index and table numbers

■10 Connection time
Ⓟ Station Car Park
🚲 Bicycle storage facility
◇ Seat reservations can be made at this station
⚠ Penalty Fare Schemes in operation on some or all services from this station
🚕 Taxi rank or cab office at station, or signposted and within 100 metres
Ⓤ Unstaffed station
[ ] Station Operator Code

Station index and table numbers

■10 Connection time
Ⓟ Station Car Park
🚲 Bicycle storage facility
◇ Seat reservations can be made at this station
⚠ Penalty Fare Schemes in operation on some or all services from this station
🚕 Taxi rank or cab office at station, or signposted and within 100 metres
Ⓤ Unstaffed station
[ ] Station Operator Code

Ryde Esplanade [IL] ◇ 🚕 167
Ryde Pier Head [IL] Ⓟ 🚲 ◇ 167
Ryde St. Johns Road [IL] Ⓟ 🚲 Ⓤ 167
Ryder Brow [NT] Ⓤ 78
Rye [SN] Ⓟ ⚠ 🚕 189, 207
Rye House [LE] ⚠ 22

S

St Albans [FC] Ⓟ 🚲 ◇ ⚠ 🚕 52, 186
St Albans Abbey [LM] Ⓟ Ⓤ 61
St Andrews Bus Station *Bus* 229
St Andrews Road [GW] Ⓟ 🚲 Ⓤ 133
St Annes-on-the-Sea [NT] Ⓟ ◇ 🚕 97
St Austell [GW] Ⓟ 🚲 ◇ 🚕 51, 135, *Bus* 135B, *Sleepers* 406
St Bees [NT] Ⓟ Ⓤ 100
St Budeaux Ferry Road [GW] Ⓤ 135, 139
St Budeaux Victoria Road [GW] Ⓤ 139
St Columb Road [GW] Ⓟ Ⓤ 142
St Denys [SW] Ⓟ 🚲 ◇ ⚠ 158, 165
St Erth [GW] Ⓟ ◇ 51, 135, 144, *Sleepers* 406
St Germans [GW] Ⓤ 135
St Helens Central [NT] Ⓟ ◇ 🚕 90
St Helens Junction [NT] Ⓟ 90
St Helier (Surrey) **[FC]** 🚲 ⚠ Ⓤ 52, 179
St Ives [GW] Ⓟ Ⓤ 135, 144
St James' Park [GW] Ⓤ 136
St James Street [LE] 🚲 ⚠ 20
St Johns [SE] ⚠ 199, 200, 203, 204
St Keyne Wishing Well Halt[GW] Ⓤ 140
St Leonards Warrior Square [SE] ■4 Ⓟ ⚠ 🚕 189, 206
St Margarets (Herts.) [LE] Ⓟ ⚠ 🚕 22
St Margarets (Greater London) **[SW]** 🚲 ◇ ⚠ 🚕 149
St Mary Cray [SE] Ⓟ ⚠ 52, 195, 196, 212
St Michaels [ME] Ⓟ ⚠ 103
St Neots [FC] Ⓟ 🚲 ⚠ 🚕 25
St Neots Cross Keys Mall *Bus* 65C
St Neots Square *Bus* 65C
St Pancras International (see London)
Salford Central [NT] 82, 94, 95
Salford Crescent [NT] 82, 94, 95
Salfords [SN] ◇ ⚠ 186
Salhouse [LE] Ⓟ 🚲 Ⓤ 16
Salisbury [SW] Ⓟ 🚲 ◇ ⚠ 🚕 123, 158, 160
Saltaire [NT] Ⓤ 36
Saltash [GW] Ⓟ 🚲 Ⓤ 135
Saltburn [NT] Ⓤ 44
Saltcoats [SR] Ⓟ 🚲 🚕 221
Saltmarshe [NT] Ⓟ Ⓤ 29
Salwick [NT] Ⓤ 97
Sampford Courtenay Ⓤ 136
Sandal & Agbrigg [NT] Ⓟ 🚲 Ⓤ 31
Sandbach [NT] Ⓟ 🚲 84
Sanderstead [SN] Ⓟ ⚠ 184
Sandhills [ME] ⚠ 103
Sandhurst [GW] Ⓤ 148
Sandling [SE] Ⓟ 207
Sandown [IL] Ⓟ 🚲 Ⓤ 167
Sandplace [GW] Ⓤ 140
Sandringham Norwich Gates *Bus* 17A
Sandringham Visitor Centre *Bus* 17A
Sandwell & Dudley [LM] Ⓟ 🚲 ◇ ⚠ 🚕 66, 68, 74
Sandwich [SE] Ⓟ 207
Sandy [FC] Ⓟ 🚲 ⚠ 25
Sankey for Penketh [NT] Ⓟ 89
Sanquhar [SR] Ⓟ 🚲 Ⓤ 216
Sarn [AW] Ⓟ Ⓤ 128
Saundersfoot [AW] Ⓤ 128
Saunderton [CH] Ⓟ 🚲 ⚠ Ⓤ 115
Sawbridgeworth [LE] Ⓟ ⚠ 22
Saxilby [EM] Ⓟ 🚲 Ⓤ 18, 30
Saxmundham [LE] Ⓟ 🚲 Ⓤ 13
Scarborough [TP] Ⓟ 🚲 ◇ 🚕 26, 39, 43
Scotscalder [SR] Ⓟ 🚲 Ⓤ 239
Scotstounhill [SR] Ⓟ 🚲 226
Scrabster *Ship* 239A
Scunthorpe [TP] Ⓟ ◇ 🚕 29
Sea Mills [GW] 🚲 Ⓤ 133
Seaford [SN] Ⓟ 🚲 ⚠ 🚕 189
Seaforth & Litherland [ME] ⚠ 🚕 103
Seaham [NT] Ⓟ Ⓤ 44
Seamer [TP] Ⓟ Ⓤ 39, 43
Seascale [NT] Ⓟ Ⓤ 100
Seaton Carew [NT] Ⓟ 🚲 Ⓤ 44
Seer Green [CH] Ⓟ 🚲 ⚠ 115
Selby [TP] Ⓟ 🚲 ◇ 🚕 26, 29, 39, 40, 41
Selhurst [SN] ■4 🚲 ◇ ⚠ 176, 177
Selkirk *Bus* 65G
Sellafield [NT] Ⓟ Ⓤ 100
Selling [SE] Ⓟ Ⓤ 212
Selly Oak [LM] Ⓟ 🚲 ◇ ⚠ 69
Settle [NT] Ⓟ ◇ 36
Seven Kings [LE] 🚲 ⚠ 5
Seven Sisters [LE] ⚠ 21, 22
Sevenoaks [SE] ■4 Ⓟ ◇ ⚠ 🚕 52, 195, 204, 206, 207
Severn Beach [GW] 🚲 Ⓤ 133
Severn Tunnel Junction [AW] Ⓟ 🚲 ◇ 123, 132
Shalford [GW] Ⓟ Ⓤ 148
Shanklin [IL] Ⓟ 🚲 ◇ 🚕 167
Shaw & Crompton [NT] Ⓟ 🚲 95
Shawford [SW] Ⓟ 🚲 Ⓤ 158
Shawlands [SR] 🚲 Ⓤ 223
Sheerness-on-Sea [SE] 🚲 🚕 212
Sheffield [EM] ■7 Ⓟ 🚲 ◇ 🚕
Barnsley 34
Birmingham 51
Bournemouth 51
Bristol 51
Cambridge 49
Cardiff 51
Chesterfield 53
Cleethorpes 29
Darlington 26
Derby 53
Doncaster 29
Edinburgh 26
Exeter 51
Gatwick Airport 53
Glasgow 26
Goole 29
Grimsby 29
Huddersfield 34
Hull 29
Ipswich 49
Leeds 31
Leicester 53
Lincoln 30
Liverpool 89
London 53
Luton 53
Manchester 78
Manchester Airport 78
Meadowhall 29
Newcastle 26
New Mills 78
Newport (South Wales) 51
Norwich 49
Nottingham 53
Oxford 51
Paignton 51
Penistone 34
Penzance 51
Peterborough 49
Plymouth 51
Reading 51
Retford 30
Rotherham 29
Scunthorpe 29
Southampton 51
Stockport 78
Torquay 51
Wakefield 31
Warrington 89
York 29
Shelford [LE] ⚠ 22
Shenfield [LE] ■3 Ⓟ 🚲 ◇ ⚠ 🚕 5, 11, 13, 14
Shenstone [LM] Ⓟ ⚠ 69
Shepherd's Bush [LO] ⚠ 66, 176, 177, 186
Shepherds Well [SE] Ⓟ 212

Station index and table numbers

- **[10]** Connection time
- Ⓟ Station Car Park
- 🚲 Bicycle storage facility
- ◇ Seat reservations can be made at this station
- ⚠ Penalty Fare Schemes in operation on some or all services from this station
- 🚕 Taxi rank or cab office at station, or signposted and within 100 metres
- Ⓤ Unstaffed station
- [ ] Station Operator Code

Station index and table numbers

■10 Connection time
Ⓟ Station Car Park
🚲 Bicycle storage facility
◇ Seat reservations can be made at this station
⚠ Penalty Fare Schemes in operation on some or all services from this station
🚕 Taxi rank or cab office at station, or signposted and within 100 metres
ⓤ Unstaffed station
[ ] Station Operator Code

Station index and table numbers

■10 Connection time
Ⓟ Station Car Park
🚲 Bicycle storage facility
◇ Seat reservations can be made at this station
⚠ Penalty Fare Schemes in operation on some or all services from this station
🚕 Taxi rank or cab office at station, or signposted and within 100 metres
ⓤ Unstaffed station
[ ] Station Operator Code

■10 Connection time
Ⓟ Station Car Park
🚲 Bicycle storage facility
◇ Seat reservations can be made at this station
⚠ Penalty Fare Schemes in operation on some or all services from this station
🚕 Taxi rank or cab office at station, or signposted and within 100 metres
Ⓤ Unstaffed station
[ ] Station Operator Code

Station index and table numbers

U

V

W

Station index and table numbers

(10) Connection time
Ⓟ Station Car Park
🚲 Bicycle storage facility
◇ Seat reservations can be made at this station
⚠ Penalty Fare Schemes in operation on some or all services from this station
🚕 Taxi rank or cab office at station, or signposted and within 100 metres
Ⓤ Unstaffed station
[ ] Station Operator Code

- Reading 51
- Rhyl 81
- Runcorn East 81
- St Helens 90
- Scarborough 39
- Sheffield 89
- Southampton 51
- Stafford 65
- Stockport 89
- Torquay 51
- Widnes 89
- Wigan 65
- Wolverhampton 65
- York 39

Warwick [CH] Ⓟ 🚲 ◇ ⚠ 🚕 71, 115, 116
Warwick Parkway [CH] Ⓟ 🚲 ◇ ⚠ 🚕 71, 115, 116
Watchet (West Somerset Ry) *Bus* 135E
Water Orton [LM] Ⓤ 57
Waterbeach [FC] Ⓟ 🚲 ⚠ Ⓤ 17
Wateringbury [SE] Ⓟ Ⓤ 208
Waterloo (London) **[NR]** (see London)
Waterloo (Merseyside) [ME] ⚠ 103
Waterloo East [SE] (see London)
Waterlooville Precinct *Bus* 156B
Watford High Street [LO] ⚠ 60
Watford Junction [LM] Ⓟ 🚲 ◇ ⚠ 🚕

- Aberdeen 65, *Sleepers* 402
- Bangor (Gwynedd) 65
- Birmingham 66
- Birmingham International 66
- Blackpool North 65
- Bletchley 66
- Brighton 66, 176, 186
- Carlisle 65, *Sleepers* 400, 401
- Clapham Junction 66, 186
- Coventry 66
- Crewe 65
- Dundee 65, *Sleepers* 402
- East Croydon 66, 176, 177, 186
- Edinburgh 65, *Sleepers* 400
- Fort William *Sleepers* 404
- Gatwick Airport 66, 176, 186
- Glasgow 65, *Sleepers* 401
- Haywards Heath 66
- Holyhead 65
- Inverness 65, *Sleepers* 403
- Kensington (Olympia) 66, 176, 177, 186
- Liverpool 65
- London 60, 66, 67
- Manchester 65
- Manchester Airport 65
- Milton Keynes Central 66, 176, 177
- Motherwell 65, *Sleepers* 401
- Northampton 66, 186
- Oxenholme Lake District 65
- Perth 65, *Sleepers* 403
- Preston 65
- Rugby 66
- St. Albans 61
- Stafford 65
- Stirling *Sleepers* 403
- Stoke-on-Trent 65
- Wolverhampton 66

Watford North [LM] Ⓤ 61
Watlington [FC] ⚠ Ⓤ 17
Watton-at-Stone [FC] ⚠ 24
Waun-gron Park [AW] Ⓤ 130
Wavertree Technology Park [NT] 🚲 90
Wealdstone [LT] (see Harrow & Wealdstone)
Wedgwood Old Road Bridge *Bus* 67
Weeley [LE] 🚲 ⚠ Ⓤ 11
Weeton [NT] Ⓟ Ⓤ 35
Welham Green [FC] Ⓟ ⚠ 24
Welling [SE] Ⓟ ⚠ 200
Wellingborough [EM] Ⓟ 🚲 ◇ 🚕 53
Wellington (Shropshire) [LM] Ⓟ ◇ 🚕 75
Welshpool [AW] Ⓟ Ⓤ 75
Welwyn Garden City [FC] (4) ◇ ⚠ 🚕 24, 25
Welwyn North [FC] Ⓟ 🚲 ⚠ 🚕 24, 25
Wem [AW] Ⓟ Ⓤ 131
Wembley Central [LT] ⚠ 60, 66, 176, 177
Wembley Stadium [CH] ⚠ Ⓤ 115
Wembley (North) [LT] (see North Wembley)
Wemyss Bay [SR] Ⓟ 🚲 🚕 219, *Ship* 219B
Wendover [CH] Ⓟ 🚲 ◇ ⚠ 🚕 114
Wennington [NT] Ⓟ Ⓤ 36
Wesham [NT] (see Kirkham & Wesham)
West Allerton [NT] 89, 91
West Brompton [LT] ⚠ 66, 176, 177, 186
West Byfleet [SW] Ⓟ 🚲 ◇ ⚠ 🚕 149, 155
West Calder [SR] Ⓟ 🚲 Ⓤ 225
West Croydon [SN] (4) ◇ ⚠ 🚕 177, 178, 182
West Drayton [GW] Ⓟ ⚠ 🚕 117
West Dulwich [SE] 🚲 ⚠ 195
West Ealing [GW] (3) ⚠ 117
West Ham [LT] ⚠ 1
West Hampstead [LO] ⚠ 59, 176
West Hampstead Thameslink [FC] ◇ ⚠ 52
West Horndon [CC] Ⓟ 🚲 ◇ ⚠ 🚕 1
West Kilbride [SR] Ⓟ 🚲 🚕 Ⓤ 221
West Kirby [ME] 🚲 ⚠ 🚕 106
West Malling [SE] Ⓟ 🚲 ⚠ 🚕 196
West Norwood [SN] (4) ◇ ⚠ 177, 178
West Ruislip [CH] (3) Ⓟ 🚲 ⚠ 115
West Runton [LE] 🚲 Ⓤ 16
West St Leonards [SE] Ⓟ 206
West Sutton [FC] ⚠ Ⓤ 52, 179, 182
West Wickham [SE] Ⓟ 🚲 ⚠ 🚕 203
West Worthing [SN] Ⓟ 🚲 ⚠ 188
Westbury (Wilts.) **[GW]** Ⓟ 🚲 ◇ 🚕 123, 135, 160
Westcliff [CC] Ⓟ 🚲 ◇ ⚠ 🚕 1
Westcombe Park [SE] ⚠ 200
Westenhanger [SE] Ⓟ Ⓤ 207
Wester Hailes [SR] Ⓟ 🚲 Ⓤ 225
Westerfield [LE] 🚲 Ⓤ 13
Westerton [SR] Ⓟ 🚲 226, 227, *Sleepers* 404
Westgate-on-Sea [SE] 🚲 212
Westham [SN] (see Pevensey & Westham)
Westhoughton [NT] Ⓤ 82
Westhumble [SN] (see Boxhill & Westhumble)
Weston Milton [GW] Ⓟ 🚲 Ⓤ 134
Weston-super-Mare [GW] Ⓟ 🚲 ◇ 🚕 51, 125, 134, 135
Wetheral [NT] Ⓟ Ⓤ 48
Weybridge [SW] Ⓟ 🚲 ◇ ⚠ 🚕 149, 155
Weymouth [SW] Ⓟ 🚲 ◇ ⚠ 🚕 123, 158
Whaley Bridge [NT] Ⓟ 86
Whalley [NT] Ⓟ Ⓤ 94
Whatstandwell [EM] Ⓟ Ⓤ 56
Whifflet [SR] Ⓟ 🚕 Ⓤ 220, 224, 226
Whimple [SW] Ⓟ 🚲 Ⓤ 160
Whinhill [SR] 🚲 Ⓤ 219
Whiston [NT] Ⓟ 90
Whitby [NT] Ⓟ ◇ 🚕 Ⓤ 45
Whitby Bus Station 🚕 *Bus* 26G
Whitchurch (Cardiff) [AW] Ⓤ 130
Whitchurch (Hants.) [SW] Ⓟ 🚲 ◇ ⚠ 160
Whitchurch (Shrops) [AW] Ⓟ Ⓤ 131
White Hart Lane [LE] ⚠ 21
White Notley [LE] 🚲 ⚠ Ⓤ 11
Whitecraigs [SR] Ⓟ 🚲 223
Whitehaven [NT] Ⓟ ◇ 100
Whitland [AW] Ⓟ Ⓤ 128
Whitley Bridge [NT] Ⓟ Ⓤ 32
Whitlock's End [LM] ⚠ Ⓤ 71
Whitstable [SE] Ⓟ 🚕 212
Whittlesea [LE] Ⓟ Ⓤ 14, 17
Whittlesford Parkway [LE] Ⓟ 🚲 ⚠ 22
Whitton [SW] 🚲 ◇ ⚠ 149
Whitwell [EM] Ⓤ 55
Whyteleafe [SN] Ⓟ 🚲 ⚠ 181

Station index and table numbers

[10] Connection time
Ⓟ Station Car Park
🚲 Bicycle storage facility
◇ Seat reservations can be made at this station
⚠ Penalty Fare Schemes in operation on some or all services from this station
🚕 Taxi rank or cab office at station, or signposted and within 100 metres
Ⓤ Unstaffed station
[ ] Station Operator Code

Whyteleafe South [SN] Ⓟ 🚲 ⚠ 181
Wick [SR] Ⓟ 🚲 ◇ 🚕 239
Wickford [LE] [2] Ⓟ 🚲 ⚠ 🚕 5
Wickham Market [LE] Ⓟ 🚲 Ⓤ 13
Widdrington [NT] Ⓟ 🚲 Ⓤ 48
Widnes [NT] Ⓟ 🚕 49, 89
Widney Manor [LM] Ⓟ ⚠ 71
Wigan
- **North Western [VT]** Ⓟ ◇ 🚕
- **Wallgate [NT]** 🚲 🚕

Barrow-in-Furness 65
Birmingham 65
Blackpool 90
Bolton 82
Bournemouth 51
Bristol 51
Carlisle 65
Crewe 65
Edinburgh 65
Exeter 51
Glasgow 65
Kirkby 82
Lancaster 65
Liverpool 82, 90
London 65
Manchester 82
Milton Keynes Central 65
Manchester Airport 82
Paignton 51
Penzance 51
Plymouth 51
Preston 65
Oxenholme Lake District 65
Oxford 51
Reading 51
St Helens 90
Southampton 51
Southport 82
Stafford 65
Stockport 82
Torquay 51
Warrington 65
Wolverhampton 65
Windermere 65

Wigton [NT] Ⓟ 🚕 Ⓤ 100
Wildmill [AW] Ⓤ 128
Willesden Junction [LO] ⚠ 59, 60, 176
Williamwood [SR] 🚲 223
Willington [EM] Ⓤ 57
Wilmcote [LM] ⚠ Ⓤ 71, 115
Wilmslow [NT] Ⓟ 🚲 ◇ 🚕 51, 65, 84, 85, 131
Wilnecote [LM] Ⓤ 57
Wilpshire [NT] (see Ramsgreave and Wilpshire)
Wimbledon [SW] [6] Ⓟ 🚲 ◇ ⚠ 🚕 52, 152, 155, 179, 182
Wimbledon Chase [FC] ⚠ Ⓤ 52, 179
Winchelsea [SN] Ⓤ 189
Winchester [SW] Ⓟ 🚲 ◇ ⚠ 🚕 51, 158
Winchfield [SW] Ⓟ 🚲 ◇ ⚠ 155
Winchmore Hill [FC] ⚠ 24
Windermere [TP] Ⓟ ◇ 🚕 65, 82, 83
Windsor & Eton Central [GW] ⚠ 🚕 119
Windsor & Eton Riverside [SW] Ⓟ 🚲 ◇ ⚠ 🚕 149
Winnersh [SW] 🚲 ◇ ⚠ 149
Winnersh Triangle [SW] ◇ ⚠ 149
Winsford [LM] Ⓟ ◇ 91
Wisbech *Bus* 26A
Wishaw [SR] Ⓟ 🚲 226
Witham [LE] [2] Ⓟ 🚲 ◇ ⚠ 🚕 11, 13, 14
Witley [SW] Ⓟ 🚲 ⚠ 156
Witney Market Place *Bus* 116C
Witton [LM] ⚠ 70
Wivelsfield [SN] [4] 🚲 ⚠ 52, 186, 189
Wivenhoe [LE] [3] Ⓟ 🚲 ⚠ 🚕 11
Woburn Sands [LM] Ⓤ 64
Woking [SW] Ⓟ 🚲 ◇ ⚠ 🚕

Aldershot 155
Basingstoke 155
Bournemouth 158
Bristol 160
Exeter 160
Fareham 158
Guildford 156
Heathrow Airport *Bus* 158A
London 149, 155, 156
Portsmouth 156
Salisbury 160
Southampton 158
Surbiton 155
Weymouth 158

Wokingham [SW] Ⓟ 🚲 ◇ ⚠ 🚕 148, 149
Woldingham [SN] Ⓟ 🚲 ⚠ 🚕 184
Wolverhampton [VT] [7] Ⓟ 🚲 ◇ ⚠ 🚕

Bangor (Gwynedd) 65
Birmingham 68
Birmingham International 68
Bournemouth 51
Bristol 51
Carlisle 65
Chester 65, 75
Coventry 68
Crewe 65
Edinburgh 65
Exeter 51
Glasgow 65
Holyhead 65
Liverpool 65
London 66
Macclesfield 84
Manchester 65
Manchester Airport 65
Oxenholme Lake District 65
Oxford 51
Paignton 51
Penzance 51
Plymouth 51
Preston 65
Reading 51
Rugby 66
Shrewsbury 74
Southampton 51
Stafford 68
Stockport 65
Stoke-on-Trent 65
Torquay 51
Walsall 70
Watford 66
Wrexham 75

Wolverton [LM] Ⓟ 🚲 66
Wombwell [NT] Ⓟ Ⓤ 34
Wood End [LM] ⚠ Ⓤ 71
Wood Street [LE] ⚠ 20
Woodbridge [LE] Ⓟ 🚲 🚕 Ⓤ 13
Woodgrange Park [LO] 🚲 ⚠ 62
Woodhall [SR] 🚲 219
Woodham Ferrers [LE] (South Woodham Ferrers)
Woodhouse [NT] Ⓟ Ⓤ 30
Woodlesford [NT] Ⓟ 🚲 Ⓤ 32, 34
Woodley [NT] Ⓟ Ⓤ 78
Woodmansterne [SN] ⚠ 181
Woodsmoor [NT] 86
Wool [SW] Ⓟ 🚲 ◇ ⚠ 🚕 158
Woolston [SW] Ⓟ 🚲 ◇ ⚠ 165
Woolwich Arsenal [SE] [4] Ⓟ ◇ ⚠ 🚕 200
Woolwich Dockyard [SE] ⚠ 200
Wootton Wawen [LM] ⚠ Ⓤ 71
Worcester Foregate Street [LM] [7] ◇ ⚠ 🚕 71, 126
Worcester Shrub Hill [LM] [7] Ⓟ ◇ ⚠ 🚕 57, 71, 126
Worcester Park [SW] Ⓟ 🚲 ◇ ⚠ 🚕 152
Workington [NT] Ⓟ ◇ 100
Workington (Bus Station) 🚕 *Bus* 65F
Worksop [NT] Ⓟ ◇ 30, 55
Worle [GW] Ⓟ 🚲 Ⓤ 134
Worplesdon [SW] Ⓟ 🚲 ◇ ⚠ 155, 156
Worstead [LE] Ⓟ 🚲 Ⓤ 16
Worthing [SN] [4] Ⓟ 🚲 ◇ ⚠ 🚕 123, 188
Wrabness [LE] Ⓟ 🚲 Ⓤ 11
Wraysbury [SW] Ⓟ ⚠ Ⓤ 149
Wrenbury [AW] Ⓟ Ⓤ 131
Wressle [NT] Ⓤ 29
Wrexham Central [AW] Ⓤ 101
Wrexham General [AW] Ⓟ ◇ 🚕 65, 75, 101
Wrotham [SE] (see Borough Green & Wrotham)
Wroxham [LE] (see Hoveton & Wroxham)
Wye [SE] Ⓟ 207

Station index and table numbers

10 Connection time
Ⓟ Station Car Park
🚲 Bicycle storage facility
◇ Seat reservations can be made at this station
⚠ Penalty Fare Schemes in operation on some or all services from this station
🚕 Taxi rank or cab office at station, or signposted and within 100 metres
Ⓤ Unstaffed station
[ ] Station Operator Code

Network Diagram for Tables 1, 4

DM-1/06
Design BAJS

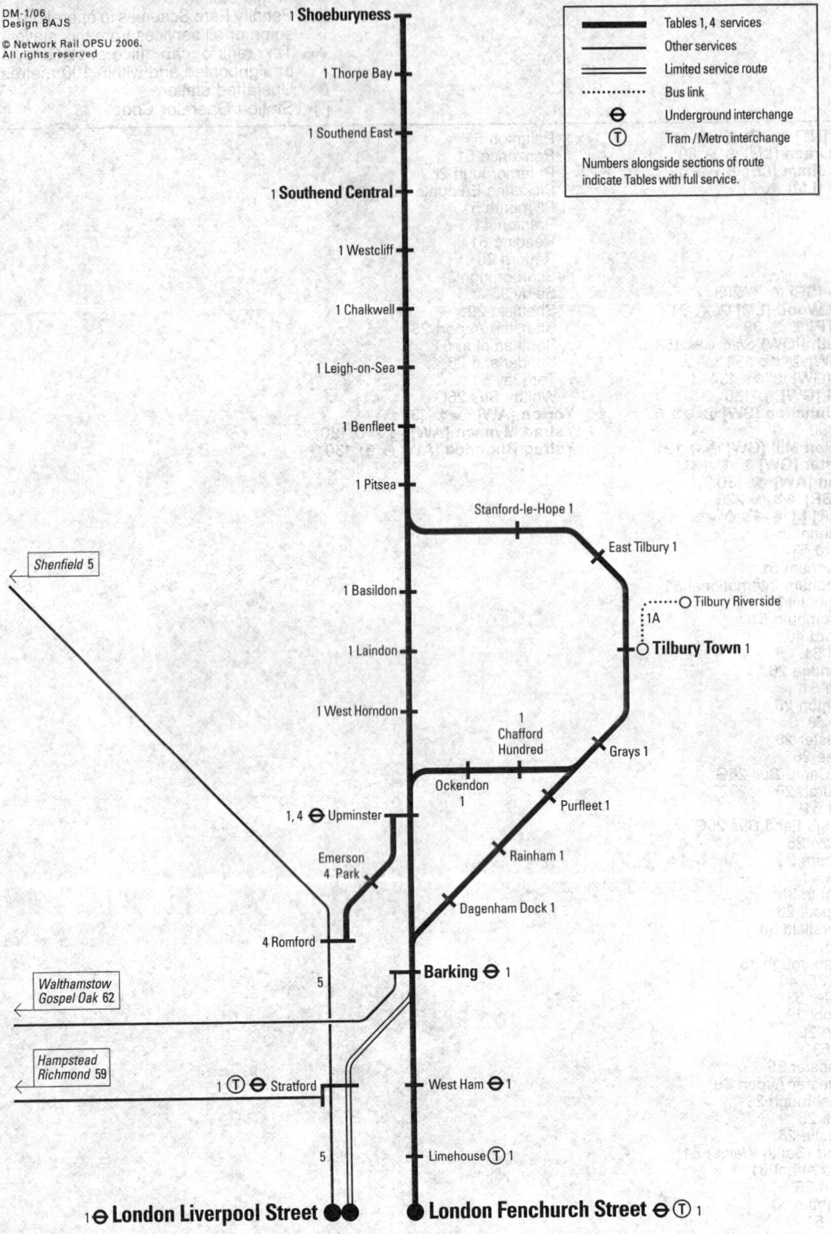
1 Shoeburyness
1 Thorpe Bay
1 Southend East
1 Southend Central
1 Westcliff
1 Chalkwell
1 Leigh-on-Sea
1 Benfleet
1 Pitsea
Stanford-le-Hope 1
East Tilbury 1
Tilbury Riverside
1A
Tilbury Town 1
Shenfield 5
1 Basildon
1 Laindon
1 West Horndon
1 Chafford Hundred
Grays 1
Ockendon 1
Purfleet 1
1, 4 Upminster
Emerson Park 4
Rainham 1
Dagenham Dock 1
4 Romford
Barking 1
5
Walthamstow Gospel Oak 62
Hampstead Richmond 59
1 Stratford
West Ham 1
5
Limehouse 1
1 London Liverpool Street
London Fenchurch Street 1
Tables 1, 4 services
Other services
Limited service route
Bus link
Underground interchange
Tram / Metro interchange
Numbers alongside sections of route indicate Tables with full service.

London → Southend Central and Shoeburyness

Network diagram - see first page of Table I

Miles	Miles	Miles			CC MO	CC MX	CC MX	CC MO	CC MX	CC MX	CC MX	CC MX	CC MO		CC MX	CC MX	CC MX	CC MX	CC MO	CC MX	CC MX	CC	CC	CC
0	0	—	**London Fenchurch Street** 7	⊖ d	22p50	22p50	23p05	23p10	23p10		23p20	23p35	23p40		23p40	23p50	00 01		00 10	00 15	00 25		05 10	
1¾	1¾	—	Limehouse	d	22p54	22p54	23p09	23p14	23p14		23p24	23p39	23p44		23p44	23p54			00 14	00 19	00 29		05 14	
4¾	4¾	—	West Ham	⊖ d	22p59	22p59	23p14	23p19	23p19		23p29	23p44	23p49		23p49	23p59	00 09		00 19	00 24	00 34		05 19	
—	—	—	**London Liverpool Street** 15	⊖ d																				
—	—	—	Stratford 7	⊖ d																				
7½	7½	—	Barking	⊖ d	23p04	23p05	23p20	23p24	23p25		23p35	23p50	23p54		23p55	00 05	00 15		00 24	00 30	00 40		05 25	05 45
15¼	—	0	Upminster	⊖ d	23p12	23p14		23p32	23p34		23p44		00 02		00 04	00 14	00 24		00 32		00 49	05 32	05 34	
—	—	3	Ockendon	d	23p18	23p19					23p49					00 19						05 37		
—	—	5	Chafford Hundred	d	23p21	23p23					23p53					00 23						05 41		
19¼	—	—	West Horndon	d				23p37	23p39				00 07		00 09				00 37		00 54		05 39	
22¾	—	—	Laindon	d				23p42	23p44				00 12		00 16		00 32		00 42		00 59		05 44	
24½	—	—	Basildon	d				23p45	23p47				00 15		00 19		00 35		00 45		01 02		05 47	
—	10½	—	Dagenham Dock	d			23p25					23p55								00 35				05 50
—	12¾	—	Rainham	d			23p29					23p59								00 39				05 54
—	16	—	Purfleet	d			23p34			←		00 04								00 44				05 59
—	19¾	7½	Grays	d	23p25	23p27	23p42			23p42	23p57	00a10				00 27		←		00a50		05a45		06 05
—	21½	—	**Tilbury Town** 3	d	23p28	23p30	→			23p45	00 01					00 30		00 30						→
—	25¼	—	East Tilbury	d	23p34	23p36				23p51	00 06					→		00 36						
—	27¼	—	Stanford-le-Hope	d	23p37	23p40				23p55	00 10							00 40						
26½	32¼	—	Pitsea	d	23p45	23p48		23p49	23p52	00b06	00 18		00 19		00 22			00 48	00 49		01 06		05 51	
29¼	35	—	Benfleet	d	23p49	23p52		23p52	23p56	00 10	00 22		00 22		00 26		00 42	00 52	00 52		01 10		05 55	
32½	38¼	—	Leigh-on-Sea	d	23p53	23p56		23p57	23p59	00 15	00 27		00 27		00 31		00 46	00 56	00 57		01 14		06 00	
34	39¾	—	Chalkwell	d	23p56	23p59		23p59	00 03	00 18	00 30		00 29		00 34		00 49	00 59	00 59		01 17		06 03	
34¾	40½	—	Westcliff	d	23p58	00 02		00 02	00 06	00 20	00 32		00 32		00 36		00 52	01 02	01 02		01 20		06 05	
35¾	41½	—	**Southend Central**	a	00 01	00 05		00 05	00 09	00 23	00 35		00 34		00 39		00 55	01 05	01 04		01 23		06 08	
—	—	—		d	00 01	00 05		00 06	00 09	00 23	00 35		00 36		00 40		00 55	01 05	01 06		01 23		06 08	
36½	42¼	—	Southend East	d	00 03	00 07		00 08	00 11	00 26	00 38		00 38		00 42		00 57	01 07	01 08		01 25		06 10	
38	43¾	—	Thorpe Bay	d	00 06	00 11		00 10	00 15	00 29	00 41		00 40		00 46		01 01	01 11	01 10		01 29		06 14	
39½	45¼	—	**Shoeburyness**	a	00 13	00 17		00 18	00 21	00 36	00 48		00 48		00 52		01 07	01 17	01 18		01 35		06 18	

		CC		CC	CC	CC	CC	CC	CC	CC	CC	CC		CC	CC	CC	CC	CC	CC	CC	CC	CC		CC
London Fenchurch Street 7	⊖ d	05 40						06 10	06 20		06 40			06 44	06 50	07 00	07 09	07 13	07 17	07 30	07 40	07 42		07 48
Limehouse	d	05 44						06 14	06 24		06 44			06 48	06 54		07 13				07 44			
West Ham	⊖ d	05 49						06 19	06 29		06 49			06 53	06 59	07 08	07 18		07 25	07 38	07 49	07 52		
London Liverpool Street 15	⊖ d																							
Stratford 7	⊖ d																							
Barking	⊖ d	05 55			06 05			06 25	06 35	06 52	06 55			07 00	07 05	07 14	07 24	07 26	07 31	07 44	07 55	07 57		
Upminster	⊖ d	06 04				06 10	06 32	06 34			07 04			07c12		07 23	07 33		07 41	07 53	08 04			08e10
Ockendon	d					06a15	06 37							07 17					07 47					08 19
Chafford Hundred	d						06 41							07 21					07 51					08 23
West Horndon	d	06 09						06 39			07 09						07 38				08 09			→
Laindon	d	06 14						06 44			07 14						07 43				08 14			
Basildon	d	06 17						06 47			07 17					07 33	07 46			08 03	08 17			
Dagenham Dock	d				06 10				06 40	06 57					07 10			07 31				08 02		
Rainham	d				06 14				06 44	07 01					07 14			07 35				08 06		
Purfleet	d			←	06 19				06 49	07 06		←			07 19			07 40				08 12		
Grays	d			06 05	06 25		06a46		06 55	07 12		07 12		07a25	07f28			07 46	07 55			08 17		
Tilbury Town 3	d			06 08	06 28				06 58	→		07 15			07 31				07 59			→		
East Tilbury	d			06 14	06 34				07 04			07 21			07 37				08 05					
Stanford-le-Hope	d			06 18	06 38				07 08			07 25			07 41			07 56	08 09					
Pitsea	d	06 21		06 27	06a46			06 51	07 16		07 21	07a33			07a48		07 50	08a03	08a16		08 21			
Benfleet	d	06 25		06 32				06 55	07 20		07 25					07 39	07 54			08 09	08 25			
Leigh-on-Sea	d	06 30		06 36				07 00	07 24		07 30					07 44	07 58			08 14	08 30			
Chalkwell	d	06 33		06 39				07 03	07 27		07 33					07 47	08 01			08 17	08 33			
Westcliff	d	06 35		06 42				07 05	07 30		07 35					07 49	08 04			08 19	08 35			
Southend Central	a	06 38		06 44				07 08	07 32		07 38					07 52	08 06			08 22	08 38			
	d	06 38		06 44				07 08	07 33		07 38					07 52	08 07			08 22	08 38			
Southend East	d	06 40		06 46				07 10	07 35		07 40					07 54	08 09			08 24	08 40			
Thorpe Bay	d	06 44		06 50				07 14	07 38		07 44					07 58	08 12			08 28	08 44			
Shoeburyness	a	06 48		06 54				07 18	07 43		07 48					08 02	08 17			08 32	08 48			

		CC	CC	CC	CC	CC	CC	CC	CC	CC		CC	CC	CC	CC	CC	CC	CC	CC	CC		CC	CC	CC
London Fenchurch Street 7	⊖ d	07 52	08 00			08 05	08 10		08 15	08 20		08 30		08 40	08 50	08 54	09 00		09 10	09 16		09 20	09 30	
Limehouse	d	07 56				08 09	08 14			08 24				08 44	08 54				09 14	09 20		09 24		
West Ham	⊖ d	08 01	08 08				08 19			08 29		08 38		08 49	08 59		09 08		09 19	09 25		09 29	09 38	
London Liverpool Street 15	⊖ d																							
Stratford 7	⊖ d																							
Barking	⊖ d	08 07	08 14			08 18	08 25		08 29	08 35		08 44		08 55	09 06	09 09	09 16		09 25	09 31		09 35	09 44	
Upminster	⊖ d	08 16	08 23				08 34		08g41			08 53		09 04		09 18	09 25		09 34			09 45	09 53	
Ockendon	d				←				08 46							09 23						09 50		
Chafford Hundred	d				08 23				08 50							09 27						09 54		
West Horndon	d	08 21					08 39							09 09					09 39					
Laindon	d	08a27	08 31				08 44					09 01		09 14			09 34		09 44				10 01	
Basildon	d		08 34				08 47					09 04		09 17			09 37		09 47				10 04	
Dagenham Dock	d					08 23				08 40					09 11					09 36				
Rainham	d					08 27				08 44					09 15					09 40				
Purfleet	d			←		08 32		←		08 49			←		09 20			←		09 45				←
Grays	d			08 17	08 27	08 38		08 38	08a54	08 57			08 57		09 27	09a33		09 27		09 51		09 58		09 51
Tilbury Town 3	d			08 21		→		08 42		→			09 00		→			09 30		→		10 02		09 54
East Tilbury	d			08 27				08 48					09 06					09 36				→		10 00
Stanford-le-Hope	d			08 31	08 37			08 52					09 10					09 40						10 04
Pitsea	d		08 38	08g41	08a45		08 51	08a59				09 07	09 18	09 21				09 48	09 51					10 12
Benfleet	d		08 42	08 45			08 55					09 10	09 22	09 26			09 43	09 52	09 55				10 10	10 16
Leigh-on-Sea	d		08 46	08 50			09 00					09 15	09 26	09 30			09 48	09 56	10 00				10 15	10 20
Chalkwell	d		08 49	08 53			09 03					09 18	09 29	09 33			09 51	09 59	10 03				10 18	10 23
Westcliff	d		08 52	08 55			09 05					09 20	09 32	09 36			09 53	10 02	10 05				10 20	10 26
Southend Central	a		08 54	08 58			09 08					09 23	09 35	09 38			09 56	10 05	10 08				10 23	10 29
	d		08 55				09 08					09 23		09 38			09 56		10 08				10 23	
Southend East	d		08 57				09 10					09 25		09 40			09 58		10 10				10 25	
Thorpe Bay	d		09 00				09 14					09 29		09 44			10 02		10 14				10 29	
Shoeburyness	a		09 05				09 18					09 36		09 48			10 06		10 18				10 34	

For general notes see front of timetable
For details of catering facilities see Directory of Train Operators

b Arr. 0003
c Arr. 0709
e Arr. 0807
f Arr. 0725
g Arr. 0838

London → Southend Central and Shoeburyness

Network diagram - see first page of Table 1

		CC	CC	CC	CC	CC	CC	CC	CC	
London Fenchurch Street 7	⊖ d	09 35	09 40		09 50	10 00		10 05	10 10	
Limehouse	d	09 39	09 44		09 54			10 09	10 14	
West Ham	⊖ d	09 44	09 49		09 59	10 08		10 14	10 19	
London Liverpool Street 15	⊖ d									
Stratford 7	⊖ d									
Barking	⊖ d	09 50	09 55		10 05	10 14		10 20	10 25	
Upminster	⊖ d		10 04		10 15	10 23			10 34	
Ockendon	d				10 20					
Chafford Hundred	d				10 24					
West Horndon	d		10 09						10 39	
Laindon	d		10 14			10 31			10 44	
Basildon	d		10 17			10 34			10 47	
Dagenham Dock	d	09 55						10 25		
Rainham	d	09 59						10 29		
Purfleet	d	10 04						10 34		
Grays	d	10a10		←	10 28		←	10a40		
Tilbury Town 3	d			10 02	10 32		10 32			
East Tilbury	d			10 08	→		10 38			
Stanford-le-Hope	d			10 12			10 42			
Pitsea	d		10 21	10b25			10c54		10 51	
Benfleet	d		10 25	10 29		10 40	→		10 55	
Leigh-on-Sea	d		10 30	10 34		10 45			10 59	
Chalkwell	d		10 33	10 37		10 48			11 02	
Westcliff	d		10 35	10 39		10 50			11 05	
Southend Central	a		10 38	10 42		10 53			11 07	
	d		10 38			10 53			11 08	
Southend East	d		10 40			10 55			11 10	
Thorpe Bay	d		10 44			10 59			11 14	
Shoeburyness	a		10 48			11 04			11 18	

		CC	CC	CC	CC	CC		CC	CC	CC	CC	CC	CC	CC	CC
London Fenchurch Street 7	⊖ d		10 20	10 30		10 35		10 40	10 50	11 00		11 05	11 10	11 20	11 30
Limehouse	d		10 24			10 39		10 44	10 54			11 09	11 14	11 24	
West Ham	⊖ d		10 29	10 38		10 44		10 49	10 59	11 08		11 14	11 19	11 29	11 38
London Liverpool Street 15	⊖ d														
Stratford 7	⊖ d														
Barking	⊖ d		10 35	10 44		10 50		10 55	11 05	11 14		11 20	11 25	11 35	11 44
Upminster	⊖ d		10 44	10 53				11 04	11 14	11 23			11 34	11 44	11 53
Ockendon	d		10 49						11 19					11 49	
Chafford Hundred	d		10 53						11 23					11 53	
West Horndon	d							11 09					11 39		
Laindon	d			11 01				11 14		11 31			11 44		12 01
Basildon	d			11 04				11 17		11 34			11 47		12 04
Dagenham Dock	d					10 55						11 25			
Rainham	d					10 59						11 29			
Purfleet	d					11 04						11 34			
Grays	d		10 57		←	11a10			11 27		←	11a40		11 57	
Tilbury Town 3	d		11 00		11 00				11 30		11 30			12 00	
East Tilbury	d		→		11 06				→		11 36			→	
Stanford-le-Hope	d	←			11 10						11 40				
Pitsea	d	10 54			11 18			11 21			11 48		11 51		
Benfleet	d	10 58		11 10	11 22			11 25		11 40	11 52		11 55		12 10
Leigh-on-Sea	d	11 03		11 15	11 26			11 30		11 45	11 56		12 00		12 15
Chalkwell	d	11 06		11 18	11 29			11 33		11 48	11 59		12 03		12 18
Westcliff	d	11 08		11 20	11 32			11 35		11 50	12 02		12 05		12 20
Southend Central	a	11 11		11 23	11 35			11 38		11 53	12 05		12 08		12 23
	d			11 23				11 38		11 53			12 08		12 23
Southend East	d			11 25				11 40		11 55			12 10		12 25
Thorpe Bay	d			11 29				11 44		11 59			12 14		12 29
Shoeburyness	a			11 34				11 48		12 04			12 18		12 34

		CC	CC	and at the same minutes past each hour until		CC	CC	CC	CC	CC	CC	CC	CC	CC
London Fenchurch Street 7	⊖ d		11 35			14 40	14 50	15 00		15 05	15 10	15 20	15 25	15 30
Limehouse	d		11 39			14 44	14 54			15 09	15 14	15 24		
West Ham	⊖ d		11 44			14 49	14 59	15 08		15 14	15 19	15 29	15 33	15 38
London Liverpool Street 15	⊖ d													
Stratford 7	⊖ d													
Barking	⊖ d		11 50			14 55	15 05	15 14		15 20	15 25	15 35	15 39	15 44
Upminster	⊖ d					15 04	15 14	15 23			15 34	15 44	15 48	15 53
Ockendon	d						15 19					15 49		
Chafford Hundred	d						15 23					15 53		
West Horndon	d					15 09					15 39			
Laindon	d					15 14		15 31			15 44		15 56	16 01
Basildon	d					15 17		15 34			15 47		15 59	16 04
Dagenham Dock	d		11 55							15 25				
Rainham	d		11 59							15 29				
Purfleet	d		12 04							15 34				
Grays	d	←	12a10				15 27		←	15a40		15 57		
Tilbury Town 3	d	12 00					15 30		15 30			→		
East Tilbury	d	12 06					→		15 36					
Stanford-le-Hope	d	12 10							15 40					
Pitsea	d	12 18				15 21			15 48		15 51		16 03	
Benfleet	d	12 22				15 25		15 40	15 52		15 55		16 07	16 10
Leigh-on-Sea	d	12 26				15 30		15 45	15 56		16 00		16a12	16 15
Chalkwell	d	12 29				15 33		15 48	15 59		16 03			16 18
Westcliff	d	12 32				15 35		15 50	16 02		16 05			16 20
Southend Central	a	12 35				15 38		15 53	16 05		16 08			16 23
	d					15 38		15 53			16 08			16 23
Southend East	d					15 40		15 55			16 10			16 25
Thorpe Bay	d					15 44		15 59			16 14			16 29
Shoeburyness	a					15 48		16 04			16 18			16 34

			CC	CC	CC	CC	CC	CC	CC	CC
London Fenchurch Street 7	⊖ d		15 35	15 40		15 50	15 55	16 00	16 10	16 13
Limehouse	d		15 39	15 44		15 54	15 59		16 14	16 17
West Ham	⊖ d		15 44	15 49		15 59	16 04	16 08	16 19	16 22
London Liverpool Street 15	⊖ d									
Stratford 7	⊖ d									
Barking	⊖ d		15 50	15 54		16 05	16 10	16 14	16 25	16 28
Upminster	⊖ d			16 02		16 14		16 23	16 34	
Ockendon	d					16 19				
Chafford Hundred	d					16 23				
West Horndon	d			16 07					16 39	
Laindon	d			16 12					16 44	
Basildon	d			16 15				16 33	16 47	
Dagenham Dock	d		15 55				16 15			16 33
Rainham	d		15 59				16 19			16 37
Purfleet	d		16 04		←		16 24			16 43
Grays	d		16a10		15 57	16 27	16a33			16 49
Tilbury Town 3	d				16 00	16 31				16 52
East Tilbury	d				16 06	16 37				16 58
Stanford-le-Hope	d				16 10	16 41				17 02
Pitsea	d			16 19	16e22	16a48			16 51	17a12
Benfleet	d			16 22	16 26			16 40	16 55	
Leigh-on-Sea	d			16 27	16 30			16 45	17 00	
Chalkwell	d			16 29	16 33			16 48	17 03	
Westcliff	d			16 32	16 36			16 50	17 05	
Southend Central	a			16 34	16 41			16 53	17 08	
	d			16 35				16 53	17 08	
Southend East	d			16 37				16 55	17 10	
Thorpe Bay	d			16 39				16 59	17 14	
Shoeburyness	a			16 44				17 05	17 20	

		CC	CC	CC		CC	CC	CC	CC	CC	CC	CC	CC	CC
London Fenchurch Street 7	⊖ d	16 20	16 28	16 30		16 33	16 37	16 45	16 48	16 54	17 00		17 02	17 05
Limehouse	d	16 24		16 34		16 37	16 41	16 49	16 52	16 58				17 09
West Ham	⊖ d	16 29	16 36	16 39		16 42	16 46		16 57	17 03				
London Liverpool Street 15	⊖ d													
Stratford 7	⊖ d													
Barking	⊖ d	16 35		16 45		16 48	16 52	16 59	17 03	17 09			17 15	17 19
Upminster	⊖ d	16 45		16 55			17 02	17 08	17 13				17 24	
Ockendon	d	16 50					17 08						17 29	
Chafford Hundred	d	16 54					17 12						17 33	
West Horndon	d			17 00					17 18					
Laindon	d		16 56	17a08				17 17	17a26					17 35
Basildon	d		16 59					17 20						17 38
Dagenham Dock	d					16 53				17 14				
Rainham	d					16 57				17 18				
Purfleet	d					17 03				17 24		←		
Grays	d	16 59				17 09	17a18			17 30		17 09	17a40	
Tilbury Town 3	d	17 02				→				→		17 12		
East Tilbury	d	17 08										17 18		
Stanford-le-Hope	d	17a15										17 22		
Pitsea	d							17 24				17a32		17 42
Benfleet	d		17 06					17 28			17 33			17 46
Leigh-on-Sea	d		17 11					17 33			17 37			17 51
Chalkwell	d		17 14					17 36			17 40			17 54
Westcliff	d		17 16					17 38			17 43			17 56
Southend Central	a		17 19					17 41			17 45			17 59
	d		17 19					17 41			17 45			17 59
Southend East	d		17 21					17 43			17 47			18 01
Thorpe Bay	d		17 24					17 46			17 51			18 04
Shoeburyness	a		17 31					17 53			17 59			18 11

			CC	CC	CC	CC	CC	CC	CC	CC	CC
London Fenchurch Street 7	⊖ d		17 07	17 11	17 15	17 18		17 20	17 22		17 26
Limehouse	d		17 12	17 16	17 19			17 24	17 27		17 30
West Ham	⊖ d		17 17						17 32		
London Liverpool Street 15	⊖ d										
Stratford 7	⊖ d										
Barking	⊖ d		17 22	17 25				17 34	17 37		17 40
Upminster	⊖ d		17 31			17 39			17 46		
Ockendon	d										
Chafford Hundred	d										
West Horndon	d		17 36						17 51		
Laindon	d		17a43					17 50	17a58		
Basildon	d					17 50		17 54			
Dagenham Dock	d			17 30							17 45
Rainham	d			17 34						←	17 49
Purfleet	d			17 39			←			17 39	17 54
Grays	d			→			17 30			17 48	18 00
Tilbury Town 3	d						17 33			17 51	→
East Tilbury	d						17 39			17 57	
Stanford-le-Hope	d						17 43			18 01	
Pitsea	d					17 53	17a53	17 57		18a11	
Benfleet	d				17 52	17 58		18 02			
Leigh-on-Sea	d				17 56	18 02		18 06			
Chalkwell	d				17 59	18 05		18 09			
Westcliff	d				18 02	18 08		18 12			
Southend Central	a				18 04	18 13		18 14			
	d				18 04			18 15			
Southend East	d				18 06			18 17			
Thorpe Bay	d				18 10			18 20			
Shoeburyness	a				18 16			18 28			

For general notes see front of timetable
For details of catering facilities see Directory of Train Operators

b Arr. 1019
c Arr. 1049
e Arr. 1618

London → Southend Central and Shoeburyness

Network diagram - see first page of Table I

		CC	CC		CC	CC	CC	CC	CC	CC	CC	CC	CC		CC	CC	CC	CC	CC	CC	CC	CC	CC	CC
London Fenchurch Street 7	⊖ d	17 30	17 32		17 35	17 37	17 41	17 45		17 47	17 50	17 53	17 56		18 00		18 02	18 06	18 09	18 12	18 20			18 22
Limehouse	d				17 39	17 42	17 45	17 49		17 52		17 57	18 00				18 06	18 10	18 13	18 16				18 26
West Ham	⊖ d					17 47					17 58				18 08				18 18	18 21				
London Liverpool Street 15	⊖ d																							
Stratford 7	⊖ d																							
Barking	⊖ d		17 45		17 49	17 52	17 55					18 07	18 10				18 16	18 20	18 24	18 28				
Upminster	⊖ d		17 54			18 01				18 09	18 11						18 26		18 33					18 43
Ockendon	d		18 00							18 14							18 32							18 48
Chafford Hundred	d		18 04							18 18							18 36							18 52
West Horndon	d					18 06						18 19							18 38					
Laindon	d				18 05	18a13						18 25						18 36	18 42		18 46			
Basildon	d				18 08						18 23	18 28			18 33			18 40	18 46		18 50			
Dagenham Dock	d						18 00						18 15							18 33				
Rainham	d						18 04						18 19			←				18 37		←		
Purfleet	d						18 09 →		←				18 24 →			18 09				18 42		18 24	←	
Grays	d		18a10						18 00	18a24						18 18	18 41 →			18 48 →		18 32	18 41	18 57 →
Tilbury Town 3	d								18 04							18 21						18 35	18 44	
East Tilbury	d								18 10							18 27						18 41	18 50	
Stanford-le-Hope	d								18 14							18 31						18 46	18 54	
Pitsea	d				18 12				18a23		18 26	18 32			18 37	18a41		18 43	18 49			18b56	19a04	
Benfleet	d	18 07			18 16			18 22			18 31	18 36			18 40			18 48	18 53		18 57	19 01		
Leigh-on-Sea	d	18 11			18 21			18 26			18 35	18 41			18 46			18 52	18 58		19 02	19 05		
Chalkwell	d	18 14			18 24			18 29			18 38	18 44			18 49			18 55	19 00		19 05	19 08		
Westcliff	d	18 17			18 26			18 32			18 41	18 47			18 51			18 58	19 03		19 07	19 11		
Southend Central	a	18 19			18 29			18 34			18 43	18 49			18 54			19 00	19 05		19 10	19 16		
	d	18 19			18 29			18 34			18 43	18 49			18 54			19 00	19 06		19 10			
Southend East	d	18 21			18 31			18 36			18 45	18 51			18 56			19 02	19 08		19 12			
Thorpe Bay	d	18 25			18 34			18 40			18 49	18 55			18 59			19 06	19 10		19 15			
Shoeburyness	a	18 31			18 41			18 49			18 55	19 01			19 06			19 12	19 17		19 24			

		CC		CC	CC	CC	CC	CC	CC	CC	CC	CC		CC	CC	CC	CC	CC	CC	CC	CC	CC		CC
London Fenchurch Street 7	⊖ d	18 25				18 30	18 33	18 40	18 45		18 51	19 00		19 02	19 05		19 08	19 10		19 20	19 30			19 32
Limehouse	d	18 29				18 34	18 37		18 50		18 54				19 09		19 12	19 14		19 24				
West Ham	⊖ d	18 34						18 48	18 55		18 59			19 10			19 17	19 19		19 29				19 40
London Liverpool Street 15	⊖ d																							
Stratford 7	⊖ d																							
Barking	⊖ d	18 40				18 45	18 47		19 00		19 05			19 16	19 19		19 23	19 25		19 35				19 46
Upminster	⊖ d	18 50					18 56		19 09					19 26	19 30			19 34		19 44	19 50			19 55
Ockendon	d						19 03							19 33						19 49				
Chafford Hundred	d						19 08							19 38						19 53				
West Horndon	d	18 55							19 14									19 39						20 00
Laindon	d	19 00							19 19			19 26						19 44						20a06
Basildon	d	19 04						19 12	19 22						19 40			19 47			20 00			
Dagenham Dock	d					18 50					19 10						19 28							
Rainham	d					18 54					19 14					←	19 32							
Purfleet	d			←	←	18 59				←	19 20 →					19 20	19 37		←					
Grays	d			18 48	18 57	19 05 →	19a14			19 05				19 46 →		19 27	19a43		19 46	19 57		←		
Tilbury Town 3	d			18 52	19 00					19 09						19 30			19 50	20 00 →		20 00		
East Tilbury	d			18 58	19 06					19 15						19 36			19 56			20 06		
Stanford-le-Hope	d			19 02	19 10					19 19						19 40			20 00			20 10		
Pitsea	d	19 08		19a11	19a22				19 26	19a28					19 44	19 48		19 51	20a07			20 18		
Benfleet	d	19 12						19 19	19 30			19 32			19 48	19 52		19 55			20 06	20 22		
Leigh-on-Sea	d	19 16						19 24	19 34			19 36			19 52	19 56		20 00			20 11	20 27		
Chalkwell	d	19 19						19 27	19 37			19 39			19 55	19 59		20 03			20 14	20 30		
Westcliff	d	19 22						19 29	19 39			19 42			19 58	20 02		20 05			20 16	20 32		
Southend Central	a	19 24						19 32	19 42			19 44			20 00	20 07		20 08			20 19	20 35		
	d	19 24						19 32	19 42			19 44			20 00			20 08			20 19			
Southend East	d	19 26						19 34	19 44			19 47			20 02			20 10			20 21			
Thorpe Bay	d	19 30						19 37	19 46			19 51			20a06			20 14			20 25			
Shoeburyness	a	19 36						19 44	19 53			19 58						20 18			20 29			

		CC	CC	CC	CC	CC	CC	CC	CC	CC		CC	CC	CC	CC	CC	CC	CC	CC	CC		CC	CC	CC
London Fenchurch Street 7	⊖ d	19 35	19 40	19 50	20 00		20 05	20 10	20 20	20 30				20 40	20 50	21 00		21 05	21 10	21 20		21 30		
Limehouse	d	19 39	19 44	19 54			20 09	20 14	20 24					20 44	20 54			21 09	21 14	21 24				
West Ham	⊖ d	19 44	19 49	19 59	20 08		20 14	20 19	20 29	20 38				20 49	20 59	21 08		21 14	21 19	21 29		21 38		
London Liverpool Street 15	⊖ d												20 35											21 35
Stratford 7	⊖ d												20 42											21 42
Barking	⊖ d	19 50	19 55	20 05	20 14		20 20	20 25	20 35	20 44			20 50	20 55	21 05	21 14		21 20	21 25	21 35		21 44		21 50
Upminster	⊖ d		20 04	20 14	20 23			20 34	20 44	20 53				21 04	21 14	21 23			21 34	21 44		21 53		
Ockendon	d			20 19					20 49						21 19					21 49				
Chafford Hundred	d			20 23					20 53						21 23					21 53				
West Horndon	d		20 09					20 39						21 09					21 39					
Laindon	d		20 14		20 31			20 44		21 01				21 14		21 31			21 44			22 01		
Basildon	d		20 17		20 34			20 47		21 04				21 17		21 34			21 47			22 04		
Dagenham Dock	d	19 55					20 25						20 55					21 25						21 55
Rainham	d	19 59					20 29						20 59					21 29						21 59
Purfleet	d	20 04					20 34						21 04					21 34						22 04
Grays	d	20a10		20 27		←	20a40		20 57			←	21a10		21 27		←	21a40		21 57			←	22a11
Tilbury Town 3	d			20 30 →		20 30			21 00 →			21 00			21 30 →		21 30			22 00 →			22 00	
East Tilbury	d					20 36						21 06					21 36						22 06	
Stanford-le-Hope	d					20 40						21 10					21 40						22 10	
Pitsea	d		20 21			20 48		20 51				21 18		21 21			21 48		21 51				22 18	
Benfleet	d		20 26		20 40	20 52		20 55		21 10		21 22		21 25		21 40	21 52		21 55			22 10	22 22	
Leigh-on-Sea	d		20 30		20 45	20 56		21 00		21 15		21 26		21 30		21 45	21 56		22 00			22 15	22 26	
Chalkwell	d		20 33		20 48	20 59		21 03		21 18		21 29		21 33		21 48	21 59		22 03			22 18	22 29	
Westcliff	d		20 36		20 50	21 02		21 05		21 20		21 32		21 35		21 50	22 02		22 05			22 20	22 32	
Southend Central	a		20 38		20 53	21 05		21 08		21 23		21 35		21 38		21 53	22 05		22 08			22 23	22 35	
	d		20 38		20 53			21 08		21 23				21 38		21 53			22 08			22 23		
Southend East	d		20 40		20 55			21 10		21 25				21 40		21 56			22 10			22 25		
Thorpe Bay	d		20 44		20 59			21 14		21 29				21 44		21 58			22 14			22 29		
Shoeburyness	a		20 48		21 04			21 18		21 34				21 48		22 04			22 18			22 34		

For general notes see front of timetable
For details of catering facilities see
Directory of Train Operators

b Arr. 1853

London → Southend Central and Shoeburyness

Network diagram - see first page of Table I

		CC	CC	CC	CC	CC	CC	CC	CC		CC	CC	CC	CC	CC	CC	CC	CC	CC		CC	CC		
London Fenchurch Street 7	d	21 40	21 50	22 00		22 05	22 10	22 20	22 35		22 40	22 50	23 00		23 05	23 10		23 20	23 35		23 40	23 50		
Limehouse	d	21 44	21 54			22 09	22 14	22 24	22 39		22 44	22 54			23 09	23 14		23 24	23 39		23 44	23 54		
West Ham	d	21 49	21 59	22 08		22 14	22 19	22 29	22 44		22 49	22 59	23 08		23 14	23 19		23 29	23 44		23 49	23 59		
London Liverpool Street 15	d																							
Stratford 7	d																							
Barking	d	21 55	22 05	22 14		22 20	22 25	22 35	22 50		22 55	23 05	23 14		23 20	23 25		23 35	23 50		23 55	00 05		
Upminster	d	22 04	22 14	22 23			22 34	22 44			23 04	23 14	23 23			23 34		23 44			00 04	00 14		
Ockendon	d		22 19					22 49				23 19						23 49				00 19		
Chafford Hundred	d		22 23					22 53				23 23						23 53				00 23		
West Horndon	d	22 09					22 39				23 09					23 39					00 09			
Laindon	d	22 14		22 31			22 44				23 14		23 31			23 44					00 16			
Basildon	d	22 17		22 34			22 47				23 17		23 34			23 47					00 19			
Dagenham Dock	d					22 25			22 55						23 25				23 55					
Rainham	d					22 29			22 59						23 29				23 59					
Purfleet	d					22 34			23 04						23 34		←		00 04					
Grays	d		22 27		←	22a40		22 57	23a11			23 27		←	23 42		23 42	23 57	00a10			00 27		
Tilbury Town 3	d		22 30		22 30			23 00				23 30		23 30	→		23 45	00 01				00 30		
East Tilbury	d		→		22 36			23 06				→		23 36			23 51	00 06				00 36		
Stanford-le-Hope	d				22 40			23 10						23 40			23 55	00 10				00 40		
Pitsea	d	22 21			22 48		22 51	23 18			23 22			23 48		23 52	00b06	00 18			00 22	00 48		
Benfleet	d	22 25		22 40	22 52		22 55	23 22			23 26		23 41	23 52		23 56	00 10	00 22			00 26	00 52		
Leigh-on-Sea	d	22 30		22 45	22 56		23 00	23 26			23 30		23 45	23 56		23 59	00 15	00 27			00 31	00 56		
Chalkwell	d	22 33		22 48	22 59		23 03	23 29			23 33		23 48	23 59		00 03	00 18	00 30			00 34	00 59		
Westcliff	d	22 35		22 50	23 02		23 05	23 32			23 36		23 51	00 02		00 06	00 20	00 32			00 36	01 02		
Southend Central	a	22 38		22 52	23 05		23 08	23 35			23 39		23 54	00 05		00 09	00 23	00 35			00 39	01 05		
	d	22 38		22 53	23 05		23 08	23 35			23 39		23 54	00 05		00 09	00 23	00 35			00 40	01 05		
Southend East	d	22 40		22 55	23 07		23 10	23 37			23 41		23 56	00 07		00 11	00 26	00 38			00 42	01 07		
Thorpe Bay	d	22 44		22 59	23 10		23 14	23 41			23 45		23 59	00 11		00 15	00 29	00 41			00 46	01 11		
Shoeburyness	a	22 48		23 04	23 15		23 18	23 47			23 51		00 06	00 17		00 21	00 36	00 48			00 52	01 17		

Saturdays

		CC	CC	CC	CC	CC	CC	CC		CC	CC	CC	CC	CC	CC	CC		CC	CC	CC	CC	CC	CC	CC
London Fenchurch Street 7	d	22p50	23p05	23p10		23p20	23p35	23p40		23p50	00 01		00 15	00 25				05 10	05 35	05 50	06 05	06 10	06 20	06 35
Limehouse	d	22p54	23p09	23p14		23p24	23p39	23p44		23p54			00 19	00 29				05 14	05 39	05 54	06 09	06 14	06 24	06 39
West Ham	d	22p59	23p14	23p19		23p29	23p44	23p49		23p59	00 09		00 24	00 34				05 19	05 44	05 59	06 14	06 19	06 29	06 44
London Liverpool Street 15	d																							
Stratford 7	d																							
Barking	d	23p05	23p20	23p25		23p35	23p50	23p55		00 05	00 15		00 30	00 40				05 24	05 49	06 04	06 19	06 24	06 34	06 49
Upminster	d	23p14		23p34		23p44		00 04		00 14	00 24			00 49	05 05	05 27		05 32		06 12		06 32	06 42	
Ockendon	d	23p19				23p49				00 19					05a12	05 32				06 18			06 48	
Chafford Hundred	d	23p23				23p53				00 23						05 36				06 21			06 51	
West Horndon	d			23p39				00 09						00 54				05 37				06 37		
Laindon	d			23p44				00 16			00 32			00 59				05 42				06 42		
Basildon	d			23p47				00 19			00 35			01 02				05 45				06 45		
Dagenham Dock	d		23p25				23p55						00 35						05 54		06 24			06 54
Rainham	d		23p29				23p59						00 39						05 57		06 27			06 57
Purfleet	d		23p34		←		00 04						00 44						06 03		06 33			07 03
Grays	d	23p27	23p42		23p42	23p57	00a10			00 27		←	00a50			05a42			06a12	06 25	06a42		06 55	07a12
Tilbury Town 3	d	23p30	→		23p45	00 01				00 30		00 30								06 28			06 58	
East Tilbury	d	23p36			23p51	00 06				→		00 36								06 34			07 04	
Stanford-le-Hope	d	23p40			23p55	00 10						00 40								06 37			07 07	
Pitsea	d	23p48		23p52	00b06	00 18		00 22				00 48		01 06				05 50		06 45		06 49	07 15	
Benfleet	d	23p52		23p56	00 10	00 22		00 26			00 42	00 52		01 10				05 54		06 49		06 52	07 19	
Leigh-on-Sea	d	23p56		23p59	00 15	00 27		00 31			00 46	00 56		01 14				05 58		06 53		06 57	07 23	
Chalkwell	d	23p59		00 03	00 18	00 30		00 34			00 49	00 59		01 17				06 01		06 56		06 59	07 26	
Westcliff	d	00 02		00 06	00 20	00 32		00 36			00 52	01 02		01 20				06 03		06 58		07 02	07 28	
Southend Central	a	00 05		00 09	00 23	00 35		00 39			00 55	01 05		01 23				06 06		07 04		07 05	07 34	
	d	00 05		00 09	00 23	00 35		00 40			00 55	01 05		01 23				06 07				07 06		
Southend East	d	00 07		00 11	00 26	00 38		00 42			00 57	01 07		01 25				06 09				07 08		
Thorpe Bay	d	00 11		00 15	00 29	00 41		00 46			01 01	01 11		01 29				06 12				07 10		
Shoeburyness	a	00 17		00 21	00 36	00 48		00 52			01 07	01 17		01 35				06 19				07 18		

		CC	CC		CC	CC	CC	CC	CC	CC	CC		CC	CC	CC	CC	CC	CC	CC			CC	CC	CC
London Fenchurch Street 7	d	06 40	06 50		07 05	07 10	07 20	07 35	07 40	07 50	08 05		08 10	08 20	08 35	08 40	08 50	09 00				09 05	09 10	09 20
Limehouse	d	06 44	06 54		07 09	07 14	07 24	07 39	07 44	07 54	08 09		08 14	08 24	08 39	08 44	08 54					09 09	09 14	09 24
West Ham	d	06 49	06 59		07 14	07 19	07 29	07 44	07 49	07 59	08 14		08 19	08 29	08 44	08 49	08 59	09 08				09 14	09 19	09 29
London Liverpool Street 15	d																							
Stratford 7	d																							
Barking	d	06 54	07 04		07 19	07 24	07 34	07 49	07 54	08 04	08 19		08 24	08 34	08 49	08 54	09 04	09 13				09 19	09 24	09 34
Upminster	d	07 02	07 12			07 32	07 42		08 02	08 12			08 32	08 42		09 02	09 12	09 21					09 32	09 42
Ockendon	d		07 18				07 48			08 18				08 48			09 18							09 48
Chafford Hundred	d		07 21				07 51			08 21				08 51			09 21							09 51
West Horndon	d	07 07				07 37			08 07				08 37			09 07							09 37	
Laindon	d	07 12				07 42			08 12				08 42			09 12		09 29					09 42	
Basildon	d	07 15				07 45			08 15				08 45			09 15		09 32					09 45	
Dagenham Dock	d				07 24			07 54			08 24				08 54							09 24		
Rainham	d				07 27			07 57			08 27				08 57							09 27		
Purfleet	d				07 33			08 03			08 33				09 03							09 33		
Grays	d		07 25		07a42		07 55	08a12		08 25	08a42			08 55	09a12		09 25		←			09a42		09 55
Tilbury Town 3	d		07 28				07 58			08 28				08 58			09 28		09 28					09 58
East Tilbury	d		07 34				08 04			08 34				09 04			→		09 34					→
Stanford-le-Hope	d		07 37				08 07			08 37				09 07					09 37					
Pitsea	d	07 19	07 45			07 49	08 15		08 19	08 45			08 49	09 15		09 19			09 45				09 49	
Benfleet	d	07 22	07 49			07 52	08 19		08 22	08 49			08 52	09 19		09 22		09 38	09 49				09 52	
Leigh-on-Sea	d	07 27	07 53			07 57	08 23		08 27	08 53			08 57	09 23		09 27		09 42	09 53				09 57	
Chalkwell	d	07 29	07 56			07 59	08 26		08 29	08 56			08 59	09 26		09 29		09 45	09 56				09 59	
Westcliff	d	07 32	07 58			08 02	08 28		08 32	08 58			09 02	09 28		09 32		09 47	09 58				10 02	
Southend Central	a	07 35	08 04			08 05	08 34		08 35	09 04			09 05	09 34		09 35		09 50	10 04				10 05	
	d	07 36				08 06			08 36				09 06			09 36		09 50					10 06	
Southend East	d	07 38				08 08			08 38				09 08			09 38		09 52					10 08	
Thorpe Bay	d	07 40				08 10			08 40				09 10			09 40		09 55					10 10	
Shoeburyness	a	07 48				08 18			08 48				09 18			09 48		10 02					10 18	

For general notes see front of timetable
For details of catering facilities see Directory of Train Operators

b Arr. 0003

Table 1

London → Southend Central and Shoeburyness

Saturdays

Network diagram - see first page of Table 1

	CC	CC	CC	CC	CC	CC	CC	
London Fenchurch Street 7 ⊖ d	09 30		09 35	09 40	09 50	10 00		
Limehouse d			09 39	09 44	09 54			
West Ham ⊖ d	09 38		09 44	09 49	09 59	10 08		
London Liverpool Street 15 ⊖ d								
Stratford 7 ⊖ d								
Barking ⊖ d	09 43		09 49	09 54	10 04	10 13		
Upminster ⊖ d	09 51			10 02	10 12	10 21		
Ockendon d					10 18			
Chafford Hundred d					10 21			and at
West Horndon d				10 07				
Laindon d	09 59			10 12		10 29		the same
Basildon d	10 02			10 15		10 32		
Dagenham Dock d			09 54					minutes
Rainham d			09 57					
Purfleet d			10 03					past
Grays d		←	10a12		10 25		←	
Tilbury Town 3 d		09 58			10 28 →		10 28	each
East Tilbury d		10 04					10 34	
Stanford-le-Hope d		10 07					10 37	hour until
Pitsea d		10 15		10 19			10 45	
Benfleet d	10 08	10 19		10 22		10 38	10 49	
Leigh-on-Sea d	10 12	10 23		10 27		10 42	10 53	
Chalkwell d	10 15	10 26		10 29		10 45	10 56	
Westcliff d	10 17	10 28		10 32		10 47	10 58	
Southend Central a	10 20	10 34		10 35		10 50	11 04	
d	10 20			10 36		10 50		
Southend East d	10 22			10 38		10 52		
Thorpe Bay d	10 25			10 40		10 55		
Shoeburyness a	10 32			10 48		11 02		

		CC	CC	CC	CC	CC	CC	CC		CC	CC	CC	CC	CC
London Fenchurch Street 7 ⊖ d		20 05	20 10	20 20	20 35	20 40	20 50	21 00			21 05	21 10	21 20	21 35
Limehouse d		20 09	20 14	20 24	20 39	20 44	20 54				21 09	21 14	21 24	21 39
West Ham ⊖ d		20 14	20 19	20 29	20 44	20 49	20 59	21 08			21 14	21 19	21 29	21 44
London Liverpool Street 15 ⊖ d														
Stratford 7 ⊖ d														
Barking ⊖ d		20 19	20 24	20 34	20 49	20 54	21 04	21 13			21 19	21 24	21 34	21 49
Upminster ⊖ d			20 32	20 42		21 02	21 12	21 21				21 32	21 42	
Ockendon d				20 48			21 18						21 48	
Chafford Hundred d				20 51			21 21						21 51	
West Horndon d			20 37			21 07						21 37		
Laindon d			20 42			21 12		21 29				21 42		
Basildon d			20 45			21 15		21 32				21 45		
Dagenham Dock d		20 24			20 54						21 24			21 54
Rainham d		20 27			20 57						21 27			21 57
Purfleet d		20 33			21 03						21 33			22 03
Grays d		20a42		20 55	21a12		21 25			←	21a42		21 55	22a12
Tilbury Town 3 d				20 58			21 28 →			21 28			21 58	
East Tilbury d				21 04						21 34			22 04	
Stanford-le-Hope d				21 07						21 37			22 07	
Pitsea d			20 49	21 15		21 19				21 45		21 49	22 15	
Benfleet d			20 52	21 19		21 22		21 38		21 49		21 52	22 19	
Leigh-on-Sea d			20 57	21 23		21 27		21 42		21 53		21 57	22 23	
Chalkwell d			20 59	21 26		21 29		21 45		21 56		21 59	22 26	
Westcliff d			21 02	21 28		21 32		21 47		21 58		22 02	22 28	
Southend Central a			21 05	21 34		21 35		21 50		22 04		22 05	22 34	
d			21 06			21 36		21 50				22 06		
Southend East d			21 08			21 38		21 52				22 08		
Thorpe Bay d			21 10			21 40		21 55				22 10		
Shoeburyness a			21 18			21 48		22 02				22 18		

	CC	CC	CC	CC		CC	CC	CC	CC	CC	CC	CC
London Fenchurch Street 7 ⊖ d	21 40	21 50	22 00			22 05	22 10	22 20	22 35	22 40	22 50	23 05
Limehouse d	21 44	21 54				22 09	22 14	22 24	22 39	22 44	22 54	23 09
West Ham ⊖ d	21 49	21 59	22 08			22 14	22 19	22 29	22 44	22 49	22 59	23 14
London Liverpool Street 15 ⊖ d												
Stratford 7 ⊖ d												
Barking ⊖ d	21 54	22 04	22 13			22 19	22 24	22 34	22 49	22 54	23 04	23 19
Upminster ⊖ d	22 02	22 12	22 21				22 32	22 42		23 02	23 12	
Ockendon d		22 18						22 48			23 18	
Chafford Hundred d		22 21						22 51			23 21	
West Horndon d	22 07						22 37			23 07		
Laindon d	22 12		22 29				22 42			23 12		
Basildon d	22 15		22 32				22 45			23 15		
Dagenham Dock d						22 24			22 54			23 24
Rainham d						22 27			22 57			23 27
Purfleet d						22 33			23 03			23 33
Grays d		22 25		←		22a42		22 55	23a12		23 25	23 38 →
Tilbury Town 3 d		22 28 →		22 28				22 58			23 28	
East Tilbury d				22 34				23 04			23 34	
Stanford-le-Hope d				22 37				23 07			23 37	
Pitsea d	22 19			22 45			22 49	23 15		23 19	23 45	
Benfleet d	22 22		22 38	22 49			22 52	23 19		23 22	23 49	
Leigh-on-Sea d	22 27		22 42	22 53			22 57	23 23		23 27	23 53	
Chalkwell d	22 29		22 45	22 56			22 59	23 26		23 29	23 56	
Westcliff d	22 32		22 47	22 58			23 02	23 28		23 32	23 58	
Southend Central a	22 35		22 50	23 04			23 05	23 31		23 35	00 01	
d	22 36		22 50				23 06	23 31		23 36	00 01	
Southend East d	22 38		22 52				23 08	23 33		23 38	00 03	
Thorpe Bay d	22 40		22 55				23 10	23 36		23 40	00 06	
Shoeburyness a	22 48		23 02				23 18	23 43		23 48	00 13	

		CC	CC	CC	CC	CC	CC	CC			
London Fenchurch Street 7 ⊖ d		23 10		23 20	23 35	23 40		23 50			
Limehouse d		23 14		23 24	23 39	23 44		23 54			
West Ham ⊖ d		23 19		23 29	23 44	23 49		23 59			
London Liverpool Street 15 ⊖ d											
Stratford 7 ⊖ d											
Barking ⊖ d		23 24		23 34	23 49	23 54		00 04			
Upminster ⊖ d		23 32		23 42		00 02		00 12			
Ockendon d				23 48				00 18			
Chafford Hundred d				23 51				00 21			
West Horndon d		23 37				00 07					
Laindon d		23 42				00 12					
Basildon d		23 45				00 15					
Dagenham Dock d					23 54						
Rainham d					23 57						
Purfleet d			←		00 03		←				
Grays d			23 38	23 55	00 08 →		00 08	00 25			
Tilbury Town 3 d			23 41	23 58			00 11	00 28			
East Tilbury d			23 47	00 04			00 17	00 34			
Stanford-le-Hope d			23 50	00 07			00 20	00 37			
Pitsea d		23 49	23 58	00 15		00 19	00 28	00 45			
Benfleet d		23 52	00 01	00 19		00 22	00 31	00 49			
Leigh-on-Sea d		23 57	00 06	00 23		00 27	00 36	00 53			
Chalkwell d		23 59	00 08	00 26		00 29	00 38	00 56			
Westcliff d		00 02	00 11	00 28		00 32	00 41	00 58			
Southend Central a		00 05	00 13	00 31		00 35	00 43	01 01			
d		00 06	00 14	00 31		00 36	00 44	01 01			
Southend East d		00 08	00 16	00 33		00 38	00 46	01 03			
Thorpe Bay d		00 10	00 18	00 36		00 40	00 48	01 06			
Shoeburyness a		00 18	00 26	00 43		00 48	00 56	01 13			

Sundays

	CC	CC	CC	CC	CC	CC	CC	CC	CC	CC	CC	CC
London Fenchurch Street 7 ⊖ d	22p50	23p05	23p10		23p20	23p35	23p40		23p50	00 10	00 40	06 40
Limehouse d	22p54	23p09	23p14		23p24	23p39	23p44		23p54	00 14	00 44	06 44
West Ham ⊖ d	22p59	23p14	23p19		23p29	23p44	23p49		23p59	00 19	00 49	06 49
London Liverpool Street 15 ⊖ d												
Stratford 7 ⊖ d												
Barking ⊖ d	23p04	23p19	23p24		23p34	23p49	23p54		00 04	00 24	00 54	06 54
Upminster ⊖ d	23p12		23p32		23p42		00 02		00 12	00 32	01 02	07 02
Ockendon d	23p18				23p48				00 18			
Chafford Hundred d	23p21				23p51				00 21			
West Horndon d			23p37				00 07			00 37	01 07	07 07
Laindon d			23p42				00 12			00 42	01 12	07 12
Basildon d			23p45				00 15			00 45	01 15	07 15
Dagenham Dock d		23p24				23p54						
Rainham d		23p27				23p57						
Purfleet d		23p33		←		00 03		←				
Grays d	23p25	23p38 →		23p38	23p55	00 08 →		00 08	00 25			
Tilbury Town 3 d	23p28			23p41	23p58			00 11	00 28			
East Tilbury d	23p34			23p47	00 04			00 17	00 34			
Stanford-le-Hope d	23p37			23p50	00 07			00 20	00 37			
Pitsea d	23p45		23p49	23p58	00 15		00 19	00 28	00 45	00 49	01 19	07 19
Benfleet d	23p49		23p52	00 01	00 19		00 22	00 31	00 49	00 52	01 22	07 22
Leigh-on-Sea d	23p53		23p57	00 06	00 23		00 27	00 36	00 53	00 57	01 27	07 27
Chalkwell d	23p56		23p59	00 08	00 26		00 29	00 38	00 56	00 59	01 29	07 29
Westcliff d	23p58		00 02	00 11	00 28		00 32	00 41	00 58	01 02	01 32	07 32
Southend Central a	00 01		00 05	00 13	00 31		00 35	00 43	01 01	01 05	01 35	07 34
d	00 01		00 06	00 14	00 31		00 36	00 44	01 01	01 06	01 36	07 36
Southend East d	00 03		00 08	00 16	00 33		00 38	00 46	01 03	01 08	01 38	07 38
Thorpe Bay d	00 06		00 10	00 18	00 36		00 40	00 48	01 06	01 10	01 40	07 40
Shoeburyness a	00 13		00 18	00 26	00 43		00 48	00 56	01 13	01 18	01 48	07 48

	CC	CC	CC	CC	CC	CC	CC	CC	CC	CC	CC
London Fenchurch Street 7 ⊖ d		07 10	07 40	07 50	08 10			08 40	08 50	09 10	
Limehouse d		07 14	07 44	07 54	08 14			08 44	08 54	09 14	
West Ham ⊖ d		07 19	07 49	07 59	08 19			08 49	08 59	09 19	
London Liverpool Street 15 ⊖ d											
Stratford 7 ⊖ d											
Barking ⊖ d	07 04	07 24	07 54	08 04	08 24	08 29	08 34	08 54	09 04	09 24	09 29
Upminster ⊖ d	07 12	07 32	08 02	08 12	08 32		08 42	09 02	09 12	09 32	
Ockendon d	07 18			08 18			08 48		09 18		
Chafford Hundred d	07 21			08 21			08 51		09 21		
West Horndon d		07 37	08 07		08 37			09 07		09 37	
Laindon d		07 42	08 12		08 42			09 12		09 42	
Basildon d		07 45	08 15		08 45			09 15		09 45	
Dagenham Dock d						08 33					09 33
Rainham d						08 37					09 37
Purfleet d						08 42					09 42
Grays d	07 25			08 25		08a50	08 55		09 25		09a50
Tilbury Town 3 d	07 28			08 28			08 58		09 28		
East Tilbury d	07 34			08 34			09 04		09 34		
Stanford-le-Hope d	07 37			08 37			09 07		09 37		
Pitsea d	07 45	07 49	08 19	08 45	08 49		09 15	09 19	09 45	09 49	
Benfleet d	07 49	07 52	08 22	08 49	08 52		09 19	09 22	09 49	09 52	
Leigh-on-Sea d	07 53	07 57	08 27	08 53	08 57		09 23	09 27	09 53	09 57	
Chalkwell d	07 56	07 59	08 29	08 56	08 59		09 26	09 29	09 56	09 59	
Westcliff d	07 58	08 02	08 32	08 58	09 02		09 28	09 32	09 58	10 02	
Southend Central a	08 04	08 05	08 34	09 04	09 05		09 34	09 35	10 04	10 05	
d		08 06	08 36		09 06			09 36		10 06	
Southend East d		08 08	08 38		09 08			09 38		10 08	
Thorpe Bay d		08 10	08 40		09 10			09 40		10 10	
Shoeburyness a		08 18	08 48		09 18			09 48		10 18	

For general notes see front of timetable
For details of catering facilities see Directory of Train Operators

London → Southend Central and Shoeburyness

Network diagram - see first page of Table 1

		CC	CC	CC		CC	CC	CC	CC	CC		CC	CC	CC	CC	CC	CC	CC	CC	CC	CC		
London Fenchurch Street 7	⊖ ⛴ d		09 40	09 50		10 10		10 20	10 40	10 50		21 10		21 20	21 40	21 50	22 10	22 40	22 50	23 10	23 40		
Limehouse	⛴ d		09 44	09 54		10 14		10 24	10 44	10 54		21 14		21 24	21 44	21 54	22 14	22 44	22 54	23 14	23 44		
West Ham	⊖ d		09 49	09 59		10 19		10 29	10 49	10 59		21 19		21 29	21 49	21 59	22 19	22 49	22 59	23 19	23 49		
London Liverpool Street 15	⊖ d																						
Stratford 7	⊖ ⛴ d																						
Barking	⊖ d	09 34	09 54	10 04		10 24	10 29	10 34	10 54	11 04		21 24	21 29	21 34	21 54	22 04	22 24	22 54	23 04	23 24	23 54		
Upminster	⊖ d	09 42	10 02	10 12		10 32		10 42	11 02	11 12		21 32		21 42	22 02	22 12	22 32	23 02	23 12	23 32	00 02		
Ockendon	d	09 48		10 18				10 48		11 18	and at			21 48		22 18			23 18				
Chafford Hundred	d	09 51		10 21				10 51		11 21				21 51		22 21			23 21				
West Horndon	d		10 07			10 37			11 07		the same	21 37			22 07		22 37	23 07		23 37	00 07		
Laindon	d		10 12			10 42			11 12		minutes	21 42			22 12		22 42	23 12		23 42	00 12		
Basildon	d		10 15			10 45			11 15			21 45			22 15		22 45	23 15		23 45	00 15		
Dagenham Dock	d						10 33				past		21 33										
Rainham	d						10 37						21 37										
Purfleet	d						10 42				each		21 42										
Grays	d	09 55		10 25			10a50	10 55		11 25	hour until		21a50	21 55		22 25			23 25				
Tilbury Town 3	d	09 58		10 28				10 58		11 28				21 58		22 28			23 28				
East Tilbury	d	10 04		10 34				11 04		11 34				22 04		22 34			23 34				
Stanford-le-Hope	d	10 07		10 37				11 07		11 37				22 07		22 37			23 37				
Pitsea	d	10 15	10 19	10 45		10 49		11 15	11 19	11 45		21 49		22 15	22 19	22 45	22 49	23 19	23 45	23 49	00 19		
Benfleet	d	10 19	10 22	10 49		10 52		11 19	11 22	11 49		21 52		22 19	22 22	22 49	22 52	23 22	23 49	23 52	00 22		
Leigh-on-Sea	d	10 23	10 27	10 53		10 57		11 23	11 27	11 53		21 57		22 23	22 27	22 53	22 57	23 27	23 53	23 57	00 27		
Chalkwell	d	10 26	10 29	10 56		10 59		11 26	11 29	11 56		21 59		22 26	22 29	22 56	22 59	23 29	23 56	23 59	00 29		
Westcliff	d	10 28	10 32	10 58		11 02		11 28	11 32	11 58		22 02		22 28	22 32	22 58	23 02	23 32	23 58	00 02	00 32		
Southend Central	a	10 34	10 35	11 04		11 05		11 34	11 35	12 04		22 05		22 31	22 35	23 01	23 05	23 35	00 01	00 05	00 34		
	d		10 36			11 06			11 36			22 06		22 31	22 36	23 01	23 06	23 36	00 01	00 06	00 36		
Southend East	d		10 38			11 08			11 38			22 08		22 33	22 38	23 03	23 08	23 38	00 03	00 08	00 38		
Thorpe Bay	d		10 40			11 10			11 40			22 10		22 36	22 40	23 06	23 10	23 40	00 06	00 10	00 40		
Shoeburyness	a		10 48			11 18			11 48			22 18		22 43	22 48	23 13	23 18	23 48	00 13	00 18	00 48		

For general notes see front of timetable
For details of catering facilities see Directory of Train Operators

Shoeburyness and Southend Central → London

Network diagram - see first page of Table I

Miles	Miles	Miles	Station		CC MX	CC MX	CC	CC	CC	CC	CC	CC	CC	CC	CC	CC	CC	CC	CC	CC	CC	CC	CC	CC
0	0	—	**Shoeburyness**	d		23p05		04 20		04 40	04 59		05 13	05 24			05 28		05 45		05 58			06 04
1½	1½	—	Thorpe Bay	d		23p09		04 24		04 44	05 03		05 17	05 28			05 32		05 49	05 58	06 02			06 08
3	3	—	Southend East	d		23p12		04 27		04 47	05 06		05 20	05 31			05 35		05 52	06 01	06 05			06 11
3¾	3¾	—	**Southend Central**	a		23p14		04 29		04 49	05 08		05 22	05 33			05 37		05 54	06 03	06 07			06 13
—	—	—		d	22p50	23p15		04 29		04 50	05 09		05 23	05 34			05 38	05 47	05 55	06 04	06 08			06 14
4¾	4¾	—	Westcliff	d	22p53	23p17		04 31		04 52	05 11		05 25	05 36			05 40	05 49	05 57	06 06	06 10			06 16
5½	5½	—	Chalkwell	d	22p55	23p19		04 34		04 54	05 13		05 27	05 38			05 42	05 51	05 59	06 08	06 12			06 18
7	7	—	Leigh-on-Sea	d	22p58	23p22		04 37		04 57	05 16		05 30	05 41			05 45	05 54	06 02	06 11	06 15			06 21
10¼	10¼	—	Benfleet	d	23p03	23p27		04 41		05 02	05 21		05 35	05 46			05 50	05 59	06 07	06 16	06 20			06 26
13	13	—	Pitsea	d	23p07	23p32		04 45		05 06	05 25		05 39	05 50			05 54	06 04	06 11	06b24				06 30
—	18	—	Stanford-le-Hope	d	23p14		04 29			05 14			05 46				06 01	06 11		06 31				
—	20	—	East Tilbury	d	23p18		04 33			05 18			05 50				06 05	06 15		06 35			←	
—	23¾	—	**Tilbury Town 3**	d	23p24		04 39			05 24			05 56		←		06 11	06 21		06 41			06 21	
—	25½	0	Grays	d	23p27		04 42		05 12	05 27		05 50	06 00		06 00		06 15	→		06 45		06 28	06 25	
—	29¼	—	Purfleet	d						05 33			→		06 05		06 20			→		06 33		
—	32½	—	Rainham	d						05 38					06 10		06 25					06 39		
—	34¾	—	Dagenham Dock	d						05 41					06 14		06 29					06 42		
15	—	—	Basildon	d		23p36		04 50			05 29			05 54					06 16		06 27			06 35
16¾	—	—	Laindon	d		23p39		04 53			05 32			05 57					06 19		06 31			06 38
20¼	—	—	West Horndon	d		23p44		04 58			05 37			06 02					06 24					06 43
—	—	2½	Chafford Hundred	d	23p31		04 46		05 16			05 54											06 30	
—	—	4½	Ockendon	d	23p35		04 50		05 20			05 58				06 20							06c37	
24¼	—	7½	Upminster	⊖ d	23p42	23p50	04 57	05 04	05a25		05 42	06 03		06 08		06a25			06 30				06 43	06 49
32	37¾	—	Barking	⊖ d	23p50	23p58	05 06	05 13		05 47	05 51	06 12		06 16	06 20		06 35		06 38			06 49		06 58
—	—	—	Stratford 7	⊖ a			05 13																	
—	—	—	**London Liverpool Street 15**	⊖ a			05 23																	
35	40¾	—	West Ham	⊖ d	23p56	00 04		05 18		05 53	05 57	06 17		06 22	06 26		06 41		06 43			06 54	06 57	07 03
37¾	43½	—	Limehouse	d	00 01	00 09		05 23		05 58	06 02	06 22		06 27	06 31		06 46		06 48		06 54	06 59	07 02	
39½	45¼	—	**London Fenchurch Street 7**	⊖ a	00 05	00 14		05 30		06 04	06 08	06 29		06 31	06 37		06 52		06 53		07 01	07 06	07 08	07 14

Station		CC	CC	CC	CC		CC	CC	CC	CC	CC	CC	CC	CC	CC	CC	CC	CC	CC	CC	CC	CC	CC	CC
Shoeburyness	d		06 13		06 17			06 28			06 32	06 46					06 53			07 05				
Thorpe Bay	d	06 13	06 17		06 21			06 32			06 36	06 50					06 57			07 09			07 14	
Southend East	d	06 16	06 20		06 24			06 35			06 39	06 53					07 00			07 12			07 17	
Southend Central	a	06 18	06 22		06 26			06 37			06 41	06 55					07 02			07 14			07 19	
	d	06 19	06 23		06 27			06 38			06 42	06 56					07 03		07 10	07 15			07 20	
Westcliff	d	06 21	06 25		06 29			06 40			06 44	06 58					07 05		07 12	07 17			07 22	
Chalkwell	d	06 23	06 27		06 31			06 42			06 46	07 00					07 07		07 14	07 19			07 24	
Leigh-on-Sea	d	06 26	06 30		06 34			06 45			06 49	07 03					07 10		07 18	07 22			07 27	
Benfleet	d	06 31	06 35		06 39			06 50			06 54	07 08					07 15		07 22	07 27			07 32	
Pitsea	d	06e39			06 43					06 55	06 58				07 02	07 15	07 19		07 27				07 36	
Stanford-le-Hope	d	06 46								07 02					07 09	07 22			07 34					
East Tilbury	d	06 50							←	07 06					07 13	07 26			07 38					
Tilbury Town 3	d	06 56		←					06 56	07 12			←		07 20	07 32		←	07 44					←
Grays	d	→		06 45			06 51		07 00	07 16			07 16		07 24	07 36		07 24	07 48		07 32			07 36
Purfleet	d			06 51					07 05	→			07 21		→	→			→		07 37			
Rainham	d			06 56					07 11				07 27								07 43			
Dagenham Dock	d			07 00					07 14				07 30								07 46			
Basildon	d		06 42		06 48			06 57			07 03	07 15					07 24						07 41	
Laindon	d				06 51						07 06			07 22			07 27					07 37	07 44	
West Horndon	d				06 56						07 11			07 27								07 42		
Chafford Hundred	d						06 55											07 28						07 40
Ockendon	d						07 00											07 32						07f48
Upminster	⊖ d				07 02		07 06	07 10			07 17			07 32				07 39				07 48		07 54
Barking	⊖ d		07 00	07 06	07 11		07 15		07 21		07 27		07 37	07 41			07 45	07 48			07 54	07 56	08 01	
Stratford 7	⊖ a																							
London Liverpool Street 15	⊖ a																							
West Ham	⊖ d		07 07	07 12			07 20	07 23	07 26					07 46								08 02		
Limehouse	d			07 17	07 20		07 25		07 32		07 36		07 46	07 51			07 54			08 00	08 03	08 08	08 10	
London Fenchurch Street 7	⊖ a		07 17	07 23	07 26		07 32	07 34	07 38		07 42	07 46	07 52	07 58			08 00	08 03		08 07	08 10	08 14	08 17	08 19

Station		CC	CC	CC	CC	CC	CC		CC	CC	CC	CC	CC	CC	CC	CC	CC	CC	CC	CC	CC	CC	CC	CC
Shoeburyness	d	07 20					07 24			07 35							07 50			07 54		08 05		
Thorpe Bay	d	07 24					07 28			07 39				07 43			07 54			07 58		08 09		
Southend East	d	07 27					07 31			07 42				07 46			07 57			08 01		08 12		
Southend Central	a	07 29					07 33			07 44				07 48			07 59			08 03		08 14		
	d	07 30					07 34			07 45				07 49			08 00			08 04		08 15		
Westcliff	d	07 32					07 36			07 47				07 51			08 02			08 06		08 17		
Chalkwell	d	07 34					07 38			07 49				07 53			08 04			08 08		08 19		
Leigh-on-Sea	d	07 37					07 41			07 52				07 56			08 07			08 11		08 22		
Benfleet	d	07 42					07 46			07 57				08 01			08 12			08 16		08 27		
Pitsea	d				07 42	07 49	07 50						07 54	08 05					08 13	08 20				
Stanford-le-Hope	d				07 49	07 56			07 44				08 02						08 20		08 12			
East Tilbury	d				07 53								08 06						08 24		08 16			
Tilbury Town 3	d		←		07 59						←		08 12			←			08 30		08 22		←	
Grays	d		07 48		08 03	08 07			07 54		08 03		08 16			08 16			08 34		08 26		08 34	
Purfleet	d		07 53		→						08 08		→			08 21			→				08 40	
Rainham	d		07 59								08 14					08 27							08 45	
Dagenham Dock	d		08 02								08 17					08 30							08 49	
Basildon	d						07 55							08 10						08 25				
Laindon	d			07 52			07 58					08 08		08 13				08 23		08 28				08 38
West Horndon	d			07 57								08 13			←			08 28						08 43
Chafford Hundred	d					08 11			07 59						08 11						08 30			
Ockendon	d					→			08 03						08 18						08 34			
Upminster	⊖ d			08 03					08 10	08 14		08 18			08 25		08 29	08 33			08 41			08 49
Barking	⊖ d		08 09	08 12			08 15		08 19		08 24	08 27		08 30		08 37		08 43		08 46	08 51		08 55	08 58
Stratford 7	⊖ a																							
London Liverpool Street 15	⊖ a																							
West Ham	⊖ d			08 17								08 32						08 48					09 01	09 04
Limehouse	d	08 16	08 19	08 22			08 25			08 31	08 34	08 37		08 39		08 46	08 48	08 53		08 56			09 06	09 09
London Fenchurch Street 7	⊖ a	08 22	08 25	08 28			08 32		08 34	08 37	08 40	08 43		08 46	08 48	08 52	08 55	08 59		09 02	09 06	09 08	09 12	09 15

For general notes see front of timetable
For details of catering facilities see Directory of Train Operators

b Arr. 0620
c Arr. 0634
e Arr. 0635
f Arr. 0744

Shoeburyness and Southend Central → London

Network diagram - see first page of Table I

		CC	CC	CC	CC	CC	CC	CC	CC		CC	CC	CC	CC	CC	CC		CC	CC	CC	CC	CC	CC	CC
Shoeburyness	d		08 10		08 25						08 40							09 05			09 20		09 35	
Thorpe Bay	d		08 14		08 29						08 44							09 09			09 24		09 39	
Southend East	d		08 17		08 32						08 47							09 12			09 27		09 42	
Southend Central	a		08 19		08 34						08 49							09 14			09 29		09 44	
	d		08 20		08 34						08 50			09 06				09 15		09 20	09 30		09 45	
Westcliff	d		08 22		08 36						08 52			09 08				09 17		09 23	09 32		09 47	
Chalkwell	d		08 24		08 39						08 54			09 11				09 19		09 25	09 34		09 49	
Leigh-on-Sea	d		08 27		08 42						08 57			09 14				09 22		09 28	09 37		09 52	
Benfleet	d		08 32		08 47						09 02			09 19				09 27		09 33	09 42		09 57	
Pitsea	d	08 34	08 36		08 51				08 54		09 06					09 08		09 32		09 37			10 02	
Stanford-le-Hope	d	08 41		08 32					09 01							09 16				09 44				
East Tilbury	d	08 45		08 36		←			09 05							09 20				09 48		←		
Tilbury Town 3	d	08 51		08 42		08 51			09 11			←				09 26				09 54		09 54		
Grays	d	→		08 46		08 56	09 03		09 15			09 15				09 29			09 46	→		09 57		10 16
Purfleet	d			08 51			09 08		→			09 20							09 51					10 21
Rainham	d			08 57			09 13					09 26							09 56					10 26
Dagenham Dock	d			09 00			09 17					09 29							10 00					10 30
Basildon	d		08 41		08 55						09 11			09 26				09 36			09 49		10 06	
Laindon	d		08 44					09 04			09 14		09 17		09 31			09 39			09 52		10 09	
West Horndon	d							09 10					09 22					09 44					10 14	
Chafford Hundred	d					09 01										09 34						10 01		
Ockendon	d					09 05										09 38						10 05		
Upminster	⊖ d		08 54		09 06	09 11		09 16					09 28		09 41	09 45		09 50			10 00	10 10	10 20	
Barking	⊖ d		09 03	09 07		09 20	09 23	09 25			09 30	09 35	09 37	09 43	09 50	09 54		09 58	10 06		10 08	10 18	10 28	10 36
Stratford 7	⊖ a																							
London Liverpool Street 15	⊖ a																							
West Ham	⊖ d		09 08			09 25	09 29	09 31					09 43	09 49	09 56	09 59		10 04	10 11		10 16	10 26	10 34	10 41
Limehouse	d		09 14	09 17	09 23	09 30	09 34	09 36				09 44		09 54	10 01	10 04		10 09	10 16			10 31	10 39	10 46
London Fenchurch Street 7	⊖ a		09 20	09 26	09 29	09 38	09 40	09 43			09 45	09 51	09 53	10 00	10 07	10 09		10 14	10 21		10 24	10 35	10 43	10 51

		CC	CC	CC		CC	CC	CC	CC	CC	CC	CC	CC		CC	CC	CC	CC	CC	CC	CC	CC	CC
Shoeburyness	d		09 50			15 05			15 20		15 35				15 50		16 05			16 15			16 28
Thorpe Bay	d		09 54			15 09			15 24		15 39				15 54		16 09			16 19			16 32
Southend East	d		09 57			15 12			15 27		15 42				15 57		16 12			16 22			16 35
Southend Central	a		09 59			15 14			15 29		15 44				15 59		16 14			16 24			16 37
	d	09 50	10 00			15 15		15 20	15 30		15 45		15 48		16 00		16 15		16 19	16 25	16 33		16 38
Westcliff	d	09 53	10 02			15 17		15 23	15 32		15 47		15 50		16 02		16 17		16 21	16 27	16 35		16 40
Chalkwell	d	09 55	10 04			15 19		15 25	15 34		15 49		15 53		16 04		16 19		16 23	16 29	16 37		16 42
Leigh-on-Sea	d	09 58	10 07			15 22		15 28	15 37		15 52		15 56		16 07		16 22		16 26	16 32	16 40		16 45
Benfleet	d	10 03	10 12		and at the same minutes past each hour until	15 27		15 33	15 42		15 57		16 00		16 12		16 27		16 31	16 37	16 45		16 50
Pitsea	d	10 07				15 32		15 37			16 02		16 04				16 31		16 35		16 49		16 54
Stanford-le-Hope	d	10 14						15 44					16 11						16 42				
East Tilbury	d	10 18		←				15 48		←			16 15			←			16 46				
Tilbury Town 3	d	10 24		10 24				15 54		15 54			16 21			16 21			16 52				
Grays	d	→		10 27			15 46	→		15 57		16 16	→			16 26		16 39	→			16 52	
Purfleet	d						15 51					16 21						16 44				16 57	
Rainham	d						15 56					16 26						16 49				17 02	
Dagenham Dock	d						16 00					16 30						16 53				17 06	
Basildon	d		10 19			15 36			15 49		16 06				16 19		16 35			16 43	16 53		16 58
Laindon	d		10 22			15 39			15 52		16 09						16 38						17 01
West Horndon	d					15 44					16 14						16 43						17 06
Chafford Hundred	d			10 31						16 01						16 30							
Ockendon	d			10 35						16 05						16 34							
Upminster	⊖ d		10 30	10 40		15 50			16 00	16 10	16 20				16 30	16 41	16 48			16 54			17 11
Barking	⊖ d		10 38	10 48		15 58	16 06		16 08	16 18	16 28	16 36			16 38	16 49	16 57	17 00		17 03		17b16	17 20
Stratford 7	⊖ a																						
London Liverpool Street 15	⊖ a																						
West Ham	⊖ d		10 46	10 56		16 04	16 11		16 17	16 26	16 34				16 44		17 02			17 09		17 22	
Limehouse	d			11 01		16 09	16 16			16 31	16 39						17 08	17 10		17 14			17 29
London Fenchurch Street 7	⊖ a		10 54	11 05		16 13	16 21		16 26	16 36	16 43	16 48			16 52	17 03	17 12	17 15		17 18	17 24	17 30	17 33

		CC	CC	CC	CC	CC	CC	CC	CC	CC	CC	CC	CC	CC	CC	CC		CC	CC	CC	CC	CC	CC	CC
Shoeburyness	d				16 49		16 56				17 10					17 30				17 45				18 05
Thorpe Bay	d				16 53		17 00				17 14					17 34				17 49				18 09
Southend East	d				16 56		17 03				17 17					17 37				17 52				18 12
Southend Central	a				16 58		17 05				17 19					17 39				17 54				18 14
	d			16 54	16 59		17 06				17 19					17 40				17 55				18 15
Westcliff	d			16 56	17 01		17 08				17 21					17 42				17 57				18 17
Chalkwell	d			16 59	17 03		17 10				17 24					17 44				17 59				18 19
Leigh-on-Sea	d			17 02	17 06		17 13				17 27					17 47				18 02				18 22
Benfleet	d			17 06	17 11		17 18				17 32					17 52				18 07				18 27
Pitsea	d		16 56	17 10	17 15		17 22			17 24	17 36				17 43	17 56			17 59	18 11			18 31	18 32
Stanford-le-Hope	d		17 03						17 19	17 32					17 50				18 06				18 38	
East Tilbury	d	←	17 07					←	17 23	17 36					17 54				18 10		←		18 42	
Tilbury Town 3	d	16 52	17 13					17 13	17 29	17 42				←	18 00			←	18 16		18 16		18 48	
Grays	d	16 57	→			17 22		17 19	17 32	17 49		17 44		17 49	18 04			18 04	→		18 20	18 28	→	
Purfleet	d					17 27			17 38	→		17 49			→			18 09				18 33		
Rainham	d					17 32			17 43			17 54						18 14				18 38		
Dagenham Dock	d					17 36			17 46			17 58						18 18				18 42		
Basildon	d			17 14	17 19		17 26				17 40					18 00				18 15				18 36
Laindon	d			17 17							17 44		17 47			18 05				18 18				18 39
West Horndon	d			17 22									17 52			18 10				18 23				18 44
Chafford Hundred	d	17 01						17 23						17 53							18 25			
Ockendon	d	17 07						17c30						17 59							18 31			
Upminster	⊖ d	17 15		17 28	17 31			17 38					17 58	18 06		18 15				18 30	18 38			18 50
Barking	⊖ d	17 25		17 36	17 40	17 42		17 47	17 52			18 04	18 06	18 14		18 24		18 26		18 38		18 48		18 58
Stratford 7	⊖ a																							
London Liverpool Street 15	⊖ a																							
West Ham	⊖ d	17 31					17 49		17 58			18 09	18 12			18 29		18 32		18 44		18 53		19 04
Limehouse	d								18 03				18 17					18 37		18 49		18 58		19 09
London Fenchurch Street 7	⊖ a	17 39		17 49	17 52	17 54	17 58	18 00	18 09		18 11	18 18	18 21	18 27		18 38		18 41		18 53	19 00	19 03		19 13

For general notes see front of timetable
For details of catering facilities see Directory of Train Operators

b Arr. 1712
c Arr. 1727

Shoeburyness and Southend Central → London

Network diagram - see first page of Table 1

Station		CC	CC	CC	CC	CC	CC	CC	CC	CC	CC	CC	CC	CC	CC	CC	CC	CC		CC	CC	CC	CC	CC
Shoeburyness	d		18 20			18 35			18 50		19 05		19 20			19 35				19 50			20 05	
Thorpe Bay	d		18 24			18 39			18 54		19 09		19 24			19 39				19 54			20 09	
Southend East	d		18 27			18 42			18 57		19 12		19 27			19 42				19 57			20 12	
Southend Central	a		18 29			18 44			18 59		19 15		19 29			19 44				19 59			20 14	
	d	18 20	18 30			18 45		18 49	19 00		19 15	19 20	19 30			19 45		19 50		20 00			20 15	20 20
Westcliff	d	18 23	18 32			18 47		18 51	19 02		19 17	19 23	19 32			19 47		19 53		20 02			20 17	20 23
Chalkwell	d	18 25	18 34			18 49		18 53	19 04		19 19	19 25	19 34			19 49		19 55		20 04			20 19	20 25
Leigh-on-Sea	d	18 28	18 37			18 52		18 56	19 07		19 22	19 28	19 37			19 52		19 58		20 07			20 22	20 28
Benfleet	d	18 33	18 42			18 57		19 01	19 12		19 27	19 33	19 42			19 57		20 03		20 12			20 27	20 33
Pitsea	d	18 37				19 02		19 05			19 32	19 37				20 02		20 07					20 32	20 37
Stanford-le-Hope	d	18 44						19 12				19 44						20 14						20 44
East Tilbury	d	18 48		←	←			19 16		←		19 48			←			20 18			←			20 48
Tilbury Town 3	d	18 54		18 54	18 48			19 22		19 22		19 54			19 54			20 24			20 24			20 54
Grays	d	→		18 57	18b54		19 18	→		19 25		→		19 48	19 57		20 16	→			20 27			→
Purfleet	d			19 04			19 23							19 53			20 21							
Rainham	d			19 09			19 28							19 58			20 26							
Dagenham Dock	d			19 12			19 32							20 02			20 30							
Basildon	d		18 49			19 06			19 19		19 36		19 49			20 06				20 19			20 36	
Laindon	d		18 52			19 09			19 22		19 39		19 52			20 09				20 22			20 39	
West Horndon	d					19 14					19 44					20 14							20 44	
Chafford Hundred	d				18 59					19 29					20 01						20 31			
Ockendon	d				19 04					19 34					20 05						20 35			
Upminster	⊖ d		19 00		19 10	19 20			19 30	19 40	19 50		20 00		20 10	20 20				20 30	20 40		20 50	
Barking	⊖ d		19 08	19 18	19 18	19 28	19 37		19 38	19 48	19 58		20 08	20c11	20 18	20 28	20 36			20 38	20 48	20 50	20 58	
Stratford 7	⊖ ⛴ a													20 20								21 00		
London Liverpool Street 15	⊖ a													20 30								21 10		
West Ham	⊖ d		19 16		19 26	19 34	19 43		19 46	19 56	20 04		20 16		20 26	20 34	20 41			20 46	20 56		21 04	
Limehouse	⛴ d			19 27		19 39	19 48			20 01	20 09				20 31	20 39	20 46				21 01		21 09	
London Fenchurch Street 7	⊖ ⛴ a		19 24	19 32	19 38	19 43	19 53		19 55	20 05	20 13		20 25		20 35	20 43	20 51			20 54	21 05		21 13	

Station		CC	CC	CC	CC	CC	CC	CC	CC	CC	CC	CC	CC	CC	CC	CC	CC	CC	CC	CC	CC	CC		
Shoeburyness	d	20 20			20 35			21 05			21 20		21 35			22 05			22 35			23 05		
Thorpe Bay	d	20 24			20 39			21 09			21 24		21 39			22 09			22 39			23 09		
Southend East	d	20 27			20 42			21 12			21 27		21 42			22 12			22 42			23 12		
Southend Central	a	20 29			20 44			21 14			21 29		21 45			22 14			22 44			23 14		
	d	20 30			20 45		20 50	21 15		21 20	21 30		21 45		21 50	22 15		22 20	22 45	22 50		23 15		
Westcliff	d	20 32			20 47		20 53	21 17		21 23	21 32		21 47		21 53	22 17		22 23	22 47	22 53		23 17		
Chalkwell	d	20 34			20 49		20 55	21 19		21 25	21 34		21 49		21 55	22 19		22 25	22 49	22 55		23 19		
Leigh-on-Sea	d	20 37			20 52		20 58	21 22		21 28	21 37		21 52		21 58	22 22		22 28	22 52	22 58		23 22		
Benfleet	d	20 42			20 57		21 03	21 27		21 33	21 42		21 57		22 03	22 27		22 33	22 57	23 03		23 27		
Pitsea	d				21 02		21 07	21 32		21 37			22 02		22 07	22 32		22 37	23 02	23 07		23 32		
Stanford-le-Hope	d						21 14			21 44					22 14			22 44		23 14				
East Tilbury	d			←			21 18			21 48		←			22 18			22 48		23 18				
Tilbury Town 3	d			20 54			21 24			21 54		21 54			22 24			22 54		23 24				
Grays	d		20 46	20 57		21 16	21 27		21 46	→		21 57		22 16	22 27		22 46	22 57		23 27	23 31			
Purfleet	d		20 51			21 21			21 51					22 21			22 51				23 36			
Rainham	d		20 56			21 26			21 56					22 26			22 56				23 41			
Dagenham Dock	d		21 00			21 30			22 00					22 30			23 00				23 45			
Basildon	d	20 49			21 06			21 36			21 49		22 06			22 36			23 06			23 36		
Laindon	d	20 52			21 09			21 39			21 52		22 09			22 39			23 09			23 39		
West Horndon	d				21 14			21 44					22 14			22 44			23 14			23 44		
Chafford Hundred	d			21 01			21 31					22 01			22 31			23 01		23 31				
Ockendon	d			21 05			21 35					22 05			22 35			23 05		23 35				
Upminster	⊖ d	21 00		21 10	21 20		21 40	21 50			22 00	22 10	22 20		22 42	22 50		23 12	23 20	23 42		23 50		
Barking	⊖ d	21 08	21e11	21 18	21 28	21 36	21 48	21 58	22 06		22 08	22 18	22 28	22 36	22 50	22 58	23 06	23 20	23 28	23 50	23 51	23 58		
Stratford 7	⊖ ⛴ a		21 20																		23 57			
London Liverpool Street 15	⊖ a		21 30																		00 07			
West Ham	⊖ d	21 16		21 26	21 34	21 41	21 56	22 04	22 11		22 16	22 26	22 34	22 41	22 56	23 04	23 11	23 26	23 34	23 56		00 04		
Limehouse	⛴ d			21 31	21 39	21 46	22 01	22 09	22 16			22 31	22 39	22 46	23 01	23 09	23 16	23 31	23 39	00 01		00 09		
London Fenchurch Street 7	⊖ ⛴ a	21 24		21 35	21 43	21 51	22 05	22 13	22 21		22 24	22 35	22 43	22 52	23 05	23 13	23 22	23 35	23 43	00 05		00 14		

Saturdays

Station		CC	CC	CC	CC	CC	CC	CC		CC	CC	CC	CC	CC	CC	CC		CC	CC	CC	CC	CC	CC	CC
Shoeburyness	d		23p05		04 20		05 05				05 35			06 05				06 35			07 05			07 35
Thorpe Bay	d		23p09		04 23		05 08				05 38			06 08				06 38			07 08			07 38
Southend East	d		23p12		04 26		05 11				05 41			06 11				06 41			07 11			07 41
Southend Central	a		23p14		04 28		05 13				05 43			06 13				06 43			07 13			07 43
	d	22p50	23p15		04 29		05 14			05 20	05 44		05 50	06 14		06 20		06 44		06 50	07 14		07 20	07 44
Westcliff	d	22p53	23p17		04 31		05 16			05 23	05 46		05 53	06 16		06 23		06 46		06 53	07 16		07 23	07 46
Chalkwell	d	22p55	23p19		04 33		05 18			05 25	05 48		05 55	06 18		06 25		06 48		06 55	07 18		07 25	07 48
Leigh-on-Sea	d	22p58	23p22		04 36		05 21			05 28	05 51		05 58	06 21		06 28		06 51		06 58	07 21		07 28	07 51
Benfleet	d	23p03	23p27		04 40		05 25			05 32	05 55		06 02	06 25		06 32		06 55		07 02	07 25		07 32	07 55
Pitsea	d	23p07	23p32		04 44		05 29			05 36	05 59		06 06	06 29		06 36		06 59		07 06	07 29		07 36	07 59
Stanford-le-Hope	d	23p14		04 29						05 42			06 12			06 42				07 12			07 42	
East Tilbury	d	23p18		04 32						05 45			06 15			06 45				07 15			07 45	
Tilbury Town 3	d	23p24		04 38						05 51			06 21			06 51				07 21			07 51	
Grays	d	23p27		04 41				05 48		05 54		06 18	06 24		06 48	06 54			07 18	07 24		07 48	07 54	
Purfleet	d							05 53				06 23			06 53				07 23			07 53		
Rainham	d							05 58				06 28			06 58				07 28			07 58		
Dagenham Dock	d							06 02				06 32			07 02				07 32			08 02		
Basildon	d		23p36		04 47		05 32				06 02			06 32				07 02			07 32			08 02
Laindon	d		23p39		04 50		05 35				06 05			06 35				07 05			07 35			08 05
West Horndon	d		23p44		04 55		05 40				06 10			06 40				07 10			07 40			08 10
Chafford Hundred	d	23p31		04 45						05 59			06 29			06 59				07 29			07 59	
Ockendon	d	23p35		04 49		05 16				06 02			06 32			07 02				07 32			08 02	
Upminster	⊖ d	23p42	23p50	04a57	05 02	05a23	05 46			06 09	06 16		06 39	06 46		07 09		07 16		07 39	07 46		08 09	08 16
Barking	⊖ d	23p50	23p58		05 10		05 54	06 08		06 17	06 24	06 38	06 47	06 54	07 08	07 17		07 24	07 38	07 47	07 54	08 08	08 17	08 24
Stratford 7	⊖ ⛴ a																							
London Liverpool Street 15	⊖ a																							
West Ham	⊖ d	23p56	00 04		05 16		06 00	06 14		06 23	06 30	06 44	06 53	07 00	07 14	07 23		07 30	07 44	07 53	08 00	08 14	08 23	08 30
Limehouse	⛴ d	00 01	00 09		05 21		06 05	06 19		06 28	06 35	06 49	06 58	07 05	07 19	07 28		07 35	07 49	07 58	08 05	08 19	08 28	08 35
London Fenchurch Street 7	⊖ ⛴ a	00 05	00 14		05 27		06 12	06 26		06 34	06 42	06 56	07 04	07 12	07 26	07 34		07 42	07 56	08 04	08 12	08 26	08 34	08 42

For general notes see front of timetable
For details of catering facilities see Directory of Train Operators

b Arr. 1851
c Arr. 2008
e Arr. 2106

Table 1

Saturdays

Shoeburyness and Southend Central → London

Network diagram - see first page of Table 1

	CC	CC		CC	CC		CC	CC	CC	CC	CC	CC	CC	CC	CC	CC			CC	CC	CC	CC
Shoeburyness d		07 50					08 05		08 20			08 35		08 50					20 05			20 35
Thorpe Bay d		07 53					08 08		08 23			08 38		08 53					20 08			20 38
Southend East d		07 56					08 11		08 26			08 41		08 56					20 11			20 41
Southend Central a		07 58					08 13		08 28			08 43		08 58					20 13			20 43
d	07 50	07 59					08 14	08 20	08 29			08 44	08 50	08 59					20 14		20 20	20 44
Westcliff d	07 53	08 01					08 16	08 23	08 31			08 46	08 53	09 01					20 16		20 23	20 46
Chalkwell d	07 55	08 03					08 18	08 25	08 33			08 48	08 55	09 03					20 18		20 25	20 48
Leigh-on-Sea d	07 58	08 06					08 21	08 28	08 36			08 51	08 58	09 06			and at		20 21		20 28	20 51
Benfleet d	08 02	08 10					08 25	08 32	08 40			08 55	09 02	09 10					20 25		20 32	20 55
Pitsea d	08 06						08 29	08 36				08 59	09 06				the same		20 29		20 36	20 59
Stanford-le-Hope d	08 12							08 42					09 12								20 42	
East Tilbury d	08 15				←			08 45			←		09 15			←	minutes				20 45	
Tilbury Town 3 d	08 21				08 21			08 51			08 51		09 21			09 21					20 51	
Grays d	→			08 18	08 24			→		08 48	08 54		→		09 18	09 24	past			20 48	20 54	
Purfleet d				08 23						08 53					09 23					20 53		
Rainham d				08 28						08 58					09 28		each			20 58		
Dagenham Dock d				08 32						09 02					09 32					21 02		
Basildon d		08 16					08 32		08 46			09 02		09 16			hour until		20 32			21 02
Laindon d		08 19					08 35		08 49			09 05		09 19					20 35			21 05
West Horndon d							08 40					09 10							20 40			21 10
Chafford Hundred d					08 29						08 59					09 29					20 59	
Ockendon d					08 32						09 02					09 32					21 02	
Upminster ⊖ d		08 28			08 39		08 46		08 58		09 09	09 16		09 28		09 39			20 46		21 09	21 16
Barking ⊖ d		08 36		08 38	08 47		08 54		09 06	09 08	09 17	09 24		09 36	09 38	09 47			20 54	21 08	21 17	21 24
Stratford 7 ⊖ a																						
London Liverpool Street 15 ⊖ a																						
West Ham ⊖ d		08 42		08 44	08 53		09 00		09 12	09 14	09 23	09 30		09 42	09 44	09 53			21 00	21 14	21 23	21 30
Limehouse d				08 49	08 58		09 05			09 19	09 28	09 35			09 49	09 58			21 05	21 19	21 28	21 35
London Fenchurch Street 7 ⊖ a		08 53		08 56	09 04		09 12		09 23	09 26	09 34	09 42		09 53	09 56	10 04			21 12	21 26	21 34	21 42

	CC	CC	CC	CC	CC		CC	CC	CC	CC	CC	CC	CC		CC	CC	CC	CC	CC	CC			
Shoeburyness d		20 50			21 05				21 35			22 05				22 35			23 05				
Thorpe Bay d		20 53			21 08				21 38			22 08				22 38			23 08				
Southend East d		20 56			21 11				21 41			22 11				22 41			23 11				
Southend Central a		20 58			21 13				21 43			22 13				22 43			23 13				
d	20 50	20 59			21 14			21 20	21 44		21 50	22 14			22 20	22 44		22 50	23 14	23 20			
Westcliff d	20 53	21 01			21 16			21 23	21 46		21 53	22 16			22 23	22 46		22 53	23 16	23 23			
Chalkwell d	20 55	21 03			21 18			21 25	21 48		21 55	22 18			22 25	22 48		22 55	23 18	23 25			
Leigh-on-Sea d	20 58	21 06			21 21			21 28	21 51		21 58	22 21			22 28	22 51		22 58	23 21	23 28			
Benfleet d	21 02	21 10			21 25			21 32	21 55		22 02	22 25			22 32	22 55		23 02	23 25	23 32			
Pitsea d	21 06				21 29			21 36	21 59		22 06	22 29			22 36	22 59		23 06	23 29	23 36			
Stanford-le-Hope d	21 12							21 42			22 12				22 42			23 12		23 42			
East Tilbury d	21 15			←				21 45			22 15				22 45			23 15		23 45			
Tilbury Town 3 d	21 21			21 21				21 51			22 21				22 51			23 21		23 51			
Grays d	→		21 18	21 24			21 48	21 54		22 18	22 24		22 48		22 54		23 18	23 24		23 54			
Purfleet d			21 23				21 53			22 23			22 53				23 23						
Rainham d			21 28				21 58			22 28			22 58				23 28						
Dagenham Dock d			21 32				22 02			22 32			23 02				23 32						
Basildon d		21 16			21 32				22 02			22 32				23 02			23 32				
Laindon d		21 19			21 35				22 05			22 35				23 05			23 35				
West Horndon d					21 40				22 10			22 40				23 10			23 40				
Chafford Hundred d				21 29				21 59			22 29				22 59			23 29		23 59			
Ockendon d				21 32				22 02			22 32				23 02			23 32		00 02			
Upminster ⊖ d		21 28		21 39	21 46			22 09	22 16		22 39	22 46			23 09	23 16		23 39	23 46	00 08			
Barking ⊖ d		21 36	21 38	21 47	21 54		22 08	22 17	22 24	22 38	22 47	22 54	23 08		23 17	23 24	23a39	23 47	23 55	00a18			
Stratford 7 ⊖ a																							
London Liverpool Street 15 ⊖ a																							
West Ham ⊖ d		21 42	21 44	21 53	22 00		22 14	22 23	22 30	22 44	22 53	23 00	23 14		23 23	23 30		23 53	00 01				
Limehouse d			21 49	21 58	22 05		22 19	22 28	22 35	22 49	22 58	23 05	23 19		23 28	23 35		23 58	00 06				
London Fenchurch Street 7 ⊖ a		21 53	21 56	22 04	22 12		22 26	22 34	22 42	22 56	23 04	23 12	23 26		23 34	23 42		00 04	00 12				

Sundays

	CC		CC		CC		CC		CC		CC		CC		CC		CC			CC	CC	CC	CC
Shoeburyness d	23p05				05 35		06 05		06 11		06 35		07 05		07 11		07 35			08 05			08 35
Thorpe Bay d	23p08				05 38		06 08		06 14		06 38		07 08		07 14		07 38			08 08			08 38
Southend East d	23p11				05 41		06 11		06 17		06 41		07 11		07 17		07 41			08 11			08 41
Southend Central a	23p13				05 43		06 13		06 19		06 43		07 13		07 19		07 43			08 13			08 43
d	23p14		23p20		05 44		06 14		06 20		06 44		07 14		07 20		07 44			08 14	08 20		08 44
Westcliff d	23p16		23p23		05 46		06 16		06 23		06 46		07 16		07 23		07 46			08 16	08 23		08 46
Chalkwell d	23p18		23p25		05 48		06 18		06 25		06 48		07 18		07 25		07 48			08 18	08 25		08 48
Leigh-on-Sea d	23p21		23p28		05 51		06 21		06 28		06 51		07 21		07 28		07 51			08 21	08 28		08 51
Benfleet d	23p25		23p32		05 55		06 25		06 32		06 55		07 25		07 32		07 55			08 25	08 32		08 55
Pitsea d	23p29		23p36		05 59		06 29		06 36		06 59		07 29		07 36		07 59			08 29	08 36		08 59
Stanford-le-Hope d			23p42						06 42						07 42						08 42		
East Tilbury d			23p45						06 45						07 45						08 45		
Tilbury Town 3 d			23p51						06 51						07 51						08 51		
Grays d			23p54						06 54						07 54						08 54	08 59	
Purfleet d																						09 04	
Rainham d																						09 09	
Dagenham Dock d																						09 13	
Basildon d	23p32				06 02		06 32				07 02		07 32				08 02			08 32			09 02
Laindon d	23p35				06 05		06 35				07 05		07 35				08 05			08 35			09 05
West Horndon d	23p40				06 10		06 40				07 10		07 40				08 10			08 40			09 10
Chafford Hundred d			23p59						06 59						07 59						08 59		
Ockendon d			00 02						07 02						08 02						09 02		
Upminster ⊖ d	23p46		00 08		06 16		06 46		07 09		07 16		07 46		08 09		08 16			08 46	09 09		09 16
Barking ⊖ d	23p55		00a18		06 25		06 55		07 17		07 25		07 55		08 17		08 25			08 55	09 17	09a20	09 25
Stratford 7 ⊖ a																							
London Liverpool Street 15 ⊖ a																							
West Ham ⊖ d	00 01				06 31		07 01		07 23		07 31		08 01		08 23		08 31			09 01	09 23		09 31
Limehouse d	00 06				06 36		07 06		07 28		07 36		08 06		08 28		08 36			09 06	09 28		09 36
London Fenchurch Street 7 ⊖ a	00 12				06 42		07 12		07 34		07 42		08 12		08 34		08 42			09 12	09 34		09 42

For general notes see front of timetable
For details of catering facilities see
Directory of Train Operators

Table I

Sundays

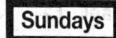

Shoeburyness and Southend Central → London

Network diagram - see first page of Table I

Station		CC	and at the same minutes past each hour until	CC	CC	CC	CC	CC	CC	CC
Shoeburyness	d			21 05			21 35	22 05		22 35
Thorpe Bay	d			21 08			21 38	22 08		22 38
Southend East	d			21 11			21 41	22 11		22 41
Southend Central	a			21 13			21 43	22 13		22 43
	d	08 50		21 14	21 20		21 44	22 14	22 20	22 44
Westcliff	d	08 53		21 16	21 23		21 46	22 16	22 23	22 46
Chalkwell	d	08 55		21 18	21 25		21 48	22 18	22 25	22 48
Leigh-on-Sea	d	08 58		21 21	21 28		21 51	22 21	22 28	22 51
Benfleet	d	09 02		21 25	21 32		21 55	22 25	22 32	22 55
Pitsea	d	09 06		21 29	21 36		21 59	22 29	22 36	22 59
Stanford-le-Hope	d	09 12			21 42				22 42	
East Tilbury	d	09 15			21 45				22 45	
Tilbury Town [3]	d	09 21			21 51				22 51	
Grays	d	09 24			21 54	21 59			22 54	
Purfleet	d					22 04				
Rainham	d					22 09				
Dagenham Dock	d					22 13				
Basildon	d			21 32			22 02	22 32		23 02
Laindon	d			21 35			22 05	22 35		23 05
West Horndon	d			21 40			22 10	22 40		23 10
Chafford Hundred	d	09 29			21 59				22 59	
Ockendon	d	09 32			22 02				23 02	
Upminster (Underground)	d	09 39		21 46	22 09		22 16	22 46	23 09	23 16
Barking (Underground)	d	09 47		21 55	22 17	22a20	22 25	22 55	23 17	23 25
Stratford [7] (Underground) (ferry)	a									
London Liverpool Street [15] (Underground)	a									
West Ham (Underground)	d	09 53		22 01	22 23		22 31	23 01	23 23	23 31
Limehouse (ferry)	d	09 58		22 06	22 28		22 36	23 06	23 28	23 36
London Fenchurch Street [7] (Underground) (ferry)	a	10 04		22 12	22 34		22 42	23 12	23 34	23 42

For general notes see front of timetable
For details of catering facilities see Directory of Train Operators

Table 1A

Mondays to Fridays

Tilbury Town — Tilbury Riverside

Bus Service

Network diagram - see first page of Table I

Mondays to Fridays

		CC	CC	CC	CC	CC	CC	CC	CC	CC	CC		CC	CC	and every 30 minutes until	CC	CC	CC	CC	CC	CC	CC	CC	
London Fenchurch Street 7	⊖ d		05b10	05 40	06 20	06 50	07 17	07 42	08 20	08 50	09 16		09 20	10 20		14 50	15 20		16 13	16 33	17 11	17 41	18 12	
Tilbury Town 3	d	05 40	06 18	06 50	07 18	07 45	08 13	08 38	09 03	09 33	10 03		10 33	11 03		15 33	16 03	16 33	17 03	17 33	18 00	18 30	19 00	
Tilbury Riverside	a	05 47	06 25	06 57	07 25	07 52	08 20	08 45	09 10	09 40	10 10		10 40	11 10		15 40	16 10	16 40	17 10	17 40	18 07	18 37	19 07	

Saturdays

		CC		CC		CC			CC	CC	and every 30 minutes until		CC		CC									
London Fenchurch Street 7	⊖ d					06 20			06 50	07 20			17 50		18 20									
Tilbury Town 3	d	05 40		06 15		07 01			07 31	08 01			18 31		19 01									
Tilbury Riverside	a	05 47		06 22		07 08			07 38	08 08			18 38		19 08									

Mondays to Fridays

		CC	CC	CC	CC	CC	CC	CC	CC	CC		CC	CC	and every 30 minutes until	CC	CC	CC	CC	CC	CC	CC	CC	CC	
Tilbury Riverside	d	05 50	06 30	07 00	07 30	07 55	08 23	08 50	09 12	09 42		10 12	10 42		15 12	15 42	16 12	16 40	17 15	17 45	18 15	18 40	19 10	
Tilbury Town 3	a	05 57	06 37	07 07	07 37	08 02	08 30	08 57	09 19	09 49		10 19	10 49		15 19	15 49	16 19	16 47	17 22	17 52	18 22	18 47	19 17	
London Fenchurch Street 7	⊖ a	06 52	07 23	07 52	08 25	08 52	09 26	09 51	10 09	10 37		11 05	11 35		16 05	16 36		17 39	18 09	18 41		19 32	20 05	

Saturdays

		CC		CC		CC		CC		CC			CC	CC	and every 30 minutes until		CC		CC					
Tilbury Riverside	d	05 50		06 30		07 10		07 50		08 09			08 39	09 09			18 39		19 09					
Tilbury Town 3	a	05 57		06 37		07 17		07 57		08 16			08 46	09 16			18 46		19 16					
London Fenchurch Street 7	⊖ a	07 04		07 34		08 04				09 04			09 34	10 04			19 34		20 04					

For general notes see front of timetable
For details of catering facilities see Directory of Train Operators

For full services between Tilbury Town and London Fenchurch Street refer to Table I

b Change at Barking and Tilbury Town

No Sunday Service

Table 4

Mondays to Fridays

Romford — Upminster

Network diagram - see first page of Table I

Miles			LE	LE	LE	LE	LE	LE	LE	LE	LE		LE	LE
0	Romford	d	06 12	06 42	07 06	07 30	07 54	08 18	08 42	09 12	09 42	and every 30 minutes until	19 12	19 42
2	Emerson Park	d	06 16	06 46	07 10	07 34	07 58	08 22	08 46	09 16	09 46		19 16	19 46
3½	Upminster ⊖	a	06 20	06 50	07 14	07 38	08 02	08 26	08 50	09 20	09 50		19 20	19 50

Saturdays

		LE	LE	LE	LE	LE	LE	LE	LE		LE	LE
Romford	d	06 12	06 42	07 12	07 42	08 12	08 42	09 12	09 42	and every 30 minutes until	19 12	19 42
Emerson Park	d	06 16	06 46	07 16	07 46	08 16	08 46	09 16	09 46		19 16	19 46
Upminster ⊖	a	06 20	06 50	07 20	07 50	08 20	08 50	09 20	09 50		19 20	19 50

Mondays to Fridays

Miles			LE	LE	LE	LE	LE	LE	LE	LE	LE		LE	LE
0	Upminster ⊖	d	06 24	06 54	07 18	07 42	08 06	08 30	08 54	09 24	09 54	and every 30 minutes until	19 24	19 54
1½	Emerson Park	d	06 28	06 58	07 22	07 46	08 10	08 34	08 58	09 28	09 58		19 28	19 58
3½	Romford	a	06 32	07 02	07 26	07 50	08 14	08 38	09 02	09 32	10 02		19 32	20 02

Saturdays

		LE	LE	LE	LE	LE	LE	LE	LE		LE	LE
Upminster ⊖	d	06 24	06 54	07 24	07 54	08 24	08 54	09 24	09 54	and every 30 minutes until	19 24	19 54
Emerson Park	d	06 28	06 58	07 28	07 58	08 28	08 58	09 28	09 58		19 28	19 58
Romford	a	06 32	07 02	07 32	08 02	08 32	09 02	09 32	10 02		19 32	20 02

For general notes see front of timetable
For details of catering facilities see
Directory of Train Operators

No Sunday Service

Network Diagram for Tables 5, 10, 11

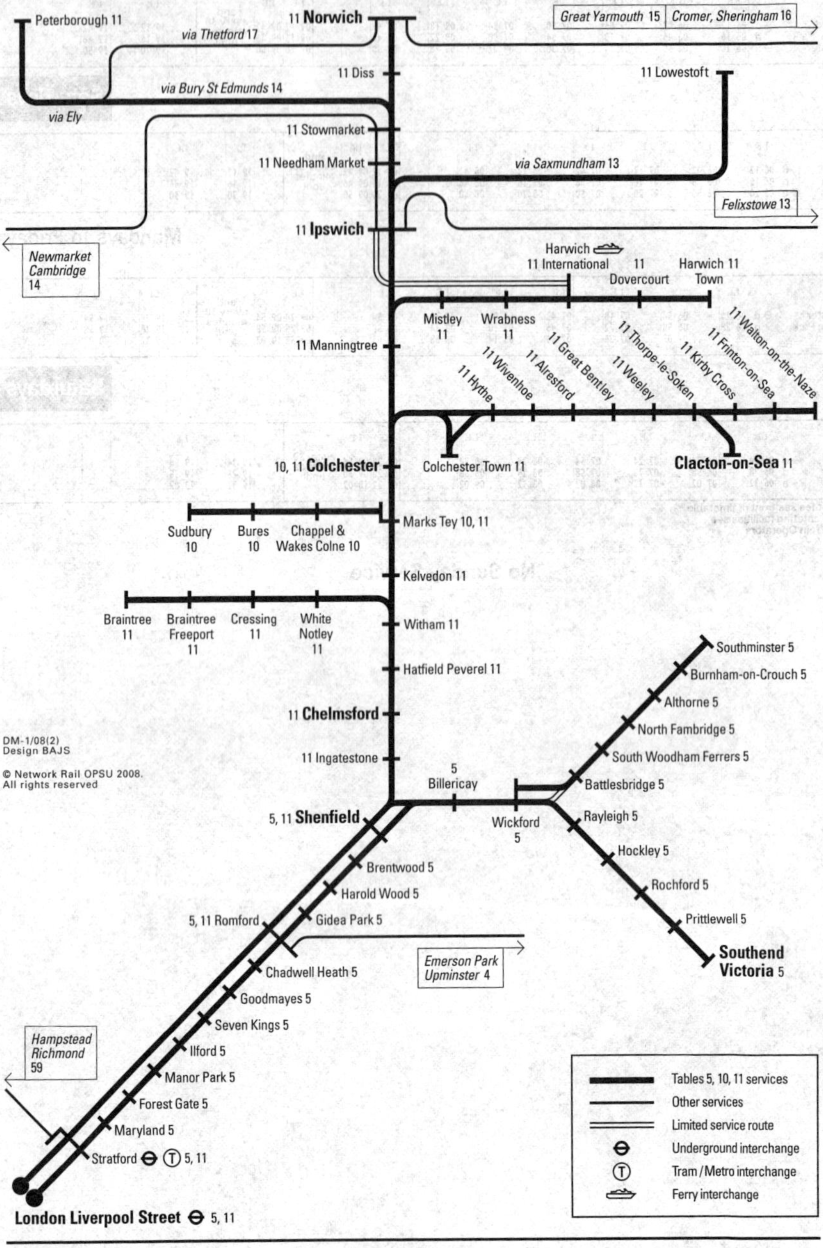

Peterborough 11
via Thetford 17
11 Norwich
Great Yarmouth 15
Cromer, Sheringham 16
via Bury St Edmunds 14
via Ely
11 Diss
11 Lowestoft
11 Stowmarket
11 Needham Market
via Saxmundham 13
Felixstowe 13
11 Ipswich
Newmarket
Cambridge
14
Harwich
11 International
11
Dovercourt
Harwich 11
Town
Mistley
11
Wrabness
11
11 Manningtree
11 Hythe
11 Wivenhoe
11 Alresford
11 Great Bentley
11 Weeley
11 Thorpe-le-Soken
11 Kirby Cross
11 Frinton-on-Sea
11 Walton-on-the-Naze
10, 11 Colchester
Colchester Town 11
Clacton-on-Sea 11
Sudbury
10
Bures
10
Chappel &
Wakes Colne 10
Marks Tey 10, 11
Kelvedon 11
Braintree
11
Braintree
Freeport
11
Cressing
11
White
Notley
11
Witham 11
Hatfield Peverel 11
Southminster 5
Burnham-on-Crouch 5
Althorne 5
North Fambridge 5
South Woodham Ferrers 5
11 Chelmsford
11 Ingatestone
5
Billericay
Battlesbridge 5
5, 11 Shenfield
Wickford
5
Rayleigh 5
Hockley 5
Rochford 5
Prittlewell 5
Southend
Victoria 5
Brentwood 5
Harold Wood 5
5, 11 Romford
Gidea Park 5
Emerson Park
Upminster 4
Chadwell Heath 5
Goodmayes 5
Seven Kings 5
Hampstead
Richmond
59
Ilford 5
Manor Park 5
Forest Gate 5
Maryland 5
Stratford 5, 11
London Liverpool Street 5, 11
Tables 5, 10, 11 services
Other services
Limited service route
Underground interchange
Tram / Metro interchange
Ferry interchange

DM-1/08(2)
Design BAJS

London → Shenfield, Southminster and Southend Victoria

Network diagram - see first page of Table 5

Miles	Miles			LE MX 1	LE MO 1	LE MO	LE MX	LE MX 1	LE MO 1	LE MX	LE MO 1	LE MX	LE MO	LE MX 1	LE MO 1	LE MX 1	LE MX	LE MX	LE MO	LE MO 1	LE MX 1 A	LE MX 1	LE MX	LE MO	LE 1
0	—	**London Liverpool Street 15** ⊖	d	23p15	23p15	23p35	23p37	23p45	23p45	23p52	00 02	00 02	00 05	00 15	00 15	00 18	00 22	00 35	00 35	00 45	00 46	00 50	00 55	00 55	05 23
4	—	Stratford 7 ⊖	d	23p22	23p22	23p42	23p44	23p52	23p52	23p58	00 09	00 09	00 12	00 22	00 22	00 25	00 29	00 42	00 42	00 52	00 55	00 57	01 02	01 02	05 32
4½	—	Maryland	d			23p43	23p45			23p59		00 10	00 13				00 30	00 43	00 43				01 03	01 03	
5¼	—	Forest Gate	d			23p45	23p47			00 02		00 12	00 15				00 32	00 45	00 45				01 05	01 05	
6¼	—	Manor Park	d			23p47	23p49			00 04		00 14	00 17				00 34	00 47	00 47				01 07	01 07	
7¼	—	Ilford 2	d			23p50	23p52			00 07		00 17	00 20				00 37	00 50	00 50				01 10	01 10	
8½	—	Seven Kings	d			23p53	23p55			00 10		00 20	00 23				00 40	00 53	00 53				01 13	01 13	
9¼	—	Goodmayes	d			23p55	23p57			00 12		00 22	00 25				00 42	00 55	00 55				01 15	01 15	
10	—	Chadwell Heath	d			23p57	23p59			00 14		00 24	00 27				00 44	00 57	00 57				01 17	01 17	
12½	—	Romford	d		23p33	23p59	00 02		00 03	00 17		00 27	00 30	00 32	00 33		00 47	01 00	01 00	01 03		01 08	01 20	01 20	05 40
13½	—	Gidea Park 2	d		23p37	00 04	00 06		00 07	00 21		00a31	00a36		00 37		00 51	01a04	01a06	01 07	01 07		01 24	01 24	
15	—	Harold Wood	d		23p40	00 07	00 09		00 10	00 24					00 40		00 54			01 10			01 27	01 27	
18¼	—	Brentwood	d		23p44	00 11	00 13		00 14	00 28					00 44		00 58			01 14			01 31	01 31	
20¼	—	**Shenfield 3**	a	23p39	23p50	00 16	00 20	00 09	00 20	00 35	00 30			00 44	00 50	00 47	01 03			01 20	01 17	01 20	01 36	01 38	05 50
—	—		d	23p40	23p50			00 10	00 20					00 45	00 50					01 20		01 20			
24¼	—	Billericay	d	23p46	23p56			00 16	00 26					00 51	00 56					01 26		01 26			
29	0	**Wickford 2**	d	23p51	00 01			00 21	00 31					00 56	01 01					01 31		01 31			
—	2½	Battlesbridge	d																						
—	5	South Woodham Ferrers	d																						
—	8¼	North Fambridge	d																						
—	11¼	Althorne	d																						
—	14¼	Burnham-on-Crouch	d																						
—	16½	**Southminster**	a																						
33	—	Rayleigh	d	23p56	00 06			00 26	00 36					01 01	01 06					01 36		01 36			
36	—	Hockley	d	00 01	00 11			00 31	00 41					01 06	01 11					01 41		01 41			
38¾	—	Rochford	d	00 04	00 14			00 34	00 44					01 09	01 14					01 44		01 44			
41	—	Prittlewell	d	00 08				00 38						01 13								01 48			
41½	—	**Southend Victoria**	a	00 15	00 24			00 45	00 54					01 20	01 24					01 54		01 55			

		LE 1	LE 1	LE		LE	LE 1	LE 1	LE 1	LE 1	LE	LE 1	LE	LE 1	LE	LE	LE 1	LE	LE 1	LE	LE 1	LE	LE 1	LE 1	LE
London Liverpool Street 15 ⊖	d			05 28		05 39	05 52	05 55	06 02		06 02	06 12	06 12	06 15	06 22	06 32	06 34	06 42	06 48	06 52	06 55	07 02	07 04	07 08	07 12
Stratford 7 ⊖	d			05 35		05 46	06a01	06 02	06 09		06 09	06 19	06 19	06 22	06 29	06 39	06 41	06 49	06 55	06 59	07 02	07 09	07 11	07 15	07 19
Maryland	d					05 47					06 10		06 20		06 30	06 40		06 50		07 00		07 10			07 20
Forest Gate	d					05 49					06 12		06 22		06 32	06 42		06 52		07 02		07 12			07 22
Manor Park	d					05 51					06 14		06 24		06 34	06 44		06 54		07 04		07 14			07 24
Ilford 2	d			05 40		05 54					06 17		06 27		06 37	06 47		06 57		07 07		07 17			07 27
Seven Kings	d			05 42		05 57					06 20		06 30		06 40	06 50		07 00		07 10		07 20			07 30
Goodmayes	d					05 59					06 22		06 32		06 42	06 52		07 02		07 12		07 22			07 32
Chadwell Heath	d					06 01					06 24		06 34		06 44	06 54		07 04		07 14		07 24			07 34
Romford	d			05 48		06 04			06 17		06 27		06 37		06 47	06 57	06 49	07 07		07 17		07 27		07 23	07 37
Gidea Park 2	d			05 51		06 08					06 31		06 41		06 51	07 01		07 11		07 21		07 31			07 41
Harold Wood	d			05 54		06 11					06 34		06 44		06 54	07 04		07 14		07 24		07 34			07 44
Brentwood	d			05 59		06 15					06 38		06 48		06 58	07 08		07 18		07 28		07 38			07 48
Shenfield 3	a			06 04		06 22		06 19	06 27		06 45	06 36	06 55	06 40	07 05	07 15	07 00	07 25	07 12	07 35	07 20	07 45	07 28	07 33	07 55
	d		05 58	06 04				06 20		06 35				06 40			07 00				07 20				
Billericay	d		06 04	06 10				06 26		06 41				06 46			07 06				07 26				
Wickford 2	d	05 20	06 10	06 15				06 31		06 47				06 51			07 11				07 31				
Battlesbridge	d	05 24	06 14							06 51															
South Woodham Ferrers	d	05 28	06 18							06 55															
North Fambridge	d	05b45	06 25							07c07															
Althorne	d	05 50	06 30							07 12															
Burnham-on-Crouch	d	05 55	06 35							07 17															
Southminster	a	06 00	06 40							07 22															
Rayleigh	d			06 21				06 36						06 56			07 16				07 36				
Hockley	d			06 25				06 41						07 01			07 21				07 41				
Rochford	d			06 29				06 44						07 04			07 24				07 44				
Prittlewell	d			06 32				06 48						07 08			07 28				07 48				
Southend Victoria	a			06 36				06 51						07 11			07 31				07 51				

		LE 1	LE 1	LE 1	LE	LE 1		LE	LE 1	LE 1	LE	LE 1	LE	LE 1	LE 1	LE	LE 1	LE	LE 1	LE 1	LE	LE 1	LE	LE 1	LE 1
London Liverpool Street 15 ⊖	d		07 15	07 18	07 22	07 27		07 32	07 34	07 40	07 42	07 48	07 52	07 55	08 02	08 02	08 08	08 12	08 14	08 18	08 22		08 32	08 35	08 38
Stratford 7 ⊖	d		07 22	07 25	07 29			07 39	07 41	07 47	07 49	07 55	07 59	08 02		08 09	08 15	08 19	08 21	08 25	08 29		08 39	08 42	
Maryland	d				07 30			07 40			07 50		08 00			08 10		08 20			08 30		08 40		
Forest Gate	d				07 32			07 42			07 52		08 02			08 12		08 22			08 32		08 42		
Manor Park	d				07 34			07 44			07 54		08 04			08 14		08 24			08 34		08 44		
Ilford 2	d				07 37			07 47			07 57		08 07			08 17		08 27			08 37		08 47		
Seven Kings	d				07 40			07 50			08 00		08 10			08 20		08 30			08 40		08 50		
Goodmayes	d				07 42			07 52			08 02		08 12			08 22		08 32			08 42		08 52		
Chadwell Heath	d				07 44			07 54			08 04		08 14			08 24		08 34			08 44		08 54		
Romford	d				07 47			07 57	07 49		08 07		08 17		08 16	08 27		08 37	08 29		08 47		08 57		
Gidea Park 2	d				07 51			08 01			08 11		08 21			08 31		08 41			08 51		09 01		
Harold Wood	d				07 54			08 04			08 14		08 24			08 34		08 44			08 54		09 04		
Brentwood	d				07 58			08 08			08 18		08 28			08 38		08 48			08 58		09 08		
Shenfield 3	a		07 40	07 41	08 05	07 50		08 15	08 00	08 06	08 25	08 12	08 35	08 19	08 26	08 45	08 31	08 55	08 40	08 41	09 05		09 15	08 59	09 02
	d		07 41						08 00	08 08				08 20					08 40			09 08		09 00	
Billericay	d		07 47						08 06	08 14				08 26					08 46			09 14		09 06	
Wickford 2	d	07 35	07 52						08 11	08 20				08 31					08 51			09 20		09 11	
Battlesbridge	d	07 39								08 24												09 24			
South Woodham Ferrers	d	07 43								08 28												09 28			
North Fambridge	d	07 51								08 34												09 34			
Althorne	d	07 56								08 39												09 39			
Burnham-on-Crouch	d	08 01								08 44												09 44			
Southminster	a	08 06								08 49												09 49			
Rayleigh	d		07 57						08 16					08 36					08 56					09 16	
Hockley	d		08 02						08 21					08 41					09 01					09 21	
Rochford	d		08 05						08 24					08 44					09 04					09 24	
Prittlewell	d		08 09						08 28					08 48					09 08					09 28	
Southend Victoria	a		08 14						08 31					08 51					09 11					09 31	

For general notes see front of timetable
For details of catering facilities see Directory of Train Operators

A To Colchester (Table 11)
b Arr. 0534
c Arr. 0701

London → Shenfield, Southminster and Southend Victoria

Network diagram - see first page of Table 5

		LE	LE 1	LE	LE 1	LE	LE 1	LE		LE 1	LE 1	LE	LE	LE 1	LE 1	LE	LE 1	LE	LE 1		LE	LE 1	LE	LE 1	LE 1
London Liverpool Street 15	⊖ d	08 42	08 48	08 52	08 55	09 02	09 08	09 12		09 15	09 18	09 22	09 32	09 34	09 40	09 42	09 48	09 52	09 55		10 02	10 08	10 12	10 15	10 18
Stratford 7	⊖ d	08 49	08 55	08 59	09 02	09 09	09 15	09 19		09 22	09 25	09 29	09 39	09 41	09 47	09 49	09 55	09 59	10 02		10 09	10 15	10 19	10 22	10 25
Maryland	d	08 50		09 00		09 10		09 20				09 30	09 40			09 50		10 00			10 10		10 20		
Forest Gate	d	08 52		09 02		09 12		09 22				09 32	09 42			09 52		10 02			10 12		10 22		
Manor Park	d	08 54		09 04		09 14		09 24				09 34	09 44			09 54		10 04			10 14		10 24		
Ilford 2	d	08 57		09 07		09 17		09 27				09 37	09 47			09 57		10 07			10 17		10 27		
Seven Kings	d	09 00		09 10		09 20		09 30				09 40	09 50			10 00		10 10			10 20		10 30		
Goodmayes	d	09 02		09 12		09 22		09 32				09 42	09 52			10 02		10 12			10 22		10 32		
Chadwell Heath	d	09 04		09 14		09 24		09 34				09 44	09 54			10 04		10 14			10 24		10 34		
Romford	d	09 07		09 17		09 27	09 23	09 37				09 47	09 57	09 49		10 07		10 17			10 27	10 23	10 37		
Gidea Park 2	d	09 11		09 21		09 31		09 41				09 51	10 01			10 11		10 21			10 31		10 41		
Harold Wood	d	09 14		09 24		09 34		09 44				09 54	10 04			10 14		10 24			10 34		10 44		
Brentwood	d	09 18		09 28		09 38		09 48				09 58	10 08			10 18		10 28			10 38		10 48		
Shenfield 3	a	09 25	09 12	09 35	09 19	09 45	09 33	09 55		09 39	09 41	10 05	10 15	10 00	10 05	10 25	10 12	10 35	10 19		10 45	10 33	10 55	10 39	10 41
	d				09 20					09 40				10 00	10 08				10 20					10 40	
Billericay	d				09 26					09 46				10 06	10 14				10 26					10 46	
Wickford 2	d				09 31					09 51				10 11	10 20				10 31					10 51	
Battlesbridge	d														10 24										
South Woodham Ferrers	d														10 28										
North Fambridge	d														10 34										
Althorne	d														10 39										
Burnham-on-Crouch	d														10 44										
Southminster	a														10 49										
Rayleigh	d				09 36					09 56				10 16					10 36					10 56	
Hockley	d				09 41					10 01				10 21					10 41					11 01	
Rochford	d				09 44					10 04				10 24					10 44					11 04	
Prittlewell	d				09 48					10 08				10 28					10 48					11 08	
Southend Victoria	a				09 51					10 11				10 31					10 51					11 11	

		LE	LE 1	LE	LE 1	LE	LE 1	LE	LE 1		LE	LE 1		LE	LE 1	LE 1	LE	LE 1	LE 1	LE	LE 1	LE	LE 1	LE
London Liverpool Street 15	⊖ d	10 22		10 32	10 34	10 42	10 48	10 52	10 55		15 02	15 08		15 12	15 15	15 18	15 22	15 32		15 32	15 34	15 42	15 48	15 52
Stratford 7	⊖ d	10 29		10 39	10 41	10 49	10 55	10 59	11 02		15 09	15 15		15 19	15 22	15 25	15 29			15 39	15 41	15 49	15 55	15 59
Maryland	d	10 30		10 40		10 50		11 00			15 10			15 20			15 30			15 40		15 50		16 00
Forest Gate	d	10 32		10 42		10 52		11 02			15 12			15 22			15 32			15 42		15 52		16 02
Manor Park	d	10 34		10 44		10 54		11 04			15 14			15 24			15 34			15 44		15 54		16 04
Ilford 2	d	10 37		10 47		10 57		11 07			15 17			15 27			15 37			15 47		15 57		16 07
Seven Kings	d	10 40		10 50		11 00		11 10			15 20			15 30			15 40			15 50		16 00		16 10
Goodmayes	d	10 42		10 52		11 02		11 12		and at	15 22			15 32			15 42			15 52		16 02		16 12
Chadwell Heath	d	10 44		10 54		11 04		11 14			15 24			15 34			15 44			15 54		16 04		16 14
Romford	d	10 47		10 57	10 49	11 07		11 17		the same	15 27	15 23		15 37			15 47			15 57	15 49	16 07		16 17
Gidea Park 2	d	10 51		11 01		11 11		11 21			15 31			15 41			15 51			16 01		16 11		16 21
Harold Wood	d	10 54		11 04		11 14		11 24		minutes	15 34			15 44			15 54			16 04		16 14		16 24
Brentwood	d	10 58		11 08		11 18		11 28			15 38			15 48			15 58			16 08		16 18		16 28
Shenfield 3	a	11 05		11 15	11 00	11 25	11 12	11 35	11 19	past	15 45	15 33		15 55	15 39	15 41	16 05	15 54		16 15	16 00	16 25	16 12	16 35
	d		11 08		11 00				11 20	each					15 40				16 08		16 00			
Billericay	d		11 14		11 06				11 26						15 46				16 14		16 06			
Wickford 2	d		11 20		11 11				11 31	hour until					15 51				16 20		16 11			
Battlesbridge	d		11 24																16 24					
South Woodham Ferrers	d		11 28																16 28					
North Fambridge	d		11 34																16 34					
Althorne	d		11 39																16 39					
Burnham-on-Crouch	d		11 44																16 44					
Southminster	a		11 49																16 49					
Rayleigh	d				11 16				11 36						15 56						16 16			
Hockley	d				11 21				11 41						16 01						16 21			
Rochford	d				11 24				11 44						16 04						16 24			
Prittlewell	d				11 28				11 48						16 08						16 28			
Southend Victoria	a				11 31				11 51						16 11						16 31			

		LE 1	LE	LE 1	LE 1	LE	LE 1	LE	LE 1	LE	LE 1	LE 1	LE 1	LE	LE		LE 1	LE	LE 1	LE	LE 1	LE	LE 1	LE	LE 1
London Liverpool Street 15	⊖ d	15 55	16 02	16 02	16 10	16 12	16 17	16 22	16 25	16 32	16 34		16 40	16 42	16 46		16 47	16 52	16 55	16 56	17 02	17 02	17 04	17 06	17 08
Stratford 7	⊖ d	16 02	16 09	16 10	16 18	16 19	16 25	16 29	16 33	16 39	16 42		16 48	16 49	16 53		16 55	16 59	17 03	17 03		17 09	17 12	17 13	17a16
Maryland	d		16 10			16 20		16 30		16 40					16 55					17 05				17 15	
Forest Gate	d		16 12			16 22		16 32		16 42					16 57					17 07				17 17	
Manor Park	d		16 14			16 24		16 34		16 44					16 59					17 09				17 19	
Ilford 2	d		16 17			16 27		16 37		16 47				16 55	17 02			17 05		17 12		17 15		17 22	
Seven Kings	d		16 20			16 30		16 40		16 50				16 58				17 08				17 18			
Goodmayes	d		16 22			16 32		16 42		16 52				17 00				17 10				17 20			
Chadwell Heath	d		16 24			16 34		16 44		16 54				17 02	17 06			17 12		17 16		17 22		17 26	
Romford	d		16 27			16 37		16 47		16 57				17 06	17 10			17 16		17 20		17 26		17 30	
Gidea Park 2	d		16 31			16 41		16 51		17 01				17a11	17 14			17a21		17 24		17a31		17 34	
Harold Wood	d		16 34			16 44		16 54		17 04					17 17					17 27				17 37	
Brentwood	d		16 38			16 48		16 58		17 08					17 21					17 31				17 41	
Shenfield 3	a	16 19	16 45	16 25	16 34	16 55	16 40	17 05	16 50	17 15	16 57		17 04		17 29		17 10		17 20	17 39	17 24		17 29	17 49	
	d	16 20			16 35				16 50				17 05						17 20				17 29		
Billericay	d	16 26			16 41				16 56				17 11						17 26				17 36		
Wickford 2	d	16 31			16 46				17 01			17 07	17 16						17 31				17 42		
Battlesbridge	d											17 11													
South Woodham Ferrers	d											17 15													
North Fambridge	d											17 21													
Althorne	d											17 26													
Burnham-on-Crouch	d											17 31													
Southminster	a											17 36													
Rayleigh	d	16 36			16 51				17 06				17 21						17 36				17 47		
Hockley	d	16 41			16 56				17 11				17 26						17 41				17 52		
Rochford	d	16 44			16 59				17 14				17 29						17 44				17 55		
Prittlewell	d	16 48			17 03				17 18				17 33						17 48				17 59		
Southend Victoria	a	16 51			17 09				17 23				17 39						17 53				18 04		

For general notes see front of timetable
For details of catering facilities see
Directory of Train Operators

London → Shenfield, Southminster and Southend Victoria

Network diagram - see first page of Table 5

		LE	LE 1	LE 1	LE	LE 1	LE 1	LE	LE 1	LE	LE 1	LE	LE 1	LE	LE 1	LE	LE		LE 1	LE 1	LE	LE	LE 1	LE	LE 1
London Liverpool Street 15 ⊖	d	17 12	17 12	17 15	17 16	17 17	17 22	17 22	17 25	17 26	17 32	17 32	17 34	17 36	17 38	17 39	17 42		17 42	17 45	17 46	17 49	17 52	17 52	17 54
Stratford 7 ⊖	d	17 19	17a20		17 23			17 29	17 33	17 33		17 39	17 42	17 43	17a46	17 46	17 49		17a50	17 53	17 53	17 56		17 59	
Maryland	d				17 25					17 35				17 45							17 55				
Forest Gate	d				17 27					17 37		17 42					17 52							18 02	
Manor Park	d				17 29					17 39						17 50						18 00			
Ilford 2	d	17 25			17 32			17 35		17 42		17 46		17 50		17 53	17 56				18 00	18 03		18 06	
Seven Kings	d	17 28						17 38				17 49		17 52		17 56	17 59				18 02	18 06		18 09	
Goodmayes	d	17 30						17 40				17 51		17 54		17 58	18 01				18 04	18 08		18 11	
Chadwell Heath	d	17 32			17 36			17 42		17 46		17 53		17 56		18 00	18 03				18 06	18 10		18 13	
Romford	d	17 36			17 40			17 46		17 50		17 57		18 00		18 04	18 07				18 10	18 14		18 17	
Gidea Park 2	d	17a41			17 44			17a51		17 54		18a02		18 04		18a09	18a12				18 14	18 18		18a22	
Harold Wood	d				17 47					17 57				18 07							18 17	18 21			
Brentwood	d				17 51					18 01				18 11							18 21	18 25			
Shenfield 3	a				17 59	17 41	17 44		17 51	18 09	17 54		17 59	18 19						18 10	18 29	18 31	18 14		
	d					17 42			17 52				17 59							18 11		18 35			
Billericay	d			17 44		17 48			17 58				18 06							18 17		18 41			
Wickford 2	d			17 50		17 54			18 04				18 12							18 23		18 47			18 29
Battlesbridge	d																								18 33
South Woodham Ferrers	d			17 57																					18 37
North Fambridge	d			18 03																					18 43
Althorne	d			18 08																					18 48
Burnham-on-Crouch	d			18 13																					18 53
Southminster	a			18 20																					19 00
Rayleigh	d					17 59			18 09				18 17							18 28		18 53			
Hockley	d					18 04			18 14				18 22							18 33		18 57			
Rochford	d					18 07			18 17				18 25							18 36		19 01			
Prittlewell	d					18 11			18 21				18 29							18 40		19 04			
Southend Victoria	a					18 16			18 26				18 34							18 45		19 10			

		LE 1	LE	LE	LE 1	LE 1	LE	LE 1	LE	LE 1	LE 1	LE	LE 1	LE	LE 1	LE	LE	LE 1	LE 1		LE	LE 1	LE	LE 1	LE 1
London Liverpool Street 15 ⊖	d	17 56	17 56	18 02	18 02	18 04	18 06	18 08	18 12	18 12	18 15	18 16	18 22	18 22	18 25	18 26	18 32	18 32	18 35		18 38	18 38	18 42	18 42	18 45
Stratford 7 ⊖	d		18 03	18 09	18a10	18 13	18 13	18a16	18 19	18a20	18 23	18 23		18 29	18 33	18 33	18 39	18a40	18 43		18 45	18 46	18 49	18 50	18 53
Maryland	d		18 05				18 15					18 25				18 35	18 40				18 46		18 50		
Forest Gate	d		18 07				18 17					18 27				18 37	18 42				18 48		18 52		
Manor Park	d		18 09				18 19					18 29				18 39	18 44				18 50		18 54		
Ilford 2	d		18 12	18 15			18 22		18 25			18 32		18 35		18 42	18 47				18 53		18 57		
Seven Kings	d			18 18					18 28					18 38			18 50				18 56		19 00		
Goodmayes	d			18 20					18 30					18 40			18 52				18 58		19 02		
Chadwell Heath	d		18 16	18 22			18 26		18 32			18 36		18 42		18 46	18 54				19 00		19 04		
Romford	d		18 20	18 26			18 30		18 36			18 40		18 46		18 50	18 57				19 03		19 07		
Gidea Park 2	d		18 24	18a31			18 34		18a41			18 44		18a51		18 54	19 01				19a09		19 11		
Harold Wood	d		18 27				18 37					18 47				18 57	19 04						19 14		
Brentwood	d		18 31				18 41					18 51				19 01	19 08						19 18		
Shenfield 3	a	18 21	18 39			18 29	18 49				18 40	18 59	18 44		18 50	19 09	19 15		19 00			19 01	19 25		19 10
	d	18 22				18 29					18 41				18 51				19 01						19 11
Billericay	d	18 28				18 36					18 47				18 57				19 07						19 17
Wickford 2	d	18 34				18 42					18 53				19 03				19 13					19 17	19 23
Battlesbridge	d																							19 22	
South Woodham Ferrers	d																							19 26	
North Fambridge	d																							19 32	
Althorne	d																							19 37	
Burnham-on-Crouch	d																							19 42	
Southminster	a																							19 49	
Rayleigh	d	18 39				18 47					18 58				19 08				19 18						19 28
Hockley	d	18 44				18 52					19 03				19 13				19 23						19 33
Rochford	d	18 47				18 55					19 06				19 16				19 26						19 36
Prittlewell	d	18 51				18 59					19 10				19 20				19 30						19 40
Southend Victoria	a	18 56				19 04					19 15				19 25				19 35						19 45

		LE	LE 1	LE	LE 1	LE	LE 1	LE	LE 1	LE	LE 1	LE 1	LE	LE	LE 1	LE 1	LE	LE 1	LE	LE 1	LE 1		LE	LE 1	LE
London Liverpool Street 15 ⊖	d	18 46	18 48	18 52	18 55	18 56	19 02	19 02	19 08	19 12	19 15	19 18	19 22	19 32	19 35	19 38	19 42	19 48	19 52		19 55		20 02	20 08	20 12
Stratford 7 ⊖	d	18 53		18 59	19 03	19 03	19 09	19 09	19a15	19 19	19 22	19 25	19 29	19 39	19 42	19 45	19 49	19 55	19 59		20 03		20 09	20 15	20 19
Maryland	d			19 00				19 10		19 20			19 30	19 40			19 50		20 00				20 10		20 20
Forest Gate	d	18 55		19 02		19 05		19 12		19 22			19 32	19 42			19 52		20 02				20 12		20 22
Manor Park	d	18 57		19 04		19 07		19 14		19 24			19 34	19 44			19 54		20 04				20 14		20 24
Ilford 2	d	19 00		19 07		19 10		19 17		19 27			19 37	19 47			19 57		20 07				20 17		20 27
Seven Kings	d	19 03		19 10		19 13		19 20		19 30			19 40	19 50			20 00		20 10				20 20		20 30
Goodmayes	d	19 05		19 12		19 15		19 22		19 32			19 42	19 52			20 02		20 12				20 22		20 32
Chadwell Heath	d	19 07		19 14		19 17		19 24		19 34			19 44	19 54			20 04		20 14				20 24		20 34
Romford	d	19 10		19 17		19 20		19 27		19 37			19 47	19 57			20 07		20 17				20 27		20 37
Gidea Park 2	d	19 14		19 21		19a26		19 31		19 41			19 51	20 01			20 11		20 21				20 31		20 41
Harold Wood	d	19 17		19 24				19 34		19 44			19 54	20 04			20 14		20 24				20 34		20 44
Brentwood	d	19 21		19 28				19 38		19 48			19 58	20 08			20 18		20 28				20 38		20 48
Shenfield 3	a	19 29	19 11	19 35	19 20		19 25	19 45		19 55	19 39	19 41	20 05	20 15	19 59	20 01	20 25	20 12	20 35		20 20		20 45	20 31	20 55
	d				19 21						19 40				20 00						20 20				
Billericay	d				19 27						19 46				20 06						20 26				
Wickford 2	d				19 33						19 51				20 11					20 20	20 31				
Battlesbridge	d																			20 24					
South Woodham Ferrers	d																			20 28					
North Fambridge	d																			20 34					
Althorne	d																			20 39					
Burnham-on-Crouch	d																			20 44					
Southminster	a																			20 49					
Rayleigh	d				19 38						19 56				20 16						20 36				
Hockley	d				19 43						20 01				20 21						20 41				
Rochford	d				19 46						20 04				20 24						20 44				
Prittlewell	d				19 50						20 08				20 28						20 48				
Southend Victoria	a				19 55						20 11				20 31						20 51				

For general notes see front of timetable
For details of catering facilities see Directory of Train Operators

London → Shenfield, Southminster and Southend Victoria

Network diagram - see first page of Table 5

Station		LE 1	LE 1	LE	LE 1	LE	LE 1	CC	LE 1	LE	LE 1	LE	LE 1	LE	LE 1	LE	LE 1	LE 1	LE	LE 1	LE	LE 1	CC		LE
London Liverpool Street 15 ⊖	d	20 15	20 18	20 22		20 32	20 34	20 35	20 38	20 42	20 48	20 52	20 55	21 02	21 08	21 12	21 15	21 18	21 22		21 32	21 34	21 35		21 42
Stratford 7 ⊖	d	20 22	20 25	20 29		20 39	20 41	20a42	20 45	20 49	20 55	20 59	21 02	21 09	21 15	21 19	21 22	21 25	21 29		21 39	21 41	21a42		21 49
Maryland	d			20 30		20 40				20 50		21 00		21 10		21 20			21 30		21 40				21 50
Forest Gate	d			20 32		20 42				20 52		21 02		21 12		21 22			21 32		21 42				21 52
Manor Park	d			20 34		20 44				20 54		21 04		21 14		21 24			21 34		21 44				21 54
Ilford 2	d			20 37		20 47				20 57		21 07		21 17		21 27			21 37		21 47				21 57
Seven Kings	d			20 40		20 50				21 00		21 10		21 20		21 30			21 40		21 50				22 00
Goodmayes	d			20 42		20 52				21 02		21 12		21 22		21 32			21 42		21 52				22 02
Chadwell Heath	d			20 44		20 54				21 04		21 14		21 24		21 34			21 44		21 54				22 04
Romford	d			20 47		20 57	20 49			21 07		21 17		21 27	21 23	21 37			21 47		21 57	21 49			22 07
Gidea Park 2	d			20 51		21 01				21 11		21 21		21 31		21 41			21 51		22 01				22 11
Harold Wood	d			20 54		21 04				21 14		21 24		21 34		21 44			21 54		22 04				22 14
Brentwood	d			20 58		21 08				21 18		21 28		21 38		21 48			21 58		22 08				22 18
Shenfield 3	a	20 39	20 41	21 05		21 15	21 00		21 01	21 25	21 12	21 35	21 19	21 45	21 33	21 53	21 39	21 41	22 05		22 15	22 00			22 25
	d	20 40			21 08		21 00						21 20				21 40			22 08		22 00			
Billericay	d	20 46			21 14		21 06						21 26				21 46			22 14		22 06			
Wickford 2	d	20 51			21 20		21 11						21 31				21 51			22 20		22 11			
Battlesbridge	d				21 24															22 24					
South Woodham Ferrers	d				21 28															22 28					
North Fambridge	d				21 34															22 34					
Althorne	d				21 39															22 39					
Burnham-on-Crouch	d				21 44															22 44					
Southminster	a				21 49															22 49					
Rayleigh	d	20 56					21 16						21 36				21 56					22 16			
Hockley	d	21 01					21 21						21 41				22 01					22 21			
Rochford	d	21 04					21 24						21 44				22 04					22 24			
Prittlewell	d	21 08					21 28						21 48				22 08					22 28			
Southend Victoria	a	21 11					21 31						21 51				22 11					22 31			

Station		LE 1	LE	LE 1	LE 1	LE	LE 1	LE 1	LE	LE	LE 1	LE 1	LE 1	LE	LE 1	LE	LE 1	LE 1	LE	LE	LE 1	LE 1	LE		
London Liverpool Street 15 ⊖	d	21 48	21 52	21 55	22 00	22 07	22 15	22 18	22 22	22 37		22 45	22 48	22 52	23 00	23 07	23 15	23 18	23 22	23 37	23 45	23 48	23 52		
Stratford 7 ⊖	d	21 55	21 59	22 02		22 14	22 22	22 25	22 29	22 44		22 52	22 55	22 59	23 07	23 14	23 22	23 25	23 29	23 44	23 52	23 55	23 58		
Maryland	d		22 00			22 15			22 30	22 45				23 00		23 15			23 30	23 45			23 59		
Forest Gate	d		22 02			22 17			22 32	22 47				23 02		23 17			23 32	23 47			00 02		
Manor Park	d		22 04			22 19			22 34	22 49				23 04		23 19			23 34	23 49			00 04		
Ilford 2	d		22 07			22 22			22 37	22 52				23 07		23 22			23 37	23 52			00 07		
Seven Kings	d		22 10			22 25			22 40	22 55				23 10		23 25			23 40	23 55			00 10		
Goodmayes	d		22 12			22 27			22 42	22 57				23 12		23 27			23 42	23 57			00 12		
Chadwell Heath	d		22 14			22 29			22 44	22 59				23 14		23 29			23 44	23 59			00 14		
Romford	d		22 17			22 32			22 47	23 02				23 17		23 32			23 47	00 02			00 17		
Gidea Park 2	d		22 21			22 36			22 51	23 06				23 21		23 36			23 51	00 06			00 21		
Harold Wood	d		22 24			22 39			22 54	23 09				23 24		23 39			23 54	00 09			00 24		
Brentwood	d		22 28			22 43			22 58	23 13				23 28		23 43			23 58	00 13			00 28		
Shenfield 3	a	22 12	22 35	22 19	22 22	22 50	22 39	22 41	23 05	23 20		23 09	23 12	23 35	23 23	23 50	23 39	23 41	00 05	00 20	00 09	00 12	00 35		
	d			22 20			22 40					23 10					23 40				00 10				
Billericay	d			22 26			22 46					23 16					23 46				00 16				
Wickford 2	d			22 31			22 51				22 58	23 21					23 51				00 21				
Battlesbridge	d										23 02														
South Woodham Ferrers	d										23 06														
North Fambridge	d										23 12														
Althorne	d										23 17														
Burnham-on-Crouch	d										23 22														
Southminster	a										23 27														
Rayleigh	d			22 36			22 56					23 26					23 56				00 26				
Hockley	d			22 41			23 01					23 31					00 01				00 31				
Rochford	d			22 44			23 04					23 34					00 04				00 34				
Prittlewell	d			22 48			23 08					23 38					00 08				00 38				
Southend Victoria	a			22 51			23 11					23 45					00 15				00 45				

For general notes see front of timetable
For details of catering facilities see Directory of Train Operators

London → Shenfield, Southminster and Southend Victoria

Network diagram - see first page of Table 5

		LE 1	LE	LE 1	LE	LE		LE 1	LE 1	LE	LE	LE 1 A		LE 1	LE	LE 1	LE 1	LE		LE	LE 1	LE 1	LE	LE 1	LE
London Liverpool Street 15 ⊖	d	23p15	23p37	23p45	23p52	00 02		00 15	00 18	00 22	00 35	00 46		00 50	00 55	05 23		05 28		05 28	05 30		05 42	06 00	06 04
Stratford 7 ⊖	d	23p22	23p44	23p52	23p58	00 09		00 22	00 25	00 29	00 42	00 55		00 57	01 02	05a32		05 35		05a36	05 37		05 49	06 07	06 11
Maryland	d		23p45		23p59	00 10				00 30	00 43				01 03								05 50		
Forest Gate	d		23p47		00 02	00 12				00 32	00 45				01 05								05 52		
Manor Park	d		23p49		00 04	00 14				00 34	00 47				01 07								05 54		
Ilford 2	d		23p52		00 07	00 17				00 37	00 50				01 10			05 40					05 57		
Seven Kings	d		23p55		00 10	00 20				00 40	00 53				01 13			05 42					06 00		
Goodmayes	d		23p57		00 12	00 22				00 42	00 55				01 15								06 02		
Chadwell Heath	d		23p59		00 14	00 24				00 44	00 57				01 17								06 04		
Romford	d		00 02		00 17	00 27		00 32		00 47	01 00			01 08	01 20			05 48			05 45		06 07	06 15	
Gidea Park 2	d		00 06		00 21	00a31				00 51	01a04	01 07			01 24			05 51					06 11		
Harold Wood	d		00 09		00 24					00 54					01 27			05 54					06 14		
Brentwood	d		00 13		00 28					00 58					01 31			05 59					06 18		
Shenfield 3	a	23p39	00 20	00 09	00 35			00 44	00 47	01 03		01 17		01 20	01 36			06 04			05 55		06 23	06 25	06 30
	d	23p40		00 10				00 45						01 20				06 04				06 08			06 30
Billericay	d	23p46		00 16				00 51						01 26				06 10				06 14			06 36
Wickford 2	d	23p51		00 21				00 56						01 31			05 39	06 15				06 20			06 41
Battlesbridge	d																05 43					06 24			
South Woodham Ferrers	d																05 47					06 28			
North Fambridge	d																05 53					06 34			
Althorne	d																05 58					06 39			
Burnham-on-Crouch	d																06 03					06 44			
Southminster	a																06 08					06 49			
Rayleigh	d	23p56		00 26				01 01						01 36				06 21							06 46
Hockley	d	00 01		00 31				01 06						01 41				06 25							06 51
Rochford	d	00 04		00 34				01 09						01 44				06 29							06 54
Prittlewell	d	00 08		00 38				01 13						01 48				06 32							06 58
Southend Victoria	a	00 15		00 45				01 20						01 55				06 36							07 02

		LE		LE 1	LE 1	LE 1	LE 1	LE		LE 1	LE 1	LE	LE 1	LE		LE 1	LE 1	LE	LE 1	LE		LE 1	LE	LE 1	LE
London Liverpool Street 15 ⊖	d	06 12		06 18	06 23	06 34		06 42		06 48	06 55	07 02	07 08	07 12		07 15	07 18	07 22		07 32		07 34	07 42	07 48	07 52
Stratford 7 ⊖	d	06 19		06 25	06a32	06 41		06 49		06 55	07 02	07 09	07 15	07 19		07 22	07 25	07 29		07 39		07 41	07 49	07 55	07 59
Maryland	d	06 20						06 50				07 10		07 20				07 30		07 40			07 50		08 00
Forest Gate	d	06 22						06 52				07 12		07 22				07 32		07 42			07 52		08 02
Manor Park	d	06 24						06 54				07 14		07 24				07 34		07 44			07 54		08 04
Ilford 2	d	06 27						06 57				07 17		07 27				07 37		07 47			07 57		08 07
Seven Kings	d	06 30						07 00				07 20		07 30				07 40		07 50			08 00		08 10
Goodmayes	d	06 32						07 02				07 22		07 32				07 42		07 52			08 02		08 12
Chadwell Heath	d	06 34						07 04				07 24		07 34				07 44		07 54			08 04		08 14
Romford	d	06 37				06 49		07 07				07 27	07 23	07 37				07 47		07 57		07 49	08 07		08 17
Gidea Park 2	d	06 41						07 11				07 31		07 41				07 51		08 01			08 11		08 21
Harold Wood	d	06 44						07 14				07 34		07 44				07 54		08 04			08 14		08 24
Brentwood	d	06 48						07 18				07 38		07 48				07 58		08 08			08 18		08 28
Shenfield 3	a	06 53		06 41		07 00		07 23		07 12	07 19	07 43	07 33	07 53		07 39	07 41	08 03		08 13		08 00	08 23	08 12	08 33
	d					07 00	07 08				07 20					07 40			08 08			08 00			
Billericay	d					07 06	07 14				07 26					07 46			08 14			08 06			
Wickford 2	d					07 11	07 20				07 31					07 51			08 20			08 11			
Battlesbridge	d						07 24												08 24						
South Woodham Ferrers	d						07 28												08 28						
North Fambridge	d						07 34												08 34						
Althorne	d						07 39												08 39						
Burnham-on-Crouch	d						07 44												08 44						
Southminster	a						07 49												08 49						
Rayleigh	d					07 16					07 36					07 56						08 16			
Hockley	d					07 21					07 41					08 01						08 21			
Rochford	d					07 24					07 44					08 04						08 24			
Prittlewell	d					07 28					07 48					08 08						08 28			
Southend Victoria	a					07 31					07 51					08 11						08 31			

		LE 1		LE	LE 1	LE	LE 1	LE 1	LE	LE 1	LE	LE 1	LE	LE 1	LE	LE 1	and at the same minutes past each hour until		LE	LE 1	LE	LE 1	LE 1	LE
London Liverpool Street 15 ⊖	d	07 55		08 02	08 08	08 12	08 15	08 18	08 22		08 32	08 34	08 42	08 48	08 52	08 55			20 02	20 08	20 12	20 15	20 18	20 22
Stratford 7 ⊖	d	08 02		08 09	08 15	08 19	08 22	08 25	08 29		08 39	08 41	08 49	08 55	08 59	09 02			20 09	20 15	20 19	20 22	20 25	20 29
Maryland	d			08 10		08 20			08 30		08 40		08 50		09 00				20 10		20 20			20 30
Forest Gate	d			08 12		08 22			08 32		08 42		08 52		09 02				20 12		20 22			20 32
Manor Park	d			08 14		08 24			08 34		08 44		08 54		09 04				20 14		20 24			20 34
Ilford 2	d			08 17		08 27			08 37		08 47		08 57		09 07				20 17		20 27			20 37
Seven Kings	d			08 20		08 30			08 40		08 50		09 00		09 10				20 20		20 30			20 40
Goodmayes	d			08 22		08 32			08 42		08 52		09 02		09 12				20 22		20 32			20 42
Chadwell Heath	d			08 24		08 34			08 44		08 54		09 04		09 14				20 24		20 34			20 44
Romford	d			08 27	08 23	08 37			08 47		08 57	08 49	09 07		09 17				20 27	20 23	20 37			20 47
Gidea Park 2	d			08 31		08 41			08 51		09 01		09 11		09 21				20 31		20 41			20 51
Harold Wood	d			08 34		08 44			08 54		09 04		09 14		09 24				20 34		20 44			20 54
Brentwood	d			08 38		08 48			08 58		09 08		09 18		09 28				20 38		20 48			20 58
Shenfield 3	a	08 19		08 43	08 33	08 53	08 39	08 41	09 03		09 13	09 00	09 23	09 12	09 33	09 19			20 43	20 33	20 53	20 39	20 41	21 03
	d	08 20					08 40			09 08		09 00				09 20						20 40		
Billericay	d	08 26					08 46			09 14		09 06				09 26						20 46		
Wickford 2	d	08 31					08 51			09 20		09 11				09 31						20 51		
Battlesbridge	d									09 24														
South Woodham Ferrers	d									09 28														
North Fambridge	d									09 34														
Althorne	d									09 39														
Burnham-on-Crouch	d									09 44														
Southminster	a									09 49														
Rayleigh	d	08 36					08 56					09 16				09 36						20 56		
Hockley	d	08 41					09 01					09 21				09 41						21 01		
Rochford	d	08 44					09 04					09 24				09 44						21 04		
Prittlewell	d	08 48					09 08					09 28				09 48						21 08		
Southend Victoria	a	08 51					09 11					09 31				09 51						21 11		

For general notes see front of timetable
For details of catering facilities see Directory of Train Operators

A To Colchester (Table 11)

London → Shenfield, Southminster and Southend Victoria

Network diagram - see first page of Table 5

		LE 1		LE	LE 1	LE 1	LE	LE 1		LE	LE 1	LE 1	LE	LE 1		LE 1	LE	LE	LE 1	LE 1		LE 1	LE	LE 1	LE
London Liverpool Street 15 ⊖	d			20 32	20 34	20 38	20 42	20 48		20 52	20 55	21 04	21 07	21 15		21 18	21 22	21 37	21 45	21 48			21 52	22 00	22 07
Stratford 7 ⊖	d			20 39	20 41	20 45	20 49	20 55		20 59	21 02	21 11	21 14	21 22		21 25	21 29	21 44	21 52	21 55			21 59	22 07	22 14
Maryland	d			20 40			20 50			21 00			21 15				21 30	21 45					22 00		22 15
Forest Gate	d			20 42			20 52			21 02			21 17				21 32	21 47					22 02		22 17
Manor Park	d			20 44			20 54			21 04			21 19				21 34	21 49					22 04		22 19
Ilford 2	d			20 47			20 57			21 07			21 22				21 37	21 52					22 07		22 22
Seven Kings	d			20 50			21 00			21 10			21 25				21 40	21 55					22 10		22 25
Goodmayes	d			20 52			21 02			21 12			21 27				21 42	21 57					22 12		22 27
Chadwell Heath	d			20 54			21 04			21 14			21 29				21 44	21 59					22 14		22 29
Romford	d			20 57	20 49		21 07			21 17		21 19	21 32				21 47	22 02					22 17		22 32
Gidea Park 2	d			21 01			21 11			21 21			21 36				21 51	22 06					22 21		22 36
Harold Wood	d			21 04			21 14			21 24			21 39				21 54	22 09					22 24		22 39
Brentwood	d			21 08			21 18			21 28			21 43				21 58	22 13					22 28		22 43
Shenfield 3	a			21 13	20 59	21 02	21 23	21 12		21 33	21 19	21 33	21 48	21 43		21 45	22 03	22 18	22 13	22 15			22 33	22 27	22 48
	d	21 08			21 00						21 20			21 43					22 13			22 22			
Billericay	d	21 14			21 06						21 26			21 49					22 19			22 28			
Wickford 2	d	21 20			21 11						21 31			21 54					22 24			22 34			
Battlesbridge	d	21 24																				22 38			
South Woodham Ferrers	d	21 28																				22 42			
North Fambridge	d	21 34																				22 48			
Althorne	d	21 39																				22 53			
Burnham-on-Crouch	d	21 44																				22 58			
Southminster	a	21 49																				23 03			
Rayleigh	d				21 16						21 36			21 59					22 29						
Hockley	d				21 21						21 41			22 04					22 34						
Rochford	d				21 24						21 44			22 07					22 37						
Prittlewell	d				21 28						21 48			22 11					22 41						
Southend Victoria	a				21 31						21 51			22 14					22 44						

		LE 1	LE 1	LE		LE	LE 1	LE 1	LE	LE 1		LE	LE 1	LE 1	LE	LE		LE 1	LE 1	LE					
London Liverpool Street 15 ⊖	d	22 15	22 18	22 22		22 37	22 45	22 48	22 52	23 00		23 07	23 15	23 18	23 22	23 37		23 45	23 48	23 52					
Stratford 7 ⊖	d	22 22	22 25	22 29		22 44	22 52	22 55	22 59	23 07		23 14	23 22	23 25	23 29	23 44		23 52	23 55	23 58					
Maryland	d			22 30		22 45			23 00			23 15			23 30	23 45				23 59					
Forest Gate	d			22 32		22 47			23 02			23 17			23 32	23 47				00 02					
Manor Park	d			22 34		22 49			23 04			23 19			23 34	23 49				00 04					
Ilford 2	d			22 37		22 52			23 07			23 22			23 37	23 52				00 07					
Seven Kings	d			22 40		22 55			23 10			23 25			23 40	23 55				00 10					
Goodmayes	d			22 42		22 57			23 12			23 27			23 42	23 57				00 12					
Chadwell Heath	d			22 44		22 59			23 14			23 29			23 44	23 59				00 14					
Romford	d			22 47		23 02			23 17			23 32			23 47	00 02				00 17					
Gidea Park 2	d			22 51		23 06			23 21			23 36			23 51	00 06				00 21					
Harold Wood	d			22 54		23 09			23 24			23 39			23 54	00 09				00 24					
Brentwood	d			22 58		23 13			23 28			23 43			23 58	00 13				00 28					
Shenfield 3	a	22 43	22 45	23 03		23 18	23 13	23 15	23 33	23 27		23 48	23 43	23 45	00 03	00 18		00 13	00 15	00 33					
	d	22 43					23 13						23 43					00 13							
Billericay	d	22 49					23 19						23 49					00 19							
Wickford 2	d	22 54					23 24						23 54					00 24							
Battlesbridge	d																								
South Woodham Ferrers	d																								
North Fambridge	d																								
Althorne	d																								
Burnham-on-Crouch	d																								
Southminster	a																								
Rayleigh	d	22 59					23 29						23 59					00 29							
Hockley	d	23 04					23 34						00 04					00 34							
Rochford	d	23 07					23 37						00 07					00 37							
Prittlewell	d	23 11					23 41						00 11					00 41							
Southend Victoria	a	23 14					23 48						00 18					00 48							

For general notes see front of timetable
For details of catering facilities see Directory of Train Operators

London → Shenfield, Southminster and Southend Victoria

Network diagram - see first page of Table 5

		LE 1	LE	LE 1	LE	LE		LE 1	LE 1	LE	LE	LE 1		LE	LE	LE	LE 1	LE 1		LE	LE 1	LE 1	LE 1	LE	LE 1
London Liverpool Street 15	⊖ d	23p15	23p37	23p45	23p52	00 02		00 15	00 18	00 22	00 32	00 50		00 55	06 35	07 05		07 15		07 35		07 45	08 02	08 05	08 15
Stratford 7	⊖ d	23p22	23p44	23p52	23p58	00 09		00 22	00 25	00 29	00 39	00 57		01 02	06 42	07 12		07 22		07 42		07 52	08 09	08 12	08 22
Maryland	d		23p45		23p59	00 10				00 30	00 40			01 03	06 43	07 13				07 43				08 13	
Forest Gate	d		23p47		00 02	00 12				00 32	00 42			01 05	06 45	07 15				07 45				08 15	
Manor Park	d		23p49		00 04	00 14				00 34	00 44			01 07	06 47	07 17				07 47				08 17	
Ilford 2	d		23p52		00 07	00 17				00 37	00 47			01 10	06 50	07 20				07 50				08 20	
Seven Kings	d		23p55		00 10	00 20				00 40	00 50			01 13	06 53	07 23				07 53				08 23	
Goodmayes	d		23p57		00 12	00 22				00 42	00 52			01 15	06 55	07 25				07 55				08 25	
Chadwell Heath	d		23p59		00 14	00 24				00 44	00 54			01 17	06 57	07 27				07 57				08 27	
Romford	d		00 02		00 17	00 27		00 32		00 47	00 57	01 08		01 20	07 00	07 30		07 33		08 00		08 03		08 30	08 33
Gidea Park 2	d		00 06		00 21	00a31				00 51	01a01			01 24	07 04	07 34		07 37		08 04		08 07		08 34	08 37
Harold Wood	d		00 09		00 24					00 54				01 27	07 07	07 37		07 40		08 07		08 10		08 37	08 40
Brentwood	d		00 13		00 28					00 58				01 31	07 11	07 41		07 44		08 11		08 14		08 41	08 44
Shenfield 3	a	23p43	00 18	00 13	00 33			00 44	00 47	01 03		01 20		01 36	07 16	07 46		07 50		08 16		08 20	08 30	08 46	08 50
	d	23p43		00 13				00 45				01 20						07 50				08 20			08 50
Billericay	d	23p49		00 19				00 51				01 26						07 56				08 26			08 56
Wickford 2	d	23p54		00 24				00 56				01 31					07 30	08 01			08 05	08 31			09 01
Battlesbridge	d																07 34				08 09				
South Woodham Ferrers	d																07 38				08 13				
North Fambridge	d																07 44				08 20				
Althorne	d																07 49				08 25				
Burnham-on-Crouch	d																07 54				08 30				
Southminster	a																07 59				08 35				
Rayleigh	d	23p59		00 29				01 01				01 36						08 06				08 36			09 06
Hockley	d	00 04		00 34				01 06				01 41						08 11				08 41			09 11
Rochford	d	00 07		00 37				01 09				01 44						08 14				08 44			09 14
Prittlewell	d	00 11		00 41				01 13				01 48													
Southend Victoria	a	00 18		00 48				01 20				01 55						08 22				08 52			09 22

		LE 1		LE	LE 1	LE 1	LE		LE 1	LE	LE 1	LE	LE 1	LE	LE 1	LE 1	LE			LE 1	LE	LE 1	LE	LE 1
London Liverpool Street 15	⊖ d	08 32		08 35		08 45	08 47		09 02	09 05	09 15	09 17	09 32	09 35		09 45	09 47	and at the same minutes past each hour until		19 02	19 05	19 15	19 17	19 32
Stratford 7	⊖ d	08 39		08 42		08 52	08 54		09 09	09 12	09 22	09 24	09 39	09 42		09 52	09 54			19 09	19 12	19 22	19 24	19 39
Maryland	d			08 43						09 13				09 43							19 13			
Forest Gate	d			08 45			08 57			09 15		09 27		09 45			09 57				19 15		19 27	
Manor Park	d			08 47			08 59			09 17		09 29		09 47			09 59				19 17		19 29	
Ilford 2	d			08 50			09 02			09 20		09 32		09 50			10 02				19 20		19 32	
Seven Kings	d			08 53			09 04			09 23		09 34		09 53			10 04				19 23		19 34	
Goodmayes	d			08 55			09 06			09 25		09 36		09 55			10 06				19 25		19 36	
Chadwell Heath	d			08 57			09 08			09 27		09 38		09 57			10 08				19 27		19 38	
Romford	d			09 00		09 03	09 12			09 30	09 33	09 42		10 00		10 03	10 12				19 30	19 33	19 42	
Gidea Park 2	d			09 04		09 07	09a17			09 34	09 37	09a47		10 04		10 07	10a17				19 34	19 37	19a47	
Harold Wood	d			09 07		09 10				09 37	09 40			10 07		10 10					19 37	19 40		
Brentwood	d			09 11		09 14				09 41	09 44			10 11		10 14					19 41	19 44		
Shenfield 3	a	09 00		09 16		09 20			09 30	09 46	09 50		10 00	10 16		10 20				19 30	19 46	19 50		20 00
	d					09 20					09 50					10 20						19 50		
Billericay	d					09 26					09 56					10 26						19 56		
Wickford 2	d				09 05	09 31					10 01				10 05	10 31						20 01		
Battlesbridge	d				09 09										10 09									
South Woodham Ferrers	d				09 13										10 13									
North Fambridge	d				09 20										10 20									
Althorne	d				09 25										10 25									
Burnham-on-Crouch	d				09 30										10 30									
Southminster	a				09 35										10 35									
Rayleigh	d					09 36					10 06					10 36						20 06		
Hockley	d					09 41					10 11					10 41						20 11		
Rochford	d					09 44					10 14					10 44						20 14		
Prittlewell	d																							
Southend Victoria	a					09 52					10 22					10 52						20 22		

		LE	LE 1		LE 1	LE	LE 1	LE 1	LE		LE 1	LE	LE 1	LE	LE 1		LE 1	LE	LE 1	LE	LE 1		LE	LE 1	LE
London Liverpool Street 15	⊖ d	19 35			19 45	19 47	20 00	20 02	20 05		20 15	20 17	20 32	20 35			20 45	20 47	21 02	21 05	21 15		21 17	21 32	21 35
Stratford 7	⊖ d	19 42			19 52	19 54		20 09	20 12		20 22	20 24	20 39	20 42			20 52	20 54	21 09	21 12	21 22		21 24	21 39	21 42
Maryland	d	19 43							20 13					20 43						21 13					21 43
Forest Gate	d	19 45				19 57			20 15			20 27		20 45				20 57		21 15			21 27		21 45
Manor Park	d	19 47				19 59			20 17			20 29		20 47				20 59		21 17			21 29		21 47
Ilford 2	d	19 50				20 02			20 20			20 32		20 50				21 02		21 20			21 32		21 50
Seven Kings	d	19 53				20 04			20 23			20 34		20 53				21 04		21 23			21 34		21 53
Goodmayes	d	19 55				20 06			20 25			20 36		20 55				21 06		21 25			21 36		21 55
Chadwell Heath	d	19 57				20 08			20 27			20 38		20 57				21 08		21 27			21 38		21 57
Romford	d	20 00			20 03	20 12			20 30		20 33	20 42		21 00			21 03	21 12		21 30	21 33		21 42		22 00
Gidea Park 2	d	20 04			20 07	20a17			20 34		20 37	20a47		21 04			21 07	21a17		21 34	21 37		21a47		22 04
Harold Wood	d	20 07			20 10				20 37		20 40			21 07			21 10			21 37	21 40				22 07
Brentwood	d	20 11			20 14				20 41		20 44			21 11			21 14			21 41	21 44				22 11
Shenfield 3	a	20 16			20 20		20 27	20 30	20 46		20 50		21 00	21 16			21 20		21 30	21 46	21 50			22 00	22 16
	d				20 20						20 50						21 20				21 50				
Billericay	d				20 26						20 56						21 26				21 56				
Wickford 2	d		20 05		20 31						21 01				21 05		21 31				22 01				
Battlesbridge	d		20 09												21 09										
South Woodham Ferrers	d		20 13												21 13										
North Fambridge	d		20 20												21 20										
Althorne	d		20 25												21 25										
Burnham-on-Crouch	d		20 30												21 30										
Southminster	a		20 35												21 35										
Rayleigh	d				20 36						21 06						21 36				22 06				
Hockley	d				20 41						21 11						21 41				22 11				
Rochford	d				20 44						21 14						21 44				22 14				
Prittlewell	d																								
Southend Victoria	a				20 52						21 22						21 52				22 22				

For general notes see front of timetable
For details of catering facilities see Directory of Train Operators

Table 5

Sundays

London → Shenfield, Southminster and Southend Victoria

Network diagram - see first page of Table 5

		LE 1	LE 1	LE	LE 1		LE	LE 1	LE	LE 1	LE		LE 1	LE 1	LE	LE 1	LE 1		LE	LE 1					
London Liverpool Street 15 ⊖	d		21 45	21 47	22 02		22 05	22 15	22 17	22 32	22 35		22 45	23 02	23 05	23 15	23 32		23 35	23 45					
Stratford 7 ⊖	d		21 52	21 54	22 09		22 12	22 22	22 24	22 39	22 42		22 52	23 09	23 12	23 22	23 39		23 42	23 52					
Maryland	d						22 13				22 43				23 13				23 43						
Forest Gate	d			21 57			22 15		22 27		22 45				23 15				23 45						
Manor Park	d			21 59			22 17		22 29		22 47				23 17				23 47						
Ilford 2	d			22 02			22 20		22 32		22 50				23 20				23 50						
Seven Kings	d			22 04			22 23		22 34		22 53				23 23				23 53						
Goodmayes	d			22 06			22 25		22 36		22 55				23 25				23 55						
Chadwell Heath	d			22 08			22 27		22 38		22 57				23 27				23 57						
Romford	d		22 03	22 12			22 30	22 33	22 42		23 00		23 03		23 30	23 33			23 59	00 03					
Gidea Park 2	d		22 07	22a17			22 34	22 37	22a47		23 04		23 07		23 34	23 37			00 04	00 07					
Harold Wood	d		22 10				22 37	22 40			23 07		23 10		23 37	23 40			00 07	00 10					
Brentwood	d		22 14				22 41	22 44			23 11		23 14		23 41	23 44			00 11	00 14					
Shenfield 3	a		22 20		22 30		22 46	22 50		23 00	23 16		23 20	23 30	23 46	23 50	00 01		00 16	00 20					
	d		22 20					22 50					23 20			23 50				00 20					
Billericay	d		22 26					22 56					23 26			23 56				00 26					
Wickford 2	d	22 05	22 31					23 01					23 31			00 01				00 31					
Battlesbridge	d	22 09																							
South Woodham Ferrers	d	22 13																							
North Fambridge	d	22 20																							
Althorne	d	22 25																							
Burnham-on-Crouch	d	22 30																							
Southminster	a	22 35																							
Rayleigh	d		22 36					23 06					23 36			00 06				00 36					
Hockley	d		22 41					23 11					23 41			00 11				00 41					
Rochford	d		22 44					23 14					23 44			00 14				00 44					
Prittlewell	d																								
Southend Victoria	a		22 52					23 24					23 54			00 24				00 54					

For general notes see front of timetable
For details of catering facilities see Directory of Train Operators

Southend Victoria, Southminster and Shenfield → London

Network diagram - see first page of Table 5

Miles	Miles			LE MX	LE MO	LE MX	LE	CC	LE	LE	LE	LE 1 A	LE	LE 1	LE		LE 1	LE 1	LE	LE	LE	LE 1	LE 1	LE	LE 1
0	—	**Southend Victoria**	d				04 02			04 32				05 06			05 26						05 46		
½	—	Prittlewell	d				04 04			04 34				05 08			05 28						05 48		
2¾	—	Rochford	d				04 08			04 38				05 12			05 32						05 52		
5½	—	Hockley	d				04 12			04 42				05 16			05 36						05 56		
8¼	—	Rayleigh	d				04 16			04 46				05 20			05 40						06 00		
—	0	**Southminster**	d																			05 30			
—	2¼	Burnham-on-Crouch	d																			05 34			
—	5¼	Althorne	d																			05 39			
—	8¼	North Fambridge	d																			05 45			
—	11½	South Woodham Ferrers	d																			05 50			
—	14	Battlesbridge	d																			05 54			
12½	16½	**Wickford 2**	d				04 21			04 51				05 25			05 45					06a00	06 05		
17¼	—	Billericay	d				04 28			04 58				05 31			05 51						06 11		
21¼	—	**Shenfield 3**	a				04 39			05 09				05 38			05 58						06 18		
—	—		d	23p29	23p43	23p44	04 39			05 09		05 26	05 29	05 38	05 44		05 58	06 02		06 04	06 14		06 18	06 24	06 26
23½	—	Brentwood	d	23p32	23p46	23p47	04 42			05 12			05 32		05 47					06 07	06 17			06 27	
26½	—	Harold Wood	d	23p37	23p51	23p52	04 47			05 17			05 37		05 52					06 12	06 22			06 32	
28	—	Gidea Park 2	d	23p41	23p55	23p56	04 51			05 21		05 33	05 41		05 56				06 06	06 16	06 26			06 36	
29	—	Romford	d	23p43	23p57	23p58	04 53			05 23			05 43		05 58				06 08	06 18	06 28			06 38	
31½	—	Chadwell Heath	d	23p47	00 01	00 02	04 57			05 27			05 47		06 02				06 12	06 22	06 32			06 42	
32¼	—	Goodmayes	d	23p49	00 03	00 04	04 59			05 29			05 49		06 04				06 14	06 24	06 34			06 44	
33	—	Seven Kings	d	23p51	00 05	00 06	05 01			05 31		05 38	05 51		06 06				06 16	06 26	06 36			06 46	
34¼	—	Ilford 2	d	23p54	00 08	00 09	05 04		05 09	05 34	05 39		05 54		06 09				06 19	06 29	06 39			06 49	
35¼	—	Manor Park	d	23p56	00 10	00 11			05 11		05 41		05 56		06 11				06 21	06 31	06 41			06 51	
36¼	—	Forest Gate	d	23p58	00 12	00 13			05 13		05 43		05 58		06 13				06 23	06 33	06 43			06 53	
37	—	Maryland	d	23p59	00 14	00 15			05 15		05 45		06 00		06 15				06 25	06 35	06 45			06 55	
37½	—	Stratford 7 ⊖	d	00 02	00 16	00 17	05 09	05 13	05 17	05 39	05 47	05s44	06 02	05s53	06 17		06s15	06s18	06 27	06 37	06 47		06s32	06 57	06s41
41½	—	**London Liverpool Street 15** ⊖	a	00 12	00 25	00 27	05 17	05 23	05 25	05 47	05 55	05 57	06 12	06 01	06 27		06 24	06 27	06 35	06 47	06 57		06 41	07 07	06 49

		LE 1	LE	LE 1	LE	LE		LE 1	LE 1	LE	LE	LE	LE	LE	LE 1	LE 1	LE	LE	LE 1		LE 1	LE 1	LE 1	LE	LE
Southend Victoria	d	06 01						06 16				06 29				06 40						06 56			
Prittlewell	d	06 03						06 18				06 31				06 42						06 58			
Rochford	d	06 07						06 22				06 35				06 46						07 02			
Hockley	d	06 11						06 26				06 39				06 50						07 06			
Rayleigh	d	06 15						06 30				06 43				06 54						07 10			
Southminster	d								06 10														06 52		
Burnham-on-Crouch	d								06 14														06 56		
Althorne	d								06 19														07 01		
North Fambridge	d								06 26														07 08		
South Woodham Ferrers	d								06 32														07 14		
Battlesbridge	d								06 36														07 18		
Wickford 2	d	06 20						06 35	06 41			06 48				06 59						07 15	07 23		
Billericay	d	06 26						06 42	06 48			06 55				07 05						07 22	07 30		
Shenfield 3	a	06 33						06 48	06 54			07 01				07 12						07 28			
	d	06 33	06 34	06 39		06 44		06 48	06 54		06 54	07 01		07 04	07 06	07 12		07 15	07 16		07 20	07 28			07 28
Brentwood	d		06 37			06 47					06 57			07 07				07 18							07 31
Harold Wood	d		06 42			06 52					07 02			07 12				07 23							07 36
Gidea Park 2	d		06 46		06 49	06 56				06 59	07 06		07 09	07 16			07 22	07 28						07 34	07 40
Romford	d		06 48		06 51	06 58				07 01	07 08		07 11	07 18			07 24	07 30						07 36	07 42
Chadwell Heath	d		06 52		06 55	07 02				07 05	07 12		07 15	07 22			07 28	07 34						07 40	07 46
Goodmayes	d				06 57					07 07			07 17	07 24			07 30	07 36						07 42	07 48
Seven Kings	d				06 59					07 09			07 19	07 26			07 32	07 38						07 44	07 50
Ilford 2	d		06 57		07 02	07 07				07 12	07 17		07 22	07 29			07 35	07 41						07 47	07 53
Manor Park	d				07 05					07 15			07 25				07 38							07 50	
Forest Gate	d				07 07					07 17			07 27				07 40							07 52	
Maryland	d				07 09					07 19			07 29				07 42							07 54	
Stratford 7 ⊖	d	06s47	07 03	06s56	07 11	07 14		07s05	07s11	07 21	07 24	07s18	07 31	07 35		07s29	07 44	07 47	07s33		07s37	07s45		07 56	07 59
London Liverpool Street 15 ⊖	a	06 56	07 13	07 07	07 21	07 24		07 16	07 24	07 31	07 34	07 29	07 41	07 45	07 33	07 40	07 54	07 57	07 44		07 48	07 57	08 01	08 06	08 09

		LE 1	LE 1	LE	LE 1	LE 1	LE	LE	LE 1	LE		LE	LE	LE	LE 1	LE	LE 1	LE 1	LE 1	LE 1	LE	LE	LE		LE 1
Southend Victoria	d		07 17			07 09								07 21	07 25			07 33							07 40
Prittlewell	d		07 19			07 11								07 23	07 27			07 35							07 42
Rochford	d		07 23			07 15								07 27	07 31			07 39							07 46
Hockley	d		07 27			07 19								07 31	07 35			07 43							07 50
Rayleigh	d		07 31			07 23								07 35	07 39			07 47							07 54
Southminster	d																			07 35					
Burnham-on-Crouch	d																			07 39					
Althorne	d																			07 44					
North Fambridge	d																			07 50					
South Woodham Ferrers	d																			07b58					
Battlesbridge	d																								
Wickford 2	d		07 36			07 28								07 40	07 44			07 52		08 06					07 59
Billericay	d		07 43			07 35								07 47	07 51			07 59		08 13					08 06
Shenfield 3	a					07 42								07 55	07 58			08 06							08 13
	d	07 32		07 34	07 38	07 42		07 44	07 50			07 50		07 56	07 58	08 00	08 02	08 06	08 08				08 10		08 13
Brentwood	d			07 37				07 47				07 53		07 59		08 03							08 13		
Harold Wood	d			07 42				07 52				07 58		08 04		08 08							08 18		
Gidea Park 2	d			07 46			07 49	07 56		07 59		08 02	08 05	08 09		08 12					08 15	08 19	08 22		
Romford	d			07 48			07 51	07 58		08 01		08 04	08 07	08 11		08 14					08 17	08 21	08 24		
Chadwell Heath	d			07 52			07 55	08 02		08 05		08 08	08 11	08 15		08 18					08 21	08 25	08 28		
Goodmayes	d			07 54			07 57	08 04		08 07		08 10	08 13	08 17		08 20					08 23	08 27	08 30		
Seven Kings	d			07 56			07 59	08 06		08 09		08 12	08 15	08 19		08 22					08 25	08 29	08 32		
Ilford 2	d			07 59			08 02	08 09		08 12		08 15	08 18	08 22		08 25					08 28	08 32	08 35		
Manor Park	d						08 05						08 21								08 31				
Forest Gate	d						08 07						08 23								08 33				
Maryland	d						08 09						08 25								08 35				
Stratford 7 ⊖	d			08 05	07s55	08s00	08 11	08 15		08 18		08 21	08 27	08 30	08s15	08 33			08s25		08 37	08 40	08 43		08s30
London Liverpool Street 15 ⊖	a	07 59	08 14	08 15	08 06	08 12	08 21	08 25	08 16	08 28		08 31	08 37	08 40	08 26	08 43	08 28	08 32	08 36	08 46	08 47	08 50	08 53		08 44

For general notes see front of timetable
For details of catering facilities see
Directory of Train Operators

A From Colchester (Table 11)
b Arr. 0755

Southend Victoria, Southminster and Shenfield → London

Network diagram - see first page of Table 5

		LE 1	LE	LE	LE	LE 1	LE 1	LE	LE	LE	LE 1	LE 1	LE 1		LE	LE	LE 1	LE	LE 1	LE 1	LE 1	LE	LE	LE 1	LE 1
Southend Victoria	d					07 53					08 03		08 11							08 26				08 46	
Prittlewell	d					07 55					08 05		08 13							08 28				08 48	
Rochford	d					07 59					08 09		08 17							08 32				08 52	
Hockley	d					08 03					08 13		08 21							08 36				08 56	
Rayleigh	d					08 07					08 17		08 25							08 40				09 00	
Southminster	d																				08 17				
Burnham-on-Crouch	d																				08 21				
Althorne	d																				08 26				
North Fambridge	d																				08 34				
South Woodham Ferrers	d																				08 40				
Battlesbridge	d																				08 44				
Wickford 2	d					08 12					08 22		08 30							08 45	08 49			09 05	
Billericay	d					08 19					08 29		08 37							08 52	08 56			09 12	
Shenfield 3	a					08 26					08 36		08 44							08 59	09 03			09 19	
	d	08 20			08 20	08 26	08 32			08 34	08 36	08 40	08 44			08 44	08 52	08 54	08 55	08 59	09 03	09 04	09 14	09 19	09 22
Brentwood	d				08 23					08 37						08 47		08 57				09 07	09 17		
Harold Wood	d				08 28					08 42						08 52		09 02				09 12	09 22		
Gidea Park 2	d			08 29	08 32				08 39	08 46						08 56		09 06				09 16	09 26		
Romford	d			08 31	08 34				08 41	08 48			08 52			08 58		09 08				09 18	09 28		
Chadwell Heath	d			08 35	08 38				08 45	08 52						09 02		09 12				09 22	09 32		
Goodmayes	d			08 37	08 40				08 47	08 54						09 04		09 14				09 24	09 34		
Seven Kings	d			08 39	08 42				08 49	08 56						09 06		09 16				09 26	09 36		
Ilford 2	d		08 38	08 42	08 45			08 48	08 52	08 59					09 02	09 09		09 19				09 29	09 39		
Manor Park	d		08 41					08 51							09 05			09 21				09 31	09 41		
Forest Gate	d		08 43					08 53							09 07			09 23				09 33	09 43		
Maryland	d		08 45					08 55							09 09			09 25				09 35	09 45		
Stratford 7	⊖ d		08 47	08 50	08 53	08s44	08s49	08 57	09 00	09 05	08s53		09s03		09 11	09 15	09s09	09 27		09s16	09s20	09 37	09 47	09s36	09s39
London Liverpool Street 15	⊖ a	08 48	08 57	09 00	09 03	08 56	09 01	09 07	09 10	09 15	09 04	09 06	09 14		09 21	09 25	09 20	09 37	09 22	09 28	09 31	09 47	09 57	09 47	09 50

		LE	LE 1	LE		LE 1	LE 1	LE	LE 1	LE	LE 1	LE 1	LE	LE 1	LE	LE 1	LE		LE		LE 1	LE 1	LE	LE 1	LE
Southend Victoria	d					09 06					09 26					09 46					10 06				
Prittlewell	d					09 08					09 28					09 48					10 08				
Rochford	d					09 12					09 32					09 52					10 12				
Hockley	d					09 16					09 36					09 56					10 16				
Rayleigh	d					09 20					09 40					10 00					10 20				
Southminster	d											09 17													
Burnham-on-Crouch	d											09 21													
Althorne	d											09 26													
North Fambridge	d											09 34													
South Woodham Ferrers	d											09 39													
Battlesbridge	d											09 43													
Wickford 2	d					09 25					09 45	09 49				10 05					10 25				
Billericay	d					09 31					09 51	09 55				10 11					10 31				
Shenfield 3	a					09 38					09 58	10 02				10 18					10 38				
	d	09 24	09 25	09 34		09 38	09 40	09 44	09 54	09 54	09 58	10 02	10 04	10 10	10 14	10 18	10 24		10 34		10 38	10 40	10 44	10 51	10 54
Brentwood	d	09 27		09 37				09 47		09 57			10 07		10 17		10 27		10 37				10 47		10 57
Harold Wood	d	09 32		09 42				09 52		10 02			10 12		10 22		10 32		10 42				10 52		11 02
Gidea Park 2	d	09 36		09 46				09 56		10 06			10 16		10 26		10 36		10 46				10 56		11 06
Romford	d	09 38		09 48			09 48	09 58		10 08			10 18		10 28	10 26	10 38		10 48				10 58	10 59	11 08
Chadwell Heath	d	09 42		09 52				10 02		10 12			10 22		10 32		10 42		10 52				11 02		11 12
Goodmayes	d	09 44		09 54				10 04		10 14			10 24		10 34		10 44		10 54				11 04		11 14
Seven Kings	d	09 46		09 56				10 06		10 16			10 26		10 36		10 46		10 56				11 06		11 16
Ilford 2	d	09 49		09 59				10 09		10 19			10 29		10 39		10 49		10 59				11 09		11 19
Manor Park	d	09 51		10 01				10 11		10 21			10 31		10 41		10 51		11 01				11 11		11 21
Forest Gate	d	09 53		10 03				10 13		10 23			10 33		10 43		10 53		11 03				11 13		11 23
Maryland	d	09 55		10 05				10 15		10 25			10 35		10 45		10 55		11 05				11 15		11 25
Stratford 7	⊖ d	09 57		10 07		09s52	09s57	10 17	10s08	10 27	10s13	10s16	10 37	10s24	10 47	10s34	10 57		11 07		10s52	10s55	11 17	11s07	11 27
London Liverpool Street 15	⊖ a	10 07	09 52	10 15		10 04	10 05	10 25	10 17	10 37	10 22	10 25	10 47	10 33	10 57	10 44	11 07		11 17		11 01	11 03	11 27	11 18	11 37

		LE 1	LE 1	LE	LE 1	LE	LE 1	LE	LE	and at the same minutes past each hour until		LE 1	LE 1	LE	LE 1	LE	LE 1	LE 1	LE	LE 1	LE	LE 1	LE	LE 1
Southend Victoria	d	10 26					10 46					15 06					15 26					15 46		
Prittlewell	d	10 28					10 48					15 08					15 28					15 48		
Rochford	d	10 32					10 52					15 12					15 32					15 52		
Hockley	d	10 36					10 56					15 16					15 36					15 56		
Rayleigh	d	10 40					11 00					15 20					15 40					16 00		
Southminster	d		10 17															15 17						
Burnham-on-Crouch	d		10 21															15 21						
Althorne	d		10 26															15 26						
North Fambridge	d		10 34															15 34						
South Woodham Ferrers	d		10 39															15 39						
Battlesbridge	d		10 43															15 43						
Wickford 2	d	10 45	10 49				11 05					15 25					15 45	15 49				16 05		
Billericay	d	10 51	10 55				11 11					15 31					15 51	15 55				16 11		
Shenfield 3	a	10 58	11 02				11 18					15 38					15 58	16 02				16 18		
	d	10 58		11 04	11 10	11 14	11 18	11 24	11 34			15 38	15 40	15 44	15 51	15 54	15 58		16 04	16 12	16 14	16 18	16 24	16 25
Brentwood	d			11 07		11 17		11 27	11 37					15 47		15 57			16 07		16 17		16 27	
Harold Wood	d			11 12		11 22		11 32	11 42					15 52		16 02			16 12		16 22		16 32	
Gidea Park 2	d			11 16		11 26		11 36	11 46					15 56		16 06			16 16		16 26		16 36	
Romford	d			11 18		11 28	11 26	11 38	11 48					15 58	15 59	16 08			16 18		16 28	16 26	16 38	
Chadwell Heath	d			11 22		11 32		11 42	11 52					16 02		16 12			16 22		16 32		16 42	
Goodmayes	d			11 24		11 34		11 44	11 54					16 04		16 14			16 24		16 34		16 44	
Seven Kings	d			11 26		11 36		11 46	11 56					16 06		16 16			16 26		16 36		16 46	
Ilford 2	d			11 29		11 39		11 49	11 59					16 09		16 19			16 29		16 39		16 49	
Manor Park	d			11 31		11 41		11 51	12 01					16 11		16 21			16 31		16 41		16 51	
Forest Gate	d			11 33		11 43		11 53	12 03					16 13		16 23			16 33		16 43		16 53	
Maryland	d			11 35		11 45		11 55	12 05					16 15		16 25			16 35		16 45		16 55	
Stratford 7	⊖ d	11s12		11 37	11s24	11 47	11s34	11 57	12 07			15s52	15s55	16 17	16s07	16 27	16s12		16 37	16s26	16 47	16s34	16 57	16s40
London Liverpool Street 15	⊖ a	11 24		11 47	11 33	11 57	11 43	12 07	12 17			16 01	16 03	16 27	16 18	16 37	16 21		16 47	16 35	16 57	16 43	17 07	16 49

For general notes see front of timetable
For details of catering facilities see
Directory of Train Operators

Southend Victoria, Southminster and Shenfield → London

Network diagram - see first page of Table 5

		LE		LE 1	LE 1	LE	LE 1	LE 1	LE	LE	LE 1	LE 1	LE 1	LE	LE		LE 1	LE	LE	LE 1	LE	LE	LE 1	LE 1	LE
Southend Victoria	d			16 06				16 21				16 35					16 51							17 06	
Prittlewell	d			16 08				16 23				16 37					16 53							17 08	
Rochford	d			16 12				16 27				16 41					16 57							17 12	
Hockley	d			16 16				16 31				16 45					17 01							17 16	
Rayleigh	d			16 20				16 35				16 49					17 05							17 20	
Southminster	d										16 17														
Burnham-on-Crouch	d										16 21														
Althorne	d										16 26														
North Fambridge	d										16 34														
South Woodham Ferrers	d										16 39														
Battlesbridge	d										16 43														
Wickford 2	d			16 25				16 40			16a50	16 54					17 10							17 25	
Billericay	d			16 31				16 46				17 00					17 16							17 31	
Shenfield 3	a			16 38				16 53				17 07					17 23							17 38	
	d	16 34		16 38	16 40	16 44	16 51	16 53	16 54	17 04		17 07	17 12		17 14		17 23		17 24	17 27		17 34	17 36	17 38	
Brentwood	d	16 37				16 47			16 57	17 07					17 17				17 27			17 37			
Harold Wood	d	16 42				16 52			17 02	17 12					17 22				17 32			17 42			
Gidea Park 2	d	16 46				16 56			17 06	17 16				17 22	17 26			17 32	17 36		17 42	17 46			17 52
Romford	d	16 48			16 48	16 58			17 08	17 18				17 24	17 28			17 34	17 38		17 44	17 48			17 54
Chadwell Heath	d	16 52				17 02			17 12	17 22					17 32				17 42			17 52			
Goodmayes	d	16 54				17 04			17 14	17 24					17 34				17 44			17 54			
Seven Kings	d	16 56				17 06			17 16	17 26					17 36				17 46			17 56			
Ilford 2	d	16 59				17 09			17 19	17 29				17 31	17 39			17 41	17 49		17 51	17 59			18 01
Manor Park	d	17 01				17 11			17 21					17 34				17 44			17 54				18 04
Forest Gate	d	17 03				17 13			17 23					17 36				17 46			17 56				18 06
Maryland	d	17 05				17 15			17 25					17 38				17 48			17 58				18 08
Stratford 7 ⊖	d	17 07		16s52	16s56	17 17	17s05	17s08	17 27	17 34			17s26	17 40	17 44		17s37	17 50	17 54		18 00	18 05	17s50	17s53	18 10
London Liverpool Street 15 ⊖	a	17 17		17 03	17 05	17 27	17 15	17 18	17 37	17 44		17 29	17 38	17 48	17 54		17 46	17 58	18 04	17 49	18 09	18 15	18 00	18 02	18 18

		LE	LE 1	LE 1	LE 1	LE 1		LE	LE	LE	LE	LE 1	LE 1	LE	LE	LE 1	LE	LE	LE 1		LE	LE 1	LE 1	LE	LE 1
Southend Victoria	d					17 21						17 36				17 51						18 06			
Prittlewell	d					17 23						17 38				17 53						18 08			
Rochford	d					17 27						17 42				17 57						18 12			
Hockley	d					17 31						17 46				18 01						18 16			
Rayleigh	d					17 35						17 50				18 05						18 20			
Southminster	d			17 05															17 47						
Burnham-on-Crouch	d			17 09															17 51						
Althorne	d			17 14															17 56						
North Fambridge	d			17 21															18 03						
South Woodham Ferrers	d			17 26															18 08						
Battlesbridge	d			17 30															18 12						
Wickford 2	d			17 36		17 40						17 55				18 10			18 18			18 25			
Billericay	d			17 42		17 46						18 01				18 16			18 24			18 31			
Shenfield 3	a			17 49		17 53						18 08				18 23			18 31			18 38			
	d	17 44	17 46	17 49	17 51	17 53			17 54		18 04	18 08	18 12		18 14	18 23		18 24	18 31		18 34	18 38	18 40	18 44	18 51
Brentwood	d	17 47							17 57		18 07				18 17			18 27			18 37			18 47	
Harold Wood	d	17 52							18 02		18 12				18 22			18 32			18 42			18 52	
Gidea Park 2	d	17 56						18 02	18 06	18 12	18 16			18 22	18 26		18 32	18 36			18 46			18 56	
Romford	d	17 58			17 59			18 04	18 08	18 14	18 18			18 24	18 28		18 34	18 38			18 48			18 58	18 59
Chadwell Heath	d	18 02							18 12		18 22				18 32			18 42			18 52			19 02	
Goodmayes	d	18 04							18 14		18 24				18 34			18 44			18 54			19 04	
Seven Kings	d	18 06							18 16		18 26				18 36			18 46			18 56			19 06	
Ilford 2	d	18 09						18 11	18 19	18 21	18 29			18 31	18 39		18 41	18 49			18 59			19 09	
Manor Park	d							18 14		18 24				18 34			18 44	18 51			19 01			19 11	
Forest Gate	d							18 16		18 26				18 36			18 46	18 53			19 03			19 13	
Maryland	d							18 18		18 28				18 38			18 48	18 55			19 05			19 15	
Stratford 7 ⊖	d	18 15	18s02	18s03	18s07	18s12		18 20	18 24	18 30	18 34	18s22	18s26	18 40	18 44	18s37	18 50	18 57	18s46		19 07	18s52	18s55	19 17	19s07
London Liverpool Street 15 ⊖	a	18 25	18 11	18 14	18 20	18 21		18 28	18 34	18 38	18 44	18 31	18 36	18 48	18 54	18 46	18 58	19 07	18 55		19 17	19 01	19 05	19 27	19 16

		LE	LE 1	LE	LE 1	LE 1	LE	LE 1	LE 1	LE		LE	LE 1	LE 1	LE	LE 1	CC	LE	LE 1	LE 1	LE	LE 1	LE		LE 1
Southend Victoria	d		18 26						18 46				19 06						19 26						19 46
Prittlewell	d		18 28						18 48				19 08						19 28						19 48
Rochford	d		18 32						18 52				19 12						19 32						19 52
Hockley	d		18 36						18 56				19 16						19 36						19 56
Rayleigh	d		18 40						19 00				19 20						19 40						20 00
Southminster	d					18 27														19 17					
Burnham-on-Crouch	d					18 31														19 21					
Althorne	d					18 36														19 26					
North Fambridge	d					18 43														19 34					
South Woodham Ferrers	d					18 48														19 39					
Battlesbridge	d					18 52														19 43					
Wickford 2	d		18 45			18 58			19 05				19 25						19 45	19 49					20 05
Billericay	d		18 51			19 04			19 11				19 31						19 51	19 55					20 11
Shenfield 3	a		18 58			19 11			19 18				19 38						19 58	20 03					20 18
	d	18 54	18 58	19 04	19 10		19 14	19 16	19 18	19 24		19 34	19 38	19 40	19 44	19 51		19 54	19 58		20 04	20 10	20 14		20 18
Brentwood	d	18 57		19 07			19 17			19 27		19 37			19 47			19 57			20 07		20 17		
Harold Wood	d	19 02		19 12			19 22			19 32		19 42			19 52			20 02			20 12		20 22		
Gidea Park 2	d	19 06		19 16			19 26			19 36		19 46			19 56			20 06			20 16		20 26		
Romford	d	19 08		19 18			19 28		19 26	19 38		19 48			19 58	19 59		20 08			20 18		20 28		20 26
Chadwell Heath	d	19 12		19 22			19 32			19 42		19 52			20 02			20 12			20 22		20 32		
Goodmayes	d	19 14		19 24			19 34			19 44		19 54			20 04			20 14			20 24		20 34		
Seven Kings	d	19 16		19 26			19 36			19 46		19 56			20 06			20 16			20 26		20 36		
Ilford 2	d	19 19		19 29			19 39			19 49		19 59			20 09			20 19			20 29		20 39		
Manor Park	d	19 21		19 31			19 41			19 51		20 01			20 11			20 21			20 31		20 41		
Forest Gate	d	19 23		19 33			19 43			19 53		20 03			20 13			20 23			20 33		20 43		
Maryland	d	19 25		19 35			19 45			19 55		20 05			20 15			20 25			20 35		20 45		
Stratford 7 ⊖	d	19 27	19s12	19 37	19s24		19 47		19s35	19 57		20 07	19s52	19s55	20 17	20s07	20 20	20 27	20s12		20 37	20s24	20 47		20s34
London Liverpool Street 15 ⊖	a	19 37	19 21	19 47	19 33		19 57	19 40	19 44	20 07		20 17	20 01	20 04	20 27	20 16	20 30	20 37	20 21		20 47	20 33	20 57		20 43

For general notes see front of timetable
For details of catering facilities see
Directory of Train Operators

Southend Victoria, Southminster and Shenfield → London

Network diagram - see first page of Table 5

		LE	CC 1	LE	LE 1	LE 1	LE	LE 1	CC	LE	LE 1	LE 1	LE		LE 1	LE	LE 1	LE	LE	LE 1	LE 1	LE	LE 1	LE 1	LE
Southend Victoria	d				20 06						20 26						20 46			21 06					
Prittlewell	d				20 08						20 28						20 48			21 08					
Rochford	d				20 12						20 32						20 52			21 12					
Hockley	d				20 16						20 36						20 56			21 16					
Rayleigh	d				20 20						20 40						21 00			21 20					
Southminster	d											20 17													
Burnham-on-Crouch	d											20 21													
Althorne	d											20 26													
North Fambridge	d											20 34													
South Woodham Ferrers	d											20 39													
Battlesbridge	d											20 43													
Wickford 2	d				20 25						20 45	20 49					21 05			21 25					
Billericay	d				20 31						20 51	20 55					21 11			21 31					
Shenfield 3	a				20 38						20 58	21 02					21 18			21 38					
	d	20 24		20 34	20 38	20 40	20 44	20 51		20 54	20 58		21 04		21 10	21 14	21 18	21 24	21 34	21 38	21 40	21 44	21 51	21 58	21 59
Brentwood	d	20 27		20 37			20 47			20 57			21 07			21 17		21 27	21 37			21 47			22 02
Harold Wood	d	20 32		20 42			20 52			21 02			21 12			21 22		21 32	21 42			21 52			22 07
Gidea Park 2	d	20 36		20 46			20 56			21 06			21 16			21 26		21 36	21 46			21 56			22 11
Romford	d	20 38		20 48			20 58	20 59		21 08			21 18			21 28	21 26	21 38	21 48			21 58	21 59		22 13
Chadwell Heath	d	20 42		20 52			21 02			21 12			21 22			21 32		21 42	21 52			22 02			22 17
Goodmayes	d	20 44		20 54			21 04			21 14			21 24			21 34		21 44	21 54			22 04			22 19
Seven Kings	d	20 46		20 56			21 06			21 16			21 26			21 36		21 46	21 56			22 06			22 21
Ilford 2	d	20 49		20 59			21 09			21 19			21 29			21 39		21 49	21 59			22 09			22 24
Manor Park	d	20 51		21 01			21 11			21 21			21 31			21 41		21 51	22 01			22 11			22 26
Forest Gate	d	20 53		21 03			21 13			21 23			21 33			21 43		21 53	22 03			22 13			22 28
Maryland	d	20 55		21 05			21 15			21 25			21 35			21 45		21 55	22 05			22 15			22 30
Stratford 7 ⊖	d	20 57	21 00	21 07	20s52	20s55	21 17	21s07	21 20	21 27	21s12		21 37		21s24	21 47	21s34	21 57	22 07	21s52	21s55	22 17	22s10	22s12	22 32
London Liverpool Street 15 ⊖	a	21 07	21 10	21 17	21 01	21 04	21 27	21 17	21 30	21 37	21 21		21 47		21 33	21 57	21 43	22 07	22 17	22 01	22 03	22 27	22 19	22 23	22 42

		LE 1	LE 1	LE 1		LE	LE	LE 1	LE 1	LE	LE 1	LE	LE 1	LE 1	LE 1	LE	CC		LE	LE 1	LE 1	LE			
Southend Victoria	d		21 36					22 06						22 36						23 06					
Prittlewell	d		21 38					22 08						22 38						23 08					
Rochford	d		21 42					22 12						22 42						23 12					
Hockley	d		21 46					22 16						22 46						23 16					
Rayleigh	d		21 50					22 20						22 50						23 20					
Southminster	d	21 17											22 17								22 56				
Burnham-on-Crouch	d	21 21											22 21								23 00				
Althorne	d	21 26											22 26								23 05				
North Fambridge	d	21 34											22 34								23 12				
South Woodham Ferrers	d	21 39											22 39								23 17				
Battlesbridge	d	21 43											22 43								23 21				
Wickford 2	d	21 49	21 55					22 25					22a49	22 55						23 25	23 29				
Billericay	d	21 55	22 01					22 31						23 01						23 31	23 35				
Shenfield 3	a	22 02	22 08					22 38						23 08						23 38	23 42				
	d		22 08	22 11		22 14	22 29	22 38	22 40	22 44	22 51	22 59		23 08	23 10	23 14			23 29	23 38	23 42	23 44			
Brentwood	d					22 17	22 32			22 47		23 02				23 17			23 32			23 47			
Harold Wood	d					22 22	22 37			22 52		23 07				23 22			23 37			23 52			
Gidea Park 2	d					22 26	22 41			22 56		23 11				23 26			23 41			23 56			
Romford	d					22 28	22 43			22 58	22 59	23 13				23 28			23 43		23 50	23 58			
Chadwell Heath	d					22 32	22 47			23 02		23 17				23 32			23 47			00 02			
Goodmayes	d					22 34	22 49			23 04		23 19				23 34			23 49			00 04			
Seven Kings	d					22 36	22 51			23 06		23 21				23 36			23 51			00 06			
Ilford 2	d					22 39	22 54			23 09		23 24				23 39			23 54			00 09			
Manor Park	d					22 41	22 56			23 11		23 26				23 41			23 56			00 11			
Forest Gate	d					22 43	22 58			23 13		23 28				23 43			23 58			00 13			
Maryland	d					22 45	23 00			23 15		23 30				23 45			23 59			00 15			
Stratford 7 ⊖	d		22s22	22s27		22 47	23 02	22s52	22s55	23 17	23s07	23 32		23s22	23s25	23 47	23 57		00 02	23s54	23s58	00 17			
London Liverpool Street 15 ⊖	a		22 31	22 36		22 57	23 12	23 01	23 03	23 27	23 16	23 42		23 31	23 34	23 57	00 07		00 12	00 03	00 07	00 27			

For general notes see front of timetable
For details of catering facilities see
Directory of Train Operators

Table 5

Saturdays

Southend Victoria, Southminster and Shenfield → London

Network diagram - see first page of Table 5

		LE	LE	LE	LE	LE	LE	LE [1] A	LE [1]	LE [1]	LE	LE [1]	LE	LE [1]	LE	LE [1]	LE	LE	LE	LE [1]	LE [1]	LE [1]	LE [1]	LE	LE
Southend Victoria	d			04 02		04 32			05 06			05 36				06 06						06 26			
Prittlewell	d			04 04		04 34			05 08			05 38				06 08						06 28			
Rochford	d			04 08		04 38			05 12			05 42				06 12						06 32			
Hockley	d			04 12		04 42			05 16			05 46				06 16						06 36			
Rayleigh	d			04 16		04 46			05 20			05 50				06 20						06 40			
Southminster	d																						06 17		
Burnham-on-Crouch	d																						06 21		
Althorne	d																						06 26		
North Fambridge	d																						06 34		
South Woodham Ferrers	d																						06 39		
Battlesbridge	d																						06 43		
Wickford [2]	d			04 21		04 51			05 25			05 55				06 25						06 45	06 49		
Billericay	d			04 28		04 58			05 31			06 01				06 31						06 51	06 55		
Shenfield [3]	a			04 39		05 09			05 38			06 08				06 38						06 58	07 02		
	d	23p29	23p44	04 39		05 09		05 26	05 38		05 44	06 08		06 11	06 14	06 38			06 44	06 47	06 51	06 58			07 04
Brentwood	d	23p32	23p47	04 42		05 12					05 47				06 17				06 47						07 07
Harold Wood	d	23p37	23p52	04 47		05 17					05 52				06 22				06 52						07 12
Gidea Park [2]	d	23p41	23p56	04 51		05 21		05 33			05 56		06 16		06 26		06 36	06 46	06 56					07 06	07 16
Romford	d	23p43	23p58	04 53		05 23			05 46		05 58	06 16	06 18	06 19	06 28		06 38	06 48	06 58		06 59			07 08	07 18
Chadwell Heath	d	23p47	00 02	04 57		05 27					06 02		06 22		06 32		06 42	06 52	07 02					07 12	07 22
Goodmayes	d	23p49	00 04	04 59		05 29					06 04		06 24		06 34		06 44	06 54	07 04					07 14	07 24
Seven Kings	d	23p51	00 06	05 01		05 31		05 38			06 06		06 26		06 36		06 46	06 56	07 06					07 16	07 26
Ilford [2]	d	23p54	00 09	05 04	05 09	05 34	05 39				06 09		06 29		06 39		06 49	06 59	07 09					07 19	07 29
Manor Park	d	23p56	00 11		05 11		05 41				06 11		06 31		06 41		06 51	07 01	07 11					07 21	07 31
Forest Gate	d	23p58	00 13		05 13		05 43				06 13		06 33		06 43		06 53	07 03	07 13					07 23	07 33
Maryland	d	23p59	00 15		05 15		05 45				06 15		06 35		06 45		06 55	07 05	07 15					07 25	07 35
Stratford [7] ⊖	d	00 02	00 17	05 09	05 17	05 39	05 47	05s44	05s54	06 05	06 17	06s24	06 37	06s27	06 47	06s52	06 57	07 07	07 17	07s01	07s07	07s12		07 27	07 37
London Liverpool Street [15] ⊖	a	00 12	00 27	05 17	05 25	05 47	05 55	05 57	06 03	06 14	06 25	06 33	06 45	06 36	06 55	07 01	07 05	07 15	07 25	07 10	07 16	07 21		07 35	07 45

		LE [1]	LE [1]	LE	LE	LE	LE [1]	LE [1]	LE	LE [1]	LE	LE [1]	LE [1]	LE	LE [1]	LE [1]	LE	LE [1]	LE	LE	LE [1]	LE [1]	LE	LE [1]	LE
Southend Victoria	d		06 46				07 06					07 26						07 46			08 06				
Prittlewell	d		06 48				07 08					07 28						07 48			08 08				
Rochford	d		06 52				07 12					07 32						07 52			08 12				
Hockley	d		06 56				07 16					07 36						07 56			08 16				
Rayleigh	d		07 00				07 20					07 40						08 00			08 20				
Southminster	d												07 17												
Burnham-on-Crouch	d												07 21												
Althorne	d												07 26												
North Fambridge	d												07 34												
South Woodham Ferrers	d												07 39												
Battlesbridge	d												07 43												
Wickford [2]	d		07 05				07 25					07 45	07 49					08 05			08 25				
Billericay	d		07 11				07 31					07 51	07 55					08 11			08 31				
Shenfield [3]	a		07 18				07 38					07 58	08 02					08 18			08 38				
	d	07 10	07 18		07 24	07 34	07 38	07 40	07 44	07 51	07 54	07 58		08 04	08 10	08 14	08 14	08 18	08 24	08 34	08 38	08 40	08 44	08 51	08 54
Brentwood	d				07 27	07 37			07 47		07 57			08 07			08 17		08 27	08 37			08 47		08 57
Harold Wood	d				07 32	07 42			07 52		08 02			08 12			08 22		08 32	08 42			08 52		09 02
Gidea Park [2]	d			07 26	07 36	07 46			07 56		08 06			08 16			08 26		08 36	08 46			08 56		09 06
Romford	d		07 26	07 28	07 38	07 48			07 58	07 59	08 08			08 18			08 28	08 26	08 38	08 48			08 58	08 59	09 08
Chadwell Heath	d			07 32	07 42	07 52			08 02		08 12			08 22			08 32		08 42	08 52			09 02		09 12
Goodmayes	d			07 34	07 44	07 54			08 04		08 14			08 24			08 34		08 44	08 54			09 04		09 14
Seven Kings	d			07 36	07 46	07 56			08 06		08 16			08 26			08 36		08 46	08 56			09 06		09 16
Ilford [2]	d			07 39	07 49	07 59			08 09		08 19			08 29			08 39		08 49	08 59			09 09		09 19
Manor Park	d			07 41	07 51	08 01			08 11		08 21			08 31			08 41		08 51	09 01			09 11		09 21
Forest Gate	d			07 43	07 53	08 03			08 13		08 23			08 33			08 43		08 53	09 03			09 13		09 23
Maryland	d			07 45	07 55	08 05			08 15		08 25			08 35			08 45		08 55	09 05			09 15		09 25
Stratford [7] ⊖	d	07s24	07s34	07 47	07 57	08 07	07s52	07s55	08 17	08s07	08 27	08s12		08 37	08s24	08s30	08 47	08s34	08 57	09 07	08s52	08s55	09 17	09s07	09 27
London Liverpool Street [15] ⊖	a	07 33	07 43	07 55	08 05	08 15	08 01	08 03	08 25	08 16	08 35	08 21		08 45	08 33	08 39	08 55	08 43	09 05	09 15	09 01	09 03	09 25	09 16	09 35

			LE [1]	LE [1]	LE	LE [1]	LE	LE [1]	LE	LE	LE [1]	LE [1]	LE	LE [1]	LE		LE [1]	LE [1]	LE	LE [1]	LE	LE [1]	LE	LE
Southend Victoria	d		08 26					08 46			09 06					and at the same minutes past each hour until	18 26					18 46		
Prittlewell	d		08 28					08 48			09 08						18 28					18 48		
Rochford	d		08 32					08 52			09 12						18 32					18 52		
Hockley	d		08 36					08 56			09 16						18 36					18 56		
Rayleigh	d		08 40					09 00			09 20						18 40					19 00		
Southminster	d			08 17														18 17						
Burnham-on-Crouch	d			08 21														18 21						
Althorne	d			08 26														18 26						
North Fambridge	d			08 34														18 34						
South Woodham Ferrers	d			08 39														18 39						
Battlesbridge	d			08 43														18 43						
Wickford [2]	d		08 45	08 49				09 05			09 25						18 45	18 49				19 05		
Billericay	d		08 51	08 55				09 11			09 31						18 51	18 55				19 11		
Shenfield [3]	a		08 58	09 02				09 18			09 38						18 58	19 02				19 18		
	d		08 58		09 04	09 10	09 14	09 18	09 24	09 34	09 38	09 40	09 44	09 51	09 54		18 58		19 04	19 13	19 14	19 18	19 24	19 34
Brentwood	d				09 07		09 17		09 27	09 37			09 47		09 57				19 07		19 17		19 27	19 37
Harold Wood	d				09 12		09 22		09 32	09 42			09 52		10 02				19 12		19 22		19 32	19 42
Gidea Park [2]	d				09 16		09 26		09 36	09 46			09 56		10 06				19 16		19 26		19 36	19 46
Romford	d				09 18		09 28	09 26	09 38	09 48			09 58	09 59	10 08				19 18		19 28	19 26	19 38	19 48
Chadwell Heath	d				09 22		09 32		09 42	09 52			10 02		10 12				19 22		19 32		19 42	19 52
Goodmayes	d				09 24		09 34		09 44	09 54			10 04		10 14				19 24		19 34		19 44	19 54
Seven Kings	d				09 26		09 36		09 46	09 56			10 06		10 16				19 26		19 36		19 46	19 56
Ilford [2]	d				09 29		09 39		09 49	09 59			10 09		10 19				19 29		19 39		19 49	19 59
Manor Park	d				09 31		09 41		09 51	10 01			10 11		10 21				19 31		19 41		19 51	20 01
Forest Gate	d				09 33		09 43		09 53	10 03			10 13		10 23				19 33		19 43		19 53	20 03
Maryland	d				09 35		09 45		09 55	10 05			10 15		10 25				19 35		19 45		19 55	20 05
Stratford [7] ⊖	d		09s12		09 37	09s24	09 47	09s34	09 57	10 07	09s52	09s55	10 17	10s07	10 27		19s12		19 37	19s27	19 47	19s34	19 57	20 07
London Liverpool Street [15] ⊖	a		09 21		09 45	09 33	09 55	09 43	10 05	10 15	10 01	10 03	10 25	10 16	10 35		19 21		19 45	19 37	19 55	19 43	20 05	20 15

For general notes see front of timetable
For details of catering facilities see Directory of Train Operators

A From Colchester (Table 11)

Southend Victoria, Southminster and Shenfield → London

Network diagram - see first page of Table 5

		LE 1	LE 1	LE	LE 1	LE	LE 1	LE 1	LE	LE 1	LE	LE 1	LE	LE	LE 1	LE 1	LE	LE 1	LE	LE 1	LE 1	LE 1	LE	LE	LE 1
Southend Victoria	d	19 06					19 26					19 46			20 06						20 36				21 06
Prittlewell	d	19 08					19 28					19 48			20 08						20 38				21 08
Rochford	d	19 12					19 32					19 52			20 12						20 42				21 12
Hockley	d	19 16					19 36					19 56			20 16						20 46				21 16
Rayleigh	d	19 20					19 40					20 00			20 20						20 50				21 20
Southminster	d							19 17												20 17					
Burnham-on-Crouch	d							19 21												20 21					
Althorne	d							19 26												20 26					
North Fambridge	d							19 34												20 34					
South Woodham Ferrers	d							19 39												20 39					
Battlesbridge	d							19 43												20 43					
Wickford 2	d	19 25					19 45	19 49				20 05			20 25					20 49	20 55				21 25
Billericay	d	19 31					19 51	19 55				20 11			20 31					20 55	21 01				21 31
Shenfield 3	a	19 38					19 58	20 02				20 18			20 38					21 02	21 08				21 38
	d	19 38	19 40	19 44	19 51	19 54	19 58		20 04	20 10	20 14	20 18	20 24	20 34	20 38	20 40	20 44	20 51	20 59		21 08	21 11	21 14	21 29	21 38
Brentwood	d			19 47		19 57			20 07		20 17		20 27	20 37			20 47		21 02				21 17	21 32	
Harold Wood	d			19 52		20 02			20 12		20 22		20 32	20 42			20 52		21 07				21 22	21 37	
Gidea Park 2	d			19 56		20 06			20 16		20 26		20 36	20 46			20 56		21 11				21 26	21 41	
Romford	d			19 58	19 59	20 08			20 18		20 28	20 26	20 38	20 48			20 58	20 59	21 13				21 28	21 43	
Chadwell Heath	d			20 02		20 12			20 22		20 32		20 42	20 52			21 02		21 17				21 32	21 47	
Goodmayes	d			20 04		20 14			20 24		20 34		20 44	20 54			21 04		21 19				21 34	21 49	
Seven Kings	d			20 06		20 16			20 26		20 36		20 46	20 56			21 06		21 21				21 36	21 51	
Ilford 2	d			20 09		20 19			20 29		20 39		20 49	20 59			21 09		21 24				21 39	21 54	
Manor Park	d			20 11		20 21			20 31		20 41		20 51	21 01			21 11		21 26				21 41	21 56	
Forest Gate	d			20 13		20 23			20 33		20 43		20 53	21 03			21 13		21 28				21 43	21 58	
Maryland	d			20 15		20 25			20 35		20 45		20 55	21 05			21 15		21 30				21 45	22 00	
Stratford 7 ⊖ ⛴	d	19s52	19s55	20 17	20s07	20 27	20s12		20 37	20s24	20 47	20s34	20 57	21 07	20s52	20s55	21 17	21s07	21 32		21s22	21s25	21 47	22 02	21s52
London Liverpool Street 15 ⊖	a	20 01	20 03	20 25	20 16	20 35	20 21		20 45	20 33	20 55	20 43	21 05	21 15	21 01	21 03	21 29	21 16	21 44		21 35	21 38	21 59	22 14	22 05

		LE 1	LE	LE 1	LE 1	LE	LE 1	LE 1	LE 1	LE	LE	LE 1	LE 1	LE 1	LE	LE 1	LE	LE 1	LE 1	LE	LE	LE 1	LE	LE 1	
Southend Victoria	d							21 36				22 06						22 36				23 06			
Prittlewell	d							21 38				22 08						22 38				23 08			
Rochford	d							21 42				22 12						22 42				23 12			
Hockley	d							21 46				22 16						22 46				23 16			
Rayleigh	d							21 50				22 20						22 50				23 20			
Southminster	d						21 17							21 59										23 07	
Burnham-on-Crouch	d						21 21							22 03										23 11	
Althorne	d						21 26							22 08										23 16	
North Fambridge	d						21 34							22 14										23 22	
South Woodham Ferrers	d						21 39							22 19										23 27	
Battlesbridge	d						21 43							22 23										23 31	
Wickford 2	d						21 49	21 55				22 25		22 29				22 55				23 25		23a37	
Billericay	d						21 55	22 01				22 31		22 35				23 01				23 31			
Shenfield 3	a						22 02	22 08				22 38		22 42				23 08				23 38			
	d	21 40	21 44	21 51	21 58	21 59		22 08	22 11	22 14	22 29	22 38	22 40		22 44	22 51	22 59	23 08	23 10	23 14	23 29	23 38	23 44		
Brentwood	d		21 47			22 02				22 17	22 32				22 47		23 02			23 17	23 32		23 47		
Harold Wood	d		21 52			22 07				22 22	22 37				22 52		23 07			23 22	23 37		23 52		
Gidea Park 2	d		21 56			22 11				22 26	22 41				22 56		23 11			23 26	23 41		23 56		
Romford	d		21 58	21 59		22 13				22 28	22 43				22 58	22 59	23 13			23 28	23 43		23 58		
Chadwell Heath	d		22 02			22 17				22 32	22 47				23 02		23 17			23 32	23 47		00 02		
Goodmayes	d		22 04			22 19				22 34	22 49				23 04		23 19			23 34	23 49		00 04		
Seven Kings	d		22 06			22 21				22 36	22 51				23 06		23 21			23 36	23 51		00 06		
Ilford 2	d		22 09			22 24				22 39	22 54				23 09		23 24			23 39	23 54		00 09		
Manor Park	d		22 11			22 26				22 41	22 56				23 11		23 26			23 41	23 56		00 11		
Forest Gate	d		22 13			22 28				22 43	22 58				23 13		23 28			23 43	23 58		00 13		
Maryland	d		22 15			22 30				22 45	23 00				23 15		23 30			23 45	23 59		00 15		
Stratford 7 ⊖ ⛴	d	21s54	22 17	22s07	22s12	22 32		22s22	22s25	22 47	23 02	22s52	22s55		23 17	23s07	23 32	23s22	23s25	23 47	00 02	23s54	00 17		
London Liverpool Street 15 ⊖	a	22 07	22 29	22 20	22 25	22 44		22 35	22 38	22 59	23 14	23 05	23 07		23 29	23 20	23 44	23 35	23 38	23 59	00 14	00 07	00 29		

For general notes see front of timetable
For details of catering facilities see
Directory of Train Operators

Sundays

Southend Victoria, Southminster and Shenfield → London

Network diagram - see first page of Table 5

		LE	LE 1	LE	LE		LE	LE	LE 1	LE		LE 1	LE	LE 1	LE		LE 1	LE	LE 1	LE		LE 1	LE	LE 1	LE 1
Southend Victoria	d								06 18					06 48					07 18						07 52
Prittlewell	d																								
Rochford	d								06 22					06 52					07 22						07 56
Hockley	d								06 26					06 56					07 26						08 00
Rayleigh	d								06 30					07 00					07 30						08 04
Southminster	d																								
Burnham-on-Crouch	d																								
Althorne	d																								
North Fambridge	d																								
South Woodham Ferrers	d																								
Battlesbridge	d																								
Wickford 2	d								06 35					07 05					07 35						08 09
Billericay	d								06 41					07 11					07 41						08 15
Shenfield 3	a								06 52					07 22					07 52						08 22
	d	23p29		23p44				06 43	06 53			07 07	07 13	07 23			07 37	07 43	07 53			08 07	08 13	08 18	08 23
Brentwood	d	23p32		23p47				06 46	06 56				07 16	07 26				07 46	07 56				08 16		08 26
Harold Wood	d	23p37		23p52				06 51	07 01				07 21	07 31				07 51	08 01				08 21		08 31
Gidea Park 2	d	23p41		23p56	05 55		06 25	06 55	07 05	07 11			07 25	07 35	07 41			07 55	08 05	08 11			08 25		08 35
Romford	d	23p43		23p58	05 57		06 27	06 57	07 07	07 13			07 27	07 37	07 43			07 57	08 07	08 13			08 27		08 37
Chadwell Heath	d	23p47		00 02	06 01		06 31	07 01		07 17			07 31		07 47			08 01		08 17			08 31		
Goodmayes	d	23p49		00 04	06 03		06 33	07 03		07 19			07 33		07 49			08 03		08 19			08 33		
Seven Kings	d	23p51		00 06	06 05		06 35	07 05		07 21			07 35		07 51			08 05		08 21			08 35		
Ilford 2	d	23p54		00 09	06 08		06 38	07 08		07 24			07 38		07 54			08 08		08 24			08 38		
Manor Park	d	23p56		00 11	06 10		06 40	07 10		07 26			07 40		07 56			08 10		08 26			08 40		
Forest Gate	d	23p58		00 13	06 12		06 42	07 12		07 28			07 42		07 58			08 12		08 28			08 42		
Maryland	d	23p59		00 15	06 14		06 44	07 14					07 44					08 14					08 44		
Stratford 7 ⊖ ⛴	d	00 02	00 05	00 17	06 16		06 46	07 16	07 19	07 31		07s34	07 46	07 49	08 01		08s04	08 16	08 19	08 31		08s34	08 46	08s49	08 49
London Liverpool Street 15 ⊖	a	00 14	00 14	00 29	06 26		06 56	07 24	07 27	07 41		07 42	07 54	07 57	08 11		08 12	08 24	08 27	08 41		08 42	08 54	08 59	08 59

		LE	LE 1		LE	LE 1	LE 1	LE		LE 1	LE		LE 1	LE	LE 1	LE	LE 1	LE 1	LE	LE 1	LE			LE 1
Southend Victoria	d						08 22						08 52					09 22						20 52
Prittlewell	d																							
Rochford	d						08 26						08 56					09 26						20 56
Hockley	d						08 30						09 00					09 30						21 00
Rayleigh	d						08 34						09 04					09 34						21 04
Southminster	d					08 05											09 05							
Burnham-on-Crouch	d					08 09											09 09					and at the same minutes past each hour until		
Althorne	d					08 14											09 14							
North Fambridge	d					08 20											09 20							
South Woodham Ferrers	d					08 25											09 25							
Battlesbridge	d					08 29											09 29							
Wickford 2	d					08a35	08 39						09 09				09a35	09 39						21 09
Billericay	d						08 45						09 15					09 45						21 15
Shenfield 3	a						08 52						09 22					09 52						21 22
	d		08 41		08 43		08 53			09 11	09 13		09 23		09 41	09 43		09 53		10 11	10 13			21 23
Brentwood	d				08 46		08 56				09 16		09 26			09 46		09 56			10 16			21 26
Harold Wood	d				08 51		09 01				09 21		09 31			09 51		10 01			10 21			21 31
Gidea Park 2	d	08 41			08 55		09 05	09 11			09 25		09 35	09 41		09 55		10 05	10 11		10 25			21 35
Romford	d	08 43			08 57		09 07	09 13			09 27		09 37	09 43		09 57		10 07	10 13		10 27			21 37
Chadwell Heath	d	08 47			09 01			09 17			09 31			09 47		10 01			10 17		10 31			
Goodmayes	d	08 49			09 03			09 19			09 33			09 49		10 03			10 19		10 33			
Seven Kings	d	08 51			09 05			09 21			09 35			09 51		10 05			10 21		10 35			
Ilford 2	d	08 54			09 08			09 24			09 38			09 54		10 08			10 24		10 38			
Manor Park	d	08 56			09 10			09 26			09 40			09 56		10 10			10 26		10 40			
Forest Gate	d	08 58			09 12			09 28			09 42			09 58		10 12			10 28		10 42			
Maryland	d				09 14						09 44					10 14					10 44			
Stratford 7 ⊖ ⛴	d	09 01	09s04		09 16		09 19	09 31		09s34	09 46		09 49	10 01	10s04	10 16		10 21	10 31	10s34	10 46			21 49
London Liverpool Street 15 ⊖	a	09 11	09 12		09 24		09 29	09 41		09 42	09 54		09 59	10 11	10 12	10 24		10 31	10 41	10 42	10 54			21 59

		LE 1	LE	LE 1	LE 1		LE 1	LE	LE 1	LE 1		LE	LE 1	LE 1	LE 1		LE 1	LE	LE 1	LE 1		LE			
Southend Victoria	d				21 22				21 52					22 22					22 52						
Prittlewell	d																								
Rochford	d				21 26				21 56					22 26					22 56						
Hockley	d				21 30				22 00					22 30					23 00						
Rayleigh	d				21 34				22 04					22 34					23 04						
Southminster	d			21 05									22 05							22 45					
Burnham-on-Crouch	d			21 09									22 09							22 49					
Althorne	d			21 14									22 14							22 54					
North Fambridge	d			21 20									22 20							23 00					
South Woodham Ferrers	d			21 25									22 25							23 05					
Battlesbridge	d			21 29									22 29							23 09					
Wickford 2	d			21a35	21 39				22 09				22a35	22 39					23 09	23 15					
Billericay	d				21 45				22 15					22 45					23 15						
Shenfield 3	a				21 52				22 22					22 52					23 22	23 26					
	d	21 41	21 43		21 53		22 11	22 13	22 23	22 41		22 43		22 53			23 11	23 13	23 23			23 43			
Brentwood	d		21 46		21 56			22 16	22 26			22 46		22 56				23 16	23 26			23 46			
Harold Wood	d		21 51		22 01			22 21	22 31			22 51		23 01				23 21	23 31			23 51			
Gidea Park 2	d		21 55		22 05			22 25	22 35			22 55		23 05				23 25	23 35			23 55			
Romford	d		21 57		22 07			22 27	22 37			22 57		23 07				23 27	23 37			23 57			
Chadwell Heath	d		22 01					22 31				23 01						23 31				00 01			
Goodmayes	d		22 03					22 33				23 03						23 33				00 03			
Seven Kings	d		22 05					22 35				23 05						23 35				00 05			
Ilford 2	d		22 08					22 38				23 08						23 38				00 08			
Manor Park	d		22 10					22 40				23 10						23 40				00 10			
Forest Gate	d		22 12					22 42				23 12						23 42				00 12			
Maryland	d		22 14					22 44				23 14						23 44				00 14			
Stratford 7 ⊖ ⛴	d	22s04	22 16		22 19		22s34	22 46	22 49	23s04		23 16		23 19	23 22		23s34	23 46	23 49			00 16			
London Liverpool Street 15 ⊖	a	22 12	22 24		22 29		22 42	22 54	22 59	23 12		23 24		23 31	23 36		23 42	23 54	23 59			00 25			

For general notes see front of timetable
For details of catering facilities see Directory of Train Operators

Marks Tey — Sudbury

Network diagram - see first page of Table 5

Miles			LE	LE	LE	LE	LE	LE	LE	LE	LE	LE	LE	LE	LE	LE	LE	LE	LE	LE
0	**Colchester 4**	d	05 48	06 29	07 18	08 18	09 17	10 17	11 17	12 17	13 17	14 17	15 17	15 48	16 53	17 49	18 49	19 33	20 15	21 17
—	London Liverpool Street 15	⊖ d	.	05 25	06 38	07 38	08 38	09 38	10 38	11 38	12 38	13 38	14 38	15 18	16 15	17 08	18 02	18 38	19 38	20 38
5	Marks Tey 2	d	05 57	06 53	07 40	08 33	09 33	10 33	11 33	12 33	13 33	14 33	15 31	16 17	17 07	18 05	18 59	19 45	20 33	21 33
8¼	Chappel & Wakes Colne	d	06 03	06 59	.	08 39	09 39	10 39	11 39	12 39	13 39	14 39	15 37	16 23	17 13	18 11	19 05	19 51	20 39	21 39
11¾	Bures	d	06 09	07 05	.	08 45	09 45	10 45	11 45	12 45	13 45	14 45	15 43	16 29	17 19	18 17	19 11	19 57	20 45	21 45
16¾	**Sudbury**	a	06 16	07 12	07 56	08 52	09 52	10 52	11 52	12 52	13 52	14 52	15 52	16 36	17 26	18 24	19 20	20 06	20 52	21 52

Saturdays

		LE	LE	LE	LE	LE	LE	LE	LE	LE	LE	LE	LE	LE	LE	LE	LE
Colchester 4	d	06 17	07 17	08 17	09 17	10 17	11 17	12 17	13 17	14 17	15 17	16 17	17 17	18 17	19 17	20 17	21 17
London Liverpool Street 15	⊖ d	05 30	06 38	07 38	08 38	09 38	10 38	11 38	12 38	13 38	14 38	15 38	16 38	17 38	18 38	19 38	20 38
Marks Tey 2	d	06 33	07 33	08 33	09 33	10 33	11 33	12 33	13 33	14 33	15 33	16 33	17 33	18 33	19 33	20 33	21 33
Chappel & Wakes Colne	d	06 39	07 39	08 39	09 39	10 39	11 39	12 39	13 39	14 39	15 39	16 39	17 39	18 39	19 39	20 39	21 39
Bures	d	06 45	07 45	08 45	09 45	10 45	11 45	12 45	13 45	14 45	15 45	16 45	17 45	18 45	19 45	20 45	21 45
Sudbury	a	06 52	07 52	08 52	09 52	10 52	11 52	12 52	13 52	14 52	15 52	16 52	17 52	18 52	19 52	20 52	21 52

Sundays

		LE	LE	LE	LE	LE	LE	LE	LE	LE	LE	LE	LE	LE	LE	LE
Colchester 4	d	07 07	08 06	09 06	10 06	11 06	12 06	13 06	14 06	15 06	16 06	17 06	18 06	19 06	20 06	21 06
London Liverpool Street 15	⊖ d	.	.	08 02	09 02	10 02	11 02	12 02	13 02	14 02	15 02	16 02	17 02	18 02	19 02	20 02
Marks Tey 2	d	07 15	08 15	09 15	10 15	11 15	12 15	13 15	14 15	15 15	16 15	17 15	18 15	19 15	20 15	21 15
Chappel & Wakes Colne	d	07 21	08 21	09 21	10 21	11 21	12 21	13 21	14 21	15 21	16 21	17 21	18 21	19 21	20 21	21 21
Bures	d	07 27	08 27	09 27	10 27	11 27	12 27	13 27	14 27	15 27	16 27	17 27	18 27	19 27	20 27	21 27
Sudbury	a	07 34	08 34	09 34	10 34	11 34	12 34	13 34	14 34	15 34	16 34	17 34	18 34	19 34	20 34	21 34

Mondays to Fridays

Miles			LE	LE	LE	LE	LE	LE	LE	LE	LE	LE	LE	LE	LE	LE	LE	LE	LE	LE	LE
0	**Sudbury**	d	05 30	06 30	07 17	08 00	09 00	10 00	11 00	12 00	13 00	14 00	15 00	15 54	16 40	17 31	18 31	19 22	20 08	21 00	22 00
5	Bures	d	05 37	06 37	07 24	08 07	09 07	10 07	11 07	12 07	13 07	14 07	15 07	16 01	.	17 38	18 38	19x29	20x15	21 07	22 07
8½	Chappel & Wakes Colne	d	05 43	06 43	07 30	08 13	09 13	10 13	11 13	12 13	13 13	14 13	15 13	16 07	.	17 44	18 44	19x35	20x21	21 13	22 13
11¾	Marks Tey 2	a	05 49	06 49	07 36	08 19	09 19	10 19	11 19	12 19	13 19	14 19	15 19	16 13	16 56	17 50	18 50	19 41	20 27	21 19	22 19
—	London Liverpool Street 15	⊖ a	06 49	07 51	08 48	09 22	10 17	11 18	12 16	13 16	14 16	15 16	16 18	17 15	17 49	18 49	19 47	20 46	21 33	22 19	23 16
16¾	**Colchester 4**	a	06 32	07 04	07 56	08 38	09 37	10 37	11 37	12 37	13 37	14 37	15 37	16 41	17 09	18 03	19 03	20 08	20 38	21 38	22 30

Saturdays

		LE	LE	LE	LE	LE	LE	LE	LE	LE	LE	LE	LE	LE	LE	LE	LE
Sudbury	d	07 00	08 00	09 00	10 00	11 00	12 00	13 00	14 00	15 00	16 00	17 00	18 00	19 00	20 00	21 00	22 00
Bures	d	07 07	08 07	09 07	10 07	11 07	12 07	13 07	14 07	15 07	16 07	17 07	18 07	19 07	20 07	21 07	22 07
Chappel & Wakes Colne	d	07 13	08 13	09 13	10 13	11 13	12 13	13 13	14 13	15 13	16 13	17 13	18 13	19 13	20 13	21 13	22 13
Marks Tey 2	a	07 19	08 19	09 19	10 19	11 19	12 19	13 19	14 19	15 19	16 19	17 19	18 19	19 19	20 19	21 19	22 19
London Liverpool Street 15	⊖ a	08 16	09 16	10 16	11 16	12 16	13 16	14 16	15 16	16 16	17 16	18 16	19 16	20 16	21 16	22 20	23 20
Colchester 4	a	07 37	08 37	09 37	10 37	11 37	12 37	13 37	14 37	15 37	16 37	17 37	18 36	19 36	20 37	21 37	22 30

Sundays

		LE	LE	LE	LE	LE	LE	LE	LE	LE	LE	LE	LE	LE	LE	LE
Sudbury	d	07 40	08 40	09 40	10 40	11 40	12 40	13 40	14 40	15 40	16 40	17 40	18 40	19 40	20 40	21 40
Bures	d	07 47	08 47	09 47	10 47	11 47	12 47	13 47	14 47	15 47	16 47	17 47	18 47	19 47	20 47	21 47
Chappel & Wakes Colne	d	07 53	08 53	09 53	10 53	11 53	12 53	13 53	14 53	15 53	16 53	17 53	18 53	19 53	20 53	21 53
Marks Tey 2	a	07 59	08 59	09 59	10 59	11 59	12 59	13 59	14 59	15 59	16 59	17 59	18 59	19 59	20 59	21 59
London Liverpool Street 15	⊖ a	09 12	10 12	11 12	12 12	13 12	14 12	15 12	16 12	17 12	18 12	19 12	20 12	21 12	22 12	23 12
Colchester 4	a	.	09 12	10 12	11 12	12 12	13 12	14 12	15 12	16 12	17 12	18 12	19 12	20 12	21 12	22 09

For general notes see front of timetable
For details of catering facilities see Directory of Train Operators

London → Chelmsford, Colchester, Walton-on-Naze, Clacton, Harwich, Ipswich and Norwich

Network diagram - see first page of Table 5

Miles	Miles	Miles	Miles	Miles			LE MX 1 ◇ ☕	LE MO 1 ◇ ☕	LE MX 1	LE MO 1	LE FO 1	LE MFX 1	LE MX 1 ◇ ☕	LE MO 1 ◇	LE MO 1	LE MX 1	LE MO 1	LE MX 1	LE MX 1	LE A	LE 1		LE 1	LE A	LE 1
0	—	—	—	—	**London Liverpool Street 15** ⊖	d	22p30	22p30	23p00	23p02	23p18	23p18	23p30	23p30	23p32	23p48	00 02	00 18	00 46						
4	—	—	—	—	Stratford 7 ⊖	d	22b38		23p07	23p09	23p25	23p25	23b38		23p39	23p55	00 09	00 25	00 55						
12¼	—	—	—	—	Romford	d																			
20¼	—	—	—	—	Shenfield 3	d		22b57	23p24	23p31	23p42	23p42		23b57	00 01	00 12	00 31	00 47	01 17						
23½	—	—	—	—	Ingatestone	d				23p35	23p46	23p46				00 16	00 35	00 51	01 21						
29¾	—	—	—	—	**Chelmsford 3**	d	23p03		23p33	23p42	23p53	23p53	00 03		00 10	00 23	00 42	00 58	01 28						
36	—	—	—	—	Hatfield Peverel	d				23p49						00 30	00 49	01 05							
38½	0	—	—	—	**Witham 2**	d			23p42	23p54	00 03	00 03			00 19	00 35	00 54	01 10	01 38				05 21		
—	3	—	—	—	White Notley	d																	05 28		
—	4¼	—	—	—	Cressing	d																	05 30		
—	5½	—	—	—	Braintree Freeport	d																	05 33		
—	6¼	—	—	—	**Braintree**	a																	05 37		
42¼	—	—	—	—	Kelvedon	d				23p59						00 40	00 59	01 15							
46¾	—	—	—	—	Marks Tey 2	d				00 04					00 27	00 45	01 04	01 20							
51¾	—	—	—	—	**Colchester 4**	a	23p22	23p23	23p56	00 12	00 17	00 21	00 23	00 27	00 40	00 57	01 18	01 32	02 03						
—	0	0	—	—		d	23p23	23p24	23p57	00 12	00 17		00 23	00 28							05 35				05 43
—	—	2¼	—	—	Colchester Town	a																			
—	—	—	—	—		d																			
—	2¾	3¼	—	—	Hythe	d																			
—	—	5¾	—	—	Wivenhoe 3	d					00 25														
—	—	7½	—	—	Alresford (Essex)	d					00 28														
—	—	9¾	—	—	Great Bentley	d					00 32														
—	—	12½	—	—	Weeley	d																			
—	—	14¾	—	—	Thorpe-le-Soken 1	a					00 37														
—	—	—	0	—		d					00 37														
—	—	—	4¾	—	**Clacton-on-Sea**	a					00 51														
—	—	17¼	—	—	Kirby Cross	d																			
—	—	18½	—	—	Frinton-on-Sea	d																			
—	—	19¾	—	—	**Walton-on-the-Naze**	a																			
59½	—	—	—	0	Manningtree 2	d	23p32	23p33	00 04	00 20			00 32	00 37							05 44				05 51
—	—	—	—	1¾	Mistley	d																			05 55
—	—	—	—	5¼	Wrabness	d																			06 00
—	—	—	—	9¼	Harwich International	d																			06 09
—	—	—	—	10¾	Dovercourt	d																			06 12
—	—	—	—	11¼	**Harwich Town**	a																			06 14
68¾	—	—	—	—	**Ipswich**	a	23p42	23p42	00 20	00 36			00 44	00 46							05 55				
—	—	—	—	—		d	23p43	23p44					00 44	00 48						05 10	06 01			06 13	
—	—	—	—	—	**Lowestoft**	a																			
77	—	—	—	—	Needham Market	d														05 20				06 23	
80¾	—	—	—	—	Stowmarket	d	23p54	23p55					00 55	00 59						05a25	06 12			06a28	
—	—	—	—	—	**Peterborough 8**	a															07 39				
95	—	—	—	—	Diss	d	00 07	00 07					01 08	01 11											
115	—	—	—	—	**Norwich**	a	00 45	00 39					01 45	01 43											

		LE 1	LE 1	LE 1	LE A	LE 1	LE 1	LE 1	LE 1	LE 1	LE 1 ◇	LE 1	LE 1	LE 1	LE 1		LE 1 ◇	LE 1	LE 1 ◇	LE 1	LE 1	LE 1 ◇	LE A	LE 1	LE 1
London Liverpool Street 15 ⊖	d							05 23			06 00		06 02	06 12			06 25		06 38	06 48		07 00			
Stratford 7 ⊖	d							05 32					06 09	06 19			06u33			06 55					
Romford	d							05 40					06 17												
Shenfield 3	d							05 51			06u23		06 28	06 37					07u02	07 12		07u23			
Ingatestone	d							05 55						06 41						07 16					
Chelmsford 3	d							06 02					06 37	06 49			06 57		07 12	07 23					←
Hatfield Peverel	d							06 09						06 55						07 30					07 30
Witham 2	d							06 14	06 16				06 46	07 03			07 07		07 21	→					07 36
White Notley	d								06 23					07 10											
Cressing	d								06 25					07 12											
Braintree Freeport	d								06 28					07 15											
Braintree	a								06 32					07 20											
Kelvedon	d							06 19					06 51						07 27						
Marks Tey 2	d							06 24					06 56						07 33						07 47
Colchester 4	a							06 32			06 48		07 04				07 20		07 41			07 49			07 56
	d	05 55	06 22					06 33		06 45	06 50		07 04		07 18		07 22	07 26	07 41		07 48	07 50			
Colchester Town	a									06 52								07 33			07 55				
	d																	07 37							
Hythe	d												07 09					07 41							
Wivenhoe 3	d							06 40					07 13		07 25			07 45							
Alresford (Essex)	d												07 16		07 29			07 49							
Great Bentley	d												07 20		07 33			07 53							
Weeley	d												07 23					07 56							
Thorpe-le-Soken 1	a							06 50					07 27		07 39			08 00							
	d			06 26			06 41	06 50				07 20	07 27		07 39			08 00							
Clacton-on-Sea	a							07 00					07 36					08 10							
Kirby Cross	d			06 30			06c49					07 24			07e46										
Frinton-on-Sea	d			06 33			06 52					07 27			07 49										
Walton-on-the-Naze	a			06 38			06 57					07 32			07 55										
Manningtree 2	d	06 03	06 31			06 36					06 59						07 32		07 50			07 59		07 35	
Mistley	d					06 40																		07 39	
Wrabness	d					06 45																		07 44	
Harwich International	d					06 52																	07 47	07 51	
Dovercourt	d					06 55																		07 54	
Harwich Town	a					06 57																		07 56	
Ipswich	a	06 17	06 41								07 08						07 41		07 59			08 08	08 15		
	d		06 42		06 52						07 09						07 42		08 02			08 09	08 16		
Lowestoft	a																								
Needham Market	d				07 02																		08 26		
Stowmarket	d		06 53		07a07						07 20						07 53		08 13			08 20	08a31		
Peterborough 8	a																		09 37						
Diss	d		07 05								07 32						08 05					08 32			
Norwich	a		07 27								07 54						08 27					08 54			

For general notes see front of timetable
For details of catering facilities see Directory of Train Operators

A To Cambridge (Table 14)
b Previous night.
Stops to pick up only
c Arr. 0645
e Arr. 0743

London → Chelmsford, Colchester, Walton-on-Naze, Clacton, Harwich, Ipswich and Norwich

Network diagram - see first page of Table 5

		LE 1	LE 1	LE 1	LE 1	LE 1 ◇	LE 1	LE 1	LE 1 ◇		LE 1	LE 1	LE 1 ◇	LE	LE 1		LE 1	LE 1	LE 1	LE 1 ◇	LE 1	LE 1	LE 1	LE 1	LE 1
						☕							☕ A	A						☕					
London Liverpool Street 15 ⊖	d	07 04	07 08	07 18	07 27	07 30			07 38		07 48		08 00		08 02		08 08		08 18	08 30			08 38	08 48	
Stratford 7 ⊖	d	07 11	07 15	07 25		07u38					07 55						08 15		08 25	08u38				08 55	
Romford	d		07 23												08 16										
Shenfield 3	d	07 28	07 34	07 42	07 51				08u02		08 12		08u23		08 26		08 32		08 42				09 02	09 12	
Ingatestone	d			07 46							08 16						08 36		08 46					09 16	
Chelmsford 3	d	07 37	07 43	07 53	08 00	08 04			08 12		08 23				08 35		08 43		08 53	09 02			09 12	09 23	
Hatfield Peverel	d							←			08 30													09 30	
Witham 2	d	07 47	07 52	08 03	08b12			08 12	08 22		08c38				08 44		08 52		09 03				09 21	09 37	
White Notley	d	07 54			→						08 44													09 43	
Cressing	d	07 56									08 47													09 46	
Braintree Freeport	d	07 59									08 49													09 48	
Braintree	a	08 04									08 54													09 53	
Kelvedon	d			08 07				08 19											09 07						
Marks Tey 2	d			08 13				08 24	08 30										09 13				09 29		
Colchester 4	a		08 06	08 20		08 23		08 32	08 38				08 49		08 58		09 06		09 20	09 23			09 37		
	d		08 06	08 21		08 24		08 32	08 38			08 46	08 50		09 02	09 04	09 07	09 14		09 24		09 30	09 38		
Colchester Town	a							08 40				08 53			09 09							09 37			
	d											08 57													
Hythe	d		08 11									09 00													
Wivenhoe 3	d		08 15									09 04					09 14								
Alresford (Essex)	d		08 18									09 08													
Great Bentley	d		08 22									09 12													
Weeley	d											09 16													
Thorpe-le-Soken 1	a		08 27									09 19					09 24				←				
	d		08 27				08 29					09 26					09 24				09 26				
Clacton-on-Sea	a		08 37									→					09 34								
Kirby Cross	d						08 33														09 30				
Frinton-on-Sea	d						08 36														09 33				
Walton-on-the-Naze	a						08 41														09 39				
Manningtree 2	d			08 29		08 34							08 59			09 12		09 22		09 34			09 46		
Mistley	d			08 33														09 26							
Wrabness	d			08 38														09 31							
Harwich International	d			08 46														09 39							
Dovercourt	d			08 49														09 42							
Harwich Town	a			08 51														09 44							
Ipswich	a					08 43			08 56				09 08			09 23				09 43			09 58		
	d					08 44			09 02				09 09	09 16						09 44					10 02
Lowestoft	a								10 32																
Needham Market	d													09 26											
Stowmarket	d					08 55								09a31						09 55					10 13
Peterborough 8	a																								11 37
Diss	d					09 07							09 30							10 07					
Norwich	a					09 27							09 52							10 27					

		LE 1	LE 1 ◇		LE 1	LE	LE 1	LE 1	LE 1 ◇	LE 1	LE 1	LE 1 ◇	LE 1	LE 1	LE 1 ◇	LE 1	LE	LE 1	LE 1		LE 1 ◇	LE 1	LE 1	LE 1 ◇	LE 1
			☕			A			☕						☕		A				☕				
London Liverpool Street 15 ⊖	d		09 00				09 08	09 18	09 30			09 38	09 48		10 00			10 08	10 18		10 30			10 38	10 48
Stratford 7 ⊖	d						09 15	09 25	09u38				09 55					10 15	10 25		10u38				10 55
Romford	d						09 23											10 23							
Shenfield 3	d		09u23				09 34	09 42				10u02	10 12		10u23			10 34	10 42					11u02	11 12
Ingatestone	d												10 16												11 16
Chelmsford 3	d						09 43	09 51	10 02			10 12	10 23					10 43	10 51		11 02			11 12	11 23
Hatfield Peverel	d												10 30												11 30
Witham 2	d						09 52	10 00				10 21	10 36					10 52	11 00					11 21	11 36
White Notley	d												10 43												11 43
Cressing	d												10 45												11 45
Braintree Freeport	d												10 48												11 48
Braintree	a												10 53												11 53
Kelvedon	d							10 05											11 05						
Marks Tey 2	d							10 10				10 29							11 10					11 29	
Colchester 4	a		09 49				10 06	10 18	10 21			10 37			10 49			11 06	11 18		11 21			11 37	
	d	09 46	09 50		10 00		10 07	10 21	10 24		10 30	10 38		10 46	10 50	11 00		11 07	11 18		11 22		11 30	11 38	
Colchester Town	a	09 53			10 07						10 37			10 53		11 07							11 37		
	d	09 57												10 57											
Hythe	d	10 00												11 00											
Wivenhoe 3	d	10 04					10 14							11 04				11 14							
Alresford (Essex)	d	10 08												11 08											
Great Bentley	d	10 12												11 12											
Weeley	d	10 16												11 16											
Thorpe-le-Soken 1	a	10 19					10 24			←				11 19				11 24				←			
	d	10 26					10 24			10 26				11 26				11 24				11 26			
Clacton-on-Sea	a	→					10 34							→				11 34							
Kirby Cross	d									10 30												11 30			
Frinton-on-Sea	d									10 33												11 33			
Walton-on-the-Naze	a									10 39												11 39			
Manningtree 2	d		09 59					10 29	10 34						10 59				11 26		11 31				
Mistley	d							10 33											11 30						
Wrabness	d							10 38											11 35						
Harwich International	d							10 47											11 44						
Dovercourt	d							10 50											11 47						
Harwich Town	a							10 52											11 49						
Ipswich	a		10 08						10 43			10 56			11 08						11 41			11 56	
	d		10 09			10 16			10 44			11 02			11 09		11 16				11 42			12 02	
Lowestoft	a											12 32													
Needham Market	d					10 26											11 26								
Stowmarket	d					10a31			10 55								11a31				11 53			12 13	
Peterborough 8	a																							13 37	
Diss	d		10 30						11 07						11 30						12 05				
Norwich	a		10 52						11 27						11 52						12 27				

For general notes see front of timetable
For details of catering facilities see Directory of Train Operators

A To Cambridge (Table 14)
b Arr. 0809
c Arr. 0835

London → Chelmsford, Colchester, Walton-on-Naze, Clacton, Harwich, Ipswich and Norwich

Network diagram - see first page of Table 5

		LE 1	LE 1 ◇ ☕	LE 1	LE A	LE 1	LE 1	LE 1 ◇ ☕	LE 1	LE 1	LE 1 ◇	LE 1	LE 1		LE 1 ◇ ☕	LE 1	LE A	LE 1	LE 1	LE 1 ◇ ☕	LE 1	LE 1	LE 1 ◇	LE 1	LE 1
London Liverpool Street 15	⊖ d		11 00			11 08	11 18	11 30			11 38	11 48			12 00			12 08	12 18	12 30			12 38	12 48	
Stratford 7	⊖ ⛴ d					11 15	11 25	11u38				11 55						12 15	12 25	12u38				12 55	
Romford	d					11 23												12 23							
Shenfield 3	d		11u23			11 34	11 42				12u02	12 12			12u23			12 34	12 42				13u02	13 12	
Ingatestone	d											12 16												13 16	
Chelmsford 3	d					11 43	11 51	12 02			12 12	12 23						12 43	12 51	13 02			13 12	13 23	
Hatfield Peverel	d											12 30												13 30	
Witham 2	d					11 52	12 00				12 21	12 36						12 52	13 00				13 21	13 36	
White Notley	d											12 43												13 43	
Cressing	d											12 45												13 45	
Braintree Freeport	d											12 48												13 48	
Braintree	a											12 53												13 53	
Kelvedon	d						12 05												13 05						
Marks Tey 2	d						12 10				12 29								13 10				13 29		
Colchester 4	a		11 49			12 06	12 18	12 21			12 37				12 49			13 06	13 18	13 21			13 37		
	d	11 46	11 50	12 00		12 07	12 18	12 22		12 30	12 38		12 46		12 50	13 00		13 07	13 18	13 22		13 30	13 38		13 46
Colchester Town	a	11 53		12 07						12 37			12 53			13 07						13 37			13 53
	d	11 57											12 57												13 57
Hythe	d	12 00											13 00												14 00
Wivenhoe 3	d	12 04				12 14							13 04					13 14							14 04
Alresford (Essex)	d	12 08											13 08												14 08
Great Bentley	d	12 12											13 12												14 12
Weeley	d	12 16											13 16												14 16
Thorpe-le-Soken 1	a	12 19				12 24			←				13 19					13 24			←				14 19
	d	12 26				12 24			12 26				13 26					13 24			13 26				14 26
Clacton-on-Sea	a	→				12 34							→					13 34							→
Kirby Cross	d								12 30												13 30				
Frinton-on-Sea	d								12 33												13 33				
Walton-on-the-Naze	a								12 39												13 39				
Manningtree 2	d		11 59				12 26	12 31							12 59				13 26	13 31					
Mistley	d						12 30												13 30						
Wrabness	d						12 35												13 35						
Harwich International	d						12 44												13 44						
Dovercourt	d						12 47												13 47						
Harwich Town	a						12 49												13 49						
Ipswich	a		12 08					12 41			12 56				13 08					13 41			13 56		
	d		12 09		12 16			12 42			13 02				13 09		13 16			13 42			14 02		
Lowestoft	a										14 32														
Needham Market	d				12 26												13 26								
Stowmarket	d				12a31			12 53									13a31			13 53			14 13		
Peterborough 8	a																						15 37		
Diss	d		12 30					13 05							13 30					14 05					
Norwich	a		12 52					13 27							13 52					14 27					

		LE 1 ◇ ☕	LE 1	LE A	LE 1	LE 1	LE 1 ◇ ☕		LE 1	LE 1	LE 1 ◇	LE 1	LE 1	LE 1 ◇ ☕	LE 1	LE A	LE 1	LE 1	LE 1 ◇ ☕	LE 1	LE 1	LE 1 ◇	LE 1		LE 1
London Liverpool Street 15	⊖ d	13 00			13 08	13 18	13 30				13 38	13 48		14 00			14 08	14 18	14 30			14 38	14 48		
Stratford 7	⊖ ⛴ d				13 15	13 25	13u38					13 55					14 15	14 25	14u38				14 55		
Romford	d				13 23												14 23								
Shenfield 3	d	13u23			13 34	13 42					14u02	14 12		14u23			14 34	14 42				15u02	15 12		
Ingatestone	d											14 16											15 16		
Chelmsford 3	d				13 43	13 51	14 02				14 12	14 23					14 43	14 51	15 02			15 12	15 23		
Hatfield Peverel	d											14 30											15 30		
Witham 2	d				13 52	14 00					14 21	14 36					14 52	15 00				15 21	15 36		
White Notley	d											14 43											15 43		
Cressing	d											14 45											15 45		
Braintree Freeport	d											14 48											15 48		
Braintree	a											14 53											15 53		
Kelvedon	d					14 05												15 05							
Marks Tey 2	d					14 10					14 29							15 10				15 29			
Colchester 4	a	13 49			14 06	14 18	14 21				14 37			14 49			15 06	15 18	15 21			15 37			
	d	13 50	14 00		14 07	14 18	14 22			14 30	14 38		14 46	14 50	15 00		15 07	15 18	15 22		15 30	15 38			15 46
Colchester Town	a		14 07							14 37			14 53		15 07						15 37				15 53
	d												14 57												15 57
Hythe	d												15 00												16 00
Wivenhoe 3	d				14 14								15 04				15 14								16 04
Alresford (Essex)	d												15 08												16 08
Great Bentley	d												15 12												16 12
Weeley	d												15 16												16 16
Thorpe-le-Soken 1	a				14 24				←				15 19				15 24			←					16 19
	d				14 24				14 26				15 26				15 24			15 26					16 26
Clacton-on-Sea	a				14 34								→				15 34								→
Kirby Cross	d								14 30											15 30					
Frinton-on-Sea	d								14 33											15 33					
Walton-on-the-Naze	a								14 39											15 39					
Manningtree 2	d	13 59				14 26	14 31							14 59				15 26	15 31						
Mistley	d					14 30												15 30							
Wrabness	d					14 35												15 35							
Harwich International	d					14 44												15 44							
Dovercourt	d					14 47												15 47							
Harwich Town	a					14 49												15 49							
Ipswich	a	14 08					14 41				14 56			15 08					15 41			15 56			
	d	14 09		14 16			14 42				15 02			15 09		15 16			15 42			16 02			
Lowestoft	a										16 32														
Needham Market	d			14 26												15 26									
Stowmarket	d			14a31			14 53									15a31			15 53			16 13			
Peterborough 8	a																					17 37			
Diss	d	14 30					15 05							15 30					16 05						
Norwich	a	14 52					15 27							15 52					16 27						

For general notes see front of timetable
For details of catering facilities see
Directory of Train Operators

A To Cambridge (Table 14)

London → Chelmsford, Colchester, Walton-on-Naze, Clacton, Harwich, Ipswich and Norwich

Network diagram - see first page of Table 5

Station		LE	LE	LE	LE	LE	LE	LE	LE	LE	LE	LE	LE	LE	LE	LE		LE	LE	LE	LE	LE	LE	LE	
		1 ◊	1		1	1	R 1	1	1	1	R 1	1	R 1	1	1	1		1		R 1	1	1	R 1	1	
				A															A						
		☕					☕						☕							☕					
London Liverpool Street 15 ⊖	d	15 00			15 08	15 18	15 30		15 32		15 38	15 48	16 00		16 02	16 15		16 17		16 30			16 32	16 34	
Stratford 7 ⊖	d				15 15	15 25						15 55			16 10			16 25						16 42	
Romford	d				15 23																				
Shenfield 3	d	15u23			15 34	15 42			15 55		16u02	16 12			16 25			16 40					16u54	16 57	
Ingatestone	d								15 59			16 16						16 44							
Chelmsford 3	d				15 43	15 51	15 59		16 06		16u12	16 23	16 31		16 36	16 45		16 53						17 08	
Hatfield Peverel	d								16 13			16 30												17 15	
Witham 2	d				15 52	16 00			16 19		16 23	16 36			16 45			17a06					17 13	17 21	
White Notley	d											16 43												17 28	
Cressing	d											16 45												17 30	
Braintree Freeport	d											16 48												17 33	
Braintree	a											16 53												17 40	
Kelvedon	d					16 05			16 24						16 50	16 56									
Marks Tey 2	d					16 10					16 32					17 01									
Colchester 4	a	15 49			16 06	16 18	16 21		16 37		16 41		16 49		17 01	17 09				17 17			17 26		
	d	15 50	16 00		16 07	16 18	16 22			16 41	16 41		16 50	16 54	17 02	17 13				17 18		17 24	17 26		
Colchester Town	a		16 07							16 48				17 01								17 31			
	d									16 52												17 35			
Hythe	d									16 55					17 06							17 38			
Wivenhoe 3	d				16 14					16 59					17 10							17 42			
Alresford (Essex)	d									17 03												17 46			
Great Bentley	d									17 07												17 50			
Weeley	d									17 11												17 54			
Thorpe-le-Soken 1	a				16 24			←		17 14					17 20						←	17 57			
	d				16 24			16 26		17 22 →					17 20						17 22	18 04 →			
Clacton-on-Sea	a				16 34										17 32										
Kirby Cross	d							16 30													17 26				
Frinton-on-Sea	d							16 33													17 29				
Walton-on-the-Naze	a							16 39													17 35				
Manningtree 2	d	15 59				16 26	16 31						16 59			17 21							17 35		
Mistley	d					16 30										17 25									
Wrabness	d					16 35										17 30									
Harwich International	d					16 44										17 38									
Dovercourt	d					16 47										17 41									
Harwich Town	a					16 49										17 45									
Ipswich	a	16 08					16 41				16 58		17 08							17 33			17 47		
	d	16 09		16 16			16 42				17 02		17 09						17 16	17 34			17 49		
Lowestoft	a										18 33														
Needham Market	d			16 26															17 26				17 58		
Stowmarket	d			16a31			16 53						17 20						17a31	17 45			18 03		
Peterborough 8	a																						19 42		
Diss	d	16 30					17 05						17 32							17 57					
Norwich	a	16 52					17 27						17 55							18 20					

Station		LE		LE	LE	LE	LE	LE	LE	LE		LE	LE	LE	LE	LE	LE	LE	LE	LE	LE	LE	LE	LE	LE
		1		1	R 1	1	1	1	1			1	1	1	1	1	R 1	1	1	1	1	1	R 1	1	1
										A															
					☕												☕						☕		
London Liverpool Street 15 ⊖	d	16 45		16 47	17 00				17 02			17 08	17 12	17 20	17 22		17 30	17 32		17 38	17 42		17 50		
Stratford 7 ⊖	d			16 55								17 16	17 20							17 46	17 50				
Romford	d																								
Shenfield 3	d			17 10					17 24						17 44			17 54							
Ingatestone	d			17 14											17 48										
Chelmsford 3	d	17 15		17 23					17 35				17 44	17 51	17 58			18 05			18 14				
Hatfield Peverel	d												17 51								18 21				
Witham 2	d			17a36					17 45			17 50	17a59		18 09			18 15		18 20	→				
White Notley	d														18 16										
Cressing	d														18 18										
Braintree Freeport	d														18 21										
Braintree	a														18 28										
Kelvedon	d	17 26							17 50			17 54						18 20		18 24					
Marks Tey 2	d	17 31							17 55			18 00								18 30					
Colchester 4	a	17 39							18 03			18 08		18 11				18 31		18 38			18 42		
	d	17 43	17 47				17 49	17 51	18 03			18 08		18 11				18 34		18 38		18 42	18 43		
Colchester Town	a						17 56											18 42							←
	d						18 00											18 48 →							18 48
Hythe	d	17 47					18 03					18 13								18 43					
Wivenhoe 3	d	17 51					18 07					18 17								18 47		18 51			18 55
Alresford (Essex)	d						18 11					18 20										18 54			18 59
Great Bentley	d						18 15					18 24										18 58			19 03
Weeley	d						18 19																		19 07
Thorpe-le-Soken 1	a	18 02				←	18 22					18 29							←	18 57		19 03			19 11
	d	18 02				18 04	18 31 →					18 29							18 31	18 57		19 04			19 11
Clacton-on-Sea	a	18 13										18 41								19 08					19 22
Kirby Cross	d					18 08													18 35			19 08			
Frinton-on-Sea	d					18 11													18 38			19 11			
Walton-on-the-Naze	a					18 17													18 44			19 16			
Manningtree 2	d		17 55					17 59	18 11					18 19		18 23	18 27						18 52	18 57	
Mistley	d		17 59													18 27								19 01	
Wrabness	d		18 04													18 32								19 06	
Harwich International	d		18 12						18a29							18 39								19 13	
Dovercourt	d		18 15													18 42								19 16	
Harwich Town	a		18 19													18 46								19 18	
Ipswich	a				17 58			18 10						18 33			18 36						19 01		
	d				17 59					18 16							18 37						19 03		
Lowestoft	a																								
Needham Market	d									18 26															
Stowmarket	d									18a31							18 48								
Peterborough 8	a																								
Diss	d				18 20												19 00								
Norwich	a				18 42												19 23						19 44		

For general notes see front of timetable
For details of catering facilities see Directory of Train Operators

A To Cambridge (Table 14)

London → Chelmsford, Colchester, Walton-on-Naze, Clacton, Harwich, Ipswich and Norwich

Network diagram - see first page of Table 5

		LE 1	LE 1	LE R 1 ☕		LE 1	LE A	LE 1	LE 1	LE 1	LE R 1 ☕	LE 1	LE R 1 ☕	LE 1	LE 1	LE 1	LE 1	LE 1	LE 1	LE 1		LE 1	LE R 1 ☕	LE 1	LE 1
London Liverpool Street 15 ⊖	d		17 52	18 00				18 02	18 08	18 12	18 20	18 22	18 30				18 32	18 38				18 48	19 00	19 02	
Stratford 7 ⊖	d							18 10	18 16	18 20							18 40	18 46						19 09	
Romford	d																								
Shenfield 3	d		18 14									18 44						19 01				19 11		19 26	
Ingatestone	d		18 18									18 48										19 15			
Chelmsford 3	d	←	18 28					18 35	18 40	18 44		18 58					19 05	19 13				19 24		19 35	
Hatfield Peverel	d	18 21								18 51						←	19 12							19 41	
Witham 2	d	18b30	18a41					18 45	18 50	18 57		19c11				19 11	19 18	19 23				19 34		19 47	
White Notley	d									19 04		→												19 54	
Cressing	d									19 06														19 56	
Braintree Freeport	d									19 09														19 59	
Braintree	a									19 16														20 04	
Kelvedon	d	18 36						18 50	18 54							19 17	19 23	19 27							
Marks Tey 2	d							18 55	19 00							19 23		19 33							
Colchester 4	a	18 48		18 51				19 03	19 08		19 11		19 22			19 31	19 34	19 41				19 50	19 51		
	d	18 52		18 53		18 56		19 03	19 08		19 12		19 23			19 31	19 34	19 41		19 46			19 53		
Colchester Town	a					19 03														19 53					
	d																			19 57					
Hythe	d								19 13									19 46		20 00					
Wivenhoe 3	d	18 59							19 17							19 39		19 50		20 04					
Alresford (Essex)	d	19 03														19 42				20 08					
Great Bentley	d	19 07														19 46				20 12					
Weeley	d															19 49				20 16					
Thorpe-le-Soken 1	a	19 15							19 27							19 53		20 00		20 19					
	d	19 15							19 27						19 29	19 53		20 00	20 04	20 28					
Clacton-on-Sea	a	19 26							19 38							20 04		20 11		→					
Kirby Cross	d														19 33				20 08						
Frinton-on-Sea	d														19 36				20 11						
Walton-on-the-Naze	a														19 41				20 16						
Manningtree 2	d			19 02				19 11			19 21			19 27			19 42						20 02		
Mistley	d													19 31											
Wrabness	d													19 36											
Harwich International	d													19 43											
Dovercourt	d													19 46											
Harwich Town	a													19 48											
Ipswich	a			19 11				19 24			19 30		19 39				19 56						20 11		
	d			19 12			19 16				19 32		19 40										20 12		20 16
Lowestoft	a																								
Needham Market	d						19 26																		20 25
Stowmarket	d			19 23			19a31						19 51										20 23		20 30
Peterborough 8	a																								21 58
Diss	d			19 35									20 03										20 35		
Norwich	a			19 58							20 14		20 26										20 57		

		LE 1	LE 1	LE 1	LE R 1 ☕	LE R 1	LE 1	LE 1	LE 1	LE 1	LE 1 ◇ ☕	LE A	LE 1	LE 1		LE	LE 1	LE 1 ◇ ☕	LE 1	LE 1	LE	LE 1	LE 1 ◇	LE B	LE 1
London Liverpool Street 15 ⊖	d		19 08	19 18	19 30	19 32		19 38	19 48		20 00		20 08				20 18	20 30	20 38	20 48			21 00		21 08
Stratford 7 ⊖	d		19 15	19 25				19 45	19 55				20 15				20 25	20u38	20 45	20 55					21 15
Romford	d																								21 23
Shenfield 3	d			19 42		19u55		20 02	20 12				20 32				20 42		21 02	21 12			21u23		21 34
Ingatestone	d			19 46					20 16								20 46			21 16					
Chelmsford 3	d		19 39	19 53	20 00			20 11	20 23				20 41				20 53	21 03	21 11	21 23					21 43
Hatfield Peverel	d								20 30											21 30					
Witham 2	d		19 50	20 03		20 12		20 20	20 36				20 50				21 03		21 20	21 36					21 52
White Notley	d								20 43											21 43					
Cressing	d								20 45											21 45					
Braintree Freeport	d								20 48											21 48					
Braintree	a								20 53											21 53					
Kelvedon	d		19 54					20 25					20 55						21 25						
Marks Tey 2	d		20 00					20 30					21 00						21 30						
Colchester 4	a		20 08	20 16	20 20	20 25		20 38			20 49		21 08				21 16	21 22	21 38				21 49		22 06
	d		20 08	20 17	20 21	20 26		20 38		20 46	20 50		21 09				21 17	21 23	21 38			21 46	21 50		22 07
Colchester Town	a									20 53												21 53			
	d									20 57												21 57			
Hythe	d									21 00												22 00			
Wivenhoe 3	d		20 16							21 04			21 16									22 04			22 14
Alresford (Essex)	d									21 08												22 08			
Great Bentley	d									21 12												22 12			
Weeley	d									21 16												22 16			
Thorpe-le-Soken 1	a		20 26				←			21 19			21 26	←								22 19			22 24
	d		20 26				20 28			21 28			21 26	21 28								22 26			22 24
Clacton-on-Sea	a		20 35							→			21 36									→			22 34
Kirby Cross	d						20 32							21 32											
Frinton-on-Sea	d						20 35							21 35											
Walton-on-the-Naze	a						20 41							21 41											
Manningtree 2	d	20 07		20 25	20 30						20 59						21 25	21 32	21 46				21 58		
Mistley	d	20 11		20 29													21 29								
Wrabness	d	20 16		20 34													21 34				←				
Harwich International	d	20 23		20 42												21 34	21 42		22a02		21 34				
Dovercourt	d	20 26		20 45												→	21 45								
Harwich Town	a	20 28		20 47													21 47								
Ipswich	a				20 40	20 44		20 57			21 08							21 42			22 00		22 07		
	d				20 41	20 52					21 09	21 16						21 43					22 15	22 16	
Lowestoft	a					22 22																	23 45		
Needham Market	d											21 26												22 26	
Stowmarket	d				20 52						21 20	21a31						21 54						22a31	
Peterborough 8	a																								
Diss	d				21 04						21 32							22 06							
Norwich	a				21 26						21 54							22 28							

For general notes see front of timetable
For details of catering facilities see Directory of Train Operators

A To Cambridge (Table 14)
B To Bury St Edmunds (Table 14)
b Arr. 1826
c Arr. 1907

London → Chelmsford, Colchester, Walton-on-Naze, Clacton, Harwich, Ipswich and Norwich

Network diagram - see first page of Table 5

		LE	LE	LE	LE	LE	LE	LE		LE	LE	LE	LE	LE	LE	LE	LE	LE	LE	LE	LE	LE	LE
																				ThFO	ThFX		
		1	1 ◇	1	1	1		1		1	1	1	1	1 ◇	1	1	1	1	1	1	1	1 ◇	1
							A																
			☕											☕								☕	
London Liverpool Street 15 ⊖	d	21 18	21 30					21 38		21 48	22 00		22 18	22 30		22 48	23 00			23 18	23 18	23 30	23 48
Stratford 7 ⊖ ⛴	d	21 25	21u38							21 55			22 25	22u38		22 55	23 07			23 25	23 25	23u38	23 55
Romford	d																						
Shenfield 3	d	21 42						22u02		22 12	22 22		22 42			23 12	23 24			23 42	23 42		00 12
Ingatestone	d									22 16						23 16				23 46	23 46		00 16
Chelmsford 3	d	21 51	22 03					22u12		22 23	22 31		22 51	23 03		23 23	23 33			23 53	23 53	00 03	00 23
Hatfield Peverel	d									22 30						23 30							00 30
Witham 2	d	22 00						22 21		22 36	22 40		23 00			23 35	23 42		23 44	00 03	00 03		00 35
White Notley	d									22 43									23 50				
Cressing	d									22 45									23 53				
Braintree Freeport	d									22 48									23 55				
Braintree	a									22 53								⟵	23 59				
Kelvedon	d	22 05											23 05			23 40		23 40					00 40
Marks Tey 2	d	22 10					22 21	22 29					23 10			⟶		23 45					00 45
Colchester 4	a	22 18	22 22			⟵	22 30	22 37			22 54		23 18	23 22			23 56	23 57		00 17	00 21	00 23	00 57
	d	22 26	22 23			22 26		22 38			22 54	22 58	23 19	23 23			23 57			00 17		00 23	
Colchester Town	a	⟶										23 05											
	d											23 09											
Hythe	d											23 12											
Wivenhoe 3	d					22 33						23 16	23 26							00 25			
Alresford (Essex)	d					22 36						23 20	23 29							00 28			
Great Bentley	d					22 40						23 24	23 33							00 32			
Weeley	d											23 28											
Thorpe-le-Soken 1	a				⟵	22 46						23 31	23 39							00 37			
	d				22 26	22 46						23 31	23 39							00 37			
Clacton-on-Sea	a											23 41	23 48							00 51			
Kirby Cross	d				22 30	22 51																	
Frinton-on-Sea	d				22 33	22 54																	
Walton-on-the-Naze	a				22 39	23 00																	
Manningtree 2	d		22 32	22 38							23 02			23 32	23 38		00 04					00 32	
Mistley	d			22 42											23 42								
Wrabness	d			22 47											23 47								
Harwich International	d			22 54											23 54								
Dovercourt	d			22 57											23 57								
Harwich Town	a			22 59											23 59								
Ipswich	a		22 42					22 56			23 14			23 42			00 20					00 44	
	d		22 43											23 43								00 44	
Lowestoft	a																						
Needham Market	d																						
Stowmarket	d		22 54											23 54								00 55	
Peterborough 8	a																						
Diss	d		23 07											00 07								01 08	
Norwich	a		23 29											00 45								01 45	

For general notes see front of timetable
For details of catering facilities see Directory of Train Operators

A From Sudbury (Table 10)

Table 11

Saturdays

London → Chelmsford, Colchester, Walton-on-Naze, Clacton, Harwich, Ipswich and Norwich

Network diagram - see first page of Table 5

		LE	LE	LE	LE	LE	LE	LE	LE	LE	LE	LE	LE	LE		LE	LE	LE	LE	LE	LE	LE	LE	LE	LE
		1 ◇	1	1	1 ◇	1	1	1		1	1	1		1		1	1	1	1		1	1	1	1 ◇	1
									A				A							A					
		☕			☕																				
London Liverpool Street 15 ⊖	d	22p30	23p00	23p18	23p30	23p48	00 18	00 46									05 30					06 00	06 18	06 30	
Stratford 7 ⊖	d	22b38	23p07	23p25	23b38	23p55	00 25	00 55									05 37					06 07	06 25	06u38	
Romford	d																05 45					06 15			
Shenfield 3	d		23p24	23p42		00 12	00 47	01 17									05 56					06 26	06 42		
Ingatestone	d			23p46		00 16	00 51	01 21									06 00					06 30			
Chelmsford 3	d	23p03	23p33	23p53	00 03	00 23	00 58	01 28									06 07					06 37	06 51	07 02	
Hatfield Peverel	d					00 30	01 05										06 14					06 44			
Witham 2	d		23p42	00 03		00 35	01 10	01 38				05 36					06 19	06 25				06 49	07 00		
White Notley	d											05 43						06 32							
Cressing	d											05 45						06 34							
Braintree Freeport	d											05 48						06 37							
Braintree	a											05 52						06 41							
Kelvedon	d					00 40	01 15										06 24						07 05		
Marks Tey 2	d					00 45	01 20										06 29						07 10		
Colchester 4	a	23p22	23p56	00 17	00 23	00 57	01 32	02 03									06 37					07 03	07 18	07 21	
	d	23p23	23p57	00 17	00 23					05 18	05 38			06 18			06 37				06 46	07 07	07 18	07 22	
Colchester Town	a																				06 53				
	d																				06 57				
Hythe	d																				07 00				
Wivenhoe 3	d			00 25																	07 04	07 14			
Alresford (Essex)	d			00 28																	07 08				
Great Bentley	d			00 32																	07 12				
Weeley	d																				07 16				
Thorpe-le-Soken 1	a			00 37																	07 19	07 24			←
	d			00 37												06 26					07 26	07 24			07 26
Clacton-on-Sea	a			00 51																	→	07 34			
Kirby Cross	d															06 30									07 30
Frinton-on-Sea	d															06 33									07 33
Walton-on-the-Naze	a															06 38									07 39
Manningtree 2	d	23p32	00 04		00 32					05 26	05 46			06 26			06 45						07 26	07 31	
Mistley	d									05 30				06 30									07 30		
Wrabness	d									05 35				06 35									07 35		
Harwich International	d									05 44				06 44									07 44		
Dovercourt	d									05 47				06 47									07 47		
Harwich Town	a									05 49				06 49									07 49		
Ipswich	a	23p42	00 20		00 44						05 58						06 56							07 41	
	d	23p43			00 44				05 10		06 00		06 14						07 09	07 16				07 42	
Lowestoft	a																								
Needham Market	d								05 20				06 24							07 26					
Stowmarket	d	23p54			00 55				05a25		06 11		06a29						07 20	07a31				07 53	
Peterborough 8	a										07 37														
Diss	d	00 07			01 08														07 32					08 05	
Norwich	a	00 45			01 45														07 52					08 27	

For general notes see front of timetable
For details of catering facilities see Directory of Train Operators

A To Cambridge (Table 14)

b Previous night.

u Stops to pick up only

Table 11

Saturdays

London → Chelmsford, Colchester, Walton-on-Naze, Clacton, Harwich, Ipswich and Norwich

Network diagram - see first page of Table 5

		LE	LE	LE	LE	LE		LE	LE	LE	LE	LE	LE	LE	LE	LE	LE	LE	LE	LE		LE	LE	LE	LE
		1 ◇	1	1	1 ◇			1	1	1	1 ◇	1	1	1 ◇	1	1	1 ◇	1		1		1	1 ◇	1	1
						A													A						
											☕						☕						☕		
London Liverpool Street 15 ⊖	d	06 38		06 48	07 00				07 08	07 18	07 30			07 38	07 48		08 00			08 08		08 18	08 30		
Stratford 7 ⊖	d			06 55					07 15	07 25	07u38				07 55					08 15		08 25	08u38		
Romford	d								07 23											08 23					
Shenfield 3	d	07u02		07 12	07u23				07 34	07 42				08u02	08 12		08u23			08 34		08 42			
Ingatestone	d			07 16											08 16										
Chelmsford 3	d	07 12		07 23					07 43	07 51	08 02			08 12	08 23					08 43		08 51	09 02		
Hatfield Peverel	d			07 30											08 30										
Witham 2	d	07 21		07 36					07 52	08 00				08 21	08 36					08 52		09 00			
White Notley	d			07 43											08 43										
Cressing	d			07 45											08 45										
Braintree Freeport	d			07 48											08 48										
Braintree	a			07 53											08 53										
Kelvedon	d									08 05												09 05			
Marks Tey 2	d	07 29								08 10				08 29								09 10			
Colchester 4	a	07 37			07 49				08 06	08 18	08 21			08 37			08 49			09 06		09 18	09 21		
	d	07 38	07 46		07 50			08 00	08 07	08 18	08 22		08 30	08 38		08 46	08 50	09 00		09 07		09 18	09 22		09 30
Colchester Town	a		07 53					08 07					08 37			08 53		09 07							09 37
	d		07 57													08 57									
Hythe	d		08 00													09 00									
Wivenhoe 3	d		08 04						08 14							09 04				09 14					
Alresford (Essex)	d		08 08													09 08									
Great Bentley	d		08 12													09 12									
Weeley	d		08 16													09 16									
Thorpe-le-Soken 1	a		08 19						08 24			←				09 19				09 24				←	
	d		08 26						08 24			08 26				09 26				09 24				09 26	
Clacton-on-Sea	a		→						08 34							→				09 34					
Kirby Cross	d											08 30												09 30	
Frinton-on-Sea	d											08 33												09 33	
Walton-on-the-Naze	a											08 39												09 39	
Manningtree 2	d	07 46			07 59					08 26	08 31						08 59					09 26	09 31		
Mistley	d									08 30												09 30			
Wrabness	d									08 35												09 35			
Harwich International	d					07 47				08 44												09 44			
Dovercourt	d									08 47												09 47			
Harwich Town	a									08 49												09 49			
Ipswich	a	07 58			08 08	08 15					08 41			08 56			09 08						09 41		
	d	08 02			08 09	08 16					08 42			09 02			09 09		09 16				09 42		
Lowestoft	a													10 32											
Needham Market	d					08 26													09 26						
Stowmarket	d	08 13				08a31					08 53								09a31				09 53		
Peterborough 8	a	09 38																							
Diss	d				08 30						09 05						09 30						10 05		
Norwich	a				08 52						09 27						09 52						10 27		

		LE	LE	LE	LE	LE	LE	LE	LE	LE	LE	LE		LE	LE	LE	LE	LE	LE	LE	LE	LE	LE	LE	LE
		1 ◇	1	1	1 ◇	1		1	1	1 ◇	1	1		R 1	1	1	R 1	1		1	1	1 ◇	1	1	R 1
							A										B		A						
					☕					☕							☕					☕			
London Liverpool Street 15 ⊖	d	08 38	08 48		09 00			09 08	09 18	09 30				09 38	09 48		10 00			10 08	10 18	10 30			10 38
Stratford 7 ⊖	d		08 55					09 15	09 25	09u38					09 55					10 15	10 25	10u38			
Romford	d							09 23												10 23					
Shenfield 3	d	09u02	09 12		09u23			09 34	09 42					10u02	10 12		10u23			10 34	10 42				11u02
Ingatestone	d		09 16												10 16										
Chelmsford 3	d	09 12	09 23					09 43	09 51	10 02				10 12	10 23					10 43	10 51	11 02			11 12
Hatfield Peverel	d		09 30												10 30										
Witham 2	d	09 21	09 36					09 52	10 00					10 21	10 36					10 52	11 00				11 21
White Notley	d		09 43												10 43										
Cressing	d		09 45												10 45										
Braintree Freeport	d		09 48												10 48										
Braintree	a		09 53												10 53										
Kelvedon	d								10 05												11 05				
Marks Tey 2	d	09 29							10 10					10 29							11 10				11 29
Colchester 4	a	09 37			09 49			10 06	10 18	10 21				10 37			10 49			11 06	11 18	11 21			11 37
	d	09 38		09 46	09 50	10 00		10 07	10 18	10 22		10 30		10 38		10 46	10 50	11 00		11 07	11 18	11 22		11 30	11 38
Colchester Town	a			09 53		10 07						10 37				10 53		11 07						11 37	
	d			09 57												10 57									
Hythe	d			10 00												11 00									
Wivenhoe 3	d			10 04				10 14								11 04				11 14					
Alresford (Essex)	d			10 08												11 08									
Great Bentley	d			10 12												11 12									
Weeley	d			10 16												11 16									
Thorpe-le-Soken 1	a			10 19				10 24			←					11 19				11 24			←		
	d			10 26				10 24			10 26					11 26				11 24			11 26		
Clacton-on-Sea	a			→				10 34								→				11 34					
Kirby Cross	d										10 30												11 30		
Frinton-on-Sea	d										10 33												11 33		
Walton-on-the-Naze	a										10 39												11 39		
Manningtree 2	d	09 46			09 59				10 26	10 31							10 59				11 26	11 31			
Mistley	d								10 30												11 30				
Wrabness	d								10 35												11 35				
Harwich International	d								10 44												11 44				
Dovercourt	d								10 47												11 47				
Harwich Town	a								10 49												11 49				
Ipswich	a	09 58			10 08					10 41				10 56			11 08					11 41			11 56
	d	10 02			10 09		10 16			10 42				11 02			11 09		11 16			11 42			12 02
Lowestoft	a													12 32											
Needham Market	d						10 26												11 26						
Stowmarket	d	10 13					10a31			10 53									11a31			11 53			12 13
Peterborough 8	a	11 37																							13 37
Diss	d				10 30					11 05							11 30					12 05			
Norwich	a				10 52					11 27							11 52					12 27			

For general notes see front of timetable
For details of catering facilities see
Directory of Train Operators

A To Cambridge (Table 14)

B Until 26 September to Great Yarmouth (Table 15).
☕ to Norwich, until 26 September.
☕ from 3 October

London → Chelmsford, Colchester, Walton-on-Naze, Clacton, Harwich, Ipswich and Norwich

Network diagram - see first page of Table 5

		LE 1	LE 1	LE 1 ◇ ⊏P		LE 1	LE A	LE 1	LE 1	LE 1 ◇ ⊏P	LE 1	LE 1	LE R 1	LE 1	LE 1	LE R 1 B ⊏P	LE 1	LE A		LE 1	LE 1	LE 1 ◇ ⊏P	LE 1	LE 1	LE R 1
London Liverpool Street 15 ⊖	d	10 48		11 00				11 08	11 18	11 30			11 38	11 48		12 00				12 08	12 18	12 30			12 38
Stratford 7 ⊖	d	10 55						11 15	11 25	11u38				11 55						12 15	12 25	12u38			
Romford	d							11 23												12 23					
Shenfield 3	d	11 12		11u23				11 34	11 42				12u02	12 12		12u23				12 34	12 42				13u02
Ingatestone	d	11 16												12 16											
Chelmsford 3	d	11 23						11 43	11 51	12 02			12 12	12 23						12 43	12 51	13 02			13 12
Hatfield Peverel	d	11 30												12 30											
Witham 2	d	11 36						11 52	12 00				12 21	12 36						12 52	13 00				13 21
White Notley	d	11 43												12 43											
Cressing	d	11 45												12 45											
Braintree Freeport	d	11 48												12 48											
Braintree	a	11 53												12 53											
Kelvedon	d								12 05												13 05				
Marks Tey 2	d								12 10				12 29								13 10				13 29
Colchester 4	a			11 49				12 06	12 18	12 21			12 37			12 49				13 06	13 18	13 21			13 37
	d		11 46	11 50		12 00		12 07	12 18	12 22		12 30	12 38		12 46	12 50	13 00			13 07	13 18	13 22		13 30	13 38
Colchester Town	a		11 53			12 07						12 37			12 53		13 07							13 37	
	d		11 57												12 57										
Hythe	d		12 00												13 00										
Wivenhoe 3	d		12 04					12 14							13 04					13 14					
Alresford (Essex)	d		12 08												13 08										
Great Bentley	d		12 12												13 12										
Weeley	d		12 16												13 16										
Thorpe-le-Soken 1	a		12 19					12 24			←				13 19					13 24			←		
	d		12 26					12 24			12 26				13 26					13 24			13 26		
Clacton-on-Sea	a		→					12 34							→					13 34					
Kirby Cross	d										12 30												13 30		
Frinton-on-Sea	d										12 33												13 33		
Walton-on-the-Naze	a										12 39												13 39		
Manningtree 2	d			11 59					12 26	12 31						12 59					13 26	13 31			
Mistley	d								12 30												13 30				
Wrabness	d								12 35												13 35				
Harwich International	d								12 44												13 44				
Dovercourt	d								12 47												13 47				
Harwich Town	a								12 49												13 49				
Ipswich	a			12 08						12 41			12 56			13 08						13 41			13 56
	d			12 09			12 16			12 42			13 02			13 09		13 16				13 42			14 02
Lowestoft	a												14 32												
Needham Market	d						12 26											13 26							
Stowmarket	d						12a31			12 53								13a31				13 53			14 13
Peterborough 8	a																								15 37
Diss	d			12 30						13 05						13 30						14 05			
Norwich	a			12 52						13 27						13 52						14 27			

		LE 1	LE 1	LE 1 ◇ ⊏P	LE 1	LE A	LE 1	LE 1	LE 1 ◇ ⊏P	LE 1		LE 1	LE R 1	LE 1	LE 1	LE 1 ◇ ⊏P	LE 1	LE A	LE 1	LE 1	LE 1 ◇ ⊏P	LE 1	LE 1	LE 1 ◇	LE 1
London Liverpool Street 15 ⊖	d	12 48		13 00			13 08	13 18	13 30				13 38	13 48		14 00			14 08	14 18	14 30			14 38	14 48
Stratford 7 ⊖	d	12 55					13 15	13 25	13u38					13 55					14 15	14 25	14u38				14 55
Romford	d						13 23												14 23						
Shenfield 3	d	13 12		13u23			13 34	13 42					14u02	14 12		14u23			14 34	14 42				15u02	15 12
Ingatestone	d	13 16												14 16											15 16
Chelmsford 3	d	13 23					13 43	13 51	14 02				14 12	14 23					14 43	14 51	15 02			15 12	15 23
Hatfield Peverel	d	13 30												14 30											15 30
Witham 2	d	13 36					13 52	14 00					14 21	14 36					14 52	15 00				15 21	15 36
White Notley	d	13 43												14 43											15 43
Cressing	d	13 45												14 45											15 45
Braintree Freeport	d	13 48												14 48											15 48
Braintree	a	13 53												14 53											15 53
Kelvedon	d							14 05												15 05					
Marks Tey 2	d							14 10					14 29							15 10				15 29	
Colchester 4	a			13 49			14 06	14 18	14 21				14 37			14 49			15 06	15 18	15 21			15 37	
	d		13 46	13 50	14 00		14 07	14 18	14 22			14 30	14 38		14 46	14 50	15 00		15 07	15 18	15 22		15 30	15 38	
Colchester Town	a		13 53		14 07							14 37			14 53		15 07						15 37		
	d		13 57												14 57										
Hythe	d		14 00												15 00										
Wivenhoe 3	d		14 04				14 14								15 04				15 14						
Alresford (Essex)	d		14 08												15 08										
Great Bentley	d		14 12												15 12										
Weeley	d		14 16												15 16										
Thorpe-le-Soken 1	a		14 19				14 24			←					15 19				15 24			←			
	d		14 26				14 24			14 26					15 26				15 24			15 26			
Clacton-on-Sea	a		→				14 34								→				15 34						
Kirby Cross	d									14 30												15 30			
Frinton-on-Sea	d									14 33												15 33			
Walton-on-the-Naze	a									14 39												15 39			
Manningtree 2	d			13 59				14 26	14 31							14 59				15 26	15 31				
Mistley	d							14 30												15 30					
Wrabness	d							14 35												15 35					
Harwich International	d							14 44												15 44					
Dovercourt	d							14 47												15 47					
Harwich Town	a							14 49												15 49					
Ipswich	a			14 08					14 41				14 56			15 08					15 41			15 56	
	d			14 09		14 16			14 42				15 02			15 09		15 16			15 42			16 02	
Lowestoft	a												16 32												
Needham Market	d					14 26												15 26							
Stowmarket	d					14a31			14 53									15a31			15 53			16 13	
Peterborough 8	a																							17 37	
Diss	d			14 30					15 05							15 30					16 05				
Norwich	a			14 52					15 27							15 52					16 27				

For general notes see front of timetable
For details of catering facilities see
Directory of Train Operators

A To Cambridge (Table 14)
B Until 26 September to Great Yarmouth (Table 15).
⊏P to Norwich, until 26 September.
⊏P from 3 October

Table 11

Saturdays

London → Chelmsford, Colchester, Walton-on-Naze, Clacton, Harwich, Ipswich and Norwich

Network diagram - see first page of Table 5

Station																									
		LE		LE	LE	LE	LE	LE	LE	LE	LE	LE R	LE	LE	LE	LE		LE	LE	LE	LE	LE	LE	LE R	LE
		1		1 ◇	1		1	1	1 ◇	1	1	1	1	1	1 ◇	1			1	1	1 ◇	1	1	1	1
						A												A							
				☕					☕						☕						☕				
London Liverpool Street 15 ⊖	d			15 00			15 08	15 18	15 30			15 38	15 48		16 00				16 08	16 18	16 30			16 38	16 48
Stratford 7 ⊖	d						15 15	15 25	15u38				15 55						16 15	16 25	16u38				16 55
Romford	d						15 23												16 23						
Shenfield 3	d			15u23			15 34	15 42				16u02	16 12		16u23				16 34	16 42				17u02	17 12
Ingatestone	d												16 16												17 16
Chelmsford 3	d						15 43	15 51	16 02			16 12	16 23						16 43	16 51	17 02			17 12	17 23
Hatfield Peverel	d												16 30												17 30
Witham 2	d						15 52	16 00				16 21	16 36						16 52	17 00				17 21	17 36
White Notley	d												16 43												17 43
Cressing	d												16 45												17 45
Braintree Freeport	d												16 48												17 48
Braintree	a												16 53												17 53
Kelvedon	d							16 05												17 05					
Marks Tey 2	d							16 10				16 29								17 10				17 29	
Colchester 4	a			15 49			16 06	16 18	16 21			16 37			16 49				17 06	17 18	17 21			17 37	
	d	15 46		15 50	16 00		16 07	16 18	16 22		16 30	16 38		16 46	16 50	17 00			17 07	17 18	17 22		17 30	17 38	
Colchester Town	a	15 53			16 07						16 37			16 53		17 07							17 37		
	d	15 57												16 57											
Hythe	d	16 00												17 00											
Wivenhoe 3	d	16 04					16 14							17 04					17 14						
Alresford (Essex)	d	16 08												17 08											
Great Bentley	d	16 12												17 12											
Weeley	d	16 16												17 16											
Thorpe-le-Soken 1	a	16 19					16 24			←				17 19					17 24			←			
	d	16 26					16 24			16 26				17 26					17 24			17 26			
Clacton-on-Sea	a	→					16 34							→					17 34						
Kirby Cross	d									16 30												17 30			
Frinton-on-Sea	d									16 33												17 33			
Walton-on-the-Naze	a									16 39												17 39			
Manningtree 2	d			15 59				16 26	16 31						16 59					17 26	17 31				
Mistley	d							16 30												17 30					
Wrabness	d							16 35												17 35					
Harwich International	d							16 44												17 44					
Dovercourt	d							16 47												17 47					
Harwich Town	a							16 49												17 49					
Ipswich	a			16 08					16 41			16 56			17 08						17 41			17 56	
	d			16 09		16 16			16 42			17 02			17 09			17 16			17 42			18 02	
Lowestoft	a											18 32													
Needham Market	d					16 26												17 26							
Stowmarket	d					16a31			16 53						17 20			17a31			17 53			18 13	
Peterborough 8	a																							19 37	
Diss	d			16 30					17 05						17 32						18 05				
Norwich	a			16 52					17 27						17 52						18 27				

Station																									
		LE	LE	LE	LE	LE	LE	LE		LE	LE	LE	LE R	LE	LE	LE	LE	LE	LE	LE	LE	LE		LE	LE
		1	1 ◇	1		1	1	1 ◇		1	1	1	1	1	1	1 ◇	1		1	1	1 ◇	1		1	1
					A													A							
			☕					☕								☕					☕				
London Liverpool Street 15 ⊖	d		17 00			17 08	17 18	17 30				17 38	17 46	17 48		18 00			18 08	18 18	18 30				18 38
Stratford 7 ⊖	d					17 15	17 25	17u38						17 55					18 15	18 25	18u38				
Romford	d					17 23													18 23						
Shenfield 3	d		17u23			17 34	17 42					18u02		18 12		18u23			18 34	18 42					19u02
Ingatestone	d													18 16											
Chelmsford 3	d					17 43	17 51	18 02				18 11	18u16	18 23					18 43	18 51	19 02				19 11
Hatfield Peverel	d													18 30											
Witham 2	d					17 52	18 00					18 21		18 36					18 52	19 00					19 21
White Notley	d													18 43											
Cressing	d													18 45											
Braintree Freeport	d													18 48											
Braintree	a													18 53											
Kelvedon	d						18 05													19 05					
Marks Tey 2	d						18 10					18 28								19 10					19 28
Colchester 4	a		17 49			18 06	18 18	18 21				18 36	18 39			18 49			19 06	19 18	19 21				19 36
	d	17 46	17 50	18 00		18 07	18 18	18 22			18 30		18 40		18 46	18 50	19 00		19 07	19 18	19 22			19 30	
Colchester Town	a	17 53		18 07							18 37				18 53		19 07							19 37	
	d	17 57													18 57										
Hythe	d	18 00													19 00										
Wivenhoe 3	d	18 04				18 14									19 04				19 14						
Alresford (Essex)	d	18 08													19 08										
Great Bentley	d	18 12													19 12										
Weeley	d	18 16													19 16										
Thorpe-le-Soken 1	a	18 19				18 24				←					19 19				19 24			←			
	d	18 26				18 24				18 26					19 26				19 24			19 26			
Clacton-on-Sea	a	→				18 34									→				19 34						
Kirby Cross	d									18 30												19 30			
Frinton-on-Sea	d									18 33												19 33			
Walton-on-the-Naze	a									18 39												19 39			
Manningtree 2	d		17 59				18 26	18 31								18 59				19 26	19 31				
Mistley	d						18 30													19 30					
Wrabness	d						18 35													19 35					
Harwich International	d						18 44													19 44					
Dovercourt	d						18 47													19 47					
Harwich Town	a						18 49													19 49					
Ipswich	a		18 08					18 41					18 56			19 08					19 41				
	d		18 09		18 16			18 42					19 02			19 09		19 16			19 42				
Lowestoft	a												20 32												
Needham Market	d				18 26													19 26							
Stowmarket	d				18a31			18 53										19a32			19 53				
Peterborough 8	a																								
Diss	d		18 30					19 05								19 30					20 05				
Norwich	a		18 52					19 27								19 52					20 27				

For general notes see front of timetable
For details of catering facilities see Directory of Train Operators

A To Cambridge (Table 14)

London → Chelmsford, Colchester, Walton-on-Naze, Clacton, Harwich, Ipswich and Norwich

Network diagram - see first page of Table 5

		LE R 1	LE 1	LE 1	LE 1 ◊ ☕	LE A	LE 1	LE 1	LE 1 ◊ ☕	LE 1	LE R 1	LE 1	LE 1	LE 1 ◊ ☕		LE 1	LE 1	LE	LE 1	LE 1 ◊ ☕	LE 1	LE 1	LE	LE 1	LE 1 ◊
London Liverpool Street 15 ⊖	d	18 46	18 48		19 00		19 08	19 18	19 30		19 38		19 48	20 00		20 08			20 18	20 30	20 38	20 48			21 00
Stratford 7 ⊖ ⛴	d		18 55				19 15	19 25	19u38				19 55			20 15			20 25	20u38	20 45	20 55			
Romford	d						19 23									20 23									
Shenfield 3	d		19 12		19u23		19 34	19 42			20u02		20 12	20u23		20 34			20 42		21 02	21 12			21u23
Ingatestone	d		19 16										20 16									21 16			
Chelmsford 3	d	19u16	19 23				19 43	19 51	20 03		20 12		20 23			20 43			20 51	21 03	21 12	21 23			
Hatfield Peverel	d		19 30										20 30									21 30			
Witham 2	d		19 36				19 52	20 00			20 21		20 36			20 52			21 00		21 21	21 36			
White Notley	d		19 43										20 43									21 43			
Cressing	d		19 45										20 45									21 45			
Braintree Freeport	d		19 48										20 48									21 48			
Braintree	a		19 53										20 53									21 53			
Kelvedon	d							20 05											21 05						
Marks Tey 2	d							20 10			20 29								21 10		21 29				
Colchester 4	a	19 39			19 49		20 06	20 18	20 22		20 37			20 49		21 06			21 18	21 22	21 37				21 49
	d	19 40		19 46	19 50		20 07	20 18	20 23		20 38	20 46		20 50		21 07			21 18	21 23	21 38			21 46	21 50
Colchester Town	a			19 53								20 53												21 53	
	d			19 57								20 57												21 57	
Hythe	d			20 00								21 00												22 00	
Wivenhoe 3	d			20 04			20 14					21 04				21 14								22 04	
Alresford (Essex)	d			20 08								21 08												22 08	
Great Bentley	d			20 12								21 12												22 12	
Weeley	d			20 16								21 16												22 16	
Thorpe-le-Soken 1	a			20 19			20 24			←		21 19				21 24	←							22 19	
	d			20 26			20 24			20 26		21 26				21 24	21 26							22 26	
Clacton-on-Sea	a			→			20 34					→				21 34								→	
Kirby Cross	d									20 30							21 30								
Frinton-on-Sea	d									20 33							21 33								
Walton-on-the-Naze	a									20 39							21 39								
Manningtree 2	d				19 59			20 26	20 32					20 59					21 26	21 32	21 46				21 58
Mistley	d							20 30											21 30						
Wrabness	d							20 35											21 35				←		
Harwich International	d							20 44										21 34	21 44		22a02		21 34		
Dovercourt	d							20 47										→	21 47						
Harwich Town	a							20 49											21 49						
Ipswich	a	19 56			20 08				20 42		20 56			21 08						21 42			22 00		22 09
	d	20 02			20 09	20 16			20 43		21 02			21 09						21 43					22 15
Lowestoft	a										22 32														23 45
Needham Market	d					20 26																			
Stowmarket	d	20 13				20a31			20 54											21 54					
Peterborough 8	a	21 37																							
Diss	d				20 30				21 06					21 30						22 06					
Norwich	a				20 52				21 28					21 52						22 28					

		LE B	LE 1	LE 1	LE 1 ◊ ☕	LE C		LE 1	LE 1	LE 1	LE 1	LE 1	LE 1	LE 1	LE 1 ◊ ☕	LE 1	LE 1	LE 1	LE 1	LE 1		LE 1 ◊ ☕	LE 1		
London Liverpool Street 15 ⊖	d		21 04	21 18	21 30					21 34		21 48	22 00	22 18	22 30		22 48	23 00		23 18		23 30	23 48		
Stratford 7 ⊖ ⛴	d		21 11	21 25								21 55	22 07	22 25			22 55	23 07		23 25			23 55		
Romford	d		21 19																						
Shenfield 3	d		21 34	21 46						22u02		22 16	22 28	22 46			23 16	23 28		23 46			00 16		
Ingatestone	d											22 20					23 20			23 50			00 20		
Chelmsford 3	d		21 43	21 55	22 04					22 12		22 27	22 37	22 55	23 04		23 27	23 37		23 57		00 04	00 27		
Hatfield Peverel	d											22 34					23 34						00 34		
Witham 2	d		21 52	22 04						22 21		22 40	22 46	23 04			23 39	23 46	23 48	00 07			00 39		
White Notley	d											22 47							23 54						
Cressing	d											22 49							23 57						
Braintree Freeport	d											22 52							23 59						
Braintree	a											22 57							00 03						
Kelvedon	d			22 09										23 09			23 44						00 44		
Marks Tey 2	d			22 14		22 21				22 29				23 14			23 49						00 49		
Colchester 4	a		22 06	22 22	22 25	22 30				22 37			23 00	23 22	23 25		00 01	00 01		00 25		00 28	01 01		
	d		22 07		22 26					22 38	22 46		23 00	23 23	23 26			00 01				00 29			
Colchester Town	a										22 53														
	d										22 57														
Hythe	d										23 00														
Wivenhoe 3	d		22 14								23 04			23 30											
Alresford (Essex)	d										23 08			23 33											
Great Bentley	d										23 12			23 37											
Weeley	d										23 16														
Thorpe-le-Soken 1	a		22 24						←		23 19			23 43											
	d		22 24						22 26		23 19			23 43											
Clacton-on-Sea	a		22 34								23 29			23 52											
Kirby Cross	d								22 30																
Frinton-on-Sea	d								22 33																
Walton-on-the-Naze	a								22 39																
Manningtree 2	d				22 35			22 38					23 08		23 35	23 38		00 08				00 38			
Mistley	d							22 42								23 42									
Wrabness	d							22 47								23 47									
Harwich International	d							22 54								23 54									
Dovercourt	d							22 57								23 57									
Harwich Town	a							22 59								23 59									
Ipswich	a				22 45					22 56			23 20		23 45			00 24				00 48			
	d	22 17			22 46										23 46							00 50			
Lowestoft	a																								
Needham Market	d	22 27																							
Stowmarket	d	22a32			22 57										23 57							01 01			
Peterborough 8	a																								
Diss	d				23 10										00 10							01 14			
Norwich	a				23 32										00 32							01 36			

For general notes see front of timetable
For details of catering facilities see Directory of Train Operators

A To Cambridge (Table 14)
B To Bury St Edmunds (Table 14)
C From Sudbury (Table 10)

Table 11

Sundays

London → Chelmsford, Colchester, Walton-on-Naze, Clacton, Harwich, Ipswich and Norwich

Network diagram - see first page of Table 5

		LE	LE	LE	LE	LE	LE	LE	LE	LE	LE	LE	LE	LE	LE	LE	LE	LE	LE	LE	LE	LE
		1 ◇	1	1	1 ◇	1	1	1	1	1	1			1	1	1	1	1	1	1 ◇	1	1
									A			B	C									
		☕			☕																	
London Liverpool Street 15 ⊖	d	22p30	23p00	23p18	23p30	23p48	00 18											08 02		08 30	08 32	
Stratford 7 ⊖ ⛴	d		23p07	23p25		23p55	00 25											08 09			08 39	
Romford	d																					
Shenfield 3	d		23p28	23p46		00 16	00 47											08 31		08u57	09 01	
Ingatestone	d			23p50		00 20	00 51											08 35				
Chelmsford 3	d	23p04	23p37	23p57	00 04	00 27	00 58											08 42			09 10	
Hatfield Peverel	d					00 34	01 05											08 49				
Witham 2	d		23p46	00 07		00 39	01 10	07 33								08 23		08 54			09 19	09 23
White Notley	d							07 39								08 29						09 29
Cressing	d							07 42								08 32						09 32
Braintree Freeport	d							07 44								08 34						09 34
Braintree	a							07 48								08 38						09 38
Kelvedon	d					00 44	01 15											08 59				
Marks Tey 2	d					00 49	01 20											09 04			09 27	
Colchester 4	a	23p25	00 01	00 25	00 28	01 01	01 32											09 12		09 23	09 35	
	d	23p26	00 01		00 29					07 40	08 12			08 18	08 35			09 12		09 24	09 35	
Colchester Town	a																					
	d																					
Hythe	d																					
Wivenhoe 3	d														08 43						09 43	
Alresford (Essex)	d														08 46						09 46	
Great Bentley	d														08 50						09 50	
Weeley	d																					
Thorpe-le-Soken 1	a														08 55						09 55	
	d														08 55		08 57				09 55	
Clacton-on-Sea	a														09 07						10 05	
Kirby Cross	d																09 01					
Frinton-on-Sea	d																09 04					
Walton-on-the-Naze	a																09 09					
Manningtree 2	d	23p35	00 08		00 38					07 48	08 20			08 26				09 20	09 26	09 33		
Mistley	d													08 30					09 30			
Wrabness	d													08 35					09 35			
Harwich International	d												08 30	08 42					09 42			
Dovercourt	d													08 45					09 45			
Harwich Town	a													08 47					09 47			
Ipswich	a	23p45	00 24		00 48					08 00	08 32		08 55					09 32		09 42		
	d	23p46			00 50				07 55			08 45	09 02							09 44		
Lowestoft	a																					
Needham Market	d												09 12									
Stowmarket	d	23p57			01 01				08 07			08a58	09a17							09 55		
Peterborough 8	a								09 36													
Diss	d	00 10			01 14															10 07		
Norwich	a	00 32			01 36															10 29		

For general notes see front of timetable
For details of catering facilities see Directory of Train Operators

A Until 6 September
B To Bury St Edmunds (Table 14)
C To Cambridge (Table 14)

Sundays

London → Chelmsford, Colchester, Walton-on-Naze, Clacton, Harwich, Ipswich and Norwich

Network diagram - see first page of Table 5

		LE 1	LE 1	LE 1	LE 1	LE 1 ◇ ☕		LE 1	LE 1	LE A	LE 1	LE 1	LE 1		LE 1 ◇ ☕	LE 1	LE 1	LE 1	LE 1	LE 1		LE 1	LE 1 ◇ ☕	LE 1	LE 1
London Liverpool Street 15 ⊖	d			09 02		09 30		09 32				10 02			10 30	10 32				11 02			11 30	11 32	
Stratford 7 ⊖ ⛴	d			09 09				09 39				10 09				10 39				11 09				11 39	
Romford	d																								
Shenfield 3	d			09 31		09u57		10 01				10 31			10u57	11 01				11 31			11u57	12 01	
Ingatestone	d			09 35								10 35								11 35					
Chelmsford 3	d			09 42				10 10				10 42				11 10				11 42				12 10	
Hatfield Peverel	d			09 49								10 49								11 49					
Witham 2	d			09 54				10 19	10 23			10 54				11 19	11 23			11 54				12 19	12 23
White Notley	d								10 29								11 29								12 29
Cressing	d								10 32								11 32								12 32
Braintree Freeport	d								10 34								11 34								12 34
Braintree	a								10 38								11 38								12 38
Kelvedon	d			09 59								10 59								11 59					
Marks Tey 2	d			10 04				10 27				11 04				11 27				12 04				12 27	
Colchester 4	a			10 12		10 23		10 35				11 12			11 23	11 35				12 12			12 23	12 35	
	d			10 12		10 24		10 35				11 12			11 24	11 35				12 12			12 24	12 35	
Colchester Town	a																								
	d																								
Hythe	d																								
Wivenhoe 3	d							10 43								11 43								12 43	
Alresford (Essex)	d							10 46								11 46								12 46	
Great Bentley	d							10 50								11 50								12 50	
Weeley	d																								
Thorpe-le-Soken 1	a							10 55								11 55								12 55	
	d		09 57					10 55			10 57					11 55			11 57					12 55	
Clacton-on-Sea	a							11 05								12 05								13 05	
Kirby Cross	d		10 01								11 01								12 01						
Frinton-on-Sea	d		10 04								11 04								12 04						
Walton-on-the-Naze	a		10 09								11 09								12 09						
Manningtree 2	d			10 20	10 26	10 33						11 20	11 26		11 33					12 20		12 26	12 33		
Mistley	d				10 30								11 30									12 30			
Wrabness	d				10 35								11 35									12 35			
Harwich International	d				10 42								11 42									12 42			
Dovercourt	d				10 45								11 45									12 45			
Harwich Town	a				10 47								11 47									12 47			
Ipswich	a			10 32		10 42						11 32			11 42					12 32			12 42		
	d	09 55				10 44				11 02					11 44			11 55					12 44		
Lowestoft	a																								
Needham Market	d									11 12															
Stowmarket	d	10 07				10 55				11a17					11 55			12 07					12 55		
Peterborough 8	a	11 36																13 36							
Diss	d					11 07									12 07								13 07		
Norwich	a					11 29									12 29								13 29		

		LE A	LE 1	LE 1	LE 1		LE 1 ◇ ☕	LE 1	LE 1	LE 1	LE 1	LE 1		LE 1	LE 1 ◇ ☕	LE 1	LE 1	LE A	LE 1		LE 1	LE 1	LE 1 ◇ ☕	LE 1	LE 1
London Liverpool Street 15 ⊖	d			12 02			12 30	12 32				13 02			13 30	13 32					14 02		14 30	14 32	
Stratford 7 ⊖ ⛴	d			12 09				12 39				13 09				13 39					14 09			14 39	
Romford	d																								
Shenfield 3	d			12 31			12u57	13 01				13 31			13u57	14 01					14 31		14u57	15 01	
Ingatestone	d			12 35								13 35									14 35				
Chelmsford 3	d			12 42				13 10				13 42				14 10					14 42			15 10	
Hatfield Peverel	d			12 49								13 49									14 49				
Witham 2	d			12 54				13 19	13 23			13 54				14 19	14 23				14 54			15 19	15 23
White Notley	d								13 29								14 29								15 29
Cressing	d								13 32								14 32								15 32
Braintree Freeport	d								13 34								14 34								15 34
Braintree	a								13 38								14 38								15 38
Kelvedon	d			12 59								13 59									14 59				
Marks Tey 2	d			13 04				13 27				14 04				14 27					15 04			15 27	
Colchester 4	a			13 12			13 23	13 35				14 12			14 23	14 35					15 12		15 23	15 35	
	d			13 12			13 24	13 35				14 12			14 24	14 35					15 12		15 24	15 35	
Colchester Town	a																								
	d																								
Hythe	d																								
Wivenhoe 3	d							13 43								14 43								15 43	
Alresford (Essex)	d							13 46								14 46								15 46	
Great Bentley	d							13 50								14 50								15 50	
Weeley	d																								
Thorpe-le-Soken 1	a							13 55								14 55								15 55	
	d		12 57					13 55			13 57					14 55			14 57					15 55	
Clacton-on-Sea	a							14 05								15 05								16 05	
Kirby Cross	d		13 01								14 01								15 01						
Frinton-on-Sea	d		13 04								14 04								15 04						
Walton-on-the-Naze	a		13 09								14 09								15 09						
Manningtree 2	d			13 20	13 26		13 33					14 20		14 26	14 33						15 20	15 26	15 33		
Mistley	d				13 30									14 30								15 30			
Wrabness	d				13 35									14 35								15 35			
Harwich International	d				13 42									14 42								15 42			
Dovercourt	d				13 45									14 45								15 45			
Harwich Town	a				13 47									14 47								15 47			
Ipswich	a			13 32			13 42					14 32			14 42						15 32		15 42		
	d	13 02					13 44			13 55					14 44			15 02					15 44		
Lowestoft	a																								
Needham Market	d	13 12																15 12							
Stowmarket	d	13a17					13 55			14 07					14 55			15a17					15 55		
Peterborough 8	a									15 36															
Diss	d						14 07								15 07								16 07		
Norwich	a						14 29								15 29								16 29		

For general notes see front of timetable
For details of catering facilities see Directory of Train Operators

A To Cambridge (Table 14)

Sundays

London → Chelmsford, Colchester, Walton-on-Naze, Clacton, Harwich, Ipswich and Norwich

Network diagram - see first page of Table 5

		LE 1	LE 1	LE 1	LE 1	LE 1 ◇ ☕	LE 1	LE 1	LE A	LE 1	LE 1	LE 1	LE 1 ◇ ☕	LE 1	LE 1	LE 1	LE 1	LE 1	LE 1	LE 1 ◇ ☕	LE 1	LE 1
London Liverpool Street 15 ⊖	d			15 02		15 30	15 32				16 02		16 30	16 32				17 02		17 30	17 32	
Stratford 7 ⊖ ⛴	d			15 09			15 39				16 09			16 39				17 09			17 39	
Romford	d																					
Shenfield 3	d			15 31		15u57	16 01				16 31		16u57	17 01				17 31		17u57	18 01	
Ingatestone	d			15 35							16 35							17 35				
Chelmsford 3	d			15 42			16 10				16 42			17 10				17 42			18 10	
Hatfield Peverel	d			15 49							16 49							17 49				
Witham 2	d			15 54			16 19	16 23			16 54			17 19	17 23			17 54			18 19	18 23
White Notley	d							16 29							17 29							18 29
Cressing	d							16 32							17 32							18 32
Braintree Freeport	d							16 34							17 34							18 34
Braintree	a							16 38							17 38							18 38
Kelvedon	d			15 59							16 59							17 59				
Marks Tey 2	d			16 04			16 27				17 04			17 27				18 04			18 27	
Colchester 4	a			16 12		16 23	16 35				17 12		17 23	17 35				18 12		18 23	18 35	
	d			16 12		16 24	16 35				17 12		17 24	17 35				18 12		18 24	18 35	
Colchester Town	a																					
	d																					
Hythe	d																					
Wivenhoe 3	d						16 43							17 43							18 43	
Alresford (Essex)	d						16 46							17 46							18 46	
Great Bentley	d						16 50							17 50							18 50	
Weeley	d																					
Thorpe-le-Soken 1	a						16 55							17 55							18 55	
	d		15 57				16 55			16 57				17 55			17 57				18 55	
Clacton-on-Sea	a						17 05							18 05							19 05	
Kirby Cross	d		16 01							17 01							18 01					
Frinton-on-Sea	d		16 04							17 04							18 04					
Walton-on-the-Naze	a		16 09							17 09							18 09					
Manningtree 2	d			16 20	16 26	16 33					17 20	17 26	17 33					18 20	18 26	18 33		
Mistley	d				16 30							17 30							18 30			
Wrabness	d				16 35							17 35							18 35			
Harwich International	d				16 42							17 42							18 42			
Dovercourt	d				16 45							17 45							18 45			
Harwich Town	a				16 47							17 47							18 47			
Ipswich	a			16 32		16 42					17 32		17 42					18 32		18 42		
	d	15 55				16 44			17 02				17 44			17 55				18 44		
Lowestoft	a																					
Needham Market	d								17 12													
Stowmarket	d	16 07				16 55			17a17				17 55			18 07				18 55		
Peterborough 8	a	17 31														19 32						
Diss	d					17 07							18 07							19 07		
Norwich	a					17 29							18 29							19 29		

		LE A	LE 1	LE 1	LE 1	LE 1 ◇ ☕	LE 1	LE 1 ◇ ☕	LE 1	LE 1	LE 1	LE 1	LE 1 ◇ ☕	LE 1	LE 1	LE A	LE 1	LE	LE 1	LE 1	LE	LE 1
London Liverpool Street 15 ⊖	d			18 02		18 30	18 32	19 00			19 02		19 30	19 32					20 00	20 02		
Stratford 7 ⊖ ⛴	d			18 09			18 39				19 09			19 39						20 09		
Romford	d																					
Shenfield 3	d			18 31		18u57	19 01				19 31		19u57	20 01					20 27	20 31		
Ingatestone	d			18 35							19 35									20 35		
Chelmsford 3	d			18 42			19 10				19 42			20 10					20 37	20 42		
Hatfield Peverel	d			18 49							19 49									20 49		
Witham 2	d			18 54			19 19		19 23		19 54			20 19	20 23					20 54		
White Notley	d								19 29						20 29							
Cressing	d								19 32						20 32							
Braintree Freeport	d								19 34						20 34							
Braintree	a								19 38						20 38							
Kelvedon	d			18 59							19 59									20 59		
Marks Tey 2	d			19 04			19 27				20 04			20 27						21 04		
Colchester 4	a			19 12		19 23	19 35				20 12		20 23	20 35					20 55	21 12		
	d			19 12		19 24	19 35				20 12		20 24	20 35					20 56	21 12		
Colchester Town	a																					
	d																					
Hythe	d																					
Wivenhoe 3	d						19 43							20 43								
Alresford (Essex)	d						19 46							20 46								
Great Bentley	d						19 50							20 50								
Weeley	d																					
Thorpe-le-Soken 1	a						19 55							20 55								
	d		18 57				19 55			19 57				20 55			20 57					
Clacton-on-Sea	a						20 05							21 05								
Kirby Cross	d		19 01							20 01							21 01					
Frinton-on-Sea	d		19 04							20 04							21 04					
Walton-on-the-Naze	a		19 09							20 09							21 09					
Manningtree 2	d			19 20	19 26	19 33					20 20	20 26	20 33						21 04	21 20		21 26
Mistley	d				19 30							20 30										21 30
Wrabness	d				19 35							20 35									←	21 35
Harwich International	d				19 42							20 42						21 10 →	21a22		21 10	21 42
Dovercourt	d				19 45							20 45										21 45
Harwich Town	a				19 47							20 47										21 47
Ipswich	a			19 32		19 42		20 04			20 32		20 42							21 32	21 37	
	d	19 02				19 44		20 06					20 44			21 02						
Lowestoft	a																					
Needham Market	d	19 12														21 12						
Stowmarket	d	19a17				19 55		20 17					20 55			21a17						
Peterborough 8	a																					
Diss	d					20 07		20 29					21 07									
Norwich	a					20 29		20 51					21 29									

For general notes see front of timetable
For details of catering facilities see
Directory of Train Operators

A To Cambridge (Table 14)

Table 11

Sundays

London → Chelmsford, Colchester, Walton-on-Naze, Clacton, Harwich, Ipswich and Norwich

Network diagram - see first page of Table 5

		LE		LE	LE	LE	LE	LE	LE		LE	LE	LE	LE	LE	LE		LE	LE	LE	LE	LE			
		1 ◇		1	1	1		1	1		1 ◇	1	1	1	1	1 ◇		1	1	1	1 ◇	1			
							A																		
London Liverpool Street 15 ⊖	d	20 30		20 32				21 02			21 30	21 32			22 02	22 30		22 32		23 02	23 30	23 32			
Stratford 7 ⊖	d			20 39				21 09				21 39			22 09			22 39		23 09		23 39			
Romford	d																								
Shenfield 3	d	20u57		21 01				21 31			21u57	22 01			22 31	22u57		23 01		23 31	23u57	00 01			
Ingatestone	d							21 35							22 35					23 35					
Chelmsford 3	d			21 10				21 42				22 10			22 42			23 10		23 42		00 10			
Hatfield Peverel	d							21 49							22 49					23 49					
Witham 2	d			21 19	21 23			21 54				22 19	22 23		22 54			23 19	23 23	23 54		00 19			
White Notley	d				21 29								22 29						23 29						
Cressing	d				21 32								22 32						23 32						
Braintree Freeport	d				21 34								22 34						23 34						
Braintree	a				21 38								22 38						23 38						
Kelvedon	d							21 59							22 59					23 59					
Marks Tey 2	d			21 27			22 00	22 04				22 27			23 04			23 27		00 04		00 27			
Colchester 4	a	21 23		21 35			22 09	22 12			22 23	22 35			23 12	23 23		23 35		00 12	00 27	00 40			
	d	21 24		21 35				22 12			22 24	22 35			23 12	23 24		23 35		00 12	00 28				
Colchester Town	a																								
	d																								
Hythe	d																								
Wivenhoe 3	d			21 43								22 43						23 43							
Alresford (Essex)	d			21 46								22 46						23 46							
Great Bentley	d			21 50								22 50						23 50							
Weeley	d																								
Thorpe-le-Soken 1	a			21 55								22 55						23 55							
	d			21 55		21 57						22 55		22 57				23 55							
Clacton-on-Sea	a			22 05								23 05						00 05							
Kirby Cross	d					22 01								23 01											
Frinton-on-Sea	d					22 04								23 04											
Walton-on-the-Naze	a					22 09								23 09											
Manningtree 2	d	21 33						22 20	22 26		22 33				23 20	23 33				00 20	00 37				
Mistley	d								22 30																
Wrabness	d								22 35																
Harwich International	d								22 42																
Dovercourt	d								22 45																
Harwich Town	a								22 47																
Ipswich	a	21 42						22 32			22 42				23 32	23 42				00 36	00 46				
	d	21 44									22 44					23 44					00 48				
Lowestoft	a																								
Needham Market	d																								
Stowmarket	d	21 55									22 55					23 55					00 59				
Peterborough 8	a																								
Diss	d	22 07									23 07					00 07					01 11				
Norwich	a	22 29									23 29					00 39					01 43				

For general notes see front of timetable
For details of catering facilities see Directory of Train Operators

A From Sudbury (Table 10)

Norwich, Ipswich, Harwich, Clacton, Walton-on-Naze, Colchester and Chelmsford → London

Network diagram - see first page of Table 5

Miles	Miles	Miles	Miles	Miles			LE MX [1]	LE MO A	LE [1]	LE [1]	LE [1] ◊	LE [1]	LE [1]	LE [1]	LE [1]	LE [1]	LE [R] [1] ☕	LE [1]	LE B	LE [1]	LE [1]	LE [R] [1] ☕	LE [1]	LE [1]	LE [1]
0	—	—	—	—	**Norwich**	d											05 10					05 40			
20	—	—	—	—	Diss	d											05 28					05 58			
—	—	—	—	—	**Peterborough** [8]	d																			
34¼	—	—	—	—	Stowmarket	d		00 04									05 40		05 57			06 10			
38	—	—	—	—	Needham Market	d		00 09											06 03						
—	—	—	—	—	**Lowestoft**	d																			
46¼	—	—	—	—	**Ipswich**	a		00 21									05 51		06 15			06 21			
—	—	—	—	—		d					05 23						05 53					06 23			
—	0	—	—	—	**Harwich Town**	d									05 37										
—	½	—	—	—	Dovercourt	d									05 39										
—	1¾	—	—	—	Harwich International	d									05 42										
—	5½	—	—	—	Wrabness	d									05 48										
—	9½	—	—	—	Mistley	d									05 53										
55½	11¼	—	—	—	Manningtree [2]	d					05 33				05a58		06 03					06 33			
—	—	0	—	—	**Walton-on-the-Naze**	d								05 38							06 10				
—	—	1¼	—	—	Frinton-on-Sea	d								05 41							06 13				
—	—	2½	—	—	Kirby Cross	d								05 44							06 16				
—	—	—	0	—	**Clacton-on-Sea**	d							05 20					05 44							06 17
—	—	5	4¾	—	Thorpe-le-Soken [1]	a							05 27	05 50				05 51			06 22				06 25
—	—	—	—	—		d							05 27					05 51							06 25
—	—	7¼	—	—	Weeley	d												05 55							
—	—	10	—	—	Great Bentley	d												05 59							
—	—	12¼	—	—	Alresford (Essex)	d												06 03							
—	—	14	—	—	Wivenhoe [3]	d							05 38					06 06							06 36
—	—	16½	—	—	Hythe	d												06 10							06 40
—	—	18	—	—	Colchester Town	a																			
—	—	—	—	—		d														06 21					
63¼	0	19¾	—	—	**Colchester** [4]	a					05 43		05 47				06 13	06 17		06 28		06 43			06 47
—	—	—	—	—		d			04 45	05 21	05 43		05 48				06 15	06 18		06 29		06 45			06 48
68½	—	—	—	—	Marks Tey [2]	d			04 51	05 27			05 54							06 35					06 54
72¾	—	—	—	—	Kelvedon	d			04 56	05 32			06 00					06 28		06 41					07 00
—	—	—	—	0	**Braintree**	d	00 03					05 45												06 42	
—	—	—	—	¾	Braintree Freeport	d	00 05					05 47												06 44	
—	—	—	—	2	Cressing	d	00 08					05 50												06 47	
—	—	—	—	3½	White Notley	d	00 11					05 53												06 50	
76½	—	—	—	6¼	**Witham** [2]	d	00a18		05 01	05 37	05 56	06a01	06 05			06 15	06 27	06 33		06 46				06 58	07 05
79	—	—	—	—	Hatfield Peverel	d			05 05	05 41						06 19								07 02	
85¼	—	—	—	—	**Chelmsford** [3]	d			05 12	05 48	06 05		06 14			06 26		06 42		06 55			07 03	07 09	07 14
91½	—	—	—	—	Ingatestone	d			05 19	05 55						06 33		06 48					07 10		
94¾	—	—	—	—	Shenfield [3]	a			05 25	06 01			06 25			06 39				07 06			07 16	07 20	
102¾	—	—	—	—	Romford	a																			
111¾	—	—	—	—	Stratford [7] ⊖ ⛴	a			05s44	06s18	06s29		06s41			06s56	06s59	07s08				07s26	07s33	07s37	07s40
115	—	—	—	—	**London Liverpool Street** [15] ⊖	a			05 57	06 27	06 41		06 49			07 07	07 10	07 20		07 33		07 37	07 44	07 48	07 51

		LE [1]	LE [1]	LE [1]	LE [1]	LE [1]	LE [1]	LE [R] [1] ☕	LE [1]	LE [1]	LE [1]	LE [1]	LE [1]	LE [1]	LE B	LE [R] [1] ☕	LE [1]	LE [1]	LE [1]	LE [1]	LE [1]	LE [1]	LE [R] [1] ☕		LE [1]
Norwich	d							06 10								06 25							06 40		
Diss	d							06 28								06 43							06 58		
Peterborough [8]	d																								
Stowmarket	d							06 40							06 44	06 55							07 10		
Needham Market	d																								
Lowestoft	d																								
Ipswich	a							06 51							07 00	07 06							07 21		
	d		06 38					06 53							07 00	07 08							07 23		
Harwich Town	d	06 22												07 08											
Dovercourt	d	06 24												07 10											
Harwich International	d	06 27											07 10	07 13	07a25										
Wrabness	d	06 33												07 19											
Mistley	d	06 38												07 24							←				
Manningtree [2]	d	06 43	06 48					07 03					07b25 →	07a29		07 18					07 25		07 33		
Walton-on-the-Naze	d						06 43													07 04					
Frinton-on-Sea	d						06 46													07 07					
Kirby Cross	d						06 49													07 10					
Clacton-on-Sea	d			06 34		06 38				06 47									07 04						
Thorpe-le-Soken [1]	a			06 42		06 46	06 54			06 55	←								07 12	07 16					
	d			06 42		06 46	07 01 →			06 55	07 01								07 12						
Weeley	d					06 50					07 05														
Great Bentley	d					06 53					07 08														
Alresford (Essex)	d					06 58					07 13														
Wivenhoe [3]	d			06 53		07 01				07 06	07 16								07 23			←			
Hythe	d					07 05				07 10	07 20 →											07 20			
Colchester Town	a					07 09						←										07 24			
	d				06 59	07 13 →						07 13										07 28			
Colchester [4]	a	06 53	06 58	07 02	07 06			07 13		07 17		07 22				07 28			07 32		07 37	07 38	07 43		
	d		06 59	07 03	07 07			07 15		07 18						07 30			07 33		07 37		07 45		
Marks Tey [2]	d				07 13					07 24											07 43				
Kelvedon	d			07 13						07 30									07 43						
Braintree	d																	07 27							
Braintree Freeport	d																	07 29							
Cressing	d																	07 32							
White Notley	d								←									07 35							←
Witham [2]	d		07 11	07 18	07b28 →				07 28	07 35								07 43	07 48		07c58 →				07 58
Hatfield Peverel	d								07 32																08 02
Chelmsford [3]	d		07 20	07 27					07 39								07 49	07 53	07 57						08 09
Ingatestone	d		07 26														07 56								
Shenfield [3]	a		07 32	07 38					07 50								08 02		08 08						08 20
Romford	a																								
Stratford [7] ⊖ ⛴	a			07s55						08s09									08s25						
London Liverpool Street [15] ⊖	a		07 59	08 06				08 09	08 16	08 20						08 23	08 28	08 30	08 36				08 39		08 48

For general notes see front of timetable
For details of catering facilities see Directory of Train Operators

A From Cambridge (Table 14)
B From Bury St Edmunds (Table 14)
b Arr. 0722
c Arr. 0752

Norwich, Ipswich, Harwich, Clacton, Walton-on-Naze, Colchester and Chelmsford → London

Network diagram - see first page of Table 5

		LE	LE	LE	LE	LE	LE	LE	LE	LE	LE	LE	LE	LE	LE	LE	LE	LE	LE	LE	LE	LE	LE	LE	LE
				R					R							R									
		1	1	1		1	1	1	1	1	1	1	1		1	1	1	1 ◇	1	1	1	1	1 ◇	1	1
					A									B		C									
				☕					☕									☕					☕		
Norwich	d			06 55					07 10							07 30		07 40					08 00		
Diss	d			07 13					07 28									07 58					08 17		
Peterborough 8	d																								
Stowmarket	d			07 25					07 40					07 45				08 10					08 29		
Needham Market	d													07 50											
Lowestoft	d																								
Ipswich	a			07 36					07 51					08 02		08 07		08 22					08 40		
	d			07 38					07 53							08 18		08 23					08 42		
Harwich Town	d																08 00								
Dovercourt	d																08 02								
Harwich International	d				07 47												08 06								
Wrabness	d				07 53												08 12								
Mistley	d				07a59												08 17								
Manningtree 2	d			07 48					08 03								08 22	08 33					08 52		
Walton-on-the-Naze	d		07 40												08 09							08 45			
Frinton-on-Sea	d		07 43												08 12							08 48			
Kirby Cross	d		07 46												08 15							08 51			
Clacton-on-Sea	d	07 09									07 45									08 15					08 50
Thorpe-le-Soken 1	a	07 17	07 51								07 52		←		08 21					08 22		08 56			08 57
	d	07 17	07 56								07 52		07 56							08 22		09 01			08 57
Weeley	d	07 21	→										08 00									→			
Great Bentley	d	07 24											08 03							08 28					
Alresford (Essex)	d	07 28											08 08							08 32					
Wivenhoe 3	d	07 32									08 03		08 11							08 35					09 07
Hythe	d	07 36											08 15												
Colchester Town	a												08 19												
	d							08 02				←	08 23									08 45			
Colchester 4	a	07 44		07 58				08 09	08 13		08 16	08 09	08 32				08 32	08 43		08 44	08 52		09 01		09 17
	d	07 49		08 00			08 03	→	08 15		08 18						08 37	08 45		08 48			09 03		09 17
Marks Tey 2	d						08 09				08 24									08 54					09 23
Kelvedon	d	07 59					08 15				08 30									09 00					09 29
Braintree	d									08 12														09 00	
Braintree Freeport	d									08 14														09 02	
Cressing	d									08 17														09 05	
White Notley	d									08 20														09 08	
Witham 2	d	08 04					08 20			08 28	08 35						08 49		08 58	09 05				09 15	09 34
Hatfield Peverel	d									08 32									09 02					09 20	
Chelmsford 3	d	08 13				08 19	08 29			08 39	08 44						08 58	09 02	09 09	09 14				09 27	09 43
Ingatestone	d					08 26				08 46									09 16					09 33	
Shenfield 3	a					08 32	08 40			08 52	08 55								09 22	09 25			09s29	09 40	09 54
Romford	a																							09 48	
Stratford 7 ⊖ ⛴	a	08s39				08s49			08s59	09s09								09s28	09s39					09s57	10s08
London Liverpool Street 15 ⊖	a	08 50		08 55		09 01	09 06		09 10	09 20	09 22					09 25	09 33	09 40	09 50	09 52			09 56	10 05	10 17

		LE	LE	LE	LE	LE	LE	LE	LE	LE	LE	LE	LE	LE	LE	LE	LE	LE		LE	LE	LE	LE	LE	LE
				R				R			R									R					
		1		1	1	1	1	1	1	1	1	1	1	1		1 ◇	1	1		1	1	1	1 ◇	1	1
			B												B										
				☕							☕					☕							☕		
Norwich	d			08 30							09 00					09 30							10 00		
Diss	d			08 47							09 17					09 47							10 17		
Peterborough 8	d							07 46																	
Stowmarket	d		08 45					09 12			09 29				09 45								10 29		
Needham Market	d		08 51												09 50										
Lowestoft	d																			08 58					
Ipswich	a		09 03	09 07				09 26			09 40				10 03	10 07				10 26			10 40		
	d			09 08				09 30			09 42					10 08				10 30			10 42		
Harwich Town	d				09 00												10 00								
Dovercourt	d				09 02												10 02								
Harwich International	d				09 06												10 06								
Wrabness	d				09 12												10 12								
Mistley	d				09 17												10 17								
Manningtree 2	d			09 18	09 22						09 52					10 18	10 22						10 52		
Walton-on-the-Naze	d									09 45												10 45			
Frinton-on-Sea	d									09 48												10 48			
Kirby Cross	d									09 51												10 51			
Clacton-on-Sea	d												09 50												10 50
Thorpe-le-Soken 1	a					←				09 56			09 57					←				10 56			10 57
	d					09 01				10 01			09 57					10 01				11 01			10 57
Weeley	d					09 05				→								10 05				→			
Great Bentley	d					09 08												10 08							
Alresford (Essex)	d					09 13												10 13							
Wivenhoe 3	d					09 16							10 07					10 16							11 07
Hythe	d					09 20												10 20							
Colchester Town	a					09 24												10 24							
	d	09 15				09 28			09 45					10 15				10 28			10 45				
Colchester 4	a	09 22		09 27	09 32	09 37		09 48	09 52		10 01		10 17	10 22		10 27	10 32	10 37		10 48	10 52		11 01		11 17
	d			09 29	09 33		09 44	09 49			10 03		10 17			10 29	10 33			10 49			11 03		11 17
Marks Tey 2	d				09 39								10 23				10 39								11 23
Kelvedon	d				09 44												10 44								
Braintree	d											10 00												11 00	
Braintree Freeport	d											10 02												11 02	
Cressing	d											10 05												11 05	
White Notley	d											10 08												11 08	
Witham 2	d				09 49		09 56	10 02				10 15	10 31				10 49			11 02				11 15	11 31
Hatfield Peverel	d											10 20												11 20	
Chelmsford 3	d			09 47	09 58		10 05	10s10				10 27	10 40			10 46	10 58			11 11				11 27	11 40
Ingatestone	d						10 12					10 33												11 33	
Shenfield 3	a				10 09			10s22			10s29	10 40	10 51				11 09			11s22			11s29	11 40	11 51
Romford	a												10 59												11 59
Stratford 7 ⊖ ⛴	a			10s11	10s24		10s32					10s55	11s07			11s10	11s24							11s55	12s07
London Liverpool Street 15 ⊖	a			10 24	10 33		10 41	10 46			10 54	11 03	11 18			11 24	11 33			11 45			11 54	12 03	12 16

For general notes see front of timetable
For details of catering facilities see Directory of Train Operators

A To Cambridge (Table 14)
B From Cambridge (Table 14)
C From Great Yarmouth (Table 15)

Norwich, Ipswich, Harwich, Clacton, Walton-on-Naze, Colchester and Chelmsford → London

Network diagram - see first page of Table 5

		LE 1	LE A	LE 1 ◇ ☕	LE 1	LE 1	LE 1 ◇	LE 1	LE 1	LE 1 ◇ ☕	LE 1	LE 1	LE 1	LE A	LE 1 ◇ ☕	LE 1	LE 1	LE 1 ◇	LE 1	LE 1	LE 1 ◇ ☕	LE 1	LE 1	LE 1	LE A
Norwich	d			10 30						11 00					11 30						12 00				
Diss	d			10 47						11 17					11 47						12 17				
Peterborough 8	d						09 45																		
Stowmarket	d		10 45				11 12			11 29				11 45							12 29				12 45
Needham Market	d		10 50											11 50											12 50
Lowestoft	d																	10 58							
Ipswich	a		11 03	11 07			11 25			11 40				12 03	12 07			12 26			12 40				13 03
	d			11 08			11 30			11 42					12 08			12 30			12 42				
Harwich Town	d				11 00											12 00									
Dovercourt	d				11 02											12 02									
Harwich International	d				11 06											12 06									
Wrabness	d				11 12											12 12									
Mistley	d				11 17											12 17									
Manningtree 2	d			11 18	11 22					11 52					12 18	12 22					12 52				
Walton-on-the-Naze	d								11 45											12 45					
Frinton-on-Sea	d								11 48											12 48					
Kirby Cross	d								11 51											12 51					
Clacton-on-Sea	d											11 50											12 50		
Thorpe-le-Soken 1	a					←			11 56			11 57					←			12 56			12 57		
	d					11 01			12 01 →			11 57					12 01			13 01 →			12 57		
Weeley	d					11 05											12 05								
Great Bentley	d					11 08											12 08								
Alresford (Essex)	d					11 13											12 13								
Wivenhoe 3	d					11 16						12 07					12 16						13 07		
Hythe	d					11 20											12 20								
Colchester Town	a					11 24											12 24								
	d	11 15				11 28		11 45					12 15				12 28		12 45					13 15	
Colchester 4	a	11 22		11 27	11 32	11 37	11 48	11 52		12 01		12 17	12 22		12 27	12 32	12 37	12 48	12 52		13 01		13 17	13 22	
	d			11 29	11 33		11 49			12 03		12 17			12 29	12 33		12 49			13 03		13 17		
Marks Tey 2	d				11 39							12 23				12 39							13 23		
Kelvedon	d				11 44											12 44									
Braintree	d										12 00											13 00			
Braintree Freeport	d										12 02											13 02			
Cressing	d										12 05											13 05			
White Notley	d										12 08											13 08			
Witham 2	d				11 49		12 02				12 15	12 31				12 49		13 02				13 15	13 31		
Hatfield Peverel	d										12 20											13 20			
Chelmsford 3	d			11 46	11 58		12 11				12 27	12 40			12 46	12 58		13 11				13 27	13 40		
Ingatestone	d										12 33											13 33			
Shenfield 3	a				12 09		12s22			12s29	12 40	12 51				13 09		13s22			13s29	13 40	13 51		
Romford	a											12 59											13 59		
Stratford 7 ⊖	a			12s10	12s24						12s55	13s07			13s10	13s24						13s55	14s07		
London Liverpool Street 15 ⊖	a			12 24	12 33		12 45			12 54	13 03	13 16			13 24	13 33		13 45			13 54	14 03	14 16		

		LE 1 ◇ ☕	LE 1	LE 1	LE 1 ◇	LE 1	LE 1	LE 1 ◇ ☕	LE 1	LE 1	LE 1	LE A	LE 1 ◇ ☕	LE 1		LE 1	LE 1 ◇	LE 1	LE 1	LE 1 ◇ ☕	LE 1	LE 1	LE 1	LE A	LE 1 ◇ ☕
Norwich	d	12 30						13 00					13 30							14 00					14 30
Diss	d	12 47						13 17					13 47							14 17					14 47
Peterborough 8	d				11 45																				
Stowmarket	d				13 12			13 29				13 45								14 29				14 45	
Needham Market	d											13 50												14 50	
Lowestoft	d																12 58								
Ipswich	a	13 07			13 25			13 40				14 03	14 07				14 26			14 40				15 03	15 07
	d	13 08			13 30			13 42					14 08				14 30			14 42					15 08
Harwich Town	d		13 00											14 00											
Dovercourt	d		13 02											14 02											
Harwich International	d		13 06											14 06											
Wrabness	d		13 12											14 12											
Mistley	d		13 17											14 17											
Manningtree 2	d	13 18	13 22					13 52					14 18	14 22						14 52					15 18
Walton-on-the-Naze	d						13 45												14 45						
Frinton-on-Sea	d						13 48												14 48						
Kirby Cross	d						13 51												14 51						
Clacton-on-Sea	d									13 50												14 50			
Thorpe-le-Soken 1	a			←			13 56			13 57						←			14 56			14 57			
	d			13 01			14 01 →			13 57						14 01			15 01 →			14 57			
Weeley	d			13 05												14 05									
Great Bentley	d			13 08												14 08									
Alresford (Essex)	d			13 13												14 13									
Wivenhoe 3	d			13 16						14 07						14 16						15 07			
Hythe	d			13 20												14 20									
Colchester Town	a			13 24												14 24									
	d			13 28		13 45					14 15					14 28		14 45					15 15		
Colchester 4	a	13 27	13 32	13 37	13 48	13 52		14 01		14 17	14 22		14 27	14 32		14 37	14 48	14 52		15 01		15 17	15 22		15 27
	d	13 29	13 33		13 49			14 03		14 17			14 29	14 33			14 49			15 03		15 17			15 29
Marks Tey 2	d		13 39							14 23				14 39								15 23			
Kelvedon	d		13 44											14 44											
Braintree	d								14 00												15 00				
Braintree Freeport	d								14 02												15 02				
Cressing	d								14 05												15 05				
White Notley	d								14 08												15 08				
Witham 2	d		13 49		14 02				14 15	14 31				14 49			15 02				15 15	15 31			
Hatfield Peverel	d								14 20												15 20				
Chelmsford 3	d	13 46	13 58		14 11				14 27	14 40			14 46	14 58			15 11				15 27	15 40			15 46
Ingatestone	d								14 33												15 33				
Shenfield 3	a		14 09		14s22			14s29	14 40	14 51				15 09			15s22			15s29	15 40	15 51			
Romford	a									14 59												15 59			
Stratford 7 ⊖	a	14s10	14s24						14s55	15s07			15s10	15s24							15s55	16s07			16s10
London Liverpool Street 15 ⊖	a	14 24	14 33		14 45			14 54	15 03	15 16			15 24	15 34			15 45			15 54	16 03	16 18			16 24

For general notes see front of timetable
For details of catering facilities see Directory of Train Operators

A From Cambridge (Table 14)

Norwich, Ipswich, Harwich, Clacton, Walton-on-Naze, Colchester and Chelmsford → London

Network diagram - see first page of Table 5

		LE 1	LE 1	LE 1	LE 1	LE 1	LE 1	LE 1 ◇	LE 1	LE 1	LE	LE 1	LE 1 ◇	LE 1	LE 1	LE 1	LE 1	LE 1	LE 1 ◇	LE 1	LE 1	LE 1	LE 1	LE	LE 1 ◇
											A													A	
								☕					☕						☕						☕
Norwich	d							15 00					15 30						16 00						16 30
Diss	d							15 17					15 47						16 18						16 48
Peterborough [8]	d			13 45																					
Stowmarket	d			15 12				15 29			15 45								16 30					16 45	
Needham Market	d										15 50													16 50	
Lowestoft	d																								
Ipswich	a			15 25				15 40			16 03		16 07						16 41					17 03	17 07
	d			15 26				15 42					16 08				16 30		16 42						17 08
Harwich Town	d	15 00														16 05									
Dovercourt	d	15 02														16 07									
Harwich International	d	15 06														16 11									
Wrabness	d	15 12														16 17									
Mistley	d	15 17														16 22									
Manningtree [2]	d	15 22						15 52					16 18			16 27			16 52						17 18
Walton-on-the-Naze	d						15 45											16 43							
Frinton-on-Sea	d						15 48											16 46							
Kirby Cross	d						15 51											16 49							
Clacton-on-Sea	d									15 50													16 48		
Thorpe-le-Soken [1]	a		←				15 56			15 57					←			16 54					16 55		
	d		15 01				16 01 →			15 57					16 01			17 01 →					16 55		
Weeley	d		15 05												16 05										
Great Bentley	d		15 08												16 08										
Alresford (Essex)	d		15 13												16 13										
Wivenhoe [3]	d		15 16							16 07					16 16								17 05		
Hythe	d		15 20												16 20								17 09		
Colchester Town	a		15 24												16 24										
	d		15 28			15 45						16 15			16 28						17 05				
Colchester [4]	a	15 32	15 37	15 43		15 52		16 01		16 17		16 22	16 27		16 38	16 40	16 48		17 01		17 12		17 17		17 27
	d	15 36			15 47			16 03		16 17			16 29	16 33		16 53			17 03				17 17		17 29
Marks Tey [2]	d				15 54					16 23				16 39		16 59							17 23		
Kelvedon	d	15 45			16 00									16 44											
Braintree	d								16 00											17 00					
Braintree Freeport	d								16 02											17 02					
Cressing	d								16 05											17 05					
White Notley	d								16 08											17 08					
Witham [2]	d	15 49			16 05				16 15	16 31				16 49		17 07				17 15		17 21	17 31		
Hatfield Peverel	d								16 20													17 25			
Chelmsford [3]	d	15 58			16 14				16 27	16 40			16 46	16 58		17 16				17 25		17 32	17 40		17 46
Ingatestone	d	16 05							16 33					17 05								17 39			
Shenfield [3]	a	16 11			16 25			16s29	16 40	16 51				17 11		17 27			17s30	17 36		17 45	17 51		
Romford	a								16 48														17 59		
Stratford [7] ⊖ ⛴	a	16s26			16s40				16s56	17s05			17s10	17s26						17s50		18s02	18s07		18s12
London Liverpool Street [15] ⊖	a	16 35			16 49			16 54	17 05	17 15			17 24	17 38		17 49			17 54	18 00		18 11	18 20		18 24

		LE 1	LE 1	LE 1	LE 1 ◇	LE 1	LE 1 ◇	LE 1	LE 1	LE 1		LE	LE 1 ◇	LE 1	LE 1	LE 1	LE 1 ◇	LE 1	LE 1 ◇	LE 1	LE 1	LE 1	LE 1	LE	LE 1
												A												A	
							☕						☕						☕						
Norwich	d						17 00						17 30						18 00						
Diss	d						17 18						17 48						18 17						
Peterborough [8]	d				15 45																				
Stowmarket	d				17 12		17 30					17 46	18 00						18 29					18 46	
Needham Market	d											17 52												18 52	
Lowestoft	d																16 58								
Ipswich	a				17 27		17 41					18 03	18 11				18 26		18 40					19 03	
	d				17 30		17 42						18 11				18 30		18 42			18 56			
Harwich Town	d	17 00						17 53										18 25					18 53		
Dovercourt	d	17 02						17 55										18 27					18 55		
Harwich International	d	17 06						17 58										18 30					18 58		
Wrabness	d	17 12						18 04										18 36					19 04		
Mistley	d	17 17						18 09										18 41					19 09		
Manningtree [2]	d	17 22					17 52	18a14					18 21					18a46	18 52			19 06	19a14		
Walton-on-the-Naze	d					17 39										18 27									
Frinton-on-Sea	d					17 42										18 30									
Kirby Cross	d					17 45										18b36									
Clacton-on-Sea	d									17 45											18 45				
Thorpe-le-Soken [1]	a		←			17 50				17 52				←		18 42					18 52				
	d		17 01			17 56 →				17 52				17 56							18 52				
Weeley	d		17 05											18 00											
Great Bentley	d		17 08							17 58				18 03							18 58				
Alresford (Essex)	d		17 13							18 02				18 08							19 02				
Wivenhoe [3]	d		17 16							18 05				18 11							19 05				
Hythe	d		17 20											18 15											
Colchester Town	a		17 24											18 19											
	d		17 28											18 23											19 15
Colchester [4]	a	17 32	17 37		17 48		18 01			18 14			18 30	18 32			18 48		19 01		19 14	19 17			19 22
	d	17 33			17 49		18 03			18 15			18 32	18 35			18 49		19 03		19 15				19 33 →
Marks Tey [2]	d	17 39			17 55					18 21							18 55				19 21				
Kelvedon	d	17 44								18 26				18 44							19 26				
Braintree	d			17 44											18 36										
Braintree Freeport	d			17 46											18 38										
Cressing	d			17 49											18 41										
White Notley	d			17 52											18 44										
Witham [2]	d	17 49		18 00	18 04				18 15	18 31				18 49	18 52		19 04			19 15	19 31				
Hatfield Peverel	d								18 20											19 20					
Chelmsford [3]	d	17 58		18 09	18 13				18 27	18 40			18 49	18 58	19 02		19 13			19 27	19 40				
Ingatestone	d	18 05							18 33						19 09					19 33					
Shenfield [3]	a	18 11			18s25		18s29		18 40	18 51				19 09	19 15		19s24		19s29	19 40	19 51				
Romford	a									18 59											19 59				
Stratford [7] ⊖ ⛴	a	18s26							18s55	19s07			19s15	19s24						19s55	20s07				
London Liverpool Street [15] ⊖	a	18 36		18 41	18 49		18 54		19 05	19 16			19 27	19 33	19 40		19 47		19 54	20 04	20 16				

For general notes see front of timetable
For details of catering facilities see Directory of Train Operators

A From Cambridge (Table 14)
b Arr. 1833

Norwich, Ipswich, Harwich, Clacton, Walton-on-Naze, Colchester and Chelmsford → London

Network diagram - see first page of Table 5

		LE 1	LE 1 ◇	LE 1	LE 1	LE 1	LE 1 ◇	LE 1	LE 1	LE 1 ◇	LE 1	LE 1	LE 1	LE	LE 1	LE 1	LE 1	LE 1	LE 1 ◇	LE 1	LE 1 ◇	LE 1	LE 1	LE 1	LE 1
			🍴							🍴				A							🍴				
Norwich	d		18 30							19 00											20 00				
Diss	d		18 47							19 17											20 17				
Peterborough 8	d						17 45																		
Stowmarket	d						19 12			19 29				19 45							20 29				
Needham Market	d													19 50											
Lowestoft	d																		18 43						
Ipswich	a		19 07				19 25			19 40				20 03					20 16		20 40				
	d		19 08				19 27	19 35		19 42					20 08				20 30		20 42				
Harwich Town	d								19 28							20 00							20 33		21 00
Dovercourt	d								19 30							20 02							20 35		21 02
Harwich International	d								19 33							20 06							20 38		21 06
Wrabness	d								19 39							20 12							20 44		21 12
Mistley	d								19 44							20 17							20 49		21 17
Manningtree 2	d		19 18				19 37	19 46	19a49	19 52					20 18	20 22					20 52		20 56		21 22 →
Walton-on-the-Naze	d				18 49	19 25											19 52	20 24		20 45					
Frinton-on-Sea	d				18 52	19 28											19 55	20 27		20 48					
Kirby Cross	d				18 55	19b34											19 58	20c33		20 51					
Clacton-on-Sea	d												19 45											20 50	
Thorpe-le-Soken 1	a				19 00	19 40							19 52				20 03	20 39		20 56				20 57	
	d				19 02								19 52				20 04			21 01 →				20 57	
Weeley	d				19 06												20 08								
Great Bentley	d				19 09								19 58				20 11								
Alresford (Essex)	d				19 14								20 02				20 16								
Wivenhoe 3	d				19 17								20 05				20 19							21 07	
Hythe	d				19 21												20 23								
Colchester Town	a				19 25												20 27								
	d				19 29												20 31								
Colchester 4	a		19 27	←	19 38		19 47	19 57		20 01			20 14		20 28	20 32	20 40		20 48		21 01		21 06	21 17	
	d		19 29	19 33			19 48			20 03			20 15		20 29	20 33			20 49		21 03			21 17	
Marks Tey 2	d			19 39			19 54						20 21			20 39								21 23	
Kelvedon	d			19 44									20 26			20 44									
Braintree	d	19 25										20 10										21 00			
Braintree Freeport	d	19 27										20 12										21 02			
Cressing	d	19 30										20 15										21 05			
White Notley	d	19 33										20 18										21 08			
Witham 2	d	19 41		19 49			20 02				20 15	20a25	20 31			20 49			21 02			21 15		21 31	
Hatfield Peverel	d										20 20											21 20			
Chelmsford 3	d	19 50	19 46	19 58			20 11				20 27		20 40		20 46	20 58			21 11			21 27		21 40	
Ingatestone	d										20 33											21 33			
Shenfield 3	a			20 09			20s23			20s29	20 40		20 51			21 09			21s23		21s29	21 40		21 51	
Romford	a												20 59											21 59	
Stratford 7 ⊖ ⛴	a		20s10	20s24							20s55		21s07		21s10	21s24						21s55		22s10	
London Liverpool Street 15 ⊖	a	20 23	20 24	20 33			20 46			20 54	21 04		21 17		21 21	21 33			21 46		21 54	22 03		22 19	

		LE	LE 1	LE 1	LE 1	LE 1 ◇	LE 1	LE 1 ◇	LE 1	LE 1	LE 1	LE	LE 1	LE 1	LE 1	LE 1	LE 1	LE 1 ◇	LE 1	LE 1	LE 1	LE 1	LE
		A						🍴				A											A
Norwich	d							21 00										22 00				23 05	
Diss	d							21 17										22 17				23 22	
Peterborough 8	d					19 46															22 05		
Stowmarket	d	20 45				21 08		21 29				21 46						22 29			23 24	23 34	23 46
Needham Market	d	20 50										21 52											23 52
Lowestoft	d																					
Ipswich	a	21 03				21 25		21 40				22 03						22 40			23 37	23 48	00 03
	d	21 04	21 08			21 27		21 42					22 08					22 42		23 22	23 38		
Harwich Town	d										21 54								23 05				
Dovercourt	d										21 56								23 07				
Harwich International	d	21a28									21 59								23 10				
Wrabness	d										22 05								23 16				
Mistley	d			←							22 10								23 21				
Manningtree 2	d		21 18	21 22		21 37		21 52			22a15		22 18					22 52	23a26	23 31	23 48		
Walton-on-the-Naze	d						21 45										22 43						
Frinton-on-Sea	d						21 48										22 46						
Kirby Cross	d						21 51										22e52						
Clacton-on-Sea	d									21 50						22 24							
Thorpe-le-Soken 1	a				←		21 56			21 57				←		22 31	22 58						
	d				21 01		22 01 →			21 57				22 01		22 31							
Weeley	d				21 05									22 05		22 35							
Great Bentley	d				21 08									22 08		22 39							
Alresford (Essex)	d				21 13									22 13		22 43							
Wivenhoe 3	d				21 16					22 07				22 16		22 46							
Hythe	d				21 20									22 20		22 50							
Colchester Town	a				21 24									22 24									
	d				21 28									22 28									
Colchester 4	a		21 28	21 32	21 37	21 48		22 01		22 17			22 28	22 37		22 57		23 01		23 41	23 58		
	d		21 29	21 33		21 49		22 03		22 17			22 29					23 03					
Marks Tey 2	d			21 39						22 23			22 35										
Kelvedon	d			21 44									22 40										
Braintree	d								22 00						22 57								
Braintree Freeport	d								22 02						22 59								
Cressing	d								22 05						23 02								
White Notley	d								22 08						23 05								
Witham 2	d			21 49		22 02			22 15	22 31			22 45		23a12			23 15					
Hatfield Peverel	d								22 20				22 49										
Chelmsford 3	d		21 46	21 58		22 11			22 27	22 40			22 56					23 24					
Ingatestone	d								22 33				23 03										
Shenfield 3	a		21 58	22 11		22s22		22s29	22 40	22 51			23 09					23s36					
Romford	a									22 59													
Stratford 7 ⊖ ⛴	a		22s12	22s27					22s55	23s07			23s25					23s52					
London Liverpool Street 15 ⊖	a		22 23	22 36		22 46		22 54	23 03	23 16			23 34					00 03					

For general notes see front of timetable
For details of catering facilities see Directory of Train Operators

A From Cambridge (Table 14)
b Arr. 1931
c Arr. 2030
e Arr. 2249

Table 11

Saturdays

Norwich, Ipswich, Harwich, Clacton, Walton-on-Naze, Colchester and Chelmsford → London

Network diagram - see first page of Table 5

		LE	LE	LE	LE	LE	LE	LE	LE	LE	LE	LE	LE	LE	LE	LE	LE	LE	LE	LE	LE	LE	LE
		1	1	1	1	1	1 ◇	1	1	1 ◇	1	1	1	1	1 ◇	1	1	1	1			1 ◇	1
																					A		
							ꟾP			ꟾP					ꟾP							ꟾP	
Norwich	d						05 00			05 30					06 00							06 30	
Diss	d						05 17			05 47					06 17							06 47	
Peterborough 8	d																						
Stowmarket	d						05 29								06 29						06 45		
Needham Market	d																				06 50		
Lowestoft	d																						
Ipswich	a						05 40			06 07					06 40						07 03	07 07	
	d						05 42			06 08			06 30		06 42					07 00		07 08	
Harwich Town	d										06 00							07 00					
Dovercourt	d										06 02							07 02					
Harwich International	d										06 06							07 06	07 15	07a25			
Wrabness	d										06 12							07 12					
Mistley	d										06 17							07 17					←
Manningtree 2	d						05 52			06 18	06 22				06 52			07 22	07 28			07 18	07 22
Walton-on-the-Naze	d				05 45									06 45				→	→				
Frinton-on-Sea	d				05 48									06 48									
Kirby Cross	d				05 51									06 51									
Clacton-on-Sea	d								05 50								06 50						
Thorpe-le-Soken 1	a				05 56				05 57			←		06 56			06 57						
	d				06 01				05 57			06 01		07 01			06 57						
Weeley	d				→							06 05		→									
Great Bentley	d											06 08											
Alresford (Essex)	d											06 13											
Wivenhoe 3	d								06 07			06 16					07 07						
Hythe	d											06 20											
Colchester Town	a											06 24											
	d											06 28											
Colchester 4	a						06 01		06 17	06 27	06 32	06 37	06 48		07 01		07 17					07 27	07 32
	d		04 45	05 30			06 03	06 06	06 17	06 29	06 33		06 49		07 03		07 17					07 29	07 33
Marks Tey 2	d		04 51	05 36				06 12	06 23		06 39						07 23						07 39
Kelvedon	d		04 56	05 41				06 17			06 44												07 44
Braintree	d	00 03				06 00										07 00							
Braintree Freeport	d	00 05				06 02										07 02							
Cressing	d	00 08				06 05										07 05							
White Notley	d	00 11				06 08										07 08							
Witham 2	d	00a18	05 01	05 46		06a15		06 22	06 31		06 49		07 02			07 15	07 31						07 49
Hatfield Peverel	d		05 05	05 50				06 26								07 20							
Chelmsford 3	d		05 12	05 57				06 33	06 40	06 46	06 58		07 11			07 27	07 40					07 46	07 58
Ingatestone	d		05 19	06 04				06 40								07 33							
Shenfield 3	a		05 25	06 10			06s29	06 46	06 51		07 09		07s22		07s29	07 40	07 51						08 09
Romford	a			06 19					06 59								07 59						
Stratford 7 ⊖	a		05s44	06s27				07s01	07s07	07s10	07s24					07s55	08s07					08s10	08s24
London Liverpool Street 15 ⊖	a		05 57	06 36			06 54	07 10	07 16	07 24	07 33		07 45		07 54	08 03	08 16					08 24	08 33

For general notes see front of timetable
For details of catering facilities see Directory of Train Operators

A From Bury St Edmunds (Table 14)

Table 11

Saturdays

Norwich, Ipswich, Harwich, Clacton, Walton-on-Naze, Colchester and Chelmsford → London

Network diagram - see first page of Table 5

		LE	LE	LE	LE	LE	LE	LE	LE	LE	LE	LE	LE	LE	LE	LE	LE	LE	LE	LE	LE	LE	LE
				R											R								
		1	1	1	1	1 ◇	A	1	1	1	B	1 ◇	1	1	1	1	1	1	1 ◇	1	1	1	B
						🍴						🍴							🍴				
Norwich	d					07 00						07 30							08 00				
Diss	d					07 17						07 47							08 17				
Peterborough 8	d																						
Stowmarket	d					07 29					07 45								08 29				08 45
Needham Market	d										07 50												08 50
Lowestoft	d			05 58											06 58								
Ipswich	a			07 26		07 40					08 03	00 07			08 26				08 40				09 03
	d			07 30		07 42						08 08			08 30				08 42				
Harwich Town	d												08 00										
Dovercourt	d												08 02										
Harwich International	d						07 47						08 06										
Wrabness	d						07 53						08 12										
Mistley	d		←				07a59						08 17										
Manningtree 2	d		07 28			07 52						08 18	08 22						08 52				
Walton-on-the-Naze	d				07 45													08 45					
Frinton-on-Sea	d				07 48													08 48					
Kirby Cross	d				07 51													08 51					
Clacton-on-Sea	d								07 50												08 50		
Thorpe-le-Soken 1	a	←			07 56				07 57					←				08 56			08 57		
	d	07 01			08 01 →				07 57					08 01				09 01 →			08 57		
Weeley	d	07 05												08 05									
Great Bentley	d	07 08												08 08									
Alresford (Essex)	d	07 13												08 13									
Wivenhoe 3	d	07 16							08 07					08 16							09 07		
Hythe	d	07 20												08 20									
Colchester Town	a	07 24												08 24									
	d	07 28								08 15				08 28			08 45					09 15	
Colchester 4	a	07 37	07 38	07 48		08 01			08 17	08 22		08 27	08 32	08 37	08 48		08 52		09 01		09 17	09 22	
	d		07 41	07 49		08 03			08 17			08 29	08 33		08 49	08 52			09 03		09 17		
Marks Tey 2	d								08 23				08 39								09 23		
Kelvedon	d												08 44										
Braintree	d							08 00												09 00			
Braintree Freeport	d							08 02												09 02			
Cressing	d							08 05												09 05			
White Notley	d							08 08												09 08			
Witham 2	d			08 02				08 15	08 31				08 49			09 04				09 15	09 31		
Hatfield Peverel	d							08 20												09 20			
Chelmsford 3	d		08 02	08 11				08 27	08 40			08 46	08 58		09s06	09 13				09 27	09 40		
Ingatestone	d							08 33												09 33			
Shenfield 3	a		08 13	08s22		08s29		08 40	08 51				09 09			09s24			09s29	09 40	09 51		
Romford	a								08 59												09 59		
Stratford 7 ⊖ ⛴	a		08s30					08s55	09s07			09s10	09s24							09s55	10s07		
London Liverpool Street 15 ⊖	a		08 39	08 45		08 54		09 03	09 16			09 24	09 33		09 38	09 47			09 54	10 03	10 16		

		LE	LE	LE	LE	LE	LE	LE	LE	LE	LE	LE	LE	LE	LE	LE	LE	LE	LE	LE	LE	LE	LE
					R												R						
		1 ◇	1	1	1	1	1	1	1 ◇	1	1	1	B	1 ◇	1	1	1	1	1	1	1 ◇	1	1
		🍴							🍴					🍴							🍴		
Norwich	d	08 30							09 00					09 30							10 00		
Diss	d	08 47							09 17					09 47							10 17		
Peterborough 8	d				07 45																		
Stowmarket	d				09 12				09 29				09 45								10 29		
Needham Market	d												09 50										
Lowestoft	d																08 58						
Ipswich	a	09 07			09 25				09 40				10 03	10 07			10 26				10 40		
	d	09 08			09 30				09 42					10 08			10 30				10 42		
Harwich Town	d		09 00												10 00								
Dovercourt	d		09 02												10 02								
Harwich International	d		09 06												10 06								
Wrabness	d		09 12												10 12								
Mistley	d		09 17												10 17								
Manningtree 2	d	09 18	09 22						09 52					10 18	10 22						10 52		
Walton-on-the-Naze	d							09 45												10 45			
Frinton-on-Sea	d							09 48												10 48			
Kirby Cross	d							09 51												10 51			
Clacton-on-Sea	d										09 50												10 50
Thorpe-le-Soken 1	a			←				09 56			09 57					←				10 56			10 57
	d			09 01				10 01 →			09 57					10 01				11 01 →			10 57
Weeley	d			09 05												10 05							
Great Bentley	d			09 08												10 08							
Alresford (Essex)	d			09 13												10 13							
Wivenhoe 3	d			09 16							10 07					10 16							11 07
Hythe	d			09 20												10 20							
Colchester Town	a			09 24												10 24							
	d			09 28			09 45					10 15				10 28			10 45				
Colchester 4	a	09 27	09 32	09 37	09 48		09 52		10 01		10 17	10 22		10 27	10 32	10 37	10 48		10 52		11 01		11 17
	d	09 29	09 33		09 49	09 52			10 03		10 17			10 29	10 33		10 49	10 52			11 03		11 17
Marks Tey 2	d		09 39								10 23				10 39								11 23
Kelvedon	d		09 44												10 44								
Braintree	d									10 00												11 00	
Braintree Freeport	d									10 02												11 02	
Cressing	d									10 05												11 05	
White Notley	d									10 08												11 08	
Witham 2	d		09 49			10 04				10 15	10 31				10 49			11 04				11 15	11 31
Hatfield Peverel	d									10 20												11 20	
Chelmsford 3	d	09 46	09 58		10s06	10 13				10 27	10 40			10 46	10 58		11s06	11 13				11 27	11 40
Ingatestone	d									10 33												11 33	
Shenfield 3	a		10 09			10s24			10s29	10 40	10 51				11 09			11s24			11s29	11 40	11 51
Romford	a										10 59												11 59
Stratford 7 ⊖ ⛴	a	10s10	10s24							10s55	11s07			11s10	11s24							11s55	12s07
London Liverpool Street 15 ⊖	a	10 24	10 33		10 38	10 47			10 54	11 03	11 16			11 24	11 33		11 42	11 47			11 54	12 03	12 16

For general notes see front of timetable
For details of catering facilities see
Directory of Train Operators

A To Cambridge (Table 14)
B From Cambridge (Table 14)

Table 11

Saturdays

Norwich, Ipswich, Harwich, Clacton, Walton-on-Naze, Colchester and Chelmsford → London

Network diagram - see first page of Table 5

		LE	LE	LE	LE	LE	LE	LE	LE	LE	LE	LE	LE	LE	LE	LE	LE	LE	LE	LE	LE	LE	LE
		1	A	1 ◇ ☕	1	1	R 1	1	1	R 1 B ☕	1	1	1	A	1 ◇ ☕	1	1	R 1	1	1	1 ◇ ☕	1	1
Norwich	d			10 30						11 00					11 30						12 00		
Diss	d			10 47						11 17					11 47						12 17		
Peterborough 8	d						09 55																
Stowmarket	d		10 45				11 14			11 29				11 45							12 29		
Needham Market	d		10 50											11 50									
Lowestoft	d																	10 58					
Ipswich	a		11 03	11 07			11 27			11 40				12 03	12 07			12 26			12 40		
	d			11 08			11 30			11 42					12 08			12 30			12 42		
Harwich Town	d				11 00											12 00							
Dovercourt	d				11 02											12 02							
Harwich International	d				11 06											12 06							
Wrabness	d				11 12											12 12							
Mistley	d				11 17											12 17							
Manningtree 2	d			11 18	11 22					11 52					12 18	12 22					12 52		
Walton-on-the-Naze	d								11 45											12 45			
Frinton-on-Sea	d								11 48											12 48			
Kirby Cross	d								11 51											12 51			
Clacton-on-Sea	d											11 50											12 50
Thorpe-le-Soken 1	a					←			11 56			11 57					←			12 56			12 57
	d					11 01			12 01 →			11 57					12 01			13 01 →			12 57
Weeley	d					11 05											12 05						
Great Bentley	d					11 08											12 08						
Alresford (Essex)	d					11 13											12 13						
Wivenhoe 3	d					11 16						12 07					12 16						13 07
Hythe	d					11 20											12 20						
Colchester Town	a					11 24											12 24						
	d	11 15				11 28		11 45					12 15				12 28		12 45				
Colchester 4	a	11 22		11 27	11 32	11 37	11 48	11 52		12 01		12 17	12 22		12 27	12 32	12 37	12 48	12 52		13 01		13 17
	d			11 29	11 33		11 49			12 03		12 17			12 29	12 33		12 49			13 03		13 17
Marks Tey 2	d				11 39							12 23				12 39							13 23
Kelvedon	d				11 44											12 44							
Braintree	d										12 00											13 00	
Braintree Freeport	d										12 02											13 02	
Cressing	d										12 05											13 05	
White Notley	d										12 08											13 08	
Witham 2	d				11 49		12 02				12 15	12 31				12 49		13 02				13 15	13 31
Hatfield Peverel	d										12 20											13 20	
Chelmsford 3	d			11 46	11 58		12 11				12 27	12 40			12 46	12 58		13 11				13 27	13 40
Ingatestone	d										12 33											13 33	
Shenfield 3	a				12 09		12s22			12s29	12 40	12 51				13 09		13s22			13s29	13 40	13 51
Romford	a											12 59											13 59
Stratford 7 ⊖ ⛴	a			12s10	12s24						12s55	13s07			13s10	13s24						13s55	14s07
London Liverpool Street 15 ⊖	a			12 24	12 33		12 45			12 54	13 03	13 16			13 24	13 33		13 45			13 54	14 03	14 16

		LE	LE	LE	LE	LE	LE	LE	LE	LE	LE	LE	LE	LE	LE	LE	LE	LE	LE	LE	LE	LE	LE
		1	A	1 ◇ ☕	1	1	1 ◇	1	1	1 ◇ ☕	1	1	1	A	1 ◇ ☕	1	1	1 ◇	1	1	R 1 B ☕	1	1
Norwich	d			12 30						13 00					13 30						14 00		
Diss	d			12 47						13 17					13 47						14 17		
Peterborough 8	d						11 45																
Stowmarket	d		12 45				13 12			13 29				13 45							14 29		
Needham Market	d		12 50											13 50									
Lowestoft	d																	12 58					
Ipswich	a		13 03	13 07			13 27			13 40				14 03	14 07			14 26			14 40		
	d			13 08			13 30			13 42					14 08			14 30			14 42		
Harwich Town	d				13 00											14 00							
Dovercourt	d				13 02											14 02							
Harwich International	d				13 06											14 06							
Wrabness	d				13 12											14 12							
Mistley	d				13 17											14 17							
Manningtree 2	d			13 18	13 22					13 52					14 18	14 22					14 52		
Walton-on-the-Naze	d								13 45											14 45			
Frinton-on-Sea	d								13 48											14 48			
Kirby Cross	d								13 51											14 51			
Clacton-on-Sea	d											13 50											14 50
Thorpe-le-Soken 1	a					←			13 56			13 57					←			14 56			14 57
	d					13 01			14 01 →			13 57					14 01			15 01 →			14 57
Weeley	d					13 05											14 05						
Great Bentley	d					13 08											14 08						
Alresford (Essex)	d					13 13											14 13						
Wivenhoe 3	d					13 16						14 07					14 16						15 07
Hythe	d					13 20											14 20						
Colchester Town	a					13 24											14 24						
	d	13 15				13 28		13 45					14 15				14 28		14 45				
Colchester 4	a	13 22		13 27	13 32	13 37	13 48	13 52		14 01		14 17	14 22		14 27	14 32	14 37	14 48	14 52		15 01		15 17
	d			13 29	13 33		13 49			14 03		14 17			14 29	14 33		14 49			15 03		15 17
Marks Tey 2	d				13 39							14 23				14 39							15 23
Kelvedon	d				13 44											14 44							
Braintree	d										14 00											15 00	
Braintree Freeport	d										14 02											15 02	
Cressing	d										14 05											15 05	
White Notley	d										14 08											15 08	
Witham 2	d				13 49		14 02				14 15	14 31				14 49		15 02				15 15	15 31
Hatfield Peverel	d										14 20											15 20	
Chelmsford 3	d			13 46	13 58		14 11				14 27	14 40			14 46	14 58		15 11				15 27	15 40
Ingatestone	d										14 33											15 33	
Shenfield 3	a				14 09		14s22			14s29	14 40	14 51				15 09		15s22			15s29	15 40	15 51
Romford	a											14 59											15 59
Stratford 7 ⊖ ⛴	a			14s10	14s24						14s55	15s07			15s10	15s24						15s55	16s07
London Liverpool Street 15 ⊖	a			14 24	14 33		14 45			14 54	15 03	15 16			15 24	15 33		15 45			15 54	16 03	16 16

For general notes see front of timetable
For details of catering facilities see
Directory of Train Operators

A From Cambridge (Table 14)

B Until 26 September from Great Yarmouth (Table 15).
☕ from Norwich, until 26 September.
☕ from 3 October

Norwich, Ipswich, Harwich, Clacton, Walton-on-Naze, Colchester and Chelmsford → London

Network diagram - see first page of Table 5

		LE 1	LE A	LE 1◇ ☕	LE 1	LE 1	LE 1◇	LE 1	LE 1	LE 1◇ ☕	LE 1		LE 1	LE 1	LE A	LE 1◇ ☕	LE 1	LE 1	LE 1◇	LE 1	LE 1	LE 1◇ ☕		LE 1	LE 1
Norwich	d			14 30						15 00						15 30						16 00			
Diss	d			14 47						15 17						15 47						16 17			
Peterborough 8	d						13 45																		
Stowmarket	d		14 45				15 12			15 29					15 45							16 29			
Needham Market	d		14 50												15 50										
Lowestoft	d																		14 58						
Ipswich	a		15 03	15 07			15 25			15 40					16 03	16 07			16 26			16 40			
	d			15 08			15 30			15 42						16 08			16 30			16 42			
Harwich Town	d				15 00												16 00								
Dovercourt	d				15 02												16 02								
Harwich International	d				15 06												16 06								
Wrabness	d				15 12												16 12								
Mistley	d				15 17												16 17								
Manningtree 2	d			15 18	15 22					15 52						16 18	16 22					16 52			
Walton-on-the-Naze	d								15 45												16 45				
Frinton-on-Sea	d								15 48												16 48				
Kirby Cross	d								15 51												16 51				
Clacton-on-Sea	d												15 50												16 50
Thorpe-le-Soken 1	a					←			15 56				15 57					←			16 56				16 57
	d					15 01			16 01 →				15 57					16 01			17 01 →				16 57
Weeley	d					15 05												16 05							
Great Bentley	d					15 08												16 08							
Alresford (Essex)	d					15 13												16 13							
Wivenhoe 3	d					15 16							16 07					16 16							17 07
Hythe	d					15 20												16 20							
Colchester Town	a					15 24												16 24							
	d	15 15				15 28		15 45						16 15				16 28		16 45					
Colchester 4	a	15 22		15 27	15 32	15 37	15 48	15 52		16 01			16 17	16 22		16 27	16 32	16 37	16 48	16 52		17 01			17 17
	d			15 29	15 33		15 49			16 03			16 17			16 29	16 33		16 49			17 03			17 17
Marks Tey 2	d				15 39								16 23				16 39								17 23
Kelvedon	d				15 44												16 44								
Braintree	d										16 00													17 00	
Braintree Freeport	d										16 02													17 02	
Cressing	d										16 05													17 05	
White Notley	d										16 08													17 08	
Witham 2	d				15 49		16 02				16 15		16 31				16 49		17 02					17 15	17 31
Hatfield Peverel	d										16 20													17 20	
Chelmsford 3	d			15 46	15 58		16 11				16 27		16 40			16 46	16 58		17 11					17 27	17 40
Ingatestone	d										16 33													17 33	
Shenfield 3	a				16 09		16s22			16s29	16 40		16 51				17 09		17s22			17s29		17 40	17 51
Romford	a												16 59												17 59
Stratford 7 ⊖ ⛴	a			16s10	16s24						16s55		17s07			17s10	17s24							17s55	18s07
London Liverpool Street 15 ⊖	a			16 24	16 33		16 45			16 54	17 03		17 16			17 24	17 33		17 45			17 54		18 03	18 16

		LE 1	LE A	LE 1◇ ☕	LE 1	LE 1	LE 1◇	LE 1	LE 1	LE 1◇ ☕	LE 1		LE 1	LE 1	LE A	LE 1◇ ☕	LE 1	LE 1	LE 1◇	LE 1	LE 1	LE 1◇ ☕		LE 1	LE 1
Norwich	d			16 30						17 00						17 30						18 00			
Diss	d			16 47						17 17						17 47						18 17			
Peterborough 8	d						15 45																		
Stowmarket	d		16 45				17 12			17 29					17 46	17 59						18 29			
Needham Market	d		16 50												17 52										
Lowestoft	d																		16 58						
Ipswich	a		17 03	17 07			17 27			17 40					18 03	18 10			18 26			18 40			
	d			17 08			17 30			17 42						18 11			18 30			18 42			
Harwich Town	d				17 00												18 03								
Dovercourt	d				17 02												18 05								
Harwich International	d				17 06												18 09								
Wrabness	d				17 12												18 15								
Mistley	d				17 17												18 20								
Manningtree 2	d			17 18	17 22					17 52						18 21	18 25					18 52			
Walton-on-the-Naze	d								17 45												18 45				
Frinton-on-Sea	d								17 48												18 48				
Kirby Cross	d								17 51												18 51				
Clacton-on-Sea	d												17 50												18 50
Thorpe-le-Soken 1	a					←			17 56				17 57					←			18 56				18 57
	d					17 01			18 01 →				17 57					18 01			19 01 →				18 57
Weeley	d					17 05												18 05							
Great Bentley	d					17 08												18 08							
Alresford (Essex)	d					17 13												18 13							
Wivenhoe 3	d					17 16							18 07					18 16							19 07
Hythe	d					17 20												18 20							
Colchester Town	a					17 24												18 24							
	d	17 15				17 28		17 45						18 15				18 28		18 45					
Colchester 4	a	17 22		17 27	17 32	17 37	17 48	17 52		18 01			18 17	18 22		18 30	18 35	18 37	18 48	18 52		19 01			19 17
	d			17 29	17 33		17 49			18 03			18 17			18 32	18 36		18 49			19 03			19 17
Marks Tey 2	d				17 39								18 23				18 42								19 23
Kelvedon	d				17 44												18 47								
Braintree	d										18 00													19 00	
Braintree Freeport	d										18 02													19 02	
Cressing	d										18 05													19 05	
White Notley	d										18 08													19 08	
Witham 2	d				17 49		18 02				18 15		18 31				18 52		19 02					19 15	19 31
Hatfield Peverel	d										18 20													19 20	
Chelmsford 3	d			17 46	17 58		18 11				18 27		18 40			18 49	19 01		19 11					19 27	19 40
Ingatestone	d										18 33													19 33	
Shenfield 3	a				18 09		18s22			18s29	18 40		18 51				19 12		19s22			19s29		19 40	19 51
Romford	a												18 59												19 59
Stratford 7 ⊖ ⛴	a			18s10	18s24						18s55		19s07			19s15	19s27							19s55	20s07
London Liverpool Street 15 ⊖	a			18 24	18 33		18 45			18 54	19 03		19 16			19 26	19 37		19 45			19 54		20 03	20 16

For general notes see front of timetable
For details of catering facilities see
Directory of Train Operators

A From Cambridge (Table 14)

Saturdays

Norwich, Ipswich, Harwich, Clacton, Walton-on-Naze, Colchester and Chelmsford → London

Network diagram - see first page of Table 5

Station		LE 1	LE A	LE 1 ◇ ☕	LE 1	LE 1	LE 1 ◇	LE 1	LE 1	LE 1 ◇ ☕	LE 1	LE 1	LE A	LE 1	LE 1	LE 1	LE 1 ◇	LE 1	LE 1 ◇ ☕	LE 1	LE 1	LE 1	LE A
Norwich	d			18 30						19 00									20 00				
Diss	d			18 47						19 17									20 17				
Peterborough 8	d						17 45																
Stowmarket	d		18 46				19 12			19 29			19 45						20 29				20 45
Needham Market	d		18 52										19 50										20 50
Lowestoft	d																18 58						
Ipswich	a		19 03	19 07			19 25			19 40			20 03				20 26		20 40				21 03
	d			19 08			19 27			19 42				20 08			20 30		20 42				21 04
Harwich Town	d				19 00										20 00							21 00	
Dovercourt	d				19 02										20 02							21 02	
Harwich International	d				19 06										20 06							21 06	21a28
Wrabness	d				19 12										20 12							21 12	
Mistley	d				19 17										20 17							21 17	
Manningtree 2	d			19 18	19 22		19 37			19 52				20 18	20 22				20 52			21 22 →	
Walton-on-the-Naze	d								19 45									20 45					
Frinton-on-Sea	d								19 48									20 48					
Kirby Cross	d								19 51									20 51					
Clacton-on-Sea	d											19 50									20 50		
Thorpe-le-Soken 1	a					←			19 56			19 57				←		20 56			20 57		
	d					19 01			20 01 →			19 57				20 01		21 01 →			20 57		
Weeley	d					19 05										20 05							
Great Bentley	d					19 08										20 08							
Alresford (Essex)	d					19 13										20 13							
Wivenhoe 3	d					19 16						20 07				20 16					21 07		
Hythe	d					19 20										20 20							
Colchester Town	a					19 24										20 24							
	d	19 15				19 28		19 45								20 28							
Colchester 4	a	19 22		19 27	19 32	19 37	19 48	19 52		20 01		20 17		20 28	20 32	20 37	20 48		21 01		21 17		
	d			19 29	19 33		19 49			20 03		20 17		20 29	20 33		20 49		21 03		21 17		
Marks Tey 2	d				19 39							20 23			20 39						21 23		
Kelvedon	d				19 44										20 44								
Braintree	d										20 00									21 00			
Braintree Freeport	d										20 02									21 02			
Cressing	d										20 05									21 05			
White Notley	d										20 08									21 08			
Witham 2	d				19 49		20 02				20 15	20 31			20 49		21 02			21 15	21 31		
Hatfield Peverel	d										20 20									21 20			
Chelmsford 3	d			19 46	19 58		20 11				20 27	20 40		20 46	20 58		21 11			21 27	21 40		
Ingatestone	d										20 33									21 33			
Shenfield 3	a				20 09		20s22			20s29	20 40	20 51			21 10		21s22		21s29	21 40	21 51		
Romford	a											20 59									21 59		
Stratford 7 ⊖	a			20s10	20s24						20s55	21s07		21s10	21s25					21s54	22s07		
London Liverpool Street 15 ⊖	a			20 24	20 33		20 45			20 54	21 03	21 16		21 19	21 38		21 49		21 58	22 07	22 20		

Station		LE 1	LE 1	LE 1	LE 1 ◇	LE 1	LE 1 ◇ ☕	LE 1	LE 1	LE 1	LE A	LE 1	LE 1	LE 1	LE 1	LE 1 ◇	LE A	LE 1	LE 1	LE 1	LE 1	LE 1
Norwich	d						21 00									22 00						23 05
Diss	d						21 17									22 17						23 22
Peterborough 8	d				19 45																21 45	
Stowmarket	d				21 12		21 29				21 45					22 29	22 46				23 17	23 34
Needham Market	d										21 50						22 52				23 22	
Lowestoft	d																					
Ipswich	a				21 27		21 40				22 03					22 40	23 03				23 32	23 50
	d	21 08			21 27		21 42					22 08				22 42				23 26	23 35	
Harwich Town	d									21 54									23 10			
Dovercourt	d									21 56									23 12			
Harwich International	d									21 59									23 15			
Wrabness	d									22 05									23 21			
Mistley	d		←							22 10									23 26			
Manningtree 2	d	21 18	21 22		21 37		21 52			22a15		22 18				22 52			23a31	23 35	23 45	
Walton-on-the-Naze	d					21 45									22 45							
Frinton-on-Sea	d					21 48									22 48							
Kirby Cross	d					21 51									22 51							
Clacton on-Sea	d								21 50					22 25								
Thorpe-le-Soken 1	a			←		21 56			21 57				←	22 32	22 57							
	d			21 01		22 01 →			21 57				22 01	22 32								
Weeley	d			21 05									22 05	22 36								
Great Bentley	d			21 08									22 08	22 40								
Alresford (Essex)	d			21 13									22 13	22 44								
Wivenhoe 3	d			21 16					22 07				22 16	22 47								
Hythe	d			21 20									22 20	22 51								
Colchester Town	a			21 24									22 24									
	d			21 28									22 28									
Colchester 4	a	21 28	21 32	21 37	21 48		22 01		22 17			22 28	22 37	22 58		23 01				23 45	23 56	
	d	21 29	21 33		21 49		22 03		22 17			22 29				23 03						
Marks Tey 2	d		21 39						22 23			22 35										
Kelvedon	d		21 44									22 40										
Braintree	d							22 00										23 07				
Braintree Freeport	d							22 02										23 09				
Cressing	d							22 05										23 12				
White Notley	d							22 08										23 15				
Witham 2	d		21 49		22 02			22 15	22 31			22 45				23 15		23a22				
Hatfield Peverel	d							22 20				22 49										
Chelmsford 3	d	21 46	21 58		22 11			22 27	22 40			22 56				23 24						
Ingatestone	d							22 33				23 03										
Shenfield 3	a	21 58	22 10		22s22		22s29	22 40	22 51			23 09				23s36						
Romford	a								22 59													
Stratford 7 ⊖	a	22s12	22s25					22s55	23s07			23s25				23s52						
London Liverpool Street 15 ⊖	a	22 25	22 38		22 49		22 58	23 07	23 20			23 38				00 07						

For general notes see front of timetable
For details of catering facilities see Directory of Train Operators

A From Cambridge (Table 14)

Table 11

Sundays

Norwich, Ipswich, Harwich, Clacton, Walton-on-Naze, Colchester and Chelmsford → London

Network diagram - see first page of Table 5

		LE 1	LE 1	LE 1	LE	LE 1	LE 1	LE 1	LE 1 ◇	LE 1	LE	LE 1	LE 1	LE 1	LE 1 ◇	LE 1	LE 1	LE 1	LE 1	LE 1	LE 1 ◇	LE 1	LE 1	LE 1	LE 1
					A				☕						☕						☕				
Norwich	d								07 00						08 00						09 00				
Diss	d								07 17						08 17						09 17				
Peterborough 8	d																								
Stowmarket	d								07 29						08 29						09 29				
Needham Market	d																								
Lowestoft	d																								
Ipswich	a								07 40						08 40						09 40				
	d								07 42		07 45	08 08			08 42			09 08			09 42			10 08	
Harwich Town	d																08 53						09 53		
Dovercourt	d																08 55						09 55		
Harwich International	d						07 25				08a10						08 58						09 58		
Wrabness	d																09 04						10 04		
Mistley	d																09 09						10 09		
Manningtree 2	d						07 38		07 52			08 18			08 52		09a14	09 18			09 52		10a14	10 18	
Walton-on-the-Naze	d												08 30						09 30						10 30
Frinton-on-Sea	d												08 33						09 33						10 33
Kirby Cross	d												08 36						09 36						10 36
Clacton-on-Sea	d									07 36						08 36						09 36			
Thorpe-le-Soken 1	a									07 43			08 42			08 43			09 42			09 43			10 42
	d									07 43						08 43						09 43			
Weeley	d																								
Great Bentley	d									07 49						08 49						09 49			
Alresford (Essex)	d									07 53						08 53						09 53			
Wivenhoe 3	d									07 56						08 56						09 56			
Hythe	d																								
Colchester Town	a																								
	d																								
Colchester 4	a						07 48		08 01	08 06		08 29			09 01	09 06		09 29			10 01	10 06		10 29	
	d			06 56	07 07	07 26	07 49		08 03	08 06		08 30			09 03	09 06		09 30			10 03	10 06		10 30	
Marks Tey 2	d			07 02	07a14	07 32				08 12		08 36				09 12		09 36				10 12		10 36	
Kelvedon	d			07 07		07 37						08 41						09 41						10 41	
Braintree	d	00 07						08 00						09 00						10 00					
Braintree Freeport	d	00 09						08 02						09 02						10 02					
Cressing	d	00 12						08 05						09 05						10 05					
White Notley	d	00 15						08 08						09 08						10 08					
Witham 2	d	00a22		07 12		07 42		08a16		08 20		08 46		09a16		09 20		09 46		10a16		10 20		10 46	
Hatfield Peverel	d			07 16		07 46						08 50						09 50						10 50	
Chelmsford 3	d		06 53	07 23		07 53	08 07			08 29		08 57				09 29		09 57				10 29		10 57	
Ingatestone	d		07 00	07 30		08 00						09 04						10 04						11 04	
Shenfield 3	a		07 06	07 36		08 06	08 18		08s29	08 40		09 10			09s29	09 40		10 10			10s29	10 40		11 10	
Romford	a																								
Stratford 7 ⊖ ⛴	a		07s34	08s04		08s34	08s49			09s04		09s34				10s04		10s34				11s04		11s34	
London Liverpool Street 15 ⊖	a		07 42	08 12		08 42	08 59		09 03	09 12		09 42			10 01	10 12		10 42			11 03	11 12		11 42	

For general notes see front of timetable
For details of catering facilities see Directory of Train Operators

A To Sudbury (Table 10)

Table 11

Sundays

Norwich, Ipswich, Harwich, Clacton, Walton-on-Naze, Colchester and Chelmsford → London

Network diagram - see first page of Table 5

		LE		LE	LE	LE	LE	LE	LE	LE	LE	LE	LE	LE	LE	LE	LE	LE	LE	LE	LE	LE	LE	LE	LE
		A		[1]	[1] ◇ 🍴	[1]	[1]	[1]	[1] B	[1]	[1]	[1] ◇ 🍴	[1]	[1]	[1]	[1]	C	[1]	[1] ◇ 🍴	[1]	[1]	[1]	[1]	[1]	[1]
Norwich	d				10 00							11 00							12 00						
Diss	d				10 17							11 17							12 17						
Peterborough [8]	d								09 46														11 46		
Stowmarket	d	10 17			10 29				11 12			11 29					12 17		12 29				13 12		
Needham Market	d	10 22															12 22								
Lowestoft	d																								
Ipswich	a	10 34			10 40				11 25			11 40					12 34		12 40				13 25		
	d				10 42			11 08				11 42			12 08				12 42			13 08			
Harwich Town	d						10 53							11 53							12 53				
Dovercourt	d						10 55							11 55							12 55				
Harwich International	d						10 58							11 58							12 58				
Wrabness	d						11 04							12 04							13 04				
Mistley	d						11 09							12 09							13 09				
Manningtree [2]	d				10 52		11a14	11 18				11 52		12a14	12 18				12 52		13a14	13 18			
Walton-on-the-Naze	d									11 30						12 30								13 30	
Frinton-on-Sea	d									11 33						12 33								13 33	
Kirby Cross	d									11 36						12 36								13 36	
Clacton-on-Sea	d					10 36							11 36							12 36					
Thorpe-le-Soken [1]	a					10 43				11 42			11 43			12 42				12 43				13 42	
	d					10 43							11 43							12 43					
Weeley	d																								
Great Bentley	d					10 49							11 49							12 49					
Alresford (Essex)	d					10 53							11 53							12 53					
Wivenhoe [3]	d					10 56							11 56							12 56					
Hythe	d																								
Colchester Town	a																								
	d																								
Colchester [4]	a				11 01	11 06		11 29				12 01	12 06		12 29				13 01	13 06		13 29			
	d				11 03	11 06		11 30				12 03	12 06		12 30				13 03	13 06		13 30			
Marks Tey [2]	d					11 12		11 36					12 12		12 36					13 12		13 36			
Kelvedon	d							11 41							12 41							13 41			
Braintree	d			11 00							12 00							13 00							14 00
Braintree Freeport	d			11 02							12 02							13 02							14 02
Cressing	d			11 05							12 05							13 05							14 05
White Notley	d			11 08							12 08							13 08							14 08
Witham [2]	d			11a16		11 20		11 46			12a16		12 20		12 46			13a16		13 20		13 46			14a16
Hatfield Peverel	d							11 50							12 50							13 50			
Chelmsford [3]	d					11 29		11 57					12 29		12 57					13 29		13 57			
Ingatestone	d							12 04							13 04							14 04			
Shenfield [3]	a				11s29	11 40		12 10				12s29	12 40		13 10				13s29	13 40		14 10			
Romford	a																								
Stratford [7] ⊖	a					12s04		12s34					13s04		13s34					14s04		14s34			
London Liverpool Street [15] ⊖	a				12 01	12 12		12 42				13 01	13 12		13 42				14 01	14 12		14 42			

		LE	LE	LE		LE	LE	LE	LE	LE	LE	LE	LE	LE	LE	LE	LE	LE	LE	LE	LE	LE	LE	LE	LE
		[1] ◇ 🍴	[1]	[1]		[1]	[1]	C	[1]	[1] ◇ 🍴	[1]	[1]	[1]	[1]	[1]	[1]	[1] ◇ 🍴	[1]	[1]	[1]	[1]	C	[1]	R [1] 🍴	[1]
Norwich	d	13 00								14 00							15 00							16 00	
Diss	d	13 17								14 17							15 17							16 17	
Peterborough [8]	d													13 46											
Stowmarket	d	13 29						14 17		14 29				15 12			15 29					16 17		16 29	
Needham Market	d							14 22														16 22			
Lowestoft	d																								
Ipswich	a	13 40						14 34		14 40				15 27			15 40					16 34		16 40	
	d	13 42				14 08				14 42			15 08				15 42			16 08				16 42	
Harwich Town	d			13 53								14 53							15 53						
Dovercourt	d			13 55								14 55							15 55						
Harwich International	d			13 58								14 58							15 58						
Wrabness	d			14 04								15 04							16 04						
Mistley	d			14 09								15 09							16 09						
Manningtree [2]	d	13 52		14a14		14 18				14 52		15a14	15 18				15 52		16a14	16 18				16 52	
Walton-on-the-Naze	d						14 30								15 30						16 30				
Frinton-on-Sea	d						14 33								15 33						16 33				
Kirby Cross	d						14 36								15 36						16 36				
Clacton-on-Sea	d		13 36								14 36							15 36							16 36
Thorpe-le-Soken [1]	a		13 43				14 42				14 43				15 42			15 43			16 42				16 43
	d		13 43								14 43							15 43							16 43
Weeley	d																								
Great Bentley	d		13 49								14 49							15 49							16 49
Alresford (Essex)	d		13 53								14 53							15 53							16 53
Wivenhoe [3]	d		13 56								14 56							15 56							16 56
Hythe	d																								
Colchester Town	a																								
	d																								
Colchester [4]	a	14 01	14 06			14 29				15 01	15 06		15 29				16 01	16 06		16 29				17 01	17 06
	d	14 03	14 06			14 30				15 03	15 06		15 30				16 03	16 06		16 30				17 03	17 06
Marks Tey [2]	d		14 12			14 36					15 12		15 36					16 12		16 36					17 12
Kelvedon	d					14 41							15 41							16 41					
Braintree	d								15 00							16 00							17 00		
Braintree Freeport	d								15 02							16 02							17 02		
Cressing	d								15 05							16 05							17 05		
White Notley	d								15 08							16 08							17 08		
Witham [2]	d		14 20			14 46			15a16		15 20		15 46			16a16		16 20		16 46			17a16		17 20
Hatfield Peverel	d					14 50							15 50							16 50					
Chelmsford [3]	d		14 29			14 57					15 29		15 57					16 29		16 57					17 29
Ingatestone	d					15 04							16 04							17 04					
Shenfield [3]	a	14s29	14 40			15 10				15s29	15 40		16 10				16s29	16 40		17 10				17s29	17 40
Romford	a																								
Stratford [7] ⊖	a		15s04			15s34					16s04		16s34					17s04		17s34					18s04
London Liverpool Street [15] ⊖	a	15 01	15 12			15 42				16 01	16 12		16 42				17 01	17 12		17 42				18 01	18 12

For general notes see front of timetable
For details of catering facilities see Directory of Train Operators

A From Bury St Edmunds (Table 14)
B Until 6 September
C From Cambridge (Table 14)

Table 11

Sundays

Norwich, Ipswich, Harwich, Clacton, Walton-on-Naze, Colchester and Chelmsford → London

Network diagram - see first page of Table 5

Station		LE 1	LE 1 ◇	LE 1	LE 1	LE 1		LE 1	LE 1 ◇	LE 1	LE 1	LE 1	LE 1	LE	LE 1	LE 1 ◇	LE 1	LE 1	LE 1	LE 1	LE 1	LE 1	LE 1 ◇	LE 1	LE 1
			☕						☕					A		☕							☕		
Norwich	d		16 20						17 00							18 00							19 00		
Diss	d		16 37						17 17							18 17							19 17		
Peterborough 8	d				15 46															17 46					
Stowmarket	d		16 49		17 12				17 29					18 17		18 29				19 12			19 29		
Needham Market	d													18 22											
Lowestoft	d																								
Ipswich	a		17 00		17 25				17 40					18 34		18 40				19 27			19 40		
	d		17 03	17 08					17 42			18 08				18 42			19 08				19 42		
Harwich Town	d	16 53									17 53							18 53							19 53
Dovercourt	d	16 55									17 55							18 55							19 55
Harwich International	d	16 58									17 58							18 58							19 58
Wrabness	d	17 04									18 04							19 04							20 04
Mistley	d	17 09									18 09							19 09							20 09
Manningtree 2	d	17a14		17 18					17 52		18a14	18 18				18 52		19a14	19 18				19 52		20a14
Walton-on-the-Naze	d					17 30							18 30								19 30				
Frinton-on-Sea	d					17 33							18 33								19 33				
Kirby Cross	d					17 36							18 36								19 36				
Clacton-on-Sea	d									17 36							18 36							19 36	
Thorpe-le-Soken 1	a					17 42				17 43			18 42				18 43				19 42			19 43	
	d									17 43							18 43							19 43	
Weeley	d																								
Great Bentley	d									17 49							18 49							19 49	
Alresford (Essex)	d									17 53							18 53							19 53	
Wivenhoe 3	d									17 56							18 56							19 56	
Hythe	d																								
Colchester Town	a																								
	d																								
Colchester 4	a		17 19	17 29					18 01	18 06		18 29				19 01	19 06		19 29				20 01	20 06	
	d		17 21	17 30					18 03	18 06		18 30				19 03	19 06		19 30				20 03	20 06	
Marks Tey 2	d			17 36						18 12		18 36					19 12		19 36					20 12	
Kelvedon	d			17 41								18 41							19 41						
Braintree	d							18 00							19 00							20 00			
Braintree Freeport	d							18 02							19 02							20 02			
Cressing	d							18 05							19 05							20 05			
White Notley	d							18 08							19 08							20 08			
Witham 2	d			17 46				18a16		18 20		18 46			19a16		19 20		19 46			20a16		20 20	
Hatfield Peverel	d			17 50								18 50							19 50						
Chelmsford 3	d			17 57						18 29		18 57					19 29		19 57					20 29	
Ingatestone	d			18 04								19 04							20 04						
Shenfield 3	a			18 10					18s29	18 40		19 10				19s29	19 40		20 10				20s29	20 40	
Romford	a																								
Stratford 7 ⊖ ⛴	a			18s34						19s04		19s34					20s04		20s34					21s04	
London Liverpool Street 15 ⊖	a		18 28	18 42					19 01	19 12		19 42				20 01	20 12		20 42				21 01	21 12	

Station		LE 1	LE 1	LE 1	LE 1	LE	LE 1 ◇	LE 1	LE 1	LE 1	LE 1	LE 1	LE 1 ◇	LE 1	LE 1	LE 1	LE 1	LE 1	LE	LE 1	LE 1 ◇	LE 1	LE 1		
						A	☕												A						
Norwich	d						20 00						21 00								22 00		23 05		
Diss	d						20 17						21 17								22 17		23 22		
Peterborough 8	d									19 44															
Stowmarket	d					20 17	20 29			21 05			21 29						22 17		22 29		23 34		
Needham Market	d					20 22													22 22						
Lowestoft	d																								
Ipswich	a					20 34	20 40			21 18			21 40						22 34		22 40		23 48		
	d	20 08				20 35	20 42		21 08	21 19			21 42				22 08				22 42				
Harwich Town	d				20 53											21 53						22 53			
Dovercourt	d				20 55											21 55						22 55			
Harwich International	d				20 58	21a02										21 58						22 58			
Wrabness	d				21 04											22 04						23 04			
Mistley	d				21 09											22 09						23 09			
Manningtree 2	d	20 18			21a14		20 52		21 18	21 29			21 52			22a14	22 18				22 52	23 14			
Walton-on-the-Naze	d		20 30								21 30				22 13										
Frinton-on-Sea	d		20 33								21 33				22 16										
Kirby Cross	d		20 36								21 36				22 19										
Clacton-on-Sea	d							20 36						21 36				22 20							
Thorpe-le-Soken 1	a		20 42					20 43			21 42			21 43	22 25			22 27							
	d							20 43						21 43				22 27							
Weeley	d																								
Great Bentley	d							20 49						21 49											
Alresford (Essex)	d							20 53						21 53											
Wivenhoe 3	d							20 56						21 56				22 37							
Hythe	d																								
Colchester Town	a																								
	d																								
Colchester 4	a	20 29					21 01	21 06	21 29	21 40			22 01	22 06			22 29	22 47			23 01	23 24			
	d	20 30					21 03	21 06	21 30				22 03	22 06			22 30				23 03				
Marks Tey 2	d	20 36						21 12	21 36					22 12			22 36								
Kelvedon	d	20 41							21 41								22 41								
Braintree	d			21 00								22 00								22 56					
Braintree Freeport	d			21 02								22 02								22 58					
Cressing	d			21 05								22 05								23 01					
White Notley	d			21 08								22 08								23 04					
Witham 2	d	20 46		21a16				21 20	21 46			22a16		22 20			22 46			23a12	23 15				
Hatfield Peverel	d	20 50							21 50								22 50								
Chelmsford 3	d	20 57						21 29	21 57					22 29			22 57				23 24				
Ingatestone	d	21 04							22 04								23 04								
Shenfield 3	a	21 10					21s29	21 40	22 10				22s29	22 40			23 10				23s36				
Romford	a																								
Stratford 7 ⊖ ⛴	a	21s34						22s04	22s34					23s04			23s34				23s57				
London Liverpool Street 15 ⊖	a	21 42					22 01	22 12	22 42				23 01	23 12			23 42				00 07				

For general notes see front of timetable
For details of catering facilities see Directory of Train Operators

A From Cambridge (Table 14)

Network Diagram for Tables 13, 14, 15, 16, 17

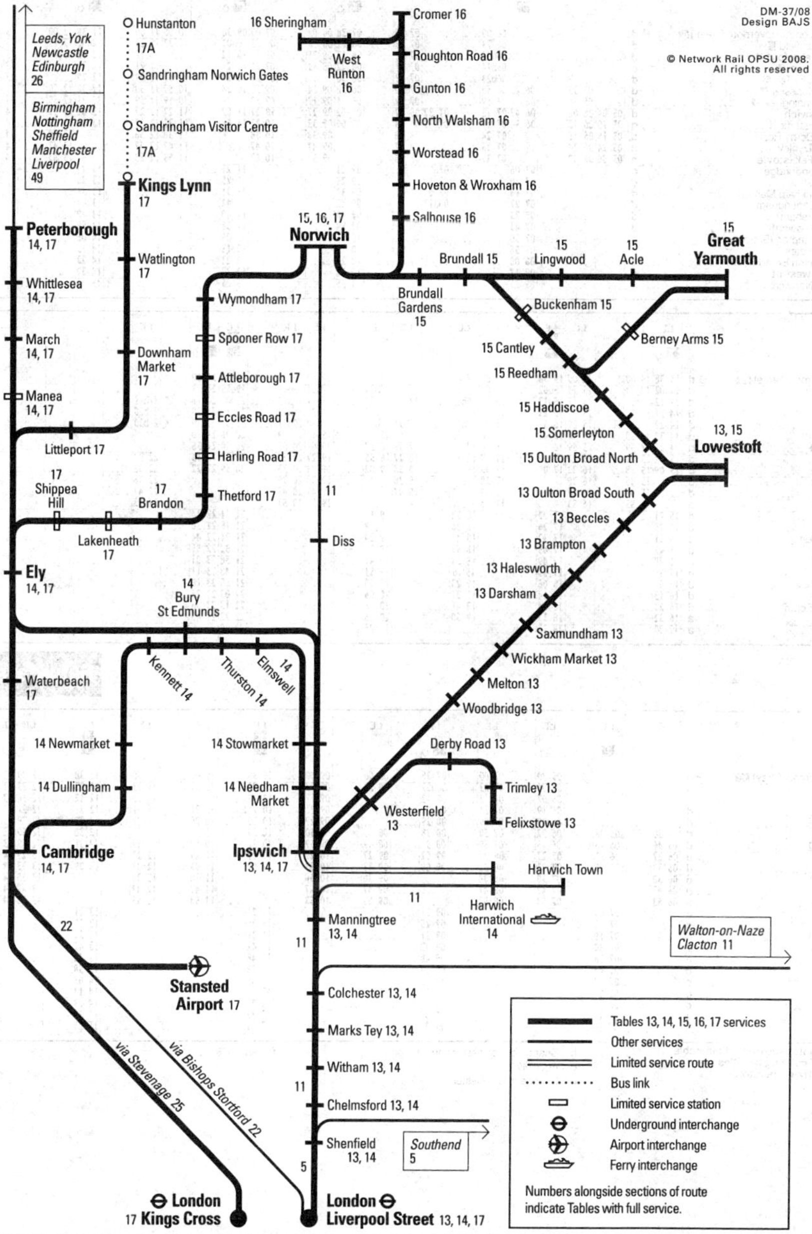

DM-37/08
Design BAJS
Leeds, York
Newcastle
Edinburgh
26
Birmingham
Nottingham
Sheffield
Manchester
Liverpool
49
Hunstanton
17A
Sandringham Norwich Gates
Sandringham Visitor Centre
17A
Kings Lynn 17
16 Sheringham
West Runton 16
Cromer 16
Roughton Road 16
Gunton 16
North Walsham 16
Worstead 16
Hoveton & Wroxham 16
Salhouse 16
15, 16, 17 Norwich
Peterborough 14, 17
Watlington 17
Whittlesea 14, 17
Wymondham 17
Spooner Row 17
March 14, 17
Downham Market 17
Attleborough 17
Manea 14, 17
Eccles Road 17
Littleport 17
Harling Road 17
17 Shippea Hill
17 Brandon
Thetford 17
Lakenheath 17
Ely 14, 17
Brundall 15
Brundall Gardens 15
15 Lingwood
15 Acle
15 Great Yarmouth
Buckenham 15
Berney Arms 15
15 Cantley
15 Reedham
15 Haddiscoe
15 Somerleyton
15 Oulton Broad North
13, 15 Lowestoft
13 Oulton Broad South
13 Beccles
13 Brampton
13 Halesworth
13 Darsham
Saxmundham 13
Wickham Market 13
Melton 13
Woodbridge 13
11
Diss
14 Bury St Edmunds
Kennett 14
Thurston 14
Elmswell 14
Waterbeach 17
14 Newmarket
14 Stowmarket
14 Dullingham
14 Needham Market
Derby Road 13
Trimley 13
Westerfield 13
Felixstowe 13
Cambridge 14, 17
Ipswich 13, 14, 17
Harwich Town
11
Harwich International 14
Manningtree 13, 14
22
11
Walton-on-Naze
Clacton 11
Stansted Airport 17
Colchester 13, 14
Marks Tey 13, 14
Witham 13, 14
11
Chelmsford 13, 14
via Stevenage 25
via Bishops Stortford 22
Shenfield 13, 14
Southend 5
5
London Kings Cross 17
London Liverpool Street 13, 14, 17
Tables 13, 14, 15, 16, 17 services
Other services
Limited service route
Bus link
Limited service station
Underground interchange
Airport interchange
Ferry interchange
Numbers alongside sections of route indicate Tables with full service.

Ipswich → Felixstowe and Lowestoft

Network diagram - see first page of Table 13

Mondays to Fridays

Miles	Miles			LE	LE		LE 1	LE		LE	LE		LE 1 ◇	LE		LE	LE 1 ◇		LE	LE		LE 1 ◇	LE		LE
—	—	London Liverpool Street 15 ⊖	d					06 00			07 00		07 38	08 02		09 00	09 38		10 00	11 00		11 38	12 00		13 00
—	—	Shenfield 3	d					06 23			07 23		08u02	08 26		09 23	10u02		10 23	11 23		12u02	12 23		13 23
—	—	Chelmsford 3	d					06b02			07 12		08 12	08 35		09 12	10 12			11 12		12 12			13 12
—	—	Witham 2	d					06b14			07 21		08 22	08 44		09 21	10 21			11 21		12 21			13 21
—	—	Marks Tey 2	d					06b24			07 33		08 30			09 29	10 29			11 29		12 29			13 29
—	—	Colchester 4	d		05 35		06 22	06 50			07 50		08 38	09 04		09 50	10 38		10 50	11 50		12 38	12 50		13 50
—	—	Manningtree 2	d		05 44		06 31	06 59			07 59		08 34	09 12		09 59	10 34		10 59	11 59		12 31	12 59		13 59
0	—	**Ipswich**	d	05 04	06 04		06 47	07 13		07 32	08 27		09 02	09 27		10 27	11 02		11 27	12 27		13 02	13 27		14 27
3½	0	Westerfield	d	05 10	06 10		06 54	07 19		07 39	08 33		09 09	09 33		10 33	11 09		11 33	12 33		13 09	13 33		14 33
—	2½	Derby Road	d	05 15	06 15			07 24			08 38			09 38		10 38			11 38	12 38			13 38		14 38
—	10½	Trimley	d	05 24	06 24			07 33			08 47			09 47		10 47			11 47	12 47			13 47		14 47
—	12¼	**Felixstowe**	a	05 30	06 30			07 39			08 53			09 53		10 53			11 53	12 53			13 53		14 53
10¼	—	Woodbridge	d				07 06			07c55			09 21				11 21					13 21			
11½	—	Melton	d				07 10			07 59			09 25				11 25					13 25			
15¾	—	Wickham Market	d				07 16			08 05			09 31				11 31					13 31			
22½	—	Saxmundham	d				07 27			08a17			09 42				11 42					13 42			
26¾	—	Darsham	d				07 33						09 48				11 48					13 48			
32	—	Halesworth	d				07 43						09 58				11 58					13 58			
36	—	Brampton (Suffolk)	d				07 50						10 05				12 05					14 05			
40¼	—	Beccles	d				07 58						10 13				12 13					14 13			
46¾	—	Oulton Broad South	d				08 08						10 23				12 23					14 23			
49	—	**Lowestoft**	a				08 17						10 32				12 32					14 32			
—	—	Norwich	a				09 25						11 25				13 25					15 25			

		LE 1 ◇	LE		LE	LE R 1		LE	LE		LE	LE		LE	LE		LE R 1	LE 1 ◇		LE					
London Liverpool Street 15 ⊖	d	13 38	14 00		15 00	15 38		16 00	17 00			17 30		18 00	19 00		19 32	21 00							
Shenfield 3	d	14u02	14 23		15 23	16u02		16 02	16 54			17b24		17b54	19b01		19u55	21u23							
Chelmsford 3	d	14 12			15 12	16u12		16 31	16b45		17b15	17 51		18b14	19b13		20e00	21 11		21b11					
Witham 2	d	14 21			15 21	16 23		16 23	17 13			17b45		18b30	19b23		20 12	21 20		21b20					
Marks Tey 2	d	14 29			15 29	16 32		16 32	17b01		17b31	17b55		18b30	19b33		20 00	21 30		21b30					
Colchester 4	d	14 38	14 50		15 50	16 41		16 50	17 26		17 51	18 11		18 53	19 53		20 26	21 50							
Manningtree 2	d	14 31	14 59		15 59	16 31		16 59	17 35		17 59	18 27		19 02	20 02		20 30	21 58							
Ipswich	d	15 02	15 27		16 27	17 02		17 27	18 13		18 27	18 55		19 27	20 27		20 52	22 15		22 27					
Westerfield	d	15 09	15 33		16 33	17 09		17 33	18 20		18 33	19 02		19 33	20 33		20 59	22 22		22 33					
Derby Road	d		15 38		16 38			17 38			18 38			19 38	20 38					22 38					
Trimley	d		15 47		16 47			17 47			18 47			19 47	20 47					22 47					
Felixstowe	a		15 53		16 53			17 53			18 53			19 53	20 53					22 53					
Woodbridge	d	15 21				17 22			18 32			19 14					21 11	22 34							
Melton	d	15 25				17 26			18 36			19 18					21 15	22 38							
Wickham Market	d	15 31				17 32			18 42			19 24					21 21	22 44							
Saxmundham	d	15 42				17 43			18 53			19 35					21 32	22 55							
Darsham	d	15 48				17 49			18 59			19 41					21 38	23 01							
Halesworth	d	15 58				17 59			19f16			19 51					21 48	23 11							
Brampton (Suffolk)	d	16 05				18 06			19 23			19 58					21 55	23 18							
Beccles	d	16 13				18 14			19 31			20 06					22 03	23 26							
Oulton Broad South	d	16 23				18 24			19 41			20 16					22 13	23 36							
Lowestoft	a	16 32				18 33			19 50			20 25					22 22	23 45							
Norwich	a	17 30				19 30						21 25					23 28								

Saturdays

		LE		LE 1		LE		LE		LE 1 ◇		LE		LE		LE R 1		LE		LE		LE R 1		LE	LE
London Liverpool Street 15 ⊖	d					05 30		07 00		07 38		08 00		09 00		09 38		10 00		11 00		11 38		12 00	13 00
Shenfield 3	d					05 56		07 23		08u02		08 23		09 23		10u02		10 23		11 23		12u02		12 23	13 23
Chelmsford 3	d					06 07		07 12		08 12				09 12		10 12		10 12		11 12		12 12		12 12	13 12
Witham 2	d					06 19		07 21		08 21				09 21		10 21		10 21		11 21		12 21		12 21	13 21
Marks Tey 2	d					06 29		07 29		08 29				09 29		10 29		10 29		11 29		12 29		12 29	13 29
Colchester 4	d	05 38		05 38		06 37		07 50		08 38		08 50		09 50		10 38		10 50		11 50		12 38		12 50	13 50
Manningtree 2	d	05 46		05 46		06 45		07 59		08 31		08 59		09 59		10 31		10 59		11 59		12 31		12 59	13 59
Ipswich	d	06 27		06 50		07 27		08 27		09 02		09 27		10 27		11 02		11 27		12 27		13 02		13 27	14 27
Westerfield	d	06 33		06 57		07 33		08 33		09 09		09 33		10 33		11 09		11 33		12 33		13 09		13 33	14 33
Derby Road	d	06 38				07 38		08 38				09 38		10 38				11 38		12 38				13 38	14 38
Trimley	d	06 47				07 47		08 47				09 47		10 47				11 47		12 47				13 47	14 47
Felixstowe	a	06 53				07 53		08 53				09 53		10 53				11 53		12 53				13 53	14 53
Woodbridge	d			07 09						09 21						11 21						13 21			
Melton	d			07 13						09 25						11 25						13 25			
Wickham Market	d			07 19						09 31						11 31						13 31			
Saxmundham	d			07 30						09 42						11 42						13 42			
Darsham	d			07 36						09 48						11 48						13 48			
Halesworth	d			07 46						09 58						11 58						13 58			
Brampton (Suffolk)	d			07 53						10 05						12 05						14 05			
Beccles	d			08 01						10 13						12 13						14 13			
Oulton Broad South	d			08 11						10 23						12 23						14 23			
Lowestoft	a			08 20						10 32						12 32						14 32			
Norwich	a			09 25						11 25						13 25						15 25			

For general notes see front of timetable
For details of catering facilities see Directory of Train Operators

b Change at Colchester and Ipswich
c Arr. 0749
e Change at Colchester
f Arr. 1908

Table 13

Saturdays

Ipswich → Felixstowe and Lowestoft

Network diagram - see first page of Table 13

		LE R 1	LE	LE	LE R 1	LE	LE	LE R 1	LE	LE	LE R 1	LE 1 ◇	LE
London Liverpool Street 15	⊖ d	13 38	14 00	15 00	15 38	16 00	17 00	17 46	18 00	19 00	19 38	21 00	
Shenfield 3	d	14u02	14 23	15 23	16u02	16 23	17 23	18b02	18 23	19 23	20u02	21u23	
Chelmsford 3	d	14 12	14 12	15 12	16 12	16 12	17 12	18u16	18 16	19 16	20 12	21 12	21c12
Witham 2	d	14 21	14 21	15 21	16 21	16 21	17 21	18 21	18c21	19c21	20 21	21 21	21c21
Marks Tey 2	d	14 29	14 29	15 29	16 29	16 29	17 29	18 28	18c28	19c28	20 29	21 29	21c29
Colchester 4	d	14 38	14 50	15 50	16 38	16 50	17 50	18 40	18 50	19 50	20 38	21 50	
Manningtree 2	d	14 31	14 59	15 59	16 31	16 59	17 59	18 31	18 59	19 59	20 32	21 58	
Ipswich	d	15 02	15 27	16 27	17 02	17 27	18 27	19 02	19 27	20 27	21 02	22 15	22 27
Westerfield	d	15 09	15 33	16 33	17 09	17 33	18 33	19 09	19 33	20 33	21 09	22 22	22 33
Derby Road	d		15 38	16 38		17 38	18 38		19 38	20 38			22 38
Trimley	d		15 47	16 47		17 47	18 47		19 47	20 47			22 47
Felixstowe	a		15 53	16 53		17 53	18 53		19 53	20 53			22 53
Woodbridge	d	15 21			17 21			19 21			21 21	22 34	
Melton	d	15 25			17 25			19 25			21 25	22 38	
Wickham Market	d	15 31			17 31			19 31			21 31	22 44	
Saxmundham	d	15 42			17 42			19 42			21 42	22 55	
Darsham	d	15 48			17 48			19 48			21 48	23 01	
Halesworth	d	15 58			17 58			19 58			21 58	23 11	
Brampton (Suffolk)	d	16 05			18 05			20 05			22 05	23 18	
Beccles	d	16 13			18 13			20 13			22 13	23 26	
Oulton Broad South	d	16 23			18 23			20 23			22 23	23 36	
Lowestoft	a	16 32			18 32			20 32			22 32	23 45	
Norwich	a	17 30			19 30			21 25			23 28		

Sundays

		LE 1	LE A	LE	LE	LE	LE	LE 1	LE	LE	LE	LE	LE	LE 1	LE	LE	LE 1	LE
London Liverpool Street 15	⊖ d	08 30	09 30	10 30		11 30	12 30	12 30	13 30	14 30		15 30	16 30	16 30	17 30	18 30	18 30	20 30
Shenfield 3	d	08 57	09 57	10 57		11 57	12 57	12 57	13 57	14 57		15 57	16 57	16 57	17 57	18 57	18 57	20 57
Chelmsford 3	d	08 42	09 42	10 42		11 42	12 42	12 42	13 42	14 42		15 42	16 42	16 42	17 42	18 42	18 42	20 42
Witham 2	d	08 54	09 54	10 54		11 54	12 54	12 54	13 54	14 54		15 54	16 54	16 54	17 54	18 54	18 54	20 54
Marks Tey 2	d	09 04	10 04	11 04		12 04	13 04	13 04	14 04	15 04		16 04	17 04	17 04	18 04	19 04	19 04	21 04
Colchester 4	d	09 24	10 24	11 24		12 24	13 24	13 24	14 24	15 24		16 24	17 24	17 24	18 24	19 24	19 24	21 24
Manningtree 2	d	09 33	10 33	11 33		12 33	13 33	13 33	14 33	15 33		16 33	17 33	17 33	18 33	19 33	19 33	21 33
Ipswich	d	10 00	10 55	11 55	12 00	12 55	13 55	14 00	14 55	15 55	16 00	16 55	17 55	18 00	18 55	19 55	20 00	22 00
Westerfield	d	10 07	11 01	12 01	12 07	13 01	14 01	14 07	15 01	16 01	16 07	17 01	18 01	18 07	19 01	20 01	20 07	22 07
Derby Road	d		11 06	12 06		13 06	14 06		15 06	16 06		17 06	18 06		19 06	20 06		
Trimley	d		11 15	12 15		13 15	14 15		15 15	16 15		17 15	18 15		19 15	20 15		
Felixstowe	a		11 21	12 21		13 21	14 21		15 21	16 21		17 21	18 21		19 21	20 21		
Woodbridge	d	10 19			12 19			14 19			16 19			18 19			20 19	22 19
Melton	d	10 23			12 23			14 23			16 23			18 23			20 23	22 23
Wickham Market	d	10 29			12 29			14 29			16 29			18 29			20 29	22 29
Saxmundham	d	10 40			12 40			14 40			16 40			18 40			20 40	22 40
Darsham	d	10 46			12 46			14 46			16 46			18 46			20 46	22 46
Halesworth	d	10 56			12 56			14 56			16 56			18 56			20 56	22 56
Brampton (Suffolk)	d	11 03			13 03			15 03			17 03			19 03			21 03	23 03
Beccles	d	11 11			13 11			15 11			17 11			19 11			21 11	23 11
Oulton Broad South	d	11 21			13 21			15 21			17 21			19 21			21 21	23 21
Lowestoft	a	11 30			13 30			15 30			17 30			19 30			21 30	23 30
Norwich	a	12 33			14 33			16 33			18 33			20 33			22 33	00 13

For general notes see front of timetable
For details of catering facilities see Directory of Train Operators

A Until 6 September
b Change at Colchester
c Change at Colchester and Ipswich

Lowestoft and Felixstowe → Ipswich

Network diagram - see first page of Table 13

Miles	Miles			LE	LE	LE	LE [R] [1]	LE	LE	LE	LE	LE [R] [1]	LE	LE	LE [1] ◇	LE	LE	LE [1] ◇
—	—	Norwich	d				05 45					07 54			09 57			11 57
0	—	**Lowestoft**	d		05 31		06 44					08 58			10 58			12 58
2¼	—	Oulton Broad South	d		05 38		06 51					09 05			11 05			13 05
8½	—	Beccles	d		05 47		07 00					09 14			11 14			13 14
13	—	Brampton (Suffolk)	d		05 55		07 08					09 22			11 22			13 22
17	—	Halesworth	d		06 03		07 16					09 30			11 30			13 30
22½	—	Darsham	d		06 11		07 24					09 38			11 38			13 38
26½	—	Saxmundham	d		06 19		07 32		08 21			09 46			11 46			13 46
33¼	—	Wickham Market	d		06 28		07 41		08 30			09 55			11 55			13 55
37¼	—	Melton	d		06 35		07 48		08 37			10 02			12 02			14 02
38¾	—	Woodbridge	d		06 40		07 53		08 42			10 07			12 07			14 07
—	0	**Felixstowe**	d	05 34		06 38		07 50		08 56	09 56		10 56	11 56		12 56	13 56	
—	1¾	Trimley	d	05 37		06 41		07 53		08 59	09 59		10 59	11 59		12 59	13 59	
—	9¾	Derby Road	d	05 47		06 51		08 03		09 09	10 09		11 09	12 09		13 09	14 09	
45½	12¼	Westerfield	d	05 52	06 51	06 56	08 04	08 08	08 53	09 14	10 14	10 18	11 14	12 14	12 18	13 14	14 14	14 18
49	—	**Ipswich**	a	06 00	06 59	07 03	08 12	08 16	09 01	09 22	10 22	10 26	11 22	12 22	12 26	13 22	14 22	14 26
—	—	Manningtree [2]	a	06 32		07 17	08 32		09 17	09 51	10 51	10 51	11 51		12 51	13 51		14 51
—	—	Colchester [4]	a	06 43		07 28	08 43		09 27	09 48	10 48	10 48	11 48		12 48	13 48		14 48
—	—	Marks Tey [2]	a	06b54		07b43	08b54		09b39	10b23	11b23	11 23	12b23	13b23	13 23	14b23	15b23	15 23
—	—	Witham [2]	a	07b05		07b47	09b05		09b49	10 02	11 02	11 02	12 02		13 02	14 02		15 02
—	—	Chelmsford [3]	a	07b14		07b56	09 02		09 46	10 10	11 10	11 10	12 10		13 10	14 10		15 10
—	—	Shenfield [3]	a	07 32		08b08	09b25		10b09	10 22	11 22	11s22	12 22		13s22	14 22		15s22
—	—	London Liverpool Street [15]	⊖ a	07 37		08 23	09 25		10 24	10 46	11 45	11 45	12 45		13 45	14 45		15 45

		LE	LE	LE	LE	LE	LE [1] ◇	LE	LE [1] ◇	LE	LE	LE	LE
Norwich	d			13 57			15 57		16 57			19 57	
Lowestoft	d			14 58			16 58		18 43			20 58	
Oulton Broad South	d			15 05			17 05		18 50			21 05	
Beccles	d			15 14			17 14		18 59			21 14	
Brampton (Suffolk)	d			15 22			17 22		19 07			21 22	
Halesworth	d			15 30			17 30		19 15			21 30	
Darsham	d			15 38			17 38		19 23			21 38	
Saxmundham	d			15 46			17 46		19c36			21 46	
Wickham Market	d			15 55			17 55		19 45			21 55	
Melton	d			16 02			18 02		19 52			22 02	
Woodbridge	d			16 07			18 07		19 57			22 07	
Felixstowe	d	14 56	15 56		16 56	17 56		18 56		19 56	20 56		22 56
Trimley	d	14 59	15 59		16 59	17 59		18 59		19 59	20 59		22 59
Derby Road	d	15 09	16 09		17 09	18 09		19 09		20 09	21 09		23 09
Westerfield	d	15 14	16 14	16 18	17 14	18 14	18 18	19 14	20 08	20 14	21 14	22 18	23 14
Ipswich	a	15 22	16 22	16 26	17 22	18 22	18 26	19 22	20 16	20 22	21 22	22 26	23 22
Manningtree [2]	a	15 51		16 51	17 51		18 51	19 36	20 51	20 51	21 36	22 51	23 47
Colchester [4]	a	15 43		16 48	17 48		18 48	19 47	20 48	20 48	21 48	23 01	23 58
Marks Tey [2]	a	15b54		16 59	17 55		18 55	19 54	21 23	21b23	22b23		
Witham [2]	a	16b04		17 06	18 03		19 03	20 02	21 02	21 02	22 02	23 15	
Chelmsford [3]	a	16b13		17 15	18 13		19 12	20 11	21 10	21 10	22 10	23 24	
Shenfield [3]	a	16b24		17 27	18 25		19s24	20 23	21s23	21 23	22 22	23 36	
London Liverpool Street [15]	⊖ a	16b48		17 49	18 49		19 47	20 46	21 46	21 46	22 46	00 03	

Saturdays

		LE	LE [R] [1]	LE	LE [R] [1]	LE	LE	LE [R] [1]	LE	LE	LE [R] [1]	LE	LE	LE [1] ◇
Norwich	d				05 49			07 54			09 57			11 57
Lowestoft	d		05 58		06 58			08 58			10 58			12 58
Oulton Broad South	d		06 05		07 05			09 05			11 05			13 05
Beccles	d		06 14		07 14			09 14			11 14			13 14
Brampton (Suffolk)	d		06 22		07 22			09 22			11 22			13 22
Halesworth	d		06 30		07 30			09 30			11 30			13 30
Darsham	d		06 38		07 38			09 38			11 38			13 38
Saxmundham	d		06 46		07 46			09 46			11 46			13 46
Wickham Market	d		06 55		07 55			09 55			11 55			13 55
Melton	d		07 02		08 02			10 02			12 02			14 02
Woodbridge	d		07 07		08 07			10 07			12 07			14 07
Felixstowe	d	06 56		07 56		08 56	09 56		10 56	11 56		12 56	13 56	
Trimley	d	06 59		07 59		08 59	09 59		10 59	11 59		12 59	13 59	
Derby Road	d	07 09		08 09		09 09	10 09		11 09	12 09		13 09	14 09	
Westerfield	d	07 14	07 18	08 14	08 18	09 14	10 14	10 18	11 14	12 14	12 18	13 14	14 14	14 18
Ipswich	a	07 22	07 26	08 22	08 26	09 22	10 22	10 26	11 22	12 22	12 26	13 22	14 22	14 26
Manningtree [2]	a	07 51	07 51	08 51	08 51	09 51	10 51	10 51	11 51	12 51	12 51	13 51		14 51
Colchester [4]	a	07 48	07 48	08 48	08 48	09 48	10 48	10 48	11 48	12 48	12 48	13 48		14 48
Marks Tey [2]	a	08b23	08 23	09b23	09 23	10b23	11b23	11 23	12b23	13b23	13 23	14b23	15b23	15 23
Witham [2]	a	08 02	08 02	09b04	09 04	10b04	11b04	11 04	12 02	13 02	13 02	14 02		15 02
Chelmsford [3]	a	08 10	08 10	09 06	09s06	10 06	11 06	11s06	12 10	13 10	13 10	14 10		15 10
Shenfield [3]	a	08 22	08s22	09b24	09e24	10b24	11b24	11e24	12 22	13 22	13s22	14 22		15s22
London Liverpool Street [15]	⊖ a	08 45	08 45	09 38	09 38	10 38	11 42	11 42	12 45	13 45	13 45	14 45		15 45

For general notes see front of timetable
For details of catering facilities see Directory of Train Operators

b Change at Ipswich and Colchester
c Arr. 1930
e Change at Colchester

Table 13

Saturdays

Lowestoft and Felixstowe → Ipswich

Network diagram - see first page of Table 13

		LE	LE	LE 1 ◇	LE	LE	LE 1 ◇	LE	LE	LE 1 ◇	LE	LE	LE
Norwich	d			13 57			15 57			17 57		19 57	
Lowestoft	d			14 58			16 58			18 58		20 58	
Oulton Broad South	d			15 05			17 05			19 05		21 05	
Beccles	d			15 14			17 14			19 14		21 14	
Brampton (Suffolk)	d			15 22			17 22			19 22		21 22	
Halesworth	d			15 30			17 30			19 30		21 30	
Darsham	d			15 38			17 38			19 38		21 38	
Saxmundham	d			15 46			17 46			19 46		21 46	
Wickham Market	d			15 55			17 55			19 55		21 55	
Melton	d			16 02			18 02			20 02		22 02	
Woodbridge	d			16 07			18 07			20 07		22 07	
Felixstowe	d	14 56	15 56		16 56	17 56		18 56	19 56		20 56		22 56
Trimley	d	14 59	15 59		16 59	17 59		18 59	19 59		20 59		22 59
Derby Road	d	15 09	16 09		17 09	18 09		19 09	20 09		21 09		23 09
Westerfield	d	15 14	16 14	16 18	17 14	18 14	18 18	19 14	20 14	20 18	21 14	22 18	23 14
Ipswich	a	15 22	16 22	16 26	17 22	18 22	18 26	19 22	20 22	20 26	21 22	22 26	23 22
Manningtree 2	a	15 51		16 51	17 51		18 51	19 36		20 51	21 37	22 51	23 35
Colchester 4	a	15 48		16 48	17 48		18 48	19 48		20 48	21 48	23 01	23 45
Marks Tey 2	a	16b23	17b23	17 23	18b23	19b23	19 23	20b23	21b23	21 23	22b23		
Witham 2	a	16 02		17 02	18 02		19 02	20 02		21 02	22 02	23 15	
Chelmsford 3	a	16 10		17 10	18 10		19 10	20 10		21 10	22 10	23 24	
Shenfield 3	a	16 22		17s22	18 22		19s22	20 22		21s22	22 22	23 36	
London Liverpool Street 15	⊖ a	16 45		17 45	18 45		19 45	20 45		21 49	22 49	00 07	

Sundays

		LE 1	LE	LE A	LE	LE 1	LE	LE	LE	LE	LE	LE 1	LE	LE	LE 1	LE	LE	LE
Norwich	d	07 25	08 57			10 57			12 57			14 57			16 57			18 57
Lowestoft	d	08 05	10 05			12 05			14 05			16 05			18 05			20 05
Oulton Broad South	d	08 12	10 12			12 12			14 12			16 12			18 12			20 12
Beccles	d	08 21	10 21			12 21			14 21			16 21			18 21			20 21
Brampton (Suffolk)	d	08 29	10 29			12 29			14 29			16 29			18 29			20 29
Halesworth	d	08 37	10 37			12 37			14 37			16 37			18 37			20 37
Darsham	d	08 45	10 45			12 45			14 45			16 45			18 45			20 45
Saxmundham	d	08 53	10 53			12 53			14 53			16 53			18 53			20 53
Wickham Market	d	09 02	11 02			13 02			15 02			17 02			19 02			21 02
Melton	d	09 09	11 09			13 09			15 09			17 09			19 09			21 09
Woodbridge	d	09 14	11 14			13 14			15 14			17 14			19 14			21 14
Felixstowe	d			11 25	12 25		13 25	14 25		15 25	16 25		17 25	18 25		19 25	20 25	
Trimley	d			11 28	12 28		13 28	14 28		15 28	16 28		17 28	18 28		19 28	20 28	
Derby Road	d			11 38	12 38		13 38	14 38		15 38	16 38		17 38	18 38		19 38	20 38	
Westerfield	d	09 25	11 25	11 43	12 43	13 25	13 43	14 43	15 25	15 43	16 43	17 25	17 43	18 43	19 25	19 43	20 43	21 25
Ipswich	a	09 33	11 33	11 50	12 50	13 33	13 50	14 50	15 33	15 50	16 50	17 33	17 50	18 50	19 33	19 50	20 50	21 33
Manningtree 2	a	09 51	11 51	12 18	13 18	13 51	14 18	15 18	15 51	16 18	17 18	17 51	18 18	19 18	19 51	20 18	21 18	21 51
Colchester 4	a	10 01	12 01	12 29	13 29	14 01	14 29	15 29	16 01	16 29	17 19	18 01	18 29	19 29	20 01	20 29	21 29	22 01
Marks Tey 2	a	10b12	12b12	12 36	13 36	14b12	14 36	15 36	16b12	16 36	17 36	18b12	18 36	19 36	20b12	20 36	21 36	22b12
Witham 2	a	10b20	12b20	12 46	13 46	14b20	14 46	15 46	16b20	16 46	17 46	18b20	18 46	19 46	20b20	20 46	21 46	22b20
Chelmsford 3	a	10b29	12b29	12 57	13 57	14b29	14 57	15 57	16b29	16 57	17 57	18b29	18 57	19 57	20b29	20 57	21 57	22b29
Shenfield 3	a	10 29	12 29	13 10	14 10	14 29	15 10	16 10	16 29	17 10	18 10	18 29	19 10	20 10	20 29	21 10	22 10	22 29
London Liverpool Street 15	⊖ a	11 03	13 01	13 42	14 42	15 01	15 42	16 42	17 01	17 42	18 28	19 01	19 42	20 42	21 01	21 42	22 42	23 01

For general notes see front of timetable
For details of catering facilities see Directory of Train Operators

A Until 6 September
b Change at Ipswich and Colchester

Ipswich → Bury St Edmunds, Cambridge, Ely and Peterborough

Network diagram - see first page of Table 13

Mondays to Fridays

Miles	Miles	Miles	Station		LE	LE [1]	LE	LE	LE [1] ◇	LE	LE	LE [1]	LE	LE	LE [1] ◇
—	—	—	London Liverpool Street [15] ⊖	d					06 38		08 00	08 38	09 00	10 00	10 38
—	—	—	Shenfield	d					07u02		08 23	09 02	09 23	10 23	11u02
—	—	—	Chelmsford	d					07 12		08 12	09 12		10 12	11 12
—	—	—	Witham	d					07 21		08 22	09 21		10 21	11 21
—	—	—	Marks Tey	d					07 33		08 30	09 29		10 29	11 29
—	—	—	Colchester	d		05 35		06 22	07 41		08 50	09 38	09 50	10 50	11 38
—	—	—	Manningtree	d		05 44		06 31	07 50		08 59	09 46	09 59	10 59	
—	—	0	Harwich International	d						07 47					
0	—	18	**Ipswich**	d	05 10	06 01	06 13	06 52	08 02	08 16	09 16	10 02	10 16	11 16	12 02
8¼	—	—	Needham Market	d	05 20		06 23	07 02		08 26	09 26		10 26	11 26	
12	—	—	Stowmarket	d	05 26	06 12	06 29	07 08	08 13	08 32	09 32	10 13	10 32	11 32	12 13
17¾	—	—	Elmswell	d	05 35		06 38	07 18		08 41	09 41		10 41	11 41	
22¼	—	—	Thurston	d	05 41		06 44	07 24		08 47	09 47		10 47	11 47	
26¼	—	—	Bury St Edmunds	a	05 47	06 28	06 50	07 30	08 29	08 53	09 53	10 29	10 53	11 53	12 29
—	—	—		d	05 49	06 28	06 51	07 30	08 29	08 55	09 55	10 29	10 55	11 55	12 29
36	0	—	Kennett	d	06 00		07 02	07 42			10 06			12 06	
41	—	—	Newmarket	d	06 10		07 13	07 51		09 15	10 17		11 15	12 17	
44¼	—	—	Dullingham	d	06 15		07 18	08b00		09 20			11 20		
55¼	—	—	**Cambridge**	a	06 33		07 37	08 19		09 39	10 39		11 39	12 39	
70	14¾	—	**Ely** [6]	d		07 00			08 58			10 58			12 58
79¾	—	—	Manea	d											
85¼	—	—	March	d		07 16			09 15			11 15			13 15
93¼	—	—	Whittlesea	d		07 27			09 26			11 26			13 26
99¼	—	—	**Peterborough** [8]	a		07 39			09 37			11 37			13 37

Station		LE	LE	LE [1] ◇	LE	LE	LE [1] ◇	LE	LE	LE [R] [1]	LE	LE	LE [1]	LE	LE
London Liverpool Street [15] ⊖	d	11 00	12 00	12 38	13 00	14 00	14 38	15 00	16 00	16 32	17 00	18 00	19 00	20 00	21 00
Shenfield	d	11 23	12 23	13u02	13 23	14 23	15u02	15 23	16 02	16u54	16 54	17c54	19c01	20 02	21 23
Chelmsford	d		12 12	13 12		14 12	15 12		16 31	16e45	17c15	18c14	19c13	20 11	21c11
Witham	d		12 21	13 21		14 21	15 21		16 23	17 13	17 13	18c30	19c23	20 20	21c20
Marks Tey	d		12 29	13 29		14 29	15 29		16 32	17 01	17c31	18c30	19c33	20 30	21c30
Colchester	d	11 50	12 50	13 38	13 50	14 50	15 38	15 50	16 50	17 26	17 51	18 53	19 53	20 50	21 50
Manningtree	d	11 59	12 59		13 59	14 59		15 59	16 59	17 35	17 59	19 02	20 02	20 59	21 58
Harwich International	d														21 34
Ipswich	d	12 16	13 16	14 02	14 16	15 16	16 02	16 16	17 16	17 49	18 16	19 16	20 16	21 16	22 16
Needham Market	d	12 26	13 26		14 26	15 26		16 26	17 26	17 58	18 26	19 26	20 25	21 26	22 26
Stowmarket	d	12 32	13 32	14 13	14 32	15 32	16 13	16 32	17 32	18 03	18 32	19 32	20 30	21 32	22 32
Elmswell	d	12 41	13 41		14 41	15 41		16 41	17 41	18 12	18 41	19 41	20 39	21 41	22 41
Thurston	d	12 47	13 47		14 47	15 47		16 47	17 47	18 17	18 47	19 47	20 44	21 47	22 47
Bury St Edmunds	a	12 53	13 53	14 29	14 53	15 53	16 29	16 53	17 53	18 23	18 53	19 53	20 50	21 53	22 54
	d	12 55	13 55	14 29	14 55	15 55	16 29	16 55	17 55	18 23	18 55	19 55	20 50	21 55	
Kennett	d		14 06			16 06			18 06			20 06		22 06	
Newmarket	d	13 15	14 17		15 15	16 17		17 17	18 17		19 15	20 17		22 15	
Dullingham	d	13 20			15 20						19 20			22 20	
Cambridge	a	13 39	14 39		15 39	16 39		17 39	18 39		19 39	20 39		22 39	
Ely [6]	d			14 58			16 58			19f01			21 19		
Manea	d														
March	d			15 15			17 15			19 17			21 36		
Whittlesea	d			15 26			17 26			19 29			21 47		
Peterborough [8]	a			15 37			17 37			19 42			21 58		

Saturdays

Station		LE	LE [1]	LE	LE	LE [1] ◇	LE	LE	LE [1] ◇	LE	LE	LE [R] [1]	LE	LE
London Liverpool Street [15] ⊖	d				05 30	06 38	07g00	08 00	08 38	09 00	10 00	10 38	11 00	12 00
Shenfield	d				05 56	07u02	07g23	08 23	09u02	09 23	10 23	11u02	11 23	12 23
Chelmsford	d				06 07	07 12		08 12	09 12		10 12	11 12	11 12	12 12
Witham	d				06 19	07 21		08 21	09 21		10 21	11 21	11 21	12 21
Marks Tey	d				06 29	07 29		08 29	09 29		10 29	11 29	11 29	12 29
Colchester	d		05 38		06 37	07 38	07g50	08 50	09 38	09 50	10 50	11 38	11 50	12 50
Manningtree	d		05 46		06 45	07 46	07g59	08 59	09 46	09 59	10 59		11 59	12 59
Harwich International	d						07 47							
Ipswich	d	05 10	06 00	06 14	07 16	08 02	08 16	09 16	10 02	10 16	11 16	12 02	12 16	13 16
Needham Market	d	05 20		06 24	07 26		08 26	09 26		10 26	11 26		12 26	13 26
Stowmarket	d	05 26	06 11	06 30	07 32	08 13	08 32	09 32	10 13	10 32	11 32	12 13	12 32	13 32
Elmswell	d	05 35		06 39	07 41		08 41	09 41		10 41	11 41		12 41	13 41
Thurston	d	05 41		06 45	07 47		08 47	09 47		10 47	11 47		12 47	13 47
Bury St Edmunds	a	05 47	06 27	06 51	07 53	08 29	08 53	09 53	10 29	10 53	11 53	12 29	12 53	13 53
	d	05 49	06 27	06 53	07 55	08 29	08 55	09 55	10 29	10 55	11 55	12 29	12 55	13 55
Kennett	d	06 00		07 04	08 06			10 06			12 06			14 06
Newmarket	d	06 10		07 15	08 17		09 15	10 17		11 15	12 17		13 15	14 17
Dullingham	d	06 15		07 20	08 22		09 20			11 20			13 20	
Cambridge	a	06 36		07 39	08 39		09 39	10 39		11 39	12 39		13 39	14 39
Ely [6]	d		06 57			08 58			10 58			12 58		
Manea	d													
March	d		07 14			09 16			11 15			13 15		
Whittlesea	d		07 25			09 27			11 26			13 26		
Peterborough [8]	a		07 37			09 38			11 37			13 37		

For general notes see front of timetable
For details of catering facilities see Directory of Train Operators

- b Arr. 0757
- c Change at Colchester and Ipswich
- e Change at Colchester
- f Arr. 1852
- g Change at Ipswich

Table 14

Saturdays

Ipswich → Bury St Edmunds, Cambridge, Ely and Peterborough

Network diagram - see first page of Table 13

		LE R 1	LE	LE	LE 1 ◊	LE	LE	LE R 1	LE	LE	LE R 1	LE	LE
London Liverpool Street 15	⊖ d	12 38	13 00	14 00	14 38	15 00		16 38	17 00	18 00	18 46	19 00	21 00
Shenfield	d	13u02	13 23	14 23	15u02	15 23		17u02	17 23	18 23	19b02	19 23	21 23
Chelmsford	d	13 12	13 12	14 12	15 12		16 12	17 12	17 12	18 16	19u16	19 16	21c12
Witham	d	13 21	13 21	14 21	15 21		16 21	17 21	17 21	18c21	19 21	19c21	21c21
Marks Tey	d	13 29	13 29	14 29	15 29		16 29	17 29	17 29	18c28	19 28	19c28	21c29
Colchester	d	13 38	13 50	14 50	15 38	15 50		17 38	17 50	18 50	19 40	19 50	21 50
Manningtree	d		13 59	14 59		15 59			17 59	18 59		19 59	21 58
Harwich International	d												21 34
Ipswich	d	14 02	14 16	15 16	16 02	16 16	17 16	18 02	18 16	19 16	20 02	20 16	22 17
Needham Market	d		14 26	15 26		16 26	17 26		18 26	19 26		20 26	22 27
Stowmarket	d	14 13	14 32	15 32	16 13	16 32	17 32	18 13	18 32	19 32	20 13	20 32	22 33
Elmswell	d		14 41	15 41		16 41	17 41		18 41	19 42		20 41	22 42
Thurston	d		14 47	15 47		16 47	17 47		18 47	19 48		20 47	22 48
Bury St Edmunds	a	14 29	14 53	15 53	16 29	16 53	17 53	18 29	18 53	19 53	20 29	20 53	22 55
	d	14 29	14 55	15 55	16 29	16 55	17 55	18 29	18 55	19 55	20 29	20 55	
Kennett	d			16 06			18 06			20 06		21 06	
Newmarket	d		15 15	16 17		17 17	18 17		19 15	20 17		21 15	
Dullingham	d		15 20						19 20			21 20	
Cambridge	a		15 39	16 39		17 39	18 39		19 39	20 39		21 39	
Ely 6	d	14 58			16 58			18 58			20 58		
Manea	d												
March	d	15 15			17 15			19 15			21 15		
Whittlesea	d	15 26			17 26			19 26			21 26		
Peterborough 8	a	15 37			17 37			19 37			21 37		

Sundays

		LE 1 A	LE	LE	LE 1	LE	LE 1	LE	LE 1	LE	LE 1	LE	LE 1	LE	LE
London Liverpool Street 15	⊖ d														
Shenfield	d														
Chelmsford	d				08 42	09 42	10 42	11 42	12 42	13 42	14 42	15 42	16 42	17 42	19 42
Witham	d				08 54	09 54	10 54	11 54	12 54	13 54	14 54	15 54	16 54	17 54	19 54
Marks Tey	d				09 04	10 04	11 04	12 04	13 04	14 04	15 04	16 04	17 04	18 04	20 04
Colchester	d		08 12												
Manningtree	d		08 20												
Harwich International	d			08 30											
Ipswich	d	07 55	08 45	09 02	09 55	11 02	11 55	13 02	13 55	15 02	15 55	17 02	17 55	19 02	21 02
Needham Market	d			09 12		11 12		13 12		15 12		17 12		19 12	21 12
Stowmarket	d	08 07	08 59	09 18	10 07	11 18	12 07	13 18	14 07	15 18	16 07	17 18	18 07	19 18	21 18
Elmswell	d			09 27		11 27		13 27		15 27		17 27		19 27	21 27
Thurston	d			09 33		11 33		13 33		15 33		17 33		19 33	21 33
Bury St Edmunds	a	08 22	09 17	09 39	10 22	11 39	12 22	13 39	14 22	15 39	16 22	17 39	18 22	19 39	21 39
	d	08 23		09 40	10 23	11 40	12 23	13 40	14 23	15 40	16 23	17 40	18 23	19 40	21 40
Kennett	d			09 51		11 51		13 51		15 51		17 51		19 51	21 51
Newmarket	d			10 00		12 00		14 00		16 00		18 00		20 00	22 00
Dullingham	d			10 05		12 05		14 05		16 05		18 05		20 05	22 05
Cambridge	a			10 24		12 24		14 24		16 24		18 24		20 24	22 24
Ely 6	d	08 52			10 52		12 52		14 52		16 52		18 52		
Manea	d														
March	d	09 09			11 09		13 09		15 09		17 09		19 09		
Whittlesea	d	09 20			11 20		13 20		15 20		17 20		19 20		
Peterborough 8	a	09 36			11 36		13 36		15 36		17 31		19 32		

For general notes see front of timetable
For details of catering facilities see Directory of Train Operators

A Until 6 September
b Change at Colchester
c Change at Colchester and Ipswich

Peterborough, Ely, Cambridge and Bury St Edmunds → Ipswich

Network diagram - see first page of Table 13

Mondays to Fridays

Miles	Miles	Miles	Station		LE MO	LE	LE	LE	LE	LE R 1	LE	LE	LE 1 ◇	LE	LE	LE 1 ◇	LE	LE	LE 1
0	—	—	Peterborough 8	d						07 46			09 45			11 45			13 45
6	—	—	Whittlesea	d						07 54			09 53			11 53			13 53
14	—	—	March	d						08 05			10 04			12 04			14 04
19¼	—	—	Manea	d															
29¼	0	—	Ely 6	d						08 30			10b26			12c30			14 30
45	—	—	Cambridge	d	23p00			06 41	07 43		08 43	09 43		10 43	11 43		12 43	13 43	
56	—	—	Dullingham	d	23p16				08 00			09 59			11 59			13 59	
58½	—	—	Newmarket	d	23p21			07 01	08 04		09 03	10 04		11 03	12 04		13 03	14 04	
63¼	14¾	—	Kennett	d	23p29			07 09			09 11			11 11			13 11		
73¼	—	—	Bury St Edmunds	a	23p41			07 21	08 23	08 55	09 23	10 23	10 51	11 23	12 23	12 55	13 23	14 23	14 55
—	—	—		d	23p42	05 36	06 22	07 23	08 24	08 56	09 23	10 23	10 56	11 23	12 23	12 56	13 23	14 23	14 56
77¼	—	—	Thurston	d	23p48	05 42	06 28	07 30	08 30		09 30	10 30		11 30	12 30		13 30	14 30	
81¼	—	—	Elmswell	d	23p55	05 49	06 35	07 36	08 37		09 36	10 36		11 36	12 36		13 36	14 36	
87¼	—	—	Stowmarket	d	00 04	05 57	06 44	07 45	08 45	09 12	09 45	10 45	11 12	11 45	12 45	13 12	13 45	14 45	15 12
90¾	—	—	Needham Market	d	00 09	06 03		07 50	08 51		09 50	10 50		11 50	12 50		13 50	14 50	
99¼	—	0	Ipswich	a	00 21	06 15	07 00	08 02	09 03	09 26	10 03	11 03	11 25	12 03	13 03	13 25	14 03	15 03	15 25
—	—	18	Harwich International	a			07 25												
—	—	—	Manningtree	a		06 32	07e17		09 17	09 51	10 17	11 17	11 51	12 17	13 17	13 51	14 17	15 17	15 51
—	—	—	Colchester	a		06 43	07e28		09 27	09 48	10 27	11 27	11 48	12 27	13 27	13 48	14 27	15 27	15 43
—	—	—	Marks Tey	a		06f54	07f43	08f54	09f39	10 23	10f39	11f39	12 23	12f39	13f39	14 23	14f39	15f54	15 54
—	—	—	Witham	a		07f05	07f47	09f05	09f49	10 02	10f49	11f49	12 02	12f49	13f49	14 02	14f49	15f49	16 04
—	—	—	Chelmsford	a		07f14	07f56		09 46	10s10	10 45	11 45	12 10	12 45	13 45	14 10	14 45	15 45	16 13
—	—	—	Shenfield	a		07 32	08f08	09f25	10f09	10s22	11f09	12f09	12s22	13f09	14f09	14s22	15f09	16f11	16 24
—	—	—	London Liverpool Street 15 ⊖	a		07 37	08e23	09 25	10 24	10 46	11 24	12 24	12 45	13 24	14 24	14 45	15 24	16 24	16 48

Station		LE	LE	LE 1 ◇	LE	LE	LE 1 ◇	LE	LE	LE 1 ◇	LE	LE 1	LE
Peterborough 8	d			15 45			17 45			19 46		22 05	
Whittlesea	d			15 53			17 53			19 54		22 13	
March	d			16 04			18 04			20 05		22 24	
Manea	d												
Ely 6	d			16g30			18h30			20 27		22 42	
Cambridge	d	14 43	15 43		16 43	17 43		18 43	19 43		20 43		22 43
Dullingham	d		15 59		16 59	17 59			19 59		20 59		22 59
Newmarket	d	15 03	16 04		17 04	18 04		19 03	20 04		21 04		23 04
Kennett	d	15 11			17 12	18 12		19 11			21 12		23 12
Bury St Edmunds	a	15 23	16 23	16 55	17 24	18 24	18 55	19 23	20 23	20 52	21 24	23 07	23 24
	d	15 23	16 23	16 56	17 25	18 25	18 56	19 23	20 23	20 52	21 25	23 08	23 25
Thurston	d	15 30	16 30		17 31	18 31		19 30	20 30		21 31		23 31
Elmswell	d	15 36	16 36		17 38	18 38		19 36	20 36		21 38		23 38
Stowmarket	d	15 45	16 45	17 12	17 46	18 46	19 12	19 45	20 45	21 08	21 46	23 24	23 46
Needham Market	d	15 50	16 50		17 52	18 52		19 50	20 50		21 52		23 52
Ipswich	a	16 03	17 03	17 27	18 03	19 03	19 25	20 03	21 03	21 25	22 03	23 37	00 03
Harwich International	a								21 28				
Manningtree	a	16 17	17 17	17 51		19 17	19 36	20 18	21e18	21 36	22 18	23 47	
Colchester	a	16 27	17 27	17 48		19 27	19 47	20 28	21e28	21 48	22 28	23 58	
Marks Tey	a	16f39	17f39	17 55	18 55	19f39	19 54	20f39	21f39	22 23	22 35		
Witham	a	16f49	17f49	18 03	18f49	19f49	20 02	20f49	21f49	22 02	22 45		
Chelmsford	a	16 45	17 45	18 13		19 45	20 11	20 46	21e46	22 10	22 56		
Shenfield	a	17f11	18f11	18s25	19f09	20f09	20s23	21f09	21e58	22s22	23 09		
London Liverpool Street 15 ⊖	a	17 24	18 24	18 49		20 24	20 46	21 21	22e23	22 46	23 34		

Saturdays

Station		LE	LE	LE	LE R 1	LE	LE	LE R 1	LE	LE	LE 1 ◇	LE	LE	LE 1 ◇
Peterborough 8	d				07 45			09 55			11 45			13 45
Whittlesea	d				07 53			10 03			11 53			13 53
March	d				08 04			10 14			12 04			14 04
Manea	d													
Ely 6	d				08j30			10 32			12c30			14k30
Cambridge	d		06 43	07 43		08 43	09 43		10 43	11 43		12 43	13 43	
Dullingham	d			07 59			09 59			11 59			13 59	
Newmarket	d		07 03	08 04		09 03	10 04		11 03	12 04		13 03	14 04	
Kennett	d		07 11			09 11			11 11			13 11		
Bury St Edmunds	a		07 23	08 23	08 55	09 23	10 23	10 57	11 23	12 23	12 55	13 23	14 23	14 55
	d	06 23	07 23	08 23	08 56	09 23	10 23	10 58	11 23	12 23	12 56	13 23	14 23	14 56
Thurston	d	06 30	07 30	08 30		09 30	10 30		11 30	12 30		13 30	14 30	
Elmswell	d	06 36	07 36	08 36		09 36	10 36		11 36	12 36		13 36	14 36	
Stowmarket	d	06 45	07 45	08 45	09 12	09 45	10 45	11 14	11 45	12 45	13 12	13 45	14 45	15 12
Needham Market	d	06 50	07 50	08 50		09 50	10 50		11 50	12 50		13 50	14 50	
Ipswich	a	07 03	08 03	09 03	09 25	10 03	11 03	11 27	12 03	13 03	13 27	14 03	15 03	15 25
Harwich International	a													
Manningtree	a	07 17	08 17	09 17	09 51	10 17	11 17	11 51	12 17	13 17	13 51	14 17	15 17	15 51
Colchester	a	07 27	08 27	09 27	09 48	10 27	11 27	11 48	12 27	13 27	13 48	14 27	15 27	15 48
Marks Tey	a	07f39	08f39	09f39	10 23	10f39	11f39	12 23	12f39	13f39	14 23	14f39	15f39	16 23
Witham	a	07f49	08f49	09f49	10 04	10f49	11f49	12 02	12f49	13f49	14 02	14f49	15f49	16 02
Chelmsford	a	07 45	08 45	09 45	10s06	10 45	11 45	12 10	12 45	13 45	14 10	14 45	15 45	16 10
Shenfield	a	08f09	09f09	10f09	10m24	11f09	12f09	12s22	13f09	14f09	14s22	15f09	16f09	16s22
London Liverpool Street 15 ⊖	a	08 24	09 24	10 24	10 38	11 24	12 24	12 45	13 24	14 24	14 45	15 24	16 24	16 45

For general notes see front of timetable
For details of catering facilities see Directory of Train Operators

- b Arr. 1023
- c Arr. 1222
- e Change at Ipswich
- f Change at Ipswich and Colchester
- g Arr. 1622
- h Arr. 1822
- j Arr. 0822
- k Arr. 1422
- m Change at Colchester

Table 14

Saturdays

Peterborough, Ely, Cambridge and Bury St Edmunds → Ipswich

Network diagram - see first page of Table 13

		LE	LE	LE 1 ◇	LE	LE	LE 1 ◇	LE	LE	LE 1 ◇	LE	LE	LE 1
Peterborough 8	d			15 45			17 45			19 45			21 45
Whittlesea	d			15 53			17 53			19 53			21 53
March	d			16 04			18 04			20 04			22 04
Manea	d												
Ely 6	d			16b30			18c30			20e30			22f30
Cambridge	d	14 43	15 43		16 43	17 43		18 43	19 43		20 43	21 43	
Dullingham	d		15 59		16 59	17 59			19 59			21 59	
Newmarket	d	15 03	16 04		17 04	18 04		19 03	20 04		21 03	22 04	
Kennett	d	15 11			17 12	18 12		19 11			21 11	22 12	22 47
Bury St Edmunds	a	15 23	16 23	16 55	17 24	18 24	18 55	19 23	20 23	20 55	21 23	22 24	22 57
	d	15 23	16 23	16 56	17 25	18 25	18 56	19 23	20 23	20 56	21 23	22 25	22 58
Thurston	d	15 30	16 30		17 31	18 31		19 30	20 30		21 30	22 31	23 03
Elmswell	d	15 36	16 36		17 38	18 38		19 36	20 36		21 36	22 38	23 09
Stowmarket	d	15 45	16 45	17 12	17 46	18 46	19 12	19 45	20 45	21 12	21 45	22 46	23 17
Needham Market	d	15 50	16 50		17 52	18 52		19 50	20 50		21 50	22 52	23 22
Ipswich	a	16 03	17 03	17 27	18 03	19 03	19 25	20 03	21 03	21 27	22 03	23 03	23 32
Harwich International	a								21 28				
Manningtree	a	16 17	17 17	17 51		19 17	19 36	20 17	21g18	21 37	22 18	23 35	23 44
Colchester	a	16 27	17 27	17 48		19 27	19 48	20 28	21g28	21 48	22 28	23 45	23 56
Marks Tey	a	16h39	17h39	18 23	18h42	19h39	20 23	20h39	21h39	22 23	22 35		
Witham	a	16h49	17h49	18 02	18h52	19h49	20 02	20h49	21h49	22 02	22 45		
Chelmsford	a	16 45	17 45	18 10		19 45	20 10	20 46	21g46	22 10	22 56		
Shenfield	a	17h09	18h09	18s22	19h12	20h09	20s22	21h10	21g58	22s22	23 09		
London Liverpool Street 15 ⊖	a	17 24	18 24	18 45		20 24	20 45	21 19	22g25	22 49	23 38		

Sundays

		LE	LE 1 A	LE	LE 1	LE	LE 1	LE	LE 1	LE	LE 1	LE	LE 1	LE	LE
Peterborough 8	d		09 46		11 46		13 46		15 46		17 46		19 44		
Whittlesea	d		09 54		11 54		13 54		15 54		17 54		19 52		
March	d		10 05		12 05		14 05		16 05		18 05		20 03		
Manea	d														
Ely 6	d		10 30		12 30		14 30		16 30		18j30		20 22		
Cambridge	d			11 12		13 12		15 12		17 12		19 12		21 12	23 00
Dullingham	d			11 28		13 28		15 28		17 28		19 28		21 28	23 16
Newmarket	d			11 34		13 34		15 34		17 34		19 34		21 34	23 21
Kennett	d			11 42		13 42		15 42		17 42		19 42		21 42	23 29
Bury St Edmunds	a		10 55	11 54	12 55	13 54	14 55	15 54	16 55	17 54	18 55	19 54	20 47	21 54	23 41
	d	09 55	10 56	11 55	12 56	13 55	14 56	15 55	16 56	17 55	18 56	19 55	20 47	21 55	23 42
Thurston	d	10 01		12 01		14 01		16 01		18 01		20 01		22 01	23 48
Elmswell	d	10 08		12 08		14 08		16 08		18 08		20 08		22 08	23 55
Stowmarket	d	10 17	11 12	12 17	13 12	14 17	15 12	16 17	17 12	18 17	19 12	20 17	21 05	22 17	00 04
Needham Market	d	10 22		12 22		14 22		16 22		18 22		20 22		22 22	00 09
Ipswich	a	10 34	11 25	12 34	13 25	14 34	15 27	16 34	17 25	18 34	19 27	20 34	21 18	22 34	00 21
Harwich International	a											21 02			
Manningtree	a	10 51	11 51	12 51	13 51	14 51	15 51	16 51	17 51	18 51	19 51	20g51	21 28		
Colchester	a	11 01	12 01	13 01	14 01	15 01	16 01	17 01	18 01	19 01	20 01	21g01	21 40		
Marks Tey	a	11h12	12h12	13h12	14h12	15h12	16h12	17h12	18h12	19h12	20h12	21h12	22 12		
Witham	a	11h20	12h20	13h20	14h20	15h20	16h20	17h20	18h20	19h20	20h20	21h20	22 20		
Chelmsford	a	11h29	12h29	13h29	14h29	15h29	16h29	17h29	18h29	19h29	20h29	21h29	22 29		
Shenfield	a	11 29	12 29	13 29	14 29	15 29	16 29	17 29	18 29	19 29	20 29	21g29	22 29		
London Liverpool Street 15 ⊖	a	12 01	13 01	14 01	15 01	16 01	17 01	18 01	19 01	20 01	21 01	22g01	23 01		

For general notes see front of timetable
For details of catering facilities see Directory of Train Operators

A Until 6 September
b Arr. 1622
c Arr. 1822
e Arr. 2026
f Arr. 2222
g Change at Ipswich
h Change at Ipswich and Colchester
j Arr. 1827

Norwich → Great Yarmouth and Lowestoft

Network diagram - see first page of Table 13

Miles	Miles	Miles			LE [1]	LE	LE [1]	LE	LE		LE	LE [1]	LE	LE	LE		LE	LE	LE	LE	LE		LE	LE	LE	LE [1]
—	—	—	London Liverpool Street [15] ⊖	d										06 25			07 30	08 00	08 30	09 00	09 30		10 00	10 30	11 00	11 30
0	0	0	**Norwich**	d	05 15	05 45	06 24	06 34	06 57		07 05	07 36	07 54	08 36	08 57		09 36	09 57	10 36	10 57	11 36		11 57	12 36	12 57	13 36
4¾	4¾	4¾	Brundall Gardens	d		05 52		06 41			07 12		08 01	08 43			09 43		10 43		11 43			12 43		13 43
5¾	5¾	5¾	Brundall	d	05 23	05 55	06 32	06 44	07 05		07 15	07 44	08 04	08 46			09 46	10 05	10 46		11 46		12 05	12 46		13 46
8	—	—	Lingwood	d				06 49			07 20			08 51			09 51				11 51			12 51		13 51
10½	—	—	Acle	d				06 54			07b27			08 55			09 55				11 55			12 55		13 55
—	7¾	7¾	Buckenham	d																						
—	10	10	Cantley	d		06 01			07 11			07 50	08 10					10 11	10 52				12 11			
—	12¼	12¼	Reedham (Norfolk)	d		06 06	06 41		07 16			07 55	08 15					10 16	10 57				12 16			
—	16	—	Berney Arms	d								08x01							11x03							
18¼	20½	—	**Great Yarmouth**	a	05 46			07 07			07 40	08 12		09 08			10 08		11 13		12 08			13 08		14 08
—	—	16¼	Haddiscoe	d		06 14			07 24				08 23					10 24					12 24			
—	—	18	Somerleyton	d		06 18			07 28				08 27					10 28					12 28			
—	—	22	Oulton Broad North	d		06 24	06 56		07 34				08 33		09 26			10 34		11 26			12 34		13 26	
—	—	23½	**Lowestoft**	a		06 30	07 03		07 41				08 38		09 36			10 41		11 33			12 41		13 33	

		LE	LE	LE [1]		LE [1]	LE	LE [1]	LE [1]	LE		LE	LE [1]	LE [1]	LE [1]	LE		LE	LE [1]	LE	LE	LE [1]	LE [1]	LE		
London Liverpool Street [15] ⊖	d	12 00	12 30	13 00		13 30	14 00	14 30	15 00			15 30	15 30	16 30	17 00	17 30		17 50	18 30		19 30	19 30	20 30			
Norwich	d	13 57	14 36	14 57		15 36	15 57	16 40	16 57	17 05		17 36	17 57	18 40	18 57	19 36		19 57	20 40	20 57	21 40	21 57	22 40	23 00		
Brundall Gardens	d		14 43			15 43		16 47		17 12		17 43		18 47		19 43			20 47		21 47					
Brundall	d	14 05	14 46			15 46	16 05	16 50	17 05	17 15		17 46	18 05	18 50	19 05	19 46		20 05	20 50	21 05	21 50	22 05	22 48	23 08		
Lingwood	d		14 51			15 51		16 54		17 20		17 51		18 55		19 51			20 55		21 55			23 13		
Acle	d		14 55			15 55		16 59		17c27		17 55		18 59		19 55			20 59		21 59			23 17		
Buckenham	d																									
Cantley	d	14 11		15 09			16 11		17 11				18 11		19 11			20 11		21 11		22 11	22 54			
Reedham (Norfolk)	d	14 16		15 14			16 16		17 16				18 16		19 16			20 16		21 16		22 16	22 59			
Berney Arms	d																									
Great Yarmouth	a		15 08			16 08		17 12		17 40		18 08		19 12		20 08			21 12		22 12			23 30		
Haddiscoe	d	14 24					16 24		17 24				18 24		19 24			20 24				22 24	23 07			
Somerleyton	d	14 28					16 28		17 28				18 28		19 28			20 28				22 28	23 11			
Oulton Broad North	d	14 34		15 29			16 34		17 34				18 34		19 34			20 34		21 31		22 34	23 17			
Lowestoft	a	14 41		15 36			16 41		17 41				18 41		19 41			20 41		21 38		22 41	23 24			

Saturdays

		LE	LE	LE	LE	LE	LE	LE		LE	LE	LE	LE	LE A	LE	LE		LE A	LE	LE	LE [R] [1] B ⊡	LE	LE	LE A		LE
London Liverpool Street [15] ⊖	d									06 30	07 00	07 30	08 00		08 30	09 00			09 30	10 00	10 00	10 30	11 00			11 30
Norwich	d	05 36	05 49	06 36	06 55	07 05	07 36	07 54		08 36	08 57	09 36	09 57	10 06	10 36	10 57		11 13	11 36	11 57	12 06	12 36	12 57	13 18		13 36
Brundall Gardens	d		05 56	06 43		07 12		08 01		08 43		09 43			10 43				11 43			12 43				13 43
Brundall	d	05 44	05 59	06 46	07 03	07 15	07 44	08 04		08 46		09 46	10 05		10 46				11 46	12 05		12 46				13 46
Lingwood	d			06 51		07 20				08 51		09 51							11 51			12 51				13 51
Acle	d			06 55		07b27				08 55		09 55							11 55			12 55				13 55
Buckenham	d												10x09													
Cantley	d		06 05		07 09		07 50	08 10					10 13		10 52					12 11						
Reedham (Norfolk)	d	05 52	06 10		07 14		07 55	08 15					10 17		10 57					12 16						
Berney Arms	d						08x01								11x03											
Great Yarmouth	a	06 08		07 08		07 40	08 12			09 08		10 08		10 38	11 13			11 43	12 08		12 40	13 08		13 48		14 08
Haddiscoe	d		06 18		07 22			08 23					10 26							12 24						
Somerleyton	d		06 22		07 26			08 27					10 29							12 28						
Oulton Broad North	d		06 28		07 32			08 33			09 26		10 35			11 26				12 34			13 26			
Lowestoft	a		06 34		07 38			08 38			09 33		10 41			11 33				12 41			13 33			

		LE	LE [R] [1] B ⊡	LE	LE	LE A	LE	LE		LE	LE	LE	LE	LE	LE	LE	LE	LE	LE	LE	LE	LE	LE [1]	LE		
London Liverpool Street [15] ⊖	d	12 00	12 00	12 30	13 00		13 30	14 00		14 30	15 00		15 30	16 00	16 30	17 00	17 30	18 00	18 30	19 00	19 30	20 00	20 30			
Norwich	d	13 57	14 18	14 36	14 57	15 18	15 36	15 57		16 40	16 57	17 05	17 36	17 57	18 40	18 57	19 36	19 57	20 40	20 57	21 40	21 57	22 40	23 00		
Brundall Gardens	d			14 43			15 43			16 47		17 12	17 43		18 47		19 43		20 47		21 47					
Brundall	d	14 05		14 46			15 46	16 05		16 50	17 05	17 15	17 46	18 05	18 50	19 05	19 46	20 05	20 50	21 05	21 50	22 05	22 48	23 08		
Lingwood	d			14 51			15 51			16 55		17 20	17 51		18 55		19 51		20 55		21 55			23 13		
Acle	d			14 55			15 55			16 59		17c27	17 55		18 59		19 55		20 59		21 59			23 17		
Buckenham	d																									
Cantley	d	14 11			15 09			16 11			17 11			18 11		19 11		20 11		21 11		22 11	22 54			
Reedham (Norfolk)	d	14 16			15 14			16 16			17 16			18 16		19 16		20 16		21 16		22 16	22 59			
Berney Arms	d																									
Great Yarmouth	a		14 52	15 08		15 48	16 08			17 12		17 40	18 08		19 12		20 08		21 12		22 12			23 30		
Haddiscoe	d	14 24						16 24			17 24			18 24		19 24		20 24				22 24	23 07			
Somerleyton	d	14 28						16 28			17 28			18 28		19 28		20 28				22 28	23 11			
Oulton Broad North	d	14 34			15 29			16 34			17 34			18 34		19 34		20 34		21 31		22 34	23 17			
Lowestoft	a	14 41			15 36			16 41			17 41			18 41		19 41		20 41		21 38		22 41	23 24			

For general notes see front of timetable
For details of catering facilities see Directory of Train Operators

A Until 26 September
B Until 26 September. ⊡ to Norwich

b Arr. 0724
c Arr. 1724

Table 15

Sundays

Norwich → Great Yarmouth and Lowestoft

Network diagram - see first page of Table 13

		LE [1]	LE	LE	LE [1]	LE	LE	LE [1]	LE	LE	LE	LE	LE	LE [1]
London Liverpool Street [15] ⊖	d						*08 30*	*08 30*	*09 30*	*10 30*		*11 30*	*12 30*	*12 30*
Norwich	d	07 25	07 36	08 45	08 57	09 36	10 45	10 57	11 36	12 45	12 57	13 36	14 45	14 57
Brundall Gardens	d			08 52			10 52			12 52			14 52	
Brundall	d		07 44	08 55	09 05	09 44	10 55	11 05	11 44	12 55	13 05	13 44	14 55	15 05
Lingwood	d			09 00			11 00			13 00			15 00	
Acle	d			09 04			11 04			13 04			15 04	
Buckenham	d					09x48			11x48					
Cantley	d		07 50		09 11	09 52		11 11	11 52		13 11	13 50		15 11
Reedham (Norfolk)	d		07 55		09 16	09 56		11 16	11 56		13 16	13 55		15 16
Berney Arms	d		08x01			10x03			12x03			14x01		
Great Yarmouth	a		08 12	09 17		10 13	11 17		12 13	13 17		14 12	15 17	
Haddiscoe	d				09 24			11 24			13 24			15 24
Somerleyton	d				09 28			11 28			13 28			15 28
Oulton Broad North	d	07 53			09 34			11 34			13 34			15 34
Lowestoft	a	07 59			09 40			11 40			13 40			15 40

		LE A	LE B	LE	LE [1] A	LE [1] B	LE	LE	LE	LE	LE	LE [1]	LE	LE
London Liverpool Street [15] ⊖	d	*13 30*	*13 30*	*14 30*	*14 30*	*14 30*	*15 30*	*16 30*		*17 30*	*18 30*	*19 00*	*19 30*	*20 30*
Norwich	d	15 36	15 36	16 45	16 57	16 57	17 36	18 45	18 57	19 36	20 45	20 57	21 36	22 36
Brundall Gardens	d			16 52				18 52			20 52			22 43
Brundall	d	15 44	15 44	16 55	17 05	17 05	17 44	18 55	19 05	19 44	20 55	21 05	21 44	22 46
Lingwood	d			17 00				19 00			21 00			22 51
Acle	d			17 04				19 04			21 04			22 55
Buckenham	d	15x48	15x48		17x09									
Cantley	d	15 52	15 52		17 13	17 13	17 50		19 11	19 50		21 11	21 50	
Reedham (Norfolk)	d	15 56	15 56		17 17	17 17	17 55		19 16	19 55		21 16	21 55	
Berney Arms	d	16x03												
Great Yarmouth	a	16 13	16 13	17 17			18 10	19 17		20 10	21 17		22 10	23 08
Haddiscoe	d				17 26	17 26			19 24			21 24		
Somerleyton	d				17 29	17 29			19 28			21 28		
Oulton Broad North	d				17 35	17 35			19 34			21 34		
Lowestoft	a				17 41	17 41			19 40			21 40		

For general notes see front of timetable
For details of catering facilities see Directory of Train Operators

A Until 6 September
B From 13 September

Lowestoft and Great Yarmouth → Norwich

Network diagram - see first page of Table 13

Mondays to Fridays

Miles	Miles	Miles			LE	LE	LE	LE	LE	LE	LE	LE	LE	LE	LE	LE	LE	LE	LE	LE		LE	LE	LE	LE	LE
					MX	MO																				
					1			1	R 1				1		1											
0	—	—	**Lowestoft**	d	23p30	23p35	05 36			06 40			07 40	07 55		08 42		09 42		10 50			11 42		12 50	
1½	—	—	Oulton Broad North	d	23p34	23p39	05 40			06 44			07 44	07 59		08 46		09 46		10 54			11 46		12 54	
5¼	—	—	Somerleyton	d			05 46			06 50			07 50			08 52		09 52					11 52			
7¼	—	—	Haddiscoe	d			05 49			06 53			07 54			08 55		09 55					11 55			
—	0	0	**Great Yarmouth**	d				05 55	06 40		07 17	07 44			08 17		09 17		10 17			11 17		12 17		13 17
—	—	4½	Berney Arms	d																						
11¼	—	8¼	Reedham (Norfolk)	d	23p51	23p54	05 58			07 02			08 03	08 14		09 04		10 04					12 04			
13½	—	10½	Cantley	d	23p55		06 02			07 06			08 07	08 19		09 08		10 08					12 08			
15¾	—	12¾	Buckenham	d																						
—	8	—	Acle	d				06 06	06b54		07 27	07 54			08 27		09 27		10 27			11 27		12 27		13 27
—	10½	—	Lingwood	d				06 11	06 59		07 32	07 59			08 32		09 32		10 32			11 32		12 32		13 32
17¾	12¾	14¾	Brundall	d	00 01	00 03	06 08	06 15	07 03	07 12	07 36	08 03	08 13		08 36	09 14	09 36	10 14	10 36			11 36	12 14	12 36		13 36
18¾	13¾	15¾	Brundall Gardens	d				06 18		07 15	07 39	08 06			08 39		09 39		10 39			11 39		12 39		13 39
23½	18½	20½	**Norwich**	a	00 12	00 13	06 19	06 28	07 14	07 25	07 50	08 19	08 25	08 38	08 50	09 25	09 50	10 28	10 50	11 25		11 50	12 25	12 50	13 25	13 50
—	—	—	London Liverpool Street 15 ⊖	a			08 23	08 39	09 25	09 25	09 56		10 24		10 54	11 24	11 54		12 54	13 24		13 54	14 24	14 54	15 24	15 54

		LE	LE	LE	LE	LE	LE	LE	LE	LE	LE	LE	LE	LE	LE	LE	LE	LE	LE	LE	LE	LE	LE	LE		
			1	1		1	1		1			1		1	1	1			1			1		1		
										A	B															
Lowestoft	d	13 42		14 50		15 42		16 47				17 47		18 47		19 47		20 50		21 42		22 45		23 30		
Oulton Broad North	d	13 46		14 54		15 46		16 51				17 51		18 51		19 51		20 54		21 46		22 49		23 34		
Somerleyton	d	13 52				15 52		16 57				17 57		18 57		19 57				21 52		22 55				
Haddiscoe	d	13 55				15 55		17 00				18 00		19 00		20 00				21 55		22 58				
Great Yarmouth	d		14 12		15 17		16 17		17 17	17 47	17 47		18 17		19 17		20 17		21 17		22 17		23 33			
Berney Arms	d		14x19							17x54																
Reedham (Norfolk)	d	14 04	14 26			16 04		17 09		18 01	18 01	18 09		19 09		20 09				22 04		23 07	23 46	23 51		
Cantley	d	14 08	14 30			16 08		17 13		18 05	18 05	18 13		19 13		20 13				22 08		23 11		23 55		
Buckenham	d																									
Acle	d				15 27		16 27		17 27				18 27		19 27		20 27		21 27		22 27					
Lingwood	d				15 32		16 32		17 32				18 32		19 32		20 32		21 32		22 32					
Brundall	d	14 14	14 36		15 36	16 14	16 36	17 19	17 36	18 12	18 12	18 19	18 36	19 19	19 36	20 19	20 36		21 36	22 14	22 36	23 17	23 54	00 01		
Brundall Gardens	d		14 39		15 39		16 39		17 39				18 39		19 39		20 39		21 39		22 39					
Norwich	a	14 25	14 49	15 25	15 50	16 25	16 50	17 30	17 54	18 23	18 23	18 30	18 52	19 30	19 52	20 30	20 50	21 25	21 50	22 25	22 50	23 28	00 05	00 12		
London Liverpool Street 15 ⊖	a	16 24	16 54	17 24	17 54	18 24	18 54		19 54	20 24	20 24	20 54	20 54		21 54	22 54	22 54		00 03							

Saturdays

		LE	LE	LE	LE	LE	LE	LE	LE	LE	LE	LE	LE		LE	LE	LE	LE	LE	LE	LE	LE	LE	LE	LE	LE
		1										R 1										R 1				
												C ⊥P			D			D				C ⊥P			D	
Lowestoft	d	23p30		06 40			07 42		08 42		09 42					10 50			11 42		12 50			13 42		
Oulton Broad North	d	23p34		06 44			07 46		08 46		09 46					10 54			11 46		12 54			13 46		
Somerleyton	d			06 50			07 52		08 52		09 52								11 52					13 52		
Haddiscoe	d			06 53			07 55		08 55		09 55								11 55					13 55		
Great Yarmouth	d		06 17		07 17	07 44		08 17		09 17		10 08	10 17		10 42		11 17	11 47		12 17		13 10	13 17		13 58	14 12
Berney Arms	d																									14x19
Reedham (Norfolk)	d	23p51		07 02			08 04		09 04		10 04								12 04					14 04		14 26
Cantley	d	23p55		07 06			08 08		09 08		10 08								12 08					14 08		14 30
Buckenham	d																									
Acle	d		06 27		07 27	07 54		08 27		09 27			10 27				11 27			12 27			13 27			
Lingwood	d		06 32		07 32	07 59		08 32		09 32			10 32				11 32			12 32			13 32			
Brundall	d	00 01	06 36	07 12	07 36	08 03	08 14	08 36	09 14	09 36	10 14		10 36				11 36		12 14	12 36			13 36	14 14		14 36
Brundall Gardens	d		06 39	07 15	07 39	08 06		08 39		09 39			10 39				11 39			12 39			13 39			14 39
Norwich	a	00 12	06 50	07 25	07 50	08 19	08 25	08 50	09 25	09 50	10 25	10 44	10 52		11 08	11 25	11 50	12 16	12 25	12 50	13 25	13 44	13 52	14 25	14 35	14 49
London Liverpool Street 15 ⊖	a		08 54	09 24	09 54		10 24	10 54	11 24	11 54	12 24	12 54	12 54			13 24	13 54		14 24	14 54	15 24	15 54	15 54	16 24		16 54

		LE	LE		LE	LE	LE	LE	LE	LE	LE	LE	LE	LE	LE	LE	LE	LE	LE	LE	LE	LE	LE	LE		
																		1						1		
						D				D	E															
Lowestoft	d	14 50			15 42			16 47				17 47		18 47		19 47		20 50		21 42		22 45		23 30		
Oulton Broad North	d	14 54			15 46			16 51				17 51		18 51		19 51		20 54		21 46		22 49		23 34		
Somerleyton	d				15 52			16 57				17 57		18 57		19 57				21 52		22 55				
Haddiscoe	d				15 55			17 00				18 00		19 00		20 00				21 55		22 58				
Great Yarmouth	d		15 17			16 02	16 17		17 17	17 47	17 47		18 17		19 17		20 17		21 17		22 17		23 33			
Berney Arms	d									17x54																
Reedham (Norfolk)	d				16 04			17 09		18 01	18 01	18 09		19 09		20 09				22 04		23 07	23 46	23 51		
Cantley	d				16 08			17 13		18 05	18 05	18 13		19 13		20 13				22 08		23 11		23 55		
Buckenham	d				16x11																					
Acle	d		15 27				16 27		17 27				18 27		19 27		20 27		21 27		22 27					
Lingwood	d		15 32				16 32		17 32				18 32		19 32		20 32		21 32		22 32					
Brundall	d		15 36		16 14		16 36	17 19	17 36	18 12	18 12	18 19	18 36	19 19	19 36	20 19	20 36		21 36	22 14	22 36	23 17	23 54	00 01		
Brundall Gardens	d		15 39				16 39		17 39				18 39		19 39		20 39		21 39		22 39					
Norwich	a	15 25	15 50		16 25	16 33	16 50	17 30	17 50	18 23	18 23	18 30	18 52	19 30	19 50	20 30	20 50	21 25	21 50	22 25	22 50	23 28	00 05	00 12		
London Liverpool Street 15 ⊖	a	17 24	17 54		18 24		18 54		19 54	20 24	20 24		20 54		21 58		22 58	00 07	00 07							

For general notes see front of timetable
For details of catering facilities see Directory of Train Operators

A Until 25 September
B From 28 September
C Until 26 September. ⊥P from Norwich
D Until 26 September
E From 3 October
b Arr. 0650

Sundays

Lowestoft and Great Yarmouth → Norwich

Network diagram - see first page of Table 13

		LE 1	LE	LE	LE 1	LE	LE	LE 1	LE	LE	LE	LE	LE	LE 1
Lowestoft	d	23p30			09 50			11 50			13 50			15 50
Oulton Broad North	d	23p34			09 54			11 54			13 54			15 54
Somerleyton	d				10 00			12 00			14 00			16 00
Haddiscoe	d				10 03			12 03			14 03			16 03
Great Yarmouth	d		08 20	09 22		10 18	11 22		12 18	13 22		14 20	15 22	
Berney Arms	d		08x27			10x25			12x25			14x27		
Reedham (Norfolk)	d	23p51	08 34		10 12	10 32		12 12	12 32		14 12	14 34		16 12
Cantley	d	23p55	08 38		10 16	10 36		12 16	12 36		14 16	14 38		16 16
Buckenham	d				10x20	10x40			12x40					
Acle	d			09 32			11 32			13 32			15 32	
Lingwood	d			09 37			11 37			13 37			15 37	
Brundall	d	00 01	08 45	09 41	10 24	10 44	11 41	12 22	12 44	13 41	14 22	14 45	15 41	16 22
Brundall Gardens	d			09 44			11 44			13 44			15 44	
Norwich	a	00 12	08 55	09 55	10 34	10 55	11 55	12 33	12 55	13 55	14 33	14 55	15 55	16 33
London Liverpool Street 15 ⊖	a		*11 03*	*12 01*	*13 01*	*13 01*	*14 01*	*15 01*	*15 01*	*16 01*		*17 01*	*18 01*	*19 01*

		LE A	LE B	LE	LE	LE	LE	LE 1	LE	LE	LE 1	LE	LE	LE
Lowestoft	d				17 50			19 50			21 50			23 35
Oulton Broad North	d				17 54			19 54			21 54			23 39
Somerleyton	d				18 00			20 00			22 00			
Haddiscoe	d				18 03			20 03			22 03			
Great Yarmouth	d	16 18	16 18	17 22		18 18	19 22		20 22	21 22		22 22	23 20	
Berney Arms	d	16x25												
Reedham (Norfolk)	d	16 32	16 32		18 12	18 30		20 12	20 34		22 12	22 34	23 32	23 54
Cantley	d	16 36	16 36		18 16	18 34		20 16	20 38		22 16	22 38	23 36	
Buckenham	d	16x40												
Acle	d			17 32			19 32			21 32				
Lingwood	d			17 37			19 37			21 37				
Brundall	d	16 44	16 44	17 41	18 22	18 41	19 41	20 22	20 45	21 41	22 22	22 45	23 43	00 03
Brundall Gardens	d			17 44			19 44			21 44			23 45	
Norwich	a	16 55	16 55	17 55	18 33	18 52	19 55	20 33	20 55	21 55	22 33	22 55	23 55	00 13
London Liverpool Street 15 ⊖	a	*19 01*	*19 01*	*20 01*		*21 01*	*22 01*	*23 01*	*23 01*	*00 07*				

For general notes see front of timetable
For details of catering facilities see
Directory of Train Operators

A Until 6 September
B From 13 September

Table 16

Mondays to Saturdays

Norwich—Cromer and Sheringham

Network diagram - see first page of Table 13

Miles			LE SX	LE SO	LE SO	LE SX	LE	LE	LE	LE	LE	LE	LE	LE	LE	LE	LE	LE	LE	LE	LE
—	London Liverpool Street 15	⊖ d						06b00	07 30	08 30	09 30	10 30	11 30	12 30	13 30	14 30	15 30	17c00	17 30	19 00	20 30
0	**Norwich**	d	05 20	05 20	05 45	05 50	07 15	08 23	09 45	10 45	11 45	12 45	13 45	14 45	15 45	16 45	17 45	18 47	19 45	21 15	22 45
6	Salhouse	d		05 30	05 55	06 00	07 25	08 33	09 55		11 55		13 55		15 55	16 55	17 55		19 55	21 25	22 55
8¾	Hoveton & Wroxham	d	05 34	05 35	06 00	06 05	07 30	08 38	10 00	10 59	12 00	12 59	14 00	14 59	16 00	17 00	18 00	19 00	20 00	21 30	23 00
13	Worstead	d		05 42	06 07	06 12	07 37	08 45		11 06		13 06		15 06	16 07	17 07	18 07	19 07	20 07	21 37	23 07
16	North Walsham	a	05 44	05 48	06 13	06 18	07 43	08 51	10 10	11 11	12 10	13 11	14 10	15 11	16 13	17 13	18 13	19 13	20 13	21 43	23 13
—		d	05 44	05 48	06 13	06 21	07 46	08 53	10 13	11 14	12 13	13 14	14 13	15 14	16 15	17 15	18 16	19 15	20 16	21 43	23 13
19¾	Gunton	d		05 54	06 19	06 27	07 52	08 59	10 19		12 19		14 19		16 21	17 21	18 22	19 21	20 22	21 49	23 19
23¼	Roughton Road	d		06 01	06 26	06 34	07 59	09 06		11 25		13 25		15 25	16 28	17 28	18 29	19 28	20 29	21 56	23 26
26½	**Cromer**	a	05 59	06 06	06 31	06 39	08 04	09 11	10 29	11 30	12 29	13 30	14 29	15 30	16 33	17 33	18 34	19 33	20 34	22 01	23 31
—		d	06 06	06 10	06 36	06 46	08 07	09 15	10 33	11 33	12 33	13 33	14 33	15 33	16 36	17 36	18 37	19 36	20 37	22 04	23 34
28¾	West Runton	d	06 10	06 14	06 40	06 50	08 11	09 19	10 37	11 37	12 37	13 37	14 37	15 37	16 40	17 40	18 41	19 40	20 41	22 08	23 38
30½	**Sheringham**	a	06 15	06 19	06 45	06 55	08 15	09 23	10 42	11 42	12 42	13 42	14 42	15 42	16 45	17 45	18 45	19 45	20 45	22 13	23 43

Sundays

		LE	LE A	LE	LE A	LE	LE A	LE	LE A	LE	LE A	LE	LE A	LE
London Liverpool Street 15	⊖ d			08 30	09 30	10 30	11 30	12 30	13 30	14 30	15 30	16 30	17 30	18 30
Norwich	d	08 36	09 45	10 36	11 45	12 36	13 45	14 36	15 45	16 36	17 45	18 36	19 45	20 36
Salhouse	d	08 46		10 46		12 46		14 46		16 46		18 46		20 46
Hoveton & Wroxham	d	08 51	09 59	10 51	11 59	12 51	13 59	14 51	15 59	16 51	17 59	18 51	19 59	20 51
Worstead	d	08 58		10 58		12 58		14 58		16 58		18 58		20 58
North Walsham	a	09 04	10 09	11 04	12 09	13 04	14 09	15 04	16 09	17 04	18 09	19 04	20 09	21 04
	d	09 04	10 11	11 07	12 11	13 07	14 11	15 07	16 11	17 07	18 11	19 07	20 11	21 07
Gunton	d	09 10		11 13		13 13		15 13		17 13		19 13		21 13
Roughton Road	d	09 17		11 20		13 20		15 20		17 20		19 20		21 20
Cromer	a	09 22	10 26	11 25	12 26	13 25	14 26	15 25	16 26	17 25	18 26	19 25	20 26	21 25
	d	09 26	10 30	11 29	12 30	13 29	14 30	15 29	16 30	17 29	18 30	19 29	20 30	21 29
West Runton	d	09 30		11 33		13 33		15 33		17 33		19 33		21 33
Sheringham	a	09 35	10 38	11 38	12 38	13 38	14 38	15 38	16 38	17 38	18 38	19 38	20 38	21 38

Mondays to Saturdays

Miles			LE MX	LE SX	LE SO	LE SX	LE	LE	LE	LE	LE	LE	LE	LE	LE	LE	LE	LE	LE	LE	LE	LE	LE
0	**Sheringham**	d	23p46		06 22	06 32	07 17	08 25	09 46	10 46	11 46	12 46	13 46	14 46	15 46	16 49	17 48	18 49	19 48	20 49	22 16	23 46
1¾	West Runton	d	23p50		06 26	06 36	07 21	08 29	09 50	10 50	11 50	12 50	13 50	14 50	15 50	16 53	17 52	18 53	19 52	20 53	22 20	23 50
4	**Cromer**	a	23p54		06 30	06 40	07 25	08 33	09 54	10 54	11 54	12 54	13 54	14 54	15 54	16 57	17 56	18 57	19 56	20 57	22 24	23 54
—		d	23p57	06 03	06 33	06 43	07 28	08 36	09 57	10 57	11 57	12 57	13 57	14 57	15 57	17 00	17 59	19 00	19 59	21 00	22 27	23 57
7	Roughton Road	d		06 08	06 38	06 48	07 33	08 41	10 02		12 02		14 02	15 02	16 02		18 04		20 04	21 05	22 32	
10¾	Gunton	d		06 15	06 45	06 55	07 40	08 48		11 08		13 08			16 09		18 11		20 11	21 12	22 39	
14½	North Walsham	a	00 12	06 20	06 50	07 00	07 45	08 53	10 12	11 13	12 12	13 13	14 12	15 13	16 15	17 15	18 16	19 15	20 16	21 17	22 44	00 12
—		d	00 12	06 21	06 51	07 01	07 46	08 54	10 13	11 14	12 13	13 14	14 13	15 14	16 15	17 15	18 17	19 15	20 17	21 18	22 45	00 12
17½	Worstead	d		06 25	06 55	07 05	07 50	08 58	10 17		12 17		14 17		16 20		18 21		20 21	21 22	22 49	
21¾	Hoveton & Wroxham	d	00 22	06 33	07 03	07 13	07 58	09 06	10 25	11 24	12 25	13 24	14 25	15 24	16 27	17 26	18 29	19 26	20 29	21 30	22 57	00 22
24½	Salhouse	d		06 38	07 08	07 18	08 03	09 11		11 29		13 29		15 29	16 32		18 34		20 34	21 35	23 02	
30½	**Norwich**	a	00 37	06 49	07 19	07 29	08 14	09 22	10 41	11 41	12 41	13 41	14 41	15 41	16 44	17 41	18 45	19 41	20 45	21 46	23 13	00 37
—	London Liverpool Street 15	⊖ a		08 55	09 24	09 40	10 24	11 24	12 54	13 54	14 54	15 54	16 54	17 54	18 54	19 54	20 54	21e54	22f54	00g03		

Sundays

		LE	LE	LE A	LE	LE A	LE	LE A	LE	LE A	LE	LE A	LE	LE A	LE
Sheringham	d	23p46	09 43	10 43	11 43	12 43	13 43	14 43	15 43	16 43	17 43	18 43	19 43	20 43	21 43
West Runton	d	23p50	09 47		11 47		13 47		15 47		17 47		19 47		21 47
Cromer	a	23p54	09 51	10 49	11 51	12 49	13 51	14 49	15 51	16 49	17 51	18 49	19 51	20 49	21 51
	d	23p57	09 54	10 53	11 54	12 53	13 54	14 53	15 54	16 53	17 54	18 53	19 54	20 53	21 54
Roughton Road	d		09 59		11 59		13 59		15 59		17 59		19 59		21 59
Gunton	d		10 06		12 06		14 06		16 06		18 06		20 06		22 06
North Walsham	a	00 12	10 11	11 07	12 11	13 07	14 11	15 07	16 11	17 07	18 11	19 07	20 11	21 07	22 11
	d	00 12	10 12	11 08	12 12	13 08	14 12	15 08	16 12	17 08	18 12	19 08	20 12	21 08	22 12
Worstead	d		10 16		12 16		14 16		16 16		18 16		20 16		22 16
Hoveton & Wroxham	d	00 22	10 24	11 18	12 24	13 18	14 24	15 18	16 24	17 18	18 24	19 18	20 24	21 18	22 24
Salhouse	d		10 29		12 29		14 29		16 29		18 29		20 29		22 29
Norwich	a	00 37	10 40	11 33	12 40	13 33	14 40	15 33	16 40	17 33	18 40	19 33	20 40	21 33	22 40
London Liverpool Street 15	⊖ a		13 01	14 01	15 01	16 01	17 01	18 01	19 01	20 01	21 01	22 01	23 01	00 07	

For general notes see front of timetable
For details of catering facilities see Directory of Train Operators

A Until 6 September
b Mondays to Fridays only
c Saturdays dep. 1630
e Saturdays arr. 2158
f Saturdays arr. 2258
g Saturdays arr. 0007

London, Norwich and Cambridge → Ely, Kings Lynn and Peterborough

Network Diagram - see first page of Table 13

Miles	Miles			FC MX 1	FC MO 1	XC 1 ◇ A	XC 1 ◇ A	LE 1	LE 1	FC 1	XC 1	EM ◇ B	LE 1	XC 1 ◇ A	FC 1	LE 1	LE 1	LE 1		EM ◇ B	FC 1	XC 1 ◇	FC 1	LE 1	XC 1	LE 1
—	—	**London Liverpool Street**	d																							
—	0	**London Kings Cross**	d	23p15	23p15										05 45						06 45		07 15			
—	—	Ipswich	d										06 01													
—	—	Stansted Airport	d				05 21							06 06								07 21				
—	—	**Norwich**	d						05 33			05 50					06 33			06 52						07 37
10¾	—	Wymondham	d						05 45			06 02					06 45									07 49
12¾	—	Spooner Row	d																							
16	—	Attleborough	d						05 52			06 09					06 52									07 56
19¾	—	Eccles Road	d																							
22¾	—	Harling Road	d																							
30½	—	Thetford	d						06 05			06 23					07 05			07 20						08 09
37¾	—	Brandon	d						06 13								07 13									08 17
41½	—	Lakenheath	d																							
47	—	Shippea Hill	d																							
—	58	**Cambridge**	d	00 13	00 19	05 15	05 55	06 05		06 18	06 22			06 52	06 58	07 05		07 22			07 35	08 00	08 04	08 12	08 22	
—	63¼	Waterbeach	d	00 19	00 25					06 24					07 04						07 41		08 10			
53	72¾	**Ely 3**	a	00 29	00 38	05 29	06 09	06 19	06 30	06 33	06 36	06 45	06 57	07 06	07 13	07 19	07 30	07 38		07 41	07 51	08 14	08 19	08 26	08 36	08 37
—	—	**Cambridge**	a						06 51								07 51									08 55
—	—	**Ely 3**	d			05 30	06 10			06 33	06 37	06 51	07 00	07 08	07 13					07 44	07 51	08 15	08 21		08 37	
—	78¼	Littleport	d							06 43					07 20						07 58		08 28			
—	88½	Downham Market	d							06 52					07 29						08 07		08 37			
—	93¼	Watlington	d							07 00					07 35						08 13		08 43			
—	99¼	**Kings Lynn**	a							07 10					07 45						08 23		08 53			
62¾	—	Manea	d				06x20																			
68¼	—	March	d			05 46	06 28				06 53	07 07	07 16	07 26						08 01		08 31			08 53	
76¼	—	Whittlesea	d			05 58	06 39						07 27	07 39						08 12						
82¼	—	**Peterborough 3**	a			06 08	06 50				07 16	07 25	07 39	07 51						08 23		08 49			09 11	

		EM ◇	FC 1	LE 1 ◇	XC 1 ◇	LE 1	LE 1	FC 1	EM ◇	XC 1 ◇	LE 1		XC 1	LE 1	FC 1	EM ◇	LE 1	XC 1 ◇	LE 1	LE 1	FC 1	EM ◇	XC 1 ◇	LE 1	XC 1	LE 1
London Liverpool Street	d			06 38																						
London Kings Cross	d		07 45					08 45							09 45						10 45					
Ipswich	d			08 02													10 02									
Stansted Airport	d				08 21					09 21								10 20					11 25			
Norwich	d	07 57					08 40		08 57					09 40		09 57				10 40		10 57				11 40
Wymondham	d						08 52							09 52						10 52						11 52
Spooner Row	d																									
Attleborough	d						08 59							09 59						10 59						11 59
Eccles Road	d																									
Harling Road	d																									
Thetford	d	08 24					09 12		09 24					10 12		10 24				11 12		11 24				12 12
Brandon	d						09 20							10 20						11 20						12 20
Lakenheath	d																									
Shippea Hill	d																									
Cambridge	d		08 38		09 00	09 12		09 35		10 00	10 12		10 22		10 34			11 00	11 12		11 33		12 00	12 12	12 22	
Waterbeach	d		08 44					09 41							10 40						11 39					
Ely 6	a	08 45	08 53	08 58	09 14	09 26	09 38	09 50	09 45	10 14	10 26		10 36	10 37	10 49	10 48	10 58	11 14	11 26	11 37	11 48	11 46	12 14	12 26	12 36	12 37
Cambridge	a						09 58							10 58						11 58						12 58
Ely 6	d	08 49	08 54	08 58	09 15			09 50	09 52	10 15			10 37		10 49	10 52	10 58	11 15			11 48	11 52	12 15		12 37	
Littleport	d		09 01					09 57							10 56						11 55					
Downham Market	d		09 10					10 06							11 05						12 04					
Watlington	d		09 16					10 12							11 11						12 10					
Kings Lynn	a		09 25					10 21							11 20						12 20					
Manea	d																									
March	d	09 07		09 15	09 31					10 32			10 53				11 15	11 31					12 31		12 53	
Whittlesea	d			09 26													11 26									
Peterborough 8	a	09 25		09 37	09 51				10 26	10 50			11 11			11 24	11 37	11 51				12 24	12 50		13 11	

For general notes see front of timetable
For details of catering facilities see Directory of Train Operators

A To Birmingham New Street (Table 49)
B To Liverpool Lime Street (Table 49)

London, Norwich and Cambridge → Ely, Kings Lynn and Peterborough

Network Diagram - see first page of Table 13

		FC	EM	LE		XC	LE	LE	FC	EM	XC	LE	XC	LE	FC	EM	LE	XC	LE	LE		FC	FC	EM	XC	LE
		1	◇ 🍴	1 ◇		1 ◇ 🍴	1	1	1	◇ 🍴	1 ◇ 🍴	1	1	1	1	◇ 🍴	1 ◇	1 ◇ 🍴	1	1		1	1	◇ 🍴	1 ◇ 🍴	1
London Liverpool Street	d			10 38													12 38									
London Kings Cross	d	11 45							12 45						13 45								14 45			
Ipswich	d			12 02													14 02									
Stansted Airport	d					12 25					13 25							14 25							15 20	
Norwich	d		11 57					12 40		12 57				13 40		13 57				14 40				14 57		
Wymondham	d							12 52						13 52						14 52						
Spooner Row	d																									
Attleborough	d							12 59						13 59						14 59						
Eccles Road	d																									
Harling Road	d																									
Thetford	d		12 24					13 12		13 24				14 12		14 24				15 12				15 24		
Brandon	d							13 20						14 20						15 20						
Lakenheath	d																									
Shippea Hill	d																									
Cambridge	d	12 33				13 00	13 12		13 33		14 00	14 12	14 22		14 33			15 00	15 12			15 24	15 35		16 00	16 12
Waterbeach	d	12 39							13 39						14 39							15 30	15 41			
Ely 6	a	12 48	12 45	12 58		13 14	13 26	13 38	13 48	13 46	14 14	14 26	14 36	14 40	14 48	14 45	14 58	15 14	15 26	15 37		15 40	15 50	15 45	16 14	16 26
Cambridge	a							13 58						14 58						15 58						
Ely 6	d	12 48	12 52	12 58		13 15			13 48	13 52	14 15		14 37		14 50	14 52	14 58	15 15					15 50	15 52	16 15	
Littleport	d	12 55							13 55						14 57								15 57			
Downham Market	d	13 04							14 04						15 06								16 06			
Watlington	d	13 10							14 10						15 12								16 12			
Kings Lynn	a	13 20							14 20						15 21								16 21			
Manea	d																									
March	d			13 15		13 31					14 31		14 53				15 15	15 31							16 31	
Whittlesea	d			13 26													15 26									
Peterborough 8	a		13 25	13 37		13 51				14 25	14 50		15 11			15 25	15 37	15 50						16 25	16 49	

		LE	FC	XC	FC	EM	LE	XC	LE	LE	LE	EM	FC		XC	FC	LE	LE	LE	LE	EM	FC	LE	XC	FC	LE
		1	1	1 A	1	◇ B 🍴	1 ◇	1 ◇ 🍴	1	1		◇ C 🍴	1		1 ◇ A 🍴	1	1	1	1	1	◇ D	1	R 1	1 ◇ 🍴	1	1
London Liverpool Street	d						14 38			15 58								16 58					16 32			17 58
London Kings Cross	d				15 45								16 44			17 14						17 44			18 14	
Ipswich	d						16 02																17 49			
Stansted Airport	d							16 25							17 18									18 21		
Norwich	d	15 40				15 52					16 38	16 57							17 35		17 54					
Wymondham	d	15 52									16 50	17 09							17 47		18 06					
Spooner Row	d										16x54															
Attleborough	d	15 59				16 09					16 59								17 54		18 13					
Eccles Road	d					16 14													17 59							
Harling Road	d					16 18													18 03							
Thetford	d	16 12				16 27					17 12	17 27							18 12		18 27					
Brandon	d	16 20									17 20								18 20							
Lakenheath	d																									
Shippea Hill	d																									
Cambridge	d		16 24	16 30	16 35			17 00	17 12	17 22			17 39		17 51	18 05	18 09	18 14		18 24		18 39		19 00	19 05	19 19
Waterbeach	d		16 30		16 41					17 28			17 45					18 20		18 30		18 45				19 25
Ely 6	a	16 37	16 40	16 44	16 50	16 48	16 58	17 14	17 26	17 38	17 38	17 48	17 55		18 06	18 20	18 26	18 30	18 38	18 40	18 48	18 55	18 52	19 14	19 18	19 34
Cambridge	a	16 58									17 58								18 58							
Ely 6	d			16 45	16 50	16 52	16 58	17 15				17 52	17 56		18 06			18 30			18 52	18 56	19 01	19 15	19 22	19 35
Littleport	d				16 57								18 03					18 37				19 03				19 42
Downham Market	d				17 06								18 12					18 47				19 12			19 38	19 52
Watlington	d				17 12								18 18					18 53				19 18				19 58
Kings Lynn	a				17 21								18 28					19 05				19 28			19 56	20 10
Manea	d			16 55											18x17											
March	d			17 03			17 15	17 31							18 25						19 08		19 17	19 31		
Whittlesea	d						17 26																19 29			
Peterborough 8	a			17 21		17 27	17 37	17 50				18 25			18 50						19 31		19 42	19 51		

For general notes see front of timetable
For details of catering facilities see Directory of Train Operators

A To Birmingham New Street (Table 49)
B To Liverpool Lime Street (Table 49)
C To Manchester Piccadilly (Table 49)
D To Nottingham (Table 49)

London, Norwich and Cambridge → Ely, Kings Lynn and Peterborough

Network Diagram - see first page of Table 13

		LE	LE	EM	FC	XC		LE	LE	LE	FC	XC	LE	FC	LE	FC	FC	LE	FC	LE	FC	LE	FC	FC		
																FO	FX						FO	FX		
		1	1	◇	1	1 ◇ 🍴		1	1	1	1	1 ◇ 🍴	1	1	1	1	1	1	1	1	1	1	1	1		
London Liverpool Street	d							18 58																		
London Kings Cross	d				18 44						19 45			20 15		20 45	20 45		21 15		22 15		23 15	23 15		
Ipswich	d												20 16													
Stansted Airport	d					19 21						20 21														
Norwich	d	18 40		18 57						19 45								21 15				22 40				
Wymondham	d	18 52								19 57								21 27				22 52				
Spooner Row	d																									
Attleborough	d	18 59								20 04								21 34				22 59				
Eccles Road	d																									
Harling Road	d																									
Thetford	d	19 12		19 24						20 17								21 47				23 12				
Brandon	d	19 20								20 25								21 55				23 20				
Lakenheath	d																									
Shippea Hill	d																									
Cambridge	d		19 25		19 39	20 00		20 15	20 20		20 40	21 00		21 10	21 13	21 35	21 35		22 10	22 55	23 10		00 13	00 13		
Waterbeach	d				19 45			20 21			20 46			21 16		21 41	21 41		22 16		23 16		00 19	00 19		
Ely 6	a	19 37	19 39	19 48	19 55	20 14		20 30	20 35	20 44	20 55	21 14	21 19	21 25	21 29	21 52	21 54	22 14	22 25	23 09	23 25	23 38	00 28	00 29		
Cambridge	a	19 58								21 04								22 33				00 02				
Ely 6	d			19 52	19 56	20 15		20 31			20 55	21 15	21 19	21 25		21 53			22 25		23 25		00 29			
Littleport	d				20 03			20 38			21 02			21 32		22 00			22 32		23 32		00 36			
Downham Market	d				20 12			20 47			21 11			21 41		22 09			22 41		23 41		00 45			
Watlington	d				20 18			20 53			21 17			21 47		22 14			22 47		23 47		00 50			
Kings Lynn	a				20 28			21 05			21 26			21 56		22 24			22 56		23 56		01 00			
Manea	d																									
March	d					20 31						21 31	21 36													
Whittlesea	d												21 47													
Peterborough 8	a			20 26		20 49						21 49	21 58													

Saturdays

		FC	XC	XC	LE		LE	XC	FC	EM		LE	XC	LE	LE		EM	FC	XC	LE		LE	LE	XC	FC	EM
		1	1 ◇	1 ◇	1		1	1	1	◇		1	1 ◇	1	1		◇	1	1 ◇	1		1	1	1	1	◇
								A		B							B							A		
			🍴	🍴						🍴			🍴				🍴		🍴							🍴
London Liverpool Street	d																					06 58				
London Kings Cross	d	23p15																06 45							07 45	
Ipswich	d											06 00														
Stansted Airport	d			05 25									06 25						07 25							
Norwich	d						05 38			05 52					06 40		06 52						07 40			07 57
Wymondham	d						05 50			06 04					06 52								07 52			
Spooner Row	d																									
Attleborough	d						05 57			06 11					06 59								07 59			
Eccles Road	d																									
Harling Road	d																									
Thetford	d						06 10			06 25					07 12		07 20						08 12			08 24
Brandon	d						06 18								07 20								08 20			
Lakenheath	d																									
Shippea Hill	d																									
Cambridge	d	00 13	05 15	05 55	06 08			06 26	06 32				06 56	07 00				07 33	08 00	08 12		08 20		08 26	08 33	
Waterbeach	d	00 19							06 38									07 39				08 26			08 39	
Ely 6	a	00 28	05 29	06 09	06 22		06 35	06 40	06 47	06 46		06 56	07 10	07 14	07 37		07 41	07 48	08 14	08 26		08 36	08 37	08 41	08 48	08 47
Cambridge	a						06 55								07 58								08 58			
Ely 6	d	00 29	05 30	06 10				06 41	06 47	06 51		06 57	07 11				07 44	07 48	08 15					08 41	08 48	08 54
Littleport	d	00 36							06 54									07 55							08 55	
Downham Market	d	00 45							07 03									08 04							09 04	
Watlington	d	00 50							07 09									08 09							09 10	
Kings Lynn	a	01 00							07 20									08 21							09 21	
Manea	d			06x20																						
March	d		05 46	06 28				06 57		07 07		07 14	07 29				08 01		08 31					08 57		09 11
Whittlesea	d		05 58	06 39								07 25	07 40				08 12									
Peterborough 8	a		06 08	06 50				07 15		07 25		07 37	07 51				08 25		08 50					09 16		09 28

For general notes see front of timetable
For details of catering facilities see Directory of Train Operators

A Until 11 July and from 12 September
B To Liverpool Lime Street (Table 49)

London, Norwich and Cambridge → Ely, Kings Lynn and Peterborough

Network Diagram - see first page of Table 13

		LE	XC	LE	LE	FC	EM	XC	LE	XC	LE	FC	EM	LE	XC	LE	LE	FC	EM	XC	LE
		1 ◇	1 ◇	1	1	1	◇	1 ◇	1	1	1	1	◇	1 ◇	1 ◇	1	1	1	◇	1 ◇	1
										A											
			🛒				🛒	🛒					🛒		🛒				🛒	🛒	
London Liverpool Street	d	06 38												08 38							
London Kings Cross	d					08 45						09 45						10 45			
Ipswich	d	08 02												10 02							
Stansted Airport	d		08 25					09 25							10 25					11 25	
Norwich	d				08 40		08 57				09 40		09 57				10 40		10 57		
Wymondham	d				08 52						09 52						10 52				
Spooner Row	d																				
Attleborough	d				08 59						09 59						10 59				
Eccles Road	d																				
Harling Road	d																				
Thetford	d				09 12		09 24				10 12		10 24				11 12		11 24		
Brandon	d				09 20						10 20						11 20				
Lakenheath	d										10x25										
Shippea Hill	d																				
Cambridge	d		09 00	09 12		09 33		10 00	10 12	10 22		10 33			11 00	11 12		11 33		12 00	12 12
Waterbeach	d					09 39						10 39						11 39			
Ely 6	a	08 58	09 14	09 26	09 37	09 48	09 45	10 14	10 26	10 36	10 38	10 48	10 46	10 58	11 14	11 26	11 38	11 48	11 46	12 14	12 26
Cambridge	a				09 58						10 58						11 58				
Ely 6	d	08 58	09 15			09 48	09 51	10 15		10 37		10 48	10 53	10 58	11 15			11 48	11 53	12 15	
Littleport	d					09 55						10 55						11 55			
Downham Market	d					10 04						11 04						12 04			
Watlington	d					10 10						11 10						12 10			
Kings Lynn	a					10 21						11 21						12 21			
Manea	d																				
March	d	09 16	09 31					10 31		10 53				11 15	11 31					12 31	
Whittlesea	d	09 27												11 26							
Peterborough 8	a	09 38	09 50				10 25	10 50		11 11			11 24	11 37	11 51				12 24	12 50	

		XC	FC	LE	FC	EM	LE	XC	LE	LE	FC	EM	EM	XC	LE	XC	LE	FC	EM	LE	XC
							R													R	
		1	1	1	1	◇	1	1 ◇	1	1	1	◇	◇	1 ◇	1	1	1	1	◇	1	1 ◇
		A										A	B			A					
						🛒		🛒				🛒	🛒	🛒					🛒		🛒
London Liverpool Street	d						10 38													12 38	
London Kings Cross	d				11 45						12 45							13 45			
Ipswich	d						12 02													14 02	
Stansted Airport	d							12 25						13 25							14 25
Norwich	d			11 40		11 57				12 40		12 57	12 57				13 40		13 57		
Wymondham	d			11 52						12 52							13 52				
Spooner Row	d																				
Attleborough	d			11 59						12 59							13 59				
Eccles Road	d																				
Harling Road	d																				
Thetford	d			12 12		12 24				13 12		13 24	13 24				14 12		14 24		
Brandon	d			12 20						13 20							14 20				
Lakenheath	d																				
Shippea Hill	d																				
Cambridge	d	12 22			12 33			13 00	13 12		13 33			14 00	14 12	14 22		14 33			15 00
Waterbeach	d		12 36		12 39						13 39							14 39			
Ely 6	a	12 36		12 37	12 48	12 45	12 58	13 14	13 26	13 37	13 48	13 46	13 46	14 14	14 26	14 36	14 37	14 48	14 45	14 58	15 14
Cambridge	a		12 44	12 58						13 58							14 58				
Ely 6	d	12 37			12 48	12 54	12 58	13 15			13 48	13 53	13 53	14 15		14 37		14 48	14 53	14 58	15 15
Littleport	d				12 55						13 55							14 55			
Downham Market	d				13 04						14 04							15 04			
Watlington	d				13 10						14 10							15 10			
Kings Lynn	a				13 21						14 21							15 21			
Manea	d																				
March	d	12 53					13 15	13 31						14 31		14 53				15 15	15 31
Whittlesea	d						13 26													15 26	
Peterborough 8	a	13 11				13 26	13 37	13 51				14 25	14 27	14 50		15 11			15 25	15 37	15 51

		LE	LE	FC	EM	XC	LE	XC	LE	FC	EM	LE	XC	LE	LE	FC	EM	XC	LE	LE	FC	EM
		1	1	1	◇	1 ◇	1	1	1	1	◇	1 ◇	1 ◇	1	1	1	◇	1 ◇	1	1	1	◇
								A			C						C					D
					🛒	🛒					🛒		🛒				🛒	🛒				
London Liverpool Street	d											14 38										
London Kings Cross	d			14 45						15 45						16 45					17 45	
Ipswich	d											16 02										
Stansted Airport	d					15 25							16 25					17 25				
Norwich	d		14 40		14 57				15 35		15 52				16 38		16 57			17 35		17 54
Wymondham	d		14 52						15 47						16 50		17 09			17 47		18 06
Spooner Row	d														16x54							
Attleborough	d		14 59						15 54		16 09				16 59					17 54		18 13
Eccles Road	d								15 59											17 59		
Harling Road	d								16 03											18 03		
Thetford	d		15 12		15 24				16 12		16 23				17 12		17 27			18 12		18 27
Brandon	d		15 20						16 20						17 20					18 20		
Lakenheath	d																					
Shippea Hill	d																					
Cambridge	d	15 12		15 33		16 00	16 12	16 22		16 33			17 00	17 12		17 33		18 00	18 12		18 40	
Waterbeach	d			15 39						16 39						17 39					18 46	
Ely 6	a	15 26	15 37	15 48	15 48	16 14	16 26	16 36	16 37	16 48	16 47	16 58	17 14	17 26	17 37	17 48	17 48	18 14	18 26	18 37	18 55	18 48
Cambridge	a		15 58						16 58						17 58					18 58		
Ely 6	d			15 48	15 52	16 15		16 37		16 48	16 52	16 58	17 15			17 48	17 52	18 15			18 55	18 54
Littleport	d			15 55						16 55						17 55					19 03	
Downham Market	d			16 04						17 04						18 04					19 12	
Watlington	d			16 10						17 10						18 10					19 17	
Kings Lynn	a			16 21						17 21						18 21					19 26	
Manea	d																	18x25				
March	d					16 31		16 53				17 15	17 31					18 33				19 10
Whittlesea	d											17 26										
Peterborough 8	a				16 25	16 50		17 11			17 26	17 37	17 51				18 25	18 50				19 29

For general notes see front of timetable
For details of catering facilities see Directory of Train Operators

A Until 11 July and from 12 September
B 18 July to 5 September
C To Manchester Piccadilly (Table 49)
D To Nottingham (Table 49)

Table 17

Saturdays

London, Norwich and Cambridge → Ely, Kings Lynn and Peterborough

Network Diagram - see first page of Table 13

		LE R 1		XC 1 ◇	FC 1	LE 1	LE 1		EM ◇	FC 1	XC 1 ◇	LE 1		XC 1 A	LE 1	FC 1	LE R 1	LE 1	LE 1	FC 1	LE 1	FC 1	LE 1	FC 1		
London Liverpool Street	d	16 38															18 46									
London Kings Cross	d				18 15					18 45						19 45				20 45		21 52		23 12		
Ipswich	d	18 02															20 02									
Stansted Airport	d			18 25							19 25															
Norwich	d						18 40		18 57						19 40				20 40				22 40			
Wymondham	d						18 52								19 52				20 52				22 52			
Spooner Row	d																									
Attleborough	d						18 59								19 59				20 59				22 59			
Eccles Road	d																									
Harling Road	d																									
Thetford	d						19 12		19 24						20 12				21 12				23 12			
Brandon	d						19 20								20 20				21 20				23 20			
Lakenheath	d																									
Shippea Hill	d						19x28																			
Cambridge	d			19 00	19 04	19 12				19 40	20 00	20 12		20 22		20 40		21 12		21 40	22 30	22 55		00 19		
Waterbeach	d									19 46						20 46				21 46		23 00		00 25		
Ely 6	a	18 58		19 14	19 18	19 26	19 37		19 47	19 55	20 14	20 26		20 36	20 37	20 55	20 58	21 26	21 37	21 55	22 44	23 10	23 37	00 34		
Cambridge	a						19 58								20 58				21 58				23 58			
Ely 6	d	18 58		19 15					19 53	19 55	20 15			20 37		20 55	20 58			21 55		23 10		00 34		
Littleport	d									20 03						21 03				22 03		23 17		00 41		
Downham Market	d									20 12						21 12				22 12		23 26		00 50		
Watlington	d									20 17						21 17				22 17		23 31		00 56		
Kings Lynn	a									20 26						21 26				22 26		23 40		01 07		
Manea	d																									
March	d	19 15		19 31							20 31			20 53			21 15									
Whittlesea	d	19 26															21 26									
Peterborough 8	a	19 37		19 50					20 25		20 50			21 11			21 37									

Sundays

		FC 1	LE 1 B	FC 1 B	FC 1 C	FC 1	LE 1	EM ◇ B	LE 1	LE 1	XC 1 ◇	FC 1	EM ◇		XC 1 ◇	FC 1	LE 1	LE 1	LE 1	XC 1 ◇	LE 1	FC 1	LE 1	XC 1 ◇	LE 1	FC 1
London Liverpool Street	d																									
London Kings Cross	d	23p12		07 52	07b26	09 15						10 15				11 15						12 15				13 15
Ipswich	d		07 55						09 55									11 55								
Stansted Airport	d										10 25				11 25					12 25				13 25		
Norwich	d						09 15	09 33					10 47				11 15				12 15				13 15	
Wymondham	d						09 27										11 27				12 27				13 27	
Spooner Row	d																									
Attleborough	d						09 34										11 34				12 34				13 34	
Eccles Road	d																									
Harling Road	d																									
Thetford	d						09 47	10 00					11 14				11 47				12 47				13 47	
Brandon	d						09 55										11 55				12 55				13 55	
Lakenheath	d						10x00										12x00									
Shippea Hill	d																									
Cambridge	d	00 19		09 07	09 07	10 05				10 46	10 56	11 05			11 56	12 05			12 46	12 56		13 05	13 46	13 56		14 05
Waterbeach	d	00 25		09 13	09 13	10 10						11 10				12 10						13 10				14 10
Ely 6	a	00 34	08 51	09 22	09 22	10 19	10 19	10 25	10 51	11 00	11 10	11 19	11 35		12 11	12 19	12 19	12 51	13 00	13 10	13 17	13 19	14 00	14 10	14 17	14 19
Cambridge	a						10 36										12 36				13 34				14 34	
Ely 6	d	00 34	08 52	09 22	09 22	10 19		10 32	10 52		11 11	11 19	11 39		12 11	12 19		12 52		13 11		13 19		14 11		14 19
Littleport	d	00 41		09 29	09 29	10 26						11 26				12 26						13 26				14 26
Downham Market	d	00 50		09 38	09 38	10 35						11 35				12 35						13 35				14 35
Watlington	d	00 56		09 43	09 43	10 40						11 40				12 40						13 41				14 40
Kings Lynn	a	01 07		09 52	09 52	10 50						11 50				12 50						13 50				14 50
Manea	d																									
March	d		09 09						11 09		11 27				12 28			13 09		13 27				14 27		
Whittlesea	d		09 20						11 20									13 20								
Peterborough 8	a		09 36					11 09	11 36		11 50		12 16		12 50			13 36		13 50				14 50		

For general notes see front of timetable
For details of catering facilities see Directory of Train Operators

A Until 11 July and from 12 September
B Until 6 September
C From 13 September

b Bus service Kings Cross to Finsbury Park

Table 17

Sundays

London, Norwich and Cambridge → Ely, Kings Lynn and Peterborough

Network Diagram - see first page of Table 13

		EM ◇	LE [1]		LE [1]	XC [1] ◇	LE [1]	FC [1]	EM ◇	LE [1]	XC [1] ◇ A	XC [1] ◇ B	XC [1] ◇ C	LE [1]	FC [1]	EM ◇		LE [1]	LE [1]	XC [1] ◇ D	XC [1] ◇ C	LE [1]	FC [1]	EM ◇	LE [1]	XC [1] ◇ D
London Liverpool Street	d																									
London Kings Cross	d							14 15							15 15								16 15			
Ipswich	d		13 55															15 55								
Stansted Airport	d					14 25					15 25	15 25	15 25							16 25	16 25					17 25
Norwich	d	13 49					14 15		14 47					15 15		15 53						16 15		16 57		
Wymondham	d						14 27							15 27								16 27				
Spooner Row	d																									
Attleborough	d						14 34							15 34								16 34				
Eccles Road	d																									
Harling Road	d																									
Thetford	d	14 16					14 47		15 14					15 47		16 20						16 47		17 24		
Brandon	d						14 55							15 55								16 55				
Lakenheath	d													16x00												
Shippea Hill	d																									
Cambridge	d				14 46	14 56		15 05		15 38	15 56	15 56	15 56		16 05				16 42	16 56	16 56		17 05		17 42	17 56
Waterbeach	d							15 10							16 10								17 10			
Ely [6]	a	14 42	14 51		15 00	15 11	15 17	15 19	15 40	15 52	16 10	16 10	16 11	16 14	16 19			16 51	16 56	17 10	17 11	17 12	17 19	17 45	17 56	18 10
Cambridge	a						15 34							16 33								17 32				
Ely [6]	d	14 45	14 52			15 11		15 19	15 48		16 11	16 11	16 11		16 19			16 52		17 11	17 11		17 19	17 48		18 11
Littleport	d							15 26							16 26								17 26			
Downham Market	d							15 35							16 35								17 35			
Watlington	d							15 40							16 40								17 40			
Kings Lynn	a							15 50							16 50								17 50			
Manea	d																									
March	d		15 09			15 28					16 27	16 27	16 27					17 09		17 27	17 27					18 27
Whittlesea	d		15 20															17 20								
Peterborough [8]	a	15 24	15 36			15 50			16 22		16 46	16 50	16 50			17 10		17 31		17 50	17 50			18 25		18 51

		XC [1] ◇ C	LE [1]	FC [1]	EM ◇	LE [1]		LE [1]	XC [1] ◇ D	XC [1] ◇ C	LE [1]	FC [1]	EM ◇	LE [1]	XC [1] ◇ D	XC [1] ◇ C	FC [1]	LE [1]	FC [1]	EM ◇	LE [1]	FC [1]	FC [1]	FC [1]		
London Liverpool Street	d																									
London Kings Cross	d			17 15								18 15					19 15		20 15			21 15	22 15	23 15		
Ipswich	d					17 55																				
Stansted Airport	d	17 25							18 25	18 25					19 25	19 25										
Norwich	d		17 15		17 56						18 15		18 57					20 15		20 52						
Wymondham	d		17 27								18 27							20 27								
Spooner Row	d																									
Attleborough	d		17 34								18 34							20 34								
Eccles Road	d																									
Harling Road	d																									
Thetford	d		17 47		18 23						18 47		19 24					20 47		21 19						
Brandon	d		17 55								18 55							20 55								
Lakenheath	d																									
Shippea Hill	d																									
Cambridge	d	17 56		18 04				18 42	18 56	18 56		19 05		19 48	19 56	19 56	20 05		21 05		21 48	22 04	23 11	00 19		
Waterbeach	d			18 10								19 10					20 10		21 10			22 10	23 17	00 25		
Ely [6]	a	18 11	18 12	18 19	18 44	18 51		18 56	19 10	19 11	19 12	19 19	19 45	20 02	20 10	20 11	20 19	21 12	21 19	21 40	22 02	22 19	23 26	00 38		
Cambridge	a		18 32								19 32							21 32								
Ely [6]	d	18 11		18 19	18 48	18 52			19 11	19 11		19 19	19 49		20 11	20 11	20 19		21 19	21 44		22 19	23 26			
Littleport	d			18 26								19 26					20 26		21 26			22 26	23 33			
Downham Market	d			18 35								19 35					20 35		21 35			22 35	23 42			
Watlington	d			18 40								19 40					20 40		21 40			22 40	23 47			
Kings Lynn	a			18 50								19 50					20 50		21 50			22 50	23 59			
Manea	d																									
March	d	18 27				19 09			19 27	19 27					20 27	20 27										
Whittlesea	d					19 20																				
Peterborough [8]	a	18 51			19 24	19 32			19 50	19 50			20 28		20 50	20 50				22 20						

For general notes see front of timetable
For details of catering facilities see Directory of Train Operators

A 19 July to 6 September. To Birmingham New Street (Table 57)
B Until 12 July
C From 13 September
D Until 6 September

Peterborough, Kings Lynn and Ely → Cambridge, Norwich and London

Network Diagram - see first page of Table 13

Miles	Miles			FC	LE	LE	FC	LE	LE	FC	EM	LE	FC	LE	LE	XC	FC	LE	EM	FC	LE	LE	LE	XC
				1	1	1	1	1	1	1	◇ A (T)	1	1	1	1	1 ◇ B	1	1	◇ A (T)	1	1	R 1	1	1 ◇ (T)
0	—	**Peterborough 8**	d								06 27					07 10			07 35			07 46		08 18
6	—	Whittlesea	d													07 18						07 54		
14	—	March	d								06 43					07 29			07 51			08 05		08 34
19¼	—	Manea	d													07x37								
—	0	**Kings Lynn**	d		05 19		05 52		06 18				06 52				07 23			07 55				
—	6	Watlington	d		05 26		05 59		06 25				06 59				07 30			08 02				
—	10¾	Downham Market	d		05 33		06 05		06 32				07 05				07 36			08 08				
—	21	Littleport	d		05 42		06 14		06 41				07 14				07 45			08 17				
29¼	26½	**Ely 6**	a		05 51		06 22		06 49		07 01		07 22			07 51	07 54		08 11	08 25		08 30		08 52
—	—	**Cambridge**	d			06 05						07 05									08 12			
—	—	**Ely 6**	d	05 26	05 52	06 20	06 22	06 30	06 50	06 54	07 05	07 20	07 22	07 30	07 33	07 52	07 54	08 03	08 15	08 25	08 28	08 30	08 38	08 53
—	36	Waterbeach	d	05 35	06 01		06 32		06 59				07 32				08 04	08 12		08 35				
—	41¼	**Cambridge**	a	05 44	06 10		06 40	06 51	07 08	07 11			07 40	07 47	07 51	08 07	08 14	08 21		08 44			08 55	09 08
35¼	—	Shippea Hill	d									07x29												
40¾	—	Lakenheath	d																					
44½	—	Brandon	d			06 36					07 20	07 39									08 44			
51¾	—	Thetford	d			06 45					07 29	07 48							08 37		08 53			
59½	—	Harling Road	d			06 53						07 56												
62½	—	Eccles Road	d			06 57						08 00												
66¼	—	Attleborough	d			07 03					07 43	08 06							08 51		09 07			
69½	—	Spooner Row	d									08x11												
72	—	Wymondham	d			07 10					07 50	08 15							08 58		09 14			
82¼	—	**Norwich**	a			07 30					08 13	08 30							09 13		09 30			
—	—	Stansted Airport	a													08 45								09 45
—	—	Ipswich	a																			09 26		
—	99¼	**London Kings Cross**	a	06 38			07 39			08 06			08 39				09 12			09 42				
—	—	London Liverpool Street	a		07 34				08 34					09 19				09 49				10 46		

		FC	LE	FC	XC	LE	EM	XC	EM	LE	LE	FC	LE	XC	EM	FC	LE	XC	LE	XC	EM	LE	FC
		1	1	1	1	1	◇ C (T)	1 ◇ (T)	◇ (T)	1 ◇	1	1	1	1 ◇ (T)	◇ (T)	1	1	1	1	1 ◇ (T)	◇ (T)	1 ◇	1
Peterborough 8	d				08 54		08 59	09 18	09 40	09 45				10 18	10 44			10 58		11 18	11 38	11 45	
Whittlesea	d									09 53												11 53	
March	d				09 10			09 34		10 04				10 34				11 13		11 34		12 04	
Manea	d																						
Kings Lynn	d	08 27		08 59								09 59				10 56							11 56
Watlington	d	08 34		09 06								10 06				11 03							12 03
Downham Market	d	08 40		09 12								10 12				11 09							12 09
Littleport	d	08 49		09 21								10 21				11 18							12 18
Ely 6	a	08 57		09 29	09 35		09 41	09 53	10 13	10 23		10 29		10 52	11 16	11 26		11 31		11 52	12 11	12 22	12 26
Cambridge	d		09 12								10 12						11 12						
Ely 6	d	08 57	09 27	09 29	09 35	09 38	09 44	09 53	10 16	10 26	10 27	10 29	10 38	10 52	11 19	11 26	11 27	11 32	11 38	11 53	12 15	12 30	12 26
Waterbeach	d	09 07		09 38								10 38				11 35						→	12 35
Cambridge	a	09 16		09 47	09 51	09 58		10 09				10 47	10 58	11 08		11 44		11 50	11 58	12 08			12 44
Shippea Hill	d																						
Lakenheath	d																						
Brandon	d		09 43								10 43						11 43						
Thetford	d		09 52				10 05		10 39		10 52				11 41		11 52				12 36		
Harling Road	d																						
Eccles Road	d																						
Attleborough	d		10 06								11 06						12 06						
Spooner Row	d		10x11																				
Wymondham	d		10 15								11 13						12 13						
Norwich	a		10 30				10 43		11 13		11 30				12 13		12 30				13 13		
Stansted Airport	a							10 45						11 45						12 45			
Ipswich	a									11 25													
London Kings Cross	a	10 13		10 46								11 39				12 33							13 33
London Liverpool Street	a									12 45													

		LE	LE	LE	XC	EM	FC	LE	XC	LE	XC	EM	FC	LE	LE	LE	XC	EM	FC	LE	LE	XC	XC	FC
		1	1 ◇	1	1 ◇ (T)	◇ (T)	1	1	1	1	1 ◇ (T)	◇ (T)	1	1	1	1	1 ◇ (T)	◇ (T)	1	1	1	1	1 ◇ (T)	1
Peterborough 8	d				12 18	12 43			12 55		13 18	13 40			13 45		14 18	14 40				14 52	15 18	
Whittlesea	d														13 53									
March	d				12 34				13 10		13 34				14 04		14 34					15 10	15 34	
Manea	d																							
Kings Lynn	d						12 56						13 56						14 56					
Watlington	d						13 03						14 03						15 03					
Downham Market	d						13 09						14 09						15 09					
Littleport	d						13 18						14 18						15 18					
Ely 6	a				12 52	13 16	13 26		13 32		13 52	14 13	14 26		14 29		14 52	15 13	15 26			15 41	15 52	
Cambridge	d	12 12	←					13 12						14 12						15 12				
Ely 6	d	12 27	12 30	12 38	12 52	13 20	13 26	13 29	13 32	13 38	13 53	14 16	14 26	14 27	14 30	14 40	14 53	15 16	15 26	15 27	15 38	15 41	15 53	16 02
Waterbeach	d						13 35						14 35						15 35					16 11
Cambridge	a			12 58	13 08		13 44		13 50	13 58	14 08		14 44			14 58	15 08		15 44		15 58	15 57	16 08	16 19
Shippea Hill	d																							
Lakenheath	d																							
Brandon	d	12 43						13 45						14 43						15 43				
Thetford	d	12 52				13 41		13 54				14 37		14 52				15 37		15 52				
Harling Road	d																							
Eccles Road	d																							
Attleborough	d	13 06						14 08						15 06						16 06				
Spooner Row	d																							
Wymondham	d	13 13						14 15						15 13						16 13				
Norwich	a	13 30				14 13		14 30				15 13		15 30				16 13		16 30				
Stansted Airport	a				13 45						14 45						15 45						16 45	
Ipswich	a		13 25												15 25									
London Kings Cross	a						14 33						15 33						16 33					
London Liverpool Street	a		14 45																					

For general notes see front of timetable
For details of catering facilities see Directory of Train Operators

A From Nottingham (Table 49)
B From Birmingham New Street (Table 49)
C From Mansfield Woodhouse (Table 55)

Peterborough, Kings Lynn and Ely → Cambridge, Norwich and London

Network Diagram - see first page of Table 13

		EM ◇	LE 1 ◇	FC 1		LE 1	LE 1 ◇	LE 1	XC 1 ◇	EM ◇	FC 1	LE 1	LE		XC 1 ◇	FC 1	LE 1	LE 1 ◇	FC 1	LE 1	XC 1 ◇	FC 1		LE 1	EM ◇	XC 1 ◇
															A											
Peterborough 8	d	15 35	15 45						16 18	16 36					17 18			17 45			18 18				18 42	18 59
Whittlesea	d		15 53												17 26			17 53								
March	d		16 04						16 34						17 37			18 04			18 34				18 58	19 15
Manea	d														17x44											
Kings Lynn	d			15 56							16 54					17 36						18 36				
Watlington	d			16 03							17 01					17 43						18 43				
Downham Market	d			16 09							17 07					17 49						18 49				
Littleport	d			16 18							17 16					17 58						18 58				
Ely 6	a	16 08	16 22	16 26					16 52	17 09	17 24				17 58	18 06		18 22			18 52	19 06			19 24	19 32
Cambridge	d					16 12	←					17 12					18 09		18 39					19 19		
Ely 6	d	16 12	16 30	16 26		16 27	16 30	16 38	16 53	17 13	17 24	17 27	17 39		17 59	18 06	18 24	18 30		18 39	18 53	19 06			19 27	19 33
Waterbeach	d		→	16 35							17 33					18 15			18a45			19 15		19a25		
Cambridge	a			16 44				16 58	17 08		17 43		17 58		18 16	18 22				18 58	19 08	19 22				19 55
Shippea Hill	d																									
Lakenheath	d																									
Brandon	d					16 43						17 43					18 40									
Thetford	d	16 33				16 52				17 34		17 52					18 48								19 49	
Harling Road	d																									
Eccles Road	d																									
Attleborough	d					17 06						18 06					19 02									
Spooner Row	d																									
Wymondham	d					17 13						18 13					19 09									
Norwich	a	17 13				17 30				18 13		18 30					19 25								20 22	
Stansted Airport	a								17 45						18 50						19 45					
Ipswich	a						17 27											19 25								
London Kings Cross	a			17 38							18 38					19 34						20 33				
London Liverpool Street	a						18 49											20 46								

		LE 1	LE 1	XC 1 ◇	FC 1	EM ◇	LE 1 ◇	LE 1		LE 1	XC 1 ◇	FC 1	LE 1	XC 1	XC 1 ◇	FC 1	EM ◇		LE 1	LE 1	XC 1 ◇	FC 1	LE 1	LE 1		
																	B									
Peterborough 8	d			19 18		19 37	19 46				20 18			20 59	21 18		21 37			22 05	22 18					
Whittlesea	d						19 54													22 13						
March	d			19 34			20 05				20 34			21 14	21 34					22 24	22 34					
Manea	d																									
Kings Lynn	d				19 39							20 39				21 36						22 32				
Watlington	d				19 46							20 46				21 43						22 39				
Downham Market	d				19 52							20 52				21 49						22 45				
Littleport	d				20 01							21 01				21 58						22 54				
Ely 6	a			19 52	20 09	20 13	20 26				20 52	21 09		21 34	21 52	22 06	22 10			22 42	22 52	23 02				
Cambridge	d		19 25					20 20					21 13										22 55			
Ely 6	d	19 38	19 40	19 53	20 09	20 16	20 27	20 36		20 45	20 53	21 09	21 29	21 34	21 53	22 06	22 14		22 14	22 42	22 53	23 02	23 10	23 38		
Waterbeach	d				20 18							21 18				22 15						23 11				
Cambridge	a	19 58		20 08	20 26					21 04	21 08	21 27		21 54	22 08	22 23			22 33		23 10	23 19		00 02		
Shippea Hill	d																									
Lakenheath	d																									
Brandon	d		19 56					20 52					21 45										23 26			
Thetford	d		20 04			20 37		21 00					21 54				22 35						23 34			
Harling Road	d																									
Eccles Road	d																									
Attleborough	d		20 18					21 15					22 08				22 49						23 48			
Spooner Row	d																									
Wymondham	d		20 25					21 23					22 15				22 56						23 55			
Norwich	a		20 42			21 13		21 38					22 31				23 18						00 12			
Stansted Airport	a			20 45							21 45				22 45											
Ipswich	a						21 25													23 37						
London Kings Cross	a				21 30							22 30				23 35						00 42				
London Liverpool Street	a						22 46																			

For general notes see front of timetable
For details of catering facilities see
Directory of Train Operators

A From Birmingham New Street (Table 49)
B From Liverpool Lime Street (Table 49)

Peterborough, Kings Lynn and Ely → Cambridge, Norwich and London

Network Diagram - see first page of Table 13

		FC	LE	FC	LE	EM	LE	FC	LE	XC	EM	LE	FC	LE	LE	LE	XC	LE	EM	FC	LE	XC
		1	1	1	1	◇ 🛒	1	1	1	1 ◇ 🛒	◇ 🛒	R 1	1	1	R 1	1	1 ◇ A 🛒	1	◇ 🛒	1	1	1 A
Peterborough 8	d					06 27				07 13	07 35	07 45					08 18		08 46			08 58
Whittlesea	d									07 21		07 53										
March	d					06 43				07 32	07 51	08 04					08 34					09 14
Manea	d									07x39												
Kings Lynn	d			05 56				06 56					07 56							08 56		
Watlington	d			06 03				07 03					08 03							09 03		
Downham Market	d			06 09				07 09					08 09							09 09		
Littleport	d			06 18				07 18					08 18							09 18		
Ely 6	a			06 26		07 01		07 26		07 52	08 13	08 22	08 26				08 52		09 19	09 26		09 32
Cambridge	d		06 08				07 00							08 12	←						09 12	
Ely 6	d	05 26	06 23	06 26	06 35	07 06	07 15	07 26	07 38	07 53	08 17	08 30	08 26	08 27	08 30	08 38	08 53	09 11	09 22	09 26	09 29	09 33
Waterbeach	d	05 35		06 35				07 35				→	08 35					09 20		09 35		
Cambridge	a	05 44		06 44	06 55			07 44	07 58	08 08			08 44			08 58	09 08	09 28		09 44		09 50
Shippea Hill	d						07x23															
Lakenheath	d																					
Brandon	d		06 39			07 22	07 33							08 43							09 45	
Thetford	d		06 48			07 30	07 42				08 39			08 52					09 44		09 54	
Harling Road	d		06 56				07 50															
Eccles Road	d		07 00				07 54															
Attleborough	d		07 06			07 44	08 00				08 53			09 06							10 08	
Spooner Row	d						08x05															
Wymondham	d		07 13			07 51	08 09				09 00			09 13							10 15	
Norwich	a		07 29			08 13	08 24				09 18			09 30					10 19		10 30	
Stansted Airport	a									08 45							09 45					
Ipswich	a														09 25							
London Kings Cross	a	06 38		07 34				08 33					09 33							10 34		
London Liverpool Street	a														10 38			10 43				

		LE	FC	XC	EM	FC	LE	LE	LE	XC	EM	FC	LE	XC	LE	XC	EM	LE	FC	LE	LE	LE
		1	1	1 ◇ 🛒	◇ 🛒	1	1	R 1	1	1 ◇ 🛒	◇ 🛒	1	1	1 A	1	1 ◇ 🛒	◇ 🛒	1 ◇	1	1	1 ◇	1
Peterborough 8	d			09 21	09 46			09 55		10 18	10 44			10 58		11 18	11 38	11 45				
Whittlesea	d							10 03										11 53				
March	d			09 37				10 14		10 34				11 14		11 34		12 04				
Manea	d																					
Kings Lynn	d		09 30			09 56						10 56							11 56			
Watlington	d					10 03						11 03							12 03			
Downham Market	d		09 41			10 09						11 09							12 09			
Littleport	d					10 18						11 18							12 18			
Ely 6	a		09 58	09 58	10 19	10 26		10 32		10 52	11 17	11 26		11 32		11 52	12 11	12 22	12 26			
Cambridge	d						10 12						11 12							12 12	←	
Ely 6	d	09 38	09 58	09 58	10 22	10 26	10 29	10 32	10 38	10 53	11 22	11 26	11 29	11 33	11 38	11 53	12 15	12 30	12 26	12 27	12 30	12 38
Waterbeach	d					10 35						11 35						→	12 36			
Cambridge	a	09 58	10 12	10 16		10 44			10 58	11 08		11 44		11 50	11 58	12 08			12 44			12 58
Shippea Hill	d																					
Lakenheath	d																					
Brandon	d						10 45						11 45							12 43		
Thetford	d				10 44		10 54				11 44		11 54				12 36			12 52		
Harling Road	d																					
Eccles Road	d																					
Attleborough	d						11 08						12 08							13 06		
Spooner Row	d																					
Wymondham	d						11 15						12 15							13 13		
Norwich	a				11 18		11 30				12 18		12 30				13 13			13 30		
Stansted Airport	a			10 45						11 45						12 45						
Ipswich	a							11 27													13 27	
London Kings Cross	a		11 05			11 35						12 33							13 35			
London Liverpool Street	a							12 45													14 45	

For general notes see front of timetable
For details of catering facilities see
Directory of Train Operators

A Until 11 July and from 12 September

Peterborough, Kings Lynn and Ely → Cambridge, Norwich and London

Network Diagram - see first page of Table 13

		XC 1 ◇ 🍴	EM ◇ 🍴	FC 1	LE 1	XC 1 A	LE 1	XC 1 ◇ 🍴	EM ◇ 🍴	LE 1 ◇	FC 1	LE 1	LE 1 ◇	LE 1	XC 1 ◇ 🍴	EM ◇ 🍴	FC 1	LE 1	XC 1 A	LE 1	XC 1 ◇ 🍴	EM ◇ 🍴
Peterborough 8	d	12 18	12 40			12 58		13 18	13 38	13 45					14 18	14 41			14 55		15 18	15 36
Whittlesea	d									13 53												
March	d	12 34				13 14		13 34		14 04					14 34				15 11		15 34	
Manea	d																					
Kings Lynn	d			12 56							13 56						14 56					
Watlington	d			13 03							14 03						15 03					
Downham Market	d			13 09							14 09						15 09					
Littleport	d			13 18							14 18						15 18					
Ely 6	a	12 52	13 13	13 26		13 32		13 52	14 11	14 22	14 26				14 52	15 14	15 26		15 30		15 52	16 09
Cambridge	d				13 12							14 12	←					15 12				
Ely 6	d	12 53	13 17	13 26	13 28	13 32	13 38	13 53	14 15	14 30	14 26	14 27	14 30	14 38	14 53	15 17	15 26	15 27	15 31	15 38	15 53	16 13
Waterbeach	d			13 35						→	14 35						15 35					
Cambridge	a	13 08		13 44		13 50	13 58	14 08			14 44			14 58	15 08		15 44		15 50	15 58	16 08	
Shippea Hill	d																					
Lakenheath	d																	15x40				
Brandon	d				13 45							14 43						15 45				
Thetford	d		13 39		13 54				14 36			14 52				15 38		15 54				16 34
Harling Road	d																					
Eccles Road	d																					
Attleborough	d				14 08							15 06						16 08				
Spooner Row	d																					
Wymondham	d				14 15							15 13						16 15				
Norwich	a		14 13		14 30				15 13			15 30				16 13		16 30				17 13
Stansted Airport	a	13 45						14 45							15 45						16 45	
Ipswich	a												15 25									
London Kings Cross	a			14 33							15 33						16 35					
London Liverpool Street	a												16 45									

		LE 1 ◇	FC 1	LE 1	LE 1 ◇	LE 1	XC 1 ◇ 🍴	EM ◇ 🍴	FC 1	LE 1	LE 1	XC 1 ◇ 🍴	LE 1 ◇	FC 1	LE 1	LE 1 ◇	LE 1	XC 1 ◇ 🍴	FC 1	EM ◇ 🍴	LE 1	LE 1
Peterborough 8	d	15 45					16 18	16 40				17 18	17 45					18 18		18 42		
Whittlesea	d	15 53										17 27	17 53									
March	d	16 04					16 34					17 38	18 04					18 34		19 01		
Manea	d											17x45										
Kings Lynn	d		15 56						16 56					17 56					18 34			
Watlington	d		16 03						17 03					18 03					18 41			
Downham Market	d		16 09						17 09					18 09					18 47			
Littleport	d		16 18						17 18					18 18					18 56			
Ely 6	a	16 22	16 26				16 52	17 13	17 26			17 59	18 22	18 26				18 52	19 04	19 20		
Cambridge	d			16 12	←					17 12					18 12	←					19 12	
Ely 6	d	16 30	16 26	16 27	16 30	16 38	16 53	17 17	17 26	17 27	17 38	18 00	18 30	18 26	18 27	18 30	18 38	18 53	19 05	19 23	19 29	19 38
Waterbeach	d	→	16 35						17 35				→	18 35					19 15			
Cambridge	a		16 44			16 58	17 08		17 44		17 58	18 16		18 44			18 58	19 08	19 21			19 58
Shippea Hill	d																					
Lakenheath	d																					
Brandon	d			16 43						17 43					18 43						19 45	
Thetford	d			16 52				17 38		17 52					18 52					19 44	19 54	
Harling Road	d																					
Eccles Road	d																					
Attleborough	d			17 06						18 06					19 06						20 08	
Spooner Row	d																					
Wymondham	d			17 13						18 13					19 13						20 15	
Norwich	a			17 30				18 18		18 30					19 30					20 18	20 30	
Stansted Airport	a						17 45					18 53						19 45				
Ipswich	a				17 27											19 25						
London Kings Cross	a		17 34						18 34					19 33					20 32			
London Liverpool Street	a				18 45											20 45						

		XC 1 ◇ 🍴	FC 1	EM ◇ 🍴	LE 1	LE 1 ◇	LE 1	XC 1 ◇ 🍴	FC 1	LE 1	XC 1 A	LE 1	XC 1 ◇ 🍴	FC 1	EM ◇ B 🍴	EM ◇ C 🍴	LE 1	LE 1	XC 1 ◇ 🍴	LE 1	FC 1
Peterborough 8	d	19 18		19 37		19 45		20 18			20 54		21 18		21 36	21 39	21 45		22 18		
Whittlesea	d					19 53											21 53				
March	d	19 34				20 04		20 34			21 10		21 34				22 04		22 34		
Manea	d																				
Kings Lynn	d		19 34						20 34					21 34							23 15
Watlington	d		19 41						20 41					21 41							23 22
Downham Market	d		19 47						20 47					21 47							23 28
Littleport	d		19 56						20 56					21 56							23 37
Ely 6	a	19 52	20 04	20 12		20 26		20 52	21 05		21 28		21 52	22 05	22 10	22 12	22 22		22 54		23 44
Cambridge	d				20 12					21 12								22 30			
Ely 6	d	19 53	20 05	20 16	20 27	20 30	20 38	20 53	21 05	21 27	21 28	21 38	21 53	22 05	22 14	22 19	22 30	22 45	22 55	23 38	23 44
Waterbeach	d		20 15						21 15					22 15							23 54
Cambridge	a	20 08	20 21				20 58	21 08	21 21		21 50	21 58	22 08	22 21					23 10	23 58	00 02
Shippea Hill	d																				
Lakenheath	d																				
Brandon	d				20 43					21 43								23 01			
Thetford	d			20 36	20 52					21 52					22 35	22 41		23 09			
Harling Road	d																				
Eccles Road	d																				
Attleborough	d				21 06					22 06					22 49	22 55		23 23			
Spooner Row	d																				
Wymondham	d				21 13					22 13					22 56	23 02		23 30			
Norwich	a			21 13	21 30					22 30					23 18	23 20		23 45			
Stansted Airport	a	20 45						21 45					22 45								
Ipswich	a					21 27											23 32				
London Kings Cross	a		21 32						22 34					23 47							
London Liverpool Street	a					22 49															

For general notes see front of timetable
For details of catering facilities see Directory of Train Operators

A Until 11 July and from 12 September

B Until 11 July and from 12 September. From Liverpool Lime Street (Table 49)

C 18 July to 5 September. From Liverpool Lime Street (Table 49)

Peterborough, Kings Lynn and Ely → Cambridge, Norwich and London

Network Diagram - see first page of Table 13

		FC 1	FC 1	LE 1	LE 1 A	FC 1	LE 1	EM ◇ B		FC 1	LE 1	LE 1	FC 1	LE 1	LE 1	EM ◇ A		FC 1	XC 1 ◇ C	XC 1 ◇ D	LE 1	LE 1	EM ◇ E	LE 1		FC 1
Peterborough 8	d				09 46			11 09				11 46				12 53			13 18	13 23			13 43	13 46		
Whittlesea	d				09 54							11 54												13 54		
March	d				10 05			11 25				12 05							13 34	13 39				14 05		
Manea	d																									
Kings Lynn	d	08 28	09 28			10 28				11 28			12 28					13 26								14 26
Watlington	d	08 35	09 35			10 35				11 35			12 35					13 33								14 33
Downham Market	d	08 41	09 41			10 41				11 41			12 41					13 39								14 39
Littleport	d	08 50	09 50			10 50				11 50			12 50					13 48								14 48
Ely 6	a	08 58	09 58		10 29	10 58		11 48		11 58		12 28	12 58			13 32		13 56	13 58	13 58			14 21	14 30		14 56
Cambridge	d						10 46							12 46							13 46					
Ely 6	d	08 58	09 58	10 19	10 30	10 58	11 02	11 56		11 58	12 19	12 30	12 58	13 02	13 17	13 36		13 56	13 58	13 58	14 02	14 17	14 28	14 30		14 56
Waterbeach	d	09 07	10 07			11 07				12 07			13 07					14 05								15 05
Cambridge	a	09 16	10 16	10 36		11 16				12 16	12 36		13 16		13 34			14 14	14 17	14 17		14 34				15 14
Shippea Hill	d																									
Lakenheath	d						11x15							13x15												
Brandon	d						11 20	12 12						13 20							14 18					
Thetford	d						11 29	12 20						13 29		13 57					14 26		14 49			
Harling Road	d																									
Eccles Road	d																									
Attleborough	d						11 43	12 34						13 43							14 40					
Spooner Row	d																									
Wymondham	d						11 50	12 41						13 50							14 47					
Norwich	a						12 09	13 05						14 09		14 35					15 09		15 28			
Stansted Airport	a																		14 47	14 47						
Ipswich	a				11 25							13 25												15 27		
London Kings Cross	a	10 08	11 08			12 08				13 08			14 09					15 05								16 03
London Liverpool Street	a																									

		XC 1 ◇	LE 1	LE 1	EM ◇	LE 1	FC 1	XC 1 ◇ A		XC 1 ◇ G	LE 1	LE 1	EM ◇	XC 1 ◇	LE 1	FC 1		LE 1	EM ◇ H	EM ◇ J	XC 1 ◇	LE 1	FC 1	LE 1		LE 1
Peterborough 8	d	14 18			14 42			15 18		15 18		15 46	16 05	16 18					16 53	16 58	17 18					17 46
Whittlesea	d											15 54														17 54
March	d	14 34						15 34		15 34		16 05		16 34							17 34					18 05
Manea	d																									
Kings Lynn	d						15 26									16 28							17 28			
Watlington	d						15 33									16 35							17 35			
Downham Market	d						15 39									16 41							17 41			
Littleport	d						15 48									16 50							17 50			
Ely 6	a	14 58			15 21		15 56	15 58		16 02		16 28	16 38	16 52		16 58			17 31	17 31	17 52		17 58			18 27
Cambridge	d		14 46			15 38									16 42							17 42				
Ely 6	d	14 58	15 02	15 17	15 28	15 53	15 56	15 58		16 02	16 14	16 30	16 41	16 53	16 57	16 58		17 12	17 35	17 35	17 52	17 57	17 58	18 12		18 30
Waterbeach	d						16 05									17 07							18 07			
Cambridge	a	15 17		15 34			16 14	16 17		16 17	16 33			17 08		17 16		17 32			18 07		18 16	18 32		
Shippea Hill	d																									
Lakenheath	d					16x06																				
Brandon	d		15 18			16 12									17 13							18 13				
Thetford	d		15 26		15 49	16 20							17 02		17 21				17 56	17 56		18 21				
Harling Road	d																									
Eccles Road	d																									
Attleborough	d		15 40			16 34									17 35							18 35				
Spooner Row	d																									
Wymondham	d		15 47			16 41									17 42							18 42				
Norwich	a		16 09		16 35	16 58							17 35		17 59				18 29	18 29		18 59				
Stansted Airport	a	15 47						16 47		16 47				17 45							18 45					
Ipswich	a											17 25														19 27
London Kings Cross	a						17 03									18 08							19 08			
London Liverpool Street	a																									

For general notes see front of timetable
For details of catering facilities see Directory of Train Operators

A Until 6 September
B Until 6 September. From Nottingham (Table 49)
C Until 12 July and from 13 September
D 19 July to 6 September
E From Nottingham (Table 19)
G From 13 September
H Until 12 July
J From 19 July

Table 17

Sundays

Peterborough, Kings Lynn and Ely → Cambridge, Norwich and London

Network Diagram - see first page of Table 13

		EM	XC	XC	LE	FC	LE	EM		XC	FC	LE	XC	LE	EM	XC	FC	LE	XC	FC	XC	LE	XC	FC
		◇	1 ◇	1 ◇	1	1	1	◇		1 ◇	1	1	1 ◇	1	◇	1 ◇	1	1	1 ◇	1	1 ◇	1	1 ◇	1
			A	B						A			B						A		B			
		🍴	🍴	🍴				🍴		🍴			🍴		🍴	🍴			🍴		🍴		🍴	
Peterborough 8	d	17 53	18 18	18 20				18 47		19 18			19 39	19 44	19 58	20 18			21 18		21 22		22 18	
Whittlesea	d													19 52										
March	d		18 34	18 36						19 34			19 56	20 03		20 34			21 34		21 38		22 34	
Manea	d																							
Kings Lynn	d					18 28					19 28						20 28			21 28				22 28
Watlington	d					18 35					19 35						20 35			21 35				22 35
Downham Market	d					18 41					19 41						20 41			21 41				22 41
Littleport	d					18 50					19 50						20 50			21 50				22 50
Ely 6	a	18 31	18 52	18 54		18 58		19 20		19 52	19 58		20 13	20 21	20 31	20 52	20 58		21 52	21 58	22 01		22 52	22 58
Cambridge	d				18 42							19 48										21 48		
Ely 6	d	18 35	18 53	18 55	18 57	18 58	19 12	19 25		19 52	19 58	20 03	20 14	20 22	20 35	20 52	20 58	21 12	21 52	21 58	22 02	22 03	22 52	22 58
Waterbeach	d					19 07					20 07						21 07			22 07				23 07
Cambridge	a		19 08	19 10		19 16	19 32			20 07	20 16		20 31			21 07	21 16	21 32	22 07	22 16	22 17		23 12	23 15
Shippea Hill	d																							
Lakenheath	d																							
Brandon	d				19 13							20 19										22 19		
Thetford	d	18 56			19 21			19 49				20 27			20 56							22 27		
Harling Road	d																							
Eccles Road	d																							
Attleborough	d				19 35							20 41			21 10							22 41		
Spooner Row	d																							
Wymondham	d				19 42							20 48			21 17							22 48		
Norwich	a	19 29			19 59			20 28				21 09			21 35							23 05		
Stansted Airport	a		19 45	19 47						20 45			21 17			21 45			22 45		22 47			
Ipswich	a													21 18										
London Kings Cross	a					20 08					21 08						22 08			23 19				00 32
London Liverpool Street	a																							

For general notes see front of timetable
For details of catering facilities see Directory of Train Operators

A Until 12 July and from 13 September
B 19 July to 6 September

Kings Lynn → Sandringham and Hunstanton
Bus Service

Mondays to Fridays

This service is operated by First Eastern Counties.
Telephone Lo-call 08456-020-121

		FC	FC	FC	FC	FC	FC	FC	FC	FC	FC	FC	FC	FC	FC	FC	FC	FC
London Kings Cross	⊖ 17 d				06 45		07 15		07 45				08 45				09 45	
London Liverpool Street	⊖ 17 d				05b58				06b58				07b58				08b58	
Cambridge	17 d			06 22	07 35		08 04		08 38				09 35				10 34	
Kings Lynn	d	06 25	06 55	07 28	08 35	08 50	09 05	09 20	09 35	09 50	10 05	10 20	10 35	10 50	11 05	11 20	11 35	11 50
Sandringham Visitor Centre	a					09 12		09 42		10 12		10 42		11 12		11 42		12 12
Sandringham Norwich Gates	a			07 51		09 14		09 44		10 14		10 44		11 14		11 44		12 14
Hunstanton Bus Station	a	07 14	07 44	08 21	09 25	09 44	09 55	10 14	10 25	10 44	10 55	11 14	11 25	11 44	11 55	12 14	12 25	12 44

		FC		FC	FC	FC	FC	FC	FC	FC	FC	FC	FC	FC	FC	FC	FC	FC	FC	FC
London Kings Cross	⊖ 17 d		and at the same minutes past each hour until		12 45		13 45				14 45				15 45			16 44	17 44	18 44
London Liverpool Street	⊖ 17 d				11b58		12b58				13b58				14b28			15b58	16 58	18 58
Cambridge	17 d				13 33		14 33				15 35				16 35			17 40	18 39	20 15
Kings Lynn	d	12 05		14 20	14 30	15 05	15 35	15 50	16 05	16 20	16 35	16 50	17 05	17 20	17 35	17 50	18 20	19 00	20 00	21 30
Sandringham Visitor Centre	a			14 42		15 27		16 12		16 42		17 12		17 42		18 12				
Sandringham Norwich Gates	a			14 44		15 29		16 14		16 44		17 14		17 44		18 14				
Hunstanton Bus Station	a	12 55		15 14	15 20	15 59	16 25	16 44	16 55	17 14	17 25	17 44	17 55	18 14	18 25	18 41	19 03	19 40	20 40	22 10

		FC
London Kings Cross	⊖ 17 d	20c15
London Liverpool Street	⊖ 17 d	19e28
Cambridge	17 d	21f10
Kings Lynn	d	23 00
Sandringham Visitor Centre	a	
Sandringham Norwich Gates	a	
Hunstanton Bus Station	a	23 40

Saturdays

This service is operated by First Eastern Counties.
Telephone Lo-call 08456-020-121

		FC	FC	FC	FC	FC	FC	FC	FC	FC	FC	FC		FC	FC	FC	FC	FC
London Kings Cross	⊖ 17 d			06 45				07 45				08 45	and at the same minutes past each hour until				13 45	
London Liverpool Street	⊖ 17 d			05b58				06b58				07b58					12b58	
Cambridge	17 d		06 32	07 33				08 33				09 33					14 33	
Kings Lynn	d	06 35	07 35	08 35	08 50	09 05	09 20	09 35	09 50	10 05	10 20	10 35		14 50	15 05	15 20	15 35	15 50
Sandringham Visitor Centre	a				09 12		09 42		10 12		10 42			15 12	15 27	15 42		16 12
Sandringham Norwich Gates	a				09 14		09 44		10 14		10 44			15 14	15 29	15 44		16 14
Hunstanton Bus Station	a	07 25	08 25	09 25	09 44	09 55	10 14	10 25	10 44	10 55	11 14	11 25		15 44	15 59	16 14	16 25	16 44

		FC	FC	FC	FC	FC	FC	FC	FC	FC	FC	FC	FC	FC
London Kings Cross	⊖ 17 d			14 45				15 45			16 45	17 45	18 45	20 45
London Liverpool Street	⊖ 17 d			13b58				14b58			15b58	16b58	17b58	19b58
Cambridge	17 d			15 33				16 33			17 33	18 38	19 40	21 40
Kings Lynn	d	16 05	16 20	16 35	16 50	17 05	17 20	17 35	17 50	18 20	19 00	20 00	21 30	23 00
Sandringham Visitor Centre	a		16 42		17 12		17 42		18 12					
Sandringham Norwich Gates	a		16 44		17 14		17 44		18 14					
Hunstanton Bus Station	a	16 55	17 14	17 25	17 44	17 55	18 14	18 25	18 41	19 03	19 40	20 40	22 10	23 40

Sundays

This service is operated by First Eastern Counties.
Telephone Lo-call 08456-020-121

		FC	FC	FC	FC	FC	FC	FC	FC	FC	FC	FC	FC	FC
London Kings Cross	⊖ 17 d			07 52	09 15	10 15	11 15	12 15	13 15	14 15	15 15	18 15	19 15	21 15
London Liverpool Street	⊖ 17 d				08b28	09b28	10b28	11b28		13b28	14b28	17b28	18b28	20b28
Cambridge	17 d			09 07	10 05	11 05	12 05	13 05		15 05	16 05	19 04	20 05	22 04
Kings Lynn	d	08 50	09 50	10 50	11 50	12 50	13 50	14 50	15 50	16 50	17 50	20 00	21 30	23 00
Sandringham Visitor Centre	a	09 12	10 12	11 12	12 12	13 12	14 12	15 12	16 12	17 12	18 12			
Sandringham Norwich Gates	a	09 14	10 14	11 14	12 14	13 14	14 14	15 14	16 14	17 14	18 14			
Hunstanton Bus Station	a	09 42	10 42	11 42	12 42	13 42	14 42	15 42	16 42	17 42	18 42	20 40	22 10	23 40

For general notes see front of timetable
For details of catering facilities see Directory of Train Operators

b Change at Cambridge and Kings Lynn
c Fridays dep. 2045
e Change at Cambridge and Kings Lynn. Fridays dep. 1958
f Fridays dep. 2135

Hunstanton and Sandringham → Kings Lynn
Bus Service

This service is operated by First Eastern Counties.
Telephone Lo-call 08456-020-121

		FC	FC		FC	FC		FC		FC	FC	FC	FC			FC	FC		FC	FC		FC	FC	FC
Hunstanton Bus Station	d	06 30	07 16		07 48	08 33		08 48		09 03	09 18	09 33	09 48	and at the same minutes past each hour until		14 03	14 18		14 33	14 48		15 18	15 25	16 03
Sandringham Norwich Gates	d	06 55	07 43					09 15			09 45		10 15				14 45			15 15		15 45	15 56	
Sandringham Visitor Centre	d							09 17			09 47		10 17				14 47			15 17		15 47	15 58	
Kings Lynn	a	07 20	08 10		08 40	09 25		09 44		09 55	10 14	10 25	10 44			14 55	15 14		15 25	15 44		16 14	16 25	16 55
Cambridge	17 a	08 44	09 16		09 47			10 47					11 44							16 44			17 43	
London Liverpool Street	⊖ 17 a		10b43		11b43			12b43					13b43							18b44			19b13	
London Kings Cross	⊖ 17 a	09 42	10 13		10 46			11 39					12 33							17 35			18 38	

		FC		FC	FC		FC	FC		FC	FC		FC	FC		FC	FC		FC	FC		FC		
Hunstanton Bus Station	d	16 18		16 33	16 48		17 08	17 18		17 33	17 48		18 03	18 44		19 14	19 44		20 44	22 14		23 44		
Sandringham Norwich Gates	d	16 45			17 15			17 45			18 15													
Sandringham Visitor Centre	d	16 47			17 17			17 47			18 17													
Kings Lynn	a	17 14		17 25	17 44		18 00	18 14		18 25	18 44		18 55	19 22		19 52	20 22		21 22	22 52		00 22		
Cambridge	17 a			18 22						19 22				20 26			21 27		22 23					
London Liverpool Street	⊖ 17 a			20b13						21b14				22b13			23b13		23b43					
London Kings Cross	⊖ 17 a			19 34						20 33				21 30			22 30		23 35					

Saturdays

This service is operated by First Eastern Counties.
Telephone Lo-call 08456-020-121

		FC		FC		FC		FC			FC	FC	FC	FC			FC		FC		FC		FC	FC
Hunstanton Bus Station	d	06 30		07 30		08 33		08 48			09 03	09 18	09 33	09 48	and at the same minutes past each hour until		16 03		16 18		16 33		16 48	17 03
Sandringham Norwich Gates	d	06 55		07 55				09 15				09 45		10 15					16 45				17 15	
Sandringham Visitor Centre	d							09 17				09 47		10 17					16 47				17 17	
Kings Lynn	a	07 20		08 20		09 25		09 44			09 55	10 14	10 25	10 44			16 55		17 14		17 25		17 44	17 55
Cambridge	17 a	08 44		09 44		10 12		10 44						11 44									18 44	
London Liverpool Street	⊖ 17 a	10b43				11b43		12b43						13b43										
London Kings Cross	⊖ 17 a	09 33		10 34		11 05		11 35						12 33									19 33	

		FC		FC		FC		FC		FC		FC		FC		FC		FC		FC				
Hunstanton Bus Station	d	17 18		17 33		17 48		18 03		18 44		19 14		19 44		20 44		22 14		23 44				
Sandringham Norwich Gates	d	17 45				18 15																		
Sandringham Visitor Centre	d	17 47				18 17																		
Kings Lynn	a	18 14		18 25		18 44		18 55		19 22		19 52		20 22		21 22		22 52		00 22				
Cambridge	17 a			19 21						20 21				21 21		22 21		00 03						
London Liverpool Street	⊖ 17 a			20b43						21b43				22b43		23b43								
London Kings Cross	⊖ 17 a			20 32						21 32				22 34		23 47								

Sundays

This service is operated by First Eastern Counties.
Telephone Lo-call 08456-020-121

		FC		FC		FC		FC		FC		FC		FC		FC		FC		FC	FC	FC	FC	
Hunstanton Bus Station	d	09 47		10 47		11 47		12 47		13 47		14 47		15 47		16 47		17 47		18 47	20 44	22 14	23 44	
Sandringham Norwich Gates	d	10 14		11 14		12 14		13 14		14 14		15 14		16 14		17 14		18 14		19 14				
Sandringham Visitor Centre	d	10 16		11 16		12 16		13 16		14 16		15 16		16 16		17 16		18 16						
Kings Lynn	a	10 40		11 40		12 40		13 40		14 40		15 40		16 40		17 40		18 40		19 38	21 22	22 52	00 22	
Cambridge	17 a	12 16		13 16		14 14		15 14		16 14		17 16		18 16		19 16		20 16		21 16	22 16			
London Liverpool Street	⊖ 17 a	13b43		14b43		15b43		16b43		17b43		18b43		19b43		20b43		21b43		22b43	23b43			
London Kings Cross	⊖ 17 a	13 08		14 09		15 05		16 03		17 03		18 08		19 08		20 08		21 08		22 08	23 19			

For general notes see front of timetable
For details of catering facilities see Directory of Train Operators

b Change at Kings Lynn and Cambridge

Network Diagram for Tables 18, 19, 27, 29, 30

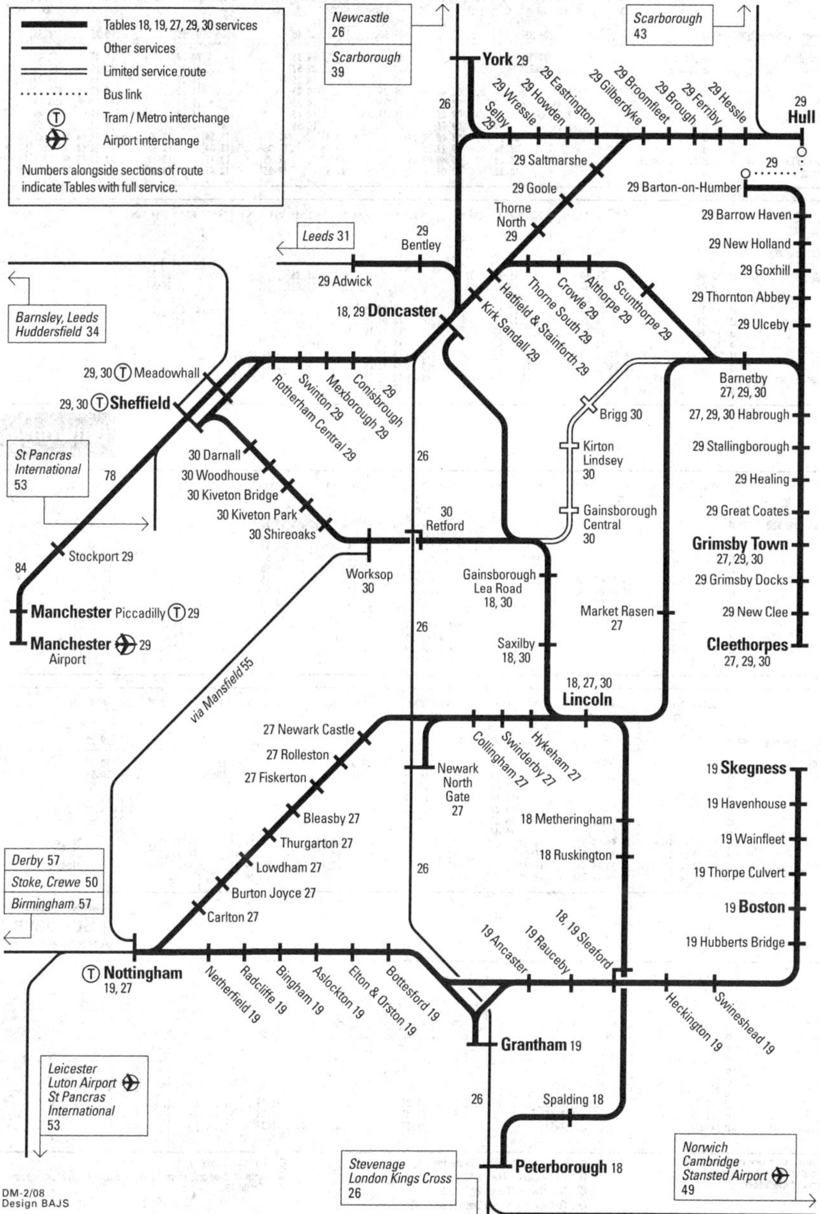

Tables 18, 19, 27, 29, 30 services
Other services
Limited service route
Bus link
Tram / Metro interchange
Airport interchange
Numbers alongside sections of route indicate Tables with full service.
Newcastle 26
Scarborough 39
Scarborough 43
York 29
29 Selby
29 Wressle
29 Howden
29 Eastrington
29 Gilberdyke
29 Broomfleet
29 Brough
29 Ferriby
29 Hessle
29 Hull
29 Saltmarshe
29 Goole
Thorne North 29
29 Barton-on-Humber
29 Barrow Haven
29 New Holland
29 Goxhill
29 Thornton Abbey
29 Ulceby
Leeds 31
29 Bentley
29 Adwick
18, 29 Doncaster
Kirk Sandall 29
Hatfield & Stainforth 29
Thorne South 29
Crowle 29
Althorpe 29
Scunthorpe 29
Barnsley, Leeds Huddersfield 34
29, 30 Meadowhall
29, 30 Sheffield
Rotherham Central 29
Swinton 29
Mexborough 29
Conisbrough 29
Barnetby 27, 29, 30
Brigg 30
27, 29, 30 Habrough
29 Stallingborough
29 Healing
29 Great Coates
Grimsby Town 27, 29, 30
29 Grimsby Docks
29 New Clee
Cleethorpes 27, 29, 30
St Pancras International 53
78
30 Darnall
30 Woodhouse
30 Kiveton Bridge
30 Kiveton Park
30 Shireoaks
26
30 Retford
Kirton Lindsey 30
Gainsborough Central 30
Worksop 30
Gainsborough Lea Road 18, 30
Market Rasen 27
Saxilby 18, 30
Stockport 29
84
Manchester Piccadilly 29
Manchester Airport 29
via Mansfield 55
18, 27, 30 Lincoln
27 Newark Castle
27 Rolleston
27 Fiskerton
Bleasby 27
Thurgarton 27
Lowdham 27
Burton Joyce 27
Carlton 27
Newark North Gate 27
Collingham 27
Swinderby 27
Hykeham 27
18 Metheringham
18 Ruskington
19 Skegness
19 Havenhouse
19 Wainfleet
19 Thorpe Culvert
19 Boston
19 Hubberts Bridge
Derby 57
Stoke, Crewe 50
Birmingham 57
Nottingham 19, 27
Netherfield 19
Radcliffe 19
Bingham 19
Aslockton 19
Elton & Orston 19
Bottesford 19
19 Ancaster
19 Rauceby
18, 19 Sleaford
Heckington 19
Swineshead 19
Grantham 19
Leicester Luton Airport St Pancras International 53
Spalding 18
Peterborough 18
Stevenage London Kings Cross 26
Norwich Cambridge Stansted Airport 49

DM-2/08
Design BAJS

Peterborough → Sleaford, Lincoln and Doncaster

Network Diagram - see first page of Table 18

Mondays to Fridays

Miles			EM A	NT	EM B		EM	EM	NT C		EM	NT C	EM		NT C	EM	NT C		EM	EM	NT C		EM	NT C	EM D	NT C
—	London Kings Cross 15	⊖ d						06 35					07 30			08 40				09 35			10 35		11 35	
0	Peterborough 8	d	06 30					07 30					08 33			09 35				10 38			11 48		12 41	
16½	Spalding	d	06a56					07a56					08 57			09 57				11 01			12 10		13 03	
35½	Sleaford	a											09 25			10 25				11 29			12 38		13 31	
—		d			06 57		07 42				08 46		09 25			10 25				11 30			12 42		13 32	
40	Ruskington	d			07 04		07 49				08 53		09 33			10 33				11 37			12 50		13 39	
47¼	Metheringham	d			07 14		07 59				09 03		09 43			10 43				11 47			12 59		13 49	
56¾	Lincoln	a			07 27		08 12				09 16		09 59			10 59				12 04			13 14		14 05	
—		d		07 04					08 27		09 18	09 27			10 27		11 27		11 54		12 27		13 17	13 27		14 27
62¾	Saxilby	d		07 14					08 36		09 27	09 36			10 36		11 36		12 04		12 36		13 26	13 36		14 36
72¼	Gainsborough Lea Road	d		07a26					08 49		09 40	09 49			10 49		11 49		12 17		12 49		13 39	13 49		14 49
93½	Doncaster 7	a							10 36		10 08	11 35			12 35		13 35		12 47		14 35		14 15	15 36		16 35

		EM		NT C	NT E	EM		NT	EM	EM		NT	EM	EM		EM	NT	NT		EM	EM	NT				
London Kings Cross 15	⊖ d	12 30				14 10			15 30	16 35						17 30					19 03					
Peterborough 8	d	13 40				15 10			16 25	17 32						18 36					20 28					
Spalding	d	14 02				15 32			16 49	17a58						19a02					20a54					
Sleaford	a	14 30				16 00			17 17																	
	d	14 32				16 14			17 18				17 54	19 00						20 07						
Ruskington	d	14 39				16 22			17 25				18 01	19 07						20 14						
Metheringham	d	14 49				16 32			17 35				18 11	19 17						20 24						
Lincoln	a	15 05				16 48			17 51				18 27	19 32						20 41						
	d			15 27	16 27			17 22				18 24	18 29	19 32			19 43	20 27				21 27				
Saxilby	d			15 36	16 36			17 31				18 33	18 41	19 41			19 52	20 36				21 36				
Gainsborough Lea Road	d			15 49	16 49			17a43				18a45	18 57	19 53			20a04	20a48				21a48				
Doncaster 7	a			17 35	18 38								19 25	20 23												

Saturdays

		EM G	NT		EM B	EM		EM	NT C		EM	NT C		EM	NT C		EM	NT C		EM	NT C		EM	NT C		EM D
London Kings Cross 15	⊖ d							06 15						07 10			08 30						10 40			11 30
Peterborough 8	d	06 30						07 30						08 33			09 33						11 48			12 41
Spalding	d	06a56						07a56						08 57			09 57						12 10			13 03
Sleaford	a													09 25			10 25						12 38			13 31
	d				06 57	07 42								09 25			10 25						12 42			13 32
Ruskington	d				07 04	07 49								09 33			10 33						12 50			13 39
Metheringham	d				07 14	07 59								09 43			10 43						12 59			13 49
Lincoln	a				07 27	08 12								09 59			10 59						13 14			14 05
	d		07 04						08 27		09 15	09 27			10 27			11 27		11 54	12 27			13 27		
Saxilby	d		07 14						08 36		09 24	09 36			10 36			11 36		12 04	12 36			13 36		
Gainsborough Lea Road	d		07a26						08 49		09 37	09 49			10 49			11 49		12 17	12 49			13 49		
Doncaster 7	a								10 36		10 07	11 35			12 35			13 35		12 47	14 35			15 36		

		EM	NT C		EM	NT C		NT	EM		NT	EM		EM	NT		EM	EM	EM	NT	NT	EM	EM	NT		
London Kings Cross 15	⊖ d								14 00			15 00		16 30					17 40				19 30			
Peterborough 8	d								15 11			16 25		17 30					18 36				20 27			
Spalding	d								15 33			16 49		17a56					19a02				20a54			
Sleaford	a								16 02			17 17														
	d								16 14			17 18					17 54	19 00				20 07				
Ruskington	d								16 22			17 25					18 01	19 07				20 14				
Metheringham	d								16 32			17 35					18 11	19 17				20 24				
Lincoln	a								16 48			17 51					18 27	19 32				20 41				
	d	14 10	14 27		15 10	15 27		16 27			17 22				18 24			19 32		19 43	20 27			21 24		
Saxilby	d	14 19	14 36		15 20	15 36		16 36			17 31				18 33			19 41		19 52	20 36			21 33		
Gainsborough Lea Road	d	14 32	14 49		15 32	15 49		16 49			17a43				18a45			19 53		20a04	20a48			21a45		
Doncaster 7	a	15 01	16 35		16 01	17 35		18 38										20 23								

Sundays

		NT					NT					NT					NT									
London Kings Cross 15	⊖ d																									
Peterborough 8	d																									
Spalding	d																									
Sleaford	a																									
	d																									
Ruskington	d																									
Metheringham	d																									
Lincoln	a																									
	d	15 15					17 35					19 35					21 15									
Saxilby	d	15 25					17 45					19 45					21 25									
Gainsborough Lea Road	d	15a37					17a57					19a57					21a37									
Doncaster 7	a																									

For general notes see front of timetable
For details of catering facilities see Directory of Train Operators

- **A** From Nottingham (Table 19)
- **B** To Leicester (Table 53)
- **C** To Adwick (Table 29)
- **D** To Newark North Gate (Table 27)
- **E** To Hull (Table 29)
- **G** Until 11 July and from 12 September from Nottingham (Table 19)

Doncaster, Lincoln and Sleaford → Peterborough

Network Diagram - see first page of Table 18

Miles			NT	EM	EM	EM	EM A	NT	NT	EM	NT	EM	NT	EM	EM	NT	EM	NT	EM B	EM	NT	EM
0	**Doncaster** 7	d	.	.	.	.	.	.	.	.	.	.	09 01	.	10 22	10 02	.	11 02	.	13 04	11 58	.
21¼	Gainsborough Lea Road	d	06 25	.	.	.	.	07 38	08 24	.	09 38	.	10 38	.	10 52	11 38	.	12 38	.	13 30	13 39	.
30¾	Saxilby	d	06 37	.	.	.	.	07 51	08 37	.	09 51	.	10 51	.	11 05	11 51	.	12 51	.	13 43	13 51	.
36¾	**Lincoln**	a	06 53	.	.	.	.	08 06	08 52	.	10 06	.	11 06	.	11 16	12 06	.	13 06	.	13 54	14 06	.
—		d	.	.	07 05	.	08 00	.	.	09 10	.	10 15	.	11 10	.	.	12 08	.	13 30	.	.	14 41
46¼	Metheringham	d	.	.	07 17	.	08 12	.	.	09 22	.	10 27	.	11 22	.	.	12 20	.	13 42	.	.	14 53
53½	Ruskington	d	.	.	07 27	.	08 22	.	.	09 32	.	10 37	.	11 32	.	.	12 30	.	13 52	.	.	15 03
58	Sleaford	a	.	.	07 36	.	08 31	.	.	09 41	.	10 50	.	11 41	.	.	12 39	.	14 01	.	.	15 13
—		d	.	.	.	.	08 34	.	.	09 42	.	10 50	.	11 42	.	.	12 42	.	14 02	.	.	15 16
77	Spalding	d	.	07 00	.	08 00	09 02	.	.	10 07	.	11 15	.	12 07	.	.	13 07	.	14 27	.	.	15 41
93½	**Peterborough** 8	a	.	07 25	.	08 25	09 27	.	.	10 31	.	11 41	.	12 34	.	.	13 32	.	14 53	.	.	16 09
—	London Kings Cross 15	⊖ a	.	*08 33*	.	*09 26*	*10 40*	.	.	*11 51*	.	*12 42*	.	*13 43*	.	.	*14 44*	.	*15 58*	.	.	*17 15*

		NT	EM	EM	EM B	NT	NT	EM C	EM	NT	EM	NT	EM	EM	NT	EM	EM D	EM E	NT	EM
Doncaster 7	d	12 59	.	14 27	.	14 01	15 02	.	.	16 02	.	17 01	.	.	.	19 34	.	.	.	20 33
Gainsborough Lea Road	d	14 38	.	14 54	.	15 38	16 38	.	.	17 38	.	18 38	.	.	19 39	20 00	.	.	20 42	21 00
Saxilby	d	14 51	.	15 07	.	15 51	16 51	.	.	17 51	.	18 51	.	.	19 52	20 13	.	.	20 55	21 14
Lincoln	a	15 06	.	15 18	.	16 09	17 06	.	.	18 06	.	19 07	.	.	20 06	20 26	.	.	21 10	21 26
	d	.	15 12	.	16 03	.	.	17 15	.	.	18 12	.	19 10	.	.	.	.	20 48	.	.
Metheringham	d	.	15 24	.	16 15	.	.	17 28	.	.	18 24	.	19 22	.	.	.	.	21 01	.	.
Ruskington	d	.	15 34	.	16 25	.	.	17 38	.	.	18 34	.	19 32	.	.	.	.	21 10	.	.
Sleaford	a	.	15 43	.	16 34	.	.	17 47	.	.	18 43	.	19 41	.	.	.	.	21 19	.	.
	d	.	.	.	16 34	.	.	.	.	.	.	.	.	.	.	.	.	.	.	.
Spalding	d	.	.	.	16 59	.	.	.	18 02	.	.	.	.	19 53	.	.	21 00	.	.	.
Peterborough 8	a	.	.	.	17 24	.	.	.	18 27	.	.	.	.	20 21	.	.	21 26	.	.	.
London Kings Cross 15	⊖ a	.	.	.	*18 54*	.	.	.	*19 59*	.	.	.	.	*21 33*	.	.	*23 32*	.	.	.

Saturdays

		NT	EM	EM	EM	EM A	NT	NT	NT	EM	NT	EM	EM	NT	NT	EM B	EM	NT	EM	NT
Doncaster 7	d	.	.	.	.	.	.	.	.	.	09 01	.	10 26	10 02	11 02	.	13 04	12 02	.	13 01
Gainsborough Lea Road	d	06 25	.	.	.	.	07 38	08 24	09 38	.	10 38	.	10 52	11 38	12 38	.	13 30	13 38	.	14 38
Saxilby	d	06 37	.	.	.	.	07 51	08 37	09 51	.	10 51	.	11 05	11 51	12 51	.	13 43	13 51	.	14 51
Lincoln	a	06 53	.	.	.	.	08 06	08 52	10 06	.	11 06	.	11 16	12 06	13 06	.	13 54	14 06	.	15 06
	d	.	.	07 05	.	08 00	.	.	.	10 15	.	11 10	.	.	.	13 30	.	.	14 41	.
Metheringham	d	.	.	07 17	.	08 12	.	.	.	10 27	.	11 22	.	.	.	13 42	.	.	14 53	.
Ruskington	d	.	.	07 27	.	08 22	.	.	.	10 37	.	11 32	.	.	.	13 52	.	.	15 03	.
Sleaford	a	.	.	07 36	.	08 31	.	.	.	10 50	.	11 41	.	.	.	14 01	.	.	15 13	.
	d	.	.	.	.	08 34	.	.	.	10 50	.	11 42	.	.	.	14 02	.	.	15 16	.
Spalding	d	.	07 00	.	08 00	09 02	.	.	.	11 15	.	12 07	.	.	.	14 27	.	.	15 41	.
Peterborough 8	a	.	07 25	.	08 25	09 27	.	.	.	11 41	.	12 32	.	.	.	14 52	.	.	16 07	.
London Kings Cross 15	⊖ a	.	*08 40*	.	*09 51*	*10 44*	.	.	.	*12 42*	.	*13 44*	.	.	.	*16 03*	.	.	*17 33*	.

		EM	EM B	NT	NT	EM	EM	EM	NT	EM	NT	EM	EM	NT	EM J	EM E	NT	EM
Doncaster 7	d	15 07	.	14 01	15 02	.	16 27	.	16 00	.	17 01	.	.	18 02	.	.	.	20 33
Gainsborough Lea Road	d	15 33	.	15 45	16 38	.	16 56	.	17 38	.	18 38	.	.	19 39	.	.	20 42	21 00
Saxilby	d	15 46	.	15 58	16 51	.	17 09	.	17 51	.	18 51	.	.	19 52	.	.	20 55	21 14
Lincoln	a	15 57	.	16 09	17 06	.	17 20	.	18 06	.	19 07	.	.	20 06	.	.	21 10	21 26
	d	.	16 03	.	.	17 15	.	.	.	18 12	.	19 10	.	.	.	20 48	.	.
Metheringham	d	.	16 15	.	.	17 28	.	.	.	18 24	.	19 22	.	.	.	21 01	.	.
Ruskington	d	.	16 25	.	.	17 38	.	.	.	18 34	.	19 32	.	.	.	21 10	.	.
Sleaford	a	.	16 34	.	.	17 47	.	.	.	18 43	.	19 41	.	.	.	21 19	.	.
	d	.	16 34	.	.	.	.	.	.	.	.	.	.	.	.	.	.	.
Spalding	d	.	16 59	.	.	.	.	18 02	.	.	.	.	19 53	.	20 58	.	.	.
Peterborough 8	a	.	17 24	.	.	.	.	18 27	.	.	.	.	20 21	.	21 23	.	.	.
London Kings Cross 15	⊖ a	.	*18 28*	.	.	.	.	*19 40*	.	.	.	.	*21 48*	.	*22 47*	.	.	.

Sundays

		NT	NT	NT	NT
Doncaster 7	d	.	.	.	.
Gainsborough Lea Road	d	14 26	16 54	18 54	20 18
Saxilby	d	14 39	17 07	19 07	20 31
Lincoln	a	14 54	17 21	19 22	20 45
	d	.	.	.	.
Metheringham	d	.	.	.	.
Ruskington	d	.	.	.	.
Sleaford	a	.	.	.	.
	d	.	.	.	.
Spalding	d	.	.	.	.
Peterborough 8	a	.	.	.	.
London Kings Cross 15	⊖ a	.	.	.	.

For general notes see front of timetable
For details of catering facilities see Directory of Train Operators

A From Nottingham (Table 27)
B From Newark North Gate (Table 27)
C From Leicester (Table 53)
D To Nottingham (Table 49)
E To Boston (Table 19)
J To Nottingham (Table 19)

Skegness → Grantham and Nottingham

Network Diagram - see first page of Table 18

Miles	Miles			EM	EM	EM A	EM ◇ B ⚲	EM	EM ◇ ⚲	EM	EM ◇ ⚲	EM	EM ◇ ⚲	EM	EM ◇ ⚲	EM	EM ◇ ⚲	EM
0	—	**Skegness**	d					07 08		08 10		09 05		10 15		11 15		12 15
3¼	—	Havenhouse	d					07 13										
5	—	Wainfleet	d					07 17		08 18		09 13		10 23		11 23		12 23
7	—	Thorpe Culvert	d					07 21										
23¾	—	**Boston**	d		06 14			07 45		08 45		09 40		10 50		11 50		12 50
27½	—	Hubberts Bridge	d					07 51										
30¾	—	Swineshead	d					07 56										
35¾	—	Heckington	d		06 28			08 02		08 59		09 54		11 04		12 04		13 04
40½	—	**Sleaford**	d		06 36	06 57		08 11		09 07		10 02		11 12		12 12		13 12
42½	—	Rauceby	d					08 15						11 21				
46¼	0	Ancaster	d		06 45			08 21										
57¾	—	**Grantham 7**	a		07 04			08 42		09 35		10 31		11 41		12 41		13 41
—	—	London Kings Cross 15	⊖ a		*08 33*			*10 10*		*10 51*		*11 51*		*13 10*		*14 20*		*15 20*
—	—	**Grantham 7**	d	06 10	07 10		07 58	08 45	08 58	09 40	09 58	10 34	11 13	11 45	11 56	12 45	12 58	13 45
65¼	12¾	Bottesford	d	06 21	07 21		08 11			09 52				11 56				13 56
67¾	—	Elton & Orston	d	06 25														
69½	—	Aslockton	d	06 29	07 27		08 17					10 50						
71¾	—	Bingham	d	06 33	07 31		08 21	09 02		10 00		10 54		12 04		13 02		14 04
75¼	—	Radcliffe (Notts)	d	06 39	07 37		08 27							12 09				
77	—	Netherfield	d		07 41		08 31											
80¼	—	**Nottingham 8**	a	06 54	07 53	08 30	08 38	09 22	09 36	10 18	10 36	11 13	11 43	12 23	12 36	13 22	13 36	14 22

		EM ◇ ⚲	EM	EM ◇ ⚲	EM	EM ◇ ⚲	EM	EM ◇ ⚲	EM	EM ◇ ⚲	EM	EM ◇ ⚲	EM	EM ◇	EM	EM ◇	EM	EM
Skegness	d		13 15		14 15		15 09		16 10		17 30		18 14		19 14		20 15	21 00
Havenhouse	d								16 15									
Wainfleet	d		13 23		14 23		15 17		16 19		17 38		18 22		19 22		20 23	21 08
Thorpe Culvert	d								16 23									
Boston	d		13 50		14 50		15 44		16 46		18 05		18 49		19 49		20 50	21 35
Hubberts Bridge	d						15 50											
Swineshead	d						15 55											
Heckington	d		14 04		15 04		16 01		17 04		18 19		19 04		20 03		21 04	
Sleaford	d		14 13		15 12		16 10		17 13		18 27		19 13		20 12		21 12	21 58
Rauceby	d						16 14											
Ancaster	d						16 20											
Grantham 7	a		14 42		15 41		16 41		17 42				19 41		20 41		21 43	
London Kings Cross 15	⊖ a		*16 22*		*17 04*		*18 12*		*19 12*				*21 03*		*22 04*		*23 32*	
Grantham 7	d	13 58	14 45	14 58	15 45	15 58	16 45	16 58	17 45	17 59		18 58	19 45	20 03	20 45	20 58	21 47	
Bottesford	d				15 56				17 56				19 56				21 58	
Elton & Orston	d																	
Aslockton	d												20 02					
Bingham	d		15 02		16 04		17 02		18 04		19 03		20 06		21 02		22 06	22 33
Radcliffe (Notts)	d												20 12					
Netherfield	d												20 16					
Nottingham 8	a	14 36	15 22	15 36	16 22	16 36	17 22	17 36	18 22	18 36	19 22	19 36	20 28	20 37	21 22	21 35	22 24	22 52

Saturdays

		EM	EM	EM A	EM ◇ B ⚲	EM	EM ◇ ⚲	EM	EM ◇ ⚲	EM	EM ◇ ⚲	EM	EM ◇ ⚲	EM C	EM D	EM ◇ ⚲	EM C	EM D	EM ◇ ⚲	EM E
Skegness	d					07 08		08 15		09 15		10 15		11 15	11 15		12 15	12 15		13 15
Havenhouse	d					07 13														
Wainfleet	d					07 17		08 23		09 23		10 23		11 23	11 23		12 23	12 23		13 23
Thorpe Culvert	d					07 21														
Boston	d		06 14			07 45		08 50		09 50		10 50		11 50	11 50		12 50	12 50		13 50
Hubberts Bridge	d					07 51														
Swineshead	d					07 56														
Heckington	d		06 28			08 02		09 04		10 05		11 04		12 04	12 07		13 04	13 07		14 04
Sleaford	d		06 36	06 57		08 11		09 12		10 14		11 12		12 12	12 15		13 12	13 15		14 13
Rauceby	d					08 15						11 21								
Ancaster	d		06 45			08 21														
Grantham 7	a		07 06			08 42		09 41		10 43		11 41		12 41	12 42		13 41	13 42		14 42
London Kings Cross 15	⊖ a		*08 40*			*10 20*		*11 33*		*12 24*		*13b10*		*14 27*	*14 27*		*15 42*	*15 42*		
Grantham 7	d	06 10	07 10		07 58	08 45	08 58	09 45	09 58	10 45	10 58	11 45	11 58	12 45	12 45	12 58	13 45	13 45	13 58	14 45
Bottesford	d	06 21	07 21		08 11			09 56				11 56					13 56	13 55		
Elton & Orston	d	06 25																		
Aslockton	d	06 29	07 27		08 17															
Bingham	d	06 33	07 31		08 21	09 02		10 04		11 03		12 04		13 02	13 02		14 04	14 04		15 02
Radcliffe (Notts)	d	06 39	07 37		08 27							12 09								
Netherfield	d		07 41		08 31															
Nottingham 8	a	06 54	07 53	08 30	08 38	09 22	09 36	10 22	10 36	11 22	11 35	12 23	12 36	13 22	13 22	13 36	14 22	14 22	14 36	15 22

For general notes see front of timetable
For details of catering facilities see Directory of Train Operators

A To Leicester (Table 53)
B From Norwich (Table 17) to Liverpool Lime Street (Table 49)
C Until 11 July and from 12 September
D 18 July to 5 September
E From 12 September
b 18 July to 5 September arr. 1311

Saturdays

Skegness → Grantham and Nottingham

Network Diagram - see first page of Table 18

		EM ◇ 🍴	EM	EM ◇ 🍴	EM A	EM B	EM ◇ 🍴	EM	EM ◇ 🍴	EM	EM ◇ 🍴	EM	EM ◇	EM	EM ◇	EM	EM C	EM
Skegness	d		14 15		15 09	15 09		16 10		17 30		18 14		19 19		20 15		21 09
Havenhouse	d							16 15										
Wainfleet	d		14 23		15 17	15 17		16 19		17 38		18 22		19 27		20 23		21 17
Thorpe Culvert	d							16 23										
Boston	d		14 50		15 44	15 44		16 46		18 05		18 49		19 54		20 50		21 44
Hubberts Bridge	d				15 50	15 50												
Swineshead	d				15 55	15 55												
Heckington	d		15 06		16 01	16 03		17 04		18 19		19 04		20 10		21 04		
Sleaford	d		15 14		16 10	16 11		17 13		18 27		19 13		20 18		21 12		22 05
Rauceby	d				16 14	16 15												
Ancaster	d				16 20	16 21												
Grantham 7	a		15 42		16 41	16 41		17 42				19 41		20 45		21 43		
London Kings Cross 15 ⊖	a		*17 33*		*18 10*	*18 10*		*20 12*				*21 15*		*22 47*				
Grantham 7	d	14 58	15 46	15 58	16 45	16 45	16 58	17 45	18 03		18 58	19 45	20 03	20 48	20 58	21 47	22 02	
Bottesford	d		15 57					17 56				19 56				21 58		
Elton & Orston	d																	
Aslockton	d											20 02						
Bingham	d		16 05		17 02	17 02		18 04		19 03		20 06		21 05		22 06		22 39
Radcliffe (Notts)	d											20 12						
Netherfield	d											20 16						
Nottingham 8	a	15 36	16 23	16 36	17 22	17 22	17 36	18 22	18 36	19 22	19 36	20 28	20 37	21 24	21 32	22 24	22 32	22 57

Sundays

until 6 September

		EM	EM	EM ◇ 🍴	EM	EM ◇ D 🍴	EM	EM	EM ◇ 🍴	EM	EM ◇ 🍴	EM E	EM ◇ G 🍴	EM ◇ H 🍴	EM ◇ 🍴	EM	EM ◇	EM	EM ◇ 🍴	EM	EM ◇
Skegness	d		10 14		11 08		12 27	14 08		15 04		16 22				18 07		19 15		20 43	
Havenhouse	d																				
Wainfleet	d		10 22		11 16		12 35	14 16		15 12		16 30				18 15		19 23		20 51	
Thorpe Culvert	d																				
Boston	d	09 06	10 49		11 43		13 02	14 43		15 42		16 57				18 42		19 50		21 18	
Hubberts Bridge	d																				
Swineshead	d																				
Heckington	d	09 20	11 03		11 57		13 16	14 57		15 56		17 11				18 56		20 04		21 32	
Sleaford	d	09 28	11 11		12 05		13 24	15 05		16 04		17 19				19 04		20 12		21 41	
Rauceby	d																				
Ancaster	d																				
Grantham 7	a	09 57	11 40		12 34			15 35		16 33						19 33		20 41		22 10	
London Kings Cross 15 ⊖	a	*12 19*	*13 14*		*13 50*			*17 18*		*17 55*						*21 01*		*22 16*		*23 50*	
Grantham 7	d	10 01	11 45	11 56	12 39	12 47		15 40	15 59	16 37	16 56		17 55	17 59	19 01	19 37	19 57	20 45	21 03	22 13	22 51
Bottesford	d		11 56			12 58															
Elton & Orston	d																				
Aslockton	d		12 02			13 04															
Bingham	d	10 18	12 06		12 56	13 09	14 00	15 57		16 54		17 55	18 14	18 16		19 54		21 02		22 30	
Radcliffe (Notts)	d		12 12			13 14															
Netherfield	d		12 16			13 18															
Nottingham 8	a	10 37	12 27	12 33	13 15	13 26	14 19	16 17	16 28	17 13	17 25	18 13	18 29	18 31	19 30	20 14	20 31	21 21	21 35	22 49	23 26

Sundays

from 13 September

		EM ◇ D 🍴	EM	EM	EM ◇ 🍴	EM ◇ 🍴	EM	EM ◇ J 🍴	EM ◇ 🍴	EM	EM ◇	EM	EM ◇ 🍴	EM	EM ◇
Skegness	d			14 08			16 17			18 07		19 15			
Havenhouse	d														
Wainfleet	d			14 16			16 25			18 15		19 23			
Thorpe Culvert	d														
Boston	d		12 13	14 43			16 52			18 42		19 50			
Hubberts Bridge	d														
Swineshead	d														
Heckington	d		12 27	14 57			17 06			18 56		20 04			
Sleaford	d		12 35	15 05			17 14			19 04		20 12		21 41	
Rauceby	d														
Ancaster	d														
Grantham 7	a		13 07	15 35			17 43			19 33		20 41		22 10	
London Kings Cross 15 ⊖	a		*14 44*	*17 18*			*19 52*			*21 01*		*22 16*		*23 50*	
Grantham 7	d	12 47		15 40	15 59	16 56	17 47	17 55	19 01	19 37	19 57	20 45	21 03	22 13	22 51
Bottesford	d	12 58													
Elton & Orston	d														
Aslockton	d	13 04													
Bingham	d	13 09		15 57			18 04	18 14		19 54		21 02		22 30	
Radcliffe (Notts)	d	13 14													
Netherfield	d	13 18													
Nottingham 8	a	13 26		16 17	16 28	17 25	18 23	18 29	19 30	20 14	20 31	21 21	21 35	22 49	23 26

For general notes see front of timetable
For details of catering facilities see Directory of Train Operators

A Until 11 July and from 12 September

B 18 July to 5 September

C From Spalding (Table 18)

D From Norwich to Liverpool Lime Street (Table 49)

E To Derby (Table 57)

G Until 12 July. From Norwich to Manchester Piccadilly (Table 49)

H From 19 July. From Norwich to Manchester Piccadilly (Table 49)

J From Norwich to Manchester Piccadilly (Table 49)

Table 19

Nottingham and Grantham → Skegness

Network Diagram - see first page of Table 18

Miles	Miles			EM A	EM	EM	EM	EM	EM ◇ 🛒	EM ◇ 🛒	EM	EM ◇ 🛒	EM	EM ◇ 🛒	EM	EM ◇ 🛒	EM	EM ◇ 🛒
0	—	**Nottingham 8**	d	05 10		05 50	06 45	07 35	07 52	08 34	08 45	09 34	09 55	10 34	10 45	11 34	11 45	12 34
4½	—	Netherfield	d								08 51							
5	—	Radcliffe (Notts)	d								08 56							
8½	—	Bingham	d	05 24		06 04	06 59	07 49			09 02		10 09		10 59		11 59	
10¾	—	Aslockton	d	05 28							09 06							
14½	—	Elton & Orston	d															
15	0	Bottesford	d	05 35		06 13	07 08	07 58			09 12				11 08			
22½	—	**Grantham 7**	a	05 49		06 27	07 22	08 12	08 23	09 07	09 26	10 06		11 05	11 22	12 05	12 19	13 06
—	—	London Kings Cross 15	⊖ d				*06 00*	*06 35*			*07 30*				*10 10*		*11 10*	
—	—	**Grantham 7**	d			06 31	07 26	08 16			09 36				11 26		12 23	
34	12¾	Ancaster	d					08 34										
37¾	—	Rauceby	d					08 40										
40	—	**Sleaford**	d			06 57	07 52	08 45			10 04		10 44		11 52		12 49	
44½	—	Heckington	d			07 04	07 59	08 52			10 11		10 51		11 59		12 56	
49½	—	Swineshead	d				08 05											
52¾	—	Hubberts Bridge	d				08 10											
56½	—	**Boston**	d		06 25	07 24	08 20	09 12			10 29		11 11		12 18		13 15	
73¼	—	Thorpe Culvert	d			07 46												
75¼	—	Wainfleet	d		06 49	07 51	08 45	09 36			10 53		11 35		12 43		13 40	
77	—	Havenhouse	d			07 54												
80¼	—	**Skegness**	a		07 03	08 06	08 59	09 51			11 08		11 50		12 57		13 54	

		EM	EM ◇ 🛒	EM	EM ◇ 🛒	EM	EM ◇ 🛒	EM	EM B	EM	EM ◇ C 🛒	EM	EM ◇ 🛒	EM	EM ◇ 🛒	EM D	EM
Nottingham 8	d	12 45	13 34	13 45	14 34	14 45	15 34	15 45	16 14	16 45	17 34	17 45	18 34	18 45	20 34		20 51
Netherfield	d							15 51		16 51							
Radcliffe (Notts)	d	12 55						15 56		16 56		17 55					21 01
Bingham	d	13 01		13 59		14 59		16 02		17 02	17 48	18 01		18 59			21 07
Aslockton	d			14 03				16 06		17 06	17 52	18 05					21 11
Elton & Orston	d									17 10							
Bottesford	d	13 09				15 08		16 12		17 14		18 12		19 08			21 17
Grantham 7	a	13 23	14 05	14 21	15 05	15 22	16 05	16 25		17 28	18 09	18 25	19 05	19 21	21 05		21 32
London Kings Cross 15	⊖ d	*12 10*		*12 35*		*14 10*		*15 10*		*16 10*		*17 03*		*18 03*			*20 03*
Grantham 7	d	13 27		14 25		15 26		16 29		17 32		18 29		19 24			21 36
Ancaster	d	13 45								17 50				19 42			
Rauceby	d									17 56				19 48			
Sleaford	d	13 55		14 51		15 52		16 55	17a47	18 01		18 55		19 53		21 20	22 01
Heckington	d	14 02		14 58		15 59		17 02		18 08		19 02		20 00			22 08
Swineshead	d					16 05											
Hubberts Bridge	d					16 10											
Boston	d	14 21		15 17		16 20		17 21		18 26		19 21		20 17		21a53	22a29
Thorpe Culvert	d							17 43									
Wainfleet	d	14 46		15 42		16 45		17 48		18 51		19 46		20 41			
Havenhouse	d							17 51									
Skegness	a	15 00		15 56		16 59		18 03		19 05		20 00		20 55			

Saturdays

		EM ◇ E 🛒	EM G	EM	EM	EM H	EM J	EM	EM	EM ◇ 🛒	EM ◇ 🛒	EM H
Nottingham 8	d	05 10	05 10		05 50	06 45	06 45	06 55	07 30	07 45	08 34	08 45
Netherfield	d											08 51
Radcliffe (Notts)	d											08 56
Bingham	d	05 24	05 24		06 04	06 59	06 59		07 44			09 02
Aslockton	d	05 28	05 28									09 06
Elton & Orston	d											
Bottesford	d	05 35	05 35		06 13	07 08	07 08		07 53			09 12
Grantham 7	a	05 48	05 49		06 27	07 22	07 23		08 07	08 15	09 07	09 26
London Kings Cross 15	⊖ d								*07 00*			*08 10*
Grantham 7	d				06 31	07 26	07 26		08 16			09 30
Ancaster	d								08 34			
Rauceby	d								08 40			
Sleaford	d				06 57	07 52	07 52	08a34	08 45			09 56
Heckington	d				07 04	07 59	07 59		08 52			10 03
Swineshead	d					08 05	08 05					
Hubberts Bridge	d					08 10	08 10					
Boston	d			06 25	07 24	08 20	08 20		09 12			10 22
Thorpe Culvert	d				07 46							
Wainfleet	d			06 49	07 51	08 45	08 45		09 36			10 47
Havenhouse	d				07 54							
Skegness	a			07 03	08 06	08 59	08 59		09 51			11 01

		EM J	EM ◇ 🛒	EM K	EM ◇ H 🛒	EM ◇ J 🛒	EM H	EM J	EM ◇ 🛒	EM H	EM J	EM ◇ 🛒
Nottingham 8	d	08 45	09 34	09 55	10 34	10 34	10 45	10 45	11 34	11 45	11 50	12 34
Netherfield	d	08 51										
Radcliffe (Notts)	d	08 56										
Bingham	d	09 02		10 09			10 59	10 59		11 59	12 05	
Aslockton	d	09 06										
Elton & Orston	d											
Bottesford	d	09 12					11 08	11 08				
Grantham 7	a	09 27	10 07		11 06	11 07	11 22	11 28	12 06	12 19	12 28	13 06
London Kings Cross 15	⊖ d	*08 10*					*10 10*	*10 10*		*11 10*	*11 10*	
Grantham 7	d	09 30					11 26	11 31		12 23	12 31	
Ancaster	d											
Rauceby	d											
Sleaford	d	09 56		10 44			11 52	11 57		12 49	12 57	
Heckington	d	10 03		10 51			11 59	12 04		12 56	13 04	
Swineshead	d											
Hubberts Bridge	d											
Boston	d	10 22		11 11			12 18	12 24		13 15	13 24	
Thorpe Culvert	d											
Wainfleet	d	10 47		11 35			12 43	12 48		13 40	13 48	
Havenhouse	d											
Skegness	a	11 01		11 50			12 57	13 03		13 54	14 03	

For general notes see front of timetable
For details of catering facilities see Directory of Train Operators

A To Spalding (Table 18)
B From Leicester (Table 53)
C From Liverpool Lime Street to Norwich (Table 49)
D From Lincoln (Table 18)
E 18 July to 5 September. To Norwich (Table 17)
G Until 11 July and from 12 September. To Spalding (Table 18)
H Until 11 July and from 12 September
J 18 July to 5 September
K From 12 September

Table 19

Nottingham and Grantham → Skegness

Network Diagram - see first page of Table 18

Saturdays

		EM	EM	EM	EM	EM	EM	EM	EM	EM	EM	EM	EM	EM	EM	EM	EM	EM	EM	EM	EM	EM
		A	B	C	◇	D	C	◇	D	C	◇ D	◇ C			◇ E		◇		◇ D	◇ C	G	
Nottingham	d	12 45	12 45	12 45	13 34	13 45	13 50	14 34	14 45	14 45	15 34	15 34	15 45	16 45	17 34	17 45	18 34	18 45	20 34	20 34		20 51
Netherfield	d												15 51	16 51								
Radcliffe (Notts)	d	12 55	12 55	12 55									15 56	16 56		17 55						21 01
Bingham	d	13 01	13 01	13 01		13 59	14 05		14 59	14 59			16 02	17 02	17 48	18 01		18 59				21 07
Aslockton	d					14 03	14 09						16 06	17 06	17 52	18 05						21 11
Elton & Orston	d													17 10								
Bottesford	d	13 09	13 09	13 09					15 08	15 08			16 12	17 14		18 12		19 08				21 17
Grantham	a	13 25	13 25	13 28	14 05	14 21	14 28	15 06	15 22	15 23	16 05	16 06	16 25	17 28	18 10	18 26	19 05	19 28	21 05	21 09		21 31
London Kings Cross	⊖ d	*12 10*	*12 10*	*12 10*		*13 10*	*13 10*		*13 48*	*13 48*			*14 30*	*15 30*		*17 05*		*17 40*				*20 00*
Grantham	d	13 29	13 29	13 31		14 23	14 31		15 26	15 27			16 29	17 32		18 30		19 31				21 36
Ancaster	d													17 50				19 49				
Rauceby	d													17 56				19 55				
Sleaford	d	13 55	13 55	13 57		14 51	14 57		15 52	15 53			16 55	18 01		18 56		20 00			21 20	22 04
Heckington	d	14 02	14 02	14 04		14 58	15 04		15 59	16 00			17 02	18 08		19 03		20 07				22 11
Swineshead	d								16 05	16 06												
Hubberts Bridge	d								16 10	16 11												
Boston	d	14 21	14 23	14 23		15 17	15 23		16 20	16 21			17 21	18 26		19 22		20 24			21a53	22a32
Thorpe Culvert	d												17 43									
Wainfleet	d	14 46	14 48	14 48		15 42	15 48		16 45	16 46			17 48	18 51		19 47		20 48				
Havenhouse	d												17 51									
Skegness	a	15 00	15 02	15 02		15 56	16 02		16 59	17 00			18 03	19 05		20 01		21 02				

Sundays
until 6 September

		EM	EM	EM	EM	EM	EM	EM	EM	EM	EM	EM	EM	EM	EM	EM	EM	EM	EM	EM	EM	EM
					◇		◇		◇ H	◇			◇		◇ J	◇ K	◇ E		◇ L	◇ N		◇
Nottingham	d		09 00	09 40	09 52	11 09	11 45	11 55	12 39	13 41	14 03	14 56	15 47	16 21	16 45	16 45	17 36	18 17	18 43	18 47	19 48	20 44
Netherfield	d													16 27			17 42					
Radcliffe (Notts)	d													16 32			17 46					
Bingham	d		09 14	09 54		11 23		12 11	12 53		14 17	15 10		16 38			17 52	18 31	18 57	19 01	20 02	20 58
Aslockton	d													16 42			17 56					
Elton & Orston	d																					
Bottesford	d													16 48			18 03					
Grantham	a			10 14	10 25	11 44	12 16	12 29	13 13	14 12	14 37	15 31	16 18	17 03	17 15	17 23	18 16	18 51	19 16	19 21	20 22	21 18
London Kings Cross	⊖ d			*09 00*		*10 10*		*11 10*			*13 10*	*14 10*		*15 44*				*17 44*			*19 10*	
Grantham	d			10 18		11 49		12 35			14 41	15 36		17 07				18 55			20 26	
Ancaster	d																					
Rauceby	d																					
Sleaford	d		09 49	10 44		12 15		13 01			15 09	16 04		17 36				19 21			20 52	
Heckington	d		09 56	10 51		12 22		13 08			15 16	16 11		17 43				19 28			20 59	
Swineshead	d																					
Hubberts Bridge	d																					
Boston	d	09 31	10 16	11 10		12 41		13 27			15 39	16 31		18 02				19 50			21a20	
Thorpe Culvert	d																					
Wainfleet	d	09 55	10 40	11 35		13 06		13 52			16 03	16 55		18 27				20 14				
Havenhouse	d																					
Skegness	a	10 07	10 55	11 49		13 20		14 06			16 18	17 10		18 41				20 29				

Sundays
from 13 September

		EM	EM	EM	EM	EM	EM	EM	EM	EM	EM	EM	EM	EM
			◇ H		◇		◇		◇	◇ E		◇ E		◇
Nottingham	d	11 55	12 39		13 41	14 56	15 52	16 21	16 45	17 36	18 31	18 47	19 48	20 44
Netherfield	d							16 27		17 42				
Radcliffe (Notts)	d							16 32		17 46				
Bingham	d	12 11	12 53			15 10		16 38		17 52	18 45	19 01	20 02	20 58
Aslockton	d							16 42		17 56				
Elton & Orston	d													
Bottesford	d							16 48		18 03				
Grantham	a	12 29	13 13		14 12	15 31	16 23	17 03	17 15	18 16	19 08	19 21	20 22	21 18
London Kings Cross	⊖ d	*11 10*		*12 10*		*14 10*		*15 44*			*18 00*		*19 10*	
Grantham	d	12 35		13 50		15 36		17 07			19 13		20 26	
Ancaster	d													
Rauceby	d													
Sleaford	d	13 01		14 16		16 04		17 36			19 41		20a54	
Heckington	d	13 08		14 23		16 11		17 43			19 48			
Swineshead	d													
Hubberts Bridge	d													
Boston	d	13 27		14 43		16 31		18 02			20a10			
Thorpe Culvert	d													
Wainfleet	d	13 52		15 07		16 55		18 27						
Havenhouse	d													
Skegness	a	14 06		15 22		17 10		18 41						

For general notes see front of timetable
For details of catering facilities see Directory of Train Operators

A From 12 September
B Until 11 July
C 18 July to 5 September
D Until 11 July and from 12 September
E From Liverpool Lime Street to Norwich (Table 49)
G From Lincoln (Table 18)
H To Norwich (Table 49)
J Until 12 July
K From 19 July
L From 19 July. From Liverpool Lime Street (Table 49) to Norwich (Table 17)
N Until 12 July. From Liverpool Lime Street (Table 49) to Norwich (Table 17)

Network Diagram for Tables 20, 21, 22

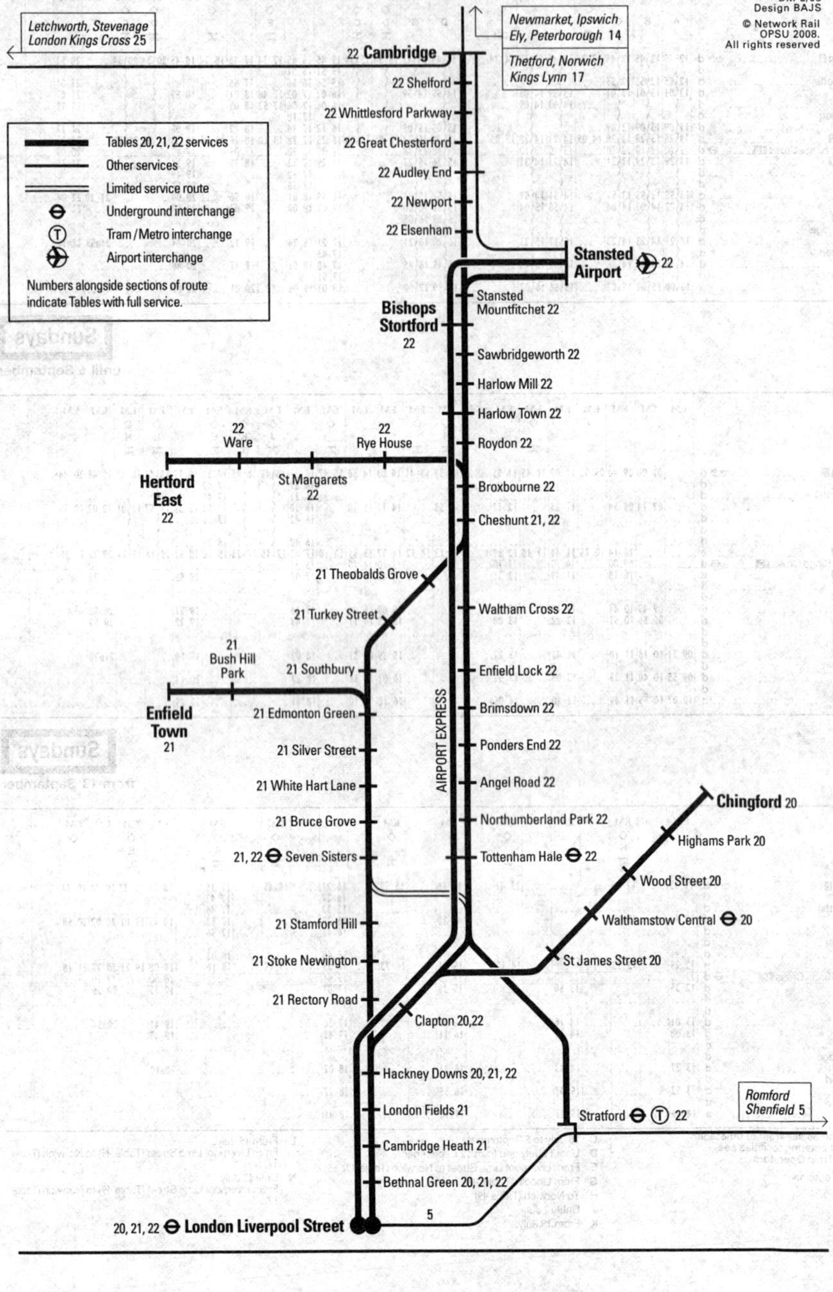
Letchworth, Stevenage
London Kings Cross 25
Newmarket, Ipswich
Ely, Peterborough 14
Thetford, Norwich
Kings Lynn 17
22 Cambridge
22 Shelford
22 Whittlesford Parkway
22 Great Chesterford
22 Audley End
22 Newport
22 Elsenham
Stansted Airport 22
Stansted Mountfitchet 22
Bishops Stortford 22
Sawbridgeworth 22
Harlow Mill 22
Harlow Town 22
Roydon 22
22 Ware
22 Rye House
Hertford East 22
St Margarets 22
Broxbourne 22
Cheshunt 21, 22
21 Theobalds Grove
21 Turkey Street
Waltham Cross 22
21 Bush Hill Park
21 Southbury
Enfield Lock 22
Enfield Town 21
21 Edmonton Green
Brimsdown 22
AIRPORT EXPRESS
21 Silver Street
Ponders End 22
21 White Hart Lane
Angel Road 22
Chingford 20
21 Bruce Grove
Northumberland Park 22
Highams Park 20
21, 22 Seven Sisters
Tottenham Hale 22
Wood Street 20
Walthamstow Central 20
21 Stamford Hill
21 Stoke Newington
St James Street 20
21 Rectory Road
Clapton 20,22
Hackney Downs 20, 21, 22
London Fields 21
Stratford 22
Romford
Shenfield 5
Cambridge Heath 21
Bethnal Green 20, 21, 22
5
20, 21, 22 London Liverpool Street
Tables 20, 21, 22 services
Other services
Limited service route
Underground interchange
Tram / Metro interchange
Airport interchange
Numbers alongside sections of route indicate Tables with full service.

London → Chingford

Network diagram - see first page of Table 20

Mondays to Fridays

Miles			LE MX	LE	LE MX	LE	LE MX	LE	LE	LE	LE	LE	LE	LE	LE	LE	LE	LE	LE	LE
0	**London Liverpool Street** [15]	⊖ d	23p48	00 03	00 18	00 33	00 48	01 03	06 03	06 33	07 03	07 30	07 48	08 00	08 18	08 33	08 48	09 03	09 18	09 33
1¼	Bethnal Green	d	23p51	00 06	00 21	00 36			06 06	06 36	07 06	07 33	07 51	08 03	08 21	08 36	08 51	09 06	09 21	09 36
3	Hackney Downs	d	23p55	00 10	00 25	00 40	00 55	01 10	06 10	06 40	07 10	07 37	07 55	08 07	08 25	08 40	08 55	09 10	09 25	09 40
4	Clapton	d	23p58	00 13	00 28	00 43	00 58	01 13	06 13	06 43	07 13	07 40	07 58	08 10	08 28	08 43	08 58	09 13	09 28	09 43
5¾	St James Street	d	00 01	00 16	00 32	00 47	01 02	01 17	06 16	06 46	07 16	07 44	08 01	08 14	08 31	08 46	09 01	09 16	09 31	09 46
6¼	Walthamstow Central	⊖ d	00 03	00 18	00 34	00 49	01 04	01 19	06 18	06 48	07 18	07 46	08 03	08 16	08 33	08 48	09 03	09 18	09 33	09 48
7	Wood Street	d	00 05	00 20	00 36	00 51	01 06	01 21	06 20	06 50	07 20	07 48	08 05	08 18	08 35	08 50	09 05	09 20	09 35	09 50
8½	Highams Park	d	00 08	00 23	00 39	00 54	01 09	01 24	06 23	06 53	07 23	07 51	08 08	08 21	08 38	08 53	09 08	09 23	09 38	09 53
10½	**Chingford**	a	00 14	00 29	00 44	00 59	01 14	01 29	06 29	06 59	07 29	07 56	08 14	08 26	08 44	08 59	09 15	09 30	09 44	10 00

		LE	LE	LE	LE		LE	LE	LE	LE	LE	LE	LE	LE	LE	LE	LE	LE	LE	LE
London Liverpool Street [15]	⊖ d	09 48	10 03	10 18	10 33	and every 15 minutes until	15 48	16 03	16 18	16 33	16 48	17 03	17 18	17 33	17 48	18 03	18 18	18 33	18 48	19 03
Bethnal Green	d	09 51	10 06	10 21	10 36		15 51	16 06		16 36		17 06		17 36		18 06		18 36		19 06
Hackney Downs	d	09 55	10 10	10 25	10 40		15 55	16 10	16 25	16 40	16 55	17 10	17 25	17 40	17 55	18 10	18 25	18 40	18 55	19 10
Clapton	d	09 58	10 13	10 28	10 43		15 58	16 13	16 28	16 43	16 58	17 13	17 28	17 43	17 58	18 13	18 28	18 43	18 58	19 13
St James Street	d	10 01	10 16	10 31	10 46		16 01	16 16	16 31	16 46	17 01	17 16	17 31	17 46	18 01	18 16	18 31	18 46	19 01	19 16
Walthamstow Central	⊖ d	10 03	10 18	10 33	10 48		16 03	16 19	16 34	16 49	17 04	17 19	17 34	17 49	18 04	18 19	18 34	18 49	19 04	19 18
Wood Street	d	10 05	10 20	10 35	10 50		16 05	16 21	16 36	16 51	17 06	17 21	17 36	17 51	18 06	18 21	18 36	18 51	19 06	19 20
Highams Park	d	10 08	10 23	10 38	10 53		16 08	16 24	16 39	16 54	17 09	17 24	17 39	17 54	18 09	18 24	18 39	18 54	19 09	19 23
Chingford	a	10 14	10 29	10 44	10 59		16 14	16 31	16 46	17 01	17 16	17 31	17 46	18 01	18 16	18 31	18 46	19 01	19 16	19 29

		LE	LE	LE	LE	LE	LE	LE	LE	LE	LE	LE	LE	LE	LE	LE	LE	LE	LE	LE
London Liverpool Street [15]	⊖ d	19 18	19 33	19 48	20 03	20 18	20 33	20 48	21 03	21 18	21 33	21 48	22 03	22 18	22 33	22 48	23 03	23 18	23 33	23 48
Bethnal Green	d		19 36	19 51	20 06	20 21	20 36	20 51	21 06	21 21	21 36	21 51	22 06	22 21	22 36	22 51	23 06	23 21		23 51
Hackney Downs	d	19 25	19 40	19 55	20 10	20 25	20 40	20 55	21 10	21 25	21 40	21 55	22 10	22 25	22 40	22 55	23 10	23 25		23 55
Clapton	d	19 28	19 43	19 58	20 13	20 28	20 43	20 58	21 13	21 28	21 43	21 58	22 13	22 28	22 43	22 58	23 13	23 28		23 58
St James Street	d	19 31	19 46	20 01	20 16	20 31	20 46	21 01	21 16	21 31	21 46	22 01	22 16	22 31	22 46	23 01	23 16	23 31		00 01
Walthamstow Central	⊖ d	19 33	19 48	20 03	20 18	20 33	20 48	21 03	21 18	21 33	21 48	22 03	22 18	22 33	22 48	23 03	23 18	23 33	23 44	00 03
Wood Street	d	19 35	19 50	20 05	20 20	20 35	20 50	21 05	21 20	21 35	21 50	22 05	22 20	22 35	22 50	23 05	23 20	23 35		00 05
Highams Park	d	19 38	19 53	20 08	20 23	20 38	20 53	21 08	21 23	21 38	21 53	22 08	22 23	22 38	22 53	23 08	23 23	23 38		00 08
Chingford	a	19 44	19 59	20 14	20 29	20 44	20 59	21 14	21 29	21 44	21 59	22 14	22 29	22 44	22 59	23 14	23 29	23 44	23 54	00 14

Saturdays

		LE	LE	LE	LE	LE	LE	LE	LE	LE	LE	LE		LE	LE	LE	LE	LE	LE
London Liverpool Street [15]	⊖ d	23p48	00 03	00 18	00 33	00 48	01 03	06 03	06 33	06 48	07 03	07 18	and every 15 minutes until	22 33	22 48	23 03	23 18	23 33	23 48
Bethnal Green	d	23p51	00 06	00 21	00 36			06 06	06 36	06 51	07 06	07 21		22 36	22 51	23 06	23 21		23 51
Hackney Downs	d	23p55	00 10	00 25	00 40	00 55	01 10	06 10	06 40	06 55	07 10	07 25		22 40	22 55	23 10	23 25		23 55
Clapton	d	23p58	00 13	00 28	00 43	00 58	01 13	06 13	06 43	06 58	07 13	07 28		22 43	22 58	23 13	23 28		23 58
St James Street	d	00 01	00 16	00 32	00 47	01 02	01 17	06 16	06 46	07 01	07 16	07 31		22 46	23 01	23 16	23 31		00 01
Walthamstow Central	⊖ d	00 03	00 18	00 34	00 49	01 04	01 19	06 18	06 48	07 03	07 18	07 33		22 48	23 03	23 18	23 33	23 44	00 03
Wood Street	d	00 05	00 20	00 36	00 51	01 06	01 21	06 20	06 50	07 05	07 20	07 35		22 50	23 05	23 20	23 35		00 05
Highams Park	d	00 08	00 23	00 39	00 54	01 09	01 24	06 23	06 53	07 08	07 23	07 38		22 53	23 08	23 23	23 38		00 08
Chingford	a	00 14	00 29	00 44	00 59	01 14	01 29	06 29	06 59	07 14	07 29	07 44		22 59	23 14	23 29	23 44	23 54	00 14

Sundays

		LE	LE	LE	LE	LE	LE	LE	LE	LE	LE	LE	LE	LE	LE		LE
London Liverpool Street [15]	⊖ d	23p48	00 03	00 18	00 33	01 03	07 33	08 03	08 33	08 48	09 03	09 18	09 33	09 48	10 03	and every 15 minutes until	18 18
Bethnal Green	d	23p51	00 06	00 21	00 36							09 21	09 36	09 51	10 06		18 21
Hackney Downs	d	23p55	00 10	00 25	00 40	01 10	07 40	08 10	08 40	08 55	09 10	09 25	09 40	09 55	10 10		18 25
Clapton	d	23p58	00 13	00 28	00 43	01 13	07 43	08 13	08 43	08 58	09 13	09 28	09 43	09 58	10 13		18 28
St James Street	d	00 01	00 16	00 32	00 47	01 17	07 46	08 16	08 46	09 01	09 16	09 31	09 46	10 01	10 16		18 31
Walthamstow Central	⊖ d	00 03	00 18	00 34	00 49	01 19	07 48	08 18	08 48	09 03	09 18	09 33	09 48	10 03	10 18		18 33
Wood Street	d	00 05	00 20	00 36	00 51	01 21	07 50	08 20	08 50	09 05	09 20	09 35	09 50	10 05	10 20		18 35
Highams Park	d	00 08	00 23	00 39	00 54	01 24	07 53	08 23	08 53	09 08	09 23	09 38	09 53	10 08	10 23		18 38
Chingford	a	00 14	00 29	00 44	00 59	01 29	07 59	08 29	08 59	09 14	09 29	09 44	09 59	10 14	10 29		18 44

		LE	LE	LE	LE	LE	LE	LE	LE	LE	LE	LE	LE
London Liverpool Street [15]	⊖ d	18 33	18 48	19 03	19 33	20 03	20 33	21 03	21 33	22 03	22 33	23 03	23 33
Bethnal Green	d	18 36	18 51	19 06	19 36	20 06	20 36	21 06	21 36	22 06	22 36	23 06	23 36
Hackney Downs	d	18 40	18 55	19 10	19 40	20 10	20 40	21 10	21 40	22 10	22 40	23 10	23 40
Clapton	d	18 43	18 58	19 13	19 43	20 13	20 43	21 13	21 43	22 13	22 43	23 13	23 43
St James Street	d	18 46	19 01	19 16	19 46	20 16	20 46	21 16	21 46	22 16	22 46	23 16	23 46
Walthamstow Central	⊖ d	18 48	19 03	19 18	19 48	20 18	20 48	21 18	21 48	22 18	22 48	23 18	23 48
Wood Street	d	18 50	19 05	19 20	19 50	20 20	20 50	21 20	21 50	22 20	22 50	23 20	23 50
Highams Park	d	18 53	19 08	19 23	19 53	20 23	20 53	21 23	21 53	22 23	22 53	23 23	23 53
Chingford	a	18 59	19 14	19 29	19 59	20 29	20 59	21 29	21 59	22 29	22 59	23 29	23 59

For general notes see front of timetable
For details of catering facilities see Directory of Train Operators

Chingford → London

Network diagram - see first page of Table 20

Miles			LE	LE	LE	LE	LE	LE	LE	LE	LE	LE	LE	LE	LE	LE	LE	LE
0	**Chingford**	d	05 10	05 25	05 40	05 55	06 10	06 25	06 42	06 57	07 12	07 27	07 42	07 54	08 12	08 27	08 32	08 42
2	Highams Park	d	05 14	05 29	05 44	05 59	06 14	06 29	06 46	07 01	07 16	07 31	07 46	07 58	08 16	08 31	08 36	08 46
3½	Wood Street	d	05 17	05 32	05 47	06 02	06 17	06 33	06 50	07 05	07 20	07 35	07 50	08 02	08 20	08 35	08 40	08 50
4¼	Walthamstow Central	⊖ d	05 19	05 34	05 49	06 04	06 19	06 35	06 52	07 07	07 22	07 37	07 52	08 04	08 22	08 37	08 42	08 52
4¾	St James Street	d	05 21	05 36	05 51	06 06	06 21	06 38	06 55	07 10	07 25	07 40	07 55	08 07	08 25	08 40		08 55
6½	Clapton	d	05 24	05 39	05 54	06 09	06 24	06 41	06 58	07 13	07 28	07 43	07 58	08 10	08 28	08 43		08 58
7½	Hackney Downs	d	05 28	05 43	05 58	06 13	06 28	06 45	07 02	07 17	07 32	07 47	08 02	08 14	08 32	08 47		09 02
9¼	Bethnal Green	d	05 32	05 47	06 02	06 17	06 32	06 49		07 21		07 51		08 18		08 51		
10½	**London Liverpool Street** 15	⊖ a	05 36	05 51	06 07	06 21	06 36	06 53	07 12	07 27	07 42	07 57	08 12	08 24	08 42	08 57	09 00	09 12

		LE	LE	LE	LE	LE	LE	LE		LE	LE	LE	LE
Chingford	d	08 57	09 12	09 27	09 40	09 55	10 10	10 25	and	22 40	22 55	23 10	23 25
Highams Park	d	09 01	09 16	09 31	09 44	09 59	10 14	10 29	every 15	22 44	22 59	23 14	23 29
Wood Street	d	09 05	09 20	09 35	09 47	10 02	10 17	10 32	minutes	22 47	23 02	23 17	23 32
Walthamstow Central	⊖ d	09 07	09 22	09 37	09 49	10 04	10 19	10 34	until	22 49	23 04	23 19	23 34
St James Street	d	09 10	09 25	09 40	09 51	10 06	10 21	10 36		22 51	23 06	23 21	23 36
Clapton	d	09 13	09 28	09 43	09 54	10 09	10 24	10 39		22 54	23 09	23 24	23 39
Hackney Downs	d	09 17	09 32	09 47	09 58	10 13	10 28	10 43		22 58	23 13	23 28	23 43
Bethnal Green	d	09 21		09 51	10 02	10 17	10 32	10 47		23 02	23 17	23 32	23 47
London Liverpool Street 15	⊖ a	09 27	09 42	09 57	10 07	10 21	10 36	10 51		23 06	23 21	23 36	23 51

Saturdays

		LE	LE	LE	LE	LE	LE		LE	LE	LE	LE
Chingford	d	05 10	05 25	05 40	05 55	06 10	06 25	and	22 40	22 55	23 10	23 25
Highams Park	d	05 14	05 29	05 44	05 59	06 14	06 29	every 15	22 44	22 59	23 14	23 29
Wood Street	d	05 17	05 32	05 47	06 02	06 17	06 32	minutes	22 47	23 02	23 17	23 32
Walthamstow Central	⊖ d	05 19	05 34	05 49	06 04	06 19	06 34	until	22 49	23 04	23 19	23 34
St James Street	d	05 21	05 36	05 51	06 06	06 21	06 36		22 51	23 06	23 21	23 36
Clapton	d	05 24	05 39	05 54	06 09	06 24	06 39		22 54	23 09	23 24	23 39
Hackney Downs	d	05 28	05 43	05 58	06 13	06 28	06 43		22 58	23 13	23 28	23 43
Bethnal Green	d	05 32	05 47	06 02	06 17	06 32	06 47		23 02	23 17	23 32	23 47
London Liverpool Street 15	⊖ a	05 36	05 51	06 06	06 21	06 36	06 51		23 06	23 22	23 36	23 51

Sundays

		LE	LE	LE	LE	LE	LE	LE	LE	LE	LE	LE	LE	LE	LE		LE
Chingford	d	06 40	06 55	07 10	07 25	07 40	07 55	08 10	08 25	08 40	08 55	09 10	09 25	09 40	09 55	and	18 10
Highams Park	d	06 44	06 59	07 14	07 29	07 44	07 59	08 14	08 29	08 44	08 59	09 14	09 29	09 44	09 59	every 15	18 14
Wood Street	d	06 47	07 02	07 17	07 32	07 47	08 02	08 17	08 32	08 47	09 02	09 17	09 32	09 47	10 02	minutes	18 17
Walthamstow Central	⊖ d	06 49	07 04	07 19	07 34	07 49	08 04	08 19	08 34	08 49	09 04	09 19	09 34	09 49	10 04	until	18 19
St James Street	d	06 51	07 06	07 21	07 36	07 51	08 06	08 21	08 36	08 51	09 06	09 21	09 36	09 51	10 06		18 21
Clapton	d	06 54	07 09	07 24	07 39	07 54	08 09	08 24	08 39	08 54	09 09	09 24	09 39	09 54	10 09		18 24
Hackney Downs	d	06 58	07 13	07 28	07 43	07 58	08 13	08 28	08 43	08 58	09 13	09 28	09 43	09 58	10 13		18 28
Bethnal Green	d										09 17	09 32	09 47	10 02	10 17		18 32
London Liverpool Street 15	⊖ a	07 06	07 21	07 37	07 52	08 06	08 21	08 38	08 51	09 06	09 21	09 36	09 51	10 06	10 21		18 36

		LE	LE	LE	LE	LE	LE	LE	LE	LE	LE	LE
Chingford	d	18 25	18 40	19 10	19 40	20 10	20 40	21 10	21 40	22 10	22 40	23 10
Highams Park	d	18 29	18 44	19 14	19 44	20 14	20 44	21 14	21 44	22 14	22 44	23 14
Wood Street	d	18 32	18 47	19 17	19 47	20 17	20 47	21 17	21 47	22 17	22 47	23 17
Walthamstow Central	⊖ d	18 34	18 49	19 19	19 49	20 19	20 49	21 19	21 49	22 19	22 49	23 19
St James Street	d	18 36	18 51	19 21	19 51	20 21	20 51	21 21	21 51	22 21	22 51	23 21
Clapton	d	18 39	18 54	19 24	19 54	20 24	20 54	21 24	21 54	22 24	22 54	23 24
Hackney Downs	d	18 43	18 58	19 28	19 58	20 28	20 58	21 28	21 58	22 28	22 58	23 28
Bethnal Green	d	18 47	19 02	19 32	20 02	20 32	21 02	21 32	22 02	22 32	23 02	23 32
London Liverpool Street 15	⊖ a	18 51	19 06	19 36	20 06	20 36	21 06	21 36	22 06	22 36	23 06	23 36

For general notes see front of timetable
For details of catering facilities see Directory of Train Operators

London → Cheshunt (via Seven Sisters) and Enfield Town

Network diagram - see first page of Table 20

Miles	Miles	Station		LE MX A	LE MX	LE	LE	LE	LE	LE	LE	LE	LE	LE	LE	LE	LE	LE	LE	LE
0	0	**London Liverpool Street** 15	⊖ d	23p45	00 01	05 45	06 00	06 14	06 21	06 30	06 44	06 51	07 00	07 18	07 21	07 33	07 44	07 51	08 03	08 14
1¼	1¼	Bethnal Green	d	23p48	00 03	05 48	06 03		06 24	06 33		06 54	07 03		07 24	07 36		07 54	08 06	
1¾	1¾	Cambridge Heath	d	23p50	00 05	05 50	06 05		06 26	06 35		06 56	07 05		07 26	07 38		07 56	08 08	
2½	2½	London Fields	d	23p52	00 07	05 52	06 07		06 28	06 37		06 58	07 07		07 28	07 40		07 58	08 10	
3	3	Hackney Downs	d	23p54	00 09	05 54	06 09	06 22	06 30	06 39	06 52	07 00	07 09	07 25	07 30	07 42	07 52	08 00	08 12	08 22
3¾	3¾	Rectory Road	d	23p57	00 12	05 57	06 12	06 24	06 33	06 42	06 54	07 03	07 12		07 33	07 45	07 54	08 03	08 15	08 24
4¼	4¼	Stoke Newington	d	23p58	00 13	05 58	06 13	06 26	06 34	06 43	06 56	07 04	07 13		07 34	07 46	07 56	08 04	08 16	08 26
5	5	Stamford Hill	d	23p59	00 15	06 00	06 15	06 28	06 36	06 45	06 58	07 06	07 15		07 36	07 48	07 58	08 06	08 18	08 28
5½	5½	Seven Sisters	⊖ d	00 02	00 17	06 02	06 17	06 30	06 38	06 47	07 00	07 08	07 17	07 30	07 38	07 50	08 00	08 08	08 20	08 30
6¼	6¼	Bruce Grove	d	00 04	00 19	06 04	06 19	06 32	06 40	06 49	07 02	07 10	07 19	07 32	07 40	07 52	08 02	08 10	08 22	08 32
7¼	7¼	White Hart Lane	d	00 06	00 21	06 06	06 21	06 34	06 42	06 51	07 04	07 12	07 21	07 34	07 42	07 54	08 04	08 12	08 24	08 34
8	8	Silver Street	d	00 08	00 23	06 08	06 23	06 36	06 44	06 53	07 06	07 14	07 23	07 36	07 44	07 56	08 06	08 14	08 26	08 36
8½	8½	Edmonton Green	d	00 10	00 25	06 10	06 25	06 38	06 46	06 55	07 08	07 16	07 25	07 38	07 46	07 58	08 08	08 16	08 28	08 38
—	9¾	Bush Hill Park	d		00 28		06 28		06 49	06 58		07 19	07 28		07 49	08 01		08 19	08 31	
—	10¾	**Enfield Town**	a		00 33		06 33		06 54	07 03		07 24	07 33		07 54	08 06		08 24	08 36	
10½	—	Southbury	d	00 14		06 14		06 41			07 11			07 41			08 11			08 41
12¼	—	Turkey Street	d	00 17		06 17		06 44			07 14			07 44			08 14			08 44
13½	—	Theobalds Grove	d	00 19		06 19		06 47			07 17			07 47			08 17			08 47
14½	—	**Cheshunt**	a	00 22		06 24		06 51			07 21			07 51			08 21			08 51

Station		LE	LE	LE	LE	LE	LE	LE	LE	LE		LE	LE	LE	LE	LE	LE	LE	LE
London Liverpool Street 15	⊖ d	08 21	08 30	08 44	08 51	09 00	09 15	09 30	09 45	10 00	and at the same minutes past each hour until	15 15	15 30	15 45	16 00	16 15	16 20	16 30	16 38
Bethnal Green	d	08 24	08 33		08 54	09 03	09 18	09 33	09 48	10 03		15 18	15 33	15 48	16 03	16 18	16 23	16 33	
Cambridge Heath	d	08 26	08 35		08 56	09 05	09 20	09 35	09 50	10 05		15 20	15 35	15 50	16 05	16 20	16 25	16 35	16 43
London Fields	d	08 28	08 37		08 58	09 07	09 22	09 37	09 52	10 07		15 22	15 37	15 52	16 07	16 22	16 27	16 37	16 45
Hackney Downs	d	08 30	08 39	08 52	09 00	09 09	09 24	09 39	09 54	10 09		15 24	15 39	15 54	16 09	16 24	16 29	16 39	16 47
Rectory Road	d	08 33	08 42	08 54	09 03	09 12	09 27	09 42	09 57	10 12		15 27	15 42	15 57	16 12	16 27	16 32	16 42	16 49
Stoke Newington	d	08 34	08 43	08 56	09 04	09 13	09 28	09 43	09 58	10 13		15 28	15 43	15 58	16 13	16 28	16 33	16 43	16 51
Stamford Hill	d	08 36	08 45	08 58	09 06	09 15	09 30	09 45	10 00	10 15		15 30	15 45	16 00	16 15	16 30	16 35	16 45	16 53
Seven Sisters	⊖ d	08 38	08 47	09 00	09 08	09 17	09 32	09 47	10 02	10 17		15 32	15 47	16 02	16 17	16 33	16 38	16 48	16 56
Bruce Grove	d	08 40	08 49	09 02	09 10	09 19	09 34	09 49	10 04	10 19		15 34	15 49	16 04	16 19	16 35	16 40	16 50	16 58
White Hart Lane	d	08 42	08 51	09 04	09 12	09 21	09 36	09 51	10 06	10 21		15 36	15 51	16 06	16 21	16 37	16 42	16 52	17 00
Silver Street	d	08 44	08 53	09 06	09 14	09 23	09 38	09 53	10 08	10 23		15 38	15 53	16 08	16 23	16 39	16 44	16 54	17 02
Edmonton Green	d	08 46	08 55	09 08	09 16	09 25	09 40	09 55	10 10	10 25		15 40	15 55	16 10	16 25	16 41	16 46	16 56	17 04
Bush Hill Park	d	08 49	08 58		09 19	09 28		09 58		10 28			15 58		16 28		16 49	16 59	
Enfield Town	a	08 54	09 03		09 24	09 33		10 03		10 33			16 03		16 34		16 55	17 06	
Southbury	d			09 11			09 44		10 14			15 44		16 14		16 45			17 08
Turkey Street	d			09 14			09 47		10 17			15 47		16 17		16 48			17 11
Theobalds Grove	d			09 17			09 49		10 19			15 49		16 19		16 50			17 14
Cheshunt	a			09 21			09 54		10 24			15 54		16 24		16 56			17 19

Station		LE	LE	LE	LE	LE	LE	LE	LE	LE	LE	LE	LE	LE	LE	LE	LE	LE	LE	LE
London Liverpool Street 15	⊖ d	16 50	17 00	17 08	17 20	17 30	17 38	17 50	18 00	18 08	18 20	18 30	18 38	18 50	19 00	19 08	19 20	19 30	19 45	20 00
Bethnal Green	d	16 53	17 03		17 23	17 33		17 53	18 03		18 23	18 33		18 53	19 03		19 23	19 33	19 48	20 03
Cambridge Heath	d	16 55	17 05	17 13	17 25	17 35	17 43	17 55	18 05	18 13	18 25	18 35	18 43	18 55	19 05	19 13	19 25	19 35	19 50	20 05
London Fields	d	16 57	17 07	17 15	17 27	17 37	17 45	17 57	18 07	18 15	18 27	18 37	18 45	18 57	19 07	19 15	19 27	19 37	19 52	20 07
Hackney Downs	d	16 59	17 09	17 17	17 29	17 39	17 47	17 59	18 09	18 17	18 29	18 39	18 47	18 59	19 09	19 17	19 29	19 39	19 54	20 09
Rectory Road	d	17 02	17 12	17 19	17 32	17 42	17 49	18 02	18 12	18 19	18 32	18 42	18 49	19 02	19 12	19 19	19 32	19 42	19 57	20 12
Stoke Newington	d	17 03	17 13	17 21	17 33	17 43	17 51	18 03	18 13	18 21	18 33	18 43	18 51	19 03	19 13	19 21	19 33	19 43	19 58	20 13
Stamford Hill	d	17 05	17 15	17 23	17 35	17 45	17 53	18 05	18 15	18 23	18 35	18 45	18 53	19 05	19 15	19 23	19 35	19 45	20 00	20 15
Seven Sisters	⊖ d	17 08	17 18	17 26	17 38	17 48	17 56	18 08	18 18	18 26	18 38	18 48	18 56	19 08	19 18	19 26	19 38	19 47	20 02	20 17
Bruce Grove	d	17 10	17 20	17 28	17 40	17 50	17 58	18 10	18 20	18 28	18 40	18 50	18 58	19 10	19 20	19 28	19 40	19 49	20 04	20 19
White Hart Lane	d	17 12	17 22	17 30	17 42	17 52	18 00	18 12	18 22	18 30	18 42	18 52	19 00	19 12	19 22	19 30	19 42	19 51	20 06	20 21
Silver Street	d	17 14	17 24	17 32	17 44	17 54	18 02	18 14	18 24	18 32	18 44	18 54	19 02	19 14	19 24	19 32	19 44	19 53	20 08	20 23
Edmonton Green	d	17 16	17 26	17 34	17 46	17 56	18 04	18 16	18 26	18 34	18 46	18 56	19 04	19 16	19 26	19 34	19 46	19 55	20 10	20 25
Bush Hill Park	d	17 19	17 29		17 49	17 59		18 19	18 29		18 49	18 59		19 19	19 29		19 49	19 58		20 28
Enfield Town	a	17 25	17 36		17 55	18 06		18 25	18 36		18 55	19 06		19 25	19 35		19 54	20 03		20 33
Southbury	d			17 38			18 08			18 38			19 08			19 38			20 14	
Turkey Street	d			17 41			18 11			18 41			19 11			19 41			20 17	
Theobalds Grove	d			17 44			18 14			18 44			19 14			19 44			20 19	
Cheshunt	a			17 49			18 19			18 49			19 19			19 48			20 24	

Station		LE	LE	LE	LE	LE	LE	LE	LE	LE	LE	LE	LE	LE	LE	LE A
London Liverpool Street 15	⊖ d	20 15	20 30	20 45	21 00	21 15	21 30	21 45	22 00	22 15	22 30	22 45	23 00	23 15	23 30	23 45
Bethnal Green	d	20 18	20 33	20 48	21 03	21 18	21 33	21 48	22 03	22 18	22 33	22 48	23 03	23 18	23 33	23 48
Cambridge Heath	d	20 20	20 35	20 50	21 05	21 20	21 35	21 50	22 05	22 20	22 35	22 50	23 05	23 20	23 35	23 50
London Fields	d	20 22	20 37	20 52	21 07	21 22	21 37	21 52	22 07	22 22	22 37	22 52	23 07	23 22	23 37	23 52
Hackney Downs	d	20 24	20 39	20 54	21 09	21 24	21 39	21 54	22 09	22 24	22 39	22 54	23 09	23 24	23 39	23 54
Rectory Road	d	20 27	20 42	20 57	21 12	21 27	21 42	21 57	22 12	22 27	22 42	22 57	23 12	23 27	23 42	23 57
Stoke Newington	d	20 28	20 43	20 58	21 13	21 28	21 43	21 58	22 13	22 28	22 43	22 58	23 13	23 28	23 43	23 58
Stamford Hill	d	20 30	20 45	21 00	21 15	21 30	21 45	22 00	22 15	22 30	22 45	23 00	23 15	23 30	23 45	23 59
Seven Sisters	⊖ d	20 32	20 47	21 02	21 17	21 32	21 47	22 02	22 17	22 32	22 47	23 02	23 17	23 32	23 47	00 02
Bruce Grove	d	20 34	20 49	21 04	21 19	21 34	21 49	22 04	22 19	22 34	22 49	23 04	23 19	23 34	23 49	00 04
White Hart Lane	d	20 36	20 51	21 06	21 21	21 36	21 51	22 06	22 21	22 36	22 51	23 06	23 21	23 36	23 51	00 06
Silver Street	d	20 38	20 53	21 08	21 23	21 38	21 53	22 08	22 23	22 38	22 53	23 08	23 23	23 38	23 53	00 08
Edmonton Green	d	20 40	20 55	21 10	21 25	21 40	21 55	22 10	22 25	22 40	22 55	23 10	23 25	23 40	23 55	00 10
Bush Hill Park	d		20 58		21 28		21 58		22 28		22 58		23 28		23 58	
Enfield Town	a		21 03		21 33		22 03		22 33		23 03		23 33		00 03	
Southbury	d	20 44		21 14		21 44		22 14		22 44		23 14		23 44		00 14
Turkey Street	d	20 47		21 17		21 47		22 17		22 47		23 17		23 47		00 17
Theobalds Grove	d	20 49		21 19		21 49		22 19		22 49		23 19		23 49		00 19
Cheshunt	a	20 54		21 24		21 54		22 24		22 54		23 24		23 54		00 22

For general notes see front of timetable
For details of catering facilities see Directory of Train Operators

A To Bishops Stortford (Table 22)

Table 21

Saturdays

London → Cheshunt (via Seven Sisters) and Enfield Town

Network diagram - see first page of Table 20

	LE A	LE	LE	LE	LE	LE	LE	LE	LE	LE		LE	LE	LE	LE	LE	LE	LE
London Liverpool Street [15] ⊖ d	23p45	00 01	05 15	05 28	05 45	06 00	06 15	06 30	06 45	07 00		22 15	22 30	22 45	23 00	23 15	23 30	23 45
Bethnal Green d	23p48	00 03	05 18		05 48	06 03	06 18	06 33	06 48	07 03		22 18	22 33	22 48	23 03	23 18	23 33	23 48
Cambridge Heath d	23p50	00 05	05 20		05 50	06 05	06 20	06 35	06 50	07 05		22 20	22 35	22 50	23 05	23 20	23 35	23 50
London Fields d	23p52	00 07	05 22		05 52	06 07	06 22	06 37	06 52	07 07		22 22	22 37	22 52	23 07	23 22	23 37	23 52
Hackney Downs d	23p54	00 09	05 24		05 54	06 09	06 24	06 39	06 54	07 09	and at	22 24	22 39	22 54	23 09	23 24	23 39	23 54
Rectory Road d	23p57	00 12	05 27		05 57	06 12	06 27	06 42	06 57	07 12	the same	22 27	22 42	22 57	23 12	23 27	23 42	23 57
Stoke Newington d	23p58	00 13	05 28		05 58	06 13	06 28	06 43	06 58	07 13		22 28	22 43	22 58	23 13	23 28	23 43	23 58
Stamford Hill d	23p59	00 15	05 30		06 00	06 15	06 30	06 45	07 00	07 15	minutes	22 30	22 45	23 00	23 15	23 30	23 45	23 59
Seven Sisters ⊖ d	00 02	00 17	05 32	05 50	06 02	06 17	06 32	06 47	07 02	07 17		22 32	22 47	23 02	23 17	23 32	23 47	00 02
Bruce Grove d	00 04	00 19	05 34	05 52	06 04	06 19	06 34	06 49	07 04	07 19	past	22 34	22 49	23 04	23 19	23 34	23 49	00 04
White Hart Lane d	00 06	00 21	05 36	05 54	06 06	06 21	06 36	06 51	07 06	07 21	each	22 36	22 51	23 06	23 21	23 36	23 51	00 06
Silver Street d	00 08	00 23	05 38	05 56	06 08	06 23	06 38	06 53	07 08	07 23		22 38	22 53	23 08	23 23	23 38	23 53	00 08
Edmonton Green d	00 10	00 25	05 40	05 58	06 10	06 25	06 40	06 55	07 10	07 25	hour until	22 40	22 55	23 10	23 25	23 40	23 55	00 10
Bush Hill Park d		00 28		06 01		06 28		06 58		07 28			22 58		23 28		23 58	
Enfield Town a		00 33		06 06		06 33		07 03		07 33			23 03		23 33		00 03	
Southbury d	00 14		05 44		06 14		06 44		07 14			22 44		23 14		23 44		00 14
Turkey Street d	00 17		05 47		06 17		06 47		07 17			22 47		23 17		23 47		00 17
Theobalds Grove d	00 19		05 49		06 19		06 49		07 19			22 49		23 19		23 49		00 19
Cheshunt a	00 22		05 54		06 24		06 54		07 24			22 54		23 24		23 54		00 24

Sundays

	LE	LE	LE	LE B	LE	LE B	LE	LE B	LE	LE B	LE	LE B	LE
London Liverpool Street [15] ⊖ d	23p45	00 01	07 30	07 52	08 00	08 22	08 30	08 52	09 00	09 22	09 30	09 52	10 00
Bethnal Green d	23p48	00 03									09 33		10 03
Cambridge Heath d	23p50	00 05									09 35		10 05
London Fields d	23p52	00 07									09 37		10 07
Hackney Downs d	23p54	00 09	07 39	07 59	08 09	08 29	08 39	08 59	09 09	09 29	09 39	09 59	10 09
Rectory Road d	23p57	00 12	07 42		08 12		08 42		09 12		09 42		10 12
Stoke Newington d	23p58	00 13	07 43		08 13		08 43		09 13		09 43		10 13
Stamford Hill d	23p59	00 15	07 45		08 15		08 45		09 15		09 45		10 15
Seven Sisters ⊖ d	00 02	00 17	07 47	08 04	08 17	08 34	08 47	09 04	09 17	09 34	09 47	10 04	10 17
Bruce Grove d	00 04	00 19	07 49		08 19		08 49		09 19		09 49		10 19
White Hart Lane d	00 06	00 21	07 51		08 21		08 51		09 21		09 51		10 21
Silver Street d	00 08	00 23	07 53		08 23		08 53		09 23		09 53		10 23
Edmonton Green d	00 10	00 25	07 55	08 08	08 25	08 38	08 55	09 08	09 25	09 38	09 55	10 08	10 25
Bush Hill Park d		00 28	07 58		08 28		08 58		09 28		09 58		10 28
Enfield Town a		00 33	08 03		08 33		09 03		09 33		10 03		10 33
Southbury d	00 14			08 12		08 42		09 12		09 42		10 12	
Turkey Street d	00 17			08 15		08 45		09 15		09 45		10 15	
Theobalds Grove d	00 19			08 17		08 47		09 17		09 47		10 17	
Cheshunt a	00 24			08 20		08 52		09 20		09 52		10 20	

	LE B		LE	LE B	LE	LE B	LE	LE B	LE	LE B	LE	LE B	LE
London Liverpool Street [15] ⊖ d	10 22		18 30	19 00	19 30	20 00	20 30	21 00	21 30	22 00	22 30	23 00	23 30
Bethnal Green d			18 33	19 03	19 33	20 03	20 33	21 03	21 33	22 03	22 33	23 03	23 33
Cambridge Heath d			18 35	19 05	19 35	20 05	20 35	21 05	21 35	22 05	22 35	23 05	23 35
London Fields d			18 37	19 07	19 37	20 07	20 37	21 07	21 37	22 07	22 37	23 07	23 37
Hackney Downs d	10 29	and at	18 39	19 09	19 39	20 09	20 39	21 09	21 39	22 09	22 39	23 09	23 39
Rectory Road d		the same	18 42	19 12	19 42	20 12	20 42	21 12	21 42	22 12	22 42	23 12	23 42
Stoke Newington d			18 43	19 13	19 43	20 13	20 43	21 13	21 43	22 13	22 43	23 13	23 43
Stamford Hill d		minutes	18 45	19 15	19 45	20 15	20 45	21 15	21 45	22 15	22 45	23 15	23 45
Seven Sisters ⊖ d	10 34		18 47	19 17	19 47	20 17	20 47	21 17	21 47	22 17	22 47	23 17	23 47
Bruce Grove d		past	18 49	19 19	19 49	20 19	20 49	21 19	21 49	22 19	22 49	23 19	23 49
White Hart Lane d		each	18 51	19 21	19 51	20 21	20 51	21 21	21 51	22 21	22 51	23 21	23 51
Silver Street d			18 53	19 23	19 53	20 23	20 53	21 23	21 53	22 23	22 53	23 23	23 53
Edmonton Green d	10 38	hour until	18 55	19 25	19 55	20 25	20 55	21 25	21 55	22 25	22 55	23 25	23 55
Bush Hill Park d			18 58		19 58		20 58		21 58		22 58		23 58
Enfield Town a			19 03		20 03		21 03		22 03		23 03		00 03
Southbury d	10 42			19 29		20 29		21 29		22 29		23 29	
Turkey Street d	10 45			19 32		20 32		21 32		22 32		23 32	
Theobalds Grove d	10 47			19 34		20 34		21 34		22 34		23 34	
Cheshunt a	10 52			19 37		20 37		21 37		22 37		23 37	

For general notes see front of timetable
For details of catering facilities see Directory of Train Operators

A To Bishops Stortford (Table 22)
B To Hertford East (Table 22)

Cheshunt (via Seven Sisters) and Enfield Town → London

Network diagram - see first page of Table 20

Miles	Miles			LE MX	LE MO A	LE MX 1	LE MX 1	LE MO 1	LE MX 1	LE MO 1	LE MX 1	LE	LE	LE	LE	LE	LE	LE	LE	LE	LE	LE
0	—	**Cheshunt**	d	23p31	23p31	23p51			23p58			05 16		06 01			06 33			07 03		
1	—	Theobalds Grove	d	23p34	23p34							05 19		06 04			06 36			07 06		
2¼	—	Turkey Street	d	23p36	23p36							05 21		06 06			06 38			07 08		
4	—	Southbury	d	23p39	23p39							05 24		06 09			06 41			07 11		
—	0	**Enfield Town**	d										05 52		06 20	06 32		06 48	07 02		07 18	07 32
—	1	Bush Hill Park	d										05 55		06 23	06 35		06 51	07 05		07 21	07 35
6	2¼	Edmonton Green	d	23p43	23p43							05 28	05 58	06 13	06 26	06 38	06 45	06 54	07 08	07 15	07 24	07 38
6½	2¾	Silver Street	d	23p45	23p45							05 30	06 00	06 15	06 28	06 40	06 47	06 56	07 10	07 17	07 26	07 40
7¼	3½	White Hart Lane	d	23p47	23p47							05 32	06 02	06 17	06 30	06 42	06 49	06 58	07 12	07 19	07 28	07 42
8¼	4½	Bruce Grove	d	23p49	23p49							05 34	06 04	06 19	06 32	06 44	06 51	07 00	07 14	07 21	07 30	07 44
9	5¼	Seven Sisters	⊖ d	23p51	23p51	00 04	00 07	00 08	00 11	00 21	00 21	05 36	06 06	06 21	06 35	06 47	06 55	07 03	07 17	07 25	07 33	07 47
9½	5¾	Stamford Hill	d	23p53	23p53							05 38	06 08	06 23	06 37	06 49	06 57	07 05	07 19	07 27	07 35	07 49
10¼	6½	Stoke Newington	d	23p55	23p55							05 40	06 10	06 25	06 39	06 51	06 59	07 07	07 21	07 29	07 37	07 51
10¾	7	Rectory Road	d	23p56	23p56							05 41	06 11	06 26	06 41	06 53	07 00	07 09	07 23	07 30	07 39	07 53
11½	7¾	Hackney Downs	d	23p59	23p59				00 16			05 44	06 14	06 29	06 45	06 58	07 04	07 13	07 28	07 34	07 43	07 58
12	8¼	London Fields	d	00 01	00 01							05 46	06 16	06 31	06 47	07 00	07 06	07 15	07 30	07 36	07 45	08 00
12¾	9	Cambridge Heath	d	00 03	00 03							05 48	06 18	06 33	06 49	07 02	07 08	07 17	07 32	07 38	07 47	08 02
13¼	9½	Bethnal Green	d	00 05	00 05							05 50	06 20	06 35	06 51		07 10	07 19		07 40	07 49	
14½	10¾	**London Liverpool Street 15**	⊖ a	00 10	00 11	00 18	00 22	00 22	00 25	00 35	00 36	05 55	06 25	06 40	06 55	07 10	07 16	07 25	07 40	07 46	07 55	08 10

		LE	LE	LE	LE	LE	LE	LE	LE	LE	LE	LE	LE	LE	LE	LE	LE		LE	LE
Cheshunt	d	07 33			08 03			08 33			09 03			09 31		10 01		and at	15 31	
Theobalds Grove	d	07 36			08 06			08 36			09 06			09 34		10 04		the same	15 34	
Turkey Street	d	07 38			08 08			08 38			09 08			09 36		10 06		minutes	15 36	
Southbury	d	07 41			08 11			08 41			09 11			09 39		10 09		past	15 39	
Enfield Town	d		07 50	08 02		08 18	08 33		08 48	09 02		09 18	09 29		09 52		10 22	each		15 52
Bush Hill Park	d		07 53	08 05		08 21	08 36		08 51	09 05		09 21	09 32		09 55		10 25	hour until		15 55
Edmonton Green	d	07 45	07 56	08 08	08 15	08 24	08 39	08 45	08 54	09 08	09 15	09 24	09 35	09 43	09 58	10 13	10 28		15 43	15 58
Silver Street	d	07 47	07 58	08 10	08 17	08 26	08 41	08 47	08 56	09 10	09 17	09 26	09 37	09 45	10 00	10 15	10 30		15 45	16 00
White Hart Lane	d	07 49	08 00	08 12	08 19	08 28	08 43	08 49	08 58	09 12	09 19	09 28	09 39	09 47	10 02	10 17	10 32		15 47	16 02
Bruce Grove	d	07 51	08 02	08 14	08 21	08 30	08 45	08 51	09 00	09 14	09 21	09 30	09 41	09 49	10 04	10 19	10 34		15 49	16 04
Seven Sisters	⊖ d	07 55	08 05	08 17	08 25	08 33	08 48	08 55	09 03	09 17	09 25	09 33	09 43	09 51	10 06	10 21	10 36		15 51	16 06
Stamford Hill	d	07 57	08 07	08 19	08 27	08 35	08 50	08 57	09 05	09 19	09 27	09 35	09 45	09 53	10 08	10 23	10 38		15 53	16 08
Stoke Newington	d	07 59	08 09	08 21	08 29	08 37	08 52	08 59	09 07	09 21	09 29	09 37	09 47	09 55	10 10	10 25	10 40		15 55	16 10
Rectory Road	d	08 00	08 10	08 23	08 30	08 39	08 54	09 00	09 09	09 23	09 30	09 39	09 49	09 56	10 11	10 26	10 41		15 56	16 11
Hackney Downs	d	08 04	08 14	08 28	08 34	08 43	08 58	09 04	09 13	09 28	09 34	09 43	09 52	09 59	10 14	10 29	10 44		15 59	16 14
London Fields	d	08 06	08 16	08 30	08 36	08 45	09 00	09 06	09 15	09 30	09 36	09 45	09 54	10 01	10 16	10 31	10 46		16 01	16 16
Cambridge Heath	d	08 08	08 18	08 32	08 38	08 47	09 02	09 08	09 17	09 32	09 38	09 47	09 56	10 03	10 18	10 33	10 48		16 03	16 18
Bethnal Green	d	08 10	08 20		08 40	08 49		09 10	09 19		09 40	09 49		10 05	10 20	10 35	10 50		16 05	16 20
London Liverpool Street 15	⊖ a	08 16	08 26	08 40	08 46	08 55	09 10	09 16	09 25	09 40	09 46	09 55	10 03	10 10	10 25	10 40	10 55		16 11	16 25

		LE	LE	LE	LE	LE	LE	LE	LE	LE	LE	LE	LE	LE	LE	LE	LE	LE	LE	LE	LE	LE
Cheshunt	d	16 01		16 31			17 01			17 31			18 01			18 31			19 01			19 31
Theobalds Grove	d	16 04		16 34			17 04			17 34			18 04			18 34			19 04			19 34
Turkey Street	d	16 06		16 36			17 06			17 36			18 06			18 36			19 06			19 36
Southbury	d	16 09		16 39			17 09			17 39			18 09			18 39			19 09			19 39
Enfield Town	d		16 22		16 52	17 00		17 22	17 30		17 52	18 00		18 22	18 30		18 52	19 00		19 22	19 30	
Bush Hill Park	d		16 25		16 55	17 03		17 25	17 33		17 55	18 03		18 25	18 33		18 55	19 03		19 25	19 33	
Edmonton Green	d	16 13	16 28	16 43	16 58	17 06	17 13	17 28	17 36	17 43	17 58	18 06	18 13	18 28	18 36	18 43	18 58	19 06	19 13	19 28	19 36	19 43
Silver Street	d	16 15	16 30	16 45	17 00	17 08	17 15	17 30	17 38	17 45	18 00	18 08	18 15	18 30	18 38	18 45	19 00	19 08	19 15	19 30	19 38	19 45
White Hart Lane	d	16 17	16 32	16 47	17 02	17 10	17 17	17 32	17 40	17 47	18 02	18 10	18 17	18 32	18 40	18 47	19 02	19 10	19 17	19 32	19 40	19 47
Bruce Grove	d	16 19	16 34	16 49	17 04	17 12	17 19	17 34	17 42	17 49	18 04	18 12	18 19	18 34	18 42	18 49	19 04	19 12	19 19	19 34	19 42	19 49
Seven Sisters	⊖ d	16 21	16 36	16 51	17 06	17 14	17 21	17 36	17 44	17 51	18 06	18 14	18 21	18 36	18 44	18 51	19 06	19 14	19 21	19 36	19 44	19 51
Stamford Hill	d	16 23	16 38	16 53	17 08		17 23	17 38		17 53	18 08		18 23	18 38		18 53	19 08		19 23	19 38		19 53
Stoke Newington	d	16 25	16 40	16 55	17 10	17 17	17 25	17 40	17 47	17 55	18 10	18 17	18 25	18 40	18 47	18 55	19 10	19 17	19 25	19 40	19 47	19 55
Rectory Road	d	16 26	16 41	16 56	17 11		17 26	17 41		17 56	18 11		18 26	18 41		18 56	19 11		19 26	19 41		19 56
Hackney Downs	d	16 29	16 44	16 59	17 14	17 20	17 29	17 44	17 50	17 59	18 14	18 20	18 29	18 44	18 50	18 59	19 14	19 20	19 29	19 44	19 50	19 59
London Fields	d	16 31	16 46	17 01	17 16		17 31	17 46		18 01	18 16		18 31	18 46		19 01	19 16		19 31	19 46		20 01
Cambridge Heath	d	16 33	16 48	17 03	17 18		17 33	17 48		18 03	18 18		18 33	18 48		19 03	19 18		19 33	19 48		20 03
Bethnal Green	d	16 35	16 50	17 05	17 20		17 35	17 50		18 05	18 20		18 35	18 50		19 05	19 20		19 35	19 50		20 05
London Liverpool Street 15	⊖ a	16 40	16 56	17 10	17 26	17 29	17 40	17 56	17 59	18 11	18 26	18 29	18 40	18 56	18 59	19 11	19 26	19 29	19 41	19 55	19 59	20 11

		LE	LE	LE	LE	LE	LE	LE	LE	LE	LE	LE	LE	LE	LE	LE	LE	LE 1	LE 1
Cheshunt	d		20 01		20 31		21 01		21 31		22 01		22 31		23 01		23 31	23 51	23 58
Theobalds Grove	d		20 04		20 34		21 04		21 34		22 04		22 34		23 04		23 34		
Turkey Street	d		20 06		20 36		21 06		21 36		22 06		22 36		23 06		23 36		
Southbury	d		20 09		20 39		21 09		21 39		22 09		22 39		23 09		23 39		
Enfield Town	d	19 52		20 22		20 52		21 22		21 52		22 22		22 52		23 22			
Bush Hill Park	d	19 55		20 25		20 55		21 25		21 55		22 25		22 55		23 25			
Edmonton Green	d	19 58	20 13	20 28	20 43	20 58	21 13	21 28	21 43	21 58	22 13	22 28	22 43	22 58	23 13	23 28	23 43		
Silver Street	d	20 00	20 15	20 30	20 45	21 00	21 15	21 30	21 45	22 00	22 15	22 30	22 45	23 00	23 15	23 30	23 45		
White Hart Lane	d	20 02	20 17	20 32	20 47	21 02	21 17	21 32	21 47	22 02	22 17	22 32	22 47	23 02	23 17	23 32	23 47		
Bruce Grove	d	20 04	20 19	20 34	20 49	21 04	21 19	21 34	21 49	22 04	22 19	22 34	22 49	23 04	23 19	23 34	23 49		
Seven Sisters	⊖ d	20 06	20 21	20 36	20 51	21 06	21 21	21 36	21 51	22 06	22 21	22 36	22 51	23 06	23 21	23 36	23 51	00 04	00 11
Stamford Hill	d	20 08	20 23	20 38	20 53	21 08	21 23	21 38	21 53	22 08	22 23	22 38	22 53	23 08	23 23	23 38	23 53		
Stoke Newington	d	20 10	20 25	20 40	20 55	21 10	21 25	21 40	21 55	22 10	22 25	22 40	22 55	23 10	23 25	23 40	23 55		
Rectory Road	d	20 11	20 26	20 41	20 56	21 11	21 26	21 41	21 56	22 11	22 26	22 41	22 56	23 11	23 26	23 41	23 56		
Hackney Downs	d	20 14	20 29	20 44	20 59	21 14	21 29	21 44	21 59	22 14	22 29	22 44	22 59	23 14	23 29	23 44	23 59		00 16
London Fields	d	20 16	20 31	20 46	21 01	21 16	21 31	21 46	22 01	22 16	22 31	22 46	23 01	23 16	23 31	23 46	00 01		
Cambridge Heath	d	20 18	20 33	20 48	21 03	21 18	21 33	21 48	22 03	22 18	22 33	22 48	23 03	23 18	23 33	23 48	00 03		
Bethnal Green	d	20 20	20 35	20 50	21 05	21 20	21 35	21 50	22 05	22 20	22 35	22 50	23 05	23 20	23 35	23 50	00 05		
London Liverpool Street 15	⊖ a	20 25	20 40	20 55	21 10	21 25	21 40	21 55	22 10	22 25	22 40	22 55	23 10	23 25	23 40	23 55	00 10	00 18	00 25

For general notes see front of timetable
For details of catering facilities see Directory of Train Operators

A From Hertford East (Table 22)

Table 21

Cheshunt (via Seven Sisters) and Enfield Town → London

Network diagram - see first page of Table 20

Saturdays

		LE	LE 1	LE 1	LE 1	LE 1	LE 1 A	LE	LE	LE	LE	LE	LE		LE	LE	LE	LE	LE	LE
Cheshunt	d	23p31	23p51		23p58		05 16	06 01		06 31		07 01			22 31		23 01		23 31	
Theobalds Grove	d	23p34					05 19	06 04		06 34		07 04			22 34		23 04		23 34	
Turkey Street	d	23p36					05 21	06 06		06 36		07 06			22 36		23 06		23 36	
Southbury	d	23p39					05 24	06 09		06 39		07 09		and at	22 39		23 09		23 39	
Enfield Town	d								06 22		06 52		07 22	the same		22 52		23 22		23 52
Bush Hill Park	d								06 25		06 55		07 25			22 55		23 25		23 55
Edmonton Green	d	23p43					05 28	06 13	06 28	06 43	06 58	07 13	07 28	minutes	22 43	22 58	23 13	23 28	23 43	23 58
Silver Street	d	23p45					05 30	06 15	06 30	06 45	07 00	07 15	07 30		22 45	23 00	23 15	23 30	23 45	23 59
White Hart Lane	d	23p47					05 32	06 17	06 32	06 47	07 02	07 17	07 32	past	22 47	23 02	23 17	23 32	23 47	00 02
Bruce Grove	d	23p49					05 34	06 19	06 34	06 49	07 04	07 19	07 34	each	22 49	23 04	23 19	23 34	23 49	00 04
Seven Sisters	⊖ d	23p51	00 04	00 07	00 11	00 21	05 36	06 21	06 36	06 51	07 06	07 21	07 36	hour until	22 51	23 06	23 21	23 36	23 51	00 06
Stamford Hill	d	23p53					05 38	06 23	06 38	06 53	07 08	07 23	07 38		22 53	23 08	23 23	23 38	23 53	00 08
Stoke Newington	d	23p55					05 40	06 25	06 40	06 55	07 10	07 25	07 40		22 55	23 10	23 25	23 40	23 55	00 10
Rectory Road	d	23p56					05 41	06 26	06 41	06 56	07 11	07 26	07 41		22 56	23 11	23 26	23 41	23 56	00 11
Hackney Downs	d	23p59			00 16		05 45	06 29	06 44	06 59	07 14	07 29	07 44		22 59	23 14	23 29	23 44	23 59	00 14
London Fields	d	00 01						06 31	06 46	07 01	07 16	07 31	07 46		23 01	23 16	23 31	23 46	00 01	00 16
Cambridge Heath	d	00 03						06 33	06 48	07 03	07 18	07 33	07 48		23 03	23 18	23 33	23 48	00 03	00 18
Bethnal Green	d	00 05					05 49	06 35	06 50	07 05	07 20	07 35	07 50		23 05	23 20	23 35	23 50	00 05	00 20
London Liverpool Street 15	⊖ a	00 10	00 18	00 22	00 25	00 36	05 54	06 40	06 55	07 10	07 25	07 40	07 55		23 10	23 25	23 40	23 55	00 10	00 25

Sundays

		LE	LE	LE	LE B	LE	LE B	LE	LE B	LE	LE B		LE	LE B	LE
Cheshunt	d	23p31			08 15		08 45		09 15		09 45			18 15	
Theobalds Grove	d	23p34			08 18		08 48		09 18		09 48			18 18	
Turkey Street	d	23p36			08 21		08 51		09 21		09 51			18 21	
Southbury	d	23p39			08 24		08 54		09 24		09 54	and at		18 24	
Enfield Town	d		23p52	07 57		08 27		08 57		09 27		the same	17 57		18 27
Bush Hill Park	d		23p55	08 00		08 30		09 00		09 30			18 00		18 30
Edmonton Green	d	23p43	23p58	08 03	08 27	08 33	08 57	09 03	09 27	09 33	09 57	minutes	18 03	18 27	18 33
Silver Street	d	23p45	23p59	08 05		08 35		09 05		09 35			18 05		18 35
White Hart Lane	d	23p47	00 02	08 07		08 37		09 07		09 37		past	18 07		18 37
Bruce Grove	d	23p49	00 04	08 09		08 39		09 09		09 39			18 09		18 39
Seven Sisters	⊖ d	23p51	00 06	08 11	08 33	08 41	09 03	09 11	09 33	09 41	10 03	each	18 11	18 33	18 41
Stamford Hill	d	23p53	00 08	08 13		08 43		09 13		09 43		hour until	18 13		18 43
Stoke Newington	d	23p55	00 10	08 15		08 45		09 15		09 45			18 15		18 45
Rectory Road	d	23p56	00 11	08 16		08 46		09 16		09 46			18 16		18 46
Hackney Downs	d	23p59	00 14	08 19	08 39	08 49	09 09	09 19	09 39	09 49	10 09		18 19	18 39	18 49
London Fields	d	00 01	00 16					09 21		09 51			18 21		18 51
Cambridge Heath	d	00 03	00 18					09 23		09 53			18 23		18 53
Bethnal Green	d	00 05	00 20					09 25		09 55			18 25		18 55
London Liverpool Street 15	⊖ a	00 10	00 25	08 30	08 48	09 00	09 18	09 30	09 48	10 00	10 18		18 30	18 48	19 00

		LE B	LE	LE B	LE	LE B	LE	LE B	LE	LE B	LE	LE B
Cheshunt	d	18 45		19 31		20 31		21 31		22 31		23 31
Theobalds Grove	d	18 48		19 34		20 34		21 34		22 34		23 34
Turkey Street	d	18 51		19 36		20 36		21 36		22 36		23 36
Southbury	d	18 54		19 39		20 39		21 39		22 39		23 39
Enfield Town	d		19 08		20 08		21 08		22 08		23 08	
Bush Hill Park	d		19 11		20 11		21 11		22 11		23 11	
Edmonton Green	d	18 57	19 13	19 43	20 13	20 43	21 13	21 43	22 13	22 43	23 13	23 43
Silver Street	d		19 15	19 45	20 15	20 45	21 15	21 45	22 15	22 45	23 15	23 45
White Hart Lane	d		19 17	19 47	20 17	20 47	21 17	21 47	22 17	22 47	23 17	23 47
Bruce Grove	d		19 19	19 49	20 19	20 49	21 19	21 49	22 19	22 49	23 19	23 49
Seven Sisters	⊖ d	19 03	19 21	19 51	20 21	20 51	21 21	21 51	22 21	22 51	23 21	23 51
Stamford Hill	d		19 23	19 53	20 23	20 53	21 23	21 53	22 23	22 53	23 23	23 53
Stoke Newington	d		19 25	19 55	20 25	20 55	21 25	21 55	22 25	22 55	23 25	23 55
Rectory Road	d		19 27	19 56	20 27	20 56	21 27	21 56	22 27	22 56	23 27	23 56
Hackney Downs	d	19 09	19 30	19 59	20 30	20 59	21 30	21 59	22 30	22 59	23 30	23 59
London Fields	d		19 32	20 01	20 32	21 01	21 32	22 01	22 32	23 01	23 32	00 01
Cambridge Heath	d		19 34	20 03	20 34	21 03	21 34	22 03	22 34	23 03	23 34	00 03
Bethnal Green	d		19 36	20 05	20 36	21 05	21 36	22 05	22 36	23 05	23 36	00 05
London Liverpool Street 15	⊖ a	19 18	19 41	20 11	20 41	21 11	21 41	22 11	22 41	23 11	23 41	00 11

For general notes see front of timetable
For details of catering facilities see
Directory of Train Operators

A From Cambridge (Table 22)
B From Hertford East (Table 22)

London → Broxbourne, Hertford East, Bishops Stortford, Stansted Airport and Cambridge

Network diagram - see first page of Table 20

Miles	Miles			LE MO [1]	LE MX [1]	LE MO	LE MO [1]	LE MX [1]	LE MX [1]	LE MO [1]	LE MO	LE MX [1]	LE MX	LE [1]	LE MX		LE MO [1]	LE MFO [1]	XC [1] ◇ 🛒	LE [1]	LE [1]	LE [1]	LE	XC [1] ◇ 🛒	LE [1]
0	—	**London Liverpool Street** [15]	Θ d		22p58	23p00	23p25	23p25	23p28	23p28		23p40	23p45	23p58			03 40	04 10		04 40	05 10				05 25
1¼	—	Bethnal Green	d			23p03							23p48		←										
3	—	Hackney Downs	d			23p09						23p46	23p54		23p54										
—	0	Stratford [7]	Θ d	22p45									→												
4	—	Clapton	d									23p49													
—	6¾	Seven Sisters	Θ d			23p17									00 02										
6	—	Tottenham Hale	Θ d	22p55	23p10		23p37	23b37	23p40	23p40		23p53		00 10						04u52	05u22				05u37
7	—	Northumberland Park	d									23p55													
7¾	—	Angel Road	d																						
10	—	Ponders End	d	22p59						23p44		23p59													
10¾	—	Brimsdown	d	23p02						23p47		00 02													
11¾	—	Enfield Lock	d	23p04						23p49		00 04													
12¾	—	Waltham Cross	d	23p07						23p52		00 07													
14	—	Cheshunt	d	23p09	23p18	23p37			23p48	23p54		00 09		00 18	00 22										
17¼	—	Broxbourne [3]	a	23p14	23p22	23p42			23p52	23p59	←	00 14		00 22	00 27										
—	0		d	23p19	23p22	00 02			23p52	23p59	00 02	00 14		00 22	00 27								05 40		
—	1¾	Rye House	d			→					00 05	00 17											05 43		
—	3	St Margarets (Herts)	d								00 08	00 20											05 46		
—	5	Ware	d								00 12	00 24											05 50		
—	7	**Hertford East**	a								00 19	00 31											05 56		
20	—	Roydon	d	23p24	23p26									00 26											
22¾	—	Harlow Town	d	23p28	23p30		23p52	23p54	23p58	00 05				00 30	00 34					05 10	05 37				05 55
24½	—	Harlow Mill	d	23p31	23p33									00 33											
26¾	—	Sawbridgeworth	d	23p34	23p37				00 03	00 10				00 37							05 42				
30¼	—	**Bishops Stortford**	a	23p41	23p44		00 02	00 04	00 10	00 17				00 44	00 47					05 20	05 49				06 05
—	—		d	23p42	23p44		00 03	00 04	00 11											05 20	05 50	05 55			06 05
33¾	0	Stansted Mountfitchet	d	23p46	23p48				00 15											05 24		05 59			
—	3¾	**Stansted Airport**	✈ a				00 12	00 13									04 30	05 00		05 39	05 59				06 15
—	—		✈ d																05 21					06 06	
35½	8¼	Elsenham	d	23p50	23p52				00 19													06 03			
40	—	Newport (Essex)	d	23p55	23p57				00 24													06 08			
41¾	—	Audley End	d	23p58	23p59				00 27										05 33			06 11		06 23	
45¾	—	Great Chesterford	d	00 03	00 05				00 32													06 16			
49	—	Whittlesford Parkway	d	00 08	00 10				00 37													06 21			
52½	—	Shelford	d	00 12	00 14				00 41													06 25			
55¾	—	**Cambridge**	a	00 19	00 21				00 48										05 53			06 32		06 38	

		LE [1]	LE [1]	LE	LE [1]	LE [1]		LE [1]	LE [1]	LE [1]	LE [1]	LE [1]	LE [1]	XC [1] ◇ 🛒	LE [1]	LE [1]	LE	LE [1]	LE [1]		LE [1] 🛒	LE [1]	LE	LE [1] 🛒	LE [1]
London Liverpool Street [15]	Θ d	05 28	05 40	05 42	05 52	05 55		05 58		06 10	06 12	06 25	06 28		06 40		06 42	06 55	06 58		07 10		07 12	07 25	07 28
Bethnal Green	d																								
Hackney Downs	d			05 49					←		06 18						06 49						07 19		
Stratford [7]	Θ d				06 03				06 03													07 02			
Clapton	d				→																				
Seven Sisters	Θ d																								
Tottenham Hale	Θ d	05 40	05u52	05 55		06u07		06 10	06 15	06u22	06 25	06u37	06 40		06u52		06 55	07u07	07 10		07u22	07 13	07 25	07u37	07 40
Northumberland Park	d								06 17													07 15			
Angel Road	d								06 19													07 17			
Ponders End	d			05 59							06 29						06 59						07 29		
Brimsdown	d			06 02							06 32						07 02						07 32		
Enfield Lock	d			06 04					06 24		06 34						07 04					07 22	07 34		
Waltham Cross	d			06 07							06 37						07 07						07 37		
Cheshunt	d	05 48		06 09				06 18	06 28		06 39		06 48				07 09		07 18			07 26	07 39		07 48
Broxbourne [3]	a	05 53		06 14				06 22	06 32		06 44		06 52				07 14		07 22			07 30	07 44		07 52
	d	05 53		06 14				06 24	06 36		06 44		06 54				07 14		07 22			07 34	07 44		07 52
Rye House	d								06 39		06 47						07 17						07 47		
St Margarets (Herts)	d								06 42		06 50						07 20						07 50		
Ware	d								06 46		06 54						07 24						07 54		
Hertford East	a			06 27					06 53		07 01					←	07 31						08 01		
Roydon	d	05 57						06 28					06 58			06 58			07 26						07 56
Harlow Town	d	06 01				06 25		06 32				06 55	→			07c08		07 24	07 30			07 40		07 54	08 00
Harlow Mill	d	06 04						06 35								07 11			07 33						08 03
Sawbridgeworth	d	06 07						06 38								07 14			07 37						08 07
Bishops Stortford	a	06 14	06 18					06 45		06 49					07 15	07 21			07 44		07 47	07 51			08 14
	d	06 14	06 18					06 45		06 49					07 18	07 26			07 44		07 48				08 14
Stansted Mountfitchet	d	06 19	06 23					06 50							07 23	07 30			07 48						08 18
Stansted Airport	✈ a		06 29			06 43				06 59		07 13			07 30			07 42			07 59			08 13	
	✈ d													07 21											
Elsenham	d	06 22						06 53								07 34			07 52						08 22
Newport (Essex)	d	06 28						06 59								07 39			07 57						08 27
Audley End	d	06 31						07 02						07 37		07 42			08 00						08 30
Great Chesterford	d	06 36						07 07								07 47			08 05						08 35
Whittlesford Parkway	d	06 40						07 11								07 52			08 10						08 40
Shelford	d	06 45						07 16								07 56			08 14						08 44
Cambridge	a	06 58						07 25						07 57		08 06			08 23						08 55

For general notes see front of timetable
For details of catering facilities see Directory of Train Operators

b Previous night.
Stops to pick up only

c Arr. 0702

London → Broxbourne, Hertford East, Bishops Stortford, Stansted Airport and Cambridge

Network diagram - see first page of Table 20

	LE 1	XC 1◇ 🛒	LE 1 🛒	LE 1	LE 1 🛒	LE 1	LE 1 🛒	LE 1	LE 1		LE 1	LE 1 🛒	LE 1	XC 1◇ 🛒	LE 1 🛒	LE	LE 1 🛒	LE 1	LE 1 🛒	LE 1	LE	LE 1 🛒		LE 1
London Liverpool Street 15 ⊖ d			07 40	07 42	07 55	07 58	08 10		08 12			08 25	08 28		08 40	08 42	08 55	08 58	09 10		09 12	09 25		09 28
Bethnal Green d																								
Hackney Downs d				07 48					08 18							08 49					09 19			
Stratford 7 ⊖ d	07 33							08 03			08 20									08 58				
Clapton d																								
Seven Sisters ⊖ d																								
Tottenham Hale ⊖ d	07 43		07u52	07 55	08u07	08 10	08u22	08 13	08 25		08 29	08u37	08 40		08u52	08 55	09u07	09 10	09u22	09 14	09 25	09u37		09 40
Northumberland Park d	07 45							08 15			08 32									09 16				
Angel Road d	07 47							08 17			08 34									09 18				
Ponders End d				07 59					08 29							08 59					09 29			
Brimsdown d				08 02					08 32							09 02					09 32			
Enfield Lock d	07 52			08 04				08 22	08 34		08 39					09 04				09 23	09 34			
Waltham Cross d				08 07					08 37							09 07					09 37			
Cheshunt d	07 56			08 09		08 18		08 26	08 39		08 42		08 48			09 09		09 18		09 27	09 39			09 48
Broxbourne 3 a	08 00			08 14		08 22		08 30	08 44		08 47		08 52			09 14		09 22		09 31	09 44			09 52
d				08 14		08 22		08 34	08 44				08 52			09 14		09 22		09 35	09 44			09 52
Rye House d				08 17					08 47							09 17					09 47			
St Margarets (Herts) d				08 20					08 50							09 20					09 50			
Ware d				08 24					08 54							09 24					09 54			
Hertford East a				08 31					09 01							09 31					10 01			
Roydon d						08 26												09 26						
Harlow Town d					08 24	08 30		08 40				08 54	08 58				09 24	09 30		09 41		09 54		09 58
Harlow Mill d						08 33												09 33						
Sawbridgeworth d						08 37							09 03					09 37						10 03
Bishops Stortford a			08 18			08 44	08 47	08 52					09 11		09 16			09 44	09 47	09 52				10 10
d			08 18			08 44	08 48						09 11		09 18			09 44	09 48					10 11
Stansted Mountfitchet d			08 23			08 48									09 23			09 48						
Stansted Airport ✈ a			08 30		08 42		09 00					09 12			09 30		09 42		09 57			10 12		
✈ d		08 21												09 21										
Elsenham d						08 52												09 52						
Newport (Essex) d						08 57												09 57						
Audley End d		08 37				09 00							09 23	09 37				10 00						10 23
Great Chesterford d						09 05												10 05						
Whittlesford Parkway d						09 10							09 30					10 10						10 30
Shelford d						09 14												10 14						
Cambridge a		08 57				09 24							09 42	09 58				10 24						10 41

	XC 1◇ 🛒	LE 1 🛒	LE 1	LE 1	LE 1 🛒	LE 1	LE 1 🛒	LE 1	LE 1	LE 1 🛒	LE 1	XC 1◇ 🛒		LE 1 🛒	LE 1	LE 1	LE 1 🛒	LE 1	LE 1 🛒	LE 1	LE 1 🛒	LE 1	XC 1◇ 🛒	LE 1 🛒
London Liverpool Street 15 ⊖ d		09 40		09 42	09 55	09 58	10 10		10 12	10 25	10 28			10 40		10 42	10 55	10 58	11 10	11 12	11 25	11 28		11 40
Bethnal Green d																								
Hackney Downs d				09 48					10 18							10 48				11 18				
Stratford 7 ⊖ d			09 25					09 55							10 33									
Clapton d																								
Seven Sisters ⊖ d																								
Tottenham Hale ⊖ d		09u52	09 44	09 55	10u07	10 10	10u22	10 13	10 25	10u37	10 40			10u52	10 43	10 55	11u07	11 10	11u22	11 25	11u37	11 40		11u52
Northumberland Park d			09 46					10 15							10 45									
Angel Road d			09 48																					
Ponders End d				09 59					10 29							10 59				11 29				
Brimsdown d				10 02					10 32							11 02				11 32				
Enfield Lock d			09 53	10 04				10 21	10 34						10 51	11 04				11 34				
Waltham Cross d				10 07					10 37							11 07				11 37				
Cheshunt d			09 57	10 09		10 18		10 25	10 39		10 48				10 55	11 09		11 18		11 39		11 48		
Broxbourne 3 a			10 01	10 14		10 22		10 29	10 44		10 52				10 59	11 14		11 22		11 44		11 52		
d			10 05	10 14		10 22		10 33	10 44		10 52				11 03	11 14		11 22		11 44		11 52		
Rye House d				10 17					10 47							11 17				11 47				
St Margarets (Herts) d				10 20					10 50							11 20				11 50				
Ware d				10 24					10 54							11 24				11 54				
Hertford East a				10 31					11 01							11 31				12 01				
Roydon d			10 09			10 26									11 08			11 26						
Harlow Town d			10 13		10 24	10 30		10 40		10 54	10 58				11 12		11 24	11 30			11 54	11 58		
Harlow Mill d			10 16			10 33									11 15			11 33						
Sawbridgeworth d			10 20			10 37					11 03				11 18			11 37				12 03		
Bishops Stortford a		10 15	10 27			10 44	10 47	10 51			11 10			11 15	11 25			11 44	11 47			12 10		12 15
d		10 15	10 27			10 44	10 48				11 11			11 15	11 26			11 44	11 48			12 11		12 15
Stansted Mountfitchet d			10 31			10 48									11 30			11 48						
Stansted Airport ✈ a		10 30	10 39		10 42		10 57			11 12				11 25	11 39		11 42		11 57		12 12			12 25
✈ d	10 20											11 25											12 25	
Elsenham d						10 52												11 52						
Newport (Essex) d						10 57												11 57						
Audley End d	10 36					11 00					11 23	11 37						12 00				12 23	12 37	
Great Chesterford d						11 05												12 05						
Whittlesford Parkway d						11 10					11 30							12 10				12 30		
Shelford d						11 14												12 14						
Cambridge a	10 58					11 21					11 40	11 58						12 21				12 40	12 58	

For general notes see front of timetable
For details of catering facilities see Directory of Train Operators

London → Broxbourne, Hertford East, Bishops Stortford, Stansted Airport and Cambridge

Network diagram - see first page of Table 20

		LE	LE	LE		LE	LE	LE	LE	LE	XC	LE	LE	LE	LE	LE	LE		LE	LE	LE	XC	LE	LE	LE
		1	1	1		1	1	1	1	1	1 ◇	1	1	1	1	1	1		1	1	1	1 ◇	1	1	1
				🍴			🍴		🍴		🍴	🍴			🍴		🍴			🍴		🍴	🍴		
London Liverpool Street 15	⊖ d		11 42	11 55		11 58	12 10	12 12	12 25	12 28		12 40		12 42	12 55	12 58	13 10		13 12	13 25	13 28		13 40		13 42
Bethnal Green	d																								
Hackney Downs	d		11 48					12 18						12 48					13 18						13 48
Stratford 7	⊖ ⛴ d	11 33											12 33											13 33	
Clapton	d																								
Seven Sisters	⊖ d																								
Tottenham Hale	⊖ d	11 43	11 55	12u07		12 10	12u22	12 25	12u37	12 40		12u52	12 43	12 55	13u07	13 10	13u22		13 25	13u37	13 40		13u52	13 43	13 55
Northumberland Park	d	11 45											12 45											13 45	
Angel Road	d																								
Ponders End	d		11 59					12 29						12 59					13 29						13 59
Brimsdown	d		12 02					12 32						13 02					13 32						14 02
Enfield Lock	d	11 51	12 04					12 34					12 51	13 04					13 34					13 51	14 04
Waltham Cross	d		12 07					12 37						13 07					13 37						14 07
Cheshunt	d	11 55	12 09			12 18		12 39		12 48			12 55	13 09		13 18			13 39		13 48			13 55	14 09
Broxbourne 3	a	11 59	12 14			12 22		12 44		12 52			12 59	13 14		13 22			13 44		13 52			13 59	14 14
	d	12 03	12 14			12 22		12 44		12 52			13 03	13 14		13 22			13 44		13 52			14 03	14 14
Rye House	d		12 17					12 47						13 17					13 47						14 17
St Margarets (Herts)	d		12 20					12 50						13 20					13 50						14 20
Ware	d		12 24					12 54						13 24					13 54						14 24
Hertford East	a		12 31					13 01						13 31					14 01						14 31
Roydon	d	12 08				12 26							13 08			13 26								14 08	
Harlow Town	d	12 12		12 24		12 30			12 54	12 58			13 12		13 24	13 30				13 54	13 58			14 12	
Harlow Mill	d	12 15				12 33							13 15			13 33								14 15	
Sawbridgeworth	d	12 18				12 37				13 03			13 18			13 37					14 03			14 18	
Bishops Stortford	a	12 25				12 44	12 47			13 10		13 15	13 25			13 44	13 47				14 10		14 15	14 25	
	d	12 26				12 44	12 48			13 11		13 15	13 26			13 44	13 48				14 11		14 15	14 26	
Stansted Mountfitchet	d	12 30				12 48							13 30			13 48								14 30	
Stansted Airport	✈ a	12 39		12 42			12 57		13 12			13 25	13 39		13 42		13 57			14 12			14 25	14 39	
	✈ d										13 25											14 25			
Elsenham	d					12 52										13 52									
Newport (Essex)	d					12 57										13 57									
Audley End	d					13 00				13 23	13 37					14 00					14 23	14 37			
Great Chesterford	d					13 05										14 05									
Whittlesford Parkway	d					13 10				13 30						14 10					14 30				
Shelford	d					13 14										14 14									
Cambridge	a					13 21				13 40	13 58					14 21					14 40	14 58			

		LE	LE	LE	LE	LE	LE	XC		LE	LE	LE	LE	LE	LE	LE	LE	LE	XC	LE	LE		LE	LE	LE
		1	1	1	1	1	1	1 ◇		1	1	1	1	1	1	1	1	1	1 ◇	1	1		1	1	1
																									A
		🍴		🍴		🍴		🍴		🍴			🍴		🍴		🍴		🍴	🍴				🍴	
London Liverpool Street 15	⊖ d	13 55	13 58	14 10	14 12	14 25	14 28			14 40		14 42	14 55	14 58	15 10	15 12	15 25	15 28		15 40			15 42	15 55	15 58
Bethnal Green	d																								
Hackney Downs	d				14 18							14 48				15 18							15 48		
Stratford 7	⊖ ⛴ d										14 33										15 33				
Clapton	d																								
Seven Sisters	⊖ d																								
Tottenham Hale	⊖ d	14u07	14 10	14u22	14 25	14u37	14 40			14u52	14 43	14 55	15u07	15 10	15u22	15 25	15u37	15 40		15u52	15 43		15 55	16u07	16 10
Northumberland Park	d										14 45										15 45				
Angel Road	d																				15 47				
Ponders End	d				14 29							14 59				15 29							15 59		
Brimsdown	d				14 32							15 02				15 32							16 02		
Enfield Lock	d				14 34						14 51	15 04				15 34					15 52		16 04		
Waltham Cross	d				14 37							15 07				15 37							16 07		
Cheshunt	d		14 18		14 39		14 48				14 55	15 09		15 18		15 39		15 48			15 56		16 09		16 18
Broxbourne 3	a		14 22		14 44		14 52				14 59	15 14		15 22		15 44		15 52			16 00		16 14		16 22
	d		14 22		14 44		14 52				15 03	15 14		15 22		15 44		15 52			16 04		16 14		16 22
Rye House	d				14 47							15 17				15 47							16 17		
St Margarets (Herts)	d				14 50							15 20				15 50							16 20		
Ware	d				14 54							15 24				15 54							16 24		
Hertford East	a				15 01							15 31				16 01							16 31		
Roydon	d		14 26								15 08			15 26							16 08				16 26
Harlow Town	d	14 24	14 30			14 54	14 58				15 12		15 24	15 30			15 54	15 58			16 12			16 24	16 30
Harlow Mill	d		14 33								15 15			15 33							16 15				16 33
Sawbridgeworth	d		14 37				15 03				15 18			15 37				16 03			16 19				16 37
Bishops Stortford	a		14 44	14 47			15 10			15 15	15 25			15 44	15 47			16 10		16 15	16 26				16 44
	d		14 44	14 48			15 11			15 15	15 26			15 44	15 48			16 11		16 15	16 26				16 44
Stansted Mountfitchet	d		14 48								15 30			15 48				16 15			16 30				16 48
Stansted Airport	✈ a	14 42		14 57		15 12				15 29	15 39		15 42		15 59		16 12			16 25	16 39			16 42	
	✈ d							15 20											16 25						
Elsenham	d		14 52											15 52				16 19							16 52
Newport (Essex)	d		14 57											15 58				16 24							16 57
Audley End	d		15 00				15 23	15 37						16 02				16 27	16 37						17 00
Great Chesterford	d		15 05											16 07				16 32							17 05
Whittlesford Parkway	d		15 10				15 30							16 12				16 37							17 10
Shelford	d		15 14											16 16				16 41							17 14
Cambridge	a		15 21				15 40	15 58						16 28				16 49	16 58						17 21

For general notes see front of timetable
For details of catering facilities see Directory of Train Operators

A To Ely (Table 17)

London → Broxbourne, Hertford East, Bishops Stortford, Stansted Airport and Cambridge

Network diagram - see first page of Table 20

		LE [1]	LE	LE [1]	LE [1]	LE	XC [1] ◊	LE [1]	LE [1]	LE	LE [1]	LE [1] A		LE	LE [1]	LE [1]	LE	LE [1]	LE [1]	LE	XC [1] ◊	LE [1]	LE [1]	LE	LE [1]
		🛒		🛒			🛒	🛒			🛒				🛒			🛒			🛒	🛒			🛒
London Liverpool Street [15] ⊖	d	16 10	16 12	16 25	16 28			16 40	16 43	16 45	16 55	16 58			17 10	17 13	17 15	17 25	17 28			17 40	17 43	17 45	17 55
Bethnal Green	d																								
Hackney Downs	d		16 18							16 51							17 21							17 51	
Stratford [7] ⊖ ⛴	d					16 32								17 02						17 32					
Clapton	d																								
Seven Sisters ⊖	d																								
Tottenham Hale ⊖	d	16u22	16 25	16u37	16 40	16 43		16u52	16 55	16 58	17u07	17 10		17 13	17u22	17 25	17 28	17u37	17 40	17 43		17u52	17 55	17 58	18u07
Northumberland Park	d					16 45								17 15						17 45					
Angel Road	d					16 47								17 17						17 47					
Ponders End	d		16 29							17 02							17 32							18 02	
Brimsdown	d		16 32							17 05							17 35							18 05	
Enfield Lock	d		16 34			16 52				17 07				17 22			17 37			17 52				18 07	
Waltham Cross	d		16 37			16 55				17 10				17 25			17 40			17 55				18 10	
Cheshunt	d		16 39			16 57			17 04	17 12				17 27		17 34	17 42			17 57			18 04	18 12	
Broxbourne [3]	a		16 44		16 51	17 04			17 08	17 17		17 24		17 32		17 39	17 47		17 54	18 04			18 08	18 17	
	d		16 44		16 52				17 09	17 17		17 25		17 35		17 39	17 50		17 54				18 09	18 17	
Rye House	d		16 48							17 21				17 39			17 54							18 21	
St Margarets (Herts)	d		16 51							17 24				17 42			17 57							18 24	
Ware	d		16 55							17 28				17 48			18 01							18 28	
Hertford East	a		17 03							17 36				17 56			18 09							18 36	
Roydon	d								17 13							17 43							18 13		
Harlow Town	d			16 54	16 59				17 18		17 27	17 32				17 48		17 54				18 10	18 18		18 27
Harlow Mill	d								17 21							17 51							18 21		
Sawbridgeworth	d				17 04				17 24							17 54			18 04				18 24		
Bishops Stortford	a	16 47			17 11			17 17	17 31			17 42			17 47	18 01		18 05	18 11			18 20	18 31		18 36
	d	16 48			17 11			17 18	17 32			17 42			17 48	18 02		18 06	18 11			18 20	18 32		18 36
Stansted Mountfitchet	d				17 15				17 36						17 52	18 06							18 36		
Stansted Airport ✈	a	17 01		17 14				17 32			17 47				18 01			18 17				18 32			18 56
✈	d						17 18														18 21				
Elsenham	d								17 40							18 10							18 40		
Newport (Essex)	d								17 45							18 15							18 45		
Audley End	d				17 25		17 33		17 49			17 55				18 19			18 24		18 37		18 49		
Great Chesterford	d								17 54							18 24							18 54		
Whittlesford Parkway	d				17 33				17 58			18 03				18 28			18 32				18 58		
Shelford	d								18 03							18 33							19 03		
Cambridge	a				17 44		17 49		18 12			18 13				18 42			18 45		18 58		19 12		

		LE [1] A	LE		LE [1]	LE [1]	LE	LE [1]	LE [1]	XC [1] ◊	LE [1]	LE	LE [1]	LE	LE [1]	LE [1] A		LE [1]	LE	LE [1]	LE [1]	LE [1]	LE [1]	XC [1] ◊	LE [1]
					🛒			🛒		🛒	🛒				🛒			🛒				🛒		🛒	🛒
London Liverpool Street [15] ⊖	d	17 58			18 10	18 13	18 15	18 25	18 28		18 40		18 43	18 45	18 55	18 58		19 10		19 13	19 15	19 25	19 28		19 40
Bethnal Green	d																								
Hackney Downs	d						18 21							18 51							19 21				
Stratford [7] ⊖ ⛴	d		18 02									18 32							19 02						
Clapton	d																								
Seven Sisters ⊖	d																								
Tottenham Hale ⊖	d	18 10	18 13		18u22	18 25	18 28	18u37	18 40		18u52	18 43	18 55	18 58	19u07	19 10		19u22	19 13	19 25	19 28	19u37	19 40		19u52
Northumberland Park	d		18 15									18 45							19 15						
Angel Road	d		18 17									18 47							19 17						
Ponders End	d						18 32							19 02							19 32				
Brimsdown	d						18 35							19 05							19 35				
Enfield Lock	d		18 22				18 37					18 52		19 07					19 22		19 37				
Waltham Cross	d		18 25				18 40					18 55		19 10					19 25		19 40				
Cheshunt	d		18 27			18 34	18 42					18 57	19 04	19 12					19 27	19 34	19 42		19 49		
Broxbourne [3]	a	18 24	18 32			18 39	18 47		18 54			19 02	19 09	19 17		19 24			19 32	19 39	19 47		19 54		
	d	18 25	18 35			18 39	18 47		18 55			19 05	19 09	19 17		19 25			19 35	19 39	19 47		19 54		
Rye House	d		18 39				18 51							19 21							19 50				
St Margarets (Herts)	d		18 42				18 54							19 24							19 53				
Ware	d		18 48				18 58							19 28							19 57				
Hertford East	a		18 56				19 06							19 36							20 04				
Roydon	d					18 43						19 10	19 13							19 43			19 59		
Harlow Town	d					18 48		18 57	19 02			19 14	19 18		19 27	19 32			19 42	19 48		19 57	20 03		
Harlow Mill	d					18 51						19 17	19 21							19 51			20 06		
Sawbridgeworth	d	18 35				18 54			19 07			19 20	19 24						19 47	19 54			20 09		
Bishops Stortford	a	18 42			18 47	19 01			19 14		19 18	19 27	19 31			19 42		19 47	19 56	20 01			20 16		20 20
	d	18 42			18 48	19 02			19 14		19 18	19 28	19 32			19 42		19 47		20 02			20 17		20 21
Stansted Mountfitchet	d				18 52	19 06					19 23	19 32	19 36							20 06			20 21		
Stansted Airport ✈	a				19 01			19 17			19 32	19 41			19 47			19 57				20 15			20 30
✈	d									19 21														20 21	
Elsenham	d					19 10							19 40							20 10			20 25		
Newport (Essex)	d					19 15							19 45							20 15			20 30		
Audley End	d	18 55				19 19			19 27	19 37			19 49			19 55				20 19			20 33	20 37	
Great Chesterford	d					19 24							19 54							20 24			20 38		
Whittlesford Parkway	d	19 03				19 28			19 35				19 58			20 03				20 28			20 43		
Shelford	d					19 33							20 03							20 33			20 47		
Cambridge	a	19 16				19 42			19 46	19 58			20 13			20 14				20 40			20 56	20 58	

For general notes see front of timetable
For details of catering facilities see Directory of Train Operators

A To Kings Lynn (Table 17)

London → Broxbourne, Hertford East, Bishops Stortford, Stansted Airport and Cambridge

Network diagram - see first page of Table 20

		LE 1	LE 1	LE 1 🚲	LE 1	LE 1 🚲	LE 1		LE 1 🚲	LE 1	XC 1 ◇ 🚲	LE 1 🚲	LE 1	LE 1	LE 1 🚲	LE 1	LE 1 🚲	LE 1	LE 1 🚲	LE 1		XC 1 ◇ 🚲	LE 1 🚲	LE 1	LE 1
London Liverpool Street 15	⊖ d		19 42	19 55	19 58	20 10	20 12		20 25	20 28		20 40		20 42	20 55	20 58	21 10	21 12	21 25	21 28			21 40		21 42
Bethnal Green	d																								
Hackney Downs	d		19 48				20 18							20 48				21 18							21 48
Stratford 7	⊖ ⛴ d	19 33											20 33											21 33	
Clapton	d																								
Seven Sisters	⊖ d																								
Tottenham Hale	⊖ d	19 43	19 55	20u07	20 10	20u22	20 25		20u37	20 40		20u52	20 43	20 55	21u07	21 10	21u22	21 25	21u37	21 40			21u52	21 43	21 55
Northumberland Park	d	19 45											20 45											21 45	
Angel Road	d																								
Ponders End	d		19 59				20 29							20 59				21 29							21 59
Brimsdown	d		20 02				20 32							21 02				21 32							22 02
Enfield Lock	d	19 51	20 04				20 34						20 51	21 04				21 34						21 51	22 04
Waltham Cross	d		20 07				20 37							21 07				21 37							22 07
Cheshunt	d	19 55	20 09		20 18		20 39			20 48			20 55	21 09		21 18		21 39		21 48				21 55	22 09
Broxbourne 3	a	19 59	20 14		20 22		20 44			20 52			20 59	21 14		21 22		21 44		21 52				21 59	22 14
	d	20 03	20 14		20 22		20 44			20 52			21 03	21 14		21 22		21 44		21 52				22 03	22 14
Rye House	d		20 17				20 47							21 17				21 47							22 17
St Margarets (Herts)	d		20 20				20 50							21 20				21 50							22 20
Ware	d		20 24				20 54							21 24				21 54							22 24
Hertford East	a		20 31				21 01							21 31				22 01							22 31
Roydon	d	20 08			20 26								21 08			21 26								22 08	
Harlow Town	d	20 12		20 24	20 30				20 54	20 58			21 12		21 24	21 30			21 54	21 58				22 12	
Harlow Mill	d	20 15			20 33								21 15			21 33								22 15	
Sawbridgeworth	d	20 18			20 37					21 03			21 18			21 37				22 03				22 18	
Bishops Stortford	a	20 25			20 44	20 48				21 10		21 15	21 25			21 44	21 47			22 10			22 15	22 25	
	d	20 26			20 44	20 48				21 11		21 15	21 26			21 44	21 48			22 11			22 15	22 26	
Stansted Mountfitchet	d	20 30			20 48				21 05				21 30			21 48			22 05					22 30	
Stansted Airport	✈ a	20 39		20 42		20 58			21 13			21 25	21 39		21 42		21 57		22 13				22 25	22 39	
	✈ d										21 25											22 25			
Elsenham	d				20 52											21 52									
Newport (Essex)	d				20 57											21 57									
Audley End	d				21 00					21 23	21 37					22 00				22 23		22 37			
Great Chesterford	d				21 05											22 05									
Whittlesford Parkway	d				21 10					21 30						22 10				22 30					
Shelford	d				21 14											22 14									
Cambridge	a				21 22					21 40	21 58					22 21				22 40		22 55			

		LE 1 🚲	LE 1	XC 1 ◇ 🚲	LE 1	LE 1	LE 1	LE 1	LE 1	LE 1	LE 1		LE 1	LE 1	LE 1	LE 1	LE 1	LE 1	LE	LE FX 1	LE FO 1	LE			
London Liverpool Street 15	⊖ d	21 55	21 58		22 10	22 12	22 25	22 28	22 40		22 42		22 55	22 58	23 12	23 25	23 28	23 40	23 45	23 58	23 58	←			
Bethnal Green	d																		23 48						
Hackney Downs	d					22 18					22 48				23 18			23 46	23 54 →			23 54			
Stratford 7	⊖ ⛴ d									22 33															
Clapton	d																	23 49							
Seven Sisters	⊖ d																					00 02			
Tottenham Hale	⊖ d	22u07	22 10		22u22	22 25	22u37	22 40	22u52	22 43	22 55		23u07	23 10	23 25	23u37	23 40	23 53		00 10	00 10				
Northumberland Park	d									22 45								23 55							
Angel Road	d																								
Ponders End	d					22 29					22 59				23 29			23 59							
Brimsdown	d					22 32					23 02				23 32			00 02							
Enfield Lock	d					22 34				22 51	23 04				23 34			00 04							
Waltham Cross	d					22 37					23 07				23 37			00 07							
Cheshunt	d		22 18			22 39		22 48		22 55	23 09			23 18	23 39		23 48	00 09		00 18	00 18	00 22			
Broxbourne 3	a		22 22			22 44		22 52		22 59	23 14			23 22	23 44		23 52	00 14		00 22	00 22	00 27			
	d		22 22			22 44		22 52		23 03	23 14			23 22	23 44		23 52	00 14		00 22	00 22	00 27			
Rye House	d					22 47					23 17				23 47			00 17							
St Margarets (Herts)	d					22 50					23 20				23 50			00 20							
Ware	d					22 54					23 24				23 54			00 24							
Hertford East	a					23 01					23 31				00 01			00 31							
Roydon	d		22 26							23 08				23 26						00 26	00 26				
Harlow Town	d	22 24	22 30				22 54	22 58		23 12			23 24	23 30		23 54	23 58			00 30	00 30	00 34			
Harlow Mill	d		22 33							23 15				23 33						00 33	00 33				
Sawbridgeworth	d		22 37					23 03		23 18				23 37			00 03			00 37	00 37				
Bishops Stortford	a		22 44		22 47			23 10	23 15	23 26				23 44		00 04	00 10			00 44	00 44	00 47			
	d		22 44		22 48			23 11	23 15					23 44		00 04	00 11				00 44				
Stansted Mountfitchet	d		22 48				23 05						23 35	23 48			00 15				00 48				
Stansted Airport	✈ a	22 42			22 57		23 13		23 25				23 43			00 13									
	✈ d			22 57																					
Elsenham	d		22 52											23 52			00 19				00 52				
Newport (Essex)	d		22 57											23 57			00 24				00 57				
Audley End	d		23 00	23 10				23 23						23 59			00 27				01 00				
Great Chesterford	d		23 05											00 05			00 32				01 05				
Whittlesford Parkway	d		23 10					23 30						00 10			00 37				01 10				
Shelford	d		23 14											00 14			00 41								
Cambridge	a		23 22	23 32				23 40						00 21			00 48				01 19				

For general notes see front of timetable
For details of catering facilities see
Directory of Train Operators

London → Broxbourne, Hertford East, Bishops Stortford, Stansted Airport and Cambridge

Network diagram - see first page of Table 20

		LE 1	LE 1	LE 1	LE 1	LE	LE 1	LE	LE 1	XC 1 ◇	LE 1		LE 1	LE 1	LE 1	LE 1	LE 1	XC 1 ◇	LE 1	LE 1	LE 1	LE 1		LE 1	LE 1
																	A								
										bike								bike							
London Liverpool Street 15	⊖ d	22p58	23p25	23p28	23p40	23p45	23p58		04 10		04 40			05 10	05 23	05 25	05 28		05 40		05 42	05 55		05 58	06 10
Bethnal Green	d					23p48		⟵																	
Hackney Downs	d				23p46	23p54		23p54												⟵	05 48				
Stratford 7	⊖ d					⟶									05 33 ⟶		05 37			05 33					
Clapton	d				23p49																				
Seven Sisters	⊖ d							00 02									05a50								
Tottenham Hale	⊖ d	23p10	23b37	23p40	23p53		00 10				04u52			05u22		05u37			05u52	05 43	05 55	06u07		06 10	06u22
Northumberland Park	d				23p55															05 45					
Angel Road	d																								
Ponders End	d				23p59																05 59				
Brimsdown	d				00 02																06 02				
Enfield Lock	d				00 04															05 51	06 04				
Waltham Cross	d				00 07																06 07				
Cheshunt	d	23p18		23p48	00 09		00 18	00 22												05 55	06 09			06 18	
Broxbourne 3	a	23p22		23p52	00 14		00 22	00 27												05 59	06 14			06 22	
	d	23p22		23p52	00 14		00 22	00 27												06 03	06 14			06 22	
Rye House	d				00 17																06 17				
St Margarets (Herts)	d				00 20																06 20				
Ware	d				00 24																06 24				
Hertford East	a				00 31																06 31				
Roydon	d	23p26					00 26													06 08				06 26	
Harlow Town	d	23p30	23p54	23p58			00 30	00 34			05 10			05 37		05 55				06 12		06 24		06 30	
Harlow Mill	d	23p33					00 33													06 15				06 33	
Sawbridgeworth	d	23p37		00 03			00 37							05 42						06 18				06 37	
Bishops Stortford	a	23p44	00 04	00 10			00 44	00 47			05 20			05 49		06 05			06 15	06 25				06 44	06 47
	d	23p44	00 04	00 11			00 44				05 20		05 42	05 50		06 06			06 15	06 26				06 44	06 48
Stansted Mountfitchet	d	23p48		00 15			00 48				05 24		05 46							06 30				06 48	
Stansted Airport	✈ a		00 13						05 00		05 39		05 53	05 59		06 15			06 25	06 39		06 42			06 57
	✈ d									05 25								06 25							
Elsenham	d	23p52		00 19			00 52																	06 52	
Newport (Essex)	d	23p57		00 24			00 57																	06 57	
Audley End	d	23p59		00 27			01 00			05 37								06 37						07 00	
Great Chesterford	d	00 05		00 32			01 05																	07 05	
Whittlesford Parkway	d	00 10		00 37			01 10																	07 10	
Shelford	d	00 14		00 41																				07 14	
Cambridge	a	00 21		00 48			01 19			05 54								06 55						07 21	

		LE 1	LE 1	LE 1	LE 1	XC 1 ◇	LE 1	LE 1	LE 1	LE 1	LE 1		LE 1	LE 1	LE 1	LE 1	XC 1 ◇	LE 1	LE 1	LE 1	LE 1	LE 1		LE 1	LE 1
											B														
						bike							bike		bike		bike	bike			bike			bike	
London Liverpool Street 15	⊖ d	06 12	06 23	06 25	06 28		06 40		06 42	06 55	06 58		07 10	07 12	07 25	07 28		07 40		07 42	07 55	07 58		08 10	08 12
Bethnal Green	d																								
Hackney Downs	d	06 18						⟵	06 48					07 18						07 48					08 18
Stratford 7	⊖ d		06 33 ⟶					06 33											07 33						
Clapton	d																								
Seven Sisters	⊖ d																								
Tottenham Hale	⊖ d	06 25		06u37	06 40		06u52	06 43	06 55	07u07	07 10		07u22	07 25	07u37	07 40		07u52	07 43	07 55	08u07	08 10		08u22	08 25
Northumberland Park	d							06 45											07 45						
Angel Road	d																								
Ponders End	d	06 29							06 59					07 29						07 59					08 29
Brimsdown	d	06 32							07 02					07 32						08 02					08 32
Enfield Lock	d	06 34						06 51	07 04					07 34					07 51	08 04					08 34
Waltham Cross	d	06 37							07 07					07 37						08 07					08 37
Cheshunt	d	06 39			06 48			06 55	07 09		07 18			07 39		07 48			07 55	08 09		08 18			08 39
Broxbourne 3	a	06 44			06 52			06 59	07 14		07 22			07 44		07 52			07 59	08 14		08 22			08 44
	d	06 44			06 52			07 03	07 14		07 22			07 44		07 52			08 03	08 14		08 22			08 44
Rye House	d	06 47							07 17					07 47						08 17					08 47
St Margarets (Herts)	d	06 50							07 20					07 50						08 20					08 50
Ware	d	06 54							07 24					07 54						08 24					08 54
Hertford East	a	07 01							07 31					08 01						08 31					09 01
Roydon	d							07 08			07 26								08 08			08 26			
Harlow Town	d			06 54	06 58			07 12		07 24	07 30				07 54	07 58			08 12		08 24	08 30			
Harlow Mill	d							07 15			07 33								08 15			08 33			
Sawbridgeworth	d				07 03			07 18			07 37					08 03			08 18			08 37			
Bishops Stortford	a				07 10		07 15	07 25			07 44		07 47			08 10		08 15	08 25			08 44		08 47	
	d				07 11		07 15	07 26			07 44		07 48			08 11		08 15	08 26			08 44		08 48	
Stansted Mountfitchet	d			07 05				07 30			07 48				08 05				08 30			08 48			
Stansted Airport	✈ a			07 13			07 25	07 39		07 42			07 57		08 13			08 25	08 39		08 42			08 57	
	✈ d					07 25											08 25								
Elsenham	d										07 52											08 52			
Newport (Essex)	d										07 57											08 57			
Audley End	d				07 23	07 37					08 00					08 23	08 37					09 00			
Great Chesterford	d										08 05											09 05			
Whittlesford Parkway	d				07 30						08 10					08 30						09 10			
Shelford	d				07 35											08 35									
Cambridge	a				07 42	07 55					08 19					08 42	08 58					09 19			

For general notes see front of timetable
For details of catering facilities see Directory of Train Operators

A To Enfield Town (Table 21)
B To Ely (Table 17)

b Previous night.
u Stops to pick up only

London → Broxbourne, Hertford East, Bishops Stortford, Stansted Airport and Cambridge

Network diagram - see first page of Table 20

		LE	LE	XC	LE	LE	LE	LE	LE	LE	LE	LE	LE	XC	LE	LE	LE	LE	LE	LE	LE	LE	LE
		1	1	1 ◇	1	1	1	1	1	1	1	1	1	1 ◇	1	1	1	1	1	1	1	1	1
		🚲		🚲	🚲			🚲		🚲		🚲		🚲	🚲			🚲		🚲		🚲	
London Liverpool Street 15 ⊖	d	08 25	08 28		08 40		08 42	08 55	08 58	09 10	09 12	09 25	09 28		09 40		09 42	09 55	09 58	10 10	10 12	10 25	10 28
Bethnal Green	d																						
Hackney Downs	d						08 48				09 18						09 48				10 18		
Stratford 7 ⊖	d					08 33										09 33							
Clapton	d																						
Seven Sisters ⊖	d																						
Tottenham Hale ⊖	d	08u37	08 40		08u52	08 43	08 55	09u07	09 10	09u22	09 25	09u37	09 40		09u52	09 43	09 55	10u07	10 10	10u22	10 25	10u37	10 40
Northumberland Park	d					08 45										09 45							
Angel Road	d																						
Ponders End	d						08 59				09 29						09 59				10 29		
Brimsdown	d						09 02				09 32						10 02				10 32		
Enfield Lock	d					08 51	09 04				09 34					09 51	10 04				10 34		
Waltham Cross	d						09 07				09 37						10 07				10 37		
Cheshunt	d		08 48			08 55	09 09		09 18		09 39		09 48			09 55	10 09		10 18		10 39		10 48
Broxbourne 3	a		08 52			08 59	09 14		09 22		09 44		09 52			09 59	10 14		10 22		10 44		10 52
	d		08 52			09 03	09 14		09 22		09 44		09 52			10 03	10 14		10 22		10 44		10 52
Rye House	d						09 17				09 47						10 17				10 47		
St Margarets (Herts)	d						09 20				09 50						10 20				10 50		
Ware	d						09 24				09 54						10 24				10 54		
Hertford East	a						09 31				10 01						10 31				11 01		
Roydon	d					09 08			09 26							10 08			10 26				
Harlow Town	d	08 54	08 58			09 12		09 24	09 30			09 54	09 58			10 12		10 24	10 30			10 54	10 58
Harlow Mill	d					09 15			09 33							10 15			10 33				
Sawbridgeworth	d		09 03			09 18			09 37				10 03			10 18			10 37				11 03
Bishops Stortford	a		09 10		09 15	09 25			09 44	09 47			10 10		10 15	10 25			10 44	10 47			11 10
	d		09 11		09 15	09 26			09 44	09 48			10 11		10 15	10 26			10 44	10 48			11 11
Stansted Mountfitchet	d	09 05				09 30			09 48			10 05				10 30			10 48			11 05	
Stansted Airport ✈	a	09 13			09 25	09 39		09 42		09 57		10 13			10 25	10 39		10 42		10 57		11 13	
✈	d			09 25										10 25									
Elsenham	d								09 52										10 52				
Newport (Essex)	d								09 57										10 57				
Audley End	d		09 23	09 37					10 00				10 23	10 37					11 00				11 23
Great Chesterford	d								10 05										11 05				
Whittlesford Parkway	d		09 30						10 10				10 30						11 10				11 30
Shelford	d		09 35						10 14										11 14				
Cambridge	a		09 42	09 58					10 21				10 40	10 58					11 21				11 40

		XC	LE	LE	LE	LE	LE	LE	LE	LE	LE	XC	LE	LE	LE	LE	LE	LE	LE	LE	LE	XC	LE
		1 ◇	1	1	1	1	1	1	1	1	1	1 ◇	1	1	1	1	1	1	1	1	1	1 ◇	1
		🚲	🚲			🚲		🚲		🚲		🚲	🚲			🚲		🚲		🚲		🚲	🚲
London Liverpool Street 15 ⊖	d		10 40		10 42	10 55	10 58	11 10	11 12	11 25	11 28		11 40		11 42	11 55	11 58	12 10	12 12	12 25	12 28		12 40
Bethnal Green	d																						
Hackney Downs	d				10 48				11 18						11 47				12 18				
Stratford 7 ⊖	d			10 33										11 33									
Clapton	d																						
Seven Sisters ⊖	d																						
Tottenham Hale ⊖	d		10u52	10 43	10 55	11u07	11 10	11u22	11 25	11u37	11 40		11u52	11 43	11 55	12u07	12 10	12u22	12 25	12u37	12 40		12u52
Northumberland Park	d			10 45										11 45									
Angel Road	d																						
Ponders End	d				10 59				11 29						11 59				12 29				
Brimsdown	d				11 02				11 32						12 02				12 32				
Enfield Lock	d			10 51	11 04				11 34					11 51	12 04				12 34				
Waltham Cross	d				11 07				11 37						12 07				12 37				
Cheshunt	d			10 55	11 09		11 18		11 39		11 48			11 55	12 09		12 18		12 39		12 48		
Broxbourne 3	a			10 59	11 14		11 22		11 44		11 52			11 59	12 14		12 22		12 44		12 52		
	d			11 03	11 14		11 22		11 44		11 52			12 03	12 14		12 22		12 44		12 52		
Rye House	d				11 17				11 47						12 17				12 47				
St Margarets (Herts)	d				11 20				11 50						12 20				12 50				
Ware	d				11 24				11 54						12 24				12 54				
Hertford East	a				11 31				12 01						12 31				13 01				
Roydon	d			11 08			11 26							12 08			12 26						
Harlow Town	d			11 12		11 24	11 30			11 54	11 58			12 12		12 24	12 30			12 54	12 58		
Harlow Mill	d			11 15			11 33							12 15			12 33						
Sawbridgeworth	d			11 18			11 37				12 03			12 18			12 37				13 03		
Bishops Stortford	a		11 15	11 25			11 44	11 47			12 10		12 15	12 25			12 44	12 47			13 10		13 15
	d		11 15	11 26			11 44	11 48			12 11		12 15	12 26			12 44	12 48			13 11		13 15
Stansted Mountfitchet	d			11 30			11 48			12 05				12 30			12 48			13 05			
Stansted Airport ✈	a		11 25	11 39		11 42		11 57		12 13			12 25	12 39		12 42		12 57		13 13			13 25
✈	d	11 25										12 25										13 25	
Elsenham	d						11 52										12 52						
Newport (Essex)	d						11 57										12 57						
Audley End	d	11 37					12 00				12 23	12 37					13 00				13 23	13 37	
Great Chesterford	d						12 05										13 05						
Whittlesford Parkway	d						12 10				12 30						13 10				13 30		
Shelford	d						12 14										13 14						
Cambridge	a	11 58					12 21				12 40	12 58					13 21				13 40	13 58	

For general notes see front of timetable
For details of catering facilities see Directory of Train Operators

London → Broxbourne, Hertford East, Bishops Stortford, Stansted Airport and Cambridge

Network diagram - see first page of Table 20

		LE 1	LE 1	LE 1	LE 1	LE 1	LE 1	LE 1	LE 1	XC 1 ◇	LE 1	LE 1	LE 1	LE 1	LE 1	LE 1	LE 1	LE 1	LE 1	XC 1 ◇	LE 1	LE 1	LE 1
				⊥		⊥		⊥		⊥	⊥			⊥		⊥		⊥		⊥	⊥		
London Liverpool Street [15] ⊖	d		12 42	12 55	12 58	13 10	13 12	13 25	13 28		13 40		13 42	13 55	13 58	14 10	14 12	14 25	14 28		14 40		14 42
Bethnal Green	d																						
Hackney Downs	d		12 48				13 18						13 48				14 18						14 48
Stratford [7] ⊖	d	12 33										13 33										14 33	
Clapton	d																						
Seven Sisters ⊖	d																						
Tottenham Hale ⊖	d	12 43	12 55	13u07	13 10	13u22	13 25	13u37	13 40		13u52	13 43	13 55	14u07	14 10	14u22	14 25	14u37	14 40		14u52	14 43	14 55
Northumberland Park	d	12 45										13 45										14 45	
Angel Road	d																						
Ponders End	d		12 59				13 29						13 59				14 29						14 59
Brimsdown	d		13 02				13 32						14 02				14 32						15 02
Enfield Lock	d	12 51	13 04				13 34					13 51	14 04				14 34					14 51	15 04
Waltham Cross	d		13 07				13 37						14 07				14 37						15 07
Cheshunt	d	12 55	13 09		13 18		13 39		13 48			13 55	14 09		14 18		14 39		14 48			14 55	15 09
Broxbourne [3]	a	12 59	13 14		13 22		13 44		13 52			13 59	14 14		14 22		14 44		14 52			14 59	15 14
	d	13 03	13 14		13 22		13 44		13 52			14 03	14 14		14 22		14 44		14 52			15 03	15 14
Rye House	d		13 17				13 47						14 17				14 47						15 17
St Margarets (Herts)	d		13 20				13 50						14 20				14 50						15 20
Ware	d		13 24				13 54						14 24				14 54						15 24
Hertford East	a		13 31				14 01						14 31				15 01						15 31
Roydon	d	13 08			13 26							14 08			14 26							15 08	
Harlow Town	d	13 12		13 24	13 30			13 54	13 58			14 12		14 24	14 30			14 54	14 58			15 12	
Harlow Mill	d	13 15			13 33							14 15			14 33							15 15	
Sawbridgeworth	d	13 18			13 37				14 03			14 18			14 37				15 03			15 18	
Bishops Stortford	a	13 25			13 44	13 47			14 10		14 15	14 25			14 44	14 47			15 10		15 15	15 25	
	d	13 26			13 44	13 48			14 11		14 15	14 26			14 44	14 48			15 11		15 15	15 26	
Stansted Mountfitchet	d	13 30			13 48			14 05				14 30			14 48			15 05				15 30	
Stansted Airport ✈	a	13 39		13 42		13 57		14 13			14 25	14 39		14 42		14 57		15 13			15 25	15 39	
✈	d									14 25										15 25			
Elsenham	d				13 52										14 52								
Newport (Essex)	d				13 57										14 57								
Audley End	d				14 00				14 23	14 37					15 00				15 23	15 37			
Great Chesterford	d				14 05										15 05								
Whittlesford Parkway	d				14 10				14 30						15 10				15 30				
Shelford	d				14 14										15 14								
Cambridge	a				14 21				14 40	14 58					15 21				15 40	15 58			

		LE 1	LE 1	LE 1	LE 1	LE 1	LE 1	XC 1 ◇	LE 1	LE 1	LE 1	LE 1	LE 1	LE 1	LE 1	LE 1	LE 1	XC 1 ◇	LE 1	LE 1	LE 1	LE 1	LE 1
		⊥		⊥		⊥		⊥	⊥			⊥		⊥		⊥		⊥	⊥			⊥	
London Liverpool Street [15] ⊖	d	14 55	14 58	15 10	15 12	15 25	15 28		15 40		15 42	15 55	15 58	16 10	16 12	16 25	16 28		16 40		16 42	16 55	16 58
Bethnal Green	d																						
Hackney Downs	d				15 18						15 48				16 18						16 48		
Stratford [7] ⊖	d									15 33										16 33			
Clapton	d																						
Seven Sisters ⊖	d																						
Tottenham Hale ⊖	d	15u07	15 10	15u22	15 25	15u37	15 40		15u52	15 43	15 55	16u07	16 10	16u22	16 25	16u37	16 40		16u52	16 43	16 55	17u07	17 10
Northumberland Park	d									15 45										16 45			
Angel Road	d																						
Ponders End	d				15 29						15 59				16 29						16 59		
Brimsdown	d				15 32						16 02				16 32						17 02		
Enfield Lock	d				15 34					15 51	16 04				16 34					16 51	17 04		
Waltham Cross	d				15 37						16 07				16 37						17 07		
Cheshunt	d		15 18		15 39		15 48			15 55	16 09		16 18		16 39		16 48			16 55	17 09		17 18
Broxbourne [3]	a		15 22		15 44		15 52			15 59	16 14		16 22		16 44		16 52			16 59	17 14		17 22
	d		15 22		15 44		15 52			16 03	16 14		16 22		16 44		16 52			17 03	17 14		17 22
Rye House	d				15 47						16 17				16 47						17 17		
St Margarets (Herts)	d				15 50						16 20				16 50						17 20		
Ware	d				15 54						16 24				16 54						17 24		
Hertford East	a				16 01						16 31				17 01						17 31		
Roydon	d		15 26							16 08			16 26							17 08			17 26
Harlow Town	d	15 24	15 30			15 54	15 58			16 12		16 24	16 30			16 54	16 58			17 12		17 24	17 30
Harlow Mill	d		15 33							16 15			16 33							17 15			17 33
Sawbridgeworth	d		15 37				16 03			16 18			16 37				17 03			17 18			17 37
Bishops Stortford	a		15 44	15 47			16 10		16 15	16 25			16 44	16 47			17 10		17 15	17 25			17 44
	d		15 44	15 48			16 11		16 15	16 26			16 44	16 48			17 11		17 15	17 26			17 44
Stansted Mountfitchet	d		15 48			16 05				16 30			16 48			17 05				17 30			17 48
Stansted Airport ✈	a	15 42		15 57		16 13			16 25	16 39		16 42		16 57		17 13			17 25	17 39		17 42	
✈	d							16 25										17 25					
Elsenham	d		15 52										16 52										17 52
Newport (Essex)	d		15 57										16 57										17 57
Audley End	d		16 00				16 23	16 37					17 00				17 23	17 37					18 00
Great Chesterford	d		16 05										17 05										18 05
Whittlesford Parkway	d		16 10				16 30						17 10				17 30						18 10
Shelford	d		16 14										17 14										18 14
Cambridge	a		16 21				16 40	16 58					17 21				17 40	17 58					18 21

For general notes see front of timetable
For details of catering facilities see Directory of Train Operators

London → Broxbourne, Hertford East, Bishops Stortford, Stansted Airport and Cambridge

Network diagram - see first page of Table 20

		LE 1 🛒	LE 1	LE 1 🛒	LE 1	XC 1 ◇ 🛒	LE 1 🛒	LE 1	LE 1	LE 1 🛒	LE 1	LE 1 🛒	LE 1	LE 1 🛒	LE 1	XC 1 ◇ 🛒	LE 1 🛒	LE 1	LE 1	LE 1 🛒	LE 1	LE 1 🛒	LE 1
London Liverpool Street 15 ⊖	d	17 10	17 12	17 25	17 28		17 40		17 42	17 55	17 58	18 10	18 12	18 25	18 28		18 40		18 42	18 55	18 58	19 10	19 12
Bethnal Green	d																						
Hackney Downs	d		17 18						17 48				18 18						18 48				19 18
Stratford 7 ⊖	d							17 33										18 33					
Clapton	d																						
Seven Sisters ⊖	d																						
Tottenham Hale ⊖	d	17u22	17 25	17u37	17 40		17u52	17 43	17 55	18u07	18 10	18u22	18 25	18u37	18 40		18u52	18 43	18 55	19u07	19 10	19u22	19 25
Northumberland Park	d							17 45										18 45					
Angel Road	d																						
Ponders End	d		17 29						17 59				18 29						18 59				19 29
Brimsdown	d		17 32						18 02				18 32						19 02				19 32
Enfield Lock	d		17 34					17 51	18 04				18 34					18 51	19 04				19 34
Waltham Cross	d		17 37						18 07				18 37						19 07				19 37
Cheshunt	d		17 39		17 48			17 55	18 09		18 18		18 39		18 48			18 55	19 09		19 18		19 39
Broxbourne 3	a		17 44		17 52			17 59	18 14		18 22		18 44		18 52			18 59	19 14		19 22		19 44
	d		17 44		17 52			18 03	18 14		18 22		18 44		18 52			19 03	19 14		19 22		19 44
Rye House	d		17 47						18 17				18 47						19 17				19 47
St Margarets (Herts)	d		17 50						18 20				18 50						19 20				19 50
Ware	d		17 54						18 24				18 54						19 24				19 54
Hertford East	a		18 01						18 31				19 01						19 31				20 01
Roydon	d							18 08			18 26							19 08			19 26		
Harlow Town	d			17 54	17 58			18 12		18 24	18 30			18 54	18 58			19 12		19 24	19 30		
Harlow Mill	d							18 15			18 33							19 15			19 33		
Sawbridgeworth	d				18 03			18 18			18 37				19 03			19 18			19 37		
Bishops Stortford	a	17 47			18 10		18 15	18 25			18 44	18 47			19 10		19 15	19 25			19 44	19 47	
	d	17 48			18 11		18 15	18 26			18 44	18 48			19 11		19 15	19 26			19 44	19 48	
Stansted Mountfitchet	d			18 05				18 30			18 48			19 05				19 30			19 48		
Stansted Airport ✈	a	17 57		18 13			18 25	18 39		18 42		18 57		19 13			19 25	19 39		19 42		19 57	
✈	d					18 25										19 25							
Elsenham	d										18 52										19 52		
Newport (Essex)	d										18 57										19 57		
Audley End	d				18 23	18 37					19 00				19 23	19 37					20 00		
Great Chesterford	d										19 05										20 05		
Whittlesford Parkway	d				18 30						19 10				19 30						20 10		
Shelford	d										19 14										20 14		
Cambridge	a				18 40	18 58					19 21				19 40	19 58					20 21		

		LE 1 🛒	LE 1	XC 1 ◇ 🛒	LE 1 🛒	LE 1	LE 1	LE 1 🛒	LE 1	LE 1 🛒	LE 1	LE 1 🛒	LE 1	XC 1 ◇ 🛒	LE 1 🛒	LE 1	LE 1	LE 1 🛒	LE 1	LE 1 🛒	LE 1	LE 1 🛒	LE 1
London Liverpool Street 15 ⊖	d	19 25	19 28		19 40		19 42	19 55	19 58	20 10	20 12	20 25	20 28		20 40		20 42	20 55	20 58	21 10	21 12	21 25	21 28
Bethnal Green	d																						
Hackney Downs	d						19 48				20 18						20 48				21 18		
Stratford 7 ⊖	d					19 33										20 33							
Clapton	d																						
Seven Sisters ⊖	d																						
Tottenham Hale ⊖	d	19u37	19 40		19u52	19 43	19 55	20u07	20 10	20u22	20 25	20u37	20 40		20u52	20 43	20 55	21u07	21 10	21u22	21 25	21u37	21 40
Northumberland Park	d					19 45										20 45							
Angel Road	d																						
Ponders End	d						19 59				20 29						20 59				21 29		
Brimsdown	d						20 02				20 32						21 02				21 32		
Enfield Lock	d					19 51	20 04				20 34					20 51	21 04				21 34		
Waltham Cross	d						20 07				20 37						21 07				21 37		
Cheshunt	d		19 48			19 55	20 09		20 18		20 39		20 48			20 55	21 09		21 18		21 39		21 48
Broxbourne 3	a		19 52			19 59	20 14		20 22		20 44		20 52			20 59	21 14		21 22		21 44		21 52
	d		19 52			20 03	20 14		20 22		20 44		20 52			21 03	21 14		21 22		21 44		21 52
Rye House	d						20 17				20 47						21 17				21 47		
St Margarets (Herts)	d						20 20				20 50						21 20				21 50		
Ware	d						20 24				20 54						21 24				21 54		
Hertford East	a						20 31				21 01						21 31				22 01		
Roydon	d					20 08			20 26							21 08			21 26				
Harlow Town	d	19 54	19 58			20 12		20 24	20 30			20 54	20 58			21 12		21 24	21 30			21 54	21 58
Harlow Mill	d					20 15			20 33							21 15			21 33				
Sawbridgeworth	d		20 03			20 18			20 37				21 03			21 18			21 37				22 03
Bishops Stortford	a		20 10		20 15	20 25			20 44	20 47			21 10		21 15	21 25			21 44	21 47			22 10
	d		20 11		20 15	20 26			20 44	20 48			21 11		21 15	21 26			21 44	21 48			22 11
Stansted Mountfitchet	d	20 05				20 30			20 48			21 05				21 30			21 48			22 05	
Stansted Airport ✈	a	20 13			20 25	20 39		20 42		20 57		21 13			21 25	21 39		21 42		21 57		22 13	
✈	d			20 25										21 25									
Elsenham	d								20 52										21 52				
Newport (Essex)	d								20 57										21 57				
Audley End	d		20 23	20 38					21 00				21 23	21 38					22 00				22 23
Great Chesterford	d								21 05										22 05				
Whittlesford Parkway	d		20 30						21 10				21 30						22 10				22 30
Shelford	d								21 14										22 14				
Cambridge	a		20 40	21 01					21 21				21 40	22 01					22 21				22 40

For general notes see front of timetable
For details of catering facilities see Directory of Train Operators

Saturdays

London → Broxbourne, Hertford East, Bishops Stortford, Stansted Airport and Cambridge

Network diagram - see first page of Table 20

		XC [1] ◇ 🚲	LE [1] 🚲	LE [1]	LE [1]	LE [1] 🚲	LE [1]	LE [1]	LE [1]	LE [1]	LE [1]		XC [1] ◇ 🚲	LE [1]	LE [1]	LE [1]	LE [1]	LE [1]	LE [1]	LE [1]	LE [1]	LE [1]	LE [1]		
London Liverpool Street [15] ⊖	d		21 40		21 42	21 55	21 58	22 10	22 12	22 25	22 28			22 40		22 42	22 55	22 58	23 10	23 25	23 28	23 40	23 58		
Bethnal Green	d																								
Hackney Downs	d				21 48				22 18							22 48			23 16			23 46			
Stratford [7] ⊖	d			21 33											22 33										
Clapton	d																					23 49			
Seven Sisters ⊖	d																								
Tottenham Hale ⊖	d		21u52	21 43	21 55	22u07	22 10	22u22	22 25	22u37	22 40			22u52	22 43	22 55	23u07	23 10	23 23	23u37	23 40	23 53	00 10		
Northumberland Park	d			21 45											22 45				23 25			23 55			
Angel Road	d																								
Ponders End	d				21 59				22 29							22 59			23 29			23 59			
Brimsdown	d				22 02				22 32							23 02			23 32			00 02			
Enfield Lock	d			21 51	22 04				22 34						22 51	23 04			23 34			00 04			
Waltham Cross	d				22 07				22 37							23 07			23 37			00 07			
Cheshunt	d			21 55	22 09		22 18		22 39		22 48				22 55	23 09		23 18	23 39		23 48	00 09	00 18		
Broxbourne [3]	a			21 59	22 14		22 22		22 44		22 52				22 59	23 14		23 22	23 44		23 52	00 14	00 22		
	d			22 03	22 14		22 22		22 44		22 52				23 03	23 14		23 22	23 44		23 52	00 14	00 22		
Rye House	d				22 17				22 47							23 17			23 47			00 17			
St Margarets (Herts)	d				22 20				22 50							23 20			23 50			00 20			
Ware	d				22 24				22 54							23 24			23 54			00 24			
Hertford East	a				22 31				23 01							23 31			00 01			00 31			
Roydon	d			22 08			22 26								23 08			23 26					00 26		
Harlow Town	d			22 12		22 24	22 30			22 54	22 58				23 12		23 24	23 30		23 54	23 58		00 30		
Harlow Mill	d			22 15			22 33								23 15			23 33					00 33		
Sawbridgeworth	d			22 18			22 37				23 03				23 18			23 37			00 03		00 37		
Bishops Stortford	a		22 15	22 25			22 44	22 47			23 10			23 15	23 26			23 44		00 04	00 10		00 44		
	d		22 15	22 26			22 44	22 48			23 11			23 15				23 44		00 04	00 11		00 44		
Stansted Mountfitchet	d			22 30			22 48			23 05								23 48					00 48		
Stansted Airport ✈	a		22 25	22 39		22 42		22 57		23 13				23 25			23 42			00 13					
✈	d	22 25											23 25												
Elsenham	d						22 52											23 52					00 52		
Newport (Essex)	d						22 57											23 57					00 57		
Audley End	d	22 38					23 00				23 23		23 38					23 59			00 23		01 00		
Great Chesterford	d						23 05											00 05					01 05		
Whittlesford Parkway	d						23 10				23 30							00 10			00 30		01 10		
Shelford	d						23 14											00 14							
Cambridge	a	23 01					23 21				23 40		23 53					00 21			00 40		01 19		

Sundays

		LE [1]	LE [1]	LE [1]	LE [1]	LE [1]	LE [1]	LE [1]	LE [1]	LE [1]	LE [1]	LE [1]	LE [1]	LE [1]	LE [1] 🚲	LE [1] 🚲	LE [1] 🚲		LE	LE [1]	LE [1]	LE	LE [1] 🚲	LE [1]	LE [1] 🚲
London Liverpool Street [15] ⊖	d	22p58	23p25	23p28	23p40	23p58	04 10	04 40	05 10	05 40	06 10	06 25	06 40	06 55	07 10	07 25	07 40			07 43		07 52	07 55		08 10
Bethnal Green	d																								
Hackney Downs	d				23p46																	07 59			
Stratford [7] ⊖	d																								
Clapton	d				23p49																				
Seven Sisters ⊖	d																					08 04			
Tottenham Hale ⊖	d	23p10	23b37	23p40	23p53	00 10		04u52	05u22	05u52	06u22	06u37	06u52	07 07	07 22	07 37	07 52			07 55			08 07		08 22
Northumberland Park	d				23p55																				
Angel Road	d																								
Ponders End	d				23p59															07 59					
Brimsdown	d				00 02															08 02					
Enfield Lock	d				00 04															08 04	←				
Waltham Cross	d				00 07															08 07 →	08 07				
Cheshunt	d	23p18		23p48	00 09	00 18															08 09	08 20			
Broxbourne [3]	a	23p22		23p52	00 14	00 22															08 14	08 25			
	d	23p22		23p52	00 14	00 22													07 57		08 19	08 25			
Rye House	d				00 17														08 00			08 28			
St Margarets (Herts)	d				00 20														08 03			08 31			
Ware	d				00 24														08 07			08 35			
Hertford East	a				00 31														08 14			08 42		←	
Roydon	d	23p26				00 26															08 24 →			08 24	
Harlow Town	d	23p30	23p54	23p58		00 30		05 07	05 37	06 10		06 52		07 22		07 52							08 22	08 28	
Harlow Mill	d	23p33				00 33																		08 31	
Sawbridgeworth	d	23p37		00 03		00 37																		08 34	
Bishops Stortford	a	23p44	00 04	00 10		00 44		05 17	05 47	06 20	06 45		07 15		07 45		08 15							08 41	08 45
	d	23p44	00 04	00 11		00 44		05 18	05 48	06 21	06 46		07 16		07 46		08 16							08 42	08 46
Stansted Mountfitchet	d	23p48				00 48		05 22				07 03				08 03								08 46	
Stansted Airport ✈	a		00 13				04 58	05 29	05 57	06 30	06 55	07 12	07 25	07 40	07 55	08 13	08 25						08 40		08 55
✈	d																								
Elsenham	d	23p52				00 52																		08 50	
Newport (Essex)	d	23p57				00 57																		08 55	
Audley End	d	23p59		00 23		01 00																		08 58	
Great Chesterford	d	00 05				01 05																		09 03	
Whittlesford Parkway	d	00 10		00 30		01 10																		09 08	
Shelford	d	00 14																						09 12	
Cambridge	a	00 21		00 40		01 19																		09 19	

For general notes see front of timetable
For details of catering facilities see
Directory of Train Operators

b Previous night.
Stops to pick up only

London → Broxbourne, Hertford East, Bishops Stortford, Stansted Airport and Cambridge

Network diagram - see first page of Table 20

		LE	LE 1 🛒	LE 1	LE	LE 1 🛒	LE 1	LE	LE 1 🛒	LE 1	LE 1 🛒	LE		LE 1 🛒	LE 1	LE	XC 1 ◇ 🛒	LE 1 🛒	LE 1	LE	LE 1 🛒	LE 1	LE 1 🛒	LE	LE 1 🛒
London Liverpool Street [15]	⊖ d	08 22	08 25	08 28		08 40		08 52	08 55		09 10	09 22		09 25	09 28			09 40		09 52	09 55		10 10	10 22	10 25
Bethnal Green	d				←											←									
Hackney Downs	d	08 29			08 29			08 59				09 29				09 29				09 59				10 29	
Stratford [7]	⊖ ⛴ d	→					08 45					→							09 45					→	
Clapton	d																								
Seven Sisters	⊖ d				08 34			09 04								09 34				10 04					
Tottenham Hale	⊖ d		08 37	08 40		08 52	08 55		09 07		09 22			09 37	09 40			09 52	09 55		10 07		10 22		10 37
Northumberland Park	d																								
Angel Road	d																								
Ponders End	d						08 59												09 59						
Brimsdown	d						09 02												10 02						
Enfield Lock	d						09 04												10 04						
Waltham Cross	d						09 07												10 07						
Cheshunt	d			08 49	08 52		09 09	09 20							09 49	09 52			10 09	10 20					
Broxbourne [3]	a			08 53	08 57		09 14	09 25							09 53	09 57			10 14	10 25					
	d			08 53	08 57		09 19	09 25							09 53	09 57			10 19	10 25					
Rye House	d				09 00			09 28								10 00				10 28					
St Margarets (Herts)	d				09 03			09 31								10 03				10 31					
Ware	d				09 07			09 35								10 07				10 35					
Hertford East	a				09 14			09 42		←						10 14				10 42		←			
Roydon	d						09 24			09 24									10 24			10 24			
Harlow Town	d		08 52	08 59			→		09 22	09 28				09 52	09 59				→		10 22	10 28			10 52
Harlow Mill	d									09 31												10 31			
Sawbridgeworth	d			09 04						09 34					10 04							10 34			
Bishops Stortford	a			09 11		09 15				09 41	09 45				10 11			10 15				10 41	10 45		
	d			09 12		09 16				09 42	09 46				10 12			10 16				10 42	10 46		
Stansted Mountfitchet	d		09 03							09 46				10 03								10 46			11 03
Stansted Airport	✈ a		09 12			09 25			09 40		09 55			10 12				10 25			10 40		10 55		11 12
	✈ d																10 25								
Elsenham	d									09 50												10 50			
Newport (Essex)	d									09 55												10 55			
Audley End	d			09 24						09 58					10 24		10 39					10 58			
Great Chesterford	d									10 03												11 03			
Whittlesford Parkway	d			09 31						10 08					10 31							11 08			
Shelford	d									10 12												11 12			
Cambridge	a			09 41						10 19					10 41		10 54					11 19			

		LE 1	LE	XC 1 ◇ 🛒	LE 1 🛒	LE 1	LE		LE 1 🛒	LE 1	LE 1 🛒	LE	LE 1 🛒	LE 1	LE	XC 1 ◇ 🛒	LE 1 🛒	LE 1	LE	LE 1 🛒	LE 1	LE 1 🛒	LE	LE 1 🛒	LE 1
London Liverpool Street [15]	⊖ d	10 28			10 40		10 52		10 55		11 10	11 22	11 25	11 28			11 40		11 52	11 55		12 10	12 22	12 25	12 28
Bethnal Green	d		←												←										
Hackney Downs	d		10 29				10 59					11 29			11 29				11 59				12 29		
Stratford [7]	⊖ ⛴ d					10 45						→						11 45					→		
Clapton	d																								
Seven Sisters	⊖ d		10 34				11 04								11 34				12 04						
Tottenham Hale	⊖ d	10 40			10 52	10 55			11 07		11 22		11 37	11 40			11 52	11 55		12 07		12 22		12 37	12 40
Northumberland Park	d																								
Angel Road	d																								
Ponders End	d					10 59												11 59							
Brimsdown	d					11 02												12 02							
Enfield Lock	d					11 04												12 04							
Waltham Cross	d					11 07												12 07							
Cheshunt	d	10 49	10 52			11 09	11 20							11 49	11 52			12 09	12 20						12 49
Broxbourne [3]	a	10 53	10 57			11 14	11 25							11 53	11 57			12 14	12 25						12 53
	d	10 53	10 57			11 19	11 25							11 53	11 57			12 19	12 25						12 53
Rye House	d		11 00				11 28								12 00				12 28						
St Margarets (Herts)	d		11 03				11 31								12 03				12 31						
Ware	d		11 07				11 35								12 07				12 35						
Hertford East	a		11 14				11 42			←					12 14				12 42		←				
Roydon	d					11 24				11 24								12 24			12 24				
Harlow Town	d	10 59				→			11 22	11 28			11 52	11 59				→		12 22	12 28			12 52	12 59
Harlow Mill	d									11 31											12 31				
Sawbridgeworth	d	11 04								11 34				12 04							12 34				13 04
Bishops Stortford	a	11 11			11 15					11 41	11 45			12 11			12 15				12 41	12 45			13 11
	d	11 12			11 16					11 42	11 46			12 12			12 16				12 42	12 46			13 12
Stansted Mountfitchet	d									11 46			12 03								12 46			13 03	
Stansted Airport	✈ a				11 25				11 40		11 55		12 12				12 25			12 40		12 55		13 12	
	✈ d			11 25												12 25									
Elsenham	d									11 50											12 50				
Newport (Essex)	d									11 55											12 55				
Audley End	d	11 24		11 39						11 58				12 24		12 39					12 58				13 24
Great Chesterford	d									12 03											13 03				
Whittlesford Parkway	d	11 31								12 08				12 31							13 08				13 31
Shelford	d									12 12											13 12				
Cambridge	a	11 41		11 55						12 19				12 41		12 54					13 19				13 41

For general notes see front of timetable
For details of catering facilities see Directory of Train Operators

London → Broxbourne, Hertford East, Bishops Stortford, Stansted Airport and Cambridge

Network diagram - see first page of Table 20

		LE		XC 1◇ 🍴	LE 1 🍴	LE 1	LE	LE 1 🍴	LE 1	LE 1 🍴	LE	LE 1 🍴	LE 1	LE	XC 1◇ 🍴	LE 1 🍴	LE 1	LE	LE 1 🍴		LE 1	LE 1 🍴	LE	LE 1 🍴	LE 1
London Liverpool Street 15 ⊖	d				12 40		12 52	12 55		13 10	13 22	13 25	13 28			13 40		13 52	13 55			14 10	14 22	14 25	14 28
Bethnal Green	d	←												←											
Hackney Downs	d	12 29					12 59				13 29 →			13 29				13 59					14 29 →		
Stratford 7 ⊖	d					12 45											13 45								
Clapton	d																								
Seven Sisters ⊖	d	12 34					13 04							13 34				14 04							
Tottenham Hale ⊖	d				12 52	12 55		13 07		13 22		13 37	13 40			13 52	13 55		14 07			14 22		14 37	14 40
Northumberland Park	d																								
Angel Road	d																								
Ponders End	d					12 59											13 59								
Brimsdown	d					13 02											14 02								
Enfield Lock	d					13 04											14 04								
Waltham Cross	d					13 07											14 07								
Cheshunt	d	12 52				13 09	13 20						13 49	13 52			14 09	14 20							14 49
Broxbourne 3	a	12 57				13 14	13 25						13 53	13 57			14 14	14 25							14 53
	d	12 57				13 19	13 25						13 53	13 57			14 19	14 25							14 53
Rye House	d	13 00					13 28							14 00				14 28							
St Margarets (Herts)	d	13 03					13 31							14 03				14 31							
Ware	d	13 07					13 35							14 07				14 35							
Hertford East	a	13 14					13 42		←					14 14				14 42			←				
Roydon	d					13 24 →			13 24								14 24 →				14 24				
Harlow Town	d							13 22	13 28			13 52	13 59						14 22		14 28			14 52	14 59
Harlow Mill	d								13 31												14 31				
Sawbridgeworth	d								13 34				14 04								14 34				15 04
Bishops Stortford	a				13 15				13 41	13 45			14 11			14 15					14 41	14 45			15 11
	d				13 16				13 42	13 46			14 12			14 16					14 42	14 46			15 12
Stansted Mountfitchet	d								13 46			14 03									14 46			15 03	
Stansted Airport ✈	a				13 25			13 40		13 55		14 12				14 25			14 40			14 55		15 12	
✈	d			13 25											14 25										
Elsenham	d								13 50												14 50				
Newport (Essex)	d								13 55												14 55				
Audley End	d			13 39					13 58				14 24		14 39						14 58				15 24
Great Chesterford	d								14 03												15 03				
Whittlesford Parkway	d								14 08				14 31								15 08				15 31
Shelford	d								14 12												15 12				
Cambridge	a			13 54					14 19				14 41		14 55						15 19				15 41

		LE	XC 1◇ 🍴	LE 1 🍴	LE 1	LE	LE 1 🍴	LE 1	LE 1 🍴	LE	LE 1 🍴	LE 1	LE	XC 1◇ 🍴		LE 1 🍴	LE 1	LE	LE 1 🍴	LE 1	LE 1 🍴	LE	LE 1 🍴	LE 1	LE
London Liverpool Street 15 ⊖	d			14 40		14 52	14 55		15 10	15 22	15 25	15 28				15 40		15 52	15 55		16 10	16 22	16 25	16 28	
Bethnal Green	d	←											←												←
Hackney Downs	d	14 29				14 59				15 29 →			15 29					15 59				16 29 →			16 29
Stratford 7 ⊖	d				14 45												15 45								
Clapton	d																								
Seven Sisters ⊖	d	14 34				15 04							15 34					16 04							16 34
Tottenham Hale ⊖	d			14 52	14 55		15 07		15 22		15 37	15 40				15 52	15 55		16 07		16 22		16 37	16 40	
Northumberland Park	d																								
Angel Road	d																								
Ponders End	d				14 59												15 59								
Brimsdown	d				15 02												16 02								
Enfield Lock	d				15 04												16 04								
Waltham Cross	d				15 07												16 07								
Cheshunt	d	14 52			15 09	15 20						15 49	15 52				16 09	16 20						16 49	16 52
Broxbourne 3	a	14 57			15 14	15 25						15 53	15 57				16 14	16 25						16 53	16 57
	d	14 57			15 19	15 25						15 53	15 57				16 19	16 25						16 53	16 57
Rye House	d	15 00				15 28							16 00					16 28							17 00
St Margarets (Herts)	d	15 03				15 31							16 03					16 31							17 03
Ware	d	15 07				15 35							16 07					16 35							17 07
Hertford East	a	15 14				15 42		←					16 14					16 42		←					17 14
Roydon	d				15 24 →			15 24									16 24 →			16 24					
Harlow Town	d						15 22	15 28			15 52	15 59							16 22	16 28			16 52	16 59	
Harlow Mill	d							15 31												16 31					
Sawbridgeworth	d							15 34				16 04								16 34				17 04	
Bishops Stortford	a			15 15				15 41	15 45			16 11				16 15				16 41	16 45			17 11	
	d			15 16				15 42	15 46			16 12				16 16				16 42	16 46			17 12	
Stansted Mountfitchet	d							15 46			16 03									16 46			17 03		
Stansted Airport ✈	a			15 25			15 40		15 55		16 12					16 25			16 40		16 55		17 12		
✈	d		15 25											16 25											
Elsenham	d							15 50												16 50					
Newport (Essex)	d							15 55												16 55					
Audley End	d		15 39					15 58				16 24		16 39						16 58				17 24	
Great Chesterford	d							16 03												17 03					
Whittlesford Parkway	d							16 08				16 31								17 08				17 31	
Shelford	d							16 12												17 12					
Cambridge	a		15 54					16 19				16 41		16 55						17 19				17 41	

For general notes see front of timetable
For details of catering facilities see
Directory of Train Operators

London → Broxbourne, Hertford East, Bishops Stortford, Stansted Airport and Cambridge

Network diagram - see first page of Table 20

Station		XC 1◇ (trolley)	LE 1 (trolley)	LE 1	LE	LE 1 (trolley)	LE 1	LE 1 (trolley)	LE		LE 1 (trolley)	LE 1	LE	XC 1◇ (trolley)	LE 1 (trolley)	LE 1	LE	LE 1 (trolley)	LE 1	LE 1 (trolley)	LE	LE 1 (trolley)	LE 1	LE	XC 1◇ (trolley)
London Liverpool Street 15 ⊖	d		16 40		16 52	16 55		17 10	17 22		17 25	17 28			17 40		17 52	17 55		18 10	18 22	18 25	18 28		
Bethnal Green	d												←											←	
Hackney Downs	d				16 59				17 29				17 29				17 59				18 29			18 29	
Stratford 7 ⊖ ⛴	d			16 45					→							17 45					→				
Clapton	d																								
Seven Sisters ⊖	d				17 04								17 34				18 04							18 34	
Tottenham Hale ⊖	d		16 52	16 55		17 07		17 22			17 37	17 40			17 52	17 55		18 07		18 22		18 37	18 40		
Northumberland Park	d																								
Angel Road	d																								
Ponders End	d			16 59												17 59									
Brimsdown	d			17 02												18 02									
Enfield Lock	d			17 04												18 04									
Waltham Cross	d			17 07												18 07									
Cheshunt	d			17 09	17 20							17 49	17 52			18 09	18 20						18 49	18 52	
Broxbourne 3	a			17 14	17 25							17 53	17 57			18 14	18 25						18 53	18 57	
	d			17 19	17 25							17 53	17 57			18 19	18 25						18 53	18 57	
Rye House	d				17 28								18 00				18 28							19 00	
St Margarets (Herts)	d				17 31								18 03				18 31							19 03	
Ware	d				17 35								18 07				18 35							19 07	
Hertford East	a				17 42		←						18 14				18 42		←					19 14	
Roydon	d			17 24			17 24									18 24			18 24						
Harlow Town	d			→		17 22	17 28				17 52	17 59				→		18 22	18 28			18 52	18 59		
Harlow Mill	d						17 31												18 31						
Sawbridgeworth	d						17 34					18 04							18 34				19 04		
Bishops Stortford	a		17 15				17 41	17 45				18 11			18 15				18 41	18 45			19 11		
	d		17 16				17 42	17 46				18 12			18 16				18 42	18 46			19 12		
Stansted Mountfitchet	d						17 46				18 03								18 46			19 03			
Stansted Airport ✈	a		17 25			17 43		17 55			18 12				18 25			18 43		18 55		19 12			
✈	d	17 25												18 25											19 25
Elsenham	d						17 50												18 50						
Newport (Essex)	d						17 55												18 55						
Audley End	d	17 39					17 58					18 24		18 39					18 58				19 24		19 39
Great Chesterford	d						18 03												19 03						
Whittlesford Parkway	d						18 08					18 31							19 08				19 31		
Shelford	d						18 12												19 12						
Cambridge	a	17 54					18 19					18 41		18 54					19 19				19 41		19 54

Station		LE 1 (trolley)	LE 1 (trolley)	LE 1		LE	LE 1 (trolley)	LE 1 (trolley)	LE 1	XC 1◇ (trolley)	LE 1 (trolley)	LE	LE 1 (trolley)	LE 1	LE	LE 1 (trolley)	LE 1 (trolley)	LE 1	XC 1◇ A (trolley)	LE 1 (trolley)	XC 1◇ B (trolley)		LE	LE 1 (trolley)	LE 1
London Liverpool Street 15 ⊖	d	18 40	18 55			19 00	19 10	19 25	19 28		19 40		19 55		20 00	20 10	20 25	20 28		20 40				20 55	
Bethnal Green	d					19 03									20 03										
Hackney Downs	d					19 09									20 09										
Stratford 7 ⊖ ⛴	d			18 45										19 45											20 45
Clapton	d																								
Seven Sisters ⊖	d					19 17									20 17										
Tottenham Hale ⊖	d	18 52	19 07	18 55			19 22	19 37	19 40		19 52		20 07	19 55		20 22	20 37	20 40		20 52				21 07	20 55
Northumberland Park	d																								
Angel Road	d																								
Ponders End	d			18 59										19 59											20 59
Brimsdown	d			19 02										20 02											21 02
Enfield Lock	d			19 04										20 04											21 04
Waltham Cross	d			19 07										20 07											21 07
Cheshunt	d			19 09		19 37			19 48					20 09	20 37			20 48							21 09
Broxbourne 3	a			19 14		19 42			19 52			←		20 14	20 42			20 52					←		21 14
	d			19 19		19 55			19 52			19 55		20 19	20 55			20 52					20 55		21 19
Rye House	d					→						19 59			→								20 59		
St Margarets (Herts)	d											20 02											21 02		
Ware	d											20 06											21 06		
Hertford East	a											20 12											21 12		
Roydon	d			19 24										20 24											21 24
Harlow Town	d		19 22	19 28				19 52	19 58				20 22	20 28			20 52	20 58						21 22	21 28
Harlow Mill	d			19 31										20 31											21 31
Sawbridgeworth	d			19 34					20 03					20 34				21 03							21 34
Bishops Stortford	a	19 15		19 41			19 45		20 10		20 15			20 41		20 45		21 10		21 15					21 41
	d	19 16		19 42			19 46		20 11		20 16			20 42		20 46		21 11		21 16					21 42
Stansted Mountfitchet	d			19 46				20 03						20 46			21 03								21 46
Stansted Airport ✈	a	19 25	19 40				19 55	20 12			20 25		20 40			20 55	21 12			21 27				21 40	
✈	d									20 25									21 18		21 27				
Elsenham	d			19 50										20 50					⌇		⌇				21 50
Newport (Essex)	d			19 55										20 55					⌇		⌇				21 55
Audley End	d			19 58					20 23	20 38				20 58				21 23	21 33		21 40				21 58
Great Chesterford	d			20 03										21 03					⌇		⌇				22 03
Whittlesford Parkway	d			20 08					20 30					21 08				21 30	⌇		⌇				22 08
Shelford	d			20 12										21 12					⌇		⌇				22 12
Cambridge	a			20 19					20 40	20 55				21 19				21 40	21 50		21 59				22 19

For general notes see front of timetable
For details of catering facilities see Directory of Train Operators

A Until 12 July and from 13 September
B 19 July to 6 September

Table 22

Sundays

London → Broxbourne, Hertford East, Bishops Stortford, Stansted Airport and Cambridge

Network diagram - see first page of Table 20

		LE	LE	LE	LE	XC	LE	LE	LE	LE	LE	LE	LE	LE	LE	LE	LE	LE	LE	LE	LE	LE	LE
			1	1	1	1 ◇	1		1	1		1	1	1	1		1	1		1	1		1
			🛒	🛒		🛒	🛒		🛒														
London Liverpool Street 15	⊖ d	21 00	21 10	21 25	21 28		21 40		21 55		22 00	22 10	22 25	22 28	22 40		22 55		23 00	23 25	23 28		23 58
Bethnal Green	d	21 03									22 03								23 03				
Hackney Downs	d	21 09									22 09								23 09				
Stratford 7	⊖ d									21 45								22 45					
Clapton	d																						
Seven Sisters	⊖ d	21 17									22 17								23 17				
Tottenham Hale	⊖ d		21 22	21 37	21 40		21 52		22 07	21 55		22 22	22 37	22 40	22 52		23 07	22 55		23 37	23 40		00 10
Northumberland Park	d																						
Angel Road	d																						
Ponders End	d									21 59								22 59			23 44		
Brimsdown	d									22 02								23 02			23 47		
Enfield Lock	d									22 04								23 04			23 49		
Waltham Cross	d									22 07								23 07			23 52		
Cheshunt	d	21 37			21 48					22 09	22 37			22 48				23 09	23 37		23 54		00 18
Broxbourne 3	a	21 42			21 52			←		22 14	22 42			22 52		←		23 14	23 42		23 59	←	00 22
	d	21 55			21 52			21 55		22 19	22 55			22 52		22 55		23 19	00 02		23 59	00 02	00 22
Rye House	d	→						21 59			→					22 59			→			00 05	
St Margarets (Herts)	d							22 02								23 02						00 08	
Ware	d							22 06								23 06						00 12	
Hertford East	a							22 12								23 12						00 19	
Roydon	d									22 24								23 24					00 26
Harlow Town	d			21 52	21 58				22 22	22 28			22 52	22 58			23 22	23 28		23 52	00 05		00 30
Harlow Mill	d									22 31								23 31					00 33
Sawbridgeworth	d				22 03					22 34				23 03				23 34			00 10		00 37
Bishops Stortford	a		21 45		22 10		22 15			22 41		22 45		23 10	23 15			23 41		00 02	00 17		00 44
	d		21 46		22 11		22 16			22 42		22 46		23 11	23 16			23 42		00 03			
Stansted Mountfitchet	d			22 03						22 46			23 03					23 46					
Stansted Airport	✈ a		21 55	22 12			22 27		22 40			22 55	23 12		23 25		23 40			00 12			
	✈ d					22 18																	
Elsenham	d									22 50								23 50					
Newport (Essex)	d									22 55								23 55					
Audley End	d				22 23	22 33				22 58				23 23				23 58					
Great Chesterford	d									23 03								00 03					
Whittlesford Parkway	d				22 30					23 08				23 30				00 08					
Shelford	d									23 12								00 12					
Cambridge	a				22 40	22 50				23 19				23 40				00 19					

For general notes see front of timetable
For details of catering facilities see Directory of Train Operators

Cambridge, Stansted Airport, Bishops Stortford, Hertford East and Broxbourne → London

Network diagram - see first page of Table 20

Miles	Miles			LE	LE	LE	LE	LE	LE	LE	LE	LE	LE	LE	XC	LE	LE	LE	LE	LE	XC	LE	LE	LE	LE
				MO	MX	MX	MO	MX	MO	MX			MFO	MFO				MFO	MFX						
					1	1	1	1	1	1	1	1	1	1	1 ◇	1	1	1	1	1	1 ◇	1	1		1
0	—	**Cambridge**	d		22p51										04 32	04 48					05 17	05 21			
3¼	—	Shelford	d		22p56																	05 26			
6¾	—	Whittlesford Parkway	d		23p00											04 55						05 30			
10	—	Great Chesterford	d		23p04																	05 34			
14	—	Audley End	d		23p10										04 46	05 03					05 35	05 40			
15¾	—	Newport (Essex)	d		23p13																	05 43			
20¼	0	Elsenham	d		23p19																	05 49			
—	4½	**Stansted Airport** ✈	a												05 03						05 50				
—	—	✈	d			23p30	23p30		23p45	23p45	23p59	00 30	01 00	01 30				05 30					06 00		
22½	8¼	Stansted Mountfitchet	d		23p22																	05 52	06 06		
25½	—	**Bishops Stortford**	a		23p28	23p39	23p39				00 08	00 39				05 16		05 39				05 58	06 10		
—	—		d		23p28	23p39	23p39				00 08	00 39				05 16		05 39	05 39	05 45		05 58	06 10		06 14
29	—	Sawbridgeworth	d		23p32											05 21				05 49		06 03			06 18
31¼	—	Harlow Mill	d		23p36											05 24				05 53		06 06			
33	—	Harlow Town	d		23p39		23p47		23p59	23p59	00 16	00 47				05 27		05 47	05 47	05 56		06 10	06 18		06 23
35¾	—	Roydon	d		23p43											05 31				06 00		06 14			
—	0	**Hertford East**	d	22p57				23p39									05 25							06 05	
—	2	Ware	d	23p01				23p43									05 29							06 09	
—	4	St Margarets (Herts)	d	23p05				23p47									05 33							06 13	
—	5¼	Rye House	d	23p08				23p50									05 36							06 16	
38½	7	Broxbourne 3	a	23p12	23p47			23p54								05 36	05 40	05 53	05 53	06 04		06 18		06 21	06 30
—	—		d	23p26	23p47			23p54								05 36	05 40	05 53	05 53	06 04		06 18		06 25	06 39
41¾	—	Cheshunt	d	23p31	23p51			23p58								05 41	05 44	05 57	05 57	06 08		06 23		06 30	⟶
43	—	Waltham Cross	d														05 47			06 10				06 32	
44	—	Enfield Lock	d														05 49			06 13				06 35	
45	—	Brimsdown	d														05 52			06 15				06 37	
45¾	—	Ponders End	d														05 54			06 17				06 39	
48	—	Angel Road	d														05 57			06 21					
48¾	—	Northumberland Park	d														05 59			06 23					
49¾	—	Tottenham Hale ⊖	d													05 49	06 03	06 07	06 07	06 26		06 31	06 34	06 45	
—	0	Seven Sisters ⊖	d	23p51	00 04	00 07	00 08	00 11	00 21	00 21															
51¾	—	Clapton	d																						
—	6¾	Stratford 7 ⊖ ⛴	a																	06 39					
52¾	—	Hackney Downs	d	23p59				00 16									06 08							06 51	
54½	—	Bethnal Green	d	00 05																					
55¾	—	**London Liverpool Street** 15 ⊖	a	00 11	00 18	00 22	00 22	00 25	00 35	00 36	00 51	01 21	01 50	02 20	.	06 03	06 17	06 23	06 23	.	.	06 47	06 49	07 02	

		LE	LE	LE		LE	LE	LE	LE	LE	LE	LE	LE	LE	XC	LE	LE	LE	LE	LE	LE	LE	LE	LE	LE
		1	1	1		1	1		1	1	1	1	1	1	1 ◇			1	1		1	1		1	1
										A														A	
Cambridge	d	05 41				05 51				06 18			06 21		06 32			06 48			06 51			07 18	
Shelford	d	05 46				05 56							06 26								06 56				
Whittlesford Parkway	d	05 50				06 00				06 25			06 30					06 55			07 00			07 25	
Great Chesterford	d	05 54				06 04							06 34								07 04				
Audley End	d	06 00				06 10				06 34			06 40		06 46			07 04			07 10			07 34	
Newport (Essex)	d	06 03				06 13							06 43								07 13				
Elsenham	d	06 09				06 19							06 49								07 19				
Stansted Airport ✈	a														07 08										
✈	d		06 15				06 30				06 43			07 00					07 15			07 30			07 43
Stansted Mountfitchet	d	06 12				06 22					06 49		06 52								07 22				07 49
Bishops Stortford	a	06 18	06 24			06 28	06 39			06 47	06 53		06 58	07 09				07 17	07 24		07 28	07 39		07 47	07 54
	d	06 18	06 24			06 28	06 39		06 42	06 48	06 54		06 58	07 09				07 17	07 24		07 28	07 39		07 48	07 54
Sawbridgeworth	d					06 33			06 46				07 03					07 22			07 33				
Harlow Mill	d					06 36			06 50				07 06								07 36				
Harlow Town	d	06 27				06 40	06 47		06 53	06 57	07 02		07 10					07 27	07 32		07 40			07 57	08 02
Roydon	d					06 44			06 57				07 14								07 44				
Hertford East	d							06 35								07 09	07 15						07 39		
Ware	d							06 39								07 13	07 19						07 43		
St Margarets (Herts)	d							06 43								07 17	07 23						07 47		
Rye House	d							06 46								07 20	07 26						07 50		
Broxbourne 3	a	06 33		⟵		06 48		06 51	07 02	07 04		⟵	07 18	07 22		07 25	07 30	07 33		⟵	07 48	07 52	07 55	08 03	
	d	06 34		06 39		06 48		06 55	07 11	07 05		07 11	07 18	07 22		07 25	07 40	07 34		07 40	07 48	07 52	07 55	08 04	
Cheshunt	d			06 43		06 53		07 00	⟶		07 12	07 15		07 27		07 30	⟶			07 44	07 53		08 00		
Waltham Cross	d			06 46				07 02				07 18				07 32				07 47		07 58	08 02		
Enfield Lock	d			06 48				07 05				07 20				07 35				07 49			08 05		
Brimsdown	d							07 07						07 31		07 37				07 52		08 02	08 07		
Ponders End	d							07 09						07 33		07 39						08 04	08 09		
Angel Road	d			06 53								07 25													
Northumberland Park	d			06 55								07 27								07 57					
Tottenham Hale ⊖	d	06 48	06 51	06 58	.	07 01	07 04	07 15	.	07 18	07 21	07 30	07 33	07 38	.	07 45	.	07 48	07 51	08 00	08 03	08 10	08 15	08 18	08 21
Seven Sisters ⊖	d																								
Clapton	d																								
Stratford 7 ⊖ ⛴	a			07 12								07 44								08 13					
Hackney Downs	d							07 21								07 51							08 21		
Bethnal Green	d																								
London Liverpool Street 15 ⊖	a	07 04	07 07	.	.	07 18	07 21	07 32	.	07 34	07 37	.	07 49	07 59	.	08 02	.	08 04	08 07	.	08 19	08 28	08 32	08 34	08 37

For general notes see front of timetable
For details of catering facilities see Directory of Train Operators

A From Kings Lynn (Table 17)

Cambridge, Stansted Airport, Bishops Stortford, Hertford East and Broxbourne → London

Network diagram - see first page of Table 20

		LE	LE 1	LE 1	XC 1 ◇	LE		LE	LE 1	LE 1	LE	LE 1	LE 1	LE	LE 1	LE 1	XC 1 ◇	LE	LE 1	LE 1	LE 1	LE 1	LE 1	LE 1	LE 1
										🛒		A	🛒			🛒			A	🛒			🛒		
Cambridge	d		07 21		07 29				07 48			07 51			08 18		08 09		08 21						08 51
Shelford	d		07 26									07 56							08 26						08 56
Whittlesford Parkway	d		07 30						07 55			08 00			08 25				08 30						09 00
Great Chesterford	d		07 34									08 04							08 34						09 04
Audley End	d		07 40		07 44				08 04			08 10			08 34		08 24		08 40						09 10
Newport (Essex)	d		07 43									08 13							08 43						09 13
Elsenham	d		07 49									08 19							08 49						09 19
Stansted Airport ✈	a				08 08												08 45								
✈	d			08 00						08 15			08 30			08 45				09 00			09 15		
Stansted Mountfitchet	d		07 52									08 22				08 51			08 52						09 22
Bishops Stortford	a		07 58	08 09					08 17			08 28	08 39		08 48				08 58	09 09					09 28
	d		07 58	08 09				08 12	08 17			08 28	08 39		08 48				08 58	09 09		09 14			09 28
Sawbridgeworth	d		08 03					08 16	08 22			08 33							09 03			09 18			09 32
Harlow Mill	d		08 06					08 20				08 36							09 06			09 22			09 36
Harlow Town	d		08 10					08 23	08 27	08 31		08 40			08 57	09 02			09 10			09 25	09 30		09 39
Roydon	d		08 14					08 27				08 44							09 14			09 29			09 43
Hertford East	d					08 09								08 39							09 09				
Ware	d					08 13								08 43							09 13				
St Margarets (Herts)	d					08 17								08 47							09 17				
Rye House	d					08 20								08 50							09 20				
Broxbourne 3	a		08 18			08 25		08 32	08 34		←	08 48		08 55	09 03				09 18		09 25	09 34			09 47
	d	08 10	08 18			08 25		08 40	08 35		08 40	08 48		08 55	09 04			09 10	09 18		09 25	09 37		←	09 47
Cheshunt	d	08 14	08 23			08 30		→			08 44	08 53		09 00				09 14	09 23		09 30	09 42		09 42	09 51
Waltham Cross	d	08 17				08 32					08 47			09 02				09 17			09 32	→			
Enfield Lock	d	08 19				08 35					08 49			09 05				09 19			09 35			09 45	
Brimsdown	d					08 37								09 07							09 37				
Ponders End	d					08 39								09 09							09 39				
Angel Road	d	08 24									08 54							09 24						09 50	
Northumberland Park	d	08 26									08 56							09 26						09 52	
Tottenham Hale ⊖	d	08 29	08 32	08 35		08 45			08 48	08 51	08 59	09 02	09 05	09 15	09 18	09 21		09 29	09 32	09 35	09 45		09 48	09 56	10 00
Seven Sisters ⊖	d																								
Clapton	d																								
Stratford 7 ⊖	a	08 43									09 13							09 43						10 08	
Hackney Downs	d					08 51								09 21							09 51				
Bethnal Green	d																								
London Liverpool Street 15 ⊖	a		08 49	08 52		09 02			09 04	09 07		09 19	09 22	09 32	09 34	09 37			09 49	09 52	10 00		10 05		10 13

		LE 1	LE	LE 1	XC 1 ◇	LE 1	LE 1	LE		LE 1	LE 1	LE 1	LE 1	LE 1	LE 1	LE 1	XC 1 ◇	LE 1	LE 1	LE 1	LE 1	LE 1	LE 1	LE 1	LE 1
		🛒		🛒	🛒		🛒				🛒			🛒		🛒	🛒		🛒			🛒			🛒
Cambridge	d				09 10	09 32							09 48				10 10	10 32						10 48	
Shelford	d												09 53											10 53	
Whittlesford Parkway	d					09 39							10b00					10 39						11c00	
Great Chesterford	d												10 04											11 04	
Audley End	d				09 24	09 47							10 10				10 24	10 47						11 10	
Newport (Essex)	d												10 13											11 13	
Elsenham	d												10 19											11 19	
Stansted Airport ✈	a				09 45												10 45								
✈	d	09 30		09 45			10 00				10 15			10 30		10 45			11 00		11 03	11 15			11 30
Stansted Mountfitchet	d			09 51									10 22								11 09			11 22	
Bishops Stortford	a	09 39				10 00	10 09						10 28	10 39				11 00	11 09		11 13			11 28	11 39
	d	09 39				10 00	10 09			10 14			10 28	10 39				11 00	11 09		11 14			11 28	11 39
Sawbridgeworth	d					10 05				10 18			10 32					11 05			11 18			11 32	
Harlow Mill	d									10 22			10 36								11 22			11 36	
Harlow Town	d			10 02		10 10				10 25	10 30		10 39			11 00		11 10			11 25	11 30		11 39	
Roydon	d									10 29			10 43								11 29			11 43	
Hertford East	d		09 39					10 09							10 39					11 09					
Ware	d		09 43					10 13							10 43					11 13					
St Margarets (Herts)	d		09 47					10 17							10 47					11 17					
Rye House	d		09 50					10 20							10 50					11 20					
Broxbourne 3	a		09 54			10 16		10 24		10 34			10 47		10 54			11 16		11 24	11 34			11 47	
	d		09 54			10 16		10 24		10 37		←	10 47		10 54			11 16		11 24	11 37		←	11 47	
Cheshunt	d		09 58			10 20		10 28		10 42		10 42	10 51		10 58			11 20		11 28	11 42		11 42	11 51	
Waltham Cross	d		10 01					10 31		→					11 01					11 31	→				
Enfield Lock	d		10 03					10 33				10 45			11 03					11 33			11 45		
Brimsdown	d		10 06					10 36							11 06					11 36					
Ponders End	d		10 08					10 38							11 08					11 38					
Angel Road	d																								
Northumberland Park	d											10 51											11 51		
Tottenham Hale ⊖	d	10 03	10 14	10 17		10 29	10 32	10 44			10 47	10 55	11 00	11 03	11 14	11 17		11 29	11 32	11 44		11 47	11 55	12 00	12 03
Seven Sisters ⊖	d																								
Clapton	d																								
Stratford 7 ⊖	a											11 05											12 05		
Hackney Downs	d		10 20					10 50							11 20					11 50					
Bethnal Green	d																								
London Liverpool Street 15 ⊖	a	10 18	10 28	10 31		10 43	10 46	10 58			11 01		11 13	11 17	11 28	11 31		11 43	11 46	11 58		12 01		12 13	12 17

For general notes see front of timetable
For details of catering facilities see Directory of Train Operators

A From Ely (Table 17)
b Arr. 0957
c Arr. 1057

Cambridge, Stansted Airport, Bishops Stortford, Hertford East and Broxbourne → London

Network diagram - see first page of Table 20

		LE	LE	XC	LE	LE	LE	LE	LE	LE		LE	LE	LE	LE	XC	LE	LE	LE	LE	LE	LE	LE	LE	LE
		[1]	[1] 🛒	[1] ◊ 🛒	[1]	[1] 🛒	[1]	[1]	[1] 🛒	[1]		[1]	[1] 🛒	[1]	[1] 🛒	[1] ◊ 🛒	[1]	[1] 🛒	[1]	[1]	[1] 🛒	[1]	[1]	[1] 🛒	[1]
Cambridge	d			11 10	11 32							11 51				12 10	12 32						12 51		
Shelford	d											11 56											12 56		
Whittlesford Parkway	d				11 39							12 00					12 39						13 00		
Great Chesterford	d											12 04											13 04		
Audley End	d			11 24	11 47							12 10				12 24	12 47						13 10		
Newport (Essex)	d											12 13											13 13		
Elsenham	d											12 19											13 19		
Stansted Airport ✈	a			11 45												12 45									
✈	d		11 45			12 00		12 03	12 15				12 30		12 45			13 00		13 03	13 15			13 30	
Stansted Mountfitchet	d							12 09				12 22								13 09			13 22		
Bishops Stortford	a				12 00	12 09		12 13				12 28	12 39				13 00	13 09		13 13			13 28	13 39	
	d				12 00	12 09		12 14				12 28	12 39				13 00	13 09		13 14			13 28	13 39	
Sawbridgeworth	d				12 05			12 18				12 32					13 05			13 18			13 32		
Harlow Mill	d							12 22				12 36								13 22			13 36		
Harlow Town	d		12 00		12 10			12 25	12 30			12 39			13 00		13 10			13 25	13 30		13 39		
Roydon	d							12 29				12 43								13 29			13 43		
Hertford East	d	11 39					12 09							12 39					13 09						13 39
Ware	d	11 43					12 13							12 43					13 13						13 43
St Margarets (Herts)	d	11 47					12 17							12 47					13 17						13 47
Rye House	d	11 50					12 20							12 50					13 20						13 50
Broxbourne [3]	a	11 54			12 16		12 24	12 34				12 47		12 54			13 16		13 24	13 34			13 47		13 54
	d	11 54			12 16		12 24	12 37		←		12 47		12 54			13 16		13 24	13 37		←	13 47		13 54
Cheshunt	d	11 58			12 20		12 28	12 42		12 42		12 51		12 58			13 20		13 28	13 42		13 42	13 51		13 58
Waltham Cross	d	12 01					12 31	→						13 01					13 31	→					14 01
Enfield Lock	d	12 03					12 33			12 45				13 03					13 33			13 45			14 03
Brimsdown	d	12 06					12 36							13 06					13 36						14 06
Ponders End	d	12 08					12 38							13 08					13 38						14 08
Angel Road	d																								
Northumberland Park	d									12 51												13 51			
Tottenham Hale ⊖	d	12 14	12 17		12 29	12 32	12 44		12 47	12 55		13 00	13 03	13 14	13 17		13 29	13 32	13 44		13 47	13 55	14 00	14 03	14 14
Seven Sisters ⊖	d																								
Clapton	d																								
Stratford [7] ⊖	a									13 05												14 05			
Hackney Downs	d	12 20					12 50							13 20					13 50						14 20
Bethnal Green	d																								
London Liverpool Street [15] ⊖	a	12 28	12 31		12 43	12 46	12 58		13 01			13 13	13 17	13 28	13 31		13 43	13 46	13 58		14 01		14 13	14 17	14 28

		LE	XC	LE	LE MFO	LE MFX	LE	LE	LE	LE	LE MFO	LE MFX		LE	LE	LE	XC	LE	LE	LE	LE	LE	LE	LE	LE
		[1] 🛒	[1] ◊ 🛒	[1]	[1] 🛒	[1] 🛒	[1]	[1]	[1] 🛒	[1]	[1]	[1]		[1] 🛒	[1]	[1] 🛒	[1] ◊ 🛒	[1]	[1] 🛒	[1]	[1]	[1] 🛒	[1]	[1]	[1] 🛒
Cambridge	d		13 10	13 32							13 51	13 51					14 10	14 32						14 51	
Shelford	d										13 56	13 56												14 56	
Whittlesford Parkway	d			13 39							14 00	14 00						14 39						15 00	
Great Chesterford	d										14 04	14 04												15 04	
Audley End	d		13 24	13 47							14 10	14 10					14 24	14 47						15 10	
Newport (Essex)	d										14 13	14 13												15 13	
Elsenham	d										14 19	14 19												15 19	
Stansted Airport ✈	a		13 45														14 45								
✈	d	13 45			14 00	14 00		14 03	14 15					14 30		14 45			15 00		15 03	15 15			15 30
Stansted Mountfitchet	d							14 09			14 22	14 22									15 09			15 22	
Bishops Stortford	a			14 00	14 09	14 09		14 13			14 28	14 28		14 39				15 00	15 09		15 13			15 28	15 39
	d			14 00	14 09	14 09		14 14			14 28	14 28		14 39				15 00	15 09		15 14			15 28	15 39
Sawbridgeworth	d			14 05				14 18			14 32	14 32						15 05			15 18			15 32	
Harlow Mill	d							14 22			14 36	14 36									15 22			15 36	
Harlow Town	d	14 00		14 10				14 25	14 30		14 39	14 39				15 00		15 10			15 25	15 30		15 39	
Roydon	d							14 29			14 43	14 43									15 29			15 43	
Hertford East	d						14 09								14 39					15 09					
Ware	d						14 13								14 43					15 13					
St Margarets (Herts)	d						14 17								14 47					15 17					
Rye House	d						14 20								14 50					15 20					
Broxbourne [3]	a			14 16			14 24	14 34			14 47	14 47			14 54			15 16		15 24	15 34			15 47	
	d			14 16			14 24	14 37		←	14 47	14 47			14 54			15 16		15 24	15 37		←	15 47	
Cheshunt	d			14 20			14 28	14 42		14 42	14 51	14 51			14 58			15 20		15 28	15 42		15 42	15 51	
Waltham Cross	d						14 31	→							15 01					15 31	→				
Enfield Lock	d						14 33			14 45					15 03					15 33			15 45		
Brimsdown	d						14 36								15 06					15 36					
Ponders End	d						14 38								15 08					15 38					
Angel Road	d																						15 50		
Northumberland Park	d									14 51													15 52		
Tottenham Hale ⊖	d	14 17		14 29	14 32	14 32	14 44		14 47	14 55	15 00	15 00		15 03	15 14	15 17		15 29	15 32	15 44		15 47	15 56	16 00	16 03
Seven Sisters ⊖	d																								
Clapton	d																								
Stratford [7] ⊖	a									15 05													16 06		
Hackney Downs	d						14 50								15 20					15 50					
Bethnal Green	d																								
London Liverpool Street [15] ⊖	a	14 31		14 43	14 46	14 48	14 58		15 01		15 13	15 15		15 17	15 28	15 31		15 45	15 47	15 58		16 01		16 13	16 17

For general notes see front of timetable
For details of catering facilities see Directory of Train Operators

Cambridge, Stansted Airport, Bishops Stortford, Hertford East and Broxbourne → London

Network diagram - see first page of Table 20

		LE 1	LE 1	LE 1 🍴	XC 1 ◇ 🍴	LE 1	LE 1	LE 1 🍴	LE 1	LE 1	LE 1 🍴	LE 1	LE 1	LE 1 🍴		LE 1	LE 1 🍴	XC 1 ◇ 🍴	LE 1	LE 1	LE 1 🍴	LE 1	LE 1	LE 1 🍴	LE 1
Cambridge	d				15 10		15 21						15 51					16 10		16 21					
Shelford	d						15 26						15 56							16 26					
Whittlesford Parkway	d						15 30						16 00							16 30					
Great Chesterford	d						15 34						16 04							16 34					
Audley End	d				15 24		15 40						16 10					16 24		16 40					
Newport (Essex)	d						15 43						16 13							16 43					
Elsenham	d						15 49						16 19							16 49					
Stansted Airport ✈	a				15 45													16 45							
✈	d			15 45				16 00		16 03	16 15			16 30			16 45				17 00		17 03	17 15	
Stansted Mountfitchet	d						15 52			16 09			16 22							16 52			17 09		
Bishops Stortford	a						15 58	16 09		16 13			16 28	16 39						16 58	17 09		17 13		
	d		15 48				15 58	16 09		16 14			16 28	16 39						16 58	17 09		17 14		
Sawbridgeworth	d						16 02			16 18			16 32							17 02			17 18		
Harlow Mill	d						16 06			16 22			16 36							17 06			17 22		
Harlow Town	d		15 56	16 00			16 09			16 25	16 30		16 39				17 00			17 09			17 25	17 30	
Roydon	d						16 13			16 29			16 43							17 13			17 29		
Hertford East	d	15 39							16 09							16 39						17 12			
Ware	d	15 43							16 13							16 43						17 16			
St Margarets (Herts)	d	15 47							16 17							16 47						17 20			
Rye House	d	15 50							16 20							16 50						17 23			
Broxbourne 3	a	15 54	16 03				16 17		16 24	16 34			16 47			16 54				17 17		17 27	17 34		
	d	15 54	16 07				16 17		16 24	16 37		⟵	16 47			16 54			17 09	17 17		17 27	17 37		⟵
Cheshunt	d	15 58	16 12				16 21		16 28	16 42		16 42	16 51			16 58			17 13	17 21		17 31	17 42		17 42
Waltham Cross	d	16 01				⟵			16 31	⟶						17 01						17 34	⟶		
Enfield Lock	d	16 03	16 15			16 15			16 33			16 45				17 03			17 17			17 36			17 45
Brimsdown	d	16 06	⟶						16 36							17 06						17 39			
Ponders End	d	16 08							16 38							17 08						17 41			
Angel Road	d					16 20						16 50							17 22						17 50
Northumberland Park	d					16 22						16 52							17 24						17 52
Tottenham Hale ⊖	d	16 14		16 17		16 26	16 30	16 33	16 44		16 47	16 56	17 00	17 03		17 14	17 17		17 27	17 30	17 33	17 46		17 49	17 56
Seven Sisters ⊖	d																								
Clapton	d																								
Stratford 7 ⊖ ⛴	a					16 39						17 10							17 40						18 10
Hackney Downs	d	16 20							16 50							17 20						17 52			
Bethnal Green	d																								
London Liverpool Street 15 ⊖	a	16 29		16 31			16 43	16 48	16 58		17 03		17 13	17 17		17 30	17 32			17 44	17 48	18 01		18 03	

		LE 1	LE 1 🍴	LE 1	LE 1 🍴	XC 1 ◇ 🍴	LE 1	LE 1	LE 1 🍴	LE 1	LE 1 🍴	LE 1	LE 1	LE 1 🍴	LE 1	LE 1 🍴		XC 1 ◇ 🍴	LE 1	LE 1 🍴	LE 1	LE 1 🍴	LE 1	LE 1	LE 1 🍴
Cambridge	d	16 51				17 10		17 21					17 51					18 18	18 21					18 51	
Shelford	d	16 56						17 26					17 56						18 26					18 56	
Whittlesford Parkway	d	17 00						17 30					18 00						18 30					19 00	
Great Chesterford	d	17 04						17 34					18 04						18 34					19 04	
Audley End	d	17 10				17 24		17 40					18 10					18 32	18 40					19 10	
Newport (Essex)	d	17 13						17 43					18 13						18 43					19 13	
Elsenham	d	17 19						17 49					18 19						18 49					19 19	
Stansted Airport ✈	a					17 45												18 50							
✈	d		17 30		17 45				18 00		18 15			18 30		18 45				19 00		19 15			19 30
Stansted Mountfitchet	d	17 22						17 52	18 06				18 22						18 52	19 06				19 22	
Bishops Stortford	a	17 28	17 39					17 58	18 10				18 28	18 39					18 58	19 10				19 28	19 39
	d	17 28	17 39					17 58	18 11				18 28	18 39					19 00	19 11				19 28	19 39
Sawbridgeworth	d	17 32						18 02					18 32						19 05					19 32	
Harlow Mill	d	17 36						18 06					18 36											19 36	
Harlow Town	d	17 39			18 00			18 09			18 30		18 39			19 00			19 10			19 30		19 39	
Roydon	d	17 43						18 13					18 43											19 43	
Hertford East	d			17 40						18 13		18 18			18 40						19 12		19 18		
Ware	d			17 44								18 22			18 44						19 16		19 22		
St Margarets (Herts)	d			17 48								18 26			18 48						19 20		19 26		
Rye House	d			17 51								18 29			18 51						19 23		19 29		
Broxbourne 3	a	17 47		17 55				18 17		18 27		18 33	18 47		18 57				19 16		19 27		19 33	19 47	
	d	17 47		17 55			18 09	18 17		18 27		18 37	18 47		18 57				19 16		19 27		19 37	19 47	
Cheshunt	d	17 51		17 59			18 13	18 21		18 31		18 42	18 51		19 01				19 20		19 31		19 42	19 51	
Waltham Cross	d			18 02						18 34					19 04						19 34				
Enfield Lock	d			18 04			18 17			18 36		18 45			19 06						19 36		19 45		
Brimsdown	d			18 07						18 39					19 09						19 39				
Ponders End	d			18 09						18 41					19 11						19 41				
Angel Road	d						18 22					18 50											19 50		
Northumberland Park	d						18 24					18 52											19 52		
Tottenham Hale ⊖	d	18 00	18 03	18 14	18 18		18 27	18 30	18 33	18 46	18 49	18 56	19 00	19 03	19 16	19 19			19 29	19 32	19 46	19 49	19 56	20 00	20 03
Seven Sisters ⊖	d																								
Clapton	d																								
Stratford 7 ⊖ ⛴	a						18 40					19 10											20 06		
Hackney Downs	d			18 20						18 52					19 22						19 52				
Bethnal Green	d																								
London Liverpool Street 15 ⊖	a	18 13	18 17	18 31	18 33			18 44	18 48	19 01	19 03		19 13	19 17	19 31	19 33			19 43	19 46	20 01	20 03		20 13	20 17

For general notes see front of timetable
For details of catering facilities see Directory of Train Operators

Cambridge, Stansted Airport, Bishops Stortford, Hertford East and Broxbourne → London

Network diagram - see first page of Table 20

Station		LE	LE	XC	LE	LE	LE	LE	LE	LE	LE	LE	LE	LE	XC	LE	LE	LE		LE	LE	LE	LE	LE	LE
		1	1 🚲	1 ◇ 🚲	1	1 🚲	1	1	1 🚲	1	1	1 🚲	1	1 🚲	1 ◇ 🚲	1	1	1		1	1	1	1	1	1
Cambridge	d			19 10	19 21						19 51				20 10	20 32							20 51		
Shelford	d				19 26						19 56												20 56		
Whittlesford Parkway	d				19 30						20 00					20 39							21 00		
Great Chesterford	d				19 34						20 04												21 04		
Audley End	d			19 24	19 40						20 10				20 24	20 47							21 10		
Newport (Essex)	d				19 43						20 13												21 13		
Elsenham	d				19 49						20 19												21 19		
Stansted Airport ✈	a			19 45											20 45										
	d		19 45			20 00		20 03	20 15			20 30		20 45			21 00			21 03	21 15			21 30	
Stansted Mountfitchet	d				19 53			20 09			20 22									21 09			21 22		
Bishops Stortford	a				20 00	20 09		20 13			20 28	20 39				21 00	21 09			21 13			21 28	21 39	
	d				20 00	20 09		20 14			20 28	20 39				21 00	21 09			21 14			21 28	21 39	
Sawbridgeworth	d				20 05			20 18			20 32					21 05				21 18			21 32		
Harlow Mill	d							20 22			20 36									21 22			21 36		
Harlow Town	d		20 00		20 10			20 25	20 30		20 39			21 00		21 10				21 25	21 30		21 39		
Roydon	d							20 29			20 43									21 29			21 43		
Hertford East	d	19 40					20 10						20 39					21 09							21 39
Ware	d	19 44					20 14						20 43					21 13							21 43
St Margarets (Herts)	d	19 48					20 18						20 47					21 17							21 47
Rye House	d	19 51					20 21						20 50					21 20							21 50
Broxbourne 3	a	19 57			20 16		20 25	20 34			20 47		20 54			21 16		21 24		21 34			21 47		21 54
	d	19 57			20 16		20 25	20 40		←	20 47		20 54			21 16		21 24		21 37		←	21 47		21 54
Cheshunt	d	20 01			20 20		20 29	20 45		20 45	20 51		20 58			21 20		21 28		21 42		21 42	21 51		21 58
Waltham Cross	d	20 03					20 32	→					21 01					21 31		→					22 01
Enfield Lock	d	20 06					20 34			20 48			21 03					21 33				21 45			22 03
Brimsdown	d	20 08					20 37						21 06					21 36							22 06
Ponders End	d	20 10					20 39						21 08					21 38							22 08
Angel Road	d																								
Northumberland Park	d									20 54												21 51			
Tottenham Hale ⊖	d	20 15	20 18		20 29	20 32	20 45		20 48	20 57	21 00	21 03	21 14	21 17		21 29	21 32	21 44			21 47	21 55	22 00	22 03	22 14
Seven Sisters ⊖	d																								
Clapton	d																								
Stratford 7 ⊖ ⛴	a									21 08												22 05			
Hackney Downs	d	20 22					20 50						21 20					21 50							22 20
Bethnal Green	d																								
London Liverpool Street 15 ⊖	a	20 31	20 33		20 45	20 47	21 01		21 03		21 14	21 17	21 28	21 31		21 43	21 46	21 58			22 01		22 13	22 17	22 28

Station		LE	XC	LE	LE	LE	LE	LE	LE	LE	LE	LE	XC	LE	LE	LE	LE	LE	LE	LE	LE	LE	LE		
		1	1 ◇ 🚲	1	1	1	1	1	1	1	1	1	1 ◇ 🚲	1	1	1	1	1	1	1	1	1	1		
Cambridge	d		21 10	21 32					21 51				22 10	22 32					22 51						
Shelford	d								21 56										22 56						
Whittlesford Parkway	d			21 39					22 00					22 39					23 00						
Great Chesterford	d								22 04										23 04						
Audley End	d		21 24	21 47					22 10				22 24	22 47					23 10						
Newport (Essex)	d								22 13										23 13						
Elsenham	d								22 19										23 19						
Stansted Airport ✈	a		21 45										22 45												
	d	21 45			22 00		22 03	22 15		22 30		22 45			23 00		23 03	23 15		23 30		23 45	23 59		
Stansted Mountfitchet	d						22 09		22 22								23 09		23 22						
Bishops Stortford	a			22 00	22 09		22 13		22 28	22 39				23 00	23 09		23 13		23 28	23 39			00 08		
	d			22 00	22 09				22 28	22 39				23 00	23 09				23 28	23 39			00 08		
Sawbridgeworth	d			22 05					22 32					23 05					23 32						
Harlow Mill	d								22 36										23 36						
Harlow Town	d	22 00		22 10				22 30	22 39			23 00		23 10				23 30	23 39			23 59	00 16		
Roydon	d								22 43										23 43						
Hertford East	d					22 09					22 39					23 09					23 39				
Ware	d					22 13					22 43					23 13					23 43				
St Margarets (Herts)	d					22 17					22 47					23 17					23 47				
Rye House	d					22 20					22 50					23 20					23 50				
Broxbourne 3	a			22 16		22 24			22 47		22 54			23 16		23 24			23 47		23 54				
	d			22 16		22 24			22 47		22 54			23 16		23 24			23 47		23 54				
Cheshunt	d			22 20		22 28			22 51		22 58			23 20		23 28			23 51		23 58				
Waltham Cross	d					22 31					23 01					23 31									
Enfield Lock	d					22 33					23 03					23 33									
Brimsdown	d					22 36					23 06					23 36									
Ponders End	d					22 38					23 08					23 38									
Angel Road	d																								
Northumberland Park	d																								
Tottenham Hale ⊖	d	22 17		22 29	22 32	22 44		22 47	23 00	23 03	23 14	23 17		23 29	23 32	23 44		23 47							
Seven Sisters ⊖	d																		00 04	00 07	00 11	00 21			
Clapton	d																								
Stratford 7 ⊖ ⛴	a																								
Hackney Downs	d					22 50					23 20					23 50					00 16				
Bethnal Green	d																								
London Liverpool Street 15 ⊖	a	22 31		22 43	22 46	22 58		23 01	23 13	23 17	23 28	23 31		23 43	23 46	23 58		00 01	00 18	00 22	00 25	00 36	00 51		

For general notes see front of timetable
For details of catering facilities see Directory of Train Operators

Table 22

Saturdays

Cambridge, Stansted Airport, Bishops Stortford, Hertford East and Broxbourne → London

Network diagram - see first page of Table 20

		LE 1	LE 1	LE 1	LE 1	LE 1	LE 1	LE 1	LE 1	LE 1	LE 1	XC 1 ◇ 🚲	LE 1	LE 1	LE 1	LE 1	LE 1	XC 1 ◇ 🚲	LE 1	LE 1	LE 1	LE 1	LE 1	LE 1	XC 1 ◇ 🚲
Cambridge	d	22p51								04 25		04 56		05 21				05 42			05 51				06 25
Shelford	d	22p56												05 26							05 56				
Whittlesford Parkway	d	23p00								04 32				05 30							06 00				
Great Chesterford	d	23p04												05 34							06 04				
Audley End	d	23p10								04 40				05 40				05 56			06 10				06 39
Newport (Essex)	d	23p13												05 43							06 13				
Elsenham	d	23p19												05 49							06 19				
Stansted Airport ✈	a											05 20						06 11							06 55
✈	d		23p30		23p45	23p59	00 30	01 00	01 30				05 30		06 00		06 03		06 15			06 30		06 45	
Stansted Mountfitchet	d	23p22												05 52			06 09				06 22			06 51	
Bishops Stortford	a	23p28	23p39			00 08	00 39			04 53			05 39	05 58	06 09		06 13				06 28	06 39			
	d	23p28	23p39			00 08	00 39			04 53	05 15		05 39	05 58	06 09		06 14				06 28	06 39			
Sawbridgeworth	d	23p32								04 58	05 19			06 02			06 18				06 32				
Harlow Mill	d	23p36								05 01	05 23			06 06			06 22				06 36				
Harlow Town	d	23p39			23p59	00 16	00 47			05 04	05 26			06 09			06 25		06 30		06 39			07 02	
Roydon	d	23p43								05 08	05 30			06 13			06 29				06 43				
Hertford East	d			23p39												06 09							06 39		
Ware	d			23p43												06 13							06 43		
St Margarets (Herts)	d			23p47												06 17							06 47		
Rye House	d			23p50												06 20							06 50		
Broxbourne 3	a	23p47		23p54						05 12	05 34			06 17		06 24	06 34				06 47		06 54		
	d	23p47		23p54						05 12	05 34			06 17		06 24	06 37			←	06 47		06 54		
Cheshunt	d	23p51		23p58						05 16	05 38			06 21		06 28	06 42			06 42	06 51		06 58		
Waltham Cross	d										05 40					06 31	→						07 01		
Enfield Lock	d										05 43					06 33				06 45			07 03		
Brimsdown	d										05 45					06 36							07 06		
Ponders End	d										05 47					06 38							07 08		
Angel Road	d																								
Northumberland Park	d										05 51									06 51					
Tottenham Hale ⊖	d										05 55		06 01	06 30	06 33	06 44			06 47	06 55	07 00	07 03	07 14	07 17	
Seven Sisters ⊖	d	00 04	00 07	00 11	00 21					05 36															
Clapton	d																								
Stratford 7 ⊖	a										06 04									07 05					
Hackney Downs	d			00 16						05 45						06 50							07 20		
Bethnal Green	d									05 49															
London Liverpool Street 15 ⊖	a	00 18	00 22	00 25	00 36	00 51	01 21	01 50	02 20	05 54	06 14		06 15	06 43	06 47	06 58			07 01		07 13	07 17	07 28	07 31	

		LE 1	LE 1	LE 1	LE 1	LE 1	LE 1	LE 1	LE 1	LE 1	LE 1	XC 1 ◇ 🚲	LE 1	LE 1	LE 1	LE 1	LE 1 🚲	LE 1	LE 1	LE 1 🚲	LE 1		LE 1 🚲	XC 1 ◇ A 🚲	LE 1
Cambridge	d	06 32						06 51				07 25	07 32						07 51					08 10	08 32
Shelford	d							06 56											07 56						
Whittlesford Parkway	d	06 39						07 00					07 39						08 00						08 39
Great Chesterford	d							07 04											08 04						
Audley End	d	06 47						07 10				07 39	07 47						08 10					08 24	08 47
Newport (Essex)	d							07 13											08 13						
Elsenham	d							07 19											08 19						
Stansted Airport ✈	a											07 55												08 45	
✈	d		07 00		07 03	07 15			07 30		07 45			08 00		08 03	08 15			08 30			08 45		
Stansted Mountfitchet	d				07 09			07 22			07 51					08 09			08 22				08 51		
Bishops Stortford	a	07 00	07 09		07 13			07 28	07 39				08 00	08 09		08 13			08 28	08 39					09 00
	d	07 00	07 09		07 14			07 28	07 39				08 00	08 09		08 14			08 28	08 39					09 00
Sawbridgeworth	d	07 05			07 18			07 32					08 05			08 18			08 32						09 05
Harlow Mill	d				07 22			07 36								08 22			08 36						
Harlow Town	d	07 10			07 25	07 30		07 39			08 02		08 10			08 25	08 30		08 39				09 02		09 10
Roydon	d				07 29			07 43								08 29			08 43						
Hertford East	d			07 09						07 39					08 09						08 39				
Ware	d			07 13						07 43					08 13						08 43				
St Margarets (Herts)	d			07 17						07 47					08 17						08 47				
Rye House	d			07 20						07 50					08 20						08 50				
Broxbourne 3	a	07 16		07 24	07 34			07 47		07 54			08 16		08 24	08 34			08 47		08 54				09 16
	d	07 16		07 24	07 37		←	07 47		07 54			08 16		08 24	08 37		←	08 47		08 54				09 16
Cheshunt	d	07 20		07 28	07 42		07 42	07 51		07 58			08 20		08 28	08 42		08 42	08 51		08 58				09 20
Waltham Cross	d			07 31	→					08 01					08 31	→					09 01				
Enfield Lock	d			07 33			07 45			08 03					08 33			08 45			09 03				
Brimsdown	d			07 36						08 06					08 36						09 06				
Ponders End	d			07 38						08 08					08 38						09 08				
Angel Road	d																								
Northumberland Park	d						07 51											08 51							
Tottenham Hale ⊖	d	07 29	07 32	07 44		07 47	07 55	08 00	08 03	08 14	08 17		08 29	08 32	08 44		08 47	08 55	09 00	09 03	09 14		09 17		09 29
Seven Sisters ⊖	d																								
Clapton	d																								
Stratford 7 ⊖	a						08 05											09 05							
Hackney Downs	d			07 50						08 20					08 50						09 20				
Bethnal Green	d																								
London Liverpool Street 15 ⊖	a	07 43	07 46	07 58		08 01		08 13	08 17	08 28	08 31		08 43	08 46	08 58		09 01		09 13	09 17	09 28		09 31		09 43

For general notes see front of timetable
For details of catering facilities see Directory of Train Operators

A Until 11 July and from 12 September

Table 22

Saturdays

Cambridge, Stansted Airport, Bishops Stortford, Hertford East and Broxbourne → London

Network diagram - see first page of Table 20

		LE 1	LE 1	LE 1	LE 1	LE 1	LE 1	LE 1	LE 1	LE 1	XC 1 ◇	LE 1	LE 1	LE 1	LE 1	LE 1	LE 1	LE 1	LE 1	LE 1	LE 1	XC 1 ◇	LE 1	LE 1	LE 1
												A													
		🚲			🚲			🚲		🚲	🚲		🚲			🚲			🚲		🚲	🚲		🚲	
Cambridge	d						08 51				09 10	09 32						09 51				10 18	10 32		
Shelford	d						08 56											09 56							
Whittlesford Parkway	d						09 00					09 39						10 00					10 39		
Great Chesterford	d						09 04											10 04							
Audley End	d						09 10				09 24	09 47						10 10				10 32	10 47		
Newport (Essex)	d						09 13											10 13							
Elsenham	d						09 19											10 19							
Stansted Airport ✈	a										09 45											10 50			
✈	d	09 00		09 03	09 15			09 30		09 45			10 00		10 03	10 15			10 30		10 45			11 00	
Stansted Mountfitchet	d			09 09			09 22			09 51					10 09			10 22			10 51				
Bishops Stortford	a	09 09		09 13			09 28	09 39				10 00	10 09		10 13			10 28	10 39				11 00	11 09	
	d	09 09		09 14			09 28	09 39				10 00	10 09		10 14			10 28	10 39				11 00	11 09	
Sawbridgeworth	d			09 18			09 32					10 05			10 18			10 32					11 05		
Harlow Mill	d			09 22			09 36								10 22			10 36							
Harlow Town	d			09 25	09 30		09 39			10 02		10 10			10 25	10 30		10 39			11 02		11 10		
Roydon	d			09 29			09 43								10 29			10 43							
Hertford East	d		09 09						09 39					10 09						10 39					11 09
Ware	d		09 13						09 43					10 13						10 43					11 13
St Margarets (Herts)	d		09 17						09 47					10 17						10 47					11 17
Rye House	d		09 20						09 50					10 20						10 50					11 20
Broxbourne 3	a		09 24	09 34			09 47		09 54			10 16		10 24	10 34			10 47		10 54			11 16		11 24
	d		09 24	09 37		⟵	09 47		09 54			10 16		10 24	10 37		⟵	10 47		10 54			11 16		11 24
Cheshunt	d		09 28	09 42		09 42	09 51		09 58			10 20		10 28	10 42		10 42	10 51		10 58			11 20		11 28
Waltham Cross	d		09 31	⟶					10 01					10 31	⟶					11 01					11 31
Enfield Lock	d		09 33			09 45			10 03					10 33			10 45			11 03					11 33
Brimsdown	d		09 36						10 06					10 36						11 06					11 36
Ponders End	d		09 38						10 08					10 38						11 08					11 38
Angel Road	d																								
Northumberland Park	d					09 51											10 51								
Tottenham Hale ⊖	d	09 32	09 44		09 47	09 55	10 00	10 03	10 14	10 17		10 29	10 32	10 44		10 47	10 55	11 00	11 03	11 14	11 17		11 29	11 32	11 44
Seven Sisters ⊖	d																								
Clapton	d																								
Stratford 7 ⊖	a					10 05											11 05								
Hackney Downs	d		09 50						10 20					10 50						11 20					11 50
Bethnal Green	d																								
London Liverpool Street 15 ⊖	a	09 46	09 58		10 01		10 13	10 17	10 28	10 31		10 43	10 46	10 58		11 01		11 13	11 17	11 28	11 31		11 43	11 46	11 58

		LE 1	LE 1	LE 1	LE 1	LE 1	LE 1	LE 1	XC 1 ◇	LE 1	LE 1	LE 1	LE 1	LE 1	LE 1	LE 1	LE 1	LE 1	LE 1	XC 1 ◇		LE 1	LE 1	LE 1	LE 1
			🚲			🚲		🚲	🚲		🚲			🚲			🚲		🚲	🚲			🚲		
Cambridge	d				10 51				11 10	11 32						11 51				12 10		12 32			
Shelford	d				10 56											11 56									
Whittlesford Parkway	d				11 00					11 39						12 00						12 39			
Great Chesterford	d				11 04											12 04									
Audley End	d				11 10				11 24	11 47						12 10				12 24		12 47			
Newport (Essex)	d				11 13											12 13									
Elsenham	d				11 19											12 19									
Stansted Airport ✈	a								11 45											12 45					
✈	d	11 03	11 15			11 30		11 45			12 00		12 03	12 15			12 30		12 45				13 00		13 03
Stansted Mountfitchet	d	11 09			11 22			11 51					12 09			12 22			12 51						13 09
Bishops Stortford	a	11 13			11 28	11 39				12 00	12 09		12 13			12 28	12 39					13 00	13 09		13 13
	d	11 14			11 28	11 39				12 00	12 09		12 14			12 28	12 39					13 00	13 09		13 14
Sawbridgeworth	d	11 18			11 32					12 05			12 18			12 32						13 05			13 18
Harlow Mill	d	11 22			11 36								12 22			12 36									13 22
Harlow Town	d	11 25	11 30		11 39			12 02		12 10			12 25	12 30		12 39			13 02			13 10			13 25
Roydon	d	11 29			11 43								12 29			12 43									13 29
Hertford East	d						11 39					12 09						12 39						13 09	
Ware	d						11 43					12 13						12 43						13 13	
St Margarets (Herts)	d						11 47					12 17						12 47						13 17	
Rye House	d						11 50					12 20						12 50						13 20	
Broxbourne 3	a	11 34			11 47		11 54			12 16		12 24	12 34			12 47		12 54				13 16		13 24	13 34
	d	11 37		⟵	11 47		11 54			12 16		12 24	12 37		⟵	12 47		12 54				13 16		13 24	13 37
Cheshunt	d	11 42		11 42	11 51		11 58			12 20		12 28	12 42		12 42	12 51		12 58				13 20		13 28	13 42
Waltham Cross	d	⟶					12 01					12 31	⟶					13 01						13 31	⟶
Enfield Lock	d			11 45			12 03					12 33			12 45			13 03						13 33	
Brimsdown	d						12 06					12 36						13 06						13 36	
Ponders End	d						12 08					12 38						13 08						13 38	
Angel Road	d																								
Northumberland Park	d			11 51											12 51										
Tottenham Hale ⊖	d		11 47	11 55	12 00	12 03	12 14	12 17		12 29	12 32	12 44		12 47	12 55	13 00	13 03	13 14	13 17			13 29	13 32	13 44	
Seven Sisters ⊖	d																								
Clapton	d																								
Stratford 7 ⊖	a			12 05											13 05										
Hackney Downs	d						12 20					12 50						13 20						13 50	
Bethnal Green	d																								
London Liverpool Street 15 ⊖	a		12 01		12 13	12 17	12 28	12 31		12 43	12 46	12 58		13 01		13 13	13 17	13 28	13 31			13 43	13 46	13 58	

For general notes see front of timetable
For details of catering facilities see Directory of Train Operators

A From Ely (Table 17)

Cambridge, Stansted Airport, Bishops Stortford, Hertford East and Broxbourne → London

Network diagram - see first page of Table 20

		LE	LE	LE	LE	LE	LE	XC	LE	LE	LE	LE	LE	LE	LE	LE	LE	LE	XC	LE	LE	LE	LE	LE	LE
		1 🛒	1	1	1 🛒	1	1 🛒	1◇ 🛒	1	1 🛒	1	1	1 🛒	1	1	1 🛒	1	1 🛒	1◇ 🛒	1	1 🛒	1	1	1 🛒	1
Cambridge	d			12 51				13 10	13 32						13 51				14 10	14 32					
Shelford	d			12 56											13 56										
Whittlesford Parkway	d			13 00					13 39						14 00					14 39					
Great Chesterford	d			13 04											14 04										
Audley End	d			13 10				13 24	13 47						14 10				14 24	14 47					
Newport (Essex)	d			13 13											14 13										
Elsenham	d			13 19											14 19										
Stansted Airport ✈	a							13 45											14 45						
	d	13 15			13 30		13 45			14 00		14 03	14 15			14 30		14 45			15 00		15 03	15 15	
Stansted Mountfitchet	d			13 22			13 51					14 09			14 22			14 51					15 09		
Bishops Stortford	a			13 28	13 39				14 00	14 09		14 13			14 28	14 39				15 00	15 09		15 13		
	d			13 28	13 39				14 00	14 09		14 14			14 28	14 39				15 00	15 09		15 14		
Sawbridgeworth	d			13 32					14 05			14 18			14 32					15 05			15 18		
Harlow Mill	d			13 36								14 22			14 36								15 22		
Harlow Town	d	13 30		13 39			14 02		14 10			14 25	14 30		14 39			15 02		15 10			15 25	15 30	
Roydon	d			13 43								14 29			14 43								15 29		
Hertford East	d					13 39					14 09						14 39					15 09			
Ware	d					13 43					14 13						14 43					15 13			
St Margarets (Herts)	d					13 47					14 17						14 47					15 17			
Rye House	d					13 50					14 20						14 50					15 20			
Broxbourne 3	a			13 47		13 54			14 16		14 24	14 34			14 47		14 54			15 16		15 24	15 34		
	d		←	13 47		13 54			14 16		14 24	14 37		←	14 47		14 54			15 16		15 24	15 37		←
Cheshunt	d		13 42	13 51		13 58			14 20		14 28	14 42		14 42	14 51		14 58			15 20		15 28	15 42		15 42
Waltham Cross	d					14 01					14 31	→					15 01					15 31	→		
Enfield Lock	d		13 45			14 03					14 33			14 45			15 03					15 33			15 45
Brimsdown	d					14 06					14 36						15 06					15 36			
Ponders End	d					14 08					14 38						15 08					15 38			
Angel Road	d																								
Northumberland Park	d		13 51											14 51											15 51
Tottenham Hale ⊖	d	13 47	13 55	14 00	14 03	14 14	14 17		14 29	14 32	14 44		14 47	14 55	15 00	15 03	15 14	15 17		15 29	15 32	15 44		15 47	15 55
Seven Sisters ⊖	d																								
Clapton	d																								
Stratford 7 ⊖	a		14 05											15 05											16 05
Hackney Downs	d					14 20					14 50						15 20					15 50			
Bethnal Green	d																								
London Liverpool Street 15 ⊖	a	14 01		14 13	14 17	14 28	14 31		14 43	14 46	14 58		15 01		15 13	15 17	15 28	15 31		15 43	15 46	15 58		16 01	

		LE	LE	LE	LE	XC	LE	LE	LE	LE	LE	LE	LE	LE	LE	LE	XC	LE	LE		LE	LE	LE	LE	LE
		1	1 🛒	1	1 🛒	1◇ 🛒	1	1 🛒	1	1	1 🛒	1	1	1 🛒	1	1 🛒	1◇ 🛒	1	1 🛒		1	1	1 🛒	1	1
Cambridge	d	14 51				15 10	15 32						15 51				16 10	16 32							16 51
Shelford	d	14 56											15 56												16 56
Whittlesford Parkway	d	15 00					15 39						16 00					16 39							17 00
Great Chesterford	d	15 04											16 04												17 04
Audley End	d	15 10				15 24	15 47						16 10				16 24	16 47							17 10
Newport (Essex)	d	15 13											16 13												17 13
Elsenham	d	15 19											16 19												17 19
Stansted Airport ✈	a					15 45											16 45								
	d		15 30		15 45			16 00		16 03	16 15			16 30		16 45			17 00			17 03	17 15		
Stansted Mountfitchet	d	15 22			15 51					16 09			16 22			16 51						17 09			17 22
Bishops Stortford	a	15 28	15 39				16 00	16 09		16 13			16 28	16 39				17 00	17 09			17 13			17 28
	d	15 28	15 39				16 00	16 09		16 14			16 28	16 39				17 00	17 09			17 14			17 28
Sawbridgeworth	d	15 32					16 05			16 18			16 32					17 05				17 18			17 32
Harlow Mill	d	15 36								16 22			16 36									17 22			17 36
Harlow Town	d	15 39			16 02		16 10			16 25	16 30		16 39			17 02		17 10				17 25	17 30		17 39
Roydon	d	15 43								16 29			16 43									17 29			17 43
Hertford East	d			15 39					16 09						16 39						17 09				
Ware	d			15 43					16 13						16 43						17 13				
St Margarets (Herts)	d			15 47					16 17						16 47						17 17				
Rye House	d			15 50					16 20						16 50						17 20				
Broxbourne 3	a	15 47		15 54			16 16		16 24	16 34			16 47		16 54			17 16			17 24	17 34			17 47
	d	15 47		15 54			16 16		16 24	16 37		←	16 47		16 54			17 16			17 24	17 37		←	17 47
Cheshunt	d	15 51		15 58			16 20		16 28	16 42		16 42	16 51		16 58			17 20			17 28	17 42		17 42	17 51
Waltham Cross	d			16 01					16 31	→					17 01						17 31	→			
Enfield Lock	d			16 03					16 33			16 45			17 03						17 33			17 45	
Brimsdown	d			16 06					16 36						17 06						17 36				
Ponders End	d			16 08					16 38						17 08						17 38				
Angel Road	d																								
Northumberland Park	d											16 51												17 51	
Tottenham Hale ⊖	d	16 00	16 03	16 14	16 17		16 29	16 32	16 44		16 47	16 55	17 00	17 03	17 14	17 17		17 29	17 32		17 44		17 47	17 55	18 00
Seven Sisters ⊖	d																								
Clapton	d																								
Stratford 7 ⊖	a											17 05												18 05	
Hackney Downs	d			16 20					16 50						17 20						17 50				
Bethnal Green	d																								
London Liverpool Street 15 ⊖	a	16 13	16 17	16 28	16 31		16 43	16 46	16 58		17 01		17 13	17 17	17 28	17 31		17 43	17 46		17 58		18 01		18 13

For general notes see front of timetable
For details of catering facilities see Directory of Train Operators

Table 22

Saturdays

Cambridge, Stansted Airport, Bishops Stortford, Hertford East and Broxbourne → London

Network diagram - see first page of Table 20

		LE	LE	LE	XC	LE	LE	LE	LE	LE	LE	LE	LE	LE	LE	XC	LE	LE	LE	LE	LE	LE	LE	LE	LE
		1	1	1	1 ◊	1	1	1	1	1	1	1	1	1	1	1 ◊	1	1	1	1	1	1	1	1	1
		🚲		🚲	🚲		🚲			🚲			🚲		🚲	🚲		🚲			🚲			🚲	
Cambridge	d				17 10	17 32						17 51				18 20	18 32						18 51		
Shelford	d											17 56											18 56		
Whittlesford Parkway	d					17 39						18 00					18 39						19 00		
Great Chesterford	d											18 04											19 04		
Audley End	d				17 24	17 47						18 10				18 34	18 47						19 10		
Newport (Essex)	d											18 13											19 13		
Elsenham	d											18 19											19 19		
Stansted Airport ✈	a				17 45											18 53									
✈	d	17 30		17 45			18 00		18 03	18 15			18 30		18 45			19 00		19 03	19 15			19 30	
Stansted Mountfitchet	d			17 51					18 09			18 22			18 51					19 09			19 22		
Bishops Stortford	a	17 39				18 00	18 09		18 13			18 28	18 39				19 00	19 09		19 13			19 28	19 39	
	d	17 39				18 00	18 09		18 14			18 28	18 39				19 00	19 09		19 14			19 28	19 39	
Sawbridgeworth	d					18 05			18 18			18 32					19 05			19 18			19 32		
Harlow Mill	d								18 22			18 36								19 22			19 36		
Harlow Town	d			18 02		18 10			18 25	18 30		18 39			19 02		19 10			19 25	19 30		19 39		
Roydon	d								18 29			18 43								19 29			19 43		
Hertford East	d		17 39					18 09						18 39					19 09						19 39
Ware	d		17 43					18 13						18 43					19 13						19 43
St Margarets (Herts)	d		17 47					18 17						18 47					19 17						19 47
Rye House	d		17 50					18 20						18 50					19 20						19 50
Broxbourne 3	a		17 54			18 16		18 24	18 34			18 47		18 54			19 16		19 24	19 34			19 47		19 54
	d		17 54			18 16		18 24	18 37		←	18 47		18 54			19 16		19 24	19 37		←	19 47		19 54
Cheshunt	d		17 58			18 20		18 28	18 42		18 42	18 51		18 58			19 20		19 28	19 42		19 42	19 51		19 58
Waltham Cross	d		18 01					18 31	→					19 01					19 31	→					20 01
Enfield Lock	d		18 03					18 33			18 45			19 03					19 33			19 45			20 03
Brimsdown	d		18 06					18 36						19 06					19 36						20 06
Ponders End	d		18 08					18 38						19 08					19 38						20 08
Angel Road	d																								
Northumberland Park	d										18 51											19 51			
Tottenham Hale ⊖	d	18 03	18 14	18 17		18 29	18 32	18 44		18 47	18 55	19 00	19 03	19 14	19 17		19 29	19 32	19 44		19 47	19 55	20 00	20 03	20 14
Seven Sisters ⊖	d																								
Clapton	d																								
Stratford 7 ⊖	a										19 05											20 05			
Hackney Downs	d		18 20					18 50						19 20					19 50						20 20
Bethnal Green	d																								
London Liverpool Street 15 ⊖	a	18 17	18 28	18 31		18 43	18 46	18 58		19 01		19 13	19 17	19 28	19 31		19 43	19 46	19 58		20 01		20 13	20 17	20 28

		LE	XC	LE	LE	LE	LE	LE	LE	LE	LE	LE	LE	XC	LE	LE	LE	LE	LE	LE	LE	LE	LE	LE	XC
		1	1 ◊	1	1	1	1	1	1	1	1	1	1	1 ◊	1	1	1	1	1	1	1	1	1	1	1 ◊
		🚲	🚲		🚲			🚲			🚲		🚲	🚲											🚲
Cambridge	d		19 10	19 32						19 51				20 10	20 32						20 51				21 10
Shelford	d									19 56											20 56				
Whittlesford Parkway	d			19 39						20 00					20 39						21 00				
Great Chesterford	d									20 04											21 04				
Audley End	d		19 24	19 47						20 10				20 24	20 47						21 10				21 24
Newport (Essex)	d									20 13											21 13				
Elsenham	d									20 19											21 19				
Stansted Airport ✈	a		19 45											20 45											21 45
✈	d	19 45			20 00		20 03	20 15			20 30		20 45			21 00		21 03	21 15			21 30		21 45	
Stansted Mountfitchet	d	19 51					20 09			20 22			20 51					21 09			21 22			21 51	
Bishops Stortford	a			20 00	20 09		20 13			20 28	20 39				21 00	21 09		21 13			21 28	21 39			
	d			20 00	20 09		20 14			20 28	20 39				21 00	21 09		21 14			21 28	21 39			
Sawbridgeworth	d			20 05			20 18			20 32					21 05			21 18			21 32				
Harlow Mill	d						20 22			20 36								21 22			21 36				
Harlow Town	d	20 02		20 10			20 25	20 30		20 39			21 02		21 10			21 25	21 30		21 39			22 02	
Roydon	d						20 29			20 43								21 29			21 43				
Hertford East	d					20 09						20 39					21 09						21 39		
Ware	d					20 13						20 43					21 13						21 43		
St Margarets (Herts)	d					20 17						20 47					21 17						21 47		
Rye House	d					20 20						20 50					21 20						21 50		
Broxbourne 3	a			20 16		20 24	20 34			20 47		20 54			21 16		21 24	21 34			21 47		21 54		
	d			20 16		20 24	20 37		←	20 47		20 54			21 16		21 24	21 37		←	21 47		21 54		
Cheshunt	d			20 20		20 28	20 42		20 42	20 51		20 58			21 20		21 28	21 42		21 42	21 51		21 58		
Waltham Cross	d					20 31	→					21 01					21 31	→					22 01		
Enfield Lock	d					20 33			20 45			21 03					21 33			21 45			22 03		
Brimsdown	d					20 36						21 06					21 36						22 06		
Ponders End	d					20 38						21 08					21 38						22 08		
Angel Road	d																								
Northumberland Park	d								20 51											21 51					
Tottenham Hale ⊖	d	20 17		20 29	20 32	20 44		20 47	20 55	21 00	21 03	21 14	21 17		21 29	21 32	21 44		21 47	21 55	22 00	22 03	22 14	22 17	
Seven Sisters ⊖	d																								
Clapton	d																								
Stratford 7 ⊖	a								21 05											22 05					
Hackney Downs	d					20 50						21 20					21 50						22 20		
Bethnal Green	d																								
London Liverpool Street 15 ⊖	a	20 31		20 43	20 46	20 58		21 01		21 13	21 17	21 28	21 31		21 43	21 46	21 58		22 01		22 13	22 17	22 28	22 31	

For general notes see front of timetable
For details of catering facilities see Directory of Train Operators

Table 22

Saturdays

Cambridge, Stansted Airport, Bishops Stortford, Hertford East and Broxbourne → London

Network diagram - see first page of Table 20

		LE 1	LE 1	LE 1	LE 1	LE 1	LE 1	LE 1	LE 1	LE 1	XC 1 ◇ ⚒	LE 1	LE 1	LE 1	LE 1	LE 1	LE 1	LE 1	LE 1	LE 1	LE 1	LE 1	LE 1	
Cambridge	d	21 32					21 51				22 10	22 32						22 51						
Shelford	d						21 56											22 56						
Whittlesford Parkway	d	21 39					22 00					22 39						23 00						
Great Chesterford	d						22 04											23 04						
Audley End	d	21 47					22 10				22 24	22 47						23 10						
Newport (Essex)	d						22 13											23 13						
Elsenham	d						22 19											23 19						
Stansted Airport ✈	a										22 45													
✈	d		22 00		22 03	22 15		22 30		22 45			23 00		23 03	23 15				23 30		23 45	23 59	
Stansted Mountfitchet	d				22 09		22 22			22 51					23 09			23 22						
Bishops Stortford	a	22 00	22 09		22 13		22 28	22 39				23 00	23 09		23 13			23 28		23 39			00 08	
	d	22 00	22 09				22 28	22 39				23 00	23 09		23 14			23 28		23 39			00 08	
Sawbridgeworth	d	22 05					22 32					23 05			23 18			23 32						
Harlow Mill	d						22 36								23 22			23 36						
Harlow Town	d	22 10				22 30	22 39			23 02		23 10			23 25	23 30		23 39				23 59	00 16	
Roydon	d						22 43								23 29			23 43						
Hertford East	d			22 09					22 39					23 09							23 39			
Ware	d			22 13					22 43					23 13							23 43			
St Margarets (Herts)	d			22 17					22 47					23 17							23 47			
Rye House	d			22 20					22 50					23 20							23 50			
Broxbourne 3	a	22 16		22 24			22 47		22 54			23 16		23 24	23 34			23 47			23 54			
	d	22 16		22 24			22 47		22 54			23 16		23 24	23 37		←	23 47			23 54			
Cheshunt	d	22 20		22 28			22 51		22 58			23 20		23 28	23 42		23 42	23 51			23 58			
Waltham Cross	d			22 31					23 01					23 31	→						00 01			
Enfield Lock	d			22 33					23 03					23 33			23 45				00 03			
Brimsdown	d			22 36					23 06					23 36							00 06			
Ponders End	d			22 38					23 08					23 38							00 08			
Angel Road	d																							
Northumberland Park	d						22 58										23 51		←					
Tottenham Hale	Θ d	22 29	22 32	22 44		22 47	23 01	23 03	23 14	23 17		23 29	23 32	23 44		23 47	23 55	23 59	23 55	00 03	00 14	00 17		
Seven Sisters	Θ d																→							
Clapton	d																							
Stratford 7	Θ ⛴ a																		00 04					
Hackney Downs	d			22 50					23 20					23 50							00 20			
Bethnal Green	d																							
London Liverpool Street 15	Θ a	22 43	22 46	22 58		23 01	23 15	23 18	23 28	23 31		23 43	23 46	23 58		00 01		00 13	00 14	00 17	00 28	00 31	00 51	

Sundays

		LE 1	LE 1	LE 1	LE 1	LE 1	LE 1	LE 1	LE 1	LE 1	LE 1	LE 1	LE 1	LE 1		LE 1	LE 1	LE	LE 1	LE 1	LE 1	LE	LE 1 ⚒	LE	LE 1
Cambridge	d																			07 32					07 51
Shelford	d																								07 56
Whittlesford Parkway	d																			07 39					08 00
Great Chesterford	d																								08 04
Audley End	d																			07 47					08 10
Newport (Essex)	d																								08 13
Elsenham	d																								08 19
Stansted Airport ✈	a																								
✈	d	23p03	23p30		23p45	23p59	00 30	05 30	06 00	06 30		07 00	07 15			07 30			07 45		08 00		08 15		
Stansted Mountfitchet	d	23p09																	07 51						08 22
Bishops Stortford	a	23p13	23p39			00 08	00 39	05 39	06 09	06 39		07 09				07 39				08 00	08 09				08 28
	d	23p14	23p39			00 08	00 39	05 39	06 09	06 39	06 42	07 09		07 28		07 39				08 00	08 09				08 28
Sawbridgeworth	d	23p18									06 46			07 32						08 05					08 32
Harlow Mill	d	23p22												07 36											08 36
Harlow Town	d	23p25			23p59	00 16	00 47	05 47	06 17	06 47	06 51	07 17	07 30	07 39					08 02	08 10			08 30		08 39
Roydon	d	23p29												07 43											08 43
Hertford East	d			23p39														07 55						08 25	
Ware	d			23p43														07 59						08 29	
St Margarets (Herts)	d			23p47														08 03						08 33	
Rye House	d			23p50														08 06						08 36	
Broxbourne 3	a	23p34		23p54							06 57			07 48			←	08 11		08 16				08 41	08 48
	d	23p37		23p54							06 57			07 52			07 52	08 11		08 16				08 41	08 52
Cheshunt	d	23p42		23p58							07 01			→			07 57	08 15		08 20				08 45	→
Waltham Cross	d			00 01							07 04						07 59								
Enfield Lock	d	23p45		00 03							07 06						08 02								
Brimsdown	d			00 06							07 09						08 04								
Ponders End	d			00 08							07 11						08 06								
Angel Road	d																								
Northumberland Park	d	23p51																							
Tottenham Hale	Θ d	23p55	00 03	00 14	00 17			06 04	06 33	07 03	07 17	07 33	07 46			08 01	08 12		08 17	08 29	08 32	←	08 46		
Seven Sisters	Θ d																	08 33				08 33		09 03	
Clapton	d																	→							
Stratford 7	Θ ⛴ a	00 04															08 23								
Hackney Downs	d			00 20																		08 39		09 09	
Bethnal Green	d																							→	
London Liverpool Street 15	Θ a	00 14	00 17	00 28	00 31	00 51	01 21	06 17	06 46	07 16	07 30	07 46	08 00			08 15			08 31	08 43	08 46	08 48	09 03		

For general notes see front of timetable
For details of catering facilities see
Directory of Train Operators

Table 22

Sundays

Cambridge, Stansted Airport, Bishops Stortford, Hertford East and Broxbourne → London

Network diagram - see first page of Table 20

		LE 1 ⚮	LE	LE 1	LE	LE 1 ⚮		LE 1	LE 1 ⚮	LE	LE 1 ⚮	LE	LE 1	LE 1 ⚮	LE	LE 1	LE 1 ⚮	XC 1 ◇ ⚮	LE	LE 1		LE 1 ⚮	LE	LE 1 ⚮	LE
Cambridge	d							08 32					08 51					09 15		09 32					
Shelford	d												08 56												
Whittlesford Parkway	d							08 39					09 00							09 39					
Great Chesterford	d												09 04												
Audley End	d							08 47					09 10					09 28		09 47					
Newport (Essex)	d												09 13												
Elsenham	d												09 19												
Stansted Airport ✈	a																	09 45							
✈	d	08 30				08 45			09 00		09 15			09 30			09 45					10 00		10 15	
Stansted Mountfitchet	d					08 51							09 22				09 51								
Bishops Stortford	a	08 39						09 00	09 09				09 28	09 39						10 00		10 09			
	d	08 39						09 00	09 09				09 28	09 39						10 00		10 09			
Sawbridgeworth	d							09 05					09 32							10 05					
Harlow Mill	d												09 36												
Harlow Town	d					09 02		09 10			09 30		09 39				10 02			10 10				10 30	
Roydon	d												09 43												
Hertford East	d				08 55							09 25							09 55						10 25
Ware	d				08 59							09 29							09 59						10 29
St Margarets (Herts)	d				09 03							09 33							10 03						10 33
Rye House	d				09 06							09 36							10 06						10 36
Broxbourne 3	a			←	09 11			09 16				09 41	09 48			←			10 11	10 16					10 41
	d			08 52	09 11			09 16				09 41	09 52			09 52			10 11	10 16					10 41
Cheshunt	d			08 57	09 15			09 20				09 45	→			09 57			10 15	10 20					10 45
Waltham Cross	d			08 59												09 59									
Enfield Lock	d			09 02												10 02									
Brimsdown	d			09 04												10 04									
Ponders End	d			09 06												10 06									
Angel Road	d																								
Northumberland Park	d																								
Tottenham Hale ⊖	d	09 01		09 12		09 17		09 29	09 32	←	09 46			10 01		10 12	10 17			10 29		10 32	←	10 46	
Seven Sisters ⊖	d				09 33 →					09 33		10 03							10 33 →				10 33		11 03
Clapton	d																								
Stratford 7 ⊖ 🚢	a		←	09 23											←	10 23									
Hackney Downs	d		09 09							09 39		10 09 →			10 09								10 39		11 09 →
Bethnal Green	d																								
London Liverpool Street 15 ⊖	a	09 15	09 18			09 31		09 43	09 46	09 48	10 01			10 15	10 18		10 31			10 43		10 46	10 48	11 01	

		LE 1	LE 1 ⚮	LE	LE 1	LE 1 ⚮	XC 1 ◇ ⚮	LE	LE 1	LE 1 ⚮	LE	LE 1 ⚮		LE	LE 1	LE 1 ⚮	LE	LE 1	LE 1 ⚮	XC 1 ◇ ⚮	LE	LE 1	LE 1 ⚮	LE	LE 1 ⚮
Cambridge	d	09 51					10 15		10 32						10 51					11 15		11 32			
Shelford	d	09 56													10 56										
Whittlesford Parkway	d	10 00							10 39						11 00							11 39			
Great Chesterford	d	10 04													11 04										
Audley End	d	10 10					10 28		10 47						11 10					11 28		11 47			
Newport (Essex)	d	10 13													11 13										
Elsenham	d	10 19													11 19										
Stansted Airport ✈	a						10 45													11 45					
✈	d		10 30			10 45				11 00		11 15				11 30			11 45				12 00		12 15
Stansted Mountfitchet	d	10 22				10 51									11 22				11 51						
Bishops Stortford	a	10 28	10 39						11 00	11 09					11 28	11 39						12 00	12 09		
	d	10 28	10 39						11 00	11 09					11 28	11 39						12 00	12 09		
Sawbridgeworth	d	10 32							11 05						11 32							12 05			
Harlow Mill	d	10 36													11 36										
Harlow Town	d	10 39				11 02			11 10			11 30			11 39				12 02			12 10			12 30
Roydon	d	10 43													11 43										
Hertford East	d							10 55						11 25							11 55				
Ware	d							10 59						11 29							11 59				
St Margarets (Herts)	d							11 03						11 33							12 03				
Rye House	d							11 06						11 36							12 06				
Broxbourne 3	a	10 48			←			11 11	11 16					11 41	11 48			←			12 11	12 16			
	d	10 52			10 52			11 11	11 16					11 41	11 52			11 52			12 11	12 16			
Cheshunt	d	→			10 57			11 15	11 20					11 45	→			11 57			12 15	12 20			
Waltham Cross	d				10 59													11 59							
Enfield Lock	d				11 02													12 02							
Brimsdown	d				11 04													12 04							
Ponders End	d				11 06													12 06							
Angel Road	d																								
Northumberland Park	d																								
Tottenham Hale ⊖	d		11 01		11 12	11 17			11 29	11 32	←	11 46				12 01		12 12	12 17			12 29	12 32	←	12 46
Seven Sisters ⊖	d							11 33 →			11 33			12 03							12 33 →			12 33	
Clapton	d																								
Stratford 7 ⊖ 🚢	a			←	11 23												←	12 23							
Hackney Downs	d			11 09							11 39			12 09 →			12 09							12 39	
Bethnal Green	d																								
London Liverpool Street 15 ⊖	a		11 15	11 18		11 31			11 43	11 46	11 48	12 01				12 15	12 18		12 31			12 43	12 46	12 48	13 01

For general notes see front of timetable
For details of catering facilities see
Directory of Train Operators

Table 22

Sundays

Cambridge, Stansted Airport, Bishops Stortford, Hertford East and Broxbourne → London

Network diagram - see first page of Table 20

		LE	LE 1	LE 1 ⚲		LE	LE 1	LE 1 ⚲	XC 1 ◇ ⚲	LE	LE 1	LE 1 ⚲	LE	LE 1 ⚲	LE	LE 1	LE 1 ⚲	LE		LE 1	LE 1 ⚲	XC 1 ◇ ⚲	LE	LE 1	LE 1 ⚲
Cambridge	d		11 51						12 15		12 32					12 51						13 15		13 32	
Shelford	d		11 56													12 56									
Whittlesford Parkway	d		12 00								12 39					13 00								13 39	
Great Chesterford	d		12 04													13 04									
Audley End	d		12 10						12 28		12 47					13 10						13 28		13 47	
Newport (Essex)	d		12 13													13 13									
Elsenham	d		12 19													13 19									
Stansted Airport ✈	a								12 45													13 45			
✈	d			12 30				12 45				13 00		13 15			13 30				13 45				14 00
Stansted Mountfitchet	d		12 22					12 51								13 22					13 51				
Bishops Stortford	a		12 28	12 39							13 00	13 09				13 28	13 39							14 00	14 09
	d		12 28	12 39							13 00	13 09				13 28	13 39							14 00	14 09
Sawbridgeworth	d		12 32								13 05					13 32								14 05	
Harlow Mill	d		12 36													13 36									
Harlow Town	d		12 39					13 02			13 10			13 30		13 39					14 02			14 10	
Roydon	d		12 43													13 43									
Hertford East	d	12 25								12 55					13 25								13 55		
Ware	d	12 29								12 59					13 29								13 59		
St Margarets (Herts)	d	12 33								13 03					13 33								14 03		
Rye House	d	12 36								13 06					13 36								14 06		
Broxbourne 3	a	12 41	12 48				←			13 11	13 16				13 41	13 48				←			14 11	14 16	
	d	12 41	12 52				12 52			13 11	13 16				13 41	13 52				13 52			14 11	14 16	
Cheshunt	d	12 45	→				12 57			13 15	13 20				13 45	→				13 57			14 15	14 20	
Waltham Cross	d						12 59													13 59					
Enfield Lock	d						13 02													14 02					
Brimsdown	d						13 04													14 04					
Ponders End	d						13 06													14 06					
Angel Road	d																								
Northumberland Park	d																								
Tottenham Hale	⊖ d			13 01			13 12	13 17			13 29	13 32	←	13 46			14 01			14 12	14 17			14 29	14 32
Seven Sisters	⊖ d	13 03								13 33			13 33		14 03								14 33		
Clapton	d									→													→		
Stratford 7	⊖ ⛴ a					←	13 23											←		14 23					
Hackney Downs	d	13 09				13 09							13 39		14 09			14 09							
Bethnal Green	d	→													→										
London Liverpool Street 15	⊖ a			13 15		13 18		13 31			13 43	13 46	13 48	14 01			14 15	14 18			14 31			14 43	14 46

		LE	LE 1 ⚲	LE	LE 1	LE 1 ⚲	LE	LE 1	LE 1 ⚲	XC 1 ◇ ⚲		LE	LE 1	LE 1 ⚲	LE	LE 1 ⚲	LE	LE 1	LE 1 ⚲	LE	LE 1	LE 1 ⚲	XC 1 ◇ ⚲	LE	LE 1
Cambridge	d				13 51					14 18			14 32					14 51					15 18		15 32
Shelford	d				13 56													14 56							
Whittlesford Parkway	d				14 00								14 39					15 00							15 39
Great Chesterford	d				14 04													15 04							
Audley End	d				14 10					14 31			14 47					15 10					15 31		15 47
Newport (Essex)	d				14 13													15 13							
Elsenham	d				14 19													15 19							
Stansted Airport ✈	a									14 47													15 47		
✈	d		14 15			14 30			14 45					15 00		15 15			15 30			15 45			
Stansted Mountfitchet	d				14 22				14 51									15 22				15 51			
Bishops Stortford	a				14 28	14 39							15 00	15 09				15 28	15 39						16 00
	d				14 28	14 39							15 00	15 09				15 28	15 39						16 00
Sawbridgeworth	d				14 32								15 05					15 32							16 05
Harlow Mill	d				14 36													15 36							
Harlow Town	d		14 30		14 39				15 02				15 10			15 30		15 39				16 02			16 10
Roydon	d				14 43													15 43							
Hertford East	d			14 25								14 55					15 25							15 55	
Ware	d			14 29								14 59					15 29							15 59	
St Margarets (Herts)	d			14 33								15 03					15 33							16 03	
Rye House	d			14 36								15 06					15 36							16 06	
Broxbourne 3	a			14 41	14 48			←				15 11	15 16				15 41	15 48			←			16 11	16 16
	d			14 41	14 52			14 52				15 11	15 16				15 41	15 52			15 52			16 11	16 16
Cheshunt	d			14 45	→			14 57				15 15	15 20				15 45	→			15 57			16 15	16 20
Waltham Cross	d							14 59													15 59				
Enfield Lock	d							15 02													16 02				
Brimsdown	d							15 04													16 04				
Ponders End	d							15 06													16 06				
Angel Road	d																								
Northumberland Park	d																								
Tottenham Hale	⊖ d	←	14 46			15 01		15 12	15 17				15 29	15 32	←	15 46			16 01		16 12	16 17			16 29
Seven Sisters	⊖ d	14 33		15 03								15 33			15 33		16 03							16 33	
Clapton	d											→												→	
Stratford 7	⊖ ⛴ a						←	15 23												←	16 23				
Hackney Downs	d	14 39		15 09			15 09								15 39		16 09			16 09					
Bethnal Green	d			→													→								
London Liverpool Street 15	⊖ a	14 48	15 01			15 15	15 18		15 31				15 43	15 46	15 48	16 01			16 15	16 18		16 31			16 43

For general notes see front of timetable
For details of catering facilities see
Directory of Train Operators

Table 22

Sundays

Cambridge, Stansted Airport, Bishops Stortford, Hertford East and Broxbourne → London

Network diagram - see first page of Table 20

		LE 1 ☕		LE	LE 1 ☕	LE	LE 1	LE 1 ☕	LE	LE 1	LE 1 ☕	XC 1 ◇ A ☕	XC 1 ◇ B ☕	LE	LE 1	LE 1 ☕		LE	LE 1 ☕	LE	LE 1	LE 1 ☕	LE	LE 1	LE 1 ☕
Cambridge	d						15 51					16 17	16 18		16 32						16 51				
Shelford	d						15 56														16 56				
Whittlesford Parkway	d						16 00								16 39						17 00				
Great Chesterford	d						16 04														17 04				
Audley End	d						16 10					16 31	16 31		16 47						17 10				
Newport (Essex)	d						16 13														17 13				
Elsenham	d						16 19														17 19				
Stansted Airport ✈	a											16 47	16 47												
	d	16 00			16 15			16 30			16 45					17 00			17 15			17 30			17 45
Stansted Mountfitchet	d						16 22				16 51										17 22				17 51
Bishops Stortford	a	16 09					16 28	16 39							17 00	17 09					17 28	17 39			
	d	16 09					16 28	16 39							17 00	17 09					17 28	17 39			
Sawbridgeworth	d						16 32								17 05						17 32				
Harlow Mill	d						16 36														17 36				
Harlow Town	d				16 30		16 39				17 02				17 10				17 30		17 39				18 02
Roydon	d						16 43														17 43				
Hertford East	d					16 25								16 55						17 25					
Ware	d					16 29								16 59						17 29					
St Margarets (Herts)	d					16 33								17 03						17 33					
Rye House	d					16 36								17 06						17 36					
Broxbourne 3	a					16 41	16 48			←				17 11	17 16					17 41	17 48			←	
	d					16 41	16 52			16 52				17 11	17 16					17 41	17 52			17 52	
Cheshunt	d					16 45	→			16 57				17 15	17 20					17 45	→			17 57	
Waltham Cross	d									16 59														17 59	
Enfield Lock	d									17 02														18 02	
Brimsdown	d									17 04														18 04	
Ponders End	d									17 06														18 06	
Angel Road	d																								
Northumberland Park	d																								
Tottenham Hale	⊖ d	16 32		←	16 46			17 01		17 12	17 17				17 29	17 32		←	17 46			18 01		18 12	18 17
Seven Sisters	⊖ d			16 33		17 03								17 33 →				17 33		18 03					
Clapton	d																								
Stratford 7	⊖ ⛴ a								←	17 23													←	18 23	
Hackney Downs	d			16 39		17 09 →			17 09									17 39		18 09 →			18 09		
Bethnal Green	d																								
London Liverpool Street 15	⊖ a	16 46		16 48	17 01			17 15	17 18		17 31				17 43	17 46		17 48	18 01			18 15	18 18		18 31

		XC 1 ◇ ☕	LE	LE 1	LE 1 ☕	LE	LE 1 ☕	LE		LE 1	LE 1 ☕	LE	LE	LE 1	LE 1 ☕	XC 1 ◇ ☕	LE 1	LE 1 ☕	LE 1 ☕	LE	LE 1	LE 1 ☕		LE 1	LE 1 ☕
Cambridge	d	17 10		17 32						17 51						18 10	18 32				18 51				
Shelford	d									17 56											18 56				
Whittlesford Parkway	d			17 39						18 00							18 39				19 00				
Great Chesterford	d									18 04											19 04				
Audley End	d	17 24		17 47						18 10						18 24	18 47				19 10				
Newport (Essex)	d									18 13											19 13				
Elsenham	d									18 19											19 19				
Stansted Airport ✈	a	17 45														18 45									
	d				18 00		18 15				18 30				18 45			19 00	19 15			19 30			19 45
Stansted Mountfitchet	d									18 22					18 51						19 22				19 51
Bishops Stortford	a			18 00	18 09					18 28	18 39						19 00	19 09			19 28	19 39			
	d			18 00	18 09					18 28	18 39						19 00	19 09			19 28	19 39			
Sawbridgeworth	d			18 05						18 32							19 05				19 32				
Harlow Mill	d									18 36											19 36				
Harlow Town	d			18 10			18 30			18 39					19 02		19 10		19 30		19 39				20 02
Roydon	d									18 43											19 43				
Hertford East	d		17 55					18 25				18 57													
Ware	d		17 59					18 29				19 01													
St Margarets (Herts)	d		18 03					18 33				19 05													
Rye House	d		18 06					18 36				19 08													
Broxbourne 3	a		18 11	18 16				18 41		18 48		19 12		←			19 16			←	19 48			←	
	d		18 11	18 16				18 41		18 52		19 26		18 52			19 16			19 26	19 52			19 52	
Cheshunt	d		18 15	18 20				18 45		→		→		18 57			19 20			19 31	→			19 57	
Waltham Cross	d													18 59										19 59	
Enfield Lock	d													19 02										20 02	
Brimsdown	d													19 04										20 04	
Ponders End	d													19 06										20 06	
Angel Road	d																								
Northumberland Park	d																								
Tottenham Hale	⊖ d			18 29	18 32	←	18 46				19 01			19 12	19 17		19 29	19 32	19 46			20 01		20 12	20 17
Seven Sisters	⊖ d		18 33 →			18 33		19 03												19 51					
Clapton	d																								
Stratford 7	⊖ ⛴ a												←	19 23										20 23	
Hackney Downs	d					18 39		19 09 →					19 09							19 59					
Bethnal Green	d																			20 05					
London Liverpool Street 15	⊖ a			18 43	18 46	18 48	19 01				19 15		19 18		19 31		19 43	19 46	20 00	20 11		20 15			20 31

For general notes see front of timetable
For details of catering facilities see Directory of Train Operators

A From 19 July
B Until 12 July

Table 22

Sundays

Cambridge, Stansted Airport, Bishops Stortford, Hertford East and Broxbourne → London

Network diagram - see first page of Table 20

		XC	XC	LE	LE	LE	LE	LE	LE	LE	LE	LE	XC	LE		LE	XC	LE	LE	LE	LE	LE	LE	LE	XC
		1 ◇	1 ◇		1	1	1		1	1	1	1	1 ◇			1	1 ◇	1	1		1	1	1	1	1 ◇
		A	B										A				B								
		🍴	🍴			🍴	🍴			🍴		🍴	🍴				🍴								🍴
Cambridge	d	19 10	19 12		19 32				19 51				20 10			20 32	20 35				20 51				21 10
Shelford	d								19 56												20 56				
Whittlesford Parkway	d				19 39				20 00							20 39					21 00				
Great Chesterford	d								20 04												21 04				
Audley End	d	19 24	19 26		19 47				20 10				20 24			20 47	20 52				21 10				21 24
Newport (Essex)	d								20 13												21 13				
Elsenham	d								20 19												21 19				
Stansted Airport ✈	a	19 45	19 47										20 45				21 17								21 45
✈	d					20 00	20 15			20 30		20 45						21 00	21 15			21 30		21 45	
Stansted Mountfitchet	d								20 22			20 51									21 22			21 51	
Bishops Stortford	a				20 00	20 09			20 28	20 39						21 00		21 09			21 28	21 39			
	d				20 00	20 09			20 28	20 39						21 00		21 09			21 28	21 39			
Sawbridgeworth	d				20 05				20 32							21 05					21 32				
Harlow Mill	d								20 36												21 36				
Harlow Town	d				20 10		20 30		20 39			21 02				21 10			21 30		21 39			22 02	
Roydon	d								20 43												21 43				
Hertford East	d			19 57										20 57											
Ware	d			20 01										21 01											
St Margarets (Herts)	d			20 05										21 05											
Rye House	d			20 08										21 08											
Broxbourne 3	a			20 12	20 16			←	20 48		←			21 12		21 16				←	21 48		←		
	d			20 26	20 16			20 26	20 52		20 52			21 26		21 16				21 26	21 52		21 52		
Cheshunt	d			→	20 20			20 31	→		20 57			→		21 20				21 31	→		21 57		
Waltham Cross	d										20 59												21 59		
Enfield Lock	d										21 02												22 02		
Brimsdown	d										21 04												22 04		
Ponders End	d										21 06												22 06		
Angel Road	d																								
Northumberland Park	d																								
Tottenham Hale ⊖	d				20 29	20 32	20 46			21 01	21 12	21 17				21 29		21 32	21 46			22 01	22 12	22 17	
Seven Sisters ⊖	d							20 51												21 51					
Clapton	d																								
Stratford 7 ⊖ DLR	a										21 23												22 23		
Hackney Downs	d							20 59												21 59					
Bethnal Green	d							21 05												22 05					
London Liverpool Street 15 ⊖	a				20 43	20 46	21 00	21 11		21 15		21 31				21 43		21 46	22 00	22 11		22 15		22 31	

		LE	LE	LE	LE	LE		LE	LE	LE	LE	XC	XC	LE	LE	LE	LE	LE	LE	LE	LE	LE	LE		
			1	1	1			1	1	1	1	1 ◇	1 ◇		1	1	1	1		1	1	1	1		
												A	B												
												🍴	🍴												
Cambridge	d		21 32					21 51				22 10	22 17			22 32				22 51					
Shelford	d							21 56												22 56					
Whittlesford Parkway	d		21 39					22 00								22 39				23 00					
Great Chesterford	d							22 04												23 04					
Audley End	d		21 47					22 10				22 24	22 31			22 47				23 10					
Newport (Essex)	d							22 13												23 13					
Elsenham	d							22 19												23 19					
Stansted Airport ✈	a											22 45	22 47												
✈	d			22 00	22 15				22 30		22 45						23 00	23 15			23 30	23 45	23 59		
Stansted Mountfitchet	d							22 22			22 51									23 22					
Bishops Stortford	a		22 00	22 09				22 28	22 39							23 00	23 09			23 28	23 39		00 08		
	d		22 00	22 09				22 28	22 39							23 00	23 09				23 39		00 08		
Sawbridgeworth	d		22 05					22 32								23 05									
Harlow Mill	d							22 36																	
Harlow Town	d		22 10		22 30			22 39			23 02					23 10		23 30			23 47	23 59	00 16		
Roydon	d							22 43																	
Hertford East	d	21 57												22 57											
Ware	d	22 01												23 01											
St Margarets (Herts)	d	22 05												23 05											
Rye House	d	22 08												23 08											
Broxbourne 3	a	22 12	22 16			←		22 48		←				23 12		23 16			←						
	d	22 26	22 16			22 26		22 52		22 52				23 26		23 16			23 26						
Cheshunt	d	→	22 20			22 31		→		22 57				→		23 20			23 31						
Waltham Cross	d									22 59															
Enfield Lock	d									23 02															
Brimsdown	d									23 04															
Ponders End	d									23 06															
Angel Road	d																								
Northumberland Park	d														←										
Tottenham Hale ⊖	d		22 29	22 32	22 46				23 01	23 12	23 17				23 12	23 29	23 32	23 46							
Seven Sisters ⊖	d					22 51				→									23 51		00 08	00 21			
Clapton	d																								
Stratford 7 ⊖ DLR	a														23 22										
Hackney Downs	d					22 59													23 59						
Bethnal Green	d					23 05													00 05						
London Liverpool Street 15 ⊖	a		22 43	22 46	23 00	23 11			23 15		23 31				23 36	23 43	23 46	00 01	00 11		00 22	00 35	00 51		

For general notes see front of timetable
For details of catering facilities see Directory of Train Operators

A Until 12 July and from 13 September
B 19 July to 6 September

Network Diagram for Tables 24, 25

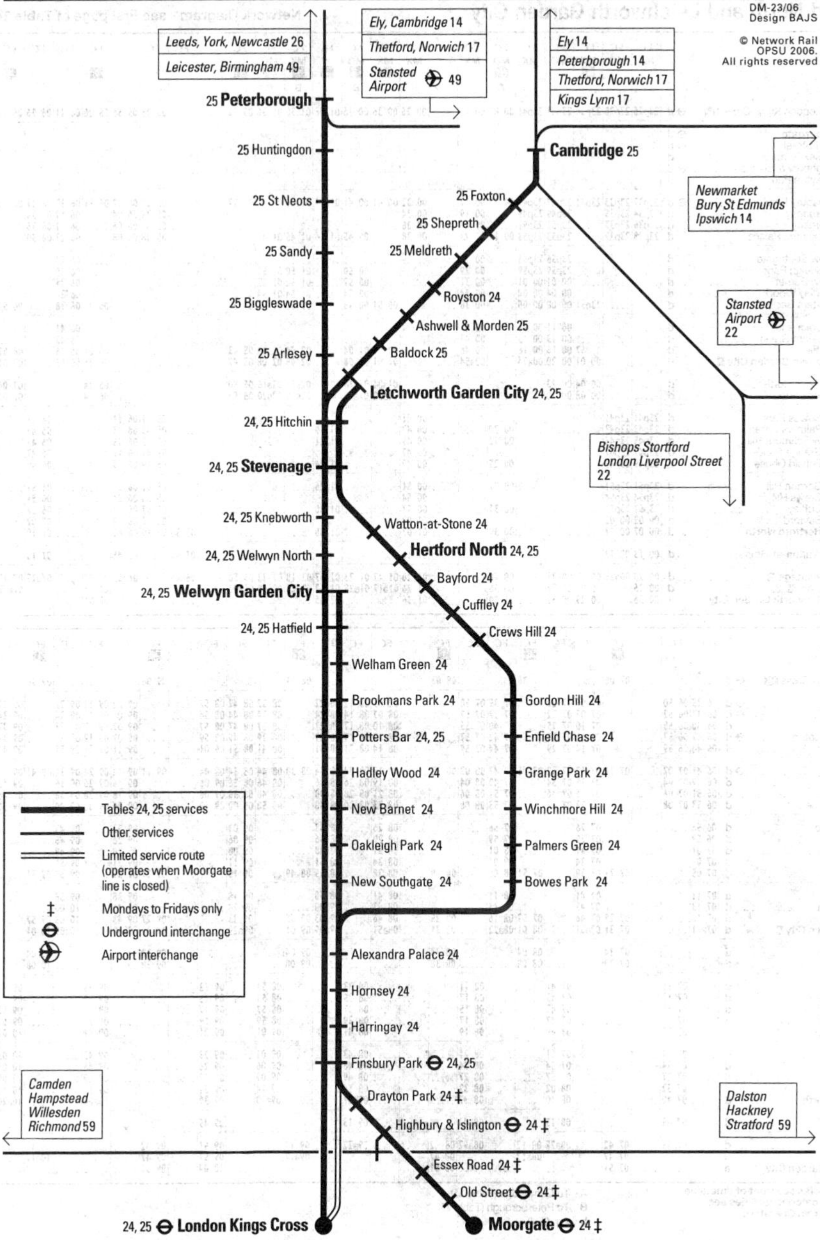

DM-23/06
Design BAJS
© Network Rail
OPSU 2006.
All rights reserved
Leeds, York, Newcastle 26
Leicester, Birmingham 49
Ely, Cambridge 14
Thetford, Norwich 17
Stansted Airport 49
Ely 14
Peterborough 14
Thetford, Norwich 17
Kings Lynn 17
25 Peterborough
25 Huntingdon
Cambridge 25
25 St Neots
25 Foxton
25 Shepreth
Newmarket
Bury St Edmunds
Ipswich 14
25 Sandy
25 Meldreth
Royston 24
25 Biggleswade
Ashwell & Morden 25
Stansted Airport 22
25 Arlesey
Baldock 25
Letchworth Garden City 24, 25
24, 25 Hitchin
Bishops Stortford
London Liverpool Street
22
24, 25 Stevenage
24, 25 Knebworth
Watton-at-Stone 24
24, 25 Welwyn North
Hertford North 24, 25
Bayford 24
24, 25 Welwyn Garden City
Cuffley 24
24, 25 Hatfield
Crews Hill 24
Welham Green 24
Brookmans Park 24
Gordon Hill 24
Potters Bar 24, 25
Enfield Chase 24
Hadley Wood 24
Grange Park 24
New Barnet 24
Winchmore Hill 24
Oakleigh Park 24
Palmers Green 24
New Southgate 24
Bowes Park 24
Tables 24, 25 services
Other services
Limited service route (operates when Moorgate line is closed)
‡ Mondays to Fridays only
Underground interchange
Airport interchange
Alexandra Palace 24
Hornsey 24
Harringay 24
Finsbury Park 24, 25
Camden
Hampstead
Willesden
Richmond 59
Drayton Park 24 ‡
Highbury & Islington 24 ‡
Dalston
Hackney
Stratford 59
Essex Road 24 ‡
Old Street 24 ‡
24, 25 London Kings Cross
Moorgate 24 ‡

London → Welwyn Garden City, Hertford North and Letchworth Garden City

Saturday service operates on Bank Holiday Mondays

Network Diagram - see first page of Table 24

Miles	Miles			FC	FC	FC	FC	FC	FC	FC	FC	FC	FC	FC	FC	FC	FC	FC	FC	FC	FC	FC	FC	FC
				MX	MO	MX	MO	MX	MO	MX	MX	MX	MO		MX	MO								
						[1]			[1]			[1]	[1]	[1]	[1]	[1]	[1]				[1]			[1]
									A				B		B	B								
0	—	London Kings Cross [15]	⊖ d	23p26	23p28	23p36	23p41	23p41	00 07	00 11	00 26	00 36	00 36	01 06	01 36	01 36	05 22		05 26	05 56	06 06	06 11	06 26	06 36
—	0	**Moorgate**	⊖ d																					
—	½	Old Street	⊖ d																					
—	1¾	Essex Road	d																					
—	2¼	Highbury & Islington	⊖ d																					
—	2¾	Drayton Park	d																					
2½	3½	Finsbury Park	⊖ d	23p32	23p33	23p41	23p47	23p47	00 12	00 17	00 32	00 41	00 41	01 11	01 41	01 41	05 27		05 32	06 02	06 11	06 17	06 32	06 41
3½	4½	Harringay	d	23p34	23p35		23p49	23p49		00 19	00 34								05 34	06 04		06 19	06 34	
4	5	Hornsey	d	23p36	23p37		23p51	23p51		00 21	00 36								05 36	06 06		06 21	06 36	
5	6	Alexandra Palace	d	23p38	23p39		23p53	23p53	00 17	00 23	00 38		00 45	01 16	01 45	01 45			05 38	06 08		06 23	06 38	
6½	—	New Southgate	d				23p56	23p56		00 26												06 26		
8½	—	Oakleigh Park	d				23p59	23p59		00 29			00 50		01 50	01 50						06 29		
9¼	—	New Barnet	d				00 01	00 01		00 31			00 52		01 52	01 52						06 31		
10½	—	Hadley Wood	d				00 04	00 04		00 34			00 54		01 54	01 54						06 34		
12¾	—	Potters Bar	d			23p51	00 08	00 08		00 38		00 51	00 58		01 58	01 58	05 37				06 21	06 38		06 51
14½	—	Brookmans Park	d				00 11	00 11		00 41												06 41		
15¼	—	Welham Green	d				00 13	00 13		00 43												06 43		
17¾	—	Hatfield	d			23p57	00 16	00 16		00 46		00 57	01 04		02 04	02 04	05 43				06 27	06 46		06 57
20¼	—	**Welwyn Garden City [4]**	d			00 01	00 20	00a24		00a54		01 01	01 08		02 08	02 08	05 47				06 31	06a53		07 01
22	—	Welwyn North	d			00 04	00 23					01s04	01s16		02s11	02s16	05 50				06 34			07 04
25	—	Knebworth	d			00 08	00 28					01s08	01s20		02s15	02s20	05 54				06 38			07 08
—	6¾	Bowes Park	d	23p41	23p41						00 41								05 41	06 11			06 41	
—	7¾	Palmers Green	d	23p43	23p43				00 20		00 43			01 19					05 43	06 13			06 43	
—	8¾	Winchmore Hill	d	23p45	23p45				00 22		00 45			01 21					05 45	06 15			06 45	
—	9½	Grange Park	d	23p47	23p47						00 47								05 47	06 17			06 47	
—	10¼	Enfield Chase	d	23p49	23p49				00 25		00 49			01 24					05 49	06 19			06 49	
—	11	Gordon Hill	d	23p51	23p51				00 27		00 51			01 26					05 51	06 21			06 51	
—	12½	Crews Hill	d	23p54	23p54						00 54								05 54	06 24			06 54	
—	14¼	Cuffley	d	23p57	23p57				00 31		00 57			01 30					05 57	06 27			06 57	
—	17¾	Bayford	d	00 02	00 02						01 02								06 02	06 32			07 02	
—	20¾	**Hertford North**	d	00 07	00 07				00 39		01 07			01 38				05 50	06a10	06 40			07 10	
—	25	Watton-at-Stone	d	00 13	00 13						01 13							05 55		06 45			07 15	
27½	30	**Stevenage [4]**	d	00 20	00a25	00 12	00 31		00 48		01 20	01 12	01 23	01 47	02 18	02 23	05 58	06a05		06a55	06 42		07a25	07 12
31¾	34¼	Hitchin [4]	d	00 26		00 20	00 37		00 56		01 26	01a17	01a28	01 52	02a23	02a28	06a06				06 47			07a17
34¾	37¼	**Letchworth Garden City**	a	00 36		00 29	00 52		01 00		01 36			02 06							06 51			

		FC	FC	FC	FC	FC	FC	FC	FC	FC	FC	FC	FC	FC	FC	FC	FC	FC	FC	FC	FC	FC	FC
				[1]			[1]			[1]				[1]				[1]				[1]	
London Kings Cross [15]	⊖ d			07 06			07 36			08 03				08 33				09 06				09 36	
Moorgate	⊖ d	06 35	06 50		07 05	07 20		07 35	07 50		08 05	08 12	08 22		08 32	08 42	08 52		09 02	09 12	09 22		09 32
Old Street	⊖ d	06 37	06 52		07 07	07 22		07 37	07 52		08 07	08 14	08 24		08 34	08 44	08 54		09 04	09 14	09 24		09 34
Essex Road	d	06 40	06 55		07 10	07 25		07 40	07 55		08 10	08 17	08 27		08 37	08 47	08 57		09 07	09 17	09 27		09 37
Highbury & Islington	⊖ d	06 42	06 57		07 12	07 27		07 42	07 57		08 12	08 19	08 29		08 39	08 49	08 59		09 09	09 19	09 29		09 39
Drayton Park	d	06 44	06 59		07 14	07 29		07 44	07 59		08 14	08 21	08 31		08 41	08 51	09 01		09 11	09 21	09 31		09 41
Finsbury Park	⊖ d	06 47	07 02	07 11	07 17	07 32	07 41	07 47	08 02	08 08	08 17	08 24	08 34	08 38	08 44	08 54	09 04	09 11	09 14	09 24	09 34	09 41	09 44
Harringay	d	06 49	07 04		07 19	07 34		07 49	08 04		08 19	08 26	08 36		08 46	08 56	09 06		09 16	09 26	09 36		09 46
Hornsey	d	06 51	07 06		07 21	07 36		07 51	08 06		08 21	08 28	08 38		08 48	08 58	09 08		09 18	09 28	09 38		09 48
Alexandra Palace	d	06 53	07 08		07 23	07 38		07 53	08 08		08 23	08 30	08 40		08 50	09 00	09 10		09 20	09 30	09 40		09 50
New Southgate	d	06 56			07 26			07 56			08 26		08 43			09 03			09 23		09 43		
Oakleigh Park	d	06 59			07 29			07 59			08 29		08 46			09 06			09 26		09 46		
New Barnet	d	07 01			07 31			08 01			08 31		08 48			09 08			09 28		09 48		
Hadley Wood	d	07 04			07 34			08 04			08 34		08 51			09 11			09 31		09 51		
Potters Bar	d	07 08		07 21	07 38		07 51	08 08		08 19	08 38		08 55	08 49		09 15		09 21	09 35		09 55	09 51	
Brookmans Park	d	07 11			07 41			08 11			08 41		08 58			09 18			09 38		09 58		
Welham Green	d	07 13			07 43			08 13			08 43		09 00			09 20			09 40		10 00		
Hatfield	d	07 16		07 27	07 46		07 57	08 16		08 25	08 46		09 03	08 55		09 23		09 27	09 43		10 03	09 57	
Welwyn Garden City [4]	d	07a21		07 31	07a51		08 01	08a22		08 31	08a51		09a09	09 01		09a29		09 31	09a49		10a09	10 01	
Welwyn North	d			07 34			08 04			08 34				09 04				09 34				10 04	
Knebworth	d			07 38			08 08			08 38				09 08				09 38				10 08	
Bowes Park	d		07 11			07 41			08 11			08 33			08 53		09 13			09 33			09 53
Palmers Green	d		07 13			07 43			08 13			08 35			08 55		09 15			09 35			09 55
Winchmore Hill	d		07 15			07 45			08 15			08 37			08 57		09 17			09 37			09 57
Grange Park	d		07 17			07 47			08 17			08 39			08 59		09 19			09 39			09 59
Enfield Chase	d		07 19			07 49			08 19			08 41			09 01		09 21			09 41			10 01
Gordon Hill	d		07 21			07 51			08 21			08 43			09 03		09 23			09 43			10 03
Crews Hill	d		07 24			07 54			08 24			08 46			09 06		09 26			09 46			10 06
Cuffley	d		07 27			07 57			08 27			08 49			09 09		09 29			09 49			10 09
Bayford	d		07 32			08 02			08 32			08 54			09 14		09 34			09 54			10 14
Hertford North	d		07 40			08 10			08 37			09b07			09a20		09 39			10a00			10a20
Watton-at-Stone	d		07 45			08 15			08 43			09 13					09 45						
Stevenage [4]	d		07a55	07 42		08a22	08 12		08a52	08 42		09a22		09 12			09 51	09 42				10 12	
Hitchin [4]	d			07 47			08a17			08 47				09a17			09 57	09 47				10a17	
Letchworth Garden City	a			07 51						08 51							10 04	09 51					

For general notes see front of timetable
For details of catering facilities see Directory of Train Operators

A To Cambridge (Table 25)
B To Peterborough (Table 25)
b Arr. 0859

London → Welwyn Garden City, Hertford North and Letchworth Garden City

Saturday service operates on Bank Holiday Mondays

Network Diagram - see first page of Table 24

		FC	FC	FC 1		FC	FC	FC	FC 1	FC	FC	FC		FC 1	FC	FC	FC	FC 1	FC	FC		FC	FC 1	FC	FC	FC
London Kings Cross 15	⊖ d			10 06					10 36					11 06				11 36					12 06			
Moorgate	⊖ d	09 42	09 52			10 02	10 12	10 22		10 32	10 42	10 52			11 02	11 12	11 22		11 32	11 42		11 52		12 02	12 12	12 22
Old Street	⊖ d	09 44	09 54			10 04	10 14	10 24		10 34	10 44	10 54			11 04	11 14	11 24		11 34	11 44		11 54		12 04	12 14	12 24
Essex Road	d	09 47	09 57			10 07	10 17	10 27		10 37	10 47	10 57			11 07	11 17	11 27		11 37	11 47		11 57		12 07	12 17	12 27
Highbury & Islington	⊖ d	09 49	09 59			10 09	10 19	10 29		10 39	10 49	10 59			11 09	11 19	11 29		11 39	11 49		11 59		12 09	12 19	12 29
Drayton Park	d	09 51	10 01			10 11	10 21	10 31		10 41	10 51	11 01			11 11	11 21	11 31		11 41	11 51		12 01		12 11	12 21	12 31
Finsbury Park	⊖ d	09 54	10 04	10 11		10 14	10 24	10 34	10 41	10 44	10 54	11 04		11 11	11 14	11 24	11 34	11 41	11 44	11 54		12 04	12 11	12 14	12 24	12 34
Harringay	d	09 56	10 06			10 16	10 26	10 36		10 46	10 56	11 06			11 16	11 26	11 36		11 46	11 56		12 06		12 16	12 26	12 36
Hornsey	d	09 58	10 08			10 18	10 28	10 38		10 48	10 58	11 08			11 18	11 28	11 38		11 48	11 58		12 08		12 18	12 28	12 38
Alexandra Palace	d	10 00	10 10			10 20	10 30	10 40		10 50	11 00	11 10			11 20	11 30	11 40		11 50	12 00		12 10		12 20	12 30	12 40
New Southgate	d	10 03				10 23		10 43			11 03				11 23		11 43			12 03				12 23		12 43
Oakleigh Park	d	10 06				10 26		10 46			11 06				11 26		11 46			12 06				12 26		12 46
New Barnet	d	10 08				10 28		10 48			11 08				11 28		11 48			12 08				12 28		12 48
Hadley Wood	d	10 11				10 31		10 51			11 11				11 31		11 51			12 11				12 31		12 51
Potters Bar	d	10 15		10 21		10 35		10 55	10 51		11 15			11 21	11 35		11 55	11 51		12 15			12 21	12 35		12 55
Brookmans Park	d	10 18				10 38		10 58			11 18				11 38		11 58			12 18				12 38		12 58
Welham Green	d	10 20				10 40		11 00			11 20				11 40		12 00			12 20				12 40		13 00
Hatfield	d	10 23		10 27		10 43		11 03	10 57		11 23			11 27	11 43		12 03	11 57		12 23			12 27	12 43		13 03
Welwyn Garden City 4	d	10a29		10 31		10a49		11a09	11 01		11a29			11 31	11a49		12a09	12 01		12a29			12 31	12a49		13a09
Welwyn North	d			10 34					11 04					11 34				12 04					12 34			
Knebworth	d			10 38					11 08					11 38				12 08					12 38			
Bowes Park	d		10 13				10 33			10 53		11 13				11 33			11 53			12 13			12 33	
Palmers Green	d		10 15				10 35			10 55		11 15				11 35			11 55			12 15			12 35	
Winchmore Hill	d		10 17				10 37			10 57		11 17				11 37			11 57			12 17			12 37	
Grange Park	d		10 19				10 39			10 59		11 19				11 39			11 59			12 19			12 39	
Enfield Chase	d		10 21				10 41			11 01		11 21				11 41			12 01			12 21			12 41	
Gordon Hill	d		10 23				10 43			11 03		11 23				11 43			12 03			12 23			12 43	
Crews Hill	d		10 26				10 46			11 06		11 26				11 46			12 06			12 26			12 46	
Cuffley	d		10 29				10 49			11 09		11 29				11 49			12 09			12 29			12 49	
Bayford	d		10 34				10 54			11 14		11 34				11 54			12 14			12 34			12 54	
Hertford North	d		10 39				11a00			11a20		11 39				12a00			12a20			12 39			13a00	
Watton-at-Stone	d		10 45									11 45										12 45				
Stevenage 4	d		10 51	10 42					11 12			11 51		11 42				12 12				12 51	12 42			
Hitchin 4	d		10 57	10 47					11a17			11 57		11 47				12a17				12 57	12 47			
Letchworth Garden City	a		11 04	10 51								12 04		11 51								13 04	12 51			

		FC 1	FC	FC	FC		FC 1	FC	FC	FC	FC 1	FC	FC		FC	FC 1	FC	FC	FC	FC 1	FC		FC	FC	FC 1	FC
London Kings Cross 15	⊖ d	12 36					13 06				13 36					14 06				14 36					15 06	
Moorgate	⊖ d		12 32	12 42	12 52			13 02	13 12	13 22		13 32	13 42		13 52		14 02	14 12	14 22		14 32		14 42	14 52		15 02
Old Street	⊖ d		12 34	12 44	12 54			13 04	13 14	13 24		13 34	13 44		13 54		14 04	14 14	14 24		14 34		14 44	14 54		15 04
Essex Road	d		12 37	12 47	12 57			13 07	13 17	13 27		13 37	13 47		13 57		14 07	14 17	14 27		14 37		14 47	14 57		15 07
Highbury & Islington	⊖ d		12 39	12 49	12 59			13 09	13 19	13 29		13 39	13 49		13 59		14 09	14 19	14 29		14 39		14 49	14 59		15 09
Drayton Park	d		12 41	12 51	13 01			13 11	13 21	13 31		13 41	13 51		14 01		14 11	14 21	14 31		14 41		14 51	15 01		15 11
Finsbury Park	⊖ d	12 41	12 44	12 54	13 04		13 11	13 14	13 24	13 34	13 41	13 44	13 54		14 04	14 11	14 14	14 24	14 34	14 41	14 44		14 54	15 04	15 11	15 14
Harringay	d		12 46	12 56	13 06			13 16	13 26	13 36		13 46	13 56		14 06		14 16	14 26	14 36		14 46		14 56	15 06		15 16
Hornsey	d		12 48	12 58	13 08			13 18	13 28	13 38		13 48	13 58		14 08		14 18	14 28	14 38		14 48		14 58	15 08		15 18
Alexandra Palace	d		12 50	13 00	13 10			13 20	13 30	13 40		13 50	14 00		14 10		14 20	14 30	14 40		14 50		15 00	15 10		15 20
New Southgate	d			13 03				13 23		13 43			14 03				14 23		14 43				15 03			15 23
Oakleigh Park	d			13 06				13 26		13 46			14 06				14 26		14 46				15 06			15 26
New Barnet	d			13 08				13 28		13 48			14 08				14 28		14 48				15 08			15 28
Hadley Wood	d			13 11				13 31		13 51			14 11				14 31		14 51				15 11			15 31
Potters Bar	d	12 51		13 15			13 21	13 35		13 55	13 51		14 15			14 21	14 35		14 55	14 51			15 15		15 21	15 35
Brookmans Park	d			13 18				13 38		13 58			14 18				14 38		14 58				15 18			15 38
Welham Green	d			13 20				13 40		14 00			14 20				14 40		15 00				15 20			15 40
Hatfield	d	12 57		13 23			13 27	13 43		14 03	13 57		14 23			14 27	14 43		15 03	14 57			15 23		15 27	15 43
Welwyn Garden City 4	d	13 01		13a29			13 31	13a49		14a10	14 01		14a29			14 31	14a49		15a09	15 01			15a29		15 31	15a49
Welwyn North	d	13 04					13 34				14 04					14 34				15 04					15 34	
Knebworth	d	13 08					13 38				14 08					14 38				15 08					15 38	
Bowes Park	d		12 53		13 13				13 33			13 53			14 13			14 33			14 53			15 13		
Palmers Green	d		12 55		13 15				13 35			13 55			14 15			14 35			14 55			15 15		
Winchmore Hill	d		12 57		13 17				13 37			13 57			14 17			14 37			14 57			15 17		
Grange Park	d		12 59		13 19				13 39			13 59			14 19			14 39			14 59			15 19		
Enfield Chase	d		13 01		13 21				13 41			14 01			14 21			14 41			15 01			15 21		
Gordon Hill	d		13 03		13 23				13 43			14 03			14 23			14 43			15 03			15 23		
Crews Hill	d		13 06		13 26				13 46			14 06			14 26			14 46			15 06			15 26		
Cuffley	d		13 09		13 29				13 49			14 09			14 29			14 49			15 09			15 29		
Bayford	d		13 14		13 34				13 54			14 14			14 34			14 54			15 14			15 34		
Hertford North	d		13a20		13 39				14a00			14a20			14 39			15a00			15a20			15 39		
Watton-at-Stone	d				13 45										14 45									15 45		
Stevenage 4	d	13 12			13 51		13 42				14 12				14 51	14 42				15 12				15 51	15 42	
Hitchin 4	d	13a17			13 57		13 47				14a17				14 57	14 47				15a17				15 57	15 47	
Letchworth Garden City	a				14 04		13 51								15 04	14 51								16 04	15 51	

For general notes see front of timetable
For details of catering facilities see Directory of Train Operators

London → Welwyn Garden City, Hertford North and Letchworth Garden City

Saturday service operates on Bank Holiday Mondays

Network Diagram - see first page of Table 24

	FC	FC	FC	FC	FC		FC	FC	FC	FC	FC	FC	FC		FC	FC	FC	FC	FC	FC	FC		FC	FC	FC
			1						1						1	4E		1	1						
London Kings Cross 15 ⊖ d			15 36		15 46				16 06						16 32			16 50	16 54		16 57				
Moorgate ⊖ d	15 12	15 22		15 32			15 42	15 52		16 02	16 08	16 18	16 23			16 28	16 38			16 48			16 53	16 58	17 03
Old Street ⊖ d	15 14	15 24		15 34			15 44	15 54		16 04	16 10	16 20	16 25			16 30	16 40			16 50			16 55	17 00	17 05
Essex Road d	15 17	15 27		15 37			15 47	15 57		16 07	16 13	16 23	16 28			16 33	16 43			16 53			16 58	17 03	17 08
Highbury & Islington ⊖ d	15 19	15 29		15 39			15 49	15 59		16 09	16 16	16 26	16 31			16 36	16 46			16 56			17 01	17 06	17 11
Drayton Park d	15 21	15 31		15 41			15 51	16 01		16 11	16 17	16 27	16 32			16 37	16 47			16 57			17 02	17 07	17 12
Finsbury Park ⊖ d	15 24	15 34	15 41	15 44	15 51		15 54	16 04	16 11	16 14	16 20	16 30	16 35		16 37	16 40	16 50	16 55	16 59	17 00	17 03		17 05	17 10	17 15
Harringay d	15 26	15 36		15 46			15 56	16 06		16 16	16 23	16 33				16 43	16 53						17 08		17 18
Hornsey d	15 28	15 38		15 48			15 58	16 08		16 18	16 25	16 35				16 45	16 55						17 10		17 20
Alexandra Palace d	15 30	15 40		15 50			16 00	16 10		16 20	16 28	16 38	16 41			16 47	16 58						17 12	17 16	17 23
New Southgate d		15 43					16 03			16 23						16 50					17 08		17 15		
Oakleigh Park d		15 46					16 06			16 26						16 54					17 11		17 19		
New Barnet d		15 48					16 08			16 28						16 56					17 13		17 21		
Hadley Wood d		15 51					16 11			16 31						16 59							17 24		
Potters Bar d		15 55	15 51		16 01		16 15		16 21	16 35					16 48	17 03					17 19		17 28		
Brookmans Park d		15 58					16 18			16 38						17 06							17 31		
Welham Green d		16 00					16 20			16 40						17 08							17 33		
Hatfield d		16 03	15 57		16 07		16 23		16 27	16 43					16 54	17 11			17 15		17 25		17 36		
Welwyn Garden City 4 d		16a09	16 01		16a12		16a29		16 32	16a49					16 59	17a16			17 19		17a30		17a41		
Welwyn North d			16 04						16 35						17 03			17 11	17 22						
Knebworth d			16 08						16 39						17 07				17 26						
Bowes Park d	15 33			15 53				16 13			16 30		16 44				17 00			17 07					17 25
Palmers Green d	15 35			15 55				16 15			16 32	16 41	16 46				17 02			17 09				17 19	17 27
Winchmore Hill d	15 37			15 57				16 17			16 35	16 44	16 49				17 05			17 12				17 22	17 30
Grange Park d	15 39			15 59				16 19			16 37		16 51				17 07			17 14					17 32
Enfield Chase d	15 41			16 01				16 21			16 39	16 47	16 53				17 09			17 16				17 26	17 34
Gordon Hill d	15 43			16 03				16 23			16 41	16a51	16 55				17 11			17 18				17a31	17 37
Crews Hill d	15 46			16 06				16 26			16 44						17 14								17 40
Cuffley d	15 49			16 09				16 29			16 47		17 00				17 17			17 23					17 43
Bayford d	15 54			16 14				16 34			16 52						17 22								17 48
Hertford North d	16b09			16a20				16 39			16a58		17 09				17a28			17 33					17a53
Watton-at-Stone d	16 15							16 45					17 15							17 38					
Stevenage 4 d	16a23		16 12					16a53	16 43				17a23		17 11			17 17	17 36	17a46					
Hitchin 4 d			16a17						16 49						17 17			17a23	17 42						
Letchworth Garden City a									16 53						17 21				17 47						

	FC	FC	FC	FC	FC	FC		FC	FC	FC	FC	FC	FC	FC		FC	FC	FC	FC	FC	FC	FC		FC	FC
	1		1								1								1	1					
London Kings Cross 15 ⊖ d	17 14		17 22		17 27						17 52		17 57						18 22	18 23		18 27			
Moorgate ⊖ d		17 08		17 18		17 23		17 28	17 33	17 38		17 48		17 53		17 58	18 03	18 08			18 18			18 23	18 28
Old Street ⊖ d		17 10		17 20		17 25		17 30	17 35	17 40		17 50		17 55		18 00	18 05	18 10			18 20			18 25	18 30
Essex Road d		17 13		17 23		17 28		17 33	17 38	17 43		17 53		17 58		18 03	18 08	18 13			18 23			18 28	18 33
Highbury & Islington ⊖ d		17 16		17 26		17 31		17 36	17 41	17 46		17 56		18 01		18 06	18 11	18 16			18 26			18 31	18 36
Drayton Park d		17 17		17 27		17 32		17 37	17 42	17 47		17 57		18 02		18 07	18 12	18 17			18 27			18 32	18 37
Finsbury Park ⊖ d	17 19	17 20	17 28	17 30	17 33	17 35		17 40	17 45	17 50	17 58	18 00	18 03	18 05		18 10	18 15	18 20	18 28		18 30	18 33		18 35	18 40
Harringay d		17 23				17 38			17 48	17 53				18 08			18 18	18 23						18 38	
Hornsey d		17 25				17 40			17 50	17 55				18 10			18 20	18 25						18 40	
Alexandra Palace d		17 27				17 42		17 46	17 53	17 57				18 12		18 16	18 23	18 27						18 42	18 46
New Southgate d		17 30			17 38	17 45				18 00			18 08	18 15				18 30				18 38		18 45	
Oakleigh Park d		17 34			17 41	17 49				18 04			18 11	18 19				18 34				18 41		18 49	
New Barnet d		17 36			17 43	17 51				18 06			18 13	18 21				18 36				18 43		18 51	
Hadley Wood d		17 39				17 54				18 09				18 24				18 39						18 54	
Potters Bar d		17 43			17 49	17 58				18 13			18 19	18 28				18 43				18 49		18 58	
Brookmans Park d		17 46				18 01				18 16				18 31				18 46						19 01	
Welham Green d		17 48				18 03				18 18				18 33				18 48						19 03	
Hatfield d		17 51			17 55	18 06				18 21			18 25	18 36				18 51				18 55		19 06	
Welwyn Garden City 4 d		17a56	17 47		18a00	18a11				18a26	18 17		18a30	18a41				18a56	18 47			19a00		19a11	
Welwyn North d			17 51								18 21								18 51	18 41					
Knebworth d	17 35		17 55								18 25								18 55						
Bowes Park d				17 37					17 55			18 07					18 25				18 37				
Palmers Green d				17 39				17 49	17 57			18 09				18 19	18 27				18 39				18 49
Winchmore Hill d				17 42				17 52	18 00			18 12				18 22	18 30				18 42				18 52
Grange Park d				17 44					18 02			18 14					18 32				18 44				
Enfield Chase d				17 46				17 56	18 04			18 16				18 26	18 34				18 46				18 56
Gordon Hill d				17 48				18 03	18 07			18 18				18 28	18 37				18 48				18 58
Crews Hill d									18 10								18 40								
Cuffley d				17 53				18 04	18 13			18 23				18 33	18 43				18 53				19 03
Bayford d									18 18								18 48								
Hertford North d				18 03				18a12	18a23			18 33				18a42	18a53				19 03				19a12
Watton-at-Stone d				18 08								18 38									19 08				
Stevenage 4 d	17 40		18 04	18a16							18 34	18a46							19 04		19 16				
Hitchin 4 d	17a45		18 10								18 40								19 10	18 51	19 22				
Letchworth Garden City a			18 16								18 46								19 16	18 55	19 27				

For general notes see front of timetable
For details of catering facilities see
Directory of Train Operators

b Arr. 1559

London → Welwyn Garden City, Hertford North and Letchworth Garden City

Saturday service operates on Bank Holiday Mondays

Network Diagram - see first page of Table 24

	FC	FC 1	FC	FC 1	FC	FC	FC	FC	FC 1	FC	FC	FC 1	FC	FC	FC	FC	FC	FC 1	FC	FC	FC 1	FC
London Kings Cross 15 ⊖ d		18 44		18 52		18 57			19 18			19 36		19 40				20 06			20 36	
Moorgate ⊖ d	18 35		18 40		18 50		18 55	19 02		19 12	19 22		19 32		19 37	19 42	19 52		20 07	20 12		20 32
Old Street ⊖ d	18 37		18 42		18 52		18 57	19 04		19 14	19 24		19 34		19 39	19 44	19 54		20 09	20 14		20 34
Essex Road d	18 40		18 45		18 55		19 00	19 07		19 17	19 27		19 37		19 42	19 47	19 57		20 12	20 17		20 37
Highbury & Islington ⊖ d	18 43		18 48		18 58		19 03	19 10		19 20	19 30		19 40		19 45	19 50	19 59		20 14	20 19		20 39
Drayton Park d	18 44		18 49		18 59		19 04	19 11		19 21	19 31		19 41		19 46	19 51	20 01		20 16	20 21		20 41
Finsbury Park ⊖ d	18 47	18 49	18 52	18 58	19 02	19 03	19 07	19 14	19 23	19 24	19 34	19 41	19 44	19 45	19 49	19 54	20 04	20 11	20 19	20 24	20 41	20 44
Harringay d	18 50		18 55				19 10	19 17		19 27	19 37				19 52	19 57	20 06		20 21	20 26		20 46
Hornsey d	18 52		18 57				19 12	19 19		19 29	19 39				19 54	19 59	20 08		20 23	20 28		20 48
Alexandra Palace d	18 55		18 59		19 08		19 14	19 22		19 31	19 42				19 56	20 02	20 10		20 25	20 30		20 50
New Southgate d			19 02			19 08	19 17			19 34					19 59				20 28			
Oakleigh Park d			19 06			19 11	19 21			19 38					20 03				20 31			
New Barnet d			19 08			19 13	19 23			19 40					20 05				20 33			
Hadley Wood d			19 11			19 16	19 26			19 43					20 08				20 36			
Potters Bar d			19 15			19 20	19 30		19 34	19 47				19 57	20 12			20 21	20 40		20 51	
Brookmans Park d			19 18				19 33			19 50					20 15				20 43			
Welham Green d			19 20				19 35			19 52					20 17				20 45			
Hatfield d			19 23	19 14		19 27	19 38		19 42	19 55				20 03	20 20			20 27	20 48		20 57	
Welwyn Garden City 4 d			19a28	19 18		19a32	19a43		19 48	20a00		20b00		20a09	20a25			20 31	20a54		21 01	
Welwyn North d				19 22					19 52			20 04						20 34			21 04	
Knebworth d		19 05		19 26					19 56			20 08						20 38			21 08	
Bowes Park d	18 57				19 09			19 24			19 44		19 51			20 04	20 13			20 33		20 53
Palmers Green d	18 59				19 11			19 26			19 46		19 53			20 06	20 15			20 35		20 55
Winchmore Hill d	19 02				19 14			19 29			19 49		19 56			20 09	20 17			20 37		20 57
Grange Park d	19 04				19 16			19 31			19 51		19 58			20 11	20 19			20 39		20 59
Enfield Chase d	19 06				19 18			19 33			19 53		20 00			20 13	20 21			20 41		21 01
Gordon Hill d	19 09				19 20			19 36			19 56		20 03			20 16	20 23			20 43		21 03
Crews Hill d	19 12							19 39					20 06				20 26			20 46		21 06
Cuffley d	19 15				19 25			19 42			20 00		20 09			20 20	20 29			20 49		21 09
Bayford d	19 20							19 47					20 14				20 34			20 54		21 14
Hertford North d	19a25				19 35			19a52			20 10		20a19			20a30	20 40			21c10		21a20
Watton-at-Stone d					19 40						20 15						20 45			21 15		
Stevenage 4 d		19 10		19 36	19a52				20 04		20 23	20 12					20a53	20 42		21 23	21 12	
Hitchin 4 d		19a15		19 42					20 10		20 27	20 17						20 47		21 28	21 17	
Letchworth Garden City a				19 47					20 15		20 35	20 23						20 51		21 34	21 23	

	FC	FC	FC 1	FC	FC	FC 1	FC	FC	FC	FC 1	FC	FC	FC 1	FC	FC	FC 1	FC	FC	FC 1	FC
London Kings Cross 15 ⊖ d			21 06			21 36				22 06	22 11	22 26	22 36	22 41	22 56	23 06	23 11	23 26	23 36	23 41
Moorgate ⊖ d	20 37	20 52		21 07	21 12		21 32	21 37	21 52											
Old Street ⊖ d	20 39	20 54		21 09	21 14		21 34	21 39	21 54											
Essex Road d	20 42	20 57		21 12	21 17		21 37	21 42	21 57											
Highbury & Islington ⊖ d	20 44	20 59		21 14	21 19		21 39	21 44	21 59											
Drayton Park d	20 46	21 01		21 16	21 21		21 41	21 46	22 01											
Finsbury Park ⊖ d	20 49	21 04	21 11	21 19	21 24	21 41	21 44	21 49	22 04	22 11	22 17	22 32	22 41	22 47	23 02	23 11	23 17	23 32	23 41	23 47
Harringay d	20 51	21 06		21 21	21 26		21 46	21 51	22 06		22 19	22 34		22 49	23 04		23 19	23 34		23 49
Hornsey d	20 53	21 08		21 23	21 28		21 48	21 53	22 08		22 21	22 36		22 51	23 06		23 21	23 36		23 51
Alexandra Palace d	20 55	21 10		21 25	21 30		21 50	21 55	22 10		22 23	22 38		22 53	23 08		23 23	23 38		23 53
New Southgate d	20 58			21 28				21 58			22 26			22 56			23 26			23 56
Oakleigh Park d	21 01			21 31				22 01			22 29			22 59			23 29			23 59
New Barnet d	21 03			21 33				22 03			22 31			23 01			23 31			00 01
Hadley Wood d	21 06			21 36				22 06			22 34			23 04			23 34			00 04
Potters Bar d	21 10		21 21	21 40		21 51		22 10		22 21	22 38		22 51	23 08		23 21	23 38		23 51	00 08
Brookmans Park d	21 13			21 43				22 13			22 41			23 11			23 41			00 11
Welham Green d	21 15			21 45				22 15			22 43			23 13			23 43			00 13
Hatfield d	21 18		21 27	21 48		21 57		22 18		22 27	22 46		22 57	23 16		23 27	23 46		23 57	00 16
Welwyn Garden City 4 d	21a24		21 31	21a54		22 01		22a24		22 31	22a51		23 01	23a24		23 31	23a54		00 01	00a24
Welwyn North d			21 34			22 04				22 34			23 04			23 34			00 04	
Knebworth d			21 38			22 08				22 38			23 08			23 38			00 08	
Bowes Park d		21 13			21 33		21 53		22 13			22 41			23 11			23 41		
Palmers Green d		21 15			21 35		21 55		22 15			22 43			23 13			23 43		
Winchmore Hill d		21 17			21 37		21 57		22 17			22 45			23 15			23 45		
Grange Park d		21 19			21 39		21 59		22 19			22 47			23 17			23 47		
Enfield Chase d		21 21			21 41		22 01		22 21			22 49			23 19			23 49		
Gordon Hill d		21 23			21 43		22 03		22 23			22 51			23 21			23 51		
Crews Hill d		21 26			21 46		22 06		22 26			22 54			23 24			23 54		
Cuffley d		21 29			21 49		22 09		22 29			22 57			23 27			23 57		
Bayford d		21 34			21 54		22 14		22 34			23 02			23 32			00 02		
Hertford North d		21a40			22e07		22a20		22a40			23 07			23a38			00 07		
Watton-at-Stone d					22 13							23 13						00 13		
Stevenage 4 d			21 42		22 20	22 12				22 42		23 20	23 12			23 42		00 20	00 12	
Hitchin 4 d			21 47		22 25	22 17				22 50		23 28	23 20			23 50		00 26	00 20	
Letchworth Garden City a			21 51		22 33	22 23				22 54		23 36	23 26			23 54		00 36	00 29	

For general notes see front of timetable
For details of catering facilities see Directory of Train Operators

b Arr. 1957
c Arr. 2059
e Arr. 2159

London → Welwyn Garden City, Hertford North and Letchworth Garden City

Network Diagram - see first page of Table 24

		FC	FC 1	FC	FC	FC	FC 1	FC 1	FC	FC 1	FC 1	FC	FC	FC 1	FC	FC	FC 1	FC	FC	FC 1	FC	FC	FC 1	FC
London Kings Cross 15 ⊖	d	23p26	23p36	23p41	00 11	00 26	00 36	01 06	01 11	01 36	05 22	05 26	05 56	06 06	06 11	06 26	06 36	06 41	06 56	07 06	07 11	07 26	07 36	07 41
Finsbury Park ⊖	d	23p32	23p41	23p47	00 17	00 32	00 41	01 11	01 17	01 41	05 27	05 32	06 02	06 11	06 17	06 32	06 41	06 47	07 02	07 11	07 17	07 32	07 41	07 47
Harringay	d	23p34		23p49	00 19	00 34			01 19			05 34	06 04		06 19	06 34		06 49	07 04		07 19	07 34		07 49
Hornsey	d	23p36		23p51	00 21	00 36			01 21			05 36	06 06		06 21	06 36		06 51	07 06		07 21	07 36		07 51
Alexandra Palace	d	23p38		23p53	00 23	00 38		01 16	01 23	01 45		05 38	06 08		06 23	06 38		06 53	07 08		07 23	07 38		07 53
New Southgate	d			23p56	00 26				01 26						06 26			06 56			07 26			07 56
Oakleigh Park	d			23p59	00 29				01 29	01 50					06 29			06 59			07 29			07 59
New Barnet	d			00 01	00 31				01 31	01 52					06 31			07 01			07 31			08 01
Hadley Wood	d			00 04	00 34				01 34	01 54					06 34			07 04			07 34			08 04
Potters Bar	d		23p51	00 08	00 38		00 51		01 38	01 58	05 37			06 21	06 38		06 51	07 08		07 21	07 38		07 51	08 08
Brookmans Park	d			00 11	00 41				01 41						06 41			07 11			07 41			08 11
Welham Green	d			00 13	00 43				01 43						06 43			07 13			07 43			08 13
Hatfield	d		23p57	00 16	00 46		00 57		01 46	02 04	05 43			06 27	06 46		06 57	07 16		07 27	07 46		07 57	08 16
Welwyn Garden City 4	d		00 01	00a24	00a54		01 01		01a54	02 08	05 47			06 31	06a51		07 01	07a21		07 31	07a51		08 01	08a21
Welwyn North	d		00 04				01s04			02s11	05 50			06 34			07 04			07 34			08 04	
Knebworth	d		00 08				01s08			02s15	05 54			06 38			07 08			07 38			08 08	
Bowes Park	d	23p41				00 41						05 41	06 11			06 41			07 11			07 41		
Palmers Green	d	23p43				00 43		01 19				05 43	06 13			06 43			07 13			07 43		
Winchmore Hill	d	23p45				00 45		01 21				05 45	06 15			06 45			07 15			07 45		
Grange Park	d	23p47				00 47						05 47	06 17			06 47			07 17			07 47		
Enfield Chase	d	23p49				00 49		01 24				05 49	06 19			06 49			07 19			07 49		
Gordon Hill	d	23p51				00 51		01 26				05 51	06 21			06 51			07 21			07 51		
Crews Hill	d	23p54				00 54						05 54	06 24			06 54			07 24			07 54		
Cuffley	d	23p57				00 57		01 30				05 57	06 27			06 57			07 27			07 57		
Bayford	d	00 02				01 02						06 02	06 32			07 02			07 32			08 02		
Hertford North	d	00 07				01 07		01 38				06a08	06a38			07 07			07a38			08 07		
Watton-at-Stone	d	00 13				01 13										07 13						08 13		
Stevenage 4	d	00 20	00 12			01 20	01 12	01 47		02 18	05 58			06 42		07a20	07 12			07 42		08a20	08 12	
Hitchin 4	d	00 26	00 20			01 26	01a17	01 52		02a23	06a06			06 47			07a17			07 47			08a17	
Letchworth Garden City	a	00 36	00 29			01 36		02 06						06 51						07 51				

		FC	FC 1	FC	FC	FC 1	FC	FC	FC 1	FC	FC	FC 1	FC	FC	FC 1	FC	FC	FC 1	FC	FC	FC 1	FC	FC	FC 1	FC
London Kings Cross 15 ⊖	d	07 56	08 06	08 11	08 26	08 36	08 41	08 56	09 06	09 11	09 26	09 36	09 41	09 56	10 06	10 11	10 26	10 36	10 41	10 56	11 06	11 11	11 26	11 36	11 41
Finsbury Park ⊖	d	08 02	08 11	08 17	08 32	08 41	08 47	09 02	09 11	09 17	09 32	09 41	09 47	10 02	10 11	10 17	10 32	10 41	10 47	11 02	11 11	11 17	11 32	11 41	11 47
Harringay	d	08 04		08 19	08 34		08 49	09 04		09 19	09 34		09 49	10 04		10 19	10 34		10 49	11 04		11 19	11 34		11 49
Hornsey	d	08 06		08 21	08 36		08 51	09 06		09 21	09 36		09 51	10 06		10 21	10 36		10 51	11 06		11 21	11 36		11 51
Alexandra Palace	d	08 08		08 23	08 38		08 53	09 08		09 23	09 38		09 53	10 08		10 23	10 38		10 53	11 08		11 23	11 38		11 53
New Southgate	d			08 26			08 56			09 26			09 56			10 26			10 56			11 26			11 56
Oakleigh Park	d			08 29			08 59			09 29			09 59			10 29			10 59			11 29			11 59
New Barnet	d			08 31			09 01			09 31			10 01			10 31			11 01			11 31			12 01
Hadley Wood	d			08 34			09 04			09 34			10 04			10 34			11 04			11 34			12 04
Potters Bar	d		08 21	08 38		08 51	09 08		09 21	09 38		09 51	10 08		10 21	10 38		10 51	11 08		11 21	11 38		11 51	12 08
Brookmans Park	d			08 41			09 11			09 41			10 11			10 41			11 11			11 41			12 11
Welham Green	d			08 43			09 13			09 43			10 13			10 43			11 13			11 43			12 13
Hatfield	d		08 27	08 46		08 57	09 16		09 27	09 46		09 57	10 16		10 27	10 46		10 57	11 16		11 27	11 46		11 57	12 16
Welwyn Garden City 4	d		08 31	08a51		09 01	09a21		09 31	09a51		10 01	10a21		10 31	10a51		11 01	11a21		11 31	11a51		12 01	12a21
Welwyn North	d		08 34			09 04			09 34			10 04			10 34			11 04			11 34			12 04	
Knebworth	d		08 38			09 08			09 38			10 08			10 38			11 08			11 38			12 08	
Bowes Park	d	08 11			08 41			09 11			09 41			10 11			10 41			11 11			11 41		
Palmers Green	d	08 13			08 43			09 13			09 43			10 13			10 43			11 13			11 43		
Winchmore Hill	d	08 15			08 45			09 15			09 45			10 15			10 45			11 15			11 45		
Grange Park	d	08 17			08 47			09 17			09 47			10 17			10 47			11 17			11 47		
Enfield Chase	d	08 19			08 49			09 19			09 49			10 19			10 49			11 19			11 49		
Gordon Hill	d	08 21			08 51			09 21			09 51			10 21			10 51			11 21			11 51		
Crews Hill	d	08 24			08 54			09 24			09 54			10 24			10 54			11 24			11 54		
Cuffley	d	08 27			08 57			09 27			09 57			10 27			10 57			11 27			11 57		
Bayford	d	08 32			09 02			09 32			10 02			10 32			11 02			11 32			12 02		
Hertford North	d	08a38			09 07			09a38			10 07			10a38			11 07			11a38			12 07		
Watton-at-Stone	d				09 13						10 13						11 13						12 13		
Stevenage 4	d		08 42		09a20	09 12			09 42		10a20	10 12			10 42		11a20	11 12			11 42		12a20	12 12	
Hitchin 4	d		08 47			09a17			09 47			10a17			10 47			11a17			11 47			12a17	
Letchworth Garden City	a		08 51						09 51						10 51						11 51				

For general notes see front of timetable
For details of catering facilities see Directory of Train Operators

There is no service between Moorgate and Finsbury Park on Saturdays

Table 24

Saturdays

London → Welwyn Garden City, Hertford North and Letchworth Garden City

Network Diagram - see first page of Table 24

	FC	FC 1	FC	FC	FC 1	FC	FC	FC 1	FC	FC	FC 1	FC	FC	FC 1	FC	FC	FC 1	FC	FC	FC 1	FC	FC	FC 1	FC
London Kings Cross [15] ⊖ d	11 56	12 06	12 11	12 26	12 36	12 41	12 56	13 06	13 11	13 26	13 36	13 41	13 56	14 06	14 11	14 26	14 36	14 41	14 56	15 06	15 11	15 26	15 36	15 41
Finsbury Park ⊖ d	12 02	12 11	12 17	12 32	12 41	12 47	13 02	13 11	13 17	13 32	13 41	13 47	14 02	14 11	14 17	14 32	14 41	14 47	15 02	15 11	15 17	15 32	15 41	15 47
Harringay d	12 04		12 19	12 34		12 49	13 04		13 19	13 34		13 49	14 04		14 19	14 34		14 49	15 04		15 19	15 34		15 49
Hornsey d	12 06		12 21	12 36		12 51	13 06		13 21	13 36		13 51	14 06		14 21	14 36		14 51	15 06		15 21	15 36		15 51
Alexandra Palace d	12 08		12 23	12 38		12 53	13 08		13 23	13 38		13 53	14 08		14 23	14 38		14 53	15 08		15 23	15 38		15 53
New Southgate d			12 26			12 56			13 26			13 56			14 26			14 56			15 26			15 56
Oakleigh Park d			12 29			12 59			13 29			13 59			14 29			14 59			15 29			15 59
New Barnet d			12 31			13 01			13 31			14 01			14 31			15 01			15 31			16 01
Hadley Wood d			12 34			13 04			13 34			14 04			14 34			15 04			15 34			16 04
Potters Bar d		12 21	12 38		12 51	13 08		13 21	13 38		13 51	14 08		14 21	14 38		14 51	15 08		15 21	15 38		15 51	16 08
Brookmans Park d			12 41			13 11			13 41			14 11			14 41			15 11			15 41			16 11
Welham Green d			12 43			13 13			13 43			14 13			14 43			15 13			15 43			16 13
Hatfield d		12 27	12 46		12 57	13 16		13 27	13 46		13 57	14 16		14 27	14 46		14 57	15 16		15 27	15 46		15 57	16 16
Welwyn Garden City [4] d		12 31	12a51		13 01	13a21		13 31	13a51		14 01	14a21		14 31	14a51		15 01	15a21		15 31	15a51		16 01	16a21
Welwyn North d		12 34			13 04			13 34			14 04			14 34			15 04			15 34			16 04	
Knebworth d		12 38			13 08			13 38			14 08			14 38			15 08			15 38			16 08	
Bowes Park d	12 11			12 41			13 11			13 41			14 11			14 41			15 11			15 41		
Palmers Green d	12 13			12 43			13 13			13 43			14 13			14 43			15 13			15 43		
Winchmore Hill d	12 15			12 45			13 15			13 45			14 15			14 45			15 15			15 45		
Grange Park d	12 17			12 47			13 17			13 47			14 17			14 47			15 17			15 47		
Enfield Chase d	12 19			12 49			13 19			13 49			14 19			14 49			15 19			15 49		
Gordon Hill d	12 21			12 51			13 21			13 51			14 21			14 51			15 21			15 51		
Crews Hill d	12 24			12 54			13 24			13 54			14 24			14 54			15 24			15 54		
Cuffley d	12 27			12 57			13 27			13 57			14 27			14 57			15 27			15 57		
Bayford d	12 32			13 02			13 32			14 02			14 32			15 02			15 32			16 02		
Hertford North d	12a38			13 07			13a38			14 07			14a38			15 07			15a38			16 07		
Watton-at-Stone d				13 13						14 13						15 13						16 13		
Stevenage [4] d		12 42		13a20	13 12			13 42		14a20	14 12			14 42		15a20	15 12			15 42		16a20	16 12	
Hitchin [4] d		12 47			13a17			13 47			14a17			14 47			15a17			15 47			16a17	
Letchworth Garden City a		12 51						13 51						14 51						15 51				

	FC	FC 1	FC	FC	FC 1	FC	FC	FC 1	FC	FC	FC 1	FC	FC	FC 1	FC	FC	FC 1	FC	FC	FC 1	FC	FC	FC 1	FC
London Kings Cross [15] ⊖ d	15 56	16 06	16 11	16 26	16 36	16 41	16 56	17 06	17 11	17 26	17 36	17 41	17 56	18 06	18 11	18 26	18 36	18 41	18 56	19 06	19 11	19 26	19 36	19 41
Finsbury Park ⊖ d	16 02	16 11	16 17	16 32	16 41	16 47	17 02	17 11	17 17	17 32	17 41	17 47	18 02	18 11	18 17	18 32	18 41	18 47	19 02	19 11	19 17	19 32	19 41	19 47
Harringay d	16 04		16 19	16 34		16 49	17 04		17 19	17 34		17 49	18 04		18 19	18 34		18 49	19 04		19 19	19 34		19 49
Hornsey d	16 06		16 21	16 36		16 51	17 06		17 21	17 36		17 51	18 06		18 21	18 36		18 51	19 06		19 21	19 36		19 51
Alexandra Palace d	16 08		16 23	16 38		16 53	17 08		17 23	17 38		17 53	18 08		18 23	18 38		18 53	19 08		19 23	19 38		19 53
New Southgate d			16 26			16 56			17 26			17 56			18 26			18 56			19 26			19 56
Oakleigh Park d			16 29			16 59			17 29			17 59			18 29			18 59			19 29			19 59
New Barnet d			16 31			17 01			17 31			18 01			18 31			19 01			19 31			20 01
Hadley Wood d			16 34			17 04			17 34			18 04			18 34			19 04			19 34			20 04
Potters Bar d		16 21	16 38		16 51	17 08		17 21	17 38		17 51	18 08		18 21	18 38		18 51	19 08		19 21	19 38		19 51	20 08
Brookmans Park d			16 41			17 11			17 41			18 11			18 41			19 11			19 41			20 11
Welham Green d			16 43			17 13			17 43			18 13			18 43			19 13			19 43			20 13
Hatfield d		16 27	16 46		16 57	17 16		17 27	17 46		17 57	18 16		18 27	18 46		18 57	19 16		19 27	19 46		19 57	20 16
Welwyn Garden City [4] d		16 31	16a51		17 01	17a21		17 31	17a51		18 01	18a21		18 31	18a51		19 01	19a21		19 31	19a51		20 01	20a21
Welwyn North d		16 34			17 04			17 34			18 04			18 34			19 04			19 34			20 04	
Knebworth d		16 38			17 08			17 38			18 08			18 38			19 08			19 38			20 08	
Bowes Park d	16 11			16 41			17 11			17 41			18 11			18 41			19 11			19 41		
Palmers Green d	16 13			16 43			17 13			17 43			18 13			18 43			19 13			19 43		
Winchmore Hill d	16 15			16 45			17 15			17 45			18 15			18 45			19 15			19 45		
Grange Park d	16 17			16 47			17 17			17 47			18 17			18 47			19 17			19 47		
Enfield Chase d	16 19			16 49			17 19			17 49			18 19			18 49			19 19			19 49		
Gordon Hill d	16 21			16 51			17 21			17 51			18 21			18 51			19 21			19 51		
Crews Hill d	16 24			16 54			17 24			17 54			18 24			18 54			19 24			19 54		
Cuffley d	16 27			16 57			17 27			17 57			18 27			18 57			19 27			19 57		
Bayford d	16 32			17 02			17 32			18 02			18 32			19 02			19 32			20 02		
Hertford North d	16a38			17 07			17a38			18 07			18a38			19 07			19a38			20 07		
Watton-at-Stone d				17 13						18 13						19 13						20 13		
Stevenage [4] d		16 42		17a20	17 12			17 42		18a20	18 12			18 42		19a20	19 12			19 42		20a20	20 12	
Hitchin [4] d		16 47			17a17			17 47			18a17			18 47			19a17			19 47			20a17	
Letchworth Garden City a		16 51						17 51						18 51						19 51				

	FC	FC 1	FC	FC	FC 1	FC	FC	FC 1	FC	FC	FC 1	FC	FC	FC 1	FC	FC	FC 1	FC	FC	FC 1	FC	FC	FC
London Kings Cross [15] ⊖ d	19 56	20 06	20 11	20 26	20 36	20 41	20 56	21 06	21 11	21 26	21 36	21 41	21 56	22 06	22 11	22 26	22 36	22 41	22 56	23 06	23 17	23 26	23 41
Finsbury Park ⊖ d	20 02	20 11	20 17	20 32	20 41	20 47	21 02	21 11	21 17	21 32	21 41	21 47	22 02	22 11	22 17	22 32	22 41	22 47	23 02	23 11	23 23	23 32	23 46
Harringay d	20 04		20 19	20 34		20 49	21 04		21 19	21 34		21 49	22 04		22 19	22 34		22 49	23 04		23 25	23 34	23 48
Hornsey d	20 06		20 21	20 36		20 51	21 06		21 21	21 36		21 51	22 06		22 21	22 36		22 51	23 06		23 27	23 36	23 50
Alexandra Palace d	20 08		20 23	20 38		20 53	21 08		21 23	21 38		21 53	22 08		22 23	22 38		22 53	23 08		23 29	23 38	23 52
New Southgate d			20 26			20 56			21 26			21 56			22 26			22 56			23 32		23 55
Oakleigh Park d			20 29			20 59			21 29			21 59			22 29			22 59			23 35		23 58
New Barnet d			20 31			21 01			21 31			22 01			22 31			23 01			23 37		00 01
Hadley Wood d			20 34			21 04			21 34			22 04			22 34			23 04			23 40		00 03
Potters Bar d		20 21	20 38		20 51	21 08		21 21	21 38		21 51	22 08		22 21	22 38		22 51	23 08		23 21	23 44		00 07
Brookmans Park d			20 41			21 11			21 41			22 11			22 41			23 11			23 47		00 10
Welham Green d			20 43			21 13			21 43			22 13			22 43			23 13			23 49		00 13
Hatfield d		20 27	20 46		20 57	21 16		21 27	21 46		21 57	22 16		22 27	22 46		22 57	23 16		23 27	23 52		00 15
Welwyn Garden City [4] d		20 31	20a51		21 01	21a21		21 31	21a51		22 01	22a21		22 31	22a53		23 01	23a23		23b37	00a02		00c30
Welwyn North d		20 34			21 04			21 34			22 04			22 34			23 04			23 42			00 33
Knebworth d		20 38			21 08			21 38			22 08			22 38			23 08			23 46			00 38
Bowes Park d	20 11			20 41			21 11			21 41			22 11			22 41			23 11			23 41	
Palmers Green d	20 13			20 43			21 13			21 43			22 13			22 43			23 13			23 43	
Winchmore Hill d	20 15			20 45			21 15			21 45			22 15			22 45			23 15			23 45	
Grange Park d	20 17			20 47			21 17			21 47			22 17			22 47			23 17			23 47	
Enfield Chase d	20 19			20 49			21 19			21 49			22 19			22 49			23 19			23 49	
Gordon Hill d	20 21			20 51			21 21			21 51			22 21			22 51			23 21			23 51	
Crews Hill d	20 24			20 54			21 24			21 54			22 24			22 54			23 24			23 54	
Cuffley d	20 27			20 57			21 27			21 57			22 27			22 57			23 27			23 57	
Bayford d	20 32			21 02			21 32			22 02			22 32			23 02			23 32			00 02	
Hertford North d	20a38			21 07			21a38			22 07			22a38			23 07			23a38			00 07	
Watton-at-Stone d				21 13						22 13						23 13						00 13	
Stevenage [4] d		20 42		21a20	21 12			21 42		22a20	22 12			22 42		23a24	23 12			23 51		00 22	00 43
Hitchin [4] d		20 47			21a17			21 47			22a17			22 47			23 17			23 58		00 31	00 51
Letchworth Garden City a		20 51						21 51						22 51			23 28			00 02		00 36	00 59

For general notes see front of timetable
For details of catering facilities see Directory of Train Operators

b Arr. 2330
c Arr. 0021

There is no service between Moorgate and Finsbury Park on Saturdays

Table 24

Sundays

London → Welwyn Garden City, Hertford North and Letchworth Garden City

Network Diagram - see first page of Table 24

		FC	FC	FC 1 A	FC	FC	FC 1 B	FC 1 C	FC	FC	FC	FC	FC	FC	FC 1 B	FC 1 C	FC	FC	FC	FC	FC 1	FC	FC	FC	FC	FC 1
London Kings Cross 15 ⊖	d	23p26	23p41	00 07	00 11	00 26	00 36	00 36	00 41	05 56	06 11	06 26	06 41	06 56	07 06		07 11	07 26	07 41	07 56	08 06	08 11	08 26	08 41	08 56	09 06
Finsbury Park ⊖	d	23p32	23p46	00 12	00 17	00 32	00 41	00 41	00 47	06 02	06 17	06 32	06 47	07 02	07 11		07 17	07 32	07 47	08 02	08 11	08 17	08 32	08 47	09 02	09 11
Harringay	d	23p34	23p48		00 19	00 34			00 49	06 04	06 19	06 34	06 49	07 04			07 19	07 34	07 49	08 04		08 19	08 34	08 49	09 04	
Hornsey	d	23p36	23p50		00 21	00 36			00 51	06 06	06 21	06 36	06 51	07 06			07 21	07 36	07 51	08 06		08 21	08 36	08 51	09 06	
Alexandra Palace	d	23p38	23p52	00 17	00 23	00 38			00 53	06 08	06 23	06 38	06 53	07 08			07 23	07 38	07 53	08 08		08 23	08 38	08 53	09 08	
New Southgate	d		23p55		00 26				00 56		06 26		06 56				07 26		07 56			08 26		08 56		
Oakleigh Park	d		23p58		00 29				00 59		06 29		06 59				07 29		07 59			08 29		08 59		
New Barnet	d		00 01		00 31				01 01		06 31		07 01				07 31		08 01			08 31		09 01		
Hadley Wood	d		00 03		00 34				01 04		06 34		07 04				07 34		08 04			08 34		09 04		
Potters Bar	d		00 07		00 38		00 51	00 51	01 08		06 38		07 08		07 21	07 21	07 38		08 08		08 21	08 38		09 08		09 21
Brookmans Park	d		00 10		00 41				01 11		06 41		07 11				07 41		08 11			08 41		09 11		
Welham Green	d		00 13		00 43				01 13		06 43		07 13				07 43		08 13			08 43		09 13		
Hatfield	d		00 15		00 46		00 57	00 57	01 16		06 46		07 16		07 27	07 27	07 46		08 16		08 27	08 46		09 16		09 27
Welwyn Garden City 4	d		00b30		00a58		01 03	01 03	01a26		06a55		07a25		07 33	07 33	07a55		08a25		08 31	08a55		09a21		09 31
Welwyn North	d		00 33				01s06	01s06							07 36	07 36					08 34					09 34
Knebworth	d		00 38				01s10	01s10							07 40	07 40					08 38					09 38
Bowes Park	d	23p41				00 41				06 11		06 41		07 11				07 41		08 11			08 41		09 11	
Palmers Green	d	23p43		00 20		00 43				06 13		06 43		07 13				07 43		08 13			08 43		09 13	
Winchmore Hill	d	23p45		00 22		00 45				06 15		06 45		07 15				07 45		08 15			08 45		09 15	
Grange Park	d	23p47				00 47				06 17		06 47		07 17				07 47		08 17			08 47		09 17	
Enfield Chase	d	23p49		00 25		00 49				06 19		06 49		07 19				07 49		08 19			08 49		09 19	
Gordon Hill	d	23p51		00 27		00 51				06 21		06 51		07 21				07 51		08 21			08 51		09 21	
Crews Hill	d	23p54				00 54				06 24		06 54		07 24				07 54		08 24			08 54		09 24	
Cuffley	d	23p57		00 31		00 57				06 27		06 57		07 27				07 57		08 27			08 57		09 27	
Bayford	d	00 02				01 02				06 32		07 02		07 32				08 02		08 32			09 02		09 32	
Hertford North	d	00 07		00 39		01a10				06a40		07 07		07a40				08 07		08a39			09 07		09a38	
Watton-at-Stone	d	00 13										07 12						08 12					09 13			
Stevenage 4	d	00 22	00 43	00 48			01 16	01 16				07a22			07 45	07 45		08a23			08 42		09a20			09 42
Hitchin 4	d	00 31	00 51	00 56			01 23	01a23							07 52	07 52					08 47					09 47
Letchworth Garden City	a	00 36	00 59	01 03			01 30								07 56	07 56					08 54					09 51

		FC	FC	FC	FC	FC 1	FC	FC	FC	FC	FC 1	FC	FC	FC	FC	FC 1	FC	FC	FC	FC	FC 1	FC	FC	FC	FC	FC 1
London Kings Cross 15 ⊖	d	09 11	09 26	09 41	09 56	10 06	10 11	10 26	10 41	10 56	11 06	11 11	11 26	11 41	11 56	12 06	12 11	12 26	12 41	12 56	13 06	13 11	13 26	13 41	13 56	14 06
Finsbury Park ⊖	d	09 17	09 32	09 47	10 02	10 11	10 17	10 32	10 47	11 02	11 11	11 17	11 32	11 47	12 02	12 11	12 17	12 32	12 47	13 02	13 11	13 17	13 32	13 47	14 02	14 11
Harringay	d	09 19	09 34	09 49	10 04		10 19	10 34	10 49	11 04		11 19	11 34	11 49	12 04		12 19	12 34	12 49	13 04		13 19	13 34	13 49	14 04	
Hornsey	d	09 21	09 36	09 51	10 06		10 21	10 36	10 51	11 06		11 21	11 36	11 51	12 06		12 21	12 36	12 51	13 06		13 21	13 36	13 51	14 06	
Alexandra Palace	d	09 23	09 38	09 53	10 08		10 23	10 38	10 53	11 08		11 23	11 38	11 53	12 08		12 23	12 38	12 53	13 08		13 23	13 38	13 53	14 08	
New Southgate	d	09 26		09 56			10 26		10 56			11 26		11 56			12 26		12 56			13 26		13 56		
Oakleigh Park	d	09 29		09 59			10 29		10 59			11 29		11 59			12 29		12 59			13 29		13 59		
New Barnet	d	09 31		10 01			10 31		11 01			11 31		12 01			12 31		13 01			13 31		14 01		
Hadley Wood	d	09 34		10 04			10 34		11 04			11 34		12 04			12 34		13 04			13 34		14 04		
Potters Bar	d	09 38		10 08		10 21	10 38		11 08		11 21	11 38		12 08		12 21	12 38		13 08		13 21	13 38		14 08		14 21
Brookmans Park	d	09 41		10 11			10 41		11 11			11 41		12 11			12 41		13 11			13 41		14 11		
Welham Green	d	09 43		10 13			10 43		11 13			11 43		12 13			12 43		13 13			13 43		14 13		
Hatfield	d	09 46		10 16		10 27	10 46		11 16		11 27	11 46		12 16		12 27	12 46		13 16		13 27	13 46		14 16		14 27
Welwyn Garden City 4	d	09a51		10a21		10 31	10a51		11a21		11 31	11a51		12a21		12 31	12a51		13a21		13 31	13a51		14a21		14 31
Welwyn North	d					10 34					11 34					12 34					13 34					14 34
Knebworth	d					10 38					11 38					12 38					13 38					14 38
Bowes Park	d		09 41		10 11			10 41		11 11			11 41		12 11			12 41		13 11			13 41		14 11	
Palmers Green	d		09 43		10 13			10 43		11 13			11 43		12 13			12 43		13 13			13 43		14 13	
Winchmore Hill	d		09 45		10 15			10 45		11 15			11 45		12 15			12 45		13 15			13 45		14 15	
Grange Park	d		09 47		10 17			10 47		11 17			11 47		12 17			12 47		13 17			13 47		14 17	
Enfield Chase	d		09 49		10 19			10 49		11 19			11 49		12 19			12 49		13 19			13 49		14 19	
Gordon Hill	d		09 51		10 21			10 51		11 21			11 51		12 21			12 51		13 21			13 51		14 21	
Crews Hill	d		09 54		10 24			10 54		11 24			11 54		12 24			12 54		13 24			13 54		14 24	
Cuffley	d		09 57		10 27			10 57		11 27			11 57		12 27			12 57		13 27			13 57		14 27	
Bayford	d		10 02		10 32			11 02		11 32			12 02		12 32			13 02		13 32			14 02		14 32	
Hertford North	d		10 07		10a38			11 07		11a38			12 07		12a38			13 07		13a38			14 07		14a38	
Watton-at-Stone	d		10 13					11 13					12 13					13 13					14 13			
Stevenage 4	d		10a20			10 42		11a20			11 42		12a20			12 42		13a20			13 42		14a20			14 42
Hitchin 4	d					10 47					11 47					12 47					13 47					14 47
Letchworth Garden City	a					10 51					11 51					12 51					13 51					14 51

For general notes see front of timetable
For details of catering facilities see Directory of Train Operators

A To Cambridge (Table 25)
B Until 6 September
C From 13 September

b Arr. 0021

There is no service between Moorgate and Finsbury Park on Sundays

Sundays

London → Welwyn Garden City, Hertford North and Letchworth Garden City

Network Diagram - see first page of Table 24

		FC	FC	FC	FC	FC 1	FC	FC	FC	FC	FC 1	FC	FC	FC	FC	FC 1	FC	FC	FC	FC	FC 1	FC	FC	FC	FC	FC 1
London Kings Cross 15	⊖ d	14 11	14 26	14 41	14 56	15 06	15 11	15 26	15 41	15 56	16 06	16 11	16 26	16 41	16 56	17 06	17 11	17 26	17 41	17 56	18 06	18 11	18 26	18 41	18 56	19 06
Finsbury Park	⊖ d	14 17	14 32	14 47	15 02	15 11	15 17	15 32	15 47	16 02	16 11	16 17	16 32	16 47	17 02	17 11	17 17	17 32	17 47	18 02	18 11	18 17	18 32	18 47	19 02	19 11
Harringay	d	14 19	14 34	14 49	15 04		15 19	15 34	15 49	16 04		16 19	16 34	16 49	17 04		17 19	17 34	17 49	18 04		18 19	18 34	18 49	19 04	
Hornsey	d	14 21	14 36	14 51	15 06		15 21	15 36	15 51	16 06		16 21	16 36	16 51	17 06		17 21	17 36	17 51	18 06		18 21	18 36	18 51	19 06	
Alexandra Palace	d	14 23	14 38	14 53	15 08		15 23	15 38	15 53	16 08		16 23	16 38	16 53	17 08		17 23	17 38	17 53	18 08		18 23	18 38	18 53	19 08	
New Southgate	d	14 26		14 56			15 26		15 56			16 26		16 56			17 26		17 56			18 26		18 56		
Oakleigh Park	d	14 29		14 59			15 29		15 59			16 29		16 59			17 29		17 59			18 29		18 59		
New Barnet	d	14 31		15 01			15 31		16 01			16 31		17 01			17 31		18 01			18 31		19 01		
Hadley Wood	d	14 34		15 04			15 34		16 04			16 34		17 04			17 34		18 04			18 34		19 04		
Potters Bar	d	14 38		15 08		15 21	15 38		16 08		16 21	16 38		17 08		17 21	17 38		18 08		18 21	18 38		19 08		19 21
Brookmans Park	d	14 41		15 11			15 41		16 11			16 41		17 11			17 41		18 11			18 41		19 11		
Welham Green	d	14 43		15 13			15 43		16 13			16 43		17 13			17 43		18 13			18 43		19 13		
Hatfield	d	14 46		15 16		15 27	15 46		16 16		16 27	16 46		17 16		17 27	17 46		18 16		18 27	18 46		19 16		19 27
Welwyn Garden City 4	d	14a51		15a21		15 31	15a51		16a21		16 31	16a51		17a21		17 31	17a51		18a21		18 31	18a51		19a21		19 31
Welwyn North	d					15 34					16 34					17 34					18 34					19 34
Knebworth	d					15 38					16 38					17 38					18 38					19 38
Bowes Park	d		14 41		15 11			15 41		16 11			16 41		17 11			17 41		18 11			18 41		19 11	
Palmers Green	d		14 43		15 13			15 43		16 13			16 43		17 13			17 43		18 13			18 43		19 13	
Winchmore Hill	d		14 45		15 15			15 45		16 15			16 45		17 15			17 45		18 15			18 45		19 15	
Grange Park	d		14 47		15 17			15 47		16 17			16 47		17 17			17 47		18 17			18 47		19 17	
Enfield Chase	d		14 49		15 19			15 49		16 19			16 49		17 19			17 49		18 19			18 49		19 19	
Gordon Hill	d		14 51		15 21			15 51		16 21			16 51		17 21			17 51		18 21			18 51		19 21	
Crews Hill	d		14 54		15 24			15 54		16 24			16 54		17 24			17 54		18 24			18 54		19 24	
Cuffley	d		14 57		15 27			15 57		16 27			16 57		17 27			17 57		18 27			18 57		19 27	
Bayford	d		15 02		15 32			16 02		16 32			17 02		17 32			18 02		18 32			19 02		19 32	
Hertford North	d		15 07		15a38			16 07		16a38			17 07		17a38			18 07		18a38			19 07		19a38	
Watton-at-Stone	d		15 13					16 13					17 13					18 13					19 13			
Stevenage 4	d		15a20			15 42		16a20			16 42		17a20			17 42		18a20			18 42		19a20			19 42
Hitchin 4	d					15 47					16 47					17 47					18 47					19 47
Letchworth Garden City	a					15 51					16 51					17 51					18 51					19 51

		FC	FC	FC	FC	FC 1	FC	FC	FC	FC	FC 1	FC	FC	FC	FC	FC 1	FC	FC	FC	FC	FC 1	FC	FC	FC		
London Kings Cross 15	⊖ d	19 11	19 26	19 41	19 56	20 06	20 11	20 26	20 41	20 56	21 06	21 11	21 26	21 41	21 56	22 06	22 11	22 26	22 41	22 56	23 06	23 19	23 28	23 41		
Finsbury Park	⊖ d	19 17	19 32	19 47	20 02	20 11	20 17	20 32	20 47	21 02	21 11	21 17	21 32	21 47	22 02	22 11	22 17	22 32	22 47	23 02	23 11	23 25	23 33	23 47		
Harringay	d	19 19	19 34	19 49	20 04		20 19	20 34	20 49	21 04		21 19	21 34	21 49	22 04		22 19	22 34	22 49	23 04		23 27	23 35	23 49		
Hornsey	d	19 21	19 36	19 51	20 06		20 21	20 36	20 51	21 06		21 21	21 36	21 51	22 06		22 21	22 36	22 51	23 06		23 29	23 37	23 51		
Alexandra Palace	d	19 23	19 38	19 53	20 08		20 23	20 38	20 53	21 08		21 23	21 38	21 53	22 08		22 23	22 38	22 53	23 08		23 31	23 39	23 53		
New Southgate	d	19 26		19 56			20 26		20 56			21 26		21 56			22 26		22 56			23 34		23 56		
Oakleigh Park	d	19 29		19 59			20 29		20 59			21 29		21 59			22 29		22 59			23 37		23 59		
New Barnet	d	19 31		20 01			20 31		21 01			21 31		22 01			22 31		23 01			23 39		00 01		
Hadley Wood	d	19 34		20 04			20 34		21 04			21 34		22 04			22 34		23 04			23 42		00 04		
Potters Bar	d	19 38		20 08		20 21	20 38		21 08		21 21	21 38		22 08		22 21	22 38		23 08		23 21	23 46		00 08		
Brookmans Park	d	19 41		20 11			20 41		21 11			21 41		22 11			22 41		23 11			23 49		00 11		
Welham Green	d	19 43		20 13			20 43		21 13			21 43		22 13			22 43		23 13			23 51		00 13		
Hatfield	d	19 46		20 16		20 27	20 46		21 16		21 27	21 46		22 16		22 27	22 46		23 16		23 27	23 54		00 16		
Welwyn Garden City 4	d	19a51		20a21		20 31	20a51		21a21		21 31	21a51		22a21		22 31	22a54		23a24		23 31	00a04		00 20		
Welwyn North	d					20 34					21 34					22 34					23 36			00 23		
Knebworth	d					20 38					21 38					22 38					23 40			00 28		
Bowes Park	d		19 41		20 11			20 41		21 11			21 41		22 11			22 41		23 11			23 41			
Palmers Green	d		19 43		20 13			20 43		21 13			21 43		22 13			22 43		23 13			23 43			
Winchmore Hill	d		19 45		20 15			20 45		21 15			21 45		22 15			22 45		23 15			23 45			
Grange Park	d		19 47		20 17			20 47		21 17			21 47		22 17			22 47		23 17			23 47			
Enfield Chase	d		19 49		20 19			20 49		21 19			21 49		22 19			22 49		23 19			23 49			
Gordon Hill	d		19 51		20 21			20 51		21 21			21 51		22 21			22 51		23 21			23 51			
Crews Hill	d		19 54		20 24			20 54		21 24			21 54		22 24			22 54		23 24			23 54			
Cuffley	d		19 57		20 27			20 57		21 27			21 57		22 27			22 57		23 27			23 57			
Bayford	d		20 02		20 32			21 02		21 32			22 02		22 32			23 02		23 32			00 02			
Hertford North	d		20 07		20a38			21 07		21a38			22 07		22a38			23 07		23a38			00 07			
Watton-at-Stone	d		20 13					21 13					22 13					23 13					00 13			
Stevenage 4	d		20a20			20 42		21a20			21 42		22a20			22 42		23a20			23 43		00a25	00 31		
Hitchin 4	d					20 47					21 47					22 47					23 53			00 37		
Letchworth Garden City	a					20 51					21 51					22 51					23 57			00 52		

For general notes see front of timetable
For details of catering facilities see
Directory of Train Operators

There is no service between Moorgate and Finsbury Park on Sundays

Letchworth Garden City, Hertford North and Welwyn Garden City → London

Saturday service operates on Bank Holiday Mondays

Network Diagram - see first page of Table 24

Miles	Miles			FC	FC	FC	FC	FC	FC	FC	FC	FC	FC	FC	FC	FC	FC	FC	FC	FC	FC	FC	FC	FC	FC	FC
				MX	MO	MO	MX																			
						1	1		1	1		1			1			1					1		1	
									A	A																
0	0	**Letchworth Garden City**	d	23p18		23p39	23p50				04 50	05 29	05 20		05 59	05 48		06 19				06 27			06 57	
3	3	Hitchin 4	d	23p22		23p43	23p54		04 13	04 58	04 54	05 33	05 24		06 03	05 52		06 24				06 31	06 46		07 01	
7¼	7¼	**Stevenage 4**	d	23p27	23p29	23p48	23p59		04 18	05 04	04 59	05 39	05 29		06 09	05 57	06 10	06 30				06 36	06 52		07 07	
—	12¼	Watton-at-Stone	d	23p34	23p36						05 06		05 36			06 04	06 17					06 42				
—	16½	**Hertford North**	d	23p40	23p42				04 28		05 12		05 42			06 10	06 25				06 34	06 50				
—	19½	Bayford	d	23p44	23p46						05 16		05 46			06 14					06 38					
—	23	Cuffley	d	23p49	23p51				04 35		05 21		05 51			06 19	06 32				06 43	06 57				
—	24¾	Crews Hill	d	23p52	23p54						05 24		05 54			06 22					06 46					
—	26¼	Gordon Hill	d	23p55	23p57				04 39		05 27		05 57			06 25	06 37				06 49	07 02				07 09
—	27	Enfield Chase	d	23p57	23p59				04 41		05 29		05 59			06 27	06 39				06 52	07 04				07 12
—	27¾	Grange Park	d	23p59	00 01						05 31		06 01			06 29					06 54					07 14
—	28½	Winchmore Hill	d	00 01	00 03						05 33		06 03			06 31	06 41				06 56	07 06				07 16
—	29½	Palmers Green	d	00 03	00 05						05 35		06 05			06 33	06 44				06 58	07 09				07 18
—	30½	Bowes Park	d	00 06	00 08						05 38		06 08			06 36					07 01					07 21
9¾	—	Knebworth	d			23p51	00 02			05 07		05 43			06 13			06 33					06 55		07 11	
12¾	—	Welwyn North	d			23p55	00 06			05 11		05 47			06 17			06 37					06 59			
14½	—	**Welwyn Garden City 4**	d			23p58	00 09	04 15		05 15		05 50		05 58	06 20			06 40	06 25	06 35			07 03	06 50		
17	—	Hatfield	d			00 01	00 12	04 19		05 19		05 53		06 02	06 23			06 44	06 29	06 39				06 54		
19¼	—	Welham Green	d											06 06					06 33					06 58		
20¼	—	Brookmans Park	d					04 24						06 08					06 35					07 00		
22	—	Potters Bar	d			00 07	00 18	04 27		05 25		05 59		06 11	06 29			06 49	06 38	06 46				07 03		
24¼	—	Hadley Wood	d											06 15					06 42	06 49				07 07		
25¼	—	New Barnet	d					04 32		05 29				06 17					06 44	06 52				07 09		
26¼	—	Oakleigh Park	d					04 34		05 31				06 19					06 46	06 54				07 11		
28¼	—	New Southgate	d					04 37		05 34				06 22					06 49	06 57				07 14		
29¾	31¼	Alexandra Palace	d	00 08	00 10			04 40		05 37	05 40		06 10	06 25		06 38			06 52		07 03			07 17		07 23
30¾	32¼	Hornsey	d	00 10	00 12			04 42			05 42		06 12	06 27		06 40			06 54		07 05			07 19		07 25
31¼	32¾	Harringay	d	00 12	00 14			04 44			05 44		06 14	06 29		06 42			06 56		07 07			07 21		07 27
32¼	33¾	Finsbury Park	⊖ d	00 15	00 17	00 20	00 29	04 47	04s50	05 41	05 47	06 08	06 17	06 32	06 38	06 45	06 51	06 58	06 59	07 03	07 10	07 17	07 17	07 24	07 27	07 30
—	34½	Drayton Park	d										06 19	06 34		06 47	06 53		07 01		07 12	07 19		07 26		07 32
—	35	Highbury & Islington	⊖ d										06 20	06 35		06 49	06 55		07 03		07 14	07 21		07 28		07 34
—	35½	Essex Road	d										06 22	06 37		06 51	06 57		07 05		07 16	07 23		07 30		07 36
—	36¾	Old Street	⊖ d										06 25	06 40		06 54	07 00		07 08		07 19	07 26		07 33		07 39
—	37¼	**Moorgate**	⊖ a										06 30	06 45		07 00	07 05		07 13		07 24	07 30		07 39		07 44
34¾	—	London Kings Cross 15	⊖ a	00 26	00 27	00 32	00 42	04 56	05 04	05 55	05 58	06 18			06 48			07 07		07 10			07 25		07 35	

		FC	FC	FC	FC	FC	FC	FC	FC	FC	FC	FC	FC	FC	FC	FC	FC	FC	FC	FC	FC	FC	FC	FC	FC
					1						1				1					1	1				
Letchworth Garden City	d	06 48			07 04					07 20	07 32				07 47					07 57	08 02				
Hitchin 4	d	06 52			07 08					07 24	07 36				07 51					08 01	08 06				
Stevenage 4	d	06 58		07 04	07 14					07 30	07 42		07 35							08 07	08 12		08 05		
Watton-at-Stone	d			07 11									07 42										08 12		
Hertford North	d		07 04	07 18			07 25		07 33			07 38	07 50			07 55			08 05				08 20		08 27
Bayford	d		07 08									07 42							08 09						
Cuffley	d		07 13	07 25			07 32		07 40			07 47	07 57			08 02			08 14				08 27		08 34
Crews Hill	d		07 16									07 50							08 17						
Gordon Hill	d		07 19	07 30			07 37		07 45			07 53	08 02			08 07		08 15	08 20				08 32		08 39
Enfield Chase	d		07 22	07 32			07 39		07 47			07 56	08 04			08 09		08 17	08 22				08 34		08 41
Grange Park	d		07 24				07 41		07 49			07 58				08 11		08 19	08 24						08 43
Winchmore Hill	d		07 26	07 34			07 43		07 51			08 00				08 13		08 21	08 26						08 45
Palmers Green	d		07 28	07 37			07 45		07 53			08 02				08 15		08 23	08 28						08 47
Bowes Park	d		07 31				07 48		07 56			08 05	08 08			08 18		08 26	08 31				08 38		08 50
Knebworth	d				07 18						07 46									08 11	08 16				
Welwyn North	d				07 22						07 50				07 59						08 20				
Welwyn Garden City 4	d	07 08			07 26	07 16		07 30		07 42	07 54			07 47			07 58				08 24	08 14		08 18	
Hatfield	d	07 12			07 30	07 20		07 34		07 46				07 51			08 02					08 18		08 22	
Welham Green	d					07 24		07 38						07 55			08 06							08 26	
Brookmans Park	d					07 26		07 40						07 57			08 08							08 28	
Potters Bar	d	07 18				07 29		07 43		07 52				08 00			08 11					08 25		08 31	
Hadley Wood	d					07 33		07 47						08 04			08 15							08 35	
New Barnet	d	07 23				07 36		07 49		07 57				08 06			08 18					08 29		08 37	
Oakleigh Park	d	07 25				07 38		07 51		07 59				08 08			08 20					08 31		08 39	
New Southgate	d	07 28				07 41		07 54		08 02				08 11			08 23					08 34		08 42	
Alexandra Palace	d		07 33			07 44	07 50		07 58			08 07	08 11	08 14		08 20		08 28	08 33			08 37	08 41	08 45	08 52
Hornsey	d		07 35			07 46	07 52		08 00				08 13	08 16		08 22	08 26	08 30					08 43	08 47	08 54
Harringay	d		07 37			07 48	07 54		08 02				08 15	08 18		08 24	08 28	08 32					08 45	08 49	08 56
Finsbury Park	⊖ d	07 34	07 40	07 44	07 46	07 51	07 57	08 01	08 06	08 09	08 09	08 12	08 18	08 22		08 27	08 31	08 35	08 39		08 39	08 42	08 48	08 52	08 59
Drayton Park	d		07 42	07 46		07 53	07 59	08 03	08 08			08 14	08 20	08 24		08 29	08 33	08 37	08 41				08 50	08 54	09 01
Highbury & Islington	⊖ d		07 44	07 48		07 55	08 01	08 05	08 10			08 16	08 22	08 26		08 31	08 35	08 39	08 43				08 52	08 56	09 03
Essex Road	d		07 46	07 50		07 57	08 03	08 07	08 12			08 18	08 24	08 28		08 33	08 37	08 41	08 45				08 54	08 58	09 05
Old Street	⊖ d		07 49	07 53		08 00	08 06	08 10	08 15			08 21	08 27	08 31		08 36	08 40	08 44	08 48				08 57	09 01	09 08
Moorgate	⊖ a		07 54	07 59		08 05	08 11	08 16	08 20			08 27	08 32	08 36		08 41	08 46	08 50	08 55				09 02	09 06	09 13
London Kings Cross 15	⊖ a	07 42			07 56					08 17	08 18				08 19					08 36	08 49	08 50			

For general notes see front of timetable
For details of catering facilities see Directory of Train Operators

A From Peterborough (Table 25)

Saturday service operates on Bank Holiday Mondays

Letchworth Garden City, Hertford North and Welwyn Garden City → London

Network Diagram - see first page of Table 24

	FC	FC	FC	FC	FC	FC	FC	FC 1	FC	FC	FC	FC	FC 1	FC	FC	FC	FC 1	FC	FC	FC	FC 1	FC	FC	FC	FC 1
Letchworth Garden City d								09 00					09 29				09 59	09 50			10 29				
Hitchin 4 d				08 39				09 04					09 33				10 03	09 54			10 33				11 03
Stevenage 4 d				08 45	08 34			09 10	09 04				09 39		09 34		10 09	09 59			10 39				11 09
Watton-at-Stone d					08 41				09 11						09 41			10 06							
Hertford North d					08 48				09 17			09 32			09 52			10 12		10 32			10 52		
Bayford d					08 52				09 22			09 36			09 56			10 16		10 36			10 56		
Cuffley d					08 57				09 26			09 41			10 01			10 21		10 41			11 01		
Crews Hill d					09 00				09 29			09 44			10 04			10 24		10 44			11 04		
Gordon Hill d			08 55		09 03	09 12			09 32			09 47			10 07			10 27		10 47			11 07		
Enfield Chase d			08 57		09 05	09 14			09 34			09 49			10 09			10 29		10 49			11 09		
Grange Park d			08 59		09 07	09 16			09 36			09 51			10 11			10 31		10 51			11 11		
Winchmore Hill d			09 01		09 09	09 18			09 38			09 53			10 13			10 33		10 53			11 13		
Palmers Green d			09 03		09 12	09 21			09 41			09 55			10 15			10 35		10 55			11 15		
Bowes Park d			09 06		09 14	09 23			09 43			09 58			10 18			10 38		10 58			11 18		
Knebworth d				08 49				09 13					09 43				10 13				10 43				11 13
Welwyn North d				08 53				09 17					09 47				10 17				10 47				11 17
Welwyn Garden City 4 d	08 29	08 42		08 58			09 03	09 20		09 23	09 40		09 50	09 43		10 03	10 20		10 23		10 50	10 43		11 03	11 20
Hatfield d	08 33	08 46		09 02			09 07	09 24		09 27	09 43		09 53	09 47		10 07	10 23		10 27		10 53	10 47		11 07	11 23
Welham Green d	08 37						09 11			09 31				09 51		10 11			10 31			10 51		11 11	
Brookmans Park d	08 39						09 13			09 33				09 53		10 13			10 33			10 53		11 13	
Potters Bar d	08 42	08 53					09 16	09 30		09 36	09 49		09 59	09 56		10 16	10 29		10 36		10 59	10 56		11 16	11 29
Hadley Wood d	08 46						09 20			09 40				10 00		10 20			10 40			11 00		11 20	
New Barnet d	08 49	08 57					09 22			09 42				10 02		10 22			10 42			11 02		11 22	
Oakleigh Park d	08 51	08 59					09 24			09 44				10 04		10 24			10 44			11 04		11 24	
New Southgate d	08 54	09 02					09 27			09 47				10 07		10 27			10 47			11 07		11 27	
Alexandra Palace d	08 57	09 05	09 08		09 17	09 26	09 30		09 46	09 50		10 00		10 10	10 20	10 30		10 40	10 50	11 00		11 10	11 20	11 30	
Hornsey d	08 59		09 10		09 19	09 28	09 32		09 48	09 52		10 02		10 12	10 22	10 32		10 42	10 52	11 02		11 12	11 22	11 32	
Harringay d	09 01		09 12		09 21	09 30	09 34		09 50	09 54		10 04		10 14	10 24	10 34		10 44	10 54	11 04		11 14	11 24	11 34	
Finsbury Park ⊖ d	09 03	09 10	09 15	09 19	09 24	09 32	09 37	09 41	09 53	09 57	10 01	10 07	10 08	10 17	10 27	10 37	10 41	10 47	10 57	11 07	11 08	11 17	11 27	11 37	11 41
Drayton Park d	09 05		09 17		09 26	09 34	09 39		09 55	09 59		10 09		10 19	10 29	10 39		10 49	10 59	11 09		11 19	11 29	11 39	
Highbury & Islington ⊖ d	09 07		09 19		09 28	09 36	09 40		09 56	10 00		10 10		10 20	10 30	10 40		10 50	11 00	11 10		11 20	11 30	11 40	
Essex Road d	09 09		09 21		09 30	09 38	09 42		09 58	10 02		10 12		10 22	10 32	10 42		10 52	11 02	11 12		11 22	11 32	11 42	
Old Street ⊖ d	09 12		09 24		09 33	09 41	09 45		10 01	10 05		10 15		10 25	10 35	10 45		10 55	11 05	11 15		11 25	11 35	11 45	
Moorgate ⊖ a	09 18		09 29		09 38	09 46	09 50		10 06	10 10		10 20		10 30	10 40	10 50		11 00	11 10	11 20		11 30	11 40	11 50	
London Kings Cross 15 ⊖ a		09 18		09 27				09 50			10 10		10 19				10 49				11 19				11 49

	FC	FC		FC	FC 1	FC	FC	FC	FC 1	FC	FC	FC	FC 1	FC	FC	FC	FC 1	FC	FC	FC	FC 1	FC	FC	FC	FC 1
Letchworth Garden City d	10 50				11 29					11 50			12 29					12 50			13 29				
Hitchin 4 d	10 54				11 33				12 03	11 54			12 33				13 03	12 54			13 33				14 03
Stevenage 4 d	10 59				11 39				12 09	11 59			12 39				13 09	12 59			13 39				14 09
Watton-at-Stone d	11 06									12 06								13 06							
Hertford North d	11 12			11 32			11 52			12 12		12 32			12 52			13 12		13 32			13 52		
Bayford d	11 16			11 36			11 56			12 16		12 36			12 56			13 16		13 36			13 56		
Cuffley d	11 21			11 41			12 01			12 21		12 41			13 01			13 21		13 41			14 01		
Crews Hill d	11 24			11 44			12 04			12 24		12 44			13 04			13 24		13 44			14 04		
Gordon Hill d	11 27			11 47			12 07			12 27		12 47			13 07			13 27		13 47			14 07		
Enfield Chase d	11 29			11 49			12 09			12 29		12 49			13 09			13 29		13 49			14 09		
Grange Park d	11 31			11 51			12 11			12 31		12 51			13 11			13 31		13 51			14 11		
Winchmore Hill d	11 33			11 53			12 13			12 33		12 53			13 13			13 33		13 53			14 13		
Palmers Green d	11 35			11 55			12 15			12 35		12 55			13 15			13 35		13 55			14 15		
Bowes Park d	11 38			11 58			12 18			12 38		12 58			13 18			13 38		13 58			14 18		
Knebworth d					11 43				12 13				12 43				13 13				13 43				14 13
Welwyn North d					11 47				12 17				12 47				13 17				13 47				14 17
Welwyn Garden City 4 d		11 23			11 50	11 43		12 03	12 20		12 23		12 50	12 43		13 03	13 20		13 23		13 50	13 43		14 03	14 20
Hatfield d		11 27			11 53	11 47		12 07	12 23		12 27		12 53	12 47		13 07	13 23		13 27		13 53	13 47		14 07	14 23
Welham Green d		11 31				11 51		12 11			12 31			12 51		13 11			13 31			13 51		14 11	
Brookmans Park d		11 33				11 53		12 13			12 33			12 53		13 13			13 33			13 53		14 13	
Potters Bar d		11 36			11 59	11 56		12 16	12 29		12 36		12 59	12 56		13 16	13 29		13 36		13 59	13 56		14 16	14 29
Hadley Wood d		11 40				12 00		12 20			12 40			13 00		13 20			13 40			14 00		14 20	
New Barnet d		11 42				12 02		12 22			12 42			13 02		13 22			13 42			14 02		14 22	
Oakleigh Park d		11 44				12 04		12 24			12 44			13 04		13 24			13 44			14 04		14 24	
New Southgate d		11 47				12 07		12 27			12 47			13 07		13 27			13 47			14 07		14 27	
Alexandra Palace d	11 40	11 50		12 00		12 10	12 20	12 30		12 40	12 50	13 00		13 10	13 20	13 30		13 40	13 50	14 00		14 10	14 20	14 30	
Hornsey d	11 42	11 52		12 02		12 12	12 22	12 32		12 42	12 52	13 02		13 12	13 22	13 32		13 42	13 52	14 02		14 12	14 22	14 32	
Harringay d	11 44	11 54		12 04		12 14	12 24	12 34		12 44	12 54	13 04		13 14	13 24	13 34		13 44	13 54	14 04		14 14	14 24	14 34	
Finsbury Park ⊖ d	11 47	11 57		12 07	12 11	12 17	12 27	12 37	12 41	12 47	12 57	13 07	13 08	13 17	13 27	13 37	13 41	13 47	13 57	14 07	14 08	14 17	14 27	14 37	14 41
Drayton Park d	11 49	11 59		12 09		12 19	12 29	12 39		12 49	12 59	13 09		13 19	13 29	13 39		13 49	13 59	14 09		14 19	14 29	14 39	
Highbury & Islington ⊖ d	11 50	12 00		12 10		12 20	12 30	12 40		12 50	13 00	13 10		13 20	13 30	13 40		13 50	14 00	14 10		14 20	14 30	14 40	
Essex Road d	11 52	12 02		12 12		12 22	12 32	12 42		12 52	13 02	13 12		13 22	13 32	13 42		13 52	14 02	14 12		14 22	14 32	14 42	
Old Street ⊖ d	11 55	12 05		12 15		12 25	12 35	12 45		12 55	13 05	13 15		13 25	13 35	13 45		13 55	14 05	14 15		14 25	14 35	14 45	
Moorgate ⊖ a	12 00	12 10		12 20		12 30	12 40	12 50		13 00	13 10	13 20		13 30	13 40	13 50		14 00	14 10	14 20		14 30	14 40	14 50	
London Kings Cross 15 ⊖ a					12 19				12 49				13 19				13 49				14 19				14 49

For general notes see front of timetable
For details of catering facilities see Directory of Train Operators

Letchworth Garden City, Hertford North and Welwyn Garden City → London

Saturday service operates on Bank Holiday Mondays

Network Diagram - see first page of Table 24

		FC	FC	FC	FC 1	FC	FC	FC	FC 1	FC	FC	FC	FC 1	FC	FC		FC	FC 1	FC	FC	FC	FC	FC 1	FC	FC	FC
Letchworth Garden City	d	13 50			14 29					14 50			15 29						15 50				16 29	16 20		
Hitchin 4	d	13 54			14 33				15 03	14 54			15 33					16 03	15 54				16 33	16 24		
Stevenage 4	d	13 59			14 39				15 09	14 59			15 39					16 09	15 59				16 39	16 29		
Watton-at-Stone	d	14 06								15 06									16 06					16 36		
Hertford North	d	14 12		14 32			14 52			15 12		15 33			15 53				16 13			16 33		16 43		16 53
Bayford	d	14 16		14 36			14 56			15 16		15 37			15 57				16 17			16 37		16 47		16 57
Cuffley	d	14 21		14 41			15 01			15 21		15 42			16 02				16 22			16 42		16 52		17 02
Crews Hill	d	14 24		14 44			15 04			15 24		15 45			16 05				16 25			16 45		16 55		17 05
Gordon Hill	d	14 27		14 47			15 07			15 27		15 48			16 08				16 28			16 48		16 58		17 08
Enfield Chase	d	14 29		14 49			15 09			15 29		15 50			16 10				16 30			16 50		17 00		17 10
Grange Park	d	14 31		14 51			15 11			15 31		15 52			16 12				16 32			16 52				17 12
Winchmore Hill	d	14 33		14 53			15 13			15 33		15 54			16 14				16 34			16 54		17 02		17 14
Palmers Green	d	14 35		14 55			15 15			15 35		15 56			16 16				16 36			16 56		17 05		17 16
Bowes Park	d	14 38		14 58			15 18			15 38		15 59			16 19				16 39			16 59				17 19
Knebworth	d				14 43				15 13				15 43					16 13					16 43			
Welwyn North	d				14 47				15 17				15 47					16 17					16 47			
Welwyn Garden City 4	d		14 23		14 50	14 43		15 03	15 20		15 24		15 50	15 44			16 04	16 20		16 24	16 40		16 51		16 44	
Hatfield	d		14 27		14 53	14 47		15 07	15 23		15 28		15 53	15 48			16 08	16 23		16 28	16 43		16 55		16 48	
Welham Green	d		14 31			14 51		15 11			15 32			15 52			16 12			16 32					16 52	
Brookmans Park	d		14 33			14 53		15 13			15 34			15 54			16 14			16 34					16 54	
Potters Bar	d		14 36		14 59	14 56		15 16	15 29		15 37		15 59	15 57			16 17	16 29		16 37	16 49		17 01		16 57	
Hadley Wood	d		14 40			15 00		15 20			15 41			16 01			16 21			16 41					17 01	
New Barnet	d		14 42			15 02		15 22			15 43			16 03			16 23			16 43					17 03	
Oakleigh Park	d		14 44			15 04		15 24			15 45			16 05			16 25			16 45					17 05	
New Southgate	d		14 47			15 07		15 27			15 48			16 08			16 28			16 48					17 08	
Alexandra Palace	d	14 40	14 50	15 00		15 10	15 20	15 30		15 40	15 51	16 01		16 11	16 21		16 31		16 41	16 51		17 01			17 11	17 21
Hornsey	d	14 42	14 52	15 02		15 12	15 22	15 32		15 42	15 53	16 03		16 13	16 23		16 33		16 43	16 53		17 03			17 13	17 23
Harringay	d	14 44	14 54	15 04		15 14	15 24	15 34		15 44	15 55	16 05		16 15	16 25		16 35		16 45	16 55		17 05			17 15	17 25
Finsbury Park	⊖ d	14 47	14 57	15 07	15 11	15 17	15 27	15 37	15 41	15 47	15 58	16 08	16 11	16 18	16 28		16 38	16 38	16 48	16 58	17 01	17 08	17 11	17 12	17 18	17 28
Drayton Park	d	14 49	14 59	15 09		15 19	15 29	15 39		15 49	16 00	16 10		16 20	16 30		16 40		16 50	17 00		17 10		17 14	17 20	17 30
Highbury & Islington	⊖ d	14 50	15 00	15 10		15 20	15 30	15 40		15 50	16 01	16 11		16 21	16 31		16 41		16 51	17 01		17 11		17 15	17 21	17 31
Essex Road	d	14 52	15 02	15 12		15 22	15 32	15 42		15 52	16 03	16 13		16 23	16 33		16 43		16 53	17 03		17 13		17 17	17 23	17 33
Old Street	⊖ d	14 55	15 05	15 15		15 25	15 35	15 45		15 55	16 06	16 16		16 26	16 36		16 46		16 56	17 06		17 16		17 20	17 26	17 36
Moorgate	⊖ a	15 00	15 10	15 20		15 30	15 40	15 50		16 00	16 12	16 21		16 31	16 41		16 51		17 01	17 11		17 21		17 26	17 31	17 41
London Kings Cross 15	⊖ a				15 20				15 50				16 21					16 49			17 10		17 21			

		FC	FC 1	FC	FC	FC	FC	FC 1	FC	FC	FC	FC	FC 1	FC	FC	FC	FC 1	FC	FC	FC	FC 1	FC	FC	FC	FC 1	FC
Letchworth Garden City	d							17 29									18 29								19 29	
Hitchin 4	d		17 03					17 33					18 11				18 33				19 11				19 33	
Stevenage 4	d		17 09	16 59				17 39		17 29	17 53		18 17		18 23		18 39		18 53		19 17				19 39	
Watton-at-Stone	d			17 06						17 36	18 00				18 30				19 00							
Hertford North	d			17 13		17 36				17 43	18 06			18 18	18 36			18 48	19 06			19 18	19 36			19 48
Bayford	d			17 17						17 47				18 22				18 52				19 22				19 52
Cuffley	d			17 22		17 43				17 52	18 13			18 27	18 43			18 57	19 13			19 27	19 43			19 57
Crews Hill	d			17 25						17 55				18 30				19 00				19 30				20 00
Gordon Hill	d			17 28	17 38	17 48				17 58	18 18			18 33	18 48			19 03	19 18			19 33	19 48			20 03
Enfield Chase	d			17 30	17 40	17 50				18 00	18 20			18 35	18 50			19 05	19 20			19 35	19 50			20 05
Grange Park	d			17 32	17 42					18 02				18 37				19 07				19 37				20 07
Winchmore Hill	d			17 34	17 44	17 52				18 04	18 22			18 39	18 52			19 09	19 22			19 39	19 52			20 09
Palmers Green	d			17 36	17 46	17 55				18 06	18 25			18 41	18 55			19 11	19 25			19 41	19 55			20 11
Bowes Park	d			17 39	17 49					18 09				18 44				19 14				19 44				20 14
Knebworth	d		17 13					17 43					18 21				18 43				19 21				19 43	
Welwyn North	d		17 17					17 47					18 25				18 47				19 25				19 47	
Welwyn Garden City 4	d	17 04	17 21				17 34	17 51	17 44			18 04	18 28			18 34	18 51			19 04	19 28			19 34	19 50	
Hatfield	d	17 08	17 25				17 38	17 55	17 48			18 08	18 32			18 38	18 55			19 08	19 32			19 38	19 53	
Welham Green	d	17 12					17 42					18 12				18 42				19 12				19 42		
Brookmans Park	d	17 14					17 44					18 14				18 44				19 14				19 44		
Potters Bar	d	17 17	17 31				17 47	18 01	17 55			18 17	18 38			18 47	19 01			19 17	19 38			19 47	19 59	
Hadley Wood	d	17 21					17 51					18 21				18 51				19 21				19 51		
New Barnet	d	17 23					17 53					18 23				18 53				19 23				19 53		
Oakleigh Park	d	17 25					17 55					18 25				18 55				19 25				19 55		
New Southgate	d	17 28					17 58					18 28				18 58				19 28				19 58		
Alexandra Palace	d	17 31		17 41	17 51		18 01			18 11		18 31		18 46		19 01		19 16		19 31		19 46		20 01		20 16
Hornsey	d	17 33		17 43	17 53		18 03			18 13		18 33		18 48		19 03		19 18		19 33		19 48		20 03		20 18
Harringay	d	17 35		17 45	17 55		18 05			18 15		18 35		18 50		19 05		19 20		19 35		19 50		20 05		20 20
Finsbury Park	⊖ d	17 38	17 41	17 48	17 58	18 02	18 08	18 11	18 07	18 18	18 32	18 38	18 47	18 53	19 02	19 08	19 11	19 23	19 32	19 38	19 47	19 53	20 02	20 08	20 11	20 23
Drayton Park	d	17 40		17 50	18 00	18 04	18 10			18 20	18 34	18 40		18 55	19 04	19 10		19 25	19 34	19 40		19 55	20 04	20 10		20 25
Highbury & Islington	⊖ d	17 41		17 51	18 01	18 05	18 11			18 21	18 35	18 41		18 56	19 05	19 11		19 26	19 35	19 41		19 56	20 05	20 11		20 26
Essex Road	d	17 43		17 53	18 03	18 07	18 13			18 23	18 37	18 43		18 58	19 07	19 13		19 28	19 37	19 43		19 58	20 07	20 13		20 28
Old Street	⊖ d	17 46		17 56	18 06	18 10	18 16			18 26	18 40	18 46		19 01	19 10	19 16		19 31	19 40	19 46		20 01	20 10	20 16		20 31
Moorgate	⊖ a	17 51		18 01	18 12	18 16	18 22			18 31	18 45	18 51		19 06	19 15	19 21		19 36	19 45	19 51		20 06	20 15	20 21		20 36
London Kings Cross 15	⊖ a		17 50					18 20	18 17				18 58				19 21				19 58				20 19	

For general notes see front of timetable
For details of catering facilities see
Directory of Train Operators

Letchworth Garden City, Hertford North and Welwyn Garden City → London

Saturday service operates on Bank Holiday Mondays

Network Diagram - see first page of Table 24

		FC	FC 1	FC	FC	FC 1	FC	FC	FC 1	FC	FC	FC 1	FC	FC	FC 1	FC	FC	FC 1	FC	FC	FC	FC 1	FC	FC 1
Letchworth Garden City	d					20 29	20 20					21 29	21 20					22 29	22 20				23 18	23 50
Hitchin 4	d		20 03			20 33	20 24		21 03			21 33	21 24		22 11			22 33	22 24			23 16	23 22	23 54
Stevenage 4	d		20 09	19 59		20 39	20 29		21 09	20 59		21 39	21 29		22 17			22 39	22 29			23 22	23 27	23 59
Watton-at-Stone	d			20 06			20 36			21 06			21 36						22 36				23 34	
Hertford North	d			20 12			20 42			21 12			21 42			22 12			22 42		23 10		23 40	
Bayford	d			20 16			20 46			21 16			21 46			22 16			22 46		23 14		23 44	
Cuffley	d			20 21			20 51			21 21			21 51			22 21			22 51		23 19		23 49	
Crews Hill	d			20 24			20 54			21 24			21 54			22 24			22 54		23 22		23 52	
Gordon Hill	d			20 27			20 57			21 27			21 57			22 27			22 57		23 25		23 55	
Enfield Chase	d			20 29			20 59			21 29			21 59			22 29			22 59		23 27		23 57	
Grange Park	d			20 31			21 01			21 31			22 01			22 31			23 01		23 29		23 59	
Winchmore Hill	d			20 33			21 03			21 33			22 03			22 33			23 03		23 31		00 01	
Palmers Green	d			20 35			21 05			21 35			22 05			22 35			23 05		23 33		00 03	
Bowes Park	d			20 38			21 08			21 38			22 08			22 38			23 08		23 36		00 06	
Knebworth	d		20 13			20 43			21 13			21 43			22 20			22 43				23 25		00 02
Welwyn North	d		20 17			20 47			21 17			21 47			22 24			22 47				23 29		00 06
Welwyn Garden City 4	d	19 58	20 20		20 28	20 50		20 58	21 20		21 28	21 50		21 58	22 27		22 30	22 50		23 00		23 32		00 09
Hatfield	d	20 02	20 23		20 32	20 53		21 02	21 23		21 32	21 53		22 02	22 30		22 34	22 53		23 04		23 35		00 12
Welham Green	d	20 06			20 36			21 06			21 36			22 06			22 38			23 08				
Brookmans Park	d	20 08			20 38			21 08			21 38			22 08			22 40			23 10				
Potters Bar	d	20 11	20 29		20 41	20 59		21 11	21 29		21 41	21 59		22 11	22 36		22 43	22 59		23 13		23 41		00 18
Hadley Wood	d	20 15			20 45			21 15			21 45			22 15			22 47			23 17				
New Barnet	d	20 17			20 47			21 17			21 47			22 17			22 49			23 19				
Oakleigh Park	d	20 19			20 49			21 19			21 49			22 19			22 51			23 21				
New Southgate	d	20 22			20 52			21 22			21 52			22 22			22 54			23 24				
Alexandra Palace	d	20 25		20 40	20 55		21 10	21 25		21 40	21 55		22 10	22 25		22 40	22 57		23 10	23 27	23 38		00 08	
Hornsey	d	20 27		20 42	20 57		21 12	21 27		21 42	21 57		22 12	22 27		22 42	22 59		23 12	23 29	23 40		00 10	
Harringay	d	20 29		20 44	20 59		21 14	21 29		21 44	21 59		22 14	22 29		22 44	23 01		23 14	23 31	23 42		00 12	
Finsbury Park	⊖ d	20 32	20 38	20 47	21 02	21 11	21 17	21 32	21 38	21 47	22 02	22 11	22 17	22 32	22 44	22 47	23 04	23 11	23 17	23 34	23 45	23s51	00 15	00 29
Drayton Park	d	20 34		20 49	21 04		21 19	21 34		21 49														
Highbury & Islington	⊖ d	20 35		20 50	21 05		21 20	21 35		21 50														
Essex Road	d	20 37		20 52	21 07		21 22	21 37		21 52														
Old Street	⊖ d	20 40		20 55	21 10		21 25	21 40		21 55														
Moorgate	⊖ a	20 45		21 00	21 15		21 30	21 45		22 00														
London Kings Cross 15	⊖ a		20 49			21 19			21 48		22 10	22 19	22 26	22 40	22 56	22 55	23 12	23 21	23 25	23 42	23 53	00 04	00 26	00 42

Saturdays

		FC	FC 1	FC	FC 1 A	FC 1 A	FC	FC 1	FC	FC	FC 1	FC	FC	FC 1	FC	FC		FC 1	FC	FC	FC 1	FC	FC	FC 1	FC	FC
Letchworth Garden City	d	23p18	23p50				04 50	05 29	05 20					06 29							07 29					
Hitchin 4	d	23p22	23p54		04 13	04 58	04 54	05 33	05 24		06 03			06 33				07 03			07 33			08 03		
Stevenage 4	d	23p27	23p59		04 18	05 04	04 59	05 39	05 29		06 09			06 39	06 29			07 09			07 39	07 29		08 09		
Watton-at-Stone	d	23p34					05 06		05 36						06 36							07 36				
Hertford North	d	23p40			04 28		05 12		05 42			06 12			06 42				07 12			07 42			08 12	
Bayford	d	23p44					05 16		05 46			06 16			06 46				07 16			07 46			08 16	
Cuffley	d	23p49			04 35		05 21		05 51			06 21			06 51				07 21			07 51			08 21	
Crews Hill	d	23p52					05 24		05 54			06 24			06 54				07 24			07 54			08 24	
Gordon Hill	d	23p55			04 39		05 27		05 57			06 27			06 57				07 27			07 57			08 27	
Enfield Chase	d	23p57			04 41		05 29		05 59			06 29			06 59				07 29			07 59			08 29	
Grange Park	d	23p59					05 31		06 01			06 31			07 01				07 31			08 01			08 31	
Winchmore Hill	d	00 01					05 33		06 03			06 33			07 03				07 33			08 03			08 33	
Palmers Green	d	00 03					05 35		06 05			06 35			07 05				07 35			08 05			08 35	
Bowes Park	d	00 06					05 38		06 08			06 38			07 08				07 38			08 08			08 38	
Knebworth	d		00 02			05 07		05 43			06 13			06 43				07 13			07 43			08 13		
Welwyn North	d		00 06			05 11		05 47			06 17			06 47				07 17			07 47			08 17		
Welwyn Garden City 4	d		00 09	04 15		05 15		05 50		05 58	06 20		06 28	06 50		06 58		07 20		07 28	07 50		07 58	08 20		08 28
Hatfield	d		00 12	04 19		05 19		05 53		06 02	06 23		06 32	06 53		07 02		07 23		07 32	07 53		08 02	08 23		08 32
Welham Green	d									06 06			06 36			07 06				07 36			08 06			08 36
Brookmans Park	d			04 24						06 08			06 38			07 08				07 38			08 08			08 38
Potters Bar	d		00 18	04 27		05 25		05 59		06 11	06 29		06 41	06 59		07 11		07 29		07 41	07 59		08 11	08 29		08 41
Hadley Wood	d									06 15			06 45			07 15				07 45			08 15			08 45
New Barnet	d			04 32		05 29				06 17			06 47			07 17				07 47			08 17			08 47
Oakleigh Park	d			04 34		05 31				06 19			06 49			07 19				07 49			08 19			08 49
New Southgate	d			04 37		05 34				06 22			06 52			07 22				07 52			08 22			08 52
Alexandra Palace	d	00 08		04 40		05 37	05 40		06 10	06 25		06 40	06 55		07 10	07 25			07 40	07 55		08 10	08 25		08 40	08 55
Hornsey	d	00 10		04 42			05 42		06 12	06 27		06 42	06 57		07 12	07 27			07 42	07 57		08 12	08 27		08 42	08 57
Harringay	d	00 12		04 44			05 44		06 14	06 29		06 44	06 59		07 14	07 29			07 44	07 59		08 14	08 29		08 44	08 59
Finsbury Park	⊖ d	00 15	00 29	04 47	04s50	05 41	05 47	06 08	06 17	06 32	06 41	06 47	07 02	07 08	07 17	07 32		07 41	07 47	08 02	08 08	08 17	08 32	08 41	08 47	09 02
London Kings Cross 15	⊖ a	00 26	00 42	04 56	05 04	05 55	05 58	06 21	06 25	06 40	06 49	06 55	07 10	07 19	07 25	07 40		07 49	07 55	08 10	08 19	08 25	08 40	08 49	08 55	09 10

For general notes see front of timetable
For details of catering facilities see Directory of Train Operators

A From Peterborough (Table 25)

There is no service between Finsbury Park and Moorgate on Saturdays

Saturdays

Letchworth Garden City, Hertford North and Welwyn Garden City → London

Network Diagram - see first page of Table 24

	FC 1	FC	FC	FC 1	FC	FC	FC 1	FC		FC	FC 1	FC	FC	FC 1	FC	FC	FC 1	FC	FC	FC 1	FC	FC	FC 1	FC	FC
Letchworth Garden City d	08 29						09 29							10 29						11 29					
Hitchin 4 d	08 33			09 03			09 33				10 03			10 33			11 03			11 33			12 03		
Stevenage 4 d	08 39	08 29		09 09			09 39	09 29			10 09			10 39	10 29		11 09			11 39	11 29		12 09		
Watton-at-Stone d		08 36						09 36							10 36						11 36				
Hertford North d		08 42			09 12			09 42				10 12			10 42			11 12			11 42			12 12	
Bayford d		08 46			09 16			09 46				10 16			10 46			11 16			11 46			12 16	
Cuffley d		08 51			09 21			09 51				10 21			10 51			11 21			11 51			12 21	
Crews Hill d		08 54			09 24			09 54				10 24			10 54			11 24			11 54			12 24	
Gordon Hill d		08 57			09 27			09 57				10 27			10 57			11 27			11 57			12 27	
Enfield Chase d		08 59			09 29			09 59				10 29			10 59			11 29			11 59			12 29	
Grange Park d		09 01			09 31			10 01				10 31			11 01			11 31			12 01			12 31	
Winchmore Hill d		09 03			09 33			10 03				10 33			11 03			11 33			12 03			12 33	
Palmers Green d		09 05			09 35			10 05				10 35			11 05			11 35			12 05			12 35	
Bowes Park d		09 08			09 38			10 08				10 38			11 08			11 38			12 08			12 38	
Knebworth d	08 43			09 13			09 43				10 13			10 43			11 13			11 43			12 13		
Welwyn North d	08 47			09 17			09 47				10 17			10 47			11 17			11 47			12 17		
Welwyn Garden City 4 d	08 50		08 58	09 20		09 28	09 50			09 58	10 20		10 28	10 50		10 58	11 20		11 28	11 50		11 58	12 20		12 28
Hatfield d	08 53		09 02	09 23		09 32	09 53			10 02	10 23		10 32	10 53		11 02	11 22		11 32	11 53		12 02	12 23		12 32
Welham Green d			09 06			09 36				10 06			10 36			11 06			11 36			12 06			12 36
Brookmans Park d			09 08			09 38				10 08			10 38			11 08			11 38			12 08			12 38
Potters Bar d	08 59		09 11	09 29		09 41	09 59			10 11	10 29		10 41	10 59		11 11	11 29		11 41	11 59		12 11	12 29		12 41
Hadley Wood d			09 15			09 45				10 15			10 45			11 15			11 45			12 15			12 45
New Barnet d			09 17			09 47				10 17			10 47			11 17			11 47			12 17			12 47
Oakleigh Park d			09 19			09 49				10 19			10 49			11 19			11 49			12 19			12 49
New Southgate d			09 22			09 52				10 22			10 52			11 22			11 52			12 22			12 52
Alexandra Palace d		09 10	09 25		09 40	09 55		10 10		10 25		10 40	10 55		11 10	11 25		11 40	11 55		12 10	12 25		12 40	12 55
Hornsey d		09 12	09 27		09 42	09 57		10 12		10 27		10 42	10 57		11 12	11 27		11 42	11 57		12 12	12 27		12 42	12 57
Harringay d		09 14	09 29		09 44	09 59		10 14		10 29		10 44	10 59		11 14	11 29		11 44	11 59		12 14	12 29		12 44	12 59
Finsbury Park ⊖ d	09 08	09 17	09 32	09 41	09 47	10 02	10 08	10 17		10 32	10 41	10 47	11 02	11 08	11 17	11 32	11 40	11 47	12 02	12 08	12 17	12 32	12 41	12 47	13 02
London Kings Cross 15 ⊖ a	09 20	09 25	09 40	09 49	09 55	10 10	10 19	10 25		10 40	10 49	10 55	11 10	11 19	11 25	11 40	11 48	11 55	12 10	12 19	12 25	12 40	12 49	12 55	13 10

	FC 1		FC	FC	FC 1	FC	FC	FC 1	FC	FC	FC 1	FC	FC	FC 1	FC	FC	FC 1		FC	FC	FC 1	FC	FC	FC 1	FC
Letchworth Garden City d	12 29							13 29						14 29							15 29				
Hitchin 4 d	12 33				13 03			13 33			14 03			14 33			15 03				15 33			16 03	
Stevenage 4 d	12 39		12 29		13 09			13 39	13 29		14 09			14 39	14 29		15 09				15 39	15 29		16 09	
Watton-at-Stone d			12 36						13 36						14 36							15 36			
Hertford North d			12 42			13 12			13 42			14 12			14 42				15 12			15 42			16 12
Bayford d			12 46			13 16			13 46			14 16			14 46				15 16			15 46			16 16
Cuffley d			12 51			13 21			13 51			14 21			14 51				15 21			15 51			16 21
Crews Hill d			12 54			13 24			13 54			14 24			14 54				15 24			15 54			16 24
Gordon Hill d			12 57			13 27			13 57			14 27			14 57				15 27			15 57			16 27
Enfield Chase d			12 59			13 29			13 59			14 29			14 59				15 29			15 59			16 29
Grange Park d			13 01			13 31			14 01			14 31			15 01				15 31			16 01			16 31
Winchmore Hill d			13 03			13 33			14 03			14 33			15 03				15 33			16 03			16 33
Palmers Green d			13 05			13 35			14 05			14 35			15 05				15 35			16 05			16 35
Bowes Park d			13 08			13 38			14 08			14 38			15 08				15 38			16 08			16 38
Knebworth d	12 43				13 13			13 43			14 13			14 43			15 13				15 43			16 13	
Welwyn North d	12 47				13 17			13 47			14 17			14 47			15 17				15 47			16 17	
Welwyn Garden City 4 d	12 50			12 58	13 20		13 28	13 50		13 58	14 20		14 28	14 50		14 58	15 20			15 28	15 50		15 58	16 20	
Hatfield d	12 53			13 02	13 23		13 32	13 53		14 02	14 23		14 32	14 53		15 02	15 23			15 32	15 53		16 02	16 23	
Welham Green d				13 06			13 36			14 06			14 36			15 06				15 36			16 06		
Brookmans Park d				13 08			13 38			14 08			14 38			15 08				15 38			16 08		
Potters Bar d	12 59			13 11	13 30		13 41	13 59		14 11	14 29		14 41	14 59		15 11	15 29			15 41	15 59		16 11	16 29	
Hadley Wood d				13 15			13 45			14 15			14 45			15 15				15 45			16 15		
New Barnet d				13 17			13 47			14 17			14 47			15 17				15 47			16 17		
Oakleigh Park d				13 19			13 49			14 19			14 49			15 19				15 49			16 19		
New Southgate d				13 22			13 52			14 22			14 52			15 22				15 52			16 22		
Alexandra Palace d			13 10	13 25		13 40	13 55		14 10	14 25		14 40	14 55		15 10	15 25			15 40	15 55		16 10	16 25		16 40
Hornsey d			13 12	13 27		13 42	13 57		14 12	14 27		14 42	14 57		15 12	15 27			15 42	15 57		16 12	16 27		16 42
Harringay d			13 14	13 29		13 44	13 59		14 14	14 29		14 44	14 59		15 14	15 29			15 44	15 59		16 14	16 29		16 44
Finsbury Park ⊖ d	13 08		13 17	13 32	13 41	13 47	14 02	14 08	14 17	14 32	14 41	14 47	15 02	15 08	15 17	15 32	15 41		15 47	16 02	16 08	16 17	16 32	16 41	16 47
London Kings Cross 15 ⊖ a	13 19		13 25	13 40	13 49	13 55	14 10	14 19	14 25	14 40	14 49	14 55	15 10	15 19	15 25	15 40	15 49		15 55	16 10	16 19	16 25	16 40	16 49	16 55

For general notes see front of timetable
For details of catering facilities see
Directory of Train Operators

There is no service between Finsbury Park and Moorgate on Saturdays

Table 24

Saturdays

Letchworth Garden City, Hertford North and Welwyn Garden City → London

Network Diagram - see first page of Table 24

		FC	FC 1	FC	FC	FC 1	FC	FC	FC 1	FC	FC		FC 1	FC	FC	FC 1	FC	FC	FC 1	FC	FC	FC 1	FC	FC	FC 1	FC
Letchworth Garden City	d		16 29						17 29							18 29						19 29				
Hitchin 4	d		16 33			17 03			17 33				18 03			18 33			19 03			19 33			20 03	
Stevenage 4	d		16 39	16 29		17 09			17 39	17 29			18 09			18 39	18 29		19 09			19 39	19 29		20 09	
Watton-at-Stone	d			16 36						17 36							18 36						19 36			
Hertford North	d			16 42			17 12			17 42				18 12			18 42			19 12			19 42			20 12
Bayford	d			16 46			17 16			17 46				18 16			18 46			19 16			19 46			20 16
Cuffley	d			16 51			17 21			17 51				18 21			18 51			19 21			19 51			20 21
Crews Hill	d			16 54			17 24			17 54				18 24			18 54			19 24			19 54			20 24
Gordon Hill	d			16 57			17 27			17 57				18 27			18 57			19 27			19 57			20 27
Enfield Chase	d			16 59			17 29			17 59				18 29			18 59			19 29			19 59			20 29
Grange Park	d			17 01			17 31			18 01				18 31			19 01			19 31			20 01			20 31
Winchmore Hill	d			17 03			17 33			18 03				18 33			19 03			19 33			20 03			20 33
Palmers Green	d			17 05			17 35			18 05				18 35			19 05			19 35			20 05			20 35
Bowes Park	d			17 08			17 38			18 08				18 38			19 08			19 38			20 08			20 38
Knebworth	d		16 43			17 12			17 42				18 13			18 43			19 13			19 43			20 13	
Welwyn North	d		16 47			17 17			17 47				18 17			18 47			19 17			19 47			20 17	
Welwyn Garden City 4	d	16 28	16 50		16 58	17 20		17 28	17 50		17 58		18 20		18 28	18 50		18 58	19 20		19 28	19 50		19 58	20 20	
Hatfield	d	16 32	16 53		17 02	17 23		17 32	17 53		18 02		18 23		18 32	18 53		19 02	19 23		19 32	19 53		20 02	20 23	
Welham Green	d	16 36			17 06			17 36			18 06				18 36			19 06			19 36			20 06		
Brookmans Park	d	16 38			17 08			17 38			18 08				18 38			19 08			19 38			20 08		
Potters Bar	d	16 41	16 59		17 11	17 29		17 41	17 59		18 11		18 29		18 41	18 59		19 11	19 29		19 41	19 59		20 11	20 29	
Hadley Wood	d	16 45			17 15			17 45			18 15				18 45			19 15			19 45			20 15		
New Barnet	d	16 47			17 17			17 47			18 17				18 47			19 17			19 47			20 17		
Oakleigh Park	d	16 49			17 19			17 49			18 19				18 49			19 19			19 49			20 19		
New Southgate	d	16 52			17 22			17 52			18 22				18 52			19 22			19 52			20 22		
Alexandra Palace	d	16 55		17 10	17 25		17 40	17 55		18 10	18 25			18 40	18 55		19 10	19 25		19 40	19 55		20 10	20 25		20 40
Hornsey	d	16 57		17 12	17 27		17 42	17 57		18 12	18 27			18 42	18 57		19 12	19 27		19 42	19 57		20 12	20 27		20 42
Harringay	d	16 59		17 14	17 29		17 44	17 59		18 14	18 29			18 44	18 59		19 14	19 29		19 44	19 59		20 14	20 29		20 44
Finsbury Park ⊖	d	17 02	17 08	17 17	17 32	17 41	17 47	18 02	18 08	18 17	18 32		18 41	18 47	19 02	19 08	19 17	19 32	19 41	19 47	20 02	20 08	20 17	20 32	20 41	20 47
London Kings Cross 15 ⊖	a	17 10	17 19	17 25	17 40	17 50	17 55	18 10	18 19	18 25	18 40		18 49	18 55	19 10	19 19	19 25	19 40	19 49	19 55	20 10	20 19	20 25	20 40	20 50	20 55

		FC	FC 1	FC		FC	FC 1	FC	FC	FC 1	FC	FC	FC 1	FC	FC	FC	FC 1	FC	FC 1 A	FC 1 B	FC	FC	FC 1 C	FC 1 D		
Letchworth Garden City	d		20 29							21 29							22 29						23 37	23 37		
Hitchin 4	d		20 33				21 03			21 33			22 03				22 33		23 03	23 03			23 41	23 41		
Stevenage 4	d		20 39	20 29			21 09			21 39	21 29		22 09			22 29	22 39		23 09	23 09		23 29	23 46	23 46		
Watton-at-Stone	d			20 36							21 36					22 36						23 36				
Hertford North	d			20 42				21 12			21 42			22 12		22 42					23 12	23 42				
Bayford	d			20 46				21 16			21 46			22 16		22 46					23 16	23 46				
Cuffley	d			20 51				21 21			21 51			22 21		22 51					23 21	23 51				
Crews Hill	d			20 54				21 24			21 54			22 24		22 54					23 24	23 54				
Gordon Hill	d			20 57				21 27			21 57			22 27		22 57					23 27	23 57				
Enfield Chase	d			20 59				21 29			21 59			22 29		22 59					23 29	23 59				
Grange Park	d			21 01				21 31			22 01			22 31		23 01					23 31	00 01				
Winchmore Hill	d			21 03				21 33			22 03			22 33		23 03					23 33	00 03				
Palmers Green	d			21 05				21 35			22 05			22 35		23 05					23 35	00 05				
Bowes Park	d			21 08				21 38			22 08			22 38		23 08					23 38	00 08				
Knebworth	d		20 43				21 13			21 43			22 13				22 43		23 13	23 13			23 49	23 49		
Welwyn North	d		20 47				21 17			21 47			22 17				22 47		23 17	23 17			23 53	23 53		
Welwyn Garden City 4	d	20 28	20 50			20 58	21 20		21 28	21 50		21 58	22 20		22 28		22 50	22 58	23 20	23 20			23 56	23 56		
Hatfield	d	20 32	20 53			21 02	21 23		21 32	21 53		22 02	22 23		22 32		22 53	23 02	23 23	23 23			23 59	23 59		
Welham Green	d	20 36				21 06			21 36			22 06			22 36			23 06								
Brookmans Park	d	20 38				21 08			21 38			22 08			22 38			23 08								
Potters Bar	d	20 41	20 59			21 11	21 29		21 41	21 59		22 11	22 29		22 41		22 59	23 11	23 29	23a31			00 05	00 05		
Hadley Wood	d	20 45				21 15			21 45			22 15			22 45			23 15								
New Barnet	d	20 47				21 17			21 47			22 17			22 47			23 17								
Oakleigh Park	d	20 49				21 19			21 49			22 19			22 49			23 19								
New Southgate	d	20 52				21 22			21 52			22 22			22 52			23 22								
Alexandra Palace	d	20 55		21 10		21 25		21 40	21 55		22 10	22 25		22 40	22 55	23 10		23 25			23 40	00 10		00a19		
Hornsey	d	20 57		21 12		21 27		21 42	21 57		22 12	22 27		22 42	22 57	23 12		23 27			23 42	00 12				
Harringay	d	20 59		21 14		21 29		21 44	21 59		22 14	22 29		22 44	22 59	23 14		23 29			23 44	00 14				
Finsbury Park ⊖	d	21 02	21 08	21 17		21 32	21 41	21 47	22 02	22 08	22 17	22 32	22 41	22 47	23 02	23 17	23s16	23 32	23s45		23 47	00 17	00s23			
London Kings Cross 15 ⊖	a	21 10	21 19	21 25		21 40	21 49	21 55	22 10	22 19	22 25	22 40	22 49	22 55	23 10	23 25	23 30	23 42	23 53		23 58	00 25	00 34			

For general notes see front of timetable
For details of catering facilities see Directory of Train Operators

A Until 5 September. From Peterborough (Table 25)

B From 12 September. From Peterborough (Table 25)

C Until 5 September

D From 12 September. From Cambridge (Table 25)

There is no service between Finsbury Park and Moorgate on Saturdays

Table 24

Sundays

Letchworth Garden City, Hertford North and Welwyn Garden City → London

Network Diagram - see first page of Table 24

		FC	FC 1 A	FC 1 B	FC A	FC C	FC A	FC C	FC C	FC A	FC A	FC A	FC C	FC A	FC C	FC 1 C	FC 1 A	FC A	FC C	FC	FC	FC	FC 1	FC	FC	FC
Letchworth Garden City	d		23p37	23p37													07 23						08 29			
Hitchin [4]	d		23p41	23p41												07 28	07 27						08 33			
Stevenage [4]	d	23p29	23p46	23p46												07 33	07 35	07 29	07 29				08 39	08 29		
Watton-at-Stone	d	23p36																07 36	07 36					08 36		
Hertford North	d	23p42			06 12	06 12			06 42	06 42		07 12	07 12					07 42	07 42		08 12			08 42		09 12
Bayford	d	23p46			06 16	06 16			06 43	06 46		07 16	07 16					07 46	07 46		08 16			08 46		09 16
Cuffley	d	23p51			06 21	06 21			06 48	06 51		07 21	07 21					07 51	07 51		08 21			08 51		09 21
Crews Hill	d	23p54			06 24	06 24			06 51	06 54		07 24	07 24					07 54	07 54		08 24			08 54		09 24
Gordon Hill	d	23p57			06 27	06 27			06 54	06 57		07 27	07 27					07 57	07 57		08 27			08 57		09 27
Enfield Chase	d	23p59			06 29	06 29			06 56	06 59		07 29	07 29					07 59	07 59		08 29			08 59		09 29
Grange Park	d	00 01			06 31	06 31			06 58	07 01		07 31	07 31					08 01	08 01		08 31			09 01		09 31
Winchmore Hill	d	00 03			06 33	06 33			07 00	07 03		07 33	07 33					08 03	08 03		08 33			09 03		09 33
Palmers Green	d	00 05			06 35	06 35			07 02	07 05		07 35	07 35					08 05	08 05		08 35			09 05		09 35
Bowes Park	d	00 08			06 38	06 38			07 05	07 08		07 38	07 38					08 08	08 08		08 38			09 08		09 38
Knebworth	d		23p49	23p49												07 37	07 40						08 43			
Welwyn North	d		23p53	23p53												07 40	07 43						08 47			
Welwyn Garden City [4]	d		23p56	23p56			06 28	06 28			06 58			07 28	07 26	07 43	07 46			07 58		08 28	08 50		08 58	
Hatfield	d		23p59	23p59			06 32	06 32			07 02			07 32	07 30					08 02		08 32	08 53		09 02	
Welham Green	d						06 36	06 36			07 06			07 36	07 34					08 06		08 36			09 06	
Brookmans Park	d						06 38	06 38			07 08			07 38	07 36					08 08		08 38			09 08	
Potters Bar	d		00 05	00 05			06 41	06 41			07 11			07 41	07 39					08 11		08 41	08 59		09 11	
Hadley Wood	d						06 45	06 45			07 15			07 45	07 43					08 15		08 45			09 15	
New Barnet	d						06 47	06 47			07 17			07 47	07 45					08 17		08 47			09 17	
Oakleigh Park	d						06 49	06 49			07 19			07 49	07 47					08 19		08 49			09 19	
New Southgate	d						06 52	06 52			07 22			07 52	07 50					08 22		08 52			09 22	
Alexandra Palace	d	00 10		00a19	06 40	06 40	06 55	06 55	07 07	07 10	07 25	07 40	07 40	07 55	07 53			08 10	08 10	08 25	08 40	08 55		09 10	09 25	09 40
Hornsey	d	00 12			06 42	06 42	06 57	06 57	07 09	07 12	07 27	07 42	07 42	07 57	07 55			08 12	08 12	08 27	08 42	08 57		09 12	09 27	09 42
Harringay	d	00 14			06 44	06 44	06 59	06 59	07 11	07 14	07 29	07 44	07 44	07 59	07 57			08 14	08 14	08 29	08 44	08 59		09 14	09 29	09 44
Finsbury Park	⊖ d	00 17	00s23		06 47	06a49	07 02	07a04	07a17	07 17	07 32	07 47	07a49	08 02	08a03	08a05	08 10	08 17	08a19	08 32	08 47	09 02	09 11	09 17	09 32	09 47
London Kings Cross [15]	⊖ a	00 25	00 34		06 57		07 13			07 29	07 45	07 57		08 15			08 18	08 27		08 40	08 55	09 10	09 19	09 25	09 40	09 55

		FC	FC 1	FC	FC	FC	FC	FC 1	FC	FC		FC	FC	FC 1	FC	FC	FC	FC	FC 1	FC	FC	FC	FC	FC 1	FC	FC
Letchworth Garden City	d		09 29					10 29						11 29					12 29					13 29		
Hitchin [4]	d		09 33					10 33						11 33					12 33					13 33		
Stevenage [4]	d		09 39	09 29				10 39	10 29					11 39	11 29				12 39	12 29				13 39	13 29	
Watton-at-Stone	d			09 36					10 36						11 36					12 36					13 36	
Hertford North	d			09 42		10 12			10 42			11 12			11 42		12 12			12 42		13 12			13 42	
Bayford	d			09 46		10 16			10 46			11 16			11 46		12 16			12 46		13 16			13 46	
Cuffley	d			09 51		10 21			10 51			11 21			11 51		12 21			12 51		13 21			13 51	
Crews Hill	d			09 54		10 24			10 54			11 24			11 54		12 24			12 54		13 24			13 54	
Gordon Hill	d			09 57		10 27			10 57			11 27			11 57		12 27			12 57		13 27			13 57	
Enfield Chase	d			09 59		10 29			10 59			11 29			11 59		12 29			12 59		13 29			13 59	
Grange Park	d			10 01		10 31			11 01			11 31			12 01		12 31			13 01		13 31			14 01	
Winchmore Hill	d			10 03		10 33			11 03			11 33			12 03		12 33			13 03		13 33			14 03	
Palmers Green	d			10 05		10 35			11 05			11 35			12 05		12 35			13 05		13 35			14 05	
Bowes Park	d			10 08		10 38			11 08			11 38			12 08		12 38			13 08		13 38			14 08	
Knebworth	d		09 43					10 43						11 43					12 43					13 43		
Welwyn North	d		09 47					10 47						11 47					12 47					13 47		
Welwyn Garden City [4]	d	09 28	09 50		09 58		10 28	10 50		10 58			11 28	11 50		11 58		12 28	12 50		12 58		13 28	13 50		13 58
Hatfield	d	09 32	09 53		10 02		10 32	10 53		11 02			11 32	11 53		12 02		12 32	12 53		13 02		13 32	13 53		14 02
Welham Green	d	09 36			10 06		10 36			11 06			11 36			12 06		12 36			13 06		13 36			14 06
Brookmans Park	d	09 38			10 08		10 38			11 08			11 38			12 08		12 38			13 08		13 38			14 08
Potters Bar	d	09 41	09 59		10 11		10 41	10 59		11 11			11 41	11 59		12 11		12 41	12 59		13 11		13 41	13 59		14 11
Hadley Wood	d	09 45			10 15		10 45			11 15			11 45			12 15		12 45			13 15		13 45			14 15
New Barnet	d	09 47			10 17		10 47			11 17			11 47			12 17		12 47			13 17		13 47			14 17
Oakleigh Park	d	09 49			10 19		10 49			11 19			11 49			12 19		12 49			13 19		13 49			14 19
New Southgate	d	09 52			10 22		10 52			11 22			11 52			12 22		12 52			13 22		13 52			14 22
Alexandra Palace	d	09 55		10 10	10 25	10 40	10 55		11 10	11 25		11 40	11 55		12 10	12 25	12 40	12 55		13 10	13 25	13 40	13 55		14 10	14 25
Hornsey	d	09 57		10 12	10 27	10 42	10 57		11 12	11 27		11 42	11 57		12 12	12 27	12 42	12 57		13 12	13 27	13 42	13 57		14 12	14 27
Harringay	d	09 59		10 14	10 29	10 44	10 59		11 14	11 29		11 44	11 59		12 14	12 29	12 44	12 59		13 14	13 29	13 44	13 59		14 14	14 29
Finsbury Park	⊖ d	10 02	10 11	10 17	10 32	10 47	11 02	11 11	11 17	11 32		11 47	12 02	12 11	12 17	12 32	12 47	13 02	13 11	13 17	13 32	13 47	14 02	14 11	14 17	14 32
London Kings Cross [15]	⊖ a	10 10	10 19	10 25	10 40	10 55	11 10	11 18	11 25	11 40		11 55	12 10	12 18	12 25	12 40	12 55	13 10	13 19	13 25	13 40	13 55	14 10	14 19	14 25	14 40

For general notes see front of timetable
For details of catering facilities see Directory of Train Operators

A Until 6 September
B From 13 September. From Cambridge (Table 25)
C From 13 September

There is no service between Finsbury Park and Moorgate on Sundays

Table 24

Sundays

Letchworth Garden City, Hertford North and Welwyn Garden City → London

Network Diagram - see first page of Table 24

	FC	FC	FC 1	FC	FC	FC	FC	FC 1	FC	FC	FC	FC	FC 1	FC	FC	FC	FC	FC 1	FC	FC	FC	FC	FC 1	FC	FC
Letchworth Garden City d			14 29					15 29					16 29					17 29					18 29		
Hitchin 4 d			14 33					15 33					16 33					17 33					18 33		
Stevenage 4 d			14 39	14 29				15 39	15 29				16 39	16 29				17 39	17 29				18 39	18 29	
Watton-at-Stone d				14 36					15 36					16 36					17 36					18 36	
Hertford North d	14 12			14 42		15 12			15 42		16 12			16 42		17 12			17 42		18 12			18 42	
Bayford d	14 16			14 46		15 16			15 46		16 16			16 46		17 16			17 46		18 16			18 46	
Cuffley d	14 21			14 51		15 21			15 51		16 21			16 51		17 21			17 51		18 21			18 51	
Crews Hill d	14 24			14 54		15 24			15 54		16 24			16 54		17 24			17 54		18 24			18 54	
Gordon Hill d	14 27			14 57		15 27			15 57		16 27			16 57		17 27			17 57		18 27			18 57	
Enfield Chase d	14 29			14 59		15 29			15 59		16 29			16 59		17 29			17 59		18 29			18 59	
Grange Park d	14 31			15 01		15 31			16 01		16 31			17 01		17 31			18 01		18 31			19 01	
Winchmore Hill d	14 33			15 03		15 33			16 03		16 33			17 03		17 33			18 03		18 33			19 03	
Palmers Green d	14 35			15 05		15 35			16 05		16 35			17 05		17 35			18 05		18 35			19 05	
Bowes Park d	14 38			15 08		15 38			16 08		16 38			17 08		17 38			18 08		18 38			19 08	
Knebworth d			14 43					15 43					16 43					17 43					18 43		
Welwyn North d			14 47					15 47					16 47					17 47					18 47		
Welwyn Garden City 4 d		14 28	14 50		14 58		15 28	15 50		15 58		16 28	16 50		16 58		17 28	17 50		17 58		18 28	18 50		18 58
Hatfield d		14 32	14 53		15 02		15 32	15 53		16 02		16 32	16 53		17 02		17 32	17 53		18 02		18 32	18 53		19 02
Welham Green d		14 36			15 06		15 36			16 06		16 36			17 06		17 36			18 06		18 36			19 06
Brookmans Park d		14 38			15 08		15 38			16 08		16 38			17 08		17 38			18 08		18 38			19 08
Potters Bar d		14 41	15 00		15 11		15 41	15 59		16 11		16 41	16 59		17 11		17 41	17 59		18 11		18 41	18 59		19 11
Hadley Wood d		14 45			15 15		15 45			16 15		16 45			17 15		17 45			18 15		18 45			19 15
New Barnet d		14 47			15 17		15 47			16 17		16 47			17 17		17 47			18 17		18 47			19 17
Oakleigh Park d		14 49			15 19		15 49			16 19		16 49			17 19		17 49			18 19		18 49			19 19
New Southgate d		14 52			15 22		15 52			16 22		16 52			17 22		17 52			18 22		18 52			19 22
Alexandra Palace d	14 40	14 55		15 10	15 25	15 40	15 55		16 10	16 25	16 40	16 55		17 10	17 25	17 40	17 55		18 10	18 25	18 40	18 55		19 10	19 25
Hornsey d	14 42	14 57		15 12	15 27	15 42	15 57		16 12	16 27	16 42	16 57		17 12	17 27	17 42	17 57		18 12	18 27	18 42	18 57		19 12	19 27
Harringay d	14 44	14 59		15 14	15 29	15 44	15 59		16 14	16 29	16 44	16 59		17 14	17 29	17 44	17 59		18 14	18 29	18 44	18 59		19 14	19 29
Finsbury Park ⊖ d	14 47	15 02	15 12	15 17	15 32	15 47	16 02	16 11	16 17	16 32	16 47	17 02	17 11	17 17	17 32	17 47	18 02	18 11	18 17	18 32	18 47	19 02	19 11	19 17	19 32
London Kings Cross 15 ⊖ a	14 55	15 10	15 22	15 25	15 40	15 55	16 10	16 18	16 25	16 40	16 55	17 10	17 19	17 25	17 40	17 55	18 10	18 19	18 25	18 40	18 55	19 10	19 18	19 25	19 40

	FC	FC	FC 1	FC	FC	FC	FC	FC 1	FC	FC	FC	FC	FC 1	FC	FC	FC	FC	FC 1	FC	FC	FC	FC	FC 1		
Letchworth Garden City d			19 29					20 29					21 29					22 29					23 39		
Hitchin 4 d			19 33					20 33					21 33					22 33					23 43		
Stevenage 4 d			19 39	19 29				20 39	20 29				21 39	21 29				22 39	22 29			23 29	23 48		
Watton-at-Stone d				19 36					20 36					21 36					22 36			23 36			
Hertford North d	19 12			19 42		20 12			20 42		21 12			21 42		22 12			22 42		23 12	23 42			
Bayford d	19 16			19 46		20 16			20 46		21 16			21 46		22 16			22 46		23 16	23 46			
Cuffley d	19 21			19 51		20 21			20 51		21 21			21 51		22 21			22 51		23 21	23 51			
Crews Hill d	19 24			19 54		20 24			20 54		21 24			21 54		22 24			22 54		23 24	23 54			
Gordon Hill d	19 27			19 57		20 27			20 57		21 27			21 57		22 27			22 57		23 27	23 57			
Enfield Chase d	19 29			19 59		20 29			20 59		21 29			21 59		22 29			22 59		23 29	23 59			
Grange Park d	19 31			20 01		20 31			21 01		21 31			22 01		22 31			23 01		23 31	00 01			
Winchmore Hill d	19 33			20 03		20 33			21 03		21 33			22 03		22 33			23 03		23 33	00 03			
Palmers Green d	19 35			20 05		20 35			21 05		21 35			22 05		22 35			23 05		23 35	00 05			
Bowes Park d	19 38			20 08		20 38			21 08		21 38			22 08		22 38			23 08		23 38	00 08			
Knebworth d			19 43					20 43					21 43					22 43					23 51		
Welwyn North d			19 47					20 47					21 47					22 47					23 55		
Welwyn Garden City 4 d		19 28	19 50		19 58		20 28	20 50		20 58		21 28	21 50		21 58		22 28	22 50		22 58			23 58		
Hatfield d		19 32	19 53		20 02		20 32	20 53		21 02		21 32	21 53		22 02		22 32	22 53		23 02			00 01		
Welham Green d		19 36			20 06		20 36			21 06		21 36			22 06		22 36			23 06					
Brookmans Park d		19 38			20 08		20 38			21 08		21 38			22 08		22 38			23 08					
Potters Bar d		19 41	19 59		20 11		20 44	20 59		21 11		21 41	21 59		22 11		22 41	22 59		23 11			00 07		
Hadley Wood d		19 45			20 15		20 47			21 15		21 45			22 15		22 45			23 15					
New Barnet d		19 47			20 17		20 50			21 17		21 47			22 17		22 47			23 17					
Oakleigh Park d		19 49			20 19		20 52			21 19		21 49			22 19		22 49			23 19					
New Southgate d		19 52			20 22		20 55			21 22		21 52			22 22		22 52			23 22					
Alexandra Palace d	19 40	19 55		20 10	20 25	20 40	20 58		21 10	21 25	21 40	21 55		22 10	22 25	22 40	22 55		23 10	23 25	23 40	00 10			
Hornsey d	19 42	19 57		20 12	20 27	20 42	21 00		21 12	21 27	21 42	21 57		22 12	22 27	22 42	22 57		23 12	23 27	23 42	00 12			
Harringay d	19 44	19 59		20 14	20 29	20 44	21 02		21 14	21 29	21 44	21 59		22 14	22 29	22 44	22 59		23 14	23 29	23 44	00 14			
Finsbury Park ⊖ d	19 47	20 02	20 11	20 17	20 32	20 47	21 04	21 11	21 17	21 32	21 47	22 02	22 11	22 17	22 32	22 47	23 02	23 11	23 17	23 32	23 47	00 17	00 20		
London Kings Cross 15 ⊖ a	19 55	20 10	20 18	20 25	20 40	20 56	21 10	21 18	21 25	21 40	21 55	22 10	22 19	22 25	22 40	22 58	23 12	23 23	23 27	23 44	23 57	00 27	00 32		

For general notes see front of timetable
For details of catering facilities see
Directory of Train Operators

There is no service between Finsbury Park and Moorgate on Sundays

First Capital Connect will run a Saturday service on Bank Holiday Mondays

London → Stevenage, Cambridge and Peterborough

Network Diagram - see first page of Table 24

Miles	Miles	Station		FC	FC	FC	FC	FC	FC	FC	FC	FC	FC	FC	FC	FC	FC	FC	FC	FC	FC	FC	FC	GR	FC	FC
				MO	MX	MO	MX	MO	MX	MO	MX	MX	MO	MX	MO	MX	MX	MO		MX	MO					
																								R		
				1	1	1	1	1	1	1	1			1	1	1		1		1	1	1	1	1	1	1
						A													B				C			
																								☕		
0	0	**London Kings Cross 15** ⊖	d	23p06	23p06	23p15			23p22	23p25	23p36	23p26	23p41	00 07	00 07	00 36	00 26	00 36	01 06	01 36	01 36	05 22	05 45	06 00		06 06
2½	2½	Finsbury Park ⊖	d	23p11	23p11				23p27	23p30	23p41	23p32	23p47	00 12	00 12	00 41	00 32	00 41	01 11	01 41	01 41	05 27	05 50			06 11
12¾	12¾	Potters Bar	d	23p21	23p21						23p51		00 08			00 51		00 58		01 58	01 58	05 37				06 21
17¾	17¾	Hatfield	d	23p27	23p27		←	←			23p57		00 16			00 57		01 04		02 04	02 04	05 43				06 27
20¼	20¼	Welwyn Garden City 4	d	23p31	23p31		23p31	23p31			00 01		00 20			01 01		01 08		02 08	02 08	05 47				→
22	22	Welwyn North	d	→	→		23p34	23p36			00 04		00 23			01s04		01s16		02s11	02s16	05 50				
25	25	Knebworth	d				23p38	23p40			00 08		00 28			01s08		01s20		02s15	02s20	05 54				
—	—	Hertford North	d									00 07			00 39		01 07		01 38							
27½	27½	**Stevenage 4**	d				23p42	23p43	23p46	23p49	00 12	00 20	00 31	00 35	00 48	01 12	01 20	01 23	01 47	02 18	02 23	05 58	06 08	06 19		
31¾	31¾	Hitchin 4	d				23p50	23p53	23p54	00 04	00 20	00 26	00 37	00 43	00 56	01 17	01 26	01 28	01 52	02 23	02 28	06 06	06 13			
34¾	—	Letchworth Garden City	d			23p52	23p54	23p57			00a29	00a36	00a52	00 47	01 00		01a36		02a06				06 17			
36¾	—	Baldock	d				23p58	23p59						00 51	01 04								06 20			
41	—	Ashwell & Morden	d				00 03	00 05						00 56	01 09								06 25			
45	—	Royston	d			00 01	00 07	00 10						01 00	01 13								06 30			
48	—	Meldreth	d				00 11	00 13						01 04	01 17								06 34			
50	—	Shepreth	d				00 14	00 16						01 07	01 20								06 37			
51	—	Foxton	d				00 17	00 18						01 10	01 23								06 40			
58	—	**Cambridge**	a			00 19	00 29	00 35						01 25	01 39								06 55			
—	37	Arlesey	d						23p59	00 10						01s28		01s37				06 11			←	
—	41	Biggleswade	d						00 04	00 15						01s33		01s42		02s38	02s40	06 16			06 16	
—	44	Sandy	d						00 08	00 18						01s37		01s46				→			06 20	
—	51½	St Neots	d						00 15	00 26						01s45		01s53		02s48	02s50				06 28	
—	58¾	Huntingdon	a						00 26	00 33						01s55		02s04		02s59	03s01				06 35	
—	—		d						00 26	00 33															06 35	
—	76¼	**Peterborough 8**	a						00 42	00 58						02 17		02 26		03 21	03 23			06 50	06 54	

Station		GR		FC	FC	GR	FC	FC	FC	FC	GR	FC	GR	FC	FC	FC	FC	GR	FC	FC	FC	FC	FC	GR	FC	GR
		R				R					R		R					R						R		R
		1		1	1	1	1	1	1	1	1	1	1	1	1	1	1	1	1	1	1	1	1	1	1	1
		☕ 🛒				☕					☕ 🛒		☕ 🛒					☕ 🛒						☕ 🛒		☕ 🛒
London Kings Cross 15 ⊖	d	06 15			06 22	06 35		06 36	06 45	06 52	07 00	07 06	07 10		07 15		07 22	07 30		07 36	07 45		07 52	08 00	08 03	08 10
Finsbury Park ⊖	d				06 27			06 41		06 57		07 11					07 27			07 41			07 57		08 08	
Potters Bar	d			←				06 51				07 21				←				07 51					08 19	
Hatfield	d			06 27				06 57				07 27				07 27				07 57					08 25	
Welwyn Garden City 4	d			06 31				07 01				→				07 31				08 01					08 31	
Welwyn North	d			06 34				07 04								07 34				08 04					08 34	
Knebworth	d			06 38				07 08								07 38				08 08					08 38	
Hertford North	d																					←				
Stevenage 4	d	06 34		06 42	06 46			07 12		07 17	07 19		07 29			07 42	07 46	07 50		08 12		08 12	08 17		08 42	
Hitchin 4	d			06 47	06 51			07 17		07 22						07 47	07 51			→		08 17	08 22		08 47	
Letchworth Garden City	d			06 51						07 26						07 51							08 26		→	
Baldock	d			06 55						07 29						07 55							08 29			
Ashwell & Morden	d			07 00						07 34						08 00							08 34			
Royston	d			07 06						07 39						08 06							08 39			
Meldreth	d			07 10						07 43						08 10							08 43			
Shepreth	d			07 13						07 46						08 13							08 46			
Foxton	d			07 16						07 48						08 16							08 48			
Cambridge	a			07 29			←		07 32	08 02					08 02	08 29					08 35		09 02			
Arlesey	d				06 56		06 56	07 23						←			07 56		←			08 23				
Biggleswade	d				→		07 01	07 28						07 28			08 01		08 01			08 28				
Sandy	d						07 05	→						07 32			→		08 05			08 32				
St Neots	d						07 12							07 39					08 12			08 39				
Huntingdon	a						07 20							07 47					08 20			08 47				
	d						07 20							07 47					08 20			08 47				
Peterborough 8	a	07 05				07 21	07 38				07 51		08 00	08 09				08 21	08 38			09 13		08 46		08 59

Station		FC		FC	GR	FC	GR	FC	FC	FC	FC	FC	GR	FC	GR	FC	FC	GR	FC	FC	GR	FC	FC	FC	FC	FC
					R		R						R		R			R			R					
		1		1	1	1	1	1	1	1	1	1	1	1	1	1	1	1	1		1	1	1	1	1	1
					☕ 🛒		☕						☕ 🛒		☕			☕ 🛒			☕ 🛒					
London Kings Cross 15 ⊖	d	08 15		08 22	08 30	08 33	08 40			08 45		08 52	09 00	09 06	09 10	09 15	09 22	09 30			09 35		09 36	09 45		09 52
Finsbury Park ⊖	d			08 27		08 38						08 57		09 11			09 27			09 04			09 41			09 57
Potters Bar	d					08 49								09 21									09 51			
Hatfield	d					08 55								09 27									09 57			
Welwyn Garden City 4	d					09 01								09 31									10 01			
Welwyn North	d					09 04								09 34									10 04			
Knebworth	d					09 08								09 38									10 08			
Hertford North	d										←									09 39					←	
Stevenage 4	d			08 46	08 49	09 12			←		09 12	09 16		09 42			09 46	09 49	←	09 51	09 54		10 12		10 12	10 16
Hitchin 4	d			08 51		→			08 47		09 17	09 21		09 47			09 51		09 47	09 57			→		10 17	10 21
Letchworth Garden City	d								08 54			09 25		→					09 51	10a04						10 25
Baldock	d								08 57			09 28							09 55							10 28
Ashwell & Morden	d								09 02										10 00							
Royston	d								09 07			09 36							10 04							10 36
Meldreth	d								09 11										10 08							
Shepreth	d								09 14										10 11							
Foxton	d								09 16										10 14							
Cambridge	a	09 03							09 29	09 31		09 54				10 03			10 29					10 31		10 54
Arlesey	d			08 56				←			09 23														10 23	
Biggleswade	d			09 01				09 01			09 28						09 59					←			10 28	
Sandy	d			→				09 05			09 32						10 03					10 03			10 32	
St Neots	d							09 12			09 39						→					10 10			10 39	
Huntingdon	a							09 20			09 47											10 18			10 47	
	d							09 20			09 47											10 18			10 47	
Peterborough 8	a				09 20		09 27	09 38			10 04		09 46		09 57			10 20			10 26	10 35			11 05	

For general notes see front of timetable
For details of catering facilities see Directory of Train Operators

A To Ely (Table 17)
B First Class accommodation available Tuesdays to Fridays
C To Kings Lynn (Table 17)

First Capital Connect will run a Saturday service on Bank Holiday Mondays

London → Stevenage, Cambridge and Peterborough

Network Diagram - see first page of Table 24

		GR		FC	GR	FC	FC	GR	GR	FC	FC	FC	FC	FC	FC	FC	GR	FC	GR	FC	FC	GR	FC	FC	GR	FC
		R 1 A		1	R 1	1	1	R 1 B	R 1	1	1		1	1	1	1	R 1	1	R 1	1	1	R 1	1		R 1	1
London Kings Cross 15 ⊖	d	10 00		10 06	10 10	10 15	10 22	10 30	10 35				10 36	10 45		10 52	11 00	11 06	11 10	11 15	11 22	11 30			11 35	
Finsbury Park ⊖	d			10 11			10 27					10 04	10 41			10 57		11 11			11 27			11 04		
Potters Bar	d			10 21									10 51					11 21								
Hatfield	d			10 27									10 57					11 27								
Welwyn Garden City 4	d			10 31									11 01					11 31								
Welwyn North	d			10 34									11 04					11 34								
Knebworth	d			10 38									11 08					11 38								
Hertford North	d											10 39			←									11 39		
Stevenage 4	d			10 42			10 46				←	10 51	11 12		11 12	11 16		11 42			11 46	11 50	←	11 51	11 54	
Hitchin 4	d			10 47			10 51				10 47	10 57	→		11 17	11 21		11 47			11 51		11 47	11 57		
Letchworth Garden City	d			→							10 51	11a04				11 25		→					11 51	12a04		
Baldock	d										10 55					11 28							11 55			
Ashwell & Morden	d										11 00												12 00			
Royston	d										11 04					11 36							12 04			
Meldreth	d										11 08												12 08			
Shepreth	d										11 11												12 11			
Foxton	d										11 14												12 14			
Cambridge	a					11 02					11 29			11 31		11 54				12 01			12 27			
Arlesey	d									←					11 23											
Biggleswade	d						10 59			10 59					11 28						11 59					←
Sandy	d						→			11 03					11 32						12 03					12 03
St Neots	d									11 10					11 39						→					12 10
Huntingdon	a									11 18					11 47											12 18
	d									11 18					11 47											12 18
Peterborough 8	a	10 45			10 56			11 16	11 22	11 34					12 04		11 45		11 56			12 21			12 27	12 34

		FC		FC	FC	FC	GR	FC	GR	FC	FC	FC	FC	GR	FC	FC	FC	FC	FC	GR	FC	GR	FC	FC	GR	FC
		1		1	1	1	R 1 C	1	R 1	1	1	1		R 1	1	1	1	1	1	R 1	1	R 1	1	1	R 1	1
London Kings Cross 15 ⊖	d	11 36		11 45		11 52	12 00	12 06	12 10	12 15		12 22		12 30		12 36	12 45		12 52	13 00	13 06	13 10	13 15	13 22	13 35	
Finsbury Park ⊖	d	11 41				11 57		12 11				12 27	12 04			12 41			12 57		13 11			13 27		
Potters Bar	d	11 51						12 21			←					12 51					13 21					
Hatfield	d	11 57						12 27			12 27					12 57					13 27					
Welwyn Garden City 4	d	12 01						→			12 31					13 01					13 31					
Welwyn North	d	12 04									12 34					13 04					13 34					
Knebworth	d	12 08									12 38					13 08					13 38					
Hertford North	d				←								12 39					←								
Stevenage 4	d	12 12			12 12	12 16			12 29		12 42	12 46	12 51			13 12		13 12	13 16		13 42			13 46		
Hitchin 4	d	→			12 17	12 21					12 47	12 51	12 57			→		13 17	13 21		13 47			13 51		
Letchworth Garden City	d					12 25					12 51		13a04						13 25		→					
Baldock	d					12 28					12 55								13 28							
Ashwell & Morden	d										13 00															
Royston	d					12 36					13 04								13 36							
Meldreth	d										13 08															
Shepreth	d										13 11															
Foxton	d										13 14															
Cambridge	a			12 31		12 54				13 02	13 27				←		13 31		13 54				14 01			←
Arlesey	d				12 23							12 56			12 56			13 23						13 56		13 56
Biggleswade	d				12 28							→			13 01			13 28						→		14 01
Sandy	d				12 32										13 05			13 32								14 05
St Neots	d				12 39										13 12			13 39								14 12
Huntingdon	a				12 47										13 20			13 47								14 20
	d				12 47										13 20			13 47								14 20
Peterborough 8	a				13 07		12 46		13 00					13 16	13 36			14 05		13 45		13 57			14 24	14 36

		FC		FC	FC	FC	FC	FC	FC	GR	FC	FC	GR	FC	FC	FC	FC	FC	FC	FC	FC	GR	FC	FC	GR	FC
		1			1	1	1	1	1	R 1	1	1	R 1	1	1		1	1	1	1	1	R 1	1	1	R 1	1
London Kings Cross 15 ⊖	d				13 36	13 45		13 52	14 06	14 10	14 15	14 22	14 30				14 36	14 45		14 52	15 06	15 10	15 15	15 22	15 30	
Finsbury Park ⊖	d			13 04	13 41			13 57	14 11			14 27				14 04	14 41			14 57	15 11			15 27		
Potters Bar	d				13 51				14 21								14 51				15 21					
Hatfield	d				13 57				14 27								14 57				15 27					
Welwyn Garden City 4	d				14 01				14 31								15 01				15 31					
Welwyn North	d				14 04				14 34								15 04				15 34					
Knebworth	d				14 08				14 38								15 08				15 38					
Hertford North	d			13 39			←									14 39			←							
Stevenage 4	d	←		13 51	14 12		14 12	14 16	14 42			14 46			←	14 51	15 12		15 12	15 16	15 42			15 46		←
Hitchin 4	d	13 47		13 57	→		14 17	14 21	14 47			14 51			14 47	14 57	→		15 17	15 21	15 47			15 51		15 47
Letchworth Garden City	d	13 51		14a04				14 25	→						14 51	15a04				15 25	→					15 51
Baldock	d	13 55						14 28							14 55					15 28						15 55
Ashwell & Morden	d	14 00													15 00											16 00
Royston	d	14 04						14 36							15 04					15 36						16 04
Meldreth	d	14 08													15 08											16 08
Shepreth	d	14 11													15 11											16 11
Foxton	d	14 14													15 14											16 14
Cambridge	a	14 27				14 31		14 54			15 04			←	15 29			15 31		15 54			16 03			16 30
Arlesey	d						14 23					14 56		14 56					15 23					15 56		
Biggleswade	d						14 28					→		15 01					15 28					→		
Sandy	d						14 32							15 05					15 32							
St Neots	d						14 39							15 12					15 39							
Huntingdon	a						14 47							15 20					15 47							
	d						14 47							15 20					15 47							
Peterborough 8	a						15 05			14 56			15 16	15 36					16 04			15 56			16 16	

For general notes see front of timetable
For details of catering facilities see Directory of Train Operators

A The Flying Scotsman
B The Northen Lights
C The Highland Chieftain

First Capital Connect will run a Saturday service on Bank Holiday Mondays

London → Stevenage, Cambridge and Peterborough

Network Diagram - see first page of Table 24

	FC		GR	FC	FC	FC	FC	FC	FC	GR	FC	FC	FC	FC	FC	GR	FC	FC	FC	FC	FC	FC	FC	GR	FC
	1		R 1	1	1	1	1	1	1	R 1	1	1	1	1	1	R 1	1	1	1	1	1	1	1	R 1	1
																			A						
London Kings Cross 15 ⊖ d			15 35		15 36	15 45		15 52	16 06	16 10	16 15	16 17		16 22	16 32	16 35	16 40		16 44			16 50	16 54	17 03	17 10
Finsbury Park ⊖ d	15 04				15 41			15 57	16 11					16 27	16 37							16 55	16 59		
Potters Bar d					15 51				16 21				←		16 48										
Hatfield d					15 57				16 27 →				16 27		16 54						←		17 15		
Welwyn Garden City 4 d					16 01								16 32		16 59 →						16 59		17 19 →		
Welwyn North d					16 04								16 35								17 03	17 11			
Knebworth d					16 08								16 39								17 07				
Hertford North d	15 39						←																		
Stevenage 4 d	15 51		15 54		16 12 →		16 12	16 16				16 38	16 43	16 47				←			17 11	17 17			
Hitchin 4 d	15 57						16 17	16 21					16 49 →	16 53				16 49			17 17	17 23			17 33
Letchworth Garden City d	16a04							16 25				16 47						16 53	17 10		17 24				
Baldock d								16 28				16 50						16 57			17 28				
Ashwell & Morden d								16 33				16 55						17 02			17 33				
Royston d								16 37				17a02						17 06	17 20		17 37				
Meldreth d																		17 10			17 41				
Shepreth d																		17 13			17 44				
Foxton d																		17 16			17 47				
Cambridge a				←		16 31		16 54			17 04							17 30	17 35		18 02				
Arlesey d				15 56			16 23							16 58								17 28 →			
Biggleswade d				16 01			16 28							17 03			17 07			←					
Sandy d				16 05			16 32							17 07 →						17 07					
St Neots d				16 12			16 39										17 17			17 22					17 50 →
Huntingdon a				16 20			16 47										17 25			17 31					
d				16 20			16 47										17 25								
Peterborough 8 a			16 26	16 37			17 04			16 56						17 24	17 43							17 51	

	FC		FC	FC	GR	FC	FC	FC	GR	FC	FC	FC	FC	FC	FC	GR	FC	FC	FC	GR	FC	FC	FC	FC	FC
	1		1	1	R 1	1	1	1	R 1	1	1	1	1	1	1	R 1	1	1	1	R 1	1	1	1	1	1
	B				C				✕																
London Kings Cross 15 ⊖ d	17 14			17 14	17 19		17 22	17 23	17 30			17 40	17 44		17 44	17 49	17 52		17 53	18 03		18 10	18 14		18 14
Finsbury Park ⊖ d				17 19			17 28								17 49		17 58								18 19
Potters Bar d																									
Hatfield d			←											←										←	
Welwyn Garden City 4 d			17 19				17 47 →							17 47			18 17 →							18 17	
Welwyn North d			17 22											17 51										18 21	
Knebworth d			17 26	17 35										17 55										18 25	
Hertford North d																									
Stevenage 4 d			17 36	17 40				17 43						18 04	18 09				18 13					18 34	18 39
Hitchin 4 d			17 42	17 46								18 03		18 10	18 16							18 33		18 40	18 46
Letchworth Garden City d			17 47					17 52						18 16					18 22					18 46	
Baldock d			17 51					17 55											18 25						
Ashwell & Morden d			17 56					18 00											18 30						
Royston d	17 48		18 01					18a07						18 28					18a37					18 58	
Meldreth d			18 05											18 32										19 02	
Shepreth d			18 08											18 35										19 05	
Foxton d			18 10											18 37										19 07	
Cambridge a	18 03		18 24			←					←		18 31	18 55							←		19 01	19 22	
Arlesey d				17 51 →		17 28					17 51				18 21 →						18 21				18 51 →
Biggleswade d						17 33					17 56										18 26				
Sandy d						17 37				←	18 00							←			18 30				
St Neots d						17 46				17 50	18 08	18 20 →						18 20			18 38	18 50 →			
Huntingdon a						17 53				17 57	18 16							18 28			18 45				
d						17 54				17 58	18 16							18 28			18 46				
Peterborough 8 a					18 06	18 12			18 16	18 22	18 33					18 37		18 50		18 54	19 03				

	GR		FC	FC	GR	FC	FC	FC	FC	FC	FC	FC	FC	GR	GR	FC	FC	FC	FC	FC	FC	GR	FC	FC	FC
	R 1		1	1	R 1	1	1	1	1	1	1	1	1	R 1	R 1	1	1	1	1	1	1	R 1	1	1	1
	✕							A						✕	✕							✕			
London Kings Cross 15 ⊖ d	18 19			18 23	18 35		18 40	18 44	18 22	18 44	18 52	18 53		19 00	19 03		19 10	19 15		19 18	19 22	19 33			
Finsbury Park ⊖ d									18 28	18 49	18 58		18 30							19 23	19 27				
Potters Bar d																				19 34					
Hatfield d											19 14								←	19 42					←
Welwyn Garden City 4 d									18 47		19 18 →								19 18	19 48 →					19 48
Welwyn North d				18 41					18 51										19 22						19 52
Knebworth d									18 55	19 05									19 26						19 56
Hertford North d													19 03												
Stevenage 4 d									19 04	19 10		19 13	19 16						19 36		19 47				20 04
Hitchin 4 d				18 51					19 10	19 16			19 22				19 34		19 42		19 53				20 10
Letchworth Garden City d				18 55					19 16			19 22	19a27					19 41	19 47						20 15
Baldock d				18 59								19 25							19 51						20 19
Ashwell & Morden d				19 04								19 30							19 56						20 24
Royston d				19a11				19 18	19 28			19a37						19 51	20 01						20 29
Meldreth d									19 32										20 05						20 33
Shepreth d									19 35										20 08						20 36
Foxton d									19 37										20 10						20 38
Cambridge a						←		19 33	19 52							←		20 08	20 24					←	20 52
Arlesey d						18 51				19 21 →						19 21					19 58 →			19 58	
Biggleswade d						18 56	19 08									19 26								20 03	
Sandy d			←			19 00										19 30							←	20 07	
St Neots d			18 50			19 08	19 18									19 38	19 52 →						19 52	20 15	
Huntingdon a			18 57			19 15	19 25									19 45							20 00	20 23	
d			18 58			19 16	19 26									19 46							20 00	20 23	
Peterborough 8 a	19 06		19 14		19 25	19 32	19 43							19 46	19 52	20 03						20 22	20 24	20 40	

For general notes see front of timetable
For details of catering facilities see Directory of Train Operators

A To Kings Lynn (Table 17)
B To Ely (Table 17)
C **The Hull Executive**

First Capital Connect will run a Saturday service on Bank Holiday Mondays

London → Stevenage, Cambridge and Peterborough

Network Diagram - see first page of Table 24

		FC		FC	FC	FC	GR	GR	FC	FC	FC	FC	FC	GR	FC	FC	FC	FC	FC	GR	FC	FC	FC	FC	FC	FC
		1		1	1		R 1	R 1	1	1	1	1	1	R 1	1	1	1	1	1	R 1		1	1	1	1	1
				A							A													A		
							☕ 🍴	☕ 🍴						☕ 🍴						☕ 🍴						
London Kings Cross 15 ⊖	d	19 36		19 45	19 52		20 00	20 03	20 06	20 07	20 15		20 22	20 33			20 36	20 45	20 52	21 00		21 06	21 07	21 15		21 22
Finsbury Park ⊖	d	19 41			19 57	19 34			20 11				20 27				20 41		20 57		20 24	21 11				21 27
Potters Bar	d								20 21								20 51					21 21				
Hatfield	d								20 27			←					20 57					21 27			←	
Welwyn Garden City 4	d	20 00							20 31			20 31					21 01					21 31			21 31	
Welwyn North	d	20 04							→			20 34					21 04					→			21 34	
Knebworth	d	20 08										20 38					21 08								21 38	
Hertford North	d					20 10															21 10					
Stevenage 4	d	20 12			20 17	20 23						20 42	20 47		←		21 12		21 16	21 20	21 23				21 42	21 47
Hitchin 4	d	20 17			20 23	20 27						20 47	20 53		20 17		21 17		21 21		21 28				21 47	21 53
Letchworth Garden City	d	→		20 10		20a35					20 40	20 51			20 23		21a23		21 28		21a34			21 40	21 51	
Baldock	d											20 55							21 31						21 55	
Ashwell & Morden	d											21 00							21 36						22 00	
Royston	d			20 20							20 50	21 04							21 41					21 50	22 04	
Meldreth	d											21 08							21 44						22 08	
Shepreth	d											21 11							21 47						22 11	
Foxton	d											21 14							21 50						22 14	
Cambridge	a			20 35							21 05	21 27				←		21 32	22 03					22 05	22 27	
Arlesey	d				20 28								20 58		20 23	20 58										21 58
Biggleswade	d				20 33								→		20 28	21 03							21 35			→
Sandy	d				20 37										20 32	21 08										
St Neots	d				20 45					20 41					20 40	21 15							21 44			
Huntingdon	a				20 54					20 49					20 55	21 23							21 51			
	d				20 55					20 49					20 55	21 23							21 51			
Peterborough 8	a				21 26		20 46	20 52		21 05				21 20	21 26	21 40				21 53			22 07			

		GR		FC	FC	FC	FC	GR	FC	FC	FC	FC	FC	FC	FC	FC	FC	FC	FC	FC	GR	FC	FC	FC		
		R 1		1	1	1		R 1	1	1	1	1	1	1	1		1	1	1	1	R 1	1	1			
											A							B								
		☕ 🍴						☕													☕					
London Kings Cross 15 ⊖	d	21 30			21 36	21 52		22 00	22 06	22 07	22 15		22 22	22 36	22 52	22 26	23 06	23 15		23 22	23 30		23 36	23 26		
Finsbury Park ⊖	d				21 41	21 57	21 24		22 11				22 27	22 41	22 57	22 32	23 11			23 27			23 41	23 32		
Potters Bar	d				21 51				22 21					22 51			23 21						23 51			
Hatfield	d				21 57				22 27			←		22 57			23 27		←				23 57			
Welwyn Garden City 4	d				22 01				22 31			22 31		23 01			23 31		23 31				00 01			
Welwyn North	d				22 04				→			22 34		23 04			→		23 34				00 04			
Knebworth	d				22 08							22 38		23 08					23 38				00 08			
Hertford North	d						22 07									23 07								00 07		
Stevenage 4	d				22 12	22 16	22 20					22 42	22 46	23 12	23 16	23 20			23 42	23 46			00 12	00 20		
Hitchin 4	d				22 17	22 21	22 25					22 50	22 54	23 20	23 24	23 28			23 50	23 54			00 20	00 26		
Letchworth Garden City	d				22a23	22 28	22a33				22 40	22 54		23a26	23 31	23a36		23 44	23 54				00a29	00a36		
Baldock	d					22 31						22 58			23 34				23 58							
Ashwell & Morden	d					22 36						23 03			23 39				00 03							
Royston	d					22 41					22 50	23 07			23 44			23 54	00 07							
Meldreth	d											23 11							00 11							
Shepreth	d											23 14							00 14							
Foxton	d											23 17							00 17							
Cambridge	a			←		22 58					23 05	23 29			00 01			00 10	00 29			←				
Arlesey	d			21 58									22 59							23 59		23 59				
Biggleswade	d			22 03						22 35			23 04							→		00 04				
Sandy	d			22 07									23 08									00 08				
St Neots	d			22 15						22 44			23 15									00 15				
Huntingdon	a			22 23						22 51			23 26									00 26				
	d			22 23						22 51			23 26									00 26				
Peterborough 8	a	22 16		23 40				22 46		23 17			23 42								00s23	00 42				

For general notes see front of timetable
For details of catering facilities see Directory of Train Operators

A To Kings Lynn (Table 17)

B Fridays to Kings Lynn (Table 17). Mondays to Thursdays to Ely (Table 17)

London → Stevenage, Cambridge and Peterborough

Network Diagram - see first page of Table 24

		FC	FC	FC	FC	FC	FC	FC	FC	FC	FC	FC	FC	FC	FC	GR	FC	FC	FC	FC	FC	FC	GR	FC	GR	FC
		1	1	1		1	1	1	1		1	1	1	1	1	R 1	1	1	1	1	1	1	R 1	1	R 1	1
London Kings Cross 15 ⊖	d	23p06	23p22	23p36	23p26	00 01	00 07	00 31	00 36	00 26	01 06	01 36	05 22	05 45	06 06	06 15		06 22	06 36	06 45		06 52	07 00	07 06	07 10	07 22
Finsbury Park ⊖	d	23p11	23p27	23p41	23p32		00 12		00 41	00 32	01 11	01 41	05 27	05 50	06 11			06 27	06 41			06 57		07 11		07 27
Potters Bar	d	23p21		23p51					00 51			01 58	05 37		06 21		←		06 51					07 21		
Hatfield	d	23p27		23p57					00 57			02 04	05 43		06 27		06 27		06 57					07 27		
Welwyn Garden City 4	d	23p31		00 01					01 01			02 08	05 47		→		06 31		07 01					07 31		
Welwyn North	d	23p34		00 04					01s04			02s11	05 50				06 34		07 04					07 34		
Knebworth	d	23p38		00 08					01s08			02s15	05 54				06 38		07 08					07 38		
Hertford North	d				00 07					01 07	01 38										←					
Stevenage 4	d	23p42	23p46	00 12	00 20	00s20	00 35	00s50	01 12	01 20	01 47	02 18	05 58	06 08		06 34	06 42	06 46	07 12		07 12	07 16		07 42		07 46
Hitchin 4	d	23p50	23p54	00 20	00 26	00s35	00 43	01s05	01 17	01 26	01 52	02 23	06 06	06 13			06 47	06 51	→		07 17	07 21		07 47		07 51
Letchworth Garden City	d	23p54		00a29	00a36		00 47	01s08		01a36	02a06			06 16			06 51					07 25		07 51		
Baldock	d	23p58					00 50							06 19			06 55					07 28		07 55		
Ashwell & Morden	d	00 03					00 55							06 24			07 00					07 33		08 00		
Royston	d	00 07					01 00	01s17						06 29			07 04					07 37		08 04		
Meldreth	d	00 11					01 04							06 32			07 08					07 41		08 08		
Shepreth	d	00 14					01 07							06 35			07 11					07 44		08 11		
Foxton	d	00 17					01 10							06 38			07 14					07 46		08 14		
Cambridge	a	00 29					01 25	01 34						06 50			07 27			07 31		07 59		08 27		
Arlesey	d		23p59						01s28				06 11					06 56			07 23					07 56
Biggleswade	d		00 04			00s44			01s33			02s38	06 16					07 01			07 28					08 01
Sandy	d		00 08						01s37				06 20					07 05			07 32					08 05
St Neots	d		00 15			00s53			01s45			02s48	06 28					07 12			07 39					08 12
Huntingdon	a		00 26			01s04			01s55			02s59	06 35					07 20			07 47					08 20
	d		00 26										06 35					07 20			07 47					08 20
Peterborough 8	a		00 42			01 24			02 17			03 21	06 56			07 05		07 36			08 05		07 45		07 56	08 38

		FC	FC	FC	GR	FC	GR	FC	FC	FC	GR	FC	FC	FC	FC	FC	FC	GR	FC	FC	FC	GR	FC	FC	FC	FC
		1	1	1	R 1	1	R 1	1	1	1	R 1	1	1	1	1	1	1	R 1	1	1	1	R 1	1	1	1	1
London Kings Cross 15 ⊖	d	07 36	07 45	07 52	08 00	08 06	08 10		08 15	08 22	08 30			08 36	08 45		08 52	09 00	09 06	09 15	09 22	09 30			09 36	09 45
Finsbury Park ⊖	d	07 41		07 57		08 11				08 27				08 41			08 57		09 11		09 27				09 41	
Potters Bar	d	07 51				08 21								08 51					09 21						09 51	
Hatfield	d	07 57				08 27								08 57					09 27						09 57	
Welwyn Garden City 4	d	08 01				08 31								09 01					09 31						10 01	
Welwyn North	d	08 04				08 34								09 04					09 34						10 04	
Knebworth	d	08 08				08 38								09 08					09 38						10 08	
Hertford North	d															←										
Stevenage 4	d	08 12		08 16	08 20	08 42				08 46	08 49		←	09 12		09 12	09 16		09 42		09 46	09 49		←	10 12	
Hitchin 4	d	08 17		08 21		08 47				08 51			08 47	→		09 17	09 21		09 47		09 51			09 47	→	
Letchworth Garden City	d			08 25		→							08 51				09 25		→					09 51		
Baldock	d			08 28									08 55				09 28							09 55		
Ashwell & Morden	d												09 00											10 00		
Royston	d			08 36									09 04				09 36							10 04		
Meldreth	d												09 08											10 08		
Shepreth	d												09 11											10 11		
Foxton	d												09 14											10 14		
Cambridge	a		08 31	08 54					09 02				09 27		09 31		09 54			10 01				10 27		10 31
Arlesey	d	08 23						←		08 56		←				09 23					09 56		←			
Biggleswade	d	08 28						08 28		09 01		09 01				09 28					10 01		10 01			
Sandy	d	→						08 32		→		09 05				09 32					→		10 05			
St Neots	d							08 39				09 12				09 39							10 12			
Huntingdon	a							08 47				09 20				09 47							10 20			
	d							08 47				09 20				09 47							10 20			
Peterborough 8	a				08 51		08 57	09 05			09 20	09 38				10 05		09 45				10 20	10 36			

		FC	FC	GR	FC	GR	FC	FC	GR	FC	GR	FC	FC	FC	FC	FC	GR	FC	GR	FC	FC		GR	FC	FC	FC
		1	1	R 1 A	1	R 1	1	1	R 1 B	1	R 1	1	1	1	1	1	R 1	1	R 1	1	1		R 1	1	1	1
London Kings Cross 15 ⊖	d		09 52	10 00	10 06	10 10	10 15	10 22	10 30	10 36	10 40			10 45		10 52	11 00	11 06	11 10	11 15	11 22		11 30			11 36
Finsbury Park ⊖	d		09 57		10 11			10 27		10 41						10 57		11 11			11 27					11 41
Potters Bar	d				10 21					10 51								11 21								11 51
Hatfield	d				10 27					10 57								11 27								11 57
Welwyn Garden City 4	d				10 31					11 01								11 31								12 01
Welwyn North	d				10 34					11 04								11 34								12 04
Knebworth	d				10 38					11 08								11 38								12 08
Hertford North	d	←													←											
Stevenage 4	d	10 12	10 16		10 42			10 46		11 12			←		11 12	11 16		11 42			11 46		11 50		←	12 12
Hitchin 4	d	10 17	10 21		10 47			10 51		→			10 47		11 17	11 21		11 47			11 51				11 47	→
Letchworth Garden City	d		10 25		→								10 51			11 25		→							11 51	
Baldock	d		10 28										10 55			11 28									11 55	
Ashwell & Morden	d												11 00												12 00	
Royston	d		10 36										11 04			11 36									12 04	
Meldreth	d												11 08												12 08	
Shepreth	d												11 11												12 11	
Foxton	d												11 14												12 14	
Cambridge	a		10 54				11 01					←	11 27	11 31		11 54				12 02					12 27	
Arlesey	d	10 23						10 56				10 56			11 23						11 56			←		
Biggleswade	d	10 28						→				11 01			11 28						12 01			12 01		
Sandy	d	10 32										11 05			11 32						→			12 05		
St Neots	d	10 39										11 12			11 39									12 12		
Huntingdon	a	10 47										11 20			11 47									12 20		
	d	10 47										11 20			11 47									12 20		
Peterborough 8	a	11 04		10 46		10 56			11 16		11 26	11 38			12 05		11 45		11 56				12 21	12 39		

For general notes see front of timetable
For details of catering facilities see
Directory of Train Operators

A The Flying Scotsman
B The Northern Lights

London → Stevenage, Cambridge and Peterborough

Network Diagram - see first page of Table 24

	FC	FC	FC	GR	FC	GR	FC	FC	GR	FC	FC	FC	FC	FC	FC	GR	FC	GR	FC	FC	GR	FC	FC	FC	FC
				R		R			R							R		R			R				
	1	1	1	1	1	1	1	1	1	1	1	1	1	1	1	1	1	1	1	1	1	1	1	1	1
				A																					
London Kings Cross 15 ⊖ d	11 45		11 52	12 00	12 06	12 10	12 15	12 22	12 30			12 36	12 45		12 52	13 00	13 06	13 10	13 15	13 22	13 30			13 36	13 45
Finsbury Park ⊖ d			11 57		12 11			12 27				12 41			12 57		13 11			13 27				13 41	
Potters Bar d					12 21							12 51					13 21							13 51	
Hatfield d					12 27							12 57					13 27							13 57	
Welwyn Garden City 4 d					12 31							13 01					13 31							14 01	
Welwyn North d					12 34							13 04					13 34							14 04	
Knebworth d					12 38							13 08					13 38							14 08	
Hertford North d		←												←											
Stevenage 4 d		12 12	12 16		12 42			12 46			←	13 12 →		13 12	13 16		13 42			13 46	13 49		←	14 12 →	
Hitchin 4 d		12 17	12 21		12 47 →			12 51			12 47			13 17	13 21		13 47 →			13 51			13 47		
Letchworth Garden City d			12 25								12 51				13 25								13 51		
Baldock d			12 28								12 55				13 28								13 55		
Ashwell & Morden d											13 00												14 00		
Royston d			12 36								13 04				13 36								14 04		
Meldreth d											13 08												14 08		
Shepreth d											13 11												14 11		
Foxton d											13 14												14 14		
Cambridge a	12 31		12 54				13 01			←	13 27		13 31		13 54				14 01				14 27		14 31
Arlesey d		12 23						12 56 →		12 56				13 23						13 56		←			
Biggleswade d		12 28								13 01				13 28						14 01 →		14 01			
Sandy d		12 32								13 05				13 32								14 05			
St Neots d		12 39								13 12				13 39								14 12			
Huntingdon a		12 47								13 20				13 47								14 20			
d		12 47								13 20				13 47								14 20			
Peterborough 8 a		13 05		12 46		12 56			13 16	13 36				14 05		13 45		13 56			14 20	14 38			

	FC	FC	GR	FC	FC	FC	GR	FC	FC	FC	FC	FC	FC	GR	FC	FC	FC	GR	FC	FC	FC	FC	FC	FC	GR
			R				R							R				R							R
	1	1	1	1	1	1	1	1	1	1	1	1	1	1	1	1	1	1	1	1	1	1	1	1	1
London Kings Cross 15 ⊖ d		13 52	14 00	14 06	14 15	14 22	14 30			14 36	14 45		14 52	15 00	15 06	15 15	15 22	15 30			15 36	15 45		15 52	16 00
Finsbury Park ⊖ d		13 57		14 11		14 27				14 41			14 57		15 11		15 27				15 41			15 57	
Potters Bar d				14 21						14 51					15 21						15 51				
Hatfield d				14 27						14 57					15 27						15 57				
Welwyn Garden City 4 d				14 31						15 01					15 31						16 01				
Welwyn North d				14 34						15 04					15 34						16 04				
Knebworth d				14 38						15 08					15 38						16 08				
Hertford North d	←											←											←		
Stevenage 4 d	14 12	14 16		14 42		14 46			←	15 12 →		15 12	15 16		15 42		15 46	15 49		←	16 12 →		16 12	16 16	
Hitchin 4 d	14 17	14 21		14 47 →		14 51			14 47			15 17	15 21		15 47 →		15 51			15 47			16 17	16 21	
Letchworth Garden City d		14 25							14 51				15 25							15 51				16 25	
Baldock d		14 28							14 55				15 28							15 55				16 28	
Ashwell & Morden d									15 00											16 00					
Royston d		14 36							15 04				15 36							16 04				16 36	
Meldreth d									15 08											16 08					
Shepreth d									15 11											16 11					
Foxton d									15 14											16 14					
Cambridge a		14 54			15 01			←	15 27		15 31		15 54			16 04				16 27		16 31		16 54	
Arlesey d	14 23					14 56 →		14 56				15 23					15 56		←				16 23		
Biggleswade d	14 28							15 01				15 28					16 01 →		16 01				16 28		
Sandy d	14 32							15 05				15 32							16 05				16 32		
St Neots d	14 39							15 12				15 39							16 12				16 39		
Huntingdon a	14 47							15 20				15 47							16 20				16 47		
d	14 47							15 20				15 47							16 20				16 47		
Peterborough 8 a	15 05		14 46				15 16	15 36				16 04		15 45				16 20	16 36				17 04		16 46

	FC	FC	FC	GR	FC	FC	FC	FC	FC	FC	GR	FC	FC	FC	FC	GR	FC	GR	FC	FC	FC	FC	FC	GR	GR
				R							R					R		R						R	R
	1	1	1	1	1	1	1	1	1	1	1	1	1	1	1	1	1	1	1	1	1	1	1	1	1
																					B				
London Kings Cross 15 ⊖ d	16 06	16 15	16 22	16 30			16 36	16 45		16 52	17 00	17 06	17 10	17 15	17 22	17 30	17 36	17 40			17 45		17 52	18 00	18 03
Finsbury Park ⊖ d	16 11		16 27				16 41			16 57		17 11			17 27		17 41						17 57		
Potters Bar d	16 21						16 51					17 21					17 51								
Hatfield d	16 27						16 57					17 27					17 57								
Welwyn Garden City 4 d	16 31						17 01					17 31					18 01								
Welwyn North d	16 34						17 04					17 34					18 04								
Knebworth d	16 38						17 08					17 38					18 08								
Hertford North d									←													←			
Stevenage 4 d	16 42		16 46			←	17 12 →		17 12	17 16		17 42			17 46	17 50	18 12 →			←		18 12	18 16		
Hitchin 4 d	16 47 →		16 51			16 47			17 17	17 21		17 47 →			17 51					17 47		18 17	18 21		
Letchworth Garden City d						16 51				17 25										17 51			18 25		
Baldock d						16 55				17 28										17 55			18 28		
Ashwell & Morden d						17 00														18 00					
Royston d						17 04				17 36										18 04	18 18		18 36		
Meldreth d						17 08														18 08					
Shepreth d						17 11														18 11					
Foxton d						17 14														18 14					
Cambridge a		17 01			←	17 27		17 31		17 54				18 01						18 27	18 35		18 54		
Arlesey d			16 56 →		16 56				17 23						17 56				←			18 23			
Biggleswade d					17 01				17 28						18 01 →				18 01			18 28			
Sandy d					17 05				17 32										18 05			18 32			
St Neots d					17 12				17 39				17 44						18 12			18 39			
Huntingdon a					17 20				17 47				17 52						18 20			18 47			
d					17 20				17 47				17 52						18 20			18 47			
Peterborough 8 a				17 16	17 36				18 04		17 45		18 08			18 21		18 27	18 36			19 05		18 46	18 52

For general notes see front of timetable
For details of catering facilities see
Directory of Train Operators

A The Highland Chieftain
B To Kings Lynn (Table 17)

Table 25

Saturdays

London → Stevenage, Cambridge and Peterborough

Network Diagram - see first page of Table 24

		FC	FC	FC	FC	FC	GR	FC	GR	FC	FC	FC	FC	GR	FC	FC	FC	GR	FC	FC	FC	FC	FC	FC	GR	FC
							R		R					R				R							R	
		1	1	1	1	1	1	1	1	1	1	1	1	1	1	1	1	1	1	1	1	1	1	1	1	1
											A											A				
London Kings Cross 15 ⊖	d	18 06	18 08	18 15		18 22	18 35	18 36	18 40		18 45		18 52	19 00	19 06	19 15	19 22	19 30			19 36	19 45		19 52	20 00	20 06
Finsbury Park ⊖	d	18 11				18 27		18 41					18 57		19 11		19 27				19 41			19 57		20 11
Potters Bar	d	18 21			←			18 51							19 21						19 51					20 21
Hatfield	d	18 27			18 27			18 57							19 27						19 57					20 27
Welwyn Garden City 4	d	→			18 31			19 01							19 31						20 01					20 31
Welwyn North	d				18 34			19 04							19 34						20 04					20 34
Knebworth	d				18 38			19 08							19 38						20 08					20 38
Hertford North	d											←											←			
Stevenage 4	d		18 27		18 42	18 46		19 12				19 12	19 16	19 19	19 42		19 46			←	20 12		20 12	20 16		20 42
Hitchin 4	d		18 32		18 47	18 51		→				19 17	19 21		19 47		19 51			19 47	→		20 17	20 21		20 47
Letchworth Garden City	d				18 51								19 25		→					19 51				20 25		20 51
Baldock	d				18 55								19 28							19 55				20 28		20 55
Ashwell & Morden	d				19 00															20 00						21 00
Royston	d				19 04						19 18		19 36							20 04		20 18		20 36		21 04
Meldreth	d				19 08															20 08						21 08
Shepreth	d				19 11															20 11						21 11
Foxton	d				19 14															20 14						21 14
Cambridge	a			19 01	19 27					←	19 35		19 54			20 01			←	20 27		20 35		20 54		21 27
Arlesey	d					18 56				18 56		19 23					19 56		19 56				20 23			
Biggleswade	d					→				19 01		19 28					→		20 01				20 28			
Sandy	d									19 05		19 32							20 05				20 32			
St Neots	d		18 46							19 12		19 39							20 12				20 39			
Huntingdon	a		18 53							19 20		19 47							20 20				20 47			
	d		18 53							19 20		19 47							20 20				20 47			
Peterborough 8	a		19 09				19 21		19 26	19 36		20 05		19 50				20 16	20 36				21 05		20 46	

		FC	GR	FC	FC	FC	FC	FC	FC	FC	FC	FC	FC	FC	FC	FC	FC	FC	FC	FC	FC	FC	FC	FC		
			R																							
		1	1	1	1	1	1	1	1	1	1	1	1	1	1	1	1	1	1	1			1			
						A				B	C	A						A								
London Kings Cross 15 ⊖	d	20 22	20 30		20 36	20 45	20 52	21 06	21 22	21 36	21 36	21 52	22 06	22 22	22 36	22 52	23 06	23 12		23 22	23 26	23 41	23 52			
Finsbury Park ⊖	d	20 27			20 41		20 57	21 11	21 27	21 41	21 41	21 57	22 11	22 27	22 41	22 57	23 11	23 17		23 27	23 32	23 46	23 57			
Potters Bar	d				20 51			21 21		21 51	21 51		22 21		22 51		23 21					00 07				
Hatfield	d				20 57			21 27		21 57	21 57		22 27		22 57		23 27					00 15		←		
Welwyn Garden City 4	d				21 01			21 31		22 01	22 01		22 31		23 01		23b37		←			00c30		00c30		
Welwyn North	d				21 04			21 34		22 04	22 04		22 34		23 04		23 42		23 42			→		00 33		
Knebworth	d				21 08			21 38		22 08	22 08		22 38		23 08		→		23 46					00 38		
Hertford North	d																				00 07					
Stevenage 4	d	20 46			21 12		21 16	21 42	21 46	22 12	22 12	22 16	22 42	22 46	23 12	23 20			23 51	23 58	00 22			00 43		
Hitchin 4	d	20 51			21 17		21 21	21 47	21 51	22 17	22 17	22 21	22 47	22 51	23 17	23 30			23 58	00 05	00 31		00s36	00 51		
Letchworth Garden City	d						21 25	21 51				22 25	22 51		23a28			23 50	00 02		00a36			00a59		
Baldock	d						21 28	21 55				22 28	22 55						00 06							
Ashwell & Morden	d							22 00					23 00						00 11							
Royston	d					21 18	21 36	22 04				22 36	23 04					23 59	00 15							
Meldreth	d							22 08					23 08						00 18							
Shepreth	d							22 11					23 11						00 21							
Foxton	d							22 14					23 14						00 25							
Cambridge	a			←		21 35	21 54	22 27				22 51	23 28					00 19	00 41							
Arlesey	d	20 56		20 56	21 23				21 56	22 23	22 23			22 56		23 36				00 10						
Biggleswade	d	→		21 01	21 28				22 01	22 28	22 28			23 01		23 41				00 15			00s45			
Sandy	d			21 05	21 32				22 05	22 32	22 32			23 05		23 44				00 19						
St Neots	d			21 12	21 39				22 12	22 39	22 39			23 12		23 52				00 26			00s54			
Huntingdon	a			21 20	21 47				22 20	22 47	22 47			23 20		23 59				00 34			01s02			
	d			21 20	21 47				22 20	22 47	22 47			23 20		23 59				00 34						
Peterborough 8	a		21 16	21 36	22 05				22 36	23 05	23 06			23 43		00 20				00 54			01 21			

For general notes see front of timetable
For details of catering facilities see Directory of Train Operators

A To Kings Lynn (Table 17)
B From 12 September
C Until 5 September

b Arr. 2330
c Arr. 0021

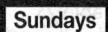

London → Stevenage, Cambridge and Peterborough

Network Diagram - see first page of Table 24

		FC 1	FC 1	FC	FC	FC 1	FC 1	FC	FC 1	FC 1 A	FC A (bus)	FC 1 B	FC 1 A	FC 1 B	FC 1 A	FC 1 B	FC 1 B	FC 1 A	FC 1 C	FC 1 D	FC 1 A	FC 1 B	FC 1 A
London Kings Cross 15 ⊖	d	23p06	23p22	23p26	23p41	23p52	00 04		00 07	00 36		00 36	06 52		07 06			07 22	07 52		08 06		08 22
Finsbury Park ⊖	d	23p11	23p27	23p32	23p46	23p57	00 09		00 12	00 41		00 41	06 57	06 57	07 11		07 27	07 27	07 58	07 58	08 11	08 11	08 27
Potters Bar	d	23p21			00 07					00 51		00 51		07 08	07 21	07 21					08 21	08 21	
Hatfield	d	23p27			00 15			←		00 57		00 57			07 27	07 27					08 27	08 27	
Welwyn Garden City 4	d	23b37			00c30			00c30		01 03		01 03			07 33	07 33					08 31	08 31	
Welwyn North	d	23p42			→			00 33		01s06		01s06			07 36	07 36					08 34	08 34	
Knebworth	d	23p46						00 38		01s10		01s10			07 40	07 40					08 38	08 38	
Hertford North	d			00 07					00 39														
Stevenage 4	d	23p51	23p58	00 22			00 35	00 43	00 48	01 16		01 16	07 17	07 17	07 45	07 45	07 50	07 50	08 16	08 16	08 42	08 42	08 46
Hitchin 4	d	23p58	00 05	00 31		00s36	00 42	00 51	00 56	01 23		01 23	07 26	07 26	07 52	07 52	08 00	08 00	08 30	08 30	08 47	08 47	08 51
Letchworth Garden City	d	00 02		00a36			00s49	00a59	01 03	01a30	01 35		07 34	07 34	07 56	07 56			08 33	08 33	08 54	08 54	
Baldock	d	00 06							01 07				07 37	07 37	07 59	07 59			08 36	08 36	08 57	08 57	
Ashwell & Morden	d	00 11							01 12						08 04	08 04					09 02	09 02	
Royston	d	00 15					00s58		01 16				07 45	07 45	08 09	08 09			08 44	08 44	09 07	09 07	
Meldreth	d	00 18							01 20						08 13	08 13					09 13	09 13	
Shepreth	d	00 21							01 23						08 16	08 16					09 16	09 16	
Foxton	d	00 25							01 26						08 18	08 18					09 18	09 18	
Cambridge	a	00 41					01 14		01 42				08 03	08 04	08 34	08 34			09 03	09 03	09 31	09 31	
Arlesey	d		00 10								01 47	01s30					08 05	08 05					08 56
Biggleswade	d		00 15			00s45					02 07	01s35					08 10	08 10					09 01
Sandy	d		00 19								02 17	01s39					08 14	08 14					09 05
St Neots	d		00 26			00s54					02 37	01s47					08 21	08 21					09 12
Huntingdon	a		00 34			01s02					03 07	01s54					08 29	08 29					09 20
	d		00 34								03 07						08 29	08 29					09 20
Peterborough 8	a		00 54			01 21					03 47	02 16					08 50	08 50					09 39

		FC 1 B	FC 1	GR R 1	FC 1	GR R 1	FC 1	FC 1	GR R 1	FC 1	FC 1	FC 1	GR R 1 E	FC 1	GR R 1	FC 1	FC 1	GR R 1	FC 1	FC 1	FC 1	GR R 1 G	FC 1
London Kings Cross 15 ⊖	d		08 52	09 00	09 06	09 10	09 15	09 22	09 30			09 52	10 00	10 06	10 10	10 15	10 22	10 30			10 52	11 00	11 06
Finsbury Park ⊖	d	08 27	08 57		09 11			09 27				09 57		10 11			10 27				10 57		11 11
Potters Bar	d				09 21									10 21									11 21
Hatfield	d				09 27									10 27									11 27
Welwyn Garden City 4	d				09 31									10 31									11 31
Welwyn North	d				09 34									10 34									11 34
Knebworth	d				09 38									10 38									11 38
Hertford North	d																						
Stevenage 4	d	08 46	09 16	09 20	09 42			09 46			←	10 16		10 42			10 46	10 49		←	11 16		11 42
Hitchin 4	d	08 51	09 21		09 47			09 51			09 47	10 21		10 47			10 51			10 47	11 21		11 47
Letchworth Garden City	d		09 25		→						09 51	10 25		→						10 51	11 25		→
Baldock	d		09 28								09 55	10 28								10 55	11 28		
Ashwell & Morden	d										10 00									11 00			
Royston	d		09 36								10 04	10 36								11 04	11 36		
Meldreth	d										10 08									11 08			
Shepreth	d										10 11									11 11			
Foxton	d										10 14									11 14			
Cambridge	a		09 54				10 00			←	10 27	10 54				11 00				11 27	11 54		
Arlesey	d	08 56						09 56		09 56							10 56		←				
Biggleswade	d	09 01						→		10 01							11 01		11 01				
Sandy	d	09 05								10 05							→		11 05				
St Neots	d	09 12								10 12									11 12				
Huntingdon	a	09 20								10 20									11 20				
	d	09 20								10 20									11 20				
Peterborough 8	a	09 39		09 49		09 57			10 14	10 36			10 45		10 59			11 18	11 36			11 44	

For general notes see front of timetable
For details of catering facilities see
Directory of Train Operators

A Until 6 September

B From 13 September

C Until 6 September. To Kings Lynn (Table 17)

D From 13 September. To Kings Lynn (Table 17)

E **The Flying Scotsman**

G **The Northern Lights**

b Previous night. Arr. 2330

c Arr. 0021

London → Stevenage, Cambridge and Peterborough

Network Diagram - see first page of Table 24

	GR	FC	FC	FC	FC	GR	FC	GR	FC	FC	FC	GR	FC	FC	GR	FC	GR	FC	FC	GR	FC	FC
	R 1	1	1	1	1	R 1	1	R 1	1	1	1	R 1	1	1	R 1	1	R 1	1	1	R 1	1	1
												A						B				
London Kings Cross 15 ⊖ d	11 10	11 15		11 22	11 52	12 00	12 06	12 10	12 15		12 22	12 30		12 52	13 00	13 06	13 10	13 15	13 22	13 30		13 52
Finsbury Park ⊖ d				11 27	11 57		12 11				12 27			12 57		13 11			13 27			13 57
Potters Bar d							12 21			←						13 21						
Hatfield d							12 27			12 27						13 27						
Welwyn Garden City 4 d							→			12 31						13 31						
Welwyn North d										12 34						13 34						
Knebworth d										12 38						13 38						
Hertford North d																						
Stevenage 4 d			←	11 46	12 16			12 29		12 42	12 46			13 16	13 19	13 42			13 46	13 49		14 16
Hitchin 4 d			11 47	11 51	12 21					12 47	12 51			13 21		13 47			13 51			14 21
Letchworth Garden City d			11 51		12 25					12 51				13 25		13 51						14 25
Baldock d			11 55		12 28					12 55				13 28		13 55						14 28
Ashwell & Morden d			12 00							13 00						14 00						
Royston d			12 04		12 36					13 04				13 36		14 04						14 36
Meldreth d			12 08							13 08						14 08						
Shepreth d			12 11							13 11						14 11						
Foxton d			12 14							13 14						14 14						
Cambridge a		12 00	12 27		12 54				13 02	13 27			←	13 54		14 27		14 02				14 54
Arlesey d				11 56							12 56		12 56						13 56		←	
Biggleswade d				12 01							→		13 01						14 01		14 01	
Sandy d				12 05									13 05						→		14 05	
St Neots d				12 12									13 12								14 12	
Huntingdon a				12 20									13 20								14 20	
Huntingdon d				12 20									13 20								14 20	
Peterborough 8 a	11 54			12 36		12 44		12 58				13 14	13 36		13 50		13 56			14 18	14 37	

	GR	FC	GR	FC	FC	GR	FC	FC	FC	GR	FC	GR	FC	FC	GR	FC	FC	FC	GR	FC	GR	FC
	R 1	1	R 1	1	1	R 1	1	1	1	R 1	1	R 1	1	1	R 1	1	1	1	R 1	1	R 1	1
London Kings Cross 15 ⊖ d	14 00	14 06	14 10	14 15	14 22	14 30			14 52	15 00	15 06	15 10	15 15	15 22	15 30			15 52	16 00	16 06	16 10	16 15
Finsbury Park ⊖ d		14 11			14 27				14 57		15 11			15 27				15 57		16 11		
Potters Bar d		14 21									15 21									16 21		
Hatfield d		14 27									15 27									16 27		
Welwyn Garden City 4 d		14 31									15 31									→		
Welwyn North d		14 34									15 34											
Knebworth d		14 38									15 38											
Hertford North d																						
Stevenage 4 d		14 42			14 46			←	15 16	15 19	15 42			15 46			←	16 16			16 29	
Hitchin 4 d		14 47			14 51			14 47	15 21		15 47			15 51			15 47	16 21				
Letchworth Garden City d		→						14 51	15 25		→						15 51	16 25				
Baldock d								14 55	15 28								15 55	16 28				
Ashwell & Morden d								15 00									16 00					
Royston d								15 04	15 36								16 04	16 36				
Meldreth d								15 08									16 08					
Shepreth d								15 11									16 11					
Foxton d								15 14									16 14					
Cambridge a				15 00			←	15 27	15 54				16 00			←	16 27	16 54				17 02
Arlesey d					14 56		14 56							15 56		15 56						
Biggleswade d					→		15 01							→		16 01						
Sandy d							15 05									16 05						
St Neots d							15 12									16 12						
Huntingdon a							15 20									16 20						
Huntingdon d							15 20									16 20						
Peterborough 8 a	14 44		14 54			15 14	15 36			15 49		15 54			16 14	16 38			16 44		16 58	

	FC	FC	GR	GR	FC	FC	GR	FC	GR	FC	FC	GR	FC	FC	FC	GR	FC	GR	FC	FC	GR	GR
	1	1	R 1	R 1	1	1	R 1	1	R 1	1	1	R 1	1	1	1	R 1	1	R 1	1	1	R 1	R 1
London Kings Cross 15 ⊖ d		16 22	16 30	16 40		16 52	17 00	17 06	17 10	17 15	17 22	17 30			17 52	18 00	18 06	18 10	18 15	18 22	18 30	18 40
Finsbury Park ⊖ d		16 27				16 57		17 11			17 27				17 57		18 11			18 27		
Potters Bar d	←							17 21									18 21					
Hatfield d	16 27							17 27									18 27					
Welwyn Garden City 4 d	16 31							17 31									18 31					
Welwyn North d	16 34							17 34									18 34					
Knebworth d	16 38							17 38									18 38					
Hertford North d																						
Stevenage 4 d	16 42	16 46	16 49			17 16		17 42			17 46	17 49		←	18 16		18 42			18 46	18 50	
Hitchin 4 d	16 47	16 51				17 21		17 47			17 51			17 47	18 21		18 47			18 51		
Letchworth Garden City d	16 51					17 25		→						17 51	18 25		→					
Baldock d	16 55					17 28								17 55	18 28							
Ashwell & Morden d	17 00													18 00								
Royston d	17 04					17 36								18 04	18 36							
Meldreth d	17 08													18 08								
Shepreth d	17 11													18 11								
Foxton d	17 14													18 14								
Cambridge a	17 27					17 54				18 00				18 27	18 54				19 00			
Arlesey d		16 56			←						17 56		←							18 56		
Biggleswade d		17 01			17 01						18 01		18 01							19 01		
Sandy d		→			17 05						→		18 05							→		
St Neots d					17 12								18 12									
Huntingdon a					17 20								18 20									
Huntingdon d					17 20								18 20									
Peterborough 8 a			17 18	17 24	17 36		17 46		17 54			18 18	18 38			18 44		18 54			19 19	19 25

For general notes see front of timetable
For details of catering facilities see Directory of Train Operators

A **The Highland Chieftain**
B To Kings Lynn (Table 17)

Table 25 | **Sundays**

London → Stevenage, Cambridge and Peterborough

Network Diagram - see first page of Table 24

	FC	FC	FC	GR	FC	GR	FC		FC	GR	GR	FC	FC	FC	GR		GR	FC	FC	FC	GR	FC	FC		FC
				R		R				R	R				R		R				R				
	1	1	1	1	1	1	1		1	1	1	1	1	1	1		1	1	1	1	1	1	1		1
				🍴		🍴				🍴	🍴				🍴		🍴				🍴				
London Kings Cross 15 ⊖ d			18 52	19 00	19 06	19 10	19 15		19 22	19 30	19 35			19 52	20 00		20 03	20 06	20 15	20 22	20 30				20 52
Finsbury Park ⊖ d			18 57		19 11				19 27					19 57				20 11		20 27					20 57
Potters Bar d					19 21													20 21							
Hatfield d					19 27													20 27							
Welwyn Garden City 4 d					19 31													20 31							
Welwyn North d					19 34													20 34							
Knebworth d					19 38													20 38							
Hertford North d																									
Stevenage 4 d		←	19 16		19 42				19 46	19 49	19 54		←	20 16				20 42		20 46			←		21 16
Hitchin 4 d		18 47	19 21		19 47				19 51				19 47	20 21				20 47		20 51			20 47		21 21
Letchworth Garden City d		18 51	19 25		→								19 51	20 25				→					20 51		21 25
Baldock d		18 55	19 28										19 55	20 28									20 55		21 28
Ashwell & Morden d		19 00											20 00										21 00		
Royston d		19 04	19 36										20 04	20 36									21 04		21 36
Meldreth d		19 08											20 08										21 08		
Shepreth d		19 11											20 11										21 11		
Foxton d		19 14											20 14										21 14		
Cambridge a		19 27	19 54				20 00						20 27	20 54					21 00			←	21 27		21 54
Arlesey d	←								19 56			←								20 56 →		20 56			
Biggleswade d	19 01								20 01 →			20 01										21 01			
Sandy d	19 05											20 05										21 05			
St Neots d	19 12											20 12										21 12			
Huntingdon a	19 20											20 20										21 20			
d	19 20											20 20										21 20			
Peterborough 8 a	19 36			19 44		19 55				20 18	20 24	20 36			20 44		20 50				21 14	21 36			

	GR	FC	FC	FC	GR	FC	FC		FC	GR	FC	GR	FC	FC	FC		FC	FC	FC	FC	FC	FC			
	R				R					R		R													
	1	1	1	1	1	1	1		1	1	1	1	1	1	1		1	1	1	1	1				
																			A						
	🍴				🍴					🍴		🍴													
London Kings Cross 15 ⊖ d	21 00	21 06	21 15	21 22	21 30				21 52	22 00	22 06	22 10	22 15		22 22		22 52	23 06	23 15		23 25	23 41			
Finsbury Park ⊖ d		21 11		21 27					21 57		22 11				22 27		22 57	23 11			23 30	23 47			
Potters Bar d		21 21									22 21							23 21				00 08			
Hatfield d		21 27									22 27							23 27		←		00 16			
Welwyn Garden City 4 d		21 31									22 31							23 31 →		23 31		00 20			
Welwyn North d		21 34									22 34									23 36		00 23			
Knebworth d		21 38									22 38									23 40		00 28			
Hertford North d																									
Stevenage 4 d		21 42		21 46			←		22 16		22 42			←	22 46		23 16			23 43	23 49	00 31			
Hitchin 4 d		21 47		21 51			21 47		22 21		22 47			22 47	22 51		23 26			23 53	00 04	00 37			
Letchworth Garden City d		→					21 51		22 25		→			22 51			23 30		23 52	23 57		00a52			
Baldock d							21 55		22 28					22 55			23 33			23 59					
Ashwell & Morden d							22 00							23 00						00 05					
Royston d							22 04		22 36					23 04			23 41		00 01	00 10					
Meldreth d							22 08							23 08						00 13					
Shepreth d							22 11							23 11						00 16					
Foxton d							22 14							23 14						00 18					
Cambridge a			22 00			←	22 27		22 54				23 10	23 29			00 01		00 19	00 35					
Arlesey d				21 56 →		21 56									22 56						00 10				
Biggleswade d						22 01									23 01						00 15				
Sandy d						22 05									23 05						00 18				
St Neots d						22 12									23 12						00 26				
Huntingdon a						22 20									23 27						00 33				
d						22 20									23 27						00 33				
Peterborough 8 a	21 45				22 14	22 36				22 44		22s59			23 49						00 58				

For general notes see front of timetable
For details of catering facilities see
Directory of Train Operators

A To Ely (Table 17)

First Capital Connect will run a Saturday service on Bank Holiday Mondays

Peterborough, Cambridge and Stevenage → London

Network Diagram - see first page of Table 24

Miles	Miles			FC MX	FC MO	FC MX	FC MO	FC MX	FC	FC	FC	FC	FC	FC	FC	FC	FC		FC	FC	FC	FC	GR	FC	FC	FC
					1		1	1	1		1			1		1	1		1	1	1	1	R 1	1		1
							A	A											B							
0	—	**Peterborough** 8	d		22p51				03 30		04 12					05 12					05 40	06 00	06 10			
17½	—	Huntingdon	a		23p05				03 44		04 26					05 26					05 54	06 14				
—	—		d		23p05				03 44		04 26					05 26					05 55	06 15				
24¾	—	St Neots	d		23p12				03 51		04 34					05 34					06 03	06 23				
32¼	—	Sandy	d		23p20						04 41					05 41						06 31				
35¼	—	Biggleswade	d		23p23				04 01		04 45					05 45						06 35				
39¼	—	Arlesey	d		23p28						04 50					05 50						06 40				
—	0	**Cambridge**	d				23p15	23p19											05 45					05 48		06 15
—	7	Foxton	d					23p28																05 57		
—	8	Shepreth	d					23p31																05 59		
—	10	Meldreth	d					23p34																06 02		
—	13	Royston	d				23p29	23p38						05 16			05 46		05 59					06 06		06 29
—	17	Ashwell & Morden	d					23p42						05 21			05 51							06 11		
—	21¼	Baldock	d					23p47						05 26			05 56							06 16		
—	23¼	Letchworth Garden City	d	23p18			23p39	23p50		04 50			05 20	05 29	05 48		05 59		06 09					06 19	06 27	06 39
44½	26	Hitchin 4	d	23p22	23p34	←	23p43	23p54	04 13	04 54	04 58	←	05 24	05 33	05 52	05 58	06 03				06 19	06 46		06 24	06 31	06 43
48¾	30¼	**Stevenage** 4	d	23p27	23p39	23p27	23p48	23p59	04 18	04 59	05 04	04 59	05 29	05 39	05 57	06 03	06 09				06 25	→		06 30	06 36	06 48
—	—	Hertford North	a	→		23p40			04 28	→		05 12	05 42		06 10										06 49	
51½	33	Knebworth	d				23p51	00 02			05 07			05 43			06 13			←				06 33		
54¼	36	Welwyn North	d				23p55	00 06			05 11			05 47			06 17			06 17				06 37		
56	37¾	Welwyn Garden City 4	d				23p58	00 09			05 15			05 50			→			06 20				06 40		
58½	40¼	Hatfield	d				00 01	00 12			05 19			05 53						06 23				06 44		
63½	45¼	Potters Bar	d				00 07	00 18			05 25			05 59						06 29				06 49		
73¾	55½	Finsbury Park ⊖	d		00 05	00 15	00 20	00 29	04s50		05 41	05 47	06a16	06 08	06a44	06 21				06 38	06 44			06 58	07a15	07 06
76¼	58	**London Kings Cross** 15 ⊖	a		00 14	00 26	00 32	00 42	05 04		05 55	05 58		06 18		06 30			06 38	06 48	06 52		07 00	07 07		07 15

		FC	FC	FC	FC	GR	FC	FC	FC		FC	FC	FC	GR	FC	FC	FC	FC	FC	FC	FC	FC	GR	FC		FC
		1		1	1	R 1	1	1	1			1	1	R 1	1		1	1	1	1	1	1	R 1			1
									A											B						
						☕								☕									☕ 🍴			
Peterborough 8	d			06 21	06 32	06 40							06 54	07 00							07 06	07 14	07 20			
Huntingdon	a			06 35	06 46								07 08								07 20	07 28				
	d			06 36	06 47								07 09				←				07 23	07 32				
St Neots	d			06 44	06 55								07 17				07 17				07 32	07 40				
Sandy	d				07 03							←	→								07 40	→				
Biggleswade	d			06 53	07 07							07 07									07 44					
Arlesey	d				→							07 12									→					
Cambridge	d							06 27	06 45										06 57	07 15						
Foxton	d							06 37											07 07							
Shepreth	d							06 40											07 10							
Meldreth	d							06 43											07 13							
Royston	d						06 44	06 50	06 59									07 14	07 21	07 29						
Ashwell & Morden	d						06 48	06 55										07 18								
Baldock	d						06 53	07 00										07 23								
Letchworth Garden City	d	←	06 48				06 57	07 04	07 09							07 20		07 27	07 32							
Hitchin 4	d	06 46	06 52				07 01	07 08				07 18				07 24		07 31	07 36							
Stevenage 4	d	06 52	06 58				07 07	07 14				07 24				07 30	07 36	07 37	07 42							
Hertford North	a																									←
Knebworth	d	06 55					07 11	07 18							←				07 46							07 46
Welwyn North	d	06 59						07 22							07 22				→							07 50
Welwyn Garden City 4	d	07 03	07 08					→			←				07 26	07 42								←		07 54
Hatfield	d		07 12								07 12				07 30	07 46								07 46		
Potters Bar	d		→								07 18					→								07 52		
Finsbury Park ⊖	d	07 17					07 27				07 34	07 41			07 46			07 56						08 09		08 09
London Kings Cross 15 ⊖	a	07 25		07 28		07 30	07 35		07 38		07 42	07 50		07 53	07 56		07 59	08 04		08 06			08 13	08 17		08 18

		FC	FC	FC	FC	FC	GR	FC	FC	FC	GR	FC	FC	FC	GR		FC	FC	FC	FC	FC	FC	FC	GR	FC	FC
		1	1	1	1	1	R 1	1	1	1	R 1	1	1	1	R 1		1	1	1		1		1	R 1	1	1
										A									A							
							☕ 🍴				☕ 🍴				✕ 🍴									☕ 🍴		
Peterborough 8	d				07 26	07 33	07 40				07 50			07 58	08 04								08 16	08 33		
Huntingdon	a				07 40	07 47								08 12									08 31			
	d		←		07 40	07 50								08 12				←					08 31			
St Neots	d		07 40		07 48	07 58								08 20				08 20					08 38			
Sandy	d			←		08 06							←	→									08 46		←	
Biggleswade	d			07 44	07 56	08 10							08 10										08 49		08 49	
Arlesey	d			07 49		→							08 15										→		08 54	
Cambridge	d								07 26	07 45							07 54		08 15							08 25
Foxton	d								07 36								08 04									08 35
Shepreth	d								07 39								08 06									08 37
Meldreth	d								07 43								08 09									08 40
Royston	d	07 34						07 43	07 51	07 59							08 14		08 29		08 34					08 46
Ashwell & Morden	d	07 38						07 48									08 18				08 38					08 51
Baldock	d	07 43						07 53									08 23				08 43					08 56
Letchworth Garden City	d	07 47						07 57	08 02								08 27		08 39		08 47					09 00
Hitchin 4	d	07 51		07 55				08 01	08 06				08 21				08 31			08 39	08 51				09 00	09 04
Stevenage 4	d		07 59	08 01				08 07	08 12				08 27					08 39		08 45	08 57				09 05	09 10
Hertford North	a											←														
Knebworth	d							08 11	08 16			08 16								08 49		←				09 13
Welwyn North	d	07 59							→			08 20								08 53		08 53				09 17
Welwyn Garden City 4	d											08 24								→		08 58				→
Hatfield	d																					09 02				
Potters Bar	d																									
Finsbury Park ⊖	d			08 19								08 39	08 46								09 15	09 19			09 23	
London Kings Cross 15 ⊖	a	08 19	08 22	08 29	08 31		08 33	08 36		08 39	08 43	08 49	08 56		08 59		09 00	09 03	09 12		09 23	09 27		09 26	09 32	

For general notes see front of timetable
For details of catering facilities see Directory of Train Operators

A From Kings Lynn (Table 17)
B From Ely (Table 17)

First Capital Connect will run a Saturday service on Bank Holiday Mondays

Peterborough, Cambridge and Stevenage → London

Network Diagram - see first page of Table 24

	FC	FC	GR	FC	FC	FC		FC	FC	FC	FC	GR	FC	FC	FC	FC	GR	FC	FC	FC	GR		FC	FC	FC
			R									R					R				R				
	1	1	1	1	1	1		1	1	1	1	1		1	1	1	1	1	1	1	1		1	1	1
	A		B																A						
			☕ 🛒									☕ 🛒					☕ 🛒				☕ 🛒				
Peterborough (8) d		08 45	08 51							09 15	09 23	09 26				09 44	09 48				10 05				
Huntingdon a		08 59								09 29	09 38					09 58									
Huntingdon d		09 00								09 30	09 41					09 59									
St Neots d		09 07								09 37	09 49					10 06		←							
Sandy d		09 15			←						09 57					10 14		09 57					←		
Biggleswade d		09 18			09 18					09 45	→					10 17		10 01					10 17		
Arlesey d		→			09 23											→		10 06					10 22		
Cambridge d	08 45					08 54		09 20						09 26					09 50					09 55	10 20
Foxton d						09 04																		10 05	
Shepreth d						09 06																		10 07	
Meldreth d						09 09																		10 10	
Royston d	08 59					09 15								09 43					10 04					10 15	
Ashwell & Morden d						09 20																		10 20	
Baldock d						09 25								09 51										10 25	
Letchworth Garden City d	09 09					09 29			←				09 50	09 54	09 59				10 14					10 29	
Hitchin (4) d					09 29	09 33			09 33				09 54	09 58	10 03			10 12					10 28	10 33	
Stevenage (4) d					09 34	→			09 39	09 56		09 57	09 59	10 03	10 09			10 18					10 33	→	
Hertford North a													10 12												
Knebworth d				←					09 43						10 13										
Welwyn North d				09 17					09 47						10 17					←					
Welwyn Garden City (4) d				09 20					09 50						10 20					10 20					
Hatfield d				09 24					09 53						→					10 23					
Potters Bar d				09 30					09 59											10 29					
Finsbury Park ⊖ d				09 41	09 52				10 08				10a47	10 21						10 41			10 51		
London Kings Cross (15) ⊖ a	09 42		09 45	09 50	10 02			10 13	10 19	10 22		10 25		10 30			10 40	10 45	10 46	10 49	10 59		11 02		11 10

	FC	GR	FC	FC	FC	GR	FC	FC	FC	GR	FC	FC	GR		FC	FC	FC	GR	FC	GR	FC	FC	FC	FC	GR
		R				R				R			R					R		R					R
	1	1	1		1	1	1	1	1	1	1	1	1		1	1	1	1	1	1		1	1	1	1
		☕ 🛒				☕ 🛒				☕ 🛒			☕					✕ 🛒		☕ 🛒					☕ 🛒
Peterborough (8) d	10 15	10 18				10 37			10 46	10 57			11 06				11 14	11 17		11 31				11 44	11 49
Huntingdon a	10 29								11 00								11 28							11 58	
Huntingdon d	10 33								11 00								11 33							12 00	
St Neots d	10 41							←	11 07								11 41							12 07	
Sandy d	10 48							10 48	11 15		←						11 48							12 15	
Biggleswade d	→							10 52	11 18		11 18						→							12 18	
Arlesey d								10 57	→															→	
Cambridge d					10 26		10 50					10 55			11 15							11 26	11 45		
Foxton d												11 05													
Shepreth d												11 07													
Meldreth d												11 10													
Royston d					10 43							11 15										11 43			
Ashwell & Morden d												11 20													
Baldock d					10 51							11 25										11 51			
Letchworth Garden City d			←	10 50	10 54							11 29				←					11 50	11 54			
Hitchin (4) d			10 33	10 54	10 58			11 03			11 28	11 33				11 33					11 54	11 58			
Stevenage (4) d			10 39	10 59	11 03	11 06		11 09			11 33	→				11 39		11 47			11 59	12 03			
Hertford North a				11 12																	12 12				
Knebworth d			10 43					11 13								11 43									
Welwyn North d			10 47					11 17								11 47			←						
Welwyn Garden City (4) d			10 50					11 20								11 50			11 50						
Hatfield d			10 53					11 23								→			11 53						
Potters Bar d			10 59					11 29											11 59						
Finsbury Park ⊖ d			11 08	11a46	11 21			11 41			11 51								12 11		12a46	12 21			
London Kings Cross (15) ⊖ a		11 14	11 19		11 30	11 34	11 39	11 49		11 51	12 00		12 03		12 04			12 17	12 19	12 25		12 30	12 33		12 42

	FC	FC	FC	FC	GR		FC	FC	FC	FC	GR	FC	FC	GR	FC	FC	FC	GR	FC	GR		FC	FC	FC	FC
					R						R			R				R		R					
	1	1	1	1	1		1		1	1	1	1	1	1	1	1	1	1	1	1		1		1	1
					☕ 🛒						☕ 🛒			☕ 🛒				☕ 🛒		☕ 🛒					
Peterborough (8) d					12 14					12 18	12 29		12 43	12 47				13 06		13 12					
Huntingdon a										12 33			12 57												
Huntingdon d										12 33			13 00												
St Neots d	←									12 41			13 07			←									
Sandy d	11 48	←								12 48			13 15			13 15									
Biggleswade d	11 52	12 18								12 52			→			13 18									
Arlesey d	11 57									12 57															
Cambridge d			11 55	12 15					12 28			12 45					12 55		13 15					13 28	13 45
Foxton d			12 05														13 05								
Shepreth d			12 07														13 07								
Meldreth d			12 10														13 10								
Royston d			12 15						12 43								13 15							13 43	
Ashwell & Morden d			12 20														13 20								
Baldock d			12 25						12 51								13 25							13 51	
Letchworth Garden City d			12 29					12 50	12 54								13 29					←	13 50	13 54	
Hitchin (4) d	12 03	12 28	12 33					12 54	12 58	13 03					←	13 28	13 33					13 33	13 54	13 58	
Stevenage (4) d	12 09	12 33	12 39		12 43			12 59	13 03	13 09				13 16	13 09	13 33	→					13 39	13 59	14 03	
Hertford North a								13 12		→													14 12		
Knebworth d	12 13		12 43												13 13							13 43			
Welwyn North d	12 17		12 47				←								13 17							13 47			
Welwyn Garden City (4) d	12 20		12 50				12 50								13 20							13 50			
Hatfield d	12 23		→				12 53								13 23							13 53			
Potters Bar d	12 29						12 59								13 29							13 59			
Finsbury Park ⊖ d	12 41	12 51					13 08	13a46	13 21						13 41	13 51						14 08	14a46	14 21	
London Kings Cross (15) ⊖ a	12 49	13 00		13 03	13 10		13 19		13 30		13 22	13 33		13 43	13 49	14 00		14 02	14 05	14 10		14 19		14 30	14 33

For general notes see front of timetable
For details of catering facilities see
Directory of Train Operators

A From Kings Lynn (Table 17)
B The Hull Executive

First Capital Connect will run a Saturday service on Bank Holiday Mondays

Peterborough, Cambridge and Stevenage → London

Network Diagram - see first page of Table 24

		FC	FC	GR	FC	GR	FC	FC	GR	FC	FC	FC	FC		FC	FC	GR	FC	GR	FC	GR	FC	FC	FC	FC	FC
		1	1	R 1	1	R 1	1	1	R 1	1	1		1		1	1	R 1	1	R 1	1	R 1	1	1	1	1	1
Peterborough 8	d	13 18	13 43	13 47		14 03			14 10							14 18	14 43	14 45	14 50		15 06					15 18
Huntingdon	a	13 32	13 57													14 32		15 01								15 32
	d	13 33	13 59													14 33		15 01								15 33
St Neots	d	13 41	14 06				←									14 41		15 08								15 41
Sandy	d	13 48	14 14				14 14									14 48		15 16				←				15 48
Biggleswade	d	13 52	→				14 17									14 52		15 19				15 19				→
Arlesey	d	13 57					14 22									14 57		→				15 24				
Cambridge	d							13 55		14 15			14 28		14 45								14 55	15 15		
Foxton	d							14 05															15 05			
Shepreth	d							14 07															15 07			
Meldreth	d							14 10															15 10			
Royston	d							14 15					14 43										15 15			
Ashwell & Morden	d							14 20															15 20			
Baldock	d							14 25					14 51										15 25			
Letchworth Garden City	d							14 29			←	14 50	14 54										15 29		←	
Hitchin 4	d	14 03					14 28	14 33			14 33	14 54	14 58			15 03						15 30	15 33		15 33	
Stevenage 4	d	14 09		14 17			14 33	→			14 39	14 59	15 03			15 09	15 12					15 35	→		15 39	
Hertford North	a											15 12														
Knebworth	d	14 13									14 43					15 13									15 43	
Welwyn North	d	14 17			←						14 47					15 17				←					15 47	
Welwyn Garden City 4	d	14 20			14 20						14 50					15 20				15 20					15 50	
Hatfield	d	→			14 23						14 53					→				15 23					15 53	
Potters Bar	d				14 29						14 59									15 29					15 59	
Finsbury Park	⊖ d				14 41		14 51				15 11	15a46	15 21							15 41		15 53			16 11	
London Kings Cross 15	⊖ a			14 44	14 49	14 57	15 00		15 05	15 07	15 20		15 30		15 33		15 40		15 44	15 50	15 58	16 02		16 08	16 21	

		GR	FC	FC	FC		FC	FC	GR	FC	GR	FC	FC	FC	FC	FC	FC	GR	FC	FC		FC	FC	GR	GR	FC
		R 1	1		1		1	1	R 1	1	R 1	1		1	1	1	1	R 1	1	1		1	1	R 1	R 1	1
											A													B		
Peterborough 8	d	15 23	15 44						15 47		16 02	16 14						16 19					16 45	16 48	16 52	
Huntingdon	a		15 58									16 28											16 59			
	d		15 59									16 33											16 59			
St Neots	d		16 06					←				16 41		←									17 06			←
Sandy	d		16 14					15 48				16 48		16 14									17 14			16 48
Biggleswade	d		→					15 52				→		16 17									17 17			16 52
Arlesey	d							15 57						16 22									→			16 57
Cambridge	d				15 26		15 45								15 55	16 15				16 24		16 45				
Foxton	d														16 05					16 33						
Shepreth	d														16 07					16 35						
Meldreth	d														16 10					16 38						
Royston	d				15 43										16 15					16 43						
Ashwell & Morden	d														16 20					16 47						
Baldock	d				15 51										16 25					16 52						
Letchworth Garden City	d			15 50	15 54								16 20		16 29		←			16 55						
Hitchin 4	d			15 54	15 58			16 03					16 24	16 28	16 33		16 33			17 00						17 03
Stevenage 4	d	15 52		15 59	16 03			16 09	16 17				16 29	16 33	→		16 39	16 48		17 05						17 09
Hertford North	a			16 12									16 42													
Knebworth	d							16 13									16 43									17 13
Welwyn North	d							16 17		←							16 47		←							17 17
Welwyn Garden City 4	d							16 20		16 20							16 51		16 51							17 21
Hatfield	d							→		16 23							→		16 55							17 25
Potters Bar	d									16 29									17 01							17 31
Finsbury Park	⊖ d			16a47	16 21					16 38			17a11	16 51					17 11	17 23						17 41
London Kings Cross 15	⊖ a	16 22			16 30		16 33		16 46	16 49	16 57			17 01		17 06		17 15	17 21	17 33		17 38		17 41	17 46	17 50

		FC	FC	GR	FC	FC	FC	FC	GR	FC	FC	FC		GR	FC	FC	FC	FC	FC	FC	GR	FC	FC	FC	FC	GR
		1	1	R 1	1	1	1	1	R 1	1	1	1		R 1	1	1	1	1	1	1	R 1	1	1	1	1	R 1
																			C							
Peterborough 8	d			17 04				17 20	17 28			17 56		18 02						18 20	18 26				18 44	19 07
Huntingdon	a							17 34				18 11								18 34					18 58	
	d							17 41			18 04	18 12								18 41					18 59	
St Neots	d							17 48			18 11	18 19								18 48					19 06	
Sandy	d	←						17 56				18 27						←		18 56					19 14	
Biggleswade	d	17 17						18 00				18 30						18 30		19 00					19 17	
Arlesey	d	17 22						18 05				→						18 35		19 05					→	
Cambridge	d		16 55		17 15		17 26			17 45						17 55	18 15		18 26				18 45			
Foxton	d		17 05				17 35									18 05			18 35							
Shepreth	d		17 07				17 37									18 07			18 37							
Meldreth	d		17 10				17 40									18 10			18 40							
Royston	d		17 15				17 46									18 15			18 46							
Ashwell & Morden	d		17 20				17 51									18 20			18 51							
Baldock	d		17 25				17 56									18 25			18 56							
Letchworth Garden City	d		17 29			←	17 59									18 29			18 59							
Hitchin 4	d	17 28	17 33			17 33	18 03	18 11			18 29				←	18 33		18 42	19 03	19 11				←		
Stevenage 4	d	17 33	→	17 34		17 39	18 09	18 17			18 35				18 17	18 39		18 48	19 09	19 17				19 17		
Hertford North	a							→												→						
Knebworth	d					17 43									18 21	18 43								19 21		
Welwyn North	d					17 47									18 25	18 47						←		19 25		
Welwyn Garden City 4	d					17 51									18 28	18 51						18 51		19 28		
Hatfield	d					17 55									18 32	→						18 55		19 32		
Potters Bar	d					18 01									18 38							19 01		19 38		
Finsbury Park	⊖ d	17 51				18 11	18 27				18 54				18 47			19 06	19 27			19 11		19 47		
London Kings Cross 15	⊖ a	18 00		18 04	18 08	18 20	18 35		18 24	18 38	19 01			18 54	18 58		19 05	19 15	19 34		19 19	19 21	19 38	19 58		19 59

For general notes see front of timetable
For details of catering facilities see Directory of Train Operators

A The Northern Lights
B The Flying Scotsman
C From Kings Lynn (Table 17)

First Capital Connect will run a Saturday service on Bank Holiday Mondays

Peterborough, Cambridge and Stevenage → London

Network Diagram - see first page of Table 24

		FC	FC	FC		FC	FC	GR	FC	GR	FC	FC	FC	FC	GR	FC	FC	FC	FC		FC	FC	GR	GR	FC	GR
								R		R					R								R	R		R
		1	1	1		1	1	1	1	1	1	1	1	1	1	1		1	1		1	1	1	1	1	1
												A									A					
								☕ 🛒		☕ 🛒					✕ 🛒								☕ 🛒	☕		✕ 🛒
Peterborough 8	d						19 15	19 20		19 26	19 41				19 46							20 16	20 28	20 38		20 46
Huntingdon	a						19 29				19 56											20 31				
	d						19 33				19 59											20 33				
St Neots	d						19 41				20 06			←				←				20 41				
Sandy	d	←					19 48				20 14			19 48				20 14				20 48				
Biggleswade	d	19 17					→				→			19 52				20 17				20 52				
Arlesey	d	19 22												19 57				20 22				20 57				
Cambridge	d		18 55	19 15								19 24	19 45						19 55		20 28				20 45	
Foxton	d		19 05									19 33							20 05							
Shepreth	d		19 07									19 35							20 07							
Meldreth	d		19 10									19 38							20 10							
Royston	d		19 15									19 43							20 15		20 43					
Ashwell & Morden	d		19 20									19 47							20 20							
Baldock	d		19 25									19 52							20 25		20 51					
Letchworth Garden City	d		19 29			←						19 55					20 20		20 29		20 54					
Hitchin 4	d	19 28	19 33			19 33						20 00		20 03			20 24	20 28	20 33		20 58	21 03				
Stevenage 4	d	19 33	→			19 39		19 50				20 05		20 09	20 16		20 29	20 33	20 39		21 03	21 09				21 17
Hertford North	a																20 42					→				
Knebworth	d					19 43								20 13					20 43							
Welwyn North	d					19 47			←					20 17		←			20 47							
Welwyn Garden City 4	d					19 50			19 50					20 20		20 20			20 50							
Hatfield	d					→			19 53					→		20 23			20 53							
Potters Bar	d								19 59							20 29			20 59							
Finsbury Park ⊖	d	19 52							20 11			20 23				20 38	21a16	20 51	21 11		21 21					
London Kings Cross 15 ⊖	a	20 03		20 10				20 18	20 19	20 21		20 33	20 40		20 44	20 49		21 00	21 19		21 30		21 20	21 33	21 37	21 44

		FC	FC	FC	FC	GR	FC	FC	GR	FC	FC		FC	FC	FC	FC	FC	GR	FC	FC	FC	GR	FC	FC		
						R			R									R				R				
		1		1	1	1	1	1	1		1		1	1		1		1	1	1		1		1		
											A								A					A		
						☕			☕ 🛒									☕				☕ 🛒				
Peterborough 8	d				20 55	21 10			21 21					21 28				22 15		22 30		22 59				
Huntingdon	a				21 09									21 42						22 44						
	d				21 12									21 42						22 44						
St Neots	d				21 19									21 49						22 51						
Sandy	d				21 27		←							21 57						22 59						
Biggleswade	d				21 30		21 30							22 00						23 02						
Arlesey	d				→		21 35							22 05						23 07						
Cambridge	d			20 55							21 28		21 45			21 55			22 28					23 19		
Foxton	d			21 05												22 05								23 28		
Shepreth	d			21 07												22 07								23 31		
Meldreth	d			21 10												22 10								23 34		
Royston	d			21 15							21 43					22 15			22 43					23 38		
Ashwell & Morden	d			21 20												22 20								23 42		
Baldock	d			21 25							21 51					22 25			22 51					23 47		
Letchworth Garden City	d		21 20	21 29							21 54				22 20	22 29			22 54		23 18			23 50		
Hitchin 4	d	←	21 24	21 33			21 41				21 58			22 11	22 24	22 33	←		22 58	23 16	23 22			23 54		
Stevenage 4	d	21 09	21 29	21 39			21 47		21 52	←	22 03			22 17	22 29	22 39	22 29	22s51	23 03	23 22	23 27	23s35	←	23 59		
Hertford North	a		21 42							21 42					→		22 42				23 40		23 40			
Knebworth	d	21 13	→	21 43										22 20		22 43				23 25	→			00 02		
Welwyn North	d	21 17		21 47				←						22 24		22 47				23 29				00 06		
Welwyn Garden City 4	d	21 20		21 50				21 50						22 27		22 50				23 32				00 09		
Hatfield	d	21 23		→				21 53						22 30		22 53				23 35				00 12		
Potters Bar	d	21 29						21 59						22 36		22 59				23 41				00 18		
Finsbury Park ⊖	d	21 38					22 05	22 11		22 17	22 21			22 44		23 11	23 17		23 21	23s51			00 15	00 29		
London Kings Cross 15 ⊖	a	21 48				22 04	22 14	22 19	22 20	22 26	22 30		22 35	22 56		23 21	23 25	23 32	23 35	00 04		00 15	00 26	00 42		

For general notes see front of timetable
For details of catering facilities see
Directory of Train Operators

A From Kings Lynn (Table 17)

Peterborough, Cambridge and Stevenage → London

Network Diagram - see first page of Table 24

		FC	FC 1 A	FC 1	FC	FC 1	FC	FC	FC 1	FC	FC 1 B		FC 1	FC 1	FC 1	FC 1	FC 1	GR R 1 ☕ 🛒	FC 1	FC 1	FC 1	GR R 1 ☕ 🛒		FC 1	FC 1	FC 1
Peterborough 8	d			03 30		04 12							05 14	05 45			06 18	06 37			06 45	07 09				
Huntingdon	a			03 44		04 26							05 28	05 59			06 32				06 59					
	d			03 44		04 26							05 28	05 59			06 33				06 59					
St Neots	d			03 51		04 34							05 36	06 06			06 41				07 06					
Sandy	d					04 41							05 43	06 14			06 48				07 14					
Biggleswade	d			04 01		04 45							05 47	06 17			06 52				07 17					
Arlesey	d					04 50							05 52	06 22			06 57				07 22					
Cambridge	d		23p19								05 45				05 55	06 28			06 45					06 55	07 28	07 45
Foxton	d		23p28												06 05									07 05		
Shepreth	d		23p31												06 07									07 07		
Meldreth	d		23p34												06 10									07 10		
Royston	d		23p38						05 16		05 59				06 15	06 43								07 15	07 43	
Ashwell & Morden	d		23p42						05 21						06 20									07 20		
Baldock	d		23p47						05 26						06 25	06 51								07 25	07 51	
Letchworth Garden City	d	23p18	23p50		04 50			05 20	05 29		06 09				06 29	06 54								07 29	07 54	
Hitchin 4	d	23p22	23p54	04 13	04 54	04 58	←	05 24	05 33	←			06 03	06 28	06 33	06 58	07 03			←	07 28			07 33	07 58	
Stevenage 4	d	23p27	23p59	04 18	04 59 →	05 04	04 59	05 29 →	05 39	05 29			06 09	06 33	06 39	07 03	07 09 →			07 09	07 33			07 39	08 03	
Hertford North	a	23p40		04 28			05 12			05 42																
Knebworth	d		00 02			05 07			05 43				06 13		06 43					07 13				07 43		
Welwyn North	d		00 06			05 11			05 47				06 17		06 47					07 17				07 47		
Welwyn Garden City 4	d		00 09			05 15			05 50				06 20		06 50					07 20				07 50		
Hatfield	d		00 12			05 19			05 53				06 23		06 53					07 23				07 53		
Potters Bar	d		00 18			05 25			05 59				06 29		06 59					07 29				07 59		
Finsbury Park ⊖	d	00 15	00 29	04s50		05 41	05 47		06 08	06 17			06 41	06 51	07 08	07 21				07 41	07 51			08 08	08 21	
London Kings Cross 15 ⊖	a	00 26	00 42	05 04		05 55	05 58		06 21	06 25	06 38		06 49	07 02	07 19	07 32		07 29	07 34	07 49	07 59	08 04		08 19	08 32	08 33

		FC 1	FC 1	GR R 1 ☕	FC 1	FC 1	FC 1	GR R 1 ☕ 🛒	FC 1	FC 1		FC 1	FC 1	GR R 1 ☕ 🛒	GR R 1 ☕ 🛒	FC 1	FC 1	FC 1	GR R 1 ☕ 🛒	GR R 1 ☕ 🛒	FC 1		FC 1	FC 1	FC 1	GR R 1 ☕ 🛒
Peterborough 8	d	07 18	07 44	07 48				08 09					08 18	08 26	08 32			08 45	08 57	09 07					09 12	09 16
Huntingdon	a	07 32	07 58										08 32					08 59							09 26	
	d	07 33	07 59										08 33					08 59							09 26	
St Neots	d	07 41	08 06										08 41					09 06							→	
Sandy	d	07 48	08 14			←							08 48					09 14			←					
Biggleswade	d	07 52	08 17			08 17							08 52					09 17			09 17					
Arlesey	d	07 57	→			08 22							08 57					→			09 22					
Cambridge	d						07 55		08 15			08 28				08 45							08 55	09 15		
Foxton	d						08 05																09 05			
Shepreth	d						08 07																09 07			
Meldreth	d						08 10																09 10			
Royston	d						08 15					08 43											09 15			
Ashwell & Morden	d						08 20																09 20			
Baldock	d						08 25					08 51											09 25			
Letchworth Garden City	d						08 29			←		08 54											09 29			
Hitchin 4	d	08 03			←	08 28	08 33			08 33		08 58	09 03				←				09 28		09 33			
Stevenage 4	d	08 09			08 09	08 33	→			08 39		09 03	09 09				09 09				09 33		09 39			09 45
Hertford North	a	→											→													
Knebworth	d				08 13					08 43							09 13						09 43			
Welwyn North	d				08 17					08 47							09 17						09 47			
Welwyn Garden City 4	d				08 20					08 50							09 20						09 50			
Hatfield	d				08 23					08 53							09 23						→			
Potters Bar	d				08 29					08 59							09 29									
Finsbury Park ⊖	d				08 41	08 51				09 08		09 21					09 41				09 51					
London Kings Cross 15 ⊖	a			08 40	08 49	09 02		09 03	09 05	09 20		09 32		09 18	09 26	09 33	09 49		09 51	10 00	10 02			10 05		10 13

		FC 1	FC 1	GR R 1 ☕ 🛒	GR R 1 ☕ 🛒	FC 1	FC 1	FC 1	FC 1		FC 1	GR R 1 ☕ 🛒	GR R 1 ☕ 🛒	FC 1	FC 1	FC 1	FC 1	FC 1	GR R 1 ☕ 🛒	FC 1		GR R 1 ☕ 🛒	FC 1	FC 1	FC 1	GR R 1 ☕ 🛒
Peterborough 8	d			09 26	09 33						09 45	09 52	10 06			10 14		10 18	10 32						10 45	10 54
Huntingdon	a	←									09 59					10 28		10 33							10 59	
	d	09 26							09 33		09 59					10 28		10 33							10 59	
St Neots	d	09 34							09 41		10 06					10 36		10 41						←	11 06	
Sandy	d								09 48		10 14			←				10 48						10 48	11 14	
Biggleswade	d								09 52		10 17			10 17				→						10 52	11 17	
Arlesey	d								09 57		→			10 22										10 57	→	
Cambridge	d					09 28	09 45	09 55							10 15					10 28			10 45			
Foxton	d							10 05																		
Shepreth	d							10 07																		
Meldreth	d							10 10																		
Royston	d					09 43		10 15												10 43						
Ashwell & Morden	d							10 20																		
Baldock	d					09 51		10 25												10 51						
Letchworth Garden City	d					09 54		10 29									←			10 54						
Hitchin 4	d					09 58		10 33	10 03					10 28			10 33			10 58		←		11 03		
Stevenage 4	d					10 03		→	10 09					10 33			10 39		11 02	11 03		11 02		11 09		
Hertford North	a																		→							
Knebworth	d								10 13								10 43							11 13		
Welwyn North	d		←						10 17								10 47							11 17		
Welwyn Garden City 4	d		09 50						10 20								10 50							11 20		
Hatfield	d		09 53						10 23								10 53							11 22		
Potters Bar	d		09 59						10 29								10 59							11 29		
Finsbury Park ⊖	d		10 08			10 21			10 41					10 51			11 08			11 21				11 40		
London Kings Cross 15 ⊖	a	10 15	10 19	10 20	10 26	10 32	10 34		10 49			10 44	10 58	11 02	11 05	11 15	11 19			11 32		11 33	11 35	11 48		11 50

For general notes see front of timetable
For details of catering facilities see
Directory of Train Operators

A From Kings Lynn (Table 17)
B From Ely (Table 17)

Peterborough, Cambridge and Stevenage → London

Network Diagram - see first page of Table 24

		FC	FC	FC	FC	FC	GR	FC		GR	FC	FC	FC	GR	FC	FC	FC	FC	FC		GR	FC	FC	GR	FC	FC
							R			R				R							R			R		
		1	1	1	1	1	1	1		1	1	1	1	1	1	1	1	1	1		1	1	1	1	1	1
							☕			☕				☕							☕			☕		
							🍴			🍴											🍴			🍴		
Peterborough 8	d					11 16	11 21			11 32			11 45	11 50					12 15		12 19			12 34		
Huntingdon	a					11 30							11 59						12 29							
	d					11 33							11 59						12 33							
St Neots	d					11 41							12 06		←				12 41							←
Sandy	d	←				11 48							12 14		11 48	←			12 48							12 48
Biggleswade	d	11 17				→							12 17		11 52	12 17			→							12 52
Arlesey	d	11 22											→		11 57	12 22										12 57
Cambridge	d		10 55	11 15							11 28	11 45					11 55	12 15					12 28		12 45	
Foxton	d		11 05														12 05									
Shepreth	d		11 07														12 07									
Meldreth	d		11 10														12 10									
Royston	d		11 15								11 43						12 15						12 43			
Ashwell & Morden	d		11 20														12 20									
Baldock	d		11 25								11 51						12 25						12 51			
Letchworth Garden City	d		11 29		←						11 54						12 29					←	12 54			
Hitchin 4	d	11 28	11 33		11 33						11 58				12 03	12 28	12 33					12 33	12 58			13 03
Stevenage 4	d	11 33	→		11 39		11 50				12 03				12 09	12 33	→					12 39	13 03	13 03		13 09
Hertford North	a																									→
Knebworth	d				11 43										12 13							12 43				
Welwyn North	d				11 47			←							12 17							12 47				
Welwyn Garden City 4	d				11 50			11 50							12 20							12 50				
Hatfield	d				→			11 53							12 23							12 53				
Potters Bar	d							11 59							12 29							12 59				
Finsbury Park ⊖	d	11 51						12 08			12 21				12 41	12 51						13 08	13 21			
London Kings Cross 15 ⊖	a	12 02		12 03			12 17	12 19		12 24	12 32	12 33		12 42	12 49	13 02		13 03			13 11	13 19	13 32	13 33	13 35	

		FC	GR	FC	GR	FC	FC		FC	FC	FC	FC	FC	FC	GR	FC	FC	FC		FC	GR	FC	FC	FC	GR	FC
			R		R										R						R				R	
		1	1	1	1	1	1		1	1	1	1	1	1	1	1	1	1		1	1	1	1	1	1	1
			☕		☕										☕						☕				☕	
					🍴										🍴						🍴				🍴	
Peterborough 8	d	12 45	12 50		13 07								13 18	13 42	13 47						14 14			14 18	14 29	
Huntingdon	a	12 59											13 32	13 56										14 32		
	d	12 59											13 33	13 59										14 33		
St Neots	d	13 06											13 41	14 06			←							14 41		
Sandy	d	13 14				←							13 48	14 14			14 14							14 48		
Biggleswade	d	13 17				13 17							13 52	→			14 17							14 52		
Arlesey	d	→				13 22							13 57				14 22							14 57		
Cambridge	d						12 55		13 15		13 28	13 45						13 55		14 15			14 28			14 45
Foxton	d						13 05											14 05								
Shepreth	d						13 07											14 07								
Meldreth	d						13 10											14 10								
Royston	d						13 15				13 43							14 15					14 43			
Ashwell & Morden	d						13 20											14 20								
Baldock	d						13 25				13 51							14 25					14 51			
Letchworth Garden City	d						13 29			←	13 54							14 29				←	14 54			
Hitchin 4	d			←		13 28	13 33			13 33	13 58		14 03				14 28	14 33				14 33	14 58	15 03		
Stevenage 4	d			13 09		13 33	→			13 39	14 03		14 09		14 16		14 33	→				14 39	15 03	15 09		
Hertford North	a																							→		
Knebworth	d			13 13						13 43			14 13									14 43				
Welwyn North	d			13 17						13 47			14 17			←						14 47				
Welwyn Garden City 4	d			13 20						13 50			14 20			14 20						14 50				
Hatfield	d			13 23						13 53			→			14 23						14 53				
Potters Bar	d			13 30						13 59						14 29						14 59				
Finsbury Park ⊖	d			13 41		13 51				14 08	14 21					14 41	14 51					15 08	15 21			
London Kings Cross 15 ⊖	a		13 44	13 49	13 59	14 02			14 03	14 19	14 32	14 33			14 43	14 49	15 02			15 03	15 10	15 19	15 32		15 21	15 33

		FC	GR	FC	FC	FC		GR	FC	FC	FC	FC	GR	FC	FC	GR	FC		FC	FC	FC	FC	FC	FC	GR	FC
			R					R					R			R									R	
		1	1	1	1	1		1	1	1	1	1	1	1	1	1	1		1	1	1	1	1	1	1	1
								A																		
			☕					☕					☕			☕									☕	
			🍴					🍴					🍴			🍴									🍴	
Peterborough 8	d	14 45	14 49					15 04				15 18	15 39		15 45	15 50								16 18	16 35	
Huntingdon	a	14 59										15 32			15 59									16 32		
	d	14 59										15 33			15 59									16 33		
St Neots	d	15 06										15 41			16 06				←					16 41		
Sandy	d	15 14			←							15 48			16 14				16 14					16 48		
Biggleswade	d	15 17			15 17							15 52			→				16 17					→		
Arlesey	d	→			15 22							15 57							16 22							
Cambridge	d					14 55			15 15		15 28			15 45						15 55	16 15		16 28			16 45
Foxton	d					15 05														16 05						
Shepreth	d					15 07														16 07						
Meldreth	d					15 10														16 10						
Royston	d					15 15					15 43									16 15			16 43			
Ashwell & Morden	d					15 20														16 20						
Baldock	d					15 25					15 51									16 25			16 51			
Letchworth Garden City	d					15 29				←	15 54									16 29		←	16 54			
Hitchin 4	d			←	15 28	15 33				15 33	15 58	16 03					←		16 28	16 33		16 33	16 58			
Stevenage 4	d			15 09	15 33	→				15 39	16 03	16 09				16 21	16 09		16 33	→		16 39	17 03		17 06	
Hertford North	a											→														
Knebworth	d			15 13						15 43							16 13					16 43				
Welwyn North	d			15 17						15 47							16 17					16 47				
Welwyn Garden City 4	d			15 20						15 50							16 20					16 50				
Hatfield	d			15 23						15 53							16 23					16 53				
Potters Bar	d			15 29						15 59							16 29					16 59				
Finsbury Park ⊖	d			15 41	15 51					16 08	16 21						16 41		16 51			17 08	17 21			
London Kings Cross 15 ⊖	a		15 42	15 49	16 02			16 03	16 07	16 19	16 29		16 34	16 35		16 47	16 49		17 02		17 03	17 19	17 32		17 33	17 34

For general notes see front of timetable
For details of catering facilities see
Directory of Train Operators

A The Highland Chieftain

Peterborough, Cambridge and Stevenage → London

Network Diagram - see first page of Table 24

		FC	FC	GR	FC		FC	FC	FC	GR	FC	FC	FC	GR	FC	FC		GR	FC	FC	FC	FC	FC	FC	FC	FC
				R						R				R				R								
		1	1	1	1		1	1	1	1	1	1	1	1	1	1		1	1	1	1	1	1	1	1	1
				A																						
				☕🍴						☕🍴				☕🍴				☕🍴								
Peterborough 8	d		16 43	16 46						17 12			17 18	17 36		17 45		17 50								18 18
Huntingdon	a		16 57										17 32			17 59										18 32
	d		16 59										17 33			17 59										18 33
St Neots	d	←	17 06				←						17 41			18 06				←						18 41
Sandy	d	16 48	17 14				17 14						17 48			18 14				18 14						18 48
Biggleswade	d	16 52	→				17 17						17 52			→				18 17						18 52
Arlesey	d	16 57					17 22						17 57							18 22						18 57
Cambridge	d							16 55	17 15			17 28			17 45						17 55	18 15		18 28	18 45	
Foxton	d							17 05													18 05					
Shepreth	d							17 07													18 07					
Meldreth	d							17 10													18 10					
Royston	d							17 15				17 43									18 15			18 43		
Ashwell & Morden	d							17 20													18 20					
Baldock	d							17 25				17 51									18 25			18 51		
Letchworth Garden City	d							17 29			←	17 54									18 29		←	18 54		
Hitchin 4	d	17 03					17 28	17 33			17 33	17 58	18 03						←	18 28	18 33		18 33	18 58		19 03
Stevenage 4	d	17 09		17 16			17 33	→			17 39	18 03	18 09					18 19	18 09	18 33	→		18 39	19 03		19 09
Hertford North	a												→													→
Knebworth	d	17 12									17 42								18 13				18 43			
Welwyn North	d	17 17			←						17 47								18 17				18 47			
Welwyn Garden City 4	d	17 20			17 20						17 50								18 20				18 50			
Hatfield	d	→			17 23						17 53								18 23				18 53			
Potters Bar	d				17 29						17 59								18 29				18 59			
Finsbury Park	⊖ d				17 41		17 51				18 08	18 21							18 41	18 51			19 08	19 21		
London Kings Cross 15	⊖ a			17 43	17 50		18 03		18 05	18 10	18 19	18 32		18 28	18 34			18 46	18 49	19 02		19 03	19 19	19 32	19 33	

		FC	GR	FC		FC	FC	FC	GR	FC	FC	FC	GR	FC	FC		FC	FC	FC	GR	FC	FC	FC	FC	FC	GR
			R						R				R							R						R
		1	1	1		1	1	1	1	1	1	1	1	1	1		1	1	1	1	1	1	1	1	1	1
											B											B				
			☕🍴						☕🍴				☕🍴							☕🍴						☕🍴
Peterborough 8	d	18 43	18 48						19 12			19 18	19 38				19 45		20 14	20 19					20 45	20 51
Huntingdon	a	18 57										19 32					19 59		20 29						20 59	
	d	18 59										19 33					19 59		20 33						20 59	
St Neots	d	19 06										19 41			←		20 06		20 41					←	21 06	
Sandy	d	19 14				←						19 48			19 48		20 14		20 48					20 48	21 14	
Biggleswade	d	19 17				19 17						→			19 52		20 17		→					20 52	→	
Arlesey	d	→				19 22									19 57		20 22							20 57		
Cambridge	d						18 55	19 15			19 28			19 45				19 55				20 28	20 45			
Foxton	d						19 05											20 05								
Shepreth	d						19 07											20 07								
Meldreth	d						19 10											20 10								
Royston	d						19 15				19 43							20 15				20 43				
Ashwell & Morden	d						19 20											20 20								
Baldock	d						19 25				19 51							20 25				20 51				
Letchworth Garden City	d						19 29				19 54							20 29				20 54				
Hitchin 4	d			←		19 28	19 33				19 58				20 03		20 28	20 33				20 58		21 03		
Stevenage 4	d			19 09		19 33	19 39		19 43		20 03		20 07		20 09		20 33	20 39		20 48		21 03		21 09		21 20
Hertford North	a																									
Knebworth	d			19 13			19 43								20 13			20 43						21 13		
Welwyn North	d			19 17			19 47			←					20 17			20 47			←			21 17		
Welwyn Garden City 4	d			19 20			19 50			19 50					20 20			20 50			20 50			21 20		
Hatfield	d			19 23			→			19 53					20 23			→			20 53			→		
Potters Bar	d			19 29						19 59					20 29						20 59					
Finsbury Park	⊖ d			19 41		19 51				20 08	20 21				20 41		20 51				21 08	21 21				
London Kings Cross 15	⊖ a		19 40	19 49		20 02		20 03	20 12	20 19	20 32		20 35	20 36	20 50		21 02			21 15	21 19	21 32	21 34			21 48

		FC	FC		FC	FC	FC	GR	FC	FC	FC	FC	GR	FC		FC	FC	FC	FC	FC	FC	FC	FC	FC		
								R					R													
		1	1		1	1	1	1	1	1	1	1	1	1		1	1	1	1	1	1	1	1	1		
									B									B	C	D	C	D	C	E		
								☕🍴					☕													
Peterborough 8	d					21 17		21 21				21 45	21 51						22 18	22 18	22 42	22 42				
Huntingdon	a					21 31						21 59							22 32	22 32	22 56	22 56				
	d					21 33						21 59							22 33	22 33	22 56	22 56				
St Neots	d		←			21 41					←	22 06				←			22 41	22 41	23 03	23 03				
Sandy	d		21 14			21 48					21 48	22 14				22 14			22 48	22 48	23 11	23 11				
Biggleswade	d		21 17			→					21 52	→				22 17			22 52	22 52	23 14	23 14				
Arlesey	d		21 22								21 57					22 22			22 57	22 57	23 19	23 19				
Cambridge	d				20 55				21 28	21 45							21 55	22 28					23 06	23 06		
Foxton	d				21 05												22 05						23 15	23 15		
Shepreth	d				21 07												22 07						23 18	23 18		
Meldreth	d				21 10												22 10						23 21	23 21		
Royston	d				21 15				21 43								22 15	22 43					23 25	23 25		
Ashwell & Morden	d				21 20												22 20						23 29	23 29		
Baldock	d				21 25				21 51								22 25	22 51					23 34	23 34		
Letchworth Garden City	d				21 29				21 54								22 29	22 54					23 37	23 37		
Hitchin 4	d		21 28		21 33				21 58		22 03					22 28	22 33	22 58	23 03	23 03	23 25	23 25	23 41	23 41		
Stevenage 4	d		21 33		21 39			21 54	22 03		22 09		22 20			22 33	22 39	23 03	23 09	23 09	23 30	23 30	23 46	23 46		
Hertford North	a																									
Knebworth	d				21 43						22 13						22 43		23 13	23 13			23 49	23 49		
Welwyn North	d	←			21 47		←				22 17			←			22 47		23 17	23 17			23 53	23 53		
Welwyn Garden City 4	d	21 20			21 50		21 50				22 20			22 20			22 50		23 20	23 20			23 56	23 56		
Hatfield	d	21 23			→		21 53				→			22 23			22 53		23 23	23 23			23 59	23 59		
Potters Bar	d	21 29					21 59							22 29			22 59		23 29	23a31		23u47	00 05	00a05		
Finsbury Park	⊖ d	21 41	21 51				22 08		22 21					22 41		23s07	23s16	23s34	23s45		23 55	23 55	00s23			
London Kings Cross 15	⊖ a	21 49	22 02				22 19	22 20	22 34	22 34			22 47	22 49		23 16	23 30	23 47	23 53		00 11	00 11	00 34			

For general notes see front of timetable
For details of catering facilities see
Directory of Train Operators

A **The Flying Scotsman**
B From Kings Lynn (Table 17)
C Until 5 September
D From 12 September
E From 12 September. To Alexandra Palace (Table 24)

Table 25

Sundays

Peterborough, Cambridge and Stevenage → London

Network Diagram - see first page of Table 24

		FC	FC	FC	FC	FC	FC	FC	FC	FC	FC	FC	FC	FC	FC	FC	FC	FC	FC	FC	FC	GR	FC
																						R	
		1			1	1	1	1		1	1	1	1	1	1	1	1	1	1	1	1	1	1
		A	A	A	A	B	A	B	A	B	A												
			(bus)	(bus)					(bus)													(catering)	
Peterborough 8	d		04 07	05 07	05 50	05 50			06 07	06 45			07 45			08 45					09 45	09 53	
Huntingdon	a		04 47	05 47	06 04	06 04			06 47	06 59			07 59			08 59					09 59		
	d		04 47	05 47	06 04	06 04			06 47	06 59			07 59			08 59					09 59		
St Neots	d		05 17	06 17	06 11	06 11			07 17	07 06			08 06			09 06					10 06		
Sandy	d		05 37	06 37	06 19	06 19			07 37	07 14			08 14			09 14					10 14		←
Biggleswade	d		05 47	06 47	06 22	06 22			07 47	07 17			08 17			09 17					10 17		10 17
Arlesey	d		06 07	07 07	06 27	06 27			08a07	07 22			08 22			09 22					→		10 22
Cambridge	d	23p06					06 28	06 28				07 28		07 55	08 28		08 55	09 20		09 28			
Foxton	d	23p15												08 05			09 05						
Shepreth	d	23p18												08 07			09 07						
Meldreth	d	23p21												08 10			09 10						
Royston	d	23p25					06 43	06 43				07 43		08 15	08 43		09 15			09 43			
Ashwell & Morden	d	23p29												08 20			09 20						
Baldock	d	23p34					06 51	06 51				07 51		08 25	08 51		09 25			09 51			
Letchworth Garden City	d	23p37	06a19	07a19			06 54	06 54			07 23	07 54		08 29	08 54		09 29		←	09 54			
Hitchin 4	d	23p41			06 33	06 33	06 58	06 58		07 28	07 27	07 58	08 28	08 33	08 58	09 28	09 33		09 33	09 58			10 28
Stevenage 4	d	23p46			06 41	06 41	07 03	07 03		07 33	07 35	08 03	08 33	08 39	09 03	09 33	→		09 39	10 03			10 33
Hertford North	a																						
Knebworth	d	23p49								07 37	07 40			08 43					09 43				
Welwyn North	d	23p53								07 40	07 43			08 47					09 47				
Welwyn Garden City 4	d	23p56								07 43	07 46			08 50					09 50				
Hatfield	d	23p59												08 53					09 53				
Potters Bar	d	00 05												08 59					09 59				
Finsbury Park	⊖ d	00s23			07 09	07a10	07 31	07a32		08a05	08 10	08s34	08 51	09 11	09 21	09 51			10 11	10 21			10 51
London Kings Cross 15	⊖ a	00 34			07 17		07 39				08 18	08 45	09 00	09 19	09 30	10 00		10 08	10 19	10 30		10 48	11 01

		FC	FC	FC	GR	FC	FC	GR	FC	FC	FC	FC	GR	FC	GR	FC	FC	FC	GR	FC	FC	FC	GR
					R			R					R		R				R				R
		1	1	1	1	1	1	1	1	1	1	1	1	1	1	1	1	1	1	1	1	1	1
					(catering)			(catering)					(catering)		(catering)				(catering)				(catering)
Peterborough 8	d				10 24		10 45	11 02					11 25		11 45	11 42			12 16			12 42	12 45
Huntingdon	a						10 59									11 56						12 56	
	d						10 59									11 59						12 59	
St Neots	d						11 06									12 06						13 06	
Sandy	d						11 14		←							12 14						13 14	
Biggleswade	d						11 17		11 17							12 17						13 17	
Arlesey	d						→		11 22							12 22						→	
Cambridge	d	09 55	10 20			10 28				10 55	11 20			11 28			11 55	12 20			12 28		
Foxton	d	10 05								11 05							12 05						
Shepreth	d	10 07								11 07							12 07						
Meldreth	d	10 10								11 10							12 10						
Royston	d	10 15				10 43				11 15				11 43			12 15				12 43		
Ashwell & Morden	d	10 20								11 20							12 20						
Baldock	d	10 25				10 51				11 25				11 51			12 25				12 51		
Letchworth Garden City	d	10 29		←		10 54				11 29		←		11 54			12 29			←	12 54		
Hitchin 4	d	10 33		10 33		10 58			11 28	11 33		11 33		11 58		12 28	12 33			12 33	12 58		
Stevenage 4	d	→		10 39	10 55	11 03			11 33	→		11 39	11 55	12 03		12 33	→			12 39	13 03		
Hertford North	a																						
Knebworth	d			10 43								11 43								12 43			
Welwyn North	d			10 47								11 47								12 47			
Welwyn Garden City 4	d			10 50								11 50								12 50			
Hatfield	d			10 53								11 53								12 53			
Potters Bar	d			10 59								11 59								12 59			
Finsbury Park	⊖ d			11 11		11 21			11 51			12 11		12 21		12 51				13 11	13 21		
London Kings Cross 15	⊖ a		11 08	11 18	11 23	11 30		11 55	12 00		12 08	12 18	12 23	12 30	12 40	13 00		13 08	13 14	13 19	13 30		13 39

For general notes see front of timetable
For details of catering facilities see Directory of Train Operators

A Until 6 September
B From 13 September

Sundays

Peterborough, Cambridge and Stevenage → London

Network Diagram - see first page of Table 24

		FC	FC	GR	FC	FC	FC	FC		FC	FC	GR	GR	FC	FC	FC		GR	FC	FC	FC	FC	GR	FC		FC
				R								R	R					R					R			
		1	1	1	1	1	1	1		1	1	1	1	1	1	1		1	1	1	1	1	1	1		1
				🍴								🍴	🍴					🍴					🍴			
Peterborough 8	d			13 06				13 42				14 11	14 22			14 45		14 48					15 36			15 44
Huntingdon	a							13 56								14 59										15 58
	d							13 59								14 59										15 59
St Neots	d							14 06								15 06										16 06
Sandy	d	←						14 14								15 14			←							16 14
Biggleswade	d	13 17						14 17								15 17			15 17							→
Arlesey	d	13 22						14 22								→			15 22							
Cambridge	d		12 55		13 20		13 28			13 55	14 15				14 28					14 55	15 14			15 28		
Foxton	d		13 05							14 05										15 05						
Shepreth	d		13 07							14 07										15 07						
Meldreth	d		13 10							14 10										15 10						
Royston	d		13 15				13 43			14 15					14 43					15 15				15 43		
Ashwell & Morden	d		13 20							14 20										15 20						
Baldock	d		13 25				13 51			14 25					14 51					15 25				15 51		
Letchworth Garden City	d		13 29			←	13 54			14 29				←	14 54					15 29		←		15 54		
Hitchin 4	d	13 28	13 33			13 33	13 58	14 28		14 33				14 33	14 58				15 28	15 33		15 33		15 58		
Stevenage 4	d	13 33	→	13 36		13 39	14 03	14 33		→				14 39	15 03				15 33	→		15 39		16 03		
Hertford North	a																									
Knebworth	d					13 43								14 43								15 43				
Welwyn North	d					13 47								14 47								15 47				
Welwyn Garden City 4	d					13 50								14 50								15 50				
Hatfield	d					13 53								14 53								15 53				
Potters Bar	d					13 59								15 00								15 59				
Finsbury Park ⊖	d	13 51				14 11	14 21	14 51						15 12	15 21				15 52			16 11		16 21		
London Kings Cross 15 ⊖	a	14 00		14 04	14 09	14 19	14 30	15 00			15 05	15 09	15 16	15 22	15 30			15 42	16 00		16 03	16 18	16 29	16 34		

		GR	FC	FC	FC	FC	GR	FC		FC	FC	GR	GR	FC	FC	FC		GR	FC	FC	FC	GR	GR	FC	GR	FC
		R					R					R	R					R				R	R		R	
		1	1	1	1	1	1	1		1	1	1	1	1	1	1		1	1	1	1	1	1	1	1	1
												A						B								
		🍴					🍴					🍴	🍴					🍴				🍴	🍴		🍴	
Peterborough 8	d	15 47					16 19				16 45	16 51	17 02					17 18			17 41	17 45	18 02			
Huntingdon	a										16 59										17 56					
	d										16 59										17 59					
St Neots	d		←								17 06			←							18 06			←		
Sandy	d		16 14								17 14			17 14							18 14			18 14		
Biggleswade	d		16 17								→			17 17							→			18 17		
Arlesey	d		16 22											17 22										18 22		
Cambridge	d			15 55	16 15					16 28					16 55	17 20				17 28						17 55
Foxton	d			16 05											17 05											18 05
Shepreth	d			16 07											17 07											18 07
Meldreth	d			16 10											17 10											18 10
Royston	d			16 15						16 43					17 15					17 43						18 15
Ashwell & Morden	d			16 20											17 20											18 20
Baldock	d			16 25						16 51					17 25					17 51						18 25
Letchworth Garden City	d			16 29		←				16 54					17 29				←	17 54						18 29
Hitchin 4	d		16 28	16 33		16 33				16 58				17 28	17 33				17 33	17 58				18 28		18 33
Stevenage 4	d	16 18	16 33	→		16 39	16 49			17 03		17 21		17 33	→				17 39	18 03		18 16		18 33	18 48	→
Hertford North	a																									
Knebworth	d					16 43													17 43							
Welwyn North	d					16 47		←											17 47							
Welwyn Garden City 4	d					16 50		16 50											17 50							
Hatfield	d					→		16 53											17 53							
Potters Bar	d							16 59											17 59							
Finsbury Park ⊖	d		16 51					17 11		17 21				17 51					18 11	18 21				18 51		
London Kings Cross 15 ⊖	a	16 46	17 00		17 03		17 18	17 19		17 30		17 49	17 55	18 00		18 08		18 15	18 19	18 30		18 43	18 55	19 00	19 16	

		FC	FC	GR	FC	FC	GR	GR		FC	FC	FC	GR	FC	GR	FC		GR	FC	GR	GR	FC	FC	GR		FC
				R			R	R					R		R			R		R	R			R		
		1	1	1	1	1	1	1		1	1	1	1	1	1	1		1	1	1	1	1	1	1		1
				🍴			🍴	🍴					🍴		🍴			🍴		🍴	🍴			🍴		
Peterborough 8	d			18 27		18 45	18 51	18 59					19 19		19 29			19 33	19 42	19 45	20 02					
Huntingdon	a					18 59													19 56							
	d					18 59													19 59							
St Neots	d					19 06				←									20 06			←				
Sandy	d					19 14				19 14									20 14			20 14				
Biggleswade	d					→				19 17									→			20 17				
Arlesey	d									19 22												20 22				
Cambridge	d	18 20			18 28						18 55	19 20				19 28							19 55			20 20
Foxton	d										19 05												20 05			
Shepreth	d										19 07												20 07			
Meldreth	d										19 10												20 10			
Royston	d				18 43						19 15					19 43							20 15			
Ashwell & Morden	d										19 20												20 20			
Baldock	d				18 51						19 25					19 51							20 25			
Letchworth Garden City	d		←		18 54						19 29			←		19 54							20 29			
Hitchin 4	d		18 33		18 58					19 28	19 33			19 33		19 58						20 28	20 33	←		
Stevenage 4	d		18 39		19 03		19 21			19 33	→			19 39		20 03		20 07		20 18	20 33	20 33	→	20 33		
Hertford North	a																				→					
Knebworth	d		18 43											19 43												
Welwyn North	d		18 47											19 47												
Welwyn Garden City 4	d		18 50											19 50												
Hatfield	d		18 53											19 53												
Potters Bar	d		18 59											19 59												
Finsbury Park ⊖	d		19 11		19 21					19 51				20 11		20 21						20 51				
London Kings Cross 15 ⊖	a	19 08	19 18	19 21	19 29		19 48	19 52		20 00		20 08	20 14	20 18	20 23	20 30		20 34		20 43		21 00		21 01		21 08

For general notes see front of timetable
For details of catering facilities see
Directory of Train Operators

A The Flying Scotsman
B The Highland Chieftain

Table 25

Peterborough, Cambridge and Stevenage → London

Network Diagram - see first page of Table 24

		FC	GR	FC	FC	GR	FC	FC		FC	GR	FC	FC	GR	FC	FC		GR	FC	FC	GR	FC	FC	FC		
			R			R					R			R				R			R					
		1	1	1	1	1	1	1		1	1	1	1	1	1	1		1	1	1	1	1	1	1		
																								A		
			☕ 🛒			☕ 🛒					☕ 🛒			☕				☕ 🛒			☕ 🛒					
Peterborough 8	d		20 23		20 45	20 48					21 18			21 36	21 45			22 04			22 44		22 51			
Huntingdon	a				20 59										21 59								23 05			
	d				20 59										21 59								23 05			
St Neots	d				21 06		←								22 06								23 12			
Sandy	d				21 14		21 14								22 14								23 20			
Biggleswade	d				→		21 17								22 17								23 23			
Arlesey	d						21 22								22 22								23 28			
Cambridge	d			20 28				20 55		21 20			21 28			21 55			22 20			22 41		23 15		
Foxton	d							21 05								22 05										
Shepreth	d							21 07								22 07										
Meldreth	d							21 10								22 10										
Royston	d			20 43				21 15					21 43			22 15						22 55		23 29		
Ashwell & Morden	d							21 20								22 20										
Baldock	d			20 51				21 25					21 51			22 25						23 03				
Letchworth Garden City	d	←		20 54				21 29					21 54			22 29				←		23 06		23 39		
Hitchin 4	d	20 33		20 58			21 28	21 33					21 58		22 28	22 33				22 33		23 11	23 34	23 43		
Stevenage 4	d	20 39	20 54	21 03		21 20	21 33	21 39			21 48		22 03	22 09	22 33	→		22 34		22 39		23 16	23 39	23 48		
Hertford North	a																									
Knebworth	d	20 43						21 43												22 43				23 51		
Welwyn North	d	20 47						21 47				←								22 47				23 55		
Welwyn Garden City 4	d	20 50						21 50				21 50								22 50				23 58		
Hatfield	d	20 53						→				21 53								22 53				00 01		
Potters Bar	d	20 59										21 59								22 59				00 07		
Finsbury Park ⊖	d	21 11		21 21			21 51					22 11	22 21		22 56					23 11		23 38	00 05	00 20		
London Kings Cross 15 ⊖	a	21 18	21 25	21 30		21 47	22 00			22 08	22 16	22 19	22 32	22 37	23 09			23 14	23 19	23 23	23 50	23 54	00 14	00 32		

For general notes see front of timetable
For details of catering facilities see
Directory of Train Operators

A From Kings Lynn (Table 17)

Route Diagram for Table 26

DM-2/09
Design BAJS

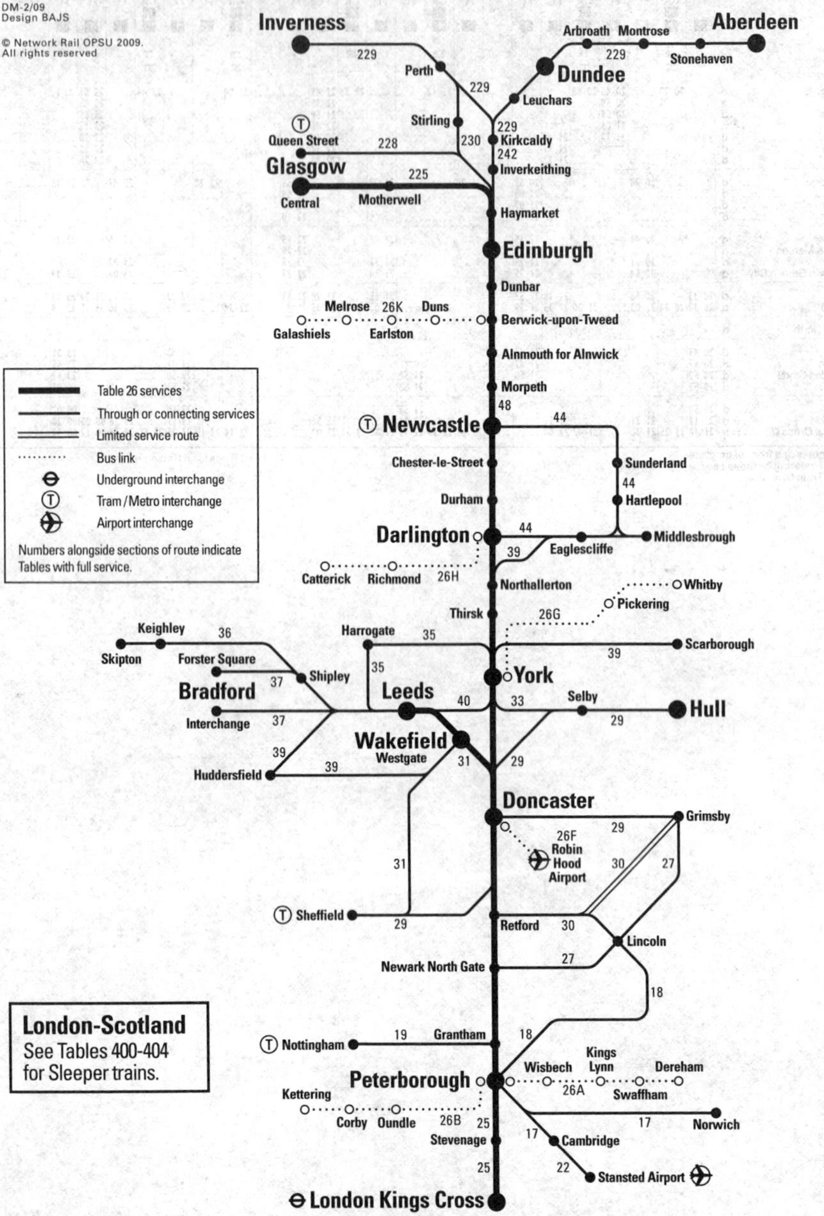

London-Scotland
See Tables 400-404 for Sleeper trains.

London → Humberside, Yorkshire, North East England and Scotland

Route Diagram - see first page of Table 26

					NT	XC	GR	NT	TP	GR	NT	TP	XC	TP	GR	TP	NT	XC	GR	GR	TP	GR	XC	EM	GR	TP
						1 ◇	R 1		1 ◇	R 1		1 ◇	1 ◇	1 ◇	R 1	1 ◇		1 ◇	R 1	R 1	1 ◇	R 1	1 ◇	◇	R 1	1 ◇
					A			B			C	D	E			G	C	H			J		H	K		G
Miles	Miles	Miles					⊡			⊡ ✕			✕		⊡ ✕	✕		✕	⊡	∅ ✕	✕	⊡	✕	✕	∅ ✕	✕
0	—	—	**London Kings Cross 15** ⊖	d															06 00	06 15		06 35			07 00	
27½	—	—	**Stevenage 4**	d															06 19	06 34					07 19	
76¼	—	—	**Peterborough 8**	a															06 50	07 05		07 21			07 51	
—	—	—	Norwich	d																				05 50		
—	—	—	Stansted Airport	d																*05 21*						
—	—	—	Cambridge	d															*05 15*	*05 55*					*06 26*	
—	—	—	**Peterborough 8**	d															06 51	07 06		07 21		07 27	07 51	
105½	—	—	**Grantham 7**	a															07 10	07 25		07 40		07 58		
—	—	—		d															07 10	07 25		07 40				
120	—	—	**Newark North Gate 7**	a															07 22	07 37						
—	—	—	Lincoln	a																*08 15*						
—	—	—	Grimsby Town	a																*09 15*		*09b42*				
—	—	—	**Newark North Gate 7**	d															07 22	07 37						
138½	—	—	**Retford 10**	d															07 37	07 52						
156	0	—	**Doncaster 7**	a															07 51	08 07		08 12				
—	—	—	Selby	a																						
—	—	—	Hull	a																		*09 13*				
—	19¾	—	**Wakefield Westgate 7**	a															08 10			08 36				
—	—	—	Huddersfield	a															*09 04*			*09c25*				
—	29¾	—	**Leeds 10**	a															08 32			08 52				
—	—	—	Shipley	a															*09 01*			*09 21*				
—	—	—	Bradford Forster Square	a															*09e11*			*09e28*				
—	—	—	Keighley	a															*09 11*			*09 50*				
—	—	—	Skipton	a															*09 24*			*10 07*				
—	—	—	Sheffield 7	d						*05 29*			06 40					07 12		*07 24*			07 54			
—	—	—	**Doncaster 7**	d						06 15			07 06							08 08			08 26			
188½	—	—	**York 8**	a						06 35			07 27							08 31			08 47		08 56	
—	—	—	Scarborough	a																					*10 32*	
—	—	—	Harrogate	a																*09 18*					*09 43*	
—	—	—	Leeds 10	d						*05 40*		06 35	*06 38*	*06 55*	07 10	07 50		07 57			08 12					08 27
—	—	—	Hull	d									*06f00*							*07 07*						
—	—	—	**York 8**	d					05 54	06 37		07 06	07 29	07 34	07 37	08 23		08 27		08 33	08 42		08 50		08 58	09 03
210¾	—	—	Thirsk	d					06 10			07 22		07 54		08 39										
218¼	—	—	Northallerton	d					06 18			07 30		08 01		08 49					09 03					09 24
232½	—	—	**Darlington 7**	a					06 29	07 05		07 41	07 55		08 05			08 55		09 02	09 14		09 20		09 30	09 36
—	—	—	Eaglescliffe	a																						
—	—	—	Middlesbrough	a					07 01	*07 50*		*08 12*		08 34		09 21							*09 57*			*10 23*
—	—	—	**Darlington 7**	d				06 14		07 06	07 20	07 42	07 56		08 05		08 15	08 56		09 03	09 15		09 22		09 31	09 37
254½	—	—	**Durham**	d				06 35		07 23	07 41	07 59	08 16		08 23		08 36	09 13		09 20	09 31		09 38			09 54
260¼	—	—	Chester-le-Street	d				06 42			07 48	08 05					08 43						09 45			
268½	—	—	**Newcastle 8**	a				06 55		07 39	08 02	08 18	08 39		08 39		09 00	09 26		09 36	09 49		10 00		10 02	10 10
—	—	—	Hartlepool	a																						
—	—	—	Sunderland	a				*07 49*				*08 49*					*09 49*									*10 49*
—	—	—	**Newcastle 8**	d	05 45		06 25			07 41					08 41			09 29		09 38					10 04	
285	—	—	Morpeth	d	06 05		06 38			*08a20*					08 55			09 42							*10a35*	
303¼	—	—	Alnmouth for Alnwick	d	06a22		06 52			08 07								09 56								
335½	—	—	**Berwick-upon-Tweed**	d			07 14			08 29					09 30					10 21					10 47	
363¾	—	—	Dunbar	d		06 39	07 38			08 52					09 54											
393	—	—	**Edinburgh 10**	a		07 09	08 05			09 19					10 20			11 02		11 09					11 32	
—	—	0	**Edinburgh**	d		07 26	08 08			09 22					10 27										11 38	
394¼	—	1¼	Haymarket	d		07 30	08 13			09 27					10 32										11 43	
437½	—	—	Motherwell	a		08 09	08 59			10 05															12 25	
450¼	—	—	**Glasgow Central 15**	a		08 29	09 22			10 29					*11g19*			*12h05*		*12h19*					12 47	
—	—	—	Stirling	a		*08j22*	*09j23*			*10j23*					*11j23*					*12 22*					*12j53*	
—	—	—	Perth	a		*09k36*	*09j48*			*10j52*					*11j54*					*12 52*					*13k36*	
—	—	—	**Inverness**	a			*11j54*			*13m37*										*15 06*						
—	—	13¼	Inverkeithing	a		*07j53*	*09j00*			*09j52*					10 47					*11 42*					*12j11*	
—	—	26	Kirkcaldy	a		*08j02*	*09j06*			*10j08*					11 04					*12 23*					*12j34*	
—	—	51	Leuchars 3	a		*08j32*	*09j23*			*11j03*					11 28					*12 23*					*13j03*	
—	—	59¼	**Dundee**	a		*08j44*	*09j36*			*10j32*					11 43					*12 36*					*13j18*	
—	—	76¼	Arbroath	a		*09j01*	*09j53*			*10j49*					12 01					*12 53*						
—	—	90	Montrose	a		*09j16*	*10n31*			*11j04*					12 17					*13n33*						
—	—	114¼	Stonehaven	a		*09j37*	*10j29*			*11j25*					12 42					*13 26*						
—	—	130½	**Aberdeen**	a		*09j57*	*10j53*			*11j45*					13 07					*13 46*						

For general notes see front of timetable
For details of catering facilities see Directory of Train Operators

- **A** To Chathill (Table 48)
- **B** From Middlesbrough (Table 44)
- **C** From Saltburn (Table 44)
- **D** From Manchester Piccadilly (Table 39)
- **E** From Derby (Table 51)
- **G** From Manchester Airport (Table 39)
- **H** From Birmingham New Street (Table 51)
- **J** From Liverpool Lime Street (Table 39). ✕ to York
- **K** To Liverpool Lime Street (Table 49)
- **b** Change at Doncaster. 22 June to 4 September arr. 1020, by bus
- **c** Change at Leeds
- **e** Bradford Interchange
- **f** Change at Selby and York
- **g** Glasgow Queen Street. Change at Edinburgh
- **h** Glasgow Queen Street
- **j** Change at Edinburgh
- **k** Change at Edinburgh and Stirling
- **m** Change at Edinburgh and Perth
- **n** Change at Edinburgh and Arbroath

London → Humberside, Yorkshire, North East England and Scotland

Route Diagram - see first page of Table 26

		TP	XC	GR	HT	GR	XC	EM	GR		GR	TP	GC	TP	XC	GR	GR	XC	EM	TP	GR	GR	TP	XC	GR	GR
				R	BHX	R			R		R		R			R	R				R	R			R	R
		1 ◇	1 ◇	1	1 ◇	1	1 ◇	◇	1		1	1 ◇	1	1 ◇	1 ◇	1	1	1 ◇	◇	1 ◇	1	1	1 ◇	1 ◇	1	1
		A	B				B	C				A		A	D			E	C	A			A	G		
		⊥	⊥	🍽 ⊥	⊠	🍽 ⊥	⊥	⊥	🍽 ⊥		⊘ ⊥	⊥	🍽	⊥	⊥	🍽 ⊥	⊘ ⊥	⊥	⊥	⊥	🍽	⊘ ⊥	⊥	⊥	🍽	⊘ ⊥
London Kings Cross 15 ⊖	d			07 10	07 20	07 30			07 35		08 00		08 04			08 10	08 30				08 40	09 00			09 10	09 30
Stevenage 4	d			07 29	07u44	07 50			07 56								08 49									09 49
Peterborough 8	a			08 00		08 21					08 46					08 59	09 20				09 27	09 46			09 57	10 20
Norwich	d							06 52											07 57							
Stansted Airport	d			06 06												07 21										08 21
Cambridge	d			06 52							07b05					08 00	08 22									09 00
Peterborough 8	d			08 01		08 21		08 30			08 46					08 59	09 21		09 27		09 28	09 47			09 57	10 21
Grantham 7	a				08 28	08 45		08 58											09 57		09 49					
	d				08 29	08 45															09 49					
Newark North Gate 7	a			08 28													09 48									10 48
Lincoln	a					09c59											10 21				10c59					
Grimsby Town	a					10e44											11 21					11f42				
Newark North Gate 7	d			08 28													09 48									10 48
Retford 10	d				08 50																10 12					
Doncaster 7	a			08 58	09 05	09 16															10 27	10 35				11 12
Selby	a				09 21																					
Hull	a				10 04	10 49																11 53				
Wakefield Westgate 7	a			09 16					09 30							10 01					10 51				10 57	
Huddersfield	a			10 04					10g25							10g58					11g45				11g58	
Leeds 10	a			09 36					09 46							10 21					11 09				11 18	
Shipley	a			10 01					10 07							10 51					11 39				11 51	
Bradford Forster Square	a			10h09					10h28							10h57					11h42				11h57	
Keighley	a			10 11					10 20							11 11					11 51				12 20	
Skipton	a			10 24					10 37							11 24					12 07				12 37	
Sheffield 7	d		08 21			08 25	08 54								09 21			09 54						10 21		10 24
Doncaster 7	d					09 17	09 22											10 17				10 35				11 12
York 8	a					09 40	09 48				09 53		10 02				10 34	10 40				11 02				11 37
Scarborough	a												11 30									12 30				
Harrogate	a								10 33				10 43			11 33						11 43			12 03	
Leeds 10	d	08 57	09 05				09 12					09 27		09 57	10 05			10 12		10 27			10 57	11 05		
Hull	d										08j40			09 02										10j12		
York 8	d	09 26	09 37			09 42	09 51				09 55	10 00	10 14	10 26	10 31		10 36	10 43		10 54		11 03	11 26	11 32		11 41
Thirsk	d	09 46											10 30	10 46									11 46			
Northallerton	d	09 57										10 21	10 39	10 55						11 15			11 55			12 00
Darlington 7	a		10 04			10 12	10 17				10 22	10 32			10 59		11 05	11 12		11 27		11 33		11 58		12 14
Eaglescliffe	a												10 57													
Middlesbrough	a	10 30									10 54	11 22		11 30						12 00			12 30	12 31		
Darlington 7	d		10 05			10 12	10 19				10 23	10 33			11 01		11 06	11 14		11 28		11 34		12 00		12 14
Durham	d		10 22				10 35				10 40	10 50			11 18		11 23	11 30		11 45				12 23		12 32
Chester-le-Street	d											10 56														
Newcastle 8	a		10 36			10 44	10 57				10 58	11 10			11 32		11 42	11 54		12 00		12 03		12 36		12 50
Hartlepool	a												11 20													
Sunderland	a											11 49	11 50									12 49				
Newcastle 8	d		10 39								10 59				11 34							12 05		12 40		
Morpeth	d										11a35											12a36				13a23
Alnmouth for Alnwick	d														12 01							12 31				
Berwick-upon-Tweed	d		11 21								11 42											12 53		13 22		
Dunbar	d		11 44																					13 45		
Edinburgh 10	a		12 13								12 31				13 10							13 38		14 14		
Edinburgh	d																					13 41				
Haymarket	d																									
Motherwell	a																					14 26				
Glasgow Central 15	a		13k19								13k35				14k19							14 47		15k20		
Stirling	a		13 23								13 53				14 23							14m53		15 23		
Perth	a		14n36								14n36				14 52							15n36				
Inverness	a														17 05											
Inverkeithing	a		12 52								13 11				14 01							14m11				
Kirkcaldy	a		13 08								13 33				14 23							14m33				
Leuchars 3	a		13 23								14 03				14 23							15m03		15 23		
Dundee	a		13 35								14 18				14 35							15m18		15 37		
Arbroath	a		13 52												14 52									15 54		
Montrose	a		14 07												15q37									16 08		
Stonehaven	a		14 28												15 26									16 30		
Aberdeen	a		14 53												15 46									16 50		

For general notes see front of timetable
For details of catering facilities see Directory of Train Operators

- **A** From Manchester Airport (Table 39)
- **B** From Birmingham New Street (Table 51)
- **C** To Liverpool Lime Street (Table 49)
- **D** From Bristol Temple Meads (Table 51)
- **E** From Guildford (Table 51)
- **G** From Plymouth (Table 51)
- **b** Change at Ely and Peterborough
- **c** Change at Peterborough
- **e** Change at Doncaster. 22 June to 4 September arr. 1115, by bus
- **f** Change at Doncaster. 22 June to 4 September arr. 1210, by bus
- **g** Change at Leeds
- **h** Bradford Interchange
- **j** Change at Selby and York
- **k** Glasgow Queen Street
- **m** Change at Edinburgh
- **n** Change at Edinburgh and Stirling
- **q** Change at Edinburgh and Arbroath

London → Humberside, Yorkshire, North East England and Scotland

Route Diagram - see first page of Table 26

		GR	HT	EM	XC	GR	XC	TP	TP	GR	GR	XC	GR	EM	XC	GR	XC	TP	GR	GC	TP	XC	GR	XC	EM
		R 1	1 ◇	◇	1 ◇	R 1	1 ◇	1 ◇	1 ◇	R 1	R 1	1 ◇	R 1	◇	1 ◇	R 1	1 ◇	1 ◇	R 1	R 1	1 ◇	1 ◇	R 1	1 ◇	◇
				A	B	C	B	D	D		E	G		A	B		B	D			D	G		B	A
		🍽 ✕	⊠	✕	✕	Ø ✕	✕	✕	✕	🍽 ✕	Ø ✕	✕	🍽	✕	✕	Ø ✕	✕	✕	🍽 ✕	🍽	✕	✕	🍽 ✕	✕	✕
London Kings Cross 15 ⊖	d	09 35	09 48			10 00				10 10	10 30		10 35			11 00			11 10	11 27			11 30		
Stevenage 4	d	09 54	10u09								10 12					10 46							11 50		
Peterborough 8	a	10 26				10 45				10 56	11 16		11 22			11 45			11 56				12 21		
Norwich	d			08 57										09 57											10 57
Stansted Airport	d										09 21												10 20		
Cambridge	d					09b12					10 00		10 22			10b34							11 00		
Peterborough 8	d	10 27		10 30		10 45				10 56	11 17		11 23	11 27		11 46			11 56				12 21		12 25
Grantham 7	a	10 46	10 54	11 12						11 16			11 42	11 55					12 15						12 58
	d	10 46	10 55							11 16			11 42						12 15						
Newark North Gate 7	a									11 28			11 55						12 27				12 50		
Lincoln	a	12c04									13 14		12 35										13 30		
Grimsby Town	a		12e45										13 36												
Newark North Gate 7	d									11 28			11 55						12 27				12 50		
Retford 10	d		11 17							11 43															
Doncaster 7	a	11 17	11 32							11 58			12 18						12 58				13 14		
Selby	a		11 51																						
Hull	a		12 32							13 06			13 52						14 08						
Wakefield Westgate 7	a	11 36								12 16			12 36						13 17						
Huddersfield	a	12f25								13 03			13f25						14 04						
Leeds 10	a	11 55								12 36			12 54						13 41						
Shipley	a	12 21								13 01			13 21						14 07						
Bradford Forster Square	a	12g28								13g11			13g28						14g11						
Keighley	a	12 50								13 11			13 51						14 20						
Skipton	a	13 07								13 24			14 09						14 37						
Sheffield 7 ⛴	d				10 54							11 21			11 54							12 21	12 24	12 54	
Doncaster 7	d				11 17										12 17								13 15	13 24	
York 8	a				11 45	11 53					12 26				12 45	12 51				13 19			13 39	13 46	
Scarborough	a										13 30									14 30					
Harrogate	a					12 43				13 33						13 43			14 33						
Leeds 10	d				11 12			11 27	11 57		11 41	12 05			12 12			12 27			12 57	13 05		13 12	
Hull	d								11 05												11h38				
York 8	d				11 47	11 54		12 01	12 26		12 29	12 34			12 45	12 52		12 59		13 22	13 26	13 32	13 42	13 50	
Thirsk	d								12 46											13 38	13 46				
Northallerton	d							12 22	12 55									13 20		13 47	13 55				
Darlington 7	a				12 20	12 25		12 33				13 00			13 13	13 20		13 31				14 00	14 10	14 16	
Eaglescliffe	a																			14 04					
Middlesbrough	a				12 53			13 17	13 30							13 56					14 30	14 32		14 55	
Darlington 7	d				12 21	12 26	←	12 34				13 02			13 15	13 20	←	13 32				14 02	14 11	14 18	
Durham	d				12j45		12 45	12 50				13 19			13 31		13 31	13 48				14 19	14 28	14 35	
Chester-le-Street	d				→		12 51								→			13 54						14 42	
Newcastle 8 ⛴	a					12 55	13 05	13 08			13 22	13 33				13 50	13 51	14 09				14 36	14 47	14 56	
Hartlepool	a																			14 23					
Sunderland ⛴	a										13 49							14 49		14 50					
Newcastle 8 ⛴	d					12 57					13 24	13 35				13 51						14 40			
Morpeth	d																14a34								
Alnmouth for Alnwick	d											14 01													
Berwick-upon-Tweed	d															14 34						15 22			
Dunbar	d																					15 45			
Edinburgh 10	a					14 25					14 53	15k10				15 19						16 16			
Edinburgh	d										15 00					15 22									
Haymarket	d										15 04														
Motherwell	a											16 06				16 06									
Glasgow Central 15	a					15m37					16n07	16m19				16 27						17m21			
Stirling	a										15q53					16q23									
Perth	a					15 53					16r36					16q53						17 52			
Inverness	a															19t34									
Inverkeithing	a					14 52					15 18					15q52						16 51			
Kirkcaldy	a					15 08					15 35					16q08						17 07			
Leuchars 3	a										16 00					16q23						17 24			
Dundee	a										16 18					16q35						17 38			
Arbroath	a										16 35					16q53						18 01			
Montrose	a										16 51					17q08						18 16			
Stonehaven	a										17 14					17q32						18 40			
Aberdeen	a										17 37					17q52						19 00			

For general notes see front of timetable
For details of catering facilities see Directory of Train Operators

- A To Liverpool Lime Street (Table 49)
- B From Reading (Table 51)
- C **The Flying Scotsman**
- D From Manchester Airport (Table 39)
- E **The Northern Lights**
- G From Plymouth (Table 51)
- b Change at Ely and Peterborough
- c Change at Peterborough
- e Change at Doncaster. 22 June to 4 September arr. 1310, by bus
- f Change at Leeds
- g Bradford Interchange
- h Change at Selby and York
- j Arr. 1238
- k From 7 September arr. 1514
- m Glasgow Queen Street
- n Glasgow Queen Street. Change at Edinburgh
- q Change at Edinburgh
- r Change at Edinburgh and Stirling
- t Change at Edinburgh and Perth

Table 26 — Mondays to Fridays

London → Humberside, Yorkshire, North East England and Scotland

Route Diagram - see first page of Table 26

		GR	HT	TP	GR	TP	TP	XC	GR	GR	XC	GR	EM	TP	GR	XC	TP	TP	GR	GR	XC		HT	XC	GR	EM
		R 1	1 ◇	1 ◇	R 1	1 ◇	1 ◇	1 ◇	R 1	R 1	1 ◇	R 1	◇	1 ◇	R 1	1 ◇	1 ◇	1 ◇	R 1	R 1	1 ◇		1 ◇	1 ◇	R 1	◇
				A	B	A	A	C			D		E	A		D	A	A			G			D		E
			⊠		Ø				Ø	Ø					Ø				Ø	Ø			⊠			
London Kings Cross 15 ⊖	d	11 35	11 48		12 00				12 10	12 30		12 35			13 00				13 10	13 30			13 33		13 35	
Stevenage 4	d	11 54							12 29			12 57			*12 46*										*13 12*	
Peterborough 8	a	12 27			12 46				13 00	13 16					13 45				13 57						14 24	
Norwich	d												11 57													12 57
Stansted Airport	d								*11 25*																*12 25*	
Cambridge	d				*11b12*				*12 00*				*12c22*		*12b33*										*13 00*	
Peterborough 8	d	12 27			12 47				13 01	13 17			13 26		13 46				13 58						14 25	14 26
Grantham 7	a	12 46	12 53						13 20			13 42	13 56						14 17				14 34		14 44	14 56
	d	12 46	12 54						13 20			13 42							14 17				14 35		14 44	
Newark North Gate 7	a	12 58										13 55							14 29						15 00	
Lincoln	a	*14e05*																	*15 00*							
Grimsby Town	a		*14f45*												*15g42*				*15 57*							
Newark North Gate 7	d	12 58										13 55							14 29						15 01	
Retford 10	d		13 16						13 42											14 48			14 56			
Doncaster 7	a		13 29						13 57	14 06		14 20			14 33				14 53	15 02			15 11		15 25	
Selby	a		13 44																				15 27			
Hull	a		14 25							*15 07*					*15 51*								16 10			
Wakefield Westgate 7	a	13 37							14 14			14 39							15 14	*15 42*					15 51	
Huddersfield	a	*14h25*							*15 04*			*15h45*							*16 04*						*16h45*	
Leeds 10	a	13 55							14 35			15 01							15 35	*16 02*					16 09	
Shipley	a	*14 21*							*15 01*			*15 37*							*16 07*						*16 37*	
Bradford Forster Square	a	*14j28*							*15j11*			*15j42*							*16j10*						*16j42*	
Keighley	a	*14 50*							*15 11*			*15 50*							*16 20*						*16 51*	
Skipton	a	*15 07*							*15 24*			*16 07*							*16 37*						*17 07*	
Sheffield 7	d							13 21		*13 11*	13 54									*14 11*	14 21			14 54		
Doncaster 7	d									14 07	14 19				14 34					15 03				15 17		
York 8	a				14 00					14 34	14 43				14 58					15 26				15 40		
Scarborough	a				*15 30*															*16 30*						
Harrogate	a				*14 43*				*15 33*						*15 43*				*16 33*							
Leeds 10	d			13 27			13 57	14 05			*14 12*			14 27	*14 27*			14 57		*14 41*	15 05			*15 12*		
Hull	d							*13 12*									←									
York 8	d			13 54	14 02		14 26	14 33		14 36	14 48			14 54 →	15 00		14 54	15 26		15 28	15 34			15 44		
Thirsk	d					←	14 43											15 46								
Northallerton	d			14 16 →		14 16	14 54			14 58							15 23	15 55								
Darlington 7	a					14 27		14 58		15 11	15 16				15 27		15 34			16 01	16 06			16 11		
Eaglescliffe	a																									
Middlesbrough	a					*15 22*	15 30				*15 55*						*16 23*	16 30								
Darlington 7	d					14 34		15 00		15 11	15 18				15 28	←	15 35			16 01	16 07			16 13		
Durham	d					14 50		15 16		15 29	15 35 →					15 35	15 51				16 25			16 30		
Chester-le-Street	d																15 57									
Newcastle 8	a				14 58	15 06		15 31		15 47					15 57	15 58	16 12			16 31	16 37			16 51		
Hartlepool	a																									
Sunderland	a					*15 49*											*16 49*				*17k14*					
Newcastle 8	d				15 00			15 35							15 59					16 32	16 40					
Morpeth	d					*15a35*		15 48								*16a36*										
Alnmouth for Alnwick	d							16 02												16 58						
Berwick-upon-Tweed	d														16 42						17 26					
Dunbar	d																				17 49					
Edinburgh 10	a				16 27			17 09							17 33					18 04	18 13					
Edinburgh	d				16 33										17 39						18 16					
Haymarket	d				16 38										17 44						18 21					
Motherwell	a														18 23											
Glasgow Central 15	a				*17m36*			*18n22*							18 41					*19n06*	*19m21*					
Stirling	a				17 19			*18 06*							*18q53*						*19q25*					
Perth	a				18 00			*18r52*							*19r42*						*20q02*					
Inverness	a				20 08			*21 03*																		
Inverkeithing	a				*17q03*			*17 46*							*18q12*						18 36					
Kirkcaldy	a				*17q26*			*18 15*							*18q35*						18 58					
Leuchars 3	a				*18q12*			*18 34*							*19q11*						19 29					
Dundee	a				*18q34*			*18 47*							*19q27*						19 44					
Arbroath	a							*19 04*													20 01					
Montrose	a							*19 21*													20 15					
Stonehaven	a							*19 43*													20 35					
Aberdeen	a							*20 06*													20 57					

For general notes see front of timetable
For details of catering facilities see Directory of Train Operators

- **A** From Manchester Airport (Table 39)
- **B** **The Highland Chieftain**
- **C** From Penzance (Table 135)
- **D** From Reading (Table 51)
- **E** To Liverpool Lime Street (Table 49)
- **G** From Plymouth (Table 51)
- **b** Change at Ely and Peterborough
- **c** Change at Ely
- **e** Change at Peterborough
- **f** Change at Doncaster. 22 June to 4 September arr. 1510, by bus
- **g** Change at Doncaster. 22 June to 4 September arr. 1610, by bus
- **h** Change at Leeds
- **j** Bradford Interchange
- **k** From 7 September arr. 1 minute earlier
- **m** Glasgow Queen Street. Change at Edinburgh
- **n** Glasgow Queen Street
- **q** Change at Edinburgh
- **r** Change at Edinburgh and Stirling

London → Humberside, Yorkshire, North East England and Scotland

Route Diagram - see first page of Table 26

		GR	NT	GR	GR	TP	XC	EM	GR	XC	GR	XC	TP	XC
		R 1		R 1	R 1	1 ◇	1 ◇	◇	R 1	1 ◇	R 1	1 ◇	1 ◇	1 ◇
			A			B	C	D		E		E	B	G
London Kings Cross 15 ⊖	d	14 00		14 10	14 30				14 35		15 00			
Stevenage 4	d			13 46	14 12				14 54					
Peterborough 8	a			14 56	15 16									
Norwich	d							13 57						
Stansted Airport	d				13 25									
Cambridge	d			13b12	14 00									
Peterborough 8	d			14 56	15 16			15 26						
Grantham 7	a			15 15				15 55						
	d			15 15										
Newark North Gate 7	a			15 27										
Lincoln	a			16 03										
Grimsby Town	a	16c46							17e42					
Newark North Gate 7	d			15 27										
Retford 10	d													
Doncaster 7	a	15 29		15 55					16 09					
Selby	a													
Hull	a	16 49							17 14					
Wakefield Westgate 7	a			16 15					16 30					
Huddersfield	a			17 04					17g25					
Leeds 10	a			16 35					16 48					
Shipley	a			17 07					17 21					
Bradford Forster Square	a			17h10					17h28					
Keighley	a			17 21					17 51					
Skipton	a			17 37					18 07					
Sheffield 7	d						15 21			15 54				16 21
Doncaster 7	d	15 30								16 17				
York 8	a	15 53			16 21					16 40	16 44			
Scarborough	a						17 30				18 17			
Harrogate	a	16 43									17 26			
Leeds 10	d				15 27	15 57	16 05			16 12			16 27	17 05
Hull	d				15 06									16 10
York 8	d	15 55			16 22	16 26	16 32			16 43	16 46		16 58	17 33
Thirsk	d					16 46							17 14	
Northallerton	d					16 55							17 22	
Darlington 7	a	16 23			16 50		16 57			17 08			17 36	17 59
Eaglescliffe	a													
Middlesbrough	a	16 54			17 23	17 30				17 59			18 28	
Darlington 7	d				16 51		16 59			17 15		←	17 38	18 02
Durham	d				17 08		17 15			17 32 →		17 32	17 55	18 18
Chester-le-Street	d											17 41	18 01	
Newcastle 8	a	16 53			17 26		17 34				17 38	17 54	18 16	18 36
Hartlepool	a													
Sunderland	a	17j50											18 49	
Newcastle 8	d	16 54	17 15				17 36				17 40			18 43
Morpeth	d		17 36								18a07		18a49	
Alnmouth for Alnwick	d		18a18				18 02							
Berwick-upon-Tweed	d	17 38									18 27			19 25
Dunbar	d													19 48
Edinburgh 10	a	18 26					19 03				19 13			20 15
Edinburgh	d	18 30					19 07				19 18			20 15
Haymarket	d	18 35					19 12				19 22			20 20
Motherwell	a						19 55				19 59			
Glasgow Central 15	a	19k36					20 25				20 18			21k22
Stirling	a	19m25									20m23			21m23
Perth	a	20m02									20m53			
Inverness	a										23m14			
Inverkeithing	a	18 54					19m44				19m54			20 33
Kirkcaldy	a	19 11									20m10			20 49
Leuchars 3	a	19 38									20m28			21 21
Dundee	a	19 52									20m40			21 45
Arbroath	a	20 10									20m57			
Montrose	a	20 26									21m12			
Stonehaven	a	20 49									21m33			
Aberdeen	a	21 12									21m53			

		GR	GR	TP	XC	GR	EM	GR	TP	XC	HT	GR	GR FX
		R 1	R 1	1 ◇	1 ◇	R 1	◇	R 1	1 ◇	1 ◇	1 ◇	R 1	R 1
				H	E		D		B	G			
London Kings Cross 15 ⊖	d	15 10	15 30			15 35		16 00			16 05	16 10	16 30
Stevenage 4	d	14 46	15 12			15 54							16 49
Peterborough 8	a	15 56	16 16			16 26						16 56	
Norwich	d						14 57						
Stansted Airport	d		14 25										
Cambridge	d	14b33	15 00									15b24	
Peterborough 8	d	15 57	16 17			16 26	16 27					16 56	
Grantham 7	a	16 18				16 45	16 58				17 06	17 15	17 34
	d	16 18				16 45					17 07	17 15	17 34
Newark North Gate 7	a	16 29										17 27	17 46
Lincoln	a		17 51									18 03	
Grimsby Town	a							18f44					
Newark North Gate 7	d	16 29										17 27	17 46
Retford 10	d	16 45									17 28		
Doncaster 7	a	17 00	17 08			17 19		17 29			17 41		18 09
Selby	a										17 59		
Hull	a	18 06									18 40		19 09
Wakefield Westgate 7	a	17 18				17 36						18 04	
Huddersfield	a	18 05				18g25						18g57	
Leeds 10	a	17 36				17 56						18 23	
Shipley	a	18 02				18 21						18 52	
Bradford Forster Square	a	18h10				18h28						18h57	
Keighley	a	18 16				18 50						19 15	
Skipton	a	18 33				19 07						19 33	
Sheffield 7	d		16 11		16 54					17 21			
Doncaster 7	d		17 09		17 17			17 30					18 10
York 8	a		17 34		17 40			17 54					18 33
Scarborough	a		18 51										19 33
Harrogate	a	18 33						18 43				19 33	
Leeds 10	d		16 57	17 12					17 57	18 05			
Hull	d												
York 8	d		17 36	17 43	17 46			17 56	18 26	18 33			18 39
Thirsk	d			18 00					18 46				
Northallerton	d		17 56	18 10					18 55				19 00
Darlington 7	a		18 09		18 15			18 26		19 00			19 13
Eaglescliffe	a												
Middlesbrough	a			18 42				18 56	19 30	19 55			
Darlington 7	d		18 10		18 17			18 27		19 02			19 13
Durham	d		18 27		18 34					19 19			19 31
Chester-le-Street	d												
Newcastle 8	a		18 45		18 55			18 57		19 34			19 49
Hartlepool	a												
Sunderland	a							19j50					
Newcastle 8	d		18 46					18 59		19 38			
Morpeth	d												
Alnmouth for Alnwick	d		19 13							20 06			
Berwick-upon-Tweed	d							19 43					
Dunbar	d												
Edinburgh 10	a		20 26					20 29		21 12			
Edinburgh	d							20 32		21 14			
Haymarket	d							20 37		21 19			
Motherwell	a									22 04			
Glasgow Central 15	a							21k50		22 35			
Stirling	a												
Perth	a		22 00										
Inverness	a												
Inverkeithing	a							20 51					
Kirkcaldy	a							21 08					
Leuchars 3	a							21 33					
Dundee	a							21 47					
Arbroath	a							22 05					
Montrose	a							22 21					
Stonehaven	a							22 44					
Aberdeen	a							23 07					

For general notes see front of timetable
For details of catering facilities see Directory of Train Operators

- A From MetroCentre to Chathill (Table 48)
- B From Manchester Airport (Table 39)
- C From Penzance (Table 135)
- D To Liverpool Lime Street (Table 49)
- E From Reading (Table 51)
- G From Plymouth (Table 51)
- H From Liverpool Lime Street (Table 39)
- b Change at Ely and Peterborough
- c Change at Doncaster. 22 June to 4 September arr. 1720, by bus
- e Change at Doncaster. 22 June to 4 September arr. 1820, by bus
- f Change at Doncaster. 22 June to 4 September arr. 1920, by bus
- g Change at Leeds
- h Bradford Interchange
- j From 7 September arr. 1 minute earlier
- k Glasgow Queen Street. Change at Edinburgh
- m Change at Edinburgh

Table 26

Mondays to Fridays

London → Humberside, Yorkshire, North East England and Scotland

Route Diagram - see first page of Table 26

		GR	GR	EM		GC	GR	TP	XC	GR	GR	GR	TP	XC	GR	EM	XC	GR	GR	XC	GR	GR	GR	TP	XC	GR
		FO R 1	R 1	◇ A		R 1 B	R 1	1 ◇ C	1 ◇ D	R 1	R 1 E	R 1	1 ◇ C	1 ◇ G	R 1	◇ H	1 ◇ D	R 1	R 1	1 ◇ D	R 1	R 1	R 1	1 ◇ C	1 ◇ J	FX R 1
London Kings Cross 15 ⊖	d	16 30	16 35			16 50	17 00			17 03	17 19	17 30			17 33			17 49	18 00			18 03	18 19			18 30
Stevenage 4	d	16 49	16 12												17 52			17 18				17 40				18 50
Peterborough 8	a		17 24							17 51	18 06	18 16						18 37				18 54	19 06			
Norwich	d			15 52												16 57										
Stansted Airport	d		15 20								16 25												17 18			
Cambridge	d		16 00							16b35	17 00							17b22					17 51			
Peterborough 8	d		17 25	17 28						17 51	18 07	18 17				18 26		18 39				18 54	19 07			
Grantham 7	a	17 34		17 59						18 10					18 40	18 52		19 04			⟵	19 15				19 35
	d	17 34								18 10					18 40			19 05 ⟶			19 05	19 15				19 35
Newark North Gate 7	a	17 46									18 35										19 17		19 34			
Lincoln	a		19c07							19e32											19 51					
Grimsby Town	a									19f58									20g42		20 52					
Newark North Gate 7	d	17 46									18 35										19 17		19 34			
Retford 10	d		18 04												19 02											19 57
Doncaster 7	a	18 09	18 19							18 41	19 04				19 17				19 28		19 41	19 48				20 14
Selby	a										19 20															
Hull	a	19 09	19 48								20 00										20 55	21 06				
Wakefield Westgate 7	a		18 36							19 00					19 34						20 01	20 07				
Huddersfield	a		19h25							19h59					20h25							20h59				
Leeds 10	a		18 55							19 20					19 52						20 21	20 24				
Shipley	a		19 21							20 07					20s11							21 07				
Bradford Forster Square	a		19j28							19j57					20 22							20j57				
Keighley	a		19 41							20 20					20k50							20s57				
Skipton	a		19 54							20 35					21k06							21 13				
Sheffield 7	d								17 47					18 21			18 54								19 26	19 30
Doncaster 7	d	18 10															19 19		19 28							20 15
York 8	a	18 33				18 44	18 51					19 23					19 44		19 51				20 22			20 39
Scarborough	a	19 33										20 30											21 30			
Harrogate	a						19 43												20 43							
Leeds 10	d					18 12		18 27	18 35				18 57	19 05			19 12						19 27	19 57	20 09	20 12
Hull	d					17 18																		19 10		
York 8	d	18 39				18 47	18 53	18 56	19 01			19 25	19 31	19 37			19 47		19 53				20 23	20 29	20 37	20 44
Thirsk	d					19 05							19 47											20 45		
Northallerton	d	19 00				19 16		19 21					19 58											20 53		21 03
Darlington 7	a	19 13					19 21	19 33	19 38			19 52		20 04			20 12		20 22				20 51		21 07	21 16
Eaglescliffe	a					19 33																				
Middlesbrough	a						19 55					20 35	20 30						20 55					21 25		
Darlington 7	d	19 13					19 21	19 34	19 39			19 53		20 05			20 14		20 23				20 51		21 09	21 16
Durham	d	19 31						19 50	19 56			20 10		20 23			20 31						21 09		21 26	21 34
Chester-le-Street	d							19 56	20 02																	
Newcastle 8	a	19 49					19 52	20 10	20 18			20 26		20 38			20 48		20 52				21 27		21 39	21 52
Hartlepool	a					20 00																				
Sunderland	a					20 35						21 04								⟵						
Newcastle 8	d	19 49					19 54					20 29		20 40			20 58 ⟶		20 54	20 58					21 48	
Morpeth	d											20 44							21a26	21 14						
Alnmouth for Alnwick	d											21 00								21 28					22 12	
Berwick-upon-Tweed	d											21 22		21 28					21 37	21 48					22 33	
Dunbar	d											21 46		21 52												
Edinburgh 10	a	21 16					21 21					22 14		22 22					22 23	22 35					23 23	
Edinburgh	d																		22 26							
Haymarket	d																		22 30							
Motherwell	a																		23 13							
Glasgow Central 15	a	22m22					22m50					23m30							23 32	00m03						
Stirling	a						22 23												23n24							
Perth	a						23 03												00n07						00 23	
Inverness	a																									
Inverkeithing	a						22 11												23n01	23 31						
Kirkcaldy	a						22 12												23n23	23 53						
Leuchars 3	a						22 34													00 23						
Dundee	a						22 48													00 39						
Arbroath	a						23 05																			
Montrose	a						23 23																			
Stonehaven	a						23 45																			
Aberdeen	a						00 08																			

For general notes see front of timetable
For details of catering facilities see Directory of Train Operators

- **A** To Liverpool Lime Street (Table 49)
- **B** **The 21st Century Limited**
- **C** From Manchester Airport (Table 39)
- **D** From Reading (Table 51)
- **E** **The Hull Executive**
- **G** From Plymouth (Table 51)
- **H** To Manchester Piccadilly (Table 49)
- **J** From Plymouth (Table 51). ⚭ to Leeds
- **b** Change at Ely and Peterborough
- **c** Change at Retford
- **e** Change at Grantham and Sleaford
- **f** Change at Doncaster. 22 June to 4 September arr. 2025, by bus
- **g** Change at Doncaster. 22 June to 4 September arr. 2110, by bus
- **h** Change at Leeds
- **j** Bradford Interchange
- **k** Change at Shipley
- **m** Glasgow Queen Street
- **n** Change at Edinburgh

London → Humberside, Yorkshire, North East England and Scotland

Route Diagram - see first page of Table 26

		GR	GR	XC	HT	EM	GR	GR	TP	GR	GR	GR	XC	EM	GR	GR	HT	GR	XC	GR	TP	GR	GR	GR
		FO					FX	FO			FO						BHX							
		R 1	R 1	1 ◇	1 ◇	◇	R 1	R 1	1 ◇	R 1	R 1	R 1	1 ◇	◇	R 1	R 1	1 ◇	R 1	1 ◇	R 1	1 ◇	R 1	R 1	R 1
				A		B			C				D	B					D		C			
		✕ ⫫	Ø ⫫	⫫	⊠		✕ ⫫	✕ ⫫		✕ ⫫	☕ ⫫	✕ ⫫			Ø ⫫	Ø ⫫	⊠	☕ ⫫		Ø ⫫		☕ ⫫	☕	☕
London Kings Cross 15 ⊖	d	18 30	18 35		18 50		19 00	19 00		19 03	19 30	19 33			20 00	20 03	20 30	20 33		21 00		21 30	22 00	23 30
Stevenage 4	d	18 50	18 09				18 39	18 39				19 10			19b15	19 47				21 20			21 46	
Peterborough 8	a		19 25				19 46	19 46		19 52		20 22			20 46	20 52		21 20		21 53		22 16	22 46	00s23
Norwich	d					17 54								18 57								19c45		
Stansted Airport	d											18 21						19 21				20 21		
Cambridge	d						18c24	18c24				19 00			19c25			20 00				21 00		
Peterborough 8	d		19 25			19 31	19 47	19 47		19 53		20 22		20 28	20 46	20 53		21 20		21 54		22 17	22 47	
Grantham 7	a	19 35			19 55	20 01	20 06	20 06				20 41		20 56		21 14	21 30	21 39				22 38	23 08	00s44
	d	19 35			19 56		20 06	20 06				20 41				21 14	21 32	21 39				22 38	23 08	
Newark North Gate 7	a		19 52							20 22		20 53				21 26		21 51		22 23		22 49	23 19	00s56
Lincoln	a									20 56												23 40		
Grimsby Town	a				21e44							22f46			23g10			23h57						
Newark North Gate 7	d		19 54							20 22		20 53				21 26		21 51		22 23		22 49	23 19	
Retford 10	d	19 57			20 18										21 23		21 53					23 05		
Doncaster 7	a	20 14	20 18		20 30		20 38	20 38		20 47		21 19			21 38	21 51	22 11	22 17		22 47		23 24	23 49	01s24
Selby	a				20 46												22 29							
Hull	a				21 28										22 57		23 13							
Wakefield Westgate 7	a		20 38		21j10					21 15		21 37				22 13		22 35				23 42		
Huddersfield	a		21k25		21m59					22 05		22k25						23 15						03k56
Leeds 10	a		20 55		21j27					21 35		21 55				22 33		22 53				23 59		02 37
Shipley	a		21 38							22 07		22 37				23 07		23 31						
Bradford Forster Square	a		21n28		21q57							22n28						23n29						
Keighley	a		21 50							22 20		22 50				23 20		23 44						
Skipton	a		22 07							22 36		23 10				23 39		00 01						
Sheffield 7	d	19 30		19 54									20 54						21 54	22 11				
Doncaster 7	d	20 15		20 22			20 38	20 38					21 22		21 39				22 31	22 48			23 49	
York 8	a	20 39		20 46			21 01	21 01			21 21		21 45		22 01				22 59	23 13			00 41	
Scarborough	a														23 06									
Harrogate	a						21 43	21 43							22 45			00 06						
Leeds 10	d	20 12		20 12					20 45						21 12					21 51	22 42			
Hull	d								19r56															
York 8	d	20 44		20 51			21 03	21 03	21 14		21 23		21 47		22 03					23 14	23 20			
Thirsk	d								21 30												23 35			
Northallerton	d	21 03							21 38						22 23						23 55			
Darlington 7	a	21 16		21 20			21 30	21 30	21 49		21 54		22 13		22 35					23 49	00 06		01 26	
Eaglescliffe	a																							
Middlesbrough	a						22 09	22 09							23 10									
Darlington 7	d	21 16		21 22			21 31	21 31	21 50		21 54		22 14		22 36					23 50	00 08			
Durham	d	21 34		21 39			21 49	21 49	22 08		22 13		22 31		22 53					00 07	00 24		01a44	
Chester-le-Street	d			21 46									22 37											
Newcastle 8	a	21 52		22 00			22 07	22 07	22 23		22 31		22 56		23 16					00 41	00 56		02 23	
Hartlepool	a																							
Sunderland	a																							
Newcastle 8	d	21 53						22 08																
Morpeth	d							22 22																
Alnmouth for Alnwick	d							22 38																
Berwick-upon-Tweed	d	22 37						23 00																
Dunbar	d																							
Edinburgh 10	a	23 30						23 54																
Edinburgh	d																							
Haymarket	d																							
Motherwell	a																							
Glasgow Central 15	a																							
Stirling	a																							
Perth	a																							
Inverness	a																							
Inverkeithing	a																							
Kirkcaldy	a																							
Leuchars 3	a																							
Dundee	a																							
Arbroath	a																							
Montrose	a																							
Stonehaven	a																							
Aberdeen	a																							

For general notes see front of timetable
For details of catering facilities see Directory of Train Operators

- **A** From Reading (Table 51). ⫫ to Doncaster
- **B** To Nottingham (Table 19)
- **C** From Manchester Airport (Table 39)
- **D** From Reading (Table 51)
- **b** Change at Hitchin and Peterborough
- **c** Change at Ely and Peterborough
- **e** Change at Doncaster. 22 June to 4 September arr. 2210, by bus
- **f** Until 19 June and from 7 September only. Change at Doncaster
- **g** 22 June to 4 September only. Change at Doncaster. By bus
- **h** Change at Doncaster. 22 June to 4 September arr. 0015, by bus
- **j** Change at Doncaster
- **k** Change at Leeds
- **m** Change at Doncaster and Leeds
- **n** Bradford Interchange
- **q** Bradford Interchange. Change at Doncaster and Leeds
- **r** Change at Selby and York

Table 26

Saturdays

London → Humberside, Yorkshire, North East England and Scotland

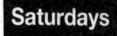

Route Diagram - see first page of Table 26

	NT	TP	XC	GR	GR	NT	TP	TP	GR	XC	TP	NT	XC	GR	TP	XC	EM	TP	GR	TP	XC	GR	XC	EM
		1◇	1◇	R 1	R 1		1◇	1◇	R 1	1◇	1◇		1◇	R 1	1◇	1◇	◇	1◇	R 1	1◇	1◇	R 1	1◇	◇
	A					B	C			D	E	B	G			G	H	E		E	G		G	H
London Kings Cross 15 ⊖ d														06 15					07 00			07 10		
Stevenage 4 d														06 34					06 46					
Peterborough 8 a														07 05					07 45			07 56		
Norwich d																	05 52							06 52
Stansted Airport d														05b25										
Cambridge d														05b55			06c26		06e32					
Peterborough 8 d														07 06			07 27		07 46			07 56		08 30
Grantham 7 a														07 25			07 56		08 05			08 15		08 58
d														07 25					08 05			08 15		
Newark North Gate 7 a														07 37					08 17			08 27		
Lincoln a																			09 02			09f59		
Grimsby Town a														09g42					10h20			10j44		
Newark North Gate 7 d														07 37					08 17			08 27		
Retford 10 d														07 52								08 42		
Doncaster 7 a														08 07					08 41			08 57		
Selby a																								
Hull a														09 13					09 55			10 10		
Wakefield Westgate 7 a														08 56								09 15		
Huddersfield a																						10 04		
Leeds 10 a																						09 36		
Shipley a																						10 01		
Bradford Forster Square a																						10k10		
Keighley a																						10 11		
Skipton a																						10 24		
Sheffield 7 d					05 29					06 49			07 12	07 24		07 54					08 21		08 54	
Doncaster 7 d					06 20					07 17				08 08		08 25			08 42				09 23	
York 8 a					06 40					07 39				08 31		08 49			09 04				09 45	
Scarborough a																			10m32					
Harrogate a										08 29				09 17		09 43						10 33		
Leeds 10 d					05 19		06 35	06 55	07 10		07 50		07 57		08 12			08 27		08 57	09 07		09 12	
Hull d								06n00			06 57													
York 8 d		05 54			06 42		07 06	07 32	07 35	07 42	08 23		08 28	08 33	08 42	08 51		08 57	09 06	09 26	09 34		09 47	
Thirsk d		06 10					07 22	07 54			08 45									09 46				
Northallerton d		06 18			07 01		07 30	08 04			08 56				09 03			09 18		09 55				
Darlington 7 a		06 29			07 15		07 41		08 04	08 09			08 54	09 00	09 14	09 18		09 29	09 35		09 59		10 13	
Eaglescliffe a																								
Middlesbrough a		07 01			08 02			08 36		09 21	09 32				09 53				10 16	10 30			10 52	
Darlington 7 d					07 15	07 20	07 42		08 05	08 11		08 15	08 55	09 01	09 15	09 20		09 30	09 36		10 01		10 14	
Durham d					07 33	07 41	07 59		08 22	08 29		08 36	09 12	09 18	09 31	09 36		09 46			10 17		10 31	
Chester-le-Street d						07 48	08 05					08 43				09 43								
Newcastle 8 a					07 50	08 02	08 18		08 43	08 51		09 00	09 26	09 34	09 49	09 59		10 02	10 05		10 33		10 51	
Hartlepool a																								
Sunderland a							08 49					09 49							10 49					
Newcastle 8 d	06 05			06 30	07 52				08 45				09 29	09 36					10 07		10 36			
Morpeth d	06 25			06 43	08 06	08a44							09 42						10a35					
Alnmouth for Alnwick d	06a43			06 57	08 20								09 56											
Berwick-upon-Tweed d				07 19	08 42				09 29					10 21					10 50		11 18			
Dunbar d				07 43	09 06				09 53												11 41			
Edinburgh 10 a				08 09	09 32				10 21				11 02	11 10					11 37		12 12			
Edinburgh d			07 25	08 12	09 38				10 27										11 39					
Haymarket d			07 29		09 42				10 32										11 43					
Motherwell a			08 15	08 57	10 27														12 28					
Glasgow Central 15 a			08 35	09 15	10 48				11q37				12r05	12r19					12 50		13r19			
Stirling a				09t23	10t54				11t23					12 22					12t53		13 23			
Perth a				09t48	11v34				11t54					12 52					13v36		14v36			
Inverness a				11t54										15 06										
Inverkeithing a				09t00	10t12				10 47					12 01					12t11		12 52			
Kirkcaldy a				09t06	10t33				11 04					12 23					12t34		13 08			
Leuchars 3 a				09t23	11t03				11 28					12 23					13t03		13 23			
Dundee a				09t36	11t20				11 43					12 36					13t18		13 35			
Arbroath a				09t53					12 01					12 53							13 52			
Montrose a				10w31					12 17					13w33							14 07			
Stonehaven a				10t29					12 42					13 26							14 28			
Aberdeen a				10t53					13 07					13 46							14 48			

For general notes see front of timetable
For details of catering facilities see Directory of Train Operators

- **A** To Chathill (Table 48)
- **B** From Saltburn (Table 44)
- **C** From Manchester Piccadilly (Table 39)
- **D** From Derby (Table 51)
- **E** From Manchester Airport (Table 39)
- **G** From Birmingham New Street (Table 51)
- **H** To Liverpool Lime Street (Table 49)
- **b** Until 11 July and from 12 September only
- **c** Change at Ely. 18 July to 5 September dep. 0608
- **e** Change at Ely and Peterborough
- **f** Change at Peterborough
- **g** Until 20 June and from 12 September change at Doncaster. 27 June to 5 September change at Retford arr. 1000
- **h** 27 June to 5 September only. Change at Doncaster, by bus
- **j** Until 20 June and from 12 September only; change at Doncaster
- **k** Bradford Interchange. Until 11 July arr. 1012
- **m** 18 July to 5 September arr. 1015
- **n** Change at Selby and York
- **q** Glasgow Queen Street. Change at Edinburgh
- **r** Glasgow Queen Street
- **t** Change at Edinburgh
- **v** Change at Edinburgh and Stirling
- **w** Change at Edinburgh and Arbroath

Table 26

Saturdays

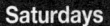

London → Humberside, Yorkshire, North East England and Scotland

Route Diagram - see first page of Table 26

	TP	GC	GR	TP	EM	EM	TP	XC	GR	GR	XC	EM	TP	GR	TP	XC	GR	GR	XC	TP	HT	EM	GR
	1◇	R 1	R 1	1◇	1◇	1◇	1◇	1◇	R 1	R 1	1◇	◇	1◇	R 1	1◇	1◇	R 1	R 1	1◇	1◇	1◇	◇	R 1
	A		Ø	A	B	C	A	D			E	G	A	Ø	A	H			J	A	⊠	G	K
London Kings Cross 15 ⊖ d		07 57	08 00						08 10	08 30				09 00			09 05	09 30			09 34		10 00
Stevenage 4 d			08 20						07 46	08 49							09 24	09 49					
Peterborough 8 a			08 51						08 57	09 20				09 45				10 20					10 46
Norwich d												07 57										08 57	
Stansted Airport d			06b25							07b25								08b25					
Cambridge d			07c00							08e00				08c33				09f00					09c12
Peterborough 8 d			08 51						08 57	09 21		09 30		09 46				10 21				10 28	10 46
Grantham 7 a									09 16	09 40		09 58						10 40			10 44	10 58	
d									09 16	09 40								10 40			10 44		
Newark North Gate 7 a									09 28								10 18						
Lincoln a									10 21	10g59											12h06		
Grimsby Town a			11j15						11 21	11k42				12j10									12m44
Newark North Gate 7 d									09 28								10 18						
Retford 10 d														10 24							11 06		
Doncaster 7 a			09 37						09 56	10 11				10 39			10 47	11 13			11 24		11 32
Selby a																					11 39		
Hull a			10 50							11 12				11 53			12 08				12 20		12 50
Wakefield Westgate 7 a									10 14								11 11						
Huddersfield a									11 04								12 04						
Leeds 10 a									10 35								11 35						
Shipley a									11 01								12 07						
Bradford Forster Square a									11n11								12q10						
Keighley a									11 11								12 20						
Skipton a									11 24								12 37						
Sheffield 7 d					09 21	09 21		09 21		09 25	09 54					10 21		10 24	10 54				
Doncaster 7 d			09 37		09 55	09 55				10 12	10 20			10 40				11 14	11 20				11 32
York 8 a		09 57	10 01		10 16	10 16				10 39	10 44			11 03				11 39	11 44				11 56
Scarborough a					11 06	11 30								12r30									13t30
Harrogate a			10 43						11 33					11 43			12 33						12 43
Leeds 10 d	09 27						09 57	10 07			10 12		10 27		10 57	11 07			11 12	11 27			
Hull d	08v40						09 02									10v06							
York 8 d	09 56	10 00	10 03				10 26	10 34		10 42	10 47		10 54	11 04	11 26	11 34		11 41	11 47	11 54			11 57
Thirsk d		10 21		←			10 46								11 43								
Northallerton d	10 25 →	10 32		10 25			10 55						11 15		11 55					12 16			12 20
Darlington 7 a			10 30	10 36				10 59		11 11	11 16		11 27	11 33		11 59		12 09	12 14	12 27			12 32
Eaglescliffe a		10 48																					
Middlesbrough a				11 09			11 30				11 55				12 30	12 32				12 58			13 23
Darlington 7 d			10 31	10 37				11 01		11 11	11 17		11 28	11 33		12 01		12 10	12 16	12 28			12 33
Durham d			10 48	10 54				11 17			11 34		11 45			12 17		12 27	12 35	12 45			
Chester-le-Street d				11 00															12 42				
Newcastle 8 a			11 04	11 14				11 32		11 43	11 54		12 00	12 02		12 33		12 44	12 55	13 00			13 02
Hartlepool a		11 20																					
Sunderland a		11 50		11 49										12 49									13 49
Newcastle 8 d			11 08					11 36		11 45				12 03		12 36		12 46					13 04
Morpeth d			11a35											12a35									13a36
Alnmouth for Alnwick d			11 34					12 00															
Berwick-upon-Tweed d										12 28						13 18		13 29					
Dunbar d																13 41							
Edinburgh 10 a			12 40					13 06		13 16				13 28		14 12		14 16					14 32
Edinburgh d														13 40									
Haymarket d														13 44									
Motherwell a														14 27									
Glasgow Central 15 a			13w49							14w19				14 47				15w20					15w37
Stirling a			13 53							14 23				14y53				15 23					
Perth a			14z36							14 52				15z36				15 53					
Inverness a										17 05													
Inverkeithing a			13 17					13 41						14y01				14 52					15 12
Kirkcaldy a			13 33					14 23						14y23				15 08					
Leuchars 3 a			14 03							14 23				15y03				15 23					
Dundee a			14 18							14 35				15y18				15 37					
Arbroath a										14 52								15 54					
Montrose a										15L37								16 08					
Stonehaven a										15 26								16 30					
Aberdeen a										15 46								16 50					

For general notes see front of timetable
For details of catering facilities see Directory of Train Operators

- **A** From Manchester Airport (Table 39)
- **B** Until 5 September. From St Pancras International (Table 53)
- **C** From 12 September. From St Pancras International (Table 53)
- **D** From Bristol Temple Meads (Table 51)
- **E** From Guildford (Table 51)
- **G** To Liverpool Lime Street (Table 49)
- **H** From Plymouth (Table 51)
- **J** From Bournemouth (Table 51)
- **K** **The Flying Scotsman**
- **L** Change at Edinburgh and Arbroath
- **b** Until 11 July and from 12 September only
- **c** Change at Ely and Peterborough
- **e** 18 July to 5 September dep. 0700
- **f** 18 July to 5 September dep. 0833
- **g** Change at Peterborough
- **h** Change at Retford
- **j** 27 June to 5 September only; by bus from Doncaster
- **k** Until 20 June and from 12 September only; change at Doncaster
- **m** Change at Doncaster. 27 June to 5 September arr. 1310, by bus
- **n** Bradford Interchange. Until 11 July arr. 1112
- **q** Bradford Interchange. Until 11 July arr. 1212
- **r** 18 July to 5 September arr. 1215
- **t** 18 July to 5 September arr. 1315
- **v** Change at Selby and York
- **w** Glasgow Queen Street
- **y** Change at Edinburgh
- **z** Change at Edinburgh and Stirling

London → Humberside, Yorkshire, North East England and Scotland

Route Diagram - see first page of Table 26

		TP	GR	GR	XC	EM	XC	GR	TP	GR	TP	TP	GR	GC	XC	GR	XC	HT	EM	TP	GR	XC	TP	TP
		1◇ A	R 1	R 1 B	1◇ C	◇ D	1◇ E	R 1	1◇ A	R 1	1◇ A	1◇ A	R 1	R 1	1◇ C	R 1 Ø	1◇ E	1◇	◇ D	1◇ A	R 1 G Ø	1◇ E	1◇ A	1◇ A
London Kings Cross 15 ⊖	d		10 10	10 30				10 40		11 00			11 10	11 27		11 30		11 48			12 00			
Stevenage 4	d			10 12						10 46						11 50								
Peterborough 8	a		10 56	11 16				11 26		11 45			11 56			12 21					12 46			
Norwich	d					09 57													10 57					
Stansted Airport	d			09b25												10b25								
Cambridge	d			10c00				10c22		10e33						11f00					11e12			
Peterborough 8	d		10 56	11 18		11 25		11 27		11 46			11 56			12 21			12 25		12 47			
Grantham 7	a		11 15			11 57		11 48					12 16			12 42		12 49	12 58					
	d		11 15					11 48					12 16			12 42		12 49						
Newark North Gate 7	a		11 27										12 28											
Lincoln	a		12 35					13g14					13 30					14h06						
Grimsby Town	a		13 36							13j42								14k44						
Newark North Gate 7	d		11 27										12 28											
Retford 10	d												12 43					13 13						
Doncaster 7	a		11 53					12 19		12 33			12 58			13 14		13 26						
Selby	a																	13 42						
Hull	a		13 07							13 50			14 10					14 22						
Wakefield Westgate 7	a		12 13										13 16											
Huddersfield	a		13 03										14 04											
Leeds 10	a		12 35										13 35											
Shipley	a		13 01										14 03											
Bradford Forster Square	a		13m10										14n11											
Keighley	a		13 11										14 13											
Skipton	a		13 24										14 26											
Sheffield 7 ⛴	d				11 21		11 54	11 41							12 21	12 24	12 54							
Doncaster 7	d						12 18	12 20		12 34						13 15	13 21							
York 8	a			12 27			12 44	12 47		12 56				13 25		13 39	13 44				13 56			
Scarborough	a													14 30										
Harrogate	a		13 33							13 43			14 33								14 43			
Leeds 10	d	11 57		11q41	12 07		12 12		12 27			12 57		12r41	13 07		13 12			13 27				13 57
Hull	d	11 08									←				11t38									
York 8	d	12 26		12 29	12 34		12 47	12 49	12 54 →	12 58	12 54	13 26		13 30	13 34	13 41	13 49			13 54	13 57			14 26 →
Thirsk	d	12 46										13 43		13 51									←	
Northallerton	d	12 55									13 23	13 55		14 09						14 23 →			14 23	
Darlington 7	a				13 01		13 12	13 17		13 25	13 34				13 59	14 09	14 16						14 34	
Eaglescliffe	a													14 26										
Middlesbrough	a	13 30					13 57	13 57			14 18	14 30					14 58						15 27	
Darlington 7	d				13 03		13 14	13 17		13 26	13 35				14 01	14 09	14 17					←	14 34	
Durham	d				13 19		13 30	13 35			13 52				14 17	14 27	14 35 →					14 35	14 50	
Chester-le-Street	d										13 58											14 42		
Newcastle 8 ⛴	a			13 25	13 33		13 50	13 53		13 59	14 12				14 32	14 43					14 54	14 55	15 08	
Hartlepool	a													14 45										
Sunderland ⛴	a										14 49			15 15									15 50	
Newcastle 8 ⛴	d			13 26	13 36					14 01					14 36	14 45					14 58			
Morpeth	d									14a36												15a35		
Alnmouth for Alnwick	d				14 00																			
Berwick-upon-Tweed	d									14 44					15 18						15 42			
Dunbar	d														15 41									
Edinburgh 10	a			14 53	15 09					15 29					16 10	16 18					16 30			
Edinburgh	d			15 00						15 36											16 33			
Haymarket	d			15 04						15 41											16 38			
Motherwell	a									16 27														
Glasgow Central 15	a			16v07	16w19					16 50						17w21					17v36			
Stirling	a			15y53	16 23					16y53											17 19			
Perth	a			16z36	16 53					17z36						17 52					18 00			
Inverness	a				19H34											20 08					20 08			
Inverkeithing	a			15 18	15 42					16y01						16 51					17y10			
Kirkcaldy	a			15 35	16 08					16y23						17 07					17y37			
Leuchars 3	a			16 00	16 23					17y03						17 24					18y12			
Dundee	a			16 18	16 35					17y20						17 38					18y34			
Arbroath	a			16 35	16 53											18 01								
Montrose	a			16 51	17 08											18 16								
Stonehaven	a			17 14	17 32											18 40								
Aberdeen	a			17 37	17 52											19 00								

For general notes see front of timetable
For details of catering facilities see Directory of Train Operators

- **A** From Manchester Airport (Table 39)
- **B** **The Northern Lights**
- **C** From Plymouth (Table 51)
- **D** To Liverpool Lime Street (Table 49)
- **E** From Reading (Table 51)
- **G** **The Highland Chieftain**
- **H** Change at Edinburgh and Perth
- **b** Until 11 July and from 12 September only
- **c** 18 July to 5 September dep. 0912
- **e** Change at Ely and Peterborough
- **f** 18 July to 5 September dep. 1033
- **g** Change at Peterborough
- **h** Change at Retford
- **j** Change at Doncaster. 27 June to 5 September arr. 1410, by bus
- **k** Change at Doncaster. 27 June to 5 September arr. 1510, by bus
- **m** Bradford Interchange. Until 11 July arr. 1312
- **n** Bradford Interchange. Until 11 July arr. 1412
- **q** Until 11 July dep. 1143
- **r** Until 11 July dep. 1243
- **t** Change at Selby and York
- **v** Glasgow Queen Street. Change at Edinburgh
- **w** Glasgow Queen Street
- **y** Change at Edinburgh
- **z** Change at Edinburgh and Stirling

Table 26

London → Humberside, Yorkshire, North East England and Scotland

Route Diagram - see first page of Table 26

	XC	GR	GR	EM	TP	XC	TP	GR	TP	TP	XC	GR	GR	XC	HT	EM	GR	TP	NT	XC	XC	GR	EM
		R	R					R				R	R				R					R	
	1 ◇	1	1	◇	1 ◇	1 ◇	1 ◇	1	1 ◇	1 ◇	1 ◇	1	1	1 ◇	1 ◇	◇	1	1 ◇		1 ◇	1 ◇	1	◇
	A			B	C	D	C		C	C	E			D		G		C	H	J	D		B
	╤	Ø ╤	Ø ╤	╤	╤	╤	╤	Ø ╤	╤	╤	╤	Ø ╤	⊡ ╤	╤	⊠	╤	⊡ ╤			╤	╤	⊡ ╤	╤
London Kings Cross 15 ⊖ d		12 10	12 30					13 00				13 10	13 30		13 48		14 00					14 30	
Stevenage 4 d			12 12					12 46					13 49									14 12	
Peterborough 8 a		12 56	13 16					13 45				13 56	14 20				14 46					15 16	
Norwich d				11 57												12 57							13 57
Stansted Airport d			11b25										12b25									13b25	
Cambridge d			12c00	12e22				12f33					13g00				13f12					14h00	
Peterborough 8 d		12 56	13 16	13 28				13 46				13 56	14 21			14 26	14 47					15 16	15 26
Grantham 7 a		13 15	13 35	13 56								14 16	14 40		14 47	14 57						15 35	15 57
d		13 15	13 35									14 16	14 40		14 47							15 35	
Newark North Gate 7 a		13 27										14 28	14 52									15 47	
Lincoln a												15 00	16 03		16j09		16 48						
Grimsby Town a								15k42				15 57					16m44						
Newark North Gate 7 d		13 27										14 28	14 52									15 47	
Retford 10 d												14 43			15 12							16 02	
Doncaster 7 a		13 52	14 07					14 33				14 58			15 26		15 35					16 20	
Selby a															15 42								
Hull a			15n10					15 51				16 07			16 22		16 50						
Wakefield Westgate 7 a		14 13	14 42									15 15										16 38	
Huddersfield a		15 10	15q45									16 04										17r45	
Leeds 10 a		14 35	15 02									15 35										17 01	
Shipley a		15 01	15q37									16 07										17 37	
Bradford Forster Square a		15t11	15v42									16w10										17y42	
Keighley a		15 11	15q50									16 20										17 51	
Skipton a		15 24	16q07									16 37										18 07	
Sheffield 7 ⛴ d	13 21		13 11			13 54					14 21			14 54						15 21	15 54		
Doncaster 7 d			14 07			14 18		14 34						15 18			15 36				16 18		
York 8 a			14 34			14 44		14 58					15 38	15 44			15 59				16 44		
Scarborough a	15 30							16 30									17 30						
Harrogate a		15 33						15 43				16 33					16 43					17 47	
Leeds 10 d	14 07					14 12	14 27			14 57	15 07			15 12				15 57		16 07	16 12		
Hull d	13 12				⟵				⟵								14 51						
York 8 d	14 34		14 36		14 26	14 47	14 54 ⟶	15 00	14 54	15 26	15 34		15 41	15 47			16 01	16 26		16 34	16 47		
Thirsk d					14 46					15 47								16 46					
Northallerton d			14 55		15 00				15 23	15 55								16 55					
Darlington 7 a	14 59		15 08			15 15		15 27	15 34		15 59		16 08	16 13			16 29			16 59	17 12		
Eaglescliffe a																							
Middlesbrough a					15 35				16 22	16 30				16 52			17 26	17 33			17 54		
Darlington 7 d	15 01		15 08			15 16		15 28	15 35		16 01		16 09	16 15			16 29			17 01	17 14		
Durham d	15 17		15 26			15 33		15 45	15 51		16 17		16 26	16 33						17 17	17 30		
Chester-le-Street d									15 57												17 37		
Newcastle 8 ⛴ a	15 32		15 42			15 51		16 01	16 12		16 32		16 42	16 51			16 59			17 32	17 53		
Hartlepool a																							
Sunderland ⛴ a									16 49				17 14				17z50						
Newcastle 8 ⛴ d	15 36		15 43					16 03			16 36		16 44				17 01		17 10	17 36			
Morpeth d	15 49							16a36											17 32	18a06			
Alnmouth for Alnwick d	16 03							16 30											18a00	18 02			
Berwick-upon-Tweed d								16 52			17 18												
Dunbar d											17 41												
Edinburgh 10 a	17 14		17 19					17 38			18 05		18 12				18 28			19 07			
Edinburgh d								17 40			18 08						18 32			19 10			
Haymarket d								17 45			18 13						18 37			19 14			
Motherwell a								18 28												20 00			
Glasgow Central 15 a			18K22					18 50			19L06		19K21				19L36			20 29			
Stirling a			18 23					18N53					19 23				19N53			20N23			
Perth a			18 58					19Q42									20N02			20N53			
Inverness a			21 03																	23N14			
Inverkeithing a			18 08								18 25		18 48				18 54			19N44			
Kirkcaldy a			18 15								18 40						19 11			20N10			
Leuchars 3 a			18 34								19 11						19 38			20N28			
Dundee a			18 47								19 24						19 52			20N40			
Arbroath a			19 04								19 41						20 10			20N57			
Montrose a			19 21								20 01						20 26			21N12			
Stonehaven a			19 43								20 22						20 49			21N33			
Aberdeen a			20 06								20 46						21 12			21N53			

For general notes see front of timetable
For details of catering facilities see Directory of Train Operators

- **A** From Penzance (Table 51)
- **B** To Liverpool Lime Street (Table 49)
- **C** From Manchester Airport (Table 39)
- **D** From Reading (Table 51)
- **E** From Plymouth (Table 51)
- **G** To Liverpool (Table 49)
- **H** From MetroCentre to Chathill (Table 48)
- **J** From Penzance (Table 135)
- **K** Glasgow Queen Street
- **L** Glasgow Queen Street. Change at Edinburgh
- **N** Change at Edinburgh
- **Q** Change at Edinburgh and Stirling
- **b** Until 11 July and from 12 September only
- **c** 18 July to 5 September dep. 1112
- **e** Change at Ely. 18 July to 5 September dep. 1212
- **f** Change at Ely and Peterborough
- **g** 18 July to 5 September dep. 1233
- **h** 18 July to 5 September dep. 1312
- **j** Change at Retford
- **k** Change at Doncaster. 27 June to 5 September arr. 1610, by bus
- **m** Change at Doncaster. 27 June to 5 September arr. 1720, by bus
- **n** From 12 September arr. 1512
- **q** Change at Doncaster and Leeds
- **r** Change at Leeds
- **t** Bradford Interchange. Until 11 July arr. 1512
- **v** Bradford Interchange. Change at Doncaster and Leeds
- **w** Bradford Interchange. Until 11 July arr. 1612
- **y** Bradford Interchange
- **z** From 12 September arr. 1749

Saturdays

London → Humberside, Yorkshire, North East England and Scotland

Route Diagram - see first page of Table 26

		GR	TP	TP	XC	XC	GR	XC	EM	GR	TP	XC		GR	EM	GC	TP	GR	TP	XC	GC	TP	HT	XC	GR	XC
		R 1	1 ◇	1 ◇	1 ◇	1 ◇	R 1	1 ◇	◇	R 1	1 ◇	1 ◇		R 1	◇	R 1	1 ◇	R 1	1 ◇	1 ◇	R 1	1 ◇	1 ◇	1 ◇	R 1	1 ◇
			A	A	B	C		D	E		A	G			H	J	A		A	D	J	A		G		D
London Kings Cross 15 ⊖	d	15 00					15 30			16 00				16 30		16 50		17 00					17 05		17 30	
Stevenage 4	d	14 46					15 49							16 12				16 46							17 50	
Peterborough 8	a	15 45					16 20			16 46				17 16				17 45							18 21	
Norwich	d								14 57						15 52											
Stansted Airport	d						14b25							15b25											16b25	
Cambridge	d	14c33					15e00			15c12				16f00	16g22			16c33							17h00	
Peterborough 8	d	15 46					16 21		16 27	16 46				17 16	17 27			17 46							18 21	
Grantham 7	a						16 40		16 58					17 35	18 01								18 10		18 42	
	d						16 40							17 35									18 10		18 42	
Newark North Gate 7	a						16 52							17 47											18 54	
Lincoln	a	17 51												18 33									19j32			
Grimsby Town	a	17k42								18m44				19 29									19n58			
Newark North Gate 7	d						16 52							17 47											18 54	
Retford 10	d													18 02									18 31			
Doncaster 7	a	16 32					17 16			17 35				18 17				18 33					18 46		19 17	
Selby	a																						19 07			
Hull	a	17 53								18 57				19 15									19 47			
Wakefield Westgate 7	a						17 33							18 35											19 35	
Huddersfield	a						18q25							19q25											20q25	
Leeds 10	a						17 53							18 53											19 51	
Shipley	a						18 21							19 21											20 18	
Bradford Forster Square	a						18r28							19t28											20v28	
Keighley	a						18 50							19 41											20s17	
Skipton	a						19 07							19 54											20 31	
Sheffield 7 ⛴	d				16 21	16 21		16 54				17 21						17 41		17 47				18 21		18 54
Doncaster 7	d	16 32						17 21		17 35								18 34								19 20
York 8	a	16 56						17 44		18 01						18 46		18 56								19 44
Scarborough	a	18 29								19 30										20 30						
Harrogate	a	17 49					19 03			18 43				20 03						19 43						
Leeds 10	d		16 27	16 57	17 07	17 07		17 12			17 57	18 07				18 12	18 27			18 35		18 57		19 07		19 12
Hull	d			16 10												17 18										
York 8	d	16 57	17 02	17 26	17 33	17 33		17 47		18 03	18 26	18 34				18 48	18 56	18 58		19 04	←	19 26		19 34		19 47
Thirsk	d		17 20	17 40							18 44					19 20			←		19 20	19 42				
Northallerton	d		17 28	17 51						18 22	18 55					→	19 21		19 21		19 29	19 50				
Darlington 7	a	17 27	17 39		18 00	18 00		18 12		18 35		19 01					→	19 25	19 33	19 37				20 03		20 12
Eaglescliffe	a																				19 48					
Middlesbrough	a		18 27	18 32				19 00			19 30	19 52										20 23				
Darlington 7	d	17 27	17 40		18 01	18 01		18 14		18 35		19 02						19 26	19 34	19 39				20 04		20 14
Durham	d	17 45	17 57		18 17	18 17		18 30				19 20						19 43	19 50	19 55				20 22		20 30
Chester-le-Street	d		18 03																19 56	20 02						
Newcastle 8 ⛴	a	18 01	18 17		18 37	18 37		18 50		19 05		19 35						19 59	20 10	20 18				20 33		20 45
Hartlepool	a																				20 07					
Sunderland ⛴	a		18 49							19 50											20 34					21 20
Newcastle 8 ⛴	d	18 02			18 42	18 42				19 06		19 37						20 01						20 36		20 50
Morpeth	d		18a49																20a45							21 03
Alnmouth for Alnwick	d											20 04														21 17
Berwick-upon-Tweed	d	18 45			19 26	19 26				19 49														21 20		21 38
Dunbar	d				19 50	19 50												21 05						21 43		
Edinburgh 10	a	19 34			20 15	20 15				20 37		21 10						21 31						22 15		22 28
Edinburgh	d	19 39			20 22	20 22						21 10						21 39								
Haymarket	d	19 43			20 26	20 26						21 14						21 43								
Motherwell	a	20 22										21 55						22 26								
Glasgow Central 15	a	20 44			21w22	21w22				21y50		22 23						22 46						23y30		
Stirling	a	20z53			21z23	21z23						22z23												23 24		
Perth	a	21K42			22z00	22z00						23z03						23z34								00 07
Inverness	a																									
Inverkeithing	a	20z12			20 43	20 43				21 14								22z11								23 01
Kirkcaldy	a	20z44			20 59	21 00				21 44		22z04						22z53								23 23
Leuchars 3	a	21z14			21 31	21 35				22 14		22z28						23z28								
Dundee	a	21z30			21 52	21 57				22 30		22z42						23z44								
Arbroath	a				22 24	22 24						22z59														
Montrose	a				22 39	22 39						23z14														
Stonehaven	a				23 00	23 00						23z38														
Aberdeen	a				23 20	23 20						23z58														

For general notes see front of timetable
For details of catering facilities see Directory of Train Operators

- **A** From Manchester Airport (Table 39)
- **B** From 12 September. From Plymouth (Table 51)
- **C** Until 5 September. From Newquay (Table 135)
- **D** From Reading (Table 51)
- **E** To Liverpool Lime Street (Table 49)
- **G** From Plymouth (Table 51)
- **H** To Manchester Piccadilly (Table 49)
- **J** **The 21st Century Limited**
- **K** Change at Edinburgh and Stirling
- **b** Until 11 July and from 12 September only
- **c** Change at Ely and Peterborough
- **e** 18 July to 5 September dep. 1433
- **f** 18 July to 5 September dep. 1512
- **g** Change at Ely. 18 July to 5 September dep. 1612
- **h** 18 July to 5 September dep. 1633
- **j** Change at Grantham and Sleaford
- **k** Change at Doncaster. 27 June to 5 September arr. 1820, by bus
- **m** Change at Doncaster. 27 June to 5 September arr. 1920, by bus
- **n** Change at Doncaster. 27 June to 5 September arr. 2025, by bus
- **q** Change at Leeds
- **r** Bradford Interchange
- **t** Bradford Interchange. Until 11 July Bradford Forster Square arr. 1930, change at Leeds
- **v** Bradford Interchange. Until 11 July arr. 2030
- **w** Glasgow Queen Street. Change at Edinburgh
- **y** Glasgow Queen Street
- **z** Change at Edinburgh

Table 26

London → Humberside, Yorkshire, North East England and Scotland

Route Diagram - see first page of Table 26

	EM		GR	GR	TP	XC	GR	GR	GR	XC	GR	EM	GR	TP		GR	HT	XC	EM	GR	GR	XC	EM		
	◇ A		R 1	R 1	1 ◇ B	1 ◇ C	R 1	R 1	R 1	1 ◇ D	R 1	◇ E	R 1	1 ◇ B		R 1	1 ◇	1 ◇ D	◇ E	R 1	R 1	1 ◇ D	G		
London Kings Cross 15 ⊖ d			17 40	18 00			18 03	18 30	18 35		18 40		19 00			19 30	19 41			20 00	20 30				
Stevenage 4 d			17 12						18 27				19 19							19 46	20 12				
Peterborough 8 a			18 27	18 46			18 52		19 21		19 26		19 50			20 16				20 46	21 16				
Norwich d	16 57											17 54							18 57						
Stansted Airport d									17b25							18b25					19b25				
Cambridge d				17c12					18e00				18c12			19f00				19c12	20g00		20g22		
Peterborough 8 d	18 26		18 27	18 46			18 52		19 21		19 27	19 31	19 51			20 16			20 27	20 46	21 17		21 27		
Grantham 7 a	18 55		18 48					19 30				19 59				20 35	20 41		20 58	21 05	21 38		22 00		
Grantham d			18 48					19 30								20 35	20 43			21 05	21 38				
Newark North Gate 7 a			19 00				19 20				19 55					20 47				21 17	21 49				
Lincoln a			20h41								20 56										22 40				
Grimsby Town a				20j42							21k44		22m10				22n44				23q49				
Newark North Gate 7 d			19 00				19 20				19 55					20 47				21 17	21 49				
Retford 10 d											20 11						21 05			21 32					
Doncaster 7 a			19 24	19 33				20 01	20 08		20 27		20 39			21 11	21 20			21 47	22 14				
Selby a											20 43						21 35								
Hull a				20 52				21 04			21 27		21 45				22 16			22 58					
Wakefield Westgate 7 a							20 00	20 19			21r13						22r00			22 05	22 39				
Huddersfield a							20t59	21 05			22v05									22t59	23w49				
Leeds 10 a							20 22	20 35			21r33						22r18			22 24	22 58				
Shipley a								20s56			22y07									23 07	23y31				
Bradford Forster Square a							20z57	21 06			22H28									22J57	23K30				
Keighley a								21L20			22y20									23 20	23y44				
Skipton a								21L36			22y36									23 39	00y01				
Sheffield 7 d						19 21				19 54						20 15		20 54			21 14	21 54			
Doncaster 7 d			19 25	19 34					20 08	20 18			20 40			21 12		21 26			22 14	22 20			
York 8 a			19 54	20 00					20 34	20 40			21 03			21 38		21 48			22 38	22 48			
Scarborough a				21 30														23 02							
Harrogate a				20 43				21t54										22 29			23y58				
Leeds 10 d				19 15	19 57	20 07				20 12				20 45		20 48		21 12			21 45				
Hull d					18 46									19N56											
York 8 d			19 56	20 02	20 26	20 34			20 41	20 45			21 06	21 11		21 42		21 51			22 39				
Thirsk d					20 43									21 28											
Northallerton d					20 51								21 26	21 36											
Darlington 7 a			20 23	20 30		21 04			21 09	21 14			21 40	21 47		22 09		22 21			23 07				
Eaglescliffe a																									
Middlesbrough a			20 55		21 25					22 09								22 57							
Darlington 7 d			20 24	20 31		21 05			21 09	21 15			21 41	21 48		22 10		22 23			23 08				
Durham d			20 41			21 22			21 27	21 33			21 58	22 05		22 27		22 44			23 25				
Chester-le-Street d										21 40								22 51							
Newcastle 8 ⛴ a			21 00	21 02		21 33			21 45	21 55			22 16	22 20		22 45		23 10			23 46				
Hartlepool a																									
Sunderland ⛴ a																									
Newcastle 8 ⛴ d				21 03		21 36																			
Morpeth d				21 19																					
Alnmouth for Alnwick d				21 35		22 00																			
Berwick-upon-Tweed d				21 57		22 21																			
Dunbar d																									
Edinburgh 10 a				22 44		23 09																			
Edinburgh d																									
Haymarket d																									
Motherwell a																									
Glasgow Central 15 a				00Q03		00Q28																			
Stirling a						00 23																			
Perth a																									
Inverness a																									
Inverkeithing a				23 31		23 41																			
Kirkcaldy a				23 53																					
Leuchars 3 a				00 23																					
Dundee a				00 39																					
Arbroath a																									
Montrose a																									
Stonehaven a																									
Aberdeen a																									

For general notes see front of timetable
For details of catering facilities see Directory of Train Operators

- **A** To Manchester Piccadilly (Table 49)
- **B** From Manchester Airport (Table 39)
- **C** From Plymouth (Table 51)
- **D** From Reading (Table 51)
- **E** To Nottingham (Table 19)
- **G** From Spalding (Table 18) to Nottingham (Table 19)
- **H** Bradford Interchange. Change at Doncaster and Leeds. Until 11 July arr. 2230
- **J** Bradford Interchange. Until 11 July arr. 2259
- **K** Until 5 September only. Bradford Interchange. Change at Doncaster and Leeds. 18 July to 5 September arr. 2329
- **L** Change at Shipley
- **N** Change at Selby and York
- **Q** Glasgow Queen Street
- **b** Until 11 July and from 12 September only
- **c** Change at Ely and Peterborough
- **e** 18 July to 5 September dep. 1712
- **f** 18 July to 5 September dep. 1812
- **g** 18 July to 5 September dep. 1912
- **h** Change at Grantham and Sleaford
- **j** Change at Doncaster. 27 June to 5 September arr. 2110, by bus
- **k** Until 20 June and from 12 September only. Change at Doncaster
- **m** 27 June to 5 September only; by bus from Doncaster
- **n** Change at Doncaster. 27 June to 5 September arr. 2310, by bus
- **q** Change at Doncaster. 27 June to 5 September arr. 0015, by bus
- **r** Change at Doncaster
- **t** Change at Leeds
- **v** Change at Doncaster and Wakefield Westgate
- **w** Change at Doncaster and Leeds. 12 September arr. 2355. Sundays arr. 0035, by bus from Leeds
- **y** Change at Doncaster and Leeds
- **z** Bradford Interchange. Until 11 July arr. 2059

Sundays until 6 September

London → Humberside, Yorkshire, North East England and Scotland

Route Diagram - see first page of Table 26

		GR	TP	GR	TP	XC	GR	TP	XC	TP	GR	TP	GC	GR	GR	GR	TP	EM	XC	TP	GR	EM
		R		R			R				R		R	R	R	R					R	
		1	1 ◇	1	1 ◇	1 ◇	1	1 ◇	1 ◇	1 ◇	1	1 ◇	1	1	1	1	1 ◇	1 ◇	1 ◇	1 ◇	1	◇
			A		A		B	A				A				C	A	D	E	G		H
London Kings Cross 15 ⊖	d										09 00		09 07	09 10	09 30	10 00					10 10	
Stevenage 4	d										09 20					09 46						
Peterborough 8	a										09 49			09 57	10 14	10 45					10 59	
Norwich	d																					09 33
Stansted Airport	d																					
Cambridge	d																					
Peterborough 8	d										09 49			09 57	10 14	10 46					10 59	11 11
Grantham 7	a										10 11										11 21	11 52
	d										10 11										11 21	
Newark North Gate 7	a													10 31		11 16						
Lincoln	a															12 00						
Grimsby Town	a															12 53						
Newark North Gate 7	d													10 31		11 16						
Retford 10	d													10 46							11 43	
Doncaster 7	a										10 44			11 02	11 05	11 41					11 59	
Selby	a																					
Hull	a										11 46											
Wakefield Westgate 7	a													11 20							12 18	
Huddersfield	a													12b16							13b16	
Leeds 10	a													11 39							12 36	
Shipley	a													12 19							13 19	
Bradford Forster Square	a													12c16							13e16	
Keighley	a													12 32							13 32	
Skipton	a													12 49							13 48	
Sheffield 7	d						08 45		09 21		09 52				10 26			11 31	11 21			
Doncaster 7	d						09 43				10 44				11 06	11 41		11 53				
York 8	a						10 05				11 07		11 14		11 29	12 05		12 15				
Scarborough	a														12 32							
Harrogate	a															12 50					13 28	
Leeds 10	d		07 40		08 40	09 08	09 12	09 40	10 08	10 12		10 40				11 12	11 40		12 08	12 12		
Hull	d						08 54															
York 8	d		08 21	09 00	09 09	09 37	10 06	10 13	10 36	10 45	11 09	11 15	11 18		11 30	12 06	12 15		12 36	12 40		
Thirsk	d		08 37							11 04			11 35							13 02		
Northallerton	d		08 45	09 20	09 30			10 35		11 12		11 35	11 44				12 35			13 10		
Darlington 7	a		08 57	09 32	09 41	10 03	10 33	10 46	11 02		11 36	11 47			11 58	12 34	12 46		13 01			
Eaglescliffe	a												12 02									
Middlesbrough	a		09 26		11f03			11 30		11 48		12 24							13 35	13 44		
Darlington 7	d			09 33	09 42	10 04	10 34	10 47	11 04		11 37	11 47			11 58	12 34	12 47		13 03			
Durham	d			09 50	09 58	10 21	10 51	11 08	11 20		11 54	12 03				12 52	13 03		13 19			
Chester-le-Street	d																					
Newcastle 8	a			10 06	10 18	10 35	11 09	11 23	11 35		12 10	12 20			12 28	13 08	13 20		13 34			
Hartlepool	a												12 21									
Sunderland	a					11 22			12 21				12 51		13 22				14 21			
Newcastle 8	d			10 10		10 38	11 11		11 38		12 15				12 31	13 09			13 36			
Morpeth	d			10 25																		
Alnmouth for Alnwick	d			10 41					12 02										14 01			
Berwick-upon-Tweed	d			11 03		11 20	11 54				12 58											
Dunbar	d			11 27		11 43																
Edinburgh 10	a			11 57		12 07	12 38		13 08		13 46				14 02	14 35			15 07			
Edinburgh	d	09 10		12 03		12 12	12 42															
Haymarket	d	09 14		12 07		12 16	12 47															
Motherwell	a			12 47		12 53	13 32															
Glasgow Central 15	a			13 05		13 19	13 54		14g23		14g51				15g22	15g51			16g22			
Stirling	a					13h24			14 28						15 24				16 24			
Perth	a					14j46			15 12						16j45							
Inverness	a					17j50			17 38													
Inverkeithing	a	09 31		12h38		13h00	13h40		14 10		14 21				14 40	15 38			16 17			
Kirkcaldy	a	09 48		13h03		13h16	14h04		14 27						15 02	16 02			16 41			
Leuchars 8	a	10 13				13h39	14h35									16 33			17 05			
Dundee	a	10 27				13h52	14h50									16 48			17 24			
Arbroath	a	10 45				14h09	15k27									17k27			17 41			
Montrose	a	11 01				14h24	15k41									17k41			17 59			
Stonehaven	a	11 24				14h45	16k06									18k03			18 22			
Aberdeen	a	11 47				15h05	16k26									18k23			18 46			

For general notes see front of timetable
For details of catering facilities see Directory of Train Operators

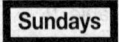

- **A** From Manchester Airport (Table 39)
- **B** From Leeds (Table 31)
- **C** **The Flying Scotsman**
- **D** Until 12 July. From Leicester (Table 53)
- **E** From Birmingham New Street (Table 51)
- **G** From Liverpool Lime Street (Table 39)
- **H** To Liverpool Lime Street (Table 49)
- **b** Change at Leeds
- **c** Bradford Interchange. From 19 July arr. 1214
- **e** Bradford Interchange. From 19 July arr. 1314
- **f** Change at Darlington and Thornaby
- **g** Glasgow Queen Street
- **h** Change at Edinburgh
- **j** Change at Edinburgh and Stirling
- **k** Change at Edinburgh and Dundee

Table 26

Sundays

London → Humberside, Yorkshire, North East England and Scotland

until 6 September

Route Diagram - see first page of Table 26

		GR	HT	GR	TP	XC	GR	EM	GR	TP	GR	GR	XC	TP	XC	GR	TP	XC	GR	GR	XC	GC
		R 1	1 ◇	R 1	1 ◇	1 ◇	R 1	◇	R 1	1 ◇	R 1	R 1	1 ◇	1 ◇	1 ◇	R 1	1 ◇	1 ◇	R 1	R 1	1 ◇	R 1
				A	B	C		D		B		E	C	G	H		B	J			H	
London Kings Cross 15 ⊖	d	10 30	10 44	11 00			11 10		12 00		12 10	12 30				13 00			13 10	13 30		13 45
Stevenage 4	d	10 49							11 46		12 29					13 19			12 46	13 49		
Peterborough 8	a	11 18		11 44			11 54		12 44		12 58	13 14				13 50			13 56	14 18		
Norwich	d							10 47								11b15						
Stansted Airport	d								10 25		11 25									12 25		
Cambridge	d	10b05							11b05		11 56					12b05				12 56		
Peterborough 8	d	11 19		11 45			11 54	12 18	12 44		12 59	13 15				13 51			13 57	14 19		
Grantham 7	a		11 45				12 16	12 46			13 21								14 19			
	d		11 46				12 16				13 21								14 19			
Newark North Gate 7	a						12 28		13 14										14 31			
Lincoln	a								14 02		14c54											
Grimsby Town	a		13e45	14f10					15f10			15g45				16f10				16g45		
Newark North Gate 7	d						12 28		13 14										14 31			
Retford 10	d		12 07				12 43				13 43											
Doncaster 7	a	12 09	12 23	12 38			12 59		13 41		13 59	14 07				14 41			14 56	15 09		
Selby	a		12 41																			
Hull	a		13 21	13 48					14 59							15 57						
Wakefield Westgate 7	a						13 17				14 16								15 14			
Huddersfield	a						14h16				15h27								16h16			
Leeds 10	a						13 36				14 36								15 33			
Shipley	a						14 19				15 09								16 19			
Bradford Forster Square	a						14j16				15k16								16m16			
Keighley	a						14 32				15 20								16 32			
Skipton	a						14 48				15 33								16 48			
Sheffield 7	d			11n31		12 21			13 11			13 24	13 21		13 51	14 11		14 21		14 28	14 51	
Doncaster 7	d	12 10		12 39					13 42			14 09			14 15	14 42				15 10	15 15	
York 8	a	12 35		13 05					14 04			14 33			14 43	15 05				15 34	15 43	15 51
Scarborough	a	13 32		14 32												16 32						
Harrogate	a								14 52		15 28								16 28			
Leeds 10	d				12 40	13 08			13 12	13 40		13 57	14 08	14 12			14 40	15 08			15 12	
Hull	d			11 54								13 27								14 28		
York 8	d	12 44		13 07	13 15	13 36			14 06	14 15		14 35	14 39	14 40	14 46	15 07	15 15	15 36		15 38	15 46	15 54
Thirsk	d													15 02								16 10
Northallerton	d				13 35				14 25	14 35				15 10			15 35					16 20
Darlington 7	a	13 11		13 35	13 46	14 01			14 38	14 46		15 03	15 07		15 15	15 34	15 46	16 01		16 07	16 12	
Eaglescliffe	a																					16 39
Middlesbrough	a					14 32				15 27			15 41	15 52	16 04	16 04					16 41	
Darlington 7	d	13 12		13 35	13 47	14 03			14 38	14 47		15 03	15 09		15 17	15 35	15 47	16 03		16 08	16 14	
Durham	d			13 53	14 03	14 19			14 56	15 03			15 25		15 33	15 54	16 03	16 19		16 25	16 31	
Chester-le-Street	d				14 09																	
Newcastle 8	a	13 41		14 09	14 22	14 34			15 12	15 20		15 33	15 38		15 51	16 10	16 20	16 34		16 42	16 50	
Hartlepool	a																					16 58
Sunderland	a	14 21				15 22									16 21						17 22	17 36
Newcastle 8	d	13 43		14 13		14 36			15 14			15 34	15 41			16 11		16 38		16 44		
Morpeth	d												15 54							16 59		
Alnmouth for Alnwick	d												16 08							17 15		
Berwick-upon-Tweed	d	14 26				15 20			15 57									17 20		17 37		
Dunbar	d					15 43												17 43				
Edinburgh 10	a	15 10		15 41		16 12			16 46			17 00	17 14			17 37		18 07		18 25		
Edinburgh	d	15 13		16 00								17 12				17 41		18 10				
Haymarket	d	15 18		16 04								17 16				17 45		18 15				
Motherwell	a	15 56														18 24						
Glasgow Central 15	a	16 14		16q51		17r22			17r52				18r22			18 44		19q22				
Stirling	a	16t24				17 24						17 52	18 24					19t25				
Perth	a											18 28	19v15					20v46				
Inverness	a											20 44	21v34									
Inverkeithing	a	16t17		16w24					17 22			17t37				18t07		18 27				
Kirkcaldy	a	16t41		16 41					17 38			17t59				18t23		18 43				
Leuchars 3	a			17 05					18 01			18t30						19 13				
Dundee	a			17 24					18 14			18t46						19 28				
Arbroath	a			17 41					18 31			19y27						19 45				
Montrose	a			17 59					18 46			19y41						19 59				
Stonehaven	a			18 22					19 07			20y05						20 22				
Aberdeen	a			18 46					19 30			20y29						20 47				

For general notes see front of timetable
For details of catering facilities see Directory of Train Operators

- **A** **The Northern Lights**
- **B** From Manchester Airport (Table 39)
- **C** From Bristol Temple Meads (Table 51)
- **D** To Liverpool Lime Street (Table 49)
- **E** **The Highland Chieftain**
- **G** From Liverpool Lime Street (Table 39)
- **H** From Birmingham New Street (Table 51)
- **J** From Plymouth (Table 51)
- **b** Change at Ely and Peterborough
- **c** Change at Retford
- **e** Change at Doncaster. From 28 June arr. 1405, by bus
- **f** From 28 June only. Change at Doncaster. By bus
- **g** Until 21 June only. Change at Doncaster
- **h** Change at Leeds
- **j** Bradford Interchange. From 19 July arr. 1414
- **k** Bradford Interchange. From 19 July arr. 1514
- **m** Bradford Interchange. From 19 July arr. 1614
- **n** From 19 July dep. 1121, change at York
- **q** Glasgow Queen Street. Change at Edinburgh
- **r** Glasgow Queen Street
- **t** Change at Edinburgh
- **v** Change at Edinburgh and Stirling
- **w** By changing at Edinburgh, passengers may arrive at 1617
- **y** Change at Edinburgh and Dundee

Table 26

Sundays

until 6 September

London → Humberside, Yorkshire, North East England and Scotland

Route Diagram - see first page of Table 26

		GR	TP	XC	TP	GR		GR	XC	HT	EM	GR		TP	XC	GR	XC	GR		HT	EM	GR	TP	XC		GR
		R 1	1 ◇	1 ◇	1 ◇	R 1		R 1	1 ◇	1 ◇	◇	R 1		1 ◇	1 ◇	R 1	1 ◇	R 1		1 ◇	◇	R 1	1 ◇	1 ◇		R 1
			A	B	C				D		E			A	G		H				E		A	B		
London Kings Cross 15 ⊖	d	14 00				14 10		14 30		14 44		15 00				15 10		15 30		15 44		16 00				16 10
Stevenage 4	d											15 19				*14 46*				16u04						16 29
Peterborough 8	a	14 44				14 54		15 14				15 49				15 54		16 14				16 44				16 58
Norwich	d							*12b15*			13 49										14 47					
Stansted Airport	d							*13 25*										*14 25*								*15 25*
Cambridge	d							*13 56*										*14 56*				*15b05*				*15 56*
Peterborough 8	d	14 45				14 54		15 14			15 26	15 49				15 55		16 15			16 24	16 45				16 59
Grantham 7	a					15 16				15 46	15 56					16 17		16 39		16 48	16 54					
	d					15 16				15 47						16 18		16 39		16 49						
Newark North Gate 7	a					15 28										16 30		16 50								
Lincoln	a															*17 08*		*18 20*								*19c22*
Grimsby Town	a	*17e10*								*17f45*										*18g45*		*19e10*				
Newark North Gate 7	d					15 28										16 31		16 50								
Retford 10	d					15 43				16 08										17 10						17 39
Doncaster 7	a	15 38				15 59		16 08		16 22						16 57		17 14		17 25		17 39				17 55
Selby	a									16 41										17 50						
Hull	a	*16 50*								17 21										18 32						*18 57*
Wakefield Westgate 7	a					16 17										17 14				*18h12*						18 12
Huddersfield	a					*17j27*										*18j16*										*19j24*
Leeds 10	a					16 36										17 34										18 32
Shipley	a					*17 19*										*18 19*										*19 19*
Bradford Forster Square	a					*17k16*										*18m16*										*19n03*
Keighley	a					*17 32*										*18 32*										*19 32*
Skipton	a					*17 48*										*18 48*										*19 48*
Sheffield 7	d			15 21				15 28	15 51						16 21		16 51							17 21		
Doncaster 7	d	15 39						16 09	16 17								17 15	17 20				17 40				
York 8	a	16 04						16 35	16 40			17 03					17 42	17 46				18 04				
Scarborough	a											*18 32*														
Harrogate	a	*16 50*				*17 28*						*17 50*				*18 28*						*18 50*				*19 28*
Leeds 10	d		15 40	16 08	16 12									16 40	17 08			*17 12*					17 40	18 08		
Hull	d											*16 01*												*17 23*		
York 8	d	16 06	16 15	16 36	16 40			16 42	16 46			17 05		17 14	17 36		17 44	17 47				18 07	18 14	18 36		
Thirsk	d				17 02																					
Northallerton	d		16 35		17 10									17 35									18 35			
Darlington 7	a	16 34	16 46	17 01				17 09	17 14			17 32		17 46	18 01		18 10	18 15				18 35	18 46	19 01		
Eaglescliffe	a																									
Middlesbrough	a				17 43				*17 49*									*18 53*								
Darlington 7	d	16 34	16 47	17 03				17 10	17 15			17 33		17 47	18 03		18 11	18 16				18 35	18 47	19 03		
Durham	d		17 03	17 19					17 33					18 03	18 19		18 28	18 33					19 03	19 19		
Chester-le-Street	d								17 40					18 09												
Newcastle 8	a	17 04	17 20	17 34				17 39	17 53			18 02		18 22	18 34		18 47	18 52				19 05	19 20	19 34		
Hartlepool	a																									
Sunderland	a							*18 21*										*19 22*								
Newcastle 8	d	17 07		17 38				17 41				18 05			18 38							19 07		19 40		
Morpeth	d																									
Alnmouth for Alnwick	d			18 02																				20 05		
Berwick-upon-Tweed	d							18 28				18 48			19 20											
Dunbar	d														19 43											
Edinburgh 10	a	18 33		19 08				19 14				19 33			20 07							20 35		21 11		
Edinburgh	d	18 42										19 37			20 12									21 12		
Haymarket	d	18 47										19 42			20 16									21 16		
Motherwell	a											20 19			20 53									21 53		
Glasgow Central 15	a	*19q51*						*20r22*				20 37			21 17							*21r55*		22 19		
Stirling	a							20 24							*21t23*									*22t24*		
Perth	a														*22v46*											
Inverness	a																									
Inverkeithing	a	19 01										*20t17*										*21 18*				
Kirkcaldy	a	19 18										*20t59*										*21 34*				
Leuchars 3	a	19 43																				*22 04*				
Dundee	a	19 57																				*22 17*				
Arbroath	a	20 15																				*22 34*				
Montrose	a	20 31																				*22 49*				
Stonehaven	a	20 54																				*23 10*				
Aberdeen	a	21 17																				*23 33*				

For general notes see front of timetable
For details of catering facilities see Directory of Train Operators

- **A** From Manchester Airport (Table 39)
- **B** From Plymouth (Table 51)
- **C** From Liverpool Lime Street (Table 39)
- **D** From Guildford (Table 51)
- **E** To Liverpool Lime Street (Table 49)
- **G** From Penzance (Table 135)
- **H** From Reading (Table 51)
- **b** Change at Ely and Peterborough
- **c** Change at Retford
- **e** From 28 June only. Change at Doncaster. By bus
- **f** Change at Doncaster. From 28 June arr. 1810, by bus
- **g** Until 21 June only. Change at Doncaster
- **h** Change at Doncaster
- **j** Change at Leeds
- **k** Bradford Interchange. From 19 July arr. 1714
- **m** Bradford Interchange. From 19 July arr. 1814
- **n** Bradford Interchange. From 19 July arr. 1923
- **q** Glasgow Queen Street. Change at Edinburgh
- **r** Glasgow Queen Street
- **t** Change at Edinburgh
- **v** Change at Edinburgh and Stirling

Table 26

Sundays

until 6 September

London → Humberside, Yorkshire, North East England and Scotland

Route Diagram - see first page of Table 26

	EM	TP	GR	TP	XC	GR	GR	TP	XC	XC	GR	XC	GR	HT	EM	GR	TP	GR	GC	XC	GR
			R			R	R				R		R			R		R			R
	◇	1 ◇	1	1 ◇	1 ◇	1	1	1 ◇	1 ◇	1 ◇	1	1 ◇	1	1 ◇	◇	1	1 ◇	1	1	1 ◇	1
	A	B		B	C			D	C	E		C			A		D			G	
London Kings Cross 15 ⊖ d			16 30			16 40	17 00				17 10		17 30	17 44		18 00		18 10	18 20		18 30
Stevenage 4 d			16 49										17 49								18 50
Peterborough 8 a			17 18			17 24	17 46				17 54		18 18			18 44		18 54			19 19
Norwich d	15 53														16 57						
Stansted Airport d													*16 25*								*17 25*
Cambridge d							*16b05*						*16 56*			*17b05*					*17 56*
Peterborough 8 d	17 14		17 19			17 25	17 46				17 54		18 19		18 30	18 45		18 55			19 19
Grantham 7 a	17 58					17 47					18 17			18 45	18 59	19 06					
d						17 47					18 17			18 46		19 06					
Newark North Gate 7 a							18 16						18 49					19 25			
Lincoln a													*19 48*					*20 21*			
Grimsby Town a			*19c45*				*20e10*							*20c45*		*21e10*					
Newark North Gate 7 d							18 16						18 49					19 26			
Retford 10 d														19 07				19 42			
Doncaster 7 a			18 10				18 42				18 50		19 14	19 23		19 42		19 58			20 12
Selby a														19 40							
Hull a							*19 55*							20 22							
Wakefield Westgate 7 a						18 38					19 07			*19f58*				20 16			
Huddersfield a						*19g27*					*20g00*			*21h00*							
Leeds 10 a						18 59					19 27			*20f20*				20 39			
Shipley a						*19 45*					*20 19*			*20h45*				*21 19*			
Bradford Forster Square a						*19j54*					*20k03*			*20m54*				*21n27*			
Keighley a											*20 32*							*21 32*			
Skipton a											*20 48*							*21 48*			
Sheffield 7 d			*17 28*		17 51			*17 34*	←	18 21		18 51							*18 57*	19 21	
Doncaster 7 d			18 11		18 15 ↪		18 43		18 15			19 17	19 20			19 42					20 12
York 8 a			18 34				19 05		19 21			19 42	19 45			20 07			20 23		20 39
Scarborough a			*19 32*				*20 32*												*21 32*		
Harrogate a							*19 50*				*20 28*					*20 50*					
Leeds 10 d		18 12						18 40	18 57	19 08		*19 12*					19 40			20 08	
Hull d				←												*19 04*					
York 8 d		18 40 →	18 42	18 40			19 07	19 14	19 24	19 36		19 45	19 47			20 08	20 13		20 25	20 35	20 40
Thirsk d				18 59													20 30		20 42		
Northallerton d			19 01	19 07				19 35					20 08				20 38		20 50		21 00
Darlington 7 a			19 15				19 35	19 46	19 51	20 03		20 10	20 20			20 36				21 03	21 13
Eaglescliffe a																			21 12		
Middlesbrough a			*19 57*	19 40									*20 57*				21 12				
Darlington 7 d			19 15				19 36	19 47	19 53	20 04		20 12	20 21			20 36				21 04	21 13
Durham d			19 33				19 53	20 03	20 09	20 22		20 28	20 38							21 22	21 31
Chester-le-Street d								20 09	20 18												
Newcastle 8 ⛴ a			19 51				20 09	20 22	20 30	20 37		20 43	20 56			21 06				21 37	21 47
Hartlepool a																			21 36		
Sunderland ⛴ a			*20 21*																22 06		
Newcastle 8 ⛴ d							20 11			20 39		20 49				21 07				21 39	21 53
Morpeth d												21 02									
Alnmouth for Alnwick d												21 16				21 35				22 07	
Berwick-upon-Tweed d							20 54			21 25		21 37				21 57				22 30	22 37
Dunbar d										21 50											23 01
Edinburgh 10 a							21 38			22 20		22 25				22 44				23 19	23 29
Edinburgh d							21 41														
Haymarket d							21 45														
Motherwell a							22 23														
Glasgow Central 15 a							22 45									*23q55*				*00q25*	
Stirling a												*23 27*									
Perth a												*00 07*									
Inverness a																					
Inverkeithing a							*22r17*													*23 58*	
Kirkcaldy a							*23r05*														
Leuchars 3 a							*23r40*														
Dundee a							*23r56*														
Arbroath a																					
Montrose a																					
Stonehaven a																					
Aberdeen a																					

For general notes see front of timetable
For details of catering facilities see Directory of Train Operators

- **A** To Manchester Piccadilly (Table 49)
- **B** From Liverpool Lime Street (Table 39)
- **C** From Reading (Table 51)
- **D** From Manchester Airport (Table 39)
- **E** From Newquay (Table 51)
- **G** From Plymouth (Table 51)
- **b** Change at Ely and Peterborough
- **c** Until 21 June only. Change at Doncaster
- **e** From 28 June only. Change at Doncaster. By bus
- **f** Change at Doncaster
- **g** Change at Leeds
- **h** Change at Doncaster and Leeds
- **j** Until 12 July change at Leeds. From 19 July Bradford Interchange arr. 1953, change at Leeds
- **k** Bradford Interchange. From 19 July arr. 2014
- **m** Change at Doncaster and Leeds. From 19 July Bradford Interchange arr. 2053
- **n** Bradford Interchange. From 19 July arr. 2125
- **q** Glasgow Queen Street
- **r** Change at Edinburgh

Sundays

until 6 September

London → Humberside, Yorkshire, North East England and Scotland

Route Diagram - see first page of Table 26

Station		XC	GR	EM	GR	TP	GR	GR	XC	GR	EM	GR	TP	GR	HT	GR	GR	GR	EM	GR	GR
		A		B		C			A		B		D						B		
London Kings Cross 15 ⊖	d		18 40		19 00		19 10	19 30		19 35		20 00		20 03	20 10	20 30	21 00	21 30		22 00	22 10
Stevenage 4	d							19 49		19 54					20u30		20 46			21 46	
Peterborough 8	a		19 25		19 44		19 55	20 18		20 24		20 44		20 50		21 14	21 45	22 14		22 44	22s59
Norwich	d			17 56							18 57								20 52		
Stansted Airport	d							18b25								19c25					
Cambridge	d				18e04			18b56				19e04				19f56				21e05	
Peterborough 8	d		19 25	19 26	19 44		19 56	20 19		20 25	20 30	20 44		20 50		21 14	21 46	22 15	22 22	22 45	
Grantham 7	a		19 47	19 56			20 19				21 01				21 18	21 36		22 39	22 50		23s31
	d		19 47				20 19								21 19	21 36		22 39			
Newark North Gate 7	a						20 30									21 48		22 50			23s42
Lincoln	a															22 27		23 46			
Grimsby Town	a				21g45					22h45		23j10					23k58				
Newark North Gate 7	d						20 30									21 48		22 50			
Retford 10	d														21 40	22 03		23 06			
Doncaster 7	a		20 20		20 35		20 56	21 09		21 16		21 36			21 54	22 19	22 42	23 27		23 42	00s12
Selby	a						21 15								22 09						
Hull	a		21 23				21 56								22 50		00 02				
Wakefield Westgate 7	a		20 38					21 27						21 57		22 37					
Huddersfield	a		21m27											22m57		23m59					02m56
Leeds 10	a		20 59					21 46						22 16		23 00		00 24			01 18
Shipley	a		21 45					22 19						22 45		23 21					
Bradford Forster Square	a		21 54					22n27						22 54		23q43					
Keighley	a							22 32								23 34					
Skipton	a							22 48								23 50					
Sheffield 7	d	19 51							20 51	20 28			21 03				21r51			22 30	
Doncaster 7	d	20 18			20 35				21 21	21 23		21 36					22 43			23 45	
York 8	a	20 44			21 00				21 42	21 47		22 00					23 09			00 39	
Scarborough	a											23 02									
Harrogate	a		21 51		21 58			23 00								23 59					
Leeds 10	d	20 12				20 40				21 12			22 12								
Hull	d								20 22												
York 8	d	20 47			21 02	21 08			21 44	21 48		22 02	22 42				23 11				
Thirsk	d					21 26							23 06								
Northallerton	d					21 34							23 16				23 47				
Darlington 7	a	21 18			21 30	21 46			22 10	22 26		22 43	23 32				23 59			01 32	
Eaglescliffe	a																				
Middlesbrough	a				22 07					23 10											
Darlington 7	d	21 19			21 30	21 46			22 11	22 27		22 43	23 33				23 59				
Durham	d	21 37				22 03			22 28	22 44		23 01	23 49				00 17			01a50	
Chester-le-Street	d	21 46																			
Newcastle 8	a	21 59			22 02	22 20			22 43	23 14		23 34	00 21				00 50			02 25	
Hartlepool	a																				
Sunderland	a																				
Newcastle 8	d																				
Morpeth	d																				
Alnmouth for Alnwick	d																				
Berwick-upon-Tweed	d																				
Dunbar	d																				
Edinburgh 10	a																				
Edinburgh	d																				
Haymarket	d																				
Motherwell	a																				
Glasgow Central 15	a																				
Stirling	a																				
Perth	a																				
Inverness	a																				
Inverkeithing	a																				
Kirkcaldy	a																				
Leuchars 3	a																				
Dundee	a																				
Arbroath	a																				
Montrose	a																				
Stonehaven	a																				
Aberdeen	a																				

For general notes see front of timetable
For details of catering facilities see Directory of Train Operators

A From Reading (Table 51)
B To Nottingham (Table 19)
C From Manchester Airport (Table 39)
D From Liverpool Lime Street (Table 39)

b From 19 July dep. Stansted Airport 1725, Cambridge 1804
c Until 12 July only
e Change at Ely and Peterborough
f From 19 July dep. 1904
g Change at Doncaster. From 28 June arr. 2210, by bus
h Until 21 June only. Change at Doncaster

j From 28 June only. Change at Doncaster. By bus
k Change at Doncaster. From 28 June arr. 0025, by bus
m Change at Leeds
n Bradford Interchange. From 19 July arr. 2225
q Bradford Interchange
r Change at York

Table 26

Sundays

London → Humberside, Yorkshire, North East England and Scotland

from 13 September

Route Diagram - see first page of Table 26

	GR	TP	GR	TP	XC	GR	TP	XC	TP	GR	TP	GC	GR	GR	GR	TP	XC	EM	TP	GR	GR
	R 1	1 ◇	R 1	1 ◇	1 ◇	R 1	1 ◇	1 ◇	1 ◇	R 1	1 ◇	R 1	R 1	R 1	R 1	1 ◇	1 ◇	1 ◇	1 ◇	R 1	R 1
						A	B		C		B				D	B	E	G	C		
London Kings Cross 15 ⊖ d										09 00		09 07	09 10	09 30	10 00					10 10	10 30
Stevenage 4 d										09 20					09 46						10 49
Peterborough 8 a										09 49			09 57	10 14	10 45					10 59	11 18
Norwich d																					
Stansted Airport d																					
Cambridge d																					
Peterborough 8 d										09 49			09 57	10 14	10 46					10 59	11 19
Grantham 7 a										10 11										11 21	
Grantham 7 d										10 11										11 21	
Newark North Gate 7 a													10 31		11 16						
Lincoln a															12 02						
Grimsby Town a																					
Newark North Gate 7 d													10 31		11 16						
Retford 10 d													10 46							11 43	
Doncaster 7 a										10 44			11 02	11 05	11 41					11 59	12 09
Selby a																					
Hull a										11 46											
Wakefield Westgate 7 a													11 20							12 18	
Huddersfield a													12b20							13b20	
Leeds 10 a													11 39							12 36	
Shipley a													12 19							13 19	
Bradford Forster Square a													12c14							13c14	
Keighley a													12 32							13 32	
Skipton a													12 49							13 48	
Sheffield 7 🚌 d						08 45		09 21		09 52				10 26			11 21	11 31			
Doncaster 7 d						09 43				10 44				11 06	11 41			11 53			12 10
York 8 a						10 05				11 07		11 14		11 29	12 05			12 15			12 35
Scarborough a														12 32							
Harrogate a															12 50					13 28	
Leeds 10 d		07e10		08 40	09 08	09 12	09 46	10 08	10 18		10 40				11 18	11 40	12 08		12 12		
Hull d						08 54															
York 8 d		08 21	09 00	09 09	09 37	10 06	10 13	10 36	10 45	11 09	11 15	11 18		11 30	12 06	12 15	12 36		12 40		12 44
Thirsk d		08 37							11 04			11 35							13 02		
Northallerton d		08 45	09 20	09 30			10 35		11 12		11 35	11 44				12 35			13 10		
Darlington 7 a		08 57	09 32	09 41	10 03	10 33	10 46	11 02		11 36	11 46			11 58	12 34	12 46	13 01				13 11
Eaglescliffe a												12 02									
Middlesbrough a		09 26		11f18			11 30		11 48		12 24						13 35		13 44		
Darlington 7 d			09 33	09 42	10 04	10 34	10 47	11 04		11 37	11 47			11 58	12 34	12 47	13 03				13 12
Durham d			09 50	09 58	10 21	10 51	11 08	11 20		11 54	12 03				12 52	13 03	13 19				
Chester-le-Street d																					
Newcastle 8 🚌 a			10 06	10 18	10 35	11 09	11 23	11 35		12 10	12 20			12 28	13 08	13 20	13 34				13 41
Hartlepool a												12 21									
Sunderland 🚌 a					11 22			12 21				12 51		13 22			14 21				14 21
Newcastle 8 🚌 d			10 10		10 38	11 11		11 38		12 15				12 31	13 09		13 36				13 43
Morpeth d			10 25																		
Alnmouth for Alnwick d			10 41					12 02									14 01				
Berwick-upon-Tweed d			11 03		11 20	11 54				12 58											14 26
Dunbar d			11 27		11 43																
Edinburgh 10 a			11 57		12 07	12 38		13 08		13 46				14 02	14 35		15 07				15 10
Edinburgh d	09 10		12 03		12 12	12 42															15 13
Haymarket d	09 14		12 07		12 16	12 47															15 18
Motherwell a			12 47		12 53	13 32															15 56
Glasgow Central 15 a			13 05		13 19	13 54		14g23		14g51				15g22	15g51		16g22				16 14
Stirling a					13h24			14 28						15 24			16 24				16h24
Perth a					14j46			15 12						16j45							
Inverness a					17j50			17 38													
Inverkeithing a	09 31		12h38		13h00	13h40		14 10		14 21				14 40	15 38		16 17				16h17
Kirkcaldy a	09 48		13h03		13h16	14h04		14 27						15 02	16 02		16 41				
Leuchars 3 a	10 13				13h39	14h35									16 33		17 05				
Dundee a	10 27				13h52	14h50									16 48		17 24				
Arbroath a	10 45				14h09	15k27									17k27		17 41				
Montrose a	11 01				14h24	15k41									17k41		17 59				
Stonehaven a	11 24				14h45	16k06									18k03		18 22				
Aberdeen a	11 47				15h05	16k26									18k23		18 46				

For general notes see front of timetable
For details of catering facilities see Directory of Train Operators

A From Leeds (Table 31)
B From Manchester Airport (Table 39)
C From Liverpool Lime Street (Table 39)
D **The Flying Scotsman**
E From Birmingham New Street (Table 51)
G From Leicester (Table 53)
b Change at Leeds
c Bradford Interchange
e By bus
f Change at Darlington and Thornaby. 13 September arr. 1103
g Glasgow Queen Street
h Change at Edinburgh
j Change at Edinburgh and Stirling
k Change at Edinburgh and Dundee

Table 26

Sundays

from 13 September

London → Humberside, Yorkshire, North East England and Scotland

Route Diagram - see first page of Table 26

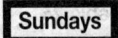

		HT	GR	TP	XC	GR	EM	GR	TP	GR	GR	XC	TP	XC	GR	TP	XC	GR	GR	XC	GC
		1 ◇	R 1	1 ◇	1 ◇	R 1	◇	R 1	1 ◇	R 1	R 1	1 ◇	1 ◇	1 ◇	R 1	1 ◇	1 ◇	R 1	R 1	1 ◇	R 1
			A	B	C		D		B		E	C	G	H		B	J			H	
London Kings Cross 15 ⊖	d	10 44	11 00			11 10		12 00		12 10	12 30				13 00			13 10	13 30		13 45
Stevenage 4	d							11 46		12 29					13 19			12 46	13 49		
Peterborough 8	a		11 44			11 54		12 44		12 58	13 14				13 50			13 56	14 18		
Norwich	d		09b15				10 47								11b15						
Stansted Airport	d							10 25		11 25									12 25		
Cambridge	d		10b05					11b05		11 56					12b05				12 56		
Peterborough 8	d		11 45			11 54	12 18	12 44		12 59	13 15				13 51			13 57	14 19		
Grantham 7	a	11 45				12 16	12 46			13 21								14 19			
	d	11 46				12 16				13 21								14 19			
Newark North Gate 7	a					12 28		13 14										14 31			
Lincoln	a							14 02		14c54											
Grimsby Town	a	13e45									15e45								16e45		
Newark North Gate 7	d					12 28		13 14										14 31			
Retford 10	d	12 07				12 43				13 43											
Doncaster 7	a	12 23	12 38			12 59		13 41		13 59	14 07				14 41			14 56	15 09		
Selby	a	12 41																			
Hull	a	13 21	13 48					14 59							15 57						
Wakefield Westgate 7	a	13e17				13 17				14 16								15 14			
Huddersfield	a					14f20				15f20								16f20			
Leeds 10	a					13 36				14 36								15 33			
Shipley	a					14 19				15 09								16 19			
Bradford Forster Square	a					14g14				15g14								16g14			
Keighley	a					14 32				15 20								16 32			
Skipton	a					14 48				15 33								16 48			
Sheffield 7 ⛴	d				12 21			13 11			13 24	13 21		13 51	14 11		14 21		14 28	14 51	
Doncaster 7	d		12 39					13 42			14 09			14 15	14 42				15 10	15 15	
York 8	a		13 05		13 32			14 04			14 33	14 32		14 43	15 05				15 34	15 43	15 51
Scarborough	a		14 32												16 32						
Harrogate	a							14 52		15 28								16 28			
Leeds 10	d			12 40	13 08			13 12	13 40		13 57	14 08	14 14			14 40	15 08			15 12	
Hull	d		11 54								13j27								14 28		
York 8	d		13 07	13 15	13 36			14 06	14 15		14 35	14 39	14 40	14 46	15 07	15 15	15 36		15 38	15 46	15 54
Thirsk	d												15 02								16 10
Northallerton	d			13 35				14 25	14 35				15 10			15 35					16 20
Darlington 7	a		13 35	13 46	14 01			14 38	14 46		15 03	15 07		15 15	15 34	15 46	16 01		16 07	16 12	
Eaglescliffe	a																				16 39
Middlesbrough	a				14 32							15 41	15 52		16 04					16 41	
Darlington 7	d		13 35	13 47	14 03			14 38	14 47		15 03	15 09		15 17	15 35	15 47	16 03		16 08	16 14	
Durham	d		13 53	14 03	14 19			14 56	15 03			15 25		15 33	15 54	16 03	16 19		16 25	16 31	
Chester-le-Street	d			14 09																	
Newcastle 8 ⛴	a		14 09	14 22	14 34			15 12	15 20		15 33	15 38		15 51	16 10	16 20	16 34		16 42	16 50	
Hartlepool	a																				16 58
Sunderland ⛴	a				15 22									16 21						17 22	17 36
Newcastle 8 ⛴	d		14 13		14 36			15 14			15 34	15 41			16 11		16 38		16 44		
Morpeth	d											15 54					16 58		16 59		
Alnmouth for Alnwick	d											16 08							17 15		
Berwick-upon-Tweed	d				15 20			15 57									17 20		17 37		
Dunbar	d				15 43												17 43				
Edinburgh 10	a		15 41		16 12			16 46			17 00	17 14			17 37		18 07		18 25		
Edinburgh	d		16 00								17 12				17 41		18 10				
Haymarket	d		16 04								17 16				17 45		18 15				
Motherwell	a														18 24						
Glasgow Central 15	a		16k51		17m22			17m52				18m22			18 44		19k22				
Stirling	a				17 24						17 52	18 24					19n25				
Perth	a										18 28	19q15					20q46				
Inverness	a										20 44	21q34									
Inverkeithing	a		16 24					17 22			17n37				18n07		18 27				
Kirkcaldy	a		16 41					17 38			17n59				18n23		18 43				
Leuchars 3	a		17 05					18 01			18n30						19 13				
Dundee	a		17 24					18 14			18n46						19 28				
Arbroath	a		17 41					18 31			19r27						19 45				
Montrose	a		17 59					18 46			19r41						19 59				
Stonehaven	a		18 22					19 07			20r05						20 22				
Aberdeen	a		18 46					19 30			20r29						20 47				

For general notes see front of timetable
For details of catering facilities see Directory of Train Operators

- **A** **The Northern Lights**
- **B** From Manchester Airport (Table 39)
- **C** From Bristol Temple Meads (Table 51)
- **D** To Liverpool Lime Street (Table 49)
- **E** **The Highland Chieftain**
- **G** From Liverpool Lime Street (Table 39)
- **H** From Birmingham New Street (Table 51)
- **J** From Plymouth (Table 51) (from 8 November from Birmingham New Street) (Table 51)
- **b** Change at Ely and Peterborough
- **c** Change at Retford
- **e** Change at Doncaster
- **f** Change at Leeds
- **g** Bradford Interchange
- **h** Change at Doncaster and Leeds
- **j** 13 September only
- **k** Glasgow Queen Street. Change at Edinburgh
- **m** Glasgow Queen Street
- **n** Change at Edinburgh
- **q** Change at Edinburgh and Stirling
- **r** Change at Edinburgh and Dundee

Table 26

Sundays

from 13 September

London → Humberside, Yorkshire, North East England and Scotland

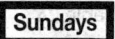

Route Diagram - see first page of Table 26

		GR	TP	XC	TP	GR	GR	XC	HT	EM	GR	TP	XC	GR	XC	GR	HT	EM	GR	TP	XC
		R				R	R				R			R		R			R		
		1	1 ◇	1 ◇	1 ◇	1	1	1 ◇	1 ◇	◇	1	1 ◇	1 ◇	1	1 ◇	1	1 ◇	◇	1	1 ◇	1 ◇
			A	B	C			D		E		A	G		H			E		A	B
									⊠								⊠				
London Kings Cross 15 ⊖	d	14 00				14 10	14 30		14 44		15 00			15 10		15 30	15 44		16 00		
Stevenage 4	d										15 19			14 46			16u04				
Peterborough 8	a	14 44				14 54	15 14				15 49			15 54		16 14			16 44		
Norwich	d						12b15			13 49								14 47			
Stansted Airport	d						13 25									14 25					
Cambridge	d						13 56									14 56			15b05		
Peterborough 8	d	14 45				14 54	15 14			15 26	15 49			15 55		16 15		16 24	16 45		
Grantham 7	a					15 16			15 46	15 56				16 17		16 39	16 48	16 54			
	d					15 16			15 47					16 18		16 39	16 49				
Newark North Gate 7	a					15 28								16 30		16 50					
Lincoln	a								17c21					17 08							
Grimsby Town	a								17e45								18e45				
Newark North Gate 7	d					15 28								16 31		16 50					
Retford 10	d					15 43			16 08								17 10				
Doncaster 7	a	15 38				15 59	16 08		16 22					16 57		17 14	17 25		17 39		
Selby	a								16 41								17 50				
Hull	a	16 50							17 21								18 32				
Wakefield Westgate 7	a					16 17								17 14							
Huddersfield	a					17f20								18f20							
Leeds 10	a					16 36								17 34							
Shipley	a					17g19								18 19							
Bradford Forster Square	a					17h14								18h14							
Keighley	a					17j32								18 32							
Skipton	a					17j48								18 48							
Sheffield 7	d			15 21			15 28	15 51					16 21		16 51						17 21
Doncaster 7	d	15 39					16 09	16 17							17 15	17 20			17 40		
York 8	a	16 04					16 35	16 40			17 03				17 42	17 46			18 04		
Scarborough	a										18 32		18 32								
Harrogate	a	16 50				17 28					17 50			18 28					18 50		
Leeds 10	d		15 40	16 08	16 12							16 40	17 08			17 12				17 40	18 08
Hull	d											16k01									17 23
York 8	d	16 06	16 15	16 36	16 40		16 42	16 46			17 05	17 14	17 36		17 44	17 47			18 07	18 14	18 36
Thirsk	d				17 02																
Northallerton	d		16 35		17 10							17 35								18 35	
Darlington 7	a	16 34	16 46	17 01			17 09	17 14			17 32	17 46	18 01		18 10	18 15			18 35	18 46	19 01
Eaglescliffe	a																				
Middlesbrough	a				17 43			17 49								18 53					
Darlington 7	d	16 34	16 47	17 03			17 10	17 15			17 33	17 47	18 03		18 11	18 16			18 35	18 47	19 03
Durham	d		17 03	17 19				17 33				18 03	18 19		18 28	18 33				19 03	19 19
Chester-le-Street	d							17 40				18 09									
Newcastle 8	a	17 04	17 20	17 34			17 39	17 53			18 02	18 22	18 34		18 47	18 52			19 05	19 20	19 34
Hartlepool	a																				
Sunderland	a						18 21									19 22					
Newcastle 8	d	17 07		17 38			17 41				18 05		18 38						19 07		19 40
Morpeth	d																				
Alnmouth for Alnwick	d			18 02																	20 05
Berwick-upon-Tweed	d						18 28				18 48		19 20								
Dunbar	d												19 43								
Edinburgh 10	a	18 33		19 08			19 14				19 33		20 07						20 35		21 11
Edinburgh	d	18 42									19 37		20 12								21 12
Haymarket	d	18 47									19 42		20 16								21 16
Motherwell	a										20 19		20 53								21 53
Glasgow Central 15	a	19m51					20n22				20 37		21 17						21n55		22 19
Stirling	a						20 24						21q23								22q24
Perth	a												22r46								
Inverness	a																				
Inverkeithing	a	19 01									20q17								21 18		
Kirkcaldy	a	19 18									20q59								21 34		
Leuchars 3	a	19 43																	22 04		
Dundee	a	19 57																	22 17		
Arbroath	a	20 15																	22 34		
Montrose	a	20 31																	22 49		
Stonehaven	a	20 54																	23 10		
Aberdeen	a	21 17																	23 33		

For general notes see front of timetable
For details of catering facilities see Directory of Train Operators

- **A** From Manchester Airport (Table 39)
- **B** From Plymouth (Table 51) (from 8 November from Birmingham New Street) (Table 51)
- **C** From Liverpool Lime Street (Table 39)
- **D** From Guildford (Table 51)
- **E** To Liverpool Lime Street (Table 49)
- **G** From Penzance (Table 135) (from 8 November from Birmingham New Street) (Table 51)
- **H** From Reading (Table 51)
- **b** Change at Ely and Peterborough
- **c** Change at Retford
- **e** Change at Doncaster
- **f** Change at Leeds
- **g** From 8 November arr. 1714
- **h** Bradford Interchange
- **j** From 8 November arr. Keigthley 1724, Skipton 1737
- **k** 13 September only
- **m** Glasgow Queen Street. Change at Edinburgh
- **n** Glasgow Queen Street
- **q** Change at Edinburgh
- **r** Change at Edinburgh and Stirling

Table 26

Sundays

from 13 September

London → Humberside, Yorkshire, North East England and Scotland

Route Diagram - see first page of Table 26

	GR	EM	GR	TP	GR	GR	TP	XC	XC	GR	XC	GR	HT	EM	GR	TP	GR	GC	XC	GR	XC
	R 1	◇	R 1	1 ◇	R 1	R 1	1 ◇	1 ◇	1 ◇	R 1	1 ◇	R 1	1 ◇	◇	R 1	1 ◇	R 1	1	1 ◇	R 1	1 ◇
		A		B			C	D	E		D			A		C			G		D
London Kings Cross [15] ⊖ d	16 10		16 30		16 40	17 00				17 10		17 30	17 44		18 00		18 10	18 20		18 30	
Stevenage [4] d	16 29		16 49									17 49								18 50	
Peterborough [8] a	16 58		17 18		17 24	17 46				17 54		18 18			18 44		18 54			19 19	
Norwich d		15 53												16 57							
Stansted Airport d	*15 25*											*16 25*								*17 25*	
Cambridge d	*15 56*					*16b05*						*16 56*			*17b05*					*17 56*	
Peterborough [8] d	16 59	17 14	17 19		17 25	17 46				17 54		18 19		18 30	18 45		18 55			19 19	
Grantham [7] a		17 52			17 47					18 17			18 45	18 59	19 06						
d					17 47					18 17			18 46		19 06						
Newark North Gate [7] a						18 16						18 49					19 25				
Lincoln a	*19c22*											*19 48*					*20c45*				
Grimsby Town a			*19e45*										*20e45*								
Newark North Gate [7] d						18 16						18 49					19 26				
Retford [10] d	17 39												19 07				19 42				
Doncaster [7] a	17 55		18 10			18 42				18 50		19 14	19 23		19 42		19 58			20 12	
Selby a													19 40								
Hull a	*18 57*					*19 55*							20 22								
Wakefield Westgate [7] a	18 12				18 38					19 07			*19e58*				20 16				
Huddersfield a	*19f20*									*20f02*			*21g02*								
Leeds [10] a	18 32				18 59					19 27			*20e20*				20 39				
Shipley a	*19 19*				*19 45*					*20 19*			*20g45*				*21 19*				
Bradford Forster Square a	*19h23*				*19h53*					*20h14*			*20j53*				*21h25*				
Keighley a	*19 32*									*20 32*							*21 32*				
Skipton a	*19 48*									*20 48*							*21 48*				
Sheffield [7] d			*17 28*					17 51	18 21		18 51								19 21		19 51
Doncaster [7] d			18 11			18 43		18 15			19 17	19 20			19 42					20 12	20 18
York [8] a			18 34			19 05		19 21			19 42	19 45			20 07			20 23		20 39	20 44
Scarborough a						*20 32*												*21 32*			
Harrogate a	*19 28*					*19 50*				*20 28*					*20 50*						
Leeds [10] d							18 40	18 57	19 08		*19 12*					19 40			20 08		*20 12*
Hull d															*19k04*						
York [8] d			18 42	18 40		19 07	19 14	19 24	19 36		19 45	19 47			20 08	20 13		20 25	20 35	20 40	20 47
Thirsk d				18 59												20 30		20 42			
Northallerton d			19 01	19 07			19 35					20 08				20 38		20 50		21 00	
Darlington [7] a			19 15			19 35	19 46	19 51	20 03		20 10	20 20			20 36				21 03	21 13	21 18
Eaglescliffe a																		21 12			
Middlesbrough a			*19 57*	19 40								*20 57*				21 12					
Darlington [7] d			19 15			19 36	19 47	19 53	20 04		20 12	20 21			20 36				21 04	21 13	21 19
Durham d			19 33			19 53	20 03	20 09	20 22		20 28	20 38							21 22	21 31	21 37
Chester-le-Street d							20 09	20 18													21 46
Newcastle [8] a			19 51			20 09	20 22	20 30	20 37		20 43	20 56			21 06				21 37	21 47	21 59
Hartlepool a																		21 36			
Sunderland a			*20 21*															22 06			
Newcastle [8] d						20 11			20 39		20 49				21 07				21 39	21 53	
Morpeth d											21 02										
Alnmouth for Alnwick d											21 16				21 35				22 07		
Berwick-upon-Tweed d						20 54			21 25		21 37				21 57				22 30	22 37	
Dunbar d									21 50											23 01	
Edinburgh [10] a						21 38			22 20		22 25				22 44				23 19	23 29	
Edinburgh d						21 41															
Haymarket d						21 45															
Motherwell a						22 23															
Glasgow Central [15] a						22 45									*23m55*				*00m25*		
Stirling a											23 27										
Perth a											*00 07*										
Inverness a																					
Inverkeithing a						22n17													23 58		
Kirkcaldy a						23n05															
Leuchars [3] a						23n40															
Dundee a						23n56															
Arbroath a																					
Montrose a																					
Stonehaven a																					
Aberdeen a																					

For general notes see front of timetable
For details of catering facilities see Directory of Train Operators

- **A** To Manchester Piccadilly (Table 49)
- **B** From Liverpool Lime Street (Table 39)
- **C** From Manchester Airport (Table 39)
- **D** From Reading (Table 51)
- **E** From Penzance (Table 135) (from 8 November from Birmingham New Street) (Table 51)
- **G** From Plymouth (Table 51) (from 8 November from Birmingham New Street) (Table 51)
- **b** Change at Ely and Peterborough
- **c** Change at Retford
- **e** Change at Doncaster
- **f** Change at Leeds
- **g** Change at Doncaster and Leeds
- **h** Bradford Interchange
- **j** Bradford Interchange. Change at Doncaster and Leeds
- **k** 13 September only
- **m** Glasgow Queen Street
- **n** Change at Edinburgh

Sundays

from 13 September

London → Humberside, Yorkshire, North East England and Scotland

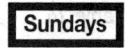

Route Diagram - see first page of Table 26

		GR		EM	GR	TP	GR		GR	XC	GR	EM		GR	TP	GR	HT		GR	GR	GR	EM	GR	GR		
		R 1 ⊏P ⚒		◇ A	R 1 ⊏P ⚒	1 ◇ B	R 1 ⊏P ⚒		R 1 ⊏P ⚒	1 ◇ C ⚒	R 1 ⊘ ⚒	◇ A ⚒		R 1 ⊏P ⚒	1 ◇ D	R 1 ⊏P ⚒	1 ◇ ⊠		R 1 ⊏P ⚒	R 1 ⊏P ⚒	R 1 ⊏P ⚒	◇ A	R 1 ⊏P ⚒	R 1 ⊏P ⚒		
London Kings Cross 15 ⊖	d	18 40			19 00		19 10		19 30		19 35			20 00		20 03	20 10		20 30	21 00	21 30		22 00	22 10		
Stevenage 4	d								19 49		19 54						20u30			20 46			21 46			
Peterborough 8	a	19 25			19 44		19 55		20 18		20 24			20 44		20 50			21 14	21 45	22 14		22 44	22s59		
Norwich	d			17 56								18 57										20 52				
Stansted Airport	d								18 25										19 25							
Cambridge	d				18b04				18 56					19b04					19 56				21b05			
Peterborough 8	d	19 25		19 26	19 44		19 56		20 19		20 25	20 30		20 44		20 50			21 14	21 46	22 15	22 22	22 45			
Grantham 7	a	19 47		19 56			20 19					21 01					21 18		21 36		22 39	22 50		23s31		
	d	19 47					20 19										21 19		21 36		22 39					
Newark North Gate 7	a						20 30												21 48		22 50			23s42		
Lincoln	a																				23 46					
Grimsby Town	a				21c45						22c45									23c58						
Newark North Gate 7	d						20 30												21 48		22 50					
Retford 10	d																21 40		22 03		23 06					
Doncaster 7	a	20 20			20 35		20 56		21 09		21 16			21 36			21 54		22 19	22 42	23 27		23 42	00s12		
Selby	a						21 15										22 09									
Hull	a	21 23					21 56										22 50			00 02						
Wakefield Westgate 7	a	20 38							21 27							21 57			22 37							
Huddersfield	a	22e02														22e57			00e02					02e56		
Leeds 10	a	20 59							21 46							22 16			23 00		00 24			01 18		
Shipley	a	21f45							22 19							22 45			23 21							
Bradford Forster Square	a	21f54							22g25							22 54			23g43							
Keighley	a								22 32										23 34							
Skipton	a								22 48										23 50							
Sheffield 7 ⛴	d									20 51										21h51			22 30			
Doncaster 7	d				20 35					21 21	21 23			21 36						22 43			23 45			
York 8	a				21 00					21 42	21 47			22 00						23 09			00 39			
Scarborough	a													23 02												
Harrogate	a	21 51			21 58				23 00										23 59							
Leeds 10	d					20 40					21 12				22 12											
Hull	d									20 22																
York 8	d				21 02	21 08				21 44	21 48			22 02	22 42					23 11						
Thirsk	d					21 26									23 06											
Northallerton	d					21 34									23 16					23 47						
Darlington 7	a				21 30	21 46				22 10	22 26			22 43	23 32					23 59			01 32			
Eaglescliffe	a																									
Middlesbrough	a				22 07						23 10															
Darlington 7	d				21 30	21 46				22 11	22 27			22 43	23 33					23 59			01a50			
Durham	d					22 03				22 28	22 44			23 01	23 49					00 17						
Chester-le-Street	d																									
Newcastle 8 ⛴	a				22 02	22 20				22 43	23 14			23 34	00 21					00 50			02 25			
Hartlepool	a																									
Sunderland ⛴	a																									
Newcastle 8 ⛴	d																									
Morpeth	d																									
Alnmouth for Alnwick	d																									
Berwick-upon-Tweed	d																									
Dunbar	d																									
Edinburgh 10	a																									
Edinburgh	d																									
Haymarket	d																									
Motherwell	a																									
Glasgow Central 15	a																									
Stirling	a																									
Perth	a																									
Inverness	a																									
Inverkeithing	a																									
Kirkcaldy	a																									
Leuchars 3	a																									
Dundee	a																									
Arbroath	a																									
Montrose	a																									
Stonehaven	a																									
Aberdeen	a																									

For general notes see front of timetable
For details of catering facilities see Directory of Train Operators

A To Nottingham (Table 19)
B From Manchester Airport (Table 39)
C From Reading (Table 51)
D From Liverpool Lime Street (Table 39)
b Change at Ely and Peterborough
c Change at Doncaster
e Change at Leeds
f From 8 November arr. Shipley 2146, Bradford Forster Square 2155
g Bradford Interchange
h Change at York

Table 26

Mondays to Fridays

Scotland, North East England, Yorkshire and Humberside → London

Route Diagram - see first page of Table 26

Miles	Miles	Miles			GR	EM	GR	GR	GR	GR	GR	GR	GR	TP	GR	HT		GR	HT	TP	GR	XC	TP	GR	GR	GR
									MO	MX																
					1 ◇		R 1	R 1	R 1	R 1	R 1	R 1	R 1	1 ◇	R 1	BHX 1 ◇		R 1	BHX 1 ◇	1 ◇	R 1	1 ◇	1 ◇	R 1	R 1	R 1
						A								B						C		D	C		E	
–	–	0	**Aberdeen**	d																						
–	–	16¼	Stonehaven	d																						
–	–	40½	Montrose	d																						
–	–	54¼	Arbroath	d																						
–	–	71¼	**Dundee**	d																						
–	–	79½	Leuchars 3	d																						
–	–	104½	Kirkcaldy	d																						
–	–	117¼	Inverkeithing	d																						
–	–	–	**Inverness**	d																						
–	–	–	Perth	d																						
–	–	–	Stirling	d																						
0	–	–	**Glasgow Central 15**	d																						
12¾	–	–	Motherwell	d																						
56	–	129¼	Haymarket	d																						
57¼	–	130½	**Edinburgh 10**	a																						
–	–	–	**Edinburgh**	d																						
86½	–	–	Dunbar	d																						
114¾	–	–	**Berwick-upon-Tweed**	d																						
147	–	–	Alnmouth for Alnwick	d																						
165½	–	–	Morpeth	d																						
181¾	–	–	**Newcastle 8**	a																						
–	–	–	Sunderland	d																						
–	–	–	Hartlepool	d																						
–	–	–	**Newcastle 8**	d					04 20	04 30		05 25			06 00					06 13		06 21		06 30		
190	–	–	Chester-le-Street	d																		06 32				
195¾	–	–	**Durham**	d					04 34	04 44		05 38			06 12					06 29		06 39		06 44		
217¾	–	–	**Darlington 7**	a					04 51	05 01		05 55			06 29					06 45		06 55		07 01		
–	–	–	Middlesbrough	d										05 57												
–	–	–	Eaglescliffe	d																						
–	–	–	**Darlington 7**	d					04 52	05 02		05 56			06 30					06 46		06 56	←	07 02		
231¾	–	–	Northallerton	d					05 18	05 28		06 08		06 25						06 58 →			06 58	07 13		
239½	–	–	Thirsk	d										06 33									07 06			
261¾	–	–	**York 8**	a					05 53	05 54		06 28		06 51	06 57							07 22	07 30	07 34		
–	–	–	Hull	a					*08b20*	*08b20*												*08 46*				
–	–	–	Leeds 10	a					*06 49*	*06 49*				07 20	*07 49*								08 04			
–	–	–	Harrogate	d														*06c06*			*06 30*			*06 45*		
–	–	–	Scarborough	d																				*06 30*		
–	–	–	**York 8**	d					06 00	06 00		06 30			07 00							07 27		07 36		
294¼	–	–	**Doncaster 7**	a					06 22	06 22		06 53										07 49				
–	–	–	Sheffield 7	a					*07 06*	*07 06*		*07 40*										08 20				
–	–	–	Skipton	d									*05 48*					*06e02*			*06 18*					06 55
–	–	–	Keighley	d									*06 01*					*06e15*			*06 31*					07u05
–	–	–	Bradford Forster Square	d									*06 01*					06 30			*06f48*					*07g05*
–	–	–	Shipley	d									*06 13*					06u35			*06 44*					07u14
–	0	–	**Leeds 10**	d			05 05	05 30			06 05	*06 15*	06 40					07 00			07 20					07 40
–	–	–	Huddersfield	d							*05 32*							*06c11*			*06 41*					*06c56*
–	10	–	**Wakefield Westgate 7**	d			05 17	05 42			06 18	*06 27*	06 52					07 12			07 32					07 52
–	–	–	Hull	d					*05 20*	*05 20*						06 25									07 00	
–	–	–	Selby	d								*06 18*				07 00									07 32	
–	29¾	–	**Doncaster 7**	d			05 35	06 00	06 23	06 23		06 54				07 18		07 30	←						07 55	
311¾	–	–	**Retford 10**	d			05 50				06 48					07 32 →			07 32							08 19
330¼	–	–	**Newark North Gate 7**	a			06 05	06 24	06 46	06 46	07 03		07 29													08 34
–	–	–	Grimsby Town	d								*05h26*	*05 56*					*06j00*							*06k26*	*07 03*
–	–	–	Lincoln	d			*05 26*						*06 53*													*07 59*
–	–	–	**Newark North Gate 7**	d			06 05	06 24	06 46	06 46	07 04		07 29													08 34
344¾	–	–	**Grantham 7**	a			06 18	06 37	06 59	06 59	07 16	07 25							07 56						08 29	
–	–	–		d		05 50	06 18	06 37	06 59	06 59	07 17	07 25							07 57						08 29	
374	–	–	**Peterborough 8**	a		06 25	06 37	06 58	07 18	07 18	07 37	07 45			08 03						08 32				08 50	
–	–	–	Cambridge	a				*08 07*	*08m44*	*08m44*	*08m55*				*09 08*						*09 51*				*10 09*	
–	–	–	Stansted Airport	a				*08 45*							*09 45*										*10 45*	
–	–	–	Norwich	a					*09 13*	*09 13*					*10m30*											
–	–	–	**Peterborough 8**	d			06 40	07 00	07 20	07 20	07 40	07 50			08 04						08 33				08 51	
422¾	–	–	**Stevenage 4**	a	06 10		*07 35*	*07 58*	*08 26*	*08 26*		*08 38*			*09 05*						*09 34*			*09 06*	*09 56*	
450¼	–	–	**London Kings Cross 15** ⊖	a	07 00		07 30	07 53	08 13	08 13	08 33	08 43	08 46		08 59			09 07	09 17		09 26			09 35	09 45	09 51

For general notes see front of timetable
For details of catering facilities see Directory of Train Operators

- **A** From Nottingham (Table 19) to Spalding (Table 18)
- **B** To Manchester Airport (Table 39)
- **C** To Liverpool Lime Street (Table 39)
- **D** To Reading (Table 51)
- **E** **The Hull Executive**
- **b** Change at York and Selby
- **c** Change at Leeds
- **e** Change at Shipley
- **f** Bradford Interchange
- **g** Bradford Interchange. Change at Leeds
- **h** Change at Doncaster. 22 June to 4 September dep. 0505, by bus
- **j** 22 June to 4 September only; by bus to Doncaster
- **k** Until 19 June and from 7 September only; change at Doncaster
- **m** Change at Peterborough and Ely

Scotland, North East England, Yorkshire and Humberside → London

Route Diagram - see first page of Table 26

		EM	XC	GR	GR	GR	GC	EM	TP	XC	TP	GR	HT	GR	XC	GR	NT	GR	TP	XC	EM	GR	GR	XC
		◇	1 ◇	R 1	R 1	R 1	R 1	◇	1 ◇	1 ◇	1 ◇	R 1	1 ◇	R 1	1 ◇	R 1		R 1	1 ◇	1 ◇	◇	R 1	R 1	1 ◇
		A	B				C	D	E	G	E				B		H		E	G	J			B
Aberdeen	d																							
Stonehaven	d																							
Montrose	d																							
Arbroath	d																							
Dundee	d																							
Leuchars 3	d																							
Kirkcaldy	d																					05 53		
Inverkeithing	d																					06 16		
Inverness	d																							
Perth	d																					05 10		
Stirling	d																			05 30				
Glasgow Central 15	d																					06b00		06 00
Motherwell	d																							
Haymarket	d																							06 55
Edinburgh 10	a																							06 59
Edinburgh	d				05 50							06 00			06 08					06 44		07 00		07 08
Dunbar	d											06 20												07 28
Berwick-upon-Tweed	d				06 29							06 43			06 49					07 23		07 42		07 51
Alnmouth for Alnwick	d											07 03			07 10		07 23			07 47				
Morpeth	d											07 19					07 49			08 01				
Newcastle 8	a				07 16							07 38			07 43		08 14			08 19		08 30		08 38
Sunderland	d						06 41													07 55				
Hartlepool	d						07 08																	
Newcastle 8	d		06 44	07 00	07 20					07 23	07 26	07 40			07 44	07 52				08 24		08 32		08 40
Chester-le-Street	d										07 36									08 33				
Durham	d		06 55	07 12						07 37	07 43					08 04				08 40		08 45		08 52
Darlington 7	a		07 12	07 29						07 52	07 59				08 11	08 22				08 55		09 04		09 11
Middlesbrough	d			06 49					07 23							07 42				08 02		08 25		
Eaglescliffe	d						07 28												←					
Darlington 7	d		07 12	07 30						07 55	08 00				08 12	08 22			08 00	08 57		09 05		09 12
Northallerton	d						07 45		07 53		→								08 12					
Thirsk	d						07 56		08 01										08 20					
York 8	a		07 41	07 58	08 09		08 17		08 19	08 23		08 34			08 41	08 50			08 55	09 24		09 34		09 41
Hull	a											10c04												10 56
Leeds 10	a		08 08				09 02		08 52	09 04					09 08				09 23	10 04				10 08
Harrogate	d			07 05		07 28						07 49		07 51				08 14				08 16	08 30	
Scarborough	d			07 00								07 38												
York 8	d			08 00	08 11		08 21			08 27		08 36				08 52				09 27		09 35		
Doncaster 7	a									08 50						09 16				09 54		10 03		
Sheffield 7	a		08 51							09 20					09 51	10 05				10 20				10 51
Skipton	d					07 08								07 47				07 56					08 43	
Keighley	d					07 21								08 00				08 09					08 56	
Bradford Forster Square	d					07e20								08e06				08 26					09e03	
Shipley	d					07 35								08 13				08 33					09 09	
Leeds 10	d					08 05								08 40				09 05					09 40	
Huddersfield	d					07f26								07f57				08 37					08f57	
Wakefield Westgate 7	d					08 17								08 52				09 18					09 52	
Hull	d												08 12									08 56		
Selby	d												08 45											
Doncaster 7	d					08 37							09 02	09 12		09 17		09 36				10 04	10 15	
Retford 10	d												09 16					09 51						
Newark North Gate 7	a													09 37		09 43		10 06					10 38	
Grimsby Town	d					07g26												08h00				08g36		
Lincoln	d												08j27			09 11								
Newark North Gate 7	d													09 37		09 43		10 06					10 38	
Grantham 7	a				09 00							09 28	09 41			09 55						10 36		
	d	08 25			09 00			09 11				09 28	09 42			09 55					10 08	10 38		
Peterborough 8	a	08 57				09 26		09 38				09 47		10 05		10 15		10 36			10 42	10 57	11 06	
Cambridge	a					10k47								11 08				11k44					12 08	
Stansted Airport	a													11 45									12 45	
Norwich	a	10 43						11 13													12 13			
Peterborough 8	d					09 26						09 48		10 05		10 18		10 37				10 57	11 06	
Stevenage 4	a					09 57												11 06						
London Kings Cross 15 ⊖	a			09 55	10 10	10 25	10 31					10 40	10 51	10 59		11 14		11 34				11 51	12 03	

For general notes see front of timetable
For details of catering facilities see Directory of Train Operators

- A From Mansfield Woodhouse (Table 55)
- B To Plymouth (Table 51)
- C **The Zephyr**
- D From Nottingham (Table 49)
- E To Manchester Airport (Table 39)
- G To Reading (Table 51)
- H From Chathill (Table 48)
- J From Liverpool Lime Street (Table 49)
- b Glasgow Queen Street
- c Change at York and Selby
- e Bradford Interchange
- f Change at Leeds
- g Until 19 June and from 7 September only; change at Doncaster
- h 22 June to 4 September only; by bus to Doncaster
- j Change at Retford
- k Change at Peterborough and Ely

Scotland, North East England, Yorkshire and Humberside → London

Route Diagram - see first page of Table 26

		TP	GR	GR	EM	TP	GR	XC	HT		GR	GR	XC	TP	EM	TP	XC	GR	GR	XC	TP	GR		EM	GR	TP
			R	R			R				R	R						R	R			R			R	
		1 ◇	1	1	◇	1 ◇	1	1 ◇	1 ◇		1	1	1 ◇	1 ◇	◇	1 ◇	1 ◇	1	1	1 ◇	1 ◇	1		◇	1	1 ◇
		A			B	A		C					D	A	B	A	C			D	A			B		A
		🛒	✕ 🛒	☕ 🛒	🛒	🛒	⊘ 🛒	🛒	⊠		☕ 🛒	☕ 🛒	🛒	🛒	🛒	🛒	🛒	⊘ 🛒	☕ 🛒	🛒	🛒	⊘ 🛒		🛒	✕ 🛒	🛒
Aberdeen	d																	05b56								
Stonehaven	d																	06b12								
Montrose	d																	06b34								
Arbroath	d																	06b48								
Dundee	d						06b05						06 32					07b08		07 35						
Leuchars 3	d						06b16						06 46					07b20		07 48						
Kirkcaldy	d						06b49						07 21					07b54		08 20		08 28				
Inverkeithing	d						07b19						07 42					08b16		08 35		08 49				
Inverness	d																									
Perth	d						05c16						06b14					07c03				07c15				
Stirling	d						06b36						06b36					07b49				08 05				
Glasgow Central 15	d						06 50						07e00					07 50		08e00		08f30				
Motherwell	d						07 04											08 04		08b04						
Haymarket	d						07 46						08 01					08 49		08 54						
Edinburgh 10	a						07 52						08 05					08 56		08 58						
Edinburgh	d						08 00						08 10					09 00		09 07		09 30				
Dunbar	d																			09 28						
Berwick-upon-Tweed	d												08 52					09 39		09 51		10 10				
Alnmouth for Alnwick	d						08 56																			
Morpeth	d																									
Newcastle 8	a						09 29						09 40					10 31		10 38		10 59				
Sunderland	d		08 30													09 30						10 30				10 30
Hartlepool	d																									
Newcastle 8	d		09 00			09 12	09 30	09 33					09 43			10 15	10 25	10 34		10 43		11 01				11 15
Chester-le-Street	d					09 21																				
Durham	d		09 12			09 27		09 48					09 55			10 27	10 41	10 47		10 55						11 27
Darlington 7	a		09 30			09 43	09 58	10 04					10 12			10 43	10 56	11 05		11 10		11 28				11 43
Middlesbrough	d	09 00	08 55											09 59				10 24			11 00	10 54				10 54
Eaglescliffe	d																									
Darlington 7	d		09 31			09 44	09 58	10 05					10 12			10 44	10 58	11 06		11 10		11 29				11 44
Northallerton	d	09 27	09 43			09 56								10 27		10 56					11 27					11 56
Thirsk	d	09 35												10 35							11 35					
York 8	a	09 55	10 05			10 21	10 27	10 32					10 41	10 54		11 21	11 24	11 33		11 41	11 55	11 58				12 21
Hull	a		11g34																	13 02		13g34				
Leeds 10	a	10 23				10 53		11 04					11 08	11 23		11 53	12 04			12 08	12 23	12 49				12 53
Harrogate	d		09 05								09 44	10 14							10 44			11 05			11 14	
Scarborough	d		08 47															09 47				10 47				
York 8	d		10 06				10 29	10 34									11 27	11 35				11 59				
Doncaster 7	a		10 30				10 53	10 57									11 51	12 00								
Sheffield 7	a		11 08				11 41	11 20					11 51				12 20			12 51						
Skipton	d										09 48								10 48						10 59	
Keighley	d										10 01								11 01						11 09	
Bradford Forster Square	d			09 31							10h04	10 31							11h05						11 31	
Shipley	d			09 39							10 14	10 39							11 14						11 39	
Leeds 10	d			10 05							10 40	11 05							11 40						12 05	
Huddersfield	d			09 35							09j57	10 35							10j57						11 35	
Wakefield Westgate 7	d			10 18							10 52	11 17							11 54						12 17	
Hull	d			09 25			09 56		10 12			10 22						10 57							11 22	
Selby	d								10 47																	
Doncaster 7	d		10 30	10 35			10 53		11 05		11 13	11 37						12 00	12 12						12 36	
Retford 10	d						11 08		11 20																12 51	
Newark North Gate 7	a			10 59							11 41								12 37							
Grimsby Town	d			09 28			09k36					10m10						10k36							11m10	
Lincoln	d			10 23														11 10							11n27	
Newark North Gate 7	d			10 59							11 41								12 37							
Grantham 7	a			11 11					11 40		11 54	12 09													13 14	
	d			11 11	11 06				11 40		11 54	12 09			12 07									13 06	13 14	
Peterborough 8	a		11 16	11 31	11 36		11 48				12 13	12 28			12 42			12 46	13 05			13 11		13 38		
Cambridge	a			12q44			13 08					13q44						13 50				14 08				
Stansted Airport	a						13 45															14 45				
Norwich	a				13 13										14 13									15 13		
Peterborough 8	d		11 17	11 31			11 49				12 14	12 29						12 47	13 06			13 12				
Stevenage 4	a		11 47	12 33							12 43							13 16				14 08				
London Kings Cross 15	⊖ a		12 17	12 25			12 42		12 44		13 10	13 22						13 43	14 02			14 10			14 20	

For general notes see front of timetable
For details of catering facilities see Directory of Train Operators

- **A** To Manchester Airport (Table 39)
- **B** From Liverpool Lime Street (Table 49)
- **C** To Reading (Table 51)
- **D** To Plymouth (Table 51)
- **b** Change at Edinburgh
- **c** Change at Stirling and Edinburgh
- **e** Glasgow Queen Street. Change at Edinburgh
- **f** Glasgow Queen Street
- **g** Change at York and Selby
- **h** Bradford Interchange
- **j** Change at Leeds
- **k** Until 19 June and from 7 September only; change at Doncaster
- **m** 22 June to 4 September only; by bus to Doncaster
- **n** Change at Retford
- **q** Change at Peterborough and Ely

Scotland, North East England, Yorkshire and Humberside → London

Route Diagram - see first page of Table 26

		XC	GR	XC	GR	GR	EM	HT	GR	TP	TP	XC		GR	XC	TP	GR	GR	GC	GR	EM	TP	GR	XC	XC	TP
		1◇	R 1	1◇	R 1	R 1	◇	1◇	R 1	1◇	1◇	1◇		R 1	1◇	1◇	R 1	R 1	R 1	R 1	◇	1◇	R 1	1◇	1◇	1◇
		A		B			C			D	D	A			B	D	E				C	D		A	B	D
Aberdeen	d			07b13	07 52										08 20								09 07			
Stonehaven	d			07b29	08 09										08 38											
Montrose	d			07b54	08 32										08 59								09 46			
Arbroath	d			08b08	08 48										09 15								10 00			
Dundee	d			08b27	09 06										09 33		09b42						10 17			
Leuchars 3	d			08b39	09 20										09 47		09b55						10 29			
Kirkcaldy	d			09b12	09 44										10 17		10b27						10 42			
Inverkeithing	d			09b33	10 01									10b08	10 32		10b43						11 10			
Inverness	d			04b57	06b46												07 55									
Perth	d			07b59	08b47												09 55									
Stirling	d			08b36	09b06									09b36			10 30						10 36			
Glasgow Central 15	d			09 00	09c30									09 50	10c00		10c30						11e00			
Motherwell	d			09 15										10 04												
Haymarket	d			09 54	10 19									10 48	10 54		11 09									
Edinburgh 10	a			09 59	10 25									10 56	11 01		11 15									
Edinburgh	d			10 08	10 30									11 00	11 08		11 30						12 00		12 05	
Dunbar	d														11 28											
Berwick-upon-Tweed	d													11 39	11 51								12 39			
Alnmouth for Alnwick	d			11 05										12 00											13 06	
Morpeth	d			11 20																						
Newcastle 8	a			11 37	11 57									12 34	12 38		12 58						13 27		13 36	
Sunderland	d										11 30						12 30		12 30							
Hartlepool	d																		12 54							
Newcastle 8	d	11 27	11 30	11 40	11 59						12 15	12 19		12 35	12 43		13 01					13 15	13 29	13 34	13 44	
Chester-le-Street	d											12 28														
Durham	d	11 39	11 44	11 52							12 27	12 35		12 48	12 55							13 27		13 46	13 52	
Darlington 7	a	11 55	12 01	12 09							12 43	12 51		13 06	13 11							13 43	13 55	14 02	14 12	
Middlesbrough	d		11 24							12 00				12 24		12 50						12 57		13 25		13 50
Eaglescliffe	d																		13 16							
Darlington 7	d	11 56	12 02	12 11							12 44	12 53		13 06	13 12							13 44	13 56	14 03	14 12	
Northallerton	d									12 27	12 56					13 17			13 38			13 56				14 17
Thirsk	d									12 35						13 25			13 47							14 25
York 8	a	12 24	12 30	12 41	12 50					12 55	13 21	13 24		13 35	13 41	13 49	13 52		14 07			14 21	14 24	14 29	14 41	14 48
Hull	a													14 48												
Leeds 10	a		13 04	13 08						13 23	13 53	14 04			14 07	14 23	14 49					14 53		15 04	15 08	15 23
Harrogate	d				12 05				12 14								13 07			13 14						
Scarborough	d				11 47												12 47									
York 8	d	12 27	12 32		12 53							13 26		13 36			13 54		14 10				14 26	14 32		
Doncaster 7	a	12 50	12 54									13 53		14 02									14 49	14 55		
Sheffield 7	a	13 20		13 51								14 20			14 51									15 20	15 51	
Skipton	d					11 48			12 14									12 48								
Keighley	d					12 01			12 24									13 01								
Bradford Forster Square	d					12f05			12 31									13f05		13 31						
Shipley	d					12 14			12 39									13 14		13 39						
Leeds 10	d					12 40			13 05									13 40		14 05						
Huddersfield	d					11g57			12 35									12g57		13 35						
Wakefield Westgate 7	d					12 52			13 18									13 53		14 18						
Hull	d		11 55					12 45	12 22					12 57									13 25			
Selby	d							13 20																		
Doncaster 7	d		12 55			13 14		13 37	13 38					14 03				14 15					14 50			
Retford 10	d								13 55																	
Newark North Gate 7	a					13 42			14 10														15 13			
Grimsby Town	d		11h36					12j10						12h36									13k36			
Lincoln	d		12 08			12 23			12m27									13 30					14 05			
Newark North Gate 7	d					13 42			14 10														15 13			
Grantham 7	a							14 08	14 23											15 03			15 26			
	d						14 07	14 09	14 23											15 03	15 07		15 26			
Peterborough 8	a		13 42		14 02	14 09	14 38		14 42					14 49				15 05		15 22	15 34		15 45			
Cambridge	a					15 08			15 57									16 08		16n44						
Stansted Airport	a					15 45												16 45								
Norwich	a						16 13														17 13					
Peterborough 8	d		13 47		14 03	14 10			14 43					14 50				15 06		15 23			15 47			
Stevenage 4	a		14 17			15 08			15 12											15 52			16 17			
London Kings Cross 15 ⊖	a		14 44		14 57	15 05		15 20	15 40					15 44			15 50	15 58	16 05	16 22			16 46			

For general notes see front of timetable
For details of catering facilities see Directory of Train Operators

A To Reading (Table 51)
B To Penzance (Table 135)
C From Liverpool Lime Street (Table 49)
D To Manchester Airport (Table 39)
E **The Highland Chieftain**
b Change at Edinburgh
c Glasgow Queen Street. Change at Edinburgh
e Glasgow Queen Street
f Bradford Interchange
g Change at Leeds
h Until 19 June and from 7 September only; change at Doncaster
j 22 June to 4 September only; by bus to Doncaster
k Change at Doncaster. 22 June to 4 September dep. 1310, by bus
m Change at Retford
n Change at Peterborough and Ely

Scotland, North East England, Yorkshire and Humberside → London

Route Diagram - see first page of Table 26

		GR		GR	GR	EM	GR	TP	XC	GR	GR	XC	TP	GR	HT		GR	TP	XC	GR	GR	XC	TP	GR	TP	GR
		R 1		R 1	R 1	◇	R 1	1 ◇	1 ◇	R 1	R 1	1 ◇	1 ◇	R 1	1 ◇		R 1	1 ◇	1 ◇	R 1	R 1	1 ◇	1 ◇	R 1	1 ◇	R 1
		A				B		C	D	E		G	H					C	D			G	C		C	
Aberdeen	d	09 52																		11 05						12b07
Stonehaven	d	10 09																		11 21						12b26
Montrose	d	10 32																		11 46						12c17
Arbroath	d	10 49																		12 00						13b00
Dundee	d	11 06										11 30								12 17		12 34				13b17
Leuchars 3	d	11 20										11 45								12 29		12 46				13b29
Kirkcaldy	d	11 44								12b00		12 17								13 00		13 18				14b00
Inverkeithing	d	12 01								12b21		12 33								13 21		13 34				14b21
Inverness	d																			09e18						10b47
Perth	d	10b57																		11 59						13b01
Stirling	d	11b06								11b36										12 36						13b36
Glasgow Central 15	d	11f30								11 50		12g00								13g00						13 50
Motherwell	d									12 06																14 05
Haymarket	d	12 19								12 49																14 49
Edinburgh 10	a	12 25								12 56																14 56
Edinburgh	d	12 30								13 00		13 06								14 00		14 08				15 00
Dunbar	d											13 28														
Berwick-upon-Tweed	d									13 41		13 51								14 39						
Alnmouth for Alnwick	d																					15 05				
Morpeth	d																									
Newcastle 8	a	13 57								14 30		14 38								15 28		15 35				16 26
Sunderland	d	13 30						13 30										14h28							15 30	
Hartlepool	d																									
Newcastle 8	d	14 00					14 05	14 12	14 27	14 34		14 40		14 55				15 12	15 22	15 30		15 40		15 55	16 06	16 28
Chester-le-Street	d																	15 21							16 15	
Durham	d						14 17	14 24	14 40			14 52		15 07				15 27	15 34			15 52		16 08	16 21	
Darlington 7	a						14 36	14 43	14 55	15 03		15 10		15 24				15 43	15 50	16 01		16 10		16 26	16 39	
Middlesbrough	d						13 55			14 24			14 50					14 55				15 27	15 50			
Eaglescliffe	d																									
Darlington 7	d						14 37	14 44	14 57	15 04		15 10		15 25				15 44	15 51	16 02		16 12		16 26	16 39 →	
Northallerton	d						14 49	14 56					15 17					15 56					16 17			
Thirsk	d												15 25										16 25			
York 8	a	14 51					15 09	15 21	15 26	15 33		15 41	15 51	15 52				16 21	16 23	16 30		16 41	16 51	16 54		17 20
Hull	a	15 58												17 27										18 29		
Leeds 10	a	15 49						15 53	16 04			16 08	16 23	16 49				16 53		17 04		17 07	17 23	17 49		
Harrogate	d	14 05									14 44						15 14				15 44			16 05		
Scarborough	d	13 47												14 47										15 47		
York 8	d	14 53					15 11		15 29	15 35				15 54					16 25	16 32				16 56		17 21
Doncaster 7	a						15 35		15 54	15 59									16 48					17 19		
Sheffield 7	a						16 08		16 20			16 51							17 18			17 51		18 08		
Skipton	d			13 48	13 58						14 48						15 10				15 48					
Keighley	d			14 01	14 09						15 01						15 20				16 01					
Bradford Forster Square	d			14j05	14 31						15j05						15 31				16j05					
Shipley	d			14 14	14 39						15 14						15 39				16 14					
Leeds 10	d			14 40	15 05						15 40						16 05				16 40					
Huddersfield	d			13k57	14 35						14k57						15 35				15k57					
Wakefield Westgate 7	d			14 52	15 17						15 52						16 17				16 52					
Hull	d			13 57			14 25			14 57					15 18		15 25				15 57					
Selby	d														15 57											
Doncaster 7	d			15 15			15 36			16 00					16 15		16 36				17 10			17 20		
Retford 10	d						15 51								16 34											
Newark North Gate 7	a			15 41			16 06										17 00				17 33			17 44		
Grimsby Town	d			13 52			14m10			14n36							15m00				16 03					
Lincoln	d			14 48											15q27						16 57					
Newark North Gate 7	d			15 41			16 06										17 00				17 33			17 44		
Grantham 7	a			15 54			16 19							16 44	16 55									17 57		
	d			15 54		16 07	16 19							16 44	16 55									17 57		
Peterborough 8	a	16 01			16 18	16 34				16 47	16 51			17 04			17 27				18 01					18 26
Cambridge	a	17 08			17r43									18 16			18r58				19 08					19r58
Stansted Airport	a	17 45												18 50							19 45					
Norwich	a					18 13								19r27												
Peterborough 8	d	16 02			16 19					16 48	16 52			17 04			17 28				18 02					18 26
Stevenage 4	a				16 48									17 34	17s46		18 47				19 17			18 42		19 32
London Kings Cross 15 ⊖	a	16 57		17 04	17 15		17 28			17 41	17 46			18 04	18 12		18 24			18 27	18 54			19 12		19 19

For general notes see front of timetable
For details of catering facilities see Directory of Train Operators

A **The Northern Lights**
B From Liverpool Lime Street (Table 49)
C To Manchester Airport (Table 39)
D To Reading (Table 51)
E **The Flying Scotsman**
G To Plymouth (Table 51)
H To Manchester Piccadilly (Table 39)
b Change at Edinburgh
c Change at Arbroath and Edinburgh
e Change at Perth and Edinburgh
f Glasgow Queen Street. Change at Edinburgh
g Glasgow Queen Street
h From 7 September dep. 1429
j Bradford Interchange
k Change at Leeds
m 22 June to 4 September only; by bus to Doncaster
n Until 19 June and from 7 September only; change at Doncaster
q Change at Retford
r Change at Peterborough and Ely

Scotland, North East England, Yorkshire and Humberside → London

Route Diagram - see first page of Table 26

		TP	GR	EM	XC		HT	GR	XC	TP	GR	GR	TP	XC	EM	GR	GR	XC		TP	GC	GR	GR	XC	GR	GR
		1◇	R 1	◇	1◇		1◇	R 1	1◇	1◇	R 1	R 1	1◇	1◇	◇	R 1	R 1	1◇		1◇	R 1	R 1	R 1	1◇	R 1	R 1
		A		B	C				D	E			A	G	B			H		A				J		
Aberdeen	d															13 06										14b07
Stonehaven	d															13 22										14b23
Montrose	d															13 44										14c17
Arbroath	d															13 58										15b00
Dundee	d								13 34							14 17		14 34								15b17
Leuchars 3	d								13 46							14 29		14 46								15b29
Kirkcaldy	d								14 18							15 00		15 18								16b00
Inverkeithing	d								14 34							15 22		15 34								16b21
Inverness	d																									12b54
Perth	d															13 58										15b00
Stirling	d															14 36										15b36
Glasgow Central 15	d								14e00							15e00										15 50
Motherwell	d																									16 04
Haymarket	d																									16 50
Edinburgh 10	a																									16 56
Edinburgh	d								15 08							16 00		16 07								17 00
Dunbar	d								15 28							16 20										
Berwick-upon-Tweed	d								15 51							16 43										
Alnmouth for Alnwick	d																	17 09								18 00
Morpeth	d																	17 24								
Newcastle 8	a								16 38							17 31		17 40								18 32
Sunderland	d												16 30								17 30					
Hartlepool	d																				17 56					
Newcastle 8	d				16 32				16 40		16 55		17 01	17 17		17 32		17 40					18 10	18 20		18 35
Chester-le-Street	d				16 41									17 26										18 29		
Durham	d				16 48				16 52		17 07		17 13	17 33				17 55					18 22	18 36		
Darlington 7	a	←			17 04				17 11		17 25		17 29	17 48		17 59		18 11					18 39	18 54		19 03
Middlesbrough	d	15 55			16 19					16 50				16 57				17 24		17 50			17 55	18 24		
Eaglescliffe	d																				18 15					
Darlington 7	d	16 39			17 05				17 12		17 25		17 30	17 50		17 59		18 12					18 40	18 56		19 04
Northallerton	d	16 50								17 17			17 42							18 17	18 36		18 51			
Thirsk	d	16 58								17 25										18 25	18 45					
York 8	a	17 27			17 31				17 41	17 50	17 53		18 06	18 18		18 28		18 41		18 51	19 04		19 11	19 25		19 33
Hull	a												19 32										20f39			
Leeds 10	a	17 53			18 04				18 09	18 23			18 35			19 04		19 09		19 35				20 04		
Harrogate	d		16 14					16 44				17 14					17 50				18 05					
Scarborough	d										16 47										17 47					
York 8	d				17 34						17 55			18 24		18 31					19 06		19 13	19 29		19 35
Doncaster 7	a				17 57						18 20			18 49		18 53							19 37	19 55		19 59
Sheffield 7	a				18 20				18 51		19 08			19 21				19 51					20 18	20 20		
Skipton	d		16 12					16 49				16 58					17 49									
Keighley	d		16 22					17 02				17 08					18 02									
Bradford Forster Square	d		16 31					17g04				17 31					18g04					18 27				18h27
Shipley	d		16 39					17 15				17 39					18 14					18 34				18h34
Leeds 10	d		17 05					17 40				18 05					18 40					19 05				19 05
Huddersfield	d		16 35					16j57				17 35					17j57					18 40				18k40
Wakefield Westgate 7	d		17 17					17 52				18 17					18 52					19 17				
Hull	d						17 06									17 52						18 22				18 53
Selby	d						17 43									18 26										
Doncaster 7	d		17 37				18 03	18 11			18 21	18 35				18 54	19 11					19 35	19 37			20 00
Retford 10	d		17 57				18 17				18 36															
Newark North Gate 7	a							18 34			18 51					19 17	19 34					20 05			←	
Grimsby Town	d		16m00				16n36					17m05				17n36						18m10			18 28	18n36
Lincoln	d						17q22				18 18														19 25	
Newark North Gate 7	d							18 34			18 51					19 17	19 34					20 05 →			20 05	
Grantham 7	a						18 37	18 47									19 49								20 17	
	d			18 12			18 37	18 47							19 07		19 49								20 17	
Peterborough 8	a			18 41				19 06			19 19	19 25			19 36	19 45							20 27		20 37	20 46
Cambridge	a							20 08				21r04				21 08										21 54
Stansted Airport	a							20 45								21 45										
Norwich	a			20 22											21 13	22r31										
Peterborough 8	d							19 07			19 20	19 26				19 46							20 28		20 38	20 46
Stevenage 4	a		19 00				19s24				19 50					20 16	20 35									21 17
London Kings Cross 15 ⊖	a		19 29				19 49	19 59			20 18	20 21				20 44	21 03				21 09		21 20		21 33	21 44

For general notes see front of timetable
For details of catering facilities see Directory of Train Operators

- **A** To Manchester Airport (Table 39)
- **B** From Liverpool Lime Street (Table 49)
- **C** To Reading (Table 51)
- **D** To Plymouth (Table 51)
- **E** To Manchester Piccadilly (Table 39)
- **G** To Guildford (Table 51)
- **H** To Bristol Temple Meads (Table 51)
- **J** To Birmingham New Street (Table 51)
- **b** Change at Edinburgh
- **c** Change at Arbroath and Edinburgh
- **e** Glasgow Queen Street
- **f** Change at York and Selby
- **g** Bradford Interchange
- **h** Change at Leeds and Doncaster
- **j** Change at Leeds
- **k** Change at Wakefield Westgate and Doncaster
- **m** 22 June to 4 September only; by bus to Doncaster
- **n** Until 19 June and from 7 September only; change at Doncaster
- **q** Change at Retford
- **r** Change at Peterborough and Ely

Scotland, North East England, Yorkshire and Humberside → London

Route Diagram - see first page of Table 26

		HT	GR	XC	TP	TP	GR	XC		EM	GR	XC	TP	NT	GR	GR	TP	TP	TP	NT	GR		GR	XC		
		BHX	R				R				R				R	R					R		R			
		1 ◇	1	1 ◇	1 ◇	1 ◇	1	1 ◇		◇	1	1 ◇	1 ◇		1	1	1 ◇	1 ◇	1 ◇		1		1	1 ◇		
				A		B		C		D		C	B	E		G	H		B	J						
		⊠	🍽	☕			⌀ ☕	☕		☕	🍽	☕			🍽	🍽 ☕					🍽		🍽			
Aberdeen	d						14 49								15b33	16c01					18 16					
Stonehaven	d						15 06								15b49	16c18					18 33					
Montrose	d						15 29								16b11						18 56					
Arbroath	d						15 45								16b25	16c55					19 12					
Dundee	d			15 35			16 03								16 50	17c26					19 30					
Leuchars 3	d			15 47			16 17								17 02	17c39					19 44					
Kirkcaldy	d			16 19			16 45					17 00			17 48	18c13					20 08					
Inverkeithing	d			16 35			17 01					17 22			18 04	18c29					20 24					
Inverness	d														14e51								16c56			
Perth	d						15c59								17 00								19c09			
Stirling	d						16c06					16 36			17 06	17c36							19c36			
Glasgow Central 15	d			16f00			16g30					17f00			17f15	17 50							19 50	20 48		
Motherwell	d															18 05							20 04	21 08		
Haymarket	d						17 20									18 49					20s42		20 49	21 52		
Edinburgh 10	a						17 27									18 56					20 48		20 55	22 02		
Edinburgh	d			17 08			17 30					18 05			18 35	19 00							21 00			
Dunbar	d			17 28			17 54					18 25			18 57	19 24							21 20			
Berwick-upon-Tweed	d			17 51			18 17					18 48			19 20	19 47							21 43			
Alnmouth for Alnwick	d											19 08		19 20	19 42								22 05			
Morpeth	d													19 45	19 59					21 34			22 22			
Newcastle 8 ⛴	a			18 39			19 07					19 40		20 06	20 20	20 36				21 56			22 43			
Sunderland ⛴	d						18 30									19 27			20 27	21 27						
Hartlepool	d																									
Newcastle 8 ⛴	d			18 40		18 58	19 08	19 25				19 43				20 38			21 47	22 00			22 45			
Chester-le-Street	d							19 37												22 09						
Durham	d			18 52		19 10		19 44				19 55				20 51			22 00	22 18			23 00			
Darlington 7	a			19 11		19 26	19 36	20 02				20 12				21 08			22 16	22 38			23 17			
Middlesbrough	d				19 00			19 25					20 00				20 50	21 40					21 55			
Eaglescliffe	d																									
Darlington 7	d			19 12		19 27	19 36	20 04				20 12	20 31			21 09		22 08	22 17				23 18			
Northallerton	d				19 27	19 38							20 42				21 19	22 19	22 28				23s44			
Thirsk	d				19 35								20 50					22 27								
York 8	a			19 41	19 58	20 02	20 05	20 30				20 41	21 10			21 38	21 44	22 54	23 04				00 16			
Hull	a																23 08									
Leeds 10	a			20 09		20 35	20 52	21 04				21 07	21 35			22 51	22 07		23 33				02h31			
Harrogate	d		18 44				19 05				19 44					20 05										
Scarborough	d						18 47									20 37										
York 8	d						20 09	20 32								21 40										
Doncaster 7	a						20 31	20 55								22 02										
Sheffield 7 ⛴	a			20 51			21 17	21 22				21 51				22 54	00 02									
Skipton	d		18 48								19 48															
Keighley	d		19 01								20 01															
Bradford Forster Square	d		19j05								20j04															
Shipley	d		19 14								20 14															
Leeds 10	d		19 40								20 40															
Huddersfield	d		18k57								19k45															
Wakefield Westgate 7	d		19 52								20 55															
Hull	d	19 18									20 03					20 56										
Selby	d	19 53																								
Doncaster 7	d	20 10	20 14				20 32				21 12					22 03										
Retford 10	d										21 27															
Newark North Gate 7	a		20 37								21 42					22 26										
Grimsby Town	d										19m36					20n36										
Lincoln	d										20q27															
Newark North Gate 7	d		20 37								21 42					22 26										
Grantham 7	a	20 41	20 50								21 55					22 39										
	d	20 41	20 50							21 08	21 55					22 39										
Peterborough 8	a		21 09				21 20			21 35	22 14					22 58										
Cambridge	a		22 08				22r33																			
Stansted Airport	a		22 45																							
Norwich	a									23 18																
Peterborough 8	d		21 10				21 21				22 15					22 59										
Stevenage 4	a	21s30					21 52				22s51					23s35										
London Kings Cross 15 ⊖	a	21 58	22 04				22 20				23 32					00 15										

For general notes see front of timetable
For details of catering facilities see Directory of Train Operators

- **A** To Bristol Temple Meads (Table 51)
- **B** To Manchester Airport (Table 39)
- **C** To Birmingham New Street (Table 51)
- **D** From Liverpool Lime Street (Table 49)
- **E** From Chathill to Hexham (Table 48)
- **G** NXEC cannot guarantee connections with London Underground services
- **H** To Manchester Piccadilly (Table 39)
- **J** To Middlesbrough (Table 44)
- **b** Change at Dundee and Edinburgh
- **c** Change at Edinburgh
- **e** Change at Perth and Edinburgh
- **f** Glasgow Queen Street
- **g** Glasgow Queen Street. Change at Edinburgh
- **h** Saturday mornings arr. 0218
- **j** Bradford Interchange
- **k** Change at Leeds
- **m** Change at Doncaster. 22 June to 4 September dep. 1910, by bus
- **n** Change at Doncaster. 22 June to 4 September dep. 2010, by bus
- **q** Change at Retford
- **r** Change at Peterborough and Ely

Table 26

Saturdays

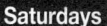

Scotland, North East England, Yorkshire and Humberside → London

Route Diagram - see first page of Table 26

		EM		GR	GR	GR	TP	GR		GR	GR	TP	EM	XC	TP	GR		GR	XC	GR	GR	GR	TP	XC		EM
		◇ A		R 1	R 1 ⊘	R 1	1 ◇ C	R 1		R 1	R 1	1 ◇ D	◇ E	1 ◇ G	1 ◇ D	R 1		R 1	1 ◇ H	R 1	R 1 ⊘	R 1 ⊘	1 ◇ C	1 ◇ G		◇ E
Aberdeen	d																									
Stonehaven	d																									
Montrose	d																									
Arbroath	d																									
Dundee	d																									
Leuchars 3	d																									
Kirkcaldy	d																									
Inverkeithing	d																									
Inverness	d																									
Perth	d																									
Stirling	d																									
Glasgow Central 15	d																									
Motherwell	d																									
Haymarket	d																									
Edinburgh 10	a																									
Edinburgh	d																									
Dunbar	d																									
Berwick-upon-Tweed	d																									
Alnmouth for Alnwick	d																									
Morpeth	d																									
Newcastle 8	a																									
Sunderland	d																									
Hartlepool	d																									
Newcastle 8	d				04 30			06 00				06 13		06 20		06 35			06 40	07 00				07 25		
Chester-le-Street	d													06 32												
Durham	d				04 45			06 12				06 29		06 39		06 48			06 56	07 12				07 38		
Darlington 7	a				05 02			06 29				06 45		06 55		07 06			07 11	07 29				07 53		
Middlesbrough	d						05 57													06 49			07 21			
Eaglescliffe	d																									
Darlington 7	d				05 03			06 30				06 46		06 56	←	07 06			07 13	07 30				07 55		
Northallerton	d				05 30		06 25					06 58			06 58					07 41			07 48			
Thirsk	d						06 33					→			07 06								07 56			
York 8	a				05 57		06 51	06 57						07 23	07 30	07 34			07 42	08 01			08 17	08 22		
Hull	a				08b20			08 46																10b34		
Leeds 10	a				06 49		07 20	07 49							08 04				08 08	08 49			08 52			
Harrogate	d									06 06						06 45				07 14		07 44				
Scarborough	d															06 34				07 04						
York 8	d				06 00			07 00						07 25		07 36				08 03				08 27		
Doncaster 7	a				06 22			07 22						07 48		07 59								08 50		
Sheffield 7	a				07 06			08 00						08 18					08 51					09 20		
Skipton	d									05 48								06 55			07c01					
Keighley	d									06 01								07u07			07c15					
Bradford Forster Square	d									06e26								07f05			07 33	07e34				
Shipley	d									06 13								07u18			07u38					
Leeds 10	d			05 05		06 10		06 19		07 00								07 40			08 05	08 15				
Huddersfield	d									06g11								06g56			07 32					
Wakefield Westgate 7	d			05 17		06 22		06 33		07 12								07 52			08 18					
Hull	d				05 20			06 07			06 50															
Selby	d							06 15			07 23															
Doncaster 7	d			05 35	06 23	06 40		07 23		07 30	07 40					08 00						08 45				
Retford 10	d			05 50		06 55												08 20								
Newark North Gate 7	a			06 05		07 10				07 53						08 24		08 34			08 54					
Grimsby Town	d					05h15		05j26		06h00	06j26							07 03				07j26				
Lincoln	d			05 26														07 59								
Newark North Gate 7	d			06 05		07 10				07 53						08 24		08 34			08 54					
Grantham 7	a			06 17		07 23				08 06						08 37		08 46			09 06					
	d	05 51		06 17		07 23				08 06			08 16			08 37		08 46			09 06					09 11
Peterborough 8	a	06 21		06 37	07 09	07 42		08 09		08 26	08 32		08 44			08 57		09 06		09 15	09 26	09 32				09 44
Cambridge	a			08k08	08m44			09 08			09m44							10q16				10m44				
Stansted Airport	a			08r45				09 45																		
Norwich	a	08 13			09 18								10 19													11 18
Peterborough 8	d			06 37	07 09	07 48		08 09		08 26	08 32					08 57		09 07		09 16	09 26	09 33				
Stevenage 4	a			07 33	08 08			09 08			09 33									09 45		10 33				
London Kings Cross 15 ⊖	a			07 29	08 04	08 40		09 03		09 18	09 26					09 51		10 00		10 13	10 20	10 26				

For general notes see front of timetable
For details of catering facilities see Directory of Train Operators

- **A** From Nottingham (Table 19)
- **C** To Manchester Airport (Table 39)
- **D** To Liverpool Lime Street (Table 39)
- **E** From Nottingham (Table 19)
- **G** To Reading (Table 51)
- **H** To Penzance (Table 135) (from 12 September to Plymouth) (Table 51)
- **b** Change at York and Selby
- **c** Change at Shipley
- **e** Bradford Interchange
- **f** Bradford Interchange. Change at Leeds
- **g** Change at Leeds
- **h** 27 June to 5 September only; by bus to Doncaster
- **j** Until 20 June and from 12 September only. Change at Doncaster
- **k** 18 July to 5 September arr. 0844, change at Peterborough and Ely
- **m** Change at Peterborough and Ely
- **q** 18 July to 5 September arr. 1044, change at Peterborough and Ely
- **r** Until 11 July and from 12 September only

Table 26

Saturdays

Scotland, North East England, Yorkshire and Humberside → London

Route Diagram - see first page of Table 26

		GR	GC	TP	XC	GC	HT	GR		TP	NT	GR	XC	EM	GR	XC		TP	GR	GR	TP	XC	EM	GR		HT
		R 1	R 1	1 ◇	1 ◇	R 1	1 ◇	R 1		1 ◇		R 1	1 ◇	◇	R 1	1 ◇		1 ◇	R 1	R 1	1 ◇	1 ◇	◇	R 1		1 ◇
			A	B	C	A				B	D		E	G		C		B			B	E	G			
		Ø					⊠	Ø				Ø			Ø											⊠
Aberdeen	d																									
Stonehaven	d																									
Montrose	d																									
Arbroath	d																									
Dundee	d																							06b05		
Leuchars 3	d																							06b16		
Kirkcaldy	d																		06 16					06b49		
Inverkeithing	d																		06 39					07b14		
Inverness	d																									
Perth	d																		05 35							
Stirling	d												05 30											06b36		
Glasgow Central 15	d														06c00									06 50		
Motherwell	d																							07 05		
Haymarket	d																							07 49		
Edinburgh 10	a																							07 56		
Edinburgh	d				06 12			06 15					06 55		07 00	07 05			07 30					08 00		
Dunbar	d							06 35								07 25										
Berwick-upon-Tweed	d				06 51			06 58					07 35		07 40	07 48			08 09							
Alnmouth for Alnwick	d				07 11			07 18			07 34		07 55											08 58		
Morpeth	d							07 34			08 00		08 09													
Newcastle 8	a				07 41			07 53			08 25		08 27		08 31	08 38			08 58					09 31		
Sunderland	d		06 53										07 55								08 31					
Hartlepool	d		07 17																							
Newcastle 8	d	07 30		07 33	07 44			07 54					08 30		08 33	08 40			09 00		09 12	09 25		09 32		
Chester-le-Street	d			07 42												08 49					09 21					
Durham	d	07 42		07 49	07 56								08 42		08 46	08 56			09 13		09 27	09 37				
Darlington 7	a	07 59		08 05	08 12			08 21					08 58		09 04	09 12			09 30		09 43	09 54		10 00		
Middlesbrough	d							07 42					08 02		08 25			09 00								
Eaglescliffe	d		07 45																							
Darlington 7	d	08 00		08 06	08 13	←		08 21		←			08 59		09 04	09 13			09 31		09 44	09 56		10 01		
Northallerton	d		08 06	08 18						08 18								09 27	09 42		09 56					
Thirsk	d		08 15	→		08 15				08 26								09 35								
York 8	a	08 28	→		08 41	08 44		08 50		08 57			09 26		09 33	09 41		09 55	10 03		10 21	10 22		10 29		
Hull	a															10 56			11e34							
Leeds 10	a	09 04			09 07					09 23			10 04			10 08		10 23	10 49		10 53			11 04		
Harrogate	d					07 49						08 00			08 16				09 05	09 18						
Scarborough	d					07 47													08 47							
York 8	d	08 30				08 47		08 51					09 28		09 35				10 05			10 25		10 31		
Doncaster 7	a	08 54						09 15					09 51		10 01				10 28			10 48		10 52		
Sheffield 7	a	09 41			09 51			10 05					10 20			10 51			11 08			11 20		11 41		
Skipton	d											07 56							08f18	08 48						
Keighley	d											08 09							08f31	09 01						
Bradford Forster Square	d											08 31							08g34	09 31						
Shipley	d											08 38							08f44	09 39						
Leeds 10	d							08 19				09 05							09 19	10 05						
Huddersfield	d											08 37							08f45	09 35						
Wakefield Westgate 7	d							08 34				09 17							09 33	10 18						
Hull	d	07 36					08 02	08 08							08 56					09 25				09 56		10 06
Selby	d						08 37																			10 41
Doncaster 7	d	08 55					09 01	09 15				09 35			10 03				10 29	10 36				10 55		11 02
Retford 10	d	09 10					09h21																	11 10		11 17
Newark North Gate 7	a											10 00								11 00						
Grimsby Town	d											08j00			08k36					09 28				09k36		
Lincoln	d	08 00					08m27					09 11								10 23						10m27
Newark North Gate 7	d											10 00								11 00						
Grantham 7	a						09 42					10 12								11 12						11 38
	d						09 42					10 12		10 09						11 12			11 07			11 38
Peterborough 8	a	09 51						10 06				10 32		10 42	10 54				11 20	11 32			11 36	11 49		
Cambridge	a							11 08				11q44			12 08					12q44				13 08		
Stansted Airport	a							11 45							12 45									13 45		
Norwich	a													12 18									13 13			
Peterborough 8	d	09 52						10 06				10 32			10 54				11 21	11 32				11 50		
Stevenage 4	a											11 02			11w47				11 50	12 33						
London Kings Cross 15 ⊖	a	10 44				10 48	10 52	10 58				11 33			11 50				12 17	12 24				12 42		12 47

For general notes see front of timetable
For details of catering facilities see Directory of Train Operators

A The Zephyr
B To Manchester Airport (Table 39)
C To Plymouth (Table 51)
D From Chathill (Table 48)
E To Reading (Table 51)
G From Liverpool Lime Street (Table 49)
b Change at Edinburgh
c Glasgow Queen Street
e Change at York and Selby
f Change at Leeds and Doncaster
g Bradford Interchange. Change at Leeds and Doncaster
h Arr. 0916
j 27 June to 5 September only; by bus to Doncaster
k Until 20 June and from 12 September only. Change at Doncaster
m Change at Retford
n 18 July to 5 September arr. 1144, change at Peterborough and Ely
q Change at Peterborough and Ely
w 18 July to 5 September arr. 1150

Scotland, North East England, Yorkshire and Humberside → London

Route Diagram - see first page of Table 26

		XC	TP	GR	GR	TP	XC	EM	GR	XC	TP	GR	EM	GR	TP	XC	GR	XC	TP	GR	GR	TP	XC
		1 ◇	1 ◇	R 1	R 1	1 ◇	1 ◇	◇	R 1	1 ◇	1 ◇	R 1	◇	R 1	1 ◇	1 ◇	R 1	1 ◇	1 ◇	R 1	R 1	1 ◇	1 ◇
		A	B			B	C	D		E	B		D		B	C		G	B			B	C
Aberdeen	d			05 56													07b13			07 52			
Stonehaven	d			06 12													07b29			08 09			
Montrose	d			06 34													07b54			08 32			
Arbroath	d			06 48													08b08			08 48			
Dundee	d			07 08						07 35		07 35					08b27			09 06			
Leuchars 3	d			07 20						07 48							08b39			09 20			
Kirkcaldy	d			07 49						08 20		08 28					08b41			09 44			
Inverkeithing	d			07 54					08b08	08 35		08 49					09b09			10 01			
Inverness	d																04b57			06b46			
Perth	d			06 55								07c15					07b59			08b47			
Stirling	d			07 16								08 05					08b36			09b06			
Glasgow Central 15	d	07 00		07e30					07 50	08f00		08e30					08 50	09 00		09f30			
Motherwell	d								08 04								09 04						
Haymarket	d	07 54							08 49	08 54							09 46	09 55		10 21			
Edinburgh 10	a	07 59							08 56	08 58							09 53	09 59		10 27			
Edinburgh	d	08 05		08 35					09 00	09 05		09 30					10 00	10 05		10 30			
Dunbar	d									09 25													
Berwick-upon-Tweed	d	08 47		09 14					09 41	09 47		10 10											
Alnmouth for Alnwick	d	09 09																11 04					
Morpeth	d																	11 19					
Newcastle 8	a	09 39		10 02					10 31	10 38		10 58					11 27	11 39		11 58			
Sunderland	d			09 29								10 30								11 30			
Hartlepool	d																						
Newcastle 8	d	09 40		10 03		10 12	10 25		10 32	10 44		11 00			11 15	11 20	11 29	11 40		12 00		12 15	12 22
Chester-le-Street	d																						12 31
Durham	d	09 55				10 27	10 38		10 45	10 56					11 27	11 34	11 42	11 55		12 13		12 27	12 38
Darlington 7	a	10 10		10 31		10 43	10 54		11 03	11 12		11 26			11 43	11 54	12 00	12 10		12 31		12 43	12 53
Middlesbrough	d		10 00	09 39					10 24		11 00	10 54					11 24		12 00	11 55		11 55	
Eaglescliffe	d																						
Darlington 7	d	10 12		10 31		10 44	10 56		11 03	11 13		11 27			11 44	11 56	12 01	12 12		12 31		12 44	12 55
Northallerton	d		10 27			10 56					11 27				11 56				12 27			12 56	
Thirsk	d		10 35								11 35								12 35				
York 8	a	10 41	10 54	10 59		11 21	11 24		11 32	11 41	11 55	11 57			12 21	12 22	12 30	12 41	12 55	13 00		13 21	13 24
Hull	a									12 54		13g34											14 45
Leeds 10	a	11 08	11 23	11 49		11 53	12 04		12 04	12 08	12 23	12h49			12 53		13 04	13 09	13 23	13 49		13 53	
Harrogate	d			10 05	10 14							11 05		11 14						12 05	12 14		
Scarborough	d			09 47								10 47								11 47			
York 8	d			11 00			11 27		11 33			11 59				12 25	12 31			13 02			13 27
Doncaster 7	a			11 24			11 50		11 57			12 20				12 50	12 55						13 52
Sheffield 7	a	11 51		12 08			12 20			12 51		13 08				13 20		13 51					14 20
Skipton	d			09j18	09 57							10j18		10 48							12 14		
Keighley	d			09j31	10 08							10j31		11 01							12 24		
Bradford Forster Square	d			09k34	10 31							10k34		11 31							12 31		
Shipley	d			09j44	10 39							10j44		11 39							12 39		
Leeds 10	d			10 19	11 05							11 19		12 05							13 05		
Huddersfield	d			09j45	10 35							10j45		11 35							12 35		
Wakefield Westgate 7	d			10 32	11 17							11 32		12 17							13 17		
Hull	d				10 22				10 57					11 22			11 55				12 22		
Selby	d																						
Doncaster 7	d			11 24	11 39				11 57			12 21		12 35			12 57				13 38		
Retford 10	d													12 50									
Newark North Gate 7	a				12 01									13 05							14 01		
Grimsby Town	d				10m10				10n36					11 28			11n36				12m10		
Lincoln	d								11q10					12 23									
Newark North Gate 7	d				12 01									13 05							14 01		
Grantham 7	a			11 55	12 14				12 28					13 17									
	d			11 55	12 14			12 07	12 28				13 06	13 17									
Peterborough 8	a			12 19	12 33			12 38	12 49			13 07	13 35				13 43			14 13	14 29		
Cambridge	a			13r44					13t50			14 08									15r44		
Stansted Airport	a											14 45											
Norwich	a							14 13					15 13										
Peterborough 8	d			12 19	12 34				12 50			13 07					13 47			14 14	14 29		
Stevenage 4	a				13 03							14 08					14 16				15 33		
London Kings Cross 15 ⊖	a			13 11	13 33				13 44			13 59		14 27			14 43			15 10	15 21		

For general notes see front of timetable
For details of catering facilities see Directory of Train Operators

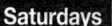

- **A** To Newquay (Table 135) (from 12 September to Plymouth) (Table 51)
- **B** To Manchester Airport (Table 39)
- **C** To Reading (Table 51)
- **D** From Liverpool Lime Street (Table 49)
- **E** To Plymouth (Table 51)
- **G** To Penzance (Table 135)
- **b** Change at Edinburgh
- **c** Change at Stirling and Edinburgh
- **e** Glasgow Queen Street
- **f** Glasgow Queen Street. Change at Edinburgh
- **g** Change at York and Selby
- **h** Until 11 July arr. 1250
- **j** Change at Leeds and Doncaster
- **k** Bradford Interchange. Change at Leeds and Doncaster
- **m** 27 June to 5 September only; by bus to Doncaster
- **n** Until 20 June and from 12 September only. Change at Doncaster
- **q** Change at Peterborough
- **r** Change at Peterborough and Ely
- **t** 18 July to 5 September arr. 1444, change at Peterborough and Ely

Scotland, North East England, Yorkshire and Humberside → London

Route Diagram - see first page of Table 26

		EM ◇ A	GR R 1	HT 1 ◇	XC 1 ◇ B	TP 1 ◇ C	GR R 1 D	GC R 1	EM ◇ A	GR R 1	TP 1 ◇ C	XC 1 ◇ E
Aberdeen	d				08 20							
Stonehaven	d				08 38							
Montrose	d				08 59							
Arbroath	d				09 15							
Dundee	d				09 33		09b42					
Leuchars 3	d				09 47		09b55					
Kirkcaldy	d				10 17		10b27					
Inverkeithing	d		10b08		10 32		10b43					
Inverness	d						07 55					
Perth	d						09 55					
Stirling	d		09b36				10 30					
Glasgow Central 15	d		09 50		10c00		10c15					
Motherwell	d		10 04									
Haymarket	d		10 49		10 52		11 09					
Edinburgh 10	a		10 56		10 58		11 15					
Edinburgh	d		11 00		11 05		11 30					
Dunbar	d				11 25							
Berwick-upon-Tweed	d		11 39		11 48							
Alnmouth for Alnwick	d						12 28					
Morpeth	d											
Newcastle 8	a		12 31		12 38		13 02					
Sunderland	d						12 30	12 30				
Hartlepool	d							12 54				
Newcastle 8	d		12 33		12 44		13 04				13 15	13 27
Chester-le-Street	d											
Durham	d		12 46		12 56						13 27	13 39
Darlington 7	a		13 03		13 12						13 43	13 56
Middlesbrough	d		12 20		12 20	12 50					12 55	
Eaglescliffe	d							13 13				
Darlington 7	d		13 04		13 13						13 44	13 58
Northallerton	d					13 17		13 31			13 56	
Thirsk	d					13 25		13 42				
York 8	a		13 32		13 41	13 49	13 55	14 03			14 21	14 24
Hull	a											
Leeds 10	a		14 04		14 08	14 23		14 49			14 53	15 04
Harrogate	d						13 05			13 14		
Scarborough	d						12 47					
York 8	d		13 34				13 57	14 05				14 27
Doncaster 7	a		13 58									14 50
Sheffield 7	a				14 51							15 20
Skipton	d									12 48		
Keighley	d									13 01		
Bradford Forster Square	d									13 31		
Shipley	d									13 39		
Leeds 10	d									14 05		
Huddersfield	d									13 35		
Wakefield Westgate 7	d									14 17		
Hull	d		12 57	13 05						13 25		
Selby	d			13 40								
Doncaster 7	d		13 58	14 04						14 35		
Retford 10	d			14 19						14 50		
Newark North Gate 7	a									15 05		
Grimsby Town	d		12f36							13g10		
Lincoln	d			13j27			13 30			14 05		
Newark North Gate 7	d									15 05		
Grantham 7	a		14 29	14 39						15 18		
	d	14 07	14 29	14 39					15 07	15 18		
Peterborough 8	a	14 39	14 49				15 04		15 34	15 38		
Cambridge	a						16k44					
Stansted Airport	a											
Norwich	a	16 13							17 13			
Peterborough 8	d		14 49				15 04			15 39		
Stevenage 4	a						16 08					
London Kings Cross 15 ⊖	a		15 42	15 50			16 03	16 04		16 34		

		GR R 1	XC 1 ◇ B	TP 1 ◇ C	GR R 1 G	GR R 1	EM ◇ A	TP 1 ◇ C	XC 1 ◇ E	GR R 1 H	HT 1 ◇	XC 1 ◇ J
Aberdeen	d	09 07			09 52							
Stonehaven	d				10 09							
Montrose	d	09 46			10 32							
Arbroath	d	10 00			10 49							
Dundee	d	10 17			11 06							11 30
Leuchars 3	d	10 29			11 20							11 45
Kirkcaldy	d	10 42			11 44					12b00		12 17
Inverkeithing	d	11 10			12 01					12b21		12 33
Inverness	d	07 55										
Perth	d	09 55			10b57							
Stirling	d	10 36			11b06					11b36		
Glasgow Central 15	d	10e45	11e00		11c30					11 50		12e00
Motherwell	d									12 04		
Haymarket	d				12 19					12 49		
Edinburgh 10	a				12 25					12 56		
Edinburgh	d	12 00	12 05		12 30					13 00		13 05
Dunbar	d											13 25
Berwick-upon-Tweed	d	12 39										13 48
Alnmouth for Alnwick	d		13 05									
Morpeth	d											
Newcastle 8	a	13 27	13 35		13 57					14 27		14 38
Sunderland	d							13 30				
Hartlepool	d											
Newcastle 8	d	13 31	13 44		13 59			14 15	14 22	14 29		14 44
Chester-le-Street	d											
Durham	d	13 44	13 56		14 12			14 27	14 34	14 42		14 56
Darlington 7	a	14 01	14 12		14 30			14 43	14 51	14 59		15 12
Middlesbrough	d	13 24		14 00	13 55					14 23		
Eaglescliffe	d											
Darlington 7	d	14 02	14 13		14 30			14 44	14 52	15 00		15 13
Northallerton	d	14 13		14 27				14 56				
Thirsk	d			14 35								
York 8	a	14 35	14 41	14 55	14 59			15 21	15 23	15 28		15 41
Hull	a			16 03								
Leeds 10	a		15 08	15 23	15 49			15 53		16 04		16 08
Harrogate	d				14 05	14 14						
Scarborough	d				13 47							
York 8	d	14 37			15 01				15 26	15 30		
Doncaster 7	a	15 03							15 51	15 55		
Sheffield 7	a		15 51						16 20			16 51
Skipton	d					13 58						
Keighley	d					14 09						
Bradford Forster Square	d					14 31						
Shipley	d					14 39						
Leeds 10	d					15 05						
Huddersfield	d					14 35						
Wakefield Westgate 7	d					15 17						
Hull	d	13 57				14 25				14 57	15 06	
Selby	d										15 42	
Doncaster 7	d	15 04				15 35				15 55	16 02	
Retford 10	d										16 17	
Newark North Gate 7	a					16 02						
Grimsby Town	d	13f36				13h52				14f36		
Lincoln	d					14 48				14 41	15j27	
Newark North Gate 7	d					16 02						
Grantham 7	a					16 15					16 37	
	d					16 15	16 07				16 37	
Peterborough 8	a	15 50				16 34	16 38			16 42		
Cambridge	a	17 08								18 16		
Stansted Airport	a	17 45								18 53		
Norwich	a						18 18			19r30		
Peterborough 8	d	15 50				16 35				16 46		
Stevenage 4	a	16 21				17 06				17 16		
London Kings Cross 15 ⊖	a	16 47			16 58	17 33				17 43	17 45	

For general notes see front of timetable
For details of catering facilities see Directory of Train Operators

- **A** From Liverpool Lime Street (Table 49)
- **B** To Penzance (Table 135)
- **C** To Manchester Airport (Table 39)
- **D** **The Highland Chieftain**
- **E** To Reading (Table 51)
- **G** **The Northern Lights**
- **H** **The Flying Scotsman**
- **J** To Plymouth (Table 51)
- **b** Change at Edinburgh
- **c** Glasgow Queen Street. Change at Edinburgh
- **e** Glasgow Queen Street
- **f** Until 20 June and from 12 September only. Change at Doncaster
- **g** 27 June to 5 September only; by bus to Doncaster
- **h** 27 June to 5 September dep. 1410; by bus to Doncaster
- **j** Change at Retford
- **k** Change at Peterborough and Ely
- **r** Until 11 July and from 12 September only. Change at Peterborough and Ely

Scotland, North East England, Yorkshire and Humberside → London

Route Diagram - see first page of Table 26

		TP 1◇ A	GR R 1	GR R 1	TP 1◇ B	XC 1◇ C	GR R 1	XC 1◇ D	TP 1◇ B	EM ◇ E	TP 1◇ B	XC 1◇ C	GR R 1	GR R 1	XC 1◇ D	EM 1◇ G	TP 1◇ A	TP 1◇ B	XC 1◇ H	EM ◇ E	GR R 1	HT 1◇	GR R 1
Aberdeen	d						11 05						12b07								13 06		
Stonehaven	d						11 21						12b26								13 22		
Montrose	d						11 46						12c17								13 44		
Arbroath	d						12 00						13b00								13 58		
Dundee	d						12 17						13b17		13 34						14 17		
Leuchars 3	d						12 29						13b29		13 46						14 29		
Kirkcaldy	d		12 39				13 00						14b00		14 18						15 00		
Inverkeithing	d		12 55				13 21						14b21		14 34						15 22		
Inverness	d		09e18										10b47										
Perth	d		11 59										13b01								13 58		
Stirling	d		12 06				12 36						13b36								14 36		
Glasgow Central 15	d		12f15				12f45	13f00					13 50		14f00						15f00		
Motherwell	d												14 04										
Haymarket	d												14 49										
Edinburgh 10	a												14 56										
Edinburgh	d		13 30				14 00	14 05					15 00		15 05						16 00		
Dunbar	d														15 25								
Berwick-upon-Tweed	d		14 09				14 39								15 48						16 39		
Alnmouth for Alnwick	d							15 05															
Morpeth	d																						
Newcastle 8 ⛴	a		14 57				15 26	15 35					16 27		16 38						17 27		
Sunderland ⛴	d		14g31								15 30							16 30					
Hartlepool	d																						
Newcastle 8 ⛴	d		14 59		15 09	15 25	15 28	15 44			16 06	16 22	16 29		16 44			17 01	17 22		17 29		
Chester-le-Street	d				15 18						16 15	16 31							17 31				
Durham	d				15 25	15 38	15 42	15 56			16 21	16 38	16 42		16 56			17 13	17 38				
Darlington 7	a		15 25		15 41	15 54	16 03	16 12			16 39	16 54	16 59		17 12			17 29	17 53		17 58		
Middlesbrough	d	14 50			14 55		15 27		15 50		15 55		16 24				17 00				17 25		
Eaglescliffe	d																						
Darlington 7	d		15 26		15 42	15 56	16 04	16 13			16 39	16 56	17 00		17 13			17 30	17 55		17 59		
Northallerton	d	15 17			15 53				16 17		16 50						17 27	17 42					
Thirsk	d	15 25							16 25		16 58						17 35						
York 8	a	15 51	15 55		16 17	16 22	16 32	16 41	16 51		17 18	17 22	17 29		17 41		17 55	18 06	18 22		18 27		
Hull	a	17 27							18 21								19 28						
Leeds 10	a	16 23	16 49		16 53		17 04	17 08	17 23		17 53		18 04		18 08		18 23	18 35			19 04		
Harrogate	d		15 05	15 14			15h14						16 05	16 44									17 50
Scarborough	d		14 47										15 47										
York 8	d		15 57			16 25	16 34					17 25	17 31			17 49			18 25		18 29		
Doncaster 7	a		16 20			16 51	16 57					17 50	17 54			18 16			18 48		18 51	19 04	
Sheffield 7 ⛴	a		17 08			17 20		17 51				18 20	18 41		18j51	18 44			19 18		19 42		
Skipton	d		14h18	15 10									15h18	16 49									17 49
Keighley	d		14h31	15 21									15h31	17 02									18 02
Bradford Forster Square	d		14k34	15 31									15k34	17m04									18n04
Shipley	d		14h45	15 39									15h44	17 15									18 14
Leeds 10	d		15 19	16 05									16 19	17 40									18 40
Huddersfield	d		14h45	15 35									15h45	16q57									17q57
Wakefield Westgate 7	d		15 32	16 17									16 32	17 52									18 54
Hull	d			15 25			15 57						16 54								17 55	18 12	
Selby	d																				18 26	18 47	
Doncaster 7	d		16 21	16 38			16 58						17 55	18 10							18 52	19 05	19 14
Retford 10	d			16 53										18 25								19 20	19 29
Newark North Gate 7	a			17 08									18 18	18 40									19 44
Grimsby Town	d			15r28			15t36						16v36								17w36		
Lincoln	d			16y03									16 57	17r22								18r24	
Newark North Gate 7	d			17 08									18 18	18 40									19 44
Grantham 7	a		16 52				17 29							18 52								19 40	19 56
	d		16 52				17 29			18 15				18 52						19 05		19 40	19 56
Peterborough 8	a		17 11	17 36			17 48			18 42			18 46	19 12						19 34	19 38		20 18
Cambridge	a			18z44			19 08						20 08	20z58							21 08		21L50
Stansted Airport	a						19 45						20 45								21 45		
Norwich	a									20 18										21 13	22U30		
Peterborough 8	d		17 12	17 36			17 50						18 48	19 12							19 38		20 19
Stevenage 4	a						18 19							19 43							20 07		20 48
London Kings Cross 15 ⊖	a		18 10	18 28			18 46						19 40	20 12							20 35	20 46	21 15

For general notes see front of timetable
For details of catering facilities see Directory of Train Operators

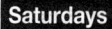

- **A** To Manchester Piccadilly (Table 39)
- **B** To Manchester Airport (Table 39)
- **C** To Reading (Table 51)
- **D** To Plymouth (Table 51)
- **E** From Liverpool Lime Street (Table 49)
- **G** To St Pancras International (Table 53). Until 5 September starts Scarborough dep. 1703
- **H** To Guildford (Table 51)
- **L** 18 July to 5 September arr. 2208
- **U** Change at Peterborough and Ely. 18 July to 5 September arr. 2320
- **b** Change at Edinburgh
- **c** Change at Arbroath and Edinburgh
- **e** Change at Perth and Edinburgh
- **f** Glasgow Queen Street
- **g** From 12 September dep. 1330
- **h** Change at Leeds and Doncaster
- **j** By changing at York, passengers may arrive at 1844
- **k** Bradford Interchange. Change at Leeds and Doncaster
- **m** Bradford Interchange. Until 11 July dep. 1705
- **n** Bradford Interchange. Until 11 July dep. 1805
- **q** Change at Leeds
- **r** Change at Retford
- **t** Until 20 June and from 12 September only. Change at Doncaster
- **v** Change at Doncaster. 27 June to 5 September dep. 1600, by bus
- **w** Change at Doncaster. 27 June to 5 September dep. 1705, by bus
- **y** Change at Peterborough
- **z** Change at Peterborough and Ely

Scotland, North East England, Yorkshire and Humberside → London

Route Diagram - see first page of Table 26

		XC	TP	GC	XC	GR	XC	TP	TP	GR	EM	XC	EM	GR	XC	TP	NT	TP	GR	TP	NT	XC
				R		R				R				R					R			
		1◇	1◇	1	1◇	1	1◇	1◇	1◇	1	◇	1◇	◇	1	1◇	1◇		1◇	1	1◇		1◇
		A	B		C		C		B		D	C	E		C	B	G	H	J	K	L	
Aberdeen	d					14b07				14 49									16b01			
Stonehaven	d					14b23				15 06									16b18			
Montrose	d					14c17				15 29									16c11			
Arbroath	d					15b00				15 45									16b55			
Dundee	d	14 34				15b17				16 03									17b26			
Leuchars 3	d	14 46				15b29				16 17									17b39			
Kirkcaldy	d	15 18				16b00				16 45					17 00				18b13			
Inverkeithing	d	15 34				16b21				17 01									18b29			
Inverness	d					12b54													14e51			
Perth	d					15b00				15b59					15 59				17b00			
Stirling	d					15b36				16b06					16 36				17b36			
Glasgow Central 15	d					15 50	16f00			16g15					17f00				17 50			21 00
Motherwell	d					16 04	15 38												18 04			
Haymarket	d					16 49				17 20									18 48			22 01
Edinburgh 10	a					16 56				17 25									18 56			22 10
Edinburgh	d	16 05				17 00	17 05			17 30					18 05				19 00			
Dunbar	d						17 25			17 50					18 25				19 20			
Berwick-upon-Tweed	d						17 48			18 13					18 48				19 46			
Alnmouth for Alnwick	d	17 05				17 58									19 08		19 24		20 08			
Morpeth	d	17 20															19 49		20 25			
Newcastle 8	a	17 38				18 32	18 40			19 05					19 41		20 12		20 46			
Sunderland	d			17 30						18 30									19 27		20 27	
Hartlepool	d			17 56																		
Newcastle 8	d	17 44			18 22	18 34	18 43		18 52	19 06		19 25			19 43				20 47		21 50	
Chester-le-Street	d				18 31																21 59	
Durham	d	17 56			18 38	18 47	18 56		19 04			19 37			19 56				21 00		22 08	
Darlington 7	a	18 12			18 54	19 04	19 12		19 20	19 34		19 53			20 12				21 18		22 29	
Middlesbrough	d		18 07		18 24			19 00		18 53		18 53			19 25	20 10		20 50		21 50		
Eaglescliffe	d			18 28																		
Darlington 7	d	18 13			18 56	19 05	19 13		19 22	19 34		19 54			20 13				21 18	22 19		
Northallerton	d		18 35	18 45				19 27	19 36							20 37		21 17	21 30	22 30		
Thirsk	d		18 43	18 54				19 35								20 45				22 38		
York 8	a	18 41	19 03	19 13	19 22	19 34	19 41	19 58	20 02	20 04		20 20			20 41	21 07		21 41	21 51	22 57		
Hull	a			20h39						21 22						23h21						
Leeds 10	a	19 08	19 35		20 04		20 08		20 35	20 54		21 04			21 08	21 35		22 05	22 51	23 33		
Harrogate	d			18 05						19 05												
Scarborough	d			17 45						18 47												
York 8	d			19 16	19 25	19 36				20 06									21 52			
Doncaster 7	a				19 50	20 03				20 29									22 17			
Sheffield 7	a	19 51			20 20		20 51			21 17		21 20			21 51	23 02			23 05			
Skipton	d									18j28				19 18								
Keighley	d									18j38				19 31								
Bradford Forster Square	d									18k34				19m34								
Shipley	d									18j48				19 44								
Leeds 10	d									19 22				20 15								
Huddersfield	d									18j45				19 35								
Wakefield Westgate 7	d									19 32				20 31								
Hull	d					18 53								19 24								
Selby	d																					
Doncaster 7	d					20 04				20 30				20 48								
Retford 10	d													21 03								
Newark North Gate 7	a													21 18								
Grimsby Town	d					18n36								19q36								
Lincoln	d													19r43								
Newark North Gate 7	d													21 18								
Grantham 7	a													21 31								
	d										21 07		21 10	21 31								
Peterborough 8	a					20 51				21 21	21 34		21 37	21 50								
Cambridge	a					22 08								23 10								
Stansted Airport	a					22 45																
Norwich	a									23 20	23 18		23 20									
Peterborough 8	d					20 51				21 21				21 51								
Stevenage 4	a					21 20				21 54				22 20								
London Kings Cross 15 ⊖	a			21 16		21 48				22 20				22 47								

For general notes see front of timetable
For details of catering facilities see Directory of Train Operators

- **A** To Bristol Temple Meads (Table 57)
- **B** To Manchester Airport (Table 39)
- **C** To Birmingham New Street (Table 51)
- **D** Until 11 July and from 12 September. From Liverpool Lime Street (Table 49)
- **E** 18 July to 5 September. From Liverpool Lime Street (Table 49)
- **G** From Chathill to Hexham (Table 48)
- **H** To Manchester Piccadilly (Table 39)
- **J** To Leeds (Table 31)
- **K** Until 5 September to Manchester Airport (Table 39)
- **L** To Middlesbrough (Table 44)
- **b** Change at Edinburgh
- **c** Change at Arbroath and Edinburgh
- **e** Change at Perth and Edinburgh
- **f** Glasgow Queen Street
- **g** Glasgow Queen Street. Change at Edinburgh
- **h** Change at York and Selby
- **j** Change at Leeds and Doncaster
- **k** Bradford Interchange. Change at Leeds and Doncaster
- **m** Bradford Interchange
- **n** Change at Doncaster. 27 June to 5 September dep. 1810, by bus
- **q** Until 20 June and from 12 September change at Doncaster. 27 June to 5 September dep. 1920, change at Retford
- **r** Change at Retford

Table 26

Sundays

Scotland, North East England, Yorkshire and Humberside → London

until 6 September

Route Diagram - see first page of Table 26

		GR R 1	GR R 1	TP 1◇ A	GR R 1	EM ◇ B	XC 1◇ C	GR R 1	GR R 1	HT 1◇	XC 1◇ C	GC R 1	TP 1◇ D	GC R 1	GR R 1	TP 1◇ A	XC 1◇ E	GR R 1	EM ◇ G	GR R 1	GR R 1	TP 1◇ A
Aberdeen	d																					
Stonehaven	d																					
Montrose	d																					
Arbroath	d																					
Dundee	d																				07 25	
Leuchars 3	d																				07 37	
Kirkcaldy	d																				08 08	
Inverkeithing	d																				08 30	
Inverness	d																					
Perth	d																					
Stirling	d																					
Glasgow Central 15	d																	07b50				
Motherwell	d																					
Haymarket	d																					
Edinburgh 10	a																					
Edinburgh	d																08 50	09 00			09 30	
Dunbar	d																					
Berwick-upon-Tweed	d																09 33	09 39				
Alnmouth for Alnwick	d																					
Morpeth	d																					
Newcastle 8	a																10 21	10 28			10 55	
Sunderland	d											09 10					09 28					10 28
Hartlepool	d											09 34										
Newcastle 8	d		08 00	08 06				09 00	09 30		09 25		09 33				10 25	10 30			10 57	11 03
Chester-le-Street	d												09 42									
Durham	d		08 12	08 18				09 12			09 38		09 48				10 38				11 10	11 15
Darlington 7	a		08 30	08 35				09 29	09 58		09 53		10 04				10 54	10 59				11 31
Middlesbrough	d							08 45					09 15			10 15	10 00					10 53
Eaglescliffe	d											09 55										
Darlington 7	d		08 30	08 35				09 30	09 59		09 55		10 05				10 55	10 59				11 32
Northallerton	d			08 47				09 43				10 12	10 16	←		10 42						11 42
Thirsk	d											10 26		10 26		10 51						
York 8	a		08 58	09 11				10 03	10 27		10 22	→	10 41	10 45		11 10	11 24	11 28			11 51	12 07
Hull	a										11 38						13 03				13 03	
Leeds 10	a			09 38				10 37			10 51		11 08	11 32		11 38	11 52	12 08				12 38
Harrogate	d														09 53					10 53		
Scarborough	d								09 20		09 20										10 50	
York 8	d		09 00				09 28	10 04	10 28					10 47				11 29			11 53	
Doncaster 7	a		09 24				10 28	10 28	10 53		11 28						12 28	11 53				
Sheffield 7	a		09c55				10 54	11 07			11 53		12 29				12 54					
Skipton	d				08 35					09e15										10 15		
Keighley	d				08 48					09e28										10 28		
Bradford Forster Square	d				09 02				09f21						10 02			10g25		11 02		
Shipley	d				09 10					09e40					10 08			10e08		11 10		
Leeds 10	d	08 25			09 40				10 00	10h09					10 40			11 00		11 40		
Huddersfield	d	07j12			09j04										09j51			10e12		10j43		
Wakefield Westgate 7	d	08 37			09 52				10 12	10h22					10 52			11 12		11 52		
Hull	d				08 42				09 41	10 12								10 41				
Selby	d									10 47												
Doncaster 7	d	08 55	09 25		10 10			10 28	10 53	11 04					11 13			11 53		12 10		
Retford 10	d		09 40							11 19					11 28							
Newark North Gate 7	a	09 18			10 32			10 51							11 42						12 36	
Grimsby Town	d								09k36									10k36				
Lincoln	d														11 05							
Newark North Gate 7	d	09 18			10 32			10 51							11 42						12 36	
Grantham 7	a	09 31	10 02					11 03		11 38					11 54					12 40		
	d	09 31	10 02			10 30		11 03		11 39					11 54				12 18	12 41		
Peterborough 8	a	09 53	10 24		11 02	11 06		11 25	11 43						12 16			12 40	12 50		13 06	
Cambridge	a		12m16						13m16									14m14			14 17	
Stansted Airport	a																				14 47	
Norwich	a					13 05			14m09										14 35			
Peterborough 8	d	09 53	10 24		11 02			11 25	11 45						12 16			12 45			13 06	
Stevenage 4	a		10 55					11 55							13 33						13 36	
London Kings Cross 15 ⊖	a	10 48	11 23		11 55			12 23	12 40	12 48				12 51	13 14			13 39		13 50	14 04	

For general notes see front of timetable
For details of catering facilities see Directory of Train Operators

A To Manchester Airport (Table 39)
B From Nottingham (Table 49)
C To Plymouth (from 12 July to Birmingham New Street) (Table 51)
D To Liverpool Lime Street (Table 39)
E To Plymouth (Table 51)
G From Sheffield (Table 49)
b Glasgow Queen Street
c From 19 July arr. 1009
e Change at Leeds and Doncaster
f Bradford Interchange. Change at Leeds and Doncaster. From 19 July dep. 0920
g Bradford Interchange. Change at Leeds and Doncaster
h Change at Doncaster
j Change at Leeds
k Change at Doncaster. From 28 June dep. 26 mins earlier, by bus
m Change at Peterborough and Ely

Table 26

Sundays
until 6 September

Scotland, North East England, Yorkshire and Humberside → London

Route Diagram - see first page of Table 26

		EM		XC	GR	HT	GR		GR	GR	XC	TP		EM	XC	GR	GR		TP	GR	TP	XC		GR	XC	GR
					R		R		R	R						R	R			R				R		R
		◇		1◇	1	1◇	1		1	1	1◇	1◇		◇	1◇	1	1		1◇	1	1◇	1◇		1	1◇	1
		A		B							B	C		D	E				G		C	H			B	
Aberdeen	d																									
Stonehaven	d																									
Montrose	d																									
Arbroath	d																									
Dundee	d																			09 25						
Leuchars 3	d																			09 37						
Kirkcaldy	d																			10 08						
Inverkeithing	d																			10 30						
Inverness	d																									
Perth	d																			09 27						
Stirling	d								09 05											10 02						
Glasgow Central 15	d			08b30											09b30										10b30	10 50
Motherwell	d																									11 05
Haymarket	d																									11 48
Edinburgh 10	a																									11 54
Edinburgh	d			09 50	10 00				10 30						10 50	11 00				11 30					11 50	12 00
Dunbar	d														11 10											
Berwick-upon-Tweed	d				10 39				11 09						11 33											12 39
Alnmouth for Alnwick	d			10 47																					12 47	
Morpeth	d			11 02																12 40						
Newcastle 8	a			11 19	11 30				11 58						12 20	12 26				12 59					13 17	13 29
Sunderland	d								11 28											12 28						
Hartlepool	d																									
Newcastle 8	d			11 25	11 32				12 00			12 05			12 25	12 32				13 01	13 06	13 15		13 24	13 28	13 32
Chester-le-Street	d																					13 23				
Durham	d			11 37								12 17			12 37	12 45					13 18	13 30			13 40	13 45
Darlington 7	a			11 53					12 26			12 33			12 53	13 02				13 27	13 34	13 46		13 51	13 56	14 04
Middlesbrough	d								11 24							12 25			12 45							13 25
Eaglescliffe	d																									
Darlington 7	d			11 54					12 27			12 34			12 54	13 03				13 28	13 35	13 47		13 51	13 57	14 05
Northallerton	d																		13 12	13 39						
Thirsk	d																		13 22							
York 8	a			12 22	12 28				12 55			13 07			13 22	13 35			13 42	14 00	14 12	14 14		14 19	14 25	14 34
Hull	a										←	14 21														15 40
Leeds 10	a			12 51 →	13 08						12 51	13 38			13 51				14 08		14 38				14 51	15 08
Harrogate	d				11 30		11 53										12 53							13 30		
Scarborough	d								11 50						11 50											
York 8	d				12 29				12 57							13 37				14 02		14 19		14 22		14 36
Doncaster 7	a				12 54				13 20		13 28					14 00				14 25		14 44		14 48		14 59
Sheffield 7	a										13 55				14 44	14 52				15 03		15 18			15 42	
Skipton	d					11c15			11c30								12 15									
Keighley	d					11c28			11c40								12 28									
Bradford Forster Square	d					11e25			12c02							12e25	13 02									
Shipley	d					11c40			12c08								13 08									
Leeds 10	d				12 00	12f09	12 40									13 00	13 40									
Huddersfield	d				11c12	11c12	11g43									12c12	12g43									
Wakefield Westgate 7	d				12 12	12f22	12 52									13 12	13 52									
Hull	d				11 41	12 12										12 41								13 41		
Selby	d					12 47																				
Doncaster 7	d				12 54	13 06	13 11		13 21	←						14 01	14 10			14 26				14 48		15 00
Retford 10	d					13 21	13h34 →			13 34																
Newark North Gate 7	a									13 48							14 33									
Grimsby Town	d				11j36											12k10				12m15				13j36		
Lincoln	d									13 00																
Newark North Gate 7	d									13 48							14 33									
Grantham 7	a				13 26	13 40				14 00										14 56						
	d	13 14			13 26	13 40				14 00				14 14						14 56						
Peterborough 8	a	13 41							14 10	14 22				14 41		14 48								15 35		15 47
Cambridge	a								15 17	16n14						16 17										17q08
Stansted Airport	a								15 47							16 47										17r45
Norwich	a	15 28												16 35												17 35
Peterborough 8	d								14 11	14 22						14 48								15 36		15 47
Stevenage 4	a				14 16	14s29				15 33							15 28									16 18
London Kings Cross 15 ⊖	a				14 44	14 54			15 09	15 16						15 42	15 55			16 10				16 29		16 46

For general notes see front of timetable
For details of catering facilities see Directory of Train Operators

- **A** From Nottingham (Table 49)
- **B** To Penzance (Table 135)
- **C** To Manchester Airport (Table 39)
- **D** From Sheffield (Table 49)
- **E** To Plymouth (Table 51)
- **G** To Liverpool Lime Street (Table 39)
- **H** To Reading (Table 51)
- **b** Glasgow Queen Street
- **c** Change at Leeds and Doncaster
- **e** Bradford Interchange. Change at Leeds and Doncaster
- **f** Change at Doncaster
- **g** Change at Leeds
- **h** Arr. 1326
- **j** Change at Doncaster. From 28 June dep. 26 mins earlier, by bus
- **k** From 28 June only; by bus to Doncaster
- **m** From 28 June only. Change at Doncaster. By bus
- **n** Change at Peterborough and Ely
- **q** From 19 July arr. 1716, change at Peterborough and Ely
- **r** Until 12 July only

Sundays

until 6 September

Scotland, North East England, Yorkshire and Humberside → London

Route Diagram - see first page of Table 26

		HT	GR	GR	TP	XC	GC	GR	EM	GR	TP	GR	TP	XC	XC	GR	EM	GR	HT	GR	GR
		1 ◇	R 1	R 1	1 ◇	1 ◇	R 1	R 1	◇	R 1	1 ◇	R 1	1 ◇	1 ◇	1 ◇	R 1	◇	R 1	1 ◇	R 1	R 1
			A		B	C		D	E		G	H	B	J	C		E				
		⊠	☕ 🍴	☕ 🍴		🍴	☕	☕ 🍴	🍴	☕ 🍴		☕ 🍴		🍴	🍴	☕ 🍴	🍴	☕ 🍴	⊠	☕ 🍴	☕ 🍴
Aberdeen	d		09 48												11 12						11 47
Stonehaven	d		10 05												11 29						12 04
Montrose	d		10 28												11 50						12 27
Arbroath	d		10 44												12 06						12 43
Dundee	d		11 02									11b25			12 25						13 01
Leuchars 3	d		11 16									11b37			12 38						13 15
Kirkcaldy	d		11 40									12b08			13 03						13 39
Inverkeithing	d		11 56									12b30			13 18						13 55
Inverness	d											09 38									
Perth	d											11 56									
Stirling	d		11b06									12 33									13b06
Glasgow Central 15	d					11 37									12c30	12 50					13c00
Motherwell	d					11 56										13 05					
Haymarket	d		12 18			12 38						13 13			13 37	13 50					14 19
Edinburgh 10	a		12 24			12 43						13 18			13 42	13 55					14 24
Edinburgh	d		12 30			12 50		13 00				13 30		13 33	13 50	14 00					14 30
Dunbar	d					13 11															
Berwick-upon-Tweed	d					13 33		13 39				14 11		14 18							
Alnmouth for Alnwick	d		13 29											14 38	14 49						
Morpeth	d																				
Newcastle 8	a		14 00			14 22		14 30				15 00		15 08	15 19	15 25					15 59
Sunderland	d		13 28				13 42					14 28									15 28
Hartlepool	d						14 06														
Newcastle 8	d		14 02		14 08	14 25		14 32				15 01	15 07	15 18	15 25	15 30				15 50	16 01
Chester-le-Street	d												15 16								
Durham	d				14 20	14 37						15 15	15 22	15 30	15 37						16 14
Darlington 7	a		14 29		14 36	14 53		14 58				15 32	15 39	15 46	15 53	15 59				16 20	16 32
Middlesbrough	d										14 45	14 38									15 50
Eaglescliffe	d						14 34														
Darlington 7	d		14 30		14 37	14 54		14 59				15 33	15 40	15 47	15 54	15 59				16 20	16 32
Northallerton	d				14 48		14 53	15 10			15 12									16 32	
Thirsk	d						15 06				15 21										
York 8	a		15 00		15 12	15 22	15 28	15 31			15 41	16 02	16 13	16 15	16 22	16 28				16 52	17 01
Hull	a							16 41													18 10
Leeds 10	a				15 38	15 51					16 08		16 38		16 51	17 08					
Harrogate	d									14 53						15 30					
Scarborough	d		13 50																	15 50	
York 8	d		15 02				15 31	15 34				16 03		16 20		16 29				16 53	17 03
Doncaster 7	a							15 57				16 28		16 48		16 53				17 18	17 27
Sheffield 7	a					16 41		16 52				17 07		17 18	17 41	17 54				18 01	18 07
Skipton	d	13e15								14 15								15 15			
Keighley	d	13e28								14 28								15 28			
Bradford Forster Square	d	13f25		14 02						15 02								16g02			
Shipley	d	13e40		14 08						15 08								16 08			
Leeds 10	d	14h09		14 40						15 40								16 40			
Huddersfield	d	13e12		13j43						14j43								15j43			
Wakefield Westgate 7	d	14h22		14 52						15 52								16 52			
Hull	d	14 10						14 41								15 41			16 21		
Selby	d	14 45																	16 56		
Doncaster 7	d	15 05		15 10				15 58		16 10		16 28				16 53		17 10	17 15	17 19	17 28
Retford 10	d	15 20		15 25															17 30		
Newark North Gate 7	a			15 39				16 20												17 46	
Grimsby Town	d			14 03				14k36								15k36					
Lincoln	d			15 00																15 50	
Newark North Gate 7	d			15 39				16 20												17 46	
Grantham 7	a	15 40		15 52						16 40								17 40	17 49		
	d	15 40		15 52					16 20	16 40							17 25	17 40	17 49		
Peterborough 8	a			16 13				16 51	16m56	17 01		17 18				17 40	17 52	18 02			18 26
Cambridge	a			18n07						18q07								19r08			20t16
Stansted Airport	a									18q45								19r45			
Norwich	a								18 29								19 29				
Peterborough 8	d			16 19				16 51		17 02		17 18				17 45		18 02			18 27
Stevenage 4	a			16 49				17 21								18 16				18 48	
London Kings Cross 15 ⊖	a	16 50	17 11	17 18			17 24	17 49		17 55		18 15				18 43		18 55	19 06	19 16	19 21

For general notes see front of timetable
For details of catering facilities see Directory of Train Operators

- **A** **The Northern Lights**
- **B** To Manchester Airport (Table 39)
- **C** To Plymouth (Table 51)
- **D** **The Flying Scotsman**
- **E** From Liverpool Lime Street (Table 49)
- **G** To Liverpool Lime Street (Table 39)
- **H** **The Highland Chieftain**
- **J** To Reading (Table 51)
- **b** Change at Edinburgh
- **c** Glasgow Queen Street. Change at Edinburgh
- **e** Change at Leeds and Doncaster
- **f** Bradford Interchange. Change at Leeds and Doncaster
- **g** Until 12 July change at Leeds. From 19 July Bradford Interchange dep. 1603, change at Leeds
- **h** Change at Doncaster
- **j** Change at Leeds
- **k** Change at Doncaster. From 28 June dep. 26 mins earlier, by bus
- **m** Until 12 July arr. 1651
- **n** From 19 July arr. 1816, change at Peterborough and Ely
- **q** From 19 July arr. Cambridge 1910, Stansted Airport 1947
- **r** From 19 July arr. 2 minutes later
- **t** Change at Peterborough and Ely

Sundays

until 6 September

Scotland, North East England, Yorkshire and Humberside → London

Route Diagram - see first page of Table 26

		GR	TP	EM	XC	XC	GR	GR	EM	TP	TP	GR	GR	GR	GR	XC	XC	GR	EM	GR	TP	GR
		R 1	1 ◇	◇	1 ◇	1 ◇	R 1	R 1	1 ◇	1 ◇	1 ◇	R 1	R 1	R 1	R 1	1 ◇	1 ◇	R 1	◇	R 1	1 ◇	R 1
			A	B	C	D			E	G	A					H	J		B		A	
Aberdeen	d																					13 50
Stonehaven	d																					14 07
Montrose	d																					14 30
Arbroath	d																					14 46
Dundee	d												13 25									15 04
Leuchars 3	d												13 37									15 18
Kirkcaldy	d												14 08									15 42
Inverkeithing	d												14 30									15 58
Inverness	d																					
Perth	d												13b05									
Stirling	d												14 06									15c06
Glasgow Central 15	d					13 45							14e00				14e30	14 50				15f00
Motherwell	d					14 01												15 05				
Haymarket	d					14 43												15 50				16 20
Edinburgh 10	a					14 47												15 55				16 25
Edinburgh	d					14 50	15 00						15 30				15 50	16 00				16 30
Dunbar	d					15 10																
Berwick-upon-Tweed	d					15 33	15 39						16 09									17 09
Alnmouth for Alnwick	d																16 47					17 32
Morpeth	d												16 43				17 02					
Newcastle 8	a					16 20	16 31						17 02				17 20	17 27				18 07
Sunderland	d												16 28								17 28	
Hartlepool	d																					
Newcastle 8	d		16 08		16 18	16 25	16 33				16 52		17 04		17 12	17 18	17 25	17 30			17 57	18 10
Chester-le-Street	d										17 01					17 26						
Durham	d		16 20		16 30	16 37	16 46				17 08				17 24	17 33	17 37				18 09	
Darlington 7	a		16 36		16 46	16 53	17 03				17 25		17 30		17 42	17 49	17 54	17 59			18 25	
Middlesbrough	d									16 45	16 49					17 14					17 49	
Eaglescliffe	d																					
Darlington 7	d		16 37		16 47	16 54	17 04				17 26		17 31		17 42	17 50	17 55	17 59			18 26	
Northallerton	d		16 48							17 12	17 38		17 42									
Thirsk	d									17 21												
York 8	a		17 12		17 17	17 22	17 34			17 41	18 00		18 04		18 10	18 16	18 23	18 28			18 59	19 04
Hull	a																				20 09	
Leeds 10	a		17 38			17 51				18 08	18 38		18 38				18 51	19 05			19 38	19 38
Harrogate	d						16 30	16 53										17 30		17 53		
Scarborough	d												16 50									17 50
York 8	d				17 20		17 36		17 40				18 05		18 12	18 20		18 29				19 05
Doncaster 7	a				17 46		18 00		18 05				18 31		18 37	18 48		18 53				19 31
Sheffield 7	a				18 16	18g40	18 52		18 28				19 07			19 15	19 40	19 55				20 07
Skipton	d	16 15																		17 15		
Keighley	d	16 28																		17 28		
Bradford Forster Square	d	16h25						17 02												18 02		
Shipley	d	16 40						17 09												18 08		
Leeds 10	d	17 05						17 40												18 40		
Huddersfield	d	16j33						16j43												17j43		
Wakefield Westgate 7	d	17 18						17 52												18 52		
Hull	d						16 41					17 30						17 41				
Selby	d											18 05										
Doncaster 7	d	17 36					18 03					18 23	18 31	←	18 37			18 53		19 10		19 31
Retford 10	d	17 51										18k44 →		18 44								
Newark North Gate 7	a	18 05													19 02							
Grimsby Town	d						16m36								17n10			17q36				
Lincoln	d	17 25												17r35								
Newark North Gate 7	d	18 05													19 02							
Grantham 7	a							18 37						19 06						19 40		
	d			18 18				18 37						19 06					19t16	19 40		
Peterborough 8	a			18 45			18 50	18 59					19 18	19 28	19 33			19 40	19 56	20 01		20 22
Cambridge	a							20v07												21 07		
Stansted Airport	a							20w45												21 45		
Norwich	a			20 28															21 35			
Peterborough 8	d						18 51	18 59					19 19	19 29	19 33			19 45		20 02		20 23
Stevenage 4	a	19 02					19 21								20 07			20 18		20 32		20 54
London Kings Cross 15 ⊖	a	19 33					19 48	19 52					20 14	20 23	20 34			20 43		21 01		21 25

For general notes see front of timetable
For details of catering facilities see Directory of Train Operators

- **A** To Manchester Airport (Table 39)
- **B** From Liverpool Lime Street (Table 49)
- **C** To Reading (Table 51)
- **D** To Plymouth (Table 51)
- **E** To St Pancras International (Table 53)
- **G** To Liverpool Lime Street (Table 39)
- **H** To Southampton Central (Table 51)
- **J** To Bristol Temple Meads (Table 51)
- **b** Change at Stirling and Edinburgh
- **c** Change at Edinburgh
- **e** Glasgow Queen Street
- **f** Glasgow Queen Street. Change at Edinburgh
- **g** By changing at York, passengers may arrive at 1828
- **h** Bradford Interchange. From 19 July dep. 1626
- **j** Change at Leeds
- **k** Arr. 1838
- **m** Change at Doncaster. From 28 June dep. 26 mins earlier, by bus
- **n** From 28 June only; by bus to Doncaster
- **q** Until 21 June only; change at Doncaster
- **r** Change at Retford
- **t** Until 12 July dep. 1923
- **v** From 19 July arr. 2031
- **w** From 19 July arr. 2117

Table 26

Scotland, North East England, Yorkshire and Humberside → London

Sundays

until 6 September

Route Diagram - see first page of Table 26

		HT	XC	XC	GR	TP	GR	TP	GC	GR	XC	GR	TP	TP	GR	NT	TP	GR	GR
					R		R		R	R		R			R			R	R
		1◇	1◇	1◇	1	1◇	1	1◇	1	1	1◇	1	1◇	1◇	1		1◇	1	1
			A	B		C		D			A			E		G	E		
		⊠	🛒	🛒	🍴🛒		🍴🛒		🍴	🍴	🛒	⊘🛒			🍴🛒			🍴🛒	🍴🛒
Aberdeen	d											15 10						17 10	
Stonehaven	d											15 26						17 26	
Montrose	d											15 48						17 48	
Arbroath	d											16 02						18 02	
Dundee	d						15 25					16 25						18 19	
Leuchars 3	d						15 37					16 37						18 31	
Kirkcaldy	d				16b03		16 08					17 02			17b07			18 56	19b07
Inverkeithing	d				16b19		16 30					17 18			17b45			19 12	19b45
Inverness	d				13b25														16c15
Perth	d				15b25										15c05			17c05	18c27
Stirling	d						16 06								17b06			18 06	19b12
Glasgow Central 15	d				15 50		16e00				16e30				17 50			18e30	19 50
Motherwell	d				16 05						16 05				18 05				20 04
Haymarket	d				16 44										18 46				20 45
Edinburgh 10	a				16 51										18 52				20 50
Edinburgh	d			16 50	17 00		17 30				17 50	18 00			19 00			20 00	21 00
Dunbar	d			17 10							18 11				19 20			20 20	21 21
Berwick-upon-Tweed	d			17 33								18 39						20 43	21 44
Alnmouth for Alnwick	d										18 51	19 03							22 06
Morpeth	d																	21 17	
Newcastle 8	a			18 20	18 26		18 53				19 20	19 33			20 29			21 38	22 41
Sunderland	d							18 28	18 42					19 28		20 28			
Hartlepool	d								19 06										
Newcastle 8	d		18 18	18 25	18 29		18 55	19 06			19 25	19 35		20 07	20 31	21 06		21 40	
Chester-le-Street	d		18 26	18 33												21 15			
Durham	d		18 33	18 40	18 43		19 08	19 17			19 39	19 48		20 19		21 24		21 53	
Darlington 7	a		18 49	18 56	19 00		19 25	19 34			19 55	20 05		20 35	20 57	21 44		22 10	
Middlesbrough	d					18 45	18 37	18 53					20 07				22 07	20 56	
Eaglescliffe	d								19 25										
Darlington 7	d		18 50	18 57	19 01		19 26	19 35			19 56	20 06		20 36	20 58			22 11	
Northallerton	d					19 14	19 39		19 48				20 34	20 48			22 34	22 41	
Thirsk	d					19 23			19 57				20 42				22 42		
York 8	a		19 16	19 25	19 29	19 42	20 00	20 09	20 13		20 24	20 34	21 02	21 12	21 26		23 09	23 19	
Hull	a														22 39				
Leeds 10	a			19 51		20 08		20 38			20 51	21 08		21 38	22 32		23 38		
Harrogate	d				18 30					18 53		19 30			20 30				
Scarborough	d						18 50								19 50				
York 8	d		19 20		19 31		20 02		20 15		20 28	20 36			21 28				
Doncaster 7	a		19 48		19 53		20 25					20 59			21 51				
Sheffield 7	a		20 15	20 40	20 53		21 07				21 44	21 56			22 58				
Skipton	d									19 24									
Keighley	d									19 37									
Bradford Forster Square	d									19f25					19g44				
Shipley	d									19 49									
Leeds 10	d									20 15					20 20				
Huddersfield	d									19h43									
Wakefield Westgate 7	d									20 27					20 33				
Hull	d	18 48													20 30				
Selby	d	19 23																	
Doncaster 7	d	19 43			19 54		20 26			20 47		21 00			21 52				
Retford 10	d	19 58										21 15							
Newark North Gate 7	a				20 16							21 29							
Grimsby Town	d	18j10			18k25					19m36		20 07			20m36				
Lincoln	d				19 24							21 00							
Newark North Gate 7	d				20 16							21 34							
Grantham 7	a	20 18					20 56								22 22				
	d	20 18					20 56								22 22				
Peterborough 8	a				20 46		21 17			21 35		22 03			22 43				
Cambridge	a				22n07							23 12							
Stansted Airport	a				22n45														
Norwich	a				23q05														
Peterborough 8	d				20 48		21 18			21 36		22 04			22 44				
Stevenage 4	a	21s09			21 20		21 48			22 09		22 34			23 39				
London Kings Cross 15 ⊖	a	21 34			21 47		22 16		22 17	22 37		23 14			23 50				

For general notes see front of timetable
For details of catering facilities see Directory of Train Operators

- **A** To Birmingham New Street (Table 51)
- **B** To Bristol Temple Meads (Table 51)
- **C** To Liverpool Lime Street (Table 39)
- **D** To Manchester Piccadilly (Table 39)
- **E** To Manchester Airport (Table 39)
- **G** To Saltburn (Table 44)
- **b** Change at Edinburgh
- **c** Change at Stirling and Edinburgh
- **e** Glasgow Queen Street
- **f** Bradford Interchange. From 19 July dep. 1944
- **g** Bradford Interchange. Change at Leeds and Doncaster
- **h** Change at Leeds
- **j** From 28 June only; by bus to Doncaster
- **k** Until 21 June dep. 1836, change at Doncaster
- **m** Change at Doncaster. From 28 June dep. 26 mins earlier, by bus
- **n** From 19 July arr. Cambridge 2217, Stansted Airport 2247
- **q** Until 12 July only. Change at Peterborough and Ely

Sundays

from 13 September

Scotland, North East England, Yorkshire and Humberside → London

Route Diagram - see first page of Table 26

		GR	GR	TP	GR		XC	GR	GR	HT		XC	GC	TP	GC		TP	GR	XC	GR		GR	GR	XC	TP	EM
		R 1	R 1	1 ◇	R 1		1 ◇	R 1	R 1	1 ◇		1 ◇	R 1	1 ◇	R 1		1 ◇	R 1	1 ◇	R 1		R 1	R 1	1 ◇	1 ◇	◇
				A			B					B		C			A		B					B	A	D
		▭ ⌶	⊘ ⌶		▭ ⌶		⌶	▭ ⌶	▭ ⌶	⊠		⌶	▭		▭			▭ ⌶	⌶	▭ ⌶		▭ ⌶	▭ ⌶	⌶		⌶
Aberdeen	d																									
Stonehaven	d																									
Montrose	d																									
Arbroath	d																									
Dundee	d																						*07 25*			
Leuchars 3	d																						*07 37*			
Kirkcaldy	d																						*08 08*			
Inverkeithing	d																						*08 30*			
Inverness	d																									
Perth	d																									
Stirling	d																									
Glasgow Central 15	d																			*07b50*						
Motherwell	d																									
Haymarket	d																									
Edinburgh 10	a																									
Edinburgh	d																		08 50	09 00			09 30			
Dunbar	d																									
Berwick-upon-Tweed	d																		09 33	09 39						
Alnmouth for Alnwick	d																									
Morpeth	d																									
Newcastle 8	a																		10 21	10 28			10 55			
Sunderland	d												09 10						*09 28*						*10 28*	
Hartlepool	d												09 34													
Newcastle 8	d		08 00	08 06				09 00	09 30			09 25		09 33					10 25	10 30			10 57		11 03	
Chester-le-Street	d													09 42												
Durham	d		08 12	08 18				09 12				09 38		09 48					10 38				11 10		11 15	
Darlington 7	a		08 30	08 35				09 29	09 58			09 53		10 04					10 54	10 59					11 31	
Middlesbrough	d							*08 45*						*09 15*			10 15								*10 53*	
Eaglescliffe	d												09 55													
Darlington 7	d		08 30	08 35				09 30	09 59			09 55		10 05					10 55	10 59					11 32	
Northallerton	d			08 47				09 43					10 12	10 16	←		10 42								11 42	
Thirsk	d												10 26		10 26		10 51									
York 8	a		08 58	09 11				10 03	10 27			10 22	→	10 41	10 45		11 10		11 24	11 28			11 51		12 07	
Hull	a											*11 38*								*13c03*				←		
Leeds 10	a			09 38				*10 38*				10 51		11 08	*11 32*		11 38		11 52 →	*12 08*				11 52	12 38	
Harrogate	d																	*09 53*				*10 53*				
Scarborough	d								*09 20*														*10 50*			
York 8	d		09 00				09 28	10 04	10 28			10 28			10 47					11 29			11 53			
Doncaster 7	a		09 24				10 28	10 28	10 53	11 03		11 28								11 53				12 28		
Sheffield 7	a		*09e55*				10 54	*11 07*		*11 51*		11 53		*12 29*										12 54	*13 49*	
Skipton	d				*08 35*					*09f15*												*10 15*				
Keighley	d				*08 48*					*09f28*												*10 28*				
Bradford Forster Square	d				*09 02*				*09g20*									*10h03*		*10g25*		*11 02*				
Shipley	d				*09 10*					*09f40*								*10 08*		*10f08*		*11 10*				
Leeds 10	d	08 25			09 40				*10 00*	*10j09*								10 40		*11 00*		11 40				
Huddersfield	d	*06k25*			*07k40*				*09f17*									*09m54*		*09f54*		*10m54*				
Wakefield Westgate 7	d	08 37			09 52				*10 12*	*10j22*								10 52		*11 12*		11 52				
Hull	d				*08 42*				*09 41*	10 12										*10 41*						
Selby	d									10 47																
Doncaster 7	d	08 55	09 25		10 10			10 28	10 53	11 04								11 13		11 53		12 10				
Retford 10	d		09 40							11 19								11 28								
Newark North Gate 7	a	09 18			10 32			10 51										11 42					12 36			
Grimsby Town	d								*09j36*											*10j36*						
Lincoln	d																	*11 05*								
Newark North Gate 7	d	09 18			10 32			10 51										11 42					12 36			
Grantham 7	a	09 31	10 02					11 03		11 38								11 54				12 40				
	d	09 31	10 02					11 03		11 39								11 54				12 41				13 14
Peterborough 8	a	09 53	10 24		11 02			11 25	11 43									12 16		12 40			13 06			13 41
Cambridge	a								*13n16*														*14 17*			
Stansted Airport	a																						*14 47*			
Norwich	a								*14n09*																	15 28
Peterborough 8	d	09 53	10 24		11 02			11 25	11 45									12 16		12 45			13 06			
Stevenage 4	a		10 55					11 55										*13 33*					13 36			
London Kings Cross 15 ⊖	a	10 48	11 23		11 55			12 23	12 40	12 48					12 51			13 14		13 39		13 50	14 04			

For general notes see front of timetable
For details of catering facilities see Directory of Train Operators

- **A** To Manchester Airport (Table 39)
- **B** To Plymouth (from 8 November to Birmingham New Street (Table 51)
- **C** To Liverpool Lime Street (Table 39)
- **D** From Nottingham (Table 49)
- **b** Glasgow Queen Street
- **c** 13 September only
- **e** From 8 November arr. 1009
- **f** Change at Leeds and Doncaster
- **g** Bradford Interchange. Change at Leeds and Doncaster
- **h** Bradford Interchange
- **j** Change at Doncaster
- **k** Change at Leeds. By bus
- **m** Change at Leeds
- **n** Change at Peterborough and Ely

Table 26

Sundays

from 13 September

Scotland, North East England, Yorkshire and Humberside → London

Route Diagram - see first page of Table 26

	XC	GR	HT	GR	GR	GR	XC	TP	EM	XC	GR	GR	TP	GR	TP	XC	GR	XC	GR	HT
	1 ◇	R 1	1 ◇	R 1	R 1	R 1	1 ◇	1 ◇	◇	1 ◇	R 1	R 1	1 ◇	R 1	1 ◇	1 ◇	R 1	1 ◇	R 1	1 ◇
	A						A	B	C	D			E		B	G		A		
Aberdeen d																				
Stonehaven d																				
Montrose d																				
Arbroath d																				
Dundee d														09 25						
Leuchars 3 d														09 37						
Kirkcaldy d														10 08						
Inverkeithing d														10 30						
Inverness d																				
Perth d														09 27						
Stirling d					09 05									10 02						
Glasgow Central 15 d	08b30									09b30								10b30	10 50	
Motherwell d																			11 05	
Haymarket d																			11 48	
Edinburgh 10 a																			11 54	
Edinburgh d	09 50	10 00			10 30					10 50	11 00			11 30				11 50	12 00	
Dunbar d										11 10										
Berwick-upon-Tweed d		10 39			11 09					11 33									12 39	
Alnmouth for Alnwick d	10 47																	12 47		
Morpeth d	11 02													12 40						
Newcastle 8 a	11 19	11 30			11 58					12 20	12 26			12 59				13 17	13 29	
Sunderland d					11 28									12 28						
Hartlepool d																				
Newcastle 8 d	11 25	11 32			12 00			12 05		12 25	12 32			13 01	13 06	13 15	13 24	13 28	13 32	
Chester-le-Street d																13 23				
Durham d	11 37							12 17		12 37	12 45				13 18	13 30		13 40	13 45	
Darlington 7 a	11 53				12 26			12 33		12 53	13 02			13 27	13 34	13 46	13 51	13 56	14 04	
Middlesbrough d					11 24						12 25		12 45						13 25	
Eaglescliffe d																				
Darlington 7 d	11 54				12 27			12 34		12 54	13 03			13 28	13 35	13 47	13 51	13 57	14 05	
Northallerton d													13 12	13 39						
Thirsk d													13 22							
York 8 a	12 22	12 28			12 55			13 07		13 22	13 35		13 42	14 00	14 12	14 14	14 19	14 25	14 34	
Hull a							←	14 21						15c40						
Leeds 10 a	12 51	13 08					12 51	13 38		13 51			14 08		14 38			14 51	15 08	
Harrogate d	→	11 30		11 53								12 53					13 30			
Scarborough d					11 50															
York 8 d		12 29			12 57						13 37			14 02		14 19	14 22		14 36	
Doncaster 7 a		12 54	13 05		13 20		13 28				14 00			14 25		14 44	14 48		14 59	
Sheffield 7 a							13 55			14 44	14 52			15 03		15 18		15 42		
Skipton d			11e15		11f30							12 15								13e15
Keighley d			11e28		11f40							12 28								13e28
Bradford Forster Square d					12e02						12g25	13h02								13g25
Shipley d			11e40		12e08							13j08								
Leeds 10 d			12k09	12 40							13 00	13 40								14k09
Huddersfield d											11e58	12m30								13e30
Wakefield Westgate 7 d		12 12	12k22	12 52							13 12	13 52								14k22
Hull d		11 41	12 12								12 41						13 41			14 10
Selby d			12 47																	14 45
Doncaster 7 d		12 54	13 06	13 11	13 21	←					14 01	14 10		14 26			14 48		15 00	15 05
Retford 10 d			13 21	13n34		13 34														15 20
Newark North Gate 7 a				→		13 48						14 33								
Grimsby Town d		11k36															13k36			
Lincoln d						13 00														
Newark North Gate 7 d						13 48						14 33								
Grantham 7 a		13 26	13 40			14 00								14 56						15 40
d		13 26	13 40			14 00			14 14					14 56						15 40
Peterborough 8 a					14 10	14 22			14 41		14 48						15 35		15 47	
Cambridge a					15 17	16q14					16 17								17 08	
Stansted Airport a					15 47						16 47								17 45	
Norwich a									16 35										17 35	
Peterborough 8 d					14 11	14 22					14 48						15 36		15 47	
Stevenage 4 a		14 16	14s29			15 33						15 28							16 18	
London Kings Cross 15 ⊖ a		14 44	14 54		15 09	15 16					15 42	15 55		16 10			16 29		16 46	16 50

For general notes see front of timetable
For details of catering facilities see Directory of Train Operators

- **A** To Penzance (Table 135) (from 8 November to Birmingham New Street) (Table 51)
- **B** To Manchester Airport (Table 39)
- **C** From Sheffield (Table 49)
- **D** To Plymouth (from 8 November to Birmingham New Street (Table 51)
- **E** To Liverpool Lime Street (Table 39)
- **G** To Reading (Table 51)
- **b** Glasgow Queen Street
- **c** 13 September only
- **e** Change at Leeds and Doncaster
- **f** Change at Leeds and Doncaster. From 8 November dep. Skipton 1115, Keighley 1128
- **g** Bradford Interchange. Change at Leeds and Doncaster
- **h** Until 1 November change at Leeds. From 8 November departs Bradford Interchange, change at Leeds
- **j** From 8 November dep. 1240
- **k** Change at Doncaster
- **m** Change at Leeds
- **n** Arr. 1326
- **q** Change at Peterborough and Ely

Sundays

from 13 September

Scotland, North East England, Yorkshire and Humberside → London

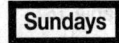

Route Diagram - see first page of Table 26

		GR	GR	TP	XC	XC	GC	GR	EM	GR	TP	GR	XC	TP	XC	GR	EM	GR	HT	GR	EM
		R 1	R 1	1 ◇	1 ◇	1 ◇	R 1	R 1	◇	R 1	1 ◇	R 1	1 ◇	1 ◇	1 ◇	R 1	◇	R 1	1 ◇	R 1	1 ◇
		A		B	C	D		E	G		H	J	K	B	D		G				L
Aberdeen	d	09 48													11 12						
Stonehaven	d	10 05													11 29						
Montrose	d	10 28													11 50						
Arbroath	d	10 44													12 06						
Dundee	d	11 02										*11b25*			12 25						
Leuchars 3	d	11 16										*11b37*			12 38						
Kirkcaldy	d	11 40										*12b08*			13 03						
Inverkeithing	d	11 56										*12b30*			13 18						
Inverness	d											09 38									
Perth	d											11 56									
Stirling	d	*11b06*										12 33									
Glasgow Central 15	d					11 37									*12c30*	12 50					
Motherwell	d					11 57										13 05					
Haymarket	d	12 18				12 38						13 13			13 37	13 50					
Edinburgh 10	a	12 24				12 43						13 18			13 42	13 55					
Edinburgh	d	12 30				12 50		13 00				13 30	13 33		13 50	14 00					
Dunbar	d					13 11															
Berwick-upon-Tweed	d					13 33		13 39				14 11	14 18								
Alnmouth for Alnwick	d	13 29											14 38		14 49						
Morpeth	d																				
Newcastle 8	a	14 00				14 22		14 30				15 00	15 08		15 19	15 25					
Sunderland	d	*13 28*					13 42					*14 28*									
Hartlepool	d						14 06														
Newcastle 8	d	14 02		14 08	14 18	14 25		14 32				15 01	15 18	15 07	15 25	15 30				15 50	
Chester-le-Street	d													15 16							
Durham	d			14 20	14 30	14 37						15 15	15 30	15 22	15 37						
Darlington 7	a	14 29		14 36	14 46	14 53		14 58				15 32	15 46	15 39	15 53	15 59				16 20	
Middlesbrough	d										14 45	*14 38*									
Eaglescliffe	d						14 34														
Darlington 7	d	14 30		14 37	14 47	14 54		14 59				15 33	15 47	15 40	15 54	15 59				16 20	
Northallerton	d			14 48			14 53	15 10			15 12									16 32	
Thirsk	d						15 06				15 21										
York 8	a	15 00		15 12	15 16	15 22	15 28	15 31			15 41	16 02	16 15	16 13	16 22	16 28				16 52	
Hull	a							*16 41*													
Leeds 10	a			15 38		15 51					16 08			16 38	16 51	*17 08*					
Harrogate	d									*14 53*						*15 30*					
Scarborough	d	*13 50*																		*15 50*	
York 8	d	15 02			15 20		15 31	15 34				16 03	16 20			16 29				16 53	17 00
Doncaster 7	a				15 46			15 57				16 28	16 48			16 53				17 18	17 21
Sheffield 7	a				16 15	16 41		*16 52*				*17 07*	17 18		17 41						17 47
Skipton	d									*14 15*								*15 15*			
Keighley	d									*14 28*								*15 28*			
Bradford Forster Square	d		*14 02*							*15 02*								*16e03*			
Shipley	d		*14 08*							*15 08*								*16 08*			
Leeds 10	d		14 40							15 40								16 40			
Huddersfield	d									*14f30*								*15f30*			
Wakefield Westgate 7	d		14 52							15 52								16 52			
Hull	d							*14 41*								*15 41*			16 21		
Selby	d																		16 56		
Doncaster 7	d		15 10					15 58		16 10		16 28				16 53		17 10	17 15	17 19	
Retford 10	d		15 25																17 30		
Newark North Gate 7	a		15 39					16 20												17 46	
Grimsby Town	d							*14g36*								*15g36*					
Lincoln	d		*15 00*																*15h15*		
Newark North Gate 7	d		15 39					16 20												17 46	
Grantham 7	a		15 52							16 40								17 40		17 49	
	d		15 52						16 25	16 40							17 25	17 40		17 49	
Peterborough 8	a		16 13					16 51	16 56	17 01		17 18				17 40	17 52	18 02			
Cambridge	a									*18 07*								*19 08*			
Stansted Airport	a									*18 45*								*19 45*			
Norwich	a								18 29								19 29				
Peterborough 8	d		16 19					16 51		17 02		17 18				17 45		18 02			
Stevenage 4	a		16 49					17 21								18 16				18 48	
London Kings Cross 15 ⊖	a	17 11	17 18				17 24	17 49		17 55		18 15				18 43		18 55	19 06	19 16	

For general notes see front of timetable
For details of catering facilities see Directory of Train Operators

A **The Northern Lights**
B To Manchester Airport (Table 39)
C To Reading (Table 51)
D To Plymouth (from 8 November to Birmingham New Street (Table 51)
E **The Flying Scotsman**
G From Liverpool Lime Street (Table 49)
H To Liverpool Lime Street (Table 39)
J **The Highland Chieftain**
K From Edinburgh to Reading (Table 51)
L To St Pancras International (Table 53)
b Change at Edinburgh
c Glasgow Queen Street. Change at Edinburgh
e Bradford Interchange
f Change at Leeds
g Change at Doncaster
h Change at Retford

Table 26

Sundays

from 13 September

Scotland, North East England, Yorkshire and Humberside → London

Route Diagram - see first page of Table 26

		GR	GR	TP	EM	XC	XC	GR	GR	TP	TP	GR	GR	GR	GR	XC	XC	GR	EM	GR	TP	GR
		R 1	R 1	1 ◇	◇	1 ◇	1 ◇	R 1	R 1	1 ◇	1 ◇	R 1	R 1	R 1	R 1	1 ◇	1 ◇	R 1	◇	R 1	1 ◇	R 1
				A	B	C	D			E	A					G	H		B		A	
Aberdeen	d	11 47																				13 50
Stonehaven	d	12 04																				14 07
Montrose	d	12 27																				14 30
Arbroath	d	12 43																				14 46
Dundee	d	13 01											13 25									15 04
Leuchars 3	d	13 15											13 37									15 18
Kirkcaldy	d	13 39											14 08									15 42
Inverkeithing	d	13 55											14 30									15 58
Inverness	d																					
Perth	d												13b05									
Stirling	d	13c06											14 06									15c06
Glasgow Central 15	d	13e00					13 45						14f00				14f30	14 50				15e00
Motherwell	d						14 01											15 05				
Haymarket	d	14 19					14 43											15 50				16 20
Edinburgh 10	a	14 24					14 47											15 55				16 25
Edinburgh	d	14 30					14 50	15 00					15 30				15 50	16 00				16 30
Dunbar	d						15 10															
Berwick-upon-Tweed	d						15 33	15 39					16 09									17 09
Alnmouth for Alnwick	d																16 47					17 32
Morpeth	d												16 43				17 02					
Newcastle 8	a	15 59					16 20	16 31					17 02				17 20	17 27				18 07
Sunderland	d	15 28											16 28								17 28	
Hartlepool	d																					
Newcastle 8	d	16 01		16 08		16 18	16 25	16 33			16 52		17 04		17 12	17 18	17 25	17 30			17 57	18 10
Chester-le-Street	d										17 01					17 26						
Durham	d	16 14		16 20		16 30	16 37	16 46			17 08				17 24	17 33	17 37				18 09	
Darlington 7	a	16 32		16 36		16 46	16 53	17 03			17 25		17 30		17 42	17 49	17 54	17 59			18 25	
Middlesbrough	d	15 50								16 45	16 49					17 14					17 49	
Eaglescliffe	d																					
Darlington 7	d	16 32		16 37		16 47	16 54	17 04			17 26		17 31		17 42	17 50	17 55	17 59			18 26	
Northallerton	d			16 48						17 12	17 38		17 42									
Thirsk	d									17 21												
York 8	a	17 01		17 12		17 17	17 22	17 34		17 41	18 00		18 04		18 10	18 16	18 23	18 28			18 59	19 04
Hull	a	18g10																			20 09	
Leeds 10	a			17 38			17 51			18 08	18 38		18 38			18h56	18 51	19 08			19 38	19 38
Harrogate	d							16 30	16 53									17 30		17 53		
Scarborough	d																					17 50
York 8	d	17 03				17 20		17 36					18 05		18 12	18 20		18 29				19 05
Doncaster 7	a	17 27				17 46		18 00					18 31		18 37	18 48		18 53				19 31
Sheffield 7	a	18 07				18 16	18 40	18 52					19 07			19 15	19 40	19 55				20 07
Skipton	d		16 15																	17j15		
Keighley	d		16 28																	17j28		
Bradford Forster Square	d		16k26						17 02											18 02		
Shipley	d		16 40						17 09											18 08		
Leeds 10	d		17 05						17 40											18 40		
Huddersfield	d		16m30																	17m30		
Wakefield Westgate 7	d		17 18						17 52											18 52		
Hull	d							16 41				17 30						17 41				
Selby	d											18 05										
Doncaster 7	d	17 28	17 36					18 03				18 23	18 31	←	18 37			18 53		19 10		19 31
Retford 10	d		17 51									18n44 →		18 44								
Newark North Gate 7	a		18 05												19 02							
Grimsby Town	d							16q36										17q36				
Lincoln	d													17r35								
Newark North Gate 7	d		18 05												19 02							
Grantham 7	a								18 37					19 06						19 40		
	d				18 18				18 37					19 06					19 23	19 40		
Peterborough 8	a	18 26			18 45			18 50	18 59				19 18	19 28	19 33			19 40	19 56	20 01		20 22
Cambridge	a								20 07											21 07		
Stansted Airport	a								20 45											21 45		
Norwich	a				20 28				21t09										21 35			
Peterborough 8	d	18 27						18 51	18 59				19 19	19 29	19 33			19 45		20 02		20 23
Stevenage 4	a		19 02					19 21							20 07			20 18		20 32		20 54
London Kings Cross 15 ⊖	a	19 21	19 33					19 48	19 52				20 14	20 23	20 34			20 43		21 01		21 25

For general notes see front of timetable
For details of catering facilities see Directory of Train Operators

- **A** To Manchester Airport (Table 39)
- **B** From Liverpool Lime Street (Table 49)
- **C** To Reading (Table 51)
- **D** To Plymouth (from 8 November to Birmingham New Street (Table 51)
- **E** To Liverpool Lime Street (Table 39)
- **G** To Southampton Central (Table 51)
- **H** To Bristol Temple Meads (from 8 November to Birmingham New Street) (Table 51)
- **b** Change at Stirling and Edinburgh
- **c** Change at Edinburgh
- **e** Glasgow Queen Street. Change at Edinburgh
- **f** Glasgow Queen Street
- **g** 13 September only
- **h** From 8 November arr. 1851
- **j** From 8 November dep. Skipton 1732, Keighley 1742
- **k** Bradford Interchange
- **m** Change at Leeds
- **n** Arr. 1838
- **q** Change at Doncaster
- **r** Change at Retford
- **t** Change at Peterborough and Ely

Scotland, North East England, Yorkshire and Humberside → London

Route Diagram - see first page of Table 26

		HT		XC	XC	GR	TP		GR	TP	GC	GR		XC	GR	TP	TP		GR	NT	TP	GR		GR		
		1◇		1◇	1◇	R 1	1◇		R 1	1◇	R 1	R 1		1◇	R 1	1◇	1◇		R 1		1◇	R 1		R 1		
				A	B		C			D				A			E			G	E					
Aberdeen	d														15 10							17 10				
Stonehaven	d														15 26							17 26				
Montrose	d														15 48							17 48				
Arbroath	d														16 02							18 02				
Dundee	d								15 25						16 25							18 19				
Leuchars 3	d								15 37						16 37							18 31				
Kirkcaldy	d					16b03			16 08						17 02				17b07			18 56		19b07		
Inverkeithing	d					16b19			16 30						17 18				17b45			19 12		19b45		
Inverness	d					13b25																		16c15		
Perth	d					15b25																17c05		18c27		
Stirling	d								16 06										17b06			18 06		19b12		
Glasgow Central 15	d				15e30	15 50			16e00					16e30					17 50			18e30		19 50		
Motherwell	d					16 05													18 05					20 04		
Haymarket	d					16 44													18 46					20 45		
Edinburgh 10	a					16 51													18 52					20 50		
Edinburgh	d				16 50	17 00			17 30					17 50	18 00				19 00			20 00		21 00		
Dunbar	d				17 10									18 11					19 20			20 20		21 21		
Berwick-upon-Tweed	d				17 33										18 39							20 43		21 44		
Alnmouth for Alnwick	d													18 51	19 03									22 06		
Morpeth	d																					21 17				
Newcastle 8	a				18 20	18 26			18 53					19 20	19 33				20 29			21 38		22 41		
Sunderland	d									18 28	18 42						19 28			20 28						
Hartlepool	d										19 06															
Newcastle 8	d			18 18	18 25	18 29			18 55	19 06				19 25	19 35		20 07		20 31	21 06		21 40				
Chester-le-Street	d			18 26	18 33															21 15						
Durham	d			18 33	18 40	18 43			19 08	19 17				19 39	19 48		20 19			21 24		21 53				
Darlington 7	a			18 49	18 56	19 00			19 25	19 34				19 55	20 05		20 35		20 57	21 44		22 10				
Middlesbrough	d						18 45			18 53						20 07					22 07					
Eaglescliffe	d										19 25															
Darlington 7	d			18 50	18 57	19 01			19 26	19 35				19 56	20 06		20 36		20 58			22 11				
Northallerton	d						19 14		19 39		19 48					20 34	20 48				22 34	22 41				
Thirsk	d						19 23				19 57					20 42					22 42					
York 8	a			19 16	19 25	19 29	19 42		20 00	20 09	20 13			20 24	20 34	21 02	21 12		21 26		23 09	23 19				
Hull	a																22 39		22 39							
Leeds 10	a				19 51		20 08			20 38				20 51	21 08		21 38		22 32		23 38					
Harrogate	d					18 30						18 53			19 30				20 30							
Scarborough	d																		19 50							
York 8	d			19 20		19 31			20 02		20 15				20 36				21 28							
Doncaster 7	a			19 48		19 53			20 25						20 59				21 51							
Sheffield 7	a			20 15	20 40	20 53			21 07					21 44	21 56				22 58							
Skipton	d											19 24														
Keighley	d											19 37														
Bradford Forster Square	d											19f44														
Shipley	d											19 49														
Leeds 10	d											20 15							20 20							
Huddersfield	d											19g30														
Wakefield Westgate 7	d											20 27							20 33							
Hull	d	18 48																	20 30							
Selby	d	19 23																								
Doncaster 7	d	19 43				19 54			20 26			20 47			21 00				21 52							
Retford 10	d	19 58													21 15											
Newark North Gate 7	a					20 16									21 29											
Grimsby Town	d					18h36						19h36							20h36							
Lincoln	d														21 00											
Newark North Gate 7	d					20 16									21 34											
Grantham 7	a	20 18							20 56										22 22							
	d	20 18							20 56										22 22							
Peterborough 8	a					20 46			21 17			21 35			22 03				22 43							
Cambridge	a					22 07									23 12											
Stansted Airport	a					22 45																				
Norwich	a					23j05																				
Peterborough 8	d					20 48			21 18			21 36			22 04				22 44							
Stevenage 4	a	21s09				21 20			21 48			22 09			22 34				23 39							
London Kings Cross 15 ⊖	a	21 34				21 47			22 16		22 17	22 37			23 14				23 50							

For general notes see front of timetable
For details of catering facilities see Directory of Train Operators

A To Birmingham New Street (Table 51)
B To Bristol Temple Meads (from 8 November to Birmingham New Street) (Table 51)
C To Liverpool Lime Street (Table 39)
D To Manchester Piccadilly (Table 39)
E To Manchester Airport (Table 39)
G To Saltburn (Table 44)
b Change at Edinburgh
c Change at Stirling and Edinburgh
e Glasgow Queen Street
f Bradford Interchange
g Change at Leeds
h Change at Doncaster
j Change at Peterborough and Ely

Table 26A

Mondays to Saturdays

Peterborough — Wisbech, Kings Lynn, Swaffham and Dereham

Bus Service

		GR	GR	GR	GR	GR	GR	GR	GR	GR	GR	GR	GR	GR	GR	GR	GR	GR
		SX	SX															
Peterborough	d	06 43	07 13	07 48	08 18	08 48	09 18	09 48	10 18	10 48	11 18	11 48	12 18	12 48	13 18	13 48	14 18	14 48
Wisbech Bus Station	d	07 30	08 00	08 35	09 05	09 35	10 05	10 35	11 05	11 35	12 05	12 35	13 05	13 35	14 05	14 35	15 05	15 35
Kings Lynn Bus Station	d	08 07	08 37	09 07	09 37	10 07	10 37	11 07	11 37	12 07	12 37	13 07	13 37	14 07	14 37	15 07	15 37	16 07
Swaffham Market Place	d	08 42	09 12	09 42	10 12	10 42	11 12	11 42	12 12	12 42	13 12	13 42	14 12	14 42	15 12	15 42	16 12	16 42
Dereham Market Place	a	09 13	09 43	10 13	10 43	11 13	11 43	12 13	12 43	13 13	13 43	14 13	14 43	15 13	15 43	16 13	16 43	17 13

		GR	GR	GR	GR	GR	GR	GR	GR	GR	GR	GR	GR	GR				
Peterborough	d	15 18	15 48	16 18	16 48	17 18	17 48	18 18	18 48	19 18	20 18	21 18	22 18	23 18				
Wisbech Bus Station	d	16 05	16 35	17 05	17 35	18 05	18 35	19 05	19 35	20 05	21 05	22 05	23 05	00 05				
Kings Lynn Bus Station	d	16 37	17 07	17 37	18 07	18 37	19a07	19 37	20a07	20 37	21 37	22a37	23a37	00a37				
Swaffham Market Place	d	17 12	17 42	18 12	18 42	19 12		20 12		21 12	22 12							
Dereham Market Place	a	17 43	18 13	18 43	19 13	19 43		20 43		21 43	22 43							

Sundays

		GR	GR	GR	GR	GR	GR	GR	GR	GR	GR	GR	GR	GR	GR	GR	GR
Peterborough	d	08 18	09 18	10 18	11 18	12 18	13 18	14 18	15 18	16 18	17 18	18 18	19 18	20 18	21 18	22 18	23 18
Wisbech Bus Station	d	09 05	10 05	11 05	12 05	13 05	14 05	15 05	16 05	17 05	18 05	19 05	20 05	21 05	22 05	23 05	00 05
Kings Lynn Bus Station	d	09 37	10 37	11 37	12 37	13 37	14 37	15 37	16 37	17 37	18 37	19 37	20 37	21 37	22a37	23a37	00a37
Swaffham Market Place	d	10 12	11 12	12 12	13 12	14 12	15 12	16 12	17 12	18 12	19 12	20 12	21 12	22 12			
Dereham Market Place	a	10 43	11 43	12 43	13 43	14 43	15 43	16 43	17 43	18 43	19 43	20 43	21 43	22 43			

Mondays to Saturdays

		GR	GR	GR	GR	GR	GR	GR	GR	GR	GR	GR	GR	GR	GR	GR	GR	GR
		SX	SX					SX	SO	SX	SO							
Dereham Market Place	d							07 19	07 24	07 49	07 54	08 24	08 54	09 24	09 54	10 24	10 54	11 24
Swaffham Market Place	d							07 49	07 54	08 19	08 24	08 54	09 24	09 54	10 24	10 54	11 24	11 54
Kings Lynn Bus Station	d	05 24	05 54	06 29	06 59	07 29	07 59	08 29	08 29	08 59	08 59	09 29	09 59	10 29	10 59	11 29	11 59	12 29
Wisbech Bus Station	d	05 56	06 26	07 01	07 31	08 01	08 31	09 01	09 01	09 31	09 31	10 01	10 31	11 01	11 31	12 01	12 31	13 01
Peterborough	a	06 38	07 08	07 43	08 13	08 43	09 13	09 43	09 43	10 13	10 13	10 43	11 13	11 43	12 13	12 43	13 13	13 43

		GR	GR	GR	GR	GR	GR	GR	GR	GR	GR	GR	GR	GR	GR	GR
Dereham Market Place	d	11 54	12 24	12 54	13 24	13 54	14 24	14 54	15 24	15 54	16 24	16 54	17 54	18 54	19 54	20 54
Swaffham Market Place	d	12 24	12 54	13 24	13 54	14 24	14 54	15 24	15 54	16 24	16 54	17 24	18 24	19 24	20 24	21 24
Kings Lynn Bus Station	d	12 59	13 29	13 59	14 29	14 59	15 29	15 59	16 29	16 59	17 29	17 59	18 59	19 59	20 59	21 59
Wisbech Bus Station	d	13 31	14 01	14 31	15 01	15 31	16 01	16 31	17 01	17 31	18 01	18 31	19 31	20 31	21 31	22 31
Peterborough	a	14 13	14 43	15 13	15 43	16 13	16 43	17 13	17 43	18 13	18 43	19 13	20 13	21 13	22 13	23 13

Sundays

		GR	GR	GR	GR	GR	GR	GR	GR	GR	GR	GR	GR	GR	GR	GR	GR
Dereham Market Place	d				08 54	09 54	10 54	11 54	12 54	13 54	14 54	15 54	16 54	17 54	18 54	19 54	20 54
Swaffham Market Place	d				09 24	10 24	11 24	12 24	13 24	14 24	15 24	16 24	17 24	18 24	19 24	20 24	21 24
Kings Lynn Bus Station	d	06 59	07 59	08 59	09 59	10 59	11 59	12 59	13 59	14 59	15 59	16 59	17 59	18 59	19 59	20 59	21 59
Wisbech Bus Station	d	07 31	08 31	09 31	10 31	11 31	12 31	13 31	14 31	15 31	16 31	17 31	18 31	19 31	20 31	21 31	22 31
Peterborough	a	08 13	09 13	10 13	11 13	12 13	13 13	14 13	15 13	16 13	17 13	18 13	19 13	20 13	21 13	22 13	23 13

For general notes see front of timetable
For details of catering facilities see
Directory of Train Operators

Sunday service operates on Bank Holiday Monday

Peterborough — Oundle, Corby and Kettering
Bus Service

		GR	GR	GR	GR	GR	GR	GR	GR	GR	GR	GR	GR	GR	GR
Peterborough §	d	07 05	07 40	09 10	10 10	11 10	12 10	13 10	14 10	15 10	16 10	17 10	18 30	19 30	20 30
Oundle Market Place	a	07 27	08 22	09 32	10 32	11 32	12 32	13 32	14 32	15 32	16 32	17 32	18 57	19 57	20 57
Corby George Street	a	08 05	09 05	10 05	11 05	12 05	13 05	14 05	15 05	16 05	17 05	18 05	19 25	20 25	21 25
Kettering Library	a	08 35	09 35	10 35	11 35	12 35	13 35	14 35	15 35	16 35	17 35	18 35	19 55	20 55	21 55

Sundays

		GR	GR	GR	GR	GR	GR
Peterborough §	d	10 10	12 10	14 10	16 10	18 10	20 10
Oundle Market Place	a	10 37	12 37	14 37	16 37	18 37	20 37
Corby George Street	a	11 05	13 05	15 05	17 05	19 05	21 05
Kettering Library	a	11 35	13 35	15 35	17 35	19 35	21 33

Mondays to Saturdays

		GR	GR	GR	GR	GR	GR	GR	GR	GR	GR	GR	GR	GR	GR
Kettering Library	d	05 30	06 00	07 05	08 45	09 45	10 45	11 45	12 45	13 45	14 45	15 45	16 50	17 55	18 55
Corby George Street	d	05 55	06 25	07 30	09 10	10 10	11 10	12 10	13 10	14 10	15 10	16 10	17 15	18 20	19 20
Oundle Market Place	d	06 23	06 53	07 58	09 38	10 38	11 38	12 38	13 38	14 38	15 38	16 38	17 43	18 48	19 48
Peterborough §	a	06 40	07 25	08 30	10 00	11 00	12 00	13 00	14 00	15 00	16 00	17 00	18 05	19 10	20 20

Sundays

		GR	GR	GR	GR	GR	GR
Kettering Library	d	08 15	10 15	12 15	14 15	16 15	18 15
Corby George Street	d	08 40	10 40	12 40	14 40	16 40	18 40
Oundle Market Place	d	09 08	11 08	13 08	15 08	17 08	19 08
Peterborough §	a	09 40	11 40	13 40	15 40	17 40	19 40

For general notes see front of timetable
For details of catering facilities see Directory of Train Operators

§ Peterborough Queensgate Bus Station

Table 26F

Doncaster → Robin Hood Airport

Bus Service

		GR	GR		GR	GR		GR	GR		GR	GR		GR	GR		GR	GR		GR	GR		GR		GR	GR
Doncaster Interchange	d	05 35	05 55	.....	06 00	06 25	.....	06 35	06 50	.....	06 55	07 25	.....	07 35	07 45	.....	07 55	08 05	.....	08 15	08 30	.....	08 35	.....	09 00	09 05
Robin Hood Airport	a	05 59	06 20	.	06 25	06 50	.	06 59	07 15	.	07 20	07 50	.	07 59	08 10	.	08 20	08 30	.	08 40	08 55	.	08 59	.	09 25	09 30

		GR	GR	GR	and at the same minutes past each hour until			GR	GR		GR	GR		GR	GR		GR	GR		GR	GR		GR	GR		GR
Doncaster Interchange	d	09 20	09 35	09 40			.....	14 40	15 00	.....	15 05	15 20	.....	15 35	15 45	.....	16 05	16 10	.....	16 25	16 35	.....	16 40	16 55	.....	17 10
Robin Hood Airport	a	09 45	09 59	10 05			.	15 05	15 25	.	15 30	15 45	.	15 59	16 10	.	16 30	16 39	.	16 54	16 59	.	17 09	17 24	.	17 39

		GR	GR		GR	GR		GR		GR	GR	GR	and at the same minutes past each hour until			GR	GR		GR							
Doncaster Interchange	d	17 15	17 30	.....	17 35	17 50	.....	18 10	.....	18 15	18 35	18 40			.....	21 40	22 35	.....	23 00	.....	.....	.....	.....	.....	.....	.....
Robin Hood Airport	a	17 40	17 59	.	17 59	18 18	.	18 35	.	18 40	18 59	19 05			.	22 05	22 59	.	23 25	.	.	.	.	.	.	.

Saturdays

		GR	GR		GR	GR		GR	GR		GR	GR		GR	GR		GR	GR			GR	GR	GR			
Doncaster Interchange	d	05 35	05 55	.....	06 00	06 35	.....	06 40	06 50	.....	07 35	07 40	.....	07 55	08 10	.....	08 35	08 40	.....	.....	09 05	09 10	09 35	.....	.....	.....
Robin Hood Airport	a	05 59	06 20	.	06 25	06 59	.	07 05	07 15	.	07 59	08 05	.	08 20	08 35	.	08 59	09 05	.	.	09 30	09 35	09 59	.	.	.

		GR	and at the same minutes past each hour until			GR	GR		GR	GR		GR	GR			GR	GR	GR	and at the same minutes past each hour until			GR	GR		GR	
Doncaster Interchange	d	09 40			.....	16 40	17 10	.....	17 15	17 35	.....	17 40	18 10	.....	.....	18 15	18 35	18 40			.....	21 40	22 35	.....	23 00	.....
Robin Hood Airport	a	10 05			.	17 05	17 35	.	17 40	17 59	.	18 05	18 35	.	.	18 40	18 59	19 05			.	22 05	22 59	.	23 25	.

Sundays

		GR	GR	GR	GR	GR	GR	GR	GR	GR	GR	GR	GR	GR	GR	GR	GR	GR	GR	GR	GR	GR	GR	GR		
Doncaster Interchange	d	08 35	09 35	09 40	10 35	10 40	11 35	11 40	12 35	12 40	13 40	14 35	14 40	15 35	15 40	16 35	16 40	17 35	17 40	18 40	19 40	20 40	21 40	23 00	.....	.....
Robin Hood Airport	a	08 59	09 59	10 05	10 59	11 05	11 59	12 05	12 59	13 05	14 05	14 59	15 05	15 59	16 05	16 59	17 05	17 59	18 05	19 05	20 05	21 05	22 05	23 25	.	.

For general notes see front of timetable
For details of catering facilities see
Directory of Train Operators

Robin Hood Airport → Doncaster

Bus Service

		GR	GR	GR	GR	GR	GR	GR	GR	GR	GR	GR	GR		GR		GR	GR	GR	GR	and at the same minutes past each hour until	GR	GR	GR	GR
Robin Hood Airport	d	06 05	06 25	06 38	07 05	07 08	07 23	07 25	07 53	08 05	08 08	08 25	08 28	.....	08 48	.....	09 05	09 08	09 28	09 35		15 48	16 05	16 08	16 38
Doncaster Interchange	a	06 30	06 55	07 03	07 30	07 33	07 54	07 55	08 24	08 30	08 39	08 55	08 59	.	09 15	.	09 30	09 33	09 53	10 05		16 13	16 30	16 33	17 03

		GR	GR	GR	GR	GR		GR	GR	GR	GR	GR	GR		GR	GR	GR	and at the same minutes past each hour until	GR	GR	GR	GR	GR		
Robin Hood Airport	d	16 45	16 58	17 05	17 18	17 38	.....	17 45	17 58	18 05	18 28	18 45	18 58	.....	19 05	19 28	19 45		21 45	22 05	22 28	23 05	23 43	.....	.....
Doncaster Interchange	a	17 20	17 23	17 30	17 43	18 03	.	18 15	18 23	18 30	18 53	19 15	19 23	.	19 30	19 53	20 15		22 15	22 30	22 53	23 30	00 08	.	.

Saturdays

		GR	GR	GR	GR	GR		GR	GR	GR	GR	GR			GR	GR	GR	GR	and at the same minutes past each hour until	GR		GR	GR	GR	GR
Robin Hood Airport	d	06 05	06 25	06 38	07 05	07 28	.....	07 25	08 05	08 28	08 25	08 58	.....	.....	09 05	09 28	09 35	09 58		15 58	.....	16 05	16 28	16 45	16 58
Doncaster Interchange	a	06 30	06 55	07 03	07 30	07 53	.	07 55	08 30	08 53	08 55	09 23	.	.	09 30	09 53	10 05	10 23		16 23	.	16 30	16 53	17 20	17 23

		GR	GR	GR		GR	GR	GR	GR	GR			GR	GR	GR	and at the same minutes past each hour until	GR	GR		GR	GR	GR			
Robin Hood Airport	d	17 05	17 28	17 45	.....	17 58	18 05	18 28	18 45	18 58	.....	.....	19 05	19 28	19 45		21 45	22 05	.....	22 28	23 05	23 43	.....	.....	.....
Doncaster Interchange	a	17 30	17 53	18 15	.	18 23	18 30	18 53	19 15	19 23	.	.	19 30	19 53	20 15		22 15	22 30	.	22 53	23 30	00 08	.	.	.

Sundays

		GR	GR	GR	GR	GR	GR	GR	GR	GR	GR	GR	GR	GR	GR	GR	GR	GR	GR	GR	GR	GR	GR	GR	GR	
Robin Hood Airport	d	09 05	09 28	10 05	10 28	11 05	11 28	12 05	12 28	13 28	14 05	14 28	15 05	15 28	16 05	16 28	17 05	17 28	18 05	18 28	19 28	20 28	21 28	22 28	23 43	.....
Doncaster Interchange	a	09 30	09 53	10 30	10 53	11 30	11 53	12 30	12 53	13 53	14 30	14 53	15 30	15 53	16 30	16 53	17 30	17 53	18 30	18 53	19 53	20 53	21 53	22 53	00 08	.

For general notes see front of timetable
For details of catering facilities see
Directory of Train Operators

York — Pickering and Whitby

Bus Service

		GR	GR	GR	GR	GR	GR	GR	GR	GR	GR	GR	GR	GR
York	d	06 46	08 18	09 20	10 01	10 22	11 22	12 22	13 22	14 22	15 22	16 24	17 34	18 31
Eden Camp	a	08 02	09 22	10 22	10 57	11 22	12 22	13 22	14 22	15 22	16 22	17 27	18 32	19 27
Flamingo Land	a			10 35		11 35								
Pickering Eastgate	a	08 16	09 36	10 43	11 09	11 43	12 36	13 36	14 36	15 36	16 36	17 41	18 46	19 41
Whitby Bus Station	a		10 37		11 51	12 44		14 37		16 37	17 37		19 41	

Saturdays

		GR	GR	GR	GR	GR	GR	GR	GR	GR	GR	GR	GR
York	d	08 22	09 22	09 56	10 22	11 22	12 22	13 22	14 22	15 22	16 22	17 34	18 27
Eden Camp	a	09 22	10 22	10 52	11 22	12 22	13 22	14 22	15 22	16 22	17 22	18 27	19 27
Flamingo Land	a		10 35		11 35								
Pickering Eastgate	a	09 36	10 43	11 04	11 43	12 36	13 36	14 36	15 36	16 36	17 36	18 41	19 41
Whitby Bus Station	a	10 37		11 46	12 44		14 37		16 37	17 37		19 42	

Sundays

		GR	GR	GR	GR	GR	GR
York	d	09 22	09 52	09 56	12 52	14 52	16 12
Eden Camp	a	10 22	10 52	10 52	13 52	15 52	17 12
Flamingo Land	a	10 35	11 05				
Pickering Eastgate	a	10 48		11 06	14 06	16 06	17 26
Whitby Bus Station	a			12 07	15 07	17 07	18 27

Mondays to Fridays

		GR	GR	GR	GR	GR	GR	GR	GR	GR	GR	GR	GR	GR	GR	GR
Whitby Bus Station	d					11 06	12 31	13 06		15 06			17 31	18 16		20 16
Pickering Eastgate	d	06 47	08 37	09 07	11 07	12 07	13 13	14 07	15 07	16 07		17 57	18 13	19 17	19 57	21 17
Flamingo Land	d										17 12	18 15				
Eden Camp	d	07 03	08 53	09 23	11 23	12 23	13 23	14 23	15 23	16 23	17 23	18 26	18 23	19 33	20 13	21 33
York	a	08 06	09 56	10 26	12 26	13 26	14 26	15 26	16 26	17 27	18 27	19 23	19 23	20 30	21 30	22 30

Saturdays

		GR	GR	GR	GR	GR	GR	GR	GR	GR	GR	GR	GR	GR	GR	GR
Whitby Bus Station	d					11 06	12 31	13 06		15 06			17 31	18 16		20 16
Pickering Eastgate	d	07 07	08 37	09 07	11 07	12 07	13 13	14 07	15 07	16 07		17 57	18 13	19 17	19 57	21 17
Flamingo Land	d										17 12	18 15				
Eden Camp	d	07 23	08 53	09 23	11 23	12 23	13 23	14 23	15 23	16 23	17 23	18 26	18 23	19 33	20 13	21 33
York	a	08 26	09 56	10 26	12 26	13 26	14 26	15 26	16 26	17 26	18 25	19 23	19 23	20 30	21 30	22 30

Sundays

		GR	GR	GR	GR	GR	GR	GR
Whitby Bus Station	d			12 26	15 46		17 46	18 46
Pickering Eastgate	d	08 57	10 57	13 27	16 47		18 47	19 47
Flamingo Land	d					17 52		
Eden Camp	d	09 13	11 13	13 43	17 03	18 03	19 03	20 03
York	a	10 26	12 26	14 46	18 06	19 03	20 03	21 00

For general notes see front of timetable
For details of catering facilities see Directory of Train Operators

Darlington — Richmond and Catterick

Bus Service

Mondays to Fridays

		GR	GR	GR	GR	GR		GR	GR	GR	GR	GR	GR
		SX											
		🚌	🚌	🚌	🚌	🚌		🚌	🚌	🚌	🚌	🚌	🚌
Darlington	d	06 23	06 53	07 33	08 03	08 33	and every 30 minutes until	17 33	18 03	19 03	20 03	21 03	23 03
Richmond (Market)	a	06 54	07 24	08 04	08 34	09 04		18 04	18 36	19 36	20 36	21 36	23 36
Catterick Garrison Tesco	a	07 05	07 35	08 15	08 45	09 15		18 15	18 47	19 47	20 47	21 47	23 47
Catterick Camp Centre	a	07 07	07 37	08 17	08 47	09 17		18 17	18 49	19 49	20 49	21 49	23 49
Catterick Garrison Kemmel	a	07 15	07 45	08 25	08 55	09 25		18 25	18 57	19 57	20 57	21 57	23 57

Sundays

		GR	GR	GR	GR	GR	GR	GR	GR	GR	GR	GR	GR	GR	GR	GR
		🚌	🚌	🚌	🚌	🚌	🚌	🚌	🚌	🚌	🚌	🚌	🚌	🚌	🚌	🚌
Darlington	d	09 03	10 03	11 03	12 03	13 03	14 03	15 03	16 03	17 03	18 03	19 03	20 03	21 03	22 03	23 03
Richmond (Market)	a	09 34	10 34	11 34	12 34	13 34	14 34	15 34	16 34	17 34	18 36	19 36	20 36	21 36	22 36	23 36
Catterick Garrison Tesco	a	09 45	10 45	11 45	12 45	13 45	14 45	15 45	16 45	17 45	18 47	19 47	20 47	21 47	22 47	23 47
Catterick Camp Centre	a	09 47	10 47	11 47	12 47	13 47	14 47	15 47	16 47	17 47	18 49	19 49	20 49	21 49	22 49	23 49
Catterick Garrison Kemmel	a	09 55	10 55	11 55	12 55	13 55	14 55	15 55	16 55	17 55	18 57	19 57	20 57	21 57	22 57	23 57

Mondays to Fridays

		GR	GR	GR	GR	GR	GR	GR	GR	GR		GR	GR	GR	GR	GR	GR	GR
		SX	SX	SX	SO	SX	SO											
		🚌	🚌	🚌	🚌	🚌	🚌	🚌	🚌	🚌		🚌	🚌	🚌	🚌	🚌	🚌	🚌
Catterick Garrison Kemmel	d	06 22	06 52	07 22	07 27	07 52	07 57	08 32	09 02	09 32	and every 30 minutes until	17 32	18 02	18 32	19 02	20 02	21 02	22 02
Catterick Camp Centre	d	06 30	07 00	07 30	07 35	08 00	08 05	08 40	09 10	09 40		17 40	18 10	18 40	19 10	20 10	21 10	22 10
Catterick Garrison Tesco	d	06 32	07 02	07 32	07 37	08 02	08 07	08 42	09 12	09 42		17 42	18 12	18 42	19 12	20 12	21 12	22 12
Richmond (Market)	d	06 44	07 14	07 44	07 49	08 14	08 19	08 54	09 24	09 54		17 54	18 24	18 54	19 24	20 24	21 24	22 24
Darlington	a	07 15	07 45	08 20	08 20	08 45	08 50	09 25	09 55	10 25		18 25	18 55	19 25	19 57	20 57	21 57	22 57

Sundays

		GR	GR	GR	GR	GR	GR	GR	GR	GR	GR	GR	GR	GR	GR
		🚌	🚌	🚌	🚌	🚌	🚌	🚌	🚌	🚌	🚌	🚌	🚌	🚌	🚌
Catterick Garrison Kemmel	d	09 02	10 02	11 02	12 02	13 02	14 02	15 02	16 02	17 02	18 02	19 02	20 02	21 02	22 02
Catterick Camp Centre	d	09 10	10 10	11 10	12 10	13 10	14 10	15 10	16 10	17 10	18 10	19 10	20 10	21 10	22 10
Catterick Garrison Tesco	d	09 12	10 12	11 12	12 12	13 12	14 12	15 12	16 12	17 12	18 12	19 12	20 12	21 12	22 12
Richmond (Market)	d	09 24	10 24	11 24	12 24	13 24	14 24	15 24	16 24	17 24	18 24	19 24	20 24	21 24	22 24
Darlington	a	09 55	10 55	11 55	12 55	13 55	14 55	15 55	16 55	17 55	18 55	19 57	20 57	21 57	22 57

For general notes see front of timetable
For details of catering facilities see Directory of Train Operators

Berwick-upon-Tweed — Scottish Border Towns
Bus Service

This service is operated by First Lowland under contract to Scottish Borders Council. Telephone: 01835 824000

		XC	XC	XC	XC	XC	XC	XC	XC	XC
Berwick-upon-Tweed	d	06 57	08 12	09 52	10 52	12 52	15 07	17 47	18 47	20 22
Duns	a	07 30	08 45	10 25	11 25	13 25	15 40	18 20	19 20	20 55
Earlston	a	08 08	09 33	11 03	12 03	14 03	16 28	18 58	19 58	21 33
Melrose	a	08 22	09 47	11 15	12 15	14 15	16 40	19 10	20 10	21 45
Galashiels Bus Station	a	08 40	10 02	11 30	12 30	14 30	16 55	19 25	20 25	22 00

Saturdays

This service is operated by First Lowland under contract to Scottish Borders Council. Telephone: 01835 824000

		XC	XC	XC	XC	XC	XC
Berwick-upon-Tweed	d	08 22	10 52	12 52	15 17	17 17	19 17
Duns	a	08 55	11 25	13 25	15 50	17 50	19 50
Earlston	a	09 33	12 03	14 03	16 28	18 28	20 28
Melrose	a	09 47	12 15	14 15	16 40	18 40	20 40
Galashiels Bus Station	a	10 02	12 30	14 30	16 55	18 55	20 55

Sundays

This service is operated by First Lowland under contract to Scottish Borders Council. Telephone: 01835 824000

		XC	XC	XC	XC	XC	XC
Berwick-upon-Tweed	d	10 52	12 52	15 17	17 42	19 07	20 37
Duns	a	11 25	13 40	15 50	18 30	19 55	21 10
Earlston	a	12 03	14 18	16 28	19 08	20 33	21 48
Melrose	a	12 15	14 30	16 40	19 20	20 45	22 00
Galashiels Bus Station	a	12 30	14 45	16 55	19 35	21 00	22 15

Mondays to Fridays

This service is operated by First Lowland under contract to Scottish Borders Council. Telephone: 01835 824000

		XC	XC	XC	XC	XC	XC	XC	XC
Galashiels Bus Station	d	06 25	07 40	08 10	10 50	12 50	14 40	16 32	17 20
Melrose	d	06 40	07 55	08 28	11 05	13 05	14 55	16 50	17 35
Earlston	d	06 52	08 07	08 40	11 17	13 17	15 07	17 02	17 47
Duns	d	07 30	08 50	09 20	11 55	13 55	15 55	17 40	18 30
Berwick-upon-Tweed	a	08 01	09 26	09 56	12 26	14 26	16 26	18 11	19 01

Saturdays

This service is operated by First Lowland under contract to Scottish Borders Council. Telephone: 01835 824000

		XC	XC	XC	XC	XC	XC
Galashiels Bus Station	d	06 35	08 20	10 50	12 50	14 50	17 20
Melrose	d	06 50	08 35	11 05	13 05	15 05	17 35
Earlston	d	07 02	08 47	11 17	13 17	15 17	17 52
Duns	d	07 40	09 25	11 55	13 55	15 55	18 30
Berwick-upon-Tweed	a	08 11	09 56	12 26	14 26	16 26	19 01

Sundays

This service is operated by First Lowland under contract to Scottish Borders Council. Telephone: 01835 824000

		XC	XC	XC	XC	XC	XC
Galashiels Bus Station	d	08 50	10 50	12 35	14 50	16 35	18 35
Melrose	d	09 05	11 05	12 50	15 05	16 50	18 50
Earlston	d	09 17	11 17	13 02	15 17	17 02	19 02
Duns	d	09 55	11 55	13 40	15 55	17 40	19 40
Berwick-upon-Tweed	a	10 26	12 26	14 26	16 26	18 26	20 26

For general notes see front of timetable
For details of catering facilities see Directory of Train Operators

Cleethorpes → Lincoln → Newark → Nottingham

Network Diagram - see first page of Table 18

Miles	Miles			EM	EM	EM 1 ◇ A	EM B	EM	EM C	EM	EM C	EM	EM C	EM C	EM	EM C	EM C	EM D
0	—	**Cleethorpes**	d		05 49													
3¼	—	**Grimsby Town**	d		05 56			07 03				09 28			11 28			
11¼	—	Habrough	d		06 06			07 13				09 38			11 38			
17¾	—	Barnetby	d		06 15			07 22				09 47			11 47			
32¼	—	Market Rasen	d		06 32			07 39				10 03			12 03			
47	—	**Lincoln**	a		06 51			07 57				10 22			12 22			
—	—		d	05 26	06 53	07 08	07 29	07 59	08 35	09 11	09 31	10 23	10 36	11 42	12 23	12 30	13 40	14 05
51	—	Hykeham	d	05 34	07 01		07 36		08 43				10 44			12 38		
55¾	—	Swinderby	d	05 40	07 07		07 42		08 49				10 50			12 44		
58½	0	Collingham	d	05 45	07 12	07 23	07 47	08 15	08 54	09 26		10 40	10 55		12 40	12 48		14 21
—	5	**Newark North Gate 7**	a	05 56	07 22			08 25		09 36		10 52			12 52			14 33
—	—	London Kings Cross 15	⊖ a	*07 30*	*08 46*			*09 51*		*11 14*		*12 25*			*15 05*			*16 46*
—	—	**Newark North Gate 7**	d	05 59														
63½	—	**Newark Castle**	d	06 09		07 33	07 56		09 04		09 54		11 03	12 04		12 57	14 05	
67	—	Rolleston	d	06 16			08 03				10 01					13 04		
68	—	Fiskerton	d	06 18			08 05				10 03					13 06		
69¾	—	Bleasby	d	06 22			08 08				10 07					13 09		
70¾	—	Thurgarton	d	06 25			08 11				10 10					13 12		
71½	—	Lowdham	d	06 29			08 15		09 18		10 14		11 17	12 18		13 17	14 17	
75¾	—	Burton Joyce	d	06 34			08 19				10 19							
77¾	—	Carlton	d	06 38			08 23				10 23					13 23		
80¾	—	**Nottingham 8**	a	06 45		07 57	08 30		09 30		10 30		11 29	12 30		13 30	14 30	

		EM C	EM	EM C	EM C	EM	EM C	EM	EM C	EM	EM	EM	EM	EM
Cleethorpes	d												21 15	
Grimsby Town	d		13 52			16 03				18 28			21 22	
Habrough	d		14 02			16 12				18 38			21 31	
Barnetby	d		14 11			16 21				18 49			21 40	
Market Rasen	d		14 27			16 36				19 04			21 55	
Lincoln	a		14 47			16 55				19 23			22 18	
	d	14 35	14 48	15 30	16 35	16 57	17 28	18 18	18 35	19 25	20 45	21 40		22 28
Hykeham	d			15 37	16 43		17 36			19 33				22 36
Swinderby	d			15 43	16 49		17 42			19 39				22 42
Collingham	d		15 04	15 48	16 54	17 12	17 47	18 34		19 44	21 00			22 47
Newark North Gate 7	a		15 14			17 25		18 44		19 54				
London Kings Cross 15	⊖ a		*17 04*			*18 54*		*20 18*		*21 33*				
Newark North Gate 7	d													
Newark Castle	d	15 01		15 57	17 03		17 56		19 03		21 10	22 05		22 57
Rolleston	d			16 04			18 03							
Fiskerton	d			16 06			18 05							23 05
Bleasby	d			16 10			18 09							23 08
Thurgarton	d			16 12			18 12							
Lowdham	d	15 14		16 16	17 17		18 16		19 16		21 23	22 18		23 13
Burton Joyce	d	15 19					18 20							23 17
Carlton	d	15 23		16 23			18 23							23 21
Nottingham 8	a	15 30		16 30	17 30		18 31		19 29		21 39	22 34		23 33

Saturdays

		EM	EM 1 ◇ A	EM B	EM	EM C	EM	EM C	EM	EM C	EM C	EM	EM C	EM C
Cleethorpes	d													
Grimsby Town	d				07 03				09 28			11 28		
Habrough	d				07 13				09 38			11 38		
Barnetby	d				07 22				09 47			11 47		
Market Rasen	d				07 39				10 03			12 03		
Lincoln	a				07 57				10 22			12 22		
	d	05 26	07 08	07 29	07 59	08 35	09 11	09 31	10 23	10 36	11 42	12 23	12 30	13 40
Hykeham	d	05 34		07 36		08 43				10 44			12 38	
Swinderby	d	05 40		07 42		08 49				10 50			12 44	
Collingham	d	05 45	07 23	07 47	08 15	08 54	09 26		10 40	10 55		12 40	12 48	
Newark North Gate 7	a	05 56			08 25		09 36		10 52			12 52		
London Kings Cross 15	⊖ a	*07 29*			*10 00*		*11 33*		*12 24*			*14 27*		
Newark North Gate 7	d	05 59												
Newark Castle	d	06 09	07 35	07 56		09 04		09 54		11 03	12 04		12 57	14 05
Rolleston	d	06 16		08 03				10 01					13 04	
Fiskerton	d	06 18		08 05				10 03					13 06	
Bleasby	d	06 22		08 08				10 07					13 09	
Thurgarton	d	06 25		08 11				10 10					13 12	
Lowdham	d	06 29		08 15		09 18		10 14		11 17	12 18		13 17	14 17
Burton Joyce	d	06 34		08 19				10 19						
Carlton	d	06 38		08 23				10 23					13 23	
Nottingham 8	a	06 45	07 58	08 30		09 30		10 30		11 29	12 30		13 30	14 30

For general notes see front of timetable
For details of catering facilities see Directory of Train Operators

A To St Pancras International (Table 53)
B From Sleaford (Table 18) to Leicester (Table 53)
C To Leicester (Table 53)
D From Peterborough (Table 18)

From Monday 28 September a revised service will be in operation due to seasonal difficulties. Some trains will be retimed between 1 and 3 minutes. Passengers should check with National Rail Enquiries for precise times.

From Saturday 3 October a revised service will be in operation due to seasonal difficulties. Some trains will be retimed between 1 and 3 minutes. Passengers should check with National Rail Enquiries for precise times.

Table 27

Saturdays

Cleethorpes → Lincoln → Newark → Nottingham

Network Diagram - see first page of Table 18

		EM A	EM B	EM	EM B	EM B	EM	EM B	EM B	EM	EM	EM	EM
Cleethorpes	d												
Grimsby Town	d			13 52			16 03			18 28		19 45	
Habrough	d			14 02			16 12			18 38		19 54	
Barnetby	d			14 11			16 21			18 49		20 03	
Market Rasen	d			14 27			16 36			19 04		20 18	
Lincoln	a			14 47			16 55			19 23		20 37	
	d	14 05	14 35	14 48	15 30	16 35	16 57	17 28	18 35	19 25	19 35		20 45
Hykeham	d				15 37	16 43		17 36		19 33			
Swinderby	d				15 43	16 49		17 42		19 39			
Collingham	d	14 21		15 04	15 48	16 54	17 12	17 47		19 44			21 00
Newark North Gate 7	a	14 33		15 14			17 25			19 54			
London Kings Cross 15 ⊖	a	*16 34*		*17 33*			*19 40*			*22 47*			
Newark North Gate 7	d												
Newark Castle	d		15 01		15 57	17 03		17 56	19 02		20 03		21 10
Rolleston	d				16 04			18 03					
Fiskerton	d				16 06			18 05					
Bleasby	d				16 10			18 09					
Thurgarton	d				16 12			18 12					
Lowdham	d		15 14		16 16	17 17		18 16	19 16		20 16		21 23
Burton Joyce	d		15 19					18 20					
Carlton	d		15 23		16 23			18 23					
Nottingham 8	a		15 30		16 30	17 30		18 31	19 29		20 30		21 39

Sundays

until 6 September

		EM	EM	EM	EM	EM	EM	EM	EM	EM	EM	EM	EM	EM
Cleethorpes	d			13 56						18 18		19 54		
Grimsby Town	d			14 03						18 25		20 07		
Habrough	d			14 13						18 35		20 17		
Barnetby	d			14 22						18 44		20 26		
Market Rasen	d			14 37						18 59		20 41		
Lincoln	a			14 56						19 18		20 58		
	d	11 05	13 00	15 00	15 50	17 10	17 25	18 10	19 10	19 24	20 10	21 00	21 26	22 10
Hykeham	d			15 08		17 18		18 18	19 18		20 18	21 08		22 18
Swinderby	d			15 14		17 24		18 24	19 24		20 24	21 14		22 24
Collingham	d	11 20	13 15	15 18		17 28		18 28	19 28		20 28	21 18		22 28
Newark North Gate 7	a	11 30	13 25	15 28	16 14		17 49			19 48		21 27	21 50	
London Kings Cross 15 ⊖	a	*13 14*	*15 16*	*17 18*	*19b14*		*19 33*			*21 47*		*23 14*		
Newark North Gate 7	d			15 32								21 31		
Newark Castle	d			15 42		17 38		18 39	19 40		20 40	21 40		22 39
Rolleston	d							18 45						22 45
Fiskerton	d							18 47						22 47
Bleasby	d							18 51						22 50
Thurgarton	d							18 54						22 53
Lowdham	d			15 55		17 51		18 58	19 52		20 52	21 53		22 58
Burton Joyce	d							19 02						23 02
Carlton	d							19 06						23 05
Nottingham 8	a			16 11		18 08		19 17	20 08		21 08	22 09		23 17

Sundays

from 13 September

		EM	EM	EM	EM	EM	EM	EM	EM
Cleethorpes	d								
Grimsby Town	d								
Habrough	d								
Barnetby	d								
Market Rasen	d								
Lincoln	a								
	d	11 05	13 00	15 00	18 10	19 10	20 10	21 00	22 10
Hykeham	d			15 08	18 18	19 18	20 18	21 08	22 18
Swinderby	d			15 14	18 24	19 24	20 24	21 14	22 24
Collingham	d	11 20	13 15	15 18	18 28	19 28	20 28	21 18	22 28
Newark North Gate 7	a	11 30	13 25	15 28				21 27	
London Kings Cross 15 ⊖	a	*13 14*	*15 16*	*17 18*				*23 14*	
Newark North Gate 7	d			15 32				21 31	
Newark Castle	d			15 42	18 39	19 40	20 40	21 40	22 39
Rolleston	d				18 45				22 45
Fiskerton	d				18 47				22 47
Bleasby	d				18 51				22 50
Thurgarton	d				18 54				22 53
Lowdham	d			15 55	18 58	19 52	20 52	21 53	22 58
Burton Joyce	d				19 02				23 02
Carlton	d				19 06				23 05
Nottingham 8	a			16 11	19 17	20 08	21 08	22 09	23 17

For general notes see front of timetable
For details of catering facilities see Directory of Train Operators

A From Peterborough (Table 18)
B To Leicester (Table 53)
b From 19 July arr. 1916

From Saturday 3 October a revised service will be in operation due to seasonal difficulties. Some trains will be retimed between 1 and 3 minutes. Passengers should check with National Rail Enquiries for precise times.

Nottingham → Newark → Lincoln → Cleethorpes

Network Diagram - see first page of Table 18

Miles	Miles	Station		EM	EM	EM A	EM	EM	EM B	EM C	EM	EM C	EM C	EM	EM C	EM A	EM C	EM
0	—	**Nottingham** 8	d		05 55	06 55			08 05	09 23		10 29	11 17		12 27		13 17	
3	—	Carlton	d		06 01	07 01			08 13	09 29			11 23				13 23	
5	—	Burton Joyce	d		06 05	07 05			08 17				11 27				13 27	
9¼	—	Lowdham	d		06 10	07 10			08 21	09 36		10 40	11 32		12 38		13 32	
10	—	Thurgarton	d		06 14	07 14			08 25				11 36				13 36	
11	—	Bleasby	d		06 17	07 17			08 28				11 39				13 39	
12¾	—	Fiskerton	d		06 20	07 20			08 32				11 42				13 42	
13¾	—	Rolleston	d		06 22	07 22			08 34				11 45				13 44	
17¼	—	**Newark Castle**	d		06 30	07 29			08 41	09 50		10 58	11 51		12 53		13 51	
—	—	**Newark North Gate** 7	a															
—	—	London Kings Cross 15 ⊖	d				*06 15*				*08 30*			*10 35*		*11 30*		*13 10*
—	0	**Newark North Gate** 7	d				07 45	08 31			09 57			12 04		13 02		14 36
22¼	5	Collingham	d		06 40	07 39	07 54	08 40			10 05	11 08	12 01	12 13		13 11	14 00	14 44
25	—	Swinderby	d		06 44		07 59	08 45				11 12		12 17			14 05	
29¾	—	Hykeham	d		06 50		08 05	08 51				11 18		12 24			14 11	
33¾	—	**Lincoln**	a		07 04	07 58	08 15	09 02	09 08	10 17	10 21	11 30	12 21	12 35	13 20	13 30	14 23	15 00
—	—		d	05 57			08 17				10 23			12 37				15 01
48½	—	Market Rasen	d	06 13			08 34				10 40			12 54				15 17
63½	—	Barnetby	a	06 30			08 51				10 56			13 11				15 33
69½	—	Habrough	a	06 41			09 01				11 06			13 21				15 42
77½	—	**Grimsby Town**	a	06 56			09 15				11 21			13 36				15 57
80¾	—	**Cleethorpes**	a															

Station		EM C	EM A	EM C	EM D	EM	EM	EM	EM	EM	EM	EM C	EM	EM 1 ◇ E ⊡	EM
Nottingham 8	d	14 29		15 27	16 14			17 17	17 50	18 15		19 25		20 29	22 25
Carlton	d			15 33	16 20			17 23		18 21					22 31
Burton Joyce	d				16 24			17 27		18 25					22 35
Lowdham	d	14 40		15 40	16 29			17 32	18 01	18 30		19 36		20 40	22 40
Thurgarton	d				16 33			17 36		18 34					
Bleasby	d				16 36			17 39		18 37					22 45
Fiskerton	d				16 39			17 42		18 40					22 48
Rolleston	d				16 42			17 45		18 43					
Newark Castle	d	14 55		15 53	16 48			17 53	18 14	18 50		19 50		20 57	22 56
Newark North Gate 7	a														23 05
London Kings Cross 15 ⊖	d		*14 10*				*16 10*				*17 49*		*19 03*		*21 30*
Newark North Gate 7	d		15 36				17 34				19 24		20 30		23 08
Collingham	d		15 45	16 03	16 58		17 42	18 02	18 25	18 59	19 33		20 39	21 05	23 17
Swinderby	d			16 07				18 07	18 29	19 04					23 22
Hykeham	d			16 13				18 13	18 35	19 10					23 28
Lincoln	a	15 22	16 03	16 25	17 14		18 03	18 26	18 48	19 22	19 51	20 17	20 56	21 24	23 40
	d					17 21					19 55				
Market Rasen	d					17 37					20 12				
Barnetby	a					17 53					20 30				
Habrough	a					18 02					20 40				
Grimsby Town	a					18 17					20 52				
Cleethorpes	a										21 02				

Saturdays

Station		EM	EM	EM A	EM	EM	EM	EM C	EM	EM C	EM C	EM	EM C	EM A
Nottingham 8	d		05 55	06 55			08 01	09 23		10 29	11 17		12 27	
Carlton	d		06 01	07 01			08 08	09 29			11 23			
Burton Joyce	d		06 05	07 05			08 12				11 27			
Lowdham	d		06 10	07 10			08 17	09 36		10 40	11 32		12 38	
Thurgarton	d		06 14	07 14			08 21				11 36			
Bleasby	d		06 17	07 17			08 24				11 39			
Fiskerton	d		06 20	07 20			08 27				11 42			
Rolleston	d		06 22	07 22			08 30				11 45			
Newark Castle	d		06 30	07 29			08 37	09 50		10 58	11 51		12 53	
Newark North Gate 7	a													
London Kings Cross 15 ⊖	d					*07 00*			*08 10*			*10 10*		*11 10*
Newark North Gate 7	d					08 31			09 57			12 04		13 02
Collingham	d		06 40	07 39		08 40			10 05	11 08	12 01	12 13		13 11
Swinderby	d		06 44			08 45				11 12		12 17		
Hykeham	d		06 50			08 51				11 18		12 24		
Lincoln	a		07 04	07 58		09 02	09 08	10 17	10 21	11 30	12 21	12 35	13 20	13 30
	d	05 57			08 17				10 23			12 37		
Market Rasen	d	06 13			08 34				10 40			12 54		
Barnetby	a	06 30			08 51				10 56			13 11		
Habrough	a	06 41			09 01				11 06			13 21		
Grimsby Town	a	06 56			09 15				11 21			13 36		
Cleethorpes	a													

For general notes see front of timetable
For details of catering facilities see Directory of Train Operators

A To Peterborough (Table 18)
B From Worksop (Table 55)
C From Leicester (Table 53)
D From Leicester (Table 53) to Sleaford (Table 18)
E From St Pancras International (Table 53)

From Monday 28 September a revised service will be in operation due to seasonal difficulties. Some trains will be retimed between 1 and 3 minutes. Passengers should check with National Rail Enquiries for precise times.

From Saturday 3 October a revised service will be in operation due to seasonal difficulties. Some trains will be retimed between 1 and 3 minutes. Passengers should check with National Rail Enquiries for precise times.

Saturdays

Nottingham → Newark → Lincoln → Cleethorpes

Network Diagram - see first page of Table 18

		EM	EM	EM	EM	EM	EM	EM	EM	EM	EM	EM	EM	EM	EM
												1 ◇			
		A		A	B	A	A		A		A	C		A	A
												🍽			
Nottingham 8	🚌 d	13 17		14 29		15 27	16 14		17 17		18 15	19 29		20 29	21 25
Carlton	d	13 23				15 33	16 20		17 23		18 21				
Burton Joyce	d	13 27					16 24		17 27		18 25				21 33
Lowdham	d	13 32		14 40		15 40	16 29		17 32		18 30	19 40		20 40	21 37
Thurgarton	d	13 36					16 33		17 36		18 34				
Bleasby	d	13 39					16 36		17 39		18 37				21 42
Fiskerton	d	13 42					16 39		17 42		18 40				21 46
Rolleston	d	13 44					16 42		17 45		18 43				
Newark Castle	d	13 51		14 55		15 53	16 48		17 53		18 50	19 59		20 57	21 57
Newark North Gate 7	a														22 06
London Kings Cross 15	⊖ d		*13 10*		*13 30*					*16 30*			*18 40*		*20 30*
Newark North Gate 7	d		14 36		15 36					18 05			20 30		22 09
Collingham	d	14 00	14 44		15 45	16 03	16 58		18 02	18 14	18 59	20 08	20 39	21 05	22 18
Swinderby	d	14 05				16 07			18 07		19 04				22 22
Hykeham	d	14 11				16 13			18 13		19 10				22 28
Lincoln	a	14 23	15 00	15 22	16 03	16 25	17 14		18 26	18 33	19 22	20 26	20 56	21 24	22 40
	d		15 01					17 21		18 33			20 58		
Market Rasen	d		15 17					17 37		18 49			21a15		
Barnetby	a		15 33					17 53		19 05					
Habrough	a		15 42					18 02		19 14					
Grimsby Town	a		15 57					18 17		19 29					
Cleethorpes	a														

Sundays

until 6 September

		EM	EM	EM	EM	EM	EM	EM	EM	EM	EM	EM	EM	EM
Nottingham 8	🚌 d			15 29		16 35		17 30	18 37		19 37	20 37		22 26
Carlton	d							17 36						22 32
Burton Joyce	d							17 39						22 35
Lowdham	d			15 39		16 45		17 43	18 47		19 47	20 47		22 40
Thurgarton	d							17 47						22 44
Bleasby	d							17 50						22 47
Fiskerton	d							17 54						22 50
Rolleston	d							17 56						22 52
Newark Castle	d			15 55		17 00		18 05	19 02		20 02	21 02		23 01
Newark North Gate 7	a								19 12					23 11
London Kings Cross 15	⊖ d	*10 00*	*12 00*		*15 10*		*15 30*		*17 30*	*18 10*			*20 30*	*21 30*
Newark North Gate 7	d	11 35	13 35		16 37		17 56		19 17	19 55			22 00	23 15
Collingham	d	11 43	13 43	16 04	16 45	17 09		18 14	19 25		20 11	21 11	22 09	23 23
Swinderby	d				16 50	17 14		18 19	19 30		20 16	21 16		23 28
Hykeham	d				16 56	17 20		18 25	19 36		20 22	21 22		23 34
Lincoln	a	12 00	14 02	16 21	17 08	17 32	18 20	18 38	19 48	20 21	20 34	21 34	22 27	23 46
	d	12 02		16 23			18 22							
Market Rasen	d	12 18		16 39			18 38							
Barnetby	a	12 33		16 54			18 53							
Habrough	a	12 41		17 02			19 01							
Grimsby Town	a	12 53		17 14			19 13							
Cleethorpes	a	13 16		17 23			19 24							

Sundays

from 13 September

		EM	EM	EM	EM	EM	EM	EM	EM
Nottingham 8	🚌 d			16 35	17 30	18 37	19 37	20 37	22 26
Carlton	d				17 36				22 32
Burton Joyce	d				17 39				22 35
Lowdham	d			16 45	17 43	18 47	19 47	20 47	22 40
Thurgarton	d				17 47				22 44
Bleasby	d				17 50				22 47
Fiskerton	d				17 54				22 50
Rolleston	d				17 56				22 52
Newark Castle	d			17 00	18 05	19 02	20 02	21 02	23 01
Newark North Gate 7	a					19 12			23 11
London Kings Cross 15	⊖ d	*10 00*	*12 00*			*17 30*			*21 30*
Newark North Gate 7	d	11 35	13 35			19 17			23 15
Collingham	d	11 43	13 43	17 09	18 14	19 25	20 11	21 11	23 23
Swinderby	d			17 14	18 19	19 30	20 16	21 16	23 28
Hykeham	d			17 20	18 25	19 36	20 22	21 22	23 34
Lincoln	a	12 02	14 02	17 32	18 38	19 48	20 34	21 34	23 46
	d								
Market Rasen	d								
Barnetby	a								
Habrough	a								
Grimsby Town	a								
Cleethorpes	a								

For general notes see front of timetable
For details of catering facilities see Directory of Train Operators

A From Leicester (Table 53)
B To Peterborough (Table 18)
C From St Pancras International (Table 53)

From Saturday 3 October a revised service will be in operation due to seasonal difficulties. Some trains will be retimed between 1 and 3 minutes. Passengers should check with National Rail Enquiries for precise times.

Hull and Cleethorpes → Doncaster → Meadowhall, Sheffield, Manchester and Manchester Airport
Cleethorpes → Barton-on-Humber

Network Diagram - see first page of Table 18

Miles	Miles	Miles	Miles	Miles			TP	EM	NT	NT	NT	NT	TP	NT	EM	NT	NT	TP	XC	NT	XC	NT	NT	HT
																	BHX							BHX
							1 ◇	1 ◇					1 ◇					1 ◇	1 ◇		1 ◇			1 ◇
								A		B					C			D	E	G	H		B	
								⊠					⚲				🚌	⚲	⚲		⚲			⊠
0	0	—	—	—	**Hull**	d					05 20							06 00				06 07		06 25
4¾	4¾	—	—	—	Hessle	d																06 14		
7½	7½	—	—	—	Ferriby	d																06 19		
10½	10½	—	—	—	Brough	d					05 32							06 12				06 24		06 37
14½	14½	—	—	—	Broomfleet	d																		
17	17	—	—	—	Gilberdyke	d												06 19				06 32		
—	19¾	—	—	—	Eastrington	d																		
—	22¼	—	—	—	Howden	d												06 26						06 49
—	25	—	—	—	Wressle	d																		
—	31	—	—	—	**Selby**	a												06 35						06 59
—	—	—	—	—		d						06 18						06 35						07 00
—	—	—	—	—	York 8	33 a												*07 20*						
20¾	—	—	—	—	Saltmarshe	d																06 38		
23¾	—	—	—	—	Goole	d					05 47											06 43		
31	—	—	—	—	Thorne North	d					05 56											06 51		
—	—	0	0	—	**Cleethorpes**	d							05 18		05 49	06 00								
—	—	1½	1½	—	New Clee	d																		
—	—	2¼	2¼	—	Grimsby Docks	d																		
—	—	3¼	3¼	—	**Grimsby Town**	a							05 25		05 55	06 08								
—	—	—	—	—		d							05 26		05 56	06 08								
—	—	5¼	5¼	—	Great Coates	d																		
—	—	6¼	6¼	—	Healing	d										06 15								
—	—	7½	7½	—	Stallingborough	d										06 18								
—	—	11¼	11¼	—	Habrough	d							05 36		06 06	06 24								
—	—	—	13	—	Ulceby	d										06 28								
—	—	—	15¾	—	Thornton Abbey	d																		
—	—	—	17¼	—	Goxhill	d										06 35								
—	—	—	19¼	—	New Holland	d										06 40								
—	—	—	20¾	—	Barrow Haven	d										06 43								
—	—	—	22¾	—	**Barton-on-Humber**	a										06 48								
—	—	—	—	—	Barton-on-Humber	🚌 d											06 53							
—	—	—	—	—	Hull Paragon Interchange	🚌 a											07 18							
—	—	17¾	—	—	Barnetby	d							05 45		06a15									
—	—	29	—	—	**Scunthorpe**	a							06 00											
—	—	—	—	—		d							06 00											
—	—	32¼	—	—	Althorpe	d							06 05											
—	—	36¼	—	—	Crowle	d							06 11											
—	—	42¼	—	—	Thorne South	d							06 20											
34¼	—	45¼	—	—	Hatfield & Stainforth	d					06 03		06 25									06 57		
37	—	48	—	—	Kirk Sandall	d					06 10											07 02		
—	—	—	—	0	Adwick	31 d																		
—	—	—	—	2¼	Bentley (S.Yorks)	31 d																		
41	49¼	52	—	4	**Doncaster 7**	31 a					06 16	06 38	06 38									07 12		07 16
—	—	—	—	—	London Kings Cross 15	⊖ 26 a					*08 13*		*08 43*											09b17
—	—	—	—	—	York 8	26 d							*06 00*							*06 30*	06 32			
—	—	—	—	—	**Doncaster 7**	d	05 40	05 57	06 00		06 25		06 40						06 45	07 02				
45¾	—	—	—	—	Conisbrough	d			06 07		06 32									07 09				
48	—	—	—	—	Mexborough	d			06 11		06 36									07 13				
49¼	—	—	—	—	Swinton (S.Yorks)	d			06 14	06 22	06 39									07 16			07 29	
53¾	—	—	—	—	Rotherham Central	d			06 22	06 31	06 46			←						07 27			07 41	
56½	—	—	—	—	**Meadowhall**	🚋 d	05 58		06 27	06 37	06 52		06 58	06 52						07 33			07 47	
60	—	—	—	—	**Sheffield 7**	🚋 a	06 08	06 18	06 38	06 47	→		07 06	07 07					07 11	07 40	07 50		07 57	
—	—	—	—	—		d	06 11						07 09											
96¾	—	—	—	—	Stockport	78 a	06 53						07 53					08c22	*08 24*					
102¾	—	—	—	—	**Manchester Piccadilly 10**	78 🚋 a	07 02						08 02					08 05	*08 36*					
112½	—	—	—	—	**Manchester Airport**	85 ✈ a	07 26						08 29					*08 42*						

For general notes see front of timetable
For details of catering facilities see Directory of Train Operators

A From Leeds (Table 31) to St Pancras International (Table 53)
B From Leeds (Table 31)
C To Newark North Gate (Table 27)
D To Liverpool Lime Street (Table 39)
E From Leeds to Reading (Table 51)
G To Worksop (Table 30)
H To Plymouth (Table 51)
b By changing at Doncaster, passengers may arrive at 0907
c Change at Manchester Piccadilly

Hull and Cleethorpes → Doncaster → Meadowhall, Sheffield, Manchester and Manchester Airport
Cleethorpes → Barton-on-Humber

Network Diagram - see first page of Table 18

	TP	TP	EM	NT	NT	NT	NT	XC	NT	XC	GR	NT	NT	NT	TP	NT	TP	NT	XC	NT	NT	NT	XC
							BHX				R												
	1 ◇	1 ◇						1 ◇		1 ◇	1				1 ◇		1 ◇		1 ◇				1 ◇
			A					B		C	D		E	G		H		J	B	K	J	K	L
							bus																
	catering	catering						catering		catering	catering				catering		catering		catering				catering
Hull d	06 35				06 40						07 00			07 07	07 33			07 36			08 04		
Hessle d					06 47													07 43					
Ferriby d					06 52													07 48					
Brough d	06 47				06 57						07 12			07 19	07 45			07 53			08 16		
Broomfleet d																		07 58					
Gilberdyke d					07 04									07 26				08 03					
Eastrington d														07 31									
Howden d														07 35	07 56								
Wressle d														07 40									
Selby a	07 07										07 32			07 48	08 06								
d	07 07										07 32			07 48	08 07								
York 8 33 a														08 21									
Saltmarshe d					07 10													08 08					
Goole d					07 15													08 13			08 30		
Thorne North d					07 24													08 22					
Cleethorpes d		06 18				07 00											07 18						
New Clee d																							
Grimsby Docks d						07 05																	
Grimsby Town a		06 25				07 07											07 25						
d		06 26	07 03			07 08											07 26						
Great Coates d						07 12																	
Healing d						07 15																	
Stallingborough d						07 18																	
Habrough d		06 36	07 13			07 24											07 36						
Ulceby d						07 28																	
Thornton Abbey d						07 32																	
Goxhill d						07 35																	
New Holland d						07 40																	
Barrow Haven d						07 43																	
Barton-on-Humber a						07 48																	
Barton-on-Humber (bus) d							07 53																
Hull Paragon Interchange (bus) a							08 18																
Barnetby d		06 45	07a22														07 45						
Scunthorpe a		07 00															08 00						
d		07 00											07 34				08 00			08 10			
Althorpe d													07 39							08 15			
Crowle d													07 45							08 21			
Thorne South d													07 53							08 30			
Hatfield & Stainforth d					07 30								07 59					08 28		08 35			
Kirk Sandall d					07 34								08 03					08 33		08 39			
Adwick 31 d		06 53		07 29								07 54					08 11		08b35				
Bentley (S.Yorks) 31 d		06 57		07 33								07 57					08 15		08b39				
Doncaster 7 31 a		07 33		07 37	07 45						07 53	08 01	08 14				08 30	08 43		08 52	08 55		
London Kings Cross 15 ⊖ 26 a											09 45						10 25						
York 8 26 d								07 27		07 44									08 27			←	08 44
Doncaster 7 d		07 35		07 39	07 46			07 52				08 16					08 41		08 51	09 01	08 56	09 01	
Conisbrough d				07 46	07 53							08 23								→		09 08	
Mexborough d				07 50	07 57				←			08 27										09 12	
Swinton (S.Yorks) d				07 53	08 00				08 00			08 30				08 34						09 15	
Rotherham Central d				08 00	→				08 12			08 42				08 47						09 27	
Meadowhall (tram) d		07 53		08 06					08 22			08 49				08 55	09 01				09 15	09 33	
Sheffield 7 (tram) a		08 00		08 18				08 20	08 32	08 51		08 58				09 05	09 08		09 20		09 26	09 41	09 51
d		08 05															09 11						
Stockport 78 a	08c57	08 53							09 25						09c57		09 53				10 25		
Manchester Piccadilly 10 78 (tram) a	08 36	09 02							09 36						09 36		10 02				10 36		
Manchester Airport 85 (air) a	09 07	09 33													10 07		10 26						

For general notes see front of timetable
For details of catering facilities see Directory of Train Operators

A To Newark North Gate (Table 27)
B From Newcastle to Reading (Table 51)
C From Newcastle to Plymouth (Table 51)
D **The Hull Executive**
E To Adwick (Table 31)
G From Beverley (Table 43)
H From Leeds (Table 31)
J From Bridlington (Table 43)
K To Lincoln (Table 30)
L From Edinburgh to Plymouth (Table 51)
b Change at Doncaster
c Change at Manchester Piccadilly

until 19 June and from 7 September

Hull and Cleethorpes → Doncaster → Meadowhall, Sheffield, Manchester and Manchester Airport
Cleethorpes → Barton-on-Humber

Network Diagram - see first page of Table 18

		HT	NT	NT	NT	TP	TP	NT	NT	NT	XC	NT	EM	XC	NT	NT	NT	NT	TP	TP	NT	XC	NT	XC
										BHX														
		[1]◇				[1]◇	[1]◇				[1]◇			[1]◇					[1]◇	[1]◇		[1]◇		[1]◇
			A		B			C		🚌	D	E	G	H		A		J			C	K	E	L
		⊠				⊼	⊼				⊼			⊼					⊼	⊼		⊼		⊼
Hull	d	08 12			08 29	08 40		08 56							09 02			09 25	09 40		09 56			
Hessle	d				08 36													09 32						
Ferriby	d				08 41													09 37						
Brough	d	08 24			08 46	08 52		09 08							09 14			09 42	09 52		10 08			
Broomfleet	d																							
Gilberdyke	d				08 53										09 21			09 49						
Eastrington	d																							
Howden	d	08 36													09 28									
Wressle	d																							
Selby	a	08 45				09 10									09 38				10 10					
	d	08 45				09 11									09 38				10 11					
York [8]	33 a					*09 46*									10 07									
Saltmarshe	d																							
Goole	d				09 02			09 22										09 58			10 22			
Thorne North	d				09 10													10 06						
Cleethorpes	d						08 28		09 00											09 28				
New Clee	d								09x03															
Grimsby Docks	d								09 05															
Grimsby Town	a						08 35		09 08											09 35				
	d						08 36		09 08				09 28							09 36				
Great Coates	d								09 12															
Healing	d								09 15															
Stallingborough	d								09 18															
Habrough	d						08 46		09 24				09 38											
Ulceby	d								09 28															
Thornton Abbey	d								09 32															
Goxhill	d								09 35															
New Holland	d								09 40															
Barrow Haven	d								09 43															
Barton-on-Humber	a								09 48															
Barton-on-Humber	🚌 d									09 53														
Hull Paragon Interchange	🚌 a									10 18														
Barnetby	d						08 55						09a47							09 55				
Scunthorpe	a						09 10													10 10				
	d						09 10					09 17								10 10			10 18	
Althorpe	d											09 22											10 23	
Crowle	d											09 29											10 29	
Thorne South	d											09 37											10 38	
Hatfield & Stainforth	d				09 17							09 42						10 12					10 43	
Kirk Sandall	d				09 21							09 47						10 17					10 47	
Adwick	31 d			09 13													10 13							
Bentley (S.Yorks)	31 d			09 17													10 17							
Doncaster [7]	31 a	09 02		09 22	09 31		09 40	09 46				09 57					10 22	10 27		10 40	10 46		10 58	
London Kings Cross [15]	⊖ 26 a	10 51		*11 34*								*11 51*					*12 17*	*12 25*			*12 42*			
York [8]	26 d			*08 52*							09 27			09 44			*09 35*			*10 06*		10 34	*10 29*	10 44
Doncaster [7]	d			09 24			09 42	09 48			09 56	10 02					10 24			10 42	10 48	10 58	11 02	
Conisbrough	d			09 31								10 09					10 31						11 09	
Mexborough	d			09 35								10 13					10 35						11 13	
Swinton (S.Yorks)	d		09 35	09 42								10 16				10 34	10 41						11 16	
Rotherham Central	d		09 44	09 50								10 27				10 44	10 49						11 27	
Meadowhall	⇌ d		09 50	09 55			10 01	10 07				10 33				10 50	10 57			11 01	11 06		11 33	
Sheffield [7]	⇌ a		10 00	10 05			10 08	10 20			10 20	10 41		10 51		11 00	11 05			11 08	11 20	11 20	11 41	11 51
	d						10 11													11 11				
Stockport	78 a					*10b57*	10 53				*11 25*								*11b57*	11 53		*12 25*		
Manchester Piccadilly [10]	78 ⇌ a					10 36	11 02				*11 36*								11 36	12 02		*12 36*		
Manchester Airport	85 ⇄ a					*11 07*	11 26												*12 07*	12 26				

For general notes see front of timetable
For details of catering facilities see Directory of Train Operators

A From Leeds (Table 31)
B From Scarborough (Table 43)
C From Bridlington (Table 43)
D From Edinburgh to Reading (Table 51)
E To Lincoln (Table 30)
G To Newark North Gate (Table 27)
H From Glasgow Central to Plymouth (Table 51)
J From Beverley (Table 43)
K From Newcastle to Reading (Table 51)
L From Dundee to Plymouth (Table 51)
b Change at Manchester Piccadilly

Table 29

Mondays to Fridays

until 19 June and from 7 September

Hull and Cleethorpes → Doncaster → Meadowhall, Sheffield, Manchester and Manchester Airport
Cleethorpes → Barton-on-Humber

Network Diagram - see first page of Table 18

		HT	NT	NT	TP	NT	TP	NT	NT BHX	EM	NT		XC	NT	NT	XC	NT	NT	NT	NT	TP	TP	NT	XC
		1◇			1◇		1◇						1◇			1◇					1◇	1◇		1◇
				A						B	C		D	E	G	H		A					C	D
		☒			ꝏ		ꝏ		🚌				ꝏ			ꝏ					ꝏ	ꝏ		ꝏ
Hull	d	10 12	10 22		10 38						10 57						11 05			11 22	11 38		11 55	
Hessle	d		10 29																	11 29				
Ferriby	d		10 34																	11 34				
Brough	d	10 24	10 39		10 50						11 09						11 18			11 39	11 50		12 07	
Broomfleet	d																							
Gilberdyke	d		10 46																	11 46				
Eastrington	d																							
Howden	d	10 36																						
Wressle	d																							
Selby	a	10 46			11 08												11 38				12 08			
	d	10 47			11 09												11 39				12 09			
York 8 33	a	*11 20*															12 10				*13 15*			
Saltmarshe	d																			11 52				
Goole	d		10 55								11 23									11 58			12 22	
Thorne North	d		11 03																	12 06				
Cleethorpes	d						10 28	11 00														11 28		
New Clee	d							11x03																
Grimsby Docks	d							11 05																
Grimsby Town	a						10 35	11 08														11 35		
	d						10 36	11 08		11 28												11 36		
Great Coates	d							11 12																
Healing	d							11 15																
Stallingborough	d							11 18																
Habrough	d						10 46	11 24		11 38														
Ulceby	d							11 28																
Thornton Abbey	d							11 32																
Goxhill	d							11 35																
New Holland	d							11 40																
Barrow Haven	d							11 43																
Barton-on-Humber	a							11 48																
Barton-on-Humber 🚌	d								11 53															
Hull Paragon Interchange 🚌	a								12 18															
Barnetby	d						10 55			11a47												11 55		
Scunthorpe	a						11 10															12 10		
	d						11 10								11 17							12 10		
Althorpe	d														11 22									
Crowle	d														11 28									
Thorne South	d														11 37									
Hatfield & Stainforth	d		11 09												11 42					12 12				
Kirk Sandall	d		11 14												11 46					12 17				
Adwick 31	d					11 16													12 12					
Bentley (S.Yorks) 31	d					11 20													12 16					
Doncaster 7 31	a	11 04	11 24			11 25	11 40				11 46				11 58				12 23	12 27		12 40	12 46	
London Kings Cross 15 ⊖ 26	a	12 44				*13 22*					*13 43*				*14 02*					*14 20*			*14 44*	
York 8 26	d												11 27	11 02		11 44			*11 35*					12 27
Doncaster 7	d					11 27	11 42				11 48		11 54		11 58				12 24			12 42	12 48	12 55
Conisbrough	d					11 34									12 06				12 31					
Mexborough	d					11 38									12 10				12 35					
Swinton (S.Yorks)	d			11 34		11 41								12 02	12 16			12 34	12 42					
Rotherham Central	d			11 45		11 50								12 11	12 27			12 45	12 50					
Meadowhall 🚊	d			11 50		11 55	12 01				12 06			12 16	12 33			12 50	12 55			13 01	13 06	
Sheffield 7 🚊	a			12 00		12 05	12 08				12 20		12 20	12 26	12 41	12 51		13 00	13 05			13 08	13 20	13 20
	d						12 11															13 11		
Stockport 78	a				*12b57*		12 53							*13 25*							*13b57*	13 53		*14 25*
Manchester Piccadilly 10 78 🚊	a				12 36		13 02							*13 36*							13 36	14 02		*14 36*
Manchester Airport 85 ✈	a				*13 07*		13 26														*14 07*	14 26		

For general notes see front of timetable
For details of catering facilities see Directory of Train Operators

A From Leeds (Table 31)
B To Newark North Gate (Table 27)
C From Bridlington (Table 43)
D From Newcastle to Reading (Table 51)
E Via Pontefract Baghill (Table 33)
G To Lincoln (Table 30)
H From Dundee (Table 229) to Plymouth (Table 51)
b Change at Manchester Piccadilly

Table 29

Mondays to Fridays

until 19 June and from 7 September

Hull and Cleethorpes → Doncaster → Meadowhall, Sheffield, Manchester and Manchester Airport
Cleethorpes → Barton-on-Humber

Network Diagram - see first page of Table 18

		NT	XC	NT	NT	NT	TP	HT	TP	NT	NT	NT BHX	XC	NT	XC	NT	NT	NT	NT	TP	TP	EM	NT	XC
			1◇				1◇	1◇	1◇				1◇		1◇					1◇	1◇			1◇
		A	B	C						D			E	A	G		C					H	J	E
												🚌												
			🍴				🍴	☒	🍴				🍴		🍴					🍴	🍴			🍴
Hull	d					12 22	12 38	12 45		12 57						13 12			13 25	13 38			13 57	
Hessle	d					12 29													13 32					
Ferriby	d					12 34													13 37					
Brough	d					12 39	12 50	12 57		13 09						13 24			13 42	13 50			14 09	
Broomfleet	d					12 44																		
Gilberdyke	d					12 49										13 31			13 49					
Eastrington	d															13 36								
Howden	d							13 09								13 41								
Wressle	d															13 46								
Selby	a						13 08	13 19								13 54				14 08				
	d						13 09	13 20								13 54				14 09				
York 8	33 a															14 25								
Saltmarshe	d																							
Goole	d					12 58				13 23									13 58				14 23	
Thorne North	d					13 06													14 06					
Cleethorpes	d								12 28		13 00										13 28			
New Clee	d										13x03													
Grimsby Docks	d										13 05													
Grimsby Town	a								12 35		13 08										13 35			
	d								12 36		13 08										13 36	13 52		
Great Coates	d										13 12													
Healing	d										13 15													
Stallingborough	d										13 18													
Habrough	d										13 24											14 02		
Ulceby	d										13 28													
Thornton Abbey	d										13 32													
Goxhill	d										13 35													
New Holland	d										13 40													
Barrow Haven	d										13 43													
Barton-on-Humber	a										13 48													
Barton-on-Humber	🚌 d											13 53												
Hull Paragon Interchange	🚌 a											14 18												
Barnetby	d								12 55												13 55	14a11		
Scunthorpe	a								13 10												14 10			
	d	12 17							13 10					13 18							14 10			
Althorpe	d	12 22												13 23										
Crowle	d	12 28												13 29										
Thorne South	d	12 37												13 38										
Hatfield & Stainforth	d	12 42				13 14								13 43					14 14					
Kirk Sandall	d	12 46				13 19								13 47					14 18					
Adwick	31 d				13 12													14 14						
Bentley (S.Yorks)	31 d				13 16													14 18						
Doncaster 7	31 a	12 59			13 23	13 29		13 37	13 40	13 46				13 58				14 22	14 29		14 40		14 46	
London Kings Cross 15	⊖ 26 a	15 05						15 20		15 44				15 58							16 46			
York 8	26 d		12 44		12 32								13 26		13 44			13 36						14 32
Doncaster 7	d	12 59			13 23				13 42	13 48			13 55	14 01				14 24			14 42		14 48	14 57
Conisbrough	d	13 09			13 31									14 09				14 31						
Mexborough	d	13 13			13 35									14 13				14 35						
Swinton (S.Yorks)	d	13 16		13 34	13 41									14 16			14 34	14 41						
Rotherham Central	d	13 27		13 45	13 50									14 27			14 45	14 50						
Meadowhall	d	13 33		13 50	13 55				14 01	14 06				14 33			14 50	14 55			15 01		15 06	
Sheffield 7	a	13 41	13 51	14 00	14 05				14 08	14 20			14 20	14 41	14 51		15 00	15 05			15 08		15 19	15 20
	d								14 11												15 11			
Stockport	78 a						14b57		14 53				15 25							15b57	15 53			16 25
Manchester Piccadilly 10	78 a				15 32		14 36		15 02				15 36							15 36	16 02			16 36
Manchester Airport	85 a						15 07		15 26											16 07	16 26			

For general notes see front of timetable
For details of catering facilities see Directory of Train Operators

- **A** To Lincoln (Table 30)
- **B** From Glasgow Central (Table 51) to Penzance (Table 135)
- **C** From Leeds (Table 31)
- **D** From Scarborough (Table 43)
- **E** From Newcastle to Reading (Table 51)
- **G** From Aberdeen (Table 229) to Penzance (Table 135)
- **H** To Newark North Gate (Table 27)
- **J** From Bridlington (Table 43)
- **b** Change at Manchester Piccadilly

Hull and Cleethorpes → Doncaster → Meadowhall, Sheffield, Manchester and Manchester Airport
Cleethorpes → Barton-on-Humber

Network Diagram - see first page of Table 18

		NT	XC	NT	NT	NT	TP	TP	NT	NT	NT	XC	NT	NT	XC	NT	HT	NT	NT	NT	TP	TP	NT	EM
											BHX													
			1 ◇				1 ◇	1 ◇				1 ◇			1 ◇		1 ◇				1 ◇	1 ◇		
		A	B	C					D			E	G	A	H			C	J				K	L
											🚌													
			⚲				⚲	⚲				⚲			⚲		☒				⚲	⚲		
Hull	d					14 25	14 38		14 57							15 06	15 18			15 25	15 40		15 57	
Hessle	d					14 32														15 32				
Ferriby	d					14 37														15 37				
Brough	d					14 42	14 50		15 09							15 18	15 30			15 42	15 52		16 09	
Broomfleet	d																							
Gilberdyke	d					14 49														15 49				
Eastrington	d																							
Howden	d																15 42							
Wressle	d																							
Selby	a						15 08									15 37	15 56				16 10			
	d						15 09									15 38	15 57				16 11			
York 8	33 a															16 06								
Saltmarshe	d																							
Goole	d					14 58			15 23											15 58			16 23	
Thorne North	d					15 06														16 06				
Cleethorpes	d							14 28		15 00												15 28		
New Clee	d									15x03														
Grimsby Docks	d									15 05														
Grimsby Town	a							14 35		15 08												15 35		
	d							14 36		15 09												15 36		16 03
Great Coates	d									15 13														
Healing	d									15 16														
Stallingborough	d									15 19														
Habrough	d							14 46		15 25														16 12
Ulceby	d									15 28														
Thornton Abbey	d									15 33														
Goxhill	d									15 36														
New Holland	d									15 40														
Barrow Haven	d									15 43														
Barton-on-Humber	a									15 49														
Barton-on-Humber	🚌 d										15 56													
Hull Paragon Interchange	🚌 a										16 21													
Barnetby	d							14 55														15 55		16a21
Scunthorpe	a							15 10														16 10		
	d	14 18						15 10						15 17								16 10		
Althorpe	d	14 23												15 22										
Crowle	d	14 29												15 28										
Thorne South	d	14 38												15 37										
Hatfield & Stainforth	d	14 43				15 12								15 42						16 12				
Kirk Sandall	d	14 47				15 17								15 46						16 17				
Adwick	31 d				15 13														16 13					
Bentley (S.Yorks)	31 d				15 17														16 17					
Doncaster 7	31 a	14 58			15 22	15 27		15 40	15 46					15 58			16 15		16 23	16 27		16 40	16 46	
London Kings Cross 15	⊖ 26 a	*17 04*				*17 30*			*17 41*								18 12			*18 24*				
York 8	26 d		14 44					*15 11*				15 29	15 02		15 44				*15 35*					
Doncaster 7	d	15 02			15 24			15 42	15 48			15 55		16 02					16 24			16 42	16 47	
Conisbrough	d	15 10			15 31									16 09					16 31					
Mexborough	d	15 14			15 35									16 13					16 35					
Swinton (S.Yorks)	d	15 17		15 34	15 41								16 01	16 16				16 34	16 41					
Rotherham Central	d	15 27		15 43	15 50								16 10	16 27				16 43	16 50					
Meadowhall	🚋 d	15 33		15 50	15 55			16 01	16 07				16 18	16 33				16 50	16 55			17 01	17 06	
Sheffield 7	🚋 a	15 41	15 51	16 00	16 05			16 08	16 20			16 20	16 25	16 41	16 51			17 00	17 05			17 08	⟶	
	d							16 10														17 11		
Stockport	78 a						16b57	16 52					*17 25*								17b57	17 53		
Manchester Piccadilly 10	78 🚋 a				*17 29*		16 36	17 02					*17 37*						*18 31*		17 37	18 02		
Manchester Airport	85 ✈ a						*17 07*	17 32													*18 12*	18 26		

For general notes see front of timetable
For details of catering facilities see Directory of Train Operators

A To Lincoln (Table 30)
B From Edinburgh (Table 51) to Penzance (Table 135)
C From Leeds (Table 31)
D From Scarborough (Table 43)
E From Newcastle to Reading (Table 51)
G Via Pontefract Baghill (Table 33)
H From Edinburgh to Plymouth (Table 51)
J To Retford (Table 30)
K From Bridlington (Table 43)
L To Newark North Gate (Table 27)
b Change at Manchester Piccadilly

Table 29

Mondays to Fridays

until 19 June and from 7 September

Hull and Cleethorpes → Doncaster → Meadowhall, Sheffield, Manchester and Manchester Airport
Cleethorpes → Barton-on-Humber

Network Diagram - see first page of Table 18

		XC	NT	NT	XC	NT	NT	NT	NT	TP	TP	NT	NT	NT BHX	XC	NT	TP	XC	HT	NT	NT	TP	EM	NT
		1 ◇			1 ◇					1 ◇	1 ◇				1 ◇		1 ◇	1 ◇	1 ◇			1 ◇		
		A	B	C	D		E		G			H			A		J	D		E			K	H
														🚌										
		🍴			🍴					🍴	🍴				🍴			🍴	☒			🍴		
Hull	d					16 10			16 27	16 40		16 54					17 01		17 06					17 18
Hessle	d								16 34															17 25
Ferriby	d								16 39															17 30
Brough	d					16 22			16 44	16 52		17 06					17 13		17 19					17 35
Broomfleet	d								16 49															17 40
Gilberdyke	d					16 29			16 54			17 13												17 45
Eastrington	d																							17 49
Howden	d					16 36													17 32					17 54
Wressle	d																							17 59
Selby	a					16 46				17 10							17 31		17 42					18 06
	d					16 47				17 11									17 43					18 07
York 8 33	a					17 13																		18 36
Saltmarshe	d								16 59															
Goole	d								17 04			17 22												
Thorne North	d								17 13															
Cleethorpes	d										16 28		17 00									17 28		
New Clee	d																							
Grimsby Docks	d												17 05											
Grimsby Town	a										16 35		17 07									17 35		
	d										16 36		17 08									17 36	18 28	
Great Coates	d												17 12											
Healing	d												17 15											
Stallingborough	d												17 18											
Habrough	d												17 24									17 46	18 38	
Ulceby	d												17 28											
Thornton Abbey	d												17 32											
Goxhill	d												17 35											
New Holland	d												17 40											
Barrow Haven	d												17 43											
Barton-on-Humber	a												17 48											
Barton-on-Humber 🚌	d													17 57										
Hull Paragon Interchange 🚌	a													18 23										
Barnetby	d										16 55											17 55	18a46	
Scunthorpe	a										17 10											18 10		
	d			16 18							17 10					17 18						18 10		
Althorpe	d			16 23												17 23								
Crowle	d			16 29												17 29								
Thorne South	d			16 38												17 38								
Hatfield & Stainforth	d			16 43					17 19							17 43								
Kirk Sandall	d			16 47					17 23							17 47								
Adwick 31	d							*16 53*			*17 09*										*17 53*	*18 14*		
Bentley (S.Yorks) 31	d							*16 57*			*17 14*										*17 57*	*18 18*		
Doncaster 7 31	a			16 58					17 34		17 40	17 47				17 58			18 01			18 40		
London Kings Cross 15 ⊖ 26	a			*18 54*												*19 59*			*19 49*					
York 8 26	d	16 25			16 44						*16 56*				17 34			17 44				*17 55*		
Doncaster 7	d	16 53		17 01				17 24			17 42	17 48			17 58	18 02					18 26	18 42		
Conisbrough	d			17 09				17 31								18 09					18 33			
Mexborough	d			17 13				17 35								18 13					18 37			
Swinton (S.Yorks)	d			17 16			17 34	17 42								18 16				18 34	18 42			
Rotherham Central	d		⟵	17 27			17 44	17 50								18 27				18 45	18 49			
Meadowhall 🚋	d		17 06	17 33			17 50	17 57			18 01	18 06				18 33				18 49	18 57	19 01		
Sheffield 7 🚋	a	17 18	17 19	17 41	17 51		18 00	18 04			18 08	18 19			18 20	18 43		18 51		19 00	19 06	19 08		
	d										18 10											19 11		
Stockport 78	a		*18 25*							*18b57*	18 53				*19 25*							19 53		
Manchester Piccadilly 10 78 🚋	a		*18 36*							18 37	19 02				*19 36*						*20 32*	20 02		
Manchester Airport 85 ✈	a		*19c08*							*19 13*	19 28				*20c07*							20 35		

For general notes see front of timetable
For details of catering facilities see Directory of Train Operators

A From Newcastle to Reading (Table 51)
B From Bridlington (Table 43)
C To Lincoln (Table 30)
D From Edinburgh to Plymouth (Table 51)
E From Leeds (Table 31)
G From Scarborough (Table 43)
H From Beverley (Table 43)
J To Huddersfield (Table 39)
K To Newark North Gate (Table 27)
b Change at Manchester Piccadilly
c Change at Sheffield and Manchester Piccadilly

Table 29

Mondays to Fridays

until 19 June and from 7 September

Hull and Cleethorpes → Doncaster → Meadowhall, Sheffield, Manchester and Manchester Airport
Cleethorpes → Barton-on-Humber

Network Diagram - see first page of Table 18

		NT	NT	XC	NT	NT	TP	XC	NT	NT	NT	TP	NT	NT	NT	NT	XC	TP	NT	XC	NT	NT	HT	NT
																BHX							BHX	
				1 ◇			1 ◇	1 ◇				1 ◇					1 ◇	1 ◇		1 ◇			1 ◇	
		A	B	C	A			D		E						bus	G	H	J	D		E		B
				trolley			trolley	trolley				trolley					trolley			trolley			⊠	
Hull	d	17 42	17 52				17 58		18 22				18 53					18 59			19 10		19 18	19 24
Hessle	d	17 49							18 29															19 31
Ferriby	d	17 54							18 34															19 36
Brough	d	17 59	18 04				18 10		18 39				19 05					19 11			19 22		19 30	19 41
Broomfleet	d																							
Gilberdyke	d	18 06							18 46												19 29			19 48
Eastrington	d																							
Howden	d																				19 36		19 43	
Wressle	d																							
Selby	a		18 25				18 30											19 29			19 46		19 52	
	d		18 26				18 31														19 47		19 53	
York 8	33 a																				20 16			
Saltmarshe	d	18 12			←																			
Goole	d	18 19			18 19				18 55				19 19											19 58
Thorne North	d	→			18 28				19 03															20 06
Cleethorpes	d											18 28			19 00									
New Clee	d																							
Grimsby Docks	d														19 05									
Grimsby Town	a											18 35			19 07									
	d											18 36			19 08									
Great Coates	d														19 12									
Healing	d														19 15									
Stallingborough	d														19 18									
Habrough	d											18 46			19 24									
Ulceby	d														19 28									
Thornton Abbey	d														19 32									
Goxhill	d														19 35									
New Holland	d														19 40									
Barrow Haven	d														19 43									
Barton-on-Humber	a														19 48									
Barton-on-Humber	bus d															19 55								
Hull Paragon Interchange	bus a															20 20								
Barnetby	d											18 55												
Scunthorpe	a											19 10												
	d					18 18						19 10		19 15										
Althorpe	d					18 23								19 20										
Crowle	d					18 29								19 26										
Thorne South	d					18 38								19 34										
Hatfield & Stainforth	d				18 34	18 46			19 12					19 40										20 14
Kirk Sandall	d				18 39	18 50			19 16					19 44										20 19
Adwick	31 d										18 53													
Bentley (S.Yorks)	31 d										18 57													
Doncaster 7	31 a		18 45		18 51	19 03			19 27			19 40	19 46	19 56									20 10	20 29
London Kings Cross 15	⊖ 26 a		20 44			21 03			21 20				21 44										21 58	
York 8	26 d			18 24				18 44			18 31		19 13				19 29			19 44				
Doncaster 7	d		18 47	18 52	18 55						19 28	19 42	19 49				19 57		20 03					
Conisbrough	d				19 02						19 35								20 10					
Mexborough	d				19 06						19 39								20 14					
Swinton (S.Yorks)	d				19 09					19 34	19 43								20 17			20 34		
Rotherham Central	d				19 19					19 45	19 50								20 28			20 43		
Meadowhall	d		19 06		19 25					19 50	19 57	20 01	20 07						20 33			20 51		
Sheffield 7	a		19 17	19 21	19 35			19 51		19 59	20 06	20 08	20 18				20 20		20 41	20 51		21 02		
	d											20 11												
Stockport	78 a				20 25		20b22					20 53					21 20							
Manchester Piccadilly 10	78 a				20 36		19 57					21 02					21 32							
Manchester Airport	85 a				21c07		20 53					21 35					22c10							

For general notes see front of timetable
For details of catering facilities see Directory of Train Operators

A From Beverley (Table 43)
B From Scarborough (Table 43)
C From Newcastle to Guildford (Table 51)
D From Edinburgh to Bristol Temple Meads (Table 51)
E From Leeds (Table 31)
G From Newcastle to Birmingham New Street (Table 51)
H To Leeds (Table 39)
J To Worksop (Table 30)
b Change at Manchester Piccadilly
c Change at Sheffield and Manchester Piccadilly

Hull and Cleethorpes → Doncaster → Meadowhall, Sheffield, Manchester and Manchester Airport
Cleethorpes → Barton-on-Humber

Network Diagram - see first page of Table 18

	TP	TP	XC	NT	NT	XC	NT	NT	TP	NT	NT	NT	NT	EM	NT	NT	TP	NT	NT	NT	NT
												ThFO									
	1◇	1◇	1◇			1◇			1◇								1◇				
		A	B		C	D	E					🚌		G				E			E
Hull d		19 56			20 03								20 56				21 33			22 20	
Hessle d					20 10															22 27	
Ferriby d					20 15															22 32	
Brough d		20 08			20 20								21 08				21 45			22 37	
Broomfleet d																					
Gilberdyke d					20 27												21 52				
Eastrington d																					
Howden d																					
Wressle d																					
Selby a		20 26															22 07				
d																	22 07				
York 8 33 a		*21 00*																			
Saltmarshe d																					
Goole d					20 36								21 22		21 35					22 51	
Thorne North d					20 44										21 44					23 00	
Cleethorpes d	19 28								20 28		21 00			21 15							
New Clee d																					
Grimsby Docks d											21 05										
Grimsby Town a	19 35								20 35		21 07			21 21							
d	19 36								20 36		21 08			21 22							
Great Coates d											21 12										
Healing d											21 15										
Stallingborough d											21 18										
Habrough d	19 46										21 24			21 31							
Ulceby d											21 27										
Thornton Abbey d											21 32										
Goxhill d											21 35										
New Holland d											21 39										
Barrow Haven d											21 42										
Barton-on-Humber a											21 48										
Barton-on-Humber 🚌 d												21 55									
Hull Paragon Interchange 🚌 a												22 20									
Barnetby d	19 55								20 55					21a40							
Scunthorpe a	20 10								21 10												
d	20 10			20 21					21 10							21 31			22 21		
Althorpe d				20 26												21 36			22 26		
Crowle d				20 32												21 42			22 32		
Thorne South d				20 41												21 51			22 41		
Hatfield & Stainforth d				20 46	20 51										21 49	21 56			22 46	23 06	
Kirk Sandall d				20 50	20 56										21 54	22 01			22 50	23 10	
Adwick 31 d	*19 53*							*20 55*												*22 02*	
Bentley (S.Yorks) 31 d	*19 59*							*20 59*												*22 06*	
Doncaster 7 31 a	20 40			21 01	21 05				21 40				21 45		22 06	22 11			23 02	23 21	
London Kings Cross 15 ⊖ 26 a					*23 32*								*00 15*								
York 8 26 d	*20 09*		*20 32*			*20 44*										*21 40*					
Doncaster 7 d	20 42		20 57		21 07			21 30	21 42				21 48			22 13				23 22	
Conisbrough d	20 48				21 14			21 37		←						22 20				23 29	
Mexborough d	20 52				21 18			21 41		21 41						22 24				23 33	
Swinton (S.Yorks) d	20 55				21 21		21 35	→		21 44						22 29		22 34		23 36	23 55
Rotherham Central d	21 01				21 28		21 44			21 55						22 38		22 45		23 45	00 03
Meadowhall 🚋 d	21 07				21 35		21 52		21 58	22 03			22 09			22 44		22 52		23 54	00 08
Sheffield 7 🚋 a	21 17		21 24		21 46	21 51	22 07		22 08	22 11			22 21			22 54		23 02		00 04	00 23
d									22 11												
Stockport 78 a									22 53				*23 47*								
Manchester Piccadilly 10 78 🚋 a									23 02				*00 02*				*23 37*				
Manchester Airport 85 ✈ a									23 26				*01b10*				*00 22*				

For general notes see front of timetable
For details of catering facilities see Directory of Train Operators

A To Leeds (Table 40)
B From Newcastle to Birmingham New Street (Table 51)
C From Bridlington (Table 43)
D From Edinburgh to Birmingham New Street (Table 51)
E From Leeds (Table 31)
G To Lincoln (Table 27)
b Change at Sheffield and Manchester Piccadilly

Table 29

Mondays to Fridays
22 June to 4 September

Hull and Cleethorpes → Doncaster → Meadowhall, Sheffield, Manchester and Manchester Airport
Cleethorpes → Barton-on-Humber

Network Diagram - see first page of Table 18

		TP	EM	NT	NT	NT	TP	TP	TP	NT	NT	TP	XC	NT	XC	NT	NT	NT BHX	NT	HT BHX	TP	TP	TP	EM
		1 ◇	1 ◇						1 ◇			1 ◇	1 ◇		1 ◇					1 ◇	1 ◇			
			A		B							C	D	E	G				B					H
							🚌	🚌								🚌		🚌				🚌	🚌	
			⊠						⊼			⊼	⊼		⊼					⊠	⊼			
Hull	d					05 20						06 00					06 07			06 25	06 35			
Hessle	d																06 14							
Ferriby	d																06 19							
Brough	d					05 32						06 12					06 24			06 37	06 47			
Broomfleet	d																							
Gilberdyke	d											06 19					06 32							
Eastrington	d																							
Howden	d											06 26								06 49				
Wressle	d																							
Selby	a											06 35								06 59	07 07			
	d										06 18	06 35								07 00	07 07			
York 8	33 a											*07 20*												
Saltmarshe	d																06 38							
Goole	d					05 47											06 43							
Thorne North	d					05 56											06 51							
Cleethorpes	d							04 45														04 50	05 40	05 49
New Clee	d																							
Grimsby Docks	d																							
Grimsby Town	a																					05 10		05 55
	d							05u05														05 15	06u00	05 56
Great Coates	d																							
Healing	d																							
Stallingborough	d																							
Habrough	d																					05 40		06 06
Ulceby	d																							
Thornton Abbey	d																							
Goxhill	d																							
New Holland	d																							
Barrow Haven	d																							
Barton-on-Humber	a																							
Barton-on-Humber	🚌 d																	06 53						
Hull Paragon Interchange	🚌 a																	07 18						
Barnetby	d							05u30														05 55		06a15
Scunthorpe	a																					06 20		
	d						05 20									06 00						06 25		
Althorpe	d						05 35									06 10								
Crowle	d						05 45									06 20								
Thorne South	d						06 00									06 35								
Hatfield & Stainforth	d					06 03	06 10									06a50	06 57							
Kirk Sandall	d					06 10											07 02							
Adwick	31 d																							
Bentley (S.Yorks)	31 d																							
Doncaster 7	31 a					06 16	06 25	06 25			06 38						07 12			07 16		07 20	07 20	
London Kings Cross 15	⊖ 26 a					*08 13*					*08 43*						*09 07*			09b17				
York 8	26 d								*06 00*					*06 30*	06 32									
Doncaster 7	d	05 40	05 57	06 00		06 25			06 40				06 45	07 02										
Conisbrough	d			06 07		06 32								07 09										
Mexborough	d			06 11		06 36								07 13										
Swinton (S.Yorks)	d			06 14	06 22	06 39								07 16					07 29					
Rotherham Central	d			06 22	06 31	06 46				⟵				07 27					07 41					
Meadowhall	🚋 d	05 58		06 27	06 37	06 52			06 58	06 52				07 33					07 47					
Sheffield 7	🚋 a	06 08	06 18	06 38	06 47	⟶			07 06	07 07			07 11	07 40	07 50				07 57					
	d	06 11							07 09															
Stockport	78 a	06 53							07 53			08c22	*08 24*								*08c57*			
Manchester Piccadilly 10	78 🚋 a	07 02							08 02			08 05	*08 36*								08 36			
Manchester Airport	85 ✈ a	07 32							08 29			*08 42*									*09 07*			

For general notes see front of timetable
For details of catering facilities see Directory of Train Operators

- **A** From Leeds (Table 31) to St Pancras International (Table 53)
- **B** From Leeds (Table 31)
- **C** To Liverpool Lime Street (Table 39)
- **D** From Leeds to Reading (Table 51)
- **E** To Worksop (Table 30)
- **G** To Plymouth (Table 51)
- **H** To Newark North Gate (Table 27)
- **b** By changing at Doncaster, passengers may arrive at 0907
- **c** Change at Manchester Piccadilly

Table 29

Mondays to Fridays

22 June to 4 September

Hull and Cleethorpes → Doncaster → Meadowhall, Sheffield, Manchester and Manchester Airport
Cleethorpes → Barton-on-Humber

Network Diagram - see first page of Table 18

Station		TP	NT	NT		XC	NT	GR	XC	NT	NT	NT	NT	TP	TP	TP	EM	NT	TP	NT	XC	NT	NT	NT
		1 ◇				1 ◇		R 1	1 ◇					1 ◇					1 ◇		1 ◇			
						A		B	C		D		E				G	H		J	A		K	J
												bus			bus	bus						bus		
Hull	d			06 40				07 00			07 07			07 33						07 36				08 04
Hessle	d			06 47																07 43				
Ferriby	d			06 52																07 48				
Brough	d			06 57				07 12			07 19			07 45						07 53				08 16
Broomfleet	d																			07 58				
Gilberdyke	d			07 04							07 26									08 03				
Eastrington	d										07 31													
Howden	d										07 35			07 56										
Wressle	d										07 40													
Selby	a							07 32			07 48			08 06										
	d							07 32			07 48			08 07										
York 8	33 a										08 21													
Saltmarshe	d			07 10																08 08				
Goole	d			07 15																08 13				08 30
Thorne North	d			07 24									07 53							08 22			08 27	
Cleethorpes	d														05 50	06 35								
New Clee	d																							
Grimsby Docks	d																							
Grimsby Town	a														06 10	06 55								
	d														06 15	07 00	07 03							
Great Coates	d																							
Healing	d																							
Stallingborough	d																							
Habrough	d														06 40		07 13							
Ulceby	d																							
Thornton Abbey	d																							
Goxhill	d																							
New Holland	d																							
Barrow Haven	d																							
Barton-on-Humber	a																							
Barton-on-Humber	bus d																							
Hull Paragon Interchange	bus a																							
Barnetby	d														06 55		07a22							
Scunthorpe	a														07 20									
	d											06 55			07 25							07 35		
Althorpe	d											07 05										07 45		
Crowle	d											07 15										07 55		
Thorne South	d											07 30										08 10		
Hatfield & Stainforth	d			07 30								07a50	07 59							08 28		08a30	08 35	
Kirk Sandall	d			07 34									08 03							08 33			08 39	
Adwick	31 d	*06 53*	07 29							07 54									*08 11*		08b35			
Bentley (S.Yorks)	31 d	*06 57*	07 33							07 57									*08 15*		08b39			
Doncaster 7	31 a		07 37	07 45				07 53		08 01			08 14		08 25	08 25				08 43			08 52	08 55
London Kings Cross 15	⊖ 26 a							09 45								*10 25*								
York 8	26 d					07 27			07 44												08 27			
Doncaster 7	d	07 35	07 39	07 46		07 52				08 16									08 41		08 51		09 01 →	08 56
Conisbrough	d		07 46	07 53						08 23														
Mexborough	d		07 50	07 57			←			08 27														
Swinton (S.Yorks)	d		07 53	08 00			08 00			08 30								08 34						
Rotherham Central	d		08 00	→			08 12			08 42								08 47						
Meadowhall	d	07 53	08 06				08 22			08 49								08 55	09 01					09 15
Sheffield 7	a	08 00	08 18			08 20	08 32		08 51	08 58								09 05	09 08		09 20			09 26
	d	08 05																	09 11					
Stockport	78 a	08 53					*09 25*							09c57					09 53					*10 25*
Manchester Piccadilly 10	78 a	09 02					*09 36*							09 36				*10 32*	10 02					*10 36*
Manchester Airport	85 a	09 33												*10 07*					10 26					

For general notes see front of timetable
For details of catering facilities see Directory of Train Operators

A From Newcastle to Reading (Table 51)
B **The Hull Executive**
C From Newcastle to Plymouth (Table 51)
D From Beverley (Table 43)
E To Adwick (Table 31)
G To Newark North Gate (Table 27)
H From Leeds (Table 31)
J From Bridlington (Table 43)
K To Lincoln (Table 30)
b Change at Doncaster
c Change at Manchester Piccadilly

Table 29

Mondays to Fridays

22 June to 4 September

Hull and Cleethorpes → Doncaster → Meadowhall, Sheffield, Manchester and Manchester Airport
Cleethorpes → Barton-on-Humber

Network Diagram - see first page of Table 18

		NT	TP	HT	XC	NT	NT	TP		NT	NT	TP	TP	NT	TP	TP	NT	XC	NT	TP	NT	XC	NT	NT
											BHX													
				1◇	1◇										1◇	1◇		1◇				1◇		
		A			B	C								D			E	G			A	H		C
			bus					bus			bus	bus	bus						bus	bus				
				⊠	catering										catering	catering		catering				catering		
Hull	d			08 12										08 29	08 40		08 56						09 02	
Hessle	d													08 36										
Ferriby	d													08 41										
Brough	d			08 24										08 46	08 52		09 08						09 14	
Broomfleet	d																							
Gilberdyke	d													08 53									09 21	
Eastrington	d																							
Howden	d			08 36																			09 28	
Wressle	d																							
Selby	a			08 45											09 10								09 38	
	d			08 45											09 11								09 38	
York 8	33 a														*09 46*								10 07	
Saltmarshe	d																							
Goole	d													09 02			09 22							
Thorne North	d													09 10							09 37			
Cleethorpes	d							06 50		07 00			07 35											
New Clee	d																							
Grimsby Docks	d									07 05														
Grimsby Town	a							07 10		07 07		←	07 55											
	d							07 15		07 08		07 15	08 00											
Great Coates	d							→		07 12														
Healing	d									07 15														
Stallingborough	d									07 18														
Habrough	d									07 24		07 40												
Ulceby	d									07 28														
Thornton Abbey	d									07 32														
Goxhill	d									07 35														
New Holland	d									07 40														
Barrow Haven	d									07 43														
Barton-on-Humber	a									07 48														
Barton-on-Humber (bus)	d										07 53													
Hull Paragon Interchange (bus)	a										08 18													
Barnetby	d											07 55												
Scunthorpe	a											08 20												
	d		07 55									08 25							08 45	09 05				
Althorpe	d																		08 55					
Crowle	d																		09 05					
Thorne South	d																		09 20					
Hatfield & Stainforth	d													09 17					09a35		09 42			
Kirk Sandall	d													09 21							09 47			
Adwick	31 d						09 13																	
Bentley (S.Yorks)	31 d						09 17																	
Doncaster 7	31 a		08 55	09 02			09 22					09 25	09 25	09 31			09 46			09 55	09 57			
London Kings Cross 15	⊖ 26 a			10 51			*11 34*														*11 51*			
York 8	26 d	←			08 44		*08 52*											09 27				09 44		
Doncaster 7	d	09 01					09 24									09 42	09 48	09 56			10 02			
Conisbrough	d	09 08					09 31														10 09			
Mexborough	d	09 12					09 35														10 13			
Swinton (S.Yorks)	d	09 15				09 35	09 42														10 16			10 34
Rotherham Central	d	09 27				09 44	09 50														10 27			10 44
Meadowhall (tram)	d	09 33				09 50	09 55									10 01	10 07				10 33			10 50
Sheffield 7 (tram)	a	09 41			09 51	10 00	10 05									10 08	10 20	10 20			10 41	10 51		11 00
	d															10 11								
Stockport	78 a														*10b57*	10 53		*11 25*						
Manchester Piccadilly 10	78 (tram) a						*11 32*								10 36	11 02		*11 36*						
Manchester Airport	85 (plane) a														*11 07*	11 26								

For general notes see front of timetable
For details of catering facilities see Directory of Train Operators

- **A** To Lincoln (Table 30)
- **B** From Edinburgh to Plymouth (Table 51)
- **C** From Leeds (Table 31)
- **D** From Scarborough (Table 43)
- **E** From Bridlington (Table 43)
- **G** From Edinburgh to Reading (Table 51)
- **H** From Glasgow Central to Plymouth (Table 51)
- **b** Change at Manchester Piccadilly

22 June to 4 September

Hull and Cleethorpes → Doncaster → Meadowhall, Sheffield, Manchester and Manchester Airport
Cleethorpes → Barton-on-Humber

Network Diagram - see first page of Table 18

		NT	TP	TP	NT	TP	TP	NT	XC	NT	TP	NT		XC	HT	NT	NT	NT BHX	NT	NT	TP	EM	TP	TP
						1 ◇	1 ◇		1 ◇					1 ◇	1 ◇						1 ◇			
					A			B	C			D		E					G			H		
			Bus	Bus						Bus	Bus							Bus					Bus	Bus
						Trolley	Trolley		Trolley					Trolley	Restaurant						Trolley			
Hull	d				09 25	09 40		09 56							10 12	10 22					10 38			
Hessle	d				09 32											10 29								
Ferriby	d				09 37											10 34								
Brough	d				09 42	09 52		10 08							10 24	10 39					10 50			
Broomfleet	d																							
Gilberdyke	d				09 49											10 46								
Eastrington	d																							
Howden	d														10 36									
Wressle	d																							
Selby	a					10 10									10 46						11 08			
	d					10 11									10 47						11 09			
York 8	33 a														*11 20*									
Saltmarshe	d																							
Goole	d				09 58			10 22								10 55								
Thorne North	d				10 06							10 37				11 03								
Cleethorpes	d		08 00	08 45													09 00						09 00	09 45
New Clee	d																09x03							
Grimsby Docks	d																09 05							
Grimsby Town	a		08 20	09 05													09 08						09 20	10 05
	d		08 25	09 10													09 08					09 28	09 25	10 10
Great Coates	d																09 12							
Healing	d																09 15							
Stallingborough	d																09 18							
Habrough	d		08 50														09 24					09 38	09 50	
Ulceby	d																09 28							
Thornton Abbey	d																09 32							
Goxhill	d																09 35							
New Holland	d																09 40							
Barrow Haven	d																09 43							
Barton-on-Humber	a																09 48							
Barton-on-Humber (Bus)	d																	09 53						
Hull Paragon Interchange (Bus)	a																	10 18						
Barnetby	d		09 05																			09a47	10 05	
Scunthorpe	a		09 30																				10 30	
	d		09 35							09 45	10 05												10 35	
Althorpe	d									09 55														
Crowle	d									10 05														
Thorne South	d									10 20														
Hatfield & Stainforth	d				10 12					10a35		10 43				11 09								
Kirk Sandall	d				10 17							10 47				11 14								
Adwick	31 d	10 13																		11 16				
Bentley (S.Yorks)	31 d	10 17																		11 20				
Doncaster 7	31 a	10 22	10 25	10 25	10 27			10 46			10 55	10 58			11 04	11 24				11 25			11 25	11 25
London Kings Cross 15	⊖ 26 a	*12 17*			*12 25*			*12 42*							12 44									*13 22*
York 8	26 d	*09 35*					*10 06*		10 34			*10 29*		10 44										
Doncaster 7	d	10 24					10 42	10 48	10 58			11 02								11 27				
Conisbrough	d	10 31										11 09								11 34				
Mexborough	d	10 35										11 13								11 38				
Swinton (S.Yorks)	d	10 41										11 16							11 34	11 41				
Rotherham Central	d	10 49										11 27							11 45	11 50				
Meadowhall	d	10 57					11 01	11 06				11 33							11 50	11 55				
Sheffield 7	a	11 05					11 08	11 20	11 20			11 41		11 51					12 00	12 05				
	d						11 11																	
Stockport	78 a					*11b57*	11 53		*12 25*												*12b57*			
Manchester Piccadilly 10	78 a					11 36	12 02		*12 36*											*13 32*	12 36			
Manchester Airport	85 a					*12 07*	12 26														*13 07*			

For general notes see front of timetable
For details of catering facilities see Directory of Train Operators

- **A** From Beverley (Table 43)
- **B** From Bridlington (Table 43)
- **C** From Newcastle to Reading (Table 51)
- **D** To Lincoln (Table 30)
- **E** From Dundee (Table 229)to Plymouth (Table 51)
- **G** From Leeds (Table 31)
- **H** To Newark North Gate (Table 27)
- **b** Change at Manchester Piccadilly

Table 29

Mondays to Fridays

22 June to 4 September

Hull and Cleethorpes → Doncaster → Meadowhall, Sheffield, Manchester and Manchester Airport
Cleethorpes → Barton-on-Humber

Network Diagram - see first page of Table 18

		TP	NT	XC	NT	NT	TP	NT	XC	NT	NT	NT	TP	TP	NT	TP		NT	NT BHX	EM	TP	NT	XC	NT
		1 ◇		1 ◇					1 ◇							1 ◇					1 ◇		1 ◇	
			A	B	C			D	E		G									H		A	B	
						🚌	🚌						🚌	🚌					🚌					🚌
		🍴		🍴					🍴							🍴					🍴		🍴	
Hull	d		10 57							11 05					11 22	11 38						11 55		
Hessle	d														11 29									
Ferriby	d														11 34									
Brough	d		11 09							11 18					11 39	11 50						12 07		
Broomfleet	d																							
Gilberdyke	d														11 46									
Eastrington	d																							
Howden	d																							
Wressle	d																							
Selby	a									11 38						12 08								
	d									11 39						12 09								
York 8	33 a									12 10						*13 15*								
Saltmarshe	d														11 52									
Goole	d		11 23												11 58							12 22		
Thorne North	d							11 36							12 06									
Cleethorpes	d												10 00	10 45				11 00						
New Clee	d																	11x03						
Grimsby Docks	d																	11 05						
Grimsby Town	a												10 20	11 05				11 08						
	d												10 25	11 10				11 08		11 28				
Great Coates	d																	11 12						
Healing	d																	11 15						
Stallingborough	d																	11 18						
Habrough	d												10 50					11 24		11 38				
Ulceby	d																	11 28						
Thornton Abbey	d																	11 32						
Goxhill	d																	11 35						
New Holland	d																	11 40						
Barrow Haven	d																	11 43						
Barton-on-Humber	a																	11 48						
Barton-on-Humber	🚌 d																		11 53					
Hull Paragon Interchange	🚌 a																		12 18					
Barnetby	d												11 05							11a47				
Scunthorpe	a												11 30											
	d					10 45	11 05						11 35											11 45
Althorpe	d					10 55																		11 55
Crowle	d					11 05																		12 05
Thorne South	d					11 20																		12 20
Hatfield & Stainforth	d					11a35		11 42							12 12									12a35
Kirk Sandall	d							11 46							12 17									
Adwick	31 d											12 12												
Bentley (S.Yorks)	31 d											12 16												
Doncaster 7	31 a		11 46				11 55	11 58				12 23	12 25	12 25	12 27							12 46		
London Kings Cross 15	⊖ 26 a		*13 43*					*14 02*							*14 20*							*14 44*		
York 8	26 d			11 27	11 02				11 44			*11 35*											12 27	
Doncaster 7	d	11 42	11 48	11 54				11 58				12 24									12 42	12 48	12 55	
Conisbrough	d							12 06				12 31												
Mexborough	d							12 10				12 35												
Swinton (S.Yorks)	d				12 02			12 16			12 34	12 42												
Rotherham Central	d				12 11			12 27			12 45	12 50												
Meadowhall	🚋 d	12 01	12 06		12 16			12 33			12 50	12 55									13 01	13 06		
Sheffield 7	🚋 a	12 08	12 20	12 20	12 26			12 41	12 51		13 00	13 05									13 08	13 20	13 20	
	d	12 11																			13 11			
Stockport	78 a	12 53			*13 25*											*13b57*					13 53		*14 25*	
Manchester Piccadilly 10	78 🚋 a	13 02			*13 36*											13 36					14 02		*14 36*	
Manchester Airport	85 ✈ a	13 26														*14 07*					14 26			

For general notes see front of timetable
For details of catering facilities see Directory of Train Operators

- **A** From Bridlington (Table 43)
- **B** From Newcastle to Reading (Table 51)
- **C** Via Pontefract Baghill (Table 33)
- **D** To Lincoln (Table 30)
- **E** From Dundee (Table 229) to Plymouth (Table 51)
- **G** From Leeds (Table 31)
- **H** To Newark North Gate (Table 27)
- **b** Change at Manchester Piccadilly

Table 29

Mondays to Fridays
22 June to 4 September

Hull and Cleethorpes → Doncaster → Meadowhall, Sheffield, Manchester and Manchester Airport Cleethorpes → Barton-on-Humber

Network Diagram - see first page of Table 18

	TP	NT	XC	NT	NT	TP	TP	NT	TP	TP	HT	NT	XC	NT	TP	NT	XC	NT	NT		NT	TP	TP
			1◇						1◇	1◇	1◇		1◇				1◇						
		A	B	C								D	E			A	G	C					
	bus					bus	bus							bus	bus							bus	bus
			trolley						trolley	trolley	⊠		trolley				trolley						
Hull d								12 22	12 38		12 45	12 57									13 12		
Hessle d								12 29															
Ferriby d								12 34															
Brough d								12 39	12 50		12 57	13 09									13 24		
Broomfleet d								12 44															
Gilberdyke d								12 49													13 31		
Eastrington d																					13 36		
Howden d											13 09										13 41		
Wressle d																					13 46		
Selby a									13 08		13 19										13 54		
d									13 09		13 20										13 54		
York 8 33 a																					14 25		
Saltmarshe d																							
Goole d								12 58				13 23											
Thorne North d		12 37						13 06								13 37							
Cleethorpes d						11 00	11 45															12 00	12 45
New Clee d																							
Grimsby Docks d																							
Grimsby Town a						11 20	12 05															12 20	13 05
d						11 25	12 10															12 25	13 10
Great Coates d																							
Healing d																							
Stallingborough d																							
Habrough d						11 50																12 50	
Ulceby d																							
Thornton Abbey d																							
Goxhill d																							
New Holland d																							
Barrow Haven d																							
Barton-on-Humber a																							
Barton-on-Humber bus d																							
Hull Paragon Interchange bus a																							
Barnetby d						12 05																13 05	
Scunthorpe a						12 30																13 30	
d	12 05					12 35								12 45	13 05							13 35	
Althorpe d														12 55									
Crowle d														13 05									
Thorne South d														13 20									
Hatfield & Stainforth d		12 42						13 14						13a35		13 42							
Kirk Sandall d		12 47						13 19								13 47							
Adwick 31 d					13 12														14 14				
Bentley (S.Yorks) 31 d					13 16														14 18				
Doncaster 7 31 a	12 55	12 59			13 23	13 25	13 25	13 29			13 37	13 46			13 55	13 58			14 22			14 25	14 25
London Kings Cross 15 ⊖ 26 a		*15 05*									15 20	*15 44*				*15 58*							*16 46*
York 8 26 d			12 44		*12 32*								13 26				13 44		*13 36*				
Doncaster 7 d		12 59			13 23					13 42		13 48	13 55			14 01			14 24				
Conisbrough d		13 09			13 31											14 09			14 31				
Mexborough d		13 13			13 35											14 13			14 35				
Swinton (S.Yorks) d		13 16		13 34	13 41											14 16		14 34	14 41				
Rotherham Central d		13 27		13 45	13 50											14 27		14 45	14 50				
Meadowhall tram d		13 33		13 50	13 55					14 01		14 06				14 33		14 50	14 55				
Sheffield 7 tram a		13 41	13 51	14 00	14 05					14 08		14 20	14 20			14 41	14 51	15 00	15 05				
d										14 11													
Stockport 78 a									*14b57*	14 53			*15 25*										
Manchester Piccadilly 10 78 tram a					*15 32*				14 36	15 02			*15 36*										
Manchester Airport 85 ✈ a									*15 07*	15 26													

For general notes see front of timetable
For details of catering facilities see Directory of Train Operators

A To Lincoln (Table 30)
B From Glasgow Central (Table 51) to Penzance (Table 135)
C From Leeds (Table 31)
D From Scarborough (Table 43)
E From Newcastle to Reading (Table 51)
G From Aberdeen (Table 229)to Penzance (Table 135)
b Change at Manchester Piccadilly

Hull and Cleethorpes → Doncaster → Meadowhall, Sheffield, Manchester and Manchester Airport
Cleethorpes → Barton-on-Humber

Network Diagram - see first page of Table 18

		NT	TP	TP	NT	XC	NT	TP	NT	NT	NT	XC	NT	NT	TP	EM	TP	NT	TP	TP	NT	XC	NT	NT
											BHX													
			1 ◇	1 ◇		1 ◇						1 ◇							1 ◇	1 ◇		1 ◇		
					A	B			C			D	E			G					H	B	J	
							🚌	🚌			🚌				🚌		🚌							🚌
			🍴	🍴		🍴						🍴							🍴	🍴		🍴		
Hull	d	13 25	13 38		13 57													14 25	14 38		14 57			
Hessle	d	13 32																14 32						
Ferriby	d	13 37																14 37						
Brough	d	13 42	13 50		14 09													14 42	14 50		15 09			
Broomfleet	d																							
Gilberdyke	d	13 49																14 49						
Eastrington	d																							
Howden	d																							
Wressle	d																							
Selby	a		14 08																15 08					
	d		14 09																15 09					
York 8	33 a																							
Saltmarshe	d																							
Goole	d	13 58			14 23													14 58			15 23			
Thorne North	d	14 06							14 37									15 06						
Cleethorpes	d									13 00					13 00		13 45							
New Clee	d									13x03														
Grimsby Docks	d									13 05														
Grimsby Town	a									13 08					13 20		14 05							
	d									13 08					13 25	13 52	14 10							
Great Coates	d									13 12														
Healing	d									13 15														
Stallingborough	d									13 18														
Habrough	d									13 24					13 50	14 02								
Ulceby	d									13 28														
Thornton Abbey	d									13 32														
Goxhill	d									13 35														
New Holland	d									13 40														
Barrow Haven	d									13 43														
Barton-on-Humber	a									13 48														
Barton-on-Humber	🚌 d										13 53													
Hull Paragon Interchange	🚌 a										14 18													
Barnetby	d														14 05	14a11								
Scunthorpe	a														14 30									
	d						13 45	14 05							14 35									14 45
Althorpe	d						13 55																	14 55
Crowle	d						14 05																	15 05
Thorne South	d						14 20																	15 20
Hatfield & Stainforth	d	14 14					14a35		14 42									15 12						15a35
Kirk Sandall	d	14 18							14 47									15 17						
Adwick	31 d													15 13										
Bentley (S.Yorks)	31 d													15 17										
Doncaster 7	31 a	14 29			14 46			14 55	14 58					15 22	15 25		15 25	15 27			15 46			
London Kings Cross 15	⊖ 26 a								*17 04*									*17 30*			*17 41*			
York 8	26 d					14 32						14 44								*15 11*		15 29	15 02	
Doncaster 7	d			14 42	14 48	14 57			15 02					15 24						15 42	15 48	15 55		
Conisbrough	d								15 10					15 31										
Mexborough	d								15 14					15 35										
Swinton (S.Yorks)	d								15 17				15 34	15 41									16 01	
Rotherham Central	d								15 27				15 43	15 50									16 10	
Meadowhall	⛴ d			15 01	15 06				15 33				15 50	15 55						16 01	16 07		16 18	
Sheffield 7	⛴ a			15 08	15 19	15 20			15 41			15 51	16 00	16 05						16 08	16 20	16 20	16 25	
	d			15 11																16 10				
Stockport	78 a		*15b57*	15 53		*16 25*													*16b57*	16 52			*17 25*	
Manchester Piccadilly 10	78 ⛴ a		15 36	16 02		*16 36*								*17 29*					16 36	17 02			*17 37*	
Manchester Airport	85 ✈ a		*16 07*	16 26															*17 07*	17 32				

For general notes see front of timetable
For details of catering facilities see Directory of Train Operators

- **A** From Bridlington (Table 43)
- **B** From Newcastle to Reading (Table 51)
- **C** To Lincoln (Table 30)
- **D** From Edinburgh (Table 51) to Penzance (Table 135)
- **E** From Leeds (Table 31)
- **G** To Newark North Gate (Table 27)
- **H** From Scarborough (Table 43)
- **J** Via Pontefract Baghill (Table 33)
- **b** Change at Manchester Piccadilly

22 June to 4 September

Hull and Cleethorpes → Doncaster → Meadowhall, Sheffield, Manchester and Manchester Airport
Cleethorpes → Barton-on-Humber

Network Diagram - see first page of Table 18

		TP	NT		XC	NT	HT	NT	NT	TP	TP	NT	TP	TP	NT	XC	NT	NT	TP	NT	XC	NT	NT	NT
					1 ◇		1 ◇						1 ◇	1 ◇		1 ◇					1 ◇			
			A		B			C	D						E	G	E			A	B		C	
		🚌								🚌	🚌							🚌	🚌					
					🛒		⊠						🛒	🛒		🛒					🛒			
Hull	d					15 06	15 18					15 25	15 40		15 57							16 10		
Hessle	d											15 32												
Ferriby	d											15 37												
Brough	d					15 18	15 30					15 42	15 52		16 09							16 22		
Broomfleet	d																							
Gilberdyke	d											15 49										16 29		
Eastrington	d																							
Howden	d						15 42															16 36		
Wressle	d																							
Selby	a					15 37	15 56						16 10									16 46		
	d					15 38	15 57						16 11									16 47		
York 8	33 a					16 06																17 13		
Saltmarshe	d																							
Goole	d											15 58			16 23									
Thorne North	d		15 36									16 06								16 37				
Cleethorpes	d									13 50	14 35													
New Clee	d																							
Grimsby Docks	d																							
Grimsby Town	a									14 10	14 55													
	d									14 15	15 00													
Great Coates	d																							
Healing	d																							
Stallingborough	d																							
Habrough	d									14 40														
Ulceby	d																							
Thornton Abbey	d																							
Goxhill	d																							
New Holland	d																							
Barrow Haven	d																							
Barton-on-Humber	a																							
Barton-on-Humber	🚌 d																							
Hull Paragon Interchange	🚌 a																							
Barnetby	d									14 55														
Scunthorpe	a									15 20														
	d	15 00								15 25								15 40	15 55					
Althorpe	d																	15 50						
Crowle	d																	16 00						
Thorne South	d																	16 15						
Hatfield & Stainforth	d		15 42									16 12						16a35		16 43				
Kirk Sandall	d		15 46									16 17								16 47				
Adwick	31 d								16 13															*16 53*
Bentley (S.Yorks)	31 d								16 17															*16 57*
Doncaster 7	31 a	15 55	15 58				16 15		16 23	16 25	16 25	16 27			16 46				16 55	16 58				
London Kings Cross 15	⊖ 26 a						18 12					*18 24*								*18 54*				
York 8	26 d				15 44				*15 35*							16 25					16 44			
Doncaster 7	d		16 02						16 24					16 42	16 47	16 53				17 01				17 24
Conisbrough	d		16 09						16 31											17 09				17 31
Mexborough	d		16 13						16 35											17 13				17 35
Swinton (S.Yorks)	d		16 16					16 34	16 41											17 16			17 34	17 42
Rotherham Central	d		16 27					16 43	16 50								←			17 27			17 44	17 50
Meadowhall	🚋 d		16 33					16 50	16 55					17 01	17 06		17 06			17 33			17 50	17 57
Sheffield 7	🚋 a		16 41		16 51			17 00	17 05					17 08	→	17 18	17 19			17 41	17 51		18 00	18 04
	d													17 11										
Stockport	78 a												17b57	17 53			*18 25*							
Manchester Piccadilly 10	78 🚋 a								*18 31*				17 37	18 02			*18 36*							
Manchester Airport	85 ✈ a												*18 12*	18 26			*19c08*							

For general notes see front of timetable
For details of catering facilities see Directory of Train Operators

- **A** To Lincoln (Table 30)
- **B** From Edinburgh to Plymouth (Table 51)
- **C** From Leeds (Table 31)
- **D** To Retford (Table 30)
- **E** From Bridlington (Table 43)
- **G** From Newcastle to Reading (Table 51)
- **b** Change at Manchester Piccadilly
- **c** Change at Sheffield and Manchester Piccadilly

Hull and Cleethorpes → Doncaster → Meadowhall, Sheffield, Manchester and Manchester Airport
Cleethorpes → Barton-on-Humber

Network Diagram - see first page of Table 18

	TP	NT	NT BHX	TP	TP	EM		NT	TP	TP	NT	XC	NT	TP	NT	TP	HT	XC	NT	NT	TP	TP	TP
									1 ◇	1 ◇		1 ◇				1 ◇	1 ◇	1 ◇					1 ◇
						A		B			C	D				E		G	H				
	bus		bus	bus	bus								bus	bus							bus	bus	
Hull d								16 27	16 40		16 54					17 01	17 06						
Hessle d								16 34															
Ferriby d								16 39															
Brough d								16 44	16 52		17 06					17 13	17 19						
Broomfleet d								16 49															
Gilberdyke d								16 54			17 13												
Eastrington d																							
Howden d																	17 32						
Wressle d																							
Selby a									17 10							17 31	17 42						
d									17 11								17 43						
York 8 33 a																							
Saltmarshe d								16 59															
Goole d								17 04			17 22												
Thorne North d								17 13							17 38								
Cleethorpes d	14 50	15 00			15 35																15 55	16 40	
New Clee d		15x03																					
Grimsby Docks d		15 05																					
Grimsby Town a	15 10	15 08		←	15 55																16 15	17 00	
d	15 15	15 09		15 15	16 00	16 03															16 20	17 05	
Great Coates d	→	15 13																					
Healing d		15 16																					
Stallingborough d		15 19																					
Habrough d		15 25		15 40		16 12															16 45		
Ulceby d		15 28																					
Thornton Abbey d		15 33																					
Goxhill d		15 36																					
New Holland d		15 40																					
Barrow Haven d		15 43																					
Barton-on-Humber a		15 49																					
Barton-on-Humber bus d			15 56																				
Hull Paragon Interchange bus a			16 21																				
Barnetby d				15 55		16a21															17 00		
Scunthorpe a				16 20																	17 25		
d				16 25									16 40	16 55							17 30		
Althorpe d													16 50										
Crowle d													17 00										
Thorne South d													17 15										
Hatfield & Stainforth d								17 19					17a35		17 43								
Kirk Sandall d								17 23							17 47								
Adwick 31 d										17 09										17 53			18 14
Bentley (S.Yorks) 31 d										17 14										17 57			18 18
Doncaster 7 31 a				17 25	17 25			17 34			17 47			17 55	17 58		18 01				18 25	18 25	
London Kings Cross 15 ⊖ 26 a					19 29										19 59		19 49						
York 8 26 d										16 56		17 34						17 44					17 55
Doncaster 7 d										17 42	17 48	17 58			18 02					18 26			18 42
Conisbrough d															18 09					18 33			
Mexborough d															18 13					18 37			
Swinton (S.Yorks) d															18 16				18 34	18 42			
Rotherham Central d															18 27				18 45	18 49			
Meadowhall d										18 01	18 06				18 33				18 49	18 57			19 01
Sheffield 7 a										18 08	18 19	18 20			18 43			18 51	19 00	19 06			19 08
d										18 10													19 11
Stockport 78 a									18b57	18 53		19 25											19 53
Manchester Piccadilly 10 78 a									18 37	19 02		19 36								20 32			20 02
Manchester Airport 85 a									19 13	19 28		20c07											20 35

For general notes see front of timetable
For details of catering facilities see Directory of Train Operators

- **A** To Newark North Gate (Table 27)
- **B** From Scarborough (Table 43)
- **C** From Beverley (Table 43)
- **D** From Newcastle to Reading (Table 51)
- **E** To Huddersfield (Table 39)
- **G** From Edinburgh to Plymouth (Table 51)
- **H** From Leeds (Table 31)
- **b** Change at Manchester Piccadilly
- **c** Change at Sheffield and Manchester Piccadilly

Table 29

Mondays to Fridays

22 June to 4 September

Hull and Cleethorpes → Doncaster → Meadowhall, Sheffield, Manchester and Manchester Airport
Cleethorpes → Barton-on-Humber

Network Diagram - see first page of Table 18

		NT	NT	NT	XC	NT	NT	TP	NT	NT	NT		TP	XC	NT	NT	TP	TP	NT	TP	NT	NT	TP	NT
											BHX													
					1 ◇								1 ◇	1 ◇						1 ◇				
		A	A	B	C	A								D	E									
							(bus)	(bus)			(bus)						(bus)	(bus)				(bus)	(bus)	
					(trolley)								(trolley)	(trolley)						(trolley)				
Hull	d	17 18	17 42	17 52									17 58						18 22		18 53			
Hessle	d	17 25	17 49																18 29					
Ferriby	d	17 30	17 54																18 34					
Brough	d	17 35	17 59	18 04									18 10						18 39		19 05			
Broomfleet	d	17 40																						
Gilberdyke	d	17 45	18 06																18 46					
Eastrington	d	17 49																						
Howden	d	17 54																						
Wressle	d	17 59																						
Selby	a	18 06		18 25									18 30											
	d	18 07		18 26									18 31											
York 8	33 a	18 36																						
Saltmarshe	d		18 12			←																		
Goole	d		18 19			18 19													18 55		19 19			
Thorne North	d		→			18 28			18 36										19 03					19 33
Cleethorpes	d									17 00							17 00	17 45						
New Clee	d																							
Grimsby Docks	d									17 05														
Grimsby Town	a									17 07							17 20	18 05						
	d									17 08							17 25	18 10						
Great Coates	d									17 12														
Healing	d									17 15														
Stallingborough	d									17 18														
Habrough	d									17 24							17 50							
Ulceby	d									17 28														
Thornton Abbey	d									17 32														
Goxhill	d									17 35														
New Holland	d									17 40														
Barrow Haven	d									17 43														
Barton-on-Humber	a									17 48														
Barton-on-Humber (bus)	d										17 57													
Hull Paragon Interchange (bus)	a										18 23													
Barnetby	d																18 05							
Scunthorpe	a																18 30							
	d						17 45	18 05									18 35					18 45	19 05	
Althorpe	d						17 55															18 55		
Crowle	d						18 05															19 05		
Thorne South	d						18 20															19 20		
Hatfield & Stainforth	d					18 34	18a35		18 45										19 12			19a35		19 40
Kirk Sandall	d					18 39			18 50										19 16					19 44
Adwick	31 d															*18 53*								
Bentley (S.Yorks)	31 d															*18 57*								
Doncaster 7	31 a			18 45		18 51		18 55	19 01								19 25	19 25	19 27		19 46		19 55	19 56
London Kings Cross 15	⊖ 26 a			*20 44*					*21 03*									*21 20*			*21 44*			
York 8	26 d				18 24									18 44		*18 31*					*19 13*			
Doncaster 7	d			18 47	18 52	18 55										19 28				19 42	19 49			
Conisbrough	d					19 02										19 35								
Mexborough	d					19 06										19 39								
Swinton (S.Yorks)	d					19 09									19 34	19 43								
Rotherham Central	d					19 19									19 45	19 50								
Meadowhall (tram)	d			19 06		19 25									19 50	19 57				20 01	20 07			
Sheffield 7 (tram)	a			19 17	19 21	19 35								19 51	19 59	20 06				20 08	20 18			
	d																			20 11				
Stockport	78 a					20 25							20b22							20 53				
Manchester Piccadilly 10	78 (tram) a					20 36							19 57							21 02				
Manchester Airport	85 (plane) a					21c07							20 53							21 35				

For general notes see front of timetable
For details of catering facilities see Directory of Train Operators

- **A** From Beverley (Table 43)
- **B** From Scarborough (Table 43)
- **C** From Newcastle to Guildford (Table 51)
- **D** From Edinburgh to Bristol Temple Meads (Table 51)
- **E** From Leeds (Table 31)
- **b** Change at Manchester Piccadilly
- **c** Change at Sheffield and Manchester Piccadilly

Hull and Cleethorpes → Doncaster → Meadowhall, Sheffield, Manchester and Manchester Airport
Cleethorpes → Barton-on-Humber

Network Diagram - see first page of Table 18

	XC	NT	TP	XC	NT	EM	HT	TP	TP	NT	NT	NT	NT	TP		XC	NT	TP	NT	TP	NT	XC	NT
							BHX						BHX										
	1 ◇		1 ◇	1 ◇			1 ◇							1 ◇		1 ◇				1 ◇		1 ◇	
	A	B	C	D		E				G	H					A				J	K	L	H
								Bus	Bus				Bus				Bus	Bus					
	Trolley			Trolley			⊠																
Hull d			18 59		19 10		19 18			19 24										19 56	20 03		
Hessle d										19 31											20 10		
Ferriby d										19 36											20 15		
Brough d			19 11		19 22		19 30			19 41										20 08	20 20		
Broomfleet d																							
Gilberdyke d					19 29					19 48											20 27		
Eastrington d																							
Howden d					19 36		19 43																
Wressle d																							
Selby a			19 29		19 46		19 52													20 26			
Selby d					19 47		19 53																
York 8 33 a					20 16															*21 00*			
Saltmarshe d																							
Goole d										19 58											20 36		
Thorne North d										20 06									20 40		20 44		
Cleethorpes d								18 00	18 45			19 00											
New Clee d																							
Grimsby Docks d												19 05											
Grimsby Town a								18 20	19 05			19 07											
Grimsby Town d						18 28		18 25	19 10			19 08											
Great Coates d												19 12											
Healing d												19 15											
Stallingborough d												19 18											
Habrough d						18 38		18 50				19 24											
Ulceby d												19 28											
Thornton Abbey d												19 32											
Goxhill d												19 35											
New Holland d												19 40											
Barrow Haven d												19 43											
Barton-on-Humber a												19 48											
Barton-on-Humber Bus d													19 55										
Hull Paragon Interchange Bus a													20 20										
Barnetby d						18a46		19 05															
Scunthorpe a								19 30															
Scunthorpe d								19 35									19 50	20 05					
Althorpe d																	20 00						
Crowle d																	20 10						
Thorne South d																	20 25						
Hatfield & Stainforth d										20 14							20a40		20 46		20 51		
Kirk Sandall d										20 19									20 50		20 56		
Adwick 31 d														*19 53*									
Bentley (S.Yorks) 31 d														*19 59*									
Doncaster 7 31 a							20 10	20 25	20 25	20 29								20 55	21 01		21 05		
London Kings Cross 15 ⊖ 26 a							21 58														*23 32*		
York 8 26 d	19 29			19 44										*20 09*		20 32						20 44	
Doncaster 7 d	19 57	20 03												20 42		20 57					21 07		
Conisbrough d		20 10												20 48							21 14		
Mexborough d		20 14												20 52							21 18		
Swinton (S.Yorks) d		20 17									20 34			20 55							21 21		21 35
Rotherham Central d		20 28									20 43			21 01							21 28		21 44
Meadowhall Tram d		20 33									20 51			21 07							21 35		21 52
Sheffield 7 Tram a	20 20	20 41		20 51							21 02			21 17		21 22					21 46	21 51	22 07
Sheffield 7 d																							
Stockport 78 a	*21 20*																						
Manchester Piccadilly 10 78 Tram a	*21 32*																						
Manchester Airport 85 ✈ a	*22b10*																						

For general notes see front of timetable
For details of catering facilities see Directory of Train Operators

A From Newcastle to Birmingham New Street (Table 51)
B To Worksop (Table 30)
C To Leeds (Table 39)
D From Edinburgh to Bristol Temple Meads (Table 51)
E To Newark North Gate (Table 27)
G From Scarborough (Table 43)
H From Leeds (Table 31)
J To Leeds (Table 40)
K From Bridlington (Table 43)
L From Edinburgh to Birmingham New Street (Table 51)
b Change at Sheffield and Manchester Piccadilly

Hull and Cleethorpes → Doncaster → Meadowhall, Sheffield, Manchester and Manchester Airport
Cleethorpes → Barton-on-Humber

Network Diagram - see first page of Table 18

	NT	TP	TP	TP	NT	NT	NT	NT	TP	NT	TP	NT	NT	EM	TP	NT	NT	NT	NT		NT		
				1 ◇									ThFO	A	1 ◇	B					B		
		Bus	Bus					Bus	Bus		Bus		Bus				Bus						
Hull d						20 56									21 33				22 20				
Hessle d																			22 27				
Ferriby d																			22 32				
Brough d						21 08									21 45				22 37				
Broomfleet d																							
Gilberdyke d															21 52								
Eastrington d																							
Howden d																							
Wressle d																							
Selby a															22 07								
Selby d															22 07								
York 8 33 a																							
Saltmarshe d																							
Goole d						21 22	21 35												22 51				
Thorne North d							21 44			21 51								22 40	23 00				
Cleethorpes d		19 00	19 45								20 30	21 00		21 15									
New Clee d																							
Grimsby Docks d												21 05											
Grimsby Town a		19 20	20 05								20 50	21 07		21 21									
Grimsby Town d		19 25	20 10								20 55	21 08		21 22									
Great Coates d												21 12											
Healing d												21 15											
Stallingborough d												21 18											
Habrough d		19 50										21 24		21 31									
Ulceby d												21 27											
Thornton Abbey d												21 32											
Goxhill d												21 35											
New Holland d												21 39											
Barrow Haven d												21 42											
Barton-on-Humber a												21 48											
Barton-on-Humber (Bus) d													21 55										
Hull Paragon Interchange (Bus) a													22 20										
Barnetby d		20 05									21 25			21a40									
Scunthorpe a		20 30									21 50												
Scunthorpe d		20 35						21 00	21 05		21 55						21 50						
Althorpe d								21 10									22 00						
Crowle d								21 20									22 10						
Thorne South d								21 35									22 25						
Hatfield & Stainforth d							21 49	21a50		21 56							22a40	22 46	23 06				
Kirk Sandall d							21 54			22 01								22 50	23 10				
Adwick 31 d	*20 55*																		22 02				
Bentley (S.Yorks) 31 d	*20 59*																		22 06				
Doncaster 7 31 a		21 25	21 25			21 45	22 06		21 55	22 11	22 45							23 02	23 21				
London Kings Cross 15 ⊖ 26 a						*00 15*																	
York 8 26 d										*21 40*													
Doncaster 7 d	21 30			21 42		21 48				22 13									23 22				
Conisbrough d	21 37				←					22 20									23 29				
Mexborough d	21 41 →				21 41					22 24									23 33				
Swinton (S.Yorks) d					21 44					22 29						22 34			23 36		23 55		
Rotherham Central d					21 55					22 38						22 45			23 45		00 03		
Meadowhall d				21 58	22 03	22 09				22 44						22 52			23 54		00 08		
Sheffield 7 a				22 08	22 11	22 21				22 54						23 02			00 04		00 23		
Sheffield 7 d				22 11																			
Stockport 78 a				22 53		*23 47*																	
Manchester Piccadilly 10 78 a				23 02		*00 02*									23 37								
Manchester Airport 85 a				23 26		*01b10*									*00 22*								

For general notes see front of timetable
For details of catering facilities see Directory of Train Operators

A To Lincoln (Table 27)
B From Leeds (Table 31)
b Change at Sheffield and Manchester Piccadilly

Hull and Cleethorpes → Doncaster → Meadowhall, Sheffield, Manchester and Manchester Airport
Cleethorpes → Barton-on-Humber

until 20 June and from 12 September

Network Diagram - see first page of Table 18

		TP	NT	NT	NT	TP	NT	TP	NT	XC	NT	XC	NT	TP	NT	TP	EM	NT	NT	NT	NT	GR	NT	XC
		1 ◇				1 ◇		1 ◇		1 ◇		1 ◇		1 ◇		1 ◇						R 1		1 ◇
								A		B		C			D		E				🚌			G
						🍴		🍴		🍴		🍴				🍴						🍴 🍴		🍴
Hull	d			05 20				06 00					06 07	06 35				06 40				06 50		
Hessle	d												06 14					06 47						
Ferriby	d												06 19					06 52						
Brough	d			05 32				06 12					06 24	06 47				06 57				07 02		
Broomfleet	d																							
Gilberdyke	d							06 19					06 31					07 04						
Eastrington	d																							
Howden	d							06 26																
Wressle	d																							
Selby	a							06 35						07 07								07 23		
	d				06 15			06 35						07 07								07 23		
York 8	33 a							*07 20*																
Saltmarshe	d												06 37					07 10					←	
Goole	d			05 47									06 42					07 15 →					07 15	
Thorne North	d			05 56									06 51										07 24	
Cleethorpes	d					05 18	06 00									06 18				07 00				
New Clee	d																							
Grimsby Docks	d																			07 05				
Grimsby Town	a					05 25	06 08									06 25				07 07				
	d					05 26	06 08									06 26	07 03			07 08				
Great Coates	d																			07 12				
Healing	d						06 15													07 15				
Stallingborough	d						06 18													07 18				
Habrough	d					05 36	06 24									06 36	07 13			07 24				
Ulceby	d						06 28													07 28				
Thornton Abbey	d																			07 32				
Goxhill	d						06 35													07 35				
New Holland	d						06 40													07 40				
Barrow Haven	d						06 43													07 43				
Barton-on-Humber	a						06 48													07 48				
Barton-on-Humber	🚌 d																				07 53			
Hull Paragon Interchange	🚌 a																				08 18			
Barnetby	d					05 45										06 45	07a22							
Scunthorpe	a					06 00										07 00								
	d					06 00										07 00								
Althorpe	d					06 05																		
Crowle	d					06 11																		
Thorne South	d					06 20																		
Hatfield & Stainforth	d			06 03		06 25							06 57										07 30	
Kirk Sandall	d			06 10									07 01										07 34	
Adwick	31 d															*06 53*			07 29					
Bentley (S.Yorks)	31 d															*06 57*			07 33					
Doncaster 7	31 a			06 16	06 36	06 38							07 14			07 33			07 37			07 40	07 45	
London Kings Cross 15	⊖ 26 a			*08 04*									*09 03*			*09 26*						09 26	*09 51*	
York 8	26 d					*06 00*						*06 09*				*07 00*								*07 25*
Doncaster 7	d	05 40	06 00	06 25		06 40				06 47	07 02					07 35			07 39				07 46	07 52
Conisbrough	d		06 07	06 32							07 09								07 46				07 53	
Mexborough	d		06 11	06 36							07 13								07 50				07 57	
Swinton (S.Yorks)	d		06 14	06 39							07 16				07 29				07 53				08 00	
Rotherham Central	d		06 22	06 46					←		07 27				07 41				08 00				→	
Meadowhall	🚋 d	05 58	06 27	06 52		06 58			06 52		07 33				07 47	07 53			08 06					
Sheffield 7	🚋 a	06 08	06 38	→		07 06			07 07	07 15	07 45	07 51			07 57	08 00			08 18					08 18
	d	06 11				07 09										08 05								
Stockport	78 a	06 53				07 53		*08b22*		*08 24*				*08b57*		08 53								
Manchester Piccadilly 10	78 🚋 a	07 02				08 02		08 05		*08 36*				08 36		09 02								
Manchester Airport	85 ⇄ a	07 26				08 29		*08 42*						*09 08*		09 26								

For general notes see front of timetable
For details of catering facilities see Directory of Train Operators

- **A** To Liverpool Lime Street (Table 39)
- **B** From Leeds to Reading (Table 51)
- **C** To Plymouth (Table 51)
- **D** From Leeds (Table 31)
- **E** To Newark North Gate (Table 27)
- **G** From Newcastle to Reading (Table 51)
- **b** Change at Manchester Piccadilly

Table 29

Saturdays

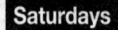

Hull and Cleethorpes → Doncaster → Meadowhall, Sheffield, Manchester and Manchester Airport
Cleethorpes → Barton-on-Humber

until 20 June and from 12 September

Network Diagram - see first page of Table 18

		NT	NT	XC	NT	NT	TP	NT	TP		NT	NT	HT	XC	NT	HT	NT	XC	NT	NT	NT	TP	TP	NT
				1 ◇			1 ◇		1 ◇				1 ◇	1 ◇		1 ◇		1 ◇				1 ◇	1 ◇	
		A		B		C		D			E	G		H	E		G	J	D		K			E
				🍴			🍴		🍴				⊠	🍴		⊠		🍴				🍴	🍴	
Hull	d					06 57	07 33				07 36		08 02		08 08						08 28	08 40		08 56
Hessle	d										07 43										08 35			
Ferriby	d										07 48										08 40			
Brough	d					07 09	07 45				07 53		08 14		08 20						08 45	08 52		09 08
Broomfleet	d										07 58													
Gilberdyke	d					07 17					08 03										08 52			
Eastrington	d					07 21										←								
Howden	d					07 26	07 56						08 26 →			08 26								
Wressle	d					07 31																		
Selby	a					07 40	08 06									08 36						09 10		
	d					07 40	08 07									08 37						09 11		
York 8	33 a					08 15																*09 46*		
Saltmarshe	d										08 08													
Goole	d										08 13				08 34						09 01			09 22
Thorne North	d										08 22										09 09			
Cleethorpes	d								07 18														08 28	
New Clee	d																							
Grimsby Docks	d																							
Grimsby Town	a								07 25														08 35	
	d								07 26														08 36	
Great Coates	d																							
Healing	d																							
Stallingborough	d																							
Habrough	d								07 36														08 46	
Ulceby	d																							
Thornton Abbey	d																							
Goxhill	d																							
New Holland	d																							
Barrow Haven	d																							
Barton-on-Humber	a																							
Barton-on-Humber	🚌 d																							
Hull Paragon Interchange	🚌 a																							
Barnetby	d								07 45														08 55	
Scunthorpe	a								08 00														09 10	
	d	07 34							08 00			08 10											09 10	
Althorpe	d	07 39										08 15												
Crowle	d	07 45										08 21												
Thorne South	d	07 53										08 30												
Hatfield & Stainforth	d	07 59									08 28	08 35									09 15			
Kirk Sandall	d	08 03									08 32	08 39									09 20			
Adwick	31 d				08 07				*08 12*					*08b35*						09 13				
Bentley (S.Yorks)	31 d				08 11				*08 16*					*08b39*						09 17				
Doncaster 7	31 a	08 13			08 15				08 30		08 43	08 52			08 57	09 00				09 22	09 30		09 40	09 46
London Kings Cross 15	⊖ 26 a								*10 26*		*10 44*				*10 58*	10 52	←			*11 33*				*11 50*
York 8	26 d			07 44	*07 36*									08 27			*08 30*	08 44		*08 51*				
Doncaster 7	d				08 17				08 41			09 01 →		08 53	08 59		09 01			09 24			09 42	09 48
Conisbrough	d				08 24												09 08			09 31				
Mexborough	d		←		08 28												09 12			09 35				
Swinton (S.Yorks)	d		08 00		08 31			08 34									09 15		09 35	09 42				
Rotherham Central	d		08 12		08 41			08 47									09 27		09 44	09 50				
Meadowhall	🚊 d		08 22		08 49			08 55	09 01						09 19		09 33		09 50	09 55			10 01	10 07
Sheffield 7	🚊 a		08 32	08 51	08 58			09 05	09 08					09 20	09 28		09 41	09 51	10 00	10 05			10 08	10 20
	d								09 11														10 11	
Stockport	78 a		*09 25*				09c57		09 53						*10 25*							10c57	10 53	
Manchester Piccadilly 10	78 🚊 a		*09 36*				09 36	*10 32*	10 02						*10 36*					*11 32*		10 36	11 02	
Manchester Airport	85 ✈ a						*10 07*		10 26													*11 07*	11 26	

For general notes see front of timetable
For details of catering facilities see Directory of Train Operators

- **A** To Adwick (Table 31)
- **B** From Newcastle to Penzance (Table 135) (from 12 September to Plymouth) (Table 51)
- **C** From Beverley (Table 43)
- **D** From Leeds (Table 31)
- **E** From Bridlington (Table 43)
- **G** To Lincoln (Table 30)
- **H** From Newcastle to Reading (Table 51)
- **J** From Edinburgh to Plymouth (Table 51)
- **K** From Scarborough (Table 43)
- **b** Change at Doncaster
- **c** Change at Manchester Piccadilly

Table 29

Saturdays

Hull and Cleethorpes → Doncaster → Meadowhall, Sheffield, Manchester and Manchester Airport
Cleethorpes → Barton-on-Humber

until 20 June and from 12 September

Network Diagram - see first page of Table 18

		NT	NT	XC	NT	EM	XC	NT	NT	NT	NT	TP	TP	NT	XC	NT	XC	NT		HT	NT	NT	TP	NT
				1 ◇			1 ◇					1 ◇	1 ◇		1 ◇		1 ◇			1 ◇			1 ◇	
				A	B	C	D		E		G			H	J	B	K	E						
			🚌																					
				🛒			🛒						🛒		🛒		🛒			⊠			🛒	
Hull	d							09 02			09 25	09 40		09 56						10 06		10 22		
Hessle	d										09 32											10 29		
Ferriby	d										09 37											10 34		
Brough	d							09 14			09 42	09 52		10 08						10 18		10 39		
Broomfleet	d																							
Gilberdyke	d							09 21			09 49											10 46		
Eastrington	d																							
Howden	d							09 28												10 30				
Wressle	d																							
Selby	a							09 38				10 10								10 40				
	d							09 38				10 11								10 41				
York 8	33 a							10 10												*11 20*				
Saltmarshe	d																							
Goole	d										09 58			10 22								10 55		
Thorne North	d										10 06											11 03		
Cleethorpes	d	09 00											09 28										10 28	11 00
New Clee	d	09x03																						11x03
Grimsby Docks	d	09 05																						11 05
Grimsby Town	a	09 08											09 35										10 35	11 08
	d	09 08				09 28							09 36										10 36	11 08
Great Coates	d	09 12																						11 12
Healing	d	09 15																						11 15
Stallingborough	d	09 18																						11 18
Habrough	d	09 24				09 38																	10 46	11 24
Ulceby	d	09 28																						11 28
Thornton Abbey	d	09 32																						11 32
Goxhill	d	09 35																						11 35
New Holland	d	09 40																						11 40
Barrow Haven	d	09 43																						11 43
Barton-on-Humber	a	09 48																						11 48
Barton-on-Humber	🚌 d		09 53																					
Hull Paragon Interchange	🚌 a		10 18																					
Barnetby	d					09a47							09 55										10 55	
Scunthorpe	a												10 10										11 10	
	d				09 17								10 10			10 18							11 10	
Althorpe	d				09 22											10 23								
Crowle	d				09 29											10 29								
Thorne South	d				09 37											10 38								
Hatfield & Stainforth	d				09 42						10 12					10 43						11 08		
Kirk Sandall	d				09 47						10 17					10 47						11 14		
Adwick	31 d									10 10											11 08			
Bentley (S.Yorks)	31 d									10 14											11 12			
Doncaster 7	31 a				09 57					10 19	10 27		10 40	10 46		10 58				11 01	11 19	11 25	11 40	
London Kings Cross 15	⊖ 26 a									*12 14*	*12 24*			*12 42*		*13 10*				12 47		*13 33*		
York 8	26 d			09 28			09 44			*09 35*			*10 05*		10 25	*10 31*	10 44						*11 00*	
Doncaster 7	d			09 53	10 02					10 23			10 42	10 48	10 53	11 02					11 24		11 42	
Conisbrough	d				10 09					10 31						11 09					11 31			
Mexborough	d				10 13					10 35						11 13					11 35			
Swinton (S.Yorks)	d				10 16				10 34	10 41						11 16		11 34			→			
Rotherham Central	d				10 27				10 44	10 50						11 27		11 45						
Meadowhall	🚋 d				10 33				10 50	10 57			11 01	11 06		11 33		11 50					11 59	
Sheffield 7	🚋 a			10 20	10 41		10 51		11 00	11 06			11 08	11 20	11 20	11 41	11 51	12 00					12 08	
	d												11 11										12 11	
Stockport	78 a			*11 25*								*11b57*	11 53		*12 25*								12 53	
Manchester Piccadilly 10	78 🚋 a			*11 36*						*12 32*		11 36	12 02		*12 36*								13 02	
Manchester Airport	85 ✈ a											*12 07*	12c26										13 33	

For general notes see front of timetable
For details of catering facilities see Directory of Train Operators

A From Edinburgh to Reading (Table 51)
B To Lincoln (Table 30)
C To Newark North Gate (Table 27)
D From Edinburgh to Plymouth (Table 51)
E From Leeds (Table 31)
G From Beverley (Table 43)
H From Bridlington (Table 43)
J From Newcastle to Reading (Table 51)
K From Glasgow Central to Newquay (Table 135) (from 12 September to Plymouth) (Table 51)
b Change at Manchester Piccadilly
c From 7 November arr. 7 mins. later

Saturdays

Hull and Cleethorpes → Doncaster → Meadowhall, Sheffield, Manchester and Manchester Airport
Cleethorpes → Barton-on-Humber

until 20 June and from 12 September

Network Diagram - see first page of Table 18

	NT	NT	NT	EM	TP	NT	XC	NT	NT	XC	NT	NT	NT	NT	TP	TP	NT	XC	NT	XC	NT	NT	NT
					1 ◇		1 ◇			1 ◇					1 ◇	1 ◇		1 ◇		1 ◇			
		A		B		C	D	E	G	H		J					C	D	G	K	J		
	🚌						🍴			🍴					🍴	🍴		🍴		🍴			
Hull d					10 38	10 57					11 08			11 22	11 38		11 55						12 22
Hessle d														11 29									12 29
Ferriby d														11 34									12 34
Brough d					10 50	11 09					11 20			11 39	11 50		12 08						12 39
Broomfleet d																							12 44
Gilberdyke d														11 46									12 49
Eastrington d																							
Howden d																							
Wressle d																							
Selby a					11 08						11 39				12 08								
d					11 09						11 40				12 09								
York 8 33 a											12 10				*13 23*								
Saltmarshe d														11 52									
Goole d						11 23								11 58			12 22						12 58
Thorne North d														12 06									13 06
Cleethorpes d		11 13														11 28							
New Clee d																							
Grimsby Docks d																							
Grimsby Town a		11 19														11 35							
d		11 20		11 28												11 36							
Great Coates d																							
Healing d																							
Stallingborough d																							
Habrough d		11 30		11 38																			
Ulceby d																							
Thornton Abbey d																							
Goxhill d																							
New Holland d																							
Barrow Haven d																							
Barton-on-Humber a																							
Barton-on-Humber 🚌 d	11 53																						
Hull Paragon Interchange 🚌 a	12 18																						
Barnetby d		11a39 →		11a47												11 55							
Scunthorpe a																12 10							
d									11 17							12 10			12 17				
Althorpe d									11 22										12 22				
Crowle d									11 28										12 28				
Thorne South d									11 37										12 37				
Hatfield & Stainforth d									11 42					12 12					12 42				13 12
Kirk Sandall d									11 46					12 17					12 46				13 17
Adwick 31 d													12 12									13 12	
Bentley (S.Yorks) 31 d													12 16									13 16	
Doncaster 7 31 a						11 46			11 58				12 22	12 27		12 40	12 46		12 59			13 23	13 27
London Kings Cross 15 ⊖ 26 a						*13 44*			*13 59*					*14 27*			*14 43*						*15 21*
York 8 26 d							11 27	11 01		11 44			*11 33*			*11 59*		12 25		12 44		*12 31*	
Doncaster 7 d						11 48	11 55		12 02				12 24			12 42	12 48	12 52	13 01			13 23	
Conisbrough d			←						12 09				12 31						13 09			13 31	
Mexborough d			11 35						12 13				12 35						13 13			13 35	
Swinton (S.Yorks) d			11 41					12 01	12 16			12 34	12 42						13 16		13 34	13 41	
Rotherham Central d			11 55					12 11	12 27			12 45	12 50						13 27		13 45	13 50	
Meadowhall 🚊 d			12 00			12 06		12 16	12 33			12 50	12 55			13 01	13 06		13 33		13 50	13 55	
Sheffield 7 🚊 a			12 10			12 20	12 20	12 25	12 41	12 51		13 00	13 05			13 08	13 20	13 20	13 41	13 51	14 00	14 05	
d																13 11							
Stockport 78 a					12b57			*13 25*							13b57	13 53		*14 25*					
Manchester Piccadilly 10 78 🚊 a					12 36			*13 36*					*14 32*		13 36	14 02		*14 36*				*15 32*	
Manchester Airport 85 ✈ a					*13 07*										*14 07*	14c26							

For general notes see front of timetable
For details of catering facilities see Directory of Train Operators

A To Sheffield via Retford (Table 30)
B To Newark North Gate (Table 27)
C From Bridlington (Table 43)
D From Newcastle to Reading (Table 51)
E Via Pontefract Baghill (Table 33)
G To Lincoln (Table 30)
H From Dundee (Table 229) to Plymouth (Table 51)
J From Leeds (Table 31)
K From Glasgow Central (Table 51) to Penzance (Table 135)
b Change at Manchester Piccadilly
c From 7 November arr. 7 mins. later

Table 29

Saturdays

Hull and Cleethorpes → Doncaster → Meadowhall, Sheffield, Manchester and Manchester Airport
Cleethorpes → Barton-on-Humber

until 20 June and from 12 September

Network Diagram - see first page of Table 18

		TP	TP	NT	NT	NT		XC	NT	XC	HT	NT	NT	NT	NT	TP	TP	EM	NT	XC	NT	XC	NT	NT
		1◇	1◇					1◇		1◇	1◇					1◇	1◇			1◇		1◇		
				A		🚌		B	C	D		E						G	H	B	C	J	E	
		🛒	🛒					🛒		🛒	⊠						🛒			🛒		🛒		
Hull	d	12 38		12 57							13 05			13 12	13 25	13 38			13 57					
Hessle	d														13 32									
Ferriby	d														13 37									
Brough	d	12 50		13 09							13 17			13 24	13 42	13 50			14 09					
Broomfleet	d																							
Gilberdyke	d													13 31	13 49									
Eastrington	d													13 36										
Howden	d										13 29			13 40										
Wressle	d													13 45										
Selby	a	13 08									13 39			13 53		14 08								
	d	13 09									13 40			13 54		14 09								
York 8	33 a													14 26										
Saltmarshe	d																							
Goole	d			13 23											13 58				14 23					
Thorne North	d														14 06									
Cleethorpes	d		12 28		13 00												13 28							
New Clee	d				13x03																			
Grimsby Docks	d				13 05																			
Grimsby Town	a		12 35		13 08												13 35							
	d		12 36		13 08												13 36	13 52						
Great Coates	d				13 12																			
Healing	d				13 15																			
Stallingborough	d				13 18																			
Habrough	d				13 24													14 02						
Ulceby	d				13 28																			
Thornton Abbey	d				13 32																			
Goxhill	d				13 35																			
New Holland	d				13 40																			
Barrow Haven	d				13 43																			
Barton-on-Humber	a				13 48																			
Barton-on-Humber	🚌 d					13 53																		
Hull Paragon Interchange	🚌 a					14 18																		
Barnetby	d		12 55														13 55	14a11						
Scunthorpe	a		13 10														14 10							
	d		13 10						13 18								14 10				14 18			
Althorpe	d								13 23												14 23			
Crowle	d								13 29												14 29			
Thorne South	d								13 38												14 38			
Hatfield & Stainforth	d								13 43						14 12						14 43			
Kirk Sandall	d								13 47						14 17						14 47			
Adwick	31 d		*13 12*										14 14											15 13
Bentley (S.Yorks)	31 d		*13 16*										14 18											15 17
Doncaster 7	31 a		13 40	13 46					13 58		14 03		14 22		14 27		14 40		14 46		14 58			15 22
London Kings Cross 15	⊖ 26 a			*15 42*							15 50				*16 34*				*16 47*					
York 8	26 d							13 27		13 44			*13 34*							14 27		14 44		*14 37*
Doncaster 7	d		13 42	13 48				13 54	14 01				14 24				14 42		14 48	14 56	15 02			15 24
Conisbrough	d								14 09				14 31								15 10			15 31
Mexborough	d								14 13				14 35								15 14			15 35
Swinton (S.Yorks)	d								14 16			14 34	14 41								15 17		15 34	→
Rotherham Central	d								14 27			14 45	14 50								15 27		15 43	
Meadowhall	🚋 d		14 01	14 06					14 33			14 50	14 55				15 01		15 06		15 33		15 50	
Sheffield 7	🚋 a		14 08	14 20				14 20	14 41	14 51		15 00	15 05				15 08		15 20	15 20	15 41	15 51	16 00	
	d		14 11														15 11							
Stockport	78 a	*14b57*	14 53					*15 25*								*15b57*	15 53			*16 25*				
Manchester Piccadilly 10	78 🚋 a	14 36	15 02					*15 36*					*16 33*			15 36	16 02			*16 36*				
Manchester Airport	85 ✈ a	*15 07*	15c26													*16 07*	16c26							

For general notes see front of timetable
For details of catering facilities see Directory of Train Operators

A From Scarborough (Table 43)
B From Newcastle to Reading (Table 51)
C To Lincoln (Table 30)
D From Aberdeen (Table 229) to Penzance (Table 135)
E From Leeds (Table 31)
G To Newark North Gate (Table 27)
H From Bridlington (Table 43)
J From Edinburgh (Table 51) to Penzance (Table 135)
b Change at Manchester Piccadilly
c From 7 November arr. 7 mins. later

Table 29

Saturdays

until 20 June and from 12 September

Hull and Cleethorpes → Doncaster → Meadowhall, Sheffield, Manchester and Manchester Airport
Cleethorpes → Barton-on-Humber

Network Diagram - see first page of Table 18

	NT	TP 1 ◇	TP 1 ◇	NT	NT	NT	NT A	NT	NT B	XC 1 ◇ C	NT D	NT E	XC 1 ◇ G	HT 1 ◇		NT H	NT J	NT	TP 1 ◇	TP 1 ◇	NT K	EM L	XC 1 ◇ C
			⌶			🚌				⌶			⌶	⊠					⌶	⌶			⌶
Hull d	14 25	14 38						14 51	14 57					15 06				15 25	15 40		15 57		
Hessle d	14 32																	15 32					
Ferriby d	14 37																	15 37					
Brough d	14 42	14 50						15 03	15 09					15 18				15 42	15 52		16 09		
Broomfleet d																							
Gilberdyke d	14 49																	15 49					
Eastrington d																							
Howden d														15 31									
Wressle d																							
Selby a		15 08						15 22						15 41					16 10				
d		15 09						15 22						15 42					16 11				
York 8 33 a								15 53															
Saltmarshe d																							
Goole d	14 58								15 23									15 58			16 23		
Thorne North d	15 06																	16 06					
Cleethorpes d			14 28		15 00		15 21													15 28			
New Clee d					15x03																		
Grimsby Docks d					15 05																		
Grimsby Town a			14 35		15 09		15 27													15 35			
d			14 36		15 10		15 28													15 36		16 03	
Great Coates d					15 14																		
Healing d					15 17																		
Stallingborough d					15 20																		
Habrough d			14 46		15 26		15 38															16 12	
Ulceby d					15 29																		
Thornton Abbey d					15 34																		
Goxhill d					15 37																		
New Holland d					15 41																		
Barrow Haven d					15 44																		
Barton-on-Humber a					15 50																		
Barton-on-Humber 🚌 d						15 56																	
Hull Paragon Interchange 🚌 a						16 21																	
Barnetby d			14 55				15a47													15 55		16a21	
Scunthorpe a			15 10																	16 10			
d			15 10									15 17								16 10			
Althorpe d												15 22											
Crowle d												15 28											
Thorne South d												15 37											
Hatfield & Stainforth d	15 12											15 42						16 12					
Kirk Sandall d	15 17											15 46						16 17					
Adwick 31 d																	16 13						
Bentley (S.Yorks) 31 d																	16 17						
Doncaster 7 31 a	15 27		15 40						15 46			15 58		16 01			16 23	16 28		16 40	16 46		
London Kings Cross 15 ⊖ 26 a	*17 33*								*17 43*			*18 10*		17 45				*18 28*			*18 46*		
York 8 26 d										15 26	15 11		15 44				*15 30*			*15 57*			16 25
Doncaster 7 d			15 42						15 48	15 55		16 00					16 24			16 42	16 47		16 53
Conisbrough d				←								16 09					16 31						
Mexborough d				15 35								16 13					16 35						
Swinton (S.Yorks) d				15 41							16 10	16 16				16 34	16 41						
Rotherham Central d				15b55							16 18	16 27				16 43	16 50						
Meadowhall 🚊 d			15 58	16 00					16 07		16 24	16 33				16 50	16 55			17 01	17 06		
Sheffield 7 🚊 a			16 08	16 10					16 20	16 20	16 35	16 41	16 51			17 00	17 05			17 08	17 19		17 20
d			16 10																	17 11			
Stockport 78 a		*16c57*	16 52								*17 25*								*17c57*	17 53			*18 25*
Manchester Piccadilly 10 78 🚊 a		16 36	17 02								*17 37*						*18 32*		17 37	18 02			*18 36*
Manchester Airport 85 ✈ a		*17 07*	17e32																*18 12*	18f26			

For general notes see front of timetable
For details of catering facilities see Directory of Train Operators

A To Sheffield via Retford (Table 30)
B From Scarborough (Table 43)
C From Newcastle to Reading (Table 51)
D Via Pontefract Baghill (Table 33)
E To Lincoln (Table 30)
G From Edinburgh to Plymouth (Table 51)
H From Leeds (Table 31)
J To Retford (Table 30)
K From Bridlington (Table 43)
L To Newark North Gate (Table 27)
b Arr. 1550
c Change at Manchester Piccadilly
e From 7 November arr. 1733
f From 7 November arr. 7 mins. later

Hull and Cleethorpes → Doncaster → Meadowhall, Sheffield, Manchester and Manchester Airport
Cleethorpes → Barton-on-Humber

until 20 June and from 12 September

Network Diagram - see first page of Table 18

	NT	XC	NT	NT	NT	NT	TP	TP	NT	NT	NT	XC	NT	TP	EM	XC	NT	NT	TP	EM	NT	NT	NT
		■1 ◇					■1 ◇	■1 ◇				■1 ◇		■1 ◇	■1 ◇	■1 ◇			■1 ◇				
	A	B		C		D			E		🚌	G	A	H	J	B	C			K	E	E	D
Hull d			16 10			16 27	16 40		16 54					17 01							17 18	17 42	17 55
Hessle d						16 34															17 25	17 49	
Ferriby d						16 39															17 30	17 54	
Brough d			16 22			16 44	16 52		17 06					17 13							17 35	17 59	18 07
Broomfleet d						16 49															17 40		
Gilberdyke d			16 29			16 54			17 13												17 45	18 06	
Eastrington d																					17 49		
Howden d			16 36																		17 54		
Wressle d																					17 58		
Selby a			16 46				17 10							17 31							18 06		18 25
d			16 47				17 11														18 06		18 26
York [8] 33 a			17 13																		18 36		
Saltmarshe d						16 59																18 12	
Goole d						17 04			17 22													18 19	
Thorne North d						17 13																→	
Cleethorpes d								16 28		17 00									17 28				
New Clee d																							
Grimsby Docks d										17 05													
Grimsby Town a								16 35		17 07									17 35				
d								16 36		17 08									17 36	18 28			
Great Coates d										17 12													
Healing d										17 15													
Stallingborough d										17 18													
Habrough d										17 24									17 46	18 38			
Ulceby d										17 28													
Thornton Abbey d										17 32													
Goxhill d										17 35													
New Holland d										17 40													
Barrow Haven d										17 43													
Barton-on-Humber a										17 48													
Barton-on-Humber 🚌 d											17 57												
Hull Paragon Interchange 🚌 a											18 23												
Barnetby d								16 55											17 55	18a46			
Scunthorpe a								17 10											18 10				
d	16 18							17 10					17 18						18 10				
Althorpe d	16 23												17 23										
Crowle d	16 29												17 29										
Thorne South d	16 38												17 38										
Hatfield & Stainforth d	16 43					17 19							17 43										
Kirk Sandall d	16 47					17 23							17 47										
Adwick 31 d					17 05										17b53				18 14				
Bentley (S.Yorks) 31 d					17 09										17b57				18 18				
Doncaster [7] 31 a	16 58					17 34		17 40	17 47				17 58						18 40				18 45
London Kings Cross [15] ⊖ 26 a									19 40				20 12										20 35
York [8] 26 d		16 44			16 34							17 25	17 31		17 49	17 44							
Doncaster [7] d	17 01				17 24			17 42	17 48			17 55	18 02		18 18			18 24	18 42				18 47
Conisbrough d	17 09				17 31								18 09					18 31					
Mexborough d	17 13				17 35								18 13					18 35					
Swinton (S.Yorks) d	17 16			17 34	17 42								18 16				18 34	18 41					
Rotherham Central d	17 27			17 44	17 50								18 27				18 43	18 48					
Meadowhall d	17 33			17 50	17 57			18 01	18 06				18 33				18 51	18 56	19 01				19 06
Sheffield [7] a	17 41	17 51		18 00	18 05			18 08	18 19			18 20	18 41		18 44	18 51	19 02	19 05	19 08				19 17
d								18 10											19 11				
Stockport 78 a							18c57	18 53				19 25							19 53				
Manchester Piccadilly [10] 78 a					19 32		18 37	19 02				19 36						20 32	20 02				
Manchester Airport 85 a							19 13	19e28				20f07						21f07	20 35				

For general notes see front of timetable
For details of catering facilities see Directory of Train Operators

- **A** To Lincoln (Table 30)
- **B** From Edinburgh to Plymouth (Table 51)
- **C** From Leeds (Table 31)
- **D** From Scarborough (Table 43)
- **E** From Beverley (Table 43)
- **G** From Newcastle to Reading (Table 51)
- **H** To Leeds (Table 39)
- **J** To St Pancras International (Table 53) (until 20 June from Scarborough) (Table 39)
- **K** To Newark North Gate (Table 27)
- **b** Change at Doncaster
- **c** Change at Manchester Piccadilly
- **e** From 7 November arr. 7 mins. later
- **f** Change at Sheffield and Manchester Piccadilly

Table 29

Saturdays

Hull and Cleethorpes → Doncaster → Meadowhall, Sheffield, Manchester and Manchester Airport
Cleethorpes → Barton-on-Humber

until 20 June and from 12 September

Network Diagram - see first page of Table 18

		XC	NT		NT	TP	TP	XC	HT	NT	NT	NT	TP	NT	NT	NT	NT	NT	XC	NT	TP	NT	XC	NT
		1 ◇				1 ◇	1 ◇	1 ◇	1 ◇				1 ◇						1 ◇		1 ◇		1 ◇	
		A	B			C	D	E		G						H			J		K	L	N	Q
		🛒						🛒	⊠				🛒		🚌				🛒				🛒	
Hull	d					18 03	18 03		18 12			18 24					18 46	18 53			18 59			19 24
Hessle	d											18 31												19 31
Ferriby	d											18 36												19 36
Brough	d					18 15	18 15		18 25			18 41					18 58	19 05			19 11			19 41
Broomfleet	d																							
Gilberdyke	d											18 48					19 05							19 48
Eastrington	d																							
Howden	d								18 37								19 12							
Wressle	d																							
Selby	a					18 33	18 33		18 46								19 22				19 29			
	d					18 34			18 47								19 22							
York 8	33 a																19 56							
Saltmarshe	d		←																					
Goole	d		18 19									18 57						19 19						19 58
Thorne North	d		18 28									19 05												20 06
Cleethorpes	d												18 28	19 00		19 13								
New Clee	d																							
Grimsby Docks	d													19 05										
Grimsby Town	a												18 35	19 07		19 19								
	d												18 36	19 08		19 20								
Great Coates	d													19 12										
Healing	d													19 15										
Stallingborough	d													19 18										
Habrough	d												18 46	19 24		19 30								
Ulceby	d													19 28										
Thornton Abbey	d													19 32										
Goxhill	d													19 35										
New Holland	d													19 40										
Barrow Haven	d													19 43										
Barton-on-Humber	a													19 48										
Barton-on-Humber	🚌 d														19 55									
Hull Paragon Interchange	🚌 a														20 20									
Barnetby	d												18 55			19a39								
Scunthorpe	a												19 10											
	d				18 18								19 10							19 15				
Althorpe	d				18 23															19 20				
Crowle	d				18 29															19 26				
Thorne South	d				18 38															19 35				
Hatfield & Stainforth	d		18 34		18 45							19 12								19 40				20 13
Kirk Sandall	d		18 39		18 50							19 17								19 44				20 17
Adwick	31 d										*18 53*													
Bentley (S.Yorks)	31 d										*18 57*													
Doncaster 7	31 a		18 51		19 01				19 04			19 26	19 40					19 46		19 56				20 30
London Kings Cross 15	⊖ 26 a				*21 15*				20 46											*21 48*				
York 8	26 d	18 25			*18 29*			18 44											19 25				19 44	
Doncaster 7	d	18 51			19 03						19 25		19 42					19 49	19 53			20 03		
Conisbrough	d				19 10						19 32											20 10		
Mexborough	d				19 14						19 36											20 14		
Swinton (S.Yorks)	d				19 17					19 34	19 43											20 17		
Rotherham Central	d				19 27					19 43	19 51											20 29		
Meadowhall	🚊 d				19 33					19 50	19 57		20 01					20 07				20 35		
Sheffield 7	🚊 a	19 18			19 42			19 51		19 59	20 05		20 08					20 18	20 20			20 42	20 51	
	d												20 11											
Stockport	78 a	*20 25*				20b27							20 53						*21 20*					
Manchester Piccadilly 10	78 🚊 a	*20 37*				20 05							21 02						*21 32*					
Manchester Airport	85 ✈ a	*21c17*				20 47							21 35						*22c08*					

For general notes see front of timetable
For details of catering facilities see Directory of Train Operators

- **A** From Newcastle to Guildford (Table 51)
- **B** From Beverley (Table 43)
- **C** Until 20 June. To Liverpool Lime Street (Table 39)
- **D** From 12 September. To Leeds (Table 39)
- **E** From Edinburgh to Bristol Temple Meads (Table 51)
- **G** From Leeds (Table 31)
- **H** To Sheffield via Retford (Table 30)
- **J** From Newcastle to Birmingham New Street (Table 51)
- **K** To Leeds (Table 39)
- **L** To Worksop (Table 30)
- **N** From Edinburgh to Birmingham New Street (Table 51)
- **Q** From Scarborough (Table 43)
- **b** Change at Manchester Piccadilly
- **c** Change at Sheffield and Manchester Piccadilly

Table 29

Saturdays

until 20 June and from 12 September

Hull and Cleethorpes → Doncaster → Meadowhall, Sheffield, Manchester and Manchester Airport
Cleethorpes → Barton-on-Humber

Network Diagram - see first page of Table 18

		NT	TP	EM	NT	XC	TP	NT	XC	NT	TP	NT	NT	NT	NT	NT	TP	NT	NT	NT	NT	NT
			1 ◇			1 ◇	1 ◇		1 ◇		1 ◇			bus			1 ◇					
		A		B		C	D	E	G	A								A			A	E
Hull	d						19 56	20 03				20 51					21 33					22 22
Hessle	d							20 10														
Ferriby	d							20 15														
Brough	d						20 08	20 20				21 03					21 45					22 34
Broomfleet	d																					
Gilberdyke	d							20 27									21 52					
Eastrington	d																					
Howden	d																					
Wressle	d																					
Selby	a						20 26										22 07					
	d																22 07					
York 8	33 a						21 00										22 53					
Saltmarshe	d																					
Goole	d							20 36				21 17										22 48
Thorne North	d							20 44				21 26										22 57
Cleethorpes	d		19 28								20 28		21 00									
New Clee	d																					
Grimsby Docks	d												21 05									
Grimsby Town	a		19 35								20 35		21 07									
	d		19 36	19 45							20 36		21 08									
Great Coates	d												21 12									
Healing	d												21 15									
Stallingborough	d												21 18									
Habrough	d		19 46	19 54									21 24									
Ulceby	d												21 27									
Thornton Abbey	d												21 32									
Goxhill	d												21 35									
New Holland	d												21 39									
Barrow Haven	d												21 42									
Barton-on-Humber	a												21 48									
Barton-on-Humber	bus d													21 55								
Hull Paragon Interchange	bus a													22 20								
Barnetby	d		19 55	20a03							20 55											
Scunthorpe	a		20 10								21 10											
	d		20 10		20 18						21 10					21 21				22 21		
Althorpe	d				20 23											21 26				22 26		
Crowle	d				20 30											21 32				22 32		
Thorne South	d				20 38											21 40				22 41		
Hatfield & Stainforth	d				20 43			20 51				21 32				21 46				22 46		23 03
Kirk Sandall	d				20 48			20 56				21 37				21 50				22 50		23 07
Adwick	31 d		19 53								20 57											22 50
Bentley (S.Yorks)	31 d		19 57								21 01											22 54
Doncaster 7	31 a		20 40		20 59			21 05			21 40	21 46				22 02				23 02		23 18
London Kings Cross 15	⊖ 26 a		22 47																			
York 8	26 d		20 06			20 23			20 44										21 52			
Doncaster 7	d		20 42					21 07			21 42	21 48			21 54				22 24			23 19
Conisbrough	d		20 48					21 14							22 01				22 31			23 26
Mexborough	d		20 52					21 18							22 05				22 35			23 30
Swinton (S.Yorks)	d	20 34	20 55					21 21		21 35					22 08			22 40	22 42		23 30	23 33
Rotherham Central	d	20 43	21 01					21 28		21 44					22 16			22 46	22 52		23 38	23 43
Meadowhall	tram d	20 51	21 07					21 35		21 52	21 58	22 09			22 22			22 53	22 58		23 44	23 49
Sheffield 7	tram a	21 02	21 17			21 20		21 46	21 51	22 07	22 10	22 21			22 32			23 02	23 05		23 58	23 59
	d																					
Stockport	78 a										23 21											
Manchester Piccadilly 10	78 tram a										23 43						23 37					
Manchester Airport	85 ✈ a										00b22						00 22					

For general notes see front of timetable
For details of catering facilities see Directory of Train Operators

- **A** From Leeds (Table 31)
- **B** To Lincoln (Table 27)
- **C** From Newcastle to Birmingham New Street (Table 51)
- **D** To Leeds (Table 40)
- **E** From Bridlington (Table 43)
- **G** From Edinburgh to Birmingham New Street (Table 51)
- **b** Change at Sheffield and Manchester Piccadilly

Table 29

Saturdays

Hull and Cleethorpes → Doncaster → Meadowhall, Sheffield, Manchester and Manchester Airport
Cleethorpes → Barton-on-Humber

27 June to 5 September

Network Diagram - see first page of Table 18

		TP	NT	NT	TP	TP	TP	NT	NT	TP	NT	NT	XC	NT	XC	NT	TP	TP	TP	NT	TP	NT	NT	GR
		1 ◇					1 ◇			1 ◇			1 ◇		1 ◇		1 ◇				1 ◇			R 1
										A			B		C	D								
					bus	bus					bus							bus	bus					
							trolley			trolley			trolley		trolley						trolley			trolley
Hull	d			05 20						06 00		06 07					06 35						06 40	06 50
Hessle	d											06 14											06 47	
Ferriby	d											06 19											06 52	
Brough	d			05 32						06 12		06 24					06 47						06 57	07 02
Broomfleet	d																							
Gilberdyke	d									06 19		06 31											07 04	
Eastrington	d																							
Howden	d									06 26														
Wressle	d																							
Selby	a									06 35							07 07							07 23
	d							06 15		06 35							07 07							07 23
York 8	33 a									*07 20*														
Saltmarshe	d											06 37											07 10	
Goole	d			05 47								06 42											07 15 →	
Thorne North	d			05 56								06 51												
Cleethorpes	d					04 45												04 50	05 40	06 00				
New Clee	d																							
Grimsby Docks	d																							
Grimsby Town	a																	05 10		06 08				
	d					05u05												05 15	06u00	06 08				
Great Coates	d																							
Healing	d																			06 15				
Stallingborough	d																			06 18				
Habrough	d																	05 40		06 24				
Ulceby	d																			06 28				
Thornton Abbey	d																							
Goxhill	d																			06 35				
New Holland	d																			06 40				
Barrow Haven	d																			06 43				
Barton-on-Humber	a																			06 48				
Barton-on-Humber	bus d																							
Hull Paragon Interchange	bus a																							
Barnetby	d					05u30												05 55						
Scunthorpe	a																	06 20						
	d				05 20						06 00							06 25						
Althorpe	d				05 35						06 10													
Crowle	d				05 45						06 20													
Thorne South	d				06 00						06 35													
Hatfield & Stainforth	d			06 03	06 10						06a50	06 57												
Kirk Sandall	d			06 10								07 01												
Adwick	31 d																				*06 53*	07 29		
Bentley (S.Yorks)	31 d																				*06 57*	07 33		
Doncaster 7	31 a			06 16	06 25	06 25		06 36				07 14						07 20	07 20			07 37		07 40
London Kings Cross 15	⊖ 26 a			*08 04*		*08 40*						*09 03*												09 26
York 8	26 d						*06 00*								06 09						*07 00*			
Doncaster 7	d	05 40	06 00	06 25			06 40						06 47	07 02							07 35	07 39		
Conisbrough	d		06 07	06 32										07 09								07 46		
Mexborough	d		06 11	06 36										07 13								07 50		
Swinton (S.Yorks)	d		06 14	06 39										07 16		07 29						07 53		
Rotherham Central	d		06 22	06 46					←					07 27		07 41						08 00		
Meadowhall	tram d	05 58	06 27	06 52			06 58		06 52					07 33		07 47					07 53	08 06		
Sheffield 7	tram a	06 08	06 38	→			07 06		07 07				07 15	07 45	07 51	07 57					08 00	08 18		
	d	06 11					07 09														08 05			
Stockport	78 a	06 53					07 53			*08b22*			*08 24*				*08b57*				08 53			
Manchester Piccadilly 10	78 tram a	07 02					08 02			08 05			*08 36*				08 36				09 02			
Manchester Airport	85 ✈ a	07 32					08 29			*08 42*							*09 08*				09 26			

For general notes see front of timetable
For details of catering facilities see Directory of Train Operators

A To Liverpool Lime Street (Table 39)
B From Leeds to Reading (Table 51)
C To Plymouth (Table 51)
D From Leeds (Table 31)
b Change at Manchester Piccadilly

Table 29

Saturdays

Hull and Cleethorpes → Doncaster → Meadowhall, Sheffield, Manchester and Manchester Airport
Cleethorpes → Barton-on-Humber

27 June to 5 September

Network Diagram - see first page of Table 18

		NT	XC	NT		XC	NT	NT	NT	TP	NT	NT	TP	TP	EM	NT	NT	TP	NT	NT	NT	XC	HT	TP
			1 ◇			1 ◇				1 ◇								1 ◇				1 ◇	1 ◇	
			A			B		C	D			E			G				H		J	A		
							🚌						🚌	🚌			🚌			🚌				🚌
			⚲			⚲				⚲								⚲				⚲	☒	
Hull	d								06 57	07 33									07 36				08 02	
Hessle	d																		07 43					
Ferriby	d																		07 48					
Brough	d								07 09	07 45									07 53				08 14	
Broomfleet	d																		07 58					
Gilberdyke	d								07 17										08 03					
Eastrington	d								07 21															
Howden	d								07 26	07 56													08 26 →	
Wressle	d								07 31															
Selby	a								07 40	08 06														
	d								07 40	08 07														
York 8	33 a								08 15															
Saltmarshe	d	←																	08 08					
Goole	d	07 15																	08 13					
Thorne North	d	07 24						07 53											08 22		08 29			
Cleethorpes	d												05 50	06 35		07 00								
New Clee	d																							
Grimsby Docks	d															07 05								
Grimsby Town	a												06 10	06 55		07 07								
	d												06 15	07 00	07 03	07 08								
Great Coates	d															07 12								
Healing	d															07 15								
Stallingborough	d															07 18								
Habrough	d												06 40		07 13	07 24								
Ulceby	d															07 28								
Thornton Abbey	d															07 32								
Goxhill	d															07 35								
New Holland	d															07 40								
Barrow Haven	d															07 43								
Barton-on-Humber	a															07 48								
Barton-on-Humber	🚌 d																07 53							
Hull Paragon Interchange	🚌 a																08 18							
Barnetby	d												06 55		07a22									
Scunthorpe	a												07 20											
	d						06 55						07 25							07 35				07 55
Althorpe	d						07 05													07 45				
Crowle	d						07 15													07 55				
Thorne South	d						07 30													08 10				
Hatfield & Stainforth	d	07 30					07a50	07 59											08 28	08a30	08 35			
Kirk Sandall	d	07 34						08 03											08 32		08 39			
Adwick	31 d										08 07							*08 12*				*08b35*		
Bentley (S.Yorks)	31 d										08 11							*08 16*				*08b39*		
Doncaster 7	31 a	07 45						08 13			08 15		08 25	08 25					08 43		08 52			08 55
London Kings Cross 15	⊖ 26 a	*09 51*												*10 26*					*10 44*					
York 8	26 d		07 25			07 44					*07 36*											08 27		
Doncaster 7	d	07 46	07 52								08 17							08 41			09 01 →	08 53		
Conisbrough	d	07 53									08 24													
Mexborough	d	07 57		←							08 28													
Swinton (S.Yorks)	d	08 00		08 00							08 31	08 34												
Rotherham Central	d	→		08 12							08 41	08 47												
Meadowhall	🚊 d			08 22							08 49	08 55						09 01						
Sheffield 7	🚊 a		08 18	08 32		08 51					08 58	09 05						09 08				09 20		
	d																	09 11						
Stockport	78 a			*09 25*						*09c57*								09 53						
Manchester Piccadilly 10	78 🚊 a			*09 36*						09 36		*10 32*						10 02						
Manchester Airport	85 ✈ a									*10 07*								10 26						

For general notes see front of timetable
For details of catering facilities see Directory of Train Operators

- **A** From Newcastle to Reading (Table 51)
- **B** From Newcastle (Table 51) to Penzance (Table 135)
- **C** To Adwick (Table 31)
- **D** From Beverley (Table 43)
- **E** From Leeds (Table 31)
- **G** To Newark North Gate (Table 27)
- **H** From Bridlington (Table 43)
- **J** To Lincoln (Table 30)
- **b** Change at Doncaster
- **c** Change at Manchester Piccadilly

Table 29

Saturdays

Hull and Cleethorpes → Doncaster → Meadowhall, Sheffield, Manchester and Manchester Airport
Cleethorpes → Barton-on-Humber

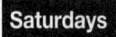

27 June to 5 September

Network Diagram - see first page of Table 18

	NT	HT	NT	XC	NT	NT	TP		TP	NT	TP	TP	NT	XC	NT	TP	NT	XC	NT	NT	NT	TP	TP
		1 ◇		1 ◇							1 ◇	1 ◇		1 ◇				1 ◇					
	A		B	C	D					E			A	G			B	C		D			
							🚌		🚌						🚌	🚌						🚌	🚌
		⊠		🍴							🍴	🍴		🍴				🍴					
Hull d	08 08									08 28	08 40		08 56						09 02				
Hessle d										08 35													
Ferriby d										08 40													
Brough d	08 20									08 45	08 52		09 08						09 14				
Broomfleet d																							
Gilberdyke d										08 52									09 21				
Eastrington d		←																					
Howden d		08 26																	09 28				
Wressle d																							
Selby a		08 36									09 10								09 38				
d		08 37									09 11								09 38				
York 8 33 a											*09 46*								10 10				
Saltmarshe d																							
Goole d	08 34									09 01			09 22										
Thorne North d										09 09							09 37						
Cleethorpes d							06 50		07 35													08 00	08 45
New Clee d																							
Grimsby Docks d																							
Grimsby Town a							07 10		07 55													08 20	09 05
d							07 15		08 00													08 25	09 10
Great Coates d																							
Healing d																							
Stallingborough d																							
Habrough d							07 40															08 50	
Ulceby d																							
Thornton Abbey d																							
Goxhill d																							
New Holland d																							
Barrow Haven d																							
Barton-on-Humber a																							
Barton-on-Humber 🚌 d																							
Hull Paragon Interchange 🚌 a																							
Barnetby d							07 55															09 05	
Scunthorpe a							08 20															09 30	
d							08 25								08 45	09 05						09 35	
Althorpe d															08 55								
Crowle d															09 05								
Thorne South d															09 20								
Hatfield & Stainforth d										09 15					09a35		09 42						
Kirk Sandall d										09 20							09 47						
Adwick 31 d						09 13															10 10		
Bentley (S.Yorks) 31 d						09 17															10 14		
Doncaster 7 31 a	08 57	09 00				09 22	09 25		09 25	09 30			09 46			09 55	09 57				10 19	10 25	10 25
London Kings Cross 15 ⊖ 26 a	*10 58*	10 52	←			*11 33*							*11 50*								*12b17*		
York 8 26 d			*08 30*	08 44		*08 51*								09 28				09 44			*09 35*		
Doncaster 7 d	08 59		09 01			09 24						09 42	09 48	09 53			10 02				10 23		
Conisbrough d			09 08			09 31											10 09				10 31		
Mexborough d			09 12			09 35											10 13				10 35		
Swinton (S.Yorks) d			09 15		09 35	09 42											10 16			10 34	10 41		
Rotherham Central d			09 27		09 44	09 50											10 27			10 44	10 50		
Meadowhall 🚋 d	09 19		09 33		09 50	09 55						10 01	10 07				10 33			10 50	10 57		
Sheffield 7 🚋 a	09 28		09 41	09 51	10 00	10 05						10 08	10 20	10 20			10 41	10 51		11 00	11 06		
d												10 11											
Stockport 78 a	*10 25*										*10c57*	10 53		*11 25*									
Manchester Piccadilly 10 78 🚋 a	*10 36*					*11 32*					10 36	11 02		*11 36*							*12 32*		
Manchester Airport 85 ✈ a											*11 07*	11 26											

For general notes see front of timetable
For details of catering facilities see Directory of Train Operators

- **A** From Bridlington (Table 43)
- **B** To Lincoln (Table 30)
- **C** From Edinburgh to Plymouth (Table 51)
- **D** From Leeds (Table 31)
- **E** From Scarborough (Table 43)
- **G** From Edinburgh to Reading (Table 51)
- **b** 27 June, 4 and 11 July arr. 1214
- **c** Change at Manchester Piccadilly

Saturdays

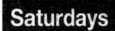

Hull and Cleethorpes → Doncaster → Meadowhall, Sheffield, Manchester and Manchester Airport
Cleethorpes → Barton-on-Humber

27 June to 5 September

Network Diagram - see first page of Table 18

		NT	TP	NT	NT	TP	EM	NT	XC	NT	TP	NT		XC	HT	NT	NT	NT	TP	TP	TP	NT	TP	NT
			1◇			1◇			1◇					1◇	1◇						1◇		1◇	
		A					B	C	D			E		G				H						C
					bus					bus	bus								bus	bus				
						trolley			trolley					trolley	⊠						trolley			
Hull	d	09 25	09 40					09 56							10 06		10 22						10 38	10 57
Hessle	d	09 32															10 29							
Ferriby	d	09 37															10 34							
Brough	d	09 42	09 52					10 08							10 18		10 39						10 50	11 09
Broomfleet	d																							
Gilberdyke	d	09 49															10 46							
Eastrington	d																							
Howden	d														10 30									
Wressle	d																							
Selby	a		10 10												10 40								11 08	
	d		10 11												10 41								11 09	
York 8 33	a														*11 20*									
Saltmarshe	d																							
Goole	d	09 58						10 22									10 55							11 23
Thorne North	d	10 06										10 37					11 03							
Cleethorpes	d			09 00															09 00	09 45				
New Clee	d			09x03																				
Grimsby Docks	d			09 05																				
Grimsby Town	a			09 08															09 20	10 05				
	d			09 08			09 28												09 25	10 10				
Great Coates	d			09 12																				
Healing	d			09 15																				
Stallingborough	d			09 18																				
Habrough	d			09 24			09 38												09 50					
Ulceby	d			09 28																				
Thornton Abbey	d			09 32																				
Goxhill	d			09 35																				
New Holland	d			09 40																				
Barrow Haven	d			09 43																				
Barton-on-Humber	a			09 48																				
Barton-on-Humber (bus)	d				09 53																			
Hull Paragon Interchange (bus)	a				10 18																			
Barnetby	d						09a47												10 05					
Scunthorpe	a																		10 30					
	d									09 45	10 05								10 35					
Althorpe	d									09 55														
Crowle	d									10 05														
Thorne South	d									10 20														
Hatfield & Stainforth	d	10 12								10a35		10 43					11 08							
Kirk Sandall	d	10 17										10 47					11 14							
Adwick 31	d															11 08								
Bentley (S.Yorks) 31	d															11 12								
Doncaster 7 31	a	10 27						10 46			10 55	10 58			11 01	11 19	11 25		11 25	11 25				11 46
London Kings Cross 15 ⊖ 26	a	*12 24*						*12 42*				*13b11*			12 47					*13 33*				*13 44*
York 8 26	d					*10 05*			10 25			*10 31*		10 44							*11 00*			
Doncaster 7	d					10 42		10 48	10 53			11 02				11 24					11 42			11 48
Conisbrough	d											11 09				11 31						←		
Mexborough	d											11 13				11 35						11 35		
Swinton (S.Yorks)	d											11 16				→		11 34				11 41		
Rotherham Central	d											11 27						11 45				11 55		
Meadowhall (tram)	d					11 01		11 06				11 33						11 50			11 59	12 00		12 06
Sheffield 7 (tram)	a					11 08		11 20	11 20			11 41		11 51				12 00			12 08	12 10		12 20
	d					11 11															12 11			
Stockport 78	a		11c57			11 53			*12 25*												12 53		*12c57*	
Manchester Piccadilly 10 78 (tram)	a		11 36			12 02			*12 36*												13 02		12 36	
Manchester Airport 85 (air)	a		*12 07*			12 26															13 33		*13 07*	

For general notes see front of timetable
For details of catering facilities see Directory of Train Operators

- **A** From Beverley (Table 43)
- **B** To Newark North Gate (Table 27)
- **C** From Bridlington (Table 43)
- **D** From Newcastle to Reading (Table 51)
- **E** To Lincoln (Table 30)
- **G** From Glasgow Central (Table 51) to Newquay (Table 135)
- **H** From Leeds (Table 31)
- **b** 27 June, 4 and 11 July arr. 1310
- **c** Change at Manchester Piccadilly

Table 29

Saturdays

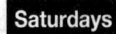

Hull and Cleethorpes → Doncaster → Meadowhall, Sheffield, Manchester and Manchester Airport
Cleethorpes → Barton-on-Humber

27 June to 5 September

Network Diagram - see first page of Table 18

		XC	NT	NT	TP	NT	XC	NT	NT	NT	TP	TP	NT	TP	NT	NT		TP	NT	XC	NT	NT	EM	TP
		1◇					1◇							1◇				1◇		1◇				
		A	B			C	D		E										G	A	H		J	
				🚌	🚌						🚌	🚌				🚌						🚌		🚌
		🍴					🍴							🍴				🍴		🍴				
Hull	d							11 08					11 22	11 38					11 55					
Hessle	d												11 29											
Ferriby	d												11 34											
Brough	d							11 20					11 39	11 50					12 08					
Broomfleet	d																							
Gilberdyke	d												11 46											
Eastrington	d																							
Howden	d																							
Wressle	d																							
Selby	a							11 39						12 08										
	d							11 40						12 09										
York 8	33 a							12 10						*13 23*										
Saltmarshe	d												11 52											
Goole	d												11 58						12 22					
Thorne North	d					11 37							12 06											
Cleethorpes	d										10 00	10 45			11 00						11 13			
New Clee	d														11x03									
Grimsby Docks	d														11 05									
Grimsby Town	a										10 20	11 05			11 08						11 19			
	d										10 25	11 10			11 08						11 20		11 28	
Great Coates	d														11 12									
Healing	d														11 15									
Stallingborough	d														11 18									
Habrough	d										10 50				11 24						11 30		11 38	
Ulceby	d														11 28									
Thornton Abbey	d														11 32									
Goxhill	d														11 35									
New Holland	d														11 40									
Barrow Haven	d														11 43									
Barton-on-Humber	a														11 48									
Barton-on-Humber	🚌 d															11 53								
Hull Paragon Interchange	🚌 a															12 18								
Barnetby	d										11 05										11a40		11a47	
Scunthorpe	a										11 30													
	d			10 45	11 05						11 35											11 45		12 05
Althorpe	d			10 55																		11 55		
Crowle	d			11 05																		12 05		
Thorne South	d			11 20																		12 20		
Hatfield & Stainforth	d			11a35		11 42							12 12									12a35		
Kirk Sandall	d					11 46							12 17											
Adwick	31 d									12 12														
Bentley (S.Yorks)	31 d									12 16														
Doncaster 7	31 a				11 55	11 58				12 22	12 25	12 25	12 27						12 46					12 55
London Kings Cross 15	⊖ 26 a					*13 59*							*14 27*						*14 43*					
York 8	26 d	11 27	11 01				11 44			*11 33*								*11 59*		12 25				
Doncaster 7	d	11 55				12 02				12 24								12 42	12 48	12 52				
Conisbrough	d					12 09				12 31														
Mexborough	d					12 13				12 35														
Swinton (S.Yorks)	d		12 01			12 16			12 34	12 42														
Rotherham Central	d		12 11			12 27			12 45	12 50														
Meadowhall	🚊 d		12 16			12 33			12 50	12 55								13 01	13 06					
Sheffield 7	🚊 a	12 20	12 25			12 41	12 51		13 00	13 05								13 08	13 20	13 20				
	d																	13 11						
Stockport	78 a		*13 25*											13b57				13 53						
Manchester Piccadilly 10	78 🚊 a		*13 36*							*14 32*				13 36				14 02						
Manchester Airport	85 ✈ a													*14 07*				14 26						

For general notes see front of timetable
For details of catering facilities see Directory of Train Operators

- **A** From Newcastle to Reading (Table 51)
- **B** Via Pontefract Baghill (Table 33)
- **C** To Lincoln (Table 30)
- **D** From Dundee to Plymouth (Table 51)
- **E** From Leeds (Table 31)
- **G** From Bridlington (Table 43)
- **H** To Sheffield via Retford (Table 30)
- **J** To Newark North Gate (Table 27)
- **b** Change at Manchester Piccadilly

Table 29

Saturdays

Hull and Cleethorpes → Doncaster → Meadowhall, Sheffield, Manchester and Manchester Airport Cleethorpes → Barton-on-Humber

27 June to 5 September

Network Diagram - see first page of Table 18

		NT	XC	NT	NT	TP	TP	NT	TP	TP	NT	XC	NT	TP	NT	XC	HT	NT	NT	NT		TP	TP	NT
			1 ◇						1 ◇	1 ◇		1 ◇				1 ◇	1 ◇							
		A	B	C							D	E			A	G		C						
						🚌	🚌						🚌	🚌								🚌	🚌	
			trolley						trolley	trolley		trolley				trolley	⊠							
Hull	d							12 22	12 38		12 57						13 05			13 12				13 25
Hessle	d							12 29																13 32
Ferriby	d							12 34																13 37
Brough	d							12 39	12 50		13 09						13 17			13 24				13 42
Broomfleet	d							12 44																
Gilberdyke	d							12 49												13 31				13 49
Eastrington	d																			13 36				
Howden	d																13 29			13 40				
Wressle	d																			13 45				
Selby	a								13 08								13 39			13 53				
	d								13 09								13 40			13 54				
York 8	33 a																			14 26				
Saltmarshe	d																							
Goole	d							12 58			13 23													13 58
Thorne North	d	12 37						13 06							13 37									14 06
Cleethorpes	d					11 00	11 45															12 00	12 45	
New Clee	d																							
Grimsby Docks	d																							
Grimsby Town	a					11 20	12 05															12 20	13 05	
	d					11 25	12 10															12 25	13 10	
Great Coates	d																							
Healing	d																							
Stallingborough	d																							
Habrough	d					11 50																12 50		
Ulceby	d																							
Thornton Abbey	d																							
Goxhill	d																							
New Holland	d																							
Barrow Haven	d																							
Barton-on-Humber	a																							
Barton-on-Humber	🚌 d																							
Hull Paragon Interchange	🚌 a																							
Barnetby	d					12 05																13 05		
Scunthorpe	a					12 30																13 30		
	d					12 35							12 45	13 05								13 35		
Althorpe	d												12 55											
Crowle	d												13 05											
Thorne South	d												13 20											
Hatfield & Stainforth	d	12 42						13 12					13a35		13 42									14 12
Kirk Sandall	d	12 46						13 17							13 47									14 17
Adwick	31 d				13 12														14 14					
Bentley (S.Yorks)	31 d				13 16														14 18					
Doncaster 7	31 a	12 59			13 23	13 25	13 25	13 27			13 46			13 55	13 58		14 03		14 22			14 25	14 25	14 27
London Kings Cross 15	⊖ 26 a						*15 21*				*15 42*						15 50							*16 34*
York 8	26 d		12 44		*12 31*							13 27				13 44			*13 34*					
Doncaster 7	d	13 01			13 23					13 42	13 48	13 54			14 01				14 24					
Conisbrough	d	13 09			13 31										14 09				14 31					
Mexborough	d	13 13			13 35										14 13				14 35					
Swinton (S.Yorks)	d	13 16		13 34	13 41										14 16			14 34	14 41					
Rotherham Central	d	13 27		13 45	13 50										14 27			14 45	14 50					
Meadowhall	🚊 d	13 33		13 50	13 55					14 01	14 06				14 33			14 50	14 55					
Sheffield 7	🚊 a	13 41	13 51	14 00	14 05					14 08	14 20	14 20			14 41	14 51		15 00	15 05					
	d									14 11														
Stockport	78 a								*14b57*	14 53		*15 25*												
Manchester Piccadilly 10	78 🚊 a				*15 32*				14 36	15 02		*15 36*							*16 33*					
Manchester Airport	85 ✈ a								*15 07*	15 26														

For general notes see front of timetable
For details of catering facilities see Directory of Train Operators

- **A** To Lincoln (Table 30)
- **B** From Glasgow Central (Table 51) to Penzance (Table 135)
- **C** From Leeds (Table 31)
- **D** From Scarborough (Table 43)
- **E** From Newcastle to Reading (Table 51)
- **G** From Aberdeen (Table 229) to Penzance (Table 135)
- **b** Change at Manchester Piccadilly

Hull and Cleethorpes → Doncaster → Meadowhall, Sheffield, Manchester and Manchester Airport
Cleethorpes → Barton-on-Humber

27 June to 5 September

Network Diagram - see first page of Table 18

		TP	NT	NT	TP	NT	XC	NT	TP	NT	XC	NT	NT	TP	EM	TP	NT	TP	TP	NT	NT	NT	XC	NT
		1 ◇			1 ◇		1 ◇				1 ◇							1 ◇	1 ◇				1 ◇	
						A	B			C	D	E			G							H	B	J
				[bus]				[bus]	[bus]					[bus]		[bus]								
					[trolley]		[trolley]				[trolley]								[trolley]				[trolley]	
Hull	d	13 38				13 57											14 25	14 38			14 51	14 57		
Hessle	d																14 32							
Ferriby	d																14 37							
Brough	d	13 50				14 09											14 42	14 50			15 03	15 09		
Broomfleet	d																							
Gilberdyke	d																14 49							
Eastrington	d																							
Howden	d																							
Wressle	d																							
Selby	a	14 08																15 08			15 22			
	d	14 09																15 09			15 22			
York [8] 33	a																				15 53			
Saltmarshe	d																							
Goole	d					14 23											14 58					15 23		
Thorne North	d									14 37							15 06							
Cleethorpes	d		13 00											13 00		13 45								
New Clee	d		13x03																					
Grimsby Docks	d		13 05																					
Grimsby Town	a		13 08											13 20		14 05								
	d		13 08											13 25	13 52	14 10								
Great Coates	d		13 12																					
Healing	d		13 15																					
Stallingborough	d		13 18																					
Habrough	d		13 24											13 50	14 02									
Ulceby	d		13 28																					
Thornton Abbey	d		13 32																					
Goxhill	d		13 35																					
New Holland	d		13 40																					
Barrow Haven	d		13 43																					
Barton-on-Humber	a		13 48																					
Barton-on-Humber [bus]	d			13 53																				
Hull Paragon Interchange [bus]	a			14 18																				
Barnetby	d													14 05	14a11									
Scunthorpe	a													14 30										
	d							13 45	14 05					14 35										
Althorpe	d							13 55																
Crowle	d							14 05																
Thorne South	d							14 20																
Hatfield & Stainforth	d							14a35		14 42							15 12							
Kirk Sandall	d									14 47							15 17							
Adwick 31	d												15 13											
Bentley (S.Yorks) 31	d												15 17											
Doncaster [7] 31	a					14 46			14 55	14 58			15 22	15 25		15 25	15 27					15 46		
London Kings Cross [15] ⊖ 26	a					*16 47*											*17 33*					*17 43*		
York [8] 26	d						14 27				14 44								14 37				15 26	15 11
Doncaster [7]	d				14 42	14 48	14 56			15 02			15 24						15 42	←		15 48	15 55	
Conisbrough	d									15 10			15 31											
Mexborough	d									15 14			15 35							15 35				
Swinton (S.Yorks)	d									15 17		15 34	→							15 41				16 10
Rotherham Central	d									15 27		15 43								15b55				16 18
Meadowhall ⇌	d				15 01	15 06				15 33		15 50							15 58	16 00		16 07		16 24
Sheffield [7] ⇌	a				15 08	15 20	15 20			15 41	15 51	16 00							16 08	16 10		16 20	16 20	16 35
	d				15 11														16 10					
Stockport 78	a	*15c57*			15 53		*16 25*											*16c57*	16 52					*17 25*
Manchester Piccadilly [10] 78 ⇌	a	15 36			16 02		*16 36*											16 36	17 02					*17 37*
Manchester Airport 85 ⇌	a	*16 07*			16 26													17 07	17 32					*18e12*

For general notes see front of timetable
For details of catering facilities see Directory of Train Operators

- **A** From Bridlington (Table 43)
- **B** From Newcastle to Reading (Table 51)
- **C** To Lincoln (Table 30)
- **D** From Edinburgh (Table 51) to Penzance (Table 135)
- **E** From Leeds (Table 31)
- **G** To Newark North Gate (Table 27)
- **H** From Scarborough (Table 43)
- **J** Via Pontefract Baghill (Table 33)
- **b** Arr. 1550
- **c** Change at Manchester Piccadilly
- **e** Change at Sheffield and Manchester Piccadilly

Table 29

Saturdays

Hull and Cleethorpes → Doncaster → Meadowhall, Sheffield, Manchester and Manchester Airport
Cleethorpes → Barton-on-Humber

27 June to 5 September

Network Diagram - see first page of Table 18

		NT	TP		NT	XC	HT	NT	NT	TP	TP	NT	TP	TP	NT	XC	NT	TP	NT	XC	TP	NT	NT	NT
						1◇	1◇						1◇	1◇		1◇				1◇				
					A	B		C	D						E	G			A	B				C
		🚌	🚌							🚌	🚌						🚌	🚌			🚌		🚌	
						⊼	⊠						⊼	⊼		⊼				⊼				
Hull	d						15 06					15 25	15 40		15 57									
Hessle	d											15 32												
Ferriby	d											15 37												
Brough	d						15 18					15 42	15 52		16 09									
Broomfleet	d																							
Gilberdyke	d											15 49												
Eastrington	d																							
Howden	d						15 31																	
Wressle	d																							
Selby	a						15 41						16 10											
	d						15 42						16 11											
York 8	33 a																							
Saltmarshe	d																							
Goole	d											15 58			16 23									
Thorne North	d				15 37							16 06							16 37					
Cleethorpes	d									13 50	14 35										14 50	15 00		
New Clee	d																					15x03		
Grimsby Docks	d																					15 05		
Grimsby Town	a									14 10	14 55										15 10	15 09		
	d									14 15	15 00										15 15 ↳	15 10		
Great Coates	d																					15 14		
Healing	d																					15 17		
Stallingborough	d																					15 20		
Habrough	d									14 40												15 26		
Ulceby	d																					15 29		
Thornton Abbey	d																					15 34		
Goxhill	d																					15 37		
New Holland	d																					15 41		
Barrow Haven	d																					15 44		
Barton-on-Humber	a																					15 50		
Barton-on-Humber	🚌 d																						15 56	
Hull Paragon Interchange	🚌 a																						16 21	
Barnetby	d									14 55														
Scunthorpe	a									15 20														
	d	14 45	15 00							15 25							15 40	15 55						
Althorpe	d	14 55															15 50							
Crowle	d	15 05															16 00							
Thorne South	d	15 20															16 15							
Hatfield & Stainforth	d	15a35			15 42							16 12					16a35		16 43					
Kirk Sandall	d				15 46							16 17							16 47					
Adwick	31 d								16 13															
Bentley (S.Yorks)	31 d								16 17															
Doncaster 7	31 a		15 55		15 58		16 01		16 23	16 25	16 25	16 28			16 46			16 55	16 58					
London Kings Cross 15	⊖ 26 a				*18 10*		17 45				*18 28*				*18 46*									
York 8	26 d					15 44			*15 30*					*15 57*		16 25				16 44				
Doncaster 7	d				16 00				16 24					16 42	16 47	16 53			17 01					
Conisbrough	d				16 09				16 31										17 09					
Mexborough	d				16 13				16 35										17 13					
Swinton (S.Yorks)	d				16 16			16 34	16 41										17 16					17 34
Rotherham Central	d				16 27			16 43	16 50										17 27					17 44
Meadowhall	🚊 d				16 33			16 50	16 55					17 01	17 06				17 33					17 50
Sheffield 7	🚊 a				16 41	16 51		17 00	17 05					17 08	17 19	17 20			17 41	17 51				18 00
	d													17 11										
Stockport	78 a												17b57	17 53										
Manchester Piccadilly 10	78 🚊 a								*18 32*				17 37	18 02										
Manchester Airport	85 ✈ a												*18 12*	18 26										

For general notes see front of timetable
For details of catering facilities see Directory of Train Operators

A To Lincoln (Table 30)
B From Edinburgh to Plymouth (Table 51)
C From Leeds (Table 31)
D To Retford (Table 30)
E From Bridlington (Table 43)
G From Newcastle to Reading (Table 51)
b Change at Manchester Piccadilly

Table 29

Saturdays

27 June to 5 September

Hull and Cleethorpes → Doncaster → Meadowhall, Sheffield, Manchester and Manchester Airport
Cleethorpes → Barton-on-Humber

Network Diagram - see first page of Table 18

		NT	NT	NT	TP	TP	EM		NT	TP	TP	NT	XC	NT	TP	NT	EM	TP	XC	NT	NT	TP	TP	TP
										1◇	1◇		1◇				1◇	1◇	1◇					1◇
				A			B		C			D	E			G	H	J	K	L				
					bus	bus								bus	bus							bus	bus	
											trolley		trolley				restaurant		trolley					trolley
Hull	d	16 10							16 27	16 40		16 54						17 01						
Hessle	d								16 34															
Ferriby	d								16 39															
Brough	d	16 22							16 44	16 52		17 06						17 13						
Broomfleet	d								16 49															
Gilberdyke	d	16 29							16 54			17 13												
Eastrington	d																							
Howden	d	16 36																						
Wressle	d																							
Selby	a	16 46								17 10								17 31						
	d	16 47								17 11														
York 8	33 a	17 13																						
Saltmarshe	d								16 59															
Goole	d								17 04			17 22												
Thorne North	d								17 13							17 37								
Cleethorpes	d			15 21		15 35																15 55	16 40	
New Clee	d																							
Grimsby Docks	d																							
Grimsby Town	a			15 27	←	15 55																16 15	17 00	
	d			15 28	15 15	16 00	16 03															16 20	17 05	
Great Coates	d																							
Healing	d																							
Stallingborough	d																							
Habrough	d			15 38	15 40		16 12															16 45		
Ulceby	d																							
Thornton Abbey	d																							
Goxhill	d																							
New Holland	d																							
Barrow Haven	d																							
Barton-on-Humber	a																							
Barton-on-Humber	bus d																							
Hull Paragon Interchange	bus a																							
Barnetby	d			15a47	15 55		16a21															17 00		
Scunthorpe	a				16 20																	17 25		
	d				16 25									16 40	16 55							17 30		
Althorpe	d													16 50										
Crowle	d													17 00										
Thorne South	d													17 15										
Hatfield & Stainforth	d								17 19					17a35		17 43								
Kirk Sandall	d								17 23							17 47								
Adwick	31 d		17 05														17b53							18 14
Bentley (S.Yorks)	31 d		17 09														17b57							18 18
Doncaster 7	31 a				17 25	17 25			17 34			17 47			17 55	17 58						18 25	18 25	
London Kings Cross 15	⊖ 26 a											19 40				20 12								
York 8	26 d		16 34										17 25			17 31	17 49		17 44					
Doncaster 7	d		17 24								17 42	17 48	17 55			18 02	18 18				18 24			18 42
Conisbrough	d		17 31													18 09					18 31			
Mexborough	d		17 35													18 13					18 35			
Swinton (S.Yorks)	d		17 42													18 16				18 34	18 41			
Rotherham Central	d		17 50													18 27				18 43	18 48			
Meadowhall	tram d		17 57								18 01	18 06				18 33				18 51	18 56			19 01
Sheffield 7	tram a		18 05								18 08	18 19	18 20			18 41	18 44		18 51	19 02	19 05			19 08
	d										18 10													19 11
Stockport	78 a									18c57	18 53		19 25											19 53
Manchester Piccadilly 10	78 tram a		19 32							18 37	19 02		19 36								20 32			20 02
Manchester Airport	85 ✈ a									19 13	19 28		20e07								21e07			20 35

For general notes see front of timetable
For details of catering facilities see Directory of Train Operators

- **A** To Sheffield via Retford (Table 30)
- **B** To Newark North Gate (Table 27)
- **C** From Scarborough (Table 43)
- **D** From Beverley (Table 43)
- **E** From Newcastle to Reading (Table 51)
- **G** To Lincoln (Table 30)
- **H** From Scarborough (Table 39) to St Pancras International (Table 53)
- **J** To Leeds (Table 39)
- **K** From Edinburgh to Plymouth (Table 51)
- **L** From Leeds (Table 31)
- **b** Change at Doncaster
- **c** Change at Manchester Piccadilly
- **e** Change at Sheffield and Manchester Piccadilly

Saturdays

Hull and Cleethorpes → Doncaster → Meadowhall, Sheffield, Manchester and Manchester Airport
Cleethorpes → Barton-on-Humber

27 June to 5 September

Network Diagram - see first page of Table 18

Station		NT	NT	NT	NT	NT	XC	NT	NT	TP	NT		TP	HT	XC	NT	NT	TP	TP	NT	TP	EM	NT	NT
							1◇						1◇	1◇	1◇						1◇			
				A	A	B	C	A					D		E	G						H		
			bus						bus	bus								bus	bus				bus	
							trolley							⊠	trolley						trolley			
Hull	d			17 18	17 42	17 55							18 03	18 12						18 24				18 46
Hessle	d			17 25	17 49															18 31				
Ferriby	d			17 30	17 54															18 36				
Brough	d			17 35	17 59	18 07							18 15	18 25						18 41				18 58
Broomfleet	d			17 40																				
Gilberdyke	d			17 45	18 06															18 48				19 05
Eastrington	d			17 49																				
Howden	d			17 54										18 37										19 12
Wressle	d			17 58																				
Selby	a			18 06		18 25							18 33	18 46										19 22
	d			18 06		18 26							18 34	18 47										19 22
York 8	33 a			18 36																				19 56
Saltmarshe	d				18 12			←																
Goole	d				18 19			18 19												18 57				
Thorne North	d				→			18 28			18 37									19 05				
Cleethorpes	d	17 00																17 00	17 45					
New Clee	d																							
Grimsby Docks	d	17 05																						
Grimsby Town	a	17 07																17 20	18 05					
	d	17 08																17 25	18 10			18 28		
Great Coates	d	17 12																						
Healing	d	17 15																						
Stallingborough	d	17 18																						
Habrough	d	17 24																17 50				18 38		
Ulceby	d	17 28																						
Thornton Abbey	d	17 32																						
Goxhill	d	17 35																						
New Holland	d	17 40																						
Barrow Haven	d	17 43																						
Barton-on-Humber	a	17 48																						
Barton-on-Humber	bus d		17 57																				19 55	
Hull Paragon Interchange	bus a		18 23																				20 20	
Barnetby	d																	18 05				18a46		
Scunthorpe	a																	18 30						
	d								17 45	18 05								18 35						
Althorpe	d								17 55															
Crowle	d								18 05															
Thorne South	d								18 20															
Hatfield & Stainforth	d							18 34	18a35		18 45									19 12				
Kirk Sandall	d							18 39			18 50									19 17				
Adwick	31 d																*18 53*							
Bentley (S.Yorks)	31 d																*18 57*							
Doncaster 7	31 a					18 45		18 51		18 55	19 01			19 04				19 25	19 25	19 26				
London Kings Cross 15	⊖ 26 a					*20 35*					*21 15*			20 46										
York 8	26 d						18 25				*18 29*				18 44									
Doncaster 7	d					18 47	18 51				19 03						19 25				19 42			
Conisbrough	d										19 10						19 32							
Mexborough	d										19 14						19 36							
Swinton (S.Yorks)	d										19 17					19 34	19 43							
Rotherham Central	d										19 27					19 43	19 51							
Meadowhall	tram d					19 06					19 33					19 50	19 57				20 01			
Sheffield 7	tram a					19 17	19 18				19 42				19 51	19 59	20 05				20 08			
	d																				20 11			
Stockport	78 a						*20 25*						20b27								20 53			
Manchester Piccadilly 10	78 tram a						*20 37*						20 05								21 02			
Manchester Airport	85 ✈ a						*21c17*						20 47								21 35			

For general notes see front of timetable
For details of catering facilities see Directory of Train Operators

- **A** From Beverley (Table 43)
- **B** From Scarborough (Table 43)
- **C** From Newcastle to Guildford (Table 51)
- **D** To Liverpool Lime Street (Table 39)
- **E** From Edinburgh to Bristol Temple Meads (Table 51)
- **G** From Leeds (Table 31)
- **H** To Newark North Gate (Table 27)
- **b** Change at Manchester Piccadilly
- **c** Change at Sheffield and Manchester Piccadilly

Table 29

Saturdays

Hull and Cleethorpes → Doncaster → Meadowhall, Sheffield, Manchester and Manchester Airport Cleethorpes → Barton-on-Humber

27 June to 5 September

Network Diagram - see first page of Table 18

		NT	TP	XC	NT	TP	NT	NT	XC	NT	TP	TP	NT	NT	TP		XC	NT	TP	NT	TP	NT	TP	NT
			1◇	1◇					1◇						1◇		1◇						1◇	
			A	B				C	D	E				G			B					H	A	J
					bus	bus					bus	bus						bus	bus		bus			
				trolley					trolley															
Hull	d	18 53	18 59											19 24									19 56	20 03
Hessle	d													19 31										20 10
Ferriby	d													19 36										20 15
Brough	d	19 05	19 11											19 41									20 08	20 20
Broomfleet	d																							
Gilberdyke	d													19 48										20 27
Eastrington	d																							
Howden	d																							
Wressle	d																							
Selby	a		19 29																				20 26	
	d																							
York 8	33 a																						*21 00*	
Saltmarshe	d																							
Goole	d	19 19												19 58										20 36
Thorne North	d						19 34							20 06						20 38				20 44
Cleethorpes	d										18 00	18 45	19 00								19 00	19 13		
New Clee	d																							
Grimsby Docks	d												19 05											
Grimsby Town	a										18 20	19 05	19 07								19 20	19 19		
	d										18 25	19 10	19 08								19 25 ↳	19 20		
Great Coates	d												19 12											
Healing	d												19 15											
Stallingborough	d												19 18											
Habrough	d										18 50		19 24									19 30		
Ulceby	d												19 28											
Thornton Abbey	d												19 32											
Goxhill	d												19 35											
New Holland	d												19 40											
Barrow Haven	d												19 43											
Barton-on-Humber	a												19 48											
Barton-on-Humber	bus d																							
Hull Paragon Interchange	bus a																							
Barnetby	d										19 05											19a38		
Scunthorpe	a										19 30													
	d				18 45	19 05					19 35							19 45	20 05					
Althorpe	d				18 55													19 55						
Crowle	d				19 05													20 05						
Thorne South	d				19 20													20 20						
Hatfield & Stainforth	d				19a35		19 40							20 13				20a35		20 43				20 51
Kirk Sandall	d						19 44							20 17						20 48				20 56
Adwick	31 d														*19 53*									
Bentley (S.Yorks)	31 d														*19 57*									
Doncaster 7	31 a	19 46				19 55	19 56				20 25	20 25		20 30					20 55	20 59				21 05
London Kings Cross 15	⊖ 26 a						*21 48*							*22 47*										
York 8	26 d			19 25					19 44						*20 06*		20 23							
Doncaster 7	d	19 49		19 53				20 03							20 42									21 07
Conisbrough	d							20 10							20 48									21 14
Mexborough	d							20 14							20 52									21 18
Swinton (S.Yorks)	d							20 17		20 34					20 55									21 21
Rotherham Central	d							20 29		20 43					21 01									21 28
Meadowhall	tram d	20 07						20 35		20 51					21 07									21 35
Sheffield 7	tram a	20 18		20 20				20 42	20 51	21 02					21 17		21 20							21 46
	d																							
Stockport	78 a			*21 20*																				
Manchester Piccadilly 10	78 tram a			*21 32*																				
Manchester Airport	85 ✈ a			*22b08*																				

For general notes see front of timetable
For details of catering facilities see Directory of Train Operators

- **A** To Leeds (Table 39)
- **B** From Newcastle to Birmingham New Street (Table 51)
- **C** To Worksop (Table 30)
- **D** From Edinburgh to Birmingham New Street (Table 51)
- **E** From Leeds (Table 31)
- **G** From Scarborough (Table 43)
- **H** To Sheffield via Retford (Table 30)
- **J** From Bridlington (Table 43)
- **b** Change at Sheffield and Manchester Piccadilly

Saturdays

Hull and Cleethorpes → Doncaster → Meadowhall, Sheffield, Manchester and Manchester Airport
Cleethorpes → Barton-on-Humber

27 June to 5 September

Network Diagram - see first page of Table 18

		TP	EM	TP	XC	NT	TP	NT	NT	NT	TP	NT	TP	NT	NT	NT	TP	NT	NT	NT	NT	NT
					1 ◇		1 ◇						1 ◇									
			A		B	C								C							C	D
		bus		bus						bus	bus				bus		bus		bus			
Hull	d							20 51					21 33									22 22
Hessle	d																					
Ferriby	d																					
Brough	d							21 03					21 45									22 34
Broomfleet	d																					
Gilberdyke	d												21 52									
Eastrington	d																					
Howden	d																					
Wressle	d																					
Selby	a												22 07									
	d												22 07									
York 8	33 a												*22 53*									
Saltmarshe	d																					
Goole	d							21 17														22 48
Thorne North	d							21 26				21 40								22 40		22 57
Cleethorpes	d			19 45													20 30	21 00				
New Clee	d																					
Grimsby Docks	d																	21 05				
Grimsby Town	a	←		20 05													20 50	21 07				
	d	19 25	19 45	20 10													20 55	21 08				
Great Coates	d																	21 12				
Healing	d																	21 15				
Stallingborough	d																	21 18				
Habrough	d	19 50	19 54															21 24				
Ulceby	d																	21 27				
Thornton Abbey	d																	21 32				
Goxhill	d																	21 35				
New Holland	d																	21 39				
Barrow Haven	d																	21 42				
Barton-on-Humber	a																	21 48				
Barton-on-Humber	bus d																		21 55			
Hull Paragon Interchange	bus a																		22 20			
Barnetby	d	20 05	20a03														21 25					
Scunthorpe	a	20 30															21 50					
	d	20 35								20 50	21 05				21 50		21 55					
Althorpe	d									21 00					22 00							
Crowle	d									21 10					22 10							
Thorne South	d									21 25					22 25							
Hatfield & Stainforth	d							21 32		21a40		21 46			22a40					22 46		23 03
Kirk Sandall	d							21 37				21 50								22 50		23 07
Adwick	31 d						*20 57*															*22 50*
Bentley (S.Yorks)	31 d						*21 01*															*22 54*
Doncaster 7	31 a	21 25		21 25				21 46			21 55	22 02					22 45			23 02		23 18
London Kings Cross 15	⊖ 26 a																					
York 8	26 d				20 44											*21 52*						
Doncaster 7	d						21 42	21 48	21 54							22 24						23 19
Conisbrough	d								22 01							22 31						23 26
Mexborough	d								22 05							22 35						23 30
Swinton (S.Yorks)	d					21 35			22 08					22 40		22 42					23 30	23 33
Rotherham Central	d					21 44			22 16					22 46		22 52					23 38	23 43
Meadowhall	tram d					21 52	21 58	22 09	22 22					22 53		22 58					23 44	23 49
Sheffield 7	tram a				21 51	22 07	22 10	22 21	22 32					23 02		23 05					23 58	23 59
	d																					
Stockport	78 a						*23 21*															
Manchester Piccadilly 10	78 tram a						*23 43*						*23 37*									
Manchester Airport	85 ✈ a						*00b22*						*00 22*									

For general notes see front of timetable
For details of catering facilities see Directory of Train Operators

A To Lincoln (Table 27)
B From Edinburgh to Birmingham New Street (Table 51)
C From Leeds (Table 31)
D From Bridlington (Table 43)
b Change at Sheffield and Manchester Piccadilly

Table 29

Sundays

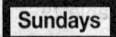

Hull and Cleethorpes → Doncaster → Meadowhall, Sheffield, Manchester and Manchester Airport
Cleethorpes → Barton-on-Humber

until 21 June and from 13 September

Network Diagram - see first page of Table 18

		NT	XC	NT	XC	NT	NT	NT	XC	NT	TP	TP	NT	TP	NT	NT	HT	NT	XC	NT	TP	TP	TP	NT
			1◇		1◇				1◇		1◇	1◇		1◇			1◇		1◇		1◇	1◇	1◇	
			A		B	C			D		E	G			H	H (bus)			J	K	E	L		C
			(trolley)		(trolley)				(trolley)								⊠		(trolley)					
Hull	d						08 42			08 54	09 00	09 00	09 41				10 12			10 41	10 58	10 58		
Hessle	d						08 49																	
Ferriby	d						08 54																	
Brough	d						08 59			09 06	09 12	09 12	09 53				10 24			10 53	11 10	11 10		
Broomfleet	d																							
Gilberdyke	d						09 06						10 00							11 00				
Eastrington	d																							
Howden	d																10 36							
Wressle	d																							
Selby	a									09 25	09 30	09 30					10 46				11 28	11 28		
	d									09 25	09 31						10 47				11 29			
York 8	33 a									09 54														
Saltmarshe	d																							
Goole	d						09 15	09 43					10 09							11 09				
Thorne North	d							09 51																
Cleethorpes	d													09 28	09 56								10 28	
New Clee	d														09x59									
Grimsby Docks	d														10 01									
Grimsby Town	a													09 35	10 04								10 35	
	d													09 36	10 04								10 36	
Great Coates	d														10 08									
Healing	d														10 11									
Stallingborough	d														10 14									
Habrough	d													09 46	10 20								10 46	
Ulceby	d														10 24									
Thornton Abbey	d														10 28									
Goxhill	d														10 31									
New Holland	d														10 36									
Barrow Haven	d														10 39									
Barton-on-Humber	a														10 45									
Barton-on-Humber (bus)	d															10 55								
Hull Paragon Interchange (bus)	a															11 19								
Barnetby	d													09 55									10 55	
Scunthorpe	a													10 10									11 10	
	d													10 10									11 10	
Althorpe	d																							
Crowle	d																							
Thorne South	d																							
Hatfield & Stainforth	d							09 57					10 21											
Kirk Sandall	d							10 02					10 26											
Adwick	31 d																	10 43						
Bentley (S.Yorks)	31 d																	10 47						
Doncaster 7	31 a						09 38	10 11					10 36	10 40			11 03			11 32			11 40	
London Kings Cross 15	⊖ 26 a						11 55	12 19						12 37			12 48						13 39	
York 8	26 d				09 00		09 00		09 28					10 02				10 23	10 28					
Doncaster 7	d	08 03	09 01	09 13	09 32		09 39	10 13	10 31					10 42				11 13	11 30	11 33			11 42	
Conisbrough	d	08 10		09 20				10 20										11 20						
Mexborough	d	08 14		09 24				10 24										11 24						
Swinton (S.Yorks)	d	08 17		09 28		09 35		10 27										11 27						11 55
Rotherham Central	d	08 25		09 35		09 48		10 35										11 35						12 06
Meadowhall	d	08 30		09 41		09 54	10 00	10 40						11 00				11 40		11 52			12 00	12 11
Sheffield 7	a	08 41	09 25	09 51	09 55	10 03	10 09	10 52	10 54					11 07				11 51	11 53	12 03			12 07	12 20
	d													11 10									12 10	
Stockport	78 a	09 52				10b52					11c27			11 52							13c16		12 52	13 25
Manchester Piccadilly 10	78 a	10 06				11b06	11b36				11 05			12 06							12 54		13 06	13 37
Manchester Airport	85 ✈ a	10 30					12b17				11 47			12 29							13 19		13 29	14e17

For general notes see front of timetable
For details of catering facilities see Directory of Train Operators

- **A** From 8 November. From Leeds to Plymouth (Table 51)
- **B** Until 1 November. From Leeds to Plymouth (Table 51)
- **C** From Leeds (Table 31)
- **D** To Plymouth (from 8 November to Birmingham New Street) (Table 51)
- **E** Until 21 June
- **G** From 13 September. To Leeds (Table 39)
- **H** Until 13 September
- **J** From Newcastle to Plymouth (from 8 November to Birmingham New Street) (Table 51)
- **K** Until 20 September from Bridlington (Table 43)
- **L** From 13 September. To Huddersfield (Table 39)
- **b** Until 21 June only
- **c** Change at Manchester Piccadilly
- **e** Change at Sheffield and Manchester Piccadilly

Table 29

Sundays

until 21 June and from 13 September

Hull and Cleethorpes → Doncaster → Meadowhall, Sheffield, Manchester and Manchester Airport
Cleethorpes → Barton-on-Humber

Network Diagram - see first page of Table 18

		NT	XC	NT	NT	NT	TP	TP		TP	NT	NT	HT	NT	XC	NT	TP	TP	TP	NT	XC	NT	NT	NT
			1 ◇				1 ◇	1 ◇		1 ◇			1 ◇		1 ◇		1 ◇	1 ◇	1 ◇		1 ◇			
			A				B	C			D	D			E	G	B	C		H	A		D	J
			trolley									bus	⊠		trolley						trolley			
Hull	d			11 41	11 54		12 00	12 00					12 12			12 41	12 58	12 58					13 27	13 41
Hessle	d																							
Ferriby	d																							
Brough	d			11 53	12 06		12 12	12 12					12 24			12 53	13 10	13 10					13 39	13 53
Broomfleet	d																							
Gilberdyke	d			12 00												13 00								14 00
Eastrington	d																							
Howden	d												12 36											
Wressle	d																							
Selby	a				12 25		12 32	12 32					12 46				13 28	13 28					13 58	
	d				12 25		12 33						12 47				13 29						13 58	
York 8	33 a				12 50																		14 22	
Saltmarshe	d																							
Goole	d	11 43		12 09												13 09						13 43		14 09
Thorne North	d	11 51																				13 51		
Cleethorpes	d									11 28	12 56													
New Clee	d										12x59													
Grimsby Docks	d										13 01													
Grimsby Town	a									11 35	13 04													
	d									11 36	13 04													
Great Coates	d										13 08													
Healing	d										13 11													
Stallingborough	d										13 14													
Habrough	d										13 20													
Ulceby	d										13 24													
Thornton Abbey	d										13 29													
Goxhill	d										13 32													
New Holland	d										13 36													
Barrow Haven	d										13 39													
Barton-on-Humber	a										13 45													
Barton-on-Humber (bus)	d											13 55												
Hull Paragon Interchange (bus)	a											14 19												
Barnetby	d									11 55														
Scunthorpe	a									12 10														
	d									12 10														
Althorpe	d																							
Crowle	d																							
Thorne South	d																							
Hatfield & Stainforth	d	11 57																				13 57		
Kirk Sandall	d	12 02																				14 02		
Adwick	31 d													12 43										
Bentley (S.Yorks)	31 d													12 47										
Doncaster 7	31 a	12 14		12 32						12 40			13 05			13 32						14 11		14 32
London Kings Cross 15	⊖ 26 a									*14 44*			14 54			*15 42*						*16 10*		
York 8	26 d	*11 29*	11 28											*12 29*	12b28	*12 57*					13 28	*13 37*		*14 02*
Doncaster 7	d	12 16	12 31							12 42				13 13	13 30	13 34			13 42			14 13		14 33
Conisbrough	d	12 23												13 20								14 20		
Mexborough	d	12 27				←								13 24								14 24		
Swinton (S.Yorks)	d	12 30				12 30								13 27						14 01		14 30		
Rotherham Central	d	→				12 38								13 36						14 09		14 37		
Meadowhall	(tram) d					12 43				13 00				13 44		13 53			14 00	14 17		14 43		14 53
Sheffield 7	(tram) a		12 54			12 55				13 07				13 52	13 55	14 04			14 07	14 25	14 44	14 52		15 03
	d									13 10									14 11					
Stockport	78 a						*14c16*			13 52							*15c16*		14 52	*15 25*				
Manchester Piccadilly 10	78 (tram) a						13 54			14 06							14 54		15 06	*15 37*				
Manchester Airport	85 (air) a						14 19			14e29							15 20		15e29	*16f17*				

For general notes see front of timetable
For details of catering facilities see Directory of Train Operators

- **A** From Edinburgh to Plymouth (from 8 November to Birmingham New Street) (Table 51)
- **B** Until 21 June
- **C** From 13 September. To Huddersfield (Table 39)
- **D** Until 13 September
- **E** From Edinburgh to Penzance (Table 135) (from 8 November to Birmingham New Street) (Table 51)
- **G** From Scarborough (from 27 September from Beverley) (Table 43)
- **H** From Leeds (Table 31)
- **J** From Scarborough (from 27 September from Bridlington) (Table 43)
- **b** By changing at Doncaster, passengers may depart at 1257
- **c** Change at Manchester Piccadilly
- **e** From 13 September arr. 5 mins. later
- **f** Change at Sheffield and Manchester Piccadilly

Table 29

Sundays

until 21 June and from 13 September

Hull and Cleethorpes → Doncaster → Meadowhall, Sheffield, Manchester and Manchester Airport
Cleethorpes → Barton-on-Humber

Network Diagram - see first page of Table 18

		TP	EM	XC	XC	HT	NT	NT	NT	TP	TP	TP	NT	NT	XC	NT		XC	NT	NT	TP	XC	XC	NT
		1◇		1◇	1◇	1◇				1◇	1◇	1◇			1◇			1◇			1◇	1◇	1◇	
			A	B	C				D	E	G		H	J 🚌	B	K		L		N		Q	U	J
				⊼	⊼	☒									⊼			⊼				⊼	⊼	
Hull	d					14 10		14 28	14 41	14 58	14 58									15 41				16 01
Hessle	d							14 35																
Ferriby	d							14 40																
Brough	d					14 22		14 45	14 53	15 10	15 10									15 53				16 13
Broomfleet	d																							
Gilberdyke	d								15 00											16 00				
Eastrington	d																							
Howden	d					14 34																		
Wressle	d																							
Selby	a					14 44		15 04		15 28	15 28													16 32
	d					14 45		15 04		15 29														16 32
York 8	33 a							15 30																16 57
Saltmarshe	d																							
Goole	d								15 09										15 43	16 09				
Thorne North	d																		15 51					
Cleethorpes	d	13 28	13 56									14 28	15 02								15 28			
New Clee	d												15x05											
Grimsby Docks	d												15 07											
Grimsby Town	a	13 35	14 02									14 35	15 10								15 35			
	d	13 36	14 03									14 36	15 10								15 36			
Great Coates	d												15 14											
Healing	d												15 17											
Stallingborough	d												15 20											
Habrough	d		14 13									14 46	15 26											
Ulceby	d												15 30											
Thornton Abbey	d												15 34											
Goxhill	d												15 37											
New Holland	d												15 42											
Barrow Haven	d												15 45											
Barton-on-Humber	a												15 50											
Barton-on-Humber	🚌 d													15 55										
Hull Paragon Interchange	🚌 a													16 19										
Barnetby	d	13 55	14a21									14 55									15 55			
Scunthorpe	a	14 10										15 10									16 10			
	d	14 10										15 10									16 10			
Althorpe	d																							
Crowle	d																							
Thorne South	d																							
Hatfield & Stainforth	d																		15 57					
Kirk Sandall	d																		16 02					
Adwick	31 d						14 43																	
Bentley (S.Yorks)	31 d						14 47																	
Doncaster 7	31 a	14 40				15 05			15 32			15 40							16 11	16 32	16 40			
London Kings Cross 15	⊖ 26 a	16 29				16 50						17 49							18 15		18 43			
York 8	26 d			14 19	14 28		14 36								15 20			15 28	15 34		16 03	16 20	16 28	
Doncaster 7	d	14 42		14 50			15 13		15 33			15 42			15 50				16 13	16 33	16 42	16 50		
Conisbrough	d						15 20												16 20					
Mexborough	d						15 24												16 24					
Swinton (S.Yorks)	d						15 30									15 55			16 29					
Rotherham Central	d						15 37									16 05			16 37					
Meadowhall	🚋 d	15 00					15 43		15 52			16 00				16 11			16 43	16 53	17 00			
Sheffield 7	🚋 a	15 07		15 18	15 42		15 51		16 01			16 07			16 15	16 21		16 41	16 52	17 03	17 07	17 18	17 41	
	d	15 11										16 11									17 11			
Stockport	78 a	15 53		16 25						17b16		16 53				17 27					17 53	18 25		
Manchester Piccadilly 10	78 🚋 a	16 06		16 37						16 54		17 06				17 37					18 06	18 37		
Manchester Airport	85 ✈ a	16c29		17e17						17 19		17 29				18e17					18 29	19e17		

For general notes see front of timetable
For details of catering facilities see Directory of Train Operators

- **A** Until 21 June. To Nottingham (Table 27)
- **B** From Newcastle to Reading (Table 51)
- **C** From Edinburgh to Penzance (Table 135) (from 8 November to Birmingham New Street) (Table 51)
- **D** Until 20 September from Bridlington (Table 43)
- **E** Until 21 June
- **G** From 13 September. To Huddersfield (Table 39)
- **H** Until 21 June and 13 September
- **J** Until 13 September
- **K** From Leeds (Table 31)
- **L** From Glasgow Central to Plymouth (from 8 November to Birmingham New Street) (Table 51)
- **N** From Scarborough (from 27 September from Bridlington) (Table 43)
- **Q** From Edinburgh to Reading (Table 51)
- **U** From Aberdeen (Table 229) to Plymouth (from 8 November to Birmingham New Street) (Table 51)
- **b** Change at Manchester Piccadilly
- **c** From 13 September arr. 5 mins. later
- **e** Change at Sheffield and Manchester Piccadilly

Hull and Cleethorpes → Doncaster → Meadowhall, Sheffield, Manchester and Manchester Airport Cleethorpes → Barton-on-Humber

until 21 June and from 13 September

Network Diagram - see first page of Table 18

		NT	HT	EM	NT	NT	TP	TP	TP	XC	NT	EM	NT	XC	NT	NT	GR	NT	TP	NT	NT	EM	XC	XC
			1 ◇	1 ◇			1 ◇	1 ◇	1 ◇	1 ◇		1 ◇		1 ◇			R 1		1 ◇				1 ◇	1 ◇
				A		B	C	D		E	G	H	J	K				L		N	Q	U	V	X
			⊠	☕						🍴		☕		🍴			☕ 🍴				🚌		🍴	🍴
Hull	d		16 21			16 41	16⌇58	16⌇58								17 23	17 30	17 41						
Hessle	d																							
Ferriby	d																							
Brough	d		16 33			16 53	17⌇10	17⌇10								17 35	17 42	17 53						
Broomfleet	d																							
Gilberdyke	d					17 00												18 00						
Eastrington	d																							
Howden	d		16 45																					
Wressle	d																							
Selby	a		16 55				17⌇28	17⌇28								17 54	18 05							
	d		16 56				17⌇29									17 54	18 05							
York 8	33 a															18 23								
Saltmarshe	d																							
Goole	d					17 09									17 43			18 09						
Thorne North	d														17 51									
Cleethorpes	d								16 28										17 28	17⌇56		18⌇18		
New Clee	d																			17x59				
Grimsby Docks	d																			18⌇01				
Grimsby Town	a								16 35										17 35	18⌇04		18⌇24		
	d								16 36										17 36	18⌇04		18⌇25		
Great Coates	d																			18⌇08				
Healing	d																			18⌇11				
Stallingborough	d																			18⌇14				
Habrough	d																		17 46	18⌇20		18⌇35		
Ulceby	d																			18⌇24				
Thornton Abbey	d																			18⌇28				
Goxhill	d																			18⌇31				
New Holland	d																			18⌇36				
Barrow Haven	d																			18⌇39				
Barton-on-Humber	a																			18⌇45				
Barton-on-Humber	🚌 d																				18⌇55			
Hull Paragon Interchange	🚌 a																				19⌇19			
Barnetby	d								16 55										17 55			18a43		
Scunthorpe	a								17 10										18 10					
	d								17 10										18 10					
Althorpe	d																							
Crowle	d																							
Thorne South	d																							
Hatfield & Stainforth	d														17 57									
Kirk Sandall	d														18 02									
Adwick	31 d	*16 43*							*16 43*															
Bentley (S.Yorks)	31 d	*16 47*							*16 47*															
Doncaster 7	31 a		17 14			17 31			17 40						18 11		18 23	18 33	18 40					
London Kings Cross 15	⊖ 26 a		19 06						*19 48*						*20 14*		20b23		*20 43*					
York 8	26 d	*16 29*		17⌇00		*17c00*			*17 03*	17 20		17⌇40	17 17	17 28	*17e36*				*18 05*				18 20	18 28
Doncaster 7	d	17 13		17⌇23		17 32			17 42	17 50		18⌇06			18 13			18 34	18 42				18 50	
Conisbrough	d	17 21													18 20									
Mexborough	d	17 25			←										18 24									
Swinton (S.Yorks)	d	17 30 →			17 30						17 55		18 11		18 30									
Rotherham Central	d				17 38						18 06		18 18		18 37									
Meadowhall	🚊 d				17 43	17 53			18 00		18 12		18 24		18 43			18 53	19 00					
Sheffield 7	🚊 a			17⌇47	17 54	18 01			18 07	18 16	18 23	18⌇28	18 35	18 40	18 52			19 03	19 07				19 15	19 40
	d								18 11										19 11					
Stockport	78 a						*19f16*		18 53			*19⌇25*							19 53				*20 25*	
Manchester Piccadilly 10	78 🚊 a						18⌇54		19 06			*19⌇37*							20 06				*20 38*	
Manchester Airport	85 ✈ a						*19⌇19*		19 29			20g17							20h29				*21g17*	

For general notes see front of timetable
For details of catering facilities see Directory of Train Operators

- **A** From 13 September. To St Pancras International (Table 53)
- **B** Until 20 September from Bridlington (Table 43)
- **C** Until 21 June
- **D** From 13 September. To Huddersfield (Table 39)
- **E** From Newcastle to Reading (Table 51)
- **G** From Leeds (Table 31)
- **H** Until 21 June. To St Pancras International (Table 53)
- **J** Via Pontefract Baghill (Table 33)
- **K** From Glasgow Central to Plymouth (from 8 November to Birmingham New Street) (Table 51)
- **L** Until 20 September from Scarborough (Table 43)
- **N** Until 13 September
- **Q** Until 21 June and 13 September
- **U** Until 21 June. To Newark North Gate (Table 27)
- **V** From Newcastle to Southampton Central (Table 51)
- **X** From Edinburgh to Bristol Temple Meads (from 8 November to Birmingham New Street) (Table 51)
- **b** By changing at Doncaster, passengers may arrive at 2014
- **c** Until 21 June dep. 1653
- **e** Until 21 June dep. 1740
- **f** Change at Manchester Piccadilly
- **g** Change at Sheffield and Manchester Piccadilly
- **h** From 13 September arr. 5 mins. later

Table 29

Sundays

until 21 June and from 13 September

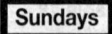

Hull and Cleethorpes → Doncaster → Meadowhall, Sheffield, Manchester and Manchester Airport
Cleethorpes → Barton-on-Humber

Network Diagram - see first page of Table 18

	NT	NT	HT	TP	TP	TP	XC	NT	XC	NT	TP	EM	NT	XC	NT	NT	NT	TP	TP	NT	NT
			1 ◇	1 ◇	1 ◇	1 ◇	1 ◇		1 ◇		1 ◇			1 ◇				1 ◇	1 ◇		
		A		B	C		D	E	G			H	B	J			K		L	E	N
			⊠				🛒		🛒												
Hull d		18 38	18 48	18 58	18 58								19 04		20 22	20 30			21 00		21 15
Hessle d																					21 22
Ferriby d																					21 27
Brough d		18 50	19 00	19 10	19 10								19 16		20 34	20 42			21 12		21 32
Broomfleet d																					
Gilberdyke d		18 57														20 49					21 39
Eastrington d																					
Howden d			19 12																		
Wressle d																					
Selby a			19 22	19 28	19 28								19 35		20 53				21 30		
Selby d			19 23	19 29									19 35		20 53						
York 8 33 a													19 59		21 20						
Saltmarshe d																					
Goole d		19 06														20 58					21 48
Thorne North d		19 14																			21 56
Cleethorpes d						18 28					19 28	19 54						20 28			
New Clee d																					
Grimsby Docks d																					
Grimsby Town a						18 35					19 35	20 00						20 35			
Grimsby Town d						18 36					19 36	20 07						20 36			
Great Coates d																					
Healing d																					
Stallingborough d																					
Habrough d											19 46	20 17						20 46			
Ulceby d																					
Thornton Abbey d																					
Goxhill d																					
New Holland d																					
Barrow Haven d																					
Barton-on-Humber a																					
Barton-on-Humber 🚌 d																					
Hull Paragon Interchange 🚌 a																					
Barnetby d						18 55					19 55	20a25						20 55			
Scunthorpe a						19 10					20 10							21 10			
Scunthorpe d						19 10					20 10							21 10			
Althorpe d																					
Crowle d																					
Thorne South d																					
Hatfield & Stainforth d		19 20																			22 02
Kirk Sandall d		19 25																			22 07
Adwick 31 d	18 43															20 54					21 43
Bentley (S.Yorks) 31 d	18 47															20 58					21 47
Doncaster 7 31 a		19 35	19 43			19 40					20 40					21 21		21 40			22 17
London Kings Cross 15 ⊖ 26 a			21 34			21 47					22 37							23 50			
York 8 26 d	18 29					19 05	19 20		19 28	19 31	20 02			20 28		20 38	20 42				21 28
Doncaster 7 d	19 15	19 37				19 42	19 50			20 14	20 42					21 23		21 42			22 20
Conisbrough d	19 22									20 21											22 27
Mexborough d	19 26									20 25											22 31
Swinton (S.Yorks) d	19 30							19 55		20 32							21 38	21 54		22 32	22 37
Rotherham Central d	19 41							20 06		20 39						21 39	21 49	22 00		22 40	22 44
Meadowhall 🚋 d	19 47	19 57				20 00		20 11		20 45	21 00					21 45	21 54	22 04		22 45	22 50
Sheffield 7 🚋 a	19 55	20 06				20 07	20 15	20 23	20 40	20 53	21 07			21 44		21 56	22 05	22 15		22 54	22 58
Sheffield 7 d						20 11					21 11										
Stockport 78 a				21b15		20 53		21 24			21 53						23 16				
Manchester Piccadilly 10 78 🚋 a				20 54		21 06		21 36			22 06						23 29				
Manchester Airport 85 ✈ a				21 19		21c29		22e17			22 29						00e17				

For general notes see front of timetable
For details of catering facilities see Directory of Train Operators

A From Bridlington (Table 43)
B Until 13 September
C From 13 September. To Huddersfield (Table 39)
D From Newcastle to Birmingham New Street (Table 51)
E From Leeds (Table 31)
G From Edinburgh to Bristol Temple Meads (from 8 November to Birmingham New Street) (Table 51)
H Until 21 June. To Nottingham (Table 27)
J From Edinburgh to Birmingham New Street (Table 51)
K Via Pontefract Baghill (Table 33)
L To Leeds (Table 39)
N From Scarborough (from 27 September from Bridlington) (Table 43)
b Change at Manchester Piccadilly
c From 13 September arr. 2130
e Change at Sheffield and Manchester Piccadilly

Table 29

Sundays

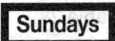

28 June to 6 September

Hull and Cleethorpes → Doncaster → Meadowhall, Sheffield, Manchester and Manchester Airport Cleethorpes → Barton-on-Humber

Network Diagram - see first page of Table 18

		NT	XC	NT	XC	NT	NT	NT	TP	TP	XC	NT	TP	NT	TP		HT	NT	XC	NT	TP	TP	TP	NT
			1 ◊		1 ◊						1 ◊		1 ◊		1 ◊		1 ◊		1 ◊		1 ◊			
			A		B	C					D								E	G				
									🚌	🚌												🚌	🚌	
			𐃒		𐃒						𐃒						⊠		𐃒					
Hull	d						08 42					08 54	09 00	09 41			10 12			10 41	10 58			
Hessle	d						08 49																	
Ferriby	d						08 54																	
Brough	d						08 59					09 06	09 12	09 53			10 24			10 53	11 10			
Broomfleet	d																							
Gilberdyke	d						09 06							10 00						11 00				
Eastrington	d																							
Howden	d																10 36							
Wressle	d																							
Selby	a											09 25	09 30				10 46				11 28			
	d											09 25	09 31				10 47				11 29			
York 8	33 a											09 54												
Saltmarshe	d																							
Goole	d						09 15	09 43						10 09						11 09				
Thorne North	d							09 51																
Cleethorpes	d								08 00	08 45												09 00	09 45	09 56
New Clee	d																							09x59
Grimsby Docks	d																							10 01
Grimsby Town	a								08 20	09 05												09 20	10 05	10 04
	d								08 25	09 10												09 25	10 10	10 04
Great Coates	d																							10 08
Healing	d																							10 11
Stallingborough	d																							10 14
Habrough	d								08 50													09 50		10 20
Ulceby	d																							10 24
Thornton Abbey	d																							10 28
Goxhill	d																							10 31
New Holland	d																							10 36
Barrow Haven	d																							10 39
Barton-on-Humber	a																							10 45
Barton-on-Humber	🚌 d																							
Hull Paragon Interchange	🚌 a																							
Barnetby	d								09 05													10 05		
Scunthorpe	a								09 30													10 30		
	d								09 35													10 35		
Althorpe	d																							
Crowle	d																							
Thorne South	d																							
Hatfield & Stainforth	d							09 57						10 21										
Kirk Sandall	d							10 02						10 26										
Adwick	31 d																	10 43						
Bentley (S.Yorks)	31 d																	10 47						
Doncaster 7	31 a						09 38	10 11	10 25	10 25				10 36			11 03			11 32		11 25	11 25	
London Kings Cross 15	⊖ 26 a						*11 55*	*12 19*						*12 37*			12 48			*13 39*				
York 8	26 d				*09 00*		*09 00*				09 28				*10 02*			*10 23*	10 28					
Doncaster 7	d	08 03	09 02	09 13	09 32		09 39	10 13			10 31				10 42			11 13	11 30	11 33				
Conisbrough	d	08 10	⌇	09 20	⌇			10 20										11 20						
Mexborough	d	08 14	⌇	09 24	⌇			10 24										11 24						
Swinton (S.Yorks)	d	08 17	⌇	09 28	⌇	09 35		10 27										11 27						
Rotherham Central	d	08 25	⌇	09 35	⌇	09 48		10 35										11 35						
Meadowhall	🚊 d	08 30	⌇	09 41	⌇	09 54	10 00	10 40							11 00			11 40		11 52				
Sheffield 7	🚊 a	08 41	09 25	09 51	09 55	10 03	10 09	10 52			10 54				11 07			11 51	11 53	12 03				
	d														11 10									
Stockport	78 a	*09 52*				*10 52*	*11b26*						*11c23*		11 52						*13e16*			
Manchester Piccadilly 10	78 🚊 a	*10 06*				*11 06*	*11 38*						11 05		12 06						12 54			
Manchester Airport	85 ✈ a	*10 30*					*12f17*						*11 47*		12 29						*13 19*			

For general notes see front of timetable
For details of catering facilities see Directory of Train Operators

A From 19 July.
From Leeds to Plymouth (Table 51)

B Until 12 July.
From Leeds to Plymouth (Table 51)

C From Leeds (Table 31)

D To Plymouth (from 19 July to Birmingham New Street) (Table 51)

E From Newcastle to Plymouth (from 19 July to Birmingham New Street) (Table 51)

G From Bridlington (Table 43)

b Until 12 July arr. 1152

c Change at Manchester Piccadilly. 28 June, 5 and 12 July arr. 1127

e Change at Manchester Piccadilly

f Change at Sheffield and Manchester Piccadilly

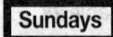

Hull and Cleethorpes → Doncaster → Meadowhall, Sheffield, Manchester and Manchester Airport
Cleethorpes → Barton-on-Humber

28 June to 6 September

Network Diagram - see first page of Table 18

	NT	TP	NT	NT	XC	NT	TP	TP		TP	NT	NT	TP	HT	NT	XC	TP	TP	NT	TP	TP	NT	NT
		1 ◇			1 ◇					1 ◇			1 ◇	1 ◇		1 ◇				1 ◇	1 ◇		
			A		B											C			D			A	
	🚌						🚌	🚌									🚌	🚌					
					╤									⊠		╤							
Hull d											11 41	11 54	12 00	12 12					12 41	12 58			13 27
Hessle d																							
Ferriby d																							
Brough d											11 53	12 06	12 12	12 24					12 53	13 10			13 39
Broomfleet d																							
Gilberdyke d											12 00								13 00				
Eastrington d																							
Howden d														12 36									
Wressle d																							
Selby a												12 25	12 32	12 46						13 28			13 58
Selby d												12 25	12 33	12 47						13 29			13 58
York 8 33 a												12 50											14 22
Saltmarshe d																							
Goole d				11 43							12 09								13 09				
Thorne North d				11 51																			
Cleethorpes d							10 00	10 45									11 00	11 45					
New Clee d																							
Grimsby Docks d																							
Grimsby Town a							10 20	11 05									11 20	12 05					
Grimsby Town d							10 25	11 10									11 25	12 10					
Great Coates d																							
Healing d																							
Stallingborough d																							
Habrough d							10 50										11 50						
Ulceby d																							
Thornton Abbey d																							
Goxhill d																							
New Holland d																							
Barrow Haven d																							
Barton-on-Humber a																							
Barton-on-Humber 🚌 d	10 55																						
Hull Paragon Interchange 🚌 a	11 19																						
Barnetby d							11 05										12 05						
Scunthorpe a							11 30										12 30						
Scunthorpe d							11 35										12 35						
Althorpe d																							
Crowle d																							
Thorne South d																							
Hatfield & Stainforth d				11 57																			
Kirk Sandall d				12 02																			
Adwick 31 d															*12 43*								
Bentley (S.Yorks) 31 d															*12 47*								
Doncaster 7 31 a				12 14			12 25	12 25			12 32			13 05			13 25	13 25	13 32				
London Kings Cross 15 ⊖ 26 a											*14 44*			14 54					*15 42*				
York 8 26 d				*11 29*	11 28										*12 29*	12b28			*12 57*				
Doncaster 7 d		11 42		12 16	12 31					12 42					13 13	13 30			13 34		13 42		
Conisbrough d				12 23											13 20								
Mexborough d				12 27		←									13 24								
Swinton (S.Yorks) d			11 55	12 30 →		12 30									13 27							14 01	
Rotherham Central d			12 06			12 38									13 36							14 09	
Meadowhall 🚊 d		12 00	12 11			12 43				13 00					13 44				13 53		14 00	14 17	
Sheffield 7 🚊 a		12 07	12 20		12 54	12 55				13 07					13 52	13 55			14 04		14 07	14 25	
Sheffield 7 d		12 10								13 10											14 11		
Stockport 78 a		12 52	*13 25*							13 52			*14c16*							*15c16*	14 52	*15 25*	
Manchester Piccadilly 10 78 🚊 a		13 06	*13 37*							14 06			13 54							14 54	15 06	*15 37*	
Manchester Airport 85 ✈ a		13 29	*14e17*							14 29			*14 19*							*15 20*	15 29	*16e17*	

For general notes see front of timetable
For details of catering facilities see Directory of Train Operators

A From Leeds (Table 31)
B From Edinburgh to Plymouth (Table 51)
C From Edinburgh (Table 51) to Penzance (Table 135)
D From Scarborough (Table 43)
b By changing at Doncaster, passengers may depart at 1257
c Change at Manchester Piccadilly
e Change at Sheffield and Manchester Piccadilly

Table 29

Sundays

28 June to 6 September

Hull and Cleethorpes → Doncaster → Meadowhall, Sheffield, Manchester and Manchester Airport
Cleethorpes → Barton-on-Humber

Network Diagram - see first page of Table 18

	XC	NT		TP	TP	NT	NT	NT	TP	XC	HT	XC	NT	TP	TP	NT	NT		TP	TP	NT	EM	XC
	1 ◇								1 ◇	1 ◇	1 ◇	1 ◇							1 ◇	1 ◇			1 ◇
	A							B		C		D					E				G	H	J
				bus	bus		bus							bus	bus								
	trolley									trolley	⊠	trolley											trolley
Hull d								13 41			14 10					14 28	14 41		14 58				
Hessle d																14 35							
Ferriby d																14 40							
Brough d								13 53			14 22					14 45	14 53		15 10				
Broomfleet d																							
Gilberdyke d								14 00									15 00						
Eastrington d																							
Howden d											14 34												
Wressle d																							
Selby a											14 44					15 04			15 28				
Selby d											14 45					15 04			15 29				
York 8 33 a																15 30			16 57				
Saltmarshe d																							
Goole d		13 43						14 09									15 09						
Thorne North d		13 51																					
Cleethorpes d				12 00	12 45	12 56								13 00	13 45							13 56	
New Clee d						12x59																	
Grimsby Docks d						13 01																	
Grimsby Town a				12 20	13 05	13 04								13 20	14 05							14 02	
Grimsby Town d				12 25	13 10	13 04								13 25	14 10							14 03	
Great Coates d						13 08																	
Healing d						13 11																	
Stallingborough d						13 14																	
Habrough d				12 50		13 20								13 50								14 13	
Ulceby d						13 24																	
Thornton Abbey d						13 29																	
Goxhill d						13 32																	
New Holland d						13 36																	
Barrow Haven d						13 39																	
Barton-on-Humber a						13 45																	
Barton-on-Humber (bus) d							13 55																
Hull Paragon Interchange (bus) a							14 19																
Barnetby d				13 05										14 05								14a21	
Scunthorpe a				13 30										14 30									
Scunthorpe d				13 35										14 35									
Althorpe d																							
Crowle d																							
Thorne South d																							
Hatfield & Stainforth d		13 57																					
Kirk Sandall d		14 02																					
Adwick 31 d													14 43										
Bentley (S.Yorks) 31 d													14 47										
Doncaster 7 31 a		14 11		14 25	14 25			14 32			15 05			15 25	15 25		15 32						
London Kings Cross 15 ⊖ 26 a		16 10						16 29			16 50						17 49						
York 8 26 d	13 28	13 37						14 02		14 19		14 28	14 36										15 28
Doncaster 7 d		14 13						14 33	14 42	14 50			15 13				15 33			15 42			
Conisbrough d		14 20											15 20										
Mexborough d		14 24											15 24										
Swinton (S.Yorks) d		14 30											15 30								15 55		
Rotherham Central d		14 37											15 37								16 05		
Meadowhall (tram) d		14 43						14 53	15 00				15 43				15 52			16 00	16 11		
Sheffield 7 (tram) a	14 44	14 52						15 03	15 07	15 18		15 42	15 51				16 01			16 07	16 21		16 41
Sheffield 7 d									15 11											16 11			
Stockport 78 a									15 53	16 25									17b16	16 53	17 27		
Manchester Piccadilly 10 78 (tram) a									16 06	16 37									16 54	17 06	17 37		
Manchester Airport 85 (plane) a									16 29	17c17									17 19	17 29	18c17		

For general notes see front of timetable
For details of catering facilities see Directory of Train Operators

A From Edinburgh to Plymouth (Table 51)

B From Scarborough (Table 43)
C From Newcastle to Reading (Table 51)
D From Edinburgh (Table 51) to Penzance (Table 135)
E From Bridlington (Table 43)
G From Leeds (Table 31)

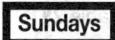

H To Nottingham (Table 27)
J From Glasgow Central to Plymouth (Table 51)
b Change at Manchester Piccadilly
c Change at Sheffield and Manchester Piccadilly

Table 29

Sundays

Hull and Cleethorpes → Doncaster → Meadowhall, Sheffield, Manchester and Manchester Airport
Cleethorpes → Barton-on-Humber

28 June to 6 September

Network Diagram - see first page of Table 18

		NT	TP	TP	NT	TP	NT	NT	TP	XC	XC	NT		NT	HT	TP	TP	NT	TP	TP	XC	NT	EM	NT
									1 ◇	1 ◇	1 ◇				1 ◇				1 ◇	1 ◇	1 ◇		1 ◇	
					A					B	C							D			E	G	H	J
			bus	bus		bus		bus								bus	bus							
										trolley	trolley				first class						trolley		restaurant	
Hull	d				15 41									16 01	16 21			16 41	16 58					
Hessle	d																							
Ferriby	d																							
Brough	d				15 53									16 13	16 33			16 53	17 10					
Broomfleet	d																							
Gilberdyke	d				16 00													17 00						
Eastrington	d																							
Howden	d														16 45									
Wressle	d																							
Selby	a													16 32	16 55				17 28					
	d													16 32	16 56				17 29					
York 8	33 a													16 57										
Saltmarshe	d																							
Goole	d	15 43			16 09													17 09						
Thorne North	d	15 51																						
Cleethorpes	d		14 00	14 45		15 00	15 02										15 45							
New Clee	d						15x05																	
Grimsby Docks	d						15 07																	
Grimsby Town	a		14 20	15 05		15 20	15 10									←	16 05							
	d		14 25	15 10		15 25	15 10									15 25	16 10							
Great Coates	d					→	15 14																	
Healing	d						15 17																	
Stallingborough	d						15 20																	
Habrough	d		14 50				15 26									15 50								
Ulceby	d						15 30																	
Thornton Abbey	d						15 34																	
Goxhill	d						15 37																	
New Holland	d						15 42																	
Barrow Haven	d						15 45																	
Barton-on-Humber	a						15 50																	
Barton-on-Humber	bus d							15 55																
Hull Paragon Interchange	bus a							16 19																
Barnetby	d		15 05													16 05								
Scunthorpe	a		15 30													16 30								
	d		15 35													16 35								
Althorpe	d																							
Crowle	d																							
Thorne South	d																							
Hatfield & Stainforth	d	15 57																						
Kirk Sandall	d	16 02																						
Adwick	31 d											*16 43*												
Bentley (S.Yorks)	31 d											*16 47*												
Doncaster 7	31 a	16 11	16 25	16 25	16 32										17 14	17 25	17 25	17 31						
London Kings Cross 15	⊖ 26 a	*18 15*			*18 43*										19 06			*19 48*						
York 8	26 d	*15 34*							*16 03*	16 20	16 28	*16 29*						*16 53*		*17 03*	17 20		17 40	17 17
Doncaster 7	d	16 13			16 33				16 42	16 50		17 13						17 32		17 42	17 50		18 06	
Conisbrough	d	16 20										17 21												
Mexborough	d	16 24										17 25												
Swinton (S.Yorks)	d	16 29										17 30										17 55		18 11
Rotherham Central	d	16 37										17 38										18 06		18 18
Meadowhall	tram d	16 43			16 53				17 00			17 43						17 53		18 00		18 12		18 24
Sheffield 7	tram a	16 52			17 03				17 07	17 18	17 41	17 54						18 01		18 07	18 16	18 23	18 28	18 35
	d								17 11											18 11				
Stockport	78 a								17 53	*18 25*									*19b16*	18 53			*19 25*	
Manchester Piccadilly 10	78 tram a								18 06	*18 37*									18 54	19 06			*19 37*	
Manchester Airport	85 rail-air a								18 29	*19c17*									*19 19*	19 29			*20c17*	

For general notes see front of timetable
For details of catering facilities see Directory of Train Operators

A From Scarborough (Table 43)
B From Edinburgh to Reading (Table 51)
C From Aberdeen to Plymouth (Table 51)
D From Bridlington (Table 43)
E From Newcastle to Reading (Table 51)
G From Leeds (Table 31)
H To St Pancras International (Table 53)
J Via Pontefract Baghill (Table 33)
b Change at Manchester Piccadilly
c Change at Sheffield and Manchester Piccadilly

Table 29

Sundays

28 June to 6 September

Hull and Cleethorpes → Doncaster → Meadowhall, Sheffield, Manchester and Manchester Airport
Cleethorpes → Barton-on-Humber

Network Diagram - see first page of Table 18

		XC	NT	NT	GR	TP		TP	NT	TP	XC	XC	NT	TP	TP	NT	NT	NT	TP	HT	XC		NT	XC
		1 ◊			**R** **1**					**1** ◊	**1** ◊	**1** ◊							**1** ◊	**1** ◊	**1** ◊			**1** ◊
		A							B		C	D				E					G		H	D
						🚌		🚌						🚌	🚌			🚌						
		🍴			🍴						🍴	🍴								⊠	🍴			🍴
Hull	d			17 23	17 30				17 41							18 38				18 48				
Hessle	d																							
Ferriby	d																							
Brough	d			17 35	17 42				17 53							18 50				19 00				
Broomfleet	d																							
Gilberdyke	d								18 00							18 57								
Eastrington	d																							
Howden	d																			19 12				
Wressle	d																							
Selby	a			17 54	18 05															19 22				
	d			17 54	18 05															19 23				
York **8**	33 a			18 23																				
Saltmarshe	d																							
Goole	d		17 43						18 09							19 06								
Thorne North	d		17 51													19 14								
Cleethorpes	d					16 00		16 45						17 00	17 45		17 56							
New Clee	d																17x59							
Grimsby Docks	d																18 01							
Grimsby Town	a					16 20		17 05						17 20	18 05		18 04							
	d					16 25		17 10						17 25	18 10		18 04							
Great Coates	d																18 08							
Healing	d																18 11							
Stallingborough	d																18 14							
Habrough	d					16 50								17 50			18 20							
Ulceby	d																18 24							
Thornton Abbey	d																18 28							
Goxhill	d																18 31							
New Holland	d																18 36							
Barrow Haven	d																18 39							
Barton-on-Humber	a																18 45							
Barton-on-Humber	🚌 d																	18 55						
Hull Paragon Interchange	🚌 a																	19 19						
Barnetby	d					17 05								18 05										
Scunthorpe	a					17 30								18 30										
	d					17 35								18 35										
Althorpe	d																							
Crowle	d																							
Thorne South	d																							
Hatfield & Stainforth	d		17 57													19 20								
Kirk Sandall	d		18 02													19 25								
Adwick	31 d												*18 43*											
Bentley (S.Yorks)	31 d												*18 47*											
Doncaster 7	31 a		18 11		18 23	18 25		18 25	18 33					19 25	19 25	19 35				19 43				
London Kings Cross **15**	⊖ 26 a		*20 14*		20b23				*20 43*											21 34				
York **8**	26 d	17 28								*18 05*	18 20	18 28	*18 29*						*19 05*		19 20			19 28
Doncaster 7	d		18 13						18 34	18 42	18 50		19 15			19 37			19 42		19 50			
Conisbrough	d		18 20										19 22											
Mexborough	d		18 24										19 26											
Swinton (S.Yorks)	d		18 30										19 30										19 55	
Rotherham Central	d		18 37										19 41										20 06	
Meadowhall	⛴ d		18 43						18 53	19 00			19 47			19 57			20 00				20 11	
Sheffield 7	⛴ a	18 40	18 52						19 03	19 07	19 15	19 40	19 55			20 06			20 07		20 15		20 23	20 40
	d									19 11									20 11					
Stockport	78 a									19 53	*20 25*								20 53				*21 24*	
Manchester Piccadilly 10	78 ⛴ a									20 06	*20 38*								21 06				*21 36*	
Manchester Airport	85 ✈ a									20 29	*21c17*								21 29				*22c17*	

For general notes see front of timetable
For details of catering facilities see Directory of Train Operators

A From Glasgow Central to Plymouth (Table 51)
B From Scarborough (Table 43)
C From Newcastle to Southampton Central (Table 51)
D From Edinburgh to Bristol Temple Meads (Table 51)
E From Bridlington (Table 43)
G From Newcastle to Birmingham New Street (Table 51)
H From Leeds (Table 31)
b By changing at Doncaster, passengers may arrive at 2014
c Change at Sheffield and Manchester Piccadilly

Table 29

Sundays

Hull and Cleethorpes → Doncaster → Meadowhall, Sheffield, Manchester and Manchester Airport
Cleethorpes → Barton-on-Humber

28 June to 6 September

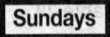

Network Diagram - see first page of Table 18

		TP	NT	TP	EM	TP	TP	NT	TP	XC	NT	NT	TP	TP	NT	EM	TP	TP	NT	TP	NT	TP
		1 ◇							1 ◇	1 ◇							1 ◇	1 ◇				
					A					B					C	D		E	G		H	
				🚌		🚌	🚌						🚌	🚌						🚌		🚌
Hull	d	18 58						19 04			20 22	20 30						21 00			21 15	
Hessle	d																				21 22	
Ferriby	d																				21 27	
Brough	d	19 10						19 16			20 34	20 42						21 12			21 32	
Broomfleet	d																					
Gilberdyke	d											20 49									21 39	
Eastrington	d																					
Howden	d																					
Wressle	d																					
Selby	a	19 28						19 35			20 53							21 30				
	d	19 29						19 35			20 53											
York 8	33 a	19 59						19 59			21 20											
Saltmarshe	d																					
Goole	d											20 58									21 48	
Thorne North	d																				21 56	
Cleethorpes	d			18 00	18 18		18 45						19 00	19 45		19 54				20 30		20 30
New Clee	d																					
Grimsby Docks	d																					
Grimsby Town	a			18 20	18 24	←	19 05						19 20	20 05		20 00						20 50
	d			18 25 →	18 25	18 25	19 10						19 25	20 10		20 07				20u55		20 55
Great Coates	d																					
Healing	d																					
Stallingborough	d																					
Habrough	d				18 35	18 50							19 50			20 17						21 20
Ulceby	d																					
Thornton Abbey	d																					
Goxhill	d																					
New Holland	d																					
Barrow Haven	d																					
Barton-on-Humber	a																					
Barton-on-Humber	🚌 d																					
Hull Paragon Interchange	🚌 a																					
Barnetby	d				18a43	19 05							20 05			20a25						21 35
Scunthorpe	a					19 30							20 30									22 00
	d					19 35							20 35									22 05
Althorpe	d																					
Crowle	d																					
Thorne South	d																					
Hatfield & Stainforth	d																				22 02	
Kirk Sandall	d																				22 07	
Adwick	31 d											20 54									21 43	
Bentley (S.Yorks)	31 d											20 58									21 47	
Doncaster 7	31 a					20 25	20 25					21 21	21 25	21 25						22 10	22 17	22 55
London Kings Cross 15	⊖ 26 a						22 37							23 50								
York 8	26 d		19 31						20 02	20 28		20 38			20 42						21 28	
Doncaster 7	d		20 14						20 42			21 23					21 42				22 20	
Conisbrough	d		20 21																		22 27	
Mexborough	d		20 25																		22 31	
Swinton (S.Yorks)	d		20 32												21 38		21 54		22 32		22 37	
Rotherham Central	d		20 39									21 39			21 49		22 00		22 40		22 44	
Meadowhall	🚊 d		20 45						21 00			21 45			21 54		22 04		22 45		22 50	
Sheffield 7	🚊 a		20 53						21 07	21 44		21 56			22 05		22 15		22 54		22 58	
	d								21 11													
Stockport	78 a	21b15							21 53						23 16							
Manchester Piccadilly 10	78 🚊 a	20 54							22 06						23 29							
Manchester Airport	85 ✈ a	21 19							22 29						00c17							

For general notes see front of timetable
For details of catering facilities see Directory of Train Operators

A To Newark North Gate (Table 27)
B From Edinburgh to Birmingham New Street (Table 51)
C Via Pontefract Baghill (Table 33)
D To Nottingham (Table 27)
E To Leeds (Table 39)
G From Leeds (Table 31)
H From Scarborough (Table 43)
b Change at Manchester Piccadilly
c Change at Sheffield and Manchester Piccadilly

until 19 June and from 7 September

Manchester Airport, Manchester, Sheffield and Meadowhall → Doncaster → Cleethorpes and Hull Barton-on-Humber → Cleethorpes

Network Diagram - see first page of Table 18

Miles	Miles	Miles	Miles	Miles	Station		NT	NT	NT	EM	NT	NT	NT	NT BHX	NT	XC	NT	NT	TP	TP	NT	NT	NT	XC
																1 ◇			1 ◇	1 ◇				1 ◇
							A		B	C			A	(bus)		D		E			B			G
																(trolley)				(trolley)				(trolley)
0	—	—	—	—	**Manchester Airport**	85 ✈ d													05 15	*05 37*				
9¾	—	—	—	—	**Manchester Piccadilly 10**	78 d													05 44	06 21				*05 50*
15¾	—	—	—	—	Stockport	78 d													05 52	*05b53*				*06 00*
52½	—	—	—	—	**Sheffield 7**	a													06 49					
—	—	—	—	—		d	05 22		05 29			06 18	06 28			06 40	06 52		06 55					07 12
56	—	—	—	—	**Meadowhall**	d	05 28		05 35			06 24	06 34				06 58		07 01				←	
58¾	—	—	—	—	Rotherham Central	d	05 34		05 41			06 30	06 40				07 05							
63¼	—	—	—	—	Swinton (S.Yorks)	d	05a42		05 49			06 39	06a51				07 15						07 15	
64½	—	—	—	—	Mexborough	d			05 52			06 42					→						07 18	
66¾	—	—	—	—	Conisbrough	d			05 56			06 46											07 22	
71½	—	—	—	—	**Doncaster 7**	a			06 06			06 56				07 04			07 22				07 30	
—	—	—	—	—	York 8	26 a			*06 35*							07 27								08 23
—	—	—	—	—	London Kings Cross 15	⊖ 26 d																		
—	0	0	—	0	**Doncaster**	31 d		05 52	06 14		06 47	06 59							07 24		07 28		07 32	
—	—	—	—	1¾	Bentley (S.Yorks)	31 a			*06 28*			07 02				*07c17*							07 35	
—	—	—	—	4	Adwick	31 a			*06 32*			07 08				*07c21*							07 40	
75½	—	4	—	—	Kirk Sandall	d			06 20		06 53										07 34			
78¼	—	6¾	—	—	Hatfield & Stainforth	d			06 25		06 58										07 39			
—	—	9¾	—	—	Thorne South	d					07 03													
—	—	15¾	—	—	Crowle	d					07 11													
—	—	19½	—	—	Althorpe	d					07 17													
—	—	23	—	—	**Scunthorpe**	a					07 26								07 49					
—	—	—	—	—		d													07 50					
—	—	34¼	—	—	Barnetby	d				06 31									08 04					
—	—	—	—	—	Hull Paragon Interchange	(bus) d								06 25										
—	—	—	—	—	Barton-on-Humber	(bus) a								06 50										
—	—	—	0	—	**Barton-on-Humber**	d									06 58									
—	—	—	2	—	Barrow Haven	d									07 03									
—	—	—	3½	—	New Holland	d									07 07									
—	—	—	5½	—	Goxhill	d									07 11									
—	—	—	7	—	Thornton Abbey	d																		
—	—	—	9¾	—	Ulceby	d									07 19									
—	—	40¾	11½	—	Habrough	d				06 41					07 23				08 12					
—	—	44½	15¼	—	Stallingborough	d									07 28									
—	—	45½	16¼	—	Healing	d									07 31									
—	—	45½	17¼	—	Great Coates	d																		
—	—	48¾	19½	—	**Grimsby Town**	a				06 56					07 37				08 26					
—	—	—	—	—		d									07 38				08 35					
—	—	49¾	20½	—	Grimsby Docks	d																		
—	—	50½	21¼	—	New Clee	d																		
—	—	52	22¾	—	**Cleethorpes**	a									07 50				08 46					
81½	—	—	—	—	Thorne North	d			06 30												07 44			
88¾	—	—	—	—	Goole	d			06 41												07 53			
92¼	—	—	—	—	Saltmarshe	d			06 46												07 58			
—	—	—	—	—	York 8	33 d														*06 09*		07 31		
—	18¼	—	—	—	**Selby**	a		06 14												07 43		07 50		
—	—	—	—	—		d														07 43		07 50		
—	24½	—	—	—	Wressle	d																07 58		
—	27	—	—	—	Howden	d														07 52		08 03		
—	30	—	—	—	Eastrington	d																08 08		
95½	32¼	—	—	—	Gilberdyke	d			06 53									07 39			08 04	08 12		
98	34¾	—	—	—	Broomfleet	d			06 57									07 43				08 16		
102	38¾	—	—	—	Brough	d			07 03									07 49		08 04	08 12	08 22		
105	41¾	—	—	—	Ferriby	d			07 07									07 53			08 16	08 27		
107¾	44½	—	—	—	Hessle	d			07 12									07 58			08 21	08 31		
112	49¼	—	—	—	**Hull**	a			07 22									08 11		08 20	08 34	08 46		

For general notes see front of timetable
For details of catering facilities see Directory of Train Operators

- **A** To Leeds (Table 31)
- **B** To Beverley (Table 43)
- **C** From Lincoln (Table 27)
- **D** From Derby to Newcastle (Table 51)
- **E** To Scarborough (Table 43)
- **G** From Birmingham New Street to Edinburgh (Table 51)
- **b** Change at Manchester Piccadilly
- **c** Change at Doncaster

Table 29

Mondays to Fridays

until 19 June and from 7 September

Manchester Airport, Manchester, Sheffield and Meadowhall → Doncaster → Cleethorpes and Hull
Barton-on-Humber → Cleethorpes

Network Diagram - see first page of Table 18

	NT A	NT	NT B	NT BHX 🚌	NT	EM C	XC 1◇ D ⊤	TP 1◇ ⊤	NT A		TP 1◇ ⊤	NT	HT BHX 1◇ ⊠	XC 1◇ E ⊤	NT	NT B	XC 1◇ D ⊤	NT G	NT BHX 🚌	NT	TP 1◇ ⊤	TP 1◇ ⊤	NT A
Manchester Airport 85 ✈ d								06 55			07 05					07b05					07 54	08 05	
Manchester Piccadilly 10 78 🚆 d								07 20			07 36					07 42					08 20	08 42	
Stockport 78 d								07 28			07c10					07 54					08 28	08c19	
Sheffield 7 🚆 a								08 10													09 08		
d	07 14	07 24	07 41				07 54	08 11	08 14					08 21	08 25	08 41	08 54	08 57			09 11		09 14
Meadowhall 🚆 d	07 21	07 30	07 47					08 17	08 23						08 31	08 47		09 03			09 17		09 21
Rotherham Central d	07 27	07 36	07 55						08 29						08 37			09 11					09 27
Swinton (S.Yorks) d	07a35	07 44	08 03						08a38						08 48			09 19					09a36
Mexborough d		07 47	08 06												08 51			09 22					
Conisbrough d		07 51	08 10												08 55			09 26					
Doncaster 7 a		08 01	08 20				08 24	08 40							09 05	09 12	09 20	09 36			09 40		
York 8 26 a		*08 31*					08 47							09 33	*09 40*		09 48						
London Kings Cross 15 ⊖ 26 d		*06 00*	*06 35*										07 20		*07 10*						*07 30*		
Doncaster 31 d		08 03	08 22					08 42				08 56	09 06		09 10	09 17		09 49 →			09 42		
Bentley (S.Yorks) 31 a		*08 19*						*08 55*							*09 17*								
Adwick 31 a		*08 25*						*09 01*							*09 21*								
Kirk Sandall d		08 09										09 02			09 18								
Hatfield & Stainforth d		08 14										09 07			09 23								
Thorne South d		08 18													09 28								
Crowle d		08 27													09 36								
Althorpe d		08 33													09 42								
Scunthorpe a		08 43						09 07							09 50						10 07		
d								09 08													10 08		
Barnetby d						08 52		09 22													10 22		
Hull Paragon Interchange 🚌 d				07 25															09 25				
Barton-on-Humber 🚌 a				07 50															09 50				
Barton-on-Humber d					08 00															09 58			
Barrow Haven d					08 05															10 03			
New Holland d					08 08															10 06			
Goxhill d					08 13															10 11			
Thornton Abbey d					08 16															10 14			
Ulceby d					08 20															10 18			
Habrough d					08 25	09 01														10 23	10 31		
Stallingborough d					08 30															10 28			
Healing d					08 33															10 31			
Great Coates d					08 36															10 34			
Grimsby Town a					08 41	09 15		09 42												10 39	10 44		
d					08 41			09 43												10 39	10 45		
Grimsby Docks d					08 44															10 42			
New Clee d					08x46															10x44			
Cleethorpes a					08 51			09 58												10 49	10 59		
Thorne North d												09 12											
Goole d			08 43									09 21				09 39							
Saltmarshe d																							
York 8 33 d													*08 43*										
Selby a											08 58		09 21									09 57	
d											08 59		09 22									09 58	
Wressle d																							
Howden d													09 32										
Eastrington d																							
Gilberdyke d												09 29											
Broomfleet d																							
Brough d			08 57									09 37	09 44			09 56						10 16	
Ferriby d												09 42											
Hessle d												09 46											
Hull a			09 13								09 31	09 59	10 04			10 10						10 34	

For general notes see front of timetable
For details of catering facilities see Directory of Train Operators

- **A** To Leeds (Table 31)
- **B** To Bridlington (Table 43)
- **C** From Newark North Gate (Table 27)
- **D** From Birmingham New Street to Newcastle (Table 51)
- **E** From Birmingham New Street to Edinburgh (Table 51)
- **G** From Worksop (Table 30)
- **b** Change at Manchester Piccadilly and Sheffield
- **c** Change at Manchester Piccadilly

Manchester Airport, Manchester, Sheffield and Meadowhall → Doncaster → Cleethorpes and Hull Barton-on-Humber → Cleethorpes

Network Diagram - see first page of Table 18

		NT	NT	NT	XC	NT	NT	NT	XC	NT	EM	TP	TP	NT	NT		NT	XC	NT	NT	XC	HT	NT	NT BHX
					1 ◇				1 ◇			1 ◇	1 ◇					1 ◇			1 ◇	1 ◇		
				A	B		C	D	E	G	H			J	G			K		L	N		G	🚌
					⊼				⊼			⊼	⊼					⊼			⊼	☒		
Manchester Airport	85 ✈ d											08 55	*09 05*											
Manchester Piccadilly 10	78 🚊 d								*08 43*			09 20	09 42	*08 45*							*09 43*			
Stockport	78 d								*08 54*			09 28	09b17								*09 54*			
Sheffield 7	🚊 a											10 08												
	d				09 21	09 24	09 29	09 41	09 54	09 57		10 11		10 14				10 21	10 24	10 41	10 54		10 57	
Meadowhall	🚊 d					09 30	09 35	09 45		10 03		10 17		10 21					10 30	10 47			11 03	
Rotherham Central	d					09 37	09 42			10 10				10 27					10 36				11 10	
Swinton (S.Yorks)	d					09 48	09 51			10 18				10a36					10 44				11 20	
Mexborough	d					09 51				10 21									10 47				11 23	
Conisbrough	d					09 55				10 25									10 51				11 27	
Doncaster 7	a					10 04		10 11	10 15	10 36		10 40							11 04	11 08	11 15		11 35	
York 8	26 a			←	10 29		10 52	*11 02*	10 40						←			11 29	*11 37*		11 45			
London Kings Cross 15	⊖ 26 d											*09 00*										09 48	*09 35*	
Doncaster	31 d	09 46		09 49		10 06		10 16		10 46 →		10 42			10 46		10 47		11 07	11 17		11 36	11 38	
Bentley (S.Yorks)	31 a			09 52		*10 17*									10 49						*11c29*		11 41	
Adwick	31 a			09 58		*10 21*									10 55						*11c33*		11 47	
Kirk Sandall	d	09 52				10 12											10 53		11 13					
Hatfield & Stainforth	d	09 57				10 17											10 58		11 18					
Thorne South	d					10 22													11 23					
Crowle	d					10 31													11 31					
Althorpe	d					10 37													11 37					
Scunthorpe	a					10 45						11 07							11 45					
	d											11 08												
Barnetby	d										10 57	11 22												
Hull Paragon Interchange	🚌 d																							11 25
Barton-on-Humber	🚌 a																							11 50
Barton-on-Humber	d																							
Barrow Haven	d																							
New Holland	d																							
Goxhill	d																							
Thornton Abbey	d																							
Ulceby	d																							
Habrough	d										11 06													
Stallingborough	d																							
Healing	d																							
Great Coates	d																							
Grimsby Town	a										11 21	11 42												
	d											11 43												
Grimsby Docks	d																							
New Clee	d																							
Cleethorpes	a											11 54												
Thorne North	d	10 02															11 03							
Goole	d	10 11						10 35									11 12			11 38				
Saltmarshe	d																							
York 8	33 d		09 53										*10 20*											
Selby	a		10 12										10 57									11 51		
	d		10 12										10 58									11 52		
Wressle	d																							
Howden	d		10 22																			12 02		
Eastrington	d																							
Gilberdyke	d	10 19	10 29														11 20							
Broomfleet	d																11 25							
Brough	d	10 27	10 37					10 49					11 16				11 31			11 52		12 15		
Ferriby	d	10 32															11 35							
Hessle	d	10 36															11 40							
Hull	a	10 49	10 56					11 06					11 34				11 53			12 09		12 32		

For general notes see front of timetable
For details of catering facilities see Directory of Train Operators

- **A** From Worksop (Table 30)
- **B** From Bristol Temple Meads to Newcastle (Table 51)
- **C** Via Pontefract Baghill (Table 33)
- **D** To Scarborough (Table 43)
- **E** From Guildford to Newcastle (Table 51)
- **G** From Lincoln (Table 30)
- **H** From Newark North Gate (Table 27)
- **J** To Leeds (Table 31)
- **K** From Plymouth to Edinburgh (Table 51)
- **L** To Bridlington (Table 43)
- **N** From Reading to Newcastle (Table 51)
- **b** Change at Manchester Piccadilly
- **c** Change at Doncaster

until 19 June and from 7 September

Manchester Airport, Manchester, Sheffield and Meadowhall → Doncaster → Cleethorpes and Hull Barton-on-Humber → Cleethorpes

Network Diagram - see first page of Table 18

		NT	TP	TP	NT	NT	NT	XC	NT	NT	XC	NT	EM	TP	TP	NT	NT	XC	NT	NT		NT BHX	NT	XC
			1 ◇	1 ◇				1 ◇			1 ◇			1 ◇	1 ◇			1 ◇						1 ◇
					A			B		C	D	E	G			A		B		H				D
			╤	╤				╤			╤			╤	╤			╤				Bus		╤
Manchester Airport 85 ✈	d		09 55	*10 05*										10 55	*11 05*									
Manchester Piccadilly 10 78	d		10 20	10 42							*10 43*			11 20	11 42	*10 45*								*11 43*
Stockport 78	d		10 28	*10b17*							*10 54*			11 28	*11b17*									*11 54*
Sheffield 7	a		11 08											12 08										
	d		11 11		11 14			11 21	11 24	11 41	11 54	11 57		12 11		12 14		12 21	12 24	12 41				12 54
Meadowhall	d		11 17		11 21				11 30	11 47		12 03		12 17		12 21			12 30	12 47				
Rotherham Central	d				11 27				11 37			12 10				12 27			12 37					
Swinton (S.Yorks)	d				11a36				11 48			12 19				12a36			12 47					
Mexborough	d								11 51			12 22							12 50					
Conisbrough	d								11 55			12 26							12 54					
Doncaster 7	a		11 40						12 04	12 11	12 15	12 35		12 40					13 04	13 11				13 20
York 8 26	a							12 29			12 45							13 29	*13 39*					13 46
London Kings Cross 15 ⊖ 26	d								*10 10*			*10 35*							*11 10*					
Doncaster 31	d		11 42			11 49			12 07	12 14		12 36		12 42			12 49		13 06	13 18				
Bentley (S.Yorks) 31	a										*12c28*	12 40												*13c30*
Adwick 31	a										*12c32*	12 45												*13c34*
Kirk Sandall	d					11 55			12 14								12 55		13 12					
Hatfield & Stainforth	d					12 00			12 19								13 00		13 17					
Thorne South	d								12 24										13 22					
Crowle	d								12 32										13 31					
Althorpe	d								12 38										13 37					
Scunthorpe	a		12 06						12 46					13 07					13 45					
	d		12 08											13 08										
Barnetby	d		12 22										13 12	13 22										
Hull Paragon Interchange (bus)	d																					13 25		
Barton-on-Humber (bus)	a																					13 50		
Barton-on-Humber	d	11 58																					13 58	
Barrow Haven	d	12 03																					14 03	
New Holland	d	12 06																					14 06	
Goxhill	d	12 11																					14 11	
Thornton Abbey	d	12 14																					14 14	
Ulceby	d	12 18																					14 18	
Habrough	d	12 23	12 31										13 21										14 23	
Stallingborough	d	12 28																					14 28	
Healing	d	12 31																					14 31	
Great Coates	d	12 34																					14 34	
Grimsby Town	a	12 39	12 45										13 36	13 42									14 39	
	d	12 39	12 46											13 43									14 39	
Grimsby Docks	d	12 42																					14 42	
New Clee	d	12x44																					14x44	
Cleethorpes	a	12 49	12 57											13 54									14 49	
Thorne North	d					12 05											13 05							
Goole	d					12 14				12 35							13 14			13 37				
Saltmarshe	d																							
York 8 33	d						11 53								*12 18*									
Selby	a			11 57			12 17								12 57									
	d			11 58			12 18								12 58									
Wressle	d																							
Howden	d						12 27																	
Eastrington	d																							
Gilberdyke	d					12 22	12 34										13 22							
Broomfleet	d																							
Brough	d			12 16		12 30	12 42			12 49					13 16		13 30			13 51				
Ferriby	d					12 35											13 35							
Hessle	d					12 39											13 39							
Hull	a			12 36		12 52	13 02			13 06					13 34		13 52			14 08				

For general notes see front of timetable
For details of catering facilities see Directory of Train Operators

- **A** To Leeds (Table 31)
- **B** From Plymouth to Edinburgh (Table 51)
- **C** To Scarborough (Table 43)
- **D** From Reading to Newcastle (Table 51)
- **E** From Lincoln (Table 30)
- **G** From Newark North Gate (Table 27)
- **H** To Bridlington (Table 43)
- **b** Change at Manchester Piccadilly
- **c** Change at Doncaster

Table 29

Mondays to Fridays

until 19 June and from 7 September

Manchester Airport, Manchester, Sheffield and Meadowhall → Doncaster → Cleethorpes and Hull Barton-on-Humber → Cleethorpes

Network Diagram - see first page of Table 18

		HT	NT	TP	TP	NT	NT	NT	XC	NT	NT	NT	XC	NT	TP	TP	NT	NT	NT	XC	NT	HT	NT	EM
		1 ◇		1 ◇	1 ◇				1 ◇				1 ◇		1 ◇	1 ◇				1 ◇		1 ◇		
			A			B			C		D	E	G	A			B	H		J				K
		☒		🍴	🍴				🍴				🍴		🍴	🍴				🍴		☒		
Manchester Airport	85 ✈ d			11 55	*12 05*										12 55	*13 05*								
Manchester Piccadilly 10	78 🚌 d			12 20	12 42								*12 43*		13 20	13 42	*12 45*							
Stockport	78 d			12 28	*12b17*								*12 54*		13 28	*13b17*								
Sheffield 7	🚌 a			13 08											14 08									
	d		12 57	13 11		13 14			13 21	13 24	13 28	13 41	13 54	13 57	14 11		14 14			14 21	14 24		14 41	
Meadowhall	🚌 d		13 03	13 17		13 21				13 30	13 35	13 46		14 03	14 17		14 21				14 30		14 47	
Rotherham Central	d		13 10			13 27				13 37	13 41			14 10			14 27				14 37			
Swinton (S.Yorks)	d		13 18			13a36				13 47	13 50			14 18			14a36				14 48			
Mexborough	d		13 21							13 50				14 21							14 51			
Conisbrough	d		13 25							13 54				14 25							14 55			
Doncaster 7	a		13 35	13 40						14 04		14 13	14 17	14 35	14 40						15 04		15 09	
York 8	26 a			*14 34*					14 29		14 51	*14 58*	14 43		*15 26*					15 29				
London Kings Cross 15	⊖ 26 d	11 48								*12 10*		*12 30*		*12 35*	*13 00*						*13 10*	13 33	*13 30*	
Doncaster	31 d	13 29	13 38	13 42				13 46		14 06		14 17		14 38	14 42			14 46			15 06	15 12	15 14	
Bentley (S.Yorks)	31 a		13 41										*14c30*	14 41							*15 17*			
Adwick	31 a		13 47										*14c34*	14 47							*15 21*			
Kirk Sandall	d							13 52		14 13								14 54			15 12			
Hatfield & Stainforth	d							13 57		14 18								14 59			15 17			
Thorne South	d									14 23											15 22			
Crowle	d									14 32											15 30			
Althorpe	d									14 38											15 36			
Scunthorpe	a			14 07						14 45					15 07						15 45			
	d			14 08											15 08									
Barnetby	d			14 22											15 22									15 34
Hull Paragon Interchange	🚌 d																							
Barton-on-Humber	🚌 a																							
Barton-on-Humber	d																							
Barrow Haven	d																							
New Holland	d																							
Goxhill	d																							
Thornton Abbey	d																							
Ulceby	d																							
Habrough	d			14 31																				15 42
Stallingborough	d																							
Healing	d																							
Great Coates	d																							
Grimsby Town	a			14 45											15 42									15 57
	d			14 46											15 43									
Grimsby Docks	d																							
New Clee	d																							
Cleethorpes	a			14 57											15 54									
Thorne North	d							14 02										15 04						
Goole	d							14 12				14 36						15 13					15 38	
Saltmarshe	d							14 17																
York 8	33 d						13 45												14 59					
Selby	a	13 44			13 57		14 09									14 57			15 19			15 27		
	d	13 45			13 58		14 09									14 58			15 19			15 28		
Wressle	d																							
Howden	d	13 55																				15 38		
Eastrington	d																							
Gilberdyke	d							14 28										15 21						
Broomfleet	d																							
Brough	d	14 08			14 16		14 29	14 36				14 52				15 16		15 29	15 39			15 53	15 58	
Ferriby	d							14 40										15 34						
Hessle	d							14 45										15 38						
Hull	a	14 25			14 34		14 48	14 56				15 07				15 34		15 51	15 58			16 10	16 12	

For general notes see front of timetable
For details of catering facilities see Directory of Train Operators

A From Lincoln (Table 30)
B To Leeds (Table 31)
C From Penzance (Table 135) to Edinburgh (Table 51)
D Via Pontefract Baghill (Table 33)
E To Bridlington (Table 43)
G From Reading to Newcastle (Table 51)
H To Scarborough (Table 43)
J From Plymouth (Table 51) to Aberdeen (Table 229)
K From Newark North Gate (Table 27)
b Change at Manchester Piccadilly
c Change at Doncaster

Manchester Airport, Manchester, Sheffield and Meadowhall → Doncaster → Cleethorpes and Hull Barton-on-Humber → Cleethorpes

Network Diagram - see first page of Table 18

		XC	NT	NT		NT	TP	TP	NT	NT	XC	NT	NT	NT	XC	NT	TP	TP	NT	NT	EM	NT	NT	XC
				BHX																		BHX		
		[1] ◇					[1] ◇	[1] ◇			[1] ◇				[1] ◇		[1] ◇	[1] ◇						[1] ◇
		A	B						C	D	E			G	A	B			C	D	H			J
				Bus																		Bus		
		Buffet					Buffet	Buffet			Buffet				Buffet		Buffet	Buffet						Buffet
Manchester Airport	85 ✈ d						13 55	14 05									14 55	15 05						
Manchester Piccadilly [10]	78 ⇌ d	13 43					14 20	14 42					14 43				15 20	15 42	14 45					
Stockport	78 d	13 54					14 28	14b17					14 54				15 28	15b17						
Sheffield [7]	⇌ a						15 08										16 08							
	d	14 54	14 57				15 11		15 14		15 21	15 24	15 41		15 54	15 57	16 11		16 14					16 21
Meadowhall	⇌ d		15 03				15 17		15 21			15 30	15 47			16 03	16 17		16 21					
Rotherham Central	d		15 10						15 27			15 37				16 10			16 27					
Swinton (S.Yorks)	d		15 18						15a36			15 47				16 18			16a36					
Mexborough	d		15 21									15 50				16 21								
Conisbrough	d		15 25									15 54				16 25								
Doncaster [7]	a	15 16	15 36				15 40					16 04	16 12		16 15	16 35	16 40							
York [8]	26 a	15 40									16 29				16 40		17 34							17 30
London Kings Cross [15]	⊖ 26 d		14 00									14 10	14 35											
Doncaster	31 d		15 38				15 42			15 46		16 09	16 18			16 38	16 42			16 46				
Bentley (S.Yorks)	31 a		15 41									16 17				16 41								
Adwick	31 a		15 47									16 21				16 47								
Kirk Sandall	d									15 52		16 15								16 52				
Hatfield & Stainforth	d									15 57		16 20								16 57				
Thorne South	d											16 25												
Crowle	d											16 34												
Althorpe	d											16 40												
Scunthorpe	a						16 07					16 48					17 07							
	d						16 08										17 08							
Barnetby	d						16 22										17 22				17 54			
Hull Paragon Interchange	Bus d			15 25																		17 30		
Barton-on-Humber	Bus a			15 50																		17 55		
Barton-on-Humber	d					15 58																	18 00	
Barrow Haven	d					16 03																	18 05	
New Holland	d					16 06																	18 08	
Goxhill	d					16 11																	18 13	
Thornton Abbey	d					16 14																	18 16	
Ulceby	d					16 18																	18 20	
Habrough	d					16 23	16 31														18 02		18 25	
Stallingborough	d					16 28																	18 30	
Healing	d					16 31																	18 33	
Great Coates	d					16 34																	18 36	
Grimsby Town	a					16 39	16 46										17 42				18 17		18 41	
	d					16 39	16 47										17 43						18 41	
Grimsby Docks	d					16 42																	18 44	
New Clee	d																							
Cleethorpes	a					16 48	16 57										17 54						18 50	
Thorne North	d									16 02										17 02				
Goole	d									16 11			16 39							17 11				
Saltmarshe	d																			17 16				
York [8]	33 d													16 12										
Selby	a							15 57						16 38				17 00						
	d							15 58						16 39				17 00						
Wressle	d													16 46										
Howden	d													16 51										
Eastrington	d																							
Gilberdyke	d									16 20				16 58						17 23				
Broomfleet	d																							
Brough	d							16 16		16 28			16 52	17 06				17 18		17 31				
Ferriby	d									16 32				17 10						17 36				
Hessle	d									16 37										17 40				
Hull	a							16 35		16 49			17 14	17 27				17 37		17 53				

For general notes see front of timetable
For details of catering facilities see Directory of Train Operators

- **A** From Reading to Newcastle (Table 51)
- **B** From Lincoln (Table 30)
- **C** To Leeds (Table 31)
- **D** To Bridlington (Table 43)
- **E** From Penzance (Table 135) to Glasgow Central (Table 51)
- **G** To Scarborough (Table 43)
- **H** From Lincoln (Table 27)
- **J** From Plymouth (Table 51) to Dundee (Table 229)
- **b** Change at Manchester Piccadilly

Table 29

Mondays to Fridays

until 19 June and from 7 September

Manchester Airport, Manchester, Sheffield and Meadowhall → Doncaster → Cleethorpes and Hull
Barton-on-Humber → Cleethorpes

Network Diagram - see first page of Table 18

	NT	NT	NT	XC	NT	NT	TP	HT		TP	NT	NT	XC	NT	NT	NT	NT	XC	TP	NT	NT	XC	TP
				1 ◇			1 ◇	1 ◇		1 ◇			1 ◇					1 ◇	1 ◇			1 ◇	1 ◇
				A	B	C					D	E	G				B	A		C	D	H	
				🍴			🍴	⊠		🍴			🍴					🍴	🍴			🍴	🍴
Manchester Airport 85 ✈ d							15 55			16 05									17 05				16 55
Manchester Piccadilly 10 78 🚆 d				15 43			16 20			16 42	15 45							16 43	17 42				17 20
Stockport 78 d				15 54			16 28			16b17								16 54	17b17				17 28
Sheffield 7 🚆 a							17 08																18 15
d	16 24	16 41		16 54		16 57	17 11				17 14		17 21	17 25	17 41			17 47		17 57	18 14	18 21	18 24
Meadowhall 🚆 d	16 30	16 47				17 03	17 17				17 21			17 31	17 47					18 03	18 21		18 29
Rotherham Central d	16 37					17 10					17 27			17 39						18 10	18 27		
Swinton (S.Yorks) d	16 47					17 18					17a36			17 47						18 18	18a36		
Mexborough d	16 50					17 21								17 50						18 21			
Conisbrough d	16 54					17 25								17 54						18 25			
Doncaster 7 a	17 07	17 11		17 15		17 35	17 40							18 07	18 13					18 38			18 53
York 8 26 a		17 54		17 40			18 33						18 31					18 58				19 30	
London Kings Cross 15 ⊖ 26 d		15 10			15 30	16 00		16 05							16 30		16 35						17 03
Doncaster 31 d		17 14			17 22	17 38	17 42	17 42				17 56			18 16		18 27			18 41			18 55
Bentley (S.Yorks) 31 a				17c30		17 41									18 30								
Adwick 31 a				17c34		17 47									18 34								
Kirk Sandall d					17 29							18 02					18 34			18 47			
Hatfield & Stainforth d					17 34							18 07					18 39			18 52			
Thorne South d					17 39												18 44						
Crowle d					17 47												18 53						
Althorpe d					17 53												18 59						
Scunthorpe a					18 01		18 07										19 07						19 22
d							18 08																19 23
Barnetby d							18 22																19 37
Hull Paragon Interchange 🚌 d																							
Barton-on-Humber 🚌 a																							
Barton-on-Humber d																							
Barrow Haven d																							
New Holland d																							
Goxhill d																							
Thornton Abbey d																							
Ulceby d																							
Habrough d							18 31																
Stallingborough d																							
Healing d																							
Great Coates d																							
Grimsby Town a							18 44																19 58
d							18 45																19 58
Grimsby Docks d																							
New Clee d																							
Cleethorpes a							18 59																20 09
Thorne North d		17 26										18 12								18 57			
Goole d		17 35										18 21			18 36					19 06			
Saltmarshe d												18 26											
York 8 33 d			17 27													18 14							
Selby a			17 45					17 59		18 04						18 43			19 00				
d			17 46					18 00		18 06						18 43			19 01				
Wressle d																18 51							
Howden d			17 55					18 10		18 16						18 56							
Eastrington d																19 00							
Gilberdyke d			18 01									18 32				19 05				19 21			
Broomfleet d												18 36											
Brough d		17 49	18 09					18 23		18 28		18 42			18 53	19 13			19 18	19 29			
Ferriby d												18 46								19 34			
Hessle d												18 51								19 38			
Hull a		18 06	18 29					18 40		18 46		19 04			19 09	19 32			19 37	19 48			

For general notes see front of timetable
For details of catering facilities see Directory of Train Operators

- **A** From Reading to Newcastle (Table 51)
- **B** From Adwick (Table 31)
- **C** From Lincoln (Table 30)
- **D** To Leeds (Table 31)
- **E** To Scarborough (Table 43)
- **G** From Plymouth to Glasgow Central (Table 51)
- **H** From Plymouth to Edinburgh (Table 51)
- **b** Change at Manchester Piccadilly
- **c** Change at Doncaster

Manchester Airport, Manchester, Sheffield and Meadowhall → Doncaster → Cleethorpes and Hull
Barton-on-Humber → Cleethorpes

Network Diagram - see first page of Table 18

		GR	NT	NT	XC	NT	NT	NT	NT	TP	TP	NT	NT	XC		NT	NT	EM	XC	NT	HT	NT	TP	NT
		R 1			1 ◇			BHX		1 ◇	1 ◇			1 ◇					1 ◇		1 ◇		1 ◇	
		A		B	C		D					E		G			H	J	K					B
Manchester Airport	85 d									17 55	*18 03*												18 55	
Manchester Piccadilly	78 d				*17 43*					18 20	18 42						*18 43*						19 18	
Stockport	78 d				*17 54*					18 28	*18b17*						*18 54*						19 26	
Sheffield	a									19 10													20 08	
	d		18 29	18 41	18 54		19 00			19 11		19 18		19 26		19 30	19 44		19 54			19 57	20 11	
Meadowhall	d		18 35	18 47			19 06			19 17		19 25				19 36	19 50					20 03	20 17	
Rotherham Central	d		18 42				19 12					19 31				19 42						20 10		
Swinton (S.Yorks)	d		18 50				19 20					19a40				19 51						20 19		
Mexborough	d		18 53				19 23									19 54						20 22		
Conisbrough	d		18 57				19 27									19 58						20 26		
Doncaster	a		19 08	19 11	19 17		19 39			19 40						20 08	20 11		20 20			20 36	20 40	
York	26 a				19 44									20 31		*20 39*			20 46					
London Kings Cross	26 d	17 19								*18 00*							*18 03*			*18 35*	18 50			
Doncaster	31 d	19 05		19 14		19 20				19 42			19 51				20 15			20 25	20 31		20 42	20 44
Bentley (S.Yorks)	31 a				*19c30*														*20c41*					
Adwick	31 a				*19c34*														*20c45*					
Kirk Sandall	d					19 27							19 57							20 31				
Hatfield & Stainforth	d					19 32							20 02							20 36				
Thorne South	d					19 36														20 41				
Crowle	d					19 45														20 50				
Althorpe	d					19 51														20 56				
Scunthorpe	a					19 59				20 07										21 04			21 07	
	d									20 08													21 08	
Barnetby	d									20 22								20 31					21 22	
Hull Paragon Interchange	bus d							19 25																
Barton-on-Humber	bus a							19 50																
Barton-on-Humber	d								19 58															
Barrow Haven	d								20 03															
New Holland	d								20 06															
Goxhill	d								20 11															
Thornton Abbey	d								20 14															
Ulceby	d								20 18															
Habrough	d								20 23									20 40					21 31	
Stallingborough	d								20 28															
Healing	d								20 31															
Great Coates	d								20 34															
Grimsby Town	a								20 39	20 42								20 52					21 44	
	d								20 39	20 43								20 52					21 45	
Grimsby Docks	d								20 42															
New Clee	d																							
Cleethorpes	a								20 48	20 55								21 02					21 59	
Thorne North	d												20 08											
Goole	d			19 34									20 17				20 36							
Saltmarshe	d																							
York	33 d										*19 23*													
Selby	a	19 20									20 00										20 46			21 01
	d	19 21									20 01										20 47			21 02
Wressle	d																							
Howden	d										20 10										20 57			
Eastrington	d																							
Gilberdyke	d												20 25											21 15
Broomfleet	d																							
Brough	d	19 43		19 49							20 22		20 33				20 49				21 09			21 23
Ferriby	d												20 37											21 28
Hessle	d												20 42											21 32
Hull	a	20 00		20 07							20 39		20 55				21 06				21 28			21 45

For general notes see front of timetable
For details of catering facilities see Directory of Train Operators

A The Hull Executive

B To Bridlington (Table 43)
C From Reading to Edinburgh (Table 51)
D From Retford (Table 30)
E To Leeds (Table 31)
G From Plymouth to Edinburgh (Table 51)
H To Beverley (Table 43)
J From Newark North Gate (Table 27)
K From Reading to Newcastle (Table 51)
b Change at Manchester Piccadilly
c Change at Doncaster

Table 29

Mondays to Fridays
until 19 June and from 7 September

Manchester Airport, Manchester, Sheffield and Meadowhall → Doncaster → Cleethorpes and Hull
Barton-on-Humber → Cleethorpes

Network Diagram - see first page of Table 18

		NT	TP	XC	NT	NT	XC	NT	NT	TP	NT	NT	HT	TP	NT	XC	TP	NT	NT	NT	NT	NT
								ThFO					BHX									
			1 ◇	1 ◇			1 ◇			1 ◇			1 ◇	1 ◇		1 ◇	1 ◇					
			A	B	C		D				E			G	C	H		C			C	
								🚌					⊠									
Manchester Airport	85 ✈ d						19b09			19 55				20 29		20b09	20 47					21 47
Manchester Piccadilly 10	78 🚢 d						19 43			20 20				21 11		20 43	21 20					22 20
Stockport	78 d						19 54			20 28				20c42		20 54	21 28					22 28
Sheffield 7	🚢 a									21 08							22 08					
	d	20 15		20 21	20 27	20 38	20 54			21 11	21 15				21 30	21 54	22 11	22 15	22 21		23 15	23 27
Meadowhall	🚢 d	20 21			20 35	20 45				21 17	21 21				21 36		22 17	22 21	22 31		23 21	23 33
Rotherham Central	d	20 27			20 41	20 52					21 27				21 42			22 27	22 37		23 27	23 39
Swinton (S.Yorks)	d	20 36			20a50	21 00					21 36				21a50			22a36	22 48		23a36	23 48
Mexborough	d	20 39				21 03					21 39								22 51			23 51
Conisbrough	d	20 43				21 07					21 43								22 55			23 55
Doncaster 7	a	20 55				21 18	21 20			21 40	21 54					22 29	22 40		23 04			00 07
York 8	26 a			21 39		22 01	21 45									22 59	23 13		00 41			
London Kings Cross 15	⊖ 26 d	19 03								19 33	20 00		20 30				20 33			21 00		
Doncaster	31 d	20 56				21 18				21 42	21 56		22 12				22 42			23 25		
Bentley (S.Yorks)	31 a						21e41				22 33											
Adwick	31 a						21e45				22 37											
Kirk Sandall	d	21 03				21 26					22 02						22 49			23 31		
Hatfield & Stainforth	d	21 08				21 31					22 07						22 53			23 36		
Thorne South	d					21 38											22 58					
Crowle	d					21 46											23 07					
Althorpe	d					21 52											23 13					
Scunthorpe	a					22 01				22 07							23 18					
	d									22 08							23 18					
Barnetby	d									22 22							23 36					
Hull Paragon Interchange	🚌 d							21 25														
Barton-on-Humber	🚌 a							21 50														
Barton-on-Humber	d								21 58													
Barrow Haven	d								22 03													
New Holland	d								22 06													
Goxhill	d								22 11													
Thornton Abbey	d								22 14													
Ulceby	d								22 18													
Habrough	d								22 23	22 31							23 44					
Stallingborough	d								22 28													
Healing	d								22 31													
Great Coates	d								22 34													
Grimsby Town	a								22 39	22 46							23 57					
	d								22 39	22 47							23 58					
Grimsby Docks	d								22 42													
New Clee	d																					
Cleethorpes	a								22 48	22 59							00 09					
Thorne North	d	21 14									22 13									23 42		
Goole	d	21a23									22 22									23a53		
Saltmarshe	d										22 26											
York 8	33 d											22 03										
Selby	a											22 22	22 29	22 44								
	d		21 27									22 22	22 30	22 44								
Wressle	d																					
Howden	d		21 36										22 40									
Eastrington	d																					
Gilberdyke	d										22 31	22 38										
Broomfleet	d																					
Brough	d		21 48								22 39	22 46	22 54	23 04								
Ferriby	d											22 51										
Hessle	d											22 55										
Hull	a		22 05								22 57	23 08	23 13	23 21								

For general notes see front of timetable
For details of catering facilities see Directory of Train Operators

A From Leeds (Table 40)
B From Plymouth (Table 51)
C To Leeds (Table 31)
D From Reading to Newcastle (Table 51)
E To Beverley (Table 43)
G From Liverpool Lime Street (Table 39)
H From Reading (Table 51)
b Change at Manchester Piccadilly and Sheffield
c Change at Manchester Piccadilly
e Change at Doncaster

Table 29

Mondays to Fridays

22 June to 4 September

Manchester Airport, Manchester, Sheffield and Meadowhall → Doncaster → Cleethorpes and Hull Barton-on-Humber → Cleethorpes

Network Diagram - see first page of Table 18

		NT	NT	NT	EM	NT	NT	TP	NT	NT	NT	NT	XC		NT	TP	NT	TP	NT	NT	NT	XC	NT	NT
						BHX																	BHX	
													1 ◇			1 ◇		1 ◇				1 ◇		
		A		B	C							A	D				E		B			G		
						[bus]		[bus]		[bus]													[bus]	
													[trolley]					[trolley]				[trolley]		
Manchester Airport	85 ✈ d															05 15		*05 37*						
Manchester Piccadilly 10	78 🚆 d															05 44		06 21				*05 50*		
Stockport	78 d															05 52		05b53				*06 00*		
Sheffield 7	🚆 a															06 49								
	d	05 22		05 29							06 18	06 28	06 40		06 52	06 55						07 12		
Meadowhall	🚆 d	05 28		05 35							06 24	06 34			06 58	07 01								
Rotherham Central	d	05 34		05 41							06 30	06 40			07 05						←			
Swinton (S.Yorks)	d	05a42		05 49							06 39	06a51			07 15 →						07 15			
Mexborough	d			05 52							06 42										07 18			
Conisbrough	d			05 56							06 46										07 22			
Doncaster 7	a			06 06							06 56		07 04			07 22					07 30			
York 8	26 a			*06 35*									07 27			*08 31*						08 23		
London Kings Cross 15	⊖ 26 d																							
Doncaster	31 d		05 52	06 14				06 30	06 47		06 59								07 28		07 32			
Bentley (S.Yorks)	31 a			*06 28*							07 02		*07c17*								07 35			
Adwick	31 a			*06 32*							07 08		*07c21*								07 40			
Kirk Sandall	d			06 20					06 53										07 34					
Hatfield & Stainforth	d			06 25					06 58	07 05									07 39					
Thorne South	d									07 15														
Crowle	d									07 30														
Althorpe	d									07 40														
Scunthorpe	a							07 20		07 55														
	d							07 20																
Barnetby	d				06 31			07 45																
Hull Paragon Interchange	[bus] d					06 25																	07 25	
Barton-on-Humber	[bus] a					06 50																	07 50	
Barton-on-Humber	d						06 58																	08 00
Barrow Haven	d						07 03																	08 05
New Holland	d						07 07																	08 08
Goxhill	d						07 11																	08 13
Thornton Abbey	d																							08 16
Ulceby	d						07 19																	08 20
Habrough	d				06 41		07 23	08 00																08 25
Stallingborough	d						07 28																	08 30
Healing	d						07 31																	08 33
Great Coates	d																							08 36
Grimsby Town	a				06 56		07 37	08 25																08 41
	d						07 38	08 25																08 41
Grimsby Docks	d																							08 44
New Clee	d																							08x46
Cleethorpes	a						07 50	08 45																08 51
Thorne North	d			06 30					07a03										07 44					
Goole	d			06 41															07 53					
Saltmarshe	d			06 46															07 58					
York 8	33 d																	*06 09*			07 31			
Selby	a		06 14															07 43			07 50			
	d																	07 43			07 50			
Wressle	d																				07 58			
Howden	d																	07 52			08 03			
Eastrington	d																				08 08			
Gilberdyke	d			06 53													07 39		08 04		08 12			
Broomfleet	d			06 57													07 43				08 16			
Brough	d			07 03													07 49	08 04	08 12		08 22			
Ferriby	d			07 07													07 53		08 16		08 27			
Hessle	d			07 12													07 58		08 21		08 31			
Hull	a			07 22													08 11	08 20	08 34		08 46			

For general notes see front of timetable
For details of catering facilities see Directory of Train Operators

- **A** To Leeds (Table 31)
- **B** To Beverley (Table 43)
- **C** From Lincoln (Table 27)
- **D** From Derby to Newcastle (Table 51)
- **E** To Scarborough (Table 43)
- **G** From Birmingham New Street to Edinburgh(Table 51)
- **b** Change at Manchester Piccadilly
- **c** Change at Doncaster

Table 29

Mondays to Fridays

22 June to 4 September

Manchester Airport, Manchester, Sheffield and Meadowhall → Doncaster → Cleethorpes and Hull Barton-on-Humber → Cleethorpes

Network Diagram - see first page of Table 18

		TP	NT	EM	TP	NT	NT	NT	TP	XC	TP	TP	TP	NT	NT	NT	TP	NT	XC	HT	NT	NT
															BHX					BHX		
									1 ◇	1 ◇		1 ◇							1 ◇	1 ◇		
			A	B				C		D								A	E			
		bus			bus		bus				bus		bus		bus		bus					bus
									trolley	trolley		trolley							trolley	⊠		
Manchester Airport	85 ✈ d								*07 05*			06 55										
Manchester Piccadilly 10	78 🚆 d								07 36			07 20										
Stockport	78 d								07b10			07 28										
Sheffield 7	🚆 a											08 10										
	d		07 14			07 24		07 41		07 54		08 11						08 14	08 21		08 25	
Meadowhall	🚆 d		07 21			07 30		07 47				08 17						08 23			08 31	
Rotherham Central	d		07 27			07 36		07 55										08 29			08 37	
Swinton (S.Yorks)	d		07a35			07 44		08 03										08a38			08 48	
Mexborough	d					07 47		08 06													08 51	
Conisbrough	d					07 51		08 10													08 55	
Doncaster 7	a					08 01		08 20		08 24		08 40									09 05	
York 8	26 a					*08 31*				08 47		*09 40*							09 33		*09 40*	
London Kings Cross 15	⊖ 26 d					*06 00*		*06 35*												07 20	*07 10*	
Doncaster	31 d	07 35			07 40	08 03		08 22			08 30		08 55	08 56			09 00			09 06	09 10	
Bentley (S.Yorks)	31 a					*08 19*						*08 55*									*09 17*	
Adwick	31 a					*08 25*						*09 01*									*09 21*	
Kirk Sandall	d					08 09								09 02							09 18	
Hatfield & Stainforth	d					08 14	08 20							09 07							09 23	09 30
Thorne South	d						08 35															09 40
Crowle	d						08 50															09 55
Althorpe	d						09 00															10 05
Scunthorpe	a				08 40		09 20				09 30						10 00					10 20
	d				08 45												10 05					
Barnetby	d			08 52	09 10												10 30					
Hull Paragon Interchange	bus d														09 25							
Barton-on-Humber	bus a														09 50							
Barton-on-Humber	d															09 58						
Barrow Haven	d															10 03						
New Holland	d															10 06						
Goxhill	d															10 11						
Thornton Abbey	d															10 14						
Ulceby	d															10 18						
Habrough	d			09 01	09 25											10 23	10 45					
Stallingborough	d															10 28						
Healing	d															10 31						
Great Coates	d															10 34						
Grimsby Town	a	09s00		09 15	09 50								10s20			10 39	11 10					
	d				09 55											10 39	11 15					
Grimsby Docks	d															10 42						
New Clee	d															10x44						
Cleethorpes	a	09 20			10 15								10 40			10 49	11 35					
Thorne North	d					08a19								09 12							09a28	
Goole	d							08 43						09 21								
Saltmarshe	d																					
York 8	33 d																			*08 43*		
Selby	a								08 58											09 21		
	d								08 59											09 22		
Wressle	d																					
Howden	d																			09 32		
Eastrington	d																					
Gilberdyke	d													09 29								
Broomfleet	d																					
Brough	d							08 57						09 37						09 44		
Ferriby	d													09 42								
Hessle	d													09 46								
Hull	a							09 13	09 31					09 59						10 04		

For general notes see front of timetable
For details of catering facilities see Directory of Train Operators

A To Leeds (Table 31)
B From Newark North Gate (Table 27)
C To Bridlington (Table 43)
D From Birmingham New Street to Newcastle (Table 51)
E From Birmingham New Street to Edinburgh(Table 51)
b Change at Manchester Piccadilly

22 June to 4 September

Manchester Airport, Manchester, Sheffield and Meadowhall → Doncaster → Cleethorpes and Hull Barton-on-Humber → Cleethorpes

Network Diagram - see first page of Table 18

	NT	XC	TP	TP	NT	NT	TP	NT	NT	TP	EM	TP	XC	NT	NT	NT	NT	XC	TP	NT	TP	TP
		[1] ◇		[1] ◇			[1] ◇						[1] ◇					[1] ◇			[1] ◇	[1] ◇
	A	B				C		D			E		G			H	J	K		L		
			Bus							Bus		Bus			Bus				Bus			
		Trolley		Trolley			Trolley						Trolley					Trolley			Trolley	Trolley
Manchester Airport 85 ✈ d				*08 05*			07 54														08 55	*09 05*
Manchester Piccadilly [10] 78 d	*07 42*			08 42			08 20											*08 43*			09 20	09 42
Stockport 78 d	*07 54*			08b19			08 28											*08 54*			09 28	09b17
Sheffield [7] a							09 08														10 08	
d	08 41	08 54				08 57	09 11	09 14					09 21	09 24		09 29	09 41	09 54		09 57	10 11	
Meadowhall d	08 47					09 03	09 17	09 21						09 30		09 35	09 45			10 03	10 17	
Rotherham Central d						09 11		09 27						09 37		09 42				10 10		
Swinton (S.Yorks) d						09 19		09a36						09 48		09 51				10 18		
Mexborough d						09 22								09 51						10 21		
Conisbrough d						09 26								09 55						10 25		
Doncaster [7] a	09 12	09 20				09 36	09 40							10 04			10 11	10 15		10 36	10 40	
York [8] 26 a		09 48											10 29			10 52	*11 02*	10 40			*11 37*	
London Kings Cross [15] ⊖ 26 d					*07 30*															*09 00*		
Doncaster 31 d	09 17		09 30		09 46	09 49				09 55		10 00		10 06			10 16		10 30	10 46		
Bentley (S.Yorks) 31 a						09 52								*10 17*						10 49		
Adwick 31 a						09 58								*10 21*						10 55		
Kirk Sandall d					09 52									10 12								
Hatfield & Stainforth d					09 57									10 17	10 25							
Thorne South d															10 35							
Crowle d															10 50							
Althorpe d															11 00							
Scunthorpe a			10 25									10 50			11 15				11 20			
d												10 55										
Barnetby d											10 57	11 20										
Hull Paragon Interchange Bus d																						
Barton-on-Humber Bus a																						
Barton-on-Humber d																						
Barrow Haven d																						
New Holland d																						
Goxhill d																						
Thornton Abbey d																						
Ulceby d																						
Habrough d											11 06	11 35										
Stallingborough d																						
Healing d																						
Great Coates d																						
Grimsby Town a										11s15	11 21	12 00										
d												12 05										
Grimsby Docks d																						
New Clee d																						
Cleethorpes a										11 35		12 25										
Thorne North d					10 02									10a23								
Goole d	09 42				10 11												10 35					
Saltmarshe d																						
York [8] 33 d									09 53													*10 20*
Selby a				09 57					10 12													10 57
d				09 58					10 12													10 58
Wressle d																						
Howden d									10 22													
Eastrington d																						
Gilberdyke d					10 19				10 29													
Broomfleet d																						
Brough d	09 56			10 16	10 27				10 37								10 49					11 16
Ferriby d					10 32																	
Hessle d					10 36																	
Hull a	10 10			10 34	10 49				10 56								11 06					11 34

For general notes see front of timetable
For details of catering facilities see Directory of Train Operators

- **A** To Bridlington (Table 43)
- **B** From Birmingham New Street to Newcastle (Table 51)
- **C** From Worksop (Table 30)
- **D** To Leeds (Table 31)
- **E** From Newark North Gate (Table 27)
- **G** From Bristol Temple Meads to Edinburgh (Table 51)
- **H** Via Pontefract Baghill (Table 33)
- **J** To Scarborough (Table 43)
- **K** From Guildford to Newcastle (Table 51)
- **L** From Lincoln (Table 30)
- **b** Change at Manchester Piccadilly

Table 29

Mondays to Fridays

22 June to 4 September

Manchester Airport, Manchester, Sheffield and Meadowhall → Doncaster → Cleethorpes and Hull Barton-on-Humber → Cleethorpes

Network Diagram - see first page of Table 18

	NT		NT	TP	NT	NT	TP	XC	NT	NT	NT	XC	TP	HT		NT	TP	TP	NT	NT	TP	EM	TP
					BHX																		
								1 ◇				1 ◇		1 ◇			1 ◇	1 ◇					
	A							B			C	D				E				A		G	
				🚌	🚌		🚌			🚌			🚌								🚌		🚌
								✠				✠		⊠			✠	✠					
Manchester Airport 85 ✈ d																	09 55	*10 05*					
Manchester Piccadilly 10 78 🚆 d	*08 45*											*09 43*					10 20	10 42					
Stockport 78 d												*09 54*					10 28	*10b17*					
Sheffield 7 🚆 a																	11 08						
d	10 14							10 21	10 24		10 41	10 54				10 57	11 11			11 14			
Meadowhall 🚆 d	10 21								10 30		10 47					11 03	11 17			11 21			
Rotherham Central d	10 27								10 36							11 10				11 27			
Swinton (S.Yorks) d	10a36								10 44							11 20				11a36			
Mexborough d									10 47							11 23							
Conisbrough d									10 51							11 27							
Doncaster 7 a									11 04		11 08	11 15				11 35	11 40						
York 8 26 a								11 29	*11 37*			11 45											
London Kings Cross 15 ⊖ 26 d														09 48		*09 35*							
Doncaster 31 d			10 47	10 55			11 00		11 07		11 17		11 30	11 36		11 38			11 49		11 55		12 00
Bentley (S.Yorks) 31 a												*11c29*				11 41							
Adwick 31 a												*11c33*				11 47							
Kirk Sandall d			10 53						11 13										11 55				
Hatfield & Stainforth d			10 58						11 18	11 25									12 00				
Thorne South d										11 35													
Crowle d										11 50													
Althorpe d										12 00													
Scunthorpe a							11 50			12 15			12 20										12 50
d							11 55																12 55
Barnetby d							12 20															13 12	13 20
Hull Paragon Interchange 🚌 d					11 25																		
Barton-on-Humber 🚌 a					11 50																		
Barton-on-Humber d						11 58																	
Barrow Haven d						12 03																	
New Holland d						12 06																	
Goxhill d						12 11																	
Thornton Abbey d						12 14																	
Ulceby d						12 18																	
Habrough d						12 23	12 35															13 21	13 35
Stallingborough d						12 28																	
Healing d						12 31																	
Great Coates d						12 34																	
Grimsby Town a				12s10		12 39	13 00														13s10	13 36	14 00
d						12 39	13 05																14 05
Grimsby Docks d						12 42																	
New Clee d						12x44																	
Cleethorpes a				12 30		12 49	13 25														13 30		14 25
Thorne North d			11 03						11a23										12 05				
Goole d			11 12								11 38								12 14				
Saltmarshe d																							
York 8 33 d																							
Selby a														11 51				11 57					
d														11 52				11 58					
Wressle d																							
Howden d														12 02									
Eastrington d																							
Gilberdyke d			11 20																12 22				
Broomfleet d			11 25																				
Brough d			11 31								11 52			12 15				12 16	12 30				
Ferriby d			11 35																12 35				
Hessle d			11 40																12 39				
Hull a			11 53								12 09			12 32				12 36	12 52				

For general notes see front of timetable
For details of catering facilities see Directory of Train Operators

- **A** To Leeds (Table 31)
- **B** From Plymouth to Edinburgh (Table 51)
- **C** To Bridlington (Table 43)
- **D** From Reading to Newcastle (Table 51)
- **E** From Lincoln (Table 30)
- **G** From Newark North Gate (Table 27)
- **b** Change at Manchester Piccadilly
- **c** Change at Doncaster

Table 29

Manchester Airport, Manchester, Sheffield and Meadowhall → Doncaster → Cleethorpes and Hull
Barton-on-Humber → Cleethorpes

Network Diagram - see first page of Table 18

		NT	XC	NT	NT	NT	XC		TP	NT	TP	TP	NT	TP	NT BHX	NT	TP	NT	XC	NT		NT	NT	XC
			1 ◊				1 ◊				1 ◊	1 ◊							1 ◊					1 ◊
			A			B	C			D								E	A				G	C
					🚌				🚌					🚌	🚌		🚌					🚌		
			🍴				🍴				🍴	🍴							🍴					🍴
Manchester Airport	85 ✈ d										10 55	*11 05*												
Manchester Piccadilly [10]	78 🚊 d						*10 43*				11 20	11 42						*10 45*						*11 43*
Stockport	78 d						*10 54*				11 28	*11b17*												*11 54*
Sheffield [7]	🚊 a										12 08													
	d		11 21	11 24		11 41	11 54			11 57	12 11							12 14	12 21	12 24			12 41	12 54
Meadowhall	🚊 d			11 30		11 47				12 03	12 17							12 21		12 30			12 47	
Rotherham Central	d			11 37						12 10								12 27		12 37				
Swinton (S.Yorks)	d			11 48						12 19								12a36		12 47				
Mexborough	d			11 51						12 22										12 50				
Conisbrough	d			11 55						12 26										12 54				
Doncaster [7]	a			12 04		12 11	12 15			12 35	12 40									13 04			13 11	13 20
York [8]	26 a		12 29				12 45												13 29	*13 39*				13 46
London Kings Cross [15]	⊖ 26 d			*10 10*						*10 35*										*11 10*				
Doncaster	31 d			12 07		12 14			12 30	12 36			12 49	12 55			13 00			13 06			13 18	
Bentley (S.Yorks)	31 a						*12c28*			12 40														*13c30*
Adwick	31 a						*12c32*			12 45														*13c34*
Kirk Sandall	d			12 14									12 55							13 12				
Hatfield & Stainforth	d			12 19	12 25								13 00							13 17		13 25		
Thorne South	d				12 35																	13 35		
Crowle	d				12 50																	13 50		
Althorpe	d				13 00																	14 00		
Scunthorpe	a				13 15				13 20								13 50					14 15		
	d																13 55							
Barnetby	d																14 20							
Hull Paragon Interchange	🚌 d														13 25									
Barton-on-Humber	🚌 a														13 50									
Barton-on-Humber	d															13 58								
Barrow Haven	d															14 03								
New Holland	d															14 06								
Goxhill	d															14 11								
Thornton Abbey	d															14 14								
Ulceby	d															14 18								
Habrough	d															14 23	14 35							
Stallingborough	d															14 28								
Healing	d															14 31								
Great Coates	d															14 34								
Grimsby Town	a													14s10		14 39	15 00							
	d															14 39	15 05							
Grimsby Docks	d															14 42								
New Clee	d															14x44								
Cleethorpes	a													14 30		14 49	15 25							
Thorne North	d			12a24									13 05							13a12				
Goole	d					12 38							13 14										13 37	
Saltmarshe	d																							
York [8]	33 d	11 53										*12 18*												
Selby	a	12 17										12 57												
	d	12 18										12 58												
Wressle	d																							
Howden	d	12 27																						
Eastrington	d																							
Gilberdyke	d	12 34											13 22											
Broomfleet	d																							
Brough	d	12 42				12 52						13 16	13 30										13 51	
Ferriby	d												13 35											
Hessle	d												13 39											
Hull	a	13 02				13 06						13 34	13 52										14 08	

For general notes see front of timetable
For details of catering facilities see Directory of Train Operators

- **A** From Plymouth to Edinburgh (Table 51)
- **B** To Scarborough (Table 43)
- **C** From Reading to Newcastle (Table 51)
- **D** From Lincoln (Table 30)
- **E** To Leeds (Table 31)
- **G** To Bridlington (Table 43)
- **b** Change at Manchester Piccadilly
- **c** Change at Doncaster

22 June to 4 September

Manchester Airport, Manchester, Sheffield and Meadowhall → Doncaster → Cleethorpes and Hull Barton-on-Humber → Cleethorpes

Network Diagram - see first page of Table 18

		HT	TP	NT	TP	TP	NT	NT	TP	TP	NT	XC	NT	NT	NT	EM	NT	XC	TP	NT	TP	TP	NT
		1 ◇			1 ◇	1 ◇						1 ◇						1 ◇			1 ◇	1 ◇	
				A							B	C			D	E	G	H		A			J
			🚌						🚌	🚌				🚌					🚌				
		⊠			🛒	🛒						🛒						🛒			🛒	🛒	
Manchester Airport	85 ✈ d				11 55	12 05															12 55	13 05	
Manchester Piccadilly 10	78 d				12 20	12 42												12 43			13 20	13 42	
Stockport	78 d				12 28	12b17												12 54			13 28	13b17	
Sheffield 7	a				13 08																14 08		
	d			12 57	13 11						13 14	13 21	13 24		13 28		13 41	13 54		13 57	14 11		
Meadowhall	d			13 03	13 17						13 21		13 30		13 35		13 46			14 03	14 17		
Rotherham Central	d			13 10							13 27		13 37		13 41					14 10			
Swinton (S.Yorks)	d			13 18							13a36		13 47		13 50					14 18			
Mexborough	d			13 21									13 50							14 21			
Conisbrough	d			13 25									13 54							14 25			
Doncaster 7	a			13 35	13 40								14 04				14 13	14 17		14 35	14 40		
York 8	26 a				14 34							14 29			14 51		14 58	14 43			15 26		
London Kings Cross 15	⊖ 26 d	11 48											12 10				12 30			12 35			13 00
Doncaster	31 d	13 29	13 30	13 38				13 46	13 55	14 00			14 06				14 17		14 30	14 38			14 46
Bentley (S.Yorks)	31 a			13 41														14c30		14 41			
Adwick	31 a			13 47														14c34		14 47			
Kirk Sandall	d							13 52					14 13										14 54
Hatfield & Stainforth	d							13 57					14 18	14 25									14 59
Thorne South	d													14 35									
Crowle	d													14 50									
Althorpe	d													15 00									
Scunthorpe	a		14 20							14 50				15 15					15 20				
	d									14 55													
Barnetby	d									15 20						15 34							
Hull Paragon Interchange	🚌 d																						
Barton-on-Humber	🚌 a																						
Barton-on-Humber	d																						
Barrow Haven	d																						
New Holland	d																						
Goxhill	d																						
Thornton Abbey	d																						
Ulceby	d																						
Habrough	d									15 35						15 42							
Stallingborough	d																						
Healing	d																						
Great Coates	d																						
Grimsby Town	a								15s10	16 00						15 57							
	d									16 05													
Grimsby Docks	d																						
New Clee	d																						
Cleethorpes	a								15 30	16 25													
Thorne North	d							14 02					14a24										15 04
Goole	d							14 12									14 38						15 13
Saltmarshe	d							14 17															
York 8	33 d						13 45																
Selby	a	13 44				13 57	14 09															14 57	
	d	13 45				13 58	14 09															14 58	
Wressle	d																						
Howden	d	13 55																					
Eastrington	d																						
Gilberdyke	d							14 28															15 21
Broomfleet	d																						
Brough	d	14 08				14 16	14 29	14 36									14 52					15 16	15 29
Ferriby	d							14 40															15 34
Hessle	d							14 45															15 38
Hull	a	14 25				14 34	14 48	14 56									15 07					15 34	15 51

For general notes see front of timetable
For details of catering facilities see Directory of Train Operators

A From Lincoln (Table 30)
B To Leeds (Table 31)
C From Penzance (Table 135) to Edinburgh (Table 51)
D Via Pontefract Baghill (Table 33)
E From Newark North Gate (Table 27)
G To Bridlington (Table 43)
H From Reading to Newcastle (Table 51)
J To Scarborough (Table 43)
b Change at Manchester Piccadilly
c Change at Doncaster

22 June to 4 September

Manchester Airport, Manchester, Sheffield and Meadowhall → Doncaster → Cleethorpes and Hull
Barton-on-Humber → Cleethorpes

Network Diagram - see first page of Table 18

		NT	TP	NT BHX	NT	TP	NT A	XC B	NT	NT	HT	NT	XC C	TP	NT D	TP	TP	NT E	TP	TP	NT A	XC G
Manchester Airport	85 d															13 55	14 05					
Manchester Piccadilly	78 d						12 45						13 43			14 20	14 42					
Stockport	78 d												13 54			14 28	14b17					
Sheffield	a															15 08						
	d						14 14	14 21	14 24			14 41	14 54		14 57	15 11					15 14	15 21
Meadowhall	d						14 21		14 30			14 47			15 03	15 17					15 21	
Rotherham Central	d						14 27		14 37						15 10						15 27	
Swinton (S.Yorks)	d						14a36		14 48						15 18						15a36	
Mexborough	d								14 51						15 21							
Conisbrough	d								14 55						15 25							
Doncaster	a								15 04			15 09	15 16		15 36	15 40						
York	26 a							15 29					15 40									16 29
London Kings Cross	26 d								13 10		13 33	13 30			14 00							
Doncaster	31 d		14 55			15 00			15 06		15 12	15 14		15 30	15 38			15 46	15 55	16 00		
Bentley (S.Yorks)	31 a								15 17						15 41							
Adwick	31 a								15 21						15 47							
Kirk Sandall	d								15 12									15 52				
Hatfield & Stainforth	d								15 17	15 25								15 57				
Thorne South	d									15 35												
Crowle	d									15 50												
Althorpe	d									16 00												
Scunthorpe	a					15 50				16 15				16 25						17 00		
	d					15 55														17 05		
Barnetby	d					16 20														17 30		
Hull Paragon Interchange	d			15 25																		
Barton-on-Humber	a			15 50																		
Barton-on-Humber	d				15 58																	
Barrow Haven	d				16 03																	
New Holland	d				16 06																	
Goxhill	d				16 11																	
Thornton Abbey	d				16 14																	
Ulceby	d				16 18																	
Habrough	d				16 23	16 35														17 45		
Stallingborough	d				16 28																	
Healing	d				16 31																	
Great Coates	d				16 34																	
Grimsby Town	a		16s10		16 39	17 00													17s20	18 10		
	d				16 39	17 05														18 15		
Grimsby Docks	d				16 42																	
New Clee	d																					
Cleethorpes	a		16 30		16 48	17 25													17 40	18 35		
Thorne North	d								15a22									16 02				
Goole	d											15 38						16 11				
Saltmarshe	d																					
York	33 d	14 59																				
Selby	a	15 19									15 27						15 57					
	d	15 19									15 28						15 58					
Wressle	d																					
Howden	d										15 38											
Eastrington	d																					
Gilberdyke	d																	16 20				
Broomfleet	d																					
Brough	d	15 39									15 53	15 58					16 16	16 28				
Ferriby	d																	16 32				
Hessle	d																	16 37				
Hull	a	15 58									16 10	16 12					16 35	16 49				

For general notes see front of timetable
For details of catering facilities see Directory of Train Operators

A To Leeds (Table 31)
B From Plymouth (Table 51) to Aberdeen (Table 229)
C From Reading to Newcastle (Table 51)
D From Lincoln (Table 30)
E To Bridlington (Table 43)
G From Penzance (Table 135) to Glasgow Central (Table 51)
b Change at Manchester Piccadilly

Table 29

Mondays to Fridays

22 June to 4 September

Manchester Airport, Manchester, Sheffield and Meadowhall → Doncaster → Cleethorpes and Hull Barton-on-Humber → Cleethorpes

Network Diagram - see first page of Table 18

		NT	NT	NT	NT	XC	TP	NT	TP	TP	EM	NT	TP	NT	NT	TP	NT	XC	NT	NT	NT	XC
														BHX								
						1 ◇			**1** ◇	**1** ◇								**1** ◇				**1** ◇
					A	B		C			D	E					G	H				B
			🚌				🚌						🚌	🚌		🚌						
						🍴			🍴	🍴								🍴				🍴
Manchester Airport	85 ✈ d								14 55	15 05												
Manchester Piccadilly 10	78 🚊 d			14 43					15 20	15 42							14 45					15 43
Stockport	78 d			14 54					15 28	15b17												15 54
Sheffield 7	🚊 a								16 08													
	d	15 24		15 41		15 54		15 57	16 11								16 14	16 21	16 24	16 41		16 54
Meadowhall	🚊 d	15 30		15 47				16 03	16 17								16 21		16 30	16 47		
Rotherham Central	d	15 37						16 10									16 27		16 37			
Swinton (S.Yorks)	d	15 47						16 18									16a36		16 47			
Mexborough	d	15 50						16 21											16 50			
Conisbrough	d	15 54						16 25											16 54			
Doncaster 7	a	16 04		16 12		16 15		16 35	16 40										17 07	17 11		17 15
York 8	26 a					16 40			17 34									17 30		17 54		17 40
London Kings Cross 15	⊖ 26 d	14 10		14 35																15 10		
Doncaster	31 d	16 09		16 18			16 30	16 38				16 46	16 55			17 00				17 14		
Bentley (S.Yorks)	31 a	16 17						16 41														17c30
Adwick	31 a	16 21						16 47														17c34
Kirk Sandall	d	16 15										16 52										
Hatfield & Stainforth	d	16 20	16 25									16 57										
Thorne South	d		16 40																			
Crowle	d		16 55																			
Althorpe	d		17 05																			
Scunthorpe	a		17 25				17 30									18 00						
	d															18 05						
Barnetby	d										17 54					18 30						
Hull Paragon Interchange	🚌 d													17 30								
Barton-on-Humber	🚌 a													17 55								
Barton-on-Humber	d														18 00							
Barrow Haven	d														18 05							
New Holland	d														18 08							
Goxhill	d														18 13							
Thornton Abbey	d														18 16							
Ulceby	d														18 20							
Habrough	d										18 02				18 25	18 45						
Stallingborough	d														18 30							
Healing	d														18 33							
Great Coates	d														18 36							
Grimsby Town	a										18 17		18s20		18 41	19 10						
	d														18 41	19 15						
Grimsby Docks	d														18 44							
New Clee	d																					
Cleethorpes	a												18 40		18 50	19 35						
Thorne North	d	16a26										17 02								17 26		
Goole	d			16 39								17 11								17 35		
Saltmarshe	d											17 16										
York 8	33 d				16 12																17 27	
Selby	a				16 38					17 00											17 45	
	d				16 39					17 00											17 46	
Wressle	d				16 46																	
Howden	d				16 51																17 55	
Eastrington	d																					
Gilberdyke	d				16 58							17 23									18 01	
Broomfleet	d																					
Brough	d			16 52	17 06					17 18		17 31								17 49	18 09	
Ferriby	d				17 10							17 36										
Hessle	d											17 40										
Hull	a			17 14	17 27					17 37		17 53								18 06	18 29	

For general notes see front of timetable
For details of catering facilities see Directory of Train Operators

- **A** To Scarborough (Table 43)
- **B** From Reading to Newcastle (Table 51)
- **C** From Lincoln (Table 30)
- **D** From Lincoln (Table 27)
- **E** To Bridlington (Table 43)
- **G** To Leeds (Table 31)
- **H** From Plymouth (Table 51) to Dundee (Table 229)
- **b** Change at Manchester Piccadilly
- **c** Change at Doncaster

Table 29

Mondays to Fridays

22 June to 4 September

Manchester Airport, Manchester, Sheffield and Meadowhall → Doncaster → Cleethorpes and Hull Barton-on-Humber → Cleethorpes

Network Diagram - see first page of Table 18

		NT	TP	NT	NT	TP	HT	TP	TP	NT	NT	TP	XC		NT	NT	NT	NT	NT	XC	TP	TP	NT	NT
						1 ◇	1 ◇	1 ◇					1 ◇							1 ◇		1 ◇		
		A			B					C	D		E					A		G			B	C
			🚌	🚌					🚌			🚌							🚌		🚌			
						🍴	⊠	🍴					🍴							🍴		🍴		
Manchester Airport	85 ✈ d					15 55		16 05														17 05		
Manchester Piccadilly 10	78 🚆 d					16 20		16 42		15 45										16 43		17 42		
Stockport	78 d					16 28		16b17												16 54		17b17		
Sheffield 7	🚊 a					17 08																		
	d				16 57	17 11				17 14			17 21		17 25	17 41				17 47			17 57	18 14
Meadowhall	🚊 d				17 03	17 17				17 21					17 31	17 47							18 03	18 21
Rotherham Central	d				17 10					17 27					17 39								18 10	18 27
Swinton (S.Yorks)	d				17 18					17a36					17 47								18 18	18a36
Mexborough	d				17 21										17 50								18 21	
Conisbrough	d				17 25										17 54								18 25	
Doncaster 7	a				17 35	17 40									18 07	18 13							18 38	
York 8	26 a					18 33							18 31							18 58				
London Kings Cross 15	⊖ 26 d	15 30			16 00		16 05									16 30		16 35						
Doncaster	31 d	17 22	17 30		17 38		17 42		17 55		17 56	18 00				18 16		18 27			18 30		18 41	
Bentley (S.Yorks)	31 a				17 41											18 30								
Adwick	31 a				17 47											18 34								
Kirk Sandall	d	17 29									18 02							18 34					18 47	
Hatfield & Stainforth	d	17 34		17 40							18 07							18 39	18 45				18 52	
Thorne South	d			17 55														18 44	18 55					
Crowle	d			18 10															19 10					
Althorpe	d			18 20															19 20					
Scunthorpe	a		18 30	18 35								19 00							19 35		19 20			
	d											19 05												
Barnetby	d											19 30												
Hull Paragon Interchange	🚌 d																							
Barton-on-Humber	🚌 a																							
Barton-on-Humber	d																							
Barrow Haven	d																							
New Holland	d																							
Goxhill	d																							
Thornton Abbey	d																							
Ulceby	d																							
Habrough	d											19 45												
Stallingborough	d																							
Healing	d																							
Great Coates	d																							
Grimsby Town	a								19s20			20 10												
	d											20 15												
Grimsby Docks	d																							
New Clee	d																							
Cleethorpes	a								19 40			20 35												
Thorne North	d	17a39									18 12							18a45					18 57	
Goole	d										18 21					18 36							19 06	
Saltmarshe	d										18 26													
York 8	33 d																18 14							
Selby	a						17 59	18 04									18 43					19 00		
	d						18 00	18 06									18 43					19 01		
Wressle	d																18 51							
Howden	d						18 10	18 16									18 56							
Eastrington	d																19 00							
Gilberdyke	d										18 32						19 05						19 21	
Broomfleet	d										18 36													
Brough	d						18 23	18 28			18 42					18 53	19 13					19 18	19 29	
Ferriby	d										18 46												19 34	
Hessle	d										18 51												19 38	
Hull	a						18 40	18 46			19 04					19 09	19 32					19 37	19 48	

For general notes see front of timetable
For details of catering facilities see Directory of Train Operators

A From Adwick (Table 31)
B From Lincoln (Table 30)
C To Leeds (Table 31)
D To Scarborough (Table 43)
E From Plymouth to Glasgow Central (Table 51)
G From Reading to Newcastle (Table 51)
b Change at Manchester Piccadilly

Manchester Airport, Manchester, Sheffield and Meadowhall → Doncaster → Cleethorpes and Hull
Barton-on-Humber → Cleethorpes

Network Diagram - see first page of Table 18

Station		XC	TP	GR	TP		NT	NT	EM	NT	NT	TP	XC	NT	TP	NT	NT	TP		TP	NT	TP	TP	NT
				R			BHX																	
		1 ◇	1 ◇	1									1 ◇					1 ◇		1 ◇				
		A		B					C		D		E				G							H
					Bus		Bus					Bus			Bus	Bus						Bus	Bus	
Manchester Airport	85 d		16 55															17 55		*18 03*				
Manchester Piccadilly 10	78 d		17 20										*17 43*					18 20		18 42				
Stockport	78 d		17 28										*17 54*					18 28		*18b17*				
Sheffield 7	a		18 15															19 10						
	d	18 21	18 24							18 29	18 41		18 54				19 00	19 11						19 18
Meadowhall	d		18 29							18 35	18 47						19 06	19 17						19 25
Rotherham Central	d									18 42							19 12							19 31
Swinton (S.Yorks)	d									18 50							19 20							19a40
Mexborough	d									18 53							19 23							
Conisbrough	d									18 57							19 27							
Doncaster 7	a		18 53							19 08	19 11		19 17				19 39	19 40						
York 8	26 a	19 30											19 44					*20 39*						
London Kings Cross 15	⊖ 26 d			17 19	*17 03*																	*18 00*		
Doncaster	31 d			19 05	19 10						19 14	19 15		19 20	19 30						19 51	19 55	20 00	
Bentley (S.Yorks)	31 a												*19c30*											
Adwick	31 a												*19c34*											
Kirk Sandall	d													19 27							19 57			
Hatfield & Stainforth	d													19 32		19 40					20 02			
Thorne South	d															19 50								
Crowle	d															20 05								
Althorpe	d															20 15								
Scunthorpe	a											20 05			20 20	20 30							20 50	
	d											20 10											20 55	
Barnetby	d								20 31			20 35											21 20	
Hull Paragon Interchange	Bus d						19 25																	
Barton-on-Humber	Bus a						19 50																	
Barton-on-Humber	d							19 58																
Barrow Haven	d							20 03																
New Holland	d							20 06																
Goxhill	d							20 11																
Thornton Abbey	d							20 14																
Ulceby	d							20 18																
Habrough	d							20 23	20 40			20 50											21 35	
Stallingborough	d							20 28																
Healing	d							20 31																
Great Coates	d							20 34																
Grimsby Town	a				20s25			20 39	20 52			21 15										21s10	22 00	
	d							20 39	20 52			21 20											22 05	
Grimsby Docks	d							20 42																
New Clee	d																							
Cleethorpes	a				20 45			20 48	21 02			21 40										21 30	22 25	
Thorne North	d													19a42							20 08			
Goole	d										19 34										20 17			
Saltmarshe	d																							
York 8	33 d																			*19 23*				
Selby	a			19 20																20 00				
	d			19 21																20 01				
Wressle	d																							
Howden	d																			20 10				
Eastrington	d																							
Gilberdyke	d																				20 25			
Broomfleet	d																							
Brough	d			19 43							19 49									20 22	20 33			
Ferriby	d																				20 37			
Hessle	d																				20 42			
Hull	a			20 00							20 07									20 39	20 55			

For general notes see front of timetable
For details of catering facilities see Directory of Train Operators

- **A** From Plymouth to Edinburgh (Table 51)
- **B** **The Hull Executive**
- **C** From Newark North Gate (Table 27)
- **D** To Bridlington (Table 43)
- **E** From Reading to Edinburgh (Table 51)
- **G** From Retford (Table 30)
- **H** To Leeds (Table 31)
- **b** Change at Manchester Piccadilly
- **c** Change at Doncaster

Table 29

Manchester Airport, Manchester, Sheffield and Meadowhall → Doncaster → Cleethorpes and Hull Barton-on-Humber → Cleethorpes

Network Diagram - see first page of Table 18

		XC	NT	NT	XC	NT	TP	NT	HT	NT		TP	NT	TP	TP	NT	NT	NT	TP	XC	NT	NT	NT	XC
																ThFO								
		1 ◇			1 ◇				1 ◇			1 ◇		1 ◇						1 ◇				1 ◇
		A		B	C								D	E						G	H			C
							🚌	🚌							🚌	🚌			🚌				🚌	
		⚯			⚯				⊠											⚯				
Manchester Airport	85 ✈ d											18 55												19b09
Manchester Piccadilly 10	78 🚆 d			18 43								19 18												19 43
Stockport	78 d			18 54								19 26												19 54
Sheffield 7	🚆 a											20 08												
	d	19 26	19 30	19 44	19 54					19 57		20 11						20 15		20 21	20 27	20 38		20 54
Meadowhall	🚆 d		19 36	19 50						20 03		20 17						20 21			20 35	20 45		
Rotherham Central	d		19 42							20 10								20 27			20 41	20 52		
Swinton (S.Yorks)	d		19 51							20 19								20 36			20a50	21 00		
Mexborough	d		19 54							20 22								20 39				21 03		
Conisbrough	d		19 58							20 26								20 43				21 07		
Doncaster 7	a		20 08	20 11	20 20					20 36		20 40						20 55				21 18		21 20
York 8	26 a	20 31	20 39		20 46															21 39		22 01		21 45
London Kings Cross 15	⊖ 26 d			18 03		18 35			18 50						19 00			19 03						
Doncaster	31 d			20 15		20 25	20 30		20 31				20 44		20 55			20 56	21 00			21 18		
Bentley (S.Yorks)	31 a				20c41																			21c41
Adwick	31 a				20c45																			21c45
Kirk Sandall	d					20 31												21 03				21 26		
Hatfield & Stainforth	d					20 36		20 45										21 08				21 31	21 40	
Thorne South	d							20 55															21 50	
Crowle	d							21 10															22 05	
Althorpe	d							21 20															22 15	
Scunthorpe	a						21 20	21 35											21 50				22 30	
	d																		21 55					
Barnetby	d																		22 20					
Hull Paragon Interchange	🚌 d															21 25								
Barton-on-Humber	🚌 a															21 50								
Barton-on-Humber	d																21 58							
Barrow Haven	d																22 03							
New Holland	d																22 06							
Goxhill	d																22 11							
Thornton Abbey	d																22 14							
Ulceby	d																22 18							
Habrough	d																22 23		22 35					
Stallingborough	d																22 28							
Healing	d																22 31							
Great Coates	d																22 34							
Grimsby Town	a														22s10		22 39		23 00					
	d																22 39		23 05					
Grimsby Docks	d																22 42							
New Clee	d																							
Cleethorpes	a														22 30		22 48		23 25					
Thorne North	d					20a42												21 14				21a38		
Goole	d			20 36														21a23						
Saltmarshe	d																							
York 8	33 d																							
Selby	a								20 46				21 01											
	d								20 47				21 02	21 27										
Wressle	d																							
Howden	d								20 57					21 36										
Eastrington	d																							
Gilberdyke	d												21 15											
Broomfleet	d																							
Brough	d			20 49					21 09				21 23	21 48										
Ferriby	d												21 28											
Hessle	d												21 32											
Hull	a			21 06					21 28				21 45	22 05										

For general notes see front of timetable
For details of catering facilities see Directory of Train Operators

- **A** From Plymouth to Edinburgh (Table 51)
- **B** To Beverley (Table 43)
- **C** From Reading to Newcastle (Table 51)
- **D** To Bridlington (Table 43)
- **E** From Leeds (Table 39)
- **G** From Plymouth (Table 51)
- **H** To Leeds (Table 31)
- **b** Change at Manchester Piccadilly and Sheffield
- **c** Change at Doncaster

Table 29

Mondays to Fridays

22 June to 4 September

Manchester Airport, Manchester, Sheffield and Meadowhall → Doncaster → Cleethorpes and Hull
Barton-on-Humber → Cleethorpes

Network Diagram - see first page of Table 18

		TP		TP	TP	NT	TP	NT	HT	TP	NT	XC	TP	TP	NT		TP	NT	NT	NT	NT		
									BHX														
				1 ◇					1 ◇	1 ◇		1 ◇	1 ◇										
						A				B	C	D			C					C			
		bus			bus		bus		☒					bus			bus						
Manchester Airport	85 ✈ d			19 55						*20 29*		*20b09*	20 47								*21 47*		
Manchester Piccadilly 10	78 d			20 20						21 11		*20 43*	21 20								*22 20*		
Stockport	78 d			20 28						20c42		*20 54*	21 28								*22 28*		
Sheffield 7	a			21 08									22 08										
	d			21 11		21 15					21 30	21 54	22 11		22 15			22 21		23 15	23 27		
Meadowhall	d			21 17		21 21					21 36		22 17		22 21			22 31		23 21	23 33		
Rotherham Central	d					21 27					21 42				22 27			22 37		23 27	23 39		
Swinton (S.Yorks)	d					21 36					21a50				22a36			22 48		23a36	23 48		
Mexborough	d					21 39												22 51			23 51		
Conisbrough	d					21 43												22 55			23 55		
Doncaster 7	a			21 40		21 54						22 29	22 40					23 04			00 07		
York 8	26 a											22 59	*23 13*					*00 41*					
London Kings Cross 15	⊖ 26 d				*20 00*				20 30					*20 33*					*21 00*				
Doncaster	31 d	21 30			21 55	21 56	22 00		22 12					22 55			23 00		23 25				
Bentley (S.Yorks)	31 a					*22 33*																	
Adwick	31 a					*22 37*																	
Kirk Sandall	d					22 02											23 10		23 31				
Hatfield & Stainforth	d					22 07											23 20		23 36				
Thorne South	d																23 30						
Crowle	d																23 45						
Althorpe	d																23 55						
Scunthorpe	a	22 20					22 50										00 10						
	d						22 55																
Barnetby	d						23 20							23s50									
Hull Paragon Interchange	bus d																						
Barton-on-Humber	bus a																						
Barton-on-Humber	d																						
Barrow Haven	d																						
New Holland	d																						
Goxhill	d																						
Thornton Abbey	d																						
Ulceby	d																						
Habrough	d						23 35																
Stallingborough	d																						
Healing	d																						
Great Coates	d																						
Grimsby Town	a				23s10		23 59							00s15									
	d						00 05																
Grimsby Docks	d																						
New Clee	d																						
Cleethorpes	a				23 30		00 25							00 35									
Thorne North	d					22 13													23 42				
Goole	d					22 22													23a53				
Saltmarshe	d					22 26																	
York 8	33 d							22 03															
Selby	a							22 22	22 29	22 44													
	d							22 22	22 30	22 44													
Wressle	d																						
Howden	d								22 40														
Eastrington	d																						
Gilberdyke	d					22 31		22 38															
Broomfleet	d																						
Brough	d					22 39		22 46	22 54	23 04													
Ferriby	d							22 51															
Hessle	d							22 55															
Hull	a					22 57		23 08	23 13	23 21													

For general notes see front of timetable
For details of catering facilities see Directory of Train Operators

A To Beverley (Table 43)
B From Liverpool Lime Street (Table 39)
C To Leeds (Table 31)
D From Reading (Table 51)

b Change at Manchester Piccadilly and Sheffield
c Change at Manchester Piccadilly

Table 29

Saturdays

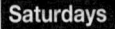

Manchester Airport, Manchester, Sheffield and Meadowhall → Doncaster → Cleethorpes and Hull Barton-on-Humber → Cleethorpes

until 20 June and from 12 September

Network Diagram - see first page of Table 18

		NT	NT	EM	NT	NT	NT	NT	NT	TP	XC	NT	TP	NT	NT		NT	XC	NT	NT	NT	NT	NT	XC
			A	B			C		D	1◇	1◇ E		1◇	A				1◇ G	C		H	Bus		1◇ J
Manchester Airport	85 d									*05 37*			05 15											
Manchester Piccadilly 10	78 d									06 21			05 44					*05 50*						
Stockport	78 d									*05b53*			05 52					*06 00*						
Sheffield 7	a												06 49											
	d		05 29			06 18	06 28				06 49	06 52	06 54					07 12	07 14	07 24	07 41			07 54
Meadowhall	d		05 35			06 24	06 34					06 58	07 01				←		07 21	07 30	07 47			
Rotherham Central	d		05 41			06 30	06 40					07 04							07 27	07 36	07 55			
Swinton (S.Yorks)	d		05 49			06 38	06a48					07 14					07 14		07a35	07 44	08 03			
Mexborough	d		05 52			06 41						→					07 17			07 47	08 06			
Conisbrough	d		05 56			06 45											07 21			07 51	08 10			
Doncaster 7	a		06 06			06 57					07 16		07 22				07 31			08 01	08 20			08 23
York 8	26 a		*06 40*								07 39							08 25		*08 31*	*09 04*			08 49
London Kings Cross 15	⊖ 26 d																				*06 15*			
Doncaster	31 d	05 50	06 14		06 47	07 00							07 24	07 30			07 32			08 03	08 22			
Bentley (S.Yorks)	31 a		*06 28*			07 03											07 35			*08 19*				
Adwick	31 a		*06 32*			07 09											07 41			*08 25*				
Kirk Sandall	d		06 20		06 53									07 36						08 09				
Hatfield & Stainforth	d		06 25		06 58									07 41						08 14				
Thorne South	d				07 03															08 18				
Crowle	d				07 11															08 27				
Althorpe	d				07 17															08 33				
Scunthorpe	a				07 25								07 49							08 43				
	d												07 50											
Barnetby	d			06 31									08 04											
Hull Paragon Interchange	Bus d																					07 25		
Barton-on-Humber	Bus a																					07 50		
Barton-on-Humber	d							06 58															08 00	
Barrow Haven	d							07 03															08 05	
New Holland	d							07 07															08 08	
Goxhill	d							07 11															08 13	
Thornton Abbey	d																						08 16	
Ulceby	d							07 19															08 20	
Habrough	d			06 41				07 23					08 12										08 25	
Stallingborough	d							07 28															08 30	
Healing	d							07 31															08 33	
Great Coates	d																						08 36	
Grimsby Town	a			06 56				07 37					08 26										08 41	
	d							07 38					08 35										08 43	
Grimsby Docks	d																						08 45	
New Clee	d																						08x48	
Cleethorpes	a							07 50					08 46										08 52	
Thorne North	d		06 30											07 46										
Goole	d		06 39											07 55							08 42			
Saltmarshe	d		06 44											08 00										
York 8	33 d									*06 05*					07 30									
Selby	a	06 10								07 43					07 50									
	d									07 43					07 50									
Wressle	d														07 58									
Howden	d									07 52					08 03									
Eastrington	d														08 08									
Gilberdyke	d		06 50						07 39					08 06	08 14									
Broomfleet	d		06 54						07 43						08 18									
Brough	d		07 00						07 49	08 04				08 14	08 24						08 56			
Ferriby	d		07 04						07 53					08 18	08 29									
Hessle	d		07 09						07 58					08 23	08 33									
Hull	a		07 22						08 11	08 20				08 36	08 46						09 13			

For general notes see front of timetable
For details of catering facilities see Directory of Train Operators

- **A** To Beverley (Table 43)
- **B** From Lincoln (Table 27)
- **C** To Leeds (Table 31)
- **D** To Scarborough (Table 43)
- **E** From Derby to Newcastle (Table 51)
- **G** From Birmingham New Street to Edinburgh(Table 51)
- **H** To Bridlington (Table 43)
- **J** From Birmingham New Street to Newcastle (Table 51)
- **b** Change at Manchester Piccadilly

Table 29

Saturdays

until 20 June and from 12 September

Manchester Airport, Manchester, Sheffield and Meadowhall → Doncaster → Cleethorpes and Hull
Barton-on-Humber → Cleethorpes

Network Diagram - see first page of Table 18

		EM	TP	TP	NT	NT	XC	NT	NT		XC	NT	NT	NT	NT	TP	TP	NT	NT	NT	EM	XC	NT	NT
		A	1 ◇	1 ◇	B		1 ◇ C		D		1 ◇ E		G	Bus		1 ◇	1 ◇	B			1 ◇ H	1 ◇ J		K
Manchester Airport 85	d		06 55	*07 05*	*06b01*											07 54	*08 05*							
Manchester Piccadilly 10 78	d		07 20	07 36	*06 35*				*07 42*							08 20	08 42	*07 44*						
Stockport 78	d		07 28	*07c04*					*07 54*							08 28	*08c19*							
Sheffield 7	a		08 10													09 08								
	d		08 11		08 14		08 21	08 25	08 41		08 54	08 57				09 11		09 14			09 21	09 21	09 25	09 31
Meadowhall	d		08 17		08e23			08 31	08 47			09 03				09 17		09 21					09 32	09 37
Rotherham Central	d				08 29			08 37				09 10						09 27					09 39	09 44
Swinton (S.Yorks)	d				08a38			08 48				09 19						09a36					09 48	09 52
Mexborough	d							08 51				09 22											09 51	
Conisbrough	d							08 55				09 26											09 55	
Doncaster 7	a		08 40					09 05	09 09		09 21	09 36				09 40					09 53		10 05	
York 8 26	a						09 30				09 45										10 16	10 30	*10 39*	10 53
London Kings Cross 15 ⊖ 26	d					*07 00*		*07 10*											*08 00*				*08 10*	
Doncaster 31	d		08 42			08 48		09 10	09 16			09 37				09 42			09 46				10 07	
Bentley (S.Yorks) 31	a		*08 53*					*09 17*				09 44											*10 17*	
Adwick 31	a		*08 59*					*09 21*				09 50											*10 21*	
Kirk Sandall	d					08 55		09 18											09 53				10 14	
Hatfield & Stainforth	d					09 00		09 23											09 58				10 19	
Thorne South	d							09 28															10 24	
Crowle	d							09 36															10 33	
Althorpe	d							09 42															10 39	
Scunthorpe	a		09 07					09 50								10 07							10 46	
	d		09 08													10 08								
Barnetby	d	08 52	09 22										09 39			10 22								
Hull Paragon Interchange (bus)	d													09 25										
Barton-on-Humber (bus)	a													09 50										
Barton-on-Humber	d														09 58									
Barrow Haven	d														10 03									
New Holland	d														10 06									
Goxhill	d														10 11									
Thornton Abbey	d														10 14									
Ulceby	d														10 18									
Habrough	d	09 01											09 48		10 23	10 31								
Stallingborough	d														10 28									
Healing	d														10 31									
Great Coates	d														10 34									
Grimsby Town	a	09 15	09 42										10 00		10 39	10 44								
	d		09 43										10 01		10 39	10 45								
Grimsby Docks	d														10 42									
New Clee	d														10x44									
Cleethorpes	a		09 58										10 13		10 49	10 59								
Thorne North	d					09 05													10 03					
Goole	d					09 14			09 39										10 12					
Saltmarshe	d																							
York 8 33	d																*08 34*			09 52				
Selby	a			08 58													09 57			10 12				
	d			08 59													09 58			10 12				
Wressle	d																							
Howden	d																			10 22				
Eastrington	d																							
Gilberdyke	d					09 22													10 20	10 29				
Broomfleet	d																							
Brough	d					09 30			09 53								10 16		10 28	10 37				
Ferriby	d					09 35													10 33					
Hessle	d					09 39													10 37					
Hull	a			09 31		09 55			10 10								10 34		10 50	10 56				

For general notes see front of timetable
For details of catering facilities see Directory of Train Operators

- **A** From Lincoln (Table 27)
- **B** To Leeds (Table 31)
- **C** From Birmingham New Street to Edinburgh (Table 51)
- **D** To Bridlington (Table 43)
- **E** From Birmingham New Street to Newcastle (Table 51)
- **G** From Sheffield via Retford (Table 30)
- **H** From St Pancras International (Table 53) (until 20 June to Scarborough) (Table 39)
- **J** From Bristol Temple Meads to Edinburgh (Table 51)
- **K** Via Pontefract Baghill (Table 33)
- **b** Change at Manchester Piccadilly and Sheffield
- **c** Change at Manchester Piccadilly
- **e** Arr. 0820

Table 29

Saturdays

until 20 June and from 12 September

Manchester Airport, Manchester, Sheffield and Meadowhall → Doncaster → Cleethorpes and Hull
Barton-on-Humber → Cleethorpes

Network Diagram - see first page of Table 18

		NT	XC	NT	EM	TP	TP	NT	NT	XC	NT	NT	XC	HT	NT	NT	NT	TP	TP	NT	NT	NT
			1 ◇			1 ◇	1 ◇			1 ◇			1 ◇	1 ◇				1 ◇	1 ◇			
		A	B	C	D			E		G		H	J		C	🚌				E		
			🍴			🍴	🍴			🍴			🍴	⊠				🍴	🍴			
Manchester Airport	85 ✈ d					08 55	*09 05*											09 55	*10 05*			
Manchester Piccadilly 10	78 🚌 d		*08 43*			09 20	09 42	*08 45*					*09 43*					10 20	10 42	*09 45*		
Stockport	78 d		*08 54*			09 28	*09b17*						*09 54*					10 28	*10b17*			
Sheffield 7	🚌 a					10 08												11 08				
	d	09 41	09 54	09 57		10 11		10 14		10 21	10 24	10 41	10 54		10 57			11 11		11 14		
Meadowhall	🚌 d	09 47		10 03		10 17		10 21			10 31	10 47			11 03			11 17		11 21		
Rotherham Central	d			10 10				10 27			10 37				11 10					11 27		
Swinton (S.Yorks)	d			10 18				10a36			10 47				11 20					11a36		
Mexborough	d			10 21							10 50				11 23							
Conisbrough	d			10 25							10 54				11 27							
Doncaster 7	a	10 11	10 18	10 36		10 40					11 04	11 09	11 16		11 35			11 41				
York 8	26 a		10 44			*11 39*				11 32	*11 39*		11 44									
London Kings Cross 15	⊖ 26 d	*08 30*							*09 00*		*09 05*			09 34				*10 00*				
Doncaster	31 d	10 22		10 37		10 42			10 46		11 07	11 18		11 24	11 38			11 42			11 46	
Bentley (S.Yorks)	31 a			10 41							*11 17*				11 41							
Adwick	31 a			10 47							*11 21*				11 47							
Kirk Sandall	d								10 52		11 13										11 52	
Hatfield & Stainforth	d								10 57		11 18										11 57	
Thorne South	d										11 23											
Crowle	d										11 31											
Althorpe	d										11 37											
Scunthorpe	a					11 07					11 45							12 07				
	d					11 08												12 08				
Barnetby	d				10 57	11 22												12 22				
Hull Paragon Interchange	🚌 d															11 25						
Barton-on-Humber	🚌 a															11 50						
Barton-on-Humber	d																11 58					
Barrow Haven	d																12 03					
New Holland	d																12 06					
Goxhill	d																12 11					
Thornton Abbey	d																12 14					
Ulceby	d																12 18					
Habrough	d				11 06												12 23	12 31				
Stallingborough	d																12 28					
Healing	d																12 31					
Great Coates	d																12 34					
Grimsby Town	a				11 21	11 42											12 39	12 44				
	d					11 43											12 39	12 45				
Grimsby Docks	d																12 42					
New Clee	d																12x44					
Cleethorpes	a					11 54											12 49	12 57				
Thorne North	d								11 02												12 02	
Goole	d	10 41							11 12			11 37									12 12	
Saltmarshe	d																					
York 8	33 d						*10 17*															11 49
Selby	a						10 57							11 39					11 57			12 09
	d						10 58							11 40					11 58			12 09
Wressle	d																					
Howden	d													11 50								12 19
Eastrington	d																					
Gilberdyke	d								11 20												12 20	12 27
Broomfleet	d								11 25													
Brough	d	10 54					11 16		11 31			11 51		12 03					12 16		12 28	12 35
Ferriby	d								11 35												12 33	
Hessle	d								11 40												12 37	
Hull	a	11 12					11 34		11 53			12 08		12 20					12 33		12 50	12 54

For general notes see front of timetable
For details of catering facilities see Directory of Train Operators

A To Scarborough (Table 43)
B From Guildford to Newcastle (Table 51)
C From Lincoln (Table 30)
D From Newark North Gate (Table 27)
E To Leeds (Table 31)
G From Plymouth to Edinburgh (Table 51)
H To Bridlington (Table 43)
J From Bournemouth to Newcastle (Table 51)
b Change at Manchester Piccadilly

Table 29

Saturdays

until 20 June and from 12 September

Manchester Airport, Manchester, Sheffield and Meadowhall → Doncaster → Cleethorpes and Hull Barton-on-Humber → Cleethorpes

Network Diagram - see first page of Table 18

		XC	NT	NT	XC	NT	EM	TP	TP	NT	NT	XC		NT	NT	NT	NT	NT	XC	HT	NT	TP	TP	NT
		1◇			1◇			1◇	1◇			1◇							1◇	1◇		1◇	1◇	
		A		B	C	D	E			G		A			H	J	(bus)		C		D			G
Manchester Airport	85 d							10 55	11 05													11 55	12 05	
Manchester Piccadilly 10	78 d				10 43			11 20	11 42	10 45									11 43			12 20	12 42	11 45
Stockport	78 d				10 54			11 28	11b17										11 54			12 28	12b17	
Sheffield 7	a							12 08														13 08		
	d	11 21	11 24	11 41	11 54	11 57		12 11		12 14		12 21		12 24	12 41				12 54		12 57	13 11		13 14
Meadowhall	d		11 31	11 47		12 03		12 17		12 21				12 31	12 47						13 03	13 17		13 21
Rotherham Central	d		11 37			12 10				12 27				12 37							13 10			13 27
Swinton (S.Yorks)	d		11 48			12 19				12a36				12 47							13 18			13a36
Mexborough	d		11 51			12 22								12 50							13 21			
Conisbrough	d		11 55			12 26								12 54							13 25			
Doncaster 7	a		12 04	12 09	12 16	12 35		12 40						13 04	13 11				13 19		13 35	13 40		
York 8	26 a	12 30			12 44							13 32		13 39					13 44			14 34		
London Kings Cross 15	⊖ 26 d		10 10			10 40		11 00						11 10						11 48				
Doncaster	31 d		12 08	12 16		12 36		12 42			12 46			13 06	13 20					13 27	13 38	13 42		
Bentley (S.Yorks)	31 a		12 17			12 40								13 17							13 41			
Adwick	31 a		12 21			12 45								13 21							13 47			
Kirk Sandall	d		12 14								12 52			13 12										
Hatfield & Stainforth	d		12 19								12 57			13 17										
Thorne South	d		12 24											13 22										
Crowle	d		12 32											13 31										
Althorpe	d		12 38											13 37										
Scunthorpe	a		12 47					13 07						13 45								14 07		
	d							13 08														14 08		
Barnetby	d						13 12	13 22								13 38						14 22		
Hull Paragon Interchange	(bus) d																13 25							
Barton-on-Humber	(bus) a																13 50							
Barton-on-Humber	d																	13 58						
Barrow Haven	d																	14 03						
New Holland	d																	14 06						
Goxhill	d																	14 11						
Thornton Abbey	d																	14 14						
Ulceby	d																	14 18						
Habrough	d						13 21									13 47		14 23				14 31		
Stallingborough	d																	14 28						
Healing	d																	14 31						
Great Coates	d																	14 34						
Grimsby Town	a						13 36	13 42								14 00		14 39				14 44		
	d							13 43								14 00		14 39				14 45		
Grimsby Docks	d																	14 42						
New Clee	d																	14x44						
Cleethorpes	a							13 54								14 11		14 49				14 57		
Thorne North	d										13 02													
Goole	d			12 35							13 11				13 39									
Saltmarshe	d																							
York 8	33 d								12 18															
Selby	a								12 57											13 42			13 57	
	d								12 58											13 43			13 58	
Wressle	d																							
Howden	d																			13 53				
Eastrington	d																							
Gilberdyke	d										13 20													
Broomfleet	d																							
Brough	d			12 49					13 16		13 28				13 53					14 05			14 16	
Ferriby	d										13 32													
Hessle	d										13 37													
Hull	a			13 07					13 34		13 50				14 10					14 22			14 34	

For general notes see front of timetable
For details of catering facilities see Directory of Train Operators

- **A** From Plymouth to Edinburgh (Table 51)
- **B** To Scarborough (Table 43)
- **C** From Reading to Newcastle (Table 51)
- **D** From Lincoln (Table 30)
- **E** From Newark North Gate (Table 27)
- **G** To Leeds (Table 31)
- **H** To Bridlington (Table 43)
- **J** From Sheffield via Retford (Table 30)
- **b** Change at Manchester Piccadilly

Table 29

Saturdays

until 20 June and from 12 September

Manchester Airport, Manchester, Sheffield and Meadowhall → Doncaster → Cleethorpes and Hull
Barton-on-Humber → Cleethorpes

Network Diagram - see first page of Table 18

		NT	NT	XC	NT	NT		NT	XC	NT	TP	TP	NT	NT	NT	XC	NT	NT	XC	HT	EM		NT	NT
				1◇					1◇		1◇	1◇				1◇			1◇	1◇				
				A		B		C	D	E			G	H		J			D		K		E	🚌
				⌶					⌶		⌶	⌶				⌶			⌶	⊠				
Manchester Airport	85 ✈ d										12b47	13 05												
Manchester Piccadilly 10	78 🚆 d								12 43		13 20	13 42	12 45						13 43					
Stockport	78 d								12 54		13 28	13c17							13 54					
Sheffield 7	🚆 a										14 08													
	d			13 21	13 24	13 28		13 41	13 54	13 57	14 11		14 14			14 21	14 24	14 41	14 54				14 57	
Meadowhall	🚆 d				13 31	13 35		13 47		14 03	14 17		14 21				14 31	14 47					15 03	
Rotherham Central	d				13 37	13 42				14 10			14 27				14 37						15 10	
Swinton (S.Yorks)	d				13 47	13 50				14 18			14a36				14 47						15 18	
Mexborough	d				13 50					14 21							14 50						15 21	
Conisbrough	d				13 54					14 25							14 54						15 25	
Doncaster 7	a				14 04			14 11	14 16	14 35	14 40						15 04	15 11	15 16				15 36	
York 8	26 a			14 30		14 51			14 44							15 32			15 44					
London Kings Cross 15	⊖ 26 d				*12 10*			*12 30*			*13 00*						*13 10*			13 48				
Doncaster	31 d		13 46		14 06			14 18		14 38	14 42			14 46			15 07	15 16		15 27			15 38	
Bentley (S.Yorks)	31 a				*14 17*					14 41							*15 17*						15 41	
Adwick	31 a				*14 21*					14 47							*15 21*						15 47	
Kirk Sandall	d		13 52		14 12									14 52			15 13							
Hatfield & Stainforth	d		13 57		14 17									14 57			15 18							
Thorne South	d				14 22												15 23							
Crowle	d				14 31												15 31							
Althorpe	d				14 37												15 37							
Scunthorpe	a				14 45						15 07						15 46							
	d										15 08													
Barnetby	d										15 22										15 34			
Hull Paragon Interchange	🚌 d																							15 25
Barton-on-Humber	🚌 a																							15 50
Barton-on-Humber	d																							
Barrow Haven	d																							
New Holland	d																							
Goxhill	d																							
Thornton Abbey	d																							
Ulceby	d																							
Habrough	d																				15 42			
Stallingborough	d																							
Healing	d																							
Great Coates	d																							
Grimsby Town	a										15 42										15 57			
	d										15 43													
Grimsby Docks	d																							
New Clee	d																							
Cleethorpes	a										15 54													
Thorne North	d		14 02											15 02										
Goole	d		14 12					14 37						15 13				15 37						
Saltmarshe	d		14 17																					
York 8	33 d	13 38													15 05									
Selby	a	14 03										14 57			15 24					15 42				
	d	14 04										14 58			15 24					15 43				
Wressle	d																							
Howden	d	14 13																		15 53				
Eastrington	d																							
Gilberdyke	d		14 26											15 21										
Broomfleet	d																							
Brough	d	14 25	14 34					14 54				15 16		15 29	15 44			15 51		16 05				
Ferriby	d		14 39											15 34										
Hessle	d		14 43											15 38										
Hull	a	14 45	14 56					15 12				15 34		15 51	16 03			16 07		16 22				

For general notes see front of timetable
For details of catering facilities see Directory of Train Operators

A From Penzance (Table 135) to Edinburgh (Table 51)
B Via Pontefract Baghill (Table 33)
C To Bridlington (Table 43)
D From Reading to Newcastle (Table 51)
E From Lincoln (Table 30)
G To Leeds (Table 31)
H To Scarborough (Table 43)
J From Plymouth (Table 51) to Aberdeen (Table 229)
K From Newark North Gate (Table 27)
b Until 31 October dep. 8 mins. later
c Change at Manchester Piccadilly

Table 29

Saturdays

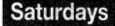

Manchester Airport, Manchester, Sheffield and Meadowhall → Doncaster → Cleethorpes and Hull Barton-on-Humber → Cleethorpes

until 20 June and from 12 September

Network Diagram - see first page of Table 18

		NT	TP	TP	NT	NT	XC	NT	NT	NT	XC	NT	TP	TP	NT		NT	NT	EM	NT	NT	NT	XC	NT
			1 ◇	1 ◇			1 ◇				1 ◇		1 ◇	1 ◇									1 ◇	
					A	B	C			D	E	G			A		B	H	J				K	
																				🚌		🚌		
			🛒				🛒				🛒		🛒										🛒	
Manchester Airport	85 ✈ d		13b47	*14 05*									14b47	*15 05*										
Manchester Piccadilly 10	78 🚉 d		14 20	14 42	*13 45*						*14 43*		15 20	15 42	*14 45*									
Stockport	78 d		14 28	*14c17*							*14 54*		15 28	*15c17*										
Sheffield 7	🚉 a		15 08										16 08											
	d		15 11		15 14		15 21	15 24	15 40		15 54	15 57	16 11		16 14								16 21	16 24
Meadowhall	🚉 d		15 17		15 21			15 31	15 46			16 03	16 17		16 21									16 31
Rotherham Central	d				15 27			15 37				16 10			16 27									16 37
Swinton (S.Yorks)	d				15a36			15 47				16 18			16a36									16 47
Mexborough	d							15 50				16 21												16 50
Conisbrough	d							15 54				16 25												16 54
Doncaster 7	a		15 40					16 04	16 11		16 16	16 35	16 40											17 08
York 8	26 a						16 30				16 44												17 31	
London Kings Cross 15	⊖ 26 d		*14 00*									*14 30*	*15 00*											
Doncaster	31 d		15 42			15 46		16 06	16 14			16 38	16 42				16 47							
Bentley (S.Yorks)	31 a										*16e30*	16 41												
Adwick	31 a										*16e34*	16 47												
Kirk Sandall	d					15 52		16 13									16 53							
Hatfield & Stainforth	d					15 57		16 18									16 58							
Thorne South	d							16 24																
Crowle	d							16 33																
Althorpe	d							16 39																
Scunthorpe	a		16 07					16 46					17 07											
	d		16 08										17 08											
Barnetby	d		16 22										17 22					17 38	17 54					
Hull Paragon Interchange	🚌 d																			17 30		19 25		
Barton-on-Humber	🚌 a																			17 55		19 50		
Barton-on-Humber	d	15 58																			18 00			
Barrow Haven	d	16 03																			18 05			
New Holland	d	16 06																			18 08			
Goxhill	d	16 11																			18 13			
Thornton Abbey	d	16 14																			18 16			
Ulceby	d	16 18																			18 20			
Habrough	d	16 23	16 31															17 47	18 02		18 25			
Stallingborough	d	16 28																			18 30			
Healing	d	16 31																			18 33			
Great Coates	d	16 34																			18 36			
Grimsby Town	a	16 39	16 44										17 42					18 01	18 17		18 41			
	d	16 39	16 45										17 43					18 02			18 41			
Grimsby Docks	d	16 42																			18 44			
New Clee	d																							
Cleethorpes	a	16 48	16 57										17 54					18 11			18 50			
Thorne North	d					16 02											17 03							
Goole	d					16 12			16 36								17 12							
Saltmarshe	d																17 17							
York 8	33 d									16 12														
Selby	a			15 57						16 38				17 00										
	d			15 58						16 39				17 00										
Wressle	d									16 46														
Howden	d									16 51														
Eastrington	d																							
Gilberdyke	d					16 20				16 58							17 23							
Broomfleet	d																							
Brough	d			16 16		16 28			16 50	17 06				17 18			17 31							
Ferriby	d					16 33				17 10							17 36							
Hessle	d					16 37											17 40							
Hull	a			16 35		16 50			17 07	17 27				17 37			17 53							

For general notes see front of timetable
For details of catering facilities see Directory of Train Operators

- **A** To Leeds (Table 31)
- **B** To Bridlington (Table 43)
- **C** From Penzance (Table 135) to Glasgow Central (Table 51)
- **D** To Scarborough (Table 43)
- **E** From Reading to Newcastle (Table 51)
- **G** From Lincoln (Table 30)
- **H** From Sheffield via Retford (Table 30)
- **J** From Lincoln (Table 27)
- **K** From Newquay (Table 135) (from 12 September from Plymouth) (Table 51) to Dundee (Table 229)
- **b** Until 31 October dep. 8 mins. later
- **c** Change at Manchester Piccadilly
- **e** Change at Doncaster

Manchester Airport, Manchester, Sheffield and Meadowhall → Doncaster → Cleethorpes and Hull Barton-on-Humber → Cleethorpes

Saturdays

until 20 June and from 12 September

Network Diagram - see first page of Table 18

Station			NT	NT	XC	NT	NT	TP	TP	NT	NT	EM	XC	NT	NT	NT	NT	XC	NT	NT	XC	TP	HT	TP
					1 ◇			1 ◇	1 ◇				1 ◇					1 ◇			1 ◇	1 ◇	1 ◇	1 ◇
					A	B	C			D		E	G				B	A	C	D	H			
					⊥			⊥					⊥					⊥			⊥		⊠	⊥
Manchester Airport	85 ✈	d						15b47	16 05													17 05		16b47
Manchester Piccadilly 10	78 🚋	d			15 43			16 20	16 42	15 45								16 43		16 45		17 42		17 20
Stockport	78	d			15 54			16 28	16c17									16 54				17c17		17 28
Sheffield 7	🚋	a						17 08																18 15
		d	16 41		16 54		16 57	17 11		17 14			17 21	17 27	17 41			17 47	17 57	18 14	18 21			18 24
Meadowhall	🚋	d	16 47				17 03	17 17		17 21				17 33	17 47				18 03	18 21				18 29
Rotherham Central		d					17 10			17 27				17 39					18 10	18 27				
Swinton (S.Yorks)		d					17 18			17a36				17 47					18 18	18a36				
Mexborough		d					17 21							17 50					18 21					
Conisbrough		d					17 25							17 54					18 25					
Doncaster 7		a	17 12		17 19		17 35	17 40						18 07	18 12				18 38					18 53
York 8	26	a			17 44								18 31		18 56			18 59			19 31			
London Kings Cross 15	⊖ 26	d					15 30	16 00							16 30								17 05	
Doncaster	31	d	17 14			17 22	17 38	17 42			17 48				18 24		18 27						18 48	18 55
Bentley (S.Yorks)	31	a			17e30		17 41								18 30									
Adwick	31	a			17e34		17 47								18 34									
Kirk Sandall		d				17 28					17 54						18 34							
Hatfield & Stainforth		d				17 33					17 59						18 39							
Thorne South		d				17 38											18 44							
Crowle		d				17 47											18 52							
Althorpe		d				17 53											18 58							
Scunthorpe		a				18 01		18 07									19 07							19 22
		d						18 08																19 23
Barnetby		d						18 22				19 06												19 37
Hull Paragon Interchange	🚌	d																						
Barton-on-Humber	🚌	a																						
Barton-on-Humber		d																						
Barrow Haven		d																						
New Holland		d																						
Goxhill		d																						
Thornton Abbey		d																						
Ulceby		d																						
Habrough		d						18 31				19 14												
Stallingborough		d																						
Healing		d																						
Great Coates		d																						
Grimsby Town		a						18 44				19 29												19 58
		d						18 45																19 58
Grimsby Docks		d																						
New Clee		d																						
Cleethorpes		a						18 59																20 09
Thorne North		d	17 28								18 04													
Goole		d	17 37								18 13				18 44									
Saltmarshe		d									18 18													
York 8	33	d		17 18												18 13								
Selby		a		17 37					17 57							18 41						19 00	19 07	
		d		17 37					17 58							18 42						19 01	19 08	
Wressle		d																						
Howden		d		17 47					18 07							18 51							19 18	
Eastrington		d														18 56								
Gilberdyke		d		17 57							18 23					19 00								
Broomfleet		d									18 27													
Brough		d	17 56	18 05					18 19		18 33				18 58	19 08						19 18	19 30	
Ferriby		d									18 37													
Hessle		d									18 42													
Hull		a	18 10	18 21					18 37		18 57				19 15	19 28						19 37	19 47	

For general notes see front of timetable
For details of catering facilities see Directory of Train Operators

A From Reading to Newcastle (Table 51)
B From Adwick (Table 31)
C From Lincoln (Table 30)
D To Leeds (Table 31)
E From Newark North Gate (Table 27)
G From Plymouth (Table 51) to Glasgow Central (Table 26)
H From Plymouth to Edinburgh (Table 51)
b Until 31 October dep. 8 mins. later
c Change at Manchester Piccadilly
e Change at Doncaster

Table 29

Saturdays

Manchester Airport, Manchester, Sheffield and Meadowhall → Doncaster → Cleethorpes and Hull Barton-on-Humber → Cleethorpes

until 20 June and from 12 September

Network Diagram - see first page of Table 18

	NT	NT		NT	XC	NT	NT	TP	TP	NT	NT	XC	NT	NT	NT	XC	NT		GR	NT	TP	NT	NT
				A	1 ◇ B	C		1 ◇	1 ◇	D		1 ◇ E		G		1 ◇ H			R 1		1 ◇	A	
Manchester Airport 85 d								17b47	18 03												18b47		
Manchester Piccadilly 10 78 d				17 43				18 20	18 42	17 45				18 43							19 18		
Stockport 78 d				17 54				18 28	18c17					18 54							19 26		
Sheffield 7 a								19 10													20 08		
d		18 29		18 41	18 54	19 00		19 11		19 14		19 21	19 30	19 44		19 54				19 57	20 11		20 15
Meadowhall d		18 35		18 47		19 06		19 17		19 21			19 36	19 50						20 03	20 17		20 20
Rotherham Central d		18 42				19 12				19 27			19 42							20 09			20 26
Swinton (S.Yorks) d		18 50				19 20				19a40			19 51							20 17			20 36
Mexborough d		18 53				19 23							19 54							20 20			20 39
Conisbrough d		18 57				19 27							19 58							20 24			20 43
Doncaster 7 a		19 08		19 10	19 18	19 39		19 40					20 09	20 11		20 16				20 36	20 40		20 56
York 8 26 a					19 44			20 34				20 31				20 40							21 38
London Kings Cross 15 ⊖ 26 d								18 00						18 30			18 35		18 40			19 00	
Doncaster 31 d	18 58	19 13		19 13				19 42			19 47			20 14			20 25		20 27		20 42	20 46	
Bentley (S.Yorks) 31 a					19e30															20 48			
Adwick 31 a					19e34															20 52			
Kirk Sandall d	19 06	19 20									19 53						20 31					20 52	
Hatfield & Stainforth d	19 11	19 25									19 58						20 36					20 57	
Thorne South d		19 30															20 41						
Crowle d		19 39															20 50						
Althorpe d		19 45															20 56						
Scunthorpe a		19 52						20 07									21 04				21 08		
d								20 08													21 08		
Barnetby d								20 22													21 22		
Hull Paragon Interchange d																							
Barton-on-Humber a																							
Barton-on-Humber d							19 58																
Barrow Haven d							20 03																
New Holland d							20 06																
Goxhill d							20 11																
Thornton Abbey d							20 14																
Ulceby d							20 18																
Habrough d							20 23														21 31		
Stallingborough d							20 28																
Healing d							20 31																
Great Coates d							20 34																
Grimsby Town a							20 39	20 42													21 44		
d							20 39	20 43													21 45		
Grimsby Docks d							20 42																
New Clee d																							
Cleethorpes a							20 48	20 55													21 59		
Thorne North d	19 16										20 03											21 02	
Goole d	19 25										20 12			20 33								21 11	
Saltmarshe d																							
York 8 33 d									19 29						20 17								
Selby a				19 34					20 00						20 36				20 43				
d				19 34					20 01						20 36				20 44				
Wressle d																							
Howden d									20 10														
Eastrington d																							
Gilberdyke d	19 33										20 22				20 50							21 19	
Broomfleet d																							
Brough d	19 41			19 54					20 22		20 30			20 47	20 58				21 06			21 27	
Ferriby d	19 46										20 35				21 02								
Hessle d	19 50										20 39				21 07								
Hull a	20 03			20 11					20 39		20 52			21 04	21 22				21 27			21 45	

For general notes see front of timetable
For details of catering facilities see Directory of Train Operators

A To Bridlington (Table 43)
B From Reading to Edinburgh (Table 51)
C From Retford (Table 30)
D To Leeds (Table 31)
E From Plymouth to Edinburgh (Table 51)
G To Beverley (Table 43)
H From Reading to Newcastle (Table 51)
b Until 31 October dep. 8 mins. later
c Change at Manchester Piccadilly
e Change at Doncaster

Table 29

Saturdays

until 20 June and from 12 September

Manchester Airport, Manchester, Sheffield and Meadowhall → Doncaster → Cleethorpes and Hull
Barton-on-Humber → Cleethorpes

Network Diagram - see first page of Table 18

		NT	TP	HT	XC	NT	NT	XC	NT	NT	TP	NT	TP	TP	NT	XC	TP	XC	NT	NT	NT
			1 ◇	1 ◇	1 ◇			1 ◇			1 ◇		1 ◇	1 ◇		1 ◇	1 ◇	1 ◇			
			A		B	C		D				E	G	H	C	J		K		C	
				☒	⚲			⚲	🚌							⚲		⚲			
Manchester Airport	85 ✈ d							19b09			19c47		20 29			20b09	20 47				21b09
Manchester Piccadilly 10	78 🚢 d							19 43			20 20		21 11			20 43	21 20				21 43
Stockport	78 d							19 54			20 28		20e42			20 54	21 28				21 52
Sheffield 7	🚢 a										21 08						22 08				
	d				20 21	20 30	20 38	20 54			21 11	21 14			21 30	21 54	22 11	22 26	22 30	22 34	23 26
Meadowhall	🚢 d					20 36	20 44				21 17	21 22			21 36		22 17		22 36	22 40	23 32
Rotherham Central	d					20 42	20 53					21 28			21 42				22 42	22 46	23 38
Swinton (S.Yorks)	d					20a50	21 05					21 40			21a50				22 50	22a53	23 46
Mexborough	d						21 08					21 43							22 53		23 49
Conisbrough	d						21 12					21 47							22 57		23 53
Doncaster 7	a						21 21	21 25			21 40	21 55				22 19	22 36	22 47	23 08		00 04
York 8	26 a				22 03			21 48				22 38				22 48					
London Kings Cross 15	⊖ 26 d			19 41								20 00					20 30				
Doncaster	31 d	21 07		21 20							21 42	21 57					22 38		23 09		
Bentley (S.Yorks)	31 a						21 31										22 55				
Adwick	31 a						21 35										22 59				
Kirk Sandall	d	21 13										22 03					22 43		23 16		
Hatfield & Stainforth	d	21 18										22 08					22 48		23 21		
Thorne South	d	21 23															22 53				
Crowle	d	21 31															23 01				
Althorpe	d	21 37															23 07				
Scunthorpe	a	21 46									22 07						23 13				
	d										22 08						23 13				
Barnetby	d										22 22						23 27				
Hull Paragon Interchange	🚌 d								21 25												
Barton-on-Humber	🚌 a								21 50												
Barton-on-Humber	d									21 58											
Barrow Haven	d									22 03											
New Holland	d									22 06											
Goxhill	d									22 11											
Thornton Abbey	d									22 14											
Ulceby	d									22 18											
Habrough	d									22 23	22 31						23 36				
Stallingborough	d									22 28											
Healing	d									22 31											
Great Coates	d									22 34											
Grimsby Town	a									22 39	22 44						23 49				
	d									22 39	22 45						23 50				
Grimsby Docks	d									22 42											
New Clee	d																				
Cleethorpes	a									22 48	22 59						00 02				
Thorne North	d											22 13							23 26		
Goole	d											22 22							23a37		
Saltmarshe	d											22 27									
York 8	33 d												21 45	21 45							
Selby	a			21 35									22 44								
	d		21 27	21 36									22 44	22 44							
Wressle	d																				
Howden	d		21 36	21 46																	
Eastrington	d																				
Gilberdyke	d											22 33									
Broomfleet	d																				
Brough	d		21 48	21 59								22 41	23 04	23 04							
Ferriby	d																				
Hessle	d																				
Hull	a		22 05	22 16								22 58	23 21	23 21							

For general notes see front of timetable
For details of catering facilities see Directory of Train Operators

- **A** From Leeds (Table 39)
- **B** From Plymouth (Table 51)
- **C** To Leeds (Table 31)
- **D** From Reading to Newcastle (Table 51)
- **E** To Beverley (Table 43)
- **G** Until 20 June. From Liverpool Lime Street (Table 39)
- **H** From 12 September. From Leeds (Table 39)
- **J** From Reading (Table 51)
- **K** From Bournemouth (from 12 September from Plymouth) (Table 51)
- **b** Change at Manchester Piccadilly and Sheffield
- **c** Until 31 October dep. 8 mins. later
- **e** Change at Manchester Piccadilly

Table 29

Saturdays

Manchester Airport, Manchester, Sheffield and Meadowhall → Doncaster → Cleethorpes and Hull
Barton-on-Humber → Cleethorpes

27 June to 5 September

Network Diagram - see first page of Table 18

		NT	NT	EM	NT	TP	NT	NT	NT	NT	NT	NT	NT	TP		XC	NT	NT	NT	NT	XC	TP	TP	NT
														1 ◇		1 ◇					1 ◇	1 ◇		
			A	B						C	D					E		A			G			C
						🚌		🚌				🚌											🚌	
																🍴					🍴			
Manchester Airport	85 ✈ d													*05 37*								05 15		
Manchester Piccadilly 10	78 🚆 d													06 21							*05 50*	05 44		
Stockport	78 d													*05b53*							*06 00*	05 52		
Sheffield 7	🚆 a																					06 49		
	d		05 29						06 18	06 28						06 49	06 52				07 12	06 54		07 14
Meadowhall	🚆 d		05 35						06 24	06 34							06 58					07 01		07 21
Rotherham Central	d		05 41						06 30	06 40							07 04		←					07 27
Swinton (S.Yorks)	d		05 49						06 38	06a48							07 14		07 14					07a35
Mexborough	d		05 52						06 41								→		07 17					
Conisbrough	d		05 56						06 45										07 21					
Doncaster 7	a		06 06						06 57							07 16			07 31			07 22		
York 8	26 a		*06 40*													07 39					08 25	*08 31*		
London Kings Cross 15	⊖ 26 d																							
Doncaster	31 d	05 50	06 14			06 30	06 47		07 00									07 30	07 32				07 35	
Bentley (S.Yorks)	31 a		*06 28*						07 03										07 35					
Adwick	31 a		*06 32*						07 09										07 41					
Kirk Sandall	d		06 20				06 53											07 36						
Hatfield & Stainforth	d		06 25				06 58	07 05										07 41						
Thorne South	d							07 15																
Crowle	d							07 30																
Althorpe	d							07 40																
Scunthorpe	a					07 20		07 55																
	d					07 20																		
Barnetby	d			06 31		07 45																		
Hull Paragon Interchange	🚌 d											07 25												
Barton-on-Humber	🚌 a											07 50												
Barton-on-Humber	d				06 58								08 00											
Barrow Haven	d				07 03								08 05											
New Holland	d				07 07								08 08											
Goxhill	d				07 11								08 13											
Thornton Abbey	d												08 16											
Ulceby	d				07 19								08 20											
Habrough	d			06 41	07 23	08 00							08 25											
Stallingborough	d				07 28								08 30											
Healing	d				07 31								08 33											
Great Coates	d												08 36											
Grimsby Town	a			06 56	07 37	08 25							08 41										09s00	
	d				07 38	08 25							08 43											
Grimsby Docks	d												08 45											
New Clee	d												08x48											
Cleethorpes	a				07 50	08 45							08 52										09 20	
Thorne North	d		06 30				07a03											07 46						
Goole	d		06 39															07 55						
Saltmarshe	d		06 44															08 00						
York 8	33 d													*06 05*						07 30				
Selby	a	06 10												07 43						07 50				
	d													07 43						07 50				
Wressle	d																			07 58				
Howden	d													07 52						08 03				
Eastrington	d																			08 08				
Gilberdyke	d		06 50								07 39							08 06		08 14				
Broomfleet	d		06 54								07 43									08 18				
Brough	d		07 00								07 49			08 04				08 14		08 24				
Ferriby	d		07 04								07 53							08 18		08 29				
Hessle	d		07 09								07 58							08 23		08 33				
Hull	a		07 22								08 11			08 20				08 36		08 46				

For general notes see front of timetable
For details of catering facilities see Directory of Train Operators

- **A** To Beverley (Table 43)
- **B** From Lincoln (Table 27)
- **C** To Leeds (Table 31)
- **D** To Scarborough (Table 43)
- **E** From Derby to Newcastle (Table 51)
- **G** From Birmingham New Street to Edinburgh (Table 51)
- **b** Change at Manchester Piccadilly

Table 29

Saturdays

27 June to 5 September

Manchester Airport, Manchester, Sheffield and Meadowhall → Doncaster → Cleethorpes and Hull
Barton-on-Humber → Cleethorpes

Network Diagram - see first page of Table 18

		EM	TP	NT	NT	NT	XC	TP	NT	TP	TP	NT	XC	NT	TP	NT	NT	TP	NT	NT	NT	XC
							1 ◇			1 ◇	1 ◇		1 ◇									1 ◇
		A				B	C		D			E	G								B	C
			[bus]		[bus]			[bus]							[bus]	[bus]		[bus]		[bus]		
							[catering]			[catering]	[catering]		[catering]									[catering]
Manchester Airport	85 d									06 55	07 05	06b01										
Manchester Piccadilly 10	78 d									07 20	07 36	06 35									07 42	
Stockport	78 d									07 28	07c04										07 54	
Sheffield 7	a									08 10												
	d			07 24		07 41	07 54			08 11		08 14	08 21						08 25		08 41	08 54
Meadowhall	d			07 30		07 47				08 17		08 23							08 31		08 47	
Rotherham Central	d			07 36		07 55						08 29							08 37			
Swinton (S.Yorks)	d			07 44		08 03						08a38							08 48			
Mexborough	d			07 47		08 06													08 51			
Conisbrough	d			07 51		08 10													08 55			
Doncaster 7	a			08 01		08 20	08 23			08 40									09 05		09 09	09 21
York 8	26 a			*08 31*		*09 04*	08 49						09 30									09 45
London Kings Cross 15	⊖ 26 d					*06 15*									*07 00*				*07 10*			
Doncaster	31 d		07 40	08 03		08 22		08 30						08 48	08 55			09 00	09 10		09 16	
Bentley (S.Yorks)	31 a			*08 19*						*08 53*									*09 17*			
Adwick	31 a			*08 25*						*08 59*									*09 21*			
Kirk Sandall	d			08 09										08 55					09 18			
Hatfield & Stainforth	d			08 14	08 20									09 00					09 23	09 30		
Thorne South	d				08 35															09 40		
Crowle	d				08 50															09 55		
Althorpe	d				09 00															10 05		
Scunthorpe	a		08 40		09 20			09 30										10 00		10 20		
	d		08 45															10 05				
Barnetby	d	08 52	09 10						09 39									10 30				
Hull Paragon Interchange	[bus] d															09 25						
Barton-on-Humber	[bus] a															09 50						
Barton-on-Humber	d																09 58					
Barrow Haven	d																10 03					
New Holland	d																10 06					
Goxhill	d																10 11					
Thornton Abbey	d																10 14					
Ulceby	d																10 18					
Habrough	d	09 01	09 25						09 48								10 23	10 45				
Stallingborough	d																10 28					
Healing	d																10 31					
Great Coates	d																10 34					
Grimsby Town	a	09 15	09 50						10 00						10s20		10 39	11 10				
	d		09 55						10 01								10 39	11 15				
Grimsby Docks	d																10 42					
New Clee	d																10x44					
Cleethorpes	a		10 15						10 13						10 40		10 49	11 35				
Thorne North	d			08a21										09 05					09a28			
Goole	d					08 42								09 14							09 39	
Saltmarshe	d																					
York 8	33 d																					
Selby	a										08 58											
	d										08 59											
Wressle	d																					
Howden	d																					
Eastrington	d																					
Gilberdyke	d													09 22								
Broomfleet	d																					
Brough	d					08 56								09 30							09 53	
Ferriby	d													09 35								
Hessle	d													09 39								
Hull	a					09 13					09 31			09 55							10 10	

For general notes see front of timetable
For details of catering facilities see Directory of Train Operators

- **A** From Lincoln (Table 27)
- **B** To Bridlington (Table 43)
- **C** From Birmingham New Street to Newcastle (Table 51)
- **D** From Sheffield via Retford (Table 30)
- **E** To Leeds (Table 31)
- **G** From Birmingham New Street to Edinburgh (Table 51)
- **b** Change at Manchester Piccadilly and Sheffield
- **c** Change at Manchester Piccadilly

Table 29

Saturdays

Manchester Airport, Manchester, Sheffield and Meadowhall → Doncaster → Cleethorpes and Hull
Barton-on-Humber → Cleethorpes

27 June to 5 September

Network Diagram - see first page of Table 18

	TP	NT	TP	TP	NT	TP	EM	NT	NT	EM	TP	XC	NT		NT	NT	NT	XC	TP	NT	TP	TP	NT
			1 ◇	1 ◇						1 ◇		1 ◇						1 ◇			1 ◇	1 ◇	
							A	B		C		D				E	G	H		J			B
	bus					bus					bus				bus				bus				
			catering							catering		catering						catering			catering	catering	
Manchester Airport 85 d			07 54	08 05																	08 55	09 05	
Manchester Piccadilly 10 78 d			08 20	08 42				07 44										08 43			09 20	09 42	08 45
Stockport 78 d			08 28	08b19														08 54			09 28	09b17	
Sheffield 7 a			09 08																		10 08		
d		08 57	09 11					09 14		09 21		09 21	09 25			09 31	09 41	09 54		09 57	10 11		10 14
Meadowhall d		09 03	09 17					09 21					09 32			09 37	09 47			10 03	10 17		10 21
Rotherham Central d		09 10						09 27					09 39			09 44				10 10			10 27
Swinton (S.Yorks) d		09 19						09a36					09 48			09 52				10 18			10a36
Mexborough d		09 22											09 51							10 21			
Conisbrough d		09 26											09 55							10 25			
Doncaster 7 a		09 36	09 40							09 53			10 05				10 11	10 18		10 36	10 40		
York 8 26 a										10 16		10 30	10 39			10 53		10 44					
London Kings Cross 15 ⊖ 26 d					08 00								08 10				08 30						
Doncaster 31 d	09 30	09 37			09 46	09 55					10 00		10 07				10 22		10 30	10 37			
Bentley (S.Yorks) 31 a		09 44											10 17							10 41			
Adwick 31 a		09 50											10 21							10 47			
Kirk Sandall d					09 53								10 14										
Hatfield & Stainforth d					09 58								10 19		10 25								
Thorne South d															10 35								
Crowle d															10 50								
Althorpe d															11 00								
Scunthorpe a	10 25										10 50				11 15				11 20				
d											10 55												
Barnetby d							10 57				11 20												
Hull Paragon Interchange bus d																							
Barton-on-Humber bus a																							
Barton-on-Humber d																							
Barrow Haven d																							
New Holland d																							
Goxhill d																							
Thornton Abbey d																							
Ulceby d																							
Habrough d							11 06				11 35												
Stallingborough d																							
Healing d																							
Great Coates d																							
Grimsby Town a						11s15	11 21				12 00												
d											12 05												
Grimsby Docks d																							
New Clee d																							
Cleethorpes a						11 35					12 25												
Thorne North d					10 03								10a25										
Goole d					10 12												10 41						
Saltmarshe d																							
York 8 33 d				08 34					09 52													10 17	
Selby a				09 57					10 12													10 57	
d				09 58					10 12													10 58	
Wressle d																							
Howden d									10 22														
Eastrington d																							
Gilberdyke d					10 20				10 29														
Broomfleet d																							
Brough d				10 16	10 28				10 37								10 54					11 16	
Ferriby d					10 33																		
Hessle d					10 37																		
Hull a				10 34	10 50				10 56								11 12					11 34	

For general notes see front of timetable
For details of catering facilities see Directory of Train Operators

A From Newark North Gate (Table 27)

B To Leeds (Table 31)

C From St Pancras International (Table 53) to Scarborough (Table 39)

D From Bristol Temple Meads to Edinburgh (Table 51)

E Via Pontefract Baghill (Table 33)

G To Scarborough (Table 43)

H From Guildford to Newcastle (Table 51)

J From Lincoln (Table 30)

b Change at Manchester Piccadilly

Table 29

Saturdays

27 June to 5 September

Manchester Airport, Manchester, Sheffield and Meadowhall → Doncaster → Cleethorpes and Hull
Barton-on-Humber → Cleethorpes

Network Diagram - see first page of Table 18

		NT	TP	NT	NT	TP	XC		NT	NT	NT	XC	HT	TP	NT	TP	TP	NT	NT	TP	EM		TP	NT
							1 ◇					1 ◇	1 ◇			1 ◇	1 ◇							
							A				B	C			D						E			G
			bus	bus		bus				bus				bus						bus			bus	
							⊼					⊼	☒			⊼	⊼							
Manchester Airport	85 ✈ d															09 55	*10 05*							
Manchester Piccadilly 10	78 ⇌ d											*09 43*				10 20	*10 42*							*09 45*
Stockport	78 d											*09 54*				10 28	*10b17*							
Sheffield 7	⇌ a															11 08								
	d						10 21		10 24		10 41	10 54			10 57	11 11								11 14
Meadowhall	⇌ d								10 31		10 47				11 03	11 17								11 21
Rotherham Central	d								10 37						11 10									11 27
Swinton (S.Yorks)	d								10 47						11 20									11a36
Mexborough	d								10 50						11 23									
Conisbrough	d								10 54						11 27									
Doncaster 7	a								11 04		11 09	11 16			11 35	11 40								
York 8	26 a						11 32		*11 39*			11 44												
London Kings Cross 15	⊖ 26 d	*09 00*							*09 05*				09 34					*10 00*						
Doncaster	31 d	10 46	10 55			11 00			11 07		11 18		11 24	11 30	11 38			11 46		11 55			12 00	
Bentley (S.Yorks)	31 a								*11 17*						11 41									
Adwick	31 a								*11 21*						11 47									
Kirk Sandall	d	10 52							11 13									11 52						
Hatfield & Stainforth	d	10 57							11 18	11 25								11 57						
Thorne South	d									11 35														
Crowle	d									11 50														
Althorpe	d									12 00														
Scunthorpe	a					11 50				12 15				12 20									12 50	
	d					11 55																	12 55	
Barnetby	d					12 20															13 12		13 20	
Hull Paragon Interchange	bus d			11 25																				
Barton-on-Humber	bus a			11 50																				
Barton-on-Humber	d				11 58																			
Barrow Haven	d				12 03																			
New Holland	d				12 06																			
Goxhill	d				12 11																			
Thornton Abbey	d				12 14																			
Ulceby	d				12 18																			
Habrough	d				12 23	12 35															13 21		13 35	
Stallingborough	d				12 28																			
Healing	d				12 31																			
Great Coates	d				12 34																			
Grimsby Town	a		12s10		12 39	13 00														13s10	13 36		14 00	
	d				12 39	13 05																	14 05 →	
Grimsby Docks	d				12 42																			
New Clee	d				12x44																			
Cleethorpes	a		12 30		12 49	13 25														13 30				
Thorne North	d	11 02							11a23									12 02						
Goole	d	11 12									11 37							12 12						
Saltmarshe	d																							
York 8	33 d																		11 49					
Selby	a												11 39				11 57		12 09					
	d												11 40				11 58		12 09					
Wressle	d																							
Howden	d												11 50						12 19					
Eastrington	d																							
Gilberdyke	d	11 20																12 20	12 27					
Broomfleet	d	11 25																						
Brough	d	11 31									11 51		12 03				12 16	12 28	12 35					
Ferriby	d	11 35																12 33						
Hessle	d	11 40																12 37						
Hull	a	11 53									12 08		12 20				12 33	12 50	12 54					

For general notes see front of timetable
For details of catering facilities see Directory of Train Operators

- **A** From Plymouth to Edinburgh (Table 51)
- **B** To Bridlington (Table 43)
- **C** From Bournemouth to Newcastle (Table 51)
- **D** From Lincoln (Table 30)
- **E** From Newark North Gate (Table 27)
- **G** To Leeds (Table 31)
- **b** Change at Manchester Piccadilly

Table 29

Saturdays

Manchester Airport, Manchester, Sheffield and Meadowhall → Doncaster → Cleethorpes and Hull
Barton-on-Humber → Cleethorpes

27 June to 5 September

Network Diagram - see first page of Table 18

	XC	NT	NT	NT	TP	NT	XC	TP	NT	TP	TP	NT	NT		TP	NT	NT	TP	XC	NT	NT	NT	XC
	1 ◇						1 ◇			1 ◇	1 ◇								1 ◇				1 ◇
	A			B		C	D		E			G							A			H	D
			🚌		🚌			🚌							🚌	🚌		🚌			🚌		
	✠						✠			✠									✠				✠
Manchester Airport 85 ✈ d										10 55	*11 05*												
Manchester Piccadilly 10 78 d							*10 43*			11 20	11 42	*10 45*											*11 43*
Stockport 78 d							*10 54*			11 28	*11b17*												*11 54*
Sheffield 7 a										12 08													
d	11 21	11 24				11 41	11 54		11 57	12 11		12 14							12 21	12 24		12 41	12 54
Meadowhall d		11 31				11 47			12 03	12 17		12 21								12 31		12 47	
Rotherham Central d		11 37							12 10			12 27								12 37			
Swinton (S.Yorks) d		11 48							12 19			12a36								12 47			
Mexborough d		11 51							12 22											12 50			
Conisbrough d		11 55							12 26											12 54			
Doncaster 7 a		12 04				12 09	12 16		12 35	12 40										13 04		13 11	13 19
York 8 26 a	12 30						12 44			*13 39*									13 32	*13 39*			13 44
London Kings Cross 15 ⊖ 26 d		*10 10*							*10 40*				*11 00*							*11 10*			
Doncaster 31 d		12 08				12 16		12 30	12 36				12 46		12 55			13 00		13 06		13 20	
Bentley (S.Yorks) 31 a		*12 17*							12 40											*13 17*			
Adwick 31 a		*12 21*							12 45											*13 21*			
Kirk Sandall d		12 14											12 52							13 12			
Hatfield & Stainforth d		12 19	12 25										12 57							13 17	13 25		
Thorne South d			12 35																		13 35		
Crowle d			12 50																		13 50		
Althorpe d			13 00																		14 00		
Scunthorpe a			13 15					13 20										13 50			14 15		
d																		13 55					
Barnetby d				13 38														14 20					
Hull Paragon Interchange 🚌 d																13 25							
Barton-on-Humber 🚌 a																13 50							
Barton-on-Humber d																	13 58						
Barrow Haven d																	14 03						
New Holland d																	14 06						
Goxhill d																	14 11						
Thornton Abbey d																	14 14						
Ulceby d																	14 18						
Habrough d				13 47													14 23	14 35					
Stallingborough d																	14 28						
Healing d																	14 31						
Great Coates d																	14 34						
Grimsby Town a				14 00	⟵										14s10		14 39	15 00					
d				14 00	14 05												14 39	15 05					
Grimsby Docks d																	14 42						
New Clee d																	14x44						
Cleethorpes a				14 11	14 25										14 30		14 49	15 25					
Thorne North d		12a24											13 02							13a23			
Goole d						12 35							13 11									13 39	
Saltmarshe d																							
York 8 33 d											*12 18*												
Selby a											12 57												
d											12 58												
Wressle d																							
Howden d																							
Eastrington d																							
Gilberdyke d													13 20										
Broomfleet d																							
Brough d						12 49					13 16		13 28									13 53	
Ferriby d													13 32										
Hessle d													13 37										
Hull a						13 07					13 34		13 50									14 10	

For general notes see front of timetable
For details of catering facilities see Directory of Train Operators

- **A** From Plymouth to Edinburgh (Table 51)
- **B** From Sheffield via Retford (Table 30)
- **C** To Scarborough (Table 43)
- **D** From Reading to Newcastle (Table 51)
- **E** From Lincoln (Table 30)
- **G** To Leeds (Table 31)
- **H** To Bridlington (Table 43)
- **b** Change at Manchester Piccadilly

Table 29

Saturdays

27 June to 5 September

Manchester Airport, Manchester, Sheffield and Meadowhall → Doncaster → Cleethorpes and Hull Barton-on-Humber → Cleethorpes

Network Diagram - see first page of Table 18

Station		HT	TP	NT	TP	TP	NT		NT	NT	XC	TP	TP	NT	NT	EM	NT	NT	XC	TP	NT		TP	TP
		1 ◇			1 ◇	1 ◇					1 ◇								1 ◇				1 ◇	1 ◇
				A			B				C					D	E	G	H		A			
			bus									bus	bus		bus					bus				
		⊠			trolley						trolley								trolley				trolley	trolley
Manchester Airport	85 ✈ d				11 55	*12 05*																	12 55	*13 05*
Manchester Piccadilly 10	78 ⇌ d				12 20	12 42	*11 45*												*12 43*				13 20	13 42
Stockport	78 d				12 28	*12b17*													*12 54*				13 28	*13b17*
Sheffield 7	⇌ a				13 08																		14 08	
	d			12 57	13 11		13 14				13 21			13 24			13 28	13 41	13 54		13 57		14 11	
Meadowhall	⇌ d			13 03	13 17		13 21							13 31			13 35	13 47			14 03		14 17	
Rotherham Central	d			13 10			13 27							13 37			13 42				14 10			
Swinton (S.Yorks)	d			13 18			13a36							13 47			13 50				14 18			
Mexborough	d			13 21										13 50							14 21			
Conisbrough	d			13 25										13 54							14 25			
Doncaster 7	a			13 35	13 40									14 04				14 11	14 16		14 35		14 40	
York 8	26 a				*14 34*						14 30						14 51		14 44					
London Kings Cross 15	⊖ 26 d	11 48												*12 10*				*12 30*						
Doncaster	31 d	13 27	13 30	13 38						13 46		13 55	14 00	14 06				14 18		14 30	14 38			
Bentley (S.Yorks)	31 a			13 41										*14 17*							14 41			
Adwick	31 a			13 47										*14 21*							14 47			
Kirk Sandall	d									13 52				14 12										
Hatfield & Stainforth	d									13 57				14 17	14 25									
Thorne South	d														14 35									
Crowle	d														14 50									
Althorpe	d														15 00									
Scunthorpe	a		14 20										14 50		15 15					15 20				
	d												14 55											
Barnetby	d												15 20			15 34								
Hull Paragon Interchange	bus d																							
Barton-on-Humber	bus a																							
Barton-on-Humber	d																							
Barrow Haven	d																							
New Holland	d																							
Goxhill	d																							
Thornton Abbey	d																							
Ulceby	d																							
Habrough	d												15 35			15 42								
Stallingborough	d																							
Healing	d																							
Great Coates	d																							
Grimsby Town	a											15s10	16 00			15 57								
	d												16 05											
Grimsby Docks	d																							
New Clee	d																							
Cleethorpes	a											15 30	16 25											
Thorne North	d									14 02				14a23										
Goole	d									14 12								14 37						
Saltmarshe	d									14 17														
York 8	33 d								13 38															
Selby	a	13 42				13 57			14 03															14 57
	d	13 43				13 58			14 04															14 58
Wressle	d																							
Howden	d	13 53							14 13															
Eastrington	d																							
Gilberdyke	d									14 26														
Broomfleet	d																							
Brough	d	14 05				14 16			14 25	14 34								14 54						15 16
Ferriby	d									14 39														
Hessle	d									14 43														
Hull	a	14 22				14 34			14 45	14 56								15 10						15 34

For general notes see front of timetable
For details of catering facilities see Directory of Train Operators

- **A** From Lincoln (Table 30)
- **B** To Leeds (Table 31)
- **C** From Penzance (Table 135) to Edinburgh (Table 51)
- **D** From Newark North Gate (Table 27)
- **E** Via Pontefract Baghill (Table 33)
- **G** To Bridlington (Table 43)
- **H** From Reading to Newcastle (Table 51)
- **b** Change at Manchester Piccadilly

Manchester Airport, Manchester, Sheffield and Meadowhall → Doncaster → Cleethorpes and Hull Barton-on-Humber → Cleethorpes

27 June to 5 September

Network Diagram - see first page of Table 18

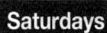

		NT	TP	NT	NT	TP	NT	XC	NT	NT	NT	NT	XC	HT		TP	NT	TP	TP	NT	TP	TP	NT	TP
								1 ◇					1 ◇	1 ◇				1 ◇	1 ◇					
		A					B	C					D				E			G			H	
			bus	bus		bus				bus						bus					bus	bus		bus
								trolley					trolley	restaurant				trolley						
Manchester Airport	85 ✈ d																	13 55	*14 05*					
Manchester Piccadilly 10	78 🚂 d						*12 45*						*13 43*					14 20	14 42					
Stockport	78 d												*13 54*					14 28	*14b17*					
Sheffield 7	🚂 a																	15 08						
	d						14 14	14 21	14 24			14 41	14 54				14 57	15 11						
Meadowhall	🚂 d						14 21		14 31			14 47					15 03	15 17						
Rotherham Central	d						14 27		14 37								15 10							
Swinton (S.Yorks)	d						14a36		14 47								15 18							
Mexborough	d								14 50								15 21							
Conisbrough	d								14 54								15 25							
Doncaster 7	a								15 04			15 11	15 16				15 36	15 40						
York 8	26 a							15 32					15 44											
London Kings Cross 15	⊖ 26 d	*13 00*							*13 10*					13 48						*14 00*				
Doncaster	31 d	14 46	14 55			15 00			15 07			15 16		15 27		15 30	15 38			15 46	15 55	16 00		
Bentley (S.Yorks)	31 a								*15 17*								15 41							
Adwick	31 a								*15 21*								15 47							
Kirk Sandall	d	14 52							15 13											15 52				
Hatfield & Stainforth	d	14 57							15 18	15 25										15 57				
Thorne South	d									15 35														
Crowle	d									15 50														
Althorpe	d									16 00														
Scunthorpe	a					15 50				16 15						16 25						17 00		
	d					15 55																17 05		
Barnetby	d					16 20																17 30	17 38	
Hull Paragon Interchange	bus d			15 25																				
Barton-on-Humber	bus a			15 50																				
Barton-on-Humber	d				15 58																			
Barrow Haven	d				16 03																			
New Holland	d				16 06																			
Goxhill	d				16 11																			
Thornton Abbey	d				16 14																			
Ulceby	d				16 18																			←
Habrough	d				16 23	16 35																17 45 →	17 47	17 45
Stallingborough	d				16 28																			
Healing	d				16 31																			
Great Coates	d				16 34																			
Grimsby Town	a		16s10		16 39	17 00															17s20		18 01	18 10
	d				16 39	17 05																	18 02	18 15
Grimsby Docks	d				16 42																			
New Clee	d																							
Cleethorpes	a		16 30		16 48	17 25															17 40		18 11	18 35
Thorne North	d	15 02							15a23											16 02				
Goole	d	15 13										15 37								16 12				
Saltmarshe	d																							
York 8	33 d										15 05													
Selby	a										15 24			15 42					15 57					
	d										15 24			15 43					15 58					
Wressle	d																							
Howden	d													15 53										
Eastrington	d																							
Gilberdyke	d	15 21																		16 20				
Broomfleet	d																							
Brough	d	15 29									15 44	15 51		16 05					16 16	16 28				
Ferriby	d	15 34																		16 33				
Hessle	d	15 38																		16 37				
Hull	a	15 51									16 03	16 07		16 22					16 35	16 50				

For general notes see front of timetable
For details of catering facilities see Directory of Train Operators

- **A** To Scarborough (Table 43)
- **B** To Leeds (Table 31)
- **C** From Plymouth (Table 51) to Aberdeen (Table 229)
- **D** From Reading to Newcastle (Table 51)
- **E** From Lincoln (Table 30)
- **G** To Bridlington (Table 43)
- **H** From Sheffield via Retford (Table 30)
- **b** Change at Manchester Piccadilly

27 June to 5 September

Manchester Airport, Manchester, Sheffield and Meadowhall → Doncaster → Cleethorpes and Hull
Barton-on-Humber → Cleethorpes

Network Diagram - see first page of Table 18

	NT A	XC 1 ◇ B (trolley)	NT	NT (bus)	NT	NT C		XC 1 ◇ D (trolley)	TP (bus)	NT E	EM G	TP 1 ◇ (trolley)	TP 1 ◇	NT H	TP (bus)	NT (bus)	NT	TP (bus)	NT A	XC 1 ◇ J (trolley)		NT	NT
Manchester Airport 85 ✈ d												14 55	*15 05*										
Manchester Piccadilly 10 78 (ship) d	*13 45*							*14 43*				15 20	15 42						*14 45*				
Stockport 78 d								*14 54*				15 28	*15b17*										
Sheffield 7 (ship) a												16 08											
d	15 14	15 21	15 24		15 40			15 54		15 57		16 11							16 14	16 20		16 24	16 41
Meadowhall (ship) d	15 21		15 31		15 46					16 03		16 17							16 21			16 31	16 47
Rotherham Central d	15 27		15 37							16 10									16 27			16 37	
Swinton (S.Yorks) d	15a36		15 47							16 18									16a36			16 47	
Mexborough d			15 50							16 21												16 50	
Conisbrough d			15 54							16 25												16 54	
Doncaster 7 a			16 04		16 11			16 16		16 35		16 40										17 08	17 12
York 8 26 a		16 30						16 44												17 31			
London Kings Cross 15 ⊖ 26 d										*14 30*				*15 00*									
Doncaster 31 d			16 06		16 14				16 30	16 38				16 47	16 55			17 00					17 14
Bentley (S.Yorks) 31 a								*16c30*		16 41													
Adwick 31 a								*16c34*		16 47													
Kirk Sandall d			16 13											16 53									
Hatfield & Stainforth d			16 18	16 25										16 58									
Thorne South d				16 40																			
Crowle d				16 55																			
Althorpe d				17 05																			
Scunthorpe a				17 25					17 30									18 00					
d																		18 05					
Barnetby d											17 54							18 30					
Hull Paragon Interchange (bus) d																17 30							
Barton-on-Humber (bus) a																17 55							
Barton-on-Humber d																	18 00						
Barrow Haven d																	18 05						
New Holland d																	18 08						
Goxhill d																	18 13						
Thornton Abbey d																	18 16						
Ulceby d																	18 20						
Habrough d											18 02						18 25	18 45					
Stallingborough d																	18 30						
Healing d																	18 33						
Great Coates d																	18 36						
Grimsby Town a											18 17				18s20		18 41	19 10					
d																	18 41	19 15					
Grimsby Docks d																	18 44						
New Clee d																							
Cleethorpes a															18 40		18 50	19 35					
Thorne North d			16a25											17 03									17 28
Goole d					16 36									17 12									17 37
Saltmarshe d														17 17									
York 8 33 d						16 12																	
Selby a						16 38							17 00										
d						16 39							17 00										
Wressle d						16 46																	
Howden d						16 51																	
Eastrington d																							
Gilberdyke d						16 58								17 23									
Broomfleet d																							
Brough d					16 50	17 06							17 18	17 31									17 56
Ferriby d						17 10								17 36									
Hessle d														17 40									
Hull a					17 07	17 27							17 37	17 53									18 10

For general notes see front of timetable
For details of catering facilities see Directory of Train Operators

A To Leeds (Table 31)
B From Penzance (Table 135) to Glasgow Central (Table 51)
C To Scarborough (Table 43)
D From Reading to Newcastle (Table 51)
E From Lincoln (Table 30)
G From Lincoln (Table 27)
H To Bridlington (Table 43)
J From Newquay (Table 135) to Dundee (Table 229)
b Change at Manchester Piccadilly
c Change at Doncaster

Manchester Airport, Manchester, Sheffield and Meadowhall → Doncaster → Cleethorpes and Hull
Barton-on-Humber → Cleethorpes

27 June to 5 September

Network Diagram - see first page of Table 18

Station			NT	XC 1◇ A 🍴	NT B	NT 🚌	TP 🚌	NT C	TP 1◇ 🍴	TP 1◇	NT	TP 🚌	EM D	TP 🚌	NT E		XC 1◇ G 🍴	NT	NT	NT	NT B	NT 🚌	XC 1◇ A 🍴	TP 🚌	NT C
Manchester Airport	85 ✈	d							15 55	*16 05*															
Manchester Piccadilly 10	78 🚆	d		*15 43*					16 20	16 42					*15 45*								*16 43*		
Stockport	78	d		*15 54*					16 28	*16b17*													*16 54*		
Sheffield 7	🚆	a							17 08																
		d		16 54				16 57	17 11						17 14		17 21	17 27	17 41				17 47		17 57
Meadowhall	🚆	d						17 03	17 17						17 21			17 33	17 47						18 03
Rotherham Central		d						17 10							17 27			17 39							18 10
Swinton (S.Yorks)		d						17 18							17a36			17 47							18 18
Mexborough		d						17 21										17 50							18 21
Conisbrough		d						17 25										17 54							18 25
Doncaster 7		a		17 19				17 35	17 40									18 07	18 12						18 38
York 8	26	a		17 44					*18 56*								18 31		*18 56*				18 59		
London Kings Cross 15	⊖ 26	d						*15 30*			*16 00*								*16 30*						
Doncaster	31	d			17 22		17 30	17 38			17 48	17 55		18 00					18 24		18 27			18 30	
Bentley (S.Yorks)	31	a		*17c30*				17 41											*18 30*						
Adwick	31	a		*17c34*				17 47											*18 34*						
Kirk Sandall		d			17 28						17 54										18 34				
Hatfield & Stainforth		d			17 33	17 40					17 59										18 39	18 45			
Thorne South		d				17 55																18 55			
Crowle		d				18 10																19 10			
Althorpe		d				18 20																19 20			
Scunthorpe		a				18 35	18 30							19 00								19 35		19 20	
		d												19 05											
Barnetby		d											19 06	19 30											
Hull Paragon Interchange	🚌	d																							
Barton-on-Humber	🚌	a																							
Barton-on-Humber		d																							
Barrow Haven		d																							
New Holland		d																							
Goxhill		d																							
Thornton Abbey		d																							
Ulceby		d																							
Habrough		d											19 14	19 45											
Stallingborough		d																							
Healing		d																							
Great Coates		d																							
Grimsby Town		a										19s20	19 29	20 10											
		d												20 15											
Grimsby Docks		d																							
New Clee		d																							
Cleethorpes		a										19 40		20 35											
Thorne North		d			17a39						18 04										18a46				
Goole		d									18 13								18 44						
Saltmarshe		d									18 18														
York 8	33	d	17 18																	18 13					
Selby		a	17 37							17 57										18 41					
		d	17 37							17 58										18 42					
Wressle		d																							
Howden		d	17 47							18 07										18 51					
Eastrington		d																		18 56					
Gilberdyke		d	17 57								18 23									19 00					
Broomfleet		d									18 27														
Brough		d	18 05							18 19	18 33								18 58	19 08					
Ferriby		d									18 37														
Hessle		d									18 42														
Hull		a	18 21							18 37	18 57								19 15	19 28					

For general notes see front of timetable
For details of catering facilities see Directory of Train Operators

A From Reading to Newcastle (Table 51)
B From Adwick (Table 31)
C From Lincoln (Table 30)
D From Newark North Gate (Table 27)
E To Leeds (Table 31)
G From Plymouth to Glasgow Central (Table 51)
b Change at Manchester Piccadilly
c Change at Doncaster

Table 29

Saturdays

27 June to 5 September

Manchester Airport, Manchester, Sheffield and Meadowhall → Doncaster → Cleethorpes and Hull Barton-on-Humber → Cleethorpes

Network Diagram - see first page of Table 18

		NT	TP	HT	XC	NT	TP		TP	NT	NT	NT	NT	NT	TP	XC	TP	NT	TP	TP	NT		TP	TP
			1 ◇	1 ◇	1 ◇		1 ◇									1 ◇			1 ◇	1 ◇				
		A			B									C		D		E						
									🚌	🚌			🚌		🚌		🚌						🚌	🚌
				⊠	⊼		⊼									⊼			⊼					
Manchester Airport	85 ✈ d		*17 05*				16 55												17 55	*18 03*				
Manchester Piccadilly 10	78 🚆 d	*16 45*	17 42				17 20							*17 43*					18 20	18 42				
Stockport	78 d		*17b17*				17 28							*17 54*					18 28	*18b17*				
Sheffield 7	🚆 a						18 15												19 10					
	d	18 14			18 21		18 24					18 29		18 41		18 54		19 00	19 11					
Meadowhall	🚆 d	18 21					18 29					18 35		18 47				19 06	19 17					
Rotherham Central	d	18 27										18 42						19 12						
Swinton (S.Yorks)	d	18a36										18 50						19 20						
Mexborough	d											18 53						19 23						
Conisbrough	d											18 57						19 27						
Doncaster 7	a						18 53					19 08		19 10		19 18		19 39	19 40					
York 8	26 a				19 31											19 44			*20 34*					
London Kings Cross 15	⊖ 26 d			17 05																	*18 00*			
Doncaster	31 d			18 48		18 58			19 10			19 13		19 13	19 15		19 30				19 47		19 55	20 00
Bentley (S.Yorks)	31 a															*19c30*								
Adwick	31 a															*19c34*								
Kirk Sandall	d					19 06						19 20									19 53			
Hatfield & Stainforth	d					19 11						19 25	19 30								19 58			
Thorne South	d												19 40											
Crowle	d												19 55											
Althorpe	d												20 05											
Scunthorpe	a												20 20		20 05		20 20							20 50
	d														20 10									20 55
Barnetby	d														20 35									21 20
Hull Paragon Interchange	🚌 d									19 25														
Barton-on-Humber	🚌 a									19 50														
Barton-on-Humber	d										19 58													
Barrow Haven	d										20 03													
New Holland	d										20 06													
Goxhill	d										20 11													
Thornton Abbey	d										20 14													
Ulceby	d										20 18													
Habrough	d										20 23				20 50									21 35
Stallingborough	d										20 28													
Healing	d										20 31													
Great Coates	d										20 34													
Grimsby Town	a								20s25		20 39				21 15								21s10	22 00
	d										20 39				21 20									22 05
Grimsby Docks	d										20 42													
New Clee	d																							
Cleethorpes	a								20 45		20 48				21 40								21 30	22 25
Thorne North	d					19 16						19a31									20 03			
Goole	d					19 25															20 12			
Saltmarshe	d																							
York 8	33 d																			*19 29*				
Selby	a		19 00	19 07										19 34						20 00				
	d		19 01	19 08										19 34						20 01				
Wressle	d																							
Howden	d			19 18																20 10				
Eastrington	d																							
Gilberdyke	d					19 33															20 22			
Broomfleet	d																							
Brough	d		19 18	19 30		19 41								19 54						20 22	20 30			
Ferriby	d					19 46															20 35			
Hessle	d					19 50															20 39			
Hull	a		19 37	19 47		20 03								20 11						20 39	20 52			

For general notes see front of timetable
For details of catering facilities see Directory of Train Operators

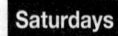

A To Leeds (Table 31)
B From Plymouth to Edinburgh (Table 51)
C To Bridlington (Table 43)
D From Reading to Edinburgh (Table 51)
E From Retford (Table 30)
b Change at Manchester Piccadilly
c Change at Doncaster

Table 29

Saturdays

Manchester Airport, Manchester, Sheffield and Meadowhall → Doncaster → Cleethorpes and Hull
Barton-on-Humber → Cleethorpes

27 June to 5 September

Network Diagram - see first page of Table 18

	NT	XC	NT	NT	NT	XC	NT	GR	TP	NT	NT	TP	NT		TP	TP	NT	NT	TP	NT	NT	NT	HT
		1 ◇				1 ◇		R 1				1 ◇				1 ◇							1 ◇
	A	B		C		D							E			G							
									🚌	🚌					🚌		🚌		🚌			🚌	
		🍴				🍴		🍴															⊠
Manchester Airport 85 ✈ d												18 55											
Manchester Piccadilly 10 78 🚇 d	*17 45*			*18 43*								19 18											
Stockport 78 d				*18 54*								19 26											
Sheffield 7 🚇 a												20 08											
d	19 14	19 21	19 30	19 44		19 54					19 57	20 11								20 15			
Meadowhall 🚇 d	19 21		19 36	19 50							20 03	20 17								20 20			
Rotherham Central d	19 27		19 42								20 09									20 26			
Swinton (S.Yorks) d	19a40		19 51								20 17									20 36			
Mexborough d			19 54								20 20									20 39			
Conisbrough d			19 58								20 24									20 43			
Doncaster 7 a			20 09	20 11		20 16					20 36	20 40								20 56			
York 8 26 a		20 31				20 40						*21 38*								*21 38*			
London Kings Cross 15 ⊖ 26 d				*18 30*			*18 35*	18 40					*19 00*										19 41
Doncaster 31 d				20 14			20 25	20 27	20 30				20 46		20 55				21 00		21 07		21 20
Bentley (S.Yorks) 31 a											*20 48*												
Adwick 31 a											*20 52*												
Kirk Sandall d							20 31						20 52								21 13		
Hatfield & Stainforth d							20 36			20 45			20 57								21 18	21 25	
Thorne South d										20 55												21 35	
Crowle d										21 10												21 50	
Althorpe d										21 20												22 00	
Scunthorpe a									21 20	21 35									21 50			22 15	
d																			21 55				
Barnetby d																			22 20				
Hull Paragon Interchange 🚌 d																	21 25						
Barton-on-Humber 🚌 a																	21 50						
Barton-on-Humber d																		21 58					
Barrow Haven d																		22 03					
New Holland d																		22 06					
Goxhill d																		22 11					
Thornton Abbey d																		22 14					
Ulceby d																		22 18					
Habrough d																		22 23	22 35				
Stallingborough d																		22 28					
Healing d																		22 31					
Great Coates d																		22 34					
Grimsby Town a															22s10			22 39	23 00				
d																		22 39	23 05				
Grimsby Docks d																		22 42					
New Clee d																							
Cleethorpes a															22 30			22 48	23 25				
Thorne North d							20a46						21 02								21a23		
Goole d				20 33									21 11										
Saltmarshe d																							
York 8 33 d					20 17																		
Selby a					20 36			20 43															21 35
d					20 36			20 44								21 27							21 36
Wressle d																							
Howden d																21 36							21 46
Eastrington d																							
Gilberdyke d					20 50								21 19										
Broomfleet d																							
Brough d				20 47	20 58			21 06					21 27			21 48							21 59
Ferriby d					21 02																		
Hessle d					21 07																		
Hull a				21 04	21 22			21 27					21 45			22 05							22 16

For general notes see front of timetable
For details of catering facilities see Directory of Train Operators

A To Leeds (Table 31)
B From Plymouth to Edinburgh (Table 51)
C To Beverley (Table 43)
D From Reading to Newcastle (Table 51)
E To Bridlington (Table 43)
G From Leeds (Table 40)

Saturdays

27 June to 5 September

Manchester Airport, Manchester, Sheffield and Meadowhall → Doncaster → Cleethorpes and Hull
Barton-on-Humber → Cleethorpes

Network Diagram - see first page of Table 18

		XC	NT	NT	XC	TP	TP		TP	NT	TP	TP	NT	XC	TP	XC	TP	TP	NT	NT	NT		
		1 ◇			1 ◇		1 ◇					1 ◇		1 ◇	1 ◇	1 ◇							
		A	B		C					D		E	B	G		H				B			
						🚌			🚌		🚌						🚌	🚌					
		🛒														🛒							
Manchester Airport	85 ✈ d				19b09		19 55					20 29		20b09	20 47						21b09		
Manchester Piccadilly 10	78 🚊 d				19 43		20 20					21 11		20 43	21 20						21 43		
Stockport	78 d				19 54		20 28					20c42		20 54	21 28						21 52		
Sheffield 7	🚊 a						21 08								22 08								
	d	20 21	20 30	20 38	20 54		21 11			21 14			21 30	21 54	22 11	22 26			22 30	22 34	23 26		
Meadowhall	🚊 d		20 36	20 44			21 17			21 22			21 36		22 17				22 36	22 40	23 32		
Rotherham Central	d		20 42	20 53						21 28			21 42						22 42	22 46	23 38		
Swinton (S.Yorks)	d		20a50	21 05						21 40			21a50						22 50	22a53	23 46		
Mexborough	d			21 08						21 43									22 53		23 49		
Conisbrough	d			21 12						21 47									22 57		23 53		
Doncaster 7	a			21 21	21 25		21 40			21 55				22 19	22 36	22 47			23 08		00 04		
York 8	26 a	22 03			21 48					22 38				22 48									
London Kings Cross 15	⊖ 26 d									20 00							20 30						
Doncaster	31 d					21 30			21 55	21 57	22 00						22 55	23 00	23 09				
Bentley (S.Yorks)	31 a			21 31											22 55								
Adwick	31 a			21 35											22 59								
Kirk Sandall	d									22 03								23 10	23 16				
Hatfield & Stainforth	d									22 08								23 20	23 21				
Thorne South	d																	23 30					
Crowle	d																	23 45					
Althorpe	d																	23 55					
Scunthorpe	a					22 20					22 50							00 10					
	d										22 55												
Barnetby	d										23 20						23s50						
Hull Paragon Interchange	🚌 d																						
Barton-on-Humber	🚌 a																						
Barton-on-Humber	d																						
Barrow Haven	d																						
New Holland	d																						
Goxhill	d																						
Thornton Abbey	d																						
Ulceby	d																						
Habrough	d										23 35												
Stallingborough	d																						
Healing	d																						
Great Coates	d																						
Grimsby Town	a								23s10		23 59						00s15						
	d										00 05												
Grimsby Docks	d																						
New Clee	d																						
Cleethorpes	a								23 30		00 25						00 35						
Thorne North	d									22 13									23 26				
Goole	d									22 22									23a37				
Saltmarshe	d									22 27													
York 8	33 d											21 45											
Selby	a											22 44											
	d											22 44											
Wressle	d																						
Howden	d																						
Eastrington	d																						
Gilberdyke	d									22 33													
Broomfleet	d																						
Brough	d									22 41		23 04											
Ferriby	d																						
Hessle	d																						
Hull	a									22 58		23 21											

For general notes see front of timetable
For details of catering facilities see Directory of Train Operators

- **A** From Plymouth (Table 51)
- **B** To Leeds (Table 31)
- **C** From Reading to Newcastle (Table 51)
- **D** To Beverley (Table 43)
- **E** From Liverpool Lime Street (Table 39)
- **G** From Reading (Table 51)
- **H** From Bournemouth to Leeds (Table 51)
- **b** Change at Manchester Piccadilly and Sheffield
- **c** Change at Manchester Piccadilly

Manchester Airport, Manchester, Sheffield and Meadowhall → Doncaster → Cleethorpes and Hull Barton-on-Humber → Cleethorpes

until 21 June and from 13 September

Network Diagram - see first page of Table 18

	NT	NT	NT	XC	NT	NT	TP	TP	NT	TP	NT	NT	NT	NT	NT	NT	XC	EM	EM	HT
				1 ◇			1 ◇	1 ◇		1 ◇							1 ◇	1 ◇		1 ◇
			A	B	C	D	E	G			H	J	K			K	L	N	Q	
Manchester Airport 85 d				07b30			08 39			08 39										
Manchester Piccadilly 10 78 d				07c57			09 11			08 58										
Stockport 78 d				08e11			08f31			09 06							09g06	09h22		
Sheffield 7 a																				
Sheffield 7 d	08 00		08 45	09 21	09 36					09 52	10 26				11 05		11 21	11 31		
Meadowhall d	08 06		08 51		09 42					09 57	10 32				11 11					
Rotherham Central d	08 12		08 57		09 48					10 02					11 17					
Swinton (S.Yorks) d	08 20		09 05		09a58					10 09					11 25					
Mexborough d	08 23		09 08							10 12					11 28					
Conisbrough d	08 27		09 12							10 17					11 32					
Doncaster 7 a	08 38		09 22							10 26	10 51				11 43			11 52		
York 8 26 a			10 05	10 33						11 07	11 29						12 32	12 15		
London Kings Cross 15 26 d											09 00									10 44
Doncaster 31 d		09 07	09 26			10 21				10 28	10 53			11 07						12 24
Bentley (S.Yorks) 31 a	09 13										11 13									
Adwick 31 a	09 17										11 17									
Kirk Sandall d		09 13												11 13						
Hatfield & Stainforth d		09 18												11 18						
Thorne South d																				
Crowle d																				
Althorpe d																				
Scunthorpe a										10 54										
Scunthorpe d										10 55										
Barnetby d										11 09									12 33	
Hull Paragon Interchange d												10 25								
Barton-on-Humber a												10 50								
Barton-on-Humber d													11 00							
Barrow Haven d													11 05							
New Holland d													11 08							
Goxhill d													11 13							
Thornton Abbey d													11 16							
Ulceby d													11 20							
Habrough d													11 25						12 41	
Stallingborough d													11 30							
Healing d													11 33							
Great Coates d													11 36							
Grimsby Town a										11 29			11 41						12 53	
Grimsby Town d										11 35			11 41						13 05	
Grimsby Docks d													11 44							
New Clee d													11x46							
Cleethorpes a										11 44			11 51						13 16	
Thorne North d		09 24	09 38											11 25						
Goole d		09a35	09 47			10 40					11 12			11a36						
Saltmarshe d																				
York 8 33 d									10 40							12 05				
Selby a							10 43		10 59							12 24				12 41
Selby d							10 43	10 46	10 59							12 24				12 42
Wressle d																				
Howden d																				12 52
Eastrington d																				
Gilberdyke d			09 58			10 48					11 23									
Broomfleet d																				
Brough d			10 06			10 56	11 01	11 04	11 19		11 31					12 44				13 04
Ferriby d																				
Hessle d																				
Hull a			10 21			11 13	11 18	11 20	11 38		11 46					13 03				13 21

For general notes see front of timetable
For details of catering facilities see Directory of Train Operators

- **A** Until 20 September to Scarborough (Table 43)
- **B** To Edinburgh (Table 26)
- **C** To Leeds (Table 31)
- **D** Until 20 September to Bridlington (Table 43)
- **E** Until 21 June. From Liverpool Lime Street (Table 39)
- **G** From 13 September. From Leeds (Table 39)
- **H** To Scarborough (from 27 September to Bridlington) (Table 43)
- **J** Until 21 June and 13 September
- **K** Until 13 September
- **L** From Birmingham New Street to Edinburgh (Table 51)
- **N** From Leicester (Table 53)
- **Q** Until 21 June. From Newark North Gate (Table 27)
- **b** Change at Manchester Piccadilly and Sheffield. Until 21 June dep. 0640
- **c** Until 21 June dep. 0745
- **e** From 13 September only
- **f** Change at Manchester Piccadilly
- **g** Until 21 June dep. 0922
- **h** Change at Manchester Piccadilly and Sheffield. Until 21 June only

Sundays

until 21 June and from 13 September

Manchester Airport, Manchester, Sheffield and Meadowhall → Doncaster → Cleethorpes and Hull Barton-on-Humber → Cleethorpes

Network Diagram - see first page of Table 18

Station		NT	TP	NT	NT	XC	NT	NT	TP	TP	NT	NT	TP	XC	NT	NT	NT	XC	TP	XC
			1 ◇			1 ◇			1 ◇	1 ◇			1 ◇	1 ◇				1 ◇	1 ◇	1 ◇
		A		B	B	C		D	E	G				C	H	A	B	J		K
				bus		trolley								trolley				trolley		trolley
Manchester Airport	85 ✈ d		10 44						11 35				11b33					12c09	12 55	
Manchester Piccadilly 10	78 ⇌ d		11 18						12 02				12 18					12 44	13 20	
Stockport	78 d		11 27						11e23				12 28					12f55	13 28	
Sheffield 7	⇌ a		12 08										13 08						14 08	
	d	11 36	12 11			12 21	12 24	12 28					13 11	13 21	13 24	13 36		13 51	14 11	14 21
Meadowhall	⇌ d	11 42	12 16				12 30	12 34					13 16		13 30	13 42			14 16	
Rotherham Central	d	11 49					12 36				←				13 36	13 49				
Swinton (S.Yorks)	d	12a00					12 48 →				12 48				13 47	13a57				
Mexborough	d										12 51				13 50					
Conisbrough	d										12 55				13 54					
Doncaster 7	a		12 39					12 54			13 03		13 35		14 02			14 13	14 35	
York 8	26 a					13 32							*14 04*	14 32	*14 33*			14 43	*15 05*	15 32
London Kings Cross 15	⊖ 26 d							*11 00*			*11 10*				*12 00*				*12 30*	
Doncaster	31 d		12 42					12 55			13 06				14 04				14 42	
Bentley (S.Yorks)	31 a										*13 13*								*15 13*	
Adwick	31 a										*13 17*								*15 17*	
Kirk Sandall	d										13 12									
Hatfield & Stainforth	d										13 17									
Thorne South	d																			
Crowle	d																			
Althorpe	d																			
Scunthorpe	a		13 09																15 09	
	d		13 10																15 10	
Barnetby	d		13 26																15 26	
Hull Paragon Interchange	bus d			13 25																
Barton-on-Humber	bus a			13 55																
Barton-on-Humber	d				14 00															
Barrow Haven	d				14 05															
New Holland	d				14 08															
Goxhill	d				14 13															
Thornton Abbey	d				14 16															
Ulceby	d				14 20															
Habrough	d		13 34		14 25															
Stallingborough	d				14 30															
Healing	d				14 33															
Great Coates	d				14 36															
Grimsby Town	a		13 45		14 41														15 45	
	d		13 46		14 41														15 46	
Grimsby Docks	d				14 44															
New Clee	d				14x46															
Cleethorpes	a		13 57		14 51														15 58	
Thorne North	d										13 25									
Goole	d							13 15			13a35				14 25					
Saltmarshe	d																			
York 8	33 d											13 23					14 42			
Selby	a								13 23			13 42					15 01			
	d								13 23	13 23		13 42					15 01			
Wressle	d																			
Howden	d																			
Eastrington	d																			
Gilberdyke	d							13 23							14 33					
Broomfleet	d																			
Brough	d							13 28	13 41	13 41		14 02			14 41		15 21			
Ferriby	d																			
Hessle	d																			
Hull	a							13 48	14 00	14 00		14 21			14 59		15 40			

For general notes see front of timetable
For details of catering facilities see Directory of Train Operators

A To Leeds (Table 31)
B Until 13 September
C From Bristol Temple Meads to Edinburgh (Table 51)
D To Scarborough (from 27 September to Bridlington) (Table 43)
E Until 21 June
G From 13 September. From Huddersfield (Table 39)
H Until 20 September to Bridlington (Table 43)
J From Birmingham New Street to Newcastle (Table 51)
K From Plymouth (from 8 November from Birmingham New Street) (Table 51) to Aberdeen (Table 229)
b Until 21 June dep. 1135
c Change at Manchester Piccadilly and Sheffield
e Change at Manchester Piccadilly
f Until 21 June dep. 1254

Table 29

Sundays

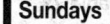

Manchester Airport, Manchester, Sheffield and Meadowhall → Doncaster → Cleethorpes and Hull
Barton-on-Humber → Cleethorpes

until 21 June and from 13 September

Network Diagram - see first page of Table 18

	NT	NT	TP	TP	NT		NT	XC	TP	XC	NT		NT	NT	NT	NT	NT		NT	XC	EM	HT	TP
			1◇	1◇				1◇	1◇	1◇										1◇		1◇	1◇
		A	B	C				D		E			G		H	J	J		K	L	N		
								🍴		🍴						🚌				🍴		☒	
Manchester Airport 85 d			13§35					13b09	13 55										14b09				14 55
Manchester Piccadilly 78 d			14§02					13 44	14 20										14 44				15 20
Stockport 78 d			13c37					13 54	14 28										14 54				15 28
Sheffield a									15 08														16 08
d	14 22	14 28						14 51	15 11	15 21	15 24		15 28		15 36				15 46	15 51			16 11
Meadowhall d	14 28	14 34							15 16		15 30		15 34		15 42				15 52				16 16
Rotherham Central d	14 34				←						15 37			←	15 48				15 58				
Swinton (S.Yorks) d	14 46				14 46						15 47			15 47	15a56				16 08				
Mexborough d	→				14 49						→			15 50									
Conisbrough d					14 53									15 54									
Doncaster a		14 56			15 03			15 13	15 39				15 55	16 04						16 15			16 39
York 26 a					*15 34*			15 43		16 32			*16 35*						17 01	16 40			
London Kings Cross ⊖ 26 d		*13 00*			*13 10*				*13 30*				*14 00*									14 44	
Doncaster 31 d		14 59			15 05				15 42				15 56									16 23	16 42
Bentley (S.Yorks) 31 a					*15 13*																		
Adwick 31 a					*15 17*																		
Kirk Sandall d					15 13																		
Hatfield & Stainforth d					15 18																		
Thorne South d																							
Crowle d																							
Althorpe d																							
Scunthorpe a									16 09														17 09
d									16 10														17 10
Barnetby d									16 26												16§54		17 26
Hull Paragon Interchange 🚌 d																15§30							
Barton-on-Humber 🚌 a																15§55							
Barton-on-Humber d																	16§15						
Barrow Haven d																	16§20						
New Holland d																	16§23						
Goxhill d																	16§28						
Thornton Abbey d																	16§31						
Ulceby d																	16§35						
Habrough d									16 34								16§40				17§02		
Stallingborough d																	16§45						
Healing d																	16§48						
Great Coates d																	16§51						
Grimsby Town a									16 45								16§56				17§14		17 45
d									16 46								16§56				17§14		17 46
Grimsby Docks d																	16§59						
New Clee d																	17x01						
Cleethorpes a									16 58								17§06				17§23		17 57
Thorne North d					15 25																		
Goole d		15 19			15a33								16 17										
Saltmarshe d																							
York 33 d							15 43																
Selby a			15§23				16 01															16 41	
d			15§23	15§23			16 02															16 42	
Wressle d																							
Howden d																						16 52	
Eastrington d																							
Gilberdyke d		15 27											16 25										
Broomfleet d																							
Brough d		15 35	15§41	15§41			16 23						16 33									17 04	
Ferriby d		15 40																					
Hessle d		15 44																					
Hull a		15 57	16§00	16§00			16 41						16 50									17 21	

For general notes see front of timetable
For details of catering facilities see Directory of Train Operators

- **A** To Scarborough (from 27 September to Beverley) (Table 43)
- **B** Until 21 June
- **C** From 13 September. From Huddersfield (Table 39)
- **D** From Birmingham New Street to Newcastle(Table 51)
- **E** From Plymouth (from 8 November from Birmingham New Street) to Edinburgh (Table 51)
- **G** To Bridlington (Table 43)
- **H** To Leeds (Table 31)
- **J** Until 13 September
- **K** Via Pontefract Baghill (Table 33)
- **L** From Guildford to Newcastle (Table 51)
- **N** Until 21 June. From Nottingham (Table 27)
- **b** Change at Manchester Piccadilly and Sheffield
- **c** Change at Manchester Piccadilly

Table 29

Sundays

Manchester Airport, Manchester, Sheffield and Meadowhall → Doncaster → Cleethorpes and Hull Barton-on-Humber → Cleethorpes

until 21 June and from 13 September

Network Diagram - see first page of Table 18

		XC	NT		NT	TP	TP	NT	NT		XC	HT	TP	XC	NT		NT	NT	NT	EM	XC		TP	NT
		1 ◇				1 ◇	1 ◇				1 ◇	1 ◇	1 ◇	1 ◇							1 ◇		1 ◇	
		A			B	C	D	E			G			H			J		K	L	G			E
																								🚌
		🍴									🍴	☒		🍴							🍴			
Manchester Airport	85 ✈ d					15 35					15b09		15 55								16b09		16 55	
Manchester Piccadilly 10	78 🚌 d					16 02					15 44		16 20								16 44		17 20	
Stockport	78 d					15c39					15 54		16 28								16 54		17 28	
Sheffield 7	🚌 a												17 08										18 08	
	d	16 21	16 24		16 28						16 51		17 11	17 21	17 24		17 28		17 36		17 51		18 11	
Meadowhall	🚌 d		16 30		16 34								17 16		17 30		17 34		17 43				18 16	
Rotherham Central	d		16 37						←						17 37			←	17 49					
Swinton (S.Yorks)	d		16 47						16 47						17 47			17 47	17a57					
Mexborough	d		→						16 50						→			17 50						
Conisbrough	d								16 54									17 54						
Doncaster 7	a				16 54				17 04		17 13		17 39				17 57	18 05			18 13		18 39	
York 8	26 a	17 32									17 42			18 32			18 34	19 05			19e21			
London Kings Cross 15	⊖ 26 d								15 10			15 44					16 10						16 30	
Doncaster	31 d				16 56				17 05			17 35	17 42				18 03						18 42	
Bentley (S.Yorks)	31 a				17 13																			
Adwick	31 a				17 17																			
Kirk Sandall	d								17 13															
Hatfield & Stainforth	d								17 18															
Thorne South	d																							
Crowle	d																							
Althorpe	d																							
Scunthorpe	a												18 09										19 09	
	d												18 10										19 10	
Barnetby	d												18 26							18 53			19 26	
Hull Paragon Interchange	🚌 d																							18 30
Barton-on-Humber	🚌 a																							18 55
Barton-on-Humber	d																							
Barrow Haven	d																							
New Holland	d																							
Goxhill	d																							
Thornton Abbey	d																							
Ulceby	d																							
Habrough	d												18 34							19 01				
Stallingborough	d																							
Healing	d																							
Great Coates	d																							
Grimsby Town	a												18 45							19 13			19 45	
	d												18 46							19 13			19 46	
Grimsby Docks	d																							
New Clee	d																							
Cleethorpes	a												18 58							19 24			19 57	
Thorne North	d								17 25															
Goole	d				17 15				17a34								18 22							
Saltmarshe	d																							
York 8	33 d							17 10																
Selby	a					17 23		17 30				17 50												
	d					17 23	17 23	17 31				17 50												
Wressle	d																							
Howden	d											18 02												
Eastrington	d																							
Gilberdyke	d				17 23												18 35							
Broomfleet	d																							
Brough	d				17 31	17 41	17 41	17 51				18 13					18 43							
Ferriby	d																							
Hessle	d																							
Hull	a				17 49	18 00	18 00	18 10				18 32					18 57							

For general notes see front of timetable
For details of catering facilities see Directory of Train Operators

A From Penzance (Table 135) (from 8 November from Birmingham New Street) to Glasgow Central (Table 51)
B Until 20 September to Scarborough (Table 43)
C Until 21 June
D From 13 September. From Huddersfield (Table 39)
E Until 13 September
G From Reading to Newcastle (Table 51)
H From Plymouth (from 8 November from Birmingham New Street) to Glasgow Central (Table 51)
J To Bridlington (Table 43)
K To Leeds (Table 31)
L Until 21 June. From Newark North Gate (Table 27)
b Change at Manchester Piccadilly and Sheffield
c Change at Manchester Piccadilly
e By changing at Doncaster, passengers may arrive at 1905

Table 29

Sundays

until 21 June and from 13 September

Manchester Airport, Manchester, Sheffield and Meadowhall → Doncaster → Cleethorpes and Hull Barton-on-Humber → Cleethorpes

Network Diagram - see first page of Table 18

		NT	XC	NT	NT	NT		TP	TP	NT	XC	HT		NT	TP	TP	TP	XC		NT	NT	XC	NT	TP
			1◇					1◇	1◇		1◇	1◇			1◇	1◇	1◇	1◇				1◇		1◇
		A	B		C			D	E		G			H		D	E	J			K	L		
Manchester Airport	85 d							17 35			17b09				17 55	18 35						18b09		18 55
Manchester Piccadilly 10	78 d							18 02			17 44				18 20	19 02						18 44		19 20
Stockport	78 d							17c39			17 54				18 28	18c39						18 54		19 28
Sheffield 7	a														19 08									20 08
	d		18 21	18 25	18 28						18 51			18 57	19 11			19 21		19 29	19 36	19 51	20 02	20 11
Meadowhall	d			18 31	18 35									19 04	19 16					19 35	19 42		20 09	20 16
Rotherham Central	d			18 37		←								19 10						19 41	19 49			
Swinton (S.Yorks)	d			18 47		18 47								19 18						19 49	19a57			
Mexborough	d			→		18 50														19 52				
Conisbrough	d					18 54														19 56				
Doncaster 7	a				18 54	19 04					19 13				19 39					20 07		20 16	20 30	20 39
York 8	26 a		19 32								19 42			20 17	20 39			20 32				20 44		
London Kings Cross 15	⊖ 26 d				17 00							17 44											18 40	19 00
Doncaster	31 d				18 55							19 24			19 42								20 30	20 42
Bentley (S.Yorks)	31 a										19e33													
Adwick	31 a										19e37													
Kirk Sandall	d				19 01																			
Hatfield & Stainforth	d				19 06																			
Thorne South	d																							
Crowle	d																							
Althorpe	d																							
Scunthorpe	a														20 10									21 09
	d														20 10									21 10
Barnetby	d														20 26									21 26
Hull Paragon Interchange	d																							
Barton-on-Humber	a																							
Barton-on-Humber	d	19 15																						
Barrow Haven	d	19 20																						
New Holland	d	19 23																						
Goxhill	d	19 28																						
Thornton Abbey	d	19 31																						
Ulceby	d	19 35																						
Habrough	d	19 40																						21 34
Stallingborough	d	19 45																						
Healing	d	19 48																						
Great Coates	d	19 51																						
Grimsby Town	a	19 56													20 45									21 45
	d	20 01													20 46									21 46
Grimsby Docks	d	20 03																						
New Clee	d	20x06																						
Cleethorpes	a	20 10													20 58									21 58
Thorne North	d				19 12																			
Goole	d				19 21																		20 49	
Saltmarshe	d																							
York 8	33 d									19 10														
Selby	a							19 23		19 29		19 40				20 16								
	d							19 23	19 23	19 30		19 40				20 16	20 16							
Wressle	d																							
Howden	d											19 52												
Eastrington	d																							
Gilberdyke	d				19 29																		20 57	
Broomfleet	d																							
Brough	d				19 37			19 44	19 44	19 50		20 03				20 34	20 34						21 05	
Ferriby	d																							
Hessle	d																							
Hull	a				19 55			20 00	20 00	20 09		20 22				20 53	20 53						21 23	

For general notes see front of timetable
For details of catering facilities see Directory of Train Operators

A Until 21 June and 13 September
B From Newquay (13 September to 1 November from Penzance) (Table 135) (from 8 November from Birmingham New Street) to Edinburgh (Table 51)
C To Beverley (Table 43)
D Until 21 June
E From 13 September. From Huddersfield (Table 39)
G From Reading to Edinburgh (Table 51)
H Via Pontefract Baghill (Table 33)
J From Plymouth (from 8 November from Birmingham New Street) to Edinburgh (Table 51)
K To Leeds (Table 31)
L From Reading to Newcastle (Table 51)
b Change at Manchester Piccadilly and Sheffield
c Change at Manchester Piccadilly
e Change at Doncaster

Table 29

Sundays

until 21 June and from 13 September

Manchester Airport, Manchester, Sheffield and Meadowhall → Doncaster → Cleethorpes and Hull Barton-on-Humber → Cleethorpes

Network Diagram - see first page of Table 18

		GR	TP		XC	NT	TP	NT	XC		TP	HT	NT	NT	TP		XC	NT	TP	NT	NT			
		R 1	1 ◇		1 ◇		1 ◇		1 ◇		1 ◇	1 ◇			1 ◇		1 ◇		1 ◇					
			A				B		C					D	E		G							
		🍴										⊠												
Manchester Airport	85 ✈ d		19 35						19b09		19 55						20b09	20 55			21 55			
Manchester Piccadilly 10	78 d		20 06						19 44		20 18						20 44	21 20			22 16			
Stockport	78 d		19c39						19 54		20 27						20 54	21 28			22 28			
Sheffield 7	a										21 08													
	d				20 21	20 28			20 51		21 11		21 24	21 36			21 51	22 26	22 30		23 41			
Meadowhall	d					20 34					21 16		21 30	21 42				22 32	22 36		23 47			
Rotherham Central	d					20 40							21 37	21 48				22 38		←	23 53			
Swinton (S.Yorks)	d					20 48							21 47	21a56				22 48		22 48	00 01			
Mexborough	d					20 51							21 50					↳		22 51	00 04			
Conisbrough	d					20 55							21 54							22 55	00 08			
Doncaster 7	a					21 05			21 19		21 39		22 03						22 56	23 04	00 19			
York 8	26 a				21 37				21 42				23 09				22 53		00 39	00 39				
London Kings Cross 15	⊖ 26 d	19 10				19 10					19 35	20 10							21 00					
Doncaster	31 d	20 58				21 06					21 42	21 55	22 04						22 58	23 07				
Bentley (S.Yorks)	31 a										21 52													
Adwick	31 a										21 56													
Kirk Sandall	d					21 12																		
Hatfield & Stainforth	d					21 17																		
Thorne South	d																							
Crowle	d																							
Althorpe	d																							
Scunthorpe	a										22 09								23 23					
	d										22 10								23 24					
Barnetby	d										22 26								23 38					
Hull Paragon Interchange	🚌 d																							
Barton-on-Humber	🚌 a																							
Barton-on-Humber	d																							
Barrow Haven	d																							
New Holland	d																							
Goxhill	d																							
Thornton Abbey	d																							
Ulceby	d																							
Habrough	d										22 34													
Stallingborough	d																							
Healing	d																							
Great Coates	d																							
Grimsby Town	a										22 45								23 58					
	d										22 46								23 59					
Grimsby Docks	d																							
New Clee	d																							
Cleethorpes	a										22 58								00 10					
Thorne North	d					21 23														23 19				
Goole	d					21a34							22 23							23 28				
Saltmarshe	d																							
York 8	33 d							21 41																
Selby	a	21 15	21 23					22 00				22 09												
	d	21 15	21 23				21 38	22 00				22 09			22 42									
Wressle	d																							
Howden	d											22 21												
Eastrington	d																							
Gilberdyke	d												22 32							23 36				
Broomfleet	d																							
Brough	d	21 36	21 44				21 56	22 20				22 31	22 40		23 00					23 44				
Ferriby	d																							
Hessle	d																							
Hull	a	21 56	22 01				22 13	22 39				22 50	22 56		23 18					00 02				

For general notes see front of timetable
For details of catering facilities see Directory of Train Operators

A Until 21 June
B From 13 September. From Huddersfield (Table 39)
C From Reading to Newcastle (Table 51)
D To Leeds (Table 31)
E From Leeds (Table 39)
G From Reading (Table 51)
b Change at Manchester Piccadilly and Sheffield
c Change at Manchester Piccadilly

Table 29

Sundays

Manchester Airport, Manchester, Sheffield and Meadowhall → Doncaster → Cleethorpes and Hull
Barton-on-Humber → Cleethorpes

28 June to 6 September

Network Diagram - see first page of Table 18

		NT	NT	NT	TP	TP	XC	NT	NT	TP	NT	NT	NT	TP	TP	TP	NT	NT	NT	NT	XC	EM	HT	NT
							1 ◇			1 ◇				1 ◇							1 ◇	1 ◇	1 ◇	
				A			B	C	D	E							A				G	H		C
					Bus	Bus	Trolley					Bus			Bus	Bus					Trolley	☕	⊠	
Manchester Airport	85 ✈ d						06b40			08 39											09b06			
Manchester Piccadilly 10	78 🚇 d						07 45			09 11				08 58							09 45			
Stockport	78 d									08c31				09 06							09b22			
Sheffield 7	🚇 a																							
	d	08 00		08 45			09 21	09 36						09 52			10 26		11 05		11 21	11 31		11 36
Meadowhall	🚇 d	08 06		08 51				09 42						09 57			10 32		11 11					11 42
Rotherham Central	d	08 12		08 57				09 48						10 02					11 17					11 49
Swinton (S.Yorks)	d	08 20		09 05				09a58						10 09					11 25					12a00
Mexborough	d	08 23		09 08										10 12					11 28					
Conisbrough	d	08 27		09 12										10 17					11 32					
Doncaster 7	a	08 38		09 22										10 26			10 51		11 43			11 52		
York 8	26 a			10 05			10 33							11 07			11 29		12e35		12 32	12 15		
London Kings Cross 15	⊖ 26 d																09 00						10 44	
Doncaster	31 d		09 07	09 26	09 40	09 45			10 21						10 40	10 45	10 53	11 07					12 24	
Bentley (S.Yorks)	31 a	09 13															11 13							
Adwick	31 a	09 17															11 17							
Kirk Sandall	d		09 13															11 13						
Hatfield & Stainforth	d		09 18															11 18						
Thorne South	d																							
Crowle	d																							
Althorpe	d																							
Scunthorpe	a					10 35										11 35								
	d					10 40										11 40								
Barnetby	d					11 05										12 05								
Hull Paragon Interchange	Bus d											10 25												
Barton-on-Humber	Bus a											10 50												
Barton-on-Humber	d												11 00											
Barrow Haven	d												11 05											
New Holland	d												11 08											
Goxhill	d												11 13											
Thornton Abbey	d												11 16											
Ulceby	d												11 20											
Habrough	d												11 25			12 20								
Stallingborough	d												11 30											
Healing	d												11 33											
Great Coates	d												11 36											
Grimsby Town	a				10 55	11 35							11 41		11 55	12 40								
	d				11 00	11 40							11 41		12 00	12 50								
Grimsby Docks	d												11 44											
New Clee	d												11x46											
Cleethorpes	a				11 20	12 00							11 51		12 20	13 10								
Thorne North	d		09 24	09 38														11 25						
Goole	d		09a35	09 47					10 40								11 12	11a36						
Saltmarshe	d																							
York 8	33 d										10 40									12 05				
Selby	a									10 43	10 59									12 24			12 41	
	d									10 43	10 59									12 24			12 42	
Wressle	d																							
Howden	d																						12 52	
Eastrington	d																							
Gilberdyke	d			09 58					10 48								11 23							
Broomfleet	d																							
Brough	d			10 06					10 56	11 01	11 19						11 31			12 44			13 04	
Ferriby	d																							
Hessle	d																							
Hull	a			10 21					11 13	11 18	11 38						11 46			13 03			13 21	

For general notes see front of timetable
For details of catering facilities see Directory of Train Operators

A To Scarborough (Table 43)
B To Edinburgh (Table 51)
C To Leeds (Table 31)
D To Bridlington (Table 43)
E From Liverpool Lime Street (Table 39)
G From Birmingham New Street to Edinburgh (Table 51)
H Until 12 July. From Leicester (Table 53)
b Change at Manchester Piccadilly and Sheffield
c Change at Manchester Piccadilly
e 28 June, 5 and 12 July arr. 1215

Table 29

Sundays

28 June to 6 September

Manchester Airport, Manchester, Sheffield and Meadowhall → Doncaster → Cleethorpes and Hull
Barton-on-Humber → Cleethorpes

Network Diagram - see first page of Table 18

		EM	TP	TP	NT	NT	XC	NT	NT	TP	TP	NT	NT	TP	TP	XC	TP	NT	NT	NT	XC	TP	TP	NT
			1 ◇				1 ◇				1 ◇			1 ◇		1 ◇					1 ◇	1 ◇		
		A					B		C							B		D	E		G			
				🚌	🚌					🚌					🚌		🚌						🚌	🚌
							trolley									trolley					trolley			
Manchester Airport	85 ✈ d		10 44								*11 35*					*11b35*					*12b09*	12 55		
Manchester Piccadilly 10	78 d		11 18								12 02			12 18							*12 44*	13 20		
Stockport	78 d		11 27								*11c27*			12 28							*12 54*	13 28		
Sheffield 7	a		12 08											13 08								14 08		
	d		12 11				12 21	12 24	12 28					13 11		13 21		13 24	13 36		13 51	14 11		
Meadowhall	d		12 16					12 30	12 34					13 16				13 30	13 42			14 16		
Rotherham Central	d							12 36				←						13 36	13 49					
Swinton (S.Yorks)	d							12 48				12 48						13 47	13a57					
Mexborough	d							→				12 51						13 50						
Conisbrough	d											12 55						13 54						
Doncaster 7	a		12 39						12 54			13 03		13 35				14 02			14 13	14 35		
York 8	26 a						13 32							*14 04*		14 32		*14 33*			14 43	*15 05*		
London Kings Cross 15	⊖ 26 d			*11 00*								*11 10*			*12 00*								*13 00*	
Doncaster	31 d			12 55					12 55	13 00		13 06			13 55		14 00	14 04					14 55	
Bentley (S.Yorks)	31 a											*13 13*												
Adwick	31 a											*13 17*												
Kirk Sandall	d											13 12												
Hatfield & Stainforth	d											13 17												
Thorne South	d																							
Crowle	d																							
Althorpe	d																							
Scunthorpe	a									13 50							14 50							
	d									13 55							14 55							
Barnetby	d	12 33								14 20							15 20							
Hull Paragon Interchange	🚌 d				13 25																			15 30
Barton-on-Humber	🚌 a				13 55																			15 55
Barton-on-Humber	d					14 00																		
Barrow Haven	d					14 05																		
New Holland	d					14 08																		
Goxhill	d					14 13																		
Thornton Abbey	d					14 16																		
Ulceby	d					14 20																		
Habrough	d	12 41				14 25				14 35							15 35							
Stallingborough	d					14 30																		
Healing	d					14 33																		
Great Coates	d					14 36																		
Grimsby Town	a	12 53		14 10		14 41				15 00					15s10		16 00						16s10	
	d	13 05		14 15		14 41				15 05							16 05							
Grimsby Docks	d					14 44																		
New Clee	d					14x46																		
Cleethorpes	a	13 16		14 35		14 51				15 25					15 30		16 25						16 30	
Thorne North	d											13 25												
Goole	d								13 15			13a35						14 25						
Saltmarshe	d																							
York 8	33 d												13 23							14 42				
Selby	a										13 23		13 42							15 01				
	d										13 23		13 42							15 01				
Wressle	d																							
Howden	d																							
Eastrington	d																							
Gilberdyke	d								13 23									14 33						
Broomfleet	d																							
Brough	d								13 28		13 41		14 02					14 41		15 21				
Ferriby	d																							
Hessle	d																							
Hull	a								13 48		14 00		14 21					14 59		15 40				

For general notes see front of timetable
For details of catering facilities see Directory of Train Operators

- **A** From Newark North Gate (Table 27)
- **B** From Bristol Temple Meads to Edinburgh (Table 51)
- **C** To Scarborough (Table 43)
- **D** To Bridlington (Table 43)
- **E** To Leeds (Table 31)
- **G** From Birmingham New Street to Newcastle (Table 51)
- **b** Change at Manchester Piccadilly and Sheffield
- **c** Change at Manchester Piccadilly. 28 June, 5 and 12 July dep. 1123

Table 29

Sundays

28 June to 6 September

Manchester Airport, Manchester, Sheffield and Meadowhall → Doncaster → Cleethorpes and Hull Barton-on-Humber → Cleethorpes

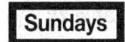

Network Diagram - see first page of Table 18

	NT	XC	NT		NT	TP	TP	NT	NT	XC	TP	EM	TP	XC	NT	NT	TP	NT	NT	NT	XC	HT	TP
		1 ◇					1 ◇			1 ◇	1 ◇			1 ◇							1 ◇	1 ◇	1 ◇
		A			B					C		D		E		G			H	J	K		
		🛒				🚌				🛒			🚌	🛒			🚌				🛒	☒	
Manchester Airport 85 ✈ d							13 35			13b09	13 55									14b09			14 55
Manchester Piccadilly 10 78 🚢 d							14 02			13 44	14 20									14 44			15 20
Stockport 78 d							13c37			13 54	14 28									14 54			15 28
Sheffield 7 🚢 a											15 08												16 08
d		14 21	14 22		14 28					14 51	15 11			15 21	15 24	15 28			15 36	15 46	15 51		16 11
Meadowhall 🚢 d			14 28		14 34						15 16				15 30	15 34			15 42	15 52			16 16
Rotherham Central d			14 34					←							15 37			←	15 48	15 58			
Swinton (S Yorks) d			14 46					14 46							15 47			15 47	15a56	16 08			
Mexborough d			→					14 49							→			15 50					
Conisbrough d								14 53										15 54					
Doncaster 7 a					14 56			15 03		15 13	15 39					15 55		16 04			16 15		16 39
York 8 26 a		15 32						15 34		15 43				16 32		16 35				17 01	16 40		
London Kings Cross 15 ⊖ 26 d								13 10					14 00									14 44	
Doncaster 31 d					14 59	15 00		15 05					15 55			15 56	16 00					16 23	
Bentley (S.Yorks) 31 a								15 13															
Adwick 31 a								15 17															
Kirk Sandall d								15 13															
Hatfield & Stainforth d								15 18															
Thorne South d																							
Crowle d																							
Althorpe d																							
Scunthorpe a						15 50											16 50						
d						15 55											16 55						
Barnetby d						16 20						16 54					17 20						
Hull Paragon Interchange 🚌 d																							
Barton-on-Humber 🚌 a																							
Barton-on-Humber d	16 15																						
Barrow Haven d	16 20																						
New Holland d	16 23																						
Goxhill d	16 28																						
Thornton Abbey d	16 31																						
Ulceby d	16 35																						
Habrough d	16 40					16 35						17 02					17 35						
Stallingborough d	16 45																						
Healing d	16 48																						
Great Coates d	16 51																						
Grimsby Town a	16 56					17 00						17 14	17s10				18 00						
d	16 56					17 05						17 14					18 05						
Grimsby Docks d	16 59																						
New Clee d	17x01																						
Cleethorpes a	17 06					17 25						17 23	17 30				18 25						
Thorne North d								15 25															
Goole d					15 19			15a33								16 17							
Saltmarshe d																							
York 8 33 d									15 43														
Selby a							15 23		16 01													16 41	
d							15 23		16 02													16 42	
Wressle d																							
Howden d																						16 52	
Eastrington d																							
Gilberdyke d					15 27											16 25							
Broomfleet d																							
Brough d					15 35		15 41		16 23							16 33						17 04	
Ferriby d					15 40																		
Hessle d					15 44																		
Hull a					15 57		16 00		16 41							16 50						17 21	

For general notes see front of timetable
For details of catering facilities see Directory of Train Operators

- **A** From Plymouth (Table 51) to Aberdeen (Table 229)
- **B** To Scarborough (Table 43)
- **C** From Birmingham New Street to Newcastle (Table 51)
- **D** From Nottingham (Table 27)
- **E** From Plymouth to Edinburgh (Table 51)
- **G** To Bridlington (Table 43)
- **H** To Leeds (Table 31)
- **J** Via Pontefract Baghill (Table 33)
- **K** From Guildford to Newcastle (Table 51)
- **b** Change at Manchester Piccadilly and Sheffield
- **c** Change at Manchester Piccadilly

Table 29

Sundays

Manchester Airport, Manchester, Sheffield and Meadowhall → Doncaster → Cleethorpes and Hull Barton-on-Humber → Cleethorpes

28 June to 6 September

Network Diagram - see first page of Table 18

		TP	XC	NT	NT	TP	TP	NT	NT	EM	XC	HT	TP	TP	NT	NT	TP	XC	NT	NT	NT	NT	XC	TP
			1◇				1◇				1◇	1◇	1◇					1◇					1◇	1◇
			A		B					C	D							E		G		H	D	
		🚌				🚌								🚌	🚌		🚌							
			🍴								🍴	⊠						🍴					🍴	
Manchester Airport	85 ✈ d						15 35				15b09		15 55										16b09	16 55
Manchester Piccadilly 10	78 🚇 d						16 02				15 44		16 20										16 44	17 20
Stockport	78 d						15c39				15 54		16 28										16 54	17 28
Sheffield 7	🚇 a												17 08											18 08
	d		16 21	16 24	16 28						16 51		17 11					17 21	17 24	17 28		17 36	17 51	18 11
Meadowhall	🚇 d			16 30	16 34								17 16						17 30	17 34		17 43		18 16
Rotherham Central	d			16 37					←										17 37		←	17 49		
Swinton (S.Yorks)	d			16 47 →					16 47										17 47 →		17 47	17a57		
Mexborough	d								16 50												17 50			
Conisbrough	d								16 54												17 54			
Doncaster 7	a				16 54				17 04		17 13		17 39							17 57	18 05		18 13	18 39
York 8	26 a		17 32								17 42							18 32		18 34	19 05		19e21	
London Kings Cross 15	⊖ 26 d								15 10			15 44		16 00						16 10				
Doncaster	31 d	16 55			16 56	17 00			17 05			17 35		17 55			18 00			18 03				
Bentley (S.Yorks)	31 a				17 13																			
Adwick	31 a				17 17																			
Kirk Sandall	d								17 13															
Hatfield & Stainforth	d								17 18															
Thorne South	d																							
Crowle	d																							
Althorpe	d																							
Scunthorpe	a					17 50											18 50							
	d					17 55											18 55							
Barnetby	d					18 20				18 53							19 20							
Hull Paragon Interchange	🚌 d														18 30									
Barton-on-Humber	🚌 a														18 55									
Barton-on-Humber	d															19 15								
Barrow Haven	d															19 20								
New Holland	d															19 23								
Goxhill	d															19 28								
Thornton Abbey	d															19 31								
Ulceby	d															19 35								
Habrough	d					18 35				19 01						19 40	19 35							
Stallingborough	d															19 45								
Healing	d															19 48								
Great Coates	d															19 51								
Grimsby Town	a	18s10				19 00				19 13				19s10		19 56	20 00							
	d					19 05				19 13						20 01	20 05							
Grimsby Docks	d															20 03								
New Clee	d															20x06								
Cleethorpes	a	18 30				19 25				19 24				19 30		20 10	20 25							
Thorne North	d								17 25															
Goole	d				17 15				17a34											18 22				
Saltmarshe	d																							
York 8	33 d							17 10																
Selby	a						17 23	17 30				17 50												
	d						17 23	17 31				17 50												
Wressle	d																							
Howden	d											18 02												
Eastrington	d																							
Gilberdyke	d				17 23															18 35				
Broomfleet	d																							
Brough	d				17 31		17 41	17 51				18 13								18 43				
Ferriby	d																							
Hessle	d																							
Hull	a				17 49		18 00	18 10				18 32								18 57				

For general notes see front of timetable
For details of catering facilities see Directory of Train Operators

- **A** From Penzance (Table 135) to Glasgow Central (Table 51)
- **B** To Scarborough (Table 43)
- **C** From Newark North Gate (Table 27)
- **D** From Reading to Newcastle (Table 51)
- **E** From Plymouth to Glasgow Central (Table 51)
- **G** To Bridlington (Table 43)
- **H** To Leeds (Table 31)
- **b** Change at Manchester Piccadilly and Sheffield
- **c** Change at Manchester Piccadilly
- **e** By changing at Doncaster, passengers may arrive at 1905

Table 29

Sundays

28 June to 6 September

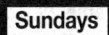

Manchester Airport, Manchester, Sheffield and Meadowhall → Doncaster → Cleethorpes and Hull
Barton-on-Humber → Cleethorpes

Network Diagram - see first page of Table 18

	TP	XC	NT	NT	TP	TP	NT	NT	XC	HT	NT	TP	TP	TP	TP	XC	NT	NT	XC	NT	TP	TP	GR
		1 ◇				1 ◇			1 ◇	1 ◇		1 ◇	1 ◇			1 ◇			1 ◇		1 ◇		R 1
		A		B					C		D					E		G	H				
	bus				bus									bus	bus							bus	
		trolley							trolley	buffet						trolley			trolley				restaurant, trolley
Manchester Airport 85 d						17 35			17b09			17 55	18 35						18b09		18 55		
Manchester Piccadilly 10 78 d						18 02			17 44			18 20	19 02						18 44		19 20		
Stockport 78 d						17c39			17 54			18 28	18c39						18 54		19 28		
Sheffield 7 a												19 08									20 08		
d		18 21	18 25	18 28					18 51		18 57	19 11				19 21	19 29	19 36	19 51	20 02	20 11		
Meadowhall d			18 31	18 35							19 04	19 16					19 35	19 42		20 09	20 16		
Rotherham Central d			18 37				←				19 10						19 41	19 49					
Swinton (S.Yorks) d			18 47 →				18 47				19 18						19 49	19a57					
Mexborough d							18 50										19 52						
Conisbrough d							18 54										19 56						
Doncaster 7 a				18 54			19 04		19 13			19 39					20 07		20 16	20 30	20 39		
York 8 26 a		19 32							19 42		20 17	20 39				20 32			20 44				
London Kings Cross 15 ⊖ 26 d	16 30				17 00					17 44					18 00					18 40		19 00	19 10
Doncaster 31 d	18 55			18 55	19 00					19 24				19 55	20 00					20 30		20 55	20 58
Bentley (S.Yorks) 31 a									19e33														
Adwick 31 a									19e37														
Kirk Sandall d				19 01																			
Hatfield & Stainforth d				19 06																			
Thorne South d																							
Crowle d																							
Althorpe d																							
Scunthorpe a					19 50										20 50								
d					19 55										20 55								
Barnetby d					20 20										21 20								
Hull Paragon Interchange bus d																							
Barton-on-Humber bus a																							
Barton-on-Humber d																							
Barrow Haven d																							
New Holland d																							
Goxhill d																							
Thornton Abbey d																							
Ulceby d																							
Habrough d					20 35										21 35								
Stallingborough d																							
Healing d																							
Great Coates d																							
Grimsby Town a	20s10				21 00									21s10	22 00							22s10	
d					21 05										22 05								
Grimsby Docks d																							
New Clee d																							
Cleethorpes a	20 30				21 25									21 30	22 25							22 30	
Thorne North d				19 12																			
Goole d				19 21																20 49			
Saltmarshe d																							
York 8 33 d								19 10															
Selby a						19 23		19 29		19 40			20 16										21 15
d						19 23		19 30		19 40			20 16										21 15
Wressle d																							
Howden d										19 52													
Eastrington d																							
Gilberdyke d				19 29																20 57			
Broomfleet d																							
Brough d				19 37		19 44		19 50		20 03			20 34							21 05			21 36
Ferriby d																							
Hessle d																							
Hull a				19 55		20 00		20 09		20 22			20 53							21 23			21 56

For general notes see front of timetable
For details of catering facilities see Directory of Train Operators

A From Newquay (Table 135) to Edinburgh (Table 51)
B To Beverley (Table 43)
C From Reading to Edinburgh (Table 51)
D Via Pontefract Baghill (Table 33)
E From Plymouth to Edinburgh (Table 51)
G To Leeds (Table 31)
H From Reading to Newcastle (Table 51)
b Change at Manchester Piccadilly and Sheffield
c Change at Manchester Piccadilly
e Change at Doncaster

Sundays

28 June to 6 September

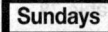

Manchester Airport, Manchester, Sheffield and Meadowhall → Doncaster → Cleethorpes and Hull Barton-on-Humber → Cleethorpes

Network Diagram - see first page of Table 18

		TP	XC	TP	TP	NT	NT	XC	TP	HT	TP	TP	NT	NT	TP	XC	NT	TP	NT	TP	TP	NT
			1 ◇	1 ◇	1 ◇			1 ◇	1 ◇	1 ◇					1 ◇	1 ◇		1 ◇				
			A	B	C			D						E	G	H						
		Bus								⊠	Bus	Bus								Bus	Bus	
Manchester Airport	85 d			19 35	19 35			19b09	19 55							20b09	20 55					21 55
Manchester Piccadilly 10	78 d			20 06	20 06			19 44	20 18							20 44	21 20					22 16
Stockport	78 d			19c39	19c39			19 54	20 27							20 54	21 28					22 28
Sheffield 7	a								21 08													
	d		20 21			20 28		20 51	21 11				21 24	21 36		21 51	22 26	22 30				23 41
Meadowhall	d					20 34			21 16				21 30	21 42			22 32	22 36				23 47
Rotherham Central	d					20 40							21 37	21 48			22 38		←			23 53
Swinton (S.Yorks)	d					20 48							21 47	21a56			22 48		22 48			00 01
Mexborough	d					20 51							21 50				→		22 51			00 04
Conisbrough	d					20 55							21 54						22 55			00 08
Doncaster 7	a					21 05		21 19	21 39				22 03					22 56	23 04			00 19
York 8	26 a		21 37					21 42					23 09			22 53			00 39			
London Kings Cross 15	⊖ 26 d					19 10				20 10	20 00									21 00		
Doncaster	31 d	21 00				21 06				21 55	21 55	22 00	22 04						23 07	23 10	23 15	
Bentley (S.Yorks)	31 a								21 52													
Adwick	31 a								21 56													
Kirk Sandall	d					21 12																
Hatfield & Stainforth	d					21 17																
Thorne South	d																					
Crowle	d																					
Althorpe	d																					
Scunthorpe	a	21 50										22 50									00s05	
	d	21 55										22 55										
Barnetby	d	22 20										23 20									00s30	
Hull Paragon Interchange	Bus d																					
Barton-on-Humber	Bus a																					
Barton-on-Humber	d																					
Barrow Haven	d																					
New Holland	d																					
Goxhill	d																					
Thornton Abbey	d																					
Ulceby	d																					
Habrough	d	22 35										23 35									00s45	
Stallingborough	d																					
Healing	d																					
Great Coates	d																					
Grimsby Town	a	23 00									23s10	23 59								00s25	01s10	
	d	23 05										00 05										
Grimsby Docks	d																					
New Clee	d																					
Cleethorpes	a	23 25									23 30	00 25								00 45	01 30	
Thorne North	d					21 23													23 19			
Goole	d					21a34							22 23						23 28			
Saltmarshe	d																					
York 8	33 d						21 41															
Selby	a			21 23	21 38		22 00			22 09												
	d			21 23	21 38		22 00			22 09					22 42							
Wressle	d																					
Howden	d									22 21												
Eastrington	d																					
Gilberdyke	d												22 32						23 36			
Broomfleet	d																					
Brough	d			21 44	21 56		22 20			22 31			22 40		23 00				23 44			
Ferriby	d																					
Hessle	d																					
Hull	a			22 01	22 13		22 39			22 50			22 56		23 18				00 02			

For general notes see front of timetable
For details of catering facilities see Directory of Train Operators

A From Plymouth (Table 51)
B Until 12 July
C From 19 July
D From Reading to Newcastle (Table 51)
E To Leeds (Table 31)
G From Leeds (Table 39)
H From Reading (Table 51)
b Change at Manchester Piccadilly and Sheffield
c Change at Manchester Piccadilly

Sheffield → Retford and Lincoln

Network Diagram - see first page of Table 18

Mondays to Fridays

Miles			NT	NT	NT	NT	NT A	NT	NT B	NT B	NT B	NT B	NT B	NT B	NT B	NT B	NT C	NT	NT	NT	NT A	NT D	NT E	NT	
—	Huddersfield	34 d					06b10		08c10	09e13	10e13	11e13	12e13	13e13	14e13	14e13		16e13		17f56	19g18	20 13	20 18		
—	Barnsley	34 d			05f23	06f38	06 58	07f40	09 14	10 14	11 14	12 14	13 14	14 14	15 14	15 14	16f40	17 14	17f40	18f55	20 06	21 12	21 11	21f24	
—	Meadowhall	34 d			05 58	06 58	07 33	08 22	09 33	10 33	11 33	12 33	13 33	14 33	15 33	16 33	16 55	17 33	18 06	19 25	20 33	21 28	21 29	22 09	
0	**Sheffield** 7	d	05 39	05 46	06 43	07 30	07 44	08 44	09 44	10 44	11 44	12 44	13 44	14 44	15 44	16 44	17 24	17 44	18 45	19 48	20 44	21 44	21 44	22 44	
2¼	Darnall	d		05 51	06 48	07 35		08 49	09 49	10 49	11 49	12 49	13 49	14 49	15 49	16 49	17 29	17 49	18 50	19 53	20 49	21 49	21 49	22 49	
5¼	Woodhouse	d		05 56	06 53	07 40		08 54	09 54	10 54	11 54	12 54	13 54	14 54	15 54	16 54	17 34	17 54	18 55	19 58	20 54	21 54	21 54	22 54	
9¼	Kiveton Bridge	d		06 03	07 00	07 47		09 01	10 01	11 01	12 01	13 01	14 01	15 01	16 01	17 01	17 41	18 01	19 02	20 05	21 01	22 01	22 01	23 01	
10¾	Kiveton Park	d	05 54	06 06	07 03	07 50	07 59	09 04	10 04	11 04	12 04	13 04	14 04	15 04	16 04	17 04	17 44	18 04	19 05	20 08	21 04	22 04	22 04	23 04	
13¾	Shireoaks	d		06 11	07 08	07 55		09 09	10 09	11 09	12 09	13 09	14 09	15 09	16 09	17 09	17 48	18 09	19 10	20 13	21 09	22 08	22 08	23 09	
15¾	Worksop	d	06 01	06h23	07 14	07 59	08a10	09 13	10 13	11 13	12 13	13 13	14 13	15 13	16 13	17 13	17 52	18 13	19 14	20 17	21a21	22 14	22 14	23a22	
23½	**Retford** 10	a	06 10	06 37	07 23	08 09		09 23	10 23	11 23	12 23	13 23	14 23	15 23	16 23	17 23	18 06	18 23	19 24	20 27		22 28	22 28		
—	London Kings Cross 15	⊖ 26 a	08 33	08 33		09 51		11 34	12 42		14 20	15 40		17 30	18 12	19 29	19 49	20 18		23 32					
—	**Retford** 10	d	06 10		07 24	08 09		09 23	10 23	11 24	12 23	13 23	14 23	15 23	16 23	17 23		18 23	19 24	20 27					
33	Gainsborough Lea Road	18 d	06 25		07 38	08 24		09 38	10 38	11 38	12 38	13 39	14 38	15 38	16 38	17 38		18 38	19 39	20 42					
42½	Saxilby	18 d	06 37		07 51	08 37		09 51	10 51	11 51	12 51	13 51	14 51	15 51	16 51	17 51		18 51	19 52	20 55					
48½	**Lincoln**	18 a	06 53		08 06	08 52		10 06	11 06	12 06	13 06	14 06	15 06	16 09	17 06	18 06		19 07	20 06	21 10					

Saturdays

		NT	NT	NT	NT	NT	NT	NT G	NT G	NT	NT	NT G	NT G	NT G	NT G	NT	NT G	NT C	NT G	NT G	NT	NT A	NT	NT	
Huddersfield	34 d					06j10		08k10	09m13	10m13		11m13	12m13	13c13	14m13		15m13		16m13	17m13		19n18	20m18		
Barnsley	34 d			05f23	06f21	06f58	07f40	09 14	10 14	11 14		12 14	13 14	14 14	15 14		16 14	16f40	17 14	18 14	18f40	20 16	21 11	21f24	
Meadowhall	34 d			05 58	06 58	07 33	08 22	09 33	10 33	11 33		12 33	13 33	14 33	15 33		16 33	16 55	17 33	18 33	19 06	20 35	21 29	22 22	
Sheffield 7	d	05 39	05 46	06 43	07 30	08 02	08 44	09 44	10 44	11 44	12 00	12 44	13 44	14 44	15 44	16 00	16 44	17 24	17 44	18 45	19 48	20 44	21 44	22 44	
Darnall	d		05 51	06 48	07 35	08 08	08 49	09 49	10 49	11 49	12 05	12 49	13 49	14 49	15 49	16 05	16 49	17 29	17 49	18 50	19 53	20 49	21 49	22 49	
Woodhouse	d		05 56	06 53	07 40	08 13	08 54	09 54	10 54	11 54	12 10	12 54	13 54	14 54	15 54	16 10	16 54	17 34	17 54	18 55	19 58	20 54	21 54	22 54	
Kiveton Bridge	d		06 03	07 00	07 47	08 20	09 01	10 01	11 01	12 01	12 17	13 01	14 01	15 01	16 01	16 17	17 01	17 41	18 01	19 02	20 05	21 01	22 01	23 01	
Kiveton Park	d	05 54	06 06	07 03	07 50	08 23	09 04	10 04	11 04	12 04	12 20	13 04	14 04	15 04	16 04	16 20	17 04	17 44	18 04	19 05	20 08	21 04	22 04	23 04	
Shireoaks	d		06 11	07 08	07 55	08 28	09 09	10 09	11 09	12 09	12 25	13 09	14 09	15 09	16 09	16 25	17 09	17 48	18 09	19 10	20 13	21 09	22 08	23 09	
Worksop	d	06 01		07 14	07 59	08 32	09 13	10 13	11 13	12 13	12 35	13 13	14 13	15 13	16 13	16 36	17 13	17 52	18 13	19 14	20 17	21a23	22 14	23a22	
Retford 10	a	06 10	06 38	07 23	08 09	08 42	09 23	10 23	11 23	12 23	12 44	13 23	14 23	15 23	16 23	16 46	17 23	18 07	18 23	19 24	20 27		22 28		
London Kings Cross 15	⊖ 26 a	08 40			10 00	10 44		12 42		14 27		15 50	16 34	17 45	18 28			20 12	20 46		22 47				
Retford 10	d	06 10		07 24	08 09	08 42	09 23	10 23	11 24	12 23	12 45	13 23	14 23	15 23	16 23	16 46	17 23		18 23	19 24	20 27				
Gainsborough Lea Road	18 d	06 25		07 38	08 24		09 38	10 38	11 38	12 38		13 38	14 38	15 45	16 38		17 38		18 38	19 39	20 42				
Saxilby	18 d	06 37		07 51	08 37		09 51	10 51	11 51	12 51		13 51	14 51	15 58	16 51		17 51		18 51	19 52	20 55				
Lincoln	18 a	06 53		08 06	08 52		10 06	11 06	12 06	13 06		14 06	15 06	16 09	17 06		18 06		19 07	20 06	21 10				
Gainsborough Central	d					08 57					13 00					17 01									
Kirton Lindsey	d					09 11					13 13					17 15									
Brigg	d					09q24					13 22					17 27									
Barnetby	29 a					09 38					13 37					17 37									
Habrough	29 a					09 48					13 47					17 47									
Grimsby Town	29 a					10 00					14 00					18 01									
Cleethorpes	29 a					10 13					14 11					18 11									

Sundays

		NT	NT	NT	NT	NT	NT
Huddersfield	34 d	11r29		14t15	15v19	17f19	19w19
Barnsley	34 d	12r17		15t12	17v12	18f12	20w12
Meadowhall	34 d	13 00		15 43	17 43	19 00	20 45
Sheffield 7	d	13 42	13 57	16 02	18 02	19 26	21 06
Darnall	d		14 03	16 07	18 07	19 31	21 11
Woodhouse	d		14 08	16 12	18 12	19 36	21 16
Kiveton Bridge	d		14 14	16 19	18 19	19 43	21 23
Kiveton Park	d		14 17	16 22	18 22	19 46	21 26
Shireoaks	d		14 22	16 26	18 26	19 50	21 30
Worksop	d	14 02	14 26	16 30	18 30	19 54	21 34
Retford 10	a	14 11	14 39	16 39	18 39	20 03	21 49
London Kings Cross 15	⊖ 26 a		16 50	19 06	21 34	23 14	
Retford 10	d	14 12		16 40	18 40	20 04	
Gainsborough Lea Road	18 d	14 26		16 54	18 54	20 18	
Saxilby	18 d	14 39		17 07	19 07	20 31	
Lincoln	18 a	14 54		17 21	19 22	20 45	

For general notes see front of timetable
For details of catering facilities see Directory of Train Operators

- **A** From Doncaster (Table 29)
- **B** From Scunthorpe (22 June to 4 September from Thorne North) (Table 29)
- **C** From Adwick (Table 29)
- **D** From 7 September
- **E** Until 4 September
- **G** From Scunthorpe (27 June to 5 September from Thorne North) (Table 29)
- **b** From 7 September dep. 0605
- **c** From 7 September dep. 0807
- **e** From 7 September dep. 5 mins earlier
- **f** Change at Meadowhall and Sheffield
- **g** From 7 September dep. 1915
- **h** Arr. 0616
- **j** Change at Meadowhall and Sheffield. From 12 September dep. 0605
- **k** From 12 September dep. 0807
- **m** From 12 September dep. 5 mins earlier
- **n** From 12 September dep. 1915
- **q** Arr. 0919
- **r** Change at Meadowhall and Sheffield. From 13 September dep. Huddersfield 1124
- **t** Change at Meadowhall and Sheffield. From 13 September dep. Huddersfield 1411
- **v** Change at Meadowhall and Sheffield. From 13 September dep. Huddersfield 1514
- **w** Change at Meadowhall and Sheffield. From 13 September dep. Huddersfield 1914

Lincoln and Retford → Sheffield

Network Diagram - see first page of Table 18

Mondays to Fridays

Miles		NT A	NT A	NT	NT B	NT B	NT B	NT B	NT B	NT B	NT B	NT B	NT B	NT C	NT	NT D	NT	NT	NT	NT	NT	NT	NT
0	**Lincoln** 18 d	.	.	07 04	.	08 27	09 27	10 27	11 27	12 27	13 27	14 27	15 27	16 27	17 22	.	18 24	19 43	20 27	.	21 27	.	.
6	Saxilby 18 d	.	.	07 14	.	08 36	09 36	10 36	11 36	12 36	13 36	14 36	15 36	16 36	17 31	.	18 33	19 52	20 36	.	21 36	.	.
15½	Gainsborough Lea Road 18 d	.	.	07 26	.	08 49	09 49	10 49	11 49	12 49	13 49	14 49	15 49	16 49	17 44	.	18 46	20 05	20 49	.	21 49	.	.
25	**Retford** 10 a	.	.	07 40	.	09 03	10 03	11 03	12 03	13 03	14 03	15 03	16 03	17 03	17 58	.	19 04	20 19	21 03	.	22 03	.	.
—	London Kings Cross 15 ⊖ 26 d	.	.	.	.	*07 20*	.	*08 40*	*10 10*	.	*12 10*	*13 33*	.	*15 10*	*16 05*	*16 35*	.	*18 30*	*18 50*	.	*20 27*	*20b27*	.
—	**Retford** 10 d	.	07 03	07 40	.	09 03	10 03	11 03	12 03	13 03	14 03	15 03	16 03	17 03	17 58	18 14	19 04	20 19	21 03	.	22 03	22 45	.
32¾	Worksop d	06 30	07 16	07 52	08 14	09 15	10 15	11 15	12 15	13 15	14 15	15 15	16 15	17 15	18 10	18 25	19 16	20 31	21 15	21 28	22 15	22 58	23 28
34¾	Shireoaks d	06 33	07 20	07 55	08 19	09 19	10 19	11 19	12 19	13 19	14 19	15 19	16 19	17 19	.	18 29	19 20	20 35	.	21 32	22 19	23 02	23 32
37¾	Kiveton Park d	06 39	07 25	08 01	08 25	09 25	10 25	11 25	12 25	13 25	14 25	15 25	16 25	17 25	.	18 34	19 26	20 41	21 23	21 38	22 25	23 08	23 38
39	Kiveton Bridge d	06 42	07 28	08 04	08 28	09 28	10 28	11 28	12 28	13 28	14 28	15 28	16 28	17 28	.	18 37	19 29	20 44	.	21 41	22 28	23 11	23 41
43¼	Woodhouse d	06 48	07 35	08 10	08 34	09 34	10 34	11 34	12 34	13 34	14 34	15 34	16 34	17 34	.	18 43	19 35	20 50	.	21 48	22 34	23 17	23 52
46¼	Darnall d	06 53	07 40	08 15	08 39	09 39	10 39	11 39	12 39	13 39	14 39	15 39	16 39	17 39	.	18 48	19 40	20 55	.	21 53	22 39	23 22	23 57
48½	**Sheffield** 7 a	07 02	07 48	08 26	08 49	09 49	10 49	11 49	12 49	13 48	14 49	15 48	16 48	17 49	18 35	18 57	19 54	21 05	21 46	22 02	22 50	23 33	00 04
—	Meadowhall 34 a	07 11	07 57	*08 46*	09 03	10 03	11 03	12 03	13 03	14 03	15 03	16 03	17 03	18 03	.	19 06	*20 16*	*21 21*	.	*22 16*	*23 20*	.	.
—	Barnsley 34 a	07 32	08 11	09c11	*09 32*	*10 32*	*11 32*	*12 32*	*13 32*	*14 32*	*15 32*	*16 32*	*17 32*	*18 33*	.	*19 33*	20c40	22c05	.	23e07	23f50	.	.
—	Huddersfield 34 a	08g49	09g49	.	10g49	11g49	12g49	13g49	14g49	15g49	16g49	17h50	18j57	19g56	.	20g55	21k56	22m57	.	00c01	.	.	.

Saturdays

	NT	NT A	NT	NT B	NT B	NT B	NT B	NT	NT B	NT B	NT B	NT B	NT	NT D	NT	NT D	NT	NT	NT	NT	NT	NT	NT	NT
Cleethorpes 29 d	.	.	.	.	.	.	.	11 13	.	.	.	.	15 21	.	.	.	.	.	19 13	.	.	.	.	.
Grimsby Town 29 d	.	.	.	.	.	.	.	11 20	.	.	.	.	15 28	.	.	.	.	.	19 20	.	.	.	.	.
Habrough 29 d	.	.	.	.	.	.	.	11 30	.	.	.	.	15 38	.	.	.	.	.	19 30	.	.	.	.	.
Barnetby 29 d	.	.	.	.	.	.	.	11 40	.	.	.	.	15 48	.	.	.	.	.	19 39	.	.	.	.	.
Brigg d	.	.	.	.	.	.	.	11 45	.	.	.	.	15 53	.	.	.	.	.	19 45	.	.	.	.	.
Kirton Lindsey d	.	.	.	.	.	.	.	11 54	.	.	.	.	16 02	.	.	.	.	.	19 54	.	.	.	.	.
Gainsborough Central d	.	.	.	.	.	.	.	12 20	.	.	.	.	16 20	.	.	.	.	.	20 12	.	.	.	.	.
Lincoln 18 d	.	.	07 04	08 27	09 27	10 27	11 27	.	12 27	13 27	14 27	15 27	.	16 27	17 22	.	18 24	19 43	.	20 27	.	21 24	.	.
Saxilby 18 d	.	.	07 14	08 36	09 36	10 36	11 36	.	12 36	13 36	14 36	15 36	.	16 36	17 31	.	18 33	19 52	.	20 36	.	21 33	.	.
Gainsborough Lea Road 18 d	.	.	07 26	08 49	09 49	10 49	11 49	.	12 49	13 49	14 49	15 49	.	16 49	17 44	.	18 46	20 05	.	20 49	.	21 46	.	.
Retford 10 a	.	.	07 40	09 03	10 03	11 03	12 03	12 35	13 03	14 03	15 03	16 03	16 35	17 03	17 58	.	19 04	20 19	20 26	21 03	.	22 00	.	.
London Kings Cross 15 ⊖ 26 d	.	.	.	*07 10*	.	*09 00*	*09 34*	.	*11 10*	*11 48*	*13 10*	*13 48*	*14 30*	.	.	*16 30*	*17 05*	.	*18 40*	.	.	*20 00*	.	.
Retford 10 d	.	07 03	07 40	09 03	10 03	11 03	12 03	12 35	13 03	14 03	15 03	16 03	16 35	17 03	17 58	18 14	19 04	20 19	20 27	21 03	.	22 00	22n45	.
Worksop d	06 30	07 16	07 52	09 15	10 15	11 15	12 15	12 47	13 15	14 15	15 15	16 15	16 47	17 15	18 10	18 25	19 16	20 31	20 38	21 15	21 28	22 12	22 58	23 28
Shireoaks d	06 33	07 20	07 55	09 19	10 19	11 19	12 19	12 51	13 19	14 19	15 19	16 19	16 51	17 19	.	18 29	19 20	20 35	20 42	.	21 32	22 16	23 02	23 32
Kiveton Park d	06 39	07 25	08 01	09 25	10 25	11 25	12 25	12 57	13 25	14 25	15 25	16 25	16 57	17 25	.	18 34	19 26	20 41	20 48	21 23	21 38	22 22	23 08	23 38
Kiveton Bridge d	06 42	07 28	08 04	09 28	10 28	11 28	12 28	13 00	13 28	14 28	15 28	16 28	17 00	17 28	.	18 37	19 29	20 44	20 51	.	21 41	22 25	23 11	23 41
Woodhouse d	06 48	07 35	08 10	09 34	10 34	11 34	12 34	13 06	13 34	14 34	15 34	16 34	17 06	17 34	.	18 43	19 35	20 50	21 01	.	21 48	22 31	23 17	23 47
Darnall d	06 53	07 40	08 15	09 39	10 39	11 39	12 39	13 11	13 39	14 39	15 39	16 39	17 11	17 39	.	18 48	19 40	20 55	21 06	.	21 53	22 36	23 22	23 52
Sheffield 7 a	07 02	07 48	08 26	09 49	10 49	11 49	12 49	13 23	13 48	14 49	15 48	16 48	17 23	17 49	18 35	18 57	19 54	21 05	21 22	21 46	22 02	22 46	23 33	00 01
Meadowhall 34 a	*07 20*	07 57	*08 46*	10 03	11 03	12 03	13 03	*13 46*	14 03	15 03	16 03	17 03	*17 46*	18 03	.	19 06	*20 16*	*21 21*	*21 36*	.	*22 16*	*23 31*	.	.
Barnsley 34 a	08c00	08 11	09c11	*10 32*	*11 32*	*12 32*	*13 32*	14c11	*14 32*	*15 32*	*16 32*	*17 32*	18c11	*18 33*	.	*19 33*	20c40	.	22c05	.	23q07	.	.	.
Huddersfield 34 a	08r49	09t49	10v49	11t49	12t49	13t49	14t49	.	15t49	16t49	17w50	18t51	.	19t51	.	20y55	21z56	.	*22 56*	.	23c59	.	.	.

Sundays

	NT	NT A	NT	NT	NT A	NT
Lincoln 18 d	.	15 15	17 35	19 35	21 15	.
Saxilby 18 d	.	15 25	17 45	19 45	21 25	.
Gainsborough Lea Road 18 d	.	15 37	17 57	19 57	21 37	.
Retford 10 a	.	15 51	18 11	20 11	21 51	.
London Kings Cross 15 ⊖ 26 d	*12 10*	.	*16 10*	*18 10*	*20 10*	*20 30*
Retford 10 d	14 50	15 51	18 11	20 11	21 51	22 24
Worksop d	15 01	16 03	18 23	20 23	22 03	22 35
Shireoaks d	15 05	16 06	18 26	20 26	22 06	22 39
Kiveton Park d	15 10	16 12	18 32	20 32	22 12	22 44
Kiveton Bridge d	15 13	16 15	18 35	20 35	22 15	22 47
Woodhouse d	15 19	16 21	18 41	20 41	22 21	22 53
Darnall d	15 24	16 26	18 46	20 46	22 26	22 58
Sheffield 7 a	15 33	16 36	18 55	20 56	22 34	23 07
Meadowhall 34 a	15 43	16 44	*19 16*	*21 16*	22 44	*23 46*
Barnsley 34 a	16 04	17 05	19c37	22c09	23 05	.
Huddersfield 34 a	16E53	18G05	20H53	.	.	.

For general notes see front of timetable
For details of catering facilities see Directory of Train Operators

- **A** To Leeds (Table 34)
- **B** To Adwick (Table 29)
- **C** To Hull (Table 29)
- **D** To Doncaster (Table 29)
- **E** From 13 September arr. 1657
- **G** From 13 September arr. 1807
- **H** Change at Sheffield and Meadowhall. From 13 September arr. 2057
- **b** Change at Retford
- **c** Change at Sheffield and Meadowhall
- **e** Change at Sheffield and Meadowhall. From 7 September arr. 2306
- **f** Mondays to Thursdays only. Change at Sheffield and Meadowhall
- **g** From 7 September arr. 3 mins later
- **h** From 7 September arr. 4 mins later
- **j** From 7 September arr. 5 mins later
- **k** Change at Sheffield and Meadowhall. From 7 September arr. 2159
- **m** Change at Sheffield and Meadowhall. From 7 September arr. 2300
- **n** Retford
- **q** Change at Sheffield and Meadowhall. From 12 September arr. 2306
- **r** Change at Sheffield and Meadowhall. From 12 September arr. 0852
- **t** From 12 September arr. 3 mins later
- **v** Change at Sheffield and Meadowhall. From 12 September arr. 1052
- **w** From 12 September arr. 4 mins later
- **y** From 12 September arr. 2100
- **z** Change at Sheffield and Meadowhall. From 12 September arr. 4 mins later

Network Diagram for Tables 31, 32, 33, 34

DM-3/09
Design BAJS

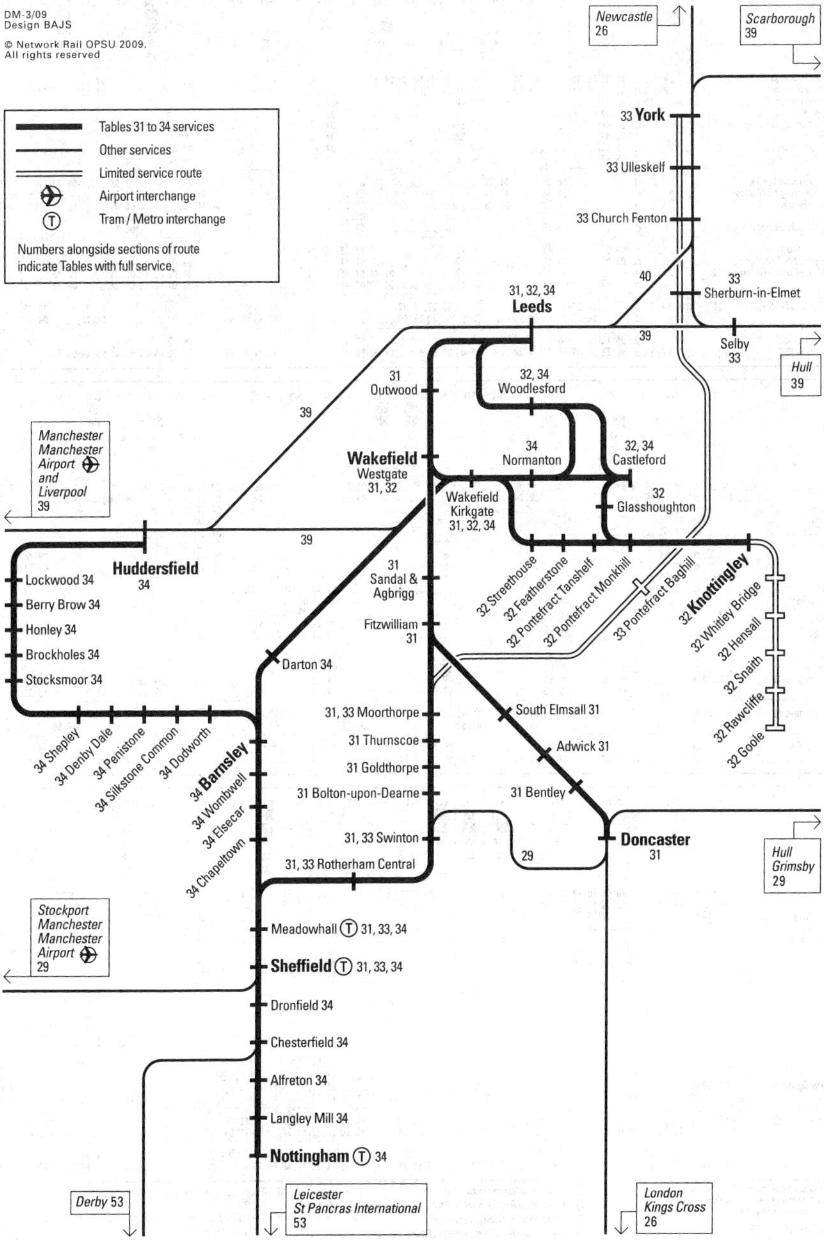
Tables 31 to 34 services
Other services
Limited service route
Airport interchange
Tram / Metro interchange
Numbers alongside sections of route indicate Tables with full service.
Newcastle 26
Scarborough 39
33 York
33 Ulleskelf
33 Church Fenton
40
33 Sherburn-in-Elmet
31, 32, 34 Leeds
39
Selby 33
Hull 39
31 Outwood
32, 34 Woodlesford
39
Manchester
Manchester Airport
and
Liverpool
39
Wakefield Westgate 31, 32
34 Normanton
32, 34 Castleford
Wakefield Kirkgate 31, 32, 34
32 Glasshoughton
39
Huddersfield 34
Lockwood 34
Berry Brow 34
Honley 34
Brockholes 34
Stocksmoor 34
31 Sandal & Agbrigg
Fitzwilliam 31
Darton 34
32 Streethouse
32 Featherstone
32 Pontefract Tanshelf
32 Pontefract Monkhill
33 Pontefract Baghill
32 Knottingley
32 Whitley Bridge
32 Hensall
32 Snaith
32 Rawcliffe
32 Goole
34 Shepley
34 Denby Dale
34 Penistone
34 Silkstone Common
34 Dodworth
34 Barnsley
34 Wombwell
34 Elsecar
34 Chapeltown
31, 33 Moorthorpe
31 Thurnscoe
31 Goldthorpe
31 Bolton-upon-Dearne
31, 33 Swinton
31, 33 Rotherham Central
South Elmsall 31
Adwick 31
31 Bentley
Doncaster 31
29
Hull
Grimsby
29
Stockport
Manchester
Manchester Airport
29
Meadowhall 31, 33, 34
Sheffield 31, 33, 34
Dronfield 34
Chesterfield 34
Alfreton 34
Langley Mill 34
Nottingham 34
Derby 53
Leicester
St Pancras International
53
London
Kings Cross
26

Sheffield, Doncaster and Wakefield → Leeds

Network Diagram - see first page of Table 31

Miles	Miles				NT	NT	NT	NT	NT	NT	NT	NT	XC	NT	NT	NT	NT	NT	NT	GR	NT	NT	GR	NT	NT
													1 ◇							R 1			R 1		
									A		B	C	D			E	C	A		G		H	G		J
													🛒							🍴			🍴		
—	0	**Sheffield 7**	29 ⇌	d	05 22	05 50		06 06		06 28	06 49	07 06	07 12		07 14	07 18						07 51		08 06	
—	3½	Meadowhall	29 ⇌	d	05 28	05 56		06 12		06 34	06 55	07 12			07 21	07 24						07 57		08 12	
—	6¾	Rotherham Central	29	d	05 34					06 40					07 27										
—	10¾	Swinton (S.Yorks)	29	d	05 42					06 51					07 35										
—	13	Bolton-upon-Dearne		d	05 46					06 56					07 39										
—	14¼	Goldthorpe		d	05 49					06 58					07 42				←						
—	15	Thurnscoe		d	05 52					07 01					07 45				07 45						
—	18½	Moorthorpe		d	05 57					07 06					→				07 50						
0	—	**Doncaster 7**		d			06 25		06 59					07 14				07 32		07 51	07 58		08 12		08 16
1¾	—	Bentley (S.Yorks)		d			06 28		07 02					07 17				07 35			08 01				08 19
4	—	Adwick		a			06 32		07 08					07 21				07 40			08 05				08 25
—	—			d			06 32							07 21							08 05				
8¾	—	South Elmsall		d			06 38							07 27							08 11				
13¼	22¼	Fitzwilliam		d	06 02		06 43			07 12				07 35					07 56		08 16				
18	27	Sandal & Agbrigg		d	06 08		06 49			07 18				07 41					08 02		08 22				
19¾	28¾	**Wakefield Westgate 7**	32, 39	a	06 12		06 53			07 22			07 36	07 45					08 06	08 10	08 26		08 36		
—	—			d	06 13		06 53			07 23			07 37	07 45			←		08 07	08 10	08 26		08 36		
—	—	Wakefield Kirkgate 4	32, 34, 39	a		06 27		06 49			07 27	07 49				07 57	07 49					08 27		08 49	
—	—			d		06 28		06 50			07 28	07 50				07 58	07 50					08 28		08 50	
22¼	31¼	Outwood		d	06 18		06 58			07 28		→		07 50					08 12		08 31			→	
29¾	38¾	**Leeds 10**	32, 34	a	06 35	06 49	07 14	07 28		07 44	07 51		07 52	08 04		08 21	08 25		08 30	08 32	08 46	08 49	08 52		

			NT	NT	XC	NT	NT	NT	NT	NT	GR	GR	NT	NT	NT	NT	NT	NT	XC	NT	GR	NT	NT	NT
					1 ◇						R 1	R 1							1 ◇		R 1			
				E	D		E				G	G			C			E	K	E	G			L
					🛒						🍴 🛒								🛒					
Sheffield 7	29 ⇌	d	08 14	08 18	08 21		←						08 51			09 06	09 14	09 18	09 21	←				09 29
Meadowhall	29 ⇌	d	08 23	08 24			08 24						08 57			09 12	09 21	09 24		09 24				09 35
Rotherham Central	29	d	08 29	→													09 27	→						09 42
Swinton (S.Yorks)	29	d	08 38														09 36							09 51
Bolton-upon-Dearne		d	08 42														09 41							
Goldthorpe		d	08 45							←							09 43						←	
Thurnscoe		d	08 48							08 48							09 46						09 46	
Moorthorpe		d	→							08 53							→						09 51	10a01
Doncaster 7		d				08 26		08 52			08 58			09 14	09 49									
Bentley (S.Yorks)		d				08 29		08 55						09 17	09 52									
Adwick		a				08 33		09 01						09 21	09 58									
		d				08 33								09 21										
South Elmsall		d				08 39								09 27										
Fitzwilliam		d				08 46				08 59				09 32									09 57	
Sandal & Agbrigg		d				08 52				09 05				09 38									10 03	
Wakefield Westgate 7	32, 39	a			08 46	08 56				09 09	09 16			09 42					09 46				10 07	
		d			08 47	08 56			←	09 09	09 16	09 30		09 42					09 47		10 01	←	10 08	
Wakefield Kirkgate 4	32, 34, 39	a					08 57		08 49				09 27			09 49				09 57		09 49		
		d					08 58		08 50				09 28			09 50				09 58		09 50		
Outwood		d				09 01				09 14				09 47		→							10 13	
Leeds 10	32, 34	a			09 02	09 14	09 19		09 25	09 30	09 36	09 46	09 49	10 02					10 02	10 18	10 21	10 25	10 30	

			NT	NT	NT	NT	NT	XC	GR	GR	NT	NT	NT	NT	NT	GR	NT	NT	NT	XC	NT	NT	NT	NT
								1 ◇	R 1	R 1						R 1				1 ◇				
							E	N	G	G	E	Q				G			E	N		E		
								🛒	🍴							🍴 🛒				🛒				
Sheffield 7	29 ⇌	d	09 51		10 06	10 14	10 18	10 21			←				10 51		11 06	11 14	11 18	11 21		←		
Meadowhall	29 ⇌	d	09 57		10 12	10 21	10 24				10 24				10 57		11 12	11 21	11 24			11 24		
Rotherham Central	29	d				10 27	→											11 27	→					
Swinton (S.Yorks)	29	d				10 36												11 36						
Bolton-upon-Dearne		d				10 41												11 41						
Goldthorpe		d				10 43								←				11 43						←
Thurnscoe		d				10 46								10 46				11 46						11 46
Moorthorpe		d				→								10 51				→						11 51
Doncaster 7		d		10 14					10 30			10 46				11 19					11 26			
Bentley (S.Yorks)		d		10 17								10 49									11 29			
Adwick		a		10 21								10 55									11 33			
		d		10 21																	11 33			
South Elmsall		d		10 27																	11 39			
Fitzwilliam		d		10 32										10 57							11 44			11 57
Sandal & Agbrigg		d		10 38										11 03							11 50			12 03
Wakefield Westgate 7	32, 39	a		10 42				10 46	10 51					11 07		11 36				11 46	11 54			12 07
		d		10 42				10 47	10 51	10 57			←	11 08		11 36				11 47	11 54		←	12 08
Wakefield Kirkgate 4	32, 34, 39	a	10 27		10 49						10 57		10 49		11 27		11 49					11 57	11 49	
		d	10 28		10 50						10 58		10 50		11 28		11 50					11 58	11 50	
Outwood		d		10 47	→									11 13			→				11 59			12 13
Leeds 10	32, 34	a	10 48	11 02				11 02	11 09	11 18	11 18		11 25	11 30	11 48	11 55				12 02	12 14	12 18	12 25	12 30

For general notes see front of timetable
For details of catering facilities see Directory of Train Operators

- **A** From Sheffield (Table 29)
- **B** From Chesterfield (Table 34)
- **C** From Worksop (Table 30)
- **D** From Birmingham New Street to Edinburgh (Table 51)
- **E** From Nottingham (Table 34)
- **G** From London Kings Cross (Table 26)
- **H** From Retford (Table 30)
- **J** From Scunthorpe (22 June to 4 September from Thorne North) (Table 29)
- **K** From Bristol Temple Meads to Edinburgh (Table 51)
- **L** To York (Table 33)
- **N** From Plymouth to Edinburgh (Table 51)
- **Q** From Lincoln (Table 30)

Sheffield, Doncaster and Wakefield → Leeds

Network Diagram - see first page of Table 31

		NT	GR	NT	GR	NT	NT	NT		XC	NT	NT	NT	NT	NT	GR	NT	GR	NT	NT		NT	XC	NT	NT
			R 1		R 1					1 ◇						R 1		R 1					1 ◇		
		A	B		B			C		D		C		A		B		B				C	E		C
Sheffield 7	29 d			11 51		12 06	12 14	12 18		12 21		←					12 51		13 06	13 14		13 18	13 21		←
Meadowhall	29 d			11 57		12 12	12 21	12 24				12 24					12 57		13 12	13 21		13 24			13 24
Rotherham Central	29 d						12 27	→												13 27		→			
Swinton (S.Yorks)	29 d						12 36													13 36					
Bolton-upon-Dearne	d						12 41													13 41					
Goldthorpe	d						12 43								←					13 43					
Thurnscoe	d						12 46								12 46					13 46					
Moorthorpe	d						→								12 51					→					
Doncaster 7	d	11 38	11 59		12 19						12 25			12 36		12 58								13 27	
Bentley (S.Yorks)	d	11 41									12 28			12 40										13 30	
Adwick	a	11 47									12 32			12 45										13 34	
	d										12 32													13 34	
South Elmsall	d										12 38													13 40	
Fitzwilliam	d										12 43				12 57									13 45	
Sandal & Agbrigg	d										12 49				13 03									13 51	
Wakefield Westgate 7	32, 39 a		12 16		12 36					12 46	12 53				13 07	13 17							13 46	13 55	
	d		12 16		12 36					12 47	12 53		←		13 08	13 17		13 37					13 47	13 55	
Wakefield Kirkgate 4	32, 34, 39 a			12 27		12 49						12 57	12 49				13 27		13 50						13 57
	d			12 28		12 50						12 58	12 50				13 28		13 50						13 58
Outwood	d					→					12 58				13 13				→					14 00	
Leeds 10	32, 34 a		12 36	12 48	12 54					13 02	13 13	13 18	13 25		13 33	13 41	13 48	13 55					14 02	14 14	14 18

		NT	NT	NT	GR	NT	NT	GR	NT	NT		NT	XC	NT	NT	NT	NT	NT	GR	NT	NT	NT		NT	NT
					R 1 Ø			R 1					1 ◇						R 1 Ø						
			A		B	G		B				C	H		C		A		B						C
Sheffield 7	29 d					13 28	13 51		14 06	14 14		14 18	14 21		←					14 51		15 06		15 14	15 18
Meadowhall	29 d					13 35	13 57		14 12	14 21		14 24			14 24					14 57		15 12		15 21	15 24
Rotherham Central	29 d					13 41				14 27		→												15 27	→
Swinton (S.Yorks)	29 d					13 50				14 36														15 36	
Bolton-upon-Dearne	d									14 41														15 41	
Goldthorpe	d			←						14 43								←						15 43	
Thurnscoe	d			13 46						14 46								14 46						15 46	
Moorthorpe	d			13 51		14a01				→								14 51						→	
Doncaster 7	d		13 38		13 57			14 21						14 27			14 38		14 53		15 14				
Bentley (S.Yorks)	d		13 41											14 30			14 41				15 17				
Adwick	a		13 47											14 34			14 47				15 21				
	d													14 34							15 21				
South Elmsall	d													14 40							15 27				
Fitzwilliam	d			13 57										14 45				14 57			15 32				
Sandal & Agbrigg	d			14 03										14 51				15 03			15 38				
Wakefield Westgate 7	32, 39 a			14 07	14 14			14 39					14 46	14 55				15 07	15 14		15 42				
	d	←		14 08	14 14			14 39					14 47	14 55		←		15 08	15 14		15 42				
Wakefield Kirkgate 4	32, 34, 39 a	13 50					14 27		14 49						14 57	14 49				15 27		15 49			
	d	13 50					14 28		14 50						14 58	14 50				15 28		15 50			
Outwood	d			14 13					→					15 00				15 13			15 47	→			
Leeds 10	32, 34 a	14 25		14 30	14 35		14 48	15 01					15 02	15 15	15 18	15 25		15 30	15 35	15 48	16 02				

		XC	GR	NT	NT	NT	NT	GR	NT	GR	NT	NT		NT	NT	NT	XC	NT	NT	NT	GR	NT	GR	NT	NT
		1 ◇	R 1					R 1		R 1							1 ◇				R 1 Ø		R 1		
		J	B	C		A		B		B		A				C	K	C			B		B		
Sheffield 7	29 d	15 21		←					15 51					16 06	16 14	16 18	16 21	←				16 51		17 06	17 14
Meadowhall	29 d			15 24					15 57					16 12	16 21	16 24		16 24				16 57		17 12	17 21
Rotherham Central	29 d														16 27	→									17 27
Swinton (S.Yorks)	29 d														16 36										17 36
Bolton-upon-Dearne	d														16 41										17 40
Goldthorpe	d						←								16 43					←					17 43
Thurnscoe	d						15 46								16 46					16 46					17 46
Moorthorpe	d						15 51								→					16 51					→
Doncaster 7	d		15 29			15 38		15 55		16 10	16 14	16 38									17 01		17 19		
Bentley (S.Yorks)	d					15 41					16 17	16 41													
Adwick	a					15 47					16 21	16 47													
	d										16 21														
South Elmsall	d										16 27														
Fitzwilliam	d						15 57				16 32									16 57					
Sandal & Agbrigg	d						16 03				16 38									17 03					
Wakefield Westgate 7	32, 39 a	15 46	15 51				16 08	16 15		16 30	16 42						16 46			17 07	17 18		17 36		
	d	15 47	15 51		←		16 08	16 15		16 30	16 42						16 47		←	17 08	17 18		17 36		
Wakefield Kirkgate 4	32, 34, 39 a			15 57	15 49				16 27					16 49				16 57	16 49			17 28		17 49	
	d			15 58	15 50				16 28					16 50				16 58	16 50			17 28		17 50	
Outwood	d						16 13				16 50			→						17 13				→	
Leeds 10	32, 34 a	16 02	16 09	16 19	16 25		16 30	16 35	16 48	16 48	17 02						17 02	17 18	17 25	17 30	17 36	17 48	17 56		

For general notes see front of timetable
For details of catering facilities see Directory of Train Operators

- **A** From Lincoln (Table 30)
- **B** From London Kings Cross (Table 26)
- **C** From Nottingham (Table 34)
- **D** From Plymouth to Edinburgh (Table 51)
- **E** From Penzance (Table 135) to Edinburgh (Table 51)
- **G** To York (Table 33)
- **H** From Plymouth (Table 51) to Aberdeen (Table 229)
- **J** From Penzance (Table 135) to Glasgow Central (Table 51)
- **K** From Plymouth (Table 51) to Dundee (Table 229)

Sheffield, Doncaster and Wakefield → Leeds

Network Diagram - see first page of Table 31

			NT		XC	NT	NT	GR	NT	NT	XC	NT	NT	GR	NT		NT	NT	XC	NT	GR	NT	NT	NT	GR	NT
					1 ◇			R 1			1 ◇			R 1					1 ◇		R 1				R 1	
			A		B		A	C		D	E			C				A	G		C	A			H	
					⊥						⊥			Ø ⊥					⊥		Ø ⊥				Ø ⊥	
Sheffield 7	29 🚊	d	17 18		17 21		←				17 47		17 51		18 06		18 14	18 18	18 21			←				18 51
Meadowhall	29 🚊	d	17 24				17 24						17 57		18 12		18 21	18 24				18 24				18 57
Rotherham Central	29	d	→														18 27	→								
Swinton (S.Yorks)	29	d															18 36									
Bolton-upon-Dearne		d															18 41									
Goldthorpe		d										←					18 43							←		
Thurnscoe		d										17 46					18 46							18 46		
Moorthorpe		d										17 51					→							18 51		
Doncaster 7		d				17 27				17 38				18 19						18 27	18 43				19 17	
Bentley (S.Yorks)		d				17 30				17 41										18 30						
Adwick		a				17 34				17 47										18 34						
		d				17 34														18 34						
South Elmsall		d				17 40														18 40						
Fitzwilliam		d				17 45						18 10								18 46				19 01		
Sandal & Agbrigg		d				17 51						18 16								18 51				19 07		
Wakefield Westgate 7	32, 39	a			17 46	17 55					18 12	18 20		18 36					18 46	18 55	19 00			19 12	19 34	
		d			17 47	17 55		18 04	←		18 13	18 20		18 36					18 47	18 56	19 00		←	19 12	19 34	
Wakefield Kirkgate 4	32, 34, 39	a					17 57		17 49				18 28		18 50							18 58	18 50			19 29
		d					17 58		17 50				18 32		18 50							18 58	18 50			19 32
Outwood		d				18 00						18 25			→					19 00				19 17		
Leeds 10	32, 34	a			18 04	18 15	18 18	18 23	18 25		18 30	18 42	18 51	18 55					19 02	19 15	19 20	19 23	19 27	19 33	19 52	19 55

			NT	NT	NT		XC	NT	NT	GR	GR	NT	NT	NT	NT	GR	NT		XC	NT	NT	NT	GR	NT	GR	NT
							1 ◇			R 1	R 1					R 1			1 ◇				R 1		R 1	
					A		G		A	C	J					C	A		K	A			C		C	
							⊥			⊡ ⊥	Ø ⊥					Ø ⊥							✕ ⊥		✕ ⊥	
Sheffield 7	29 🚊	d	19 06	19 18	19 22		19 26		←					19 51	20 06		20 18		20 21	←				20 27		21 09
Meadowhall	29 🚊	d	19 12	19 25	19 28				19 28					19 57	20 12		20 24			20 24				20 35		21 15
Rotherham Central	29	d		19 31	→												→							20 41		→
Swinton (S.Yorks)	29	d		19 40																				20 50		
Bolton-upon-Dearne		d		19 44																				20 55		
Goldthorpe		d		19 47									←											20 57		
Thurnscoe		d		19 50									19 50											21 00		
Moorthorpe		d		→									19 55											21 05		
Doncaster 7		d						19 27		19 42	19 48					20 19						20 38	20 50		21 20	
Bentley (S.Yorks)		d						19 30														20 41				
Adwick		a						19 34														20 45				
		d						19 34														20 45				
South Elmsall		d						19 40														20 51				
Fitzwilliam		d						19 46					20 05									21 01		21 11		
Sandal & Agbrigg		d						19 51					20 11									21 06		21 17		
Wakefield Westgate 7	32, 39	a					19 49	19 55		20 01	20 07		20 15			20 38			20 53			21 10	21 15	21 22	21 37	
		d					19 50	19 56		20 01	20 07	←	20 16			20 38			20 54		←	21 11	21 15	21 22	21 37	
Wakefield Kirkgate 4	32, 34, 39	a	19 50						19 58			19 50		20 28	20 49					20 57	20 49					
		d	19 50						19 58			19 50		20 28	20 50					20 58	20 50					
Outwood		d	→					20 00					20 21		→							21 15		21 27		
Leeds 10	32, 34	a					20 06	20 17	20 19	20 21	20 24	20 26	20 36	20 48		20 55			21 09	21 18	21 25	21 27	21 35	21 47	21 55	

			XC	EM	NT	NT	GR		NT	GR	NT	NT	EM	NT	NT	NT	NT	XC	EM		GR	NT	NT	NT
											FX				FX	FO						FX	FO	FX
			1 ◇	1 ◇			R 1			R 1			1 ◇					1 ◇	1 ◇		R 1			
			L	N			C			C			N					L	N		C			
				⊡			Ø ⊥			⊡ ⊥			⊡					⊥	⊡		⊡ ⊥			
Sheffield 7	29 🚊	d	21 21	21 25		←			21 30		22 06	22 15	22 19		←			22 32	22 48			23 15	23 15	23 24
Meadowhall	29 🚊	d				21 15			21 36		22 12	22 21			22 12							23 21	23 21	23 30
Rotherham Central	29	d							21 42		→	22 27										23 27	23 27	
Swinton (S.Yorks)	29	d							21 50			22 36										23 36	23 36	
Bolton-upon-Dearne		d							21 55			22 41					←					23 41	23 41	
Goldthorpe		d							21 57			22 43					22 43					23 44	23 44	
Thurnscoe		d							22 00			→					22 46					23 47	23 47	
Moorthorpe		d							22 05								22 51					23 52	23 52	
Doncaster 7		d			21 38		21 53			22 18				22 30							23 24			
Bentley (S.Yorks)		d			21 41									22 33										
Adwick		a			21 45									22 37										
		d			21 45									22 37										
South Elmsall		d			21 51									22 43										
Fitzwilliam		d			21 58				22 11					22 48			22 57							
Sandal & Agbrigg		d			22 04				22 17					22 54			23 03							
Wakefield Westgate 7	32, 39	a	21 48	21 54	22 08		22 13		22 21	22 35			22 46	22 58			23 07	23 11	23 17		23 42	00 09		00 17
		d	21 49	21 55	22 09		22 13		22 21	22 35			22 47	22 58			23 08	23 12	23 18		23 42	00 10		
Wakefield Kirkgate 4	32, 34, 39	a				21 52									22 49									00s10
		d				21 52									22 50	22 50								
Outwood		d			22 14				22 26					23 03			23 13							
Leeds 10	32, 34	a	22 08	22 12	22 28	22 28	22 33		22 46	22 53			23 05	23 18	23 28	23 28	23 30	23 30	23 36		23 59	00 30	00 30	

For general notes see front of timetable
For details of catering facilities see Directory of Train Operators

- **A** From Nottingham (Table 34)
- **B** From Plymouth to Glasgow Central (Table 51)
- **C** From London Kings Cross (Table 26)
- **D** From Lincoln (Table 30)
- **E** From Reading to Newcastle (Table 51)
- **G** From Plymouth to Edinburgh (Table 51)
- **H** From London Kings Cross to Bradford Forster Square (Table 26)
- **J** From London Kings Cross to Skipton (Table 26)
- **K** From Plymouth to York (Table 51)
- **L** From Plymouth (Table 51)
- **N** From St Pancras International (Table 53)

Saturdays

Sheffield, Doncaster and Wakefield → Leeds

Network Diagram - see first page of Table 31

	NT	NT	NT	NT	NT	XC	NT		NT	NT	NT	NT	NT	NT	NT		NT	XC	NT	NT	NT	NT	NT	GR
			A			1 ◇ B 🛒				A		C		D			E	1 ◇ B 🛒		E				R 1 G 🍴 🛒
Sheffield 7 29 🚋 d		06 06		06 28	07 06	07 12			←		07 14	07 51	08 06		08 14		08 18	08 21		←				
Meadowhall 29 🚋 d		06 12		06 34	07 12				07 12		07 21	07 57	08 12		08 23		08 24			08 24				
Rotherham Central 29 d				06 40	→						07 27				08 29		→							
Swinton (S.Yorks) 29 d				06 48							07 35				08 38									
Bolton-upon-Dearne d				06 52							07 39				08 42									
Goldthorpe d				06 55							07 42				08 45								←	
Thurnscoe d				06 58							07 45				08 48								08 48	
Moorthorpe d				07 03							07 50				→								08 53	
Doncaster 7 d	06 25		07 00				07 14			07 32				08 16					08 26		08 50			08 58
Bentley (S.Yorks) d	06 28		07 03				07 17			07 35				08 19					08 29		08 53			
Adwick a	06 32		07 09				07 21			07 41				08 25					08 33		08 59			
Adwick d	06 32						07 21												08 33					
South Elmsall d	06 38						07 27												08 39					
Fitzwilliam d	06 43			07 09			07 35				07 56								08 46				08 59	
Sandal & Agbrigg d	06 49			07 15			07 41				08 02								08 52				09 05	
Wakefield Westgate 7 32, 39 a	06 53			07 19		07 36	07 45				08 06							08 46	08 56				09 09	09 15
Wakefield Westgate d	06 53			07 19		07 37	07 45				08 07							08 47	08 56			←	09 09	09 15
Wakefield Kirkgate 4 32, 34, 39 a		06 49							07 49			08 27	08 49							08 57		08 50		
Wakefield Kirkgate d		06 50							07 50			08 28	08 50							08 58		08 50		
Outwood d	06 58			07 24			07 50				08 12		→						09 01				09 14	
Leeds 10 32, 34 a	07 14	07 28		07 44		07 52	08 04		08 25		08 30	08 49						09 02	09 14	09 19		09 25	09 30	09 36

	NT		NT	NT	NT	NT	NT	XC	NT		NT	NT	GR	NT	NT	NT	NT		NT	NT	NT	XC	NT	NT
				A			E	1 ◇ H 🛒	E				R 1 G 🍴 🛒	J			K				E	1 ◇ L 🛒	E	
Sheffield 7 29 🚋 d	08 51				09 06	09 14	09 18	09 21	←					09 31	09 51				10 06	10 14	10 18	10 21	←	
Meadowhall 29 🚋 d	08 57				09 12	09 21	09 24		09 24					09 37	09 57				10 12	10 21	10 24		10 24	
Rotherham Central 29 d						09 27	→							09 44						10 27	→			
Swinton (S.Yorks) 29 d						09 36								09 52						10 36				
Bolton-upon-Dearne d						09 41														10 41				
Goldthorpe d						09 43						←								10 43				
Thurnscoe d						09 46						09 46								10 46				
Moorthorpe d						→						09 51		10a01						→				
Doncaster 7 d			09 14	09 37									09 57			10 14	10 37							
Bentley (S.Yorks) d			09 17	09 44												10 17	10 41							
Adwick a			09 21	09 50												10 21	10 47							
Adwick d			09 21													10 21								
South Elmsall d			09 27													10 27								
Fitzwilliam d			09 32									09 57				10 32								
Sandal & Agbrigg d			09 38									10 03				10 38								
Wakefield Westgate 7 32, 39 a			09 42					09 46				10 07	10 14			10 42						10 46		
Wakefield Westgate d			09 42					09 47			←	10 08	10 16			10 42						10 47		←
Wakefield Kirkgate 4 32, 34, 39 a	09 27				09 49				09 57		09 49				10 27				10 49				10 57	10 49
Wakefield Kirkgate d	09 28				09 50				09 58		09 50				10 28				10 50				10 58	10 50
Outwood d			09 47		→							10 13				10 47			→					
Leeds 10 32, 34 a	09 49		10 02					10 03	10 18		10 25	10 30	10 35		10 48	11 02						11 02	11 18	11 25

	NT	GR	NT		NT	NT	NT	NT	NT	XC	NT		NT	NT	GR	NT	NT	NT	NT		NT	NT	XC	NT
		R 1 G 🍴 🛒				K			E	1 ◇ L 🛒	E				R 1 G 🍴 🛒			K				E	1 ◇ L 🛒	E
Sheffield 7 29 🚋 d			10 51				11 06	11 14	11 18	11 21	←					11 51			12 06		12 14	12 18	12 21	←
Meadowhall 29 🚋 d			10 57				11 12	11 21	11 24		11 24					11 57			12 12		12 21	12 24		12 24
Rotherham Central 29 d								11 27	→												12 27	→		
Swinton (S.Yorks) 29 d								11 36													12 36			
Bolton-upon-Dearne d								11 41													12 41			
Goldthorpe d	←							11 43						←							12 43			
Thurnscoe d	10 46							11 46						11 46							12 46			
Moorthorpe d	10 51							→						11 51							→			
Doncaster 7 d		10 48			11 14	11 38									11 54		12 14	12 36						
Bentley (S.Yorks) d					11 17	11 41											12 17	12 40						
Adwick a					11 21	11 47											12 21	12 45						
Adwick d					11 21												12 21							
South Elmsall d					11 27												12 27							
Fitzwilliam d	10 57				11 32									11 57			12 32							
Sandal & Agbrigg d	11 03				11 38									12 03			12 38							
Wakefield Westgate 7 32, 39 a	11 07	11 11			11 42					11 46				12 07	12 13		12 42						12 46	
Wakefield Westgate d	11 08	11 13			11 42					11 47			←	12 08	12 13		12 42						12 47	
Wakefield Kirkgate 4 32, 34, 39 a			11 27				11 49				11 57		11 49			12 27			12 49					12 57
Wakefield Kirkgate d			11 28				11 50				11 58		11 50			12 28			12 50					12 58
Outwood d	11 13				11 47		→							12 13			12 47		→					
Leeds 10 32, 34 a	11 30	11 35	11 48		12 02					12 02	12 18		12 25	12 30	12 35	12 48	13 02						13 03	13 18

For general notes see front of timetable
For details of catering facilities see Directory of Train Operators

A From Sheffield (Table 29)
B From Birmingham New Street to Edinburgh (Table 51)
C From Retford (Table 30)
D From Scunthorpe (27 June to 5 September from Thorne North) (Table 29)
E From Nottingham (Table 34)
G From London Kings Cross (Table 26)
H From Bristol Temple Meads (Table 51) to Edinburgh (Table 26)
J To York (Table 33)
K From Lincoln (Table 30)
L From Plymouth to Edinburgh (Table 51)

Sheffield, Doncaster and Wakefield → Leeds

Network Diagram - see first page of Table 31

	NT	NT	GR	NT	NT	NT	NT	NT	NT	XC	NT	NT	NT	GR	NT	NT	NT	NT	NT	NT	NT
			R 1 A			B			C	1 ◇ D	C			R 1 A	E			B			C
Sheffield 7 — 29 d				12 51			13 06	13 14	13 18	13 21	←				13 28	13 51			14 06	14 14	14 18
Meadowhall — 29 d				12 57			13 12	13 21	13 24		13 24				13 35	13 57			14 12	14 21	14 24
Rotherham Central — 29 d								13 27	→						13 42					14 27	→
Swinton (S.Yorks) — 29 d								13 36							13 50					14 36	
Bolton-upon-Dearne d								13 41												14 41	
Goldthorpe d		←						13 43					←							14 43	
Thurnscoe d		12 46						13 46					13 46							14 46	
Moorthorpe d		12 51						→					13 51		14a00					→	
Doncaster 7 d			12 59		13 14	13 38								13 53			14 14	14 38			
Bentley (S.Yorks) d					13 17	13 41											14 17	14 41			
Adwick a					13 21	13 47											14 21	14 47			
Adwick d					13 21												14 21				
South Elmsall d					13 27												14 27				
Fitzwilliam d		12 57			13 32								13 57				14 32				
Sandal & Agbrigg d		13 03			13 38								14 03				14 38				
Wakefield Westgate 7 — 32, 39 a		13 07	13 16		13 42					13 46			14 07	14 13			14 42				
Wakefield Westgate d	←	13 08	13 16		13 42					13 47		←	14 08	14 13			14 42				
Wakefield Kirkgate 4 — 32, 34, 39 a	12 49			13 27			13 50				13 57	13 50				14 27			14 49		
Wakefield Kirkgate d	12 50			13 28			13 50				13 58	13 50				14 28			14 50		
Outwood d		13 13			13 47		→						14 13				14 47		→		
Leeds 10 — 32, 34 a	13 25	13 33	13 35	13 48	14 02					14 02	14 18	14 25	14 30	14 35		14 48	15 02				

	XC	NT	NT	NT	GR	NT	NT	NT	NT	NT	NT	XC	NT	NT	NT	NT	GR	NT	NT	NT	XC	NT
	1 ◇ G	C			R 1 A			B			C	1 ◇ H	C				R 1 A			C	1 ◇ J	
Sheffield 7 — 29 d	14 21	←				14 51			15 06	15 14	15 18	15 21	←			15 51		16 06	16 14	16 18	16 21	
Meadowhall — 29 d		14 24				14 57			15 12	15 21	15 24		15 24			15 57		16 12	16 21	16 24		
Rotherham Central — 29 d										15 27	→								16 27	→		
Swinton (S.Yorks) — 29 d										15 36									16 36			
Bolton-upon-Dearne d										15 41									16 41			
Goldthorpe d				←						15 43					←				16 43			
Thurnscoe d				14 46						15 46					15 46				16 46			
Moorthorpe d				14 51						→					15 51				→			
Doncaster 7 d					14 58		15 14	15 38									16 21					16 27
Bentley (S.Yorks) d							15 17	15 41														16 30
Adwick a							15 21	15 47														16 34
Adwick d							15 21															16 34
South Elmsall d							15 27															16 40
Fitzwilliam d				14 57			15 32								15 57							16 45
Sandal & Agbrigg d				15 03			15 38								16 03							16 51
Wakefield Westgate 7 — 32, 39 a	14 46			15 07	15 15		15 42					15 46			16 08		16 38				16 46	16 55
Wakefield Westgate d	14 47		←	15 08	15 15		15 42					15 47		←	16 08		16 38				16 47	16 55
Wakefield Kirkgate 4 — 32, 34, 39 a		14 57	14 49			15 27			15 49				15 57	15 49		16 27		16 49				
Wakefield Kirkgate d		14 58	14 50			15 28			15 50				15 58	15 50		16 28		16 50				
Outwood d				15 13			15 47		→						16 13			→				17 02
Leeds 10 — 32, 34 a	15 02	15 18	15 25	15 30	15 35	15 48	16 02					16 02	16 19	16 25	16 30	16 48	17 01				17 02	17 16

	NT	NT	NT	NT	NT	GR	NT	NT	NT	XC	NT	NT	NT	NT	NT	XC	NT	GR	NT	NT	NT
	C			B		R 1 A			C	1 ◇ K		C		B		1 ◇ L		R 1 A			C
Sheffield 7 — 29 d	←				16 51		17 06	17 14	17 18	17 21		←				17 47	17 51		18 06	18 14	18 18
Meadowhall — 29 d	16 24				16 57		17 12	17 21	17 24			17 24					17 57		18 12	18 21	18 24
Rotherham Central — 29 d								17 27	→											18 27	→
Swinton (S.Yorks) — 29 d								17 36												18 36	
Bolton-upon-Dearne d								17 41												18 41	
Goldthorpe d			←					17 43							←					18 43	
Thurnscoe d			16 46					17 46							17 46					18 46	
Moorthorpe d			16 51					→							17 51					→	
Doncaster 7 d				16 38		17 16					17 27			17 38				18 18			
Bentley (S.Yorks) d				16 41							17 30			17 41							
Adwick a				16 47							17 34			17 47							
Adwick d											17 34										
South Elmsall d											17 40										
Fitzwilliam d			16 57								17 46				17 57						
Sandal & Agbrigg d			17 03								17 51				18 03						
Wakefield Westgate 7 — 32, 39 a			17 07			17 33				17 47	17 55				18 07	18 14		18 35			
Wakefield Westgate d		←	17 08			17 33				17 47	17 56		←		18 08	18 15		18 35			
Wakefield Kirkgate 4 — 32, 34, 39 a	16 57	16 49			17 28		17 49					17 57	17 49				18 28		18 50		
Wakefield Kirkgate d	16 58	16 50			17 28		17 50					17 58	17 50				18 32		18 50		
Outwood d			17 13				→				18 00				18 13				→		
Leeds 10 — 32, 34 a	17 18	17 25	17 30		17 48	17 53				18 04	18 15	18 18	18 25		18 30	18 32	18 51	18 53			

For general notes see front of timetable
For details of catering facilities see Directory of Train Operators

- **A** From London Kings Cross (Table 26)
- **B** From Lincoln (Table 30)
- **C** From Nottingham (Table 34)
- **D** From Penzance (Table 135) to Edinburgh (Table 51)
- **E** To York (Table 33)
- **G** From Plymouth (Table 51) to Aberdeen (Table 229)
- **H** From Penzance (Table 135) to Glasgow Central (Table 51)
- **J** From Newquay (Table 135) (from 12 September from Plymouth) (Table 51) to Dundee (Table 229)
- **K** From Plymouth to Glasgow Central (Table 51)
- **L** From Reading to Newcastle (Table 51)

Saturdays

Sheffield, Doncaster and Wakefield → Leeds

Network Diagram - see first page of Table 31

		XC 1◇ A	NT	NT B		NT	NT	GR R 1 C	NT	NT	NT	NT B		XC 1◇ A	NT	NT B	GR R 1 D	NT	NT	GR R 1 E		NT	NT	NT B	XC 1◇ G
Sheffield 7	29 d	18 21		←					18 51	19 06	19 14	19 18		19 21		←						19 51	20 06	20 18	20 21
Meadowhall	29 d			18 24					18 57	19 12	19 21	19 24				19 24						19 57	20 12	20 24	
Rotherham Central	29 d										19 27	→												→	
Swinton (S.Yorks)	29 d										19 40														
Bolton-upon-Dearne	d										19 44														
Goldthorpe	d						←				19 47								←						
Thurnscoe	d						18 46				19 50								19 50						
Moorthorpe	d						18 51				→								19 55						
Doncaster 7	d		18 27					19 18							19 27					20 02					
Bentley (S.Yorks)	d		18 30												19 30										
Adwick	a		18 34												19 34										
	d		18 34												19 34										
South Elmsall	d		18 40												19 40										
Fitzwilliam	d		18 45				18 57								19 45				20 01						
Sandal & Agbrigg	d		18 51				19 03								19 51				20 07						
Wakefield Westgate 7	32, 39 a	18 46	18 55				19 07	19 35						19 46	19 55				20 11	20 19					20 46
	d	18 47	18 55			←	19 08	19 35						19 47	19 55		20 00	←	20 11	20 19					20 47
Wakefield Kirkgate 4	32, 34, 39 a			18 58		18 50			19 29	19 50						19 58		19 50				20 28	20 49		
	d			18 58		18 50			19 32	19 50						19 58		19 50				20 28	20 50		
Outwood	d		19 00				19 13			→					20 00				20 16				→		
Leeds 10	32, 34 a	19 02	19 17	19 23		19 27	19 28	19 51	19 55					20 02	20 13	20 19	20 22	20 26	20 32	20 35		20 48			21 05

		NT B	NT	NT	NT	NT H		NT J	XC 1◇ K	EM 1◇ L	NT H	NT	GR R 1 D	NT J		NT	GR R 1 N	EM 1◇ L	NT	XC 1◇ Q	NT	NT	XC 1◇ U		
Sheffield 7	29 d	←			20 27	21 06		21 06	21 21	21 24	←			←		21 30		22 19		22 26		22 34	23 11		
Meadowhall	29 d	20 24			20 35	21 12		21 12			21 12			21 12		21 36						22 40			
Rotherham Central	29 d				20 42	→		→								21 42						22 46			
Swinton (S.Yorks)	29 d				20 50											21 50						22 54			
Bolton-upon-Dearne	d				20 55											21 54						22 58			
Goldthorpe	d				20 57											21 57						23 01			
Thurnscoe	d				21 00											22 00						23 04			
Moorthorpe	d				21 05											22 05						23 09			
Doncaster 7	d			20 45								21 28	21 48				22 22			22 49	22 52				
Bentley (S.Yorks)	d			20 48								21 31									22 55				
Adwick	a			20 52								21 35									22 59				
	d			20 52								21 35									22 59				
South Elmsall	d			20 58								21 41									23 05				
Fitzwilliam	d			21 03	21 11							21 51				22 11					23 10	23 15			
Sandal & Agbrigg	d			21 09	21 17							21 56				22 17					23 16	23 21			
Wakefield Westgate 7	32, 39 a			21 13	21 22				21 46	21 52		22 00	22 05			22 21	22 39	22 44		23 09	23 20	23 25			
	d		←	21 13	21 22				21 47	21 53		22 01	22 05			22 21	22 39	22 45		23 10	23 20	23 26			
Wakefield Kirkgate 4	32, 34, 39 a	20 57	20 49								21 49			21 52											
	d	20 58	20 50								21 50			21 52					22 50						
Outwood	d			21 18	21 27							22 05				22 26					23 25	23 31			
Leeds 10	32, 34 a	21 19	21 25	21 33	21 47				22 07	22 10	22 14	22 18	22 24	22 28		22 46	22 58	23 04	23b28	23 29	23 38	23 46	23 56		

Sundays

until 12 July

		NT	NT	NT	XC 1◇ V	NT		NT	GR R 1 D	NT	NT	NT B		XC 1◇ X	NT B	GR R 1 D	NT	NT B		XC 1◇ Y	NT B	GR R 1 D	NT	NT	NT B
Sheffield 7	29 d	08 39		09 17	09 21	←		09 36		10 39		11 17		11 21	←		11 36	12 16		12 21	←		12 39		13 17
Meadowhall	29 d	08 45		09 23		09 23		09 42		10 45		11 23			11 23		11 42	12 23			12 23		12 45		13 23
Rotherham Central	29 d			→				09 48				→					11 49	→							→
Swinton (S.Yorks)	29 d							09 58									12 00								
Bolton-upon-Dearne	d							10 03									12 04								
Goldthorpe	d							10 05									12 07								
Thurnscoe	d							10 08									12 10								
Moorthorpe	d							10 13									12 15								
Doncaster 7	d		09 10						11 03		11 10					12 00						13 00		13 10	
Bentley (S.Yorks)	d		09 13								11 13													13 13	
Adwick	a		09 17								11 17													13 17	
	d		09 17								11 17													13 17	
South Elmsall	d		09 23								11 23													13 23	
Fitzwilliam	d		09 28					10 19			11 28						12 21							13 28	
Sandal & Agbrigg	d		09 34					10 25			11 34						12 27							13 34	
Wakefield Westgate 7	32, 39 a		09 38		09 44			10 29	11 20		11 38			11 44		12 18	12 31			12 44		13 17		13 38	
	d		09 38		09 45			10 30	11 20		11 38			11 45		12 18	12 31			12 45		13 17		13 38	
Wakefield Kirkgate 4	32, 34, 39 a	09 29				09 52				11 29					11 52						12 52		13 29		
	d	09 32				09 55				11 30					11 53						12 53		13 30		
Outwood	d		09 43					10 35			11 43						12 36							13 43	
Leeds 10	32, 34 a	09 52	09 56		10 02	10 19		10 52	11 39	11 52	11 56			12 02	12 18	12 36	12 53			13 02	13 18	13 36	13 52	13 57	

For general notes see front of timetable
For details of catering facilities see Directory of Train Operators

- **A** From Plymouth to Edinburgh (Table 51)
- **B** From Nottingham (Table 34)
- **C** From London Kings Cross to Skipton (Table 26)
- **D** From London Kings Cross (Table 26)
- **E** From London Kings Cross to Bradford Forster Square (Table 26)
- **G** From Plymouth to York (Table 51)
- **H** Until 11 July
- **J** From 18 July
- **K** From Plymouth (Table 51)
- **L** From St Pancras International (Table 53)
- **N** From Glasgow Central (Table 26)
- **Q** From Bournemouth (from 12 September from Plymouth) (Table 51)
- **U** Until 5 September. From Penzance (Table 135)
- **V** To Edinburgh (Table 26)
- **X** From Birmingham New Street to Edinburgh (Table 51)
- **Y** From Bristol Temple Meads to Edinburgh (Table 51)
- **b** Until 11 July arr. 2312

Sheffield, Doncaster and Wakefield → Leeds

Network Diagram - see first page of Table 31

			XC	NT	GR	NT	NT	XC	NT	GR	NT	NT	NT	XC	NT	GR	NT	NT	NT	XC	NT	GR
			1◇		R 1			1◇		R 1				1◇		R 1				1◇		R 1
			A	B	C		B	D	B	C			B	E	B	C		G	B	H	B	C
Sheffield 7	29	d	13 21	←		13 36	14 17	14 21	←		14 39		15 17	15 21	←		15 36	15 46	16 17	16 21	←	
Meadowhall	29	d		13 23		13 42	14 23		14 23		14 45		15 23		15 23		15 42	15 52	16 23		16 23	
Rotherham Central	29	d				13 49	→						→				15 48	15 58	→			
Swinton (S.Yorks)	29	d				13 57											15 56	16 08				
Bolton-upon-Dearne		d				14 01											16 00					
Goldthorpe		d				14 04											16 03					
Thurnscoe		d				14 07											16 06					
Moorthorpe		d				14 12											16 11	16a17				
Doncaster 7		d			13 59					14 57		15 10				16 00						16 57
Bentley (S.Yorks)		d										15 13										
Adwick		a										15 17										
		d										15 17										
South Elmsall		d										15 23										
Fitzwilliam		d				14 17						15 28					16 17					
Sandal & Agbrigg		d				14 23						15 34					16 23					
Wakefield Westgate 7	32, 39	a	13 44		14 16	14 27		14 44		15 14		15 38		15 44		16 17	16 27			16 44		17 14
		d	13 45		14 16	14 28		14 45		15 14		15 38		15 45		16 17	16 27			16 45		17 14
Wakefield Kirkgate 4	32, 34, 39	a		13 52					14 52		15 29				15 52						16 52	
		d		13 53					14 53		15 30				15 53						16 53	
Outwood		d				14 33						15 43					16 32					
Leeds 10	32, 34	a	14 02	14 18	14 36	14 47		15 02	15 18	15 33	15 53	15 57		16 02	16 18	16 36	16 52			17 02	17 18	17 34

			NT	NT	NT	XC	NT	EM	GR	NT	XC	NT	GR	XC	NT	GR	NT	NT	NT	XC	NT	NT
						1◇		1◇	R 1		1◇		R 1	1◇		R 1				1◇		
			J		B	K	B	L	C		N	B	C	Q	B	C		G	B	E		B
Sheffield 7	29	d	16 39		17 17	17 21	←	17 34		17 36	17 51	18 17		18 21	←		18 39	18 57	19 16	19 21		←
Meadowhall	29	d	16 45		17 23		17 23			17 43		18 23			18 23		18 45	19 04	19 23			19 23
Rotherham Central	29	d			→					17 49		→						19 10	→			
Swinton (S.Yorks)	29	d								17 57								19 18				
Bolton-upon-Dearne		d								18 02												
Goldthorpe		d								18 04												
Thurnscoe		d								18 07												
Moorthorpe		d								18 12								19a28				
Doncaster 7		d		17 10					17 55		18 15					18 50					19 30	
Bentley (S.Yorks)		d		17 13																	19 33	
Adwick		a		17 17																	19 37	
		d		17 17																	19 37	
South Elmsall		d		17 23																	19 43	
Fitzwilliam		d		17 28						18 18											19 48	
Sandal & Agbrigg		d		17 34						18 24											19 54	
Wakefield Westgate 7	32, 39	a		17 38		17 45		18 06	18 12	18 28	18 33			18 47		19 07				19 48	19 58	
		d		17 38		17 46		18 07	18 12	18 29	18 34		18 38	18 48		19 07				19 49	19 58	
Wakefield Kirkgate 4	32, 34, 39	a	17 29				17 52								18 52		19 29					19 52
		d	17 30				17 53								18 53		19 30					19 57
Outwood		d		17 43						18 34											20 03	
Leeds 10	32, 34	a	17 52	17 56		18 02	18 18	18 24	18 32	18 50	18 53		18 59	19 04	19 17	19 27	19 52			20 05	20 20	20 27

			GR	NT	GR	NT	XC	NT	NT	GR	EM	NT	XC	GR	NT	NT	GR	XC	NT	GR	EM
			R 1		R 1		1◇			R 1	1◇		1◇	R 1			R 1	1◇		R 1	1◇
			C		C	B	V	B		C	L		X	C			C	Y	J	C	L
Sheffield 7	29	d		19 36		20 17	20 21	←	20 39		21 03	←	21 21			21 36		22 21	22 39		23 29
Meadowhall	29	d		19 42		20 23		20 23	20 45			20 45				21 42			22 45		
Rotherham Central	29	d		19 49		→			→							21 48					
Swinton (S.Yorks)	29	d		19 57												21 56					
Bolton-upon-Dearne		d		20 02												22 00					
Goldthorpe		d		20 04												22 03					
Thurnscoe		d		20 07												22 06					
Moorthorpe		d		20 12												22 11					
Doncaster 7		d	19 59		20 20					21 10					21 49		22 20			23 27	
Bentley (S.Yorks)		d													21 52						
Adwick		a													21 56						
		d													21 56						
South Elmsall		d													22 02						
Fitzwilliam		d		20 18											22 09	22 16					
Sandal & Agbrigg		d		20 24											22 15	22 22					
Wakefield Westgate 7	32, 39	a	20 16	20 28	20 38		20 46			21 27	21 32		21 44		22 19	22 26	22 37	22 46			23 54
		d	20 16	20 28	20 38		20 47			21 27	21 33		21 45	21 57	22 20	22 27	22 37	22 47			23 55
Wakefield Kirkgate 4	32, 34, 39	a						20 52				21 29							23 28		
		d						20 53				21 30							23 30		
Outwood		d		20 33											22 25	22 32					
Leeds 10	32, 34	a	20 39	20 52	20 59		21 03	21 18		21 46	21 49	21 54	22 06	22 16	22 39	22 52	23 00	23 09	00 08	00 24	00 31

For general notes see front of timetable
For details of catering facilities see Directory of Train Operators

- **A** From Bristol Temple Meads to Edinburgh (Table 51)
- **B** From Nottingham (Table 34)
- **C** From London Kings Cross (Table 26)
- **D** From Plymouth (Table 51) to Aberdeen (Table 229)
- **E** From Plymouth to Edinburgh (Table 51)
- **G** To York (Table 33)
- **H** From Penzance (Table 135) to Glasgow Central (Table 51)
- **J** From Lincoln (Table 30)
- **K** From Plymouth to Glasgow Central (Table 51)
- **L** From St Pancras International (Table 53)
- **N** From Reading to Newcastle (Table 51)
- **Q** From Newquay (Table 135) to Edinburgh (Table 51)
- **V** From Plymouth to York (Table 51)
- **X** From Plymouth (Table 51)
- **Y** From Penzance (Table 135)

Sundays

from 19 July

Sheffield, Doncaster and Wakefield → Leeds

Network Diagram - see first page of Table 31

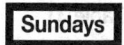

Station		NT	NT	NT	XC	NT	NT	NT	NT	GR	NT	NT		XC	NT	NT	GR	NT	NT	XC	NT	NT	GR	NT	NT
					1 ◇ A (trolley)					R 1 B (restaurant) (trolley)		C		1 ◇ D (trolley)		C	R 1 B (restaurant) (trolley)		C	1 ◇ E (trolley)	C		R 1 B (restaurant) (trolley)		C
Sheffield 7 29 (bus)	d	08 39		09 17	09 21		←	09 36	10 39			11 17		11 21		←		11 36	12 16	12 21	←	12 39			13 17
Meadowhall 29 (bus)	d	08 45		09 23			09 23	09 42	10 45			11 23				11 23		11 42	12 23		12 23	12 45			13 23
Rotherham Central 29	d			→				09 48				→						11 49	→						→
Swinton (S.Yorks) 29	d							09 58										12 00							
Bolton-upon-Dearne	d							10 03										12 04							
Goldthorpe	d							10 05										12 07							
Thurnscoe	d							10 08										12 10							
Moorthorpe	d							10 13										12 15							
Doncaster 7	d		09 10							11 03	11 10						12 00						13 00	13 10	
Bentley (S.Yorks)	d		09 13								11 13													13 13	
Adwick	a		09 17								11 17													13 17	
	d		09 17								11 17													13 17	
South Elmsall	d		09 23								11 23													13 23	
Fitzwilliam	d		09 28					10 19			11 28							12 21						13 28	
Sandal & Agbrigg	d		09 34					10 25			11 34							12 27						13 34	
Wakefield Westgate 7 32, 39	a		09 38		09 44			10 29		11 20	11 38			11 44			12 18	12 31		12 44			13 17	13 38	
	d		09 38		09 45	←		10 30		11 20	11 38			11 45	←		12 18	12 31		12 45			13 17	13 38	
Wakefield Kirkgate 4 32, 34, 39	a	09 29				09 29	09 55		11 29						11 29	11 52					12 52	13 29			
	d	09 30				09 30	09 55		11 30						11 30	11 53					12 53	13 30			
Outwood	d	→	09 43					10 35	→		11 43							12 36				→		13 43	
Leeds 10 32, 34	a		09 56		10 02	10 04	10 15	10 52		11 39	11 56			12 02	12 05	12 18	12 36	12 53		13 02	13 18		13 36	13 57	

Station		XC		NT	NT	GR	NT	NT	XC	NT	GR	NT	NT	NT		XC	NT	NT	GR	NT	NT	NT	XC	NT	GR
		1 ◇ E (trolley)			C	R 1 B (restaurant) (trolley)		C	1 ◇ G (trolley)	C	R 1 B (restaurant) (trolley)			C		1 ◇ H (trolley)		C	R 1 B (restaurant) (trolley)		J	C	1 ◇ K (trolley)	C	R 1 B (restaurant) (trolley)
Sheffield 7 29 (bus)	d	13 21			←		13 36	14 17	14 21	←		14 39		15 17		15 21		←		15 36	15 46	16 17	16 21	←	
Meadowhall 29 (bus)	d				13 23		13 42	14 23		14 23		14 45		15 23				15 23		15 42	15 52	16 23		16 23	
Rotherham Central 29	d						13 49	→						→						15 48	15 58	→			
Swinton (S.Yorks) 29	d						13 57													15 56	16 08				
Bolton-upon-Dearne	d						14 01													16 00					
Goldthorpe	d						14 04													16 03					
Thurnscoe	d						14 07													16 06					
Moorthorpe	d						14 12													16 11	16a17				
Doncaster 7	d					13 59					14 57		15 10						16 00						16 57
Bentley (S.Yorks)	d												15 13												
Adwick	a												15 17												
	d												15 17												
South Elmsall	d												15 23												
Fitzwilliam	d						14 17						15 28							16 17					
Sandal & Agbrigg	d						14 23						15 34							16 23					
Wakefield Westgate 7 32, 39	a	13 44				14 16	14 27		14 44		15 14		15 38			15 44			16 17	16 27			16 44		17 14
	d	13 45		←		14 16	14 28		14 45		15 14		15 38			15 45	←		16 17	16 27			16 45		17 14
Wakefield Kirkgate 4 32, 34, 39	a			13 29	13 52					14 52		15 29					15 29	15 52						16 52	
	d			13 30	13 53					14 53		15 30					15 30	15 53						16 53	
Outwood	d						14 33					→	15 43							16 32					
Leeds 10 32, 34	a	14 02		14 04	14 18	14 36	14 47		15 02	15 18	15 33		15 57			16 02	16 04	16 18	16 36	16 52			17 02	17 18	17 34

Station		NT	NT	NT		XC	NT	NT	EM	GR	NT	XC	GR	EM	NT	XC		NT	GR	NT	NT	NT	XC	NT	NT
		L		C		1 ◇ N (trolley)	L	C	1 ◇ Q (restaurant)	R 1 B (restaurant) (trolley)		1 ◇ U (trolley)	R 1 B (restaurant) (trolley)	1 ◇ V (restaurant)	C	1 ◇ X (trolley)		C	R 1 B (restaurant) (trolley)		J	C	1 ◇ H (trolley)	C	
Sheffield 7 29 (bus)	d	16 39		17 17		17 21		←	17 34		17 36	17 51		18 08	18 17	18 21		←		18 39	18 57	19 16	19 21	←	
Meadowhall 29 (bus)	d	16 45		17 23				17 23			17 43				18 23			18 23		18 45	19 04	19 23		19 23	
Rotherham Central 29	d			→							17 49				→						19 10	→			
Swinton (S.Yorks) 29	d										17 57										19 18				
Bolton-upon-Dearne	d										18 02														
Goldthorpe	d										18 04														
Thurnscoe	d										18 07														
Moorthorpe	d										18 12										19a28				
Doncaster 7	d		17 10							17 55		18 15							18 50						19 30
Bentley (S.Yorks)	d		17 13																						19 33
Adwick	a		17 17																						19 37
	d		17 17																						19 37
South Elmsall	d		17 23																						19 43
Fitzwilliam	d		17 28								18 18														19 48
Sandal & Agbrigg	d		17 34								18 24														19 54
Wakefield Westgate 7 32, 39	a		17 38			17 45			18 06	18 12	18 28	18 33		18 42		18 47			19 07				19 48		19 58
	d		17 38			17 46	←		18 07	18 12	18 29	18 34	18 38	18 43		18 48			19 07				19 49		19 58
Wakefield Kirkgate 4 32, 34, 39	a	17 29					17 29	17 52										18 52		19 29				19 52	
	d	17 30					17 30	17 53										18 53		19 30				19 53	
Outwood	d	→	17 43								18 34														20 03
Leeds 10 32, 34	a		17 56			18 02	18 05	18 18	18 25	18 32	18 50	18 53	18 59	19 00		19 05		19 18	19 27	20 05			20 05	20 18	20 20

For general notes see front of timetable
For details of catering facilities see Directory of Train Operators

- **A** To Edinburgh (Table 26)
- **B** From London Kings Cross (Table 26)
- **C** From Nottingham (Table 34)
- **D** From Birmingham New Street to Edinburgh (Table 51)
- **E** From Bristol Temple Meads to Edinburgh (Table 51)
- **G** From Plymouth (Table 51) (from 8 November from Birmingham New Street) to Aberdeen (Table 229)
- **H** From Plymouth (from 8 November from Birmingham New Street) to Edinburgh (Table 51)
- **J** To York (Table 33)
- **K** From Penzance (Table 135) (from 8 November from Birmingham New Street) to Glasgow Central (Table 51)
- **L** From Lincoln (Table 30)
- **N** From Plymouth (8 November from Birmingham New Street) to Glasgow Central (Table 51)
- **Q** Until 6 September. From St Pancras International (Table 53)
- **U** From Reading to Newcastle (Table 51)
- **V** From 13 September. From St Pancras International (Table 53)
- **X** From Newquay (13 September to 1 November from Penzance (Table 135), from 8 November from Birmingham New Street) to Edinburgh (Table 51)

Sundays

from 19 July

Sheffield, Doncaster and Wakefield → Leeds

Network Diagram - see first page of Table 31

		GR	NT	GR	NT	XC		XC	NT	NT	GR	EM	NT	XC	GR	NT	NT	GR	EM	XC	NT	GR	EM	
		R 1		R 1		1 ◇		1 ◇			R 1	1 ◇		1 ◇	R 1			R 1	1 ◇	1 ◇		R 1	1 ◇	
		A		A	B	C		D	B		A	E		G	A			A	H	J	K	A	E	
Sheffield 7	29 d		19 36		20 17	20 21		20 23	←	20 39		21 03		21 21			21 36		22 18	22 21	22 39		23 44	
Meadowhall	29 d		19 42		20 23 →				20 23	20 45							21 42				22 45			
Rotherham Central	29 d		19 49														21 48							
Swinton (S.Yorks)	29 d		19 57														21 56							
Bolton-upon-Dearne	d		20 02														22 00							
Goldthorpe	d		20 04														22 03							
Thurnscoe	d		20 07														22 06							
Moorthorpe	d		20 12														22 11							
Doncaster 7	d	19 59		20 20							21 10					21 49		22 20				23 27		
Bentley (S.Yorks)	d															21 52								
Adwick	a															21 56								
	d															21 56								
South Elmsall	d															22 02								
Fitzwilliam	d		20 18													22 09	22 16							
Sandal & Agbrigg	d		20 24													22 15	22 22							
Wakefield Westgate 7	32, 39 a	20 16	20 28	20 38		20 46		20 49			21 27	21 32		21 44		22 19	22 26	22 37	22 43	22 46			00 12	
	d	20 16	20 28	20 38		20 47		20 50			21 27	21 33	←	21 45	21 57	22 20	22 27	22 37	22 44	22 47			00 13	
Wakefield Kirkgate 4	32, 34, 39 a								20 52	21 29			21 29								23 28			
	d								20 53	21 30			21 30								23 30			
Outwood	d		20 33							→						22 25	22 32							
Leeds 10	32, 34 a	20 39	20 52	20 59		21 03		21 05	21 16		21 46	21 50	22 04	22 06	22 16	22 39	22 52	23 00	23 01	23 08	00 04	00 24	00 49	

For general notes see front of timetable
For details of catering facilities see Directory of Train Operators

A From London Kings Cross (Table 26)
B From Nottingham (Table 34)
C Until 6 September. From Plymouth to York (Table 51)
D From 13 September. From Plymouth (from 8 November from Birmingham New Street) to York (Table 51)
E Until 6 September. From St Pancras International (Table 53)
G From Plymouth (from 8 November from Birmingham New Street) (Table 51)
H From 13 September. From St Pancras International (Table 53)
J From Penzance (Table 135) (from 8 November from Birmingham New Street (Table 51)
K From Lincoln (Table 30)

Leeds → Wakefield, Doncaster and Sheffield

Network Diagram - see first page of Table 31

Miles	Miles				GR	EM	GR	NT	XC	NT	NT	GR	NT	XC	NT	EM	NT	GR	NT	GR	XC		NT	NT	NT	NT
					R 1	1◇	R 1		1◇			R 1		1◇		1◇		R 1		R 1	1◇					
					A	B	A		C			A	D	E		B		A		G	H				D	J
					🍽	⊠	🍽		🛒					🛒		🍽				✕ 🛒	🛒					
0	0	**Leeds 10**	32, 34	d	05 05	05 25	05 30	05 33	06 00			06 05	06 05	06 15	06 19	06 34	06 38	06 40	06 43	07 00	07 05				07 05	
7½	7½	Outwood		d				05 44							06 28				06 54					←		
—	—	Wakefield Kirkgate 4	32, 34, 39	a									06 21				07 07							07 07	07 23	
—	—			d							06 04		06 21				07 08							07 08	07 23	
10	10	**Wakefield Westgate 7**	32, 39	a	05 17	05 36	05 42	05 49	06 11			06 18		06 26	06 32	06 45	→	06 52	06 58	07 12	07 17					
—	—			d	05 17	05 37	05 42	05 49	06 12					06 27	06 33	06 46			06 58	07 12	07 18					
11¾	11¾	Sandal & Agbrigg		d				05 53							06 36				07 02							
16½	16½	Fitzwilliam		d				06 00							06 42				07 09							
21	—	South Elmsall		d											06 47											
25¾	—	Adwick		a											06 53											
—	—			d											06 53											07 29
28	—	Bentley (S.Yorks)		d											06 57											07 33
29¾	—	**Doncaster 7**		a	05 35	05 55	06 00							06 43	07 07					07 29						07 37
—	20¼	Moorthorpe		d				06 06		←									07 14				←			
—	23¾	Thurnscoe		d				06 12		06 12									07 20				07 20			
—	24½	Goldthorpe		d				→		06 14									→				07 22			
—	25¾	Bolton-upon-Dearne		d						06 17													07 25			
—	28	Swinton (S.Yorks)	29	a						06 22													07 29			
—	32½	Rotherham Central	29	a						06 30													07 39			
—	35¼	Meadowhall	29 🚋	a						06 37	06 41		06 49										07 46	07 48	07 53	
—	38¾	**Sheffield 7**	29 🚋	a		06 18			06 39	06 47	06 55		07 00	07 11		07 25					07 50		07 57	07 57	08 05	

			GR	NT	NT	NT	NT	GR	NT	NT	NT	GR	XC	NT	NT	NT	NT		NT	NT	NT	GR	NT	NT	GR	NT
			R 1					R 1				R 1	1◇									R 1			R 1	
			A	J				K			D	L	N			D						A		J	A	
												🍽 🛒	🛒									🍽 🛒			🍽 🛒	
Leeds 10	32, 34	d	07 20		07 27	07 29	07 35	07 40	07 47		08 02	08 05	08 11						08 19	08 32	08 37	08 40	08 48		09 05	
Outwood		d			07 36				07 59	←						←			08 28				08 59			←
Wakefield Kirkgate 4	32, 34, 39	a				08 00	07 54			08 00	08 23					08 23				09 03	08 54					09 03
		d				08 04	07 55			08 04	08 23					08 23				09 04	08 55					09 04
Wakefield Westgate 7	32, 39	a	07 32		07 42	→		07 52	08 03		→	08 17	08 22						08 33	→		08 52	09 03		09 18	
		d			07 42				08 03			08 17	08 23						08 34			08 52	09 03		09 18	
Sandal & Agbrigg		d			07 45				08 07										08 37				09 07			
Fitzwilliam		d			07 51				08 14										08 43				09 14			
South Elmsall		d			08 06														08 48							
Adwick		a			08 11														08 54							
		d		07 54	08 11									08 35					08 54					09 13		
Bentley (S.Yorks)		d		07 57	08 15									08 39					08 58					09 17		
Doncaster 7		a		08 01	08 24							08 36		08 44			←		09 07			09 11		09 22	09 35	
Moorthorpe		d							08 19								08 19						09 20			
Thurnscoe		d							→								08 25						09 26			
Goldthorpe		d															08 27						→			
Bolton-upon-Dearne		d															08 30									
Swinton (S.Yorks)	29	a															08 34									
Rotherham Central	29	a													←		08 47									
Meadowhall	29 🚋	a					08 31			08 45					08 45	08 52	08 54				09 28					09 46
Sheffield 7	29 🚋	a					08 39			→			08 51		08 55	09 02	09 05				09 37					→

			NT	XC	NT	NT	NT	NT	NT	NT	GR	NT	NT		GR	NT	NT	XC	NT	NT	NT	NT	NT	NT	GR	NT
				1◇							R 1				R 1			1◇							R 1	
			D	Q			D				A		J		A		D	U			D				A	
				🛒							🍽				🍽 🛒			🛒							🍽 🛒	
Leeds 10	32, 34	d	09 05	09 11				09 19	09 32	09 37	09 40	09 48			10 05		10 05	10 11				10 19	10 32	10 37	10 40	10 48
Outwood		d					←	09 28				09 59				←					←	10 28				10 59
Wakefield Kirkgate 4	32, 34, 39	a	09 23				09 23		10 01	09 54						10 01	10 23				10 23		11 01	10 54		
		d	09 23				09 23		10 04	09 55						10 04	10 23				10 23		11 04	10 55		
Wakefield Westgate 7	32, 39	a	→	09 23				09 32	→		09 52	10 03			10 18		→	10 23				10 32	→		10 52	11 03
		d		09 23				09 32			09 52	10 03			10 18			10 23				10 32			10 52	11 03
Sandal & Agbrigg		d						09 35				10 07										10 35				11 07
Fitzwilliam		d						09 42				10 14										10 42				11 14
South Elmsall		d						09 47														10 47				
Adwick		a						09 52														10 52				
		d						09 53					10 13									10 53				
Bentley (S.Yorks)		d						09 57					10 17									10 57				
Doncaster 7		a						10 08			10 14		10 22		10 35							11 07			11 12	
Moorthorpe		d				←						10 19								←						11 19
Thurnscoe		d				09 26						10 25								10 25						11 25
Goldthorpe		d				09 28						→								10 27						→
Bolton-upon-Dearne		d				09 31														10 30						
Swinton (S.Yorks)	29	a				09 35														10 34						
Rotherham Central	29	a			←	09 44													←	10 44						
Meadowhall	29 🚋	a			09 46	09 50	09 52			10 27						10 46			10 46	10 50	10 52			11 27		
Sheffield 7	29 🚋	a		09 51	09 56	10 00	10 02			10 37						→		10 51	10 56	11 00	11 02			11 37		

For general notes see front of timetable
For details of catering facilities see Directory of Train Operators

- **A** To London Kings Cross (Table 26)
- **B** To St Pancras International (Table 53)
- **C** To Plymouth (Table 51)
- **D** To Nottingham (Table 34)
- **E** To Reading (Table 51)
- **G** From Bradford Forster Square to London Kings Cross (Table 26)
- **H** From York to Plymouth (Table 51)
- **J** To Sheffield (Table 29)
- **K** From Skipton to London Kings Cross (Table 26)
- **L** From Harrogate to London Kings Cross (Table 26)
- **N** From Newcastle to Plymouth (Table 51)
- **Q** From Edinburgh to Plymouth (Table 51)
- **U** From Glasgow Central to Plymouth (Table 51)

Leeds → Wakefield, Doncaster and Sheffield

Network Diagram - see first page of Table 31

	NT	GR	NT	NT	XC	NT	NT		NT	NT	NT	NT	NT	GR	NT	NT	GR	NT	NT	XC	NT	NT	NT	NT
		R 1			1 ◇									R 1			R 1			1 ◇				
	A	B		C	D				C			E		B		A	B		C	D			C	
Leeds 10 32, 34 d		11 05		11 05	11 11					11 19	11 32		11 37	11 40	11 48		12 05		12 05	12 11				12 19
Outwood d			←						←	11 28					11 59			←					←	12 28
Wakefield Kirkgate 4 32, 34, 39 a			11 01	11 23					11 23		12 01		11 54					12 01	12 23				12 23	
d			11 04	11 23					11 23		12 04		11 55					12 04	12 23				12 23	
Wakefield Westgate 7 32, 39 a		11 17		→	11 23					11 32	→			11 54	12 03		12 17		→	12 23				12 32
d		11 17			11 23					11 32				11 54	12 03		12 17			12 23				12 32
Sandal & Agbrigg d										11 35					12 07									12 35
Fitzwilliam d										11 42					12 14									12 42
South Elmsall d										11 47														12 47
Adwick a										11 52														12 52
d	11 16									11 53						12 12								12 53
Bentley (S.Yorks) d	11 20									11 57						12 16								12 57
Doncaster 7 a	11 25	11 37								12 07				12 12		12 23	12 36							13 07
Moorthorpe d							←					11 51			12 19							←		
Thurnscoe d							11 25								12 25							12 25		
Goldthorpe d							11 27								→							12 27		
Bolton-upon-Dearne d							11 30															12 30		
Swinton (S.Yorks) 29 a							11 34					12 01										12 34		
Rotherham Central 29 a						←	11 44					12 10									←	12 44		
Meadowhall 29 a			11 46			11 46	11 50		11 52			12 16	12 27					12 46			12 46	12 50	12 52	
Sheffield 7 29 a			→		11 51	11 56	12 00		12 02			12 26	12 37					→		12 51	12 56	13 00	13 02	

	NT	NT	GR		NT	NT	GR	NT	NT	XC	NT	NT	NT	NT	NT	NT	GR	NT	GR	NT	NT		XC	NT
			R 1				R 1			1 ◇							R 1		R 1				1 ◇	
			B			A	B		C	G			C				B		B		C		H	
Leeds 10 32, 34 d	12 32	12 37	12 40		12 48		13 05		13 05	13 11				13 19	13 32	13 37	13 40	13 48	14 05		14 05		14 11	
Outwood d					12 59			←					←	13 28				13 59		←				
Wakefield Kirkgate 4 32, 34, 39 a	13 01	12 54						13 01	13 23				13 23		14 01	13 54				14 01	14 23			
d	13 04	12 55						13 04	13 23				13 23		14 04	13 55				14 04	14 23			
Wakefield Westgate 7 32, 39 a	→		12 52		13 03		13 18		→	13 23				13 32	→		13 53	14 03	14 18		→		14 23	
d			12 52		13 03		13 18			13 23				13 32			13 53	14 03					14 23	
Sandal & Agbrigg d					13 07									13 35				14 07						
Fitzwilliam d					13 14									13 42				14 14						
South Elmsall d														13 47										
Adwick a														13 52										
d						13 12								13 53										
Bentley (S.Yorks) d						13 16								13 57										
Doncaster 7 a			13 11			13 23	13 37							14 07			14 13							
Moorthorpe d					13 19							←						14 19						
Thurnscoe d					13 25							13 25						14 25						
Goldthorpe d					→							13 27						→						
Bolton-upon-Dearne d												13 30												
Swinton (S.Yorks) 29 a												13 34												
Rotherham Central 29 a											←	13 44												←
Meadowhall 29 a		13 27						13 46			13 46	13 50	13 52			14 27				14 46				14 46
Sheffield 7 29 a		13 37						→		13 51	13 56	14 00	14 02			14 37				→			14 51	14 56

	NT	NT	NT	NT	NT	NT	GR	NT	GR	NT	NT	XC	NT	NT	NT	NT	NT		NT	NT	NT	GR	NT	NT
							R 1		R 1			1 ◇										R 1		
		C	A				B		B		C	J			C	A				E		B		K
Leeds 10 32, 34 d				14 19	14 32	14 37	14 40	14 48	15 05		15 05	15 11					15 19		15 32		15 37	15 40	15 48	
Outwood d		←		14 28				14 59		←					←		15 28						15 59	
Wakefield Kirkgate 4 32, 34, 39 a		14 23			15 01	14 54				15 01	15 23				15 23				16 01		15 54			
d		14 23			15 04	14 55				15 04	15 23				15 23				16 04		15 55			
Wakefield Westgate 7 32, 39 a				14 32	→		14 52	15 03	15 17		→	15 23					15 32		→			15 52	16 03	
d				14 32			14 52	15 03				15 23					15 32						16 03	
Sandal & Agbrigg d				14 35				15 07									15 35						16 07	
Fitzwilliam d				14 42				15 14									15 42						16 14	
South Elmsall d				14 47													15 47							
Adwick a				14 52													15 52							
d			14 14	14 53												15 13	15 53							16 13
Bentley (S.Yorks) d			14 18	14 57												15 17	15 57							16 17
Doncaster 7 a			14 22	15 07			15 11									15 22	16 07							16 23
Moorthorpe d	←							15 19						←						15 51			16 19	
Thurnscoe d	14 25							15 25						15 25									16 25	
Goldthorpe d	14 27							→						15 27									→	
Bolton-upon-Dearne d	14 30													15 30										
Swinton (S.Yorks) 29 a	14 34													15 34						16 01				
Rotherham Central 29 a	14 44												←	15 42						16 10				
Meadowhall 29 a	14 50	14 52				15 27				15 46			15 46	15 50	15 52					16 17	16 27			
Sheffield 7 29 a	15 00	15 02				15 37				→		15 51	15 56	16 00	16 02					16 25	16 37			

For general notes see front of timetable
For details of catering facilities see Directory of Train Operators

- **A** To Sheffield (Table 29)
- **B** To London Kings Cross (Table 26)
- **C** To Nottingham (Table 34)
- **D** From Dundee (Table 229) to Plymouth (Table 51)
- **E** From York (Table 33)
- **G** From Glasgow Central (Table 51) to Penzance (Table 135)
- **H** From Aberdeen (Table 229) to Penzance (Table 135)
- **J** From Edinburgh (Table 51) to Penzance (Table 135)
- **K** To Retford (Table 30)

Leeds → Wakefield, Doncaster and Sheffield

Network Diagram - see first page of Table 31

		GR	NT	NT	XC	NT	NT	NT	NT	NT	NT	GR	NT	NT		GR	NT	NT	XC	NT	NT	NT	NT	NT	NT
		R 1			1 ◇							R 1				R 1			1 ◇						
		A		B	C			B				A	D			A		B	C				B		
		Ø 🛒			🛒							Ø 🛒				Ø 🛒			🛒						
Leeds 10	32, 34 d	16 05		16 05	16 11				16 19	16 32	16 37	16 40		16 48		17 05		17 05	17 11			17 19		17 32	17 37
Outwood	d		←					←	16 28					16 59			←					17 28	←		
Wakefield Kirkgate 4	32, 34, 39 a		16 01	16 23				16 23		17 01	16 54						17 01	17 22					17 22	18 01	17 54
	d		16 04	16 23				16 23		17 04	16 55						17 04	17 23					17 23	18 04	17 55
Wakefield Westgate 7	32, 39 a	16 17		→	16 23				16 32	→		16 52		17 03		17 17		→	17 23			17 32		→	
	d	16 17			16 23				16 32			16 52		17 03		17 17			17 23			17 32			
Sandal & Agbrigg	d								16 35					17 07								17 35			
Fitzwilliam	d								16 42					17 14								17 42			
South Elmsall	d								16 47													17 47			
Adwick	a								16 52													17 52			
	d								16 53				17 09									17 53			
Bentley (S.Yorks)	d								16 57				17 14									17 57			
Doncaster 7	a	16 36							17 07			17 10	17 19			17 36						18 07			
Moorthorpe	d						←							17 19							←				
Thurnscoe	d						16 25							17 25							17 25				
Goldthorpe	d						16 27							→							17 27				
Bolton-upon-Dearne	d						16 30														17 30				
Swinton (S.Yorks)	29 a						16 34														17 34				
Rotherham Central	29 a					←	16 43													←	17 44				
Meadowhall	29 a		16 46			16 46	16 50	16 52			17 25						17 46			17 46	17 50		17 51		18 27
Sheffield 7	29 a		→		16 51	16 56	17 00	17 02			17 37						→		17 51	17 56	18 00		18 02		18 37

		GR	NT	NT	GR	NT	NT	XC	NT	NT		NT	NT	NT	GR	NT	NT	GR	NT	NT	XC	NT	NT	NT	NT
		R 1			R 1			1 ◇							R 1			R 1			1 ◇				
		A	D		A		B	C					B		A			A		B	E				B
		Ø 🛒			Ø 🛒			🛒							🍽 🛒			🍽			🛒				
Leeds 10	32, 34 d	17 40		17 46	18 05		18 05	18 11				18 19		18 32	18 40	18 43	18 48	19 05		19 05	19 11			19 19	
Outwood	d			17 57		←						18 28	←				18 59		←					19 28	←
Wakefield Kirkgate 4	32, 34, 39 a					18 01	18 23						18 23	19 04		18 59			19 04	19 23					19 23
	d					18 04	18 23						18 23	19 04		18 59			19 04	19 23					19 23
Wakefield Westgate 7	32, 39 a	17 52		18 01	18 17		→	18 23				18 32		→	18 52		19 03	19 17		→	19 23			19 32	
	d	17 52		18 03	18 17			18 23				18 32			18 52		19 03	19 17			19 23			19 32	
Sandal & Agbrigg	d			18 07								18 35					19 07							19 35	
Fitzwilliam	d			18 14								18 42					19 14							19 42	
South Elmsall	d											18 47												19 47	
Adwick	a											18 52												19 52	
	d		18 14									18 53												19 53	
Bentley (S.Yorks)	d		18 18									18 57												19 59	
Doncaster 7	a	18 10	18 25		18 34							19 07			19 10			19 34						20 07	
Moorthorpe	d			18 19						←							19 19						←		
Thurnscoe	d			18 25						18 25							19 25						19 25		
Goldthorpe	d			→						18 27							→						19 27		
Bolton-upon-Dearne	d									18 30													19 30		
Swinton (S.Yorks)	29 a									18 34													19 34		
Rotherham Central	29 a								←	18 44												←	19 44		
Meadowhall	29 a					18 46			18 46	18 49			18 52			19 33			19 46			19 46	19 50		19 52
Sheffield 7	29 a					→		18 51	18 56	19 00			19 03			19 43			→		19 51	19 58	19 59		20 04

		NT	GR	NT	NT	XC		NT	NT	NT	NT	NT	GR	NT	XC	NT	NT	NT	NT	NT	NT	NT	NT		
			R 1			1 ◇							R 1		1 ◇										
			A			E							A		G										
			🍽										🍽												
Leeds 10	32, 34 d	19 37	19 40	19 43	19 48	20 11				20 21	20 30	20 37	20 40	20 48	21 11			21 28	21 37	21 48	22 37	22 39	23 09		
Outwood	d				19 59			←		20 30				20 59		←		21 37		21 59		22 48	23 20		
Wakefield Kirkgate 4	32, 34, 39 a	20 06		19 59				20 06			20 46	21 06				21 06			22 06		23 10				
	d	20 07		20 00				20 07			20 46	21 07				21 07			22 07		23 10				
Wakefield Westgate 7	32, 39 a	→	19 52		20 03	20 22				20 34		→	20 55	21 03	21 22			21 41		22 03		22 53	23 24		
	d		19 52		20 03	20 23				20 34			20 55	21 03	21 23			21 42		22 03		22 54	23 24		
Sandal & Agbrigg	d				20 07					20 37				21 07				21 45		22 07		22 57	23 28		
Fitzwilliam	d				20 14					20 44				21 13				21 51		22 14		23 03	23 35		
South Elmsall	d									20 49								21 56				23 08			
Adwick	a									20 54								22 02				23 14			
	d									20 55								22 02				23 14			
Bentley (S.Yorks)	d									20 59								22 06				23 18			
Doncaster 7	a		20 13							21 09			21 12					22 16				23 27			
Moorthorpe	d				20 19				←					21 20			←			22 19			23 40		
Thurnscoe	d				20 25				20 25					21 26			21 26			22 25			23 46		
Goldthorpe	d				→				20 27					→			21 28			22 27			23 48		
Bolton-upon-Dearne	d								20 30								21 31			22 30			23 51		
Swinton (S.Yorks)	29 a								20 34								21 35			22 34			23 55		
Rotherham Central	29 a								20 42								21 44			22 46			00 02		
Meadowhall	29 a			20 33				20 45	20 51		21 17					21 45	21 52		22b46	22 52	23 51		00 08		
Sheffield 7	29 a			20 44		20 51		20 58	21 02		21 30				21 51	21 58	22 05		22 58	23 02	00 02		00 23		

For general notes see front of timetable
For details of catering facilities see Directory of Train Operators

- **A** To London Kings Cross (Table 26)
- **B** To Nottingham (Table 34)
- **C** From Edinburgh to Plymouth (Table 51)
- **D** To Scunthorpe (22 June to 4 September to Thorne North) (Table 29)
- **E** From Edinburgh to Bristol Temple Meads (Table 51)
- **G** From Edinburgh to Birmingham New Street (Table 51)
- **b** Fridays arr. 2247

Table 31 — Saturdays

Leeds → Wakefield, Doncaster and Sheffield

Network Diagram - see first page of Table 31

Station	Table		GR R 1 A 🍽 🛒	XC 1◊ B 🛒	GR R 1 A 🍽	XC 1◊ C 🛒	NT	EM 1◊ D 🍽	NT	NT	GR R 1 A 🍽 🛒	XC 1◊ E 🛒	NT	NT	NT G	NT H	NT H	NT		NT	EM 1◊ D 🍽	NT	GR R 1 J 🍽 🛒	NT	GR R 1 K	NT G
Leeds 10	32, 34	d	05 05	06 00	06 10	06 15	06 19	06 34	06 38	06 43	07 00	07 05			07 05			07 26		07 29	07 34	07 35	07 40	07 47	08 05	08 05
Outwood		d					06 28			06 54				←				07 35						07 59		
Wakefield Kirkgate 4	32, 34, 39	a							07 07					07 07	07 23					08 00		07 54				08 23
		d							07 08					07 08	07 23					08 04		07 55				08 23
Wakefield Westgate 7	32, 39	a	05 17	06 11	06 22	06 28	06 33	06 45	→	06 58	07 12	07 17						07 39		→	07 45		07 52	08 03	08 18	→
		d	05 17	06 12	06 22	06 29	06 33	06 46		06 58	07 12	07 18						07 39			07 46			08 03		
Sandal & Agbrigg		d					06 36			07 02								07 42						08 07		
Fitzwilliam		d					06 42			07 09								07 49						08 14		
South Elmsall		d					06 47											08 06								
Adwick		a					06 52											08 12								
		d					06 53									07 29	08 07	08 12								
Bentley (S.Yorks)		d					06 57									07 33	08 11	08 16								
Doncaster 7		a	05 34		06 40	06 46	07 07				07 30					07 37	08 15	08 24								
Moorthorpe		d								07 14			←											08 19		
Thurnscoe		d								07 20			07 20											→		
Goldthorpe		d								→			07 22													
Bolton-upon-Dearne		d											07 25													
Swinton (S.Yorks)	29	a											07 29													
Rotherham Central	29	a											07 39													
Meadowhall	29 🚋	a											07 46	07 48	07 53							08 31				
Sheffield 7	29 🚋	a		06 45		07 15		07 22				07 51	07 57	07 57	08 05						08 21	08 39				

Station	Table		XC 1◊ L 🛒	NT	NT	NT G	NT	NT	NT	NT	NT	NT H	GR R 1 A ⊘ 🛒		NT	NT G	XC 1◊ N 🛒	NT	NT	NT G	NT	NT	NT	NT	NT H	GR R 1 A 🍽 🛒
Leeds 10	32, 34	d	08 11					08 19	08 32	08 37	08 48		09 05			09 05	09 11				09 19	09 32	09 37	09 48		10 05
Outwood		d		←		←		08 28			08 59				←					←	09 28			09 59		
Wakefield Kirkgate 4	32, 34, 39	a		08 00		08 23			09 03	08 54					09 03	09 23				09 23		10 01	09 54			
		d		08 04		08 23			09 04	08 55					09 04	09 23				09 23		10 04	09 55			
Wakefield Westgate 7	32, 39	a	08 22					08 33	→		09 03		09 17			→	09 22				09 33	→		10 03		10 18
		d	08 23					08 34			09 03		09 17				09 23				09 33			10 03		10 18
Sandal & Agbrigg		d						08 37			09 07										09 36			10 07		
Fitzwilliam		d						08 43			09 14										09 42			10 14		
South Elmsall		d						08 48													09 47					
Adwick		a						08 54													09 52					
		d			08 35			08 54				09 13									09 53				10 10	
Bentley (S.Yorks)		d			08 39			08 58				09 17									09 57				10 14	
Doncaster 7		a			08 44		←	09 07				09 22	09 35								10 07				10 19	10 36
Moorthorpe		d					08 19				09 20								←					10 19		
Thurnscoe		d					08 25				09 26								09 26					10 25		
Goldthorpe		d					08 27				→								09 28					→		
Bolton-upon-Dearne		d					08 30												09 31							
Swinton (S.Yorks)	29	a					08 34												09 35							
Rotherham Central	29	a					08 47											←	09 44							
Meadowhall	29 🚋	a		08 45		08 52	08 54			09 28					09 46			09 46	09 50	09 52			10 27			
Sheffield 7	29 🚋	a	08 51	08 55		09 02	09 05			09 37					→		09 51	09 56	10 00	10 02			10 37			

Station	Table		NT	NT G	XC 1◊ N 🛒	NT	NT	NT G		NT	NT	NT	NT	NT H	GR R 1 A 🍽 🛒	NT	NT G	XC 1◊ Q 🛒	NT	NT	NT G	NT	NT	NT U	NT	NT
Leeds 10	32, 34	d		10 05	10 11					10 19	10 32	10 37	10 48		11 05		11 05	11 11				11 19	11 32		11 37	11 48
Outwood		d	←					←		10 28			10 59			←					←	11 28				11 59
Wakefield Kirkgate 4	32, 34, 39	a	10 01	10 23				10 23			11 01	10 54				11 01	11 23				11 23		12 01		11 54	
		d	10 04	10 23				10 23			11 04	10 55				11 04	11 23				11 23		12 04		11 55	
Wakefield Westgate 7	32, 39	a		→	10 22					10 32	→		11 03		11 17		→	11 22				11 32	→			12 03
		d			10 23					10 32			11 03		11 17			11 23				11 32				12 03
Sandal & Agbrigg		d								10 35			11 07									11 35				12 07
Fitzwilliam		d								10 42			11 14									11 42				12 14
South Elmsall		d								10 47												11 47				
Adwick		a								10 52												11 52				
		d								10 53				11 08								11 53				
Bentley (S.Yorks)		d								10 57				11 12								11 57				
Doncaster 7		a								11 07				11 19	11 38							12 07				
Moorthorpe		d					←						11 19							←				11 49		12 19
Thurnscoe		d					10 25						11 25							11 25						12 25
Goldthorpe		d					10 27						→							11 27						→
Bolton-upon-Dearne		d					10 30													11 30						
Swinton (S.Yorks)	29	a					10 34													11 34				11 59		
Rotherham Central	29	a				←	10 44												←	11 44				12 10		
Meadowhall	29 🚋	a	10 46			10 46	10 50	10 52				11 27				11 46			11 46	11 50	11 52			12 16	12 27	
Sheffield 7	29 🚋	a	→		10 51	10 56	11 00	11 02				11 37				→		11 51	11 56	12 00	12 02			12 25	12 37	

For general notes see front of timetable
For details of catering facilities see Directory of Train Operators

- **A** To London Kings Cross (Table 26)
- **B** To Plymouth (Table 51)
- **C** To Reading (Table 51)
- **D** To St Pancras International (Table 53)
- **E** From York to Plymouth (Table 51)
- **G** To Nottingham (Table 34)
- **H** To Sheffield (Table 29)
- **J** From Skipton to London Kings Cross (Table 26)
- **K** From Bradford Forster Square to London Kings Cross (Table 26)
- **L** From Newcastle to Penzance (Table 135)
- **N** From Edinburgh to Plymouth (Table 51)
- **Q** From Glasgow Central (Table 26) to Newquay (Table 135) (from 12 September to Plymouth (Table 51))
- **U** From York (Table 33)

Table 31

Saturdays

Leeds → Wakefield, Doncaster and Sheffield

Network Diagram - see first page of Table 31

Station		NT		GR	NT	NT	XC	NT	NT	NT	NT	NT	NT	NT	NT	GR	NT	NT	XC		NT	NT	NT	NT	NT
		A		R 1 B		C	1 ◇ D			C					A	R 1 B		C	1 ◇ E				C		
Leeds 10	32, 34 d			12 05		12 05	12 11				12 19	12 32	12 37	12 48		13 05		13 05	13 11					13 19	13 32
Outwood	d				←					←	12 28			12 59			←						←	13 28	
Wakefield Kirkgate 4	32, 34, 39 a				12 01	12 23				12 23		13 01	12 54				13 01	13 23					13 23		14 01
	d				12 04	12 23				12 23		13 04	12 55				13 04	13 23					13 23		14 04
Wakefield Westgate 7	32, 39 a			12 17		→	12 22				12 32	→		13 03		13 17		→	13 22					13 32	→
	d			12 17			12 23				12 32			13 03		13 17			13 23					13 32	
Sandal & Agbrigg	d										12 35			13 07										13 35	
Fitzwilliam	d										12 42			13 14										13 42	
South Elmsall	d										12 47													13 47	
Adwick	a										12 52													13 52	
	d	12 12									12 53				13 12									13 53	
Bentley (S.Yorks)	d	12 16									12 57				13 16									13 57	
Doncaster 7	a	12 22		12 34							13 07				13 23	13 37								14 07	
Moorthorpe	d								←					13 19								←			
Thurnscoe	d								12 25					13 25 →								13 25			
Goldthorpe	d								12 27													13 27			
Bolton-upon-Dearne	d								12 30													13 30			
Swinton (S.Yorks)	29 a								12 34													13 34			
Rotherham Central	29 a							←	12 44												←	13 44			
Meadowhall	29 ⛴ a				12 46 →			12 46	12 50	12 52			13 27				13 46 →				13 46	13 50	13 52		
Sheffield 7	29 ⛴ a						12 51	12 56	13 00	13 02			13 37						13 51		13 56	14 00	14 02		

Station		NT	NT	NT	GR	NT	NT	XC	NT	NT	NT	NT	NT	NT		NT	NT	GR	NT	NT	XC	NT	NT	NT	NT
				A	R 1 B		C	1 ◇ G			C						A	R 1 B		C	1 ◇ H			C	
Leeds 10	32, 34 d	13 37	13 48		14 05		14 05	14 11				14 19	14 32	14 37		14 48		15 05		15 05	15 11				15 19
Outwood	d		13 59			←					←	14 28				14 59			←					←	15 28
Wakefield Kirkgate 4	32, 34, 39 a	13 54				14 01	14 23				14 23		15 01	14 54					15 01	15 23				15 23	
	d	13 55				14 04	14 23				14 23		15 04	14 55					15 04	15 23				15 23	
Wakefield Westgate 7	32, 39 a		14 03		14 17		→	14 22				14 32	→			15 03		15 17		→	15 22				15 32
	d		14 03		14 17			14 23				14 32				15 03		15 17			15 23				15 32
Sandal & Agbrigg	d		14 07									14 35				15 07									15 35
Fitzwilliam	d		14 14									14 42				15 14									15 42
South Elmsall	d											14 47													15 47
Adwick	a											14 52													15 52
	d			14 14								14 53					15 13								15 53
Bentley (S.Yorks)	d			14 18								14 57					15 17								15 57
Doncaster 7	a			14 22	14 34							15 07					15 22	15 35							16 07
Moorthorpe	d		14 19							←						15 19							←		
Thurnscoe	d		14 25 →							14 25						15 25 →							15 25		
Goldthorpe	d									14 27													15 27		
Bolton-upon-Dearne	d									14 30													15 30		
Swinton (S.Yorks)	29 a									14 34													15 34		
Rotherham Central	29 a								←	14 44												←	15 42		
Meadowhall	29 ⛴ a	14 27				14 46 →			14 46	14 50	14 52			15 27					15 46 →			15 46	15 50	15 52	
Sheffield 7	29 ⛴ a	14 37						14 51	14 56	15 00	15 02			15 37							15 51	15 56	16 00	16 02	

Station		NT	NT	NT	NT	NT	GR	NT	NT		XC	NT	NT	NT	NT	NT	NT	NT	NT	NT	NT	XC	NT	NT	NT
			J			K	R 1 B		C		1 ◇ L			C				N			C	1 ◇ L			
Leeds 10	32, 34 d	15 32		15 37	15 48		16 05		16 05		16 11				16 19	16 32	16 37		16 48		17 05	17 11			17 19
Outwood	d				15 59			←						←	16 28				16 59	←					17 28
Wakefield Kirkgate 4	32, 34, 39 a	16 01		15 54				16 01	16 23					16 23		17 01	16 54			17 01	17 22				
	d	16 04		15 55				16 04	16 23					16 23		17 04	16 55			17 04	17 23				
Wakefield Westgate 7	32, 39 a	→			16 03		16 17		→		16 22				16 32	→			17 03		→	17 22			17 32
	d				16 03		16 17				16 23				16 32				17 03			17 23			17 32
Sandal & Agbrigg	d				16 07										16 35				17 07						17 35
Fitzwilliam	d				16 14										16 42				17 14						17 42
South Elmsall	d														16 47										17 47
Adwick	a														16 52										17 52
	d					16 13									16 53			17 05							17 53
Bentley (S.Yorks)	d					16 17									16 57			17 09							17 57
Doncaster 7	a					16 23	16 38								17 07			17 14							18 07
Moorthorpe	d		16 01		16 19								←						17 19					←	
Thurnscoe	d				16 25 →								16 25						17 25 →					17 25	
Goldthorpe	d												16 27											17 27	
Bolton-upon-Dearne	d												16 30											17 30	
Swinton (S.Yorks)	29 a		16 10										16 34											17 34	
Rotherham Central	29 a		16 17									←	16 43										←	17 44	
Meadowhall	29 ⛴ a		16 23	16 27				16 46 →				16 46	16 50	16 52			17 25			17 46 →			17 46	17 50	
Sheffield 7	29 ⛴ a		16 35	16 37							16 51	16 56	17 00	17 02			17 37					17 51	17 56	18 00	

For general notes see front of timetable
For details of catering facilities see Directory of Train Operators

A To Sheffield (Table 29)
B To London Kings Cross (Table 26)
C To Nottingham (Table 34)
D From Dundee to (Table 229) to Plymouth (Table 51)
E From Glasgow Central (Table 51) to Penzance (Table 135)
G From Aberdeen (Table 229) to Penzance (Table 135)
H From Edinburgh (Table 51) to Penzance (Table 135)
J From York (Table 33)
K To Retford (Table 30)
L From Edinburgh to Plymouth (Table 51)
N To Scunthorpe (27 June to 5 September to Thorne North) (Table 29)

Saturdays

Leeds → Wakefield, Doncaster and Sheffield

Network Diagram - see first page of Table 31

	NT A	NT	NT		GR R 1 B 🍽 🛒	NT	NT C	NT	NT A	XC 1 ◇ D 🛒	NT	NT	NT	NT A	NT	NT	GR R 1 B 🍽 🛒	NT	NT	NT A		XC 1 ◇ E 🛒	NT	NT
Leeds [10] 32, 34 d		17 32	17 37		17 40	17 46			18 05	18 11			18 19		18 32	18 37	18 40	18 48		19 05		19 11		
Outwood d	←					17 57		←					18 27	←				18 59	←					
Wakefield Kirkgate [4] 32, 34, 39 a	17 22	18 01	17 54					18 01	18 23					18 23	19 04	18 54			19 04	19 23				
d	17 23	18 04 →	17 55					18 04	18 23 →					18 23	19 04 →	18 55			19 04	19 23 →				
Wakefield Westgate [7] 32, 39 a					17 52	18 01				18 22			18 31				18 54	19 03				19 22		
d					17 52	18 01				18 23			18 32				18 54	19 03				19 23		
Sandal & Agbrigg d						18 05							18 35					19 07						
Fitzwilliam d						18 12							18 42					19 14						
South Elmsall d													18 47											
Adwick a													18 53											
d							18 14						18 53											
Bentley (S.Yorks) d							18 18						18 57											
Doncaster [7] a					18 09		18 25						19 07				19 12							
Moorthorpe d						18 17						←						19 19						←
Thurnscoe d						18 23 →						18 23						19 25 →						19 25
Goldthorpe d												18 25												19 27
Bolton-upon-Dearne d												18 28												19 30
Swinton (S.Yorks) 29 a												18 34												19 34
Rotherham Central 29 a											←	18 43											←	19 43
Meadowhall 29 🚋 a	17 51		18 27					18 46 →			18 46	18 50		18 52		19 27			19 46 →				19 46	19 50
Sheffield [7] 29 🚋 a	18 02		18 37							18 51	18 56	19 00		19 03		19 37						19 51	19 58	19 59

	NT	NT A	NT	NT	NT	XC 1 ◇ G	NT	NT	GR R 1 B 🍽	NT	NT	NT	NT	XC 1 ◇ G	NT	NT	NT	NT	NT	NT	NT H	NT		
Leeds [10] 32, 34 d	19 22		19 37	19 43	19 48	20 11			20 15	20 21	20 30	20 37	20 48	21 11			21 34	21 37	21 48	22 16	22 37	22 44		
Outwood d	19 28				19 59		←			20 30			20 59		←		21 43		21 59	22 25		22 55		
Wakefield Kirkgate [4] 32, 34, 39 a		←	20 06	19 59			20 06				20 46	21 06			21 06			22 06			23 10			
d		19 23	20 07 →	20 00			20 07				20 46	21 07 →			21 07			22 07						
Wakefield Westgate [7] 32, 39 a	19 32				20 03	20 22			20 31	20 36			21 03	21 22			21 47		22 03	22 29		22 59		
d	19 32				20 03	20 23			20 31	20 36			21 03	21 23			21 47		22 03	22 30		22 59		
Sandal & Agbrigg d	19 35				20 07					20 39			21 07				21 50		22 07	22 33		23 03		
Fitzwilliam d	19 42				20 14					20 46			21 13				21 57		22 14	22 39		23 10		
South Elmsall d	19 47									20 51							22 02			22 44				
Adwick a	19 53									20 56							22 07			22 50				
d	19 53									20 57							22 08			22 50				
Bentley (S.Yorks) d	19 57									21 01							22 12			22 54				
Doncaster [7] a	20 10								20 48	21 09							22 22			23 04				
Moorthorpe d					20 19			←					21 20			←			22 19			23 15		
Thurnscoe d					20 25 →			20 25					21 26 →			21 26			22 25			23 21		
Goldthorpe d								20 27								21 28			22 27			23 23		
Bolton-upon-Dearne d								20 30								21 31			22 30			23 26		
Swinton (S.Yorks) 29 a								20 34								21 35			22 40			23 30		
Rotherham Central 29 a								20 42								21 44			22 46			23 37		
Meadowhall 29 🚋 a		19 52		20 29			20 45	20 51			21 17				21 45	21 52		22 46	22 52			23 43		
Sheffield [7] 29 🚋 a		20 04		20 41		20 51	20 58	21 02			21 28			21 51	21 58	22 07		22 58	23 02			23 58		

Sundays

until 12 July

	XC 1 ◇ J 🛒	GR R 1 B 🍽 🛒	NT	NT		NT A	XC 1 ◇ J 🛒	NT	GR R 1 K 🍽 🛒		NT A	GR R 1 B 🍽 🛒	EM 1 ◇ L 🍽	NT A		XC 1 ◇ N 🛒	NT	NT A	EM 1 ◇ L 🍽		NT	GR R 1 B 🍽 🛒	NT A	XC 1 ◇ Q 🛒
Leeds [10] 32, 34 d	08 05	08 25	08 37	08 49		08 55	09 00		09 05			09 40	09 44	09 54		10 00	10 09		10 20		10 28	10 40	10 51	11 00
Outwood d				09 00							←						10 18	←						
Wakefield Kirkgate [4] 32, 34, 39 a			08 54			09 11					09 11			10 09				10 09			10 44		11 06	
d			09 00			09 14 →					09 14			10 11 →				10 11			10 46		11 13 →	
Wakefield Westgate [7] 32, 39 a	08 20	08 37		09 04			09 12		09 17			09 52	09 57			10 11	10 22		10 31			10 52		11 11
d	08 21	08 37		09 04			09 13		09 17			09 52	09 58			10 12	10 22		10 32			10 52		11 12
Sandal & Agbrigg d				09 08													10 25							
Fitzwilliam d				09 15													10 32							
South Elmsall d																	10 37							
Adwick a																	10 42							
d																	10 43							
Bentley (S.Yorks) d																	10 47							
Doncaster [7] a		08 54					09 31		09 37			10 09				10 28	10 57					11 12		11 28
Moorthorpe d				09 20				←																
Thurnscoe d				09 26 →				09 26																
Goldthorpe d								09 28																
Bolton-upon-Dearne d								09 31																
Swinton (S.Yorks) 29 a								09 35																
Rotherham Central 29 a								09 44																
Meadowhall 29 🚋 a			09 41					09 53			09 54							10 51			11 32			
Sheffield [7] 29 🚋 a	08 52		09 55				09 55	10 03			10 04		10 25			10 54		11 00	11 02		11 44			11 53

For general notes see front of timetable
For details of catering facilities see Directory of Train Operators

- **A** To Nottingham (Table 34)
- **B** To London Kings Cross (Table 26)
- **C** To Scunthorpe (27 June to 5 September to Thorne North) (Table 29)
- **D** From Edinburgh to Plymouth (Table 51)
- **E** From Edinburgh to Bristol Temple Meads (Table 51)
- **G** From Edinburgh to Birmingham New Street (Table 51)
- **H** From 18 July. Also stops at Normanton 2301
- **J** To Plymouth (Table 51)
- **K** To Glasgow Central (Table 26)
- **L** To St Pancras International (Table 53)
- **N** From York to Plymouth (Table 51)
- **Q** From Newcastle to Plymouth (Table 51)

Table 31

Sundays

until 12 July

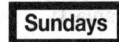

Leeds → Wakefield, Doncaster and Sheffield

Network Diagram - see first page of Table 31

		NT	NT	NT	GR	XC	NT	NT	GR	NT	XC	NT	NT	GR	NT	XC	EM	NT	NT	NT
					R 1	1◇			R 1		1◇			R 1		1◇	1◇			
		A		A	B	C		A	B		D			B	A	C	E		A	
Leeds 10	32, 34 d		11 09	11 29	11 40	12 00	12 09	12 29	12 40	12 43	13 00		13 09	13 40	13 48	14 00	14 05	14 09		14 26
Outwood	d	←	11 20				12 18					←	13 20					14 18	←	
Wakefield Kirkgate 4	32, 34, 39 a	11 06		11 46				12 46		13 00		13 00			14 05				14 05	14 42
	d	11 13		11 46				12 46		13 02		13 02			14 11				14 11	14 46
Wakefield Westgate 7	32, 39 a		11 24		11 52	12 11	12 22		12 52	→	13 11		13 24	13 52	→	14 11	14 17	14 22		→
	d		11 24		11 52	12 12	12 22		12 52		13 12		13 24	13 52		14 12	14 18	14 22		
Sandal & Agbrigg	d		11 28				12 25						13 28					14 25		
Fitzwilliam	d		11 35				12 32						13 35					14 32		
South Elmsall	d						12 37											14 37		
Adwick	a						12 42											14 42		
	d						12 43											14 43		
Bentley (S.Yorks)	d						12 47											14 47		
Doncaster 7	a				12 09	12 28	12 57		13 11		13 28			14 09				14 57		
Moorthorpe	d		11 40										13 40							
Thurnscoe	d		11 46										13 46							
Goldthorpe	d		11 48										13 48							
Bolton-upon-Dearne	d		11 51										13 51							
Swinton (S.Yorks)	29 a		11 55										14 00							
Rotherham Central	29 a		12 05										14 08							
Meadowhall	29 a	11 46	12 11	12 17				13 18				13 47	14 14						14 54	
Sheffield 7	29 a	11 56	12 20	12 29		12 54		13 29			13 55	13 58	14 25			14 44	14 55		15 06	

		GR	XC	NT	NT	NT	GR	XC	NT	NT	NT	GR	NT	XC	NT	GR	NT	NT	GR	NT	XC
		R 1	1◇				R 1	1◇				R 1		1◇		R 1			R 1		1◇
		B	D		A		B	G	A			B	A	H		B	A		B	J	G
Leeds 10	32, 34 d	14 40	15 00		15 05	15 09	15 40	16 00	16 05	16 09	16 27	16 40	16 54	17 00		17 05		17 09	17 40		18 00
Outwood	d			←		15 20				16 18					←		←	17 20			
Wakefield Kirkgate 4	32, 34, 39 a			14 42	15 22				16 21		16 43		17 09		16 43		17 09				
	d			14 46	15 22				16 22		16 46		17 11		16 46		17 11				
Wakefield Westgate 7	32, 39 a	14 52	15 11			15 24	15 52	16 11		16 22	→	16 52	→	17 11		17 18		17 24	17 52		18 11
	d	14 52	15 12			15 24	15 52	16 12		16 22		16 52		17 12		17 18		17 24			18 12
Sandal & Agbrigg	d					15 28				16 25								17 28			
Fitzwilliam	d					15 35				16 32								17 35			
South Elmsall	d									16 37											
Adwick	a									16 42											
	d									16 43											
Bentley (S.Yorks)	d									16 47											
Doncaster 7	a	15 10					16 09			16 57		17 10				17 35					
Moorthorpe	d					15 40												17 40		18 02	
Thurnscoe	d					15 46												17 46			
Goldthorpe	d					15 48												17 48			
Bolton-upon-Dearne	d					15 51												17 51			
Swinton (S.Yorks)	29 a					15 55												17 55		18 11	
Rotherham Central	29 a					16 05												18 05		18 18	
Meadowhall	29 a			15 35	15 55	16 10			16 56						17 34		17 55	18 11		18 23	
Sheffield 7	29 a		15 42	15 45	16 05	16 21		16 41	17 05					17 41	17 44		18 05	18 23		18 35	18 40

		NT	NT	NT	GR	XC	NT	NT	NT	XC	GR	NT	NT	XC	NT	NT	NT	NT
					R 1	1◇				1◇	R 1			1◇				
		A			B	K		A		K	B			L	J			
Leeds 10	32, 34 d	18 05	18 09	18 28	18 40	19 00		19 04	19 09	20 00	20 15	20 20	20 28	21 00		21 09	21 40	22 28
Outwood	d		18 18				←		19 20			20 29				21 18	21 51	
Wakefield Kirkgate 4	32, 34, 39 a	18 21		18 43			18 43	19 20					20 44					22 44
	d	18 22		18 45			18 45	19 20					20 46					22 46
Wakefield Westgate 7	32, 39 a		18 22	→	18 52	19 11			19 24	20 11	20 27	20 33		21 11		21 22	21 55	
	d		18 22		18 52	19 12			19 24	20 12	20 27	20 33		21 12		21 22	21 55	
Sandal & Agbrigg	d		18 25						19 28			20 36				21 25	21 59	
Fitzwilliam	d		18 32						19 35			20 43				21 32	22 06	
South Elmsall	d		18 37									20 48				21 37		
Adwick	a		18 42									20 53				21 42		
	d		18 43									20 54				21 43		
Bentley (S.Yorks)	d		18 47									20 58				21 47		
Doncaster 7	a		18 57		19 09						20 47	21 08				21 55		
Moorthorpe	d								19 40						21 29		22 11	
Thurnscoe	d								19 46								22 17	
Goldthorpe	d								19 48								22 19	
Bolton-upon-Dearne	d								19 51								22 22	
Swinton (S.Yorks)	29 a								19 55						21 38		22 32	
Rotherham Central	29 a								20 04						21 48		22 39	
Meadowhall	29 a	18 56					19 32	19 54	20 11				21 33		21 54		22 45	23 31
Sheffield 7	29 a	19 05				19 40	19 43	20 04	20 23	20 40			21 42	21 44	22 05		22 54	23 42

For general notes see front of timetable
For details of catering facilities see Directory of Train Operators

A To Nottingham (Table 34)
B To London Kings Cross (Table 26)
C From Edinburgh to Plymouth (Table 51)
D From Edinburgh (Table 51) to Penzance (Table 135)
E To St Pancras International (Table 53)
G From Glasgow Central to Plymouth (Table 51)
H From Aberdeen (Table 229) to Plymouth (Table 51)
J From York (Table 33)
K From Edinburgh to Bristol Temple Meads (Table 51)
L From Edinburgh to Birmingham New Street (Table 51)

Sundays

from 19 July

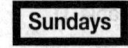

Leeds → Wakefield, Doncaster and Sheffield

Network Diagram - see first page of Table 31

			XC	XC	GR	XC	NT		EM	NT	XC	NT	GR		EM	NT	NT	NT	EM		GR	EM	XC	NT	NT	NT
			1 ◇	1 ◇	R 1	1 ◇			1 ◇		1 ◇		R 1		1 ◇				1 ◇		R 1	1 ◇	1 ◇			
				A	B	C			D		E	J	G		H			J	D		B	H	K	J		
Leeds 10	32, 34	d	07 45	08 10	08 25	08 30	08 34		08 46	08 49	09 00	09 05	09 05		09 11				09 35		09 40	09 54	10 00	10 02	10 09	10 17
Outwood		d								09 00						←		←							10 18	
Wakefield Kirkgate 4	32, 34, 39	a					09 03					09 21				09 03		09 21						10 18		10 46
		d					09 03					09 21				09 03		09 21						10 18		10 46
Wakefield Westgate 7	32, 39	a	07 59	08 21	08 37	08 42	→		08 57	09 04	09 11	→	09 17		09 22				09 46		09 52	10 05	10 11		10 22	
		d	08 00	08 22	08 37	08 43			08 58	09 04	09 12		09 17		09 23				09 47		09 52	10 06	10 12		10 22	
Sandal & Agbrigg		d								09 08															10 25	
Fitzwilliam		d								09 15															10 32	
South Elmsall		d																							10 37	
Adwick		a																							10 42	
		d																							10 43	
Bentley (S.Yorks)		d																							10 47	
Doncaster 7		a			08 54	08 59					09 31		09 37								10 09		10 28		10 57	
Moorthorpe		d								09 20							←									
Thurnscoe		d								09 26							09 26									
Goldthorpe		d								→							09 28									
Bolton-upon-Dearne		d															09 31									
Swinton (S.Yorks)	29	a															09 35									
Rotherham Central	29	a															09 44									
Meadowhall	29	a														09b47	09 53	09c55						10 51		11 32
Sheffield 7	29	a	08 30	08 52		09 25			09 29		09 55				09 51	09 55	10 03	10 04	10 21			10 33	10 54	11 00		11 44

			GR		NT	XC	NT	NT	NT		GR	XC	NT	NT	NT		GR	XC	EM	XC	NT		NT	GR	XC	EM
			R 1			1 ◇					R 1	1 ◇					R 1	1 ◇	1 ◇	1 ◇				R 1	1 ◇	1 ◇
			B		J	L	J		J		B	N		J			B	Q	D	Q				B	N	H
Leeds 10	32, 34	d	10 40		10 57	11 00		11 09	11 29		11 40	12 00	12 09	12 29	12 34		12 40	13 00	13 05				13 09	13 40	14 00	14 05
Outwood		d					←	11 20					12 18								←		13 20			
Wakefield Kirkgate 4	32, 34, 39	a			11 13		11 13		11 46					12 46	13 03						13 03					
		d			11 13		11 13		11 46					12 46	13 03						13 03					
Wakefield Westgate 7	32, 39	a	10 52		→	11 11		11 24			11 52	12 11	12 22		→		12 52	13 11	13 16	←			13 24	13 52	14 11	14 17
		d	10 52			11 12		11 24			11 52	12 12	12 22				12 52	13 12	13 17	13 12			13 24	13 52	14 12	14 18
Sandal & Agbrigg		d						11 28					12 25					→					13 28			
Fitzwilliam		d						11 35					12 32										13 35			
South Elmsall		d											12 37													
Adwick		a											12 42													
		d											12 43													
Bentley (S.Yorks)		d											12 47													
Doncaster 7		a	11 12			11 28					12 09	12 28	12 57				13 11			13 28				14 09		
Moorthorpe		d						11 40															13 40			
Thurnscoe		d						11 46															13 46			
Goldthorpe		d						11 48															13 48			
Bolton-upon-Dearne		d						11 51															13 51			
Swinton (S.Yorks)	29	a						11 55															14 00			
Rotherham Central	29	a						12 05															14 08			
Meadowhall	29	a					11 46	12 11	12 17					13 18							13 47		14 14			
Sheffield 7	29	a				11 53	11 56	12 20	12 29			12 54		13 29					13 49	13 55	13 58		14 25		14 44	14 55

			NT	NT	NT		GR	XC	NT	NT	NT		GR	XC	NT	NT	NT		GR	XC	NT	GR	NT		NT	GR
							R 1	1 ◇					R 1	1 ◇					R 1	1 ◇		R 1				R 1
			J				B	Q		J			B	U	J				B	V		B	J			B
Leeds 10	32, 34	d	14 05	14 09	14 17		14 40	15 00		15 05	15 09		15 40	16 00	16 05	16 09	16 17		16 40	17 00		17 05	17 05		17 09	17 40
Outwood		d		14 18					←		15 20					16 18					←				17 20	
Wakefield Kirkgate 4	32, 34, 39	a	14 21		14 46				14 46	15 22					16 21		16 46				16 46		17 21			
		d	14 21		14 46				14 46	15 22					16 22		16 46				16 46		17 21			
Wakefield Westgate 7	32, 39	a		14 22	→		14 52	15 11			15 24		15 52	16 11		16 22	→		16 52	17 11		17 18			17 24	17 52
		d		14 22			14 52	15 12			15 24		15 52	16 12		16 22			16 52	17 12		17 18			17 24	
Sandal & Agbrigg		d		14 25							15 28					16 25									17 28	
Fitzwilliam		d		14 32							15 35					16 32									17 35	
South Elmsall		d		14 37												16 37										
Adwick		a		14 42												16 42										
		d		14 43												16 43										
Bentley (S.Yorks)		d		14 47												16 47										
Doncaster 7		a		14 57			15 10						16 09			16 57			17 10			17 35				
Moorthorpe		d									15 40														17 40	
Thurnscoe		d									15 46														17 46	
Goldthorpe		d									15 48														17 48	
Bolton-upon-Dearne		d									15 51														17 51	
Swinton (S.Yorks)	29	a									15 55														17 55	
Rotherham Central	29	a									16 05														18 05	
Meadowhall	29	a	14 54						15 35	15 55	16 10				16 56						17 34		17 55		18 11	
Sheffield 7	29	a	15 06					15 42	15 45	16 05	16 21			16 41	17 05					17 41	17 44		18 05		18 23	

For general notes see front of timetable
For details of catering facilities see Directory of Train Operators

- **A** Until 1 November. To Plymouth (Table 51)
- **B** To London Kings Cross (Table 26)
- **C** From 8 November. To Plymouth (Table 51)
- **D** From 13 September. To St Pancras International (Table 53)
- **E** 13 September to 1 November. To Plymouth (Table 51)
- **G** To Glasgow Central (Table 26)
- **H** Until 6 September. To St Pancras International (Table 53)
- **J** To Nottingham (Table 34)
- **K** From York to Birmingham New Street (13 September to 1 November to Plymouth) (Table 51)
- **L** From Newcastle to Birmingham New Street (13 September to 1 November to Plymouth) (Table 51)
- **N** From Edinburgh to Plymouth (from 8 November to Birmingham New Street) (Table 51)
- **Q** From Edinburgh to Penzance (Table 135) (from 8 November to Birmingham New Street) (Table 51)
- **U** From Glasgow Central to Plymouth (from 8 November to Birmingham New Street) (Table 51)
- **V** From Aberdeen to Plymouth (Table 229) (from 8 November to Birmingham New Street) (Table 51)
- **b** From 13 September arr. 0941
- **c** From 13 September arr. 0954

Sundays

from 19 July

Leeds → Wakefield, Doncaster and Sheffield

Network Diagram - see first page of Table 31

	NT	XC	NT	NT	NT		GR	XC	NT	NT	NT		XC	GR	NT	NT	XC		NT	NT	NT	NT		
		1◇					R 1	1◇					1◇	R 1			1◇							
	A	B	C				D	E		C			E	D			G		A					
		✠					✕ ✠	✠						✕										
Leeds 10 32, 34 d		18 00	18 05	18 09	18 17		18 40	19 00		19 04	19 09		20 00	20 15	20 17	20 20	21 00			21 09	21 40	22 17		
Outwood d				18 18					←		19 20					20 29				21 18	21 51			
Wakefield Kirkgate 4 32, 34, 39 a			18 21		18 45				18 45	19 20					20 46							22 46		
d			18 22		18 45				18 45	19 20					20 46							22 46		
Wakefield Westgate 7 32, 39 a		18 11		18 22	→		18 52	19 11			19 24		20 11	20 27		20 33	21 11			21 22	21 55			
d		18 12		18 22			18 52	19 12			19 24		20 12	20 27		20 33	21 12			21 22	21 55			
Sandal & Agbrigg d				18 25							19 28					20 36				21 25	21 59			
Fitzwilliam d				18 32							19 35					20 43				21 32	22 06			
South Elmsall d				18 37												20 48				21 37				
Adwick a				18 42												20 53				21 42				
d				18 43												20 54				21 43				
Bentley (S.Yorks) d				18 47												20 58				21 47				
Doncaster 7 a				18 57			19 09							20 47		21 08				21 55				
Moorthorpe d	18 02										19 40								21 29		22 11			
Thurnscoe d											19 46										22 17			
Goldthorpe d											19 48										22 19			
Bolton-upon-Dearne d											19 51										22 22			
Swinton (S.Yorks) 29 a	18 11										19 55								21 38		22 32			
Rotherham Central 29 a	18 18										20 04								21 48		22 39			
Meadowhall 29 🚋 a	18 23		18 56						19 32	19 54	20 11				21 33				21 54		22 45	23 31		
Sheffield 7 29 🚋 a	18 35	18 40	19 05					19 40	19 43	20 04	20 23		20 40		21 42		21 44		22 05		22 54	23 42		

For general notes see front of timetable
For details of catering facilities see Directory of Train Operators

A From York (Table 33)
B From Glasgow Central to Plymouth (from 8 November to Birmingham New Street) (Table 51)
C To Nottingham (Table 34)
D To London Kings Cross (Table 26)
E From Edinburgh to Bristol Temple Meads (from 8 November to Birmingham New Street) (Table 51)
G From Edinburgh to Birmingham New Street (Table 51)

Table 32

Leeds and Wakefield → Pontefract, Knottingley and Goole

Mondays to Saturdays

Network Diagram - see first page of Table 31

Miles	Miles	Station		NT SX	NT	NT A	NT		NT	NT A	NT SO	NT SX		NT	NT A	NT	NT		NT A	NT	NT	NT A		NT	NT
0	—	**Leeds** 10	31, 34 d	05 46		06 38	07 00			07 29	08 00	08 05			08 32	09 00			09 32	10 00		10 32		11 00	
6	—	Woodlesford	34 d	05 54		06 46	07 08			07 37	08 08	08 15			08 40	09 08			09 40	10 08		10 40		11 08	
10¾	—	Castleford	a	06 03		06 54	07 19			07 45	08 17	08 24			08 48	09 17			09 48	10 18		10 48		11 17	
—	—		34 d	06 05		06 57	07 19			07 48	08 19	08 26			08 51	09 19			09 51	10 19		10 51		11 19	
12¼	—	Glasshoughton	d	06 10			07 24				08 24	08 31				09 24				10 24				11 24	
—	0	**Wakefield Westgate** 7	31, 39 d		06 24																				
—	1	Wakefield Kirkgate 4	31, 34, 39 a		06 29	07 07				08 00					09 03				10 01			11 01			
—	—		d		06 31				07 31					08 31			09 31				10 31				11 31
—	5¼	Streethouse	d		06 38				07 39					08 39			09 39				10 39				11 39
—	7	Featherstone	d		06 42				07 43					08 43			09 43				10 43				11 43
—	9	Pontefract Tanshelf	d		06 45				07 46					08 46			09 46				10 46				11 46
14	9¾	Pontefract Monkhill	a	06 14	06 48		07 28		07 50		08 28	08 35		08 49		09 28	09 49			10 28	10 49			11 28	11 49
—	—		d	06 14	06 48		07 28		07 50		08 28	08 35		08 49		09 28	09 49			10 28	10 49			11 28	11 49
16	—	**Knottingley**	a	06 20	06 56		07 36		07 59		08 36	08 44		08 56		09 37	09 56			10 36	10 56			11 35	11 56
—	—		d																						
20¼	—	Whitley Bridge	d																						
22	—	Hensall	d																						
25¾	—	Snaith	d																						
28½	—	Rawcliffe	d																						
32½	—	**Goole**	a																						

Station		NT A	NT	NT	NT A		NT	NT	NT A	NT		NT	NT A	NT	NT		NT A	NT	NT	NT A		NT	NT	NT A	NT
Leeds 10	31, 34 d	11 32	12 00		12 32		13 00		13 32	14 00			14 32	15 00			15 32	16 00		16 32		17 16		17 32	18 00
Woodlesford	34 d	11 40	12 08		12 40		13 08		13 40	14 08			14 40	15 08			15 40	16 08		16 40		17 24		17 40	18 08
Castleford	a	11 48	12 17		12 48		13 17		13 48	14 17			14 48	15 17			15 48	16 17		16 48		17 33		17 48	18 17
	34 d	11 51	12 19		12 51		13 19		13 51	14 19			14 51	15 19			15 51	16 19		16 51		17 35		17 51	18 19
Glasshoughton	d		12 24				13 24			14 24				15 24				16 24				17 40			18 24
Wakefield Westgate 7	31, 39 d																								
Wakefield Kirkgate 4	31, 34, 39 a	12 01			13 01				14 01				15 01				16 01			17 01				18 01	
	d			12 31				13 31				14 31			15 31				16 31				17 31		
Streethouse	d			12 39				13 39				14 39			15 39				16 39				17 39		
Featherstone	d			12 43				13 43				14 43			15 43				16 43				17 43		
Pontefract Tanshelf	d			12 46				13 46				14 46			15 46				16 46				17 46		
Pontefract Monkhill	a		12 28	12 49			13 28	13 49		14 28		14 49		15 28	15 49			16 28	16 49			17 44	17 49		18 28
	d		12 28	12 49			13 28	13 49		14 28		14 49		15 28	15 49			16 28	16 49			17 44	17 49		18 28
Knottingley	a		12 35	12 56			13 35	13 56		14 35		14 56		15 35	15 56			16 35	16 56			17 50	17 57		18 35
	d																					17 51			
Whitley Bridge	d																					17 57			
Hensall	d																					18 01			
Snaith	d																					18 08			
Rawcliffe	d																					18 12			
Goole	a																					18 26			

Station		NT	NT A		NT	NT	NT A	NT		NT	NT A	NT	NT		NT A	NT B	NT SX	NT SO C		NT SO D Bus	NT E				
Leeds 10	31, 34 d		18 32		19 00		19 37	20 05			20 37	21 05			21 37	22 05					22 37				
Woodlesford	34 d		18 40		19 08		19 45	20 13			20 45	21 13			21 45	22 13					22 45				
Castleford	a		18 48		19 18		19 53	20 22			20 53	21 22			21 53	22 22					22 53				
	34 d		18 51		19 20		19 56	20 24			20 56	21 24			21 56	22 24					22 56				
Glasshoughton	d				19 24			20 29				21 29				22 28									
Wakefield Westgate 7	31, 39 d												21 57				23 04	23 04		23 04					
Wakefield Kirkgate 4	31, 34, 39 a		19 04				20 06				21 06		22 00		22 06		23 07	23 07		23 09	23 10				
	d	18 33				19 33				20 54			22 00				23 07	23 07		23 09					
Streethouse	d	18 41				19 41				21 02			22 08				23 15	23 15		23 22					
Featherstone	d	18 45				19 45				21 06			22 12				23 19	23 19		23 27					
Pontefract Tanshelf	d	18 48				19 48				21 09			22 16				23 23	23 23		23 33					
Pontefract Monkhill	a	18 51			19 28	19 51		20 33		21 12		21 33	22 18			22 33	23 25	23 29		23 37					
	d	18 51			19 28	19 51		20 33		21 12		21 33	22 19			22 33	23 26								
Knottingley	a	18 58			19 35	19 58		20 40		21 19		21 40	22 25			22 40	23 32								
	d																								
Whitley Bridge	d																								
Hensall	d																								
Snaith	d																								
Rawcliffe	d																								
Goole	a																								

Sundays

until 12 July

Station		NT G Bus	NT Bus		NT G Bus	NT Bus		NT G Bus	NT Bus		NT G Bus	NT Bus		NT G Bus	NT Bus		NT G Bus	NT Bus		NT G Bus	NT Bus		NT G Bus	NT H Bus			
Leeds 10	34 d	07 55	08 55		09 40	10 40		11 55	12 40		13 40	14 40		15 40	16 40		17 40	18 40		19 40	20 55		21 40	22 40			
Woodlesford	34 d	08 15	09 15		10 00	11 00		12 15	13 00		14 00	15 00		16 00	17 00		18 00	19 00		20 00	21 15		22 00	23s00			
Castleford	34 a	08 30	09 30		10 15	11 15		12 30	13 15		14 15	15 15		16 15	17 15		18 15	19 15		20 15	21 30		22 15	23 15			
	d		09 30			11 15			13 15			15 15			17 15			19 15			21 30						
Glasshoughton	d		09 35			11 20			13 20			15 20			17 20			19 20			21 35						
Pontefract Monkhill	d		09 42			11 27			13 27			15 27			17 27			19 27			21 42						
Knottingley	a		09 51			11 36			13 36			15 36			17 36			19 36			21 51						

For general notes see front of timetable
For details of catering facilities see Directory of Train Operators

A To Sheffield (Table 34)
B All Mondays to Fridays, also Saturdays from 18 July
C From 18 July
D Until 11 July
E All Mondays to Fridays, also Saturdays from 18 July. Mondays to Fridays to Sheffield (Table 34)
G To Wakefield Kirkgate (Table 31)
H To Normanton arr. 2327

Table 32

Sundays

from 19 July

Leeds and Wakefield → Pontefract, Knottingley and Goole

Network Diagram - see first page of Table 31

		NT	NT	NT	NT	NT	NT	NT	NT	NT	NT	NT	NT	NT	NT	NT
		A		A		A		A		A		A		A		A
Leeds 10	34 d	08 34	09 34	10 17	11 17	12 34	13 17	14 17	15 17	16 17	17 17	18 17	19 17	20 17	21 17	22 17
Woodlesford	34 d	08 42	09 42	10 25	11 25	12 42	13 25	14 25	15 25	16 25	17 25	18 25	19 25	20 25	21 25	22 25
Castleford	34 a	08 50	09 50	10 33	11 33	12 50	13 33	14 33	15 33	16 33	17 33	18 33	19 35	20 33	21 33	22 33
	d	.	09 53	.	11 36	.	13 36	.	15 36	.	17 36	.	19 36	.	21 36	.
Glasshoughton	d		09 57		11 40		13 40		15 40		17 40		19 40		21 40	
Pontefract Monkhill	d	.	10 02	.	11 45	.	13 45	.	15 45	.	17 45	.	19 45	.	21 45	.
Knottingley	a		10 08		11 52		13 52		15 52		17 52		19 52		21 52	

For general notes see front of timetable
For details of catering facilities see Directory of Train Operators

A To Sheffield (Table 34)

Goole, Knottingley and Pontefract → Wakefield and Leeds

Network Diagram - see first page of Table 31

Miles	Miles			NT SX	NT A	NT	NT SX	NT SX	NT SO	NT B	NT	NT	NT A	NT	NT	NT A	NT	NT	NT A	NT	NT
0	—	**Goole**	d					07 04	07 09												
4	—	Rawcliffe	d					07 11	07 16												
6¾	—	Snaith	d					07 16	07 21												
10½	—	Hensall	d					07 23	07 28												
12¼	—	Whitley Bridge	d					07 30	07 30												
16½	—	**Knottingley**	a					07 38	07 39												
—	—		d	06 25		06 58		07 38	07 39		07 53	08 16		08 53	09 16		09 53	10 16		10 53	11 16
18½	0	Pontefract Monkhill	a	06 29		07 02		07 43	07 43		07 57	08 20		08 57	09 20		09 57	10 20		10 57	11 20
—	—		d	06 29		07 02		07 43	07 43		07 57	08 20		08 57	09 20		09 57	10 20		10 57	11 20
—	¾	Pontefract Tanshelf	d			07 05					08 00			09 00			10 00			11 00	
—	2¾	Featherstone	d			07 08					08 03			09 03			10 03			11 03	
—	4½	Streethouse	d			07 12					08 07			09 07			10 07			11 07	
—	8¾	Wakefield Kirkgate 4 31, 34, 39	a			07 24					08 18			09 18			10 18			11 18	
—	—		d		06 50					07 50			08 50			09 50			10 50		
—	9¾	**Wakefield Westgate** 7 ... 31, 39	a																		
20	—	Glasshoughton	d	06 34				07 48	07 48			08 25			09 25			10 25			11 25
21½	—	Castleford	a	06 38	07 00			07 54	07 54	08 00		08 30	09 00		09 29	10 00		10 30	11 00		11 29
—	—	34	d	06 41	07 02		07 38	07 55	07 55	08 02		08 32	09 02		09 32	10 02		10 32	11 02		11 32
26½	—	Woodlesford 34	d	06 50	07 12		07 47	08 04	08 04	08 12		08 41	09 12		09 41	10 12		10 41	11 12		11 41
32½	—	**Leeds** 10 31, 34	a	07 04	07 28		08 01	08 19	08 19	08 25		08 54	09 25		09 53	10 25		10 55	11 25		11 53

		NT A	NT	NT	NT A	NT	NT	NT A	NT	NT	NT A	NT	NT	NT A	NT	NT	NT A	NT	NT	NT A	NT
Goole	d																				
Rawcliffe	d																				
Snaith	d																				
Hensall	d																				
Whitley Bridge	d																				
Knottingley	a																				
	d		11 53	12 16		12 53	13 16		13 53	14 16		14 53	15 16		15 53	16 16		16 53	17 14		18 02
Pontefract Monkhill	a		11 57	12 20		12 57	13 20		13 57	14 20		14 57	15 20		15 57	16 20		16 57	17 18		18 06
	d		11 57	12 20		12 57	13 20		13 57	14 20		14 57	15 20		15 57	16 20		16 57	17 18		18 06
Pontefract Tanshelf	d		12 00			13 00			14 00			15 00			16 00			17 00			18 09
Featherstone	d		12 03			13 03			14 03			15 03			16 03			17 03			18 12
Streethouse	d		12 07			13 07			14 07			15 07			16 07			17 07			18 16
Wakefield Kirkgate 4 31, 34, 39	a		12 18			13 18			14 18			15 18			16 19			17 18			18 27
	d	11 50			12 50			13 50			14 50			15 50			16 50			17 50	
Wakefield Westgate 7 ... 31, 39	a																				
Glasshoughton	d			12 25			13 25			14 25			15 25			16 25			17 23		
Castleford	a	12 00		12 29	13 00		13 29	14 00		14 29	15 00		15 29	16 00		16 29	17 00		17 27	18 00	
34	d	12 02		12 32	13 02		13 32	14 02		14 32	15 02		15 32	16 02		16 32	17 02		17 30	18 02	
Woodlesford 34	d	12 12		12 41	13 12		13 41	14 12		14 41	15 12		15 41	16 12		16 41	17 12		17 41	18 12	
Leeds 10 31, 34	a	12 25		12 53	13 25		13 53	14 25		14 53	15 25		15 53	16 25		16 55	17 25		17 53	18 25	

		NT	NT A	NT	NT	NT A	NT	NT	NT A	NT	NT	NT C	NT D	NT SO E	NT G	NT	NT D
Goole	d				18 49												
Rawcliffe	d				18 56												
Snaith	d				19 01												
Hensall	d				19 08												
Whitley Bridge	d				19 12												
Knottingley	a				19 20												
	d	18 39		19 02	19 21		19 53	20 16		21 16	21 23		22 16	22 16		22 30	23 05
Pontefract Monkhill	a	18 43		19 06	19 25		19 57	20 20		21 20	21 27		22 22	22 22		22 34	23 09
	d	18 43		19 06	19 25		19 57	20 20		21 20	21 27		22 22	22 22		22 34	23 09
Pontefract Tanshelf	d			19 09			20 00				21 30					22 37	
Featherstone	d			19 12			20 03				21 33					22 40	
Streethouse	d			19 16			20 07				21 37					22 44	
Wakefield Kirkgate 4 31, 34, 39	a			19 27			20 18				21 47					22 55	
	d		18 50			19 50			20 50		21 47	21 52			22 50	22 55	
Wakefield Westgate 7 ... 31, 39	a										21 52					23 01	
Glasshoughton	d	18 48			19 30			20 25		21 25			22 27	22 27			23 14
Castleford	a	18 54	19 00		19 34	20 00		20 29	21 00	21 29		22 03	22 31	22 31	23 00		23 18
34	d	18 57	19 02		19 37	20 02		20 32	21 02	21 32		22 05	22 34		23 02		23 21
Woodlesford 34	d	19 06	19 13		19 46	20 12		20 44	21 12	21 41		22 14	22 43		23 13		23 30
Leeds 10 31, 34	a	19 20	19 27		20 00	20 26		20 57	21 25	21 53		22 28	22 57		23 28		23 44

Sundays

until 12 July

		NT H (bus)	NT (bus)	NT H (bus)	NT (bus)	NT H (bus)	NT (bus)	NT H (bus)	NT (bus)	NT H (bus)	NT (bus)	NT H (bus)	NT (bus)	NT H (bus)	NT (bus)	NT H (bus)
Knottingley	d		10 35		12 35		14 35		16 35		18 35		20 35		22 35	
Pontefract Monkhill	d		10 44		12 44		14 44		16 44		18 44		20 44		22 44	
Glasshoughton	d		10 54		12 54		14 54		16 54		18 54		20 54		22 54	
Castleford	a		10 59		12 59		14 59		16 59		18 59		20 59		22 59	
34	d	09 59	10 59	11 59	12 59	13 59	14 59	15 59	16 59	17 59	18 59	19 59	20 59	21 59	22 59	23 59
Woodlesford 34	d	10 14	11 14	12 14	13 14	14 14	15 14	16 14	17 14	18 14	19 14	20 14	21 14	22 14	23 14	00 14
Leeds 10 34	a	10 34	11 34	12 34	13 34	14 34	15 34	16 34	17 34	18 34	19 34	20 34	21 34	22 34	23 34	00 34

For general notes see front of timetable
For details of catering facilities see Directory of Train Operators

A From Sheffield (Table 34)

B From Worksop (Table 30) (Saturdays from Sheffield) (Table 34)

C All Mondays to Fridays, also Saturdays from 18 July. From Sheffield (Table 34)

D All Mondays to Fridays, also Saturdays from 18 July

E Until 11 July

G All Mondays to Fridays, also Saturdays from 18 July. Mondays to Thursdays from Sheffield (Table 34)

H From Wakefield Kirkgate (Table 34)

Table 32

Sundays

from 19 July

Goole, Knottingley and Pontefract → Wakefield and Leeds

Network Diagram - see first page of Table 31

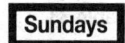

		NT	NT	NT	NT	NT	NT	NT	NT	NT	NT	NT	NT	NT	NT	NT	NT
		A		A		A		A		B		A		A		B	
Knottingley	d		10 26		12 26		14 26		16 26		18 26		20 26		22 26		
Pontefract Monkhill	d		10 30		12 30		14 30		16 30		18 30		20 30		22 30		
Glasshoughton	d		10 35		12 35		14 35		16 35		18 35		20 35		22 35		
Castleford	a		10 39		12 39		14 39		16 39		18 39		20 39		22 39		
	34 d	09 42	10 42	11 41	12 42	13 42	14 42	15 41	16 42	17 42	18 42	19 44	20 42	21 42	22 42	23 42	
Woodlesford	34 d	09 52	10 51	11 51	12 52	13 51	14 51	15 51	16 51	17 51	18 51	19 53	20 51	21 51	22 51	23 51	
Leeds 10	34 a	10 04	11 04	12 05	13 04	14 04	15 04	16 04	17 04	18 05	19 04	20 05	21 03	22 04	23 04	00 04	

For general notes see front of timetable
For details of catering facilities see
Directory of Train Operators

A From Sheffield (Table 34)
B From Lincoln (Table 30)

Table 33

Mondays to Fridays

Sheffield and Selby → York

Local services only

Network Diagram - see first page of Table 31

Miles	Miles		NT	NT A	NT B	NT B	NT	NT	NT B	NT	NT	NT	NT B	NT
0	—	**Sheffield** 7 29, 31 d								09 29				
3½	—	Meadowhall 29, 31 d								09 35				
6¼	—	Rotherham Central 29, 31 d								09 42				
10¾	—	Swinton (S.Yorks) 29, 31 d								09 51				
18½	—	Moorthorpe 31 d								10 01				
25½	—	Pontefract Baghill d								10 10				
—	—	Hull 29 d	*06 00*	07 07			*08 40*	09 02			*10 12*	11 05		*11 38*
—	0	**Selby** d	06 48	07 48			09 15	09 38			10 54	11 39		12 51
33¾	8¼	Sherburn-in-Elmet d	07 00	08 02			09 26			10 28				
36	10½	Church Fenton d	07 04		08 05	09 05			10 05	10 32			12 05	
38	12½	Ulleskelf d		08 08						10 36				
46¾	21	**York** 8 29 a	07 20	08 21	08 21	09 21	09 46	10 07	10 21	10 52	11 20	12 10	12 21	13 15

	NT B	NT	NT	NT	NT B	NT	NT B	NT A	NT B	NT	NT	NT B	NT B
Sheffield 7 29, 31 d			13 28										
Meadowhall 29, 31 d			13 35										
Rotherham Central 29, 31 d			13 41										
Swinton (S.Yorks) 29, 31 d			13 50										
Moorthorpe 31 d			14 01										
Pontefract Baghill d			14 10										
Hull 29 d		13 12		15 06		16 10		17 18		19 10	*19 56*		
Selby d		13 54		15 38		16 47		18 07		19 47	20 35		
Sherburn-in-Elmet d		14 08	14 28										
Church Fenton d	14 05		14 32		16 05		18 06		19 05			21 12	23 16
Ulleskelf d			14 36				18 10					21 16	
York 8 29 a	14 21	14 25	14 51	16 06	16 21	17 13	18 24	18 36	19 21	20 16	21 00	21 31	23 33

Saturdays

	NT	NT A	NT B	NT B	NT	NT	NT B	NT	NT	NT	NT B	NT	NT B
Sheffield 7 29, 31 d								09 31					
Meadowhall 29, 31 d								09 37					
Rotherham Central 29, 31 d								09 44					
Swinton (S.Yorks) 29, 31 d								09 52					
Moorthorpe 31 d								10 02					
Pontefract Baghill d								10 11					
Hull 29 d	*06 00*	06 57			*08 40*	09 02			*10 06*	11 08		*11 38*	
Selby d	06 48	07 40			09 15	09 38			10 54	11 40		12 51	
Sherburn-in-Elmet d	07 00	07 54			09 26			10 28				13 03	
Church Fenton d	07 04		08 05	09b07			10b07	10 33			12b07		14b07
Ulleskelf d		08 00						10 37					
York 8 29 a	07 20	08 15	08 21	09 21	09 46	10 10	10 23	10 53	11 20	12 10	12 21	13 23	14 21

	NT	NT	NT	NT B	NT	NT B	NT A	NT B	NT	NT	NT B	NT	NT B
Sheffield 7 29, 31 d		13 28											
Meadowhall 29, 31 d		13 35											
Rotherham Central 29, 31 d		13 42											
Swinton (S.Yorks) 29, 31 d		13 50											
Moorthorpe 31 d		14 00											
Pontefract Baghill d		14 09											
Hull 29 d	13 12		14 51		16 10		17 18		18 46	*19 56*		*21 33*	
Selby d	13 54		15 22		16 47		18 06		19 22	20 35		22 28	
Sherburn-in-Elmet d		14 27											
Church Fenton d		14 31		16b07		18c07		19b07			21 12		23 19
Ulleskelf d		14 35				18 11					21 16		
York 8 29 a	14 26	14 51	15 53	16 22	17 13	18 24	18 36	19 21	19 56	21 00	21 31	22 53	23 36

Sundays

	NT C	NT	NT D	NT	NT B	NT E	NT B	NT	NT E	NT	NT B	NT	NT B	NT E	NT	NT B	NT	NT G
Sheffield 7 29, 31 d										15 46					18 57			
Meadowhall 29, 31 d										15 52					19 04			
Rotherham Central 29, 31 d										15 58					19 10			
Swinton (S.Yorks) 29, 31 d										16 08					19 18			
Moorthorpe 31 d										16 18					19 28			
Pontefract Baghill d										16 26					19 37			
Hull 29 d		08 54		11 54		13 27		14 28	16 01			17 23		19 04			20 22	
Selby d		09 25		12 25		13 58		15 04	16 32			17 54		19 35			20 53	
Sherburn-in-Elmet d										16 43					19 55			
Church Fenton d	09 18		10 51		12 49		14 49			16 47	16 49		18 47		19 59	20 49		23 07
Ulleskelf d																		
York 8 29 a	09 34	09 54	11 07	12 50	13 02	14 22	15 02	15 30	16 57	17 01	17 06	18 23	19 03	19 59	20 17	21 03	21 20	23 18

For general notes see front of timetable
For details of catering facilities see Directory of Train Operators

- **A** From Beverley (Table 43)
- **B** From Blackpool North (Table 41)
- **C** From Bradford Interchange (Table 40)
- **D** From Bradford Interchange (Table 40) (from 19 July from Huddersfield) (Table 41)
- **E** Until 13 September
- **G** From Leeds (Table 40)
- **b** From 18 July dep. 2 minutes earlier
- **c** From 18 July dep. 1 minute earlier

York → Selby and Sheffield

Local services only

Network Diagram - see first page of Table 31

Miles	Miles		NT	NT A	NT	NT B	NT	NT A	NT	NT	NT	NT A	NT	NT
0	0	**York 8** 29 d	06 09	07 06	07 31	07 48	08 43	09 09	09 53	10 20	11 02	11 09	11 53	12 18
8¾	8¾	Ulleskelf d		07 15							11 12			
10¾	10¾	Church Fenton d		07a20		08a00		09a20			11 16	11a20		
12¾	12¾	Sherburn-in-Elmet d									11 20			
—	21	**Selby** a	06 30		07 50		09 06		10 12	10 40			12 17	12 38
—	—	Hull 29 a	*08 20*		08 46		*10 04*		10 56	*11 34*			13 02	*13 34*
21¼	—	Pontefract Baghill d									11 39			
28¼	—	Moorthorpe 31 a									11 51			
36	—	Swinton (S.Yorks) 29, 31 a									12 01			
40½	—	Rotherham Central 29, 31 a									12 10			
43¾	—	Meadowhall 29, 31 a									12 16			
46¾	—	**Sheffield 7** 29, 31 a									12 26			

	NT A	NT	NT	NT	NT A	NT C	NT A	NT	NT	NT A	NT	NT B	NT B	NT	NT B
York 8 29 d	13 09	13 45	14 59	15 02	15 09	16 12	17 08	17 27	18 14	19 04	19 23	20 13	21 16	22 03	23 13
Ulleskelf d				15 12					18 24				21 25		
Church Fenton d	13a20			15 16	15a20	16 23	17a20		18 28	19a15		20a24	21a31		23a28
Sherburn-in-Elmet d		13 57		15 20		16 27			18 32						
Selby a		14 09	15 19			16 38		17 45	18 43		19 44			22 22	
Hull 29 a		14 48	15 58			17 27		18 29	19 32		*20 39*			23 08	
Pontefract Baghill d				15 39											
Moorthorpe 31 a				15 51											
Swinton (S.Yorks) 29, 31 a				16 01											
Rotherham Central 29, 31 a				16 10											
Meadowhall 29, 31 a				16 17											
Sheffield 7 29, 31 a				16 25											

Saturdays

	NT	NT A	NT	NT A	NT	NT A	NT	NT	NT	NT A	NT	NT	NT A
York 8 29 d	06 05	07 06	07 30	08 09	08 34	09 09	09 52	10 17	11 01	11 09	11 49	12 18	13 09
Ulleskelf d		07 15							11 11				
Church Fenton d		07a20		08a21		09a20			11 15	11a20			13a20
Sherburn-in-Elmet d									11 19				
Selby a	06 26		07 50		08 55		10 12	10 37			12 09	12 38	
Hull 29 a	*08 20*		08 46		*10 34*		10 56	*11 34*			12 54	*13 34*	
Pontefract Baghill d									11 37				
Moorthorpe 31 a									11 49				
Swinton (S.Yorks) 29, 31 a									11 59				
Rotherham Central 29, 31 a									12 10				
Meadowhall 29, 31 a									12 16				
Sheffield 7 29, 31 a									12 25				

	NT	NT	NT A	NT	NT C	NT A	NT	NT	NT A	NT	NT B	NT	NT B	NT	NT B
York 8 29 d	13 38	15 05	15 08	15 11	16 12	17 08	17 18	18 13	19 04	19 29	20 13	20 17	21 13	21 45	23 13
Ulleskelf d				15 22				18 22					21 22		
Church Fenton d			15a20	15 26	16 23	17a20		18 27	19a15		20a24		21a28		23a28
Sherburn-in-Elmet d	13 52			15 30	16 27			18 30							
Selby a	14 03	15 24			16 38		17 37	18 41		19 50		20 36		22 05	
Hull 29 a	14 45	16 03			17 27		18 21	19 28		*20 39*		21 22		*23 21*	
Pontefract Baghill d				15 49											
Moorthorpe 31 a				16 01											
Swinton (S.Yorks) 29, 31 a				16 10											
Rotherham Central 29, 31 a				16 17											
Meadowhall 29, 31 a				16 23											
Sheffield 7 29, 31 a				16 35											

Sundays

	NT A	NT A	NT	NT A	NT D	NT	NT A	NT D	NT	NT A	NT D	NT	NT A	NT	NT A	NT	NT	NT B
York 8 29 d	08 50	09 52	10 40	11 52	12 05	13 23	13 52	14 42	15 43	15 52	17 10	17 17	17 52	19 10	19 52	20 42	21 41	21 52
Ulleskelf d																		
Church Fenton d	09a01	10a03		12a03			14a03			16a03		17 28	18a03		20a03	20 55		22a04
Sherburn-in-Elmet d												17 32				20 59		
Selby a			10 59		12 24	13 42		15 01	16 01		17 30			19 29			22 00	
Hull 29 a			11 38		13 03	14 21		15 40	16 41		18 10			20 09			22 39	
Pontefract Baghill d												17 49				21 17		
Moorthorpe 31 a												18 01				21 29		
Swinton (S.Yorks) 29, 31 a												18 11				21 38		
Rotherham Central 29, 31 a												18 18				21 48		
Meadowhall 29, 31 a												18 23				21 54		
Sheffield 7 29, 31 a												18 35				22 05		

For general notes see front of timetable
For details of catering facilities see Directory of Train Operators

A To Blackpool North (Table 41)
B To Leeds (Table 40)
C To Scarborough (Table 43)
D Until 13 September

Nottingham, Sheffield → Barnsley → Huddersfield and Leeds

Network Diagram - see first page of Table 31

Miles	Miles	Station		NT	NT A	NT B	NT	NT	NT	NT C	NT A	NT		NT	NT C	TP [1] ◇ D	NT E	NT A	NT	NT E	NT G	EM ◇ H		NT	NT J
—	—	St Pancras International	⊖ 53 d																						
0	—	**Nottingham [8]**	d																06 23			06 40			
12	—	Langley Mill	d																06 38						
18¼	—	Alfreton	d																06 46			07 02			
28¼	—	Chesterfield	d											06 26					06 58			07 13			
33½	—	Dronfield	d											06 33					07 05			07 20			
40½	—	**Sheffield [7]**	29, 31 a											06 46					07 18			07 31			
—	—		d	05 16	05 22	05 29	05 36	05 50	06 06	06 18	06 28	06 36		06 49	06 52	06 55	07 06	07 14	07 20		07 24			07 36	07 41
44	3½	**Meadowhall [4]**	29, 31 a	05 21	05 27	05 34	05 41	05 55	06 11	06 23	06 33	06 41		06 54	06 57	07 00	07 11	07 20	07 25		07 30			07 41	07 46
—	—		d	05 22			05 42	05 56	06 12			06 42		06 55			07 12		07 26					07 42	
47¾	7¼	Chapeltown	d	05 28			05 48		06 18			06 48					07 18							07 48	
51	10½	Elsecar	d	05 33					06 23								07 23								
52½	12	Wombwell	d	05 37			05 55		06 27			06 55					07 27							07 55	
56½	16	**Barnsley**	a	05 42			06 00	06 10	06 32			07 00		07 09			07 32		07 41					08 00	
—	—		d				06 01	06 10	06 33			07 01		07 12			07 33		07 42					08 01	
—	19	Dodworth	d				06 07					07 07												08 07	
—	20¼	Silkstone Common	d				06 11					07 11												08 11	
—	23½	Penistone	d				06 18					07 18												08 18	
—	27½	Denby Dale	d				06 24					07 24												08 24	
—	29¾	Shepley	d				06 29					07 29												08 29	
—	30¾	Stocksmoor	d				06 32					07 32												08 32	
—	32¾	Brockholes	d				06 36					07 36												08 36	
—	33¾	Honley	d				06 38					07 38												08 38	
—	34¾	Berry Brow	d				06 41					07 41												08 41	
—	35¾	Lockwood	d				06 44					07 44												08 44	
—	37	**Huddersfield**	a				06 49					07 49												08 49	
60	—	Darton	d						06 38								07 38								
67½	—	**Wakefield Kirkgate [4]**	31 a					06 27	06 49					07 27			07 49		07 57						
—	—		d					06 28	06 50					07 28			07 50		07 58	←					
70½	—	Normanton	d					06 33	06 54					07 33			07 54			07 54					
74	—	Castleford	a						07 00								→			08 00					
78¾	—	Woodlesford	a						07 12											08 12					
84¾	—	**Leeds [10]**	31 a					06 49	07 28					07 51					08 21	08 25					

Station		NT K	EM [1] ◇ L	NT	TP [1] ◇ D	NT A	NT	NT	NT G	NT		EM ◇ N	NT J	NT	NT Q	NT	TP [1] ◇ D	NT A	NT	NT		NT G	NT U	NT	NT V
St Pancras International	⊖ 53 d																*06 37*								
Nottingham [8]	d						07 13					07 45							08 11						
Langley Mill	d						07 30												08 31						
Alfreton	d						07 38					08 07							08 39						
Chesterfield	d		07 42				07 50					08 18							08 51						
Dronfield	d		07 49									08 25							08 58						
Sheffield [7]	29, 31 a		08 00				08 08					08 38							09 15						
	d	07 51		08 06	08 11	08 14	08 18		08 25	08 36			08 41	08 51	08 57	09 06	09 11	09 14	09 18			09 24	09 29	09 36	09 41
Meadowhall [4]	29, 31 a	07 57		08 11	08 16	08 21	08 24		08 30	08 41			08 46	08 56	09 03	09 11	09 16	09 20	09 23			09 29	09 34	09 41	09 45
	d	07 57		08 12			08 24			08 42				08 57		09 12			09 24					09 42	
Chapeltown	d			08 18						08 48						09 18								09 48	
Elsecar	d			08 23												09 23									
Wombwell	d			08 27						08 55						09 27								09 55	
Barnsley	a	08 11		08 32			08 40			09 00				09 11		09 32			09 40					10 00	
	d	08 12		08 33			08 42			09 01				09 12		09 33			09 42					10 01	
Dodworth	d									09 07														10 07	
Silkstone Common	d									09 11														10 11	
Penistone	d									09 18														10 18	
Denby Dale	d									09 24														10 24	
Shepley	d									09 29														10 29	
Stocksmoor	d									09 32														10 32	
Brockholes	d									09 36														10 36	
Honley	d									09 38														10 38	
Berry Brow	d									09 41														10 41	
Lockwood	d									09 44														10 44	
Huddersfield	a									09 49														10 49	
Darton	d			08 38												09 38									
Wakefield Kirkgate [4]	31 a	08 27		08 49			08 57							09 27		09 49			09 57						
	d	08 28		08 50			08 58	←						09 28		09 50			09 58	←					
Normanton	d			08 54				08 54								09 54				09 54					
Castleford	a			→				09 00								→				10 00					
Woodlesford	a							09 12												10 12					
Leeds [10]	31 a	08 49					09 19	09 25						09 49					10 18	10 25					

For general notes see front of timetable
For details of catering facilities see Directory of Train Operators

- **A** To Leeds (Table 31)
- **B** To Beverley (Table 43)
- **C** To Adwick (Table 29)
- **D** From Manchester Airport to Cleethorpes (22 June to 4 September to Doncaster) (Table 29)
- **E** From Worksop (Table 30)
- **G** To Scunthorpe (from 22 June to 4 September to Thorne North) (Table 29)
- **H** To Liverpool Lime Street (Table 89)
- **J** To Bridlington (Table 43)
- **K** From Retford (Table 30)
- **L** From Derby (Table 53)
- **N** To Liverpool Lime Street (Table 49)
- **Q** From Worksop (Table 30) to Adwick (Table 29)
- **U** To York (Table 33)
- **V** To Scarborough (Table 43)

From 7 September a revised Northern service will be in operation on the Huddersfield Line due to seasonal difficulties. Customers should check with NRES for precise times

Nottingham, Sheffield → Barnsley → Huddersfield and Leeds

Network Diagram - see first page of Table 31

	NT	NT	NT	TP	NT	NT	NT		NT	NT	NT	NT	NT	NT	TP	NT	NT		NT	NT	NT	NT	NT	NT
		A		1 ◇ B 🛒	C				D		E		A		1 ◇ B 🛒	C				D		G		A
St Pancras International ⊖ 53 d				*07 55*											*08 55*									
Nottingham 8 🚌 d						09 15											10 15							
Langley Mill d						09 32											10 32							
Alfreton d						09 40											10 40							
Chesterfield d						09 52											10 52							
Dronfield d						09 59											10 59							
Sheffield 7 29, 31 🚌 a						10 15											11 15							
d	09 51	09 57	10 06	10 11	10 14	10 18			10 24	10 36	10 41	10 51	10 57	11 06	11 11	11 14	11 18			11 24	11 36	11 41	11 51	11 57
Meadowhall 4 29, 31 🚌 a	09 56	10 03	10 11	10 16	10 20	10 23			10 29	10 41	10 46	10 56	11 03	11 11	11 16	11 20	11 23			11 29	11 41	11 46	11 56	12 03
🚌 d	09 57		10 12			10 24				10 42		10 57		11 12			11 24				11 42		11 57	
Chapeltown d			10 18							10 48				11 18							11 48			
Elsecar d			10 23											11 23										
Wombwell d			10 27							10 55				11 27							11 55			
Barnsley a	10 11		10 32			10 40				11 00		11 11		11 32			11 40				12 00		12 11	
d	10 12		10 33			10 42				11 01		11 12		11 33			11 42				12 01		12 12	
Dodworth d										11 07											12 07			
Silkstone Common d										11 11											12 11			
Penistone d										11 18											12 18			
Denby Dale d										11 24											12 24			
Shepley d										11 29											12 29			
Stocksmoor d										11 32											12 32			
Brockholes d										11 36											12 36			
Honley d										11 38											12 38			
Berry Brow d										11 41											12 41			
Lockwood d										11 44											12 44			
Huddersfield a										11 49											12 49			
Darton d			10 38											11 38										
Wakefield Kirkgate 4 31 a	10 27		10 49			10 57						11 27		11 49			11 57						12 27	
d	10 28		10 50			10 58	←					11 28		11 50			11 58		←				12 28	
Normanton d			10 54 →				10 54							11 54 →					11 54					
Castleford a							11 00												12 00					
Woodlesford a							11 12												12 12					
Leeds 10 31 a	10 48					11 18	11 25					11 48					12 18		12 25				12 48	

	NT	TP	NT	NT	NT		NT	NT	NT	NT	NT	NT	TP	NT	NT		NT	NT	NT	NT	NT	NT	NT	NT
		1 ◇ B 🛒	C				D		E		A		1 ◇ B 🛒	C				D	H		E		A	
St Pancras International ⊖ 53 d		*09 55*											*10 55*											
Nottingham 8 🚌 d				11 15											12 15									
Langley Mill d				11 32											12 32									
Alfreton d				11 40											12 40									
Chesterfield d				11 52											12 52									
Dronfield d				11 59											13 02									
Sheffield 7 29, 31 🚌 a				12 15											13 15									
d	12 06	12 11	12 14	12 18			12 24	12 36	12 41	12 51	12 57	13 06	13 11	13 14	13 18			13 24	13 28	13 36	13 41	13 51	13 57	14 06
Meadowhall 4 29, 31 🚌 a	12 11	12 16	12 20	12 23			12 29	12 41	12 46	12 56	13 03	13 11	13 16	13 20	13 23			13 29	13 34	13 41	13 46	13 56	14 03	14 11
🚌 d	12 12			12 24				12 42		12 57		13 12			13 24					13 42		13 57		14 12
Chapeltown d	12 18							12 48				13 18								13 48				14 18
Elsecar d	12 23											13 23												14 23
Wombwell d	12 27							12 55				13 27								13 55				14 27
Barnsley a	12 32			12 40				13 00		13 11		13 32			13 40					14 00		14 11		14 32
d	12 33			12 42				13 01		13 12		13 33			13 42					14 01		14 12		14 33
Dodworth d								13 07												14 07				
Silkstone Common d								13 11												14 11				
Penistone d								13 18												14 18				
Denby Dale d								13 24												14 24				
Shepley d								13 29												14 29				
Stocksmoor d								13 32												14 32				
Brockholes d								13 36												14 36				
Honley d								13 38												14 38				
Berry Brow d								13 41												14 41				
Lockwood d								13 44												14 44				
Huddersfield a								13 49												14 49				
Darton d	12 38											13 38												14 38
Wakefield Kirkgate 4 31 a	12 49			12 57						13 27		13 50			13 57							14 27		14 49
d	12 50			12 58	←					13 28		13 50			13 58		←					14 28		14 50
Normanton d	12 54 →				12 54							13 54 →					13 54							14 54 →
Castleford a					13 00												14 00							
Woodlesford a					13 12												14 12							
Leeds 10 31 a				13 18	13 25					13 48					14 18		14 25					14 48		

For general notes see front of timetable
For details of catering facilities see Directory of Train Operators

- **A** From Lincoln (Table 30) to Adwick (Table 29)
- **B** From Manchester Airport to Cleethorpes (22 June to 4 September to Doncaster) (Table 29)
- **C** To Leeds (Table 31)
- **D** To Scunthorpe (from 22 June to 4 September to Thorne North) (Table 29)
- **E** To Bridlington (Table 43)
- **G** To Scarborough (Table 43)
- **H** To York (Table 33)

From 7 September a revised Northern service will be in operation on the Huddersfield Line due to seasonal difficulties. Customers should check with NRES for precise times

Nottingham, Sheffield → Barnsley → Huddersfield and Leeds

Network Diagram - see first page of Table 31

Station		TP 1 ◇ A ✠	NT B	NT		NT	NT C	NT	NT D	NT	NT E	NT	TP 1 ◇ A ✠	NT B		NT	NT	NT C	NT	NT D	NT	NT E	NT	TP 1 ◇ A ✠	NT B
St Pancras International	⊖ 53 d	11 55											12 55											13 55	
Nottingham [8]	d			13 15												14 15									
Langley Mill	d			13 32												14 32									
Alfreton	d			13 40												14 40									
Chesterfield	d			13 52												14 52									
Dronfield	d			13 59												14 59									
Sheffield [7]	29, 31 a			14 15												15 15									
	d	14 11	14 14	14 18			14 24	14 36	14 41	14 51	14 57	15 06	15 11	15 14		15 18		15 24	15 36	15 41	15 51	15 57	16 06	16 11	16 14
Meadowhall [4]	29, 31 a	14 16	14 20	14 23			14 29	14 41	14 46	14 56	15 03	15 11	15 16	15 20		15 23		15 29	15 41	15 46	15 56	16 03	16 11	16 16	16 20
	d			14 24				14 42		14 57		15 12				15 24			15 42		15 57		16 12		
Chapeltown	d							14 48				15 18							15 48				16 18		
Elsecar	d											15 23											16 23		
Wombwell	d							14 55				15 27							15 55				16 27		
Barnsley	a			14 40				15 00		15 11		15 32				15 40			16 00		16 11		16 32		
	d			14 42				15 01		15 12		15 33				15 42			16 01		16 12		16 33		
Dodworth	d							15 07											16 07						
Silkstone Common	d							15 11											16 11						
Penistone	d							15 18											16 18						
Denby Dale	d							15 24											16 24						
Shepley	d							15 29											16 29						
Stocksmoor	d							15 32											16 32						
Brockholes	d							15 36											16 36						
Honley	d							15 38											16 38						
Berry Brow	d							15 41											16 41						
Lockwood	d							15 44											16 44						
Huddersfield	a							15 49											16 49						
Darton	d											15 38											16 38		
Wakefield Kirkgate [4]	31 a			14 57						15 27		15 49				15 57					16 27		16 49		
	d			14 58		←				15 28		15 50				15 58	←				16 28		16 50		
Normanton	d					14 54						15 54 →					15 54						16 54 →		
Castleford	a					15 00											16 00								
Woodlesford	a					15 12											16 12								
Leeds [10]	31 a			15 18		15 25				15 48						16 19	16 25				16 48				

Station		NT		NT	NT G	NT	NT D	NT	NT E	NT	TP 1 ◇ A ✠	NT B		NT	NT	NT G	NT	NT D	NT	NT H	NT	NT B		NT	NT
St Pancras International	⊖ 53 d										14 55													15b55	
Nottingham [8]	d	15 15												16 15										17 15	
Langley Mill	d	15 32												16 32										17 31	
Alfreton	d	15 40												16 40										17 39	
Chesterfield	d	15 52												16 56										17 52	
Dronfield	d	15 59												17 03										17 59	
Sheffield [7]	29, 31 a	16 15												17 17										18 15	
	d	16 18			16 24	16 36	16 41	16 51	16 57	17 06	17 11	17 14		17 18		17 25	17 36	17 41	17 51	17 57	18 06	18 14		18 18	
Meadowhall [4]	29, 31 a	16 23			16 29	16 41	16 46	16 56	17 03	17 11	17 16	17 20		17 23		17 30	17 41	17 46	17 56	18 03	18 12	18 20		18 23	
	d	16 24				16 42		16 57		17 12				17 24			17 42		17 57		18 12			18 24	
Chapeltown	d					16 48				17 18							17 48				18 18				
Elsecar	d					16 53				17 23							17 53				18 23				
Wombwell	d					16 57				17 27							17 57				18 27				
Barnsley	a	16 40				17 02		17 11		17 32				17 40			18 02		18 11		18 33			18 42	
	d	16 42				17 03		17 12		17 33				17 42			18 03		18 12		18 33			18 42	
Dodworth	d					17 09											18 09								
Silkstone Common	d					17 13											18 13								
Penistone	d					17 20											18c27								
Denby Dale	d					17 26											18 33								
Shepley	d					17 31											18 38								
Stocksmoor	d					17 34											18 41								
Brockholes	d					17 38											18 45								
Honley	d					17 40											18 47								
Berry Brow	d					17 43											18 50								
Lockwood	d					17 46											18 53								
Huddersfield	a					17 50											18 57								
Darton	d									17 38											18 38				
Wakefield Kirkgate [4]	31 a	16 57						17 28		17 49				17 57					18 28		18 50			18 58	
	d	16 58		←				17 28		17 50				17 58	←				18 32		18 50			18 58	←
Normanton	d			16 54						17 54 →					17 54						18 54 →				18 54
Castleford	a			17 00											18 00										19 00
Woodlesford	a			17 12											18 12										19 13
Leeds [10]	31 a	17 18		17 25				17 48						18 18	18 25				18 51					19 23	19 27

For general notes see front of timetable
For details of catering facilities see Directory of Train Operators

- **A** From Manchester Airport to Cleethorpes (22 June to 4 September to Doncaster) (Table 29)
- **B** To Leeds (Table 31)
- **C** To Scunthorpe (from 22 June to 4 September to Thorne North) (Table 29)
- **D** To Hull (Table 29)
- **E** From Lincoln (Table 30) to Adwick (Table 29)
- **G** To Doncaster (Table 29)
- **H** From Lincoln (Table 30) to Hull (Table 29)
- **b** Change at Sheffield
- **c** Arr. 1820

From 7 September a revised Northern service will be in operation on the Huddersfield Line due to seasonal difficulties. Customers should check with NRES for precise times

Nottingham, Sheffield → Barnsley → Huddersfield and Leeds

Network Diagram - see first page of Table 31

	TP	NT	NT	NT	NT	NT	NT	TP	NT		NT	NT	NT	NT	NT	NT	NT	TP	NT		NT	NT	NT	NT
	1 ◇							1 ◇										1 ◇						
	A	B		C		D		A	E				B		G		B	A			H	E		
St Pancras International ⊖ 53 d								16 55										17 55						
Nottingham 8 d											18 15												19 15	
Langley Mill d											18 32												19 32	
Alfreton d											18 40												19 40	
Chesterfield d											18 52												19 52	
Dronfield d											18 59												19 59	
Sheffield 7 29, 31 a											19 15												20 15	
d	18 24	18 29	18 36	18 41	18 51	19 00	19 06	19 11	19 18		19 22		19 30	19 36	19 44	19 51	19 57	20 11	20 06		20 15	20 27	20 18	
Meadowhall 4 29, 31 a	18 29	18 34	18 41	18 46	18 56	19 06	19 11	19 16	19 24		19 27		19 35	19 41	19 49	19 56	20 03	20 16	20 11		20 20	20 34	20 24	
d			18 42		18 57		19 12				19 28			19 42		19 57			20 12				20 24	
Chapeltown d			18 48				19 18							19 48					20 18					
Elsecar d			18 53				19 23							19 53					20 23					
Wombwell d			18 57				19 27							19 57					20 27					
Barnsley a			19 02		19 14		19 33				19 42			20 02		20 12			20 32				20 40	
d			19 08		19 14		19 33				19 42			20 08		20 12			20 33				20 42	
Dodworth d			19 14											20 14										
Silkstone Common d			19 18											20 18										
Penistone d			19 25											20 25										
Denby Dale d			19 31											20 31										
Shepley d			19 36											20 36										
Stocksmoor d			19 39											20 39										
Brockholes d			19 43											20 43										
Honley d			19 45											20 45										
Berry Brow d			19 48											20 48										
Lockwood d			19 51											20 51										
Huddersfield a			19 56											20 55										
Darton d							19 38												20 38					
Wakefield Kirkgate 4 31 a					19 29		19 50				19 58					20 28			20 49				20 57	
d					19 32		19 50				19 58	←				20 28			20 50				20 58	←
Normanton d							19 54 →					19 54							20 54 →					20 54
Castleford a												20 00												21 00
Woodlesford a												20 12												21 12
Leeds 10 31 a					19 55						20 19	20 26				20 48							21 18	21 25

	NT	NT	NT	TP	NT	NT	NT		NT	NT	NT	TP	NT	NT	NT	NT	NT		NT	NT	NT			
										FX	FO					FO				FX				
				1 ◇								1 ◇												
	J				G	E							E		B		E			K	B			
St Pancras International ⊖ 53 d							18 55												19 55	20 55	20 55			
Nottingham 8 d									20 45					21 11										
Langley Mill d														21 31										
Alfreton d														21 39										
Chesterfield d									21 28					22 00										
Dronfield d														22 07										
Sheffield 7 29, 31 a									21 54					22 19										
d	20 38	20 41	21 09	21 11	21 15	21 30	21 41			22 06	22 06	22 11	22 15		22 21		23 15		22 41	23 24	23 27			
Meadowhall 4 29, 31 a	20 44	20 47	21 14	21 16	21 21	21 35	21 46			22 11	22 11	22 16	22 21		22 30		23 20		22 46	23 29	23 32			
d		20 47	21 15				21 47			22 12	22 12								22 47	23 30				
Chapeltown d		20 53	21 21				21 53			22 18	22 18								22 53	23 36				
Elsecar d			21 26							22 23	22 23								22 58	23 41				
Wombwell d		21 00	21 30				22 00			22 27	22 27								23 02	23 45				
Barnsley a		21 06	21 35				22 05			22 32	22 32								23 07	23 50				
d		21 08	21 36				22 08			22 33									23 08	23 51				
Dodworth d		21 14					22 14												23 14					
Silkstone Common d		21 18					22 18												23 18					
Penistone d		21 25					22 25												23 25					
Denby Dale d		21 31					22 31												23 31					
Shepley d		21 36					22 36												23 36					
Stocksmoor d		21 39					22 39												23 39					
Brockholes d		21 43					22 43												23 43					
Honley d		21 45					22 45												23 45					
Berry Brow d		21 48					22 48												23 48					
Lockwood d		21 51					22 51												23 51					
Huddersfield a		21 56					22 57												00 01					
Darton d			21 41							22 38										23 56				
Wakefield Kirkgate 4 31 a			21 52							22 49										00s10				
d			21 52							22 50						22 50								
Normanton d			21 57							22 54						22 54								
Castleford a			22 03							23 00						23 00								
Woodlesford a			22 14							23 13						23 13								
Leeds 10 31 a			22 28							23 28						23 28								

For general notes see front of timetable
For details of catering facilities see Directory of Train Operators

- **A** From Manchester Airport to Cleethorpes (22 June to 4 September to Doncaster) (Table 29)
- **B** To Doncaster (Table 29)
- **C** To Bridlington (Table 43)
- **D** From Retford (Table 30) to Doncaster (Table 29)
- **E** To Leeds (Table 31)
- **G** To Beverley (Table 43)
- **H** To Goole (Table 29)
- **J** To Scunthorpe (from 22 June to 4 September to Thorne North) (Table 29)
- **K** To Wakefield Westgate (Table 31)

From 7 September a revised Northern service will be in operation on the Huddersfield Line due to seasonal difficulties. Customers should check with NRES for precise times

Nottingham, Sheffield → Barnsley → Huddersfield and Leeds

Network Diagram - see first page of Table 31

	NT	NT A	NT	NT	NT B	NT C	NT	NT B	TP 1◇ D	NT	NT C	NT E
St Pancras International ⊖ 53 d												
Nottingham 8 d												
Langley Mill d												
Alfreton d												
Chesterfield d												
Dronfield d												
Sheffield 7 29, 31 a												
d	05 16	05 29	05 43	06 06	06 18	06 28	06 36	06 52	06 54	07 06	07 14	07 24
Meadowhall 4 29, 31 a	05 21	05 34	05 48	06 11	06 23	06 33	06 41	06 57	07 00	07 11	07 20	07 30
d	05 22		05 49	06 12			06 42			07 12		
Chapeltown d	05 28		05 55	06 18			06 48			07 18		
Elsecar d	05 33		06 01	06 23						07 23		
Wombwell d	05 37		06 05	06 27			06 55			07 27		
Barnsley a	05 42		06 11	06 32			07 00			07 32		
d				06 33			07 01			07 33		
Dodworth d							07 07					
Silkstone Common d							07 11					
Penistone d							07 18					
Denby Dale d							07 24					
Shepley d							07 29					
Stocksmoor d							07 32					
Brockholes d							07 36					
Honley d							07 38					
Berry Brow d							07 41					
Lockwood d							07 44					
Huddersfield a							07 49					
Darton d				06 38						07 38		
Wakefield Kirkgate 4 31 a				06 49						07 49		
d				06 50						07 50		
Normanton d				06 54						07 54		
Castleford a				07 00						08 00		
Woodlesford a				07 12						08 12		
Leeds 10 31 a				07 28						08 25		

	EM ◇ G	NT	NT H	NT J	EM 1◇ K	NT	TP 1◇ D	NT C	NT	NT	NT E	NT
St Pancras International ⊖ 53 d												
Nottingham 8 d	06 40								07 15			
Langley Mill d									07 30			
Alfreton d	07 02								07 38			
Chesterfield d	07 13				07 42				07 50			
Dronfield d	07 20				07 49							
Sheffield 7 29, 31 a	07 31				07 59				08 08			
d		07 36	07 41	07 51		08 06	08 11	08 14	08 18		08 25	08 36
Meadowhall 4 29, 31 a		07 41	07 46	07 57		08 11	08 16	08 20	08 24		08 30	08 41
d		07 42		07 57		08 12			08 24			08 42
Chapeltown d		07 48				08 18						08 48
Elsecar d						08 23						
Wombwell d		07 55				08 27						08 55
Barnsley a		08 00		08 11		08 32			08 40			09 00
d		08 01		08 12		08 33			08 42			09 01
Dodworth d		08 07										09 07
Silkstone Common d		08 11										09 11
Penistone d		08 18										09 18
Denby Dale d		08 24										09 24
Shepley d		08 29										09 29
Stocksmoor d		08 32										09 32
Brockholes d		08 36										09 36
Honley d		08 38										09 38
Berry Brow d		08 41										09 41
Lockwood d		08 44										09 44
Huddersfield a		08 49										09 49
Darton d						08 38						
Wakefield Kirkgate 4 31 a				08 27		08 49			08 57			
d				08 28		08 50			08 58	←		
Normanton d						08 54 →				08 54		
Castleford a										09 00		
Woodlesford a										09 12		
Leeds 10 31 a				08 49					09 19	09 25		

	EM ◇ G	NT H	NT	NT B	NT		TP 1◇ D	NT C	NT	NT	NT E	NT L
St Pancras International ⊖ 53 d									*06b37*			
Nottingham 8 d	07 45								08 11			
Langley Mill d									08 32			
Alfreton d	08 07								08 40			
Chesterfield d	08 18								08 52			
Dronfield d	08 25								08 59			
Sheffield 7 29, 31 a	08 38								09 15			
d		08 41	08 51	08 57	09 06		09 11	09 14	09 18		09 25	09 31
Meadowhall 4 29, 31 a		08 46	08 56	09 03	09 11		09 16	09 20	09 23		09 32	09 37
d			08 57		09 12				09 24			
Chapeltown d					09 18							
Elsecar d					09 23							
Wombwell d					09 27							
Barnsley a			09 11		09 32				09 40			
d			09 12		09 33				09 42			
Dodworth d												
Silkstone Common d												
Penistone d												
Denby Dale d												
Shepley d												
Stocksmoor d												
Brockholes d												
Honley d												
Berry Brow d												
Lockwood d												
Huddersfield a												
Darton d					09 38							
Wakefield Kirkgate 4 31 a			09 27		09 49				09 57			
d			09 28		09 50				09 58	←		
Normanton d					09 54 →					09 54		
Castleford a										10 00		
Woodlesford a										10 12		
Leeds 10 31 a			09 49						10 18	10 25		

	NT	NT N	NT	NT Q	NT	TP 1◇ D	NT C	NT	NT	NT E	NT	NT H
St Pancras International ⊖ 53 d						*07 55*						
Nottingham 8 d								09 15				
Langley Mill d								09 32				
Alfreton d								09 40				
Chesterfield d								09 52				
Dronfield d								09 59				
Sheffield 7 29, 31 a								10 15				
d	09 36	09 41	09 51	09 57	10 06	10 11	10 14	10 18		10 24	10 36	10 41
Meadowhall 4 29, 31 a	09 41	09 46	09 56	10 03	10 11	10 16	10 20	10 23		10 29	10 41	10 46
d	09 42		09 57		10 12			10 24			10 42	
Chapeltown d	09 48				10 18						10 48	
Elsecar d					10 23							
Wombwell d	09 55				10 27						10 55	
Barnsley a	10 00		10 11		10 32			10 40			11 00	
d	10 01		10 12		10 33			10 42			11 01	
Dodworth d	10 07										11 07	
Silkstone Common d	10 11										11 11	
Penistone d	10 18										11 18	
Denby Dale d	10 24										11 24	
Shepley d	10 29										11 29	
Stocksmoor d	10 32										11 32	
Brockholes d	10 36										11 36	
Honley d	10 38										11 38	
Berry Brow d	10 41										11 41	
Lockwood d	10 44										11 44	
Huddersfield a	10 49										11 49	
Darton d					10 38							
Wakefield Kirkgate 4 31 a			10 27		10 49			10 57				
d			10 28		10 50			10 58	←			
Normanton d					10 54 →				10 54			
Castleford a									11 00			
Woodlesford a									11 12			
Leeds 10 31 a			10 48					11 18	11 25			

For general notes see front of timetable
For details of catering facilities see Directory of Train Operators

- **A** To Beverley (Table 43)
- **B** To Adwick (Table 29)
- **C** To Leeds (Table 31)
- **D** From Manchester Airport to Cleethorpes (27 June to 5 September to Doncaster) (Table 29)
- **E** To Scunthorpe (27 June to 5 September to Thorne North) (Table 29)
- **G** To Liverpool Lime Street (Table 49)
- **H** To Bridlington (Table 43)
- **J** From Retford (Table 30)
- **K** From Derby (Table 53)
- **L** To York (Table 33)
- **N** To Scarborough (Table 43)
- **Q** From Lincoln (Table 30) to Adwick (Table 29)
- **b** Change at Sheffield

From 12 September a revised Northern service will be in operation on the Huddersfield Line due to seasonal difficulties. Customers should check with NRES for precise times

Table 34

Saturdays

Nottingham, Sheffield → Barnsley → Huddersfield and Leeds

Network Diagram - see first page of Table 31

Station		NT	NT A	NT	TP 1◇ B	NT C	NT	NT	NT D	NT	NT E	NT		NT A	NT	TP 1◇ B	NT C	NT	NT	NT D	NT	NT G	NT	NT A	NT
St Pancras International ⊖ 53	d				*08 55*											*09 55*									
Nottingham [8]	d						10 15											11 15							
Langley Mill	d						10 32											11 32							
Alfreton	d						10 40											11 40							
Chesterfield	d						10 52																		
Dronfield	d						10 59																		
Sheffield [7] 29, 31	a						11 15											12 15							
	d	10 51	10 57	11 06	11 11	11 14	11 18		11 24	11 36	11 41	11 51		11 57	12 06	12 11	12 14	12 18		12 24	12 36	12 41	12 51	12 57	13 06
Meadowhall [4] 29, 31	a	10 56	11 03	11 11	11 16	11 20	11 23		11 29	11 41	11 46	11 56		12 03	12 11	12 16	12 20	12 23		12 29	12 41	12 46	12 56	13 03	13 11
	d	10 57		11 12			11 24			11 42		11 57			12 12			12 24			12 42		12 57		13 12
Chapeltown	d			11 18						11 48					12 18						12 48				13 18
Elsecar	d			11 23											12 23										13 23
Wombwell	d			11 27						11 55					12 27						12 55				13 27
Barnsley	a	11 11		11 32			11 40			12 00		12 11			12 32			12 40			13 00		13 11		13 32
	d	11 12		11 33			11 42			12 01		12 12			12 33			12 42			13 01		13 12		13 33
Dodworth	d									12 07											13 07				
Silkstone Common	d									12 11											13 11				
Penistone	d									12 18											13 18				
Denby Dale	d									12 24											13 24				
Shepley	d									12 29											13 29				
Stocksmoor	d									12 32											13 32				
Brockholes	d									12 36											13 36				
Honley	d									12 38											13 38				
Berry Brow	d									12 41											13 41				
Lockwood	d									12 44											13 44				
Huddersfield	a									12 49											13 49				
Darton	d			11 38											12 38										13 38
Wakefield Kirkgate [4] 31	a	11 27		11 49			11 57					12 27			12 49			12 57					13 27		13 50
	d	11 28		11 50			11 58	←				12 28			12 50			12 58	←				13 28		13 50
Normanton	d			11 54 →				11 54							12 54 →				12 54						13 54 →
Castleford	a							12 00											13 00						
Woodlesford	a							12 12											13 12						
Leeds [10] 31	a	11 48					12 18	12 25				12 48						13 18	13 25				13 48		

Station		TP 1◇ B	NT C	NT	NT	NT D	NT H	NT	NT G	NT	NT A	NT	TP 1◇ B	NT C	NT	NT	NT D	NT		NT J	NT	NT A	NT	TP 1◇ B	NT C
St Pancras International ⊖ 53	d	*10 55*											*11 55*											*12 55*	
Nottingham [8]	d			12 15											13 15										
Langley Mill	d			12 32											13 32										
Alfreton	d			12 40											13 40										
Chesterfield	d			12 52											13 52										
Dronfield	d			12 59											13 59										
Sheffield [7] 29, 31	a			13 15											14 15										
	d	13 11	13 14	13 18		13 24	13 28	13 36	13 41	13 51	13 57	14 06	14 11	14 14	14 18		14 24	14 36		14 41	14 51	14 57	15 06	15 11	15 14
Meadowhall [4] 29, 31	a	13 16	13 20	13 23		13 29	13 34	13 41	13 46	13 56	14 03	14 11	14 16	14 20	14 23		14 29	14 41		14 46	14 56	15 03	15 11	15 16	15 20
	d			13 24				13 42		13 57		14 12			14 24			14 42			14 57		15 12		
Chapeltown	d							13 48				14 18						14 48					15 18		
Elsecar	d											14 23											15 23		
Wombwell	d							13 55				14 27						14 55					15 27		
Barnsley	a			13 40				14 00		14 11		14 32			14 40			15 00			15 11		15 32		
	d			13 42				14 01		14 12		14 33			14 42			15 01			15 12		15 33		
Dodworth	d							14 07										15 07							
Silkstone Common	d							14 11										15 11							
Penistone	d							14 18										15 18							
Denby Dale	d							14 24										15 24							
Shepley	d							14 29										15 29							
Stocksmoor	d							14 32										15 32							
Brockholes	d							14 36										15 36							
Honley	d							14 38										15 38							
Berry Brow	d							14 41										15 41							
Lockwood	d							14 44										15 44							
Huddersfield	a							14 49										15 49							
Darton	d											14 38											15 38		
Wakefield Kirkgate [4] 31	a			13 57						14 27		14 49			14 57						15 27		15 49		
	d			13 58	←					14 28		14 50			14 58	←					15 28		15 50		
Normanton	d				13 54							14 54 →				14 54							15 54 →		
Castleford	a				14 00											15 00									
Woodlesford	a				14 12											15 12									
Leeds [10] 31	a			14 18	14 25					14 48					15 18	15 25					15 48				

For general notes see front of timetable
For details of catering facilities see Directory of Train Operators

- **A** From Lincoln (Table 30) to Adwick (Table 29)
- **B** From Manchester Airport to Cleethorpes (27 June to 5 September to Doncaster) (Table 29)
- **C** To Leeds (Table 31)
- **D** To Scunthorpe (27 June to 5 September to Thorne North) (Table 29)
- **E** To Scarborough (Table 43)
- **G** To Bridlington (Table 43)
- **H** To York (Table 33)
- **J** To Hull (Table 29)

From 12 September a revised Northern service will be in operation on the Huddersfield Line due to seasonal difficulties. Customers should check with NRES for precise times

Table 34

Saturdays

Nottingham, Sheffield → Barnsley → Huddersfield and Leeds

Network Diagram - see first page of Table 31

		NT	NT	NT	NT	NT	NT	NT	NT	TP	NT	NT	NT	NT	NT	NT	NT	NT	NT	TP	NT	NT	NT	NT	NT
										1 ◇										1 ◇					
				A		B		C		D	E			G		B		C		D	E			G	
St Pancras International	⊖ 53 d									*13 55*										*14 55*					
Nottingham 8	d	14 15										15 15										16 15			
Langley Mill	d	14 30										15 32										16 32			
Alfreton	d	14 38										15 40										16 40			
Chesterfield	d	14 52										15 51										16 51			
Dronfield	d	14 59										15 58										16 58			
Sheffield 7	29, 31 a	15 15										16 15										17 15			
	d	15 18		15 24	15 36	15 40	15 51	15 57	16 06	16 11	16 14	16 18		16 24	16 36	16 41	16 51	16 57	17 06	17 11	17 14	17 18		17 27	17 36
Meadowhall 4	29, 31 a	15 23		15 29	15 41	15 46	15 56	16 03	16 11	16 16	16 20	16 23		16 29	16 41	16 46	16 56	17 03	17 11	17 16	17 21	17 23		17 32	17 41
	d	15 24			15 42		15 57		16 12			16 24			16 42		16 57		17 12			17 24			17 42
Chapeltown	d				15 48				16 18						16 48				17 18						17 48
Elsecar	d								16 23						16 53				17 23						17 53
Wombwell	d				15 55				16 27						16 57				17 27						17 57
Barnsley	a	15 40			16 00		16 11		16 32			16 40			17 02		17 11		17 32			17 40			18 02
	d	15 42			16 01		16 12		16 33			16 42			17 03		17 12		17 33			17 42			18 03
Dodworth	d				16 07										17 09										18 09
Silkstone Common	d				16 11										17 13										18 13
Penistone	d				16 18										17 20										18 20
Denby Dale	d				16 24										17 26										18 26
Shepley	d				16 29										17 31										18 31
Stocksmoor	d				16 32										17 34										18 34
Brockholes	d				16 36										17 38										18 38
Honley	d				16 38										17 40										18 40
Berry Brow	d				16 41										17 43										18 43
Lockwood	d				16 44										17 46										18 46
Huddersfield	a				16 49										17 50										18 51
Darton	d								16 38										17 38						
Wakefield Kirkgate 4	31 a	15 57					16 27		16 49			16 57					17 27		17 49			17 57			
	d	15 58	←				16 28		16 50			16 58	←				17 28		17 50			17 58	←		
Normanton	d		15 54						16 54 →				16 54						17 54 →				17 54		
Castleford	a		16 00										17 00										18 00		
Woodlesford	a		16 12										17 12										18 12		
Leeds 10	31 a	16 19	16 25				16 48					17 18	17 25				17 48					18 18	18 25		

		NT		NT	NT	NT	NT	NT	NT	TP	NT	NT	NT	NT	NT	NT	TP	NT	NT	NT	NT	NT	NT	NT	NT
										1 ◇							1 ◇								
		B			H		E			D	A		J		K		D	E			G		L		G
St Pancras International	⊖ 53 d							*15b55*									*16 55*								
Nottingham 8	d							17 15											18 15						
Langley Mill	d							17 31											18 32						
Alfreton	d							17 39											18 40						
Chesterfield	d							17 52											18 52						
Dronfield	d							17 59											18 59						
Sheffield 7	29, 31 a							18 15											19 15						
	d	17 41		17 51	17 57	18 06	18 14	18 18		18 24	18 29	18 36	18 41	18 51	19 00	19 06	19 11	19 14	19 18		19 30	19 36	19 44	19 51	19 57
Meadowhall 4	29, 31 a	17 46		17 56	18 03	18 12	18 20	18 23		18 29	18 34	18 41	18 46	18 56	19 06	19 11	19 16	19 20	19 23		19 35	19 41	19 49	19 56	20 03
	d			17 57		18 12		18 24				18 42		18 57		19 12			19 24			19 42		19 57	
Chapeltown	d					18 18						18 48				19 18						19 48			
Elsecar	d					18 23						18 53				19 23						19 53			
Wombwell	d					18 27						18 57				19 27						19 57			
Barnsley	a			18 11		18 33		18 42				19 02		19 14		19 33			19 42			20 02		20 12	
	d			18 12		18 33		18 42				19 03		19 14		19 33			19 42			20 08		20 12	
Dodworth	d											19 09										20 14			
Silkstone Common	d											19 13										20 18			
Penistone	d											19 20										20 25			
Denby Dale	d											19 26										20 31			
Shepley	d											19 31										20 36			
Stocksmoor	d											19 34										20 39			
Brockholes	d											19 38										20 43			
Honley	d											19 41										20 45			
Berry Brow	d											19 44										20 48			
Lockwood	d											19 46										20 51			
Huddersfield	a											19 51										20 55			
Darton	d					18 38										19 38									
Wakefield Kirkgate 4	31 a			18 28		18 50		18 58						19 29		19 50			19 58					20 28	
	d			18 32		18 50		18 58	←					19 32		19 50			19 58	←				20 28	
Normanton	d					18 54 →			18 54							19 54 →				19 54					
Castleford	a								19 00											20 00					
Woodlesford	a								19 13											20 12					
Leeds 10	31 a			18 51				19 23	19 27					19 55					20 19	20 26				20 48	

For general notes see front of timetable
For details of catering facilities see Directory of Train Operators

A To Scunthorpe (27 June to 5 September to Thorne North) (Table 29)
B To Hull (Table 29)
C From Lincoln (Table 30) to Adwick (Table 29)
D From Manchester Airport to Cleethorpes (27 June to 5 September to Doncaster) (Table 29)
E To Leeds (Table 31)
G To Doncaster (Table 29)
H From Lincoln (Table 30) to Doncaster (Table 29)
J To Bridlington (Table 43)
K From Retford (Table 30) to Doncaster (Table 29)
L To Beverley (Table 43)
b Change at Sheffield

From 12 September a revised Northern service will be in operation on the Huddersfield Line due to seasonal difficulties. Customers should check with NRES for precise times

Saturdays

Nottingham, Sheffield → Barnsley → Huddersfield and Leeds

Network Diagram - see first page of Table 31

	TP 1◇ A	NT	NT B	NT	NT C	NT	NT B	NT	NT D	NT E	TP 1◇ G	NT H	NT C	NT	NT	TP 1◇ G	NT	NT J	NT C	NT E	NT	NT B
St Pancras International ⊖ 53 d			17 55								18 55							19 55				20 55
Nottingham 8 d				19 15													21 15					
Langley Mill d				19 32													21 31					
Alfreton d				19 40													21 39					
Chesterfield d				19 52													21 50					
Dronfield d				19 59													21 57					
Sheffield 7 29, 31 a				20 15													22 14					
d	20 11	20 06	20 15	20 18	20 30		20 38	20 41	21 06	21 06	21 11	21 14	21 30	21 41	22 06	22 11		22 30	22 34		22 41	23 26
Meadowhall 4 29, 31 a	20 16	20 11	20 20	20 24	20 36		20 43	20 47	21 11	21 11	21 16	21 21	21 36	21 46	22 11	22 16		22 35	22 39		22 46	23 31
d		20 12		20 24				20 47	21 12	21 12				21 47	22 12						22 47	
Chapeltown d		20 18						20 53	21 18	21 18				21 53	22 18						22 53	
Elsecar d		20 23							21 23	21 23					22 23						22 58	
Wombwell d		20 27						21 00	21 27	21 27				22 00	22 27						23 02	
Barnsley a		20 32		20 40				21 06	21 32	21 32				22 05	22 32						23 07	
d		20 33		20 42				21 08	21 33	21 33				22 08							23 08	
Dodworth d								21 14						22 14							23 14	
Silkstone Common d								21 18						22 18							23 18	
Penistone d								21 25						22 25							23 25	
Denby Dale d								21 31						22 31							23 31	
Shepley d								21 36						22 36							23 36	
Stocksmoor d								21 39						22 39							23 39	
Brockholes d								21 43						22 43							23 43	
Honley d								21 45						22 45							23 45	
Berry Brow d								21 48						22 48							23 48	
Lockwood d								21 51						22 51							23 51	
Huddersfield a								21 56						22 56							23 59	
Darton d		20 38							21 38	21 38												
Wakefield Kirkgate 4 31 a		20 49		20 57					21 49	21 52												
d		20 50		20 58		←			21 50	21 52										22 50		
Normanton d		20 54				20 54				21 57										22 54		
Castleford a		→				21 00				22 03										23 00		
Woodlesford a						21 12				22 14										23 13		
Leeds 10 31 a				21b22		21 25			22 14	22 28										23 28		

Sundays

until 12 July

	NT B	NT	NT (bus)	NT K	NT		NT C	NT	TP 1◇ L	NT K	NT		NT (bus)	NT B	NT	NT C	NT		TP 1◇ L	NT	NT J	NT K	NT	NT
St Pancras International ⊖ 53 d																								09 30
Nottingham 8 d															10 06					11 15				
Langley Mill d															10 27					11 31				
Alfreton d															10 35					11 39				
Chesterfield d															10 54					11 51				
Dronfield d															11 01					11 58				
Sheffield 7 29, 31 a															11 15					12 15				
d	08 00	08 39		08 45	09 17		09 36	09 39	09 52	10 26	10 39			11 05	11 17	11 36	11 49		12 11	12 16	12 24	12 28	12 35	12 39
Meadowhall 4 29, 31 a	08 05	08 44		08 50	09 22		09 41	09 44	09 57	10 31	10 44			11 10	11 22	11 41	11 54		12 16	12 22	12 29	12 33	12 40	12 44
d		08 45			09 23			09 45			10 45				11 23		11 55			12 23			12 41	12 45
Chapeltown d		08 51						09 51			10 51						12 01							12 55
Elsecar d		08 56						09 56			10 56						12 06							13 00
Wombwell d		09 00						10 00			11 00						12 10							13 04
Barnsley a		09 05			09 37			10 05			11 05				11 37		12 15			12 37			12 55	13 09
d		09 10			09 37			10 06			11 10				11 37		12 16			12 37			13 06	13 10
Dodworth d								10 12									12 22						13 12	
Silkstone Common d								10 16									12 26						13 16	
Penistone d								10 23									12 33						13 23	
Denby Dale d								10 29									12 39						13 29	
Shepley d								10 34									12 44						13 34	
Stocksmoor d								10 37									12 47						13 37	
Brockholes d								10 41									12 51						13 41	
Honley d								10 43									12 53						13 43	
Berry Brow d								10 46									12 56						13 46	
Lockwood d								10 49									12 59						13 49	
Huddersfield a								10 53									13 03						13 53	
Darton d		09 15									11 15													13 15
Wakefield Kirkgate 4 31 a		09 29			09 52						11 29				11 52					12 52				13 29
d		09 32	09 35		09 55						11 30		11 35		11 53					12 53				13 30
Normanton d			09 47										11 47											
Castleford a			09 59										11 59											
Woodlesford a			10 14										12 14											
Leeds 10 31 a		09 52	10 34		10 19						11 52		12 34		12 18					13 18				13 52

For general notes see front of timetable
For details of catering facilities see Directory of Train Operators

- **A** To Scunthorpe (27 June to 5 September to Thorne North) (Table 29)
- **B** To Doncaster (Table 29)
- **C** To Leeds (Table 31)
- **D** Until 11 July
- **E** From 18 July
- **G** From Manchester Airport to Cleethorpes (27 June to 5 September to Doncaster) (Table 29)
- **H** To Beverley (Table 43)
- **J** To Goole (Table 29)
- **K** To Scarborough (Table 43)
- **L** To Cleethorpes (from 28 June to Doncaster) (Table 29)
- **b** From 18 July arr. 2119

From 12 September a revised Northern service will be in operation on the Huddersfield Line due to seasonal difficulties. Customers should check with NRES for precise times

Table 34

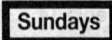

Sundays until 12 July

Nottingham, Sheffield → Barnsley → Huddersfield and Leeds

Network Diagram - see first page of Table 31

		NT	TP	NT	NT	NT	NT	TP	NT	NT	NT	NT	NT	TP	NT	NT	NT	NT	NT	NT	TP
		(bus)	1◇ A		B	C		1◇ D		E	G		(bus)	1◇ D		H	B	C	J	K	1◇ D
St Pancras International	⊖53 d						10 30					11 30								12 30	
Nottingham 8	d			12 19					13 11						14 19						
Langley Mill	d			12 35					13 27						14 35						
Alfreton	d			12 43					13 35						14 43						
Chesterfield	d			12 54					13b51						14 54						
Dronfield	d			13 01					13 58						15 01						
Sheffield 7	29, 31 a			13 15					14 15						15 15						
	d		13 11	13 17	13 24	13 36	13 39	14 11	14 17	14 22	14 28	14 39		15 11	15 17	15 24	15 28	15 36	15 39	15 46	16 11
Meadowhall 4	29, 31 a		13 16	13 22	13 29	13 41	13 44	14 16	14 22	14 27	14 33	14 44		15 16	15 22	15 29	15 33	15 41	15 43	15 51	16 16
	d			13 23			13 45		14 23			14 45			15 23				15 43		
Chapeltown	d						13 51					14 51							15 49		
Elsecar	d						13 56					14 56							15 54		
Wombwell	d						14 00					15 00							15 58		
Barnsley	a			13 37			14 05		14 37			15 05			15 37				16 04		
	d			13 37			14 06		14 37			15 10			15 37				16 04		
Dodworth	d						14 12												16 10		
Silkstone Common	d						14 16												16 14		
Penistone	d						14 23												16 21		
Denby Dale	d						14 29												16 27		
Shepley	d						14 34												16 32		
Stocksmoor	d						14 37												16 35		
Brockholes	d						14 41												16 39		
Honley	d						14 43												16 41		
Berry Brow	d						14 46												16 44		
Lockwood	d						14 49												16 47		
Huddersfield	a						14 53												16 53		
Darton	d											15 15									
Wakefield Kirkgate 4	31 a			13 52					14 52			15 29			15 52						
	d	13 35		13 53					14 53			15 30	15 35		15 53						
Normanton	d	13 47											15 47								
Castleford	a	13 59											15 59								
Woodlesford	a	14 14											16 14								
Leeds 10	31 a	14 34		14 18					15 18			15 53	16 34		16 18						

		NT	NT	NT	NT	NT	NT	TP	NT	NT	NT	NT	NT	TP	NT	NT	NT	NT	NT	NT	TP
			E	G	L	(bus)		1◇ D		H	B	C		1◇ D		H	N		(bus)	K	1◇ D
St Pancras International	⊖53 d						13 30						14 30					15 30			16 25
Nottingham 8	d	15 12							16 14						17 14						
Langley Mill	d	15 34							16 30						17 30						
Alfreton	d	15 42							16 38						17 38						
Chesterfield	d	15 53							16 50						17 49						
Dronfield	d	16 00							16 57						17 56						
Sheffield 7	29, 31 a	16 15							17 15						18 15						
	d	16 17	16 24	16 28	16 39		16 54	17 11	17 17	17 24	17 28	17 36	17 39	18 11	18 17	18 25	18 28	18 39		18 57	19 11
Meadowhall 4	29, 31 a	16 22	16 29	16 33	16 44		16 59	17 16	17 22	17 29	17 33	17 43	17 46	18 16	18 22	18 30	18 34	18 44		19 03	19 16
	d	16 23			16 45		17 00		17 23				17 46		18 23			18 45			
Chapeltown	d				16 51								17 52					18 51			
Elsecar	d				16 56								17 58					18 56			
Wombwell	d				17 00								18 01					19 00			
Barnsley	a	16 37			17 05		17 14		17 37				18 08		18 37			19 05			
	d	16 37			17 10		17 15		17 37				18 10		18 37			19 10			
Dodworth	d						17 21						18 16								
Silkstone Common	d						17 25						18 20								
Penistone	d						17 32						18 27								
Denby Dale	d						17 38						18 34								
Shepley	d						17 43						18 39								
Stocksmoor	d						17 46						18 41								
Brockholes	d						17 50						18 45								
Honley	d						17 52						18 48								
Berry Brow	d						17 55						18 51								
Lockwood	d						17 58						18 53								
Huddersfield	a						18 05						18 58								
Darton	d				17 15													19 15			
Wakefield Kirkgate 4	31 a	16 52			17 29				17 52						18 52			19 29			
	d	16 53			17 30	17 35			17 53						18 53			19 30	19 35		
Normanton	d					17 47													19 47		
Castleford	a					17 59													19 59		
Woodlesford	a					18 14													20 14		
Leeds 10	31 a	17 18			17 52	18 34			18 18						19 17			19 52	20 34		

For general notes see front of timetable
For details of catering facilities see Directory of Train Operators

A From Manchester Piccadilly to Doncaster (Table 29)
B To Bridlington (Table 43)
C To Leeds (Table 31)
D To Cleethorpes (from 28 June to Doncaster) (Table 29)
E To Goole (Table 29)
G To Scarborough (Table 43)
H To Doncaster (Table 29)
J From Retford (Table 30)
K To York (Table 33)
L From Lincoln (Table 30)
N To Beverley (Table 43)
b Arr. 1346

Table 34

Sundays

until 12 July

Nottingham, Sheffield → Barnsley → Huddersfield and Leeds

Network Diagram - see first page of Table 31

		NT	NT	NT	NT	NT		TP	NT	NT	NT	NT		TP	NT	NT	NT	NT	TP	NT	NT	NT	NT		
			A	B		C		1 ◇ D		E		bus		1 ◇ D	C	B		C	1 ◇ D		G	bus	A		
St Pancras International	⊖ 53 d					17 25								18 25				19 25					20 30		
Nottingham 8	d	18 14							19 19											21 20					
Langley Mill	d	18 30							19 35											21 41					
Alfreton	d	18 38							19 43											21 49					
Chesterfield	d	18 49							19 54											22 08					
Dronfield	d	18 56							20 01											22 15					
Sheffield 7 29, 31	a	19 15							20 15											22 32					
	d	19 16	19 29	19 36	19 39	20 02		20 11	20 17	20 28	20 39			21 11	21 24	21 36	21 43	22 26	22 30		22 39		23 41		
Meadowhall 4 29, 31	a	19 22	19 34	19 41	19 44	20 08		20 16	20 22	20 33	20 44			21 16	21 29	21 41	21 48	22 31	22 35		22 44		23 46		
	d	19 23			19 45				20 23		20 45						21 49				22 45				
Chapeltown	d				19 51						20 51						21 55				22 51				
Elsecar	d				19 56						20 56						22 00				22 56				
Wombwell	d				20 00						21 00						22 04				23 00				
Barnsley	a	19 37			20 05				20 37		21 06						22 09				23 05				
	d	19 37			20 06				20 37		21 10										23 10				
Dodworth	d				20 12																				
Silkstone Common	d				20 16																				
Penistone	d				20 23																				
Denby Dale	d				20 29																				
Shepley	d				20 34																				
Stocksmoor	d				20 37																				
Brockholes	d				20 41																				
Honley	d				20 43																				
Berry Brow	d				20 46																				
Lockwood	d				20 49																				
Huddersfield	a				20 53																				
Darton	d										21 15										23 15				
Wakefield Kirkgate 4 31	a	19 52							20 52		21 29										23 28				
	d	19 57							20 53		21 30	21 35									23 30	23 35			
Normanton	d											21 47										23 47			
Castleford	a											21 59										23 59			
Woodlesford	a											22 14										00 14			
Leeds 10 31	a	20 27							21 18		21 54	22 34									00 08	00 34			

Sundays

19 July to 6 September

		NT	NT	NT		NT	NT	NT		TP	NT	NT		NT	NT	NT		NT	TP	NT		NT	NT	NT	NT
		A		H			B			1 ◇ A	H			A		B			1 ◇ J			E	H		
St Pancras International	⊖ 53 d																								
Nottingham 8	d														10 06					11 15					
Langley Mill	d														10 27					11 31					
Alfreton	d														10 35					11 39					
Chesterfield	d														10 54					11 51					
Dronfield	d														11 01					11 58					
Sheffield 7 29, 31	a														11 15					12 15					
	d	08 00	08 39	08 45		09 17	09 36	09 39		09 52	10 26	10 39		11 05	11 17	11 36		11 49	12 11	12 16		12 24	12 28	12 35	12 39
Meadowhall 4 29, 31	a	08 05	08 44	08 50		09 22	09 41	09 44		09 57	10 31	10 44		11 10	11 22	11 41		11 54	12 16	12 22		12 29	12 33	12 40	12 44
	d		08 45			09 23		09 45				10 45			11 23			11 55		12 23				12 41	12 45
Chapeltown	d		08 51					09 51				10 51						12 01							12 55
Elsecar	d		08 56					09 56				10 56						12 06							13 00
Wombwell	d		09 00					10 00				11 00						12 10							13 04
Barnsley	a		09 05			09 37		10 05				11 05			11 37			12 15		12 37				12 55	13 09
	d		09 10			09 37		10 06				11 10			11 37			12 16		12 37				13 06	13 10
Dodworth	d							10 12										12 22						13 12	
Silkstone Common	d							10 16										12 26						13 16	
Penistone	d							10 23										12 33						13 23	
Denby Dale	d							10 29										12 39						13 29	
Shepley	d							10 34										12 44						13 34	
Stocksmoor	d							10 37										12 47						13 37	
Brockholes	d							10 41										12 51						13 41	
Honley	d							10 43										12 53						13 43	
Berry Brow	d							10 46										12 56						13 46	
Lockwood	d							10 49										12 59						13 49	
Huddersfield	a							10 53										13 03						13 53	
Darton	d		09 15									11 15													13 15
Wakefield Kirkgate 4 31	a		09 29			09 55						11 29			11 52					12 52					13 29
	d		09 30			09 55						11 30			11 53					12 53					13 30
Normanton	d		09 34									11 34													13 34
Castleford	a		09 40									11 40													13 40
Woodlesford	a		09 52									11 51													13 51
Leeds 10 31	a		10 04			10 15						12 05			12 18					13 18					14 04

For general notes see front of timetable
For details of catering facilities see Directory of Train Operators

A To Doncaster (Table 29)
B To Leeds (Table 31)
C To Hull (Table 29)
D To Cleethorpes (from 28 June to Doncaster) (Table 29)
E To Goole (Table 29)
G From Lincoln (Table 30)
H To Scarborough (Table 43)
J From Manchester Airport to Doncaster (Table 29)

Table 34

Sundays

Nottingham, Sheffield → Barnsley → Huddersfield and Leeds

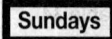

19 July to 6 September

Network Diagram - see first page of Table 31

		TP 1◇ A	NT	NT B	NT C	NT	TP 1◇ D	NT	NT E	NT G	NT	TP 1◇ D	NT	NT H	NT B	NT C	NT J	NT K	TP 1◇ D
St Pancras International	⊖ 53 d	09 30					10 30					11 30						12 30	
Nottingham 8	d		12 19					13 09					14 19						
Langley Mill	d		12 35					13 27					14 35						
Alfreton	d		12 43					13 35					14 43						
Chesterfield	d		12 54					13b51					14 54						
Dronfield	d		13 01					13 58					15 01						
Sheffield 7	29, 31 a		13 15					14 15					15 15						
	d	13 11	13 17	13 24	13 36	13 39	14 11	14 17	14 22	14 28	14 39	15 11	15 17	15 24	15 28	15 36	15 39	15 46	16 11
Meadowhall 4	29, 31 a	13 16	13 22	13 29	13 41	13 44	14 16	14 22	14 27	14 33	14 44	15 16	15 22	15 29	15 33	15 41	15 43	15 51	16 16
	d		13 23			13 45		14 23			14 45		15 23				15 43		
Chapeltown	d					13 51					14 51						15 49		
Elsecar	d					13 56					14 56						15 54		
Wombwell	d					14 00					15 00						15 58		
Barnsley	a		13 37			14 05		14 37			15 05		15 37				16 04		
	d		13 37			14 06		14 37			15 10		15 37				16 04		
Dodworth	d					14 12											16 10		
Silkstone Common	d					14 16											16 14		
Penistone	d					14 23											16 21		
Denby Dale	d					14 29											16 27		
Shepley	d					14 34											16 32		
Stocksmoor	d					14 37											16 35		
Brockholes	d					14 41											16 39		
Honley	d					14 43											16 41		
Berry Brow	d					14 46											16 44		
Lockwood	d					14 49											16 47		
Huddersfield	a					14 53											16 53		
Darton	d										15 15								
Wakefield Kirkgate 4	31 a		13 52					14 52			15 29		15 52						
	d		13 53					14 53			15 30		15 53						
Normanton	d										15 34								
Castleford	a										15 40								
Woodlesford	a										15 51								
Leeds 10	31 a		14 18					15 18			16 04		16 18						

		NT	NT E	NT G	NT L	NT	TP 1◇ D	NT	NT H	NT B	NT C	NT	TP 1◇ D	NT	NT H	NT N	NT	NT K	TP 1◇ D	NT
St Pancras International	⊖ 53 d					13 30						14 30					15 30		16 25	
Nottingham 8	d	15 12						16 14						17 12						18 13
Langley Mill	d	15 34						16 30						17 30						18 30
Alfreton	d	15 42						16 38						17 38						18 38
Chesterfield	d	15 53						16 50						17 49						18 49
Dronfield	d	16 00						16 57						17 56						18 56
Sheffield 7	29, 31 a	16 15						17 15						18 15						19 15
	d	16 17	16 24	16 28	16 39	16 54	17 11	17 17	17 24	17 28	17 36	17 39	18 11	18 17	18 25	18 28	18 39	18 57	19 11	19 16
Meadowhall 4	29, 31 a	16 22	16 29	16 33	16 44	16 59	17 16	17 22	17 29	17 33	17 43	17 46	18 16	18 22	18 30	18 34	18 44	19 03	19 16	19 22
	d	16 23			16 45	17 00		17 23				17 46		18 23			18 45			19 23
Chapeltown	d				16 51							17 52					18 51			
Elsecar	d				16 56							17 58					18 56			
Wombwell	d				17 00							18 01					19 00			
Barnsley	a	16 37			17 05	17 14		17 37				18 08		18 37			19 05			19 37
	d	16 37			17 10	17 15		17 37				18 10		18 37			19 10			19 37
Dodworth	d					17 21						18 16								
Silkstone Common	d					17 25						18 20								
Penistone	d					17 32						18 27								
Denby Dale	d					17 38						18 34								
Shepley	d					17 43						18 39								
Stocksmoor	d					17 46						18 41								
Brockholes	d					17 50						18 45								
Honley	d					17 52						18 48								
Berry Brow	d					17 55						18 51								
Lockwood	d					17 58						18 53								
Huddersfield	a					18 05						18 58								
Darton	d				17 15												19 15			
Wakefield Kirkgate 4	31 a	16 52			17 29			17 52						18 52			19 29			19 52
	d	16 53			17 30			17 53						18 53			19 30			19 53
Normanton	d				17 34												19 34			
Castleford	a				17 40												19 41			
Woodlesford	a				17 51												19 53			
Leeds 10	31 a	17 18			18 05			18 18						19 18			20 05			20 18

For general notes see front of timetable
For details of catering facilities see Directory of Train Operators

- **A** From Manchester Piccadilly to Doncaster (Table 29)
- **B** To Bridlington (Table 43)
- **C** To Leeds (Table 31)
- **D** From Manchester Airport to Doncaster (Table 29)
- **E** To Goole (Table 29)
- **G** To Scarborough (Table 43)
- **H** To Doncaster (Table 29)
- **J** From Retford (Table 30)
- **K** To York (Table 33)
- **L** From Lincoln (Table 30)
- **N** To Beverley (Table 43)
- **b** Arr. 1346

Table 34

Sundays

19 July to 6 September

Nottingham, Sheffield → Barnsley → Huddersfield and Leeds

Network Diagram - see first page of Table 31

		NT		NT	NT	NT		TP 1 ◇	NT	NT		NT	TP 1 ◇	NT		NT	NT	NT		TP 1 ◇	NT	NT	NT		
		A		B		C		D		E			D	C		B		C		A		G	A		
St Pancras International	⊖ 53 d					17 25							18 25					19 25							
Nottingham 8	d								19 19												21 20				
Langley Mill	d								19 35												21 41				
Alfreton	d								19 43												21 49				
Chesterfield	d								19 54												22 08				
Dronfield	d								20 01												22 15				
Sheffield 7	29, 31 a								20 15												22 32				
	d	19 29		19 36	19 39	20 02		20 11	20 17	20 28		20 39	21 11	21 24		21 36	21 43	22 26		22 30		22 39	23 41		
Meadowhall 4	29, 31 a	19 34		19 41	19 44	20 08		20 16	20 22	20 33		20 44	21 16	21 29		21 41	21 48	22 31		22 35		22 44	23 46		
	d				19 45				20 23			20 45					21 49					22 45			
Chapeltown	d				19 51							20 51					21 55					22 51			
Elsecar	d				19 56							20 56					22 00					22 56			
Wombwell	d				20 00							21 00					22 04					23 00			
Barnsley	a				20 05				20 37			21 06					22 09					23 05			
	d				20 06				20 37			21 10										23 10			
Dodworth	d				20 12																				
Silkstone Common	d				20 16																				
Penistone	d				20 23																				
Denby Dale	d				20 29																				
Shepley	d				20 34																				
Stocksmoor	d				20 37																				
Brockholes	d				20 41																				
Honley	d				20 43																				
Berry Brow	d				20 46																				
Lockwood	d				20 49																				
Huddersfield	a				20 53																				
Darton	d											21 15										23 15			
Wakefield Kirkgate 4	31 a								20 52			21 29										23 28			
	d								20 53			21 30										23 30			
Normanton	d											21 34										23 34			
Castleford	a											21 40										23 40			
Woodlesford	a											21 51										23 51			
Leeds 10	31 a								21 16			22 04										00 04			

Sundays

from 13 September

		NT	NT	NT		NT	NT	NT		TP 1 ◇	NT	NT		NT	NT	NT		NT	TP 1 ◇	NT		NT	NT	NT	NT
		A		H			B			J	K			A		B			L			E	K		
St Pancras International	⊖ 53 d																								
Nottingham 8	d														10 10					11 15					
Langley Mill	d														10 27					11 31					
Alfreton	d														10 35					11 39					
Chesterfield	d														10 54					11 51					
Dronfield	d														11 01					11 58					
Sheffield 7	29, 31 a														11 15					12 15					
	d	08 00	08 39	08 45		09 17	09 36	09 39		09 52	10 26	10 39		11 05	11 17	11 36		11 49	12 11	12 16		12 24	12 28	12 35	12 39
Meadowhall 4	29, 31 a	08 05	08 44	08 50		09 22	09 41	09 44		09 57	10 31	10 44		11 10	11 22	11 41		11 54	12 16	12 22		12 29	12 33	12 40	12 44
	d		08 45			09 23		09 45				10 45			11 23			11 55		12 23				12 41	12 45
Chapeltown	d		08 51					09 51				10 51						12 01							12 55
Elsecar	d		08 56					09 56				10 56						12 06							13 00
Wombwell	d		09 00					10 00				11 00						12 10							13 04
Barnsley	a		09 05			09 37		10 05				11 05			11 37			12 15		12 37				12 55	13 09
	d		09 10			09 37		10 06				11 10			11 37			12 16		12 37				13 06	13 10
Dodworth	d							10 12										12 22						13 12	
Silkstone Common	d							10 16										12 26						13 16	
Penistone	d							10 23										12 33						13 23	
Denby Dale	d							10 29										12 39						13 29	
Shepley	d							10 34										12 44						13 34	
Stocksmoor	d							10 37										12 47						13 37	
Brockholes	d							10 41										12 51						13 41	
Honley	d							10 43										12 53						13 43	
Berry Brow	d							10 46										12 56						13 46	
Lockwood	d							10 49										12 59						13 49	
Huddersfield	a							10 58										13 07						13 58	
Darton	d		09 15									11 15													13 15
Wakefield Kirkgate 4	31 a		09 29			09 55						11 29			11 52					12 52					13 29
	d		09 30			09 55						11 30			11 53					12 53					13 30
Normanton	d		09 34									11 34													13 34
Castleford	a		09 40									11 40													13 40
Woodlesford	a		09 52									11 51													13 51
Leeds 10	31 a		10 04			10 15						12 05			12 18					13 18					14 04

For general notes see front of timetable
For details of catering facilities see Directory of Train Operators

A To Doncaster (Table 29)
B To Leeds (Table 31)
C To Hull (Table 29)
D From Manchester Airport to Doncaster (Table 29)
E To Goole (Table 29)
G From Lincoln (Table 30)
H To Scarborough (Table 43) (from 27 September to Hull) (Table 29)
J To Cleethorpes (Table 29)
K To Scarborough (from 27 September to Bridlington) (Table 43)
L From Manchester Airport to Cleethorpes (Table 29)

Table 34

Sundays

from 13 September

Nottingham, Sheffield → Barnsley → Huddersfield and Leeds

Network Diagram - see first page of Table 31

		TP 1 ◇	NT	NT	NT	NT	TP 1 ◇	NT	NT	NT	NT	TP 1 ◇	NT	NT	NT	NT	NT	NT	TP 1 ◇
		A		B	C		D		E	G		D		H	J	C	K	L	D
St Pancras International	⊖ 53 d	09 30									10 30						11 30		
Nottingham 8	d		12 19					13 11					14 19						
Langley Mill	d		12 35					13 27					14 35						
Alfreton	d		12 43					13 35					14 43						
Chesterfield	d		12 54					13b51					14 54						
Dronfield	d		13 01					13 58					15 01						
Sheffield 7	29, 31 a		13 15					14 15					15 15						
	d	13 11	13 17	13 24	13 36	13 39	14 11	14 17	14 22	14 28	14 39	15 11	15 17	15 24	15 28	15 36	15 39	15 46	16 11
Meadowhall 4	29, 31 a	13 16	13 22	13 29	13 41	13 44	14 16	14 22	14 27	14 33	14 44	15 16	15 22	15 29	15 33	15 41	15 43	15 51	16 16
	d		13 23			13 45		14 23			14 45		15 23				15 43		
Chapeltown	d					13 51					14 51						15 49		
Elsecar	d					13 56					14 56						15 54		
Wombwell	d					14 00					15 00						15 58		
Barnsley	a		13 37			14 05		14 37			15 05		15 37				16 04		
	d		13 37			14 06		14 37			15 10		15 37				16 04		
Dodworth	d					14 12											16 10		
Silkstone Common	d					14 16											16 14		
Penistone	d					14 23											16 21		
Denby Dale	d					14 29											16 27		
Shepley	d					14 34											16 32		
Stocksmoor	d					14 37											16 35		
Brockholes	d					14 41											16 39		
Honley	d					14 43											16 41		
Berry Brow	d					14 46											16 44		
Lockwood	d					14 49											16 47		
Huddersfield	a					14 58											16 57		
Darton	d										15 15								
Wakefield Kirkgate 4	31 a		13 52					14 52			15 29		15 52						
	d		13 53					14 53			15 30		15 53						
Normanton	d										15 34								
Castleford	a										15 40								
Woodlesford	a										15 51								
Leeds 10	31 a		14 18					15 18			16 04		16 18						

		NT	NT	NT	NT	NT	TP 1 ◇	NT	NT	NT	NT	NT	TP 1 ◇	NT	NT	NT	NT	NT	TP 1 ◇	NT
			E	N	Q		D		H	J	C		D		H	U		L	D	
St Pancras International	⊖ 53 d				12 30							13 30	14 30						15 30	
Nottingham 8	d	15 12						16 14						17 14						18 14
Langley Mill	d	15 34						16 30						17 30						18 30
Alfreton	d	15 42						16 38						17 38						18 38
Chesterfield	d	15 53						16 50						17 49						18 49
Dronfield	d	16 00						16 57						17 56						18 56
Sheffield 7	29, 31 a	16 15						17 15						18 15						19 15
	d	16 17	16 24	16 28	16 39	16 54	17 11	17 17	17 24	17 28	17 36	17 39	18 11	18 17	18 25	18 28	18 39	18 57	19 11	19 16
Meadowhall 4	29, 31 a	16 22	16 29	16 33	16 44	16 59	17 16	17 22	17 29	17 33	17 43	17 46	18 16	18 22	18 30	18 34	18 44	19 03	19 16	19 22
	d	16 23			16 45	17 00		17 23				17 46		18 23			18 45			19 23
Chapeltown	d				16 51							17 52					18 51			
Elsecar	d				16 56							17 58					18 56			
Wombwell	d				17 00							18 01					19 00			
Barnsley	a	16 37			17 05	17 14		17 37				18 08		18 37			19 05			19 37
	d	16 37			17 10	17 15		17 37				18 10		18 37			19 10			19 37
Dodworth	d					17 21						18 16								
Silkstone Common	d					17 25						18 20								
Penistone	d					17 32						18 27								
Denby Dale	d					17 38						18 34								
Shepley	d					17 43						18 39								
Stocksmoor	d					17 46						18 41								
Brockholes	d					17 50						18 45								
Honley	d					17 52						18 48								
Berry Brow	d					17 55						18 51								
Lockwood	d					17 58						18 53								
Huddersfield	a					18 07						19 02								
Darton	d				17 15												19 15			
Wakefield Kirkgate 4	31 a	16 52			17 29			17 52						18 52			19 29			19 52
	d	16 53			17 30			17 53						18 53			19 30			19 53
Normanton	d				17 34												19 34			
Castleford	a				17 40												19 41			
Woodlesford	a				17 51												19 53			
Leeds 10	31 a	17 18			18 05			18 18						19 18			20 05			20 18

For general notes see front of timetable
For details of catering facilities see Directory of Train Operators

A From Manchester Piccadilly to Doncaster (Table 29)
B To Bridlington (Table 43) (from 27 September to Hull) (Table 29)
C To Leeds (Table 31)
D From Manchester Airport to Cleethorpes (Table 29)
E To Goole (Table 29)
G To Scarborough (from 27 September to Beverley) (Table 43)
H To Doncaster (Table 29)
J To Bridlington (Table 43)
K From Retford (Table 30)
L To York (Table 33)
N To Scarborough (Table 43) (from 27 September to Hull) (Table 29)
Q From Lincoln (Table 30)
U To Beverley (Table 43)
b Arr. 1346

Table 34

Sundays

from 13 September

Nottingham, Sheffield → Barnsley → Huddersfield and Leeds

Network Diagram - see first page of Table 31

	NT	NT	NT	NT	TP	NT	NT	NT	TP	NT	NT	NT	NT	TP	NT	NT	NT
					1 ◇				1 ◇					1 ◇			
	A	B		C	D		E		D	C	B		C	G		H	A
St Pancras International ⊖ 53 d				*16 30*								*17 30*	*18 30*				
Nottingham 8 🚌 d						19 19									21 20		
Langley Mill d						19 35									21 41		
Alfreton d						19 43									21 52		
Chesterfield d						19 54									22 08		
Dronfield d						20 01									22 15		
Sheffield 7 29, 31 🚌 a						20 15									22 32		
d	19 29	19 36	19 39	20 02	20 11	20 17	20 28	20 39	21 11	21 24	21 36	21 43	22 26	22 30		22 39	23 41
Meadowhall 4 29, 31 🚌 a	19 34	19 41	19 44	20 08	20 16	20 22	20 33	20 44	21 16	21 29	21 41	21 48	22 31	22 35		22 44	23 46
🚌 d			19 45			20 23		20 45				21 49				22 45	
Chapeltown d			19 51					20 51				21 55				22 51	
Elsecar d			19 56					20 56				22 00				22 56	
Wombwell d			20 00					21 00				22 04				23 00	
Barnsley a			20 05			20 37		21 06				22 09				23 05	
d			20 06			20 37		21 10								23 10	
Dodworth d			20 12														
Silkstone Common d			20 16														
Penistone d			20 23														
Denby Dale d			20 29														
Shepley d			20 34														
Stocksmoor d			20 37														
Brockholes d			20 41														
Honley d			20 44														
Berry Brow d			20 47														
Lockwood d			20 49														
Huddersfield a			20 57														
Darton d								21 15								23 15	
Wakefield Kirkgate 4 31 a						20 52		21 29								23 28	
d						20 53		21 30								23 30	
Normanton d								21 34								23 34	
Castleford a								21 40								23 40	
Woodlesford a								21 51								23 51	
Leeds 10 31 a						21 16		22 04								00 04	

For general notes see front of timetable
For details of catering facilities see Directory of Train Operators

A To Doncaster (Table 29)
B To Leeds (Table 31)
C To Hull (Table 29)
D From Manchester Airport to Cleethorpes (Table 29)
E To Goole (Table 29)
G To Cleethorpes (Table 29)
H From Lincoln (Table 30)

Leeds and Huddersfield → Barnsley → Sheffield, Nottingham

Network Diagram - see first page of Table 31

Miles	Miles			NT	NT	NT	TP	NT	NT	NT	NT		NT	TP	NT	NT	NT	NT	NT	TP		NT	NT	NT	NT
				MX			1 ◇							1 ◇						1 ◇					
				A			B		C	A				D ✠	E		G	A		D ✠			H		E
0	—	**Leeds** 10	31 d										06 05						06 38			07 05			
6	—	Woodlesford	d																06 46						
10¾	—	Castleford	d																06 57						
14¼	—	Normanton	d																07 03						
17¼	—	Wakefield Kirkgate 4	31 a										06 21						07 07			07 23			
—	—		d								06 04		06 21						07 08			07 23			
24¾	—	Darton	d								06 15								07 19						
—	0	**Huddersfield**	d													06 10								07 10	
—	1¼	Lockwood	d													06 13								07 13	
—	2¼	Berry Brow	d													06 16								07 16	
—	3¼	Honley	d													06 19								07 19	
—	4¼	Brockholes	d													06 22								07 22	
—	6¼	Stocksmoor	d													06 26								07 26	
—	7¼	Shepley	d													06 28								07 28	
—	9½	Denby Dale	d													06 34								07 34	
—	13½	Penistone	d													06 42								07 42	
—	16¾	Silkstone Common	d													06 47								07 47	
—	18	Dodworth	d													06 51								07 51	
28¼	21	**Barnsley**	a								06 20		06 37			06 57			07 25			07 39		07 57	
—	—		d		05 23			05 50			06 21		06 38			06 58			07 25			07 40		07 58	
32¼	25	Wombwell	d		05 28			05 55			06 26					07 03			07 30					08 03	
33¾	26½	Elsecar	d		05 32			05 59			06 30					07 07			07 34					08 07	
37	29¾	Chapeltown	d		05 37			06 04			06 35					07 12			07 39					08 12	
40¾	33½	**Meadowhall**	29, 31 🚋 a		05 43			06 10			06 41		06 49			07 20			07 48			07 53		08 20	
—	—		d	00 08	05 43		05 58	06 10	06 27	06 37	06 42		06 49	06 58	06 52	07 20	07 33	07 47	07 48	07 53		07 54	08 06	08 20	08 22
44¼	37	**Sheffield** 7	29, 31 🚋 a	00 23	05 53		06 08	06 25	06 38	06 47	06 55		07 00	07 06	07 07	07 29	07 40	07 57	07 57	08 00		08 05	08 18	08 29	08 32
—	—		d			06 00							07 03									08 05			
51¼	—	Dronfield	d			06 10							07 13									08 15			
56½	—	Chesterfield	d			06 16							07 20									08 24			
66½	—	Alfreton	d			06 30							07 33									08 35			
72¾	—	Langley Mill	d			06 37							07 40									08 42			
84¾	—	**Nottingham**	a			07 08							08 02									09 02			
—	—	St Pancras International	⊖ 53 a				*08 57*		*09 13*						*09 37*	*10 06*							*10 34*		

		NT	NT	NT	NT	NT			TP	NT	NT	NT	NT	NT	NT	NT		NT	NT	TP	NT	NT	NT	NT	NT
									1 ◇											1 ◇					
					H		A		D ✠	J				K		A			H	D ✠	J				K
Leeds 10	31 d	07 29	07 35	←		08 02						08 32	08 37		←			09 05					09 32	09 37	
Woodlesford	d	07 37										08 40											09 40		
Castleford	d	07 48		07 48								08 51			08 51								09 51		
Normanton	d	→		07 54								→			08 57								→		
Wakefield Kirkgate 4	31 a		07 54	08 00		08 23							08 54		09 03			09 23						09 54	
	d		07 55	08 04		08 23							08 55		09 04			09 23						09 55	
Darton	d			08 15											09 15										
Huddersfield	d										08 10											09 13			
Lockwood	d										08 13											09 16			
Berry Brow	d										08 16											09 19			
Honley	d										08 19											09 22			
Brockholes	d										08 22											09 25			
Stocksmoor	d										08 26											09 29			
Shepley	d										08 28											09 31			
Denby Dale	d										08 34											09 36			
Penistone	d										08 42											09 44			
Silkstone Common	d										08 47											09 49			
Dodworth	d										08 51											09 53			
Barnsley	a		08 11	08 21		08 39					08 57		09 11		09 23			09 39				10 00		10 11	
	d		08 14	08 24		08 40					08 58		09 14		09 24			09 40				10 01		10 14	
Wombwell	d			08 29							09 03				09 29							10 06			
Elsecar	d			08 33							09 07				09 33										
Chapeltown	d			08 38							09 12				09 38							10 13			
Meadowhall	29, 31 🚋 a		08 31	08 45		08 52					09 20		09 28		09 46			09 52				10 19		10 27	
	d		08 31	08 45	08 49	08 52	08 55		09 01	09 15	09 21		09 28	09 33	09 46	09 50		09 52	09 55	10 01	10 07	10 19		10 28	10 33
Sheffield 7	29, 31 🚋 a		08 39	08 55	08 58	09 02	09 05		09 08	09 26	09 30		09 37	09 41	09 56	10 00		10 02	10 05	10 08	10 20	10 30		10 37	10 41
	d					09 05												10 05							
Dronfield	d					09 15												10 15							
Chesterfield	d					09 22												10 22							
Alfreton	d					09 33												10 33							
Langley Mill	d					09 40												10 40							
Nottingham	a					10 01												11 01							
St Pancras International	⊖ 53 a								*11 34*												*12 34*				

For general notes see front of timetable
For details of catering facilities see Directory of Train Operators

A From Leeds (Table 31)
B From Doncaster to Manchester Airport (Table 29)
C From Doncaster (Table 29)
D From Cleethorpes (22 June to 4 September from Doncaster) to Manchester Airport (Table 29)
E From Hull (Table 29)
G From Doncaster (Table 29) to Worksop (Table 30)
H From Adwick (Table 29)
J From Bridlington (Table 43)
K From Scunthorpe (Table 29) (22 June to 4 September from Thorne North) to Lincoln (Table 30)

From 7 September a revised Northern service will be in operation on the Huddersfield Line due to seasonal difficulties. Customers should check with NRES for precise times

Leeds and Huddersfield → Barnsley → Sheffield, Nottingham

Network Diagram - see first page of Table 31

	NT	NT	NT	NT	TP	NT	NT	NT	NT	NT	NT	NT	NT	NT	TP	NT	NT	NT	NT	NT	NT
					1 ◇										1 ◇						
		A		B	C	D				C		A		B	E	D	G				C
					🛒										🛒						
Leeds 10 ... 31 d	⟵		10 05					10 32	10 37		⟵		11 05						11 32	11 37	
Woodlesford d								10 40											11 40		
Castleford d	09 51							10 51			10 51								11 51		
								⟶											⟶		
Normanton d	09 57										10 57										
Wakefield Kirkgate 4 ... 31 a	10 01		10 23						10 54		11 01		11 23							11 54	
d	10 04		10 23						10 55		11 04		11 23							11 55	
Darton d	10 15										11 15										
Huddersfield d							10 13											11 13			
Lockwood d							10 16											11 16			
Berry Brow d							10 19											11 19			
Honley d							10 22											11 22			
Brockholes d							10 25											11 25			
Stocksmoor d							10 29											11 29			
Shepley d							10 31											11 31			
Denby Dale d							10 36											11 36			
Penistone d							10 44											11 44			
Silkstone Common d							10 49											11 49			
Dodworth d							10 53											11 53			
Barnsley a	10 21		10 39				11 00		11 11		11 21		11 39					12 00		12 11	
d	10 24		10 40				11 01		11 14		11 24		11 40					12 01		12 14	
Wombwell d	10 29						11 06				11 29							12 06			
Elsecar d	10 33										11 33										
Chapeltown d	10 38						11 13				11 38							12 13			
Meadowhall 29, 31 🚋 a	10 46		10 52				11 19		11 27		11 46		11 52					12 19		12 27	
d	10 47	10 50	10 52	10 57	11 01	11 06	11 19		11 28	11 33	11 46	11 50	11 52	11 55	12 01	12 06	12 16	12 19		12 28	12 33
Sheffield 7 29, 31 🚋 a	10 56	11 00	11 02	11 05	11 08	11 20	11 30		11 37	11 41	11 56	12 00	12 02	12 05	12 08	12 20	12 26	12 30		12 37	12 41
d			11 05										12 05								
Dronfield d			11 15										12 15								
Chesterfield d			11 22										12 22								
Alfreton d			11 33										12 33								
Langley Mill d			11 40										12 40								
Nottingham a			12 01										13 01								
St Pancras International ⊖ 53 a						*13 34*										*14 39*					

	NT		NT	NT	TP	NT	NT	NT	NT	NT	NT		NT	NT	TP	NT	NT	NT	NT	NT	NT	NT
					1 ◇										1 ◇							
		A		B	E	D				E		A		B	E	H				C		
					🛒										🛒							
Leeds 10 ... 31 d	⟵		12 05					12 32	12 37		⟵		13 05					13 32	13 37		⟵	14 05
Woodlesford d								12 40										13 40				
Castleford d	11 51							12 51			12 51							13 51			13 51	
								⟶										⟶				
Normanton d	11 57										12 57										13 57	
Wakefield Kirkgate 4 ... 31 a	12 01		12 23						12 54		13 01		13 23						13 54		14 01	14 23
d	12 04		12 23						12 55		13 04		13 23						13 55		14 04	14 23
Darton d	12 15										13 15										14 15	
Huddersfield d							12 13										13 13					
Lockwood d							12 16										13 16					
Berry Brow d							12 19										13 19					
Honley d							12 22										13 22					
Brockholes d							12 25										13 25					
Stocksmoor d							12 29										13 29					
Shepley d							12 31										13 31					
Denby Dale d							12 36										13 36					
Penistone d							12 44										13 44					
Silkstone Common d							12 49										13 49					
Dodworth d							12 53										13 53					
Barnsley a	12 21		12 39				13 00		13 11		13 21		13 39				14 00		14 11		14 21	14 39
d	12 24		12 40				13 01		13 14		13 24		13 40				14 01		14 14		14 24	14 40
Wombwell d	12 29						13 06				13 29						14 06				14 29	
Elsecar d	12 33										13 33										14 33	
Chapeltown d	12 38						13 13				13 38						14 13				14 38	
Meadowhall 29, 31 🚋 a	12 46		12 52				13 20		13 27		13 46		13 52				14 20		14 27		14 46	14 52
d	12 46	12 50	12 52	12 55	13 01	13 06	13 20		13 28	13 33	13 46	13 50	13 52	13 55	14 01	14 06	14 20		14 28	14 33	14 46	14 52
Sheffield 7 29, 31 🚋 a	12 56	13 00	13 02	13 05	13 08	13 20	13 30		13 37	13 41	13 56	14 00	14 02	14 05	14 08	14 20	14 30		14 37	14 41	14 56	15 02
d			13 05										14 05									15 05
Dronfield d			13 15										14 15									15 15
Chesterfield d			13 22										14 22									15 22
Alfreton d			13 33										14 33									15 33
Langley Mill d			13 40										14 40									15 40
Nottingham a			14 01										15 01									16 01
St Pancras International ⊖ 53 a						*15 34*										*16 34*						

For general notes see front of timetable
For details of catering facilities see Directory of Train Operators

- **A** From Leeds (Table 31)
- **B** From Adwick (Table 29)
- **C** From Scunthorpe (Table 29) (22 June to 4 September from Thorne North) to Lincoln (Table 30)
- **D** From Bridlington (Table 43)
- **E** From Cleethorpes (22 June to 4 September from Doncaster) to Manchester Airport (Table 29)
- **G** From York (Table 33)
- **H** From Scarborough (Table 43)

From 7 September a revised Northern service will be in operation on the Huddersfield Line due to seasonal difficulties. Customers should check with NRES for precise times

Leeds and Huddersfield → Barnsley → Sheffield, Nottingham

Network Diagram - see first page of Table 31

		A	NT B	TP 1◇ C		NT D	NT	NT	NT	NT E	NT	NT A	NT		NT B	TP 1◇ C	NT G	NT H	NT	NT	NT	EM ◇ J		NT E	NT
Leeds 10	31 d							14 32	14 37				15 05							15 32	15 37				
Woodlesford	d							14 40			←									15 40					←
Castleford	d							14 51			14 51									15 51					15 51
Normanton	d							→			14 57									→					15 57
Wakefield Kirkgate 4	31 a								14 54		15 01		15 23								15 54				16 01
	d								14 55		15 04		15 23								15 55				16 04
Darton	d										15 15														16 15
Huddersfield	d						14 13												15 13						
Lockwood	d						14 16												15 16						
Berry Brow	d						14 19												15 19						
Honley	d						14 22												15 22						
Brockholes	d						14 25												15 25						
Stocksmoor	d						14 29												15 29						
Shepley	d						14 31												15 31						
Denby Dale	d						14 36												15 36						
Penistone	d						14 44												15 44						
Silkstone Common	d						14 49												15 49						
Dodworth	d						14 53												15 53						
Barnsley	a						15 00		15 11		15 21		15 39						16 00		16 11				16 21
	d						15 01		15 14		15 24		15 40						16 01		16 14				16 24
Wombwell	d						15 06				15 29								16 06						16 29
Elsecar	d										15 33														16 33
Chapeltown	d						15 13				15 38								16 13						16 38
Meadowhall	29, 31 a						15 20		15 27		15 46		15 52						16 20		16 27				16 46
	d	14 50	14 55	15 01		15 06	15 20		15 28	15 33	15 46	15 50	15 52		15 55	16 01	16 07	16 18	16 20		16 28			16 33	16 46
Sheffield 7	29, 31 a	15 00	15 05	15 08		15 19	15 30		15 37	15 41	15 56	16 00	16 02		16 05	16 08	16 20	16 25	16 30		16 37			16 41	16 56
	d												16 05									16 38			
Dronfield	d												16 15									16 48			
Chesterfield	d												16 22									16 56			
Alfreton	d												16 33									17 06			
Langley Mill	d												16 40												
Nottingham	a												17 00									17 31			
St Pancras International	⊖ 53 a					*17 34*											*18 39*								

		NT A	NT	NT K	TP 1◇ C	NT D	NT	NT	NT		NT E	EM ◇ J	NT	NT A	NT	NT L	TP 1◇ C	NT N		NT	NT	NT	NT Q	NT	NT A
Leeds 10	31 d		16 05					16 32	16 37						17 05						17 32	17 37			
Woodlesford	d							16 40					←								17 40			←	
Castleford	d							16 51					16 51								17 51			17 51	
Normanton	d							→					16 57		17 18						→			17 57	
Wakefield Kirkgate 4	31 a		16 23						16 54				17 01		17 22							17 54		18 01	
	d		16 23						16 55				17 04		17 23							17 55		18 04	
Darton	d												17 15											18 15	
Huddersfield	d						16 13													17 13					
Lockwood	d						16 16													17 16					
Berry Brow	d						16 19													17 19					
Honley	d						16 22													17 22					
Brockholes	d						16 25													17 25					
Stocksmoor	d						16 29													17 29					
Shepley	d						16 31													17 31					
Denby Dale	d						16 36													17 36					
Penistone	d						16 44													17 44					
Silkstone Common	d						16 49													17 49					
Dodworth	d						16 53													17 53					
Barnsley	a		16 39				17 00		17 11				17 21		17 39					18 00		18 11		18 21	
	d		16 40				17 01		17 14				17 24		17 40					18 01		18 14		18 24	
Wombwell	d						17 06						17 29							18 06				18 29	
Elsecar	d												17 33											18 33	
Chapeltown	d						17 13						17 38							18 13				18 38	
Meadowhall	29, 31 a		16 52				17 20		17 25				17 46		17 51					18 20		18 27		18 46	
	d	16 50	16 52	16 55	17 01	17 06	17 21		17 26		17 33		17 46	17 50	17 52	17 57	18 01	18 06		18 20		18 28	18 33	18 46	18 49
Sheffield 7	29, 31 a	17 00	17 02	17 05	17 08	17 19	17 31		17 37		17 41		17 56	18 00	18 02	18 04	18 08	18 19		18 30		18 37	18 43	18 56	19 00
	d		17 05									17 44			18 05										
Dronfield	d		17 15									17 55			18 15										
Chesterfield	d		17 22									18 01			18 22										
Alfreton	d		17 33									18 11			18 33										
Langley Mill	d		17 40												18 40										
Nottingham	a		18 01									18 33			19 00										
St Pancras International	⊖ 53 a					*19 34*												*20 38*							

For general notes see front of timetable
For details of catering facilities see Directory of Train Operators

A From Leeds (Table 31)
B From Adwick (Table 29)
C From Cleethorpes (22 June to 4 September from Doncaster) to Manchester Airport (Table 29)
D From Bridlington (Table 43)
E From Scunthorpe (Table 29) (22 June to 4 September from Thorne North) to Lincoln (Table 30)
G From Scarborough (Table 43)
H From York (Table 33)
J From Liverpool Lime Street to Norwich (Table 49)
K From Adwick (Table 29) to Retford (Table 30)
L From Doncaster (Table 29)
N From Beverley (Table 43)
Q From Scunthorpe (22 June to 4 September from Thorne North) (Table 29)

From 7 September a revised Northern service will be in operation on the Huddersfield Line due to seasonal difficulties. Customers should check with NRES for precise times

Leeds and Huddersfield → Barnsley → Sheffield, Nottingham

Network Diagram - see first page of Table 31

	NT	NT	NT	TP		NT	NT	NT	NT	NT	NT	NT	NT		NT	NT	TP	NT	NT	NT	NT	NT		NT
				1 ◇													1 ◇							
			A	B		C		D					E			A	B	G		H				
				⚲													⚲							
Leeds 10 31 d	17 43	18 05								18 32	18 43	←			19 05						19 37	19 43		←
Woodlesford d										18 40											19 45			
Castleford d										18 51		18 51									19 56			19 56
Normanton d										→		18 57									→			20 02
Wakefield Kirkgate 4 31 a		18 23									18 59	19 04			19 23							19 59		20 06
d		18 23									18 59	19 04			19 23							20 00		20 07
Darton d												19 15												20 19
Huddersfield d	18 22						17 56												19 18					
Lockwood d	18 25						17 59												19 21					
Berry Brow d	18 28						18 02												19 24					
Honley d	18 31						18 05												19 27					
Brockholes d	18 34						18 08		←										19 30					
Stocksmoor d	18 38						18 12		18 38										19 34					
Shepley d	→						18 14		18 40										19 36					
Denby Dale d							18 19		18 45										19 41					
Penistone d							18b31		18 53										19 49					
Silkstone Common d							18 36		18 58										19 54					
Dodworth d							18 40		19 02										19 58					
Barnsley a		18 39					18 47		19 09		19 15	19 24			19 40				20 05			20 16		20 24
d		18 40					18 55		19 10		19 18	19 24			19 40				20 06			20 16		20 24
Wombwell d							19 00		19 15			19 29							20 11					20 29
Elsecar d							19 04					19 33												20 33
Chapeltown d							19 09		19 22			19 38							20 18					20 38
Meadowhall 29, 31 🚋 a		18 52					19 16		19 29		19 33	19 46			19 52				20 24			20 33		20 45
d		18 52	18 57	19 01		19 06	19 16	19 25	19 30		19 34	19 46	19 50		19 52	19 57	20 01	20 07	20 26	20 33		20 34		20 46
Sheffield 7 29, 31 🚋 a		19 03	19 06	19 08		19 17	19 27	19 35	19 40		19 43	19 58	19 59		20 04	20 06	20 08	20 18	20 36	20 41		20 44		20 58
d		19 05													20 05									
Dronfield d		19 15													20 15									
Chesterfield d		19 22													20 22									
Alfreton d		19 33													20 33									
Langley Mill d		19 40													20 40									
Nottingham a		20 00													21 01									
St Pancras International ⊖ 53 a						*21 37*												*23 07*						

	NT	TP	NT	EM	NT	NT	NT	NT		TP	NT	NT	NT	NT	NT	NT	NT		NT	NT	NT			
															FX	FO								
		1 ◇		◇						1 ◇														
	E	J		K	L	N		E		B	A	G					E							
				⚲																				
Leeds 10 31 d			20 30				20 37								21 37	21 37				22 37				
Woodlesford d							20 45								21 45	21 45				22 45				
Castleford d							20 56								21 56	21 56				22 56				
Normanton d							21 02								22 02	22 02				23 01				
Wakefield Kirkgate 4 31 a			20 46				21 06								22 06	22 06				23 10				
d			20 46				21 07								22 07	22 07				23 10				
Darton d							21 18								22 18	22 21				23 24				
Huddersfield d					20 18								21 18						22 18					
Lockwood d					20 21								21 21						22 21					
Berry Brow d					20 24								21 24						22 24					
Honley d					20 27								21 27						22 27					
Brockholes d					20 30								21 30						22 30					
Stocksmoor d					20 34								21 34						22 34					
Shepley d					20 36								21 36						22 36					
Denby Dale d					20 41								21 41						22 41					
Penistone d					20 49								21 49						22 49					
Silkstone Common d					20 54								21 54						22 54					
Dodworth d					20 58								21 58						22 58					
Barnsley a			21 02		21 08		21 24						22 05		22 25	22 27			23 05	23 31				
d			21 03		21 11		21 24						22 06		22 25	22 28			23 06	23 31				
Wombwell d					21 16		21 29						22 11		22 30	22 33			23 11	23 36				
Elsecar d							21 33								22 34	22 37			23 15	23 40				
Chapeltown d					21 23		21 38						22 18		22 39	22 42			23 20	23 45				
Meadowhall 29, 31 🚋 a			21 17		21 28		21 45						22 23		22 46	22 47			23 25	23 51				
d	20 51	21 07	21 19		21 29	21 35	21 46	21 52		21 58	22 03	22 09	22 25	22 44	22 47	22 48	22 52		23 26	23 51	23 54			
Sheffield 7 29, 31 🚋 a	21 02	21 17	21 30		21 40	21 46	21 58	22 05		22 08	22 11	22 21	22 36	22 54	22 58	22 58	23 02		23 36	00 02	00 04			
d				21 38																				
Dronfield d				21 48																				
Chesterfield d				21 54																				
Alfreton d				22 05																				
Langley Mill d				22 12																				
Nottingham a				22 38																				
St Pancras International ⊖ 53 a																								

For general notes see front of timetable
For details of catering facilities see Directory of Train Operators

A From Doncaster (Table 29)
B From Cleethorpes (22 June to 4 September from Doncaster) to Manchester Airport (Table 29)
C From Scarborough (Table 43)
D From Beverley (Table 43)
E From Leeds (Table 31)
G From Hull (Table 29)
H From Doncaster (Table 29) to Worksop (Table 30)
J From Cleethorpes (22 June to 4 September from Doncaster) (Table 29)
K From Liverpool Lime Street (Table 49)
L To Retford (Table 30)
N From Bridlington (Table 43)
b Arr. 1826

From 7 September a revised Northern service will be in operation on the Huddersfield Line due to seasonal difficulties. Customers should check with NRES for precise times

Leeds and Huddersfield → Barnsley → Sheffield, Nottingham

Network Diagram - see first page of Table 31

			NT	TP	NT	NT	NT	TP	NT	NT	NT	NT	NT	TP	NT	NT	NT	NT	NT	NT	NT	NT	NT	NT	TP	NT
				1 ◇				1 ◇						1 ◇											1 ◇	
				A		B		C	D		B	E		C		G		D				G		E	C	H
								⊼						⊼											⊼	
Leeds 10	31	d											06 38		07 05				07 29	07 35	←		08 05			
Woodlesford		d											06 46						07 37							
Castleford		d											06 57						07 48 →		07 48					
Normanton		d											07 03								07 54					
Wakefield Kirkgate 4	31	a											07 07		07 23					07 54	08 00		08 23			
		d											07 08		07 23					07 55	08 04		08 23			
Darton		d											07 19								08 15					
Huddersfield		d								06 10							07 10									
Lockwood		d								06 13							07 13									
Berry Brow		d								06 16							07 16									
Honley		d								06 19							07 19									
Brockholes		d								06 22							07 22									
Stocksmoor		d								06 26							07 26									
Shepley		d								06 28							07 28									
Denby Dale		d								06 34							07 34									
Penistone		d								06 42							07 42									
Silkstone Common		d								06 47							07 47									
Dodworth		d								06 51							07 51									
Barnsley		a								06 57			07 25		07 39		07 57			08 11	08 21		08 39			
		d	05 23		05 50		06 21			06 58			07 25		07 40		07 58			08 14	08 24		08 40			
Wombwell		d	05 28		05 55		06 26			07 03			07 30				08 03				08 29					
Elsecar		d	05 32		05 59		06 30			07 07			07 34				08 07				08 33					
Chapeltown		d	05 37		06 04		06 35			07 12			07 39				08 12				08 38					
Meadowhall	29, 31 ⇌	a	05 43		06 10		06 41			07 20			07 48		07 53		08 18			08 31	08 45		08 52			
		d	05 43	05 58	06 10	06 27	06 42	06 58	06 52	07 20	07 33	07 47	07 48	07 53	07 54	08 06	08 18	08 22		08 31	08 45	08 49	08 52	08 55	09 01	09 19
Sheffield 7	29, 31 ⇌	a	05 53	06 08	06 25	06 38	06 55	07 06	07 07	07 29	07 45	07 57	07 57	08 00	08 05	08 18	08 29	08 32		08 39	08 55	08 58	09 02	09 05	09 08	09 28
		d					07 03								08 05								09 05			
Dronfield		d					07 13								08 15								09 15			
Chesterfield		d					07 20								08 24								09 22			
Alfreton		d					07 33								08 35								09 33			
Langley Mill		d					07 40								08 42								09 40			
Nottingham		a					08 02								09 02								10 01			
St Pancras International	⊖ 53	a		*08 34*					*09 34*							*10 34*									*11 34*	

			NT		NT	NT	NT	NT	NT	NT	NT	TP	NT	NT	NT	NT	NT	NT	NT	NT	NT	TP	NT	NT	NT	NT
												1 ◇										1 ◇				
							J		E		G	C	H				J		E		G	C	H			
												⊼										⊼				
Leeds 10	31	d			08 32	08 37		←		09 05					09 32	09 37		←		10 05					10 32	10 37
Woodlesford		d			08 40										09 40										10 40	
Castleford		d			08 51 →			08 51							09 51 →			09 51							10 51 →	
Normanton		d						08 57										09 57								
Wakefield Kirkgate 4	31	a				08 54		09 03		09 23						09 54		10 01		10 23						10 54
		d				08 55		09 04		09 23						09 55		10 04		10 23						10 55
Darton		d						09 15										10 15								
Huddersfield		d	08 10											09 13										10 13		
Lockwood		d	08 13											09 16										10 16		
Berry Brow		d	08 16											09 19										10 19		
Honley		d	08 19											09 22										10 22		
Brockholes		d	08 22											09 25										10 25		
Stocksmoor		d	08 26											09 29										10 29		
Shepley		d	08 28											09 31										10 31		
Denby Dale		d	08 34											09 36										10 36		
Penistone		d	08 42											09 44										10 44		
Silkstone Common		d	08 47											09 49										10 49		
Dodworth		d	08 51											09 53										10 53		
Barnsley		a	08 57			09 11		09 23		09 39				10 00		10 11		10 21		10 39				11 00		11 11
		d	08 58			09 14		09 24		09 40				10 01		10 14		10 24		10 40				11 01		11 14
Wombwell		d	09 03					09 29						10 06				10 29						11 06		
Elsecar		d	09 07					09 33										10 33								
Chapeltown		d	09 12					09 38						10 13				10 38						11 13		
Meadowhall	29, 31 ⇌	a	09 20			09 28		09 46		09 52				10 19		10 27		10 46		10 52				11 18		11 27
		d	09 21			09 28	09 33	09 46	09 50	09 52	09 55	10 01	10 07	10 19		10 28	10 33	10 47	10 50	10 52	10 57	11 01	11 06	11 19		11 28
Sheffield 7	29, 31 ⇌	a	09 30			09 37	09 41	09 56	10 00	10 02	10 05	10 08	10 20	10 30		10 37	10 41	10 56	11 00	11 02	11 06	11 08	11 20	11 29		11 37
		d								10 05										11 05						
Dronfield		d								10 15										11 15						
Chesterfield		d								10 22										11 22						
Alfreton		d								10 33										11 33						
Langley Mill		d								10 40										11 40						
Nottingham		a								11 00										12 02						
St Pancras International	⊖ 53	a											*12 34*										*13 34*			

For general notes see front of timetable
For details of catering facilities see Directory of Train Operators

A From Doncaster to Manchester Airport (Table 29)
B From Doncaster (Table 29)
C From Cleethorpes (27 June to 5 September from Doncaster) to Manchester Airport (Table 29)
D From Hull (Table 29)
E From Leeds (Table 31)
G From Adwick (Table 29)
H From Bridlington (Table 43)
J From Scunthorpe (Table 29) (27 June to 5 September from Thorne North) to Lincoln (Table 30)

From 12 September a revised Northern service will be in operation on the Huddersfield Line due to seasonal difficulties. Customers should check with NRES for precise times

Table 34 — Saturdays

Leeds and Huddersfield → Barnsley → Sheffield, Nottingham

Network Diagram - see first page of Table 31

	NT A	NT	NT B		NT	TP 1 ◇ C ✠	NT D	NT E	NT G	NT	NT	NT	NT A	NT	NT B	NT	NT D	TP 1 ◇ C ✠	NT E	NT	NT	NT	NT A	NT
Leeds 10 31 d					11 05						11 32	11 37				12 05					12 32	12 37		
Woodlesford d		←									11 40			←							12 40			←
Castleford d		10 51									11 51			11 51							12 51			12 51
Normanton d		10 57									→			11 57							→			12 57
Wakefield Kirkgate 4 31 a		11 01			11 23							11 54		12 01		12 23						12 54		13 01
d		11 04			11 23							11 55		12 04		12 23						12 55		13 04
Darton d		11 15												12 15										13 15
Huddersfield d										11 13										12 13				
Lockwood d										11 16										12 16				
Berry Brow d										11 19										12 19				
Honley d										11 22										12 22				
Brockholes d										11 25										12 25				
Stocksmoor d										11 29										12 29				
Shepley d										11 31										12 31				
Denby Dale d										11 36										12 36				
Penistone d										11 44										12 44				
Silkstone Common d										11 49										12 49				
Dodworth d										11 53										12 53				
Barnsley a		11 21			11 39					12 00		12 11		12 21		12 39				13 00		13 11		13 21
d		11 24			11 40					12 01		12 14		12 24		12 40				13 01		13 14		13 24
Wombwell d		11 29								12 06				12 29						13 06				13 29
Elsecar d		11 33												12 33										13 33
Chapeltown d		11 38								12 13				12 38						13 13				13 38
Meadowhall 29, 31 ⛴ a		11 46			11 52					12 19		12 27		12 46		12 52				13 20		13 27		13 46
d	11 33	11 46	11 50		11 52	11 59	12 00	12 06	12 16	12 19		12 28	12 33	12 46	12 50	12 52	12 55	13 01	13 06	13 20		13 28	13 33	13 46
Sheffield 7 29, 31 ⛴ a	11 41	11 56	12 00		12 02	12 08	12 10	12 20	12 25	12 30		12 37	12 41	12 56	13 00	13 02	13 05	13 08	13 20	13 30		13 37	13 41	13 56
d					12 05											13 05								
Dronfield d					12 15											13 15								
Chesterfield d					12 22											13 22								
Alfreton d					12 33											13 33								
Langley Mill d					12 40											13 40								
Nottingham a					13 00											14 00								
St Pancras International ⊖ 53 a								*14 34*											*15 34*					

	NT B	NT	NT D	TP 1 ◇ C ✠	NT H		NT	NT	NT	NT A	NT	NT B	NT	NT D	TP 1 ◇ C ✠	NT E	NT	NT	NT	NT A	NT	NT B	NT	TP 1 ◇ C ✠
Leeds 10 31 d		13 05						13 32	13 37				14 05					14 32	14 37				15 05	
Woodlesford d								13 40			←							14 40			←			
Castleford d								13 51			13 51							14 51			14 51			
Normanton d								→			13 57							→			14 57			
Wakefield Kirkgate 4 31 a		13 23							13 54		14 01		14 23						14 54		15 01		15 23	
d		13 23							13 55		14 04		14 23						14 55		15 04		15 23	
Darton d											14 15										15 15			
Huddersfield d							13 13										14 13							
Lockwood d							13 16										14 16							
Berry Brow d							13 19										14 19							
Honley d							13 22										14 22							
Brockholes d							13 25										14 25							
Stocksmoor d							13 29										14 29							
Shepley d							13 31										14 31							
Denby Dale d							13 36										14 36							
Penistone d							13 44										14 44							
Silkstone Common d							13 49										14 49							
Dodworth d							13 53										14 53							
Barnsley a		13 39					14 00		14 11		14 21		14 39				15 00		15 11		15 21		15 39	
d		13 40					14 01		14 14		14 24		14 40				15 01		15 14		15 24		15 40	
Wombwell d							14 06				14 29						15 06				15 29			
Elsecar d											14 33										15 33			
Chapeltown d							14 13				14 38						15 13				15 38			
Meadowhall 29, 31 ⛴ a		13 52					14 20		14 27		14 46		14 52				15 20		15 27		15 46		15 52	
d	13 50	13 52	13 55	14 01	14 06		14 20		14 28	14 33	14 46	14 50	14 52	14 55	15 01	15 06	15 20		15 28	15 33	15 46	15 50	15 52	15 58
Sheffield 7 29, 31 ⛴ a	14 00	14 02	14 05	14 08	14 20		14 30		14 37	14 41	14 56	15 00	15 02	15 05	15 08	15 20	15 30		15 37	15 41	15 56	16 00	16 02	16 08
d		14 05											15 05										16 05	
Dronfield d		14 15											15 15										16 15	
Chesterfield d		14 22											15 22										16 22	
Alfreton d		14 33											15 33										16 33	
Langley Mill d		14 40											15 40										16 40	
Nottingham a		15 00											16 00										17 00	
St Pancras International ⊖ 53 a					*16 34*											*17 34*								

For general notes see front of timetable
For details of catering facilities see Directory of Train Operators

- **A** From Scunthorpe (Table 29) (27 June to 5 September from Thorne North) to Lincoln (Table 30)
- **B** From Leeds (Table 31)
- **C** From Cleethorpes (27 June to 5 September from Doncaster) to Manchester Airport (Table 29)
- **D** From Adwick (Table 29)
- **E** From Bridlington (Table 43)
- **G** From York (Table 33)
- **H** From Scarborough (Table 43)

From 12 September a revised Northern service will be in operation on the Huddersfield Line due to seasonal difficulties. Customers should check with NRES for precise times

Leeds and Huddersfield → Barnsley → Sheffield, Nottingham

Network Diagram - see first page of Table 31

	NT A	NT B	NT	NT	NT C	NT	EM ◇ D		NT E	NT	NT G	NT	NT H	TP 1◇ J	NT K	NT	NT	NT	NT E	EM ◇ D	NT	NT G	NT	NT L
Leeds 10 31 d				15 32		15 37						16 05					16 32	16 37					17 05	
Woodlesford d				15 40						←							16 40				←			
Castleford d				15 51						15 51							16 51				16 51			
Normanton d				→						15 57							→				16 57		17 18	
Wakefield Kirkgate 4 31 a						15 54				16 01		16 23						16 54			17 01		17 22	
d						15 55				16 04		16 23						16 55			17 04		17 23	
Darton d										16 15											17 15			
Huddersfield d			15 13													16 13								
Lockwood d			15 16													16 16								
Berry Brow d			15 19													16 19								
Honley d			15 22													16 22								
Brockholes d			15 25													16 25								
Stocksmoor d			15 29													16 29								
Shepley d			15 31													16 31								
Denby Dale d			15 36													16 36								
Penistone d			15 44													16 44								
Silkstone Common d			15 49													16 49								
Dodworth d			15 53													16 53								
Barnsley a			16 00			16 11				16 21		16 39				17 00		17 11			17 21		17 39	
d			16 01			16 14				16 24		16 40				17 01		17 14			17 24		17 40	
Wombwell d			16 06							16 29						17 06					17 29			
Elsecar d										16 33											17 33			
Chapeltown d			16 13							16 38						17 13					17 38			
Meadowhall 29, 31 a			16 20			16 27				16 46		16 52				17 20		17 25			17 46		17 51	
d	16 00	16 07	16 20		16 24	16 28			16 33	16 46	16 50	16 52	16 55	17 01	17 06	17 21		17 26	17 33		17 46	17 50	17 51	17 57
Sheffield 7 29, 31 a	16 10	16 20	16 30		16 35	16 37			16 41	16 56	17 00	17 02	17 05	17 08	17 19	17 32		17 37	17 41		17 56	18 00	18 02	18 05
d							16 38					17 05								17 44			18 05	
Dronfield d							16 48					17 15								17 55			18 15	
Chesterfield d							16 53					17 22								17 58			18 22	
Alfreton d							17 04					17 33								18 08			18 33	
Langley Mill d												17 40											18 40	
Nottingham a							17 29					18 00								18 33			19 00	
St Pancras International ⊖53 a		*18 34*													*19 38*									

	TP 1◇ J	NT N	NT	NT	NT	NT E	NT	NT G	NT		NT L	TP 1◇ J	NT B	NT	NT	NT	NT Q	NT	NT G	NT	NT L	TP 1◇ J	NT U	NT
Leeds 10 31 d				17 32	17 37				18 05						18 32	18 37				19 05				
Woodlesford d				17 40			←								18 40			←						
Castleford d				17 51			17 51								18 51			18 51						
Normanton d				→			17 57								→			18 57						
Wakefield Kirkgate 4 31 a					17 54		18 01		18 23							18 54		19 04		19 23				
d					17 55		18 04		18 23							18 55		19 04		19 23				
Darton d							18 15											19 15						
Huddersfield d			17 13											18 13										19 18
Lockwood d			17 16											18 16										19 21
Berry Brow d			17 19											18 19										19 24
Honley d			17 22											18 22										19 27
Brockholes d			17 25											18 25										19 30
Stocksmoor d			17 29											18 29										19 34
Shepley d			17 31											18 31										19 36
Denby Dale d			17 36											18 36										19 41
Penistone d			17 44											18 44										19 49
Silkstone Common d			17 49											18 49										19 54
Dodworth d			17 53											18 53										19 58
Barnsley a			18 00		18 11		18 21		18 39					19 01		19 11		19 24		19 40				20 05
d			18 01		18 14		18 24		18 40					19 01		19 14		19 24		19 40				20 06
Wombwell d			18 06				18 29							19 06				19 29						20 11
Elsecar d							18 33											19 33						
Chapeltown d			18 13				18 38							19 13				19 38						20 18
Meadowhall 29, 31 a			18 20		18 27		18 46		18 52					19 20		19 27		19 46		19 52				20 24
d	18 01	18 06	18 20		18 28	18 33	18 46	18 51	18 52		18 56	19 01	19 06	19 20		19 28	19 33	19 46	19 50	19 52	19 57	20 01	20 07	20 24
Sheffield 7 29, 31 a	18 08	18 19	18 30		18 37	18 41	18 56	19 02	19 03		19 05	19 08	19 17	19 30		19 37	19 42	19 58	19 59	20 04	20 05	20 08	20 18	20 36
d									19 05											20 05				
Dronfield d									19 15											20 15				
Chesterfield d									19 22											20 22				
Alfreton d									19 33											20 33				
Langley Mill d									19 40											20 40				
Nottingham a									20 00											21 01				
St Pancras International ⊖53 a		*20 37*			*21 08*								*21 41*											

For general notes see front of timetable
For details of catering facilities see Directory of Train Operators

A From Adwick (Table 29)
B From Scarborough (Table 43)
C From York (Table 33)
D From Liverpool Lime Street to Norwich (Table 49)
E From Scunthorpe (Table 29) (27 June to 5 September from Thorne North) to Lincoln (Table 30)
G From Leeds (Table 31)
H From Adwick (Table 29) to Retford (Table 30)
J From Cleethorpes (27 June to 5 September from Doncaster) to Manchester Airport (Table 29)
K From Bridlington (Table 43)
L From Doncaster (Table 29)
N From Beverley (Table 43)
Q From Scunthorpe (27 June to 5 September from Thorne North) (Table 29)
U From Hull (Table 29)

From 12 September a revised Northern service will be in operation on the Huddersfield Line due to seasonal difficulties. Customers should check with NRES for precise times

Table 34

Leeds and Huddersfield → Barnsley → Sheffield, Nottingham

Saturdays

Network Diagram - see first page of Table 31

	NT	NT	NT	NT	NT	TP	NT	EM	NT	NT	NT	NT	TP	NT	NT	NT	NT	NT	NT	NT	NT	NT
						1 ◇		◇					1 ◇									
			A		B	C		D	E	G		B	C	H	J			B	J		B	G
Leeds 10 31 d	19 37	19 43					20 30				20 37						21 37					
Woodlesford d	19 45			←							20 45						21 45					
Castleford d	19 56			19 56							20 56						21 56					
Normanton d	→			20 02							21 02						22 02					
Wakefield Kirkgate 4 31 a		19 59		20 06			20 46				21 06						22 06					
d		20 00		20 07			20 46				21 07						22 07					
Darton d				20 19							21 18						22 18					
Huddersfield d									20 18							21 18				22 18		
Lockwood d									20 21							21 21				22 21		
Berry Brow d									20 24							21 24				22 24		
Honley d									20 27							21 27				22 27		
Brockholes d									20 30							21 30				22 30		
Stocksmoor d									20 34							21 34				22 34		
Shepley d									20 36							21 36				22 36		
Denby Dale d									20 41							21 41				22 41		
Penistone d									20 49							21 49				22 49		
Silkstone Common d									20 54							21 54				22 54		
Dodworth d									20 58							21 58				22 58		
Barnsley a		20 16		20 24			21 02		21 08		21 24					22 05	22 25			23 05		
d		20 16		20 24			21 03		21 11		21 24					22 06	22 25			23 06		
Wombwell d				20 29					21 16		21 29					22 11	22 30			23 11		
Elsecar d				20 33							21 33						22 34			23 15		
Chapeltown d				20 38					21 23		21 38					22 18	22 39			23 20		
Meadowhall 29, 31 🚋 a		20 29		20 45			21 17		21 28		21 45					22 23	22 46			23 26		
d		20 31	20 35	20 46	20 51	21 07	21 17		21 29	21 35	21 46	21 52	21 58	22 09	22 22	22 25	22 47	22 53	22 58	23 27	23 44	23 49
Sheffield 7 29, 31 🚋 a		20 41	20 42	20 58	21 02	21 17	21 29		21 40	21 46	21 58	22 07	22 10	22 21	22 32	22 36	22 58	23 02	23 05	23 36	23 58	23 59
d								21 38														
Dronfield d								21 48														
Chesterfield d								21 54														
Alfreton d								22 05														
Langley Mill d								22 12														
Nottingham a								22 33														
St Pancras International ⊖ 53 a																						

Sundays

until 12 July

	NT	NT	TP	NT	NT	NT	NT	NT	NT	NT	NT	NT	TP	NT	NT	NT	NT	NT	NT	TP	NT
			1 ◇										1 ◇							1 ◇	
	J		K	J	🚌		B		H		L		N		🚌		J		G	N	B
Leeds 10 31 d					07 55	08 37		08 55				09 54			09 40	10 28		10 51			
Woodlesford d					08 15										10 00						
Castleford d					08 30										10 15						
Normanton d					08 42										10 27						
Wakefield Kirkgate 4 31 a					08 54	08 54		09 11				10 09			10 39	10 44		11 06			
d						09 00		09 14				10 11				10 46		11 13			
Darton d						09 14										11 00					
Huddersfield d										09 19				10 15							
Lockwood d										09 22				10 18							
Berry Brow d										09 25				10 21							
Honley d										09 28				10 24							
Brockholes d										09 31				10 27							
Stocksmoor d										09 35				10 31							
Shepley d										09 37				10 33							
Denby Dale d										09 42				10 39							
Penistone d										09 50				10 46							
Silkstone Common d										09 55				10 52							
Dodworth d										09 59				10 55							
Barnsley a						09 20		09 33		10 06		10 30		11 03		11 07		11 32			
d						09 24		09 41		10 12		10 38		11 03		11 12		11 33			
Wombwell d						09 29				10 17						11 17					
Elsecar d						09 33				10 21						11 21					
Chapeltown d						09 38				10 26						11 26					
Meadowhall 29, 31 🚋 a						09 41		09 54		10 32		10 51		11 20		11 32		11 46			
d	08 30		09 00	09 41		09 41	09 54	09 55	10 00	10 33	10 40	10 51	11 00	11 20		11 35	11 40	11 46	11 52	12 00	12 11
Sheffield 7 29, 31 🚋 a	08 41		09 07	09 51		09 55	10 03	10 04	10 09	10 43	10 52	11 00	11 07	11 28		11 44	11 51	11 56	12 03	12 07	12 20
d		09 00						10 07				11 03						12 00			
Dronfield d		09 10						10 17				11 13						12 10			
Chesterfield d		09 17						10 24				11 20						12 18			
Alfreton d		09 28						10 35				11 31						12 29			
Langley Mill d		09 35						10 42				11 38						12 36			
Nottingham a		09 55						11 02				11 58						12 56			
St Pancras International ⊖ 53 a			*12 19*						*13 19*		*14 19*									*15 22*	

For general notes see front of timetable
For details of catering facilities see Directory of Train Operators

A From Doncaster (Table 29) to Worksop (Table 30)
B From Leeds (Table 31)
C From Cleethorpes (27 June to 5 September from Doncaster) (Table 29)
D From Liverpool Lime Street (Table 49)
E To Retford (Table 30)
G From Bridlington (Table 43)
H From Hull (Table 29)
J From Doncaster (Table 29)
K To Manchester Airport (Table 78)
L From Goole (Table 29)
N From Cleethorpes (from 28 June from Doncaster) to Manchester Airport (Table 29)

From 12 September a revised Northern service will be in operation on the Huddersfield Line due to seasonal difficulties. Customers should check with NRES for precise times

Table 34

Sundays

until 12 July

Leeds and Huddersfield → Barnsley → Sheffield, Nottingham

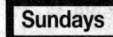

Network Diagram - see first page of Table 31

		NT	NT	NT	TP	NT	NT	NT	NT	NT	TP	NT	NT	NT	NT	NT	TP	NT	NT	NT	NT	NT
				A	1 ◇ B		C	Bus		D	1 ◇ E	G		A	D		1 ◇ B		Bus		C	H
Leeds 10	31 d	11 29				12 29		11 55	12 43							13 48			13 40	14 26		
Woodlesford	d							12 15											14 00			
Castleford	d							12 30											14 15			
Normanton	d							12 42											14 27			
Wakefield Kirkgate 4	31 a	11 46				12 46		12 54	13 00							14 05			14 39	14 42		
	d	11 46				12 46			13 02							14 11				14 46		
Darton	d								13 16											15 00		
Huddersfield	d		11 29										13 19					14 15				
Lockwood	d		11 32										13 22					14 18				
Berry Brow	d		11 35										13 25					14 21				
Honley	d		11 38										13 28					14 24				
Brockholes	d		11 41										13 31					14 27				
Stocksmoor	d		11 45										13 35					14 31				
Shepley	d		11 47										13 37					14 33				
Denby Dale	d		11 52										13 42					14 39				
Penistone	d		12 00										13 50					14 46				
Silkstone Common	d		12 05										13 55					14 52				
Dodworth	d		12 09										13 59					14 55				
Barnsley	a	12 05	12 16			13 05			13 23				14 06			14 30		15 03		15 07		
	d	12 06	12 17			13 06			13 24				14 12			14 41		15 03		15 12		
Wombwell	d		12 22						13 29				14 17							15 17		
Elsecar	d		12 26						13 33				14 21							15 21		
Chapeltown	d		12 31						13 38				14 26							15 26		
Meadowhall	29, 31 🚋 a	12 17	12 34			13 18			13 47				14 32			14 54		15 20		15 35		
	d	12 17	12 35	12 43	13 00	13 18	13 44		13 50	13 53	14 00	14 17	14 33	14 43	14 53	14 56	15 00	15 21		15 35	15 43	15 52
Sheffield 7	29, 31 🚋 a	12 29	12 47	12 55	13 07	13 29	13 52		13 58	14 04	14 07	14 25	14 47	14 52	15 03	15 06	15 07	15 28		15 45	15 51	16 01
	d	12 31				13 31										15 07						
Dronfield	d	12 42				13 41										15 17						
Chesterfield	d	12 49				13 48										15 25						
Alfreton	d	12 59				13 59										15 36						
Langley Mill	d	13 07				14 06										15 43						
Nottingham	a	13 26				14 26										16 03						
St Pancras International	⊖ 53 a				*16 15*				*16 55*					*17 59*			*18 04*					

		NT	TP	NT	NT	NT	NT	NT	TP	NT	NT	NT	NT	NT	TP	NT	NT	NT	NT	NT	NT	TP
			1 ◇ B	G		A	D		1 ◇ B	Bus		C	H		1 ◇ B	G	J		A	D		1 ◇ B
Leeds 10	31 d	15 05						16 05		15 40	16 27			16 54							18 05	
Woodlesford	d									16 00												
Castleford	d									16 15												
Normanton	d									16 27												
Wakefield Kirkgate 4	31 a	15 22						16 21		16 39	16 43			17 09							18 21	
	d	15 22						16 22			16 46			17 11							18 22	
Darton	d										17 00											
Huddersfield	d				15 19													17 19				
Lockwood	d				15 22													17 22				
Berry Brow	d				15 25													17 25				
Honley	d				15 28													17 28				
Brockholes	d				15 31													17 31				
Stocksmoor	d				15 35													17 35				
Shepley	d				15 37													17 37				
Denby Dale	d				15 42													17 47				
Penistone	d				15 50													17 54				
Silkstone Common	d				15 55													18 00				
Dodworth	d				15 59													18 03				
Barnsley	a	15 41			16 06			16 41			17 07			17 30				18 11			18 41	
	d	15 42			16 12			16 42			17 12			17 41				18 12			18 42	
Wombwell	d				16 17						17 17							18 17				
Elsecar	d				16 21						17 21							18 21				
Chapeltown	d				16 26						17 26							18 26				
Meadowhall	29, 31 🚋 a	15 55			16 32			16 56			17 34			17 55				18 32			18 56	
	d	15 56	16 00	16 11	16 33	16 43	16 53	16 56	17 00		17 35	17 43	17 53	17 56	18 00	18 12	18 24	18 33	18 43	18 53	18 56	19 00
Sheffield 7	29, 31 🚋 a	16 05	16 07	16 21	16 43	16 52	17 03	17 05	17 07		17 44	17 54	18 01	18 05	18 07	18 23	18 35	18 44	18 52	19 03	19 05	19 07
	d	16 07						17 07						18 07							19 07	
Dronfield	d	16 17						17 17						18 17							19 17	
Chesterfield	d	16 25						17 24						18 25							19 25	
Alfreton	d	16 36						17 35						18 36							19 36	
Langley Mill	d	16 43						17 43						18 43							19 43	
Nottingham	a	17 03						18 03						19 03							20 03	
St Pancras International	⊖ 53 a		*19 04*						*20 04*						*21 27*							*22 27*

For general notes see front of timetable
For details of catering facilities see Directory of Train Operators

A From Goole (Table 29)
B From Cleethorpes (from 28 June from Doncaster) to Manchester Airport (Table 29)
C From Doncaster (Table 29)
D From Scarborough (Table 43)
E From Doncaster to Manchester Airport (Table 29)
G From Leeds (Table 31)
H From Bridlington (Table 43)
J From York (Table 33)

Leeds and Huddersfield → Barnsley → Sheffield, Nottingham

Sundays
until 12 July

Network Diagram - see first page of Table 31

		NT	NT	NT		NT	NT	TP 1 ◇	NT	NT	NT		TP 1 ◇	NT	NT	NT	NT	TP 1 ◇	NT	NT	NT	NT	NT	
		🚌		A			B	C	D		A		C	🚌		E	G	H		D	J	🚌		
Leeds 10	31 d	17 40	18 28			19 04								19 40	20 28							21 40	22 28	
Woodlesford	d	18 00												20 00								22 00		
Castleford	d	18 15												20 15								22 15		
Normanton	d	18 27												20 27								22 27		
Wakefield Kirkgate 4	31 a	18 39	18 43			19 20								20 39	20 44							22 39	22 44	
	d		18 45			19 20									20 46								22 46	
Darton	d		18 59												21 00								23 00	
Huddersfield	d									19 19														
Lockwood	d									19 22														
Berry Brow	d									19 25														
Honley	d									19 28														
Brockholes	d									19 31														
Stocksmoor	d									19 35														
Shepley	d									19 37														
Denby Dale	d									19 42														
Penistone	d									19 50														
Silkstone Common	d									19 55														
Dodworth	d									19 59														
Barnsley	a		19 05			19 40				20 06					21 07								23 07	
	d		19 11			19 40				20 12					21 12				22 21				23 12	
Wombwell	d		19 17							20 17					21 17				22 26				23 17	
Elsecar	d		19 21							20 21					21 21				22 30				23 21	
Chapeltown	d		19 26							20 26					21 26				22 35				23 26	
Meadowhall	29, 31 🚋 a		19 32			19 54				20 34					21 33				22 40				23 31	
	d		19 33	19 47		19 54	19 57	20 00	20 11	20 34	20 45		21 00		21 33	21 45	21 54	22 00	22 41	22 45	22 50		23 32	
Sheffield 7	29, 31 🚋 a		19 43	19 55		20 04	20 06	20 07	20 23	20 43	20 53		21 07		21 42	21 56	22 05	22 11	22 51	22 54	22 58		23 42	
	d					20 06																		
Dronfield	d					20 16																		
Chesterfield	d					20 22																		
Alfreton	d					20 33																		
Langley Mill	d					20 40																		
Nottingham	a					21 01																		
St Pancras International	⊖ 53 a			*23 12*																				

Sundays
19 July to 6 September

		NT	NT	TP 1 ◇	NT		NT	NT	NT	NT		NT	NT	NT	TP 1 ◇		NT	NT	NT	NT		NT	TP 1 ◇	NT	NT
		A		K	A			D		E			L		N				A			B	N	D	
Leeds 10	31 d						08 34		09 05					10 02				10 17		10 57					11 29
Woodlesford	d						08 42											10 25							
Castleford	d						08 53											10 36							
Normanton	d						08 58											10 41							
Wakefield Kirkgate 4	31 a						09 03		09 21					10 18				10 46		11 13					11 46
	d						09 03		09 21					10 18				10 46		11 13					11 46
Darton	d						09 17											11 00							
Huddersfield	d											09 19					10 15								
Lockwood	d											09 22					10 18								
Berry Brow	d											09 25					10 21								
Honley	d											09 28					10 24								
Brockholes	d											09 31					10 27								
Stocksmoor	d											09 35					10 31								
Shepley	d											09 37					10 33								
Denby Dale	d											09 42					10 39								
Penistone	d											09 50					10 46								
Silkstone Common	d											09 55					10 52								
Dodworth	d											09 59					10 55								
Barnsley	a						09 24		09 40			10 06		10 37			11 03	11 07		11 32					12 05
	d						09 24		09 41			10 12		10 38			11 03	11 12		11 33					12 06
Wombwell	d						09 29					10 17						11 17							
Elsecar	d						09 33					10 21						11 21							
Chapeltown	d						09 38					10 26						11 26							
Meadowhall	29, 31 🚋 a						09 47		09 55			10 32		10 51			11 20	11 32		11 46					12 17
	d	08 30		09 00	09 41		09 48	09 54	09 55	10 00		10 33	10 40	10 51	11 00		11 20	11 35	11 40	11 46		11 52	12 00	12 11	12 17
Sheffield 7	29, 31 🚋 a	08 41		09 07	09 51		09 55	10 03	10 04	10 09		10 43	10 52	11 00	11 07		11 28	11 44	11 51	11 56		12 03	12 07	12 20	12 29
	d		09 00						10 07					11 03						12 00					12 31
Dronfield	d		09 10						10 17					11 13						12 10					12 42
Chesterfield	d		09 17						10 24					11 20						12 18					12 49
Alfreton	d		09 28						10 35					11 31						12 29					12 59
Langley Mill	d		09 35						10 42					11 38						12 36					13 07
Nottingham	a		09 57						11 02					11 58						12 56					13 26
St Pancras International	⊖ 53 a				*13 51*					*14 19*										*15b22*					

For general notes see front of timetable
For details of catering facilities see Directory of Train Operators

- **A** From Doncaster (Table 29)
- **B** From Bridlington (Table 43)
- **C** From Cleethorpes (from 28 June from Doncaster) to Manchester Airport (Table 29)
- **D** From Leeds (Table 31)
- **E** From Hull (Table 29)
- **G** From York (Table 33)
- **H** From Cleethorpes (from 28 June from Doncaster) (Table 29)
- **J** From Scarborough (Table 43)
- **K** To Manchester Airport (Table 29)
- **L** From Goole (Table 29)
- **N** From Doncaster to Manchester Airport (Table 29)
- **b** Change at Sheffield

Table 34

Sundays

Leeds and Huddersfield → Barnsley → Sheffield, Nottingham

19 July to 6 September

Network Diagram - see first page of Table 31

		NT	NT A	TP 1◊ B	NT	NT C	NT	NT D	TP 1◊ B	NT E	NT	NT A	NT D	NT	TP 1◊ B	NT	NT	NT C	NT G	NT
Leeds 10	31 d				12 29		12 34							14 05			14 17			15 05
Woodlesford	d						12 42										14 25			
Castleford	d						12 53										14 36			
Normanton	d						12 58										14 41			
Wakefield Kirkgate 4	31 a				12 46		13 03							14 21			14 46			15 22
	d				12 46		13 03							14 21			14 46			15 22
Darton	d						13 17										15 00			
Huddersfield	d	11 29									13 19					14 15				
Lockwood	d	11 32									13 22					14 18				
Berry Brow	d	11 35									13 25					14 21				
Honley	d	11 38									13 28					14 24				
Brockholes	d	11 41									13 31					14 27				
Stocksmoor	d	11 45									13 35					14 31				
Shepley	d	11 47									13 37					14 33				
Denby Dale	d	11 52									13 42					14 39				
Penistone	d	12 00									13 50					14 46				
Silkstone Common	d	12 05									13 55					14 52				
Dodworth	d	12 09									13 59					14 55				
Barnsley	a	12 16			13 05		13 24				14 06			14 40		15 03	15 07			15 41
	d	12 17			13 06		13 24				14 12			14 41		15 03	15 12			15 42
Wombwell	d	12 22					13 29				14 17						15 17			
Elsecar	d	12 26					13 33				14 21						15 21			
Chapeltown	d	12 31					13 38				14 26						15 26			
Meadowhall	29, 31 ⇌ a	12 34			13 18		13 47				14 32			14 54		15 20	15 35			15 55
	d	12 35	12 43	13 00	13 18	13 44	13 50	13 53	14 00	14 17	14 33	14 43	14 53	14 56	15 00	15 21	15 35	15 43	15 52	15 56
Sheffield 7	29, 31 ⇌ a	12 47	12 55	13 07	13 29	13 52	13 58	14 04	14 07	14 25	14 47	14 52	15 03	15 06	15 07	15 28	15 45	15 51	16 01	16 05
	d				13 31									15 07						16 07
Dronfield	d				13 41									15 17						16 17
Chesterfield	d				13 48									15 25						16 25
Alfreton	d				13 59									15 36						16 36
Langley Mill	d				14 06									15 43						16 43
Nottingham	a				14 26									16 05						17 03
St Pancras International	⊖ 53 a			*16 15*			*16 55*					*17 59*			*18 04*					

		TP 1◊ B	NT E	NT	NT A	NT D	NT	TP 1◊ B	NT	NT C	NT G	NT	TP 1◊ B	NT H	NT E	NT	NT A	NT D	NT	TP 1◊ B	NT
Leeds 10	31 d						16 05		16 17			17 05							18 05		18 17
Woodlesford	d								16 25												18 25
Castleford	d								16 36												18 36
Normanton	d								16 41												18 40
Wakefield Kirkgate 4	31 a						16 21		16 46			17 21							18 21		18 45
	d						16 22		16 46			17 21							18 22		18 45
Darton	d								17 00												18 59
Huddersfield	d			15 19												17 19					
Lockwood	d			15 22												17 22					
Berry Brow	d			15 25												17 25					
Honley	d			15 28												17 28					
Brockholes	d			15 31												17 31					
Stocksmoor	d			15 35												17 35					
Shepley	d			15 37												17 37					
Denby Dale	d			15 42												17 47					
Penistone	d			15 50												17 54					
Silkstone Common	d			15 55												18 00					
Dodworth	d			15 59												18 03					
Barnsley	a			16 06			16 41		17 07			17 40				18 11			18 41		19 05
	d			16 12			16 42		17 12			17 41				18 12			18 42		19 11
Wombwell	d			16 17					17 17							18 17					19 17
Elsecar	d			16 21					17 21							18 21					19 21
Chapeltown	d			16 26					17 26							18 26					19 26
Meadowhall	29, 31 ⇌ a			16 32			16 56		17 34			17 55				18 32			18 56		19 32
	d	16 00	16 11	16 33	16 43	16 53	16 56	17 00	17 35	17 43	17 53	17 56	18 00	18 24	18 12	18 33	18 43	18 53	18 56	19 00	19 33
Sheffield 7	29, 31 ⇌ a	16 07	16 21	16 43	16 52	17 03	17 05	17 07	17 44	17 54	18 01	18 05	18 07	18 35	18 23	18 44	18 52	19 03	19 05	19 07	19 43
	d						17 07					18 07							19 07		
Dronfield	d						17 17					18 17							19 17		
Chesterfield	d						17 24					18 25							19 25		
Alfreton	d						17 35					18 36							19 36		
Langley Mill	d						17 43					18 43							19 43		
Nottingham	a						18 03					19 03							20 03		
St Pancras International	⊖ 53 a	*19 04*						*20 04*					*21 27*							*22 27*	

For general notes see front of timetable
For details of catering facilities see Directory of Train Operators

A From Goole (Table 29)
B From Doncaster to Manchester Airport (Table 29)
C From Doncaster (Table 29)
D From Scarborough (Table 43)
E From Leeds (Table 31)
G From Bridlington (Table 43)
H From York (Table 33)

Table 34

Sundays

19 July to 6 September

Leeds and Huddersfield → Barnsley → Sheffield, Nottingham

Network Diagram - see first page of Table 31

		NT A	NT	NT B	TP [1] ◇ C	NT D	NT	NT A	TP [1] ◇ C	NT	NT E	NT G	TP [1] ◇ A	NT	NT D	NT H	NT
Leeds [10]	31 d		19 04							20 17							22 17
Woodlesford	d									20 25							22 25
Castleford	d									20 36							22 36
Normanton	d									20 41							22 41
Wakefield Kirkgate [4]	31 a		19 20							20 46							22 46
	d		19 20							20 46							22 46
Darton	d									21 00							23 00
Huddersfield	d						19 19										
Lockwood	d						19 22										
Berry Brow	d						19 25										
Honley	d						19 28										
Brockholes	d						19 31										
Stocksmoor	d						19 35										
Shepley	d						19 37										
Denby Dale	d						19 42										
Penistone	d						19 50										
Silkstone Common	d						19 55										
Dodworth	d						19 59										
Barnsley	a		19 40				20 06			21 07							23 07
	d		19 40				20 12			21 12				22 21			23 12
Wombwell	d						20 17			21 17				22 26			23 17
Elsecar	d						20 21			21 21				22 30			23 21
Chapeltown	d						20 26			21 26				22 35			23 26
Meadowhall	29, 31 🚈 a		19 54				20 34			21 33				22 40			23 31
	d	19 47	19 54	19 57	20 00	20 11	20 34	20 45	21 00	21 33	21 45	21 54	22 00	22 41	22 45	22 50	23 32
Sheffield [7]	29, 31 🚈 a	19 55	20 04	20 06	20 07	20 23	20 43	20 53	21 07	21 42	21 56	22 05	22 11	22 51	22 54	22 58	23 42
	d		20 06														
Dronfield	d		20 16														
Chesterfield	d		20 22														
Alfreton	d		20 33														
Langley Mill	d		20 40														
Nottingham	a		21 01														
St Pancras International	⊖ 53 a	*23 12*															

Sundays

from 13 September

		NT A	NT	TP [1] ◇ J	NT A	NT	NT D	NT	NT E	NT	NT K	NT	TP [1] ◇ L	NT	NT	NT A	NT	NT N	TP [1] ◇ L	NT D	NT
Leeds [10]	31 d					08 34		09 05				10 02			10 17		10 57				11 29
Woodlesford	d					08 42									10 25						
Castleford	d					08 53									10 36						
Normanton	d					08 58									10 41						
Wakefield Kirkgate [4]	31 a					09 03		09 21				10 18			10 46		11 13				11 46
	d					09 03		09 21				10 18			10 46		11 13				11 46
Darton	d					09 17									11 00						
Huddersfield	d									09 14				10 11							
Lockwood	d									09 17				10 14							
Berry Brow	d									09 20				10 17							
Honley	d									09 23				10 20							
Brockholes	d									09 26				10 23							
Stocksmoor	d									09 30				10 27							
Shepley	d									09 32				10 29							
Denby Dale	d									09 42				10 39							
Penistone	d									09 50				10 46							
Silkstone Common	d									09 55				10 52							
Dodworth	d									09 59				10 55							
Barnsley	a					09 24		09 40		10 06		10 37		11 03	11 07		11 32				12 05
	d					09 24		09 41		10 12		10 38		11 03	11 12		11 33				12 06
Wombwell	d					09 29				10 17					11 17						
Elsecar	d					09 33				10 21					11 21						
Chapeltown	d					09 38				10 26					11 26						
Meadowhall	29, 31 🚈 a					09 41		09 54		10 32		10 51		11 20	11 32		11 46				12 17
	d	08 30		09 00	09 41	09 41	09 54	09 55	10 00	10 33	10 40	10 51	11 00	11 20	11 35	11 40	11 46	11 52	12 00	12 11	12 17
Sheffield [7]	29, 31 🚈 a	08 41		09 07	09 51	09 55	10 03	10 04	10 09	10 43	10 52	11 00	11 07	11 28	11 44	11 51	11 56	12 03	12 07	12 20	12 29
	d		09 00					10 07				11 03					12 00				12 31
Dronfield	d		09 10					10 17				11 13					12 10				12 42
Chesterfield	d		09 17					10 24				11 20					12 18				12 49
Alfreton	d		09 28					10 35				11 31					12 29				12 59
Langley Mill	d		09 35					10 42				11 38					12 36				13 07
Nottingham	a		09 57					11 02				11 58					12 56				13 26
St Pancras International	⊖ 53 a			*13 19*					*14 19*				*15 15*						*16 15*		

For general notes see front of timetable
For details of catering facilities see Directory of Train Operators

A From Doncaster (Table 29)
B From Bridlington (Table 43)
C From Doncaster to Manchester Airport (Table 29)
D From Leeds (Table 31)
E From Hull (Table 29)
G From York (Table 33)
H From Scarborough (Table 43)
J To Manchester Airport (Table 29)
K From Goole (Table 29)
L From Cleethorpes to Manchester Airport (Table 29)
N From Bridlington (Table 43) (from 27 September from Hull) (Table 29)

Table 34

Sundays

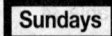

Leeds and Huddersfield → Barnsley → Sheffield, Nottingham

from 13 September

Network Diagram - see first page of Table 31

Station		NT	NT A	TP 1 ◇ B	NT	NT C	NT	NT D	TP 1 ◇ E	NT G	NT	NT A	NT H	NT	TP 1 ◇ B	NT	NT	NT C	NT J	NT
Leeds 10	31 d				12 29		12 34							14 05			14 17			15 05
Woodlesford	d						12 42										14 25			
Castleford	d						12 53										14 36			
Normanton	d						12 58										14 41			
Wakefield Kirkgate 4	31 a				12 46		13 03							14 21			14 46			15 22
	d				12 46		13 03							14 21			14 46			15 22
Darton	d						13 17										15 00			
Huddersfield	d	11 24									13 14					14 11				
Lockwood	d	11 27									13 17					14 14				
Berry Brow	d	11 30									13 20					14 17				
Honley	d	11 33									13 23					14 20				
Brockholes	d	11 36									13 26					14 23				
Stocksmoor	d	11 40									13 30					14 27				
Shepley	d	11 42									13 32					14 29				
Denby Dale	d	11 52									13 42					14 39				
Penistone	d	12 00									13 50					14 46				
Silkstone Common	d	12 05									13 55					14 52				
Dodworth	d	12 09									13 59					14 55				
Barnsley	a	12 16			13 05		13 24				14 06			14 40		15 03	15 07			15 41
	d	12 17			13 06		13 24				14 12			14 41		15 03	15 12			15 42
Wombwell	d	12 22					13 29				14 17						15 17			
Elsecar	d	12 26					13 33				14 21						15 21			
Chapeltown	d	12 31					13 38				14 26						15 26			
Meadowhall	29, 31 🚋 a	12 34			13 18		13 47				14 32			14 54		15 20	15 35			15 55
	d	12 35	12 43	13 00	13 18	13 44	13 50	13 53	14 00	14 17	14 33	14 43	14 53	14 56	15 00	15 21	15 35	15 43	15 52	15 56
Sheffield 7	29, 31 🚋 a	12 47	12 55	13 07	13 29	13 52	13 58	14 04	14 07	14 25	14 47	14 52	15 03	15 06	15 07	15 28	15 45	15 51	16 01	16 05
	d				13 31									15 07						16 07
Dronfield	d				13 41									15 17						16 17
Chesterfield	d				13 48									15 25						16 25
Alfreton	d				13 59									15 36						16 36
Langley Mill	d				14 06									15 43						16 43
Nottingham	a				14 26									16 03						17 03
St Pancras International	⊖ 53 a			*16 55*			*17 59*								*18 59*			*19 59*		

Station		TP 1 ◇ B	NT G	NT	NT A	NT H	NT	TP 1 ◇ B	NT	NT C	NT K	NT	TP 1 ◇ B	NT G	NT L	NT	NT A	NT N	NT	TP 1 ◇ B	NT
Leeds 10	31 d						16 05		16 17			17 05							18 05		18 17
Woodlesford	d								16 25												18 25
Castleford	d								16 36												18 36
Normanton	d								16 41												18 40
Wakefield Kirkgate 4	31 a						16 21		16 46			17 21							18 21		18 45
	d						16 22		16 46			17 21							18 22		18 45
Darton	d								17 00												18 59
Huddersfield	d			15 14												17 19					
Lockwood	d			15 17												17 22					
Berry Brow	d			15 20												17 25					
Honley	d			15 23												17 28					
Brockholes	d			15 26												17 31					
Stocksmoor	d			15 30												17 35					
Shepley	d			15 32												17 37					
Denby Dale	d			15 42												17 47					
Penistone	d			15 50												17 54					
Silkstone Common	d			15 55												18 00					
Dodworth	d			15 59												18 03					
Barnsley	a			16 06			16 41		17 07			17 40				18 11			18 41		19 05
	d			16 12			16 42		17 12			17 41				18 12			18 42		19 11
Wombwell	d			16 17					17 17							18 17					19 17
Elsecar	d			16 21					17 21							18 21					19 21
Chapeltown	d			16 26					17 26							18 26					19 26
Meadowhall	29, 31 🚋 a			16 32			16 56		17 34			17 55				18 32			18 56		19 32
	d	16 00	16 11	16 33	16 43	16 53	16 56	17 00	17 35	17 43	17 53	17 56	18 00	18 12	18 24	18 33	18 43	18 53	18 56	19 00	19 33
Sheffield 7	29, 31 🚋 a	16 07	16 21	16 43	16 52	17 03	17 05	17 07	17 44	17 54	18 01	18 05	18 07	18 23	18 35	18 44	18 52	19 03	19 05	19 07	19 43
	d						17 07					18 07							19 07		
Dronfield	d						17 17					18 17							19 17		
Chesterfield	d						17 24					18 25							19 25		
Alfreton	d						17 35					18 36							19 36		
Langley Mill	d						17 43					18 43							19 43		
Nottingham	a						18 03					19 03							20 03		
St Pancras International	⊖ 53 a								*21 27*				*22 27*							*23 10*	

For general notes see front of timetable
For details of catering facilities see Directory of Train Operators

- **A** From Goole (Table 29)
- **B** From Cleethorpes to Manchester Airport (Table 29)
- **C** From Doncaster (Table 29)
- **D** From Scarborough (from 27 September from Beverley (Table 43)
- **E** From Doncaster to Manchester Airport (Table 29)
- **G** From Leeds (Table 31)
- **H** From Scarborough (from 27 September from Bridlington) (Table 43)
- **J** From Bridlington (Table 43) (from 27 September from Hull) (Table 29)
- **K** From Bridlington (from 27 September from Hull) (Table 29)
- **L** From York (Table 33)
- **N** From Scarborough (from 27 September from Hull) (Table 29)

Table 34

Sundays

from 13 September

Leeds and Huddersfield → Barnsley → Sheffield, Nottingham

Network Diagram - see first page of Table 31

	NT	NT	NT	TP	NT	NT	NT	TP	NT	NT	NT	TP	NT	NT	NT	NT
				1 ◇				1 ◇				1 ◇				
	A		B	C	D		A	C		E	G	H		D	J	
Leeds 10 31 d		19 04							20 17							22 17
Woodlesford d									20 25							22 25
Castleford d									20 36							22 36
Normanton d									20 41							22 41
Wakefield Kirkgate 4 31 a		19 20							20 46							22 46
d		19 20							20 46							22 46
Darton d									21 00							23 00
Huddersfield d						19 14										
Lockwood d						19 17										
Berry Brow d						19 20										
Honley d						19 23										
Brockholes d						19 26										
Stocksmoor d						19 30										
Shepley d						19 32										
Denby Dale d						19 42										
Penistone d						19 50										
Silkstone Common d						19 55										
Dodworth d						19 59										
Barnsley a		19 40				20 06			21 07							23 07
d		19 40				20 12			21 12				22 21			23 12
Wombwell d						20 17			21 17				22 26			23 17
Elsecar d						20 21			21 21				22 30			23 21
Chapeltown d						20 26			21 26				22 35			23 26
Meadowhall 29, 31 a		19 54				20 34			21 33				22 40			23 31
d	19 47	19 54	19 57	20 00	20 11	20 34	20 45	21 00	21 33	21 45	21 54	22 00	22 41	22 45	22 50	23 32
Sheffield 7 29, 31 a	19 55	20 04	20 06	20 07	20 23	20 43	20 53	21 07	21 42	21 56	22 05	22 11	22 51	22 54	22 58	23 42
d		20 06														
Dronfield d		20 16														
Chesterfield d		20 22														
Alfreton d		20 33														
Langley Mill d		20 40														
Nottingham a		21 01														
St Pancras International ⊖ 53 a																

For general notes see front of timetable
For details of catering facilities see Directory of Train Operators

- **A** From Doncaster (Table 29)
- **B** From Bridlington (Table 43)
- **C** From Cleethorpes to Manchester Airport (Table 29)
- **D** From Leeds (Table 31)
- **E** From Hull (Table 29)
- **G** From York (Table 33)
- **H** From Cleethorpes (Table 29)
- **J** From Scarborough (from 27 September from Bridlington) (Table 43)

Network Diagram for Tables 35, 36, 37, 38

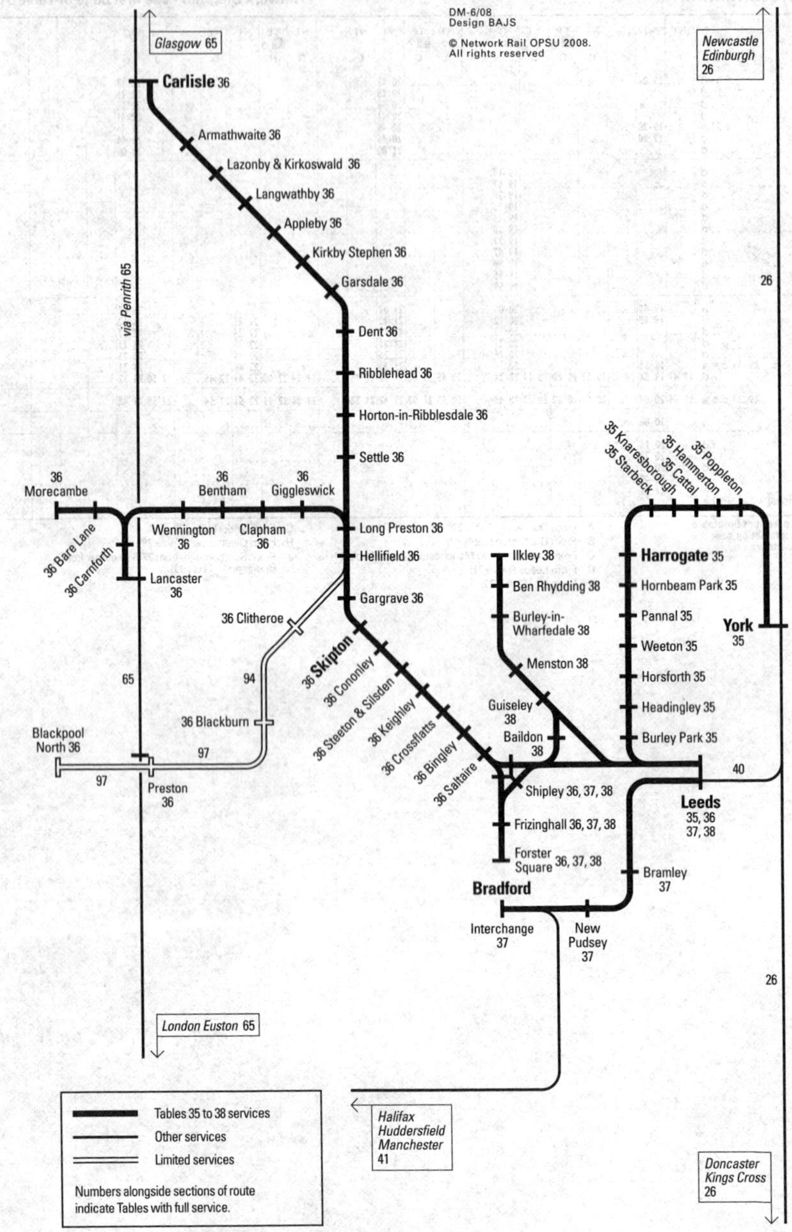

DM-6/08
Design BAJS
© Network Rail OPSU 2008.
All rights reserved
Glasgow 65
Newcastle
Edinburgh
26
Carlisle 36
Armathwaite 36
Lazonby & Kirkoswald 36
Langwathby 36
Appleby 36
Kirkby Stephen 36
Garsdale 36
Dent 36
Ribblehead 36
Horton-in-Ribblesdale 36
Settle 36
via Penrith 65
26
36
Morecambe
36
Bentham
36
Giggleswick
Wennington
36
Clapham
36
Long Preston 36
Hellifield 36
36 Bare Lane
36 Carnforth
Lancaster
36
Gargrave 36
36 Clitheroe
35 Knaresborough
35 Starbeck
35 Hammerton
35 Cattal
35 Poppleton
Harrogate 35
Hornbeam Park 35
Pannal 35
Weeton 35
Horsforth 35
Headingley 35
Burley Park 35
York
35
Ilkley 38
Ben Rhydding 38
Burley-in-Wharfedale 38
Menston 38
Guiseley
38
Baildon
38
65
94
36 Skipton
36 Cononley
36 Steeton & Silsden
36 Keighley
36 Crossflatts
36 Bingley
36 Saltaire
36 Blackburn
Blackpool
North 36
97
97
Preston
36
Shipley 36, 37, 38
Frizinghall 36, 37, 38
Forster
Square 36, 37, 38
Bradford
40
Leeds
35, 36
37, 38
Bramley
37
Interchange
37
New
Pudsey
37
26
London Euston 65
Tables 35 to 38 services
Other services
Limited services
Numbers alongside sections of route indicate Tables with full service.
Halifax
Huddersfield
Manchester
41
Doncaster
Kings Cross
26

Table 35

Mondays to Fridays

York → Harrogate → Leeds

Network Diagram - see first page of Table 35

Miles			NT	NT	NT	GR R 1 A	NT	NT	NT	NT	NT	NT	NT	NT	NT	NT	NT	NT	NT	NT
0	**York** 8	40 d					06 52				07 57		08 45	09 10		10 11		11 11		12 11
3	Poppleton	d					06 56				08 01		08 50	09 14		10 15		11 15		12 15
8¾	Hammerton	d					07 04				08 09		08 58	09 22		10 23		11 23		12 23
10¼	Cattal	d					07 07				08 12		09 01	09 26		10 26		11 26		12 26
16¾	**Knaresborough**	a					07 15				08 21		09 09	09 34		10 34		11 34		12 34
—		d			07 00		07 24	07 42	07 56		08 21	08 56	09 10	09 35	10 05	10 35	11 05	11 35	12 05	12 35
18¼	Starbeck	d			07 03		07 27	07 45	07 59		08 24	08 59	09 13	09 38	10 08	10 38	11 08	11 38	12 08	12 38
20½	**Harrogate**	a			07 08		07 32	07 50	08 04		08 29	09 04	09 18	09 43	10 13	10 43	11 13	11 43	12 13	12 43
—		d	06 06	06 30	07 11	07 28	07 40	07 51	08 06	08 14	08 30	09 05	09 19	09 44	10 14	10 44	11 14	11 44	12 14	12 44
21½	Hornbeam Park	d	06 08	06 32	07 14		07 42	07 54		08 17	08 33		09 22	09 47	10 17	10 47	11 17	11 47	12 17	12 47
23¾	Pannal	d	06 13	06 37	07 19		07 47	07 59		08 22	08 38		09 27	09 52	10 22	10 52	11 22	11 52	12 22	12 52
27	Weeton	d	06 18	06 42	07 23		07 51	08 03		08 26	08 42		09 31	09 56	10 26	10 56	11 26	11 56	12 26	12 56
33	Horsforth	d	06 28	06 50	07 32	07u46	08 00	08 12	08 22	08 35	08 51	09 21	09 40	10 05	10 35	11 05	11 35	12 05	12 35	13 05
35¾	Headingley	d	06 32	06 54	07 36		08 04	08 16	08 26	08 39	08 55	09 25	09 44	10 09	10 39	11 09	11 39	12 09	12 39	13 09
36½	Burley Park	d	06 34	06 56	07 38		08 06	08 18	08 29	08 41	08 57	09 27	09 47	10 11	10 41	11 11	11 41	12 11	12 41	13 11
38¾	**Leeds** 10	40 a	06 44	07 08	07 48	07 57	08 17	08 29	08 40	08 52	09 08	09 37	09 56	10 22	10 52	11 22	11 52	12 22	12 52	13 22

		NT	NT	NT	NT	NT	NT	NT	NT	NT	NT	NT	NT	NT	NT	NT	NT	NT	NT
York 8	40 d		13 11		14 11		15 11		16 11		16 54	17 17		18 11		19 11	20 11	21 11	22 11
Poppleton	d		13 15		14 15		15 15		16 15		16 58	17 21		18 15		19 15	20 15	21 16	22 15
Hammerton	d		13 23		14 23		15 23		16 23		17 06	17 29		18 23		19 23	20 23	21 23	22 23
Cattal	d		13 26		14 26		15 26		16 26		17 09	17 32		18 26		19 26	20 26	21 27	22 27
Knaresborough	a		13 34		14 34		15 34		16 34		17 17	17 40		18 34		19 34	20 34	21 34	22 35
	d	13 05	13 35	14 05	14 35	15 05	15 35	16 05	16 35	17 05	17 18	17 41	18 05	18 35	19 05	19 35	20 35	21 35	22 36
Starbeck	d	13 08	13 38	14 08	14 38	15 08	15 38	16 08	16 38	17 08	17 21	17 44	18 12	18 38	19 08	19 38	20 38	21 39	22 40
Harrogate	a	13 13	13 43	14 13	14 43	15 13	15 43	16 13	16 43	17 14	17 26	17 49	18 17	18 43	19 13	19 43	20 43	21 43	22 45
	d	13 14	13 44	14 14	14 44	15 14	15 44	16 14	16 44	17 14	17 37	17 50	18 18	18 44	19 14	19 44	20 44	21 45	22 47
Hornbeam Park	d	13 17	13 47	14 17	14 47	15 17	15 47	16 17	16 47	17 17	17 39	17 53	18 21	18 47	19 17	19 47	20 47	21 48	22 49
Pannal	d	13 22	13 52	14 22	14 52	15 22	15 52	16 22	16 52	17 22	17 44	17 58	18 26	18 52	19 22	19 52	20 52	21 53	22 54
Weeton	d	13 26	13 56	14 26	14 56	15 26	15 56	16 26	16 56	17 26	17 49	18 02	18 30	18 56	19 26	19 56	20 56	21 58	22 59
Horsforth	d	13 35	14 05	14 35	15 05	15 35	16 05	16 35	17 05	17 38	17 57	18 11	18 39	19 05	19 35	20 05	21 05	22 06	23 08
Headingley	d	13 39	14 09	14 39	15 09	15 39	16 09	16 39	17 09	17 42	18 01	18 15	18 43	19 09	19 39	20 09	21 09	22 10	23 12
Burley Park	d	13 41	14 11	14 41	15 11	15 41	16 11	16 41	17 11	17 44	18 03	18 17	18 45	19 11	19 41	20 11	21 11	22 13	23 15
Leeds 10	40 a	13 52	14 22	14 52	15 22	15 52	16 22	16 52	17 22	17 55	18 17	18 28	18 55	19 22	19 52	20 22	21 22	22 23	23 24

Saturdays

		NT	NT	NT	GR R 1 A	NT	NT	NT	NT	NT	NT	NT	NT	NT	NT
York 8	40 d			06 53			07 57		08 45	09 10		10 11		11 11	
Poppleton	d			06 57			08 01		08 49	09 14		10 15		11 15	
Hammerton	d			07 05			08 09		08 57	09 22		10 23		11 23	
Cattal	d			07 08			08 12		09 00	09 26		10 26		11 26	
Knaresborough	a			07 16			08 21		09 08	09 34		10 34		11 34	
	d		06 47	07 21		07 51	08 21	08 51	09 09	09 35	10 05	10 35	11 05	11 35	12 05
Starbeck	d		06 50	07 24		07 54	08 24	08 54	09 12	09 38	10 08	10 38	11 08	11 38	12 08
Harrogate	a		06 55	07 29		07 59	08 29	08 59	09 17	09 43	10 13	10 43	11 13	11 43	12 13
	d	06 06	06 56	07 31	07 44	08 00	08 30	09 00	09 18	09 44	10 14	10 44	11 14	11 44	12 14
Hornbeam Park	d	06 08	06 59	07 33		08 03	08 33	09 03	09 21	09 47	10 17	10 47	11 17	11 47	12 17
Pannal	d	06 13	07 04	07 38		08 08	08 38	09 08	09 26	09 52	10 22	10 52	11 22	11 52	12 22
Weeton	d	06 18	07 08	07 42		08 12	08 42	09 12	09 30	09 56	10 26	10 56	11 26	11 56	12 26
Horsforth	d	06 28	07 17	07 51		08 21	08 51	09 21	09 39	10 05	10 35	11 05	11 35	12 05	12 35
Headingley	d	06 32	07 21	07 55		08 25	08 55	09 25	09 43	10 09	10 39	11 09	11 39	12 09	12 39
Burley Park	d	06 34	07 23	07 57		08 27	08 57	09 27	09 47	10 11	10 41	11 11	11 41	12 11	12 41
Leeds 10	40 a	06 44	07 34	08 08	08 10	08 38	09 08	09 37	09 55	10 22	10 52	11 22	11 52	12 22	12 52

		NT	NT	NT	NT	NT	NT	NT	NT	NT	NT	NT	NT	NT	NT	NT	NT	NT
York 8	40 d	12 11		13 11		14 11		15 11		16 11		16 54	17 17		18 11	19 11	20 11	21 57
Poppleton	d	12 15		13 15		14 15		15 15		16 15		16 58	17 21		18 15	19 15	20 15	22 01
Hammerton	d	12 23		13 23		14 23		15 23		16 23		17 06	17 29		18 23	19 23	20 23	22 09
Cattal	d	12 26		13 26		14 26		15 26		16 26		17 09	17 32		18 26	19 26	20 26	22 12
Knaresborough	a	12 34		13 34		14 34		15 34		16 34		17 17	17 40		18 34	19 34	20 34	22 20
	d	12 35	13 05	13 35	14 05	14 35	15 05	15 35	16 05	16 35	17 05	17 18	17 41	18 05	18 35	19 35	20 35	22 21
Starbeck	d	12 38	13 08	13 38	14 08	14 38	15 08	15 38	16 08	16 38	17 08	17 21	17 44	18 12	18 38	19 38	20 38	22 24
Harrogate	a	12 43	13 13	13 43	14 13	14 43	15 13	15 43	16 13	16 43	17 14	17 26	17 49	18 17	18 43	19 43	20 43	22 29
	d	12 44	13 14	13 44	14 14	14 44	15 14	15 44	16 14	16 44	17 14	17 30	17 50	18 18	18 44	19 44	20 44	22 37
Hornbeam Park	d	12 47	13 17	13 47	14 17	14 47	15 17	15 47	16 17	16 47	17 17	17 32	17 53	18 21	18 47	19 47	20 47	22 39
Pannal	d	12 52	13 22	13 52	14 22	14 52	15 22	15 52	16 22	16 52	17 22	17 37	17 58	18 26	18 52	19 52	20 52	22 44
Weeton	d	12 56	13 26	13 56	14 26	14 56	15 26	15 56	16 26	16 56	17 26	17 42	18 02	18 30	18 56	19 56	20 56	22 49
Horsforth	d	13 05	13 35	14 05	14 35	15 05	15 35	16 05	16 35	17 05	17 38	17 50	18 11	18 39	19 05	20 05	21 05	22 57
Headingley	d	13 09	13 39	14 09	14 39	15 09	15 39	16 09	16 39	17 09	17 42	17 54	18 15	18 43	19 09	20 09	21 09	23 01
Burley Park	d	13 11	13 41	14 11	14 41	15 11	15 41	16 11	16 41	17 11	17 44	17 57	18 17	18 45	19 11	20 11	21 11	23 04
Leeds 10	40 a	13 22	13 52	14 22	14 52	15 22	15 52	16 22	16 52	17 22	17 55	18 07	18 28	18 55	19 22	20 22	21 22	23 14

For general notes see front of timetable
For details of catering facilities see
Directory of Train Operators

A To London Kings Cross (Table 26)

Table 35

Sundays

York → Harrogate → Leeds

Network Diagram - see first page of Table 35

		NT	NT	NT	NT	NT	NT	NT	NT	NT	NT	NT	NT
York 8	40 d				12 18	14 20	16 18	17 17	18 17	19 17	20 18	21 26	
Poppleton	d				12 22	14 24	16 22	17 21	18 21	19 21	20 22	21 30	
Hammerton	d				12 30	14 32	16 30	17 29	18 29	19 29	20 30	21 38	
Cattal	d				12 33	14 35	16 33	17 32	18 32	19 32	20 33	21 41	
Knaresborough	a				12 41	14 43	16 41	17 40	18 40	19 40	20 41	21 49	
	d			11 42	12 42	14 44	16 42	17 42	18 42	19 42	20 42	21 50	
Starbeck	d			11 45	12 45	14 47	16 45	17 45	18 45	19 45	20 45	21 53	
Harrogate	a			11 50	12 50	14 52	16 50	17 50	18 50	19 50	20 50	21 58	
	d	09 53	10 53	11 53	12 53	14 53	16 53	17 53	18 53	19 53	20 53	22 02	23 05
Hornbeam Park	d	09 56	10 56	11 56	12 56	14 56	16 56	17 56	18 56	19 56	20 56	22 04	23 08
Pannal	d	10 01	11 01	12 01	13 01	15 01	17 01	18 01	19 01	20 01	21 01	22 09	23 13
Weeton	d	10 05	11 05	12 05	13 05	15 05	17 05	18 05	19 05	20 05	21 05	22 14	23 17
Horsforth	d	10 14	11 14	12 14	13 14	15 14	17 14	18 14	19 14	20 14	21 14	22 22	23 26
Headingley	d	10 18	11 18	12 18	13 18	15 18	17 18	18 18	19 18	20 18	21 18	22 26	23 30
Burley Park	d	10 20	11 20	12 20	13 20	15 20	17 20	18 20	19 20	20 20	21 20	22 29	23 32
Leeds 10	40 a	10 30	11 30	12 30	13 30	15 30	17 30	18 30	19 30	20 30	21 30	22 40	23 43

For general notes see front of timetable
For details of catering facilities see
Directory of Train Operators

Leeds → Harrogate → York

Network Diagram - see first page of Table 35

Miles	Station		NT	NT	NT	NT	NT	NT	NT	NT	NT	NT	NT	NT	NT	NT	NT	NT	NT	NT
0	**Leeds** 10	40 d	06 09	06 29	07 13	07 43	07 59	08 29	08 59	09 29	09 59	10 29	10 59	11 29	11 59	12 29	12 59	13 29	13 59	14 29
2¼	Burley Park	d	06 13	06 33	07 17	07 47	08 03	08 33	09 03	09 33	10 03	10 33	11 03	11 33	12 03	12 33	13 03	13 33	14 03	14 33
3	Headingley	d	06 16	06 36	07 20	07 50	08 06	08 36	09 06	09 36	10 06	10 36	11 06	11 36	12 06	12 36	13 06	13 36	14 06	14 36
5¾	Horsforth	d	06 21	06 41	07 25	07 55	08 11	08 41	09 11	09 41	10 11	10 41	11 11	11 41	12 11	12 41	13 11	13 41	14 11	14 41
11¾	Weeton	d	06 29	06 49	07 33		08 19	08 49	09 19	09 49	10 19	10 49	11 19	11 49	12 19	12 49	13 19	13 49	14 19	14 49
15	Pannal	d	06 35	06 55	07 39		08 25	08 55	09 25	09 55	10 25	10 55	11 25	11 55	12 25	12 55	13 25	13 55	14 25	14 55
17¼	Hornbeam Park	d	06 40	07 00	07 44	08 10	08 30	09 00	09 30	10 00	10 30	11 00	11 30	12 00	12 30	13 00	13 30	14 00	14 30	15 00
18¼	**Harrogate**	a	06 43	07 04	07 49	08 13	08 33	09 03	09 33	10 03	10 33	11 03	11 33	12 03	12 33	13 05	13 33	14 03	14 33	15 03
—		d	06 45	07 05	07 49	08 16	08 34	09 05	09 35	10 05	10 35	11 05	11 35	12 05	12 35	13 07	13 35	14 05	14 35	15 05
20½	Starbeck	d	06 49	07 08	07 52	08 19	08 38	09 08	09 38	10 08	10 38	11 08	11 38	12 08	12 38	13 10	13 38	14 08	14 38	15 08
22	**Knaresborough**	a	06 54	07 15	07 59	08 25	08 45	09 14	09 45	10 14	10 45	11 14	11 45	12 14	12 45	13 16	13 45	14 14	14 45	15 14
—		d	06 55	07 19	07 59	08 28		09 15		10 14		11 14		12 14		13 16		14 14		15 14
28½	Cattal	d	07 03	07 27	08 07	08 36		09 23		10 22		11 22		12 22		13 24		14 22		15 22
30	Hammerton	d	07 06	07 30	08 11	08 39		09 27		10 26		11 26		12 26		13 28		14 26		15 26
35¾	Poppleton	d	07 13	07 37	08 18	08 46		09 34		10 33		11 33		12 33		13 35		14 33		15 33
38¾	**York** 3	40 a	07 21	07 48	08 27	08 58		09 47		10 46		11 45		12 45		13 45		14 44		15 47

Station		NT	NT	NT	NT	NT	NT	NT	NT	NT	NT	NT	NT	NT	NT	NT	NT	NT
Leeds 10	40 d	14 59	15 29	15 59	16 29	16 42	16 59	17 13	17 29	17 44	17 59	18 29	18 59	19 29	20 29	21 29	22 29	23 29
Burley Park	d	15 03	15 33	16 03	16 33	16 46	17 03	17 17	17 33	17 48	18 03	18 33	19 03	19 33	20 33	21 33	22 33	23 33
Headingley	d	15 06	15 36	16 06	16 36	16 49	17 06	17 20	17 36	17 51	18 06	18 36	19 06	19 36	20 36	21 36	22 36	23 36
Horsforth	d	15 11	15 41	16 11	16 41	16a55	17 11	17 25	17 41	17 56	18 11	18 41	19 11	19 41	20 41	21 41	22 41	23 41
Weeton	d	15 19	15 49	16 19	16 49		17 19	17 33	17 49		18 19	18 49	19 19	19 49	20 49	21 49	22 49	23 49
Pannal	d	15 25	15 55	16 25	16 55		17 25	17 39	17 55		18 25	18 55	19 25	19 55	20 55	21 55	22 55	23 55
Hornbeam Park	d	15 30	16 00	16 30	17 00		17 30	17 44	18 00		18 30	19 00	19 30	20 00	21 00	22 00	23 01	23 59
Harrogate	a	15 33	16 03	16 33	17 03		17 33	17 47	18 03	18 15	18 33	19 03	19 33	20 03	21 03	22 03	23 08	00 06
	d	15 35	16 05	16 35	17 08		17 35	17 49	18 05	18 16	18 35	19 05	19 35	20 05	21 05	22 05		
Starbeck	d	15 38	16 08	16 38	17 11		17 38	17 52	18 08	18 20	18 39	19 08	19 38	20 08	21 08	22 08		
Knaresborough	a	15 45	16 14	16 45	17 17		17 45	18 00	18 14	18 26	18 45	19 14	19 45	20 14	21 14	22 15		
	d		16 14		17 21				18 14			19 14		20 14	21 14			
Cattal	d		16 22		17 29				18 22			19 22		20 22	21 22			
Hammerton	d		16 26		17 32				18 26			19 26		20 26	21 26			
Poppleton	d		16 33		17 39				18 33			19 33		20 33	21 33			
York 8	40 a		16 45		17 48				18 46			19 45		20 44	21 47			

Saturdays

Station		NT	NT	NT	NT	NT	NT	NT	NT	NT	NT	NT	NT	NT	NT
Leeds 10	40 d	06 07	06 37	07 13	07 39	07 54	08 29	08 59	09 29	09 59	10 29	10 59	11 29	11 59	12 29
Burley Park	d	06 11	06 41	07 17	07 43	07 58	08 33	09 03	09 33	10 03	10 33	11 03	11 33	12 03	12 33
Headingley	d	06 14	06 44	07 20	07 46	08 01	08 36	09 06	09 36	10 06	10 36	11 06	11 36	12 06	12 36
Horsforth	d	06 19	06 49	07 25	07 51	08 06	08 41	09 11	09 41	10 11	10 41	11 11	11 41	12 11	12 41
Weeton	d	06 27	06 57	07 33	07 59	08 14	08 49	09 19	09 49	10 19	10 49	11 19	11 49	12 19	12 49
Pannal	d	06 33	07 03	07 39	08 05	08 20	08 55	09 25	09 55	10 25	10 55	11 25	11 55	12 25	12 55
Hornbeam Park	d	06 38	07 08	07 44	08 10	08 25	09 00	09 30	10 00	10 30	11 00	11 30	12 00	12 30	13 00
Harrogate	a	06 41	07 11	07 49	08 13	08 28	09 03	09 33	10 03	10 33	11 03	11 33	12 03	12 33	13 03
	d	06 45	07 14	07 49	08 16	08 29	09 05	09 35	10 05	10 35	11 05	11 35	12 05	12 35	13 05
Starbeck	d	06 49	07 17	07 52	08 19	08 33	09 08	09 38	10 08	10 38	11 08	11 38	12 08	12 38	13 08
Knaresborough	a	06 54	07 23	07 59	08 25	08 40	09 14	09 45	10 14	10 45	11 14	11 45	12 14	12 45	13 14
	d	06 55	07 23	07 59	08 28		09 15		10 14		11 14		12 14		13 14
Cattal	d	07 03	07 31	08 07	08 36		09 23		10 22		11 22		12 22		13 22
Hammerton	d	07 07	07 35	08 11	08 39		09 27		10 26		11 26		12 26		13 26
Poppleton	d	07 14	07 42	08 19	08 46		09 34		10 33		11 33		12 33		13 33
York 8	40 a	07 21	07 51	08 27	08 59		09 45		10 45		11 45		12 45		13 42

Station		NT	NT	NT	NT	NT	NT	NT	NT	NT	NT	NT	NT	NT	NT	NT	NT	NT	NT
Leeds 10	40 d	12 59	13 29	13 59	14 29	14 59	15 29	15 59	16 29	16 59	17 13	17 29	17 59	18 29	19 29	20 29	21 20	22 29	23 21
Burley Park	d	13 03	13 33	14 03	14 33	15 03	15 33	16 03	16 33	17 03	17 17	17 33	18 03	18 33	19 33	20 33	21 24	22 33	23 25
Headingley	d	13 06	13 36	14 06	14 36	15 06	15 36	16 06	16 36	17 06	17 20	17 36	18 06	18 36	19 36	20 36	21 27	22 36	23 28
Horsforth	d	13 11	13 41	14 11	14 41	15 11	15 41	16 11	16 41	17 11	17 25	17 41	18 11	18 41	19 41	20 41	21 32	22 41	23 33
Weeton	d	13 19	13 49	14 19	14 49	15 19	15 49	16 19	16 49	17 19	17 33	17 49	18 19	18 49	19 49	20 49	21 40	22 49	23 41
Pannal	d	13 25	13 55	14 25	14 55	15 25	15 55	16 25	16 55	17 25	17 39	17 55	18 25	18 55	19 55	20 55	21 46	22 55	23 47
Hornbeam Park	d	13 30	14 00	14 30	15 00	15 30	16 00	16 30	17 00	17 30	17 44	18 00	18 30	19 00	20 00	21 00	21 51	23 00	23 52
Harrogate	a	13 33	14 03	14 33	15 03	15 33	16 03	16 33	17 03	17 33	17 47	18 03	18 33	19 03	20 03	21 03	21 54	23 06	23 58
	d	13 35	14 05	14 35	15 05	15 35	16 05	16 35	17 08	17 35	17 49	18 05	18 35	19 05	20 05	21 05	21 56		
Starbeck	d	13 38	14 08	14 38	15 08	15 38	16 08	16 38	17 11	17 38	17 52	18 08	18 38	19 08	20 08	21 08	21 59		
Knaresborough	a	13 45	14 14	14 45	15 14	15 45	16 14	16 45	17 17	17 45	18 00	18 14	18 45	19 14	20 14	21 14	22 06		
	d		14 14		15 14		16 14		17 21			18 14		19 14	20 14	21 14			
Cattal	d		14 22		15 22		16 22		17 29			18 22		19 22	20 22	21 22			
Hammerton	d		14 26		15 26		16 26		17 33			18 26		19 26	20 26	21 31			
Poppleton	d		14 33		15 33		16 33		17 40			18 33		19 33	20 33	21 38			
York 8	40 a		14 46		15 46		16 45		17 47			18 46		19 45	20 45	21 48			

For general notes see front of timetable
For details of catering facilities see Directory of Train Operators

Table 35

Sundays

Leeds → Harrogate → York

Network Diagram - see first page of Table 35

		NT	NT	NT	NT	NT	NT	NT	NT	NT	NT	NT	NT
Leeds 10	40 d	09 54	10 54	12 54	14 54	15 54	16 54	17 54	18 54	19 54	21 16	22 23	23 22
Burley Park	d	09 59	10 59	12 59	14 59	15 59	16 59	17 59	18 59	19 59	21 21	22 28	23 27
Headingley	d	10 01	11 01	13 01	15 01	16 01	17 01	18 01	19 01	20 01	21 23	22 30	23 29
Horsforth	d	10 07	11 07	13 07	15 07	16 07	17 07	18 07	19 07	20 07	21 29	22 36	23 35
Weeton	d	10 14	11 14	13 14	15 14	16 14	17 14	18 14	19 14	20 14	21 37	22 43	23 42
Pannal	d	10 20	11 20	13 20	15 20	16 20	17 20	18 20	19 20	20 20	21 43	22 49	23 48
Hornbeam Park	d	10 25	11 25	13 25	15 25	16 25	17 25	18 25	19 25	20 25	21 48	22 54	23 53
Harrogate	a	10 31	11 28	13 28	15 28	16 28	17 28	18 28	19 28	20 28	21 51	23 00	23 59
	d	…	11 30	13 30	15 30	16 30	17 30	18 30	19 30	20 30	21 53	…	…
Starbeck	d	.	11 34	13 34	15 34	16 34	17 34	18 34	19 34	20 34	21 57	.	.
Knaresborough	a	…	11 39	13 39	15 39	16 39	17 39	18 39	19 39	20 39	22 03	…	…
	d	.	11 40	13 40	15 40	16 45	17 44	18 44	19 44	20 45	.	.	.
Cattal	d	…	11 48	13 48	15 48	16 53	17 52	18 52	19 52	20 53	…	…	…
Hammerton	d	.	11 51	13 51	15 51	16 56	17 55	18 55	19 55	20 56	.	.	.
Poppleton	d	…	11 58	13 58	15 58	17 03	18 02	19 02	20 02	21 03	…	…	…
York 8	40 a	.	12 07	14 08	16 08	17 10	18 10	19 12	20 12	21 15	.	.	.

For general notes see front of timetable
For details of catering facilities see Directory of Train Operators

Leeds and Bradford → Skipton, Lancaster, Morecambe and Carlisle

Network Diagram - see first page of Table 35

Miles	Miles	Miles			NT	NT	NT	NT	NT	NT	NT	NT	NT	NT	NT	NT	NT	NT	NT	NT	NT	NT	NT
—	—	—	London Kings Cross 15	⊖ 26 d																*06 00*			*06 35*
0	0	—	**Leeds 10**	37 d		05 55		06 21			06 56		07 25		07 51		08 19	08 25		08 49	08 56		09 26
—	—	0	**Bradford Forster Square**	37 d			06 10	*06 15*	06 40		*06 55*	07 15		07 42	*07 46*	08 11	*08 16*		08 41	*08 46*		09 11	*09 16*
—	—	1¾	Frizinghall	37 d			06 13	*06 18*	06 43		*06 58*	07 18		07 45	*07 49*	08 14	*08 19*		08 44	*08 49*		09 14	*09 19*
10¾	10¾	2¾	Shipley	37 a		06 07	06 17	06 32	06 47		07 08	07 22	07 36	07 49	08 02	08 18	08 31	08 37	08 48	09 01	09 07	09 18	09 37
—	—	—		d		06 08	06 19	06 33	06 48		07 08	07 23	07 37	07 50	08 03	08 19	08 32	08 37	08 49	09 02	09 09	09 19	09 38
11½	11½	—	Saltaire	d		06 10	06 21	06 35	06 50		07 10	07 25	07 39	07 52	08 05	08 21		08 39	08 51		09 11	09 21	09 40
13¾	13¾	—	Bingley	d		06 14	06 25	06 39	06 54		07 14	07 29	07 43	07 56	08 09	08 25	08 37	08 43	08 55	09 06	09 15	09 25	09 44
14½	14½	—	Crossflatts	d		06 16	06 27	06 41	06 56		07 16	07 31	07 45	07 58	08 11	08 27		08 45	08 57		09 17	09 27	09 46
17	17	—	Keighley	d		06 21	06 32	06 45	07 01		07 20	07 36	07 49	08 03	08 15	08 32	08 43	08 49	09 02	09 12	09 21	09 32	09 50
20	20	—	Steeton & Silsden	d		06 26	06 36	06 49	07 05		07 24	07 40	07 53	08 07	08 19	08 36		08 53	09 06		09 25	09 36	09 54
23¼	23¼	—	Cononley	d		06 30	06 40	06 53	07 09		07 28	07 44	07 57	08 11	08 23	08 40		08 57	09 10		09 29	09 40	09 58
26¼	26¼	—	**Skipton**	a		06 38	06 48	07 00	07 17		07 37	07 51	08 05	08 19	08 32	08 47	08 55	09 07	09 18	09 24	09 37	09 47	10 07
—	—	—		d	05 40												09 00			09 26			
30	30	—	Gargrave	d	05 45												09 05			09 32			
36¼	36¼	—	Hellifield	d	05 55												09 14			09 40			
37½	37½	—	Long Preston	d	05 58												09 17			09 43			
—	41¼	—	Giggleswick	d	06 08												09 25						
—	48	—	Clapham (Nth Yorkshire)	d	06 16												09 33						
—	51¼	—	Bentham	d	06 22												09 39						
—	54½	—	Wennington	d	06 27												09 44						
—	64	—	Carnforth	83 a	06 43												10 00						
—	70¼	—	**Lancaster 6**	65, 83, 98 a	06 53												10 12						
—	72¾	—	Bare Lane	98 a	*07 31*												10 33						
—	75½	—	**Morecambe**	98 a	*07 36*												10 40						
41¼	—	—	Settle	d																09 50			
47½	—	—	Horton-in-Ribblesdale	d																09 58			
52¼	—	—	Ribblehead	d																10 06			
58¼	—	—	Dent	d																10 16			
61¾	—	—	Garsdale	d																10 21			
71½	—	—	Kirkby Stephen	d						07 28										10 34			
82¼	—	—	Appleby	d						07 40										10 47			
93¼	—	—	Langwathby	d						07 54										11 01			
97½	—	—	Lazonby & Kirkoswald	d						08 00										11 07			
103	—	—	Armathwaite	d						08 08										11 15			
113	—	—	**Carlisle 8**	65 a						08 24										11 34			
—	—	—	Glasgow Central 15	65 a	*09 45*					*10 36*							*13b01*			*13 01*			

		NT	NT	NT	NT	NT A	NT	NT	NT	NT	NT	NT	NT	NT	NT	NT	NT	NT	NT	NT	NT	NT	NT
London Kings Cross 15	⊖ 26 d		*07 10*			*07c20*						*08 40*				*09 35*		*10 10*			*10 35*		
Leeds 10	37 d		09 47	09 56		10 19	10 26		10 49	10 56		11 26		11 56		12 26		12 49	12 56		13 26		13 49
Bradford Forster Square	37 d	09 41	*09 46*		10 11	*10 16*		10 41	*10 46*		11 11	*11 16*	11 41	*11 46*	12 11	*12 16*	12 41	*12 46*		13 11	*13 16*	13 41	*13 46*
Frizinghall	37 d	09 44	*09 49*		10 14	*10 19*		10 44	*10 49*		11 14	*11 19*	11 44	*11 49*	12 14	*12 19*	12 44	*12 49*		13 14	*13 19*	13 44	*13 49*
Shipley	37 a	09 48	10 01	10 07	10 18	10 31	10 37	10 48	11 01	11 07	11 18	11 39	11 48	12 07	12 18	12 37	12 48	13 01	13 07	13 18	13 37	13 48	14 03
	d	09 49	10 02	10 08	10 19	10 32	10 38	10 49	11 02	11 08	11 19	11 39	11 49	12 08	12 19	12 38	12 49	13 02	13 08	13 19	13 38	13 49	14 03
Saltaire	d	09 51		10 10	10 21		10 40	10 51		11 10	11 21	11 41	11 51	12 10	12 21	12 40	12 51		13 10	13 21	13 41	13 51	
Bingley	d	09 55	10 06	10 14	10 25	10 37	10 44	10 55	11 06	11 14	11 25	11 45	11 55	12 14	12 25	12 44	12 55	13 06	13 14	13 25	13 45	13 55	14 08
Crossflatts	d	09 57		10 16	10 27		10 46	10 57		11 16	11 27	11 47	11 57	12 16	12 27	12 46	12 57		13 16	13 27	13 47	13 57	
Keighley	d	10 02	10 12	10 20	10 32	10 42	10 50	11 02	11 12	11 20	11 32	11 51	12 02	12 20	12 32	12 50	13 02	13 12	13 20	13 32	13 51	14 02	14 14
Steeton & Silsden	d	10 06		10 24	10 36		10 54	11 06		11 24	11 36	11 55	12 06	12 24	12 36	12 54	13 06		13 24	13 36	13 55	14 06	
Cononley	d	10 10		10 28	10 40		10 58	11 10		11 28	11 40	11 59	12 10	12 28	12 40	12 58	13 10		13 28	13 40	13 59	14 10	
Skipton	a	10 17	10 24	10 37	10 47	10 55	11 07	11 17	11 24	11 37	11 47	12 07	12 19	12 37	12 47	13 07	13 17	13 24	13 37	13 47	14 09	14 17	14 26
	d		10 26			11 00			11 26									13 26					14 34
Gargrave	d					11 05												13 31					14 39
Hellifield	d					11 14			11 37									13 40					14 48
Long Preston	d					11 17												13 42					14 51
Giggleswick	d					11 25																	14 59
Clapham (Nth Yorkshire)	d					11 33																	15 07
Bentham	d					11 39																	15 13
Wennington	d					11 44																	15 18
Carnforth	83 a					12 00																	15 34
Lancaster 6	65, 83, 98 a					12 11																	15 47
Bare Lane	98 a					12 34																	16 03
Morecambe	98 a					12 39																	16 09
Settle	d		10 44						11 46									13 48					
Horton-in-Ribblesdale	d								11 54									13 57					
Ribblehead	d								12 02									14 05					
Dent	d								12 12									14 14					
Garsdale	d								12 17									14 20					
Kirkby Stephen	d		11 22						12 30									14 32					
Appleby	d		11 36						12 43									14 45					
Langwathby	d								12 57									14 59					
Lazonby & Kirkoswald	d								13 03									15 04					
Armathwaite	d								13 11									15 12					
Carlisle 8	65 a		12 17						13 29									15 32					
Glasgow Central 15	65 a		*14 01*			*15b17*			*15 17*									*17 18*					*19b19*

For general notes see front of timetable
For details of catering facilities see Directory of Train Operators

A To Heysham Port (Table 98)
b Change at Lancaster
c Change at Doncaster and Leeds

Leeds and Bradford → Skipton, Lancaster, Morecambe and Carlisle

Network Diagram - see first page of Table 35

		NT	NT	NT		NT	NT	NT	NT	NT	NT	NT	NT		NT	NT	NT	NT	NT	NT	NT	NT		NT	NT
London Kings Cross 15	⊖ 26 d	*11 10*		*11b30*			*12 10*			*12 35*		*13 10*			*13 35*			*14 10*		*14 35*		*15 10*			
Leeds 10	37 d	13 56		14 26			14 49	14 56		15 26		15 56			16 26		16 39	16 56		17 26		17 50		17 56	
Bradford Forster Square	37 d		14 11	*14 16*		14 41	*14 46*		15 11	*15 16*	15 41	*15 46*	16 11		*16 16*	16 40		*16 45*	17 11	*17 16*	17 38	*17 46*			18 11
Frizinghall	37 d		14 14	*14 19*		14 44	*14 49*		15 14	*15 19*	15 44	*15 49*	16 14		*16 19*	16 43		*16 48*	17 14	*17 19*	17 41	*17 49*			18 14
Shipley	37 a	14 07	14 18	14 37		14 48	15 01	15 07	15 18	15 37	15 48	16 07	16 18		16 37	16 48	16 53	17 07	17 18	17 37	17 45	18 02		18 08	18 18
	d	14 08	14 19	14 38		14 49	15 02	15 08	15 19	15 38	15 49	16 08	16 19		16 38	16 49	16 55	17 08	17 19	17 38	17 46	18 03		18 08	18 19
Saltaire	d	14 10	14 21	14 40		14 51		15 10	15 21	15 40	15 51	16 10	16 22		16 40	16 52		17 10	17 22	17 40	17 49	18 05			18 21
Bingley	d	14 14	14 25	14 44		14 55	15 06	15 14	15 25	15 44	15 55	16 14	16 26		16 44	16 56	17 03	17 14	17 26	17 44	17 53	18 09		18 17	18 25
Crossflatts	d	14 16	14 27	14 46		14 57		15 16	15 27	15 46	15 57	16 16	16 28		16 47	16 58		17 17	17 28	17 47	17 55	18 12			18 27
Keighley	d	14 20	14 32	14 50		15 02	15 12	15 20	15 32	15 50	16 02	16 20	16 33		16 51	17 03	17 10	17 21	17 33	17 51	18 00	18 16		18 24	18 32
Steeton & Silsden	d	14 24	14 36	14 54		15 06		15 24	15 36	15 54	16 06	16 24	16 37		16 56	17 07		17 26	17 37	17 56	18 04	18 21		18 29	18 36
Cononley	d	14 28	14 40	14 58		15 10		15 28	15 40	15 58	16 10	16 28	16 41		17 00	17 11		17 30	17 41	18 00	18 08	18 25			18 40
Skipton	a	14 37	14 47	15 07		15 17	15 24	15 37	15 47	16 07	16 17	16 37	16 49		17 07	17 19	17 23	17 37	17 49	18 07	18 16	18 33		18 40	18 47
	d						15 26										17 24							18 41	
Gargrave	d																17 30							18 46	
Hellifield	d						15 37										17 39							18 55	
Long Preston	d																17 42							18 57	
Giggleswick	d																17 49								
Clapham (Nth Yorkshire)	d																17 57								
Bentham	d																18 04								
Wennington	d																18 09								
Carnforth	83 a																18 29								
Lancaster 6	65, 83, 98 a																18 42								
Bare Lane	98 a																18 55								
Morecambe	98 a																19 01								
Settle	d						15 45																	19 03	
Horton-in-Ribblesdale	d						15 53																	19 12	
Ribblehead	d						16 01																	19 20	
Dent	d						16 11																	19 29	
Garsdale	d						16 16																	19 35	
Kirkby Stephen	d						16 29																	19 47	
Appleby	d						16 41																	20 00	
Langwathby	d						16 55																	20 14	
Lazonby & Kirkoswald	d						17 01																	20 19	
Armathwaite	d						17 09																	20 27	
Carlisle 8	65 a						17 28																	20 47	
Glasgow Central 15	65 a						*19 19*										*21c17*							*22 39*	

		NT	NT	NT	NT	NT	NT	NT	NT		NT	NT	GR R 1 ⊘ 🍴	NT	NT	NT	NT	NT		NT	NT	NT	NT		
London Kings Cross 15	⊖ 26 d	*15 35*				*16 35*			*17 03*			*17e33*	18 03			*18 35*	*19 03*			*19 33*	*20 03*		*20 33*		
Leeds 10	37 d	18 26		18 50		19 19	19 25		19 56			20 26	20 33	20 55		21 26	21 56			22 26	22 56		23 18		
Bradford Forster Square	37 d	*18 16*	18 41	*18 46*	19 07			19 36	*19 41*		20 07	*20 25*		*20 38*	21 05	*21 25*	*21 38*	22 05		*22 25*	*22 38*	23 09	*23 20*		
Frizinghall	37 d	*18 19*	18 44	*18 49*	19 10			19 39	*19 44*		20 10	*20 28*		*20 41*	21 08	*21 28*	*21 41*	22 08		*22 28*	*22 41*	23 12	*23 23*		
Shipley	37 a	18 38	18 48	19 03	19 14	19 31	19 37	19 43	20 07		20 15	20 37		21 07	21 12	21 38	22 07	22 12		22 37	23 07	23 16	23 31		
	d	18 38	18 49	19 03	19 15	19 32	19 38	19 44	20 08		20 15	20 38		21 08	21 14	21 38	22 08	22 14		22 38	23 08	23 17	23 32		
Saltaire	d	18 40	18 51	19 05	19 17		19 40	19 46	20 10		20 17	20 40		21 10	21 16	21 40	22 10	22 16		22 40	23 10	23 19	23 34		
Bingley	d	18 44	18 55	19 09	19 21	19 36	19 44	19 50	20 14		20 21	20 44		21 14	21 20	21 44	22 14	22 20		22 44	23 14	23 23	23 38		
Crossflatts	d	18 46	18 57	19 11	19 23		19 46	19 52	20 16		20 23	20 46		21 16	21 22	21 46	22 16	22 22		22 46	23 16	23 25	23 40		
Keighley	d	18 50	19 02	19 15	19 28	19 42	19 50	19 57	20 20		20 28	20 50	20s57	21 20	21 27	21 50	22 20	22 27		22 50	23 20	23 30	23 44		
Steeton & Silsden	d	18 54	19 06	19 19	19 32		19 54	20 01	20 24		20 32	20 54		21 24	21 31	21 54	22 24	22 31		22 54	23 24	23 34	23 48		
Cononley	d	18 58	19 10	19 23	19 36		19 58	20 05	20 28		20 36	20 58		21 28	21 35	21 58	22 28	22 35		22 58	23 28	23 38	23 52		
Skipton	a	19 07	19 17	19 33	19 44	19 54	20 06	20 12	20 35		20 46	21 06	21 13	21 36	21 42	22 07	22 36	22 42		23 10	23 39	23 45	00 01		
	d					20 00																			
Gargrave	d					20 06																			
Hellifield	d					20 15																			
Long Preston	d					20 18																			
Giggleswick	d																								
Clapham (Nth Yorkshire)	d																								
Bentham	d																								
Wennington	d																								
Carnforth	83 a																								
Lancaster 6	65, 83, 98 a																								
Bare Lane	98 a																								
Morecambe	98 a																								
Settle	d					20 24																			
Horton-in-Ribblesdale	d					20 32																			
Ribblehead	d					20a42																			
Dent	d																								
Garsdale	d																								
Kirkby Stephen	d																								
Appleby	d																								
Langwathby	d																								
Lazonby & Kirkoswald	d																								
Armathwaite	d																								
Carlisle 8	65 a																								
Glasgow Central 15	65 a																								

For general notes see front of timetable
For details of catering facilities see Directory of Train Operators

b Change at Doncaster and Leeds
c Change at Lancaster
e Change at Shipley

Table 36

Saturdays

Leeds and Bradford → Skipton, Lancaster, Morecambe and Carlisle

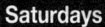

Network Diagram - see first page of Table 35

		NT	NT	NT	NT	NT	NT	NT	NT	NT	NT	NT	NT	NT	NT	NT	NT	NT	NT	NT A	NT	NT
London Kings Cross 15	⊖ 26 d														*06b15*		*07 10*					
Leeds 10	37 d	05 55		06 19	06 56		07 56		08 19	08 25		08 49	08 56		09 26		09 47	09 56		10 19	10 26	
Bradford Forster Square	37 d		06 10	*06 15*		07 11	*07 15*	08 11	*08 16*		08 41	*08 46*		09 11	*09 16*	09 41	*09 46*		10 11	*10 16*		10 41
Frizinghall	37 d		06 13	*06 18*		07 14	*07 18*	08 14	*08 19*		08 44	*08 49*		09 14	*09 19*	09 44	*09 49*		10 14	*10 19*		10 44
Shipley	37 a	06 07	06 17	06 31	07 08	07 18	08 08	08 18	08 31	08 37	08 48	09 01	09 07	09 18	09 37	09 48	10 01	10 07	10 18	10 31	10 37	10 48
	d	06 08	06 19	06 32	07 08	07 19	08 08	08 19	08 32	08 37	08 49	09 02	09 09	09 19	09 38	09 49	10 02	10 08	10 19	10 32	10 38	10 49
Saltaire	d	06 10	06 21		07 10	07 21	08 10	08 21		08 39	08 51		09 11	09 21	09 40	09 51		10 10	10 21		10 40	10 51
Bingley	d	06 14	06 25	06 36	07 14	07 25	08 14	08 25	08 37	08 43	08 55	09 06	09 15	09 25	09 44	09 55	10 06	10 14	10 25	10 37	10 44	10 55
Crossflatts	d	06 16	06 27		07 16	07 27	08 16	08 27		08 45	08 57		09 17	09 27	09 46	09 57		10 16	10 27		10 46	10 57
Keighley	d	06 21	06 32	06 42	07 20	07 32	08 20	08 32	08 43	08 49	09 02	09 12	09 21	09 32	09 50	10 02	10 12	10 20	10 32	10 42	10 50	11 02
Steeton & Silsden	d	06 26	06 36		07 24	07 36	08 24	08 36		08 53	09 06		09 25	09 36	09 54	10 06		10 24	10 36		10 54	11 06
Cononley	d	06 30	06 40		07 28	07 40	08 28	08 40		08 57	09 10		09 29	09 40	09 58	10 10		10 28	10 40		10 58	11 10
Skipton	a	06 38	06 48	06 55	07 37	07 47	08 37	08 47	08 55	09 07	09 18	09 24	09 37	09 47	10 07	10 17	10 24	10 37	10 47	10 55	11 07	11 17
	d	06 40		06 56					09 00			09 26					10 26			11 00		
Gargrave	d	06 45							09 05			09 32								11 05		
Hellifield	d	06 54		07 08					09 14			09 40								11 14		
Long Preston	d	06 57							09 17			09 43								11 17		
Giggleswick	d	07 07							09 25											11 25		
Clapham (Nth Yorkshire)	d	07 15							09 33											11 33		
Bentham	d	07 21							09 39											11 39		
Wennington	d	07 26							09 44											11 44		
Carnforth	83 a	07 42							10 00											12 00		
Lancaster 6	65, 83, 98 a	07 52							10 12											12 11		
Bare Lane	98 a	*08 41*							10 33											12 31		
Morecambe	98 a	*08 46*							10 40											12 36		
Settle	d			07 15								09 50					10 44					
Horton-in-Ribblesdale	d			07 24								09 58										
Ribblehead	d			07 32								10 06										
Dent	d			07 41								10 16										
Garsdale	d			07 47								10 21										
Kirkby Stephen	d			07 59								10 34					11 22					
Appleby	d			08 12								10 47					11 36					
Langwathby	d			08 26								11 01										
Lazonby & Kirkoswald	d			08 31								11 07										
Armathwaite	d			08 39								11 15										
Carlisle 8	65 a			08 58								11 34					12 17					
Glasgow Central 15	65 a	*11 03*		*11 03*					*13c01*			*13 01*					*14 01*			*15c01*		

		NT	NT	NT	NT	NT	NT	NT	NT	NT	NT	NT	NT	NT	NT	NT B	NT C	NT	NT	NT	NT
London Kings Cross 15	⊖ 26 d	*08 10*					*09 05*				*10 10*					*11 10*	*11 10*				
Leeds 10	37 d	10 49	10 56		11 26		11 56		12 26		12 49	12 56		13 26		13 49	13 49	13 56		14 26	
Bradford Forster Square	37 d	*10 46*		11 11	*11 16*	11 41	*11 46*	12 11	*12 16*	12 41	*12 46*		13 11	*13 16*	13 41	*13 46*	*13 46*		14 11	*14 16*	14 41
Frizinghall	37 d	*10 49*		11 14	*11 19*	11 44	*11 49*	12 14	*12 19*	12 44	*12 49*		13 14	*13 19*	13 44	*13 49*	*13 49*		14 14	*14 19*	14 44
Shipley	37 a	11 01	11 07	11 18	11 39	11 48	12 07	12 18	12 37	12 48	13 01	13 07	13 18	13 37	13 48	14 03	14 03	14 07	14 18	14 37	14 48
	d	11 02	11 08	11 19	11 39	11 49	12 08	12 19	12 38	12 49	13 02	13 08	13 19	13 38	13 49	14 03	14 03	14 08	14 19	14 38	14 49
Saltaire	d		11 10	11 21	11 41	11 51	12 10	12 21	12 40	12 51		13 10	13 21	13 41	13 51			14 10	14 21	14 40	14 51
Bingley	d	11 06	11 14	11 25	11 45	11 55	12 14	12 25	12 44	12 55	13 06	13 14	13 25	13 45	13 55	14 08	14 08	14 14	14 25	14 44	14 55
Crossflatts	d		11 16	11 27	11 47	11 57	12 16	12 27	12 46	12 57		13 16	13 27	13 47	13 57			14 16	14 27	14 46	14 57
Keighley	d	11 12	11 20	11 32	11 51	12 02	12 20	12 32	12 50	13 02	13 12	13 20	13 32	13 51	14 02	14 14	14 14	14 20	14 32	14 50	15 02
Steeton & Silsden	d		11 24	11 36	11 55	12 06	12 24	12 36	12 54	13 06		13 24	13 36	13 55	14 06			14 24	14 36	14 54	15 06
Cononley	d		11 28	11 40	11 59	12 10	12 28	12 40	12 58	13 10		13 28	13 40	13 59	14 10			14 28	14 40	14 58	15 10
Skipton	a	11 24	11 37	11 47	12 07	12 20	12 37	12 47	13 07	13 17	13 24	13 37	13 47	14 09	14 17	14 26	14 26	14 37	14 47	15 07	15 17
	d	11 26									13 26					14 34	14 34				
Gargrave	d										13 31					14 39	14 39				
Hellifield	d	11 37									13 40					14 48	14 48				
Long Preston	d										13 42					14 51	14 51				
Giggleswick	d															14 59	14 59				
Clapham (Nth Yorkshire)	d															15 07	15 07				
Bentham	d															15 13	15 13				
Wennington	d															15 18	15 18				
Carnforth	83 a															15 34	15 34				
Lancaster 6	65, 83, 98 a															15 45	15 45				
Bare Lane	98 a															15 55	16 00				
Morecambe	98 a															16 02	16 06				
Settle	d	11 46									13 48										
Horton-in-Ribblesdale	d	11 54									13 57										
Ribblehead	d	12 02									14 05										
Dent	d	12 12									14 14										
Garsdale	d	12 17									14 20										
Kirkby Stephen	d	12 30									14 32										
Appleby	d	12 43									14 45										
Langwathby	d	12 57									14 59										
Lazonby & Kirkoswald	d	13 03									15 04										
Armathwaite	d	13 11									15 12										
Carlisle 8	65 a	13 29									15 32										
Glasgow Central 15	65 a	*15 01*									*17 01*					*18c01*	*19c01*				

For general notes see front of timetable
For details of catering facilities see Directory of Train Operators

A To Heysham Port (Table 98)
B Until 31 October
C From 7 November

b Change at Doncaster and Leeds
c Change at Lancaster

Leeds and Bradford → Skipton, Lancaster, Morecambe and Carlisle

Network Diagram - see first page of Table 35

		NT	NT	NT		NT	NT	NT	NT A	NT		NT	NT	NT	NT	NT		NT	NT	NT B	NT	NT		NT	NT
London Kings Cross 15	⊖ 26 d	12 10				12b30		13 10										14 30						15 30	
Leeds 10	37 d	14 49	14 56			15 26		15 56				16 26		16 39	16 56			17 26		17 50	17 56			18 26	
Bradford Forster Square	37 d	14 46		15 11		15 16	15 41	15 46		16 11		16 16	16 40		16 44	17 11		17 16	17 41	17 46	17 46	18 11		18 16	18 41
Frizinghall	37 d	14 49		15 14		15 19	15 44	15 49		16 14		16 19	16 43		16 48	17 14		17 19	17 44	17 49	17 49	18 14		18 19	18 44
Shipley	37 a	15 01	15 07	15 18		15 37	15 48	16 07		16 18		16 37	16 48	16 53	17 07	17 18		17 37	17 48	18 02	18 08	18 18		18 38	18 48
	d	15 02	15 08	15 19		15 38	15 49	16 08		16 19		16 38	16 49	16 55	17 08	17 19		17 38	17 49	18 03	18 08	18 19		18 38	18 49
Saltaire	d		15 10	15 21		15 40	15 51	16 10		16 22		16 40	16 52		17 10	17 22		17 40	17 51		18 10	18 21		18 40	18 51
Bingley	d	15 06	15 14	15 25		15 44	15 55	16 14		16 26		16 44	16 56	17 03	17 14	17 26		17 44	17 55	18 08	18 14	18 25		18 44	18 55
Crossflatts	d		15 16	15 27		15 46	15 57	16 16		16 28		16 47	16 58		17 17	17 28		17 47	17 57		18 17	18 27		18 46	18 57
Keighley	d	15 12	15 20	15 32		15 50	16 02	16 20		16 33		16 51	17 03	17 10	17 21	17 33		17 51	18 02	18 14	18 21	18 32		18 50	19 02
Steeton & Silsden	d		15 24	15 36		15 54	16 06	16 24		16 37		16 56	17 07		17 26	17 37		17 56	18 06	18 19	18 26	18 36		18 54	19 06
Cononley	d		15 28	15 40		15 58	16 10	16 28		16 41		17 00	17 11		17 30	17 41		18 00	18 10		18 30	18 40		18 58	19 10
Skipton	a	15 24	15 37	15 47		16 07	16 17	16 37		16 49		17 07	17 19	17 24	17 37	17 49		18 07	18 17	18 29	18 39	18 47		19 07	19 17
	d	15 26							16 45					17 25						18 35					
Gargrave	d								16 50					17 31						18 40					
Hellifield	d	15 37							16 59					17 40						18 49					
Long Preston	d								17 01					17 43						18 51					
Giggleswick	d													17 50											
Clapham (Nth Yorkshire)	d													17 58											
Bentham	d													18 05											
Wennington	d													18 10											
Carnforth	83 a													18 26											
Lancaster 6	65, 83, 98 a													18 38											
Bare Lane	98 a													18 53											
Morecambe	98 a													18 59											
Settle	d	15 45							17 07											18 57					
Horton-in-Ribblesdale	d	15 53							17 16											19 06					
Ribblehead	d	16 01							17 24											19 14					
Dent	d	16 11							17 33											19 23					
Garsdale	d	16 16							17 39											19 29					
Kirkby Stephen	d	16 29							17 51											19 41					
Appleby	d	16 41							18 04											19 54					
Langwathby	d	16 55							18 18											20 08					
Lazonby & Kirkoswald	d	17 01							18 23											20 13					
Armathwaite	d	17 09							18 31											20 21					
Carlisle 8	65 a	17 28							18 51											20 41					
Glasgow Central 15	65 a	19 01							21 01					21c01						22 01					

		NT	NT	NT	NT	NT		GR R 1	NT	NT	NT	NT		NT	NT	NT	NT	NT		NT	NT	NT		
London Kings Cross 15	⊖ 26 d			16 30				17 30				18e30				18b40				20 00		20b30		
Leeds 10	37 d	18 56		19 19	19 25			19 57		20 06	20 26	20 55			21 26	21 56		22 26		22 56		23 18		
Bradford Forster Square	37 d	18 46	19 07			19 36			20 07		20 25	20 38		21 05	21 25	21 38	22 05	22 25		22 38	23 05	23 20		
Frizinghall	37 d	18 49	19 10			19 39			20 10		20 28	20 41		21 08	21 28	21 41	22 08	22 28		22 41	23 08	23 23		
Shipley	37 a	19 07	19 14	19 31	19 37	19 43			20 15	20 18	20 37	21 07		21 12	21 38	22 07	22 12	22 37		23 07	23 12	23 31		
	d	19 08	19 15	19 32	19 38	19 44			20 15	20 20	20 38	21 08		21 14	21 38	22 08	22 14	22 38		23 08	23 14	23 32		
Saltaire	d	19 10	19 17		19 40	19 46			20 17	20 22	20 40	21 10		21 16	21 40	22 10	22 16	22 40		23 10	23 16	23 34		
Bingley	d	19 14	19 21	19 36	19 44	19 50			20 21	20 26	20 44	21 14		21 20	21 44	22 14	22 20	22 44		23 14	23 20	23 38		
Crossflatts	d	19 16	19 23		19 46	19 52			20 23	20 28	20 46	21 16		21 22	21 46	22 16	22 22	22 46		23 16	23 22	23 40		
Keighley	d	19 20	19 28	19 42	19 50	19 57		20s17	20 28	20 33	20 50	21 20		21 27	21 50	22 20	22 27	22 50		23 20	23 27	23 44		
Steeton & Silsden	d	19 24	19 32		19 54	20 01			20 32	20 37	20 54	21 24		21 31	21 54	22 24	22 31	22 54		23 24	23 31	23 48		
Cononley	d	19 28	19 36		19 58	20 05			20 36	20 41	20 58	21 28		21 35	21 58	22 28	22 35	22 58		23 28	23 35	23 52		
Skipton	a	19 37	19 44	19 54	20 06	20 12		20 31	20 47	20 49	21 06	21 36		21 42	22 07	22 36	22 42	23 10		23 39	23 41	00 01		
	d			20 00																				
Gargrave	d			20 06																				
Hellifield	d			20 15																				
Long Preston	d			20 18																				
Giggleswick	d																							
Clapham (Nth Yorkshire)	d																							
Bentham	d																							
Wennington	d																							
Carnforth	83 a																							
Lancaster 6	65, 83, 98 a																							
Bare Lane	98 a																							
Morecambe	98 a																							
Settle	d			20 24																				
Horton-in-Ribblesdale	d			20 32																				
Ribblehead	d			20a42																				
Dent	d																							
Garsdale	d																							
Kirkby Stephen	d																							
Appleby	d																							
Langwathby	d																							
Lazonby & Kirkoswald	d																							
Armathwaite	d																							
Carlisle 8	65 a																							
Glasgow Central 15	65 a																							

For general notes see front of timetable
For details of catering facilities see Directory of Train Operators

A From 7 November
B Until 31 October
b Change at Doncaster and Leeds
c Change at Lancaster
e Change at Shipley

Leeds and Bradford → Skipton, Lancaster, Morecambe and Carlisle

Network Diagram - see first page of Table 35

Station		NT	NT	NT	NT		NT	NT	NT	NT		NT	NT	NT	NT		NT	NT	NT	NT		NT	NT	NT	NT
		A	B	C	C		C	D	D				A						B	C		C	C		
					(bus)		(bus)	(trolley)	(trolley)													(bus)	(bus)		
London Kings Cross 15	⊖ 26 d														*09 10*			*10 10*						*11 10*	
Leeds 10	37 d	08 40	09 00	09 00						10 08		*10*b*34*	10 51	11 08	12 08		*12*b*34*	13 08	13 15	13 44				14 08	*14*b*34*
Bradford Forster Square	37 d		*09 02*	*09 02*						*10 02*		10 48		*11 02*	*12 02*		12 48	*13 02*		*13 36*				*14 02*	14 48
Frizinghall	37 d		*09 05*	*09 05*						*10 05*		10 51		*11 05*	*12 05*		12 51	*13 05*		*13 39*				*14 05*	14 51
Shipley	37 a	08 52	09 13	09 13						10 19		10 54	11 03	11 19	12 19		12 54	13 19	13 28	13 56				14 19	14 54
	d	08 53	09 14	09 14						10 20		10 55	11 04	11 20	12 20		12 55	13 20	13 29	13 57				14 20	14 55
Saltaire	d	08 55	09 16	09 16						10 22		10 57		11 22	12 22		12 57	13 22						14 22	14 57
Bingley	d	08 59	09 20	09 20						10 26		11 01	11 09	11 26	12 26		13 01	13 26	13 34	14 01				14 26	15 01
Crossflatts	d	09 01	09 22	09 22						10 28		11 03		11 28	12 28		13 03	13 28						14 28	15 03
Keighley	d	09 06	09 28	09 28						10 32		11 08	11 14	11 32	12 32		13 08	13 32	13 39	14 07				14 32	15 08
Steeton & Silsden	d	09 11	09 32	09 32						10 36		11 12		11 36	12 36		13 12	13 36						14 36	15 12
Cononley	d	09 16	09 37	09 37						10 40		11 16		11 40	12 40		13 16	13 40						14 40	15 16
Skipton	a	09 23	09 44	09 44						10 48		11 23	11 27	11 48	12 49		13 23	13 48	13 53	14 19				14 48	15 23
	d	09 26	09 46	09 46									11 29						13 54	14 21					
Gargrave	d	09 31											11 35						14 00	14 26					
Blackpool North	97 d							08 36																	
Preston 8	94, 97 d							09 05	10 00																
Blackburn	94 d							09 27	10 22																
Clitheroe	94 d							09 51	10 45																
Hellifield	d	09 40	09 57	09 57				10 15	11 08				11 44						14 08	14 35					
Long Preston	d	09 43											11 46						14 11	14 38					
Giggleswick	d	09 52											11 54												
Clapham (Nth Yorkshire)	d	10 00											12 02												
Bentham	d	10 06											12 08												
Wennington	d	10 11											12 13												
Carnforth	83 a	10 28											12 30												
Lancaster 6	65, 83, 98 a	10 39											12 44												
Bare Lane	98 a	10 51											13 05												
Morecambe	98 a	10 55											13 09												
Settle	d		10 06	10 06				10 23	11 17										14 17	14 44					
Horton-in-Ribblesdale	d		10 15	10 15				10 32	11 26										14 26	14 53					
Ribblehead	d		10 23	10 23				10 40	11 34										14 34	15 01					
Dent	d		10 33	10 33				10 50	11 44										14 44	15 11					
Garsdale	d		10 39	10 39				10 56	11 49										14 50	15 16					
Kirkby Stephen	d		10 52	10 52				11 09	12 02										15 03	15 29					
Appleby	d		11 05	11a06	11 16		11 16	11 22	12 16										15 15	15a46		15 56	15 56		
Langwathby	d		11 19				11 41	11 36	12 30										15 29				16 21		
Lazonby & Kirkoswald	d		11 25				11 51	11 42	12 36										15 35				16 31		
Armathwaite	d		11 33				12 06	11 50	12 44										15 43				16 46		
Carlisle 8	65 a		11 49		12 16		12 31	12 10	12 59										16 00			16 56	17 11		
Glasgow Central 15	65 a		*13*c*29*					*13*e*59*	*15 06*										*18 03*						

Station		NT	NT		NT	NT	NT	NT		NT	NT	NT	NT		NT	NT	NT	NT	NT	NT	NT	NT	NT		
							C	C		C			B												
								(bus)		(bus)															
London Kings Cross 15	⊖ 26 d	*12 10*			*13 10*		*14 10*				*14 10*				*15 10*		*16 10*	*17 10*		*18 10*	*19 30*		*20 30*		
Leeds 10	37 d	14 57	15 08		16 08	*16*b*35*	17 02				17 08	17 21	17 33		18 08	*18*b*34*	19 08	20 08	*20*b*34*	21 08	22 08	*22*b*34*	23 10		
Bradford Forster Square	37 d		*15 02*		*16 02*	16 48	*17 02*				*17 02*				*18 02*	18 48	*19 02*	*20 02*	20 48	*21 02*	*22 02*	22 48	*23 02*		
Frizinghall	37 d		*15 05*		*16 05*	16 51	*17 05*				*17 05*				*18 05*	18 51	*19 05*	*20 05*	20 51	*21 05*	*22 05*	22 51	*23 05*		
Shipley	37 a	15 09	15 19		16 19	16 54	17 14				17 19	17 33	17 45		18 19	18 54	19 19	20 19	20 54	21 19	22 19	22 54	23 21		
	d	15 10	15 20		16 20	16 55	17 15				17 20	17 34	17 46		18 20	18 55	19 20	20 20	20 55	21 20	22 20	22 55	23 22		
Saltaire	d		15 22		16 22	16 57					17 22				18 22	18 57	19 22	20 22	20 57	21 22	22 22	22 57	23 24		
Bingley	d	15 15	15 26		16 26	17 01	17 19				17 26	17 39	17 50		18 26	19 01	19 26	20 26	21 01	21 26	22 26	23 01	23 28		
Crossflatts	d		15 28		16 28	17 03					17 28				18 28	19 03	19 28	20 28	21 03	21 28	22 28	23 03	23 30		
Keighley	d	15 20	15 32		16 32	17 08	17 25				17 32	17 44	17 56		18 32	19 08	19 32	20 32	21 08	21 32	22 32	23 08	23 34		
Steeton & Silsden	d		15 36		16 36	17 12					17 36				18 36	19 12	19 36	20 36	21 12	21 36	22 36	23 12	23 38		
Cononley	d		15 40		16 40	17 16					17 40				18 40	19 16	19 40	20 40	21 16	21 40	22 40	23 16	23 42		
Skipton	a	15 33	15 48		16 48	17 23	17 37				17 48	17 57	18 08		18 48	19 23	19 48	20 48	21 23	21 48	22 48	23 23	23 50		
	d	15 36					17 40					18 00	18 11												
Gargrave	d	15 41										18 05													
Blackpool North	97 d																								
Preston 8	94, 97 d																								
Blackburn	94 d																								
Clitheroe	94 d																								
Hellifield	d	15 50					17 51					18 14	18 22												
Long Preston	d	15 53										18 18													
Giggleswick	d	16 00										18 25													
Clapham (Nth Yorkshire)	d	16 08										18 33													
Bentham	d	16 15										18 39													
Wennington	d	16 20										18 44													
Carnforth	83 a	16 36										19 00													
Lancaster 6	65, 83, 98 a	16 46										19 14													
Bare Lane	98 a	16 56										19 26													
Morecambe	98 a	17 01										19 30													
Settle	d						17 59						18 30												
Horton-in-Ribblesdale	d						18 08						18 39												
Ribblehead	d						18 16						18 47												
Dent	d						18 26						18 57												
Garsdale	d						18 31						19 02												
Kirkby Stephen	d						18 44						19 15												
Appleby	d						19a01	19 10		19 10			19 28												
Langwathby	d									19 35			19 42												
Lazonby & Kirkoswald	d									19 45			19 48												
Armathwaite	d									20 00			19 56												
Carlisle 8	65 a							20 10		20 25			20 13												
Glasgow Central 15	65 a												*22 07*												

For general notes see front of timetable
For details of catering facilities see Directory of Train Operators

A Until 13 September
B Until 1 November
C From 8 November
D Until 6 September

b Change at Shipley
c 13 September to 1 November arr. 1436
e 19 July to 6 September arr. 1410

Carlisle, Morecambe, Lancaster and Skipton → Bradford and Leeds

Network Diagram - see first page of Table 35

Miles	Miles	Miles	Station		NT	NT	NT	NT	NT	GR R 1	NT		NT	NT	NT	NT	NT	NT	NT		NT	NT	NT	NT	NT
—	—	—	Glasgow Central 15	65 d														04 25				04 25			
0	—	—	**Carlisle 8**	65 d														06 20							
10	—	—	Armathwaite	d														06 34							
15½	—	—	Lazonby & Kirkoswald	d														06 41							
19¾	—	—	Langwathby	d														06 47							
30¾	—	—	Appleby	d														07 02							
41½	—	—	Kirkby Stephen	d														07a17							
51¼	—	—	Garsdale	d																					
54¾	—	—	Dent	d																					
60¾	—	—	Ribblehead	d													07 14								
65½	—	—	Horton-in-Ribblesdale	d													07 21								
71¾	—	—	Settle	d													07 29								
—	0	—	**Morecambe**	98 d																		06 19			
—	1¾	—	Bare Lane	98 d																		06 23			
—	4¼	—	**Lancaster 6**	65, 83, 98 d																		07 10			
—	11½	—	Carnforth	83 d																		07 20			
—	21	—	Wennington	d																		07 34			
—	24¼	—	Bentham	d																		07 39			
—	27½	—	Clapham (Nth Yorkshire)	d																		07 46			
—	34¼	—	Giggleswick	d																		07 54			
75½	38	—	Long Preston	d													07 34					08 02			
76¾	39¼	—	Hellifield	d													07 37					08 06			
83	45½	—	Gargrave	d													07 46					08 14			
86¾	49¼	—	**Skipton**	a													07 54					08 23			
—	—	—		d	05 48	06 02	06 18	06 27	06 42	06 55	07 01		07 08	07 24	07 32	07 47	07 56		08 01		08 15	08 27	08 32	08 43	09 02
89¾	52¼	—	Cononley	d	05 52	06 06	06 22	06 31	06 46		07 05		07 12	07 28	07 36	07 51			08 05		08 19		08 36	08 47	09 06
93	55½	—	Steeton & Silsden	d	05 56	06 10	06 26	06 35	06 51		07 10		07 17	07 33	07 41	07 56	08 04		08 10		08 24		08 40	08 51	09 10
96	58½	—	Keighley	d	06 01	06 15	06 31	06 40	06 56	07u05	07 15		07 21	07 37	07 45	08 00	08 09		08 14		08 28	08 37	08 45	08 56	09 15
98½	61	—	Crossflatts	d	06 04	06 18	06 34	06 43	07 00		07 19		07 26	07 41	07 49	08 04			08 18		08 32		08 48	08 59	09 18
99¼	61¾	—	Bingley	d	06 07	06 21	06 37	06 46	07 02		07 22		07 28	07 44	07 52	08 07	08 14		08 21		08 35	08 42	08 51	09 02	09 21
101½	64	—	Saltaire	d	06 10	06 24	06 40	06 49	07 06		07 25		07 32	07 48	07 56	08 11			08 25		08 39		08 54	09 05	09 24
102¼	64¾	0	Shipley	a	06 12	06 27	06 42	06 53	07 08		07 28		07 34	07 50	07 58	08 13	08 18		08 27		08 41	08 46	08 58	09 07	09 27
—	—	—		37 d	06 13	06 28	06 44	06 53	07 09	07u14	07 28		07 35	07 50	08 00	08 13	08 19		08 28		08 41	08 47	08 58	09 08	09 28
—	—	1	Frizinghall	37 a		06 32		06 57	07 17		07 32		07 49		08 03		08 25		08 31		08 50	08 54	09 02	09 21	09 32
—	—	2¾	**Bradford Forster Square**	37 a		06 38		07 03	07 22		07 39		07 56		08 09		08 31		08 38		08 56	09 00	09 09	09 27	09 38
113	75½	—	**Leeds 10**	37 a	06 27	06b52	06 58	07b16	07 23	07 29			07 49	08 05	08b24	08 27	08 37		08b49		08 56	09 04		09 23	09b53
—	—	—	London Kings Cross 15	⊖ 26 a	08 46	09b07	09 26			09 51			10 25			10 59	11 34							12 03	

Station		NT	NT	NT	NT		NT	NT	NT	NT	NT	NT	NT		NT	NT	NT	NT	NT	NT	NT		NT	NT	NT
Glasgow Central 15	65 d									07 10							08c40								
Carlisle 8	65 d									08 53															
Armathwaite	d									09 07															
Lazonby & Kirkoswald	d									09 14															
Langwathby	d									09 20															
Appleby	d									09 35															
Kirkby Stephen	d									09 48															
Garsdale	d									10 02															
Dent	d									10 07															
Ribblehead	d									10 17															
Horton-in-Ribblesdale	d									10 24															
Settle	d									10 32															
Morecambe	98 d																10 41								
Bare Lane	98 d																10 45								
Lancaster 6	65, 83, 98 d																11 00								
Carnforth	83 d																11 10								
Wennington	d																11 24								
Bentham	d																11 30								
Clapham (Nth Yorkshire)	d																11 37								
Giggleswick	d																11 45								
Long Preston	d																11 53								
Hellifield	d									10 39							11 57								
Gargrave	d																12 05								
Skipton	a									10 54							12 14								
	d	09 18	09 32	09 48	10 02		10 18	10 32	10 48	10 59	11 02	11 18	11 33		11 48	12 02	12 14	12 18	12 32	12 48	13 02		13 18	13 32	13 48
Cononley	d	09 22	09 36	09 52	10 06		10 22	10 36	10 52		11 06	11 22	11 37		11 52	12 06		12 22	12 36	12 52	13 06		13 22	13 36	13 52
Steeton & Silsden	d	09 26	09 40	09 56	10 10		10 26	10 40	10 56		11 10	11 26	11 41		11 56	12 10		12 26	12 40	12 56	13 10		13 26	13 40	13 56
Keighley	d	09 31	09 45	10 01	10 15		10 31	10 45	11 01	11 09	11 15	11 31	11 46		12 01	12 15	12 24	12 31	12 45	13 01	13 15		13 31	13 45	14 01
Crossflatts	d	09 34	09 48	10 04	10 18		10 34	10 48	11 04		11 18	11 34	11 49		12 04	12 18		12 34	12 48	13 04	13 18		13 34	13 48	14 04
Bingley	d	09 37	09 51	10 07	10 21		10 37	10 51	11 07	11 13	11 21	11 37	11 52		12 07	12 21		12 37	12 51	13 07	13 21		13 37	13 51	14 07
Saltaire	d	09 40	09 54	10 10	10 24		10 40	10 54	11 10		11 24	11 40	11 55		12 10	12 24		12 40	12 54	13 10	13 24		13 40	13 54	14 10
Shipley	a	09 42	09 58	10 12	10 27		10 42	10 57	11 12	11 18	11 28	11 42	11 58		12 14	12 27	12 32	12 42	12 57	13 12	13 27		13 42	13 57	14 12
	37 d	09 44	09 58	10 14	10 28		10 44	10 58	11 14	11 18	11 28	11 44	11 58		12 14	12 28	12 32	12 44	12 58	13 14	13 28		13 44	13 58	14 14
Frizinghall	37 a	09 54	10 02	10 24	10 32		10 54	11 02	11 24		11 32	11 54	12 02		12 24	12 32	12 47	12 54	13 02	13 24	13 32		13 54	14 02	14 24
Bradford Forster Square	37 a	10 00	10 08	10 30	10 38		11 00	11 08	11 30		11 38	12 00	12 10		12 30	12 38	12 53	13 00	13 08	13 30	13 38		14 00	14 08	14 30
Leeds 10	37 a	09 59	10b24	10 28	10b53		10 58	11b24	11 28	11 36	11b55	11 58	12b24		12 29		12 54	12 58	13b24	13 28	13b54		13 58	14b24	14 28
London Kings Cross 15	⊖ 26 a			13 10					14 02	14 20					15 05		15 40			15 58					17 04

For general notes see front of timetable
For details of catering facilities see Directory of Train Operators

b Change at Shipley
c Change at Lancaster

Table 36

Mondays to Fridays

Carlisle, Morecambe, Lancaster and Skipton → Bradford and Leeds

Network Diagram - see first page of Table 35

		NT	NT	NT	NT	NT	NT	NT A	NT	NT	NT	NT	NT	NT	NT	NT	NT	NT	NT	NT	NT	NT
Glasgow Central 15	65 d	*10 10*						*10b40*					*12 40*				*13 40*					
Carlisle 8	65 d	11 51											14 00				15 03					
Armathwaite	d	12 05											14 14									
Lazonby & Kirkoswald	d	12 12											14 21									
Langwathby	d	12 18											14 27									
Appleby	d	12 33											14 43				15 40					
Kirkby Stephen	d	12 46											14 56				15 53					
Garsdale	d	12 59											15 09									
Dent	d	13 04											15 14									
Ribblehead	d	13 14											15 23									
Horton-in-Ribblesdale	d	13 20											15 30									
Settle	d	13 28											15 39				16 35					
Morecambe	98 d							13 29													16 19	
Bare Lane	98 d							13 36													16 23	
Lancaster 6	65, 83, 98 d							13 48														
Carnforth	83 d							13 58													16 32	
Wennington	d							14 12													16 46	
Bentham	d							14 18													16 52	
Clapham (Nth Yorkshire)	d							14 25													16 59	
Giggleswick	d							14 33													17 10	
Long Preston	d	13 34						14 40													17 18	
Hellifield	d	13 37						14 44					15 48								17 22	
Gargrave	d	13 45						14 52													17 30	
Skipton	a	13 55						15 03					16 05				16 55				17 39	
	d	13 58	14 02	14 18	14 32	14 48	15 00	15 10	15 18	15 32	15 48	16 02	16 12	16 18	16 36	16 49	16 58	17 02	17 19	17 28	17 40	17 49
Cononley	d		14 06	14 22	14 36	14 52	15 04		15 22	15 36	15 52	16 06		16 22	16 40	16 53		17 06	17 23	17 32		17 53
Steeton & Silsden	d		14 10	14 27	14 40	14 56	15 08		15 26	15 40	15 56	16 10		16 26	16 44	16 57		17 10	17 27	17 36		17 57
Keighley	d	14 09	14 15	14 31	14 45	15 01	15 13	15 20	15 31	15 45	16 01	16 15	16 22	16 31	16 49	17 02	17 08	17 15	17 32	17 41	17 50	18 02
Crossflatts	d		14 18	14 35	14 48	15 04	15 16		15 34	15 48	16 04	16 18		16 34	16 52	17 05		17 18	17 35	17 44		18 05
Bingley	d	14 13	14 21	14 38	14 51	15 07	15 19	15 25	15 37	15 51	16 07	16 21	16 26	16 37	16 55	17 08	17 15	17 21	17 38	17 47		18 08
Saltaire	d		14 24	14 42	14 54	15 10	15 22		15 40	15 54	16 10	16 24		16 40	16 58	17 11		17 24	17 41	17 50		18 11
Shipley	a	14 18	14 28	14 44	14 57	15 12	15 25	15 30	15 42	15 57	16 12	16 27	16 31	16 42	17 02	17 13	17 20	17 28	17 43	17 53	17 58	18 13
	37 d	14 18	14 28	14 45	14 58	15 14	15 28	15 30	15 44	15 58	16 14	16 28	16 31	16 44	17 02	17 15	17 20	17 28	17 45	17 56	17 58	18 14
Frizinghall	37 a		14 32	*14 54*	15 02	*15 24*	15 32	*15 47*	*15 55*	16 02	*16 24*	16 31	*16 47*	*16 52*	17 06	*17 24*		17 32	*17 52*	17 59	*18 17*	*18 24*
Bradford Forster Square	37 a		14 38	*15 00*	15 08	*15 30*	15 38	*15 53*	*16 01*	16 08	*16 30*	16 36	*16 53*	*16 58*	17 12	*17 30*		17 38	*17 58*	18 05	*18 23*	*18 31*
Leeds 10	37 a	14 37	*14c53*	15 01	*15c24*	15 28		15 47	15 58	*16c24*	16 28	*16c53*	16 51	16 58	*17c24*	17 29	17 40	*17c55*	18 00		18 15	18 29
London Kings Cross 15	⊖ 26 a			*18e12*				*18 24*			*18 54*		*19 29*			*19 59*	*20 21*					*21 03*

		NT	NT	NT	NT	NT	NT	NT	NT	NT	NT	NT	NT	NT	NT	NT	NT	NT	NT	NT	NT
Glasgow Central 15	65 d			*14 40*								*16 40*									
Carlisle 8	65 d			16 18								18 07									
Armathwaite	d			16 32								18 21									
Lazonby & Kirkoswald	d			16 39								18 28									
Langwathby	d			16 45								18 34									
Appleby	d			17 01								18 49									
Kirkby Stephen	d			17 14								19 02									
Garsdale	d			17 27								19 15									
Dent	d			17 32								19 20									
Ribblehead	d			17 42								19 30						21 00			
Horton-in-Ribblesdale	d			17 48								19 36						21 06			
Settle	d			17 57								19 44						21 14			
Morecambe	98 d													19 08							
Bare Lane	98 d													19 12							
Lancaster 6	65, 83, 98 d													19 24							
Carnforth	83 d													19 34							
Wennington	d													19 48							
Bentham	d													19 54							
Clapham (Nth Yorkshire)	d													20 01							
Giggleswick	d													20 09							
Long Preston	d			18 03										20 17				21 20			
Hellifield	d			18 06								19 52		20 21				21 23			
Gargrave	d			18 14										20 29				21 31			
Skipton	a			18 23								20 07		20 38				21 40			
	d	18 02	18 16	18 28	18 32	18 48	19 00	19 18	19 32	19 48	19 54	20 07	20 18	20 42	20 48	20 54	21 18		21 48	21 54	22 18
Cononley	d	18 06	18 20		18 36	18 52	19 04	19 22	19 36	19 52	19 58		20 22		20 52	20 58	21 22		21 52	21 58	22 22
Steeton & Silsden	d	18 10	18 25		18 40	18 56	19 08	19 26	19 40	19 56	20 02		20 26		20 56	21 02	21 26		21 56	22 02	22 26
Keighley	d	18 15	18 29	18 38	18 45	19 01	19 13	19 31	19 45	20 01	20 07	20 17	20 31	20 52	21 01	21 07	21 31		22 01	22 07	22 31
Crossflatts	d	18 18	18 33		18 48	19 04	19 16	19 34	19 48	20 04	20 10		20 34		21 04	21 10	21 34		22 04	22 10	22 34
Bingley	d	18 21	18 35	18 42	18 51	19 07	19 19	19 37	19 51	20 07	20 13	20 22	20 37		21 07	21 13	21 37		22 07	22 13	22 37
Saltaire	d	18 24	18 39		18 54	19 10	19 22	19 40	19 54	20 10	20 16		20 40		21 10	21 16	21 40		22 10	22 16	22 40
Shipley	a	18 28	18 42	18 48	18 58	19 12	19 25	19 42	19 57	20 12	20 19	20 27	20 42	20 59	21 12	21 19	21 42		22 13	22 19	22 42
	37 d	18 28	18 44	18 48	18 58	19 14	19 26	19 44	19 58	20 14	20 20	20 28	20 43	20 59	21 14	21 19	21 43		22 14	22 19	22 43
Frizinghall	37 a	18 32	*18 54*		19 02	*19 24*	19 29		20 01		20 24		*20 51*			21 23	*21 51*			22 23	*22 51*
Bradford Forster Square	37 a	18 38	*19 01*		19 08	*19 30*	19 35		20 08		20 32		*20 57*			21 29	*21 57*			22 31	*22 57*
Leeds 10	37 a	*18c48*	18 59	19 07	*19c26*	19 29	*19c55*	19 59		20 28		20 44	21 00	21 17	21 30		21 59		22 32		23 01
London Kings Cross 15	⊖ 26 a					*22 04*				*23 32*											

For general notes see front of timetable
For details of catering facilities see Directory of Train Operators

A From Heysham Port (Table 98)
b Change at Lancaster
c Change at Shipley
e Change at Leeds and Doncaster

Table 36

Saturdays

Carlisle, Morecambe, Lancaster and Skipton → Bradford and Leeds

Network Diagram - see first page of Table 35

		NT	NT	NT	GR R 1	NT	NT	NT	NT	NT	NT	NT	NT	NT	NT	NT	NT	NT	NT	NT	NT
Glasgow Central 15	65 d																05 50		06 30		
Carlisle 8	65 d																		07 52		
Armathwaite	d																		08 06		
Lazonby & Kirkoswald	d																		08 13		
Langwathby	d																		08 19		
Appleby	d																		08 34		
Kirkby Stephen	d																		08 47		
Garsdale	d																		09 00		
Dent	d																		09 05		
Ribblehead	d								07 14										09 15		
Horton-in-Ribblesdale	d								07 21										09 21		
Settle	d								07 29										09 29		
Morecambe	98 d																07 38				
Bare Lane	98 d																07 42				
Lancaster 6	65, 83, 98 d																08 24				
Carnforth	83 d																08 34				
Wennington	d																08 48				
Bentham	d																08 53				
Clapham (Nth Yorkshire)	d																09 00				
Giggleswick	d																09 08				
Long Preston	d								07 34								09 16				
Hellifield	d								07 37								09 20		09 37		
Gargrave	d								07 46								09 28				
Skipton	a								07 54								09 37		09 53		
	d	05 48	06 02	06 47	06 55	07 01	07 32	07 47	07 56	08 01	08 18	08 32	08 48	09 02	09 18	09 32	09 42	09 48	09 57	10 02	10 18
Cononley	d	05 52	06 06	06 51		07 05	07 36	07 51		08 05	08 22	08 36	08 52	09 06	09 22	09 36		09 52		10 06	10 22
Steeton & Silsden	d	05 56	06 10	06 56		07 10	07 41	07 56	08 04	08 10	08 27	08 40	08 56	09 10	09 26	09 40		09 56		10 10	10 26
Keighley	d	06 01	06 15	07 00	07u07	07 15	07 45	08 00	08 09	08 14	08 31	08 45	09 01	09 15	09 31	09 45	09 52	10 01	10 08	10 15	10 31
Crossflatts	d	06 04	06 18	07 04		07 19	07 49	08 04		08 18	08 35	08 48	09 04	09 18	09 34	09 48		10 04		10 18	10 34
Bingley	d	06 07	06 21	07 07		07 22	07 52	08 07	08 14	08 21	08 38	08 51	09 07	09 21	09 37	09 51	09 58	10 07	10 12	10 21	10 37
Saltaire	d	06 10	06 24	07 10		07 25	07 56	08 11		08 25	08 42	08 54	09 10	09 24	09 40	09 54		10 10		10 24	10 40
Shipley	a	06 12	06 27	07 13		07 28	07 58	08 13	08 18	08 27	08 44	08 57	09 12	09 27	09 42	09 58	10 02	10 12	10 18	10 27	10 42
	37 d	06 13	06 28	07 13	07u18	07 28	08 00	08 13	08 19	08 28	08 44	08 58	09 14	09 28	09 44	09 58	10 02	10 14	10 19	10 28	10 44
Frizinghall	37 a		06 32	07 24		07 32	08 03		08 25	08 31	08 54	09 02	09 24	09 32	09 54	10 02	10 17	10 24		10 32	10 54
Bradford Forster Square	37 a		06 38	07 30		07 39	08 09		08 31	08 38	09 00	09 09	09 31	09 38	10 00	10 08	10 23	10 30		10 38	11 00
Leeds 10	37 a	06 27	07b23	07 27	07 33	07b53	08b24	08 27	08 37	08b53	08 58	09b26	09 28	09b53	09 59		10 22	10 27	10 34	10b53	10 58
London Kings Cross 15	⊖ 26 a	09 18			10 00	10b20			11 33		12c14		12 24		13c10				13 33		13c59

		NT	NT	NT	NT	NT	NT	NT	NT	NT	NT	NT	NT	NT	NT	NT	NT	NT	NT	NT
Glasgow Central 15	65 d					08 00				08e40								10 10		
Carlisle 8	65 d					09 26												11 51		
Armathwaite	d					09 40												12 05		
Lazonby & Kirkoswald	d					09 47												12 12		
Langwathby	d					09 53												12 18		
Appleby	d					10 08												12 33		
Kirkby Stephen	d					10 21												12 46		
Garsdale	d					10 35												12 59		
Dent	d					10 40												13 04		
Ribblehead	d					10 49												13 14		
Horton-in-Ribblesdale	d					10 56												13 20		
Settle	d					11 04												13 28		
Morecambe	98 d									10 41										
Bare Lane	98 d									10 45										
Lancaster 6	65, 83, 98 d									11 00										
Carnforth	83 d									11 10										
Wennington	d									11 24										
Bentham	d									11 30										
Clapham (Nth Yorkshire)	d									11 37										
Giggleswick	d									11 45										
Long Preston	d									11 53								13 34		
Hellifield	d					11 11				11 57								13 37		
Gargrave	d									12 05								13 45		
Skipton	a					11 26				12 14								13 55		
	d	10 32	10 48	11 02	11 18	11 28	11 33	11 48	12 02	12 14	12 18	12 32	12 48	13 02	13 18	13 32	13 48	13 58	14 02	14 18
Cononley	d	10 36	10 52	11 06	11 22		11 37	11 52	12 06		12 22	12 36	12 52	13 06	13 22	13 36	13 52		14 06	14 22
Steeton & Silsden	d	10 40	10 56	11 10	11 26		11 41	11 56	12 10		12 26	12 40	12 56	13 10	13 26	13 40	13 56		14 10	14 27
Keighley	d	10 45	11 01	11 15	11 31	11 38	11 46	12 01	12 15	12 24	12 31	12 45	13 01	13 15	13 31	13 45	14 01	14 09	14 15	14 31
Crossflatts	d	10 48	11 04	11 18	11 34		11 49	12 04	12 18		12 34	12 48	13 04	13 18	13 34	13 48	14 04		14 18	14 35
Bingley	d	10 51	11 07	11 21	11 37	11 42	11 52	12 07	12 21		12 37	12 51	13 07	13 21	13 37	13 51	14 07	14 13	14 21	14 38
Saltaire	d	10 54	11 10	11 24	11 40		11 55	12 10	12 24		12 40	12 54	13 10	13 24	13 40	13 54	14 10		14 24	14 42
Shipley	a	10 57	11 12	11 27	11 42	11 49	11 58	12 14	12 27	12 32	12 42	12 57	13 12	13 27	13 42	13 57	14 12	14 18	14 28	14 44
	37 d	10 58	11 14	11 28	11 44	11 49	11 58	12 14	12 28	12 32	12 44	12 58	13 14	13 28	13 44	13 58	14 14	14 18	14 28	14 45
Frizinghall	37 a	11 02	11 24	11 32	11 54		12 02	12 24	12 32	12 47	12 54	13 02	13 24	13 32	13 54	14 02	14 24		14 32	14 54
Bradford Forster Square	37 a	11 08	11 30	11 38	12 00		12 10	12 30	12 38	12 53	13 00	13 08	13 30	13 38	14 00	14 08	14 30		14 38	15 00
Leeds 10	37 a	11b24	11 28	11b55	11 58	12 06	12b24	12 29		12 54	12 58	13b24	13 28	13b54	13 58	14b24	14 28	14 37	14b53	14 59
London Kings Cross 15	⊖ 26 a		14 27							15 21			16 34					17 33		18c10

For general notes see front of timetable
For details of catering facilities see Directory of Train Operators

b Change at Shipley
c Change at Leeds and Doncaster
e Change at Lancaster

Table 36

Saturdays

Carlisle, Morecambe, Lancaster and Skipton → Bradford and Leeds

Network Diagram - see first page of Table 35

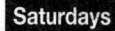

		NT	NT	NT	NT A	NT	NT	NT	NT	NT B	NT	NT C	NT	NT	NT	NT	NT	NT	NT	NT	NT
Glasgow Central [15]	65 d				11b40					12 40		12 40						14 00			
Carlisle [8]	65 d									14 00		14 26						15 49			
Armathwaite	d									14 14		14 40									
Lazonby & Kirkoswald	d									14 21		14 47									
Langwathby	d									14 27		14 53									
Appleby	d									14 43		15 09						16 26			
Kirkby Stephen	d									14 56		15 22						16 39			
Garsdale	d									15 09		15 35									
Dent	d									15 14		15 40									
Ribblehead	d									15 23		15 49									
Horton-in-Ribblesdale	d									15 30		15 56									
Settle	d									15 39		16 04						17 16			
Morecambe	98 d				13 29															16 19	
Bare Lane	98 d				13 36															16 24	
Lancaster [6]	65, 83, 98 d				13 48															16 40	
Carnforth	83 d				13 58															16 50	
Wennington	d				14 12															17 04	
Bentham	d				14 18															17 09	
Clapham (Nth Yorkshire)	d				14 25															17 16	
Giggleswick	d				14 33															17 25	
Long Preston	d				14 43															17 33	
Hellifield	d				14 46					15 49		16 11								17 36	
Gargrave	d				14 55															17 44	
Skipton	a				15 03					16 05		16 26						17 38		17 54	
	d	14 32	14 48	15 00	15 10	15 18	15 32	15 48	16 02		16 18	16 28	16 33	16 49	17 02	17 19	17 30	17 41	17 49	17 58	18 02
Cononley	d	14 36	14 52	15 04		15 22	15 36	15 52	16 06		16 22		16 37	16 53	17 06	17 23	17 34		17 53		18 06
Steeton & Silsden	d	14 40	14 56	15 08		15 26	15 40	15 56	16 10		16 26		16 41	16 57	17 10	17 27	17 38		17 57		18 10
Keighley	d	14 45	15 01	15 13	15 21	15 31	15 45	16 01	16 15		16 31	16 38	16 46	17 02	17 15	17 32	17 43	17 51	18 02	18 08	18 15
Crossflatts	d	14 48	15 04	15 16		15 34	15 48	16 04	16 18		16 34		16 49	17 05	17 18	17 35	17 46		18 05		18 18
Bingley	d	14 51	15 07	15 19	15 26	15 37	15 51	16 07	16 21		16 37	16 42	16 52	17 08	17 21	17 38	17 49	17 55	18 08	18 14	18 21
Saltaire	d	14 54	15 10	15 22		15 40	15 54	16 10	16 24		16 40		16 55	17 11	17 24	17 41	17 52		18 11		18 24
Shipley	a	14 58	15 12	15 26	15 31	15 43	15 57	16 12	16 27		16 42	16 49	16 59	17 13	17 27	17 43	17 55	18 00	18 13	18 19	18 28
	37 d	14 58	15 14	15 28	15 31	15 44	15 58	16 14	16 28		16 44	16 49	16 59	17 15	17 28	17 45	17 56	18 00	18 14	18 19	18 28
Frizinghall	37 a	15 02	15 24	15 32	15 47	15 55	16 02	16 24	16 32		16 52		17 03	17 24	17 32	17 54	18 00	18 17	18 24		18 32
Bradford Forster Square	37 a	15 08	15 30	15 38	15 53	16 01	16 08	16 30	16 38		16 59		17 08	17 30	17 38	18 00	18 08	18 23	18 31		18 38
Leeds [10]	37 a	15c24	15 28		15 47	15 58	16c24	16 28	16c53		16 58	17 07	17c24	17 29	17c55	18 00		18 17	18 29	18 39	18c52
London Kings Cross [15]	⊖ 26 a				18 28	19e40								20 12					21 15		

		NT	NT	NT	NT	NT	NT	NT	NT	NT	NT	NT	NT	NT	NT	NT	NT	NT	NT	NT
Glasgow Central [15]	65 d		14 40								16 40									
Carlisle [8]	65 d		16 18								18 00									
Armathwaite	d		16 32								18 14									
Lazonby & Kirkoswald	d		16 39								18 21									
Langwathby	d		16 45								18 28									
Appleby	d		17 01								18 42									
Kirkby Stephen	d		17 14								18 56									
Garsdale	d		17 27								19 09									
Dent	d		17 32								19 15									
Ribblehead	d		17 42								19 24						21 00			
Horton-in-Ribblesdale	d		17 48								19 31						21 06			
Settle	d		17 57								19 39						21 14			
Morecambe	98 d												19 09							
Bare Lane	98 d												19 13							
Lancaster [6]	65, 83, 98 d												19 24							
Carnforth	83 d												19 35							
Wennington	d												19 49							
Bentham	d												19 54							
Clapham (Nth Yorkshire)	d												20 01							
Giggleswick	d												20 10							
Long Preston	d		18 03										20 18				21 20			
Hellifield	d		18 06								19 47		20 21				21 23			
Gargrave	d		18 14										20 29				21 31			
Skipton	a		18 23								20 02		20 38				21 40			
	d	18 16	18 28	18 32	18 48	19 00	19 18	19 32	19 48	19 54	20 07	20 18	20 38	20 48	20 54	21 18		21 48	21 54	22 18
Cononley	d	18 20		18 36	18 52	19 04	19 22	19 36	19 52	19 58		20 22		20 52	20 58	21 22		21 52	21 58	22 22
Steeton & Silsden	d	18 25		18 40	18 56	19 08	19 26	19 40	19 56	20 02		20 26		20 56	21 02	21 26		21 56	22 02	22 26
Keighley	d	18 29	18 38	18 45	19 01	19 13	19 31	19 45	20 01	20 07	20 17	20 31	20 48	21 01	21 07	21 31		22 01	22 07	22 31
Crossflatts	d	18 33		18 48	19 04	19 16	19 34	19 48	20 04	20 10		20 33		21 04	21 10	21 34		22 04	22 10	22 34
Bingley	d	18 35	18 42	18 51	19 07	19 19	19 37	19 51	20 07	20 13	20 22	20 37	20 53	21 07	21 13	21 37		22 07	22 13	22 37
Saltaire	d	18 39		18 54	19 10	19 22	19 40	19 54	20 10	20 16		20 39		21 10	21 16	21 40		22 10	22 16	22 40
Shipley	a	18 42	18 48	18 58	19 12	19 25	19 42	19 57	20 12	20 20	20 27	20 41	20 57	21 12	21 19	21 42		22 12	22 19	22 42
	37 d	18 44	18 48	18 58	19 14	19 26	19 44	19 58	20 14	20 20	20 28	20 43	20 57	21 14	21 19	21 43		22 14	22 19	22 43
Frizinghall	37 a	18 54		19 02	19 24	19 29		20 01		20 24		20 51	21 05		21 23	21 51			22 23	22 51
Bradford Forster Square	37 a	19 01		19 08	19 30	19 35		20 08		20 32		20 57	21 12		21 29	21 57			22 31	22 57
Leeds [10]	37 a	18 59	19 06	19c26	19 29	19c55	19 59		20 28		20 44	21 00	21 16	21 30		21 59		22 32		23 01
London Kings Cross [15]	⊖ 26 a		22e17				22 47													

For general notes see front of timetable
For details of catering facilities see Directory of Train Operators

A From Heysham Port (Table 98)
B From 7 November
C Until 31 October

b Change at Lancaster. From 7 November dep. 1040
c Change at Shipley
e Change at Leeds and Doncaster

Table 36

Sundays

Carlisle, Morecambe, Lancaster and Skipton → Bradford and Leeds

Network Diagram - see first page of Table 35

	NT	NT	NT	NT	NT	NT A	NT	NT	NT B [bus]	NT B [bus]	NT B	NT	NT	NT C	NT	NT	NT	NT A	NT D	NT	NT
Glasgow Central 15 65 d																		11 51			
Carlisle 8 65 d						09 25			10 00	10 15								13 51			
Armathwaite d						09 39			10 25									14 05			
Lazonby & Kirkoswald d						09 46			10 40									14 12			
Langwathby d						09 53			10 50									14 19			
Appleby d						10 07			11 15	11 15	11 24							14 33			
Kirkby Stephen d						10 21					11 37							14 47			
Garsdale d						10 34					11 51							15 00			
Dent d						10 40					11 56							15 06			
Ribblehead d						10 49					12 06							15 15			
Horton-in-Ribblesdale d						10 56					12 13							15 22			
Settle d						11 04					12 21							15 30			
Morecambe 98 d														12 20					14 46		
Bare Lane 98 d														12 24					14 50		
Lancaster 6 65, 83, 98 d														12 48							
Carnforth 83 d														12 58					15 00		
Wennington d														13 12					15 14		
Bentham d														13 17					15 20		
Clapham (Nth Yorkshire) d														13 24					15 26		
Giggleswick d														13 32					15 35		
Long Preston d						11 10					12 27			13 40				15 36	15 45		
Hellifield d						11 13					12 30			13 44				15 39	15 48		
Clitheroe 94 a																					
Blackburn 94, 97 a																					
Preston 8 97 a																					
Blackpool North 97 a																					
Gargrave d						11 21					12 38			13 52				15 47	15 57		
Skipton a						11 30					12 46			14 01				15 55	16 05		
Skipton d	08 35	09 15	09 36	10 15	11 15	11 30	11 37	12 15			12 54	13 15	13 37	14 02	14 15	15 15	15 37	15 57	16 08	16 15	17 15
Cononley d	08 39	09 19	09 40	10 19	11 19		11 41	12 19				13 19	13 41		14 19	15 19	15 41			16 19	17 19
Steeton & Silsden d	08 44	09 23	09 44	10 23	11 23		11 45	12 23				13 23	13 45		14 23	15 23	15 45			16 23	17 23
Keighley d	08 48	09 28	09 49	10 28	11 28	11 40	11 50	12 28			13 04	13 28	13 50	14 12	14 28	15 28	15 50	16 07	16 18	16 28	17 28
Crossflatts d	08 52	09 31	09 52	10 31	11 31		11 53	12 31				13 31	13 53		14 31	15 31	15 53			16 31	17 31
Bingley d	08 54	09 34	09 55	10 34	11 34	11 44	11 56	12 34			13 08	13 34	13 56	14 16	14 34	15 34	15 56	16 11	16 23	16 34	17 34
Saltaire d	08 58	09 37	09 58	10 37	11 37		11 59	12 37				13 37	13 59		14 37	15 37	15 59			16 37	17 37
Shipley a	09 00	09 39	10 01	10 39	11 39	11 49	12 02	12 39			13 13	13 39	14 02	14 21	14 39	15 39	16 02	16 16	16 27	16 39	17 39
Shipley 37 d	09 00	09 40	10 01	10 40	11 40	11 49	12 02	12 40			13 14	13 40	14 02	14 21	14 40	15 40	16 02	16 16	16 29	16 40	17 40
Frizinghall 37 a		09 48	10 05	10 48	11 48		12 06	12 48			13 22	13b48	14 06		14 48	15 48	16 06			16 48	17 51
Bradford Forster Square 37 a		09 54	10 12	10 54	11 54		12 12	12 54			13 28	13b54	14 12		14 54	15 54	16 12			16 55	17 58
Leeds 10 37 a	09 14	09 54	10c22	10 54	11 54	12 06	12c22	12 54			13 34	13 54	14e22	14 39	14 54	15 54	16c22	16 33	16 47	16 54	17 54
London Kings Cross 15 ⊖ 26 a	11 55	12f48		13 50	14f54	15f09		15 55				16f50			17 55	18 55				19 33	21 01

	NT B [bus]	NT B [bus]	NT B	NT	NT	NT E [trolley]	NT A	NT	NT	NT	NT	NT E [trolley]	NT B [bus]	NT B [bus]	NT B	NT	NT	NT	NT	NT
Glasgow Central 15 65 d						13 56	15 06					15 55								
Carlisle 8 65 d	14 40	14 55				15 35	16 37					17 39	17 50	18 05						
Armathwaite d	15 05					15 51	16 51					17 53	18 15							
Lazonby & Kirkoswald d	15 20					15 58	16 58					18 01	18 30							
Langwathby d	15 30					16 05	17 05					18 07	18 40							
Appleby d	15 55	15 55	16 05			16 20	17 20					18 23	19 05	19 05	19 15					
Kirkby Stephen d			16 18			16 34	17 34					18 36			19 28					
Garsdale d			16 32			16 47	17 47					18 50			19 42					
Dent d			16 37			16 53	17 53					18 55			19 47					
Ribblehead d			16 47			17 02	18 02					19 05			19 57					
Horton-in-Ribblesdale d			16 54			17 09	18 09					19 12			20 04					
Settle d			17 02			17 21	18 19					19 20			20 13					
Morecambe 98 d								17 45									20 00			
Bare Lane 98 d								17 49									20 04			
Lancaster 6 65, 83, 98 d								18 04									20 20			
Carnforth 83 d								18 14									20 30			
Wennington d								18 28									20 44			
Bentham d								18 33									20 49			
Clapham (Nth Yorkshire) d								18 40									20 56			
Giggleswick d								18 49									21 05			
Long Preston d			17 07					18 57									21 13			
Hellifield d			17 10			17 30	18 26	19 00				19 30			20 21		21 16			
Clitheroe 94 a						17 55						19 55								
Blackburn 94, 97 a						18 23						20 22								
Preston 8 97 a						18 50						20 47								
Blackpool North 97 a												21 16								
Gargrave d			17 18					19 09									21 24			
Skipton a			17 27				18 41	19 17							20 36		21 33			
Skipton d			17 32	17 37	18 15		18 43	19 18	19 24	19 37	20 15				20 38	21 15	21 33	21 39	22 15	23 15
Cononley d				17 41	18 19				19 28	19 41	20 19					21 19		21 43	22 19	23 19
Steeton & Silsden d				17 45	18 23				19 32	19 45	20 23					21 23		21 47	22 23	23 23
Keighley d			17 42	17 50	18 28		18 53	19 28	19 37	19 50	20 28				20 48	21 28	21 43	21 52	22 28	23 28
Crossflatts d				17 53	18 31				19 40	19 53	20 31					21 31		21 55	22 31	23 31
Bingley d			17 46	17 56	18 34		18 57	19 32	19 43	19 56	20 34				20 53	21 34	21 48	21 58	22 34	23 34
Saltaire d				17 59	18 37				19 46	19 59	20 37					21 37		22 01	22 37	23 37
Shipley a			17 51	18 02	18 39		19 02	19 37	19 48	20 02	20 39				20 57	21 39	21 53	22 04	22 39	23 40
Shipley 37 d			17 51	18 02	18 40		19 03	19 38	19 49	20 02	20 40				20 59	21 40	21 54	22 04	22 40	23 40
Frizinghall 37 a				18 06	18 48			19 48		20 06	20 48				21 17	21g48		22 08	22 48	
Bradford Forster Square 37 a				18 12	18 54			19 54		20 12	20 54				21 23	21g54		22 14	22 54	
Leeds 10 37 a			18 09	18c23	18 54		19 20	19 56	20 03	20c22	20 54				21 17	21 54	22 10		22 54	23 58
London Kings Cross 15 ⊖ 26 a			21 01						22 37											

For general notes see front of timetable
For details of catering facilities see Directory of Train Operators

- **A** Until 1 November
- **B** From 8 November
- **C** Until 13 September
- **D** Until 13 September. From Lancaster (Table 98)
- **E** Until 6 September
- **b** From 8 November arr. Frizinghall 1354, Bradford Forster Square 1400
- **c** Change at Shipley
- **e** Change at Shipley. From 8 November arr. 1425
- **f** Change at Leeds and Doncaster
- **g** From 8 November arr. 1 min. later

Leeds → Shipley and Bradford

Network Diagram - see first page of Table 35

Miles	Miles			NT	NT	NT	NT	NT	NT	NT	NT	NT	NT		NT	NT	NT	NT	NT	NT	NT	NT	NT	NT		NT
0	0	Leeds 10	d	05 08	05 51	05 55	06 03		06 21	06 22		06 37			06 49	06 51	06 56	07 08		07 22		07 25	07 37			07 39
10¾	—	Shipley	a			06 07			06 32						07 01		07 08					07 36				07 50
—	—		d					06 28			06 41		06 53		07 02				07 15		07 28			07 47		07 51
11¾	—	Frizinghall	d					06 32			06 44		06 57		07 04				07 17		07 32			07 49		07 53
—	4	Bramley	d	05 15	05 58					06 29		06 44						07 15		07 29			07 44			
—	5¾	New Pudsey	d	05 20	06 02		06 13			06 34		06 49				07 01		07 20		07 34			07 49			
—	9½	Bradford Interchange	a	05 28	06 13		06 21			06 42		06 57				07 11		07 28		07 43			07 57			
13½	—	Bradford Forster Square	a					06 38			06 50		07 03		07 10				07 22		07 39			07 56		07 59

		NT	NT	NT	NT	NT	NT	NT	NT	NT	NT		NT	NT	NT	NT	NT	NT	NT	NT	NT	NT		NT	NT	NT
Leeds 10	d	07 51		07 51	08 08		08 10		08 19	08 22	08 25		08 37		08 40		08 49	08 51	08 56	09 08		09 10		09 22		09 26
Shipley	a			08 02			08 22		08 31		08 37				08 51		09 01		09 07			09 21				09 37
	d		08 00			08 13	08 23	08 28						08 48	08 52	08 58					09 18	09 22			09 28	
Frizinghall	d		08 03			08 16	08 25	08 31						08 50	08 54	09 02					09 21	09 24			09 32	
Bramley	d				08 15					08 29			08 44							09 15				09 29		
New Pudsey	d	08 01			08 20					08 34			08 49					09 00		09 20				09 34		
Bradford Interchange	a	08 09			08 28					08 42			08 57					09 11		09 28				09 42		
Bradford Forster Square	a		08 09			08 22	08 31	08 38						08 56	09 00	09 09					09 27	09 31			09 38	

		NT	NT	NT	NT	NT	NT	NT	NT	NT		NT	NT	NT	NT	NT	NT	NT	NT	NT	NT		NT	NT	NT	NT
Leeds 10	d	09 37		09 40		09 47	09 51	09 56	10 08			10 10		10 19	10 22	10 26	10 37		10 40		10 49		10 51	10 56	11 08	
Shipley	a			09 51		10 01		10 07				10 21		10 31		10 37			10 51		11 01			11 07		
	d		09 44	09 52	09 58					10 14		10 22	10 28					10 44	10 52	10 58						11 14
Frizinghall	d		09 47	09 54	10 02					10 17		10 24	10 32					10 47	10 54	11 02						11 17
Bramley	d	09 44							10 15						10 29		10 44								11 15	
New Pudsey	d	09 49					10 01		10 20						10 34		10 49						11 01		11 20	
Bradford Interchange	a	09 57					10 09		10 28						10 42		10 57						11 10		11 28	
Bradford Forster Square	a		09 53	10 00	10 08					10 23		10 30	10 38					10 53	11 00	11 08						11 23

		NT	NT	NT	NT	NT	NT	NT	NT		NT	NT	NT	NT	NT	NT	NT	NT	NT	NT		NT	NT	NT	NT	NT
Leeds 10	d	11 10	11 22		11 26	11 37		11 40	11 51			11 56	12 08		12 10	12 22		12 26	12 37			12 40		12 49	12 51	12 56
Shipley	a	11 21			11 39			11 51				12 07			12 21			12 37				12 51		13 01		13 07
	d	11 22		11 28			11 44	11 52			11 58			12 14	12 22		12 28			12 44		12 52	12 58			
Frizinghall	d	11 24		11 32			11 47	11 54			12 02			12 17	12 24		12 32			12 47		12 54	13 02			
Bramley	d		11 29			11 44							12 15			12 29			12 44							
New Pudsey	d		11 34			11 49			12 01				12 20			12 34			12 49						13 01	
Bradford Interchange	a		11 42			11 57			12 11				12 28			12 42			12 57						13 11	
Bradford Forster Square	a	11 30		11 38			11 53	12 00			12 10			12 24	12 30		12 38			12 53		13 00	13 08			

		NT	NT	NT	NT	NT	NT	NT		NT	NT	NT	NT	NT	NT	NT	NT	NT	NT		NT	NT	NT	NT	NT	NT
Leeds 10	d	13 08		13 10	13 22		13 26	13 37			13 40		13 49	13 51	13 56	14 08		14 10	14 22			14 26	14 37		14 40	
Shipley	a			13 21			13 37				13 51		14 03		14 07			14 21				14 37			14 51	
	d		13 14	13 22		13 28				13 44	13 52	13 58					14 14	14 22			14 28			14 44	14 52	14 58
Frizinghall	d		13 17	13 24		13 32				13 47	13 54	14 02					14 17	14 24			14 32			14 47	14 54	15 02
Bramley	d	13 15			13 29			13 44								14 15			14 29				14 44			
New Pudsey	d	13 20			13 34			13 49						14 01		14 20			14 34				14 49			
Bradford Interchange	a	13 28			13 42			13 57						14 11		14 28			14 42				14 57			
Bradford Forster Square	a		13 23	13 30		13 38				13 53	14 00	14 08					14 23	14 30			14 38			14 53	15 00	15 08

		NT	NT	NT	NT	NT	NT		NT	NT	NT	NT	NT	NT	NT	NT	NT	NT		NT	NT	NT	NT	NT	NT	NT
Leeds 10	d	14 49	14 51	14 56	15 08		15 10		15 22		15 26	15 37		15 40	15 51		15 56	16 08			16 10	16 22		16 26		16 35
Shipley	a	15 01		15 07			15 21				15 37			15 52			16 07				16 21			16 37		16 49
	d					15 14	15 22			15 28			15 44	15 52		15 58				16 14	16 22		16 28		16 44	16 49
Frizinghall	d					15 17	15 24			15 32			15 47	15 55		16 02				16 17	16 24		16 31		16 47	16 52
Bramley	d				15 15				15 29			15 44						16 15				16 29				
New Pudsey	d		15 01		15 20				15 34			15 49			16 01			16 20				16 34				
Bradford Interchange	a		15 11		15 28				15 42			15 57			16 10			16 28				16 42				
Bradford Forster Square	a					15 23	15 30			15 38			15 53	16 01		16 08				16 23	16 30		16 36		16 53	16 58

		NT	NT	NT	NT	NT		NT	NT	NT	NT	NT	NT	NT	NT	NT	NT		NT	NT	NT	NT	NT	NT	NT	NT
Leeds 10	d	16 37	16 39	16 51		16 56		17 08		17 10	17 22		17 26		17 36	17 37			17 50	17 51	17 56	18 08		18 10	18 22	
Shipley	a		16 53			17 07				17 21			17 37		17 49				18 02		18 08			18 21		
	d				17 02				17 15	17 22		17 28		17 44	17 50		17 56						18 14	18 22		18 28
Frizinghall	d				17 06				17 17	17 24		17 32		17 46	17 52		17 59						18 17	18 24		18 32
Bramley	d	16 44						17 15			17 29					17 44						18 15			18 30	
New Pudsey	d	16 49		17 01				17 20			17 34					17 49				18 01		18 20			18 35	
Bradford Interchange	a	16 57		17 10				17 28			17 42					17 57				18 10		18 28			18 43	
Bradford Forster Square	a				17 12				17 23	17 30		17 38		17 53	17 58		18 05						18 23	18 31		18 38

For general notes see front of timetable
For details of catering facilities see Directory of Train Operators

Leeds → Shipley and Bradford

Network Diagram - see first page of Table 35

Mondays to Fridays

		NT	NT	NT	NT		NT	NT	NT	NT	NT	NT	NT	NT	NT	NT		NT	NT	NT	NT	NT	GR	NT	NT	NT
																							R 1 A			
Leeds 10	d	18 26	18 37		18 40			18 50	18 51	19 08		19 10		19 19	19 22	19 25		19 37			19 51	19 56	19 59	20 08		
Shipley	a	18 38			18 52			19 03				19 21		19 31		19 37						20 07	20s11			
	d			18 44	18 52		18 58				19 14	19 22	19 26						19 44	19 58					20 20	20 28
Frizinghall	d			18 46	18 55		19 02				19 17	19 24	19 29						19 47	20 01					20 24	20 30
Bramley	d		18 44							19 15					19 30			19 44						20 15		
New Pudsey	d		18 49						19 01	19 20					19 35			19 49			20 01			20 20		
Bradford Interchange	a		18 57						19 10	19 28					19 44			19 57			20 10			20 28		
Bradford Forster Square	a			18 52	19 01		19 08				19 23	19 30	19 35						19 53	20 08			20 22		20 32	20 36

		NT	NT	NT		NT	NT	NT	NT	NT	NT	NT	NT	NT	NT		NT	NT	NT	NT	NT	NT	NT	NT		
Leeds 10	d	20 26	20 37				20 55	21 08		21 26	21 37			21 56	22 08			22 26	22 37			22 56	23 08	23 18		
Shipley	a	20 37					21 07			21 38				22 07				22 37				23 07		23 31		
	d			20 48		21 03			21 19			21 48	22 03				22 19			22 48	23 03					
Frizinghall	d			20 51		21 05			21 23			21 51	22 05				22 23			22 51	23 05					
Bramley	d		20 44					21 15			21 44				22 15				22 44				23 15			
New Pudsey	d		20 49					21 20			21 49				22 20				22 49				23 20			
Bradford Interchange	a		20 57					21 28			21 57				22 28				22 57				23 29			
Bradford Forster Square	a			20 57		21 12			21 29			21 57	22 11				22 31			22 57	23 13					

Saturdays

		NT	NT	NT	NT	NT	NT	NT	NT		NT	NT	NT	NT	NT	NT	NT	NT		NT	NT	NT	NT	NT	NT	NT
					B											B	C									
Leeds 10	d	05 37	05 51	05 55	06 03	06 16		06 19	06 37			06 51	06 56	07 08	07 10	07 22	07 23			07 37		07 51		07 56	08 08	08 10
Shipley	a			06 07				06 31					07 08		07 21									08 08		08 22
	d						06 28				06 44				07 22			07 28			07 47		08 00			08 23
Frizinghall	d						06 32				06 47				07 24			07 32			07 49		08 03			08 25
Bramley	d	05 44	05 58			06 23			06 44					07 15		07 29	07 30			07 44					08 15	
New Pudsey	d	05 49	06 02		06 13	06 28			06 49			07 01		07 20		07 34	07 35			07 49		08 01			08 20	
Bradford Interchange	a	05b59	06 13		06 21	06b38			06b59			07b13		07 28		07 43	07 45			07b59		08 12			08b30	
Bradford Forster Square	a						06 38				06 55				07 30			07 39			07 56		08 09			08 31

		NT	NT	NT		NT	NT	NT	NT	NT	NT	NT	NT		NT	NT	NT	NT	NT	NT	NT	NT		NT	NT	NT
Leeds 10	d		08 19	08 22		08 25	08 37		08 40		08 49	08 51	08 56		09 08		09 10	09 22		09 26	09 37			09 40		09 47
Shipley	a		08 31			08 37			08 51		09 01		09 07				09 21			09 37				09 51		10 01
	d	08 28						08 44	08 52	08 58						09 14	09 22		09 28			09 44		09 52	09 58	
Frizinghall	d	08 31						08 46	08 54	09 02						09 17	09 24		09 32			09 47		09 54	10 02	
Bramley	d			08 29			08 44								09 15			09 29			09 44					
New Pudsey	d			08 34			08 49					09 00			09 20			09 34			09 49					
Bradford Interchange	a			08b44			08 57					09 12			09 28			09 42			09 57					
Bradford Forster Square	a	08 38						08 53	09 00	09 09						09 24	09 31		09 38			09 53		10 00	10 08	

		NT	NT	NT	NT	NT	NT	NT		NT	NT	NT	NT	NT	NT	NT	NT		NT	NT	NT	NT	NT	NT	NT	NT
Leeds 10	d	09 51	09 56	10 08		10 10		10 19		10 22	10 26	10 37		10 40		10 49	10 51		10 56	11 08		11 10	11 22		11 26	11 37
Shipley	a		10 07			10 21		10 31			10 37			10 51		11 01			11 07			11 21			11 39	
	d				10 14	10 22	10 28						10 44	10 52	10 58						11 14	11 22		11 28		
Frizinghall	d				10 17	10 24	10 32						10 47	10 54	11 02						11 17	11 24		11 32		
Bramley	d			10 15						10 29		10 44								11 15			11 29			11 44
New Pudsey	d	10 01		10 20						10 34		10 49					11 01			11 20			11 34			11 49
Bradford Interchange	a	10b12		10 28						10 42		10 57					11b12			11 28			11 42			11 57
Bradford Forster Square	a				10 23	10 30	10 38						10 53	11 00	11 08						11 23	11 30		11 38		

		NT	NT		NT	NT	NT	NT	NT	NT	NT	NT		NT	NT	NT	NT	NT	NT	NT	NT		NT	NT	NT	NT
Leeds 10	d		11 40			11 51	11 56	12 08		12 10	12 22			12 26	12 37		12 40		12 49	12 51	12 56		13 08		13 10	13 22
Shipley	a		11 51				12 07			12 21				12 37			12 51		13 01		13 07				13 21	
	d	11 44	11 52		11 58				12 14	12 22		12 28				12 44	12 52	12 58						13 14	13 22	
Frizinghall	d	11 47	11 54		12 02				12 17	12 24		12 32				12 47	12 54	13 02						13 17	13 24	
Bramley	d							12 15			12 29				12 44								13 15			13 29
New Pudsey	d					12 01		12 20			12 34				12 49					13 01			13 20			13 34
Bradford Interchange	a					12b12		12 28			12 42				12 57					13b12			13 28			13 42
Bradford Forster Square	a	11 53	12 00		12 10				12 24	12 30		12 38				12 53	13 00	13 08						13 23	13 30	

For general notes see front of timetable
For details of catering facilities see
Directory of Train Operators

A From London Kings Cross (Table 26)
B From 18 July
C Until 11 July

b From 18 July arr. 2 mins. earlier

Table 37

Saturdays

Leeds → Shipley and Bradford

Network Diagram - see first page of Table 35

		NT	NT	NT	NT	NT	NT		NT	NT	NT	NT	NT	NT	NT	NT		NT	NT	NT	NT	NT	NT	NT	NT	NT
Leeds 10	d		13 26	13 37		13 40			13 49	13 51	13 56	14 08		14 10	14 22			14 26	14 37		14 40		14 49	14 51	14 56	15 08
Shipley	a		13 37			13 51			14 03		14 07			14 21				14 37			14 51		15 01		15 07	
	d	13 28			13 44	13 52	13 58						14 14	14 22		14 28				14 44	14 52	14 58				
Frizinghall	d	13 32			13 47	13 54	14 02						14 17	14 24		14 32				14 47	14 54	15 02				
Bramley	d			13 44								14 15			14 29				14 44							15 15
New Pudsey	d			13 49						14 01		14 20			14 34				14 49					15 01		15 20
Bradford Interchange	a			13 57						14b12		14 28			14 42				14 57					15b12		15 28
Bradford Forster Square	a	13 38			13 53	14 00	14 08						14 23	14 30		14 38				14 53	15 00	15 08				

		NT		NT	NT	NT	NT	NT	NT	NT	NT		NT	NT	NT	NT	NT	NT	NT	NT		NT	NT	NT	NT	NT
Leeds 10	d			15 10	15 22		15 26	15 37		15 40			15 51	15 56	16 08		16 10	16 22		16 26			16 35	16 37	16 39	16 51
Shipley	a			15 21			15 37			15 52				16 07			16 21			16 37			16 49		16 53	
	d	15 14		15 22		15 28			15 44	15 52	15 58					16 14	16 22		16 28			16 44	16 49			
Frizinghall	d	15 17		15 24		15 32			15 47	15 55	16 02					16 17	16 24		16 32			16 47	16 52			
Bramley	d				15 29			15 44							16 15			16 29						16 44		
New Pudsey	d				15 34			15 49					16 01		16 20			16 34						16 49		17 01
Bradford Interchange	a				15 42			15 57					16b12		16 28			16 42						16 57		17b12
Bradford Forster Square	a	15 23		15 30		15 38			15 53	16 01	16 08					16 23	16 30		16 38			16 53	16 59			

		NT	NT	NT	NT	NT		NT	NT	NT	NT	NT	NT	NT	NT A		NT	NT	NT	NT	NT	NT	NT	NT		NT
Leeds 10	d		16 56	17 08		17 10		17 22		17 26	17 37		17 40		17 50		17 51	17 56	18 08		18 10	18 22		18 26		18 37
Shipley	a		17 07			17 21				17 37			17 51		18 02			18 08			18 21			18 38		
	d	16 59			17 15	17 22			17 28			17 45	17 52	17 56						18 14	18 22		18 28			
Frizinghall	d	17 03			17 17	17 24			17 32			17 47	17 54	18 00						18 17	18 24		18 32			
Bramley	d			17 15				17 29			17 44								18 15			18 30				18 44
New Pudsey	d			17 20				17 34			17 49						18 01		18 20			18 35				18 49
Bradford Interchange	a			17 28				17 42			17 57						18b12		18 28			18 43				18c59
Bradford Forster Square	a	17 08			17 23	17 30			17 38			17 53	18 00	18 08						18 23	18 31		18 38			

		NT	NT	NT	NT	NT	NT	NT	NT		NT	NT	NT	NT	NT	NT	NT	NT		NT	NT	NT	NT	NT	NT	NT
Leeds 10	d		18 40		18 51	18 56	19 08		19 10			19 19	19 22	19 25	19 37			19 51		20 06	20 08			20 26	20 37	
Shipley	a		18 52			19 07			19 21			19 31		19 37						20 18				20 37		
	d	18 44	18 52	18 58				19 14	19 22		19 26					19 44	19 58					20 20	20 28			20 48
Frizinghall	d	18 46	18 55	19 02				19 17	19 24		19 29					19 47	20 01					20 24	20 30			20 51
Bramley	d						19 15						19 30		19 44						20 15				20 44	
New Pudsey	d				19 01		19 20						19 35		19 49			20 01			20 20				20 49	
Bradford Interchange	a				19b12		19b30						19 44		19b59			20b12			20b30				20b59	
Bradford Forster Square	a	18 52	19 01	19 08				19 23	19 30		19 35					19 53	20 08					20 32	20 36			20 57

		GR R 1 B	NT	NT		NT	NT	NT	NT	NT	NT	NT	NT		NT	NT	NT	NT	NT	NT	NT C	NT D		NT		
Leeds 10	d	20 43		20 55		21 08		21 26	21 37			21 56	22 08			22 26	22 37			22 56	23 00	23 08		23 18		
Shipley	a	20s56		21 07				21 38				22 07				22 37				23 07				23 31		
	d		21 03				21 19			21 48	22 03				22 19			22 48	23 03							
Frizinghall	d		21 05				21 23			21 51	22 05				22 23			22 51	23 05							
Bramley	d					21 15			21 44				22 15				22 44				23 07	23 15				
New Pudsey	d					21 20			21 49				22 20				22 49				23 12	23 20				
Bradford Interchange	a					21b30			21b59				22b30				22b59				23 20	23c30				
Bradford Forster Square	a	21 06	21 12				21 29			21 57	22 11				22 31			22 57	23 13							

Sundays

until 12 July

		NT	NT	NT	NT	NT		NT	NT	NT	NT	NT		NT	NT	NT	NT	NT		NT	NT	NT	NT	NT		NT
Leeds 10	d	08 03	08 21	08 34	08 40	08 45		09 00	09 23	09 34	09 54				10 08	10 12	10 34	10 51		10 54	11 08	11 12	11 34	11 54		
Shipley	a			08 45	08 52			09 13		09 45					10 19		10 45	11 03			11 19		11 45			
	d			08 46						09 46		10 01		10 15			10 46						11 46			12 02
Frizinghall	d			08 48						09 48		10 05		10 18			10 48						11 48			12 06
Bramley	d	08 10	08 28			08 52			09 30		10 01					10 19				11 01		11 19		12 01		
New Pudsey	d	08 15	08 33			08 57			09 35		10 06					10 24				11 06		11 24		12 06		
Bradford Interchange	a	08 25	08 43			09 05			09 45		10 16					10 34				11 16		11 34		12 16		
Bradford Forster Square	a			08 54						09 54		10 12		10 24			10 54						11 54			12 12

For general notes see front of timetable
For details of catering facilities see Directory of Train Operators

A Until 31 October
B From London Kings Cross (Table 26)
C From 12 September
D Until 5 September

b From 18 July arr. 2 mins. earlier
c From 18 July arr. 1 min. earlier

Sundays

until 12 July

Leeds → Shipley and Bradford

Network Diagram - see first page of Table 35

		NT	NT	NT	NT	NT		NT	NT	NT	NT	NT		NT	NT	NT	NT	NT		NT	NT	NT	NT	NT		NT
Leeds 10	d		12 08	12 12	12 34	12 54		13 08	13 12	13 15	13 34	13 54				14 08	14 12	14 34		14 54	14 57	15 08	15 12	15 34		15 54
Shipley	a		12 19		12 45			13 19		13 28	13 45					14 19		14 45			15 09	15 19		15 45		
	d	12 15			12 46						13 46			14 02	14 15			14 46						15 46		
Frizinghall	d	12 18			12 48						13 48			14 06	14 18			14 48						15 48		
Bramley	d			12 19		13 01			13 19			14 01					14 19			15 01			15 19			16 01
New Pudsey	d			12 24		13 06			13 24			14 06					14 24			15 06			15 24			16 06
Bradford Interchange	a			12 34		13 16			13 34			14 16					14 34			15 16			15 34			16 16
Bradford Forster Square	a	12 24			12 54						13 54			14 12	14 24			14 54						15 54		

		NT	NT	NT	NT	NT		NT	NT	NT	NT	NT		NT	NT	NT	NT	NT		NT	NT	NT	NT	NT		NT
Leeds 10	d			16 08	16 12	16 35		16 54	17 08	17 12	17 21	17 33		17 37	17 54			18 08		18 12	18 34	18 42	19 03	19 08		19 34
Shipley	a			16 19		16 46			17 19		17 33	17 45		17 49				18 19			18 45			19 19		19 45
	d	16 02	16 15			16 46								17 49		18 02	18 15				18 46					19 46
Frizinghall	d	16 06	16 18			16 48								17 51		18 06	18 18				18 48					19 48
Bramley	d				16 19			17 01		17 19					18 01					18 19			19 10			
New Pudsey	d				16 24			17 06		17 24					18 06					18 24		18 52	19 15			
Bradford Interchange	a				16 34			17 16		17 34					18 16					18 34		19 03	19 25			
Bradford Forster Square	a	16 12	16 24			16 55								17 58		18 12	18 24				18 54					19 54

		NT	NT	NT	NT	NT		NT	NT	NT	NT	NT		NT	NT	NT	NT	NT		NT	NT	NT	NT	NT		
Leeds 10	d	19 42		20 03		20 08		20 12	20 34	20 42	21 04	21 08		21 34	21 35		22 05			22 08	22 34	22 35	23 10	23 22		
Shipley	a					20 19			20 45			21 19		21 45						22 19	22 45		23 21			
	d		20 02		20 15				20 46					21 46		22 04		22 15			22 46					
Frizinghall	d		20 06		20 18				20 48					21 48		22 08		22 18			22 48					
Bramley	d			20 10				20 19			21 12				21 43		22 12					22 43		23 29		
New Pudsey	d	19 51		20 15				20 24		20 51	21 17				21 47		22 17					22 47		23 34		
Bradford Interchange	a	20 03		20 25				20 35		21 03	21 27				21 57		22 27					22 58		23 43		
Bradford Forster Square	a		20 12		20 24				20 54					21 54		22 14		22 24			22 54					

Sundays

19 July to 6 September

		NT	NT	NT	NT	NT	NT	NT	NT	NT	NT	NT	NT	NT		NT	NT	NT	NT	NT	NT	NT	NT	NT	NT	NT
Leeds 10	d	08 02	08 21	08 34	08 40	08 45	09 00	09 02	09 18	09 34	09 35	09 53				10 08	10 12	10 34	10 35	10 51	10 53	11 08	11 12	11 34	11 35	11 53
Shipley	a			08 45	08 52		09 13			09 45						10 19		10 45		11 03		11 19		11 45		
	d			08 46						09 46			10 01	10 15				10 46						11 46		
Frizinghall	d			08 48						09 48			10 05	10 18				10 48						11 48		
Bramley	d	08 10	08 28					09 09	09 25			10 01					10 19				11 01		11 19			12 01
New Pudsey	d	08 15	08 33			08 54		09 14	09 30		09 44	10 06					10 24		10 44		11 06		11 24		11 44	12 06
Bradford Interchange	a	08 23	08 41			09 03		09 22	09 38		09 53	10 14					10 32		10 53		11 14		11 32		11 53	12 14
Bradford Forster Square	a			08 54						09 54			10 12	10 24				10 54						11 54		

		NT	NT	NT	NT		NT	NT	NT	NT	NT	NT	NT	NT	NT	NT	NT	NT	NT		NT	NT	NT	NT	NT	NT
Leeds 10	d			12 08	12 12		12 34	12 35	12 53	13 08	13 12	13 15	13 34	13 35	13 53			14 08	14 12		14 34	14 35	14 53	14 57	15 08	15 12
Shipley	a			12 19			12 45			13 19		13 28	13 45					14 19			14 45			15 09	15 19	
	d	12 02	12 15				12 46						13 46			14 02	14 15				14 46					
Frizinghall	d	12 06	12 18				12 48						13 48			14 06	14 18				14 48					
Bramley	d				12 19				13 01		13 19				14 01				14 19				15 01			15 19
New Pudsey	d				12 24			12 44	13 06		13 24			13 44	14 06				14 24			14 44	15 06			15 24
Bradford Interchange	a				12 32			12 53	13 14		13 32			13 53	14 14				14 32			14 53	15 14			15 32
Bradford Forster Square	a	12 12	12 24				12 54						13 54			14 12	14 24				14 54					

		NT	NT	NT	NT	NT	NT	NT	NT	NT		NT	NT	NT	NT	NT	NT	NT	NT	NT	NT	NT	NT	NT		NT
Leeds 10	d	15 34	15 35	15 53			16 08	16 12	16 35	16 35		16 53	17 08	17 12	17 21	17 33	17 35	17 37	17 53			18 08	18 12	18 34		18 35
Shipley	a	15 45					16 19			16 46			17 19		17 33	17 45		17 49				18 19		18 45		
	d	15 46			16 02	16 15				16 46								17 49		18 02	18 15			18 46		
Frizinghall	d	15 48			16 06	16 18				16 48								17 51		18 06	18 18			18 48		
Bramley	d			16 01				16 19				17 01		17 19					18 01				18 19			
New Pudsey	d		15 44	16 06				16 24	16 44			17 06		17 24			17 44		18 06				18 24			18 44
Bradford Interchange	a		15 53	16 14				16 32	16 53			17 14		17 32			17 53		18 14				18 32			18 53
Bradford Forster Square	a	15 54			16 12	16 24				16 55								17 58		18 12	18 24			18 54		

		NT	NT	NT	NT	NT	NT	NT	NT	NT	NT	NT	NT	NT	NT	NT	NT	NT	NT	NT	NT	NT	NT	NT		
Leeds 10	d	19 02	19 08	19 34	19 35	19 53			20 08	20 12	20 34	20 35	21 04	21 08	21 34	21 35		22 05		22 08	22 34	22 35	23 10	23 22		
Shipley	a		19 19	19 45					20 19		20 45			21 19	21 45					22 19	22 45		23 21			
	d			19 46			20 02	20 15			20 46				21 46		22 04		22 15		22 46					
Frizinghall	d			19 48			20 06	20 18			20 48				21 48		22 08		22 18		22 48					
Bramley	d	19 10				20 01				20 19			21 12			21 43		22 12				22 43		23 29		
New Pudsey	d	19 15			19 44	20 06				20 24		20 44	21 17			21 47		22 17				22 47		23 34		
Bradford Interchange	a	19 23			19 53	20 14				20 33		20 53	21 25			21 56		22 25				22 56		23 43		
Bradford Forster Square	a			19 54			20 12	20 24			20 54				21 54		22 14		22 24		22 54					

For general notes see front of timetable
For details of catering facilities see
Directory of Train Operators

Table 37

Sundays

13 September to 1 November

Leeds → Shipley and Bradford

Network Diagram - see first page of Table 35

		NT	NT	NT	NT A	NT	NT	NT	NT	NT	NT	NT	NT	NT		NT	NT	NT	NT	NT A	NT	NT	NT	NT	NT	NT
Leeds 10	d	08 02	08 21	08 34	08 40	08 45	09 00	09 02	09 23	09 34	09 35	09 53				10 08	10 12	10 34	10 35	10 51	10 53	11 08	11 12	11 34	11 35	11 53
Shipley	a			08 45	08 52		09 13			09 45						10 19		10 45		11 03		11 19		11 45		
	d			08 46						09 46			10 01	10 15				10 46						11 46		
Frizinghall	d			08 48						09 48			10 05	10 18				10 48						11 48		
Bramley	d	08 10	08 28					09 09	09 30			10 01					10 19				11 01		11 19			12 01
New Pudsey	d	08 15	08 33			08 54		09 14	09 35		09 44	10 06					10 24		10 44		11 06		11 24		11 44	12 06
Bradford Interchange	a	08 23	08 41			09 03		09 22	09 43		09 53	10 14					10 32		10 53		11 14		11 32		11 53	12 14
Bradford Forster Square	a			08 54						09 54			10 12	10 24				10 54						11 54		

		NT	NT	NT	NT		NT	NT	NT	NT	NT	NT	NT	NT	NT	NT	NT	NT	NT		NT	NT	NT	NT	NT	NT
Leeds 10	d			12 08	12 12		12 34	12 35	12 53	13 08	13 12	13 15	13 34	13 35	13 53			14 08	14 12		14 34	14 35	14 53	14 57	15 08	15 12
Shipley	a			12 19			12 45			13 19		13 28	13 45					14 19			14 45			15 09	15 19	
	d	12 02	12 15				12 46						13 46			14 02	14 15				14 46					
Frizinghall	d	12 06	12 18				12 48						13 48			14 06	14 18				14 48					
Bramley	d				12 19				13 01		13 19				14 01				14 19				15 01			15 19
New Pudsey	d				12 24			12 44	13 06		13 24			13 44	14 06				14 24			14 44	15 06			15 24
Bradford Interchange	a				12 32			12 53	13 14		13 32			13 53	14 14				14 32			14 53	15 14			15 32
Bradford Forster Square	a	12 12	12 24				12 54						13 54			14 12	14 24				14 54					

		NT	NT	NT	NT	NT	NT	NT	NT	NT		NT	NT	NT	NT	NT	NT	NT	NT	NT	NT	NT	NT	NT		NT
Leeds 10	d	15 34	15 35	15 53			16 08	16 12	16 35	16 35		16 53	17 08	17 12	17 21	17 33	17 35	17 37	17 53			18 08	18 12	18 34		18 35
Shipley	a	15 45					16 19			16 46			17 19		17 33	17 45		17 49				18 19		18 45		
	d	15 46			16 02	16 15				16 46								17 49		18 02	18 15			18 46		
Frizinghall	d	15 48			16 06	16 18				16 48								17 51		18 06	18 18			18 48		
Bramley	d			16 01				16 19				17 01		17 19					18 01				18 19			
New Pudsey	d		15 44	16 06				16 24	16 44			17 06		17 24			17 44		18 06				18 24			18 44
Bradford Interchange	a		15 53	16 14				16 32	16 53			17 14		17 32			17 53		18 14				18 32			18 53
Bradford Forster Square	a	15 54			16 12	16 24				16 55								17 58		18 12	18 24			18 54		

		NT	NT	NT	NT	NT	NT	NT	NT	NT	NT	NT	NT	NT	NT	NT	NT	NT	NT	NT	NT	NT	NT	NT
Leeds 10	d	19 02	19 08	19 34	19 35	19 53			20 08	20 12	20 34	20 35	21 04	21 08	21 34	21 35		22 05		22 08	22 34	22 35	23 10	23 22
Shipley	a		19 19	19 45					20 19		20 45			21 19	21 45					22 19	22 45		23 21	
	d			19 46			20 02	20 15			20 46				21 46		22 04		22 15		22 46			
Frizinghall	d			19 48			20 06	20 18			20 48				21 48		22 08		22 18		22 48			
Bramley	d	19 10				20 01				20 19			21 12			21 43		22 12				22 43		23 29
New Pudsey	d	19 15			19 44	20 06				20 24		20 44	21 17			21 47		22 17				22 47		23 34
Bradford Interchange	a	19 23			19 53	20 14				20 33		20 53	21 25			21 56		22 25				22 56		23 43
Bradford Forster Square	a			19 54			20 12	20 24			20 54				21 54		22 14		22 24		22 54			

Sundays

from 8 November

		NT	NT	NT	NT	NT	NT	NT	NT	NT	NT	NT	NT	NT		NT	NT	NT	NT	NT	NT	NT	NT	NT	NT	NT
Leeds 10	d	08 02	08 21	08 34	08 45	09 00	09 02	09 23	09 34	09 35	09 53			10 08		10 12	10 34	10 35	10 53	11 08	11 12	11 34	11 35	11 53		
Shipley	a			08 45		09 13			09 45					10 19			10 45			11 19		11 45				
	d			08 46					09 46			10 01	10 15				10 46					11 46			12 02	12 15
Frizinghall	d			08 48					09 48			10 05	10 18				10 48					11 48			12 06	12 18
Bramley	d	08 10	08 28				09 09	09 30			10 01					10 19			11 01		11 19			12 01		
New Pudsey	d	08 15	08 33		08 54		09 14	09 35		09 44	10 06					10 24		10 44	11 06		11 24		11 44	12 06		
Bradford Interchange	a	08 23	08 41		09 03		09 22	09 43		09 53	10 14					10 32		10 53	11 14		11 32		11 53	12 14		
Bradford Forster Square	a			08 54					09 54			10 12	10 24				10 54					11 54			12 12	12 24

		NT	NT	NT	NT		NT	NT	NT	NT	NT	NT	NT	NT	NT	NT	NT	NT	NT		NT	NT	NT	NT	NT	NT
Leeds 10	d	12 08	12 12	12 34	12 35		12 53		13 08	13 12	13 35		13 44	13 53			14 08	14 12	14 34		14 35	14 53	14 57	15 08	15 12	15 34
Shipley	a	12 19		12 45					13 19				13 56				14 19		14 45				15 09	15 19		15 45
	d			12 46				13 19				13 52			14 02	14 15			14 46							15 46
Frizinghall	d			12 48				13 22				13 54			14 06	14 18			14 48							15 48
Bramley	d		12 19				13 01			13 19				14 01				14 19				15 01			15 19	
New Pudsey	d		12 24		12 44		13 06			13 24	13 44			14 06				14 24			14 44	15 06			15 24	
Bradford Interchange	a		12 32		12 53		13 14			13 32	13 53			14 14				14 32			14 53	15 14			15 32	
Bradford Forster Square	a			12 54				13 28				14 00			14 12	14 24			14 54							15 54

		NT	NT	NT	NT	NT	NT	NT	NT	NT		NT	NT	NT	NT	NT	NT	NT	NT	NT	NT	NT	NT	NT		NT
Leeds 10	d	15 35	15 53			16 08	16 12	16 35	16 35	16 53		17 02	17 08	17 12	17 21	17 35	17 37	17 53			18 08	18 12	18 34	18 35		19 02
Shipley	a					16 19			16 46			17 14	17 19		17 33		17 49				18 19		18 45			
	d			16 02	16 15				16 46								17 49		18 02	18 15			18 46			
Frizinghall	d			16 06	16 18				16 48								17 51		18 06	18 18			18 48			
Bramley	d		16 01				16 19			17 01				17 19				18 01				18 19				19 10
New Pudsey	d	15 44	16 06				16 24	16 44		17 06				17 24		17 44		18 06				18 24		18 44		19 15
Bradford Interchange	a	15 53	16 14				16 32	16 53		17 14				17 32		17 53		18 14				18 32		18 53		19 23
Bradford Forster Square	a			16 12	16 24				16 55								17 58		18 12	18 24			18 54			

For general notes see front of timetable
For details of catering facilities see
Directory of Train Operators

A 13 September

Sundays

from 8 November

Leeds → Shipley and Bradford

Network Diagram - see first page of Table 35

		NT	NT	NT	NT	NT	NT	NT	NT	NT	NT	NT	NT	NT	NT	NT	NT	NT	NT	NT	NT	NT	NT	NT		
Leeds 10	d	19 08	19 34	19 35	19 53	.....	.....	20 08	20 12	20 34	20 35	21 04	.....	21 08	21 34	21 35	.....	22 05	.....	22 08	22 34	22 35	23 10	23 22	.....	.....
Shipley	a	19 19	19 45	.	.	.	.	20 19	.	20 45	.	.	.	21 19	21 46	.	.	.	.	22 19	22 45	.	23 21	.	.	.
	d	.....	19 46	.....	.....	20 02	20 15	.....	.....	20 46	.....	.....	21 14	.....	21 47	.....	22 04	.....	22 15	.....	22 46	.....	.....	.....	.....	.....
Frizinghall	d	.	19 48	.	.	20 06	20 18	.	.	20 48	.	.	21 17	.	21 49	.	22 08	.	22 18	.	22 48	.	.	.	.	.
Bramley	d	.....	.....	.....	20 01	.....	.....	.....	20 19	.....	.....	21 12	.....	.....	.....	21 43	.....	22 12	.....	.....	.....	22 43	.....	23 29	.....	.....
New Pudsey	d	.	.	19 44	20 06	.	.	.	20 24	.	20 44	21 17	.	.	.	21 47	.	22 17	.	.	.	22 47	.	23 34	.	.
Bradford Interchange	a	.....	.....	19 53	20 14	.....	.....	.....	20 33	.....	20 53	21 25	.....	.....	.....	21 56	.....	22 25	.....	.....	.....	22 56	.....	23 43	.....	.....
Bradford Forster Square	a	.	19 54	.	.	20 12	20 24	.	.	20 54	.	.	21 23	.	21 55	.	22 14	.	22 24	.	22 54	.	.	.	.	.

For general notes see front of timetable
For details of catering facilities see
Directory of Train Operators

Bradford and Shipley → Leeds

Network Diagram - see first page of Table 35

Miles	Miles			NT MX	NT	NT	NT	NT	NT	GR R 1 A ✕	NT	NT	NT	NT	NT		NT	NT	GR R 1 A	NT	NT	NT	NT	NT	NT	NT
0	—	**Bradford Forster Square**	d		06 01		06 10	06 15		06 30		06 40	06 44		06 55					07 11	07 15				07 42	
—	0	**Bradford Interchange**	d	00 37					06 18					06 48				07 05				07 20		07 34		
—	3½	New Pudsey	d						06 27					06 57				07 14				07 28		07 42		
—	5½	Bramley	d						06 31					07 01				07 18						07 46		
1¾	—	Frizinghall	d		06 04		06 13	06 18				06 43	06 47		06 58					07 14	07 18				07 45	
2¾	—	**Shipley**	a		06 08		06 17	06 22				06 47	06 51		07 02					07 18	07 22				07 49	
—	—		d		06 08	06 13				06u35	06 44				07 02		07 09		07u14				07 35			07 50
13½	9½	**Leeds** 10	a	00 55	06 22	06 27			06 42	06 52	06 58			07 09	07 16		07 23	07 27	07 29			07 39	07 49	07 57		08 05

		NT	NT	NT	NT		NT	NT	NT	NT	NT	NT	NT	NT	NT	NT	NT	NT		NT	NT	NT	NT	NT	NT	NT
Bradford Forster Square	d	07 46		07 59				08 11		08 16		08 26				08 41	08 46				09 01		09 11	09 16		09 31
Bradford Interchange	d		07 50				08 06				08 20		08 34					08 50				09 03			09 20	
New Pudsey	d		07 58				08 14				08 28		08 42					08 58				09 12			09 27	
Bramley	d		08 02				08 18						08 46					09 02				09 16				
Frizinghall	d	07 49		08 02				08 14		08 19		08 29				08 44	08 49				09 04		09 14	09 19		09 34
Shipley	a	07 53		08 06				08 18		08 23		08 33				08 48	08 53				09 08		09 18	09 23		09 38
	d			08 07	08 13				08 19			08 33		08 41	08 47					09 08	09 09					09 39
Leeds 10	a		08 10	08 24	08 27		08 30		08 37		08 39	08 49	08 56	08 56	09 04			09 12		09 23	09 26	09 27			09 39	09 53

		NT	NT	NT	NT	NT	NT	NT		NT	NT	NT	NT	NT	NT	NT	NT	NT	NT	NT	NT		NT	NT	NT	NT
Bradford Forster Square	d			09 41	09 46		10 01				10 11	10 16		10 31			10 41	10 46		11 01					11 11	11 16
Bradford Interchange	d	09 34				09 50		10 04					10 20		10 34				10 50		11 05					
New Pudsey	d	09 42				09 58		10 12					10 28		10 42				10 58		11 13					
Bramley	d	09 46				10 02		10 16							10 46				11 02		11 17					
Frizinghall	d			09 44	09 49		10 04				10 14	10 19		10 34			10 44	10 49		11 04					11 14	11 19
Shipley	a			09 48	09 53		10 08				10 18	10 23		10 38			10 48	10 53		11 08					11 18	11 23
	d		09 44				10 09			10 14				10 39		10 44				11 09			11 14	11 18		
Leeds 10	a	09 58	09 59			10 12	10 24	10 25		10 28			10 40	10 53	10 58	10 58			11 13	11 24	11 27		11 28	11 36		

		NT	NT	NT	NT	NT	NT	NT	NT	NT	NT		NT	NT	NT	NT	NT	NT	NT	NT	NT	NT	NT	NT		NT
Bradford Forster Square	d		11 31			11 41	11 46		12 01				12 11	12 16			12 31			12 41	12 46		13 01			
Bradford Interchange	d	11 20		11 34				11 50		12 05					12 19			12 34				12 50		13 05		
New Pudsey	d	11 28		11 42				11 58		12 13					12 28			12 42				12 58		13 13		
Bramley	d			11 46				12 02		12 17								12 46				13 02		13 17		
Frizinghall	d		11 34			11 44	11 49		12 04				12 14	12 19			12 34			12 44	12 49		13 04			
Shipley	a		11 38			11 48	11 53		12 08				12 18	12 23			12 38			12 48	12 53		13 08			
	d		11 39		11 44				12 09		12 14					12 32	12 39		12 44				13 09			13 14
Leeds 10	a	11 39	11 55	11 58	11 58			12 12	12 24	12 27	12 29				12 39	12 54	12 55	12 58	12 58			13 12	13 24	13 27		13 28

		NT	NT	NT	NT	NT	NT	NT	NT	NT	NT	NT	NT		NT	NT	NT	NT	NT	NT	NT	NT	NT	NT	NT	NT
Bradford Forster Square	d	13 11	13 16		13 31			13 41	13 46		14 01					14 11	14 16		14 31			14 41	14 46		15 01	
Bradford Interchange	d			13 19		13 34				13 50		14 05						14 20		14 34				14 50		15 05
New Pudsey	d			13 28		13 42				13 58		14 13						14 28		14 42				14 58		15 13
Bramley	d					13 46				14 02		14 17								14 46				15 02		15 17
Frizinghall	d	13 14	13 19		13 34			13 44	13 49		14 04					14 14	14 19		14 34			14 44	14 49		15 04	
Shipley	a	13 18	13 23		13 38			13 48	13 53		14 08					14 18	14 23		14 38			14 48	14 53		15 08	
	d				13 39		13 44				14 09		14 14		14 18				14 39		14 45				15 09	
Leeds 10	a			13 38	13 54	13 58	13 58			14 12	14 24	14 27	14 28		14 37			14 39	14 53	14 58	15 01			15 12	15 24	15 26

		NT	NT		NT	NT	NT	NT	NT	NT	NT	NT	NT	NT	NT	NT		NT	NT	NT	NT	NT	NT	NT	NT	NT
Bradford Forster Square	d		15 11		15 16			15 31			15 41	15 46		16 01				16 11	16 16			16 31			16 40	16 45
Bradford Interchange	d					15 19			15 34				15 50		16 05					16 19			16 34			
New Pudsey	d					15 28			15 42				15 58		16 13					16 28			16 42			
Bramley	d								15 46				16 02		16 17								16 46			
Frizinghall	d		15 14		15 19			15 34			15 44	15 49		16 04				16 14	16 19			16 34			16 43	16 48
Shipley	a		15 18		15 23			15 38			15 48	15 53		16 08				16 18	16 23			16 38			16 48	16 52
	d	15 14					15 30	15 39		15 44				16 09		16 14					16 31	16 39		16 44		
Leeds 10	a	15 28				15 39	15 47	15 53	15 58	15 58			16 12	16 24	16 27	16 28				16 39	16 51	16 53	16 58	16 58		

For general notes see front of timetable
For details of catering facilities see Directory of Train Operators

A To London Kings Cross (Table 26)

Bradford and Shipley → Leeds

Network Diagram - see first page of Table 35

Mondays to Fridays

		NT	NT	NT	NT	NT		NT	NT	NT	NT	NT	NT	NT	NT	NT	NT	NT	NT		NT	NT	NT	NT	NT	NT
Bradford Forster Square	d		17 01			17 11				17 16	17 31			17 38	17 46			18 01				18 11	18 16		18 27	
Bradford Interchange	d	16 50		17 04				17 19				17 34				17 50			18 04					18 19		18 34
New Pudsey	d	16 58		17 13				17 28				17 42				17 58			18 13					18 28		18 42
Bramley	d	17 02		17 17								17 46				18 02			18 17							18 46
Frizinghall	d		17 04			17 14				17 19	17 34			17 41	17 49			18 04				18 14	18 19		18 30	
Shipley	a		17 08			17 18				17 23	17 38			17 45	17 53			18 08				18 18	18 23		18 34	
	d		17 09		17 15				17 20		17 39		17 45				17 58	18 09			18 14				18 34	
Leeds 10	a	17 12	17 24	17 27	17 29			17 39	17 40		17 55	17 58	18 00			18 12	18 15	18 24	18 27		18 29			18 39	18 48	18 56

		NT	NT	NT	NT	NT	NT	NT	NT		NT	NT	NT	NT	NT	NT	NT	NT	NT	NT	NT	NT		NT	NT	NT
Bradford Forster Square	d			18 41	18 46		19 01				19 07		19 31		19 36		19 41				20 07				20 25	
Bradford Interchange	d					18 52		19 05				19 19		19 34				19 50		20 04		20 19				
New Pudsey	d					19 00		19 13				19 28		19 42				19 58		20 13		20 28				
Bramley	d					19 04		19 17						19 46				20 02		20 17						
Frizinghall	d			18 44	18 49		19 04				19 10		19 34		19 39		19 44				20 10				20 28	
Shipley	a			18 48	18 53		19 08				19 14		19 38		19 43		19 48				20 15				20 32	
	d	18 44	18 48				19 09		19 14				19 39			19 44			20 14					20 28		20 43
Leeds 10	a	18 59	19 07			19 13	19 26	19 28	19 29			19 40	19 55	19 58		19 59		20 12	20 28	20 30		20 38		20 44		21 00

		NT	NT	NT	NT	NT	NT	NT	NT	NT	NT	NT		NT	NT	NT	NT	NT	NT	NT	NT	NT	NT	NT		
Bradford Forster Square	d		20 38			21 05		21 25			21 38			22 05			22 25			22 38		23 09	23 20			
Bradford Interchange	d	20 37			21 04					21 37		22 04				22 19		22 37			23 04			23 37		
New Pudsey	d	20 46			21 13					21 46		22 13				22 28		22 46			23 13			23 45		
Bramley	d	20 50			21 17					21 50		22 17						22 50			23 17			23 49		
Frizinghall	d		20 41			21 08		21 28			21 41			22 08			22 28			22 41		23 12	23 23			
Shipley	a		20 45			21 12		21 32			21 45			22 12			22 32			22 45		23 16	23 27			
	d			20 59			21 14		21 43						22 14				22 43							
Leeds 10	a	21 01		21 17	21 25		21 30		21 59	22 01		22 25			22 32	22 41		23 01	23 01		23 27			00 01		

Saturdays

		NT	NT	NT	NT	NT	NT	NT	NT	NT	GR R 1 A	NT	NT	NT	GR R 1 A	NT	NT	NT	NT	NT	NT	NT	NT	NT	NT	NT
Bradford Forster Square	d		06 01		06 10	06 15		07 01				07 11	07 15		07 33			07 59			08 11		08 16		08 31	
Bradford Interchange	d	00 37					06 26		07 05					07 20		07 34	07 50			08 05				08 20		08 34
New Pudsey	d						06 35		07 14					07 28		07 42	07 58			08 14				08 28		08 42
Bramley	d						06 39		07 18							07 46	08 02			08 18						08 46
Frizinghall	d		06 04		06 13	06 18		07 04				07 14	07 18					08 02			08 14		08 19		08 34	
Shipley	a		06 08		06 17	06 22		07 08				07 18	07 22					08 06			08 18		08 23		08 38	
	d		06 08	06 13				07 09		07 13	07u18				07u38			08 07	08 13			08 19			08 38	
Leeds 10	a	00 55	06 22	06 27			06 48	07 23	07 27	07 28	07 33			07 39	07 53	07 57	08 11	08 24	08 27	08b30		08 37		08 39	08 53	08 56

		NT	NT	NT	NT	NT	NT	NT	NT	NT	NT	NT	NT	NT	NT	NT	NT	NT	NT	NT	NT	NT	NT	NT	NT	NT
Bradford Forster Square	d		08 41	08 46		09 01			09 11	09 16		09 31			09 41	09 46			10 01			10 11		10 16		10 31
Bradford Interchange	d				08 50		09 04				09 20		09 34				09 50			10 05					10 19	
New Pudsey	d				08 58		09 13				09 27		09 42				09 58			10 13					10 28	
Bramley	d				09 02		09 17						09 46				10 02			10 17						
Frizinghall	d		08 44	08 49		09 04			09 14	09 19		09 34			09 44	09 49			10 04			10 14		10 19		10 34
Shipley	a		08 48	08 53		09 08			09 18	09 23		09 38			09 48	09 53			10 08			10 18		10 23		10 38
	d	08 44				09 09		09 14				09 39		09 44				10 02	10 09		10 14		10 19			10 39
Leeds 10	a	08 58			09 12	09 26	09 27	09 28			09 39	09 53	09 58	09 59			10 12	10 22	10 27	10 27	10 27		10 34		10 39	10 53

		NT	NT	NT	NT	NT	NT	NT	NT	NT	NT	NT	NT	NT	NT	NT	NT	NT	NT	NT	NT	NT	NT	NT	NT	NT
Bradford Forster Square	d			10 41	10 46		11 01			11 11	11 16		11 31			11 41		11 46		12 01			12 11	12 16		
Bradford Interchange	d	10 34				10 50		11 05				11 20		11 34					11 50		12 05				12 19	
New Pudsey	d	10 42				10 58		11 13				11 28		11 42					11 58		12 13				12 28	
Bramley	d	10 46				11 02		11 17						11 46					12 02		12 17					
Frizinghall	d			10 44	10 49		11 04			11 14	11 19		11 34			11 44		11 49		12 04			12 14	12 19		
Shipley	a			10 48	10 53		11 08			11 18	11 23		11 38			11 48		11 53		12 08			12 18	12 23		
	d		10 44				11 09		11 14				11 39		11 44		11 49			12 09		12 14				12 32
Leeds 10	a	10 58	10 58			11 12	11 24	11 27	11 28			11 39	11 55	11 58	11 58		12 06		12 12	12 24	12 27	12 29			12 39	12 54

For general notes see front of timetable
For details of catering facilities see
Directory of Train Operators

A To London Kings Cross (Table 26)
b Until 11 July arr. 3 mins. earlier

Table 37

Bradford and Shipley → Leeds

Saturdays

Network Diagram - see first page of Table 35

		NT	NT	NT	NT	NT	NT	NT	NT	NT	NT	NT	NT	NT	NT	NT	NT	NT	NT	NT	NT	NT	NT	NT	NT	NT
Bradford Forster Square	d	12 31			12 41	12 46		13 01			13 11	13 16		13 31			13 41	13 46		14 01				14 11	14 16	
Bradford Interchange	d		12 34				12 50		13 05				13 19		13 34				13 50		14 05					14 19
New Pudsey	d		12 42				12 58		13 13				13 28		13 42				13 58		14 13					14 28
Bramley	d		12 46				13 02		13 17						13 46				14 02		14 17					
Frizinghall	d	12 34			12 44	12 49		13 04			13 14	13 19		13 34			13 44	13 49		14 04				14 14	14 19	
Shipley	a	12 38			12 48	12 53		13 08			13 18	13 23		13 38			13 48	13 53		14 08				14 18	14 23	
	d	12 39		12 44				13 09		13 14				13 39		13 44				14 09		14 14	14 18			
Leeds 10	a	12 55	12 58	12 58			13 12	13 24	13 27	13 28			13 39	13 54	13 58	13 58			14 12	14 24	14 27	14 28	14 37			14 39

		NT	NT	NT	NT	NT	NT	NT	NT	NT	NT	NT	NT	NT	NT	NT	NT	NT	NT	NT	NT	NT	NT	NT	NT	NT
Bradford Forster Square	d	14 31			14 41	14 46		15 01			15 11	15 16			15 31			15 41	15 46		16 01			16 11	16 16	
Bradford Interchange	d		14 34				14 50		15 05				15 19			15 34				15 50		16 05				16 19
New Pudsey	d		14 42				14 58		15 13				15 28			15 42				15 58		16 13				16 28
Bramley	d		14 46				15 02		15 17							15 46				16 02		16 17				
Frizinghall	d	14 34			14 44	14 49		15 04			15 14	15 19			15 34			15 44	15 49		16 04			16 14	16 19	
Shipley	a	14 38			14 48	14 53		15 08			15 18	15 23			15 38			15 48	15 53		16 08			16 18	16 23	
	d	14 39		14 45				15 09		15 14				15 31	15 39		15 44				16 09		16 14			
Leeds 10	a	14 53	14b58	14 59			15 12	15 24	15 27	15 28			15 39	15 47	15 54	15 58	15 58			16 12	16 24	16 27	16 28			16 39

		NT	NT	NT	NT	NT A	NT	NT	NT	NT	NT	NT	NT	NT	NT	NT	NT	NT	NT	NT	NT	NT	NT	NT	NT	NT
Bradford Forster Square	d	16 31			16 40		16 44		17 01			17 11	17 16		17 31			17 41	17 46			18 01			18 11	
Bradford Interchange	d			16 34				16 50		17 04				17 19		17 34				17 50			18 04			
New Pudsey	d			16 42				16 58		17 13				17 28		17 42				17 58			18 13			
Bramley	d			16 46				17 02		17 17						17 46				18 02			18 17			
Frizinghall	d	16 34			16 43		16 48		17 04			17 14	17 19		17 34			17 44	17 49			18 04			18 14	
Shipley	a	16 38			16 48		16 51		17 08			17 18	17 23		17 38			17 48	17 53			18 08			18 18	
	d	16 39	16 44			16 49			17 09		17 15				17 39		17 45				18 00	18 09		18 14		18 19
Leeds 10	a	16 53	16 58	16b58		17 07		17 12	17 24	17 27	17 29			17 39	17 55	17 58	18 00			18 12	18 17	18 24	18 28	18 29		18 39

		NT	NT	NT	NT	NT	NT	NT	NT	NT	NT	NT	NT	NT	NT	NT	NT	NT	NT	NT	NT	NT	NT	NT	NT	NT
Bradford Forster Square	d	18 16		18 31				18 41	18 46		19 01			19 07		19 31		19 36		19 41				20 07		
Bradford Interchange	d		18 19		18 34					18 50		19 05			19 19		19 34				19 50		20 04		20 19	
New Pudsey	d		18 28		18 42					18 58		19 13			19 28		19 42				19 58		20 13		20 28	
Bramley	d				18 46					19 02		19 17					19 46				20 02		20 17			
Frizinghall	d	18 19		18 34				18 44	18 49		19 04			19 10		19 34		19 39		19 44				20 10		
Shipley	a	18 23		18 38				18 48	18 53		19 08			19 14		19 38		19 43		19 48				20 15		
	d			18 38		18 44	18 48				19 09		19 14			19 39			19 44			20 14				20 28
Leeds 10	a		18 40	18 52	18 56	18 59	19 06			19 13	19 26	19 28	19 29		19 39	19 55	19 58		19 59		20c15	20 28	20b30		20e42	20 44

		NT	NT	NT	NT	NT	NT	NT	NT	NT	NT	NT	NT	NT	NT	NT	NT B	NT	NT	NT	NT	NT	NT	NT	NT C
Bradford Forster Square	d	20 25			20 38			21 05		21 25			21 38		22 05			22 25			22 38		23 05	23 20	
Bradford Interchange	d			20 37			21 04					21 37		22 04			22 19			22 37		23 04			23 37
New Pudsey	d			20 46			21 13					21 46		22 13			22 28			22 46		23 13			23 46
Bramley	d			20 50			21 17					21 50		22 17						22 50		23 17			23 50
Frizinghall	d	20 28			20 41			21 08		21 28			21 41		22 08			22 28			22 41		23 08	23 23	
Shipley	a	20 32			20 45			21 12		21 32			21 45		22 12			22 32			22 45		23 12	23 27	
	d		20 43			20 57			21 14		21 43					22 14			22 43						
Leeds 10	a		21 00	21 01		21 16	21 26		21 30		21 59	22b01		22 26		22 32	22 39		23 01	23b01		23 27			23 59

Sundays

until 12 July

		NT	NT	NT	NT	NT		NT	NT	NT	NT	NT		NT	NT	NT	NT	NT		NT	NT	NT	NT	NT		NT
Bradford Forster Square	d			09 02				10 02				10 38		10 48		11 02						12 02				12 38
Bradford Interchange	d	08 31			09 21				10 02	10 25					11 02		11 25			11 44			12 25			
New Pudsey	d	08 39			09 30				10 10	10 33					11 10		11 33			11 52			12 33			
Bramley	d	08 43			09 34				10 14	10 37							11 37			11 56			12 37			
Frizinghall	d			09 05				10 05				10 41		10 51		11 05						12 05				12 41
Shipley	a			09 08				10 08				10 44		10 54		11 09						12 08				12 44
	d		09 00	09 10		09 40		10 08			10 40					11 10		11 40			11 49	12 08		12 40		
Leeds 10	a	08 51	09 14	09 24	09 42	09 54		10 22	10 24	10 46	10 54				11 21	11 24	11 46	11 54		12 05	12 06	12 22	12 48	12 54		

For general notes see front of timetable
For details of catering facilities see
Directory of Train Operators

- **A** Until 31 October
- **B** From 18 July
- **C** Until 11 July
- **b** Until 11 July arr. 2 mins. earlier
- **c** From 18 July arr. 3 mins. earlier
- **e** Until 11 July arr. 4 mins. earlier

Table 37

Sundays

until 12 July

Bradford and Shipley → Leeds

Network Diagram - see first page of Table 35

		NT	NT	NT	NT	NT		NT	NT	NT	NT	NT		NT	NT	NT	NT	NT		NT	NT	NT	NT	NT		NT
Bradford Forster Square	d		12 48	13 02					14 02					14 38		14 48	15 02					16 02				
Bradford Interchange	d	12 44			13 25			13 44			14 25				14 44			15 25			15 44					16 25
New Pudsey	d	12 52			13 33			13 52			14 33				14 52			15 33			15 52					16 33
Bramley	d	12 56			13 37			13 56			14 37				14 56			15 37			15 56					16 37
Frizinghall	d		12 51	13 05					14 05					14 41		14 51	15 05					16 05				
Shipley	a		12 54	13 08					14 08					14 44		14 54	15 08					16 08				
	d			13 08		13 40			14 08	14 21		14 40					15 08			15 40		16 08	16 16	16 29		
Leeds 10	a	13 05		13 22	13 46	13 54		14 05	14 22	14 39	14 48	14 54			15 05		15 24	15 46		15 54	16 05	16 22	16 33	16 47		16 48

		NT	NT	NT	NT	NT		NT	NT	NT	NT	NT		NT	NT	NT	NT	NT		NT	NT	NT	NT	NT		NT
Bradford Forster Square	d		16 38		16 48	17 02					18 02				18 38		18 48			19 02						20 02
Bradford Interchange	d			16 44				17 25		17 44		18 25				18 44					19 25			19 44		
New Pudsey	d			16 52				17 33		17 52		18 33				18 52					19 33			19 52		
Bramley	d			16 56				17 37		17 56		18 37				18 56					19 37			19 56		
Frizinghall	d		16 41		16 51	17 05					18 05				18 41		18 51			19 05						20 05
Shipley	a		16 44		16 54	17 08					18 08				18 44		18 54			19 08						20 08
	d	16 40				17 09			17 40		18 08			18 40				19 03		19 08		19 38	19 49			20 08
Leeds 10	a	16 54		17 05		17 23		17 46	17 54	18 05	18 23	18 47		18 54		19 07		19 20		19 22	19 47	19 56	20 03	20 11		20 22

		NT	NT	NT	NT	NT		NT	NT	NT	NT	NT		NT	NT	NT	NT	NT		NT	NT	NT	NT	NT		
Bradford Forster Square	d				20 38	20 48		21 02						22 02				22 38		22 48	23 02					
Bradford Interchange	d	20 07	20 31						21 07		21 38				22 02	22 32						23 02		23 49		
New Pudsey	d	20 15	20 39						21 15		21 46				22 10	22 40						23 10		23 57		
Bramley	d		20 43								21 50					22 44								00 01		
Frizinghall	d				20 41	20 51		21 05						22 05				22 41		22 51	23 05					
Shipley	a				20 44	20 54		21 08						22 08				22 44		22 54	23 08					
	d			20 40				21 08		21 40		21 54		22 08			22 40				23 08		23 40			
Leeds 10	a	20 26	20 52	20 54				21 24	21 27	21 54	21 58	22 10		22 22	22 22	22 53	22 54				23 22	23 22	23 58	00 10		

Sundays

19 July to 6 September

		NT	NT	NT	NT	NT	NT	NT	NT	NT	NT	NT	NT	NT		NT	NT	NT	NT	NT	NT	NT	NT	NT	NT	NT
Bradford Forster Square	d				09 02			10 02				10 38	10 48			11 02						12 02			12 38	
Bradford Interchange	d	00 03	08 31			09 20			10 02	10 25				11 02			11 25		11 44		12 02		12 25			12 44
New Pudsey	d	00 12	08 39			09 29			10 10	10 33				11 10			11 33		11 53		12 10		12 33			12 53
Bramley	d	00 16	08 43			09 33			10 14	10 37							11 37		11 57				12 37			12 57
Frizinghall	d				09 05			10 05				10 41	10 51			11 05						12 05			12 41	
Shipley	a				09 08			10 08				10 44	10 54			11 09						12 08			12 44	
	d			09 00	09 10		09 40	10 08			10 40					11 10		11 40		11 49		12 08		12 40		
Leeds 10	a	00 27	08 51	09 14	09 24	09 42	09 54	10 22	10 24	10 46	10 54			11 21		11 24	11 48	11 54	12 05	12 06	12 22	12 22	12 47	12 54		13 06

		NT	NT	NT	NT		NT	NT	NT	NT	NT	NT	NT	NT	NT	NT	NT	NT	NT		NT	NT	NT	NT	NT	NT
Bradford Forster Square	d	12 48		13 02						14 02				14 38		14 48		15 02					16 02			
Bradford Interchange	d		13 02		13 25			13 44	14 02			14 25			14 44		15 02		15 25			15 44		16 03		
New Pudsey	d		13 10		13 33			13 53	14 11			14 33			14 53		15 10		15 33			15 53		16 11		
Bramley	d				13 37			13 57				14 37			14 57				15 37			15 57				
Frizinghall	d	12 51		13 05						14 05				14 41		14 51		15 05					16 05			
Shipley	a	12 54		13 08						14 08				14 44		14 54		15 08					16 08			
	d			13 08			13 40			14 08	14 21		14 40					15 08			15 40		16 08		16 16	16 29
Leeds 10	a		13 22	13 22	13 46		13 54	14 06	14 22	14 22	14 39	14 48	14 54		15 06		15 22	15 24	15 46		15 54	16 06	16 22	16 22	16 33	16 47

		NT	NT	NT	NT	NT	NT	NT	NT	NT		NT	NT	NT	NT	NT	NT	NT	NT	NT	NT	NT	NT	NT		NT
Bradford Forster Square	d			16 38		16 48		17 02						18 02			18 38		18 48			19 02				
Bradford Interchange	d	16 26			16 44		17 02		17 25			17 44	18 02		18 25			18 44			19 02		19 25			
New Pudsey	d	16 34			16 53		17 10		17 33			17 53	18 10		18 33			18 53			19 10		19 33			
Bramley	d	16 38			16 57				17 37			17 57			18 37			18 57					19 37			
Frizinghall	d			16 41		16 51		17 05						18 05			18 41		18 51			19 05				
Shipley	a			16 44		16 54		17 08						18 08			18 44		18 54			19 08				
	d		16 40					17 09		17 40				18 08		18 40				19 03		19 08		19 38		19 49
Leeds 10	a	16 48	16 54		17 05		17 21	17 23	17 46	17 54		18 05	18 21	18 23	18 46	18 54		19 06		19 20	19 21	19 22	19 47	19 56		20 03

		NT	NT	NT	NT	NT	NT	NT	NT	NT	NT	NT	NT	NT	NT	NT	NT	NT	NT	NT	NT	NT	NT	NT		
Bradford Forster Square	d		20 02				20 38	20 48		21 02						22 02			22 38	22 48	23 02					
Bradford Interchange	d	19 44		20 02	20 25				21 02		21 26		21 44		22 02		22 26					23 04	23 25			
New Pudsey	d	19 53		20 10	20 33				21 10		21 34		21 53		22 10		22 34					23 12	23 33			
Bramley	d	19 57			20 37						21 38		21 57				22 38						23 37			
Frizinghall	d		20 05				20 41	20 51		21 05						22 05			22 41	22 51	23 05					
Shipley	a		20 08				20 44	20 54		21 08						22 08			22 44	22 54	23 08					
	d		20 08			20 40				21 08		21 40		21 54		22 08		22 40			23 08			23 40		
Leeds 10	a	20 05	20 22	20 23	20 47	20 54			21 22	21 24	21 48	21 54	22 05	22 10	22 22	22 22	22 47	22 54			23 22	23 26	23 46	23 58		

For general notes see front of timetable
For details of catering facilities see
Directory of Train Operators

Sundays

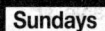

13 September to 1 November

Bradford and Shipley → Leeds

Network Diagram - see first page of Table 35

		NT	NT	NT	NT	NT	NT	NT	NT	NT	NT	NT	NT	NT		NT	NT	NT	NT	NT	NT	NT	NT	NT	NT	NT
Bradford Forster Square	d				09 02			10 02				10 38	10 48			11 02						12 02			12 38	
Bradford Interchange	d	00 03	08 31			09 20			10 03	10 25				11 02			11 25		11 44		12 02		12 25			12 44
New Pudsey	d	00 12	08 39			09 29			10 11	10 33				11 10			11 33		11 53		12 10		12 33			12 53
Bramley	d	00 16	08 43			09 33			10 15	10 37							11 37		11 57				12 37			12 57
Frizinghall	d				09 05			10 05				10 41	10 51			11 05						12 05			12 41	
Shipley	a				09 08			10 08				10 44	10 54			11 09						12 08			12 44	
	d			09 00	09 10		09 40	10 08			10 40					11 10		11 40		11 49		12 08		12 40		
Leeds 10	a	00 27	08 51	09 14	09 24	09 42	09 54	10 22	10 24	10 46	10 54			11 21		11 24	11 48	11 54	12 05	12 06	12 22	12 22	12 47	12 54		13 06

		NT	NT	NT	NT		NT	NT	NT	NT	NT A	NT	NT	NT	NT	NT	NT	NT	NT		NT	NT	NT	NT	NT	NT A
Bradford Forster Square	d	12 48		13 02						14 02				14 38		14 48		15 02					16 02			
Bradford Interchange	d		13 02		13 25			13 44	14 02			14 25			14 44		15 02		15 25			15 44		16 03		
New Pudsey	d		13 10		13 33			13 53	14 11			14 33			14 53		15 10		15 33			15 53		16 11		
Bramley	d				13 37			13 57				14 37			14 57				15 37			15 57				
Frizinghall	d	12 51		13 05						14 05				14 41		14 51		15 05					16 05			
Shipley	a	12 54		13 08						14 08				14 44		14 54		15 08					16 08			
	d			13 08			13 40			14 08	14 21		14 40					15 08			15 40		16 08		16 16	16 29
Leeds 10	a		13 22	13 22	13 46		13 54	14 06	14 22	14 22	14 39	14 48	14 54		15 06		15 22	15 24	15 46		15 54	16 06	16 22	16 22	16 33	16 47

		NT	NT	NT	NT	NT	NT	NT	NT	NT		NT	NT	NT	NT	NT	NT	NT	NT	NT	NT	NT	NT	NT		NT
Bradford Forster Square	d			16 38		16 48		17 02						18 02			18 38		18 48			19 02				
Bradford Interchange	d	16 26			16 44		17 02		17 25			17 44	18 02		18 25			18 44			19 02		19 25			
New Pudsey	d	16 34			16 53		17 10		17 33			17 53	18 10		18 33			18 53			19 10		19 33			
Bramley	d	16 38			16 57				17 37			17 57			18 37			18 57					19 37			
Frizinghall	d			16 41		16 51		17 05						18 05			18 41		18 51			19 05				
Shipley	a			16 44		16 54		17 08						18 08			18 44		18 54			19 08				
	d		16 40					17 09		17 40				18 08		18 40				19 03		19 08		19 38		19 49
Leeds 10	a	16 48	16 54		17 05		17 21	17 23	17 46	17 54		18 05	18 21	18 23	18 46	18 54		19 06		19 20	19 21	19 22	19 47	19 56		20 03

		NT	NT	NT	NT	NT	NT	NT	NT	NT	NT	NT	NT	NT	NT	NT	NT	NT	NT	NT	NT	NT	NT	NT		
Bradford Forster Square	d		20 02				20 38	20 48		21 02						22 02			22 38	22 48	23 02					
Bradford Interchange	d	19 44		20 02	20 25				21 02		21 26		21 44		22 02		22 26					23 04	23 25			
New Pudsey	d	19 53		20 10	20 33				21 10		21 34		21 53		22 10		22 34					23 12	23 33			
Bramley	d	19 57			20 37						21 38		21 57				22 38						23 37			
Frizinghall	d		20 05				20 41	20 51		21 05						22 05			22 41	22 51	23 05					
Shipley	a		20 08				20 44	20 54		21 08						22 08			22 44	22 54	23 08					
	d		20 08			20 40				21 08		21 40		21 54		22 08		22 40			23 08			23 40		
Leeds 10	a	20 05	20 22	20 23	20 47	20 54			21 22	21 24	21 48	21 54	22 05	22 10	22 22	22 22	22 47	22 54			23 22	23 26	23 46	23 58		

Sundays

from 8 November

		NT	NT	NT	NT	NT	NT	NT	NT	NT	NT	NT	NT	NT		NT	NT	NT	NT	NT	NT	NT	NT	NT	NT	NT
Bradford Forster Square	d				09 02			10 02				10 38	10 48			11 02					12 02			12 38		12 48
Bradford Interchange	d	00 03	08 31			09 20			10 03	10 25				11 02			11 25		11 44	12 02		12 25			12 44	
New Pudsey	d	00 12	08 39			09 29			10 11	10 33				11 10			11 33		11 53	12 10		12 33			12 53	
Bramley	d	00 16	08 43			09 33			10 15	10 37							11 37		11 57			12 37			12 57	
Frizinghall	d				09 05			10 05				10 41	10 51			11 05					12 05			12 41		12 51
Shipley	a				09 08			10 08				10 44	10 54			11 09					12 08			12 44		12 54
	d			09 00	09 10		09 40	10 08			10 40					11 10		11 40			12 08		12 40			
Leeds 10	a	00 27	08 51	09 14	09 24	09 42	09 54	10 22	10 24	10 46	10 54			11 21		11 24	11 48	11 54	12 05	12 22	12 22	12 47	12 54		13 06	

		NT	NT	NT	NT		NT	NT	NT	NT	NT	NT	NT	NT	NT	NT	NT	NT	NT		NT	NT	NT	NT	NT	NT
Bradford Forster Square	d		13 02					13 36			14 02			14 38		14 48		15 02					16 02			
Bradford Interchange	d	13 02			13 25				13 44	14 02		14 25			14 44		15 02		15 25			15 44		16 03	16 26	
New Pudsey	d	13 10			13 33				13 53	14 11		14 33			14 53		15 10		15 33			15 53		16 11	16 34	
Bramley	d				13 37				13 57			14 37			14 57				15 37			15 57			16 38	
Frizinghall	d		13 05					13 39			14 05			14 41		14 51		15 05					16 05			
Shipley	a		13 08					13 42			14 08			14 44		14 54		15 08					16 08			
	d			13 14			13 40				14 08		14 40					15 08			15 40		16 08			16 40
Leeds 10	a	13 22		13 34	13 46		13 54		14 06	14 22	14 25	14 48	14 54		15 06		15 22	15 24	15 46		15 54	16 06	16 22	16 22	16 48	16 54

		NT	NT	NT	NT	NT	NT	NT	NT	NT		NT	NT	NT	NT	NT	NT	NT	NT	NT	NT	NT	NT	NT		NT
Bradford Forster Square	d	16 38		16 48		17 02							18 02			18 38		18 48		19 02						20 02
Bradford Interchange	d		16 44		17 02		17 25		17 44			18 02		18 25			18 44		19 02		19 25			19 44		
New Pudsey	d		16 53		17 10		17 33		17 53			18 10		18 33			18 53		19 10		19 33			19 53		
Bramley	d		16 57				17 37		17 57					18 37			18 57				19 37			19 57		
Frizinghall	d	16 41		16 51		17 05							18 05			18 41		18 51		19 05						20 05
Shipley	a	16 44		16 54		17 08							18 08			18 44		18 54		19 08						20 08
	d					17 09		17 40		17 51			18 08		18 40					19 08		19 38	19 49			20 08
Leeds 10	a		17 05		17 21	17 23	17 46	17 54	18 05	18 09		18 21	18 23	18 46	18 54		19 06		19 21	19 22	19 47	19 56	20 03	20 05		20 22

For general notes see front of timetable
For details of catering facilities see
Directory of Train Operators

A 13 September

Table 37

Sundays

from 8 November

Bradford and Shipley → Leeds

Network Diagram - see first page of Table 35

		NT	NT	NT	NT	NT	NT	NT	NT	NT	NT	NT	NT	NT	NT	NT	NT	NT	NT	NT	NT	NT	NT	NT		
Bradford Forster Square	d				20 38	20 48			21 02			21 37				22 02			22 38	22 48	23 02					
Bradford Interchange	d	20 02	20 25	.	.	.	.	21 02	.	21 26	.	.	21 44	.	22 02	.	22 26	.	.	.	.	23 04	23 25	.	.	.
New Pudsey	d	20 10	20 33					21 10		21 34			21 53		22 10		22 34					23 12	23 33			
Bramley	d	.	20 37	.	.	.	.	.	.	21 38	.	.	21 57	.	.	.	22 38	.	.	.	.	.	23 37	.	.	.
Frizinghall	d				20 41	20 51			21 05			21 40				22 05			22 41	22 51	23 05					
Shipley	a	.	.	.	20 44	20 54	.	.	21 08	.	.	21 43	.	.	.	22 08	.	.	22 44	22 54	23 08	.	.	.	.	.
	d			20 40			20 59				21 40	21 44		21 54		22 08		22 40			23 08			23 40		
Leeds 10	a	20 23	20 47	20 54	.	.	21 17	21 22	.	21 48	21 54	21 58	22 05	22 10	22 22	22 23	22 47	22 54	.	.	23 22	23 26	23 46	23 58	.	.

For general notes see front of timetable
For details of catering facilities see
Directory of Train Operators

Leeds and Bradford → Ilkley

Network Diagram - see first page of Table 35

Miles	Miles			NT	NT	NT SX	NT SX	NT	NT SX	NT SO	NT SX	NT SX	NT SX	NT	NT	NT	NT	NT	NT	NT	NT	NT	NT	NT	NT
0	—	**Leeds** 10	d	06 02		06 27		07 02			07 29	07 35		08 02		08 32		09 02		09 32		10 02		10 32	
—	0	**Bradford Forster Square**	37 d		06 15		06 44		07 11	07 15			07 46		08 16		08 46		09 16		09 46		10 16		10 46
—	1¾	Frizinghall	37 d		06 18		06 47		07 14	07 18			07 49		08 19		08 49		09 19		09 49		10 19		10 49
—	2¾	Shipley	37 d		06 22		06 51		07 18	07 23			07 53		08 23		08 53		09 23		09 53		10 23		10 53
—	4¼	Baildon	d		06 25		06 54		07 21	07 26			07 56		08 26		08 56		09 26		09 56		10 26		10 56
10¼	7½	Guiseley	d	06 14	06 31	06 41	07 00	07 14	07 27	07 32	07 42	07 50	08 02	08 14	08 32	08 44	09 02	09 14	09 32	09 45	10 02	10 14	10 32	10 44	11 02
11½	8¾	Menston	d	06 17	06 34	06 44	07 03	07 17	07 30	07 35	07 45	07 53	08 05	08 17	08 35	08 47	09 05	09 17	09 35	09 48	10 05	10 17	10 35	10 47	11 05
13	10¼	Burley-in-Wharfedale	d	06 20	06 37	06 47	07 06	07 20	07 33	07 38	07 48	07 56	08 09	08 20	08 38	08 50	09 08	09 20	09 38	09 52	10 08	10 20	10 38	10 50	11 08
15¼	12½	Ben Rhydding	d	06 23	06 40	06 51	07 09	07 24	07 36	07 41	07 52	07 59	08 12	08 23	08 41	08 53	09 11	09 24	09 41	09 55	10 11	10 23	10 41	10 53	11 11
16¼	13½	**Ilkley**	a	06 29	06 46	06 56	07 15	07 29	07 42	07 47	07 57	08 05	08 18	08 29	08 49	09 02	09 17	09 33	09 47	10 01	10 17	10 30	10 47	10 59	11 17

		NT	NT	NT		NT	NT	NT	NT	NT	NT	NT	NT	NT	NT	NT	NT	NT	NT	NT	NT	NT	NT	NT	NT
Leeds 10	d	11 02		11 32			12 02		12 32		13 02		13 32		14 02		14 32		15 02		15 32		16 02		16 32
Bradford Forster Square	37 d		11 16			11 46		12 16		12 46		13 16		13 46		14 16		14 46		15 16		15 46		16 16	
Frizinghall	37 d		11 19			11 49		12 19		12 49		13 19		13 49		14 19		14 49		15 19		15 49		16 19	
Shipley	37 d		11 23			11 53		12 23		12 53		13 23		13 53		14 23		14 53		15 23		15 53		16 23	
Baildon	d		11 26			11 56		12 26		12 56		13 26		13 56		14 26		14 56		15 26		15 56		16 26	
Guiseley	d	11 14	11 32	11 44		12 02	12 14	12 32	12 44	13 02	13 14	13 32	13 44	14 02	14 14	14 32	14 44	15 02	15 14	15 32	15 44	16 02	16 14	16 32	16 44
Menston	d	11 17	11 35	11 47		12 05	12 17	12 35	12 47	13 05	13 17	13 35	13 47	14 05	14 17	14 35	14 47	15 05	15 17	15 35	15 47	16 05	16 17	16 35	16 47
Burley-in-Wharfedale	d	11 20	11 38	11 50		12 08	12 20	12 38	12 50	13 08	13 20	13 38	13 50	14 08	14 20	14 38	14 50	15 08	15 20	15 38	15 50	16 08	16 20	16 38	16 50
Ben Rhydding	d	11 23	11 41	11 53		12 11	12 23	12 41	12 53	13 11	13 23	13 41	13 53	14 11	14 23	14 41	14 53	15 11	15 23	15 41	15 53	16 11	16 23	16 41	16 53
Ilkley	a	11 29	11 47	12 00		12 17	12 29	12 47	13 00	13 17	13 29	13 47	13 59	14 17	14 29	14 47	15 01	15 17	15 29	15 47	15 59	16 17	16 29	16 47	17 00

		NT	NT	NT SX	NT SO	NT SX	NT	NT	NT	NT	NT	NT	NT	NT	NT	NT	NT	NT	NT	NT	NT	NT	NT		
Leeds 10	d		17 02	17 15			17 32		18 02		18 32		19 02	19 32		20 02		21 06		22 06		23 15			
Bradford Forster Square	37 d	16 44			17 16	17 16		17 46		18 16		18 46			19 41		20 38		21 38		22 38		23 20		
Frizinghall	37 d	16 48			17 19	17 19		17 49		18 19		18 49			19 44		20 41		21 41		22 41		23 23		
Shipley	37 d	16 52			17 23	17 25		17 53		18 23		18 53			19 48		20 45		21 45		22 45		23 27		
Baildon	d	16 55			17 26	17 28		17 57		18 26		18 56			19 51		20 48		21 48		22 48		23 30		
Guiseley	d	17 01	17 14	17 28	17 32	17 35	17 44	18 02	18 14	18 32	18 44	19 02	19 14	19 44	19 56	20 14	20 54	21 18	21 54	22 18	22 54	23 27	23 36		
Menston	d	17 04	17 17	17 31	17 35	17 38	17 47	18 05	18 17	18 35	18 47	19 05	19 17	19 47	19 59	20 17	20 57	21 21	21 57	22 21	22 57	23 30	23 39		
Burley-in-Wharfedale	d	17 07	17 20	17 34	17 38	17 42	17 51	18 08	18 20	18 38	18 50	19 08	19 20	19 50	20 02	20 20	21 00	21 24	22 00	22 24	23 00	23 33	23 42		
Ben Rhydding	d	17 10	17 23	17 37	17 41	17 46	17 54	18 12	18 23	18 41	18 53	19 11	19 24	19 53	20 06	20 23	21 03	21 27	22 03	22 27	23 03	23 36	23 45		
Ilkley	a	17 17	17 29	17 43	17 47	17 51	18 00	18 17	18 30	18 47	19 01	19 17	19 29	20 00	20 12	20 30	21 09	21 33	22 09	22 34	23 09	23 42	23 51		

Sundays

		NT	NT	NT	NT	NT	NT	NT	NT	NT	NT	NT	NT	NT	NT	NT	NT	NT	NT	NT	NT	NT	NT		
Leeds 10	d	09 12	10 12		11 12	12 12		13 12	14 12		15 12	16 12		17 12	18 12		19 12	20 12		21 12	22 12		23 14		
Bradford Forster Square	37 d			10 38			12 38			14 38			16 38			18 38			20 38			22 38			
Frizinghall	37 d			10 41			12 41			14 41			16 41			18 41			20 41			22 41			
Shipley	37 d			10 44			12 44			14 44			16 44			18 44			20 44			22 44			
Baildon	d			10 47			12 47			14 47			16 47			18 47			20 47			22 47			
Guiseley	d	09 23	10 23	10 52	11 23	12 23	12 52	13 23	14 23	14 52	15 23	16 23	16 52	17 23	18 23	18 52	19 23	20 23	20 52	21 23	22 23	22 52	23 25		
Menston	d	09 26	10 26	10 55	11 26	12 26	12 55	13 26	14 26	14 55	15 26	16 26	16 55	17 26	18 26	18 55	19 26	20 26	20 55	21 26	22 26	22 55	23 28		
Burley-in-Wharfedale	d	09 29	10 29	10 58	11 29	12 29	12 58	13 29	14 29	14 58	15 29	16 29	16 58	17 29	18 29	18 58	19 29	20 29	20 58	21 29	22 29	22 58	23 31		
Ben Rhydding	d	09 33	10 33	11 02	11 33	12 33	13 02	13 33	14 33	15 02	15 33	16 33	17 02	17 33	18 33	19 02	19 33	20 33	21 02	21 33	22 33	23 02	23 35		
Ilkley	a	09 38	10 38	11 07	11 38	12 38	13 07	13 38	14 38	15 07	15 38	16 38	17 07	17 38	18 38	19 07	19 38	20 38	21 07	21 38	22 38	23 07	23 40		

For general notes see front of timetable
For details of catering facilities see
Directory of Train Operators

Ilkley → Bradford and Leeds

Network Diagram - see first page of Table 35

Miles	Miles			NT	NT SX	NT SO	NT SX	NT SX	NT	NT	NT SX	NT SX	NT SX	NT SO	NT SX	NT SO	NT SX	NT	NT SO	NT SX
0	0	**Ilkley**	d	06 09	06 17	06 19	06 40	06 50	07 10	07 22	07 40	07 50	08 05	08 10	08 17	08 21	08 24	08 40	08 51	08 54
1	1	Ben Rhydding	d	06 11	06 19	06 21	06 42	06 52	07 12	07 24	07 42	07 52	08 07	08 12	08 19	08 23	08 26	08 42	08 53	08 56
3¼	3¼	Burley-in-Wharfedale	d	06 17	06 25	06 27	06 48	06 58	07 18	07 30	07 48	07 58	08 13	08 18	08 25	08 29	08 32	08 48	08 59	09 02
4¾	4¾	Menston	d	06 20	06 28	06 30	06 51	07 01	07 21	07 33	07 51	08 01	08 16	08 21	08 28	08 32	08 35	08 51	09 02	09 05
6	6	Guiseley	d	06 23	06 31	06 34	06 54	07 04	07 24	07 36	07 54	08 04	08 19	08 24	08 31	08 35	08 39	08 54	09 05	09 08
—	9¼	Baildon	d		06 36	06 39		07 09		07 41		08 09				08 40	08 44		09 10	09 13
—	10¾	Shipley	37 a		06 41	06 44		07 14		07 47		08 12				08 43	08 47		09 14	09 18
—	11¾	Frizinghall	37 a		06 44	06 47		07 17		07 49		08 16				08 46	08 50		09 17	09 21
—	13½	**Bradford Forster Square**	37 a		06 50	06 55		07 22		07 56		08 22				08 53	08 56		09 24	09 27
16¼	—	**Leeds** 10	a	06 39			07 10		07 38		08 09		08 34	08 39	08 46			09 11		

		NT	NT	NT	NT	NT	NT	NT	NT	NT	NT	NT	NT	NT	NT	NT	NT	NT	NT	NT
Ilkley	d	09 10	09 21	09 40	09 51	10 10	10 21	10 40	10 51	11 10	11 21	11 40	11 51	12 10	12 21	12 40	12 51	13 10	13 21	13 40
Ben Rhydding	d	09 12	09 23	09 42	09 53	10 12	10 23	10 42	10 53	11 12	11 23	11 42	11 53	12 12	12 23	12 42	12 53	13 12	13 23	13 42
Burley-in-Wharfedale	d	09 18	09 29	09 48	09 59	10 18	10 29	10 48	10 59	11 18	11 29	11 48	11 59	12 18	12 29	12 48	12 59	13 18	13 29	13 48
Menston	d	09 21	09 32	09 51	10 02	10 21	10 32	10 51	11 02	11 21	11 32	11 51	12 02	12 21	12 32	12 51	13 02	13 21	13 32	13 51
Guiseley	d	09 24	09 35	09 54	10 05	10 25	10 35	10 54	11 05	11 24	11 35	11 54	12 05	12 24	12 35	12 54	13 05	13 24	13 35	13 54
Baildon	d		09 40		10 10		10 40		11 10		11 40		12 10		12 40		13 10		13 40	
Shipley	37 a		09 44		10 14		10 44		11 14		11 44		12 14		12 44		13 14		13 44	
Frizinghall	37 a		09 47		10 17		10 47		11 17		11 47		12 17		12 47		13 17		13 47	
Bradford Forster Square	37 a		09 53		10 23		10 53		11 23		11 53		12 24		12 53		13 23		13 53	
Leeds 10	a	09 39		10b08		10c39		11 08		11 39		12 08		12 39		13 08		13 38		14 09

		NT	NT	NT	NT	NT	NT	NT	NT	NT	NT SO	NT SX	NT	NT	NT	NT SO	NT SX	NT	NT SO
Ilkley	d	13 51	14 10	14 21	14 40	14 51	15 10	15 21	15 40	15 51	16 10	16 12	16 21	16 40	16 51	17 10	17 14	17 21	17 40
Ben Rhydding	d	13 53	14 12	14 23	14 42	14 53	15 12	15 23	15 42	15 53	16 12	16 14	16 23	16 42	16 53	17 12	17 16	17 23	17 42
Burley-in-Wharfedale	d	13 59	14 18	14 29	14 48	14 59	15 18	15 29	15 48	15 59	16 18	16 20	16 29	16 48	16 59	17 18	17 22	17 29	17 48
Menston	d	14 02	14 21	14 32	14 51	15 02	15 21	15 32	15 51	16 02	16 21	16 23	16 32	16 51	17 02	17 21	17 25	17 32	17 51
Guiseley	d	14 05	14 24	14 35	14 54	15 05	15 24	15 35	15 54	16 05	16 24	16 27	16 35	16 54	17 05	17 24	17 29	17 35	17 54
Baildon	d	14 10		14 40		15 10		15 40		16 10			16 40		17 10			17 40	
Shipley	37 a	14 14		14 44		15 14		15 44		16 14			16 44		17 14			17 43	
Frizinghall	37 a	14 17		14 47		15 17		15 47		16 17			16 47		17 17			17 46	
Bradford Forster Square	37 a	14 23		14 53		15 23		15 53		16 23			16 53		17 23			17 53	
Leeds 10	a		14 39		15 10		15 40		16 08		16 38	16 46		17 09		17 38	17 44		18 09

		NT SX	NT	NT SX	NT	NT	NT	NT	NT	NT	NT	NT	NT	NT	NT	NT	NT	NT	NT
Ilkley	d	17 42	17 51	18 04	18 10	18 21	18 40	18 51	19 10	19 21	19 40	20 05	20 21	20 40	21 21	21 40	22 21	22 40	23 21
Ben Rhydding	d	17 44	17 53	18 06	18 12	18 23	18 42	18 53	19 12	19 23	19 42	20 07	20 23	20 42	21 23	21 42	22 23	22 42	23 23
Burley-in-Wharfedale	d	17 50	17 59	18 12	18 18	18 29	18 48	18 59	19 18	19 29	19 48	20 13	20 29	20 48	21 29	21 48	22 29	22 48	23 29
Menston	d	17 53	18 02	18 15	18 21	18 32	18 51	19 02	19 21	19 32	19 51	20 16	20 32	20 51	21 32	21 51	22 32	22 51	23 32
Guiseley	d	17 56	18 05	18 18	18 24	18 35	18 54	19 05	19 24	19 35	19 54	20 19	20 35	20 54	21 35	21 54	22 35	22 54	23 35
Baildon	d		18 10			18 40		19 10		19 40		20 24		20 59		21 59		22 59	
Shipley	37 a		18 14			18 43		19 14		19 44		20 27		21 03		22 02		23 02	
Frizinghall	37 a		18 17			18 46		19 17		19 47		20 30		21 05		22 05		23 05	
Bradford Forster Square	37 a		18 23			18 52		19 23		19 53		20 36		21 12		22 11		23 13	
Leeds 10	a	18 16		18 35	18 40		19 09		19 40		20 09		20 53		21 49		22 49		23 49

Sundays

		NT	NT	NT	NT	NT	NT	NT	NT	NT	NT	NT	NT	NT	NT	NT	NT	NT	NT	NT	NT	NT	NT
Ilkley	d	09 30	09 53	10 21	11 21	11 53	12 21	13 21	13 53	14 21	15 21	15 53	16 21	17 21	17 53	18 21	19 21	19 53	20 21	21 21	21 53	22 21	23 21
Ben Rhydding	d	09 32	09 55	10 23	11 23	11 55	12 23	13 23	13 55	14 23	15 23	15 55	16 23	17 23	17 55	18 23	19 23	19 55	20 23	21 23	21 55	22 23	23 23
Burley-in-Wharfedale	d	09 38	10 01	10 29	11 29	12 01	12 29	13 29	14 01	14 29	15 29	16 01	16 29	17 29	18 01	18 29	19 29	20 01	20 29	21 29	22 01	22 29	23 29
Menston	d	09 41	10 04	10 32	11 32	12 04	12 32	13 32	14 04	14 32	15 32	16 04	16 32	17 32	18 04	18 32	19 32	20 04	20 32	21 32	22 04	22 32	23 32
Guiseley	d	09 44	10 07	10 35	11 35	12 07	12 35	13 35	14 07	14 35	15 35	16 07	16 35	17 35	18 07	18 35	19 35	20 07	20 35	21 35	22 07	22 35	23 35
Baildon	d		10 12			12 12			14 12			16 12			18 12			20 12			22 12		
Shipley	37 a		10 15			12 15			14 15			16 15			18 15			20 15			22 15		
Frizinghall	37 a		10 18			12 18			14 18			16 18			18 18			20 18			22 18		
Bradford Forster Square	37 a		10 24			12 24			14 24			16 24			18 24			20 24			22 24		
Leeds 10	a	09 58		10 49	11 49		12 49	13 49		14 49	15 49		16 49	17 49		18 49	19 49		20 49	21 49		22 49	23 49

For general notes see front of timetable
For details of catering facilities see Directory of Train Operators

b Saturdays arr. 3 mins later
c Saturdays arr. 2 mins later

Network Diagram for Tables 39, 40, 41, 43

DM-7/08
Design BAJS

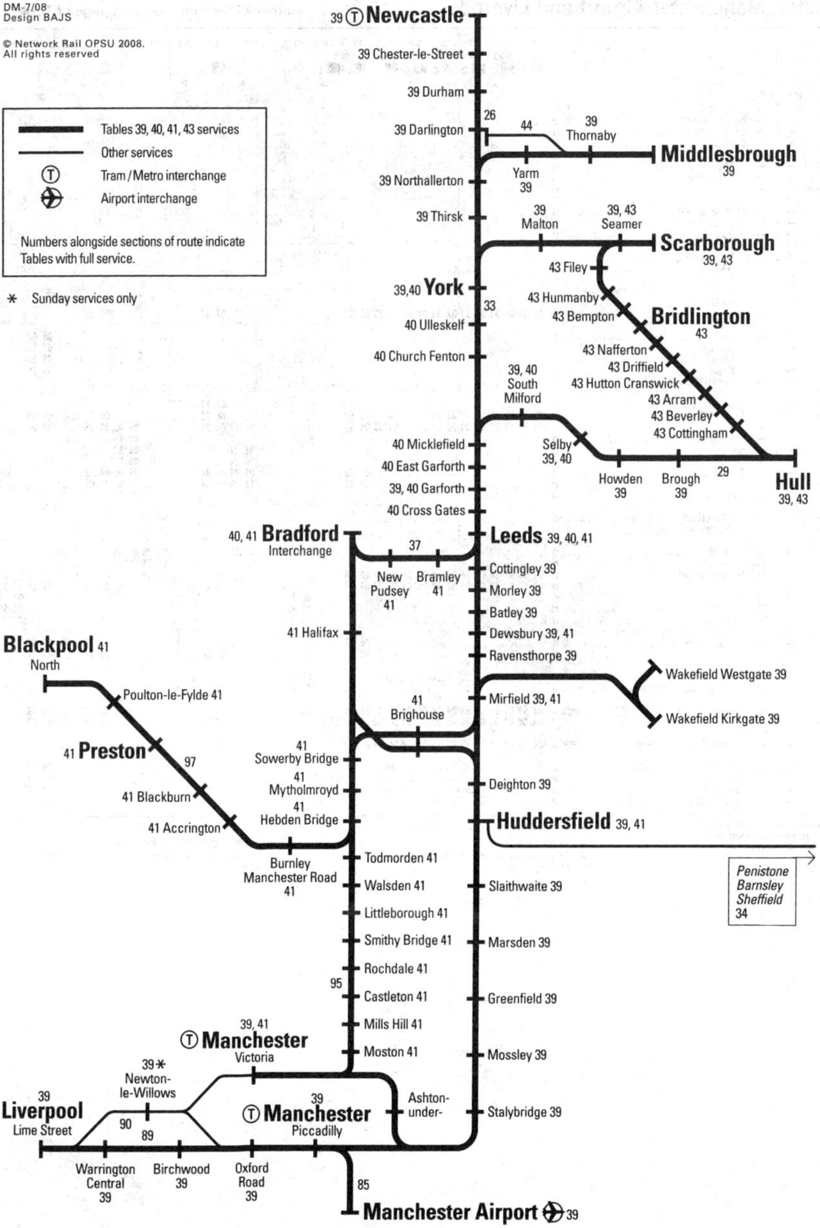
Tables 39, 40, 41, 43 services
Other services
Tram / Metro interchange
Airport interchange
Numbers alongside sections of route indicate Tables with full service.
* Sunday services only
39 Newcastle
39 Chester-le-Street
39 Durham
39 Darlington
26
44
39 Thornaby
Middlesbrough 39
Yarm 39
39 Northallerton
39 Thirsk
39 Malton
39, 43 Seamer
Scarborough 39, 43
43 Filey
39,40 York
43 Hunmanby
43 Bempton
Bridlington 43
33
40 Ulleskelf
40 Church Fenton
43 Nafferton
43 Driffield
43 Hutton Cranswick
43 Arram
43 Beverley
43 Cottingham
39, 40 South Milford
Selby 39, 40
40 Micklefield
40 East Garforth
39, 40 Garforth
40 Cross Gates
Howden 39
Brough 39
29
Hull 39, 43
40, 41 Bradford Interchange
37
Leeds 39, 40, 41
New Pudsey 41
Bramley 41
Cottingley 39
Morley 39
Batley 39
Dewsbury 39, 41
Ravensthorpe 39
41 Halifax
Blackpool 41 North
Wakefield Westgate 39
Mirfield 39, 41
Wakefield Kirkgate 39
Poulton-le-Fylde 41
41 Brighouse
41 Preston
97
41 Sowerby Bridge
41 Mytholmroyd
41 Blackburn
Deighton 39
41 Hebden Bridge
41 Accrington
Huddersfield 39, 41
Burnley Manchester Road 41
Todmorden 41
Walsden 41
Slaithwaite 39
Penistone Barnsley Sheffield 34
Littleborough 41
Smithy Bridge 41
Marsden 39
Rochdale 41
95
Castleton 41
Greenfield 39
Mills Hill 41
39, 41 Manchester Victoria
Moston 41
Mossley 39
39* Newton-le-Willows
39 Liverpool Lime Street
90
89
39 Manchester Piccadilly
Ashton-under-
Stalybridge 39
Warrington Central 39
Birchwood 39
Oxford Road 39
85
Manchester Airport 39

Newcastle, Middlesbrough, Scarborough, York, Hull, Leeds and Wakefield → Huddersfield → Manchester, Manchester Airport and Liverpool

Network Diagram - see first page of Table 39

Miles	Miles	Miles	Miles	Miles			TP MX 1◇	TP MO 1◇	TP MO 1◇	TP MX 1◇	TP MX 1◇	TP MO 1◇	TP 1◇	TP 1◇	NT		NT A	TP 1◇	NT B	NT	NT	TP 1◇ 🍴	NT	TP 1◇ C 🍴	NT
0	—	—	—	—	**Newcastle** 8	d																*04b30*			
8¼	—	—	—	—	Chester-le-Street	d																			
14	—	—	—	—	Durham	d																*04b44*			
—	—	0	—	—	**Middlesbrough**	d																			
—	—	3¼	—	—	Thornaby	d																			
—	—	8½	—	—	Yarm	d																			
36	—	—	—	—	**Darlington** 7	d																*05b02*			
50	—	20¾	—	—	Northallerton	d																*05b28*			
57¾	—	28½	—	—	Thirsk	d																			
—	—	—	0	—	**Scarborough**	d																			
—	—	—	2¾	—	Seamer	d																			
—	—	—	21	—	Malton	d																			
80	—	50¾	42	—	**York** 8	a																			
—	—	—	—	—		d	01 46	01 52	02 52	02 52	04 00	04 22	05 26					05 57				06 28			
—	0	—	—	—	**Hull**	d																		06 00	
—	10½	—	—	—	Brough	d																		06 12	
—	22¼	—	—	—	Howden	d																		06 26	
—	31	—	—	—	Selby	d																		06 35	
—	38¾	—	—	—	South Milford	d																			
98½	44½	—	60¼	—	Garforth	d												06 12							
105½	51¾	—	67½	—	**Leeds** 10	a	02 31	02 18	03 18	03 33	04 47	04 49	05 52					06 22				06 53		07 00	
—	—	—	—	—		d	02 35	02 20	03 20	03 35	04 52	04 52	05 55				06 13	06 25			06 43	06 55		07 08	
108½	—	—	—	—	Cottingley	d															06 48				
110	—	—	—	—	Morley	d											06 21				06 52				
113¼	—	—	—	—	Batley	d											06 26				06 57				
114¾	—	—	—	—	**Dewsbury**	a							06 06				06 29	06 36			07 00	07 06			
—	—	—	—	—		d							06 06				06 29	06 36			07 01	07 06			
116	—	—	—	—	Ravensthorpe	d															07 04				
—	—	—	—	0	**Wakefield Westgate**	d														06 30					
—	—	—	—	1	Wakefield Kirkgate	d														06 35			←		
117¾	—	—	—	10½	Mirfield	d											06a35			06 48	07 08		07 08		
120¾	—	—	—	13½	Deighton	d														06 55	→		07 16		
122¾	—	—	—	15½	**Huddersfield**	a	02 56	02 56	03 56	03 56	05 27	05 27	06 14					06 44		06 59		07 15	07 20	07 25	
—	—	—	—	—		d	02 59	02 59	03 59	03 59	05 28	05 28	06 15		06 29			06 45	06 57			07 16		07 26	07 33
127¼	—	—	—	20	Slaithwaite	d									06 36				07 04						07 40
129¾	—	—	—	22½	Marsden	d									06 42				07c12						07e55 →
135¾	—	—	—	28½	Greenfield	d									06 50				07 20						
138	—	—	—	30¾	Mossley (Grtr Manchester)	d									06 54				07 24						
140¾	—	—	—	33½	**Stalybridge**	a							06 33		06 59			07 03	07 29			07 34		07 43	
—	—	—	—	—		d							06 33		07 00			07 04	07 30			07 34		07 44	
—	—	—	—	34¾	Ashton-under-Lyne	d									07 04				07 34						
—	—	—	—	41¼	**Manchester Victoria** ⛴	a									07 17				07 47						
148¼	—	—	—	—	**Manchester Piccadilly** 10 ⛴	a	03 59	03 59	04 58	04 58	06 02	06 02	06 50					07 19				07 51		08 05	
—	—	—	—	—		d	04 00	04 00	05 00	05 00	06 08	06 08	06 54	07 07				07 23				07 54		08 07	
—	—	—	—	—	**Manchester Airport** ✈	a	04 15	04 15	05 15	05 15	06 24	06 24	07 12					07 42				08 12			
148¾	—	—	—	—	Manchester Oxford Road	a			*05f52*	*05f52*	*06f35*	*06f35*		07 09				*07f37*						08 09	
161¼	—	—	—	—	Birchwood	a			*06g54*	*06g54*	*07g04*	*07g04*		07 24										08 24	
164½	—	—	—	—	Warrington Central	a			*07g01*	*07g01*	*07g12*	*07g12*		07 29				*07f53*						08 29	
183	—	—	—	—	**Liverpool Lime Street** 10	a			*07g47*	*07g47*	*07f49*	*07f49*		07 57				*08f31*						08 57	

For general notes see front of timetable
For details of catering facilities see Directory of Train Operators

- **A** To Manchester Victoria (Table 41)
- **B** To Southport (Table 82)
- **C** Also stops at Gilberdyke 0619
- **b** Mondays dep. 10 minutes earlier
- **c** Arr. 0709
- **e** Arr. 0745
- **f** Change at Manchester Piccadilly
- **g** Change at Manchester Piccadilly and Manchester Oxford Road

Newcastle, Middlesbrough, Scarborough, York, Hull, Leeds and Wakefield → Huddersfield → Manchester, Manchester Airport and Liverpool

Network Diagram - see first page of Table 39

		NT	TP		NT	TP	NT	NT	NT	NT	TP	NT	TP		NT	NT	NT	TP	TP	NT	NT	TP	NT		TP
			1 ◇			**1** ◇					**1** ◇		**1** ◇					**1** ◇	**1** ◇			**1** ◇			**1** ◇
		A							B								A			B					
			🛒			🛒					🛒		🛒					🛒	🛒			🛒			🛒
Newcastle 8	d		*05b25*								*06c00*		06 13					*06c44*				*07c20*			*07c23*
Chester-le-Street	d												*06c32*												
Durham	d		*05b38*								*06c12*		06 29					*06e56*				*07c12*			*07c37*
Middlesbrough	d		05 57																			07 23			
Thornaby	d		06 02																			07 28			
Yarm	d		06 10																			07 38			
Darlington 7	d		*05 56*								*06c30*		06 46					*07e14*				*07c30*			*07c55*
Northallerton	d		06 25										06 58									07 53			
Thirsk	d		06 33										07 06									08 01			
Scarborough	d										06 30							07 00							07 38
Seamer	d										06 35							07 05							07 43
Malton	d										06 53							07 23							08 01
York 8	a		06 51								07 20		07 30					07 51				08 19			08 28
	d		06 54								07 23		07 40					07 54				08 24			08 40
Hull	d					06 35													07 33						
Brough	d					06 47													07 45						
Howden	d					*06 49*													07 56						
Selby	d					07 07													08 07						
South Milford	d																								
Garforth	d		07 09			07 24												08 13				08 41			
Leeds 10	a		07 20			07 35					07 52		08 04					08 23	08 37			08 52			09 04
	d	07 13	07 23			07 38				07 43	07 55		08 08				08 13	08 25	08 40		08 43	08 55			09 08
Cottingley	d									07 48							08 18				08 48				
Morley	d	07 21								07 52							08 22				08 52				
Batley	d	07 26								07 57							08 27				08 57				
Dewsbury	a	07 29	07 34							08 00	08 06						08 30	08 36			09 00	09 06			
	d	07 29	07 34							08 01	08 06						08 31	08 36			09 01	09 06			
Ravensthorpe	d									08 04							08 34				09 04				
Wakefield Westgate	d								07 29											08 29					
Wakefield Kirkgate	d								07 35			←								08 35			←		
Mirfield	d	07 35							07 50	08 08		08 08					08 37			08 51	09 08		09 08		
Deighton	d								07 56	→		08 13								08 57	→		09 16		
Huddersfield	a		07 43			07 56			08 03		08 15	08 20	08 25					08 44	08 58	09 04		09 15	09 20		09 25
	d		07 44			07 57		08 02			08 16		08 26		08 30			08 45	08 59			09 16			09 26
Slaithwaite	d				←			08 09							08 37										
Marsden	d				07 55			08 15							08 43										
Greenfield	d				08 03			08 23							08 51										
Mossley (Grtr Manchester)	d				08 07			08 27							08 55										
Stalybridge	a		08 01		08 12	08 17		08 32					08 43		09 00										09 43
	d		08 02		08 13	08 17	08 22	08 33					08 44		09 01	09 22									09 44
Ashton-under-Lyne	d				08 17		08 26	08 37							09 05	09 26									
Manchester Victoria	a				08 31		08 36	08 52							09 20	09 37									
Manchester Piccadilly 10	a		08 19			08 36					08 51		09 05					09 19	09 36			09 49			10 05
	d		08 24								08 54		09 07					09 24				09 54			10 07
Manchester Airport ✈	a		08 42			*09 07*					09 12							09 42	*10 07*			10 12			
Manchester Oxford Road	a		*08f33*			*08 48*					*09f03*		09 09					*09f40*	*09 48*			*10f03*			10 09
Birchwood	a		*09g03*										09 24												10 24
Warrington Central	a		*08f57*										09 29					*09f57*							10 29
Liverpool Lime Street 10	a		*09f31*				09 43				*09f48*		09 57			10 43		*10f31*				*10f48*			10 57

For general notes see front of timetable
For details of catering facilities see Directory of Train Operators

- **A** To Manchester Victoria (Table 41)
- **B** To Leeds (Table 41)
- **b** Change at Northallerton
- **c** Change at York
- **e** Change at York. From 7 September dep. Durham 0655, Darlington 0712
- **f** Change at Manchester Piccadilly
- **g** Change at Manchester Piccadilly and Manchester Oxford Road

Newcastle, Middlesbrough, Scarborough, York, Hull, Leeds and Wakefield → Huddersfield → Manchester, Manchester Airport and Liverpool

Network Diagram - see first page of Table 39

		NT	NT	NT	TP	TP	NT	NT	TP	NT		TP	NT	NT	NT	TP	TP	NT	NT	TP		NT	TP		NT
					1 ◇	1 ◇			1 ◇			1 ◇				1 ◇	1 ◇			1 ◇			1 ◇		
				A			B								A			B							
					⚲	⚲			⚲			⚲				⚲	⚲			⚲			⚲		
Newcastle 8 ⛴	d				07 26				07 52			08b24				08c43				09 12			09b33		
Chester-le-Street	d				07 36							08b33								09 21					
Durham	d				07 43				08 04			08b40				08c55				09 27			09b48		
Middlesbrough	d															09 00									
Thornaby	d															09 05									
Yarm	d															09 13									
Darlington 7	d				08 00				08 22			08b57								09 44			10b05		
Northallerton	d				08 12											09 27				09 56					
Thirsk	d				08 20											09 35									
Scarborough	d											08 47											09 47		
Seamer	d											08 52											09 52		
Malton	d											09 10											10 10		
York 8	a				08 55							09 37				09 55				10 21			10 37		
	d				08 58				09 28			09 40				09 58				10 28			10 40		
Hull	d					08 40											09 40								
Brough	d					08 52											09 52								
Howden	d					*08 36*											*09 28*								
Selby	d					09 11											10 11								
South Milford	d																								
Garforth	d				09 13											10 13									
Leeds 10	a				09 23	09 34			09 53			10 04				10 23	10 37			10 53			11 04		
	d			09 13	09 25	09 40		09 43	09 55			10 08			10 13	10 25	10 40		10 43	10 55			11 08		
Cottingley	d			09 18				09 48											10 48						
Morley	d			09 22				09 52							10 21				10 52						
Batley	d			09 27				09 57							10 26				10 57						
Dewsbury	a			09 30	09 36			10 00	10 06						10 29	10 36			11 00	11 06					
	d			09 31	09 36			10 01	10 06						10 29	10 36			11 01	11 06					
Ravensthorpe	d							10 04											11 04						
Wakefield Westgate	d						09 29											10 29							
Wakefield Kirkgate	d						09 35			←								10 35				←			
Mirfield	d			09a36			09 51	10 08		10 08					10 35			10 51	11 08			11 08			
Deighton	d						09 57	→		10 14								10 58	→			11 14			
Huddersfield	a				09 45	09 58	10 04		10 15	10 21		10 25				10 45	10 58	11 04		11 15		11 22	11 25		
	d	09 30			09 46	09 59			10 16			10 26	10 30			10 46	10 59			11 16			11 26		11 30
Slaithwaite	d	09 37											10 37												11 37
Marsden	d	09 43											10 43												11 43
Greenfield	d	09 51											10 51												11 51
Mossley (Grtr Manchester)	d	09 55											10 55												11 55
Stalybridge	a	10 00										10 43	11 00										11 43		12 00
	d	10 01	10 22									10 44	11 01	11 22									11 44		12 01
Ashton-under-Lyne	d	10 05	10 26										11 05	11 26											12 05
Manchester Victoria ⛴	a	10 20	10 36										11 20	11 35											12 20
Manchester Piccadilly 10 ⛴	a				10 19	10 36			10 49			11 05				11 19	11 36			11 49			12 05		
	d				10 24				10 54			11 07				11 24				11 54			12 07		
Manchester Airport ✈	a				10 42	*11 07*			11 12							11 42	*12 07*			12 12					
Manchester Oxford Road	a				10e40	*10 48*			11e03			11 09				11e40	*11 48*			12e03			12 09		
Birchwood	a											11 24											12 24		
Warrington Central	a				10e57							11 29				11e57							12 29		
Liverpool Lime Street 10	a		11 43		11e31				11e48			11 57		12 43		12e31				12e48			12 57		

For general notes see front of timetable
For details of catering facilities see Directory of Train Operators

- **A** To Manchester Victoria (Table 41)
- **B** To Leeds (Table 41)
- **C** To Wakefield Westgate
- **b** Change at York
- **c** Change at York. From 7 September dep. 3 minutes earlier
- **e** Change at Manchester Piccadilly

Newcastle, Middlesbrough, Scarborough, York, Hull, Leeds and Wakefield → Huddersfield → Manchester, Manchester Airport and Liverpool

Network Diagram - see first page of Table 39

		NT	NT	TP	TP	NT	NT	TP		NT	TP	NT	NT	NT	TP	TP	NT	NT		TP	NT	TP	NT	NT	NT
				1 ◇	1 ◇			1 ◇			1 ◇				1 ◇	1 ◇				1 ◇		1 ◇			
						A								B			A								B
				🛒	🛒			🛒			🛒				🛒	🛒				🛒		🛒			
Newcastle 8 ⛴	d			*09b43*				10 15			*10b25*				*10b43*					11 15		*11b30*			
Chester-le-Street	d																								
Durham	d			*09c55*				10 27			*10b41*				*10b55*					11 27		*11b44*			
Middlesbrough	d			09 59											11 00										
Thornaby	d			10 04											11 05										
Yarm	d			10 12											11 13										
Darlington 7	d			*10c12*				10 44			*10b58*				*11e10*					11 44		*12b02*			
Northallerton	d			10 27				10 56							11 27					11 56					
Thirsk	d			10 35											11 35										
Scarborough	d										10 47											11 47			
Seamer	d										10 52											11 52			
Malton	d										11 10											12 10			
York 8	a			10 54				11 21			11 37				11 55					12 21		12 37			
	d			10 58				11 28			11 40				11 58					12 28		12 39			
Hull	d				10 38											11 38									
Brough	d				10 50											11 50									
Howden	d				*10 36*																				
Selby	d				11 09											12 09									
South Milford	d																								
Garforth	d			11 13											12 13										
Leeds 10	a			11 23	11 33			11 53			12 04				12 23	12 33				12 53		13 04			
	d		11 13	11 25	11 40		11 43	11 55			12 08			12 13	12 25	12 40		12 43		12 55		13 08			13 13
Cottingley	d						11 48											12 48							
Morley	d		11 21				11 52							12 21				12 52							13 21
Batley	d		11 26				11 57							12 26				12 57							13 26
Dewsbury	a		11 29	11 36			12 00	12 06						12 29	12 36			13 00		13 06					13 29
	d		11 29	11 36			12 01	12 06						12 29	12 36			13 01		13 06					13 29
Ravensthorpe	d						12 04											13 04							
Wakefield Westgate	d					11 29											12 29								
Wakefield Kirkgate	d					11 34				←							12 35				←				
Mirfield	d		11a35			11 49	12 08			12 08				12a35			12 50	13 08			13 08				13a35
Deighton	d					11 57	→			12 17							12 56	→			13 14				
Huddersfield	a			11 45	11 58	12 04		12 15		12 21	12 25				12 45	12 58	13 03			13 15	13 21	13 25			
	d			11 46	11 59			12 16			12 26	12 30			12 46	12 58				13 16		13 26	13 30		
Slaithwaite	d											12 37											13 37		
Marsden	d											12 43											13 43		
Greenfield	d											12 51											13 51		
Mossley (Grtr Manchester)	d											12 55											13 55		
Stalybridge	a										12 43	13 00										13 43	14 00		
	d	12 22									12 44	13 01	13 22									13 44	14 01	14 22	
Ashton-under-Lyne	d	12 26										13 05	13 26										14 05	14 26	
Manchester Victoria ⛴	a	12 35										13 20	13 35										14 20	14 35	
Manchester Piccadilly 10 ⛴	a			12 19	12 36			12 49			13 05				13 19	13 36				13 49		14 05			
	d			12 24				12 54			13 07				13 24					13 54		14 07			
Manchester Airport ✈	a			12 42	*13 07*			13 12							13 42	*14 07*				14 12					
Manchester Oxford Road	a			*12f40*	*12 48*			*13f03*			13 09				*13f40*	*13 48*				*14f03*		14 09			
Birchwood	a										13 24											14 24			
Warrington Central	a			*12f57*							13 29				*13f57*							14 29			
Liverpool Lime Street 10	a	13 43		*13f31*				*13f48*			13 57		14 43		*14f31*					*14f48*		14 57		15 43	

For general notes see front of timetable
For details of catering facilities see Directory of Train Operators

A To Leeds (Table 41)
B To Manchester Victoria (Table 41)
b Change at York
c Change at York. From 7 September dep. 1 minute earlier
e Change at York. From 7 September dep. 2 minutes later
f Change at Manchester Piccadilly

Newcastle, Middlesbrough, Scarborough, York, Hull, Leeds and Wakefield → Huddersfield → Manchester, Manchester Airport and Liverpool

Network Diagram - see first page of Table 39

		TP	TP	NT	NT	TP		NT	TP	NT	NT	NT	TP	TP	NT	NT		TP	NT	TP	NT	NT	NT	TP	TP
		1 ◇	1 ◇	A		1 ◇			1 ◇			B	1 ◇	1 ◇	A			1 ◇		1 ◇			B	1 ◇	1 ◇
		✕	✕			✕			✕				✕	✕				✕		✕				✕	✕
Newcastle [8]	d	11b59				12 15			12b19				12b42					13 15		13b34				13b44	
Chester-le-Street	d								12b28																
Durham	d	11b52				12 27			12b35				12b53					13 27		13b46				13b52	
Middlesbrough	d	12 00											12 50											13 50	
Thornaby	d	12 05											12 55											13 55	
Yarm	d	12 13											13 03											14 03	
Darlington [7]	d					12 44			12b53				13c11					13 44		14b03					
Northallerton	d	12 27				12 56							13 17					13 56						14 17	
Thirsk	d	12 35											13 25					13 47						14 25	
Scarborough	d								12 47											13 47					
Seamer	d								12 52											13 52					
Malton	d								13 10											14 10					
York [8]	a	12 55				13 21			13 37				13 49					14 21		14 37				14 48	
	d	12 58				13 28			13 40				13 58					14 28		14 40				14 58	
Hull	d		12 38											13 38											14 38
Brough	d		12 50											13 50											14 50
Howden	d													13 41											
Selby	d		13 09											14 09											15 09
South Milford	d																								
Garforth	d	13 13											14 13											15 13	
Leeds [10]	a	13 23	13 33			13 53			14 04				14 23	14 33				14 53		15 04				15 23	15 33
	d	13 25	13 40		13 43	13 55			14 08			14 13	14 25	14 40		14 43		14 55		15 08			15 13	15 25	15 40
Cottingley	d				13 48											14 48									
Morley	d				13 52							14 21				14 52							15 21		
Batley	d				13 57							14 26				14 57							15 26		
Dewsbury	a	13 36			14 00	14 06						14 29	14 36			15 00		15 06					15 29	15 36	
	d	13 36			14 01	14 06						14 29	14 36			15 01		15 06					15 29	15 36	
Ravensthorpe	d				14 04											15 04									
Wakefield Westgate	d			13 29											14 29										
Wakefield Kirkgate	d			13 35				←							14 35				←						
Mirfield	d			13 51	14 08 →			14 08				14a35			14 51	15 08 →			15 08				15a35		
Deighton	d			13 57				14 14							14 57				15 16						
Huddersfield	a	13 45	13 58	14 04		14 15		14 21	14 25				14 45	14 58	15 04			15 15	15 21	15 25				15 45	15 58
	d	13 46	13 59			14 16			14 26	14 30			14 46	14 59				15 16		15 26	15 30			15 46	15 59
Slaithwaite	d									14 37											15 37				
Marsden	d									14 43											15 43				
Greenfield	d									14 51											15 51				
Mossley (Grtr Manchester)	d									14 55											15 55				
Stalybridge	a								14 43	15 00										15 43	16 00				
	d								14 44	15 01	15 22									15 44	16 01	16 22			
Ashton-under-Lyne	d									15 05	15 26										16 05	16 26			
Manchester Victoria	a									15 20	15 35										16 21	16 35			
Manchester Piccadilly [10]	a	14 19	14 36			14 49			15 05				15 19	15 36				15 49		16 05				16 19	16 36
	d	14 24				14 54			15 07				15 24					15 54		16 07				16 24	
Manchester Airport	a	14 42	*15 07*			15 12							15 42	*16 07*				16 12						16 42	*17 07*
Manchester Oxford Road	a	*14e40*	*14 48*			*15e03*			15 09				*15e40*	*15 48*				*16e03*		16 09				*16e40*	*16 48*
Birchwood	a								15 24											16 24					
Warrington Central	a	*14e57*							15 29				*15e57*							16 29				*16e57*	
Liverpool Lime Street [10]	a	*15e31*				*15e48*			15 57		16 43		*16e31*					*16e48*		16 57		17 43		*17e31*	

For general notes see front of timetable
For details of catering facilities see Directory of Train Operators

A To Leeds (Table 41)
B To Manchester Victoria (Table 41)
b Change at York
c Change at York. From 7 September dep. 1 minute later
e Change at Manchester Piccadilly

Newcastle, Middlesbrough, Scarborough, York, Hull, Leeds and Wakefield → Huddersfield → Manchester, Manchester Airport and Liverpool

Network Diagram - see first page of Table 39

		NT	NT	TP	NT	NT	TP	NT	NT	TP	TP	NT	NT	TP	NT	TP	NT	NT	TP	TP	NT	NT	NT
				1 ◇			1 ◇			1 ◇	1 ◇			1 ◇		1 ◇			1 ◇	1 ◇			
		A				B	C	D				A						D				A	E
				🛒			🛒			🛒	🛒			🛒		🛒			🛒	🛒			
Newcastle [8]	d			14 12			14b27			14b40				15 12		15b30			15b40				
Chester-le-Street	d													15 21									
Durham	d			14 24			14b40			14b52				15 27		15b34			15b52				
Middlesbrough	d									14 50									15 50				
Thornaby	d									14 55									15 55				
Yarm	d									15 03									16 03				
Darlington [7]	d			14 44			14b57							15 44		16b02							
Northallerton	d			14 56						15 17				15 56					16 17				
Thirsk	d									15 25									16 25				
Scarborough	d						14 47									15 47							
Seamer	d						14 52									15 52							
Malton	d						15 10									16 10							
York [8]	a			15 21			15 37			15 51				16 21		16 37			16 51				
	d			15 28			15 40			15 58				16 28		16 40			16 58				
Hull	d										15 40									16 40			
Brough	d										15 52									16 52			
Howden	d										15 42									16 36			
Selby	d										16 11									17 11			
South Milford	d																						
Garforth	d									16 13									17 13				
Leeds [10]	a			15 53			16 04			16 23	16 35			16 53		17 04			17 23	17 34			
	d		15 43	15 55			16 08	16 13		16 25	16 40		16 43	16 55		17 08		17 13	17 26	17 40			17 43
Cottingley	d		15 48					16 18					16 48					17 18					17 48
Morley	d		15 52					16 22					16 52					17 22					17 52
Batley	d		15 57					16 27					16 57					17 27					17 57
Dewsbury	a		16 00	16 06				16 30		16 36			17 00	17 06				17 30	17 36				18 00
	d		16 01	16 06				16 31		16 36			17 01	17 06				17 31	17 36				18 01
Ravensthorpe	d		16 04					16 34					17 04					17 34					18 04
Wakefield Westgate	d	15 29										16 29										17 29	
Wakefield Kirkgate	d	15 35			←							16 35			←							17 35	
Mirfield	d	15 51	16 08		16 08			16a37				16 51	17 08		17 08			17a37				17 52	18 08
Deighton	d	15 57	→		16 14							16 57	→		17 14							17 57	→
Huddersfield	a	16 04		16 15	16 21		16 25			16 45	16 58	17 04		17 15	17 21	17 25			17 45	17 58		18 05	
	d			16 16			16 26		16 30	16 46	16 59			17 16		17 26	17 30		17 46	17 59	18 04		
Slaithwaite	d								16 37								17 37				18 11		
Marsden	d								16 43								17 43				18 17		
Greenfield	d								16 51								17 51						
Mossley (Grtr Manchester)	d								16 55								17 55						
Stalybridge	a						16 43		17 00		17 18					17 43	18 00			18 18	18 30		
	d					16 42	16 44		17 01		17 18					17 44	18 01			18 18	18 31		
Ashton-under-Lyne	d					16 46			17 05								18 05				18 35		
Manchester Victoria	a					16 58			17 22								18 20				18 49		
Manchester Piccadilly [10]	a			16 49			17 05			17 21	17 37			17 49		18 05			18 19	18 37			
	d			16 54			17 07							17 54		18 07			18 24				
Manchester Airport	a			17 12			17 48			17 53				18 12					18 42				
Manchester Oxford Road	a			17c03			17 09			17 40	17 52			18c03		18 09			18c40	18 52			
Birchwood	a						17 24			17 57						18 24							
Warrington Central	a						17 29			18 03						18 29			18c57				
Liverpool Lime Street [10]	a			17c48			18 00			18 35						18 59			19c35				

For general notes see front of timetable
For details of catering facilities see Directory of Train Operators

A To Leeds (Table 41)
B To Southport (Table 82)
C Also stops at Hunts Cross 1740
D To Manchester Victoria (Table 41)
E To Sheffield (Table 34)
b Change at York
c Change at Manchester Piccadilly

Newcastle, Middlesbrough, Scarborough, York, Hull, Leeds and Wakefield → Huddersfield → Manchester, Manchester Airport and Liverpool

Network Diagram - see first page of Table 39

		TP		NT	TP	TP	NT	NT	TP	TP	NT	NT		TP	NT	TP	NT	NT	TP	NT	TP	TP		TP	NT
		1 ◇			1 ◇	1 ◇			1 ◇	1 ◇				1 ◇		1 ◇			1 ◇		1 ◇	1 ◇		1 ◇	
				A				B																	
		🍽				🍽			🍽	🍽				🍽											
Newcastle [8]	d	16 06				16b32				17 01						17b32			17c43			18b20			
Chester-le-Street	d	16 15				16b41										17b26						18b29			
Durham	d	16 21				16b48				17 13						17b33			17c54			18b36			
Middlesbrough	d								16 50										17 50					19 00	
Thornaby	d								16 55										17 55					19 05	
Yarm	d								17 03										18 03					19 13	
Darlington [7]	d	16 39				17b05				17 30						17b59						18b56			
Northallerton	d	16 50							17 17	17 42									18 17			18b51		19 27	
Thirsk	d	16 58							17 25										18 25			18b45		19 35	
Scarborough	d					16 47										17 47						18 47			
Seamer	d					16 52										17 52						18 52			
Malton	d					17 10										18 10						19 10			
York [8]	a	17 27				17 37			17 50	18 06						18 37			18 51			19 37		19 58	
	d	17 28				17 40			17 58	18 09						18 40			19 10			19 39			
Hull	d				17 01									17 58							18 59				
Brough	d				17 13									18 10							19 11				
Howden	d													17 54											
Selby	d				17 32									18 31							19 30				
South Milford	d																								
Garforth	d								18 13										19 25						
Leeds [10]	a	17 53			17 58	18 04			18 23	18 35				18 53		19 04			19 35		19 56	20 04			
	d	17 55			18 02	18 08		18 13	18 25	18 40		18 43		18 55		19 08		19 13	19 40			20 08			
Cottingley	d							18 18				18 48						19 18							
Morley	d							18 22				18 52						19 22							
Batley	d							18 27				18 57						19 27							
Dewsbury	a	18 06			18 13			18 30	18 36			19 00		19 06				19 30	19 51						
	d	18 06			18 13			18 31	18 36			19 01		19 06				19 31	19 51						
Ravensthorpe	d							18 34				19 04						19 34							
Wakefield Westgate	d										18 29									19 29					
Wakefield Kirkgate	d			←							18 34				←					19 34					
Mirfield	d			18 08				18a37			18 51	19 08			19 08			19 38		19 51					
Deighton	d			18 13							19 00	→			19 13			19 45		20 01					
Huddersfield	a	18 15		18 21	18 23	18 25			18 45	18 57	19 05			19 15	19 20	19 25		19 49	19 59	20 05		20 25			
	d	18 16				18 26	18 30		18 46	18 58				19 16		19 26	19 30		20 00			20 26			20 30
Slaithwaite	d						18 38										19 37								20 37
Marsden	d						18 43										19 43								20 43
Greenfield	d						18 51										19 51								20 51
Mossley (Grtr Manchester)	d						18 55										19 55								20 55
Stalybridge	a					18 43	19 01									19 43	20 00					20 43			21 00
	d					18 44	19 01									19 44	20 01					20 44			21 01
Ashton-under-Lyne	d						19 05										20 05								21 05
Manchester Victoria	a						19 20										20 20								21 20
Manchester Piccadilly [10]	a	18 49				19 05			19 21	19 33				19 57		20 05			20 33			21 05			
	d	18 54				19 07				19 40						20 07			20 40			21 07			
Manchester Airport ✈	a	19 13				19 47			19 53	19 59						20 53			20 57			21 47			
Manchester Oxford Road	a	19e03				19 09			19 36	19e48						20 09			20e48			21 09			
Birchwood	a					19 24			20f11							20 24						21 24			
Warrington Central	a					19 29			19 57							20 29						21 29			
Liverpool Lime Street [10]	a	19e48				19 57			20 35	20e48						20 59						21 57			

For general notes see front of timetable
For details of catering facilities see Directory of Train Operators

A To Sheffield (Table 34)
B To Manchester Victoria (Table 41)
b Change at York
c Change at York. From 7 September dep. Newcastle 1740, Durham 1752
e Change at Manchester Piccadilly
f Change at Manchester Piccadilly and Manchester Oxford Road

Newcastle, Middlesbrough, Scarborough, York, Hull, Leeds and Wakefield → Huddersfield → Manchester, Manchester Airport and Liverpool

Network Diagram - see first page of Table 39

		NT	TP 1 ◇	NT	TP 1 ◇	TP 1 ◇	NT	NT	TP 1 ◇	TP 1 ◇		NT	TP 1 ◇	NT	NT	TP 1 ◇ A	TP 1 ◇	TP 1 ◇	NT	NT		NT	TP 1 ◇		
Newcastle 8	d		18 58			19b25			19c43														21 47		
Chester-le-Street	d					19b37																			
Durham	d		19 10			19b44			19e56														22 00		
Middlesbrough	d								20 00				20 50				21 40								
Thornaby	d								20 05				20 55				21 45								
Yarm	d												21 03												
Darlington 7	d		19 27			20b04			20 31								22 08						22 17		
Northallerton	d		19 38						20 42				21 19				22 19						22 28		
Thirsk	d		19 35						20 50								22 27								
Scarborough	d					19 47				20 37								22 07							
Seamer	d					19 52				20 42								22 12							
Malton	d					20 10				21 00								22 30							
York 8	a		20 02			20 37			21 10	21 28			21 44				22 54	22 57					23 04		
	d		20 10			20 40			21 10				21 45										23 07		
Hull	d				19 56											21 33									
Brough	d				20 08											21 45									
Howden	d				19 43																				
Selby	d				20 27											22 07									
South Milford	d				20 36											22 17									
Garforth	d																								
Leeds 10	a		20 35		20 56	21 04			21 35				22 07			22 35							23 33		
	d	20 13	20 40			21 08		21 13	21 40				22 08		22 18	22 40						23 13	23 35		
Cottingley	d	20 18						21 18							22 23							23 18			
Morley	d	20 22						21 22							22 27							23 22			
Batley	d	20 27						21 27							22 32							23 27			
Dewsbury	a	20 30	20 51					21 30	21 51						22 35	22 51						23 30	23 46		
	d	20 31	20 51					21 31	21 51						22 36	22 51						23 31	23 46		
Ravensthorpe	d	20 34						21 34							22 39							23 34			
Wakefield Westgate	d			20 29								21 29								22 42					
Wakefield Kirkgate	d			20 34								21 35								22 47					
Mirfield	d	20 37		20 50				21 38				21 48			22 44					23 03		23 38			
Deighton	d	20 44		21 00				21 45				22 01			22 49					23 11		23 45			
Huddersfield	a	20 51	20 59	21 05		21 25		21 49	21 59			22 05	22 25		22 54	22 59				23 15		23 49	23 55		
	d		21 00			21 26	21 30		22 00				22 26	22 34		23 00			23 05				23 56		
Slaithwaite	d						21 37							22 41					23 12						
Marsden	d						21 43							22 47					23 18						
Greenfield	d						21 51							22 55					23 26						
Mossley (Grtr Manchester)	d						21 55							22 59					23 30						
Stalybridge	a					21 43	22 00						22 43	23 04					23 35						
	d					21 44	22 01						22 44	23 05					23 36						
Ashton-under-Lyne	d						22 05							23 09					23 40						
Manchester Victoria	a						22 20							23 24					23 53						
Manchester Piccadilly 10	a		21 33			22 05			22 33				23 05			23 37							00 54		
	d		21 40			22 07			22 40														00 54		
Manchester Airport	a		21 57			22 47			22 57							00 22							01 10		
Manchester Oxford Road	a		21f48			22 09			22f48																
Birchwood	a					22 24			23g54																
Warrington Central	a					22 29			00g01																
Liverpool Lime Street 10	a		22f48			22 58			00g41																

For general notes see front of timetable
For details of catering facilities see Directory of Train Operators

A Also stops at Gilberdyke 2152
b Change at York
c Change at Darlington
e Change at Darlington. From 7 September dep. 1 minute earlier
f Change at Manchester Piccadilly
g Change at Manchester Piccadilly and Manchester Oxford Road

Newcastle, Middlesbrough, Scarborough, York, Hull, Leeds and Wakefield → Huddersfield → Manchester, Manchester Airport and Liverpool

Network Diagram - see first page of Table 39

		TP	TP	TP	TP	TP	TP	TP	TP	NT	NT	TP	NT	TP	NT	NT	NT	NT	TP	NT	TP	NT	NT	NT	TP
		1◇	1◇	1◇	1◇	1◇	1◇	1◇	1◇			1◇		1◇					1◇		1◇				1◇
									A		B						C								
									🍴												🍴				🍴
Newcastle 8 🚢	d							*04 30*											*06b00*		06 13				*06b42*
Chester-le-Street	d																				*06b32*				
Durham	d							*04 45*											*06b12*		06 29				*06b56*
Middlesbrough	d											05 57													
Thornaby	d											06 02													
Yarm	d											06 10													
Darlington 7	d							*05 03*											*06b30*		06 46				*07b13*
Northallerton	d							*05 30*				06 25							*06b25*		06 58				
Thirsk	d											06 33									07 06				
Scarborough	d																		06 34						07 04
Seamer	d																		06 39						07 09
Malton	d																		06 57						07 27
York 8	a											06 51							07 24		07 30				07 55
	d	01 52	02 46	03 52	05 26		05 57	06 28				06 54							07 28		07 40				07 58
Hull	d								06 00					06 35											
Brough	d								06 12					06 47											
Howden	d								06 26																
Selby	d								06 35					07 07											
South Milford	d																								
Garforth	d						06 12					07 09													08 13
Leeds 10	a	02 18	03 12	04 34	05 52		06 22	06 53	07 00			07 20		07 35					07 52		08 04				08 23
	d	02 20	03 14	04 47	05 55		06 25	06 55	07 08		07 13	07 23		07 38				07 43	07 55		08 08			08 13	08 25
Cottingley	d																	07 48						08 18	
Morley	d										07 21							07 52						08 22	
Batley	d										07 26							07 57						08 27	
Dewsbury	a				06 06		06 36	07 06			07 29	07 34						08 00	08 06					08 30	08 36
	d				06 06		06 36	07 06			07 29	07 34						08 01	08 06					08 31	08 36
Ravensthorpe	d																	08 04						08 34	
Wakefield Westgate	d																07 29								
Wakefield Kirkgate	d																07 35			←					
Mirfield	d										07a35						07 50	08 08		08 08				08a37	
Deighton	d																07 56	→		08 13					
Huddersfield	a	02 56	03 50	05 27	06 14		06 44	07 15	07 25			07 43		07 56			08 03		08 15	08 20	08 25				08 44
	d	02 56	04 04	05 28	06 15		06 45	07 16	07 26	07 33		07 44		07 57		08 02			08 16		08 26	08 30			08 45
Slaithwaite	d									07 40			←			08 09						08 37			
Marsden	d									07c55			07 55			08 15						08 43			
Greenfield	d									→			08 03			08 23						08 51			
Mossley (Grtr Manchester)	d												08 07			08 27						08 55			
Stalybridge	a				06 33		07 03	07 34	07 43			08 01	08 12	08 17		08 32					08 43	09 00			
	d				06 33		07 04	07 34	07 44			08 02	08 13	08 17	08 22	08 33					08 44	09 01	09 22		
Ashton-under-Lyne	d												08 17		08 26	08 37						09 05	09 26		
Manchester Victoria 🚢	a												08 31		08 35	08 52						09 20	09 35	09 53	
Manchester Piccadilly 10 🚢	a	03 42	04 52	06 02	06 50		07 19	07 51	08 05			08 19		08 36					08 51		09 05				09 19
	d	03 44	04 54	06 08	06 54	07 07	07 23	07 54	08 07			08 24							08 54		09 07				09 24
Manchester Airport ✈	a	04 00	05 10	06 24	07 12		07 42	08 12				08 42		*09 08*					09 12						09 42
Manchester Oxford Road	a		*05e52*	*06e35*		07 09	*07e37*		08 09			*08e40*		*08 48*					*09e03*		09 09				*09e40*
Birchwood	a		*06f49*			07 24			08 24												09 24				
Warrington Central	a		*06f56*			07 29	*07e53*		08 29			*08e57*									09 29				*09e57*
Liverpool Lime Street 10	a		*07f40*	*07e49*		07 57	*08e31*		08 57			*09e31*			09 43				*09e48*		09 57		10 43		*10e31*

For general notes see front of timetable
For details of catering facilities see Directory of Train Operators

- **A** Also stops at Gilberdyke 0619. 🍴 from Leeds
- **B** To Manchester Victoria (Table 41)
- **C** From 18 July to Leeds (Table 41)
- **b** Change at York
- **c** Arr. 0745
- **e** Change at Manchester Piccadilly
- **f** Change at Manchester Piccadilly and Manchester Oxford Road

Table 39

Saturdays

Newcastle, Middlesbrough, Scarborough, York, Hull, Leeds and Wakefield → Huddersfield → Manchester, Manchester Airport and Liverpool

Network Diagram - see first page of Table 39

		TP	NT	NT	TP	NT	TP		NT	NT	NT	TP	TP	NT	NT	TP	NT	TP	NT	NT	NT	TP	TP	NT	NT
		1 ◊			1 ◊		1 ◊					1 ◊	1 ◊			1 ◊		1 ◊				1 ◊	1 ◊		
			A								D			A							D			A	
		🍴			🍴		🍴					🍴	🍴			🍴						🍴			
Newcastle 8	d				*07b00*		*07c30*					07 33				*07 54*		*08c30*				*08c40*			
Chester-le-Street	d											07 42										*08c49*			
Durham	d				*07b12*		*07c42*					07 49				*07 56*		*08c42*				*08c56*			
Middlesbrough	d				07 21																	09 00			
Thornaby	d				07 26																	09 05			
Yarm	d				07 34																	09 13			
Darlington 7	d				*07 30*		*08c00*					08 06				*08 21*		*08c59*							
Northallerton	d				07 48							08 18										09 27			
Thirsk	d				07 56							08 26										09 35			
Scarborough	d						07 47											08 47							
Seamer	d						07 52											08 52							
Malton	d						08 10											09 10							
York 8	a				08 17		08 37					08 57						09 37				09 55			
	d				08 24		08 40					08 58				09 28		09 40				09 58			
Hull	d	07 33											08 40										09 40		
Brough	d	07 45											08 52										09 52		
Howden	d	07 56											*08 26*										*09 28*		
Selby	d	08 07											09 11										10 11		
South Milford	d																								
Garforth	d											09 13										10 13			
Leeds 10	a	08 37			08 52		09 04					09 23	09 34			09 53		10 04				10 23	10 37		
	d	08 40		08 43	08 55		09 08				09 13	09 25	09 40		09 43	09 55		10 08			10 13	10 25	10 40		10 43
Cottingley	d			08 48							09 18				09 48										10 48
Morley	d			08 52							09 22				09 52						10 21				10 52
Batley	d			08 57							09 27				09 57						10 26				10 57
Dewsbury	a			09 00	09 06						09 30	09 36			10 00	10 06					10 29	10 36			11 00
	d			09 01	09 06						09 31	09 36			10 01	10 06					10 29	10 36			11 01
Ravensthorpe	d			09 04											10 04										11 04
Wakefield Westgate	d		08 29											09 29										10 29	
Wakefield Kirkgate	d		08 35			←								09 35			←							10 35	
Mirfield	d		08 51	09 08		09 08					09a36			09 51	10 08		10 08				10a35			10 51	11 08
Deighton	d		08 57	→		09 14								09 57	→		10 14							10 58	→
Huddersfield	a	08 58	09 04		09 15	09 21	09 25					09 45	09 58	10 04		10 15	10 21	10 25				10 45	10 58	11 04	
	d	08 59			09 16		09 26		09 30			09 46	09 59			10 16		10 26	10 30			10 46	10 59		
Slaithwaite	d								09 37										10 37						
Marsden	d								09 43										10 43						
Greenfield	d								09 51										10 51						
Mossley (Grtr Manchester)	d								09 55										10 55						
Stalybridge	a						09 43		10 00									10 43	11 00						
	d						09 44		10 01	10 22								10 44	11 01	11 22					
Ashton-under-Lyne	d								10 05	10 26									11 05	11 26					
Manchester Victoria	⛴ a								10 20	10 35									11 20	11 35					
Manchester Piccadilly 10	⛴ a	09 36			09 49		10 05					10 19	10 36			10 49		11 05				11 19	11 36		
	d				09 54		10 07					10 24				10 54		11 07				11 24			
Manchester Airport	✈ a	*10 07*			10 12							10 42	*11 07*			11 12						11 42	*12 07*		
Manchester Oxford Road	a	*09 48*			*10e03*		10 09					*10e40*	*10 48*			*11e03*		11 09				*11e40*	*11 48*		
Birchwood	a						10 24											11 24							
Warrington Central	a						10 29					*10e57*						11 29				*11e57*			
Liverpool Lime Street 10	a				*10e48*		10 57			11 43		*11e31*				*11e48*		11 57		12 43		*12e31*			

For general notes see front of timetable
For details of catering facilities see Directory of Train Operators

A From 18 July to Leeds (Table 41)
B From 10 October
D To Manchester Victoria (Table 41)
b Change at Northallerton
c Change at York
e Change at Manchester Piccadilly

Newcastle, Middlesbrough, Scarborough, York, Hull, Leeds and Wakefield → Huddersfield → Manchester, Manchester Airport and Liverpool

Network Diagram - see first page of Table 39

		TP	NT	TP	NT	NT	NT	TP	TP	TP	NT	NT	TP	NT	TP	NT	NT	NT	TP	TP	NT	NT	TP	TP	NT
		1 ◇		1 ◇				1 ◇	1 ◇	1 ◇			1 ◇		1 ◇				1 ◇	1 ◇			1 ◇	1 ◇	
							A			B	C							A			C			B	
		⚒		⚒				⚒					⚒		⚒				⚒	⚒			⚒		
Newcastle 8	d	09 12		09b32				09b40					10 12		10b32				10b44				11 15		
Chester-le-Street	d	09 21																							
Durham	d	09 27		09b37				09b55					10 27		10b45				10b56				11 27		
Middlesbrough	d							10 00											11 00						
Thornaby	d							10 05											11 05						
Yarm	d							10 13											11 13						
Darlington 7	d	09 44		10b01									10 44		11b03								11 44		
Northallerton	d	09 56						10 27					10 56						11 27				11 56		
Thirsk	d							10 35											11 35						
Scarborough	d			09 47						10 30					10 47									11 37	
Seamer	d			09 52											10 52										
Malton	d			10 10											11 10										
York 8	a	10 21		10 37				10 54		11 15			11 21		11 37				11 55				12 21	12 24	
	d	10 28		10 40				10 58					11 28		11 40				11 58				12 28		
Hull	d								10 38											11 38					
Brough	d								10 50											11 50					
Howden	d								*10 30*																
Selby	d								11 09											12 09					
South Milford	d																								
Garforth	d							11 13											12 13						
Leeds 10	a	10 53		11 04				11 23	11 33				11 53		12 04				12 23	12 33			12 53		
	d	10 55		11 08			11 13	11 25	11 40			11 43	11 55		12 08			12 13	12 25	12 40		12 43	12 55		
Cottingley	d											11 48										12 48			
Morley	d						11 21					11 52						12 21				12 52			
Batley	d						11 26					11 57						12 26				12 57			
Dewsbury	a	11 06					11 29	11 36				12 00	12 06					12 29	12 36			13 00	13 06		
	d	11 06					11 29	11 36				12 01	12 06					12 29	12 36			13 01	13 06		
Ravensthorpe	d											12 04										13 04			
Wakefield Westgate	d										11 29										12 29				
Wakefield Kirkgate	d		←								11 34			←							12 35				←
Mirfield	d		11 08				11a35				11 49	12 08 →		12 08				12a35			12 50	13 08 →			13 08
Deighton	d		11 14								11 57			12 14							12 56				13 14
Huddersfield	a	11 15	11 21	11 25				11 45	11 58		12 04		12 15	12 21	12 25				12 45	12 58	13 03		13 15		13 21
	d	11 16		11 26	11 30			11 46	11 59				12 16		12 26	12 30			12 46	12 58			13 16		
Slaithwaite	d				11 37											12 37									
Marsden	d				11 43											12 43									
Greenfield	d				11 51											12 51									
Mossley (Grtr Manchester)	d				11 55											12 55									
Stalybridge	a			11 43	12 00										12 43	13 00									
	d			11 44	12 01	12 22									12 44	13 01	13 22								
Ashton-under-Lyne	d				12 05	12 26										13 05	13 26								
Manchester Victoria	a				12 20	12 35										13 20	13 35								
Manchester Piccadilly 10	a	11 49		12 05				12 19	12 36				12 49		13 05				13 19	13 36			13 49		
	d	11 54		12 07				12 24					12 54		13 07				13 24				13 54		
Manchester Airport ✈	a	12 12						12 42	*13 07*				13 12						13 42	*14 07*			14 12		
Manchester Oxford Road	a	*12c03*		12 09				*12c40*	*12 48*				*13c03*		13 09				*13c40*	*13 48*			*14c03*		
Birchwood	a			12 24									*13c24*		13 24										
Warrington Central	a			12 29				*12c57*					*13c29*		13 29				*13c57*						
Liverpool Lime Street 10	a	*12c48*		12 57		13 43		*13c31*					*13c48*		13 57		14 43		*14c31*				*14c48*		

For general notes see front of timetable
For details of catering facilities see Directory of Train Operators

A To Manchester Victoria (Table 41)
B 18 July to 5 September
C From 18 July to Leeds (Table 41)

b Change at York
c Change at Manchester Piccadilly

Table 39

Saturdays

Newcastle, Middlesbrough, Scarborough, York, Hull, Leeds and Wakefield → Huddersfield → Manchester, Manchester Airport and Liverpool

Network Diagram - see first page of Table 39

		TP	NT	NT	NT	TP	TP	NT	NT	TP	NT	TP	NT	NT	NT	TP	TP	NT	NT	TP	NT	TP	NT	NT	NT
		1 ◇				1 ◇	1 ◇			1 ◇		1 ◇				1 ◇	1 ◇			1 ◇		1 ◇			
					A			B							A			B					C		A
						[catering]	[catering]			[catering]		[catering]				[catering]				[catering]		[catering]			
Newcastle 8	d	11b29				11b40				12 15		12b33				12b44				13 15		13b27			
Chester-le-Street	d											12b31													
Durham	d	11b42				11b55				12 27		12b46				12b56				13 27		13b39			
Middlesbrough	d					12 00										12 50									
Thornaby	d					12 05										12 55									
Yarm	d					12 13										13 03									
Darlington 7	d	12b01								12 44		13b04								13 44		13b58			
Northallerton	d					12 27				12 56						13 17				13 56					
Thirsk	d					12 35										13 25				13 42					
Scarborough	d	11 47										12 47										13 47			
Seamer	d	11 52										12 52										13 52			
Malton	d	12 10										13 10										14 10			
York 8	a	12 37				12 55				13 21		13 37				13 49				14 21		14 38			
	d	12 40				12 58				13 28		13 40				13 58				14 28		14 40			
Hull	d						12 38										13 38								
Brough	d						12 50										13 50								
Howden	d																13 40								
Selby	d						13 09										14 09								
South Milford	d																								
Garforth	d					13 13										14 13									
Leeds 10	a	13 04				13 23	13 33			13 53		14 04				14 23	14 33			14 53		15 04			
	d	13 08			13 13	13 25	13 40		13 43	13 55		14 08			14 13	14 25	14 37		14 43	14 55		15 08			15 13
Cottingley	d								13 48										14 48						
Morley	d				13 21				13 52						14 21				14 52						15 21
Batley	d				13 26				13 57						14 26				14 57						15 26
Dewsbury	a				13 29	13 36			14 00	14 06					14 29	14 36			15 00	15 06					15 29
	d				13 29	13 36			14 01	14 06					14 29	14 36			15 01	15 06					15 29
Ravensthorpe	d								14 04										15 04						
Wakefield Westgate	d							13 29										14 38							
Wakefield Kirkgate	d							13 35			←							14 44			←				
Mirfield	d				13a35			13 51	14 08		14 08				14a35			14 57	15 08		15 08				15a35
Deighton	d							13 57	→		14 14							15 03	→		15 14				
Huddersfield	a	13 25				13 45	13 58	14 04		14 15	14 21	14 25				14 45	14 55	15 10		15 15	15 21	15 25			
	d	13 26	13 30			13 46	13 59			14 16		14 26	14 30			14 46	14 56			15 16		15 26	15 30		
Slaithwaite	d		13 37										14 37										15 37		
Marsden	d		13 43										14 43										15 43		
Greenfield	d		13 51										14 51										15 51		
Mossley (Grtr Manchester)	d		13 55										14 55										15 55		
Stalybridge	a	13 43	14 00									14 43	15 00									15 43	16 00		
	d	13 44	14 01	14 22								14 44	15 01	15 22								15 44	16 01	16 22	
Ashton-under-Lyne	d		14 05	14 26									15 05	15 26									16 05	16 26	
Manchester Victoria	a		14 20	14 35									15 20	15 35									16 20	16 35	
Manchester Piccadilly 10	a	14 05				14 19	14 36			14 49		15 05				15 19	15 36			15 49		16 05			
	d	14 07				14 24				14 54		15 07				15 24				15 54		16 07			
Manchester Airport	a					14 42	15 07			15 12						15 42	16 07			16 12					
Manchester Oxford Road	a	14 09				14c40	14 48			15c03		15 09				15c40	15 48			16c03		16 09			
Birchwood	a	14 24										15 24										16 24			
Warrington Central	a	14 29				14c57						15 29				15c57						16 29			
Liverpool Lime Street 10	a	14 57		15 43		15c31				15c48		15 57		16 43		16c31				16c48		16 57		17 43	

For general notes see front of timetable
For details of catering facilities see Directory of Train Operators

- **A** To Manchester Victoria (Table 41)
- **B** From 18 July to Leeds (Table 41)
- **C** Until 3 October
- **b** Change at York
- **c** Change at Manchester Piccadilly

Table 39

Saturdays

Newcastle, Middlesbrough, Scarborough, York, Hull, Leeds and Wakefield → Huddersfield → Manchester, Manchester Airport and Liverpool

Network Diagram - see first page of Table 39

		TP	TP	NT	NT	TP	NT	TP	NT	NT	TP	TP	NT	NT	NT	TP	NT	NT	TP	NT	NT	TP	TP	NT	NT
		1 ◇	**1** ◇			**1** ◇		**1** ◇			**1** ◇	**1** ◇				**1** ◇			**1** ◇			**1** ◇	**1** ◇		
				A				B		C				A							C			A	
		🛒				🛒		🛒			🛒	🛒				🛒			🛒			🛒			
Newcastle 8	d	13b44				14 15		14b29			14b44					15 09			15b28			15b44			
Chester-le-Street	d															15 18									
Durham	d	13b56				14 27		14b42			14b56					15 25			15b42			15b56			
Middlesbrough	d	14 00									14 50											15 50			
Thornaby	d	14 05									14 55											15 55			
Yarm	d	14 13									15 03											16 03			
Darlington 7	d					14 44		15b00								15 42			16b04						
Northallerton	d	14 27				14 56					15 17					15 53						16 17			
Thirsk	d	14 35									15 25											16 25			
Scarborough	d							14 47											15 47						
Seamer	d							14 52											15 52						
Malton	d							15 10											16 10						
York 8	a	14 55				15 21		15 37			15 51					16 17			16 37			16 51			
	d	14 58				15 28		15 40			15 58					16 28			16 40			16 58			
Hull	d		14 38									15 40											16 40		
Brough	d		14 50									15 52											16 52		
Howden	d											*15 31*											*16 36*		
Selby	d		15 09									16 11											17 11		
South Milford	d																								
Garforth	d	15 13									16 13											17 13			
Leeds 10	a	15 23	15 33			15 53		16 04			16 23	16 35				16 53			17 04			17 23	17 34		
	d	15 25	15 40		15 43	15 55		16 08		16 13	16 25	16 40			16 43	16 55			17 08		17 13	17 26	17 40		17 43
Cottingley	d				15 48					16 18					16 48						17 18				17 48
Morley	d				15 52					16 22					16 52						17 22				17 52
Batley	d				15 57					16 27					16 57						17 27				17 57
Dewsbury	a	15 36			16 00	16 06				16 30	16 36				17 00	17 06					17 30	17 36			18 00
	d	15 36			16 01	16 06				16 31	16 36				17 01	17 06					17 31	17 36			18 01
Ravensthorpe	d				16 04					16 34					17 04						17 34				18 04
Wakefield Westgate	d			15 29										16 29										17 29	
Wakefield Kirkgate	d			15 35			←							16 35			←							17 35	
Mirfield	d			15 51	16 08		16 08			16a37				16 51	17 08		17 08				17a38			17 52	18 08
Deighton	d			15 57	→		16 15							16 57	→		17 14							17 57	→
Huddersfield	a	15 45	15 58	16 04		16 15	16 21	16 25			16 45	16 58		17 04		17 15	17 21		17 25			17 45	17 58	18 05	
	d	15 46	15 59			16 16		16 26	16 30		16 46	16 59	17 04			17 16			17 26	17 30		17 46	17 59		
Slaithwaite	d								16 37				17 11							17 37					
Marsden	d								16 43				17a17							17 43					
Greenfield	d								16 51											17 51					
Mossley (Grtr Manchester)	d								16 55											17 55					
Stalybridge	a							16 43	17 00			17 18							17 43	18 00			18 18		
	d							16 44	17 01			17 18						17 22	17 44	18 01			18 18		
Ashton-under-Lyne	d								17 05									17 26		18 05					
Manchester Victoria	a								17 20									17 35		18 20					
Manchester Piccadilly 10	a	16 19	16 36			16 49		17 05			17 21	17 37				17 49			18 05			18 19	18 37		
	d	16 24				16 54		17 07								17 54			18 07			18 24			
Manchester Airport	a	16 42	*17 07*			17 12		*17 48*			*17 53*					18 12						18 42			
Manchester Oxford Road	a	*16c40*	*16 48*			*17c03*		17 09			*17 40*	*17 52*				*18c03*			18 09			*18c40*	*18 52*		
Birchwood	a							17 24			*17 57*								18 24						
Warrington Central	a	*16c57*						17 29			*18 03*								18 29			*18c57*			
Liverpool Lime Street 10	a	*17c31*				*17c48*		18 00			*18 35*							18 43	18 59			*19c35*			

For general notes see front of timetable
For details of catering facilities see Directory of Train Operators

- **A** From 18 July to Leeds (Table 41)
- **B** Also stops at Hunts Cross 1740
- **C** To Manchester Victoria (Table 41)
- **b** Change at York
- **c** Change at Manchester Piccadilly

Table 39

Saturdays

Newcastle, Middlesbrough, Scarborough, York, Hull, Leeds and Wakefield → Huddersfield → Manchester, Manchester Airport and Liverpool

Network Diagram - see first page of Table 39

		TP	TP	NT	NT	TP	EM	NT	NT	TP	TP	NT	NT	TP	TP	TP	TP	NT	NT	TP	NT	TP	TP	TP	NT
		1◇	1◇			1◇	1◇			1◇	1◇			1◇	1◇	1◇	1◇			1◇		1◇	1◇	1◇	
							A	B						C	D	D	C								
Newcastle 8	d	16 06				16b29				16b44	17 01					17b29	17b29			17b44			18b22		
Chester-le-Street	d	16 15				16b31										17b31	17b31						18b31		
Durham	d	16 21				16b42				16b56	17 13					17b38	17b38			17b56			18b38		
Middlesbrough	d									17 00										18 07				19 00	
Thornaby	d									17 05										18 12				19 05	
Yarm	d									17 13										18 20				19 13	
Darlington 7	d	16 39				17b00					17 30					17b59	17b59						18b56		
Northallerton	d	16 50				16b50				17 27	17 42									18 35			18b45	19 27	
Thirsk	d	16 58								17 35										18 43			18b54	19 35	
Scarborough	d					16 47	17 03									17 45	17 45						18 47		
Seamer	d					16 52										17 50	17 50						18 52		
Malton	d					17 10										18 08	18 08						19 10		
York 8	a	17 18				17 37	17 46			17 55	18 06					18 35	18 35			19 03			19 37	19 58	
	d	17 28				17 40				17 58	18 09					18 38	18 38			19 10			19 40		
Hull	d		17 01											18 03	18 03							18 59			
Brough	d		17 13											18 15	18 15							19 11			
Howden	d													17 54	17 54							19 12			
Selby	d		17 32											18 34	18 34							19 30			
South Milford	d																								
Garforth	d									18 13										19 25					
Leeds 10	a	17 53	17 58			18 04				18 23	18 35			18 58	19 00	19 04	19 04			19 35		19 56	20 04		
	d	17 55				18 08		18 13		18 25	18 40		18 43		19 08		19 08		19 13	19 40			20 08		
Cottingley	d							18 18					18 48						19 18						
Morley	d							18 22					18 52						19 22						
Batley	d							18 27					18 57						19 27						
Dewsbury	a	18 06						18 30		18 36	18 51		19 00						19 30	19 51					
	d	18 06						18 31		18 36	18 51		19 01						19 31	19 51					
Ravensthorpe	d							18 34					19 04						19 34						
Wakefield Westgate	d											18 29									19 29				
Wakefield Kirkgate	d			←								18 34									19 34				
Mirfield	d			18 08				18a37				18 51	19 08						19 38		19 51				
Deighton	d			18 13								18 57	19 12						19 45		20 00				
Huddersfield	a	18 15		18 21		18 25				18 45	18 59	19 04	19 19		19 25		19 25		19 49	19 59	20 04		20 25		
	d	18 16				18 26			18 31	18 46	19 00				19 26		19 26	19 30		20 00			20 26		20 30
Slaithwaite	d								18 38									19 37							20 37
Marsden	d								18 43									19 43							20 43
Greenfield	d								18 51									19 51							20 51
Mossley (Grtr Manchester)	d								18 55									19 55							20 55
Stalybridge	a					18 43			19 00						19 43		19 43	20 00					20 43		21 00
	d				18 22	18 44			19 01						19 44		19 44	20 01					20 44		21 01
Ashton-under-Lyne	d				18 26				19 05									20 05							21 05
Manchester Victoria	a				18 35				19 20									20 20							21 20
Manchester Piccadilly 10	a	18 49				19 05				19 21	19 33				20 05		20 05			20 33			21 05		
	d	18 54				19 07					19 40				20 07		20 07			20 40			21 07		
Manchester Airport	a	19 13								19 50	19 59				20 47		20 47			20 57			21 47		
Manchester Oxford Road	a	19c03				19 09				19 36	19c48				20 09		20 09			20c48			21 09		
Birchwood	a					19 24				20e11					20 24		20 24						21 24		
Warrington Central	a					19 29				19 57					20 29		20 29						21 29		
Liverpool Lime Street 10	a	19c48			19 43	19 57				20 34	20c48				20 59		20 59						21 57		

For general notes see front of timetable
For details of catering facilities see Directory of Train Operators

A Until 5 September. To St Pancras International (Table 53)
B To Manchester Victoria (Table 41)
C From 12 September
D Until 5 September

b Change at York
c Change at Manchester Piccadilly
e Change at Manchester Piccadilly and Manchester Oxford Road

Newcastle, Middlesbrough, Scarborough, York, Hull, Leeds and Wakefield → Huddersfield → Manchester, Manchester Airport and Liverpool

Network Diagram - see first page of Table 39

		NT	TP	NT	TP	TP	NT	NT	TP	NT	TP	NT	NT	TP	NT	NT	TP	NT	NT	TP	TP	TP	TP
			1 ◇		1 ◇	1 ◇			1 ◇		1 ◇			1 ◇			1 ◇			1 ◇	1 ◇	1 ◇	
														A				B	C	B	C	B	B 🚌
Newcastle 8 🚢	d		18 52			19b25			19b43												20c47	20c47	
Chester-le-Street	d																						
Durham	d		19 04			19b37			19b56												21c00	21c00	
Middlesbrough	d								20 10		20 50										21 50	21 50	
Thornaby	d								20 15		20 55										21 55	21 55	
Yarm	d								20 23		21 03												
Darlington 7	d		19 22			19b54															22 19	22 19	
Northallerton	d		19 36						20 37		21 17										22 30	22 30	
Thirsk	d		19 35						20 45												22 38	22 38	
Scarborough	d					19 47											22 07						
Seamer	d					19 52											22 12						
Malton	d					20 10											22 30						
York 8	a		20 02			20 37			21 07		21 41						22 57				22 57	22 57	
	d		20 10			20 40			21 10		21 42										23 07	23 07	
Hull	d				19 56									21 33									
Brough	d				20 08									21 45									
Howden	d																						
Selby	d				20 27									22 07									
South Milford	d				20 36									22 17									
Garforth	d																						
Leeds 10	a		20 35		20 56	21 04			21 35		22 05			22 35							23 33	23 33	
	d	20 13	20 40			21 08		21 13	21 40		22 08		22 17	22 40				23 05	23 13		23 35		23 45
Cottingley	d	20 18						21 18					22 22					23 10	23 18				
Morley	d	20 22						21 22					22 26					23 14	23 22				
Batley	d	20 27						21 27					22 31					23 19	23 27				
Dewsbury	a	20 30	20 51					21 30	21 51				22 34	22 51				23 22	23 30		23 46		00 10
	d	20 31	20 51					21 31	21 51				22 35	22 51				23 23	23 31		23 46		00 10
Ravensthorpe	d	20 34						21 34					22 38					23 26	23 34				
Wakefield Westgate	d			20 29						21 29						22 42							
Wakefield Kirkgate	d			20 35						21 35						22 47							
Mirfield	d	20 38		20 51				21 38		21 48			22 42			23 00		23 30	23 38				
Deighton	d	20 44		21 01				21 45		22 01			22 48			23 08		23 37	23 45				
Huddersfield	a	20 48	20 59	21 05		21 25		21 49	21 59	22 05	22 25		22 53	22 59		23 12		23 41	23 49		23 55		00 35
	d	20 48	21 00			21 26	21 30		22 00		22 26	22 30		23 00	23 05					23 56	23 56		
Slaithwaite	d	20 55					21 37					22 37			23 12								
Marsden	d	21a02					21 43					22 43			23 18								
Greenfield	d						21 51					22 51			23 26								
Mossley (Grtr Manchester)	d						21 55					22 55			23 30								
Stalybridge	a					21 43	22 00				22 43	23 00			23 35								
	d					21 44	22 01				22 44	23 01			23 36								
Ashton-under-Lyne	d						22 05					23 05			23 40								
Manchester Victoria 🚢	a						22 20					23 20			23 53								
Manchester Piccadilly 10 🚢	a		21 33			22 05			22 33		23 05			23 37						00 30	00 41		
	d		21 40			22 07			22 40											00 33	00 45		
Manchester Airport ✈	a		21 57						22 57					00 22						00 48	01 00		
Manchester Oxford Road	a		21e48			22 09			22e48														
Birchwood	a					22 24			23f47														
Warrington Central	a					22 29			23f54														
Liverpool Lime Street 10	a		22f48			22 58			00f34														

For general notes see front of timetable
For details of catering facilities see Directory of Train Operators

- **A** Also stops at Gilberdyke 2152
- **B** From 12 September
- **C** Until 5 September
- **b** Change at York
- **c** Change at Darlington
- **e** Change at Manchester Piccadilly
- **f** Change at Manchester Piccadilly and Manchester Oxford Road

Table 39

Sundays

until 6 September

Newcastle, Middlesbrough, Scarborough, York, Hull and Leeds → Huddersfield → Manchester, Manchester Airport and Liverpool

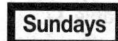

Network Diagram - see first page of Table 39

		TP 1◇	TP 1◇	TP 1◇		TP 1◇	TP 1◇	TP 1◇		TP 1◇	NT	TP 1◇		NT	TP 1◇	TP 1◇		TP 1◇	NT	TP 1◇		NT	TP 1◇	NT	TP 1◇
Newcastle 8	d														08 06					08b55			09 33		
Chester-le-Street	d																						09 42		
Durham	d														08 18					09b07			09 48		
Middlesbrough	d																								10 15
Thornaby	d																								10 20
Yarm	d																								10 28
Darlington 7	d														08 35					09b25			10 05		
Northallerton	d														08 47					09b39			10 16		10 42
Thirsk	d																								10 51
Scarborough	d																			09 20					
Seamer	d																			09 25					
Malton	d																			09 43					
York 8	a														09 11					10 10			10 41		11 10
	d	02 44	03 59	05 12		06 12	07 12			08 10		08 40			09 15					10 15			10 45		11 15
Hull	d															09 00									
Brough	d															09 12									
Howden	d																								
Selby	d															09 31									
South Milford	d															09 40									
Garforth	d																								
Leeds 10	a	03 10	04 25	05 38		06 38	07 38			08 38		09 05			09 38	09 58				10 37			11 08		11 38
	d	03 10	04 25	05 40		06 40	07 40			08 40	08 44	09 10			09 40	10 06				10 40		10 44	11 10		11 40
Cottingley	d										08 49											10 49			
Morley	d										08 53											10 53			
Batley	d										08 58											10 58			
Dewsbury	a			05 51		06 51	07 51			08 51	09 01				09 51					10 51		11 01			11 51
	d			05 51		06 51	07 51			08 51	09 02				09 51					10 51		11 02			11 51
Ravensthorpe	d										09 05											11 05			
Wakefield Westgate	d																								
Wakefield Kirkgate	d																								
Mirfield	d										09 09											11 09			
Deighton	d										09 16											11 15			
Huddersfield	a	03 29	04 44	06 00		07 00	08 00			09 00	09 20	09 27			10 00	10 25				11 00		11 20	11 27		12 00
	d	03 30	04 45	06 01		07 01	08 01			09 01		09 28		09 37	10 01	10 26			10 37	11 00			11 28	11 37	12 01
Slaithwaite	d													09 44					10 44					11 44	
Marsden	d													09 50					10 50					11 50	
Greenfield	d													09 58					10 58					11 58	
Mossley (Grtr Manchester)	d													10 02					11 02					12 02	
Stalybridge	a					07 18	08 18			09 18		09 45		10 07		10 45			11 07				11 45	12 07	
	d					07 19	08 19			09 19		09 46		10 08		10 46			11 08				11 46	12 08	
Ashton-under-Lyne	d													10 12					11 12					12 12	
Manchester Victoria	a													10 26					11 26					12 26	
Manchester Piccadilly 10	a	04 02	05 17	06 34		07 34	08 34			09 34		10 05			10 34	11 05				11 34			12 05		12 34
	d	04 06	05 21	06 38		07 38	08 38	09 07		09 38		10 07			10 38			11 07		11 38			12 07		12 38
Manchester Airport ✈	a	04 23	05 38	06 55		07 55	08 55			09 55					10 55	11 47				11 55					12 55
Manchester Oxford Road	a					07c54	08e48	09 09		09e48		10 09			10e52	11 18		11 09		11e48			12 09		12e48
Birchwood	a					08f25		09 24				10 24				12g04		11 24					12 24		
Warrington Central	a					08f30		09 29				10 29				11h58		11 29					12 29		
Liverpool Lime Street 10	a					09f09	09e53	09 57		10e55		10 57			11e53	12h30		11 59		12e53			12 57		13e53

For general notes see front of timetable
For details of catering facilities see Directory of Train Operators

b Change at York

c Change at Manchester Piccadilly. By bus

e Change at Manchester Piccadilly

f Change at Manchester Piccadilly and Manchester Oxford Road. By bus to Manchester Oxford Road

g Change at Manchester Piccadilly and Manchester Oxford Road

h Until 12 July arr. Warrington Central 12.09, Liverpool Lime Street 1248, change at Manchester Piccadilly and Manchester Oxford Road

Table 39

Sundays
until 6 September

Newcastle, Middlesbrough, Scarborough, York, Hull and Leeds → Huddersfield → Manchester, Manchester Airport and Liverpool

Network Diagram - see first page of Table 39

		TP 1 ◇	TP 1 ◇	NT	TP 1 ◇	NT	TP 1 ◇	NT	TP 1 ◇	NT	TP 1 ◇	TP 1 ◇	TP 1 ◇	NT	TP 1 ◇	NT	TP 1 ◇	NT	TP 1 ◇
Newcastle 8	d		10b30		11 03				11b32		12 05		12b32		13 06		13 28		13b32
Chester-le-Street	d																13 23		
Durham	d		10b38		11 15				11b37		12 17		12b45		13 18		13 40		13b45
Middlesbrough	d												12 45						
Thornaby	d												12 50						
Yarm	d												12 58						
Darlington 7	d		10b59		11 32						12 34		13b03		13 35		13 57		14b05
Northallerton	d				11 42								13 12		13 39				
Thirsk	d												13 22						
Scarborough	d		10 50						11 50										13 50
Seamer	d		10 56						11 55										13 55
Malton	d		11 15						12 13										14 13
York 8	a		11 42		12 07				12 40		13 07		13 42		14 12				14 40
	d		11 45		12 15				12 45		13 15		13 45		14 15		14 33		14 45
Hull	d	10 58					12 00					12 58							
Brough	d	11 10					12 12					13 10							
Howden	d	10 36										12 36							
Selby	d	11 29					12 33					13 29							
South Milford	d	11 38										13 38							
Garforth	d																		
Leeds 10	a	11 56	12 08		12 38		12 56		13 08		13 38	13 56	14 08		14 38		14 56		15 08
	d	11 59	12 10		12 40	12 44	12 59		13 10		13 40	13 59	14 10		14 40	14 44	14 59		15 10
Cottingley	d					12 49										14 49			
Morley	d					12 53										14 53			
Batley	d					12 58										14 58			
Dewsbury	a				12 51	13 01		←			13 51				14 51	15 01			
	d				12 51	13 02 →		13 02			13 51				14 51	15 02			
Ravensthorpe	d							13 05								15 05			
Wakefield Westgate	d																		
Wakefield Kirkgate	d																	←	
Mirfield	d							13 09								15 09 →		15 09	
Deighton	d							13 20										15 20	
Huddersfield	a	12 16	12 27		13 00		13 16	13 24	13 27		14 00	14 16	14 27		15 00		15 16	15 24	15 27
	d	12 17	12 28	12 37	13 01		13 17		13 28	13 37	14 01	14 17	14 28	14 37	15 01		15 17		15 28
Slaithwaite	d			12 44						13 44				14 44					
Marsden	d			12 50						13 50				14 50					
Greenfield	d			12 58						13 58				14 58					
Mossley (Grtr Manchester)	d			13 02						14 02				15 02					
Stalybridge	a		12 45	13 07					13 45	14 07			14 45	15 07					15 45
	d		12 46	13 08					13 46	14 08			14 46	15 08					15 46
Ashton-under-Lyne	d			13 12						14 12				15 12					
Manchester Victoria	a			13 26						14 26				15 26					
Manchester Piccadilly 10	a	12 54	13 05		13 34		13 54		14 05		14 34	14 54	15 05		15 34		15 54		16 05
	d		13 07		13 38				14 07		14 38		15 07		15 38				16 07
Manchester Airport	a	13 19	13 47		13 55		14 19		14 47		14 55	15 20	15 47		15 55		16 19		16 47
Manchester Oxford Road	a		13 09		13c48				14 09		14c48		15 09		15c48				16 09
Birchwood	a		13 24						14 24				15 24						16 24
Warrington Central	a		13 29						14 29				15 29						16 29
Liverpool Lime Street 10	a		13 57		14c53				14 57		15c53		15 57		16c53				16 57

For general notes see front of timetable
For details of catering facilities see Directory of Train Operators

b Change at York
c Change at Manchester Piccadilly

Table 39

Sundays

until 6 September

Newcastle, Middlesbrough, Scarborough, York, Hull and Leeds → Huddersfield → Manchester, Manchester Airport and Liverpool

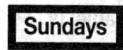

Network Diagram - see first page of Table 39

		NT	TP 1◇	TP 1◇	TP 1◇	NT	TP 1◇	NT	TP 1◇	NT	TP 1◇	NT	TP 1◇	TP 1◇	TP 1◇	TP 1◇	NT	TP 1◇	NT	TP 1◇
Newcastle 8	d		14 08		14b32		15 07		15 25		15b30		16 08			16b33		16 52		17 25
Chester-le-Street	d						15 16											17 01		17 26
Durham	d		14 20		14b37		15 22		15 37		15b37		16 20			16b46		17 08		17 37
Middlesbrough	d				14 45											16 45				
Thornaby	d				14 50											16 50				
Yarm	d				14 58											16 58				
Darlington 7	d		14 37		14b59		15 40		15 54		15b59		16 37			17b04		17 26		17 55
Northallerton	d		14 48		15 12		15 12						16 48			17 12		17 38		17 42
Thirsk	d				15 21											17 21				
Scarborough	d										15 50				16 50					
Seamer	d										15 55									
Malton	d										16 13									
York 8	a		15 12		15 41		16 13				16 40		17 12		17 37	17 41		18 00		
	d		15 15		15 45		16 15		16 33		16 45		17 15			17 45		18 15		18 33
Hull	d			14 58										16 58						
Brough	d			15 10										17 10						
Howden	d			14 34										16 45						
Selby	d			15 29										17 29						
South Milford	d			15 38										17 38						
Garforth	d																			
Leeds 10	a		15 38	15 56	16 08		16 38		16 56		17 08		17 38	17 56		18 08		18 38		18 56
	d		15 40	15 59	16 10		16 40	16 44	16 59		17 10		17 40	17 59		18 10		18 40	18 44	18 59
Cottingley	d							16 49											18 49	
Morley	d							16 53											18 53	
Batley	d							16 58											18 58	
Dewsbury	a		15 51				16 51	17 01					17 51					18 51	19 01	
	d		15 51				16 51	17 02					17 51					18 51	19 02	
Ravensthorpe	d							17 05											19 05	
Wakefield Westgate	d																			
Wakefield Kirkgate	d									←										
Mirfield	d							17 09 →		17 09									19 09 →	
Deighton	d									17 20										
Huddersfield	a		16 00	16 16	16 27		17 00		17 16	17 24	17 27		18 00	18 16		18 27		19 00		19 16
	d	15 37	16 01	16 17	16 28	16 37	17 01		17 17		17 28	17 37	18 01	18 17		18 28	18 37	19 01		19 17
Slaithwaite	d	15 44				16 44						17 44					18 44			
Marsden	d	15 50				16 50						17 50					18 50			
Greenfield	d	15 58				16 58						17 58					18 58			
Mossley (Grtr Manchester)	d	16 02				17 02						18 02					19 02			
Stalybridge	a	16 07			16 46	17 07					17 45	18 07				18 45	19 07			
	d	16 08			16 46	17 08					17 46	18 08				18 46	19 08			
Ashton-under-Lyne	d	16 12				17 12						18 12					19 12			
Manchester Victoria	a	16 26				17 26						18 26					19 26			
Manchester Piccadilly 10	a		16 34	16 54	17 05		17 34		17 54		18 05		18 34	18 54		19 05		19 34		19 54
	d		16 38		17 07		17 38				18 07		18 38			19 07		19 38		
Manchester Airport	a		16 55	17 19	17 47		17 55		18 19		18 47		18 55	19 19		19 47		19 55		20 19
Manchester Oxford Road	a		16c48		17 09		17c48				18 09		18c48			19 09		19c48		
Birchwood	a				17 24						18 24					19 24				
Warrington Central	a				17 29						18 29					19 29				
Liverpool Lime Street 10	a		17c53		17 57		18c53				18 57		19c53			19 57		20c53		

For general notes see front of timetable
For details of catering facilities see Directory of Train Operators

b Change at York
c Change at Manchester Piccadilly

Table 39

Sundays

until 6 September

Newcastle, Middlesbrough, Scarborough, York, Hull and Leeds → Huddersfield → Manchester, Manchester Airport and Liverpool

Network Diagram - see first page of Table 39

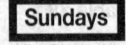

Station		NT		TP 1 ◇	NT	TP 1 ◇		TP 1 ◇	TP 1 ◇	TP 1 ◇		NT	TP 1 ◇	NT		TP 1 ◇	TP 1 ◇	NT	TP 1 ◇	TP 1 ◇	TP 1 ◇	NT	TP 1 ◇		
Newcastle 8 🚢	d			17b30		17 57				18b29			19 06			19b35			20 07		20b31				
Chester-le-Street	d									18b33															
Durham	d					18 09				18b43			19 17			19b48			20 19						
Middlesbrough	d									18 45							20 07						22 07		
Thornaby	d									18 50							20 12						22 12		
Yarm	d									18 58							20 20						22 20		
Darlington 7	d			17b59		18 26				19b01			19 35			20b06			20 36		20b58				
Northallerton	d									19 14			19 39				20 34		20 48				22 34		
Thirsk	d									19 23							20 42						22 42		
Scarborough	d			17 50					18 50							19 50					21 20				
Seamer	d			17 55												19 55					21 25				
Malton	d			18 13												20 13					21 43				
York 8	a			18 40		18 59			19 37	19 42			20 09			20 40	21 02		21 12		22 10		23 09		
	d			18 45		19 15				19 45			20 15			20 45			21 15		22 12		23 12		
Hull	d							18 58												21 00					
Brough	d							19 10												21 12					
Howden	d							19 12																	
Selby	d							19 29												21 31					
South Milford	d							19 38												21 40					
Garforth	d																								
Leeds 10	a			19 08		19 38		19 56		20 08			20 38			21 08			21 38	21 59	22 38		23 38		
	d			19 10		19 40		19 59		20 10			20 40	20 44		21 10			21 40		22 40	22 44	23 40		
Cottingley	d													20 49								22 49			
Morley	d													20 53								22 53			
Batley	d													20 58								22 58			
Dewsbury	a					19 51							20 51	21 01					21 51			23 01	23 51		
	d					19 51							20 51	21 02					21 51			23 02	23 51		
Ravensthorpe	d													21 05								23 05			
Wakefield Westgate	d																								
Wakefield Kirkgate	d	⟵																							
Mirfield	d	19 09												21 09								23 09			
Deighton	d	19 20												21 15								23 16			
Huddersfield	a	19 24		19 27		20 00		20 16		20 27			21 00	21 19		21 27			22 00		22 57	23 20	23 59		
	d			19 28	19 37	20 01		20 17		20 28		20 37	21 01	21 19		21 28		21 37	22 01		22 58		00 01		
Slaithwaite	d				19 44							20 44		21 26				21 44							
Marsden	d				19 50							20 50		21a33				21 50							
Greenfield	d				19 58							20 58						21 58							
Mossley (Grtr Manchester)	d				20 02							21 02						22 02							
Stalybridge	a			19 45	20 07					20 45		21 07	21 18					22 07	22 18		23 18				
	d			19 46	20 08					20 46		21 08	21 19					22 08	22 19		23 19				
Ashton-under-Lyne	d				20 12							21 12						22 12							
Manchester Victoria 🚢	a				20 26							21 26						22 26							
Manchester Piccadilly 10 🚢	a			20 05		20 34		20 54		21 05			21 36			22 05			22 34		23 36		00 43		
	d			20 07		20 38				21 07						22 07			22 38				00 44		
Manchester Airport ✈	a			20 47		20 55		21 19		21 47			22 17						22 55		00 17		01 00		
Manchester Oxford Road	a			20 09		20c48				21 09			21 48			22 09			22c48						
Birchwood	a			20 24						21 24						22 24									
Warrington Central	a			20 29						21 29						22 29									
Liverpool Lime Street 10	a			20 57		21c53				21 57			22 53			22 57			23c53						

For general notes see front of timetable
For details of catering facilities see Directory of Train Operators

b Change at York
c Change at Manchester Piccadilly

Table 39

Sundays

from 13 September

Newcastle, Middlesbrough, Scarborough, York, Hull and Leeds → Huddersfield → Manchester, Manchester Airport and Liverpool

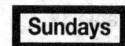

Network Diagram - see first page of Table 39

		TP (bus)	TP (bus)	TP (bus)		TP (bus)	TP 1 ◇	TP 1 ◇		TP 1 ◇	NT	TP 1 ◇		TP 1 ◇	TP 1 ◇	NT		TP 1 ◇	NT	TP 1 ◇		NT	TP 1 ◇	TP (bus)	TP 1 ◇
Newcastle 8 (ship)	d											08 06						08b55		09 33					
Chester-le-Street	d																			09 42					
Durham	d											08 18						09b07		09 48					
Middlesbrough	d																						10 15		
Thornaby	d																						10 20		
Yarm	d																						10 28		
Darlington 7	d											08 35						09b25		10 05					
Northallerton	d											08 47						09b39		10 16			10 42		
Thirsk	d																						10 51		
Scarborough	d																	09 20							
Seamer	d																	09 25							
Malton	d																	09 43							
York 8	a											09 11						10 10		10 41			11 10		
	d	02 00	03 15	04 45		06 15				08 30		09 15			09 45			10 15		10 45			11 15		
Hull	d													09 00											10 58
Brough	d													09 12											11 10
Howden	d																								*10 36*
Selby	d													09 31											11 29
South Milford	d													09 40											11 38
Garforth	d																								
Leeds 10	a	02 45	04 00	05 30		07 00				08 55		09 38		09 58	10 08			10 38		11 08			11 38		11 56
	d	02 45	04 00	05 30		07 00				09 00		09 40			10 10			10 40	10 44	11 10			11 40		11 59
Cottingley	d																		10 49						
Morley	d																		10 53						
Batley	d																		10 58						
Dewsbury	a			05 55		07 25						09 51						10 51	11 01				11 51		12 10
	d			05 55		07 25						09 51						10 51	11 02				11 51		12 10
Ravensthorpe	d																		11 05						
Mirfield	d																		11 09						
Deighton	d																		11 15						
Huddersfield	a	03 20	04 35	06 30		08 00				09 18		10 02						11 02	11 20				12 02		12 20
	d	03 20	04 35	06 30		08 00				09 22		10 03						11 04					12 04	12 10	
Slaithwaite	d																								
Marsden	d																								
Greenfield	d																								
Mossley (Grtr Manchester)	d																								
Stalybridge	a			07 15		08 45																		12 55	
	d			07 15		08 45					10 08					11 08						12 08			
Ashton-under-Lyne	d										10 12					11 12						12 12			
Manchester Victoria (ship)	a									10 08	10 26	10 53			11 04	11 26		11 53		12 04		12 26	12 53		
	d						09 15	10 14		10 15		10 54			11 09			11 54		12 09			12 54		
Manchester Piccadilly 10 (ship)	a	04 20	05 35	07 35		09 05		10 33				11 09						12 09					13 09		
	d	04 20	05 35	07 35		09 05		10 39				11 10						12 10					13 10		
Manchester Airport (plane)	a	04 45	06 00	08 00		09 30		10 53				11 25						12 25					13 25		
Manchester Oxford Road	a																								
Newton-le-Willows	a						09 33			10 33					11 27					12 27					
Birchwood	a																								
Warrington Central	a						*10c05*			*11c05*					*12c00*					*13c00*					
Liverpool Lime Street 10	a						09 57			10 57					11 57					12 57					

For general notes see front of timetable
For details of catering facilities see Directory of Train Operators

b Change at York
c By bus

Sundays

from 13 September

Newcastle, Middlesbrough, Scarborough, York, Hull and Leeds → Huddersfield → Manchester, Manchester Airport and Liverpool

Network Diagram - see first page of Table 39

		TP 1 ◇	NT	TP 1 ◇	NT	TP 1 ◇	TP 1 ◇	NT	NT	TP 1 ◇	TP (bus)	TP 1 ◇	TP 1 ◇	NT	TP 1 ◇	NT	TP 1 ◇	TP 1 ◇	NT
Newcastle 8	d	10b30		11 03			11b32			12 05			12b32		13 06		13 28	13b32	
Chester-le-Street	d																13 23		
Durham	d	10b38		11 15			11b37			12 17			12b45		13 18		13 40	13b45	
Middlesbrough	d												12 45						
Thornaby	d												12 50						
Yarm	d												12 58						
Darlington 7	d	10b59		11 32						12 34			13b03		13 35			14b05	
Northallerton	d			11 42									13 12		13 39				
Thirsk	d												13 22						
Scarborough	d	10 50					11 50											13 50	
Seamer	d	10 56					11 55											13 55	
Malton	d	11 15					12 13											14 13	
York 8	a	11 42		12 07			12 40			13 07			13 42		14 12			14 40	
	d	11 45		12 15			12 45			13 15			13 45		14 15		14 33	14 45	
Hull	d					12 00						12 58							
Brough	d					12 12						13 10							
Howden	d											12 36							
Selby	d					12 33						13 29							
South Milford	d											13 38							
Garforth	d																		
Leeds 10	a	12 08		12 38		12 56	13 08			13 38		13 56	14 08		14 38		14 56	15 08	
	d	12 10		12 40	12 44	12 59	13 10			13 40		13 59	14 10		14 40	14 44	14 59	15 10	
Cottingley	d				12 49											14 49			
Morley	d				12 53											14 53			
Batley	d				12 58											14 58			
Dewsbury	a			12 51	13 01	13 10				13 51		14 10			14 51	15 01	15 10		
	d			12 51	13 02	13 10				13 51		14 10			14 51	15 02	15 10		
Ravensthorpe	d				13 05			←								15 05			←
Mirfield	d				13 09 →			13 09								15 09 →			15 09
Deighton	d							13 20											15 20
Huddersfield	a			13 02		13 20		13 24		14 02		14 20			15 02		15 20		15 24
	d			13 04						14 04	14 10				15 04				
Slaithwaite	d																		
Marsden	d																		
Greenfield	d																		
Mossley (Grtr Manchester)	d																		
Stalybridge	a										14 55								
	d		13 08						14 08					15 08					
Ashton-under-Lyne	d		13 12						14 12					15 12					
Manchester Victoria	a	13 04	13 26	13 53			14 04		14 26	14 53			15 04	15 26	15 53			16 04	
	d	13 09		13 54			14 09			14 54			15 09		15 54			16 09	
Manchester Piccadilly 10	a			14 09						15 09					16 09				
	d			14 10						15 10					16 10				
Manchester Airport	a			14 25						15 25					16 25				
Manchester Oxford Road	a																		
Newton-le-Willows	a	13 27					14 27						15 27					16 27	
Birchwood	a																		
Warrington Central	a	14c00					15c00						16c00					17c00	
Liverpool Lime Street 10	a	13 57					14 57						15 57					16 57	

For general notes see front of timetable
For details of catering facilities see Directory of Train Operators

b Change at York
c By bus

Table 39

Sundays

from 13 September

Newcastle, Middlesbrough, Scarborough, York, Hull and Leeds → Huddersfield → Manchester, Manchester Airport and Liverpool

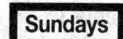

Network Diagram - see first page of Table 39

		NT	TP 1 ◇	TP 1 ◇	TP 1 ◇	NT	TP 1 ◇	NT	TP 🚌	TP 1 ◇	TP 1 ◇	NT	NT	TP 1 ◇	TP 1 ◇	TP 1 ◇	NT	TP 1 ◇	NT	TP 🚌
Newcastle 8 🚢	d		14 08		14b32		15 07			15 25	15b30			16 08		16b33		16 52		
Chester-le-Street	d						15 16											17 01		
Durham	d		14 20		14b37		15 22			15 37				16 20		16b46		17 08		
Middlesbrough	d				14 45											16 45				
Thornaby	d				14 50											16 50				
Yarm	d				14 58											16 58				
Darlington 7	d		14 37		14b59		15 40				15b59			16 37		17b04		17 26		
Northallerton	d		14 48		15 12									16 48		17 12		17 38		
Thirsk	d				15 21											17 21				
Scarborough	d										15 50									
Seamer	d										15 55									
Malton	d										16 13									
York 8	a		15 12		15 41		16 13				16 40			17 12		17 41		18 00		
	d		15 15		15 45		16 15			16 33	16 45			17 15		17 45		18 15		
Hull	d			14 58											16 58					
Brough	d			15 10											17 10					
Howden	d			14 34											16 45					
Selby	d			15 29											17 29					
South Milford	d			15 38											17 38					
Garforth	d																			
Leeds 10	a		15 38	15 56	16 08		16 38			16 56	17 08			17 38	17 56	18 08		18 38		
	d		15 40	15 59	16 10		16 40	16 44		16 59	17 10			17 40	17 59	18 10		18 40	18 44	
Cottingley	d							16 49											18 49	
Morley	d							16 53											18 53	
Batley	d							16 58											18 58	
Dewsbury	a		15 51	16 10			16 51	17 01		17 10				17 51	18 10			18 51	19 01	
	d		15 51	16 10			16 51	17 02		17 10				17 51	18 10			18 51	19 02	
Ravensthorpe	d							17 05				←							19 05	
Mirfield	d							17 09				17 09							19 09	
Deighton	d							→				17 20							→	
Huddersfield	a		16 02	16 20			17 02			17 20		17 24		18 02	18 20			19 02		
	d		16 04				17 04		17 10					18 04				19 04		19 10
Slaithwaite	d																			
Marsden	d																			
Greenfield	d																			
Mossley (Grtr Manchester)	d																			
Stalybridge	a								17 55											19 55
	d	16 08				17 08							18 08				19 08			
Ashton-under-Lyne	d	16 12				17 12							18 12				19 12			
Manchester Victoria 🚢	a	16 26	16 53		17 04	17 26	17 53				18 04		18 26	18 53		19 04	19 26	19 53		
	d		16 54		17 09		17 54				18 09			18 54		19 09		19 54		
Manchester Piccadilly 10 🚢	a		17 09				18 09							19 09				20 09		
	d		17 10				18 10							19 10				20 10		
Manchester Airport ✈	a		17 25				18 25							19 25				20 25		
Manchester Oxford Road	a																			
Newton-le-Willows	a				17 27						18 27					19 27				
Birchwood	a																			
Warrington Central	a				18c00						19c00					20c00				
Liverpool Lime Street 10	a				17 57						18 57					19 57				

For general notes see front of timetable
For details of catering facilities see
Directory of Train Operators

b Change at York
c By bus

Sundays

from 13 September

Newcastle, Middlesbrough, Scarborough, York, Hull and Leeds → Huddersfield → Manchester, Manchester Airport and Liverpool

Network Diagram - see first page of Table 39

		TP 1◇		TP 1◇	NT	NT		TP 1◇	TP 1◇	TP 1◇		NT	TP 1◇	NT		TP 1◇	TP 1◇	NT	TP 1◇	TP 1◇	TP 1◇	NT	TP 1◇		
Newcastle 8	d	17b18		17c30				17 57		18c29			19 06			19c35			20 07		20c31				
Chester-le-Street	d	17 26								18c33															
Durham	d	17b33						18 09		18c43			19 17			19c48			20 19		20c19				
Middlesbrough	d									18 45							20 07						22 07		
Thornaby	d									18 50							20 12						22 12		
Yarm	d									18 58							20 20						22 20		
Darlington 7	d	17b50		17c59				18 26		19c01			19 35			20c06			20 36		20c58				
Northallerton	d	17 42								19 14			19 39				20 34		20 48				22 34		
Thirsk	d									19 23							20 42						22 42		
Scarborough	d			17 50												19 50					21 20				
Seamer	d			17 55												19 55					21 25				
Malton	d			18 13												20 13					21 43				
York 8	a			18 40				18 59		19 42			20 09			20 40	21 02		21 12		22 10		23 09		
	d	18 33		18 45				19 15		19 45			20 15			20 45			21 15		22 12		23 12		
Hull	d								18 58											21 00					
Brough	d								19 10											21 12					
Howden	d								*19 12*																
Selby	d								19 29											21 31					
South Milford	d								19 38											21 40					
Garforth	d																								
Leeds 10	a	18 56		19 08				19 38	19 56	20 08			20 38			21 08			21 38	21 59	22 38		23 38		
	d	18 59		19 10				19 40	19 59	20 10			20 40	20 44		21 10			21 40		22 40	22 44	23 40		
Cottingley	d													20 49								22 49			
Morley	d													20 53								22 53			
Batley	d													20 58								22 58			
Dewsbury	a	19 10						19 51	20 10				20 51	21 01					21 51			23 01	23 51		
	d	19 10						19 51	20 10				20 51	21 02					21 51			23 02	23 51		
Ravensthorpe	d				←									21 05								23 05			
Mirfield	d				19 09									21 09								23 09			
Deighton	d				19 20									21 15								23 16			
Huddersfield	a	19 20			19 24			20 02	20 20				21 02	21 19					22 02		22 57	23 20	00 02		
	d							20 04					21 04	21 19					22 04		23 04		00 04		
Slaithwaite	d													21 26											
Marsden	d													21a33											
Greenfield	d																								
Mossley (Grtr Manchester)	d																								
Stalybridge	a																								
	d					20 08						21 08						22 08							
Ashton-under-Lyne	d					20 12						21 12						22 12							
Manchester Victoria	a			20 04		20 26		20 53		21 04		21 26	21 53			22 04		22 26	22 53		23s53		00s59		
	d			20 09				20 54		21 09			21 54			22 09			23 06						
Manchester Piccadilly 10	a							21 09					22 15						23 24		00 09		01 16		
	d							21 10											23 26				01 16		
Manchester Airport	a							21 25					*23 08*						23 40		*01 31*		01 31		
Manchester Oxford Road	a																								
Newton-le-Willows	a			20 27						21 27						22 27									
Birchwood	a																								
Warrington Central	a			*21e00*						*22e00*						*23e00*									
Liverpool Lime Street 10	a			20 57						21 57						22 57									

For general notes see front of timetable
For details of catering facilities see Directory of Train Operators

b From 8 November dep. Newcastle 1725, Durham 1737 and Darlington 1755

c Change at York

e By bus

Liverpool, Manchester Airport and Manchester → Huddersfield → Wakefield, Leeds, Hull, York, Scarborough, Middlesbrough and Newcastle

Network Diagram - see first page of Table 39

Miles	Miles	Miles	Miles	Miles			TP MX 1 ◇	TP MO 1 ◇	TP 1 ◇	TP 1 ◇	NT	TP 1 ◇	TP 1 ◇	NT	NT	TP 1 ◇	TP 1 ◇ 🍴	NT	NT	TP 1 ◇ 🍴	NT A	NT	TP 1 ◇ B 🍴	
0	—	—	—	—	**Liverpool Lime Street** 10	d																	06 16	
18½	—	—	—	—	Warrington Central	d																	06 38	
21¾	—	—	—	—	Birchwood	d																	06 43	
34¼	—	—	—	—	Manchester Oxford Road	d																	07 07	
—	—	—	—	—	**Manchester Airport** ✈	d	01 00	01 00		04 00			05 37							06 23				
34¾	—	—	—	—	**Manchester Piccadilly** 10 🚢	a	01 14	01 14		04 14			05 51							06 39			07 09	
—	—	—	—	—		d	01 16	01 16		04 15		05 39	05 57				06 21			06 54			07 11	
—	—	—	—	0	**Manchester Victoria** 🚢	d																06 55		
—	—	—	—	6½	Ashton-under-Lyne	d																07 05		
42¼	—	—	—	7¾	**Stalybridge**	a						05 52								07 07		07 10	07 26	
—	—	—	—	—		d						05 52							06 41	07 07		07 11	07 26	
45	—	—	—	10½	Mossley (Grtr Manchester)	d													06 45			07 15		
47¼	—	—	—	12¾	Greenfield	d													06 49			07 19		
53¼	—	—	—	18¾	Marsden	d												06 48	06 58			07 28		
55¾	—	—	—	21¼	Slaithwaite	d												06 52	07 02			07 32		
60¼	—	—	—	25¼	**Huddersfield**	a	02 14	02 14		05 13		06 10	06 26				06 54	07 00	07 10	07 25		07 40	07 44	
—	—	—	—	—		d	02 18	02 18		05 16	05 32	06 11	06 27	06 31	06 41		06 56	07 00		07 26			07 45	
62¼	—	—	—	27¾	Deighton	d					05 36			06 34	06 45			07 03						
65¼	—	—	—	30¾	Mirfield	d					05 41			06 39	06 50			07 08			07 24			
—	—	—	—	40¼	Wakefield Kirkgate	a					05 57				07 03									
—	—	—	—	41¼	**Wakefield Westgate**	a					06 05				07 10									
66¾	—	—	—	—	Ravensthorpe	d								06 42				07 11			07 27			
68¼	—	—	—	—	**Dewsbury**	a							06 36	06 46			07 05	07 15			07 31		07 54	
—	—	—	—	—		d							06 37	06 46			07 06	07 15			07 35		07 55	
69¾	—	—	—	—	Batley	d								06 49				07 18			07 38			
73	—	—	—	—	Morley	d								06 55				07 24			07 44			
74½	—	—	—	—	Cottingley	d								06 59				07 28			07 47			
77½	0	—	0	—	**Leeds** 10	a	02 40	02 56		05 37		06 32	06 53	07 08			07 19	07 38		07 48	07 55		08 10	
—	—	—	—	—		d	02 45	02 59		05 40		06 35	06 55				07 23			07 50			08 12	
84¾	7¼	—	7¼	—	Garforth	d														08 00				
—	12¾	—	—	—	South Milford	a																		
—	20¾	—	—	—	Selby	a											07 43							
—	29½	—	—	—	Howden	a											07 52							
—	41¼	—	—	—	Brough	a											08 04							
—	51¾	—	—	—	**Hull**	a											08 20							
103	—	0	25½	—	**York** 8	a	03 15	03 29		06 20		07 01	07 22							08 21			08 34	
—	—	—	—	—		d			05 54	06 38		07 06	07 25			07 34				08 23			08 38	08 42
—	—	—	46½	—	Malton	d				07 02			07 49										09 02	
—	—	—	64¾	—	Seamer	a				07 19			08 06										09 19	
—	—	—	67½	—	**Scarborough**	a				07 30			08 15										09 30	
125¼	—	22¼	—	—	Thirsk	a			06 10			07 22				07 54				08 39				
133	—	30	—	—	Northallerton	a			06 18			07 30				08 01				08 48				09 02
147	—	—	—	—	**Darlington** 7	a			06 29	07b05		07 41	08b05							09b02				09 14
—	—	42¼	—	—	Yarm	d										08 15				09 03				
—	—	47½	—	—	Thornaby	a			06 53							08 25				09 11				
—	—	50¾	—	—	**Middlesbrough**	a			07 01							08 34				09 21				
169	—	—	—	—	Durham	a				07b23		07 58	08b26							09b20				09 31
174¾	—	—	—	—	Chester-le-Street	a				07c48		08 04	08c43											09 44
183	—	—	—	—	**Newcastle** 8 🚢	a				07b39		08 18	08b39							09b36				09 49

For general notes see front of timetable
For details of catering facilities see Directory of Train Operators

A From Halifax (Table 41)
B 🍴 to York
b Change at York
c Change at York and Durham

Liverpool, Manchester Airport and Manchester → Huddersfield → Wakefield, Leeds, Hull, York, Scarborough, Middlesbrough and Newcastle

Network Diagram - see first page of Table 39

Station		NT	TP	NT	TP	NT	NT	TP	NT	NT	NT	TP	NT		TP	NT	NT	TP	TP	NT	NT	NT	TP	TP	NT
			1 ◇		1 ◇			1 ◇				1 ◇			1 ◇			1 ◇	1 ◇				1 ◇	1 ◇	
				A						B	C						A					B			A
			⊼		⊼			⊼				⊼			⊼			⊼	⊼				⊼	⊼	
Liverpool Lime Street 10	d											07 16				07 16							08 22		
Warrington Central	d											07 40											08 44		
Birchwood	d											07 45											08 49		
Manchester Oxford Road	d											08 06											09 07		
Manchester Airport ✈	d		07 05					07 35							08 05				08 35					09 05	
Manchester Piccadilly 10 ⛴	a		07 22					07 49				08 08			08 22				08 49				09 09	09 22	
	d		07 26		07 36			07 56				08 10			08 26			08 42	08 55				09 11	09 26	
Manchester Victoria ⛴	d						07 40				08 02					08 27				08 57					
Ashton-under-Lyne	d						07 49				08 12					08 37				09 07					
Stalybridge	a				07 49		07 54	08 09			08 18	08 26				08 41				09 13			09 26		
	d				07 49		07 54	08 09				08 26				08 42							09 26		
Mossley (Grtr Manchester)	d						07 59									08 46									
Greenfield	d						08 03									08 50									
Marsden	d						08 11									08 59									
Slaithwaite	d						08 16									09 03									
Huddersfield	a		07 56		08 09		08 23	08 28				08 44			08 56	09 11		09 15	09 26				09 44	09 56	
	d	07 49	07 57		08 10	08 13		08 30	08 33	08 37		08 45			08 57			09 16	09 27		09 31	09 35	09 45	09 57	
Deighton	d	07 53				08 16			08 36	08 40											09 34	09 38			
Mirfield	d	07 58		08 06		08 21			08 41	08 45							09 07				09 39	09 43			10 07
Wakefield Kirkgate	a	08 13								09 02												10 03			
Wakefield Westgate	a	08 22								09 08												10 10			
Ravensthorpe	d					08 24			08 44												09 42				
Dewsbury	a		08 06	08 11	08 19	08 27		08 39	08 48				←		09 06		09 12		09 36		09 46			10 06	10 12
	d		08 07	08 12	08 20	08 27		08 39	08 53				08 53		09 07		09 12		09 37		09 46			10 07	10 12
Batley	d			08 15		08 30			→				08 56				09 15				09 49				10 15
Morley	d			08 21		08 36							09 02				09 21				09 55				10 21
Cottingley	d			08 24		08 39							09 06								09 59				
Leeds 10	a		08 24	08 32	08 36	08 52		08 54				09 06	09 17		09 22		09 31	09 36	09 52		10 07		10 09	10 22	10 31
	d		08 27		08 38			08 57				09 12			09 27			09 38	09 57				10 12	10 27	
Garforth	d							09 05											10 05						
South Milford	a																								
Selby	a				08 58													09 57							
Howden	a				*09 31*													*10 22*							
Brough	a																	10 15							
Hull	a				09 31													10 34							
York 8	a		08 57					09 23				09 35			09 55				10 23				10 35	10 52	
	d		09 03					09 26				09 38			10 00				10 26				10 38	10 54	
Malton	d											10 02											11 02		
Seamer	a											10 19											11 19		
Scarborough	a											10 32											11 30		
Thirsk	a							09 45							*10 29*				10 45						
Northallerton	a		09 24					09 57							10 20				10 55					11 15	
Darlington 7	a		09 36					*10b04*				*10b17*			10 32				*10b59*				*11b12*	11 27	
Yarm	d							10 12											11 10						
Thornaby	a							10 22											11 20						
Middlesbrough	a							10 30											11 30						
Durham	a		09 53					*10b21*				*10b34*			10 50				*11b17*				*11b29*	11 44	
Chester-le-Street	a														10 56										
Newcastle 8 ⛴	a		10 10					*10b36*				*10b57*			11 10				*11b32*				*11b54*	12 00	

For general notes see front of timetable
For details of catering facilities see Directory of Train Operators

A From Manchester Victoria (Table 41)
B From Selby (Table 41)
C From Wigan Wallgate (Table 82)

b Change at York

Liverpool, Manchester Airport and Manchester → Huddersfield → Wakefield, Leeds, Hull, York, Scarborough, Middlesbrough and Newcastle

Network Diagram - see first page of Table 39

Station		NT	NT	TP 1 ◇	TP 1 ◇	NT		NT	TP 1 ◇	TP 1 ◇	NT	NT	NT	TP 1 ◇	TP 1 ◇	NT	NT	TP 1 ◇	TP 1 ◇	NT	NT		NT	TP 1 ◇	TP 1 ◇
								A			B						A			B					
				(trolley)	(trolley)				(trolley)	(trolley)				(trolley)	(trolley)			(trolley)	(trolley)					(trolley)	(trolley)
Liverpool Lime Street 10	d		08 44						09 22				09 46					10 22					10 46		
Warrington Central	d								09 44									10 44							
Birchwood	d								09 49									10 49							
Manchester Oxford Road	d								10 07									11 07							
Manchester Airport ✈	d				09 35					10 05					10 35				11 05						11 35
Manchester Piccadilly 10	a				09 52				10 09	10 22					10 52			11 09	11 22						11 52
	d			09 42	09 57				10 11	10 27				10 42	10 57			11 11	11 27					11 42	11 57
Manchester Victoria	d	09 27	09 57									10 27	10 57								11 27		11 57		
Ashton-under-Lyne	d	09 37	10 07									10 37	11 07								11 37		12 07		
Stalybridge	a	09 42	10 13						10 26			10 42	11 13					11 26			11 42		12 13		
	d	09 42							10 26			10 42						11 26			11 42				
Mossley (Grtr Manchester)	d	09 47										10 47									11 47				
Greenfield	d	09 51										10 51									11 51				
Marsden	d	09 59										10 59									11 59				
Slaithwaite	d	10 04										11 04									12 04				
Huddersfield	a	10 12		10 15	10 26				10 44	10 56		11 12		11 15	11 26			11 44	11 56		12 12			12 15	12 26
	d			10 16	10 27	10 31		10 35	10 45	10 57				11 16	11 27	11 31	11 35	11 45	11 57					12 16	12 27
Deighton	d					10 34		10 38								11 34	11 38								
Mirfield	d					10 39		10 43			11 07					11 39	11 43			12 07					
Wakefield Kirkgate	a							11 02									12 02								
Wakefield Westgate	a							11 08									12 08								
Ravensthorpe	d					10 42										11 42									
Dewsbury	a				10 36	10 46				11 06	11 12				11 36	11 46			12 06	12 12					12 36
	d				10 37	10 46				11 07	11 12				11 37	11 46			12 07	12 12					12 37
Batley	d					10 49					11 15					11 49				12 15					
Morley	d					10 55					11 21					11 55				12 21					
Cottingley	d					10 59										11 59									
Leeds 10	a			10 36	10 52	11 07			11 09	11 22	11 33			11 36	11 52	12 07		12 09	12 22	12 31				12 36	12 52
	d			10 38	10 57				11 12	11 27				11 38	11 57			12 12	12 27					12 38	12 57
Garforth	d				11 05										12 05										13 05
South Milford	a																								
Selby	a			10 57										11 57										12 57	
Howden	a			*12 01*										*12 27*										*13 54*	
Brough	a			11 15										12 15										13 15	
Hull	a			11 34										12 36										13 34	
York 8	a				11 23				11 35	11 52					12 23			12 35	12 52						13 23
	d				11 26				11 38	12 01					12 26			12 38	12 59						13 26
Malton	d								12 02									13 02							
Seamer	a								12 19									13 19							
Scarborough	a								12 30									13 30							
Thirsk	a				11 45										12 46				*13 37*						13 46
Northallerton	a				11 55					12 21					12 55				13 19						13 55
Darlington 7	a				*11b58*				*12b20*	12 33					*13b00*			*13b13*	13 31						*14b00*
Yarm	d				12 10										13 10										14 10
Thornaby	a				12 18										13 20										14 18
Middlesbrough	a				12 30										13 30										14 30
Durham	a				*12b22*				*12b38*	12 50					*13b18*			*13b30*	13 48						*14b18*
Chester-le-Street	a								*12b50*										13 54						
Newcastle 8	a				*12b36*				*12b55*	13 08					*13b33*			*13b50*	14 09						*14b36*

For general notes see front of timetable
For details of catering facilities see Directory of Train Operators

A From Selby (Table 41)
B From Manchester Victoria (Table 41)
b Change at York

Liverpool, Manchester Airport and Manchester → Huddersfield → Wakefield, Leeds, Hull, York, Scarborough, Middlesbrough and Newcastle

Network Diagram - see first page of Table 39

		NT	NT	TP	TP	NT	NT	NT	TP	TP	NT	NT	TP	TP		NT	NT	NT	TP	TP	NT	NT	TP	TP	NT
				1 ◇	1 ◇				1 ◇	1 ◇			1 ◇	1 ◇					1 ◇	1 ◇			1 ◇	1 ◇	
			A			B						A				B						A			B
				⊼	⊼				⊼	⊼			⊼	⊼					⊼	⊼			⊼	⊼	
Liverpool Lime Street 10	d			11 22				11 46					12 22					12 46					13 22		
Warrington Central	d			11 44									12 44										13 44		
Birchwood	d			11 49									12 49										13 49		
Manchester Oxford Road	d			12 07									13 07										14 07		
Manchester Airport ✈	d				12 05					12 35				13 05						13 35				14 05	
Manchester Piccadilly 10 ⇌	a			12 09	12 22					12 52			13 09	13 22						13 52			14 09	14 22	
	d			12 11	12 27				12 42	12 57			13 11	13 27					13 42	13 57			14 11	14 27	
Manchester Victoria ⇌	d						12 27	12 57									13 27	13 57							
Ashton-under-Lyne	d						12 37	13 07									13 37	14 07							
Stalybridge	a			12 26			12 42	13 13					13 26				13 42	14 13					14 26		
	d			12 26			12 42						13 26				13 42						14 26		
Mossley (Grtr Manchester)	d						12 47										13 47								
Greenfield	d						12 51										13 51								
Marsden	d						12 59										13 59								
Slaithwaite	d						13 04										14 04								
Huddersfield	a			12 44	12 56		13 12		13 15	13 26			13 44	13 56			14 12		14 15	14 26			14 44	14 56	
	d	12 31	12 35	12 45	12 57				13 16	13 27	13 31	13 35	13 45	13 57					14 16	14 27	14 31	14 35	14 45	14 57	
Deighton	d	12 34	12 38								13 34	13 38									14 34	14 38			
Mirfield	d	12 39	12 43			13 07					13 39	13 43				14 07					14 39	14 43			15 07
Wakefield Kirkgate	a		13 02									14 02										15 02			
Wakefield Westgate	a		13 08									14 08										15 08			
Ravensthorpe	d	12 42									13 42										14 42				
Dewsbury	a	12 46			13 06	13 12				13 36	13 46			14 06		14 12				14 36	14 46			15 06	15 12
	d	12 46			13 07	13 12				13 37	13 46			14 07		14 12				14 37	14 46			15 07	15 12
Batley	d	12 49				13 15					13 49					14 15					14 49				15 15
Morley	d	12 55				13 21					13 55					14 21					14 55				15 21
Cottingley	d	12 59									13 59										14 59				
Leeds 10	a	13 07		13 09	13 22	13 31			13 36	13 52	14 07		14 09	14 22		14 31			14 36	14 52	15 07		15 09	15 22	15 31
	d			13 12	13 27				13 38	13 57			14 12	14 27					14 38	14 57			15 12	15 27	
Garforth	d									14 05										15 05					
South Milford	a																								
Selby	a								13 57										14 57						
Howden	a																		*15 37*						
Brough	a								14 15										15 15						
Hull	a								14 34										15 34						
York 8	a			13 35	13 52					14 23			14 35	14 52						15 23			15 35	15 52	
	d			13 38	13 54					14 26			14 38	14 54						15 26			15 38		
Malton	d			14 02									15 02										16 02		
Seamer	a			14 19									15 19										16 19		
Scarborough	a			14 30									15 30										16 30		
Thirsk	a									14 42										15 46					
Northallerton	a				14 15					14 53				15 22						15 55					
Darlington 7	a			*14b16*	14 27					*14b58*			*15b16*	15 34						*16b06*			*16b11*	16 50	
Yarm	d									15 08										16 09					
Thornaby	a									15 20										16 20					
Middlesbrough	a									15 30										16 30					
Durham	a			*14b34*	14 50					*15b15*			*15b34*	15 51						*16b24*			*16b29*	17 08	
Chester-le-Street	a			*14b41*										15 57											
Newcastle 8 ⇌	a			*14b56*	15 06					*15b31*			*15b57*	16 12						*16b37*			*16b51*	17 26	

For general notes see front of timetable
For details of catering facilities see Directory of Train Operators

A From Selby (Table 41)
B From Manchester Victoria (Table 41)
b Change at York

Liverpool, Manchester Airport and Manchester → Huddersfield → Wakefield, Leeds, Hull, York, Scarborough, Middlesbrough and Newcastle

Network Diagram - see first page of Table 39

		NT	NT	TP 1 ◇	TP 1 ◇	NT	NT		TP 1 ◇	TP 1 ◇	NT	NT	NT	TP 1 ◇	TP 1 ◇	NT	NT	TP 1 ◇	TP 1 ◇	NT	NT	NT		TP 1 ◇	TP 1 ◇
							A				B						A			B					
				⚒	⚒				⚒	⚒				⚒	⚒			⚒	⚒					⚒	⚒
Liverpool Lime Street 10	d		13 46						14 22				14 46					15 22							
Warrington Central	d								14 44									15 44							
Birchwood	d								14 49									15 49							
Manchester Oxford Road	d								15 07									16 07							
Manchester Airport ✈	d				14 35					15 05					15 35				16 05						16 35
Manchester Piccadilly 10	a				14 52				15 09	15 22					15 52			16 09	16 22						16 52
	d			14 42	14 57				15 11	15 27				15 42	15 57			16 11	16 27					16 42	16 56
Manchester Victoria	d	14 27	14 58								15 00	15 27	15 57								16 17	16 27			
Ashton-under-Lyne	d	14 37	15 08									15 37	16 07								16 27	16 37			
Stalybridge	a	14 42	15 13						15 26			15 42	16 13					16 26			16 33	16 42			17 09
	d	14 42							15 26			15 42						16 26				16 42			17 09
Mossley (Grtr Manchester)	d	14 47										15 47										16 47			
Greenfield	d	14 51										15 51										16 51			
Marsden	d	14 59										15 59										16 59			
Slaithwaite	d	15 04										16 04										17 04			
Huddersfield	a	15 12		15 15	15 26				15 44	15 56		16 12		16 15	16 26			16 44	16 56			17 12		17 15	17 27
	d			15 16	15 27	15 31	15 35		15 45	15 57				16 16	16 27	16 31	16 35	16 45	16 57					17 16	17 28
Deighton	d					15 34	15 38									16 34	16 38								
Mirfield	d					15 39	15 43				16 07					16 39	16 43			17 07					
Wakefield Kirkgate	a						16 02										17 02								
Wakefield Westgate	a						16 08										17 08								
Ravensthorpe	d					15 42										16 42									
Dewsbury	a				15 36	15 46				16 06	16 12				16 36	16 46			17 06	17 12					17 36
	d				15 37	15 46				16 07	16 12				16 37	16 46			17 07	17 12					17 37
Batley	d					15 49					16 15					16 49				17 15					
Morley	d					15 55					16 21					16 55				17 21					
Cottingley	d					15 59										16 59									
Leeds 10	a			15 36	15 52	16 07			16 09	16 22	16 31			16 36	16 52	17 07		17 09	17 22	17 31				17 37	17 52
	d			15 38	15 57				16 12	16 27				16 38	16 57			17 12	17 24					17 38	17 57
Garforth	d				16 05										17 05				17 34						18 05
South Milford	a																								
Selby	a			15 57										17 00										18 04	
Howden	a			*16 51*										*17 54*										18 15	
Brough	a			16 15										17 18										18 27	
Hull	a			16 35										17 37										18 46	
York 8	a				16 23				16 35	16 54					17 22			17 38	17 57						18 24
	d				16 26				16 38	16 58					17 26			17 43	18 00						18 26
Malton	d								17 02						17 50				18 24						
Seamer	a								17 19						18 07				18 41						
Scarborough	a								17 30						18 17				18 51						
Thirsk	a				16 46					17 14								17 59							18 46
Northallerton	a				16 55					17 22					17b56			18 09							18 55
Darlington 7	a				16b57				17b08	17 36					17b59			18b15							19b00
Yarm	d				17 09													18 24							19 09
Thornaby	a				17 19													18 32							19 18
Middlesbrough	a				17 30													18 42							19 30
Durham	a				17b14				17b31	17 55					18b17			18b33							19b18
Chester-le-Street	a								17b40	18 01															
Newcastle 8	a				17b34				17b38	18 16					18b36			18b55							19b34

For general notes see front of timetable
For details of catering facilities see Directory of Train Operators

A From Selby (Table 41)
B From Manchester Victoria (Table 41)
b Change at York

Liverpool, Manchester Airport and Manchester → Huddersfield → Wakefield, Leeds, Hull, York, Scarborough, Middlesbrough and Newcastle

Network Diagram - see first page of Table 39

		NT	NT	NT	TP	NT	TP	NT	NT	TP	TP	NT	NT	NT	TP		NT	TP	NT	NT	TP	TP	NT	NT	TP
					1 ◊		1 ◊			1 ◊	1 ◊				1 ◊			1 ◊			1 ◊	1 ◊			1 ◊
			A			B		C					D						C					A	
Liverpool Lime Street 10	d			15 46	16 22									16 46	17 22										18 22
Warrington Central	d				16 44										17 44										18 44
Birchwood	d				16 49										17 49										18 49
Manchester Oxford Road	d				17 07										18 07										19 07
Manchester Airport ✈	d						17 05				17 35											18 35			
Manchester Piccadilly 10	a				17 09		17 22				17 52				18 09							18 52			19 09
	d				17 11		17 26			17 42	17 56				18 11			18 25			18 42	18 57			19 11
Manchester Victoria	d			16 57		17 15			17 27					17 57						18 27					
Ashton-under-Lyne	d			17 07		17 24			17 37					18 07						18 37					
Stalybridge	a			17 12	17 26	17 29	17 39		17 42		18 09			18 12	18 26					18 42					19 26
	d			17 12	17 26	17 29	17 39		17 42		18 09			18 12	18 26					18 42					19 26
Mossley (Grtr Manchester)	d			17 17		17 34			17 47					18 17						18 47					
Greenfield	d			17 21		17 38			17 51					18 21						18 51					
Marsden	d			17 29					17 59					18 29						18 59					
Slaithwaite	d			17 34										18 34						19 04					
Huddersfield	a			17 42	17 44	17 53	17 57		18 11	18 15	18 27			18 43	18 44			18 56		19 12	19 15	19 26			19 44
	d	17 31	17 35		17 45		17 57			18 16	18 27	18 36	18 40		18 45			18 57			19 16	19 27	19 31	19 35	19 45
Deighton	d	17 34	17 38									18 39	18 43										19 34	19 38	
Mirfield	d	17 39	17 43					18 08				18 44	18 48						19 08				19 39	19 43	
Wakefield Kirkgate	a		18 02										19 02											20 03	
Wakefield Westgate	a		18 08										19 08											20 09	
Ravensthorpe	d	17 42										18 47											19 42		
Dewsbury	a	17 46					18 06	18 13			18 37	18 51				←		19 06	19 13			19 36	19 46		
	d	17 46					18 07	18 14			18 37	18 56 →				18 56		19 07	19 13			19 37	19 46		
Batley	d	17 49						18 17								18 59			19 16				19 49		
Morley	d	17 55						18 23								19 05			19 22				19 55		
Cottingley	d	17 59														19 09							19 59		
Leeds 10	a	18 06			18 09		18 22	18 32		18 36	18 53				19 09	19 18		19 22	19 33		19 36	19 52	20 07		20 09
	d				18 12		18 27			18 38	18 57				19 12			19 27			19 38	19 57			20 12
Garforth	d										19 05											20 05			
South Milford	a									18 51											19 51				
Selby	a									19 00											20 00				
Howden	a																				20 09				
Brough	a									19 18											20 21				
Hull	a									19 37											20 39				
York 8	a				18 35		18 52				19 24				19 35			19 55				20 25			20 35
	d				18 43		18 56				19 31				19 38							20 29			20 38
Malton	d				19 07										20 02										21 02
Seamer	a				19 24										20 19										21 19
Scarborough	a				19 33										20 30										21 30
Thirsk	a				*19b04*						19 47											20 45			
Northallerton	a				*19b15*		19 20				19 58							*20 53*				20 53			*21b03*
Darlington 7	a				*19b21*		19 33				*20b04*				*20b12*			*20 51*				*21b07*			*21b16*
Yarm	d										20 12											21 07			
Thornaby	a										20 21											21 16			
Middlesbrough	a										20 30											21 25			
Durham	a				*19b50*		19 50				*20b22*				*20b30*			*21 09*				*21b25*			*21b34*
Chester-le-Street	a						19 56																		*21b45*
Newcastle 8	a				*19b52*		20 10				*20b38*				*20b48*			*21 27*				*21b39*			*21b52*

For general notes see front of timetable
For details of catering facilities see Directory of Train Operators

A From Selby (Table 41)
B From Southport (Table 82)
C From Manchester Victoria (Table 41)
D From Leeds (Table 41)
b Change at York

Liverpool, Manchester Airport and Manchester → Huddersfield → Wakefield, Leeds, Hull, York, Scarborough, Middlesbrough and Newcastle

Network Diagram - see first page of Table 39

		NT	NT	TP	TP	NT	NT	TP		NT	TP	NT	NT	TP	NT	TP	NT	NT	TP	NT	TP	TP FO	TP FX		
				1 ◇	1 ◇			1 ◇			1 ◇			1 ◇		1 ◇			1 ◇		1 ◇	1 ◇	1 ◇		
		A					B																		
Liverpool Lime Street 10	d							19 22						20 22							22 30				
Warrington Central	d							19 44						20 44							22 52				
Birchwood	d							19 49						20 49							22 57				
Manchester Oxford Road	d							20 07						21 07							23 17				
Manchester Airport ✈	d			19 20							20 20					21 20			22 22			23 18	23 18		
Manchester Piccadilly 10	a			19 36				20 09			20 36			21 09		21 36			22 36		23 19	23 34	23 34		
	d			19 42				20 11			20 42			21 11		21 42			22 42		23 21	23 38	23 38		
Manchester Victoria	d		19 27							20 27					21 27			22 08		23 00					
Ashton-under-Lyne	d		19 37							20 37					21 37			22 18		23 10					
Stalybridge	a		19 42					20 26		20 42				21 26	21 42	21 55		22 22	22 55	23 14	23 34				
	d		19 42					20 26		20 42				21 26	21 42	21 55		22 23	22 55	23 15	23 34				
Mossley (Grtr Manchester)	d		19 47							20 47					21 47			22 27		23 19					
Greenfield	d		19 51							20 51					21 51			22 31		23 23					
Marsden	d		19 59							20 59					21 59			22 40		23 32					
Slaithwaite	d		20 04							21 04					22 04			22 44		23 36					
Huddersfield	a		20 12	20 15				20 44		21 12	21 15			21 44	22 12	22 15		22 53	23 15	23 44	23 52	00 07	00 25		
	d			20 16		20 31	20 35	20 45			21 16	21 31	21 35	21 45		22 16	22 31		23 16		23 53	00 08	00 26		
Deighton	d					20 34	20 38					21 34	21 39				22 34								
Mirfield	d	20 07				20 39	20 43					21 39	21 44				22 39								
Wakefield Kirkgate	a						21 02						21 58												
Wakefield Westgate	a						21 08						22 10												
Ravensthorpe	d					20 42						21 42					22 42								
Dewsbury	a	20 12		20 25		20 46					21 25	21 46				22 25	22 46		23 25			00s17	00s35		
	d	20 12		20 26		20 46					21 26	21 46				22 26	22 46		23 26						
Batley	d	20 15				20 49						21 49					22 49								
Morley	d	20 21				20 55						21 55					22 55								
Cottingley	d					20 59						21 59					22 59								
Leeds 10	a	20 32		20 41		21 07		21 09			21 41	22 08		22 09		22 41	23 07		23 41		00 31	00 33	00 50		
	d			20 45	21 05			21 12			21 42			22 22		22 42			23 42		00 34	00 35	00 54		
Garforth	d																								
South Milford	a				21 17									22 34											
Selby	a				21 27									22 44											
Howden	a				21 36																				
Brough	a				21 48									23 03											
Hull	a				22 05									23 21											
York 8	a			21 09				21 41			22 08					23 12			00 09		01 14	01 18	01 43		
	d			21 14							22 15					23 20									
Malton	d										22 39														
Seamer	a										22 56														
Scarborough	a										23 06														
Thirsk	a			21 30												23 35									
Northallerton	a			21 38				22 22			23b55					23 55									
Darlington 7	a			21 49				22 35			23b49					00 06			01 26						
Yarm	d																								
Thornaby	a																								
Middlesbrough	a																								
Durham	a			22 07				22 53			00b07					00 24			01 44						
Chester-le-Street	a			22 36																					
Newcastle 8	a			22 23				23 16			00b41					00 56			02 23						

For general notes see front of timetable
For details of catering facilities see Directory of Train Operators

A From Manchester Victoria (Table 41)
B From Selby (Table 41)
b Change at York

Table 39

Saturdays

Liverpool, Manchester Airport and Manchester → Huddersfield → Wakefield, Leeds, Hull, York, Scarborough, Middlesbrough and Newcastle

Network Diagram - see first page of Table 39

		TP	TP	TP	TP	TP	TP	NT		NT	TP	TP	NT	TP	NT	NT		TP	TP	TP	NT	TP	NT	NT	TP
		1 ◇	1 ◇	1 ◇	1 ◇	1 ◇	1 ◇				1 ◇	1 ◇		1 ◇				1 ◇	1 ◇	1 ◇	A	1 ◇			1 ◇
														(trolley)				(trolley)		(trolley)		(trolley)			(trolley)
Liverpool Lime Street 10	d																	06 16							
Warrington Central	d																	06 38							
Birchwood	d																	06 43							
Manchester Oxford Road	d																	07 07							
Manchester Airport ✈	d	01 00		04 00			05 37							06 23						07 05					07 33
Manchester Piccadilly 10	a	01 14		04 14			05 51							06 39				07 09		07 22					07 48
	d	01 16		04 15		05 39	05 57					06 21		06 54				07 11		07 26		07 36			07 55
Manchester Victoria	d															06 55								07 40	
Ashton-under-Lyne	d															07 05								07 49	
Stalybridge	a					05 52								07 07		07 10		07 26				07 49		07 54	08 08
	d					05 52								07 07		07 11		07 26				07 49		07 54	08 09
Mossley (Grtr Manchester)	d															07 15								07 59	
Greenfield	d															07 19								08 03	
Marsden	d												07 00			07 28								08 11	
Slaithwaite	d												07 04			07 32								08 16	
Huddersfield	a	01 57		04 56		06 10	06 26					06 54	07 12	07 25		07 41		07 44		07 56		08 09		08 24	08 28
	d	01 58		04 57		06 11	06 27	06 31		06 41		06 56		07 26	07 32			07 45		07 57		08 10	08 14		08 30
Deighton	d							06 34		06 45					07 36								08 17		
Mirfield	d							06 39		06 50					07 41						08 06		08 23		
Wakefield Kirkgate	a									07 03					07 57										
Wakefield Westgate	a									07 10					08 08										
Ravensthorpe	d							06 42															08 26		
Dewsbury	a						06 36	06 46				07 05						07 54		08 06	08 11	08 19	08 29		08 39
	d						06 37	06 46				07 06						07 55		08 07	08 12	08 20	08 30		08 39
Batley	d							06 49													08 15		08 33		
Morley	d							06 55													08 21		08 39		
Cottingley	d							06 59													08 24		08 42		
Leeds 10	a	02 47		05 18		06 32	06 53	07 07				07 19		07 48				08 10		08 24	08 33	08 36	08 51		08 54
	d	02 52		05 19		06 35	06 55					07 23		07 50				08 12		08 27		08 38			08 57
Garforth	d													08 00											09 05
South Milford	a																								
Selby	a											07 43										08 58			
Howden	a											07 52													
Brough	a											08 04													
Hull	a											08 20										09 31			
York 8	a	03 22		06 02		07 03	07 22							08 21				08 34		08 54					09 23
	d		05 54		06 38	07 06	07 25				07 32			08 23				08 38	08 42	08 57					09 26
Malton	d				07 02		07 49											09 02							
Seamer	a				07 19		08 06											09 19							
Scarborough	a				07 30		08 15											09 30							
Thirsk	a		06 10			07 22	*07b54*				07 54			08 45											09 45
Northallerton	a		06 18	*07 01*		07 30	*08b04*				08 04			08 56					09 02	09 17					09 54
Darlington 7	a		06 29	*07 15*		07 41	*08b04*							*09b00*					09 14	09 29					*09b59*
Yarm	d										08 18			09 11											10 10
Thornaby	a		06 53								08 27			09 22											10 20
Middlesbrough	a		07 01								08 36			09 32											10 30
Durham	a			*07 33*		07 58	*08b22*							*09b18*					09 31	09 46					*10b16*
Chester-le-Street	a					08 04	*08c43*												*09 42*						
Newcastle 8	a			*07 50*		08 18	*08b43*							*09b34*					09 49	10 02					*10b33*

For general notes see front of timetable
For details of catering facilities see Directory of Train Operators

A From Manchester Victoria (Table 41)
b Change at York
c Change at York and Durham

Liverpool, Manchester Airport and Manchester → Huddersfield → Wakefield, Leeds, Hull, York, Scarborough, Middlesbrough and Newcastle

Network Diagram - see first page of Table 39

		NT		NT	NT	TP	TP	NT	TP	NT		NT	TP	NT	NT	EM	TP	NT		NT	TP	TP	NT	NT	NT
						1◇	1◇		1◇				1◇			1◇	1◇				1◇	1◇			
					A	B						C			D	E				A			C		
							⊼		⊼							⊡	⊼				⊼	⊼			
Liverpool Lime Street 10	d	06 46					07 16			07 16											08 22				08 44
Warrington Central	d						07 40														08 44				
Birchwood	d						07 45														08 49				
Manchester Oxford Road	d						08 06														09 07				
Manchester Airport ✈	d								08 05								08 35					09 05			
Manchester Piccadilly 10	a						08 08		08 22								08 49				09 09	09 22			
	d						08 10		08 26				08 42				08 57				09 11	09 26			
Manchester Victoria	d	07 57								08 27				08 57										09 27	09 57
Ashton-under-Lyne	d	08 07								08 37				09 07										09 37	10 07
Stalybridge	a	08 13					08 26			08 41				09 13							09 26			09 42	10 13
	d						08 26			08 42											09 26			09 42	
Mossley (Grtr Manchester)	d									08 46														09 47	
Greenfield	d									08 50														09 51	
Marsden	d									08 59														09 59	
Slaithwaite	d									09 03														10 04	
Huddersfield	a						08 44		08 56	09 11			09 15				09 26				09 44	09 56		10 12	
	d			08 33	08 37		08 45		08 57				09 16				09 27	09 31		09 35	09 45	09 57			
Deighton	d			08 36	08 40													09 34		09 38					
Mirfield	d			08 41	08 45							09 07						09 39		09 43			10 07		
Wakefield Kirkgate	a				09 02															10 03					
Wakefield Westgate	a				09 08															10 10					
Ravensthorpe	d			08 44														09 42							
Dewsbury	a			08 48				←	09 06			09 12					09 36	09 46				10 06	10 12		
	d			08 53 →				08 53	09 07			09 12			09 25		09 37	09 46				10 07	10 12		
Batley	d							08 56				09 15						09 49					10 15		
Morley	d							09 02				09 21						09 55					10 21		
Cottingley	d							09 06										09 59							
Leeds 10	a						09 06	09 16	09 22			09 31	09 36		09 41		09 52	10 07			10 09	10 22	10 31		
	d						09 12		09 27				09 38		09 43		09 57				10 12	10 27			
Garforth	d														09 55		10 05								
South Milford	a																								
Selby	a												09 57												
Howden	a												*10 22*												
Brough	a												10 15												
Hull	a												10 34												
York 8	a						09 35		09 52						10 23		10 23				10 35	10 52			
	d					09 28	09 38		09 56							10 24	10 26				10 38	10 54			
Malton	d						10 02														11 02				
Seamer	a						10 19														11 19				
Scarborough	a					10 15	10 32									11 06					11 30				
Thirsk	a								*10 20*								10 45								
Northallerton	a								10 25								10 55					11 15			
Darlington 7	a						*10b13*		10 36								*10b59*				*11b16*	11 27			
Yarm	d																11 10								
Thornaby	a																11 20								
Middlesbrough	a																11 30								
Durham	a						*10b30*		10 53								*11b16*				*11b33*	11 44			
Chester-le-Street	a								10 59																
Newcastle 8	a						*10b51*		11 14								*11b32*				*11b54*	12 00			

For general notes see front of timetable
For details of catering facilities see Directory of Train Operators

- **A** From 18 July from Selby (Table 41)
- **B** 18 July to 5 September
- **C** From Manchester Victoria (Table 41)
- **D** Until 11 July. From Blackpool North (Table 41)
- **E** Until 5 September. From St Pancras International (Table 53)
- **b** Change at York

Liverpool, Manchester Airport and Manchester → Huddersfield → Wakefield, Leeds, Hull, York, Scarborough, Middlesbrough and Newcastle

Network Diagram - see first page of Table 39

		TP	NT	TP		NT	NT	TP	TP	TP	NT	NT		NT	TP	NT	TP	NT	NT	TP		TP	TP	NT	NT
		1 ◇		1 ◇				1 ◇	1 ◇	1 ◇					1 ◇		1 ◇			1 ◇		1 ◇	1 ◇		
			A				B	C			D					A			B	C				D	
		🛒		🛒					🛒						🛒		🛒					🛒	🛒		
Liverpool Lime Street 10	d								09 22					09 46								10 22			
Warrington Central	d								09 44													10 44			
Birchwood	d								09 49													10 49			
Manchester Oxford Road	d								10 07													11 07			
Manchester Airport ✈	d			09 35						10 05							10 35						11 05		
Manchester Piccadilly 10 🚊	a			09 52					10 09	10 22							10 52					11 09	11 22		
	d	09 42		09 57					10 11	10 27					10 42		10 57					11 11	11 27		
Manchester Victoria 🚊	d											10 27		10 57											11 27
Ashton-under-Lyne	d											10 37		11 07											11 37
Stalybridge	a								10 26			10 42		11 13								11 26			11 42
	d								10 26			10 42										11 26			11 42
Mossley (Grtr Manchester)	d											10 47													11 47
Greenfield	d											10 51													11 51
Marsden	d											10 59													11 59
Slaithwaite	d											11 04													12 04
Huddersfield	a	10 15		10 26					10 44	10 56		11 12			11 15		11 26					11 44	11 56		12 12
	d	10 16		10 27		10 31	10 35		10 45	10 57					11 16		11 27	11 31	11 35			11 45	11 57		
Deighton	d					10 34	10 38											11 34	11 38						
Mirfield	d					10 39	10 43				11 07							11 39	11 43					12 07	
Wakefield Kirkgate	a						11 02												12 02						
Wakefield Westgate	a						11 08												12 08						
Ravensthorpe	d					10 42												11 42							
Dewsbury	a			10 36		10 46				11 06	11 12						11 36	11 46					12 06	12 12	
	d		10 25	10 37		10 46				11 07	11 12					11 25	11 37	11 46					12 07	12 12	
Batley	d					10 49					11 15							11 49						12 15	
Morley	d					10 55					11 21							11 55						12 21	
Cottingley	d					10 59												11 59							
Leeds 10	a	10 36	10 41	10 52		11 07			11 09	11 22	11 31				11 36	11 41	11 52	12 07				12 09	12 22	12 31	
	d	10 38	10 43	10 57					11 12	11 27					11 38	11 43	11 57					12 12	12 27		
Garforth	d		10 55	11 05												11 55	12 05								
South Milford	a																								
Selby	a	10 57													11 57										
Howden	a	*11 49*													*12 19*										
Brough	a	11 15													12 15										
Hull	a	11 34													12 33										
York 8	a		11 19	11 23					11 35	11 52						12 21	12 23					12 35	12 52		
	d			11 26				11 28	11 38	11 54							12 26			12 28		12 38	12 54		
Malton	d								12 02													13 02			
Seamer	a								12 19													13 19			
Scarborough	a							12 15	12 30											13 15		13 30			
Thirsk	a			11 42													12 46								
Northallerton	a			11 55						12 15							12 55						13 23		
Darlington 7	a			*11b59*					*12b14*	12 27							*13b01*					*13b12*	13 34		
Yarm	d			12 10													13 10								
Thornaby	a			12 18													13 20								
Middlesbrough	a			12 30													13 30								
Durham	a			*12b16*					*12b34*	12 45							*13b18*					*13b29*	13 51		
Chester-le-Street	a								*12b41*														13 57		
Newcastle 8 🚊	a			*12b33*					*12b55*	13 00						*13 25*	*13b33*					*13b50*	14 12		

For general notes see front of timetable
For details of catering facilities see Directory of Train Operators

A Until 11 July. From Blackpool North (Table 41)
B From 18 July from Selby (Table 41)
C 18 July to 5 September
D From Manchester Victoria (Table 41)
b Change at York

Liverpool, Manchester Airport and Manchester → Huddersfield → Wakefield, Leeds, Hull, York, Scarborough, Middlesbrough and Newcastle

Network Diagram - see first page of Table 39

		NT	TP	NT	TP	NT		NT	TP	TP	NT	NT	NT	TP		NT	TP	NT	NT	TP	TP	NT		NT	NT
			1 ◊		1 ◊				1 ◊	1 ◊				1 ◊			1 ◊			1 ◊	1 ◊				
				A				B			C					A			B			C			
					🛒				🛒	🛒							🛒			🛒	🛒				
Liverpool Lime Street 10	d	10 46							11 22				11 46							12 22					12 46
Warrington Central	d								11 44											12 44					
Birchwood	d								11 49											12 49					
Manchester Oxford Road	d								12 07											13 07					
Manchester Airport ✈	d				11 35					12 05							12 35				13 05				
Manchester Piccadilly 10 ⛴	a				11 52				12 09	12 22							12 52			13 09	13 22				
	d		11 42		11 57				12 11	12 27				12 42			12 57			13 11	13 27				
Manchester Victoria ⛴	d	11 57										12 27	12 57											13 27	13 57
Ashton-under-Lyne	d	12 07										12 37	13 07											13 37	14 07
Stalybridge	a	12 13							12 26			12 42	13 13							13 26				13 42	14 13
	d								12 26			12 42								13 26				13 42	
Mossley (Grtr Manchester)	d											12 47												13 47	
Greenfield	d											12 51												13 51	
Marsden	d											12 59												13 59	
Slaithwaite	d											13 04												14 04	
Huddersfield	a		12 15		12 26				12 44	12 56		13 12		13 15			13 26			13 44	13 56			14 12	
	d		12 16		12 27	12 31		12 35	12 45	12 57				13 16			13 27	13 31	13 35	13 45	13 57				
Deighton	d					12 34		12 38										13 34	13 38						
Mirfield	d					12 39		12 43			13 07							13 39	13 43			14 07			
Wakefield Kirkgate	a							13 02											14 02						
Wakefield Westgate	a							13 08											14 08						
Ravensthorpe	d					12 42												13 42							
Dewsbury	a				12 36	12 46				13 06	13 12						13 36	13 46			14 06	14 12			
	d			12 25	12 37	12 46				13 07	13 12					13 25	13 37	13 46			14 07	14 12			
Batley	d					12 49					13 15							13 49				14 15			
Morley	d					12 55					13 21							13 55				14 21			
Cottingley	d					12 59												13 59							
Leeds 10	a		12 36	12 43	12 52	13 07			13 09	13 22	13 31			13 36		13 43	13 52	14 07		14 09	14 22	14 31			
	d		12 38	12 43	12 57				13 12	13 27				13 38		13 43	13 57			14 12	14 27				
Garforth	d			12 55	13 05											13 55	14 05								
South Milford	a																								
Selby	a		12 57											13 57											
Howden	a		*13 52*											*14 13*											
Brough	a		13 15											14 15											
Hull	a		13 34											14 34											
York 8	a			13 19	13 23				13 35	13 52						14 21	14 23			14 35	14 52				
	d				13 26				13 38	13 54							14 26			14 38	14 54				
Malton	d								14 02											15 02					
Seamer	a								14 19											15 19					
Scarborough	a								14 30											15 30					
Thirsk	a				13 43												14 45								
Northallerton	a				13 55					14 22							15 00				15 22				
Darlington 7	a				*13b59*				*14b16*	14 34							*14b59*			*15b15*	15 34				
Yarm	d				14 10												15 14								
Thornaby	a				14 18												15 27								
Middlesbrough	a				14 30												15 35								
Durham	a				*14b16*				*14b34*	14 50							*15b16*			*15b32*	15 51				
Chester-le-Street	a								*14b41*												15 57				
Newcastle 8 ⛴	a				*14b32*				*14b54*	15 08							*15b32*			*15b51*	16 12				

For general notes see front of timetable
For details of catering facilities see Directory of Train Operators

A Until 11 July. From Blackpool North (Table 41)
B From 18 July from Selby (Table 41)
C From Manchester Victoria (Table 41)
b Change at York

Table 39

Saturdays

Liverpool, Manchester Airport and Manchester → Huddersfield → Wakefield, Leeds, Hull, York, Scarborough, Middlesbrough and Newcastle

Network Diagram - see first page of Table 39

		TP	NT	TP	NT	NT	TP	TP	NT	NT	NT	TP	NT	TP	NT	NT	TP	TP	NT	NT	NT	TP	NT
		1 ◇		1 ◇			1 ◇	1 ◇				1 ◇		1 ◇			1 ◇	1 ◇				1 ◇	
			A			B			C				A			B			C				A
		🛒		🛒			🛒	🛒									🛒	🛒					
Liverpool Lime Street 10	d						13 22				13 46						14 22				14 46		
Warrington Central	d						13 44										14 44						
Birchwood	d						13 49										14 49						
Manchester Oxford Road	d						14 07										15 07						
Manchester Airport ✈	d			13 35				14 05						14 35				15 05					
Manchester Piccadilly 10	a			13 52			14 09	14 22						14 52			15 09	15 22					
	d	13 42		13 57			14 11	14 27				14 42		14 57			15 11	15 27				15 42	
Manchester Victoria	d									14 27	14 57									15 27	15 57		
Ashton-under-Lyne	d									14 37	15 07									15 37	16 07		
Stalybridge	a						14 26			14 42	15 13						15 26			15 42	16 13		
	d						14 26			14 42							15 26			15 42			
Mossley (Grtr Manchester)	d									14 47										15 47			
Greenfield	d									14 51										15 51			
Marsden	d									14 59										15 59			
Slaithwaite	d									15 04										16 04			
Huddersfield	a	14 15		14 26			14 44	14 56		15 11		15 15		15 26			15 44	15 56		16 12		16 15	
	d	14 16		14 27	14 31	14 35	14 45	14 57				15 16		15 27	15 31	15 35	15 45	15 57				16 16	
Deighton	d				14 34	14 38									15 34	15 38							
Mirfield	d				14 39	14 43			15 07						15 39	15 43			16 07				
Wakefield Kirkgate	a					15 02										16 02							
Wakefield Westgate	a					15 08										16 08							
Ravensthorpe	d				14 42										15 42								
Dewsbury	a			14 36	14 46			15 06	15 12					15 36	15 46			16 06	16 12				
	d		14 25	14 37	14 46			15 07	15 12				15 25	15 37	15 46			16 07	16 12				16 25
Batley	d				14 49				15 15						15 49				16 15				
Morley	d				14 55				15 21						15 55				16 21				
Cottingley	d				14 59										15 59								
Leeds 10	a	14 36	14 41	14 52	15 07		15 09	15 22	15 31			15 36	15 41	15 52	16 07		16 09	16 22	16 31			16 36	16 41
	d	14 38	14 43	14 57			15 12	15 27				15 38	15 43	15 57			16 12	16 27				16 38	16 43
Garforth	d		14 55	15 05									15 55	16 05									16 55
South Milford	a																						
Selby	a	14 57										15 57										17 00	
Howden	a	15 52										16 51										17 47	
Brough	a	15 15										16 15										17 18	
Hull	a	15 34										16 35										17 37	
York 8	a		15 19	15 23			15 35	15 54					16 22	16 23			16 35	16 52					17 19
	d			15 26			15 38							16 26			16 38	17 02					
Malton	d						16 02										17 02						
Seamer	a						16 19										17 19						
Scarborough	a						16 30										17 30						
Thirsk	a			15 46										16 44				17 20					
Northallerton	a			15 55										16 55				17 28					
Darlington 7	a			15b59			16b13							16b59			17b12	17 39					
Yarm	d			16 09										17 09									
Thornaby	a			16 21										17 22									
Middlesbrough	a			16 30										17 33									
Durham	a			16b16			16b32							17b16			17b29	17 56					
Chester-le-Street	a																17b36	18 02					
Newcastle 8	a			16b32			16b51							17b32			17b53	18 17					

For general notes see front of timetable
For details of catering facilities see Directory of Train Operators

A Until 11 July. From Blackpool North (Table 41)
B From 18 July from Selby (Table 41)
C From Manchester Victoria (Table 41)
b Change at York

Table 39

Saturdays

Liverpool, Manchester Airport and Manchester → Huddersfield → Wakefield, Leeds, Hull, York, Scarborough, Middlesbrough and Newcastle

Network Diagram - see first page of Table 39

		TP 1◇		NT	NT	TP 1◇	TP 1◇	NT	NT	TP 1◇		NT	TP 1◇	NT	NT	NT	NT	TP 1◇		TP 1◇	NT	NT	TP 1◇	NT	TP 1◇
					A			B				C				A					B			C	
Liverpool Lime Street 10	d					15 22								15 46				16 22							
Warrington Central	d					15 44												16 44							
Birchwood	d					15 49												16 49							
Manchester Oxford Road	d					16 07												17 07							
Manchester Airport	d	15 35					16 05						16 35							17 05					17 35
Manchester Piccadilly 10	a	15 52				16 09	16 22						16 52					17 09		17 22					17 52
	d	15 57				16 11	16 27			16 42			16 56					17 11		17 26			17 42		17 56
Manchester Victoria	d								16 27					16 57								17 27			
Ashton-under-Lyne	d								16 37					17 07								17 37			
Stalybridge	a					16 26			16 42				17 09	17 13				17 26		17 39		17 42			18 09
	d					16 26			16 42				17 09					17 26		17 39		17 43			18 09
Mossley (Grtr Manchester)	d								16 47													17 47			
Greenfield	d								16 51													17 51			
Marsden	d								16 59								17 29					18 00			
Slaithwaite	d								17 04								17 33					18 04			
Huddersfield	a	16 26				16 44	16 56		17 12	17 15			17 27				17 41	17 44		17 57		18 12	18 15		18 27
	d	16 27		16 31	16 35	16 45	16 57			17 16			17 28		17 31	17 35		17 45		17 57			18 16		18 27
Deighton	d			16 34	16 38										17 34	17 38									
Mirfield	d			16 39	16 43			17 07							17 39	17 43					18 07				
Wakefield Kirkgate	a				17 02											18 02									
Wakefield Westgate	a				17 08											18 08									
Ravensthorpe	d			16 42											17 42										
Dewsbury	a	16 36		16 46			17 06	17 12					17 36		17 46					18 06	18 12				18 37
	d	16 37		16 46			17 07	17 12				17 25	17 37		17 46					18 07	18 13			18 25	18 37
Batley	d			16 49				17 15							17 49						18 16				
Morley	d			16 55				17 21							17 55						18 22				
Cottingley	d			16 59											17 59										
Leeds 10	a	16 52		17 07		17 09	17 22	17 31		17 37		17 42	17 52		18 06			18 09		18 22	18 33		18 36	18 41	18 53
	d	16 57				17 12	17 24			17 38		17 43	17 57					18 12		18 27			18 38	18 43	18 57
Garforth	d	17 05					17 34					17 55	18 05											18 55	19 05
South Milford	a																						18 51		
Selby	a									17 57													19 00		
Howden	a									18 06													*19 17*		
Brough	a									18 18													19 18		
Hull	a									18 37													19 37		
York 8	a	17 22				17 35	17 57					18 24	18 24					18 35		18 52				19 21	19 24
	d	17 26				17 38							18 26					18 38		18 56					19 26
Malton	d					18 02												19 02							
Seamer	a					18 19												19 19							
Scarborough	a					18 29												19 30							
Thirsk	a	17 40											18 44					*19b19*							19 42
Northallerton	a	17 51				*18b22*							18 55							19 20					19 50
Darlington 7	a	*18c00*				*18b12*							*19b01*					*19b25*		19 33					*20b03*
Yarm	d	18 07											19 09												20 04
Thornaby	a	18 26											19 18												20 12
Middlesbrough	a	18 32											19 30												20 23
Durham	a	*18e18*				*18b29*							*19b19*					*19b43*		19 50					*20b21*
Chester-le-Street	a																			19 56					
Newcastle 8	a	*18b37*				*18b50*							*19b35*					*19b59*		20 10					*20b33*

For general notes see front of timetable
For details of catering facilities see Directory of Train Operators

- **A** From 18 July from Selby (Table 41)
- **B** From Manchester Victoria (Table 41)
- **C** Until 11 July. From Blackpool North (Table 41)
- **b** Change at York
- **c** Change at York. From 12 September arr. 1759
- **e** Change at York. From 12 September arr. 1816

Liverpool, Manchester Airport and Manchester → Huddersfield → Wakefield, Leeds, Hull, York, Scarborough, Middlesbrough and Newcastle

Network Diagram - see first page of Table 39

		NT	NT	NT		TP	NT	NT	TP	NT	TP	NT		NT	TP	NT	NT	NT	TP	NT		TP	NT	NT	TP
						1 ◇			1 ◇		1 ◇				1 ◇				1 ◇			1 ◇			1 ◇
				A			B			C				A		B		D		D				A	
Liverpool Lime Street 10	d	16 46				17 22									18 22										19 22
Warrington Central	d					17 44									18 44										19 44
Birchwood	d					17 49									18 49										19 49
Manchester Oxford Road	d					18 07									19 07										20 07
Manchester Airport ✈	d										18 35								19 19						
Manchester Piccadilly 10	a					18 09					18 52				19 09				19 36						20 09
	d					18 11			18 42		18 57				19 11				19 42						20 11
Manchester Victoria	d	17 57						18 27									19 27								
Ashton-under-Lyne	d	18 07						18 37									19 37								
Stalybridge	a	18 13				18 26		18 42							19 26		19 42								20 26
	d					18 26		18 42							19 26		19 42								20 26
Mossley (Grtr Manchester)	d							18 47									19 47								
Greenfield	d							18 51									19 51								
Marsden	d							18 59									19 59								
Slaithwaite	d							19 04									20 04								
Huddersfield	a					18 44		19 12	19 15		19 26				19 44		20 12		20 15						20 44
	d		18 31	18 35		18 45			19 16		19 27	19 31		19 35	19 45				20 16				20 31	20 35	20 45
Deighton	d		18 34	18 39								19 34		19 38									20 34	20 38	
Mirfield	d		18 39	18 44			19 08					19 39		19 43		20 07							20 39	20 43	
Wakefield Kirkgate	a			19 02										20 03										21 02	
Wakefield Westgate	a			19 08										20 09										21 08	
Ravensthorpe	d		18 42									19 42											20 42		
Dewsbury	a		18 46			18 55	19 13				19 36	19 46				20 12			20 25				20 46		
	d		18 46			18 55	19 13			19 25	19 37	19 46				20 13		20 20	20 26				20 46		
Batley	d		18 49				19 16					19 49				20 16							20 49		
Morley	d		18 55				19 22					19 55				20 22							20 55		
Cottingley	d		18 59									19 59											20 59		
Leeds 10	a		19 07			19 10	19 32		19 36	19 43	19 52	20 07			20 09	20b34		20 36	20 41	←			21 07		21 09
	d					19 12			19 38	19 43	19 57				20 12			20 48 →	20 45	20 48		21 05			21 12
Garforth	d									19 55	20 05									21 00					
South Milford	a								19 51													21 17			
Selby	a								20 00													21 27			
Howden	a								20 09													21 36			
Brough	a								20 21													21 48			
Hull	a								20 39													22 05			
York 8	a					19 35				20 21	20 25				20 35				21 09	21 31					21 41
	d					19 38					20 26				20 38				21 11						
Malton	d					20 02									21 02										
Seamer	a					20 19									21 19										
Scarborough	a					20 30									21 30										
Thirsk	a										20 43								21 28						
Northallerton	a					20c51					20 51				21c26				21 36						
Darlington 7	a					20c12					21c04				21c14				21 47	22 09					22 21
Yarm	d										21 05														
Thornaby	a										21 14														
Middlesbrough	a										21 25														
Durham	a					20c29					21c21				21c32				22 04	22 27					22 41
Chester-le-Street	a														21c39										22 50
Newcastle 8	a					20c45					21c33				21c55				22 20	22 45					23 10

For general notes see front of timetable
For details of catering facilities see Directory of Train Operators

A From 18 July from Selby (Table 41)
B From Manchester Victoria (Table 41)
C Until 11 July. From Blackpool North (Table 97)
D Until 11 July. From Blackpool North (Table 41)
b From 11 July arr. 3 mins earlier
c Change at York

Table 39

Saturdays

Liverpool, Manchester Airport and Manchester → Huddersfield → Wakefield, Leeds, Hull, York, Scarborough, Middlesbrough and Newcastle

Network Diagram - see first page of Table 39

		NT	TP	NT	NT	TP		TP	NT	TP	TP	NT	NT	NT		TP	NT	TP	TP	TP	TP	TP			
			1 ◇			1 ◇		1 ◇		1 ◇	1 ◇					1 ◇		1 ◇	1 ◇		1 ◇				
						A		B		A		A	B					B	A	A bus	B	A bus			
Liverpool Lime Street 10	d					20 22		20 22										22 30	22 30						
Warrington Central	d					20 44		20 44										22 52	22 52						
Birchwood	d					20 49		20 49										22 57	22 57						
Manchester Oxford Road	d					21 07		21 07										23 17	23 17						
Manchester Airport ✈	d		20 20								21 20					22 22					23 24	23 24			
Manchester Piccadilly 10	a		20 36			21 09		21 09			21 36					22 36		23 19	23 19		23 39	23 49			
	d		20 42			21 11		21 11			21 42					22 42		23 21	23 21		23 41	23 49			
Manchester Victoria	d	20 27							21 27					22 08			23 00								
Ashton-under-Lyne	d	20 37							21 37					22 18			23 10								
Stalybridge	a	20 42				21 26		21 26	21 41		21 55			22 22		22 55	23 14	23 34	23 34						
	d	20 42				21 26		21 26	21 42		21 55			22 23		22 55	23 15	23 34	23 34						
Mossley (Grtr Manchester)	d	20 47							21 46					22 27			23 19								
Greenfield	d	20 51							21 50					22 31			23 23								
Marsden	d	20 59		21 19					21 59					22 40			23 32								
Slaithwaite	d	21 04		21 23					22 03					22 44			23 36								
Huddersfield	a	21 12	21 15	21 30		21 44		21 44	22 12		22 15			22 53		23 15	23 44	23 52	23 52		00 25	00 49			
	d		21 16	21 31	21 35	21 45		21 45			22 16	22 19	22 31			23 16		23 53		23 59	00 26	00 49			
Deighton	d			21 34	21 39							22 23	22 34												
Mirfield	d			21 39	21 44							22 28	22 39												
Wakefield Kirkgate	a				21 58																				
Wakefield Westgate	a				22 10																				
Ravensthorpe	d			21 42								22 31	22 42												
Dewsbury	a		21 25	21 46							22 25	22 34	22 46			23 25				00 19	00s35				
	d		21 26	21 46							22 26	22 35	22 46			23 26				00 19					
Batley	d			21 49								22 38	22 49												
Morley	d			21 55								22 44	22 55												
Cottingley	d			21 59								22 47	22 59												
Leeds 10	a		21 41	22 07		22 09		22 09			22 41	22 54	23 07			23 41		00 14		00 44	00 50	01 24			
	d		21 42			22 12		22 22		22 22	22 42					23 42		00 16			00 54	01 24			
Garforth	d																								
South Milford	a							22 34		22 34															
Selby	a							22 44		22 44															
Howden	a																								
Brough	a							23 03		23 04															
Hull	a							23 21		23 21															
York 8	a		22 08			22 35					23 08					00 11		00 44			01 22	02 09			
	d		22 11																						
Malton	d		22 35																						
Seamer	a		22 52																						
Scarborough	a		23 02																						
Thirsk	a																								
Northallerton	a																								
Darlington 7	a		23b07																						
Yarm	d																								
Thornaby	a																								
Middlesbrough	a																								
Durham	a		23b25																						
Chester-le-Street	a																								
Newcastle 8	a		23b46																						

For general notes see front of timetable
For details of catering facilities see Directory of Train Operators

A From 12 September
B Until 5 September
b Change at York

Table 39

Sundays

until 6 September

Liverpool, Manchester Airport and Manchester → Huddersfield → Leeds, Hull, York, Scarborough, Middlesbrough and Newcastle

Network Diagram - see first page of Table 39

		TP	TP	TP	NT	TP	TP	TP	NT	TP	TP	TP	NT	TP	NT	TP	TP	NT	TP	TP	NT	TP	NT	TP	TP
		1 ◇	1 ◇	1 ◇		1 ◇	1 ◇	1 ◇		1 ◇	1 ◇	1 ◇		1 ◇		1 ◇	1 ◇		1 ◇	1 ◇		1 ◇		1 ◇	1 ◇
Liverpool Lime Street 10	d											08 22				09 22			10 22						11 22
Warrington Central	d											08 44				09 44			10 44						11 44
Birchwood	d											08 49				09 49			10 49						11 49
Manchester Oxford Road	d											09 07				10 07			11 07						12 07
Manchester Airport ✈	d	01 22	04 43	06 24		07 24		08 06						09 20			10 19					11 17			
Manchester Piccadilly 10	a	01 35	04 56	06 37		07 37		08 24				09 09		09 37		10 10	10 34		11 09			11 35			12 09
	d	01 42	05 02	06 42		07 42		08 32				09 11		09 42		10 11	10 42		11 11			11 42		12 02	12 11
Manchester Victoria	d								08 43						09 43			10 43					11 43		
Ashton-under-Lyne	d								08 53						09 53			10 53					11 53		
Stalybridge	a			06 54		07 54		08 45	08 57			09 24			09 57	10 24		10 57	11 24				11 57		12 24
	d			06 55		07 55		08 45	08 58			09 24			09 58	10 24		10 58	11 24				11 58		12 24
Mossley (Grtr Manchester)	d								09 02						10 02			11 02					12 02		
Greenfield	d								09 06						10 06			11 06					12 06		
Marsden	d								09 15						10 15			11 15					12 15		
Slaithwaite	d								09 19						10 19			11 19					12 19		
Huddersfield	a	02 11	05 31	07 11		08 11		09 03	09 28			09 42		10 11	10 28	10 42	11 11	11 28	11 42			12 11	12 28	12 32	12 42
	d	02 12	05 32	07 12	07 51	08 12		09 04				09 43	09 51	10 12		10 43	11 12		11 43		11 58	12 12		12 33	12 43
Deighton	d				07 54								09 54								12 01				
Mirfield	d				07 59								09 59								12 06				
Wakefield Kirkgate	a																								
Wakefield Westgate	a																								
Ravensthorpe	d				08 02								10 02								12 09				
Dewsbury	a			07 21	08 06	08 21		09 12					10 06	10 21			11 21				12 13	12 21			
	d			07 22	08 06	08 22		09 12					10 06	10 21			11 21				12 13	12 21			
Batley	d				08 09								10 09								12 16				
Morley	d				08 15								10 15								12 22				
Cottingley	d				08 19								10 19								12 26				
Leeds 10	a	02 33	05 53	07 37	08 27	08 37		09 28				10 09	10 27	10 37		11 04	11 37		12 04		12 34	12 37		12 54	13 04
	d	02 35	05 55	07 40		08 40	09 12	09 40		10 12		10 20		10 40		11 12	11 40		12 12			12 40		13 00	13 12
Garforth	d																								
South Milford	a											10 33												13 13	
Selby	a											10 43												13 23	
Howden	a																								
Brough	a											11 01												13 41	
Hull	a											11 18												14 00	
York 8	a	03 03	06 23	08 09		09 08	09 37	10 06		10 37				11 06		11 37	12 06		12 37			13 06			13 37
	d			08 21		09 09	09 40	10 13		10 40	10 45			11 15		11 43	12 15		12 40	12 45		13 15			13 40
Malton	d						10 04									12 08									14 04
Seamer	a						10 21									12 24									14 21
Scarborough	a						10 32			11 28						12 32				13 32					14 32
Thirsk	a			08 37							11 04			*11 34*					13 02						
Northallerton	a			08 45		09 30		10 35			11 12			11 35			12 35		13 10			13 35			*14b25*
Darlington 7	a			08 57		09 41	*10b33*	10 46		*11b36*				11 47		*12b34*	12 46		*13b35*			13 46			*14b38*
Yarm	d										11 27								13 24						
Thornaby	a			09 16							11 35								13 34						
Middlesbrough	a			09 26							11 48								13 44						
Durham	a			*09c50*		09 58	*10b51*	11 08		*11b54*				12 03		*12b52*	13 03		*13b53*			14 03			*14b56*
Chester-le-Street	a																					14 09			
Newcastle 8	a			*10c06*		10 18	*11b09*	11 23		*12b10*				12 20		*13b08*	13 20		*14b09*			14 22			*15b12*

For general notes see front of timetable
For details of catering facilities see Directory of Train Operators

b Change at York
c Change at Darlington

Table 39

Sundays

until 6 September

Liverpool, Manchester Airport and Manchester → Huddersfield → Leeds, Hull, York, Scarborough, Middlesbrough and Newcastle

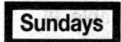

Network Diagram - see first page of Table 39

		TP 1 ◇	NT	TP 1 ◇	TP 1 ◇	NT	TP 1 ◇	NT	TP 1 ◇	TP 1 ◇	TP 1 ◇	NT	TP 1 ◇	TP 1 ◇	NT	TP 1 ◇	NT	TP 1 ◇	TP 1 ◇	TP 1 ◇	NT	TP 1 ◇	TP 1 ◇	TP 1 ◇	NT
Liverpool Lime Street 10	d				12 22					13 22				14 22					15 22				16 22		
Warrington Central	d				12 44					13 44				14 44					15 44				16 44		
Birchwood	d				12 49					13 49				14 49					15 49				16 49		
Manchester Oxford Road	d				13 07					14 07				15 07					16 07				17 07		
Manchester Airport ✈	d	12 20					13 20				14 20					15 20				16 20					
Manchester Piccadilly 10	a	12 37			13 09		13 37			14 09	14 37			15 09		15 37			16 09	16 37			17 09		
	d	12 42		13 02	13 11		13 42		14 02	14 11	14 42		15 02	15 11		15 42		16 02	16 11	16 42		17 02	17 11		
Manchester Victoria	d		12 43					13 43				14 43					15 43				16 43				
Ashton-under-Lyne	d		12 53					13 53				14 53					15 53				16 53				
Stalybridge	a		12 57		13 24			13 57		14 24		14 57		15 24			15 57		16 24		16 57		17 24		
	d		12 58		13 24			13 58		14 24		14 58		15 24			15 58		16 24		16 58		17 24		
Mossley (Grtr Manchester)	d		13 02					14 02				15 02					16 02				17 02				
Greenfield	d		13 06					14 06				15 06					16 06				17 06				
Marsden	d		13 15					14 15				15 15					16 15				17 15				
Slaithwaite	d		13 19					14 19				15 19					16 19				17 19				
Huddersfield	a	13 11	13 28	13 32	13 42		14 11	14 28	14 32	14 42	15 11	15 28	15 32	15 42		16 11	16 28	16 32	16 42	17 11	17 28	17 32	17 42		
	d	13 12		13 33	13 43	13 58	14 12		14 33	14 43	15 12		15 33	15 43	15 58	16 12		16 33	16 43	17 12		17 33	17 43		17 58
Deighton	d					14 01									16 01										18 01
Mirfield	d					14 06									16 06										18 06
Wakefield Kirkgate	a																								
Wakefield Westgate	a																								
Ravensthorpe	d					14 09									16 09										18 09
Dewsbury	a	13 21				14 13	14 21				15 21				16 13	16 21				17 21					18 13
	d	13 21				14 13	14 21				15 21				16 13	16 21				17 21					18 13
Batley	d					14 16									16 16										18 16
Morley	d					14 22									16 22										18 22
Cottingley	d					14 26									16 26										18 26
Leeds 10	a	13 37		13 54	14 04	14 34	14 37		14 54	15 04	15 37		15 54	16 04	16 34	16 37		16 54	17 04	17 37		17 54	18 04		18 34
	d	13 40		13 57	14 12		14 40		15 00	15 12	15 40		15 57	16 12		16 40		17 00	17 12	17 40		17 57	18 12		
Garforth	d																								
South Milford	a								15 13									17 13							
Selby	a								15 23									17 23							
Howden	a								*16 51*									*18 01*							
Brough	a								15 41									17 41							
Hull	a								16 00									18 00							
York 8	a	14 06		14 24	14 37		15 06			15 37	16 06		16 24	16 37		17 06			17 37	18 08		18 24	18 37		
	d	14 15			14 40		15 15			15 40	16 15			16 40		17 14			17 40	18 14			18 40	18 45	
Malton	d									16 04									18 04						
Seamer	a									16 21									18 21						
Scarborough	a									16 32									18 32					19 32	
Thirsk	a				15 02					*16b09*				17 02									18 59		
Northallerton	a	14 35			15 10		15 35			*16b19*	16 35			17 10		17 35				18 35			19 07		
Darlington 7	a	14 46			*15b15*		15 46			*16b12*	16 46			*17b14*		17 46			*18b15*	18 46			*19b35*		
Yarm	d				15 24									17 24									19 21		
Thornaby	a				15 40									17 33									19 32		
Middlesbrough	a				15 52									17 43									19 40		
Durham	a	15 03			*15b32*		16 03			*16b30*	17 03			*17b32*		18 03			*18b33*	19 03			*19b53*		
Chester-le-Street	a													*17b40*		18 09									
Newcastle 8	a	15 20			*15b51*		16 20			*16b50*	17 20			*17b53*		18 22			*18b52*	19 20			*20b09*		

For general notes see front of timetable
For details of catering facilities see Directory of Train Operators

b Change at York

Table 39

Sundays

until 6 September

Liverpool, Manchester Airport and Manchester → Huddersfield → Leeds, Hull, York, Scarborough, Middlesbrough and Newcastle

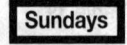

Network Diagram - see first page of Table 39

		TP 1 ◇	NT	TP 1 ◇	TP 1 ◇	TP 1 ◇	NT	TP 1 ◇	TP 1 ◇	NT	TP 1 ◇	NT	TP 1 ◇ A	TP 1 ◇ B	TP 1 ◇	TP 1 ◇	NT	TP 1 ◇	TP 1 ◇	NT	TP 1 ◇	NT	TP 1 ◇
Liverpool Lime Street 10	d				17 22				18 22						19 22			20 22					21 52
Warrington Central	d				17 44				18 44						19 44			20 44					22 14
Birchwood	d				17 49				18 49						19 49			20 49					22 19
Manchester Oxford Road	d				18 07				19 07						20 07			21 07					22 37
Manchester Airport ✈	d	17 20				18 20					19 20					20 20					21 20		
Manchester Piccadilly 10	a	17 37			18 09	18 37			19 09		19 37				20 09	20 37		21 09			21 37		22 40
	d	17 42		18 02	18 11	18 42		19 02	19 11		19 42		20 06	20 06	20 11	20 42		21 11			21 42		22 42
Manchester Victoria	d		17 43				18 43					19 43					20 43					21 43	
Ashton-under-Lyne	d		17 53				18 53					19 53					20 53					21 53	
Stalybridge	a		17 57		18 24		18 57		19 24			19 57			20 24		20 57	21 24				21 57	22 55
	d		17 58		18 24		18 58		19 24			19 58			20 24		20 58	21 24					22 55
Mossley (Grtr Manchester)	d		18 02				19 02					20 02					21 02						
Greenfield	d		18 06				19 06					20 06					21 06						
Marsden	d		18 15				19 15					20 15					21 15			21 47			
Slaithwaite	d		18 19				19 19					20 19					21 19			21 51			
Huddersfield	a	18 11	18 28	18 32	18 42	19 11	19 28	19 32	19 42		20 11	20 28	20 36	20 36	20 42	21 11	21 28	21 42		21 57	22 11		23 13
	d	18 12		18 33	18 43	19 12		19 33	19 43	19 58	20 12		20 37	20 37	20 43	21 12		21 43		21 57	22 12		23 14
Deighton	d									20 01										22 01			
Mirfield	d									20 06										22 06			
Wakefield Kirkgate	a																						
Wakefield Westgate	a																						
Ravensthorpe	d									20 09										22 09			
Dewsbury	a	18 21				19 21				20 13	20 21					21 21				22 12	22 21		23 23
	d	18 21				19 21				20 13	20 21					21 21				22 13	22 21		23 23
Batley	d									20 16										22 16			
Morley	d									20 22										22 22			
Cottingley	d									20 26										22 25			
Leeds 10	a	18 37		18 54	19 04	19 37		19 54	20 04	20 34	20 37		20 58	20 58	21 04	21 37		22 04		22 34	22 37		23 37
	d	18 40		19 00	19 12	19 40		19 57	20 12		20 40		21 04	21 04	21 12	21 40		22 12	22 20		22 40		23 40
Garforth	d																						
South Milford	a			19 13															22 33				
Selby	a			19 23				20 16					21 23	21 38					22 42				
Howden	a			19 51									22 20	22 20									
Brough	a			19 43				20 34					21 43	21 56					23 00				
Hull	a			20 00				20 53					22 01	22 13					23 18				
York 8	a	19 06			19 37	20 06			20 37		21 06				21 38	22 06		22 38			23 11		00 10
	d	19 14			19 40	20 13			20 40		21 08					22 10		22 42					
Malton	d				20 04				21 04							22 34							
Seamer	a				20 21				21 21							22 51							
Scarborough	a				20 32				21 32							23 02							
Thirsk	a					20 30					21 26							23 06					
Northallerton	a	19 35			20b06	20 38			21b34		21 34							23 16					
Darlington 7	a	19 46			20b10	21b03			21b18		21 46				22 26			23 32					01 32
Yarm	d					20 52																	
Thornaby	a					21 01																	
Middlesbrough	a					21 12																	
Durham	a	20 03			20b27	21b21			21b36		22 03				22 44			23 49					01 50
Chester-le-Street	a	20 09							21b45														
Newcastle 8	a	20 22			20b43	21b37			21b59		22 20				23 14			00 21					02 25

For general notes see front of timetable
For details of catering facilities see Directory of Train Operators

A Until 12 July
B From 19 July
b Change at York

Table 39

Sundays

from 13 September

Liverpool, Manchester Airport and Manchester → Huddersfield → Leeds, Hull, York, Scarborough, Middlesbrough and Newcastle

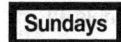

Network Diagram - see first page of Table 39

		TP 1 ◇	TP (bus)	TP (bus)	TP 1 ◇	TP (bus)	TP 1 ◇	TP 1 ◇	TP 1 ◇	NT	TP 1 ◇	NT	TP 1 ◇	TP 1 ◇	NT	TP 1 ◇	TP 1 ◇	NT	TP 1 ◇	EA (bus)
Liverpool Lime Street 10	d										08 19					09 22			10 22	
Warrington Central	d										08A05					09A10			10A10	
Birchwood	d																			
Newton-le-Willows	d										08 35					09 40			10 40	
Manchester Oxford Road	d																			
Manchester Airport ✈	d		01 35	05 00		06 10			07 40					09 03			10 03			
Manchester Piccadilly 10	a		02 00	05 25		06 35			07 53					09 18			10 18			
	d		02 00	05 25		06 35			07 55					09 20			10 20			
Manchester Victoria	a								08 09		08 56			09 35		10 03	10 35		11 03	
	d								08 30		09 05			09 38	09 43	10 05	10 38	10 43	11 05	
Ashton-under-Lyne	d														09 53			10 53		
Stalybridge	a					06 55									09 57			10 57		
	d					06 55														11 10
Mossley (Grtr Manchester)	d																			
Greenfield	d																			
Marsden	d																			
Slaithwaite	d																			
Huddersfield	a		03 00	06 25		07 40			09 15		09 53					10 53				11 55
	d		03 00	06 25		07 40			09 17	09 44	09 54					10 54				
Deighton	d									09 47										
Mirfield	d									09 52										
Ravensthorpe	d									09 55										
Dewsbury	a			06 45		08 00			09 26	09 59		←		10 24			11 21		11 58	
	d			06 45		08 00			09 26	10 03 →		10 03		10 24			11 21		11 58	
Batley	d											10 06								
Morley	d											10 12								
Cottingley	d											10 15								
Leeds 10	a		03 35	07 10		08 25			09 43		10 14	10 23		10 37		11 15	11 37		12 11	
	d	00 54	03 35	07 10			08 40	09 12	09 46		10 18		10 24	10 40		11 18	11 40		12 12	
Garforth	d																			
South Milford	a												10 36							
Selby	a												10 46							
Howden	a																			
Brough	a												11 04							
Hull	a												11 20							
York 8	a	01 46	04 20	07 55			09 08	09 37	10 10		10 42			11 06		11 41	12 06		12 37	
	d				08 21		09 09	09 40	10 13		10 45			11 15		11 43	12 15		12 40	
Malton	d							10 04								12 08				
Seamer	a							10 21								12 24				
Scarborough	a							10 32								12 32				
Thirsk	a				08 37						11 04			*11 34*					13 02	
Northallerton	a				08 45		09 30		10 35		11 12			11 35			12 35		13 10	
Darlington 7	a				08 57		09 41	*10b33*	10 46		*11b36*			11 46		*12b34*	12 46		*13b35*	
Yarm	d										11 27								13 24	
Thornaby	a				09 16						11 35								13 34	
Middlesbrough	a				09 26						11 48								13 44	
Durham	a			*09 50*			09 58	*10b51*	11 08		*11b54*			12 03		*12b52*	13 03		*13b53*	
Chester-le-Street	a																			
Newcastle 8	a			*10 06*			10 18	*11b09*	11 23		*12b10*			12 20		*13b08*	13 20		*14b09*	

For general notes see front of timetable
For details of catering facilities see Directory of Train Operators

A By bus
b Change at York

Table 39

Sundays

Liverpool, Manchester Airport and Manchester → Huddersfield → Leeds, Hull, York, Scarborough, Middlesbrough and Newcastle

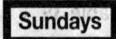

from 13 September

Network Diagram - see first page of Table 39

		NT		TP 1◇	NT	TP 1◇		TP 1◇	TP 1◇	NT		TP 1◇	TP 1◇	EA 🚌		NT	TP 1◇	NT		TP 1◇	TP 1◇	TP 1◇		NT	TP 1◇
Liverpool Lime Street 10	d							11 22					12 22								13 22				
Warrington Central	d							*11A10*					*12A10*								*13A10*				
Birchwood	d																								
Newton-le-Willows	d							11 40					12 40								13 40				
Manchester Oxford Road	d																								
Manchester Airport ✈	d			11 03					12 03								13 03					14 03			
Manchester Piccadilly 10	a			11 18					12 18								13 18					14 18			
	d			11 20					12 20								13 20					14 20			
Manchester Victoria	a			11 35				12 03	12 35				13 03				13 35				14 03	14 35			
	d			11 38	11 43			12 05	12 38	12 43			13 05				13 38	13 43			14 05	14 38		14 43	
Ashton-under-Lyne	d				11 53					12 53								13 53						14 53	
Stalybridge	a				11 57					12 57								13 57						14 57	
	d													13 10											
Mossley (Grtr Manchester)	d																								
Greenfield	d																								
Marsden	d																								
Slaithwaite	d																								
Huddersfield	a													13 55											
	d	11 58				12 30						13 30				13 58				14 30					15 30
Deighton	d	12 01														14 01									
Mirfield	d	12 06														14 06									
Ravensthorpe	d	12 09														14 09									
Dewsbury	a	12 13				12 39		12 58				13 39	13 58			14 13				14 39	14 58				15 39
	d	12 13				12 39		12 58				13 39	13 58			14 13				14 39	14 58				15 39
Batley	d	12 16														14 16									
Morley	d	12 22														14 22									
Cottingley	d	12 26														14 26									
Leeds 10	a	12 34		12 37		12 54		13 11	13 37			13 54	14 12			14 34	14 37			14 54	15 11	15 37			15 54
	d			12 40		13 00		13 12	13 40			13 57	14 14				14 40			15 00	15 12	15 40			15 57
Garforth	d																								
South Milford	a					13 13														15 13					
Selby	a					13 23														15 23					
Howden	a																			*16 51*					
Brough	a					13 41														15 41					
Hull	a					14 00														16 00					
York 8	a			13 06				13 37	14 06			14 24	14 38				15 06				15 37	16 06			16 24
	d			13 15				13 40	14 15				14 40				15 15				15 40	16 15			
Malton	d							14 04													16 04				
Seamer	a							14 21													16 21				
Scarborough	a							14 32													16 32				
Thirsk	a												15 02								*16b09*				
Northallerton	a			13 35				*14b25*	14 35				15 10				15 35				*16b19*	16 35			
Darlington 7	a			13 46				*14b38*	14 46			*15 03*	*15b15*				15 46				*16b12*	16 46			
Yarm	d												15 24												
Thornaby	a												15 40												
Middlesbrough	a												15 52												
Durham	a			14 03				*14b56*	15 03			*15 24*	*15b32*				16 03				*16b30*	17 03			*17 18*
Chester-le-Street	a			14 09																					
Newcastle 8	a			14 22				*15b12*	15 20			*15 33*	*15b51*				16 20				*16b50*	17 20			*17 34*

For general notes see front of timetable
For details of catering facilities see Directory of Train Operators

A By bus
b Change at York

Sundays

from 13 September

Liverpool, Manchester Airport and Manchester → Huddersfield → Leeds, Hull, York, Scarborough, Middlesbrough and Newcastle

Network Diagram - see first page of Table 39

		TP 1 ◇	NT	TP 1 ◇		NT	TP 1 ◇	TP 1 ◇		EA 🚌	TP 1 ◇	NT		TP 1 ◇	TP 1 ◇	NT		TP 1 ◇	NT	TP 1 ◇		TP 1 ◇	EA 🚌	TP 1 ◇	NT
Liverpool Lime Street 10	d	14 22						15 22							16 22							17 22			
Warrington Central	d	*14A10*						*15A10*							*16A10*							*17A10*			
Birchwood	d																								
Newton-le-Willows	d	14 40						15 40							16 40							17 40			
Manchester Oxford Road	d																								
Manchester Airport ✈	d			15 03							16 03							17 03						18 03	
Manchester Piccadilly 10	a			15 18							16 18							17 18						18 18	
	d			15 20							16 20							17 20						18 20	
Manchester Victoria	a	15 03		15 35				16 03			16 35				17 03			17 35				18 03		18 35	
	d	15 05		15 38		15 43		16 05			16 38	16 43			17 05			17 38	17 43			18 05		18 38	18 43
Ashton-under-Lyne	d					15 53						16 53							17 53						18 53
Stalybridge	a					15 57						16 57							17 57						18 57
	d									16 10													18 10		
Mossley (Grtr Manchester)	d																								
Greenfield	d																								
Marsden	d																								
Slaithwaite	d																								
Huddersfield	a									16 55													18 55		
	d		15 58				16 30							17 30		17 58				18 30					
Deighton	d		16 01													18 01									
Mirfield	d		16 06													18 06									
Ravensthorpe	d		16 09													18 09									
Dewsbury	a	15 58	16 13				16 39	16 58						17 39	17 58	18 13				18 39		18 58			
	d	15 58	16 13				16 39	16 58						17 39	17 58	18 13				18 39		18 58			
Batley	d		16 16													18 16									
Morley	d		16 22													18 22									
Cottingley	d		16 26													18 26									
Leeds 10	a	16 11	16 34	16 37			16 54	17 11			17 37			17 54	18 11	18 34		18 37		18 54		19 11		19 37	
	d	16 12		16 40			17 00	17 12			17 40			17 57	18 12			18 40		19 00		19 12		19 40	
Garforth	d																								
South Milford	a						17 13													19 13					
Selby	a						17 23													19 23					
Howden	a						*18 01*													*19 51*					
Brough	a						17 41													19 43					
Hull	a						18 00													20 00					
York 8	a	16 37		17 06				17 37			18 08			18 24	18 37			19 06				19 37		20 06	
	d	16 40		17 14				17 40			18 14				18 40			19 14				19 40		20 13	
Malton	d							18 04														20 04			
Seamer	a							18 21														20 21			
Scarborough	a							18 32														20 32			
Thirsk	a	17 02													18 59									20 30	
Northallerton	a	17 10		17 35							18 35				19 07			19 35				*20b06*		20 38	
Darlington 7	a	*17b14*		17 46				*18b15*			18 46				*19b35*			19 46				*20b10*			
Yarm	d	17 24													19 21									20 52	
Thornaby	a	17 33													19 32									21 01	
Middlesbrough	a	17 43													19 40									21 12	
Durham	a	*17b32*		18 03				*18b33*			19 03			*19 18*	*19b53*			20 03				*20b27*		*21b21*	
Chester-le-Street	a	*17b40*		18 09														20 09							
Newcastle 8	a	*17b53*		18 22				*18b52*			19 20			*19 51*	*20b09*			20 22				*20b43*		*21b37*	

For general notes see front of timetable
For details of catering facilities see Directory of Train Operators

A By bus
b Change at York

Table 39

Sundays

Liverpool, Manchester Airport and Manchester → Huddersfield → Leeds, Hull, York, Scarborough, Middlesbrough and Newcastle

from 13 September

Network Diagram - see first page of Table 39

		TP 1 ◇		TP 1 ◇	NT	TP 1 ◇		NT	TP 1 ◇	TP 1 ◇		TP 1 ◇	NT	TP 1 ◇		TP 1 ◇	NT	NT	TP 1 ◇	NT	TP 1 ◇	TP 1 ◇	TP 1 ◇		
Liverpool Lime Street 10	d			18 22						19 22				20 22								21 52			
Warrington Central	d			*18A10*						*19A10*				*20A10*								*21A40*			
Birchwood	d																								
Newton-le-Willows	d			18 40						19 40				20 40								22 08			
Manchester Oxford Road	d																								
Manchester Airport ✈	d					19 03						20 03							21 03		22 03		23 25		
Manchester Piccadilly 10 ⛴	a					19 18						20 18							21 18		22 16		23 38		
	d					19 20						20 20							21 20		22 18		23 40		
Manchester Victoria ⛴	a			19 03		19 35				20 03		20 35		21 03					21 35		22 32	22 30	23 53		
	d			19 05		19 38		19 43		20 05		20 38	20 43	21 05					21 38	21 43		22 38	23 55		
Ashton-under-Lyne	d							19 53					20 53							21 53					
Stalybridge	a							19 57					20 57							21 57					
	d																								
Mossley (Grtr Manchester)	d																								
Greenfield	d																								
Marsden	d																21 47								
Slaithwaite	d																21 51								
Huddersfield	a																21 57		22 23			23 23	00 40		
	d	19 30			19 58				20 30								21 57		22 26			23 26	00 43		
Deighton	d				20 01												22 01								
Mirfield	d				20 06												22 06								
Ravensthorpe	d				20 09												22 09								
Dewsbury	a	19 39		19 58	20 13				20 39	20 58				21 58			22 12		22 35			23 35			
	d	19 39		19 58	20 13				20 39	20 58				21 58			22 13		22 35			23 35			
Batley	d				20 16												22 16								
Morley	d				20 22												22 22								
Cottingley	d				20 26												22 25								
Leeds 10	a	19 54		20 11	20 34	20 37			20 54	21 11		21 37		22 10			22 34		22 51			23 51	01 04		
	d	19 57		20 12		20 40			21 04	21 12		21 40		22 12		22 20		22 43	22 53			23 54	01 07		
Garforth	d																	22 55							
South Milford	a															22 33									
Selby	a	20 16							21 38							22 42									
Howden	a								*22 20*																
Brough	a	20 34							21 56							23 00									
Hull	a	20 53							22 13							23 18									
York 8	a			20 37		21 06				21 38		22 06		22 38				23 18	23 26			00 23	01 35		
	d			20 40		21 08						22 10		22 42											
Malton	d			21 04								22 34													
Seamer	a			21 21								22 51													
Scarborough	a			21 32								23 02													
Thirsk	a					21 26								23 06											
Northallerton	a					21 34								23 16											
Darlington 7	a			*21b18*		21 46				*22 26*				23 32								*01 32*			
Yarm	d																								
Thornaby	a																								
Middlesbrough	a																								
Durham	a			*21b36*		22 03				*22 44*				23 49								*01 50*			
Chester-le-Street	a			*21b45*																					
Newcastle 8 ⛴	a			*21b59*		22 20				*23 14*				00 21								*02 25*			

For general notes see front of timetable
For details of catering facilities see Directory of Train Operators

A By bus
b Change at York

Table 40

Mondays to Fridays

York and Selby → Leeds

Network Diagram - see first page of Table 39

Miles	Miles			TP MO	TP MX	TP	TP MX	TP MO		TP	NT	TP	NT	TP		XC	TP	NT	TP	TP		NT	TP	NT	TP	XC
				1◇	1◇	1◇	1◇	1◇		1◇		1◇		1◇ 🛒		1◇ 🛒	1◇ 🛒		1◇ 🛒	1◇ 🛒			1◇ 🛒		1◇ 🛒	1◇ 🛒
0	—	**York [8]**	33 d	01 52	01 46	02 52	04 00	04 22		05 26	05 40	05 57	06 13	06 28		06 32			06 54			07 06	07 23		07 40	07 44
8¾	—	Ulleskelf	33 d																			07 15				
10¾	—	Church Fenton	33 d																			07 21				
—	0	**Selby**	d														06 35	06 41		07 07				07 26		
—	7¾	South Milford	d															06 50						07 35		
15¾	11	Micklefield	d								05 58		06 28					06 56				07 28		07 41		
17½	12¾	East Garforth	d								06 02		06 32					07 00				07 32		07 46		
18¼	13¼	Garforth	d								06 05	06 12	06 35					07 02	07 09	07 24		07 35		07 48		
21	16¼	Cross Gates	d								06 10		06 40					07 07				07 40	07 44	07 53		
25½	20¾	**Leeds [10]**	a	02 18	02 31	03b33	04 47	04 49		05 52	06 20	06 22	06 49	06 53		06 56	07 00	07 19	07 20	07 35		07 49	07 52	08 02	08 04	08 08
—	—	Bradford Interchange	37 a				05 28	05 28		06 21		06 57	07 11			07 28		07 43	07 57			08 09		08 28		

		NT	NT		TP	NT	TP	NT	TP		NT	TP	XC	NT	TP		TP	NT	TP	TP	XC		NT	TP	TP	NT
					1◇ 🛒		1◇ 🛒		1◇ 🛒			1◇ 🛒	1◇ 🛒		1◇ 🛒		1◇ 🛒		1◇ 🛒	1◇ 🛒	1◇ 🛒			1◇ 🛒	1◇ 🛒	
York [8]	33 d		07 48		07 54				08 24		08 27	08 40	08 44		08 58			09 09	09 28	09 40	09 44			09 58		10 11
Ulleskelf	33 d																									
Church Fenton	33 d		08 05															09 21								
Selby	d	07 43					08 07	08 12						08 43			09 11						09 43		10 11	
South Milford	d	07 53				←		08 22						08 53									09 52			
Micklefield	d	07 58	08 13			08 13		08 28			08 42			08 58				09 28					09 58			10 28
East Garforth	d	08 02	→			08 17		08 32			08 46			09 02				09 32					10 02			10 32
Garforth	d	08 05			08 13	08 20		08 35	08 41		08 48			09 05	09 13			09 35					10 05	10 13		10 35
Cross Gates	d	08 10				08 25		08 40			08 53			09 10				09 40					10 10			10 40
Leeds [10]	a	08 19			08 23	08 35	08 37	08 49	08 52		09 02	09 04	09 08	09 19	09 23		09 34	09 49	09 53	10 04	10 08		10 19	10 23	10 37	10 49
Bradford Interchange	37 a	08 42			08 57			09 11	09 28					09 42	09 57			10 09	10 28				10 42	10 57		11 10

		TP	TP	XC		NT	TP	TP	NT	TP		TP	XC	NT	TP	TP		NT	TP	TP	XC	NT		TP	TP	NT
		1◇ 🛒	1◇ 🛒	1◇ 🛒			1◇ 🛒	1◇ 🛒		1◇ 🛒		1◇ 🛒	1◇ 🛒		1◇ 🛒	1◇ 🛒			1◇ 🛒	1◇ 🛒	1◇ 🛒			1◇ 🛒	1◇ 🛒	
York [8]	33 d	10 28	10 40	10 44			10 58		11 09	11 28		11 40	11 44		11 58			12 13	12 28	12 39	12 44			12 58		13 09
Ulleskelf	33 d																									
Church Fenton	33 d								11 21																	13 21
Selby	d					10 43		11 09						11 43		12 09						12 43			13 09	
South Milford	d					10 53								11 52								12 53				
Micklefield	d					10 58			11 28					11 58				12 28				12 58				13 28
East Garforth	d					11 02			11 32					12 02				12 32				13 02				13 32
Garforth	d					11 05	11 13		11 35					12 05	12 13			12 35				13 05		13 13		13 35
Cross Gates	d					11 10			11 40					12 10				12 40				13 10				13 40
Leeds [10]	a	10 53	11 04	11 08		11 19	11 23	11 33	11 49	11 53		12 04	12 08	12 19	12 23	12 33		12 49	12 53	13 04	13 08	13 19		13 23	13 33	13 49
Bradford Interchange	37 a	11 28				11 42	11 57		12 11	12 28				12 42	12 57			13 11	13 28			13 42		13 57		14 11

		TP	TP	XC	NT		TP	TP	NT	TP	TP		XC	NT	TP	TP	NT		TP	TP	XC	NT	TP		TP	NT
		1◇ 🛒	1◇ 🛒	1◇ 🛒			1◇ 🛒	1◇ 🛒		1◇ 🛒	1◇ 🛒		1◇ 🛒		1◇ 🛒	1◇ 🛒			1◇ 🛒	1◇ 🛒	1◇ 🛒		1◇ 🛒		1◇ 🛒	
York [8]	33 d	13 28	13 40	13 44			13 58		14 13	14 28	14 40		14 44		14 58		15 09		15 28	15 40	15 44		15 58			16 13
Ulleskelf	33 d																									
Church Fenton	33 d																15 20									
Selby	d				13 43			14 09						14 43		15 09						15 43			16 11	
South Milford	d				13 53									14 53								15 53				
Micklefield	d				13 58				14 28					14 58			15 28					15 58				16 28
East Garforth	d				14 02				14 32					15 02			15 32					16 02				16 32
Garforth	d				14 05		14 13		14 35					15 05	15 13		15 35					16 05	16 13			16 35
Cross Gates	d				14 10				14 40					15 10			15 40					16 10				16 40
Leeds [10]	a	13 53	14 04	14 07	14 19		14 23	14 33	14 49	14 53	15 04		15 08	15 19	15 23	15 33	15 49		15 53	16 04	16 08	16 19	16 23		16 35	16 49
Bradford Interchange	37 a	14 28			14 42		14 57		15 11	15 28				15 42	15 57		16 10		16 28			16 42	16 57			17 10

		TP	TP	XC	NT	TP		TP	NT	TP	TP	TP		XC	NT	TP	NT	TP		NT	TP	TP	XC	NT		NT
		1◇ 🛒	1◇ 🛒	1◇ 🛒		1◇ 🛒		1◇ 🛒		1◇ 🛒	1◇	1◇ 🛒		1◇ 🛒		1◇ 🛒		1◇ 🛒			1◇ 🛒	1◇	1◇ 🛒			
York [8]	33 d	16 28	16 40	16 44		16 58			17 08	17 28		17 40		17 44		17 58		18 09		18 12		18 40	18 44			
Ulleskelf	33 d																									
Church Fenton	33 d								17 20																	
Selby	d				16 43			17 11			17 32				17 43		18 00				18 31			18 43		19 00
South Milford	d				16 53										17 53									18 53		
Micklefield	d				16 58				17 28						17 58					18 27				18 58		
East Garforth	d				17 02				17 32						18 02					18 31				19 02		
Garforth	d				17 05	17 13			17 35						18 05	18 13	18 18			18 33				19 05		19 15
Cross Gates	d				17 10				17 40						18 10					18 38				19 10		
Leeds [10]	a	16 53	17 04	17 07	17 20	17 23		17 34	17 49	17 53	17 58	18 04		18 09	18 19	18 23	18 31	18 35		18 49	18 53	19 04	19 09	19 21		19 27
Bradford Interchange	37 a	17 28		17 42		17 57			18 10		18 28				18 43		18 57	19 10			19 28			19 44		19 57

		NT	TP	NT	TP	TP		XC	TP	NT	TP	TP		XC	TP	NT	NT FO	TP		TP	NT	TP	NT			
			1◇		1◇	1◇		1◇ 🛒	1◇		1◇	1◇		1◇ 🛒	1◇			1◇		1◇		1◇				
York [8]	33 d	19 04	19 10			19 39		19 44	20 10	20 13		20 40		20 44	21 10	21 16	21 16	21 45			22 13	23 07	23 13			
Ulleskelf	33 d															21 25	21 25									
Church Fenton	33 d	19 21								20 25						21 31	21 31						23 28			
Selby	d				19 30						20 27									22 07						
South Milford	d			←							20 36									22 17						
Micklefield	d	19 28		19 28						20 32						21 39	21 39				22 28		23 35			
East Garforth	d	→		19 32						20 36						21 43	21 43				22 32		23 39			
Garforth	d		19 25	19 35						20 39						21 45	21 45				22 35		23 42			
Cross Gates	d			19 40						20 44						21 50	21 50				22 40		23 47			
Leeds [10]	a		19 35	19 49	19 56	20 04		20 09	20 35	20 52	20 56	21 04		21 07	21 35	21 59	21 59	22 07		22 35	22 51	23 33	23 56			
Bradford Interchange	37 a			20 10	20 28			20 57			21 28			21 57	22 28			22 57			23 29					

For general notes see front of timetable
For details of catering facilities see
Directory of Train Operators

b Mondays arr. 0318

York and Selby → Leeds

Network Diagram - see first page of Table 39

		TP	TP	TP	TP	TP	XC	NT	NT	TP	TP	NT	NT	TP	TP	NT	NT	TP	TP	XC	NT	NT	TP
		1 ◇	1 ◇	1 ◇	1 ◇	1 ◇	1 ◇			1 ◇	1 ◇			1 ◇	1 ◇			1 ◇	1 ◇	1 ◇			1 ◇
								A	B			A	B			A	B				B	A	
							trolley												trolley	trolley			trolley
York 8	33 d	01 52	02 46	03 52	05 26	05 57	06 09	06 13	06 13	06 28				06 54		07 06	07 06	07 28	07 40	07 44			07 58
Ulleskelf	33 d															07 15	07 15						
Church Fenton	33 d															07 21	07 21						
Selby	d										06 35	06 44	06 41		07 07						07 43	07 44	
South Milford	d											06 53	06 50								07 53	07 55	
Micklefield	d							06 28	06 28			06 59	06 56			07 28	07 28				07 58	08 00	
East Garforth	d							06 32	06 32			07 03	07 00			07 32	07 32				08 02	08 04	
Garforth	d					06 12		06 35	06 35			07 05	07 02	07 09		07 35	07 35				08 05	08 07	08 13
Cross Gates	d							06 40	06 40			07 10	07 07			07 40	07 40				08 10	08 12	
Leeds 10	a	02 18	03 12	04 34	05 52	06 22	06 53	06 49	06 49	06 53	07 00	07 17	07 18	07 20	07 35	07 49	07 49	07 52	08 04	08 08	08 19	08 19	08 23
Bradford Interchange	37 a			05b57	06c21	06b57			07 11		07e30	07 45	07 43	07b57	08f11	08 30	08 11	08b28			08 42	08 44	08 57

		TP	NT	NT	TP	TP	XC	NT	TP	TP	NT	NT	TP	TP	XC	NT	TP	TP	NT	NT	TP	TP	XC
		1 ◇			1 ◇	1 ◇	1 ◇		1 ◇	1 ◇			1 ◇	1 ◇	1 ◇		1 ◇	1 ◇			1 ◇	1 ◇	1 ◇
			A	B							B	A							B	A			
		trolley			trolley	trolley	trolley		trolley	trolley			trolley		trolley		trolley				trolley	trolley	trolley
York 8	33 d		08 09	08 09	08 24	08 40	08 44		08 58		09 09	09 09	09 28	09 40	09 44		09 58		10 11	10 11	10 28	10 40	10 44
Ulleskelf	33 d																						
Church Fenton	33 d		08 22	08 22							09 21	09 21											
Selby	d	08 07						08 43		09 11						09 43		10 11					
South Milford	d							08 53								09 53							
Micklefield	d		08 28	08 28				08 58			09 28	09 28				09 58			10 28	10 29			
East Garforth	d		08 32	08 32				09 02			09 32	09 32				10 02			10 32	10 33			
Garforth	d		08 35	08 35				09 05	09 13		09 35	09 35				10 05	10 13		10 35	10 36			
Cross Gates	d		08 40	08 40				09 10			09 40	09 40				10 10			10 40	10 41			
Leeds 10	a	08 37	08 49	08 49	08 52	09 04	09 07	09 19	09 23	09 34	09 49	09 50	09 53	10 04	10 08	10 19	10 23	10 37	10 49	10 49	10 53	11 04	11 08
Bradford Interchange	37 a	09 12		09 12	09 28			09 42	09 57	10b10	10 10		10 28			10 42	10 57	11b11	11 11		11 28		

		NT	TP	TP	NT	NT	TP	TP	XC	NT	TP	TP	NT	NT	TP	TP	XC	NT	TP	TP	NT	NT	TP
			1 ◇	1 ◇			1 ◇	1 ◇	1 ◇		1 ◇	1 ◇			1 ◇	1 ◇	1 ◇		1 ◇	1 ◇			1 ◇
					A	B							B	A							A	B	
			trolley				trolley	trolley	trolley		trolley	trolley			trolley		trolley		trolley	trolley			trolley
York 8	33 d		10 58		11 09	11 09	11 28	11 40	11 44		11 58		12 13	12 13	12 28	12 40	12 44		12 58		13 09	13 09	13 28
Ulleskelf	33 d																						
Church Fenton	33 d				11 21	11 21															13 21	13 21	
Selby	d	10 43		11 09						11 43		12 09						12 43		13 09			
South Milford	d	10 53								11 53								12 53					
Micklefield	d	10 58			11 28	11 28				11 58			12 28	12 28				12 58			13 28	13 28	
East Garforth	d	11 02			11 32	11 32				12 02			12 32	12 32				13 02			13 32	13 32	
Garforth	d	11 05	11 13		11 35	11 35				12 05	12 13		12 35	12 35				13 05	13 13		13 35	13 35	
Cross Gates	d	11 10			11 40	11 40				12 10			12 40	12 40				13 10			13 40	13 40	
Leeds 10	a	11 19	11 23	11 33	11 49	11 49	11 53	12 04	12 08	12 19	12 23	12 33	12 49	12 50	12 53	13 04	13 09	13 19	13 23	13 33	13 49	13 49	13 53
Bradford Interchange	37 a	11 42	11 57	12b10		12 10	12 28			12 42	12 57	13b10	13 10		13 28			13 42	13 57	14g11		14 11	14 28

		TP	XC	NT	TP	TP	NT	NT	TP	TP	XC	NT	TP	TP	NT	NT	TP	TP	XC	NT	TP	TP	NT
		1 ◇	1 ◇		1 ◇	1 ◇			1 ◇	1 ◇	1 ◇		1 ◇	1 ◇			1 ◇	1 ◇	1 ◇		1 ◇	1 ◇	
							A	B							A	B							A
		trolley	trolley		trolley				trolley	trolley	trolley		trolley				trolley	trolley	trolley		trolley	trolley	
York 8	33 d	13 40	13 44		13 58		14 13	14 13	14 28	14 40	14 44		14 58		15 08	15 08	15 28	15 40	15 44		15 58		16 13
Ulleskelf	33 d																						
Church Fenton	33 d														15 20	15 20							
Selby	d			13 43		14 09						14 43		15 09						15 43		16 11	
South Milford	d			13 53								14 53								15 53			
Micklefield	d			13 58			14 28	14 28				14 58			15 28	15 28				15 58			16 28
East Garforth	d			14 02			14 32	14 32				15 02			15 32	15 32				16 03			16 32
Garforth	d			14 05	14 13		14 35	14 35				15 05	15 13		15 35	15 35				16 05	16 13		16 35
Cross Gates	d			14 10			14 40	14 40				15 10			15 40	15 40				16 10			16 40
Leeds 10	a	14 04	14 08	14 19	14 23	14 33	14 49	14 49	14 53	15 04	15 08	15 19	15 23	15 33	15 49	15 49	15 53	16 04	16 08	16 19	16 23	16 35	16 49
Bradford Interchange	37 a			14 42	14 57	15g11		15 11	15 28			15 42	15 57	16b10		16 10	16 28			16 42	16 57	17h09	

		NT	TP	TP	XC	NT	TP	TP	NT	NT	TP	TP	TP	XC	NT	TP	TP	NT	NT	TP	TP	XC	NT
			1 ◇	1 ◇	1 ◇		1 ◇	1 ◇			1 ◇	1 ◇	1 ◇	1 ◇		1 ◇	1 ◇			1 ◇	1 ◇	1 ◇	
		B							B	A								A	B				
			trolley	trolley	trolley		trolley				trolley			trolley								trolley	
York 8	33 d	16 13	16 28	16 40	16 44		16 58		17 08	17 08	17 28		17 40	17 44		17 58	18 09	18 12	18 12		18 38	18 44	
Ulleskelf	33 d																						
Church Fenton	33 d								17 20	17 20													
Selby	d					16 43		17 11				17 32			17 43					18 34			18 43
South Milford	d					16 53									17 53								18 53
Micklefield	d	16 28				16 58			17 28	17 28					17 58			18 27	18 27				18 58
East Garforth	d	16 32				17 02			17 32	17 32					18 02			18 31	18 31				19 02
Garforth	d	16 35				17 05	17 13		17 35	17 35					18 05	18 13		18 33	18 33				19 05
Cross Gates	d	16 40				17 10			17 40	17 40					18 10			18 38	18 38				19 10
Leeds 10	a	16 49	16 53	17 04	17 08	17 19	17 23	17 34	17 49	17 50	17 53	17 58	18 04	18 08	18 19	18 23	18 35	18 49	18 49	19j00	19 04	19 08	19 21
Bradford Interchange	37 a	17 09	17 28			17 42	17 57	18h09	18 09			18 28			18 43	18g58	19b10		19 10	19k30			19 44

For general notes see front of timetable
For details of catering facilities see Directory of Train Operators

A Until 11 July
B From 18 July
b Until 11 July arr. 2 mins. later
c Until 11 July arr. 0638
e Bradford Forster Square
f Until 11 July arr. 0812
g Until 11 July arr. 1 min. later
h Until 11 July arr. 3 mins. later
j From 12 September arr. 1858
k Bradford Forster Square. From 12 September arr. Bradford Interchange 1928

Table 40

Saturdays

York and Selby → Leeds

Network Diagram - see first page of Table 39

		NT	NT	NT	TP	NT	NT	TP		TP	XC	TP	NT	TP	TP	XC		TP	NT	TP	TP	NT	TP	NT		
		1			1◇			1◇		1◇	1◇	1◇		1◇	1◇	1◇		1◇		1◇	1◇		1◇			
			A	B		A	B																			
											🛒					🛒										
York 8	33 d		19 04	19 04	19 10					19 40	19 44	20 10	20 13		20 40	20 44		21 10	21 13	21 42		22 13	23 07	23 13		
Ulleskelf	33 d																		21 22							
Church Fenton	33 d		19 21	19 21									20 25						21 28					23 28		
Selby	d	18 55						19 30						20 27							22 07					
South Milford	d					←	←							20 36							22 17					
Micklefield	d		19 28 →	19 28 →		19 28	19 28						20 32						21 36			22 28		23 35		
East Garforth	d					19 32	19 32						20 36						21 40			22 32		23 39		
Garforth	d	19 12			19 25	19 35	19 35						20 39						21 42			22 35		23 42		
Cross Gates	d					19 40	19 40						20 44						21 47			22 40		23 47		
Leeds 10	a	19 25			19 35	19 49	19 49	19 56		20 04	20 08	20 35	20 54	20 56	21 04	21 08		21 35	21 57	22 05	22 35	22 51	23 33	23 56		
Bradford Interchange	37 a	19b57			20c10	20 30	20 10	20c28			20c57			21c28		21c57		22c28	22c28	22c57	23e20	23f30				

Sundays

		TP	TP	TP	TP	TP	TP	TP	TP	TP		TP	TP	TP	TP	NT	NT	TP	XC	TP		TP	NT	NT	TP	XC
			1◇		1◇		1◇	1◇		1◇		1◇	1◇	1◇	1◇			1◇	1◇	1◇		1◇			1◇	1◇
		C	D	C	D	C	D	D	C	D		C	D	C	D	E	G					C	E	G		
		🚌		🚌		🚌			🚌										🛒							🛒
York 8	33 d	02 00	02 44	03 15	03 59	04 45	05 12	06 12	06 15	07 12		07 40	08 10	08 30	08 40	08 50	08 50	09 15	09 28			09 45	09 52	09 52	10 15	10 28
Ulleskelf	33 d																									
Church Fenton	33 d															09 02	09 02						10 04	10 04		
Selby	d																			09 31						
South Milford	d																			09 40						
Micklefield	d															09 09	09 09						10 12	10 12		
East Garforth	d															09 13	09 13						10 16	10 16		
Garforth	d															09 16	09 16						10 18	10 18		
Cross Gates	d															09 21	09 21						10 23	10 23		
Leeds 10	a	02 45	03 10	04 00	04 25	05 30	05 38	06 38	07 00	07 38		08 33	08 38	08 55	09 05	09 30	09 30	09 38	09 51	09 58		10 08	10 32	10 32	10 38	10 51
Bradford Interchange	37 a								08 23	08g25		09 03	09h45	09 43	09j45	10 16	09 53	10k14		10k32			11 16	10 53	11k14	11k32

		TP	NT	NT	TP	XC	TP		TP	NT	NT	TP	XC	TP	TP	NT	NT		TP	XC	TP	TP	NT	NT	TP	XC
		1◇			1◇	1◇	1◇		1◇			1◇	1◇	1◇	1◇				1◇	1◇	1◇	1◇			1◇	1◇
			E	G						E	G					E	G						E	G		
						🛒							🛒							🛒						🛒
York 8	33 d	10 45	10 57	10 57	11 15	11 28			11 45	11 52	11 52	12 15	12 28		12 45	12 52	12 52		13 15	13 28		13 45	13 52	13 52	14 15	14 28
Ulleskelf	33 d																									
Church Fenton	33 d									12 04	12 04												14 04	14 04		
Selby	d						11 29							12 33							13 29					
South Milford	d						11 38														13 38					
Micklefield	d		11 12	11 12						12 11	12 11					13 07	13 07						14 11	14 11		
East Garforth	d		11 16	11 16						12 15	12 15					13 11	13 11						14 15	14 15		
Garforth	d		11 18	11 18						12 18	12 18					13 13	13 13						14 18	14 18		
Cross Gates	d		11 23	11 23						12 23	12 23					13 18	13 18						14 23	14 23		
Leeds 10	a	11 08	11 32	11 32	11 38	11 52	11 56		12 08	12 32	12 32	12 38	12 51	12 56	13 08	13 27	13 27		13 38	13 51	13 56	14 08	14 32	14 32	14 38	14 51
Bradford Interchange	37 a	11m54	12 16	11 53	12k14		12k32		12m54	13 16	12 53	13k14		13k32	13m54	14 16	13 53		14k14		14k32	14m54	15 16	14 53	15k14	

		TP	TP	NT		NT	TP	XC	TP	TP	NT	NT	TP	XC		TP	TP	NT	NT	TP	XC	TP	TP	NT		NT
		1◇	1◇				1◇	1◇	1◇	1◇			1◇	1◇		1◇	1◇			1◇	1◇	1◇	1◇			
				E		G					E	G						E	G					E		G
								🛒						🛒							🛒					
York 8	33 d	14 33	14 45	14 52		14 52	15 15	15 28		15 45	15 52	15 52	16 15	16 28		16 33	16 45	16 52	16 52	17 15	17 28		17 45	17 52		17 52
Ulleskelf	33 d																									
Church Fenton	33 d										16 04	16 04												18 04		18 04
Selby	d								15 29													17 29				
South Milford	d								15 38													17 38				
Micklefield	d			15 07		15 07					16 11	16 11						17 07	17 07					18 11		18 11
East Garforth	d			15 11		15 11					16 15	16 15						17 11	17 11					18 15		18 15
Garforth	d			15 13		15 13					16 18	16 18						17 13	17 13					18 18		18 18
Cross Gates	d			15 18		15 18					16 23	16 23						17 18	17 18					18 23		18 23
Leeds 10	a	14 56	15 08	15 27		15 27	15 38	15 51	15 56	16 08	16 32	16 32	16 38	16 51		16 56	17 08	17 27	17 27	17 38	17 51	17 56	18 08	18 32		18 32
Bradford Interchange	37 a	15k32	15m54	16 16		15 53	16k14		16k32	16m55	17 16	16 53	17k14			17k32		17n58	17 53	18k14		18k32	18m54	19 03		18 53

		TP	XC	TP	TP	NT	NT	TP	XC	TP		TP	NT	NT	TP	XC	TP	NT	NT	TP	TP	NT	TP	TP		
		1◇	1◇	1◇	1◇			1◇	1◇	1◇		1◇			1◇	1◇	1◇			1◇	1◇		1◇	1◇		
						E	G						E	G				G	E							
			🛒						🛒							🛒										
York 8	33 d	18 15	18 28	18 33	18 45	18 52	18 52	19 15	19 28			19 45	19 52	19 52	20 15	20 28	20 45	20 57	20 57	21 15		21 52	22 12	23 12		
Ulleskelf	33 d																									
Church Fenton	33 d												20 04	20 04								22 04				
Selby	d									19 29											21 31					
South Milford	d									19 38											21 40					
Micklefield	d					19 07	19 07						20 12	20 12				21 12	21 12			22 12				
East Garforth	d					19 11	19 11						20 16	20 16				21 17	21 17			22 16				
Garforth	d					19 13	19 13						20 18	20 18				21 19	21 19			22 19				
Cross Gates	d					19 18	19 18						20 23	20 23				21 24	21 24			22 23				
Leeds 10	a	18 38	18 51	18 56	19 08	19 27	19 27	19 38	19 51	19 56		20 08	20 32	20 32	20 38	20 51	21 08	21 33	21 34	21 38	21 59	22 32	22 38	23 38		
Bradford Interchange	37 a	19k23	19k23		19 53	20 03	19 53	20q14	20q33	20k33		20m54	21 03	20 53		21k25	21r54	21 56	22 27	22 25	22n54		23 43			

For general notes see front of timetable
For details of catering facilities see Directory of Train Operators

- **A** Until 11 July
- **B** From 18 July
- **C** From 13 September
- **D** Until 6 September
- **E** Until 12 July
- **G** From 19 July
- **b** Until 11 July arr. 1959
- **c** Until 11 July arr. 2 mins. later
- **e** From 12 September only
- **f** Until 5 September only. 18 July to 5 September arr. 2329
- **g** 19 July to 6 September arr. 0823
- **h** 19 July to 6 September arr. 0922
- **j** 19 July to 6 September arr. 0938
- **k** Until 12 July arr. 2 mins. later
- **m** Until 12 July only. Bradford Forster Square
- **n** Bradford Forster Square
- **q** Until 12 July arr. 2025
- **r** Bradford Forster Square. From 8 November arr. 2155

Leeds → Selby and York

Network Diagram - see first page of Table 39

Miles	Miles			TP	TP	TP	TP	TP	TP	TP	TP	NT	NT	TP	GR	NT	TP	NT	NT	TP	XC	NT	TP	NT	TP	TP
				MX	MO	MX	MO	MX	MO						R											
				1◇	1◇	1◇	1◇	1◇	1◇	1◇	1◇			1◇	1		1◇			1◇	1◇		1◇		1◇	1◇
					A		B																			
															⊡ ⊼		⊼			⊼	⊼		⊼		⊼	⊼
—	—	Bradford Interchange	37 d								06b01			06 18	06b30		06 48	07 05	07 20			07 34	07 34	07 50		07b59
0	0	**Leeds** 10	d	00 34	00 53	00 54	01 07	02 45	02 59	05 40	06 35	06 38	06 48	06 55	07 10	07 13	07 23	07 29	07 41	07 50	07 57	08 00	08 12	08 15	08 27	08 38
4¼	4¼	Cross Gates	d									06 44						07 36	07 48			08 06		08 22		
7¼	7¼	Garforth	d									06 50	06 58					07 41	07 53	08 00		08 12		08 27		
8	8	East Garforth	d									06 52						07 43	07 56			08 14		08 29		
9¾	9¾	Micklefield	d									06 56						07 47	07 59			08 18		08 33		
—	12¾	South Milford	d										07 04					07 52				08 22		08 38		
—	20¾	**Selby**	a										07 20			07 40	07 43	08 04				08 36		08 55		08 58
14¾	—	Church Fenton	33 a																08 05							
16½	—	Ulleskelf	33 a																							
25½	—	**York** 8	33 a	01 14	01 22	01 43	01 35	03 15	03 29	06 20	07 01	07 15		07 22	07 35				08 21	08 21	08 23		08 34		08 57	

		NT	TP	XC	TP	NT	TP	TP	NT	TP	XC	TP	NT	TP	TP	NT	TP	XC	TP	NT	TP	TP	NT	TP	XC
			1◇	1◇	1◇		1◇	1◇		1◇	1◇	1◇		1◇	1◇		1◇	1◇	1◇		1◇	1◇		1◇	1◇
			⊼	⊼	⊼		⊼	⊼		⊼	⊼	⊼		⊼	⊼		⊼	⊼	⊼		⊼	⊼		⊼	⊼
Bradford Interchange	37 d	08 20		08b26	08 34	08 50		09 03	09 20		09b31	09 34	09 50		10 04	10 20		10b31	10 34	10 50		11 05	11 20		11b31
Leeds 10	d	08 41	08 57	09 05	09 12	09 15	09 27	09 38	09 41	09 57	10 05	10 12	10 15	10 27	10 38	10 41	10 57	11 05	11 12	11 15	11 27	11 38	11 41	11 57	12 05
Cross Gates	d	08 48				09 22			09 48				10 22			10 48				11 22			11 48		
Garforth	d	08 53	09 05			09 27			09 53	10 05			10 27			10 53	11 05			11 27			11 53	12 05	
East Garforth	d	08 56				09 29			09 56				10 29			10 56				11 29			11 56		
Micklefield	d	08 59				09 33			09 59				10 33			10 59				11 33			11 59		
South Milford	d					09 38							10 38							11 38					
Selby	a					09 53		09 57					10 54		10 57					11 55		11 57			
Church Fenton	33 a	09 05							10 05														12 05		
Ulleskelf	33 a																								
York 8	33 a	09 21	09 23	09 33	09 35		09 55		10 21	10 23	10 29	10 35		10 52		11 19	11 23	11 29	11 35		11 52		12 21	12 23	12 29

		TP	NT	TP	TP	NT	TP	XC	TP	NT	TP	TP	NT	TP	XC	TP	NT	TP	TP	NT	TP	XC	TP	NT	TP
		1◇		1◇	1◇		1◇	1◇	1◇		1◇	1◇		1◇	1◇	1◇		1◇	1◇		1◇	1◇	1◇		1◇
		⊼		⊼	⊼		⊼	⊼	⊼		⊼	⊼		⊼	⊼	⊼		⊼	⊼		⊼	⊼	⊼		⊼
Bradford Interchange	37 d	11 34	11 50		12 05	12 19		12b31	12 34	12 50		13 05	13 19		13b31	13 34	13 50		14 05	14 20		14b31	14 34	14 50	
Leeds 10	d	12 12	12 15	12 27	12 38	12 41	12 57	13 05	13 12	13 15	13 27	13 38	13 41	13 57	14 05	14 12	14 15	14 27	14 38	14 41	14 57	15 05	15 12	15 15	15 27
Cross Gates	d		12 22			12 48				13 22			13 48				14 22			14 48				15 22	
Garforth	d		12 27			12 53	13 05			13 27			13 53	14 05			14 27			14 53	15 05			15 27	
East Garforth	d		12 29			12 56				13 29			13 56				14 29			14 56				15 29	
Micklefield	d		12 33			12 59				13 33			13 59				14 33			14 59				15 33	
South Milford	d		12 38							13 38							14 38							15 38	
Selby	a		12 50		12 57					13 51		13 57					14 50		14 57					15 52	
Church Fenton	33 a												14 05												
Ulleskelf	33 a																								
York 8	33 a	12 35		12 52		13 19	13 23	13 29	13 35		13 52		14 21	14 23	14 29	14 35		14 52		15 19	15 23	15 29	15 35		15 52

		TP	NT	TP	XC	TP	NT	TP	TP	NT	TP	XC	TP	NT	TP	NT	TP	NT	NT	TP	XC	TP	NT	TP	XC
								4E																	
		1◇		1◇	1◇	1◇		1◇	1◇		1◇	1◇	1◇		1◇		1◇			1◇	1◇	1◇		1◇	1◇
		⊼		⊼	⊼	⊼		⊼	⊼		⊼	⊼	⊼		⊼		⊼			⊼	⊼	⊼		⊼	⊼
Bradford Interchange	37 d	15 05	15 19		15b31	15 34	15 50		16 05	16 19		16b31	16 34	16 50			17 04	17 19			17b31	17 34	17 50		18b01
Leeds 10	d	15 38	15 41	15 57	16 05	16 12	16 15	16 27	16 38	16 41	16 57	17 05	17 12	17 15	17 24	17 28	17 38	17 41	17 49	17 57	18 05	18 12	18 15	18 27	18 35
Cross Gates	d		15 48				16 22			16 48			17 18	17 24		17 34		17 48	17 56				18 22		
Garforth	d		15 53	16 05			16 27			16 53	17 05			17 29	17 34	17 40		17 53	18 01	18 05			18 27		
East Garforth	d		15 56				16 30			16 56				17 31		17 42		17 56	18 04				18 29		
Micklefield	d		15 59				16 34			16 59				17 35		17 46		17 59	18 08				18 33		
South Milford	d						16 39							17 40					18 12				18 38		
Selby	a	15 57					16 54		17 00					17 53			18 04		18 24				18 50		
Church Fenton	33 a		16 05															18 06							
Ulleskelf	33 a																	18 10							
York 8	33 a		16 21	16 23	16 29	16 35		16 54		17 19	17 22	17 30	17 38		17 57	18 06		18 24		18 24	18 31	18 35		18 52	18 58

		TP	NT	TP	XC	TP	NT	TP	TP	NT	TP	XC	TP	TP	NT	TP	XC	TP	TP	NT	TP	TP	NT	TP
		1◇		1◇	1◇	1◇		1◇	1◇		1◇	1◇	1◇	1◇		1◇	1◇	1◇	1◇		1◇	1◇		1◇
		⊼		⊼	⊼	⊼		⊼	⊼								⊼							
Bradford Interchange	37 d	18 04	18 19		18b27	18 34	18 52		19 05	19 19		19 34		20 04	20 19			20 37	21 04		21 37	22 04	22 19	23 04
Leeds 10	d	18 38	18 41	18 57	19 05	19 12	19 16	19 27	19 38	19 41	19 57	20 09	20 12	20 45	20 48	21 05	21 10	21 12	21 42	21 51	22 22	22 42	22 51	23 42
Cross Gates	d		18 48				19 22			19 48					20 55					21 58			22 58	
Garforth	d		18 53	19 05			19 28			19 53	20 05				21 00					22 03			23 03	
East Garforth	d		18 56				19 30			19 56					21 02					22 05			23 06	
Micklefield	d		18 59				19 34			19 59					21 06					22 09			23 10	
South Milford	d	18 51							19 51							21 18					22 35			
Selby	a	19 00							20 00							21 27					22 44			
Church Fenton	33 a		19 05												21 12								23 16	
Ulleskelf	33 a														21 16									
York 8	33 a		19 21	19 24	19 30	19 35	19 55	19 55		20 21	20 25	20 31	20 35	21 09	21 31		21 39	21 41	22 08	22 28		23 12	23 33	00 09

For general notes see front of timetable
For details of catering facilities see Directory of Train Operators

A Until 7 September
B From 14 September
b Bradford Forster Square

Table 40

Leeds → Selby and York

Network Diagram - see first page of Table 39

	TP	TP	TP	TP	TP	NT		TP	GR	NT	TP	NT	NT		TP	XC	NT	TP	NT	TP		TP	NT	NT	TP
	1 ◇	1 ◇	1 ◇	1 ◇	1 ◇			1 ◇	R 1		1 ◇				1 ◇	1 ◇		1 ◇		1 ◇		1 ◇			1 ◇
												A	B										B	A	
									🍴 🛒						🛒	🛒		🛒		🛒		🛒			🛒
Bradford Interchange 37 d					*06b01*				*06 26*			*07 05*	07 20				07 34			*07 50*		*07c59*	08 20	*08 05*	
Leeds 10 d	00 34	00 35	02 52	05 19	06 35	06 38		06 55	07 10	07 14	07 23	07 41	07 41		07 50	07 57	08 00	08 12	08 15	08 27		08 38	08 41	08 43	08 57
Cross Gates d						06 44						07 48	07 48				08 06		08 22				08 48	08 50	
Garforth d						06 50						07 53	07 53		08 00		08 12		08 27				08 53	08 55	09 05
East Garforth d						06 52						07 56	07 56				08 14		08 29				08 56	08 58	
Micklefield d						06 56						07 59	07 59				08 18		08 34				08 59	09 01	
South Milford d																	08 22		08 38						
Selby a										07 37	07 43						08 35		08 52			08 58			
Church Fenton 33 a												08 05	08 05										09 05	09 07	
Ulleskelf 33 a																									
York 8 33 a	01 14	01 18	03 22	06 02	07 03	07 15		07 22	07 34			08 21	08 21		08 21	08 25		08 34		08 54			09 21	09 21	09 23

	XC	TP	NT	TP		TP	NT	NT	TP	XC	TP		NT	TP	TP	NT	NT	TP		XC	TP	NT	TP	TP	NT
	1 ◇	1 ◇		1 ◇		1 ◇			1 ◇	1 ◇	1 ◇			1 ◇	1 ◇			1 ◇		1 ◇	1 ◇		1 ◇	1 ◇	
							B	A								B	A								B
	🛒	🛒		🛒					🛒	🛒	🛒			🛒	🛒			🛒		🛒	🛒			🛒	
Bradford Interchange 37 d	*08 34*		08 50	*08 50*		*09e04*	09 20	*09 05*		*09b31*	*09 34*		09 50		*10 05*	10 19				*10b31*	*10 34*	10 50		*11 05*	11 20
Leeds 10 d	09 07	09 12	09 15	09 27		09 38	09 41	09 43	09 57	10 07	10 12		10 15	10 27	10 38	10 41	10 43	10 57		11 07	11 12	11 15	11 27	11 38	11 41
Cross Gates d			09 22				09 48	09 50					10 22			10 48	10 50					11 22			11 48
Garforth d			09 27				09 53	09 55	10 05				10 27			10 53	10 55	11 05				11 27			11 53
East Garforth d			09 29				09 56	09 58					10 29			10 56	10 58					11 29			11 56
Micklefield d			09 33				09 59	10 01					10 33			10 59	11 01					11 33			11 59
South Milford d			09 38										10 38									11 38			
Selby a			09 53			09 57							10 53		10 57							11 54		11 57	
Church Fenton 33 a							10 05	10 07																	12 05
Ulleskelf 33 a																									
York 8 33 a	09 30	09 35		09 52			10 21	10 23	10 23	10 30	10 35			10 52		11 19	11 19	11 23		11 32	11 35		11 52		12 21

	NT	TP		XC	TP	NT	TP	TP	NT		NT	TP	XC	TP	NT	TP		TP	NT	NT	TP	XC	TP		NT
		1 ◇		1 ◇	1 ◇		1 ◇	1 ◇				1 ◇	1 ◇	1 ◇		1 ◇		1 ◇			1 ◇	1 ◇	1 ◇		
	A								B		A								B	A					
		🛒		🛒	🛒		🛒					🛒	🛒	🛒		🛒					🛒	🛒	🛒		
Bradford Interchange 37 d				*11b31*	*11 34*	11 50		*12 05*	12 19				*12b31*	*12 34*	12 50			*13 05*	13 19			*13b31*	*13 34*		13 50
Leeds 10 d	11 43	11 57		12 07	12 12	12 15	12 27	12 38	12 41		12 43	12 57	13 07	13 12	13 15	13 27		13 38	13 41	13 43	13 57	14 07	14 12		14 15
Cross Gates d	11 50					12 22			12 48		12 50				13 22				13 48	13 50					14 22
Garforth d	11 55	12 05				12 27			12 53		12 55	13 05			13 27				13 53	13 55	14 05				14 27
East Garforth d	11 58					12 29			12 56		12 58				13 29				13 56	13 58					14 29
Micklefield d	12 01					12 33			12 59		13 01				13 33				13 59	14 01					14 33
South Milford d						12 38									13 38										14 38
Selby a						12 50		12 57							13 50			13 57							14 50
Church Fenton 33 a	12 07																		14 05	14 07					
Ulleskelf 33 a																									
York 8 33 a	12 21	12 23		12 30	12 35		12 52		13 19		13 19	13 23	13 32	13 35		13 52			14 21	14 21	14 23	14 30	14 35		

	TP	TP	NT	NT	TP	XC		TP	NT	TP	TP	NT	NT		TP	XC	TP	NT	TP	TP		NT	NT	TP	XC
	1 ◇	1 ◇			1 ◇	1 ◇		1 ◇		1 ◇	1 ◇				1 ◇	1 ◇	1 ◇		1 ◇	1 ◇				1 ◇	1 ◇
			B	A								B	A									B	A		
	🛒	🛒			🛒	🛒		🛒		🛒						🛒	🛒		🛒					🛒	🛒
Bradford Interchange 37 d		*14 05*	14 19			*14f31*		*14 34*	14 50		*15 05*	15 19				*15b31*	*15 34*	15 50		*16 05*		16 19			*16g31*
Leeds 10 d	14 27	14 38	14 41	14 43	14 57	15 07		15 12	15 15	15 27	15 38	15 41	15 43		15 57	16 07	16 12	16 15	16 27	16 38		16 41	16 43	16 57	17 07
Cross Gates d			14 48	14 50					15 22			15 48	15 50					16 22				16 48	16 50		
Garforth d			14 53	14 55	15 05				15 27			15 53	15 55		16 05			16 27				16 53	16 55	17 05	
East Garforth d			14 56	14 58					15 29			15 56	15 58					16 30				16 56	16 58		
Micklefield d			14 59	15 01					15 33			15 59	16 01					16 34				16 59	17 01		
South Milford d									15 38									16 39							
Selby a		14 57							15 52		15 57							16 54		17 00					
Church Fenton 33 a												16 05	16 07												
Ulleskelf 33 a																									
York 8 33 a	14 52		15 19	15 19	15 23	15 32		15 35		15 54		16 21	16 22		16 23	16 30	16 35		16 52			17 19	17 19	17 22	17 31

	TP	NT	TP	TP		NT	NT	TP	XC	TP	NT		TP	XC	TP	NT	NT	TP		XC	TP	NT	NT	TP	TP
	1 ◇		1 ◇	1 ◇				1 ◇	1 ◇	1 ◇			1 ◇	1 ◇	1 ◇			1 ◇		1 ◇	1 ◇			1 ◇	1 ◇
						B	A									B	A					A	B	C	
									🛒					🛒						🛒					
Bradford Interchange 37 d	*16 34*	16 50		*17e04*		17 20	*17 05*		*17b31*	*17 34*	17 50			*18b01*	*18e04*	18 20	*18 05*			*18 34*		18 50	18 52		*19 05*
Leeds 10 d	17 12	17 15	17 24	17 38		17 41	17 43	17 57	18 07	18 12	18 15		18 27	18 35	18 38	18 41	18 43	18 57		19 07	19 12	19 15	19 15	19 27	19 38
Cross Gates d		17 24				17 48	17 50				18 22					18 48	18 50					19 22	19 22		
Garforth d		17 29	17 34			17 53	17 55	18 05			18 27					18 53	18 55	19 05				19 27	19 27		
East Garforth d		17 31				17 56	17 58				18 29					18 56	18 58					19 29	19 29		
Micklefield d		17 35				17 59	18 01				18 33					18 59	19 01					19 33	19 33		
South Milford d		17 40									18 38				18 51										19 51
Selby a		17 52		17 57							18 49				19 00										20 00
Church Fenton 33 a						18 06	18 07									19 05	19 07								
Ulleskelf 33 a						18 10	18 11																		
York 8 33 a	17 35		17 57			18 24	18 24	18 24	18 31	18 35			18 52	18 59		19 21	19 21	19 24		19 31	19 35	19 54	19 54	20 05	

For general notes see front of timetable
For details of catering facilities see Directory of Train Operators

- **A** Until 11 July
- **B** From 18 July
- **C** Until 5 September
- **b** Bradford Forster Square
- **c** From 18 July departs Bradford Forster Square, change at Leeds. Until 11 July Bradford Interchange dep. 0805, change at Leeds
- **e** Until 11 July dep. 1 min. later
- **f** From 18 July departs Bradford Forster Square, change at Leeds. Until 11 July Bradford Interchange dep. 1434, change at Leeds
- **g** From 18 July departs Bradford Forster Square, change at Leeds. Until 11 July Bradford Interchange dep. 1634, change at Leeds

Table 40

Saturdays

Leeds → Selby and York

Network Diagram - see first page of Table 39

	NT A	NT B		TP 1◇	XC 1◇	TP 1◇	TP 1◇	NT B	NT A		TP 1◇	TP 1◇	XC 1◇	TP 1◇	NT	TP 1◇ C		TP 1◇	TP 1◇	NT B	NT A	TP 1◇			
Bradford Interchange 37 d	19 19				19b31	19 34	20c04	20 05	20 20			20 37		21 04		21 37		21 37	22 04		22 19	23c04			
Leeds 10 d	19 41	19 43		19 57	20 07	20 12	20 45	20 48	20 48		21 05	21 12	21 15	21 42	21 45	22 12		22 22	22 42	22 54	22 54	23 42			
Cross Gates d	19 48	19 50						20 55	20 55						21 52					23 01	23 01				
Garforth d	19 53	19 55		20 05				21 00	21 00						21 57					23 06	23 06				
East Garforth d	19 56	19 58						21 02	21 02						21 59					23 09	23 09				
Micklefield d	19 59	20 01						21 06	21 06						22 03					23 13	23 13				
South Milford d											21 18							22 35							
Selby a											21 27							22 44							
Church Fenton 33 a								21 12	21 12											23 19	23 19				
Ulleskelf 33 a								21 16	21 16																
York 8 33 a	20 21	20 21		20 25	20 31	20 35	21 09	21 31	21 31			21 41	22 03	22 08	22 22	22 35			23 08	23 36	23 36	00 11			

Sundays

	TP 1◇ D	TP 1◇ D	TP 1◇ E	TP E (bus)		TP 1◇ D	TP E (bus)	TP 1◇ D	TP E (bus)		TP 1◇ D	TP 1◇	NT	GR R 1		XC 1◇	TP 1◇	TP 1◇ D	TP 1◇ E		NT G	NT H	XC 1◇	TP 1◇ D	TP 1◇ E
Bradford Interchange 37 d		00e03	00 03										08 31					09b02	09b02		09 21	09 20			
Leeds 10 d	00 16	00 54	00 54	01 24		02 35	03 35	05 55	07 10		07 40	08 40	08 54	09 05		09 08	09 12	09 40	09 46		09 47	09 49	10 08	10 12	10 18
Cross Gates d													09 00								09 54	09 55			
Garforth d													09 06								09 59	10 01			
East Garforth d													09 08								10 01	10 03			
Micklefield d													09 12								10 05	10 07			
South Milford d																									
Selby a																									
Church Fenton 33 a													09 18												
Ulleskelf 33 a																									
York 8 33 a	00 44	01 22	01 46	02 09		03 03	04 20	06 23	07 55		08 09	09 08	09 34	10 05		09 35	09 37	10 06	10 10		10 27	10 28	10 33	10 37	10 42

	TP 1◇ D		TP 1◇ E	NT D	NT E	TP 1◇		TP 1◇ D	TP 1◇ E	NT G	NT H		TP 1◇	XC 1◇	TP 1◇	NT G		NT H	TP 1◇	TP 1◇	XC 1◇		TP 1◇	NT G	NT H
Bradford Interchange 37 d				10 02	10 03			10 25	10 25		11 02		11f02	11 25		11 44		12 02	12f02	12 25				12 44	13 02
Leeds 10 d	10 20		10 24	10 27	10 27	10 40		11 12	11 18	11 25	11 25		11 40	12 08	12 12	12 25		12 25	12 40	13 00	13 08		13 12	13 25	13 25
Cross Gates d				10 33	10 33					11 32	11 32					12 32		12 32						13 32	13 32
Garforth d				10 39	10 39					11 37	11 37					12 37		12 37						13 37	13 37
East Garforth d				10 41	10 41					11 39	11 39					12 39		12 39						13 39	13 39
Micklefield d				10 45	10 45					11 43	11 43					12 43		12 43						13 43	13 43
South Milford d	10 33		10 37																	13 13					
Selby a	10 43		10 46																	13 23					
Church Fenton 33 a				10 51	10 51											12 48		12 48							
Ulleskelf 33 a																									
York 8 33 a				11 07	11 07	11 06		11 37	11 41	11 59	11 59		12 06	12 32	12 37	13 02		13 02	13 06		13 32		13 37	13 59	13 59

	TP 1◇	TP 1◇	XC 1◇		TP 1◇ D	TP 1◇ E	NT G	NT H		TP 1◇	TP 1◇	XC 1◇	TP 1◇		NT G	NT H	TP 1◇	TP 1◇		XC 1◇	TP 1◇	NT G	NT H		TP 1◇
Bradford Interchange 37 d	13f02	13 25					13 44	14 02		14f02	14 25				14 44	15 02	15f02	15 25				15 44	16 03		16f02
Leeds 10 d	13 40	13 57	14 08		14 12	14 14	14 25	14 25		14 40	15 00	15 08	15 12		15 25	15 25	15 40	15 57		16 08	16 12	16 25	16 25		16 40
Cross Gates d							14 32	14 32							15 32	15 32						16 32	16 32		
Garforth d							14 37	14 37							15 37	15 37						16 37	16 37		
East Garforth d							14 39	14 39							15 39	15 39						16 39	16 39		
Micklefield d							14 43	14 43							15 43	15 43						16 43	16 43		
South Milford d											15 13														
Selby a											15 23														
Church Fenton 33 a							14 48	14 48														16 48	16 48		
Ulleskelf 33 a																									
York 8 33 a	14 06	14 24	14 32		14 37	14 38	15 02	15 02		15 06		15 32	15 37		15 59	15 59	16 06	16 24		16 32	16 37	17 06	17 06		17 06

For general notes see front of timetable
For details of catering facilities see Directory of Train Operators

A From 18 July
B Until 11 July
C From 12 September
D Until 6 September
E From 13 September
G Until 12 July
H From 19 July
b Bradford Forster Square
c Until 11 July dep. 1 min. later
e From 23 May only. Saturdays dep. 2337
f Until 12 July only. Bradford Forster Square

Table 40

Sundays

Leeds → Selby and York

Network Diagram - see first page of Table 39

	TP 1◊	XC 1◊	TP 1◊	NT		NT	TP 1◊	TP 1◊	XC 1◊		TP 1◊	NT	NT	TP 1◊		XC 1◊	TP 1◊	XC 1◊	TP 1◊		NT	NT	TP 1◊	TP 1◊	XC 1◊
				A		B						A	B								A	B			
		🛒							🛒							🛒		🛒							🛒
Bradford Interchange .. 37 d	16b26			16 44		17 02	17c02	17 25				17 44	18 02	18c02		18 25					18 44	19 02	19c02	19 25	
Leeds 10 d	17 00	17 08	17 12	17 25		17 25	17 40	17 57	18 08		18 12	18 23	18 23	18 40		18 57	19 00	19 08	19 12		19 25	19 25	19 40	19 57	20 08
Cross Gates d				17 32		17 32						18 30	18 30								19 32	19 32			
Garforth d				17 37		17 37						18 35	18 35								19 37	19 37			
East Garforth d				17 39		17 39						18 38	18 38								19 39	19 39			
Micklefield d				17 43		17 43						18 41	18 41								19 43	19 43			
South Milford d	17 13																19 13								
Selby a	17 23																19 23							20 16	
Church Fenton 33 a												18 47	18 47												
Ulleskelf 33 a																									
York 8 33 a		17 32	17 37	18 02		18 02	18 08	18 24	18 32		18 37	19 03	19 03	19 06		19 21		19 32	19 37		20 01	20 01	20 06		20 32

	TP 1◊		NT	NT	TP 1◊	TP 1◊		TP 1◊	XC 1◊	TP 1◊	NT		NT	TP 1◊	TP 1◊	TP 1◊		TP 1◊	NT	TP 1◊	TP 1◊		TP 1◊		
			A	B		A		B			A		B					C		D	C		D		
									🛒																
Bradford Interchange .. 37 d			19 44	20 02	20c02	20 31		20 25	20e25				21 02	21c02	21f26	21g44		22h02	22j02		23c02		23 04		
Leeds 10 d	20 12		20 25	20 25	20 40	21 04		21 04	21 08	21 12	21 25		21 25	21 40	22 12	22 20		22 40	22 43	22 53	23 40		23 54		
Cross Gates d			20 32	20 32							21 32		21 32						22 49						
Garforth d			20 37	20 37							21 37		21 37						22 55						
East Garforth d			20 40	20 40							21 39		21 39						22 57						
Micklefield d			20 43	20 43							21 43		21 43						23 01						
South Milford d																22 33									
Selby a						21 23		21 38								22 42									
Church Fenton 33 a			20 49	20 49															23 07						
Ulleskelf 33 a																									
York 8 33 a	20 37		21 03	21 03	21 06				21 37	21 38	21 59		21 59	22 06	22 38			23 11	23 18	23 26	00 10		00 23		

For general notes see front of timetable
For details of catering facilities see Directory of Train Operators

- **A** Until 12 July
- **B** From 19 July
- **C** Until 6 September
- **D** From 13 September
- **b** Until 12 July dep. 1625
- **c** Until 12 July only. Bradford Forster Square
- **e** Until 12 July dep. 2031
- **f** Change at Leeds. Until 12 July dep. 2138. From 8 November Bradford Forster Square dep. 2137
- **g** From 19 July only
- **h** Change at Leeds. Until 12 July departs Bradford Forster Square. 19 July to 6 September departs Bradford Interchange
- **j** Change at Leeds. Until 12 July departs Bradford Forster Square. From 19 July departs Bradford Interchange

Leeds and Bradford → Huddersfield, Blackpool North, Rochdale and Manchester Victoria via Halifax and Brighouse

Network Diagram - see first page of Table 39

Miles	Miles	Miles	Miles	Station		NT	NT	NT	NT	NT A	NT		NT B	NT	NT	NT	NT C	NT	NT		NT	NT	NT C	NT
—	—	—	—	York 8	40 d									06 13					07 06					
—	—	—	—	Selby	40 d												06 41				07 26		07 43	
0	0	—	0	**Leeds 10**	37, 39 d	05 08	05 51	06 03	06 13	06 22		06 37			06 51	07 08	07 13	07 22	07 37	07 51		08 08	08 13	08 22	08 37
4	4	—	—	Bramley	37 d	05 15	05 58			06 29		06 44				07 15		07 29	07 44			08 15		08 29	08 44
5¾	5¾	—	—	New Pudsey	37 d	05 20	06 02	06 13		06 34		06 49			07 01	07 20		07 34	07 49	08 01		08 20		08 34	08 49
9½	9½	—	—	**Bradford Interchange**	37 a	05 28	06 13	06 21		06 42		06 57			07 11	07 28		07 43	07 57	08 09		08 28		08 42	08 57
—	—	—	—		d	05 32	06 14	06 24		06 45		07 00			07 14	07 31		07 45	08 00	08 12		08 32		08 45	09 00
17½	17½	—	—	**Halifax**	a	05 44	06 25	06 36		06 58		07 12			07 25	07 43		08 00	08 12	08 23		08 44		09 00	09 12
—	—	0	—		d	05 44	06 26	06 36			07 00	07 12			07 26	07 44		08 06	08 12	08 24		08 44		09 06	09 12
—	—	—	9¼	Dewsbury	39 d				06 29								07 29						08 31		
—	—	—	12¼	Mirfield	39 d				06 35								07 35						08 38		
—	—	5¼	16¼	Brighouse	d				06 49		07a10						07 49	08 16					08 49	09 16	
—	—	10½	—	**Huddersfield**	39 a													08 29						09 29	
21	21	—	22	Sowerby Bridge	d	05 51		06 43	06 59			07 19					07 59		08 19				08 59		09 19
25	25	—	26	Mytholmroyd	d	05 57		06 49	07 05			07 25					08 05		08 25				09 05		09 25
26¼	26¼	—	27¼	**Hebden Bridge**	a	06 00	06 37	06 52	07 08			07 28			07 37	07 55	08 08		08 28	08 35		08 56	09 08		09 28
—	—	—	—		d	06 00	06 38	06 52	07 08			07 28			07 38	07 56	08 08		08 28	08 36		08 56	09 08		09 28
—	39	—	—	Burnley Manchester Road	97 a		06 57								07 57					08 57					
—	45¼	—	—	Accrington	97 a		07 06								08 06					09 06					
—	51½	—	—	Blackburn	97 a		07 16								08 14					09 14					
—	63½	—	—	**Preston 8**	97 a		07 36								08 38					09 32					
—	78	—	—	Poulton-le-Fylde	97 a		07 54								08 56					09 50					
—	81	—	—	**Blackpool North**	97 a		08 05								09 05					10 00					
30½	—	—	—	Todmorden	d	06 08		06 59	07 15			07 36		07 44		08 04	08 15		08 36			09 04	09 15		09 36
32	—	—	—	Walsden	d	06 11		07 02				07 39		07 47					08 39						09 39
36	—	—	—	Littleborough	d	06 17		07 09	07 23			07 45		07 53			08 23		08 45				09 23		09 45
37	—	—	—	Smithy Bridge	d	06 20		07 11	07 25			07 48		07 56			08 25		08 48				09 25		09 48
39¼	—	—	—	**Rochdale**	a	06 24		07 15	07 29			07 52		08 00		08 14	08 29		08 51			09 14	09 29		09 51
—	—	—	—		95 d	06 24		07 16	07 30			07 52		08 00		08 14	08 30		08 51			09 14	09 30		09 51
41	—	—	—	Castleton	95 a	06 27		07 19	07 33			07 55		08 03		08 17	08 33						09 33		
43¾	—	—	—	Mills Hill	95 a	06 32		07 23	07 37			08 00		08 08		08 22	08 37						09 37		
45¾	—	—	—	Moston	95 a	06 35		07 27	07 40			08 03		08 11		08 25	08 40						09 40		
49¾	—	—	—	**Manchester Victoria**	95 a	06 48		07 37	07 53			08 14		08 22		08 38	08 53		09 08			09 32	09 53		10 07
—	—	—	—	Liverpool Lime Street 10	90 a	*08 13*			*09 13*					*09 43*								*10 43*			

Station		NT	NT	NT	NT C	NT		NT	NT	NT	NT C	NT	NT	NT		NT	NT C	NT	NT	NT	NT	NT C		NT	NT
York 8	40 d							09 09					10 11						11 09						12 13
Selby	40 d	08 12			08 43						09 43						10 43					11 43			
Leeds 10	37, 39 d	08 51	09 08	09 13	09 22	09 37		09 51	10 08	10 13	10 22	10 37	10 51	11 08		11 13	11 22	11 37	11 51	12 08	12 13	12 22		12 37	12 51
Bramley	37 d		09 15		09 29	09 44			10 15		10 29	10 44		11 15			11 29	11 44		12 15		12 29		12 44	
New Pudsey	37 d	09 00	09 20		09 34	09 49		10 01	10 20		10 34	10 49	11 01	11 20			11 34	11 49	12 01	12 20		12 34		12 49	13 01
Bradford Interchange	37 a	09 11	09 28		09 42	09 57		10 09	10 28		10 42	10 57	11 10	11 28			11 42	11 57	12 11	12 28		12 42		12 57	13 11
	d	09 12	09 32		09 45	10 00		10 12	10 32		10 45	11 00	11 12	11 32			11 45	12 00	12 14	12 32		12 45		13 00	13 14
Halifax	a	09 23	09 44		10 00	10 12		10 23	10 44		11 00	11 12	11 23	11 44			11 58	12 12	12 25	12 44		13 00		13 12	13 25
	d	09 24	09 44		10 06	10 12		10 24	10 44		11 06	11 12	11 24	11 44			12 06	12 12	12 26	12 44		13 06		13 12	13 26
Dewsbury	39 d			09 31						10 29						11 29					12 29				
Mirfield	39 d			09 37						10 35						11 35					12 35				
Brighouse	d			09 49	10 16					10 49	11 16					11 49	12 16				12 49	13 16			
Huddersfield	39 a				10 29						11 29						12 30					13 29			
Sowerby Bridge	d			09 59		10 19				10 59		11 19				11 59		12 19			12 59			13 19	
Mytholmroyd	d			10 05		10 25				11 05		11 25				12 05		12 25			13 05			13 25	
Hebden Bridge	a	09 35	09 56	10 08		10 28		10 35	10 56	11 08		11 28	11 35	11 56		12 08		12 28	12 37	12 56	13 08			13 28	13 37
	d	09 36	09 56	10 08		10 28		10 36	10 56	11 08		11 28	11 36	11 56		12 08		12 28	12 38	12 56	13 08			13 28	13 38
Burnley Manchester Road	97 a	09 56						10 57					11 57						12 57						13 57
Accrington	97 a	10 06						11 06					12 06						13 06						14 06
Blackburn	97 a	10 14						11 14					12 14						13 14						14 14
Preston 8	97 a	10 32						11 32					12 32						13 32						14 32
Poulton-le-Fylde	97 a	10 50						11 50					12 50						13 50						14 50
Blackpool North	97 a	11 00						12 00					13 00						14 00						15 00
Todmorden	d		10 04	10 15		10 36			11 04	11 15		11 36		12 04		12 15		12 36		13 04	13 15			13 36	
Walsden	d					10 39						11 39						12 39						13 39	
Littleborough	d			10 23		10 45				11 23		11 45				12 23		12 45			13 23			13 45	
Smithy Bridge	d			10 25		10 48				11 25		11 48				12 25		12 48			13 25			13 48	
Rochdale	a		10 14	10 29		10 51			11 14	11 29		11 51		12 14		12 29		12 51		13 14	13 29			13 51	
	95 d		10 14	10 30		10 51			11 14	11 30		11 51		12 14		12 30		12 51		13 14	13 30			13 51	
Castleton	95 a			10 33						11 33						12 33					13 33				
Mills Hill	95 a			10 37						11 37						12 37					13 37				
Moston	95 a			10 41						11 41						12 41					13 41				
Manchester Victoria	95 a		10 32	10 53		11 07			11 32	11 53		12 07		12 32		12 53		13 07		13 32	13 53			14 07	
Liverpool Lime Street 10	90 a		*11 43*						*12 43*					*13 43*						*14 43*					

For general notes see front of timetable
For details of catering facilities see Directory of Train Operators

A To Leeds (Table 39)
B To Wigan Wallgate (Table 82)
C To Wakefield Westgate (Table 39)

Leeds and Bradford → Huddersfield, Blackpool North, Rochdale and Manchester Victoria via Halifax and Brighouse

Network Diagram - see first page of Table 39

	NT	NT	NT A	NT	NT	NT	NT	NT A	NT	NT	NT	NT	NT A	NT	NT	NT	NT	NT A	NT	NT	NT	NT
York 8 40 d					13 09					14 13					15 09					16 13		
Selby 40 d			12 43					13 43					14 43					15 43				
Leeds 10 37, 39 d	13 08	13 13	13 22	13 37	13 51	14 08	14 13	14 22	14 37	14 51	15 08	15 13	15 22	15 37	15 51	16 08	16 13	16 22	16 37	16 51	17 08	17 13
Bramley 37 d	13 15		13 29	13 44		14 15		14 29	14 44		15 15		15 29	15 44		16 15		16 29	16 44		17 15	
New Pudsey 37 d	13 20		13 34	13 49	14 01	14 20		14 34	14 49	15 01	15 20		15 34	15 49	16 01	16 20		16 34	16 49	17 01	17 20	
Bradford Interchange 37 a	13 28		13 42	13 57	14 11	14 28		14 42	14 57	15 11	15 28		15 42	15 57	16 10	16 28		16 42	16 57	17 10	17 28	
d	13 32		13 45	14 00	14 14	14 32		14 45	15 00	15 14	15 32		15 45	16 00	16 13	16 32		16 45	17 00	17 12	17 32	
Halifax a	13 44		14 00	14 12	14 25	14 44		14 59	15 12	15 25	15 44		16 00	16 12	16 24	16 44		17 00	17 12	17 24	17 44	
d	13 44		14 06	14 12	14 26	14 44		15 06	15 12	15 26	15 44		16 06	16 12	16 25	16 44		17 06	17 12	17 24	17 44	
Dewsbury 39 d		13 29					14 29					15 29					16 31					17 31
Mirfield 39 d		13 35					14 35					15 35					16 38					17 38
Brighouse d		13 49	14 16				14 49	15 16				15 49	16 16				16 49	17 16				17 49
Huddersfield 39 a			14 29					15 29					16 29					17 29				
Sowerby Bridge d		13 59		14 19			14 59		15 19			15 59		16 19	16 31		16 59		17 19	17 31		17 59
Mytholmroyd d		14 05		14 25			15 05		15 25			16 05		16 25			17 05		17 25			18 05
Hebden Bridge a	13 56	14 08		14 28	14 37	14 56	15 08		15 28	15 37	15 56	16 08		16 28	16 38	16 56	17 08		17 28	17 37	17 56	18 08
d	13 56	14 08		14 28	14 38	14 56	15 08		15 28	15 38	15 56	16 08		16 28	16 38	16 56	17 08		17 28	17 38	17 56	18 08
Burnley Manchester Road 97 a					14 57					15 57					16 57					17 57		
Accrington 97 a					15 06					16 06					17 06					18 06		
Blackburn 97 a					15 14					16 14					17 14					18 14		
Preston 8 97 a					15 32					16 32					17 32					18 33		
Poulton-le-Fylde 97 a					15 50					16 50					17 56					18 50		
Blackpool North 97 a					16 00					17 00					18 06					19 00		
Todmorden d	14 04	14 15		14 36		15 04	15 15		15 36		16 04	16 15		16 36		17 04	17 15		17 36		18 04	18 15
Walsden d				14 39					15 39					16 39					17 39			18 19
Littleborough d		14 23		14 45			15 23		15 45			16 23		16 45			17 23		17 45			18 25
Smithy Bridge d		14 25		14 48			15 25		15 48			16 25		16 48			17 25		17 48			18 28
Rochdale a	14 14	14 29		14 51		15 14	15 29		15 51		16 14	16 29		16 51		17 14	17 29		17 51		18 14	18 32
95 d	14 14	14 30		14 51		15 14	15 30		15 51		16 14	16 30		16 51		17 14	17 30		17 51		18 14	18 32
Castleton 95 a		14 33					15 33					16 33					17 33					18 35
Mills Hill 95 a		14 37					15 37					16 37					17 37					18 40
Moston 95 a		14 41					15 41					16 41					17 41					18 43
Manchester Victoria 95 ⛴ a	14 32	14 53		15 08		15 32	15 53		16 07		16 32	16 53		17 07		17 32	17 53		18 07		18 32	18 54
Liverpool Lime Street 10 90 a	*15 43*					*16 43*					*17 43*	*18 13*				*18 43*					*19 43*	

	NT A	NT	NT	NT	NT	NT A	NT	NT	NT	NT A	NT	NT	NT	NT	NT	NT	NT	NT	NT
York 8 40 d			17 08									19 04							
Selby 40 d						17 43	18 00			18 43									
Leeds 10 37, 39 d	17 22	17 37	17 51	18 08	18 13	18 22	18 37	18 51	19 08	19 22	19 37	19 51	20 08	20 37	21 08	21 37	22 08	22 37	23 08
Bramley 37 d	17 29	17 44		18 15		18 30	18 44		19 15	19 30	19 44		20 15	20 44	21 15	21 44	22 15	22 44	23 15
New Pudsey 37 d	17 34	17 49	18 01	18 20		18 35	18 49	19 01	19 20	19 35	19 49	20 01	20 20	20 49	21 20	21 49	22 20	22 49	23 20
Bradford Interchange 37 a	17 42	17 57	18 10	18 28		18 43	18 57	19 10	19 28	19 44	19 57	20 10	20 28	20 57	21 28	21 57	22 28	22 57	23 29
d	17 45	18 00	18 12	18 32		18 46	19 00	19 12	19 32	19 46	20 00	20 13	20 31	21 00	21 31	22 00	22 31	23 00	23 31
Halifax a	17 58	18 12	18 24	18 44		19 00	19 12	19 23	19 44	20 00	20 12	20 24	20 44	21 12	21 44	22 12	22 44	23 12	23 44
d	18 06	18 12	18 24	18 44		19 06	19 12	19 24	19 44	20 06	20 12	20 25	20 44	21 12	21 44	22 12	22 44	23 12	23 44
Dewsbury 39 d					18 31														
Mirfield 39 d					18 38														
Brighouse d	18 16				18 49	19 16				20 16			20 55		21 55		22 55		23 55
Huddersfield 39 a	18 31					19 29				20 29			21 08		22 08		23 08		00 08
Sowerby Bridge d		18 19	18 31		18 59		19 19				20 19			21 19		22 19		23 19	
Mytholmroyd d		18 25			19 05		19 25				20 25			21 25		22 25		23 25	
Hebden Bridge a		18 28	18 37	18 56	19 08		19 28	19 35	19 56		20 28	20 36		21 28		22 28		23 28	
d		18 28	18 38	18 56	19 08		19 28	19 36	19 56		20 28	20 37		21 28		22 28		23 28	
Burnley Manchester Road 97 a			18 57					19 56				20 56							
Accrington 97 a			19 06					20 05				21 05							
Blackburn 97 a			19 14					20 14				21 14							
Preston 8 97 a			19 32					20 32				21 32							
Poulton-le-Fylde 97 a			19 50					20 50				21 50							
Blackpool North 97 a			20 00					21 00				22 00							
Todmorden d		18 36		19 04	19 15		19 36		20 04		20 36			21 36		22 36		23 36	
Walsden d		18 39			19 19		19 39				20 39			21 39		22 39		23 39	
Littleborough d		18 45			19 25		19 45				20 45			21 45		22 45		23 45	
Smithy Bridge d		18 48			19 28		19 48				20 48			21 48		22 48		23 48	
Rochdale a		18 51		19 15	19 32		19 52		20 14		20 52			21 52		22 52		23 52	
95 d		18 51		19 15	19 32		19 52		20 14		20 52			21 52		22 52		23 52	
Castleton 95 a					19 35		19 55				20 55			21 55		22 55			
Mills Hill 95 a					19 40		20 00				21 00			22 00		23 00			
Moston 95 a					19 43		20 03				21 03			22 03		23 03			
Manchester Victoria 95 ⛴ a		19 07		19 32	19 54		20 15		20 32		21 14			22 14		23 14		00 08	
Liverpool Lime Street 10 90 a				*20 43*					*21 43*		*22 43*			*23 43*					

For general notes see front of timetable
For details of catering facilities see Directory of Train Operators

A To Wakefield Westgate (Table 39)

Saturdays

until 11 July

Leeds and Bradford → Huddersfield, Blackpool North, Rochdale and Manchester Victoria via Halifax and Brighouse

Network Diagram - see first page of Table 39

		NT 🚌	NT	NT	NT 🚌	NT	NT	NT 🚌	NT	NT 🚌	NT	NT 🚌	NT	NT	NT A	NT	NT 🚌	NT 🚌	NT	NT	NT		NT 🚌	NT	NT 🚌
York [8]	40 d															06 13									
Selby	40 d																							06 44	
Leeds [10]	37, 39 d			05 37		05 51	06 03						06 16	06 37		06 58			07 08		07 13			07 23	
Bramley	37 d			05 44		05 58							06 23	06 44					07 15					07 30	
New Pudsey	37 d			05 49		06 03							06 28	06 49					07 20					07 35	
Bradford Interchange	37 a			05 59		06 13							06 38	06 59					07 28					07 45	
	d	05 20			05 40			06 00		06 20		06 40					07 10	07 25					07 40		07 55
Halifax	a	05 45			06 05			06 25		06 45		07 05					07 35	07 50					08 05		08 20
	d	05 45			06 05			06 25		06 45		07 05					07 35	07 50					08 05		08 20
Dewsbury	39 d																				07 29				
Mirfield	39 d																				07 35				
Brighouse	d																	08 05			07 49				08 40
Huddersfield	39 a																	08 25							
Sowerby Bridge	d	06 00						06 40		07 00							07 55				07 59				
Mytholmroyd	d	06 15						06 55		07 15							08 10				08 05				
Hebden Bridge	a	06 20			06 30		06 32	07 00		07 20		07 30				07 36	08 20				08 08		08 30		
	d		06 28				06 38		07 08			07 30			07 32	07 38					08 08		08 30		
Burnley Manchester Road	97 a						06 57									07 57									
Accrington	97 a						07 06									08 06									
Blackburn	97 a						07 16									08 14									
Preston [8]	97 a						07 36									08 38									
Poulton-le-Fylde	97 a						07 54									08 56									
Blackpool North	97 a						08 05									09 05									
Todmorden	d		06 35						07 15		07 36	07a50			07 44					08 04	08 15		08a50		
Walsden	d		06 38								07 39				07 47										
Littleborough	d		06 45						07 23		07 45				07 53						08 23				
Smithy Bridge	d		06 47						07 25		07 48				07 56						08 25				
Rochdale	a		06 54						07 29		07 52				08 00					08 14	08 29				
	95 d		06 55						07 30		07 52				08 00					08 14	08 30				
Castleton	95 a		06 58						07 33		07 55				08 03					08 17	08 33				
Mills Hill	95 a		07 02						07 37		08 00				08 08					08 22	08 37				
Moston	95 a		07 06						07 41		08 03				08 11					08 25	08 40				
Manchester Victoria	95 ⛴ a		07 17						07 53		08 14				08 22					08 38	08 53				
Liverpool Lime Street [10]	90 a		*08 43*						*09 13*						*09 43*										

		NT	NT	NT	NT 🚌	NT 🚌	NT		NT	NT	NT	NT 🚌	NT	NT 🚌	NT	NT	NT 🚌	NT 🚌	NT			NT	NT	NT 🚌	NT
York [8]	40 d			07 06												08 09									
Selby	40 d												07 44												08 43
Leeds [10]	37, 39 d	07 37		07 58			08 08			08 13			08 22		08 37	08 58			09 08				09 13		09 22
Bramley	37 d	07 44					08 15						08 29		08 44				09 15						09 29
New Pudsey	37 d	07 49					08 20						08 34		08 49				09 20						09 34
Bradford Interchange	37 a	07 59					08 30						08 44		08 57				09 28						09 42
	d				08 10	08 25						08 40		08 55			09 10	09 25						09 40	
Halifax	a				08 35	08 50						09 05		09 20			09 35	09 50						10 05	
	d				08 40	08 50						09 05		09 20			09 40	09 50						10 05	
Dewsbury	39 d									08 31													09 31		
Mirfield	39 d									08 38													09 37		
Brighouse	d					09 05				08 49				09 40				10 05					09 49		
Huddersfield	39 a					09 25												10 25							
Sowerby Bridge	d				08 55					08 59							09 55						09 59		
Mytholmroyd	d				09 10					09 05							10 10						10 05		
Hebden Bridge	a			08 34	09 20					09 08		09 30				09 34	10 20						10 08	10 30	
	d		08 30	08 38						09 08	09 30	09 30				09 37							10 08	10 30	
Burnley Manchester Road	97 a			08 57												09 56									
Accrington	97 a			09 06												10 06									
Blackburn	97 a			09 14												10 14									
Preston [8]	97 a			09 32												10 32									
Poulton-le-Fylde	97 a			09 50												10 50									
Blackpool North	97 a			10 00												11 00									
Todmorden	d		08 37						09 01	09 15	09 37	09a50										10 02	10 15	10a50	
Walsden	d		08 40								09 40														
Littleborough	d		08 47							09 23	09 47												10 23		
Smithy Bridge	d								09 10	09 25												10 10	10 25		
Rochdale	a		08 51						09 14	09 29	09 51											10 14	10 29		
	95 d		08 51						09 14	09 30	09 51											10 15	10 30		
Castleton	95 a									09 33													10 33		
Mills Hill	95 a									09 37													10 37		
Moston	95 a									09 40													10 41		
Manchester Victoria	95 ⛴ a		09 08						09 32	09 53	10 07											10 32	10 53		
Liverpool Lime Street [10]	90 a								*10 43*													*11 43*			

For general notes see front of timetable
For details of catering facilities see Directory of Train Operators

A To Wigan Wallgate (Table 82)

Table 41

Saturdays

until 11 July

Leeds and Bradford → Huddersfield, Blackpool North, Rochdale and Manchester Victoria via Halifax and Brighouse

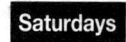

Network Diagram - see first page of Table 39

		NT 🚌	NT	NT	NT	NT	NT	NT 🚌	NT 🚌	NT	NT 🚌		NT	NT 🚌	NT	NT	NT	NT	NT 🚌		NT 🚌	NT	NT	NT 🚌	NT
York [8]	40 d				09 09												10 11								
Selby	40 d												09 43												10 43
Leeds [10]	37, 39 d		09 37		09 58		10 13			10 08			10 22		10 37		10 58					11 08	11 13		11 22
Bramley	37 d		09 44							10 15			10 29		10 44							11 15			11 29
New Pudsey	37 d		09 49							10 20			10 34		10 49							11 20			11 34
Bradford Interchange	37 a		09 57							10 28			10 42		10 57							11 28			11 42
	d	09 55						10 10	10 25		10 40			10 55					11 10		11 25			11 40	
Halifax	a	10 20						10 35	10 50		11 05			11 20					11 35		11 50			12 05	
	d	10 20						10 40	10 50		11 05			11 20					11 40		11 50			12 05	
Dewsbury	39 d						10 29																11 29		
Mirfield	39 d						10 35																11 35		
Brighouse	d	10 40					10 49		11 05					11 40							12 05		11 49		
Huddersfield	39 a								11 25												12 25				
Sowerby Bridge	d						10 59	10 55											11 55				11 59		
Mytholmroyd	d						11 05	11 10											12 10				12 05		
Hebden Bridge	a				10 34		11 08	11 20			11 30						11 34		12 20				12 08	12 30	
	d			10 30	10 38		11 08				11 30					11 30	11 38						12 08	12 30	
Burnley Manchester Road	97 a				10 57												11 57								
Accrington	97 a				11 06												12 06								
Blackburn	97 a				11 14												12 14								
Preston [8]	97 a				11 32												12 32								
Poulton-le-Fylde	97 a				11 50												12 50								
Blackpool North	97 a				12 00												13 00								
Todmorden	d			10 37		11 01	11 15				11a50					11 37		12 01					12 15	12a50	
Walsden	d			10 40												11 40									
Littleborough	d			10 47			11 23									11 47							12 23		
Smithy Bridge	d					11 10	11 25											12 10					12 25		
Rochdale	a			10 51		11 14	11 29									11 51		12 14					12 29		
	95 d			10 51		11 14	11 30									11 51		12 14					12 30		
Castleton	95 a						11 33																12 33		
Mills Hill	95 a						11 37																12 37		
Moston	95 a						11 41																12 41		
Manchester Victoria	95 ⛴ a			11 08		11 31	11 53									12 08		12 32					12 53		
Liverpool Lime Street [10]	90 a					*12 43*												*13 43*							

		NT 🚌	NT	NT	NT	NT 🚌	NT 🚌	NT	NT	NT	NT 🚌	NT	NT 🚌	NT	NT	NT	NT 🚌	NT 🚌		NT	NT	NT	NT 🚌	NT	NT 🚌
York [8]	40 d				11 09											12 13									
Selby	40 d											11 43												12 43	
Leeds [10]	37, 39 d		11 37		11 58			12 08		12 13		12 22		12 37		12 58				13 08		13 13		13 22	
Bramley	37 d		11 44					12 15				12 29		12 44						13 15				13 29	
New Pudsey	37 d		11 49					12 20				12 34		12 49						13 20				13 34	
Bradford Interchange	37 a		11 57					12 28				12 42		12 57						13 28				13 42	
	d	11 55				12 10	12 25				12 40		12 55				13 10	13 25					13 40		13 55
Halifax	a	12 20				12 35	12 50				13 05		13 20				13 35	13 50					14 05		14 20
	d	12 20				12 40	12 50				13 05		13 20				13 40	13 50					14 05		14 20
Dewsbury	39 d									12 29												13 29			
Mirfield	39 d									12 35												13 35			
Brighouse	d	12 40					13 05			12 49			13 40					14 05				13 49			14 40
Huddersfield	39 a						13 25											14 25							
Sowerby Bridge	d					12 55				12 59							13 55					13 59			
Mytholmroyd	d					13 10				13 05							14 10					14 05			
Hebden Bridge	a				12 34	13 20				13 08	13 30					13 34	14 20					14 08	14 30		
	d			12 30	12 38					13 08	13 30				13 30	13 38						14 08	14 30		
Burnley Manchester Road	97 a				12 57											13 57									
Accrington	97 a				13 06											14 06									
Blackburn	97 a				13 14											14 14									
Preston [8]	97 a				13 32											14 32									
Poulton-le-Fylde	97 a				13 50											14 50									
Blackpool North	97 a				14 00											15 00									
Todmorden	d			12 37					13 01	13 15	13a50				13 37						14 01	14 15	14a50		
Walsden	d			12 40											13 40										
Littleborough	d			12 47						13 23					13 47							14 23			
Smithy Bridge	d								13 10	13 25											14 10	14 25			
Rochdale	a			12 51					13 14	13 29					13 51						14 14	14 29			
	95 d			12 51					13 14	13 30					13 51						14 14	14 30			
Castleton	95 a									13 33												14 33			
Mills Hill	95 a									13 37												14 37			
Moston	95 a									13 41												14 41			
Manchester Victoria	95 ⛴ a			13 08					13 32	13 53					14 07						14 32	14 53			
Liverpool Lime Street [10]	90 a								*14 43*												*15 43*				

For general notes see front of timetable
For details of catering facilities see Directory of Train Operators

Table 41

Saturdays

until 11 July

Leeds and Bradford → Huddersfield, Blackpool North, Rochdale and Manchester Victoria via Halifax and Brighouse

Network Diagram - see first page of Table 39

		NT	NT	NT	NT bus	NT bus	NT	NT	NT	NT bus	NT	NT bus	NT	NT	NT	NT bus	NT bus		NT	NT	NT bus	NT	NT bus	NT	NT bus
York [8]	40 d			13 09											14 13										
Selby	40 d										13 43													14 43	
Leeds [10]	37, 39 d	13 37		13 58			14 08		14 13		14 22		14 37		14 58				15 08			15 13		15 22	
Bramley	37 d	13 44					14 15				14 29		14 44						15 15					15 29	
New Pudsey	37 d	13 49					14 20				14 34		14 49						15 20					15 34	
Bradford Interchange	37 a	13 57					14 28				14 42		14 57						15 28					15 42	
	d				14 10	14 25				14 40		14 55				15 10	15 25				15 10		15 40		15 55
Halifax	a				14 35	14 50				15 05		15 20				15 35	15 50				15 35		16 05		16 20
	d				14 40	14 50				15 05		15 20				15 40	15 50				15 40		16 05		16 20
Dewsbury	39 d								14 29													15 29			
Mirfield	39 d								14 35													15 35			
Brighouse	d					15 05			14 49			15 40					16 05					15 49			16 40
Huddersfield	39 a					15 25											16 25								
Sowerby Bridge	d				14 55				14 59							15 55					15 55	15 59			
Mytholmroyd	d				15 10				15 05							16 10					16 10	16 05			
Hebden Bridge	a			14 34	15 20				15 08	15 30					15 34	16 20					16 20	16 08	16 30		
	d		14 30	14 38					15 08	15 30				15 30	15 38							16 08	16 30		
Burnley Manchester Road	97 a			14 57											15 57										
Accrington	97 a			15 06											16 06										
Blackburn	97 a			15 14											16 14										
Preston [8]	97 a			15 32											16 32										
Poulton-le-Fylde	97 a			15 50											16 50										
Blackpool North	97 a			16 00											17 00										
Todmorden	d		14 37					15 01	15 15	15a50				15 37						16 01		16 15	16a50		
Walsden	d		14 40											15 40											
Littleborough	d		14 47						15 23					15 47								16 23			
Smithy Bridge	d							15 10	15 25											16 10		16 25			
Rochdale	a		14 51					15 14	15 29					15 51						16 14		16 29			
	95 d		14 51					15 14	15 30					15 51						16 14		16 30			
Castleton	95 a								15 33													16 33			
Mills Hill	95 a								15 37													16 37			
Moston	95 a								15 41													16 41			
Manchester Victoria	95 ⛴ a		15 08					15 32	15 53					16 08						16 32		16 53			
Liverpool Lime Street [10]	90 a							*16 43*												*17 43*		*18 13*			

		NT	NT	NT	NT bus	NT bus	NT	NT	NT	NT bus	NT	NT	NT bus	NT	NT	NT bus		NT bus	NT	NT bus	NT	NT	NT bus	NT	NT bus
York [8]	40 d			15 08											16 13										
Selby	40 d										15 43													16 43	
Leeds [10]	37, 39 d	15 37		15 59			16 08		16 13		16 22			16 37	16 58				17 08			17 13		17 22	
Bramley	37 d	15 44					16 15				16 29			16 44					17 15					17 29	
New Pudsey	37 d	15 49					16 20				16 34			16 49					17 20					17 34	
Bradford Interchange	37 a	15 57					16 28				16 42			16 57					17 28					17 42	
	d				16 10	16 25				16 40			16 55			17 10		17 25		17 55			17 40		17 55
Halifax	a				16 35	16 50				17 05			17 20			17 35		17 50		18 20			18 05		18 20
	d				16 35	16 50				17 05			17 20			17 35		17 50		18 20			18 05		18 20
Dewsbury	39 d								16 31													17 31			
Mirfield	39 d								16 38													17 38			
Brighouse	d					17 05			16 49				17 40					18 05		18 40		17 49			18 40
Huddersfield	39 a					17 25												18 25							
Sowerby Bridge	d			16 27	16 55				16 59						17 27	17 55						17 59			
Mytholmroyd	d				17 10				17 05							18 10						18 05			
Hebden Bridge	a			16 34	17 20				17 08	17 30					17 34	18 20						18 08	18 30		
	d		16 30	16 38					17 08	17 30		17 30			17 38							18 08	18 30		
Burnley Manchester Road	97 a			16 57											17 57										
Accrington	97 a			17 06											18 06										
Blackburn	97 a			17 14											18 14										
Preston [8]	97 a			17 32											18 33										
Poulton-le-Fylde	97 a			17 56											18 50										
Blackpool North	97 a			18 06											19 00										
Todmorden	d		16 37					17 01	17 15	17a50		17 37									18 03	18 15	18a50		
Walsden	d		16 40									17 40										18 19			
Littleborough	d		16 47						17 23			17 47										18 25			
Smithy Bridge	d							17 10	17 25												18 11	18 28			
Rochdale	a		16 51					17 14	17 29			17 51									18 15	18 32			
	95 d		16 51					17 14	17 30			17 51									18 16	18 32			
Castleton	95 a								17 33													18 35			
Mills Hill	95 a								17 37													18 40			
Moston	95 a								17 41													18 43			
Manchester Victoria	95 ⛴ a		17 07					17 32	17 51			18 07									18 33	18 53			
Liverpool Lime Street [10]	90 a							*18 43*													*19 43*				

For general notes see front of timetable
For details of catering facilities see Directory of Train Operators

Table 41

Saturdays

until 11 July

Leeds and Bradford → Huddersfield, Blackpool North, Rochdale and Manchester Victoria via Halifax and Brighouse

Network Diagram - see first page of Table 39

		NT	NT	NT	NT (bus)	NT (bus)	NT	NT	NT	NT (bus)	NT	NT (bus)	NT	NT	NT		NT (bus)	NT (bus)	NT	NT (bus)	NT	NT (bus)	NT	NT	NT
York 8	40 d			17 08											18 12										
Selby	40 d										17 43										18 43				
Leeds 10	37, 39 d	17 37		17 59			18 08		18 13		18 22		18 37		18 58				19 08		19 22			19 37	19 43
Bramley	37 d	17 44					18 15				18 30		18 44						19 15		19 30			19 44	
New Pudsey	37 d	17 49					18 20				18 35		18 49						19 20		19 35			19 49	
Bradford Interchange	37 a	17 57					18 28				18 43		18 59						19 30		19 44			19 59	
	d				18 10	18 25				18 40		18 55					19 10	19 25		19 40		19 55			
Halifax	a				18 35	18 50				19 05		19 20					19 35	19 50		20 05		20 20			
	d				18 35	18 50				19 05		19 30					19 35	19 50		20 05		20 30			
Dewsbury	39 d								18 31																
Mirfield	39 d								18 38																
Brighouse	d					19 05			18 49			19 50						20 05				20 50			20 04
Huddersfield	39 a					19 25												20 25							
Sowerby Bridge	d			18 27	18 55				18 59								19 55								20 14
Mytholmroyd	d				19 10				19 05								20 10								20 20
Hebden Bridge	a			18 34	19 20				19 08	19 30					19 34		20 20			20 30					20 23
	d		18 30	18 38					19 08	19 30				19 30	19 38										20 28
Burnley Manchester Road	97 a			18 57											19 56										
Accrington	97 a			19 06											20 05										
Blackburn	97 a			19 14											20 14										
Preston 8	97 a			19 32											20 32										
Poulton-le-Fylde	97 a			19 50											20 50										
Blackpool North	97 a			20 00											21 00										
Todmorden	d		18 37					19 02	19 15	19a50				19 37									20 07		20 36
Walsden	d		18 40						19 19					19 40											20 39
Littleborough	d		18 47						19 25					19 47											20 45
Smithy Bridge	d							19 11	19 28														20 15		20 48
Rochdale	a		18 51					19 15	19 32					19 52									20 19		20 52
	95 d		18 51					19 16	19 32					19 52									20 20		20 52
Castleton	95 a								19 35					19 55											20 55
Mills Hill	95 a								19 40					20 00											21 00
Moston	95 a								19 43					20 03											21 03
Manchester Victoria	95 (ship) a		19 07					19 32	19 54					20 15									20 37		21 14
Liverpool Lime Street 10	90 a							*20 43*						*21 43*											*22 43*

		NT	NT (bus)	NT (bus)	NT	NT (bus)	NT	NT	NT (bus)	NT	NT (bus)	NT (bus)	NT (bus)	NT	NT	NT (bus)	NT	NT (bus)	NT	NT	NT (bus)	NT	NT (bus)		
York 8	40 d	19 04																							
Selby	40 d																								
Leeds 10	37, 39 d	19 55			20 08		20 37	20 43		21 08				21 37	21 45		22 08		22 37	22 47		23 08			
Bramley	37 d				20 15		20 44			21 15				21 44			22 15		22 44			23 15			
New Pudsey	37 d				20 20		20 49			21 20				21 49			22 20		22 49			23 20			
Bradford Interchange	37 a				20 30		20 59			21 30				21 59			22 30		22 59			23 30			
	d		20 10	20 25		20 55			21 10		21 45	21 25	21 45			22 15		22 45			23 15		23 45		
Halifax	a		20 35	20 50		21 20			21 35		22 15	21 50	22 15			22 40		23 10			23 45		00 10		
	d		20 40	20 50		21 30			21 40			21 50				22 45		23 10			23 45		00 10		
Dewsbury	39 d																								
Mirfield	39 d																								
Brighouse	d			21 05		21 50		21 05				22 05			22 05			23 25		23 06	23 59		00 25		
Huddersfield	39 a			21 25								22 25						23 45			00 15		00 45		
Sowerby Bridge	d		20 55					21 14	21 55						22 14	23 00				23 16					
Mytholmroyd	d		21 10					21 20	22 10						22 20	23 15				23 22					
Hebden Bridge	a	20 33	21 20					21 23	22 20						22 23	23 20				23 25					
	d	20 38						21 28							22 28					23 28					
Burnley Manchester Road	97 a	20 56																							
Accrington	97 a	21 05																							
Blackburn	97 a	21 14																							
Preston 8	97 a	21 32																							
Poulton-le-Fylde	97 a	21 50																							
Blackpool North	97 a	22 00																							
Todmorden	d							21 36							22 36					23 36					
Walsden	d							21 39							22 39					23 39					
Littleborough	d							21 45							22 45					23 45					
Smithy Bridge	d							21 48							22 48					23 48					
Rochdale	a							21 52							22 52					23 52					
	95 d							21 52							22 52					23 52					
Castleton	95 a							21 55																	
Mills Hill	95 a							22 00																	
Moston	95 a							22 03																	
Manchester Victoria	95 (ship) a							22 14							23 08					00 08					
Liverpool Lime Street 10	90 a							*23 43*																	

For general notes see front of timetable
For details of catering facilities see
Directory of Train Operators

Table 41

Saturdays

from 18 July

Leeds and Bradford → Huddersfield, Blackpool North, Rochdale and Manchester Victoria via Halifax and Brighouse

Network Diagram - see first page of Table 39

		NT	NT	NT	NT	NT	NT A	NT	NT	NT	NT B	NT	NT	NT	NT	NT B	NT	NT	NT	NT	NT B	NT
York 8	40 d							06 13					07 06					08 09				
Selby	40 d										06 41					07 43					08 43	
Leeds 10	37, 39 d	05 37	05 51	06 03	06 16	06 37		06 51	07 08	07 13	07 22	07 37	07 51	08 08	08 13	08 22	08 37	08 51	09 08	09 13	09 22	09 37
Bramley	37 d	05 44	05 58		06 23	06 44			07 15		07 29	07 44		08 15		08 29	08 44		09 15		09 29	09 44
New Pudsey	37 d	05 49	06 02	06 13	06 28	06 49		07 01	07 20		07 34	07 49	08 01	08 20		08 34	08 49	09 00	09 20		09 34	09 49
Bradford Interchange	37 a	05 57	06 13	06 21	06 36	06 57		07 11	07 28		07 43	07 57	08 11	08 28		08 42	08 57	09 12	09 28		09 42	09 57
	d	06 00	06 14	06 24	06 40	07 00		07 14	07 31		07 45	08 00	08 14	08 32		08 45	09 00	09 13	09 32		09 45	10 00
Halifax	a	06 12	06 25	06 36	06 52	07 12		07 25	07 43		08 00	08 12	08 25	08 44		09 00	09 12	09 25	09 44		10 00	10 12
	d	06 12	06 26	06 36	06 52	07 12		07 26	07 44		08 06	08 12	08 26	08 44		09 06	09 12	09 25	09 44		10 06	10 12
Dewsbury	39 d									07 29					08 31					09 31		
Mirfield	39 d									07 35					08 38					09 37		
Brighouse	d									07 49	08 16				08 49	09 16				09 49	10 16	
Huddersfield	39 a										08 31					09 29					10 29	
Sowerby Bridge	d	06 19		06 43	06 59	07 19				07 59		08 19			08 59		09 19			09 59		10 19
Mytholmroyd	d	06 25		06 49	07 05	07 25				08 05		08 25			09 05		09 25			10 05		10 25
Hebden Bridge	a	06 28	06 37	06 52	07 08	07 28		07 37	07 55	08 08		08 28	08 37	08 56	09 08		09 28	09 37	09 56	10 08		10 28
	d	06 28	06 38	06 52	07 08	07 28		07 38	07 56	08 08		08 28	08 38	08 56	09 08		09 28	09 37	09 56	10 08		10 28
Burnley Manchester Road	97 a		06 57					07 57					08 57					09 56				
Accrington	97 a		07 06					08 06					09 06					10 06				
Blackburn	97 a		07 16					08 14					09 14					10 14				
Preston 8	97 a		07 36					08 38					09 32					10 32				
Poulton-le-Fylde	97 a		07 54					08 56					09 50					10 50				
Blackpool North	97 a		08 05					09 05					10 00					11 00				
Todmorden	d	06 35		06 59	07 15	07 36	07 44		08 04	08 15		08 36		09 04	09 15		09 36		10 04	10 15		10 36
Walsden	d	06 38		07 02		07 39	07 47					08 39					09 39					10 39
Littleborough	d	06 45		07 09	07 23	07 45	07 53			08 23		08 45			09 23		09 45			10 23		10 45
Smithy Bridge	d	06 47		07 11	07 25	07 48	07 56			08 25		08 48			09 25		09 48			10 25		10 48
Rochdale	a	06 54		07 15	07 29	07 52	08 00		08 14	08 29		08 51		09 14	09 29		09 51		10 14	10 29		10 51
	95 d	06 55		07 16	07 30	07 52	08 00		08 14	08 30		08 51		09 14	09 30		09 51		10 14	10 30		10 51
Castleton	95 a	06 58		07 19	07 33	07 55	08 03		08 17	08 33					09 33					10 33		
Mills Hill	95 a	07 02		07 23	07 37	08 00	08 08		08 22	08 37					09 37					10 37		
Moston	95 a	07 06		07 27	07 41	08 03	08 11		08 25	08 40					09 40					10 41		
Manchester Victoria	95 a	07 17		07 38	07 53	08 14	08 22		08 38	08 53		09 08		09 32	09 53		10 07		10 32	10 53		11 08
Liverpool Lime Street 10	90 a	*08 43*			*09 13*		*09 43*							*10 43*					*11 43*			

		NT	NT	NT	NT B	NT	NT	NT	NT	NT B	NT	NT	NT	NT	NT B	NT	NT	NT	NT	NT B	NT
York 8	40 d	09 09					10 11					11 09					12 13				
Selby	40 d				09 43					10 43					11 43					12 43	
Leeds 10	37, 39 d	09 51	10 08	10 13	10 22	10 37	10 51	11 08	11 13	11 22	11 37	11 51	12 08	12 13	12 22	12 37	12 51	13 08	13 13	13 22	13 37
Bramley	37 d		10 15		10 29	10 44		11 15		11 29	11 44		12 15		12 29	12 44		13 15		13 29	13 44
New Pudsey	37 d	10 01	10 20		10 34	10 49	11 01	11 20		11 34	11 49	12 01	12 20		12 34	12 49	13 01	13 20		13 34	13 49
Bradford Interchange	37 a	10 10	10 28		10 42	10 57	11 11	11 28		11 42	11 57	12 10	12 28		12 42	12 57	13 10	13 28		13 42	13 57
	d	10 14	10 32		10 45	11 00	11 14	11 32		11 45	12 00	12 14	12 32		12 45	13 00	13 14	13 32		13 45	14 00
Halifax	a	10 25	10 44		11 00	11 12	11 25	11 44		11 58	12 12	12 25	12 44		13 00	13 12	13 25	13 44		14 00	14 12
	d	10 26	10 44		11 06	11 12	11 26	11 44		12 06	12 12	12 26	12 44		13 06	13 12	13 26	13 44		14 06	14 12
Dewsbury	39 d			10 29					11 29					12 29					13 29		
Mirfield	39 d			10 35					11 35					12 35					13 35		
Brighouse	d			10 49	11 16				11 49	12 16				12 49	13 16				13 49	14 16	
Huddersfield	39 a				11 29					12 29					13 29					14 29	
Sowerby Bridge	d			10 59		11 19			11 59		12 19			12 59		13 19			13 59		14 19
Mytholmroyd	d			11 05		11 25			12 05		12 25			13 05		13 25			14 05		14 25
Hebden Bridge	a	10 37	10 56	11 08		11 28	11 37	11 56	12 08		12 28	12 37	12 56	13 08		13 28	13 37	13 56	14 08		14 28
	d	10 38	10 56	11 08		11 28	11 38	11 56	12 08		12 28	12 38	12 56	13 08		13 28	13 38	13 56	14 08		14 28
Burnley Manchester Road	97 a	10 57					11 57					12 57					13 57				
Accrington	97 a	11 06					12 06					13 06					14 06				
Blackburn	97 a	11 14					12 14					13 14					14 14				
Preston 8	97 a	11 32					12 32					13 32					14 32				
Poulton-le-Fylde	97 a	11 50					12 50					13 50					14 50				
Blackpool North	97 a	12 00					13 00					14 00					15 00				
Todmorden	d		11 04	11 15		11 36		12 04	12 15		12 36		13 04	13 15		13 36		14 04	14 15		14 36
Walsden	d					11 39					12 39					13 39					14 39
Littleborough	d			11 23		11 45			12 23		12 45			13 23		13 45			14 23		14 45
Smithy Bridge	d			11 25		11 48			12 25		12 48			13 25		13 48			14 25		14 48
Rochdale	a		11 14	11 29		11 51		12 14	12 29		12 51		13 14	13 29		13 51		14 14	14 29		14 51
	95 d		11 14	11 30		11 51		12 14	12 30		12 51		13 14	13 30		13 51		14 14	14 30		14 51
Castleton	95 a			11 33					12 33					13 33					14 33		
Mills Hill	95 a			11 37					12 37					13 37					14 37		
Moston	95 a			11 41					12 41					13 41					14 41		
Manchester Victoria	95 a		11 32	11 53		12 08		12 32	12 53		13 08		13 32	13 53		14 07		14 32	14 53		15 08
Liverpool Lime Street 10	90 a		*12 43*					*13 43*					*14 43*					*15 43*			

For general notes see front of timetable
For details of catering facilities see
Directory of Train Operators

A To Wigan Wallgate (Table 82)
B To Wakefield Westgate (Table 39)

Leeds and Bradford → Huddersfield, Blackpool North, Rochdale and Manchester Victoria via Halifax and Brighouse

from 18 July

Network Diagram - see first page of Table 39

		NT	NT	NT	NT A	NT	NT	NT	NT	NT A	NT	NT	NT	NT	NT A	NT	NT	NT	NT	NT A	NT
York 8	40 d	13 09					14 13					15 08					16 13				
Selby	40 d				13 43					14 43					15 43					16 43	
Leeds 10	37, 39 d	13 51	14 08	14 13	14 22	14 37	14 51	15 08	15 13	15 22	15 37	15 51	16 08	16 13	16 22	16 37	16 51	17 08	17 13	17 22	17 37
Bramley	37 d		14 15		14 29	14 44		15 15		15 29	15 44		16 15		16 29	16 44		17 15		17 29	17 44
New Pudsey	37 d	14 01	14 20		14 34	14 49	15 01	15 20		15 34	15 49	16 01	16 20		16 34	16 49	17 01	17 20		17 34	17 49
Bradford Interchange	37 a	14 11	14 28		14 42	14 57	15 11	15 28		15 42	15 57	16 10	16 28		16 42	16 57	17 09	17 28		17 42	17 57
	d	14 14	14 32		14 45	15 00	15 14	15 32		15 45	16 00	16 13	16 32		16 45	17 00	17 12	17 32		17 45	18 00
Halifax	a	14 25	14 44		14 59	15 12	15 25	15 44		15 58	16 12	16 24	16 44		17 00	17 12	17 23	17 44		17 58	18 12
	d	14 26	14 44		15 06	15 12	15 26	15 44		16 06	16 12	16 25	16 44		17 06	17 12	17 24	17 44		18 06	18 12
Dewsbury	39 d			14 29					15 29					16 31					17 31		
Mirfield	39 d			14 35					15 35					16 38					17 38		
Brighouse	d			14 49	15 16				15 49	16 16				16 49	17 16				17 49	18 16	
Huddersfield	39 a				15 29					16 29					17 29					18 30	
Sowerby Bridge	d			14 59		15 19			15 59		16 19	16 31		16 59		17 19	17 31		17 59		18 19
Mytholmroyd	d			15 05		15 25			16 05		16 25			17 05		17 25			18 05		18 25
Hebden Bridge	a	14 37	14 56	15 08		15 28	15 37	15 56	16 08		16 28	16 38	16 56	17 08		17 28	17 37	17 56	18 08		18 28
	d	14 38	14 56	15 08		15 28	15 38	15 56	16 08		16 28	16 38	16 56	17 08		17 28	17 38	17 56	18 08		18 28
Burnley Manchester Road	97 a	14 57					15 57					16 57					17 57				
Accrington	97 a	15 06					16 06					17 06					18 06				
Blackburn	97 a	15 14					16 14					17 14					18 14				
Preston 8	97 a	15 32					16 32					17 32					18 33				
Poulton-le-Fylde	97 a	15 50					16 50					17 56					18 50				
Blackpool North	97 a	16 00					17 00					18 06					19 00				
Todmorden	d		15 04	15 15		15 36		16 04	16 15		16 36		17 04	17 15		17 36		18 04	18 15		18 36
Walsden	d					15 39					16 39					17 39			18 19		18 39
Littleborough	d			15 23		15 45			16 23		16 45			17 23		17 45			18 25		18 45
Smithy Bridge	d			15 25		15 48			16 25		16 48			17 25		17 48			18 28		18 48
Rochdale	a		15 14	15 29		15 51		16 14	16 29		16 51		17 14	17 29		17 51		18 14	18 32		18 51
	95 d		15 14	15 30		15 51		16 14	16 30		16 51		17 14	17 30		17 51		18 14	18 32		18 51
Castleton	95 a			15 33					16 33					17 33					18 35		
Mills Hill	95 a			15 37					16 37					17 37					18 40		
Moston	95 a			15 41					16 41					17 41					18 43		
Manchester Victoria	95 ⛴ a		15 32	15 53		16 08		16 32	16 53		17 07		17 32	17 51		18 07		18 32	18 53		19 07
Liverpool Lime Street 10	90 a		*16 43*					*17 43*	*18 13*				*18 43*					*19 43*			

		NT	NT	NT	NT A	NT	NT	NT	NT A	NT	NT	NT	NT	NT	NT	NT	NT	NT B	NT C
York 8	40 d	17 08					18 12				19 04								
Selby	40 d				17 43				18 43										
Leeds 10	37, 39 d	17 51	18 08	18 13	18 22	18 37	18 51	19 08	19 22	19 37	19 51	20 08	20 37	21 08	21 37	22 08	22 37	23 00	23 08
Bramley	37 d		18 15		18 30	18 44		19 15	19 30	19 44		20 15	20 44	21 15	21 44	22 15	22 44	23 07	23 15
New Pudsey	37 d	18 01	18 20		18 35	18 49	19 01	19 20	19 35	19 49	20 01	20 20	20 49	21 20	21 49	22 20	22 49	23 12	23 20
Bradford Interchange	37 a	18 09	18 28		18 43	18 58	19 10	19 28	19 44	19 57	20 10	20 28	20 57	21 28	21 57	22 28	22 57	23 20	23 29
	d	18 12	18 32		18 46	19 01	19 14	19 32	19 46	20 00	20 14	20 31	21 00	21 31	22 00	22 31	23 00	23 23	23 31
Halifax	a	18 23	18 44		19 00	19 13	19 25	19 44	20 00	20 12	20 25	20 44	21 12	21 44	22 12	22 44	23 12	23 36	23 44
	d	18 24	18 44		19 06	19 13	19 26	19 44	20 06	20 12	20 26	20 44	21 12	21 44	22 12	22 44	23 12	23 36	23 44
Dewsbury	39 d			18 31															
Mirfield	39 d			18 38															
Brighouse	d			18 49	19 16				20 16			20 55		21 55		22 55		23 47	23 55
Huddersfield	39 a				19 29				20 29			21 08		22 08		23 07		23 59	00 08
Sowerby Bridge	d	18 31		18 59		19 20				20 19			21 19		22 19		23 19		
Mytholmroyd	d			19 05		19 26				20 25			21 25		22 25		23 25		
Hebden Bridge	a	18 37	18 56	19 08		19 29	19 37	19 56		20 28	20 37		21 28		22 28		23 28		
	d	18 38	18 56	19 08		19 29	19 38	19 56		20 28	20 38		21 28		22 28		23 28		
Burnley Manchester Road	97 a	18 57					19 56				20 56								
Accrington	97 a	19 06					20 05				21 05								
Blackburn	97 a	19 14					20 14				21 14								
Preston 8	97 a	19 32					20 32				21 32								
Poulton-le-Fylde	97 a	19 50					20 50				21 50								
Blackpool North	97 a	20 00					21 00				22 00								
Todmorden	d		19 04	19 15		19 36		20 04		20 36			21 36		22 36		23 36		
Walsden	d			19 19		19 39				20 39			21 39		22 39		23 39		
Littleborough	d			19 25		19 46				20 45			21 45		22 45		23 45		
Smithy Bridge	d			19 28		19 48				20 48			21 48		22 48		23 48		
Rochdale	a		19 15	19 32		19 52		20 14		20 52			21 52		22 52		23 52		
	95 d		19 16	19 32		19 53		20 14		20 52			21 52		22 52		23 52		
Castleton	95 a			19 35		19 56				20 55			21 55						
Mills Hill	95 a			19 40		20 00				21 00			22 00						
Moston	95 a			19 43		20 04				21 03			22 03						
Manchester Victoria	95 ⛴ a		19 32	19 54		20 15		20 32		21 14			22 14		23 08		00 08		
Liverpool Lime Street 10	90 a		*20 43*					*21 43*		*22 43*			*23 43*						

For general notes see front of timetable
For details of catering facilities see Directory of Train Operators

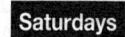

A To Wakefield Westgate (Table 39)
B From 12 September
C Until 5 September

Table 41

Sundays

until 12 July

Leeds and Bradford → Huddersfield, Blackpool North, Rochdale and Manchester Victoria via Halifax and Brighouse

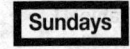

Network Diagram - see first page of Table 39

		NT (bus)	NT	NT (bus)	NT (bus)	NT		NT	NT (bus)	NT	NT	NT		NT (bus)	NT (bus)	NT	NT	NT (bus)		NT	NT (bus)	NT	NT (bus)	NT	NT
York 8	40 d																08 50								09 52
Selby	40 d																								
Leeds 10	37, 39 d		08 03			08 21		08 29		08 45	09 02	09 13				09 23	09 45			09 54		09 56		10 12	10 34
Bramley	37 d		08 10			08 28				08 52						09 30				10 01				10 19	
New Pudsey	37 d		08 15			08 33				08 57						09 35				10 06				10 24	
Bradford Interchange	37 a		08 25			08 43				09 05						09 45				10 16				10 34	
	d	08 05		08 30	08 40				08 55					09 20	09 30			09 55			10 20		10 30		
Halifax	a	08 30		08 55	09 05				09 20					09 45	09 55			10 25			10 45		10 55		
	d	08 30		08 55	09 05				09 20					09 45	09 55						10 45		10 55		
Dewsbury	39 d																								
Mirfield	39 d																								
Brighouse	d								09 35			09 32													
Huddersfield	39 a								09 55																
Sowerby Bridge	d	08 45			09 20							09 42			10 10							10 21	11 10		
Mytholmroyd	d	09 00			09 35							09 48			10 25							10 27	11 25		
Hebden Bridge	a	09 10		09 20	09 45			09 16			09 30	09 51		10 10	10 35		10 14				11 10	10 30	11 35		11 02
	d							09 17			09 31	09 53					10 20					10 45			11 19
Burnley Manchester Road	97 a										09 50						10 38								11 38
Accrington	97 a										09 59						10 47								11 47
Blackburn	97 a										10 07						10 56								11 55
Preston 8	97 a										10 27						11 13								12 13
Poulton-le-Fylde	97 a										10 45						11 31								12 31
Blackpool North	97 a										10 53						11 39								12 38
Todmorden	d							09 24				10 00										10 52			
Walsden	d							09 27				10 03										10 55			
Littleborough	d							09 34				10 10										11 02			
Smithy Bridge	d							09 36				10 12										11 04			
Rochdale	a							09 41				10 16										11 08			
	95 d							09 41				10 17										11 09			
Castleton	95 a							09 44				10 20										11 12			
Mills Hill	95 a							09 48				10 24										11 16			
Moston	95 a							09 52				10 28										11 20			
Manchester Victoria	95 (ship) a							10 02				10 38										11 30			
Liverpool Lime Street 10	90 a																								

		NT		NT (bus)	NT	NT (bus)	NT (bus)	NT		NT	NT	NT (bus)	NT	NT (bus)		NT (bus)	NT	NT	NT (bus)	NT		NT	NT (bus)	NT (bus)	NT
York 8	40 d									10 57								11 52							
Selby	40 d																								
Leeds 10	37, 39 d	10 53			10 54			11 12		11 49	11 53		11 54				12 12	12 37		12 54		13 05			13 12
Bramley	37 d				11 01			11 19					12 01				12 19			13 01					13 19
New Pudsey	37 d				11 06			11 24					12 06				12 24			13 06					13 24
Bradford Interchange	37 a				11 16			11 34					12 16				12 34			13 16					13 34
	d			10 55		11 20	11 30					11 55		12 20		12 30			12 55				13 20	13 30	
Halifax	a			11 20		11 45	11 55					12 25		12 45		12 55			13 20				13 45	13 55	
	d			11 20		11 45	11 55							12 45		12 55			13 20				13 45	13 55	
Dewsbury	39 d																								
Mirfield	39 d																								
Brighouse	d	11 20		11 35															13 35			13 25			
Huddersfield	39 a			11 55															13 55						
Sowerby Bridge	d	11 29					12 10				12 18					13 10						13 35		14 10	
Mytholmroyd	d	11 35					12 25				12 24					13 25						13 41		14 25	
Hebden Bridge	a	11 38				12 10	12 35			12 17	12 27			13 10		13 35		13 05				13 44	14 10	14 35	
	d	11 45								12 19	12 45							13 19				13 45			
Burnley Manchester Road	97 a									12 38								13 38							
Accrington	97 a									12 47								13 47							
Blackburn	97 a									12 55								13 55							
Preston 8	97 a									13 13								14 13							
Poulton-le-Fylde	97 a									13 31								14 31							
Blackpool North	97 a									13 38								14 38							
Todmorden	d	11 52									12 52											13 52			
Walsden	d	11 55									12 55											13 55			
Littleborough	d	12 02									13 02											14 02			
Smithy Bridge	d	12 04									13 04											14 04			
Rochdale	a	12 08									13 08											14 08			
	95 d	12 09									13 09											14 09			
Castleton	95 a	12 12									13 12											14 12			
Mills Hill	95 a	12 16									13 16											14 16			
Moston	95 a	12 20									13 20											14 20			
Manchester Victoria	95 (ship) a	12 30									13 30											14 30			
Liverpool Lime Street 10	90 a																								

For general notes see front of timetable
For details of catering facilities see Directory of Train Operators

Table 41

Sundays

until 12 July

Leeds and Bradford → Huddersfield, Blackpool North, Rochdale and Manchester Victoria via Halifax and Brighouse

Network Diagram - see first page of Table 39

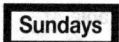

		NT	NT	NT 🚌		NT	NT 🚌	NT 🚌	NT	NT		NT 🚌	NT	NT	NT 🚌	NT 🚌		NT	NT	NT 🚌	NT	NT		NT 🚌	NT 🚌
York [8]	40 d	12 52								13 52									14 52						
Selby	40 d																								
Leeds [10]	37, 39 d	13 46	13 53			13 54			14 12	14 36			14 54	15 03				15 12	15 47		15 54	16 03			
Bramley	37 d					14 01			14 19				15 01					15 19			16 01				
New Pudsey	37 d					14 06			14 24				15 06					15 24			16 06				
Bradford Interchange	37 a					14 16			14 34				15 16					15 34			16 16				
	d			13 55			14 20	14 30				14 55			15 20	15 30				15 55				16 20	16 30
Halifax	a			14 25			14 45	14 55				15 20			15 45	15 55				16 25				16 45	16 55
	d						14 45	14 55				15 20			15 45	15 55								16 45	16 55
Dewsbury	39 d																								
Mirfield	39 d																								
Brighouse	d											15 35		15 24											
Huddersfield	39 a											15 55													
Sowerby Bridge	d		14 19					15 10						15 34		16 10						16 29			17 10
Mytholmroyd	d		14 25					15 25						15 40		16 25						16 35			17 25
Hebden Bridge	a	14 14	14 28				15 10	15 35		15 04				15 43	16 10	16 35			16 15			16 38		17 10	17 35
	d	14 19	14 45							15 19				15 45					16 19			16 45			
Burnley Manchester Road	97 a	14 38								15 38									16 38						
Accrington	97 a	14 47								15 47									16 47						
Blackburn	97 a	14 55								15 55									16 55						
Preston [8]	97 a	15 13								16 13									17 13						
Poulton-le-Fylde	97 a	15 32								16 31									17 31						
Blackpool North	97 a	15 40								16 38									17 38						
Todmorden	d		14 52											15 52								16 52			
Walsden	d		14 55											15 55								16 55			
Littleborough	d		15 02											16 02								17 02			
Smithy Bridge	d		15 04											16 04								17 04			
Rochdale	a		15 08											16 08								17 08			
	95 d		15 09											16 09								17 09			
Castleton	95 a		15 12											16 12								17 12			
Mills Hill	95 a		15 16											16 16								17 16			
Moston	95 a		15 20											16 20								17 20			
Manchester Victoria	95 a		15 30											16 30								17 30			
Liverpool Lime Street [10]	90 a																								

		NT	NT	NT 🚌	NT	NT		NT 🚌	NT 🚌	NT	NT	NT 🚌		NT	NT	NT 🚌	NT	NT 🚌		NT	NT 🚌	NT 🚌	NT	NT	NT 🚌
York [8]	40 d		15 52								16 52									17 52					
Selby	40 d																								
Leeds [10]	37, 39 d	16 12	16 35		16 54	17 03				17 12	17 46			17 54	18 03		18 12			18 34			19 03	19 16	
Bramley	37 d	16 19			17 01					17 19				18 01			18 19						19 10		
New Pudsey	37 d	16 24			17 06					17 24				18 06			18 24						19 15		
Bradford Interchange	37 a	16 34			17 16					17 34				18 16			18 34						19 25		
	d			16 55				17 20	17 30			17 55				18 20		18 40			18 55	19 20			19 40
Halifax	a			17 20				17 45	17 55			18 25				18 45		19 05			19 20	19 45			20 05
	d			17 20				17 45	17 55							18 45		19 05			19 20	19 45			20 05
Dewsbury	39 d																								
Mirfield	39 d																								
Brighouse	d			17 35		17 24															19 35			19 36	
Huddersfield	39 a			17 55																	19 55				
Sowerby Bridge	d					17 34			18 10						18 28			19 20						19 46	20 20
Mytholmroyd	d					17 40			18 25						18 34			19 35						19 52	20 35
Hebden Bridge	a		17 03			17 43		18 10	18 35		18 15				18 37	19 10		19 45		19 03		20 10		19 55	20 45
	d		17 19			17 45					18 19				18 45					19 19				19 56	
Burnley Manchester Road	97 a		17 38								18 38									19 38					
Accrington	97 a		17 47								18 47									19 47					
Blackburn	97 a		17 55								18 55									19 56					
Preston [8]	97 a		18 13								19 13									20 14					
Poulton-le-Fylde	97 a		18 31								19 31									20 32					
Blackpool North	97 a		18 38								19 38									20 39					
Todmorden	d					17 52									18 52									20 04	
Walsden	d					17 55									18 55									20 07	
Littleborough	d					18 02									19 02									20 12	
Smithy Bridge	d					18 04									19 04									20 16	
Rochdale	a					18 08									19 08									20 20	
	95 d					18 09									19 09									20 20	
Castleton	95 a					18 12									19 12									20 23	
Mills Hill	95 a					18 16									19 16									20 28	
Moston	95 a					18 20									19 20									20 31	
Manchester Victoria	95 a					18 30									19 30									20 41	
Liverpool Lime Street [10]	90 a																								

For general notes see front of timetable
For details of catering facilities see Directory of Train Operators

Leeds and Bradford → Huddersfield, Blackpool North, Rochdale and Manchester Victoria via Halifax and Brighouse

Sundays

until 12 July

Network Diagram - see first page of Table 39

		NT	NT 🚌	NT 🚌	NT	NT	NT	NT	NT 🚌	NT 🚌	NT	NT 🚌	NT	NT	NT 🚌	NT	NT 🚌	NT	NT 🚌	NT
York [8]	40 d	18 52						19 52						20 57						
Selby	40 d																			
Leeds [10]	37, 39 d	19 49			20 03	20 12	20 20	20 35			21 04		21 35	21 47		22 05		22 35		23 22
Bramley	37 d				20 10	20 19					21 12		21 43			22 12		22 43		23 29
New Pudsey	37 d				20 15	20 24					21 17		21 47			22 17		22 47		23 34
Bradford Interchange	37 a				20 25	20 35					21 27		21 57			22 27		22 58		23 43
	d		19 55	20 20					20 55	21 15		21 40			22 10		22 40		23 10	
Halifax	a		20 20	20 45					21 20	21 40		22 10			22 40		23 05		23 40	
	d		20 20	20 45					21 20	21 40					22 40		23 05			
Dewsbury	39 d																			
Mirfield	39 d																			
Brighouse	d		20 35					20 53	21 35					22 06			23 20			
Huddersfield	39 a		20 55						21 55								23 40			
Sowerby Bridge	d						20 45	21 02		21 55				22 16	22 55					
Mytholmroyd	d						20 51			22 10				22 22	23 10					
Hebden Bridge	a	20 17		21 10			20 54	21 08		22 20				22 25	23 20					
	d	20 19					20 56	21 19						22 27						
Burnley Manchester Road	97 a	20 38						21 38												
Accrington	97 a	20 47						21 47												
Blackburn	97 a	20 55						21 55												
Preston [8]	97 a	21 13						22 13												
Poulton-le-Fylde	97 a	21 31						22 31												
Blackpool North	97 a	21 38						22 38												
Todmorden	d						21 04							22 34						
Walsden	d						21 07							22 37						
Littleborough	d						21 12							22 44						
Smithy Bridge	d						21 16							22 46						
Rochdale	a						21 20							22 50						
	95 d						21 20							22 51						
Castleton	95 a						21 23							22 54						
Mills Hill	95 a						21 28							22 58						
Moston	95 a						21 31							23 02						
Manchester Victoria	95 🚊 a						21 41							23 12						
Liverpool Lime Street [10]	90 a																			

Sundays

19 July to 6 September

		NT	NT	NT	NT	NT	NT	NT	NT	NT	NT	NT	NT	NT	NT	NT	NT	NT	NT	NT	NT	NT	NT
York [8]	40 d						08 50			09 52			10 57			11 52			12 52			13 52	
Selby	40 d																						
Leeds [10]	37, 39 d	08 02	08 21	08 45	09 02	09 18	09 35	09 53	10 12	10 35	10 53	11 12	11 35	11 53	12 12	12 35	12 53	13 12	13 35	13 53	14 12	14 35	14 53
Bramley	37 d	08 10	08 28		09 09	09 25		10 01	10 19		11 01	11 19		12 01	12 19		13 01	13 19		14 01	14 19		15 01
New Pudsey	37 d	08 15	08 33	08 54	09 14	09 30	09 44	10 06	10 24	10 44	11 06	11 24	11 44	12 06	12 24	12 44	13 06	13 24	13 44	14 06	14 24	14 44	15 06
Bradford Interchange	37 a	08 23	08 41	09 03	09 22	09 38	09 53	10 14	10 32	10 53	11 14	11 32	11 53	12 14	12 32	12 53	13 14	13 32	13 53	14 14	14 32	14 53	15 14
	d		08 45	09 05	09 25	09 41	09 55	10 17	10 35	10 55	11 17	11 35	11 55	12 17	12 35	12 55	13 17	13 35	13 55	14 17	14 35	14 55	15 17
Halifax	a		08 57	09 17	09 37	09 54	10 07	10 29	10 48	11 07	11 29	11 48	12 07	12 29	12 48	13 07	13 29	13 48	14 07	14 29	14 48	15 07	15 29
	d		09 01	09 17	09 37	09 54	10 07	10 29	10 48	11 07	11 29		12 07	12 29	12 48	13 07	13 29		14 07	14 29	14 48	15 07	15 29
Dewsbury	39 d																						
Mirfield	39 d																						
Brighouse	d					10 04			10 58						12 58						14 58		
Huddersfield	39 a					10 17			11 12						13 12						15 12		
Sowerby Bridge	d		09 08		09 44			10 36			11 36			12 36			13 36			14 36			15 36
Mytholmroyd	d		09 14		09 50			10 42			11 42			12 42			13 42			14 42			15 42
Hebden Bridge	a		09 17	09 29	09 53		10 19	10 45		11 19	11 45		12 19	12 45		13 19	13 45		14 19	14 45		15 19	15 45
	d		09 17	09 30	09 53		10 20	10 45		11 20	11 45		12 20	12 45		13 19	13 45		14 20	14 45		15 19	15 45
Burnley Manchester Road	97 a			09 50			10 38			11 38			12 38			13 38			14 38			15 38	
Accrington	97 a			09 59			10 47			11 47			12 47			13 47			14 47			15 47	
Blackburn	97 a			10 07			10 56			11 55			12 55			13 55			14 55			15 55	
Preston [8]	97 a			10 27			11 13			12 13			13 13			14 13			15 13			16 13	
Poulton-le-Fylde	97 a			10 45			11 31			12 31			13 31			14 30			15 32			16 31	
Blackpool North	97 a			10 53			11 39			12 38			13 38			14 38			15 39			16 38	
Todmorden	d		09 24		10 00			10 52			11 52			12 52			13 52			14 52			15 52
Walsden	d		09 27		10 03			10 55			11 55			12 55			13 55			14 55			15 55
Littleborough	d		09 34		10 10			11 02			12 02			13 02			14 02			15 02			16 02
Smithy Bridge	d		09 36		10 12			11 04			12 04			13 04			14 04			15 04			16 04
Rochdale	a		09 41		10 16			11 08			12 08			13 08			14 08			15 08			16 08
	95 d		09 41		10 17			11 09			12 09			13 09			14 09			15 09			16 09
Castleton	95 a		09 44		10 20			11 12			12 12			13 12			14 12			15 12			16 12
Mills Hill	95 a		09 48		10 24			11 16			12 16			13 16			14 16			15 16			16 16
Moston	95 a		09 52		10 28			11 20			12 20			13 20			14 20			15 20			16 20
Manchester Victoria	95 🚊 a		10 02		10 38			11 30			12 30			13 30			14 30			15 30			16 30
Liverpool Lime Street [10]	90 a																						

For general notes see front of timetable
For details of catering facilities see Directory of Train Operators

Sundays

19 July to 6 September

Leeds and Bradford → Huddersfield, Blackpool North, Rochdale and Manchester Victoria via Halifax and Brighouse

Network Diagram - see first page of Table 39

		NT	NT	NT	NT	NT	NT	NT		NT	NT	NT	NT	NT	NT	NT	NT	NT	NT	NT	NT	NT	NT		
York 8	40 d		14 52		15 52					16 52			17 52		18 52			19 52		20 57					
Selby	40 d																								
Leeds 10	37, 39 d	15 12	15 35	15 53	16 12	16 35	16 53	17 12		17 35	17 53	18 12	18 35	19 02	19 35	19 53	20 12	20 35	21 04	21 35	22 05	22 35	23 22		
Bramley	37 d	15 19		16 01	16 19		17 01	17 19			18 01	18 19		19 10		20 01	20 19		21 12	21 43	22 12	22 43	23 29		
New Pudsey	37 d	15 24	15 44	16 06	16 24	16 44	17 06	17 24		17 44	18 06	18 24	18 44	19 15	19 44	20 06	20 24	20 44	21 17	21 47	22 17	22 47	23 34		
Bradford Interchange	37 a	15 32	15 53	16 14	16 32	16 53	17 14	17 32		17 53	18 14	18 32	18 53	19 23	19 53	20 14	20 33	20 53	21 25	21 56	22 25	22 56	23 43		
	d	15 35	15 55	16 17	16 35	16 55	17 17	17 35		17 55	18 17	18 35	18 55	19 27	19 55	20 19	20 34	20 55	21 28	21 58	22 28	22 58			
Halifax	a	15 48	16 07	16 29	16 48	17 07	17 29	17 48		18 07	18 29	18 48	19 07	19 39	20 07	20 31	20 46	21 07	21 40	22 10	22 41	23 11			
	d		16 07	16 29	16 48	17 07	17 29			18 07	18 29	18 48	19 07	19 39	20 07	20 31	20 47	21 07	21 41	22 11	22 42	23 11			
Dewsbury	39 d																								
Mirfield	39 d																								
Brighouse	d				16 58							18 58					20 57				22 52	23a22			
Huddersfield	39 a				17 12							19 12					21 12				23 04				
Sowerby Bridge	d			16 36			17 36				18 36			19 46		20 38			21 47	22 17					
Mytholmroyd	d			16 42			17 42				18 42			19 52		20 44			21 53	22 23					
Hebden Bridge	a		16 19	16 45		17 19	17 45			18 19	18 45		19 19	19 55	20 19	20 47		21 19	21 57	22 27					
	d		16 20	16 45		17 20	17 45			18 20	18 45		19 19	19 55	20 20	20 47		21 19		22 27					
Burnley Manchester Road	97 a		16 38			17 38				18 38			19 38		20 38			21 38							
Accrington	97 a		16 47			17 47				18 47			19 47		20 47			21 47							
Blackburn	97 a		16 55			17 55				18 55			19 56		20 55			21 55							
Preston 8	97 a		17 13			18 13				19 13			20 14		21 13			22 13							
Poulton-le-Fylde	97 a		17 31			18 31				19 31			20 32		21 31			22 31							
Blackpool North	97 a		17 38			18 38				19 38			20 39		21 38			22 38							
Todmorden	d			16 52			17 52				18 52			20 02		20 54				22 34					
Walsden	d			16 55			17 55				18 55			20 05		20 57				22 37					
Littleborough	d			17 02			18 02				19 02			20 11		21 03				22 44					
Smithy Bridge	d			17 04			18 04				19 04			20 14		21 06				22 46					
Rochdale	a			17 08			18 08				19 08			20 18		21 10				22 50					
	95 d			17 09			18 09				19 09			20 19		21 11				22 51					
Castleton	95 a			17 12			18 12				19 12			20 22		21 14				22 54					
Mills Hill	95 a			17 16			18 16				19 16			20 26		21 18				22 58					
Moston	95 a			17 20			18 20				19 20			20 30		21 22				23 02					
Manchester Victoria	95 ⛴ a			17 30			18 30				19 30			20 41		21 33				23 12					
Liverpool Lime Street 10	90 a																								

Sundays

from 13 September

		NT	NT	NT	NT	NT	NT	NT	NT	NT		NT	NT	NT	NT	NT	NT	NT	NT	NT		NT	NT	NT	NT
York 8	40 d						08 50			09 52				10 57			11 52			12 52				13 52	
Selby	40 d																								
Leeds 10	37, 39 d	08 02	08 21	08 45	09 02	09 23	09 35	09 53	10 12	10 35		10 53	11 12	11 35	11 53	12 12	12 35	12 53	13 12	13 35		13 53	14 12	14 35	14 53
Bramley	37 d	08 10	08 28		09 09	09 30		10 01	10 19			11 01	11 19		12 01	12 19		13 01	13 19			14 01	14 19		15 01
New Pudsey	37 d	08 15	08 33	08 54	09 14	09 35	09 44	10 06	10 24	10 44		11 06	11 24	11 44	12 06	12 24	12 44	13 06	13 24	13 44		14 06	14 24	14 44	15 06
Bradford Interchange	37 a	08 23	08 41	09 03	09 22	09 43	09 53	10 14	10 32	10 53		11 14	11 32	11 53	12 14	12 32	12 53	13 14	13 32	13 53		14 14	14 32	14 53	15 14
	d		08 45	09 05	09 25	09 46	09 55	10 19	10 35	10 55		11 17	11 35	11 55	12 17	12 35	12 55	13 17	13 35	13 55		14 17	14 35	14 55	15 17
Halifax	a		08 57	09 17	09 37	09 59	10 07	10 31	10 48	11 07		11 29	11 48	12 07	12 29	12 48	13 07	13 29	13 48	14 07		14 29	14 48	15 07	15 29
	d		09 01	09 17	09 37	09 59	10 07	10 31	10 48	11 07		11 29		12 07	12 29	12 48	13 07	13 29		14 07		14 29	14 48	15 07	15 29
Dewsbury	39 d																								
Mirfield	39 d																								
Brighouse	d					10 09			10 58							12 58							14 58		
Huddersfield	39 a					10 22			11 12							13 12							15 12		
Sowerby Bridge	d		09 08		09 44			10 39				11 38			12 38			13 38				14 38			15 38
Mytholmroyd	d		09 14		09 50			10 45				11 44			12 44			13 44				14 44			15 44
Hebden Bridge	a		09 17	09 29	09 53		10 19	10 48		11 19		11 47		12 19	12 47		13 19	13 47		14 19		14 47		15 19	15 47
	d		09 17	09 30	09 53		10 20	10 48		11 20		11 47		12 20	12 47		13 19	13 47		14 20		14 47		15 19	15 47
Burnley Manchester Road	97 a			09 50			10 38			11 38				12 38			13 38			14 38				15 38	
Accrington	97 a			09 59			10 47			11 47				12 47			13 47			14 47				15 47	
Blackburn	97 a			10 07			10 56			11 55				12 55			13 55			14 55				15 55	
Preston 8	97 a			10 27			11 13			12 13				13 13			14 13			15 13				16 13	
Poulton-le-Fylde	97 a			10 45			11 31			12 31				13 31			14 30			15 32				16 31	
Blackpool North	97 a			10 53			11 39			12 38				13 38			14 38			15 39				16 38	
Todmorden	d		09 24		10 00			10 55				11 55			12 55			13 55				14 55			15 54
Walsden	d		09 27		10 03			10 58				11 58			12 58			13 58				14 58			15 57
Littleborough	d		09 34		10 10			11 05				12 04			13 04			14 04				15 04			16 04
Smithy Bridge	d		09 36		10 12			11 07				12 07			13 07			14 07				15 07			16 06
Rochdale	a		09 41		10 16			11 11				12 11			13 11			14 11				15 11			16 10
	95 d		09 41		10 17			11 12				12 11			13 11			14 11				15 11			16 11
Castleton	95 a		09 44		10 20			11 15				12 14			13 14			14 14				15 14			16 14
Mills Hill	95 a		09 48		10 24			11 19				12 19			13 19			14 19				15 19			16 18
Moston	95 a		09 52		10 28			11 23				12 22			13 22			14 22				15 22			16 22
Manchester Victoria	95 ⛴ a		10 02		10 38			11 32				12 32			13 32			14 33				15 33			16 33
Liverpool Lime Street 10	90 a		*10 57*		*11 57*			*12 57*				*13 57*			*14 57*			*15 57*				*16 57*			*17 57*

For general notes see front of timetable
For details of catering facilities see
Directory of Train Operators

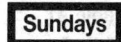

Table 41

Sundays

Leeds and Bradford → Huddersfield, Blackpool North, Rochdale and Manchester Victoria via Halifax and Brighouse

from 13 September

Network Diagram - see first page of Table 39

		NT	NT	NT	NT	NT	NT	NT		NT	NT	NT	NT	NT	NT	NT	NT	NT	NT	NT	NT	NT	NT		
York 8	40 d		14 52			15 52				16 52			17 52		18 52			19 52		20 57					
Selby	40 d																								
Leeds 10	37, 39 d	15 12	15 35	15 53	16 12	16 35	16 53	17 12		17 35	17 53	18 12	18 35	19 02	19 35	19 53	20 12	20 35	21 04	21 35	22 05	22 35	23 22		
Bramley	37 d	15 19		16 01	16 19		17 01	17 19			18 01	18 19		19 10		20 01	20 19		21 12	21 43	22 12	22 43	23 29		
New Pudsey	37 d	15 24	15 44	16 06	16 24	16 44	17 06	17 24		17 44	18 06	18 24	18 44	19 15	19 44	20 06	20 24	20 44	21 17	21 47	22 17	22 47	23 34		
Bradford Interchange	37 a	15 32	15 53	16 14	16 32	16 53	17 14	17 32		17 53	18 14	18 32	18 53	19 23	19 53	20 14	20 33	20 53	21 25	21 56	22 25	22 56	23 43		
	d	15 35	15 55	16 17	16 35	16 55	17 17	17 35		17 55	18 17	18 35	18 55	19 27	19 55	20 19	20 34	20 55	21 31	22 04	22 28	22 58			
Halifax	a	15 48	16 07	16 29	16 48	17 07	17 29	17 48		18 07	18 29	18 48	19 07	19 39	20 07	20 31	20 46	21 07	21 43	22 16	22 41	23 12			
	d		16 07	16 29	16 48	17 07	17 29			18 07	18 29	18 48	19 07	19 39	20 07	20 31	20 47	21 07	21 44	22 17	22 42	23 12			
Dewsbury	39 d																								
Mirfield	39 d																								
Brighouse	d				16 58							18 58					20 57				22 52	23a22			
Huddersfield	39 a				17 12							19 12					21 12				23 04				
Sowerby Bridge	d			16 38			17 38				18 38				19 46		20 38		21 50	22 25					
Mytholmroyd	d			16 44			17 44				18 44				19 52		20 44		21 56	22 31					
Hebden Bridge	a		16 19	16 47		17 19	17 47			18 19	18 47		19 19		19 55	20 19	20 47	21 19	21 59	22 34					
	d		16 20	16 47		17 20	17 47			18 20	18 47		19 19		19 55	20 20	20 47	21 19		22 34					
Burnley Manchester Road	97 a		16 38			17 38				18 38			19 38		20 38			21 38							
Accrington	97 a		16 47			17 47				18 47			19 47		20 47			21 47							
Blackburn	97 a		16 55			17 55				18 55			19 56		20 55			21 55							
Preston 8	97 a		17 13			18 13				19 13			20 14		21 13			22 13							
Poulton-le-Fylde	97 a		17 31			18 31				19 31			20 32		21 31			22 31							
Blackpool North	97 a		17 38			18 38				19 38			20 39		21 38			22 38							
Todmorden	d			16 55			17 55				18 55				20 02		20 54			22 42					
Walsden	d			16 58			17 58				18 58				20 05		20 57			22 45					
Littleborough	d			17 04			18 04				19 04				20 11		21 03			22 51					
Smithy Bridge	d			17 07			18 07				19 07				20 14		21 06			22 54					
Rochdale	a			17 11			18 11				19 11				20 18		21 10			22 58					
	95 d			17 11			18 11				19 11				20 19		21 11			22 58					
Castleton	95 a			17 14			18 14				19 14				20 22		21 14			23 01					
Mills Hill	95 a			17 19			18 19				19 19				20 26		21 18			23 06					
Moston	95 a			17 22			18 22				19 22				20 30		21 22			23 09					
Manchester Victoria	95 ⛴ a			17 33			18 33				19 33				20 41		21 33			23 18					
Liverpool Lime Street 10	90 a			*18 57*			*19 57*				*20 57*				*21 57*		*22 57*								

For general notes see front of timetable
For details of catering facilities see Directory of Train Operators

Manchester Victoria, Rochdale, Blackpool North and Huddersfield → Bradford and Leeds via Brighouse and Halifax

Network Diagram - see first page of Table 39

Miles	Miles	Miles	Miles			NT	NT	NT	NT	NT	NT		NT	NT	NT	NT	NT	NT		NT A	NT	NT	NT	NT	NT A
—	—	—	—	Liverpool Lime Street [10]	90 d										*05 46*						*06 46*			*07 16*	
0	—	—	—	**Manchester Victoria**	95 d			05 54			06 17		06 43		06 58		07 17	07 48			08 00		08 22	08 48	
4	—	—	—	Moston	95 d						06 23				07 04		07 23				08 06				
6	—	—	—	Mills Hill	95 d						06 28				07 09		07 28				08 11				
8¾	—	—	—	Castleton	95 d						06 33				07 14		07 33				08 16				
10½	—	—	—	**Rochdale**	95 a			06 08			06 36		06 56		07 17		07 36	08 01			08 19		08 34	09 02	
—	—	—	—		d			06 09			06 37		06 56		07 18		07 37	08 01			08 20		08 35	09 02	
12¾	—	—	—	Smithy Bridge	d			06 13			06 41				07 22		07 41				08 24		08 39		
13¾	—	—	—	Littleborough	d			06 16			06 44				07 25		07 44				08 27		08 42		
17¾	—	—	—	Walsden	d			06 22			06 50				07 31		07 50						08 48		
19¼	—	—	—	Todmorden	d			06 26			06 54		07 08		07 35		07 54	08 13			08 34		08 52	09 14	
—	0	—	—	**Blackpool North**	97 d				05 29							06 28						07 29			
—	3	—	—	Poulton-le-Fylde	97 d				05 35							06 34						07 35			
—	17½	—	—	**Preston** [8]	97 d				05 54							06 54						07 54			
—	29½	—	—	Blackburn	97 d				06 10							07 10						08 10			
—	35¾	—	—	Accrington	97 d				06 17							07 17						08 17			
—	42	—	—	Burnley Manchester Road	97 d				06 26							07 26						08 26			
23½	54¾	—	0	**Hebden Bridge**	a			06 32	06 49		07 00		07 14		07 41	07 49	08 00	08 19			08 41	08 49	08 58	09 20	
—	—	—	—		d	05 47	06 17	06 33	06 50		07 00		07 16		07 41	07 50	08 00	08 21			08 41	08 50	09 00	09 21	
24¾	56	—	1¼	Mytholmroyd	d	05 50	06 20	06 36			07 04		07 19		07 45		08 04				08 44		09 03		
28¾	60	—	5¼	Sowerby Bridge	d	05 56	06 26	06 42	06 57		07 09		07 25		07 50	07 57	08 09				08 50	08 57	09 09		
—	—	0	—	**Huddersfield**	39 d									07 29						08 21					09 23
—	—	5¼	11	Brighouse	d					07 10				07 39	07 59					08 33	08 58				09 33
—	—	—	15	Mirfield	39 a					07 24					08 06						09 06				
—	—	—	18	Dewsbury	39 a					07 31					08 11						09 12				
32¼	63½	10½	—	**Halifax**	a	06 02	06 32	06 48	07 03		07 16		07 32	07 50		08 03	08 16	08 33		08 43		09 03	09 15	09 33	09 43
—	—	—	—		d	06 03	06 33	06 49	07 03		07 16		07 33	07 50		08 03	08 16	08 33		08 48		09 03	09 16	09 33	09 48
40¼	71½	—	—	**Bradford Interchange**	a	06 16	06 46	07 03	07 17		07 31		07 47	08 03		08 17	08 31	08 47		09 01		09 17	09 31	09 47	10 01
—	—	—	—		37 d	06 18	06 48	07 05	07 20		07 34		07 50	08 06		08 20	08 34	08 50		09 03		09 20	09 34	09 50	10 04
43¾	75	—	—	New Pudsey	37 a	06 27	06 57	07 14	07 28		07 42		07 58	08 14		08 28	08 42	08 58		09 12		09 27	09 42	09 58	10 12
45¾	77	—	—	Bramley	37 a	06 30	07 00	07 17			07 46		08 02	08 18			08 46	09 02		09 16			09 46	10 02	10 16
49¾	81	—	27¼	**Leeds** [10]	37, 39 a	06 42	07 09	07 27	07 39	07 55	07 57		08 10	08 30	08 32	08 39	08 56	09 12		09 27	09 31	09 39	09 58	10 12	10 25
—	—	—	—	Selby	40 a			08 04			08 36		08 55					09 53						10 54	
—	—	—	—	York [8]	40 a				08 21							09 21						10 21			

		NT	NT		NT	NT	NT A	NT	NT	NT		NT	NT A	NT	NT	NT	NT		NT A	NT	NT	NT	NT	NT A	NT
Liverpool Lime Street [10]	90 d	*07 46*						*08 44*						*09 46*						*10 46*					*11 46*
Manchester Victoria	95 d	09 00			09 22	09 48		10 00		10 21		10 48		11 00		11 21	11 48			12 00		12 21	12 48		13 00
Moston	95 d	09 06						10 06						11 06						12 06					13 06
Mills Hill	95 d	09 11						10 11						11 11						12 11					13 11
Castleton	95 d	09 16						10 16						11 16						12 16					13 16
Rochdale	95 a	09 19			09 35	10 02		10 19		10 34		11 02		11 19		11 34	12 02			12 19		12 34	13 02		13 19
	d	09 20			09 36	10 02		10 20		10 35		11 02		11 20		11 35	12 02			12 20		12 35	13 02		13 20
Smithy Bridge	d	09 24			09 40			10 24		10 39				11 24		11 39				12 24		12 39			13 24
Littleborough	d	09 27			09 43			10 27		10 42				11 27		11 42				12 27		12 42			13 27
Walsden	d				09 49					10 48						11 48						12 48			
Todmorden	d	09 34			09 53	10 14		10 34		10 52		11 14		11 34		11 52	12 14			12 34		12 52	13 14		13 34
Blackpool North	97 d		08 29						09 29						10 29						11 29				
Poulton-le-Fylde	97 d		08 35						09 35						10 35						11 35				
Preston [8]	97 d		08 54						09 54						10 54						11 54				
Blackburn	97 d		09 10						10 10						11 10						12 10				
Accrington	97 d		09 17						10 17						11 17						12 17				
Burnley Manchester Road	97 d		09 26						10 26						11 28						12 26				
Hebden Bridge	a	09 41	09 49		09 59	10 20		10 41	10 49	10 58		11 20		11 41	11 49	11 58	12 20			12 41	12 49	12 58	13 20		13 41
	d	09 41	09 50		10 00	10 21		10 41	10 50	11 00		11 21		11 41	11 50	12 00	12 21			12 41	12 50	13 00	13 21		13 41
Mytholmroyd	d	09 44			10 03			10 44		11 03				11 44		12 03				12 44		13 03			13 44
Sowerby Bridge	d	09 50			10 09			10 50		11 09				11 50		12 09				12 50		13 09			13 50
Huddersfield	39 d						10 23						11 23						12 23					13 23	
Brighouse	d	09 58					10 33	10 58					11 33	11 58					12 33	12 58				13 34	13 58
Mirfield	39 a	10 06						11 06						12 06						13 06					14 06
Dewsbury	39 a	10 12						11 12						12 12						13 12					14 12
Halifax	a		10 02		10 15	10 33	10 43		11 02	11 15		11 33	11 43		12 02	12 15	12 33		12 43		13 02	13 15	13 33	13 44	
	d		10 03		10 16	10 33	10 49		11 03	11 16		11 33	11 49		12 03	12 16	12 33		12 49		13 03	13 16	13 33	13 49	
Bradford Interchange	a		10 17		10 31	10 47	11 02		11 17	11 31		11 47	12 02		12 17	12 31	12 47		13 02		13 17	13 31	13 47	14 02	
	37 d		10 20		10 34	10 50	11 05		11 20	11 34		11 50	12 05		12 19	12 34	12 50		13 05		13 19	13 34	13 50	14 05	
New Pudsey	37 a		10 28		10 42	10 58	11 13		11 28	11 42		11 58	12 13		12 27	12 42	12 58		13 13		13 27	13 42	13 58	14 13	
Bramley	37 a				10 46	11 02	11 17			11 46		12 02	12 17			12 46	13 02		13 17			13 46	14 02	14 17	
Leeds [10]	37, 39 a	10 31	10 40		10 58	11 13	11 27	11 33	11 39	11 58		12 12	12 27	12 31	12 39	12 58	13 12		13 27	13 31	13 38	13 58	14 12	14 27	14 31
Selby	40 a					11 55						12 50					13 51						14 50		
York [8]	40 a		11 19						12 21						13 19						14 21				

For general notes see front of timetable
For details of catering facilities see Directory of Train Operators

A From Wakefield Westgate (Table 39)

Manchester Victoria, Rochdale, Blackpool North and Huddersfield → Bradford and Leeds via Brighouse and Halifax

Network Diagram - see first page of Table 39

		NT		NT	NT	NT A	NT	NT	NT		NT	NT A	NT	NT	NT	NT		NT A	NT	NT	NT	NT	NT A		NT
Liverpool Lime Street 10	90 d						12 46						13 46						14 46						15 46
Manchester Victoria	95 ⛴ d			13 21	13 48		14 00		14 21		14 48		15 00		15 21	15 48			16 00		16 22	16 48			17 00
Moston	95 d						14 06						15 06						16 06						17 06
Mills Hill	95 d						14 11						15 11						16 11						17 11
Castleton	95 d						14 16						15 16						16 16						17 16
Rochdale	95 a			13 34	14 02		14 19		14 34		15 02		15 19		15 34	16 02			16 19		16 35	17 02			17 19
	d			13 35	14 02		14 20		14 35		15 02		15 20		15 35	16 02			16 20		16 36	17 02			17 20
Smithy Bridge	d			13 39			14 24		14 39				15 24		15 39				16 24		16 40				17 24
Littleborough	d			13 42			14 27		14 42				15 27		15 42				16 27		16 43				17 27
Walsden	d			13 48					14 48						15 48						16 49				
Todmorden	d			13 52	14 14		14 34		14 52		15 14		15 34		15 52	16 14			16 34		16 53	17 14			17 34
Blackpool North	97 d	12 29						13 29						14 29						15 29					
Poulton-le-Fylde	97 d	12 35						13 35						14 35						15 35					
Preston 8	97 d	12 54						13 54						14 54						15 54					
Blackburn	97 d	13 10						14 10						15 10						16 10					
Accrington	97 d	13 17						14 17						15 17						16 17					
Burnley Manchester Road	97 d	13 26						14 26						15 26						16 26					
Hebden Bridge	a	13 49		13 58	14 20		14 41	14 49	14 58		15 20		15 41	15 49	16 00	16 20			16 41	16 49	16 59	17 20			17 41
	d	13 50		14 00	14 21		14 41	14 50	15 00		15 21		15 41	15 50	16 01	16 21			16 41	16 50	17 00	17 21			17 41
Mytholmroyd	d			14 03			14 44		15 03				15 44		16 04				16 44		17 03				17 44
Sowerby Bridge	d			14 09			14 50		15 09				15 50		16 10				16 50		17 09				17 50
Huddersfield	39 d					14 23						15 23						16 23					17 23		
Brighouse	d					14 33	14 58					15 33	15 59					16 33	16 58				17 39		17 58
Mirfield	39 a						15 06						16 06						17 06						18 08
Dewsbury	39 a						15 12						16 12						17 12						18 13
Halifax	a	14 02		14 15	14 33	14 43		15 02	15 15		15 33	15 43		16 02	16 16	16 33		16 46		17 02	17 15	17 33	17 50		
	d	14 03		14 16	14 33	14 49		15 03	15 16		15 33	15 49		16 03	16 17	16 33		16 49		17 03	17 16	17 33	17 51		
Bradford Interchange	a	14 17		14 31	14 47	15 02		15 17	15 31		15 47	16 02		16 17	16 31	16 47		17 02		17 17	17 31	17 47	18 04		
	37 d	14 20		14 34	14 50	15 05		15 19	15 34		15 50	16 05		16 19	16 34	16 50		17 04		17 19	17 34	17 50	18 04		
New Pudsey	37 a	14 28		14 42	14 58	15 13		15 27	15 42		15 58	16 13		16 27	16 42	16 58		17 13		17 28	17 42	17 58	18 13		
Bramley	37 a			14 46	15 02	15 17			15 46		16 02	16 17			16 46	17 02		17 17			17 46	18 02	18 16		
Leeds 10	37, 39 a	14 39		14 58	15 12	15 26	15 31	15 39	15 58		16 12	16 27	16 31	16 39	16 58	17 12		17 27	17 31	17 39	17 58	18 12	18 27		18 32
Selby	40 a				15 52						16 54					17 53						18 50			
York 8	40 a	15 19						16 21						17 19						18 24					

		NT	NT	NT	NT A	NT	NT		NT	NT	NT	NT	NT	NT		NT	NT	NT	NT	NT	NT	NT	NT		
Liverpool Lime Street 10	90 d			16 16		16 46			17 10	17 35		17 48					19 12			20 12		21 12	22 12		
Manchester Victoria	95 ⛴ d		17 18	17 43		18 00			18 21	18 48		19 00		19 21			20 21			21 21		22 21	23 20		
Moston	95 d		17 24	17 49								19 06		19 27			20 27			21 27		22 27	23 27		
Mills Hill	95 d		17 29	17 54		18 09						19 11		19 32			20 32			21 32		22 32	23 32		
Castleton	95 d		17 34	17 59		18 14						19 16		19 37			20 37			21 37		22 37	23 37		
Rochdale	95 a		17 37	18 02		18 18			18 35	19 01		19 19		19 40			20 40			21 40		22 40	23 40		
	d		17 38	18 03		18 18			18 36	19 01		19 20		19 41			20 41			21 41		22 41	23 41		
Smithy Bridge	d		17 42			18 22			18 40			19 24		19 45			20 45			21 45		22 45	23 45		
Littleborough	d		17 45	18 08		18 26			18 43			19 27		19 48			20 48			21 48		22 48	23 48		
Walsden	d		17 51			18 32			18 49					19 54			20 54			21 54		22 54	23 54		
Todmorden	d		17 55	18 16		18 35			18 53	19 13		19 34		19 58			20 58			21 58		22 58	23 58		
Blackpool North	97 d	16 29					17 14						18 29						20 29						
Poulton-le-Fylde	97 d	16 35					17 20						18 35						20 35						
Preston 8	97 d	16 54					17 44						18 54						20 54						
Blackburn	97 d	17 10					18 11						19 10						21 10						
Accrington	97 d	17 17					18 19						19 17						21 17						
Burnley Manchester Road	97 d	17 26					18 28						19 26						21 28						
Hebden Bridge	a	17 49	18 01	18 22		18 42	18 49		18 59	19 19		19 41	19 49	20 04			21 04		21 50	22 04		23 04	00 04		
	d	17 50	18 01	18 23		18 42	18 50		19 00	19 20		19 41	19 50	20 05			21 05		21 51	22 05		23 04	00 04		
Mytholmroyd	d		18 05			18 45			19 03			19 44		20 08			21 08			22 08		23 08	00 08		
Sowerby Bridge	d		18 10			18 51			19 09			19 50		20 14			21 14			22 14		23 13	00 13		
Huddersfield	39 d				18 23						19 23					20 25		21 27			22 25				
Brighouse	d				18 33	18 59					19 33	19 58				20 35		21 37			22 35				
Mirfield	39 a					19 07						20 06													
Dewsbury	39 a					19 13						20 12													
Halifax	a	18 02	18 17	18 35	18 45		19 03		19 15	19 32	19 43		20 02	20 20		20 45	21 20	21 47	22 03	22 20	22 45	23 20	00 20		
	d	18 03	18 17	18 35	18 49		19 03		19 16	19 32	19 49		20 03	20 21		20 49	21 21	21 49	22 03	22 21	22 49	23 20	00 20		
Bradford Interchange	a	18 17	18 31	18 49	19 02		19 17		19 31	19 48	20 02		20 17	20 35		21 02	21 35	22 02	22 17	22 35	23 02	23 34	00 34		
	37 d	18 19	18 34	18 52	19 05		19 19		19 34	19 50	20 04		20 19	20 37		21 04	21 37	22 04	22 19	22 37	23 04	23 37	00 37		
New Pudsey	37 a	18 28	18 42	19 00	19 13		19 28		19 42	19 58	20 13		20 27	20 46		21 13	21 46	22 13	22 28	22 46	23 13	23 45			
Bramley	37 a		18 46	19 04	19 17				19 46	20 02	20 16			20 49		21 16	21 49	22 16		22 49	23 16	23 49			
Leeds 10	37, 39 a	18 39	18 56	19 13	19 28	19 33	19 40		19 58	20 12	20 30	20 32	20 38	21 01		21 25	22 01	22 25	22 41	23 01	23 27	00 01	00 55		
Selby	40 a																								
York 8	40 a	19 21		19 55			20 21						21 31						23 33						

For general notes see front of timetable
For details of catering facilities see
Directory of Train Operators

A From Wakefield Westgate (Table 39)

Table 41

Saturdays

until 11 July

Manchester Victoria, Rochdale, Blackpool North and Huddersfield → Bradford and Leeds via Brighouse and Halifax

Network Diagram - see first page of Table 39

		NT 🚌	NT	NT 🚌	NT	NT 🚌	NT 🚌	NT	NT 🚌	NT	NT	NT		NT	NT 🚌	NT	NT 🚌	NT	NT 🚌	NT 🚌	NT	NT	NT	NT	NT
Liverpool Lime Street 10	90 d																				*05 46*				
Manchester Victoria	95 d				05 40							06 21						06 43			06 58			07 17	
Moston	95 d																				07 04			07 23	
Mills Hill	95 d																				07 09			07 28	
Castleton	95 d																				07 14			07 33	
Rochdale	95 a				05 54							06 34						06 56			07 17			07 36	
	d				05 54							06 35						06 56			07 18			07 37	
Smithy Bridge	d				05 58							06 39									07 22			07 41	
Littleborough	d				06 02							06 42									07 25			07 44	
Walsden	d				06 08							06 48									07 31			07 50	
Todmorden	d				06 11							06 52						07 08			07 35			07a53	
Blackpool North	97 d									05 29												06 28			
Poulton-le-Fylde	97 d									05 35												06 34			
Preston 8	97 d									05 54												06 54			
Blackburn	97 d									06 10												07 10			
Accrington	97 d									06 17												07 17			
Burnley Manchester Road	97 d									06 26												07 26			
Hebden Bridge	a				06 18					06 49		06 58						07 14			07 41	07 49			
	d			05 45					06 30	06 50					07 05					07 30	07 41	07 50			
Mytholmroyd	d			05 55					06 40											07 40	07 45				
Sowerby Bridge	d			06 10					06 55	06 57										07 55	07 50	07 57			
Huddersfield	39 d						06 25												07 25						
Brighouse	d					06 25	06 40										07 25		07 40		07 59				
Mirfield	39 a																				08 06				
Dewsbury	39 a																				08 11				
Halifax	a			06 25		06 40	06 55		07 10						07 25		07 40		07 55	08 10					
	d	05 45		06 25		06 40	06 55		07 10						07 25		07 40		07 55	08 10					
Bradford Interchange	a	06 15		06 55		07 10	07 25		07 40						07 55		08 10		08 25	08 40					
	37 d		06 26					07 05			07 34			07 50		08 05							08 34		08 50
New Pudsey	37 a		06 35					07 14			07 42			07 58		08 14							08 42		08 58
Bramley	37 a		06 38					07 17			07 46			08 02		08 17							08 46		09 02
Leeds 10	37, 39 a		06 48					07 26		07 32	07 57			08 11		08 27					08 33	08 41	08 56		09 12
Selby	40 a										08 35														09 53
York 8	40 a									08 21												09 21			

		NT 🚌		NT	NT	NT 🚌	NT 🚌	NT 🚌	NT		NT	NT	NT	NT	NT 🚌	NT	NT	NT 🚌	NT 🚌	NT 🚌	NT	NT	NT	NT	NT
Liverpool Lime Street 10	90 d								*06 46*								*07 16*				*07 46*				
Manchester Victoria	95 d				07 47				08 00				08 22				08 48				09 00				09 22
Moston	95 d								08 06												09 06				
Mills Hill	95 d								08 11												09 11				
Castleton	95 d								08 16												09 16				
Rochdale	95 a				08 00				08 19				08 34				09 02				09 19				09 35
	d				08 00				08 20				08 35				09 02				09 20				09 36
Smithy Bridge	d								08 24				08 39								09 24				09 40
Littleborough	d								08 27				08 42								09 27				09 43
Walsden	d												08 48												09 49
Todmorden	d	07 58			08 12				08 34				08a51		08 58		09 14				09 34				09a52
Blackpool North	97 d										07 29											08 29			
Poulton-le-Fylde	97 d										07 35											08 35			
Preston 8	97 d										07 54											08 54			
Blackburn	97 d										08 10											09 10			
Accrington	97 d										08 17											09 17			
Burnley Manchester Road	97 d										08 26											09 26			
Hebden Bridge	a	08 05			08 18				08 41		08 49				09 05		09 20				09 41	09 49			
	d	08 05						08 30	08 41		08 50				09 05					09 30	09 41	09 50			
Mytholmroyd	d							08 40	08 44											09 40	09 44				
Sowerby Bridge	d							08 55	08 50		08 57									09 55	09 50				
Huddersfield	39 d						08 25												09 25						
Brighouse	d					08 25	08 40		08 58									09 25	09 40		09 58				
Mirfield	39 a								09 06												10 06				
Dewsbury	39 a								09 12		09 16										10 12	10 16			
Halifax	a	08 25				08 40	08 55	09 10							09 25			09 40	09 55	10 10					
	d	08 25				08 40	08 55	09 10							09 25			09 40	09 55	10 10					
Bradford Interchange	a	08 55				09 10	09 25	09 40							09 55			10 10	10 25	10 40					
	37 d			09 05								09 34		09 50		10 05							10 34	10 50	
New Pudsey	37 a			09 13								09 42		09 58		10 13							10 42	10 58	
Bramley	37 a			09 17								09 46		10 02		10 17							10 46	11 02	
Leeds 10	37, 39 a			09 27					09 31		09 41	09 58		10 12		10 27					10 31	10 41	10 58	11 12	
Selby	40 a													10 53										11 54	
York 8	40 a										10 23											11 19			

For general notes see front of timetable
For details of catering facilities see
Directory of Train Operators

Saturdays

until 11 July

Manchester Victoria, Rochdale, Blackpool North and Huddersfield → Bradford and Leeds via Brighouse and Halifax

Network Diagram - see first page of Table 39

		NT 🚌	NT	NT		NT 🚌	NT 🚌	NT 🚌	NT	NT	NT	NT	NT	NT 🚌	NT	NT	NT 🚌	NT 🚌		NT 🚌	NT	NT	NT	NT	NT
Liverpool Lime Street 10	90 d								*08 44*												*09 46*				
Manchester Victoria	95 ⇌ d			09 48					10 00			10 21				10 48					11 00			11 21	
Moston	95 d								10 06												11 06				
Mills Hill	95 d								10 11												11 11				
Castleton	95 d								10 16												11 16				
Rochdale	95 a			10 02					10 19			10 34				11 02					11 19			11 34	
	d			10 02					10 20			10 35				11 02					11 20			11 35	
Smithy Bridge	d								10 24			10 39									11 24			11 39	
Littleborough	d								10 27			10 42									11 27			11 42	
Walsden	d											10 48												11 48	
Todmorden	d	09 58		10 14					10 34			10a51		10 58		11 14					11 34			11a51	
Blackpool North	97 d									09 29												10 29			
Poulton-le-Fylde	97 d									09 35												10 35			
Preston 8	97 d									09 54												10 54			
Blackburn	97 d									10 10												11 10			
Accrington	97 d									10 17												11 17			
Burnley Manchester Road	97 d									10 26												11 28			
Hebden Bridge	a	10 05		10 20					10 41	10 49				11 05		11 20					11 41	11 49			
	d	10 05						10 30	10 41	10 50				11 05						11 30	11 41	11 50			
Mytholmroyd	d							10 40	10 44											11 40	11 44				
Sowerby Bridge	d							10 55	10 50											11 55	11 50				
Huddersfield	39 d						10 25											11 25							
Brighouse	d					10 25	10 40		10 58								11 25	11 40			11 58				
Mirfield	39 a								11 06												12 06				
Dewsbury	39 a								11 12	11 16											12 12	12 16			
Halifax	a	10 25				10 40	10 55	11 10						11 25			11 40	11 55		12 10					
	d	10 25				10 40	10 55	11 10						11 25			11 40	11 55		12 10					
Bradford Interchange	a	10 55				11 10	11 25	11 40						11 55			12 10	12 25		12 40					
	37 d		11 05								11 34		11 50		12 05								12 34		12 50
New Pudsey	37 a		11 13								11 42		11 58		12 13								12 42		12 58
Bramley	37 a		11 17								11 46		12 02		12 17								12 46		13 02
Leeds 10	37, 39 a		11 27						11 31	11 41	11 58		12 12		12 27						12 31	12 43	12 58		13 12
Selby	40 a												12 50												13 50
York 8	40 a									12 21												13 19			

		NT 🚌	NT	NT	NT 🚌	NT 🚌		NT 🚌	NT	NT	NT	NT	NT	NT 🚌	NT	NT		NT 🚌	NT 🚌	NT 🚌	NT	NT	NT	NT	NT
Liverpool Lime Street 10	90 d								*10 46*												*11 46*				
Manchester Victoria	95 ⇌ d			11 48					12 00			12 21				12 48					13 00			13 21	
Moston	95 d								12 06												13 06				
Mills Hill	95 d								12 11												13 11				
Castleton	95 d								12 16												13 16				
Rochdale	95 a			12 02					12 19			12 34				13 02					13 19			13 34	
	d			12 02					12 20			12 35				13 02					13 20			13 35	
Smithy Bridge	d								12 24			12 39									13 24			13 39	
Littleborough	d								12 27			12 42									13 27			13 42	
Walsden	d											12 48												13 48	
Todmorden	d	11 58		12 14					12 34			12a51		12 58		13 14					13 34			13a51	
Blackpool North	97 d									11 24												12 29			
Poulton-le-Fylde	97 d									11 31												12 35			
Preston 8	97 d									11 54												12 54			
Blackburn	97 d									12 10												13 10			
Accrington	97 d									12 17												13 17			
Burnley Manchester Road	97 d									12 26												13 26			
Hebden Bridge	a	12 05		12 20					12 41	12 49				13 05		13 20					13 41	13 49			
	d	12 05						12 30	12 41	12 50				13 05						13 30	13 41	13 50			
Mytholmroyd	d							12 40	12 44											13 40	13 44				
Sowerby Bridge	d							12 55	12 50											13 55	13 50				
Huddersfield	39 d					12 25													13 25						
Brighouse	d				12 25	12 40			12 58									13 25	13 40		13 58				
Mirfield	39 a								13 06												14 06				
Dewsbury	39 a								13 12	13 16											14 12	14 16			
Halifax	a	12 25			12 40	12 55		13 10						13 25				13 40	13 55	14 10					
	d	12 25			12 40	12 55		13 10						13 25				13 40	13 55	14 10					
Bradford Interchange	a	12 55			13 10	13 25		13 40						13 55				14 10	14 25	14 40					
	37 d		13 05								13 34		13 50		14 05								14 34		14 50
New Pudsey	37 a		13 13								13 42		13 58		14 13								14 42		14 58
Bramley	37 a		13 17								13 46		14 02		14 17								14 46		15 02
Leeds 10	37, 39 a		13 27						13 31	13 43	13 58		14 12		14 27						14 31	14 41	14 56		15 12
Selby	40 a												14 50												15 52
York 8	40 a									14 21												15 19			

For general notes see front of timetable
For details of catering facilities see Directory of Train Operators

Table 41

Saturdays

until 11 July

Manchester Victoria, Rochdale, Blackpool North and Huddersfield → Bradford and Leeds via Brighouse and Halifax

Network Diagram - see first page of Table 39

		NT 🚌	NT	NT	NT 🚌	NT 🚌	NT 🚌	NT		NT	NT	NT	NT	NT 🚌	NT	NT	NT 🚌	NT 🚌	NT 🚌	NT		NT	NT	NT	NT
Liverpool Lime Street 10	90 d							12 46												13 46					
Manchester Victoria	95 ⛴ d			13 48				14 00					14 21			14 48				15 00				15 21	
Moston	95 d							14 06												15 06					
Mills Hill	95 d							14 11												15 11					
Castleton	95 d							14 16												15 16					
Rochdale	95 a			14 02				14 19					14 34			15 02				15 19				15 34	
	d			14 02				14 20					14 35			15 02				15 20				15 35	
Smithy Bridge	d							14 24					14 39							15 24				15 39	
Littleborough	d							14 27					14 42							15 27				15 42	
Walsden	d												14 48											15 48	
Todmorden	d	13 58		14 14				14 34					14a51	14 58		15 14				15 34				15a51	
Blackpool North	97 d									13 29												14 29			
Poulton-le-Fylde	97 d									13 35												14 35			
Preston 8	97 d									13 54												14 54			
Blackburn	97 d									14 10												15 10			
Accrington	97 d									14 17												15 17			
Burnley Manchester Road	97 d									14 26												15 26			
Hebden Bridge	a	14 05		14 20				14 41		14 49				15 05		15 20				15 41		15 49			
	d	14 05					14 30	14 41		14 50				15 05					15 30	15 41		15 50			
Mytholmroyd	d						14 40	14 44											15 40	15 44					
Sowerby Bridge	d						14 55	14 50											15 55	15 50					
Huddersfield	39 d				14 25													15 25							
Brighouse	d				14 40	14 25		14 58									15 25	15 40		15 58					
Mirfield	39 a							15 06												16 06					
Dewsbury	39 a							15 12		15 16										16 12		16 16			
Halifax	a	14 25			14 55	14 40	15 10							15 25			15 40	15 55	16 10						
	d	14 25			14 55	14 40	15 10							15 25			15 40	15 55	16 10						
Bradford Interchange	a	14 55			15 25	15 10	15 40							15 55			16 10	16 25	16 40						
	37 d		15 05								15 34	15 50			16 05								16 34		16 50
New Pudsey	37 a		15 13								15 42	15 58			16 13								16 42		16 58
Bramley	37 a		15 17								15 46	16 02			16 17								16 46		17 02
Leeds 10	37, 39 a		15 27					15 31		15 41	15 58	16 12			16 27					16 31		16 41	16 56		17 12
Selby	40 a											16 54													17 52
York 8	40 a									16 22												17 19			

		NT 🚌	NT	NT	NT 🚌	NT 🚌	NT 🚌	NT	NT	NT		NT	NT	NT 🚌	NT	NT	NT 🚌	NT 🚌	NT 🚌	NT	NT	NT		NT	NT
Liverpool Lime Street 10	90 d							14 46												15 46					
Manchester Victoria	95 ⛴ d			15 48				16 00					16 21			16 48				17 00				17 18	
Moston	95 d							16 06												17 06				17 24	
Mills Hill	95 d							16 11												17 11				17 29	
Castleton	95 d							16 16												17 16				17 34	
Rochdale	95 a			16 02				16 19					16 34			17 02				17 19				17 37	
	d			16 02				16 20					16 35			17 02				17 20				17 38	
Smithy Bridge	d							16 24					16 39							17 24				17 42	
Littleborough	d							16 27					16 42							17 27				17 45	
Walsden	d												16 48											17 51	
Todmorden	d	15 58		16 14				16 34					16a51	16 58		17 14				17 34				17a54	
Blackpool North	97 d									15 29											16 29				
Poulton-le-Fylde	97 d									15 35											16 35				
Preston 8	97 d									15 54											16 54				
Blackburn	97 d									16 10											17 10				
Accrington	97 d									16 17											17 17				
Burnley Manchester Road	97 d									16 26											17 26				
Hebden Bridge	a	16 05		16 20				16 41		16 49				17 05		17 20				17 41	17 49				
	d	16 05					16 30	16 41		16 50				17 05					17 30	17 41	17 50				
Mytholmroyd	d						16 40	16 44											17 40	17 44					
Sowerby Bridge	d						16 55	16 50											17 55	17 50					
Huddersfield	39 d				16 25													17 25							
Brighouse	d				16 40	16 25		16 58									17 25	17 40		17 58					
Mirfield	39 a							17 06												18 07					
Dewsbury	39 a							17 12		17 16										18 12	18 16				
Halifax	a	16 25			16 55	16 40	17 10							17 25			17 40	17 55	18 10						
	d	16 25			16 55	16 40	17 10							17 25			17 40	17 55	18 10						
Bradford Interchange	a	16 55			17 25	17 10	17 40							17 55			18 10	18 25	18 40						
	37 d		17 05						17 34			17 50			18 05							18 34			18 50
New Pudsey	37 a		17 13						17 42			17 58			18 13							18 42			18 58
Bramley	37 a		17 17						17 46			18 02			18 17							18 46			19 02
Leeds 10	37, 39 a		17 27					17 31	17 58	17 42		18 12			18 27					18 33	18 41	18 56			19 13
Selby	40 a											18 49													
York 8	40 a									18 24											19 21				19 54

For general notes see front of timetable
For details of catering facilities see Directory of Train Operators

Saturdays

until 11 July

Manchester Victoria, Rochdale, Blackpool North and Huddersfield → Bradford and Leeds via Brighouse and Halifax

Network Diagram - see first page of Table 39

		NT 🚌	NT	NT	NT 🚌	NT 🚌	NT 🚌	NT	NT	NT	NT	NT		NT 🚌	NT	NT	NT 🚌	NT 🚌	NT 🚌	NT	NT	NT	NT	NT 🚌	NT
Liverpool Lime Street [10]	90 d			16 16				16 46			17 10					17 35				17 48					
Manchester Victoria	95 d			17 41				18 00			18 21					18 48				19 00			19 20		
Moston	95 d			17 47																19 06			19 27		
Mills Hill	95 d			17 52				18 09												19 10			19 32		
Castleton	95 d			17 57				18 14												19 15			19 37		
Rochdale	95 a			18 00				18 18			18 35					19 01				19 19			19 40		
	d			18 01				18 18			18 36					19 01				19 19			19 41		
Smithy Bridge	d							18 22			18 40									19 23			19 45		
Littleborough	d			18 06				18 26			18 43									19 27			19 48		
Walsden	d							18 32			18 49												19 54		
Todmorden	d			18 14				18 35			18a54					19 13				19 34			19a59		
Blackpool North	97 d								17 18												18 29				
Poulton-le-Fylde	97 d								17 24												18 35				
Preston [8]	97 d								17 44												18 54				
Blackburn	97 d								18 11												19 10				
Accrington	97 d								18 19												19 17				
Burnley Manchester Road	97 d								18 28												19 26				
Hebden Bridge	a			18 20				18 42	18 49							19 21				19 40	19 49				
	d	18 05					18 30	18 42	18 50					19 05					19 30	19 42	19 50			20 00	
Mytholmroyd	d						18 40	18 45											19 40	19 45					
Sowerby Bridge	d						18 55	18 51											19 55	19 51					
Huddersfield	39 d					18 25												19 25							
Brighouse	d				18 25	18 40		18 59									19 25	19 40		19 59					
Mirfield	39 a							19 07												20 07					
Dewsbury	39 a							19 13	19 17											20 12	20 17				
Halifax	a	18 25			18 40	18 55	19 10							19 25			19 40	19 55	20 10					20 20	
	d	18 25			18 40	18 55	19 10							19 25			19 40	19 55	20 10					20 25	
Bradford Interchange	a	18 55			19 10	19 25	19 40							19 55			20 10	20 25	20 40					20 55	
	37 d		19 05							19 34		19 50			20 05							20 37			21 04
New Pudsey	37 a		19 13							19 42		19 59			20 13							20 46			21 12
Bramley	37 a		19 17							19 46		20 02			20 17							20 49			21 16
Leeds [10]	37, 39 a		19 28					19 32	19 43	19 58		20 12			20 28					20 31	20 36	21 01			21 26
Selby	40 a																								
York [8]	40 a								20 21												21 31				

		NT 🚌		NT 🚌	NT 🚌	NT	NT	NT 🚌	NT 🚌	NT 🚌	NT	NT	NT 🚌	NT 🚌		NT	NT	NT	NT 🚌	NT	NT		NT 🚌	NT 🚌	
Liverpool Lime Street [10]	90 d					19 12										20 12					21 12				
Manchester Victoria	95 d					20 21										21 21					22 54				
Moston	95 d					20 27										21 27									
Mills Hill	95 d					20 32										21 32									
Castleton	95 d					20 37										21 37									
Rochdale	95 a					20 40										21 40					23 07				
	d					20 41										21 41					23 07				
Smithy Bridge	d					20 45										21 45					23 11				
Littleborough	d					20 48										21 48					23 15				
Walsden	d					20 54										21 54					23 21				
Todmorden	d	20 10				20 58										21 58					23 24				
Blackpool North	97 d											20 29													
Poulton-le-Fylde	97 d											20 35													
Preston [8]	97 d											20 54													
Blackburn	97 d											21 10													
Accrington	97 d											21 17													
Burnley Manchester Road	97 d											21 28													
Hebden Bridge	a	20 20				21 04						21 50				22 04					23 31				
	d	20 20				21 05			21 15			21 51	22 00			22 05			22 15		23 31			23 40	
Mytholmroyd	d	20 30				21 08			21 25							22 08			22 25		23 34			23 50	
Sowerby Bridge	d	20 45				21 14			21 40							22 14			22 40		23 40			00 05	
Huddersfield	39 d			20 25						21 15				22 15											
Brighouse	d			20 40		21 22				21 30				22 30		22 22					23 48				
Mirfield	39 a																								
Dewsbury	39 a																								
Halifax	a	21 00		20 55					21 55	21 45			22 20	22 45					22 55					00 20	
	d	21 00		20 55	20 40			21 25	21 55	21 45			22 25	22 45					22 55				23 50	00 20	
Bradford Interchange	a	21 30		21 25	21 10			21 55	22 25	22 15			22 55	23 15					23 25				00 20	00 50	
	37 d						21 37				22 04						22 37	23 05		23 37					
New Pudsey	37 a						21 45				22 12						22 45	23 13		23 45					
Bramley	37 a						21 49				22 16						22 49	23 17		23 49					
Leeds [10]	37, 39 a					21 46	21 59				22 26	22 27				22 47	22 59	23 27		23 59	00 12				
Selby	40 a																								
York [8]	40 a											23 36													

For general notes see front of timetable
For details of catering facilities see
Directory of Train Operators

Saturdays

from 18 July

Manchester Victoria, Rochdale, Blackpool North and Huddersfield → Bradford and Leeds via Brighouse and Halifax

Network Diagram - see first page of Table 39

	NT	NT	NT	NT		NT	NT	NT	NT		NT	NT	NT	NT		NT	NT	NT	NT		NT	NT	NT	NT
													A						A					
Liverpool Lime Street 10 90 d								*05 46*						*06 46*				*07 16*			*07 46*			
Manchester Victoria 95 d		05 54		06 21		06 43		06 58			07 17	07 48		08 00			08 22	08 48			09 00		09 22	09 48
Moston 95 d								07 04			07 23			08 06							09 06			
Mills Hill 95 d								07 09			07 28			08 11							09 11			
Castleton 95 d								07 14			07 33			08 16							09 16			
Rochdale 95 a		06 08		06 34		06 56		07 17			07 36	08 01		08 19			08 34	09 02			09 19		09 35	10 02
d		06 09		06 35		06 56		07 18			07 37	08 01		08 20			08 35	09 02			09 20		09 36	10 02
Smithy Bridge d		06 13		06 39				07 22			07 41			08 24			08 39				09 24		09 40	
Littleborough d		06 16		06 42				07 25			07 44			08 27			08 42				09 27		09 43	
Walsden d		06 22		06 48				07 31			07 50						08 48						09 49	
Todmorden d		06 26		06 52		07 08		07 35			07 54	08 13		08 34			08 52	09 14			09 34		09 53	10 14
Blackpool North 97 d			05 29						06 28							07 29						08 29		
Poulton-le-Fylde 97 d			05 35						06 34							07 35						08 35		
Preston 8 97 d			05 54						06 54							07 54						08 54		
Blackburn 97 d			06 10						07 10							08 10						09 10		
Accrington 97 d			06 17						07 17							08 17						09 17		
Burnley Manchester Road 97 d			06 26						07 26							08 26						09 26		
Hebden Bridge a		06 32	06 49	06 58		07 14		07 41	07 49		08 00	08 19		08 41		08 49	08 58	09 20			09 41	09 49	09 59	10 20
d	05 55	06 33	06 50	07 00		07 16		07 41	07 50		08 00	08 21		08 41		08 50	09 00	09 21			09 41	09 50	10 00	10 21
Mytholmroyd d	05 58	06 36		07 03		07 19		07 45			08 04			08 44			09 03				09 44		10 03	
Sowerby Bridge d	06 04	06 42	06 57	07 09		07 25		07 50	07 57		08 09			08 50		08 57	09 09				09 50		10 09	
Huddersfield 39 d							07 29						08 21						09 23					
Brighouse d							07 39	07 59					08 33	08 58					09 33		09 58			
Mirfield 39 a								08 06						09 06							10 06			
Dewsbury 39 a								08 11						09 12							10 12			
Halifax a	06 10	06 48	07 03	07 15		07 32	07 50		08 03		08 16	08 33	08 43			09 03	09 15	09 33	09 43			10 02	10 15	10 33
d	06 11	06 49	07 03	07 16		07 33	07 50		08 03		08 16	08 33	08 49			09 03	09 16	09 33	09 49			10 03	10 16	10 33
Bradford Interchange a	06 24	07 03	07 17	07 31		07 47	08 03		08 17		08 31	08 47	09 02			09 17	09 31	09 47	10 02			10 17	10 31	10 47
37 d	06 26	07 05	07 20	07 34		07 50	08 06		08 20		08 34	08 50	09 04			09 20	09 34	09 50	10 05			10 19	10 34	10 50
New Pudsey 37 a	06 35	07 14	07 28	07 42		07 58	08 14		08 28		08 42	08 58	09 13			09 27	09 42	09 58	10 13			10 27	10 42	10 58
Bramley 37 a	06 38	07 17		07 46		08 02	08 18				08 46	09 02	09 17				09 46	10 02	10 17				10 46	11 02
Leeds 10 37, 39 a	06 48	07 27	07 39	07 57		08 11	08 30	08 33	08 39		08 56	09 12	09 27	09 31		09 39	09 58	10 12	10 27		10 31	10 39	10 58	11 12
Selby 40 a				08 35								09 53						10 53						11 54
York 8 40 a			08 21						09 21							10 21						11 19		

	NT	NT		NT	NT	NT	NT		NT	NT	NT	NT		NT	NT	NT	NT		NT	NT	NT	NT		NT
	A						A							A						A				
Liverpool Lime Street 10 90 d		*08 44*							*09 46*						*10 46*						*11 46*			
Manchester Victoria 95 d		10 00			10 21	10 48			11 00		11 21	11 48			12 00		12 21		12 48		13 00			13 21
Moston 95 d		10 06							11 06						12 06						13 06			
Mills Hill 95 d		10 11							11 11						12 11						13 11			
Castleton 95 d		10 16							11 16						12 16						13 16			
Rochdale 95 a		10 19			10 34	11 02			11 19		11 34	12 02			12 19		12 34		13 02		13 19			13 34
d		10 20			10 35	11 02			11 20		11 35	12 02			12 20		12 35		13 02		13 20			13 35
Smithy Bridge d		10 24			10 39				11 24		11 39				12 24		12 39				13 24			13 39
Littleborough d		10 27			10 42				11 27		11 42				12 27		12 42				13 27			13 42
Walsden d					10 48						11 48						12 48							13 48
Todmorden d		10 34			10 52	11 14			11 34		11 52	12 14			12 34		12 52		13 14		13 34			13 52
Blackpool North 97 d				09 29						10 29						11 24						12 29		
Poulton-le-Fylde 97 d				09 35						10 35						11 31						12 35		
Preston 8 97 d				09 54						10 54						11 54						12 54		
Blackburn 97 d				10 10						11 10						12 10						13 10		
Accrington 97 d				10 17						11 17						12 17						13 17		
Burnley Manchester Road 97 d				10 26						11 28						12 26						13 26		
Hebden Bridge a		10 41		10 49	10 58	11 20			11 41	11 49	11 58	12 20			12 41	12 49	12 58		13 20		13 41	13 49		13 58
d		10 41		10 50	11 00	11 21			11 41	11 50	12 00	12 21			12 41	12 50	13 00		13 21		13 41	13 50		14 00
Mytholmroyd d		10 44			11 03				11 44		12 03				12 44		13 03				13 44			14 03
Sowerby Bridge d		10 50			11 09				11 50		12 09				12 50		13 09				13 50			14 09
Huddersfield 39 d	10 23						11 23							12 23						13 23				
Brighouse d	10 33	10 58					11 33		11 58					12 33	12 58					13 34	13 58			
Mirfield 39 a		11 06							12 06						13 06						14 06			
Dewsbury 39 a		11 12							12 12						13 12						14 12			
Halifax a	10 43			11 02	11 15	11 33	11 43			12 02	12 15	12 33		12 43		13 02	13 15		13 33	13 45		14 02		14 15
d	10 49			11 03	11 16	11 33	11 49			12 03	12 16	12 33		12 49		13 03	13 16		13 33	13 49		14 03		14 16
Bradford Interchange a	11 02			11 17	11 31	11 47	12 02			12 17	12 31	12 47		13 02		13 17	13 31		13 47	14 02		14 17		14 31
37 d	11 05			11 20	11 34	11 50	12 05			12 19	12 34	12 50		13 05		13 19	13 34		13 50	14 05		14 19		14 34
New Pudsey 37 a	11 13			11 28	11 42	11 58	12 13			12 27	12 42	12 58		13 13		13 27	13 42		13 58	14 13		14 27		14 42
Bramley 37 a	11 17				11 46	12 02	12 17				12 46	13 02		13 17			13 46		14 02	14 17				14 46
Leeds 10 37, 39 a	11 27	11 31		11 39	11 58	12 12	12 27		12 31	12 39	12 58	13 12		13 27	13 31	13 39	13 58		14 12	14 27	14 31	14 39		14 58
Selby 40 a						12 50						13 50							14 50					
York 8 40 a				12 21						13 19						14 21						15 19		

For general notes see front of timetable
For details of catering facilities see Directory of Train Operators

A From Wakefield Westgate (Table 39)

Table 41

Saturdays

from 18 July

Manchester Victoria, Rochdale, Blackpool North and Huddersfield → Bradford and Leeds via Brighouse and Halifax

Network Diagram - see first page of Table 39

		NT	NT A	NT	NT	NT	NT	NT A	NT	NT	NT	NT	NT A	NT	NT	NT	NT	NT A	NT	NT	NT
Liverpool Lime Street 10	90 d			12 46					13 46					14 46					15 46		
Manchester Victoria	95 ⛴ d	13 48		14 00		14 21	14 48		15 00		15 21	15 48		16 00		16 21	16 48		17 00		17 18
Moston	95 d			14 06					15 06					16 06					17 06		17 24
Mills Hill	95 d			14 11					15 11					16 11					17 11		17 29
Castleton	95 d			14 16					15 16					16 16					17 16		17 34
Rochdale	95 a	14 02		14 19		14 34	15 02		15 19		15 34	16 02		16 19		16 34	17 02		17 19		17 37
	d	14 02		14 20		14 35	15 02		15 20		15 35	16 02		16 20		16 35	17 02		17 20		17 38
Smithy Bridge	d			14 24		14 39			15 24		15 39			16 24		16 39			17 24		17 42
Littleborough	d			14 27		14 42			15 27		15 42			16 27		16 42			17 27		17 45
Walsden	d					14 48					15 48					16 48					17 51
Todmorden	d	14 14		14 34		14 52	15 14		15 34		15 52	16 14		16 34		16 52	17 14		17 34		17 55
Blackpool North	97 d				13 29					14 29					15 29					16 29	
Poulton-le-Fylde	97 d				13 35					14 35					15 35					16 35	
Preston 8	97 d				13 54					14 54					15 54					16 54	
Blackburn	97 d				14 10					15 10					16 10					17 10	
Accrington	97 d				14 17					15 17					16 17					17 17	
Burnley Manchester Road	97 d				14 26					15 26					16 26					17 26	
Hebden Bridge	a	14 20		14 41	14 49	14 58	15 20		15 41	15 49	16 00	16 20		16 41	16 49	16 58	17 20		17 41	17 49	18 01
	d	14 21		14 41	14 50	15 00	15 21		15 41	15 50	16 01	16 21		16 41	16 50	17 00	17 21		17 41	17 50	18 01
Mytholmroyd	d			14 44		15 03			15 44		16 04			16 44		17 03			17 44		18 05
Sowerby Bridge	d			14 50		15 09			15 50		16 10			16 50		17 09			17 50		18 10
Huddersfield	39 d		14 23					15 23					16 23					17 23			
Brighouse	d		14 33	14 58				15 33	15 58				16 33	16 58				17 33	17 58		
Mirfield	39 a			15 06					16 06					17 06					18 07		
Dewsbury	39 a			15 12					16 12					17 12					18 12		
Halifax	a	14 33	14 43		15 02	15 15	15 33	15 43		16 02	16 16	16 33	16 44		17 02	17 15	17 33	17 43		18 02	18 17
	d	14 33	14 49		15 03	15 16	15 33	15 49		16 03	16 17	16 33	16 49		17 03	17 16	17 33	17 49		18 03	18 17
Bradford Interchange	a	14 47	15 02		15 17	15 31	15 47	16 02		16 17	16 31	16 47	17 02		17 17	17 31	17 47	18 02		18 17	18 31
	37 d	14 50	15 05		15 19	15 34	15 50	16 05		16 19	16 34	16 50	17 04		17 20	17 34	17 50	18 04		18 20	18 34
New Pudsey	37 a	14 58	15 13		15 27	15 42	15 58	16 13		16 27	16 42	16 58	17 13		17 28	17 42	17 58	18 13		18 28	18 42
Bramley	37 a	15 02	15 17			15 46	16 02	16 17			16 46	17 02	17 17			17 46	18 02	18 16			18 46
Leeds 10	37, 39 a	15 12	15 27	15 31	15 39	15 58	16 12	16 27	16 31	16 39	16 58	17 12	17 27	17 31	17 39	17 58	18 12	18 27	18 33	18 40	18 56
Selby	40 a	15 52					16 54					17 52					18 49				
York 8	40 a				16 21					17 19					18 24					19 21	

		NT	NT A	NT	NT	NT	NT	NT	NT	NT	NT	NT	NT	NT	NT	NT	NT	NT
Liverpool Lime Street 10	90 d	16 16		16 46		17 10	17 35		17 48				19 12			20 12		21 12
Manchester Victoria	95 ⛴ d	17 43		18 00		18 21	18 48		19 00		19 21		20 21			21 21		22 54
Moston	95 d	17 49							19 06		19 27		20 27			21 27		
Mills Hill	95 d	17 54		18 09					19 10		19 32		20 32			21 32		
Castleton	95 d	17 59		18 14					19 15		19 37		20 37			21 37		
Rochdale	95 a	18 02		18 18		18 35	19 01		19 19		19 40		20 40			21 40		23 07
	d	18 03		18 18		18 36	19 01		19 19		19 41		20 41			21 41		23 07
Smithy Bridge	d			18 22		18 40			19 23		19 45		20 45			21 45		23 11
Littleborough	d	18 08		18 26		18 43			19 27		19 48		20 48			21 48		23 15
Walsden	d			18 32		18 49					19 54		20 54			21 54		23 21
Todmorden	d	18 16		18 35		18 53	19 13		19 34		19 58		20 58			21 58		23 24
Blackpool North	97 d				17 18					18 29					20 29			
Poulton-le-Fylde	97 d				17 24					18 35					20 35			
Preston 8	97 d				17 44					18 54					20 54			
Blackburn	97 d				18 11					19 10					21 10			
Accrington	97 d				18 19					19 17					21 17			
Burnley Manchester Road	97 d				18 28					19 26					21 28			
Hebden Bridge	a	18 22		18 42	18 49	18 59	19 19		19 40	19 49	20 04		21 04		21 50	22 04		23 31
	d	18 23		18 42	18 50	19 00	19 20		19 42	19 50	20 05		21 05		21 51	22 05		23 31
Mytholmroyd	d			18 45		19 03			19 45		20 08		21 08			22 08		23 34
Sowerby Bridge	d			18 51		19 09			19 51		20 14		21 14			22 14		23 40
Huddersfield	39 d		18 23					19 23				20 25		21 25			22 25	
Brighouse	d		18 33	18 59				19 33	19 59			20 35		21 35			22 35	
Mirfield	39 a			19 07					20 07									
Dewsbury	39 a			19 13					20 12									
Halifax	a	18 35	18 45		19 03	19 15	19 32	19 43		20 03	20 20	20 45	21 20	21 45	22 03	22 20	22 45	23 46
	d	18 35	18 49		19 03	19 16	19 32	19 49		20 03	20 21	20 49	21 21	21 49	22 03	22 21	22 49	23 47
Bradford Interchange	a	18 49	19 02		19 17	19 31	19 48	20 02		20 17	20 35	21 02	21 35	22 02	22 17	22 35	23 02	00 01
	37 d	18 52	19 05		19 19	19 34	19 50	20 04		20 20	20 37	21 04	21 37	22 04	22 19	22 37	23 04	00 03
New Pudsey	37 a	19 00	19 13		19 28	19 42	19 58	20 13		20 28	20 46	21 13	21 46	22 13	22 28	22 46	23 13	00 12
Bramley	37 a	19 04	19 17			19 46	20 02	20 16			20 49	21 16	21 49	22 16		22 49	23 16	00 15
Leeds 10	37, 39 a	19 13	19 28	19 32	19 39	19 58	20 12	20 30	20 34	20 42	21 01	21 25	22 01	22 25	22 39	23 01	23 27	00 27
Selby	40 a																	
York 8	40 a	19 54			20 21					21 31					23 36			

For general notes see front of timetable
For details of catering facilities see Directory of Train Operators

A From Wakefield Westgate (Table 39)

Table 41

Sundays

until 12 July

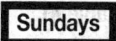

Manchester Victoria, Rochdale, Blackpool North and Huddersfield → Bradford and Leeds via Brighouse and Halifax

Network Diagram - see first page of Table 39

		NT	NT 🚌	NT	NT	NT	NT	NT 🚌	NT	NT 🚌	NT 🚌		NT	NT	NT	NT 🚌	NT	NT 🚌	NT	NT	NT 🚌	NT		NT 🚌	NT
Liverpool Lime Street [10]	90 d																								
Manchester Victoria	95 d					09 08							10 08						11 08						
Moston	95 d					09 15							10 15						11 15						
Mills Hill	95 d					09 19							10 19						11 19						
Castleton	95 d					09 24							10 24						11 24						
Rochdale	95 a					09 28							10 28						11 28						
	d					09 28							10 28						11 28						
Smithy Bridge	d					09 32							10 32						11 32						
Littleborough	d					09 36							10 36						11 36						
Walsden	d					09 42							10 42						11 42						
Todmorden	d					09 45							10 45						11 45						
Blackpool North	97 d								09 11								10 11								11 13
Poulton-le-Fylde	97 d								09 17								10 17								11 19
Preston [8]	97 d								09 37								10 37								11 38
Blackburn	97 d								09 54								10 55								11 54
Accrington	97 d								10 01								11 03								12 01
Burnley Manchester Road	97 d								10 10								11 12								12 10
Hebden Bridge	a					09 52			10 32				10 52				11 33		11 52						12 32
	d					09 52		10 00	10 32	10 40			10 52			11 00	11 34	11 40	11 52					12 00	12 32
Mytholmroyd	d					09 55		10 10					10 55			11 10			11 55					12 10	
Sowerby Bridge	d					10 01		10 25					11 01			11 25			12 01					12 25	
Huddersfield	39 d		08 50								10 35										12 35				
Brighouse	d		09 05								10 50								12 10		12 50				
Mirfield	39 a																								
Dewsbury	39 a																								
Halifax	a		09 20					10 40		11 00	11 05					11 40		12 00			13 05			12 40	
	d		09 20					10 40		11 00	11 05					11 40		12 00			13 05			12 40	
Bradford Interchange	a		09 50					11 10		11 30	11 35					12 10		12 30			13 35			13 10	
	37 d	08 31		09 21	10 02		10 25							11 25	11 44					12 25		12 44			
New Pudsey	37 a	08 39		09 30	10 10		10 33							11 33	11 52					12 33		12 52			
Bramley	37 a	08 43		09 33	10 14		10 37							11 37	11 56					12 37		12 56			
Leeds [10]	37, 39 a	08 51		09 42	10 24	10 34	10 46		11 09				11 30	11 46	12 05		12 11		12 44	12 48		13 05			13 10
Selby	40 a																								
York [8]	40 a	09 34		10 27	11 07				11 59								13 02								13 59

		NT 🚌	NT	NT	NT	NT 🚌	NT	NT 🚌	NT	NT	NT		NT 🚌	NT	NT 🚌	NT	NT	NT 🚌	NT	NT 🚌	NT	NT 🚌		NT	NT
Liverpool Lime Street [10]	90 d																								
Manchester Victoria	95 d		12 08						13 08							14 08								15 08	
Moston	95 d		12 15						13 15							14 15								15 15	
Mills Hill	95 d		12 19						13 19							14 19								15 19	
Castleton	95 d		12 24						13 24							14 24								15 24	
Rochdale	95 a		12 28						13 28							14 28								15 28	
	d		12 28						13 28							14 28								15 28	
Smithy Bridge	d		12 32						13 32							14 32								15 32	
Littleborough	d		12 36						13 36							14 36								15 36	
Walsden	d		12 42						13 42							14 42								15 42	
Todmorden	d		12 45						13 45							14 45								15 45	
Blackpool North	97 d						12 11							13 13							14 11				
Poulton-le-Fylde	97 d						12 17							13 19							14 17				
Preston [8]	97 d						12 37							13 38							14 37				
Blackburn	97 d						12 54							13 54							14 54				
Accrington	97 d						13 01							14 01							15 01				
Burnley Manchester Road	97 d						13 10							14 10							15 10				
Hebden Bridge	a		12 52				13 32		13 52					14 32		14 52					15 32			15 52	
	d	12 40	12 52			13 00	13 32	13 40	13 52				14 00	14 32	14 40	14 52				15 00	15 32	15 40		15 52	
Mytholmroyd	d		12 55			13 10			13 55				14 10			14 55				15 10				15 55	
Sowerby Bridge	d		13 01			13 25			14 01				14 25			15 01				15 25				16 01	
Huddersfield	39 d																	14 35							
Brighouse	d								14 10									14 50						16 10	
Mirfield	39 a																								
Dewsbury	39 a																								
Halifax	a	13 00				13 40		14 00					14 40		15 00			15 05		15 40		16 00			
	d	13 00				13 40		14 00					14 40		15 00			15 05		15 40		16 00			
Bradford Interchange	a	13 30				14 10		14 30					15 10		15 30			15 35		16 10		16 30			
	37 d			13 25	13 44					14 25	14 44						15 25		15 44						16 25
New Pudsey	37 a			13 33	13 52					14 33	14 52						15 33		15 52						16 33
Bramley	37 a			13 37	13 56					14 37	14 56						15 37		15 56						16 37
Leeds [10]	37, 39 a		13 30	13 46	14 05		14 08		14 44	14 48	15 05			15 11		15 30	15 46		16 05		16 11			16 44	16 48
Selby	40 a																								
York [8]	40 a						15 02							15 59							17 06				

For general notes see front of timetable
For details of catering facilities see Directory of Train Operators

Table 41

Sundays

until 12 July

Manchester Victoria, Rochdale, Blackpool North and Huddersfield → Bradford and Leeds via Brighouse and Halifax

Network Diagram - see first page of Table 39

		NT	NT 🚌	NT	NT 🚌	NT	NT	NT 🚌	NT	NT 🚌	NT		NT 🚌	NT	NT	NT	NT 🚌	NT		NT 🚌	NT	NT	NT 🚌	NT 🚌	NT
Liverpool Lime Street [10]	90 d																								
Manchester Victoria	95 🚊 d					16 08								17 08							18 08				
Moston	95 d					16 15								17 15							18 15				
Mills Hill	95 d					16 19								17 19							18 19				
Castleton	95 d					16 24								17 24							18 24				
Rochdale	95 a					16 28								17 28							18 28				
	d					16 28								17 28							18 28				
Smithy Bridge	d					16 32								17 32							18 32				
Littleborough	d					16 36								17 36							18 36				
Walsden	d					16 42								17 42							18 42				
Todmorden	d					16 45								17 45							18 45				
Blackpool North	97 d			15 13							16 11							17 11							18 11
Poulton-le-Fylde	97 d			15 19							16 17							17 17							18 17
Preston [8]	97 d			15 37							16 37							17 37							18 37
Blackburn	97 d			15 54							16 54							17 54							18 54
Accrington	97 d			16 01							17 01							18 01							19 01
Burnley Manchester Road	97 d			16 10							17 10							18 10							19 10
Hebden Bridge	a			16 32		16 52					17 32			17 52				18 32			18 52				19 32
	d		16 00	16 32	16 40	16 52				17 00	17 32		17 40	17 52			18 00	18 32		18 40	18 52			19 00	19 32
Mytholmroyd	d		16 10			16 55				17 10				17 55			18 10				18 55			19 10	
Sowerby Bridge	d		16 25			17 01				17 25				18 01			18 25				19 01			19 25	
Huddersfield	39 d							16 35															18 35		
Brighouse	d							16 50						18 10									18 50		
Mirfield	39 a																								
Dewsbury	39 a																								
Halifax	a		16 40		17 00			17 05		17 40			18 00				18 40			19 00			19 05	19 40	
	d		16 40		17 00			17 05		17 40			18 00				18 40			19 00			19 05	19 40	
Bradford Interchange	a		17 10		17 30			17 35		18 10			18 30				19 10			19 30			19 35	20 10	
	37 d	16 44					17 25		17 44						18 25	18 44						19 25			
New Pudsey	37 a	16 52					17 33		17 52						18 33	18 52						19 33			
Bramley	37 a	16 56					17 37		17 56						18 37	18 56						19 37			
Leeds [10]	37, 39 a	17 05		17 12		17 30	17 46		18 05		18 11			18 44	18 47	19 07		19 11			19 30	19 47			20 08
Selby	40 a																								
York [8]	40 a			18 02							19 03							20 01							21 03

		NT 🚌	NT	NT	NT	NT 🚌	NT	NT 🚌	NT 🚌	NT	NT		NT 🚌	NT	NT 🚌	NT	NT	NT 🚌	NT	NT 🚌	NT	NT	NT 🚌		
Liverpool Lime Street [10]	90 d																								
Manchester Victoria	95 🚊 d			19 08						20 08						21 08					22 08				
Moston	95 d			19 15						20 15						21 15					22 15				
Mills Hill	95 d			19 19						20 19						21 19					22 19				
Castleton	95 d			19 24						20 24						21 24					22 24				
Rochdale	95 a			19 28						20 28						21 28					22 28				
	d			19 28						20 28						21 28					22 28				
Smithy Bridge	d			19 32						20 32						21 32					22 32				
Littleborough	d			19 36						20 36						21 36					22 36				
Walsden	d			19 42						20 42						21 42					22 42				
Todmorden	d			19 45						20 45						21 45					22 45				
Blackpool North	97 d						19 13							20 11					21 13						
Poulton-le-Fylde	97 d						19 19							20 17					21 19						
Preston [8]	97 d						19 37							20 37					21 38						
Blackburn	97 d						19 54							20 54					21 54						
Accrington	97 d						20 01							21 01					22 01						
Burnley Manchester Road	97 d						20 10							21 10					22 10						
Hebden Bridge	a			19 52			20 32			20 52				21 32		21 52			22 32		22 52				
	d	19 40		19 52		20 00	20 32		20 40	20 52			21 00	21 32	21 40	21 52		22 00	22 32	22 40	22 52		23 00		
Mytholmroyd	d			19 55		20 10				20 55			21 10			21 55		22 10			22 55		23 10		
Sowerby Bridge	d			20 01		20 25				21 01			21 25			22 01		22 25			23 01		23 25		
Huddersfield	39 d							20 35																	
Brighouse	d			20 10				20 50								22 10									
Mirfield	39 a																								
Dewsbury	39 a																								
Halifax	a	20 00				20 40		21 05	21 00				21 40		22 00			22 40		23 00			23 40		
	d	20 00				20 40		21 05	21 00				21 40		22 00			22 40		23 00			23 40		
Bradford Interchange	a	20 30				21 10		21 35	21 30				22 10		22 30			23 10		23 30			00 10		
	37 d		19 44		20 31						21 38						22 32					23 49			
New Pudsey	37 a		19 52		20 39						21 46						22 40					23 57			
Bramley	37 a		19 56		20 43						21 50						22 44					00 01			
Leeds [10]	37, 39 a		20 08	20 42	20 52		21 08			21 30	21 58			22 09		22 44	22 53		23 09		23 30	00 10			
Selby	40 a																								
York [8]	40 a						21 59																		

For general notes see front of timetable
For details of catering facilities see
Directory of Train Operators

Table 41

Sundays

Manchester Victoria, Rochdale, Blackpool North and Huddersfield → Bradford and Leeds via Brighouse and Halifax

19 July to 6 September

Network Diagram - see first page of Table 39

		NT	NT	NT	NT	NT		NT	NT	NT	NT	NT		NT	NT	NT	NT	NT		NT	NT	NT	NT	NT	NT
Liverpool Lime Street 10	90 d																								
Manchester Victoria	95 d				09 08			10 08			11 08				12 08			13 08				14 08			15 08
Moston	95 d				09 15			10 15			11 15				12 15			13 15				14 15			15 15
Mills Hill	95 d				09 19			10 19			11 19				12 19			13 19				14 19			15 19
Castleton	95 d				09 24			10 24			11 24				12 24			13 24				14 24			15 24
Rochdale	95 a				09 28			10 28			11 28				12 28			13 28				14 28			15 28
	d				09 28			10 28			11 28				12 28			13 28				14 28			15 28
Smithy Bridge	d				09 32			10 32			11 32				12 32			13 32				14 32			15 32
Littleborough	d				09 36			10 36			11 36				12 36			13 36				14 36			15 36
Walsden	d				09 42			10 42			11 42				12 42			13 42				14 42			15 42
Todmorden	d				09 45			10 45			11 45				12 45			13 45				14 45			15 45
Blackpool North	97 d					09 11				10 11				11 13			12 11				13 13			14 11	
Poulton-le-Fylde	97 d					09 17				10 17				11 19			12 17				13 19			14 17	
Preston 8	97 d					09 37				10 37				11 38			12 37				13 38			14 37	
Blackburn	97 d					09 54				10 54				11 54			12 54				13 54			14 54	
Accrington	97 d					10 01				11 01				12 01			13 01				14 01			15 01	
Burnley Manchester Road	97 d					10 10				11 10				12 10			13 10				14 10			15 10	
Hebden Bridge	a				09 52	10 32		10 52		11 32	11 52			12 32	12 52		13 32	13 52			14 32	14 52		15 32	15 52
	d				09 52	10 32		10 52		11 32	11 52			12 32	12 52		13 32	13 52			14 32	14 52		15 32	15 52
Mytholmroyd	d				09 55			10 55			11 55				12 55			13 55				14 55			15 55
Sowerby Bridge	d				10 01			11 01			12 01				13 01			14 01				15 01			16 01
Huddersfield	39 d			09 25					11 08							13 08							15 08		
Brighouse	d			09 35					11 18							13 18							15 18		
Mirfield	39 a																								
Dewsbury	39 a																								
Halifax	a			09 47	10 08	10 44		11 08	11 29	11 44	12 08			12 44	13 08	13 28	13 44	14 08			14 44	15 08	15 28	15 44	16 08
	d		09 06	09 47	10 08	10 45		11 08	11 30	11 45	12 08	12 30		12 45	13 08	13 29	13 46	14 08		14 30	14 45	15 08	15 29	15 46	16 08
Bradford Interchange	a		09 18	09 59	10 22	10 59		11 22	11 42	11 59	12 22	12 42		12 59	13 22	13 42	14 00	14 22		14 42	14 59	15 22	15 42	16 00	16 22
	37 d	08 31	09 20	10 02	10 25	11 02		11 25	11 44	12 02	12 25	12 44		13 02	13 25	13 44	14 02	14 25		14 44	15 02	15 25	15 44	16 03	16 26
New Pudsey	37 a	08 39	09 29	10 10	10 33	11 10		11 33	11 53	12 10	12 33	12 53		13 10	13 33	13 53	14 10	14 33		14 53	15 10	15 33	15 53	16 11	16 34
Bramley	37 a	08 43	09 32	10 14	10 37			11 37	11 56		12 37	12 56			13 37	13 56		14 37		14 56		15 37	15 56		16 38
Leeds 10	37, 39 a	08 51	09 42	10 24	10 46	11 21		11 48	12 05	12 22	12 47	13 06		13 22	13 46	14 06	14 22	14 48		15 06	15 22	15 46	16 06	16 22	16 48
Selby	40 a																								
York 8	40 a	09 34	10 28	11 07		11 59				13 02				13 59			15 02				15 59			17 06	

		NT		NT	NT	NT	NT	NT		NT	NT	NT	NT	NT		NT	NT	NT	NT	NT	NT	NT	NT		
Liverpool Lime Street 10	90 d																								
Manchester Victoria	95 d				16 08			17 08				18 08				19 08		20 08			21 08		22 08		
Moston	95 d				16 15			17 15				18 15				19 15		20 15			21 15		22 15		
Mills Hill	95 d				16 19			17 19				18 19				19 19		20 19			21 19		22 19		
Castleton	95 d				16 24			17 24				18 24				19 24		20 24			21 24		22 24		
Rochdale	95 a				16 28			17 28				18 28				19 28		20 28			21 28		22 28		
	d				16 28			17 28				18 28				19 28		20 28			21 28		22 28		
Smithy Bridge	d				16 32			17 32				18 32				19 32		20 32			21 32		22 32		
Littleborough	d				16 36			17 36				18 36				19 36		20 36			21 36		22 36		
Walsden	d				16 42			17 42				18 42				19 42		20 42			21 42		22 42		
Todmorden	d				16 45			17 45				18 45				19 45		20 45			21 45		22 45		
Blackpool North	97 d			15 13			16 11				17 11			18 11			19 13			20 11		21 13			
Poulton-le-Fylde	97 d			15 19			16 17				17 17			18 17			19 19			20 17		21 19			
Preston 8	97 d			15 37			16 37				17 37			18 37			19 37			20 37		21 39			
Blackburn	97 d			15 54			16 54				17 54			18 54			19 54			20 54		21 55			
Accrington	97 d			16 01			17 01				18 01			19 01			20 01			21 01		22 02			
Burnley Manchester Road	97 d			16 10			17 10				18 10			19 10			20 10			21 10		22 12			
Hebden Bridge	a			16 32	16 52		17 32	17 52			18 32	18 52		19 32		19 52	20 32	20 52		21 32	21 52	22 34	22 52		
	d			16 32	16 52		17 32	17 52			18 32	18 52		19 32		19 52	20 32	20 52		21 32	21 52	22 34	22 52		
Mytholmroyd	d				16 55			17 55				18 55				19 55		20 55			21 55		22 55		
Sowerby Bridge	d				17 01			18 01				19 01				20 01		21 01			22 01		23 01		
Huddersfield	39 d					17 08							19 08						21 08						
Brighouse	d					17 17							19 18						21 18						
Mirfield	39 a																								
Dewsbury	39 a																								
Halifax	a			16 44	17 08	17 27	17 44	18 08			18 44	19 08	19 29	19 44		20 08	20 44	21 08	21 29	21 44	22 08	22 46	23 08		
	d	16 30		16 45	17 08	17 29	17 45	18 08		18 30	18 45	19 08	19 30	19 45		20 08	20 45	21 08	21 30	21 45	22 08	22 47	23 08		
Bradford Interchange	a	16 42		16 59	17 22	17 42	17 59	18 22		18 42	18 59	19 22	19 42	19 59		20 22	20 59	21 22	21 42	21 59	22 22	23 01	23 22		
	37 d	16 44		17 02	17 25	17 44	18 02	18 25		18 44	19 02	19 25	19 44	20 02		20 25	21 02	21 26	21 44	22 02	22 26	23 04	23 25		
New Pudsey	37 a	16 53		17 10	17 33	17 53	18 10	18 33		18 53	19 10	19 33	19 53	20 10		20 33	21 10	21 34	21 53	22 10	22 34	23 12	23 33		
Bramley	37 a	16 56			17 37	17 56		18 37		18 56		19 37	19 56			20 37		21 38	21 56		22 38		23 37		
Leeds 10	37, 39 a	17 05		17 21	17 46	18 05	18 21	18 46		19 06	19 21	19 47	20 05	20 23		20 47	21 22	21 48	22 05	22 22	22 47	23 26	23 46		
Selby	40 a																								
York 8	40 a			18 02			19 03				20 01			21 03			21 59								

For general notes see front of timetable
For details of catering facilities see Directory of Train Operators

Table 41

Sundays

from 13 September

Manchester Victoria, Rochdale, Blackpool North and Huddersfield → Bradford and Leeds via Brighouse and Halifax

Network Diagram - see first page of Table 39

		NT	NT	NT	NT	NT		NT	NT	NT	NT	NT		NT	NT	NT	NT	NT		NT	NT	NT	NT	NT	NT
Liverpool Lime Street 10	90 d				08 19			09 22			10 22				11 22			12 22				13 22			14 22
Manchester Victoria	95 d				09 08			10 08			11 08				12 08			13 08				14 08			15 08
Moston	95 d				09 15			10 15			11 15				12 15			13 15				14 15			15 15
Mills Hill	95 d				09 19			10 19			11 19				12 19			13 19				14 19			15 19
Castleton	95 d				09 24			10 24			11 24				12 24			13 24				14 24			15 24
Rochdale	95 a				09 28			10 28			11 28				12 28			13 28				14 28			15 28
	d				09 28			10 28			11 28				12 28			13 28				14 28			15 28
Smithy Bridge	d				09 32			10 32			11 32				12 32			13 32				14 32			15 32
Littleborough	d				09 36			10 36			11 36				12 36			13 36				14 36			15 36
Walsden	d				09 42			10 42			11 42				12 42			13 42				14 42			15 42
Todmorden	d				09 45			10 45			11 45				12 45			13 45				14 45			15 45
Blackpool North	97 d					09 01				10 11				11 13			12 11				13 13			14 11	
Poulton-le-Fylde	97 d					09 07				10 17				11 19			12 17				13 19			14 17	
Preston 8	97 d					09 27				10 37				11 38			12 37				13 38			14 37	
Blackburn	97 d					09 44				10 54				11 54			12 54				13 54			14 54	
Accrington	97 d					09 51				11 01				12 01			13 01				14 01			15 01	
Burnley Manchester Road	97 d					10 00				11 10				12 10			13 10				14 10			15 10	
Hebden Bridge	a				09 52	10 22		10 52		11 32	11 52			12 32	12 52		13 32	13 52			14 32	14 52		15 32	15 52
	d				09 52	10 22		10 52		11 32	11 52			12 32	12 52		13 32	13 52			14 32	14 52		15 32	15 52
Mytholmroyd	d				09 55			10 55			11 55				12 55			13 55				14 55			15 55
Sowerby Bridge	d				10 01			11 01			12 01				13 01			14 01				15 01			16 01
Huddersfield	39 d			09 26					11 08							13 08							15 08		
Brighouse	d			09 36					11 18							13 18							15 18		
Mirfield	39 a																								
Dewsbury	39 a																								
Halifax	a			09 48	10 08	10 34		11 08	11 29	11 44	12 08			12 44	13 08	13 28	13 44	14 08			14 44	15 08	15 28	15 44	16 08
	d		09 06	09 48	10 08	10 45		11 08	11 30	11 45	12 08	12 30		12 45	13 08	13 29	13 46	14 08		14 30	14 45	15 08	15 29	15 46	16 08
Bradford Interchange	a		09 18	10 00	10 22	10 59		11 22	11 42	11 59	12 22	12 42		12 59	13 22	13 42	14 00	14 22		14 42	14 59	15 22	15 42	16 00	16 22
	37 d	08 31	09 20	10 03	10 25	11 02		11 25	11 44	12 02	12 25	12 44		13 02	13 25	13 44	14 02	14 25		14 44	15 02	15 25	15 44	16 03	16 26
New Pudsey	37 a	08 39	09 29	10 11	10 33	11 10		11 33	11 53	12 10	12 33	12 53		13 10	13 33	13 53	14 10	14 33		14 53	15 10	15 33	15 53	16 11	16 34
Bramley	37 a	08 43	09 32	10 15	10 37			11 37	11 56		12 37	12 56			13 37	13 56		14 37		14 56		15 37	15 56		16 38
Leeds 10	37, 39 a	08 51	09 42	10 24	10 46	11 21		11 48	12 05	12 22	12 47	13 06		13 22	13 46	14 06	14 22	14 48		15 06	15 22	15 46	16 06	16 22	16 48
Selby	40 a																								
York 8	40 a	09 34	10 28	11 07		11 59				13 02				13 59			15 02				15 59			17 06	

		NT		NT	NT	NT	NT	NT		NT	NT	NT	NT	NT		NT	NT	NT	NT	NT	NT	NT	NT		
Liverpool Lime Street 10	90 d				15 22			16 22				17 22				18 22		19 22			20 22				
Manchester Victoria	95 d				16 08			17 08				18 08				19 08		20 08			21 08		22 08		
Moston	95 d				16 15			17 15				18 15				19 15		20 15			21 15		22 15		
Mills Hill	95 d				16 19			17 19				18 19				19 19		20 19			21 19		22 19		
Castleton	95 d				16 24			17 24				18 24				19 24		20 24			21 24		22 24		
Rochdale	95 a				16 28			17 28				18 28				19 28		20 28			21 28		22 28		
	d				16 28			17 28				18 28				19 28		20 28			21 28		22 28		
Smithy Bridge	d				16 32			17 32				18 32				19 32		20 32			21 32		22 32		
Littleborough	d				16 36			17 36				18 36				19 36		20 36			21 36		22 36		
Walsden	d				16 42			17 42				18 42				19 42		20 42			21 42		22 42		
Todmorden	d				16 45			17 45				18 45				19 45		20 45			21 45		22 45		
Blackpool North	97 d			15 13			16 11				17 11			18 11			19 13			20 11		21 13			
Poulton-le-Fylde	97 d			15 19			16 17				17 17			18 17			19 19			20 17		21 19			
Preston 8	97 d			15 37			16 37				17 37			18 37			19 37			20 37		21 39			
Blackburn	97 d			15 54			16 54				17 54			18 54			19 54			20 54		21 55			
Accrington	97 d			16 01			17 01				18 01			19 01			20 01			21 01		22 02			
Burnley Manchester Road	97 d			16 10			17 10				18 10			19 10			20 10			21 10		22 12			
Hebden Bridge	a			16 32	16 52		17 32	17 52			18 32	18 52		19 32		19 52	20 32	20 52		21 32	21 52	22 34	22 52		
	d			16 32	16 52		17 32	17 52			18 32	18 52		19 32		19 52	20 32	20 52		21 32	21 52	22 34	22 52		
Mytholmroyd	d				16 55			17 55				18 55				19 55		20 55			21 55		22 55		
Sowerby Bridge	d				17 01			18 01				19 01				20 01		21 01			22 01		23 01		
Huddersfield	39 d					17 08							19 08						21 08						
Brighouse	d					17 17							19 18						21 18						
Mirfield	39 a																								
Dewsbury	39 a																								
Halifax	a			16 44	17 08	17 27	17 44	18 08			18 44	19 08	19 28	19 44		20 08	20 44	21 08	21 29	21 44	22 08	22 46	23 08		
	d	16 30		16 45	17 08	17 29	17 45	18 08		18 30	18 45	19 08	19 29	19 45		20 08	20 45	21 08	21 30	21 45	22 08	22 47	23 08		
Bradford Interchange	a	16 42		16 59	17 22	17 42	17 59	18 22		18 42	18 59	19 22	19 42	19 59		20 22	20 59	21 22	21 42	21 59	22 22	23 01	23 22		
	37 d	16 44		17 02	17 25	17 44	18 02	18 25		18 44	19 02	19 25	19 44	20 02		20 25	21 02	21 26	21 44	22 02	22 26	23 04	23 25		
New Pudsey	37 a	16 53		17 10	17 33	17 53	18 10	18 33		18 53	19 10	19 33	19 53	20 10		20 33	21 10	21 34	21 53	22 10	22 34	23 12	23 33		
Bramley	37 a	16 56			17 37	17 56		18 37		18 56		19 37	19 56			20 37		21 38	21 56		22 38		23 37		
Leeds 10	37, 39 a	17 05		17 21	17 46	18 05	18 21	18 46		19 06	19 21	19 47	20 05	20 23		20 47	21 22	21 48	22 05	22 22	22 47	23 26	23 46		
Selby	40 a																								
York 8	40 a			18 02			19 03				20 01			21 03			21 59								

For general notes see front of timetable
For details of catering facilities see Directory of Train Operators

Mondays to Saturdays
until 5 September

Hull → Beverley, Bridlington and Scarborough

Network Diagram - see first page of Table 39

Miles			NT	TP 1◇ A	TP 1◇ B	NT	NT	NT C	NT SO	NT SX	TP 1◇ D	NT E	NT G	NT C	TP 1◇ D	NT	NT H	NT SX J	TP 1◇ D	NT	TP 1◇ D
0	**Hull**	d	06 24			06 54	07 14	07 36	07 52	07 52		08 14	08 37	09 15		09 44	10 14	10 16		10 44	
4	Cottingham	d	06 30			07 00	07 20	07 42	07 58	07 58		08 20	08 43	09 21		09 50	10 20	10 22		10 50	
8¼	**Beverley**	d	06 37			07 07	07 27	07a48	08 05	08 05		08 27	08a49	09 28		09 57	10 27	10 29		10 57	
11¼	Arram	d				07 11				08 09											
16¼	Hutton Cranswick	d				07 18	07 36		08 14	08 16		08 36		09 37		10 06				11 06	
19½	Driffield	d	06 49			07 24	07 41		08 19	08 22		08 41		09 42		10 11	10 39	10 41		11 11	
21½	Nafferton	d				07 27	07 45		08 23	08 25		08 45		09 46		10 15				11 15	
31	**Bridlington**	a	07 04			07 39	07 58		08 36	08 39		08 56		10 01		10 26	10 54	10 55		11 28	
—		d				07 49						09 00				10 36					
34½	Bempton	d				07 56						09 07				10 43					
41¾	Hunmanby	d				08 06						09 17				10 53					
44½	Filey	d				08 11						09 22				10 58					
51	Seamer	d		07 19	08 06	08 22					09 19	09 34			10 19	11 10			11 19		12 19
53¾	**Scarborough**	a		07 30	08 15	08 29					09 30	09 40			10 32	11 17			11 30		12 30

		NT C	NT	NT C	TP 1◇ D	NT	TP 1◇ D	NT C	NT	NT C	TP 1◇ D	NT	NT C	TP 1◇ D	TP 1◇ D	NT G	NT	NT	NT G	NT	TP SX 1◇ B
Hull	d	11 14	11 44	12 14		12 44		13 14	13 44	14 14		14 44	15 20			16 00	16 14	16 29	16 52	17 07	
Cottingham	d	11 20	11 50	12 20		12 50		13 20	13 50	14 20		14 50	15 26			16 07	16 21	16 36	16 59	17 14	
Beverley	d	11 27	11 57	12 27		12 57		13 27	13 57	14 27		14 57	15 33			16 13	16a27	16a42	17 05	17a20	
Arram	d					13 01										16 18					
Hutton Cranswick	d		12 06			13 08			14 06			15 06				16 25			17 14		
Driffield	d	11 39	12 11	12 39		13 14		13 39	14 11	14 39		15 11	15 45			16 30			17 20		
Nafferton	d		12 15			13 17			14 15			15 15				16 34			17 23		
Bridlington	a	11 52	12 28	12 54		13 31		13 52	14 28	14 54		15 26	16 02			16 45			17 37		
	d	12 04						14 04				15 30				16 54					
Bempton	d	12 11						14 11				15 37				17 01					
Hunmanby	d	12 21						14 21				15 47				17 11					
Filey	d	12 26						14 26				15 52				17 16					
Seamer	d	12 37			13 19		14 19	14 37			15 19	16 03		16 19	17 19	17 27					18 07
Scarborough	a	12 43			13 30		14 30	14 45			15 30	16 10		16 30	17 30	17 35					18 17

		TP SO 1◇ D	TP SX 1◇ B	NT K	NT	NT G	NT SX	NT SO	NT SX	TP SO 1◇ D	TP SX 1◇ D	TP 1◇ D	NT L	NT SX C	NT SO C	TP 1◇ D	NT C	NT G	TP SO 1◇ B	TP SX 1◇ B	NT C
Hull	d			17 30	17 44	18 00	18 25	18 45	18 50				19 14	20 10	20 14		21 09	21 48			23 00
Cottingham	d			17 37	17 51	18 07	18 31	18 51	18 56				19 20	20 16	20 21		21 15	21 54			23 06
Beverley	d			17 43	17a57	18 13	18a37	18a57	19a02				19 27	20 23	20 27		21a21	22 01			23a12
Arram	d			17 48										20 27	20 32						
Hutton Cranswick	d			17 55		18 22							19 36	20 34	20 39			22 10			
Driffield	d			18 00		18 28							19 41	20 40	20 44			22 15			
Nafferton	d			18 04		18 31							19 45	20 43	20 48			22 19			
Bridlington	a			18 15		18 45							19 57	20 57	21 01			22 32			
	d			18 18									19 59								
Bempton	d			18 25									20 06								
Hunmanby	d			18 35									20 16								
Filey	d			18 40									20 21								
Seamer	d	18 19	18 41	18 50						19 19	19 24	20 19	20 33			21 19			22 52	22 56	
Scarborough	a	18 29	18 51	18 57						19 30	19 33	20 30	20 39			21 30			23 02	23 06	

Mondays to Saturdays
from 7 September

		NT	TP 1◇ A	TP 1◇ B	NT	NT	NT C	NT SO	NT SX	TP 1◇ D	NT E	NT G	NT C	TP 1◇ D	NT	NT C	TP 1◇ D	NT	TP 1◇ D	NT C	NT
Hull	d	06 24			06 54	07 14	07 36	07 52	07 52		08 14	08 37	09 15		09 44	10 14		10 44		11 14	11 44
Cottingham	d	06 30			07 00	07 20	07 42	07 58	07 58		08 20	08 43	09 21		09 50	10 20		10 50		11 20	11 50
Beverley	d	06 38			07 07	07 28	07a50	08 06	08 06		08 28	08a50	09 29		09 57	10 28		10 58		11 27	11 58
Arram	d				07 11				08 10												
Hutton Cranswick	d				07 18	07 37		08 15	08 17		08 37		09 38		10 06			11 07			12 07
Driffield	d	06 50			07 24	07 42		08 20	08 23		08 43		09 43		10 11	10 40		11 12		11 39	12 12
Nafferton	d				07 27	07 46		08 24	08 26		08 46		09 47		10 15			11 16			12 16
Bridlington	a	07 06			07 39	08 00		08 39	08 41		09 00		10 03		10 28	10 57		11 30		11b54	12 30
	d				07 47						09 02				10 35					12 04	
Bempton	d				07 54						09 09				10 42					12 11	
Hunmanby	d				08 04						09 19				10 52					12 21	
Filey	d				08 09						09 24				10 57					12 26	
Seamer	d		07 19	08 06	08 22					09 19	09 35			10 19	11 09		11 19		12 19	12 37	
Scarborough	a		07 30	08 15	08 29					09 30	09 41			10 32	11 16		11 30		12 30	12 43	

For general notes see front of timetable
For details of catering facilities see Directory of Train Operators

A Mondays to Fridays from Manchester Airport. Saturdays from York (Table 39)
B From Manchester Airport (Table 39)
C From Sheffield (Table 29)
D From Liverpool Lime Street (Table 39)
E From Gilberdyke (Table 29)
G From Doncaster (Table 29)
H All Saturdays, also Mondays to Fridays until 19 June. From Sheffield (Table 29)
J From 22 June. From Sheffield (Table 29)
K From York (Table 33)
L Mondays to Fridays from Doncaster (Table 29)
b Saturdays arr. 1152

Mondays to Saturdays

from 7 September

Hull → Beverley, Bridlington and Scarborough

Network Diagram - see first page of Table 39

		NT	TP	NT	TP	NT	NT	NT	TP	NT	NT	NT	TP	TP	NT	NT	NT	NT	NT	TP	TP
											SX	SO								SX	SO
			1◇		1◇				1◇				1◇	1◇						1◇	1◇
		A	B		B	A		A	B		A	A	B	B	C			C		D	B
Hull	d	12 14		12 44		13 14	13 44	14 14		14 44	15 20	15 20			16 00	16 14	16 29	16 52	17 07		
Cottingham	d	12 20		12 50		13 20	13 50	14 20		14 50	15 26	15 26			16 07	16 21	16 36	16 59	17 14		
Beverley	d	12 28		12 58		13 28	13 58	14 28		14 57	15 33	15 34			16 15	16a27	16a43	17 06	17a20		
Arram	d			13 02											16 19						
Hutton Cranswick	d			13 09			14 07			15 06					16 26			17 15			
Driffield	d	12 40		13 15		13 40	14 12	14 40		15 11	15 45	15 46			16 32			17 21			
Nafferton	d			13 18			14 16			15 15					16 35			17 24			
Bridlington	a	12 56		13 33		13 55	14 30	14 56		15 28	16 03	16 02			16 48			17 39			
	d					14 04				15 30					16 54						
Bempton	d					14 11				15 37					17 01						
Hunmanby	d					14 21				15 47					17 11						
Filey	d					14 26				15 52					17 16						
Seamer	d		13 19		14 19	14 39			15 19	16 03			16 19	17 19	17 27					18 07	18 19
Scarborough	a		13 30		14 30	14 45			15 30	16 10			16 30	17 30	17 35					18 17	18 29

		TP	NT	NT	NT	NT	NT	NT	NT	TP	TP	TP	NT	NT	NT	TP	NT	NT	TP	TP	NT
		SX	SX	SO			SX	SO	SX	SO	SX			SX	SO				SO	SX	
		1◇								1◇	1◇	1◇				1◇			1◇	1◇	
		D	E	E		C				B	B	B	G	A	A	B	A	C	D	D	A
Hull	d		17 30	17 30	17 44	18 00	18 25	18 45	18 50				19 14	20 10	20 14		21 09	21 48			23 00
Cottingham	d		17 37	17 37	17 51	18 07	18 31	18 51	18 56				19 20	20 16	20 21		21 15	21 54			23 06
Beverley	d		17 45	17 45	17a58	18 14	18a38	18a58	19a03				19 28	20 24	20 28		21a23	22 02			23a13
Arram	d		17 49	17 49										20 28	20 33						
Hutton Cranswick	d		17 56	17 56		18 23							19 37	20 35	20 40			22 11			
Driffield	d		18 02	18 02		18 29							19 42	20 41	20 45			22 16			
Nafferton	d		18 05	18 05		18 32							19 46	20 44	20 49			22 20			
Bridlington	a		18 18	18 20		18 48							19 59	21 00	21 04			22 34			
	d		18 21	18 22									20 01								
Bempton	d		18 28	18 29									20 08								
Hunmanby	d		18 38	18 39									20 18								
Filey	d		18 43	18 44									20 23								
Seamer	d	18 41	18 56	18 55						19 19	19 24	20 19	20 36			21 19			22 52	22 56	
Scarborough	a	18 51	19 04	19 01						19 30	19 33	20 30	20 42			21 30			23 02	23 06	

Sundays

until 20 September

		NT	TP	NT	NT	NT	TP	NT	NT	TP	NT	NT	TP	NT	NT	NT	TP	NT	NT	NT	TP	TP	TP
			1◇				1◇			1◇			1◇				1◇				1◇	1◇	1◇
			H		A	C	B	A		B	A	A	B	A	A		B	A	A	A	B	B	D
Hull	d	09 00		09 25	10 25	11 29		12 00	13 00		14 00	15 05		16 05	16 57	17 20		18 00	19 00	20 00			
Cottingham	d	09 06		09 31	10 31	11 35		12 06	13 06		14 06	15 11		16 11	17 03	17 26		18 06	19 06	20 06			
Beverley	d	09 13		09 38	10 38	11 42		12 13	13 13		14 13	15 18		16 18	17 10	17 33		18 13	19 13	20a12			
Arram	d			09 42																			
Hutton Cranswick	d			09 49	10 47			12 22			14 22			16 27		17 42			19 22				
Driffield	d	09 25		09 55	10 52	11 54		12 27	13 25		14 27	15 30		16 32	17 22	17 47		18 25	19 27				
Nafferton	d			09 58	10 56			12 31			14 31			16 36		17 51			19 31				
Bridlington	a	09 40		10 10	11 07	12 09		12 42	13 40		14 42	15 45		16 47	17 37	18 04		18 38	19 44				
	d			10 12	11 10			12 45			14 45			16 53				18 45					
Bempton	d			10 19	11 17			12 52			14 52			17 00				18 52					
Hunmanby	d			10 29	11 27			13 02			15 02			17 10				19 02					
Filey	d			10 34	11 32			13 07			15 07			17 15				19 07					
Seamer	d		10 21	10 45	11 43		12 25	13 19		14 21	15 18		16 21	17 26			18 21	19 19			20 21	21 21	22 51
Scarborough	a		10 32	10 52	11 49		12 32	13 24		14 32	15 25		16 32	17 33			18 32	19 24			20 32	21 32	23 02

Sundays

from 27 September

		TP	TP	NT	TP	NT	NT	TP	NT	TP	NT	NT	TP	TP	TP
		1◇	1◇		1◇			1◇		1◇			1◇	1◇	1◇
		H	B	A	B	A	A	B	A	B	A	A	B	B	D
Hull	d			12 00		14 00	16 05		16 57		19 00	20 00			
Cottingham	d			12 06		14 06	16 11		17 03		19 06	20 06			
Beverley	d			12 13		14 13	16a17		17 10		19 13	20a12			
Arram	d														
Hutton Cranswick	d			12 22		14 22			17 19		19 22				
Driffield	d			12 27		14 27			17 24		19 27				
Nafferton	d			12 31		14 31			17 30		19 31				
Bridlington	a			12 44		14 44			17 41		19 44				
	d														
Bempton	d														
Hunmanby	d														
Filey	d														
Seamer	d	10 21	12 25		14 21			16 21		18 21			20 21	21 21	22 51
Scarborough	a	10 32	12 32		14 32			16 32		18 32			20 32	21 32	23 02

For general notes see front of timetable
For details of catering facilities see Directory of Train Operators

A From Sheffield (Table 29)
B From Liverpool Lime Street (Table 39)
C From Doncaster (Table 29)
D From Manchester Airport (Table 39)
E From York (Table 33)
G Mondays to Fridays from Doncaster (Table 29)
H From Leeds (Table 39)

Mondays to Saturdays
until 5 September

Scarborough, Bridlington and Beverley → Hull

Network Diagram - see first page of Table 39

Miles			NT SO A	TP SX 1◇ B	NT SX A	TP SO 1◇ B	NT SX	NT C	NT D	NT	NT C	TP SX 1◇ B	TP SO 1◇ B	TP SX 1◇ E	TP SO 1◇ E	NT D	TP 1◇ E	NT C	NT D	NT	TP 1◇ E
0	**Scarborough**	d		06 30		06 34					06 50	07 00	07 04	07 38	07 47		08 47			09 03	09 47
2¾	Seamer	d		06a35		06a39					06 55	07a05	07a09	07a43	07a52		08a52			09 08	09a52
9¼	Filey	d									07 04									09 17	
12	Hunmanby	d									07 09									09 21	
19¼	Bempton	d									07 19									09 31	
22¾	**Bridlington**	a									07 27									09 39	
—		d						06 46	07 14		07 34					08 08			09 06	09 42	
32¼	Nafferton	d						06 56	07 24		07 45					08 18			09 16	09 52	
34¼	Driffield	d						07 01	07 29		07 49					08 23			09 21	09 57	
37½	Hutton Cranswick	d						07 05	07 33		07 54					08 27			09 25	10 01	
42½	Arram	d									08 01								09 32		
45½	**Beverley**	d	06 30		06 38		06 58	07 15	07 43	07 57	08 07					08 37		09 00	09 37	10 11	
49¾	Cottingham	d	06 35		06 43		07 03	07 21	07 49	08 03	08 13					08 43		09 05	09 43	10 16	
53¾	**Hull**	a	06 44		06 53		07 12	07 31	07 59	08 13	08 23					08 53		09 14	09 53	10 26	

		NT D	NT	TP 1◇ E	NT D	NT	NT D	TP 1◇ E	NT	TP 1◇ E	NT D	NT	NT D	TP 1◇ E	NT	TP 1◇ E	NT D	NT C	TP 1◇ E	NT D	NT
Scarborough	d		10 00	10 47			11 28	11 47		12 47			13 28	13 47		14 47		14 54	15 47		
Seamer	d		10 05	10a52			11 33	11a52		12a52			13 33	13a52		14a52		14 59	15a52		
Filey	d		10 14				11 42						13 42					15 08			
Hunmanby	d		10 18				11 46						13 46					15 12			
Bempton	d		10 28				11 56						13 56					15 22			
Bridlington	a		10 36				12 04						14 04					15 30			
	d	10 12	10 42		11 12	11 42	12 12		12 42		13 12	13 42	14 12		14 42		15 12	15 40			16 14
Nafferton	d		10 52			11 52			12 52			13 52			14 52			15 50			16 24
Driffield	d	10 25	10 57		11 25	11 57	12 25		12 57		13 25	13 57	14 25		14 57		15 25	15 55			16 29
Hutton Cranswick	d		11 01			12 01			13 01			14 01			15 01			15 59			16 33
Arram	d					12 08															
Beverley	d	10 37	11 11		11 37	12 13	12 37		13 11		13 37	14 11	14 37		15 11		15 37	16 09		16 32	16 43
Cottingham	d	10 43	11 16		11 43	12 19	12 43		13 16		13 43	14 16	14 43		15 16		15 43	16 14		16 37	16 48
Hull	a	10 53	11 26		11 53	12 29	12 54		13 26		13 53	14 26	14 53		15 29		15 53	16 24		16 46	16 58

		NT A	NT G	NT D	TP 1◇ E	NT	NT	NT C	TP SO 1◇ H	TP SX 1◇ E	TP 1◇ E	NT	NT D	TP 1◇ E	NT	TP SX 1◇ J	NT	NT K	TP 1◇ J	NT
Scarborough	d			16 18	16 47			17 38	17 45	17 47	18 47			19 47	20 00	20 37			22 07	
Seamer	d			16 22	16a52			17 43	17a50	17a52	18a52			19a52	20 05	20a42			22a12	
Filey	d			16 32				17 52							20 14					
Hunmanby	d			16 36				17 56							20 19					
Bempton	d			16 46				18 06							20 28					
Bridlington	a			16 53				18 14							20 36					
	d			17 06			17 46	18 25					19 10		20 38			21 35		22 40
Nafferton	d			17 16			17 56	18 36					19 20		20 48			21 45		22 50
Driffield	d			17 20			18 01	18 40					19 25		20 53			21 50		22 55
Hutton Cranswick	d			17 24			18 05	18 45					19 29		20 57			21 54		22 59
Arram	d						18 12													
Beverley	d	17 00	17 25	17 34		18 03	18 17	18 54				19 15	19 39		21 07		21 43	22 04		23 09
Cottingham	d	17 05	17 30	17 39		18 08	18 23	19 00				19 20	19 44		21 13		21 48	22 09		23 14
Hull	a	17 14	17 39	17 49		18 18	18 33	19 12				19 30	19 54		21 23		21 58	22 19		23 25

Mondays to Saturdays
from 7 September

		NT SO A	TP SX 1◇ B	NT SX A	TP SO 1◇ B	NT SX	NT C	NT SX D	NT SO D	NT	NT C	TP SX 1◇ B	TP SO 1◇ B	TP SX 1◇ E	TP SO 1◇ E	NT D	TP 1◇ E	NT C	NT D	NT	TP 1◇ E	NT D
Scarborough	d		06 30		06 34						06 50	07 00	07 04	07 38	07 47		08 47			09 00	09 47	
Seamer	d		06a35		06a39						06 55	07a05	07a09	07a43	07a52		08a52			09 05	09a52	
Filey	d										07 04									09 14		
Hunmanby	d										07 09									09 20		
Bempton	d										07 19									09 30		
Bridlington	a										07 27									09 37		
	d						06 44	07 12	07 14		07 31					08 06			09 03	09 40		10 10
Nafferton	d						06 54	07 22	07 24		07 42					08 16			09 13	09 50		
Driffield	d						06 59	07 27	07 29		07 46					08 21			09 18	09 55		10 23
Hutton Cranswick	d						07 03	07 31	07 33		07 51					08 25			09 22	09 59		
Arram	d										07 58								09 29			
Beverley	d	06 30		06 38		06 58	07 13	07 42	07 44	07 57	08 06					08 36		09 00	09 36	10 10		10 36
Cottingham	d	06 35		06 43		07 03	07 20	07 48	07 50	08 03	08 12					08 42		09 05	09 41	10 15		10 42
Hull	a	06 45		06 53		07 14	07 32	07 59	08 00	08 13	08 23					08 53		09 14	09 53	10 26		10 53

For general notes see front of timetable
For details of catering facilities see Directory of Train Operators

- **A** To York (Table 33)
- **B** To Manchester Airport (Table 39)
- **C** To Doncaster (Table 29)
- **D** To Sheffield (Table 29)
- **E** To Liverpool Lime Street (Table 39)
- **G** Mondays to Fridays to Sheffield. Saturdays to Doncaster (Table 29)
- **H** To Leeds (Table 39)
- **J** To York (Table 39)
- **K** Saturdays to Sheffield (Table 29)

Mondays to Saturdays

from 7 September

Scarborough, Bridlington and Beverley → Hull

Network Diagram - see first page of Table 39

		NT	TP	NT	NT	NT	TP	NT	TP	NT	NT	NT	NT	TP	NT	NT	TP	NT	NT	TP	NT	NT
											SO	SX			SO	SX						
			1 ◇				1 ◇		1 ◇					1 ◇			1 ◇			1 ◇		
			A	B		B	A		A	B			B	A			A	B	C	A	B	
Scarborough	d	09 57	10 47			11 28	11 47		12 47				13b22	13 47			14 47		14 54	15 47		
Seamer	d	10 02	10a52			11 33	11a52		12a52				13 31	13a52			14a52		14 59	15a52		
Filey	d	10 11				11 42							13 40						15 08			
Hunmanby	d	10 15				11 46							13 44						15 12			
Bempton	d	10 25				11 56							13 54						15 22			
Bridlington	a	10 34				12 04							14 04						15 30			
	d	10 39		11 09	11 39	12 09		12 39		13 09	13 39	13 39	14 09		14 39	14 39		15 09	15 37			16 11
Nafferton	d	10 49			11 49			12 49			13 49	13 49			14 49	14 49			15 47			16 21
Driffield	d	10 54		11 22	11 55	12 22		12 55		13 22	13 54	13 55	14 22		14 54	14 55		15 22	15 52			16 26
Hutton Cranswick	d	10 58			12 00			13 00			13 58	14 00			14 58	15 00			15 56			16 30
Arram	d				12 07																	
Beverley	d	11 09		11 36	12 12	12 36		13 09		13 36	14 09	14 09	14 36		15 09	15 09		15 36	16 07		16 32	16 41
Cottingham	d	11 15		11 41	12 17	12 41		13 15		13 41	14 15	14 15	14 41		15 15	15 15		15 41	16 13		16 37	16 47
Hull	a	11 26		11 53	12 29	12 54		13 26		13 53	14 26	14 26	14 53		15 29	15 29		15 53	16 24		16 46	16 58

		NT	NT	NT	NT	TP	NT	NT	NT	TP	TP	TP	NT	NT	TP	NT	TP	NT	NT	NT	TP	NT
				SO	SX					SO	SX						SX		SX	SO		
						1 ◇				1 ◇	1 ◇	1 ◇			1 ◇		1 ◇				1 ◇	
		D	E	B	B	A			E	A	A	A		B	A		G			B	G	
Scarborough	d			16 15	16 15	16 47			17 38	17 45	17 47	18 47			19 47	20 00	20 37				22 07	
Seamer	d			16 19	16 20	16a52			17 43	17a50	17a52	18a52			19a52	20 05	20a42				22a12	
Filey	d			16 29	16 29				17 52							20 14						
Hunmanby	d			16 33	16 34				17 56							20 21						
Bempton	d			16 43	16 43				18 06							20 30						
Bridlington	a			16 52	16 53				18 16							20 38						
	d			17 03	17 03			17 44	18 22					19 07		20 40			21 32	21 35		22 40
Nafferton	d			17 13	17 13			17 54	18 33					19 17		20 50			21 42	21 45		22 50
Driffield	d			17 17	17 17			17 59	18 37					19 22		20 55			21 47	21 50		22 55
Hutton Cranswick	d			17 21	17 21			18 03	18 42					19 26		20 59			21 51	21 54		22 59
Arram	d							18 10														
Beverley	d	17 00	17 25	17 32	17 33		18 03	18 16	18 53				19 14	19 37		21 11		21 42	22 02	22 04		23 09
Cottingham	d	17 05	17 30	17 38	17 39		18 08	18 22	18 58				19 19	19 43		21 16		21 47	22 08	22 09		23 14
Hull	a	17 15	17 39	17 49	17 49		18 18	18 33	19 12				19 30	19 54		21 28		21 58	22 19	22 19		23 25

Sundays

until 20 September

		TP	NT	TP	NT	TP	NT	NT	TP	NT	NT	TP	NT	NT	NT	TP	NT	NT	NT	NT	TP	TP
		1 ◇		1 ◇		1 ◇			1 ◇			1 ◇				1 ◇					1 ◇	1 ◇
		H	B	A	B	A	B	B	A	B	B	A	B		B	A				B	A	J
Scarborough	d	09 20		10 50	11 14	11 50	12 08		13 50	14 08		15 50	16 08			17 50		18 08		19 37	19 50	21 20
Seamer	d	09a25		10a56	11 19	11a55	12 13		13a55	14 13		15a55	16 13			17a55		18 13		19 42	19a55	21a25
Filey	d				11 28		12 22			14 22			16 22					18 22		19 51		
Hunmanby	d				11 32		12 26			14 26			16 26					18 27		19 56		
Bempton	d				11 42		12 36			14 36			16 36					18 36		20 05		
Bridlington	a				11 50		12 44			14 44			16 44					18 44		20 13		
	d		09 53		11 53		12 53	13 53		14 53	15 50		16 53	17 21	17 53		18 14	18 53	19 57	20 15		
Nafferton	d		10 03		12 03			14 03			16 00			17 31				19 03		20 25		
Driffield	d		10 08		12 08		13 06	14 08		15 06	16 05		17 06	17 36	18 06		18 27	19 08	20 10	20 30		
Hutton Cranswick	d		10 12		12 12			14 12			16 09			17 40				19 12		20 34		
Arram	d																	19 19				
Beverley	d		10 22		12 22		13 18	14 22		15 18	16 19		17 18	17 50	18 18		18 39	19 24	20 22	20 44		
Cottingham	d		10 27		12 27		13 24	14 27		15 24	16 24		17 24	17 55	18 24		18 45	19 30	20 28	20 49		
Hull	a		10 37		12 37		13 34	14 37		15 34	16 35		17 34	18 05	18 34		18 55	19 40	20 38	20 59		

Sundays

from 27 September

		TP	TP	TP	NT	NT	TP	NT	TP	NT	TP	TP	NT	TP
		1 ◇	1 ◇	1 ◇			1 ◇		1 ◇		1 ◇	1 ◇		1 ◇
		H	A	A	B	B	A	B	A	B	A	A	B	J
Scarborough	d	09 20	10 50	11 50			13 50		15 50		17 50	19 50		21 20
Seamer	d	09a25	10a56	11a55			13a55		15a55		17a55	19a55		21a25
Filey	d													
Hunmanby	d													
Bempton	d													
Bridlington	a													
	d					12 53		14 53		17 50			20 15	
Nafferton	d					13 03		15 03		18 00			20 25	
Driffield	d					13 08		15 08		18 05			20 30	
Hutton Cranswick	d					13 12		15 12		18 09			20 34	
Arram	d													
Beverley	d				12 22	13 22		15 22		18 19			20 44	
Cottingham	d				12 27	13 27		15 27		18 24			20 49	
Hull	a				12 37	13 37		15 37		18 34			20 59	

For general notes see front of timetable
For details of catering facilities see Directory of Train Operators

A To Liverpool Lime Street (Table 39)
B To Sheffield (Table 29)
C To Doncaster (Table 29)
D To York (Table 33)
E Mondays to Fridays to Sheffield. Saturdays to Doncaster (Table 29)
G To York (Table 39)
H To Manchester Airport (Table 39)
J To Manchester Piccadilly (Table 39)
b Saturdays dep. 1326

Network Diagram for Tables 44, 45, 48

DM-24/09
Design BAJS

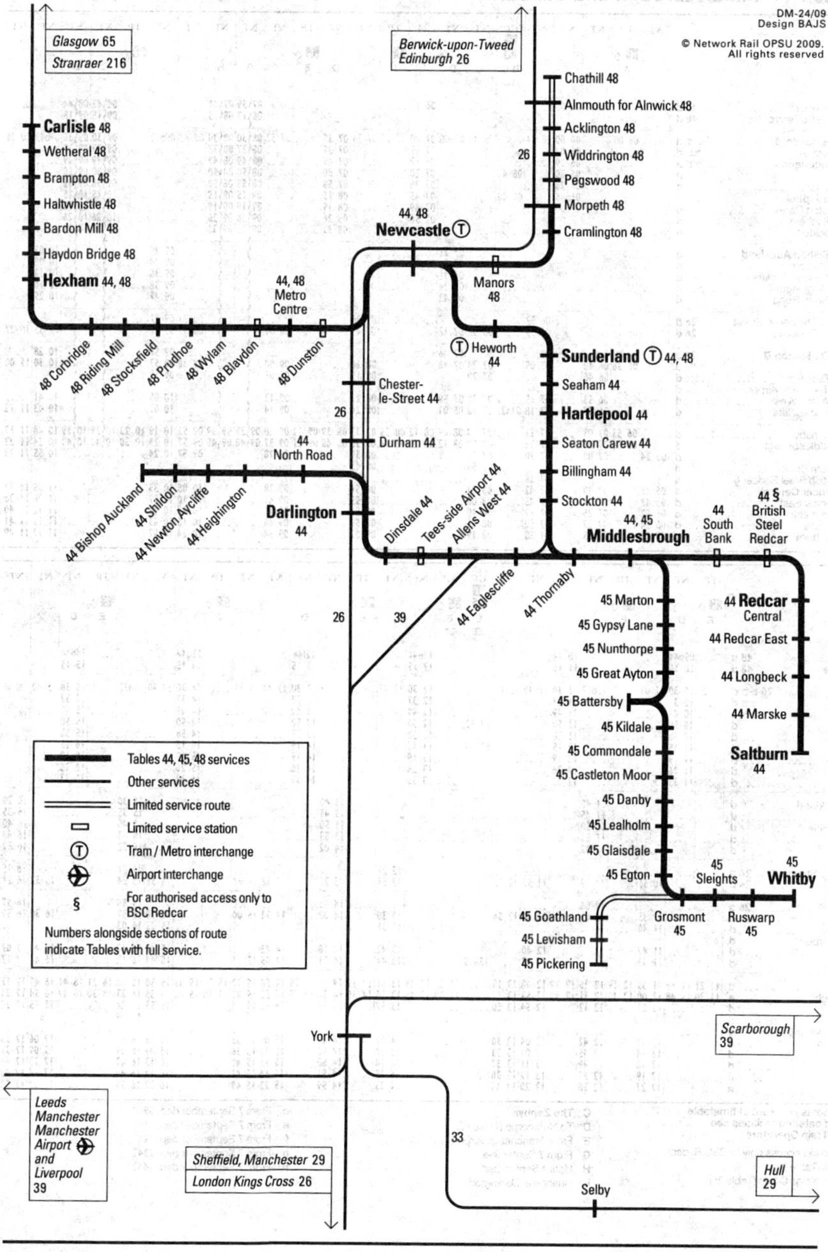
Glasgow 65
Stranraer 216
Berwick-upon-Tweed
Edinburgh 26
Chathill 48
Alnmouth for Alnwick 48
Acklington 48
26
Widdrington 48
Pegswood 48
Morpeth 48
Cramlington 48
44, 48
Newcastle
Manors 48
Carlisle 48
Wetheral 48
Brampton 48
Haltwhistle 48
Bardon Mill 48
Haydon Bridge 48
Hexham 44, 48
44, 48 Metro Centre
48 Corbridge
48 Riding Mill
48 Stocksfield
48 Prudhoe
48 Wylam
48 Blaydon
48 Dunston
Heworth 44
Sunderland 44, 48
Seaham 44
Hartlepool 44
Seaton Carew 44
Billingham 44
Stockton 44
Chester-le-Street 44
26
Durham 44
44 North Road
44 Bishop Auckland
44 Shildon
44 Newton Aycliffe
44 Heighington
Darlington 44
Dinsdale 44
Tees-side Airport 44
Allens West 44
44 Eaglescliffe
44 Thornaby
44, 45 Middlesbrough
44 South Bank
44 § British Steel Redcar
44 Redcar Central
44 Redcar East
44 Longbeck
44 Marske
Saltburn 44
26
39
45 Marton
45 Gypsy Lane
45 Nunthorpe
45 Great Ayton
45 Battersby
45 Kildale
45 Commondale
45 Castleton Moor
45 Danby
45 Lealholm
45 Glaisdale
45 Egton
45 Sleights
45 Whitby
45 Goathland
45 Levisham
45 Pickering
Grosmont 45
Ruswarp 45
Tables 44, 45, 48 services
Other services
Limited service route
Limited service station
Tram / Metro interchange
Airport interchange
For authorised access only to BSC Redcar
Numbers alongside sections of route indicate Tables with full service.
Scarborough 39
York
Leeds
Manchester
Manchester Airport
and
Liverpool
39
Sheffield, Manchester 29
London Kings Cross 26
33
Selby
Hull 29

Newcastle, Sunderland, Bishop Auckland and Darlington → Middlesbrough and Saltburn

Network Diagram - see first page of Table 44

Miles	Miles		NT	TP 1◇ A	NT	NT	NT	GC R 1 B C	NT	NT D	NT	TP 1◇ A	NT	NT D	TP 1◇ E	NT	NT G	NT H	NT	NT	TP 1◇ E	NT G	NT H	NT	NT
—	—	Hexham 48 d									06 13						07 39	07 41				08 42	08 44		
—	—	MetroCentre 48 d															08 17	08 15				09 15	09 15		
—	0	**Newcastle** 8 26 ⛴ d		06 00		06 00	06 21		06 44	07b00	07 00		07 26	07 30		07 52	08 30	08 30	08 43	09b12		09 30	09 30	09b43	10 15
—	2¾	Heworth ⛴ d				06 07					07 07			07 37			08 37	08 37				09 37	09 37		
—	12	**Sunderland** ⛴ a				06 19					07 19			07 49			08 49	08 49				09 49	09 49		
—	—	d				06 20		06 41			07 20			07 50			08 50	08 50				09 50	09 50		
—	17¼	Seaham d				06 28					07 28			07 58			08 58	08 58				09 58	09 58		
—	30	**Hartlepool** d				06a46		07 08			07 45			08 15			09 15	09 15				10 15	10 15		
—	32¼	Seaton Carew d									07 49			08 19			09 19	09 19				10 19	10 19		
—	37¼	Billingham d									07 56			08 26			09 26	09 26				10 26	10 26		
—	41¾	Stockton d									08 04			08 33			09 33	09 33				10 33	10 33		
0	—	**Bishop Auckland** d								07 21										09 25				10 03	
2¾	—	Shildon d								07 26										09 30				10 08	
5	—	Newton Aycliffe d								07 31										09 35				10 13	
6¼	—	Heighington d								07 34										09 38				10 16	
10¾	—	North Road d								07 43										09 47				10 25	
—	—	Chester-le-Street 26 d					06 32						07 36						08 33	09 21					
—	—	Durham 26 d		06 12			06 39		06 56	07 12			07 43			08 04			08 55	09 27				09 55	10 27
12	—	**Darlington** 7 26 a								07 46										09 50				10 28	
—	—	d		06 36	06 40		07 05		07 24	07 48			08 10			09 00			09 36	09 53				10 30	11 00
15¾	—	Dinsdale d			06 46				07 29				08 15			09 05				09 58					
17½	—	Tees-side Airport d																							
20	—	Allens West d			06 53		07 15		07 36	07 59			08 22			09 12				10 05				10 41	
20¾	—	Eaglescliffe d			06 57		07 18	07a27	07 38	08 01			08 24			09 14				10 07				10 43	11 12
23¾	44	Thornaby d		06 53	07 03		07 23		07 44	08 07	08 12	08 25	08 33	08 39	09 12	09 20	09 39	09 39	09 52	10 18	10 23	10 39	10 39	10 48	11 17
27	47¼	**Middlesbrough** a		07 01	07 08		07 28		07 50	08 12	08 20	08 34	08 38	08 48	09 21	09 27	09 48	09 48	09 57	10 23	10 30	10 48	10 48	10 54	11 22
—	—	d	06 34		07 08		07 30		07 51				08 39			09 28			09 57	10 24				10 55	11 23
29½	—	South Bank d							07 56				08 43												
32¾	—	British Steel Redcar § d					07 38																		
34½	—	**Redcar Central** d	06 45		07 19		07 42		08 03				08 51			09 38			10 08	10 35				11 05	11 33
35½	—	Redcar East d	06 48		07 21		07 45		08 06				08 53			09 41			10 10	10 37				11 08	11 36
37	—	Longbeck d	06 52		07 25		07 49		08 10				08 57			09 45			10 14	10 41				11 12	11 40
37½	—	Marske d	06 54		07 27		07 50		08 11				08 59			09 46			10 16	10 43				11 13	11 41
39½	—	**Saltburn** a	07 03		07 35		07 58		08 19				09 07			09 54			10 24	10 52				11 22	11 49

	TP 1◇ E	NT D	NT	TP 1◇ E	NT	NT	NT	NT	GC R 1 B	TP 1◇ E	NT	NT	TP 1◇ E	NT	NT D	NT	NT	TP 1◇ E	NT	NT	NT	TP 1◇ E	NT D	NT	NT
Hexham 48 d		09c44				10 44					11e44				12f44				13g44				14h44		
MetroCentre 48 d		10 15				11 15					12 15				13 15				14 15				15 15		
Newcastle 8 26 ⛴ d		10 30	11 01		11b27	11 30	11 40	12 15			12 30	12 42		13b29	13 30	13 44	14 12		14 30	14 40	15b22		15 30	15 40	16b06
Heworth ⛴ d		10 37				11 37					12 37				13 37				14 37				15 37		
Sunderland ⛴ a		10 49				11 49					12 49				13 49				14 49				15 49		
d		10 50				11 50			12 30		12 50				13 50				14 50				15 50		
Seaham d		10 58				11 58					12 58				13 58				14 58				15 58		
Hartlepool d		11 15				12 15			12 54		13 15				14 15				15 15				16 15		
Seaton Carew d		11 19				12 19					13 19				14 19				15 19				16 19		
Billingham d		11 26				12 26					13 26				14 26				15 26				16 26		
Stockton d		11 33				12 33					13 33				14 33				15 33				16 33		
Bishop Auckland d					11 40									13 40							15 30				16 30
Shildon d					11 45									13 45							15 35				16 35
Newton Aycliffe d					11 50									13 50							15 40				16 40
Heighington d					11 53									13 53							15 43				16 43
North Road d					12 02									14 02							15 52				16 52
Chester-le-Street 26 d												12 28									15 21				16 15
Durham 26 d			10 55		11 39		11 52	12 27				12 53		13 27		13 52	14 24			14 52	15 34			15 52	16 21
Darlington 7 26 a					12 06									14 06							15 55				16 57
d			11 35		12 07		12 30	12 56				13 30		14 08		14 32	15 00			15 30	15 57			16 30	16 59
Dinsdale d			11 40									13 35								15 35	16 03				
Tees-side Airport d																									
Allens West d			11 47				12 40					13 42		14 18		14 42				15 42	16 10			16 41	17 09
Eaglescliffe d			11 49				12 43		13a15			13 44		14 21		14 45	15 11			15 44	16 12			16 44	17 12
Thornaby d	11 21	11 39	11 55	12 19	12 25	12 39	12 48	13 12		13 21	13 39	13 51	14 19	14 26	14 39	14 50	15 17	15 21	15 39	15 50	16 18	16 21	16 41	16 49	17 17
Middlesbrough a	11 30	11 48	12 00	12 30	12 31	12 49	12 53	13 17		13 30	13 48	13 56	14 30	14 32	14 48	14 55	15 22	15 30	15 48	15 55	16 23	16 30	16 47	16 54	17 23
d			12 01		12 32		12 54	13 20				13 57		14 33		14 56	15 23			15 56	16 24			16 56	17 24
South Bank d																					16 29				
British Steel Redcar § d																									
Redcar Central d			12 11		12 42		13 04	13 30				14 07		14 43		15 06	15 33			16 06	16 36			17 06	17 35
Redcar East d			12 14		12 45		13 07	13 33				14 10		14 46		15 09	15 36			16 09	16 39			17 09	17 37
Longbeck d			12 18		12 49		13 11	13 37				14 14		14 50		15 13	15 40			16 13	16 43			17 13	17 41
Marske d			12 19		12 50		13 12	13 38				14 15		14 51		15 14	15 41			16 14	16 44			17 14	17 43
Saltburn a			12 27		12 58		13 20	13 46				14 23		14 59		15 22	15 49			16 22	16 55			17 22	17 52

For general notes see front of timetable
For details of catering facilities see Directory of Train Operators

§ For authorised access only to BSC Redcar
A From York (Table 39)
B To London Kings Cross (Table 26)
C **The Zephyr**
D To Nunthorpe (Table 45)
E From Manchester Airport (Table 39)
G From 7 September
H Until 4 September
b Change at Darlington
c From 7 September dep. 0942
e From 7 September dep. 1142
f From 7 September dep. 1242
g From 7 September dep. 1342
h From 7 September dep. 1442

Newcastle, Sunderland, Bishop Auckland and Darlington → Middlesbrough and Saltburn

Network Diagram - see first page of Table 44

	TP	NT	NT	NT	NT	GC	NT	TP	NT	NT	NT	TP	NT	NT	TP	NT	NT	NT	NT	TP	NT	NT	NT
	1 ◇ A	B		C	D	R 1 E ☕		1 ◇ G	H	J		1 ◇ A	B		1 ◇ A		H	J		1 ◇ A			K
Hexham 48 d		15b44		16 16	16 12				16 42	16 44			17 42				18 40	18 44					
MetroCentre 48 d		16 15		16 40	16 39				17 15	17 15			18 13				19 17	19 17			20 30		
Newcastle 8 26 d		16 30	16 55	16 53	16 53		17 17		17 30	17 30	17c43		18 30	18c40		19 08	19 30	19 30	19 43		20 45	20c38	22 00
Heworth d		16 37		17 00	17 00				17 37	17 37			18 37				19 37	19 37			20 52		
Sunderland a		16 49		17 14	17 13				17 49	17 50			18 49				19 49	19 50			21 04		
d		16 50		17 15	17 15	17 30			17 50	17 50			18 50				19 50	19 50			21 05		
Seaham d		16 58		17 22	17 23				17 58	17 58			18 58				19 58	19 58			21 13		
Hartlepool d		17 15		17 39	17 39	17 56			18 15	18 15			19 15				20 15	20 15			21 29		
Seaton Carew d		17 19		17 43	17 44				18 19	18 19			19 19				20 19	20 19			21 33		
Billingham d		17 26		17 50	17 51				18 26	18 26			19 26				20 26	20 26			21 40		
Stockton d		17 33		17 57	17 59				18 33	18 33			19 33				20 33	20 33			21 47		
Bishop Auckland d											18 03			19 03								21 15	
Shildon d											18 08			19 08								21 20	
Newton Aycliffe d											18 13			19 13								21 25	
Heighington d											18 16			19 16								21 28	
North Road d											18 25			19 25								21 37	
Chester-le-Street 26 d			16 41				17 26							18 29					19 37				22 09
Durham 26 d			17 07				17 33				17 54			18 52		19 10			19e56			20 51	22 18
Darlington 7 26 a											18 31			19 30								21 40	22 38
d			17 34				18 03				18 33			19 31		20 07			20 30			21 44	22 42
Dinsdale d			17 39				18 08									20 12						21 49	
Tees-side Airport d																							
Allens West d			17 46				18 15				18 43			19 42		20 19						21 56	22 53
Eaglescliffe d			17 48			18a14	18 17				18 46			19 44		20 21			20 41			21 58	22 55
Thornaby d	17 19	17 39	17 54	18 03	18 04		18 23	18 32	18 39	18 39	18 51	19 18	19 40	19 50	20 21	20 26	20 39	20 39	20 50	21 17	21 53	22 04	23 00
Middlesbrough a	17 30	17 49	17 59	18 15	18 16		18 28	18 42	18 48	18 48	18 56	19 30	19 48	19 55	20 30	20 35	20 50	20 50	20 55	21 25	22 02	22 09	23 10
d			17 59				18 30				18 59			19 56					20 55			22 09	
South Bank d			18 04																				
British Steel Redcar § d																							
Redcar Central d			18 11				18 40				19 09			20 06					21 05			22 20	
Redcar East d			18 14				18 43				19 12			20 09					21 08			22 22	
Longbeck d			18 18				18 47				19 16			20 13					21 12			22 26	
Marske d			18 19				18 48				19 17			20 14					21 13			22 28	
Saltburn a			18 27				18 56				19 26			20 23					21 22			22 37	

Saturdays

	NT	TP	NT	NT	NT	NT	GC	NT	NT	NT	TP	NT	NT	NT	TP	NT	NT	NT	TP	NT	NT	NT	NT	TP	NT
		1 ◇ L					R 1 EN ☕	B	Q	U	1 ◇ L		B		1 ◇ A				1 ◇ A	Q	U			1 ◇ A	B
Hexham 48 d									06 13	06 13										08 43	08 44				09f44
MetroCentre 48 d																				09 16	09 15				10 15
Newcastle 8 26 d		06 00		06 00	06 13	06 42		07 00	07 00	07 00		07c30	07 30	07 54		08 30	08 40	09c12		09 30	09 30	09c40	10 03		10 30
Heworth d				06 07					07 07	07 07			07 37			08 37				09 37	09 37				10 37
Sunderland a				06 19					07 19	07 19			07 49			08 49				09 49	09 49				10 49
d				06 20			06 53		07 20	07 20			07 50			08 50				09 50	09 50				10 50
Seaham d				06 28					07 28	07 28			07 58			08 58				09 58	09 58				10 58
Hartlepool d				06a46			07 17		07 45	07 45			08 15			09 15				10 15	10 15				11 15
Seaton Carew d									07 49	07 49			08 19			09 19				10 19	10 19				11 19
Billingham d									07 56	07 56			08 26			09 26				10 26	10 26				11 26
Stockton d									08 04	08 04			08 33			09 33				10 33	10 33				11 33
Bishop Auckland d												07 35						09 23				09 53			
Shildon d												07 40						09 28				09 58			
Newton Aycliffe d												07 45						09 33				10 03			
Heighington d												07 48						09 37				10 06			
North Road d												07 57						09 45				10 15			
Chester-le-Street 26 d						06 32								07 42			08 49	09 21							
Durham 26 d		06 12			06 29	06 56		07 12				07 42		07 56			08 56	09 27				09 55			
Darlington 7 26 a												08 00						09 49				10 18			
d		06 36	06 40		06 58	07 19		07 38				08 09		08 56			09 23	09 51				10 20	10 47		
Dinsdale d			06 46			07 24						08 15		09 01			09 28	09 56							
Tees-side Airport d																						10 28			
Allens West d			06 53		07 08	07 31		07 49				08 22		09 08			09 35	10 03				10 33			
Eaglescliffe d			06 55		07 11	07 32	07a44	07 51				08 27		09 10			09 37	10 05				10 35	10 59		
Thornaby d		06 53	07 01		07 16	07 39		07 56	08 09	08 12	08 27	08 33	08 39	09 16	09 23	09 39	09 45	10 11	10 21	10 39	10 39	10 45	11 04	11 21	11 39
Middlesbrough a		07 01	07 09		07 21	07 44		08 02	08 20	08 22	08 36	08 38	08 48	09 21	09 32	09 48	09 53	10 16	10 30	10 48	10 48	10 52	11 09	11 30	11 48
d	06 40		07 10		07 22	07 45						08 39		09 26			09 54	10 20				10 54	11 14		
South Bank d						07 49						08 43													
British Steel Redcar § d																									
Redcar Central d	06 50		07 20		07 32	07 57						08 51		09 36			10 04	10 30				11 04	11 24		
Redcar East d	06 53		07 23		07 35	07 59						08 53		09 39			10 07	10 33				11 07	11 27		
Longbeck d	06 57		07 27		07 39	08 03						08 57		09 43			10 11	10 37				11 11	11 31		
Marske d	06 58		07 28		07 40	08 05						08 59		09 44			10 12	10 38				11 12	11 32		
Saltburn a	07 05		07 35		07 48	08 14						09 08		09 52			10 20	10 47				11 20	11 40		

For general notes see front of timetable
For details of catering facilities see Directory of Train Operators

- § For authorised access only to BSC Redcar
- **A** From Manchester Airport (Table 39)
- **B** To Nunthorpe (Table 45)
- **C** Until 4 September. From Carlisle (Table 48)
- **D** From 7 September. From Carlisle (Table 48)
- **E** To London Kings Cross (Table 26)
- **G** From Liverpool Lime Street (Table 39)
- **H** From 7 September
- **J** Until 4 September
- **K** From Morpeth (Table 48)
- **L** From York (Table 39)
- **N** **The Zephyr**
- **Q** From 12 September
- **U** Until 5 September
- **b** From 7 September dep. 1542
- **c** Change at Darlington
- **e** From 7 September dep. 1955
- **f** From 12 September dep. 0943

Newcastle, Sunderland, Bishop Auckland and Darlington → Middlesbrough and Saltburn

Network Diagram - see first page of Table 44

	NT	TP 1◇ A	NT	NT	NT	GC R 1 B	NT	TP 1◇ A	NT C	NT D	NT	NT	TP 1◇ A
Hexham 48 d				10 44					11 43	11 44			
MetroCentre 48 d				11 15					12 16	12 15			
Newcastle 26 d	10 44		11c20	11 30	11 40		12 15		12 30	12 30	12 44	13c15	
Heworth d				11 37					12 37	12 37			
Sunderland a				11 49					12 49	12 49			
d				11 50		12 30			12 50	12 50			
Seaham d				11 58					12 58	12 58			
Hartlepool d				12 15		12 54			13 15	13 15			
Seaton Carew d				12 19					13 19	13 19			
Billingham d				12 26					13 26	13 26			
Stockton d				12 33					13 33	13 33			
Bishop Auckland d			11 40									13 26	
Shildon d			11 45									13 31	
Newton Aycliffe d			11 50									13 36	
Heighington d			11 53									13 39	
North Road d			12 02									13 48	
Chester-le-Street 26 d											12 31		
Durham 26 d	10 56		11 34		11 55		12 27				12 56	13 27	
Darlington 26 a			12 06									13 51	
d	11 30		12 06		12 35		12 58				13 31	13 53	
Dinsdale d	11 35						13 03				13 36		
Tees-side Airport d													
Allens West d	11 42				12 45		13 10				13 43	14 04	
Eaglescliffe d	11 44				12 48	13a12	13 12				13 45	14 06	
Thornaby d	11 50	12 19	12 25	12 39	12 53		13 18	13 21	13 39	13 39	13 52	14 13	14 19
Middlesbrough a	11 55	12 30	12 32	12 49	12 58		13 23	13 30	13 48	13 48	13 57	14 18	14 30
d	11 56		12 33		12 58		13 24				13 58	14 20	
South Bank d													
British Steel Redcar § d													
Redcar Central d	12 06		12 43		13 09		13 34				14 08	14 31	
Redcar East d	12 09		12 46		13 11		13 37				14 11	14 33	
Longbeck d	12 13		12 50		13 15		13 41				14 15	14 37	
Marske d	12 14		12 51		13 17		13 42				14 16	14 39	
Saltburn a	12 22		12 59		13 25		13 50				14 24	14 48	

	NT E	NT	NT	TP 1◇ A	NT C	NT D	NT	NT	TP 1◇ A	NT E	NT	NT
Hexham 48 d	12 44				13 43	13 44				14b44		
MetroCentre 48 d	13 15				14 16	14 15				15 15		
Newcastle 26 d	13 30	13 44	14 22		14 30	14 30	14 59	15c09		15 30	15 44	16 22
Heworth d	13 37				14 37	14 37				15 37		
Sunderland a	13 49				14 49	14 49				15 50		
d	13 50				14 50	14 50				15 50		
Seaham d	13 58				14 58	14 58				15 58		
Hartlepool d	14 15				15 15	15 15				16 15		
Seaton Carew d	14 19				15 19	15 19				16 19		
Billingham d	14 26				15 26	15 26				16 26		
Stockton d	14 33				15 33	15 33				16 33		
Bishop Auckland d								15 32				
Shildon d								15 37				
Newton Aycliffe d								15 42				
Heighington d								15 45				
North Road d								15 54				
Chester-le-Street 26 d								15 18				16 31
Durham 26 d		13 56	14 34				14 56	15 25			15 56	16 38
Darlington 26 a								15 58				
d		14 35	15 04				15 32	16 00			16 27	17 04
Dinsdale d							15 37					
Tees-side Airport d												
Allens West d		14 45	15 14				15 44				16 37	
Eaglescliffe d		14 48	15 17				15 46	16 12			16 40	17 15
Thornaby d	14 39	14 53	15 22	15 27	15 39	15 39	15 52	16 17	16 21	16 39	16 45	17 21
Middlesbrough a	14 48	14 58	15 27	15 35	15 48	15 48	15 57	16 22	16 30	16 47	16 52	17 26
d		14 58	15 28				15 58	16 23			16 54	17 28
South Bank d								16 27				
British Steel Redcar § d												
Redcar Central d		15 09	15 39				16 08	16 35			17 04	17 38
Redcar East d		15 11	15 41				16 11	16 37			17 07	17 41
Longbeck d		15 15	15 45				16 15	16 41			17 11	17 45
Marske d		15 17	15 47				16 16	16 43			17 12	17 46
Saltburn a		15 25	15 55				16 24	16 52			17 20	17 54

	TP 1◇ A	NT G	NT H	NT	NT J	NT	TP 1◇ A	GC R 1 B	NT C	NT D	NT	TP 1◇ A
Hexham 48 d		15 43	15 44		16 16				16 42	16 44		
MetroCentre 48 d		16 16	16 15		16 40				17 15	17 15		
Newcastle 26 d		16 30	16 30	16c44	16 53	17 22			17 29	17 30	17c44	
Heworth d		16 37	16 37		17 00				17 37	17 37		
Sunderland a		16 49	16 49		17 14				17 49	17 50		
d		16 50	16 50		17 15			17 30	17 50	17 50		
Seaham d		16 58	16 58		17 22				17 58	17 58		
Hartlepool d		17 15	17 15		17 39			17 56	18 15	18 15		
Seaton Carew d		17 19	17 19		17 43				18 19	18 19		
Billingham d		17 26	17 26		17 50				18 26	18 26		
Stockton d		17 33	17 33		17 57				18 33	18 33		
Bishop Auckland d				17 00							18 00	
Shildon d				17 05							18 05	
Newton Aycliffe d				17 10							18 10	
Heighington d				17 13							18 13	
North Road d				17 22							18 22	
Chester-le-Street 26 d						17 31						
Durham 26 d				16 56		17 38					17 56	
Darlington 26 a				17 26							18 25	
d				17 27		18 02					18 30	
Dinsdale d				17 33		18 07						
Tees-side Airport d												
Allens West d				17 40		18 14					18 41	
Eaglescliffe d				17 42		18 16		18a27			18 45	
Thornaby d	17 23	17 39	17 39	17 47	18 03	18 22	18 26		18 39	18 39	18 50	19 18
Middlesbrough a	17 33	17 49	17 49	17 54	18e15	18 27	18 32		18 48	18 48	19 00	19 30
d				17 54		18 27					19 01	
South Bank d				17 59								
British Steel Redcar § d												
Redcar Central d				18 06		18 38					19 11	
Redcar East d				18 09		18 40					19 14	
Longbeck d				18 13		18 44					19 18	
Marske d				18 14		18 46					19 19	
Saltburn a				18 23		18 54					19 28	

	NT E	NT	TP 1◇ A	NT	NT C	NT D	NT	TP 1◇ A	NT	NT	NT
Hexham 48 d	17 42				18 40	18 44					
MetroCentre 48 d	18 13				19 17	19 17				20 47	
Newcastle 26 d	18 30	18c52		19 25	19 28	19 30	19 43		20c47	21 00	21 50
Heworth d	18 37				19 36	19 37				21 08	
Sunderland a	18 49				19 50	19 50				21 20	
d	18 50				19 50	19 50				21 20	
Seaham d	18 58				19 58	19 58				21 28	
Hartlepool d	19 15				20 15	20 15				21 45	
Seaton Carew d	19 19				20 19	20 19				21 49	
Billingham d	19 26				20 26	20 26				21 56	
Stockton d	19 33				20 33	20 33				22 03	
Bishop Auckland d		18 59							21 17		
Shildon d		19 04							21 22		
Newton Aycliffe d		19 09							21 27		
Heighington d		19 12							21 30		
North Road d		19 21							21 39		
Chester-le-Street 26 d		18 31									21 59
Durham 26 d		19 04		19 37			19 56		21 00		22 08
Darlington 26 a		19 25							21 42		22 29
d		19 27		20 07			20 30		21 44		22 30
Dinsdale d				20 12					21 49		
Tees-side Airport d											
Allens West d		19 38		20 19					21 56		22 41
Eaglescliffe d		19 40		20 21			20 41		21 58		22 43
Thornaby d	19 39	19 45	20 13	20 27	20 39	20 39	20 48	21 15	22 04	22 09	22 48
Middlesbrough a	19 48	19 52	20 23	20 38	20 50	20 50	20 55	21 25	22 09	22 18	22 57
d		19 54					20 55		22 09		
South Bank d											
British Steel Redcar § d											
Redcar Central d		20 04					21 05		22 20		
Redcar East d		20 07					21 08		22 22		
Longbeck d		20 11					21 12		22 26		
Marske d		20 12					21 13		22 28		
Saltburn a		20 21					21 22		22 37		

For general notes see front of timetable
For details of catering facilities see Directory of Train Operators

§ For authorised access only to BSC Redcar
A From Manchester Airport (Table 39)
B To London Kings Cross (Table 26)
C From 12 September
D Until 5 September
E To Nunthorpe (Table 45)
G From 12 September. To Nunthorpe (Table 45)
H Until 5 September. To Nunthorpe (Table 45)
J From Carlisle (Table 48)
b From 12 September dep. 2 minutes earlier
c Change at Darlington
e From 12 September arr. 1812

Table 44

Sundays until 13 September

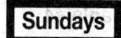

Newcastle, Sunderland, Bishop Auckland and Darlington → Middlesbrough and Saltburn

Network Diagram - see first page of Table 44

	NT A	NT	TP 1◇ B	NT A	NT	GC R 1 C	NT	NT	NT A	NT	NT	TP 1◇ D	NT	NT	NT	NT	TP 1◇ E	NT	NT	GC R 1 C	NT	NT A
Hexham 48 d																						
MetroCentre 48 d											10 48			11 48		12 48					13 48	
Newcastle 26 d		08 00	08 06				09 00	09 25	09 45	10b25	11 00		11 25	12 00	12b32	13 00			13 28		13 59	14 32
Heworth d							09 07		09 52		11 06			12 06		13 06					14 05	
Sunderland a							09 22		10 05		11 22			12 21		13 22					14 21	
d						09 10			10 06					12 21						13 42	14 21	
Seaham d									10 14					12 29							14 29	
Hartlepool d						09 34			10 31					12 45				13 30		14 06	14 45	
Seaton Carew d									10 35					12 50				13 34			14 50	
Billingham d									10 42					12 57				13 41			14 57	
Stockton d									10 49					13 04				13 48			15 04	
Bishop Auckland d				08 40						10 29					12 40							
Shildon d				08 45						10 34					12 45							
Newton Aycliffe d				08 50						10 39					12 50							
Heighington d				08 54						10 42					12 53							
North Road d				09 02						10 51					13 02							
Chester-le-Street 26 d										09 42									13 23			
Durham 26 d		08 12	08 18					09 38		10 38			11 37		12 45				13 40			14 37
Darlington 26 a				09 05						10 54					13 08			14 08				
d	08 18	08 41	09 00	09 07	09 20			10 03		11 04			12 02		13 10				14 10			15 06
Dinsdale d	08 23	08 46		09 12	09 25					11 09					13 15							
Tees-side Airport d																						
Allens West d	08 30	08 53		09 19	09 32					11 16					13 22							
Eaglescliffe d	08 32	08 55		09 21	09 34	09a54		10 14		11 18			12 13		13 24				14 21	14a33		
Thornaby d	08 38	09 01	09 16	09 31	09 43			10 20	10 55	11 24		11 35	12 19	13 09	13 30		13 34		14 27		15 09	15 22
Middlesbrough a	08 44	09 06	09 26	09 40	09 49				11 03	11 30		11 48	12 24	13 20	13 35		13 44		14 32		15 19	15 27
d		09 07			09 50					11 30			12 25		13 35				14 33			
South Bank d																						
British Steel Redcar § d																						
Redcar Central d		09 17			10 00			10 40		11 41			12 35		13 46				14 43			
Redcar East d		09 20			10 03			10 42		11 43			12 38		13 48				14 46			
Longbeck d		09 24			10 07			10 46		11 47			12 42		13 52				14 50			
Marske d		09 25			10 08			10 48		11 49			12 43		13 54				14 51			
Saltburn a		09 32			10 15			10 55		11 57			12 50		14 02				14 59			

	NT	NT	TP 1◇ E	NT	NT	NT	NT	NT	TP 1◇ E	NT	NT	NT	NT	GC R 1 C	NT	TP 1◇ E	NT	NT	TP 1◇ G	NT	NT	NT
Hexham 48 d																						
MetroCentre 48 d		14 48					15 48	16 48					17 48		18 48							
Newcastle 26 d		15 00		15 01	15 30		16 00	17 00		16b33	17 30		18 00		19 00		18 55	19b35		20 00	21 06	21 40
Heworth d		15 06					16 06	17 06					18 06		19 06					20 07		
Sunderland a		15 22					16 21	17 22					18 21		19 22					20 21		
d							16 21						18 21	18 42						20 21		
Seaham d							16 29						18 29							20 29		
Hartlepool d						16 22	16 45						18 45	19 06						20 45		
Seaton Carew d						16 26	16 50						18 50							20 50		
Billingham d						16 33	16 57						18 57							20 57		
Stockton d						16 40	17 04						19 04							21 04		
Bishop Auckland d	14 49									16 56		18 49						19 55				
Shildon d	14 54									17 01		18 54						20 00				
Newton Aycliffe d	14 59									17 06		18 59						20 05				
Heighington d	15 02									17 09		19 02						20 08				
North Road d	15 11									17 18		19 11						20 17				
Chester-le-Street 26 d					15 16						17 26						18 33				21 15	
Durham 26 d				15 15	15 37					16 46	17c37						19 08	19 48			21 24	21 53
Darlington 26 a	15 14					17 01				17 22		19 16						20 20			21 44	
d	15 16			15 42	16 19					17 24	18 31						19 32	20 32			21 45	22 45
Dinsdale d	15 21									17 29							19 37	20 37				
Tees-side Airport d																						
Allens West d	15 28									17 37							19 44	20 44				
Eaglescliffe d	15 30			15 53	16 30					17 39	18 42			19a24			19 46	20 46			21 57	22 56
Thornaby d	15 36		15 40	15 59	16 36		17 17		17 33	17 44	18 48		19 09			19 32	19 52	20 52	21 01	21 08	22 02	23 02
Middlesbrough a	15 41		15 52	16 04	16 41		17 25		17 43	17 49	18 53		19 18			19 40	19 57	20 57	21 12	21 20	22 07	23 10
d	15 42			16 05	16 45					17 50	18 54						19 58	20 58			22 08	
South Bank d																						
British Steel Redcar § d																						
Redcar Central d	15 52			16 15	16 55					18 01	19 04						20 08	21 08			22 18	
Redcar East d	15 55			16 18	16 58					18 03	19 07						20 11	21 11			22 21	
Longbeck d	15 59			16 22	17 02					18 07	19 11						20 15	21 15			22 25	
Marske d	16 00			16 23	17 03					18 09	19 12						20 16	21 16			22 26	
Saltburn a	16 08			16 30	17 11					18 17	19 19						20 23	21 24			22 34	

For general notes see front of timetable
For details of catering facilities see Directory of Train Operators

§ For authorised access only to BSC Redcar
A To Whitby (Table 45)
B From Manchester Airport (13 September from York) (Table 39)
C To London Kings Cross (Table 26)
D From York (13 September from Liverpool Lime Street) (Table 39)
E From Liverpool Lime Street (Table 39)
G From Manchester Airport (Table 39)
b Change at Darlington
c 13 September dep. 1733

Table 44

Sundays

from 20 September

Newcastle, Sunderland, Bishop Auckland and Darlington → Middlesbrough and Saltburn

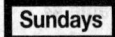

Network Diagram - see first page of Table 44

	TP 1◇ A	NT	GC R 1 B	NT	NT	NT	NT	NT	TP 1◇ C	NT	NT	NT	NT	TP 1◇ C	NT	NT	GC R 1 B	NT	NT	NT	TP 1◇ C
Hexham 48 d																					
MetroCentre 48 d								10 48			11 48		12 48					13 48		14 48	
Newcastle 8 26 d	*08 06*			09 00	*09 25*	10 00	*10b25*	11 00		*11 25*	12 00	*12b32*	13 00			*13 28*		13 59	*14b32*	15 00	
Heworth d				09 07		10 07		11 06			12 06		13 06					14 05		15 06	
Sunderland a				09 22		10 19		11 22			12 21		13 22					14 21		15 22	
d			09 10			10 20					12 21						13 42	14 21			
Seaham d						10 28					12 29							14 29			
Hartlepool d			09 34			10 45					12 45				13 30		14 06	14 45			
Seaton Carew d						10 49					12 50				13 34			14 50			
Billingham d						10 56					12 57				13 41			14 57			
Stockton d						11 03					13 04				13 48			15 04			
Bishop Auckland d							10 29					12 40							14 49		
Shildon d							10 34					12 45							14 54		
Newton Aycliffe d							10 39					12 50							14 59		
Heighington d							10 42					12 53							15 02		
North Road d							10 51					13 02							15 11		
Chester-le-Street 26 d							*09 42*									*13 23*					
Durham 26 d	*08 18*				*09 38*		*10 38*			*11 37*		*12 45*				*13 40*			*14 37*		
Darlington 7 26 a							10 54					13 08			14 08				15 14		
d	09 00	09 20			10 03		11 04			12 02		13 10				14 10			15 16		
Dinsdale d		09 25					11 09					13 15							15 21		
Tees-side Airport d																					
Allens West d		09 32					11 16					13 22							15 28		
Eaglescliffe d		09 34	09a54		10 14		11 18			12 13		13 24				14 21	14a33		15 30		
Thornaby d	09 16	09 43			10 20	11 09	11 24		11 35	12 19	13 09	13 30		13 34		14 27		15 09	15 36		15 40
Middlesbrough a	09 26	09 49				11 18	11 30		11 48	12 24	13 20	13 35		13 44		14 32		15 19	15 41		15 52
d		09 50					11 30			12 25		13 35				14 33			15 42		
South Bank d																					
British Steel Redcar § d																					
Redcar Central d		10 00			10 40		11 41			12 35		13 46				14 43			15 52		
Redcar East d		10 03			10 42		11 43			12 38		13 48				14 46			15 55		
Longbeck d		10 07			10 46		11 47			12 42		13 52				14 50			15 59		
Marske d		10 08			10 48		11 49			12 43		13 54				14 51			16 00		
Saltburn a		10 15			10 55		11 57			12 50		14 02				14 59			16 08		

	NT	NT	NT	NT	NT	TP 1◇ C	NT	NT	NT	NT	GC R 1 B	NT	TP 1◇ C	NT	NT	TP 1◇ D	NT	NT	NT
Hexham 48 d																			
MetroCentre 48 d				15 48	16 48					17 48		18 48							
Newcastle 8 26 d	*15 01*	*15 30*		16 00	17 00		*16b33*	*17 30*		18 00		19 00		*18 55*	*19 35*		20 00	21 06	*21 40*
Heworth d				16 06	17 06					18 06		19 06					20 07		
Sunderland a				16 21	17 22					18 21		19 22					20 21		
d				16 21						18 21	18 42						20 21		
Seaham d				16 29						18 29							20 29		
Hartlepool d			16 22	16 45						18 45	19 06						20 45		
Seaton Carew d			16 26	16 50						18 50							20 50		
Billingham d			16 33	16 57						18 57							20 57		
Stockton d			16 40	17 04						19 04							21 04		
Bishop Auckland d							16 56		18 49										
Shildon d							17 01		18 54										
Newton Aycliffe d							17 06		18 59										
Heighington d							17 09		19 02										
North Road d							17 18		19 11										
Chester-le-Street 26 d		*15 16*						*17 26*						*18 33*				21 15	
Durham 26 d	*15 15*	*15 37*					*16 46*	*17c33*						*19 08*	*19 48*			21 24	*21 53*
Darlington 7 26 a			17 01				17 22		19 16									21 44	
d	15 42	16 19					17 24	18 31						19 32	20 32			21 45	22 45
Dinsdale d							17 29							19 37	20 37				
Tees-side Airport d																			
Allens West d							17 37							19 44	20 44				
Eaglescliffe d	15 53	16 30					17 39	18 42			19a24			19 46	20 46			21 57	22 56
Thornaby d	15 59	16 36		17 17		17 33	17 44	18 48		19 09			19 32	19 52	20 52	21 01	21 08	22 02	23 02
Middlesbrough a	16 04	16 41		17 25		17 43	17 49	18 53		19 18			19 40	19 57	20 57	21 12	21 20	22 07	23 10
d	16 05	16 45					17 50	18 54						19 58	20 58			22 08	
South Bank d																			
British Steel Redcar § d																			
Redcar Central d	16 15	16 55					18 01	19 04						20 08	21 08			22 18	
Redcar East d	16 18	16 58					18 03	19 07						20 11	21 11			22 21	
Longbeck d	16 22	17 02					18 07	19 11						20 15	21 15			22 25	
Marske d	16 23	17 03					18 09	19 12						20 16	21 16			22 26	
Saltburn a	16 30	17 11					18 17	19 19						20 23	21 24			22 34	

For general notes see front of timetable
For details of catering facilities see Directory of Train Operators

§ For authorised access only to BSC Redcar

A From York (Table 39)
B To London Kings Cross (Table 26)
C From Liverpool Lime Street (Table 39)
D From Manchester Airport (Table 39)

b Change at Darlington
c From 8 November dep. 1737

Saltburn and Middlesbrough → Darlington, Bishop Auckland, Sunderland and Newcastle

Network Diagram - see first page of Table 44

Miles	Miles	Station		NT	TP 1◇ A	NT	NT	NT	NT B	TP 1◇ A	NT C	NT	NT	NT	NT		NT	TP 1◇ A	NT C	NT	TP 1◇ A	NT	NT	GC R 1 D	NT	TP 1◇ A
0	—	**Saltburn**	d					06 24				07 17	07 38	08 00			08 30			09 21		10 00			10 30	
2	—	Marske	d					06 28				07 21	07 42	08 04			08 34			09 25		10 04			10 34	
2½	—	Longbeck	d					06 31				07 24	07 45	08 07			08 37			09 28		10 07			10 37	
4	—	Redcar East	d					06 34				07 27	07 48	08 10			08 40			09 31		10 10			10 40	
5	—	**Redcar Central**	d					06 37				07 30	07 51	08 13			08 43			09 34		10 13			10 43	
6¾	—	British Steel Redcar §	d																							
10	—	South Bank	d														08 50									
12½	0	**Middlesbrough**	a					06 47				07 40	08 02	08 25			08 55			09 45		10 24			10 54	
—	—		d	05 45	05 57			06 49	06 56	07 23	07 32	07 42	08 02	08 25	08 32		08 55	09 00	09 32	09 46	09 59	10 24	10 32		10 54	11 00
15¾	3¼	Thornaby	d	05 50	06a02			06 54	07 02	07a28	07 37	07 47	08 07	08 30	08 37		09 00	09a05	09 37	09 51	10a04	10 29	10 37		10 59	11a05
18¾	—	Eaglescliffe	d	05 55				06 59				07 52	08 13	08 35			09 06			09 57		10 34		10 58		
19½	—	Allens West	d	05 58				07 02				07 55	08 15	08 38			09 08			09 59		10 37				
22	—	Tees-side Airport	d																							
23¾	—	Dinsdale	d					07 08				08 01	08 22									10 43				
27½	—	**Darlington** 7	a	06 14				07 20				08 11	08 31	08 54			09 24			10 17		10 54			11 19	
—	—		26 d	06 14			06 47	07 20				08 15	08 33				09 26					10 55				
—	—	Durham	26 a	06 35				07 41				08 35	09 13	09 20			09 53			10 50		11 17			11 44	
—	—	Chester-le-Street	26 a	06 42				07 48				08 43		09 44						10 56						
28¾	—	North Road	d				06 50						08 36				09 29					10 58				
33¼	—	Heighington	d				06 58						08 44				09 37					11 06				
34½	—	Newton Aycliffe	d				07 02						08 48				09 40					11 10				
36¾	—	Shildon	d				07 06						08 52				09 45					11 14				
39½	—	**Bishop Auckland**	a				07 18						08 59				09 52					11 21				
—	5½	Stockton	d						07 08		07 43				08 43				09 43				10 43			
—	10	Billingham	d						07 15		07 50				08 50				09 50				10 50			
—	15	Seaton Carew	d						07 21		07 56				08 56				09 56				10 56			
—	17¼	**Hartlepool**	d			07 03			07 27		08 02				09 02				10 02				11 02	11b23		
—	30	Seaham	d			07 18			07 42		08 17				09 17				10 17				11 17			
—	35¼	**Sunderland** ⛴	a			07 28			07 53		08 28				09 28				10 28				11 28	11 50		
—	—		d			07 30			07 55		08 29				09 30				10 30				11 30			
—	44½	Heworth ⛴	d			07 41			08 06		08 42				09 42				10 42				11 42			
—	47¼	**Newcastle** 8	26 ⛴ a	06 55		07 51		08 02	08 16		08 52	09 00	09c26	09 36	09 52		10c02		10 52	11 10		11c32	11 52		12 00	
—	—	MetroCentre	48 a			08 03			08 31		09 01								11 01				12 01			
—	—	Hexham	48 a			08 40			08e58		09f39								11g36				12h36			

Station		NT	NT	NT	TP 1◇ A		NT	NT C	TP 1◇ A	NT	NT	NT E	NT G	TP 1◇ A	NT	GC R 1 D	NT	NT		TP 1◇ H	NT	NT	NT C	TP 1◇ A	NT	NT
Saltburn	d	11 00		11 30			12 00			12 30	13 00				13 30		14 00				14 30	15 03			15 30	15 55
Marske	d	11 04		11 34			12 04			12 34	13 04				13 34		14 04				14 35	15 07			15 34	15 59
Longbeck	d	11 07		11 37			12 07			12 37	13 07				13 37		14 07				14 38	15 10			15 37	16 02
Redcar East	d	11 10		11 40			12 10			12 40	13 10				13 40		14 10				14 41	15 13			15 40	16 05
Redcar Central	d	11 13		11 43			12 13			12 43	13 13				13 43		14 13				14 44	15 16			15 43	16 08
British Steel Redcar §	d																									
South Bank	d																									
Middlesbrough	a	11 23		11 55			12 23			12 56	13 24				13 54		14 23				14 54	15 26			15 54	16 18
	d	11 24	11 32	11 55	12 00		12 24	12 32	12 50	12 57	13 25	13 32	13 32	13 50	13 55		14 24	14 32		14 50	14 55	15 27	15 32	15 50	15 55	16 19
Thornaby	d	11 30	11 37	12 00	12a05		12 29	12 37	12a55	13 02	13 30	13 37	13 37	13a55	14 00		14 29	14 37		14a55	15 00	15 32	15 37	15a55	16 00	16 24
Eaglescliffe	d	11 35					12 35			13 07	13 35					14 05	14 35					15 37			16 05	16 30
Allens West	d	11 38					12 37				13 38						14 37					15 40			16 08	16 32
Tees-side Airport	d																									
Dinsdale	d						12 44				13 44											15 46			16 14	
Darlington 7	a	11 52		12 19			12 53			13 23	13 54				14 21		14 52				15 20	15 56			16 24	16 52
	26 d						12 55										14 54					15 57				
Durham	26 a	12 22		12 50			13 18			13 48	14 18				14 50		15 15				15 51	16 24			17 08	17 14
Chester-le-Street	26 a	12 50								13 54	14 41										15 57					17 40
North Road	d						12 58										14 57					16 01				
Heighington	d						13 06										15 05					16 09				
Newton Aycliffe	d						13 10										15 09					16 12				
Shildon	d						13 14										15 13					16 16				
Bishop Auckland	a						13 21										15 19					16 24				
Stockton	d		11 43					12 43				13 43	13 43					14 43					15 43			
Billingham	d		11 50					12 50				13 50	13 50					14 50					15 50			
Seaton Carew	d		11 56					12 56				13 56	13 56					14 56					15 56			
Hartlepool	d		12 02					13 02				14 00	14 02			14 24		15 02					16 02			
Seaham	d		12 17					13 17				14 15	14 17					15 17					16 17			
Sunderland ⛴	a		12 29					13 28				14 26	14 28			14 50		15 28					16 27			
	d		12 30					13 30				14 28	14 29					15 30					16 30			
Heworth ⛴	d		12 42					13 42				14 40	14 40					15 42					16 42			
Newcastle 8	26 ⛴ a	12 36	12 51	12 55			13c33	13 51		14 09	14 36	14 49	14 49		15 06		15c31	15 51			15 57	16c37	16 51		17 26	17 34
MetroCentre	48 a		13 01					14 01				15 01	15 01					16 01					17 01			
Hexham	48 a		13j36					14k36				15 36	15 38					16 36					17 36			

For general notes see front of timetable
For details of catering facilities see Directory of Train Operators

§ For authorised access only to BSC Redcar
A To Manchester Airport (Table 39)
B To Carlisle (Table 48)
C From Nunthorpe (Table 45)
D From London Kings Cross (Table 26)
E Until 4 September
G From 7 September
H To Manchester Piccadilly (Table 39)
b Arr. 1120
c Change at Darlington
e From 7 September arr. 0901
f From 7 September arr. 0939
g From 7 September arr. 1138
h From 7 September arr. 1238
j From 7 September arr. 1338
k From 7 September arr. 1438

Saltburn and Middlesbrough → Darlington, Bishop Auckland, Sunderland and Newcastle

Network Diagram - see first page of Table 44

		NT	TP	NT	NT	NT	TP	NT		NT	NT	NT	TP	NT	GC	NT	NT	TP	NT	TP	NT	TP	NT	NT		
			1 ◇				1 ◇						1 ◇		R 1			1 ◇		1 ◇		1 ◇				
		A	B				C						D		E G			C	H	B		D				
Saltburn	d			16 30	17 00			17 30		18 00		18 30				19 00	19 30				20 30		21 30	22 40		
Marske	d			16 34	17 04			17 34		18 04		18 34				19 04	19 34				20 34		21 34	22 44		
Longbeck	d			16 37	17 07			17 37		18 07		18 37				19 07	19 37				20 37		21 37	22 47		
Redcar East	d			16 40	17 10			17 40		18 10		18 40				19 10	19 40				20 40		21 40	22 50		
Redcar Central	d			16 43	17 13			17 43		18 13		18 43				19 13	19 43				20 43		21 43	22 53		
British Steel Redcar §	d			16 46																						
South Bank	d			16 52																						
Middlesbrough	a			16 57	17 23			17 54		18 23		18 53				19 23	19 54				20 54		21 54	23 03		
	d	16 32	16 50	16 57	17 24	17 32	17 50	17 55		18 24	18 30	18 54	19 00	19 20		19 25	19 55	20 00	20 30	20 50	20 55	21 40	21 55	23 05		
Thornaby	d	16 37	16a55	17 02	17 29	17 37	17a55	18 00		18 29	18 35	18 59	19a05	19 25		19 30	20 00	20 05	20 35	20a55	21 00	21 45	22 00	23 10		
Eaglescliffe	d			17 08	17 35			18 05				19 05			19 34	19 35	20 05				21 06		22 05			
Allens West	d			17 10	17 37			18 08				19 07				19 38	20 08				21 08		22 08			
Tees-side Airport	d																									
Dinsdale	d			17 17	17 44			18 14				19 14				19 44					21 15		22 14			
Darlington 7	a			17 26	17 54			18 24		18 49		19 26				19 56	20 25	20 29			21 24	22 04	22 24	23 31		
	26 d			17 28				18 32									20 30									
Durham	26 a			*17 55*	*18 17*					*19 18*		*19 50*				*20 22*		*21 09*			*21 49*	*22 30*	*22 53*	*00 07*		
Chester-le-Street	26 a			*18 01*								*19 56*						*21 45*				*22 36*				
North Road	d			17 31				18 35									20 33									
Heighington	d			17 39				18 43									20 41									
Newton Aycliffe	d			17 43				18 47									20 45									
Shildon	d			17 47				18 51									20 49									
Bishop Auckland	a			17 55				18 58									20 56									
Stockton	d	16 44				17 43					18 41			19 31					20 41							
Billingham	d	16 51				17 50					18 48			19 38					20 48							
Seaton Carew	d	16 57				17 56					18 54			19 44					20 54							
Hartlepool	d	17 03				18 02					19 00			19 49	20 01				21 00							
Seaham	d	17 18				18 18					19 15			20b10					21 15							
Sunderland	a	17 29				18 28					19 26			20 21	20 35				21 26							
	d	17 30				18 30					19 27			20 27					21 27							
Heworth	d	17 42				18 42					19 38			20 38					21 38							
Newcastle 8	26 a	17 51		*18c16*	*18 36*	18 53				*19 34*	19 47	*20 10*		20 49		*20 38*		*21 27*	21 47		*22 07*	*22 56*	*23 16*	*00 41*		
MetroCentre	48 a	18 01									19 57															
Hexham	48 a	18 31																								

Saturdays

		NT	TP	NT	NT	NT	NT	TP	NT		NT	NT	NT	NT	NT	TP	NT	NT		TP	NT	NT	GC	NT	TP	NT
			1 ◇					1 ◇								1 ◇				1 ◇			R 1		1 ◇	
			C				A	C	J							C	J			C			E		C	
Saltburn	d					06 24					07 17	07 38	08 00		08 30			09 13			10 00			10 30		11 00
Marske	d					06 28					07 21	07 42	08 04		08 34			09 17			10 04			10 34		11 04
Longbeck	d					06 31					07 24	07 45	08 07		08 37			09 20			10 07			10 37		11 07
Redcar East	d					06 34					07 27	07 48	08 10		08 40			09 23			10 10			10 40		11 10
Redcar Central	d					06 37					07 30	07 51	08 13		08 43			09 26			10 13			10 43		11 13
British Steel Redcar §	d																									
South Bank	d														08 50											
Middlesbrough	a					06 47					07 40	08 02	08 24		08 55			09 36			10 23			10 54		11 23
	d	05 50	05 57			06 49	06 56	07 21	07 32		07 42	08 02	08 25	08 32	08 55	09 00	09 32	09 39		10 00	10 24	10 32		10 54	11 00	11 24
Thornaby	d	05 55	06a02			06 54	07 02	07a26	07 37		07 47	08 07	08 30	08 37	09 00	09a05	09 37	09 44		10a05	10 29	10 37		10 59	11a05	11 29
Eaglescliffe	d	06 00				06 59					07 56	08 13	08 35		09 06			09 49			10 34		10 49			11 35
Allens West	d	06 03				07 02					07 59	08 15	08 38		09 08			09 52			10 37					11 37
Tees-side Airport	d																									
Dinsdale	d					07 08					08 07	08 22									10 43					
Darlington 7	a	06 18				07 20					08 14	08 37	08 54		09 24			10 06			10 54			11 19		11 54
	26 d				06 48	07 20					08 15	08 38			09 24						10 57					
Durham	26 a	*07 33*				07 41					08 35	*09 11*	*09 18*		*10 16*			*10 30*			*11 16*			*11 44*		*12 16*
Chester-le-Street	26 a					07 48					08 43		*09 42*					*10 59*								*12 41*
North Road	d				06 51							08 42			09 27						11 00					
Heighington	d				06 59							08 50			09 35						11 08					
Newton Aycliffe	d				07 02							08 53			09 39						11 12					
Shildon	d				07 07							08 57			09 43						11 16					
Bishop Auckland	a				07 19							09 04			09 50						11 23					
Stockton	d						07 08		07 43					08 43			09 43					10 43				
Billingham	d						07 15		07 50					08 50			09 50					10 50				
Seaton Carew	d						07 21		07 56					08 56			09 56					10 56				
Hartlepool	d			07 03			07 27		08 02					09 02			10 02					11 02	11 21			
Seaham	d			07 18			07 42		08 17					09 17			10 17					11 17				
Sunderland	a			07 28			07 53		08 27					09 28			10 28					11 28	11 50			
	d			07 30			07 55		08 28					09 29			10 30					11 30				
Heworth	d			07 42			08 07		08 42					09 42			10 42					11 42				
Newcastle 8	26 a	*07 50*		07 53		08 02	08 17		08 51		09 00	*09c26*	09 34	09 54	*10c05*		10 52	*10 51*			*11c32*	11 52		*12 00*		*12 33*
MetroCentre	48 a			08 03			08 31		09 01								11 01					12 01				
Hexham	48 a			08 40			08e58		09f38								11g36					12h36				

For general notes see front of timetable
For details of catering facilities see Directory of Train Operators

§ For authorised access only to BSC Redcar
A To Carlisle (Table 48)
B To Manchester Piccadilly (Table 39)
C To Manchester Airport (Table 39)
D To York (Table 39)
E From London Kings Cross (Table 26)
G **The 21st Century Limited**
H From Nunthorpe (Table 45)
J Until 5 September. From Nunthorpe (Table 45)
b Arr. 2005
c Change at Darlington
e From 12 September arr. 0900
f From 12 September arr. 0939
g From 12 September arr. 1139
h From 12 September arr. 1239

Table 44

Saturdays

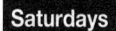

Saltburn and Middlesbrough → Darlington, Bishop Auckland, Sunderland and Newcastle

Network Diagram - see first page of Table 44

		NT	NT	TP		NT	NT	TP	NT	NT	NT	NT	NT		TP	GC	NT	NT	TP	NT	NT	NT		TP	NT	NT
				1 ◇				1 ◇							1 ◇	R 1			1 ◇					1 ◇		
				A			B	A			C	D			A	E			G			B		A		
Saltburn	d		11 30			11 56			12 30	13 00			13 30				13 58			14 30	15 00				15 30	16 00
Marske	d		11 34			12 00			12 34	13 04			13 34				14 02			14 34	15 04				15 34	16 04
Longbeck	d		11 37			12 03			12 37	13 07			13 37				14 05			14 37	15 07				15 37	16 07
Redcar East	d		11 40			12 06			12 40	13 10			13 40				14 08			14 40	15 10				15 40	16 10
Redcar Central	d		11 43			12 09			12 43	13 13			13 43				14 11			14 43	15 13				15 43	16 13
British Steel Redcar §	d																									
South Bank	d																									
Middlesbrough	a		11 54			12 19			12 54	13 23			13 53				14 21			14 54	15 23				15 53	16 23
	d	11 32	11 55	12 00		12 20	12 32	12 50	12 55	13 24	13 32	13 32	13 55		14 00		14 23	14 32	14 50	14 55	15 27	15 32		15 50	15 55	16 24
Thornaby	d	11 37	12 00	12a05		12 25	12 37	12a55	13 00	13 29	13 37	13 37	14 00		14a05		14 28	14 37	14a55	15 00	15 32	15 37		15a55	16 00	16 29
Eaglescliffe	d					12 30			13 05	13 34						14 27	14 33				15 37				16 05	16 34
Allens West	d					12 33				13 37							14 36				15 40				16 08	16 37
Tees-side Airport	d									13 41																
Dinsdale	d					12 39				13 45											15 46				16 14	
Darlington 7	a		12 20			12 49			13 21	13 55			14 20				14 50			15 20	15 55				16 24	16 51
	26 d					12 50											14 53								16 25	
Durham	26 a		12 45			13 18			13 51	14 27			14 50				15 16			15 45	16 26					17 16
Chester-le-Street	26 a								13 57	14 41										15 57						17 36
North Road	d					12 54											14 57								16 28	
Heighington	d					13 02											15 05								16 37	
Newton Aycliffe	d					13 05											15 08								16 40	
Shildon	d					13 09											15 12								16 44	
Bishop Auckland	a					13 16											15 20								16 52	
Stockton	d	11 43					12 43				13 44	13 44						14 43				15 43				
Billingham	d	11 50					12 50				13 51	13 51						14 50				15 50				
Seaton Carew	d	11 56					12 56				13 57	13 57						14 56				15 56				
Hartlepool	d	12 02					13 02				14 03	14 03				14 46		15 02				16 02				
Seaham	d	12 17					13 17				14 18	14 18						15 17				16 17				
Sunderland	a	12 29					13 28				14 29	14 29				15 15		15 28				16 27				
	d	12 30					13 30				14 31	14 31						15 30				16 30				
Heworth	d	12 42					13 42				14 42	14 42						15 42				16 42				
Newcastle 8	26 a	12 52	13 00			13b33	13 52		14 12	14 43	14 51	14 52	15 08				15b32	15 52		16 01	16 42	16 52				17 32
MetroCentre	48 a	13 01					14 01				15 01	15 01						16 01				17 01				
Hexham	48 a	13c36					14 36				15 36	15 39						16 36				17 36				

		NT	NT	TP	NT	NT	NT	TP		NT	NT	NT	TP	NT	NT	GC	NT	TP	NT	TP	NT	TP	NT	NT		
				1 ◇				1 ◇					1 ◇			R 1		1 ◇		1 ◇		1 ◇				
		H		G		B		A					J			E K		A	B	G		L				
Saltburn	d		16 30		16 59		17 28			18 00		18 28			19 00		19 35				20 30		21 30	22 40		
Marske	d		16 34		17 03		17 32			18 04		18 32			19 04		19 39				20 34		21 34	22 44		
Longbeck	d		16 37		17 06		17 35			18 07		18 35			19 07		19 42				20 37		21 37	22 47		
Redcar East	d		16 40		17 09		17 38			18 10		18 38			19 10		19 45				20 40		21 40	22 50		
Redcar Central	d		16 43		17 12		17 41			18 13		18 41			19 13		19 48				20 43		21 43	22 53		
British Steel Redcar §	d																									
South Bank	d				17 19																					
Middlesbrough	a		16 54		17 24		17 55			18 23		18 51			19 23		19 58				20 54		21 53	23 04		
	d	16 32	16 55	17 00	17 25	17 30	17 56	18 07		18 24	18 30	18 53	19 00	19 20	19 25		19 59	20 10	20 30	20 50	20 55	21 50	21 55	23 05		
Thornaby	d	16 37	17 00	17a05	17 30	17 35	18 01	18a12		18 29	18 35	18 58	19a05	19 25	19 30		20 04	20a15	20 35	20a55	21 00	21 55	22 00	23 10		
Eaglescliffe	d		17 05		17 35		18 06					19 03			19 35	19 49	20 10				21 06		22 05			
Allens West	d		17 08		17 38		18 09					19 06			19 38		20 12				21 08		22 08			
Tees-side Airport	d																									
Dinsdale	d		17 14				18 15					19 12			19 44		20 19				21 15		22 14			
Darlington 7	a		17 25		17 52		18 26			18 49		19 23			19 54		20 28				21 24	22 15	22 24	23 30		
	26 d		17 30				18 26										20 36									
Durham	26 a		17 56		18e18					19 19		19 50			20 21		21 21				21 58	22 41	23 25			
Chester-le-Street	26 a		18 02									19 56					21 39					22 50				
North Road	d		17 34				18 30										20 39									
Heighington	d		17 42				18 38										20 47									
Newton Aycliffe	d		17 45				18 41										20 51									
Shildon	d		17 49				18 45										20 55									
Bishop Auckland	a		17 58				18 53										21 02									
Stockton	d	16 43				17 41					18 41			19 31					20 41							
Billingham	d	16 50				17 48					18 48			19 38					20 48							
Seaton Carew	d	16 56				17 54					18 54			19 44					20 54							
Hartlepool	d	17 02				18 02					19 00			19 49		20 08			21 00							
Seaham	d	17 17				18 18					19 15			20f10					21 15							
Sunderland	a	17 27				18 28					19 26			20 20		20 34			21 26							
	d	17 30				18 30					19 27			20 27					21 27							
Heworth	d	17 42				18 42					19 38			20 38					21 38							
Newcastle 8	26 a	17 52	18b17		18 37	18 53	19b05			19 35	19 48	20 10		20 48	20 33		21b33		21 48		22 16	23 10	23 46			
MetroCentre	48 a	18 01									19 58															
Hexham	48 a	18 32																								

For general notes see front of timetable
For details of catering facilities see Directory of Train Operators

§ For authorised access only to BSC Redcar
A To Manchester Airport (Table 39)
B From Nunthorpe (Table 45)
C Until 5 September
D From 12 September
E From London Kings Cross (Table 26)
G To Manchester Piccadilly (Table 39)
H To Carlisle (Table 48)
J To York (Table 39)
K **The 21st Century Limited**
L Until 5 September to Manchester Airport. From 12 September to Leeds (Table 39)
b Change at Darlington
c From 12 September arr. 1339
e From 12 September arr. 1816
f Arr. 2005

Table 44

Sundays

until 13 September

Saltburn and Middlesbrough → Darlington, Bishop Auckland, Sunderland and Newcastle

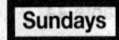

Network Diagram - see first page of Table 44

		NT	NT	NT	NT	NT	NT	TP		NT	NT	NT	NT	GC	NT	NT		TP	NT	NT	NT	NT	TP	NT		NT
								1 ◇						R 1				1 ◇					1 ◇			
							A	A						B				C					C			
Saltburn	d						09 36			10 28		11 00				12 01				13 00		14 14				
Marske	d						09 40			10 32		11 04				12 05				13 04		14 18				
Longbeck	d						09 43			10 35		11 07				12 08				13 07		14 21				
Redcar East	d						09 46			10 38		11 10				12 11				13 10		14 24				
Redcar Central	d						09 49			10 41		11 13				12 14				13 13		14 27				
British Steel Redcar §	d																									
South Bank	d																									
Middlesbrough	a						09 59			10 51		11 23				12 24				13 23		14 37				
	d		08 45		09 15	09 30	10 00	10 15		10 53		11 24	11 30			12 25		12 45		13 25	13 30	14 38	14 45			15 30
Thornaby	d		08 50		09 20	09 35	10 05	10a20		10 58		11 29	11 35			12 30		12a50		13 30	13 35	14 43	14a50			15 35
Eaglescliffe	d		08 55		09 25		10 10			11 03		11 34		12 03		12 36				13 35		14 49				
Allens West	d		08 58		09 28							11 37								13 38						
Tees-side Airport	d																									
Dinsdale	d				09 34							11 43								13 44						
Darlington 7	a		09 15		09 49		10 28			11 22		11 53				12 53				13 54		15 06				
	26 d	08 05			09 51							11 54			12 20					14 06						
Durham	26 a		09 50		10 20		11 08			11 54		12 52				13 18				14 18		15 32				
Chester-le-Street	26 a															14 09										
North Road	d	08 08			09 54							11 57								14 09						
Heighington	d	08 16			10 02							12 06								14 18						
Newton Aycliffe	d	08 19			10 05							12 09								14 21						
Shildon	d	08 24			10 10							12 13								14 25						
Bishop Auckland	a	08 34			10 20							12 19								14 31						
Stockton	d					09 41							11 41		12 36						13 41					15 41
Billingham	d					09 48							11 48		12 43						13 48					15 48
Seaton Carew	d					09 54							11 54		12 49						13 54					15 54
Hartlepool	d					10 00							12 00	12 22	12a57						14 00					16 00
Seaham	d					10 15							12 15								14 15					16 16
Sunderland	a					10 26							12 26	12 51							14 26					16 26
	d			09 28		10 28					11 28		12 28						13 28		14 28			15 28		16 28
Heworth	d			09 39		10 39					11 37		12 37						13 39		14 39			15 39		16 40
Newcastle 8	26 a		10 06	09 50	10b35	10 50	11 23			12 10	11 48	13b08	12 48			13 34			13 49	14b34	14 48	15 51		15 48		16 49
MetroCentre	48 a			10 01		11 01					11 57		12 59						13 59		14 59			15 59		16 58
Hexham	48 a																									

		NT	NT	TP	NT	GC	NT	NT		NT	NT	NT	NT	TP	NT	NT	NT	NT	TP	NT	GC	NT	TP	NT		
				1 ◇		R 1								1 ◇					1 ◇		1		1 ◇			
				C		B				D			D	C			D		E		B		A			
Saltburn	d		15 20				16 25	16 48				17 20			18 27			19 23		20 31		21 30		22 38		
Marske	d		15 24				16 29	16 52				17 24			18 31			19 27		20 35		21 34		22 42		
Longbeck	d		15 27				16 32	16 55				17 27			18 34			19 30		20 38		21 37		22 45		
Redcar East	d		15 30				16 35	16 58				17 30			18 37			19 33		20 41		21 40		22 48		
Redcar Central	d		15 33				16 38	17 01				17 33			18 40			19 36		20 44		21 43		22 51		
British Steel Redcar §	d																									
South Bank	d																									
Middlesbrough	a		15 48				16 48	17 11				17 48			18 52			19 46		20 55		21 53		23 01		
	d		15 50	16 45			16 49	17 14		17 25	17 30	17 49	18 37	18 45	18 53		19 30	19 47	20 07	20 56		21 55	22 07	23 02		
Thornaby	d		15 55	16a50			16 54	17 19		17 30	17 35	17 54	18 42	18a50	18 58		19 35	19 52	20a12	21 01		22 00	22a12	23 07		
Eaglescliffe	d		16 00			16 40	17 00	17 25		17 37		17 59	18 48					19 58		21 07	21 18	22 05		23 12		
Allens West	d		16 03							17 40		18 02	18 51					20 00				22 08				
Tees-side Airport	d																									
Dinsdale	d		16 09							17 50		18 08	18 57					20 07				22 14				
Darlington 7	a		16 20				17 18	17 43		18 05		18 18	19 07		19 25			20 17		21 24		22 26		23 30		
	26 d	15 37	16 22							18 15			19 23													
Durham	26 a		17 03				18 03	18 18		18 33		19 03	19 33		19 53			21 21		22 03		23 01		00 17		
Chester-le-Street	26 a		17 40				18 09								20 09			21 45								
North Road	d		16 25							18 18			19 26													
Heighington	d		16 33							18 26			19 34													
Newton Aycliffe	d		16 36							18 29			19 37													
Shildon	d		16 41							18 34			19 42													
Bishop Auckland	a		16 46							18 39			19 47													
Stockton	d	15 53									17 41						19 41									
Billingham	d	16 00									17 48						19 48									
Seaton Carew	d	16 06									17 54						19 54									
Hartlepool	d	16a14				17c10					18 00						20 00				21 37					
Seaham	d										18 15						20 15									
Sunderland	a					17 36					18 26						20 25				22 06					
	d				17 28						18 28					19 28	20 28									
Heworth	d				17 39						18 39					19 39	20 39									
Newcastle 8	26 a		17b04		17 48		18 02	18 34		18b52	18 48	19 05	19b51		20 09	19 52	20 49	21 06		22 20		23 34		00 50		
MetroCentre	48 a				17 59						18 59															
Hexham	48 a																									

For general notes see front of timetable
For details of catering facilities see Directory of Train Operators

§ For authorised access only to BSC Redcar

A To Manchester Airport (Table 39)
B From London Kings Cross (Table 26)
C To Liverpool Lime Street (Table 39)
D From Whitby (Table 45)
E To York (Table 39)
b Change at Darlington
c Arr. 1658

Table 44

Sundays

from 20 September

Saltburn and Middlesbrough → Darlington, Bishop Auckland, Sunderland and Newcastle

Network Diagram - see first page of Table 44

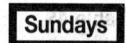

		NT	NT	NT	NT	NT	TP	NT	NT	NT	NT	GC	NT	NT	TP	NT	NT	NT	NT	TP	NT	NT
							1 ◇ A					R 1 B			1 ◇ C					1 ◇ C		
Saltburn	d							10 28		11 00				12 01			13 00		14 14			
Marske	d							10 32		11 04				12 05			13 04		14 18			
Longbeck	d							10 35		11 07				12 08			13 07		14 21			
Redcar East	d							10 38		11 10				12 11			13 10		14 24			
Redcar Central	d							10 41		11 13				12 14			13 13		14 27			
British Steel Redcar §	d																					
South Bank	d																					
Middlesbrough	a							10 51		11 23				12 24			13 23		14 37			
	d	08 45		09 15	09 30	10 00	10 15	10 53		11 24	11 30			12 25	12 45		13 25	13 30	14 38	14 45		15 30
Thornaby	d	08 50		09 20	09 35	10 05	10a20	10 58		11 29	11 35			12 30	12a50		13 30	13 35	14 43	14a50		15 35
Eaglescliffe	d	08 55		09 25		10 10		11 03		11 34		12 03		12 36			13 35		14 49			
Allens West	d	08 58		09 28						11 37							13 38					
Tees-side Airport	d																					
Dinsdale	d			09 34						11 43							13 44					
Darlington 7	a	09 15		09 49		10 28		11 22		11 53				12 53			13 54		15 06			
	26 d			09 51						11 54			12 20				14 06					
Durham	26 a	*09 50*		*10 20*		*11 08*		*11 54*		*12 52*				*13 18*			*14 18*		*15 32*			
Chester-le-Street	26 a													*14 09*								
North Road	d			09 54						11 57							14 09					
Heighington	d			10 02						12 06							14 18					
Newton Aycliffe	d			10 05						12 09							14 21					
Shildon	d			10 10						12 13							14 25					
Bishop Auckland	a			10 20						12 19							14 31					
Stockton	d				09 41						11 41		12 36					13 41				15 41
Billingham	d				09 48						11 48		12 43					13 48				15 48
Seaton Carew	d				09 54						11 54		12 49					13 54				15 54
Hartlepool	d				10 00						12 00	12 22	12a57					14 00				16 00
Seaham	d				10 15						12 15							14 15				16 16
Sunderland ⛴	a				10 26						12 26	12 51						14 26				16 26
	d		09 28		10 28				11 28		12 28					13 28		14 28			15 28	16 28
Heworth ⛴	d		09 39		10 39				11 37		12 37					13 39		14 39			15 39	16 40
Newcastle 8	26 ⛴ a	*10 06*	09 50	*10b35*	10 50	*11 23*		*12 10*	11 48	*13b08*	12 48			*13 34*		13 49	*14b34*	14 48	*15 51*		15 48	16 49
MetroCentre	48 a		10 01		11 01				11 57		12 59					13 59		14 59			15 59	16 58
Hexham	48 a																					

		NT	NT	TP	NT	GC	NT	NT	NT	NT	TP	NT	NT	NT	NT	TP	NT	GC	NT	TP	NT
				1 ◇ C		R 1 B					1 ◇ C					1 ◇ D		1 B		1 ◇ A	
Saltburn	d		15 20				16 25	16 48		17 20		18 27			19 23		20 31		21 30		22 38
Marske	d		15 24				16 29	16 52		17 24		18 31			19 27		20 35		21 34		22 42
Longbeck	d		15 27				16 32	16 55		17 27		18 34			19 30		20 38		21 37		22 45
Redcar East	d		15 30				16 35	16 58		17 30		18 37			19 33		20 41		21 40		22 48
Redcar Central	d		15 33				16 38	17 01		17 33		18 40			19 36		20 44		21 43		22 51
British Steel Redcar §	d																				
South Bank	d																				
Middlesbrough	a		15 48				16 48	17 11		17 48		18 52			19 46		20 55		21 53		23 01
	d		15 50	16 45			16 49	17 14	17 30	17 49	18 45	18 53		19 30	19 47	20 07	20 56		21 55	22 07	23 02
Thornaby	d		15 55	16a50			16 54	17 19	17 35	17 54	18a50	18 58		19 35	19 52	20a12	21 01		22 00	22a12	23 07
Eaglescliffe	d		16 00			16 40	17 00	17 25		17 59					19 58		21 07	21 18	22 05		23 12
Allens West	d		16 03							18 02					20 00				22 08		
Tees-side Airport	d																				
Dinsdale	d		16 09							18 08					20 07				22 14		
Darlington 7	a		16 20				17 18	17 43		18 18		19 25			20 17		21 24		22 26		23 30
	26 d	15 37	16 22							18 20											
Durham	26 a		*17 03*				*18 03*	*18 18*		*19 03*		*19 53*			*21 21*		*22 03*		*23 01*		*00 17*
Chester-le-Street	26 a		*17 40*				*18 09*					*20 09*			*21 45*						
North Road	d		16 25							18 23											
Heighington	d		16 33							18 31											
Newton Aycliffe	d		16 36							18 34											
Shildon	d		16 41							18 39											
Bishop Auckland	a		16 46							18 44											
Stockton	d	15 53							17 41					19 41							
Billingham	d	16 00							17 48					19 48							
Seaton Carew	d	16 06							17 54					19 54							
Hartlepool	d	16a14				17c10			18 00					20 00				21 37			
Seaham	d								18 15					20 15							
Sunderland ⛴	a					17 36			18 26					20 25				22 06			
	d				17 28				18 28				19 28	20 28							
Heworth ⛴	d				17 39				18 39				19 39	20 39							
Newcastle 8	26 ⛴ a		*17b04*		17 48		*18 02*	*18 34*	18 48	*19b05*		*20 09*	19 52	20 47	*21 06*		*22 20*		*23 34*		*00 50*
MetroCentre	48 a				17 59				18 59												
Hexham	48 a																				

For general notes see front of timetable
For details of catering facilities see Directory of Train Operators

§ For authorised access only to BSC Redcar

A To Manchester Airport (Table 39)
B From London Kings Cross (Table 26)
C To Liverpool Lime Street (Table 39)
D To York (Table 39)

b Change at Darlington
c Arr. 1658

Middlesbrough and Pickering → Whitby

Network Diagram - see first page of Table 44

Miles			NT	NT	NT	NY	NT	NT	NY	NT	NT	NY	NT	NY	NT	NT	NT
						FX			FX			FX					
				A		B		C	B		C	D	C	E		C	C
—	Newcastle	44 d	06b00	07 00	07 30		09b12	10 30		12b42	13 30		15 30		16b06	16 30	18 30
—	Darlington	44 d	06 36	07 48	08 10		09 53	11 00		13 30	14 08		15 57		16 59		18 33
0	**Middlesbrough**	d	07 08	08 13	08 49		10 38	11 49		14 16	14 49		16 47		17 40	17 54	19 49
3	Marton	d	07 13	08 18	08 54		10 43	11 54		14 21	14 54		16 52		17 45	17 59	19 54
4	Gypsy Lane	d	07 16	08 21	08 58		10 46	11 57		14 24	14 57		16 55		17 48	18 02	19 57
4½	Nunthorpe	d	07 19	08a28	09a01		10 49	12a01		14 27	15a03		16a59		17 51	18a08	20a03
8½	Great Ayton	d	07 25				10 55			14 33					17 57		
11	Battersby	a	07 31				11 01			14 39					18 03		
—		d	07 39				11 05			14 43					18 07		
12¾	Kildale	d	07 44				11 10			14 48					18 12		
16¾	Commondale	d	07 51				11 17			14 55					18 19		
18½	Castleton Moor	d	07 55				11 20			14 58					18 22		
20	Danby	d	07 58				11 23			15 01					18 25		
23½	Lealholm	d	08 05				11 30			15 08					18 32		
25½	Glaisdale	a	08 10				11 34			15 12					18 36		
—		d	08 12				11 37			15 15					18 39		
27¼	Egton	d	08 16				11 40			15 18					18 42		
—	**Pickering §**	d				09 00			12 00			15 00		16 00			
—	Levisham §	d				09 20			12 20			15 20		16 20			
—	Goathland §	d				09 48			12 50			16 10		16 50			
28¾	Grosmont	d	08 20			10 10	11 44		13 10	15 22		16 35		17 10	18 46		
32	Sleights	d	08 29				11 53			15 31					18 55		
33½	Ruswarp	d	08 34				11 58			15 36					19 00		
35	**Whitby**	a	08 41			10 35	12 05		13 35	15 43		17 00		17 35	19 07		

Saturdays

		NT	NT	NT	NY	NT	NT	NY	NT	NT	NY	NT	NY	NT	NT	NT
					G		C	G		C	H	C	J		C	C
Newcastle	44 d	06b00	07 00	07 30		09b12	10 30		12b44	13 30		15 30		16b22	16 30	18 30
Darlington	44 d	06 36	07 38	08 09		09 51	10 47		13 31	13 53		16 00		17 04		18 30
Middlesbrough	d	07 06	08 04	08 49		10 38	11 49		14 12	14 49		16 47		17 38	17 50	19 48
Marton	d	07 11	08 09	08 54		10 43	11 54		14 17	14 54		16 52		17 43	17 55	19 53
Gypsy Lane	d	07 14	08 12	08 58		10 46	11 57		14 20	14 57		16 55		17 46	17 58	19 56
Nunthorpe	d	07 17	08a18	09a01		10 49	12a01		14 23	15a01		16a59		17 49	18a01	20a01
Great Ayton	d	07 23				10 55			14 29					17 55		
Battersby	a	07 29				11 01			14 35					18 01		
	d	07 33				11 05			14 39					18 05		
Kildale	d	07 38				11 10			14 44					18 10		
Commondale	d	07 45				11 17			14 51					18 17		
Castleton Moor	d	07 49				11 20			14 54					18 20		
Danby	d	07 52				11 23			14 57					18 23		
Lealholm	d	07 59				11 30			15 04					18 30		
Glaisdale	a	08 04				11 34			15 08					18 34		
	d	08 06				11 37			15 11					18 37		
Egton	d	08 10				11 40			15 14					18 40		
Pickering §	d				09 00			12 00			15 00		16 00			
Levisham §	d				09 20			12 20			15 20		16 20			
Goathland §	d				09 48			12 50			16 10		16 50			
Grosmont	d	08 14			10 10	11 44		13 06	15 18		16 35		17 10	18 44		
Sleights	d	08 23				11 53			15 27					18 53		
Ruswarp	d	08 28				11 58			15 32					18 58		
Whitby	a	08 35			10 35	12 05		13 35	15 39		17 00		17 35	19 05		

For general notes see front of timetable
For details of catering facilities see Directory of Train Operators

§ North Yorkshire Moors Railway. For full service between Pickering, Goathland and Grosmont, please refer to separate publicity.

A From Bishop Auckland (Table 44)

B Until 1 October, 26 to 29 October. Also runs Fridays 29 May, 24 July to 4 September and Tuesdays to Thursdays 6 to 22 October

C From Hexham (Table 48)

D Until 21 May, 1 June to 16 July, 7 to 24 September and 26 to 29 October

E 25 to 29 May, 20 July to 4 September. Also runs Monday 28 September and Tuesdays to Thursdays 6 to 22 October

G Until 31 October

H 6 June, 20 June to 11 July, 12 to 26 September and 24 October

J 23 and 30 May, 13 June, 18 July to 5 September, 19 September, 3 to 31 October

b Change at Darlington and Middlesbrough

Middlesbrough and Pickering → Whitby

Network Diagram - see first page of Table 44

		NT A	NY B ☕	NT C	NT A	NY B ☕	NT A	NT A	NY B ☕
Newcastle 8	44 ⛴ d			*08 06*	09 45		*12b32*	*14 32*	
Darlington 7	44 d	08 18		09 07	*09 20*		*13 10*	15 06	
Middlesbrough	d	08 47		09 45	11 06		14 17	15 29	
Marton	d	08 52		09 50	11 11		14 22	15 34	
Gypsy Lane	d	08 55		09 53	11 14		14 25	15 37	
Nunthorpe	d	08 58		09 56	11 17		14 28	15 40	
Great Ayton	d	09 04		10 02	11 24		14 34	15 46	
Battersby	a	09 10		10 08	11 29		14 40	15 52	
	d	09 14		10 12	11 34		14 44	15 56	
Kildale	d	09 19		10 17	11 38		14 49	16 01	
Commondale	d	09 26		10 24	11 45		14 56	16 08	
Castleton Moor	d	09 29		10 27	11 49		14 59	16 11	
Danby	d	09 32		10 30	11 52		15 02	16 14	
Lealholm	d	09 39		10 37	11 58		15 09	16 21	
Glaisdale	a	09 43		10 41	12 03		15 13	16 25	
	d	09 46		10 50	12 05		15 16	16 30	
Egton	d	09 49		10 53	12 09		15 19	16 33	
Pickering §	d		09 00			12 00			16 00
Levisham §	d		09 20			12 20			16 20
Goathland §	d		09 48			12 50			16 50
Grosmont	d	09 53	10 10	10 57	12 13	13 08	15 23	16 37	17 10
Sleights	d	10 02		11 06	12 22		15 32	16 46	
Ruswarp	d	10 07		11 11	12 26		15 37	16 51	
Whitby	a	10 14	10 35	11 18	12 33	13 35	15 44	16 58	17 35

For general notes see front of timetable
For details of catering facilities see Directory of Train Operators

§ North Yorkshire Moors Railway. For full service between Pickering, Goathland and Grosmont, please refer to separate publicity.

A Until 13 September

B 20 September, 4 and 18 October, 1 November

C Until 13 September. From Bishop Auckland (Table 44)

b Change at Darlington and Middlesbrough

Whitby → Pickering and Middlesbrough

Network Diagram - see first page of Table 44

Miles			NT	NT	NT	NT	NY	NT	NT	NY	NY	NT	NT	NT	NY	NY	NY	NT	NT	NT
							FX			FX	FX				FX		MFX			
			A		A		B	A		C	D	A			E	G	H			
0	**Whitby**	d				08 52	11 00		12 41	14 00	14 45			16 05	17 30	18 00	18 00			19 15
1½	Ruswarp	d				08 56			12 45					16 09						19 19
3	Sleights	d				09 01			12 50					16 14						19 24
6¼	Grosmont	d				09 09	11 22		12 58	14 22	15 05			16 22	17 50	18 22	18 22			19 32
—	Goathland §	a					11 45			14 45	15 35				18 15	18 40				
—	Levisham §	a					12 15			15 15	16 15				18 40	19 05				
—	**Pickering §**	a					12 40			15 40	16 40				19 00	19 30				
7¾	Egton	d				09 12			13 01					16 26						19 35
9½	Glaisdale	a				09 16			13 05					16 30						19 39
—		d				09 19			13 08					16 33						19 42
11½	Lealholm	d				09 24			13 13					16 38						19 47
15	Danby	d				09 30			13 19					16 45						19 53
16½	Castleton Moor	d				09 33			13 22					16 49						19 56
18¾	Commondale	d				09 37			13 26					16 52						20 00
22¼	Kildale	d				09 44			13 33					16 59						20 07
24	Battersby	a				09 49			13 38					17 04						20 12
—		d				09 53			13 42					17 09						20 16
26½	Great Ayton	d				09 58			13 47					17 14						20 21
30½	Nunthorpe	d	07 19	08 30	09 16	10 05		12 16	13 54			15 16	17 02	17 21				18 24	20 14	20 28
31	Gypsy Lane	d	07 21	08 32	09 18	10 07		12 18	13 56			15 18	17 04	17 23				18 26	20 16	20 30
32	Marton	d	07 23	08 34	09 21	10 10		12 21	13 59			15 21	17 06	17 25				18 29	20 19	20 33
35	**Middlesbrough**	a	07 29	08 43	09 29	10 18		12 28	14 07			15 30	17 15	17 35				18 35	20 25	20 41
—	Darlington 7 44	a	*08 11*	*09 24*	*10 17*	*10 54*		*13 23*	*14 52*			*16 24*	*17 54*	*18 24*				*19 26*		*21 24*
—	Newcastle 8 44	a	08 51	*10b02*	10 52	*11b32*		13 51	*15b31*			16 51	*18b36*	*19b34*				*20b10*	21 47	*22b07*

Saturdays

		NT	NT	NT	NT	NY	NT	NT	NY	NY	NT	NT	NT	NY	NY	NT	NT	NT
		A		A		J	A		K	L	A			N	Q			
Whitby	d				08 45	11 00		12 41	14 00	14 45		15 50		17 30	18 00			19 15
Ruswarp	d				08 49			12 45				15 54						19 19
Sleights	d				08 54			12 50				15 59						19 24
Grosmont	d				09 02	11 22		12 58	14 22	15 05		16 07		17 50	18 22			19 32
Goathland §	a					11 45			14 45	15 35				18 15	18 40			
Levisham §	a					12 15			15 15	16 15				18 40	19 05			
Pickering §	a					12 45			15 40	16 40				19 00	19 30			
Egton	d				09 05			13 01				16 10						19 35
Glaisdale	a				09 09			13 05				16 14						19 39
	d				09 12			13 08				16 17						19 42
Lealholm	d				09 17			13 13				16 22						19 47
Danby	d				09 23			13 19				16 28						19 53
Castleton Moor	d				09 26			13 22				16 31						19 56
Commondale	d				09 30			13 26				16 35						20 00
Kildale	d				09 37			13 33				16 42						20 07
Battersby	a				09 42			13 38				16 47						20 12
	d				09 46			13 42				16 51						20 16
Great Ayton	d				09 51			13 47				16 56						20 21
Nunthorpe	d	07 19	08 26	09 16	09 58		12 16	13 54			15 16	17 03	17 16			18 24	20 14	20 28
Gypsy Lane	d	07 21	08 28	09 18	10 00		12 18	13 56			15 18	17 05	17 18			18 26	20 16	20 30
Marton	d	07 23	08 30	09 21	10 03		12 21	13 59			15 21	17 08	17 20			18 29	20 19	20 33
Middlesbrough	a	07 29	08 39	09 27	10 11		12 27	14 07			15 30	17 16	17 29			18 37	20 27	20 41
Darlington 7 44	a	*08 14*	*09 24*	*10 06*	*10 54*		*13 21*	*14 50*			*16 24*	*17 52*	*18 26*			*19 23*		*21 24*
Newcastle 8 44	a	08 53	*10b05*	10 52	*11b32*		13 52	*15b32*			16 52	*18b37*	18 53			*20b10*	21 48	*22b16*

For general notes see front of timetable
For details of catering facilities see Directory of Train Operators

- **§** North Yorkshire Moors Railway. For full service between Grosmont, Goathland and Pickering, please refer to separate publicity.
- **A** To Hexham (Table 48)
- **B** Until 1 October, 26 to 29 October. Also runs Fridays 29 May, 24 July to 4 September and Tuesdays to Thursdays 6 to 22 October
- **C** Until 24 September, 26 to 29 October. Also runs Fridays 29 May, 24 July to 4 September
- **D** 28 September to 1 October. Also runs Tuesdays to Thursdays 6 to 22 October
- **E** Until 21 May, 1 June to 16 July, 7 to 24 September, 26 to 29 October
- **G** 25 to 29 May, 20 July to 4 September
- **H** 29 September to 22 October. Also runs Monday 28 September
- **J** Until 31 October
- **K** Until 3 October and 17 to 31 October
- **L** 10 October
- **N** 6 June, 20 June to 11 July, 12 and 26 September, 24 October
- **Q** 23 and 30 May, 13 June, 18 July to 5 September, 19 September, 3 to 17 October and 31 October
- **b** Change at Middlesbrough and Darlington

Table 45

Sundays

Whitby → Pickering and Middlesbrough

Network Diagram - see first page of Table 44

		NT A	NY B ☕	NT A	NY B ☕	NT C	NT C	NT A	NY B ☕
Whitby	d	10 24	11 00	12 43	14 00	15 57	17 09	18 00	18 00
Ruswarp	d	10 28		12 47		16 01	17 13	18 04	
Sleights	d	10 33		12 52		16 06	17 18	18 09	
Grosmont	d	10 41	11 22	13 00	14 22	16 14	17 26	18 17	18 22
Goathland §	a		11 45		14 45				18 40
Levisham §	a		12 15		15 15				19 05
Pickering §	a		12 40		15 40				19 30
Egton	d	10 44		13 03		16 17	17 29	18 20	
Glaisdale	a	10 48		13 07		16 21	17 33	18 24	
	d	10 53		13 10		16 26	17 36	18 27	
Lealholm	d	10 58		13 15		16 31	17 41	18 32	
Danby	d	11 04		13 21		16 37	17 47	18 38	
Castleton Moor	d	11 07		13 24		16 40	17 50	18 41	
Commondale	d	11 11		13 28		16 44	17 54	18 45	
Kildale	d	11 18		13 35		16 51	18 01	18 52	
Battersby	a	11 23		13 40		16 56	18 06	18 57	
	d	11 37		13 44		17 00	18 10	19 01	
Great Ayton	d	11 42		13 49		17 05	18 15	19 06	
Nunthorpe	d	11 49		13 56		17 12	18 22	19 13	
Gypsy Lane	d	11 51		13 58		17 14	18 24	19 15	
Marton	d	11 53		14 01		17 17	18 27	19 18	
Middlesbrough	a	12 02		14 09		17 25	18 35	19 28	
Darlington 7 44	a	*12 53*		*15 06*		18 05	19 07	*20 17*	
Newcastle 8 44 ⛴	a	*13b34*		*15b51*		*18c48*	*19 51*	20 49	

For general notes see front of timetable
For details of catering facilities see Directory of Train Operators

§ North Yorkshire Moors Railway. For full service between Grosmont, Goathland and Pickering, please refer to separate publicity.

A Until 13 September
B 20 September, 18 October, 1 November
C Until 13 September. To Bishop Auckland (Table 44)

b Change at Middlesbrough and Darlington
c Change at Middlesbrough

Chathill and Morpeth → Newcastle → MetroCentre, Hexham and Carlisle

Network Diagram - see first page of Table 44

Miles	Miles			NT	NT	GR	XC	NT	NT	XC	NT	NT	NT	NT	GR	NT	NT	NT	NT	NT	NT	NT	XC	NT	NT
						R 1	1 ◇			1 ◇					R 1								1 ◇		
					A	B Ø (R)	C (R)	D		E (R)	G	H			J Ø (R)					H			K (R)		G
0	—	**Chathill**	d						07 11																
11¼	—	Alnmouth for Alnwick 26	d			07 03	07 10		07 23	07 47					08 56								11 05		
17½	—	Acklington	d						07 31																
22¾	—	Widdrington	d						07 38																
27½	—	Pegswood	d						07 44																
29½	—	**Morpeth** 26	d			07 19			07 49	08 01			08 32				09 32				10 50		11 20		
36¼	—	Cramlington	d						07 57				08 40				09 41				10 58				
45½	—	Manors	d						08 10				08 53												
46	—	**Newcastle** 3 26 ⛴	a			07 38	07 43		08 14	08 19			08 57		09 29		09 55				11 14		11 37		
—	—	Sunderland 44 ⛴	d					07 30			07 55	08 30					*09 30*			10 30					11 30
—	—	London Kings Cross 15 ⊖ 26	d													*06 15*		*07 00*		*07 30*	*08 00*				*08 30*
—	0	**Newcastle** 3 ⛴	d	06 30	06 54			07 56			08 24	08 54		09 24		09 45	10 00	10 24	10 44	10 54	11 14	11 24		11 44	11 54
48¼	2¼	Dunston	d														10 05								
49½	3½	**MetroCentre**	a					08 03			08 31	09 01		09 31		09 52	10 08	10 32	10 52	11 01	11 21	11 32		11 53	12 01
—	—		d					08 04			08 32	09 02		09 32			10 09	10 33		11 02		11 33			12 02
—	5½	Blaydon	d					08 08				09 05													
—	9¾	Wylam	d	06 44				08 14			08 40	09 12					10 17			11 10					12 10
—	12	Prudhoe	d	06 48				08 18			08 44	09 15		09 42			10 21	10 43		11 14		11 43			12 14
—	14½	Stocksfield	d	06 53				08 23			08 48	09 20					10 25			11 18					12 18
—	16¾	Riding Mill	d	06 57				08 27				09 24					10 30			11 23					12 23
—	19½	Corbridge	d	07 01				08 31				09 28					10 33			11 26					12 26
—	22¼	**Hexham**	a	07 10	07 20			08 40			08 58	09 39		09 55			10 42	10 56		11 36		11 56			12 36
—	—		d		07 20						08 59			09 55				10 56				11 56			
—	30	Haydon Bridge	d		07 29						09 08			10 04								12 05			
—	33¾	Bardon Mill	d		07 36						09 14											12 12			
—	38½	Haltwhistle	d		07 43						09 21			10 16				11 15				12 19			
—	50¾	Brampton (Cumbria)	d		07 58						09 37											12 34			
—	57½	Wetheral	d		08 07						09 45											12 43			
—	61¾	**Carlisle** 3	a		08 17						09 56			10 46				11 46				12 53			

		NT	NT	GR		NT	NT	NT	NT	NT	XC	NT	NT	NT	NT	NT	NT	NT	NT	XC	NT	NT	NT	NT	NT
				R 1		◇					1 ◇									1 ◇					
				J Ø (R)		L		G			K (R)		H				G			C (R)		G		N	
Chathill	d																								
Alnmouth for Alnwick 26	d			12 00							13 06									15 05					
Acklington	d																								
Widdrington	d																								
Pegswood	d																								
Morpeth 26	d	11 50							12 50					13 50				14 50					15 50		
Cramlington	d	11 58							12 58					13 58				14 58					15 58		
Manors	d								13 11					14 10											
Newcastle 8 26 ⛴	a	12 13		12 34					13 13		13 36			14 13				15 13		15 35			16 13		
Sunderland 44 ⛴	d							12 30					13 30				14 28					15 30			
London Kings Cross 15 ⊖ 26	d	*09 00*							*10 00*			*10 30*		*11 00*				*12 00*					*13 00*		*13 30*
Newcastle 8 ⛴	d	12 14	12 24			12 39	12 44	12 54	13 14	13 26		13 44	13 54	14 14	14 24	14 44	14 54	15 14	15 25		15 44	15 54	16 14	16 24	16 44
Dunston	d																								
MetroCentre	a	12 22	12 32			12 46	12 52	13 01	13 22	13 33		13 51	14 01	14 22	14 31	14 52	15 01	15 21	15 33		15 51	16 01	16 21	16 31	16 51
	d					12 46		13 02		13 33			14 02		14 32		15 02		15 33			16 02		16 32	
Blaydon	d																								
Wylam	d							13 10					14 10		14 40		15 10					16 10		16 40	
Prudhoe	d							13 14		13 44			14 14		14 44		15 14		15 44			16 14		16 44	
Stocksfield	d							13 18					14 18				15 18					16 18		16 48	
Riding Mill	d							13 23					14 23				15 23					16 23		16 53	
Corbridge	d							13 26					14 26				15 26					16 26		16 56	
Hexham	a					13 06		13 36		13 59			14 36		14 56		15 36		15 56			16 36		17 02	
	d					13 08				13 59					14 57				15 56					17 03	
Haydon Bridge	d														15 06				16 06					17 12	
Bardon Mill	d																		16 13						
Haltwhistle	d					13 26				14 18					15 17				16 20					17 23	
Brampton (Cumbria)	d																		16 36						
Wetheral	d																		16 44						
Carlisle 8	a					13 59				14 54					15 49				16 56					17 58	

For general notes see front of timetable
For details of catering facilities see Directory of Train Operators

A To Glasgow Central (Table 216)

B From Edinburgh to London Kings Cross (Table 26)
C From Edinburgh to Plymouth (Table 51)
D From Hartlepool (Table 44)
E From Edinburgh to Reading (Table 51)
G From Middlesbrough (Table 44)

H From Nunthorpe (Table 45)
J From Glasgow Central to London Kings Cross (Table 26)
K From Glasgow Central (Table 51) to Penzance (Table 135)
L To Stranraer (Table 216)
N To Whitehaven (Table 100)

Mondays to Fridays
until 4 September

Chathill and Morpeth → Newcastle → MetroCentre, Hexham and Carlisle

Network Diagram - see first page of Table 44

		NT	NT	NT	NT	XC	NT	NT	NT	GR	NT	NT	NT	XC	NT	NT	GR	NT	NT	NT	NT	NT	GR
		A		◇ B		1 ◇ C	D			R 1 E ✕				1 ◇ G	D		R 1 H				J		R 1 K
Chathill	d															19 08							
Alnmouth for Alnwick	26 d					17 09				18 00				19 08		19 20	19 42						22 05
Acklington	d															19 28							
Widdrington	d															19 35							
Pegswood	d															19 41							
Morpeth	26 d		16 50			17 24					18 32		19 01			19 45	19 59				21 34		22 22
Cramlington	d		16 58								18 40		19 09			19 54					21 42		
Manors	d																						
Newcastle 8	26 ⛴ a		17 12			17 42				18 32	18 55		19 25	19 40		20 06	20 20				21 56		22 43
Sunderland	44 ⛴ d	16 30					17 30					18 30			19 27				20 27	21 27			
London Kings Cross 15	⊖ 26 d			14 00			15 00					16 00				17 00		17 30	18 00	18 19		19 00	
Newcastle 8	⛴ d	16 54		17 13	17 26		17 54	18 01	18 24			19 10			19 50	20 10		20 55	21 22	21 55		22 30	
Dunston	d							18 07															
MetroCentre	a	17 01		17 20	17 33		18 01	18 10	18 31			19 17			19 57	20 17		21 03	21 29	22 04		22 37	
	d	17 02		17 20	17 34		18 01		18 32			19 18				20 18			21 30			22 38	
Blaydon	d				17 39																		
Wylam	d	17 10		17 29	17 46		18 09		18 40			19 26				20 26			21 38			22 46	
Prudhoe	d	17 14		17 32	17 49		18 13		18 44			19 30				20 30			21 42			22 50	
Stocksfield	d	17 18			17 54		18 18		18 48			19 34				20 34			21 46			22 54	
Riding Mill	d	17 23			17 58		18 22		18 53			19 39				20 39			21 51			22 59	
Corbridge	d	17 26			18 02		18 26		18 56			19 42				20 42			21 54			23 02	
Hexham	a	17 36		17 45	18 10		18 31		19 02			19 48				20 51			22 00			23 11	
	d			17 45			18 31		19 03			19 49							22 01				
Haydon Bridge	d			17 54			18 40					19 58							22 10				
Bardon Mill	d			18 01			18 47												22 16				
Haltwhistle	d			18 08			18 54		19 21			20 09							22 23				
Brampton (Cumbria)	d			18 23					19 37										22 39				
Wetheral	d			18 32					19 45										22 47				
Carlisle 8	a			18 43			19 28		19 57			20 42							22 58				

Mondays to Fridays
from 7 September

		NT	NT	GR	XC	NT	NT	XC	NT	NT	NT	NT	GR	NT		NT	NT	NT	NT	NT	NT	XC	NT	NT	NT
			L	R 1 N Ø	1 ◇ Q	U		1 ◇ V	D	A			R 1 E Ø						A			1 ◇ X		D	
Chathill	d						07 11																		
Alnmouth for Alnwick	26 d			07 03	07 10		07 23	07 47					08 56									11 05			
Acklington	d						07 31																		
Widdrington	d						07 38																		
Pegswood	d						07 44																		
Morpeth	26 d			07 19			07 49	08 01			08 32					09 32				10 50		11 20			11 50
Cramlington	d						07 57				08 40					09 41				10 58					11 58
Manors	d						08 10				08 53														
Newcastle 8	26 ⛴ a			07 38	07 43		08 14	08 19			08 57		09 29			09 55				11 14		11 37			12 13
Sunderland	44 ⛴ d					07 30			07 55	08 30						09 30			10 30					11 30	
London Kings Cross 15	⊖ 26 d													06 15			07 00		07 30	08 00				08 30	09 00
Newcastle 8	⛴ d	06 25	06 49			07 56			08 24	08 54		09 24		09 45		10 00	10 24	10 44	10 54	11 14	11 24		11 44	11 54	12 14
Dunston	d															10 05									
MetroCentre	a					08 03			08 31	09 01		09 31		09 52		10 08	10 31	10 52	11 01	11 21	11 32		11 53	12 01	12 22
	d					08 04			08 32	09 02		09 32				10 09	10 32		11 02		11 33			12 02	
Blaydon	d					08 08				09 05															
Wylam	d	06 40				08 14			08 40	09 12						10 17			11 10					12 10	
Prudhoe	d	06 44				08 18			08 44	09 15		09 42				10 21	10 42		11 14		11 43			12 14	
Stocksfield	d	06 48				08 23			08 48	09 20						10 25			11 18					12 18	
Riding Mill	d	06 53				08 27				09 24						10 30			11 23					12 23	
Corbridge	d	06 56				08 31				09 28						10 33			11 26					12 26	
Hexham	a	07 07	07 16			08 40			09 01	09 39		09 55				10 42	10 55		11 38		11 58			12 38	
	d		07 16						09 02			09 55					10 55				11 59				
Haydon Bridge	d		07 25						09 11												12 08				
Bardon Mill	d		07 32						09 17												12 14				
Haltwhistle	d		07 39						09 24			10 16					11 14				12 21				
Brampton (Cumbria)	d		07 54						09 40												12 37				
Wetheral	d		08 03						09 48												12 46				
Carlisle 8	a		08 17						10 00			10 48					11 46				12 56				

For general notes see front of timetable
For details of catering facilities see Directory of Train Operators

A From Nunthorpe (Table 45)
B To Stranraer (Table 216)
C From Edinburgh to Bristol Temple Meads (Table 51)
D From Middlesbrough (Table 44)
E From Glasgow Central to London Kings Cross (Table 26)
G From Edinburgh to Birmingham New Street (Table 51)
H From Edinburgh (Table 26)
J To Middlesbrough (Table 44)
K From Glasgow Central to York (Table 26)
L To Glasgow Central (Table 216)
N From Edinburgh to London Kings Cross (Table 26)
Q From Edinburgh to Plymouth (Table 51)
U From Hartlepool (Table 44)
V From Edinburgh to Reading (Table 51)
X From Glasgow Central (Table 51) to Penzance (Table 135)

Chathill and Morpeth → Newcastle → MetroCentre, Hexham and Carlisle

Network Diagram - see first page of Table 44

		NT	GR	NT	NT	NT		NT	NT	XC	NT	NT	NT	NT	NT	NT	NT	NT	XC	NT		NT	NT	NT	NT
			R 1	◇						1 ◇									1 ◇						
			A Ø ⌶	B		C				D ⌶		E				C			G ⌶			C		H	
Chathill	d																								
Alnmouth for Alnwick	26 d		12 00							13 06									15 05						
Acklington	d																								
Widdrington	d																								
Pegswood	d																								
Morpeth	26 d							12 50					13 50				14 50						15 50		
Cramlington	d							12 58					13 58				14 58						15 58		
Manors	d							13 11					14 10												
Newcastle 8	26 ⛴ a		12 34					13 13		13 36			14 13				15 13		15 35				16 13		
Sunderland	44 ⛴ d					12 30						13 30				14 29						15 30			
London Kings Cross 15	⊖ 26 d							*10 00*			*10 30*		*11 00*				*12 00*						*13 00*		*13 30*
Newcastle 8	⛴ d	12 24		12 39	12 44	12 54		13 14	13 26		13 44	13 54	14 14	14 24	14 44	14 54	15 14	15 25		15 44		15 54	16 14	16 24	16 44
Dunston	d																								
MetroCentre	a	12 32		12 46	12 52	13 01		13 22	13 33		13 51	14 01	14 22	14 31	14 52	15 01	15 21	15 33		15 51		16 01	16 21	16 31	16 51
	d			12 46		13 02			13 33			14 02		14 32		15 02		15 33				16 02		16 32	
Blaydon	d																								
Wylam	d					13 10						14 10		14 40		15 10						16 10		16 40	
Prudhoe	d					13 14			13 44			14 14		14 44		15 14		15 44				16 14		16 44	
Stocksfield	d					13 18						14 18				15 18						16 18		16 48	
Riding Mill	d					13 23						14 23				15 23						16 23		16 53	
Corbridge	d					13 26						14 26				15 26						16 26		16 56	
Hexham	a			13 06		13 38			14 00			14 38		14 56		15 38		15 56				16 36		17 02	
	d			13 08					14 01					14 57				15 56						17 03	
Haydon Bridge	d													15 06				16 06						17 12	
Bardon Mill	d																	16 13							
Haltwhistle	d			13 26					14 19					15 17				16 20						17 23	
Brampton (Cumbria)	d																	16 36							
Wetheral	d																	16 44							
Carlisle 8	a			13 59					14 59					15 49				16 55						17 58	

		NT	NT	NT	NT	XC	NT	NT	NT	GR	NT	NT	NT	XC	NT	NT	GR	NT	NT	NT	NT	NT	GR		
				◇		1 ◇				R 1				1 ◇			R 1						R 1		
		E		B		J ⌶	C			A ✕ ⌶				K ⌶	C		L ⊡				N		Q ⊡		
Chathill	d															19 08									
Alnmouth for Alnwick	26 d					17 09				18 00				19 08		19 20	19 42						22 05		
Acklington	d															19 28									
Widdrington	d															19 35									
Pegswood	d															19 41									
Morpeth	26 d		16 50			17 24					18 32		19 01			19 45	19 59				21 34		22 22		
Cramlington	d		16 58								18 40		19 09			19 54					21 42				
Manors	d																								
Newcastle 8	26 ⛴ a		17 12			17 40				18 32	18 55		19 25	19 40		20 06	20 20				21 56		22 43		
Sunderland	44 ⛴ d	16 30					17 30					*18 30*			19 27				*20 27*	*21 27*					
London Kings Cross 15	⊖ 26 d			*14 00*			*15 00*					*16 00*				*17 00*		*17 30*	*18 00*	*18 19*		*19 00*			
Newcastle 8	⛴ d	16 54		17 13	17 26		17 54	18 01	18 24			19 10			19 50	20 10		20 55	21 22	21 55		22 26			
Dunston	d							18 07																	
MetroCentre	a	17 01		17 20	17 33		18 01	18 10	18 31			19 17			19 57	20 17		21 03	21 29	22 04		22 33			
	d	17 02		17 20	17 34		18 01		18 32			19 18				20 18			21 30			22 34			
Blaydon	d				17 39																				
Wylam	d	17 10		17 29	17 46		18 09		18 40			19 26				20 26			21 38			22 42			
Prudhoe	d	17 14		17 32	17 49		18 13		18 44			19 30				20 30			21 42			22 46			
Stocksfield	d	17 18			17 54		18 18		18 48			19 34				20 34			21 46			22 50			
Riding Mill	d	17 23			17 58		18 22		18 53			19 39				20 39			21 51			22 55			
Corbridge	d	17 26			18 02		18 26		18 56			19 42				20 42			21 54			22 58			
Hexham	a	17 36		17 45	18 14		18 31		19 04			19 48				20 53			22 01			23 09			
	d			17 45			18 31		19 05			19 49							22 02						
Haydon Bridge	d			17 54			18 40					19 58							22 11						
Bardon Mill	d			18 01			18 47												22 17						
Haltwhistle	d			18 08			18 54		19 23			20 09							22 24						
Brampton (Cumbria)	d			18 23					19 39										22 40						
Wetheral	d			18 32					19 47										22 48						
Carlisle 8	a			18 45			19 28		19 59			20 42							23 01						

For general notes see front of timetable
For details of catering facilities see Directory of Train Operators

A From Glasgow Central to London Kings Cross (Table 26)
B To Stranraer (Table 216)
C From Middlesbrough (Table 44)
D From Edinburgh (Table 51) to Penzance (Table 135)
E From Nunthorpe (Table 45)
G From Edinburgh to Plymouth (Table 51)
H To Whitehaven (Table 100)
J From Edinburgh to Bristol Temple Meads (Table 51)
K From Edinburgh to Birmingham New Street (Table 51)
L From Edinburgh (Table 26)
N To Middlesbrough (Table 44)
Q From Glasgow Central to York (Table 26)

Table 48

Saturdays

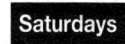

until 5 September

Chathill and Morpeth → Newcastle → MetroCentre, Hexham and Carlisle

Network Diagram - see first page of Table 44

	NT A	XC 1◇ B	GR R 1 C	NT D	NT E	NT	XC 1◇ G	NT H		NT	GR R 1 J	XC 1◇ K	NT	NT	NT	NT	NT H		NT	NT	XC 1◇ L	NT	NT E	NT
Chathill d						07 22																		
Alnmouth for Alnwick 26 d		07 11	07 18			07 34	07 55				08 58	09 09									11 04			
Acklington d						07 42																		
Widdrington d						07 49																		
Pegswood d						07 55																		
Morpeth 26 d			07 34			08 00	08 09							09 32					10 50		11 19			11 50
Cramlington d						08 08								09 40					10 58					11 58
Manors d						08 21																		
Newcastle 8 26 a		07 41	07 53			08 25	08 27				09 31	09 39		09 55					11 14		11 39			12 13
Sunderland 44 d				07 30	07 55			08 28							09 29		10 30						11 30	
London Kings Cross 15 ⊖ 26 d													06 15		07 00				08 00				08 30	09 00
Newcastle 8 d	06 35			07 56	08 24			08 53		09 24			09 44	10 00	10 24	10 44	10 54		11 14	11 22		11 44	11 54	12 14
Dunston d														10 05										
MetroCentre a				08 03	08 31			09 00		09 31			09 51	10 08	10 31	10 53	11 01		11 21	11 32		11 52	12 01	12 22
d				08 04	08 32			09 01		09 32				10 09	10 32		11 02			11 33			12 02	
Blaydon d				08 08				09 03																
Wylam d	06 49			08 14	08 40			09 10						10 17			11 10						12 10	
Prudhoe d	06 53			08 18	08 44			09 13		09 42				10 21	10 42		11 14			11 43			12 14	
Stocksfield d	06 57			08 23	08 48			09 18						10 25			11 18						12 18	
Riding Mill d	07 02			08 27				09 22						10 30			11 23						12 23	
Corbridge d	07 05			08 31				09 26						10 33			11 26						12 26	
Hexham a	07 10			08 40	08 58			09 36		09 55				10 42	10 55		11 36			11 56			12 36	
d	07 11				08 59					09 56					10 55					11 57				
Haydon Bridge d	07 20				09 08					10 05										12 06				
Bardon Mill d	07 26				09 14															12 12				
Haltwhistle d	07 33				09 21					10 16					11 14					12 19				
Brampton (Cumbria) d	07 49				09 37															12 35				
Wetheral d	07 57				09 45															12 44				
Carlisle 8 a	08 08				09 56					10 47					11 45					12 54				

	NT	NT N	NT	NT E		GR R 1 QU	NT	NT	XC 1◇ V	NT	NT H	NT	NT		NT	NT E	NT	NT	XC 1◇ X	NT	NT E	NT		NT Y
Chathill d																								
Alnmouth for Alnwick 26 d						12 28			13 05										15 05					
Acklington d																								
Widdrington d																								
Pegswood d																								
Morpeth 26 d							12 50					13 50					14 50					15 50		
Cramlington d							12 58					13 58					14 58					15 58		
Manors d							13 11																	
Newcastle 8 26 a						13 02	13 13		13 35			14 13					15 13		15 35			16 13		
Sunderland 44 d				12 30							13 30					14 31					15 30			
London Kings Cross 15 ⊖ 26 d				09 30			10 00			10 30		11 00				11 30	12 00				12 30	13 00		
Newcastle 8 d	12 24	12 39	12 44	12 54			13 14	13 24		13 44	13 54	14 14	14 24		14 44	14 54	15 14	15 24		15 44	15 54	16 14		16 24
Dunston d																								
MetroCentre a	12 31	12 46	12 52	13 01			13 22	13 31		13 51	14 01	14 22	14 32		14 52	15 01	15 21	15 31		15 51	16 01	16 21		16 31
d		12 46		13 02				13 32			14 02		14 33			15 02		15 32			16 02			16 32
Blaydon d																								
Wylam d				13 10							14 10		14 41			15 10					16 10			16 40
Prudhoe d				13 14				13 42			14 14		14 45			15 14		15 42			16 14			16 44
Stocksfield d				13 18							14 18					15 18					16 18			16 48
Riding Mill d				13 23							14 23					15 23					16 23			16 53
Corbridge d				13 26							14 26					15 26					16 26			16 56
Hexham a		13 06		13 36				13 55			14 36		14 57			15 36		15 55			16 36			17 02
d		13 08						13 56					14 58					15 56						17 03
Haydon Bridge d													15 07					16 05						17 12
Bardon Mill d																		16 11						
Haltwhistle d		13 26						14 14					15 18					16 18						17 23
Brampton (Cumbria) d																		16 34						
Wetheral d																		16 43						
Carlisle 8 a		14 00						14 45					15 49					16 54						17 58

For general notes see front of timetable
For details of catering facilities see Directory of Train Operators

- **A** To Glasgow Central (Table 216)
- **B** From Edinburgh (Table 26) to Plymouth (Table 51)
- **C** From Edinburgh to London Kings Cross (Table 26)
- **D** From Hartlepool (Table 44)
- **E** From Middlesbrough (Table 44)
- **G** From Edinburgh to Reading (Table 51)
- **H** From Nunthorpe (Table 45)
- **J** From Glasgow Central to London Kings Cross (Table 26)
- **K** From Glasgow Central (Table 51) to Newquay (Table 135)
- **L** From Glasgow Central (Table 51) to Penzance (Table 135)
- **N** To Stranraer (Table 216)
- **Q** From Inverness (Table 229) to London Kings Cross (Table 26)
- **U** **The Highland Chieftain**
- **V** From Edinburgh (Table 51) to Penzance (Table 135)
- **X** From Edinburgh to Plymouth (Table 51)
- **Y** To Whitehaven (Table 100)

Chathill and Morpeth → Newcastle → MetroCentre, Hexham and Carlisle

Saturdays

until 5 September

Network Diagram - see first page of Table 44

Station		NT	NT A	NT B	NT	NT	XC 1◇ C	NT D	NT	NT	GR R 1 E	NT	NT	NT	XC 1◇ G	NT D	NT	NT	GR R 1 H	NT	NT	NT
Chathill	d																19 12					
Alnmouth for Alnwick	26 d						17 05				17 58				19 08		19 24		20 08			
Acklington	d																19 32					
Widdrington	d																19 39					
Pegswood	d																19 45					
Morpeth	26 d				16 50		17 20					18 32		19 04			19 49		20 25		21 15	
Cramlington	d				16 58							18 40		19 12			19 58				21 23	
Manors	d																					
Newcastle 8	26 ⛴ a				17 13		17 38				18 32	18 56		19 26	19 41		20 12		20 46		21 40	
Sunderland	44 ⛴ d		16 30					17 30					*18 30*			19 27				20 27		21 27
London Kings Cross 15	⊖ 26 d		*13 30*	*14 00*						*15 00*						*16 00*	*17 00*			*18 00*		*18 35*
Newcastle 8	⛴ d	16 44	16 54	17 13		17 24		17 54	18 02	18 24			19 10			19 50	20 14	20 30		21 22		21 56
Dunston	d					17 30			18 07													
MetroCentre	a	16 51	17 01	17 20		17 32		18 01	18 12	18 31			19 17			19 58	20 21	20 39		21 29		22 04
	d		17 02	17 20		17 33		18 02		18 32			19 18				20 22			21 30		
Blaydon	d					17 37																
Wylam	d		17 10	17 29		17 44		18 10		18 40			19 26				20 30			21 38		
Prudhoe	d		17 14	17 32		17 47		18 14		18 44			19 30				20 34			21 42		
Stocksfield	d		17 18			17 52		18 18		18 48			19 34				20 38			21 46		
Riding Mill	d		17 23			17 56		18 23		18 53			19 39				20 43			21 51		
Corbridge	d		17 26			18 00		18 26		18 56			19 42				20 46			21 54		
Hexham	a		17 36	17 48		18 08		18 32		19 02			19 48				20 55			22 00		
	d			17 48				18 33		19 03			19 49							22 01		
Haydon Bridge	d			17 57				18 42					19 58							22 10		
Bardon Mill	d			18 04				18 48												22 16		
Haltwhistle	d			18 11				18 55		19 21			20 09							22 23		
Brampton (Cumbria)	d			18 26						19 37										22 39		
Wetheral	d			18 35						19 45										22 47		
Carlisle 8	a			18 46				19 29		19 57			20 42							22 57		

Saturdays

from 12 September

Station		NT J	XC 1◇ K	GR R 1 L	NT N	NT D	NT	XC 1◇ Q	NT A	NT	GR R 1 E	XC 1◇ U	NT	NT	NT	NT	NT A	NT	NT	XC 1◇ V	NT	NT D	NT
Chathill	d						07 22																
Alnmouth for Alnwick	26 d		07 11	07 18			07 34	07 55			08 58	09 09								11 04			
Acklington	d						07 42																
Widdrington	d						07 49																
Pegswood	d						07 55																
Morpeth	26 d			07 34			08 00	08 09						09 32				10 50		11 19			11 50
Cramlington	d						08 08							09 40				10 58					11 58
Manors	d						08 21																
Newcastle 8	26 ⛴ a		07 41	07 53			08 25	08 27			09 31	09 39		09 55				11 14		11 39			12 13
Sunderland	44 ⛴ d				07 30	07 55			08 28						09 29		10 30					11 30	
London Kings Cross 15	⊖ 26 d												*06 15*		*07 00*			*08 00*				*08 30*	*09 00*
Newcastle 8	⛴ d	06 35			07 56	08 24			08 53	09 24			09 44	09 57	10 24	10 44	10 54	11 14	11 22		11 44	11 54	12 14
Dunston	d													10 02									
MetroCentre	a				08 03	08 31			09 00	09 31			09 51	10 05	10 31	10 53	11 01	11 21	11 32		11 52	12 01	12 22
	d				08 04	08 32			09 01	09 32				10 06	10 32		11 02		11 33			12 02	
Blaydon	d				08 08				09 03														
Wylam	d	06 49			08 14	08 40			09 10					10 14			11 10					12 10	
Prudhoe	d	06 53			08 18	08 44			09 13	09 42				10 18	10 42		11 14		11 43			12 14	
Stocksfield	d	06 57			08 23	08 48			09 18					10 22			11 18					12 18	
Riding Mill	d	07 02			08 27				09 22					10 27			11 23					12 23	
Corbridge	d	07 05			08 31				09 26					10 30			11 26					12 26	
Hexham	a	07 10			08 40	09 00			09 36	09 57				10 41	10 57		11 39		11 58			12 39	
	d	07 11				09 01				09 58					10 57				11 59				
Haydon Bridge	d	07 20				09 10													12 08				
Bardon Mill	d	07 26				09 16													12 14				
Haltwhistle	d	07 33				09 23				10 16					11 16				12 21				
Brampton (Cumbria)	d	07 49				09 39													12 37				
Wetheral	d	07 57				09 47													12 46				
Carlisle 8	a	08 08				09 57				10 50					11 49				12 55				

For general notes see front of timetable
For details of catering facilities see Directory of Train Operators

- **A** From Nunthorpe (Table 45)
- **B** To Stranraer (Table 216)
- **C** From Edinburgh to Bristol Temple Meads (Table 51)
- **D** From Middlesbrough (Table 44)
- **E** From Glasgow Central to London Kings Cross (Table 26)
- **G** From Edinburgh to Birmingham New Street (Table 51)
- **H** From Glasgow Central to Leeds (Table 26)
- **J** To Glasgow Central (Table 216)
- **K** From Edinburgh to Plymouth (Table 51)
- **L** From Edinburgh to London Kings Cross (Table 26)
- **N** From Hartlepool (Table 44)
- **Q** From Edinburgh to Reading (Table 51)
- **U** From Glasgow Central to Plymouth (Table 51)
- **V** From Glasgow Central (Table 51) to Penzance (Table 135)

Chathill and Morpeth → Newcastle → MetroCentre, Hexham and Carlisle

from 12 September

Network Diagram - see first page of Table 44

	NT	NT	NT	NT	GR	NT	NT	XC	NT	NT	NT	NT	NT	NT	NT	NT	XC	NT	NT	NT	NT
					R 1			1 ◇									1 ◇				
		A		B	C D			E		G				B			H		B		J
Chathill d																					
Alnmouth for Alnwick 26 d					12 28			13 05									15 05				
Acklington d																					
Widdrington d																					
Pegswood d																					
Morpeth 26 d						12 50					13 50				14 50					15 50	
Cramlington d						12 58					13 58				14 58					15 58	
Manors d						13 11															
Newcastle 8 26 a					13 02	13 13		13 35			14 13				15 13		15 35			16 13	
Sunderland 44 d				12 30						13 30				14 31					15 30		
London Kings Cross 15 ⊖ 26 d				*09 30*		*10 00*			*10 30*		*11 00*			*11 30*	*12 00*				*12 30*	*13 00*	
Newcastle 8 d	12 24	12 39	12 44	12 54		13 14	13 24		13 44	13 54	14 14	14 24	14 44	14 54	15 14	15 24		15 44	15 54	16 14	16 24
Dunston d																					
MetroCentre a	12 31	12 46	12 52	13 01		13 22	13 31		13 51	14 01	14 22	14 31	14 52	15 01	15 21	15 31		15 51	16 01	16 21	16 31
d		12 46		13 02			13 32			14 02		14 32		15 02		15 32			16 02		16 32
Blaydon d																					
Wylam d				13 10						14 10		14 40		15 10					16 10		16 40
Prudhoe d				13 14			13 42			14 14		14 44		15 14		15 42			16 14		16 44
Stocksfield d				13 18						14 18				15 18					16 18		16 48
Riding Mill d				13 23						14 23				15 23					16 23		16 53
Corbridge d				13 26						14 26				15 26					16 26		16 56
Hexham a		13 06		13 39			13 55			14 36		14 56		15 39		15 56			16 36		17 02
d		13 08					13 56					14 57				15 57					17 03
Haydon Bridge d												15 07				16 06					17 12
Bardon Mill d																16 12					
Haltwhistle d		13 26					14 14					15 17				16 19					17 23
Brampton (Cumbria) d																16 35					
Wetheral d																16 44					
Carlisle 8 a		14 00					14 49					15 49				16 58					17 58

	NT	NT	NT	NT	NT	XC	NT	NT	NT	GR	NT	NT	NT	XC	NT	NT	NT	GR	NT	NT	NT
						1 ◇				R 1				1 ◇				R 1			
		G	A			K	B			L				N	B			Q			
Chathill d																19 12					
Alnmouth for Alnwick 26 d						17 05				17 58				19 08		19 24		20 08			
Acklington d																19 32					
Widdrington d																19 39					
Pegswood d																19 45					
Morpeth 26 d				16 50		17 20					18 32		19 04			19 49		20 25		21 15	
Cramlington d				16 58							18 40		19 12			19 58				21 23	
Manors d																					
Newcastle 8 26 a				17 13		17 38				18 32	18 56		19 26	19 41		20 12		20 46		21 40	
Sunderland 44 d		16 30					17 30					*18 30*			19 27				20 27		21 27
London Kings Cross 15 ⊖ 26 d		*13 30*	*14 00*						*15 00*						*16 00*	*17 00*			*18 00*		*18 35*
Newcastle 8 d	16 44	16 54	17 13		17 24		17 54	18 02	18 24			19 10			19 50	20 14	20 30		21 22		21 56
Dunston d					17 30			18 07													
MetroCentre a	16 51	17 01	17 20		17 32		18 01	18 12	18 31			19 17			19 58	20 21	20 39		21 29		22 04
d		17 02	17 20		17 33		18 02		18 32			19 18				20 22			21 30		
Blaydon d					17 37																
Wylam d		17 10	17 29		17 44		18 10		18 40			19 26				20 30			21 38		
Prudhoe d		17 14	17 32		17 47		18 14		18 44			19 30				20 34			21 42		
Stocksfield d		17 18			17 52		18 18		18 48			19 34				20 38			21 46		
Riding Mill d		17 23			17 56		18 23		18 53			19 39				20 43			21 51		
Corbridge d		17 26			18 00		18 26		18 56			19 42				20 46			21 54		
Hexham a		17 36	17 48		18 14		18 32		19 04			19 48				20 58			22 00		
d			17 48				18 33		19 05			19 49							22 01		
Haydon Bridge d			17 57				18 42					19 58							22 10		
Bardon Mill d			18 04				18 48												22 16		
Haltwhistle d			18 11				18 55		19 23			20 09							22 23		
Brampton (Cumbria) d			18 26						19 39										22 39		
Wetheral d			18 35						19 47										22 47		
Carlisle 8 a			18 46				19 29		19 59			20 42							22 57		

For general notes see front of timetable
For details of catering facilities see Directory of Train Operators

- **A** To Stranraer (Table 216)
- **B** From Middlesbrough (Table 44)
- **C** From Inverness (Table 229) to London Kings Cross (Table 26)
- **D** **The Highland Chieftain**
- **E** From Edinburgh (Table 51) to Penzance (Table 135)
- **G** From Nunthorpe (Table 45)
- **H** From Edinburgh to Plymouth (Table 51)
- **J** To Whitehaven (Table 100)
- **K** From Edinburgh to Bristol Temple Meads (Table 51)
- **L** From Glasgow Central to London Kings Cross (Table 26)
- **N** From Edinburgh to Birmingham New Street (Table 51)
- **Q** From Glasgow Central to Leeds (Table 26)

Chathill and Morpeth → Newcastle → MetroCentre, Hexham and Carlisle

Network Diagram - see first page of Table 44

	NT	NT	NT	NT	NT	NT	XC	NT	NT	NT	NT	NT	GR	NT	XC	NT	NT	GR	NT	NT	NT	XC
					A		1 ◇ B					A	R 1 C		1 ◇ B			R 1 D E			A	1 ◇ G
Chathill d																						
Alnmouth for Alnwick 26 d							10 47								12 47			13 29				14 38
Acklington d																						
Widdrington d																						
Pegswood d																						
Morpeth 26 d							11 02						12 40									
Cramlington d																						
Manors d																						
Newcastle 8 26 a							11 19						12 59		13 17			14 00				15 08
Sunderland 44 d		09 28			10 28				11 28			12 28					13 28				14 28	
London Kings Cross 15 ⊖ 26 d											*09 00*	*09 30*				*10 00*	*10 30*			*11 00*		
Newcastle 8 d	09 10	09 53	10 10	10 30	10 51	11 10		11 30	11 50	12 10	12 30	12 50		13 10		13 30	13 50		14 10	14 30	14 50	
Dunston d																						
MetroCentre a	09 17	10 01	10 17	10 37	11 01	11 17		11 37	11 57	12 17	12 37	12 59		13 17		13 37	13 59		14 17	14 37	14 59	
d	09 18		10 18			11 18				12 18				13 18					14 18			
Blaydon d																						
Wylam d	09 26		10 26			11 26				12 26				13 26					14 26			
Prudhoe d	09 30		10 30			11 30				12 30				13 30					14 30			
Stocksfield d	09 34		10 34			11 34				12 34				13 34					14 34			
Riding Mill d	09 39		10 39			11 39				12 39				13 39					14 39			
Corbridge d	09 42		10 42			11 42				12 42				13 42					14 42			
Hexham a	09 48		10 48			11 48				12 48				13 48					14 48			
d	09 49		10 49			11 49				12 49				13 49					14 49			
Haydon Bridge d	09 58		10 58							12 58												
Bardon Mill d	10 04		11 04							13 04												
Haltwhistle d	10 11		11 11			12 08				13 11				14 08					15 08			
Brampton (Cumbria) d	10 27		11 27							13 27												
Wetheral d	10 35		11 35							13 35												
Carlisle 8 a	10 45		11 45			12 38				13 45				14 38					15 40			

	NT	XC	NT	NT	NT	NT	NT	GR	NT	XC	NT	NT	GR	NT	NT	NT	XC	GR	NT	GR	GR
		1 ◇ H					A	R 1 C		1 ◇ J			R 1 D			A	1 ◇ K	R 1 C		R 1 L	R 1 N
Chathill d																					
Alnmouth for Alnwick 26 d		14 49								16 47			17 32				18 51	19 03			22 06
Acklington d																					
Widdrington d																					
Pegswood d																					
Morpeth 26 d								16 43		17 02										21 17	
Cramlington d																					
Manors d																					
Newcastle 8 26 a		15 19						17 02		17 20			18 07				19 20	19 33		21 38	22 41
Sunderland 44 d				15 28			16 28					17 28				18 28			*19 28*		
London Kings Cross 15 ⊖ 26 d			*12 00*	*12 30*		*13 00*	*13 30*				*14 00*	*14 30*		*15 00*					*16 30*		
Newcastle 8 d	15 10		15 30	15 50	16 10	16 30	16 50		17 10		17 30	17 50		18 10	18 30	18 50			20 15		
Dunston d																					
MetroCentre a	15 17		15 37	15 59	16 19	16 37	16 58		17 17		17 37	17 59		18 17	18 37	18 59			20 22		
d	15 18				16 20				17 18					18 18					20 23		
Blaydon d																					
Wylam d	15 26				16 28				17 26					18 26					20 31		
Prudhoe d	15 30				16 32				17 30					18 30					20 35		
Stocksfield d	15 34				16 36				17 34					18 34					20 39		
Riding Mill d	15 39				16 41				17 39					18 39					20 44		
Corbridge d	15 42				16 44				17 42					18 42					20 47		
Hexham a	15 48				16 50				17 48					18 48					20 53		
d	15 49				16 51				17 49					18 49					20 54		
Haydon Bridge d	15 58													18 58					21 03		
Bardon Mill d	16 04													19 04					21 09		
Haltwhistle d	16 11				17 10				18 08					19 11					21 16		
Brampton (Cumbria) d	16 27													19 27					21 32		
Wetheral d	16 35													19 35					21 40		
Carlisle 8 a	16 45				17 40				18 38					19 45					21 50		

For general notes see front of timetable
For details of catering facilities see Directory of Train Operators

A From Middlesbrough (Table 44)
B From Edinburgh to Penzance (Table 135) (from 8 November to Birmingham New Street) (Table 51)
C From Edinburgh to London Kings Cross (Table 26)
D From Aberdeen (Table 229) to London Kings Cross (Table 26)
E **The Northern Lights**
G From Edinburgh to Reading (Table 51)
H From Aberdeen (Table 229) to Plymouth (from 8 November to Birmingham New Street) (Table 51)
J From Edinburgh to Bristol Temple Meads (from 8 November to Birmingham New Street) (Table 51)
K From Edinburgh to Birmingham New Street (Table 51)
L From Edinburgh to York (Table 26)
N From Glasgow Central (Table 26)

Table 48

Carlisle, Hexham and MetroCentre → Newcastle → Morpeth and Chathill

Mondays to Fridays
until 4 September

Network Diagram - see first page of Table 44

Miles	Miles			NT	GR R 1 A	NT B	GR R 1 C	NT	NT	NT B	GR R 1 D	NT E	NT	NT B	XC 1 ◇ G	NT	NT	NT H	NT J	NT
0	—	**Carlisle 8**	d						06 25			07 13				08 29			09 33	
4¼	—	Wetheral	d						06 32			07 20				08 37				
11	—	Brampton (Cumbria)	d						06 42			07 30				08 47				
23¼	—	Haltwhistle	d						06 56			07 45				09 01			10 01	
28	—	Bardon Mill	d						07 04			07 52				09 09				
31¾	—	Haydon Bridge	d						07 09			07 57				09 14				
39½	—	**Hexham**	a						07 18			08 06				09 23			10 19	
—	—		d			06 13			07 19	07 41		08 07		08 44		09 23		09 44	10 19	
42½	—	Corbridge	d			06 17			07 23	07 45		08 11		08 48				09 48		
45	—	Riding Mill	d			06 22			07 27	07 50		08 16		08 53				09 53		
47¼	—	Stocksfield	d			06 26			07 31	07 54		08 20		08 57				09 57		
49¾	—	Prudhoe	d			06 30			07 36	07 58		08 24		09 01		09 35		10 01		
52	—	Wylam	d			06 34			07 40	08 02		08 28		09 05				10 05		
56¼	—	Blaydon	d							08 08		08 34								
58¼	0	**MetroCentre**	a						07 49	08 13		08 43		09 14		09 46		10 14	10 40	
—	—		d						07 49	08 15		08 44		09 15		09 47		10 15	10 40	11 00
59½	1¼	Dunston	d									08 47								
61¾	3½	**Newcastle 8**	a			06 52			08 04	08 25		08 57		09 27		09 59		10 25	10 55	11 09
—	—	London Kings Cross 15 ⊖ 26	a			*09 55*			*11 51*	*12 17*		*12 42*						*13 43*		*14 44*
—	—	Sunderland 44	a			07 19				08 49				09 49				10 49		
—	—	**Newcastle 8** 26	d	05 45	06 25		07 41	07 58			08 41		09 00		09 29		10 15			11 15
—	4	Manors	d																	
—	13¼	Cramlington	d	05 57				08 11					09 12				10 27			11 27
—	20	**Morpeth** 26	d	06 05	06 38			08a20			08 55		09a20		09 42		10a35			11a35
—	22	Pegswood	d																	
—	26¾	Widdrington	d																	
—	32	Acklington	d																	
—	38¼	Alnmouth for Alnwick 26	d	06 22	06a52		08a07								09a56					
—	49½	**Chathill**	a	06 38																

		NT B	XC 1 ◇ K	NT	NT	GR R 1 L	NT	NT B	NT	NT	NT	NT	NT H	XC 1 ◇ N	NT	NT	NT	NT B	NT	NT ◇ Q
Carlisle 8	d				10 33					11 34						12 30				13 37
Wetheral	d															12 37				
Brampton (Cumbria)	d															12 47				
Haltwhistle	d				11 01					12 02						13 01				14 05
Bardon Mill	d															13 09				
Haydon Bridge	d				11 12					12 13						13 14				
Hexham	a				11 21					12 22						13 23				14 23
	d	10 44			11 21			11 44		12 23			12 44			13 23		13 44		14 24
Corbridge	d	10 48						11 48					12 48					13 48		
Riding Mill	d	10 53						11 53					12 53					13 53		
Stocksfield	d	10 57						11 57					12 57					13 57		
Prudhoe	d	11 01			11 33			12 01		12 34			13 01			13 35		14 01		
Wylam	d	11 05						12 05					13 05					14 05		
Blaydon	d																			
MetroCentre	a	11 15			11 45			12 14		12 45			13 14			13 46		14 14		14 44
	d	11 15		11 30	11 45		12 05	12 15	12 30	12 45	12 40	13 00	13 15		13 30	13 47	14 00	14 15	14 30	14 45
Dunston	d																			
Newcastle 8	a	11 25		11 39	11 59		12 12	12 28	12 40	12 57	12 51	13 10	13 26		13 38	14 00	14 09	14 26	14 41	14 57
London Kings Cross 15 ⊖ 26	a			*14 57*			*15 44*				*15 50*	*16 46*			*16 57*			*17 41*	*18 04*	
Sunderland 44	a	11 49						12 49					13 49					14 49		
Newcastle 8 26	d		11 34			12 05	12 15				13 02			13 35			14 15			
Manors	d																			
Cramlington	d						12 26				13 14						14 27			
Morpeth 26	d						12a36				13a23						14a34			
Pegswood	d																			
Widdrington	d																			
Acklington	d																			
Alnmouth for Alnwick 26	d		12a01			12a31								14a01						
Chathill	a																			

For general notes see front of timetable
For details of catering facilities see Directory of Train Operators

A To Glasgow Central (Table 26)
B To Middlesbrough (Table 44)
C From Doncaster to Glasgow Central (Table 26)
D From Leeds (Table 26) to Aberdeen (Table 229)
E From Dumfries (Table 216)
G From Birmingham New Street to Edinburgh (Table 51)
H To Nunthorpe (Table 45)
J From Girvan (Table 216)
K From Bristol Temple Meads to Edinburgh (Table 51)
L From London Kings Cross to Glasgow Central (Table 26)
N From Plymouth to Edinburgh (Table 51)
Q From Stranraer (Table 216)

Table 48

Mondays to Fridays

until 4 September

Carlisle, Hexham and MetroCentre → Newcastle → Morpeth and Chathill

Network Diagram - see first page of Table 44

		NT		NT	XC	NT		NT	NT	NT		GR	NT	NT		NT	NT	XC		NT	NT	NT		NT	GR
				A	[1] ◇ B ⌶					A		[R] [1] C Ø ⌶		D			D	[1] ◇ E ⌶				A			[R] [1] C Ø ⌶
Carlisle [8]	d							14 36						15 26							16 37				
Wetheral	d																				16 44				
Brampton (Cumbria)	d																				16 54				
Haltwhistle	d							15 04						15 56							17 08				
Bardon Mill	d																				17 16				
Haydon Bridge	d													16 07							17 21				
Hexham	a							15 22						16 16							17 30				
	d			14 44				15 22		15 44				16 16			16 44				17 31	17 42			
Corbridge	d			14 48						15 48							16 48					17 46			
Riding Mill	d			14 53						15 53							16 53					17 51			
Stocksfield	d			14 57						15 57							16 57				17 40	17 55			
Prudhoe	d			15 01				15 34		16 01				16 28			17 01				17 44	17 59			
Wylam	d			15 05						16 05							17 05					18 03			
Blaydon	d																								
MetroCentre	a			15 14				15 46		16 14				16 40			17 14				17 56	18 12			
	d	15 00		15 15		15 30		15 46	16 00	16 15			16 30	16 40		17 00	17 15			17 35	17 56	18 13		18 18	
Dunston	d			15 18																					
Newcastle [8]	⛴ a	15 09		15 27		15 38		16 00	16 11	16 25			16 40	16 50		17 08	17 25			17 43	18 08	18 23		18 26	
London Kings Cross [15]	⊖ 26 a	*18 27*				*19 12*			*19 19*				*20 18*			*20 44*				*21 20*				*21 44*	
Sunderland	44 ⛴ a			15 49						16 49				17 14			17 50					18 49			
Newcastle [8]	26 ⛴ d	15 15			15 35				16 15			16 32				17 15		17 36		17 46				18 28	18 46
Manors	d								16 17							17 17				17 48				18 30	
Cramlington	d	15 27							16 28							17 28				17 59				18 41	
Morpeth	26 d	15a35			15 48				16a36							17 36				18a07				18a49	
Pegswood	d															17 40									
Widdrington	d															17 46									
Acklington	d															18 10									
Alnmouth for Alnwick	26 d				16a02							16a58				18 18		18a02							19a13
Chathill	a															18 32									

		NT	NT	XC		NT	GR	NT		XC	NT	NT		NT	XC	NT		GR	NT	NT		NT			
			D	[1] ◇ G ⌶		H	[R] [1] C ✕ ⌶	D		[1] ◇ J					[1] ◇ K			FO [R] [1] C ✕ ⌶							
Carlisle [8]	d	17 20				18 18						19 45								21 20					
Wetheral	d	17 27																		21 27					
Brampton (Cumbria)	d	17 37																		21 37					
Haltwhistle	d	17 52				18 46						20 13								21 52					
Bardon Mill	d	17 59																		21 59					
Haydon Bridge	d	18 04																		22 04					
Hexham	a	18 13				19 04						20 31								22 13					
	d	18 14	18 44			19 04						20 31				21 14				22 14		23 14			
Corbridge	d	18 18	18 48			19 09						20 36				21 18				22 18		23 18			
Riding Mill	d	18 23	18 53			19 13						20 40				21 23				22 23		23 23			
Stocksfield	d	18 27	18 57			19 17						20 44				21 27				22 27		23 27			
Prudhoe	d	18 31	19 01			19 22						20 49				21 31				22 31		23 31			
Wylam	d	18 35	19 05			19 26						20 52				21 35				22 35		23 35			
Blaydon	d		19 11																						
MetroCentre	a	18 43	19 16			19 34						21 01				21 44				22 44		23 45			
	d	18 44	19 17			19 35		20 30				21 02		21 22		21 45			22 15	22 45		23 45			
Dunston	d																								
Newcastle [8]	⛴ a	18 56	19 27			19 47		20 38				21 14		21 30		21 56			22 23	22 59		23 57			
London Kings Cross [15]	⊖ 26 a	*22 20*				*00 15*																			
Sunderland	44 ⛴ a		19 50					21 04																	
Newcastle [8]	26 ⛴ d			19 38			20 29			20 58	21 05				21 48			22 08							
Manors	d																								
Cramlington	d										21 17														
Morpeth	26 d						20 44			21 14	21a26							22 22							
Pegswood	d																								
Widdrington	d																								
Acklington	d																								
Alnmouth for Alnwick	26 d			20a06			21a00			21a28					22a12			22a38							
Chathill	a																								

For general notes see front of timetable
For details of catering facilities see Directory of Train Operators

- **A** To Nunthorpe (Table 45)
- **B** From Penzance (Table 135) to Edinburgh (Table 51)
- **C** From London Kings Cross to Edinburgh (Table 26)
- **D** To Middlesbrough (Table 44)
- **E** From Penzance (Table 135) to Glasgow Central (Table 51)
- **G** From Plymouth to Glasgow Central (Table 51)
- **H** From Glasgow Central (Table 216)
- **J** From Reading to Edinburgh (Table 51)
- **K** From Plymouth to Edinburgh (Table 51)

Carlisle, Hexham and MetroCentre → Newcastle → Morpeth and Chathill

Network Diagram - see first page of Table 44

		NT	GR R 1 A	NT B	GR R 1 C	NT	NT	NT B	GR R 1 D	NT E	NT	NT B	XC 1 ◇ G	NT	NT	NT H	NT J	NT	NT B	XC 1 ◇ K	NT	NT	GR R 1 L ⊘	NT	NT B
Carlisle 8	d						06 25			07 13				08 29			09 33					10 30			
Wetheral	d						06 32			07 20				08 37											
Brampton (Cumbria)	d						06 42			07 30				08 47											
Haltwhistle	d						06 56			07 45				09 01			10 01					10 58			
Bardon Mill	d						07 04			07 52				09 09											
Haydon Bridge	d						07 09			07 57				09 14											
Hexham	a						07 18			08 06				09 23			10 19					11 20			
	d			06 13			07 19	07 39		08 07		08 42		09 23		09 42	10 19		10 44			11 20			11 42
Corbridge	d			06 17			07 23	07 45		08 11		08 46				09 46			10 48						11 46
Riding Mill	d			06 22			07 28	07 50		08 16		08 51				09 51			10 53						11 51
Stocksfield	d			06 26			07 32	07 54		08 20		08 55				09 55			10 57						11 55
Prudhoe	d			06 32			07 36	08 00		08 24		09 00		09 35		10 00			11 01			11 32			12 00
Wylam	d			06 36			07 40	08 04		08 28		09 04				10 04			11 05						12 04
Blaydon	d							08 10		08 34															
MetroCentre	a						07 49	08 16		08 43		09 14		09 46		10 14	10 40		11 15			11 45			12 14
	d						07 50	08 17		08 44		09 15		09 47		10 15	10 40	11 00	11 15		11 30	11 46		12 05	12 15
Dunston	d									08 47															
Newcastle 8	a			06 57			08 08	08 27		08 57		09 27		09 59		10 25	10 55	11 09	11 25		11 39	11 59		12 12	12 28
London Kings Cross 15 ⊖ 26	a			*10 10*			*11 51*	*12 17*		*12 42*						*13 43*		*14 44*			*14 57*			*15 44*	
Sunderland 44	a			07 19				08 49				09 49				10 49			11 49						12 49
Newcastle 8 26	d	05 45	06 25		07 41	07 58			08 41		09 00		09 29		10 15			11 15		11 34			12 05	12 15	
Manors	d																								
Cramlington	d	05 57				08 11					09 12				10 27			11 27						12 26	
Morpeth 26	d	06 05	06 38			08a20			08 55		09a20		09 42		10a35			11a35						12a36	
Pegswood	d																								
Widdrington	d																								
Acklington	d																								
Alnmouth for Alnwick 26	d	06 22	06a52		08a07								09a56							12a01			12a31		
Chathill	a	06 38																							

		NT	NT	NT	NT	NT H	XC 1 ◇ N	NT	NT	NT	NT B	NT	NT ◇ Q	NT	NT H	XC 1 ◇ U	NT	NT	NT	NT H	GR R 1 V ⊘	NT	NT B	NT	NT B
Carlisle 8	d		11 27						12 30				13 37					14 35					15 22		
Wetheral	d								12 37																
Brampton (Cumbria)	d								12 47																
Haltwhistle	d		11 55						13 01				14 05					15 03					15 50		
Bardon Mill	d								13 09																
Haydon Bridge	d		12 06						13 14														16 01		
Hexham	a		12 18						13 23				14 23					15 21					16 12		
	d		12 19			12 42			13 23		13 42		14 24		14 42			15 21		15 42			16 12		16 42
Corbridge	d					12 46					13 46				14 46					15 46					16 46
Riding Mill	d					12 51					13 51				14 51					15 51					16 51
Stocksfield	d					12 55					13 55				14 55					15 55					16 55
Prudhoe	d		12 30			13 00			13 35		14 00				15 00			15 33		16 00			16 24		17 00
Wylam	d					13 04					14 04				15 04					16 04					17 04
Blaydon	d																								
MetroCentre	a		12 45			13 14			13 46		14 14		14 44		15 14			15 46		16 14			16 39		17 14
	d	12 30	12 45	12 40	13 00	13 15		13 30	13 47	14 00	14 15	14 30	14 45	15 00	15 15		15 30	15 46	16 00	16 15		16 30	16 39	17 00	17 15
Dunston	d														15 18										
Newcastle 8	a	12 40	12 58	12 51	13 10	13 26		13 38	13 59	14 09	14 26	14 41	14 57	15 09	15 27		15 38	15 58	16 11	16 25		16 40	16 50	17 08	17 25
London Kings Cross 15 ⊖ 26	a			*15 50*	*16 46*			*16 57*			*17 41*	*18 04*		*18 27*			*19 12*		*19 19*			*20 18*		*20 44*	
Sunderland 44	a					13 49					14 49				15 49					16 49			17 13		17 49
Newcastle 8 26	d			13 02			13 35			14 15				15 15		15 35			16 15		16 32			17 15	
Manors	d																		16 17					17 17	
Cramlington	d			13 14						14 27				15 27					16 28					17 28	
Morpeth 26	d			13a23						14a34				15a35		15 48			16a36					17 36	
Pegswood	d																							17 40	
Widdrington	d																							17 46	
Acklington	d																							18 10	
Alnmouth for Alnwick 26	d						14a01									16a02					16a58			18 18	
Chathill	a																							18 32	

For general notes see front of timetable
For details of catering facilities see Directory of Train Operators

- **A** To Glasgow Central (Table 26)
- **B** To Middlesbrough (Table 44)
- **C** From Doncaster to Glasgow Central (Table 26)
- **D** From Leeds (Table 26) to Aberdeen (Table 229)
- **E** From Dumfries (Table 216)
- **G** From Birmingham New Street to Edinburgh (Table 51)
- **H** To Nunthorpe (Table 45)
- **J** From Girvan (Table 216)
- **K** From Bristol Temple Meads to Edinburgh (Table 51)
- **L** From London Kings Cross to Glasgow Central (Table 26)
- **N** From Plymouth to Edinburgh (Table 51)
- **Q** From Stranraer (Table 216)
- **U** From Penzance (Table 135) to Edinburgh (Table 51)
- **V** From London Kings Cross to Edinburgh (Table 26)

Carlisle, Hexham and MetroCentre → Newcastle → Morpeth and Chathill

Network Diagram - see first page of Table 44

	XC 1 ◇ A	NT	NT	NT B	NT	GR R 1 C	NT	NT D	XC 1 ◇ E	NT G	GR R 1 C ✕	NT D	XC 1 ◇ H	NT	NT	NT	XC 1 ◇ J	NT	GR FO R 1 C ✕	NT	NT	NT
Carlisle d			16 29				17 12			18 18					19 41						21 18	
Wetheral d			16 36				17 19														21 25	
Brampton (Cumbria) d			16 46				17 29														21 35	
Haltwhistle d			17 03				17 44			18 46					20 09						21 50	
Bardon Mill d			17 10				17 51														21 57	
Haydon Bridge d			17 15				17 56														22 02	
Hexham a			17 27				18 09			19 04					20 26						22 13	
d			17 28	17 42			18 10	18 40		19 04					20 26			21 10			22 14	23 14
Corbridge d				17 46			18 14	18 44		19 09					20 31			21 14			22 18	23 18
Riding Mill d				17 51			18 19	18 49		19 13					20 35			21 19			22 23	23 23
Stocksfield d			17 37	17 55			18 23	18 53		19 17					20 39			21 23			22 27	23 27
Prudhoe d			17 41	17 59			18 27	18 59		19 22					20 44			21 29			22 31	23 33
Wylam d				18 03			18 31	19 03		19 26					20 47			21 33			22 35	23 37
Blaydon d								19 09														
MetroCentre a			17 56	18 12			18 43	19 16		19 34					21 00			21 44			22 44	23 49
d		17 35	17 56	18 13	18 18		18 44	19 17		19 35		20 30			21 01	21 22		21 45		22 15	22 45	23 49
Dunston d																						
Newcastle a		17 43	18 09	18 23	18 26		18 55	19 27		19 47		20 38			21 13	21 30		21 56		22 23	22 59	00 01
London Kings Cross ⊖ 26 a		*21 20*			*21 44*		*22 20*			*00 15*												
Sunderland 44 a				18 49				19 49				21 04										
Newcastle 26 d	17 36	17 46			18 28	18 46			19 38		20 29		20 58	21 05			21 48		22 08			
Manors d		17 48			18 30																	
Cramlington d		17 59			18 41									21 17								
Morpeth 26 d		18a07			18a49						20 44		21 14	21a26					22 22			
Pegswood d																						
Widdrington d																						
Acklington d																						
Alnmouth for Alnwick 26 d	18a02					19a13			20a06		21a00		21a28				22a12		22a38			
Chathill a																						

Saturdays

until 5 September

	NT	GR R 1 K	NT D	GR R 1 L	NT	NT	NT N	NT D	XC 1 ◇ Q	NT	NT	NT B	NT U	GR R 1 C	NT	NT D	XC 1 ◇ V	NT	NT	NT	NT D	NT
Carlisle d					06 25		07 13			08 29			09 33						10 33			
Wetheral d					06 32		07 20			08 37												
Brampton (Cumbria) d					06 42		07 30			08 47												
Haltwhistle d					06 56		07 45			09 01			10 01						11 02			
Bardon Mill d					07 04		07 52			09 09												
Haydon Bridge d					07 09		07 57			09 14									11 12			
Hexham a					07 18		08 06			09 23			10 19						11 21			
d			06 13		07 18		08 07	08 44		09 23		09 44	10 19			10 44			11 22		11 44	
Corbridge d			06 17		07 23		08 11	08 48				09 48				10 48					11 48	
Riding Mill d			06 22		07 27		08 16	08 53				09 53				10 53					11 53	
Stocksfield d			06 26		07 31		08 20	08 57				09 57				10 57					11 57	
Prudhoe d			06 30		07 36		08 24	09 01		09 35		10 01				11 01			11 33		12 01	
Wylam d			06 34		07 40		08 28	09 05		09 39		10 05				11 05					12 05	
Blaydon d							08 34															
MetroCentre a					07 49		08 43	09 14		09 48		10 14	10 40			11 14			11 45		12 14	
d					07 49		08 44	09 15		09 49		10 15	10 40		11 00	11 15		11 30	11 45	12 00	12 15	12 30
Dunston d							08 47															
Newcastle a			06 52		08 04		08 57	09 25		10 01		10 25	10 55		11 10	11 25		11 38	11 59	12 08	12 25	12 38
London Kings Cross ⊖ 26 a			*10 13*		*11 50*		*12 42*	*13b10*		*13 44*		*13 59*			*14 43*			*15 10*			*15 42*	
Sunderland 44 a			07 19		*08 49*			09 49				10 49				11 49					12 49	
Newcastle 26 d	06 05	06 30		07 52		08 24			09 29		10 15			11 08	11 15		11 36			12 15		
Manors d																						
Cramlington d	06 17					08 36					10 27				11 27					12 27		
Morpeth 26 d	06 25	06 43		08 06		08a44			09 42		10a35				11a35					12a35		
Pegswood d																						
Widdrington d																						
Acklington d																						
Alnmouth for Alnwick 26 d	06 43	06a57		08a20					09a56					11a34			12a00					
Chathill a	06 58																					

For general notes see front of timetable
For details of catering facilities see Directory of Train Operators

- **A** From Penzance (Table 135) to Glasgow Central (Table 51)
- **B** To Nunthorpe (Table 45)
- **C** From London Kings Cross to Edinburgh (Table 26)
- **D** To Middlesbrough (Table 44)
- **E** From Plymouth to Glasgow Central (Table 51)
- **G** From Glasgow Central (Table 216)
- **H** From Reading to Edinburgh (Table 51)
- **J** From Plymouth to Edinburgh (Table 51)
- **K** To Glasgow Central (Table 26)
- **L** From Doncaster to Glasgow Central (Table 26)
- **N** From Dumfries (Table 216)
- **Q** From Birmingham New Street to Edinburgh (Table 51)
- **U** From Girvan (Table 216)
- **V** From Bristol Temple Meads to Edinburgh (Table 51)
- **b** From 18 July arr. 1311

Table 48

Saturdays

Carlisle, Hexham and MetroCentre → Newcastle → Morpeth and Chathill

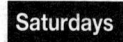

until 5 September

Network Diagram - see first page of Table 44

	NT	NT	NT	NT	NT	XC	NT		NT	NT	NT	NT	NT	NT	NT	XC	NT		NT	GR	NT	NT	NT	NT
						1 ◇							◇			1 ◇				R 1				
					A	B					C		D		A	E				G		A		C
Carlisle 8 d		11 34							12 30				13 36						14 36					15 28
Wetheral d									12 37															
Brampton (Cumbria) d									12 47															
Haltwhistle d		12 02							13 01				14 06						15 04					15 56
Bardon Mill d									13 09															
Haydon Bridge d		12 13							13 14															16 07
Hexham a		12 22							13 23				14 24						15 22					16 16
d		12 23			12 44				13 23		13 44		14 24		14 44				15 22			15 44		16 16
Corbridge d					12 48						13 48				14 48							15 48		
Riding Mill d					12 53						13 53				14 53							15 53		
Stocksfield d					12 57						13 57				14 57							15 57		
Prudhoe d		12 34			13 01				13 35		14 01				15 01				15 34			16 01		16 28
Wylam d					13 05						14 05				15 05							16 05		
Blaydon d																								
MetroCentre a		12 45			13 14				13 46		14 14		14 45		15 14				15 46			16 14		16 40
d	12 40	12 45	13 00		13 15		13 30		13 47	14 00	14 15	14 30	14 45	15 00	15 15		15 30		15 46		16 00	16 15	16 30	16 40
Dunston d															15 18									
Newcastle 8 a	12 52	12 57	13 11		13 26		13 39		14 00	14 13	14 25	14 40	14 59	15 09	15 28		15 38		16 00		16 11	16 25	16 38	16 50
London Kings Cross 15 ⊖ 26 a	*16 03*		*16 47*				*16 58*			*17 43*		*18 10*		*18 46*							*19 40*			
Sunderland 44 a					13 49						14 49				15 50							16 49		17 14
Newcastle 8 26 d				13 15		13 36				14 15				15 15		15 36				16 03	16 15			
Manors d																					16 17			
Cramlington d				13 26						14 26				15 27							16 28			
Morpeth 26 d				13a36						14a36				15a35		15 49					16a36			
Pegswood d																								
Widdrington d																								
Acklington d																								
Alnmouth for Alnwick 26 d						14a00										16a03				16a30				
Chathill a																								

	NT	NT	XC	NT	NT		NT	NT	NT	NT	XC	NT	NT	NT	XC	NT	GR	NT	XC	NT	NT	NT		
			1 ◇								1 ◇				1 ◇		R 1		1 ◇					
		C	H				A			C	J	K			L	C	N		B					
Carlisle 8 d					16 29				17 20			18 18						19 45				21 20		
Wetheral d					16 36				17 27													21 27		
Brampton (Cumbria) d					16 46				17 37													21 37		
Haltwhistle d					17 00				17 52			18 46						20 13				21 52		
Bardon Mill d					17 08				17 59													21 59		
Haydon Bridge d					17 13				18 04													22 04		
Hexham a					17 22				18 13			19 04						20 31				22 13		
d		16 44			17 22		17 42		18 14	18 44		19 04						20 31		21 14		22 14		
Corbridge d		16 48					17 46		18 18	18 48		19 09						20 36		21 18		22 18		
Riding Mill d		16 53					17 51		18 23	18 53		19 13						20 40		21 23		22 23		
Stocksfield d		16 57			17 31		17 55		18 27	18 57		19 17						20 44		21 27		22 27		
Prudhoe d		17 01			17 35		17 59		18 31	19 01		19 22						20 49		21 31		22 31		
Wylam d		17 05					18 03		18 35	19 05		19 26						20 52		21 35		22 35		
Blaydon d										19 11														
MetroCentre a		17 14			17 45		18 12		18 43	19 16		19 34						21 01		21 44		22 44		
d	17 00	17 15		17 35	17 45		18 13	18 18	18 44	19 17		19 34	20 15			20 47		21 02		21 45	22 10	22 45		
Dunston d																								
Newcastle 8 a	17 08	17 26		17 43	17 59		18 23	18 26	18 56	19 27		19 47	20 23			20 55		21 14		21 55	22 20	22 59		
London Kings Cross 15 ⊖ 26 a	*20 35*							*21 48*	*22b17*															
Sunderland 44 a		17 50					18 49			19 50						21 20								
Newcastle 8 26 d	17 10		17 36	17 44				18 28			19 37			20 24	20 50		21 03		21 36					
Manors d	17 13			17 47				18 30																
Cramlington d	17 24			17 58				18 41						20 36										
Morpeth 26 d	17 32			18a06				18a49						20a45	21 03		21 19							
Pegswood d	17 35																							
Widdrington d	17 41																							
Acklington d	17 48																							
Alnmouth for Alnwick 26 d	18 00		18a02								20a04				21a17		21a35		22a00					
Chathill a	18 19																							

For general notes see front of timetable
For details of catering facilities see Directory of Train Operators

A To Nunthorpe (Table 45)
B From Plymouth to Edinburgh (Table 51)
C To Middlesbrough (Table 44)
D From Stranraer (Table 216)
E From Penzance (Table 135) to Edinburgh (Table 51)
G From London Kings Cross to Glasgow Central (Table 26)
H From Penzance (Table 135) to Glasgow Central (Table 51)
J From Plymouth to Glasgow Central (Table 51)
K From Glasgow Central (Table 216)
L From Reading to Edinburgh (Table 51)
N From London Kings Cross to Edinburgh (Table 26)
b From 18 July arr. 2220

Table 48

Saturdays

from 12 September

Carlisle, Hexham and MetroCentre → Newcastle → Morpeth and Chathill

Network Diagram - see first page of Table 44

		NT	GR R 1 A	NT B	GR R 1 C	NT	NT	NT D	NT B	XC 1 ◇ E	NT	NT	NT G	NT H	GR R 1 J	NT	NT B	XC 1 ◇ K	NT	NT	NT	NT B	NT
Carlisle 8	d					06 25		07 13			08 29			09 33						10 28			
Wetheral	d					06 32		07 20			08 37												
Brampton (Cumbria)	d					06 42		07 30			08 47												
Haltwhistle	d					06 56		07 45			09 01			10 01						10 56			
Bardon Mill	d					07 04		07 52			09 09												
Haydon Bridge	d					07 09		07 57			09 14												
Hexham	a					07 22		08 06			09 23			10 19						11 18			
	d			06 13		07 22		08 07	08 43		09 23		09 43	10 19			10 44			11 18		11 43	
Corbridge	d			06 17		07 27		08 11	08 47				09 47				10 48					11 47	
Riding Mill	d			06 22		07 31		08 16	08 52				09 52				10 53					11 52	
Stocksfield	d			06 26		07 35		08 20	08 56				09 56				10 57					11 56	
Prudhoe	d			06 32		07 40		08 24	09 01		09 35		10 00				11 01			11 30		12 01	
Wylam	d			06 36		07 44		08 28	09 05		09 39		10 04				11 05					12 05	
Blaydon	d							08 34															
MetroCentre	a					07 56		08 43	09 15		09 48		10 14	10 40			11 14			11 45		12 15	
	d					07 56		08 44	09 16		09 49		10 15	10 40		11 00	11 15		11 30	11 45	12 00	12 16	12 30
Dunston	d							08 47															
Newcastle 8 ⛴	a			06 55		08 09		08 57	09 26		10 01		10 25	10 55		11 10	11 25		11 38	11 59	12 08	12 26	12 38
London Kings Cross 15 ⊖ 26	a			*10 44*		*11 50*		*12 42*	*13 10*		*13 44*		*13 59*			*14 43*			*15 10*		*15 42*		
Sunderland 44 ⛴	a			07 19		*08 49*			09 49				10 49				11 49					12 49	
Newcastle 8 26 ⛴	d	06 05	06 30		07 52		08 24			09 29		10 15			11 08	11 15		11 36			12 15		
Manors	d																						
Cramlington	d	06 17					08 36					10 27				11 27					12 27		
Morpeth 26	d	06 25	06 43		08 06		08a44			09 42		10a35				11a35					12a35		
Pegswood	d																						
Widdrington	d																						
Acklington	d																						
Alnmouth for Alnwick 26	d	06 43	06a57		08a20					09a56					11a34			12a00					
Chathill	a	06 58																					

		NT	NT	NT	NT	NT G	XC 1 ◇ L	NT	NT	NT	NT B	NT	NT ◇ N	NT	NT G	XC 1 ◇ Q	NT	NT	GR R 1 U	NT	NT G	NT	NT B
Carlisle 8	d		11 34						12 30				13 36					14 36					15 28
Wetheral	d								12 37														
Brampton (Cumbria)	d								12 47														
Haltwhistle	d		12 02						13 01				14 06					15 04					15 56
Bardon Mill	d								13 09														
Haydon Bridge	d		12 13						13 14														16 07
Hexham	a		12 22						13 23				14 24					15 22					16 16
	d		12 23			12 44			13 23		13 43		14 24		14 42			15 22			15 43		16 16
Corbridge	d					12 48					13 47				14 46						15 47		
Riding Mill	d					12 53					13 52				14 51						15 52		
Stocksfield	d					12 57					13 56				14 55						15 56		
Prudhoe	d		12 34			13 01			13 35		14 01				15 00			15 34			16 01		16 28
Wylam	d					13 05					14 05				15 04						16 05		
Blaydon	d																						
MetroCentre	a		12 45			13 14			13 46		14 15		14 45		15 14			15 46			16 15		16 40
	d	12 40	12 45	13 00		13 15		13 30	13 47	14 00	14 16	14 30	14 45	15 00	15 15		15 30	15 46		16 00	16 16	16 30	16 40
Dunston	d														15 18								
Newcastle 8 ⛴	a	12 52	12 57	13 11		13 26		13 39	14 00	14 13	14 26	14 40	14 59	15 09	15 28		15 38	16 00		16 11	16 26	16 38	16 50
London Kings Cross 15 ⊖ 26	a	*16 03*		*16 47*				*16 58*		*17 43*		*18 10*		*18 46*						*19 40*			
Sunderland 44 ⛴	a					13 49					14 49				15 50						16 49		17 14
Newcastle 8 26 ⛴	d				13 15		13 36			14 15				15 15		15 36			16 03	16 15			
Manors	d																			16 17			
Cramlington	d				13 26					14 26				15 27						16 28			
Morpeth 26	d				13a36					14a36				15a35		15 49				16a36			
Pegswood	d																						
Widdrington	d																						
Acklington	d																						
Alnmouth for Alnwick 26	d						14a00									16a03			16a30				
Chathill	a																						

For general notes see front of timetable
For details of catering facilities see Directory of Train Operators

- **A** To Glasgow Central (Table 26)
- **B** To Middlesbrough (Table 44)
- **C** From Doncaster to Glasgow Central (Table 26)
- **D** From Dumfries (Table 216)
- **E** From Birmingham New Street to Edinburgh (Table 51)
- **G** To Nunthorpe (Table 45)
- **H** From Girvan (Table 216)
- **J** From London Kings Cross to Edinburgh (Table 26)
- **K** From Bristol Temple Meads to Edinburgh (Table 51)
- **L** From Plymouth to Edinburgh (Table 51)
- **N** From Stranraer (Table 216)
- **Q** From Penzance (Table 135) to Edinburgh (Table 51)
- **U** From London Kings Cross to Glasgow Central (Table 26)

Table 48

Saturdays

Carlisle, Hexham and MetroCentre → Newcastle → Morpeth and Chathill

from 12 September

Network Diagram - see first page of Table 44

		NT	NT	XC	NT	NT	NT	NT	NT	NT	XC	NT	NT	NT	XC	NT	GR	NT	XC	NT	NT	NT
				1 ◇							1 ◇				1 ◇		R 1		1 ◇			
			A	B			C			A	D	E			G	A	H		J			
				✠							✠						🍴 ✠					
Carlisle 8	d					16 29			17 12			18 18						19 45				21 13
Wetheral	d					16 36			17 19													21 20
Brampton (Cumbria)	d					16 46			17 29													21 30
Haltwhistle	d					17 00			17 44			18 46						20 13				21 45
Bardon Mill	d					17 08			17 51													21 52
Haydon Bridge	d					17 13			17 56													21 57
Hexham	a					17 22			18 09			19 04						20 31				22 10
	d		16 42			17 22	17 42		18 10	18 40		19 04						20 31		21 10		22 11
Corbridge	d		16 46				17 46		18 14	18 44		19 09						20 36		21 14		22 15
Riding Mill	d		16 51				17 51		18 19	18 49		19 13						20 40		21 19		22 20
Stocksfield	d		16 55			17 31	17 55		18 23	18 53		19 17						20 44		21 23		22 24
Prudhoe	d		17 00			17 35	17 59		18 27	18 59		19 22						20 49		21 29		22 28
Wylam	d		17 04				18 03		18 31	19 03		19 26						20 52		21 33		22 32
Blaydon	d									19 09												
MetroCentre	a		17 14			17 45	18 12		18 44	19 16		19 34						21 01		21 44		22 44
	d	17 00	17 15		17 35	17 45	18 13	18 18	18 45	19 17		19 34	20 15			20 47		21 02		21 45	22 10	22 45
Dunston	d																					
Newcastle 8	⛴ a	17 08	17 26		17 43	18 01	18 23	18 26	18 56	19 27		19 47	20 23			20 55		21 13		21 55	22 20	22 59
London Kings Cross 15	⊖ 26 a	20 35						21 48	22 17													
Sunderland	44 ⛴ a		17 49				18 49			19 50						21 20						
Newcastle 8	26 ⛴ d	17 10		17 36	17 44			18 28			19 37			20 24	20 50		21 03		21 36			
Manors	d	17 13			17 47			18 30														
Cramlington	d	17 24			17 58			18 41						20 36								
Morpeth	26 d	17 32			18a06			18a49						20a45	21 03		21 19					
Pegswood	d	17 35																				
Widdrington	d	17 41																				
Acklington	d	17 48																				
Alnmouth for Alnwick	26 d	18 00		18a02							20a04				21a17		21a35		22a00			
Chathill	a	18 19																				

Sundays

		GR	NT	NT	NT	NT	XC	NT	NT	NT	NT	NT	NT	XC	NT	NT	NT	NT	NT	NT	NT	XC
		R 1					1 ◇							1 ◇								1 ◇
		K					L		A					N		A						Q
		🍴					✠							✠								✠
Carlisle 8	d			09 05				10 05			11 12				12 05			13 12			14 12	
Wetheral	d			09 12				10 12							12 12							
Brampton (Cumbria)	d			09 22				10 22							12 22							
Haltwhistle	d			09 36				10 36			11 40				12 36			13 40			14 40	
Bardon Mill	d			09 44				10 44							12 44							
Haydon Bridge	d			09 49				10 49							12 49							
Hexham	a			09 58				10 58			11 58				12 58			13 58			14 58	
	d			09 59				10 59			11 59				12 59			13 59			14 59	
Corbridge	d			10 03				11 03			12 03				13 03			14 03			15 03	
Riding Mill	d			10 08				11 08			12 08				13 08			14 08			15 08	
Stocksfield	d			10 12				11 12			12 12				13 12			14 12			15 12	
Prudhoe	d			10 16				11 16			12 16				13 16			14 16			15 16	
Wylam	d			10 20				11 20			12 20				13 20			14 20			15 20	
Blaydon	d																					
MetroCentre	a			10 29				11 29			12 29				13 29			14 29			15 29	
	d		10 10	10 30	10 48	11 10		11 30	11 48	12 10	12 30	12 48	13 10		13 30	13 48	14 10	14 30	14 48	15 10	15 30	
Dunston	d																					
Newcastle 8	⛴ a		10 18	10 40	10 56	11 18		11 40	11 56	12 18	12 40	12 57	13 18		13 40	13 56	14 18	14 40	14 56	15 18	15 40	
London Kings Cross 15	⊖ 26 a		13 39	14 04		14 44		15 09		15 42	16 10	16 29	16 46		17 11		17 49	18 15		18 43	19b14	
Sunderland	44 ⛴ a				11 22				12 21			13 22				14 21			15 22			
Newcastle 8	26 ⛴ d	10 10					11 38							13 36								15 41
Manors	d																					
Cramlington	d																					
Morpeth	26 d	10 25																				15 54
Pegswood	d																					
Widdrington	d																					
Acklington	d																					
Alnmouth for Alnwick	26 d	10a41					12a02							14a01								16a08
Chathill	a																					

For general notes see front of timetable
For details of catering facilities see Directory of Train Operators

A To Middlesbrough (Table 44)
B From Penzance (Table 135) to Glasgow Central (Table 51)
C To Nunthorpe (Table 45)
D From Plymouth to Glasgow Central (Table 51)
E From Glasgow Central (Table 216)
G From Reading to Edinburgh (Table 51)
H From London Kings Cross to Edinburgh (Table 26)
J From Plymouth to Edinburgh (Table 51)
K From York to Glasgow Central (Table 26)
L From Sheffield to Edinburgh (Table 51)
N From Birmingham New Street to Edinburgh (Table 51)
Q From Bristol Temple Meads to Edinburgh (Table 51)
b 19 July to 6 September arr. 1916

Sundays

Carlisle, Hexham and MetroCentre → Newcastle → Morpeth and Chathill

Network Diagram - see first page of Table 44

	NT		NT	NT	GR	NT	NT		XC	NT	NT	NT	NT		NT	NT	NT	XC	XC	GR	XC	NT	
					R 1				1 ◇									1 ◇	1 ◇	R 1	1 ◇		
	A				B ⊘ ✠				C ✠		A							D ✠	E	B ⊡ ✠	C		
Carlisle 8 d				15 05						16 12			17 12				18 05					20 15	
Wetheral d				15 12						.			.				18 12					.	
Brampton (Cumbria) d				15 22						.			.				18 22					.	
Haltwhistle d				15 36						16 40			17 40				18 36					20 43	
Bardon Mill d				15 44						.			.				18 44					.	
Haydon Bridge d				15 49						.			.				18 49					.	
Hexham a				15 58						16 58			17 58				18 58					20 58	
d				15 59						16 59			17 59				18 59					20 59	
Corbridge d				16 03						17 03			18 03				19 03					21 03	
Riding Mill d				16 08						17 08			18 08				19 08					21 08	
Stocksfield d				16 12						17 12			18 12				19 12					21 12	
Prudhoe d				16 16						17 16			18 16				19 16					21 16	
Wylam d				16 20						17 20			18 20				19 20					21 20	
Blaydon d																							
MetroCentre a				16 29						17 29			18 29				19 29					21 29	
d	15 48		16 10	16 30		16 48	17 10			17 30	17 48	18 10	18 30		18 48	19 10	19 30					21 30	
Dunston d																							
Newcastle 8 ⇌ a	15 58		16 18	16 40		16 56	17 18			17 40	17 55	18 18	18 40		18 56	19 18	19 40					21 43	
London Kings Cross 15 ⊖ 26 a			*19 48*			*20 14*	*20 43*				*21 25*	*21 47*	*22 16*			*23 14*	*23 50*						
Sunderland 44 ⇌ a	16 21					17 22					18 21				19 22		20 21						
Newcastle 8 26 ⇌ d					16 44				17 38									19 40	20 49	21 07	21 39		
Manors d																							
Cramlington d																							
Morpeth 26 d					16 59														21 02				
Pegswood d																							
Widdrington d																							
Acklington d																							
Alnmouth for Alnwick 26 d					17a15				18a02									20a05	21a16	21a35	22a07		
Chathill a																							

For general notes see front of timetable
For details of catering facilities see Directory of Train Operators

A To Middlesbrough (Table 44)
B From London Kings Cross to Edinburgh (Table 26)
C From Plymouth (from 8 November from Birmingham New Street) to Edinburgh (Table 51)
D From Plymouth (from 8 November from Birmingham New Street) to Glasgow Central (Table 51)
E From Reading to Edinburgh (Table 51)

Route Diagram for Table 49

DM-4/09
Design BAJS

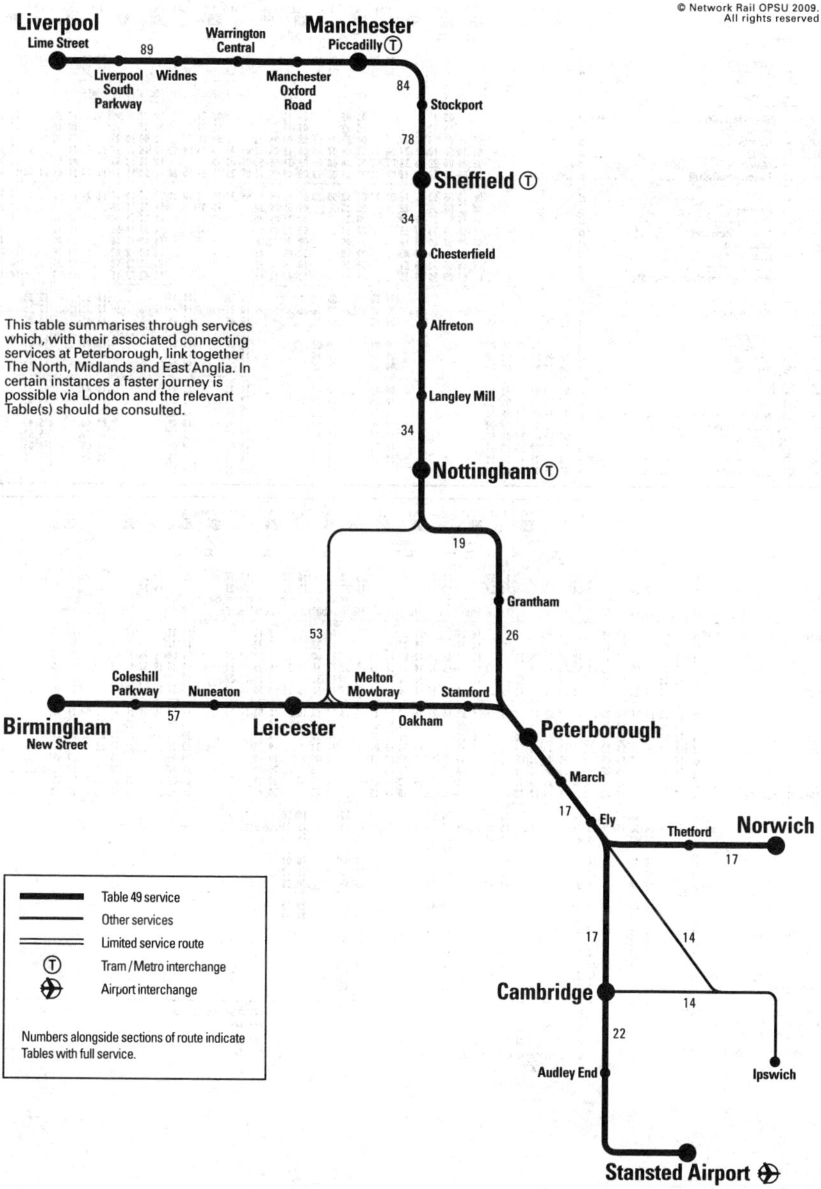

This table summarises through services which, with their associated connecting services at Peterborough, link together The North, Midlands and East Anglia. In certain instances a faster journey is possible via London and the relevant Table(s) should be consulted.

Stansted Airport → East Anglia → East Midlands → Birmingham and North West England

Route Diagram - see first page of Table 49

Miles	Miles	Miles	Miles			EM ◇	EM ◇	EM ◇	XC 1 ◇ 🛒	XC 1 ◇ 🛒	XC 1	EM ◇	XC 1 ◇ 🛒	EM ◇	XC 1 ◇ 🛒	XC 1	EM ◇	XC 1 ◇ 🛒	EM ◇	XC 1 ◇ 🛒	XC 1	EM ◇	XC 1 ◇ 🛒	EM ◇	XC 1 ◇ 🛒
0	0	—	0	**Norwich**	d							05 50		06 52			07 57		08 57			09 57		10 57	
30½	30½	—	30½	Thetford	d							06 23		07 20			08 24		09 24			10 24		11 24	
—	—	—	—	Ipswich	d								*06b01*		*06c13*		*06e13*	*08b02*		*08c16*		*08e16*	*10b02*		*10c16*
—	—	0	—	**Stansted Airport** ✈	d					05 21			06 06		07 21			08 21		09 21			10 20		11 25
—	—	10¾	—	Audley End	d					05 33			06 23		07 37			08 37		09 37			10 36		11 37
—	—	24¾	—	**Cambridge**	d				05 15	05 55	06 22		06 52	*07 05*	08 00	08 22		09 00	*09 12*	10 00	10 22		11 00	*11 12*	12 00
53¾	53¾	39½	53¾	Ely 6	d				05 30	06 10	06 37	06 51	07 08	07 44	08 15	08 37	08 49	09 15	09 52	10 15	10 37	10 52	11 15	11 52	12 15
61¼	61¼	—	61¼	March	d				05 46	06 28	06 53	07 07	07 26	08 01	08 31	08 53	09 07	09 31		10 32	10 53		11 31		12 31
75¼	75¼	—	75¼	**Peterborough 8**	a				06 08	06 50	07 16	07 25	07 51	08 23	08 49	09 11	09 25	09 51	10 26	10 50	11 11	11 24	11 51	12 24	12 50
—	—	—	—		d				06 10	06 52	07 16	07 27	07 52	08 30	08 52	09 12	09 27	09 52	10 30	10 52	11 12	11 27	11 52	12 25	12 52
87¾	—	—	—	Stamford	d				06 23	07 05	07 28		08 05		09 05	09 24		10 05		11 05	11 28		12 05		13 05
101¼	—	—	—	Oakham	d				06 39	07 21	07 44		08 21		09 21	09 40		10 21		11 21	11 44		12 21		13 21
112¾	—	—	—	Melton Mowbray	d				06 50	07 33	07 55		08 33		09 33	09 51		10 32		11 33	11 55		12 33		13 33
127¾	—	—	—	**Leicester**	d				07 09	07 49	08 16		08 49		09 49	10f16		10 49		11 49	12 16		12 49		13 49
146½	—	—	—	Nuneaton	a				07 29	08 15	08 40		09 08		10 08	10 41		11 08		12 08	12 42		13 08		14 08
158	—	—	—	Coleshill Parkway	a				07 45	08 32	08 57		09 25		10 25	10 58		11 25		12 25	12 58		13 25		14 25
167½	—	—	—	**Birmingham New Street 12**	a				08 03	08 50	09 15		09 43		10 43	11 15		11 43		12 43	13 15		13 43		14 43
—	104½	—	—	Grantham 7	d							07 58		08 58			09 58		11 13			11 56		12 58	
—	127¼	—	145	**Nottingham 8**	a				*08g16*		*09g13*	08 38	*09g26*	09 36	*10g26*	*10g59*	10 36	*11g26*	11 43	*12g26*	*12g59*	12 36	*13g26*	13 36	*14g26*
—	—	—	—		d	05 20	06 40	07 45				08 45		09 45			10 45		11 45			12 45		13 45	
—	139¼	—	157	Langley Mill	d																				
—	145½	—	163¼	Alfreton	d		07 02	08 07				09 07		10 07			11 07		12 07			13 07		14 07	
—	155½	—	173¼	Chesterfield	d	05 49	07 13	08 18				09 18		10 18			11 18		12 18			13 18		14 19	
—	167¼	—	185½	**Sheffield 7**	a	06 15	07 31	08 38				09 38		10 38			11 38		12 38			13 38		14 38	
—	—	—	—		d	06 20	07 35	08 42				09 42		10 42			11 42		12 42			13 42		14 42	
—	204½	—	222¼	Stockport	a	07 22	08 24	09 25				10 25		11 25			12 25		13 25			14 25		15 25	
—	210½	—	228¼	**Manchester Piccadilly 10**	a	07 34	08 36	09 36				10 36		11 36			12 36		13 36			14 36		15 36	
—	211	—	228¾	Manchester Oxford Road	a	07 37	08 40	09 40				10 40		11 40			12 40		13 40			14 40		15 40	
—	226¾	—	244½	Warrington Central	a	07 53	08 57	09 57				10 57		11 57			12 57		13 57			14 57		15 57	
—	233	—	250¾	Widnes	a	08 01	09 05	10 05				11 05		12 05			13 05		14 05			15 05		16 05	
—	239¾	—	257½	Liverpool South Parkway 7 ✈	a	08 18	09 15	10 15				11 15		12 15			13 15		14 15			15 15		16 15	
—	245¼	—	263	**Liverpool Lime Street 10**	a	08 31	09 31	10 31				11 31		12 31			13 31		14 31			15 31		16 31	

		XC 1	EM ◇	XC 1 ◇ 🛒	EM ◇	XC 1 ◇ 🛒	XC 1	EM ◇	XC 1 ◇ 🛒	EM ◇	XC 1 ◇ 🛒	XC 1	EM ◇	XC 1 ◇ 🛒	EM ◇	XC 1 ◇ 🛒	EM ◇	EM 1 ◇ A 🍴	XC 1 ◇ 🛒	EM ◇	XC 1 ◇ 🛒	EM B	XC 1 ◇ 🛒
Norwich	d		11 57		12 57			13 57		14 57			15 52		16 57		17 54			18 57			
Thetford	d		12 24		13 24			14 24		15 24			16 27		17 27		18 27			19 24			
Ipswich	d		*10e16*	*12b02*		*12c16*		*12e16*	*14b02*		*14c16*		*14e16*	*16b02*		*16c16*	*16e16*		*17b49*		*18c16*		*19c16*
Stansted Airport ✈	d			12 25		13 25			14 25		15 20			16 25		17 18			18 21		19 21		20 21
Audley End	d			12 37		13 37			14 37		15 37			16 37		17 33			18 37		19 37		20 37
Cambridge	d	12 22		13 00	*13 12*	14 00	14 22		15 00	*15 24*	16 00	16 30		17 00	*17 22*	17 51	*18 24*		19 00	*19 25*	20 00		21 00
Ely 6	d	12 37	12 52	13 15	13 52	14 15	14 37	14 52	15 15	15 52	16 15	16 45	16 52	17 15	17 52	18 06	18 52		19 15	19 52	20 15		21 15
March	d	12 53		13 31		14 31	14 53		15 31		16 31	17 03		17 31		18 25	19 08		19 31		20 31		21 31
Peterborough 8	a	13 11	13 25	13 51	14 25	14 50	15 11	15 25	15 50	16 25	16 49	17 21	17 27	17 50	18 25	18 50	19 31		19 51	20 26	20 49		21 49
	d	13 12	13 26	13 52	14 26	14 52	15 12	15 26	15 52	16 27	16 52	17 22	17 28	17 52	18 26	18 52	19 31		19 52	20 28	20 52	21 30	21 52
Stamford	d	13 24		14 05		15 05	15 24		16 05		17 05	17 34		18 05		19 05			20 05		21 05	21 43	22 05
Oakham	d	13 40		14 21		15 21	15 40		16 21		17 21	17 50		18 21		19 21		19 43	20 21		21 21	21 58	22 21
Melton Mowbray	d	13 51		14 33		15 33	15 51		16 33		17 33	18 01		18 33		19 33		19a55	20 33		21 33	22 11	22 33
Leicester	d	14h16		14 49		15 49	16j16		16 49		17 49	18 19		18 49		19 49			20 49		21 49		22 49
Nuneaton	a	14 42		15 08		16 08	16 42		17 08		18 16	18 45		19 08		20 08			21 08		22 08		23 08
Coleshill Parkway	a	14 59		15 25		16 25	16 58		17 25		18 32	19 01		19 25		20 25			21 25		22 25		23 25
Birmingham New Street 12	a	15 15		15 43		16 43	17 15		17 43		18 50	19 15		19 43		20 43			21 43		22 43		23 43
Grantham 7	d		13 58		14 58			15 58		16 58			17 59		18k58		20 03			20 58			
Nottingham 8	a	*14g59*	14 36	*15g26*	15 36	*16g26*	*16g59*	16 36	*17g26*	17 36	*18g30*	*19g10*	18 36	*19g27*	19 36	*20g28*	20 37		*21g29*	21 35	*22g27*	22 50	*00g14*
	d		14 45		15 45			16 45		17 45			18 45		19 40								
Langley Mill	d									18 02													
Alfreton	d		15 07		16 07			17 07		18 08			19 07		20 01								
Chesterfield	d		15 20		16 18			17 18		18 18			19 18		20 12								
Sheffield 7	a		15 38		16 38			17 34		18 38			19 39		20 28								
	d		15 42		16 42			17 40		18 42			19 42		20 32								
Stockport	a		16 25		17 25			18 25		19 25			20 25		21 20								
Manchester Piccadilly 10	a		16 36		17 37			18 36		19 36			20 36		21 32								
Manchester Oxford Road	a		16 40		17 40			18 40		19 40			20 40										
Warrington Central	a		16 57		18 03			18 57		19 57			20 57										
Widnes	a		17 05		18 11			19 05		20 05			21 05										
Liverpool South Parkway 7 ✈	a		17 15		18 21			19 18		20 15			21 19										
Liverpool Lime Street 10	a		17 31		18 35			19 35		20 35			21 35										

For general notes see front of timetable
For details of catering facilities see Directory of Train Operators

- **A** From St Pancras International (Table 53)
- **B** From Spalding (Table 18)
- **b** Change at Ely
- **c** Change at Cambridge
- **e** Change at Cambridge and Ely
- **f** Arr. 1007
- **g** Change at Leicester
- **h** Arr. 1407
- **j** Arr. 1607
- **k** Arr. 1852

Table 49

Saturdays

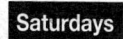

Stansted Airport → East Anglia → East Midlands → Birmingham and North West England

until 11 July and from 12 September

Route Diagram - see first page of Table 49

		EM ◇	EM ◇	XC 1 ◇	EM ◇	XC 1 ◇		XC 1	EM ◇	XC 1 ◇	EM ◇	XC 1 ◇		XC 1	EM ◇	XC 1 ◇	EM ◇	XC 1 ◇		XC 1	EM ◇	XC 1 ◇	EM ◇	XC 1 ◇	XC 1
Norwich	d								05 52		06 52				07 57		08 57				09 57		10 57		
Thetford	d								06 25		07 20				08 24		09 24				10 24		11 24		
Ipswich	d									06b00		06c14			06e14	08b02		08c16			08e16	10b02		10c16	
Stansted Airport ✈	d					05 25				06 25		07 25				08 25		09 25				10 25		11 25	
Audley End	d					05 37				06 37		07 37				08 37		09 37				10 37		11 37	
Cambridge	d			05 15		05 55		06 26		06 56	07 00	08 00		08 26		09 00	09 12	10 00		10 22		11 00	11 12	12 00	12 22
Ely 6	d			05 30		06 10		06 41	06 51	07 11	07 44	08 15		08 41	08 54	09 15	09 51	10 15		10 37	10 53	11 15	11 53	12 15	12 37
March	d			05 46		06 28		06 57	07 07	07 29	08 01	08 31		08 57	09 11	09 31		10 31		10 53		11 31		12 31	12 53
Peterborough 8	a			06 08		06 50		07 15	07 25	07 51	08 25	08 50		09 16	09 28	09 50	10 25	10 50		11 11	11 24	11 51	12 24	12 50	13 11
	d			06 10		06 52		07 16	07 27	07 52	08 30	08 52		09 16	09 30	09 52	10 28	10 52		11 12	11 25	11 52	12 25	12 52	13 12
Stamford	d			06 23		07 05		07 29		08 05		09 05		09 29		10 05		11 05		11 28		12 05		13 05	13 24
Oakham	d			06 39		07 21		07 44		08 21		09 21		09 45		10 21		11 21		11 44		12 21		13 21	13 40
Melton Mowbray	d			06 50		07 33		07 55		08 33		09 33		09 56		10 33		11 33		11 55		12 33		13 33	13 51
Leicester	d			07f16		07 49		08 16		08 49		09 49		10 16		10 49		11 49		12 16		12 49		13 49	14g16
Nuneaton	a			07 35		08 09		08 42		09 08		10 08		10 42		11 08		12 08		12 42		13 08		14 08	14 42
Coleshill Parkway	a			07 51		08 24		08 58		09 25		10 25		10 58		11 25		12 25		12 58		13 25		14 25	14 58
Birmingham New Street 12	a			08 09		08 43		09 14		09 43		10 43		11 14		11 43		12 43		13 14		13 43		14 43	15 14
Grantham 7	d								07 58		08 58				09 58		10 58				11 58		12 58		
Nottingham 8	a			08h16		08h42		09h03	08 38	09h26	09 36	10h26		10h59	10 36	11h26	11 35	12h26		12h59	12 36	13h27	13 36	14h26	14h59
	d	05 18	06 40		07 45				08 45		09 45				10 45		11 45				12 45		13 45		
Langley Mill	d																								
Alfreton	d		07 02		08 07				09 07		10 07				11 07		12 07				13 07		14 07		
Chesterfield	d	05 49	07 13		08 18				09 18		10 18				11 18		12 18				13 18		14 18		
Sheffield 7	a	06 15	07 31		08 38				09 38		10 38				11 38		12 38				13 38		14 38		
	d	06 20	07 35		08 42				09 42		10 42				11 42		12 42				13 42		14 42		
Stockport	a	07 22	08 24		09 25				10 25		11 25				12 25		13 25				14 25		15 25		
Manchester Piccadilly 10	a	07 34	08 36		09 36				10 36		11 36				12 36		13 36				14 36		15 36		
Manchester Oxford Road	a	07 37	08 40		09 40				10 40		11 40				12 40		13 40				14 40		15 40		
Warrington Central	a	07 53	08 57		09 57				10 57		11 57				12 57		13 57				14 57		15 57		
Widnes	a	08 01	09 05		10 05				11 05		12 05				13 05		14 05				15 05		16 05		
Liverpool South Parkway 7 ✈	a	08 18	09 15		10 15				11 15		12 15				13 15		14 15				15 15		16 15		
Liverpool Lime Street 10	a	08 31	09 31		10 31				11 31		12 31				13 31		14 31				15 31		16 31		

		EM ◇		XC 1 ◇	EM ◇	XC 1 ◇	XC 1	EM ◇		XC 1 ◇	EM ◇	XC 1 ◇	XC 1	EM ◇		XC 1 ◇	EM ◇	XC 1 ◇	EM ◇	XC 1 ◇	EM ◇	XC 1 ◇	XC 1		
Norwich	d	11 57			12 57			13 57			14 57			15 52			16 57		17 54		18 57				
Thetford	d	12 24			13 24			14 24			15 24			16 23			17 27		18 27		19 24				
Ipswich	d	10e16		12b02		12c16		12e16		14b02		14c16		14e16		16b02		16c16	16e16	18b02		18c16			
Stansted Airport ✈	d			12 25		13 25				14 25		15 25				16 25		17 25		18 25		19 25			
Audley End	d			12 37		13 37				14 37		15 37				16 37		17 37		18 37		19 37			
Cambridge	d			13 00	13 12	14 00	14 22			15 00	15 12	16 00	16 22			17 00	17 12	18 00	18 12	19 00	19 12	20 00	20 22		
Ely 6	d	12 54		13 15	13 53	14 15	14 37	14 53		15 15	15 52	16 15	16 37	16 52		17 15	17 52	18 15	18 54	19 15	19 53	20 15	20 37		
March	d			13 31		14 31	14 53			15 31		16 31	16 53			17 31		18 33	19 10	19 31		20 31	20 53		
Peterborough 8	a	13 26		13 51	14 25	14 50	15 11	15 25		15 51	16 25	16 50	17 11	17 26		17 51	18 25	18 50	19 29	19 50	20 25	20 50	21 11		
	d	13 28		13 52	14 26	14 52	15 12	15 26		15 52	16 27	16 52	17 12	17 27		17 52	18 26	18 52	19 31	19 52	20 27	20 52	21 12		
Stamford	d			14 05		15 05	15 24			16 05		17 05	17 24			18 05		19 05		20 05		21 05	21 24		
Oakham	d			14 21		15 21	15 40			16 21		17 21	17 40			18 21		19 21		20 21		21 21	21 40		
Melton Mowbray	d			14 33		15 33	15 51			16 33		17 33	17 51			18 33		19 33		20 33		21 33	21 51		
Leicester	d			14 49		15 49	16j16			16 49		17 49	18k16			18 49		19 49		20 49		21 49	22 16		
Nuneaton	a			15 08		16 08	16 42			17 08		18 08	18 42			19 08		20 08		21 08		22 08	22 42		
Coleshill Parkway	a			15 25		16 25	16 58			17 25		18 25	18 58			19 25		20 25		21 25		22 25	22 58		
Birmingham New Street 12	a			15 43		16 43	17 14			17 43		18 43	19 14			19 43		20 43		21 43		22 43	23 14		
Grantham 7	d	13 58			14 58			15 58			16m58			18 03			18 58		20 03		20 58				
Nottingham 8	a	14 36		15h26	15 36	16h26	16h59	16 36		17h26	17 36	18h26	18h59	18 36		19h26	19 36	20h26	20 37	21h26	21 32	22h27	23h06		
	d	14 45			15 45			16 45			17 45			18 45			19 40								
Langley Mill	d										18 03														
Alfreton	d	15 07			16 07			17 07			18 09			19 07			20 01								
Chesterfield	d	15 18			16 18			17 18			18 19			19 18			20 11								
Sheffield 7	a	15 38			16 38			17 34			18 39			19 39			20 27								
	d	15 42			16 42			17 40			18 42			19 42			20 31								
Stockport	a	16 25			17 25			18 25			19 25			20 25			21 20								
Manchester Piccadilly 10	a	16 36			17 37			18 36			19 36			20 37			21 32								
Manchester Oxford Road	a	16 40			17 40			18 40			19 40														
Warrington Central	a	16 57			18 03			18 57			19 57														
Widnes	a	17 05			18 11			19 05			20 05														
Liverpool South Parkway 7 ✈	a	17 15			18 21			19 18			20 18														
Liverpool Lime Street 10	a	17 31			18 35			19 35			20 34														

For general notes see front of timetable
For details of catering facilities see Directory of Train Operators

- **b** Change at Ely
- **c** Change at Cambridge
- **e** Change at Cambridge and Ely
- **f** Arr. 0708
- **g** Arr. 1407
- **h** Change at Leicester
- **j** Arr. 1607
- **k** Arr. 1811
- **m** Arr. 1655

Table 49

Saturdays

18 July to 5 September

Stansted Airport → East Anglia → East Midlands → Birmingham and North West England

Route Diagram - see first page of Table 49

		EM ◇	EM ◇	EM ◇	XC 🚌	XC 1 ◇ ⊼		XC 🚌	XC 🚌	XC 🚌	XC 🚌	XC 🚌		EM ◇	XC 1 ◇ ⊼	XC 1 ◇ ⊼	XC 🚌	XC 🚌		XC 🚌	EM ◇	XC 🚌	XC 🚌	XC 🚌	EM ◇
Norwich	d													05 52							06 52				07 57
Thetford	d													06 25							07 20				08 24
Ipswich	d																				*06 00*				*06b14*
Stansted Airport ✈	d														05 25	06 25									
Audley End	d														05 37	06 37									
Cambridge	d					05 15								*06 08*	05 55	06 56					*07 00*				*08 20*
Ely 6	d					05 30								06 51	06 10	07 11					07 44				08 54
March	d					05 46								07 07	06 28	07 29					08 01				09 11
Peterborough 8	a					06 08								07 25	06 50	07 51					08 25				09 28
	d					06 10		06 20	06 20		07 00	07 10		07 27	06 52	07 52		08 00		08 10	08 30		09 00	09 10	09 30
Stamford	d				05 35			06 45		07 10	07 25						08 10	08 25				09 10	09 25		
Oakham	d				06 00			07 10		07 35	07 50						08 35	08 50				09 35	09 50		
Melton Mowbray	d				06 20			07a30		07 55	08a10						08 55	09a10				09 55	10a10		
Leicester	d				07a00	07 49			07a35	08a35		08a35			08 21	09 16	09a35			09a35		10a35		10a35	
Nuneaton	a				*07 35*	08 09				*09 08*		*09 08*			08 47	09 41	*10 08*			*10 08*		*11 08*		*11 08*	
Coleshill Parkway	a				*07 51*	08 24				*09 25*		*09 25*			09 03	09 57	*10 25*			*10 25*		*11 25*		*11 25*	
Birmingham New Street 12	a				*08 09*	08 43				*09 43*		*09 43*			09 16	10 14	*10 43*			*10 43*		*11 43*		*11 43*	
Grantham 7	d													07 58							08 58				09 58
Nottingham 8 🚋	a				*08 16*				*08 42*			*09 26*		08 38						*10 26*	09 36			*11 26*	10 36
	d	05 18	06 40	07 45										08 45							09 45				10 45
Langley Mill	d																								
Alfreton	d		07 02	08 07										09 07							10 07				11 07
Chesterfield	d	05 49	07 13	08 18										09 18							10 18				11 18
Sheffield 7 🚋	a	06 15	07 31	08 38										09 38							10 38				11 38
	d	06 20	07 35	08 42										09 42							10 42				11 42
Stockport	a	07 22	08 24	09 25										10 25							11 25				12 25
Manchester Piccadilly 10 🚋	a	07 34	08 36	09 36										10 36							11 36				12 36
Manchester Oxford Road	a	07 37	08 40	09 40										10 40							11 40				12 40
Warrington Central	a	07 53	08 57	09 57										10 57							11 57				12 57
Widnes	a	08 01	09 05	10 05										11 05							12 05				13 05
Liverpool South Parkway 7 ✈	a	08 18	09 15	10 15										11 15							12 15				13 15
Liverpool Lime Street 10	a	08 31	09 31	10 31										11 31							12 31				13 31

		XC 1 ◇ ⊼		XC 🚌	XC 🚌	XC 🚌	EM ◇	XC 1 ◇ ⊼		XC 🚌	XC 🚌	XC 🚌	EM ◇	XC 1 ◇ ⊼	XC 1 ◇ ⊼	XC 🚌	XC 🚌	XC 🚌	EM ◇			XC 1 ◇ ⊼	XC 🚌	XC 🚌	XC 🚌
Norwich	d						08 57						09 57						10 57						
Thetford	d						09 24						10 24						11 24						
Ipswich	d						*08 02*						*08b16*						*10 02*						
Stansted Airport ✈	d	07 25						08 25						09 25	10 25							11 25			
Audley End	d	07 37						08 37						09 37	10 37							11 37			
Cambridge	d	08 00					*09 12*	09 00					*10 12*	10 00	11 00				*11 12*			12 00			
Ely 6	d	08 15					09 51	09 15					10 53	10 15	11 15				11 53			12 15			
March	d	08 31						09 31						10 31	11 31							12 31			
Peterborough 8	a	08 50					10 25	09 50					11 24	10 50	11 51				12 24			12 50			
	d	08 52			10 00	10 10	10 28	09 52			11 00	11 10	11 25	10 52	11 52		12 00	12 10	12 25			12 52		13 00	13 10
Stamford	d			10 10	10 25					11 10	11 25					12 10	12 25						13 10	13 25	
Oakham	d			10 35	10 50					11 35	11 50					12 35	12 50						13 35	13 50	
Melton Mowbray	d			10 55	11a10					11 55	12a10					12 55	13a10						13 55	14a10	
Leicester	d	10 16		11a35		11a35		11 16		12a35		12a35		12 16	13 16	13a35		13a35				14 16	14a35		14a35
Nuneaton	a	10 42		*12 08*		*12 08*		11 41		*13 08*		*13 08*		12 42	13 41			*14 08*				14 42	*15 08*		*15 08*
Coleshill Parkway	a	10 58		*12 25*		*12 25*		11 57		*13 25*		*13 25*		12 58	13 57			*14 25*				14 58	*15 25*		*15 25*
Birmingham New Street 12	a	11 14		*12 43*		*12 43*		12 14		*13 43*		*13 43*		13 14	14 14			*14 43*				15 14	*15 43*		*15 43*
Grantham 7	d						10 58						11 58						12 58						
Nottingham 8 🚋	a					*12 26*	11 35					*13 27*	12 36					*14 26*	13 36						*15 26*
	d						11 45						12 45						13 45						
Langley Mill	d																								
Alfreton	d						12 07						13 07						14 07						
Chesterfield	d						12 18						13 18						14 18						
Sheffield 7 🚋	a						12 38						13 38						14 38						
	d						12 42						13 42						14 42						
Stockport	a						13 25						14 25						15 25						
Manchester Piccadilly 10 🚋	a						13 36						14 36						15 36						
Manchester Oxford Road	a						13 40						14 40						15 40						
Warrington Central	a						13 57						14 57						15 57						
Widnes	a						14 05						15 05						16 05						
Liverpool South Parkway 7 ✈	a						14 15						15 15						16 15						
Liverpool Lime Street 10	a						14 31						15 31						16 31						

For general notes see front of timetable
For details of catering facilities see Directory of Train Operators

b Change at Cambridge and Ely

Table 49

Saturdays

18 July to 5 September

Stansted Airport → East Anglia → East Midlands → Birmingham and North West England

Route Diagram - see first page of Table 49

	EM ◇	XC 1 ◇ 🚲	XC 🚌		XC 🚌	XC 🚌	EM ◇	XC 1 ◇ 🚲	XC 🚌		XC 🚌	XC 🚌	EM ◇	XC 1 ◇ 🚲	XC 🚌		XC 🚌	XC 🚌	EM ◇	XC 🚌	XC 🚌		XC 🚌	EM ◇
Norwich d	11 57						12 57						13 57						14 57					15 52
Thetford d	12 24						13 24						14 24						15 24					16 23
Ipswich d	10b16						12 02						12b16						14 02					14b16
Stansted Airport ✈ d		12 25						13 25						14 25										
Audley End d		12 37						13 37						14 37										
Cambridge d	12 12	13 00					13 12	14 00					14 12	15 00					15 12					16 12
Ely 6 d	12 54	13 15					13 53	14 15					14 53	15 15					15 52					16 52
March d		13 31						14 31						15 31										
Peterborough 8 a	13 26	13 51					14 27	14 50					15 25	15 51					16 25					17 26
d	13 28	13 52			14 00	14 10	14 28	14 52			15 00	15 10	15 26	15 52			16 00	16 10	16 27		17 00		17 10	17 27
Stamford d			14 10		14 25				15 10		15 25				16 10		16 25			17 10	17 25			
Oakham d			14 35		14 50				15 35		15 50				16 35		16 50			17 35	17 50			
Melton Mowbray d			14 55		15a10				15 55		16a10				16 55		17a10			17 55	18a10			
Leicester d		15 16	15a35			15a35		16 16	16a35			16a35		17 16	17a35			17a35		18a35			18a35	
Nuneaton a		15 41	16 08			16 08		16 42	17 08			17 08		17 42	18 08					19 08			19 08	
Coleshill Parkway a		15 57	16 26			16 26		16 58	17 25			17 25		17 58	18 25					19 25			19 25	
Birmingham New Street 12 a		16 14	16 43			16 43		17 14	17 43			17 43		18 14	18 43					19 43			19 43	
Grantham 7 d	13 58						14 58						15 58						16 58					18 03
Nottingham 8 🚊 a	14 36					16 26	15 36					17 26	16 36					18 26	17 36				19 26	18 36
d	14 45						15 45						16 45						17 45					18 45
Langley Mill d																			18 03					
Alfreton d	15 07						16 07						17 07						18 09					19 07
Chesterfield d	15 18						16 18						17 18						18 19					19 18
Sheffield 7 🚊 a	15 38						16 38						17 34						18 39					19 39
d	15 42						16 42						17 40						18 42					19 42
Stockport a	16 25						17 25						18 25						19 25					20 25
Manchester Piccadilly 10 🚊 a	16 36						17 37						18 36						19 36					20 37
Manchester Oxford Road a	16 40						17 40						18 40						19 40					
Warrington Central a	16 57						18 03						18 57						19 57					
Widnes a	17 05						18 11						19 05						20 05					
Liverpool South Parkway 7 ✈ a	17 15						18 21						19 18						20 18					
Liverpool Lime Street 10 a	17 31						18 35						19 35						20 34					

	XC 1 ◇ 🚲	XC 🚌	XC 🚌	XC 🚌	EM ◇		XC 🚌	XC 🚌	XC 🚌	EM ◇	XC 1 ◇ 🚲		XC 1 ◇ 🚲	XC 🚌	XC 🚌	EM ◇	XC 1 ◇ 🚲		XC 🚌	XC 🚌	XC 1 ◇ 🚲			
Norwich d					16 57					17 54						18 57								
Thetford d					17 27					18 27						19 24								
Ipswich d					16 02					16b16						18 02								
Stansted Airport ✈ d	15 25										16 25		17 25				18 25				19 25			
Audley End d	15 37										16 37		17 37				18 37				19 37			
Cambridge d	16 00				17 12					18 12	17 00		18 00			19 12	19 00				20 00			
Ely 6 d	16 15				17 52					18 54	17 15		18 15			19 53	19 15				20 15			
March d	16 31									19 10	17 31		18 33				19 31				20 31			
Peterborough 8 a	16 49				18 25					19 29	17 51		18 50			20 25	19 50				20 49			
d	16 52		18 00	18 10	18 26			19 00	19 10	19 31	17 52		18 52	20 00	20 10	20 27	19 52			21 00	20 52			
Stamford d		18 10	18 25				19 10	19 25						20 25					20 45	21 25				
Oakham d		18 35	18 50				19 35	19 50						20 50					21 10	21 50				
Melton Mowbray d		18 55	19a10				19 55	20a10						21a10					21 30	22 10				
Leicester d	18 16	19a35		19a35			20a35		20a35		19 16		20 16		21a35		21 16		22a10	22a50	22 25			
Nuneaton a	18 42	20 08		20 08			21 08		21 08		19 42		20 42				21 42				22 51			
Coleshill Parkway a	18 58	20 25		20 25			21 25		21 25		19 58		20 58				21 58				23 07			
Birmingham New Street 12 a	19 14	20 43		20 43			21 43		21 43		20 14		21 14				22 14				23 25			
Grantham 7 d					18 58					20 03						20 58								
Nottingham 8 🚊 a				20 19	19 36				21 26	20 37					22 36	21 32			23 17	00 40				
d					19 40																			
Langley Mill d																								
Alfreton d					20 01																			
Chesterfield d					20 11																			
Sheffield 7 🚊 a					20 27																			
d					20 31																			
Stockport a					21 20																			
Manchester Piccadilly 10 🚊 a					21 32																			
Manchester Oxford Road a																								
Warrington Central a																								
Widnes a																								
Liverpool South Parkway 7 ✈ a																								
Liverpool Lime Street 10 a																								

For general notes see front of timetable
For details of catering facilities see Directory of Train Operators

b Change at Cambridge and Ely

Stansted Airport → East Anglia → East Midlands → Birmingham and North West England

Sundays
until 12 July

Route Diagram - see first page of Table 49

		EM	EM	EM	EM	XC	EM	XC	EM	XC	EM	XC	EM	XC	EM	XC	EM	XC	EM	XC	EM	XC	EM	XC	EM
		◇	◇	◇	◇	1 ◇	◇	1 ◇	◇	1 ◇	◇	1 ◇	◇	1 ◇	◇	1 ◇	◇	1 ◇	◇	1 ◇	◇	1 ◇	◇	1 ◇	◇
						🍴		🍴		🍴		🍴		🍴		🍴		🍴		🍴		🍴		🍴	
Norwich	d				09 33		10 47						13 49		14 47		15 53		16 57		17 56		18 57		20 52
Thetford	d				10 00		11 14						14 16		15 14		16 20		17 24		18 23		19 24		21 19
Ipswich	d					09b55		09c02		11b55		11c02		13b55		13c02		15b55		15c02		17b55		17c02	19c02
Stansted Airport ✈	d					10 25		11 25		12 25		13 25		14 25		15 25		16 25		17 25		18 25		19 25	
Audley End	d					10 39		11 39		12 39		13 39		14 39		15 39		16 39		17 39		18 39		19 39	
Cambridge	d				10 05	10 56	11 05	11 56		12 56		13 56		14 56	15 05	15 56		16 56	17 05	17 56	18 04	18 56	19 04	19 56	21 05
Ely 6	d				10 32	11 11	11 39	12 11		13 11		14 11	14 45	15 11	15 48	16 11		17 11	17 48	18 11	18 48	19 11	19 49	20 11	21 44
March	d					11 27		12 28		13 27		14 27		15 28		16 27		17 27		18 27		19 27		20 27	
Peterborough 8	a				11 09	11 50	12 16	12 50		13 50		14 50	15 24	15 50	16 22	16 50	17 10	17 50	18 25	18 51	19 24	19 50	20 28	20 50	22 20
	d				11 11	11 52	12 18	12 52		13 52		14 52	15 26	15 52	16 24	16 52	17 14	17 52	18 30	18 53	19 26	19 52	20 30	20 52	22 22
Stamford	d					12 05		13 05		14 05		15 05		16 05		17 05		18 05		19 06		20 05		21 05	
Oakham	d					12 21		13 21		14 21		15 21		16 21		17 21		18 21		19 22		20 21		21 21	
Melton Mowbray	d					12 33		13 33		14 33		15 33		16 32		17 32		18 33		19 33		20 33		21 33	
Leicester	d					12 49		13 49		14 49		15 49		16 48		17 48		18 49		19 49		20 49		21 49	
Nuneaton	a					13 08		14 08		15 08		16 08		17 08		18 08		19 08		20 08		21 08		22 08	
Coleshill Parkway	a					13 24		14 24		15 24		16 24		17 24		18 24		19 24		20 24		21 24		22 24	
Birmingham New Street 12	a					13 42		14 42		15 42		16 42		17 42		18 42		19 42		20 42		21 42		22 47	
Grantham 7	d				11 56		12 47						15 59		16 56		17 55		19 01		19 57		21 03		22 51
Nottingham 8 ⛴	a				12 33	14e22	13 26	15e20		16e12		17e14	16 28	18e14	17 25	18e50	18 29	19e50	19 30	20e48	20 31	21e50	21 35	23e18	23 26
	d	09 31	10 40	11 46	12 39		13 38		14 38		15 44		16 40		17 37		18 37		19 38						
Langley Mill	d				12 56		13 55		14 55				17 00		17 54		18 54								
Alfreton	d	09 53	11 03	12 08	13 04		14 03		15 03		16 04		17 08		18 02		19 02		20 00						
Chesterfield	d	10 08	11 14	12 18	13 17		14 18		15 13		16 23		17 20		18 17		19 12		20 10						
Sheffield 7 ⛴	a	10 32	11 35	12 35	13 33		14 36		15 31		16 39		17 40		18 34		19 31		20 31						
	d	10 41	11 38	12 41	13 38		14 39		15 37		16 44		17 44		18 37		19 35		20 35						
Stockport	a	11 26	12 25	13 25	14 25		15 25		16 25		17 27		18 25		19 25		20 25		21 24						
Manchester Piccadilly 10 ⛴	a	11 38	12 37	13 37	14 37		15 37		16 37		17 37		18 37		19 37		20 38		21 36						
Manchester Oxford Road	a	11 41	12 41	13 41	14 41		15 41		16 41		17 41		18 41		19 41										
Warrington Central	a	11 58	12 58	13 58	14 58		15 58		16 58		17 58		18 58		19 58										
Widnes	a	12 06	13 06	14 06	15 06		16 06		17 06		18 06		19 06		20 06										
Liverpool South Parkway 7 ✈	a	12 16	13 16	14 16	15 16		16 16		17 16		18 16		19 16		20 16										
Liverpool Lime Street 10	a	12 30	13 30	14 30	15 30		16 30		17 30		18 30		19 30		20 30										

Sundays
19 July to 6 September

		EM	EM	EM	EM		EM	XC	XC	EM		XC	XC	XC	EM		XC	XC	XC	XC		EM	XC	XC	XC
		◇	◇	◇	◇		◇	🚌	🚌	◇		1 ◇	🚌	🚌	◇		1 ◇	🚌	🚌	🚌		◇	1 ◇	🚌	🚌
												🍴					🍴						🍴		
Norwich	d						09 33								10 47										
Thetford	d						10 00								11 14										
Ipswich	d											09b55					09c02						11b55		
Stansted Airport ✈	d											10 25					11 25						12 25		
Audley End	d											10 39					11 39						12 39		
Cambridge	d						10 05					10 56			11 05		11 56						12 56		
Ely 6	d						10 32					11 11			11 39		12 11						13 11		
March	d											11 27					12 28						13 27		
Peterborough 8	a						11 09					11 50			12 16		12 50						13 50		
	d						11 11					11 52	12 00	12 10	12 18		12 52		13 00	13 10			13 52		14 00
Stamford	d							11 10	12 10				12 25					13 10	13 25					14 10	14 25
Oakham	d							11 35	12 35				12 50					13 35	13 50					14 35	14 50
Melton Mowbray	d							11 55	12 55				13a10					13 55	14a10					14 55	15a10
Leicester	d							12a35	13a35			13 42		13a35			14 18	14a35		14a35			15 19	15a35	
Nuneaton	a							13 08	14 08			14 03		14 08			14 45	15 08		15 08			15 44	16 08	
Coleshill Parkway	a							13 24	14 24			14 19		14 24			15 01	15 24		15 24			16 00	16 25	
Birmingham New Street 12	a							13 42	14 42			14 38		14 42			15 15	15 42		15 42			16 15	16 43	
Grantham 7	d						11 56								12 47										
Nottingham 8 ⛴	a						12 33	13 29				14e33		14 33	13 26		15e20			15 20			16e12		
	d	09 06	09 31	10 40	11 46		12 39			14 38					13 38							15 44			
Langley Mill	d		09 53				12 56			14 55					13 55										
Alfreton	d	09 41		11 03	12 08		13 04			15 03					14 03							16 04			
Chesterfield	d	09 51	10 08	11 14	12 18		13 17			15 13					14 18							16 23			
Sheffield 7 ⛴	a	10 16	10 30	11 35	12 35		13 33			15 31					14 36							16 39			
	d	10 41	10 41	11 38	12 41		13 38			15 37					14 39							16 44			
Stockport	a	11 26	11 25	12 25	13 25		14 25			16 25					15 25							17 27			
Manchester Piccadilly 10 ⛴	a	11 38	11 37	12 37	13 37		14 37			16 37					15 37							17 37			
Manchester Oxford Road	a	11 41	11 41	12 41	13 41		14 41			16 41					15 41							17 41			
Warrington Central	a	11 58		12 58	13 58		14 58			16 58					15 58							17 58			
Widnes	a	12 06		13 06	14 06		15 06			17 06					16 06							18 06			
Liverpool South Parkway 7 ✈	a	12 16		13 16	14 16		15 16			17 16					16 16							18 16			
Liverpool Lime Street 10	a	12 30	12 30	13 30	14 30		15 30			17 30					16 30							18 30			

For general notes see front of timetable
For details of catering facilities see Directory of Train Operators

b Change at Ely
c Change at Cambridge and Ely
e Change at Leicester

Table 49

Sundays

Stansted Airport → East Anglia → East Midlands → Birmingham and North West England

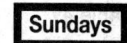

19 July to 6 September

Route Diagram - see first page of Table 49

		XC	XC 1 ◇		XC	XC	XC	EM ◇		XC 1 ◇	XC	XC	XC
Norwich	d							13 49					
Thetford	d							14 16					
Ipswich	d		11b02							13c55			
Stansted Airport	d		13 25							14 25			
Audley End	d		13 39							14 39			
Cambridge	d		13 56							14 56			
Ely 6	d		14 11					14 45		15 11			
March	d		14 27							15 28			
Peterborough 8	a		14 50					15 24		15 50			
	d	14 10	14 52			15 00	15 10	15 26		15 52		16 00	16 10
Stamford	d				15 10	15 25					16 10	16 25	
Oakham	d				15 35	15 50					16 35	16 50	
Melton Mowbray	d				15 55	16a10					16 55	17a10	
Leicester	d	15a35	16 19		16a35		16a35			17 24	17a35		17a35
Nuneaton	a	16 08	16 45		17 08		17 08			17 51	18 08		18 08
Coleshill Parkway	a	16 25	17 01		17 24		17 24			18 07	18 24		18 24
Birmingham New Street 12	a	16 43	17 15		17 42		17 42			18 20	18 42		18 42
Grantham 7	d							16 02					
Nottingham 8	a		17e14				17 14	16 31		18e14			
	d							16 34					
Langley Mill	d							17 00					
Alfreton	d							17 08					
Chesterfield	d							17 20					
Sheffield 7	a							17 40					
	d							17 44					
Stockport	a							18 25					
Manchester Piccadilly 10	a							18 37					
Manchester Oxford Road	a							18 41					
Warrington Central	a							18 58					
Widnes	a							19 06					
Liverpool South Parkway 7	a							19 16					
Liverpool Lime Street 10	a							19 30					

			EM ◇	XC 1 ◇	XC	XC		XC	EM ◇	XC 1 ◇	XC		XC
Norwich	d		14 47						15 53				
Thetford	d		15 14						16 20				
Ipswich	d			13b02						15c55			
Stansted Airport	d			15 25						16 25			
Audley End	d			15 39						16 39			
Cambridge	d		15 05	15 56						16 56			
Ely 6	d		15 48	16 11						17 11			
March	d			16 27						17 27			
Peterborough 8	a		16 22	16 46					17 10	17 50			
	d		16 24	16 52		17 00		17 10	17 14	17 52			18 00
Stamford	d				17 10	17 25					18 10		18 25
Oakham	d				17 35	17 50					18 35		18 50
Melton Mowbray	d				17 55	18a10					18 55		19a10
Leicester	d			18 16	18a35			18a35		19 20	19a35		
Nuneaton	a			18 40	19 08			19 08		19 46	20 08		
Coleshill Parkway	a			18 56	19 24			19 24		20 02	20 24		
Birmingham New Street 12	a			19 15	19 42			19 42		20 16	20 42		
Grantham 7	d		16 56						17 59				
Nottingham 8	a		17 25	18e50				19 19	18 31	20e09			
	d		17 37						18 37				
Langley Mill	d		17 54						18 54				
Alfreton	d		18 02						19 02				
Chesterfield	d		18 17						19 12				
Sheffield 7	a		18 34						19 31				
	d		18 37						19 35				
Stockport	a		19 25						20 25				
Manchester Piccadilly 10	a		19 37						20 38				
Manchester Oxford Road	a		19 41										
Warrington Central	a		19 58										
Widnes	a		20 06										
Liverpool South Parkway 7	a		20 16										
Liverpool Lime Street 10	a		20 30										

		XC	EM ◇	XC 1 ◇	XC		XC	XC	EM ◇	XC 1 ◇		XC	XC
Norwich	d		16 57						17 56				
Thetford	d		17 24						18 23				
Ipswich	d			15b02									
Stansted Airport	d			17 25						18 25			
Audley End	d			17 39						18 39			
Cambridge	d		17 05	17 56					18 04	18 56			
Ely 6	d		17 48	18 11					18 48	19 11			
March	d			18 27						19 27			
Peterborough 8	a		18 25	18 51					19 24	19 50			
	d	18 10	18 30	18 53			19 00	19 10	19 26	19 52			20 00
Stamford	d				19 10		19 25					20 10	20 25
Oakham	d				19 35		19 50					20 35	20 50
Melton Mowbray	d				19 55		20a10					20 55	21a10
Leicester	d	19a35		20 23	20a35			20a35		21 26		21a35	
Nuneaton	a	20 08		20 52	21 08			21 08		21 51		22 08	
Coleshill Parkway	a	20 24		21 07	21 24			21 24		22 09		22 24	
Birmingham New Street 12	a	20 42		21 21	21 42			21 42		22 23		22 42	
Grantham 7	d		19 01						19 57				
Nottingham 8	a	20 23	19 30	21e13				21 20	20 31				
	d		19 38										
Langley Mill	d												
Alfreton	d		20 00										
Chesterfield	d		20 10										
Sheffield 7	a		20 31										
	d		20 35										
Stockport	a		21 24										
Manchester Piccadilly 10	a		21 36										
Manchester Oxford Road	a												
Warrington Central	a												
Widnes	a												
Liverpool South Parkway 7	a												
Liverpool Lime Street 10	a												

		XC	EM ◇		XC 1 ◇	XC	XC	EM ◇		XC 1			
Norwich	d		18 57					20 52					
Thetford	d		19 24					21 19					
Ipswich	d		17 55					19b02					
Stansted Airport	d				19 25								
Audley End	d				19 39								
Cambridge	d		19 04		19 56			21 05					
Ely 6	d		19 49		20 11			21 44					
March	d				20 27								
Peterborough 8	a		20 28		20 50			22 20					
	d	20 10	20 30		20 52		21 00	22 22					
Stamford	d					21 10	21 25						
Oakham	d					21 35	21 50						
Melton Mowbray	d					21 55	22 10						
Leicester	d	21a35			22 32	22a35	22a44			22 51			
Nuneaton	a	22 08			22 56		23 10			23 10			
Coleshill Parkway	a	22 24			23 14		23 26			23 26			
Birmingham New Street 12	a	22 42			23 28		23 44			23 44			
Grantham 7	d		21 03					22 51					
Nottingham 8	a		21 35				23 40	23 26					
	d												
Langley Mill	d												
Alfreton	d												
Chesterfield	d												
Sheffield 7	a												
	d												
Stockport	a												
Manchester Piccadilly 10	a												
Manchester Oxford Road	a												
Warrington Central	a												
Widnes	a												
Liverpool South Parkway 7	a												
Liverpool Lime Street 10	a												

For general notes see front of timetable
For details of catering facilities see Directory of Train Operators

b Change at Cambridge and Ely
c Change at Ely
e Change at Leicester

Table 49

Sundays

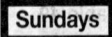

13 September to 1 November

Stansted Airport → East Anglia → East Midlands → Birmingham and North West England

Route Diagram - see first page of Table 49

		EM ◇	EM ◇	EM ◇	EM ◇	XC 1 ◇	EM ◇	EM ◇	XC 1 ◇	EM ◇	XC 1 ◇	XC 1 ◇	EM ◇	XC 1 ◇	EM ◇	XC 1 ◇	EM ◇	XC 1 ◇	EM ◇	XC 1 ◇	EM ◇	XC 1 ◇	EM ◇	XC 1 ◇	EM ◇
Norwich	d						10 47						13 49		14 47		15 53		16 57		17 56		18 57		20 52
Thetford	d						11 14						14 16		15 14		16 20		17 24		18 23		19 24		21 19
Ipswich	d					09b55			09c02		11b55	11c02		13b55		13c02		15b55		15c02		17b55		17c02	19c02
Stansted Airport ✈	d					10 25			11 25		12 25	13 25		14 25		15 25		16 25		17 25		18 25		19 25	
Audley End	d					10 39			11 39		12 39	13 39		14 39		15 39		16 39		17 39		18 39		19 39	
Cambridge	d					10 56	11 05		11 56		12 56	13 56		14 56	15 05	15 56		16 56	17 05	17 56	18 04	18 56	19 04	19 56	21 05
Ely 6	d					11 11	11 39		12 11		13 11	14 11	14 45	15 11	15 48	16 11		17 11	17 48	18 11	18 48	19 11	19 49	20 11	21 44
March	d					11 27			12 28		13 27	14 27		15 28		16 27		17 27		18 27		19 27		20 27	
Peterborough 8	a					11 50	12 16		12 50		13 50	14 50	15 24	15 50	16 22	16 50	17 10	17 50	18 25	18 51	19 24	19 50	20 28	20 50	22 20
	d					11 52	12 18		12 52		13 52	14 52	15 26	15 52	16 24	16 52	17 14	17 52	18 30	18 53	19 26	19 52	20 30	20 52	22 22
Stamford	d					12 05			13 05		14 05	15 05		16 05		17 05		18 05		19 06		20 05		21 05	
Oakham	d					12 21			13 21		14 21	15 21		16 27		17 22		18 21		19 22		20 21		21 25	
Melton Mowbray	d					12 33			13 33		14 33	15 33		16 38		17 33		18 32		19 33		20 33		21 36	
Leicester	d					12 52			13 52		14 52	15 52		17e01		17 52		18 52		19 52		20 52		21 52	
Nuneaton	a					14f18			15f18		16f18	17f18		18f18		19f18		20f18		21f18		22f18		23f20	
Coleshill Parkway	a					15f10			16f10		17f10	18f10		19f10		20f10		21f10		22f10		23f10		23f55	
Birmingham New Street 12	a					14 06			15 16		16 14	17 13		18 16		19 18		20 16		21 11		22 12		23 14	
Grantham 7	d						12 47						15 59		16 56		17 55		19 01		19 57		21 03		22 51
Nottingham 8	a					14g02	13 26				16g11	16g53	16 28	18g03	17 25	18g54	18 29	19g52	19 30	20g53	20 31	21g55	21 35		23 26
	d	09 31	10 40	11 46	12 39		13 38	14 38		15 44			16 43		17 37		18 37		19 38						
Langley Mill	d				12 56		13 55	14 55					17 00		17 54		18 54								
Alfreton	d	09 53	11 03	12 08	13 04		14 03	15 03		16 04			17 08		18 02		19 02		20 00						
Chesterfield	d	10 08	11 14	12 18	13 16		14 18	15 13		16 23			17 20		18 17		19 12		20 10						
Sheffield 7	a	10 30	11 35	12 35	13 32		14 36	15 34		16 39			17 40		18 34		19 31		20 31						
	d	10 41	11 38	12 41	13 38		14 39	15 37		16 44			17 44		18 37		19 35		20 35						
Stockport	a	11 25	12 25	13 25	14 25		15 25	16 25		17 27			18 25		19 25		20 25		21 24						
Manchester Piccadilly 10	a	11 37	12 37	13 37	14 37		15 37	16 37		17 37			18 37		19 37		20 38		21 36						
Manchester Oxford Road	a	11 41	12 41	13 41	14 41		15 41	16 41		17 41			18 41		19 41										
Warrington Central	a	11 58																							
Widnes	a	12 06																							
Liverpool South Parkway 7 ✈	a	12 16																							
Liverpool Lime Street 10	a	12 30	13 30	14 30	15 30		16 30	17 30		18 30			19 30		20 30										

Sundays

from 8 November

		EM ◇	EM ◇	EM ◇	XC 1 ◇	EM ◇	EM ◇	XC 1 ◇	EM ◇	XC 1 ◇	XC 1 ◇	EM ◇	XC 1 ◇	EM ◇	XC 1 ◇	EM ◇	XC 1 ◇	EM ◇	XC 1 ◇	EM ◇	XC 1 ◇	EM ◇	XC 1 ◇	EM ◇
Norwich	d					10 47						13 49		14 47		15 53		16 57		17 56		18 57		20 52
Thetford	d					11 14						14 16		15 14		16 20		17 24		18 23		19 24		21 19
Ipswich	d				09b55			09c02		11b55	11c02		13b55		13c02		15b55		15c02		17b55		17c02	19c02
Stansted Airport ✈	d				10 25			11 25		12 25	13 25		14 25		15 25		16 25		17 25		18 25		19 25	
Audley End	d				10 39			11 39		12 39	13 39		14 39		15 39		16 39		17 39		18 39		19 39	
Cambridge	d				10 56	11 05		11 56		12 56	13 56		14 56	15 05	15 56		16 56	17 05	17 56	18 04	18 56	19 04	19 56	21 05
Ely 6	d				11 11	11 39		12 11		13 11	14 11	14 45	15 11	15 48	16 11		17 11	17 48	18 11	18 48	19 11	19 49	20 11	21 44
March	d				11 27			12 28		13 27	14 27		15 28		16 27		17 27		18 27		19 27		20 27	
Peterborough 8	a				11 50	12 16		12 50		13 50	14 50	15 24	15 50	16 22	16 50	17 10	17 50	18 25	18 51	19 24	19 50	20 28	20 50	22 20
	d				11 52	12 18		12 52		13 52	14 52	15 26	15 52	16 24	16 52	17 14	17 52	18 30	18 53	19 26	19 52	20 30	20 52	22 22
Stamford	d				12 05			13 05		14 05	15 05		16 05		17 05		18 05		19 06		20 05		21 05	
Oakham	d				12 21			13 21		14 21	15 21		16 27		17 22		18 21		19 22		20 21		21 25	
Melton Mowbray	d				12 33			13 33		14 33	15 33		16 38		17 33		18 32		19 33		20 33		21 36	
Leicester	d				12 52			13 52		14 52	15 52		17 01		17 52		18 52		19 52		20 52		21 52	
Nuneaton	a				14f18			15f18		16f18	17 18		18f18											
Coleshill Parkway	a				15f10			16f10		17 10	18f10		19f10											
Birmingham New Street 12	a				14 06			15 16		16 14	17 13		18 16		19 19		20 16		21 12		22 12		23 14	
Grantham 7	d					12 47						15 59		16 56		17 55		19 01		19 57		21 03		22 51
Nottingham 8	a				14g02	13 26				16g11	16g53	16 28	18g03	17 25	18g54	18 29	19g52	19 30	20g53	20 31	21g55	21 35		23 26
	d	10 40	11 46	12 39		13 38	14 38		15 44			16 40		17 37		18 37		19 38						
Langley Mill	d			12 56		13 55	14 55					17 00		17 54		18 54								
Alfreton	d	11 03	12 08	13 04		14 03	15 03		16 04			17 08		18 02		19 02		20 00						
Chesterfield	d	11 14	12 18	13 16		14 18	15 13		16 23			17 20		18 17		19 12		20 10						
Sheffield 7	a	11 35	12 35	13 32		14 36	15 34		16 39			17 40		18 34		19 31		20 31						
	d	11 38	12 41	13 38		14 39	15 37		16 44			17 44		18 37		19 35		20 35						
Stockport	a	12 25	13 25	14 25		15 25	16 25		17 27			18 25		19 25		20 25		21 24						
Manchester Piccadilly 10	a	12 37	13 37	14 37		15 37	16 37		17 37			18 37		19 37		20 38		21 36						
Manchester Oxford Road	a	12 41	13 41	14 41		15 41	16 41		17 41			18 41		19 41										
Warrington Central	a	12 58	13 58	14 58		15 58	16 58		17 58			18 58		19 58										
Widnes	a	13 06	14 06	15 06		16 06	17 08		18 06			19 06		20 06										
Liverpool South Parkway 7 ✈	a	13 16	14 16	15 16		16 16	17 18		18 16			19 16		20 16										
Liverpool Lime Street 10	a	13 30	14 30	15 30		16 30	17 30		18 30			19 30		20 30										

For general notes see front of timetable
For details of catering facilities see Directory of Train Operators

b Change at Ely
c Change at Cambridge and Ely
e Arr. 1647
f By bus
g Change at Leicester

Table 49

Mondays to Fridays

North West England and Birmingham → East Midlands → East Anglia → Stansted Airport

Route Diagram - see first page of Table 49

Miles	Miles	Miles	Miles			EM	EM	XC	EM	XC	XC	EM	XC	EM	XC	EM	XC	XC	EM	XC		EM	XC	XC	EM
						◇	[1] ◇	[1] ◇	◇	[1] ◇	[1]	◇	[1] ◇	◇	[1] ◇	◇	[1]	[1] ◇	◇	[1] ◇		◇	[1]	[1] ◇	◇
							A					B													
							⊠ [trolley]			[trolley]			[trolley]		[trolley]			[trolley]		[trolley]				[trolley]	
—	0	—	0	**Liverpool Lime Street [10]**	d											06 47			07 42			08 52			09 52
—	5½	—	5½	Liverpool South Parkway [7] ✈	d											06 57			07 52			09 03			10 03
—	12¼	—	12¼	Widnes	d											07 07			08 05			09 11			10 11
—	18½	—	18½	Warrington Central	d											07 15			08 13			09 19			10 19
—	34¼	—	34¼	Manchester Oxford Road	d											07 38			08 39			09 39			10 39
—	34¾	—	34¾	**Manchester Piccadilly [10]** 🚊	d											07 42			08 43			09 43			10 43
—	40¾	—	40¾	Stockport	d											07 54			08 54			09 54			10 54
—	77½	—	77½	**Sheffield [7]** 🚊	a											08 34			09 35			10 35			11 35
—	—	—	—		d											08 38			09 38			10 38			11 38
—	89¾	—	89¾	Chesterfield	d											08 53			09 53			10 53			11 53
—	99¾	—	99¾	Alfreton	d											09 03			10 03			11 03			12 03
—	106	—	106	Langley Mill	d																				
—	118	—	118	**Nottingham [8]** 🚊	a											09 30			10 30			11 30			12 30
—	—	—	—		d	04 51			05 56	06b28	07b10	07 52		08 34	08b28	09 34	09b02	09b28	10 34	10b28		11 34	11b02	11b28	12 34
—	140¾	—	—	Grantham [7]	d							08 25		09 11		10 08			11 06			12 07			13 06
0	—	—	—	**Birmingham New Street [12]**	d			05 22		06 22	06 52		07 22		08 22		08 52	09 22		10 22			10 52	11 22	
9½	—	—	—	Coleshill Parkway	d					06 35	07 05		07 35		08 35		09 07	09 35		10 35			11 07	11 35	
21	—	—	—	Nuneaton	d			05 50		06 52	07 22		07 51		08 52		09 23	09 52		10 52			11 23	11 52	
39¾	—	—	—	**Leicester**	d			06 11		07 17	07 50		08 17		09 17		09 50	10 17		11 17			11 50	12 17	
54¾	—	—	—	Melton Mowbray	d	05 29	06 02	06 27	06 52	07 33	08 09		08 33		09 33		10 07	10 33		11 33			12 06	12 33	
66¼	—	—	—	Oakham	d	05 41	06a13	06 40	07 04	07 45	08 20		08 45		09 45		10 19	10 45		11 45			12 18	12 45	
79¾	—	—	—	Stamford	d	06 02		06 54	07 18	08 01	08 36		09 01		10 01		10 35	11 01		12 01			12 34	13 01	
92¼	170	—	187¾	**Peterborough [8]**	a	06 17		07 07	07 33	08 16	08 53	08 57	09 17	09 38	10 16	10 42	10 56	11 17	11 36	12 16		12 42	12 53	13 17	13 38
—	—	—	—		d	06 27		07 10	07 35	08 18	08 54	08 59	09 18	09 40	10 18	10 44	10 58	11 18	11 38	12 18		12 43	12 55	13 18	13 40
106¼	184	—	201¾	March	a	06 42		07 28	07 50	08 33	09 09		09 34		10 33		11 13	11 34		12 33			13 10	13 34	
113¾	191½	0	209¼	Ely [6]	a	07 01		07 51	08 11	08 52	09 35	09 41	09 53	10 13	10 52	11 16	11 31	11 52	12 11	12 52		13 16	13 32	13 52	14 13
—	—	14¾	—	**Cambridge**	a	*07 44*		08 07	*08 44*	09 08	09 51		10 09	*10 47*	11 08	*11 44*	11 50	12 08	*12 44*	13 08		*13 44*	13 50	14 08	*14 44*
—	—	28¾	—	Audley End	a			08 23		09 23			10 23		11 23			12 23		13 23				14 23	
—	—	39½	—	**Stansted Airport** ✈	a			08 45		09 45			10 45		11 45			12 45		13 45				14 45	
—	—	—	—	Ipswich	a	*10c03*		*09e26*	*09 26*	*11f03*			*11e25*	*11 25*	*13f03*	*14c03*		*13e25*	*13 25*	*15f03*		*16c03*		*15e25*	*15 25*
137	214¾	—	232¾	Thetford	a	07 28			08 36			10 05		10 38		11 41			12 36			13 40			14 37
167½	245¼	—	263	**Norwich**	a	08 13			09 13			10 43		11 13		12 13			13 13			14 13			15 13

		XC	EM	XC	XC	EM	XC	EM	XC	EM	XC	XC	EM	XC	EM	XC	XC	XC	EM	EM	XC	EM	EM	EM
		[1] ◇	◇	[1]	[1] ◇	◇	[1] ◇	◇	[1] ◇	◇	[1] ◇	[1] ◇	◇	[1] ◇	◇	[1] ◇	[1]	[1] ◇	◇	◇	[1] ◇	◇	◇	◇
		[trolley]			[trolley]		[trolley]		[trolley]		[trolley]	[trolley]		[trolley]		[trolley]		[trolley]			[trolley]			
Liverpool Lime Street [10]	d		10 52			11 52		12 52		13 52			14 52		15 52				16 52	17 52		18 52	19 52	21 37
Liverpool South Parkway [7] ✈	d		11 03			12 03		13 03		14 03			15 03		16 03				17 03	18 03		19 03	20 03	21 47
Widnes	d		11 11			12 11		13 11		14 11			15 11		16 11				17 11	18 11		19 11	20 11	21 55
Warrington Central	d		11 19			12 19		13 19		14 19			15 19		16 19				17 19	18 19		19 19	20 19	22 03
Manchester Oxford Road	d		11 39			12 39		13 39		14 39			15 39		16 39				17 39	18 39		19 39	20 39	22 24
Manchester Piccadilly [10] 🚊	d		11 43			12 43		13 43		14 43			15 43		16 43				17 43	18 43		19 43	20 43	22 28
Stockport	d		11 54			12 54		13 54		14 54			15 54		16 54				17 54	18 54		19 54	20 54	22 37
Sheffield [7] 🚊	a		12 35			13 35		14 35		15 34			16 35		17 37				18 41	19 33		20 36	21 35	22 35
	d		12 38			13 38		14 38		15 38			16 38		17 44				18 45	19 38		20 41	21 38	23 38
Chesterfield	d		12 53			13 53		14 53		15 53			16 56		18 01				19 01	19 53		20 58	21 54	00 02
Alfreton	d		13 03			14 03		15 07		16 03			17 06		18 11				19 11	20 04		21 09	22 05	
Langley Mill	d																						22 12	
Nottingham [8] 🚊	a		13 30			14 31		15 30		16 33			17 31		18 33				19 38	20 31		21 38	22 38	00 41
	d	*12b28*	13 34	*13b02*	*13b28*	14 34	*14b28*	15 34	*15b28*		*16b28*		17 34	*17b28*	18 34	*18b28*	*19b02*	*19b28*		20 34	*20b02*			
Grantham [7]	d		14 07			15 07		16 07					18 12		19 07					21 08				
Birmingham New Street [12]	d	12 22		12 52	13 22		14 22		15 22		16 22	16 52		17 22		18 22	18 52	19 22			20 22			
Coleshill Parkway	d	12 35		13 07	13 35		14 35		15 35		16 35	17 05		17 35		18 35	19 05	19 35			20 35			
Nuneaton	d	12 52		13 23	13 52		14 52		15 52		16 52	17 22		17 52		18 52	19 22	19 52			20 52			
Leicester	d	13 17		13 50	14 17		15 17		16 17		17 17	17 50		18 17		19 17	19 50	20 17			21 17			
Melton Mowbray	d	13 33		14 06	14 33		15 33		16 33		17 33	18 07		18 33		19 33	20 08	20 33			21 33			
Oakham	d	13 45		14 18	14 45		15 45		16 45		17 45	18 19		18 45		19 45	20 20	20 45			21 45			
Stamford	d	14 01		14 36	15 01		16 01		17 01		18 01	18 40		19 01		20 01	20 36	21 01			22 01			
Peterborough [8]	a	14 16	14 38	14 51	15 17	15 34	16 16	16 34	17 16		18 16	18 57	18 41	19 16	19 36	20 16	20 57	21 17		21 35	22 16			
	d	14 18	14 40	14 52	15 18	15 35	16 18	16 36	17 18		18 18	18 59	18 42	19 18	19 37	20 18	20 59	21 18		21 37	22 18			
March	a	14 33		15 09	15 34		16 33		17 36		18 33	19 14	18 58	19 33		20 33	21 14	21 34			22 33			
Ely [6]	a	14 52	15 13	15 41	15 52	16 08	16 52	17 09	17 58		18 52	19 32	19 24	19 52	20 13	20 52	21 34	21 52		22 10	22 52			
Cambridge	a	15 08	*15 44*	15 57	16 08	*16 44*	17 08	*17 43*	18 16		19 08	19 55	*19 58*	20 08	*21 04*	21 08	21 54	22 08		*22 33*	23 10			
Audley End	a	15 23			16 23		17 23		18 31		19 23			20 23		21 23		22 23						
Stansted Airport ✈	a	15 45			16 45		17 45		18 50		19 45			20 45		21 45		22 45						
Ipswich	a	*17f03*	*18c03*		*17e27*	*17 27*	*19f03*	*20c03*	*19e25*		*21f03*		*22c03*	*21e25*	*21 25*	*00c03*	*00 03*	*23e37*		*23 37*				
Thetford	a		15 37			16 33		17 33					19 49		20 36					22 34				
Norwich	a		16 13			17 13		18 13					20 22		21 13					23 18				

For general notes see front of timetable
For details of catering facilities see Directory of Train Operators

A To St Pancras International (Table 53)
B From Mansfield Woodhouse (Table 55)
b Change at Leicester
c Change at Ely and Cambridge
e Change at Ely
f Change at Cambridge

Table 49

Saturdays

until 11 July and from 12 September

North West England and Birmingham → East Midlands → East Anglia → Stansted Airport

Route Diagram - see first page of Table 49

		EM	XC	EM	XC	EM	XC		XC	EM	XC	EM	XC	XC		EM	XC	EM	XC	XC	EM		XC	EM	XC
		◇	1 ◇	◇	1 ◇	◇	1		1 ◇	◇	1 ◇	◇	1	1 ◇		◇	1 ◇	◇	1	1 ◇	◇		1 ◇	◇	1
			🛒		🛒				🛒		🛒			🛒			🛒			🛒			🛒		
Liverpool Lime Street 10	d											06 49				07 42		08 52			09 52			10 52	
Liverpool South Parkway 7 ✈	d											06 59				07 52		09 03			10 03			11 03	
Widnes	d											07 07				08 05		09 11			10 11			11 11	
Warrington Central	d											07 15				08 13		09 19			10 19			11 19	
Manchester Oxford Road	d											07 38				08 39		09 39			10 39			11 39	
Manchester Piccadilly 10	d											07 42				08 43		09 43			10 43			11 43	
Stockport	d											07 54				08 54		09 54			10 54			11 54	
Sheffield 7	a											08 34				09 35		10 35			11 35			12 35	
	d											08 38				09 38		10 38			11 38			12 38	
Chesterfield	d											08 53				09 53		10 53			11 53			12 53	
Alfreton	d											09 03				10 03		11 03			12 03			13 03	
Langley Mill	d																								
Nottingham 8	a											09 30				10 30		11 29			12 29			13 29	
	d	05 04		05 54	*06b28*	07 45	*07b02*		*07b28*	08 34	*08b28*	09 34	*09b02*	*09b28*		10 34	*10b28*	11 34	*11b02*	*11b28*	12 34		*12b28*	13 34	*13b02*
Grantham 7	d					08 16				09 11		10 09				11 07		12 07			13 06			14 07	
Birmingham New Street 12	d		05 22		06 22		06 52		07 22		08 22		08 52	09 22			10 22		10 52	11 22			12 22		12 52
Coleshill Parkway	d		05 35		06 35		07 06		07 35		08 35		09 07	09 35			10 35		11 07	11 35			12 35		13 07
Nuneaton	d		05 52		06 52		07 22		07 52		08 52		09 23	09 52			10 52		11 23	11 52			12 52		13 23
Leicester	d		06 13		07 15		07 50		08 15		09 15		09 50	10 15			11 15		11 50	12 15			13 15		13 50
Melton Mowbray	d	05 37	06 31	06 52	07 31		08 06		08 31		09 31		10 06	10 31			11 31		12 06	12 31			13 31		14 06
Oakham	d	05 49	06 43	07 04	07 43		08 18		08 43		09 43		10 18	10 43			11 43		12 18	12 43			13 43		14 18
Stamford	d	06 06	06 57	07 18	07 59		08 34		08 59		09 59		10 34	10 59			11 59		12 34	12 59			13 59		14 34
Peterborough 8	a	06 19	07 11	07 33	08 14	08 44	08 57		09 22	09 44	10 14	10 42	10 57	11 17		11 36	12 14	12 38	12 57	13 17	13 35		14 14	14 39	14 54
	d	06 27	07 13	07 35	08 18	08 46	08 58		09 23	09 46	10 18	10 44	10 58	11 18		11 38	12 18	12 40	12 58	13 18	13 38		14 18	14 41	14 55
March	a	06 42	07 31	07 50	08 33		09 13		09 39		10 33		11 13	11 34			12 33		13 13	13 34			14 33		15 10
Ely 6	a	07 01	07 52	08 11	08 52	09 19	09 32		09 58	10 19	10 52	11 17	11 32	11 52		12 11	12 52	13 13	13 32	13 52	14 11		14 52	15 14	15 30
Cambridge	a	*07 44*	08 08	*08 44*	09 08	*09 44*	09 50		10 16	*10 44*	11 08	*11 44*	11 50	12 08		*12 44*	13 08	*13 44*	13 50	14 08	*14 44*		15 08	*15 44*	15 50
Audley End	a		08 23		09 23				10 31		11 23			12 23			13 23			14 23			15 23		
Stansted Airport ✈	a		08 45		09 45				10 50		11 45			12 45			13 45			14 45			15 45		
Ipswich	a	*10c03*	*09e25*	*09 25*	*11f03*	*12c03*			*11e27*	*11 27*	*13f03*	*14c03*		*13e27*		*13 27*	*15f03*	*16c03*		*15e25*	*15 25*		*17f03*	*18c03*	
Thetford	a	07 30		08 36		09 44				10 44		11 44				12 35		13 39			14 35			15 38	
Norwich	a	08 13		09 15		10 19				11 18		12 18				13 13		14 13			15 13			16 13	

		XC	EM	XC	EM	XC		XC	EM	EM	XC	EM	XC		XC	XC	EM	EM	XC	EM	EM	EM	EM		
		1 ◇	◇	1 ◇	◇	1 ◇		1 ◇	◇	◇	1 ◇	◇	1 ◇		1	1 ◇	◇	◇	1 ◇	◇	◇	◇ A	◇ B		
		🛒		🛒		🛒		🛒			🛒		🛒			🛒			🛒						
Liverpool Lime Street 10	d		11 52		12 52				13 52	14 52		15 52					16 52	17 52		18 52	19 52	20 52	20 52		
Liverpool South Parkway 7 ✈	d		12 03		13 03				14 03	15 03		16 03					17 03	18 03		19 03	20 03	21 03	21 03		
Widnes	d		12 11		13 11				14 11	15 11		16 11					17 11	18 11		19 11	20 11	21 11	21 11		
Warrington Central	d		12 19		13 19				14 19	15 19		16 19					17 19	18 19		19 19	20 19	21 19	21 19		
Manchester Oxford Road	d		12 39		13 39				14 39	15 39		16 39					17 39	18 39		19 39	20 39	21 39	21 39		
Manchester Piccadilly 10	d		12 43		13 43				14 43	15 43		16 43					17 43	18 43		19 43	20 43	21 43	21 43		
Stockport	d		12 54		13 54				14 54	15 54		16 54					17 54	18 54		19 54	20 54	21 52	21 52		
Sheffield 7	a		13 35		14 35				15 35	16 35		17 37					18 34	19 35		20 35	21 34	22 31	22 31		
	d		13 38		14 38				15 38	16 38		17 44					18 38	19 38		20 41	21 38	22 35	22 35		
Chesterfield	d		13 53		14 53				15 53	16 53		17 58					18 53	19 53		20 59	21 54	22 51	22 51		
Alfreton	d		14 03		15 03				16 03	17 04		18 08					19 03	20 04		21 09	22 05				
Langley Mill	d																				22 12				
Nottingham 8	a		14 29		15 29				16 33	17 29		18 33					19 33	20 31		21 33	22 33	23 29	23 33		
	d	*13b28*	14 34	*14b28*	15 34	*15b28*		*16b28*		17 34	*17b28*	18 34	*18b28*		*19b02*	*19b28*		20 34	*20b02*						
Grantham 7	d		15 07		16 07					18 15		19 05						21 07							
Birmingham New Street 12	d	13 22		14 22		15 22		16 22			17 22		18 22		18 52	19 22			20 22						
Coleshill Parkway	d	13 35		14 35		15 35		16 35			17 35		18 35		19 05	19 35			20 35						
Nuneaton	d	13 52		14 52		15 52		16 52			17 52		18 52		19 22	19 52			20 52						
Leicester	d	14 15		15 15		16 15		17 15			18 15		19 15		19 50	20 15			21 15						
Melton Mowbray	d	14 31		15 31		16 31		17 31			18 31		19 31		20 07	20 31			21 31						
Oakham	d	14 43		15 43		16 43		17 43			18 43		19 43		20 18	20 43			21 43						
Stamford	d	14 59		15 59		16 59		17 59			18 59		19 59		20 34	20 59			21 59						
Peterborough 8	a	15 17	15 34	16 14	16 38	17 17		18 14		18 42	19 14	19 34	20 14		20 53	21 17		21 34	22 14						
	d	15 18	15 36	16 18	16 40	17 18		18 18		18 42	19 18	19 37	20 18		20 54	21 18		21 36	22 18						
March	a	15 34		16 33		17 37		18 33		19 01	19 33		20 33		21 09	21 34			22 33						
Ely 6	a	15 52	16 09	16 52	17 13	17 59		18 52		19 20	19 52	20 12	20 52		21 28	21 52		22 10	22 54						
Cambridge	a	16 08	*16 44*	17 08	*17 44*	18 16		19 08		*19 58*	20 08	*20 58*	21 08		21 50	22 08			23 10						
Audley End	a	16 23		17 23		18 33		19 23			20 23		21 23			22 23									
Stansted Airport ✈	a	16 45		17 45		18 53		19 45			20 45		21 45			22 45									
Ipswich	a	*17e27*	*17 27*	*19f03*	*20c03*	*19e25*		*21f03*		*22c03*	*21e27*	*21 27*	*23f03*			*23e32*		*23 32*							
Thetford	a		16 34		17 37					19 44		20 35						22 34							
Norwich	a		17 13		18 18					20 18		21 13						23 18							

For general notes see front of timetable
For details of catering facilities see Directory of Train Operators

A From 12 September
B Until 11 July
b Change at Leicester
c Change at Ely and Cambridge
e Change at Ely
f Change at Cambridge

Table 49

Saturdays

North West England and Birmingham → East Midlands → East Anglia → Stansted Airport

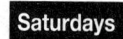

18 July to 5 September

Route Diagram - see first page of Table 49

	EM ◇	XC [1] ◇ (trolley)	XC (bus)	EM ◇	XC (bus)	XC (bus)		XC (bus)		EM ◇	XC (bus)	XC (bus)	XC (bus)		XC [1] ◇ (trolley)	EM ◇	XC (bus)	XC (bus)	XC (bus)	EM ◇	XC [1] ◇ (trolley)	XC (bus)	XC (bus)	XC (bus)
Liverpool Lime Street [10] d																				06 49				
Liverpool South Parkway [7] ✈ d																				06 59				
Widnes d																				07 07				
Warrington Central d																				07 15				
Manchester Oxford Road d																				07 38				
Manchester Piccadilly [10] (tram) d																				07 42				
Stockport d																				07 54				
Sheffield [7] (tram) a																				08 34				
d																				08 38				
Chesterfield d																				08 53				
Alfreton d																				09 03				
Langley Mill d																								
Nottingham [8] (tram) a																				09 30				
d	05 10			06 30						07 45	06 28					08 34	07 28	07 31		09 34		08 28	08 32	
Grantham [7] d	05 51									08 16						09 11				10 09				
Birmingham New Street [12] d		05 52									06 22				06 52		07 22				07 52	08 22		
Coleshill Parkway d		06 05									06 35				07 06		07 35				08 05	08 35		
Nuneaton d		06 22									06 54				07 22		07 54				08 22	08 54		
Leicester d		06 50			06 25	06 35					07 25	07 35			07 50		08 25	08 35			08 50	09 25	09 35	
Melton Mowbray d			05 50		07 00			06 50			08 00		07 50				09 00		08 50			10 00		09 50
Oakham d			06 10		07 20			07 10			08 20		08 10				09 20		09 10			10 20		10 10
Stamford d			06 35		07a50			07 35			08a50		08 35				09a50		09 35			10a50		10 35
Peterborough [8] a	06 21		07 00	07 27		08 00		08 05		08 44		09 00	09 05		09 19	09 44		10 00	10 05	10 42	10 16		11 00	11 05
d	06 27			07 35						08 46					09 21	09 46				10 44	10 18			
March a	06 42			07 50											09 36						10 33			
Ely [6] a	07 01			08 13						09 19					09 58	10 19				11 17	10 52			
Cambridge a	07 44			08 44						09 44					10 16	10 44				11 44	11 08			
Audley End a															10 31						11 23			
Stansted Airport ✈ a															10 45						11 45			
Ipswich a	10b03			09 25						12b03						11 27				14b03				
Thetford a	07 30			08 39						09 44						10 44				11 44				
Norwich a	08 13			09 18						10 19						11 18				12 18				

	XC [1] ◇ (trolley)	EM ◇	XC (bus)	XC (bus)	XC (bus)		XC [1] ◇ (trolley)	EM ◇	XC (bus)	XC (bus)	XC (bus)	XC [1] ◇ (trolley)		EM ◇	XC (bus)	XC (bus)		XC (bus)	XC [1] ◇ (trolley)	XC [1] ◇ (trolley)	EM ◇	XC (bus)	XC (bus)	
Liverpool Lime Street [10] d		07 42						08 52						09 52							10 52			
Liverpool South Parkway [7] ✈ d		07 52						09 03						10 03							11 03			
Widnes d		08 05						09 11						10 11							11 11			
Warrington Central d		08 13						09 19						10 19							11 19			
Manchester Oxford Road d		08 39						09 39						10 39							11 39			
Manchester Piccadilly [10] (tram) d		08 43						09 43						10 43							11 43			
Stockport d		08 54						09 54						10 54							11 54			
Sheffield [7] (tram) a		09 35						10 35						11 35							12 35			
d		09 38						10 38						11 38							12 38			
Chesterfield d		09 53						10 53						11 53							12 53			
Alfreton d		10 03						11 03						12 03							13 03			
Langley Mill d																								
Nottingham [8] (tram) a		10 30						11 29						12 29							13 29			
d		10 34	09 28	09 32				11 34	10 28	10 32				12 34	11 28	11 32					13 34	12 28	12 32	
Grantham [7] d		11 07						12 07						13 06							14 07			
Birmingham New Street [12] d	08 52		09 22				09 52		10 22			10 52			11 22				11 52	12 52		12 22		
Coleshill Parkway d	09 07		09 35				10 05		10 35			11 07			11 35				12 05	13 07		12 35		
Nuneaton d	09 23		09 52				10 22		10 52			11 23			11 52				12 22	13 23		12 52		
Leicester d	09 50		10 25	10 35			10 50		11 25	11 35		11 50			12 25	12 35			12 50	13 50		13 25	13 35	
Melton Mowbray d			11 00		10 50				12 00		11 50				13 00			12 50				14 00		
Oakham d			11 20		11 10				12 20		12 10				13 20			13 10				14 20		
Stamford d			11a50		11 35				12a50		12 35				13a50			13 35				14a50		
Peterborough [8] a	11 16	11 36		12 00	12 05		12 16	12 38		13 00	13 05	13 16		13 35		14 00		14 05	14 21	15 16	14 39		15 00	
d	11 18	11 38					12 18	12 40				13 18		13 38					14 22	15 18	14 41			
March a	11 34						12 33					13 34							14 38	15 34				
Ely [6] a	11 52	12 11					12 52	13 13				13 52		14 11					14 58	15 52	15 14			
Cambridge a	12 08	12 44					13 08	13 44				14 08		14 44					15 16	16 08	15 44			
Audley End a	12 23						13 23					14 23							15 31	16 23				
Stansted Airport ✈ a	12 45						13 45					14 45							15 45	16 45				
Ipswich a		13 27						16b03						15 25							18b03			
Thetford a		12 35						13 39						14 35							15 38			
Norwich a		13 13						14 13						15 13							16 13			

For general notes see front of timetable
For details of catering facilities see Directory of Train Operators

b Change at Ely and Cambridge

Table 49

Saturdays

18 July to 5 September

North West England and Birmingham → East Midlands → East Anglia → Stansted Airport

Route Diagram - see first page of Table 49

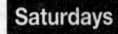

	XC	EM ◇	XC	XC		XC	XC 1 ◇	EM ◇	XC	XC			XC	XC 1 ◇	XC	EM ◇	XC	XC 1 ◇	XC 1 ◇	XC	EM ◇	XC	XC	XC
Liverpool Lime Street [10] d		11 52						12 52								13 52					14 52			
Liverpool South Parkway [7] ✈ d		12 03						13 03								14 03					15 03			
Widnes d		12 11						13 11								14 11					15 11			
Warrington Central d		12 19						13 19								14 19					15 19			
Manchester Oxford Road d		12 39						13 39								14 39					15 39			
Manchester Piccadilly [10] d		12 43						13 43								14 43					15 43			
Stockport d		12 54						13 54								14 54					15 54			
Sheffield [7] a		13 35						14 35								15 35					16 35			
d		13 38						14 38								15 38					16 38			
Chesterfield d		13 53						14 53								15 53					16 53			
Alfreton d		14 03						15 03								16 03					17 04			
Langley Mill d																								
Nottingham [8] a		14 29						15 29								16 33					17 29			
d		14 34	*13 28*	*13 32*				15 34	*14 28*	*14 32*					*15 28*		*15 32*				17 34	*16 28*	*16 32*	
Grantham [7] d		15 07						16 07													18 15			
Birmingham New Street [12] d			*13 22*				13 52		*14 22*					14 52	*15 22*			15 52	16 52			*16 22*		
Coleshill Parkway d			*13 35*				14 05		*14 35*					15 07	*15 35*			16 05	17 06			*16 35*		
Nuneaton d			*13 52*				14 22		*14 52*					15 23	*15 52*			16 22	17 22			*16 52*		
Leicester d			14 25	14 35			14 50		15 25	15 35				15 50	16 25		16 35	16 50	17 50			17 25	17 35	
Melton Mowbray d	13 50		15 00			14 50			16 00				15 50		17 00					16 50		18 00		17 50
Oakham d	14 10		15 20			15 10			16 20				16 10		17 20					17 10		18 20		18 10
Stamford d	14 35		15a50			15 35			16a50				16 35		17a50					17 35		18a50		18 35
Peterborough [8] a	15 05	15 34		16 00		16 05	16 16	16 38		17 00			17 05	17 21			18 00	18 15	19 18	18 05	18 42		19 00	19 05
d		15 36					16 18	16 40						17 22				18 18	19 18		18 42			
March a							16 33							17 41				18 33	19 34		19 01			
Ely [6] a		16 09					16 52	17 13						18 03				18 52	19 53		19 20			
Cambridge a		*16 44*					17 08	*17 44*						18 18				19 07	20 08		*19 58*			
Audley End a							17 23							18 33				19 23	20 23					
Stansted Airport ✈ a							17 45							18 53				19 45	20 45					
Ipswich a		*17 27*						*20b03*													*22b03*			
Thetford a		16 34						17 37													19 44			
Norwich a		17 13						18 18													20 18			

	EM ◇	XC	XC		XC	XC 1 ◇	XC	XC	EM ◇	XC		XC 1 ◇	EM ◇	XC	XC	XC	XC 1 ◇		XC	EM ◇	EM ◇	EM ◇		
Liverpool Lime Street [10] d	15 52								16 52				17 52							18 52	19 52	20 52		
Liverpool South Parkway [7] ✈ d	16 03								17 03				18 03							19 03	20 03	21 03		
Widnes d	16 11								17 11				18 11							19 11	20 11	21 11		
Warrington Central d	16 19								17 19				18 19							19 19	20 19	21 19		
Manchester Oxford Road d	16 39								17 39				18 39							19 39	20 39	21 39		
Manchester Piccadilly [10] d	16 43								17 43				18 43							19 43	20 43	21 43		
Stockport d	16 54								17 54				18 54							19 54	20 54	21 52		
Sheffield [7] a	17 37								18 34				19 35							20 35	21 34	22 31		
d	17 44								18 38				19 38							20 41	21 38	22 35		
Chesterfield d	17 58								18 53				19 53							20 59	21 54	22 51		
Alfreton d	18 08								19 03				20 04							21 09	22 05			
Langley Mill d																					22 12			
Nottingham [8] a	18 33								19 33				20 31							21 33	22 33	23 33		
d	18 34	*17 28*	*17 32*				*18 28*	*18 32*				*19c02*	20 34	*19 28*	*19 32*				*20 43*					
Grantham [7] d	19 05												21 10											
Birmingham New Street [12] d		*17 22*				17 52	*18 22*					18 52		*19 22*			19 52		*20 22*					
Coleshill Parkway d		*17 35*				18 05	*18 35*					19 05		*19 35*			20 06		*20 35*					
Nuneaton d		*17 52*				18 22	*18 52*					19 22		*19 52*			20 22		*20 52*					
Leicester d		18 25	18 35			18 50	19 25	19 35				19 50		20 25	20 35		20 50		21 25					
Melton Mowbray d		19 00			18 50		20 00			19 50				21 00		20 50			22 00					
Oakham d		19 20			19 10		20 20			20 10				21 20		21 10			22 20					
Stamford d		19a50			19 35		20a50			20 35				21a50		21 35			22 45					
Peterborough [8] a	19 34		20 00		20 05	20 16		21 00		21 05		21 16	21 37		22 00	22 05	22 16		23 15					
d	19 37					20 18						21 18	21 39				22 18							
March a						20 33						21 34					22 33							
Ely [6] a	20 12					20 52						21 52	22 12				22 54							
Cambridge a	*20 58*					21 08						22 08					23 15							
Audley End a						21 23						22 23												
Stansted Airport ✈ a						21 45						22 45												
Ipswich a	*21 27*											*23e32*	*23 32*											
Thetford a	20 35												22 41											
Norwich a	21 13												23 20											

For general notes see front of timetable
For details of catering facilities see Directory of Train Operators

b Change at Ely and Cambridge
c Change at Leicester
e Change at Ely

Table 49

Sundays until 12 July

North West England and Birmingham → East Midlands → East Anglia → Stansted Airport

Route Diagram - see first page of Table 49

		EM	EM	XC	EM	XC	EM	XC	EM	XC	EM	XC	EM	XC	EM	XC	EM	XC	XC	EM	XC	EM	EM	EM	EM
		◇	◇	1 ◇ 🍴	◇	1 ◇ 🍴	◇	1 ◇ 🍴	◇	1 ◇ 🍴	◇	1 ◇ 🍴	◇	1 ◇ 🍴	◇	1 ◇ 🍴	◇	1 ◇ 🍴	1 ◇ 🍴	◇	1 ◇ 🍴	◇	◇	◇	◇
Liverpool Lime Street 10	d										12 52		13 52		14 52		15 52			16 52		17 52	18 52	19 52	21 22
Liverpool South Parkway 7 ✈	d										13 03		14 03		15 03		16 03			17 03		18 03	19 03	20 03	
Widnes	d										13 11		14 11		15 11		16 11			17 11		18 11	19 11	20 11	21 39
Warrington Central	d										13 19		14 19		15 19		16 19			17 19		18 19	19 19	20 19	21 47
Manchester Oxford Road	d										13 39		14 39		15 39		16 39			17 39		18 39	19 39	20 39	22 07
Manchester Piccadilly 10	d								12 44		13 44		14 44		15 44		16 44			17 44		18 44	19 44	20 44	22 11
Stockport	d								12 54		13 54		14 54		15 54		16 54			17 54		18 54	19 54	20 54	22 28
Sheffield 7	a								13 37		14 39		15 33		16 36		17 36			18 37		19 34	20 34	21 36	23 23
	d		10 49				12 49		13 49		14 53		15 43		16 40		17 39			18 41		19 40	20 40	21 40	23 29
Chesterfield	d		11 04				13 03		14 03		15 07		15 57		16 56		17 54			18 56		19 55	20 55	21 54	23 43
Alfreton	d		11 14				13 14		14 14		15 18		16 08		17 07		18 04			19 06		20 06	21 06	22 05	23 54
Langley Mill	d										15 25		16 15		17 14		18 12			19 14		20 14	21 14	22 12	00 01
Nottingham 8	a		11 38				13 39		14 40		15 44		16 33		17 32		18 29			19 36		20 36	21 36	22 35	00 23
	d	09 52	11 45	11b19	12 39	12b15	13 41	13b14	14 45	14b30	15 47	15b36	16 45	16b18	17 36	17b34	18 47	18b10	18b44		19b46				
Grantham 7	d	10 30	12 18		13 14		14 14				16 20		17c25		18 18		19 23								
Birmingham New Street 12	d			11 22		12 22		13 22		14 22		15 22		16 22		17 22		18 22	19 22		20 22				
Coleshill Parkway	d			11 35		12 35		13 35		14 35		15 35		16 35		17 35		18 35	19 35		20 35				
Nuneaton	d			11 52		12 52		13 52		14 52		15 52		16 52		17 52		18 52	19 52		20 51				
Leicester	d			12 15		13 15		14 15		15 15		16 15		17 18		18 15		19 16	20 15		21 15				
Melton Mowbray	d			12 33		13 33		14 33		15 33		16 31		17 34		18 31		19 32	20 31		21 31				
Oakham	d			12 45		13 45		14 45		15 45		16 43		17 46		18 43		19 43	20 43		21 43				
Stamford	d			13 01		14 01		15 01		16 01		16 59		18 01		18 59		19 59	20 59		21 59				
Peterborough 8	a	11 06	12 50	13 16	13 41	14 16	14 41	15 16	16 04	16 16	16 51	17 14	17 52	18 16	18 45	19 14	19 56	20 14	21 14		22 14				
	d	11 09	12 53	13 18	13 43	14 18	14 42	15 18	16 05	16 18	16 53	17 18	17 53	18 18	18 47	19 18	19 58	20 18	21 18		22 18				
March	a	11 25		13 33		14 33		15 33		16 33		17 33		18 33		19 33		20 33	21 33		22 33				
Ely 6	a	11 48	13 32	13 58	14 21	14 58	15 21	15 58	16 38	16 52	17 31	17 52	18 31	18 52	19 20	19 52	20 31	20 52	21 52		22 52				
Cambridge	a	*12 16*	*14 14*	14 17	*15 14*	15 17	*16 14*	16 17		17 08		18 07		19 08		20 07		21 07	22 07		23 12				
Audley End	a			14 31		15 31		16 31		17 23		18 23		19 23		20 23		21 23	22 23						
Stansted Airport ✈	a			14 47		15 47		16 47		17 45		18 45		19 45		20 45		21 45	22 45						
Ipswich	a	*13 25*		*15e27*	*15 27*	*18f34*	*18f34*	*17e25*				*19e27*				*21e14*		*00f21*	*00g21*						
Thetford	a	12 20	13 57		14 48		15 48		17 02		17 56		18 55		19 48		20 55								
Norwich	a	13 05	14 35		15 28		16 35		17 35		18 29		19 29		20 28		21 35								

Sundays 19 July to 6 September

		EM	EM	XC		XC	XC	XC		EM	XC	XC		XC	XC	EM		XC	XC	XC		XC	XC	XC	XC
		◇	◇	🚌		🚌	1 ◇ 🍴	🚌		◇	🚌	🚌		1 ◇ 🍴	🚌	◇		🚌	🚌	🚌		1 ◇ 🍴	1 ◇ 🍴	🚌	🚌
Liverpool Lime Street 10	d																								
Liverpool South Parkway 7 ✈	d																								
Widnes	d																								
Warrington Central	d																								
Manchester Oxford Road	d																								
Manchester Piccadilly 10	d																								
Stockport	d																								
Sheffield 7	a																								
	d		10 49													12 49									
Chesterfield	d		11 04													13 03									
Alfreton	d		11 14													13 14									
Langley Mill	d																								
Nottingham 8	a		11 38													13 39									
	d	09 52	11 45			*10 01*	*10b01*			12 39	*11 08*			*11b08*		13 41		*12 01*				*12b01*		*13 03*	
Grantham 7	d	10 30	12 18							13 14						14 14									
Birmingham New Street 12	d						10 33				*11 22*			11 39				*12 22*				12 39	13 56	*13 22*	
Coleshill Parkway	d						10 47				*11 35*			11 54				*12 35*				12 55	14 10	*13 35*	
Nuneaton	d						11 03				*11 52*			12 10				*12 52*				13 11	14 26	*13 52*	
Leicester	d					11 45	11 33	11 50			12 35			12 41	12 50			13 25	13 35			13 38	14 55	14 25	14 35
Melton Mowbray	d			11 50				12 25				12 50			13 25			14 00		13 50				15 00	
Oakham	d			12 10				12 45				13 10			13 45			14 20		14 10				15 20	
Stamford	d			12 35				13a15				13 35			14a15			14a50		14 35				15a50	
Peterborough 8	a	11 06	12 50	13 05		13 10	13 21			13 41	14 00	14 05		14 16		14 41			15 00	15 05		15 11	16 16		16 00
	d	11 09	12 53				13 23			13 43				14 18		14 42						15 18	16 18		
March	a	11 25					13 38							14 33								15 33	16 33		
Ely 6	a	11 48	13 32				13 58			14 21				14 58		15 21						16 02	16 52		
Cambridge	a	*12 16*	*14 14*				14 17			*15 14*				15 17		*16 14*						16 17	17 08		
Audley End	a						14 31							15 31								16 32	17 23		
Stansted Airport ✈	a						14 47							15 47								16 50	17 45		
Ipswich	a	*13 25*					*15e27*			*15 27*				*18f34*		*18f34*						*17e25*			
Thetford	a	12 20	13 57							14 48						15 48									
Norwich	a	13 05	14 35							15 28						16 35									

For general notes see front of timetable
For details of catering facilities see Directory of Train Operators

b Change at Leicester
c Arr. 1715
e Change at Ely
f Change at Ely and Cambridge
g Change at Cambridge

Table 49

Sundays

19 July to 6 September

North West England and Birmingham → East Midlands → East Anglia → Stansted Airport

Route Diagram - see first page of Table 49

Station		XC 1 ◇		EM ◇	XC 🚌	EM ◇		XC 🚌	XC 🚌	XC 🚌		EM ◇	XC 🚌	XC 🚌		XC 🚌	XC 1 ◇	EM ◇		XC 🚌	XC 🚌	XC 🚌		XC 1 ◇	EM ◇
Liverpool Lime Street 10	d					12 52						13 52						14 52							15 52
Liverpool South Parkway 7 ✈	d					13 03						14 03						15 03							16 03
Widnes	d					13 11						14 11						15 11							16 11
Warrington Central	d					13 19						14 19						15 19							16 19
Manchester Oxford Road	d					13 39						14 39						15 39							16 39
Manchester Piccadilly 10	d			12 44		13 44						14 44						15 44							16 44
Stockport	d			12 54		13 54						14 54						15 54							16 54
Sheffield 7	a			13 42		14 43						15 33						16 36							17 36
	d			13 49		14 53						15 43						16 40							17 39
Chesterfield	d			14 03		15 07						15 57						16 56							17 54
Alfreton	d			14 14		15 18						16 08						17 07							18 04
Langley Mill	d					15 25						16 15						17 14							18 12
Nottingham 8	a			14 40		15 44						16 33						17 32							18 29
	d			14 45		15 47		*14 30*				16 45	*15 36*				*15b36*	17 36		*16 41*					18 43
Grantham 7	d					16 20						17 25						18 18							19 16
Birmingham New Street 12	d	14 44						*14 22*					*15 22*				15 52			*16 22*				16 52	
Coleshill Parkway	d	14 57						*14 35*					*15 35*				16 05			*16 35*				17 05	
Nuneaton	d	15 19						*14 52*					*15 52*				16 22			*16 52*				17 22	
Leicester	d	15 48						15 25	15 35				16 25	16 35			16 50			17 25	17 35			17 53	
Melton Mowbray	d				14 50			16 00		15 50			17 00			16 50				18 00		17 50			
Oakham	d				15 10			16 20		16 10			17 20			17 10				18 20		18 10			
Stamford	d				15 35			16a50		16 35			17a50			17 35				18a50		18 35			
Peterborough 8	a	17 10		16 03	16 05	16 56			17 00	17 05		17 52		18 00		18 05	18 18	18 45			19 00	19 05		19 38	19 56
	d	17 18		16 05		16 58						17 53					18 20	18 47						19 39	19 58
March	a	17 34															18 35							19 56	
Ely 6	a	17 52		16 38		17 31						18 31					18 54	19 20						20 14	20 31
Cambridge	a	18 07		*17 16*		*18 16*											19 10	*20 16*						20 31	
Audley End	a	18 23															19 25							20 52	
Stansted Airport ✈	a	18 45															19 50							21 17	
Ipswich	a					*19 27*												*21 14*							
Thetford	a			17 02		17 56						18 55						19 48							20 55
Norwich	a			17 35		18 29						19 29						20 28							21 35

Station		XC 🚌	XC 🚌	XC 🚌		XC 1 ◇	XC 🚌	XC 🚌		XC 🚌	XC 1 ◇	XC 🚌		XC 🚌	XC 🚌	EM ◇		XC 1 ◇	EM ◇	XC 🚌	EM ◇	EM ◇	EM ◇		
Liverpool Lime Street 10	d															16 52			17 52		18 52	19 52	21 22		
Liverpool South Parkway 7 ✈	d															17 03			18 03		19 03	20 03			
Widnes	d															17 11			18 11		19 11	20 11	21 39		
Warrington Central	d															17 19			18 19		19 19	20 19	21 47		
Manchester Oxford Road	d															17 39			18 39		19 39	20 39	22 07		
Manchester Piccadilly 10	d															17 44			18 44		19 44	20 44	22 11		
Stockport	d															17 54			18 54		19 54	20 54	22 28		
Sheffield 7	a															18 37			19 34		20 34	21 36	23 25		
	d															18 41			19 40		20 40	21 40	23 29		
Chesterfield	d															18 56			19 55		20 55	21 54	23 42		
Alfreton	d															19 06			20 06		21 06	22 05	23 54		
Langley Mill	d															19 14			20 14		21 14	22 12	00 01		
Nottingham 8	a															19 36			20 36		21 36	22 35	00 23		
	d	*17 47*				*18b10*	18 44				*18b44*	19 46						*19b46*							
Grantham 7	d																								
Birmingham New Street 12	d	*17 22*				17 52	*18 22*				18 52	*19 22*						19 52		*20 22*					
Coleshill Parkway	d	*17 35*				18 05	*18 35*				19 05	*19 35*						20 05		*20 35*					
Nuneaton	d	*17 52*				18 22	*18 52*				19 22	*19 52*						20 22		*20 51*					
Leicester	d	18 25	18 35			18 50	19 25	19 35			19 51	20 25		20 35				20 51		21 25					
Melton Mowbray	d	19 00		18 50			20 00			19 50		21 00			20 50					22 00					
Oakham	d	19 20		19 10			20 20			20 10		21 20			21 10					22 20					
Stamford	d	19a50		19 35			20a50			20 35		21a50			21 35					22 45					
Peterborough 8	a		20 00	20 05		20 13		21 00		21 05	21 21			22 00	22 05			22 14		23 15					
	d					20 18					21 22							22 18							
March	a					20 33					21 38							22 33							
Ely 6	a					20 52					22 01							22 52							
Cambridge	a					21 07					22 17							23 12							
Audley End	a					21 23					22 31														
Stansted Airport ✈	a					21 45					22 50														
Ipswich	a										*00c21*														
Thetford	a																								
Norwich	a																								

For general notes see front of timetable
For details of catering facilities see Directory of Train Operators

b Change at Leicester
c Change at Cambridge

Table 49

Sundays
13 September to 1 November

North West England and Birmingham → East Midlands → East Anglia → Stansted Airport

Route Diagram - see first page of Table 49

	XC 1 ◇	EM ◇	XC 1 ◇	EM ◇	XC 1 ◇	EM ◇	XC 1 ◇		EM ◇	XC 1 ◇	EM ◇	XC 1 ◇	EM ◇	XC 1 ◇	EM ◇	XC 1 ◇	EM ◇	XC 1 ◇	XC 1 ◇	EM ◇	EM ◇	EM ◇	EM ◇	
Liverpool Lime Street 10 d									12 57		13 57		14 57		15 57		16 57			17 57	18 57	19 57	21 23	
Liverpool South Parkway 7 d																								
Widnes d																								
Warrington Central d																								
Manchester Oxford Road d									13 39		14 39		15 39		16 39		17 39			18 39	19 39	20 39	22 07	
Manchester Piccadilly 10 d						12 44			13 44		14 44		15 44		16 44		17 44			18 44	19 44	20 44	22 11	
Stockport d						12 55			13 54		14 54		15 54		16 54		17 54			18 54	19 54	20 54	22 28	
Sheffield 7 a						13 37			14 39		15 37		16 36		17 36		18 37			19 34	20 34	21 36	23 23	
d				12 49		13 49			14 53		15 43		16 40		17 39		18 41			19 40	20 40	21 40	23 29	
Chesterfield d				13 03		14 03			15 07		15 57		16 56		17 54		18 56			19 55	20 55	21 54	23 43	
Alfreton d				13 14		14 14			15 18		16 08		17 07		18 04		19 06			20 06	21 06	22 05	23 54	
Langley Mill d									15 25		16 15		17 14		18 12		19 14			20 14	21 13	22 12	00 01	
Nottingham 8 a				13 39		14 38			15 44		16 33		17 32		18 29		19 36			20 36	21 35	22 36	00 23	
d	11b30	12 39	12b26	13 41	13b31	14 43	14b31		15 52	15b30	16 45	16b28	17 36	17b30	18 47			18b46	20b19					
Grantham 7 d		13 14		14 14					16 25		17c25		18 18		19 23									
Birmingham New Street 12 d	10 52		11 52		12 52		13 52			14 52		15 52		16 52		17 52		18 52	19 52					
Coleshill Parkway d	10e05		10e50		11e50		12e50			13e50		14e50		15e50		16e50		17e50	18e50					
Nuneaton d	10e45		11e45		12e45		13e45			14e45		15e45		16e45		17e45		18e45	19e45					
Leicester d	12 15		13 15		14 15		15 15			16 15		17 15		18 16		19f15		20 15	21 15					
Melton Mowbray d	12 34		13 34		14 34		15 33			16 32		17 31		18 32		19 32		20 32	21 31					
Oakham d	12 45		13 45		14 45		15 45			16 43		17 42		18 43		19 43		20 43	21 43					
Stamford d	13 01		14 01		15 01		16 01			16 59		18 01		18 59		19 59		20 59	21 59					
Peterborough 8 a	13 16	13 41	14 16	14 41	15 16	16 04	16 16		16 56	17 14	17 52	18 16	18 45	19 14	19 56	20 14		21 14	22 14					
d	13 18	13 43	14 18	14 42	15 18	16 05	16 18		16 58	17 18	17 53	18 18	18 47	19 18	19 58	20 18		21 18	22 18					
March a	13 33		14 33		15 33		16 33			17 33		18 33		19 33		20 33		21 33	22 33					
Ely 6 a	13 58	14 21	14 58	15 21	16 02	16 38	16 52		17 31	17 52	18 31	18 52	19 20	19 52	20 31	20 52		21 52	22 52					
Cambridge a	14 17	*15 14*	15 17	*16 14*	16 17		17 08			18 07		19 08		20 07		21 07		22 07	23 12					
Audley End a	14 31		15 31		16 31		17 23			18 23		19 23		20 23		21 23		22 23						
Stansted Airport a	14 47		15 47		16 47		17 45			18 45		19 45		20 45		21 45		22 45						
Ipswich a	*15g27*	*15 27*	*18h34*	*18h34*	*17g25*					*19g27*				*21g14*		*00h21*		*00j21*						
Thetford a		14 48		15 48		17 02			17 56		18 55		19 48		20 55									
Norwich a		15 28		16 35		17 35			18 29		19 29		20 28		21 35									

Sundays
from 8 November

	XC 1 ◇	EM ◇	XC 1 ◇	EM ◇	XC 1 ◇	EM ◇	XC 1 ◇	EM ◇	XC 1 ◇	EM ◇	XC 1 ◇	EM ◇	XC 1 ◇	EM ◇	XC 1 ◇	XC 1 ◇	EM ◇	XC 1 ◇	EM ◇	EM ◇	EM ◇	EM ◇		
Liverpool Lime Street 10 d								12 52		13 52		14 52		15 52			16 52		17 52	18 52	19 52	21 22		
Liverpool South Parkway 7 d								13 03		14 03		15 03		16 03			17 03		18 03	19 03	20 03			
Widnes d								13 11		14 11		15 11		16 11			17 11		18 11	19 11	20 11	21 39		
Warrington Central d								13 19		14 19		15 19		16 19			17 19		18 19	19 19	20 19	21 47		
Manchester Oxford Road d								13 39		14 39		15 39		16 39			17 39		18 39	19 39	20 39	22 07		
Manchester Piccadilly 10 d						12 44		13 44		14 44		15 44		16 44			17 44		18 44	19 44	20 44	22 11		
Stockport d						12 55		13 54		14 54		15 54		16 54			17 54		18 54	19 54	20 54	22 28		
Sheffield 7 a						13 37		14 39		15 37		16 36		17 36			18 37		19 34	20 34	21 36	23 23		
d				12 49		13 49		14 53		15 43		16 40		17 39			18 41		19 40	20 40	21 40	23 29		
Chesterfield d				13 03		14 03		15 07		15 57		16 56		17 54			18 56		19 55	20 55	21 54	23 43		
Alfreton d				13 14		14 14		15 18		16 08		17 07		18 04			19 06		20 06	21 06	22 05	23 54		
Langley Mill d								15 25		16 15		17 14		18 12			19 14		20 14	21 14	22 12	00 01		
Nottingham 8 a				13 39		14 38		15 44		16 33		17 32		18 29			19 36		20 36	21 36	23 25	00 23		
d	11b30	12 39	12b26	13 41	13b31	14 43	14b31	15 52	15b30	16 45	16b28	17 36	17b30	18 47		18b46		20b19						
Grantham 7 d		13 14		14 14				16 25		17c25		18 18		19 23										
Birmingham New Street 12 d	10 52		11 52		12 52		13 52		14 52		15 52		16 52		17 52	18 52		19 52						
Coleshill Parkway d	10e05		10e50		11e50		12e50		13e50		14e50		15e50		16e50	17e50		18e50						
Nuneaton d	10e45		11e45		12e45		13e45		14e45		15e45		16e45		17e45	18e45		19e45						
Leicester d	12k15		13k15		14k15		15k15		16k15		17k15		18m16		19f15	20k15		21k15						
Melton Mowbray d	12 34		13 34		14 34		15 33		16 32		17 31		18 32		19 32	20 32		21 31						
Oakham d	12 45		13 45		14 45		15 45		16 43		17 42		18 43		19 43	20 43		21 43						
Stamford d	13 01		14 01		15 01		16 01		16 59		18 01		18 59		19 59	20 59		21 59						
Peterborough 8 a	13 16	13 41	14 16	14 41	15 16	16 04	16 16	16 56	17 14	17 52	18 16	18 45	19 14	19 56	20 14	21 14		22 14						
d	13 18	13 43	14 18	14 42	15 18	16 05	16 18	16 58	17 18	17 53	18 18	18 47	19 18	19 58	20 18	21 18		22 18						
March a	13 33		14 33		15 33		16 33		17 33		18 33		19 33		20 33	21 33		22 33						
Ely 6 a	13 58	14 21	14 58	15 21	16 02	16 38	16 52	17 31	17 52	18 31	18 52	19 20	19 52	20 31	20 52	21 52		22 52						
Cambridge a	14 17	*15 14*	15 17	*16 14*	16 17		17 08		18 07		19 08		20 07		21 07	22 07		23 12						
Audley End a	14 31		15 31		16 31		17 23		18 23		19 23		20 23		21 23	22 23								
Stansted Airport a	14 47		15 47		16 47		17 45		18 45		19 45		20 45		21 45	22 45								
Ipswich a	*15g27*	*15 27*	*18h34*	*18h34*	*17g25*				*19g27*				*21g14*		*00h21*	*00j21*								
Thetford a		14 48		15 48		17 02		17 56		18 55		19 48		20 55										
Norwich a		15 28		16 35		17 35		18 29		19 29		20 28		21 35										

For general notes see front of timetable
For details of catering facilities see Directory of Train Operators

b Change at Leicester
c Arr. 1715
e By bus
f Arr. 1906
g Change at Ely
h Change at Ely and Cambridge
j Change at Cambridge
k Arrives 5 minutes earlier
m Arr. 1810

Network Diagram for Tables 50, 55, 56, 57

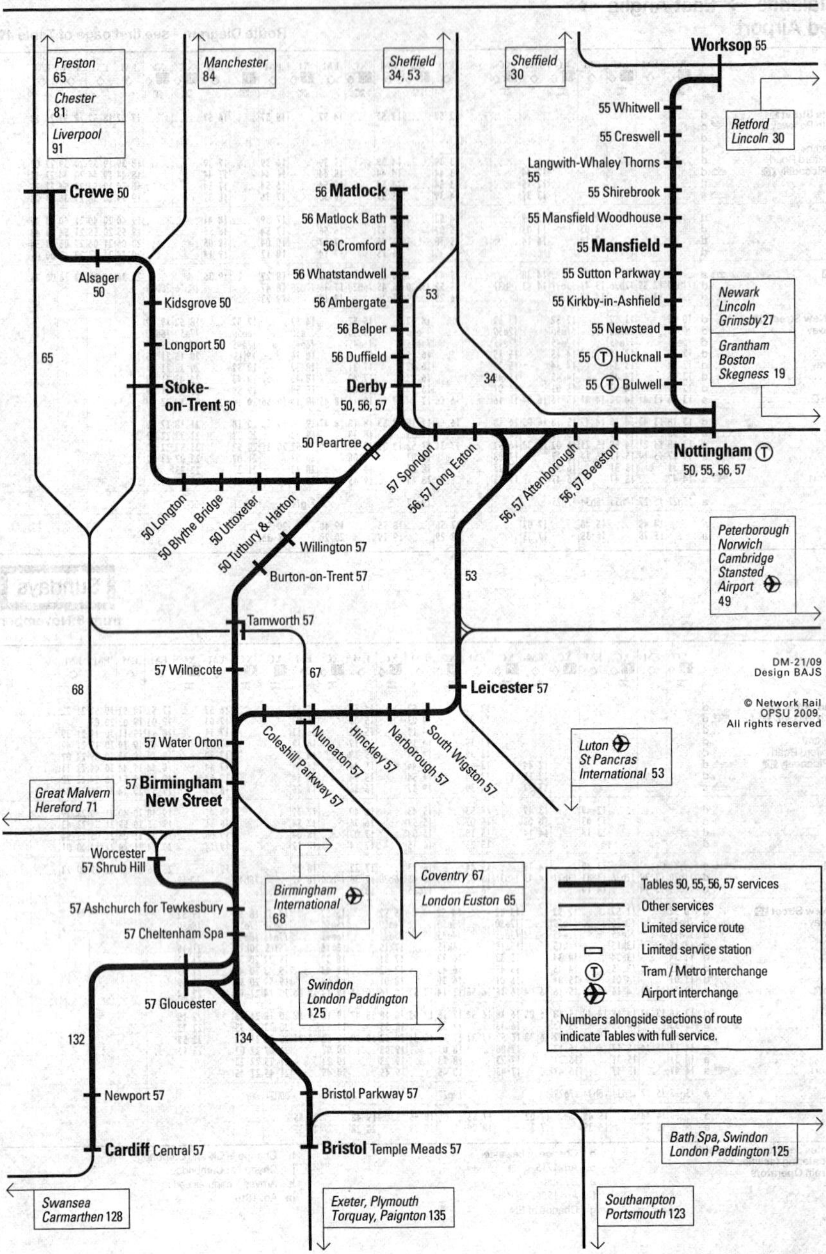

Preston 65
Chester 81
Liverpool 91
Manchester 84
Sheffield 34, 53
Sheffield 30
Worksop 55
55 Whitwell
55 Creswell
Langwith-Whaley Thorns 55
55 Shirebrook
55 Mansfield Woodhouse
55 Mansfield
55 Sutton Parkway
55 Kirkby-in-Ashfield
55 Newstead
55 Hucknall
55 Bulwell
Retford Lincoln 30
Newark Lincoln Grimsby 27
Grantham Boston Skegness 19
Crewe 50
Alsager 50
Kidsgrove 50
Longport 50
Stoke-on-Trent 50
65
56 Matlock
56 Matlock Bath
56 Cromford
56 Whatstandwell
56 Ambergate
56 Belper
56 Duffield
Derby 50, 56, 57
53
34
50 Peartree
57 Spondon
56, 57 Long Eaton
56, 57 Attenborough
56, 57 Beeston
Nottingham 50, 55, 56, 57
50 Longton
50 Blythe Bridge
50 Uttoxeter
50 Tutbury & Hatton
Willington 57
Burton-on-Trent 57
Peterborough Norwich Cambridge Stansted Airport 49
Tamworth 57
57 Wilnecote
67
68
Leicester 57
DM-21/09
Design BAJS
© Network Rail OPSU 2009. All rights reserved
57 Water Orton
57 Birmingham New Street
Coleshill Parkway 57
Nuneaton 57
Hinckley 57
Narborough 57
South Wigston 57
Luton St Pancras International 53
Great Malvern Hereford 71
Worcester 57 Shrub Hill
Birmingham International 68
Coventry 67
London Euston 65
57 Ashchurch for Tewkesbury
57 Cheltenham Spa
Swindon London Paddington 125
57 Gloucester
132
134
Newport 57
Bristol Parkway 57
Cardiff Central 57
Bristol Temple Meads 57
Bath Spa, Swindon London Paddington 125
Swansea Carmarthen 128
Exeter, Plymouth Torquay, Paignton 135
Southampton Portsmouth 123
Tables 50, 55, 56, 57 services
Other services
Limited service route
Limited service station
Tram / Metro interchange
Airport interchange
Numbers alongside sections of route indicate Tables with full service.

Table 50

Mondays to Fridays

Nottingham and Derby → Stoke-on-Trent and Crewe

Network Diagram - see first page of Table 50

Miles			NT	NT	LM 1	EM	NT	LM 1	EM	NT	LM 1 ◇		EM	NT	LM 1 ◇	EM	NT	LM 1 ◇	EM	NT	LM 1 ◇		EM	NT	LM 1 ◇	EM	NT
0	Nottingham 8 🚢	d				06 00			06 37				08 08			08 37			09 37				10 37			11 37	
16	Derby 10	d				06 40			07 40				08 42			09 40			10 40				11 40			12 40	
17¼	Peartree	d							07 44																		
27½	Tutbury & Hatton	d				06 54			07 56				08 56			09 56			10 56				11 56			12 56	
35¼	Uttoxeter	d				07 05			08 07				09 07			10 07			11 07				12 07			13 07	
46¼	Blythe Bridge	d				07 19			08 21				09 21			10 21			11 21				12 21			13 21	
49½	Longton	d				07 25			08 27				09 27			10 27			11 27				12 27			13 27	
51	Stoke-on-Trent	a				07 31			08 33				09 33			10 33			11 33				12 33			13 33	
—		d	06 30	07 17	07 26	07 33	07 57	08 13	08 34	08 58	09 13		09 34	09 58	10 13	10 34	10 58	11 13	11 34	11 58	12 13		12 34	12 58	13 13	13 34	13 58
55	Longport	d	06 34	07 21		07 39			08 40				09 40			10 40			11 40				12 40			13 40	
58¼	Kidsgrove	d	06a38	07a25	07 34	07 45	08a04	08 21	08 46	09a05	09 21		09 46	10a05	10 21	10 46	11a05	11 21	11 46	12a05	12 21		12 46	13a05	13 21	13 46	14a05
60½	Alsager	d			07 38	07 49		08 25	08 50		09 25		09 50		10 25	10 50		11 25	11 50		12 25		12 50		13 25	13 50	
66¾	Crewe 10	a			07 48	08 01		08 38	08 59		09 38		09 59		10 38	10 59		11 38	11 59		12 38		12 59		13 38	13 59	

		LM 1 ◇	EM	NT	LM 1 ◇	EM	NT		LM 1 ◇	EM	NT	LM 1 ◇	EM	NT	EM	LM 1 ◇	NT	EM	NT	EM A	EM B	NT	LM 1 ◇	EM	NT		
Nottingham 8 🚢	d		12 37			13 37				14 37			15 37		16 50			17 37		18 37	18 37			19 37			
Derby 10	d		13 40			14 40				15 40			16 40		17 40			18 40		19 40	19 40			20 40			
Peartree	d												16 44		17 44												
Tutbury & Hatton	d		13 56			14 56				15 56			16 56		17 56			18 56		19 56	19 56			20 56			
Uttoxeter	d		14 07			15 07				16 07			17 07		18 07			19 07		20 07	20 07			21 07			
Blythe Bridge	d		14 21			15 21				16 21			17 21		18 21			19 21		20 21	20 21			21 21			
Longton	d		14 27			15 27				16 27			17 27		18 27			19 27		20 27	20 27			21 27			
Stoke-on-Trent	a		14 33			15 33				16 33			17 33		18 32			19 33		20 34	20 34			21 33			
	d	14 13	14 34	14 58	15 13	15 34	15 58		16 13	16 34	16 58	17 13	17 34	17 58	18 34	18 41	18 58	19 34	19 58	20 34	20 34	20 58	21 05	21 34	22 18		
Longport	d		14 40			15 40				16 40			17 39		18 40			19 40		20 40	20 41			21 40			
Kidsgrove	d	14 21	14 46	15a05	15 21	15 46	16a05		16 21	16 46	17a05	17 21	17 46	18a05	18 46	18 49	19a05	19 46	20a05	20 46	20 46	21a05	21 14	21 46	22a25		
Alsager	d	14 25	14 50		15 25	15 50			16 25	16 50		17 25	17 50		18 50	18 53		19 50		20 50	20 50		21 18	21 50			
Crewe 10	a	14 38	14 59		15 38	15 59			16 38	16 59		17 38	17 59		18 59	19 05		19 59		20 59	20 59		21 27	21 59			

Saturdays

		NT	LM 1	EM C	EM D	NT	LM 1	EM	NT	LM 1 ◇	EM	NT	LM 1 ◇	EM	NT	LM 1 ◇	EM		NT	LM 1 ◇	EM	NT	LM 1 ◇	EM	NT	LM 1 ◇	EM
Nottingham 8 🚢	d			05 57	05 57			06 56			08 08			09 08			10 08				11 08			12 08			13 08
Derby 10	d			06 42	06 42			07 40			08 42			09 42			10 42				11 42			12 42			13 42
Peartree	d							07 44																			
Tutbury & Hatton	d			06 56	06 56			07 56			08 56			09 56			10 56				11 56			12 56			13 56
Uttoxeter	d			07 07	07 07			08 07			09 07			10 07			11 07				12 07			13 07			14 07
Blythe Bridge	d			07 21	07 21			08 21			09 21			10 21			11 21				12 21			13 21			14 21
Longton	d			07 27	07 27			08 27			09 27			10 27			11 27				12 27			13 27			14 27
Stoke-on-Trent	a			07 33	07 34			08 33			09 33			10 33			11 33				12 33			13 33			14 33
	d	06 57	07 13	07 34	07 34	07 57	08 13	08 34	08 58	09 13	09 34	09 58	10 13	10 34	10 58	11 13	11 34		11 58	12 13	12 34	12 58	13 13	13 34	13 58	14 13	14 34
Longport	d			07 40	07 41			08 40			09 40			10 40			11 40				12 40			13 40			14 40
Kidsgrove	d	07a04	07 21	07 46	07 46	08a04	08 21	08 46	09a05	09 21	09 46	10a05	10 21	10 46	11a05	11 21	11 46		12a05	12 21	12 46	13a05	13 21	13 46	14a05	14 21	14 46
Alsager	d		07 25	07 50	07 50		08 25	08 50		09 25	09 50		10 25	10 50		11 25	11 50			12 25	12 50		13 25	13 50		14 25	14 50
Crewe 10	a		07 38	08 01	08 01		08 37	08 59		09 37	09 59		10 37	11 01		11 37	12 00			12 37	13 01		13 37	14 01		14 37	15 01

		NT	LM 1 ◇	EM	NT	LM 1 ◇	EM	NT	LM 1 ◇	EM	NT	EM	LM 1 ◇	NT	LM 1 ◇	EM	NT	LM 1	EM	NT	LM 1	NT E 🚌	EM	NT G	NT E 🚌		
Nottingham 8 🚢	d			14 08			15 08			16 08		17 08				18 08			19 08				19b37				
Derby 10	d			14 42			15 42			16 42		17 42				18 42			19 42				20 42				
Peartree	d											17 45															
Tutbury & Hatton	d			14 56			15 56			16 56		17 57				18 56			19 56				20 56				
Uttoxeter	d			15 07			16 07			17 07		18 07				19 07			20 07				21 07				
Blythe Bridge	d			15 21			16 21			17 21		18 22				19 21			20 21				21 21				
Longton	d			15 27			16 27			17 27		18 27				19 27			20 27				21 27				
Stoke-on-Trent	a			15 33			16 33			17 33		18 33				19 33			20 33				21 33				
	d	14 58	15 13	15 34	15 58	16 13	16 34	16 58	17 13	17 34	17 58	18 34	18 41	18 58	19 13	19 34	19 58	20 13	20 34	20 58	21 16	21 30	21 34	22 18	22 20		
Longport	d			15 40			16 40			17 39		18 40				19 40			20 40				21 40				
Kidsgrove	d	15a05	15 21	15 46	16a05	16 21	16 46	17a05	17 21	17 46	18a05	18 46	18 49	19a05	19 21	19 46	20a05	20 21	20 46	21a05	21 24	21a55	21 46	22a25	22a45		
Alsager	d		15 25	15 50		16 25	16 50		17 25	17 50		18 50	18 53		19 25	19 50		20 25	20 50		21 28		21 50				
Crewe 10	a		15 37	16 01		16 37	17 01		17 37	17 58		18 59	19 05		19 35	20 01		20 35	21 04		21 38		22 01				

For general notes see front of timetable
For details of catering facilities see Directory of Train Operators

A From 7 September
B Until 4 September
C Until 5 September
D From 12 September

E Until 11 July
G From 18 July
b 18 July to 5 September dep. 1920

Table 50

Sundays until 12 July

Nottingham and Derby → Stoke-on-Trent and Crewe

Network Diagram - see first page of Table 50

		LM	LM	EM	LM	NT	EM	EM	LM	EM	EM	LM	NT	EM	EM	LM	NT
		🚌	🚌		1 ◇				1 ◇			1 ◇				1 ◇	
Nottingham 8	⛴ d			*14 05*			*15 05*	*16 05*		*17 00*	*18 05*			*19 05*			
Derby 10	d			14 44			15 44	16 44		17 44	18 44			19 44	20 44		
Peartree	d																
Tutbury & Hatton	d			14 58			15 58	16 58		18 00	18 58			19 58	20 58		
Uttoxeter	d			15 09			16 09	17 09		18 11	19 09			20 10	21 09		
Blythe Bridge	d			15 23			16 23	17 23		18 25	19 23			20 24	21 23		
Longton	d			15 29			16 29	17 29		18 32	19 29			20 30	21 29		
Stoke-on-Trent	a			15 35			16 35	17 37		18 38	19 36			20 37	21 36		
	d	12 20	13 40	15 36	15 41	16 01	16 36	17 37	17 41	18 39	19 37	19 41	20 01	20 37	21 36	21 43	22 39
Longport	d			15 41			16 41	17 43		18 44	19 43			20 43	21 42		
Kidsgrove	d	12 38	13 58	15 47	15 53	16a08	16 46	17 48	17 55	18 50	19 48	19 55	20a08	20 49	21 48	21 54	22a46
Alsager	d	12 52	14 12	15 52	15 58		16 51	17 52	17 58	18 54	19 52	19 59		20 53	21 52	22 00	
Crewe 10	a	13 07	14 27	16 09	16 07		17 03	18 02	18 07	19 06	20 03	20 08		21 10	22 10	22 11	

Sundays 19 July to 6 September

		LM	LM	EM	LM	NT	EM	EM	LM	EM	EM	LM	NT	EM	EM	LM	NT
		1	1 ◇		1 ◇				1 ◇			1 ◇				1 ◇	
Nottingham 8	⛴ d			*14 05*			*15 05*	*16 05*		*17 02*	*18 05*			*19 05*			
Derby 10	d			14 44			15 44	16 44		17 44	18 44			19 44	20 44		
Peartree	d																
Tutbury & Hatton	d			14 58			15 58	16 58		17 58	18 58			19 58	20 58		
Uttoxeter	d			15 09			16 09	17 09		18 09	19 09			20 09	21 09		
Blythe Bridge	d			15 23			16 23	17 23		18 23	19 23			20 23	21 23		
Longton	d			15 29			16 29	17 29		18 30	19 29			20 29	21 29		
Stoke-on-Trent	a			15 36			16 35	17 36		18 36	19 36			20 35	21 35		
	d	11 59	13 20	15 37	15 41	16 01	16 36	17 37	17 41	18 37	19 36	19 41	20 01	20 36	21 36	21 43	22 39
Longport	d			15 42			16 42	17 43		18 43	19 42			20 41	21 42		
Kidsgrove	d	12 08	13 28	15 48	15 52	16a08	16 47	17 48	17 52	18 48	19 47	19 52	20a08	20 48	21 47	21 54	22a46
Alsager	d	12 12	13 31	15 53	15 58		16 52	17 53	17 59	18 52	19 52	19 58		20 52	21 52	22 00	
Crewe 10	a	12 24	13 42	16 10	16 08		17 04	18 03	18 08	19 04	20 03	20 07		21 08	22 09	22 11	

Sundays from 13 September

		LM	LM	EM	LM	NT	EM	EM	LM	EM	EM	LM	NT	EM	EM	LM	NT
		1	1 ◇		1 ◇				1 ◇			1 ◇				1 ◇	
Nottingham 8	⛴ d			*13 20*			*14 53*	*15 10*		*17 10*	*17 23*			*19 10*	*20 10*		
Derby 10	d			14 38			15 38	16 38		17 39	18 39			19 40	20 39		
Peartree	d																
Tutbury & Hatton	d			14 52			15 52	16 52		17 55	18 56			19 54	20 54		
Uttoxeter	d			15 03			16 03	17 03		18 06	19 07			20 05	21 05		
Blythe Bridge	d			15 17			16 17	17 17		18 20	19 21			20 19	21 19		
Longton	d			15 23			16 23	17 23		18 26	19 27			20 25	21 25		
Stoke-on-Trent	a			15 30			16 29	17 30		18 33	19 33			20 32	21 36		
	d	11 59	13 20	15 31	15 41	16 01	16 30	17 31	17 41	18 33	19 34	19 41	20 01	20 32	21 36	21 43	22 39
Longport	d			15 36			16 36	17 37		18 39	19 40			20 38	21 42		
Kidsgrove	d	12 08	13 28	15 42	15 52	16a08	16 41	17 42	17 52	18 45	19 45	19 52	20a08	20 44	21 48	21 54	22a46
Alsager	d	12 12	13 31	15 47	15 58		16 46	17 47	17 59	18 49	19 49	19 58		20 48	21 52	22 00	
Crewe 10	a	12 24	13 42	16 04	16 08		16 58	17 57	18 08	19 01	20 01	20 07		21 05	22 09	22 11	

For general notes see front of timetable
For details of catering facilities see
Directory of Train Operators

Crewe and Stoke-on-Trent → Derby and Nottingham

Network Diagram - see first page of Table 50

Miles			XC 1◇	NT 1	EM	LM 1◇	EM	LM 1◇	EM	NT 1		LM 1◇	EM	NT 1	LM 1◇	EM	NT 1	LM 1◇	EM		NT 1	LM 1◇	EM	NT 1	LM 1◇	EM	NT 1
0	**Crewe 10**	d	05 47		06 07	06 35	06 58	07 33	08 07			08 33	09 07		09 33	10 07		10 33	11 07			11 33	12 07		12 33	13 07	
6¼	Alsager	d			06 16	06 44	07 07	07 41	08 16			08 41	09 16		09 41	10 16		10 41	11 16			11 41	12 16		12 41	13 16	
8½	Kidsgrove	d		06 16	06 21	06 48	07 12	07 46	08 21	08 32		08 46	09 21	09 32	09 47	10 21	10 32	10 46	11 21		11 32	11 47	12 21	12 32	12 46	13 21	13 32
11¾	Longport	d			06 27		07 18		08 27				09 27			10 27			11 27				12 27			13 27	
15¾	**Stoke-on-Trent**	a	06 07	06 26	06 31	06 57	07 22	07 54	08 31	08 42		08 54	09 31	09 42	09 55	10 31	10 42	10 54	11 31		11 42	11 55	12 31	12 42	12 54	13 31	13 42
—		d			06 33		07 24		08 33				09 33			10 33			11 33				12 33			13 33	
17¼	Longton	d			06 39		07 30		08 39				09 39			10 39			11 40				12 39			13 39	
20½	Blythe Bridge	d			06 45		07 36		08 45				09 45			10 45			11 46				12 45			13 45	
31½	Uttoxeter	d			06 58		07 49		08 58				09 58			10 58			11 58				12 58			13 58	
39¼	Tutbury & Hatton	d			07 07		07 58		09 07				10 07			11 07			12 07				13 07			14 07	
49½	Peartree	d			07 19																						
50¾	**Derby 10**	a			07 25		08 16		09 24				10 24			11 24			12 24				13 24			14 24	
66¾	**Nottingham 8**	a			08 08		09 05		10 05				11 05			12 05			13 05				14 05			15 05	

		LM 1◇	EM	NT 1		LM 1◇	EM	NT 1	LM 1◇	EM	NT 1	LM 1◇	EM		NT 1	LM 1◇	EM	NT 1	LM 1◇	EM	NT 1	NT 1	EM	NT 1	NT 1		
Crewe 10	d	13 33	14 07			14 33	15 07		15 33	16 07		16 33	17 07			17 33	18 07		18 33	19 07			20 45				
Alsager	d	13 41	14 16			14 41	15 16		15 41	16 16		16 41	17 16			17 41	18 16		18 41	19 16			20 58				
Kidsgrove	d	13 46	14 21	14 32		14 46	15 21	15 32	15 46	16 21	16 32	16 46	17 21		17 32	17 46	18 21	18 32	18 46	19 21	19 32	20 32	21 06	21 32	22 32		
Longport	d		14 27				15 27			16 27			17 27				18 27			19 27			21 12				
Stoke-on-Trent	a	13 54	14 31	14 42		14 54	15 31	15 42	15 54	16 31	16 42	16 54	17 31		17 42	17 54	18 31	18 42	18 54	19 31	19 42	20 42	21 16	21 42	22 42		
	d		14 33				15 33			16 33			17 33				18 33			19 33			21 18				
Longton	d		14 39				15 39			16 39			17 39				18 39			19 39			21 24				
Blythe Bridge	d		14 45				15 45			16 45			17 45				18 45			19 45			21 29				
Uttoxeter	d		14 58				15 58			16 58			17 58				18 58			19 58			21 42				
Tutbury & Hatton	d		15 07				16 07			17 07			18 07				19 07			20 07			21 51				
Peartree	d						16 18																				
Derby 10	a		15 24				16 23			17 24			18 24				19 24			20 24			22 10				
Nottingham 8	a		16 05				17 05			18 05			19 05				20 05			21 06			23 27				

Saturdays

		XC 1◇	NT 1	EM	LM 1◇	EM	NT 1	LM 1◇	EM	NT 1		LM 1◇	EM	NT 1	LM 1◇	EM	NT 1	LM 1◇	EM	NT 1		LM 1◇	EM	NT 1	LM 1◇	EM	NT 1
Crewe 10	d	05 47		06 07	06 38	07 07		07 33	08 07			08 33	09 07		09 33	10 07		10 33	11 07			11 33	12 07		12 33	13 07	
Alsager	d			06 16	06 47	07 16		07 41	08 16			08 41	09 16		09 41	10 16		10 41	11 16			11 41	12 16		12 41	13 16	
Kidsgrove	d		06 16	06 21	06 51	07 21	07 28	07 46	08 21	08 32		08 46	09 21	09 32	09 46	10 21	10 32	10 46	11 21	11 32		11 46	12 21	12 32	12 46	13 21	13 32
Longport	d			06 27		07 27			08 27				09 27			10 27			11 27				12 27			13 27	
Stoke-on-Trent	a	06 07	06 26	06 31	06 59	07 31	07 39	07 54	08 31	08 42		08 54	09 31	09 42	09 54	10 31	10 42	10 54	11 31	11 42		11 54	12 31	12 42	12 54	13 31	13 42
	d			06 33		07 33			08 33				09 33			10 33			11 33				12 33			13 33	
Longton	d			06 39		07 39			08 39				09 39			10 39			11 39				12 39			13 39	
Blythe Bridge	d			06 45		07 45			08 45				09 45			10 45			11 45				12 45			13 45	
Uttoxeter	d			06 58		07 58			08 58				09 58			10 58			11 58				12 58			13 58	
Tutbury & Hatton	d			07 07		08 07			09 07				10 07			11 07			12 07				13 07			14 07	
Peartree	d			07 19																							
Derby 10	a			07 25		08 24			09 24				10 24			11 24			12 24				13 24			14 24	
Nottingham 8	a			08 10		09 05			10 05				11 05			12 05			13 05				14 05			15 07	

		LM 1◇	EM	NT 1	LM 1◇	EM		NT 1	LM 1◇	EM	NT 1	LM 1◇	EM	NT 1	LM 1	EM	NT 1	LM 1	EM	NT 1	NT 1	EM	NT 1 A	NT 1 A	NT B (bus)		
Crewe 10	d	13 33	14 07		14 33	15 07			15 33	16 07		16 33	17 07		17 33	18 07		18 33	19 07			20 45					
Alsager	d	13 41	14 16		14 41	15 16			15 41	16 16		16 41	17 16		17 41	18 16		18 41	19 16			20 54					
Kidsgrove	d	13 46	14 21	14 32	14 46	15 21		15 32	15 46	16 21	16 32	16 46	17 21	17 32	17 46	18 21	18 32	18 46	19 21	19 32	20 32	21b08	21 32	22 32	23 05		
Longport	d		14 27			15 27				16 27			17 27			18 27			19 27			21 14			23a30		
Stoke-on-Trent	a	13 54	14 31	14 42	14 54	15 31		15 42	15 54	16 31	16 42	16 54	17 31	17 42	17 54	18 31	18 42	18 54	19 31	19 42	20 42	21 18	21 42	22 42			
	d		14 33			15 33				16 33			17 33			18 33			19 33			21 19					
Longton	d		14 39			15 39				16 39			17 39			18 39			19 39			21 25					
Blythe Bridge	d		14 45			15 45				16 45			17 45			18 45			19 45			21 31					
Uttoxeter	d		14 58			15 58				16 58			17 58			18 58			19 58			21 44					
Tutbury & Hatton	d		15 07			16 07				17 07			18 07			19 07			20 07			21 53					
Peartree	d					16 18																					
Derby 10	a		15 24			16 23				17 24			18 24			19 24			20 24			22 11					
Nottingham 8	a		16 05			17 05				18 05			19 05			20 05			21 05			23c33					

For general notes see front of timetable
For details of catering facilities see Directory of Train Operators

- **A** From 18 July
- **B** Until 11 July
- **b** Arr. 2059
- **c** Until 5 September only

From Monday 28 September a revised service will be in operation due to seasonal difficulties. Some trains will be retimed between 1 and 3 minutes. Passengers should check with National Rail Enquiries for precise times.

From Saturday 3 October a revised service will be in operation due to seasonal difficulties. Some trains will be retimed between 1 and 3 minutes. Passengers should check with National Rail Enquiries for precise times.

Crewe and Stoke-on-Trent → Derby and Nottingham

Sundays

until 12 July

Network Diagram - see first page of Table 50

		LM (bus)	LM 1 ◊	EM	EM	NT 1	LM 1 ◊	EM	EM	LM 1 ◊	EM	EM	NT 1	LM 1 ◊	EM	EM	NT 1
Crewe 10	d	10 35	13 38	14 04	15 05		15 38	16 10	17 08	17 38	18 09	19 08		19 36	20 10	21 16	
Alsager	d	10 52	13 46	14 13	15 14		15 46	16 19	17 18	17 46	18 18	19 18		19 44	20 19	21 25	
Kidsgrove	d	11 06	13 51	14 18	15 19	15 25	15 52	16 24	17 23	17 51	18 24	19 23	19 28	19 50	20 25	21 31	22 26
Longport	d			14 24	15 25			16 30	17 29		18 30	19 29			20 34	21 36	
Stoke-on-Trent	a	11 22	13 58	14 29	15 29	15 35	15 59	16 35	17 33	17 58	18 35	19 33	19 38	19 57	20 38	21 40	22 36
	d			14 29	15 32			16 35	17 35		18 36	19 35			20 39	21 42	
Longton	d			14 35	15 38			16 41	17 47		18 46	19 44			20 45	21 53	
Blythe Bridge	d			14 41	15 44			16 47	17 53		18 52	19 50			20 51	21 59	
Uttoxeter	d			14 53	15 56			17 00	18 05		19 04	20 03			21 04	22 12	
Tutbury & Hatton	d			15 02	16 06			17 09	18 14		19 13	20 12			21 13	22 21	
Peartree	d																
Derby 10	a			15 21	16 24			17 27	18 28		19 28	20 30			21 34	22 40	
Nottingham 8	a			*16 08*	*17 09*				*19 08*		*20 02*	*22 02*			*22 42*	*23 58*	

Sundays

19 July to 6 September

		LM 1	LM 1 ◊	LM 1 ◊	EM	EM	NT 1	LM 1 ◊	EM	EM	LM 1 ◊	EM	EM	NT 1	LM 1 ◊	EM	EM	NT 1
Crewe 10	d	10 37	11 38	13 38	14 04	15 05		15 38	16 10	17 08	17 38	18 10	19 08		19 36	20 10	21 16	
Alsager	d	10 46	11 46	13 46	14 13	15 14		15 46	16 19	17 18	17 46	18 19	19 18		19 44	20 19	21 25	
Kidsgrove	d	10 50	11 52	13 51	14 18	15 19	15 25	15 52	16 24	17 23	17 51	18 24	19 23	19 28	19 50	20 25	21 31	22 26
Longport	d				14 24	15 25			16 30	17 29		18 30	19 29			20 34	21 36	
Stoke-on-Trent	a	10 57	11 59	13 58	14 29	15 29	15 35	15 59	16 35	17 33	17 58	18 35	19 33	19 38	19 57	20 38	21 40	22 36
	d				14 29	15 32			16 35	17 35		18 37	19 35			20 40	21 42	
Longton	d				14 35	15 38			16 41	17 47		18 46	19 45			20 46	21 53	
Blythe Bridge	d				14 41	15 44			16 47	17 53		18 52	19 51			20 52	21 59	
Uttoxeter	d				14 53	15 56			17 00	18 05		19 04	20 04			21 04	22 12	
Tutbury & Hatton	d				15 02	16 06			17 09	18 14		19 13	20 13			21 13	22 21	
Peartree	d																	
Derby 10	a				15 21	16 24			17 27	18 28		19 28	20 30			21 33	22 40	
Nottingham 8	a				*16 08*	*17 09*				*19 07*		*20 07*	*21 45*			22b*15*		

Sundays

from 13 September

		LM 1	LM 1 ◊	LM 1 ◊	EM	EM	NT 1	LM 1 ◊	EM	EM	LM 1 ◊	EM	EM	NT 1	LM 1 ◊	EM	EM	NT 1
Crewe 10	d	10 38	11 38	13 38	14 04	15 05		15 38	16 09	17 08	17 38	18 10	19 08		19 36	20 10	21 16	
Alsager	d	10 47	11 46	13 46	14 13	15 14		15 46	16 19	17 18	17 46	18 19	19 19		19 44	20 20	21 25	
Kidsgrove	d	10 51	11 52	13 51	14 18	15 21	15 25	15 52	16 24	17 23	17 51	18 24	19 24	19 28	19 50	20 25	21 31	22 26
Longport	d				14 24	15 26			16 30	17 29		18 30	19 29			20 34	21 36	
Stoke-on-Trent	a	10 58	11 59	13 58	14 29	15 30	15 35	15 59	16 35	17 33	17 58	18 35	19 33	19 38	19 57	20 38	21 40	22 36
	d				14 29	15 32			16 35	17 35		18 37	19 35			20 40	21 42	
Longton	d				14 35	15 38			16 46	17 41		18 46	19 41			20 46	21 53	
Blythe Bridge	d				14 41	15 44			16 52	17 47		18 52	19 47			20 52	21 59	
Uttoxeter	d				14 53	15 56			17 05	17 59		19 04	19 59			21 04	22 12	
Tutbury & Hatton	d				15 02	16 06			17 14	18 08		19 14	20 08			21 13	22 21	
Peartree	d																	
Derby 10	a				15 21	16 24			17 35	18 24		19 33	20 27			21 33	22 40	
Nottingham 8	a				*16 01*	*17 47*			*18 57*	*19 47*		*20 57*	*21 45*			22b*15*		

For general notes see front of timetable
For details of catering facilities see Directory of Train Operators

b By bus

Route Diagram for Table 51

DM-5/09
Design BAJS

This Table summarises through services which, with their associated connecting services at Birmingham New Street, link centres in the North and South of the country. In certain instances a faster journey is possible via London and the relevant Table(s) should be consulted.

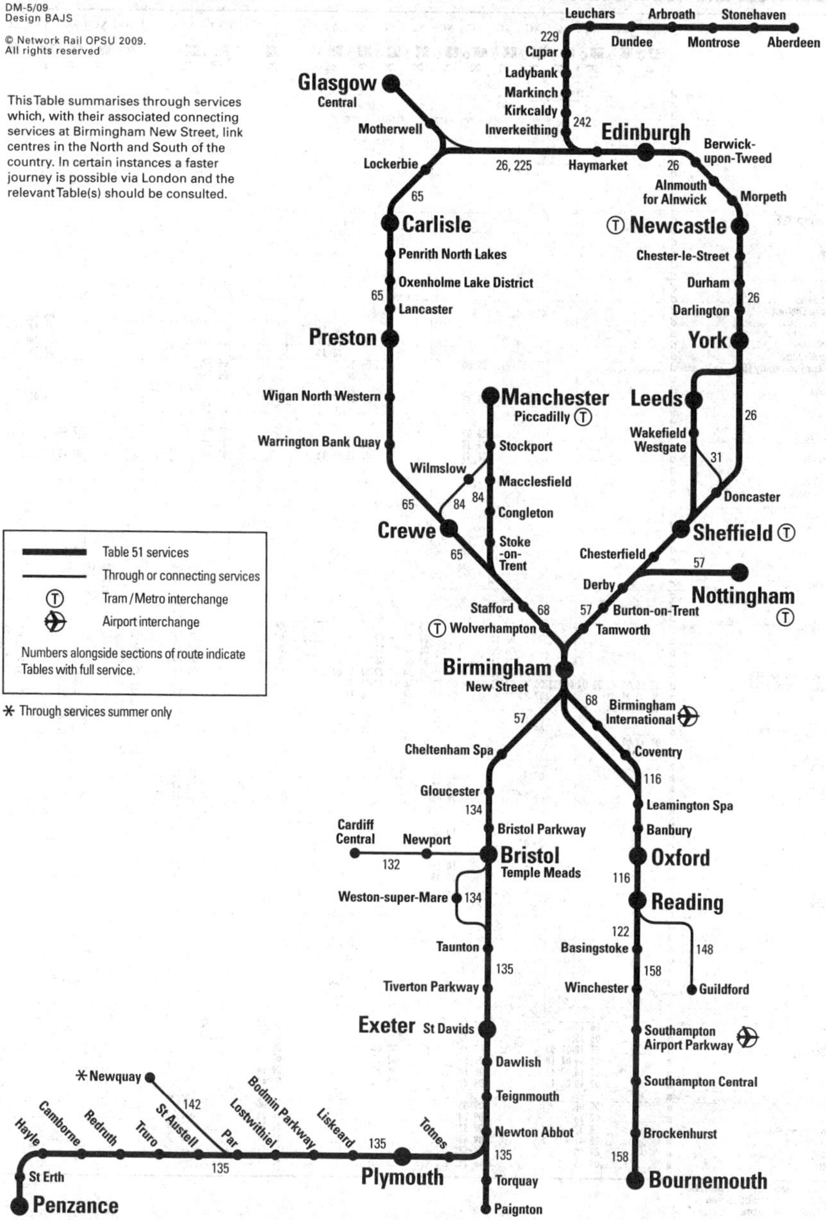

Scotland, The North East, North West England → The South West and South Coast

Route Diagram - See first page of Table 51

		XC	XC	XC	XC	XC	XC	XC	XC	XC	XC	XC	VT		XC		VT	XC		XC	XC	XC	VT	XC
		1◇	1◇	1◇	1◇	1◇	1◇	1◇	1◇	1◇	1◇	1◇	1◇		R 1		1◇	1◇		1◇	1◇	1◇	1◇	1
		⫪	⫪	⫪	⫪	⫪	⫪	⫪	⫪	⫪	⫪	⫪	⊠		⫪		⊠	⫪		⫪	⫪	⫪	⊠	
Aberdeen	d																							
Stonehaven	d																							
Montrose	d																							
Arbroath	d																							
Dundee	d																							
Leuchars [3]	d																							
Cupar	d																							
Ladybank	d																							
Markinch	d																							
Kirkcaldy	d																							
Inverkeithing	d																							
Glasgow Central [15]	d																							
Motherwell	d																							
Haymarket	d																							
Edinburgh [10]	d																							
Haymarket	d																							
Lockerbie	d																							
Carlisle [8]	d																							
Penrith North Lakes	d																							
Oxenholme Lake District	d																							
Lancaster [6]	d																						06 58	
Preston [8]	d												06 16										07 17	
Wigan North Western	d												06 27										07 28	
Warrington Bank Quay	d												06 38										07 39	
Manchester Piccadilly [10] (tram)	d							05 00				06 00					06 27					07 06		
Stockport	d											06 08					06 35							
Wilmslow	d																							
Crewe [10]	d							05 47				06 38	07 01										08 01	
Macclesfield	d																06 48							
Congleton	d																							
Stoke-on-Trent	d							06 07									07 06					07 44		
Stafford	d							06 25				06 58					07 28							
Wolverhampton [7] (tram)	d							06 41				07 15	07 32				07 45					08 15	08 32	
Dunbar	d																							
Berwick-upon-Tweed	d																							
Alnmouth for Alnwick	d																							
Morpeth	d																							
Newcastle [8]	d																							
Chester-le-Street	d																							
Durham	d																							
Darlington [7]	d																							
York [8]	d																							
Leeds [10]	d																	06 00			06 15			
Wakefield Westgate [7]	d																	06 12			06 27			
Doncaster [7]	d																				06 45			
Sheffield [7]	d										06 01							06 50			07 18			
Chesterfield	d										06 26							07 04			07 30			
Nottingham [8] (tram)	d									06 00					06 37					07 00				07 37
Derby [10]	d						06 10			06 36	06 47				07 06			07 26		07 36	07 50			08 06
Burton-on-Trent	d						06 20			06 48	06 57				07 18			07 37		07 49	08 00			08 18
Tamworth	d						06 31			07 00	07 08				07 30			07 49		08 01	08 11			08 30
Birmingham New Street [12]	a						06 52	06 58	←	07 24	07 27	07 31	07 55		07 56		08 05	08 09		08 24	08 29	08 31	08 56	08 56
Birmingham New Street [12]	d	05 00	05 42	06 04	06 33	06 42	07 12	07 04	07 12	07 30	07 33	07 42			08 04		08 10	08 12		08 30	08 33	08 42		
Cheltenham Spa	a	06 02	06 43			07 23	→		07 51	08 14		08 23						08 51		09 10		09 23		
Gloucester [7]	a	06 16	06 53							08 26										09 21				
Bristol Parkway [7]	a					07 56			08 27			08 56						09 25				09 56		
Bristol Temple Meads [10]	a					08 08			08 41			09 13						09 41				10 13		
Newport (South Wales)	a	07 11	07 52							09 11										10 11				
Cardiff Central [7]	a	07 31	08 13							09 31										10 31				
Weston-super-Mare	a																							
Taunton	a					08 42			09 15									10 16						
Tiverton Parkway	a								09 28									10 29						
Exeter St Davids [6]	a					09 07			09 43									10 46						
Dawlish	a																							
Teignmouth	a																							
Newton Abbot	a								10 03									11 08						
Torquay	a					09 35																		
Paignton	a					09 48																		
Totnes	a								10 16									11 22						
Plymouth	a								10 48									11 56						
Liskeard [6]	a																							
Bodmin Parkway	a																							
Lostwithiel	a																							
Par	a																							
Newquay	a																							
St Austell	a																							
Truro	a																							
Redruth	a																							
Camborne	a																							
Hayle	a																							
St Erth	a																							
Penzance	a																							
Birmingham International (airport)	d			06 14				07 14							08 14		08 20							
Coventry	d			06 25				07 25							08 25		08a30							
Leamington Spa [8]	d			06 38	07 00			07 38			08 00				08 38						09 00			
Banbury	a			06 54	07 18			07 54			08 18				08 54						09 18			
Oxford	a			07 14	07 41			08 14			08 41				09 14						09 41			
Reading [7]	a			07 40	08 13			08 40			09 13				09 40						10 13			
Guildford	a																							
Basingstoke	a			08 08				09 08							10 08									
Winchester	a			08 24				09 24							10 24									
Southampton Airport Parkwy (airport)	a			08 32				09 32							10 32									
Southampton Central	a			08 41				09 43							10 43									
Brockenhurst [3]	a			08 50				09 57							10 57									
Bournemouth	a			09 15				10 15							11 15									

For general notes see front of timetable
For details of catering facilities see Directory of Train Operators

Scotland, The North East, North West England → The South West and South Coast

Route Diagram - See first page of Table 51

		XC	XC	XC	XC	XC	VT	XC	XC	XC	XC	XC	XC	VT	XC	XC	XC	XC	XC	XC	VT	XC
		1◇	1◇	1◇	1◇	1◇	1◇	1	1◇	1◇	1◇	1◇	1◇	1◇	1	1◇	1◇	1◇	1◇	1◇	1◇	1
		🛒	🛒	🛒	🛒	🛒	⊠		🛒	🛒	🛒	🛒	🛒	⊠		🛒	🛒	🛒	🛒	🛒	⊠	
Aberdeen	d																					
Stonehaven	d																					
Montrose	d																					
Arbroath	d																					
Dundee	d																					
Leuchars 8	d																					
Cupar	d																					
Ladybank	d																					
Markinch	d																					
Kirkcaldy	d																					
Inverkeithing	d																					
Glasgow Central 15	d						05 50														08 00	
Motherwell	d						06 05															
Haymarket	d																					
Edinburgh 10	d													06 52			06 08		06 44			
Haymarket	d													06u56								
Lockerbie	d																					
Carlisle 8	d						07 04							08 07							09 09	
Penrith North Lakes	d						07 19							08 22								
Oxenholme Lake District	d						07 42															
Lancaster 6	d						07 57							08 57							09 57	
Preston 8	d						08 17							09 17							10 17	
Wigan North Western	d						08 28							09 28							10 28	
Warrington Bank Quay	d						08 39							09 39							10 39	
Manchester Piccadilly 10	d	07 26				08 07			08 27				09 07			09 27				10 07		
Stockport	d	07 35							08 35							09 35						
Wilmslow	d																					
Crewe 10	d						09 01							10 01							11 01	
Macclesfield	d	07 49							08 49							09 49						
Congleton	d																					
Stoke-on-Trent	d	08 07				08 44			09 07				09 44			10 07				10 44		
Stafford	d	08 25							09 25							10 25						
Wolverhampton 7	d	08 41				09 15	09 32		09 41				10 15	10 32		10 41				11 15	11 32	
Dunbar	d																					
Berwick-upon-Tweed	d																06 49		07 23			
Alnmouth for Alnwick	d																07 10		07 47			
Morpeth	d																		08 01			
Newcastle 8	d				06 21					06 44		07 23					07 44		08 24			
Chester-le-Street	d				06 32														08 33			
Durham	d				06 39					06 55		07 37							08 40			
Darlington 7	d				06 56					07 12		07 55					08 12		08 57			
York 8	d		06 32		07 27					07 44		08 27					08 44		09 27			
Leeds 10	d		07 05							08 11							09 11					
Wakefield Westgate 7	d		07 18							08 23							09 23					
Doncaster 7	d				07 52							08 51							09 56			
Sheffield 7	d		07 53		08 20					08 54		09 23					09 54		10 23			
Chesterfield	d		08 06		08 32					09 06							10 06					
Nottingham 8	d			08 08				08 37			09 08				09 37			10 08				10 37
Derby 10	d		08 28	08 37	08 53			09 07		09 28	09 37	09 53			10 06		10 28	10 37	10 53			11 06
Burton-on-Trent	d		08 38	08 49				09 19		09 38	09 49				10 18			10 49				11 18
Tamworth	d		08 49	09 01				09 30			10 01				10 30		10 48	11 01				11 30
Birmingham New Street 12	a	08 58	09 09	09 24	09 27	09 31	09 56	09 56	09 58	10 07	10 24	10 27	10 31	10 55	10 56	10 58	11 09	11 24	11 27	11 31	11 56	11 56
Birmingham New Street 12	d	09 04	09 12	09 30	09 33	09 42			10 04	10 12	10 30	10 33	10 42			11 04	11 12	11 30	11 33	11 42		
Cheltenham Spa	a		09 51	10 10		10 23				10 51	11 10		11 23				11 51	12 10		12 23		
Gloucester 7	a			10 21							11 21							12 21				
Bristol Parkway 7	a		10 26			10 56				11 26			11 56				12 26			12 56		
Bristol Temple Meads 10	a		10 41			11 13				11 38			12 13				12 41			13 13		
Newport (South Wales)	a			11 11							12 11							13 11				
Cardiff Central 7	a			11 31							12 31							13 31				
Weston-super-Mare	a					11 32																
Taunton	a		11 16			12 00				12 15							13 16					
Tiverton Parkway	a		11 29			12 13				12 28							13 29					
Exeter St Davids 6	a		11 46			12 30				12 43							13 46					
Dawlish	a					12 43																
Teignmouth	a					12 48																
Newton Abbot	a		12 08			12 56				13 03							14 08					
Torquay	a					13 07																
Paignton	a					13 20																
Totnes	a		12 22							13 16							14 22					
Plymouth	a		12 56							13 48							14 56					
Liskeard 6	a																					
Bodmin Parkway	a																					
Lostwithiel	a																					
Par	a																					
Newquay	a																					
St Austell	a																					
Truro	a																					
Redruth	a																					
Camborne	a																					
Hayle	a																					
St Erth	a																					
Penzance	a																					
Birmingham International ✈	d	09 14							10 14							11 14						
Coventry	d	09 25							10 25							11 25						
Leamington Spa 8	d	09 38			10 00				10 38			11 00				11 38			12 00			
Banbury	a	09 54			10 18				10 54			11 18				11 54			12 18			
Oxford	a	10 14			10 41				11 14			11 41				12 14			12 41			
Reading 7	a	10 40			11 13				11 40			12 13				12 40			13 13			
Guildford	a																					
Basingstoke	a	11 08							12 08							13 08						
Winchester	a	11 24							12 24							13 24						
Southampton Airport Parkway ✈	a	11 32							12 32							13 32						
Southampton Central	a	11 43							12 41							13 41						
Brockenhurst 3	a	11 57							12 56							13 56						
Bournemouth	a	12 15							13 15							14 15						

For general notes see front of timetable
For details of catering facilities see Directory of Train Operators

Scotland, The North East, North West England → The South West and South Coast

Route Diagram - See first page of Table 51

		XC	XC	XC	XC	XC	XC	VT	XC	XC	XC	XC	XC	XC	XC	VT	XC	XC	XC	XC	XC	XC	XC
														FX	FO								
		1◇	1◇	1◇	1◇	1◇	1◇	1◇	1	1◇	1◇	1◇	1◇	1◇	1◇	1◇	1	1◇	1◇	1◇	1◇	1◇	1◇
			A	B															B	A			
		[trolley]	[trolley]	[trolley]	[trolley]	[trolley]	[trolley]	[⊠]		[trolley]	[trolley]	[trolley]	[trolley]	[trolley]	[trolley]	[buffet]		[trolley]	[trolley]	[trolley]	[trolley]	[trolley]	[trolley]
Aberdeen	d																						
Stonehaven	d																						
Montrose	d																						
Arbroath	d																						
Dundee	d										06 32								07 35	07 35			
Leuchars 3	d										06 46								07 48	07 48			
Cupar	d										06 54								07 55	07 55			
Ladybank	d										07 03								08 03	08 03			
Markinch	d										07 11								08 11	08 11			
Kirkcaldy	d										07 21								08 20	08 20			
Inverkeithing	d										07 42								08 35	08 35			
Glasgow Central 15	d		06 00	06 00												10 00							
Motherwell	d																						
Haymarket	d		06 55	06 55							08 01								08 54	08 54			
Edinburgh 10	d		07 08	07 08				08 52			08 10								09 07	09 07			
Haymarket	d							08u57															
Lockerbie	d																						
Carlisle 8	d							10 07								11 09							
Penrith North Lakes	d															11 24							
Oxenholme Lake District	d							10 42															
Lancaster 6	d							10 57															
Preston 8	d							11 17								12 17							
Wigan North Western	d							11 28								12 28							
Warrington Bank Quay	d							11 39								12 39							
Manchester Piccadilly 10	d	10 27					11 07			11 27				12 07	12 07			12 27					13 07
Stockport	d	10 35								11 35								12 35					
Wilmslow	d																						
Crewe 10	d							12 01								13 01							
Macclesfield	d	10 49								11 49								12 49					
Congleton	d																						
Stoke-on-Trent	d	11 07					11 44			12 07				12 44	12 44			13 07					13 44
Stafford	d	11 25								12 25								13 25					
Wolverhampton 7	d	11 41					12 15	12 32		12 41				13 15	13 15	13 32		13 41					14 15
Dunbar	d		07 28	07 28															09 28	09 28			
Berwick-upon-Tweed	d		07 51	07 51							08 52								09 51	09 51			
Alnmouth for Alnwick	d																						
Morpeth	d																						
Newcastle 8	d		08 40	08 43		09 33					09 43		10 25						10 43	10 43		11 27	
Chester-le-Street	d																						
Durham	d		08 52	08 55		09 48					09 55		10 41						10 55	10 55		11 39	
Darlington 7	d		09 12	09 12		10 05					10 12		10 58						11 10	11 12		11 56	
York 8	d		09 44	09 44		10 34					10 44		11 27						11 44	11 44		12 27	
Leeds 10	d		10 11	10 11							11 11								12 11	12 11			
Wakefield Westgate 7	d		10 23	10 23							11 23								12 23	12 23			
Doncaster 7	d					10 58							11 54									12 55	
Sheffield 7	d		10 54	10 54		11 23					11 54		12 23						12 54	12 54		13 23	
Chesterfield	d		11 06	11 06							12 06								13 06	13 06			
Nottingham 8	d				11 08				11 37			12 08					12 37				13 08		
Derby 10	d		11 28	11 28	11 37	11 53			12 06		12 28	12 37	12 53				13 06		13 28	13 28	13 37	13 53	
Burton-on-Trent	d				11 49				12 18			12 49					13 20		13 38	13 38	13 49		
Tamworth	d				12 01				12 30		12 48	13 01					13 33				14 01		
Birmingham New Street 12	a	11 58	12 04	12 04	12 24	12 27	12 31	12 55	12 56	12 58	13 09	13 24	13 27	13 31	13 31	13 56	13 56	13 58	14 07	14 07	14 24	14 27	14 31
Birmingham New Street 12	d	12 04	12 12	12 12	12 30	12 33	12 42			13 04	13 12	13 30	13 33	13 42	13 42			14 04	14 12	14 12	14 30	14 33	14 42
Cheltenham Spa	a		12 51	12 51	13 10		13 23				13 51	14 10		14 23	14 23				14 51	14 51	15 10		15 23
Gloucester 7	a				13 21							14 21									15 21		
Bristol Parkway 7	a		13 24	13 24			13 56				14 27			14 56	14 56				15 24	15 24			15 56
Bristol Temple Meads 10	a		13 39	13 39			14 13				14 41			15 13	15 13				15 41	15 41			16 13
Newport (South Wales)	a				14 11							15 11									16 11		
Cardiff Central 7	a				14 31							15 31									16 31		
Weston-super-Mare	a																						
Taunton	a		14 15	14 15							15 16				15 44				16 15	16 15			
Tiverton Parkway	a		14 28	14 28							15 29				15 57				16 28	16 28			
Exeter St Davids 6	a		14 43	14 43							15 46				16 18				16 43	16 43			
Dawlish	a																						
Teignmouth	a																						
Newton Abbot	a		15 03	15 03							16 08								17 03	17 03			
Torquay	a																						
Paignton	a																						
Totnes	a		15 16	15 16							16 22								17 16	17 16			
Plymouth	a		15 48	15 48							16 56								17 48	17 48			
Liskeard 6	a																						
Bodmin Parkway	a																						
Lostwithiel	a																						
Par	a																						
Newquay	a																						
St Austell	a																						
Truro	a																						
Redruth	a																						
Camborne	a																						
Hayle	a																						
St Erth	a																						
Penzance	a																						
Birmingham International ✈	d	12 14								13 14								14 14					
Coventry	d	12 25								13 25								14 25					
Leamington Spa 8	d	12 38				13 00				13 38			14 00					14 38				15 00	
Banbury	a	12 54				13 18				13 54			14 18					14 54				15 18	
Oxford	a	13 14				13 41				14 14			14 41					15 14				15 41	
Reading 7	a	13 40				14 13				14 40			15 13					15 40				16 13	
Guildford	a																						
Basingstoke	a	14 08								15 07								16 08					
Winchester	a	14 24								15 24								16 24					
Southampton Airport Parkwy ✈	a	14 32								15 32								16 32					
Southampton Central	a	14 40								15 41								16 41					
Brockenhurst 3	a	14 56								15 56								16 56					
Bournemouth	a	15 15								16 15								17 15					

For general notes see front of timetable
For details of catering facilities see Directory of Train Operators

A From 7 September
B Until 4 September

Scotland, The North East, North West England → The South West and South Coast

Route Diagram - See first page of Table 51

		VT		XC	XC	XC	XC	XC	XC	VT	XC	XC	XC	XC	XC		XC	VT	XC	XC	XC	XC	XC	XC
		[1] ◇		[1]	[1] ◇	[1] ◇	[1] ◇	[1] ◇	[1] ◇	[1] ◇	[1]	[1] ◇	[1] ◇	[1] ◇	[1] ◇		[1] ◇	[1] ◇	[1]	[1] ◇	[1] ◇	[1] ◇	[1] ◇	[1] ◇
						A							A								A			
		⊡			⊼	⊼	⊼	⊼	⊼	⊡		⊼	⊼	⊼	⊼		⊼	⊡		⊼	⊼	⊼	⊼	⊼
Aberdeen	d												08 20											
Stonehaven	d												08 38											
Montrose	d												08 59											
Arbroath	d												09 15											
Dundee	d												09 33											
Leuchars [8]	d												09 47											
Cupar	d												09 54											
Ladybank	d												10 01											
Markinch	d												10 09											
Kirkcaldy	d												10 17											
Inverkeithing	d												10 32											
Glasgow Central [15]	d					09 00				12 00														
Motherwell	d					09 15																		
Haymarket	d					09 54							10 54											
Edinburgh [10]	d	10 52				10 08							11 08					12 52			12 05			
Haymarket	d	10u57																12u57						
Lockerbie	d																							
Carlisle [8]	d	12 07								13 09								14 07						
Penrith North Lakes	d																	14 22						
Oxenholme Lake District	d	12 43																						
Lancaster [6]	d	12 57								13 58								14 57						
Preston [8]	d	13 17								14 17								15 17						
Wigan North Western	d	13 28								14 28								15 28						
Warrington Bank Quay	d	13 39								14 39								15 39						
Manchester Piccadilly [10] ✈	d				13 27				14 07			14 27					15 07			15 27				16 07
Stockport	d				13 35							14 35								15 35				
Wilmslow	d																							
Crewe [10]	d	14 01								15 01								16 01						
Macclesfield	d				13 49							14 49								15 49				
Congleton	d																							
Stoke-on-Trent	d				14 07				14 44			15 07					15 44			16 07				16 44
Stafford	d				14 25							15 25								16 25				
Wolverhampton [7] ✈	d	14 32			14 41				15 15	15 32		15 41					16 15	16 32		16 41				17 15
Dunbar	d												11 28											
Berwick-upon-Tweed	d												11 51											
Alnmouth for Alnwick	d					11 05															13 06			
Morpeth	d					11 20																		
Newcastle [8]	d					11 40		12 19					12 43		13 34						13 44		14 27	
Chester-le-Street	d							12 28																
Durham	d					11 52		12 35					12 55		13 46						13 52		14 40	
Darlington [7]	d					12 11		12 53					13 12		14 03						14 12		14 57	
York [8]	d					12 44		13 26					13 44		14 32						14 44		15 29	
Leeds [10]	d					13 11							14 11								15 11			
Wakefield Westgate [7]	d					13 23							14 23								15 23			
Doncaster [7]	d							13 55							14 57								15 55	
Sheffield [7]	d					13 54		14 23					14 54		15 23						15 54		16 23	
Chesterfield	d					14 06							15 06								16 06			
Nottingham [8] ✈	d			13 37			14 08				14 37			15 08					15 37			16 08		
Derby [10]	d			14 06		14 28	14 37	14 53			15 06		15 28	15 37	15 53				16 06		16 28	16 37	16 53	
Burton-on-Trent	d			14 18			14 49				15 18		15 38	15 49					16 18			16 49		
Tamworth	d			14 30		14 48	15 01				15 30			16 01					16 30		16 48	17 01		
Birmingham New Street [12]	a	14 55		14 56	14 58	15 07	15 24	15 27	15 31	15 56	15 56	15 58	16 08	16 24	16 27		16 31	16 55	16 56	16 58	17 07	17 24	17 27	17 31
Birmingham New Street [12]	d				15 04	15 12	15 30	15 33	15 42			16 04	16 12	16 30	16 33		16 42			17 04	17 12	17 30	17 33	17 42
Cheltenham Spa	a					15 51	16 10		16 23				16 51	17 13			17 23				17 51	18 17		18 23
Gloucester [7]	a						16 21							17 25								18 28		18 35
Bristol Parkway [7]	a					16 26			16 56				17 24				17 56				18 24			19 08
Bristol Temple Meads [10]	a					16 41			17 13				17 41				18 13				18 41			19 25
Newport (South Wales)	a						17 11							18 11								19 14		
Cardiff Central [7]	a						17 31							18 31								19 35		
Weston-super-Mare	a																							
Taunton	a					17 15			17 45				18 15								19 15			
Tiverton Parkway	a					17 28			17 57				18 28								19 28			
Exeter St Davids [6]	a					17 43			18 13				18 43								19 43			
Dawlish	a								18 25															
Teignmouth	a								18 30															
Newton Abbot	a					18 10			18 38				19 04								20 04			
Torquay	a								18 50															
Paignton	a								19 01															
Totnes	a					18 23							19 17								20 17			
Plymouth	a					18 56							19 48								20 48			
Liskeard [6]	a					19 22							20 12								21 12			
Bodmin Parkway	a					19 34							20 24								21 24			
Lostwithiel	a																				21 30			
Par	a					19 44							20 35								21 37			
Newquay	a																							
St Austell	a					19 51							20 41								21 43			
Truro	a					20 08							20 59								22 01			
Redruth	a					20 24							21 14								22 13			
Camborne	a					20 32							21 21								22 22			
Hayle	a																				22 30			
St Erth	a					20 42							21 31								22 34			
Penzance	a					20 59							21 47								22 50			
Birmingham International ✈	d				15 14							16 14								17 14				
Coventry	d				15 25							16 25								17 25				
Leamington Spa [8]	d				15 38			16 00				16 38			17 00					17 38			18 00	
Banbury	a				15 54			16 18				16 54			17 18					17 54			18 18	
Oxford	a				16 14			16 41				17 14			17 41					18 14			18 41	
Reading [7]	a				16 40			17 13				17 40			18 13					18 40			19 13	
Guildford	a																							
Basingstoke	a				17 08							18 08								19 08				
Winchester	a				17 24							18 24								19 24				
Southampton Airport Parkway ✈	a				17 32							18 33								19 33				
Southampton Central	a				17 41							18 41								19 41				
Brockenhurst [3]	a				17 56							18 56								19 56				
Bournemouth	a				18 15							19 15								20 15				

For general notes see front of timetable
For details of catering facilities see Directory of Train Operators

A ⊼ to Plymouth

Scotland, The North East, North West England → The South West and South Coast

Route Diagram - See first page of Table 51

		VT	XC	XC	XC	XC			XC	XC	VT	XC	XC	XC	XC	XC	XC	XC	VT	XC		XC	XC	XC
		1 ◇	1	1 ◇	1 ◇	1 ◇			1 ◇	1 ◇	1 ◇	1	1 ◇	1 ◇	1 ◇	1 ◇	1 ◇	1 ◇	1 ◇	1		1 ◇	1 ◇	1 ◇
										B			C	B			D	E				G	H	J
		℗		⊼	⊼	⊼			⊼	⊼	℗		⊼	⊼	⊼	⊼	⊼	⊼	℗			⊼	⊼	⊼
Aberdeen	d																							
Stonehaven	d																							
Montrose	d																							
Arbroath	d																							
Dundee	d																							
Leuchars [3]	d																							
Cupar	d																							
Ladybank	d																							
Markinch	d																							
Kirkcaldy	d																							
Inverkeithing	d																							
Glasgow Central [15]	d	14 00																	16 00					
Motherwell	d																							
Haymarket	d																							
Edinburgh [10]	d				13 06						14 52			14 08									15 08	15 08
Haymarket	d										14u57													
Lockerbie	d																							
Carlisle [8]	d	15 09									16 07								17 09					
Penrith North Lakes	d										16 22													
Oxenholme Lake District	d	15 44																	17 44					
Lancaster [6]	d										16 57													
Preston [8]	d	16 17									17 17								18 17					
Wigan North Western	d	16 28									17 28								18 28					
Warrington Bank Quay	d	16 39									17 39								18 39					
Manchester Piccadilly [10] 🚊	d			16 27						17 06			17 27				18 05	18 05				18 27		
Stockport	d			16 35									17 35									18 35		
Wilmslow	d												17 44											
Crewe [10]	d	17 01									18 01								19 01					
Macclesfield	d			16 49						17 27							18 25	18 25						
Congleton	d																					18 54		
Stoke-on-Trent	d			17 07						17 44							18 44	18 44				19 07		
Stafford	d			17 25									18 25									19 25		
Wolverhampton [7] 🚊	d	17 32		17 41						18 15	18 32		18 41				19 15	19 15	19 32			19 41		
Dunbar	d				13 28																		15 28	15 28
Berwick-upon-Tweed	d				13 51																		15 51	15 51
Alnmouth for Alnwick	d													15 05										
Morpeth	d																							
Newcastle [8]	d				14 40				15 22					15 40		16 32							16 40	16 40
Chester-le-Street	d															16 41								
Durham	d				14 52				15 34					15 52		16 48							16 52	16 52
Darlington [7]	d				15 12				15 51					16 12		17 05							17 12	17 12
York [8]	d				15 44				16 25					16 44		17 34							17 44	17 44
Leeds [10]	d				16 11									17 11									18 11	18 11
Wakefield Westgate [7]	d				16 23									17 23									18 23	18 23
Doncaster [7]	d								16 53							17 58								
Sheffield [7]	d				16 54				17 23					17 54		18 23							18 54	18 54
Chesterfield	d				17 06									18 06									19 06	19 06
Nottingham [8] 🚊	d		16 37			17 08						17 37			18 08					18 37				
Derby [10]	d		17 06		17 28	17 37			17 53			18 06		18 28	18 37	18 53				19 06			19 28	19 28
Burton-on-Trent	d		17 18		17 38	17 49						18 20			18 49					19 18			19 38	19 38
Tamworth	d		17 30			18 01						18 33		18 48	19 01					19 30				
Birmingham New Street [12]	a	17 56	17 56	17 58	18 07	18 24			18 27	18 31	18 55	18 56	18 58	19 08	19 24	19 27	19 31	19 31	19 56	19 56		19 58	20 09	20 09
Birmingham New Street [12]	d			18 04	18 12	18 30			18 33	18 42			19 04	19 12	19 30	19 33	19 42	19 42				20 04	20 12	20 12
Cheltenham Spa	a				18 51	19 13				19 23				19 51	20 10		20 23	20 23					20 51	20 51
Gloucester [7]	a					19 25									20 21									
Bristol Parkway [7]	a				19 27					19 56				20 27			20 56	20 56					21 25	21 25
Bristol Temple Meads [10]	a				19 39					20 13				20 41			21 13	21 13					21 38	21 38
Newport (South Wales)	a					20 11				20 47					21 11									
Cardiff Central [7]	a					20 31				21 07					21 31									
Weston-super-Mare	a																							
Taunton	a				20 15									21 15			21 44	21 44					22 15	22 15
Tiverton Parkway	a				20 28									21 28			21 58	21 58					22 28	23 01
Exeter St Davids [6]	a				20 43									21 43			22 12	22 32					22 55	23 14
Dawlish	a																							
Teignmouth	a																							
Newton Abbot	a				21 03									22 03			22 32	22 52					23 21	23 34
Torquay	a																							
Paignton	a																							
Totnes	a				21 16									22 16			22 44	23 04					23 34	23 47
Plymouth	a				21 48									22 48			23 19	23 38					00 06	00 19
Liskeard [6]	a																							
Bodmin Parkway	a																							
Lostwithiel	a																							
Par	a																							
Newquay	a																							
St Austell	a																							
Truro	a																							
Redruth	a																							
Camborne	a																							
Hayle	a																							
St Erth	a																							
Penzance	a																							
Birmingham International ✈	d			18 14									19 14									20 14		
Coventry	d			18 25									19 25									20 25		
Leamington Spa [8]	d			18 38					19 00				19 38			20 00						20 38		
Banbury	a			18 54					19 18				19 54			20 18						20 54		
Oxford	a			19 14					19 41				20 14			20 41						21 14		
Reading [7]	a			19 40					20 13				20 40			21 13						21 40		
Guildford	a																							
Basingstoke	a			20 09									21 08									22 08		
Winchester	a			20 24									21 24									22 24		
Southampton Airport Parkwy ✈	a			20 33									21 33									22 32		
Southampton Central	a			20 41									21 41									22 41		
Brockenhurst [3]	a			20 56									21 56									22 56		
Bournemouth	a			21 15									22 21									23 21		

For general notes see front of timetable
For details of catering facilities see Directory of Train Operators

B ⊼ to Bristol Temple Meads

C ⊼ to Reading

D From 7 September. ⊼ to Bristol Temple Meads

E Until 4 September. ⊼ to Bristol Temple Meads

G ⊼ to Birmingham New Street

H Until 4 September. ⊼ to Birmingham New Street

J From 7 September. ⊼ to Birmingham New Street

Scotland, The North East, North West England → The South West and South Coast

Route Diagram - See first page of Table 51

		XC	XC	XC	VT	XC	XC	XC	XC	XC	VT	XC	XC	XC	XC	XC	VT	XC	XC	XC	XC
		1 ◇	1 ◇	1 ◇	1 ◇	1	1 ◇	1 ◇	1 ◇	1 ◇	1 ◇	1	1 ◇	1 ◇	1 ◇	1 ◇	1 ◇	1 ◇	1	1 ◇	1 ◇
			A	A			A	A							B	C				B	
		⌶	⌶	⌶	⎍		⌶	⌶		⌶	⎍			⌶	⌶	⌶	⎍			⌶	
Aberdeen	d																				
Stonehaven	d																				
Montrose	d																				
Arbroath	d																				
Dundee	d																				
Leuchars 3	d																				
Cupar	d																				
Ladybank	d																				
Markinch	d																				
Kirkcaldy	d																				
Inverkeithing	d																				
Glasgow Central 15	d										17 40										
Motherwell	d																				
Haymarket	d																				
Edinburgh 10	d				16 52			16 07							17 08		18 52			18 05	
Haymarket	d				16u57												18u57				
Lockerbie	d										18 32										
Carlisle 8	d				18 07						18 54						20 08				
Penrith North Lakes	d										19 09										
Oxenholme Lake District	d				18 42						19 32						20 42				
Lancaster 6	d				18 57						19 47						20 57				
Preston 8	d				19 17						20 08						21 17				
Wigan North Western	d				19 28						20 19						21 28				
Warrington Bank Quay	d				19 39						20 31						21 39				
Manchester Piccadilly 10	d			19 07			19 27		20 07				20 27					21 27			22 07
Stockport	d						19 35						20 35					21 35			22 16
Wilmslow	d																				
Crewe 10	d				20 01						20 54						22 01				
Macclesfield	d						19 49						20 49					21 49			22 29
Congleton	d																				
Stoke-on-Trent	d			19 44			20 07		20 44				21 07					22 07			22 47
Stafford	d						20 25				21 14		21 25					22 25			23 07
Wolverhampton 7	d			20 15	20 34		20 41		21 15		21 33		21 41				22 32	22 41			23 21
Dunbar	d														17 28					18 25	
Berwick-upon-Tweed	d														17 51					18 48	
Alnmouth for Alnwick	d							17 09												19 08	
Morpeth	d							17 24													
Newcastle 8	d		17 17					17 43		18 20					18 40	19 25				19 43	
Chester-le-Street	d		17 26							18 29						19 37					
Durham	d		17 33					17 55		18 36					18 52	19 44				19 55	
Darlington 7	d		17 50					18 12		18 56					19 12	20 04				20 12	
York 8	d		18 24					18 44		19 29					19 44	20 32				20 44	
Leeds 10	d							19 11							20 11					21 11	
Wakefield Westgate 7	d							19 23							20 23					21 23	
Doncaster 7	d		18 52							19 57						20 57					
Sheffield 7	d		19 23					19 54		20 23					20 54	21 26				22 00	
Chesterfield	d							20 06							21 06					22 24	
Nottingham 8	d	19 08				19 37						20 37							21 37		
Derby 10	d	19 37	19 53			20 06		20 28		20 53		21 06			21 28	22 00			22 10	22 45	
Burton-on-Trent	d	19 49				20 18						21 20			21 38				22 21	22 56	
Tamworth	d	20 01				20 30		20 48				21 33			21 49				22 33	23 06	
Birmingham New Street 12	a	20 24	20 27	20 31	20 55	20 56	20 58	21 07	21 36	21 40	21 51	21 57	22 00		22 07	22 54	22 55	23 03	23 05	23 34	23 40
Birmingham New Street 12	d	20 30	20 33	20 42			21 04	21 12						22 04	22 16						
Cheltenham Spa	a	21 10		21 23				21 51							23 31						
Gloucester 7	a	21 21																			
Bristol Parkway 7	a			22 00				22 23							00 04						
Bristol Temple Meads 10	a			22 19				22 41							00 18						
Newport (South Wales)	a	22 11																			
Cardiff Central 7	a	22 31																			
Weston-super-Mare	a																				
Taunton	a																				
Tiverton Parkway	a																				
Exeter St Davids 6	a																				
Dawlish	a																				
Teignmouth	a																				
Newton Abbot	a																				
Torquay	a																				
Paignton	a																				
Totnes	a																				
Plymouth	a																				
Liskeard 6	a																				
Bodmin Parkway	a																				
Lostwithiel	a																				
Par	a																				
Newquay	a																				
St Austell	a																				
Truro	a																				
Redruth	a																				
Camborne	a																				
Hayle	a																				
St Erth	a																				
Penzance	a																				
Birmingham International	d						21 14							22 14							
Coventry	d						21 25							22 25							
Leamington Spa 8	d		21 00				21 38							22 38							
Banbury	a		21 18				21 54							22 54							
Oxford	a		21 41				22 14							23 14							
Reading 7	a		22 19				22 40							23 57							
Guildford	a		22 59																		
Basingstoke	a						23 12														
Winchester	a						23 28														
Southampton Airport Parkwy	a						23 37														
Southampton Central	a						23 52														
Brockenhurst 3	a																				
Bournemouth	a																				

For general notes see front of timetable
For details of catering facilities see Directory of Train Operators

A ⌶ to Birmingham New Street
B ⌶ to Leeds
C ⌶ to York

SUMMARY OF SERVICES

Saturdays

until 5 September

Scotland, The North East, North West England → The South West and South Coast

Route Diagram - See first page of Table 51

		XC	XC	XC	XC	XC	XC	XC	XC	XC	XC	XC	XC	VT	XC	XC	XC	XC	VT	XC	XC
													R								
		1 ◇	1 ◇	1 ◇	1 ◇	1 ◇	1 ◇	1 ◇	1 ◇	1 ◇	1 ◇	1 ◇	1	1 ◇	1 ◇	1 ◇	1 ◇	1 ◇	1 ◇	1	1 ◇
Aberdeen	d																				
Stonehaven	d																				
Montrose	d																				
Arbroath	d																				
Dundee	d																				
Leuchars [3]	d																				
Cupar	d																				
Ladybank	d																				
Markinch	d																				
Kirkcaldy	d																				
Inverkeithing	d																				
Glasgow Central [15]	d																				
Motherwell	d																				
Haymarket	d																				
Edinburgh [10]	d																				
Haymarket	d																				
Lockerbie	d																				
Carlisle [8]	d																				
Penrith North Lakes	d																				
Oxenholme Lake District	d																				
Lancaster [6]	d																		06 58		
Preston [8]	d													06 17					07 17		
Wigan North Western	d													06 28					07 28		
Warrington Bank Quay	d													06 39					07 39		
Manchester Piccadilly [10]	d							05 11				06 00						07 00			07 27
Stockport	d											06 08						07 09			07 35
Wilmslow	d																				
Crewe [10]	d							05 47						07 01					08 01		
Macclesfield	d											06 21						07 25			07 49
Congleton	d																				
Stoke-on-Trent	d							06 07				06 39						07 44			08 07
Stafford	d							06 25				06 58									08 25
Wolverhampton [7]	d							06 41				07 15		07 32				08 18	08 32		08 41
Dunbar	d																				
Berwick-upon-Tweed	d																				
Alnmouth for Alnwick	d																				
Morpeth	d																				
Newcastle [8]	d																				
Chester-le-Street	d																				
Durham	d																				
Darlington [7]	d																				
York [8]	d																				
Leeds [10]	d														06 00		06 15				
Wakefield Westgate [7]	d														06 12		06 29				
Doncaster [7]	d																06 47				
Sheffield [7]	d										06 01				06 50		07 18				
Chesterfield	d										06 26				07 03		07 30				
Nottingham [8]	d									05 57			06 37			06 56				07 35	
Derby [10]	d						06 10			06 36	06 47		07 06		07 25	07 35	07 50			08 06	
Burton-on-Trent	d						06 20			06 48	06 57		07 18		07 36	07 49	08 00			08 18	
Tamworth	d						06 31			07 00	07 08		07 30		07 48	08 01	08 11			08 30	
Birmingham New Street [12]	a						06 50	06 58	⟵	07 24	07 27	07 31	07 50	07 55	08 08	08 24	08 29	08 37	08 55	08 56	08 58
Birmingham New Street [12]	d	05 00	05 42	06 04	06 33	06 42	07 12	07 04	07 12	07 30	07 33	07 42	08 04		08 12	08 30	08 33	08 42			09 04
Cheltenham Spa	a	06 02	06 41			07 23	⟶		07 51	08 10		08 23			08 51	09 10		09 24			
Gloucester [7]	a	06 13	06 54							08 21						09 21					
Bristol Parkway [7]	a					07 56			08 24			08 56			09 25			09 57			
Bristol Temple Meads [10]	a					08 11			08 38			09 13			09 38			10 13			
Newport (South Wales)	a	07 06	07 52							09 05						10 05					
Cardiff Central [7]	a	07 25	08 13							09 25						10 25					
Weston-super-Mare	a																				
Taunton	a					08 42			09 15						10 16			11 00			
Tiverton Parkway	a								09 28						10 29			11 13			
Exeter St Davids [6]	a					09 07			09 43						10 46			11 30			
Dawlish	a																				
Teignmouth	a																				
Newton Abbot	a								10 03						11 08			11 52			
Torquay	a					09 35															
Paignton	a					09 49															
Totnes	a								10 16						11 22						
Plymouth	a								10 48						11 56			12 32			
Liskeard [8]	a																	13 03			
Bodmin Parkway	a																	13 15			
Lostwithiel	a																				
Par	a																				
Newquay	a																	14 42			
St Austell	a																				
Truro	a																				
Redruth	a																				
Camborne	a																				
Hayle	a																				
St Erth	a																				
Penzance	a																				
Birmingham International ✈	d			06 14				07 14					08 14								09 14
Coventry	d			06 25				07 25					08 25								09 25
Leamington Spa [8]	d			06 38	07 00			07 38			08 00		08 38				09 00				09 38
Banbury	a			06 54	07 17			07 54			08 17		08 54				09 17				09 54
Oxford	a			07 14	07 40			08 14			08 40		09 14				09 40				10 14
Reading [7]	a			07 40	08 13			08 40			09 13		09 40				10 13				10 40
Guildford	a																				
Basingstoke	a			08 08				09 08					10 08								11 08
Winchester	a			08 24				09 24					10 24								11 24
Southampton Airport Parkway ✈	a			08 32				09 32					10 32								11 32
Southampton Central	a			08 41				09 40					10 40								11 41
Brockenhurst [3]	a			08 56				09 57					10 57								11 57
Bournemouth	a			09 15				10 15					11 15								12 15

For general notes see front of timetable
For details of catering facilities see Directory of Train Operators

Scotland, The North East, North West England → The South West and South Coast

until 5 September

Route Diagram - See first page of Table 51

Station		XC	XC	XC	XC	VT	XC	XC	XC	XC	XC	XC	VT	XC	XC	XC	XC	XC	XC	VT	XC
		1 ◇	1 ◇	1 ◇	1 ◇	1 ◇	1	1 ◇	1 ◇	1 ◇	1 ◇	1 ◇	1 ◇	1	1 ◇	1 ◇	1 ◇	1 ◇	1 ◇	1 ◇	1
Aberdeen	d																				
Stonehaven	d																				
Montrose	d																				
Arbroath	d																				
Dundee	d																				
Leuchars 3	d																				
Cupar	d																				
Ladybank	d																				
Markinch	d																				
Kirkcaldy	d																				
Inverkeithing	d																				
Glasgow Central 15	d					05 50														08 00	
Motherwell	d					06u05															
Haymarket	d																				
Edinburgh 10	d												06 52			06 12		06 55			
Haymarket	d												06u56								
Lockerbie	d																				
Carlisle 8	d					07 03							08 07							09 09	
Penrith North Lakes	d					07 18							08 22								
Oxenholme Lake District	d					07 42															
Lancaster 6	d					07 57							08 57							09 57	
Preston 8	d					08 17							09 17							10 17	
Wigan North Western	d					08 28							09 28							10 28	
Warrington Bank Quay	d					08 39							09 39							10 39	
Manchester Piccadilly 10	d				08 00			08 27				09 07			09 27				10 07		
Stockport	d				08 09			08 35							09 35						
Wilmslow	d																				
Crewe 10	d					09 01							10 01							11 01	
Macclesfield	d				08 25			08 49							09 49						
Congleton	d																				
Stoke-on-Trent	d				08 45			09 07				09 44			10 07				10 44		
Stafford	d							09 25							10 25						
Wolverhampton 7	d				09 18	09 32		09 41				10 15	10 32		10 41				11 15	11 32	
Dunbar	d																				
Berwick-upon-Tweed	d															06 51		07 35			
Alnmouth for Alnwick	d															07 11		07 55			
Morpeth	d																	08 09			
Newcastle 8	d			06 20					06 42		07 25					07 44		08 30			
Chester-le-Street	d			06 32																	
Durham	d			06 39					06 56		07 38					07 56		08 42			
Darlington 7	d			06 56					07 13		07 55					08 13		08 59			
York 8	d	06 09		07 25					07 44		08 27					08 44		09 28			
Leeds 10	d	07 05							08 11							09 11					
Wakefield Westgate 7	d	07 18							08 23							09 23					
Doncaster 7	d			07 52							08 53							09 53			
Sheffield 7	d	07 54		08 20					08 54		09 23					09 54		10 23			
Chesterfield	d	08 06		08 32					09 06							10 06					
Nottingham 8	d		08 08				08 35			09 08				09 20			10 08				10 20
Derby 10	d	08 28	08 36	08 53			09 06		09 28	09 36	09 53			09 57		10 28	10 36	10 53			10 57
Burton-on-Trent	d	08 38	08 48				09 18		09 38	09 48				10 18			10 48				11 18
Tamworth	d	08 48	09 00				09 30			10 00				10 30		10 48	11 00				11 30
Birmingham New Street 12	a	09 07	09 24	09 27	09 38	09 55	09 56	09 58	10 06	10 24	10 27	10 31	10 55	10 56	10 58	11 07	11 24	11 27	11 31	11 55	11 56
Birmingham New Street 12	d	09 12	09 30	09 33	09 42			10 04	10 12	10 30	10 33	10 42			11 04	11 12	11 30	11 33	11 42		
Cheltenham Spa	a	09 51	10 10		10 24				10 51	11 10		11 23				11 51	12 10		12 23		
Gloucester 7	a		10 21							11 21							12 21				
Bristol Parkway 7	a	10 26			10 57				11 25			11 56				12 29			12 56		
Bristol Temple Meads 10	a	10 41			11 13				11 38			12 13				12 41			13 13		
Newport (South Wales)	a		11 05							12 05							13 06				
Cardiff Central 7	a		11 25							12 25							13 25				
Weston-super-Mare	a				11 31																
Taunton	a	11 15			12 01				12 15							13 15					
Tiverton Parkway	a	11 28			12 14											13 28					
Exeter St Davids 6	a	11 43			12 31				12 42							13 43					
Dawlish	a				12 46																
Teignmouth	a				12 52																
Newton Abbot	a	12 03			13 00				13 03							14 03					
Torquay	a				13 12																
Paignton	a				13 27																
Totnes	a	12 16							13 19							14 16					
Plymouth	a	12 48							13 48							14 48					
Liskeard 6	a								14 12												
Bodmin Parkway	a								14 24												
Lostwithiel	a																				
Par	a								14 35												
Newquay	a																				
St Austell	a								14 43												
Truro	a								15 00												
Redruth	a								15 13												
Camborne	a								15 20												
Hayle	a																				
St Erth	a								15 31												
Penzance	a								15 50												
Birmingham International	d							10 14							11 14						
Coventry	d							10 25							11 25						
Leamington Spa 8	d			10 00				10 38			11 00				11 38			12 00			
Banbury	a			10 17				10 54			11 17				11 54			12 17			
Oxford	a			10 40				11 14			11 40				12 14			12 40			
Reading 7	a			11 13				11 40			12 13				12 40			13 13			
Guildford	a																				
Basingstoke	a							12 08							13 08						
Winchester	a							12 24							13 24						
Southampton Airport Parkway	a							12 32							13 32						
Southampton Central	a							12 41							13 41						
Brockenhurst 3	a							12 57							13 57						
Bournemouth	a							13 15							14 15						

For general notes see front of timetable
For details of catering facilities see Directory of Train Operators

until 5 September

Scotland, The North East, North West England → The South West and South Coast

Route Diagram - See first page of Table 51

		XC 1◇	XC 1◇	XC 1◇	XC 1◇	XC 1◇	VT 1◇	XC 1	XC 1◇	XC 1◇	XC 1◇	XC 1◇	XC 1◇	VT 1◇	XC 1	XC 1◇	XC 1◇	XC 1◇	XC 1◇	XC 1◇	VT 1◇
Aberdeen	d																				
Stonehaven	d																				
Montrose	d																				
Arbroath	d																				
Dundee	d																07 35				
Leuchars [3]	d																07 48				
Cupar	d																07 55				
Ladybank	d																08 03				
Markinch	d																08 11				
Kirkcaldy	d																08 20				
Inverkeithing	d																08 35				
Glasgow Central [15]	d									07 00				10 00							
Motherwell	d																				
Haymarket	d									07 54							08 54				
Edinburgh [10]	d		07 05				08 52			08 05							09 05				10 52
Haymarket	d						08u57														10u57
Lockerbie	d																				
Carlisle [8]	d						10 07							11 09							12 07
Penrith North Lakes	d													11 24							
Oxenholme Lake District	d						10 42														12 43
Lancaster [6]	d						10 57														12 57
Preston [8]	d						11 17							12 17							13 17
Wigan North Western	d						11 28							12 28							13 28
Warrington Bank Quay	d						11 39							12 39							13 39
Manchester Piccadilly [10]	d	10 27				11 07			11 27				12 07			12 27				13 07	
Stockport	d	10 35							11 35							12 35					
Wilmslow	d																				
Crewe [10]	d						12 01							13 01							14 01
Macclesfield	d	10 49							11 49							12 49					
Congleton	d																				
Stoke-on-Trent	d	11 07				11 44			12 07				12 44			13 07				13 44	
Stafford	d	11 25							12 25							13 25					
Wolverhampton [7]	d	11 41				12 15	12 32		12 41				13 15	13 32		13 41				14 15	14 32
Dunbar	d		07 25														09 25				
Berwick-upon-Tweed	d		07 48							08 47							09 48				
Alnmouth for Alnwick	d									09 09											
Morpeth	d																				
Newcastle [8]	d		08 40		09 25					09 40		10 25					10 44		11 20		
Chester-le-Street	d		08 49																		
Durham	d		08 56		09 37					09 55		10 38					10 56		11 34		
Darlington [7]	d		09 13		09 56					10 12		10 56					11 13		11 56		
York [8]	d		09 44		10 25					10 44		11 27					11 44		12 25		
Leeds [10]	d		10 11							11 11							12 11				
Wakefield Westgate [7]	d		10 23							11 23							12 23				
Doncaster [7]	d				10 53							11 55							12 52		
Sheffield [7]	d		10 54		11 23					11 54		12 23					12 54		13 23		
Chesterfield	d		11 06							12 06							13 06				
Nottingham [8]	d			11 08				11 20			12 08				12 20			13 08			
Derby [10]	d		11 28	11 36	11 53			11 57		12 28	12 36	12 53			12 57		13 28	13 36	13 53		
Burton-on-Trent	d		11 38	11 48				12 18			12 48				13 18		13 38	13 48			
Tamworth	d			12 00				12 30		12 48	13 00				13 30			14 00			
Birmingham New Street [12]	a	11 58	12 07	12 24	12 27	12 31	12 55	12 56	12 58	13 09	13 24	13 27	13 31	13 55	13 56	13 58	14 07	14 24	14 27	14 31	14 55
Birmingham New Street [12]	d	12 04	12 12	12 30	12 33	12 42			13 04	13 12	13 30	13 33	13 42			14 04	14 12	14 30	14 33	14 42	
Cheltenham Spa	a		12 51	13 10		13 25				13 51	14 10		14 23				14 51	15 10		15 23	
Gloucester [7]	a			13 21							14 21							15 21			
Bristol Parkway [7]	a		13 24			13 58				14 26			14 56				15 24			15 56	
Bristol Temple Meads [10]	a		13 38			14 13				14 41			15 13				15 41			16 13	
Newport (South Wales)	a			14 05							15 06							16 05			
Cardiff Central [7]	a			14 25							15 25							16 25			
Weston-super-Mare	a																				
Taunton	a		14 15							15 16			15 44				16 15				
Tiverton Parkway	a		14 28										15 56				16 28				
Exeter St Davids [6]	a		14 43							15 43			16 12				16 43				
Dawlish	a																				
Teignmouth	a																				
Newton Abbot	a		15 03							16 04			16 33				17 03				
Torquay	a												16 50								
Paignton	a												17 04								
Totnes	a		15 16							16 19							17 16				
Plymouth	a		15 48							16 47							17 48				
Liskeard [6]	a									17 15											
Bodmin Parkway	a									17 27											
Lostwithiel	a																				
Par	a																				
Newquay	a									18 49											
St Austell	a																				
Truro	a																				
Redruth	a																				
Camborne	a																				
Hayle	a																				
St Erth	a																				
Penzance	a																				
Birmingham International ✈	d	12 14							13 14							14 14					
Coventry	d	12 25							13 25							14 25					
Leamington Spa [8]	d	12 38			13 00				13 38			14 00				14 38			15 00		
Banbury	a	12 54			13 17				13 54			14 17				14 54			15 17		
Oxford	a	13 14			13 40				14 14			14 40				15 14			15 40		
Reading [7]	a	13 40			14 13				14 40			15 13				15 40			16 13		
Guildford	a																				
Basingstoke	a	14 08							15 08							16 08					
Winchester	a	14 24							15 24							16 24					
Southampton Airport Parkwy ✈	a	14 33							15 32							16 32					
Southampton Central	a	14 41							15 41							16 41					
Brockenhurst [3]	a	14 57							15 57							16 57					
Bournemouth	a	15 15							16 15							17 15					

For general notes see front of timetable
For details of catering facilities see Directory of Train Operators

Scotland, The North East, North West England → The South West and South Coast

until 5 September

Route Diagram - See first page of Table 51

		XC	XC	XC	XC	XC	XC	VT	XC	XC	XC	XC	XC	XC	VT	XC	XC	XC	XC	XC	XC	VT
		1	1◇	1◇	1◇	1◇	1◇	1◇	1	1◇	1◇	1◇	1◇	1◇	1◇	1	1◇	1◇	1◇	1◇	1◇	1◇
Aberdeen	d										08 20											
Stonehaven	d										08 38											
Montrose	d										08 59											
Arbroath	d										09 15											
Dundee	d										09 33											
Leuchars 3	d										09 47											
Cupar	d										09 54											
Ladybank	d										10 01											
Markinch	d										10 09											
Kirkcaldy	d										10 17											
Inverkeithing	d										10 32											
Glasgow Central 15	d			09 00				12 00														14 00
Motherwell	d																					
Haymarket	d			09 55							10 52											
Edinburgh 10	d			10 05							11 05				12 52			12 05				
Haymarket	d														12u57							
Lockerbie	d																					
Carlisle 8	d							13 09							14 07							15 11
Penrith North Lakes	d														14 22							
Oxenholme Lake District	d																					15 46
Lancaster 6	d							13 58							14 57							
Preston 8	d							14 17							15 17							16 17
Wigan North Western	d							14 28							15 28							16 28
Warrington Bank Quay	d							14 39							15 39							16 39
Manchester Piccadilly 10	d		13 27				14 07			14 27				15 07			15 27				16 07	
Stockport	d		13 35							14 35							15 35					
Wilmslow	d																					
Crewe 10	d							15 01							16 01							17 01
Macclesfield	d		13 49							14 49							15 49					
Congleton	d																					
Stoke-on-Trent	d		14 07				14 44			15 07				15 44			16 07				16 44	
Stafford	d		14 25							15 25							16 25					
Wolverhampton 7	d		14 41				15 15	15 32		15 41				16 15	16 32		16 41				17 15	17 32
Dunbar	d										11 25											
Berwick-upon-Tweed	d										11 48											
Alnmouth for Alnwick	d			11 04														13 05				
Morpeth	d			11 19																		
Newcastle 8	d			11 40		12 22					12 44		13 27					13 44		14 22		
Chester-le-Street	d					12 31																
Durham	d			11 55		12 38					12 56		13 39					13 56		14 34		
Darlington 7	d			12 12		12 55					13 13		13 58					14 13		14 52		
York 8	d			12 44		13 27					13 44		14 27					14 44		15 26		
Leeds 10	d			13 11							14 11							15 11				
Wakefield Westgate 7	d			13 23							14 23							15 23				
Doncaster 7	d					13 54							14 56							15 55		
Sheffield 7	d			13 54		14 23					14 54		15 23					15 54		16 23		
Chesterfield	d			14 06							15 06							16 06				
Nottingham 8	d	13 20			14 08				14 20			15 08				15 20			16 08			
Derby 10	d	13 57		14 28	14 36	14 53			14 57		15 28	15 36	15 53			15 57		16 28	16 36	16 53		
Burton-on-Trent	d	14 18			14 48				15 18		15 38	15 48				16 18			16 48			
Tamworth	d	14 30		14 48	15 00				15 30			16 00				16 30		16 48	17 00			
Birmingham New Street 12	a	14 56	14 58	15 08	15 24	15 27	15 31	15 55	15 56	15 58	16 07	16 24	16 27	16 31	16 55	16 56	16 58	17 07	17 24	17 27	17 31	17 55
Birmingham New Street 12	d		15 04	15 12	15 30	15 33	15 42			16 04	16 12	16 30	16 33	16 42			17 04	17 12	17 30	17 33	17 42	
Cheltenham Spa	a			15 51	16 10		16 23				16 51	17 10		17 23				17 51	18 17		18 23	
Gloucester 7	a				16 21							17 21							18 28		18 35	
Bristol Parkway 7	a			16 26			16 56				17 24			17 56				18 26			19 08	
Bristol Temple Meads 10	a			16 41			17 13				17 38			18 13				18 41			19 27	
Newport (South Wales)	a				17 05							18 05							19 11			
Cardiff Central 7	a				17 25							18 25							19 32			
Weston-super-Mare	a																					
Taunton	a			17 17							18 15							19 15			20 08	
Tiverton Parkway	a			17 30							18 28							19 28			20 20	
Exeter St Davids 6	a			17 47							18 43							19 43			20 36	
Dawlish	a																				20 48	
Teignmouth	a																				20 53	
Newton Abbot	a			18 09							19 03							20 03			21 01	
Torquay	a																				21 13	
Paignton	a																				21 27	
Totnes	a			18 23							19 16							20 16				
Plymouth	a			18 52							19 48							20 48				
Liskeard 6	a			19 23							20 10							21 24				
Bodmin Parkway	a			19 35							20 22							21 36				
Lostwithiel	a										20 28											
Par	a			19 46							20 35							21 47				
Newquay	a																					
St Austell	a			19 54							20 41							21 53				
Truro	a			20 12							20 59							22 11				
Redruth	a			20 24							21 10							22 29				
Camborne	a			20 31							21 17							22 35				
Hayle	a										21 25											
St Erth	a			20 41							21 29							22 45				
Penzance	a			20 59							21 46							23 02				
Birmingham International ✈	d		15 14							16 14							17 14					
Coventry	d		15 25							16 25							17 25					
Leamington Spa 8	d		15 38			16 00				16 38			17 00				17 38			18 00		
Banbury	a		15 54			16 17				16 54			17 17				17 54			18 17		
Oxford	a		16 14			16 40				17 14			17 40				18 14			18 40		
Reading 7	a		16 40			17 13				17 40			18 13				18 40			19 13		
Guildford	a																					
Basingstoke	a		17 08							18 08							19 08					
Winchester	a		17 24							18 24							19 24					
Southampton Airport Parkwy ✈	a		17 32							18 32							19 32					
Southampton Central	a		17 41							18 40							19 41					
Brockenhurst 3	a		17 57							18 57							19 57					
Bournemouth	a		18 15							19 15							20 15					

For general notes see front of timetable
For details of catering facilities see Directory of Train Operators

until 5 September

Scotland, The North East, North West England → The South West and South Coast

Route Diagram - See first page of Table 51

		XC 1	XC 1◇	XC 1◇	XC 1◇	XC 1◇	XC 1◇	VT 1◇	XC 1	XC 1◇	XC 1◇	XC 1◇	XC 1◇	XC 1◇	VT 1◇	XC 1	XC 1◇	XC 1◇	XC 1◇	XC 1◇	XC 1◇
Aberdeen	d																				
Stonehaven	d																				
Montrose	d																				
Arbroath	d																				
Dundee	d																				
Leuchars 3	d																				
Cupar	d																				
Ladybank	d																				
Markinch	d																				
Kirkcaldy	d																				
Inverkeithing	d																				
Glasgow Central 15	d														16 00						
Motherwell	d																				
Haymarket	d																				
Edinburgh 10	d			13 05				14 52			14 05							15 05			
Haymarket	d							14u57													
Lockerbie	d																				
Carlisle 8	d							16 07							17 09						
Penrith North Lakes	d							16 22													
Oxenholme Lake District	d														17 44						
Lancaster 6	d							16 57													
Preston 8	d							17 17							18 17						
Wigan North Western	d							17 28							18 28						
Warrington Bank Quay	d							17 39							18 39						
Manchester Piccadilly 10	d		16 27				17 06			17 27				18 05			18 27				19 07
Stockport	d		16 35							17 35							18 35				19 16
Wilmslow	d																				
Crewe 10	d							18 01							19 01						
Macclesfield	d		16 49				17 27							18 25							
Congleton	d									17 54							18 54				
Stoke-on-Trent	d		17 07				17 44			18 07				18 44			19 07				19 44
Stafford	d		17 25							18 25							19 25				
Wolverhampton 7	d		17 41				18 15	18 32		18 41				19 15	19 32		19 41				20 15
Dunbar	d			13 25														15 25			
Berwick-upon-Tweed	d			13 48														15 48			
Alnmouth for Alnwick	d										15 05										
Morpeth	d																				
Newcastle 8	d			14 44		15 25					15 44		16 22					16 44		17 22	
Chester-le-Street	d												16 31							17 31	
Durham	d			14 56		15 38					15 56		16 38					16 56		17 38	
Darlington 7	d			15 13		15 56					16 13		16 56					17 13		17 55	
York 8	d			15 44		16 25					16 44		17 25					17 44		18 25	
Leeds 10	d			16 11							17 11							18 11			
Wakefield Westgate 7	d			16 23							17 23							18 23			
Doncaster 7	d					16 53							17 55							18 51	
Sheffield 7	d			16 54		17 23					17 54		18 23					18 54		19 23	
Chesterfield	d			17 06							18 06							19 06			
Nottingham 8	d	16 20			17 08				17 20			18 08				18 20			19 08		
Derby 10	d	16 57		17 28	17 36	17 53			17 57		18 28	18 36	18 53			18 57		19 28	19 36	19 53	
Burton-on-Trent	d	17 18		17 38	17 48				18 18			18 48				19 18		19 38	19 48		
Tamworth	d	17 30			18 00				18 30		18 48	19 00				19 30			20 00		
Birmingham New Street 12	a	17 56	17 58	18 07	18 24	18 27	18 31	18 55	18 57	18 58	19 07	19 24	19 27	19 31	19 55	19 56	19 58	20 07	20 24	20 27	20 31
Birmingham New Street 12	d		18 04	18 12	18 30	18 33	18 42			19 04	19 12	19 30	19 33	19 42			20 04	20 12	20 30	20 33	20 42
Cheltenham Spa	a			18 51	19 10		19 23				19 51	20 10		20 23				20 51	21 10		21 23
Gloucester 7	a				19 21							20 21							21 21		
Bristol Parkway 7	a			19 26			19 56				20 26			20 56				21 23			21 57
Bristol Temple Meads 10	a			19 41			20 13				20 41			21 13				21 35			22 13
Newport (South Wales)	a				20 05		20 54					21 09							22 14		
Cardiff Central 7	a				20 25		21 16					21 32							22 39		
Weston-super-Mare	a																				
Taunton	a			20 15							21 16							22 16			
Tiverton Parkway	a			20 28							21 28							22 28			
Exeter St Davids 6	a			20 43							21 45							22 44			
Dawlish	a																				
Teignmouth	a																				
Newton Abbot	a			21 03							22 06							23 11			
Torquay	a																				
Paignton	a																				
Totnes	a			21 16							22 22							23 27			
Plymouth	a			21 48							22 55							23 59			
Liskeard 6	a																				
Bodmin Parkway	a																				
Lostwithiel	a																				
Par	a																				
Newquay	a																				
St Austell	a																				
Truro	a																				
Redruth	a																				
Camborne	a																				
Hayle	a																				
St Erth	a																				
Penzance	a																				
Birmingham International ✈	d		18 14							19 14							20 14				
Coventry	d		18 25							19 25							20 25				
Leamington Spa 8	d		18 38			19 00				19 38			20 00				20 38			21 00	
Banbury	a		18 54			19 17				19 54			20 17				20 54			21 17	
Oxford	a		19 14			19 40				20 14			20 40				21 14			21 40	
Reading 7	a		19 40			20 13				20 40			21 13				21 40			22 13	
Guildford	a																			22 59	
Basingstoke	a		20 08							21 08							22 08				
Winchester	a		20 24							21 24							22 24				
Southampton Airport Parkwy ✈	a		20 32							21 32							22 32				
Southampton Central	a		20 41							21 41							22 41				
Brockenhurst 3	a		20 57							21 57							22 57				
Bournemouth	a		21 15							22 15							23 21				

For general notes see front of timetable
For details of catering facilities see Directory of Train Operators

Scotland, The North East, North West England → The South West and South Coast

until 5 September

Route Diagram - See first page of Table 51

	VT	XC	XC	XC	XC		XC	VT	XC	XC	XC	XC	VT		XC	VT	XC	XC	XC	XC
	1 ◇	1	1 ◇	1 ◇	1 ◇		1 ◇	1 ◇	1	1 ◇	1 ◇	1 ◇	1 ◇		1 ◇	1 ◇	1	1 ◇	1 ◇	1 ◇
																			A	B
Aberdeen d																				
Stonehaven d																				
Montrose d																				
Arbroath d																				
Dundee d																				
Leuchars 3 d																				
Cupar d																				
Ladybank d																				
Markinch d																				
Kirkcaldy d																				
Inverkeithing d																				
Glasgow Central 15 d								18 00					18 40							
Motherwell d																				
Haymarket d																				
Edinburgh 10 d	16 52			16 05							17 08					18 52		18 05		
Haymarket d	16u57															18u57				
Lockerbie d																				
Carlisle 8 d	18 07							19 09					19 49			20 07				
Penrith North Lakes d													20 03			20 22				
Oxenholme Lake District d	18 42												20 26			20 45				
Lancaster 6 d	18 57							19 56					20 41			21 00				
Preston 8 d	19 17							20 17					21 01			21 20				
Wigan North Western d	19 28							20 28					21 12			21 31				
Warrington Bank Quay d	19 39							20 39					21 23			21 42				
Manchester Piccadilly 10 d			19 27				20 07			20 27		21 07							21 27	21 27
Stockport d			19 35				20 16			20 35									21 35	21 35
Wilmslow d																			21 45	
Crewe 10 d	20 01							21 01					21 44			22 04				
Macclesfield d			19 49							20 49										21 49
Congleton d																				
Stoke-on-Trent d			20 07				20 44			21 07		21 44								22 07
Stafford d			20 25							21 25			22 09			22 29			22 33	22 33
Wolverhampton 7 d	20 32		20 41				21 15	21 33		21 41		22 15	22 24			22 42			22 52	22 52
Dunbar d											17 25							18 25		
Berwick-upon-Tweed d											17 48							18 48		
Alnmouth for Alnwick d				17 05														19 08		
Morpeth d				17 20																
Newcastle 8 d				17 44	18 22						18 44				19 25			19 43		
Chester-le-Street d					18 31															
Durham d				17 56	18 38						18 56				19 37			19 56		
Darlington 7 d				18 13	18 56						19 13				19 54			20 13		
York 8 d				18 44	19 25						19 44				20 23			20 44		
Leeds 10 d				19 11							20 11							21 11		
Wakefield Westgate 7 d				19 23							20 23							21 23		
Doncaster 7 d					19 53															
Sheffield 7 d				19 54	20 23						20 54				21 23			21 54		
Chesterfield d				20 06							21 06				21 35			22 06		
Nottingham 8 d		19 20							20 20								21 37			
Derby 10 d		19 57		20 28	20 53				20 57		21 28				21 57		22 15	22 26		
Burton-on-Trent d		20 18							21 18		21 38				22 07		22 26	22 37		
Tamworth d		20 30		20 48					21 30		21 49				22 18		22 38	22 47		
Birmingham New Street 12 a	20 56	20 56	20 58	21 07	21 31		21 36	21 55	22 00	22 03	22 12	22 37	22 47		22 48	23 01	23 05	23 11	23 22	23 22
Birmingham New Street 12 d			21 04	21 12																
Cheltenham Spa a				21 51																
Gloucester 7 a																				
Bristol Parkway 7 a				22 23																
Bristol Temple Meads 10 a				22 41																
Newport (South Wales) a																				
Cardiff Central 7 a																				
Weston-super-Mare a																				
Taunton a																				
Tiverton Parkway a																				
Exeter St Davids 6 a																				
Dawlish a																				
Teignmouth a																				
Newton Abbot a																				
Torquay a																				
Paignton a																				
Totnes a																				
Plymouth a																				
Liskeard 6 a																				
Bodmin Parkway a																				
Lostwithiel a																				
Par a																				
Newquay a																				
St Austell a																				
Truro a																				
Redruth a																				
Camborne a																				
Hayle a																				
St Erth a																				
Penzance a																				
Birmingham International d			21 14																	
Coventry d			21 25																	
Leamington Spa 8 d			21 38																	
Banbury a			21 54																	
Oxford a			22 14																	
Reading 7 a			22 40																	
Guildford a																				
Basingstoke a			23 11																	
Winchester a			23 27																	
Southampton Airport Parkway a			23 35																	
Southampton Central a			23 48																	
Brockenhurst 3 a																				
Bournemouth a																				

For general notes see front of timetable
For details of catering facilities see Directory of Train Operators

A Until 11 July
B From 18 July

Scotland, The North East, North West England → The South West and South Coast

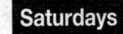

from 12 September

Route Diagram - See first page of Table 51

		XC	XC	XC	XC	XC		XC	XC	XC		XC	XC	VT	XC	XC	XC	XC	XC	VT		XC	XC	XC
		1 ◇	1 ◇	1 ◇	1 ◇	1 ◇		1 ◇	1 ◇	1 ◇		1 ◇	1 ◇	1 ◇	R 1	1 ◇	1 ◇	1 ◇	1 ◇	1 ◇		1	1 ◇	1 ◇
Aberdeen	d																							
Stonehaven	d																							
Montrose	d																							
Arbroath	d																							
Dundee	d																							
Leuchars 8	d																							
Cupar	d																							
Ladybank	d																							
Markinch	d																							
Kirkcaldy	d																							
Inverkeithing	d																							
Glasgow Central 15	d																							
Motherwell	d																							
Haymarket	d																							
Edinburgh 10	d																							
Haymarket	d																							
Lockerbie	d																							
Carlisle 8	d																							
Penrith North Lakes	d																							
Oxenholme Lake District	d																							
Lancaster 6	d																			06 58				
Preston 8	d													06 17						07 17				
Wigan North Western	d													06 28						07 28				
Warrington Bank Quay	d													06 39						07 39				
Manchester Piccadilly 10	d							05 11					06 00						07 07				07 27	
Stockport	d												06 08										07 35	
Wilmslow	d																							
Crewe 10	d							05 47						07 01						08 01				
Macclesfield	d												06 21										07 49	
Congleton	d													07 32										
Stoke-on-Trent	d							06 07					06 39						07 44				08 07	
Stafford	d							06 25					06 58										08 25	
Wolverhampton 7	d							06 41					07 15						08 15	08 32			08 41	
Dunbar	d																							
Berwick-upon-Tweed	d																							
Alnmouth for Alnwick	d																							
Morpeth	d																							
Newcastle 8	d																							
Chester-le-Street	d																							
Durham	d																							
Darlington 7	d																							
York 8	d																							06 09
Leeds 10	d															06 00		06 15						07 05
Wakefield Westgate 7	d															06 12		06 29						07 18
Doncaster 7	d																	06 47						
Sheffield 7	d											06 01				06 50		07 18						07 54
Chesterfield	d											06 26				07 03		07 30						08 06
Nottingham 8	d									05 57					06 37		06 56					07 37		
Derby 10	d									06 36		06 47			07 06	07 25	07 36	07 50				08 06		08 28
Burton-on-Trent	d									06 48		06 57			07 18	07 36	07 49	08 00				08 18		08 38
Tamworth	d									07 00		07 08			07 30	07 48	08 01	08 11				08 30		08 49
Birmingham New Street 12	a							06 58	←	07 24		07 27	07 31	07 55	07 56	08 08	08 24	08 29	08 31	08 55		08 56	08 58	09 07
Birmingham New Street 12	d	05 00	05 42	06 04	06 33	06 42		07 04	07 12	07 30		07 33	07 42		08 04	08 12	08 30	08 33	08 42				09 04	09 12
Cheltenham Spa	a	06 02	06 41			07 23			07 51	08 10			08 23			08 51	09 10		09 23					09 51
Gloucester 7	a	06 13	06 54							08 21							09 21							
Bristol Parkway 7	a					07 56			08 24				08 56			09 25			09 56					10 26
Bristol Temple Meads 10	a					08 11			08 38				09 13			09 38			10 13					10 41
Newport (South Wales)	a	07 06	07 52							09 06							10 05							
Cardiff Central 7	a	07 25	08 13							09 25							10 25							
Weston-super-Mare	a																							
Taunton	a					08 42			09 15							10 16								11 15
Tiverton Parkway	a								09 28							10 29								11 28
Exeter St Davids 6	a					09 07			09 43							10 46								11 43
Dawlish	a																							
Teignmouth	a																							
Newton Abbot	a								10 03							11 07								12 03
Torquay	a					09 37																		
Paignton	a					09 50																		
Totnes	a								10 16							11 21								12 16
Plymouth	a								10 48							11 55								12 48
Liskeard 6	a																							
Bodmin Parkway	a																							
Lostwithiel	a																							
Par	a																							
Newquay	a																							
St Austell	a																							
Truro	a																							
Redruth	a																							
Camborne	a																							
Hayle	a																							
St Erth	a																							
Penzance	a																							
Birmingham International ✈	d			06 14				07 14							08 14								09 14	
Coventry	d			06 25				07 25							08 25								09 25	
Leamington Spa 8	d			06 38	07 00			07 38				08 00			08 38			09 00					09 38	
Banbury	a			06 54	07 17			07 54				08 17			08 54			09 17					09 54	
Oxford	a			07 14	07 40			08 14				08 40			09 14			09 40					10 14	
Reading 7	a			07 40	08 13			08 40				09 13			09 40			10 13					10 40	
Guildford	a																							
Basingstoke	a			08 08				09 08							10 08								11 08	
Winchester	a			08 24				09 24							10 24								11 24	
Southampton Airport Parkwy ✈	a			08 32				09 32							10 32								11 32	
Southampton Central	a			08 41				09 40							10 40								11 41	
Brockenhurst 3	a			08 56				09 57							10 57								11 57	
Bournemouth	a			09 15				10 15							11 15								12 15	

For general notes see front of timetable
For details of catering facilities see
Directory of Train Operators

Scotland, The North East, North West England → The South West and South Coast

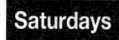

from 12 September

Route Diagram - See first page of Table 51

		XC 1◊	XC 1◊	XC 1◊	VT 1◊	XC 1	XC 1◊	XC 1◊	XC 1◊		XC 1◊	XC 1◊	VT 1◊	XC 1	XC 1◊	XC 1◊	XC 1◊	XC 1◊	XC 1◊		VT 1◊	XC 1	XC 1◊	XC 1◊
Aberdeen	d																							
Stonehaven	d																							
Montrose	d																							
Arbroath	d																							
Dundee	d																							
Leuchars 3	d																							
Cupar	d																							
Ladybank	d																							
Markinch	d																							
Kirkcaldy	d																							
Inverkeithing	d																							
Glasgow Central 15	d				05 50																08 00			
Motherwell	d				06u05																			
Haymarket	d																							
Edinburgh 10	d												06 52			06 12		06 55						07 05
Haymarket	d												06u56											
Lockerbie	d																							
Carlisle 8	d				07 03								08 07								09 09			
Penrith North Lakes	d				07 18								08 22											
Oxenholme Lake District	d				07 42																			
Lancaster 6	d				07 57								08 57								09 57			
Preston 8	d				08 17								09 17								10 17			
Wigan North Western	d				08 28								09 28								10 28			
Warrington Bank Quay	d				08 39								09 39								10 39			
Manchester Piccadilly 10	d			08 07			08 27					09 07			09 27				10 07				10 27	
Stockport	d						08 35								09 35								10 35	
Wilmslow	d																							
Crewe 10	d				09 01								10 01								11 01			
Macclesfield	d						08 49								09 49								10 49	
Congleton	d																							
Stoke-on-Trent	d			08 44			09 07					09 44			10 07				10 44				11 07	
Stafford	d						09 25								10 25								11 25	
Wolverhampton 7	d			09 15	09 32		09 41					10 15	10 32		10 41				11 15		11 32		11 41	
Dunbar	d																							07 25
Berwick-upon-Tweed	d															06 51		07 35						07 48
Alnmouth for Alnwick	d															07 11		07 55						
Morpeth	d																	08 09						
Newcastle 8	d		06 20					06 42			07 25					07 44		08 30						08 40
Chester-le-Street	d		06 32																					08 49
Durham	d		06 39					06 56			07 38					07 56		08 42						08 56
Darlington 7	d		06 56					07 13			07 55					08 13		08 59						09 13
York 8	d		07 25					07 44			08 27					08 44		09 28						09 44
Leeds 10	d							08 11								09 11								10 11
Wakefield Westgate 7	d							08 23								09 23								10 23
Doncaster 7	d		07 52								08 53							09 53						
Sheffield 7	d		08 20					08 54			09 23					09 54		10 23						10 54
Chesterfield	d		08 32					09 06								10 06								11 06
Nottingham 8	d	08 08				08 37			09 08					09 37			10 08					10 37		
Derby 10	d	08 36	08 53			09 06		09 28	09 36		09 53			10 06		10 28	10 36	10 53				11 06		11 28
Burton-on-Trent	d	08 48				09 18		09 38	09 48					10 18			10 48					11 18		11 38
Tamworth	d	09 00				09 30			10 00					10 30		10 48	11 00					11 30		
Birmingham New Street 12	a	09 24	09 27	09 31	09 55	09 56	09 58	10 07	10 24		10 27	10 31	10 55	10 56	10 58	11 07	11 24	11 27	11 31		11 55	11 56	11 58	12 07
Birmingham New Street 12	d	09 30	09 33	09 42			10 04	10 12	10 30		10 33	10 42			11 04	11 12	11 30	11 33	11 42				12 04	12 12
Cheltenham Spa	a	10 10		10 23				10 51	11 10			11 23				11 51	12 10		12 23					12 51
Gloucester 7	a	10 21							11 21								12 21							
Bristol Parkway 7	a			10 56				11 24				11 56				12 26			12 56					13 24
Bristol Temple Meads 10	a			11 13				11 38				12 13				12 41			13 13					13 38
Newport (South Wales)	a	11 05							12 05								13 06							
Cardiff Central 7	a	11 25							12 25								13 25							
Weston-super-Mare	a			11 31																				
Taunton	a			12 00				12 15								13 15								14 15
Tiverton Parkway	a			12 13				12 28								13 28								14 28
Exeter St Davids 6	a			12 28				12 43								13 43								14 43
Dawlish	a			12 41																				
Teignmouth	a			12 46																				
Newton Abbot	a			12 54				13 03								14 03								15 03
Torquay	a			13 05																				
Paignton	a			13 16																				
Totnes	a							13 16								14 16								15 16
Plymouth	a							13 48								14 48								15 48
Liskeard 6	a																							
Bodmin Parkway	a																							
Lostwithiel	a																							
Par	a																							
Newquay	a																							
St Austell	a																							
Truro	a																							
Redruth	a																							
Camborne	a																							
Hayle	a																							
St Erth	a																							
Penzance	a																							
Birmingham International ✈	d						10 14								11 14								12 14	
Coventry	d						10 25								11 25								12 25	
Leamington Spa 8	d		10 00				10 38				11 00				11 38			12 00					12 38	
Banbury	a		10 17				10 54				11 17				11 54			12 17					12 54	
Oxford	a		10 40				11 14				11 40				12 14			12 40					13 14	
Reading 7	a		11 13				11 40				12 13				12 40			13 13					13 40	
Guildford	a																							
Basingstoke	a						12 08								13 08								14 08	
Winchester	a						12 24								13 24								14 24	
Southampton Airport Parkway ✈	a						12 32								13 32								14 33	
Southampton Central	a						12 41								13 41								14 41	
Brockenhurst 3	a						12 57								13 57								14 57	
Bournemouth	a						13 15								14 15								15 15	

For general notes see front of timetable
For details of catering facilities see Directory of Train Operators

Scotland, The North East, North West England → The South West and South Coast

from 12 September

Route Diagram - See first page of Table 51

Station		XC	XC	XC	VT	VT	XC	XC	XC	XC	XC	XC	VT	XC	XC	XC	XC	XC	XC	VT	XC	XC
		1 ◇	1 ◇	1 ◇	1 ◇	1 ◇	1	1 ◇	1 ◇	1 ◇	1 ◇	1 ◇	1 ◇	1	1 ◇	1 ◇	1 ◇	1 ◇	1 ◇	1 ◇	1	1 ◇
					A	B							B							B		
Aberdeen	d																					
Stonehaven	d																					
Montrose	d																					
Arbroath	d																					
Dundee	d															07 35						
Leuchars 3	d															07 48						
Cupar	d															07 55						
Ladybank	d															08 03						
Markinch	d															08 11						
Kirkcaldy	d															08 20						
Inverkeithing	d															08 35						
Glasgow Central 15	d								07 00				10 00									
Motherwell	d																					
Haymarket	d								07 54							08 54						
Edinburgh 10	d				08 52	08 52			08 05							09 05				10 52		
Haymarket	d				08u57	08u57														10u57		
Lockerbie	d																					
Carlisle 8	d				10 07	10 07							11 09							12 07		
Penrith North Lakes	d												11 24									
Oxenholme Lake District	d				10 42	10 42														12 43		
Lancaster 6	d				10 57	10 57														12 57		
Preston 8	d				11 17	11 17							12 17							13 17		
Wigan North Western	d				11 28	11 28							12 28							13 28		
Warrington Bank Quay	d				11 39	11 39							12 39							13 39		
Manchester Piccadilly 10	d			11 07				11 27				12 07			12 27				13 07			13 27
Stockport	d							11 35							12 35							13 35
Wilmslow	d																					
Crewe 10	d				12 01	12 01							13 01							14 01		
Macclesfield	d							11 49							12 49							13 49
Congleton	d																					
Stoke-on-Trent	d			11 44				12 07				12 44			13 07				13 44			14 07
Stafford	d							12 25							13 25							14 25
Wolverhampton 7	d			12 15	12 32	12 32		12 41				13 15	13 32		13 41				14 15	14 32		14 41
Dunbar	d															09 25						
Berwick-upon-Tweed	d								08 47							09 48						
Alnmouth for Alnwick	d								09 09													
Morpeth	d																					
Newcastle 8	d		09 25						09 40		10 25					10 44		11 20				
Chester-le-Street	d																					
Durham	d		09 37						09 55		10 38					10 56		11 34				
Darlington 7	d		09 56						10 12		10 56					11 13		11 56				
York 8	d		10 25						10 44		11 27					11 44		12 25				
Leeds 10	d								11 11							12 11						
Wakefield Westgate 7	d								11 23							12 23						
Doncaster 7	d		10 53								11 55							12 52				
Sheffield 7	d		11 23						11 54		12 23					12 54		13 23				
Chesterfield	d								12 06							13 06						
Nottingham 8	d	11 08					11 37			12 08				12 37			13 08				13 37	
Derby 10	d	11 36	11 53				12 06		12 28	12 36	12 53			13 06		13 28	13 36	13 53			14 06	
Burton-on-Trent	d	11 48					12 18			12 48				13 20		13 38	13 48				14 18	
Tamworth	d	12 00					12 30		12 48	13 00				13 33			14 00				14 30	
Birmingham New Street 12	a	12 24	12 27	12 31	12 50	12 55	12 56	12 58	13 09	13 24	13 27	13 31	13 55	13 56	13 58	14 07	14 24	14 27	14 31	14 55	14 56	14 58
Birmingham New Street 12	d	12 30	12 33	12 42				13 04	13 12	13 30	13 33	13 42			14 04	14 12	14 30	14 33	14 42			15 04
Cheltenham Spa	a	13 10		13 25					13 51	14 10		14 23				14 51	15 10		15 23			
Gloucester 7	a	13 21								14 21							15 21					
Bristol Parkway 7	a			13 58					14 26			14 56				15 24			15 56			
Bristol Temple Meads 10	a			14 13					14 41			15 13				15 41			16 13			
Newport (South Wales)	a	14 05								15 06							16 05					
Cardiff Central 7	a	14 25								15 25							16 25					
Weston-super-Mare	a																					
Taunton	a								15 17							16 15						
Tiverton Parkway	a															16 28						
Exeter St Davids 6	a								15 44							16 43						
Dawlish	a																					
Teignmouth	a																					
Newton Abbot	a								16 05							17 03						
Torquay	a																					
Paignton	a																					
Totnes	a								16 19							17 16						
Plymouth	a								16 52							17 48						
Liskeard 6	a																					
Bodmin Parkway	a																					
Lostwithiel	a																					
Par	a																					
Newquay	a																					
St Austell	a																					
Truro	a																					
Redruth	a																					
Camborne	a																					
Hayle	a																					
St Erth	a																					
Penzance	a																					
Birmingham International ✈	d							13 14							14 14							15 14
Coventry	d							13 25							14 25							15 25
Leamington Spa 8	d		13 00					13 38			14 00				14 38			15 00				15 38
Banbury	a		13 17					13 54			14 17				14 54			15 17				15 54
Oxford	a		13 40					14 14			14 40				15 14			15 40				16 14
Reading 7	a		14 13					14 40			15 13				15 40			16 10				16 40
Guildford	a																					
Basingstoke	a							15 08							16 08							17 08
Winchester	a							15 24							16 24							17 24
Southampton Airport Parkwy ✈	a							15 32							16 32							17 32
Southampton Central	a							15 41							16 41							17 41
Brockenhurst 3	a							15 57							16 57							17 57
Bournemouth	a							16 15							17 15							18 15

For general notes see front of timetable
For details of catering facilities see Directory of Train Operators

A From 7 November
B Until 31 October

Table 51

SUMMARY OF SERVICES

Saturdays

Scotland, The North East, North West England → The South West and South Coast

from 12 September

Route Diagram - See first page of Table 51

		XC	XC	XC	XC	VT	VT	XC	XC	XC	XC	XC	XC	VT	XC	XC	XC	XC	XC	XC	VT	VT
		[1]◇	[1]◇	[1]◇	[1]◇	[1]◇	[1]◇	[1]	[1]◇	[1]◇	[1]◇	[1]◇	[1]◇	[1]◇	[1]	[1]◇	[1]◇	[1]◇	[1]◇	[1]◇	[1]◇	[1]◇
						A	B							B							A	B
		⊼	⊼	⊼	⊼	⊡	⊡		⊼	⊼	⊼	⊼	⊼	⊡		⊼	⊼	⊼	⊼	⊼	⊡	⊡
Aberdeen	d									08 20												
Stonehaven	d									08 38												
Montrose	d									08 59												
Arbroath	d									09 15												
Dundee	d									09 33												
Leuchars [8]	d									09 47												
Cupar	d									09 54												
Ladybank	d									10 01												
Markinch	d									10 09												
Kirkcaldy	d									10 17												
Inverkeithing	d									10 32												
Glasgow Central [15]	d	09 00					12 00															14 00
Motherwell	d																					
Haymarket	d	09 55								10 52												
Edinburgh [10]	d	10 05				10 52				11 05				12 52			12 05				12 52	
Haymarket	d					10u57								12u57							12u57	
Lockerbie	d																					
Carlisle [8]	d					12 07	13 09							14 07							14 07	15 11
Penrith North Lakes	d													14 22							14 22	
Oxenholme Lake District	d					12 43																15 46
Lancaster [6]	d					12 57	13 58							14 57							14 57	
Preston [8]	d					13 19	14 17							15 17							15 19	16 17
Wigan North Western	d						14 28							15 28								16 28
Warrington Bank Quay	d						14 39							15 39								16 39
Manchester Piccadilly [10] ⛴	d				14 07				14 27				15 07			15 27				16 07		
Stockport	d								14 35							15 35						
Wilmslow	d																					
Crewe [10]	d					15 01	15 01							16 01							17 01	17 01
Macclesfield	d								14 49							15 49						
Congleton	d																					
Stoke-on-Trent	d				14 44				15 07				15 44			16 07				16 44		
Stafford	d								15 25							16 25						
Wolverhampton [7] ⛴	d				15 15	15 32	15 32		15 41				16 15	16 32		16 41				17 15	17 32	17 32
Dunbar	d									11 25												
Berwick-upon-Tweed	d									11 48												
Alnmouth for Alnwick	d	11 04															13 05					
Morpeth	d	11 19																				
Newcastle [8]	d	11 40		12 22						12 44		13 27					13 44		14 22			
Chester-le-Street	d			12 31																		
Durham	d	11 55		12 38						12 56		13 39					13 56		14 34			
Darlington [7]	d	12 12		12 55						13 13		13 58					14 13		14 52			
York [8]	d	12 44		13 27						13 44		14 27					14 44		15 26			
Leeds [10]	d	13 11								14 11							15 11					
Wakefield Westgate [7]	d	13 23								14 23							15 23					
Doncaster [7]	d			13 54								14 56							15 55			
Sheffield [7]	d	13 54		14 23						14 54		15 23					15 54		16 23			
Chesterfield	d	14 06								15 06							16 06					
Nottingham [8] ⛴	d		14 08					14 37			15 08				15 37			16 08				
Derby [10]	d	14 29	14 36	14 53				15 06		15 28	15 36	15 53			16 06		16 28	16 36	16 53			
Burton-on-Trent	d		14 48					15 18		15 38	15 48				16 18			16 48				
Tamworth	d	14 49	15 00					15 30			16 00				16 30		16 48	17 00				
Birmingham New Street [12]	a	15 09	15 24	15 27	15 31	15 50	15 55	15 56	15 58	16 07	16 24	16 27	16 31	16 55	16 56	16 58	17 07	17 24	17 27	17 31	17 50	17 55
Birmingham New Street [12]	d	15 12	15 30	15 33	15 42				16 04	16 12	16 30	16 33	16 42			17 04	17 12	17 30	17 33	17 42		
Cheltenham Spa	a	15 51	16 10		16 23					16 51	17 10		17 23				17 51	18 17		18 23		
Gloucester [7]	a		16 21								17 21							18 28		18 35		
Bristol Parkway [7]	a	16 26			16 56					17 24			17 56				18 26			19 08		
Bristol Temple Meads [10]	a	16 41			17 11					17 38			18 13				18 41			19 27		
Newport (South Wales)	a		17 05								18 05							19 11				
Cardiff Central [7]	a		17 25								18 25							19 32				
Weston-super-Mare	a																					
Taunton	a	17 17			17 42					18 15							19 15					
Tiverton Parkway	a	17 30			17 55					18 28							19 28					
Exeter St Davids [6]	a	17 47			18 10					18 43							19 43					
Dawlish	a				18 26																	
Teignmouth	a				18 31																	
Newton Abbot	a	18 09			18 39					19 03							20 03					
Torquay	a				18 52																	
Paignton	a				19 05																	
Totnes	a	18 23								19 16							20 16					
Plymouth	a	18 52								19 48							20 48					
Liskeard [6]	a	19 23								20 10							21 24					
Bodmin Parkway	a	19 35								20 22							21 36					
Lostwithiel	a									20 28												
Par	a	19 46								20 35							21 47					
Newquay	a																					
St Austell	a	19 54								20 41							21 53					
Truro	a	20 12								20 59							22 11					
Redruth	a	20 24								21 10							22 29					
Camborne	a	20 31								21 17							22 35					
Hayle	a									21 25												
St Erth	a	20 41								21 29							22 45					
Penzance	a	20 59								21 48							23 02					
Birmingham International ✈	d								16 14							17 14						
Coventry	d								16 25							17 25						
Leamington Spa [8]	d			16 00					16 38			17 00				17 38			18 00			
Banbury	a			16 17					16 54			17 17				17 54			18 17			
Oxford	a			16 40					17 14			17 40				18 14			18 40			
Reading [7]	a			17 10					17 40			18 13				18 40			19 13			
Guildford	a																					
Basingstoke	a								18 08							19 08						
Winchester	a								18 24							19 24						
Southampton Airport Parkway ✈	a								18 32							19 32						
Southampton Central	a								18 40							19 41						
Brockenhurst [3]	a								18 57							19 57						
Bournemouth	a								19 15							20 15						

For general notes see front of timetable
For details of catering facilities see Directory of Train Operators

A From 7 November
B Until 31 October

from 12 September

Scotland, The North East, North West England → The South West and South Coast

Route Diagram - See first page of Table 51

		XC	XC	XC	XC	XC	XC	VT	XC	XC	XC	XC	XC	XC	VT	VT	XC	XC	XC	XC	XC	XC
		1	1◇	1◇	1◇	1◇	1◇	1◇	1◇	1	1◇	1◇	1◇	1◇	1◇	1◇	1	1◇	1◇	1◇	1◇	1◇
								A							B	A						
			✠	✠	✠	✠	✠	⌂	✠		✠	✠	✠	✠	⌂	⌂		✠	✠	✠	✠	✠
Aberdeen	d																					
Stonehaven	d																					
Montrose	d																					
Arbroath	d																					
Dundee	d																					
Leuchars 3	d																					
Cupar	d																					
Ladybank	d																					
Markinch	d																					
Kirkcaldy	d																					
Inverkeithing	d																					
Glasgow Central 15	d															16 00						
Motherwell	d																					
Haymarket	d																					
Edinburgh 10	d			13 05				14 52			14 05				14 52				15 05			
Haymarket	d							14u57							14u57							
Lockerbie	d																					
Carlisle 8	d							16 07							16 07	17 09						
Penrith North Lakes	d							16 22														
Oxenholme Lake District	d														16 42	17 44						
Lancaster 6	d							16 57							16 57							
Preston 8	d							17 17							17 19	18 17						
Wigan North Western	d							17 28								18 28						
Warrington Bank Quay	d							17 39								18 39						
Manchester Piccadilly 10	d		16 27				17 06		17 27					18 05				18 27				19 07
Stockport	d		16 35						17 35									18 35				19 16
Wilmslow	d																					
Crewe 10	d							18 01							19 01	19 01						
Macclesfield	d		16 49				17 27							18 25								
Congleton	d								17 54									18 54				
Stoke-on-Trent	d		17 07				17 44		18 07					18 44				19 07				19 44
Stafford	d		17 25						18 25									19 25				
Wolverhampton 7	d		17 41				18 15	18 32	18 41					19 15	19 32	19 32		19 41				20 15
Dunbar	d			13 25															15 25			
Berwick-upon-Tweed	d			13 48															15 48			
Alnmouth for Alnwick	d										15 05											
Morpeth	d																					
Newcastle 8	d			14 44		15 25					15 44		16 22						16 44		17 22	
Chester-le-Street	d												16 31								17 31	
Durham	d			14 56		15 38					15 56		16 38						16 56		17 38	
Darlington 7	d			15 13		15 56					16 13		16 56						17 13		17 55	
York 8	d			15 44		16 25					16 44		17 25						17 44		18 25	
Leeds 10	d			16 11							17 11								18 11			
Wakefield Westgate 7	d			16 23							17 23								18 23			
Doncaster 7	d					16 53							17 55								18 51	
Sheffield 7	d			16 54		17 23					17 54		18 23						18 54		19 23	
Chesterfield	d			17 06							18 06								19 06			
Nottingham 8	d	16 37			17 08					17 37		18 08					18 37			19 08		
Derby 10	d	17 06		17 28	17 36	17 53				18 06	18 28	18 36	18 53				19 06		19 28	19 36	19 53	
Burton-on-Trent	d	17 18		17 38	17 48					18 20		18 48					19 18		19 38	19 48		
Tamworth	d	17 30			18 00					18 33	18 48	19 00					19 30			20 00		
Birmingham New Street 12	a	17 56	17 58	18 07	18 24	18 27	18 31	18 55	18 58	19 00	19 07	19 24	19 27	19 31	19 56	19 55	19 56	19 58	20 07	20 24	20 27	20 31
Birmingham New Street 12	d		18 04	18 12	18 30	18 33	18 42		19 04		19 12	19 30	19 33	19 42				20 04	20 12	20 30	20 33	20 42
Cheltenham Spa	a			18 51	19 10		19 23				19 51	20 10		20 23					20 51	21 10		21 23
Gloucester 7	a				19 21							20 21								21 21		
Bristol Parkway 7	a			19 26			19 56				20 29			20 56					21 23			21 57
Bristol Temple Meads 10	a			19 41			20 13				20 42			21 13					21 35			22 13
Newport (South Wales)	a				20 05		20 54					21 09								22 14		
Cardiff Central 7	a				20 25		21 16					21 32								22 39		
Weston-super-Mare	a																					
Taunton	a			20 15							21 21			21 44					22 16			
Tiverton Parkway	a			20 28							21 33			21 56					22 28			
Exeter St Davids 6	a			20 43							21 49			22 12					22 45			
Dawlish	a																					
Teignmouth	a																					
Newton Abbot	a			21 03							22 08			22 31					23 12			
Torquay	a																					
Paignton	a																					
Totnes	a			21 16							22 21			22 43					23 27			
Plymouth	a			21 48							22 55			23 17					23 59			
Liskeard 6	a																					
Bodmin Parkway	a																					
Lostwithiel	a																					
Par	a																					
Newquay	a																					
St Austell	a																					
Truro	a																					
Redruth	a																					
Camborne	a																					
Hayle	a																					
St Erth	a																					
Penzance	a																					
Birmingham International ✈	d		18 14						19 14									20 14				
Coventry	d		18 25						19 25									20 25				
Leamington Spa 8	d		18 38			19 00			19 38				20 00					20 38			21 00	
Banbury	a		18 54			19 17			19 54				20 17					20 54			21 17	
Oxford	a		19 14			19 40			20 14				20 40					21 14			21 40	
Reading 7	a		19 40			20 13			20 40				21 13					21 40			22 13	
Guildford	a																				22 59	
Basingstoke	a		20 08						21 08									22 08				
Winchester	a		20 24						21 24									22 24				
Southampton Airport Parkwy ✈	a		20 32						21 32									22 32				
Southampton Central	a		20 41						21 41									22 41				
Brockenhurst 3	a		20 57						21 57									22 57				
Bournemouth	a		21 15						22 15									23 21				

For general notes see front of timetable
For details of catering facilities see Directory of Train Operators

A Until 31 October
B From 7 November

Scotland, The North East, North West England → The South West and South Coast

from 12 September

Route Diagram - See first page of Table 51

		VT	XC	XC	XC		XC	XC	VT	VT	XC	XC	XC	XC	VT		XC	VT	VT	XC	XC	XC
		1◇	1	1◇	1◇		1◇	1◇	1◇	1◇	1	1◇	1◇	1◇	1◇		1◇	1◇	1◇	1	1◇	1◇
		A							B	A					A			B	A			
		🍴		🛒	🛒		🛒	🛒	🍴	🍴		🛒	🛒	🛒	🍴		🛒	🍴	🍴		🛒	🛒
Aberdeen	d																					
Stonehaven	d																					
Montrose	d																					
Arbroath	d																					
Dundee	d																					
Leuchars 3	d																					
Cupar	d																					
Ladybank	d																					
Markinch	d																					
Kirkcaldy	d																					
Inverkeithing	d																					
Glasgow Central 15	d									18 00					18 40			18 00				
Motherwell	d																					
Haymarket	d																					
Edinburgh 10	d	16 52			16 05				16 52				17 05						18 52		18 05	
Haymarket	d	16u57							16u57										18u57			
Lockerbie	d																	18 52				
Carlisle 8	d	18 07							18 07	19 09					19 49			19 13	20 07			
Penrith North Lakes	d														20 03			19 28	20 22			
Oxenholme Lake District	d	18 42							18 42						20 26			19 51	20 45			
Lancaster 6	d	18 57							18 57	19 56					20 41			20 06	21 00			
Preston 8	d	19 17							19 19	20 17					21 01			20 27	21 20			
Wigan North Western	d	19 28								20 28					21 12				21 31			
Warrington Bank Quay	d	19 39								20 39					21 23				21 42			
Manchester Piccadilly 10	d			19 27				20 07				20 27		21 07								21 27
Stockport	d			19 35				20 16				20 35										21 35
Wilmslow	d																					
Crewe 10	d	20 01							21 01	21 01					21 44			22 04	22 04			
Macclesfield	d			19 49								20 49										21 49
Congleton	d																					
Stoke-on-Trent	d			20 07				20 44				21 07		21 44								22 07
Stafford	d			20 25								21 25			22 09			22 29	22 29			22 33
Wolverhampton 7	d	20 32		20 41				21 15	21 32	21 33		21 41		22 15	22 24			22 42	22 42			22 52
Dunbar	d												17 25								18 25	
Berwick-upon-Tweed	d												17 48								18 48	
Alnmouth for Alnwick	d				17 05																19 08	
Morpeth	d				17 20																	
Newcastle 8	d				17 44		18 22						18 44				19 25				19 43	
Chester-le-Street	d						18 31															
Durham	d				17 56		18 38						18 56				19 37				19 56	
Darlington 7	d				18 13		18 56						19 13				19 54				20 13	
York 8	d				18 44		19 25						19 44				20 23				20 44	
Leeds 10	d				19 11								20 11								21 11	
Wakefield Westgate 7	d				19 23								20 23								21 23	
Doncaster 7	d						19 53															
Sheffield 7	d				19 54		20 23						20 54				21 23				21 54	
Chesterfield	d				20 06								21 06				21 35				22 06	
Nottingham 8	d		19 37								20 35									21 35		
Derby 10	d		20 06		20 28		20 53				21 06		21 28				21 57			22 15	22 28	
Burton-on-Trent	d		20 18								21 20		21 38				22 07			22 26	22 38	
Tamworth	d		20 30		20 48						21 31		21 49				22 18			22 38	22 49	
Birmingham New Street 12	a	20 56	20 56	20 58	21 07		21 31	21 36	21 56	21 55	22 00	22 03	22 12	22 37	22 47		22 48	23 00	23 01	23 05	23 12	23 22
Birmingham New Street 12	d			21 04	21 12																	
Cheltenham Spa	a				21 51																	
Gloucester 7	a																					
Bristol Parkway 7	a				22 23																	
Bristol Temple Meads 10	a				22 41																	
Newport (South Wales)	a																					
Cardiff Central 7	a																					
Weston-super-Mare	a																					
Taunton	a																					
Tiverton Parkway	a																					
Exeter St Davids 6	a																					
Dawlish	a																					
Teignmouth	a																					
Newton Abbot	a																					
Torquay	a																					
Paignton	a																					
Totnes	a																					
Plymouth	a																					
Liskeard 6	a																					
Bodmin Parkway	a																					
Lostwithiel	a																					
Par	a																					
Newquay	a																					
St Austell	a																					
Truro	a																					
Redruth	a																					
Camborne	a																					
Hayle	a																					
St Erth	a																					
Penzance	a																					
Birmingham International ✈	d			21 14																		
Coventry	d			21 25																		
Leamington Spa 8	d			21 38																		
Banbury	a			21 54																		
Oxford	a			22 14																		
Reading 7	a			22 40																		
Guildford	a																					
Basingstoke	a			23 11																		
Winchester	a			23 27																		
Southampton Airport Parkwy ✈	a			23 35																		
Southampton Central	a			23 48																		
Brockenhurst 3	a																					
Bournemouth	a																					

For general notes see front of timetable
For details of catering facilities see
Directory of Train Operators

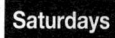

A Until 31 October
B From 7 November

Table 51

SUMMARY OF SERVICES

Sundays until 12 July

Scotland, The North East, North West England → The South West and South Coast

Route Diagram - See first page of Table 51

		XC 1◇	XC 1◇	XC 1◇	XC 1◇	XC 1◇	XC 1◇	XC 1◇	XC 1◇	XC 1◇	XC 1◇	VT 1◇	XC 1◇	XC 1◇	XC 1◇	VT 1◇	XC 1◇	XC 1◇	XC 1◇	XC 1◇
Aberdeen	d																			
Stonehaven	d																			
Montrose	d																			
Arbroath	d																			
Dundee	d																			
Leuchars 8	d																			
Cupar	d																			
Ladybank	d																			
Markinch	d																			
Kirkcaldy	d																			
Inverkeithing	d																			
Glasgow Central 15	d																			
Motherwell	d																			
Haymarket	d																			
Edinburgh 10	d																			
Haymarket	d																			
Lockerbie	d																			
Carlisle 8	d																			
Penrith North Lakes	d																			
Oxenholme Lake District	d																			
Lancaster 6	d																			
Preston 8	d											10 17				11 17				
Wigan North Western	d											10 28				11 28				
Warrington Bank Quay	d											10 39				11 39				
Manchester Piccadilly 10	d				08 27		09 27				10 26						11 26			
Stockport	d				08 36		09 36				10 35						11 36			
Wilmslow	d				08 43		09 43				10 43						11 43			
Crewe 10	d				09 04							11 03				12 01				
Macclesfield	d																			
Congleton	d																			
Stoke-on-Trent	d																			
Stafford	d				09 28		10 25				11 25						12 25			
Wolverhampton 7	d				09 41		10 41				11 41	11 41				12 34	12 41			
Dunbar	d																			
Berwick-upon-Tweed	d																			
Alnmouth for Alnwick	d																			
Morpeth	d																			
Newcastle 8	d																	09 25		
Chester-le-Street	d																			
Durham	d																	09 38		
Darlington 7	d																	09 55		
York 8	d												09 28					10 28		
Leeds 10	d					08 09		09 00					10 00					11 00		
Wakefield Westgate 7	d					08 22		09 12					10 12					11 12		
Doncaster 7	d							09 32					10 30					11 30		
Sheffield 7	d					08 55		09 57					10 57					11 57		
Chesterfield	d					09 07		10 09					11 09					12 09		
Nottingham 8	d													11 09					12 05	
Derby 10	d					09 30		10 33					11 30	11 36				12 30	12 36	
Burton-on-Trent	d							10 44					11 41	11 48					12 48	
Tamworth	d					09 49								12 00				12 48	13 00	
Birmingham New Street 12	a				09 58	10 10	10 58	11 12			11 58	12 05	12 07	12 23		12 55	12 58	13 07	13 21	
Birmingham New Street 12	d	08 52	09 04	09 52	10 04	10 14	11 04	11 12	11 30	11 33	12 04		12 12	12 30	12 33		13 04	13 12	13 30	13 33
Cheltenham Spa	a	09 50		10 51		10 55		11 50	12 10				12 50	13 10				13 50	14 10	
Gloucester 7	a			11 02					12 21					13 21					14 21	
Bristol Parkway 7	a	10 23				11 28		12 26					13 23					14 23		
Bristol Temple Meads 10	a	10 35				11 41		12 39					13 35					14 35		
Newport (South Wales)	a			11 45					13 04					14 04					15 04	
Cardiff Central 7	a			12 06					13 25					14 25					15 25	
Weston-super-Mare	a																			
Taunton	a	11 19				12 16		13 16					14 15					15 15		
Tiverton Parkway	a	11 33				12 28		13 29					14 28					15 28		
Exeter St Davids 6	a	11 48				12 47		13 47					14 44					15 44		
Dawlish	a																			
Teignmouth	a																			
Newton Abbot	a	12 08				13 08		14 08					15 03					16 03		
Torquay	a																			
Paignton	a																			
Totnes	a	12 23				13 22		14 22					15 16					16 16		
Plymouth	a	12 55				13 56		14 53					15 48					16 48		
Liskeard 6	a	13 17																		
Bodmin Parkway	a	13 29																		
Lostwithiel	a																			
Par	a	13 39																		
Newquay	a																			
St Austell	a	13 46																		
Truro	a	14 03																		
Redruth	a	14 15																		
Camborne	a	14 22																		
Hayle	a																			
St Erth	a	14 32																		
Penzance	a	14 48																		
Birmingham International ✈	d		09 14		10 14		11 14				12 14						13 14			
Coventry	d		09 25		10 25		11 25				12 25						13 25			
Leamington Spa 8	d		09 38		10 38		11 38			12 00	12 38				13 00		13 38			14 00
Banbury	a		09 54		10 54		11 54			12 18	12 54				13 18		13 54			14 18
Oxford	a		10 14		11 14		12 14			12 47	13 14				13 41		14 14			14 45
Reading 7	a		10 42		11 42		12 42			13 15	13 42				14 13		14 42			15 15
Guildford	a																			
Basingstoke	a		11 09		12 09		13 09				14 09						15 09			
Winchester	a		11 24		12 24		13 24				14 24						15 24			
Southampton Airport Parkwy ✈	a		11 33		12 33		13 33				14 33						15 33			
Southampton Central	a		11 42		12 42		13 42				14 42						15 42			
Brockenhurst 3	a		12 01		13 01		14 01				15 01						16 01			
Bournemouth	a		12 27		13 27		14 27				15 27						16 27			

For general notes see front of timetable
For details of catering facilities see Directory of Train Operators

Sundays until 12 July

Scotland, The North East, North West England → The South West and South Coast

Route Diagram - See first page of Table 51

		VT 1◇	XC 1◇	XC 1◇		XC 1◇	XC 1◇	XC 1◇	VT 1◇		XC 1◇	XC 1◇	XC 1◇	XC 1◇		XC 1◇	VT 1◇	XC 1◇	XC 1◇		XC 1◇	XC 1◇	XC 1◇	VT 1◇
Aberdeen	d																							
Stonehaven	d																							
Montrose	d																							
Arbroath	d																							
Dundee	d																							
Leuchars 8	d																							
Cupar	d																							
Ladybank	d																							
Markinch	d																							
Kirkcaldy	d																							
Inverkeithing	d																							
Glasgow Central 15	d																11 51							
Motherwell	d																							
Haymarket	d																							
Edinburgh 10	d			08 50					10 52			09 50							10 50					12 52
Haymarket	d								10u57															12u56
Lockerbie	d																							
Carlisle 8	d								12 07								13 09							14 07
Penrith North Lakes	d																							14 22
Oxenholme Lake District	d								12 43															
Lancaster 6	d	12 00							12 57								13 58							14 57
Preston 8	d	12 17							13 17								14 17							15 17
Wigan North Western	d	12 28							13 28								14 28							15 28
Warrington Bank Quay	d	12 39							13 39								14 39							15 39
Manchester Piccadilly 10	d		12 26					13 07			13 27					14 07		14 27					15 07	
Stockport	d		12 36								13 36							14 36						
Wilmslow	d		12 43					13 22																
Crewe 10	d	13 01							14 01								15 01							16 01
Macclesfield	d										13 49							14 49						
Congleton	d																							
Stoke-on-Trent	d										14 07					14 43		15 07					15 43	
Stafford	d		13 25								14 25							15 25						
Wolverhampton 7	d	13 32	13 41					14 15	14 34		14 41					15 15	15 32	15 41					16 15	16 34
Dunbar	d																		11 10					
Berwick-upon-Tweed	d			09 33															11 33					
Alnmouth for Alnwick	d											10 47												
Morpeth	d											11 02												
Newcastle 8	d			10 25								11 25							12 25			13 15		
Chester-le-Street	d																					13 23		
Durham	d			10 37								11 37							12 37			13 30		
Darlington 7	d			10 54								11 54							12 54			13 47		
York 8	d			11 28								12 28							13 28			14 19		
Leeds 10	d			12 00								13 00							14 00					
Wakefield Westgate 7	d			12 12								13 12							14 12					
Doncaster 7	d			12 30								13 30										14 50		
Sheffield 7	d			12 57								13 57		14 20					14 50			15 20		
Chesterfield	d			13 09								14 09		14 32					15 02					
Nottingham 8	d					13 05							14 05								15 05			
Derby 10	d			13 32		13 35	13 47					14 30	14 36	14 53					15 23		15 36	15 51		
Burton-on-Trent	d			13 41		13 48							14 48						15 35		15 48			
Tamworth	d					14 00						14 48	15 00								16 00			
Birmingham New Street 12	a	13 55	13 58	14 10		14 21	14 27	14 31	14 55		14 58	15 07	15 21	15 27		15 31	15 55	15 58	16 00		16 23	16 27	16 31	16 55
Birmingham New Street 12	d		14 04	14 12		14 30	14 33	14 42			15 04	15 12	15 30	15 33		15 42		16 04	16 12		16 30	16 33	16 42	
Cheltenham Spa	a			14 50		15 10		15 24				15 50	16 10			16 24			16 50		17 10		17 24	
Gloucester 7	a					15 21							16 21								17 21			
Bristol Parkway 7	a			15 25				16 00				16 23				16 57			17 23				18 02	
Bristol Temple Meads 10	a			15 38				16 13				16 35				17 13			17 35				18 14	
Newport (South Wales)	a					16 04							17 04								18 04			
Cardiff Central 7	a					16 25							17 25								18 25			
Weston-super-Mare	a																							
Taunton	a			16 16				16 45				17 15							18 19					
Tiverton Parkway	a			16 28				16 57				17 28							18 32					
Exeter St Davids 6	a			16 47				17 13				17 44							18 48					
Dawlish	a							17 25																
Teignmouth	a							17 30																
Newton Abbot	a			17 08				17 37				18 03							19 07					
Torquay	a							17 49																
Paignton	a							18 02																
Totnes	a			17 22								18 16							19 20					
Plymouth	a			17 56								18 48							19 53					
Liskeard 6	a											19 17												
Bodmin Parkway	a											19 29												
Lostwithiel	a																							
Par	a											19 39												
Newquay	a																							
St Austell	a											19 46												
Truro	a											20 07												
Redruth	a											20 18												
Camborne	a											20 25												
Hayle	a																							
St Erth	a											20 36												
Penzance	a											20 52												
Birmingham International ✈	d		14 14								15 14							16 14						
Coventry	d		14 25								15 25							16 25						
Leamington Spa 8	d		14 38				15 00				15 38			16 00				16 38				17 00		
Banbury	a		14 54				15 18				15 54			16 18				16 54				17 18		
Oxford	a		15 14				15 41				16 14			16 41				17 14				17 41		
Reading 7	a		15 42				16 13				16 42			17 15				17 42				18 13		
Guildford	a																							
Basingstoke	a		16 09								17 09							18 09						
Winchester	a		16 24								17 24							18 24						
Southampton Airport Parkway ✈	a		16 33								17 33							18 33						
Southampton Central	a		16 42								17 40							18 42						
Brockenhurst 3	a		17 01								18 01							19 01						
Bournemouth	a		17 27								18 27							19 27						

For general notes see front of timetable
For details of catering facilities see Directory of Train Operators

Scotland, The North East, North West England → The South West and South Coast

until 12 July

Route Diagram - See first page of Table 51

		XC 1◇	XC 1◇	XC 1◇	XC 1◇	XC 1◇	VT 1◇	XC 1◇	XC 1◇	XC 1◇	XC 1◇	XC 1◇	VT 1◇	XC 1◇	XC 1◇	XC 1◇	XC 1◇	XC 1◇	VT 1◇	XC 1◇
Aberdeen	d														11 12					
Stonehaven	d														11 29					
Montrose	d														11 50					
Arbroath	d														12 06					
Dundee	d														12 25					
Leuchars 3	d														12 38					
Cupar	d														12 45					
Ladybank	d																			
Markinch	d																			
Kirkcaldy	d														13 03					
Inverkeithing	d														13 18					
Glasgow Central 15	d						13 56		11 37										15 55	
Motherwell	d								11 56											
Haymarket	d								12 38						13 37					
Edinburgh 10	d		11 50						12 50		13 33		14 52		13 50					
Haymarket	d												14u57							
Lockerbie	d																			
Carlisle 8	d						15 09						16 07						17 09	
Penrith North Lakes	d												16 22							
Oxenholme Lake District	d						15 44												17 44	
Lancaster 6	d												16 57							
Preston 8	d						16 17						17 17						18 17	
Wigan North Western	d						16 28						17 28						18 28	
Warrington Bank Quay	d						16 39						17 39						18 39	
Manchester Piccadilly 10	d	15 27				16 07		16 27				17 07		17 27				18 07		18 27
Stockport	d	15 36						16 36						17 36						18 36
Wilmslow	d																			
Crewe 10	d						17 01						18 01						19 01	
Macclesfield	d	15 49						16 49						17 49						18 49
Congleton	d																			
Stoke-on-Trent	d	16 07				16 43		17 07				17 43		18 07				18 43		19 07
Stafford	d	16 25						17 25						18 25						19 25
Wolverhampton 7	d	16 41				17 15	17 32	17 41				18 15	18 32	18 41				19 15	19 32	19 41
Dunbar	d								13 10											
Berwick-upon-Tweed	d								13 33		14 18									
Alnmouth for Alnwick	d		12 47								14 38				14 47					
Morpeth	d																			
Newcastle 8	d		13 25		14 18				14 25		15 18				15 25		16 18			
Chester-le-Street	d																			
Durham	d		13 37		14 30				14 37		15 30				15 37		16 30			
Darlington 7	d		13 54		14 47				14 54		15 47				15 54		16 47			
York 8	d		14 28		15 20				15 28		16 20				16 28		17 20			
Leeds 10	d		15 00						16 00						17 00					
Wakefield Westgate 7	d		15 12						16 12						17 12					
Doncaster 7	d				15 50						16 50						17 50			
Sheffield 7	d		15 50		16 20				16 50		17 20				17 50		18 20			
Chesterfield	d		16 02						17 02						18 02					
Nottingham 8	d			16 05						17 00						18 05				
Derby 10	d		16 23	16 35	16 51				17 23	17 35	17 51				18 23	18 35	18 51			
Burton-on-Trent	d			16 48					17 35	17 48						18 48				
Tamworth	d		16 43	17 00						18 00					18 43	19 00				
Birmingham New Street 12	a	16 58	17 02	17 21	17 27	17 31	17 55	17 58	18 00	18 21	18 27	18 31	18 55	18 58	19 02	19 21	19 27	19 31	19 55	19 58
Birmingham New Street 12	d	17 04	17 12	17 30	17 29	17 42		18 04	18 12	18 30	18 33	18 42		19 04	19 12	19 30	19 33	19 42		20 04
Cheltenham Spa	a		17 50	18 10		18 24			18 50	19 13		19 24			19 50	20 10		20 24		
Gloucester 7	a			18 21		18 35				19 24						20 21				
Bristol Parkway 7	a		18 23			19 08			19 23			20 00			20 23			20 57		
Bristol Temple Meads 10	a		18 37			19 25			19 35			20 14			20 35			21 14		
Newport (South Wales)	a			19 04						20 09						21 04				
Cardiff Central 7	a			19 25						20 30						21 25				
Weston-super-Mare	a											20 36								
Taunton	a		19 15						20 16			20 58			21 15					
Tiverton Parkway	a		19 28						20 28			21 11			21 28					
Exeter St Davids 6	a		19 48						20 47			21 26			21 44					
Dawlish	a											21 42								
Teignmouth	a											21 47								
Newton Abbot	a		20 07						21 06			21 54			22 03					
Torquay	a											22 06								
Paignton	a											22 19								
Totnes	a		20 20						21 19						22 16					
Plymouth	a		20 48						21 52						22 48					
Liskeard 6	a		21 12																	
Bodmin Parkway	a		21 24																	
Lostwithiel	a																			
Par	a		21 34																	
Newquay	a																			
St Austell	a		21 41																	
Truro	a		21 58																	
Redruth	a		22 09																	
Camborne	a		22 19																	
Hayle	a																			
St Erth	a		22 30																	
Penzance	a		22 46																	
Birmingham International	d	17 14						18 14						19 14						20 14
Coventry	d	17 25						18 25						19 25						20 25
Leamington Spa 8	d	17 38			18 00			18 38			19 00			19 38				20 00		20 38
Banbury	a	17 54			18 18			18 54			19 18			19 54				20 18		20 54
Oxford	a	18 14			18 45			19 14			19 41			20 14				20 41		21 14
Reading 7	a	18 42			19 15			19 42			20 13			20 42				21 13		21 42
Guildford	a																			
Basingstoke	a	19 09						20 09						21 09						22 11
Winchester	a	19 24						20 24						21 24						22 26
Southampton Airport Parkwy	a	19 33						20 33						21 33						22 35
Southampton Central	a	19 40						20 42						21 42						22 47
Brockenhurst 3	a	20 01						21 01						22 01						
Bournemouth	a	20 27						21 27						22 27						

For general notes see front of timetable
For details of catering facilities see Directory of Train Operators

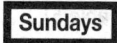

Scotland, The North East, North West England → The South West and South Coast

until 12 July

Route Diagram - See first page of Table 51

		XC	XC	XC	XC	VT	XC	XC	XC	XC	XC	XC	VT	XC	VT	XC	XC
		1 ◇	1 ◇	1 ◇	1 ◇	1 ◇	1 ◇	1 ◇	1 ◇	1 ◇	1 ◇	1 ◇	1 ◇	1 ◇	1 ◇	1 ◇	1 ◇
Aberdeen	d																
Stonehaven	d																
Montrose	d																
Arbroath	d																
Dundee	d																
Leuchars 3	d																
Cupar	d																
Ladybank	d																
Markinch	d																
Kirkcaldy	d																
Inverkeithing	d																
Glasgow Central 15	d	13 45											18 35				
Motherwell	d	14 01															
Haymarket	d	14 43															
Edinburgh 10	d	14 50				16 52		15 50			16 50				18 52	17 50	
Haymarket	d					16u56									18u57		
Lockerbie	d																
Carlisle 8	d					18 07							19 44		20 07		
Penrith North Lakes	d														20 22		
Oxenholme Lake District	d					18 42							20 19				
Lancaster 6	d					18 57							20 34		20 57		
Preston 8	d					19 17							20 55		21 17		
Wigan North Western	d					19 28							21 07		21 28		
Warrington Bank Quay	d					19 39							21 18		21 39		
Manchester Piccadilly 10	d				19 07		19 27			20 07				21 07			22 07
Stockport	d						19 36			20 16				21 16			22 16
Wilmslow	d																
Crewe 10	d					20 01							21 40		22 01		
Macclesfield	d						19 49			20 29				21 29			22 29
Congleton	d																
Stoke-on-Trent	d				19 43		20 07			20 47				21 47			22 47
Stafford	d						20 25			21 08			22 02	22 06			23 06
Wolverhampton 7	d				20 15	20 34	20 41			21 22			22 18	22 22	22 32		23 19
Dunbar	d	15 10									17 10					18 10	
Berwick-upon-Tweed	d	15 33									17 33						
Alnmouth for Alnwick	d							16 47								18 51	
Morpeth	d							17 02									
Newcastle 8	d	16 25		17 18				17 25	18 18		18 25					19 25	
Chester-le-Street	d			17 26					18 26		18 33						
Durham	d	16 37		17 33				17 37	18 33		18 37					19 37	
Darlington 7	d	16 54		17 50				17 54	18 50		18 54					19 54	
York 8	d	17 28		18 20				18 28	19 20		19 28					20 28	
Leeds 10	d	18 00						19 00			20 00					21 00	
Wakefield Westgate 7	d	18 12						19 12			20 12					21 12	
Doncaster 7	d			18 50					19 50								
Sheffield 7	d	18 50		19 20				19 50	20 20		20 50					21 50	
Chesterfield	d	19 02						20 02			21 02					22 02	
Nottingham 8	d		19 10									21 08					
Derby 10	d	19 23	19 35	19 51				20 23	21 00		21 23	21 36				22 23	
Burton-on-Trent	d	19 35	19 48								21 35	21 48				22 35	
Tamworth	d		20 00					20 43			21 46	22 00				22 46	
Birmingham New Street 12	a	20 00	20 25	20 27	20 31	20 57	20 58	21 01	21 37	21 39	22 04	22 27	22 40	22 45	22 55	23 09	23 41
Birmingham New Street 12	d	20 12		20 33	20 42		21 04	21 12		21 42	22 12						
Cheltenham Spa	a	20 50			21 24			21 50		22 24	22 50						
Gloucester 7	a																
Bristol Parkway 7	a	21 23			21 59			22 24		22 57	23 24						
Bristol Temple Meads 10	a	21 35			22 14			22 41		23 14	23 41						
Newport (South Wales)	a																
Cardiff Central 7	a																
Weston-super-Mare	a																
Taunton	a	22 15															
Tiverton Parkway	a	22 28															
Exeter St Davids 6	a	22 44															
Dawlish	a																
Teignmouth	a																
Newton Abbot	a	23 04															
Torquay	a																
Paignton	a																
Totnes	a	23 20															
Plymouth	a	23 54															
Liskeard 6	a																
Bodmin Parkway	a																
Lostwithiel	a																
Par	a																
Newquay	a																
St Austell	a																
Truro	a																
Redruth	a																
Camborne	a																
Hayle	a																
St Erth	a																
Penzance	a																
Birmingham International ✈	d						21 14										
Coventry	d						21 24										
Leamington Spa 8	d			21 00			21 35										
Banbury	a			21 18													
Oxford	a			21 38			22 08										
Reading 7	a			22 12			22 42										
Guildford	a																
Basingstoke	a			22 30													
Winchester	a																
Southampton Airport Parkwy ✈	a			23 35													
Southampton Central	a			23 47													
Brockenhurst 3	a																
Bournemouth	a																

For general notes see front of timetable
For details of catering facilities see Directory of Train Operators

Scotland, The North East, North West England → The South West and South Coast

19 July to 6 September

Route Diagram - See first page of Table 51

		XC	XC	XC	XC		XC	XC	XC	XC		XC	XC	XC	VT		XC	XC		XC		XC	XC	VT
		1◇	1◇	1◇	1◇		1◇	1◇	1◇	1◇		1◇	1◇	1◇	1◇		1◇	1◇	1◇	1◇		1◇	1◇	1◇
Aberdeen	d																							
Stonehaven	d																							
Montrose	d																							
Arbroath	d																							
Dundee	d																							
Leuchars 8	d																							
Cupar	d																							
Ladybank	d																							
Markinch	d																							
Kirkcaldy	d																							
Inverkeithing	d																							
Glasgow Central 15	d																							
Motherwell	d																							
Haymarket	d																							
Edinburgh 10	d																							
Haymarket	d																							
Lockerbie	d																							
Carlisle 8	d																							
Penrith North Lakes	d																							
Oxenholme Lake District	d																							
Lancaster 6	d																							
Preston 8	d														10 17									11 17
Wigan North Western	d														10 28									11 28
Warrington Bank Quay	d														10 39									11 39
Manchester Piccadilly 10	d			08 27					09 27								10 24							
Stockport	d			08 36					09 36								10 34							
Wilmslow	d			08 43																				
Crewe 10	d			09 04											11 01									12 01
Macclesfield	d								09 49								10 47							
Congleton	d																							
Stoke-on-Trent	d								10 07								11 07							
Stafford	d			09 25					10 25								11 25							
Wolverhampton 7	d			09 41					10 41						11 32		11 41							12 34
Dunbar	d																							
Berwick-upon-Tweed	d																							
Alnmouth for Alnwick	d																							
Morpeth	d																							
Newcastle 8	d																							
Chester-le-Street	d																							
Durham	d																							
Darlington 7	d																							
York 8	d																	09 28						
Leeds 10	d						08 09	08 30										10 00						
Wakefield Westgate 7	d						08 22	08 43										10 12						
Doncaster 7	d							09 02										10 30						
Sheffield 7	d						08 54	09 28										10 57						
Chesterfield	d						09 08	09 41										11 09						
Nottingham 8	d																						11 38	
Derby 10	d						09 30	10 03						11 06				11 30					12 06	
Burton-on-Trent	d							10 14						11 18				11 41					12 18	
Tamworth	d						09 49							11 30									12 30	
Birmingham New Street 12	a			09 58			10 10	10 41	10 58					11 51	11 55		11 58	12 07	←				12 51	12 55
Birmingham New Street 12	d	08 52	09 04	10 04	10 12		10 14	10 45	11 04	11 12		11 33	11 45	12 12			12 04		12 12	12 33		12 42	13 04	
Cheltenham Spa	a	09 50			11 10		10 55	11 50		12 10			12 50	→					13 10			13 52	14 05	
Gloucester 7	a				11 21					12 21									13 21				14 15	
Bristol Parkway 7	a	10 23					11 28	12 23					13 23									14 26		
Bristol Temple Meads 10	a	10 35					11 41	12 36					13 35									14 38		
Newport (South Wales)	a				12 04					13 04									14 04				14 58	
Cardiff Central 7	a				12 25					13 25									14 25				15 19	
Weston-super-Mare	a																							
Taunton	a	11 19					12 16	13 16					14 15									15 15		
Tiverton Parkway	a	11 33					12 28	13 29					14 28									15 28		
Exeter St Davids 6	a	11 48					12 47	13 47					14 43									15 43		
Dawlish	a																							
Teignmouth	a																							
Newton Abbot	a	12 08					13 08	14 08					15 03									16 03		
Torquay	a																							
Paignton	a																							
Totnes	a	12 23					13 22	14 22					15 16									16 16		
Plymouth	a	12 55					13 56	14 53					15 48									16 48		
Liskeard 6	a	13 17																						
Bodmin Parkway	a	13 29																						
Lostwithiel	a																							
Par	a	13 39																						
Newquay	a																							
St Austell	a	13 46																						
Truro	a	14 03																						
Redruth	a	14 15																						
Camborne	a	14 22																						
Hayle	a																							
St Erth	a	14 32																						
Penzance	a	14 48																						
Birmingham International	d		09 14	10 14					11 14								12 14							
Coventry	d		09 25	10 25					11 25								12 25							
Leamington Spa 8	d		09 38	10 38					11 38			12 00					12 38			13 00				
Banbury	a		09 54	10 54					11 54			12 18					12 54			13 18				
Oxford	a		10 14	11 14					12 14			12 47					13 14			13 41				
Reading 7	a		10 42	11 42					12 42			13 15					13 42			14 13				
Guildford	a																							
Basingstoke	a		11 09	12 09					13 09								14 09							
Winchester	a		11 24	12 24					13 24								14 24							
Southampton Airport Parkway	a		11 33	12 33					13 33								14 33							
Southampton Central	a		11 42	12 42					13 42								14 42							
Brockenhurst 8	a		12 01	13 01					14 01								15 01							
Bournemouth	a		12 27	13 27					14 27								15 27							

For general notes see front of timetable
For details of catering facilities see Directory of Train Operators

Table 51 SUMMARY OF SERVICES

Sundays

Scotland, The North East, North West England → The South West and South Coast

19 July to 6 September

Route Diagram - See first page of Table 51

		XC	XC	XC	VT	XC	XC	XC	XC	XC	VT	XC	XC	XC	XC	XC	VT	XC	XC	XC
		1◇	1◇	1◇	1◇	1◇	1◇	1◇	1◇	1◇	1◇	1◇	1◇	1◇	1◇	1◇	1◇	1◇	1◇	1◇
Aberdeen	d																			
Stonehaven	d																			
Montrose	d																			
Arbroath	d																			
Dundee	d																			
Leuchars 3	d																			
Cupar	d																			
Ladybank	d																			
Markinch	d																			
Kirkcaldy	d																			
Inverkeithing	d																			
Glasgow Central 15	d																11 51			
Motherwell	d																			
Haymarket	d																			
Edinburgh 10	d						08 50				10 52		09 50						10 50	
Haymarket	d										10u57									
Lockerbie	d																			
Carlisle 8	d										12 07						13 09			
Penrith North Lakes	d																			
Oxenholme Lake District	d										12 43									
Lancaster 6	d				12 00						12 57						13 58			
Preston 8	d				12 17						13 17						14 17			
Wigan North Western	d				12 28						13 28						14 28			
Warrington Bank Quay	d				12 39						13 39						14 39			
Manchester Piccadilly 10	d	11 27				12 26				13 07		13 27				14 07		14 27		
Stockport	d	11 36				12 36						13 36						14 36		
Wilmslow	d																			
Crewe 10	d				13 01						14 01						15 01			
Macclesfield	d	11 49				12 49						13 49						14 49		
Congleton	d																			
Stoke-on-Trent	d	12 07				13 07				13 43		14 07				14 43		15 07		
Stafford	d	12 25				13 25						14 25						15 25		
Wolverhampton 7	d	12 41			13 32	13 41				14 15	14 34	14 41				15 15	15 32	15 41		
Dunbar	d																		11 10	
Berwick-upon-Tweed	d						09 33												11 33	
Alnmouth for Alnwick	d												10 47							
Morpeth	d												11 02							
Newcastle 8	d		09 25				10 25						11 25						12 25	
Chester-le-Street	d																			
Durham	d		09 38				10 37						11 37						12 37	
Darlington 7	d		09 55				10 54						11 54						12 54	
York 8	d		10 28				11 28						12 28						13 28	
Leeds 10	d		11 00				12 00						13 00						14 00	
Wakefield Westgate 7	d		11 12				12 12						13 12						14 12	
Doncaster 7	d		11 30				12 30						13 30							
Sheffield 7	d		11 57				12 57						13 57		14 20				14 50	
Chesterfield	d		12 09				13 09						14 09		14 32				15 02	
Nottingham 8	d							13 10						14 05						15 05
Derby 10	d		12 30				13 32	13 36	13 43				14 30	14 36	14 53				15 23	15 36
Burton-on-Trent	d						13 43	13 48						14 48					15 35	15 48
Tamworth	d		12 49					14 00					14 49	15 00						16 00
Birmingham New Street 12	a	12 58	13 07		13 55	13 58	14 10	14 21	14 27	14 31	14 55	14 58	15 07	15 21	15 27	15 31	15 55	15 58	16 00	16 23
Birmingham New Street 12	d	13 04		13 33		14 04	14 12	14 30	14 33	14 42		15 04	15 12	15 30	15 33	15 42		16 04	16 12	16 30
Cheltenham Spa	a						14 51	15 10		15 24			15 50	16 10		16 24			16 50	17 10
Gloucester 7	a							15 21						16 21						17 21
Bristol Parkway 7	a						15 25			16 00			16 23			16 57			17 23	
Bristol Temple Meads 10	a						15 38			16 13			16 35			17 13			17 35	
Newport (South Wales)	a							16 04						17 04						18 04
Cardiff Central 7	a							16 25						17 25						18 25
Weston-super-Mare	a																			
Taunton	a						16 16			16 45			17 15						18 19	
Tiverton Parkway	a						16 28			16 57			17 28						18 32	
Exeter St Davids 6	a						16 47			17 13			17 44						18 48	
Dawlish	a									17 25										
Teignmouth	a									17 30										
Newton Abbot	a						17 08			17 37			18 03						19 07	
Torquay	a									17 49										
Paignton	a									18 02										
Totnes	a						17 22						18 16						19 20	
Plymouth	a						17 56						18 48						19 53	
Liskeard 6	a												19 17							
Bodmin Parkway	a												19 29							
Lostwithiel	a																			
Par	a												19 39							
Newquay	a																			
St Austell	a												19 46							
Truro	a												20 07							
Redruth	a												20 18							
Camborne	a												20 25							
Hayle	a																			
St Erth	a												20 36							
Penzance	a												20 52							
Birmingham International	d	13 14				14 14						15 14						16 14		
Coventry	d	13 25				14 25						15 25						16 25		
Leamington Spa 8	d	13 38		14 00		14 38			15 00			15 38			16 00			16 38		
Banbury	a	13 54		14 18		14 54			15 18			15 54			16 18			16 54		
Oxford	a	14 14		14 45		15 14			15 41			16 14			16 41			17 14		
Reading 7	a	14 42		15 15		15 42			16 13			16 42			17 13			17 42		
Guildford	a																			
Basingstoke	a	15 09				16 09						17 09						18 09		
Winchester	a	15 24				16 24						17 24						18 24		
Southampton Airport Parkwy	a	15 33				16 33						17 33						18 33		
Southampton Central	a	15 42				16 42						17 40						18 42		
Brockenhurst 3	a	16 01				17 01						18 01						19 01		
Bournemouth	a	16 27				17 27						18 27						19 27		

For general notes see front of timetable
For details of catering facilities see Directory of Train Operators

Table 51

SUMMARY OF SERVICES

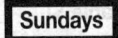

Sundays

19 July to 6 September

Scotland, The North East, North West England → The South West and South Coast

Route Diagram - See first page of Table 51

		XC	XC	VT	XC	XC	XC	XC	XC	VT	XC	XC	XC	XC	XC	VT	XC	XC	XC	XC
		1 ◇	1 ◇	1 ◇	1 ◇	1 ◇	1 ◇	1 ◇	1 ◇	1 ◇	1 ◇	1 ◇	1 ◇	1 ◇	1 ◇	1 ◇	1 ◇	1 ◇	1 ◇	1 ◇
Aberdeen	d																	11 12		
Stonehaven	d																	11 29		
Montrose	d																	11 50		
Arbroath	d																	12 06		
Dundee	d																	12 25		
Leuchars 3	d																	12 38		
Cupar	d																	12 45		
Ladybank	d																			
Markinch	d																			
Kirkcaldy	d																	13 03		
Inverkeithing	d																	13 18		
Glasgow Central 15	d									13 56		11 37								
Motherwell	d											11 56								
Haymarket	d											12 38						13 37		
Edinburgh 10	d			12 52		11 50						12 50		13 33		14 52		13 50		
Haymarket	d			12u56												14u57				
Lockerbie	d																			
Carlisle 8	d			14 07						15 09						16 07				
Penrith North Lakes	d			14 22												16 22				
Oxenholme Lake District	d									15 44										
Lancaster 6	d			14 57												16 57				
Preston 8	d			15 17						16 17						17 17				
Wigan North Western	d			15 28						16 28						17 28				
Warrington Bank Quay	d			15 39						16 39						17 39				
Manchester Piccadilly 10	d		15 07		15 27				16 07		16 27				17 07		17 27			
Stockport	d				15 36						16 36						17 36			
Wilmslow	d																			
Crewe 10	d			16 01						17 01						18 01				
Macclesfield	d				15 49						16 49						17 49			
Congleton	d																			
Stoke-on-Trent	d		15 43		16 07				16 43		17 07				17 43		18 07			
Stafford	d				16 25						17 25						18 25			
Wolverhampton 7	d		16 15	16 34	16 41				17 15	17 32	17 41				18 15	18 32	18 41			
Dunbar	d											13 10								
Berwick-upon-Tweed	d											13 33		14 18						
Alnmouth for Alnwick	d					12 47								14 38				14 47		
Morpeth	d																			
Newcastle 8	d	13 15				13 25		14 18				14 25		15 18				15 25		16 18
Chester-le-Street	d	13 23																		
Durham	d	13 30				13 37		14 30				14 37		15 30				15 37		16 30
Darlington 7	d	13 47				13 54		14 47				14 54		15 47				15 54		16 47
York 8	d	14 19				14 28		15 20				15 28		16 20				16 28		17 20
Leeds 10	d					15 00						16 00						17 00		
Wakefield Westgate 7	d					15 12						16 12						17 12		
Doncaster 7	d	14 50						15 50						16 50						17 50
Sheffield 7	d	15 20				15 50		16 20				16 50		17 20				17 50		18 20
Chesterfield	d					16 02						17 02						18 02		
Nottingham 8	d						16 10						17 05						18 05	
Derby 10	d	15 51				16 23	16 36	16 51				17 23	17 36	17 51				18 25	18 36	18 51
Burton-on-Trent	d						16 48					17 35	17 48						18 48	
Tamworth	d					16 43	17 00						18 00					18 43	19 00	
Birmingham New Street 12	a	16 27	16 31	16 55	16 58	17 02	17 21	17 27	17 31	17 55	17 58	18 00	18 21	18 27	18 31	18 55	18 58	19 02	19 21	19 27
Birmingham New Street 12	d	16 33	16 42		17 04	17 12	17 30	17 39	17 42		18 04	18 12	18 30	18 33	18 42		19 04	19 12	19 30	19 33
Cheltenham Spa	a		17 24			17 50	18 10		18 24			18 50	19 13		19 24			19 50	20 10	
Gloucester 7	a						18 21		18 35				19 24						20 21	
Bristol Parkway 7	a		18 02			18 23			19 08			19 23			20 00			20 23		
Bristol Temple Meads 10	a		18 14			18 37			19 25			19 35			20 14			20 35		
Newport (South Wales)	a						19 04						20 09						21 04	
Cardiff Central 7	a						19 25						20 30						21 25	
Weston-super-Mare	a														20 36					
Taunton	a					19 15						20 18			20 58			21 15		
Tiverton Parkway	a					19 28						20 28			21 11			21 28		
Exeter St Davids 6	a					19 48						20 47			21 26			21 44		
Dawlish	a														21 42					
Teignmouth	a														21 47					
Newton Abbot	a					20 07						21 06			21 54			22 03		
Torquay	a														22 06					
Paignton	a														22 19					
Totnes	a					20 20						21 19						22 16		
Plymouth	a					20 48						21 52						22 48		
Liskeard 6	a					21 12														
Bodmin Parkway	a					21 24														
Lostwithiel	a																			
Par	a					21 34														
Newquay	a																			
St Austell	a					21 41														
Truro	a					21 58														
Redruth	a					22 09														
Camborne	a					22 19														
Hayle	a																			
St Erth	a					22 30														
Penzance	a					22 46														
Birmingham International	d				17 14						18 14						19 14			
Coventry	d				17 25						18 25						19 25			
Leamington Spa 8	d	17 00			17 38			17 59			18 38			19 00			19 38			20 00
Banbury	a	17 18			17 54			18 18			18 54			19 18			19 54			20 18
Oxford	a	17 41			18 14			18 45			19 14			19 41			20 14			20 41
Reading 7	a	18 13			18 42			19 15			19 42			20 13			20 42			21 13
Guildford	a																			
Basingstoke	a				19 09						20 09						21 09			
Winchester	a				19 24						20 24						21 24			
Southampton Airport Parkwy	a				19 33						20 33						21 33			
Southampton Central	a				19 40						20 42						21 42			
Brockenhurst 3	a				20 01						21 01						22 01			
Bournemouth	a				20 27						21 27						22 27			

For general notes see front of timetable
For details of catering facilities see Directory of Train Operators

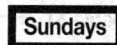

Scotland, The North East, North West England → The South West and South Coast

19 July to 6 September

Route Diagram - See first page of Table 51

		XC 1◇	VT 1◇	XC 1◇	XC 1◇	XC 1◇	XC 1◇	XC 1◇	VT 1◇	XC 1◇	XC 1◇	XC 1◇	XC 1◇	XC 1◇	VT 1◇	XC 1◇	VT 1◇	XC 1◇	XC 1◇
Aberdeen	d																		
Stonehaven	d																		
Montrose	d																		
Arbroath	d																		
Dundee	d																		
Leuchars 8	d																		
Cupar	d																		
Ladybank	d																		
Markinch	d																		
Kirkcaldy	d																		
Inverkeithing	d																		
Glasgow Central 15	d		15 55		13 45										18 35				
Motherwell	d				14 01														
Haymarket	d				14 43														
Edinburgh 10	d				14 50				16 52		15 50			16 50			18 52	17 50	
Haymarket	d								16u56								18u57		
Lockerbie	d																		
Carlisle 8	d		17 09						18 07						19 44		20 07		
Penrith North Lakes	d																20 22		
Oxenholme Lake District	d		17 44						18 42						20 19				
Lancaster 6	d								18 57						20 34		20 57		
Preston 8	d		18 17						19 17						20 55		21 17		
Wigan North Western	d		18 28						19 28						21 07		21 28		
Warrington Bank Quay	d		18 39						19 39						21 18		21 39		
Manchester Piccadilly 10	d	18 07		18 27				19 07		19 27			20 07			21 07			22 07
Stockport	d			18 36						19 36			20 16			21 16			22 16
Wilmslow	d																		
Crewe 10	d		19 01						20 01						21 40		22 01		
Macclesfield	d			18 49						19 49			20 29			21 29			22 29
Congleton	d																		
Stoke-on-Trent	d	18 43		19 07				19 43		20 07			20 47			21 47			22 47
Stafford	d			19 25						20 25			21 08		22 02	22 06			23 05
Wolverhampton 7	d	19 15	19 32	19 41				20 15	20 34	20 41			21 22		22 18	22 22	22 32		23 19
Dunbar	d				15 10									17 10				18 10	
Berwick-upon-Tweed	d				15 33									17 33					
Alnmouth for Alnwick	d										16 47							18 51	
Morpeth	d										17 02								
Newcastle 8	d				16 25		17 18				17 25	18 18		18 25				19 25	
Chester-le-Street	d						17 26					18 26		18 33					
Durham	d				16 37		17 33				17 37	18 33		18 40				19 39	
Darlington 7	d				16 54		17 50				17 55	18 50		18 57				19 56	
York 8	d				17 28		18 20				18 28	19 20		19 28				20 28	
Leeds 10	d				18 00						19 00			20 00				21 00	
Wakefield Westgate 7	d				18 12						19 12			20 12				21 12	
Doncaster 7	d						18 50					19 50							
Sheffield 7	d				18 50		19 20				19 50	20 20		20 50				21 50	
Chesterfield	d				19 02						20 02			21 02				22 02	
Nottingham 8	d					19 05													
Derby 10	d				19 23	19 36	19 51				20 23	20 51		21 23				22 23	
Burton-on-Trent	d				19 35	19 48								21 35				22 35	
Tamworth	d					20 00					20 43			21 46				22 46	
Birmingham New Street 12	a	19 31	19 55	19 58	20 00	20 25	20 27	20 31	20 57	20 58	21 02	21 30	21 39	22 04	22 40	22 45	22 55	23 05	23 41
Birmingham New Street 12	d	19 42		20 04	20 12		20 33	20 42		21 04	21 12		21 42	22 12					
Cheltenham Spa	a	20 24			20 50			21 24			21 50		22 24	22 51					
Gloucester 7	a																		
Bristol Parkway 7	a	20 57			21 23			21 59			22 24		22 57	23 24					
Bristol Temple Meads 10	a	21 14			21 35			22 14			22 41		23 13	23 41					
Newport (South Wales)	a																		
Cardiff Central 7	a																		
Weston-super-Mare	a																		
Taunton	a				22 15														
Tiverton Parkway	a				22 28														
Exeter St Davids 6	a				22 44														
Dawlish	a																		
Teignmouth	a																		
Newton Abbot	a				23 04														
Torquay	a																		
Paignton	a																		
Totnes	a				23 20														
Plymouth	a				23 54														
Liskeard 6	a																		
Bodmin Parkway	a																		
Lostwithiel	a																		
Par	a																		
Newquay	a																		
St Austell	a																		
Truro	a																		
Redruth	a																		
Camborne	a																		
Hayle	a																		
St Erth	a																		
Penzance	a																		
Birmingham International ✈	d			20 14						21 14									
Coventry	d			20 25						21 24									
Leamington Spa 8	d			20 38			21 00			21 35									
Banbury	a			20 54			21 18												
Oxford	a			21 14			21 38			22 08									
Reading 7	a			21 42			22 10			22 42									
Guildford	a																		
Basingstoke	a			22 11			22 30												
Winchester	a			22 26															
Southampton Airport Parkwy ✈	a			22 35			23 35												
Southampton Central	a			22 47			23 47												
Brockenhurst 3	a																		
Bournemouth	a																		

For general notes see front of timetable
For details of catering facilities see Directory of Train Operators

Scotland, The North East, North West England → The South West and South Coast

13 September to 1 November

Route Diagram - See first page of Table 51

		XC 1◇	XC 1◇	XC 1◇	XC 1◇	XC 1◇	XC 1◇	XC 1◇	XC 1◇	XC 1◇	XC 1◇	VT 1◇	XC 1◇	XC 1◇	XC 1◇	VT 1◇	XC 1◇	XC 1◇	XC 1◇	XC 1◇
Aberdeen	d																			
Stonehaven	d																			
Montrose	d																			
Arbroath	d																			
Dundee	d																			
Leuchars 3	d																			
Cupar	d																			
Ladybank	d																			
Markinch	d																			
Kirkcaldy	d																			
Inverkeithing	d																			
Glasgow Central 15	d																			
Motherwell	d																			
Haymarket	d																			
Edinburgh 10	d																			
Haymarket	d																			
Lockerbie	d																			
Carlisle 8	d																			
Penrith North Lakes	d																			
Oxenholme Lake District	d																			
Lancaster 6	d																			
Preston 8	d											10 17				11 17				
Wigan North Western	d											10 28				11 28				
Warrington Bank Quay	d											10 39				11 39				
Manchester Piccadilly 10	d			08 27			09 27				10 27						11 27			
Stockport	d			08 36			09 36				10 36						11 36			
Wilmslow	d			08 43																
Crewe 10	d			09 04								11 03				12 01				
Macclesfield	d						09 49				10 49						11 49			
Congleton	d																			
Stoke-on-Trent	d						10 07				11 07						12 07			
Stafford	d			09 28			10 27				11 25						12 26			
Wolverhampton 7	d			09 41			10 41				11 41	11 42				12 34	12 41			
Dunbar	d																			
Berwick-upon-Tweed	d																			
Alnmouth for Alnwick	d																			
Morpeth	d																			
Newcastle 8	d																	09 25		
Chester-le-Street	d																			
Durham	d																	09 38		
Darlington 7	d																	09 55		
York 8	d												09 28					10 28		
Leeds 10	d				08 09			09 00					10 00					11 00		
Wakefield Westgate 7	d				08 22			09 12					10 12					11 12		
Doncaster 7	d							09 30					10 30					11 30		
Sheffield 7	d				08 54			09 57					10 57					11 57		
Chesterfield	d				09 08			10 10					11 09					12 09		
Nottingham 8	d																		12 10	
Derby 10	d				09 30			10 33					11 30	11 36				12 30	12 36	
Burton-on-Trent	d							10 44					11 41	11 48					12 48	
Tamworth	d				09 49									12 00				12 49	13 00	
Birmingham New Street 12	a			09 58	10 10		10 58	11 11			11 58	12 05	12 07	12 26		12 55	12 58	13 07	13 21	
Birmingham New Street 12	d	09 04	09 12	10 04	10 12	10 30	11 04	11 12	11 30	11 33	12 04		12 12	12 30	12 33		13 04	13 12	13 30	13 33
Cheltenham Spa	a		09 49		10 51	11 10		11 51	12 10				12 50	13 10				13 50	14 12	
Gloucester 7	a					11 21			12 21					13 21					14 22	
Bristol Parkway 7	a		10 23		11 24			12 24					13 23					14 23		
Bristol Temple Meads 10	a		10 35		11 37			12 37					13 35					14 35		
Newport (South Wales)	a					12 04			13 04					14 04					15 05	
Cardiff Central 7	a					12 25			13 25					14 25					15 25	
Weston-super-Mare	a																			
Taunton	a		11 19		12 16			13 16					14 15					15 15		
Tiverton Parkway	a		11 33		12 30			13 30					14 28					15 28		
Exeter St Davids 6	a		11 48		12 47			13 47					14 44					15 44		
Dawlish	a																			
Teignmouth	a																			
Newton Abbot	a		12 08		13 08			14 08					15 03					16 03		
Torquay	a																			
Paignton	a																			
Totnes	a		12 23		13 22			14 22					15 16					16 16		
Plymouth	a		12 55		13 56			14 56					15 48					16 48		
Liskeard 6	a		13 17																	
Bodmin Parkway	a		13 29																	
Lostwithiel	a																			
Par	a		13 39																	
Newquay	a																			
St Austell	a		13 46																	
Truro	a		14 03																	
Redruth	a		14 15																	
Camborne	a		14 22																	
Hayle	a																			
St Erth	a		14 32																	
Penzance	a		14 43																	
Birmingham International ✈	d	09 14		10 14			11 14				12 14						13 14			
Coventry	d	09 25		10 25			11 25				12 25						13 25			
Leamington Spa 8	d	09 38		10 38			11 38			12 00	12 38				13 00		13 38			14 00
Banbury	a	09 54		10 54			11 54			12 18	12 54				13 18		13 54			14 18
Oxford	a	10 14		11 14			12 14			12 41	13 14				13 41		14 14			14 41
Reading 7	a	10 42		11 42			12 42			13 13	13 42				14 13		14 42			15 13
Guildford	a																			
Basingstoke	a	11 09		12 09			13 09				14 09						15 09			
Winchester	a	11 24		12 24			13 24				14 24						15 24			
Southampton Airport Parkwy ✈	a	11 33		12 33			13 33				14 33						15 33			
Southampton Central	a	11 42		12 42			13 42				14 42						15 42			
Brockenhurst 3	a	12 01		13 01			14 01				15 01						16 01			
Bournemouth	a	12 27		13 27			14 27				15 27						16 27			

For general notes see front of timetable
For details of catering facilities see Directory of Train Operators

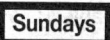

Scotland, The North East, North West England → The South West and South Coast

13 September to 1 November

Route Diagram - See first page of Table 51

		XC	VT	XC	XC	XC	XC	XC	VT	XC	XC	XC	XC	XC	VT	XC	XC	XC	XC	XC
		1◇	1◇	1◇	1◇	1◇	1◇	1◇	1◇	1◇	1◇	1◇	1◇	1◇	1◇	1◇	1◇	1◇	1◇	1◇
		⊼	⊡	⊼	⊼	⊼	⊼	⊼	⊡	⊼	⊼	⊼	⊼	⊼	⊡	⊼	⊼	⊼	⊼	⊼
Aberdeen	d																			
Stonehaven	d																			
Montrose	d																			
Arbroath	d																			
Dundee	d																			
Leuchars 3	d																			
Cupar	d																			
Ladybank	d																			
Markinch	d																			
Kirkcaldy	d																			
Inverkeithing	d																			
Glasgow Central 15	d														11 51					
Motherwell	d																			
Haymarket	d																			
Edinburgh 10	d				08 50				10 52		09 50						10 50			
Haymarket	d								10u57											
Lockerbie	d																			
Carlisle 8	d								12 07						13 09					
Penrith North Lakes	d																			
Oxenholme Lake District	d								12 43											
Lancaster 6	d		12 00						12 57						13 58					
Preston 8	d		12 17						13 17						14 17					
Wigan North Western	d		12 28						13 28						14 28					
Warrington Bank Quay	d		12 39						13 39						14 39					
Manchester Piccadilly 10 ⛴	d			12 26				13 07		13 27				14 07		14 27				15 07
Stockport	d			12 36						13 36						14 36				
Wilmslow	d																			
Crewe 10	d		13 01						14 01						15 01					
Macclesfield	d			12 49						13 49						14 49				
Congleton	d																			
Stoke-on-Trent	d			13 07				13 43		14 07				14 43		15 07				15 43
Stafford	d			13 25						14 25						15 25				
Wolverhampton 7 ⛴	d		13 32	13 41				14 15	14 34	14 41				15 15	15 32	15 41				16 15
Dunbar	d																11 10			
Berwick-upon-Tweed	d				09 33												11 33			
Alnmouth for Alnwick	d										10 47									
Morpeth	d										11 02									
Newcastle 8	d				10 25						11 25						12 25		13 15	
Chester-le-Street	d																		13 23	
Durham	d				10 38						11 37						12 37		13 30	
Darlington 7	d				10 55						11 54						12 54		13 47	
York 8	d				11 28						12 28						13 28		14 19	
Leeds 10	d				12 00						13 00						14 00			
Wakefield Westgate 7	d				12 12						13 12						14 12			
Doncaster 7	d				12 31						13 30								14 50	
Sheffield 7	d				12 57						13 57		14 22				14 50		15 20	
Chesterfield	d				13 10						14 09		14 34				15 02			
Nottingham 8 ⛴	d					13 08						14 10						15 10		
Derby 10	d				13 32	13 36	13 43				14 30	14 36	14 54				15 25	15 36	15 51	
Burton-on-Trent	d				13 43	13 48						14 48					15 35	15 48		
Tamworth	d					14 00					14 49	15 00						16 00		
Birmingham New Street 12	a		13 55	13 58	14 10	14 23	14 27	14 31	14 55	14 58	15 07	15 23	15 27	15 31	15 55	15 58	16 00	16 23	16 27	16 31
Birmingham New Street 12	d	13 42		14 04	14 12	14 30	14 33	14 42		15 04	15 12	15 30	15 33	15 42		16 04	16 12	16 30	16 33	16 42
Cheltenham Spa	a	14 23			14 52	15 10		15 24			15 50	16 10		16 24			16 50	17 10		17 24
Gloucester 7	a					15 21						16 21						17 21		
Bristol Parkway 7	a	14 56			15 25			16 00			16 23			16 57			17 23			18 02
Bristol Temple Meads 10	a	15 14			15 38			16 14			16 35			17 13			17 35			18 14
Newport (South Wales)	a					16 04						17 04						18 04		
Cardiff Central 7	a					16 25						17 25						18 25		
Weston-super-Mare	a																			
Taunton	a				16 16			16 45			17 15						18 19			
Tiverton Parkway	a				16 30			16 57			17 28						18 32			
Exeter St Davids 6	a				16 47			17 13			17 44						18 48			
Dawlish	a							17 25												
Teignmouth	a							17 30												
Newton Abbot	a				17 08			17 37			18 03						19 07			
Torquay	a							17 49												
Paignton	a							18 02												
Totnes	a				17 22						18 16						19 20			
Plymouth	a				17 56						18 44						19 53			
Liskeard 6	a										19 17									
Bodmin Parkway	a										19 29									
Lostwithiel	a																			
Par	a										19 39									
Newquay	a																			
St Austell	a										19 46									
Truro	a										20 07									
Redruth	a										20 18									
Camborne	a										20 25									
Hayle	a																			
St Erth	a										20 36									
Penzance	a										20 52									
Birmingham International ✈	d			14 14						15 14						16 14				
Coventry	d			14 25						15 25						16 25				
Leamington Spa 8	d			14 38			15 00			15 38			16 00			16 38			17 00	
Banbury	a			14 54			15 18			15 54			16 18			16 54			17 18	
Oxford	a			15 14			15 41			16 14			16 41			17 14			17 41	
Reading 7	a			15 42			16 13			16 42			17 13			17 42			18 13	
Guildford	a																			
Basingstoke	a			16 09						17 09						18 09				
Winchester	a			16 24						17 24						18 24				
Southampton Airport Parkway ✈	a			16 33						17 33						18 33				
Southampton Central	a			16 42						17 40						18 42				
Brockenhurst 3	a			17 01						18 01						19 01				
Bournemouth	a			17 27						18 27						19 27				

For general notes see front of timetable
For details of catering facilities see Directory of Train Operators

Scotland, The North East, North West England → The South West and South Coast

13 September to 1 November

Route Diagram - See first page of Table 51

Station		VT 1◇	XC 1◇	XC 1◇	XC 1◇	XC 1◇	XC 1◇	VT 1◇	XC 1◇	XC 1◇	XC 1◇	XC 1◇	XC 1◇	VT 1◇	XC 1◇	XC 1◇	XC 1◇	XC 1◇	XC 1◇	VT 1◇
Aberdeen	d															11 12				
Stonehaven	d															11 29				
Montrose	d															11 50				
Arbroath	d															12 06				
Dundee	d															12 25				
Leuchars 3	d															12 38				
Cupar	d															12 45				
Ladybank	d																			
Markinch	d																			
Kirkcaldy	d															13 03				
Inverkeithing	d															13 18				
Glasgow Central 15	d							13 56		11 37										15 55
Motherwell	d									11 57										
Haymarket	d									12 38						13 37				
Edinburgh 10	d	12 52		11 50						12 50		13 33		14 52		13 50				
Haymarket	d	12u56												14u57						
Lockerbie	d																			
Carlisle 8	d	14 07						15 09						16 07						17 09
Penrith North Lakes	d	14 22												16 22						
Oxenholme Lake District	d							15 44												17 44
Lancaster 6	d	14 57												16 57						
Preston 8	d	15 17						16 17						17 17						18 17
Wigan North Western	d	15 28						16 28						17 28						18 28
Warrington Bank Quay	d	15 39						16 39						17 39						18 39
Manchester Piccadilly 10	d		15 27				16 07		16 27				17 07		17 27				18 07	
Stockport	d		15 36						16 36						17 36					
Wilmslow	d																			
Crewe 10	d	16 01						17 01						18 01						19 01
Macclesfield	d		15 49						16 49						17 49					
Congleton	d																			
Stoke-on-Trent	d		16 07				16 43		17 07				17 43		18 07				18 43	
Stafford	d		16 25						17 25						18 25					
Wolverhampton 7	d	16 34	16 41				17 15	17 32	17 41				18 15	18 32	18 41				19 15	19 32
Dunbar	d									13 10										
Berwick-upon-Tweed	d									13 33		14 18								
Alnmouth for Alnwick	d			12 47								14 38				14 47				
Morpeth	d																			
Newcastle 8	d			13 25		14 18				14 25		15 18				15 25		16 18		
Chester-le-Street	d																			
Durham	d			13 37		14 30				14 37		15 30				15 37		16 30		
Darlington 7	d			13 55		14 47				14 54		15 47				15 54		16 47		
York 8	d			14 28		15 20				15 28		16 20				16 28		17 20		
Leeds 10	d			15 00						16 00						17 00				
Wakefield Westgate 7	d			15 12						16 12						17 12				
Doncaster 7	d					15 50						16 50						17 50		
Sheffield 7	d			15 50		16 20				16 50		17 20				17 50		18 20		
Chesterfield	d			16 02						17 02						18 02				
Nottingham 8	d				16 10						17 10						18 10			
Derby 10	d			16 25	16 36	16 51				17 25	17 36	17 51				18 25	18 36	18 51		
Burton-on-Trent	d				16 48					17 35	17 48						18 50			
Tamworth	d			16 43	17 00						18 00					18 43	19 00			
Birmingham New Street 12	a	16 55	16 58	17 02	17 23	17 25	17 31	17 55	17 58	18 00	18 23	18 26	18 31	18 55	18 58	19 03	19 23	19 27	19 31	19 55
Birmingham New Street 12	d		17 04	17 12	17 30	17 33	17 42		18 04	18 12	18 30	18 33	18 42		19 04	19 12	19 30	19 33	19 42	
Cheltenham Spa	a			17 50	18 10		18 24			18 50	19 13		19 24			19 50	20 10		20 24	
Gloucester 7	a				18 21		18 35				19 24						20 21			
Bristol Parkway 7	a			18 23			19 08			19 23			20 00			20 23			20 57	
Bristol Temple Meads 10	a			18 37			19 25			19 35			20 14			20 35			21 14	
Newport (South Wales)	a				19 04						20 09						21 04			
Cardiff Central 7	a				19 25						20 30						21 25			
Weston-super-Mare	a												20 36							
Taunton	a			19 15						20 18			20 58			21 15				
Tiverton Parkway	a			19 30						20 31			21 11			21 28				
Exeter St Davids 6	a			19 48						20 47			21 26			21 44				
Dawlish	a												21 42							
Teignmouth	a												21 47							
Newton Abbot	a			20 07						21 06			21 54			22 03				
Torquay	a												22 06							
Paignton	a												22 19							
Totnes	a			20 20						21 19						22 16				
Plymouth	a			20 48						21 52						22 48				
Liskeard 6	a			21 12																
Bodmin Parkway	a			21 24																
Lostwithiel	a																			
Par	a			21 34																
Newquay	a																			
St Austell	a			21 41																
Truro	a			21 58																
Redruth	a			22 09																
Camborne	a			22 19																
Hayle	a																			
St Erth	a			22 30																
Penzance	a			22 46																
Birmingham International ✈	d		17 14						18 14						19 14					
Coventry	d		17 25						18 25						19 25					
Leamington Spa 8	d		17 38			18 00			18 38			19 00			19 38			20 00		
Banbury	a		17 54			18 18			18 54			19 18			19 54			20 18		
Oxford	a		18 14			18 41			19 14			19 41			20 14			20 41		
Reading 7	a		18 42			19 13			19 42			20 10			20 42			21 13		
Guildford	a																			
Basingstoke	a		19 09						20 09						21 09					
Winchester	a		19 24						20 24						21 24					
Southampton Airport Parkwy ✈	a		19 33						20 33						21 33					
Southampton Central	a		19 40						20 42						21 42					
Brockenhurst 3	a		20 01						21 01						22 01					
Bournemouth	a		20 27						21 27						22 27					

For general notes see front of timetable
For details of catering facilities see Directory of Train Operators

Scotland, The North East, North West England → The South West and South Coast

13 September to 1 November

Route Diagram - See first page of Table 51

		XC 1◇		XC 1◇	XC 1◇	XC 1◇	XC 1◇		VT 1◇	XC 1◇	XC 1◇	XC 1◇		XC 1◇	XC 1◇	XC 1◇	VT 1◇		XC 1◇	VT 1◇	XC 1◇	XC 1◇		
Aberdeen	d																							
Stonehaven	d																							
Montrose	d																							
Arbroath	d																							
Dundee	d																							
Leuchars 8	d																							
Cupar	d																							
Ladybank	d																							
Markinch	d																							
Kirkcaldy	d																							
Inverkeithing	d																							
Glasgow Central 15	d			13 45													18 35							
Motherwell	d			14 01																				
Haymarket	d			14 43																				
Edinburgh 10	d			14 50					16 52		15 50					16 50				18 52	17 50			
Haymarket	d								16u56											18u57				
Lockerbie	d																							
Carlisle 8	d								18 07								19 44			20 07				
Penrith North Lakes	d																			20 22				
Oxenholme Lake District	d								18 42								20 19							
Lancaster 6	d								18 57								20 34			20 57				
Preston 8	d								19 17								20 55			21 17				
Wigan North Western	d								19 28								21 07			21 28				
Warrington Bank Quay	d								19 39								21 18			21 39				
Manchester Piccadilly 10	d	18 27					19 07			19 27					20 07				21 07			22 07		
Stockport	d	18 36								19 35					20 16				21 16			22 16		
Wilmslow	d																							
Crewe 10	d								20 01								21 40			22 01				
Macclesfield	d	18 49								19 49					20 29				21 29			22 29		
Congleton	d																							
Stoke-on-Trent	d	19 07					19 43			20 07					20 47				21 47			22 47		
Stafford	d	19 25								20 25					21 08		22 02		22 06			23 06		
Wolverhampton 7	d	19 41					20 15		20 34	20 41					21 22		22 18		22 22	22 32		23 19		
Dunbar	d			15 10												17 10					18 10			
Berwick-upon-Tweed	d			15 33												17 33								
Alnmouth for Alnwick	d										16 47													
Morpeth	d										17 02										18 51			
Newcastle 8	d			16 25		17 18					17 25			18 18		18 25					19 25			
Chester-le-Street	d					17 26								18 26		18 33								
Durham	d			16 37		17 33					17 37			18 33		18 40					19 39			
Darlington 7	d			16 54		17 50					17 55			18 50		18 57					19 56			
York 8	d			17 28		18 20					18 28			19 20		19 28					20 28			
Leeds 10	d			18 00							19 00					20 00					21 00			
Wakefield Westgate 7	d			18 12							19 12					20 12					21 12			
Doncaster 7	d					18 50								19 50										
Sheffield 7	d			18 50		19 20					19 50			20 20		20 50					21 50			
Chesterfield	d			19 02							20 02					21 02					22 04			
Nottingham 8	d				19 10							20 10												
Derby 10	d			19 25	19 36	19 51					20 25	20 36		20 51		21 23					22 25			
Burton-on-Trent	d			19 35	19 49							20 48				21 34					22 35			
Tamworth	d				20 00						20 43	21 00				21 44					22 46			
Birmingham New Street 12	a	19 58		20 03	20 23	20 27	20 31		20 57	20 58	21 02	21 23		21 27	21 39	22 03	22 40		22 45	22 55	23 05	23 41		
Birmingham New Street 12	d	20 04		20 12		20 33	20 42			21 04	21 12				21 42	22 12								
Cheltenham Spa	a			20 50			21 24				21 51				22 24	22 51								
Gloucester 7	a																							
Bristol Parkway 7	a			21 23			21 59				22 24				22 57	23 24								
Bristol Temple Meads 10	a			21 35			22 14				22 41				23 14	23 41								
Newport (South Wales)	a																							
Cardiff Central 7	a																							
Weston-super-Mare	a																							
Taunton	a			22 15																				
Tiverton Parkway	a			22 28																				
Exeter St Davids 6	a			22 44																				
Dawlish	a																							
Teignmouth	a																							
Newton Abbot	a			23 04																				
Torquay	a																							
Paignton	a																							
Totnes	a			23 20																				
Plymouth	a			23 54																				
Liskeard 6	a																							
Bodmin Parkway	a																							
Lostwithiel	a																							
Par	a																							
Newquay	a																							
St Austell	a																							
Truro	a																							
Redruth	a																							
Camborne	a																							
Hayle	a																							
St Erth	a																							
Penzance	a																							
Birmingham International ✈	d	20 14								21 14														
Coventry	d	20 25								21 24														
Leamington Spa 8	d	20 38				21 00				21 35														
Banbury	a	20 54				21 18																		
Oxford	a	21 14				21 40				22 08														
Reading 7	a	21 42				22 12				22 42														
Guildford	a																							
Basingstoke	a	22 11				22 30																		
Winchester	a	22 26																						
Southampton Airport Parkway ✈	a	22 35				23 35																		
Southampton Central	a	22 47				23 47																		
Brockenhurst 3	a																							
Bournemouth	a																							

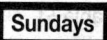

For general notes see front of timetable
For details of catering facilities see Directory of Train Operators

from 8 November

Scotland, The North East, North West England → The South West and South Coast

Route Diagram - See first page of Table 51

		XC 1◇	XC 1◇	XC 1◇	XC 1◇	XC 1◇	XC 1◇	XC 1◇	XC 1◇	XC 1◇	XC 1◇	XC 1◇	XC 1◇	XC 1◇	XC 1◇	XC 1◇	XC 1◇	XC 1◇	XC 1◇	XC 1◇
Aberdeen	d																			
Stonehaven	d																			
Montrose	d																			
Arbroath	d																			
Dundee	d																			
Leuchars 3	d																			
Cupar	d																			
Ladybank	d																			
Markinch	d																			
Kirkcaldy	d																			
Inverkeithing	d																			
Glasgow Central 15	d																			
Motherwell	d																			
Haymarket	d																			
Edinburgh 10	d																			
Haymarket	d																			
Lockerbie	d																			
Carlisle 8	d																			
Penrith North Lakes	d																			
Oxenholme Lake District	d																			
Lancaster 6	d																			
Preston 8	d																			
Wigan North Western	d																			
Warrington Bank Quay	d																			
Manchester Piccadilly 10	d					08 27			09 27				10 27					11 27		
Stockport	d					08 36			09 36				10 36					11 36		
Wilmslow	d					08 43														
Crewe 10	d					09 04														
Macclesfield	d								09 49				10 49					11 49		
Congleton	d																			
Stoke-on-Trent	d								10 07				11 07					12 07		
Stafford	d					09 28			10 27				11 25					12 26		
Wolverhampton 7	d					09 41			10 41				11 41					12 41		
Dunbar	d																			
Berwick-upon-Tweed	d																			
Alnmouth for Alnwick	d																			
Morpeth	d																			
Newcastle 8	d																		09 25	
Chester-le-Street	d																			
Durham	d																		09 38	
Darlington 7	d																		09 55	
York 8	d													09 28					10 28	
Leeds 10	d				07 45			08 30						10 00					11 00	
Wakefield Westgate 7	d				08 00			08 43						10 12					11 12	
Doncaster 7	d							09 01						10 30					11 30	
Sheffield 7	d				08 32			09 29						10 57					11 57	
Chesterfield	d				08 46			09 43						11 09					12 09	
Nottingham 8	d																			12 10
Derby 10	d				09 08			10 05						11 30	11 36				12 30	12 36
Burton-on-Trent	d							10 16						11 41	11 48					12 48
Tamworth	d				09 27										12 00				12 48	13 00
Birmingham New Street 12	a				09 47	09 58		10 43	10 59				11 59	12 12	12 26			12 58	13 12	13 21
Birmingham New Street 12	d	08 42	09 04	09 30	09 52	10 04	10 30	10 46	11 04	11 30	11 33	11 45	12 04		12 30	12 33	12 42	13 04		13 28
Cheltenham Spa	a	09 50		10 28	10 51		11 28	11 50		12 28		12 50			13 28		13 50			14 44
Gloucester 7	a			10 39			11 39			12 39					13 39					14 54
Bristol Parkway 7	a	10 23			11 24			12 23				13 23					14 25			
Bristol Temple Meads 10	a	10 35			11 37			12 36				13 35					14 37			
Newport (South Wales)	a			11 24			12 28			13 22					14 30					15 39
Cardiff Central 7	a			11 47			12 49			13 44					14 52					16 00
Weston-super-Mare	a																			
Taunton	a	11 19			12 16			13 16				14 15					15 15			
Tiverton Parkway	a	11 33			12 30			13 30				14 28					15 28			
Exeter St Davids 6	a	11 48			12 47			13 47				14 44					15 44			
Dawlish	a																			
Teignmouth	a																			
Newton Abbot	a	12 08			13 08			14 08				15 03					16 03			
Torquay	a																			
Paignton	a																			
Totnes	a	12 23			13 22			14 22				15 16					16 16			
Plymouth	a	12 55			13 56			14 56				15 49					16 49			
Liskeard 6	a	13 17																		
Bodmin Parkway	a	13 29																		
Lostwithiel	a																			
Par	a	13 39																		
Newquay	a																			
St Austell	a	13 46																		
Truro	a	14 03																		
Redruth	a	14 15																		
Camborne	a	14 22																		
Hayle	a																			
St Erth	a	14 32																		
Penzance	a	14 43																		
Birmingham International ✈	d		09 14			10 14			11 14				12 14					13 14		
Coventry	d		09 25			10 25			11 25				12 25					13 25		
Leamington Spa 8	d		09 38			10 38			11 38		12 00		12 38			13 00		13 38		
Banbury	a		09 54			10 54			11 54		12 18		12 54			13 18		13 54		
Oxford	a		10 14			11 14			12 14		12 41		13 14			13 41		14 14		
Reading 7	a		10 42			11 42			12 42		13 13		13 42			14 13		14 42		
Guildford	a																			
Basingstoke	a		11 09			12 09			13 09				14 09					15 09		
Winchester	a		11 24			12 24			13 24				14 24					15 24		
Southampton Airport Parkway ✈	a		11 33			12 33			13 33				14 33					15 33		
Southampton Central	a		11 42			12 42			13 42				14 42					15 42		
Brockenhurst 3	a		12 01			13 01			14 01				15 01					16 01		
Bournemouth	a		12 27			13 27			14 27				15 27					16 27		

For general notes see front of timetable
For details of catering facilities see Directory of Train Operators

Table 51 SUMMARY OF SERVICES

Sundays from 8 November

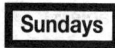

Scotland, The North East, North West England → The South West and South Coast

Route Diagram - See first page of Table 51

		XC 1◇	XC 1◇	XC 1◇	XC 1◇	XC 1◇	XC 1◇	XC 1◇	VT 1◇	XC 1◇	XC 1◇	XC 1◇	XC 1◇	XC 1◇	VT 1◇	XC 1◇	XC 1◇	XC 1◇	XC 1◇	XC 1◇
Aberdeen	d																			
Stonehaven	d																			
Montrose	d																			
Arbroath	d																			
Dundee	d																			
Leuchars 3	d																			
Cupar	d																			
Ladybank	d																			
Markinch	d																			
Kirkcaldy	d																			
Inverkeithing	d																			
Glasgow Central 15	d																			
Motherwell	d																			
Haymarket	d																			
Edinburgh 10	d				08 50						09 50				10 52		10 50			
Haymarket	d														10u57					
Lockerbie	d																			
Carlisle 8	d														12 07					
Penrith North Lakes	d																			
Oxenholme Lake District	d														12 43					
Lancaster 6	d								12 10						12 57					
Preston 8	d								12 30						13 30					
Wigan North Western	d																			
Warrington Bank Quay	d																			
Manchester Piccadilly 10	d			12 26				13 07		13 27				14 07		14 27				15 07
Stockport	d			12 36						13 36						14 36				
Wilmslow	d																			
Crewe 10	d								14 01						15 01					
Macclesfield	d			12 49						13 49						14 49				
Congleton	d																			
Stoke-on-Trent	d			13 07				13 43		14 07				14 43		15 07				15 43
Stafford	d			13 25						14 25						15 25				
Wolverhampton 7	d			13 41				14 15	14 33	14 41				15 15	15 32	15 41				16 15
Dunbar	d																11 10			
Berwick-upon-Tweed	d				09 33												11 33			
Alnmouth for Alnwick	d										10 47									
Morpeth	d										11 02									
Newcastle 8	d				10 25						11 25						12 25		13 15	
Chester-le-Street	d																		13 23	
Durham	d				10 38						11 37						12 37		13 30	
Darlington 7	d				10 55						11 54						12 54		13 47	
York 8	d				11 28						12 28						13 28		14 19	
Leeds 10	d				12 00						13 00						14 00			
Wakefield Westgate 7	d				12 12						13 12						14 12			
Doncaster 7	d				12 30						13 30								14 50	
Sheffield 7	d				12 57						13 57		14 22				14 50		15 20	
Chesterfield	d				13 09						14 09		14 34				15 02			
Nottingham 8	d					13 08						14 10						15 10		
Derby 10	d				13 32	13 36	13 43				14 30	14 35	14 54				15 25	15 35	15 51	
Burton-on-Trent	d				13 43	13 49						14 48					15 35	15 48		
Tamworth	d					14 01					14 48	15 00						16 00		
Birmingham New Street 12	a			13 58	14 12	14 22	14 27	14 31	14 55	14 58	15 12	15 23	15 27	15 31	15 55	15 58	16 05	16 23	16 27	16 31
Birmingham New Street 12	d	13 33	13 42	14 04		14 28	14 33	14 42		15 04		15 28	15 33	15 42		16 04		16 28	16 33	16 42
Cheltenham Spa	a		14 50			15 40		15 50				16 26		16 50				17 36		17 50
Gloucester 7	a					15 50						16 38						17 47		
Bristol Parkway 7	a		15 23					16 23						17 23						18 23
Bristol Temple Meads 10	a		15 36					16 35						17 35						18 35
Newport (South Wales)	a					16 44						17 28						18 42		
Cardiff Central 7	a					17 07						17 49						19 04		
Weston-super-Mare	a																			
Taunton	a		16 16					17 15						18 19						19 15
Tiverton Parkway	a		16 30					17 28						18 32						19 30
Exeter St Davids 6	a		16 47					17 44						18 48						19 48
Dawlish	a																			
Teignmouth	a																			
Newton Abbot	a		17 08					18 03						19 07						20 07
Torquay	a																			
Paignton	a																			
Totnes	a		17 22					18 16						19 20						20 20
Plymouth	a		17 56					18 44						19 53						20 48
Liskeard 6	a							19 17												21 12
Bodmin Parkway	a							19 29												21 24
Lostwithiel	a																			
Par	a							19 39												21 34
Newquay	a																			
St Austell	a							19 46												21 41
Truro	a							20 07												21 58
Redruth	a							20 18												22 09
Camborne	a							20 25												22 19
Hayle	a																			
St Erth	a							20 36												22 30
Penzance	a							20 52												22 46
Birmingham International	d			14 14						15 14						16 14				
Coventry	d			14 25						15 25						16 25				
Leamington Spa 8	d	14 00		14 38			15 00			15 38			16 00			16 38			17 00	
Banbury	a	14 18		14 54			15 18			15 54			16 18			16 54			17 18	
Oxford	a	14 41		15 14			15 41			16 14			16 41			17 14			17 41	
Reading 7	a	15 13		15 42			16 13			16 42			17 13			17 42			18 13	
Guildford	a																			
Basingstoke	a			16 09						17 09						18 09				
Winchester	a			16 24						17 24						18 24				
Southampton Airport Parkwy	a			16 33						17 33						18 33				
Southampton Central	a			16 42						17 40						18 42				
Brockenhurst 3	a			17 01						18 01						19 01				
Bournemouth	a			17 27						18 27						19 27				

For general notes see front of timetable
For details of catering facilities see Directory of Train Operators

SUMMARY OF SERVICES

Sundays

from 8 November

Scotland, The North East, North West England → The South West and South Coast

Route Diagram - See first page of Table 51

		XC 1◇	XC 1◇	XC 1◇	XC 1◇	XC 1◇	VT 1◇	XC 1◇	XC 1◇	XC 1◇	XC 1◇	XC 1◇	VT 1◇	XC 1◇	XC 1◇	XC 1◇	XC 1◇	XC 1◇	VT 1◇	XC 1◇
Aberdeen	d														11 12					
Stonehaven	d														11 29					
Montrose	d														11 50					
Arbroath	d														12 06					
Dundee	d														12 25					
Leuchars 3	d														12 38					
Cupar	d														12 45					
Ladybank	d																			
Markinch	d																			
Kirkcaldy	d														13 03					
Inverkeithing	d														13 18					
Glasgow Central 15	d								11 37										15 55	
Motherwell	d								11 57											
Haymarket	d								12 38						13 37					
Edinburgh 10	d		11 50						12 50		13 33		14 52		13 50					
Haymarket	d												14u57							
Lockerbie	d																			
Carlisle 8	d						15 07						16 07						17 09	
Penrith North Lakes	d												16 22							
Oxenholme Lake District	d						15 44												17 44	
Lancaster 6	d												16 57							
Preston 8	d						16 17						17 17						18 17	
Wigan North Western	d						16 28						17 28						18 28	
Warrington Bank Quay	d						16 39						17 39						18 39	
Manchester Piccadilly 10	d	15 27				16 07		16 27				17 07		17 27				18 07		18 27
Stockport	d	15 36						16 36						17 36						18 36
Wilmslow	d																			
Crewe 10	d						17 01						18 01						19 01	
Macclesfield	d	15 49						16 49						17 49						18 49
Congleton	d																			
Stoke-on-Trent	d	16 07				16 43		17 07				17 43		18 07				18 43		19 07
Stafford	d	16 25						17 25						18 25						19 25
Wolverhampton 7	d	16 41				17 15	17 32	17 41				18 15	18 32	18 41				19 15	19 32	19 41
Dunbar	d								13 10											
Berwick-upon-Tweed	d								13 33		14 18									
Alnmouth for Alnwick	d		12 47								14 38				14 47					
Morpeth	d																			
Newcastle 8	d		13 25		14 18				14 25		15 18				15 25		16 18			
Chester-le-Street	d																			
Durham	d		13 37		14 30				14 37		15 30				15 37		16 30			
Darlington 7	d		13 54		14 47				14 54		15 47				15 54		16 47			
York 8	d		14 28		15 20				15 28		16 20				16 28		17 20			
Leeds 10	d		15 00						16 00						17 00					
Wakefield Westgate 7	d		15 12						16 12						17 12					
Doncaster 7	d				15 50						16 50						17 50			
Sheffield 7	d		15 50		16 20				16 50		17 20				17 50		18 20			
Chesterfield	d		16 03						17 02						18 02					
Nottingham 8	d			16 10						17 10						18 10				
Derby 10	d		16 25	16 35	16 51				17 25	17 36	17 51				18 25	18 36	18 51			
Burton-on-Trent	d			16 47					17 35	17 48						18 48				
Tamworth	d		16 43	16 59						18 00					18 43	19 01				
Birmingham New Street 12	a	16 58	17 05	17 20	17 27	17 31	17 55	17 58	18 05	18 23	18 26	18 31	18 55	18 58	19 05	19 23	19 27	19 31	19 55	19 58
Birmingham New Street 12	d	17 04		17 28	17 33	17 42		18 04		18 28	18 33	18 42		19 04			19 33	19 42		20 04
Cheltenham Spa	a			18 26		18 50				19 40		19 54						20 50		
Gloucester 7	a			18 38						19 51										
Bristol Parkway 7	a					19 23						20 27						21 23		
Bristol Temple Meads 10	a					19 35						20 39						21 36		
Newport (South Wales)	a			19 25						20 39										
Cardiff Central 7	a			19 46						21 00										
Weston-super-Mare	a																			
Taunton	a					20 18						21 15						22 15		
Tiverton Parkway	a					20 31						21 28						22 28		
Exeter St Davids 6	a					20 46						21 43						22 44		
Dawlish	a																			
Teignmouth	a																			
Newton Abbot	a					21 06						22 03						23 04		
Torquay	a																			
Paignton	a																			
Totnes	a					21 19						22 16						23 20		
Plymouth	a					21 51						22 48						23 54		
Liskeard 6	a																			
Bodmin Parkway	a																			
Lostwithiel	a																			
Par	a																			
Newquay	a																			
St Austell	a																			
Truro	a																			
Redruth	a																			
Camborne	a																			
Hayle	a																			
St Erth	a																			
Penzance	a																			
Birmingham International ✈	d	17 14						18 14						19 14						20 14
Coventry	d	17 25						18 25						19 25						20 25
Leamington Spa 8	d	17 38			18 00			18 38			19 00			19 38			20 00			20 38
Banbury	a	17 54			18 18			18 54			19 18			19 54			20 18			20 54
Oxford	a	18 14			18 41			19 14			19 41			20 14			20 41			21 14
Reading 7	a	18 42			19 13			19 42			20 10			20 42			21 13			21 42
Guildford	a																			
Basingstoke	a	19 09						20 09						21 09						22 11
Winchester	a	19 24						20 24						21 24						22 26
Southampton Airport Parkwy ✈	a	19 33						20 33						21 33						22 35
Southampton Central	a	19 40						20 42						21 42						22 47
Brockenhurst 3	a	20 01						21 01						22 01						
Bournemouth	a	20 27						21 27						22 27						

For general notes see front of timetable
For details of catering facilities see Directory of Train Operators

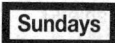

Sundays
from 8 November

Scotland, The North East, North West England → The South West and South Coast

Route Diagram - See first page of Table 51

		XC 1◇	XC 1◇	XC 1◇	XC 1◇	VT 1◇	XC 1◇	XC 1◇	XC 1◇	XC 1◇	XC 1◇	XC 1◇	VT 1◇	XC 1◇	VT 1◇	XC 1◇	XC 1◇
Aberdeen	d																
Stonehaven	d																
Montrose	d																
Arbroath	d																
Dundee	d																
Leuchars 3	d																
Cupar	d																
Ladybank	d																
Markinch	d																
Kirkcaldy	d																
Inverkeithing	d																
Glasgow Central 15	d	13 45											18 35				
Motherwell	d	14 01															
Haymarket	d	14 43															
Edinburgh 10	d	14 50				16 52		15 50				16 50			18 52	17 50	
Haymarket	d					16u56									18u57		
Lockerbie	d																
Carlisle 8	d					18 07							19 44		20 07		
Penrith North Lakes	d														20 22		
Oxenholme Lake District	d					18 42							20 19				
Lancaster 6	d					18 57							20 34		20 57		
Preston 8	d					19 17							20 55		21 17		
Wigan North Western	d					19 28							21 07		21 28		
Warrington Bank Quay	d					19 39							21 18		21 39		
Manchester Piccadilly 10	d				19 07		19 27				20 07			21 07			22 07
Stockport	d						19 36				20 16			21 16			22 16
Wilmslow	d																
Crewe 10	d					20 01							21 40		22 01		
Macclesfield	d						19 49				20 29			21 29			22 29
Congleton	d																
Stoke-on-Trent	d				19 43		20 07				20 47			21 47			22 47
Stafford	d						20 25				21 09		22 02	22 06			23 06
Wolverhampton 7	d				20 15	20 34	20 41				21 22		22 18	22 22	22 32		23 19
Dunbar	d	15 10										17 10				18 10	
Berwick-upon-Tweed	d	15 33										17 33					
Alnmouth for Alnwick	d							16 47								18 51	
Morpeth	d							17 02									
Newcastle 8	d	16 25		17 18				17 25		18 18		18 25				19 25	
Chester-le-Street	d			17 26						18 26		18 33					
Durham	d	16 37		17 33				17 37		18 33		18 40				19 39	
Darlington 7	d	16 54		17 50				17 55		18 50		18 57				19 56	
York 8	d	17 28		18 20				18 28		19 20		19 28				20 28	
Leeds 10	d	18 00						19 00				20 00				21 00	
Wakefield Westgate 7	d	18 12						19 12				20 12				21 12	
Doncaster 7	d			18 50						19 50							
Sheffield 7	d	18 50		19 20				19 50		20 20		20 50				21 50	
Chesterfield	d	19 02						20 02				21 03				22 04	
Nottingham 8	d		19 10						20 10								
Derby 10	d	19 25	19 36	19 51				20 25	20 36	20 51		21 23				22 25	
Burton-on-Trent	d	19 35	19 49						20 48			21 34				22 35	
Tamworth	d		20 00					20 44	21 00							22 46	
Birmingham New Street 12	a	20 05	20 23	20 27	20 31	20 57	20 58	21 02	21 23	21 27	21 39	21 59	22 40	22 45	22 55	23 05	23 41
Birmingham New Street 12	d			20 33	20 42		21 04				21 44						
Cheltenham Spa	a				21 50						22 50						
Gloucester 7	a																
Bristol Parkway 7	a				22 23						23 23						
Bristol Temple Meads 10	a				22 40						23 40						
Newport (South Wales)	a																
Cardiff Central 7	a																
Weston-super-Mare	a																
Taunton	a																
Tiverton Parkway	a																
Exeter St Davids 6	a																
Dawlish	a																
Teignmouth	a																
Newton Abbot	a																
Torquay	a																
Paignton	a																
Totnes	a																
Plymouth	a																
Liskeard 6	a																
Bodmin Parkway	a																
Lostwithiel	a																
Par	a																
Newquay	a																
St Austell	a																
Truro	a																
Redruth	a																
Camborne	a																
Hayle	a																
St Erth	a																
Penzance	a																
Birmingham International ✈	d						21 14										
Coventry	d						21 24										
Leamington Spa 8	d			21 00			21 35										
Banbury	a			21 18													
Oxford	a			21 40			22 08										
Reading 7	a			22 12			22 42										
Guildford	a																
Basingstoke	a			22 30													
Winchester	a																
Southampton Airport Parkwy ✈	a			23 35													
Southampton Central	a			23 47													
Brockenhurst 3	a																
Bournemouth	a																

For general notes see front of timetable
For details of catering facilities see Directory of Train Operators

South Coast and the South West → North West England, The North East and Scotland

Route Diagram - See first page of Table 51

		XC	XC	VT	XC	XC	XC	XC	XC		XC	VT	XC	XC	XC	XC	XC	XC		VT	XC	XC	XC	XC
		1◇	1◇	1◇	1	1◇	1◇	1	1◇		1◇	1◇	1	1◇	1◇	1	1◇	1◇		1◇	1◇	1◇	1◇	1◇
		⊼	⊼	☒		⊡	⊼		⊼		⊼	☒		⊼	⊼		⊼	⊼		☒	⊼	⊼		⊼
Bournemouth	d																							
Brockenhurst 3	d																							
Southampton Central	d															05 15							06 15
Southampton Airport Parkwy ✈	d															05 22							06 22
Winchester	d															05 31							06 31
Basingstoke	d															05 47							06 47
Guildford	d																			06 00			
Reading 7	d															06 10				06 40			07 10
Oxford	d															06 35				07 05			07 35
Banbury	d															06 54				07 25			07 54
Leamington Spa 8	d															07 12				07 43			08 12
Coventry	d															07 27							08 27
Birmingham International ✈	d															07 38							08 38
Penzance	d																							
St Erth	d																							
Hayle	d																							
Camborne	d																							
Redruth	d																							
Truro	d																							
St Austell	d																							
Newquay	d																							
Par	d																							
Lostwithiel	d																							
Bodmin Parkway	d																							
Liskeard 6	d																							
Plymouth	d																							
Totnes	d																							
Paignton	d																							
Torquay	d																							
Newton Abbot	d																							
Teignmouth	d																							
Dawlish	d																							
Exeter St Davids 6	d																							
Tiverton Parkway	d																							
Taunton	d																							
Weston-super-Mare	d																							
Cardiff Central 7	d																						06 40	
Newport (South Wales)	d																						06 55	
Bristol Temple Meads 10	d																06 15				07 00		
Bristol Parkway 7	d																06 25				07 10		
Gloucester 7	d																07 02					07 46	
Cheltenham Spa	d																07 12				07 42	07 56	
Birmingham New Street 12	a															07 49	07 56			08 17	08 26	08 45	08 49
Birmingham New Street 12	d	05 57	06 00	06 17	06 19	06 20	06 30	06 49	06 57		07 03	07 19	07 19	07 30	07 31	07 49	07 57	08 03		08 20	08 30	08 31	08 49	08 57
Tamworth	d		06 15		06 39		06 46	07 07			07 19		07 38	07 46		08 07		08 19					09 07	
Burton-on-Trent	d				06 51		06 56	07 19			07 29		07 50	07 57		08 19		08 29					09 19	
Derby 10	a		06 35		07 04		07 11	07 34			07 42		08 05	08 11		08 34		08 42			09 11		09 34	
Nottingham 8	a				07 41			08 08					08 35			09 05							10 05	
Chesterfield	a						07 31				08 02			08 32				09 02						
Sheffield 7	a		07 06				07 48				08 17			08 51				09 17			09 46			
Doncaster 7	a						08 24							09 20							10 15			
Wakefield Westgate 7	a		07 36								08 46							09 46						
Leeds 10	a		07 52								09 02							10 02						
York 8	a		08 23				08 47				09 33			09 48				10 29			10 40			
Darlington 7	a		08 55				09 20				10 04			10 17				10 59			11 12			
Durham	a		09 13				09 37				10 21			10 34				11 17			11 29			
Chester-le-Street	a						09 44																	
Newcastle 8	a		09 26				10 00				10 36			10 57				11 32			11 54			
Morpeth	a		09 41																					
Alnmouth for Alnwick	a		09 55															12 00						
Berwick-upon-Tweed	a										11 20													
Dunbar	a										11 43													
Wolverhampton 7	d	06 15		06 34		06 40			07 15			07 36			07 49		08 15			08 37		08 49		09 15
Stafford	a	06 29				06 53			07 29								08 29							09 29
Stoke-on-Trent	a	06 50				07 12									08 18		08 54					09 18		09 54
Congleton	a	07 02																						
Macclesfield	a	07 11				07 30									08 35		09 11							10 11
Crewe 10	a			07 07					07 50			08 07								09 07				
Wilmslow	a								08 08															
Stockport	a	07 27				07 45			08 20								09 27							10 27
Manchester Piccadilly 10	a	07 40				08 01			08 40						09 00		09 40					10 00		10 40
Warrington Bank Quay	a			07 26								08 26								09 26				
Wigan North Western	a			07 37								08 37								09 37				
Preston 8	a			07 51								08 51								09 51				
Lancaster 6	a			08 08								09 08								10 09				
Oxenholme Lake District	a			08 22																10 24				
Penrith North Lakes	a											09 44												
Carlisle 8	a			09 01								09 59								11 02				
Lockerbie	a																							
Haymarket	a			10s16																12s16				
Edinburgh 10	a		11 02	10 22							12 13							13 10		12 22				
Haymarket	a																							
Motherwell	a																							
Glasgow Central 15	a											11 16												
Inverkeithing	a																							
Kirkcaldy	a																							
Markinch	a																							
Ladybank	a																							
Cupar	a																							
Leuchars 8	a																							
Dundee	a																							
Arbroath	a																							
Montrose	a																							
Stonehaven	a																							
Aberdeen	a																							

For general notes see front of timetable
For details of catering facilities see Directory of Train Operators

South Coast and the South West → North West England, The North East and Scotland

Route Diagram - See first page of Table 51

		XC	XC	XC	VT	XC	XC	XC	XC	XC	XC	VT	XC	XC	XC	XC	XC	XC	VT	XC	XC	XC
		1◇	1	1	1◇	1◇	1◇	1◇	1◇	1◇	1	1◇	1◇	1◇	1◇	1◇	1◇	1	1◇	1◇	1◇	1◇
			A	B																		
		🛒			⊠	🛒	🛒		🛒	🛒		🍽	🛒	🛒		🛒	🛒		🍽	🛒	🛒	
Bournemouth	d								06 30							07 30						
Brockenhurst 3	d								06 49							07 49						
Southampton Central	d								07 15							08 15						
Southampton Airport Parkwy ✈	d								07 22							08 22						
Winchester	d								07 31							08 31						
Basingstoke	d								07 47							08 47						
Guildford	d																					
Reading 7	d					07 40			08 10				08 40			09 10				09 40		
Oxford	d					08 05			08 35				09 05			09 35				10 05		
Banbury	d					08 25			08 54				09 25			09 54				10 25		
Leamington Spa 8	d					08 43			09 12				09 43			10 12				10 43		
Coventry	d								09 27							10 27						
Birmingham International ✈	d								09 38							10 38						
Penzance	d																					
St Erth	d																					
Hayle	d																					
Camborne	d																					
Redruth	d																					
Truro	d																					
St Austell	d																					
Newquay	d																					
Par	d																					
Lostwithiel	d																					
Bodmin Parkway	d																					
Liskeard 6	d																					
Plymouth	d	05 20								06 25							07 25					
Totnes	d	05 45								06 50							07 50					
Paignton	d													07 00								
Torquay	d													07 06								
Newton Abbot	d	06 02								07 03				07 17			08 03					
Teignmouth	d													07 24								
Dawlish	d													07 29								
Exeter St Davids 6	d	06 23								07 23				07 43			08 23					
Tiverton Parkway	d	06 37								07 37				07 56			08 37					
Taunton	d	06 51								07 51				08 11			08 51					
Weston-super-Mare	d													08 32								
Cardiff Central 7	d						07 00	07 45							08 45							09 45
Newport (South Wales)	d						07 15	08 00							09 00							10 00
Bristol Temple Meads 10	d	07 30					08 00			08 30				09 00			09 30				10 00	
Bristol Parkway 7	d	07 40					08 10			08 40				09 10			09 40				10 10	
Gloucester 7	d							08 46							09 46							10 46
Cheltenham Spa	d	08 12					08 42	08 56		09 12				09 42	09 56		10 12				10 42	10 56
Birmingham New Street 12	a	08 56				09 17	09 26	09 45	09 49	09 56			10 17	10 26	10 45	10 49	10 56			11 17	11 26	11 45
Birmingham New Street 12	d	09 03	09 19	09 19	09 20	09 30	09 31	09 49	09 57	10 03	10 19	10 20	10 30	10 31	10 49	10 57	11 03	11 19	11 20	11 30	11 31	11 49
Tamworth	d		09 39	09 39				10 07		10 19	10 37				11 07			11 39				12 07
Burton-on-Trent	d	09 26	09 51	09 51				10 19			10 49				11 19		11 26	11 51				12 19
Derby 10	a	09 39	10 04	10 04		10 11		10 34		10 39	11 04		11 11		11 34		11 39	12 04		12 11		12 34
Nottingham 8 🚌	a		10 35	10 36				11 05			11 35				12 05			12 35				13 05
Chesterfield	a	10 02								11 02							12 02					
Sheffield 7	a	10 17				10 46				11 17			11 46				12 18			12 46		
Doncaster 7	a					11 15							12 15							13 20		
Wakefield Westgate 7	a	10 46								11 46							12 46					
Leeds 10	a	11 02								12 02							13 02					
York 8	a	11 29				11 45				12 29			12 45				13 29			13 46		
Darlington 7	a	11 58				12 20				13 00			13 13				14 00			14 16		
Durham	a	12 22				12 38				13 18			13 30				14 18			14 34		
Chester-le-Street	a					12 50														14 41		
Newcastle 8	a	12 36				13 05				13 33			13 51				14 36			14 56		
Morpeth	a																					
Alnmouth for Alnwick	a									14 00												
Berwick-upon-Tweed	a	13 21															15 21					
Dunbar	a	13 44															15 44					
Wolverhampton 7 🚌	d				09 37		09 49		10 15			10 37		10 49		11 15			11 37		11 49	
Stafford	a								10 29							11 29						
Stoke-on-Trent	a						10 18		10 54					11 18		11 54					12 18	
Congleton	a																					
Macclesfield	a								11 11							12 11						
Crewe 10	a				10 07							11 07							12 07			
Wilmslow	a																					
Stockport	a								11 27							12 27						
Manchester Piccadilly 10 🚌	a						11 00		11 40					12 00		12 40					13 00	
Warrington Bank Quay	a				10 26							11 26							12 26			
Wigan North Western	a				10 37							11 37							12 37			
Preston 8	a				10 51							11 51							12 51			
Lancaster 6	a				11 08							12 08							13 08			
Oxenholme Lake District	a											12 22							13 22			
Penrith North Lakes	a				11 44																	
Carlisle 8	a				12 00							13 01							14 01			
Lockerbie	a																					
Haymarket	a											14s16										
Edinburgh 10	a	14 14								15 10		14 22					16 16					
Haymarket	a																					
Motherwell	a																					
Glasgow Central 15	a				13 19														15 17			
Inverkeithing	a																					
Kirkcaldy	a																					
Markinch	a																					
Ladybank	a																					
Cupar	a																					
Leuchars 3	a																					
Dundee	a																					
Arbroath	a																					
Montrose	a																					
Stonehaven	a																					
Aberdeen	a																					

For general notes see front of timetable
For details of catering facilities see Directory of Train Operators

A Until 4 September
B From 7 September

South Coast and the South West → North West England, The North East and Scotland

Route Diagram - See first page of Table 51

		XC	XC	XC	VT	XC	XC	XC	XC	XC	XC	VT	XC	XC	XC	XC	XC	XC	VT	XC	XC
		1 ◇	1 ◇	1	1 ◇	1 ◇	1 ◇	1 ◇	1 ◇	1 ◇	1	1 ◇	1 ◇	1 ◇	1 ◇	1 ◇	1 ◇	1	1 ◇	1 ◇	1 ◇
										A											
		🛒	🛒		🍽	🛒	🛒		🛒	🛒		🍽	🛒	🛒		🛒	🛒		🍽	🛒	🛒
Bournemouth	d	08 45							09 45							10 45					
Brockenhurst 3	d	09 00							10 00							11 00					
Southampton Central	d	09 15							10 15							11 15					
Southampton Airport Parkwy ✈	d	09 22							10 22							11 22					
Winchester	d	09 31							10 31							11 31					
Basingstoke	d	09 47							10 47							11 47					
Guildford	d																				
Reading 7	d	10 10				10 40			11 10				11 40			12 10				12 40	
Oxford	d	10 35				11 05			11 35				12 05			12 35				13 05	
Banbury	d	10 54				11 25			11 54				12 25			12 54				13 25	
Leamington Spa 8	d	11 12				11 43			12 12				12 43			13 12				13 43	
Coventry	d	11 27							12 27							13 27					
Birmingham International ✈	d	11 38							12 38							13 38					
Penzance	d		06 28														08 28				
St Erth	d		06 36														08 36				
Hayle	d																				
Camborne	d		06 46														08 46				
Redruth	d		06 52														08 52				
Truro	d		07 04														09 04				
St Austell	d		07 20														09 20				
Newquay	d																				
Par	d		07 28														09 28				
Lostwithiel	d																				
Bodmin Parkway	d		07 39														09 39				
Liskeard 6	d		07 51														09 51				
Plymouth	d		08 25							09 25							10 25				
Totnes	d		08 50							09 50							10 50				
Paignton	d													10 05							
Torquay	d													10 11							
Newton Abbot	d		09 03							10 03				10 22			11 03				
Teignmouth	d													10 29							
Dawlish	d													10 34							
Exeter St Davids 6	d		09 23							10 23				10 48			11 23				
Tiverton Parkway	d		09 37							10 37				11 02			11 37				
Taunton	d		09 51							10 51				11 16			11 51				
Weston-super-Mare	d																				
Cardiff Central 7	d							10 45							11 45						
Newport (South Wales)	d							11 00							12 00						
Bristol Temple Meads 10	d		10 30				11 00			11 30				12 00			12 30				13 00
Bristol Parkway 7	d		10 40				11 10			11 40				12 10			12 40				13 10
Gloucester 7	d							11 46							12 46						
Cheltenham Spa	d		11 12				11 42	11 56		12 12				12 42	12 56		13 12				13 42
Birmingham New Street 12	a	11 49	11 56			12 17	12 26	12 45	12 49	12 56			13 17	13 26	13 45	13 49	13 56			14 17	14 26
Birmingham New Street 12	d	11 57	12 03	12 19	12 20	12 30	12 31	12 49	12 57	13 03	13 19	13 20	13 30	13 31	13 49	13 57	14 03	14 19	14 20	14 30	14 31
Tamworth	d		12 19	12 37				13 07			13 39				14 07		14 19	14 37			
Burton-on-Trent	d			12 49				13 19		13 26	13 51				14 19			14 49			
Derby 10	a		12 39	13 04		13 11		13 34		13 39	14 04		14 11		14 34		14 39	15 04		15 11	
Nottingham 8 🚊	a			13 35				14 05			14 35				15 05			15 35			
Chesterfield	a		13 02							14 02							15 02				
Sheffield 7	a		13 17			13 46				14 17			14 46				15 17			15 46	
Doncaster 7	a					14 17							15 16							16 15	
Wakefield Westgate 7	a		13 46							14 46							15 46				
Leeds 10	a		14 02							15 02							16 02				
York 8	a		14 29			14 43				15 29			15 40				16 29			16 40	
Darlington 7	a		14 58			15 16				16 06			16 11				16 57			17 08	
Durham	a		15 15			15 34				16 24			16 29				17 14			17 31	
Chester-le-Street	a																			17 40	
Newcastle 8	a		15 31			15 58				16 37			16 51				17 34			17 54	
Morpeth	a		15 47																		
Alnmouth for Alnwick	a		16 01														18 01				
Berwick-upon-Tweed	a									17 25											
Dunbar	a									17 48											
Wolverhampton 7 🚊	d	12 15			12 37		12 49		13 15			13 37		13 49		14 15			14 37		14 49
Stafford	a	12 29							13 29							14 29					
Stoke-on-Trent	a	12 54					13 18		13 54					14 18		14 54					15 18
Congleton	a																				
Macclesfield	a	13 11							14 11							15 11					
Crewe 10	a				13 07							14 07							15 07		
Wilmslow	a																				
Stockport	a	13 27							14 27							15 27					
Manchester Piccadilly 10 🚊	a	13 40					14 00		14 40					15 00		15 40					16 00
Warrington Bank Quay	a				13 26							14 26							15 26		
Wigan North Western	a				13 37							14 37							15 37		
Preston 8	a				13 51							14 51							15 51		
Lancaster 6	a				14 08							15 08							16 08		
Oxenholme Lake District	a											15 22									
Penrith North Lakes	a				14 44														16 44		
Carlisle 8	a				15 00							16 01							17 00		
Lockerbie	a																				
Haymarket	a				16s15														18s14		
Edinburgh 10	a		17 09		16 22					18 13							19 03		18 22		
Haymarket	a									18 19							19 11				
Motherwell	a																19 55				
Glasgow Central 15	a											17 18					20 25				
Inverkeithing	a									18 36											
Kirkcaldy	a									18 58											
Markinch	a									19 08											
Ladybank	a									19 15											
Cupar	a									19 22											
Leuchars 3	a									19 29											
Dundee	a									19 44											
Arbroath	a									20 01											
Montrose	a									20 15											
Stonehaven	a									20 35											
Aberdeen	a									20 57											

For general notes see front of timetable
For details of catering facilities see Directory of Train Operators

A 🛒 to Edinburgh

South Coast and the South West → North West England, The North East and Scotland

Route Diagram - See first page of Table 51

		XC [1]◇	XC [1]◇ ⊼	XC [1]◇ A ⊼	XC [1]	VT [1]◇ 🍽	XC [1]◇ ⊼	XC [1]◇ ⊼	XC [1]◇	XC [1]◇ ⊼	XC [1]◇ A ⊼	XC [1]	VT [1]◇ 🍽	XC [1]◇ ⊼	XC [1]◇ ⊼	XC [1]◇	XC [1]◇ ⊼	XC [1]◇ B ⊼	XC [1]	VT [1]◇ 🍽	XC [1]◇ B ⊼	XC [1]◇ ⊼
Bournemouth	d		11 45							12 45							13 45					
Brockenhurst [3]	d		12 00							13 00							14 00					
Southampton Central	d		12 15							13 15							14 15					
Southampton Airport Parkwy ✈	d		12 22							13 22							14 22					
Winchester	d		12 31							13 31							14 31					
Basingstoke	d		12 47							13 47							14 47					
Guildford	d																					
Reading [7]	d		13 10				13 40			14 10				14 40			15 10				15 40	
Oxford	d		13 35				14 05			14 35				15 05			15 35				16 05	
Banbury	d		13 54				14 25			14 54				15 25			15 54				16 25	
Leamington Spa [8]	d		14 12				14 43			15 12				15 43			16 12				16 43	
Coventry	d		14 27							15 27							16 27					
Birmingham International ✈	d		14 38							15 38							16 38					
Penzance	d							09 40														
St Erth	d							09 48														
Hayle	d							09 52														
Camborne	d							10 01														
Redruth	d							10 08														
Truro	d							10 19														
St Austell	d							10 35														
Newquay	d																					
Par	d							10 43														
Lostwithiel	d							10 50														
Bodmin Parkway	d							10 57														
Liskeard [6]	d							11 09														
Plymouth	d			11 25				11 50			12 21							13 21				
Totnes	d			11 50				12 15			12 48							13 48				
Paignton	d																					14 01
Torquay	d																					14 07
Newton Abbot	d			12 03				12 28			13 01							14 01				14 18
Teignmouth	d																					14 25
Dawlish	d																					14 30
Exeter St Davids [6]	d			12 23				12 48			13 23							14 23				14 44
Tiverton Parkway	d			12 37				13 02			13 38							14 38				14 57
Taunton	d			12 51				13 16			13 53							14 53				15 12
Weston-super-Mare	d																					15 38
Cardiff Central [7]	d	12 45							13 45							14 45						
Newport (South Wales)	d	13 00							14 00							15 00						
Bristol Temple Meads [10]	d			13 30				14 00			14 30				15 00			15 30				16 00
Bristol Parkway [7]	d			13 40				14 10			14 40				15 10			15 40				16 10
Gloucester [7]	d	13 46							14 46							15 46						
Cheltenham Spa	d	13 56		14 12				14 42	14 56		15 12				15 42	15 56		16 12				16 42
Birmingham New Street [12]	a	14 45	14 49	14 56			15 17	15 26	15 45	15 49	15 56			16 17	16 26	16 45	16 49	16 56			17 17	17 26
Birmingham New Street [12]	d	14 49	14 57	15 03	15 19	15 20	15 30	15 31	15 49	15 57	16 03	16 19	16 20	16 30	16 31	16 49	16 57	17 03	17 19	17 20	17 30	17 31
Tamworth	d	15 07			15 39				16 07		16 21	16 38				17 07			17 39			
Burton-on-Trent	d	15 19		15 26	15 51				16 19			16 51				17 19		17 28	17 51			
Derby [10]	a	15 34		15 39	16 04		16 11		16 34		16 39	17 04		17 11		17 34		17 39	18 04		18 11	
Nottingham [8] ⛴	a	16 05			16 35				17 05			17 35				18 05			18 35			
Chesterfield	a			16 02							17 03							18 02				
Sheffield [7]	a			16 17			16 46				17 19			17 45				18 18			18 49	
Doncaster [7]	a						17 15														19 17	
Wakefield Westgate [7]	a			16 46							17 46			18 12				18 46				
Leeds [10]	a			17 02							18 04			18 31				19 02				
York [8]	a			17 30			17 40				18 31			18 58				19 30			19 44	
Darlington [7]	a			17 59			18 15				19 00			19 38				20 04			20 12	
Durham	a			18 17			18 33				19 18			19 55				20 22			20 30	
Chester-le-Street	a													20 01								
Newcastle [8]	a			18 36			18 55				19 34			20 18				20 38			20 48	
Morpeth	a																				21 13	
Alnmouth for Alnwick	a										20 04										21 27	
Berwick-upon-Tweed	a			19 24														21 27			21 47	
Dunbar	a			19 47														21 51				
Wolverhampton [7] ⛴	d		15 15			15 37		15 49		16 15			16 37		16 49		17 15			17 37		17 49
Stafford	a		15 29							16 29							17 29					
Stoke-on-Trent	a		15 54					16 18		16 54					17 18		17 54					18 18
Congleton	a																					
Macclesfield	a		16 11							17 11							18 11					
Crewe [10]	a					16 07							17 07							18 07		
Wilmslow	a																					
Stockport	a		16 27							17 27							18 27					
Manchester Piccadilly [10] ⛴	a		16 40					17 00		17 40					18 00		18 40					19 00
Warrington Bank Quay	a					16 26							17 26							18 26		
Wigan North Western	a					16 37							17 37							18 37		
Preston [8]	a					16 51							17 51							18 51		
Lancaster [6]	a					17 09							18 08							19 08		
Oxenholme Lake District	a					17 24							18 22							19 23		
Penrith North Lakes	a					17 50							18 48									
Carlisle [8]	a					18 06							19 04							20 02		
Lockerbie	a																					
Haymarket	a												20s16									
Edinburgh [10]	a			20 15							21 12		20 22					22 22			22 35	
Haymarket	a			20 19							21 17											
Motherwell	a										22 04											
Glasgow Central [15]	a					19 19					22 35									21 17		
Inverkeithing	a			20 33																		
Kirkcaldy	a			20 49																		
Markinch	a			20 59																		
Ladybank	a			21 07																		
Cupar	a			21 14																		
Leuchars [3]	a			21 21																		
Dundee	a			21 45																		
Arbroath	a																					
Montrose	a																					
Stonehaven	a																					
Aberdeen	a																					

For general notes see front of timetable
For details of catering facilities see Directory of Train Operators

A ⊼ to Edinburgh
B ⊼ to Newcastle

South Coast and the South West → North West England, The North East and Scotland

Route Diagram - See first page of Table 51

		XC	XC	XC	XC	VT	XC	XC	XC	XC	XC	XC	XC	VT	XC	XC	XC	XC	XC	XC	XC	XC
																FX	FO					
		1◇	1◇	1◇	1	1◇	1◇	1◇	1◇	1◇	1◇	1	1	1◇	1◇	1◇	1◇	1◇	1◇	1◇	1◇	1◇
				A			B					C	D		E					G	G	G
			✕	✕		▭	✕	✕		✕	✕			▭	✕	✕	✕		✕	✕	✕	✕
Bournemouth	d		14 45							15 45									16 45			
Brockenhurst 3	d		15 00							16 00									17 00			
Southampton Central	d		15 15							16 15									17 15			
Southampton Airport Parkwy ✈	d		15 22							16 22									17 22			
Winchester	d		15 31							16 31									17 31			
Basingstoke	d		15 47							16 47									17 47			
Guildford	d																					
Reading 7	d		16 10				16 40			17 10					17 40				18 10		18 40	
Oxford	d		16 35				17 05			17 35					18 05				18 35		19 05	
Banbury	d		16 54				17 25			17 54					18 25				18 54		19 25	
Leamington Spa 8	d		17 12				17 43			18 12					18 43				19 12		19 43	
Coventry	d		17 27							18 27									19 27			
Birmingham International ✈	d		17 38							18 38									19 38			
Penzance	d																					
St Erth	d																					
Hayle	d																					
Camborne	d																					
Redruth	d																					
Truro	d																					
St Austell	d																					
Newquay	d																					
Par	d																					
Lostwithiel	d																					
Bodmin Parkway	d																					
Liskeard 6	d																					
Plymouth	d			14 25							15 21									16 25		
Totnes	d			14 50							15 48									16 50		
Paignton	d																					
Torquay	d																					
Newton Abbot	d			15 03							16 01									17 03		
Teignmouth	d																					
Dawlish	d																					
Exeter St Davids 6	d			15 23							16 23						16 53			17 23		
Tiverton Parkway	d			15 37							16 37						17 07			17 37		
Taunton	d			15 51							16 53						17 21			17 51		
Weston-super-Mare	d																					
Cardiff Central 7	d	15 45							16 45									17 45				
Newport (South Wales)	d	16 00							17 00									18 00				
Bristol Temple Meads 10	d			16 30				17 00			17 30					18 00	18 00			18 30		19 00
Bristol Parkway 7	d			16 40				17 10			17 40					18 10	18 10			18 40		19 10
Gloucester 7	d	16 46							17 46									18 46				
Cheltenham Spa	d	16 56		17 12				17 42	17 56		18 12					18 42	18 42	18 56		19 12		19 42
Birmingham New Street 12	a	17 45	17 49	17 56			18 17	18 26	18 45	18 49	18 56				19 17	19 26	19 26	19 45	19 49	19 56	20 17	20 28
Birmingham New Street 12	d	17 49	17 57	18 03	18 19	18 20	18 30	18 31	18 49	18 57	19 03	19 19	19 19	19 20	19 30	19 31	19 31	19 49	19 57	20 03	20 30	20 31
Tamworth	d	18 07		18 19	18 37				19 07			19 39	19 39					20 07		20 19		
Burton-on-Trent	d	18 19			18 49				19 19		19 28	19 51	19 51					20 19				
Derby 10	a	18 34		18 39	19 04		19 11		19 34		19 41	20 04	20 04		20 11			20 34		20 39	21 11	
Nottingham 8 🚌	a	19 05			19 35				20 05			20 35	20 36					21 10				
Chesterfield	a			19 02			19 29				20 02									21 02	21 34	
Sheffield 7	a			19 20			19 47				20 18				20 49					21 16	21 48	
Doncaster 7	a						20 20								21 20						22 29	
Wakefield Westgate 7	a			19 49							20 53									21 48		
Leeds 10	a			20 06							21 09									22 08		
York 8	a			20 31			20 46				21 39				21 45						22 59	
Darlington 7	a			21 07			21 20								22 13							
Durham	a			21 25			21 38								22 30							
Chester-le-Street	a						21 45								22 36							
Newcastle 8	a			21 39			22 00								22 56							
Morpeth	a																					
Alnmouth for Alnwick	a			22 11																		
Berwick-upon-Tweed	a			22 32																		
Dunbar	a																					
Wolverhampton 7 🚌	d		18 15			18 37		18 49		19 15				19 37		19 49	19 49		20 15			20 49
Stafford	a		18 29							19 29									20 29			
Stoke-on-Trent	a		18 54					19 18		19 54						20 18	20 18		20 54			21 18
Congleton	a																					
Macclesfield	a		19 11							20 11									21 11			
Crewe 10	a					19 07								20 07								
Wilmslow	a																					
Stockport	a		19 27							20 27									21 27			
Manchester Piccadilly 10 🚌	a		19 40					20 00		20 40						21 00	21 00		21 40			22 00
Warrington Bank Quay	a					19 26								20 26								
Wigan North Western	a					19 37								20 37								
Preston 8	a					19 51								20 51								
Lancaster 6	a					20 08								21 08								
Oxenholme Lake District	a													21 22								
Penrith North Lakes	a					20 44																
Carlisle 8	a					21 00								22 01								
Lockerbie	a																					
Haymarket	a					22s14																
Edinburgh 10	a			23 23		22 22																
Haymarket	a																					
Motherwell	a																					
Glasgow Central 15	a													23 17								
Inverkeithing	a																					
Kirkcaldy	a																					
Markinch	a																					
Ladybank	a																					
Cupar	a																					
Leuchars 3	a																					
Dundee	a																					
Arbroath	a																					
Montrose	a																					
Stonehaven	a																					
Aberdeen	a																					

For general notes see front of timetable
For details of catering facilities see Directory of Train Operators

A ✕ to Leeds
B ✕ to Doncaster
C Until 4 September
D From 7 September
E ✕ to Sheffield
G ✕ to Birmingham New Street

South Coast and the South West → North West England, The North East and Scotland

Route Diagram - See first page of Table 51

		XC	XC		XC	VT	XC	XC	XC	XC	XC	XC		XC MTX	XC MTO	XC	XC	XC	XC	XC	XC	XC
		1 ◇	1 ◇		1 ◇	1 ◇	1 ◇	1 ◇	1 ◇	1 ◇	1 ◇	1 ◇		1 ◇	1 ◇	1 ◇	1 ◇	1 ◇	1 ◇	1 ◇	1 ◇	1 ◇
			A		A				B		C											
Bournemouth	d		17 45						18 45								19 45					
Brockenhurst 3	d		18 00						19 00								20 00					
Southampton Central	d		18 15						19 15								20 15					
Southampton Airport Parkway	d		18 22						19 22								20 22					
Winchester	d		18 31						19 31								20 31					
Basingstoke	d		18 47						19 47								20 47					
Guildford	d																					
Reading 7	d		19 10				19 40		20 10							20 40	21 10				21 45	
Oxford	d		19 35				20 05		20 35							21 22	21 35				22 30	
Banbury	d		19 54				20 25		20 54							21 41	21 54				22 53	
Leamington Spa 8	d		20 12				20 43		21 12							22 00	22 12				23 12	
Coventry	d		20 27						21 27								22 24					
Birmingham International	d		20 38						21 38								22 34					
Penzance	d																					
St Erth	d																					
Hayle	d																					
Camborne	d																					
Redruth	d																					
Truro	d																					
St Austell	d																					
Newquay	d																					
Par	d																					
Lostwithiel	d																					
Bodmin Parkway	d																					
Liskeard 6	d																					
Plymouth	d				17 21						18 25											
Totnes	d				17 48						18 50											
Paignton	d																			20 10		
Torquay	d																			20 16		
Newton Abbot	d				18 01						19 03									20 27		
Teignmouth	d																					
Dawlish	d																					
Exeter St Davids 6	d				18 23						19 23									20 48		
Tiverton Parkway	d				18 38						19 37									21 01		
Taunton	d				18 53						19 51									21 16		
Weston-super-Mare	d																					
Cardiff Central 7	d	18 45								20 00									21 00			21 50
Newport (South Wales)	d	19 00								20 15									21 15			22 05
Bristol Temple Meads 10	d				19 30			20 00			20 30									22 00		
Bristol Parkway 7	d				19 40			20 10			20 40									22 10		
Gloucester 7	d	19 46								20 57									22 06			22 47
Cheltenham Spa	d	19 57			20 12			20 42		21 08	21 16								22 17	22 42		22 58
Birmingham New Street 12	a	20 45	20 49		20 56		21 22	21 43	21 49	21 57	22 06					22 35	22 50		23 35	23 44	23 55	00 05
Birmingham New Street 12	d	20 49	20 57		21 03	21 20			21 57			22 10		22 28	22 28			23 09				
Tamworth	d	21 09			21 21							22 28						23 28				
Burton-on-Trent	d	21 23			21 33							22 40						23 40				
Derby 10	a	21 34			21 46							22 54						23 55				
Nottingham 8	a	22 10										23 30						00 20				
Chesterfield	a				22 07																	
Sheffield 7	a				22 26																	
Doncaster 7	a																					
Wakefield Westgate 7	a				23 11																	
Leeds 10	a				23 30																	
York 8	a																					
Darlington 7	a																					
Durham	a																					
Chester-le-Street	a																					
Newcastle 8	a																					
Morpeth	a																					
Alnmouth for Alnwick	a																					
Berwick-upon-Tweed	a																					
Dunbar	a																					
Wolverhampton 7	d		21 15			21 41			22 15					22 46	22 46							
Stafford	a		21 29			21 53			22 29					22 58	22 58							
Stoke-on-Trent	a		21 54						22 54					23 20	23 20							
Congleton	a																					
Macclesfield	a		22 11						23 11													
Crewe 10	a					22 18																
Wilmslow	a																					
Stockport	a		22 25						23 25													
Manchester Piccadilly 10	a		22 40						23 40					00 15								
Warrington Bank Quay	a					22 37																
Wigan North Western	a					22 47																
Preston 8	a					23 05																
Lancaster 6	a																					
Oxenholme Lake District	a																					
Penrith North Lakes	a																					
Carlisle 8	a																					
Lockerbie	a																					
Haymarket	a																					
Edinburgh 10	a																					
Haymarket	a																					
Motherwell	a																					
Glasgow Central 15	a																					
Inverkeithing	a																					
Kirkcaldy	a																					
Markinch	a																					
Ladybank	a																					
Cupar	a																					
Leuchars 3	a																					
Dundee	a																					
Arbroath	a																					
Montrose	a																					
Stonehaven	a																					
Aberdeen	a																					

For general notes see front of timetable
For details of catering facilities see Directory of Train Operators

A to Birmingham New Street
B to Reading
C to Bristol Temple Meads

South Coast and The South West → North West England, The North East and Scotland

Route Diagram - See first page of Table 51

		XC 1◇	XC 1◇	XC 1	VT 1◇	XC 1◇	XC 1◇		XC 1	XC 1◇	XC 1◇	XC 1	VT 1◇	XC 1◇		XC 1◇	XC 1	XC 1◇	XC 1◇	VT 1◇	XC 1◇		XC 1◇	XC 1◇
Bournemouth	d																							
Brockenhurst 3	d																							
Southampton Central	d																	05 09						
Southampton Airport Parkway ✈	d																	05 16						
Winchester	d																	05 25						
Basingstoke	d																	05 41						
Guildford	d																				06 09			
Reading 7	d																	06 10			06 46			
Oxford	d																	06 36			07 12			
Banbury	d																	06 53			07 31			
Leamington Spa 8	d																	07 11			07 49			
Coventry	d																	07 27						
Birmingham International ✈	d																	07 38						
Penzance	d																							
St Erth	d																							
Hayle	d																							
Camborne	d																							
Redruth	d																							
Truro	d																							
St Austell	d																							
Newquay	d																							
Par	d																							
Lostwithiel	d																							
Bodmin Parkway	d																							
Liskeard 6	d																							
Plymouth	d																							
Totnes	d																							
Paignton	d																							
Torquay	d																							
Newton Abbot	d																							
Teignmouth	d																							
Dawlish	d																							
Exeter St Davids 6	d																							
Tiverton Parkway	d																							
Taunton	d																							
Weston-super-Mare	d																							
Cardiff Central 7	d																							06 40
Newport (South Wales)	d																							06 55
Bristol Temple Meads 10	d																		06 15				07 00	
Bristol Parkway 7	d																		06 25				07 10	
Gloucester 7	d																		07 02					07 47
Cheltenham Spa	d																		07 12				07 42	07 58
Birmingham New Street 12	a																	07 49	07 56		08 17		08 26	08 45
Birmingham New Street 12	d	05 55	05 57	06 19	06 20	06 30	06 31		06 49	06 57	07 03	07 19	07 20	07 30		07 31	07 49	07 57	08 03	08 20	08 30		08 31	08 49
Tamworth	d	06 12		06 39		06 46			07 07		07 19	07 38		07 47			08 07		08 19					09 07
Burton-on-Trent	d	06 22		06 51		06 56			07 19		07 29	07 50		07 58			08 19		08 29					09 19
Derby 10	a	06 35		07 05		07 09			07 35		07 43	08 05		08 09			08 35		08 42		09 09			09 35
Nottingham 8	a			07 40					08 10			08 36					09 05							10 05
Chesterfield	a	06 55				07 29					08 02			08 29					09 02					
Sheffield 7	a	07 09				07 48					08 17			08 46					09 17		09 46			
Doncaster 7	a					08 23								09 21							10 18			
Wakefield Westgate 7	a	07 36									08 46								09 46					
Leeds 10	a	07 52									09 02								10 02					
York 8	a	08 25				08 49					09 30			09 45					10 30		10 44			
Darlington 7	a	08 54				09 18					09 59			10 13					10 59		11 16			
Durham	a	09 11				09 35					10 16			10 30					11 16		11 33			
Chester-le-Street	a					09 42																		
Newcastle 8	a	09 26				09 59					10 33			10 51					11 32		11 54			
Morpeth	a	09 41																						
Alnmouth for Alnwick	a	09 55																	11 59					
Berwick-upon-Tweed	a										11 17													
Dunbar	a										11 40													
Wolverhampton 7	d		06 14		06 37		06 49			07 14			07 37			07 49		08 14		08 37			08 49	
Stafford	a		06 29				07 00			07 29								08 29						
Stoke-on-Trent	a		06 50				07 18									08 18		08 54					09 18	
Congleton	a		07 02																					
Macclesfield	a		07 11				07 36									08 35		09 11						
Crewe 10	a				07 07					07 50			08 07							09 07				
Wilmslow	a									08 09														
Stockport	a		07 27				07 49			08 20						08 49		09 27						
Manchester Piccadilly 10	a		07 40				08 00			08 40						09 00		09 40					10 00	
Warrington Bank Quay	a				07 26								08 27							09 26				
Wigan North Western	a				07 37								08 38							09 37				
Preston 8	a				07 51								08 52							09 51				
Lancaster 6	a				08 08								09 09							10 08				
Oxenholme Lake District	a				08 22															10 22				
Penrith North Lakes	a												09 45											
Carlisle 8	a				09 01								10 01							11 01				
Lockerbie	a																							
Haymarket	a				10s16															12s16				
Edinburgh 10	a	11 02			10 22						12 12								13 06	12 22				
Haymarket	a																							
Motherwell	a																							
Glasgow Central 15	a												11 17											
Inverkeithing	a																							
Kirkcaldy	a																							
Markinch	a																							
Ladybank	a																							
Cupar	a																							
Leuchars 8	a																							
Dundee	a																							
Arbroath	a																							
Montrose	a																							
Stonehaven	a																							
Aberdeen	a																							

For general notes see front of timetable
For details of catering facilities see Directory of Train Operators

South Coast and The South West → North West England, The North East and Scotland

until 5 September

Route Diagram - See first page of Table 51

		XC	XC	XC	VT	XC	XC		XC	XC	XC	XC	VT	XC		XC	XC	XC	XC	XC	VT		XC	XC
		1 ◇	1 ◇	1	1 ◇	1 ◇	1 ◇		1 ◇	1 ◇	1 ◇	1	1 ◇	1 ◇		1 ◇	1 ◇	1 ◇	1 ◇	1	1 ◇		1 ◇	1 ◇
		🛒	🛒		🍴	🛒	🛒			🛒	🛒		🍴	🛒		🛒		🛒	🛒		🍴		🛒	🛒
Bournemouth	d					06 25				06 37								07 45						
Brockenhurst [3]	d					06 39				06 55								08 00						
Southampton Central	d	06 15				06 53				07 15								08 15						
Southampton Airport Parkwy ✈	d	06 22				07 01				07 22								08 22						
Winchester	d	06 31				07 09				07 31								08 31						
Basingstoke	d	06 47				07 25				07 47								08 47						
Guildford	d																							
Reading [7]	d	07 10				07 45				08 10				08 40				09 10					09 40	
Oxford	d	07 36				08 15				08 36				09 07				09 36					10 07	
Banbury	d	07 53				08 35				08 53				09 25				09 53					10 25	
Leamington Spa [8]	d	08 11				08 53				09 11				09 43				10 11					10 43	
Coventry	d	08 27								09 27								10 27						
Birmingham International ✈	d	08 38								09 38								10 38						
Penzance	d																							
St Erth	d																							
Hayle	d																							
Camborne	d																							
Redruth	d																							
Truro	d																							
St Austell	d																							
Newquay	d																							
Par	d																							
Lostwithiel	d																							
Bodmin Parkway	d																							
Liskeard [6]	d																							
Plymouth	d		05 25								06 25								07 25					
Totnes	d		05 50								06 50								07 50					
Paignton	d															07 00								
Torquay	d															07 06								
Newton Abbot	d		06 03								07 03					07 18			08 03					
Teignmouth	d															07 25								
Dawlish	d															07 30								
Exeter St Davids [6]	d		06 23								07 23					07 48			08 23					
Tiverton Parkway	d		06 37								07 37								08 37					
Taunton	d		06 51								07 51					08 12			08 51					
Weston-super-Mare	d																							
Cardiff Central [7]	d						07 00		07 45								08 45							
Newport (South Wales)	d						07 14		08 00								09 00							
Bristol Temple Meads [10]	d		07 30				08 00				08 30					09 00			09 30					10 00
Bristol Parkway [7]	d		07 40				08 10				08 40					09 10			09 40					10 10
Gloucester [7]	d								08 47								09 47							
Cheltenham Spa	d		08 12				08 42		08 58		09 12					09 42	09 58		10 12					10 42
Birmingham New Street [12]	a	08 49	08 56			09 17	09 26		09 45	09 49	09 56			10 17		10 26	10 45	10 49	10 56				11 17	11 26
Birmingham New Street [12]	d	08 57	09 03	09 19	09 20	09 30	09 31		09 49	09 57	10 03	10 19	10 20	10 30		10 31	10 49	10 57	11 03	11 19	11 20		11 30	11 31
Tamworth	d			09 39					10 07		10 19	10 37					11 07			11 39				
Burton-on-Trent	d		09 26	09 51					10 19			10 49					11 19		11 26	11 51				
Derby [10]	a		09 42	10 05		10 09			10 35		10 42	11 05		11 09			11 35		11 42	12 05			12 09	
Nottingham [8] 🚊	a			10 36					11 05			11 36					12 05			12 36				
Chesterfield	a		10 02								11 02								12 02					
Sheffield [7]	a		10 17			10 46					11 17			11 46					12 17				12 46	
Doncaster [7]	a					11 16								12 16									13 19	
Wakefield Westgate [7]	a		10 46								11 46								12 46					
Leeds [10]	a		11 02								12 02								13 02					
York [8]	a		11 32			11 44					12 30			12 44					13 32				13 44	
Darlington [7]	a		11 59			12 14					13 01			13 12					13 59				14 16	
Durham	a		12 16			12 34					13 18			13 29					14 16				14 34	
Chester-le-Street	a					12 41																	14 41	
Newcastle [8]	a		12 33			12 55					13 33			13 50					14 32				14 55	
Morpeth	a																							
Alnmouth for Alnwick	a										13 59													
Berwick-upon-Tweed	a		13 17																15 17					
Dunbar	a		13 40																15 40					
Wolverhampton [7] 🚊	d	09 14			09 37		09 49			10 14			10 37			10 49		11 14			11 37			11 49
Stafford	a	09 29								10 29								11 29						
Stoke-on-Trent	a	09 54					10 18			10 54						11 18		11 54						12 18
Congleton	a																							
Macclesfield	a	10 11								11 11								12 11						
Crewe [10]	a				10 07								11 07								12 07			
Wilmslow	a																							
Stockport	a	10 27								11 27								12 27						
Manchester Piccadilly [10] 🚊	a	10 40					11 00			11 40						12 00		12 40						13 00
Warrington Bank Quay	a				10 26								11 26								12 26			
Wigan North Western	a				10 37								11 37								12 37			
Preston [8]	a				10 51								11 51								12 51			
Lancaster [6]	a				11 08								12 08								13 08			
Oxenholme Lake District	a												12 22								13 22			
Penrith North Lakes	a				11 44																			
Carlisle [8]	a				12 00								13 01								14 01			
Lockerbie	a																							
Haymarket	a												14s16											
Edinburgh [10]	a		14 12								15 09		14 22						16 10					
Haymarket	a																							
Motherwell	a																							
Glasgow Central [15]	a				13 18																15 17			
Inverkeithing	a																							
Kirkcaldy	a																							
Markinch	a																							
Ladybank	a																							
Cupar	a																							
Leuchars [3]	a																							
Dundee	a																							
Arbroath	a																							
Montrose	a																							
Stonehaven	a																							
Aberdeen	a																							

For general notes see front of timetable
For details of catering facilities see
Directory of Train Operators

until 5 September

South Coast and The South West → North West England, The North East and Scotland

Route Diagram - See first page of Table 51

		XC	XC	XC	XC	VT	XC		XC	XC	XC	XC	XC	VT		XC	XC	XC	XC	XC	XC		VT	XC
		1◇	1◇ 🛒	1◇ 🛒	1	1◇ 🍴	1◇ 🛒		1◇ 🛒	1◇	1◇ 🛒	1◇ 🛒	1	1◇ 🍴		1◇ 🛒	1◇ 🛒	1◇	1◇ 🛒	1◇ 🛒	1		1◇ 🍴	1◇ 🛒
Bournemouth	d		08 45								09 45								10 45					
Brockenhurst 3	d		09 00								10 00								11 00					
Southampton Central	d		09 15								10 15								11 15					
Southampton Airport Parkwy ✈	d		09 22								10 22								11 22					
Winchester	d		09 31								10 31								11 31					
Basingstoke	d		09 47								10 47								11 47					
Guildford	d																							
Reading 7	d		10 10				10 40				11 10					11 40			12 10					12 40
Oxford	d		10 36				11 07				11 36					12 07			12 36					13 07
Banbury	d		10 53				11 25				11 53					12 25			12 53					13 25
Leamington Spa 8	d		11 11				11 43				12 11					12 43			13 11					13 43
Coventry	d		11 27								12 27								13 27					
Birmingham International ✈	d		11 38								12 38								13 38					
Penzance	d			06 30																08 25				
St Erth	d			06 38																08 33				
Hayle	d			06 41																				
Camborne	d			06 51																08 43				
Redruth	d			06 57																08 49				
Truro	d			07 09																09 02				
St Austell	d			07 25																09 18				
Newquay	d																							
Par	d			07 32																09 26				
Lostwithiel	d			07 39																				
Bodmin Parkway	d			07 46																09 37				
Liskeard 6	d			07 58																09 49				
Plymouth	d			08 25					08 40			09 25								10 25				
Totnes	d			08 50					09 05			09 50								10 50				
Paignton	d																10 05							
Torquay	d																10 11							
Newton Abbot	d			09 03					09 18			10 03					10 22			11 03				
Teignmouth	d																10 29							
Dawlish	d																10 34							
Exeter St Davids 6	d			09 23					09 39			10 23					10 48			11 23				
Tiverton Parkway	d			09 37					09 52			10 37					11 02			11 37				
Taunton	d			09 51					10 07			10 51					11 16			11 51				
Weston-super-Mare	d								10 33															
Cardiff Central 7	d	09 45								10 45								11 45						
Newport (South Wales)	d	10 00								11 00								12 00						
Bristol Temple Meads 10	d			10 30					11 00			11 30					12 00			12 30				
Bristol Parkway 7	d			10 40					11 10			11 40					12 10			12 40				
Gloucester 7	d	10 47								11 47								12 47						
Cheltenham Spa	d	10 58		11 12					11 42	11 58		12 12					12 42	12 58		13 12				
Birmingham New Street 12	a	11 45	11 49	11 56			12 17		12 26	12 45	12 49	12 56				13 17	13 26	13 45	13 49	13 56				14 17
Birmingham New Street 12	d	11 49	11 57	12 03	12 19	12 20	12 30		12 31	12 49	12 57	13 03	13 19	13 20		13 30	13 31	13 49	13 57	14 03	14 19		14 20	14 30
Tamworth	d	12 07		12 19	12 37					13 07			13 39					14 07		14 19	14 37			
Burton-on-Trent	d	12 19			12 49					13 19		13 26	13 51					14 19			14 49			
Derby 10	a	12 35		12 42	13 05		13 09			13 35		13 42	14 05			14 09		14 35		14 42	15 05			15 09
Nottingham 8 🚊	a	13 05			13 36					14 05			14 36					15 05			15 36			
Chesterfield	a			13 02								14 02								15 02				
Sheffield 7	a			13 17			13 46					14 17				14 46				15 17				15 46
Doncaster 7	a						14 16									15 16								16 16
Wakefield Westgate 7	a			13 46								14 46								15 46				
Leeds 10	a			14 02								15 02								16 02				
York 8	a			14 30			14 44					15 32				15 44				16 30				16 44
Darlington 7	a			14 59			15 15					15 59				16 13				16 59				17 12
Durham	a			15 16			15 32					16 16				16 32				17 16				17 29
Chester-le-Street	a																							17 36
Newcastle 8	a			15 32			15 51					16 32				16 51				17 32				17 53
Morpeth	a			15 48																				
Alnmouth for Alnwick	a			16 02																18 01				
Berwick-upon-Tweed	a											17 17												
Dunbar	a											17 40												
Wolverhampton 7 🚊	d		12 14			12 37			12 49		13 14			13 37			13 49		14 14				14 37	
Stafford	a		12 29								13 29								14 29					
Stoke-on-Trent	a		12 54						13 18		13 54						14 18		14 54					
Congleton	a																							
Macclesfield	a		13 11								14 11								15 11					
Crewe 10	a					13 07								14 07									15 07	
Wilmslow	a																							
Stockport	a		13 27								14 27								15 27					
Manchester Piccadilly 10 🚊	a		13 40						14 00		14 40						15 00		15 40					
Warrington Bank Quay	a					13 26								14 26									15 26	
Wigan North Western	a					13 37								14 37									15 37	
Preston 8	a					13 51								14 51									15 51	
Lancaster 6	a					14 08								15 08									16 08	
Oxenholme Lake District	a													15 22										
Penrith North Lakes	a					14 44																	16 45	
Carlisle 8	a					15 00								16 01									17 00	
Lockerbie	a																							
Haymarket	a					16s15																	18s14	
Edinburgh 10	a			17 14		16 22						18 05								19 07			18 22	
Haymarket	a											18 11								19 13				
Motherwell	a																			20 00				
Glasgow Central 15	a													17 18						20 29				
Inverkeithing	a											18 25												
Kirkcaldy	a											18 40												
Markinch	a											18 50												
Ladybank	a											18 57												
Cupar	a											19 04												
Leuchars 3	a											19 11												
Dundee	a											19 24												
Arbroath	a											19 41												
Montrose	a											20 01												
Stonehaven	a											20 22												
Aberdeen	a											20 46												

For general notes see front of timetable
For details of catering facilities see Directory of Train Operators

South Coast and The South West → North West England, The North East and Scotland

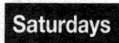

until 5 September

Route Diagram - See first page of Table 51

		XC	XC	XC	XC	XC	VT		XC	XC	XC	XC	XC	XC		VT	XC	XC	XC	XC	XC		XC	VT
		1 ◇	1 ◇	1 ◇	1 ◇	1	1 ◇		1 ◇	1 ◇	1 ◇	1 ◇	1 ◇	1		1 ◇	1 ◇	1 ◇	1 ◇	1 ◇	1 ◇		1	1 ◇
Bournemouth	d			11 45								12 45								13 45				
Brockenhurst 3	d			12 00								13 00								14 00				
Southampton Central	d			12 15								13 15								14 15				
Southampton Airport Parkway ✈	d			12 22								13 22								14 22				
Winchester	d			12 31								13 31								14 31				
Basingstoke	d			12 47								13 47								14 47				
Guildford	d																							
Reading 7	d			13 10					13 40			14 10					14 40			15 10				
Oxford	d			13 36					14 07			14 36					15 07			15 36				
Banbury	d			13 53					14 25			14 53					15 25			15 53				
Leamington Spa 8	d			14 11					14 43			15 11					15 43			16 11				
Coventry	d			14 27								15 27								16 27				
Birmingham International ✈	d			14 38								15 38								16 38				
Penzance	d																							
St Erth	d																							
Hayle	d																							
Camborne	d																							
Redruth	d																							
Truro	d																							
St Austell	d																							
Newquay	d				09 30																			
Par	d																							
Lostwithiel	d																							
Bodmin Parkway	d																							
Liskeard 6	d																							
Plymouth	d				11 21								12 21								13 25			
Totnes	d				11 48								12 48								13 50			
Paignton	d																							
Torquay	d																							
Newton Abbot	d				12 01								13 01								14 03			
Teignmouth	d																							
Dawlish	d																							
Exeter St Davids 6	d				12 23								13 23								14 23			
Tiverton Parkway	d				12 39								13 39								14 37			
Taunton	d				12 54								13 54								14 51			
Weston-super-Mare	d																							
Cardiff Central 7	d		12 45								13 45								14 45					
Newport (South Wales)	d		13 00								14 00								15 00					
Bristol Temple Meads 10	d	13 00			13 30					14 00			14 30					15 00			15 30			
Bristol Parkway 7	d	13 10			13 40					14 10			14 40					15 10			15 40			
Gloucester 7	d		13 47								14 47								15 47					
Cheltenham Spa	d	13 42	13 58		14 12					14 42	14 58		15 12					15 42	15 58		16 12			
Birmingham New Street 12	a	14 26	14 45	14 49	14 56				15 17	15 26	15 45	15 49	15 56				16 17	16 26	16 45	16 49	16 56			
Birmingham New Street 12	d	14 31	14 49	14 57	15 03	15 19	15 20		15 30	15 31	15 49	15 57	16 03	16 19		16 20	16 30	16 31	16 49	16 57	17 03		17 19	17 20
Tamworth	d		15 07			15 39					16 07		16 19	16 37					17 07				17 39	
Burton-on-Trent	d		15 19		15 26	15 51					16 19			16 49					17 19		17 26		17 51	
Derby 10	a		15 35		15 42	16 05			16 09		16 35		16 42	17 05			17 09		17 35		17 42		18 05	
Nottingham 8	a		16 05			16 36					17 05			17 36					18 05				18 36	
Chesterfield	a				16 02								17 02								18 02			
Sheffield 7	a				16 18				16 46				17 19				17 44				18 18			
Doncaster 7	a								17 19															
Wakefield Westgate 7	a				16 46								17 47				18 14				18 46			
Leeds 10	a				17 02								18 02				18 32				19 02			
York 8	a				17 31				17 44				18 31				18 59				19 31			
Darlington 7	a				18 00				18 12				19 01				19 37				20 03			
Durham	a				18 18				18 29				19 19				19 54				20 21			
Chester-le-Street	a																20 01							
Newcastle 8	a				18 37				18 50				19 35				20 18				20 33			
Morpeth	a																							
Alnmouth for Alnwick	a												20 03											
Berwick-upon-Tweed	a				19 25																21 19			
Dunbar	a				19 49																21 42			
Wolverhampton 7	d	14 49		15 14			15 37			15 49		16 14				16 37		16 49		17 14				17 37
Stafford	a			15 29								16 29								17 29				
Stoke-on-Trent	a	15 18		15 54						16 18		16 54						17 18		17 54				
Congleton	a																							
Macclesfield	a			16 11								17 11								18 11				
Crewe 10	a						16 08									17 07								18 07
Wilmslow	a																							
Stockport	a			16 27								17 27								18 27				
Manchester Piccadilly 10	a	16 00		16 40						17 00		17 40						18 00		18 40				
Warrington Bank Quay	a						16 26									17 26								18 26
Wigan North Western	a						16 37									17 37								18 37
Preston 8	a						16 51									17 51								18 51
Lancaster 6	a						17 09									18 08								19 08
Oxenholme Lake District	a						17 24									18 22								19 22
Penrith North Lakes	a															18 48								
Carlisle 8	a						18 03									19 04								20 01
Lockerbie	a																							
Haymarket	a															20s19								
Edinburgh 10	a				20 15								21 10			20 24					22 15			
Haymarket	a				20 25								21 13											
Motherwell	a												21 55											
Glasgow Central 15	a						19 17						22 23											21 17
Inverkeithing	a				20 43																			
Kirkcaldy	a				21 00																			
Markinch	a				21 10																			
Ladybank	a				21 18																			
Cupar	a				21 26																			
Leuchars 3	a				21 35																			
Dundee	a				21 57																			
Arbroath	a																							
Montrose	a																							
Stonehaven	a																							
Aberdeen	a																							

For general notes see front of timetable
For details of catering facilities see Directory of Train Operators

South Coast and The South West → North West England, The North East and Scotland

Route Diagram - See first page of Table 51

		XC	XC	XC	XC	XC	XC		VT	XC	XC	XC	XC	XC		XC	VT	XC	XC	XC	XC		XC	XC
		1◇	1◇	1◇	1◇	1◇	1		1◇	1◇	1◇	1◇	1◇	1◇		1	1◇	1◇	1◇	1◇	1◇		1◇	1◇
		🛒	🛒		🛒	🛒			🍴	🛒	🛒		🛒	🛒			🍴	🛒	🛒		🛒		🛒	🛒
Bournemouth	d				14 45								15 45								16 45			
Brockenhurst 3	d				15 00								16 00								17 00			
Southampton Central	d				15 15								16 15								17 15			
Southampton Airport Parkwy ✈	d				15 22								16 22								17 22			
Winchester	d				15 31								16 31								17 31			
Basingstoke	d				15 47								16 47								17 47			
Guildford	d																							
Reading 7	d	15 40			16 10					16 40			17 10					17 40			18 10			18 40
Oxford	d	16 07			16 36					17 07			17 36					18 07			18 36			19 07
Banbury	d	16 25			16 53					17 25			17 53					18 25			18 53			19 25
Leamington Spa 8	d	16 43			17 11					17 43			18 11					18 43			19 11			19 43
Coventry	d				17 27								18 27								19 27			
Birmingham International ✈	d				17 38								18 38								19 38			
Penzance	d																							
St Erth	d																							
Hayle	d																							
Camborne	d																							
Redruth	d																							
Truro	d																							
St Austell	d																							
Newquay	d																							
Par	d																							
Lostwithiel	d																							
Bodmin Parkway	d																							
Liskeard 6	d																							
Plymouth	d					14 25								15 25									16 25	
Totnes	d					14 50								15 50									16 50	
Paignton	d		13 47																					
Torquay	d		13 54																					
Newton Abbot	d		14 06			15 03								16 03									17 03	
Teignmouth	d		14 15																					
Dawlish	d		14 23																					
Exeter St Davids 6	d		14 38			15 23								16 23									17 23	
Tiverton Parkway	d					15 37								16 37									17 37	
Taunton	d		15 04			15 51								16 51									17 51	
Weston-super-Mare	d		15 27																					
Cardiff Central 7	d			15 45								16 45								17 45				
Newport (South Wales)	d			16 00								17 00								18 00				
Bristol Temple Meads 10	d		16 00			16 30					17 00			17 30					18 00				18 30	
Bristol Parkway 7	d		16 10			16 40					17 10			17 40					18 10				18 40	
Gloucester 7	d			16 47								17 47								18 47				
Cheltenham Spa	d		16 42	16 58		17 12					17 42	17 58		18 12					18 42	18 58			19 12	
Birmingham New Street 12	a	17 17	17 26	17 45	17 49	17 56				18 17	18 26	18 45	18 49	18 56				19 17	19 26	19 45	19 49		19 56	20 17
Birmingham New Street 12	d	17 30	17 31	17 49	17 57	18 03	18 19		18 20	18 30	18 31	18 49	18 57	19 03		19 19	19 20	19 30	19 31	19 49	19 57		20 03	20 30
Tamworth	d			18 07		18 19	18 37					19 07				19 39				20 07			20 19	20 46
Burton-on-Trent	d			18 19			18 49					19 19		19 26		19 51				20 19				20 56
Derby 10	a	18 09		18 35		18 42	19 05			19 09		19 35		19 42		20 05		20 09		20 35			20 42	21 09
Nottingham 8	a			19 05			19 36					20 05				20 36				21 05				
Chesterfield	a					19 02				19 29				20 02				20 29					21 02	21 29
Sheffield 7	a	18 47				19 18				19 51				20 18				20 49					21 18	21 44
Doncaster 7	a	19 18								20 16								21 25						22 19
Wakefield Westgate 7	a					19 46								20 46									21 46	
Leeds 10	a					20 02								21 05									22 07	
York 8	a	19 44				20 31				20 40				22 03				21 48						22 48
Darlington 7	a	20 12				21 04				21 14								22 21						
Durham	a	20 29				21 21				21 32								22 41						
Chester-le-Street	a									21 39								22 50						
Newcastle 8	a	20 45				21 33				21 55								23 10						
Morpeth	a	21 02																						
Alnmouth for Alnwick	a	21 16				21 59																		
Berwick-upon-Tweed	a	21 37				22 20																		
Dunbar	a																							
Wolverhampton 7 🚢	d		17 49		18 14				18 37		18 49		19 14				19 37		19 49		20 14			
Stafford	a				18 29								19 29								20 29			
Stoke-on-Trent	a		18 18		18 54						19 18		19 54						20 18		20 54			
Congleton	a																							
Macclesfield	a				19 11								20 11								21 11			
Crewe 10	a								19 07								20 07							
Wilmslow	a																							
Stockport	a				19 27								20 27								21 27			
Manchester Piccadilly 10 🚢	a		19 00		19 40						20 00		20 40						21 00		21 40			
Warrington Bank Quay	a								19 26								20 26							
Wigan North Western	a								19 37								20 37							
Preston 8	a								19 59								20 59							
Lancaster 6	a																							
Oxenholme Lake District	a																							
Penrith North Lakes	a																							
Carlisle 8	a																							
Lockerbie	a																							
Haymarket	a																							
Edinburgh 10	a	22 28				23 09																		
Haymarket	a																							
Motherwell	a																							
Glasgow Central 15	a																							
Inverkeithing	a																							
Kirkcaldy	a																							
Markinch	a																							
Ladybank	a																							
Cupar	a																							
Leuchars 3	a																							
Dundee	a																							
Arbroath	a																							
Montrose	a																							
Stonehaven	a																							
Aberdeen	a																							

For general notes see front of timetable
For details of catering facilities see Directory of Train Operators

Table 51 — SUMMARY OF SERVICES — Saturdays

South Coast and The South West → North West England, The North East and Scotland

until 5 September

Route Diagram - See first page of Table 51

		XC 1◇ A	XC 1◇ B	XC 1◇	XC 1◇	XC 1◇ B	XC 1◇ A	XC 1◇	XC 1◇	XC 1◇	XC 1◇ A	XC 1◇ B	XC 1◇	XC 1◇	XC 1◇	XC 1◇	XC 1◇	XC 1◇	XC 1◇	XC 1◇
		🛒	🛒		🛒	🛒	🛒	🛒	🛒	🛒	🛒	🛒	🍽		🛒	🛒	🛒		🛒	🛒
Bournemouth	d				17 45						18 45	18 45							19 45	
Brockenhurst 3	d				18 00						19 00	19 00							20 00	
Southampton Central	d				18 15						19 15	19 15							20 15	
Southampton Airport Parkway ✈	d				18 22						19 22	19 22							20 22	
Winchester	d				18 31						19 31	19 31							20 31	
Basingstoke	d				18 47						19 47	19 47							20 47	
Guildford	d																			
Reading 7	d				19 10				19 40		20 10	20 10			20 40				21 10	21 40
Oxford	d				19 36				20 07		20 36	20 36			21 07				21 36	22 07
Banbury	d				19 53				20 25		20 53	20 53			21 25				21 53	22 25
Leamington Spa 8	d				20 11				20 43		21 11	21 11			21 43				22 11	22 43
Coventry	d				20 27						21 27	21 27			21 56				22 27	
Birmingham International ✈	d				20 38						21 38	21 38			22 13				22 38	
Penzance	d												16 25							
St Erth	d												16 36							
Hayle	d																			
Camborne	d												16 47							
Redruth	d												16 54							
Truro	d												17 06							
St Austell	d												17 24							
Newquay	d					15 20	15 20													
Par	d																			
Lostwithiel	d																			
Bodmin Parkway	d					16 36	16 36						17 40							
Liskeard 6	d					16 50	16 50						17 53							
Plymouth	d					17 21	17 21						18 21			18 32				
Totnes	d					17 48	17 48						18 48			18 57				
Paignton	d									18 03										
Torquay	d									18 10										
Newton Abbot	d					18 01	18 01			18 22			19 01			19 10				
Teignmouth	d															19 17				
Dawlish	d															19 22				
Exeter St Davids 6	d					18 23	18 23			18 52			19 23			19 45				
Tiverton Parkway	d					18 37	18 37			19 05						19 58				
Taunton	d					18 51	18 51			19 20			19 49			20 14				
Weston-super-Mare	d															20 38				
Cardiff Central 7	d			18 45										20 00				20 50		
Newport (South Wales)	d			19 00										20 15				21 05		
Bristol Temple Meads 10	d	19 00	19 00			19 30	19 30			20 00			20 30			21 00				
Bristol Parkway 7	d	19 10	19 10			19 40	19 40			20 10			20 40			21 10				
Gloucester 7	d			19 47										21 06				21 49		
Cheltenham Spa	d	19 42	19 42	19 58		20 12	20 12			20 42			21 12	21 18		21 42		22 00		
Birmingham New Street 12	a	20 26	20 26	20 40	20 49	20 56	20 56	←	21 17	21 41	21 49	21 49	21 56	22 07	22 25	22 27		22 42	22 54	23 17
Birmingham New Street 12	d	20 31	20 31	20 49	21 03 →	20 57	20 57	21 03			21 57	21 57	21 57	22 10			22 31			
Tamworth	d			21 08				21 19						22 28						
Burton-on-Trent	d			21 20				21 29						22 39						
Derby 10	a			21 35				21 42					22 31	22 55						
Nottingham 8	a			22 10										23 33						
Chesterfield	a							22 07					22 52							
Sheffield 7	a							22 23					23 08							
Doncaster 7	a							22 47												
Wakefield Westgate 7	a							23 09												
Leeds 10	a							23 29					23 56							
York 8	a																			
Darlington 7	a																			
Durham	a																			
Chester-le-Street	a																			
Newcastle 8	a																			
Morpeth	a																			
Alnmouth for Alnwick	a																			
Berwick-upon-Tweed	a																			
Dunbar	a																			
Wolverhampton 7	d	20 49	20 49			21 14	21 14				22 14	22 14					22 49			
Stafford	a					21 29	21 29				22 29	22 29					23 02			
Stoke-on-Trent	a		21 18			21 49						22 50								
Congleton	a																			
Macclesfield	a		21 38			22 09						23 07								
Crewe 10	a																23 26			
Wilmslow	a	21 39					22 19				23 11						23 43			
Stockport	a	21 50	21 53			22 24	22 35				23 21	23 21					23s53			
Manchester Piccadilly 10	a	22 05	22 05			22 40	22 48				23 35	23 35					00 09			
Warrington Bank Quay	a																			
Wigan North Western	a																			
Preston 8	a																			
Lancaster 6	a																			
Oxenholme Lake District	a																			
Penrith North Lakes	a																			
Carlisle 8	a																			
Lockerbie	a																			
Haymarket	a																			
Edinburgh 10	a																			
Haymarket	a																			
Motherwell	a																			
Glasgow Central 15	a																			
Inverkeithing	a																			
Kirkcaldy	a																			
Markinch	a																			
Ladybank	a																			
Cupar	a																			
Leuchars 3	a																			
Dundee	a																			
Arbroath	a																			
Montrose	a																			
Stonehaven	a																			
Aberdeen	a																			

For general notes see front of timetable
For details of catering facilities see Directory of Train Operators

A Until 11 July
B From 18 July

South Coast and The South West → North West England, The North East and Scotland

from 12 September

Route Diagram - See first page of Table 51

		XC	XC	XC	VT	XC	XC		XC	XC	XC	XC	VT	XC		XC	XC	XC	XC	VT	XC		XC	XC
		1◇	1◇	1	1◇	1◇	1◇		1	1◇	1◇	1	1◇	1◇		1◇	1	1◇	1◇	1◇	1◇		1◇	1◇
		⊼	⊼		⊡	⊼	⊼		⊼	⊼	⊼		⊡	⊼		⊼		⊼	⊼	⊡	⊼		⊼	
Bournemouth	d																							
Brockenhurst 3	d																							
Southampton Central	d																	05 09						
Southampton Airport Parkwy ✈	d																	05 16						
Winchester	d																	05 25						
Basingstoke	d																	05 41						
Guildford	d																				06 09			
Reading 7	d																	06 10			06 46			
Oxford	d																	06 36			07 12			
Banbury	d																	06 53			07 31			
Leamington Spa 8	d																	07 11			07 49			
Coventry	d																	07 27						
Birmingham International ✈	d																	07 38						
Penzance	d																							
St Erth	d																							
Hayle	d																							
Camborne	d																							
Redruth	d																							
Truro	d																							
St Austell	d																							
Newquay	d																							
Par	d																							
Lostwithiel	d																							
Bodmin Parkway	d																							
Liskeard 6	d																							
Plymouth	d																							
Totnes	d																							
Paignton	d																							
Torquay	d																							
Newton Abbot	d																							
Teignmouth	d																							
Dawlish	d																							
Exeter St Davids 6	d																							
Tiverton Parkway	d																							
Taunton	d																							
Weston-super-Mare	d																							
Cardiff Central 7	d																							06 40
Newport (South Wales)	d																							06 55
Bristol Temple Meads 10	d																		06 15				07 00	
Bristol Parkway 7	d																		06 25				07 10	
Gloucester 7	d																		07 02					07 47
Cheltenham Spa	d																		07 12				07 42	07 58
Birmingham New Street 12	a																	07 49	07 56		08 17		08 26	08 45
Birmingham New Street 12	d	05 55	05 57	06 19	06 20	06 30	06 31		06 49	06 57	07 03	07 19	07 20	07 30		07 31	07 49	07 57	08 03	08 20	08 30		08 31	08 49
Tamworth	d	06 12		06 39		06 46			07 07		07 19	07 38		07 46			08 07		08 19					09 07
Burton-on-Trent	d	06 22		06 51		06 56			07 19		07 29	07 50		07 56			08 19		08 29					09 19
Derby 10	a	06 35		07 05		07 09			07 35		07 42	08 05		08 09			08 35		08 42		09 09			09 35
Nottingham 8 ⛴	a			07 40					08 10			08 36					09 05							10 05
Chesterfield	a	06 55				07 29					08 02			08 29					09 02					
Sheffield 7	a	07 09				07 48					08 17			08 46					09 17		09 46			
Doncaster 7	a					08 23								09 21							10 18			
Wakefield Westgate 7	a	07 36									08 46								09 46					
Leeds 10	a	07 52									09 02								10 03					
York 8	a	08 25				08 49					09 30			09 45					10 30		10 44			
Darlington 7	a	08 54				09 18					09 59			10 13					10 59		11 16			
Durham	a	09 11				09 35					10 16			10 30					11 16		11 33			
Chester-le-Street	a					09 42																		
Newcastle 8	a	09 26				09 59					10 33			10 51					11 32		11 54			
Morpeth	a	09 41																						
Alnmouth for Alnwick	a	09 55																	11 59					
Berwick-upon-Tweed	a										11 17													
Dunbar	a										11 40													
Wolverhampton 7 ⛴	d		06 14		06 37		06 49			07 14			07 37			07 49		08 14		08 37			08 49	
Stafford	a		06 29				07 00			07 29								08 29						
Stoke-on-Trent	a		06 50				07 18									08 18		08 54					09 18	
Congleton	a		07 02																					
Macclesfield	a		07 11				07 36									08 35		09 11						
Crewe 10	a				07 07					07 50			08 07							09 07				
Wilmslow	a									08 09														
Stockport	a		07 27				07 49			08 20						08 49		09 27						
Manchester Piccadilly 10 ⛴	a		07 40				08 00			08 40						09 00		09 40					10 00	
Warrington Bank Quay	a				07 26								08 27							09 26				
Wigan North Western	a				07 37								08 38							09 37				
Preston 8	a				07 51								08 52							09 51				
Lancaster 6	a				08 08								09 09							10 08				
Oxenholme Lake District	a				08 22															10 22				
Penrith North Lakes	a												09 45											
Carlisle 8	a				09 01								10 01							11 01				
Lockerbie	a																							
Haymarket	a				10s16															12s16				
Edinburgh 10	a	11 02			10 22						12 12								13 06	12 22				
Haymarket	a																							
Motherwell	a																							
Glasgow Central 15	a												11 17											
Inverkeithing	a																							
Kirkcaldy	a																							
Markinch	a																							
Ladybank	a																							
Cupar	a																							
Leuchars 3	a																							
Dundee	a																							
Arbroath	a																							
Montrose	a																							
Stonehaven	a																							
Aberdeen	a																							

For general notes see front of timetable
For details of catering facilities see Directory of Train Operators

Table 51 | **SUMMARY OF SERVICES** | **Saturdays**

South Coast and The South West → North West England, The North East and Scotland

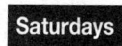

from 12 September

Route Diagram - See first page of Table 51

		XC	XC	XC	VT	VT	XC	XC	XC	XC	XC	XC	VT	XC	XC	XC	XC	XC	XC	VT	VT
		1◇	1◇	1	1◇	1◇	1◇	1◇	1◇	1◇	1◇	1	1◇	1◇	1◇	1◇	1◇	1◇	1	1◇	1◇
					A	B														A	B
		🛒	🛒		☕	☕	🛒	🛒		🛒	🛒		☕	🛒	🛒		🛒	🛒		☕	☕
Bournemouth	d						06 25			06 37							07 45				
Brockenhurst 3	d						06 39			06 55							08 00				
Southampton Central	d	06 15					06 53			07 15							08 15				
Southampton Airport Parkwy ✈	d	06 22					07 01			07 22							08 22				
Winchester	d	06 31					07 09			07 31							08 31				
Basingstoke	d	06 47					07 25			07 47							08 47				
Guildford	d																				
Reading 7	d	07 10					07 45			08 10				08 40			09 10				
Oxford	d	07 36					08 15			08 36				09 07			09 36				
Banbury	d	07 53					08 35			08 53				09 25			09 53				
Leamington Spa 8	d	08 11					08 53			09 11				09 43			10 11				
Coventry	d	08 27								09 27							10 27				
Birmingham International ✈	d	08 38								09 38							10 38				
Penzance	d																				
St Erth	d																				
Hayle	d																				
Camborne	d																				
Redruth	d																				
Truro	d																				
St Austell	d																				
Newquay	d																				
Par	d																				
Lostwithiel	d																				
Bodmin Parkway	d																				
Liskeard 6	d																				
Plymouth	d		05 25								06 25							07 25			
Totnes	d		05 50								06 50							07 50			
Paignton	d														07 00						
Torquay	d														07 06						
Newton Abbot	d		06 03								07 03				07 18			08 03			
Teignmouth	d														07 25						
Dawlish	d														07 30						
Exeter St Davids 6	d		06 23								07 23				07 48			08 23			
Tiverton Parkway	d		06 37								07 37							08 37			
Taunton	d		06 51								07 51				08 12			08 51			
Weston-super-Mare	d																				
Cardiff Central 7	d							07 00	07 45							08 45					
Newport (South Wales)	d							07 14	08 00							09 00					
Bristol Temple Meads 10	d		07 30					08 00			08 30				09 00			09 30			
Bristol Parkway 7	d		07 40					08 10			08 40				09 10			09 40			
Gloucester 7	d								08 47							09 47					
Cheltenham Spa	d		08 12					08 42	08 58		09 12				09 42	09 58		10 12			
Birmingham New Street 12	a	08 49	08 56				09 17	09 26	09 45	09 49	09 56			10 17	10 26	10 45	10 49	10 56			
Birmingham New Street 12	d	08 57	09 03	09 19	09 20	09 20	09 30	09 31	09 49	09 57	10 03	10 19	10 20	10 30	10 31	10 49	10 57	11 03	11 19	11 20	11 20
Tamworth	d			09 39					10 07		10 19	10 37				11 07			11 39		
Burton-on-Trent	d		09 26	09 51					10 19			10 49				11 19		11 26	11 51		
Derby 10	a		09 42	10 05			10 09		10 35		10 42	11 05		11 09		11 35		11 42	12 05		
Nottingham 8 🚌	a			10 36					11 05			11 36				12 05			12 36		
Chesterfield	a		10 02								11 02							12 02			
Sheffield 7	a		10 17				10 46				11 17			11 46				12 17			
Doncaster 7	a						11 16							12 16							
Wakefield Westgate 7	a		10 46								11 46							12 46			
Leeds 10	a		11 02								12 02							13 02			
York 8	a		11 32				11 44				12 30			12 44				13 32			
Darlington 7	a		11 59				12 14				13 01			13 12				13 59			
Durham	a		12 16				12 34				13 18			13 29				14 16			
Chester-le-Street	a						12 41														
Newcastle 8	a		12 33				12 55				13 33			13 50				14 32			
Morpeth	a																				
Alnmouth for Alnwick	a										13 59										
Berwick-upon-Tweed	a		13 17															15 17			
Dunbar	a		13 40															15 40			
Wolverhampton 7 🚌	d	09 14			09 37	09 37		09 49		10 14			10 37		10 49		11 14			11 37	11 37
Stafford	a	09 29								10 29							11 29				
Stoke-on-Trent	a	09 54						10 18		10 54					11 18		11 54				
Congleton	a																				
Macclesfield	a	10 11								11 11							12 11				
Crewe 10	a				10 07	10 07							11 07							12 07	12 07
Wilmslow	a																				
Stockport	a	10 27								11 27							12 27				
Manchester Piccadilly 10 🚌	a	10 40						11 00		11 40					12 00		12 40				
Warrington Bank Quay	a				10 26	10 26							11 26							12 26	
Wigan North Western	a				10 37	10 37							11 37							12 37	
Preston 8	a				10 51	10 51							11 51							12 51	13 48
Lancaster 6	a				11 08	11 08							12 08							13 08	14 08
Oxenholme Lake District	a												12 22							13 22	
Penrith North Lakes	a				11 44	11 44															14 44
Carlisle 8	a				12 00	12 00							13 01							14 01	15 00
Lockerbie	a																				
Haymarket	a												14s16								16s15
Edinburgh 10	a		14 12								15 09		14 22					16 10			16 22
Haymarket	a																				
Motherwell	a																				
Glasgow Central 15	a				13 18	13 20														15 17	
Inverkeithing	a																				
Kirkcaldy	a																				
Markinch	a																				
Ladybank	a																				
Cupar	a																				
Leuchars 3	a																				
Dundee	a																				
Arbroath	a																				
Montrose	a																				
Stonehaven	a																				
Aberdeen	a																				

For general notes see front of timetable
For details of catering facilities see Directory of Train Operators

A Until 31 October
B From 7 November

South Coast and The South West → North West England, The North East and Scotland

from 12 September

Route Diagram - See first page of Table 51

		XC	XC	XC	XC	XC	XC		VT	XC	XC	XC	XC	XC		XC	VT	VT	XC	XC	XC		XC	XC
		1 ◇	1 ◇	1 ◇	1 ◇	1 ◇	1		1 ◇	1 ◇	1 ◇	1 ◇	1 ◇	1 ◇		1	1 ◇	1 ◇	1 ◇	1 ◇	1 ◇		1 ◇	1 ◇
									A								A	B						
		⚲	⚲		⚲	⚲			🍴	⚲	⚲		⚲	⚲			🍴	🍴	⚲	⚲			⚲	⚲
Bournemouth	d				08 45								09 45										10 45	
Brockenhurst 3	d				09 00								10 00										11 00	
Southampton Central	d				09 15								10 15										11 15	
Southampton Airport Parkwy ✈	d				09 22								10 22										11 22	
Winchester	d				09 31								10 31										11 31	
Basingstoke	d				09 47								10 47										11 47	
Guildford	d																							
Reading 7	d	09 40			10 10					10 40			11 10						11 40				12 10	
Oxford	d	10 07			10 36					11 07			11 36						12 07				12 36	
Banbury	d	10 25			10 53					11 25			11 53						12 25				12 53	
Leamington Spa 8	d	10 43			11 11					11 43			12 11						12 43				13 11	
Coventry	d				11 27								12 27										13 27	
Birmingham International ✈	d				11 38								12 38										13 38	
Penzance	d					06 30																		08 28
St Erth	d					06 38																		08 36
Hayle	d					06 41																		
Camborne	d					06 51																		08 46
Redruth	d					06 57																		08 52
Truro	d					07 09																		09 04
St Austell	d					07 25																		09 20
Newquay	d																							
Par	d					07 32																		09 28
Lostwithiel	d					07 39																		
Bodmin Parkway	d					07 46																		09 39
Liskeard 6	d					07 58																		09 51
Plymouth	d					08 25								09 25										10 25
Totnes	d					08 50								09 50										10 50
Paignton	d																			10 05				
Torquay	d																			10 11				
Newton Abbot	d					09 03								10 03						10 22				11 03
Teignmouth	d																			10 29				
Dawlish	d																			10 34				
Exeter St Davids 6	d					09 23								10 23						10 48				11 23
Tiverton Parkway	d					09 37								10 37						11 02				11 37
Taunton	d					09 51								10 51						11 16				11 51
Weston-super-Mare	d																							
Cardiff Central 7	d			09 45								10 45									11 45			
Newport (South Wales)	d			10 00								11 00									12 00			
Bristol Temple Meads 10	d		10 00			10 30					11 00			11 30						12 00				12 30
Bristol Parkway 7	d		10 10			10 40					11 10			11 40						12 10				12 40
Gloucester 7	d			10 47								11 47									12 47			
Cheltenham Spa	d		10 42	10 58		11 12					11 42	11 58		12 12						12 42	12 58			13 12
Birmingham New Street 12	a	11 17	11 26	11 45	11 49	11 56				12 17	12 26	12 45	12 49	12 56					13 17	13 26	13 45		13 49	13 56
Birmingham New Street 12	d	11 30	11 31	11 49	11 57	12 03	12 19		12 20	12 30	12 31	12 49	12 57	13 03		13 19	13 20	13 20	13 30	13 31	13 49		13 57	14 03
Tamworth	d			12 07		12 19	12 37					13 07				13 39					14 07			14 19
Burton-on-Trent	d			12 19			12 49					13 19		13 26		13 51					14 19			
Derby 10	a	12 09		12 35		12 42	13 05			13 09		13 35		13 41		14 05			14 09		14 35			14 42
Nottingham 8 🚌	a			13 05			13 36					14 05				14 36					15 05			
Chesterfield	a					13 02								14 02										15 02
Sheffield 7	a	12 46				13 17				13 46				14 17					14 46					15 17
Doncaster 7	a	13 19								14 16									15 16					
Wakefield Westgate 7	a					13 46								14 46										15 46
Leeds 10	a					14 02								15 02										16 02
York 8	a	13 44				14 30				14 44				15 32					15 44					16 30
Darlington 7	a	14 16				14 59				15 15				15 59					16 13					16 59
Durham	a	14 34				15 16				15 32				16 16					16 32					17 16
Chester-le-Street	a	14 41																						
Newcastle 8	a	14 55				15 32				15 51				16 32					16 51					17 32
Morpeth	a					15 48																		
Alnmouth for Alnwick	a					16 02																		18 01
Berwick-upon-Tweed	a													17 17										
Dunbar	a													17 40										
Wolverhampton 7 🚌	d		11 49		12 14				12 37		12 49		13 14				13 37	13 37		13 49			14 14	
Stafford	a				12 29								13 29										14 29	
Stoke-on-Trent	a		12 18		12 54						13 18		13 54							14 18			14 54	
Congleton	a																							
Macclesfield	a				13 11								14 11										15 11	
Crewe 10	a								13 07								14 07	14 07						
Wilmslow	a																							
Stockport	a				13 27								14 27										15 27	
Manchester Piccadilly 10 🚌	a		13 00		13 40						14 00		14 40							15 00			15 40	
Warrington Bank Quay	a								13 26								14 26							
Wigan North Western	a								13 37								14 37							
Preston 8	a								13 51								14 51	15 48						
Lancaster 6	a								14 08								15 08	16 08						
Oxenholme Lake District	a																15 22							
Penrith North Lakes	a								14 44									16 45						
Carlisle 8	a								15 00								16 01	17 00						
Lockerbie	a																							
Haymarket	a								16s15									18s14						
Edinburgh 10	a					17 14			16 22					18 05				18 22						19 07
Haymarket	a													18 11										19 13
Motherwell	a																							20 00
Glasgow Central 15	a																17 18							20 29
Inverkeithing	a													18 25										
Kirkcaldy	a													18 40										
Markinch	a													18 50										
Ladybank	a													18 57										
Cupar	a													19 04										
Leuchars 3	a													19 11										
Dundee	a													19 24										
Arbroath	a													19 41										
Montrose	a													20 01										
Stonehaven	a													20 22										
Aberdeen	a													20 46										

For general notes see front of timetable
For details of catering facilities see Directory of Train Operators

A Until 31 October
B From 7 November

South Coast and The South West → North West England, The North East and Scotland

from 12 September

Route Diagram - See first page of Table 51

		XC	VT	XC	XC	XC	XC	XC	XC	VT	VT	XC	XC	XC	XC	XC	XC	VT	XC	XC	XC
		1	1◇	1◇	1◇	1◇	1◇	1◇	1	1◇	1◇	1◇	1◇	1◇	1◇	1◇	1	1◇	1◇	1◇	1◇
			A							B	A							A			
Bournemouth	d						11 45								12 45						
Brockenhurst 3	d						12 00								13 00						
Southampton Central	d						12 15								13 15						
Southampton Airport Parkwy ✈	d						12 22								13 22						
Winchester	d						12 31								13 31						
Basingstoke	d						12 47								13 47						
Guildford	d																				
Reading 7	d			12 40			13 10					13 40			14 10				14 40		
Oxford	d			13 07			13 36					14 07			14 36				15 07		
Banbury	d			13 25			13 53					14 25			14 53				15 25		
Leamington Spa 8	d			13 43			14 11					14 43			15 11				15 43		
Coventry	d						14 27								15 27						
Birmingham International ✈	d						14 38								15 38						
Penzance	d												09 43								
St Erth	d												09 51								
Hayle	d																				
Camborne	d												10 01								
Redruth	d												10 07								
Truro	d												10 19								
St Austell	d												10 35								
Newquay	d																				
Par	d												10 42								
Lostwithiel	d												10 49								
Bodmin Parkway	d												10 56								
Liskeard 6	d												11 08								
Plymouth	d							11 25					11 48			12 21					
Totnes	d							11 50					12 13			12 48					
Paignton	d																				
Torquay	d																				
Newton Abbot	d							12 03					12 25			13 01					
Teignmouth	d																				
Dawlish	d																				
Exeter St Davids 6	d							12 23					12 48			13 23					
Tiverton Parkway	d							12 37					13 02			13 39					
Taunton	d							12 51					13 16			13 54					
Weston-super-Mare	d																				
Cardiff Central 7	d					12 45								13 45							14 45
Newport (South Wales)	d					13 00								14 00							15 00
Bristol Temple Meads 10	d				13 00			13 30					14 00			14 30				15 00	
Bristol Parkway 7	d				13 10			13 40					14 10			14 40				15 10	
Gloucester 7	d					13 47								14 47							15 47
Cheltenham Spa	d				13 42	13 58		14 12					14 42	14 58		15 12				15 42	15 58
Birmingham New Street 12	a			14 17	14 26	14 45	14 49	14 56				15 17	15 26	15 45	15 49	15 56			16 17	16 26	16 45
Birmingham New Street 12	d	14 19	14 20	14 30	14 31	14 49	14 57	15 03	15 19	15 20	15 20	15 30	15 31	15 49	15 57	16 03	16 19	16 20	16 30	16 31	16 49
Tamworth	d	14 37				15 07			15 39					16 07		16 21	16 37				17 07
Burton-on-Trent	d	14 49				15 19		15 26	15 51					16 19			16 49				17 19
Derby 10	a	15 05		15 09		15 35		15 42	16 05			16 09		16 35		16 42	17 05		17 09		17 35
Nottingham 8	a	15 36				16 05			16 36					17 05			17 36				18 05
Chesterfield	a							16 02								17 04					
Sheffield 7	a			15 46				16 18				16 46				17 19			17 44		
Doncaster 7	a			16 16								17 19									
Wakefield Westgate 7	a							16 46								17 47			18 14		
Leeds 10	a							17 02								18 02			18 32		
York 8	a			16 44				17 31				17 44				18 31			18 59		
Darlington 7	a			17 12				17 59				18 12				19 01			19 37		
Durham	a			17 29				18 16				18 29				19 19			19 54		
Chester-le-Street	a			17 36															20 01		
Newcastle 8	a			17 53				18 37				18 50				19 35			20 18		
Morpeth	a																				
Alnmouth for Alnwick	a															20 03					
Berwick-upon-Tweed	a							19 25													
Dunbar	a							19 49													
Wolverhampton 7	d		14 37		14 49		15 14			15 37	15 37		15 49		16 14			16 37		16 49	
Stafford	a						15 29								16 29						
Stoke-on-Trent	a				15 18		15 54						16 18		16 54					17 18	
Congleton	a																				
Macclesfield	a						16 11								17 11						
Crewe 10	a		15 07							16 07	16 08							17 07			
Wilmslow	a																				
Stockport	a						16 27								17 27						
Manchester Piccadilly 10	a				16 00		16 40						17 00		17 40					18 00	
Warrington Bank Quay	a		15 26								16 26							17 26			
Wigan North Western	a		15 37								16 37							17 37			
Preston 8	a		15 51							17 48	16 51							17 51			
Lancaster 6	a		16 08							18 08	17 09							18 08			
Oxenholme Lake District	a									18 22	17 24							18 22			
Penrith North Lakes	a		16 45							18 48								18 48			
Carlisle 8	a		17 00							19 04	18 03							19 04			
Lockerbie	a																				
Haymarket	a		18s14							20s19								20s19			
Edinburgh 10	a		18 22					20 15		20 24						21 10		20 24			
Haymarket	a							20 25								21 13					
Motherwell	a															21 55					
Glasgow Central 15	a										19 17					22 23					
Inverkeithing	a							20 43													
Kirkcaldy	a							20 59													
Markinch	a							21 08													
Ladybank	a							21 16													
Cupar	a							21 23													
Leuchars 3	a							21 31													
Dundee	a							21 52													
Arbroath	a																				
Montrose	a																				
Stonehaven	a																				
Aberdeen	a																				

For general notes see front of timetable
For details of catering facilities see Directory of Train Operators

A Until 31 October
B From 7 November

from 12 September

South Coast and The South West → North West England, The North East and Scotland

Route Diagram - See first page of Table 51

		XC	XC	XC	VT	VT	XC		XC	XC	XC	XC	XC	VT		XC	XC	XC	XC	XC	XC		VT	XC
		1 ◇	1 ◇	1	1 ◇	1 ◇	1 ◇		1 ◇	1 ◇	1 ◇	1 ◇	1	1 ◇		1 ◇	1 ◇	1 ◇	1 ◇	1 ◇	1		1 ◇	1 ◇
					A	B								A									A	
		🛒	🛒		🍽	🍽	🛒		🛒		🛒	🛒		🍽		🛒	🛒		🛒	🛒			🍽	🛒
Bournemouth	d	13 45									14 45								15 45					
Brockenhurst 3	d	14 00									15 00								16 00					
Southampton Central	d	14 15									15 15								16 15					
Southampton Airport Parkway ✈	d	14 22									15 22								16 22					
Winchester	d	14 31									15 31								16 31					
Basingstoke	d	14 47									15 47								16 47					
Guildford	d																							
Reading 7	d	15 10					15 40				16 10					16 40			17 10					17 40
Oxford	d	15 36					16 07				16 36					17 07			17 36					18 07
Banbury	d	15 53					16 25				16 53					17 25			17 53					18 25
Leamington Spa 8	d	16 11					16 43				17 11					17 43			18 11					18 43
Coventry	d	16 27									17 27								18 27					
Birmingham International ✈	d	16 38									17 38								18 38					
Penzance	d																							
St Erth	d																							
Hayle	d																							
Camborne	d																							
Redruth	d																							
Truro	d																							
St Austell	d																							
Newquay	d																							
Par	d																							
Lostwithiel	d																							
Bodmin Parkway	d																							
Liskeard 6	d																							
Plymouth	d		13 25									14 25								15 25				
Totnes	d		13 50									14 50								15 50				
Paignton	d								13 53															
Torquay	d								13 59															
Newton Abbot	d		14 03						14 10			15 03								16 03				
Teignmouth	d								14 17															
Dawlish	d								14 22															
Exeter St Davids 6	d		14 23						14 36			15 23								16 23				
Tiverton Parkway	d		14 37						14 49			15 37								16 37				
Taunton	d		14 51						15 04			15 51								16 51				
Weston-super-Mare	d								15 29															
Cardiff Central 7	d									15 45								16 45						
Newport (South Wales)	d									16 00								17 00						
Bristol Temple Meads 10	d		15 30						16 00			16 30					17 00			17 30				
Bristol Parkway 7	d		15 40						16 10			16 40					17 10			17 40				
Gloucester 7	d									16 47								17 47						
Cheltenham Spa	d		16 12						16 42	16 58		17 12					17 42	17 58		18 12				
Birmingham New Street 12	a	16 49	16 56				17 17		17 26	17 45	17 49	17 56				18 17	18 26	18 45	18 49	18 56				19 17
Birmingham New Street 12	d	16 57	17 03	17 19	17 20	17 20	17 30		17 31	17 49	17 57	18 03	18 19	18 20		18 30	18 31	18 49	18 57	19 03	19 19		19 20	19 30
Tamworth	d			17 39						18 07		18 19	18 37					19 07			19 39			
Burton-on-Trent	d		17 26	17 51						18 19			18 49					19 19		19 26	19 51			
Derby 10	a		17 42	18 05			18 09			18 35		18 42	19 05			19 09		19 35		19 42	20 05			20 09
Nottingham 8 🚋	a			18 36						19 05			19 36					20 05			20 36			
Chesterfield	a		18 02									19 02				19 29				20 02				20 29
Sheffield 7	a		18 18				18 47					19 18				19 51				20 18				20 49
Doncaster 7	a						19 18									20 16								21 25
Wakefield Westgate 7	a		18 46									19 46								20 46				
Leeds 10	a		19 02									20 02								21 05				
York 8	a		19 31				19 44					20 31				20 40				22 03				21 48
Darlington 7	a		20 03				20 12					21 04				21 14								22 21
Durham	a		20 21				20 29					21 21				21 32								22 41
Chester-le-Street	a															21 39								22 50
Newcastle 8	a		20 33				20 45					21 33				21 55								23 10
Morpeth	a						21 02																	
Alnmouth for Alnwick	a						21 16					21 59												
Berwick-upon-Tweed	a		21 19				21 37					22 20												
Dunbar	a		21 42																					
Wolverhampton 7 🚋	d	17 14			17 37	17 37			17 49		18 14			18 37			18 49		19 14				19 37	
Stafford	a	17 29									18 29								19 29					
Stoke-on-Trent	a	17 54							18 18		18 54						19 18		19 54					
Congleton	a																							
Macclesfield	a	18 11									19 11								20 11					
Crewe 10	a				18 07	18 07								19 07									20 07	
Wilmslow	a																							
Stockport	a	18 27									19 27								20 27					
Manchester Piccadilly 10 🚋	a	18 40							19 00		19 40						20 00		20 40					
Warrington Bank Quay	a				18 26									19 26									20 26	
Wigan North Western	a				18 37									19 37									20 37	
Preston 8	a				18 51	19 59								19 59									20 59	
Lancaster 6	a				19 08																			
Oxenholme Lake District	a				19 22																			
Penrith North Lakes	a																							
Carlisle 8	a				20 01																			
Lockerbie	a																							
Haymarket	a																							
Edinburgh 10	a		22 15				22 28					23 09												
Haymarket	a																							
Motherwell	a																							
Glasgow Central 15	a				21 17																			
Inverkeithing	a																							
Kirkcaldy	a																							
Markinch	a																							
Ladybank	a																							
Cupar	a																							
Leuchars 3	a																							
Dundee	a																							
Arbroath	a																							
Montrose	a																							
Stonehaven	a																							
Aberdeen	a																							

For general notes see front of timetable
For details of catering facilities see Directory of Train Operators

A Until 31 October
B From 7 November

Table 51 SUMMARY OF SERVICES

Saturdays

South Coast and The South West → North West England, The North East and Scotland

from 12 September

Route Diagram - See first page of Table 51

		VT	XC	XC	XC	XC	XC		XC	XC	XC	XC	XC	XC		XC	XC	XC	XC	XC	XC	XC		
		1◇	1◇	1◇	1◇	1◇	1◇		1◇	1◇	1◇	1◇	1◇	1◇		1◇	1◇	1◇	1◇	1◇	1◇	1◇		
		A																						
Bournemouth	d				16 45						17 45					18 45					19 45			
Brockenhurst 3	d				17 00						18 00					19 00					20 00			
Southampton Central	d				17 15						18 15					19 15					20 15			
Southampton Airport Parkwy	d				17 22						18 22					19 22					20 22			
Winchester	d				17 31						18 31					19 31					20 31			
Basingstoke	d				17 47						18 47					19 47					20 47			
Guildford	d																							
Reading 7	d				18 10		18 40				19 10		19 40			20 10		20 40			21 10	21 40		
Oxford	d				18 36		19 07				19 36		20 07			20 36		21 07			21 36	22 07		
Banbury	d				18 53		19 25				19 53		20 25			20 53		21 25			21 53	22 25		
Leamington Spa 8	d				19 11		19 43				20 11		20 43			21 11		21 43			22 11	22 43		
Coventry	d				19 27						20 27					21 27		21 56			22 27			
Birmingham International	d				19 38						20 38					21 38		22 13			22 38			
Penzance	d																							
St Erth	d																							
Hayle	d																							
Camborne	d																							
Redruth	d																							
Truro	d																							
St Austell	d																							
Newquay	d																							
Par	d																							
Lostwithiel	d																							
Bodmin Parkway	d																							
Liskeard 6	d																							
Plymouth	d					16 25						17 21					18 25							
Totnes	d					16 50						17 48					18 50							
Paignton	d																							
Torquay	d																							
Newton Abbot	d					17 03						18 01					19 03							
Teignmouth	d																							
Dawlish	d																							
Exeter St Davids 6	d					17 23						18 23					19 23							
Tiverton Parkway	d					17 37						18 37					19 37							
Taunton	d					17 51						18 51					19 51							
Weston-super-Mare	d																							
Cardiff Central 7	d			17 45						18 45										20 50				
Newport (South Wales)	d			18 00						19 00										21 05				
Bristol Temple Meads 10	d		18 00			18 30			19 00			19 30		20 00			20 30							
Bristol Parkway 7	d		18 10			18 40			19 10			19 40		20 10			20 40							
Gloucester 7	d			18 47						19 47										21 49				
Cheltenham Spa	d		18 42	18 58		19 12			19 42	19 58		20 12		20 42			21 12			22 00				
Birmingham New Street 12	a		19 26	19 45	19 49	19 56	20 17		20 26	20 40	20 49	20 56	21 17	21 38		21 49	21 58	22 25		22 42	22 54	23 17		
Birmingham New Street 12	d	19 20	19 31	19 49	19 57	20 03	20 30		20 31	20 49	20 57	21 03				21 57			22 31					
Tamworth	d			20 07		20 19	20 46			21 08		21 21												
Burton-on-Trent	d			20 19			20 56			21 20		21 33												
Derby 10	a			20 35		20 42	21 09			21 36		21 46												
Nottingham 8	a			21 05						22 10														
Chesterfield	a					21 02	21 29					22 07												
Sheffield 7	a					21 18	21 43					22 23												
Doncaster 7	a						22 19					22 47												
Wakefield Westgate 7	a					21 46						23 09												
Leeds 10	a					22 07						23 29												
York 8	a						22 48																	
Darlington 7	a																							
Durham	a																							
Chester-le-Street	a																							
Newcastle 8	a																							
Morpeth	a																							
Alnmouth for Alnwick	a																							
Berwick-upon-Tweed	a																							
Dunbar	a																							
Wolverhampton 7	d	19 37	19 49		20 14				20 49		21 14					22 14			22 49					
Stafford	a				20 29						21 29					22 29			23 02					
Stoke-on-Trent	a		20 18		20 54				21 18		21 54					22 50								
Congleton	a																							
Macclesfield	a				21 11				21 37		22 11					23 07								
Crewe 10	a	20 07																	23 26					
Wilmslow	a																		23 43					
Stockport	a				21 27				21 53		22 27					23 21			23s53					
Manchester Piccadilly 10	a		21 00		21 40				22 05		22 40					23 35			00 09					
Warrington Bank Quay	a																							
Wigan North Western	a																							
Preston 8	a	21 48																						
Lancaster 6	a																							
Oxenholme Lake District	a																							
Penrith North Lakes	a																							
Carlisle 8	a																							
Lockerbie	a																							
Haymarket	a																							
Edinburgh 10	a																							
Haymarket	a																							
Motherwell	a																							
Glasgow Central 15	a																							
Inverkeithing	a																							
Kirkcaldy	a																							
Markinch	a																							
Ladybank	a																							
Cupar	a																							
Leuchars 8	a																							
Dundee	a																							
Arbroath	a																							
Montrose	a																							
Stonehaven	a																							
Aberdeen	a																							

For general notes see front of timetable
For details of catering facilities see Directory of Train Operators

A From 7 November

South Coast and The South West → North West England, The North East and Scotland

until 12 July

Route Diagram - See first page of Table 51

	VT	XC	XC	VT	XC	XC	VT	XC	XC	VT	XC	XC	XC	VT	XC	XC	XC	XC	XC	VT
	1◇	1◇	1◇	1◇	1◇	1◇	1◇	1◇	1◇	1◇	1◇	1◇	1◇	1◇	1◇	1◇	1◇	1◇	1◇	1◇
Bournemouth d																		09 40		
Brockenhurst 3 d																		09 57		
Southampton Central d												09 15						10 15		
Southampton Airport Parkway ✈ d												09 22						10 22		
Winchester d												09 31						10 31		
Basingstoke d												09 47						10 47		
Guildford d																				
Reading 7 d								09 11				10 11						11 11		
Oxford d								09 37				10 37						11 37		
Banbury d								09 53				10 53						11 53		
Leamington Spa 8 d								10 11				11 11						12 11		
Coventry d								10 28				11 28						12 28		
Birmingham International ✈ d								10 40				11 40						12 40		
Penzance d																				
St Erth d																				
Hayle d																				
Camborne d																				
Redruth d																				
Truro d																				
St Austell d																				
Newquay d																				
Par d																				
Lostwithiel d																				
Bodmin Parkway d																				
Liskeard 6 d																				
Plymouth d																	08 55			
Totnes d																	09 20			
Paignton d																				
Torquay d																				
Newton Abbot d																	09 33			
Teignmouth d																				
Dawlish d																				
Exeter St Davids 6 d																	09 55			
Tiverton Parkway d																	10 09			
Taunton d																	10 23			
Weston-super-Mare d																				
Cardiff Central 7 d																10 20				
Newport (South Wales) d																10 34				
Bristol Temple Meads 10 d									09 00				10 10				11 00			
Bristol Parkway 7 d									09 10				10 23				11 10			
Gloucester 7 d									09 46							11 18				
Cheltenham Spa d									09 57				10 56			11 29	11 42			
Birmingham New Street 12 a								10 51	10 56			11 51	11 56			12 28	12 50	12 51	←	
Birmingham New Street 12 d	08 45	09 01	09 03	09 20	10 00	10 03	10 15	10 59	11 03	11 20	11 49	12 01	12 03	12 20	12 30	12 49	13 03	13 01	13 03	13 20
Tamworth d			09 19			10 19					12 07		12 19			13 07	→			
Burton-on-Trent d			09 29			10 29			11 26		12 19					13 19			13 26	
Derby 10 a			09 42			10 42			11 41		12 34		12 42		13 09	13 31			13 42	
Nottingham 8 a											13 08					14 08				
Chesterfield a			10 02			11 02			12 02				13 02		13 29				14 02	
Sheffield 7 a			10 18			11 16			12 18				13 17		13 45				14 17	
Doncaster 7 a															14 13					
Wakefield Westgate 7 a			10 44			11 44			12 44				13 44						14 44	
Leeds 10 a			11 02			12 02			13 02				14 02						15 02	
York 8 a			11 34			12 32			13 32				14 32		14 43				15 32	
Darlington 7 a			12 03			13 01			14 01				15 07		15 15				16 01	
Durham a			12 20			13 18			14 18				15 24		15 32				16 18	
Chester-le-Street a																				
Newcastle 8 a			12 35			13 34			14 34				15 38		15 51				16 34	
Morpeth a													15 53							
Alnmouth for Alnwick a						14 00							16 07							
Berwick-upon-Tweed a			13 20						15 19										17 19	
Dunbar a			13 43						15 42										17 42	
Wolverhampton 7 d	09 04	09 19		09 37	10 18		10 32	11 17		11 37		12 19		12 36				13 19		13 37
Stafford a	09 17	09 31			10 31			11 29				12 33						13 33		
Stoke-on-Trent a																				
Congleton a																				
Macclesfield a																				
Crewe 10 a	09 43	09 56		10 12			11 07			12 07				13 07						14 09
Wilmslow a		10 14			11 11			12 05				13 08						14 09		
Stockport a		10 24			11 21			12 19				13 18						14 22		
Manchester Piccadilly 10 a		10 40			11 38			12 40				13 40						14 40		
Warrington Bank Quay a	10 01			10 31			11 26			12 26				13 26						14 28
Wigan North Western a	10 12			10 42			11 37			12 37				13 37						14 39
Preston 8 a	10 30			10 57			11 51			12 51				13 51						14 52
Lancaster 6 a							12 08			13 08				14 08						15 10
Oxenholme Lake District a							12 22			13 22										15 24
Penrith North Lakes a														14 44						
Carlisle 8 a							13 01			14 01				15 00						16 03
Lockerbie a																				
Haymarket a							14s13							16s14						
Edinburgh 10 a			14 15			15 07	14 22		16 12				17 14	16 22					18 07	
Haymarket a																			18 13	
Motherwell a																				
Glasgow Central 15 a										15 23										17 17
Inverkeithing a																			18 27	
Kirkcaldy a																			18 43	
Markinch a																			18 52	
Ladybank a																			19 00	
Cupar a																			19 06	
Leuchars 3 a																			19 13	
Dundee a																			19 28	
Arbroath a																			19 45	
Montrose a																			19 59	
Stonehaven a																			20 22	
Aberdeen a																			20 47	

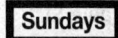

For general notes see front of timetable
For details of catering facilities see Directory of Train Operators

Table 51 — SUMMARY OF SERVICES

Sundays until 12 July

South Coast and The South West → North West England, The North East and Scotland

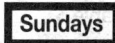

Route Diagram - See first page of Table 51

		XC	XC	XC	XC	XC	VT	XC	XC	XC	XC	XC	VT	XC	XC	XC	XC	XC	VT	XC
		1 ◇	1 ◇	1 ◇	1 ◇	1 ◇	1 ◇	1 ◇	1 ◇	1 ◇	1 ◇	1 ◇	1 ◇	1 ◇	1 ◇	1 ◇	1 ◇	1 ◇	1 ◇	1 ◇
Bournemouth	d				10 40						11 40						12 40			
Brockenhurst 3	d				10 57						11 57						12 57			
Southampton Central	d				11 15						12 15						13 15			
Southampton Airport Parkwy ✈	d				11 22						12 22						13 22			
Winchester	d				11 31						12 31						13 31			
Basingstoke	d				11 47						12 47						13 47			
Guildford	d							12 14												
Reading 7	d				12 11			12 54			13 11			13 40			14 11			14 40
Oxford	d				12 37			13 17			13 37			14 06			14 37			15 06
Banbury	d				12 53			13 35			13 53			14 25			14 53			15 25
Leamington Spa 8	d				13 11			13 53			14 11			14 43			15 11			15 43
Coventry	d				13 26						14 26						15 26			
Birmingham International ✈	d				13 38						14 38						15 38			
Penzance	d											09 30								
St Erth	d											09 38								
Hayle	d																			
Camborne	d											09 48								
Redruth	d											09 54								
Truro	d											10 06								
St Austell	d											10 24								
Newquay	d																			
Par	d											10 31								
Lostwithiel	d																			
Bodmin Parkway	d											10 42								
Liskeard 6	d											10 54								
Plymouth	d					09 55						11 25			12 00			12 25		
Totnes	d					10 20						11 50						12 50		
Paignton	d																			
Torquay	d																			
Newton Abbot	d					10 33						12 03			12 36			13 03		
Teignmouth	d																			
Dawlish	d																			
Exeter St Davids 6	d					10 55						12 23			12 57			13 23		
Tiverton Parkway	d					11 09						12 37			13 10			13 37		
Taunton	d					11 23						12 51			13 25			13 51		
Weston-super-Mare	d																			
Cardiff Central 7	d			11 20						12 20						13 50				
Newport (South Wales)	d			11 34						12 34						14 04				
Bristol Temple Meads 10	d					12 00						13 30			14 00			14 30		
Bristol Parkway 7	d					12 10						13 40			14 10			14 40		
Gloucester 7	d			12 18						13 18						14 47				
Cheltenham Spa	d			12 29		12 42				13 29		14 12			14 42	14 58		15 12		
Birmingham New Street 12	a			13 34	13 49	13 50		14 18		14 28	14 49	14 50		15 09	15 26	15 40	15 49	15 50		16 09
Birmingham New Street 12	d	13 30	13 31	13 49	14 01	14 03	14 20	14 30	14 31	14 49	15 01	15 03	15 20	15 30	15 31	15 49	16 01	16 03	16 20	16 30
Tamworth	d			14 07		14 19				15 09						16 07		16 19		
Burton-on-Trent	d			14 19						15 21		15 26				16 19				
Derby 10	a	14 09		14 34		14 42		15 05		15 34		15 42		16 05		16 34		16 42		17 05
Nottingham 8	a			15 08						16 08						17 09				
Chesterfield	a	14 29				15 02						16 02						17 02		
Sheffield 7	a	14 47				15 17		15 47				16 18		16 48				17 18		17 48
Doncaster 7	a	15 13						16 15						17 13						18 13
Wakefield Westgate 7	a					15 44						16 44						17 45		18 33
Leeds 10	a					16 02						17 02						18 02		18 53
York 8	a	15 43				16 32		16 40				17 32		17 42				18 32		19 21
Darlington 7	a	16 12				17 01		17 14				18 01		18 10				19 01		19 51
Durham	a	16 30				17 18		17 32				18 18		18 27				19 18		20 08
Chester-le-Street	a							17 40												20 18
Newcastle 8	a	16 50				17 34		17 53				18 34		18 47				19 34		20 30
Morpeth	a																			
Alnmouth for Alnwick	a					18 01												20 04		
Berwick-upon-Tweed	a											19 19								
Dunbar	a											19 42								
Wolverhampton 7	d		13 49		14 19		14 37		14 49		15 19		15 37		15 49		16 19		16u37	
Stafford	a				14 33						15 33						16 34			
Stoke-on-Trent	a		14 19		14 56				15 19		15 56				16 19		16 56			
Congleton	a																			
Macclesfield	a				15 14						16 14						17 14			
Crewe 10	a						15 09						16 09						17 09	
Wilmslow	a																			
Stockport	a				15 28						16 28						17 28			
Manchester Piccadilly 10	a		15 00		15 40				16 00		16 40				17 00		17 40			
Warrington Bank Quay	a						15 28						16 28						17 28	
Wigan North Western	a						15 39						16 39						17 39	
Preston 8	a						15 53						16 53						17 53	
Lancaster 6	a						16 10						17 10						18 10	
Oxenholme Lake District	a												17 24						18 24	
Penrith North Lakes	a						16 46												18 50	
Carlisle 8	a						17 02						18 03						19 06	
Lockerbie	a																			
Haymarket	a						18s13													
Edinburgh 10	a					19 08	18 22					20 07						21 11	20 24	
Haymarket	a											20 15						21 15		
Motherwell	a											20 53						21 53		
Glasgow Central 15	a											21 17	19 17					22 19		
Inverkeithing	a																			
Kirkcaldy	a																			
Markinch	a																			
Ladybank	a																			
Cupar	a																			
Leuchars 3	a																			
Dundee	a																			
Arbroath	a																			
Montrose	a																			
Stonehaven	a																			
Aberdeen	a																			

For general notes see front of timetable
For details of catering facilities see Directory of Train Operators

South Coast and The South West → North West England, The North East and Scotland

until 12 July

Route Diagram - See first page of Table 51

		XC	XC	XC	XC	VT	XC	XC	XC	XC	XC	XC	XC	XC	XC	XC	VT	XC	XC	XC	XC
																	R				
		1 ◇	1 ◇	1 ◇	1 ◇	1 ◇	1 ◇	1 ◇	1 ◇	1 ◇	1 ◇	1 ◇	1 ◇	1 ◇	1 ◇	1 ◇	1	1 ◇	1 ◇	1 ◇	1 ◇
Bournemouth	d			13 40						14 40					15 40						16 40
Brockenhurst 3	d			13 57						14 57					15 57						16 57
Southampton Central	d			14 15						15 15					16 15						17 15
Southampton Airport Parkwy ✈	d			14 22						15 22					16 22						17 22
Winchester	d			14 31						15 31					16 31						17 31
Basingstoke	d			14 47						15 47					16 47						17 47
Guildford	d																				
Reading 7	d			15 11			15 40			16 11		16 40			17 11			17 40			18 11
Oxford	d			15 37			16 06			16 37		17 06			17 37			18 06			18 37
Banbury	d			15 53			16 25			16 53		17 25			17 53			18 25			18 53
Leamington Spa 8	d			16 11			16 43			17 11		17 43			18 11			18 43			19 11
Coventry	d			16 26						17 26					18 26						19 26
Birmingham International ✈	d			16 38						17 38					18 38						19 38
Penzance	d												12 30								
St Erth	d												12 40								
Hayle	d												12 44								
Camborne	d												12 55								
Redruth	d												13 01								
Truro	d												13 13								
St Austell	d												13 30								
Newquay	d				11 30																
Par	d												13 37								
Lostwithiel	d												13 44								
Bodmin Parkway	d				12 41								13 51								
Liskeard 6	d				12 54								14 03								
Plymouth	d				13 21						14 21		14 35			15 21					
Totnes	d				13 48						14 48		15 00			15 48					
Paignton	d	13 08																			
Torquay	d	13 14																			
Newton Abbot	d	13 26			14 01						15 01		15 12			16 01					
Teignmouth	d	13 33																			
Dawlish	d	13 38																			
Exeter St Davids 6	d	13 51			14 23						15 23		15 33			16 23					
Tiverton Parkway	d	14 05			14 37						15 38		15 46			16 38					
Taunton	d	14 19			14 53						15 53		16 01			16 53					
Weston-super-Mare	d												16 30								
Cardiff Central 7	d		14 50						15 50					16 50						17 50	
Newport (South Wales)	d		15 04						16 04					17 04						18 04	
Bristol Temple Meads 10	d	15 00			15 30			16 00			16 30		17 00			17 30			18 00		
Bristol Parkway 7	d	15 10			15 40			16 10			16 40		17 10			17 40			18 10		
Gloucester 7	d		15 47						16 47					17 47						18 47	
Cheltenham Spa	d	15 42	15 58		16 12			16 42	16 58		17 12		17 42	17 58		18 12			18 42	18 58	
Birmingham New Street 12	a	16 26	16 40	16 49	16 50		17 09	17 26	17 40	17 49	17 50	18 09	18 27	18 40	18 49	18 56		19 09	19 26	19 40	19 49
Birmingham New Street 12	d	16 31	16 49	17 01	17 03	17 20	17 30	17 31	17 49	18 01	18 03	18 30	18 31	18 49	19 01	19 03	19 20	19 30	19 31	19 49	20 01
Tamworth	d		17 07						18 07		18 21			19 09						20 07	
Burton-on-Trent	d		17 19		17 26				18 19					19 21		19 28				20 19	
Derby 10	a		17 34		17 42		18 05		18 34		18 42	19 05		19 34		19 42		20 05		20 36	
Nottingham 8 ⛴	a		18 08						19 02					19 59						21 08	
Chesterfield	a				18 02						19 04					20 02					
Sheffield 7	a				18 19		18 46				19 20	19 39				20 18		20 38			
Doncaster 7	a						19 13					20 16						21 19			
Wakefield Westgate 7	a				18 47						19 48					20 46					
Leeds 10	a				19 04						20 05					21 03					
York 8	a				19 32		19 42				20 32	20 44				21 37		21 42			
Darlington 7	a				20 03		20 10				21 03	21 18						22 10			
Durham	a				20 21		20 27				21 21	21 36						22 27			
Chester-le-Street	a											21 45									
Newcastle 8	a				20 37		20 43				21 37	21 59						22 48			
Morpeth	a						21 01														
Alnmouth for Alnwick	a						21 15				22 05										
Berwick-upon-Tweed	a				21 23		21 36				22 28										
Dunbar	a				21 48																
Wolverhampton 7 ⛴	d	16 49		17 19		17u37		17 49		18 19			18 49		19 19		19 37		19 49		20 19
Stafford	a			17 34						18 35					19 34						20 37
Stoke-on-Trent	a	17 19		17 56				18 19		18 56			19 19		19 56				20 19		20 56
Congleton	a																				
Macclesfield	a			18 14						19 15					20 14						21 15
Crewe 10	a					18 09											20 09				
Wilmslow	a																				
Stockport	a			18 28						19 28					20 28						21 28
Manchester Piccadilly 10 ⛴	a	18 00		18 40				19 00		19 40			20 00		20 40				21 00		21 40
Warrington Bank Quay	a					18 28											20 28				
Wigan North Western	a					18 39											20 39				
Preston 8	a					18 53											20 53				
Lancaster 6	a					19 10											21 10				
Oxenholme Lake District	a					19 24											21 24				
Penrith North Lakes	a																				
Carlisle 8	a					20 03											22 03				
Lockerbie	a																22 22				
Haymarket	a																				
Edinburgh 10	a				22 20		22 25				23 19										
Haymarket	a																				
Motherwell	a																23s13				
Glasgow Central 15	a					21 17											23 35				
Inverkeithing	a																				
Kirkcaldy	a																				
Markinch	a																				
Ladybank	a																				
Cupar	a																				
Leuchars 3	a																				
Dundee	a																				
Arbroath	a																				
Montrose	a																				
Stonehaven	a																				
Aberdeen	a																				

For general notes see front of timetable
For details of catering facilities see Directory of Train Operators

Sundays

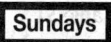

South Coast and The South West → North West England, The North East and Scotland

until 12 July

Route Diagram - See first page of Table 51

		XC	XC		XC	XC	XC	XC	VT		XC	XC	XC	XC	XC		XC	XC	XC	XC	XC			
		1 ◇	1 ◇		1 ◇	1 ◇	1 ◇	1 ◇	1 ◇		1 ◇	1 ◇	1 ◇	1 ◇	1 ◇		1 ◇	1 ◇	1 ◇	1 ◇	1 ◇			
		🛒	🛒		🛒		🛒	🛒	⊡		🛒	🛒		🛒	🛒		🛒		🛒	🛒	🛒			
Bournemouth	d						17 40							18 40					19 40					
Brockenhurst 3	d						17 57							18 57					19 57					
Southampton Central	d						18 15							19 15					20 15					
Southampton Airport Parkwy ✈	d						18 22							19 22					20 22					
Winchester	d						18 31							19 31					20 31					
Basingstoke	d						18 47							19 47					20 47					
Guildford	d																							
Reading 7	d		18 40				19 11				19 40			20 11			20 40		21 11	21 40				
Oxford	d		19 06				19 37				20 06			20 37			21 06		21 37	22 06				
Banbury	d		19 25				19 53				20 25			20 53			21 25		21 53	22 25				
Leamington Spa 8	d		19 43				20 11				20 43			21 11			21 43		22 11	22 43				
Coventry	d		19 54				20 26				20 54			21 26			21 54		22 23	22 54				
Birmingham International ✈	d		20 04				20 38				21 04			21 38			22 04		22 33	23 04				
Penzance	d							15 30																
St Erth	d							15 38																
Hayle	d																							
Camborne	d							15 48																
Redruth	d							15 54																
Truro	d							16 06																
St Austell	d							16 22																
Newquay	d																							
Par	d							16 30																
Lostwithiel	d																							
Bodmin Parkway	d							16 41																
Liskeard 6	d							16 53																
Plymouth	d	16 25						17 25							18 21									
Totnes	d	16 50						17 50							18 48									
Paignton	d											18 17												
Torquay	d											18 23												
Newton Abbot	d	17 03						18 03				18 36			19 01									
Teignmouth	d																							
Dawlish	d																							
Exeter St Davids 6	d	17 23						18 23				18 56			19 23									
Tiverton Parkway	d	17 38						18 37				19 10			19 38									
Taunton	d	17 51						18 51				19 24			19 53									
Weston-super-Mare	d																							
Cardiff Central 7	d					18 50							19 50					20 50						
Newport (South Wales)	d					19 04							20 04					21 04						
Bristol Temple Meads 10	d	18 30			19 00			19 30				20 00			20 30						22 10			
Bristol Parkway 7	d	18 40			19 10			19 40				20 10			20 40						22 20			
Gloucester 7	d					19 47							20 47					21 47						
Cheltenham Spa	d	19 12			19 42	19 58		20 12				20 42	20 58		21 12			21 58			22 52			
Birmingham New Street 12	a	19 50	20 15		20 26	20 40	20 49	20 50			21 20	21 31	21 45	21 49	21 56		22 20	22 40	23 06	23 35	23 44			
Birmingham New Street 12	d	20 03	20 30		20 31	20 49	21 01	21 03	21 20				21 49	22 01	22 03			22 49						
Tamworth	d	20 19	20 46			21 07							22 09		22 22			23 07						
Burton-on-Trent	d		20 56			21 19		21 26					22 21		22 35			23 19						
Derby 10	a	20 42	21 09			21 34		21 44					22 34		22 49			23 34						
Nottingham 8 🚌	a					22 08							23 08					23 59						
Chesterfield	a	21 02	21 29					22 02							23 13									
Sheffield 7	a	21 16	21 44					22 18							23 34									
Doncaster 7	a																							
Wakefield Westgate 7	a	21 44						22 45																
Leeds 10	a	22 08						23 08							00 49									
York 8	a		22 53																					
Darlington 7	a																							
Durham	a																							
Chester-le-Street	a																							
Newcastle 8	a																							
Morpeth	a																							
Alnmouth for Alnwick	a																							
Berwick-upon-Tweed	a																							
Dunbar	a																							
Wolverhampton 7 🚌	d				20 49		21 19		21 38					22 19										
Stafford	a						21 34		21 58					22 34										
Stoke-on-Trent	a				21 19		21 56							22 56										
Congleton	a																							
Macclesfield	a						22 14							23 13										
Crewe 10	a								22 17															
Wilmslow	a																							
Stockport	a						22 28							23 27										
Manchester Piccadilly 10 🚌	a				22 00		22 40							23 45										
Warrington Bank Quay	a								22 36															
Wigan North Western	a								22 47															
Preston 8	a								23 07															
Lancaster 6	a																							
Oxenholme Lake District	a																							
Penrith North Lakes	a																							
Carlisle 8	a																							
Lockerbie	a																							
Haymarket	a																							
Edinburgh 10	a																							
Haymarket	a																							
Motherwell	a																							
Glasgow Central 15	a																							
Inverkeithing	a																							
Kirkcaldy	a																							
Markinch	a																							
Ladybank	a																							
Cupar	a																							
Leuchars 3	a																							
Dundee	a																							
Arbroath	a																							
Montrose	a																							
Stonehaven	a																							
Aberdeen	a																							

For general notes see front of timetable
For details of catering facilities see Directory of Train Operators

Table 51 SUMMARY OF SERVICES

Sundays

19 July to 6 September

South Coast and The South West → North West England, The North East and Scotland

Route Diagram - See first page of Table 51

		VT 1◇	XC 1◇	XC 1◇	VT 1◇	XC 1◇	XC 1◇	VT 1◇	XC 1◇	XC 1◇	XC 1◇	VT 1◇	XC 1◇	XC 1◇	XC 1◇	XC 1◇	VT 1◇	XC 1◇	XC 1◇	XC 1◇	XC 1◇
Bournemouth	d																			09 40	
Brockenhurst 3	d																			09 57	
Southampton Central	d														09 15					10 15	
Southampton Airport Parkwy ✈	d														09 22					10 22	
Winchester	d														09 31					10 31	
Basingstoke	d														09 47					10 47	
Guildford	d																				
Reading 7	d									09 11					10 11					11 11	
Oxford	d									09 37					10 37					11 36	
Banbury	d									09 53					10 53					11 53	
Leamington Spa 8	d									10 11					11 11					12 11	
Coventry	d									10 28					11 28					12 28	
Birmingham International ✈	d									10 40					11 40					12 40	
Penzance	d																				
St Erth	d																				
Hayle	d																				
Camborne	d																				
Redruth	d																				
Truro	d																				
St Austell	d																				
Newquay	d																				
Par	d																				
Lostwithiel	d																				
Bodmin Parkway	d																				
Liskeard 6	d																				
Plymouth	d																		09 25		
Totnes	d																		09 50		
Paignton	d																				
Torquay	d																				
Newton Abbot	d																		10 03		
Teignmouth	d																				
Dawlish	d																				
Exeter St Davids 6	d																		10 23		
Tiverton Parkway	d																		10 37		
Taunton	d																		10 51		
Weston-super-Mare	d																				
Cardiff Central 7	d																				
Newport (South Wales)	d																				
Bristol Temple Meads 10	d								09 15					10 30					11 30		
Bristol Parkway 7	d								09 25					10 40					11 40		
Gloucester 7	d								10 01												
Cheltenham Spa	d								10 12					11 12					12 12		
Birmingham New Street 12	a								10 50	10 51	←			11 50	11 51	←			12 50	12 51	←
Birmingham New Street 12	d	08 45	09 01	09 03	09 20	10 00	10 03	10 20	11 03 →	11 01	11 03	11 20	11 49	12 03 →	12 01	12 03	12 20	12 30	13 03 →	13 01	13 03
Tamworth	d			09 19			10 19						12 07			12 19					
Burton-on-Trent	d			09 29			10 29				11 26		12 19								13 26
Derby 10	a			09 42			10 42				11 42		12 34			12 42		13 09			13 42
Nottingham 8 🚢	a												13 08								
Chesterfield	a			10 02			11 02				12 02					13 02		13 29			14 02
Sheffield 7	a			10 18			11 16				12 18					13 17		13 45			14 17
Doncaster 7	a																	14 13			
Wakefield Westgate 7	a			10 44			11 44				12 44					13 44					14 44
Leeds 10	a			11 02			12 02				13 02					14 02					15 02
York 8	a			11 34			12 32				13 32					14 32		14 43			15 32
Darlington 7	a			12 03			13 01				14 01					15 07		15 15			16 01
Durham	a			12 20			13 18				14 18					15 24		15 32			16 18
Chester-le-Street	a																				
Newcastle 8	a			12 35			13 34				14 34					15 38		15 51			16 34
Morpeth	a															15 53					
Alnmouth for Alnwick	a						14 00									16 07					
Berwick-upon-Tweed	a			13 20							15 19										17 19
Dunbar	a			13 43							15 42										17 42
Wolverhampton 7 🚢	d	09 04	09 19		09 37	10 18		10 37		11 19		11 37			12 19		12 36			13 19	
Stafford	a	09 21	09 33			10 32				11 32					12 32					13 33	
Stoke-on-Trent	a					10 51				11 52					12 52					13 56	
Congleton	a																				
Macclesfield	a					11 09				12 10					13 10					14 14	
Crewe 10	a	09 40	09 54		10 07			11 07				12 07					13 07				
Wilmslow	a		10 12																		
Stockport	a		10 21			11 22				12 26					13 28					14 28	
Manchester Piccadilly 10 🚢	a		10 40			11 38				12 40					13 41					14 40	
Warrington Bank Quay	a	09 59			10 26			11 26				12 26					13 26				
Wigan North Western	a	10 10			10 37			11 37				12 37					13 37				
Preston 8	a	10 27			10 52			11 51				12 51					13 51				
Lancaster 6	a							12 08				13 08					14 08				
Oxenholme Lake District	a							12 22				13 22									
Penrith North Lakes	a																14 44				
Carlisle 8	a							13 01				14 01					15 00				
Lockerbie	a																				
Haymarket	a							14s13									16s14				
Edinburgh 10	a			14 15			15 07	14 22			16 12					17 14	16 22				18 07
Haymarket	a																				18 13
Motherwell	a																				
Glasgow Central 15	a											15 23									
Inverkeithing	a																				18 27
Kirkcaldy	a																				18 43
Markinch	a																				18 52
Ladybank	a																				19 00
Cupar	a																				19 06
Leuchars 3	a																				19 13
Dundee	a																				19 28
Arbroath	a																				19 45
Montrose	a																				19 59
Stonehaven	a																				20 22
Aberdeen	a																				20 47

For general notes see front of timetable
For details of catering facilities see
Directory of Train Operators

South Coast and The South West → North West England, The North East and Scotland

19 July to 6 September

Route Diagram - See first page of Table 51

		VT	XC		XC	XC	XC	XC	VT		XC	XC	XC	XC	XC		VT	XC	XC	XC	XC		XC	VT
		1◇	1◇		1◇	1◇	1◇	1◇	1◇		1◇	1◇	1◇	1◇	1◇		1◇	1◇	1◇	1◇	1◇		1◇	1◇
Bournemouth	d						10 40							11 40							12 40			
Brockenhurst 3	d						10 57							11 57							12 57			
Southampton Central	d						11 15							12 15							13 15			
Southampton Airport Parkwy ✈	d						11 22							12 22							13 22			
Winchester	d						11 31							12 31							13 31			
Basingstoke	d						11 47							12 47							13 47			
Guildford	d										12 14													
Reading 7	d						12 11				12 54			13 11				13 40			14 11			
Oxford	d						12 37				13 17			13 37				14 06			14 37			
Banbury	d						12 53				13 35			13 53				14 25			14 53			
Leamington Spa 8	d						13 11				13 53			14 11				14 43			15 11			
Coventry	d						13 26							14 26							15 26			
Birmingham International ✈	d						13 38							14 38							15 38			
Penzance	d														09 30									
St Erth	d														09 38									
Hayle	d																							
Camborne	d														09 48									
Redruth	d														09 54									
Truro	d														10 06									
St Austell	d														10 24									
Newquay	d																							
Par	d														10 31									
Lostwithiel	d																							
Bodmin Parkway	d														10 42									
Liskeard 6	d														10 54									
Plymouth	d							10 25							11 25				12 00				12 25	
Totnes	d							10 50							11 50								12 50	
Paignton	d											10 50												
Torquay	d											10 56												
Newton Abbot	d							11 03				11 08			12 03				12 36				13 03	
Teignmouth	d											11 15												
Dawlish	d											11 20												
Exeter St Davids 6	d							11 23				11 32			12 23				12 57				13 23	
Tiverton Parkway	d							11 37				11 46			12 37				13 10				13 37	
Taunton	d							11 51				12 00			12 51				13 25				13 51	
Weston-super-Mare	d											12 21												
Cardiff Central 7	d					11 50							12 50							13 50				
Newport (South Wales)	d					12 04							13 04							14 04				
Bristol Temple Meads 10	d							12 30				13 00			13 30				14 00				14 30	
Bristol Parkway 7	d							12 40				13 10			13 40				14 10				14 40	
Gloucester 7	d					12 47							13 51							14 47				
Cheltenham Spa	d					12 58		13 12				13 42	14 02		14 12				14 42	14 58			15 12	
Birmingham New Street 12	a					13 40	13 49	13 50			14 18	14 26	14 45	14 49	14 50			15 09	15 26	15 40	15 49		15 50	
Birmingham New Street 12	d	13 20	13 30		13 31	13 49	14 01	14 03	14 20		14 30	14 31	14 49	15 01	15 03		15 20	15 30	15 31	15 49	16 01		16 03	16 20
Tamworth	d					14 07		14 19					15 09							16 07			16 19	
Burton-on-Trent	d					14 19							15 21		15 26					16 19				
Derby 10	a		14 09			14 34		14 42			15 05		15 34		15 42			16 05		16 34			16 42	
Nottingham 8 🚌	a					15 08							16 08							17 09				
Chesterfield	a		14 29					15 02							16 02								17 02	
Sheffield 7	a		14 47					15 17			15 47				16 18			16 48					17 18	
Doncaster 7	a		15 13								16 15							17 13						
Wakefield Westgate 7	a							15 44							16 44								17 45	
Leeds 10	a							16 02							17 02								18 02	
York 8	a		15 43					16 32			16 40				17 32			17 42					18 32	
Darlington 7	a		16 12					17 01			17 14				18 01			18 10					19 01	
Durham	a		16 30					17 18			17 32				18 18			18 27					19 18	
Chester-le-Street	a										17 40													
Newcastle 8	a		16 50					17 34			17 53				18 34			18 47						
Morpeth	a																							
Alnmouth for Alnwick	a							18 01															20 04	
Berwick-upon-Tweed	a														19 19									
Dunbar	a														19 42									
Wolverhampton 7 🚌	d	13 37			13 49		14 19		14 37			14 49		15 19			15 37		15 49		16 19			16u37
Stafford	a						14 33							15 33							16 34			
Stoke-on-Trent	a				14 19		14 56					15 19		15 56					16 19		16 56			
Congleton	a																							
Macclesfield	a						15 14							16 14							17 14			
Crewe 10	a	14 09							15 09								16 09							17 09
Wilmslow	a																							
Stockport	a						15 28							16 28							17 28			
Manchester Piccadilly 10 🚌	a				15 00		15 40					16 00		16 40					17 00		17 40			
Warrington Bank Quay	a	14 28							15 28								16 28							17 28
Wigan North Western	a	14 39							15 39								16 39							17 39
Preston 8	a	14 52							15 53								16 53							17 53
Lancaster 6	a	15 10							16 10								17 10							18 10
Oxenholme Lake District	a	15 24															17 24							18 24
Penrith North Lakes	a								16 46															18 50
Carlisle 8	a	16 03							17 02								18 03							19 06
Lockerbie	a																							
Haymarket	a								18s13															
Edinburgh 10	a							19 08	18 22						20 07								21 11	20 24
Haymarket	a														20 15								21 15	
Motherwell	a														20 53								21 53	
Glasgow Central 15	a	17 17													21 17		19 17						22 19	
Inverkeithing	a																							
Kirkcaldy	a																							
Markinch	a																							
Ladybank	a																							
Cupar	a																							
Leuchars 3	a																							
Dundee	a																							
Arbroath	a																							
Montrose	a																							
Stonehaven	a																							
Aberdeen	a																							

For general notes see front of timetable
For details of catering facilities see Directory of Train Operators

South Coast and The South West → North West England, The North East and Scotland

19 July to 6 September

Route Diagram - See first page of Table 51

		XC	XC	XC	XC	XC	VT	XC	XC	XC	XC	XC	XC	XC	XC	XC	XC	VT	XC	XC	XC
		1◇	1◇	1◇	1◇	1◇	1◇	1◇	1◇	1◇	1◇	1◇	1◇	1◇	1◇	1◇	1◇	R 1	1◇	1◇	1◇
Bournemouth	d				13 40						14 40					15 40					
Brockenhurst [3]	d				13 57						14 57					15 57					
Southampton Central	d				14 15						15 15					16 15					
Southampton Airport Parkwy ✈	d				14 22						15 22					16 22					
Winchester	d				14 31						15 31					16 31					
Basingstoke	d				14 47						15 47					16 47					
Guildford	d																				
Reading [7]	d	14 40			15 11			15 40			16 11		16 40			17 11			17 40		
Oxford	d	15 06			15 37			16 06			16 37		17 06			17 37			18 06		
Banbury	d	15 25			15 53			16 25			16 53		17 25			17 53			18 25		
Leamington Spa [8]	d	15 43			16 11			16 43			17 11		17 43			18 11			18 43		
Coventry	d				16 26						17 26					18 26					
Birmingham International ✈	d				16 38						17 38					18 38					
Penzance	d													12 30							
St Erth	d													12 40							
Hayle	d													12 44							
Camborne	d													12 55							
Redruth	d													13 01							
Truro	d													13 13							
St Austell	d													13 30							
Newquay	d					11 30															
Par	d													13 37							
Lostwithiel	d													13 44							
Bodmin Parkway	d					12 41								13 51							
Liskeard [6]	d					12 54								14 03							
Plymouth	d					13 21						14 21		14 35			15 21				
Totnes	d					13 48						14 48		15 00			15 48				
Paignton	d		13 08																		
Torquay	d		13 14																		
Newton Abbot	d		13 26			14 01						15 01		15 12			16 01				
Teignmouth	d		13 33																		
Dawlish	d		13 38																		
Exeter St Davids [6]	d		13 51			14 23						15 23		15 33			16 23				
Tiverton Parkway	d		14 05			14 37						15 37		15 46			16 37				
Taunton	d		14 19			14 53						15 53		16 01			16 53				
Weston-super-Mare	d													16 30							
Cardiff Central [7]	d			14 50						15 50					16 50						17 50
Newport (South Wales)	d			15 04						16 04					17 04						18 04
Bristol Temple Meads [10]	d		15 00			15 30			16 00			16 30		17 00			17 30			18 00	
Bristol Parkway [7]	d		15 10			15 40			16 10			16 40		17 10			17 40			18 10	
Gloucester [7]	d			15 47						16 47					17 47						18 47
Cheltenham Spa	d		15 42	15 58		16 12			16 42	16 58		17 12		17 42	17 58		18 12			18 42	18 58
Birmingham New Street [12]	a	16 09	16 26	16 40	16 49	16 50		17 09	17 26	17 40	17 49	17 50	18 09	18 27	18 40	18 49	18 56		19 09	19 26	19 40
Birmingham New Street [12]	d	16 30	16 31	16 49	17 01	17 03	17 20	17 30	17 31	17 49	18 01	18 03	18 30	18 31	18 49	19 01	19 03	19 20	19 30	19 31	19 49
Tamworth	d			17 07						18 07		18 21			19 09						20 07
Burton-on-Trent	d			17 19		17 28				18 19					19 21		19 28				20 19
Derby [10]	a	17 05		17 34		17 42		18 05		18 34		18 42	19 05		19 34		19 42		20 05		20 34
Nottingham [8]	a			18 02						19 08					20 08						21 08
Chesterfield	a					18 03						19 04					20 02				
Sheffield [7]	a	17 48				18 19		18 46				19 20	19 39				20 18		20 38		
Doncaster [7]	a	18 13						19 13					20 16						21 19		
Wakefield Westgate [7]	a	18 33				18 47						19 48					20 46				
Leeds [10]	a	18 53				19 05						20 05					21 03				
York [8]	a	19 21				19 32		19 42				20 32	20 44				21 37		21 42		
Darlington [7]	a	19 51				20 03		20 10				21 03	21 18						22 10		
Durham	a	20 08				20 21		20 27				21 21	21 36						22 27		
Chester-le-Street	a	20 18											21 45								
Newcastle [8]	a	20 30				20 37		20 43				21 37	21 59						22 48		
Morpeth	a							21 01													
Alnmouth for Alnwick	a							21 15				22 05									
Berwick-upon-Tweed	a					21 23		21 36				22 28									
Dunbar	a					21 48															
Wolverhampton [7] ⛴	d		16 49		17 19		17u37		17 49		18 19			18 49		19 19		19 37		19 49	
Stafford	a				17 34						18 35					19 34					
Stoke-on-Trent	a		17 19		17 56				18 19		18 56			19 19		19 56				20 19	
Congleton	a																				
Macclesfield	a				18 14						19 15					20 14					
Crewe [10]	a						18 09											20 09			
Wilmslow	a																				
Stockport	a				18 28						19 28					20 28					
Manchester Piccadilly [10] ⛴	a		18 00		18 40				19 00		19 40			20 00		20 40				21 00	
Warrington Bank Quay	a						18 28											20 28			
Wigan North Western	a						18 39											20 39			
Preston [8]	a						18 53											20 53			
Lancaster [6]	a						19 10											21 10			
Oxenholme Lake District	a						19 24											21 24			
Penrith North Lakes	a																				
Carlisle [8]	a						20 03											22 03			
Lockerbie	a																	22 22			
Haymarket	a																				
Edinburgh [10]	a					22 20		22 25				23 19									
Haymarket	a																				
Motherwell	a																	23s13			
Glasgow Central [15]	a						21 17											23 35			
Inverkeithing	a																				
Kirkcaldy	a																				
Markinch	a																				
Ladybank	a																				
Cupar	a																				
Leuchars [8]	a																				
Dundee	a																				
Arbroath	a																				
Montrose	a																				
Stonehaven	a																				
Aberdeen	a																				

For general notes see front of timetable
For details of catering facilities see Directory of Train Operators

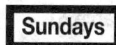

South Coast and The South West → North West England, The North East and Scotland

19 July to 6 September

Route Diagram - See first page of Table 51

		XC	XC	XC	XC	XC	XC	XC	VT	XC	XC	XC	XC	XC	XC	XC	XC	XC	XC
		1◇	1◇	1◇	1◇	1◇	1◇	1◇	1◇	1◇	1◇	1◇	1◇	1◇	1◇	1◇	1◇	1◇	1◇
		🛒	🛒	🛒	🛒		🛒	🛒	🍽	🛒	🛒		🛒	🛒	🛒		🛒	🛒	🛒
Bournemouth	d	16 40					17 40						18 40				19 40		
Brockenhurst 3	d	16 57					17 57						18 57				19 57		
Southampton Central	d	17 15					18 15						19 15				20 15		
Southampton Airport Parkway ✈	d	17 22					18 22						19 22				20 22		
Winchester	d	17 31					18 31						19 31				20 31		
Basingstoke	d	17 47					18 47						19 47				20 47		
Guildford	d																		
Reading 7	d	18 11		18 40			19 11			19 40			20 11		20 40		21 11	21 40	
Oxford	d	18 36		19 06			19 37			20 06			20 37		21 06		21 36	22 06	
Banbury	d	18 53		19 25			19 53			20 25			20 53		21 25		21 53	22 25	
Leamington Spa 8	d	19 11		19 43			20 11			20 43			21 11		21 43		22 11	22 43	
Coventry	d	19 26		19 54			20 26			20 54			21 26		21 54		22 23	22 54	
Birmingham International ✈	d	19 38		20 04			20 38			21 04			21 38		22 04		22 33	23 04	
Penzance	d							15 30											
St Erth	d							15 38											
Hayle	d																		
Camborne	d							15 48											
Redruth	d							15 54											
Truro	d							16 06											
St Austell	d							16 22											
Newquay	d																		
Par	d							16 30											
Lostwithiel	d																		
Bodmin Parkway	d							16 41											
Liskeard 6	d							16 53											
Plymouth	d		16 25					17 25						18 21					
Totnes	d		16 50					17 50						18 48					
Paignton	d										18 17								
Torquay	d										18 23								
Newton Abbot	d		17 03					18 03			18 36			19 01					
Teignmouth	d																		
Dawlish	d																		
Exeter St Davids 6	d		17 23					18 23			18 56			19 23					
Tiverton Parkway	d		17 37					18 37			19 10			19 37					
Taunton	d		17 51					18 51			19 24			19 53					
Weston-super-Mare	d																		
Cardiff Central 7	d					18 50						19 50				20 50			
Newport (South Wales)	d					19 04						20 04				21 04			
Bristol Temple Meads 10	d		18 30		19 00			19 30			20 00			20 30					22 10
Bristol Parkway 7	d		18 40		19 10			19 40			20 10			20 40					22 20
Gloucester 7	d					19 50						20 50				21 47			
Cheltenham Spa	d		19 12		19 42	20 00		20 12			20 42	21 00		21 12		21 58			22 52
Birmingham New Street 12	a	19 49	19 50	20 15	20 26	20 42	20 49	20 50		21 20	21 31	21 45	21 49	21 56	22 20	22 45	22 47	23 20	23 44
Birmingham New Street 12	d	20 01	20 03	20 30	20 31	20 49	21 01	21 03	21 20			21 49	22 01	22 03		22 49			
Tamworth	d		20 19	20 46		21 07						22 09		22 21		23 07			
Burton-on-Trent	d			20 56		21 19		21 26				22 21				23 19			
Derby 10	a		20 42	21 09		21 35		21 43				22 34		22 44		23 37			
Nottingham 8 🚌	a																		
Chesterfield	a		21 02	21 29				22 02						23 05					
Sheffield 7	a		21 16	21 44				22 18						23 21					
Doncaster 7	a																		
Wakefield Westgate 7	a		21 44					22 45											
Leeds 10	a		22 03					23 08						00 37					
York 8	a			22 53															
Darlington 7	a																		
Durham	a																		
Chester-le-Street	a																		
Newcastle 8	a																		
Morpeth	a																		
Alnmouth for Alnwick	a																		
Berwick-upon-Tweed	a																		
Dunbar	a																		
Wolverhampton 7 🚌	d	20 19			20 49		21 19		21 38				22 19						
Stafford	a	20 37					21 34		21 58				22 34						
Stoke-on-Trent	a	20 56			21 19		21 56						22 56						
Congleton	a																		
Macclesfield	a	21 15					22 14						23 13						
Crewe 10	a								22 17										
Wilmslow	a																		
Stockport	a	21 28					22 28						23 27						
Manchester Piccadilly 10 🚌	a	21 40			22 00		22 40						23 45						
Warrington Bank Quay	a								22 36										
Wigan North Western	a								22 47										
Preston 8	a								23 07										
Lancaster 6	a																		
Oxenholme Lake District	a																		
Penrith North Lakes	a																		
Carlisle 8	a																		
Lockerbie	a																		
Haymarket	a																		
Edinburgh 10	a																		
Haymarket	a																		
Motherwell	a																		
Glasgow Central 15	a																		
Inverkeithing	a																		
Kirkcaldy	a																		
Markinch	a																		
Ladybank	a																		
Cupar	a																		
Leuchars 3	a																		
Dundee	a																		
Arbroath	a																		
Montrose	a																		
Stonehaven	a																		
Aberdeen	a																		

For general notes see front of timetable
For details of catering facilities see Directory of Train Operators

South Coast and The South West → North West England, The North East and Scotland

13 September to 1 November

Route Diagram - See first page of Table 51

		VT	XC	XC	VT	XC	XC	VT	XC	XC	XC	VT	XC	XC	XC	XC	VT	XC	XC	XC	XC
		1 ◇	1 ◇	1 ◇	1 ◇	1 ◇	1 ◇	1 ◇	1 ◇	1 ◇	1 ◇	1 ◇	1 ◇	1 ◇	1 ◇	1 ◇	1 ◇	1 ◇	1 ◇	1 ◇	1 ◇
Bournemouth	d																				09 40
Brockenhurst 3	d																				09 57
Southampton Central	d														09 15						10 15
Southampton Airport Parkway ✈	d														09 22						10 22
Winchester	d														09 31						10 31
Basingstoke	d														09 47						10 47
Guildford	d																				
Reading 7	d									09 11					10 11						11 11
Oxford	d									09 37					10 37						11 37
Banbury	d									09 53					10 53						11 53
Leamington Spa 8	d									10 11					11 11						12 11
Coventry	d									10 28					11 28						12 28
Birmingham International ✈	d									10 40					11 40						12 40
Penzance	d																				
St Erth	d																				
Hayle	d																				
Camborne	d																				
Redruth	d																				
Truro	d																				
St Austell	d																				
Newquay	d																				
Par	d																				
Lostwithiel	d																				
Bodmin Parkway	d																				
Liskeard 6	d																				
Plymouth	d																			09 25	
Totnes	d																			09 50	
Paignton	d																				
Torquay	d																				
Newton Abbot	d																			10 03	
Teignmouth	d																				
Dawlish	d																				
Exeter St Davids 6	d																			10 23	
Tiverton Parkway	d																			10 37	
Taunton	d																			10 51	
Weston-super-Mare	d																				
Cardiff Central 7	d																		10 50		
Newport (South Wales)	d																		11 04		
Bristol Temple Meads 10	d								09 15					10 30						11 30	
Bristol Parkway 7	d								09 25					10 40						11 40	
Gloucester 7	d								10 01										11 51		
Cheltenham Spa	d								10 12					11 12					12 02	12 12	
Birmingham New Street 12	a								10 50	10 51	←			11 50	11 51	←			12 44	12 50	12 51
Birmingham New Street 12	d	08 45	09 01	09 03	09 20	10 00	10 03	10 15	11 03 →	11 01	11 03	11 20	11 45	12 03 →	12 01	12 03	12 20	12 30	12 45	13 03 →	13 01
Tamworth	d			09 19			10 19				11 19		12 03			12 19			13 03		
Burton-on-Trent	d			09 29			10 29				11 29		12 15						13 15		
Derby 10	a			09 42			10 42				11 42		12 28			12 40		13 09	13 31		
Nottingham 8	a												12 57						13 57		
Chesterfield	a			10 02			11 02				12 02					13 02		13 29			
Sheffield 7	a			10 18			11 16				12 18					13 17		13 43			
Doncaster 7	a																	14 13			
Wakefield Westgate 7	a			10 44			11 44				12 44					13 44					
Leeds 10	a			11 02			12 02				13 02					14 02					
York 8	a			11 34			12 32				13 32					14 32		14 43			
Darlington 7	a			12 03			13 01				14 01					15 07		15 15			
Durham	a			12 20			13 18				14 18					15 24		15 32			
Chester-le-Street	a																				
Newcastle 8	a			12 35			13 34				14 34					15 38		15 51			
Morpeth	a															15 53					
Alnmouth for Alnwick	a						14 00									16 07					
Berwick-upon-Tweed	a			13 20							15 19										
Dunbar	a			13 42							15 42										
Wolverhampton 7	d	09 04	09 19		09 37	10 18		10 32		11 19		11 37			12 19		12 36				13 19
Stafford	a	09 17	09 31			10 30				11 31					12 33						13 33
Stoke-on-Trent	a					10 51				11 51					12 52						13 56
Congleton	a																				
Macclesfield	a					11 09				12 09					13 10						14 14
Crewe 10	a	09 43	09 55		10 12			11 07				12 07					13 07				
Wilmslow	a		10 13																		
Stockport	a		10 23			11 21				12 21					13 28						14 28
Manchester Piccadilly 10	a		10 37			11 40				12 40					13 40						14 40
Warrington Bank Quay	a	10 01			10 31			11 26				12 26					13 26				
Wigan North Western	a	10 12			10 42			11 37				12 37					13 37				
Preston 8	a	10 30			10 56			11 51				12 51					13 51				
Lancaster 6	a							12 08				13 08					14 08				
Oxenholme Lake District	a							12 22				13 22									
Penrith North Lakes	a																14 44				
Carlisle 8	a							13 01				14 01					15 00				
Lockerbie	a																				
Haymarket	a							14s13									16s14				
Edinburgh 10	a			14 15			15 07	14 22			16 12					17 14	16 22				
Haymarket	a																				
Motherwell	a																				
Glasgow Central 15	a											15 23									
Inverkeithing	a																				
Kirkcaldy	a																				
Markinch	a																				
Ladybank	a																				
Cupar	a																				
Leuchars 3	a																				
Dundee	a																				
Arbroath	a																				
Montrose	a																				
Stonehaven	a																				
Aberdeen	a																				

For general notes see front of timetable
For details of catering facilities see Directory of Train Operators

South Coast and The South West → North West England, The North East and Scotland

13 September to 1 November

Route Diagram - See first page of Table 51

		XC	VT	XC	XC	XC	XC	XC	VT	XC	XC	XC	XC	XC	VT	XC	XC	XC	XC	XC	VT
		1◇	1◇	1◇	1◇	1◇	1◇	1◇	1◇	1◇	1◇	1◇	1◇	1◇	1◇	1◇	1◇	1◇	1◇	1◇	1◇
Bournemouth	d						10 40						11 40						12 40		
Brockenhurst 3	d						10 57						11 57						12 57		
Southampton Central	d						11 15						12 15						13 15		
Southampton Airport Parkway ✈	d						11 22						12 22						13 22		
Winchester	d						11 31						12 31						13 31		
Basingstoke	d						11 47						12 47						13 47		
Guildford	d									12 14											
Reading 7	d						12 11			12 54			13 11			13 40			14 11		
Oxford	d						12 37			13 17			13 37			14 06			14 37		
Banbury	d						12 53			13 36			13 53			14 25			14 53		
Leamington Spa 3	d						13 11			13 54			14 11			14 43			15 11		
Coventry	d						13 26						14 26						15 26		
Birmingham International ✈	d						13 38						14 38						15 38		
Penzance	d													09 30							
St Erth	d													09 38							
Hayle	d																				
Camborne	d													09 48							
Redruth	d													09 54							
Truro	d													10 06							
St Austell	d													10 24							
Newquay	d																				
Par	d													10 31							
Lostwithiel	d																				
Bodmin Parkway	d													10 42							
Liskeard 6	d													10 54							
Plymouth	d							10 25						11 25			12 00			12 25	
Totnes	d							10 50						11 50						12 50	
Paignton	d										10 50										
Torquay	d										10 56										
Newton Abbot	d							11 03			11 08			12 03			12 36			13 03	
Teignmouth	d										11 15										
Dawlish	d										11 20										
Exeter St Davids 6	d							11 23			11 32			12 23			12 57			13 23	
Tiverton Parkway	d							11 37			11 46			12 37			13 10			13 37	
Taunton	d							11 51			12 00			12 51			13 25			13 51	
Weston-super-Mare	d										12 22										
Cardiff Central 7	d					11 50						12 50						13 50			
Newport (South Wales)	d					12 04						13 04						14 04			
Bristol Temple Meads 10	d							12 30			13 00			13 30			14 00			14 30	
Bristol Parkway 7	d							12 40			13 10			13 40			14 10			14 40	
Gloucester 7	d					12 47						13 51						14 47			
Cheltenham Spa	d					12 58		13 12			13 42	14 02		14 12			14 42	14 58		15 12	
Birmingham New Street 12	a	←				13 40	13 49	13 50		14 20	14 26	14 44	14 49	14 50		15 09	15 26	15 40	15 49	15 50	
Birmingham New Street 12	d	13 03	13 20	13 30	13 31	13 45	14 01	14 03	14 20	14 30	14 31	14 45	15 01	15 03	15 20	15 30	15 31	15 45	16 01	16 03	16 20
Tamworth	d					14 03		14 19				15 04						16 03		16 19	
Burton-on-Trent	d	13 29				14 15						15 16		15 26				16 15			
Derby 10	a	13 42		14 09		14 28		14 42		15 02		15 32		15 42		16 02		16 27		16 42	
Nottingham 8	a					14 57						16 01						16 57			
Chesterfield	a	14 02		14 29				15 02						16 02						17 02	
Sheffield 7	a	14 17		14 43				15 17		15 47				16 18		16 48				17 18	
Doncaster 7	a			15 13						16 15						17 13					
Wakefield Westgate 7	a	14 44						15 44						16 44						17 45	
Leeds 10	a	15 02						16 02						17 02						18 02	
York 8	a	15 32		15 43				16 32		16 40				17 32		17 42				18 32	
Darlington 7	a	16 01		16 12				17 01		17 14				18 01		18 10				19 01	
Durham	a	16 18		16 30				17 18		17 32				18 18		18 27				19 18	
Chester-le-Street	a									17 40											
Newcastle 8	a	16 34		16 50				17 34		17 53				18 34		18 47				19 34	
Morpeth	a																				
Alnmouth for Alnwick	a							18 01												20 04	
Berwick-upon-Tweed	a	17 19												19 19							
Dunbar	a	17 42												19 42							
Wolverhampton 7	d		13 37		13 49		14 19		14 37		14 49		15 19		15 37		15 49		16 19		16u37
Stafford	a						14 33						15 33						16 34		
Stoke-on-Trent	a				14 19		14 56				15 19		15 56				16 19		16 56		
Congleton	a																				
Macclesfield	a						15 14						16 14						17 14		
Crewe 10	a		14 09						15 09						16 09						17 09
Wilmslow	a																				
Stockport	a						15 28						16 28						17 28		
Manchester Piccadilly 10	a				15 00		15 40				16 00		16 40				17 00		17 40		
Warrington Bank Quay	a		14 28						15 28						16 28						17 28
Wigan North Western	a		14 39						15 39						16 39						17 39
Preston 8	a		14 52						15 53						16 53						17 53
Lancaster 6	a		15 10						16 10						17 10						18 10
Oxenholme Lake District	a		15 24												17 24						18 24
Penrith North Lakes	a								16 46												18 50
Carlisle 8	a		16 03						17 02						18 03						19 06
Lockerbie	a																				
Haymarket	a								18s13												
Edinburgh 10	a	18 07						19 08	18 22					20 07						21 11	20 24
Haymarket	a	18 13												20 15						21 15	
Motherwell	a													20 53						21 53	
Glasgow Central 15	a		17 17											21 17	19 17					22 19	
Inverkeithing	a	18 27																			
Kirkcaldy	a	18 43																			
Markinch	a	18 52																			
Ladybank	a	19 00																			
Cupar	a	19 06																			
Leuchars 3	a	19 13																			
Dundee	a	19 28																			
Arbroath	a	19 45																			
Montrose	a	19 59																			
Stonehaven	a	20 22																			
Aberdeen	a	20 47																			

For general notes see front of timetable
For details of catering facilities see Directory of Train Operators

Table 51 | SUMMARY OF SERVICES | **Sundays**

South Coast and The South West → North West England, The North East and Scotland

13 September to 1 November

Route Diagram - See first page of Table 51

		XC	XC	XC	XC	XC	VT	XC	XC	XC	XC	XC	XC	XC	XC	XC	XC	VT	XC	XC	XC
																		R			
		1 ◇	1 ◇	1 ◇	1 ◇	1 ◇	1 ◇	1 ◇	1 ◇	1 ◇	1 ◇	1 ◇	1 ◇	1 ◇	1 ◇	1 ◇	1 ◇	1	1 ◇	1 ◇	1 ◇
		🛒	🛒		🛒	🛒	🍴	🛒	🛒		🛒	🛒	🛒	🛒		🛒	🛒	🍴	🛒	🛒	
Bournemouth	d				13 40						14 40					15 40					
Brockenhurst 3	d				13 57						14 57					15 57					
Southampton Central	d				14 15						15 15					16 15					
Southampton Airport Parkwy ✈	d				14 22						15 22					16 22					
Winchester	d				14 31						15 31					16 31					
Basingstoke	d				14 47						15 47					16 47					
Guildford	d																				
Reading 7	d	14 40			15 11			15 40			16 11		16 40			17 11			17 40		
Oxford	d	15 06			15 37			16 06			16 37		17 06			17 37			18 06		
Banbury	d	15 25			15 53			16 25			16 53		17 25			17 53			18 25		
Leamington Spa 8	d	15 43			16 11			16 43			17 11		17 43			18 11			18 43		
Coventry	d				16 26						17 26					18 26					
Birmingham International ✈	d				16 38						17 38					18 38					
Penzance	d					11 23								12 30							
St Erth	d					11 33								12 40							
Hayle	d													12 44							
Camborne	d					11 45								12 55							
Redruth	d					11 51								13 01							
Truro	d					12 04								13 13							
St Austell	d					12 23								13 30							
Newquay	d																				
Par	d					12 30								13 37							
Lostwithiel	d													13 44							
Bodmin Parkway	d					12 42								13 51							
Liskeard 6	d					12 55								14 03							
Plymouth	d					13 21						14 21		14 35			15 21				
Totnes	d					13 48						14 48		15 00			15 48				
Paignton	d		13 08																		
Torquay	d		13 14																		
Newton Abbot	d		13 26			14 01						15 01		15 12			16 01				
Teignmouth	d		13 33																		
Dawlish	d		13 38																		
Exeter St Davids 6	d		13 51			14 23						15 23		15 33			16 23				
Tiverton Parkway	d		14 05			14 38						15 38		15 46			16 38				
Taunton	d		14 19			14 53						15 53		16 01			16 53				
Weston-super-Mare	d													16 30							
Cardiff Central 7	d			14 50						15 50					16 50						17 50
Newport (South Wales)	d			15 04						16 04					17 04						18 04
Bristol Temple Meads 10	d		15 00			15 30			16 00			16 30		17 00			17 30			18 00	
Bristol Parkway 7	d		15 10			15 40			16 10			16 40		17 10			17 40			18 10	
Gloucester 7	d			15 47						16 47					17 47						18 47
Cheltenham Spa	d		15 42	15 58		16 12			16 42	16 56		17 12		17 42	17 58		18 12			18 42	18 58
Birmingham New Street 12	a	16 09	16 26	16 40	16 49	16 50		17 09	17 26	17 40	17 49	17 50	18 09	18 27	18 40	18 49	18 50		19 09	19 26	19 40
Birmingham New Street 12	d	16 30	16 31	16 45	17 01	17 03	17 20	17 30	17 31	17 45	18 01	18 03	18 30	18 31	18 45	19 01	19 03	19 20	19 30	19 31	19 45
Tamworth	d			17 03						18 03		18 21			19 04						20 03
Burton-on-Trent	d			17 15		17 29				18 15					19 16		19 29				20 15
Derby 10	a	17 02		17 28		17 42		18 02		18 28		18 42	19 02		19 29		19 42		20 02		20 28
Nottingham 8 🚌	a			17 57						18 57					19 57						20 57
Chesterfield	a					18 03						19 04					20 05				
Sheffield 7	a	17 48				18 19		18 46				19 20	19 39				20 21		20 38		
Doncaster 7	a	18 13						19 13					20 16						21 19		
Wakefield Westgate 7	a	18 33				18 47						19 48					20 49				
Leeds 10	a	18 53				19 05						20 05					21 05				
York 8	a	19 21				19 32		19 42				20 32	20 44				21 37		21 42		
Darlington 7	a	19 51				20 03		20 10				21 03	21 18						22 10		
Durham	a	20 08				20 21		20 27				21 21	21 36						22 27		
Chester-le-Street	a	20 18											21 45								
Newcastle 8	a	20 30				20 37		20 43				21 37	21 59						22 43		
Morpeth	a							21 01													
Alnmouth for Alnwick	a							21 15				22 05									
Berwick-upon-Tweed	a					21 23		21 36				22 28									
Dunbar	a					21 48															
Wolverhampton 7 🚌	d		16 49		17 19		17u37		17 49		18 19			18 49		19 19		19 37		19 49	
Stafford	a				17 34						18 35					19 34					
Stoke-on-Trent	a		17 19		17 56				18 19		18 56			19 19		19 56				20 19	
Congleton	a																				
Macclesfield	a				18 14						19 15					20 14					
Crewe 10	a						18 09											20 09			
Wilmslow	a																				
Stockport	a				18 28						19 28					20 28					
Manchester Piccadilly 10 🚌	a		18 00		18 40				19 00		19 40			20 00		20 40				21 00	
Warrington Bank Quay	a						18 28											20 28			
Wigan North Western	a						18 39											20 39			
Preston 8	a						18 53											20 53			
Lancaster 6	a						19 10											21 10			
Oxenholme Lake District	a						19 24											21 24			
Penrith North Lakes	a																				
Carlisle 8	a						20 03											22 03			
Lockerbie	a																	22 22			
Haymarket	a																				
Edinburgh 10	a					22 20		22 25				23 19									
Haymarket	a																				
Motherwell	a																	23s13			
Glasgow Central 15	a						21 17											23 35			
Inverkeithing	a																				
Kirkcaldy	a																				
Markinch	a																				
Ladybank	a																				
Cupar	a																				
Leuchars 3	a																				
Dundee	a																				
Arbroath	a																				
Montrose	a																				
Stonehaven	a																				
Aberdeen	a																				

For general notes see front of timetable
For details of catering facilities see
Directory of Train Operators

South Coast and The South West → North West England, The North East and Scotland

13 September to 1 November

Route Diagram - See first page of Table 51

		XC	XC	XC	XC	XC	XC		VT	XC	XC	XC	XC	XC		XC	XC	XC	XC	XC	XC			
		1 ◇	1 ◇	1 ◇	1 ◇	1 ◇	1 ◇		1 ◇	1 ◇	1 ◇	1 ◇	1 ◇	1 ◇		1 ◇	1 ◇	1 ◇	1 ◇	1 ◇	1 ◇			
Bournemouth	d	16 40				17 40							18 40						19 40					
Brockenhurst 3	d	16 57				17 57							18 57						19 57					
Southampton Central	d	17 15				18 15							19 15						20 15					
Southampton Airport Parkwy ✈	d	17 22				18 22							19 22						20 22					
Winchester	d	17 31				18 31							19 31						20 31					
Basingstoke	d	17 47				18 47							19 47						20 47					
Guildford	d																							
Reading 7	d	18 11		18 40		19 11				19 40			20 11			20 40			21 11	21 40				
Oxford	d	18 37		19 06		19 37				20 06			20 37			21 06			21 37	22 06				
Banbury	d	18 53		19 25		19 53				20 25			20 53			21 25			21 53	22 25				
Leamington Spa 8	d	19 11		19 43		20 11				20 43			21 11			21 43			22 11	22 43				
Coventry	d	19 26		19 54		20 26				20 54			21 26			21 54			22 23	22 54				
Birmingham International ✈	d	19 38		20 04		20 38				21 04			21 38			22 04			22 33	23 04				
Penzance	d						15 30																	
St Erth	d						15 38																	
Hayle	d																							
Camborne	d						15 48																	
Redruth	d						15 54																	
Truro	d						16 06																	
St Austell	d						16 24																	
Newquay	d																							
Par	d						16 31																	
Lostwithiel	d																							
Bodmin Parkway	d						16 42																	
Liskeard 6	d						16 54																	
Plymouth	d		16 25				17 25							18 21										
Totnes	d		16 50				17 50							18 48										
Paignton	d										18 17													
Torquay	d										18 23													
Newton Abbot	d		17 03				18 03				18 36			19 01										
Teignmouth	d																							
Dawlish	d																							
Exeter St Davids 6	d		17 23				18 23				18 56			19 23										
Tiverton Parkway	d		17 37				18 37				19 10			19 38										
Taunton	d		17 51				18 51				19 24			19 53										
Weston-super-Mare	d																							
Cardiff Central 7	d											19 50						20 50						
Newport (South Wales)	d											20 04						21 04						
Bristol Temple Meads 10	d		18 30		19 00		19 30				20 00			20 30							22 10			
Bristol Parkway 7	d		18 40		19 10		19 40				20 10			20 40							22 20			
Gloucester 7	d											20 50						21 47						
Cheltenham Spa	d		19 12		19 42		20 12				20 42	21 00		21 12				21 58			22 52			
Birmingham New Street 12	a	19 49	19 50	20 15	20 26	20 49	20 55			21 20	21 31	21 45	21 49	21 50		22 20		22 40	23 06	23 35	23 44			
Birmingham New Street 12	d	20 01	20 03	20 30	20 31	21 01	21 03		21 20			21 49	22 01	22 03			22 28	22 49						
Tamworth	d		20 19	20 46			21 19					22 09		22 23				23 07						
Burton-on-Trent	d			20 56			21 29					22 21		22 35				23 19						
Derby 10	a		20 42	21 09			21 42					22 34		22 48				23 37						
Nottingham 8	a											22 57												
Chesterfield	a		21 02	21 29			22 05							23 10										
Sheffield 7	a		21 16	21 44			22 19							23 27										
Doncaster 7	a																							
Wakefield Westgate 7	a		21 44				22 48																	
Leeds 10	a		22 06				23 08							00 44										
York 8	a			22 53																				
Darlington 7	a																							
Durham	a																							
Chester-le-Street	a																							
Newcastle 8	a																							
Morpeth	a																							
Alnmouth for Alnwick	a																							
Berwick-upon-Tweed	a																							
Dunbar	a																							
Wolverhampton 7	d	20 19			20 49	21 19			21 38				22 19				22 46							
Stafford	a	20 37				21 34			21 58				22 37				22 58							
Stoke-on-Trent	a	20 56			21 19	21 56							22 56											
Congleton	a																							
Macclesfield	a	21 15				22 14							23 14											
Crewe 10	a								22 17								23 24							
Wilmslow	a																23 42							
Stockport	a	21 28				22 28							23 29				23s51							
Manchester Piccadilly 10	a	21 40			22 00	22 40							23 40				00 05							
Warrington Bank Quay	a								22 36															
Wigan North Western	a								22 47															
Preston 8	a								23 07															
Lancaster 6	a																							
Oxenholme Lake District	a																							
Penrith North Lakes	a																							
Carlisle 8	a																							
Lockerbie	a																							
Haymarket	a																							
Edinburgh 10	a																							
Haymarket	a																							
Motherwell	a																							
Glasgow Central 15	a																							
Inverkeithing	a																							
Kirkcaldy	a																							
Markinch	a																							
Ladybank	a																							
Cupar	a																							
Leuchars 3	a																							
Dundee	a																							
Arbroath	a																							
Montrose	a																							
Stonehaven	a																							
Aberdeen	a																							

For general notes see front of timetable
For details of catering facilities see Directory of Train Operators

South Coast and The South West → North West England, The North East and Scotland

from 8 November

Route Diagram - See first page of Table 51

		XC 1 ◇	XC 1 ◇	VT 1 ◇	XC 1 ◇	XC 1 ◇	VT 1 ◇	XC 1 ◇	XC 1 ◇	VT 1 ◇	XC 1 ◇	XC 1 ◇	XC 1 ◇	XC 1 ◇	XC 1 ◇	XC 1 ◇	XC 1 ◇	VT 1 ◇	XC 1 ◇	XC 1 ◇
Bournemouth	d															09 40				
Brockenhurst [3]	d															09 57				
Southampton Central	d											09 15				10 15				
Southampton Airport Parkway	d											09 22				10 22				
Winchester	d											09 31				10 31				
Basingstoke	d											09 47				10 47				
Guildford	d																			
Reading [7]	d							09 11				10 11				11 11				
Oxford	d							09 37				10 37				11 37				
Banbury	d							09 53				10 53				11 53				
Leamington Spa [8]	d							10 11				11 11				12 11				
Coventry	d							10 28				11 28				12 28				
Birmingham International	d							10 40				11 40				12 40				
Penzance	d																			
St Erth	d																			
Hayle	d																			
Camborne	d																			
Redruth	d																			
Truro	d																			
St Austell	d																			
Newquay	d																			
Par	d																			
Lostwithiel	d																			
Bodmin Parkway	d																			
Liskeard [6]	d																			
Plymouth	d																			09 25
Totnes	d																			09 50
Paignton	d																			
Torquay	d																			
Newton Abbot	d																			10 03
Teignmouth	d																			
Dawlish	d																			
Exeter St Davids [6]	d																			10 23
Tiverton Parkway	d																			10 37
Taunton	d																			10 51
Weston-super-Mare	d																			
Cardiff Central [7]	d														10 25					
Newport (South Wales)	d														10 39					
Bristol Temple Meads [10]	d								08 45				10 00							11 30
Bristol Parkway [7]	d								08 55				10 10							11 40
Gloucester [7]	d								09 31						11 22					
Cheltenham Spa	d								09 42				10 42		11 33					12 12
Birmingham New Street [12]	a							10 51	10 56			11 51	11 56		12 36	12 51				13 20
Birmingham New Street [12]	d	09 01	09 03	09 20	10 00	10 03	10 20	11 01	11 03	11 20	11 45	12 01	12 03	12 30	12 45	13 01	13 03	13 20	13 30	13 31
Tamworth	d		09 19			10 19			11 19		12 03		12 19		13 03					
Burton-on-Trent	d		09 29			10 29			11 29		12 15				13 15		13 26			
Derby [10]	a		09 42			10 42			11 42		12 28		12 40	13 09	13 28		13 42		14 09	
Nottingham [8]	a										12 57				13 57					
Chesterfield	a		10 02			11 02			12 04				13 02	13 29			14 02		14 29	
Sheffield [7]	a		10 18			11 16			12 18				13 17	13 43			14 17		14 43	
Doncaster [7]	a													14 13					15 13	
Wakefield Westgate [7]	a		10 44			11 44			12 44				13 44				14 44			
Leeds [10]	a		11 02			12 02			13 02				14 02				15 02			
York [8]	a		11 34			12 32			13 32				14 32	14 43			15 32		15 43	
Darlington [7]	a		12 03			13 01			14 01				15 07	15 15			16 01		16 12	
Durham	a		12 20			13 18			14 18				15 24	15 32			16 18		16 30	
Chester-le-Street	a																			
Newcastle [8]	a		12 35			13 34			14 34				15 38	15 51			16 34		16 50	
Morpeth	a												15 53							
Alnmouth for Alnwick	a					14 00							16 07							
Berwick-upon-Tweed	a		13 20						15 19								17 19			
Dunbar	a		13 42						15 42								17 42			
Wolverhampton [7]	d	09 19		09 37	10 18		10 37	11 19		11 37		12 19				13 19		13 37		13 49
Stafford	a	09 31			10 30			11 31				12 33				13 33				
Stoke-on-Trent	a				10 51			11 51				12 52				13 56				14 19
Congleton	a																			
Macclesfield	a				11 09			12 09				13 10				14 14				
Crewe [10]	a	09 55		10 12			11 12			12 07								14 09		
Wilmslow	a	10 13																		
Stockport	a	10 23			11 21			12 21				13 28				14 28				
Manchester Piccadilly [10]	a	10 37			11 40			12 40				13 40				14 40				15 00
Warrington Bank Quay	a																			
Wigan North Western	a																			
Preston [8]	a			11 42			12 44			13 42								15 48		
Lancaster [6]	a			12 08			13 02			14 08								16 08		
Oxenholme Lake District	a			12 22			13 16													
Penrith North Lakes	a						13 42			14 44								16 44		
Carlisle [8]	a			13 01			13 59			15 00								17 01		
Lockerbie	a																			
Haymarket	a			14s13						16s14								18s13		
Edinburgh [10]	a		14 15	14 22		15 07			16 12	16 22			17 14				18 07	18 22		
Haymarket	a																18 13			
Motherwell	a																			
Glasgow Central [15]	a						15 23													
Inverkeithing	a																18 27			
Kirkcaldy	a																18 43			
Markinch	a																18 52			
Ladybank	a																19 00			
Cupar	a																19 06			
Leuchars [3]	a																19 13			
Dundee	a																19 28			
Arbroath	a																19 45			
Montrose	a																19 59			
Stonehaven	a																20 22			
Aberdeen	a																20 47			

For general notes see front of timetable
For details of catering facilities see Directory of Train Operators

South Coast and The South West → North West England, The North East and Scotland

from 8 November

Route Diagram - See first page of Table 51

		XC 1◇	XC 1◇ ⊼	XC 1◇ ⊼	XC 1◇ ⊼	XC 1◇ ⊼	XC 1◇	XC 1◇ ⊼	XC 1◇ ⊼	VT 1◇ ⊓	XC 1◇ ⊼	XC 1◇ ⊼	XC 1◇	XC 1◇ ⊼	XC 1◇ ⊼	VT 1◇ ⊓	XC 1◇ ⊼	XC 1◇ ⊼	XC 1◇	XC 1◇ ⊼
Bournemouth	d		10 40					11 40						12 40						13 40
Brockenhurst 3	d		10 57					11 57						12 57						13 57
Southampton Central	d		11 15					12 15						13 15						14 15
Southampton Airport Parkway ✈	d		11 22					12 22						13 22						14 22
Winchester	d		11 31					12 31						13 31						14 31
Basingstoke	d		11 47					12 47						13 47						14 47
Guildford	d				12 14															
Reading 7	d		12 11		12 54			13 11			13 40			14 11			14 40			15 11
Oxford	d		12 37		13 17			13 37			14 06			14 37			15 06			15 37
Banbury	d		12 53		13 36			13 53			14 25			14 53			15 25			15 53
Leamington Spa 8	d		13 11		13 54			14 11			14 43			15 11			15 43			16 11
Coventry	d		13 26					14 26						15 26						16 26
Birmingham International ✈	d		13 38					14 38						15 38						16 38
Penzance	d											09 30								
St Erth	d											09 38								
Hayle	d																			
Camborne	d											09 48								
Redruth	d											09 54								
Truro	d											10 06								
St Austell	d											10 24								
Newquay	d																			
Par	d											10 31								
Lostwithiel	d																			
Bodmin Parkway	d											10 42								
Liskeard 6	d											10 54								
Plymouth	d					10 25						11 25								
Totnes	d					10 50						11 51								
Paignton	d																	12 32		
Torquay	d																	12 38		
Newton Abbot	d					11 03						12 03						12 50		
Teignmouth	d																			
Dawlish	d																			
Exeter St Davids 6	d					11 23						12 24						13 15		
Tiverton Parkway	d					11 37						12 38						13 28		
Taunton	d					11 51						12 52						13 43		
Weston-super-Mare	d																			
Cardiff Central 7	d	11 25					12 25						13 25						14 25	
Newport (South Wales)	d	11 39					12 39						13 39						14 39	
Bristol Temple Meads 10	d					12 30						13 30						14 30		
Bristol Parkway 7	d					12 40						13 40						14 40		
Gloucester 7	d	12 22					13 22						14 22						15 22	
Cheltenham Spa	d	12 33				13 12	13 33					14 12	14 33					15 12	15 33	
Birmingham New Street 12	a	13 36	13 49		14 20	14 20	14 36	14 49			15 09	15 20	15 36	15 49			16 09	16 19	16 40	16 49
Birmingham New Street 12	d	13 45	14 01	14 03	14 30	14 31	14 45	15 01	15 03	15 20	15 30	15 31	15 45	16 01	16 03	16 20	16 30	16 31	16 45	17 01
Tamworth	d	14 03		14 19			15 05						16 03		16 19				17 03	
Burton-on-Trent	d	14 15					15 17		15 26				16 15						17 15	
Derby 10	a	14 28		14 42	15 02		15 32		15 42		16 02		16 27		16 42		17 02		17 28	
Nottingham 8	a	14 57					16 01						16 57						17 53	
Chesterfield	a			15 02					16 02						17 02					
Sheffield 7	a			15 17	15 47				16 18		16 48				17 18		17 48			
Doncaster 7	a				16 15						17 13						18 13			
Wakefield Westgate 7	a			15 44					16 44						17 44		18 33			
Leeds 10	a			16 02					17 02						18 02		18 53			
York 8	a			16 32	16 40				17 32		17 42				18 32		19 21			
Darlington 7	a			17 01	17 14				18 01		18 10				19 01		19 51			
Durham	a			17 18	17 32				18 18		18 27				19 18		20 08			
Chester-le-Street	a				17 40												20 18			
Newcastle 8	a			17 34	17 53				18 34		18 47				19 34		20 30			
Morpeth	a																			
Alnmouth for Alnwick	a			18 01											20 04					
Berwick-upon-Tweed	a								19 19											
Dunbar	a								19 42											
Wolverhampton 7	d		14 19			14 49		15 19		15 37		15 49		16 19		16u37		16 49		17 19
Stafford	a		14 33					15 33						16 34						17 34
Stoke-on-Trent	a		14 56			15 19		15 56				16 19		16 56				17 19		17 56
Congleton	a																			
Macclesfield	a		15 14					16 14						17 14						18 14
Crewe 10	a									16 09						17 09				
Wilmslow	a																			
Stockport	a		15 28					16 28						17 28						18 28
Manchester Piccadilly 10	a		15 40			16 00		16 40				17 00		17 40				18 00		18 40
Warrington Bank Quay	a									16 28						17 28				
Wigan North Western	a									16 39						17 39				
Preston 8	a									16 53						17 53				
Lancaster 6	a									17 10						18 10				
Oxenholme Lake District	a									17 24						18 24				
Penrith North Lakes	a															18 50				
Carlisle 8	a									18 03						19 06				
Lockerbie	a																			
Haymarket	a																			
Edinburgh 10	a			19 08					20 07						21 11	20 24				
Haymarket	a								20 15						21 15					
Motherwell	a								20 53						21 53					
Glasgow Central 15	a								21 17	19 17					22 19					
Inverkeithing	a																			
Kirkcaldy	a																			
Markinch	a																			
Ladybank	a																			
Cupar	a																			
Leuchars 3	a																			
Dundee	a																			
Arbroath	a																			
Montrose	a																			
Stonehaven	a																			
Aberdeen	a																			

For general notes see front of timetable
For details of catering facilities see Directory of Train Operators

from 8 November

South Coast and The South West → North West England, The North East and Scotland

Route Diagram - See first page of Table 51

		XC	VT		XC	XC	XC	XC		XC	XC	XC	XC		XC	XC	VT	XC		XC	XC	XC	XC	XC
																	R							
		[1] ◇	[1] ◇		[1] ◇	[1] ◇	[1] ◇	[1] ◇		[1] ◇	[1] ◇	[1] ◇	[1] ◇		[1] ◇	[1] ◇	[1]	[1] ◇		[1] ◇	[1] ◇	[1] ◇	[1] ◇	[1] ◇
Bournemouth	d							14 40							15 40							16 40		
Brockenhurst [3]	d							14 57							15 57							16 57		
Southampton Central	d							15 15							16 15							17 15		
Southampton Airport Parkwy ✈	d							15 22							16 22							17 22		
Winchester	d							15 31							16 31							17 31		
Basingstoke	d							15 47							16 47							17 47		
Guildford	d																							
Reading [7]	d				15 40			16 11			16 40				17 11			17 40				18 11		18 40
Oxford	d				16 06			16 37			17 06				17 37			18 06				18 37		19 06
Banbury	d				16 25			16 53			17 25				17 53			18 25				18 53		19 25
Leamington Spa [8]	d				16 43			17 11			17 43				18 11			18 43				19 11		19 43
Coventry	d							17 26							18 26							19 26		19 54
Birmingham International ✈	d							17 38							18 38							19 38		20 04
Penzance	d					11 25																		
St Erth	d					11 33																		
Hayle	d																							
Camborne	d					11 45																		
Redruth	d					11 51																		
Truro	d					12 03																		
St Austell	d					12 21																		
Newquay	d																							
Par	d					12 28																		
Lostwithiel	d																							
Bodmin Parkway	d					12 40																		
Liskeard [6]	d					12 52																		
Plymouth	d					13 25						14 25								15 25				
Totnes	d					13 50						14 50								15 50				
Paignton	d																							
Torquay	d																							
Newton Abbot	d					14 03						15 02								16 03				
Teignmouth	d																							
Dawlish	d																							
Exeter St Davids [6]	d					14 23						15 23								16 23				
Tiverton Parkway	d					14 37						15 36								16 37				
Taunton	d					14 51						15 51								16 51				
Weston-super-Mare	d																							
Cardiff Central [7]	d						15 25						16 25								17 25			
Newport (South Wales)	d						15 39						16 39								17 39			
Bristol Temple Meads [10]	d					15 30						16 30								17 30				
Bristol Parkway [7]	d					15 40						16 40								17 40				
Gloucester [7]	d						16 22						17 22								18 22			
Cheltenham Spa	d					16 12	16 33					17 12	17 33							18 12	18 33			
Birmingham New Street [12]	a				17 09	17 25	17 39	17 49			18 09	18 20	18 36		18 49			19 09		19 25	19 39	19 49		20 15
Birmingham New Street [12]	d	17 02	17 20		17 30	17 31	17 45	18 01		18 02	18 30	18 31	18 45		19 01	19 03	19 20	19 30		19 31	19 45	20 01	20 03	20 30
Tamworth	d						18 03			18 20			19 04								20 03		20 19	20 46
Burton-on-Trent	d	17 26					18 15						19 16			19 26					20 15			20 56
Derby [10]	a	17 42			18 02		18 29			18 42	19 02		19 29			19 42		20 02			20 28		20 42	21 09
Nottingham [8]	a						18 57						19 57								20 57			
Chesterfield	a	18 02								19 04						20 05							21 02	21 29
Sheffield [7]	a	18 19			18 46					19 20	19 39					20 21		20 38					21 16	21 44
Doncaster [7]	a				19 13						20 16							21 19						
Wakefield Westgate [7]	a	18 47								19 48						20 49							21 44	
Leeds [10]	a	19 05								20 05						21 05							22 06	
York [8]	a	19 32			19 42					20 32	20 44					21 37		21 42						22 53
Darlington [7]	a	20 03			20 10					21 03	21 18							22 10						
Durham	a	20 21			20 27					21 21	21 36							22 27						
Chester-le-Street	a										21 45													
Newcastle [8]	a	20 37			20 43					21 37	21 59							22 43						
Morpeth	a				21 01																			
Alnmouth for Alnwick	a				21 15					22 05														
Berwick-upon-Tweed	a	21 23			21 36					22 28														
Dunbar	a	21 48																						
Wolverhampton [7]	d		17u37			17 49		18 19				18 49			19 19		19 37			19 49		20 19		
Stafford	a							18 35							19 34							20 37		
Stoke-on-Trent	a					18 19		18 56				19 19			19 56					20 21		20 56		
Congleton	a																							
Macclesfield	a							19 15							20 14							21 15		
Crewe [10]	a		18 09														20 09							
Wilmslow	a																							
Stockport	a							19 28							20 28							21 28		
Manchester Piccadilly [10]	a					19 00		19 40				20 00			20 40					21 00		21 40		
Warrington Bank Quay	a		18 28														20 28							
Wigan North Western	a		18 39														20 39							
Preston [8]	a		18 53														20 53							
Lancaster [6]	a		19 10														21 10							
Oxenholme Lake District	a		19 24														21 24							
Penrith North Lakes	a																							
Carlisle [8]	a		20 03														22 03							
Lockerbie	a																22 22							
Haymarket	a																							
Edinburgh [10]	a	22 20			22 25					23 19														
Haymarket	a																							
Motherwell	a																23s13							
Glasgow Central [15]	a		21 17														23 35							
Inverkeithing	a																							
Kirkcaldy	a																							
Markinch	a																							
Ladybank	a																							
Cupar	a																							
Leuchars [3]	a																							
Dundee	a																							
Arbroath	a																							
Montrose	a																							
Stonehaven	a																							
Aberdeen	a																							

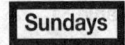

For general notes see front of timetable
For details of catering facilities see
Directory of Train Operators

South Coast and The South West → North West England, The North East and Scotland

Sundays from 8 November

Route Diagram - See first page of Table 51

		XC		XC	XC	XC	VT		XC	XC	XC	XC		XC	XC	XC	XC		XC	XC	XC			
		1 ◇		1 ◇	1 ◇	1 ◇	1 ◇		1 ◇	1 ◇	1 ◇	1 ◇		1 ◇	1 ◇	1 ◇	1 ◇		1 ◇	1 ◇	1 ◇			
		⊼			⊼	⊼	⊡		⊼	⊼		⊼		⊼	⊼	⊼			⊼	⊼	⊼			
Bournemouth	d				17 40							18 40							19 40					
Brockenhurst 3	d				17 57							18 57							19 57					
Southampton Central	d				18 15							19 15							20 15					
Southampton Airport Parkwy ✈	d				18 22							19 22							20 22					
Winchester	d				18 31							19 31							20 31					
Basingstoke	d				18 47							19 47							20 47					
Guildford	d																							
Reading 7	d				19 11				19 40			20 11				20 40			21 11	21 40				
Oxford	d				19 37				20 06			20 37				21 06			21 37	22 06				
Banbury	d				19 53				20 25			20 53				21 25			21 53	22 25				
Leamington Spa 8	d				20 11				20 43			21 11				21 43			22 11	22 43				
Coventry	d				20 26				20 54			21 26				21 54			22 23	22 54				
Birmingham International ✈	d				20 38				21 04			21 38				22 04			22 33	23 04				
Penzance	d									15 30														
St Erth	d									15 38														
Hayle	d																							
Camborne	d									15 49														
Redruth	d									15 55														
Truro	d									16 07														
St Austell	d									16 25														
Newquay	d																							
Par	d									16 32														
Lostwithiel	d																							
Bodmin Parkway	d									16 43														
Liskeard 6	d									16 55														
Plymouth	d	16 25								17 25					18 25									
Totnes	d	16 52								17 50					18 50									
Paignton	d																							
Torquay	d																							
Newton Abbot	d	17 05								18 03					19 03									
Teignmouth	d																							
Dawlish	d																							
Exeter St Davids 6	d	17 25								18 23					19 23									
Tiverton Parkway	d	17 39								18 37					19 37									
Taunton	d	17 53								18 51					19 51									
Weston-super-Mare	d																							
Cardiff Central 7	d			18 25							19 25						20 25							
Newport (South Wales)	d			18 39							19 39						20 39							
Bristol Temple Meads 10	d	18 30								19 30					20 30						22 10			
Bristol Parkway 7	d	18 40								19 40					20 40						22 20			
Gloucester 7	d			19 22							20 22						21 30							
Cheltenham Spa	d	19 12		19 34						20 12	20 33				21 12		21 41				22 52			
Birmingham New Street 12	a	20 20		20 35	20 49				21 20	21 39	21 42	21 49			22 17	22 20	22 45		23 06	23 35	23 55			
Birmingham New Street 12	d	20 31		20 45	21 01	21 03	21 20				21 46	22 01		22 03	22 28		22 49							
Tamworth	d			21 03		21 19					22 06			22 23			23 07							
Burton-on-Trent	d			21 15		21 29					22 18			22 35			23 19							
Derby 10	a			21 31		21 42					22 33			22 48			23 37							
Nottingham 8 ⛴	a																							
Chesterfield	a					22 05								23 10										
Sheffield 7	a					22 19								23 27										
Doncaster 7	a																							
Wakefield Westgate 7	a					22 48																		
Leeds 10	a					23 08								00 44										
York 8	a																							
Darlington 7	a																							
Durham	a																							
Chester-le-Street	a																							
Newcastle 8	a																							
Morpeth	a																							
Alnmouth for Alnwick	a																							
Berwick-upon-Tweed	a																							
Dunbar	a																							
Wolverhampton 7 ⛴	d	20 49			21 19		21 38					22 19			22 46									
Stafford	a				21 34		21 58					22 37			22 58									
Stoke-on-Trent	a	21 19			21 56							22 56												
Congleton	a																							
Macclesfield	a				22 14							23 14												
Crewe 10	a						22 17								23 24									
Wilmslow	a														23 42									
Stockport	a				22 28							23 29			23s51									
Manchester Piccadilly 10 ⛴	a	22 00			22 40							23 40			00 05									
Warrington Bank Quay	a						22 36																	
Wigan North Western	a						22 47																	
Preston 8	a						23 07																	
Lancaster 6	a																							
Oxenholme Lake District	a																							
Penrith North Lakes	a																							
Carlisle 8	a																							
Lockerbie	a																							
Haymarket	a																							
Edinburgh 10	a																							
Haymarket	a																							
Motherwell	a																							
Glasgow Central 15	a																							
Inverkeithing	a																							
Kirkcaldy	a																							
Markinch	a																							
Ladybank	a																							
Cupar	a																							
Leuchars 3	a																							
Dundee	a																							
Arbroath	a																							
Montrose	a																							
Stonehaven	a																							
Aberdeen	a																							

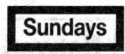

For general notes see front of timetable
For details of catering facilities see Directory of Train Operators

Network Diagram for Table 52

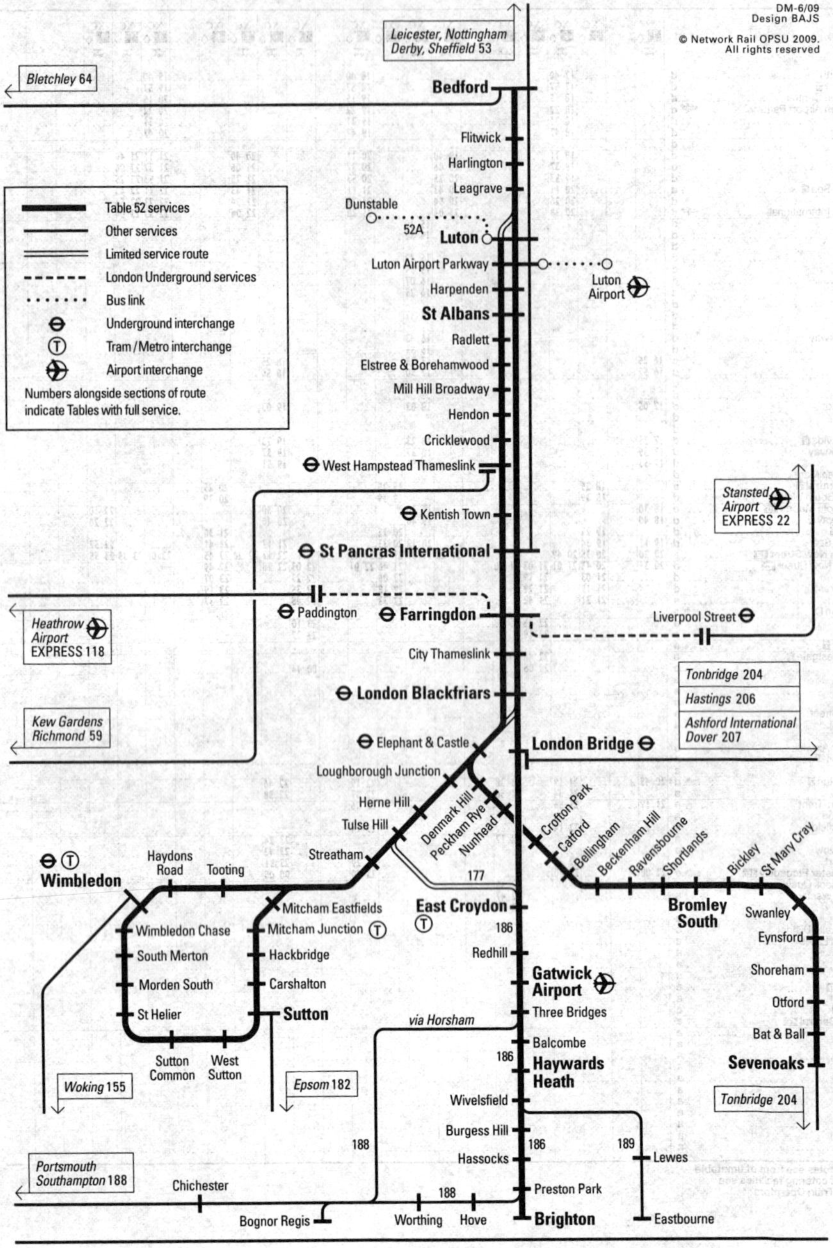

DM-6/09
Design BAJS
© Network Rail OPSU 2009. All rights reserved
Table 52 services
Other services
Limited service route
London Underground services
Bus link
Underground interchange
Tram / Metro interchange
Airport interchange
Numbers alongside sections of route indicate Tables with full service.
Leicester, Nottingham Derby, Sheffield 53
Bletchley 64
Bedford
Flitwick
Harlington
Leagrave
Dunstable
52A
Luton
Luton Airport Parkway
Luton Airport
Harpenden
St Albans
Radlett
Elstree & Borehamwood
Mill Hill Broadway
Hendon
Cricklewood
West Hampstead Thameslink
Kentish Town
St Pancras International
Stansted Airport EXPRESS 22
Paddington
Farringdon
Liverpool Street
Heathrow Airport EXPRESS 118
City Thameslink
London Blackfriars
Tonbridge 204
Hastings 206
Ashford International Dover 207
Kew Gardens Richmond 59
Elephant & Castle
London Bridge
Loughborough Junction
Herne Hill
Tulse Hill
Denmark Hill
Peckham Rye
Nunhead
Crofton Park
Catford
Bellingham
Beckenham Hill
Ravensbourne
Shortlands
Bickley
St Mary Cray
Streatham
Haydons Road
Tooting
Wimbledon
177
East Croydon
Bromley South
Swanley
Mitcham Eastfields
Wimbledon Chase
Mitcham Junction
186
Eynsford
South Merton
Hackbridge
Redhill
Morden South
Carshalton
Gatwick Airport
Shoreham
Otford
St Helier
Sutton
via Horsham
Three Bridges
Bat & Ball
Balcombe
Sutton Common
West Sutton
186
Haywards Heath
Sevenoaks
Woking 155
Epsom 182
Wivelsfield
Tonbridge 204
Burgess Hill
188
186
189
Hassocks
Lewes
Portsmouth Southampton 188
Chichester
188
Preston Park
Bognor Regis
Worthing
Hove
Brighton
Eastbourne

Bedford, Luton, St.Albans and City of London → South London, Gatwick Airport and Brighton

Network Diagram - see first page of Table 52

Miles	Miles	Miles	Miles			FC MX	FC MX	FC MO 1	FC MX 1	FC MX 1	FC MO 1	FC 1	FC 1	FC 1	FC 1	FC 1	FC 1	SE	FC 1		SN A	SN A	FC	SE	FC 1
0	0	—	—	**Bedford 7**	d			23p10	23p10	23p40	23p40	00 10	01 10	02 10	03 10	03 40	04 10		04 20						04 50
9½	—	—	—	Flitwick	d			23p19	23p19	23p49	23p49	00 19	01 19	02 19	03 19	03 49	04 19		04 29						04 59
12½	—	—	—	Harlington	d			23p23	23p23	23p53	23p53	00 23	01 23	02 23	03 23	03 53	04 23		04 33						05 03
17	—	—	—	Leagrave	d			23p29	23p29	23p59	23p59	00 29	01 29	02 29	03 29	03 59	04 29		04 39						05 09
19½	19½	—	—	**Luton 10**	d			23p34	23p34	00 04	00 04	00 34	01 34	02 34	03 34	04 04	04 34		04 44						05 14
20½	—	—	—	Luton Airport Parkway 7 ✈	d			23p36	23p36	00 06	00 06	00 36	01 36	02 36	03 36	04 06	04 36		04 46						05 16
25	—	—	—	Harpenden	d			23p42	23p42	00 12	00 12	00 42	01 42	02 42	03 42	04 12	04 42		04 52						05 22
29¾	—	—	—	**St Albans City**	d			23p48	23p48	00 18	00 18	00 48	01 48	02 48	03 48	04 18	04 48		04 58						05 28
34¼	—	—	—	Radlett	d			23p53	23p53	00 23	00 23	00 53	01 53	02 53	03 53	04 23			05 03						05 33
37¼	—	—	—	Elstree & Borehamwood	d			23p57	23p57	00 27	00 27	00 57	01 57	02 57	03 57	04 27			05 07						05 37
40½	—	—	—	Mill Hill Broadway	d			00 01	00 01	00 31	00 31	01 01	02 01	03 01	04 01	04 31			05 11						05 41
42¾	—	—	—	Hendon	d			00 04	00 04	00 34	00 34	01 04	02 04	03 04	04 04	04 34			05 14						05 44
44¾	—	—	—	Cricklewood	d			00 08	00 08	00 38	00 38	01 08	02 08	03 08	04 08	04 38			05 18						05 48
45¾	—	—	—	West Hampstead Thameslink ⊖	d			00 12	00 12	00 42	00 42	01 12	02 12	03 12	04 12	04 42	05 02		05 22						05 52
48¼	—	—	—	Kentish Town ⊖	d			00 16	00 16	00 46	00 46	01 16	02 16	03 16	04 16	04 46			05 26						05 56
49¾	—	—	—	**St Pancras International** ⊖	a			00 24	00 25	00 55	00 54	01 25	02 25	03 25	04 25										
50	—	—	—	**St Pancras International 15** ⊖	d											04 52	05 12		05 32				05 56		06 02
51	0	—	—	Farringdon 3 ⊖	d											04 57	05 17		05 37				06 01		06 07
—	1	—	—	Barbican ⊖	a																				
—	3	—	—	**Moorgate** ⊖	a																				
51¾	0	—	—	City Thameslink 3	d												05 21	05 26	05 41				06 03	06 07	06 11
52¼	0	0	0	**London Blackfriars 3** ⊖	d											05 04	05 24	05 28	05 44				06 06	06 10	06 14
1	1	—	—	Elephant & Castle ⊖	d													05 32					06 09	06 13	
3	3	—	—	Loughborough Jn	d																		06 13		
4	4	—	—	Herne Hill 4	d																		06b20		
53	—	—	—	**London Bridge 4** ⊖	d	23p28	23p58										05 31		05 51			06 00			06 21
—	5	5	5	Tulse Hill 3	d	23p40	00 10															06 17	06 26		
—	62	62	0	Streatham 4	d	23p43	00 13															06 21	06 30		
—	—	—	1	Mitcham Eastfields	d																		06 34		
—	—	2	—	Mitcham Junction 🚋	d																		06 38		
—	—	4	—	Hackbridge	d																		06 41		
—	—	4¾	—	Carshalton	d																		06 44		
—	8	—	—	Tooting	d	23p48	00 18															06 27			
—	9¼	—	—	Haydons Road	d	23p51	00 21															06 30			
—	10½	—	—	**Wimbledon 6** ⊖ 🚋	d	23p54	00 25														05 56	06 33			
—	11½	—	—	Wimbledon Chase	d	23p57	00 28														05 59	06 36			
—	12	—	—	South Merton	d	23p59	00 30														06 01	06 38			
—	12½	—	—	Morden South	d	00 01	00 32														06 03	06 40			
—	13	—	—	St Helier	d	00 03	00 34														06 05	06 42			
—	14	—	—	Sutton Common	d	00 05	00 36														06 07	06 44			
—	15	—	—	West Sutton	d	00 08	00 39														06 10	06 47			
—	16	12½	6	**Sutton (Surrey) 4**	a	00 12	00 43														06 13	06 50	06 47		
63¼	—	—	10	**East Croydon** 🚋	d											05 32	05 52		06 04						06 36
—	—	—	—	Denmark Hill 4	d													05 37						06 20	
—	—	—	—	Peckham Rye 4	d													05 39						06 23	
—	—	—	—	Nunhead 4	d													05 41						06 25	
—	—	—	—	Crofton Park	d													05 44						06 28	
—	—	—	—	Catford	d													05 46						06 30	
—	—	—	—	Bellingham	d													05 48						06 32	
—	—	—	—	Beckenham Hill	d													05 50						06 34	
—	—	—	—	Ravensbourne	d													05 52						06 36	
—	—	—	—	Shortlands	d													05 54						06 39	
—	—	—	—	Bromley South 4	d													05 58						06 42	
—	—	—	—	Bickley 4	d													06 00						06 44	
—	—	—	—	St Mary Cray	d													06 06						06 50	
—	—	—	—	Swanley 4	d													06 11						06 55	
—	—	—	—	Eynsford	d													06 15						06 59	
—	—	—	—	Shoreham (Kent)	d													06 19						07 03	
—	—	—	—	Otford 4	d													06 22						07 06	
—	—	—	—	Bat & Ball	d													06 25						07 09	
—	—	—	—	Sevenoaks 4	a													06 28						07 13	
73¾	—	—	—	Redhill	d																				
79½	—	—	—	**Gatwick Airport 10** ✈	d											05 54	06 08		06 20						06 52
82¼	—	—	—	Three Bridges 4	d											06 00	06 14		06 26						06 56
86¾	—	—	—	Balcombe	d												06 20		06 33						
90¾	—	—	—	**Haywards Heath 3**	d											06 10	06 25		06 38						07 06
93¾	—	—	—	Wivelsfield 4	d											06 14	06 29		06 42						07 10
94½	—	—	—	Burgess Hill 4	d											06 16	06 32		06 44						07 12
96½	—	—	—	Hassocks 4	d											06 19	06 35		06 47						07 15
102¼	—	—	—	Preston Park	d											06 26	06 42		06 54						07 22
103¾	—	—	—	**Brighton 10**	a											06 33	06 47		06 59						07 29

For general notes see front of timetable
For details of catering facilities see
Directory of Train Operators

A To London Bridge (Table 179)
b Arr. 0617

Bedford, Luton, St.Albans and City of London → South London, Gatwick Airport and Brighton

Network Diagram - see first page of Table 52

Station		FC 1	SN	SE	EM 1 ◇	FC	FC 1	FC 1	FC	FC 1	EM 1 ◇	FC 1	SN	FC	FC 1	FC 1	FC	FC 1	FC	EM 1 ◇	FC	SN	FC	FC
					A			B			C		D			B	E		G	H	B E	J		B G
Bedford 7	d	05 20			05 32		05 40	05 56		06 00					06 16			06 20	06 25	06 32			06 36	
Flitwick	d	05 29					05 49	06 05		06 09					06 25			06 29	06 34				06 45	
Harlington	d	05 33					05 53			06 13								06 33	06 38					
Leagrave	d	05 39					05 59			06 19								06 39	06 44					
Luton 10	d	05 44				05 48	06 04	06 16	06 18	06 24	06 24	06 29			06 36		06 38	06 44	06 49				06 56	
Luton Airport Parkway 7	✈ d	05 46			05 55	05 50	06 06		06 20	06 26		06 31					06 40	06 46	06 51					
Harpenden	d	05 52				05 56	06 12	06 22	06 26	06 32		06 37			06 42		06 46	06 52	06 57				07 02	
St Albans City	d	05 58				06 02	06 18	06 28	06 32	06 38		06 43			06 48		06 52	06 58	07 03				07 08	
Radlett	d					06 07			06 37			06 48				←	06 57		07 08					←
Elstree & Borehamwood	d					06 11			06 41			06 52		←		06 52	07 01		07 12		←			07 12
Mill Hill Broadway	d					06 15			06 45			→		06 45		06 57	07 05		→		07 05			07 17
Hendon	d					06 18			→					06 48			→				07 08			
Cricklewood	d					06 22								06 52							07 12			
West Hampstead Thameslink	⊖ d	06 12				06 25	06 32			06 52				06 55		07 04		07 12			07 15			07 24
Kentish Town	⊖ d					06 29								06 59							07 19			
St Pancras International	⊖ a				06 21						06 54									07 14				
St Pancras International 15	⊖ d	06 20				06 34	06 40	06 48		07 00				07 04	07 08	07 12		07 20			07 24		07 28	07 32
Farringdon 3	⊖ d	06 25				06 39	06 45	06 53		07 05				07 09	07 13	07 17		07 25			07 29		07 33	07 37
Barbican	⊖ a																							
Moorgate	⊖ a																							
City Thameslink 3	d	06 27		06 38		06 43	06 47	06 57		07 07				07 13	07 17	07 21		07 29			07 33		07 37	07 41
London Blackfriars 3	⊖ d	06 34		06 40		06 46	06 50	07b06		07 10				07 16	07 20	07 24		07 32			07 35		07 40	07 44
Elephant & Castle	⊖ d			06 44		06 49		07 09						07 19	07 23	07 27							07 43	07a47
Loughborough Jn	d					06 53								07 23	07 27								07 47	
Herne Hill 4	d					06 58								07 28	07 34						07a44		07 52	
London Bridge 4	⊖ d	06 43	06 30				07c01			07 16			07 00					07 40				07 31		
Tulse Hill 3	d		06 47			07 03							07 17	07 32	07 38							07 48	07 56	
Streatham 4	d		06 51			07 06							07 21	07 36	07 42							07 52	07 59	
Mitcham Eastfields	d					07 10								07 40									08 03	
Mitcham Junction	🚊 d					07 14								07 44									08 07	
Hackbridge	d					07 17								07 47									08 10	
Carshalton	d					07 20								07 50									08 13	
Tooting	d		06 56										07 25		07 46							07 56		
Haydons Road	d		06 59										07 28		07 49							07 59		
Wimbledon 6	⊖ 🚊 d		07 02										07 32		07a52							08 02		
Wimbledon Chase	d		07 10										07 35									08 05		
South Merton	d		07 12										07 37									08 07		
Morden South	d		07 14										07 39									08 09		
St Helier	d		07 16										07 41									08 11		
Sutton Common	d		07 18										07 43									08 13		
West Sutton	d		07 21										07 46									08 16		
Sutton (Surrey) 4	a		07 25			07 23							07 49	07 53								08 19	08 16	
East Croydon	🚊 d	06 56					07 16			07 32								07 56						
Denmark Hill 4	d			06 50				07 15								07 34								
Peckham Rye 4	d			06 52				07 20								07 37								
Nunhead 4	d			06 54				07 22								07 39								
Crofton Park	d			06 57				07 24								07 41								
Catford	d			06 59				07 26								07 44								
Bellingham	d			07 01				07 29								07 47								
Beckenham Hill	d			07 03				07 31								07 49								
Ravensbourne	d			07 05				07 33								07 51								
Shortlands	d			07 07				07 35								07 53								
Bromley South 4	d			07 10				07 38								07 56								
Bickley 4	d			07 13				07 40								07 58								
St Mary Cray	d			07 18				07 46								08 04								
Swanley 4	d			07 23				07 50								08 08								
Eynsford	d			07 28				07 55								08 13								
Shoreham (Kent)	d			07 31				07 58								08 16								
Otford 4	d			07 34				08 02								08 20								
Bat & Ball	d			07 37				08 05								08 23								
Sevenoaks 4	a			07 43				08 08								08 26								
Redhill	d																							
Gatwick Airport 10	✈ d	07 12					07 32			07 50								08 12						
Three Bridges 4	d	07 18					07 38			07 54								08 16						
Balcombe	d									08 00								08 22						
Haywards Heath 3	d	07 28					07 48			08 06								08 28						
Wivelsfield 4	d	07 32								08 10								08 32						
Burgess Hill 4	d	07 34					07 54			08 12								08 34						
Hassocks 4	d	07 37								08 15								08 37						
Preston Park	d	07 44								08 22								08 44						
Brighton 10	a	07 49					08 07			08 27								08 49						

For general notes see front of timetable
For details of catering facilities see Directory of Train Operators

A From Leicester (Table 53)
B TOC SE from London Blackfriars
C Mondays to Fridays Until 4 September Mondays Excepted from 8 September From Derby (Table 53)
D To London Bridge (Table 179)
E To Beckenham Junction (Table 195)
G To Bromley South (Table 195)
H From Derby (Table 53)
J To London Victoria (Table 177)
b Arr. 0700
c Arr. 0656

Bedford, Luton, St.Albans and City of London → South London, Gatwick Airport and Brighton

Network Diagram - see first page of Table 52

		FC	FC	EM	FC		FC	FC	FC	SN	FC	FC	EM	FC	FC	FC	FC	EM	SN	FC		FC	FC	FC	EM
				[1] ◇				[1]				[1]	[1] ◇	[1]				[1] ◇		[1]		[1]	[1]		[1] ◇
			A B	C ⊠ ⌶	A				D	E			G ⊠ ⌶	A H	A D	A		J ⊠	K						C ⊠ ⌶
Bedford [7]	d		06 40					06 56				07 00	07 13	07 10						07 16		07 22	07 28		
Flitwick	d		06 49					07 05				07 09								07 25		07 31	07 37		
Harlington	d		06 53									07 13								07 29		07 35			
Leagrave	d		06 59									07 19		07 26						07 35		07 41			
Luton [10]	d	06 56	07 04				07 08	07 16	07 20			07 24	07 29	07 32			07 36			07 40		07 46	07 48		07 56
Luton Airport Parkway [7] ✈	d	06 58	07 06	07 08			07 10		07 22			07 26					07 38	07 40		07 42		07 48			
Harpenden	d	07 04	07 12				07 16	07 22	07 28			07 32		07 38			07 44			07 48		07 54	07 54		
St Albans City	d	07 10	07 18				07 22	07 28	07 34			07 38		07 44		07 44	07 50			07 56		08 00	08 00		
Radlett	d	07 15					07 27		07 39							07 49	07 55					08 05			
Elstree & Borehamwood	d	07 19					07 31		07 43							07 53	07 59					08 09			
Mill Hill Broadway	d	07 24			←		07 36		07 48		←				←		08 04					→		←	
Hendon	d	07 27			07 27		07 39		07 51		07 39				07 51		08 07							08 07	
Cricklewood	d	→			07 31		→		→		07 43				07 55		→							08 11	
West Hampstead Thameslink	⊖ d				07 35						07 47				07 59	08 03								08 15	
Kentish Town	⊖ d				07 39						07 51				08 03									08 19	
St Pancras International	⊖ a			07 36									07 55					08 09							08 26
St Pancras International [15]	⊖ d		07 40		07 44			07 48			07 56	08 00		08 04	08 08	08 12				08 16			08 20	08 24	
Farringdon [3]	⊖ d		07 45		07 49			07 53			08 01	08 05		08 09	08 13	08 17				08 21			08 25	08 29	
Barbican	⊖ a																								
Moorgate	⊖ a																								
City Thameslink [3]	d		07 49		07 53			07 57			08 05	08 09		08 13	08 17	08 21				08 25			08 29	08 33	
London Blackfriars [3]	⊖ d		07 52		07 56			08 00			08 08	08 12		08a15	08 20	08 24				08 28			08 32	08 36	
Elephant & Castle	⊖ d		07a55		07 59						08 11					08 28				08 31				08 39	
Loughborough Jn	d										08 15									08 35				08 43	
Herne Hill [4]	d							08 09			08b22				08a29					08 39			08 43	08 48	
London Bridge [4]	⊖ d									08 02		08 19							08 24						
Tulse Hill [3]	d							08 13		08 19	08 26								08 38	08 43			08 47	08c57	
Streatham [4]	d									08 23	08 29								08 42	08 47				09 00	
Mitcham Eastfields	d										08 33									08 51					
Mitcham Junction	🚋 d										08 37									08 55					
Hackbridge	d										08 40									08 58					
Carshalton	d										08 43									09 01					
Tooting	d									08 27									08 46					09 06	
Haydons Road	d									08 30									08 49					09 09	
Wimbledon [6]	⊖ 🚋 d									08 33									08 55					09e17	
Wimbledon Chase	d									08 36									08 58					09 20	
South Merton	d									08 38									09 00					09 22	
Morden South	d									08 40									09 02					09 24	
St Helier	d									08 42									09 04					09 26	
Sutton Common	d									08 44									09 06					09 28	
West Sutton	d									08 47									09 09					09 31	
Sutton (Surrey) [4]	a									08 50	08 46								09 13	09 05				09 37	
East Croydon	🚋 d							08 26				08 36											09 06		
Denmark Hill [4]	d				08 06											08 35									
Peckham Rye [4]	d				08 09											08 38									
Nunhead [4]	d				08 11											08 40									
Crofton Park	d				08 13											08 42									
Catford	d				08 16											08 44									
Bellingham	d				08 19											08 47									
Beckenham Hill	d				08 21											08 49									
Ravensbourne	d				08 23											08 51									
Shortlands	d				08 25											08 53									
Bromley South [4]	d				08 28											08 56									
Bickley [4]	d				08 30											08 58									
St Mary Cray	d				08 36											09 04									
Swanley [4]	d				08 40											09 08									
Eynsford	d				08 45											09 13									
Shoreham (Kent)	d				08 48											09 16									
Otford [4]	d				08 52											09 20									
Bat & Ball	d				08 55											09 23									
Sevenoaks [4]	a				08 58											09 26									
Redhill	d																								
Gatwick Airport [10]	✈ d							08 42				08 52											09 26		
Three Bridges [4]	d							08 46				08 57											09 30		
Balcombe	d							08 52																	
Haywards Heath [3]	d							08 58				09 07											09 40		
Wivelsfield [4]	d							09 02																	
Burgess Hill [4]	d							09 04																	
Hassocks [4]	d							09 07																	
Preston Park	d							09 14																	
Brighton [10]	a							09 19				09 23											09 54		

For general notes see front of timetable
For details of catering facilities see Directory of Train Operators

A TOC SE from London Blackfriars
B To Orpington (Table 195)
C From Nottingham (Table 53)
D To Kent House (Table 195)
E To London Bridge (Table 179)
G From Melton Mowbray (Table 49)
H To Bromley South (Table 195)
J From Sheffield (Table 53)
K To London Victoria (Table 177)
b Arr. 0819
c Arr. 0852
e Arr. 0911

Bedford, Luton, St.Albans and City of London → South London, Gatwick Airport and Brighton

Network Diagram - see first page of Table 52

Station		FC 1	FC A	FC B	FC	FC	FC AB	FC 1	EM 1 ◇ C	EM 1 ◇ D	FC	FC	FC		FC	FC 1	FC	FC 1	EM 1 ◇ D	FC	FC	FC 1	FC	FC	FC 1
Bedford 7	d		07 32		07 44			07 48	07 55			07 58				08 04		08 20	08 29			08 40			08 54
Flitwick	d		07 41					07 57				08 07				08 13		08 29				08 49			09 03
Harlington	d		07 45					08 01								08 17		08 33				08 53			09 07
Leagrave	d		07 51		08 00			08 07								08 23		08 39				08 59			09 13
Luton 10	d		07 56	08 01	08 04			08 12		08 15	08 18	08 20				08 28		08 44			08 54	09 04		09 14	09 18
Luton Airport Parkway 7 ✈	d		07 58	08 03				08 14	08 12		08 20					08 30		08 46			08 56	09 06		09 16	09 20
Harpenden	d		08 04	08 09	08 10			08 20			08 26	08 26				08 36		08 52			09 02	09 12		09 22	09 26
St Albans City	d		08 12	08 15	08 16	08 06		08 26			08 32	08 32	08 22			08 44	08 42	09 00		08 58	09 08	09 18	09 13	09 29	09 34
Radlett	d	←		08 20		08 11	←				08 37		08 27		←		08 47			09 03	09 13		09 18	09 34	
Elstree & Borehamwood	d	08 09		08 24		08 15	08 24				08 41		08 31		08 41		08 51			09 07	09 17		09 22	09 38	
Mill Hill Broadway	d			→		08 20	08 29				→		08 36				08 56			09 12			09 27	09 43	
Hendon	d					08 23							08 39				08 59			09 15			09 30	09 46	
Cricklewood	d					08 27							08 43				09 03			09 19			09 34	→	
West Hampstead Thameslink ⊖	d	08 19				08 31	08 36						08 47		08 51		09 07			09 22	09 26		09 38		
Kentish Town ⊖	d					08 35							08 51				09 11			09 26			09 42		
St Pancras International ⊖	a								08 38	08 44									09 08						
St Pancras International 15 ⊖	d	08 28	08 32		08 36	08 40	08 44	08 48				08 52	08 56		09 00	09 04	09 16	09 20		09 30	09 34	09 39	09 48		09 54
Farringdon 3 ⊖	d	08 33	08 37		08 41	08 45	08 49	08 53				08 57	09 01		09 05	09 09	09 21	09 25		09 35	09 39	09 44	09 53		09 59
Barbican ⊖	a																								
Moorgate ⊖	a																								
City Thameslink 3	d	08 37	08 41		08 45	08 49	08 53	08 56				09 01	09 05		09 09	09 13	09 25	09 29		09 39	09 43	09 48	09 57		10 02
London Blackfriars 3 ⊖	d	08 40	08 44		08 48	08 52	08 56	08 59				09 04	09 08		09 12	09 16	09 28	09 34		09 42	09 46	09 50	10 00		10 05
Elephant & Castle ⊖	d	08a44	08 47		08a52	08 55	09a01					09 07	09 11		09 16		09 31			09 45	09 49		10 03		
Loughborough Jn	d					08 59						09 11	09 15				09 35				09 53		10 07		
Herne Hill 4	d					09b06						09 15	09 22				09c42				09 57		10 12		
London Bridge 4 ⊖	d							09 06								09 25		09 42				09 58			10 11
Tulse Hill 3	d					09e16						09 20	09 28				09 46				10 02		10 16		
Streatham 4	d					09 19						09 23	09 31				09 49				10 05		10 19		
Mitcham Eastfields	d					09 23											09 53						10 23		
Mitcham Junction 🚋	d					09 27											09 57						10 27		
Hackbridge	d					09 30											10 00						10 30		
Carshalton	d					09 33											10 03						10 33		
Tooting	d											09 27	09 36								10 10				
Haydons Road	d											09 30	09 39								10 13				
Wimbledon 6 ⊖ 🚋	d											09a33	09f47								10 17				
Wimbledon Chase	d												09 50								10 20				
South Merton	d												09 52								10 22				
Morden South	d												09 54								10 24				
St Helier	d												09 56								10 26				
Sutton Common	d												09 58								10 28				
West Sutton	d												10 01								10 31				
Sutton (Surrey) 4	a					09 36							10 05				10 07				10 35		10 36		
East Croydon 🚋	d							09 24								09 39		09 54				10 10			10 24
Denmark Hill 4	d		08 52												09 22					09 52					
Peckham Rye 4	d		08 55												09 25					09 55					
Nunhead 4	d		08 57												09 27					09 57					
Crofton Park	d		08 59												09 29					09 59					
Catford	d		09 01												09 31					10 01					
Bellingham	d		09 04												09 34					10 04					
Beckenham Hill	d		09 06												09 36					10 06					
Ravensbourne	d		09 08												09 38					10 08					
Shortlands	d		09 10												09 40					10 10					
Bromley South 4	d		09 13												09 43					10 13					
Bickley 4	d		09 16												09 45					10 15					
St Mary Cray	d		09 21												09 51					10 21					
Swanley 4	d		09 26												09 55					10 25					
Eynsford	d		09 30												10 00					10 30					
Shoreham (Kent)	d		09 34												10 03					10 33					
Otford 4	d		09 37												10 06					10 36					
Bat & Ball	d		09 40												10 09					10 39					
Sevenoaks 4	a		09 43												10 12					10 42					
Redhill	d																								
Gatwick Airport 10 ✈	d							09 41								09 57		10 11				10 26			10 41
Three Bridges 4	d							09 45								10 02		10 15							10 45
Balcombe	d							09 51										10 21							
Haywards Heath 3	d							09 57								10 10		10 27				10 40			10 55
Wivelsfield 4	d							10 01										10 31							10 59
Burgess Hill 4	d							10 03										10 33							11 01
Hassocks 4	d							10 06										10 36							11 04
Preston Park	d							10 13										10 43							11 11
Brighton 10	a							10 19								10 24		10 49				10 54			11 17

For general notes see front of timetable
For details of catering facilities see Directory of Train Operators

A TOC SE from London Blackfriars
B To Bromley South (Table 195)
C From Sheffield (Table 53)
D From Nottingham (Table 53)

b Arr. 0903
c Arr. 0939
e Arr. 0910
f Arr. 0944

Bedford, Luton, St.Albans and City of London → South London, Gatwick Airport and Brighton

Network Diagram - see first page of Table 52

		EM [1] ◇ A ☕	FC	FC	FC [1]	FC [1]		EM [1] ◇ B ☕	FC	FC	FC [1]	FC C	FC	FC [1]	EM [1] ◇ D ☕	FC [1]	FC	FC	FC [1]	FC C	FC		FC [1]	FC	EM [1] ◇ E ☕
Bedford [7]	d	09 02			09 10	09 18		09 18			09 24			09 40	09 48	09 48			09 54				10 10	10 18	10 18
Flitwick	d				09 19	09 27					09 33			09 49		09 57			10 03				10 19	10 27	
Harlington	d				09 23						09 37			09 53					10 07				10 23		
Leagrave	d				09 29						09 43			09 59					10 13				10 29		
Luton [10]	d	09 19			09 34	09 40				09 44	09 48			10 04	10 04	10 10		10 14	10 18				10 34	10 40	
Luton Airport Parkway [7] ✈	d				09 36			09 34		09 46	09 50			10 06				10 16	10 20				10 36		10 34
Harpenden	d				09 42	09 47				09 52	09 56			10 12		10 17		10 22	10 26				10 42	10 47	
St Albans City	d				09 48	09 54			09 43	09 59	10 03			10 18		10 24	10 14	10 29	10 34				10 48	10 54	
Radlett	d								09 48	10 04							10 19	10 34							
Elstree & Borehamwood	d								09 52	10 08							10 23	10 38							
Mill Hill Broadway	d			←					09 57	10 13			←				10 28	10 43			←				
Hendon	d			09 46					10 00	10 16			10 16				10 31	10 46			10 46				
Cricklewood	d			09 50					10 04	→			10 20				10 35	→			10 50				
West Hampstead Thameslink ⊖	d			09 54					10 10				10 24				10 38				10 54				
Kentish Town ⊖	d		09 56	10 00					10 13			10 26	10 30				10 42			10 56	11 00				
St Pancras International ⊖	a	09 47						10 00							10 30										11 01
St Pancras International [15] ⊖	d		10 00	10 04	10 09	10 14			10 18		10 24	10 30	10 34	10 39		10 44	10 48		10 54	11 00	11 04		11 09	11 14	
Farringdon [3] ⊖	d		10 05	10 09	10 14	10 19			10 23		10 29	10 35	10 39	10 44		10 49	10 53		10 59	11 05	11 09		11 14	11 19	
Barbican ⊖	a																								
Moorgate ⊖	a																								
City Thameslink [3]	d		10 09	10 13	10 17	10 22			10 27		10 32	10 39	10 43	10 47		10 52	10 57		11 02	11 09	11 13		11 17	11 22	
London Blackfriars [3] ⊖	d		10 12	10 16	10 20	10 26			10 30		10 35	10 42	10 46	10 50		10 56	11 00		11 05	11 12	11 16		11 20	11 26	
Elephant & Castle ⊖	d		10 15	10 19		10a30			10 33			10 45	10 49			11a00	11 03			11 15	11 19			11a30	
Loughborough Jn	d			10 23					10 37				10 53				11 07				11 23				
Herne Hill [4]	d			10 27					10 42				10 57				11 12				11 27				
London Bridge [4] ⊖	d				10 26						10 41			10 56					11 11				11 26		
Tulse Hill [3]	d			10 32					10 46				11 02				11 16				11 32				
Streatham [4]	d			10 35					10 49				11 05				11 19				11 35				
Mitcham Eastfields	d								10 53								11 23								
Mitcham Junction 🚋	d								10 57								11 27								
Hackbridge	d								11 00								11 30								
Carshalton	d								11 03								11 33								
Tooting	d			10 40									11 10								11 40				
Haydons Road	d			10 43									11 13								11 43				
Wimbledon [6] ⊖ 🚋	d			10 47									11 17								11 47				
Wimbledon Chase	d			10 50									11 20								11 50				
South Merton	d			10 52									11 22								11 52				
Morden South	d			10 54									11 24								11 54				
St Helier	d			10 56									11 26								11 56				
Sutton Common	d			10 58									11 28								11 58				
West Sutton	d			11 01									11 31								12 01				
Sutton (Surrey) [4]	a			11 05					11 06				11 35				11 36				12 05				
East Croydon 🚋	d				10 39						10 54			11 09					11 24				11 39		
Denmark Hill [4]	d		10 22									10 52								11 22					
Peckham Rye [4]	d		10 25									10 55								11 25					
Nunhead [4]	d		10 27									10 57								11 27					
Crofton Park	d		10 29									10 59								11 29					
Catford	d		10 31									11 01								11 31					
Bellingham	d		10 34									11 04								11 34					
Beckenham Hill	d		10 36									11 06								11 36					
Ravensbourne	d		10 38									11 08								11 38					
Shortlands	d		10 40									11 10								11 40					
Bromley South [4]	d		10 43									11 13								11 43					
Bickley [4]	d		10 45									11 15								11 45					
St Mary Cray	d		10 51									11 21								11 51					
Swanley [4]	d		10 55									11 25								11 55					
Eynsford	d		11 00									11 30								12 00					
Shoreham (Kent)	d		11 03									11 33								12 03					
Otford [4]	d		11 06									11 36								12 06					
Bat & Ball	d		11 09									11 39								12 09					
Sevenoaks [4]	a		11 12									11 42								12 12					
Redhill	d																								
Gatwick Airport [10] ✈	d				10 56						11 11			11 26					11 41				11 56		
Three Bridges [4]	d										11 15								11 45						
Balcombe	d										11 21														
Haywards Heath [3]	d				11 08						11 27			11 38					11 55				12 08		
Wivelsfield [4]	d										11 31								11 59						
Burgess Hill [4]	d										11 33								12 01						
Hassocks [4]	d										11 36								12 04						
Preston Park	d										11 43								12 11						
Brighton [10]	a				11 24						11 49			11 54					12 17				12 24		

For general notes see front of timetable
For details of catering facilities see Directory of Train Operators

A From Derby (Table 53)
B From Lincoln (Table 53)
C TOC SE from London Blackfriars
D From Corby. (Table 53)
E From Nottingham (Table 53)

Bedford, Luton, St.Albans and City of London → South London, Gatwick Airport and Brighton

Network Diagram - see first page of Table 52

		FC	FC	FC	FC	FC	FC	EM	FC	FC	FC	FC	FC	FC		EM	FC	FC	FC	FC	FC	FC	EM	FC	FC
				1			1	1 ◇			1			1		1 ◇			1			1	1 ◇		
					A			B 🍴				A				C 🍴				A			D 🍴		
Bedford 7	d			10 24			10 40	10 49			10 54			11 10		11 18			11 24			11 40	11 49		
Flitwick	d			10 33			10 49				11 03			11 19					11 33			11 49			
Harlington	d			10 37			10 53				11 07			11 23					11 37			11 53			
Leagrave	d			10 43			10 59				11 13			11 29					11 43			11 59			
Luton 10	d		10 44	10 48			11 04	11 05		11 14	11 18			11 34				11 44	11 48			12 04	12 05		12 14
Luton Airport Parkway 7 ✈	d		10 46	10 50			11 06			11 16	11 20			11 36		11 34		11 46	11 50			12 06			12 16
Harpenden	d		10 52	10 56			11 12			11 22	11 26			11 42				11 52	11 56			12 12			12 22
St Albans City	d	10 43	10 59	11 03			11 18		11 13	11 29	11 34			11 48			11 43	11 59	12 04			12 18		12 13	12 29
Radlett	d	10 48	11 04						11 18	11 34							11 48	12 04						12 18	12 34
Elstree & Borehamwood	d	10 52	11 08						11 22	11 38							11 52	12 08						12 22	12 38
Mill Hill Broadway	d	10 57	11 13			←			11 27	11 43			←				11 57	12 13			←			12 27	12 43
Hendon	d	11 00	11 16			11 16			11 30	11 46			11 46				12 00	12 16			12 16			12 30	12 46
Cricklewood	d	11 04	→			11 20			11 34	→			11 50				12 04	→			12 20			12 34	→
West Hampstead Thameslink	⊖ d	11 08				11 24			11 38				11 54				12 08				12 24			12 38	
Kentish Town	⊖ d	11 12			11 26	11 30			11 42			11 56	12 00				12 12			12 26	12 30			12 42	
St Pancras International	⊖ a							11 29								12 03							12 29		
St Pancras International 15	⊖ d	11 18		11 24	11 30	11 34	11 39		11 48		11 54	12 00	12 04	12 09			12 18		12 24	12 30	12 34	12 39		12 48	
Farringdon 3	⊖ d	11 23		11 29	11 35	11 39	11 44		11 53		11 59	12 05	12 09	12 14			12 23		12 29	12 35	12 39	12 44		12 53	
Barbican	⊖ a																								
Moorgate	⊖ a																								
City Thameslink 3	d	11 27		11 32	11 39	11 43	11 47		11 57		12 02	12 09	12 13	12 17			12 27		12 32	12 39	12 43	12 47		12 57	
London Blackfriars 3	⊖ d	11 30		11 35	11 42	11 46	11 50		12 00		12 05	12 12	12 16	12 20			12 30		12 35	12 42	12 46	12 50		13 00	
Elephant & Castle	⊖ d	11 33			11 45	11 49			12 03			12 15	12 19				12 33			12 45	12 49			13 03	
Loughborough Jn	d	11 37				11 53			12 07				12 23				12 37				12 53			13 07	
Herne Hill 4	d	11 42				11 57			12 12				12 27				12 42				12 57			13 12	
London Bridge 4	⊖ d			11 41			11 56				12 11			12 26					12 41			12 56			
Tulse Hill 3	d	11 46				12 02			12 16				12 32				12 46				13 02			13 16	
Streatham 4	d	11 49				12 05			12 19				12 35				12 49				13 05			13 19	
Mitcham Eastfields	d	11 53							12 23								12 53							13 23	
Mitcham Junction 🚊	d	11 57							12 27								12 57							13 27	
Hackbridge	d	12 00							12 30								13 00							13 30	
Carshalton	d	12 03							12 33								13 03							13 33	
Tooting	d					12 10							12 40								13 10				
Haydons Road	d					12 13							12 43								13 13				
Wimbledon 6	⊖ 🚊 d					12 17							12 47								13 17				
Wimbledon Chase	d					12 20							12 50								13 20				
South Merton	d					12 22							12 52								13 22				
Morden South	d					12 24							12 54								13 24				
St Helier	d					12 26							12 56								13 26				
Sutton Common	d					12 28							12 58								13 28				
West Sutton	d					12 31							13 01								13 31				
Sutton (Surrey) 4	a	12 06				12 35			12 36				13 05				13 06				13 35			13 36	
East Croydon	🚊 d			11 54			12 09				12 24			12 39					12 54			13 09			
Denmark Hill 4	d				11 52							12 22								12 52					
Peckham Rye 4	d				11 55							12 25								12 55					
Nunhead 4	d				11 57							12 27								12 57					
Crofton Park	d				11 59							12 29								12 59					
Catford	d				12 01							12 31								13 01					
Bellingham	d				12 04							12 34								13 04					
Beckenham Hill	d				12 06							12 36								13 06					
Ravensbourne	d				12 08							12 38								13 08					
Shortlands	d				12 10							12 40								13 10					
Bromley South 4	d				12 13							12 43								13 13					
Bickley 4	d				12 15							12 45								13 15					
St Mary Cray	d				12 21							12 51								13 21					
Swanley 4	d				12 25							12 55								13 25					
Eynsford	d				12 30							13 00								13 30					
Shoreham (Kent)	d				12 33							13 03								13 33					
Otford 4	d				12 36							13 06								13 36					
Bat & Ball	d				12 39							13 09								13 39					
Sevenoaks 4	a				12 42							13 12								13 42					
Redhill	d																								
Gatwick Airport 10	✈ d			12 11			12 26				12 41			12 56					13 11			13 26			
Three Bridges 4	d			12 15							12 45								13 15						
Balcombe	d			12 21															13 21						
Haywards Heath 3	d			12 27			12 38				12 55			13 08					13 27			13 38			
Wivelsfield 4	d			12 31							12 59								13 31						
Burgess Hill 4	d			12 33							13 01								13 33						
Hassocks 4	d			12 36							13 04								13 36						
Preston Park	d			12 43							13 11								13 43						
Brighton 10	a			12 49			12 54				13 17			13 24					13 49			13 54			

For general notes see front of timetable
For details of catering facilities see Directory of Train Operators

A TOC SE from London Blackfriars
B From Kettering (Table 53)
C From Nottingham (Table 53)
D From Corby. (Table 53)

Bedford, Luton, St.Albans and City of London → South London, Gatwick Airport and Brighton

Network Diagram - see first page of Table 52

		FC [1]	FC A	FC	FC [1]	EM [1] ◇ B (catering)	FC		FC	FC [1]	FC A	FC	FC [1]	EM [1] ◇ C (catering)	FC	FC	FC [1]	FC A	FC	FC [1]	EM [1] ◇ B (catering)	FC		FC	FC [1]
Bedford [7]	d	11 54			12 10	12 19				12 24			12 40	12 49			12 54			13 10	13 18				13 24
Flitwick	d	12 03			12 19					12 33			12 49				13 03			13 19					13 33
Harlington	d	12 07			12 23					12 37			12 53				13 07			13 23					13 37
Leagrave	d	12 13			12 29					12 43			12 59				13 13			13 29					13 43
Luton [10]	d	12 18			12 34				12 44	12 48			13 04	13 05		13 14	13 18			13 34				13 44	13 48
Luton Airport Parkway [7] ✈	d	12 20			12 36	12 35			12 46	12 50			13 06			13 16	13 20			13 36	13 34			13 46	13 50
Harpenden	d	12 26			12 42				12 52	12 56			13 12			13 22	13 26			13 42				13 52	13 56
St Albans City	d	12 34			12 48		12 43		12 59	13 04			13 18		13 13	13 29	13 34			13 48		13 43		13 59	14 04
Radlett	d						12 48		13 04						13 18	13 34						13 48		14 04	
Elstree & Borehamwood	d						12 52		13 08						13 22	13 38						13 52		14 08	
Mill Hill Broadway	d			←			12 57		13 13			←			13 27	13 43			←			13 57		14 13	
Hendon	d			12 46			13 00		13 16			13 16			13 30	13 46			13 46			14 00		14 16	
Cricklewood	d			12 50			13 04		→			13 20			13 34	→			13 50			14 04		→	
West Hampstead Thameslink	⊖ d			12 54			13 08					13 24			13 38				13 54			14 08			
Kentish Town	⊖ d		12 56	13 00			13 12				13 26	13 30			13 42			13 56	14 00			14 12			
St Pancras International	⊖ a					13 01								13 29							14 02				
St Pancras International [15]	⊖ d	12 54	13 00	13 04	13 09		13 18			13 24	13 30	13 34	13 39		13 48		13 54	14 00	14 04	14 09		14 18			14 24
Farringdon [3]	⊖ d	12 59	13 05	13 09	13 14		13 23			13 29	13 35	13 39	13 44		13 53		13 59	14 05	14 09	14 14		14 23			14 29
Barbican	⊖ a																								
Moorgate	⊖ a																								
City Thameslink [3]	d	13 02	13 09	13 13	13 17		13 27			13 32	13 39	13 43	13 47		13 57		14 02	14 09	14 13	14 17		14 27			14 32
London Blackfriars [3]	⊖ d	13 05	13 12	13 16	13 20		13 30			13 35	13 42	13 46	13 50		14 00		14 05	14 12	14 16	14 20		14 30			14 35
Elephant & Castle	⊖ d		13 15	13 19			13 33				13 45	13 49			14 03			14 15	14 19			14 33			
Loughborough Jn	d			13 23			13 37					13 53			14 07				14 23			14 37			
Herne Hill [4]	d			13 27			13 42					13 57			14 12				14 27			14 42			
London Bridge [4]	⊖ d	13 11			13 26					13 41			13 56				14 11			14 26					14 41
Tulse Hill [3]	d			13 32			13 46					14 02			14 16				14 32			14 46			
Streatham [4]	d			13 35			13 49					14 05			14 19				14 35			14 49			
Mitcham Eastfields	d						13 53								14 23							14 53			
Mitcham Junction 🚋	d						13 57								14 27							14 57			
Hackbridge	d						14 00								14 30							15 00			
Carshalton	d						14 03								14 33							15 03			
Tooting	d			13 40								14 10							14 40						
Haydons Road	d			13 43								14 13							14 43						
Wimbledon [6]	⊖ 🚋 d			13 47								14 17							14 47						
Wimbledon Chase	d			13 50								14 20							14 50						
South Merton	d			13 52								14 22							14 52						
Morden South	d			13 54								14 24							14 54						
St Helier	d			13 56								14 26							14 56						
Sutton Common	d			13 58								14 28							14 58						
West Sutton	d			14 01								14 31							15 01						
Sutton (Surrey) [4]	a			14 05			14 06					14 35			14 36				15 05			15 06			
East Croydon	🚋 d	13 24			13 39					13 54			14 09				14 24			14 39					14 54
Denmark Hill [4]	d		13 22								13 52							14 22							
Peckham Rye [4]	d		13 25								13 55							14 25							
Nunhead [4]	d		13 27								13 57							14 27							
Crofton Park	d		13 29								13 59							14 29							
Catford	d		13 31								14 01							14 31							
Bellingham	d		13 34								14 04							14 34							
Beckenham Hill	d		13 36								14 06							14 36							
Ravensbourne	d		13 38								14 08							14 38							
Shortlands	d		13 40								14 10							14 40							
Bromley South [4]	d		13 43								14 13							14 43							
Bickley [4]	d		13 45								14 15							14 45							
St Mary Cray	d		13 51								14 21							14 51							
Swanley [4]	d		13 55								14 25							14 55							
Eynsford	d		14 00								14 30							15 00							
Shoreham (Kent)	d		14 03								14 33							15 03							
Otford [4]	d		14 06								14 36							15 06							
Bat & Ball	d		14 09								14 39							15 09							
Sevenoaks [4]	a		14 12								14 42							15 12							
Redhill	d																								
Gatwick Airport [10] ✈	d	13 41			13 56					14 11			14 26				14 41			14 56					15 11
Three Bridges [4]	d	13 45								14 15							14 45								15 15
Balcombe	d									14 21															15 21
Haywards Heath [3]	d	13 55			14 08					14 27			14 38				14 55			15 08					15 27
Wivelsfield [4]	d	13 59								14 31							14 59								15 31
Burgess Hill [4]	d	14 01								14 33							15 01								15 33
Hassocks [4]	d	14 04								14 36							15 04								15 36
Preston Park	d	14 11								14 43							15 11								15 43
Brighton [10]	a	14 17			14 25					14 49			14 54				15 17			15 24					15 49

For general notes see front of timetable
For details of catering facilities see Directory of Train Operators

A TOC SE from London Blackfriars
B From Nottingham (Table 53)
C From Corby. (Table 53)

Bedford, Luton, St.Albans and City of London → South London, Gatwick Airport and Brighton

Network Diagram - see first page of Table 52

		FC	FC	FC	EM	FC	FC	FC	FC	FC	FC	EM	FC	FC	FC		FC	FC	FC	EM	FC	FC	FC	FC	FC
				1	1 ◇			1			1	1 ◇			1				1	1 ◇			1		
		A			B				A			C					A			B				A	
Bedford 7	d			13 40	13 49			13 54			14 10	14 19			14 24				14 40	14 49			14 54		
Flitwick	d			13 49				14 03			14 19				14 33				14 49				15 03		
Harlington	d			13 53				14 07			14 23				14 37				14 53				15 07		
Leagrave	d			13 59				14 13			14 29				14 43				14 59				15 13		
Luton 10	d			14 04	14 05		14 14	14 18			14 34			14 44	14 48				15 04	15 05		15 14	15 18		
Luton Airport Parkway 7 ✈	d			14 06			14 16	14 20			14 36	14 35		14 46	14 50				15 06			15 16	15 20		
Harpenden	d			14 12			14 22	14 26			14 42			14 52	14 56				15 12			15 22	15 26		
St Albans City	d			14 18		14 13	14 29	14 34			14 48		14 43	14 59	15 04				15 18		15 13	15 29	15 34		
Radlett	d					14 18	14 34						14 48	15 04							15 18	15 34			
Elstree & Borehamwood	d					14 22	14 38						14 52	15 08							15 22	15 38			
Mill Hill Broadway	d		←			14 27	14 43			←			14 57	15 13				←			15 27	15 43			←
Hendon	d		14 16			14 30	14 46			14 46			15 00	15 16				15 16			15 30	15 46			15 46
Cricklewood	d		14 20			14 34	→			14 50			15 04	→				15 20			15 34	→			15 50
West Hampstead Thameslink	⊖ d		14 24			14 38				14 54			15 08					15 24			15 38				15 54
Kentish Town	⊖ d	14 26	14 30			14 42			14 56	15 00			15 12				15 26	15 30			15 42			15 56	16 00
St Pancras International	⊖ a				14 29							15 01								15 29					
St Pancras International 15	⊖ d	14 30	14 34	14 39		14 48		14 54	15 00	15 04	15 09		15 18		15 24		15 30	15 34	15 39		15 48		15 54	16 00	16 04
Farringdon 3	⊖ d	14 35	14 39	14 44		14 53		14 59	15 05	15 09	15 14		15 23		15 29		15 35	15 39	15 44		15 53		15 59	16 05	16 09
Barbican	⊖ a																								
Moorgate	⊖ a																								
City Thameslink 3	d	14 39	14 43	14 47		14 57		15 02	15 09	15 13	15 17		15 27		15 32		15 39	15 43	15 47		15 57		16 02	16 09	16 13
London Blackfriars 3	⊖ d	14 42	14 46	14 50		15 00		15 05	15 12	15 16	15 20		15 30		15 35		15 42	15 46	15 50		16 00		16 05	16 12	16 16
Elephant & Castle	⊖ d	14 45	14 49			15 03			15 15	15 19			15 33				15 45	15 49			16 03			16 15	16 19
Loughborough Jn	d		14 53			15 07				15 23			15 37					15 53			16 07				16 23
Herne Hill 4	d		14 57			15 12				15 27			15 42					15 57			16 12				16 27
London Bridge 4	⊖ d			14 56				15 11			15 26				15 41				15 56				16 11		
Tulse Hill 3	d		15 02			15 16				15 32			15 46					16 02			16 16				16 32
Streatham 4	d		15 05			15 19				15 35			15 49					16 06			16 19				16 35
Mitcham Eastfields	d					15 23							15 53								16 23				
Mitcham Junction 🚋	d					15 27							15 57								16 27				
Hackbridge	d					15 30							16 00								16 30				
Carshalton	d					15 33							16 03								16 33				
Tooting	d		15 10							15 40								16 11							16 41
Haydons Road	d		15 13							15 43								16 14							16 44
Wimbledon 6	⊖ 🚋 d		15 17							15 47								16 17							16 47
Wimbledon Chase	d		15 20							15 50								16 20							16 50
South Merton	d		15 22							15 52								16 22							16 52
Morden South	d		15 24							15 54								16 24							16 54
St Helier	d		15 26							15 56								16 26							16 56
Sutton Common	d		15 28							15 58								16 29							16 59
West Sutton	d		15 31							16 01								16 31							17 01
Sutton (Surrey) 4	a		15 35			15 36				16 05			16 06					16 36			16 36				17 06
East Croydon	🚋 d			15 09				15 24			15 39				15 54				16 09				16 24		
Denmark Hill 4	d	14 52							15 22								15 52							16 22	
Peckham Rye 4	d	14 55							15 25								15 55							16 25	
Nunhead 4	d	14 57							15 27								15 57							16 27	
Crofton Park	d	14 59							15 29								15 59							16 29	
Catford	d	15 01							15 31								16 01							16 31	
Bellingham	d	15 04							15 34								16 04							16 34	
Beckenham Hill	d	15 06							15 36								16 06							16 36	
Ravensbourne	d	15 08							15 38								16 08							16 38	
Shortlands	d	15 10							15 40								16 10							16 40	
Bromley South 4	d	15 13							15 43								16 13							16 43	
Bickley 4	d	15 15							15 45								16 15							16 45	
St Mary Cray	d	15 21							15 51								16 21							16 51	
Swanley 4	d	15 25							15 55								16 25							16 55	
Eynsford	d	15 30							16 00								16 30							17 00	
Shoreham (Kent)	d	15 33							16 03								16 33							17 03	
Otford 4	d	15 36							16 06								16 36							17 06	
Bat & Ball	d	15 39							16 09								16 39							17 09	
Sevenoaks 4	a	15 42							16 12								16 42							17 12	
Redhill	d																								
Gatwick Airport 10 ✈	d			15 26				15 41			15 57				16 11				16 26				16 41		
Three Bridges 4	d							15 45			16 02				16 15				16 30				16 45		
Balcombe	d														16 21										
Haywards Heath 3	d			15 38				15 55			16 11				16 27				16 40				16 55		
Wivelsfield 4	d							15 59							16 31								16 59		
Burgess Hill 4	d							16 01							16 33								17 01		
Hassocks 4	d							16 04							16 36								17 04		
Preston Park	d							16 11							16 43								17 11		
Brighton 10	a			15 54				16 17			16 25				16 49				16 55				17 17		

For general notes see front of timetable
For details of catering facilities see
Directory of Train Operators

A TOC SE from London Blackfriars
B From Corby. (Table 53)
C From Nottingham (Table 53)

Bedford, Luton, St.Albans and City of London → South London, Gatwick Airport and Brighton

Network Diagram - see first page of Table 52

		FC	EM	FC	FC	FC	FC	FC		FC	FC	EM	FC	FC	FC	FC	FC	EM	FC	FC	FC	FC	FC		FC
		1	1 ◇				1				1	1 ◇			1		1	1 ◇							1
			A	B				C			C D	E			C			A		C G		C			
			⊡									⊡						⊡							
Bedford [7]	d	15 10	15 19				15 24				15 40	15 49			15 54		16 10	16 19		16 22					16 32
Flitwick	d	15 19					15 33				15 49				16 03		16 19			16 31					16 41
Harlington	d	15 23					15 37				15 53				16 07		16 23			16 35					16 45
Leagrave	d	15 29					15 43				15 59				16 13		16 29			16 42					16 51
Luton [10]	d	15 34				15 44	15 48				16 04	16 05		16 14	16 18		16 34		16 44	16 46		16 50			16 56
Luton Airport Parkway [7] ✈	d	15 36	15 35			15 46	15 50				16 06			16 16	16 20		16 36	16 35	16 46			16 52			16 58
Harpenden	d	15 42				15 52	15 56				16 12			16 22	16 26		16 42		16 52			16 58			17 04
St Albans City	d	15 48			15 43	15 59	16 04				16 18		16 13	16 29	16 34		16 48		16 58		16 43	17 04			17 10
Radlett	d				15 48	16 04							16 18	16 34					17 03		16 48		←		
Elstree & Borehamwood	d				15 52	16 08							16 22	16 38		←			17 07		16 52		17 07		
Mill Hill Broadway	d				15 57	16 13				←			16 27	16 43		16 43			→		16 57		17 12		
Hendon	d				16 00	16 16				16 16			16 30	→		16 46					17 00		17 15		
Cricklewood	d				16 04	→				16 20			16 34			16 50					17 04		17 19		
West Hampstead Thameslink	⊖ d				16 09					16 24	16 32		16 38		16 48	16 54					17 09		17 22		17 26
Kentish Town	⊖ d			16 09	16 13			16 24		16 30			16 42			16 58					17 12		17 26		
St Pancras International	⊖ a		16 01									16 29						17 00							
St Pancras International [15]	⊖ d	16 09		16 14	16 18		16 24	16 28		16 34	16 40		16 46		16 56	17 02	17 10			17 14	17 18	17 25	17 30		17 34
Farringdon [3]	⊖ d	16 14		16 19	16 23		16 29	16 33		16 39	16 45		16 51		17 01	17 07	17 15			17 19	17 23	17 30	17 35		17 39
Barbican	⊖ a																								
Moorgate	⊖ a																								
City Thameslink [3]	d	16 17		16 23	16 27		16 33	16 37		16 43	16 49		16 55		17 05	17 11	17 19			17 23	17 27	17 33	17 39		17 43
London Blackfriars [3]	⊖ d	16 20		16 26	16 30		16 36	16b42		16 46	16 52		16 58		17 10	17 14	17 22			17 26	17 30	17 36	17 42		17 46
Elephant & Castle	⊖ d			16a29	16 33			16 45		16 50	16 56		17 02		17 14	17 18				17 30	17 34	17 39	17 46		
Loughborough Jn	d				16 37					16 54	16 59		17 06			17 22					17 38		17 50		
Herne Hill [4]	d				16 42					16 58	17a03		17 10			17 26				17a36	17 42		17 54		
London Bridge [4]	⊖ d	16 26					16c46										17 32								17 52
Tulse Hill [3]	d				16e50					17 02			17 16			17 32					17 46		17 58		
Streatham [4]	d				16 54					17 05			17 20			17 35					17 50		18 01		
Mitcham Eastfields	d				16 58								17 24								17 54				
Mitcham Junction	d				17 02								17 28								17 58				
Hackbridge	d				17 05								17 31								18 01				
Carshalton	d				17 08								17 34								18 04				
Tooting	d									17 10						17 40							18 06		
Haydons Road	d									17 13						17 43							18 09		
Wimbledon [6]	⊖ d									17f19						17 47							18 13		
Wimbledon Chase	d									17 22						17 50							18 16		
South Merton	d									17 24						17 52							18 18		
Morden South	d									17 26						17 54							18 20		
St Helier	d									17 28						17 56							18 22		
Sutton Common	d									17 30						17 58							18 24		
West Sutton	d									17 33						18 01							18 27		
Sutton (Surrey) [4]	a				17 12					17 39			17 38			18 05					18 08		18 31		
East Croydon	d	16 40					17 00										17 46								18 09
Denmark Hill [4]	d							16 52							17 20							17 45			
Peckham Rye [4]	d							16 55							17 24							17 48			
Nunhead [4]	d							16 57							17 26							17 50			
Crofton Park	d							16 59							17 29							17 52			
Catford	d							17 02							17 32							17 54			
Bellingham	d							17 05							17 35							17 57			
Beckenham Hill	d							17 07							17 37							17 59			
Ravensbourne	d							17 09							17 39							18 01			
Shortlands	d							17 11							17 41							18 03			
Bromley South [4]	d							17 15							17 46							18 06			
Bickley [4]	d							17 17							17 49							18 09			
St Mary Cray	d							17 25							17 56							18 15			
Swanley [4]	d							17 30							18 01							18 20			
Eynsford	d							17 34							18 06							18 24			
Shoreham (Kent)	d							17 38							18 09							18 28			
Otford [4]	d							17 41							18 13							18 32			
Bat & Ball	d							17 44							18 16							18 36			
Sevenoaks [4]	a							17 47							18 19							18 40			
Redhill	d																18 00								
Gatwick Airport [10] ✈	d	16 56					17 16										18 12								18 25
Three Bridges [4]	d	17 00					17 21										18 18								
Balcombe	d						17 27										18 24								
Haywards Heath [3]	d	17 10					17 33										18 30								18 36
Wivelsfield [4]	d						17 37										18 34								18 40
Burgess Hill [4]	d						17 40										18 37								18 45
Hassocks [4]	d						17 44										18 41								18 49
Preston Park	d						17 51										18 48								18 57
Brighton [10]	a	17 27					17 57										18 54								19 04

For general notes see front of timetable
For details of catering facilities see Directory of Train Operators

A From Nottingham (Table 53)
B To Orpington (Table 195)
C TOC SE from London Blackfriars
D To Beckenham Junction (Table 195)
E From Corby. (Table 53)
G To Gillingham (Kent) (Table 212)
b Arr. 1639
c Arr. 1643
e Arr. 1646
f Arr. 1716

Bedford, Luton, St.Albans and City of London → South London, Gatwick Airport and Brighton

Network Diagram - see first page of Table 52

Station		EM	FC	FC	FC	FC	FC	FC	FC	FC	FC	FC	FC	FC	EM		EM	FC	FC	FC	EM	EM	FC	FC	FC
		1 ◇ A	B C	1	1 B D		B		B E		1	B		1 B	1 ◇ G		1 ◇ G		1		1 ◇ A	1 ◇ H	1	B	
Bedford 7	d	16 49			16 46				17 00		17 10			17 20	17 21				17 34		17 49		17 54		18 04
Flitwick	d				16 55				17 09		17 19			17 29					17 43				18 03		
Harlington	d				16 59				17 13		17 23			17 33					17 47				18 07		
Leagrave	d				17 05				17 19		17 29			17 39					17 53				18 13		
Luton 10	d	17 05			17 10			17 18	17 24		17 34			17 44			17 50		17 58	18 02	18 05	18 15	18 18		18 24
Luton Airport Parkway 7 ✈	d				17 12			17 20	17 26		17 36			17 46	17 34				18 00	18 04			18 20		18 26
Harpenden	d				17 18			17 26	17 32		17 42			17 52					18 06	18 10			18 26		18 32
St Albans City	d				17 25	17 18	17 28	17 32	17 38		17 48		17 44	17 58				18 02	18 12	18 16			18 32	18 28	18 38
Radlett	d					17 23	17 33	17 37					17 49					18 07		18 21				18 33	18 43
Elstree & Borehamwood	d					17 27	17 37	17 41					17 53					18 11		18 25				18 37	18 47
Mill Hill Broadway	d					17 32		17 46		←			17 58					18 15		18 29				18 41	
Hendon	d					17 35		17 49		17 49			18 01					18 18		18 32				18 44	
Cricklewood	d					17 39		→		17 53			18 05					18 22		18 36				18 48	
West Hampstead Thameslink	⊖ d				17 38	17 42	17 46			17 56			18 08	18 12				18 24	18 28	18 39				18 52	18 56
Kentish Town	⊖ d		17 34	17 38		17 46				18 00		18 08	18 12					18 28		18 43				18 56	
St Pancras International	⊖ a	17 29													18 06		18 19				18 29	18 39			
St Pancras International 15	⊖ d		17 38	17 42	17 46	17 50	17 54		17 58	18 04	18 08	18 12	18 16	18b24				18 34	18 38	18 48			18 53	19 00	19 04
Farringdon 3	⊖ d		17 43	17 47	17 51	17 55	17 59		18 03	18 09	18 13	18 17	18 21	18 29				18 39	18 43	18 53			18 57	19 05	19 09
Barbican	⊖ a																								
Moorgate	⊖ a																								
City Thameslink 3	d		17 47	17 51	17 55	17 59	18 03		18 07	18 13	18 17	18 21	18 25	18 33				18 43	18 47	18 57			19 01	19 09	19 13
London Blackfriars 3	⊖ d		17 50	17 54	17 58	18 02	18 06		18 10	18 16	18 20	18 24	18c30	18e42				18 46	18 50	19 00			19 04	19 12	19 16
Elephant & Castle	⊖ d		17 54		18a03	18 06	18 10		18 14	18 20		18 28	18 34	18 45				18 49		19 04				19 15	19 19
Loughborough Jn	d		17 58			18 10				18 24			18 38					18 53		19 08					19 23
Herne Hill 4	d		18a01	18 07		18 14			18a21	18 28			18f44					18 57		19 12					19 27
London Bridge 4	⊖ d										18 26								18 56				19 12		
Tulse Hill 3	d					18 18				18 32			18 48					19 02		19 16					19 32
Streatham 4	d					18 22				18 35			18 52					19 05		19 19					19 35
Mitcham Eastfields	d					18 26							18 56							19 23					
Mitcham Junction	🚋 d					18 30							18 59							19 27					
Hackbridge	d					18 33							19 03							19 30					
Carshalton	d					18 36							19 05							19 33					
Tooting	d									18 40								19 10							19 40
Haydons Road	d									18 43								19 13							19 43
Wimbledon 6	⊖ 🚋 d									18 47								19g19							19h49
Wimbledon Chase	d									18 50								19 22							19 52
South Merton	d									18 52								19 24							19 54
Morden South	d									18 54								19 26							19 56
St Helier	d									18 56								19 28							19 58
Sutton Common	d									18 58								19 30							20 00
West Sutton	d									19 01								19 33							20 03
Sutton (Surrey) 4	a					18 39				19 05			19 09					19 39		19 36					20 09
East Croydon	🚋 d			18 25							18 40								19 10				19 24		
Denmark Hill 4	d						18 20					18 34		18 52										19 22	
Peckham Rye 4	d						18 23					18 37		18 55										19 25	
Nunhead 4	d						18 25					18 39		18 57										19 27	
Crofton Park	d						18 28					18 42		18 59										19 29	
Catford	d						18 30					18 44		19 01										19 31	
Bellingham	d						18 33					18 47		19 04										19 34	
Beckenham Hill	d						18 35					18 49		19 06										19 36	
Ravensbourne	d						18 37					18 51		19 08										19 38	
Shortlands	d						18 39					18 53		19 10										19 40	
Bromley South 4	d						18 42					18 56		19 13										19 43	
Bickley 4	d						18 45					18 59		19 15										19 45	
St Mary Cray	d						18 51					19 04		19 21										19 51	
Swanley 4	d						18 55					19 09		19 25										19 55	
Eynsford	d						19 00					19 13		19 30										20 00	
Shoreham (Kent)	d						19 03					19 17		19 33										20 03	
Otford 4	d						19 07					19 20		19 36										20 06	
Bat & Ball	d						19 10					19 23		19 39										20 09	
Sevenoaks 4	a						19 14					19 26		19 42										20 12	
Redhill	d			18 38																					
Gatwick Airport 10	✈ d			18 51							18 56								19 27				19 41		
Three Bridges 4	d			18a56							19 02								19 32				19 45		
Balcombe	d										19 08												19 51		
Haywards Heath 3	d										19 12								19 41				19 57		
Wivelsfield 4	d																						20 01		
Burgess Hill 4	d										19 17								19 46				20 03		
Hassocks 4	d										19 21								19 49				20 06		
Preston Park	d																						20 13		
Brighton 10	a										19 34								20 00				20 18		

For general notes see front of timetable
For details of catering facilities see Directory of Train Operators

A From Corby. (Table 53)
B TOC SE from London Blackfriars
C To Beckenham Junction (Table 195)
D To Ashford International (Table 196)
E To Gillingham (Kent) (Table 212)
G From Nottingham (Table 53)
H From Sheffield (Table 53)
b Arr. 1821
c Arr. 1827
e Arr. 1836
f Arr. 1841
g Arr. 1916
h Arr. 1946

Bedford, Luton, St.Albans and City of London → South London, Gatwick Airport and Brighton

Network Diagram - see first page of Table 52

		FC 1	EM 1 ◇ A	FC	FC	FC 1	FC B	FC		EM 1 ◇ C	FC 1	FC	FC 1	FC B	FC	EM 1 ◇ A	FC	FC 1	FC B	FC	EM 1 ◇ C	FC 1	FC B		FC
Bedford 7	d	18 10	18 19			18 24		18 30		18 49	18 42		18 54			19 19		19 20			19 48	19 50			
Flitwick	d	18 19				18 33					18 51		19 03					19 29				19 59			
Harlington	d	18 23				18 37					18 55		19 07					19 33				20 03			
Leagrave	d	18 29				18 43					19 01		19 13					19 39				20 09			
Luton 10	d	18 34			18 44	18 48		18b54		19 05	19 06		19 18		19 18			19 44		19 48	20 10	20 14			20 18
Luton Airport Parkway 7 ✈	d	18 36	18 35		18 46	18 50		18 56			19 08		19 20		19 20	19 35		19 46		19 50		20 16			20 20
Harpenden	d	18 42			18 52	18 56		19 02			19 14		19 26		19 26			19 52		19 56		20 22			20 26
St Albans City	d	18 48		18 52	18 58	19 02		19 08			19 20	19 16	19 33		19 32		19 46	19 58		20 02		20 28			20 32
Radlett	d			18 57	19 03			19 13				19 21			19 37		19 51			20 07					20 37
Elstree & Borehamwood	d			19 01	19 07			19 17				19 25			19 41		19 55			20 11					20 41
Mill Hill Broadway	d				19 11		←					19 29			19 45		19 59			20 15					20 45
Hendon	d				19 14		19 14					19 32			19 48		20 02			20 18					20 48
Cricklewood	d				→		19 18					19 36			19 52		20 06			20 22					20 52
West Hampstead Thameslink	⊖ d			19 10			19 22	19 26			19 34	19 40			19 55		20 10	20 12		20 25		20 42			20 55
Kentish Town	⊖ d						19 26					19 44		19 56	20 00		20 14		20 26	20 30			20 56		21 00
St Pancras International	⊖ a		19 01							19 29						20 01					20 35				
St Pancras International 15	⊖ d	19 08		19 18		19 22	19 30	19 34			19 42	19 48	19 52	20 00	20 04		20 18	20 22	20 30	20 34		20 52	21 00		21 04
Farringdon 3	⊖ d	19 13		19 23		19 27	19 35	19 39			19 47	19 53	19 57	20 05	20 09		20 23	20 27	20 35	20 39		20 57	21 05		21 09
Barbican	⊖ a																								
Moorgate	⊖ a																								
City Thameslink 3	d	19 17		19 27		19 31	19 39	19 43			19 51	19 57	20 01	20 09	20 13		20 27	20 31	20 39	20 43		21 01	21 09		21 13
London Blackfriars 3	⊖ d	19 20		19 30		19 34	19 42	19 46			19 54	20 00	20 04	20 12	20 16		20 30	20 34	20 42	20 46		21 04	21 12		21 16
Elephant & Castle	⊖ d			19 33			19 45	19 49				20 03		20 15	20 19		20 33		20 45	20 49			21 15		21 19
Loughborough Jn	d			19 37				19 53				20 07			20 23		20 37			20 53					21 23
Herne Hill 4	d			19 42				19 57				20 12			20 27		20 42			20 57					21 27
London Bridge 4	⊖ d	19 27				19 41					20 01		20 11					20 41				21 11			
Tulse Hill 3	d			19 46				20 02				20 16			20 32		20 46			21 02					21 32
Streatham 4	d			19 49				20 05				20 19			20 35		20 49			21 05					21 35
Mitcham Eastfields	d			19 53								20 23					20 53								
Mitcham Junction	d			19 57								20 27					20 57								
Hackbridge	d			20 00								20 30					21 00								
Carshalton	d			20 03								20 33					21 03								
Tooting	d							20 10							20 40					21 10					21 40
Haydons Road	d							20 13							20 43					21 13					21 43
Wimbledon 6	⊖ d							20 17							20 47					21 17					21 47
Wimbledon Chase	d							20 20							20 50					21 20					21 50
South Merton	d							20 22							20 52					21 22					21 52
Morden South	d							20 24							20 54					21 24					21 54
St Helier	d							20 26							20 56					21 26					21 56
Sutton Common	d							20 28							20 58					21 28					21 58
West Sutton	d							20 31							21 01					21 31					22 01
Sutton (Surrey) 4	a			20 06				20 35				20 36			21 05		21 06			21 39					22 07
East Croydon	d	19 39				19 54					20 14		20 24					20 54				21 24			
Denmark Hill 4	d						19 52							20 22					20 52				21 22		
Peckham Rye 4	d						19 55							20 25					20 55				21 25		
Nunhead 4	d						19 57							20 27					20 57				21 27		
Crofton Park	d						19 59							20 29					20 59				21 29		
Catford	d						20 01							20 31					21 01				21 31		
Bellingham	d						20 04							20 34					21 04				21 34		
Beckenham Hill	d						20 06							20 36					21 06				21 36		
Ravensbourne	d						20 08							20 38					21 08				21 38		
Shortlands	d						20 10							20 40					21 10				21 40		
Bromley South 4	d						20 13							20 43					21 13				21 43		
Bickley 4	d						20 15							20 45					21 15				21 45		
St Mary Cray	d						20 21							20 51					21 21				21 51		
Swanley 4	d						20 25							20 55					21 25				21 55		
Eynsford	d						20 30							21 00					21 30				22 00		
Shoreham (Kent)	d						20 33							21 03					21 33				22 03		
Otford 4	d						20 36							21 06					21 36				22 06		
Bat & Ball	d						20 39							21 09					21 39				22 09		
Sevenoaks 4	a						20 42							21 12					21 42				22 12		
Redhill	d																								
Gatwick Airport 10 ✈	d	19 56				20 11					20 31		20 41					21 11				21 41			
Three Bridges 4	d	20 02				20 15							20 45					21 15				21 45			
Balcombe	d												20 51									21 51			
Haywards Heath 3	d	20 10				20 26					20 42		20 57					21 26				21 58			
Wivelsfield 4	d					20 30							21 01					21 30				22 02			
Burgess Hill 4	d	20 16				20 32							21 03					21 32				22 04			
Hassocks 4	d	20 20				20 35							21 06					21 35				22 08			
Preston Park	d					20 42							21 13					21 42				22 15			
Brighton 10	a	20 30				20 46					20 58		21 18					21 48				22 20			

For general notes see front of timetable
For details of catering facilities see Directory of Train Operators

A From Nottingham (Table 53)
B TOC SE from London Blackfriars
C From Corby. (Table 53)

b Arr. 1851

Bedford, Luton, St.Albans and City of London → South London, Gatwick Airport and Brighton

Network Diagram - see first page of Table 52

		EM	FC	FC	EM	FC	FC	EM	FC	FC	EM	FC	FC	FC	FC		EM	FC	EM	FC	FC	FC	FC
		1 ◇	1		1 ◇	1		1 ◇	1		1 ◇	1			1		1 ◇		1 ◇	1		1	1
		A			B			A			B						A		A				
		☕			☕			☕			☕						☕		☕				
Bedford 7	d	20 18	20 20		20 53	20 50		21 22	21 20		21 53	21 50			22 10		22 19		22 46	22 40		23 10	23 40
Flitwick	d		20 29			20 59			21 29			21 59			22 19					22 49		23 19	23 49
Harlington	d		20 33			21 03			21 33			22 03			22 23					22 53		23 23	23 53
Leagrave	d		20 39			21 09			21 39			22 09			22 29					22 59		23 29	23 59
Luton 10	d		20 44	20 48	21 08	21 14	21 18		21 44	21 48	22 09	22 14		22 18	22 34		22 35		23 01	23 04		23 34	00 04
Luton Airport Parkway 7 ✈	d	20 34	20 46	20 50		21 16	21 20	21 39	21 46	21 50		22 16		22 20	22 36		22 39			23 06		23 36	00 06
Harpenden	d		20 52	20 56		21 22	21 26		21 52	21 56		22 22		22 26	22 42					23 12		23 42	00 12
St Albans City	d		20 58	21 02		21 28	21 32		21 58	22 02		22 28		22 32	22 48					23 18		23 48	00 18
Radlett	d			21 07			21 37			22 07				22 37	22 53					23 23		23 53	00 23
Elstree & Borehamwood	d			21 11			21 41			22 11				22 41	22 57					23 27		23 57	00 27
Mill Hill Broadway	d			21 15			21 45			22 15				22 45	23 01					23 31		00 01	00 31
Hendon	d			21 18			21 48			22 18				22 48	23 04					23 34		00 04	00 34
Cricklewood	d			21 22			21 52			22 22				22 52	23 08					23 38		00 08	00 38
West Hampstead Thameslink ⊖	d		21 12	21 25		21 42	21 55		22 10	22 25		22 40		22 55	23 12					23 42		00 12	00 42
Kentish Town ⊖	d			21 30			22 00			22 29				22 59	23 16					23 46		00 16	00 46
St Pancras International ⊖	a	21 06			21 34			22 06	22 23	22 39	22 35	22 53		23 09	23 25		23 04		23 33	23 55		00 25	00 55
St Pancras International 15 ⊖	d		21 22	21 34		21 52	22 04																
Farringdon 3 ⊖	d		21 27	21 39		21 57	22 09																
Barbican ⊖	a																						
Moorgate ⊖	a																						
City Thameslink 3	d		21 31	21 43		22 01	22 13																
London Blackfriars 3 ⊖	d		21 34	21 46		22 04	22 16																
Elephant & Castle ⊖	d			21 49			22 19																
Loughborough Jn	d			21 53			22 23																
Herne Hill 4	d			21 57			22 27																
London Bridge 4 ⊖	d		21 41			22 11							22 58					23 28			23 58		
Tulse Hill 3	d			22 02			22 32						23 10					23 40			00 10		
Streatham 4	d			22 05			22 35						23 13					23 43			00 13		
Mitcham Eastfields	d																						
Mitcham Junction 🚊	d																						
Hackbridge	d																						
Carshalton	d																						
Tooting	d			22 10			22 40						23 18					23 48			00 18		
Haydons Road	d			22 13			22 43						23 21					23 51			00 21		
Wimbledon 6 ⊖ 🚊	d			22 17			22 47						23 25					23 54			00 25		
Wimbledon Chase	d			22 20			22 50						23 28					23 57			00 28		
South Merton	d			22 22			22 52						23 30					23 59			00 30		
Morden South	d			22 24			22 54						23 32					00 01			00 32		
St Helier	d			22 26			22 56						23 34					00 03			00 34		
Sutton Common	d			22 28			22 58						23 36					00 05			00 36		
West Sutton	d			22 31			23 01						23 39					00 08			00 39		
Sutton (Surrey) 4	a			22 40			23 05						23 43					00 12			00 43		
East Croydon 🚊	d		21 54			22 24																	
Denmark Hill 4	d																						
Peckham Rye 4	d																						
Nunhead 4	d																						
Crofton Park	d																						
Catford	d																						
Bellingham	d																						
Beckenham Hill	d																						
Ravensbourne	d																						
Shortlands	d																						
Bromley South 4	d																						
Bickley 4	d																						
St Mary Cray	d																						
Swanley 4	d																						
Eynsford	d																						
Shoreham (Kent)	d																						
Otford 4	d																						
Bat & Ball	d																						
Sevenoaks 4	a																						
Redhill	d																						
Gatwick Airport 10 ✈	d		22 11			22 41																	
Three Bridges 4	d		22 15			22 45																	
Balcombe	d					22 51																	
Haywards Heath 3	d		22 26			22 58																	
Wivelsfield 4	d		22 30			23 02																	
Burgess Hill 4	d		22 32			23 04																	
Hassocks 4	d		22 35			23 08																	
Preston Park	d		22 42			23 15																	
Brighton 10	a		22 48			23 20																	

For general notes see front of timetable
For details of catering facilities see Directory of Train Operators

A From Nottingham (Table 53)
B From Corby. (Table 53)

Table 52

Saturdays

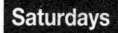

Bedford, Luton, St.Albans and City of London → South London, Gatwick Airport and Brighton

Network Diagram - see first page of Table 52

Station		FC	FC	FC [1]	FC [1]	FC	FC	FC [1]	FC [1]	FC [1]	FC [1]	FC [1]	FC
Bedford [7]	d			23p10	23p40	00 10	01 10	02 10	03 10	03 40	04 10	04 40	
Flitwick	d			23p19	23p49	00 19	01 19	02 19	03 19	03 49	04 19	04 49	
Harlington	d			23p23	23p53	00 23	01 23	02 23	03 23	03 53	04 23	04 53	
Leagrave	d			23p29	23p59	00 29	01 29	02 29	03 29	03 59	04 29	04 59	
Luton [10]	d			23p34	00 04	00 34	01 34	02 34	03 34	04 04	04 34	05 04	
Luton Airport Parkway [7] ✈	d			23p36	00 06	00 36	01 36	02 36	03 36	04 06	04 36	05 06	
Harpenden	d			23p42	00 12	00 42	01 42	02 42	03 42	04 12	04 42	05 12	
St Albans City	d			23p48	00 18	00 48	01 48	02 48	03 48	04 18	04 48	05 18	
Radlett	d			23p53	00 23	00 53	01 53	02 53	03 53	04 23	04 53	05 23	
Elstree & Borehamwood	d			23p57	00 27	00 57	01 57	02 57	03 57	04 27	04 57	05 27	
Mill Hill Broadway	d			00 01	00 31	01 01	02 01	03 01	04 01	04 31	05 01	05 31	
Hendon	d			00 04	00 34	01 04	02 04	03 04	04 04	04 34	05 04	05 34	
Cricklewood	d			00 08	00 38	01 08	02 08	03 08	04 08	04 38	05 08	05 38	
West Hampstead Thameslink ⊖	d			00 12	00 42	01 12	02 12	03 12	04 12	04 42	05 12	05 42	
Kentish Town ⊖	d			00 16	00 46	01 16	02 16	03 16	04 16	04 46	05 16	05 46	
St Pancras International ⊖	a			00 25	00 55	01 25	02 25	03 25	04 25	04 55	05 25	05 55	
St Pancras International [15] ⊖	d												
Farringdon [3] ⊖	d												
City Thameslink [3]	d												
London Blackfriars [3] ⊖	d												
Elephant & Castle ⊖	d												
Loughborough Jn	d												
Herne Hill [4]	d												
London Bridge [4] ⊖	d	23p28	23p58										06 21
Tulse Hill [3]	d	23p40	00 10										06 32
Streatham [4]	d	23p43	00 13										06 35
Mitcham Eastfields	d												
Mitcham Junction 🚋	d												
Hackbridge	d												
Carshalton	d												
Tooting	d	23p48	00 18										06 40
Haydons Road	d	23p51	00 21										06 43
Wimbledon [6] ⊖ 🚋	d	23p54	00 25										06 47
Wimbledon Chase	d	23p57	00 28										06 50
South Merton	d	23p59	00 30										06 52
Morden South	d	00 01	00 32										06 54
St Helier	d	00 03	00 34										06 56
Sutton Common	d	00 05	00 36										06 58
West Sutton	d	00 08	00 39										07 01
Sutton (Surrey) [4]	a	00 12	00 43										07 05
East Croydon 🚋	d												
Redhill	d												
Gatwick Airport [10] ✈	d												
Three Bridges [4]	d												
Balcombe	d												
Haywards Heath [3]	d												
Wivelsfield [4]	d												
Burgess Hill [4]	d												
Hassocks [4]	d												
Preston Park	d												
Brighton [10]	a												

Station		FC	FC [1]	EM [1] ◇ A 🍴	FC	FC		FC	FC [1]	FC	FC	FC	FC [1]
Bedford [7]	d	05 20	05 24	05 32				05 50	05 54			06 16	06 24
Flitwick	d	05 29	05 33					05 59	06 03			06 25	06 33
Harlington	d	05 33	05 37					06 03	06 07			06 29	06 37
Leagrave	d	05 39	05 43					06 09	06 13			06 35	06 43
Luton [10]	d	05 44	05 48					06 14	06 18			06 40	06 48
Luton Airport Parkway [7] ✈	d	05 46	05 50	05 55				06 16	06 20			06 42	06 50
Harpenden	d	05 52	05 56					06 22	06 26			06 48	06 56
St Albans City	d	05 58	06 04					06 28	06 34			06 54	07 05
Radlett	d	06 03						06 33				06 59	
Elstree & Borehamwood	d	06 07						06 37				07 03	
Mill Hill Broadway	d	06 11						06 41				07 08	
Hendon	d	06 14						06 44				07 11	
Cricklewood	d	06 18						06 48				07 15	
West Hampstead Thameslink ⊖	d	06 22						06 52				07 18	
Kentish Town ⊖	d	06 26						06 56				07 24	
St Pancras International ⊖	a	06 39	06 25	06 21				07 09	06 56				07 24
St Pancras International [15] ⊖	d											07a32	
Farringdon [3] ⊖	d												
City Thameslink [3]	d												
London Blackfriars [3] ⊖	d												
Elephant & Castle ⊖	d												
Loughborough Jn	d												
Herne Hill [4]	d				06 42					07 12			
London Bridge [4] ⊖	d					06 45					07 15		
Tulse Hill [3]	d				06 46	07b02				07 16	07c32		
Streatham [4]	d				06 49	07 05				07 19	07 35		
Mitcham Eastfields	d				06 53					07 23			
Mitcham Junction 🚋	d				06 57					07 27			
Hackbridge	d				07 00					07 30			
Carshalton	d				07 03					07 33			
Tooting	d					07 10					07 40		
Haydons Road	d					07 13					07 43		
Wimbledon [6] ⊖ 🚋	d					07 17					07 47		
Wimbledon Chase	d					07 20					07 50		
South Merton	d					07 22					07 52		
Morden South	d					07 24					07 54		
St Helier	d					07 26					07 56		
Sutton Common	d					07 28					07 58		
West Sutton	d					07 31					08 01		
Sutton (Surrey) [4]	a				07 06	07 35				07 36	08 05		
East Croydon 🚋	d												
Redhill	d												
Gatwick Airport [10] ✈	d												
Three Bridges [4]	d												
Balcombe	d												
Haywards Heath [3]	d												
Wivelsfield [4]	d												
Burgess Hill [4]	d												
Hassocks [4]	d												
Preston Park	d												
Brighton [10]	a												

For general notes see front of timetable
For details of catering facilities see Directory of Train Operators

A From Leicester (Table 53)
b Arr. 0658
c Arr. 0728

Bedford, Luton, St.Albans and City of London → South London, Gatwick Airport and Brighton

Network Diagram - see first page of Table 52

Station		FC 1	EM 1 ◇ A	FC	FC	FC	FC 1	FC 1	EM 1 ◇ B	FC	FC	FC	FC 1	FC 1		EM 1 ◇ A	FC	FC	FC	FC 1	FC 1	EM 1 ◇ B	FC	FC	FC
Bedford 7	d	06 38	06 49				06 54	07 08	07 19				07 24	07 38		07 49				07 54	08 08	08 19			
Flitwick	d	06 47					07 03	07 17					07 33	07 47						08 03	08 17				
Harlington	d	06 51					07 07	07 21					07 37	07 51						08 07	08 21				
Leagrave	d	06 57					07 13	07 27					07 43	07 57						08 13	08 27				
Luton 10	d	07 02	07 05			07 10	07 18	07 32				07 40	07 48	08 02		08 05			08 10	08 18	08 32				08 40
Luton Airport Parkway 7 ✈	d	07 04				07 12	07 20	07 34	07 35			07 42	07 50	08 04					08 12	08 20	08 34	08 35			08 42
Harpenden	d	07 10				07 18	07 26	07 40				07 48	07 56	08 10					08 18	08 26	08 40				08 48
St Albans City	d	07 17				07 24	07 35	07 47				07 54	08 05	08 17					08 24	08 35	08 47				08 54
Radlett	d					07 29						07 59							08 29						08 59
Elstree & Borehamwood	d	07 24				07 33		07 54				08 03		08 24					08 33		08 54				09 03
Mill Hill Broadway	d					07 38						08 08							08 38						09 08
Hendon	d					07 41						08 11							08 41						09 11
Cricklewood	d					07 45						08 15							08 45						09 15
West Hampstead Thameslink ⊖	d	07 33				07 48		08 03				08 18		08 33					08 48		09 03				09 18
Kentish Town ⊖	d					07 54						08 24							08 54						09 24
St Pancras International ⊖	a	07 42	07 31				07 54	08 12	08 00				08 24	08 42		08 31				08 54	09 12	09 01			
St Pancras International 15 ⊖	d					08a02						08a32							09a02						09a32
Farringdon 3 ⊖	d																								
City Thameslink 3	d																								
London Blackfriars 3 ⊖	d																								
Elephant & Castle ⊖	d																								
Loughborough Jn	d																								
Herne Hill 4	d			07 42						08 12							08 42						09 12		
London Bridge 4 ⊖	d				07 45						08 15							08 45						09 15	
Tulse Hill 3	d			07 46	08b02					08 16	08c32						08 46	09e02					09 16	09f32	
Streatham 4	d			07 49	08 05					08 19	08 35						08 49	09 05					09 19	09 35	
Mitcham Eastfields	d			07 53						08 23							08 53						09 23		
Mitcham Junction 🚊	d			07 57						08 27							08 57						09 27		
Hackbridge	d			08 00						08 30							09 00						09 30		
Carshalton	d			08 03						08 33							09 03						09 33		
Tooting	d				08 10						08 40							09 10						09 40	
Haydons Road	d				08 13						08 43							09 13						09 43	
Wimbledon 6 ⊖ 🚊	d				08 17						08 47							09 17						09 47	
Wimbledon Chase	d				08 20						08 50							09 20						09 50	
South Merton	d				08 22						08 52							09 22						09 52	
Morden South	d				08 24						08 54							09 24						09 54	
St Helier	d				08 26						08 56							09 26						09 56	
Sutton Common	d				08 28						08 58							09 28						09 58	
West Sutton	d				08 31						09 01							09 31						10 01	
Sutton (Surrey) 4	a			08 06	08 35					08 36	09 05						09 06	09 35					09 36	10 05	
East Croydon 🚊	d																								
Redhill	d																								
Gatwick Airport 10 ✈	d																								
Three Bridges 4	d																								
Balcombe	d																								
Haywards Heath 3	d																								
Wivelsfield 4	d																								
Burgess Hill 4	d																								
Hassocks 4	d																								
Preston Park	d																								
Brighton 10	a																								

For general notes see front of timetable
For details of catering facilities see Directory of Train Operators

A From Derby (Table 53)
B From Nottingham (Table 53)
b Arr. 0758
c Arr. 0828
e Arr. 0858
f Arr. 0928

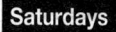

Bedford, Luton, St.Albans and City of London → South London, Gatwick Airport and Brighton

Network Diagram - see first page of Table 52

		FC 1	FC 1	EM 1 ◇ A ☕	FC	FC	FC	FC 1	FC 1	EM 1 ◇ B ☕		FC	FC	FC	FC 1	FC 1	EM 1 ◇ A ☕	FC	FC	FC	FC 1	FC 1	EM 1 ◇ C ☕	FC	FC
Bedford 7	d	08 24	08 38	08 49				08 54	09 08	09 19					09 24	09 38	09 49				09 54	10 08	10 19		
Flitwick	d	08 33	08 47					09 03	09 17						09 33	09 47					10 03	10 17			
Harlington	d	08 37	08 51					09 07	09 21						09 37	09 51					10 07	10 21			
Leagrave	d	08 43	08 57					09 13	09 27						09 43	09 57					10 13	10 27			
Luton 10	d	08 48	09 02	09 05			09 10	09 18	09 32					09 40	09 48	10 02	10 05			10 10	10 18	10 32			
Luton Airport Parkway 7 ✈	d	08 50	09 04				09 12	09 20	09 34	09 35				09 42	09 50	10 04				10 12	10 20	10 34	10 35		
Harpenden	d	08 56	09 10				09 18	09 26	09 40					09 48	09 56	10 10				10 18	10 26	10 40			
St Albans City	d	09 05	09 17				09 24	09 35	09 47					09 54	10 05	10 17				10 24	10 35	10 47			
Radlett	d						09 29							09 59						10 29					
Elstree & Borehamwood	d		09 24				09 33		09 54					10 03		10 24				10 33		10 54			
Mill Hill Broadway	d						09 38							10 08						10 38					
Hendon	d						09 41							10 11						10 41					
Cricklewood	d						09 45							10 15						10 45					
West Hampstead Thameslink ⊖	d		09 33				09 48		10 03					10 18		10 33				10 48		11 03			
Kentish Town ⊖	d						09 54							10 24						10 54					
St Pancras International ⊖	a	09 24	09 42	09 29				09 54	10 12	10 00					10 24	10 42	10 29				10 54	11 12	11 01		
St Pancras International 15 ⊖	d						10a02							10a32						11a02					
Farringdon 3 ⊖	d																								
City Thameslink 3	d																								
London Blackfriars 3 ⊖	d																								
Elephant & Castle ⊖	d																								
Loughborough Jn	d																								
Herne Hill 4	d				09 42							10 12						10 42						11 12	
London Bridge 4 ⊖	d					09 45							10 15						10 45						11 15
Tulse Hill 3	d				09 46	10b02						10 16	10c32					10 46	11e02					11 16	11f32
Streatham 4	d				09 49	10 05						10 19	10 35					10 49	11 05					11 19	11 35
Mitcham Eastfields	d				09 53							10 23						10 53						11 23	
Mitcham Junction	d				09 57							10 27						10 57						11 27	
Hackbridge	d				10 00							10 30						11 00						11 30	
Carshalton	d				10 03							10 33						11 03						11 33	
Tooting	d					10 10							10 40						11 10						11 40
Haydons Road	d					10 13							10 43						11 13						11 43
Wimbledon 6 ⊖	d					10 17							10 47						11 17						11 47
Wimbledon Chase	d					10 20							10 50						11 20						11 50
South Merton	d					10 22							10 52						11 22						11 52
Morden South	d					10 24							10 54						11 24						11 54
St Helier	d					10 26							10 56						11 26						11 56
Sutton Common	d					10 28							10 58						11 28						11 58
West Sutton	d					10 31							11 01						11 31						12 01
Sutton (Surrey) 4	a				10 06	10 35						10 36	11 05					11 06	11 35					11 36	12 05
East Croydon	d																								
Redhill	d																								
Gatwick Airport 10 ✈	d																								
Three Bridges 4	d																								
Balcombe	d																								
Haywards Heath 3	d																								
Wivelsfield 4	d																								
Burgess Hill 4	d																								
Hassocks 4	d																								
Preston Park	d																								
Brighton 10	a																								

For general notes see front of timetable
For details of catering facilities see Directory of Train Operators

A From Corby. (Table 53)
B From Lincoln (Table 53)
C From Nottingham (Table 53)
b Arr. 0958
c Arr. 1028
e Arr. 1058
f Arr. 1128

Table 52

Saturdays

Bedford, Luton, St.Albans and City of London → South London, Gatwick Airport and Brighton

Network Diagram - see first page of Table 52

		FC	FC	FC	EM	FC		FC	FC	FC	FC	EM	FC	FC	FC	FC	FC	EM	FC	FC	FC	FC	FC	EM	FC
			1	1	1 ◇					1	1	1 ◇				1	1	1 ◇				1	1	1 ◇	
					A							B						C						B	
Bedford 7	d		10 24	10 38	10 49					10 54	11 08	11 19				11 24	11 38	11 49				11 54	12 08	12 19	
Flitwick	d		10 33	10 47						11 03	11 17					11 33	11 47					12 03	12 17		
Harlington	d		10 37	10 51						11 07	11 21					11 37	11 51					12 07	12 21		
Leagrave	d		10 43	10 57						11 13	11 27					11 43	11 57					12 13	12 27		
Luton 10	d	10 40	10 48	11 02	11 05				11 10	11 18	11 32				11 40	11 48	12 02	12 05			12 10	12 18	12 32		
Luton Airport Parkway 7 ✈	d	10 42	10 50	11 04					11 12	11 20	11 34	11 35			11 42	11 50	12 04				12 12	12 20	12 34	12 35	
Harpenden	d	10 48	10 56	11 10					11 18	11 26	11 40				11 48	11 56	12 10				12 18	12 26	12 40		
St Albans City	d	10 54	11 05	11 17					11 24	11 35	11 47				11 54	12 05	12 17				12 24	12 35	12 47		
Radlett	d	10 59							11 29						11 59						12 29				
Elstree & Borehamwood	d	11 03		11 24					11 33		11 54				12 03		12 24				12 33		12 54		
Mill Hill Broadway	d	11 08							11 38						12 08						12 38				
Hendon	d	11 11							11 41						12 11						12 41				
Cricklewood	d	11 15							11 45						12 15						12 45				
West Hampstead Thameslink ⊖	d	11 18		11 33					11 48		12 03				12 18		12 33				12 48		13 03		
Kentish Town ⊖	d	11 24							11 54						12 24						12 54				
St Pancras International ⊖	a		11 24	11 42	11 29					11 54	12 12	12 01				12 24	12 42	12 29				12 54	13 12	13 01	
St Pancras International 15 ⊖	d	11a32							12a02						12a32						13a02				
Farringdon 3 ⊖	d																								
City Thameslink 3	d																								
London Blackfriars 3 ⊖	d																								
Elephant & Castle ⊖	d																								
Loughborough Jn	d																								
Herne Hill 4	d					11 42							12 12						12 42						13 12
London Bridge 4 ⊖	d							11 45						12 15						12 45					
Tulse Hill 3	d					11 46		12b02					12 16	12c32					12 46	13e02					13 16
Streatham 4	d					11 49		12 05					12 19	12 35					12 49	13 05					13 19
Mitcham Eastfields	d					11 53							12 23						12 53						13 23
Mitcham Junction 🚋	d					11 57							12 27						12 57						13 27
Hackbridge	d					12 00							12 30						13 00						13 30
Carshalton	d					12 03							12 33						13 03						13 33
Tooting	d							12 10						12 40						13 10					
Haydons Road	d							12 13						12 43						13 13					
Wimbledon 6 ⊖ 🚋	d							12 17						12 47						13 17					
Wimbledon Chase	d							12 20						12 50						13 20					
South Merton	d							12 22						12 52						13 22					
Morden South	d							12 24						12 54						13 24					
St Helier	d							12 26						12 56						13 26					
Sutton Common	d							12 28						12 58						13 28					
West Sutton	d							12 31						13 01						13 31					
Sutton (Surrey) 4	a					12 06		12 35					12 36	13 05					13 06	13 35					13 36
East Croydon 🚋	d																								
Redhill	d																								
Gatwick Airport 10 ✈	d																								
Three Bridges 4	d																								
Balcombe	d																								
Haywards Heath 3	d																								
Wivelsfield 4	d																								
Burgess Hill 4	d																								
Hassocks 4	d																								
Preston Park	d																								
Brighton 10	a																								

For general notes see front of timetable
For details of catering facilities see Directory of Train Operators

A From Kettering (Table 53)
B From Nottingham (Table 53)
C From Corby. (Table 53)
b Arr. 1158
c Arr. 1228
e Arr. 1258

Bedford, Luton, St.Albans and City of London → South London, Gatwick Airport and Brighton

Network Diagram - see first page of Table 52

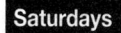

		FC		FC	FC 1	FC 1	EM 1 ◇ A	FC	FC	FC	FC 1	FC 1	EM 1 ◇ B	FC	FC	FC	FC 1	FC 1	EM 1 ◇ A	FC		FC	FC	FC 1	FC 1
Bedford 7	d				12 24	12 38	12 49				12 54	13 08	13 19				13 24	13 38	13 49					13 54	14 08
Flitwick	d				12 33	12 47					13 03	13 17					13 33	13 47						14 03	14 17
Harlington	d				12 37	12 51					13 07	13 21					13 37	13 51						14 07	14 21
Leagrave	d				12 43	12 57					13 13	13 27					13 43	13 57						14 13	14 27
Luton 10	d			12 40	12 48	13 02	13 05			13 10	13 18	13 32				13 40	13 48	14 02	14 05				14 10	14 18	14 32
Luton Airport Parkway 7 ✈	d			12 42	12 50	13 04				13 12	13 20	13 34	13 35			13 42	13 50	14 04					14 12	14 20	14 34
Harpenden	d			12 48	12 56	13 10				13 18	13 26	13 40				13 48	13 56	14 10					14 18	14 26	14 40
St Albans City	d			12 54	13 05	13 17				13 24	13 35	13 47				13 54	14 05	14 17					14 24	14 35	14 47
Radlett	d			12 59						13 29						13 59							14 29		
Elstree & Borehamwood	d			13 03		13 24				13 33		13 54				14 03		14 24					14 33		14 54
Mill Hill Broadway	d			13 08						13 38						14 08							14 38		
Hendon	d			13 11						13 41						14 11							14 41		
Cricklewood	d			13 15						13 45						14 15							14 45		
West Hampstead Thameslink ⊖	d			13 18		13 33				13 48		14 03				14 18		14 33					14 48		15 03
Kentish Town ⊖	d			13 24						13 54						14 24							14 54		
St Pancras International ⊖	a				13 24	13 42	13 29				13 54	14 12	14 01				14 24	14 42	14 29					14 54	15 12
St Pancras International 15 ⊖	d			13a32						14a02						14a32							15a02		
Farringdon 3 ⊖	d																								
City Thameslink 3	d																								
London Blackfriars 3 ⊖	d																								
Elephant & Castle ⊖	d																								
Loughborough Jn	d																								
Herne Hill 4	d							13 42						14 12						14 42					
London Bridge 4 ⊖	d	13 15							13 45						14 15							14 45			
Tulse Hill 3	d	13b32						13 46	14c02					14 16	14e32					14 46		15f02			
Streatham 4	d	13 35						13 49	14 05					14 19	14 35					14 49		15 05			
Mitcham Eastfields	d							13 53						14 23						14 53					
Mitcham Junction 🚌	d							13 57						14 27						14 57					
Hackbridge	d							14 00						14 30						15 00					
Carshalton	d							14 03						14 33						15 03					
Tooting	d	13 40							14 10						14 40							15 10			
Haydons Road	d	13 43							14 13						14 43							15 13			
Wimbledon 6 ⊖ 🚌	d	13 47							14 17						14 47							15 17			
Wimbledon Chase	d	13 50							14 20						14 50							15 20			
South Merton	d	13 52							14 22						14 52							15 22			
Morden South	d	13 54							14 24						14 54							15 24			
St Helier	d	13 56							14 26						14 56							15 26			
Sutton Common	d	13 58							14 28						14 58							15 28			
West Sutton	d	14 01							14 31						15 01							15 31			
Sutton (Surrey) 4	a	14 05						14 06	14 35					14 36	15 05					15 06		15 35			
East Croydon 🚌	d																								
Redhill	d																								
Gatwick Airport 10 ✈	d																								
Three Bridges 4	d																								
Balcombe	d																								
Haywards Heath 3	d																								
Wivelsfield 4	d																								
Burgess Hill 4	d																								
Hassocks 4	d																								
Preston Park	d																								
Brighton 10	a																								

For general notes see front of timetable
For details of catering facilities see Directory of Train Operators

A From Corby. (Table 53)
B From Nottingham (Table 53)
b Arr. 1328
c Arr. 1358
e Arr. 1428
f Arr. 1458

Bedford, Luton, St.Albans and City of London → South London, Gatwick Airport and Brighton

Network Diagram - see first page of Table 52

		EM	FC	FC	FC	FC	FC	EM	FC	FC	FC	FC	FC	EM	FC	FC		FC	FC	FC	EM	FC	FC	FC	FC
		1 ◇				1	1	1 ◇				1	1	1 ◇					1	1	1 ◇				1
		A						B						A							B				
Bedford 7	d	14 19				14 24	14 38	14 49				14 54	15 08	15 19					15 24	15 38	15 49				15 54
Flitwick	d					14 33	14 47					15 03	15 17						15 33	15 47					16 03
Harlington	d					14 37	14 51					15 07	15 21						15 37	15 51					16 07
Leagrave	d					14 43	14 57					15 13	15 27						15 43	15 57					16 13
Luton 10	d				14 40	14 48	15 02	15 05			15 10	15 18	15 32					15 40	15 48	16 02	16 05			16 10	16 18
Luton Airport Parkway 7 ✈	d	14 35			14 42	14 50	15 04				15 12	15 20	15 34	15 35				15 42	15 50	16 04				16 12	16 20
Harpenden	d				14 48	14 56	15 10				15 18	15 26	15 40					15 48	15 56	16 10				16 18	16 26
St Albans City	d				14 54	15 05	15 17				15 24	15 35	15 47					15 54	16 05	16 17				16 24	16 35
Radlett	d				14 59						15 29							15 59						16 29	
Elstree & Borehamwood	d				15 03		15 24				15 33		15 54					16 03		16 24				16 33	
Mill Hill Broadway	d				15 08						15 38							16 08						16 38	
Hendon	d				15 11						15 41							16 11						16 41	
Cricklewood	d				15 15						15 45							16 15						16 45	
West Hampstead Thameslink ⊖	d				15 18		15 33				15 48		16 03					16 18		16 33				16 48	
Kentish Town ⊖	d				15 24						15 54							16 24						16 54	
St Pancras International ⊖	a	15 01				15 24	15 42	15 29				15 54	16 12	16 01					16 24	16 42	16 29				16 54
St Pancras International 15 ⊖	d				15a32						16a02							16a32						17a02	
Farringdon 3 ⊖	d																								
City Thameslink 3	d																								
London Blackfriars 3 ⊖	d																								
Elephant & Castle ⊖	d																								
Loughborough Jn	d																								
Herne Hill 4	d		15 12						15 42						16 12							16 42			
London Bridge 4 ⊖	d			15 15						15 45						16 15							16 45		
Tulse Hill 3	d		15 16	15b32					15 46	16c02					16 16	16e32						16 46	17f02		
Streatham 4	d		15 19	15 35					15 49	16 05					16 19	16 35						16 49	17 05		
Mitcham Eastfields	d		15 23						15 53						16 23							16 53			
Mitcham Junction	d		15 27						15 57						16 27							16 57			
Hackbridge	d		15 30						16 00						16 30							17 00			
Carshalton	d		15 33						16 03						16 33							17 03			
Tooting	d			15 40						16 10						16 40							17 10		
Haydons Road	d			15 43						16 13						16 43							17 13		
Wimbledon 6 ⊖	d			15 47						16 17						16 47							17 17		
Wimbledon Chase	d			15 50						16 20						16 50							17 20		
South Merton	d			15 52						16 22						16 52							17 22		
Morden South	d			15 54						16 24						16 54							17 24		
St Helier	d			15 56						16 26						16 56							17 26		
Sutton Common	d			15 58						16 28						16 58							17 28		
West Sutton	d			16 01						16 31						17 01							17 31		
Sutton (Surrey) 4	a		15 36	16 05					16 06	16 35					16 36	17 05						17 06	17 35		
East Croydon	d																								
Redhill	d																								
Gatwick Airport 10 ✈	d																								
Three Bridges 4	d																								
Balcombe	d																								
Haywards Heath 3	d																								
Wivelsfield 4	d																								
Burgess Hill 4	d																								
Hassocks 4	d																								
Preston Park	d																								
Brighton 10	a																								

For general notes see front of timetable
For details of catering facilities see Directory of Train Operators

A From Nottingham (Table 53)
B From Corby. (Table 53)
b Arr. 1528
c Arr. 1558
e Arr. 1628
f Arr. 1658

Table 52

Saturdays

Bedford, Luton, St.Albans and City of London → South London, Gatwick Airport and Brighton

Network Diagram - see first page of Table 52

		FC 1	EM 1 ◇ A	FC	FC	FC	FC 1	FC 1	EM 1 ◇ B	FC	FC	FC		FC 1	FC 1	EM 1 ◇ A	FC	FC	FC	FC 1	FC 1	EM 1 ◇ B	FC	FC	FC
Bedford 7	d	16 08	16 19				16 24	16 38	16 49					16 54	17 08	17 19				17 24	17 38	17 49			
Flitwick	d	16 17					16 33	16 47						17 03	17 17					17 33	17 47				
Harlington	d	16 21					16 37	16 51						17 07	17 21					17 37	17 51				
Leagrave	d	16 27					16 43	16 57						17 13	17 27					17 43	17 57				
Luton 10	d	16 32				16 40	16 48	17 02	17 05			17 10		17 18	17 32				17 40	17 48	18 02	18 05			18 10
Luton Airport Parkway 7 ✈	d	16 34	16 35			16 42	16 50	17 04				17 12		17 20	17 34	17 35			17 42	17 50	18 04				18 12
Harpenden	d	16 40				16 48	16 56	17 10				17 18		17 26	17 40				17 48	17 56	18 10				18 18
St Albans City	d	16 47				16 54	17 05	17 17				17 24		17 35	17 47				17 54	18 05	18 17				18 24
Radlett	d					16 59						17 29							17 59						18 29
Elstree & Borehamwood	d	16 54				17 03		17 24				17 33			17 54				18 03		18 24				18 33
Mill Hill Broadway	d					17 08						17 38							18 08						18 38
Hendon	d					17 11						17 41							18 11						18 41
Cricklewood	d					17 15						17 45							18 15						18 45
West Hampstead Thameslink ⊖	d	17 03				17 18		17 33				17 48			18 03				18 18		18 33				18 48
Kentish Town ⊖	d					17 24						17 54							18 24						18 54
St Pancras International ⊖	a	17 12	17 01				17 24	17 42	17 29					17 54	18 12	18 01				18 24	18 42	18 29			
St Pancras International 15 ⊖	d					17a32						18a02							18a32						19a02
Farringdon 3 ⊖	d																								
City Thameslink 3	d																								
London Blackfriars 3 ⊖	d																								
Elephant & Castle ⊖	d																								
Loughborough Jn	d																								
Herne Hill 4	d			17 12						17 42							18 12						18 42		
London Bridge 4 ⊖	d				17 15						17 45							18 15						18 45	
Tulse Hill 3	d			17 16	17b32					17 46	18c02						18 16	18e32					18 46	19f02	
Streatham 4	d			17 19	17 35					17 49	18 05						18 19	18 35					18 49	19 05	
Mitcham Eastfields	d			17 23						17 53							18 23						18 53		
Mitcham Junction 🚌	d			17 27						17 57							18 27						18 57		
Hackbridge	d			17 30						18 00							18 30						19 00		
Carshalton	d			17 33						18 03							18 33						19 03		
Tooting	d				17 40						18 10							18 40						19 10	
Haydons Road	d				17 43						18 13							18 43						19 13	
Wimbledon 6 ⊖ 🚌	d				17 47						18 17							18 47						19 17	
Wimbledon Chase	d				17 50						18 20							18 50						19 20	
South Merton	d				17 52						18 22							18 52						19 22	
Morden South	d				17 54						18 24							18 54						19 24	
St Helier	d				17 56						18 26							18 56						19 26	
Sutton Common	d				17 58						18 28							18 58						19 28	
West Sutton	d				18 01						18 31							19 01						19 31	
Sutton (Surrey) 4	a			17 36	18 05					18 06	18 35						18 36	19 05					19 06	19 39	
East Croydon 🚌	d																								
Redhill	d																								
Gatwick Airport 10 ✈	d																								
Three Bridges 4	d																								
Balcombe	d																								
Haywards Heath 3	d																								
Wivelsfield 4	d																								
Burgess Hill 4	d																								
Hassocks 4	d																								
Preston Park	d																								
Brighton 10	a																								

For general notes see front of timetable
For details of catering facilities see Directory of Train Operators

A From Nottingham (Table 53)
B From Corby. (Table 53)
b Arr. 1728
c Arr. 1758
e Arr. 1828
f Arr. 1858

Bedford, Luton, St.Albans and City of London → South London, Gatwick Airport and Brighton

Network Diagram - see first page of Table 52

Station		FC 1	FC 1	EM 1 ◇ A	FC	FC	FC 1	FC		EM 1 ◇ B	FC	FC	FC 1	FC	EM 1 ◇ A	FC	FC 1	FC	EM 1 ◇ B	FC	FC 1	FC	EM 1 ◇ A	FC	FC 1
Bedford 7	d	17 54	18 08	18 19			18 22			18 51			18 50		19 21		19 20		19 53		19 50		20 21		20 20
Flitwick	d	18 03	18 17				18 31						18 59				19 29				19 59				20 29
Harlington	d	18 07	18 21				18 35						19 03				19 33				20 03				20 33
Leagrave	d	18 13	18 27				18 41						19 09				19 39				20 09				20 39
Luton 10	d	18 18	18 32				18 46	18 52		19 07			19 14	19 22			19 44	19 52	20 08		20 14	20 22			20 44
Luton Airport Parkway 7 ✈	d	18 20	18 34	18 35			18 48	18 54					19 16	19 24	19 34		19 46	19 54			20 16	20 24	20 34		20 46
Harpenden	d	18 26	18 40				18 54	19 00					19 22	19 30			19 52	20 00			20 22	20 30			20 52
St Albans City	d	18 35	18 47				19 00	19 06					19 28	19 36			19 58	20 06			20 28	20 36			20 58
Radlett	d							19 11						19 41				20 11				20 41			
Elstree & Borehamwood	d		18 54					19 15						19 45				20 15				20 45			
Mill Hill Broadway	d							19 19						19 49				20 19				20 49			
Hendon	d							19 22						19 52				20 22				20 52			
Cricklewood	d							19 26						19 56				20 26				20 56			
West Hampstead Thameslink ⊖	d		19 03				19 14	19 29					19 42	19 59			20 12	20 29			20 42	20 59			21 12
Kentish Town ⊖	d							19 33						20 03				20 33				21 03			
St Pancras International ⊖	a	18 54	19 12	18 59			19 24	19 42		19 34			19 54	20 10	20 06		20 24	20 40	20 34		20 54	21 10	21 06		21 24
St Pancras International 15 ⊖	d																								
Farringdon 3 ⊖	d																								
City Thameslink 3	d																								
London Blackfriars 3 ⊖	d																								
Elephant & Castle ⊖	d																								
Loughborough Jn	d																								
Herne Hill 4	d				19 12						19 42														
London Bridge 4 ⊖	d					19 15						19 45				20 15				20 45				21 15	
Tulse Hill 3	d				19 16	19b32					19 46	20c02				20e32				21f02				21g32	
Streatham 4	d				19 19	19 35					19 49	20 05				20 35				21 05				21 35	
Mitcham Eastfields	d				19 23						19 53														
Mitcham Junction 🚋	d				19 27						19 57														
Hackbridge	d				19 30						20 00														
Carshalton	d				19 33						20 03														
Tooting	d					19 40						20 10				20 40				21 10				21 40	
Haydons Road	d					19 43						20 13				20 43				21 13				21 43	
Wimbledon 6 ⊖ 🚋	d					19 47						20 17				20 47				21 17				21 47	
Wimbledon Chase	d					19 50						20 20				20 50				21 20				21 50	
South Merton	d					19 52						20 22				20 52				21 22				21 52	
Morden South	d					19 54						20 24				20 54				21 24				21 54	
St Helier	d					19 56						20 26				20 56				21 26				21 56	
Sutton Common	d					19 58						20 28				20 58				21 28				21 58	
West Sutton	d					20 01						20 31				21 01				21 31				22 01	
Sutton (Surrey) 4	a				19 36	20 05					20 06	20 39				21 05				21 39				22 05	
East Croydon 🚋	d																								
Redhill	d																								
Gatwick Airport 10 ✈	d																								
Three Bridges 4	d																								
Balcombe	d																								
Haywards Heath 3	d																								
Wivelsfield 4	d																								
Burgess Hill 4	d																								
Hassocks 4	d																								
Preston Park	d																								
Brighton 10	a																								

For general notes see front of timetable
For details of catering facilities see Directory of Train Operators

A From Nottingham (Table 53)
B From Corby. (Table 53)
b Arr. 1928
c Arr. 1958
e Arr. 2028
f Arr. 2058
g Arr. 2128

Table 52

Saturdays

Bedford, Luton, St.Albans and City of London → South London, Gatwick Airport and Brighton

Network Diagram - see first page of Table 52

		FC	EM 1 ◇ A ☕	FC		FC 1	FC	EM 1 ◇ B ☕	FC	FC 1	FC	EM 1 ◇ A ☕	FC	FC 1	EM 1 ◇ B ☕	FC	FC	FC 1	EM 1 ◇ B ☕	FC	FC 1	FC 1	FC 1
Bedford 7	d		20 53			20 50		21 21		21 20		21 45		21 50	22 01			22 10	22 37		22 40	23 10	23 40
Flitwick	d					20 59				21 29				21 59				22 19			22 49	23 19	23 49
Harlington	d					21 03				21 33				22 03				22 23			22 53	23 23	23 53
Leagrave	d					21 09				21 39				22 09				22 29			22 59	23 29	23 59
Luton 10	d	20 50	21 08			21 14	21 20			21 44	21 52	22 07		22 14	22 18	22 22		22 34	23 00		23 04	23 34	00 04
Luton Airport Parkway 7 ✈	d	20 52				21 16	21 22	21 37		21 46	21 54			22 16	22 21	22 24		22 36			23 06	23 36	00 06
Harpenden	d	20 58				21 22	21 28			21 52	22 00			22 22		22 30		22 42			23 12	23 42	00 12
St Albans City	d	21 04				21 28	21 34			21 58	22 06			22 28		22 36		22 48			23 18	23 48	00 18
Radlett	d	21 09					21 39				22 11					22 41		22 53			23 23	23 53	00 23
Elstree & Borehamwood	d	21 13					21 43				22 15					22 45		22 57			23 27	23 57	00 27
Mill Hill Broadway	d	21 17					21 47				22 19					22 49		23 01			23 31	00 01	00 31
Hendon	d	21 20					21 50				22 22					22 52		23 04			23 34	00 04	00 34
Cricklewood	d	21 24					21 54				22 26					22 56		23 08			23 38	00 08	00 38
West Hampstead Thameslink ⊖	d	21 27				21 42	21 57			22 12	22 29			22 42		22 59		23 12			23 42	00 12	00 42
Kentish Town ⊖	d	21 31					22 01				22 33					23 03		23 16			23 46	00 16	00 46
St Pancras International ⊖	a	21 38	21 34			21 54	22 08	22 06		22 24	22 41	22 40		22 55	22 59	23 10		23 24	23 35		23 55	00 25	00 55
St Pancras International 15 ⊖	d																						
Farringdon 3 ⊖	d																						
City Thameslink 3	d																						
London Blackfriars 3 ⊖	d																						
Elephant & Castle ⊖	d																						
Loughborough Jn	d																						
Herne Hill 4	d																						
London Bridge 4 ⊖	d			21 45					22 15				22 45				23 15			23 45			
Tulse Hill 3	d			22b02					22c32				23e02				23f32			00g02			
Streatham 4	d			22 05					22 35				23 05				23 35			00 05			
Mitcham Eastfields	d																						
Mitcham Junction 🚋	d																						
Hackbridge	d																						
Carshalton	d																						
Tooting	d			22 10					22 40				23 10				23 40			00 10			
Haydons Road	d			22 13					22 43				23 13				23 43			00 13			
Wimbledon 6 ⊖ 🚋	d			22 17					22 47				23 17				23 47			00 17			
Wimbledon Chase	d			22 20					22 50				23 20				23 50			00 20			
South Merton	d			22 22					22 52				23 22				23 52			00 22			
Morden South	d			22 24					22 54				23 24				23 54			00 24			
St Helier	d			22 26					22 56				23 26				23 56			00 26			
Sutton Common	d			22 28					22 58				23 28				23 58			00 28			
West Sutton	d			22 31					23 01				23 31				00 01			00 31			
Sutton (Surrey) 4	a			22 39					23 05				23 35				00 05			00 35			
East Croydon 🚋	d																						
Redhill	d																						
Gatwick Airport 10 ✈	d																						
Three Bridges 4	d																						
Balcombe	d																						
Haywards Heath 3	d																						
Wivelsfield 4	d																						
Burgess Hill 4	d																						
Hassocks 4	d																						
Preston Park	d																						
Brighton 10	a																						

For general notes see front of timetable
For details of catering facilities see Directory of Train Operators

A From Corby. (Table 53)
B From Nottingham (Table 53)
b Arr. 2158
c Arr. 2228
e Arr. 2258
f Arr. 2328
g Arr. 2358

Bedford, Luton, St.Albans and City of London → South London, Gatwick Airport and Brighton

Network Diagram - see first page of Table 52

Station		FC	FC	FC [1]	FC [1]	FC [1]	FC [1]	FC [1]	FC [1]	FC [1]	FC	EM [1] ◇ A ☕		FC	FC [1]	FC	EM [1] ◇ B ☕	FC	FC [1]	FC	FC [1]	EM [1] ◇ C ☕	EM [1] ◇ D ☕	FC	FC [1]
Bedford [7]	d			23p10	23p40	05 40	06 10	06 40	07 10	07 50		08 15			08 20		08 45		08 50		09 08	09 14	09 14		09 20
Flitwick	d			23p19	23p49	05 49	06 19	06 49	07 19	07 59					08 29				08 59		09 17				09 29
Harlington	d			23p23	23p53	05 53	06 23	06 53	07 23	08 03					08 33				09 03		09 21				09 33
Leagrave	d			23p29	23p59	05 59	06 29	06 59	07 29	08 09					08 39				09 09		09 27				09 39
Luton [10]	d			23p34	00 04	06 04	06 34	07 04	07 34	08 14	08 18	08 34			08 44	08 48			09 14	09 18	09 32	09 38	09 39		09 44
Luton Airport Parkway [7] ✈	d			23p36	00 06	06 06	06 36	07 06	07 36	08 16	08 20				08 46	08 50	09 07		09 16	09 20	09 34				09 46
Harpenden	d			23p42	00 12	06 12	06 42	07 12	07 42	08 22	08 26				08 52	08 56			09 22	09 26	09 40				09 52
St Albans City	d			23p48	00 18	06 18	06 48	07 18	07 48	08 28	08 32				08 58	09 02			09 28	09 32	09 46				09 58
Radlett	d			23p53	00 23	06 23	06 53	07 23	07 53		08 37					09 07				09 37					
Elstree & Borehamwood	d			23p57	00 27	06 27	06 57	07 27	07 57		08 41					09 11				09 41					
Mill Hill Broadway	d			00 01	00 31	06 31	07 01	07 31	08 01		08 45					09 15				09 45					
Hendon	d			00 04	00 34	06 34	07 04	07 34	08 04		08 48					09 18				09 48					
Cricklewood	d			00 08	00 38	06 38	07 08	07 38	08 08		08 52					09 22				09 52					
West Hampstead Thameslink ⊖	d			00 12	00 42	06 42	07 12	07 42	08 12	08 42	08 54				09 12	09 24			09 42	09 55					10 12
Kentish Town ⊖	d			00 16	00 46	06 46	07 16	07 46	08 16		09b08					09c38				10e09					
St Pancras International ⊖	a			00 25	00 55	06 54	07 24	07 54	08 24	08 54		09 19			09 24		09 49		09 54		10 08	10 19	10 19		10 24
St Pancras International [15] ⊖	d										09a16					09a46				10a16					
Farringdon [3] ⊖	d																								
City Thameslink [3]	d																								
London Blackfriars [3] ⊖	d																								
Elephant & Castle ⊖	d																								
Loughborough Jn	d																								
Herne Hill [4]	d																								
London Bridge [4] ⊖	d	23p15	23p45											09 21				09 51						10 21	
Tulse Hill [3]	d	23f32	00g02											09 32				10 02						10 32	
Streatham [4]	d	23p35	00 05											09 35				10 05						10 35	
Mitcham Eastfields	d																								
Mitcham Junction (tram)	d																								
Hackbridge	d																								
Carshalton	d																								
Tooting	d	23p40	00 10											09 40				10 10						10 40	
Haydons Road	d	23p43	00 13											09 43				10 13						10 43	
Wimbledon [6] ⊖ (tram)	d	23p47	00 17											09 47				10 17						10 47	
Wimbledon Chase	d	23p50	00 20											09 50				10 20						10 50	
South Merton	d	23p52	00 22											09 52				10 22						10 52	
Morden South	d	23p54	00 24											09 54				10 24						10 54	
St Helier	d	23p56	00 26											09 56				10 26						10 56	
Sutton Common	d	23p58	00 28											09 58				10 28						10 58	
West Sutton	d	00 01	00 31											10 01				10 31						11 01	
Sutton (Surrey) [4]	a	00 05	00 35											10 05				10 35						11 05	
East Croydon (tram)	d																								
Redhill	d																								
Gatwick Airport [10] ✈	d																								
Three Bridges [4]	d																								
Balcombe	d																								
Haywards Heath [3]	d																								
Wivelsfield [4]	d																								
Burgess Hill [4]	d																								
Hassocks [4]	d																								
Preston Park	d																								
Brighton [10]	a																								

For general notes see front of timetable
For details of catering facilities see Directory of Train Operators

A Until 12 July. From Derby (Table 53)

B Until 6 September. From Nottingham (Table 53)

C From 13 September. From Derby (Table 53)

D Until 6 September. From Derby (Table 53)

b Arr. 0858

c Arr. 0928

e Arr. 0959

f Previous night. Arr. 2328

g Arr. 2358

Sundays

Bedford, Luton, St.Albans and City of London → South London, Gatwick Airport and Brighton

Network Diagram - see first page of Table 52

Station		FC		FC 1	EM 1 ◇ A	EM 1 ◇ B	FC	FC 1	FC	FC 1	EM 1 ◇ C	FC	FC 1	FC		FC 1	EM 1 ◇ B	FC	FC 1	FC	FC 1	EM 1 ◇ D	FC	FC 1	FC
Bedford 7	d			09 38	09 43	09 45		09 50		10 08	10 14		10 20			10 38	10 45		10 50		11 08	11 14		11 20	
Flitwick	d			09 47				09 59		10 17			10 29			10 47			10 59		11 17			11 29	
Harlington	d			09 51				10 03		10 21			10 33			10 51			11 03		11 21			11 33	
Leagrave	d			09 57				10 09		10 27			10 39			10 57			11 09		11 27			11 39	
Luton 10	d	09 48		10 02				10 14	10 18	10 32	10 39		10 44	10 48		11 02			11 14	11 18	11 32	11 39		11 44	11 48
Luton Airport Parkway 7 ✈	d	09 50		10 04	10 09	10 10		10 16	10 20	10 34			10 46	10 50		11 04	11 10		11 16	11 20	11 34			11 46	11 50
Harpenden	d	09 56		10 10				10 22	10 26	10 40			10 52	10 56		11 10			11 22	11 26	11 40			11 52	11 56
St Albans City	d	10 02		10 16				10 28	10 32	10 46			10 58	11 02		11 16			11 28	11 32	11 46			11 58	12 02
Radlett	d	10 07							10 37					11 07						11 37					12 07
Elstree & Borehamwood	d	10 11							10 41					11 11						11 41					12 11
Mill Hill Broadway	d	10 15							10 46					11 16						11 46					12 16
Hendon	d	10 18							10 48					11 18						11 48					12 18
Cricklewood	d	10 22							10 52					11 22						11 52					12 22
West Hampstead Thameslink ⊖	d	10 25						10 42	10 55				11 12	11 25					11 42	11 55				12 12	12 25
Kentish Town ⊖	d	10b39							11c09					11e39						12f09					12g39
St Pancras International ⊖	a			10 38	10 49	10 49		10 54		11 08	11 19		11 24			11 38	11 49		11 54		12 08	12 19		12 24	
St Pancras International 15 ⊖	d	10a46							11a16					11a46						12a16					12a46
Farringdon 3 ⊖	d																								
City Thameslink 3	d																								
London Blackfriars 3 ⊖	d																								
Elephant & Castle ⊖	d																								
Loughborough Jn	d																								
Herne Hill 4	d																								
London Bridge 4 ⊖	d						10 51					11 21						11 51					12 21		
Tulse Hill 3	d						11 02					11 32						12 02					12 32		
Streatham 4	d						11 05					11 35						12 05					12 35		
Mitcham Eastfields	d																								
Mitcham Junction 🚋	d																								
Hackbridge	d																								
Carshalton	d																								
Tooting	d						11 10					11 40						12 10					12 40		
Haydons Road	d						11 13					11 43						12 13					12 43		
Wimbledon 6 ⊖ 🚋	d						11 17					11 47						12 17					12 47		
Wimbledon Chase	d						11 20					11 50						12 20					12 50		
South Merton	d						11 22					11 52						12 22					12 52		
Morden South	d						11 24					11 54						12 24					12 54		
St Helier	d						11 26					11 56						12 26					12 56		
Sutton Common	d						11 28					11 58						12 28					12 58		
West Sutton	d						11 31					12 01						12 31					13 01		
Sutton (Surrey) 4	a						11 35					12 05						12 35					13 05		
East Croydon 🚋	d																								
Redhill	d																								
Gatwick Airport 10 ✈	d																								
Three Bridges 4	d																								
Balcombe	d																								
Haywards Heath 3	d																								
Wivelsfield 4	d																								
Burgess Hill 4	d																								
Hassocks 4	d																								
Preston Park	d																								
Brighton 10	a																								

For general notes see front of timetable
For details of catering facilities see Directory of Train Operators

A From 13 September. From Nottingham (Table 53)

B Until 6 September From Nottingham (Table 53)

C Until 12 July and from 13 September From Derby (Table 53)

D Until 12 July and from 13 September. From 13 September from Derby (Table 53). Until 12 July from Sheffield (Table 53)

b Arr. 1029

c Arr. 1059

e Arr. 1129

f Arr. 1159

g Arr. 1229

Sundays

Bedford, Luton, St.Albans and City of London → South London, Gatwick Airport and Brighton

Network Diagram - see first page of Table 52

		FC	EM	FC		FC	FC	FC	EM	FC	FC	FC	FC	EM	FC	EM		FC	FC	FC	EM	FC	FC	FC	FC
		1	1 ◇			1		1	1 ◇		1		1	1 ◇		1 ◇		1		1	1 ◇		1		1
			A						B					C		D					E				
Bedford 7	d	11 38	11 45			11 50		12 08	12 14		12 20		12 38	12 45		12 46		12 50		13 08	13 15		13 20		13 38
Flitwick	d	11 47				11 59		12 17			12 29		12 47					12 59		13 17			13 29		13 47
Harlington	d	11 51				12 03		12 21			12 33		12 51					13 03		13 21			13 33		13 51
Leagrave	d	11 57				12 09		12 27			12 39		12 57					13 09		13 27			13 39		13 57
Luton 10	d	12 02				12 14	12 18	12 32	12 40		12 44	12 48	13 02					13 14	13 18	13 32	13 39		13 44	13 48	14 02
Luton Airport Parkway 7 ✈	d	12 04	12 09			12 16	12 20	12 34			12 46	12 50	13 04	13 10		13 10		13 16	13 20	13 34			13 46	13 50	14 04
Harpenden	d	12 10				12 22	12 26	12 40			12 52	12 56	13 10					13 22	13 26	13 40			13 52	13 56	14 10
St Albans City	d	12 16				12 28	12 32	12 46			12 58	13 02	13 16					13 28	13 32	13 46			13 58	14 02	14 16
Radlett	d						12 37					13 07							13 37					14 07	
Elstree & Borehamwood	d						12 41					13 11							13 41					14 11	
Mill Hill Broadway	d						12 46					13 16							13 46					14 16	
Hendon	d						12 48					13 18							13 48					14 18	
Cricklewood	d						12 52					13 22							13 52					14 22	
West Hampstead Thameslink ⊖	d					12 42	12 55				13 12	13 25						13 42	13 55				14 12	14 25	
Kentish Town ⊖	d						13b09					13c39							14e09					14f39	
St Pancras International ⊖	a	12 38	12 50			12 54		13 08	13 19		13 24		13 38	13 49		13 51		13 54		14 08	14 19		14 24		14 38
St Pancras International 15 ⊖	d						13a16					13a46							14a16					14a46	
Farringdon 3 ⊖	d																								
City Thameslink 3	d																								
London Blackfriars 3 ⊖	d																								
Elephant & Castle ⊖	d																								
Loughborough Jn	d																								
Herne Hill 4	d																								
London Bridge 4 ⊖	d			12 51						13 21					13 51							14 21			
Tulse Hill 3	d			13 02						13 32					14 02							14 32			
Streatham 4	d			13 05						13 35					14 05							14 35			
Mitcham Eastfields	d																								
Mitcham Junction 🚊	d																								
Hackbridge	d																								
Carshalton	d																								
Tooting	d			13 10						13 40					14 10							14 40			
Haydons Road	d			13 13						13 43					14 13							14 43			
Wimbledon 6 ⊖ 🚊	d			13 17						13 47					14 17							14 47			
Wimbledon Chase	d			13 20						13 50					14 20							14 50			
South Merton	d			13 22						13 52					14 22							14 52			
Morden South	d			13 24						13 54					14 24							14 54			
St Helier	d			13 26						13 56					14 26							14 56			
Sutton Common	d			13 28						13 58					14 28							14 58			
West Sutton	d			13 31						14 01					14 31							15 01			
Sutton (Surrey) 4	a			13 35						14 05					14 35							15 05			
East Croydon 🚊	d																								
Redhill	d																								
Gatwick Airport 10 ✈	d																								
Three Bridges 4	d																								
Balcombe	d																								
Haywards Heath 3	d																								
Wivelsfield 4	d																								
Burgess Hill 4	d																								
Hassocks 4	d																								
Preston Park	d																								
Brighton 10	a																								

For general notes see front of timetable
For details of catering facilities see Directory of Train Operators

A Until 6 September From Nottingham (Table 53)
B From Sheffield (Table 53)
C From 13 September. From Leeds (Table 53)
D Until 12 July and from 13 September From Leeds (Table 53)
E From Leeds (Table 53)
b Arr. 1259
c Arr. 1329
e Arr. 1359
f Arr. 1429

Sundays

Bedford, Luton, St.Albans and City of London → South London, Gatwick Airport and Brighton

Network Diagram - see first page of Table 52

		EM	EM	FC	FC	FC		FC	EM	FC	FC	FC	EM	FC	EM	FC	FC	FC		FC	EM	FC	FC	FC	FC
		1 ◇	1 ◇		1			1	1 ◇		1		1 ◇	1	1 ◇		1			1	1 ◇		1		1
		A	B						C				D		E						G				
Bedford 7	d	13 46	13 46		13 50			14 08	14 24		14 20		14 25	14 38	14 52		14 50			15 08	15 25		15 20		15 38
Flitwick	d				13 59			14 17			14 29			14 47			14 59			15 17			15 29		15 47
Harlington	d				14 03			14 21			14 33			14 51			15 03			15 21			15 33		15 51
Leagrave	d				14 09			14 27			14 39			14 57			15 09			15 27			15 39		15 57
Luton 10	d				14 14	14 18		14 32	14 41		14 44	14 48	14 49	15 02			15 14	15 18		15 32	15 42		15 44	15 48	16 02
Luton Airport Parkway 7 ✈	d	14 10	14 12		14 16	14 20		14 34			14 46	14 50		15 04	15 11		15 16	15 20		15 34			15 46	15 50	16 04
Harpenden	d				14 22	14 26		14 40			14 52	14 56		15 10			15 22	15 26		15 40			15 52	15 56	16 10
St Albans City	d				14 28	14 32		14 46			14 58	15 02		15 16			15 28	15 32		15 46			15 58	16 02	16 16
Radlett	d					14 37						15 07						15 37						16 07	
Elstree & Borehamwood	d					14 41						15 11						15 41						16 11	
Mill Hill Broadway	d					14 46						15 16						15 46						16 16	
Hendon	d					14 48						15 18						15 48						16 18	
Cricklewood	d					14 52						15 22						15 52						16 22	
West Hampstead Thameslink ⊖	d				14 42	14 55					15 12	15 25					15 42	15 55					16 12	16 25	
Kentish Town ⊖	d					15b09						15c39						16e09						16f39	
St Pancras International ⊖	a	14 44	14 44		14 54			15 08	15 15		15 24		15 22	15 38	15 45		15 54			16 08	16 15		16 24		16 38
St Pancras International 15 ⊖	d					15a16						15a46						16a16						16a46	
Farringdon 3 ⊖	d																								
City Thameslink 3	d																								
London Blackfriars 3 ⊖	d																								
Elephant & Castle ⊖	d																								
Loughborough Jn	d																								
Herne Hill 4	d																								
London Bridge 4 ⊖	d			14 51						15 21						15 51						16 21			
Tulse Hill 3	d			15 02						15 32						16 02						16 32			
Streatham 4	d			15 05						15 35						16 05						16 35			
Mitcham Eastfields	d																								
Mitcham Junction 🚋	d																								
Hackbridge	d																								
Carshalton	d																								
Tooting	d			15 10						15 40						16 10						16 40			
Haydons Road	d			15 13						15 43						16 13						16 43			
Wimbledon 6 ⊖ 🚋	d			15 17						15 47						16 17						16 47			
Wimbledon Chase	d			15 20						15 50						16 20						16 50			
South Merton	d			15 22						15 52						16 22						16 52			
Morden South	d			15 24						15 54						16 24						16 54			
St Helier	d			15 26						15 56						16 26						16 56			
Sutton Common	d			15 28						15 58						16 28						16 58			
West Sutton	d			15 31						16 01						16 31						17 01			
Sutton (Surrey) 4	a			15 35						16 05						16 35						17 05			
East Croydon 🚋	d																								
Redhill	d																								
Gatwick Airport 10 ✈	d																								
Three Bridges 4	d																								
Balcombe	d																								
Haywards Heath 3	d																								
Wivelsfield 4	d																								
Burgess Hill 4	d																								
Hassocks 4	d																								
Preston Park	d																								
Brighton 10	a																								

For general notes see front of timetable
For details of catering facilities see Directory of Train Operators

A Until 6 September From Nottingham (Table 53)
B From 13 September. From Nottingham (Table 53)
C From 13 September. From Sheffield (Table 53)
D Until 6 September From Sheffield (Table 53)
E From Nottingham (Table 53)
G From Sheffield (Table 53)
b Arr. 1459
c Arr. 1529
e Arr. 1559
f Arr. 1629

Sundays

Bedford, Luton, St.Albans and City of London → South London, Gatwick Airport and Brighton

Network Diagram - see first page of Table 52

	EM 1 ◇ A ☕	EM 1 ◇ B ☕	FC	FC 1	FC	EM 1 ◇ C ☕	EM 1 ◇ D ☕	FC 1	FC	FC 1	FC	EM 1 ◇ A ☕	EM 1 ◇ B ☕	FC 1	FC	FC 1	FC	EM 1 ◇ E ☕	FC 1	FC	FC 1	FC
Bedford 7 d	15 55	15 56		15 50			16 09	16 08		16 20		16 35	16 36	16 38		16 50		17 07	17 08		17 20	
Flitwick d				15 59				16 17		16 29				16 47		16 59			17 17		17 29	
Harlington d				16 03				16 21		16 33				16 51		17 03			17 21		17 33	
Leagrave d				16 09				16 27		16 39				16 57		17 09			17 27		17 39	
Luton 10 d				16 14	16 18	16 25	16 27	16 32		16 44	16 48			17 02		17 14	17 18	17 25	17 32		17 44	17 48
Luton Airport Parkway 7 ✈ d	16 14	16 13		16 16	16 20			16 34		16 46	16 50	16 53	16 54	17 04		17 16	17 20		17 34		17 46	17 50
Harpenden d				16 22	16 26			16 40		16 52	16 56			17 10		17 22	17 26		17 40		17 52	17 56
St Albans City d				16 28	16 32			16 46		16 58	17 02			17 16		17 28	17 32		17 46		17 58	18 02
Radlett d					16 37						17 07						17 37					18 07
Elstree & Borehamwood d					16 41						17 11						17 41					18 11
Mill Hill Broadway d					16 46						17 16						17 46					18 16
Hendon d					16 48						17 18						17 48					18 18
Cricklewood d					16 52						17 22						17 52					18 22
West Hampstead Thameslink ⊖ d				16 42	16 55					17 12	17 25					17 42	17 55				18 12	18 25
Kentish Town ⊖ d					17b09						17c39						18e09					18f39
St Pancras International ⊖ a	16 45	16 45		16 53		16 55	16 55	17 08		17 24		17 27	17 27	17 38		17 54		17 59	18 08		18 24	
St Pancras International 15 ⊖ d					17a16						17a46						18a16					18a46
Farringdon 3 ⊖ d																						
City Thameslink 3 d																						
London Blackfriars 3 ⊖ d																						
Elephant & Castle ⊖ d																						
Loughborough Jn d																						
Herne Hill 4 d																						
London Bridge 4 ⊖ d			16 51						17 21						17 51					18 21		
Tulse Hill 3 d			17 02						17 32						18 02					18 32		
Streatham 4 d			17 05						17 35						18 05					18 35		
Mitcham Eastfields d																						
Mitcham Junction 🚋 d																						
Hackbridge d																						
Carshalton d																						
Tooting d			17 10						17 40						18 10					18 40		
Haydons Road d			17 13						17 43						18 13					18 43		
Wimbledon 6 ⊖ 🚋 d			17 17						17 47						18 17					18 47		
Wimbledon Chase d			17 20						17 50						18 20					18 50		
South Merton d			17 22						17 52						18 22					18 52		
Morden South d			17 24						17 54						18 24					18 54		
St Helier d			17 26						17 56						18 26					18 56		
Sutton Common d			17 28						17 58						18 28					18 58		
West Sutton d			17 31						18 01						18 31					19 01		
Sutton (Surrey) 4 a			17 35						18 05						18 35					19 05		
East Croydon 🚋 d																						
Redhill d																						
Gatwick Airport 10 ✈ d																						
Three Bridges 4 d																						
Balcombe d																						
Haywards Heath 3 d																						
Wivelsfield 4 d																						
Burgess Hill 4 d																						
Hassocks 4 d																						
Preston Park d																						
Brighton 10 a																						

For general notes see front of timetable
For details of catering facilities see Directory of Train Operators

A Until 6 September. From Nottingham (Table 53)
B From 13 September. From Nottingham (Table 53)
C Until 6 September. From Sheffield (Table 53)
D From 13 September. From Sheffield (Table 53)
E From Leeds (Table 53)
b Arr. 1659
c Arr. 1729
e Arr. 1759
f Arr. 1829

Table 52

Sundays

Bedford, Luton, St.Albans and City of London → South London, Gatwick Airport and Brighton

Network Diagram - see first page of Table 52

	EM 1 ◇ A	FC 1	FC	FC 1	FC	EM 1 ◇ B	EM 1 ◇ C	FC	FC 1		FC	EM 1 ◇ A	FC	FC 1	FC	EM 1 ◇ B	EM 1 ◇ C	FC	FC 1	FC	EM 1 ◇ A		FC	FC 1
Bedford 7 d	17 40	17 38		17 50		18 11	18 12		18 20			18 40		18 50		19 09	19 10		19 20		19 40			19 50
Flitwick d		17 47		17 59					18 29					18 59					19 29					19 59
Harlington d		17 51		18 03					18 33					19 03					19 33					20 03
Leagrave d		17 57		18 09					18 39					19 09					19 39					20 09
Luton 10 d		18 02		18 14	18 18	18 29	18 29		18 44		18 48			19 14	19 18	19 27	19 29		19 44	19 48				20 14
Luton Airport Parkway 7 ✈ d	17 59	18 04		18 16	18 20				18 46		18 50	18 59		19 16	19 20				19 46	19 50	19 59			20 16
Harpenden d		18 10		18 22	18 26				18 52		18 56			19 22	19 26				19 52	19 56				20 22
St Albans City d		18 16		18 28	18 32				18 58		19 02			19 28	19 32				19 58	20 02				20 28
Radlett d					18 37						19 07				19 37					20 07				
Elstree & Borehamwood d					18 41						19 11				19 41					20 11				
Mill Hill Broadway d					18 46						19 16				19 46					20 16				
Hendon d					18 48						19 18				19 48					20 18				
Cricklewood d					18 52						19 22				19 52					20 22				
West Hampstead Thameslink ⊖ d				18 42	18 55				19 12		19 25			19 42	19 55				20 12	20 25				20 42
Kentish Town ⊖ d					18 59						19 29				19 59					20 29				
St Pancras International ⊖ a	18 29	18 38		18 54	19 09	18 59	18 59		19 24		19 39	19 29		19 54	20 09	19 59	19 59		20 24	20 39	20 29			20 54
St Pancras International 15 ⊖ d																								
Farringdon 3 ⊖ d																								
City Thameslink 3 d																								
London Blackfriars 3 ⊖ d																								
Elephant & Castle ⊖ d																								
Loughborough Jn d																								
Herne Hill 4 d																								
London Bridge 4 ⊖ d			18 51					19 21					19 51					20 21					20 51	
Tulse Hill 3 d			19 02					19 32					20 02					20 32					21 02	
Streatham 4 d			19 05					19 35					20 05					20 35					21 05	
Mitcham Eastfields d																								
Mitcham Junction 🚋 d																								
Hackbridge d																								
Carshalton d																								
Tooting d			19 10					19 40					20 10					20 40					21 10	
Haydons Road d			19 13					19 43					20 13					20 43					21 13	
Wimbledon 6 ⊖ 🚋 d			19 17					19 47					20 17					20 47					21 17	
Wimbledon Chase d			19 20					19 50					20 20					20 50					21 20	
South Merton d			19 22					19 52					20 22					20 52					21 22	
Morden South d			19 24					19 54					20 24					20 54					21 24	
St Helier d			19 26					19 56					20 26					20 56					21 26	
Sutton Common d			19 28					19 58					20 28					20 58					21 28	
West Sutton d			19 31					20 01					20 31					21 01					21 31	
Sutton (Surrey) 4 a			19 35					20 05					20 35					21 05					21 35	
East Croydon 🚋 d																								
Redhill d																								
Gatwick Airport 10 ✈ d																								
Three Bridges 4 d																								
Balcombe d																								
Haywards Heath 3 d																								
Wivelsfield 4 d																								
Burgess Hill 4 d																								
Hassocks 4 d																								
Preston Park d																								
Brighton 10 a																								

For general notes see front of timetable
For details of catering facilities see Directory of Train Operators

A From Nottingham (Table 53)

B From 13 September. From Sheffield (Table 53)

C Until 6 September. From Derby (Table 53)

Sundays

Bedford, Luton, St.Albans and City of London → South London, Gatwick Airport and Brighton

Network Diagram - see first page of Table 52

		FC	EM	FC	EM	FC	EM	EM	FC	EM	EM	FC		FC	EM	EM	EM	EM	EM	EM	FC	FC	FC	
			1 ◇	1	1 ◇	1	1 ◇	1 ◇	1	1 ◇	1 ◇	1		1	1 ◇	1 ◇	1 ◇	1 ◇	1 ◇	1 ◇		1	1	
			A		B		A	C		D	E				E	G	H	J	K	C				
Bedford 7	d		20 07	20 10	20 40	20 40	21 08	21 08	21 10	21 37	21 45	21 40		22 10	22 18	22 18	22 20	22 32	22 35	22 38	22 40	23 10	23 40	
Flitwick	d			20 19		20 49			21 19			21 49		22 19							22 49	23 19	23 50	
Harlington	d			20 23		20 53			21 23			21 53		22 23							22 53	23 23	23 54	
Leagrave	d			20 29		20 59			21 29			21 59		22 29							22 59	23 29	23 59	
Luton 10	d	20 18	20 26	20 34		21 04	21 23	21 24	21 34	21 52	21 59	22 04		22 34	22 37	22 37	22 37	22 50	22 51	22 56	23 04	23 34	00 04	
Luton Airport Parkway 7 ✈	d	20 20		20 36	20 55	21 06			21 36			22 06		22 36							23 06	23 36	00 06	
Harpenden	d	20 26		20 42		21 12			21 42			22 12		22 42							23 12	23 42	00 12	
St Albans City	d	20 32		20 48		21 18			21 48			22 18		22 48							23 18	23 48	00 18	
Radlett	d	20 37		20 53		21 23			21 53			22 23		22 53							23 23	23 53	00 23	
Elstree & Borehamwood	d	20 41		20 57		21 27			21 57			22 27		22 57							23 27	23 57	00 27	
Mill Hill Broadway	d	20 46		21 01		21 31			22 01			22 31		23 01							23 31	00 01	00 31	
Hendon	d	20 48		21 04		21 34			22 04			22 34		23 04							23 34	00 04	00 34	
Cricklewood	d	20 52		21 08		21 38			22 08			22 38		23 08							23 38	00 08	00 38	
West Hampstead Thameslink ⊖	d	20 55		21 12		21 42			22 12			22 42		23 12							23 42	00 12	00 42	
Kentish Town ⊖	d	20 59		21 16		21 46			22 16			22 46		23 16							23 46	00 16	00 46	
St Pancras International ⊖	a	21 09	20 57	21 24	21 27	21 54	21 57	21 57	22 24	22 27	22 27	22 54		23 24	23 10	23 12	23 12	23 28	23 28	23 30	23 54	00 24	00 54	
St Pancras International 15 ⊖	d																							
Farringdon 3 ⊖	d																							
City Thameslink 3	d																							
London Blackfriars 3 ⊖	d																							
Elephant & Castle ⊖	d																							
Loughborough Jn	d																							
Herne Hill 4	d																							
London Bridge 4 ⊖	d																							
Tulse Hill 3	d																							
Streatham 4	d																							
Mitcham Eastfields	d																							
Mitcham Junction (tram)	d																							
Hackbridge	d																							
Carshalton	d																							
Tooting	d																							
Haydons Road	d																							
Wimbledon 6 ⊖ (tram)	d																							
Wimbledon Chase	d																							
South Merton	d																							
Morden South	d																							
St Helier	d																							
Sutton Common	d																							
West Sutton	d																							
Sutton (Surrey) 4	a																							
East Croydon (tram)	d																							
Redhill	d																							
Gatwick Airport 10 ✈	d																							
Three Bridges 4	d																							
Balcombe	d																							
Haywards Heath 3	d																							
Wivelsfield 4	d																							
Burgess Hill 4	d																							
Hassocks 4	d																							
Preston Park	d																							
Brighton 10	a																							

For general notes see front of timetable
For details of catering facilities see Directory of Train Operators

A Until 6 September. From Nottingham (Table 53)

B From York (Table 53)

C From 13 September. From Nottingham (Table 53)

D Until 6 September. From Sheffield (Table 53)

E From 13 September. From Sheffield (Table 53)

G Until 12 July. From Sheffield (Table 53)

H 19 July to 6 September. From Sheffield (Table 53)

J Until 12 July. From Nottingham (Table 53)

K 19 July to 6 September. From Nottingham (Table 53)

Brighton, Gatwick Airport and South London → City of London, St.Albans, Luton and Bedford

Network Diagram - see first page of Table 52

Miles	Miles	Miles	Miles	Miles			FC	FC	FC	FC	FC	FC	FC	FC	FC	FC	FC	FC	FC	FC	FC	FC	SE	SE	EM
							MO [1]	MX	MX [1]	MO [1]	MX	MX [1]	MO [1]	MX									A	A	[1] ◇ B ☕
0	—	—	—	—	**Brighton [10]**	d																			
1½	—	—	—	—	Preston Park	d																			
7¼	—	—	—	—	Hassocks [4]	d																			
9¼	—	—	—	—	Burgess Hill [4]	d																			
10	—	—	—	—	Wivelsfield [4]	d																			
13	—	—	—	—	**Haywards Heath [3]**	d																			
17	—	—	—	—	Balcombe	d																			
21½	—	—	—	—	Three Bridges [4]	d																			
24¼	—	—	—	—	**Gatwick Airport [10]** ✈	d																04 25			
30	—	—	—	—	Redhill	d																04 30			
40½	—	—	0	—	**East Croydon** 🚋	d																04 47			
—	—	—	—	—	Sevenoaks [4]	d																			
—	—	—	—	—	Bat & Ball	d																			
—	—	—	—	—	Otford [4]	d																			
—	—	—	—	—	Shoreham (Kent)	d																			
—	—	—	—	—	Eynsford	d																			
—	—	—	—	—	Swanley [4]	d																			
—	—	—	—	—	St Mary Cray [4]	d																			
—	—	—	—	—	Bickley	d																	04 43	05 05	
—	—	—	—	—	Bromley South	d																	04 46	05 08	
—	—	—	—	—	Shortlands [4]	d																	04 48	05 10	
—	—	—	—	—	Ravensbourne	d																	04 51		
—	—	—	—	—	Beckenham Hill	d																	04 53		
—	—	—	—	—	Bellingham	d																	04 55		
—	—	—	—	—	Catford	d																	04 57		
—	—	—	—	—	Crofton Park	d																	04 59		
—	—	—	—	—	Nunhead [4]	d																	05 02		
—	—	—	—	—	Peckham Rye [4]	d																	05 04		
—	—	—	—	—	Denmark Hill [4]	d																	05 06		
—	0	0	—	0	**Sutton (Surrey) [4]**	d																			
—	1	—	—	—	West Sutton	d																			
—	2	—	—	—	Sutton Common	d																			
—	3	—	—	—	St Helier	d																			
—	3½	—	—	—	Morden South	d																			
—	4	—	—	—	South Merton	d																			
—	4½	—	—	—	Wimbledon Chase	d																			
—	5½	—	—	—	**Wimbledon [6]** 🚋	d																			
—	6¾	—	—	—	Haydons Road	d																			
—	8	—	—	—	Tooting	d																			
—	—	—	—	1¼	Carshalton	d																			
—	—	—	—	2	Hackbridge	d																			
—	—	—	—	4	Mitcham Junction 🚋	d																			
—	—	—	—	5	Mitcham Eastfields	d																			
—	9½	6	—	6	Streatham [4]	d																			
—	11	7½	5	—	Tulse Hill [3]	d																			
50¾	—	—	—	—	**London Bridge [4]** ⊖	d																			
—	12	8½	—	—	Herne Hill [4]	d																		05 25	
—	13	9½	—	—	Loughborough Jn	d																			
—	15	11½	—	—	Elephant & Castle	d																	05 13	05 31	
51½	16	12½	10	—	**London Blackfriars [3]** ⊖	d																05 14	05 17	05 35	
52	—	—	—	—	City Thameslink [3]	d																05 16	05a19	05a38	
—	0	—	—	—	**Moorgate** ⊖	d																			
—	2	—	—	—	Barbican ⊖	d																			
52¾	3	—	—	—	Farringdon [3] ⊖	d																05 20			
53¾	—	—	—	—	**St Pancras International [15]** ⊖	d	23p04	23p18	23p34	23p34	23p48	00 04	00 04	00 18	00 18	00 38	01 08	01 38	02 38	03 58	04 58	05b26			06 10
55½	—	—	—	—	Kentish Town ⊖	d	23p09	23p23		23p39	23p53		00 09	00 23	00 23	00 43	01 13	01 43	02 43	04 03	05 03	05 30			
58	—	—	—	—	West Hampstead Thameslink ⊖	d	23p12	23p26	23p41	23p42	23p56	00 11	00 12	00 25	00 26	00 46	01 16	01 46	02 46	04 06	05 06	05 33			
59	—	—	—	—	Cricklewood	d	23p15	23p29		23p45	23p59		00 15	00 28	00 29	00 49	01 19	01 49	02 49	04 09	05 09	05 36			
61	—	—	—	—	Hendon	d	23p18	23p31		23p48	00 02		00 18	00 31	00 32	00 52	01 22	01 52	02 52	04 12	05 12	05 39			
63¼	—	—	—	—	Mill Hill Broadway	d	23p22	23p36		23p52	00 06		00 22	00 36	00 36	00 56	01 26	01 56	02 56	04 16	05 16	05 43			
66½	—	—	—	—	Elstree & Borehamwood	d	23p26	23p39		23p56	00 10		00 26	00 39	00 40	01 00	01 30	02 00	03 00	04 20	05 20	05 47			
69½	—	—	—	—	Radlett	d	23p31	23p45		00 01	00 15		00 31	00 44	00 45	01 05	01 35	02 05	03 05	04 25	05 25	05 52			
74	—	—	—	—	**St Albans City**	d	23p37	23p51	23p55	00 07	00 21	00 25	00 38	00 50	00 52	01 11	01 42	02 11	03 11	04 31	05 31	05 58			
78¾	—	—	—	—	Harpenden	d	23p43	23p57	00 02	00 13	00 27	00 32	00 44	00 56	00 58	01 17	01 48	02 17	03 17	04 37	05 37	06 04			
83¼	—	—	—	—	Luton Airport Parkway [7] ✈	d	23p49	00 03	00 08	00 19	00 33	00 38	00 50	01 02	01 04	01 23	01 54	02 23	03 23	04 43	05 43	06 10			
84¼	30¼	—	—	—	**Luton [10]**	d	23p53	00 06	00 11	00 23	00 36	00 41	00 54	01 05	01 08	01 27	01 57	02 27	03 27	04 47	05 47	06 13			06 33
86¾	—	—	—	—	Leagrave	d	23p56	00 09	00 14	00 26	00 39	00 44	00 57	01 09	01 11	01 30	02 00	02 30	03 30	04 50	05 50	06 16			
91¼	—	—	—	—	Harlington	d	00 02	00 15	00 20	00 32	00 45	00 50	01 03	01 14	01 17	01 36	02 06	02 36	03 36	04 56	05 56	06 22			
94¼	—	—	—	—	Flitwick	d	00 06	00 19	00 24	00 36	00 49	00 54	01 07	01 18	01 21	01 40	02 10	02 40	03 40	05 00	06 00	06 26			
103¾	49¾	—	—	—	**Bedford [7]**	a	00 18	00 31	00 36	00 48	01 01	01 06	01 19	01 31	01 33	01 52	02 22	02 52	03 52	05 12	06 12	06 38			06 47

For general notes see front of timetable
For details of catering facilities see Directory of Train Operators

A From Orpington (Table 195)
B To Derby (Table 53)
b Arr. 0523

Brighton, Gatwick Airport and South London → City of London, St.Albans, Luton and Bedford

Network Diagram - see first page of Table 52

		FC [1]	EM [1] ◇ A ☕	FC B	SE C	FC [1]	EM [1] ◇ D ☕	EM [1] ◇ D ☕	FC B	SN	SE E	FC [1]	SE	FC	EM [1] ◇ D ☕	FC [1]	FC	SN	SE E	SE [1] E G	SE [1] E H	FC [1]	SE	EM [1] ◇ J ☕	FC
Brighton [10]	d					05 09						05 39				05 49						06 09			
Preston Park	d					05 13						05 43				05 53						06 13			
Hassocks [4]	d					05 19						05 49				05 59						06 19			
Burgess Hill [4]	d					05 23						05 53				06 03						06 23			
Wivelsfield [4]	d					05 26						05 56				06 05									
Haywards Heath [3]	d					05 30						06 00				06 09						06 30			
Balcombe	d											06 05										06 35			
Three Bridges [4]	d	04 55				05 40						06 12				06 20						06 40			
Gatwick Airport [10] ✈	d	05 00				05 46						06 16				06 24						06 46			
Redhill	d															06 33									
East Croydon 🚋	d	05 17				06 02						06 32				06 44						07 02			
Sevenoaks [4]	d										05 40								06 13						
Bat & Ball	d										05 43								06 16						
Otford [4]	d										05 46								06 19	06 36	06 38				
Shoreham (Kent)	d										05 49								06 22						
Eynsford	d										05 52								06 25						
Swanley [4]	d										05 57								06 31	06 49	06 49				
St Mary Cray [4]	d										06 01								06 35						
Bickley	d				05 43						06 06								06 41						
Bromley South	d				05 46						06 15								06 44	06 58	06 58				
Shortlands [4]	d				05 48						06 17								06 46						
Ravensbourne	d				05 51						06 20								06 49						
Beckenham Hill	d				05 53						06 22								06 51						
Bellingham	d				05 55						06 24								06 53						
Catford	d				05 57						06 26								06 55						
Crofton Park	d				06 00						06 28								06 58						
Nunhead [4]	d				06 02						06 31								07 00						
Peckham Rye [4]	d				06 04						06 33								07 02						
Denmark Hill [4]	d				06 07						06 35								07 05						
Sutton (Surrey) [4]	d									06 14							06 22	06 51							06 48
West Sutton	d																06 25								06 51
Sutton Common	d																06 27								06 53
St Helier	d																06 30								06 56
Morden South	d																06 32								06 58
South Merton	d																06 34								07 00
Wimbledon Chase	d																06 36								07 02
Wimbledon [6] 🚋	d													06 24			06 40								07 06
Haydons Road	d													06 26			06 42								07 08
Tooting	d													06 29			06 45								07 11
Carshalton	d									06 17								06 54							
Hackbridge	d									06 19								06 56							
Mitcham Junction 🚋	d									06 23								07 00							
Mitcham Eastfields	d									06 26															
Streatham [4]	d			05 46					06 06	06 30				06 34			06 50	07 06							07 16
Tulse Hill [3]	d			05 50					06 10	06 34				06 38			06 56	07 09							07 20
London Bridge [4] ⊖	d	05 34				06 15				06a51		06 46				06 59		07a25				07 16			
Herne Hill [4]	d			05 54					06 14					06 42			07 00								07 24
Loughborough Jn	d								06 17					06 45			07 03								07 27
Elephant & Castle	d			06 00	06 13				06 22		06 40			06 50			07 08		07 12	07 16	07 16				07 32
London Blackfriars [3] ⊖	d	05 44		06 04	06 17	06 24			06 30		06 44	06 54		06 58		07 06	07 12		07 16	07 20	07 20	07 23			07 36
City Thameslink [3]	d	05 46		06 06	06a19	06 26			06 32		06 46	06 56		07 00		07 08	07 14		07 18	07 22	07 22	07 26			07 38
Moorgate ⊖	d																								
Barbican ⊖	d																								
Farringdon [3] ⊖	d	05 50		06 10		06 30			06 36		06 50	07 00		07 04		07 12	07 18		07 22	07 28	07 28	07 29			07 44
St Pancras International [15] ⊖	d	05b56	06 37	06c16		06 34	06 55	07 00	06e42		06 54	07 04		07 08	07 30	07 16	07 22		07 26	07 32	07 32	07 33		08 00	07 48
Kentish Town ⊖	d	06 00		06 20					06 46		06 58								07 30						
West Hampstead Thameslink ⊖	d	06 03		06 23		06 41			06 49		07 01	07 11		07 15		07 25	07 29		07 33						07 57
Cricklewood	d	06 06		06 26					06 52		07 04								07 36				←		
Hendon	d	06 09		06 29					06 55		07 07		←						07 39				07 39		
Mill Hill Broadway	d	06 13		06 33					06 59		07 11		07 11						→				07 43		
Elstree & Borehamwood	d	06 17		06 37					07 03		→		07 15	07 24			07 38						07 47		
Radlett	d	06 22		06 42					07 08				07 20	07 29			07 43						07 52		
St Albans City	d	06 28		06 48		06 55			07 14			07 25	07a27	07 35		07 40	07a50			07 54	07 54	07 54	07 58		08 12
Harpenden	d	06 34		06 54		07 02			07 20			07 32		07 40		07 46				08 00	08 00	08 00			08 18
Luton Airport Parkway [7] ✈	d	06 40		07 00		07 08	07a15		07 26			07 38		07 46	07 51	07 52				08 06	08 06	08 06			08 24
Luton [10]	d	06 43	06a58	07 03		07 11		07 23	07 29			07 41		07a50		07 55				08 09	08 09	08 09	08a09	08 23	08 27
Leagrave	d	06 46		07 06		07 14			07 32			07 44				07 58				08 13	08 13	08 13			08 30
Harlington	d	06 52		07 12		07 20			07 38			07 50				08 04				08 18	08 18	08 18			08 36
Flitwick	d	06 56		07 16		07 24			07 42			07 54				08 08				08 22	08 22	08 22			08 40
Bedford [7]	a	07 08		07 29		07 36		07 38	07 54			08 06			08 06	08 20				08 34	08 34	08 34		08 37	08 52

For general notes see front of timetable
For details of catering facilities see Directory of Train Operators

A To Sheffield (Table 53)
B From Selhurst (Table 177)
C From Orpington (Table 195)
D To Nottingham (Table 53)
E TOC FC from London Blackfriars
G From 12 October. From Bearsted (Table 196)
H Until 9 October. From Bearsted (Table 196)
J To Corby. (Table 53)
b Arr. 0553
c Arr. 0613
e Arr. 0639

Brighton, Gatwick Airport and South London → City of London, St.Albans, Luton and Bedford

Network Diagram - see first page of Table 52

		SE	SE	FC [1]	SN	SE	SE	SE [1]	SE	FC	SE	EM [1] ◊	FC [1]		SN	FC	SE	SE	SE	EM [1] ◊	SE	SE	FC	SE	FC
		AB	B				AB	BC	A		B	D					BE	AB		G	BH	A		B	
Brighton [10]	d			06 23									07 00												
Preston Park	d			06 27									07 04												
Hassocks [4]	d			06 33									07 10												
Burgess Hill [4]	d			06 37									07 14												
Wivelsfield [4]	d			06 39									07 18												
Haywards Heath [3]	d			06 44									07 23												
Balcombe	d			06 50																					
Three Bridges [4]	d			06 55									07 32												
Gatwick Airport [10]	d			07 00									07 37												
Redhill	d			07 11																					
East Croydon	d			07 24									07 54												
Sevenoaks [4]	d		06 43								07 10													07 40	
Bat & Ball	d		06 46								07 13													07 43	
Otford [4]	d		06 49					07 21			07 16													07 46	
Shoreham (Kent)	d		06 52								07 19													07 49	
Eynsford	d		06 55								07 22													07 52	
Swanley [4]	d		07 01					07 31			07 28										07 55			07 58	
St Mary Cray [4]	d		07 06								07 32										08 00			08 02	
Bickley	d	07 09	07 11				07 30				07 37							07 53							
Bromley South	d	07 12	07 16				07 34	07 40			07 41							07 56			08 06			08 09	
Shortlands [4]	d	07 14	07 18				07 36				07 43							07 58							
Ravensbourne	d		07 21								07 46													08 12	
Beckenham Hill	d		07 23								07 48													08 14	
Bellingham	d		07 25								07 50							08 04						08 16	
Catford	d		07 27								07 52							08 08						08 18	
Crofton Park	d		07 29								07 55							08 10							
Nunhead [4]	d		07 32								07 57							08 13							
Peckham Rye [4]	d		07 34								08 00							08 15							
Denmark Hill [4]	d		07 37								08 02							08 18						08 26	
Sutton (Surrey) [4]	d				07 25					07 24					07 50										07 54
West Sutton	d									07 27															07 57
Sutton Common	d									07 29															07 59
St Helier	d									07 32															08 02
Morden South	d									07 34															08 04
South Merton	d									07 36															08 06
Wimbledon Chase	d									07 38															08 08
Wimbledon [6]	d									07 42													07 58		08 12
Haydons Road	d									07 44													08 00		08 14
Tooting	d									07 47													08 03		08 17
Carshalton	d				07 28										07 53										
Hackbridge	d				07 31										07 55										
Mitcham Junction	d				07 34										07 59										
Mitcham Eastfields	d				07 38																				
Streatham [4]	d				07 42					07 52					08 05								08 10		08 22
Tulse Hill [3]	d			07 35	07 46					07 56			08 05		08 09								08 14		08 26
London Bridge [4]	⊖ d				08a02										08a30										
Herne Hill [4]	d	07 32					07 50			08 01							08 13						08 22		08 31
Loughborough Jn	d	07 35					07 53			08 04							08 16						08 25		08 34
Elephant & Castle	d	07 40	07 43				07 58	08 02		08 09	08 13						08 21	08 25			08 29		08 32	08 36	08 41
London Blackfriars [3]	⊖ d	07 44	07 48	07 54			08 02	08 06		08 14	08 18		08 22				08 26	08 30			08 34		08 38	08 42	08 47
City Thameslink [3]	d	07 46	07 50	07 56			08 04	08 08		08 16	08 20		08 24				08 28	08 32			08 36		08 40	08 44	08 50
Moorgate	⊖ d																								
Barbican	⊖ d																								
Farringdon [3]	⊖ d	07 50	07 54	08 00			08 08	08 12		08 20	08 24		08 28				08 32	08 36			08 40		08 44	08 48	08 53
St Pancras International [15]	⊖ d	07 54	07 58	08 04			08 12	08 16		08 24	08 28	08 30	08 32				08 36	08 40		09 00	08 44		08 48	08 52	08 57
Kentish Town	⊖ d		08 02				08 16				08 32							08 44						08a58	09 01
West Hampstead Thameslink	⊖ d	08 01	08 05				08 19			08 33	08 37							08 49					08 55		09 04
Cricklewood	d		08 08			←	08 22		←		08 40							08 52	←			←			09 07
Hendon	d		08 11			08 11	08 25		08 25		08 43							08 55	08 43			08 55			09 10
Mill Hill Broadway	d		→			08 15	→		08 29		→					←		→	08 47			08 59			→
Elstree & Borehamwood	d	08 10				08 19			08 33	08 42						08 42			08 51			09 03	09 07		
Radlett	d	08 15				08 24			08 38	→						08 46			08 56			09 08	09 12		
St Albans City	d	08 21		08 25		08a31		08 36	08a45				08 52			08 53	08 57		09a03		09 07	09 15	09 19		
Harpenden	d	08 26		08 32				08 44									09 04				09 14	09 20	09 24		
Luton Airport Parkway [7]	d	08 32		08 38				08 50				08 51	09 00			09 02	09 10				09 20	09 26	09 30		
Luton [10]	d	08a36		08 41				08 53					09 04			09a06	09 13			09 23	09 23	09a30	09 35		
Leagrave	d			08 44				08 56									09 16				09 26		09 40		
Harlington	d			08 50				09 02									09 22				09 32		09 46		
Flitwick	d			08 54				09 06					09 14				09 26				09 36		09 50		
Bedford [7]	a			09 06				09 18				09 07	09 26				09 38			09 37	09 48		10 02		

For general notes see front of timetable
For details of catering facilities see Directory of Train Operators

- **A** From Orpington (Table 195)
- **B** TOC FC from London Blackfriars
- **C** From Ashford International (Table 196)
- **D** To Nottingham (Table 53)
- **E** From Beckenham Junction (Table 195)
- **G** To Kettering (Table 53)
- **H** From Rochester (Table 212)

Brighton, Gatwick Airport and South London → City of London, St.Albans, Luton and Bedford

Network Diagram - see first page of Table 52

	SE	FC	FC	SE	SE	EM	FC	SE	FC	SN	SE	FC	FC	SE	SE	FC	SE	EM	FC	SE	FC	FC	FC	SE
		1				1 ◊	1					1						1 ◊	1			1		
	A			A	A B	C 🍴		B			A			A	D A			E 🍴		A				
Brighton 10 d		07 24					07 50					08 02							08 16			08 36		
Preston Park d		07 28					07 54					08 06							08 20			08 40		
Hassocks 4 d		07 35					08 00					08 12							08 26			08 46		
Burgess Hill 4 d		07 39										08 16							08 30			08 50		
Wivelsfield 4 d												08 18							08 33					
Haywards Heath 3 d		07 46					08 09					08 23							08 38			09 00		
Balcombe d							08 14															09 06		
Three Bridges 4 d		07 55										08 34							08 47			09 12		
Gatwick Airport 10 ✈ d		08 01					08 22					08 38							08 52			09 16		
Redhill d		08 14																						
East Croydon 🚌 d		08 28					08 38					08 54							09 08			09 32		
Sevenoaks 4 d				07 52										08 22						08 40				
Bat & Ball d				07 55										08 25						08 43				
Otford 4 d				07 58										08 28						08 46				
Shoreham (Kent) d				08 01										08 31						08 49				
Eynsford d				08 04										08 34						08 52				
Swanley 4 d				08 10										08 40						08 58				
St Mary Cray 4 d				08 14										08 44						09 02				
Bickley d				08 20										08 49	08 55					09 06				
Bromley South d	08 18			08 23							08 45			08 52	08 58					09 09				
Shortlands 4 d	08 20			08 26							08 47			08 54	09 00					09 11				
Ravensbourne d	08 23										08 49				09 03					09 14				
Beckenham Hill d	08 25										08 51				09 05					09 16				
Bellingham d	08 27			08 32							08 54			09 00	09 07					09 18				
Catford d	08 29			08 37							08 56			09 02	09 09					09 21				
Crofton Park d				08 40							08 59				09 11					09 23				
Nunhead 4 d				08 43							09 01				09 14					09 26				
Peckham Rye 4 d	08 35			08 45							09 04			09 08	09 16					09 28				
Denmark Hill 4 d	08 37			08 48							09 07			09 11	09 19					09 31				
Sutton (Surrey) 4 d									08 20	08 51						08 47							09 06	
West Sutton d									08 23							08 50							09 09	
Sutton Common d									08 25							08 52							09 11	
St Helier d									08 28							08 55							09 14	
Morden South d									08 30							08 57							09 16	
South Merton d									08 32							08 59							09 18	
Wimbledon Chase d									08 34							09 01							09 20	
Wimbledon 6 🚌 d									08 42							09 05							09 24	
Haydons Road d									08 44							09 07							09 26	
Tooting d									08 47							09 10							09 29	
Carshalton d										08 54														
Hackbridge d										08 56														
Mitcham Junction 🚌 d										09 00														
Mitcham Eastfields d										09 03														
Streatham 4 d									08 52	09 10						09 15							09 34	
Tulse Hill 3 d		08 39					08 54		08 58	09 15						09 19			09 25				09 38	
London Bridge 4 ⊖ d										09a34		09 11										09 45		
Herne Hill 4 d		08 43			08 52		08 58		09 02							09 23							09 42	
Loughborough Jn d					08 55				09 05							09 26							09 45	
Elephant & Castle d	08 45			08 53	09 00				09 10		09 14			09 18	09 26	09 30				09 40			09 50	
London Blackfriars 3 ⊖ d	08 50	08 54		09 00	09 04		09 08		09 14		09 18	09 20		09 26	09 30	09 34			09 38	09 44		09 54	09 58	
City Thameslink 3 d	08 52	08 56		09 02	09 06		09 10		09 16		09 20	09 22		09 28	09 32	09 36			09 40	09 46		09 56	10 00	
Moorgate ⊖ d																								
Barbican ⊖ d																								
Farringdon 3 ⊖ d	08 56	09 00		09 06	09 10		09 14		09 20		09 24	09 28		09 32	09 36	09 40			09 44	09 50		10 00	10 04	
St Pancras International 15 ⊖ d	09 00	09 04		09 10	09 14	09 30	09 18		09 24		09 28	09 32		09 36	09 40	09 44		10 00	09 48	09 54		10 04	10 08	
Kentish Town ⊖ d					09 18						09 32				09a46	09 48				09 58			10 12	
West Hampstead Thameslink ⊖ d				09 17	09 21				09 31		09 37					09 51				10 01			10 15	
Cricklewood d			←		09 24			←			09 40					09 54	←			10 04	←		10 18	←
Hendon d			09 10		09 27			09 27			09 43					09 57	09 43			10 07	09 57		10 21	10 07
Mill Hill Broadway d			09 14		→			09 31			→		←			→	09 47			→	10 01		→	10 11
Elstree & Borehamwood d			09 18	09 26				09 35	09 40				09 40				09 51				10 05			10 15
Radlett d			09 23	09 31				09 40	→				09 44				09 58				10 10			10 20
St Albans City d	09 21	09 25	09a30	09 37			09 41	09 47				09 52	09a52	09 57			10 04		10 10		10 17	10 25		10a27
Harpenden d		09 32		09 42			09 46	09 54						10 04			10 09		10 16		10 24	10 32		
Luton Airport Parkway 7 ✈ d	09 29	09 38		09 48		09 51	09 52	10 00				10 00		10 10			10 15		10 22		10 30	10 38		
Luton 10 d	09 32	09 41		09a52			09 57	10a04				10 04		10 13			10a18	10 23	10 25		10a34	10 41		
Leagrave d		09 44					10 00							10 16					10 28			10 44		
Harlington d		09 50					10 06							10 22					10 34			10 50		
Flitwick d	09 43	09 54					10 10					10 13		10 26					10 38			10 54		
Bedford 7 a	09 56	10 08				10 06	10 22					10 26		10 38				10 37	10 50			11 06		

For general notes see front of timetable
For details of catering facilities see
Directory of Train Operators

A TOC FC from London Blackfriars
B From Kent House (Table 195)
C To Nottingham (Table 53)
D From Orpington (Table 195)
E To Corby. (Table 53)

Brighton, Gatwick Airport and South London → City of London, St.Albans, Luton and Bedford

Network Diagram - see first page of Table 52

Station		EM 1 ◇ A	FC 1	FC	FC	SE B	FC 1	FC	FC	SE B	EM 1 ◇ C	FC 1	FC	FC	FC 1	FC	FC	SE B	EM 1 ◇ A	FC 1	FC		FC	FC 1	FC
Brighton 10	d		09 00				09 07					09 34			09 37					10 04				10 07	
Preston Park	d						09 11								09 41									10 11	
Hassocks 4	d		09 08				09 17								09 47									10 17	
Burgess Hill 4	d		09 12				09 21								09 51									10 21	
Wivelsfield 4	d						09 23								09 53									10 23	
Haywards Heath 3	d		09 16				09 32					09 48			09 58					10 18				10 32	
Balcombe	d						09 37																	10 37	
Three Bridges 4	d		09 27				09 42								10 10									10 42	
Gatwick Airport 10	d		09 31				09 46					10 01			10 16					10 31				10 46	
Redhill	d																								
East Croydon	d		09 47				10 02					10 17			10 32					10 47				11 02	
Sevenoaks 4	d					09 12				09 34								10 04							
Bat & Ball	d					09 15				09 37								10 07							
Otford 4	d					09 18				09 40								10 10							
Shoreham (Kent)	d					09 21				09 43								10 13							
Eynsford	d					09 24				09 47								10 17							
Swanley 4	d					09 30				09 52								10 22							
St Mary Cray 4	d					09 35				09 56								10 26							
Bickley	d					09 39				10 01								10 31							
Bromley South	d					09 43				10 05								10 35							
Shortlands 4	d					09 45				10 07								10 37							
Ravensbourne	d					09 47				10 09								10 39							
Beckenham Hill	d					09 49				10 11								10 41							
Bellingham	d					09 51				10 13								10 43							
Catford	d					09 53				10 15								10 45							
Crofton Park	d					09 56				10 18								10 48							
Nunhead 4	d					09 59				10 20								10 50							
Peckham Rye 4	d					10 01				10 22								10 52							
Denmark Hill 4	d					10 04				10 25								10 55							
Sutton (Surrey) 4	d				09 38			09 37					10 06			10 07					10 36				10 37
West Sutton	d							09 40								10 10									10 40
Sutton Common	d							09 42								10 12									10 42
St Helier	d							09 45								10 15									10 45
Morden South	d							09 47								10 17									10 47
South Merton	d							09 49								10 19									10 49
Wimbledon Chase	d							09 51								10 21									10 51
Wimbledon 6	d							09 56								10 26									10 56
Haydons Road	d							09 58								10 28									10 58
Tooting	d							10 01								10 31									11 01
Carshalton	d				09 41								10 09								10 39				
Hackbridge	d				09 43								10 11								10 41				
Mitcham Junction	d				09 46								10 14								10 44				
Mitcham Eastfields	d				09 50								10 18								10 48				
Streatham 4	d				09 53			10 06					10 23			10 36					10 53				11 06
Tulse Hill 3	d				09 57			10 12					10 27			10 42					10 57				11 12
London Bridge 4	d		10 01				10 16					10 30			10 45					11 00				11 15	
Herne Hill 4	d				10 01			10 16					10 31			10 46					11 01				11 16
Loughborough Jn	d				10 04			10 19					10 34			10 49					11 04				11 19
Elephant & Castle	d				10 09	10 12		10 24		10 30			10 39			10 54		11 00			11 09				11 24
London Blackfriars 3	d		10 08		10 14	10 18	10 24	10 28		10 34		10 38	10 44		10 54	10 58		11 04		11 08	11 14			11 24	11 28
City Thameslink 3	d		10 10		10 16	10 20	10 26	10 30		10 36		10 40	10 46		10 56	11 00		11 06		11 10	11 16			11 26	11 30
Moorgate	d																								
Barbican	d																								
Farringdon 3	d		10 14		10 20	10 24	10 30	10 34		10 40		10 44	10 50		11 00	11 04		11 10		11 14	11 20			11 30	11 34
St Pancras International 15	d	10 30	10 18		10 24	10 28	10 34	10 38		10 44	11 00	10 48	10 54		11 04	11 08		11 14	11 30	11 18	11 24			11 34	11 38
Kentish Town	d				10 28	10a34		10 42		10a50			10 58			11 12		11a20			11 28				11 42
West Hampstead Thameslink	d				10 31			10 45					11 01			11 15					11 31				11 45
Cricklewood	d			←	10 34			10 48	←				11 04	←		11 18	←				11 34		←		11 48
Hendon	d			10 21	10 37			10 51	10 37				11 07	10 51		11 21	11 07				11 37		11 21		11 51
Mill Hill Broadway	d			10 25	→			→	10 41				→	10 55		→	11 11				→		11 25		→
Elstree & Borehamwood	d			10 29					10 45					10 59			11 15						11 29		
Radlett	d			10 38					10 50					11 09			11 20						11 38		
St Albans City	d		10 40	10 45			10 55		10a57			11 10		11 15	11 25		11a27			11 40			11 45	11 55	
Harpenden	d		10 46	10 50			11 00					11 16		11 20	11 32					11 46			11 50	12 02	
Luton Airport Parkway 7	d	10 51	10 52	10 56			11 06					11 22		11 26	11 38				11 51	11 52			11 56	12 08	
Luton 10	d		10 55	11a00			11 09				11 23	11 25		11a30	11 41					11 55			12a00	12 11	
Leagrave	d		10 58				11 13					11 28			11 44					11 58				12 14	
Harlington	d		11 04				11 19					11 34			11 50					12 04				12 20	
Flitwick	d		11 08				11 23					11 38			11 54					12 08				12 24	
Bedford 7	a	11 06	11 20				11 36				11 37	11 50			12 06				12 06	12 20				12 36	

For general notes see front of timetable
For details of catering facilities see Directory of Train Operators

- **A** To Nottingham (Table 53)
- **B** TOC FC from London Blackfriars
- **C** To Corby. (Table 53)

Brighton, Gatwick Airport and South London → City of London, St.Albans, Luton and Bedford

Network Diagram - see first page of Table 52

		FC	SE	EM	FC	FC	FC	FC	FC	FC	SE	EM	FC	FC	FC	FC	FC	FC	SE	EM	FC	FC	FC	FC	FC
				1 ◇	1			1				1 ◇	1			1				1 ◇	1			1	
			A	B							A	C							A	B					
				☕								☕								☕					
Brighton 10	d				10 34			10 37					11 04			11 07					11 34			11 37	
Preston Park	d							10 41								11 11								11 41	
Hassocks 4	d							10 47								11 17								11 47	
Burgess Hill 4	d							10 51								11 21								11 51	
Wivelsfield 4	d							10 53								11 23								11 53	
Haywards Heath 3	d				10 48			11 02					11 18			11 32					11 48			12 02	
Balcombe	d															11 37									
Three Bridges 4	d							11 12								11 42								12 12	
Gatwick Airport 10 ✈	d				11 01			11 16					11 31			11 46					12 01			12 16	
Redhill	d																								
East Croydon 🚊	d				11 17			11 32					11 47			12 02					12 17			12 32	
Sevenoaks 4	d		10 34								11 04								11 34						
Bat & Ball	d		10 37								11 07								11 37						
Otford 4	d		10 40								11 10								11 40						
Shoreham (Kent)	d		10 43								11 13								11 43						
Eynsford	d		10 47								11 16								11 47						
Swanley 4	d		10 52								11 22								11 52						
St Mary Cray 4	d		10 56								11 26								11 56						
Bickley	d		11 01								11 31								12 01						
Bromley South	d		11 05								11 35								12 05						
Shortlands 4	d		11 07								11 37								12 07						
Ravensbourne	d		11 09								11 39								12 09						
Beckenham Hill	d		11 11								11 41								12 11						
Bellingham	d		11 13								11 43								12 13						
Catford	d		11 15								11 45								12 15						
Crofton Park	d		11 18								11 48								12 18						
Nunhead 4	d		11 20								11 50								12 20						
Peckham Rye 4	d		11 22								11 52								12 22						
Denmark Hill 4	d		11 25								11 55								12 25						
Sutton (Surrey) 4	d					11 06			11 07					11 36			11 37					12 06			12 07
West Sutton	d								11 10								11 40								12 10
Sutton Common	d								11 12								11 42								12 12
St Helier	d								11 15								11 45								12 15
Morden South	d								11 17								11 47								12 17
South Merton	d								11 19								11 49								12 19
Wimbledon Chase	d								11 21								11 51								12 21
Wimbledon 6 🚊	d								11 26								11 56								12 26
Haydons Road	d								11 28								11 58								12 28
Tooting	d								11 31								12 01								12 31
Carshalton	d					11 09								11 39								12 09			
Hackbridge	d					11 11								11 41								12 11			
Mitcham Junction 🚊	d					11 14								11 44								12 14			
Mitcham Eastfields	d					11 18								11 48								12 18			
Streatham 4	d					11 23			11 36					11 53			12 06					12 23			12 36
Tulse Hill 3	d					11 27			11 42					11 57			12 12					12 27			12 42
London Bridge 4 ⊖	d				11 30			11 45					12 00			12 15					12 30			12 45	
Herne Hill 4	d					11 31			11 46					12 01			12 16					12 31			12 46
Loughborough Jn	d					11 34			11 49					12 04			12 19					12 34			12 49
Elephant & Castle	d		11 30			11 39			11 54		12 00			12 09			12 24		12 30			12 39			12 54
London Blackfriars 3 ⊖	d		11 34		11 38	11 44		11 54	11 58		12 04		12 08	12 14		12 24	12 28		12 34		12 38	12 44		12 54	12 58
City Thameslink 3	d		11 36		11 40	11 46		11 56	12 00		12 06		12 10	12 16		12 27	12 30		12 36		12 40	12 46		12 56	13 00
Moorgate ⊖	d																								
Barbican ⊖	d																								
Farringdon 3 ⊖	d		11 40		11 44	11 50		12 00	12 04		12 10		12 14	12 20		12 30	12 34		12 40		12 44	12 50		13 00	13 04
St Pancras International 15 ⊖	d		11 44	12 00	11 48	11 54		12 04	12 08		12 14	12 30	12 18	12 24		12 34	12 38		12 44	13 00	12 48	12 54		13 04	13 08
Kentish Town ⊖	d		11a50			11 58			12 12		12a20			12 28			12 42		12a50			12 58			13 12
West Hampstead Thameslink ⊖	d					12 01			12 15					12 31			12 45					13 01			13 15
Cricklewood	d	←				12 04	←		12 18	←				12 34	←		12 48	←				13 04	←		13 18
Hendon	d	11 37				12 07	11 51		12 21	12 07				12 37	12 21		12 51	12 37				13 07	12 51		13 21
Mill Hill Broadway	d	11 41				→	11 55		→	12 11				→	12 25		→	12 41				→	12 55		→
Elstree & Borehamwood	d	11 45					11 59			12 15					12 29			12 45					12 59		
Radlett	d	11 50					12 08			12 20					12 38			12 50					13 08		
St Albans City	d	11a57			12 10		12 15	12 25		12a27			12 40		12 45	12 55		12a57			13 10		13 15	13 25	
Harpenden	d				12 16		12 20	12 32					12 46		12 50	13 02					13 16		13 20	13 32	
Luton Airport Parkway 7 ✈	d				12 22		12 26	12 38				12 51	12 52		12 56	13 08					13 22		13 26	13 38	
Luton 10	d			12 23	12 25		12a30	12 41					12 55		13a00	13 11				13 23	13 25		13a30	13 41	
Leagrave	d				12 28			12 44					12 58			13 14					13 28			13 44	
Harlington	d				12 34			12 50					13 04			13 20					13 34			13 50	
Flitwick	d				12 38			12 54					13 08			13 24					13 38			13 54	
Bedford 7	a			12 37	12 50			13 06				13 06	13 20			13 36				13 37	13 50			14 06	

For general notes see front of timetable
For details of catering facilities see Directory of Train Operators

A TOC FC from London Blackfriars
B To Corby. (Table 53)
C To Nottingham (Table 53)

Brighton, Gatwick Airport and South London → City of London, St.Albans, Luton and Bedford

Network Diagram - see first page of Table 52

		FC	SE	EM	FC	FC	FC	FC	FC	FC	SE	EM	FC	FC	FC	FC	FC	FC	SE	EM	FC	FC	FC	FC	FC
				1 ◇	1			1				1 ◇	1			1				1 ◇	1			1	
			A	B							A	C							A	B					
Brighton 10	d				12 04			12 07					12 34			12 37					13 04			13 07	
Preston Park	d							12 11								12 41								13 11	
Hassocks 4	d							12 17								12 47								13 17	
Burgess Hill 4	d							12 21								12 51								13 21	
Wivelsfield 4	d							12 23								12 53								13 23	
Haywards Heath 3	d				12 18			12 32					12 48			13 02					13 18			13 32	
Balcombe	d							12 37																13 37	
Three Bridges 4	d							12 42								13 12								13 42	
Gatwick Airport 10 ✈	d				12 31			12 46					13 01			13 16					13 31			13 46	
Redhill	d																								
East Croydon	d				12 47			13 02					13 17			13 32					13 47			14 02	
Sevenoaks 4	d		12 04								12 34								13 04						
Bat & Ball	d		12 07								12 37								13 07						
Otford 4	d		12 10								12 40								13 10						
Shoreham (Kent)	d		12 13								12 43								13 13						
Eynsford	d		12 17								12 47								13 17						
Swanley 4	d		12 22								12 52								13 22						
St Mary Cray 4	d		12 26								12 56								13 26						
Bickley	d		12 31								13 01								13 31						
Bromley South	d		12 35								13 05								13 35						
Shortlands 4	d		12 37								13 07								13 37						
Ravensbourne	d		12 39								13 09								13 39						
Beckenham Hill	d		12 41								13 11								13 41						
Bellingham	d		12 43								13 13								13 43						
Catford	d		12 45								13 15								13 45						
Crofton Park	d		12 48								13 18								13 48						
Nunhead 4	d		12 50								13 20								13 50						
Peckham Rye 4	d		12 52								13 22								13 52						
Denmark Hill 4	d		12 55								13 25								13 55						
Sutton (Surrey) 4	d					12 36			12 37					13 06			13 07					13 36			13 37
West Sutton	d								12 40								13 10								13 40
Sutton Common	d								12 42								13 12								13 42
St Helier	d								12 45								13 15								13 45
Morden South	d								12 47								13 17								13 47
South Merton	d								12 49								13 19								13 49
Wimbledon Chase	d								12 51								13 21								13 51
Wimbledon 6	d								12 56								13 26								13 56
Haydons Road	d								12 58								13 28								13 58
Tooting	d								13 01								13 31								14 01
Carshalton	d					12 39								13 09								13 39			
Hackbridge	d					12 41								13 11								13 41			
Mitcham Junction	d					12 44								13 14								13 44			
Mitcham Eastfields	d					12 48								13 18								13 48			
Streatham 4	d					12 53			13 06					13 23			13 36					13 53			14 06
Tulse Hill 3	d					12 57			13 12					13 27			13 42					13 57			14 12
London Bridge 4 ⊖	d				13 00			13 15					13 30			13 45					14 00			14 15	
Herne Hill 4	d					13 01			13 16					13 31			13 46					14 01			14 16
Loughborough Jn	d					13 04			13 19					13 34			13 49					14 04			14 19
Elephant & Castle	d		13 00			13 09			13 24		13 30			13 39			13 54		14 00			14 09			14 24
London Blackfriars 3 ⊖	d		13 04		13 08	13 14		13 24	13 28		13 34		13 38	13 44		13 54	13 58		14 04		14 08	14 14		14 24	14 28
City Thameslink 3	d		13 06		13 10	13 16		13 27	13 30		13 36		13 40	13 46		13 56	14 00		14 06		14 10	14 16		14 26	14 30
Moorgate ⊖	d																								
Barbican ⊖	d																								
Farringdon 3 ⊖	d		13 10		13 14	13 20		13 30	13 34		13 40		13 44	13 50		14 00	14 04		14 10		14 14	14 20		14 30	14 34
St Pancras International 15 ⊖	d		13 14	13 30	13 18	13 24		13 34	13 38		13 44	14 00	13 48	13 54		14 04	14 08		14 14	14 30	14 18	14 24		14 34	14 38
Kentish Town ⊖	d		13a20			13 28			13 42		13a50			13 58			14 12		14a20			14 28			14 42
West Hampstead Thameslink ⊖	d					13 31			13 45					14 01			14 15					14 31			14 45
Cricklewood	d	←				13 34	←		13 48	←				14 04	←		14 18	←				14 34	←		14 48
Hendon	d	13 07				13 37	13 21		13 51	13 37				14 07	13 51		14 21	14 07				14 37	14 21		14 51
Mill Hill Broadway	d	13 11				→	13 25		→	13 41				→	13 55		→	14 11				→	14 25		→
Elstree & Borehamwood	d	13 15					13 29			13 45					13 59			14 15					14 29		
Radlett	d	13 20					13 38			13 50					14 08			14 20					14 38		
St Albans City	d	13a27			13 40		13 45	13 55		13a57			14 10		14 15	14 25		14a27			14 40		14 45	14 55	
Harpenden	d				13 46		13 50	14 02					14 16		14 20	14 32					14 46		14 50	15 02	
Luton Airport Parkway 7 ✈	d			13 51	13 52		13 56	14 08					14 22		14 26	14 38				14 51	14 52		14 56	15 08	
Luton 10	d				13 55		14a00	14 11				14 23	14 25		14a30	14 41					14 55		15a00	15 11	
Leagrave	d				13 58			14 14					14 28			14 44					14 58			15 14	
Harlington	d				14 04			14 20					14 34			14 50					15 04			15 20	
Flitwick	d				14 08			14 24					14 38			14 54					15 08			15 24	
Bedford 7	a			14 06	14 20			14 36				14 37	14 50			15 06				15 06	15 20			15 36	

For general notes see front of timetable
For details of catering facilities see
Directory of Train Operators

A TOC FC from London Blackfriars
B To Nottingham (Table 53)
C To Corby. (Table 53)

Brighton, Gatwick Airport and South London → City of London, St.Albans, Luton and Bedford

Network Diagram - see first page of Table 52

		FC	SE	EM	FC	FC	FC		FC	FC	FC	SE	EM	FC	FC	FC	FC	FC	FC	SE	EM	FC	FC	FC	FC
				1 ◇	1				1				1 ◇	1			1				1 ◇	1			1
			A	B								A	C							A	B				
Brighton 10	d				13 34				13 37					14 04			14 07					14 34			14 37
Preston Park	d								13 41								14 11								14 41
Hassocks 4	d								13 47								14 17								14 47
Burgess Hill 4	d								13 51								14 21								14 51
Wivelsfield 4	d								13 53								14 23								14 53
Haywards Heath 3	d				13 48				14 02					14 18			14 32					14 48			15 02
Balcombe	d																14 37								
Three Bridges 4	d								14 12								14 42								15 12
Gatwick Airport 10 ✈	d				14 01				14 16					14 31			14 46					15 01			15 16
Redhill	d																								
East Croydon	d				14 17				14 32					14 47			15 02					15 17			15 32
Sevenoaks 4	d		13 34									14 04								14 34					
Bat & Ball	d		13 37									14 07								14 37					
Otford 4	d		13 40									14 10								14 40					
Shoreham (Kent)	d		13 43									14 13								14 43					
Eynsford	d		13 47									14 17								14 47					
Swanley 4	d		13 52									14 22								14 52					
St Mary Cray 4	d		13 56									14 26								14 56					
Bickley	d		14 01									14 31								15 01					
Bromley South	d		14 05									14 35								15 05					
Shortlands 4	d		14 07									14 37								15 07					
Ravensbourne	d		14 09									14 39								15 09					
Beckenham Hill	d		14 11									14 41								15 11					
Bellingham	d		14 13									14 43								15 13					
Catford	d		14 15									14 45								15 15					
Crofton Park	d		14 18									14 48								15 18					
Nunhead 4	d		14 20									14 50								15 20					
Peckham Rye 4	d		14 22									14 52								15 22					
Denmark Hill 4	d		14 25									14 55								15 25					
Sutton (Surrey) 4	d					14 06				14 07					14 36			14 37					15 06		
West Sutton	d									14 10								14 40							
Sutton Common	d									14 12								14 42							
St Helier	d									14 15								14 45							
Morden South	d									14 17								14 47							
South Merton	d									14 19								14 49							
Wimbledon Chase	d									14 21								14 51							
Wimbledon 6	d									14 26								14 56							
Haydons Road	d									14 28								14 58							
Tooting	d									14 31								15 01							
Carshalton	d					14 09									14 39								15 09		
Hackbridge	d					14 11									14 41								15 11		
Mitcham Junction	d					14 14									14 44								15 14		
Mitcham Eastfields	d					14 18									14 48								15 18		
Streatham 4	d					14 23				14 36					14 53			15 06					15 23		
Tulse Hill 3	d					14 27				14 42					14 57			15 12					15 27		
London Bridge 4 ⊖	d				14 30				14 45					15 00			15 15					15 30			15 45
Herne Hill 4	d					14 31				14 46					15 01			15 16					15 31		
Loughborough Jn	d					14 34				14 49					15 04			15 19					15 34		
Elephant & Castle	d		14 30			14 39				14 54		15 00			15 09			15 24		15 30			15 39		
London Blackfriars 3 ⊖	d		14 34		14 38	14 44			14 54	14 58		15 04		15 08	15 14		15 24	15 28		15 34		15 38	15 44		15 54
City Thameslink 3	d		14 36		14 40	14 46			14 56	15 00		15 06		15 10	15 16		15 27	15 30		15 36		15 40	15 46		15 56
Moorgate ⊖	d																								
Barbican ⊖	d																								
Farringdon 3 ⊖	d		14 40		14 44	14 50			15 00	15 04		15 10		15 14	15 20		15 30	15 34		15 40		15 44	15 50		16 00
St Pancras International 15 ⊖	d		14 44	15 00	14 48	14 54			15 04	15 08		15 14	15 30	15 18	15 24		15 34	15 38		15 44	16 00	15 48	15 54		16 04
Kentish Town ⊖	d		14a50			14 58				15 12		15a20			15 28			15 42		15a50			15 58		
West Hampstead Thameslink ⊖	d					15 01				15 15					15 31			15 45					16 01		
Cricklewood	d	←				15 04	←			15 18	←				15 34	←		15 48	←				16 04	←	
Hendon	d	14 37				15 07	14 51			15 21	15 07				15 37	15 21		15 51	15 37				16 07	15 51	
Mill Hill Broadway	d	14 41				→	14 55			→	15 11				→	15 25		→	15 41				→	15 55	
Elstree & Borehamwood	d	14 45					14 59				15 15					15 29			15 45					15 59	
Radlett	d	14 50					15 08				15 20					15 38			15 50					16 08	
St Albans City	d	14a57			15 10		15 15		15 25		15a27			15 40		15 45	15 55		15a57			16 10		16 15	16 25
Harpenden	d				15 16		15 20		15 32					15 46		15 50	16 02					16 16		16 20	16 32
Luton Airport Parkway 7 ✈	d				15 22		15 26		15 38				15 51	15 52		15 56	16 08					16 22		16 26	16 38
Luton 10	d			15 23	15 25		15a30		15 41					15 55		16a00	16 11				16 23	16 25		16a30	16 41
Leagrave	d				15 28				15 44					15 58			16 14					16 28			16 44
Harlington	d				15 34				15 50					16 04			16 20					16 34			16 50
Flitwick	d				15 38				15 54					16 08			16 24					16 38			16 54
Bedford 7	a			15 37	15 50				16 06				16 06	16 20			16 36				16 37	16 50			17 06

For general notes see front of timetable
For details of catering facilities see Directory of Train Operators

A TOC FC from London Blackfriars
B To Corby. (Table 53)
C To Nottingham (Table 53)

Brighton, Gatwick Airport and South London → City of London, St.Albans, Luton and Bedford

Network Diagram - see first page of Table 52

		FC	FC	SE	EM	FC	FC	FC	FC	EM	FC	FC	FC	SE	FC	FC	FC	EM	FC	FC	FC	FC	SE	FC	FC
					1 ◇	1			1	1 ◇	1			1			1	1 ◇	1				1		
				A	B					C				A				B					A		
Brighton 10	d					15 04					15 07						15 34		15 37						
Preston Park	d										15 11								15 41						
Hassocks 4	d										15 17								15 47						
Burgess Hill 4	d										15 21								15 51						
Wivelsfield 4	d										15 23								15 53						
Haywards Heath 3	d					15 18					15 32						15 48		15 58						
Balcombe	d										15 37														
Three Bridges 4	d										15 42								16 07						
Gatwick Airport 10 ✈	d					15 31					15 46						16 01		16 11						
Redhill	d																								
East Croydon	d					15 47					16 02						16 17		16 27						
Sevenoaks 4	d			15 04										15 34									16 05		
Bat & Ball	d			15 07										15 37									16 08		
Otford 4	d			15 10										15 40									16 11		
Shoreham (Kent)	d			15 13										15 43									16 14		
Eynsford	d			15 17										15 47									16 18		
Swanley 4	d			15 22										15 52									16 23		
St Mary Cray 4	d			15 26										15 56									16 27		
Bickley	d			15 31										16 01									16 32		
Bromley South	d			15 35										16 05									16 35		
Shortlands 4	d			15 37										16 07									16 37		
Ravensbourne	d			15 39										16 09									16 40		
Beckenham Hill	d			15 41										16 11									16 42		
Bellingham	d			15 43										16 13									16 44		
Catford	d			15 45										16 15									16 46		
Crofton Park	d			15 48										16 18									16 48		
Nunhead 4	d			15 50										16 20									16 51		
Peckham Rye 4	d			15 52										16 22									16 53		
Denmark Hill 4	d			15 55										16 25									16 56		
Sutton (Surrey) 4	d	15 07					15 36					15 37			16 06						16 07				16 36
West Sutton	d	15 10										15 40									16 10				
Sutton Common	d	15 12										15 42									16 12				
St Helier	d	15 15										15 45									16 15				
Morden South	d	15 17										15 47									16 17				
South Merton	d	15 19										15 49									16 19				
Wimbledon Chase	d	15 21										15 51									16 21				
Wimbledon 6	d	15 26										15 56									16 28				
Haydons Road	d	15 28										15 58									16 30				
Tooting	d	15 31										16 01									16 33				
Carshalton	d						15 39								16 09										16 39
Hackbridge	d						15 41								16 11										16 41
Mitcham Junction	d						15 44								16 14										16 44
Mitcham Eastfields	d						15 48								16 18										16 48
Streatham 4	d	15 36					15 53					16 06			16 23						16 38				16 53
Tulse Hill 3	d	15 42					15 57					16 12			16 27		16 34				16 42				16 57
London Bridge 4 ⊖	d					16 00					16 15								16 42						
Herne Hill 4	d	15 46					16 01					16 16			16 31		16 38				16 46				17 01
Loughborough Jn	d	15 49					16 04					16 19			16 34						16 49				
Elephant & Castle	d	15 54		16 00			16 09		16 18			16 24		16 30	16 39		16 45				16 54	17 00	17 04		17 08
London Blackfriars 3 ⊖	d	15 58		16 04		16 08	16 14		16 22		16 26	16 30		16 36	16 44		16 50		16 54		17 00	17 04	17 08		17 12
City Thameslink 3	d	16 00		16 06		16 10	16 16		16 24		16 28	16 32		16 38	16 46		16 52		16 56		17 02	17 06	17 10		17 14
Moorgate ⊖	d																								
Barbican ⊖	d																								
Farringdon 3 ⊖	d	16 04		16 10		16 13	16 19		16 27		16 31	16 35		16 41	16 49		16 57		17 01		17 05	17 09	17 13		17 17
St Pancras International 15 ⊖	d	16 08		16 14	16 30	16 18	16 24		16 32	17 00	16 36	16 40		16 46	16 54		17 02	17 15	17 06		17 10	17 14	17 18		17 22
Kentish Town ⊖	d	16 12		16a20			16 28					16 44			16 58							17 18			
West Hampstead Thameslink ⊖	d	16 16					16 32					16 48			17 02						17 18	17 23			
Cricklewood	d	16 19	←				16 35	←				16 51	←		17 05	←				←		17 26			
Hendon	d	16 22	16 07				16 38	16 22				16 54	16 38		17 08	16 54				17 08		17 29		←	
Mill Hill Broadway	d	→	16 11				→	16 26				→	16 42		→	16 58				17 12	17 24	→		17 24	
Elstree & Borehamwood	d		16 15					16 31					16 47			17 03				17 17	→			17 29	
Radlett	d		16 20					16 38					16 51			17 07				17 21				17 33	
St Albans City	d		16a27			16 40		16 45	16 52		16 56		16a59	17 08		17a15	17 22		17 26	17a29			17 38	17 39	17 43
Harpenden	d					16 46		16 52	16 58		17 04			17 14			17 28		17 34					17 44	17 50
Luton Airport Parkway 7 ✈	d				16 51	16 52		16 58			17 10			17 20					17 40				17 46	17 50	17 56
Luton 10	d					16 55		17a02	17 04		17 13			17 23			17 34	17a40	17 43				17 50	17a54	17 59
Leagrave	d					16 59					17 17			17 27					17 47						18 03
Harlington	d					17 04					17 22			17 32					17 52						18 08
Flitwick	d					17 08			17 15		17 26			17 36			17 45		17 56				18 01		18 12
Bedford 7	a				17 06	17 20			17 28	17 33	17 38			17 48			17 58		18 08				18 14		18 24

For general notes see front of timetable
For details of catering facilities see Directory of Train Operators

A TOC FC from London Blackfriars
B To Nottingham (Table 53)
C To Corby. (Table 53)

Brighton, Gatwick Airport and South London → City of London, St.Albans, Luton and Bedford

Network Diagram - see first page of Table 52

		SE	FC	FC	FC	FC	EM	SE	EM	FC	FC	SE	FC	FC	FC		FC	FC	EM	FC	EM	FC	SE	FC	FC
				1	1		1 ◊		1 ◊	1				1	1				1 ◊		1 ◊				1
		A					B		C			A							B		D		A		
Brighton 10	d				16 07					16 22					16 30										17 04
Preston Park	d				16 11										16 34										
Hassocks 4	d				16 17										16 40										
Burgess Hill 4	d				16 21										16 44										17 14
Wivelsfield 4	d														16 46										
Haywards Heath 3	d				16 26					16 38					16 50										17 18
Balcombe	d				16 31										16 57										
Three Bridges 4	d				16 37					16 47					17 02										17 27
Gatwick Airport 10 ✈	d				16 41					16 53					17 07										17 31
Redhill	d																								
East Croydon	d				16 57					17 09					17 28										17 47
Sevenoaks 4	d	16 26										16 35											17 05		
Bat & Ball	d	16 29										16 38											17 08		
Otford 4	d	16 32										16 41											17 12		
Shoreham (Kent)	d	16 35										16 44											17 15		
Eynsford	d	16 39										16 48											17 19		
Swanley 4	d	16 46										16 54											17 24		
St Mary Cray 4	d											16 58											17 28		
Bickley	d											17 03											17 33		
Bromley South	d	16 55										17 06											17 36		
Shortlands 4	d											17 08											17 38		
Ravensbourne	d											17 11											17 41		
Beckenham Hill	d											17 13											17 43		
Bellingham	d											17 15											17 45		
Catford	d											17 17											17 47		
Crofton Park	d											17 19											17 49		
Nunhead 4	d											17 22											17 52		
Peckham Rye 4	d											17 24											17 54		
Denmark Hill 4	d											17 26											17 57		
Sutton (Surrey) 4	d					16 37							17 06							17 12				17 40	
West Sutton	d					16 40														17 15					
Sutton Common	d					16 42														17 17					
St Helier	d					16 45														17 20					
Morden South	d					16 47														17 22					
South Merton	d					16 49														17 24					
Wimbledon Chase	d					16 51														17 26					
Wimbledon 6	d					16 56														17 32					
Haydons Road	d					16 58														17 34					
Tooting	d					17 01														17 37					
Carshalton	d												17 09											17 43	
Hackbridge	d												17 11											17 45	
Mitcham Junction	d												17 14											17 48	
Mitcham Eastfields	d												17 18											17 52	
Streatham 4	d					17 06							17 23							17 42				17 57	
Tulse Hill 3	d				17 11	17 14							17 30							17 48				18 02	
London Bridge 4 ⊖	d									17 29															18 11
Herne Hill 4	d	17 06				17 18							17 36		17 46					17 54				18 06	
Loughborough Jn	d					17 21							17 39							17 57				18 09	
Elephant & Castle	d	17 12		17 16		17 26						17 34	17 44	17 48			17 58			18 02			18 06	18 14	
London Blackfriars 3 ⊖	d	17 16		17 20	17 26	17b32				17 36		17c42	17 48	17 52	17 56		18 02			18 06			18e14	18 18	18 22
City Thameslink 3	d	17 18		17 24	17 28	17 34				17 39		17 44	17 50	17 54	17 58		18 04			18 08			18 16	18 20	18 24
Moorgate ⊖	d																								
Barbican ⊖	d																								
Farringdon 3 ⊖	d	17 23		17 27	17 31	17 37				17 42		17 47	17 53	17 57	18 01		18 07			18 11			18 19	18 23	18 27
St Pancras International 15 ⊖	d	17 28		17 32	17 36	17 42	17 45		18 00	17 46		17 52	17 58	18 02	18 06		18 12		18 25	18 16	18 30		18 24	18 28	18 32
Kentish Town ⊖	d	17 32				17 46							18 02				18 16							18 32	
West Hampstead Thameslink ⊖	d	17 36				17 50						18 00	18 06				18 20						18 32	18 36	
Cricklewood	d	17 39	←			17 53		←			←		18 09				18 23	←				←		18 39	
Hendon	d	17 42 →	17 29			17 56 →		17 42			17 56		18 12 →				18 26 →	18 12				18 26		18 42 →	
Mill Hill Broadway	d		17 32					17 46			18 00	18 07						18 16				18 30			
Elstree & Borehamwood	d		17 37					17 51			18 05	18 12						18 21				18 35	18 42		
Radlett	d		17 42					17 57			18 09	18 16						18 25				18 42	18 46		
St Albans City	d		17a49	17 52	17 56			18a05		18 06	18 16	18 22		18 22	18 26			18a33		18 36		18 48	18 52		18 52
Harpenden	d			17 58	18 04					18 14	18 22	18 28		18 28	18 34					18 44		18 54	18 58		18 58
Luton Airport Parkway 7 ✈	d				18 10		18a09			18 20	18 28	18 34			18 40					18 50	18 54	19 00	19 04		
Luton 10	d			18 04	18 13				18 23	18 23	18a32	18 38		18 34	18 43				18a50	18 53		19a04	19 08		19 04
Leagrave	d				18 17					18 27		18 42			18 47					18 57			19 12		
Harlington	d				18 22					18 32		18 47			18 52					19 02			19 17		
Flitwick	d			18 15	18 26					18 36		18 51		18 45	18 56					19 06			19 21		19 15
Bedford 7	a			18 28	18 38				18 38	18 48		19 04		18 58	19 08					19 18	19 09		19 34		19 28

For general notes see front of timetable
For details of catering facilities see Directory of Train Operators

A TOC FC from London Blackfriars
B To Derby (Table 53)
C To Melton Mowbray (Table 49)
D To Lincoln (Table 53)

b Arr. 1729
c Arr. 1739
e Arr. 1809

Brighton, Gatwick Airport and South London → City of London, St.Albans, Luton and Bedford

Network Diagram - see first page of Table 52

		FC 1	FC	SN	FC	EM 1 ◇ A	SE 1 B	FC	FC	FC 1	FC 1	FC	SN	FC	EM 1 ◇ C	SE 1 B	FC	FC 1	FC	FC 1	FC	SN	FC	EM 1 ◇ A	FC 1
Brighton 10	d									17 24	17 37							18 04		18 07					18 34
Preston Park	d									17 28	17 41									18 11					
Hassocks 4	d									17 34	17 47									18 17					
Burgess Hill 4	d									17 38	17 51							18 14		18 21					
Wivelsfield 4	d									17 40										18 23					
Haywards Heath 3	d									17 46	17 56							18 18		18 32					18 48
Balcombe	d										18 02									18 37					
Three Bridges 4	d									17 56	18 12									18 42					
Gatwick Airport 10 ✈	d									18 01	18 16							18 31		18 46					19 01
Redhill	d																								
East Croydon	d									18 17	18 32							18 47		19 02					19 17
Sevenoaks 4	d						17 35									17 59									
Bat & Ball	d						17 38									18 06									
Otford 4	d						17 41									18 10									
Shoreham (Kent)	d						17 44									18 13									
Eynsford	d						17 47									18 17									
Swanley 4	d						17 53									18 22									
St Mary Cray 4	d						17 57									18 26									
Bickley	d						18 02									18 32									
Bromley South	d						18 05									18 35									
Shortlands 4	d						18 08									18 37									
Ravensbourne	d						18 10									18 39									
Beckenham Hill	d						18 12									18 41									
Bellingham	d						18 14									18 43									
Catford	d						18 16									18 45									
Crofton Park	d						18 19									18 48									
Nunhead 4	d						18 21									18 50									
Peckham Rye 4	d						18 23									18 52									
Denmark Hill 4	d						18 25									18 55									
Sutton (Surrey) 4	d		17 38	17 46				18 06				18 08	18 16						18 32		18 40	18 47			
West Sutton	d		17 41	17 49								18 11	18 19								18 43	18 51			
Sutton Common	d		17 43	17 52								18 13	18 22								18 45	18 53			
St Helier	d		17 46	17 54								18 16	18 24								18 48	18 56			
Morden South	d		17 48	17 56								18 18	18 26								18 50	18 58			
South Merton	d		17 50	17 58								18 20	18 28								18 52	19 00			
Wimbledon Chase	d		17 52	18 00								18 22	18 30								18 54	19 02			
Wimbledon 6	d		17 56	18 04								18 26	18 34								18 58	19 06			
Haydons Road	d		17 58	18 06								18 28	18 36								19 00	19 08			
Tooting	d		18 01	18 09								18 31	18 39								19 03	19 11			
Carshalton	d							18 09											18 35						
Hackbridge	d							18 11											18 37						
Mitcham Junction	d							18 14											18 40						
Mitcham Eastfields	d							18 18											18 44						
Streatham 4	d		18 06	18 13				18 23				18 36	18 45						18 49		19 08	19 16			
Tulse Hill 3	d		18 12	18 17				18 27		18 31		18 42	18 50						18 57		19 14	19 20			
London Bridge 4 ⊖	d			18a31							18 45		19a10					19 00		19 17		19a40			19 30
Herne Hill 4	d		18 18					18 31		18 38		18 48							19 01		19 18				
Loughborough Jn	d		18 21					18 34				18 51							19 04		19 21				
Elephant & Castle	d	18 22	18 26				18 32	18 39		18 45		18 56				19 02			19 09		19 26				
London Blackfriars 3 ⊖	d	18 26	18 32				18 36	18 46		18 50	18b56	19 00				19 06		19c12	19 16	19 24	19 32				19 38
City Thameslink 3	d	18 28	18 34				18 38	18 48		18 52	18 58	19 02				19 08		19 14	19 18	19 26	19 34				19 40
Moorgate ⊖	d																								
Barbican ⊖	d																								
Farringdon 3 ⊖	d	18 31	18 37				18 41	18 51		18 57	19 01	19 05				19 11		19 17	19 21	19 30	19 38				19 44
St Pancras International 15 ⊖	d	18 36	18 42			19 00	18 46	18 56		19 02	19 06	19 10			19 30	19 16		19 22	19 26	19 34	19 42			20 00	19 48
Kentish Town ⊖	d		18 46					19 00				19 14							19 30		19 46				
West Hampstead Thameslink ⊖	d		18 50					19 04				19 18						19 29	19 34	19 41	19 49				
Cricklewood	d		18 53		←			19 07	←			19 21		←			←		19 37		19 52				
Hendon	d		18 56 →		18 42			19 10 →	18 56			19 24 →		19 10			19 24		19 40		19 55 →		←		
Mill Hill Broadway	d				18 46				19 00					19 14			19 27		19 43 →				19 43		
Elstree & Borehamwood	d				18 51				19 05					19 19			19 32						19 48		
Radlett	d				18 58				19 12					19 23			19 36						19 52		
St Albans City	d	18 56			19a05		19 06		19 18	19 22	19 26			19a31		19 38	19 42	19 46		19 55			20 00		20 10
Harpenden	d	19 04					19 14		19 24	19 28	19 34					19 44	19 48	19 52		20 02			20 06		20 16
Luton Airport Parkway 7 ✈	d	19 10					19 20		19 30		19 40						19 54	19 58		20 08			20 12		20 22
Luton 10	d	19 13				19 23	19 23		19a34	19 34	19 43				19 51	19 50	19a58	20 03		20 11			20 15	20 23	20 25
Leagrave	d	19 17					19 27				19 47					19 54		20 06		20 14			20 18		20 28
Harlington	d	19 22					19 32				19 52							20 12		20 20			20 24		20 34
Flitwick	d	19 26					19 36			19 45	19 56							20 16		20 24			20 28		20 38
Bedford 7	a	19 38				19 38	19 48			19 58	20 08				20 07	20 12		20 28		20 36			20 40	20 37	20 50

For general notes see front of timetable
For details of catering facilities see Directory of Train Operators

A To Corby. (Table 53)
B TOC FC from London Blackfriars
C To Leeds (Table 53)

b Arr. 1853
c Arr. 1907

Brighton, Gatwick Airport and South London → City of London, St.Albans, Luton and Bedford

Network Diagram - see first page of Table 52

Station		SE A	FC	FC	FC 1	FC	FC	SE A	EM 1 ◇ B	FC 1	FC	FC 1	FC 1
Brighton 10	d				18 37								19 07
Preston Park	d				18 41								19 11
Hassocks 4	d				18 47								19 17
Burgess Hill 4	d				18 51								19 21
Wivelsfield 4	d				18 53								19 23
Haywards Heath 3	d				19 02								19 32
Balcombe	d												19 37
Three Bridges 4	d				19 12					19 27			19 42
Gatwick Airport 10 ✈	d				19 16					19 31			19 46
Redhill	d												
East Croydon	d				19 32					19 47			20 02
Sevenoaks 4	d	18 37						19 06					
Bat & Ball	d	18 40						19 09					
Otford 4	d	18 43						19 12					
Shoreham (Kent)	d	18 46						19 15					
Eynsford	d	18 49						19 18					
Swanley 4	d	18 58						19 24					
St Mary Cray 4	d	19 02						19 28					
Bickley	d	19 06						19 32					
Bromley South	d	19 10						19 35					
Shortlands 4	d	19 12						19 37					
Ravensbourne	d	19 14						19 40					
Beckenham Hill	d	19 16						19 42					
Bellingham	d	19 18						19 44					
Catford	d	19 20						19 46					
Crofton Park	d	19 23						19 48					
Nunhead 4	d	19 25						19 51					
Peckham Rye 4	d	19 28						19 53					
Denmark Hill 4	d	19 31						19 55					
Sutton (Surrey) 4	d			19 06		19 10						19 40	
West Sutton	d					19 13							
Sutton Common	d					19 15							
St Helier	d					19 18							
Morden South	d					19 20							
South Merton	d					19 22							
Wimbledon Chase	d					19 24							
Wimbledon 6	d					19 28							
Haydons Road	d					19 30							
Tooting	d					19 33							
Carshalton	d			19 09								19 43	
Hackbridge	d			19 11								19 45	
Mitcham Junction	d			19 14								19 48	
Mitcham Eastfields	d			19 18								19 52	
Streatham 4	d			19 23		19 38						19 56	
Tulse Hill 3	d			19 27		19 44						19 59	
London Bridge 4 ⊖	d				19 45					20 00			20 15
Herne Hill 4	d			19 32		19 48						20 03	
Loughborough Jn	d			19 35		19 51						20 07	
Elephant & Castle	d	19 38		19 40		19 56		20 00				20 11	
London Blackfriars 3 ⊖	d	19 42		19 46	19 54	20 00		20 04		20 08		20 16	20 24
City Thameslink 3	d	19 45		19 48	19 56	20 02		20 06		20 10		20 18	20 26
Moorgate ⊖	d												
Barbican ⊖	d												
Farringdon 3 ⊖	d	19 48		19 52	20 00	20 06		20 10		20 14		20 22	20 30
St Pancras International 15 ⊖	d	19 52		19 56	20 04	20 10		20 14	20 30	20 18		20 26	20 34
Kentish Town ⊖	d	19a58		20 00		20 14		20a20				20 30	
West Hampstead Thameslink ⊖	d			20 03	20 11	20 17						20 33	20 41
Cricklewood	d		←	20 06		20 20					←	20 36	
Hendon	d		19 55	20 09		20 23	←				20 23	20 39	
Mill Hill Broadway	d		19 59	20 13		→	20 13				20 27	20 43	
Elstree & Borehamwood	d		20 03	→			20 17				20 31	→	
Radlett	d		20 08				20 22				20 38		
St Albans City	d		20 15		20 25		20 30			20 40	20 45		20 55
Harpenden	d		20 20		20 32		20 36			20 46	20 50		21 02
Luton Airport Parkway 7 ✈	d		20 26		20 38		20 42		20 51	20 52	20 56		21 08
Luton 10	d		20a30		20 41		20 45			20 55	21a00		21 11
Leagrave	d				20 44		20 48			20 58			21 14
Harlington	d				20 50		20 54			21 04			21 20
Flitwick	d				20 54		20 58			21 08			21 24
Bedford 7	a				21 06		21 10		21 06	21 20			21 36

Station		FC	FC 1	SE A	EM 1 ◇ C	FC 1	FC	FC 1	FC 1	FC	FC 1	SE A	FC 1
Brighton 10	d					19 34			19 37				20 04
Preston Park	d								19 41				
Hassocks 4	d								19 47				
Burgess Hill 4	d								19 51				
Wivelsfield 4	d								19 53				
Haywards Heath 3	d					19 48			20 02				20 18
Balcombe	d												
Three Bridges 4	d								20 12				
Gatwick Airport 10 ✈	d					20 01			20 16				20 31
Redhill	d												
East Croydon	d					20 17			20 32				20 47
Sevenoaks 4	d			19 34								20 04	
Bat & Ball	d			19 37								20 07	
Otford 4	d			19 40								20 10	
Shoreham (Kent)	d			19 43								20 13	
Eynsford	d			19 46								20 16	
Swanley 4	d			19 52								20 22	
St Mary Cray 4	d			19 56								20 26	
Bickley	d			20 01								20 31	
Bromley South	d			20 05								20 35	
Shortlands 4	d			20 07								20 37	
Ravensbourne	d			20 09								20 39	
Beckenham Hill	d			20 11								20 41	
Bellingham	d			20 13								20 43	
Catford	d			20 15								20 45	
Crofton Park	d			20 18								20 48	
Nunhead 4	d			20 20								20 50	
Peckham Rye 4	d			20 22								20 52	
Denmark Hill 4	d			20 25								20 55	
Sutton (Surrey) 4	d	19 37						20 10		20 07			
West Sutton	d	19 40								20 10			
Sutton Common	d	19 42								20 12			
St Helier	d	19 45								20 15			
Morden South	d	19 47								20 17			
South Merton	d	19 49								20 19			
Wimbledon Chase	d	19 51								20 21			
Wimbledon 6	d	19 56								20 26			
Haydons Road	d	19 58								20 28			
Tooting	d	20 01								20 31			
Carshalton	d							20 13					
Hackbridge	d							20 15					
Mitcham Junction	d							20 18					
Mitcham Eastfields	d							20 22					
Streatham 4	d	20 06						20 26		20 36			
Tulse Hill 3	d	20 10						20 29		20 40			
London Bridge 4 ⊖	d					20 30			20 45				21 00
Herne Hill 4	d	20 16						20 33		20 46			
Loughborough Jn	d	20 19						20 37		20 49			
Elephant & Castle	d	20 24		20 30				20 41		20 54		21 00	
London Blackfriars 3 ⊖	d	20b30		20 34		20 38		20 46	20 54	21c00		21 04	21 08
City Thameslink 3	d	20 32		20 37		20 40		20 48	20 56	21 02		21 07	21 10
Moorgate ⊖	d												
Barbican ⊖	d												
Farringdon 3 ⊖	d	20 36		20 40		20 44		20 52	21 00	21 06		21 10	21 14
St Pancras International 15 ⊖	d	20 40		20 44	21 00	20 48		20 56	21 04	21 10		21 14	21 18
Kentish Town ⊖	d	20 44		20a50				21 00		21 14		21a20	
West Hampstead Thameslink ⊖	d	20 47						21 03	21 11	21 17			
Cricklewood	d	20 50					←	21 06		21 20			
Hendon	d	20 53	←				20 53	21 09		21 23	←		
Mill Hill Broadway	d	→	20 43				20 57	21 13		→	21 13		
Elstree & Borehamwood	d		20 47				21 01	→			21 17		
Radlett	d		20 52				21 08				21 22		
St Albans City	d		20a59			21 10	21 15		21 25		21a29		21 40
Harpenden	d					21 16	21 20		21 32				21 46
Luton Airport Parkway 7 ✈	d				21 23	21 22	21 26		21 38				21 52
Luton 10	d					21 25	21a30		21 41				21 55
Leagrave	d					21 28			21 44				21 58
Harlington	d					21 34			21 50				22 04
Flitwick	d					21 38			21 54				22 08
Bedford 7	a				21 37	21 50			22 06				22 20

For general notes see front of timetable
For details of catering facilities see Directory of Train Operators

A TOC FC from London Blackfriars
B To Nottingham (Table 53)
C To Derby (Table 53)
b Arr. 2027
c Arr. 2057

Brighton, Gatwick Airport and South London → City of London, St.Albans, Luton and Bedford

Network Diagram - see first page of Table 52

		EM	FC	FC	FC	FC	FC	EM	FC	FC	FC	FC	FC	EM	FC	FC	FC	FC	FC	EM	FC	FC	FC
		1 ◇ A		1	1		1	1 ◇ B	1		1	1	1	1 ◇ C		1			1	1 ◇ A		1	
Brighton 10	d				20 07				20 34			20 37											
Preston Park	d				20 11							20 41											
Hassocks 4	d				20 17							20 47											
Burgess Hill 4	d				20 21							20 51											
Wivelsfield 4	d				20 23							20 53											
Haywards Heath 3	d				20 32				20 48			21 02											
Balcombe	d				20 37																		
Three Bridges 4	d				20 42							21 12											
Gatwick Airport 10 ✈	d				20 46				21 01			21 16											
Redhill	d																						
East Croydon	d				21 02				21 17			21 32											
Sevenoaks 4	d																						
Bat & Ball	d																						
Otford 4	d																						
Shoreham (Kent)	d																						
Eynsford	d																						
Swanley 4	d																						
St Mary Cray 4	d																						
Bickley	d																						
Bromley South	d																						
Shortlands 4	d																						
Ravensbourne	d																						
Beckenham Hill	d																						
Bellingham	d																						
Catford	d																						
Crofton Park	d																						
Nunhead 4	d																						
Peckham Rye 4	d																						
Denmark Hill 4	d																						
Sutton (Surrey) 4	d			20 40		20 37					21 10				21 07			22 07					
West Sutton	d					20 40									21 10			22 10					
Sutton Common	d					20 42									21 12			22 12					
St Helier	d					20 45									21 15			22 15					
Morden South	d					20 47									21 17			22 17					
South Merton	d					20 49									21 19			22 19					
Wimbledon Chase	d					20 51									21 21			22 21					
Wimbledon 6	d					20 56									21b36			22 26					
Haydons Road	d					20 58									21 38			22 28					
Tooting	d					21 01									21 41			22 31					
Carshalton	d			20 43							21 13												
Hackbridge	d			20 45							21 15												
Mitcham Junction	d			20 48							21 18												
Mitcham Eastfields	d			20 52							21 22												
Streatham 4	d			20 56		21 06					21 26				21 46			22 36					
Tulse Hill 3	d			20 59		21 10					21 29				21 50			22 40					
London Bridge 4 ⊖	d				21 15				21 30			21 45						22a52					
Herne Hill 4	d			21 03		21 16					21 33				21 54								
Loughborough Jn	d			21 07		21 19					21 37				21 57								
Elephant & Castle	d			21 11		21 24					21 41				22 02								
London Blackfriars 3 ⊖	d			21 16	21 24	21c30			21 38		21 46	21 54			22 06								
City Thameslink 3	d			21 18	21 26	21 32			21 40		21 48	21 56			22 08								
Moorgate ⊖	d																						
Barbican ⊖	d																						
Farringdon 3 ⊖	d			21 22	21 30	21 36			21 44		21 52	22 00			22 12								
St Pancras International 15 ⊖	d	21 30		21 26	21 34	21 40		22 00	21 48		21 56	22 04		22 25	22 16	22 34	22 48		23 04	23 15	23 18	23 34	23 48
Kentish Town ⊖	d			21 30		21 44					22 00				22 20		22 53				23 23		23 53
West Hampstead Thameslink ⊖	d			21 33	21 41	21 47					22 03	22 11			22 23	22 41	22 56		23 11		23 26	23 41	23 56
Cricklewood	d		←	21 36		21 50				←	22 06				22 26		22 59				23 29		23 59
Hendon	d		21 23	21 39		21 53	←			21 53	22 09		←		22 29		23 02				23 31		00 02
Mill Hill Broadway	d		21 27	21 43		→	21 43			21 57	22 13		22 13		22 33		23 06				23 36		00 06
Elstree & Borehamwood	d		21 31	→			21 47			22 01	→		22 17		22 37		23 10				23 39		00 10
Radlett	d		21 38				21 52			22 08			22 22		22 42		23 15				23 45		00 15
St Albans City	d		21 45		21 55		21a59		22 10	22 15		22 25	22a29		22 48	22 55	23 21		23 25		23 51	23 55	00 21
Harpenden	d		21 50		22 02				22 16	22 20		22 32			22 54	23 02	23 27		23 32		23 57	00 02	00 27
Luton Airport Parkway 7 ✈	d	21 53	21 56		22 08				22 22	22 26		22 38		22 48	23 00	23 08	23 33		23 38		00 03	00 08	00 33
Luton 10	d		22a00		22 11			22 24	22 25	22a30		22 41			23 03	23 11	23 36		23 41	23 46	00 06	00 11	00 36
Leagrave	d				22 14				22 28			22 44			23 06	23 14	23 39		23 44		00 09	00 14	00 39
Harlington	d				22 20				22 34			22 50			23 12	23 20	23 45		23 50		00 15	00 20	00 45
Flitwick	d				22 24				22 38			22 54			23 16	23 24	23 49		23 54		00 19	00 24	00 49
Bedford 7	a	22 08			22 36			22 39	22 50			23 06		23 03	23 28	23 36	00 01		00 06	00 09	00 31	00 36	01 01

For general notes see front of timetable
For details of catering facilities see Directory of Train Operators

- **A** To Derby (Table 53)
- **B** To Nottingham (Table 53)
- **C** To Sheffield (Table 53)
- **b** Arr. 11 minutes earlier
- **c** Arr. 2127

Brighton, Gatwick Airport and South London → City of London, St.Albans, Luton and Bedford

Network Diagram - see first page of Table 52

		FC	FC 1	FC	FC 1	EM 1 ◇ A	FC	FC	FC	FC	FC	FC 1	FC 1	FC 1	FC 1		EM 1 ◇ B	FC 1	FC 1	EM 1 ◇ C	FC	EM 1 ◇ D	EM 1 ◇ D	FC 1	FC
Brighton 10	d																								
Preston Park	d																								
Hassocks 4	d																								
Burgess Hill 4	d																								
Wivelsfield 4	d																								
Haywards Heath 3	d																								
Balcombe	d																								
Three Bridges 4	d																								
Gatwick Airport 10 ✈	d																								
Redhill	d																								
East Croydon	d																								
Sutton (Surrey) 4	d																								
West Sutton	d																								
Sutton Common	d																								
St Helier	d																								
Morden South	d																								
South Merton	d																								
Wimbledon Chase	d																								
Wimbledon 6 ⊖	d																								
Haydons Road	d																								
Tooting	d																								
Carshalton	d																								
Hackbridge	d																								
Mitcham Junction	d																								
Mitcham Eastfields	d																								
Streatham 4	d																								
Tulse Hill 3	d																								
London Bridge 4 ⊖	d																								
Herne Hill 4	d																								
Loughborough Jn	d																								
Elephant & Castle	d																								
London Blackfriars 3 ⊖	d																								
City Thameslink 3	d																								
Farringdon 3 ⊖	d																								
St Pancras International 15 ⊖	d	23p18	23p34	23p48	00 04	00 15	00 18	00 38	01 08	01 38	02 38	04 04	04 34	05 04	05 34		06 10	06 04	06 18	06 37	06 34	06 55	07 00	06 48	07 04
Kentish Town ⊖	d	23p23		23p53			00 22	00 43	01 13	01 43	02 43	04 09	04 39	05 09	05 39			06 09			06 39				07 09
West Hampstead Thameslink ⊖	d	23p26	23p41	23p56	00 11		00 25	00 46	01 16	01 46	02 46	04 12	04 42	05 12	05 42			06 12	06 25		06 42			06 56	07 12
Cricklewood	d	23p29		23p59			00 28	00 49	01 19	01 49	02 49	04 15	04 45	05 15	05 45			06 15			06 45				07 15
Hendon	d	23p31		00 02			00 31	00 52	01 22	01 52	02 52	04 18	04 48	05 18	05 48			06 18			06 48				07 18
Mill Hill Broadway	d	23p36		00 06			00 35	00 56	01 26	01 56	02 56	04 22	04 52	05 22	05 52			06 22			06 52				07 22
Elstree & Borehamwood	d	23p39		00 10			00 39	01 00	01 30	02 00	03 00	04 26	04 56	05 26	05 56			06 26	06 35		06 56			07 06	07 26
Radlett	d	23p45		00 15			00 44	01 04	01 34	02 04	03 04	04 30	05 00	05 30	06 00			06 30			07 01				07 31
St Albans City	d	23p51	23p55	00 21	00 25		00 50	01 11	01 41	02 11	03 11	04 37	05 07	05 37	06 07			06 37	06 42		07 08			07 13	07 38
Harpenden	d	23p57	00 02	00 27	00 32		00 56	01 17	01 47	02 17	03 17	04 43	05 13	05 43	06 13			06 43	06 48		07 14			07 19	07 44
Luton Airport Parkway 7 ✈	d	00 03	00 08	00 33	00 38	00 46	01 02	01 23	01 53	02 23	03 23	04 49	05 19	05 49	06 19			06 49	06 54		07 18	07a15		07 25	07 50
Luton 10	d	00 06	00 11	00 36	00 41	00 50	01 05	01 27	01 57	02 27	03 27	04 53	05 23	05 53	06 23		06 33	06 53	06 57	06a58	07a24		07 23	07 28	07a54
Leagrave	d	00 09	00 14	00 39	00 44		01 08	01 30	02 00	02 30	03 30	04 56	05 26	05 56	06 26			06 56	07 00					07 31	
Harlington	d	00 15	00 20	00 45	00 50		01 14	01 36	02 06	02 36	03 36	05 02	05 32	06 02	06 32			07 02	07 06					07 37	
Flitwick	d	00 19	00 24	00 49	00 54		01 18	01 40	02 10	02 40	03 40	05 06	05 36	06 06	06 36			07 06	07 10					07 41	
Bedford 7	a	00 31	00 36	01 01	01 06	01 10	01 30	01 52	02 22	02 52	03 52	05 18	05 48	06 18	06 48		06 47	07 18	07 22				07 38	07 53	

For general notes see front of timetable
For details of catering facilities see Directory of Train Operators

A To Leicester (Table 53)
B To Derby (Table 53)
C From 12 September to York
Until 5 September to Scarborough (Table 26)
D To Nottingham (Table 53)

Table 52

Saturdays

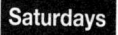

Brighton, Gatwick Airport and South London → City of London, St.Albans, Luton and Bedford

Network Diagram - see first page of Table 52

	EM 1 ◇ A	FC 1	FC	FC 1	EM 1 ◇ B	FC	FC 1		FC	FC	FC 1	EM 1 ◇ A	FC	FC 1	FC	FC	FC 1	EM 1 ◇ C	FC	FC 1	FC	FC		FC 1
Brighton 10 d																								
Preston Park d																								
Hassocks 4 d																								
Burgess Hill 4 d																								
Wivelsfield 4 d																								
Haywards Heath 3 d																								
Balcombe d																								
Three Bridges 4 d																								
Gatwick Airport 10 ✈ d																								
Redhill d																								
East Croydon d																								
Sutton (Surrey) 4 d									07 06	07 07					07 36	07 37					08 06	08 07		
West Sutton d										07 10						07 40						08 10		
Sutton Common d										07 12						07 42						08 12		
St Helier d										07 15						07 45						08 15		
Morden South d										07 17						07 47						08 17		
South Merton d										07 19						07 49						08 19		
Wimbledon Chase d										07 21						07 51						08 21		
Wimbledon 6 ⊖ d			07 00							07 30						08 00						08 30		
Haydons Road d			07 02							07 32						08 02						08 32		
Tooting d			07 05							07 35						08 05						08 35		
Carshalton d									07 09						07 39						08 09			
Hackbridge d									07 11						07 41						08 11			
Mitcham Junction d									07 14						07 44						08 14			
Mitcham Eastfields d									07 18						07 48						08 18			
Streatham 4 d			07 10						07 23	07 40					07 53	08 10					08 23	08 40		
Tulse Hill 3 d			07 17						07 27	07 47					07 57	08 17					08 27	08 47		
London Bridge 4 ⊖ d			07a30							08a00						08a30						09a00		
Herne Hill 4 d									07a31						08a01						08a31			
Loughborough Jn d																								
Elephant & Castle d																								
London Blackfriars 3 ⊖ d																								
City Thameslink 3 d																								
Farringdon 3 ⊖ d																								
St Pancras International 15 ⊖ d	07 30	07 20		07 34	08 00	07 38	07 50				08 04	08 30	08 08	08 20			08 34	09 00	08 38	08 50				09 04
Kentish Town ⊖ d						07 44							08 14						08 44					
West Hampstead Thameslink ⊖ d		07 29				07 47	07 59						08 17	08 29					08 47	08 59				
Cricklewood d						07 50							08 20						08 50					
Hendon d						07 53							08 23						08 53					
Mill Hill Broadway d						07 57							08 27						08 57					
Elstree & Borehamwood d		07 39				08 01	08 09						08 31	08 39					09 01	09 09				
Radlett d						08 06							08 36						09 06					
St Albans City d		07 46		07 55		08 12	08 16				08 25		08 42	08 46			08 55		09 12	09 16				09 25
Harpenden d		07 52		08 02		08 18	08 22				08 32		08 47	08 52			09 02		09 17	09 22				09 32
Luton Airport Parkway 7 ✈ d	07 51	07 58		08 08		08 22	08 28				08 38	08 51	08 53	08 58			09 08		09 23	09 28				09 38
Luton 10 d		08 01		08 11	08 23	08a28	08 31				08 41		08a57	09 01			09 11	09 23	09a27	09 31				09 41
Leagrave d		08 04		08 14			08 34				08 44			09 04			09 14			09 34				09 44
Harlington d		08 10		08 20			08 40				08 50			09 10			09 20			09 40				09 50
Flitwick d		08 14		08 24			08 44				08 54			09 14			09 24			09 44				09 54
Bedford 7 a	08 06	08 26		08 36	08 37		08 56				09 06	09 06		09 26			09 36	09 37		09 56				10 06

For general notes see front of timetable
For details of catering facilities see Directory of Train Operators

A To Nottingham (Table 53)
B To Corby. (Table 53)
C To Kettering (Table 53)

Brighton, Gatwick Airport and South London → City of London, St.Albans, Luton and Bedford

Network Diagram - see first page of Table 52

		EM	FC	FC	FC	FC	FC	EM	FC	FC	FC	FC	FC	EM	FC		FC	FC	FC	FC	EM	FC	FC	FC	FC
		1 ◇ A 🍴		1			1	1 ◇ B 🍴		1			1	1 ◇ A 🍴			1			1	1 ◇ B 🍴		1		
Brighton 10	d																								
Preston Park	d																								
Hassocks 4	d																								
Burgess Hill 4	d																								
Wivelsfield 4	d																								
Haywards Heath 3	d																								
Balcombe	d																								
Three Bridges 4	d																								
Gatwick Airport 10 ✈	d																								
Redhill	d																								
East Croydon	d																								
Sutton (Surrey) 4	d				08 36	08 37					09 06	09 07						09 36	09 37					10 06	10 07
West Sutton	d					08 40						09 10							09 40						10 10
Sutton Common	d					08 42						09 12							09 42						10 12
St Helier	d					08 45						09 15							09 45						10 15
Morden South	d					08 47						09 17							09 47						10 17
South Merton	d					08 49						09 19							09 49						10 19
Wimbledon Chase	d					08 51						09 21							09 51						10 21
Wimbledon 6	d					09 00						09 30							10 00						10 30
Haydons Road	d					09 02						09 32							10 02						10 32
Tooting	d					09 05						09 35							10 05						10 35
Carshalton	d				08 39						09 09							09 39						10 09	
Hackbridge	d				08 41						09 11							09 41						10 11	
Mitcham Junction	d				08 44						09 14							09 44						10 14	
Mitcham Eastfields	d				08 48						09 18							09 48						10 18	
Streatham 4	d				08 53	09 10					09 23	09 40						09 53	10 10					10 23	10 40
Tulse Hill 3	d				08 57	09 17					09 27	09 47						09 57	10 17					10 27	10 47
London Bridge 4	d					09a30						10a00							10a30						11a00
Herne Hill 4	d				09a01						09a31							10a01						10a31	
Loughborough Jn	d																								
Elephant & Castle	d																								
London Blackfriars 3	d																								
City Thameslink 3	d																								
Farringdon 3	d																								
St Pancras International 15	d	09 30	09 08	09 20			09 34	10 00	09 38	09 50			10 04	10 30	10 08		10 20			10 34	11 00	10 38	10 50		
Kentish Town	d		09 14						09 44						10 14							10 44			
West Hampstead Thameslink	d		09 17	09 29					09 47	09 59					10 17		10 29					10 47	10 59		
Cricklewood	d		09 20						09 50						10 20							10 50			
Hendon	d		09 23						09 53						10 23							10 53			
Mill Hill Broadway	d		09 27						09 57						10 27							10 57			
Elstree & Borehamwood	d		09 31	09 39					10 01	10 09					10 31		10 39					11 01	11 09		
Radlett	d		09 36						10 06						10 36							11 06			
St Albans City	d		09 42	09 46			09 55		10 12	10 16			10 25		10 42		10 46			10 55		11 12	11 16		
Harpenden	d		09 47	09 52			10 02		10 17	10 22			10 32		10 47		10 52			11 02		11 17	11 22		
Luton Airport Parkway 7 ✈	d	09 51	09 53	09 58			10 08		10 23	10 28			10 38	10 51	10 53		10 58			11 08		11 23	11 28		
Luton 10	d		09a57	10 01			10 11	10 23	10a27	10 31			10 41		10a57		11 01			11 11	11 23	11a27	11 31		
Leagrave	d			10 04			10 14			10 34			10 44				11 04			11 14			11 34		
Harlington	d			10 10			10 20			10 40			10 50				11 10			11 20			11 40		
Flitwick	d			10 14			10 24			10 44			10 54				11 14			11 24			11 44		
Bedford 7	a	10 06		10 26			10 36	10 37		10 56			11 06	11 06			11 26			11 36	11 37		11 56		

For general notes see front of timetable
For details of catering facilities see Directory of Train Operators

A To Nottingham (Table 53)
B To Corby. (Table 53)

Table 52

Saturdays

Brighton, Gatwick Airport and South London → City of London, St.Albans, Luton and Bedford

Network Diagram - see first page of Table 52

Station		FC 1	EM 1 ◇ A	FC	FC 1	FC	FC	FC 1		EM 1 ◇ B	FC	FC 1	FC	FC	FC 1	EM 1 ◇ A	FC	FC 1	FC	FC	FC 1	EM 1 ◇ B	FC		FC 1
Brighton 10	d																								
Preston Park	d																								
Hassocks 4	d																								
Burgess Hill 4	d																								
Wivelsfield 4	d																								
Haywards Heath 3	d																								
Balcombe	d																								
Three Bridges 4	d																								
Gatwick Airport 10 ✈	d																								
Redhill	d																								
East Croydon	d																								
Sutton (Surrey) 4	d					10 36	10 37						11 06	11 07					11 36	11 37					
West Sutton	d						10 40							11 10						11 40					
Sutton Common	d						10 42							11 12						11 42					
St Helier	d						10 45							11 15						11 45					
Morden South	d						10 47							11 17						11 47					
South Merton	d						10 49							11 19						11 49					
Wimbledon Chase	d						10 51							11 21						11 51					
Wimbledon 6	d						11 00							11 30						12 00					
Haydons Road	d						11 02							11 32						12 02					
Tooting	d						11 05							11 35						12 05					
Carshalton	d					10 39							11 09						11 39						
Hackbridge	d					10 41							11 11						11 41						
Mitcham Junction	d					10 44							11 14						11 44						
Mitcham Eastfields	d					10 48							11 18						11 48						
Streatham 4	d					10 53	11 10						11 23	11 40					11 53	12 10					
Tulse Hill 3	d					10 57	11 17						11 27	11 47					11 57	12 17					
London Bridge 4	d						11a30							12a00						12a30					
Herne Hill 4	d					11a01							11a31						12a01						
Loughborough Jn	d																								
Elephant & Castle	d																								
London Blackfriars 3	d																								
City Thameslink 3	d																								
Farringdon 3	d																								
St Pancras International 15	d	11 04	11 30	11 08	11 20			11 34		12 00	11 38	11 50			12 04	12 30	12 08	12 20			12 34	13 00	12 38		12 50
Kentish Town	d			11 14							11 44						12 14						12 44		
West Hampstead Thameslink	d			11 17	11 29						11 47	11 59					12 17	12 29					12 47		12 59
Cricklewood	d			11 20							11 50						12 20						12 50		
Hendon	d			11 23							11 53						12 23						12 53		
Mill Hill Broadway	d			11 27							11 57						12 27						12 57		
Elstree & Borehamwood	d			11 31	11 39						12 01	12 09					12 31	12 39					13 01		13 09
Radlett	d			11 36							12 06						12 36						13 06		
St Albans City	d	11 25		11 42	11 46			11 55			12 12	12 16			12 25		12 42	12 46			12 55		13 12		13 16
Harpenden	d	11 32		11 47	11 52			12 02			12 17	12 22			12 32		12 47	12 52			13 02		13 17		13 22
Luton Airport Parkway 7 ✈	d	11 38	11 51	11 53	11 58			12 08			12 23	12 28			12 38	12 51	12 53	12 58			13 08		13 23		13 28
Luton 10	d	11 41		11a57	12 01			12 11		12 23	12a27	12 31			12 41		12a57	13 01			13 11	13 23	13a27		13 31
Leagrave	d	11 44			12 04			12 14				12 34			12 44			13 04			13 14				13 34
Harlington	d	11 50			12 10			12 20				12 40			12 50			13 10			13 20				13 40
Flitwick	d	11 54			12 14			12 24				12 44			12 54			13 14			13 24				13 44
Bedford 7	a	12 06	12 06		12 26			12 36		12 37		12 56			13 06	13 06		13 26			13 36	13 37			13 56

For general notes see front of timetable
For details of catering facilities see Directory of Train Operators

A To Nottingham (Table 53)
B To Corby. (Table 53)

Brighton, Gatwick Airport and South London → City of London, St.Albans, Luton and Bedford

Network Diagram - see first page of Table 52

	FC	FC	FC [1]	EM [1] ◇ A 🍽	FC	FC [1]	FC	FC	FC [1]	EM [1] ◇ B 🍽	FC	FC [1]	FC	FC		FC [1]	EM [1] ◇ A 🍽	FC	FC [1]	FC	FC	FC [1]	EM [1] ◇ B 🍽	FC
Brighton [10] d																								
Preston Park d																								
Hassocks [4] d																								
Burgess Hill [4] d																								
Wivelsfield [4] d																								
Haywards Heath [3] d																								
Balcombe d																								
Three Bridges [4] d																								
Gatwick Airport [10] ✈ d																								
Redhill d																								
East Croydon 🚌 d																								
Sutton (Surrey) [4] d	12 06	12 07					12 36	12 37					13 06	13 07						13 36	13 37			
West Sutton d		12 10						12 40						13 10							13 40			
Sutton Common d		12 12						12 42						13 12							13 42			
St Helier d		12 15						12 45						13 15							13 45			
Morden South d		12 17						12 47						13 17							13 47			
South Merton d		12 19						12 49						13 19							13 49			
Wimbledon Chase d		12 21						12 51						13 21							13 51			
Wimbledon [6] ⊖ 🚌 d		12 30						13 00						13 30							14 00			
Haydons Road d		12 32						13 02						13 32							14 02			
Tooting d		12 35						13 05						13 35							14 05			
Carshalton d	12 09						12 39						13 09							13 39				
Hackbridge d	12 11						12 41						13 11							13 41				
Mitcham Junction 🚌 d	12 14						12 44						13 14							13 44				
Mitcham Eastfields d	12 18						12 48						13 18							13 48				
Streatham [4] d	12 23	12 40					12 53	13 10					13 23	13 40						13 53	14 10			
Tulse Hill [3] d	12 27	12 47					12 57	13 17					13 27	13 47						13 57	14 17			
London Bridge [4] ⊖ d		13a00						13a30						14a00							14a30			
Herne Hill [4] d	12a31						13a01						13a31							14a01				
Loughborough Jn d																								
Elephant & Castle d																								
London Blackfriars [3] ⊖ d																								
City Thameslink [3] d																								
Farringdon [3] ⊖ d																								
St Pancras International [15] ⊖ d			13 04	13 30	13 08	13 20			13 34	14 00	13 38	13 50				14 04	14 30	14 08	14 20			14 34	15 00	14 38
Kentish Town ⊖ d					13 14						13 44							14 14						14 44
West Hampstead Thameslink ⊖ d					13 17	13 29					13 47	13 59						14 17	14 29					14 47
Cricklewood d					13 20						13 50							14 20						14 50
Hendon d					13 23						13 53							14 23						14 53
Mill Hill Broadway d					13 27						13 57							14 27						14 57
Elstree & Borehamwood d					13 31	13 39					14 01	14 09						14 31	14 39					15 01
Radlett d					13 36						14 06							14 36						15 06
St Albans City d			13 25		13 42	13 46			13 55		14 12	14 16				14 25		14 42	14 46			14 55		15 12
Harpenden d			13 32		13 47	13 52			14 02		14 17	14 22				14 32		14 47	14 52			15 02		15 17
Luton Airport Parkway [7] ✈ d			13 38	13 51	13 53	13 58			14 08		14 23	14 28				14 38	14 51	14 53	14 58			15 08		15 23
Luton [10] d			13 41		13a57	14 01			14 11	14 23	14a27	14 31				14 41		14a57	15 01			15 11	15 23	15a27
Leagrave d			13 44			14 04			14 14			14 34				14 44			15 04			15 14		
Harlington d			13 50			14 10			14 20			14 40				14 50			15 10			15 20		
Flitwick d			13 54			14 14			14 24			14 44				14 54			15 14			15 24		
Bedford [7] a			14 06	14 06		14 26			14 36	14 37		14 56				15 06	15 06		15 26			15 36	15 37	

For general notes see front of timetable
For details of catering facilities see
Directory of Train Operators

A To Nottingham (Table 53)
B To Corby. (Table 53)

Table 52

Saturdays

Brighton, Gatwick Airport and South London → City of London, St.Albans, Luton and Bedford

Network Diagram - see first page of Table 52

Station		FC [1]	FC	FC	FC [1]	EM [1] ◇ A	FC	FC [1]		FC	FC	FC [1]	EM [1] ◇ B	FC	FC [1]	FC	FC	FC [1]	EM [1] ◇ A	FC	FC [1]	FC	FC		FC [1]
Brighton [10]	d																								
Preston Park	d																								
Hassocks [4]	d																								
Burgess Hill [4]	d																								
Wivelsfield [4]	d																								
Haywards Heath [3]	d																								
Balcombe	d																								
Three Bridges [4]	d																								
Gatwick Airport [10] ✈	d																								
Redhill	d																								
East Croydon	d																								
Sutton (Surrey) [4]	d		14 06	14 07						14 36	14 37					15 06	15 07					15 36	15 37		
West Sutton	d			14 10							14 40						15 10						15 40		
Sutton Common	d			14 12							14 42						15 12						15 42		
St Helier	d			14 15							14 45						15 15						15 45		
Morden South	d			14 17							14 47						15 17						15 47		
South Merton	d			14 19							14 49						15 19						15 49		
Wimbledon Chase	d			14 21							14 51						15 21						15 51		
Wimbledon [6] ⊖	d			14 30							15 00						15 30						16 00		
Haydons Road	d			14 32							15 02						15 32						16 02		
Tooting	d			14 35							15 05						15 35						16 05		
Carshalton	d		14 09							14 39						15 09						15 39			
Hackbridge	d		14 11							14 41						15 11						15 41			
Mitcham Junction	d		14 14							14 44						15 14						15 44			
Mitcham Eastfields	d		14 18							14 48						15 18						15 48			
Streatham [4]	d		14 23	14 40						14 53	15 10					15 23	15 40					15 53	16 10		
Tulse Hill [3]	d		14 27	14 47						14 57	15 17					15 27	15 47					15 57	16 17		
London Bridge [4] ⊖	d			15a00							15a30						16a00						16a30		
Herne Hill [4]	d		14a31							15a01						15a31						16a01			
Loughborough Jn	d																								
Elephant & Castle	d																								
London Blackfriars [3] ⊖	d																								
City Thameslink [3]	d																								
Farringdon [3] ⊖	d																								
St Pancras International [15] ⊖	d	14 50			15 04	15 30	15 08	15 20				15 34	16 00	15 38	15 50			16 04	16 30	16 08	16 20				16 34
Kentish Town ⊖	d						15 14							15 44						16 14					
West Hampstead Thameslink ⊖	d	14 59					15 17	15 29						15 47	15 59					16 17	16 29				
Cricklewood	d						15 20							15 50						16 20					
Hendon	d						15 23							15 53						16 23					
Mill Hill Broadway	d						15 27							15 57						16 27					
Elstree & Borehamwood	d	15 09					15 31	15 39						16 01	16 09					16 31	16 39				
Radlett	d						15 36							16 06						16 36					
St Albans City	d	15 16			15 25		15 42	15 46				15 55		16 12	16 16			16 25		16 42	16 46				16 55
Harpenden	d	15 22			15 32		15 47	15 52				16 02		16 17	16 22			16 32		16 47	16 52				17 02
Luton Airport Parkway [7] ✈	d	15 28			15 38	15 51	15 53	15 58				16 08		16 23	16 28			16 38	16 51	16 53	16 58				17 08
Luton [10]	d	15 31			15 41		15a57	16 01				16 11	16 23	16a27	16 31			16 41		16a57	17 01				17 11
Leagrave	d	15 34			15 44			16 04				16 14			16 34			16 44			17 04				17 14
Harlington	d	15 40			15 50			16 10				16 20			16 40			16 50			17 10				17 20
Flitwick	d	15 44			15 54			16 14				16 24			16 44			16 54			17 14				17 24
Bedford [7]	a	15 56			16 06	16 06		16 26				16 36	16 37		16 56			17 06	17 06		17 26				17 36

For general notes see front of timetable
For details of catering facilities see Directory of Train Operators

A To Nottingham (Table 53)
B To Corby. (Table 53)

Table 52

Saturdays

Brighton, Gatwick Airport and South London → City of London, St.Albans, Luton and Bedford

Network Diagram - see first page of Table 52

		EM	FC	FC	FC	FC	FC	EM	FC	FC	FC	FC	FC	EM	FC		FC	FC	FC	FC	EM	FC	FC	FC	FC
		1 ◇ A 🍽		1			1	1 ◇ B 🍽		1			1	1 ◇ A 🍽			1			1	1 ◇ C 🍽		1		
Brighton 10	d																								
Preston Park	d																								
Hassocks 4	d																								
Burgess Hill 4	d																								
Wivelsfield 4	d																								
Haywards Heath 3	d																								
Balcombe	d																								
Three Bridges 4	d																								
Gatwick Airport 10 ✈	d																								
Redhill	d																								
East Croydon 🚌	d																								
Sutton (Surrey) 4	d				16 06	16 07					16 36	16 37						17 06	17 07					17 36	17 37
West Sutton	d					16 10						16 40							17 10						17 40
Sutton Common	d					16 12						16 42							17 12						17 42
St Helier	d					16 15						16 45							17 15						17 45
Morden South	d					16 17						16 47							17 17						17 47
South Merton	d					16 19						16 49							17 19						17 49
Wimbledon Chase	d					16 21						16 51							17 21						17 51
Wimbledon 6 ⊖ 🚌	d					16 30						17 00							17 30						18 00
Haydons Road	d					16 32						17 02							17 32						18 02
Tooting	d					16 35						17 05							17 35						18 05
Carshalton	d				16 09						16 39							17 09						17 39	
Hackbridge	d				16 11						16 41							17 11						17 41	
Mitcham Junction 🚌	d				16 14						16 44							17 14						17 44	
Mitcham Eastfields	d				16 18						16 48							17 18						17 48	
Streatham 4	d				16 23	16 40					16 53	17 10						17 23	17 40					17 53	18 10
Tulse Hill 3	d				16 27	16 47					16 57	17 17						17 27	17 47					17 57	18 17
London Bridge 4 ⊖	d					17a00						17a30							18a00						18a30
Herne Hill 4	d				16a31						17a01							17a31						18a01	
Loughborough Jn	d																								
Elephant & Castle	d																								
London Blackfriars 3 ⊖	d																								
City Thameslink 3	d																								
Farringdon 3 ⊖	d																								
St Pancras International 15 ⊖	d	17 00	16 38	16 50			17 04	17 30	17 08	17 20			17 34	18 00	17 38		17 50			18 04	18 30	18 08	18 20		
Kentish Town ⊖	d		16 44						17 14						17 44							18 14			
West Hampstead Thameslink ⊖	d		16 47	16 59					17 17	17 29					17 47		17 59					18 17	18 29		
Cricklewood	d		16 50						17 20						17 50							18 20			
Hendon	d		16 53						17 23						17 53							18 23			
Mill Hill Broadway	d		16 57						17 27						17 57							18 27			
Elstree & Borehamwood	d		17 01	17 09					17 31	17 39					18 01		18 09					18 31	18 39		
Radlett	d		17 06						17 36						18 06							18 36			
St Albans City	d		17 12	17 16			17 25		17 42	17 46			17 55		18 12		18 16			18 25		18 42	18 46		
Harpenden	d		17 17	17 22			17 32		17 47	17 52			18 02		18 17		18 22			18 32		18 47	18 52		
Luton Airport Parkway 7 ✈	d		17 23	17 28			17 38	17 51	17 53	17 58			18 08		18 23		18 28			18 38	18 51	18 53	18 58		
Luton 10	d	17 23	17a27	17 31			17 41		17a57	18 01			18 11	18 23	18a27		18 31			18 41		18a57	19 01		
Leagrave	d			17 34			17 44			18 04			18 14				18 34			18 44			19 04		
Harlington	d			17 40			17 50			18 10			18 20				18 40			18 50			19 10		
Flitwick	d			17 44			17 54			18 14			18 24				18 44			18 54			19 14		
Bedford 7	a	17 37		17 56			18 06	18 06		18 26			18 36	18 37			18 56			19 06	19 06		19 26		

For general notes see front of timetable
For details of catering facilities see Directory of Train Operators

A To Corby. (Table 53)
B To Lincoln (Table 53)
C To Nottingham (Table 53)

Table 52

Saturdays

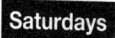

Brighton, Gatwick Airport and South London → City of London, St.Albans, Luton and Bedford

Network Diagram - see first page of Table 52

Station		FC 1	EM 1 ◇ A	FC	FC 1	FC	FC	FC 1		EM 1 ◇ B	FC	FC 1	FC	FC	FC 1	EM 1 ◇ A	FC	FC	FC	FC 1	EM 1 ◇ B	FC	FC		FC 1
Brighton 10	d																								
Preston Park	d																								
Hassocks 4	d																								
Burgess Hill 4	d																								
Wivelsfield 4	d																								
Haywards Heath 3	d																								
Balcombe	d																								
Three Bridges 4	d																								
Gatwick Airport 10 ✈	d																								
Redhill	d																								
East Croydon	d																								
Sutton (Surrey) 4	d					18 06	18 07						18 36	18 37				19 06	19 07				19 37		
West Sutton	d						18 10							18 40					19 10				19 40		
Sutton Common	d						18 12							18 42					19 12				19 42		
St Helier	d						18 15							18 45					19 15				19 45		
Morden South	d						18 17							18 47					19 17				19 47		
South Merton	d						18 19							18 49					19 19				19 49		
Wimbledon Chase	d						18 21							18 51					19 21				19 51		
Wimbledon 5 ⊖	d						18 30							19 00					19 30				20 00		
Haydons Road	d						18 32							19 02					19 32				20 02		
Tooting	d						18 35							19 05					19 35				20 05		
Carshalton	d					18 09							18 39					19 09							
Hackbridge	d					18 11							18 41					19 11							
Mitcham Junction	d					18 14							18 44					19 14							
Mitcham Eastfields	d					18 18							18 48					19 18							
Streatham 4	d					18 23	18 40						18 53	19 10				19 23	19 40				20 10		
Tulse Hill 3	d					18 27	18 47						18 57	19 17				19 27	19 47				20 17		
London Bridge 4 ⊖	d						19a00							19a30					20a00				20a30		
Herne Hill 4	d					18a31							19a01					19a31							
Loughborough Jn	d																								
Elephant & Castle	d																								
London Blackfriars 3 ⊖	d																								
City Thameslink 3	d																								
Farringdon 3 ⊖	d																								
St Pancras International 15 ⊖	d	18 34	19 00	18 38	18 50			19 04		19 30	19 08	19 20			19 34	20 00	19 48			20 04	20 30	20 18			20 34
Kentish Town ⊖	d			18 44							19 14						19 53					20 23			
West Hampstead Thameslink ⊖	d			18 47	18 59						19 17	19 29					19 56					20 26			
Cricklewood	d			18 50							19 20						19 59					20 29			
Hendon	d			18 53							19 23						20 02					20 33			
Mill Hill Broadway	d			18 57							19 27						20 06					20 37			
Elstree & Borehamwood	d			19 01	19 09						19 31	19 39					20 10					20 41			
Radlett	d			19 06							19 36						20 14					20 45			
St Albans City	d	18 55		19 12	19 16			19 25			19 42	19 46			19 55		20 20			20 25		20 51			20 55
Harpenden	d	19 02		19 17	19 22			19 32			19 47	19 52			20 02		20 26			20 32		20 57			21 02
Luton Airport Parkway 7 ✈	d	19 08		19 23	19 28			19 38		19 51	19 53	19 58			20 08		20 32			20 38	20 51	21 03			21 08
Luton 10	d	19 11	19 23	19a27	19 31			19 41			19a57	20 01			20 11	20 23	20 36			20 41		21 06			21 11
Leagrave	d	19 14			19 34			19 44				20 04			20 14		20 39			20 44		21 09			21 14
Harlington	d	19 20			19 40			19 50				20 10			20 20		20 45			20 50		21 15			21 20
Flitwick	d	19 24			19 44			19 54				20 14			20 24		20 49			20 54		21 19			21 24
Bedford 7	a	19 36	19 37		19 56			20 06		20 06		20 26			20 36	20 37	21 01			21 06	21 06	21 31			21 36

For general notes see front of timetable
For details of catering facilities see Directory of Train Operators

A To Corby. (Table 53)
B To Nottingham (Table 53)

Table 52

Saturdays

Brighton, Gatwick Airport and South London → City of London, St.Albans, Luton and Bedford

Network Diagram - see first page of Table 52

		EM	FC	FC	FC	EM	FC	FC	FC	FC	EM	FC	FC	FC	EM	FC	FC	FC	FC	FC	FC	FC	FC
		1 ◊			1	1 ◊			1		1 ◊		1		1 ◊		1			1		1	
		A				A					B				C								
		🍴				🍴					🍴				🍴								
Brighton 10	d																						
Preston Park	d																						
Hassocks 4	d																						
Burgess Hill 4	d																						
Wivelsfield 4	d																						
Haywards Heath 3	d																						
Balcombe	d																						
Three Bridges 4	d																						
Gatwick Airport 10 ✈	d																						
Redhill	d																						
East Croydon	d																						
Sutton (Surrey) 4	d			20 07				20 37				21 07				21 37			22 07				
West Sutton	d			20 10				20 40				21 10				21 40			22 10				
Sutton Common	d			20 12				20 42				21 12				21 42			22 12				
St Helier	d			20 15				20 45				21 15				21 45			22 15				
Morden South	d			20 17				20 47				21 17				21 47			22 17				
South Merton	d			20 19				20 49				21 19				21 49			22 19				
Wimbledon Chase	d			20 21				20 51				21 21				21 51			22 21				
Wimbledon 6 ⊖	d			20 30				21b00				21c30				22e00			22f30				
Haydons Road	d			20 32				21 02				21 32				22 02			22 32				
Tooting	d			20 35				21 05				21 35				22 05			22 35				
Carshalton	d																						
Hackbridge	d																						
Mitcham Junction	d																						
Mitcham Eastfields	d																						
Streatham 4	d			20 40				21 10				21 40				22 10			22 40				
Tulse Hill 3	d			20 47				21 17				21 47				22 17			22 47				
London Bridge 4 ⊖	d			21a00				21a30				22a00				22a30			23a00				
Herne Hill 4	d																						
Loughborough Jn	d																						
Elephant & Castle	d																						
London Blackfriars 3 ⊖	d																						
City Thameslink 3	d																						
Farringdon 3 ⊖	d																						
St Pancras International 15 ⊖	d	21 00	20 48		21 04	21 30	21 18		21 34	21 44	22 00		22 04	22 14	22 25		22 34	22 48		23 04	23 18	23 34	23 48
Kentish Town ⊖	d		20 53				21 23			21 49				22 19				22 53			23 23		23 53
West Hampstead Thameslink ⊖	d		20 56				21 26			21 52				22 22				22 56			23 26	23 41	23 56
Cricklewood	d		20 59				21 29			21 55				22 25				22 59			23 29		23 59
Hendon	d		21 02				21 32			21 58				22 28				23 02			23 32		00 02
Mill Hill Broadway	d		21 06				21 36			22 02				22 32				23 06			23 36		00 06
Elstree & Borehamwood	d		21 10				21 40			22 06				22 36				23 10			23 40		00 10
Radlett	d		21 14				21 44			22 10				22 40				23 14			23 44		00 14
St Albans City	d		21 20		21 25		21 50		21 55	22 16			22 26	22 46			22 56	23 20		23 26	23 50	23 57	00 20
Harpenden	d		21 26		21 32		21 56		22 02	22 22			22 32	22 52			23 02	23 26		23 32	23 56	00 03	00 26
Luton Airport Parkway 7 ✈	d		21 32		21 38	21 51	22 02		22 08	22 28			22 38	22 58	23 03		23 08	23 32		23 38	00 02	00 09	00 32
Luton 10	d	21 23	21 36		21 41		22 06		22 11	22 31	22 35		22 41	23 01			23 11	23 36		23 41	00 06	00 12	00 36
Leagrave	d		21 39		21 44		22 09		22 14	22 34			22 44	23 04			23 14	23 39		23 44	00 09	00 15	00 39
Harlington	d		21 45		21 50		22 15		22 20	22 40			22 50	23 10			23 20	23 45		23 50	00 15	00 21	00 45
Flitwick	d		21 49		21 54		22 19		22 24	22 44			22 54	23 14			23 24	23 49		23 54	00 19	00 25	00 49
Bedford 7	a	21 38	22 01		22 06	22 06	22 31		22 36	22 56	22 57		23 06	23 26	23 27		23 36	00 01		00 06	00 31	00 37	01 01

For general notes see front of timetable
For details of catering facilities see Directory of Train Operators

A To Derby (Table 53)
B Until 5 September
To Nottingham (Table 53)
C Until 11 July.
To Derby (Table 53)

b Arr. 2055
c Arr. 2125
e Arr. 2155
f Arr. 2225

Table 52

Sundays

Brighton, Gatwick Airport and South London → City of London, St.Albans, Luton and Bedford

Network Diagram - see first page of Table 52

		FC	FC [1]	FC	FC [1]	FC	FC [1]	FC [1]	FC [1]		FC [1]	FC [1]	FC [1]	FC [1]	FC [1]	EM [1] ◇ A	EM [1] ◇ B	FC [1]		EM [1] ◇ C	EM [1] ◇ D	FC [1]	FC	EM [1] ◇ A	EM [1] ◇ B
Brighton [10]	d																								
Preston Park	d																								
Hassocks [4]	d																								
Burgess Hill [4]	d																								
Wivelsfield [4]	d																								
Haywards Heath [3]	d																								
Balcombe	d																								
Three Bridges [4]	d																								
Gatwick Airport [10] ✈	d																								
Redhill	d																								
East Croydon	d																								
Sutton (Surrey) [4]	d																								
West Sutton	d																								
Sutton Common	d																								
St Helier	d																								
Morden South	d																								
South Merton	d																								
Wimbledon Chase	d																								
Wimbledon [6] ⊖	d																								
Haydons Road	d																								
Tooting	d																								
Carshalton	d																								
Hackbridge	d																								
Mitcham Junction	d																								
Mitcham Eastfields	d																								
Streatham [4]	d																								
Tulse Hill [3]	d																								
London Bridge [4] ⊖	d																								
Herne Hill [4]	d																								
Loughborough Jn	d																								
Elephant & Castle	d																								
London Blackfriars [3] ⊖	d																								
City Thameslink [3]	d																								
Farringdon [3] ⊖	d																								
St Pancras International [15] ⊖	d	23p18	23p34	23p48	00 04	00 18	00 38	01 08	01 38		06 04	07 04	07 44	08 04	08 44	09 00	09 00	09 14		09 30	09 30	09 34	09 26	10 00	10 00
Kentish Town ⊖	d	23p23		23p53		00 23	00 43	01 13	01 43		06 09	07 09		08 09											
West Hampstead Thameslink ⊖	d	23p26	23p41	23p56	00 11	00 26	00 46	01 16	01 46		06 12	07 12	07 52	08 12	08 52			09 22					09b40		
Cricklewood	d	23p29		23p59		00 29	00 49	01 19	01 49		06 15	07 15		08 15									09 44		
Hendon	d	23p32		00 02		00 32	00 52	01 22	01 52		06 18	07 18		08 18									09 47		
Mill Hill Broadway	d	23p36		00 06		00 36	00 56	01 26	01 56		06 22	07 22		08 22									09 50		
Elstree & Borehamwood	d	23p40		00 10		00 40	01 00	01 30	02 00		06 26	07 26		08 26									09 53		
Radlett	d	23p44		00 14		00 44	01 05	01 35	02 05		06 31	07 31		08 31									09 58		
St Albans City	d	23p50	23p57	00 20	00 26	00 50	01 11	01 41	02 11		06 37	07 37	08 07	08 37	09 07			09 37				09 55	10 02 10 08		
Harpenden	d	23p56	00 03	00 26	00 33	00 56	01 17	01 47	02 17		06 43	07 43	08 13	08 43	09 13			09 43				10 01	10 13		
Luton Airport Parkway [7] ✈	d	00 02	00 09	00 32	00 39	01 02	01 23	01 53	02 23		06 49	07 49	08 19	08 49	09 19	09 27	09 30	09 49				10 07	10 19	10 27	10 29
Luton [10]	d	00 06	00 12	00 36	00 42	01 06	01 27	01 57	02 27		06 53	07 53	08 23	08 53	09 23			09 53		09 59	09 59	10 11	10a23		
Leagrave	d	00 09	00 15	00 39	00 45	01 09	01 30	02 00	02 30		06 56	07 56	08 26	08 56	09 26			09 56				10 14			
Harlington	d	00 15	00 21	00 45	00 51	01 15	01 36	02 06	02 36		07 02	08 02	08 32	09 02	09 32			10 02				10 20			
Flitwick	d	00 19	00 25	00 49	00 55	01 19	01 40	02 10	02 40		07 06	08 06	08 36	09 06	09 36			10 06				10 24			
Bedford [7]	a	00 31	00 37	01 01	01 07	01 31	01 52	02 22	02 52		07 18	08 18	08 48	09 18	09 48	09 52	09 49	10 18		10 18	10 21	10 36		10 50	10 49

For general notes see front of timetable
For details of catering facilities see Directory of Train Operators

A Until 6 September
To Nottingham (Table 53)

B From 13 September.
To Nottingham (Table 53)

C From 13 September.
To Sheffield (Table 53)

D Until 6 September
To Sheffield (Table 53)

b Arr. 0932

Table 52

Sundays

Brighton, Gatwick Airport and South London → City of London, St.Albans, Luton and Bedford

Network Diagram - see first page of Table 52

		FC 1	FC	FC 1	EM 1 ◇ A ☕		EM 1 ◇ B ☕	FC 1	FC	FC 1	FC	EM 1 ◇ C ☕	EM 1 ◇ D ☕	FC 1		FC	FC 1	FC	EM 1 ◇ B ☕	EM 1 ◇ A ☕	FC 1	FC	FC 1		FC
Brighton [10]	d																								
Preston Park	d																								
Hassocks [4]	d																								
Burgess Hill [4]	d																								
Wivelsfield [4]	d																								
Haywards Heath [3]	d																								
Balcombe	d																								
Three Bridges [4]	d																								
Gatwick Airport [10] ✈	d																								
Redhill	d																								
East Croydon 🚌	d																								
Sutton (Surrey) [4]	d										10 15							10 45							11 15
West Sutton	d										10 18							10 48							11 18
Sutton Common	d										10 20							10 50							11 20
St Helier	d										10 23							10 53							11 23
Morden South	d										10 25							10 55							11 25
South Merton	d										10 27							10 57							11 27
Wimbledon Chase	d										10 29							10 59							11 29
Wimbledon [6] ⊖ 🚌	d										10 33							11 03							11 33
Haydons Road	d										10 35							11 05							11 35
Tooting	d										10 38							11 08							11 38
Carshalton	d																								
Hackbridge	d																								
Mitcham Junction 🚌	d																								
Mitcham Eastfields	d																								
Streatham [4]	d										10 43							11 13							11 43
Tulse Hill [3]	d										10 47							11 17							11 47
London Bridge [4] ⊖	d										10a59							11a29							11a59
Herne Hill [4]	d																								
Loughborough Jn	d																								
Elephant & Castle	d																								
London Blackfriars [3] ⊖	d																								
City Thameslink [3]	d																								
Farringdon [3] ⊖	d																								
St Pancras International [15] ⊖	d	10 04	09 56	10 18	10 30		10 30	10 34	10 26	10 48		11 00	11 00	11 04		10 56	11 18		11 30	11 30	11 34	11 26	11 48		
Kentish Town ⊖	d		10b10						10c40							11e10						11f40			
West Hampstead Thameslink ⊖	d		10 14	10 26					10 44	10 56						11 14	11 26					11 44	11 56		
Cricklewood	d		10 17						10 47							11 17						11 47			
Hendon	d		10 20						10 50							11 20						11 50			
Mill Hill Broadway	d		10 23						10 53							11 23						11 53			
Elstree & Borehamwood	d		10 28						10 58							11 28						11 58			
Radlett	d		10 32						11 02							11 32						12 02			
St Albans City	d	10 25	10 38	10 41				10 55	11 08	11 11				11 25		11 38	11 41				11 55	12 08	12 11		
Harpenden	d	10 31	10 43	10 47				11 01	11 13	11 17				11 31		11 43	11 47				12 01	12 13	12 17		
Luton Airport Parkway [7] ✈	d	10 37	10 49	10 53				11 07	11 19	11 23		11 29	11 29	11 37		11 49	11 53		11 56	11 57	12 07	12 19	12 23		
Luton [10]	d	10 41	10a53	10 57	11 00		11 00	11 11	11a23	11 27		11 32	11 33	11 41		11a53	11 57		11 59	12 00	12 11	12a23	12 27		
Leagrave	d	10 44		11 00				11 14		11 30				11 44			12 00				12 14		12 30		
Harlington	d	10 50		11 06				11 20		11 36				11 50			12 06				12 20		12 36		
Flitwick	d	10 54		11 10				11 24		11 40				11 54			12 10				12 24		12 40		
Bedford [7]	a	11 06		11 22	11 22		11 25	11 36		11 52		11 55	11 55	12 06			12 22		12 25	12 24	12 36		12 52		

For general notes see front of timetable
For details of catering facilities see Directory of Train Operators

- **A** From 13 September. To Sheffield (Table 53)
- **B** Until 6 September To Sheffield (Table 53)
- **C** Until 6 September To Nottingham (Table 53)
- **D** From 13 September. To Nottingham (Table 53)
- **b** Arr. 1002
- **c** Arr. 1032
- **e** Arr. 1102
- **f** Arr. 1132

Table 52

Brighton, Gatwick Airport and South London → City of London, St.Albans, Luton and Bedford

Network Diagram - see first page of Table 52

		EM	FC	FC	FC	FC	EM	FC	FC	FC	FC	EM	FC	FC	FC	FC	EM	EM	FC	FC	FC	FC	EM
		1 ◇ A ☕	1		1		1 ◇ B ☕	1		1		1 ◇ C ☕	1		1		1 ◇ D ☕	1 ◇ E ☕	1		1		1 ◇ C ☕
Brighton 10	d																						
Preston Park	d																						
Hassocks 4	d																						
Burgess Hill 4	d																						
Wivelsfield 4	d																						
Haywards Heath 3	d																						
Balcombe	d																						
Three Bridges 4	d																						
Gatwick Airport 10 ✈	d																						
Redhill	d																						
East Croydon	d																						
Sutton (Surrey) 4	d					11 45					12 15					12 45						13 15	
West Sutton	d					11 48					12 18					12 48						13 18	
Sutton Common	d					11 50					12 20					12 50						13 20	
St Helier	d					11 53					12 23					12 53						13 23	
Morden South	d					11 55					12 25					12 55						13 25	
South Merton	d					11 57					12 27					12 57						13 27	
Wimbledon Chase	d					11 59					12 29					12 59						13 29	
Wimbledon 6 ⊖	d					12 03					12 33					13 03						13 33	
Haydons Road	d					12 05					12 35					13 05						13 35	
Tooting	d					12 08					12 38					13 08						13 38	
Carshalton	d																						
Hackbridge	d																						
Mitcham Junction	d																						
Mitcham Eastfields	d																						
Streatham 4	d					12 13					12 43					13 13						13 43	
Tulse Hill 3	d					12 17					12 47					13 17						13 47	
London Bridge 4 ⊖	d					12a29					12a59					13a29						13a59	
Herne Hill 4	d																						
Loughborough Jn	d																						
Elephant & Castle	d																						
London Blackfriars 3 ⊖	d																						
City Thameslink 3	d																						
Farringdon 3 ⊖	d																						
St Pancras International 15 ⊖	d	12 00	12 04	11 56	12 18		12 30	12 34	12 26	12 48		13 00	13 04	12 56	13 18		13 30	13 30	13 34	13 26	13 48		14 00
Kentish Town ⊖	d			12b10					12c40					13e10						13f40			
West Hampstead Thameslink ⊖	d			12 14	12 26				12 44	12 56				13 14	13 26					13 44	13 56		
Cricklewood	d			12 17					12 47					13 17						13 47			
Hendon	d			12 20					12 50					13 20						13 50			
Mill Hill Broadway	d			12 23					12 53					13 23						13 53			
Elstree & Borehamwood	d			12 28					12 58					13 28						13 58			
Radlett	d			12 32					13 02					13 32						14 02			
St Albans City	d		12 25	12 38	12 41			12 55	13 08	13 11			13 25	13 38	13 41				13 55	14 08	14 11		
Harpenden	d		12 31	12 43	12 47			13 01	13 13	13 17			13 31	13 43	13 47				14 01	14 13	14 17		
Luton Airport Parkway 7 ✈	d	12 27	12 37	12 49	12 53		12 57	13 07	13 19	13 23		13 29	13 37	13 49	13 53		14 02	14 03	14 07	14 19	14 23		14 29
Luton 10	d	12 30	12 41	12a53	12 57		13 00	13 11	13a23	13 27		13 33	13 41	13a53	13 57		14 06	14 06	14 11	14a23	14 27		
Leagrave	d		12 44		13 00			13 14		13 30			13 44		14 00				14 14		14 30		
Harlington	d		12 50		13 06			13 20		13 36			13 50		14 06				14 20		14 36		
Flitwick	d		12 54		13 10			13 24		13 40			13 54		14 10				14 24		14 40		
Bedford 7	a	12 56	13 06		13 22		13 26	13 36		13 52		13 56	14 06		14 22		14 20	14 21	14 37		14 52		14 47

For general notes see front of timetable
For details of catering facilities see Directory of Train Operators

A Until 6 September To Nottingham (Table 53)
B To Sheffield (Table 53)
C To Nottingham (Table 53)
D From 13 September. To Sheffield (Table 53)
E Until 6 September. To Sheffield (Table 53)
b Arr. 1202
c Arr. 1232
e Arr. 1302
f Arr. 1332

Sundays

Brighton, Gatwick Airport and South London → City of London, St.Albans, Luton and Bedford

Network Diagram - see first page of Table 52

Station		FC	FC	FC	FC		EM	FC	FC	FC	FC	EM	EM	FC		FC	FC	FC	EM	EM	FC	FC	FC		FC
		1		1			1 ◇	1		1		1 ◇	1 ◇	1			1		1 ◇	1 ◇	1		1		
							A					B	C						D	E					
							🍴					🍴	🍴						🍴	🍴					
Brighton 10	d																								
Preston Park	d																								
Hassocks 4	d																								
Burgess Hill 4	d																								
Wivelsfield 4	d																								
Haywards Heath 3	d																								
Balcombe	d																								
Three Bridges 4	d																								
Gatwick Airport 10 ✈	d																								
Redhill	d																								
East Croydon	d																								
Sutton (Surrey) 4	d				13 45						14 15							14 45							15 15
West Sutton	d				13 48						14 18							14 48							15 18
Sutton Common	d				13 50						14 20							14 50							15 20
St Helier	d				13 53						14 23							14 53							15 23
Morden South	d				13 55						14 25							14 55							15 25
South Merton	d				13 57						14 27							14 57							15 27
Wimbledon Chase	d				13 59						14 29							14 59							15 29
Wimbledon 6 ⊖	d				14 03						14 33							15 03							15 33
Haydons Road	d				14 05						14 35							15 05							15 35
Tooting	d				14 08						14 38							15 08							15 38
Carshalton	d																								
Hackbridge	d																								
Mitcham Junction	d																								
Mitcham Eastfields	d																								
Streatham 4	d				14 13						14 43							15 13							15 43
Tulse Hill 3	d				14 17						14 47							15 17							15 47
London Bridge 4 ⊖	d				14a29						14a59							15a29							15a59
Herne Hill 4	d																								
Loughborough Jn	d																								
Elephant & Castle	d																								
London Blackfriars 3 ⊖	d																								
City Thameslink 3	d																								
Farringdon 3 ⊖	d																								
St Pancras International 15 ⊖	d	14 04	13 56	14 18			14 30	14 34	14 26	14 48		15 00	15 00	15 04		14 56	15 18		15 30	15 30	15 34	15 26	15 48		
Kentish Town ⊖	d		14b10						14c40							15e10						15f40			
West Hampstead Thameslink ⊖	d		14 14	14 26					14 44	14 56						15 14	15 26					15 44	15 56		
Cricklewood	d		14 17						14 47							15 17						15 47			
Hendon	d		14 20						14 50							15 20						15 50			
Mill Hill Broadway	d		14 23						14 53							15 23						15 53			
Elstree & Borehamwood	d		14 28						14 58							15 28						15 58			
Radlett	d		14 32						15 02							15 32						16 02			
St Albans City	d	14 25	14 38	14 41				14 55	15 08	15 11				15 25		15 38	15 41				15 55	16 08	16 11		
Harpenden	d	14 31	14 43	14 47				15 01	15 13	15 17				15 31		15 43	15 47				16 01	16 13	16 17		
Luton Airport Parkway 7 ✈	d	14 37	14 49	14 53				15 07	15 19	15 23		15 29	15 29	15 37		15 49	15 53				16 07	16 19	16 23		
Luton 10	d	14 41	14a53	14 57			15 01	15 11	15a23	15 27				15 41		15a53	15 57		15 59	16 01	16 11	16a23	16 27		
Leagrave	d	14 44		15 00				15 14		15 30				15 44			16 00				16 14		16 30		
Harlington	d	14 50		15 06				15 20		15 36				15 50			16 06				16 20		16 36		
Flitwick	d	14 54		15 10				15 24		15 40				15 54			16 10				16 24		16 40		
Bedford 7	a	15 06		15 22			15 17	15 36		15 52		15 46	15 47	16 06			16 22		16 15	16 17	16 36		16 52		

For general notes see front of timetable
For details of catering facilities see Directory of Train Operators

A To Leeds (Table 53)

B From 13 September. To Nottingham (Table 53)

C Until 6 September. To Nottingham (Table 53)

D From 13 September. To Sheffield (Table 53)

E Until 6 September. To Sheffield (Table 53)

b Arr. 1402

c Arr. 1432

e Arr. 1502

f Arr. 1532

Table 52

Sundays

Brighton, Gatwick Airport and South London → City of London, St.Albans, Luton and Bedford

Network Diagram - see first page of Table 52

		EM 1 ◇ A 🍴	FC 1	EM 1 ◇ B 🍴	FC	FC 1	FC	FC 1	FC		EM 1 ◇ A 🍴	FC 1	FC	FC 1	EM 1 ◇ C 🍴	FC	EM 1 ◇ D 🍴	FC 1		FC	FC 1	FC	EM 1 ◇ A 🍴	FC 1	FC
Brighton 10	d																								
Preston Park	d																								
Hassocks 4	d																								
Burgess Hill 4	d																								
Wivelsfield 4	d																								
Haywards Heath 3	d																								
Balcombe	d																								
Three Bridges 4	d																								
Gatwick Airport 10 ✈	d																								
Redhill	d																								
East Croydon 🚌	d																								
Sutton (Surrey) 4	d						15 45						16 15							16 45					17 15
West Sutton	d						15 48						16 18							16 48					17 18
Sutton Common	d						15 50						16 20							16 50					17 20
St Helier	d						15 53						16 23							16 53					17 23
Morden South	d						15 55						16 25							16 55					17 25
South Merton	d						15 57						16 27							16 57					17 27
Wimbledon Chase	d						15 59						16 29							16 59					17 29
Wimbledon 6 ⊖ 🚌	d						16 03						16 33							17 03					17 33
Haydons Road	d						16 05						16 35							17 05					17 35
Tooting	d						16 08						16 38							17 08					17 38
Carshalton	d																								
Hackbridge	d																								
Mitcham Junction 🚌	d																								
Mitcham Eastfields	d																								
Streatham 4	d						16 13						16 43							17 13					17 43
Tulse Hill 3	d						16 17						16 47							17 17					17 47
London Bridge 4 ⊖	d						16a29						16a59							17a29					17a59
Herne Hill 4	d																								
Loughborough Jn	d																								
Elephant & Castle	d																								
London Blackfriars 3 ⊖	d																								
City Thameslink 3	d																								
Farringdon 3 ⊖	d																								
St Pancras International 15 ⊖	d	16 00	16 04	16 30	15 56	16 18		16 34	16 26		17 00	16 48		17 04	17 30	16 56	17 30	17 18			17 34	17 26	18 00	17 48	
Kentish Town ⊖	d				16b10				16c40							17e10						17f40			
West Hampstead Thameslink ⊖	d				16 14	16 26			16 44			16 56				17 14		17 26				17 44		17 56	
Cricklewood	d				16 17				16 47							17 17						17 47			
Hendon	d				16 20				16 50							17 20						17 50			
Mill Hill Broadway	d				16 23				16 53							17 23						17 53			
Elstree & Borehamwood	d				16 28				16 58							17 28						17 58			
Radlett	d				16 32				17 02							17 32						18 02			
St Albans City	d		16 25		16 38	16 41		16 55	17 08			17 11		17 25		17 38		17 41			17 55	18 08		18 11	
Harpenden	d		16 31		16 43	16 47		17 01	17 13			17 17		17 31		17 43		17 47			18 01	18 13		18 17	
Luton Airport Parkway 7 ✈	d	16 29	16 37		16 49	16 53		17 07	17 19		17 21	17 23		17 37		17 49		17 53			18 07	18 19	18 21	18 23	
Luton 10	d		16 41	16 52	16a53	16 57		17 11	17a23			17 27		17 41	17 52	17a53	17 54	17 57			18 11	18a23		18 27	
Leagrave	d		16 44			17 00		17 14				17 30		17 44				18 00			18 14			18 30	
Harlington	d		16 50			17 06		17 20				17 36		17 50				18 06			18 20			18 36	
Flitwick	d		16 54			17 10		17 24				17 40		17 54				18 10			18 24			18 40	
Bedford 7	a	16 47	17 06	17 15		17 22		17 36			17 45	17 52		18 06	18 15		18 17	18 22			18 36		18 45	18 52	

For general notes see front of timetable
For details of catering facilities see Directory of Train Operators

A To Nottingham (Table 53)

B Until 6 September to Derby (Table 53). From 13 September to Sheffield (Table 53)

C Until 6 September. To Derby (Table 53)

D From 13 September. To Sheffield (Table 53)

b Arr. 1602

c Arr. 1632

e Arr. 1702

f Arr. 1732

Table 52

Sundays

Brighton, Gatwick Airport and South London → City of London, St.Albans, Luton and Bedford

Network Diagram - see first page of Table 52

	FC 1	EM 1 ◇ A	FC	EM 1 ◇ B		FC 1	FC	FC 1	FC	EM 1 ◇ C	FC 1	FC	FC 1		EM 1 ◇ D	FC	FC	FC	FC 1	FC	EM 1 ◇ E	FC		FC 1
Brighton 10 d																								
Preston Park d																								
Hassocks 4 d																								
Burgess Hill 4 d																								
Wivelsfield 4 d																								
Haywards Heath 3 d																								
Balcombe d																								
Three Bridges 4 d																								
Gatwick Airport 10 ✈ d																								
Redhill d																								
East Croydon d																								
Sutton (Surrey) 4 d							17 45					18 15						18 45		19 15				
West Sutton d							17 48					18 18						18 48		19 18				
Sutton Common d							17 50					18 20						18 50		19 20				
St Helier d							17 53					18 23						18 53		19 23				
Morden South d							17 55					18 25						18 55		19 25				
South Merton d							17 57					18 27						18 57		19 27				
Wimbledon Chase d							17 59					18 29						18 59		19 29				
Wimbledon 6 d							18 03					18 33						19 03		19 33				
Haydons Road d							18 05					18 35						19 05		19 35				
Tooting d							18 08					18 38						19 08		19 38				
Carshalton d																								
Hackbridge d																								
Mitcham Junction d																								
Mitcham Eastfields d																								
Streatham 4 d							18 13					18 43						19 13		19 43				
Tulse Hill 3 d							18 17					18 47						19 17		19 47				
London Bridge 4 ⊖ d							18a29					18a59						19a29		19a59				
Herne Hill 4 d																								
Loughborough Jn d																								
Elephant & Castle d																								
London Blackfriars 3 ⊖ d																								
City Thameslink 3 d																								
Farringdon 3 ⊖ d																								
St Pancras International 15 ⊖ d	18 04	18 30	17 56	18 30		18 18		18 34	18 26	19 00	18 48		19 04		19 30	18 56	19 18		19 34		20 00	19 48		20 04
Kentish Town ⊖ d			18b10						18c40							19e10	19 23					19 53		
West Hampstead Thameslink ⊖ d			18 14			18 26			18 44		18 56					19 14	19 26					19 56		
Cricklewood d			18 17						18 47							19 17	19 29					19 59		
Hendon d			18 20						18 50							19 20	19 32					20 02		
Mill Hill Broadway d			18 23						18 53							19 23	19 36					20 06		
Elstree & Borehamwood d			18 28						18 58							19 28	19 40					20 10		
Radlett d			18 32						19 02							19 32	19 44					20 14		
St Albans City d	18 25		18 38			18 41		18 55	19 08		19 11		19 25			19 38	19 50		19 55			20 20		20 25
Harpenden d	18 31		18 43			18 47		19 01	19 13		19 17		19 31			19 43	19 56		20 01			20 26		20 31
Luton Airport Parkway 7 ✈ d	18 37		18 49			18 53		19 07	19 19	19 21	19 23		19 37			19 49	20 02		20 07		20 23	20 32		20 37
Luton 10 d	18 41	18 52	18a53	18 54		18 57		19 11	19a23		19 27		19 41		19 52	19a53	20 06		20 11			20 36		20 41
Leagrave d	18 44					19 00		19 14			19 30		19 44				20 09		20 14			20 39		20 44
Harlington d	18 50					19 06		19 20			19 36		19 50				20 15		20 20			20 45		20 50
Flitwick d	18 54					19 10		19 24			19 40		19 54				20 19		20 24			20 49		20 54
Bedford 7 a	19 06	19 15		19 17		19 22		19 36		19 45	19 52		20 06		20 15		20 31		20 36		20 47	21 01		21 06

For general notes see front of timetable
For details of catering facilities see Directory of Train Operators

A Until 6 September To Derby (Table 53)
B From 13 September. To Leeds (Table 53)
C To Nottingham (Table 53)
D Until 6 September to Derby (Table 53). From 13 September to Sheffield (Table 53)
E Until 6 September. To Derby (Table 53)
b Arr. 1802
c Arr. 1832
e Arr. 1902

Table 52

Sundays

Brighton, Gatwick Airport and South London → City of London, St.Albans, Luton and Bedford

Network Diagram - see first page of Table 52

		FC	EM 1 ◇ A	FC	FC 1	FC	EM 1 ◇ B	FC	FC 1		FC	EM 1 ◇ C	FC	FC 1	FC 1	FC	FC 1	EM 1 ◇ B		FC 1	EM 1 ◇ D	FC 1	FC 1
Brighton 10	d																						
Preston Park	d																						
Hassocks 4	d																						
Burgess Hill 4	d																						
Wivelsfield 4	d																						
Haywards Heath 3	d																						
Balcombe	d																						
Three Bridges 4	d																						
Gatwick Airport 10 ✈	d																						
Redhill	d																						
East Croydon	d																						
Sutton (Surrey) 4	d	19 45				20 15					20 45					21 15							
West Sutton	d	19 48				20 18					20 48					21 18							
Sutton Common	d	19 50				20 20					20 50					21 20							
St Helier	d	19 53				20 23					20 53					21 23							
Morden South	d	19 55				20 25					20 55					21 25							
South Merton	d	19 57				20 27					20 57					21 27							
Wimbledon Chase	d	19 59				20 29					20 59					21 29							
Wimbledon 6 ⊖	d	20 03				20 33					21 03					21 33							
Haydons Road	d	20 05				20 35					21 05					21 35							
Tooting	d	20 08				20 38					21 08					21 38							
Carshalton	d																						
Hackbridge	d																						
Mitcham Junction	d																						
Mitcham Eastfields	d																						
Streatham 4	d	20 13				20 43					21 13					21 43							
Tulse Hill 3	d	20 17				20 47					21 17					21 47							
London Bridge 4 ⊖	d	20a29				20a59					21a29					21a59							
Herne Hill 4	d																						
Loughborough Jn	d																						
Elephant & Castle	d																						
London Blackfriars 3 ⊖	d																						
City Thameslink 3	d																						
Farringdon 3 ⊖	d																						
St Pancras International 15 ⊖	d		20 30	20 18	20 34		21 00	20 48	21 04			21 30	21 18	21 34	21 46		22 04	22 30		22 34	23 00	23 04	23 34
Kentish Town ⊖	d			20 23				20 53					21 23		21 53		22 09			22 39		23 09	23 39
West Hampstead Thameslink ⊖	d			20 26				20 56					21 26		21 56		22 12			22 42		23 12	23 42
Cricklewood	d			20 29				20 59					21 29		21 59		22 15			22 45		23 15	23 45
Hendon	d			20 32				21 02					21 32		22 02		22 18			22 48		23 18	23 48
Mill Hill Broadway	d			20 36				21 06					21 36		22 06		22 22			22 52		23 22	23 52
Elstree & Borehamwood	d			20 40				21 10					21 40		22 10		22 26			22 56		23 26	23 56
Radlett	d			20 44				21 14					21 44		22 14		22 31			23 01		23 31	00 01
St Albans City	d			20 50	20 55			21 20	21 25				21 50	21 55	22 20		22 37			23 07		23 37	00 07
Harpenden	d			20 56	21 01			21 26	21 31				21 56	22 01	22 26		22 43			23 13		23 43	00 13
Luton Airport Parkway 7 ✈	d			21 02	21 07		21 23	21 32	21 37				22 02	22 07	22 32		22 49	22 53		23 19	23 28	23 49	00 19
Luton 10	d		20 54	21 06	21 11			21 36	21 41			21 54	22 06	22 11	22 36		22 53			23 23		23 53	00 23
Leagrave	d			21 09	21 14			21 39	21 44				22 09	22 14	22 39		22 56			23 26		23 56	00 26
Harlington	d			21 15	21 20			21 45	21 50				22 15	22 20	22 45		23 02			23 32		00 02	00 32
Flitwick	d			21 19	21 24			21 49	21 54				22 19	22 24	22 49		23 06			23 36		00 06	00 36
Bedford 7	a		21 17	21 31	21 36		21 47	22 01	22 06			22 17	22 31	22 36	23 01		23 18	23 17		23 48	23 52	00 18	00 48

For general notes see front of timetable
For details of catering facilities see Directory of Train Operators

A Until 6 September. To Leeds (Table 53)

B Until 6 September. To Nottingham (Table 53)

C To Sheffield (Table 53)

D Until 12 July. To Derby (Table 53)

Table 52A

Luton → Dunstable

Bus Service

	FC	FC		FC	FC		FC	FC		FC	FC		FC	FC		FC	FC		FC	FC		FC	FC		FC	FC		FC
Luton ..... d	05 57	06 15	.....	06 40	07 10	.....	07 32	07 53	.....	08 06	08 27	.....	08 47	09 08	.....	09 27	09 34	.....	09 52	10 04	.....	10 22	10 34	.....	10 52	11 04	.....	11 22
Dunstable a	06 20	06 50	.	07 10	07 45	.	08 05	08 25	.	08 45	09 00	.	09 25	09 40	.	09 55	10 10	.	10 25	10 40	.	10 55	11 10	.	11 25	11 40	.	11 55

	FC	FC		FC	FC		FC	FC		FC	FC		FC	FC		FC	FC		FC	FC		FC	FC		FC	FC		FC
Luton ..... d	11 34	11 52	.....	12 04	12 22	.....	12 34	12 52	.....	13 04	13 22	.....	13 34	13 52	.....	14 04	14 22	.....	14 34	14 52	.....	15 04	15 22	.....	15 36	15 52	.....	16 04
Dunstable a	12 10	12 29	.	12 40	12 55	.	13 10	13 25	.	13 40	13 55	.	14 10	14 29	.	14 40	14 55	.	15 10	15 25	.	15 40	15 55	.	16 10	16 25	.	16 40

	FC	FC		FC	FC		FC	FC		FC	FC		FC	FC		FC	FC		FC	FC		FC	FC		FC	FC		
Luton ..... d	16 22	16 37	.....	16 50	17 07	.....	17 25	17 40	.....	17 57	18 27	.....	18 43	19 15	.....	19 30	20 02	.....	20 32	21 00	.....	21 17	21 45	.....	22 15	22 45	.....	.....
Dunstable a	16 59	17 14	.	17 34	17 46	.	18 00	18 12	.	18 32	18 55	.	19 08	19 42	.	19 54	20 32	.	21 02	21 20	.	21 41	22 09	.	22 37	23 08	.	.

Saturdays

	FC	FC		FC	FC		FC	FC		FC	FC		FC	FC		FC	FC		FC	FC		FC	FC		FC	FC		FC
Luton ..... d	05 55	06 30	.....	07 07	07 37	.....	08 07	08 37	.....	09 07	09 27	.....	09 42	10 02	.....	10 22	10 42	.....	11 02	11 22	.....	11 42	12 02	.....	12 22	12 42	.....	13 02
Dunstable a	06 13	06 48	.	07 35	08 05	.	08 40	09 10	.	09 40	09 57	.	10 15	10 35	.	10 55	11 15	.	11 35	11 55	.	12 15	12 39	.	12 55	13 15	.	13 35

	FC	FC		FC	FC		FC	FC		FC	FC		FC	FC		FC	FC		FC	FC	FC	FC	FC	FC	FC	FC		
Luton ..... d	13 22	13 42	.....	14 02	14 22	.....	14 42	15 02	.....	15 22	15 42	.....	16 02	16 13	.....	16 22	16 42	.....	17 12	17 42	19 00	19 30	20 02	20 30	21 17	21 45	.....	.....
Dunstable a	13 55	14 15	.	14 39	14 55	.	15 15	15 35	.	15 55	16 15	.	16 31	16 47	.	17 00	17 11	.	17 45	18 11	19 18	19 54	20 32	21 02	21 41	21 59	.	.

Sundays

	FC					FC					FC					FC					FC							
Luton ..... d	18 42	.....	.....	.....	.....	19 42	.....	.....	.....	.....	20 42	.....	.....	.....	.....	21 42	.....	.....	.....	.....	22 42	.....	.....	.....	.....	.....	.....	.....
Dunstable a	19 04	.	.	.	.	20 04	.	.	.	.	21 04	.	.	.	.	22 04	.	.	.	.	23 06	.	.	.	.	.	.	.

For general notes see front of timetable
For details of catering facilities see
Directory of Train Operators

Dunstable → Luton
Bus Service

		FC	FC	FC	FC	FC	FC	FC	FC	FC	FC	FC	FC	FC	FC	FC	FC	FC	FC	FC	FC	FC	FC	FC	FC	FC	FC	FC	FC
Dunstable	d	05 15	05 45	05 50	06 00	06 05	06 25	06 40	06 50	06 55	07 15	07 30	07 36	07 53	08 00	08 08	08 10	08 18	08 28	08 30	08 49	09 00	09 05	09 17	09 30	09 35	09 47	10 00	10 05
Luton	a	05 40	06 04	06 04	06 15	06 30	06 40	07 06	07 04	07 10	07 32	08 04	07 53	08 12	08 36	08 27	08 46	08 37	08 47	09 06	09 08	09 34	09 27	09 34	10 04	09 52	10 04	10 34	10 22

		FC		FC	FC	FC	FC	FC	FC	FC	FC	FC	FC	FC	FC	FC	FC	FC	FC	FC	FC	FC	FC	FC	FC	FC	FC	FC	FC
Dunstable	d	10 17	.....	10 30	10 35	10 47	11 00	11 05	11 17	11 30	11 35	11 47	12 00	12 05	12 17	12 30	12 35	12 47	13 00	13 05	13 17	13 35	13 47	14 00	14 05	14 17	14 30	14 35	14 47
Luton	a	10 34	.	11 04	10 52	11 04	11 34	11 22	11 34	12 04	11 52	12 04	12 34	12 22	12 34	13 04	12 52	13 04	13 34	13 22	13 34	13 52	14 04	14 34	14 22	14 34	15 04	14 52	15 04

		FC	FC	FC	FC	FC	FC	FC	FC	FC	FC	FC	FC	FC	FC	FC	FC	FC	FC	FC	FC	FC	FC	FC	FC		
Dunstable	d	15 00	15 05	15 19	15 35	15 40	15 47	16 05	16 10	16 20	16 33	16 40	16 50	17 08	17 10	17 20	17 23	17 40	17 40	18 10	18 20	18 45	19 15	20 15	20 45	21 45	23 08	.....	.....
Luton	a	15 34	15 22	15 36	15 52	16 15	16 04	16 22	16 47	16 37	16 50	17 17	17 07	17 25	17 47	17 59	17 40	17 57	18 17	18 27	18 51	19 16	19 44	20 35	21 10	22 07	23 31	.	.

Saturdays

		FC	FC	FC		FC	FC	FC		FC	FC	FC		FC	FC	FC		FC	FC	FC		FC	FC	FC		FC	FC	FC	FC
Dunstable	d	06 00	06 15	06 20	.....	06 50	07 00	07 15	.....	07 40	07 50	08 10	.....	08 20	08 40	08 50	.....	09 05	09 10	09 25	.....	09 30	09 45	10 00	.....	10 05	10 25	10 30	10 45
Luton	a	06 26	06 30	06 44	.	07 07	07 34	07 28	.	08 10	08 07	08 40	.	08 37	09 10	09 07	.	09 27	09 34	09 42	.	10 04	10 02	10 34	.	10 22	10 42	11 04	11 02

		FC		FC	FC	FC		FC	FC	FC		FC	FC	FC		FC	FC	FC		FC	FC	FC		FC	FC	FC		FC	FC
Dunstable	d	11 00	.....	11 05	11 25	11 30	.....	11 45	12 00	12 05	.....	12 25	12 30	12 45	.....	13 00	13 05	13 25	.....	13 30	13 45	14 00	.....	14 05	14 25	14 30	.....	14 45	15 00
Luton	a	11 34	.	11 22	11 42	12 04	.	12 02	12 34	12 22	.	12 42	13 04	13 02	.	13 34	13 22	13 42	.	14 04	14 02	14 34	.	14 22	14 42	15 04	.	15 02	15 34

		FC	FC	FC		FC	FC	FC		FC	FC	FC		FC	FC	FC		FC	FC	FC		FC	FC						
Dunstable	d	15 05	15 25	15 30	.....	15 45	16 00	16 05	.....	16 25	16 40	16 55	.....	17 10	17 23	17 40	.....	18 00	18 45	19 15	.....	20 45	23 08	.....	.....	.....	.....	.....	.....
Luton	a	15 22	15 42	16 04	.	16 02	16 34	16 22	.	16 42	17 14	17 12	.	17 44	17 40	18 10	.	18 33	19 16	19 44	.	21 10	23 31	.	.	.	.	.	.

Sundays

Dunstable	d	.....	.....	.....	.....	.....	.....	.....	.....	.....	.....	.....	.....	.....	.....	.....	.....	.....	.....	.....	.....	.....	.....	.....	.....	.....	.....	.....
Luton	a	.	.	.	.	.	.	.	.	.	.	.	.	.	.	.	.	.	.	.	.	.	.	.	.	.	.	.

For general notes see front of timetable
For details of catering facilities see
Directory of Train Operators

Route Diagram for Table 53

DM-7/09
Design BAJS

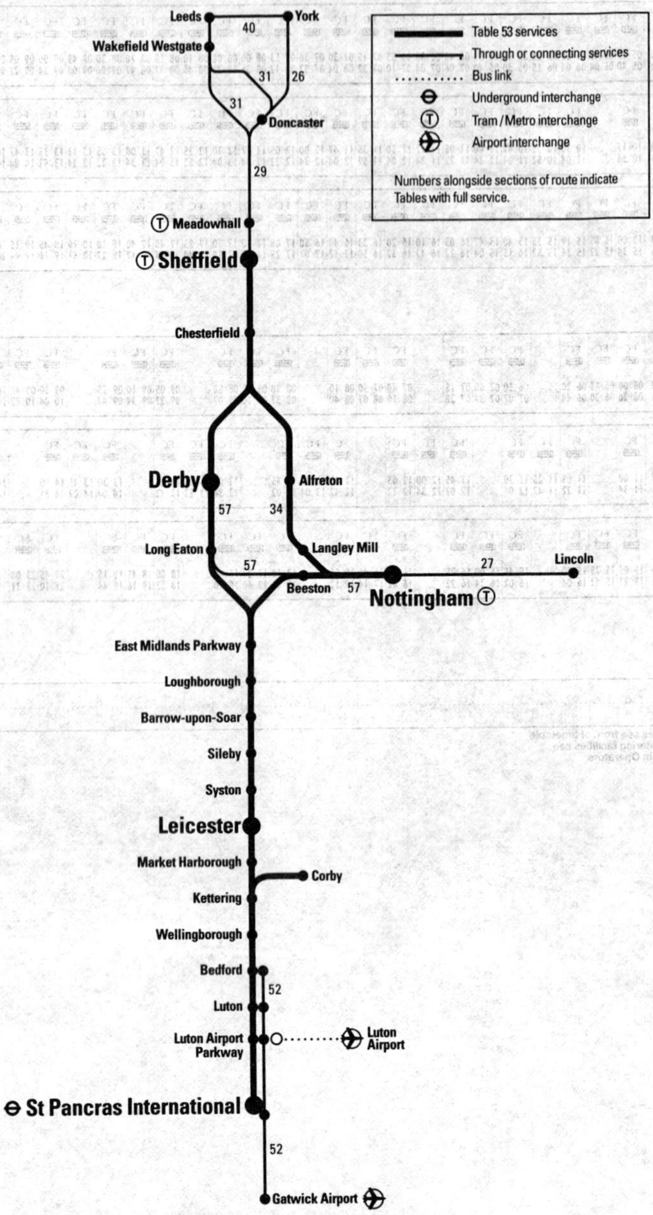
Leeds
York
40
Wakefield Westgate
31
26
31
Doncaster
29
Meadowhall
Sheffield
Chesterfield
Derby
Alfreton
57
34
Long Eaton
Langley Mill
57
27
Lincoln
Beeston
57
Nottingham
East Midlands Parkway
Loughborough
Barrow-upon-Soar
Sileby
Syston
Leicester
Market Harborough
Corby
Kettering
Wellingborough
Bedford
52
Luton
Luton Airport Parkway
Luton Airport
St Pancras International
52
Gatwick Airport
Table 53 services
Through or connecting services
Bus link
Underground interchange
Tram / Metro interchange
Airport interchange
Numbers alongside sections of route indicate Tables with full service.

London → East Midlands → Sheffield

Route Diagram - See first page of Table 53

Miles	Miles	Miles			EM ◇ C	XC [1]◇ D	NT	XC [1]◇ E	EM [1]◇	NT ◇	EM ◇	XC [1]◇ G	XC [1]◇ H	EM [1]◇	NT ◇	EM
0	0	—	**St Pancras International** ⊖	d												
—	—	—	Gatwick Airport [10] ✈	d												
29¼	29¼	—	Luton Airport Parkway [7]	d												
30¼	30¼	—	Luton [10]	d												
49¾	49¾	—	Bedford [7]	d												
65¼	65¼	—	Wellingborough	d												
72	72	—	Kettering	a												
—	—	0		d												
—	—	7½	Corby	d												
83	83	—	**Market Harborough**	d												
99¼	99¼	48½	**Leicester**	a												
—	—	—		d												06 33
103	103	—	Syston	d												06 41
105¾	105¾	—	Sileby	d												06 47
107¾	107¾	—	Barrow Upon Soar	d												06 52
111¾	111¾	—	Loughborough	d												06 57
117½	117½	—	East Midlands Parkway	d												07 08
123¼	—	—	Beeston	a												07 17
126½	—	—	**Nottingham** [8]	a												07 27
—	—	—		d	05 20					06 23	06 40				07 13	
—	—	—	Lincoln	a												
138½	—	—	Langley Mill	d						06 38					07 30	
144¾	—	—	Alfreton	d						06 46	07 02				07 38	
—	120½	—	Long Eaton	a												
—	128½	—	**Derby** [10]	a												
—	—	—		d		05 56		06 36	06 20			07 11	07 13	07 20		
155	152¾	—	Chesterfield	d	05 49	06 15	06 26		06 42	06 58	07 13	07 32	07 32	07 42	07 50	
167¼	165	—	**Sheffield** [7]	a	06 15	06 37	06 46	07 06	07 13	07 18	07 31	07 48	07 48	08 00	08 08	
—	—	—	Doncaster [7]	a		07 04	07 22		08 01		08 20	08 24	08 24	08 40		
—	—	—	Wakefield Kirkgate [4]	a			07 27			07 57					08 57	
—	—	—	Wakefield Westgate [7]	a	07 22	07e27		07 36	08f27		08f27				08g46	
—	—	—	Leeds [10]	a	07 44	07g51	07 51	07 52	08 49	08 21	08 49				09 19	
—	—	—	York [8]	a	07 27	07 27		08 23	08h31		08 47	08 47	08 47			

		XC [1]◇ E	EM ◇	XC [1]◇ G	EM	EM [1]◇	XC [1]◇ H	EM [1]◇	NT ◇	EM [1]◇	EM [1]◇	XC [1]◇ E	EM ◇	XC [1]◇ H	EM [1]◇	XC [1]◇ G	EM	EM [1]◇ J	EM [1]◇ K	EM [1]◇	EM [1]◇	NT ◇	XC [1]◇ E
St Pancras International ⊖	d					06 10		06 37		06 55					07 00			07 25	07 25	07 30	07 55		
Gatwick Airport [10] ✈	d					04 30		05 00												06 16			
Luton Airport Parkway [7]	d					06 10		06 40		07 16										07 51			
Luton [10]	d					06 33		06 59							07 23					07 29			
Bedford [7]	d					06 48									07 38					08 07			
Wellingborough	d					07 01									07 51					08 20			
Kettering	a					07 07		07 27							08 00					08 26			
	d					07 08		07 28			07 38				08 01					08 27			
Corby	d										07a47												
Market Harborough	d					07 18		07 38							08 12			08 21	08 21	08 37			
Leicester	a					07 35		07 53		08 04					08 29			08 36	08 36	08 52	09 02		
	d				07 25	07 36		07 57		08 06					08 30		08 25	08 38	08 38	08 54	09 04		
Syston	d				07 32												08 32						
Sileby	d				07 37												08 37						
Barrow Upon Soar	d				07 41												08 41						
Loughborough	d				07 46	07 47		08 07		08 17					08 41		08 47	08 48	08 48	09 04			
East Midlands Parkway	d				07 57	07 54									08 50		08 57	08 56	08 56				
Beeston	a				08 06					08 30										09 16			
Nottingham [8]	a				08 16					08 40					09 03		09 13			09 26			
	d		07 45						08 15				08 45				09 23					09 15	
Lincoln	a																10 17						
Langley Mill	d								08 31													09 32	
Alfreton	d		08 07						08 39				09 07									09 40	
Long Eaton	a					07 58												08 59	08 59				
Derby [10]	a					08 09		08 24										09 10	09 15		09 26		
	d	07 44		08 11			08 13	08 28				08 44		09 09		09 11					09 28		09 44
Chesterfield	d	08 03	08 18	08 32			08 35	08 47	08 51			09 03	09 18								09 47	09 52	10 03
Sheffield [7]	a	08 17	08 38	08 51			08 51	09 04	09 15			09 17	09 38	09 46		09 46					10 04	10 15	10 17
Doncaster [7]	a	09 05		09 20			09 20	09 40				10 04		10 15		10 15					10 40		11 04
Wakefield Kirkgate [4]	a								09 57													10 57	
Wakefield Westgate [7]	a	08 46	09f27									09 46	10f27										10 46
Leeds [10]	a	09 05	09 49						10 18			10 02	10 48									11 18	11 02
York [8]	a	09 33	09 48	09 48			09 48					10 29	10 40	10 40		10 40						11h37	11 29

For general notes see front of timetable
For details of catering facilities see Directory of Train Operators

- **A** 20 July to 7 September
- **B** Until 13 July
- **C** To Liverpool Lime Street (Table 89)
- **D** To Newcastle (Table 26)
- **E** To Edinburgh (Table 26)
- **G** Until 4 September. To Newcastle (Table 26)
- **H** From 7 September. To Newcastle (Table 26)
- **J** From 7 September
- **K** Until 4 September
- **b** Tuesdays, Wednesdays and Thursdays only. Change at Bedford
- **c** Sundays, Tuesdays and Saturdays only. Change at Bedford. Sundays dep. 2332. Mondays dep. 2319. Mondays dep. 2328
- **e** Wakefield Kirkgate. Change at Sheffield
- **f** Wakefield Kirkgate
- **g** Change at Sheffield
- **h** Change at Sheffield and Doncaster

From Monday 28 September a revised service will be in operation due to seasonal difficulties. Some trains will be retimed between 1 and 3 minutes. Passengers should check with National Rail Enquiries for precise times.

Table 53

Mondays to Fridays

London → East Midlands → Sheffield

Route Diagram - See first page of Table 53

	EM ◇	EM 1◇	EM 1◇	XC 1◇ A	XC 1◇ B	EM	EM 1◇	EM 1◇ C	EM 1◇ D	EM 1◇	EM 1◇	EM 1◇	NT ◇	XC 1◇ E	EM ◇	XC 1◇ A	XC 1◇ B	EM	EM 1◇	EM 1◇ C	EM 1◇ D	EM 1◇	EM 1◇
St Pancras International ⊖ d			08 00				08 15	08 25	08 25	08 30	08 55	09 00							09 15	09 25	09 25	09 30	09 55
Gatwick Airport 10 d			06 46							07 00		07 37										08 01	
Luton Airport Parkway 7 d			08 06							08 51		09 10										09 51	
Luton 10 d			08 23							08 27		09 23										09 32	
Bedford 7 d			08 38							09 07		09 38										10 07	
Wellingborough d			08 51							09 20		09 51										10 20	
Kettering a			09 00							09 27		10 00										10 26	
Kettering d		08 32	09 28							09 27												10 27	
Corby d		08a41	09a37																				
Market Harborough d							09 12			09 37									10 12			10 37	
Leicester a							09 29	09 34	09 34	09 53	10 02								10 29	10 33	10 33	10 54	11 02
Leicester d						09 25	09 30	09 35	09 35	09 54	10 04							10 25	10 30	10 35	10 35	10 54	11 04
Syston d						09 32												10 32					
Sileby d						09 37												10 37					
Barrow Upon Soar d						09 41												10 41					
Loughborough d						09 47		09 45	09 45	10 05								10 47		10 45	10 45	11 04	
East Midlands Parkway d						09 57	09 46	09 53	09 53									10 57	10 46	10 53	10 53		
Beeston a										10 16												11 16	
Nottingham 8 a						10 13	09 59			10 26								11 14	10 59			11 26	
Nottingham d	09 45					10 29							10 15		10 45			11 17					
Lincoln a						11 30												12 21					
Langley Mill d													10 32										
Alfreton d	10 07												10 40		11 07								
Long Eaton a								09 57	09 57											10 56	10 56		
Derby 10 a								10 08	10 15		10 26									11 07	11 15		11 26
Derby d				10 11	10 11						10 28			10 44		11 09	11 10						11 28
Chesterfield d	10 18										10 47		10 52	11 03	11 18								11 47
Sheffield 7 a	10 38			10 44	10 46						11 04		11 15	11 17	11 38	11 46	11 46						12 04
Doncaster 7 a				11 15	11 15						11 40			12 04		12 15	12 15						12 40
Wakefield Kirkgate 4 a													11 57										
Wakefield Westgate 7 a	11b27			11c27										11 46	12b27								
Leeds 10 a	11 48			11e48									12 18	12 02	12 48								
York 8 a	11 45			11 45	11 45									12 29	12 45	12 45	12 45						

	NT ◇	EM 1◇	XC 1◇ E	EM ◇	XC 1◇ A	XC 1◇ B	EM	EM 1◇	EM 1◇ C	EM 1◇ D	EM 1◇	EM 1◇	NT ◇	EM 1◇	XC 1◇ E	EM ◇	XC 1◇ G	EM	EM 1◇	EM 1◇ C	EM 1◇ D	EM 1◇	EM 1◇
St Pancras International ⊖ d		10 00						10 15	10 25	10 25	10 30	10 55		11 00					11 15	11 25	11 25	11 30	11 55
Gatwick Airport 10 d		08 38									09 16			09 46								10 16	
Luton Airport Parkway 7 d		10 10									10 51			11 06								11 51	
Luton 10 d		10 23									10 25			11 23								11 25	
Bedford 7 d		10 38									11 07			11 38								12 07	
Wellingborough d		10 51									11 20			11 51								12 20	
Kettering a		11 00									11 26			12 00								12 26	
Kettering d		11 31									11 27			12 31								12 27	
Corby d		11a40												12a40									
Market Harborough d								11 12			11 37								12 12			12 37	
Leicester a								11 29	11 33	11 33	11 52	12 02							12 29	12 33	12 33	12 53	13 02
Leicester d							11 25	11 30	11 35	11 35	11 54	12 04						12 25	12 30	12 35	12 35	12 54	13 04
Syston d							11 32											12 32					
Sileby d							11 37											12 37					
Barrow Upon Soar d							11 41											12 41					
Loughborough d							11 47		11 45	11 45	12 05							12 47		12 45	12 45	13 04	
East Midlands Parkway d							11 57	11 46	11 53	11 53								13 00	12 46	12 53	12 53		
Beeston a											12 16											13 16	
Nottingham 8 a							12 13	11 59			12 26							13 14	12 59			13 26	
Nottingham d	11 15			11 45			12 27						12 15			12 45		13 17					
Lincoln a							13 20											14 23					
Langley Mill d	11 32												12 32										
Alfreton d	11 40			12 07									12 40			13 07							
Long Eaton a									11 56	11 56										12 56	12 56		
Derby 10 a									12 07	12 15		12 26								13 07	13 15		13 26
Derby d			11 44		12 09	12 11						12 28			12 44		13 11						13 28
Chesterfield d	11 52		12 03	12 18								12 47	12 52		13 03	13 18							13 47
Sheffield 7 a	12 15		12 18	12 38	12 46	12 46						13 04	13 15		13 17	13 38	13 46						14 04
Doncaster 7 a	13 04		13 11		13 20	13 20						13 40			14 04		14 17						14 40
Wakefield Kirkgate 4 a	12 57												13 57										
Wakefield Westgate 7 a			12 46	13b27											13 46	14b27							
Leeds 10 a	13 18		13 02	13 48									14 18		14 02	14 48							
York 8 a	13f39		13 29	13 46	13 46	13 46									14 29	14 43	14 43						15f26

For general notes see front of timetable
For details of catering facilities see Directory of Train Operators

- **A** From 7 September. To Newcastle (Table 26)
- **B** Until 4 September. To Newcastle (Table 26)
- **C** From 7 September
- **D** Until 4 September
- **E** To Edinburgh (Table 26)
- **G** To Newcastle (Table 26)
- **b** Wakefield Kirkgate
- **c** Wakefield Kirkgate. Change at Sheffield
- **e** Change at Sheffield
- **f** Change at Sheffield and Doncaster

From Monday 28 September a revised service will be in operation due to seasonal difficulties. Some trains will be retimed between 1 and 3 minutes. Passengers should check with National Rail Enquiries for precise times.

Table 53

London → East Midlands → Sheffield

Route Diagram - See first page of Table 53

		NT ◇	EM 1◇	XC 1◇ A	EM ◇	XC 1◇ B	XC 1◇ C	EM	EM 1◇	EM 1◇ D	EM 1◇ E	EM 1◇	EM 1◇	NT ◇	EM 1◇	XC 1◇ G	EM ◇	XC 1◇ B	XC 1◇ C	EM	EM 1◇	EM 1◇ D	EM 1◇ E	EM 1◇
St Pancras International ⊖	d		12 00						12 15	12 25	12 25	12 30	12 55		13 00						13 15	13 25	13 25	13 30
Gatwick Airport 10 ✈	d		10 46									11 16			11 46									12 16
Luton Airport Parkway 7	d		12 08									12 51			13 08									13 51
Luton 10	d		12 23									12 25			13 23									13 25
Bedford 7	d		12 38									13 07			13 38									14 07
Wellingborough	d		12 51									13 20			13 50									14 20
Kettering	a		13 03									13 26			13 59									14 26
	d		13 31									13 27			14 15									14 27
Corby	d		13a40												14a24									
Market Harborough	d								13 12			13 37									14 12			14 37
Leicester	a								13 30	13 33	13 33	13 54	14 02								14 29	14 33	14 33	14 54
	d							13 25	13 30	13 35	13 35	13 54	14 04							14 25	14 30	14 35	14 35	14 54
Syston	d							13 32												14 32				
Sileby	d							13 37												14 37				
Barrow Upon Soar	d							13 41												14 41				
Loughborough	d							13 47		13 45	13 45	14 04								14 47		14 45	14 45	15 04
East Midlands Parkway	d							13 57	13 45	13 53	13 53									14 57	14 46	14 53	14 53	
Beeston	a											14 16												15 16
Nottingham 8	a							14 13	13 59			14 26								15 13	14 59			15 26
	d	13 15			13 45			14 29						14 15			14 45			15 27				
Lincoln	a							15 22												16 25				
Langley Mill	d	13 32												14 32										
Alfreton	d	13 40			14 07									14 40			15 07							
Long Eaton	a																							
Derby 10	a									13 56	13 56		14 26									14 56	14 56	
	d			13 44		14 09	14 11			14 07	14 15		14 28			14 44		15 09	15 11			15 07	15 15	
Chesterfield	d	13 52		14 03	14 19								14 47	14 52		15 03	15 20							
Sheffield 7	a	14 15		14 17	14 38	14 46	14 46						15 04	15 15		15 17	15 38	15 46	15 46					
Doncaster 7	a			15 04		15 16	15 16						15 40			16 04		16 15	16 15					
Wakefield Kirkgate 4	a	14 57												15 57										
Wakefield Westgate 7	a			14 46	15b27											15 46	16b27							
Leeds 10	a	15 18		15 02	15 48									16 19		16 02	16 48							
York 8	a			15 29	15 40	15 40	15 40									16 29	16 40	16 40	16 40					

		EM 1◇	EM 1◇	NT ◇	XC 1◇ H	EM ◇	EM J	EM 1◇	EM 1◇ D	XC 1◇ B	XC 1◇ C	EM 1◇ E	EM 1◇	EM 1◇	EM 1◇	NT ◇	XC 1◇ K	XC 1◇ L	EM ◇	XC 1◇ B	XC 1◇ C	EM	EM 1◇	EM 1◇ D
St Pancras International ⊖	d	13 55	14 00					14 15	14 25			14 25	14 30	14 55	15 00								15 15	15 25
Gatwick Airport 10 ✈	d		12 46										13 16		13 46									
Luton Airport Parkway 7	d		14 08										14 51		15 08									
Luton 10	d		14 23										14 25		15 23									
Bedford 7	d		14 38										15 07		15 38									
Wellingborough	d		14 51										15 20		15 51									
Kettering	a		15 00										15 26		16 00									
	d		15 01										15 27		16 01									
Corby	d		15a10												16a10									
Market Harborough	d							15 12					15 37										16 12	
Leicester	a	15 02						15 29	15 33			15 33	15 54	16 02									16 29	16 33
	d	15 04					15 25	15 30	15 35			15 35	15 54	16 04								16 25	16 30	16 35
Syston	d						15 32															16 32		
Sileby	d						15 37															16 37		
Barrow Upon Soar	d						15 41															16 41		
Loughborough	d						15 47		15 45			15 45	16 04									16 47		16 45
East Midlands Parkway	d						15 57	15 46	15 53			15 53										16 57	16 46	16 53
Beeston	a												16 16											
Nottingham 8	a						16 13	15 59					16 26									17 13	16 59	
	d			15 15		15 45	16 14									16 15			16 45			17 17		
Lincoln	a						17 14															18 26		
Langley Mill	d			15 32												16 32								
Alfreton	d			15 40		16 07										16 40			17 07					
Long Eaton	a																							
Derby 10	a	15 26							15 56			15 56		16 26										16 56
	d	15 28			15 44				16 07	16 09	16 11	16 15		16 28			16 44	16 43		17 09	17 11			17 07
Chesterfield	d	15 47		15 52	16 03	16 18								16 47		16 56	17 03	17 04	17 18					
Sheffield 7	a	16 04		16 15	16 17	16 38				16 46	16 46			17 04		17 17	17 19	17 19	17 34	17 45	17 45			
Doncaster 7	a	16 40			17 07					17 15	17 15			17 40		18 07	18 13	18 13	18 13	18 38	18 38			
Wakefield Kirkgate 4	a			16 57												17 57								
Wakefield Westgate 7	a				16 46	17b28											17 46	17 46		18 12	18 12			
Leeds 10	a			17 18	17 02	17 48										18 18	18 04	18 04		18 31	18 31			
York 8	a				17 30	17 40				17 40	17 40						18 31	18 31		18 58	18 58			

For general notes see front of timetable
For details of catering facilities see Directory of Train Operators

- **A** To Aberdeen (Table 51)
- **B** From 7 September. To Newcastle (Table 26)
- **C** Until 4 September. To Newcastle (Table 26)
- **D** From 7 September
- **E** Until 4 September
- **G** To Glasgow Central (Table 26)
- **H** To Dundee (Table 51)
- **J** To Sleaford (Table 18)
- **K** Until 4 September. To Glasgow Central (Table 26)
- **L** From 7 September. To Glasgow Central (Table 26)
- **b** Wakefield Kirkgate

From Monday 28 September a revised service will be in operation due to seasonal difficulties. Some trains will be retimed between 1 and 3 minutes. Passengers should check with National Rail Enquiries for precise times.

London → East Midlands → Sheffield

Route Diagram - See first page of Table 53

	EM 1◇ A	EM 1◇	EM 1◇	EM 1◇	NT ◇	XC 1◇ B		XC 1◇ C	EM ◇	XC 1◇ B	XC 1◇ C	EM	EM 1◇ D	EM 1◇ E	EM 1◇ A	EM 1◇	EM 1◇ G		NT ◇	XC 1◇ H	EM 1◇ E	EM ◇	XC 1◇ J	XC 1◇ K	EM 1◇ A
St Pancras International ⊖ d	15 25	15 30	15 55	16 00									16 15	16 25	16 25	16 30	16 55								
Gatwick Airport 10 ✈ d		14 16		14 46												15 16									
Luton Airport Parkway 7 d		15 51		16 08												16 51									
Luton 10 d		15 25		16 23												16 25									
Bedford 7 d		16 07		16 38												17 07									
Wellingborough d		16 20		16 51												17 20									
Kettering a		16 26		17 00												17 26									
Kettering d		16 27		17 01												17 27					18 04				18 04
Corby d				17a10																					
Market Harborough d		16 37											17 12			17 37									
Leicester a	16 33	16 54	17 02										17 29	17 35	17 35	17 54	18 02				18 27				18 27
Leicester d	16 35	16 54	17 04									17 25	17 30	17 35	17 35	17 54	18 04				18 29				18 29
Syston d												17 32													
Sileby d												17 37													
Barrow Upon Soar d												17 41													
Loughborough d	16 45	17 04										17 47		17 45	17 45	18 04					18 40				18 40
East Midlands Parkway d	16 53											17 57	17 46	17 52	17 52						18 47				18 47
Beeston a		17 16														18 17									
Nottingham 8 a		17 26										18 13	17 59			18 30									
Nottingham d					17 15				17 45			18 15							18 15			18 45			
Lincoln a												19 22													
Langley Mill d					17 31				18 02										18 32						
Alfreton d					17 39				18 08										18 40			19 07			
Long Eaton a	16 56													18 00	18 00						18 55				18 55
Derby 10 a	17 15		17 26											18 13	18 15		18 26				19 07				19 15
Derby d			17 28			17 41		17 42		18 09	18 11						18 28			18 44			19 09	19 11	
Chesterfield d			17 47		17 52	18 03		18 03	18 18								18 47		18 52	19 03		19 18	19 32	19 30	
Sheffield 7 a			18 04		18 15	18 18		18 18	18 38	18 49	18 49						19 04		19 15	19 20		19 39	19 47	19 47	
Doncaster 7 a			18 53		18 53	19 08		19 08		19 17	19 17						19 40			20 08			20 20	20 20	
Wakefield Kirkgate 4 a					18 58														19 58						
Wakefield Westgate 7 a						18 46		18 46	19b29										19c49	19 49		20b28	20e49	20e49	
Leeds 10 a					19 23	19 02		19 02	19 55										20 19	20 06		20 48			
York 8 a						19 30		19 30	19 44	19 44	19 44									20 31		20 46	20 46	20 46	

	EM 1◇	EM 1◇	EM 1◇	EM 1◇ L	NT ◇		XC 1◇	EM ◇	XC 1◇ J	XC 1◇ K		EM 1◇	EM 1◇ N	EM	EM 1◇	EM 1◇		XC 1◇	EM 1◇	EM 1◇ A	EM 1◇ E	EM 1◇	NT ◇	XC 1◇	EM
St Pancras International ⊖ d	17 00	17 15	17 30	17 55								17 45	18 00		18 15	18 25			18 30	18 55	18 55	19 00			
Gatwick Airport 10 ✈ d	15 31	15 46										16 11	16 41			16 53			17 07			17 31			
Luton Airport Parkway 7 d	16 52	17 20										18 10	18 10			18 34			18 54			19 10			
Luton 10 d	17 04	17 42											18 23			18 51			18 38			19 23			
Bedford 7 d	17 35												18 38						19 11			19 38			
Wellingborough d	17 48		18 18									18 45	18 51		19 02				19 24			19 51			
Kettering a	17 56		18 24									18 53	19 06		19 09				19 30			20 01			
Kettering d	18 08		18 26									18 56	19 10		19 10				19 32			20 01			
Corby d	18a18												19a19									20a13			
Market Harborough d		18 19	18 36									19 07				19 28				19 54	19 54				
Leicester a		18 36	18 53	19 04								19 23			19 34	19 45			19 56	20 11	20 11				
Leicester d		18 37	18 55	19 04								19 25		19 25	19 36	19 46			19 57	20 13	20 13				20 25
Syston d														19 32											20 32
Sileby d														19 37											20 37
Barrow Upon Soar d														19 41											20 41
Loughborough d			19 05									19 36		19 46	19 47	19 57				20 24	20 24				20 46
East Midlands Parkway d		18 53	19 12									19 44		19 57	19 55				20 12	20 32	20 32				20 57
Beeston a		19 02	19 17											20 07					20 17						21 05
Nottingham 8 a		19 10	19 27									19 58		20 20	20 08				20 28						21 16
Nottingham d					19 15			19 40				20 07			20 15				20 29				20 45		
Lincoln a																			21 24						
Langley Mill d					19 32										20 33										
Alfreton d					19 40			20 01							20 41										
Long Eaton a												20 22				20 06									
Derby 10 a				19 28								20 35				20 19				20 44	20 46		21 05		
Derby d				19 28			19 42		20 09	20 11								20 44		20 48	20 48		21 06	21 11	
Chesterfield d				19 47	19 52		20 03	20 12							20 53			21 03		21 09	21 09		21 28	21 34	
Sheffield 7 a				20 04	20 15		20 18	20 28	20 49	20 49					21 13			21 16		21 30	21 30		21 54	21 48	
Doncaster 7 a				20 40			21 18	21 18	21 20	21 20														22 29	
Wakefield Kirkgate 4 a					20 57																				
Wakefield Westgate 7 a							20 53								21 54			21 48							
Leeds 10 a					21 18		21 09								22 12			22 08							
York 8 a							21 39	21 45	21 45	21 45										22 59	22 59		22 59	22 59	

For general notes see front of timetable
For details of catering facilities see Directory of Train Operators

- **A** Until 4 September
- **B** From 7 September. To Edinburgh (Table 26)
- **C** Until 4 September. To Edinburgh (Table 26)
- **D** **The Robin Hood**
- **E** From 7 September
- **G** **The Master Cutler**
- **H** To Edinburgh (Table 26)
- **J** From 7 September. To Newcastle (Table 26)
- **K** Until 4 September. To Newcastle (Table 26)
- **L** **The South Yorkshireman**
- **N** To Melton Mowbray (Table 49)
- **b** Wakefield Kirkgate
- **c** Change at Sheffield
- **e** Wakefield Kirkgate. Change at Sheffield

From Monday 28 September a revised service will be in operation due to seasonal difficulties. Some trains will be retimed between 1 and 3 minutes. Passengers should check with National Rail Enquiries for precise times.

London → East Midlands → Sheffield

Route Diagram - See first page of Table 53

Mondays to Fridays

Station		EM	EM	EM	EM	EM	NT	XC	EM	EM	EM	EM	EM	EM	EM	EM	EM	EM	EM	EM	EM	EM	EM MX
		1 ◇	1 ◇	1 ◇	1 ◇	1 ◇	◇	1 ◇		1 ◇	1 ◇	1 ◇	1 ◇	1 ◇	1 ◇	1 ◇	1 ◇	1 ◇	1 ◇	1 ◇	1 ◇	1 ◇	1 ◇
		☕	☕	☕	☕	☕		🛒		☕	☕	☕	☕	☕	☕	☕	☕	☕	☕	☕	☕	☕	☕
St Pancras International ⊖	d	19 15	19 25	19 30	19 55	20 00				20 15	20 25		20 30	20 55	21 00	21 25		21 30	22 00		22 25	23 15	00 15
Gatwick Airport 10 ✈	d			*18 16*		*18 46*							*19 16*		*19 46*			*20 16*	*20 46*		*21 16*	*21 16*	
Luton Airport Parkway 7	d			19 51		*20 08*							20 51		*21 08*			21 53	*22 08*		22 48	*23 33*	00 46
Luton 10	d			*19 34*		20 23							*20 25*		21 23			*21 25*	22 24		*22 25*	23 46	00 50
Bedford 7	d			20 07		20 38							21 07		21 38			22 09	22 40		23 04	00 10	01 10
Wellingborough	d			20 20		20 51							21 20		21 51			22 22	22 53		23 17	00 23	01 31
Kettering	a		20 13			21 00							21 26		21 57			22 30	23 00		23 35	00 39	01 42
	d		20 14			21 01							21 27		21 58		22 05	22 31	23 01	23 05	23 36	00 40	01 42
Corby	d					21a10											22a14			23a14			
Market Harborough	d	20 12	20 24	20 37						21 10			21 37		22 08	22 23		22 42	23 12		23 47	00 50	
Leicester	a	20 30	20 39	20 54	21 04					21 25	21 33		21 53	22 02	22 26	22 40		23 01	23 29		00 01	01 03	02 10
	d	20 30	20 41	20 54	21 04				21 25	21 26	21 35		21 54	22 04	22 28	22 41		23 02	23 30		00 03	01 05	
Syston	d								21 32														
Sileby	d								21 37														
Barrow Upon Soar	d								21 41														
Loughborough	d		20 51	21 04					21 46		21 45		22 04		22 38	22 52		23 13	23 41		00 14	01 15	
East Midlands Parkway	d	20 45	21 01						21 57	21 43	21 53				22 46	23 01		23 24	23 50		00 22	01 23	
Beeston	a			21 18					22 07				22 16						00 04			01 36	
Nottingham 8 🚌	a	21 05		21 29					22 16	21 58		←	22 27			23 12			00 14			01 44	
	d			21 43			21 11					21 43										01 51	
Lincoln	a			→																			
Langley Mill	d						21 31					22 01											
Alfreton	d						21 39					22 09											
Long Eaton	a		21 04								21 58							23 37					
Derby 10	a		21 15		21 32						22 12			22 26	22 59			23 50			00 42	02 08	
	d				21 34			21 47						22 28							00 43		
Chesterfield	d				21 55		22 00	22 09				22 21		22 47							01 06		
Sheffield 7 🚌	a				22 16		22 19	22 26				22 37		23 04							01 21		
Doncaster 7	a													*00 07*									
Wakefield Kirkgate 4	a																						
Wakefield Westgate 7	a				22 46			23 11				23 17		*00 09*									
Leeds 10	a				23 05			23 30				23 36		*00 30*									
York 8	a																						

Saturdays

Station		EM	XC	EM	XC	EM	XC	EM	NT	EM	XC	XC	EM	XC	EM	EM	EM	EM	NT	EM
		◇	1 ◇	1 ◇	1 ◇	◇	1 ◇	1 ◇	◇		1 ◇	1 ◇	◇	1 ◇		1 ◇	1 ◇	1 ◇	◇	1 ◇
			B		C		B				D	E		B			G			
		🛒	🛒	☕	🛒	🛒	🛒	☕			🛒	🛒	🛒	🛒		☕	☕	☕		☕
St Pancras International ⊖	d															06 10	06 37			06 55
Gatwick Airport 10 ✈	d																			
Luton Airport Parkway 7	d															*06 19*				07 16
Luton 10	d															06 33	06 59			
Bedford 7	d															06 48				
Wellingborough	d															07 01				
Kettering	a															07 07	07 27			
	d															07 08	07 28	07 38		
Corby	d																	07a47		
Market Harborough	d															07 18	07 38			
Leicester	a															07 35	07 53			08 04
	d									06 36					07 25	07 36	07 55			08 06
Syston	d									06 43					07 32					
Sileby	d									06 48					07 37					
Barrow Upon Soar	d									06 52					07 41					
Loughborough	d									06 57					07 46	07 47	08 05			08 18
East Midlands Parkway	d									07 08					07 57					
Beeston	a									07 17					08 06					08 31
Nottingham 8 🚌	a									07 28					08 16					08 42
	d	05 18				06 40			07 15				07 45						08 11	
Lincoln	a																			
Langley Mill	d								07 30										08 32	
Alfreton	d					07 02			07 38				08 07						08 40	
Long Eaton	a															07 55				
Derby 10	a															08 16	08 26			
	d		05 55	06 26	06 37		07 11	07 20			07 43	07 42		08 11			08 28			
Chesterfield	d	05 49	06 31	06 45	06 56	07 13	07 30	07 42	07 50		08 03	08 03	08 18	08 30			08 47		08 52	
Sheffield 7 🚌	a	06 15	06 44	07 08	07 09	07 31	07 48	07 59	08 08		08 17	08 17	08 38	08 46			09 07		09 15	
Doncaster 7	a		07 16		*08 01*	*08 20*	08 23	*08 40*			*09 05*	*09 05*		09 21			09 53			
Wakefield Kirkgate 4	a								08 57										09 57	
Wakefield Westgate 7	a	*07 19*		*08f27*	07 36	*08f27*			*08g46*		08 46	08 46	*09f27*							
Leeds 10	a	*07 44*		*08 49*	07 52	*08 49*			09 19		09 02	09 02	*09 49*						10 18	
York 8	a	*07 39*	07 39	*08h31*	08 25	*08 49*	08 49				09 30	09 30	*09 45*	09 45			10 16		*10h39*	

For general notes see front of timetable
For details of catering facilities see Directory of Train Operators

- **B** To Newcastle (Table 26)
- **C** To Edinburgh (Table 26)
- **D** Until 5 September. To Edinburgh (Table 26)
- **E** From 12 September. To Edinburgh (Table 26)
- **G** Until 5 September to Scarborough (Table 39)
- **b** Thursdays and Fridays. Thursdays change at Luton Airport Parkway and Bedford. Fridays change at Bedford
- **c** Saturdays. Change at Luton Airport Parkway and Luton
- **e** Wednesdays. Change at Bedford
- **f** Wakefield Kirkgate
- **g** Change at Sheffield
- **h** Change at Sheffield and Doncaster

From Monday 28 September a revised service will be in operation due to seasonal difficulties. Some trains will be retimed between 1 and 3 minutes. Passengers should check with National Rail Enquiries for precise times.

From Saturday 3 October a revised service will be in operation due to seasonal difficulties. Some trains will be retimed between 1 and 3 minutes. Passengers should check with National Rail Enquiries for precise times.

Table 53

Saturdays

London → East Midlands → Sheffield

Route Diagram - See first page of Table 53

		XC	EM	XC	EM	EM	EM	EM	EM	NT	EM	XC	EM	XC	EM	EM	EM	EM	EM	EM	NT	XC	EM	XC
		1 ◇	◇	1 ◇		1 ◇	1 ◇	1 ◇	1 ◇	◇	1 ◇	1 ◇	◇	1 ◇		1 ◇	1 ◇	1 ◇	1 ◇	1 ◇	◇	1 ◇	◇	1 ◇
		A		B								A		B								A		B
		🛒	🛒	🛒		🍴	🍴	🍴	🍴		🍴	🛒	🛒	🛒		🍴	🍴	🍴	🍴	🍴		🛒	🛒	🛒
St Pancras International ⊖	d					07 00		07 30	07 55		08 00					08 15	08 25	08 30	08 55	09 00				
Gatwick Airport 10 ✈	d																							
Luton Airport Parkway 7	d					*06 54*		07 51			*08 08*							08 51		*09 08*				
Luton 10	d					07 23		*07 28*			08 23							*08 31*		09 23				
Bedford 7	d					07 38		08 07			08 38							09 07		09 38				
Wellingborough	d					07 51		08 20			08 51							09 20		09 51				
Kettering	a					08 00		08 27			09 00							09 26		10 00				
	d					08 01		08 27			09 31							09 27						
Corby	d										09a40													
Market Harborough	d					08 12		08 37								09 12		09 37						
Leicester	a					08 29		08 53	09 02							09 29	09 33	09 52	10 02					
	d				08 25	08 30	08 38	08 54	09 04						09 25	09 30	09 35	09 54	10 04					
Syston	d				08 32										09 32									
Sileby	d				08 37										09 37									
Barrow Upon Soar	d				08 41										09 41									
Loughborough	d				08 47	08 41	08 49	09 04							09 47		09 45	10 05						
East Midlands Parkway	d				08 57	08 50	08 56								09 57	09 46	09 53							
Beeston	a							09 16										10 16						
Nottingham 8 🚊	a				09 13	09 03		09 26							10 13	09 59		10 26						
	d		08 45		09 23					09 15			09 45		10 29						10 15		10 45	
Lincoln	a				10 17										11 30									
Langley Mill	d									09 32											10 32			
Alfreton	d		09 07							09 40			10 07								10 40		11 07	
Long Eaton	a						09 00										09 56							
Derby 10	a						09 20		09 26								10 16		10 26					
	d	08 44		09 11					09 28			09 44		10 11					10 28			10 44		11 11
Chesterfield	d	09 03	09 18						09 47	09 52		10 03	10 18						10 49		10 52	11 03	11 18	
Sheffield 7 🚊	a	09 17	09 38	09 46					10 04	10 15		10 17	10 38	10 46					11 04		11 15	11 17	11 38	11 46
Doncaster 7	a	*10 05*		10 18					*10 40*			*11 04*		11 16					*11b41*			*12 04*		12 16
Wakefield Kirkgate 4	a									10 57											11 57			
Wakefield Westgate 7	a	09 46	*10c27*									10 46	*11c27*									11 46	*12c27*	
Leeds 10	a	10 03	*10 48*							11 18		11 02	*11 48*								12 18	12 02	*12 48*	
York 8	a	10 30	*10 44*	10 44						*11e39*		11 32	*11 44*	11 44								12 30	*12 44*	12 44

		EM	EM	EM	EM	EM	EM	NT	EM	XC	EM	XC	EM	EM	EM	EM	EM	NT	EM	XC	EM	XC	EM
			1 ◇	1 ◇	1 ◇	1 ◇	1 ◇	◇	1 ◇	1 ◇	◇	1 ◇		1 ◇	1 ◇	1 ◇	1 ◇	◇	1 ◇	1 ◇	◇	1 ◇	
				C	D					A		B								A		B	
			🍴	🍴	🍴	🍴	🍴		🍴	🛒	🛒	🛒		🍴	🍴	🍴	🍴		🍴	🛒	🛒	🛒	
St Pancras International ⊖	d		09 15	09 25	09 25	09 30	09 55		10 00					10 15	10 25	10 30	10 55		11 00				
Gatwick Airport 10 ✈	d																						
Luton Airport Parkway 7	d					09 51			*10 08*							10 51			*11 08*				
Luton 10	d					*09 31*			10 23							*10 31*			11 23				
Bedford 7	d					10 07			10 38							11 07			11 38				
Wellingborough	d					10 20			10 51							11 20			11 51				
Kettering	a					10 26			11 00							11 26			12 00				
	d					10 27			11 31							11 27			12 31				
Corby	d								11a40										12a40				
Market Harborough	d		10 12			10 37								11 12		11 37							
Leicester	a		10 29	10 33	10 33	10 54	11 02							11 29	11 33	11 54	12 02						
	d	10 25	10 30	10 35	10 35	10 54	11 04						11 25	11 30	11 35	11 54	12 04						12 25
Syston	d	10 32											11 32										12 32
Sileby	d	10 37											11 37										12 37
Barrow Upon Soar	d	10 41											11 41										12 41
Loughborough	d	10 47		10 45	10 45	11 04							11 47		11 45	12 04							12 47
East Midlands Parkway	d	10 57	10 46	10 53	10 53								11 57	11 46	11 53								12 57
Beeston	a					11 16										12 16							
Nottingham 8 🚊	a	11 13	10 59			11 26							12 13	11 59		12 26							13 13
	d	11 17						11 15			11 45		12 27					12 15			12 45		13 17
Lincoln	a	12 21											13 20										14 23
Langley Mill	d							11 32										12 32					
Alfreton	d							11 40			12 07							12 40			13 07		
Long Eaton	a			10 56	10 56										11 56								
Derby 10	a			11 07	11 16		11 26								12 16		12 26						
	d						11 28			11 44		12 11					12 28			12 44		13 11	
Chesterfield	d						11 47			12 03	12 18						12 47	12 52		13 03	13 18		
Sheffield 7 🚊	a						12 04	12 15		12 17	12 38	12 46					13 04	13 15		13 17	13 38	13 46	
Doncaster 7	a						*12 40*			*13 04*		13 19					*13 40*			*14 04*		14 16	
Wakefield Kirkgate 4	a							12 57										13 57					
Wakefield Westgate 7	a									12 46	*13c27*									13 46	*14c27*		
Leeds 10	a							13 18		13 03	*13 48*							14 18		14 02	*14 48*		
York 8	a							*13e39*		13 32	*13 44*	13 44								14 30	*14 44*	14 44	

For general notes see front of timetable
For details of catering facilities see Directory of Train Operators

- **A** To Edinburgh (Table 26)
- **B** To Newcastle (Table 26)
- **C** From 12 September
- **D** Until 5 September
- **b** 27 June to 5 September arr. 1140
- **c** Wakefield Kirkgate
- **e** Change at Sheffield and Doncaster

From Saturday 3 October a revised service will be in operation due to seasonal difficulties. Some trains will be retimed between 1 and 3 minutes. Passengers should check with National Rail Enquiries for precise times.

Table 53

Saturdays

London → East Midlands → Sheffield

Route Diagram - See first page of Table 53

		EM	EM	EM	EM	NT	EM	XC	EM	XC		EM	EM	EM	EM	EM	NT	EM	XC	EM		XC	EM	EM	EM	EM
		1 ◇	1 ◇	1 ◇	1 ◇	◇	1 ◇	1 ◇	◇	1 ◇			1 ◇	1 ◇	1 ◇	1 ◇	◇	1 ◇	1 ◇	◇		1 ◇		1 ◇	1 ◇	1 ◇
								A		B									C			B				
St Pancras International ⊖	d	11 15	11 25	11 30	11 55		12 00						12 15	12 25	12 30	12 55		13 00						13 15	13 25	13 30
Gatwick Airport 10 ✈	d																									
Luton Airport Parkway 7	d			11 51			*12 08*								12 51			*13 08*								13 51
Luton 10	d			*11 31*			12 23								*12 31*			13 23								*13 31*
Bedford 7	d			12 07			12 38								13 07			13 38								14 07
Wellingborough	d			12 20			12 51								13 20			13 51								14 20
Kettering	a			12 26			13 00								13 26			14 00								14 26
	d			12 27			13 31								13 27			14 15								14 27
Corby	d						13a40											14a24								
Market Harborough	d	12 12		12 37									13 12		13 37									14 12		14 37
Leicester	a	12 29	12 33	12 54	13 02								13 29	13 33	13 52	14 02								14 29	14 33	14 54
	d	12 30	12 35	12 54	13 04							13 25	13 30	13 35	13 54	14 04							14 25	14 30	14 35	14 54
Syston	d											13 32											14 32			
Sileby	d											13 37											14 37			
Barrow Upon Soar	d											13 41											14 41			
Loughborough	d		12 45	13 05								13 47		13 45	14 05								14 47		14 45	15 05
East Midlands Parkway	d	12 46	12 53									13 57	13 46	13 53									14 57	14 46	14 53	
Beeston	a			13 17											14 16											15 16
Nottingham 8	a	12 59		13 27								14 13	13 59		14 26								15 13	14 59		15 26
	d					13 15			13 45			14 29					14 15			14 45			15 27			
Lincoln	a											15 22											16 25			
Langley Mill	d					13 32											14 30									
Alfreton	d					13 40			14 07								14 38			15 07						
Long Eaton	a		12 56											13 56											14 56	
Derby 10	a		13 16		13 26									14 16		14 26									15 16	
	d				13 28			13 44		14 11						14 28			14 44			15 11				
Chesterfield	d				13 47	13 52		14 03	14 18							14 47	14 52		15 03	15 18						
Sheffield 7	a				14 04	14 15		14 17	14 38	14 46						15 04	15 15		15 17	15 38		15 46				
Doncaster 7	a				*14 40*			*15 04*		15 16						*15 40*			*16 04*			16 16				
Wakefield Kirkgate 4	a					14 57											15 57									
Wakefield Westgate 7	a							14 46	15b27										15 46	16b27						
Leeds 10	a					15 18		15 02	*15 48*								16 19		16 02	*16 48*						
York 8	a							15 32	*15 44*	15 44									16 30	*16 44*		16 44				

		EM	EM	NT	XC	XC	XC		EM	XC	EM	EM	EM	EM	EM	EM	NT		XC	XC	EM	XC	EM	EM	EM	EM
		1 ◇	1 ◇	◇	1 ◇	1 ◇	1 ◇		◇	1 ◇		1 ◇	1 ◇	1 ◇	1 ◇	1 ◇	◇		1 ◇	1 ◇	◇	1 ◇		1 ◇	1 ◇	1 ◇
					D	E	G			B									H	J		B				
St Pancras International ⊖	d	13 55	14 00									14 15	14 25	14 30	14 55	15 00								15 15	15 25	15 30
Gatwick Airport 10 ✈	d																									
Luton Airport Parkway 7	d		*14 08*											14 51		*15 08*										15 51
Luton 10	d		14 23											*14 31*		15 23										*15 31*
Bedford 7	d		14 38											15 07		15 38										16 07
Wellingborough	d		14 51											15 20		15 51										16 20
Kettering	a		15 00											15 26		16 00										16 26
	d		15 01											15 27		16 01										16 27
Corby	d		15a10													16a10										
Market Harborough	d											15 12		15 37										16 12		16 37
Leicester	a	15 02										15 29	15 33	15 53	16 02									16 29	16 33	16 54
	d	15 04									15 25	15 30	15 35	15 54	16 04								16 25	16 30	16 35	16 54
Syston	d										15 32												16 32			
Sileby	d										15 37												16 37			
Barrow Upon Soar	d										15 41												16 41			
Loughborough	d										15 47		15 45	16 04									16 47		16 45	17 04
East Midlands Parkway	d										15 57	15 46	15 53										16 57	16 45	16 52	
Beeston	a													16 16												17 16
Nottingham 8	a										16 13	15 59		16 26									17 13	16 59		17 26
	d			15 15					15 45		16 14						16 15				16 45		17 17			
Lincoln	a										17 14												18 26			
Langley Mill	d			15 32													16 32									
Alfreton	d			15 40					16 07								16 40				17 07					
Long Eaton	a												15 56												16 56	
Derby 10	a	15 26											16 16		16 26										17 16	
	d	15 28			15 43	15 43	15 44			16 11					16 28				16 44	16 44		17 11				
Chesterfield	d	15 47		15 51	16 02	16 03	16 03		16 18						16 47		16 51		17 03	17 05	17 18					
Sheffield 7	a	16 04		16 15	16 18	16 18	16 18		16 38	16 46					17 04		17 15		17 19	17 19	17 34	17 44				
Doncaster 7	a	*16 40*		*17 08*	*17 12*	*17 12*	*17 12*			17 19					*17 40*				*18 07*	*18 07*	*18 12*	*18 38*				
Wakefield Kirkgate 4	a			16 57													17 57									
Wakefield Westgate 7	a				16 46	16 46	16 46		17b27										17 47	17 47		18 14				
Leeds 10	a			17 18	17 02	17 02	17 02		*17 48*								18 18		18 04	18 04		18 32				
York 8	a				17 31	17 31	17 31		*17 44*	17 44									18 31	18 31	*18c56*	18 59				

For general notes see front of timetable
For details of catering facilities see Directory of Train Operators

- **A** To Aberdeen (Table 51)
- **B** To Newcastle (Table 26)
- **C** To Glasgow Central (Table 26)
- **D** 18 July to 5 September. To Dundee (Table 51)
- **E** Until 11 July. To Dundee (Table 51)
- **G** From 12 September. To Dundee (Table 51)
- **H** Until 5 September. To Glasgow Central (Table 26)
- **J** From 12 September. To Glasgow Central (Table 26)
- **b** Wakefield Kirkgate
- **c** Change at Sheffield and Doncaster

From Saturday 3 October a revised service will be in operation due to seasonal difficulties. Some trains will be retimed between 1 and 3 minutes. Passengers should check with National Rail Enquiries for precise times.

London → East Midlands → Sheffield

Route Diagram - See first page of Table 53

		EM	EM	NT		XC	EM	XC	EM	EM	EM	EM	EM	EM		NT	XC	EM	EM	EM	XC	EM	EM	EM		EM
		1◇	1◇	◇		1◇	◇	1◇		1◇	1◇	1◇	1◇	1◇		◇	1◇	◇		1◇	1◇	1◇	1◇	1◇		1◇
						A		A									A				C					
St Pancras International	⊖ d	15 55	16 00							16 15	16 25	16 30	16 55	17 00						17 15		17 25	17 30	17 55		18 00
Gatwick Airport 10	✈ d																									
Luton Airport Parkway 7	d		16 08									16 51		17 08									17 51			18 08
Luton 10	d		16 23									16 31		17 23									17 31			18 23
Bedford 7	d		16 38									17 07		17 38									18 07			18 38
Wellingborough	d		16 51									17 20		17 51									18 20			18 51
Kettering	a		17 00									17 26		18 00									18 26			19 00
	d		17 01									17 27		18 01									18 27			19 01
Corby	d		17a10											18a10												19a10
Market Harborough	d									17 12		17 37								18 12			18 37			
Leicester	a	17 02								17 29	17 33	17 52	18 02							18 29		18 33	18 52	19 02		
	d	17 04							17 25	17 30	17 35	17 54	18 04						18 25	18 30		18 35	18 54	19 04		
Syston	d								17 32										18 32							
Sileby	d								17 37										18 37							
Barrow Upon Soar	d								17 41										18 41							
Loughborough	d								17 47		17 45	18 04							18 46			18 45	19 04			
East Midlands Parkway	d								17 57	17 46	17 53								18 57	18 46		18 53				
Beeston	a											18 17											19 16			
Nottingham 8	a								18 12	17 59		18 26							19 14	18 59			19 26			
	d			17 15			17 45		18 15							18 15		18 45					19 29			
Lincoln	a								19 22														20 26			
Langley Mill	d			17 31			18 03									18 32										
Alfreton	d			17 39			18 09									18 40		19 07								
Long Eaton	a										17 56											18 56				
Derby 10	a	17 26									18 16		18 26									19 16		19 26		
	d	17 28				17 44		18 11					18 28				18 44				19 11			19 28		
Chesterfield	d	17 47		17 52		18 03	18 19						18 47			18 52	19 03	19 18			19 30			19 47		
Sheffield 7	a	18 04		18 15		18 18	18 39	18 47					19 04			19 15	19 18	19 39			19 51			20 06		
Doncaster 7	a	18 53		18 53		19 08		19 18					19 40				20 09				20 16			20 56		
Wakefield Kirkgate 4	a			18 58												19 58										
Wakefield Westgate 7	a					18 46	19b29										19 46	20b28								
Leeds 10	a			19 23		19 02	19 55									20 19	20 02	20 48								
York 8	a					19 31	19 44	19 44									20 31	20 40			20 40			21c38		

		NT	XC	EM	XC	EM	EM	EM	EM	XC		EM	EM	EM	EM	XC	NT	XC	EM	EM		EM	NT	EM	EM	EM
		◇	1◇	◇	1◇		1◇	1◇	1◇	1◇		1◇	1◇	1◇	1◇	1◇	◇	1◇		1◇		1◇	◇	1◇	1◇	1◇
					C			D	E	G																
St Pancras International	⊖ d						18 15	18 25	18 25			18 30	18 55	19 00						19 15		19 25		19 30	19 55	20 00
Gatwick Airport 10	✈ d																									
Luton Airport Parkway 7	d											18 51		19 08										19 51		20 08
Luton 10	d											18 31		19 23										19 31		20 23
Bedford 7	d											19 07		19 38										20 07		20 38
Wellingborough	d											19 20		19 51										20 20		20 51
Kettering	a											19 26		20 00										20 26		21 00
	d											19 27		20 01										20 27		21 01
Corby	d													20a10												21a10
Market Harborough	d						19 12					19 37								20 12				20 37		
Leicester	a						19 29	19 33	19 33			19 52	20 02							20 29		20 33		20 52	21 04	
	d					19 25	19 30	19 35	19 35	19 50		19 54	20 04						20 25	20 30		20 35		20 54	21 06	
Syston	d					19 32													20 32							
Sileby	d					19 37													20 37							
Barrow Upon Soar	d					19 41													20 41							
Loughborough	d					19 47		19 45	19 45			20 07							20 47			20 45		21 05		
East Midlands Parkway	d					19 57	19 46	19 53	19 53										20 57	20 46		20 53				
Beeston	a					20 05						20 16							21 05					21 16		
Nottingham 8	a					20 16	19 59			20 19		20 26			←				21 16	20 59				21 26		
	d	19 15		19 40		20 29	20 15								20 15		20 38		21 25				21 15			
Lincoln	a					21 24	→												22 40							
Langley Mill	d	19 32													20 33		21 02						21 31			
Alfreton	d	19 40		20 01											20 41		21 10						21 39			
Long Eaton	a							19 56	20 01													20 56				
Derby 10	a							20 16	20 16				20 26									21 13			21 32	
	d		19 44		20 11								20 28			20 44		21 11							21 34	
Chesterfield	d	19 52	20 03	20 11	20 30								20 47		20 53	21 03	21 22	21 30					21 50		21 56	
Sheffield 7	a	20 15	20 18	20 27	20 49								21 00		21 14	21 18	21 40	21 43					22 14		22 16	
Doncaster 7	a		21 21	21 21	21 25								21 40					22 19								
Wakefield Kirkgate 4	a	20 57																								
Wakefield Westgate 7	a		20 46												21 52	21 46							23 09		22 44	
Leeds 10	a	21 19	21 05												22 10	22 07							23 29		23 04	
York 8	a		22 03	21 48	21 48								22c38			22e48	22 48	22 48								

For general notes see front of timetable
For details of catering facilities see Directory of Train Operators

- **A** To Edinburgh (Table 26)
- **C** To Newcastle (Table 26)
- **D** From 12 September
- **E** Until 5 September
- **G** 18 July to 5 September
- **b** Wakefield Kirkgate
- **c** Change at Sheffield and Doncaster
- **e** Change at Sheffield

From Saturday 3 October a revised service will be in operation due to seasonal difficulties. Some trains will be retimed between 1 and 3 minutes. Passengers should check with National Rail Enquiries for precise times.

Table 53

Saturdays

London → East Midlands → Sheffield

Route Diagram - See first page of Table 53

		XC	EM	EM	EM	EM	EM		EM	EM	EM	EM	EM	EM	EM	EM	EM	EM	EM	EM	EM	EM	EM	EM	EM
		1◇		1◇	1◇	1◇	1◇		1◇	1◇	1◇	1◇	1◇	1◇	1◇	1◇	1◇		1◇	1◇	1◇	1◇	1◇	1◇		
						A	B		A	B	C	D	B	A	B		D	B 🚌	C	B		C	B	C	B 🚌	B 🚌
		🍴		☕	☕	☕	☕		☕	☕	☕	☕	☕	☕	☕	☕	☕		☕	☕	☕	☕	☕	☕		
St Pancras International ⊖	d			20 15	20 25	20 30	20 30		20 55	20 55	21 00	21 00	21 00	21 25	21 25		21 30		21 30	21 30		22 00	22 00	22 25		
Gatwick Airport 10 ✈	d																									
Luton Airport Parkway 7	d					20 51	20 51				*21 08*	*21 08*	*21 08*				21 51		21 51	21 51		*22 08*	*22 08*	23 03		
Luton 10	d										21 23	21 23	21 23									22 35	22 35	*22 41*		
Bedford 7	d					21 07	21 07				21 38	21 38	21 38				22 07		22 07	22 07		22 58	22 58	23 28		
Wellingborough	d					21 20	21 20				21 51	21 51	21 51				22 20		22 20	22 20		23 16	23 16	23 41		
Kettering	a					21 26	21 26				22 00	22 00	22 00				22 26		22 26	22 26		23 23	23 23	23 49		
	d					21 27	21 27				22 01	22 01	22 01			22 05	22 27		22 27	22 27	22 59	23 24	23 24	23 50		
Corby	d															22a14					23a08					
Market Harborough	d			21 12		21 37	21 37				22 12	22 12	22 12	22 20	22 20		22 37		22 37	22 37		23 35	23 35	00 01		
Leicester	a			21 29	21 33	21 52	21 52		22 02	22 02	22 29	22 29	22 29	22 36	22 36		22 54		22 54	22 54		23 52	23 52	00 17		
	d		21 25	21 30	21 35	21 54	21 54		22 04	22 04	22 30	22 30	22 30	22 37	22 37		22 54		22 54	22 54		23 53	23 53	00 19		00 02
Syston	d		21 32																							
Sileby	d		21 37																							
Barrow Upon Soar	d		21 41																							
Loughborough	d		21 46		21 45	22 04	22 12					22 41	22 49	22 48	22 57		23 07		23 04	23 14		00 04		00 30	23 48	00a37
East Midlands Parkway	d		21 57	21 46	21 53	22 12					22 46			22 55	23 08		23 14	23 34	23 14	23 25		00 13	00 21	00 38	00a13	
Beeston	a		22 06			22 17	22 27															00 19	00 28			
Nottingham 8	a		22 16	22 01		22 27	22 36							23 06	23 19							00 29	00 38			
	d																									
Lincoln	a																									
Langley Mill	d																									
Alfreton	d																									
Long Eaton	a				21 57												23 18	23 54	23 26							
Derby 10	a				22 12				22 26	22 43	23 02	23 02	23 15				23 29	00 25	23 37	00 25				00 53		
	d	21 48							22 28	22 45																
Chesterfield	d	22 08							22 47	23 05																
Sheffield 7	a	22 23							23 00	23 18																
Doncaster 7	a	22 47							*00 04*	*00 04*																
Wakefield Kirkgate 4	a																									
Wakefield Westgate 7	a	23 09																								
Leeds 10	a	23 29																								
York 8	a																									

Sundays

until 12 July

		EM	EM	EM	EM	NT	XC	EM	EM	NT	EM	XC	EM	EM	EM	EM	NT	XC	EM	EM	EM	XC	NT	EM	XC	EM
		1◇	1◇	◇	1◇	◇	1◇	1◇	◇	◇	1◇	1◇	1◇	1◇	◇	1◇	◇	1◇	1◇	1◇	◇	1◇	◇	1◇	1◇	1◇
		D	D				E		G			E			G			E				H			J	
		☕	☕	🍴	☕		🍴	☕	🍴		☕	🍴	☕	☕	🍴	☕		🍴	☕	☕	🍴	🍴		☕	🍴	☕
St Pancras International ⊖	d	22p00	22p25								09 00		09 30			10 00			10 30					11 00		11 30
Gatwick Airport 10 ✈	d																									
Luton Airport Parkway 7	d		23p03								09 27					10 27			*10 37*					11 29		11 56
Luton 10	d	22p35									*08 53*		09 59			*10 11*			11 00					11 32		11 59
Bedford 7	d	22p58	23p28								09 52		10 21			10 50			11 25					11 55		12 25
Wellingborough	d	23p16	23p41								10 06		10 37			11 04			11 39					12 09		12 40
Kettering	a	23p24	23p50								10 14		10 43			11 12			11 46					12 15		12 47
	d	23p25	23p51		09 55						10 15		10 44	10 55		11 13			11 46	11 55				12 16		12 48
Corby	d				10a04									11a04						12a04						
Market Harborough	d										10 26		10 54			11 24			11 56					12 26		12 58
Leicester	a	00 17	00 42								10 46		11 13			11 44			12 16					12 45		13 17
	d	00 23	00 49					10 10			10 48		11 16			11 46			12 19					12 47		13 19
Syston	d																									
Sileby	d																									
Barrow Upon Soar	d																									
Loughborough	d	00 34	01 00					10 21			10 59		11 26			11 57			12 29					12 57		13 30
East Midlands Parkway	d	00 43	01 08								11 07		11 34			12 05			12 37					13 05		13 37
Beeston	a	00 49									11 13													13 10		
Nottingham 8	a	00 59									11 22					12 18								13 19		
	d			09 31		10 06			10 40	11 15					11 46		12 19				12 39		13 11			
Lincoln	a																									
Langley Mill	d					10 27				11 31							12 35				12 56		13 27			
Alfreton	d			09 53		10 35			11 03	11 39					12 08		12 43				13 04		13 35			
Long Eaton	a							10 29					11 37						12 40							13 41
Derby 10	a		01 23					10 44					11 49						12 51							13 52
	d						10 44	10 46				11 43	11 50					12 44	12 53			13 11			13 44	13 54
Chesterfield	d			10 08		10 54	11 03	11 09	11 14	11 51		12 05	12 10		12 18		12 54	13 03	13 12		13 17	13 30	13 51		14 03	14 13
Sheffield 7	a			10 32		11 15	11 16	11 28	11 35	12 15		12 18	12 29		12 35		13 15	13 17	13 28		13 33	13 45	14 15		14 17	14 28
Doncaster 7	a							11 52	*12 39*			*12 54*	*13 35*		*13 35*			*14 02*				14 13			*14 56*	
Wakefield Kirkgate 4	a					11 52				12 52							13 52						14 52			
Wakefield Westgate 7	a						11 44	*12 18*				12 44	*13b29*					13 44	*14 27*						14 44	*15b29*
Leeds 10	a					12 18	12 02	*12 36*		13 18		13 02	*13 52*				14 18	14 02	*14 47*				15 18		15 02	*15 53*
York 8	a					*12c15*	12 32	12 15				13 32	*14e04*		*14e04*		*14e33*	14 32	*14 43*		*14 43*	14 43	*15e34*		15 32	*15 43*

For general notes see front of timetable
For details of catering facilities see Directory of Train Operators

- **A** Until 11 July and from 12 September
- **B** 18 July to 5 September
- **C** Until 11 July
- **D** From 12 September
- **E** To Edinburgh (Table 26)
- **G** To Liverpool Lime Street (Table 89)
- **H** To Newcastle (Table 26)
- **J** To Aberdeen (Table 51)
- **b** Wakefield Kirkgate
- **c** Change at Sheffield
- **e** Change at Sheffield and Doncaster

From Saturday 3 October a revised service will be in operation due to seasonal difficulties. Some trains will be retimed between 1 and 3 minutes. Passengers should check with National Rail Enquiries for precise times.

Sundays

until 12 July

London → East Midlands → Sheffield

Route Diagram - See first page of Table 53

		EM	EM	XC	NT	EM	XC	EM	EM	EM	XC	NT	EM	XC	EM	EM	EM	EM	XC	NT	XC	EM	EM	EM	XC	NT
		■1 ◇	◇	■1 ◇	◇	■1 ◇	■1 ◇	◇	■1 ◇	■1 ◇	■1 ◇	◇	■1 ◇	■1 ◇	■1 ◇	■1 ◇	◇	■1 ◇	■1 ◇	◇	■1 ◇	■1 ◇	■1 ◇	◇	■1 ◇	◇
				A			B	C			A			D			C		A		D				A	
		⊏	⊤	⊤		⊏	⊤	⊤	⊏	⊏	⊤		⊏	⊤	⊏	⊏	⊤	⊏	⊤		⊤	⊏	⊏	⊤	⊤	
St Pancras International ⊖	d					12 00			12 30				13 00		13 30			14 00				14 30				
Gatwick Airport 10 ✈	d																									
Luton Airport Parkway 7	d					12 27			12 57				13 29		14 03			14 29				*14 37*				
Luton 10	d					12 30			13 00				13 33		14 06			*14 11*				15 01				
Bedford 7	d					12 56			13 26				13 56		14 21			14 47				15 17				
Wellingborough	d					13 10			13 40				14 10		14 35			15 00				15 31				
Kettering	a					13 16			13 48				14 16		14 42			15 07				15 38				
	d	12 55				13 17			13 49	13 55			14 17		14 43	14 55		15 08				15 39	15 45			
Corby.	d	13a04								14a04						15a04							15a54			
Market Harborough	d					13 27			14 00				14 27		14 54			15 18				15 50				
Leicester	a					13 46			14 20				14 46		15 16			15 37				16 17				
	d					13 48			14 22				14 48		15 18			15 39				16 19				
Syston	d																									
Sileby	d																									
Barrow Upon Soar	d																									
Loughborough	d					13 58			14 33				14 58		15 29			15 49				16 30				
East Midlands Parkway	d					14 06			14 41				15 06		15 37			15 57				16 38				
Beeston	a					14 13							15 12					16 05								
Nottingham 8	a					14 22							15 20					16 12								
	d		13 38		14 19			14 38				15 12					15 44			16 14				16 40		17 14
Lincoln	a																									
Langley Mill	d		13 55		14 35			14 55				15 34								16 30				17 00		17 30
Alfreton	d		14 03		14 43			15 03				15 42					16 04			16 38				17 08		17 38
Long Eaton	a								14 45						15 41							16 42				
Derby 10	a								15 00						15 56							16 55				
	d			14 11			14 44		15 01		15 07			15 44	15 57				16 05		16 44	16 56			17 07	
Chesterfield	d		14 18	14 30	14 54		15 03	15 13	15 22			15 53		16 03	16 18		16 23			16 50	17 03	17 17		17 20		17 49
Sheffield 7	a		14 36	14 47	15 15		15 17	15 31	15 37		15 47	16 15		16 18	16 33		16 39		16 48	17 15	17 18	17 32		17 40	17 48	18 15
Doncaster 7	a			15 13			*15 55*				16 15			*16 54*					17 13		*17 57*				18 13	
Wakefield Kirkgate 4	a				15 52							16 52								17 52						18 52
Wakefield Westgate 7	a						15 44							16 44							17 45	18 06		*18 33*	18 33	
Leeds 10	a				16 18		16 02					17 18		17 02						18 18	18 02	18 24		*18 53*	18 53	19 17
York 8	a		*15 43*	15 43	*16b35*		16 32		*16 40*		16 40			17 32	*17 42*		*17 42*		17 42	*18b34*	18 32	*19b05*		*19b05*	19 21	

		EM	XC	EM	EM	EM	XC	EM	EM	NT	XC	EM	EM	EM	EM	EM	XC	EM	NT	XC	EM	EM	EM	EM	EM	XC
		■1 ◇	■1 ◇	■1 ◇	■1 ◇	◇	■1 ◇	■1 ◇	■1 ◇	◇	■1 ◇	■1 ◇	◇	■1 ◇	■1 ◇	■1 ◇	■1 ◇	■1 ◇	◇	■1 ◇	■1 ◇	◇	■1 ◇	■1 ◇	■1 ◇	■1 ◇
			B				B				B						A									A
		⊏	⊤	⊏	⊏	⊤	⊤	⊏	⊏		⊤	⊏	⊤	⊏	⊏	⊏	⊤	⊏		⊤	⊏	⊤	⊏	⊏	⊏	⊤
St Pancras International ⊖	d	15 00		15 30				16 00	16 25			16 30		16 55		17 00		17 25			17 30		17 55		18 00	
Gatwick Airport 10 ✈	d																									
Luton Airport Parkway 7	d	15 29		*15 37*				16 29				*16 37*				17 21					*17 37*				18 21	
Luton 10	d	*15 11*		16 01				*16 11*				16 52				*17 11*					17 52				*18 11*	
Bedford 7	d	15 47		16 17				16 47				17 15				17 45					18 15				18 45	
Wellingborough	d	16 01		16 31				17 00				17 28				17 58					18 28				18 58	
Kettering	a	16 08		16 38				17 07				17 35				18 05					18 35				19 05	
	d	16 09		16 39	16 45			17 08				17 36			17 50	18 06					18 36			18 50	19 06	
Corby.	d				16a54										17a59									18a59		
Market Harborough	d	16 20		16 50				17 18				17 46				18 16					18 46				19 16	
Leicester	a	16 41		17 11				17 37	17 47			18 08		18 21		18 35		18 44			19 09		19 20		19 35	
	d	16 43		17 12				17 39	17 49			18 10		18 22		18 37		18 46			19 11		19 21		19 37	
Syston	d																									
Sileby	d																									
Barrow Upon Soar	d																									
Loughborough	d	16 54		17 24				17 49				18 20				18 47					19 21				19 47	
East Midlands Parkway	d	17 02		17 32				17 57	18 05			18 28		18 36		18 55		19 00			19 29		19 35		19 55	
Beeston	a							18 06								19 00									20 01	
Nottingham 8	a	17 14						18 14						18 50		19 07							19 50		20 08	
	d					17 37				18 14			18 37						19 19			19 38				
Lincoln	a																									
Langley Mill	d					17 54				18 30			18 54						19 35							
Alfreton	d					18 02				18 38			19 02						19 43			20 00				
Long Eaton	a			17 36								18 31									19 32					
Derby 10	a			17 51					18 17			18 48						19 14			19 49					
	d		17 44	17 53			18 07		18 19		18 44						19 04	19 16		19 43						20 06
Chesterfield	d		18 04			18 17			18 40	18 49	19 05		19 12					19 35	19 54	20 03		20 10				
Sheffield 7	a		18 19	18 29		18 34	18 46		18 57	19 15	19 20		19 31				19 39	19 49	20 15	20 18		20 31				20 38
Doncaster 7	a		*18 54*				19 13		*19 39*		*20 07*						20 16	*20 30*		*21 05*						21 19
Wakefield Kirkgate 4	a									19 52									20 52							
Wakefield Westgate 7	a		18 47	*19c29*							19 48									20 46		*21c29*				
Leeds 10	a		19 04	*19 52*						20 27	20 05								21 18	21 03						
York 8	a		19 32	*19 42*		*19 42*	19 42				20 32		*20 44*				20 44			21 37		*21 42*				21 42

For general notes see front of timetable
For details of catering facilities see
Directory of Train Operators

A To Newcastle (Table 26)
B To Edinburgh (Table 26)
C To Liverpool Lime Street (Table 89)
D To Glasgow Central (Table 26)

b Change at Sheffield and Doncaster
c Wakefield Kirkgate

Table 53

London → East Midlands → Sheffield

Sundays until 12 July

Route Diagram - See first page of Table 53

		EM 1◇	NT ◇	XC 1◇	EM 1◇	EM 1◇	EM 1◇	EM 1◇	XC 1◇	EM 1◇	XC 1◇	EM 1◇	NT ◇	EM 1◇	EM 1◇	EM 1◇	EM 1◇	EM 1◇	EM 1◇	XC 1◇	EM 1◇	EM 1◇	EM 1◇	EM 1◇
St Pancras International ⊖	d	18 25			18 30	18 55		19 00		19 25		19 30		19 55		20 00	20 25	20 30			21 00	21 30	22 30	23 00
Gatwick Airport 10 ✈	d																							
Luton Airport Parkway 7	d				18 37			19 21				19 37				20 23		20 37			21 23	21 37	22 53	23 28
Luton 10	d				18 52			19 11				19 52				20 11		20 54			21 11	21 54	22 36	22 53
Bedford 7	d				19 15			19 45				20 15				20 48		21 18			21 47	22 17	23 17	23 52
Wellingborough	d				19 28			19 58				20 28				21 00		21 31			22 00	22 30	23 31	00 06
Kettering	a				19 35			20 05				20 35				21 07		21 38			22 07	22 37	23 37	00 12
	d				19 36		19 45	20 06				20 36			20 46	21 08		21 39	21 55		22 08	22 38	23 38	00 13
Corby	d						19a54								20a55				22a04					
Market Harborough	d				19 46			20 16				20 46				21 18		21 50			22 18	22 48	23 48	00 23
Leicester	a	19 47			20 05	20 17		20 35		20 47		21 05		21 17		21 37	21 47	22 11			22 37	23 07	00 07	00 42
	d	19 49			20 07	20 20		20 37		20 49		21 07		21 19		21 39	21 49	22 13			22 39	23 09	00 09	00 44
Syston	d																							
Sileby	d																							
Barrow Upon Soar	d																							
Loughborough	d				20 17			20 47				21 17		21 30		21 49	22 01				22 49	23 19	00 19	00 54
East Midlands Parkway	d	20 08			20 25	20 34		20 55		21 05		21 25		21 39		21 57	22 09	22 29			22 57	23 27	00 27	01 02
Beeston	a							21 02								22 03					23 10		00 40	
Nottingham 8	a					20 48		21 12						21 50		22 11					23 18		00 48	
	d		20 13										21 20											
Lincoln	a																							
Langley Mill	d		20 29										21 41											
Alfreton	d		20 37										21 49											
Long Eaton	a				20 28							21 28										23 38		
Derby 10	a	20 20			20 48					21 17		21 44					22 22	22 43				23 49		01 21
	d	20 22		20 43					21 11	21 19	21 44							22 48		22 51		23 51		
Chesterfield	d	20 43	20 48	21 03					21 30	21 40	22 03		22 08					23 09		23 14		00 10		
Sheffield 7	a	20 58	21 14	21 16					21 44	21 55	22 18		22 32					23 27		23 34		00 24		
Doncaster 7	a	21 39		22 03							22 56									00 19				
Wakefield Kirkgate 4	a																							
Wakefield Westgate 7	a	21 32		21 44							22 45		23b28					23 54		00 12				
Leeds 10	a	21 49		22 08							23 08		00 08					00 31		00 49				
York 8	a								22 53		00c39													

Sundays 19 July to 6 September

		EM 1◇	EM ◇ A	EM 1◇	NT ◇	XC 1◇ B	EM ◇ A	NT ◇	EM 1◇	XC 1◇ B	EM ◇ A	EM 1◇	EM 1◇	NT ◇	EM 1◇	XC 1◇ B	EM ◇	EM 1◇	EM 1◇	XC 1◇ C		NT ◇	EM 1◇	XC 1◇ D	EM ◇	EM 1◇
St Pancras International ⊖	d	22p00							09 00			09 30			10 00			10 30					11 00			11 30
Gatwick Airport 10 ✈	d																									
Luton Airport Parkway 7	d								09 27						10 27			10 37					11 29			11 56
Luton 10	d	22p35							08 53			09 59			10 11			11 00					11 32			11 59
Bedford 7	d	22p58							09 52			10 21			10 50			11 25					11 55			12 25
Wellingborough	d	23p16							10 06			10 37			11 04			11 39					12 09			12 40
Kettering	a	23p23							10 14			10 43			11 12			11 46					12 15			12 47
	d	23p24		09 55					10 15			10 44	10 55		11 13			11 46	11 55				12 16			12 48
Corby	d			10a04									11a04						12a04							
Market Harborough	d	23p35							10 26			10 54			11 24			11 56					12 26			12 58
Leicester	a	23p52							10 46			11 13			11 44			12 16					12 45			13 17
	d	23p53							10 48			11 16			11 46			12 19					12 47			13 19
Syston	d																									
Sileby	d																									
Barrow Upon Soar	d																									
Loughborough	d	00 12																								
East Midlands Parkway	d	00 23							11 13			11 41			12 10			12 43					13 12			13 44
Beeston	a	00 30							11 22														13 18			
Nottingham 8	a	00 40							11 35						12 26								13 26			
	d		09 06		10 06		10 40	11 15			11 46			12 19			12 39					13 09			13 38	
Lincoln	a																									
Langley Mill	d				10 27			11 31						12 35			12 56					13 27			13 55	
Alfreton	d		09 41		10 35		11 03	11 39			12 08			12 43			13 04					13 35			14 03	
Long Eaton	a											11 52						12 47								13 48
Derby 10	a											12 04						12 58								14 00
	d					10 44				11 44		12 05				12 44		13 02		13 11				13 44		14 04
Chesterfield	d		09 51		10 54	11 03	11 14	11 51		12 05	12 18	12 25		12 54		13 03	13 17	13 22		13 30		13 51		14 03	14 18	14 24
Sheffield 7	a		10 16		11 15	11 16	11 35	12 15		12 18	12 35	12 40		13 15		13 17	13 33	13 37		13 45		14 15		14 17	14 36	14 39
Doncaster 7	a		10 51			12 39	12 39			12 54		13 35				14 02				14 13				14 56		
Wakefield Kirkgate 4	a				11 52			12 52						13 52								14 52				
Wakefield Westgate 7	a		11c20			11 44				12 44						13 44								14 44		
Leeds 10	a		11c39		12 18	12 02		13 18		13 02				14 18		14 02						15 18		15 02		
York 8	a		11c29			12 32				13 32		14c04		14c33		14 32		14 43		14 43		15c34		15 32		15 43

For general notes see front of timetable
For details of catering facilities see Directory of Train Operators

- **A** To Liverpool Lime Street (Table 89)
- **B** To Edinburgh (Table 26)
- **C** To Newcastle (Table 26)
- **D** To Aberdeen (Table 51)
- **b** Wakefield Kirkgate
- **c** Change at Sheffield and Doncaster

Sundays

19 July to 6 September

London → East Midlands → Sheffield

Route Diagram - See first page of Table 53

		EM	XC	NT	EM	XC	EM	EM	EM	XC	NT	EM	XC	EM	EM	EM	EM		XC	NT	XC	EM	EM	EM	XC	NT
		1 ◇	1 ◇	◇	1 ◇	1 ◇	◇	1 ◇	1 ◇	1 ◇	◇	1 ◇	1 ◇	1 ◇	1 ◇	◇	1 ◇		1 ◇	◇	1 ◇	1 ◇	1 ◇	◇	1 ◇	◇
			A			B	C			A			D			C			A		D				A	
		🍴	🛒		🍴	🛒	🛒	🍴	🍴	🛒		🍴	🛒	🍴	🍴	🛒	🍴		🛒		🛒	🍴	🍴	🛒	🛒	
St Pancras International ⊖	d				12 00			12 30				13 00		13 30			14 00					14 30				
Gatwick Airport 10 ✈	d																									
Luton Airport Parkway 7	d				12 27			12 57				13 29		14 03			14 29					*14 37*				
Luton 10	d				12 30			13 00				13 33		14 06			*14 11*					15 01				
Bedford 7	d				12 56			13 26				13 56		14 21			14 47					15 17				
Wellingborough	d				13 10			13 40				14 10		14 35			15 00					15 31				
Kettering	a				13 16			13 48				14 16		14 42			15 07					15 38				
	d	12 55			13 17			13 49	13 55			14 17		14 43	14 55		15 08					15 39	15 45			
Corby.	d	13a04							14a04						15a04								15a54			
Market Harborough	d				13 27			14 00				14 27		14 54			15 18					15 50				
Leicester	a				13 46			14 20				14 46		15 16			15 37					16 17				
	d				13 48			14 22				14 48		15 18			15 39					16 19				
Syston	d																									
Sileby	d																									
Barrow Upon Soar	d																									
Loughborough	d							14 33				14 58		15 29			15 49					16 30				
East Midlands Parkway	d				14 13			14 41				15 06		15 37			15 57					16 38				
Beeston	a				14 19							15 12					16 05									
Nottingham 8 🚌	a				14 29							15 18					16 12									
	d			14 19			14 38				15 12					15 44				16 14				16 34		17 12
Lincoln	a																									
Langley Mill	d			14 35			14 55				15 34									16 30				17 00		17 30
Alfreton	d			14 43			15 03				15 42					16 04				16 38				17 08		17 38
Long Eaton	a							14 45						15 41								16 42				
Derby 10	a							15 00						15 56								16 55				
	d		14 11			14 44		15 01		15 07			15 44	15 57					16 05		16 44	16 56			17 05	
Chesterfield	d		14 30	14 54		15 03	15 13	15 22			15 53		16 03	16 18		16 23				16 50	17 03	17 17		17 20		17 49
Sheffield 7 🚌	a		14 47	15 15		15 17	15 31	15 37		15 47	16 15		16 18	16 33		16 39			16 48	17 15	17 18	17 32		17 40	17 48	18 15
Doncaster 7	a		15 13			*15 55*				16 15			*16 54*						17 13		*17 57*				18 13	
Wakefield Kirkgate 4	a			15 52							16 52									17 52						18 52
Wakefield Westgate 7	a					15 44							16 44								17 45	18 06		*18 33*	18 33	
Leeds 10	a			16 18		16 02					17 18		17 02							18 18	18 02	18 25		*18 53*	18 53	19 18
York 8	a		15 43	*16b35*		16 32		*16 40*		16 40			17 32	*17 42*		*17 42*			17 42	*18b34*	18 32	*19b05*		19b05	19 21	

		EM	XC	EM	EM	EM	XC	EM	EM	NT	XC	EM	EM	EM		EM	EM	XC	EM	NT	XC	EM	EM	EM	EM	EM
		1 ◇	1 ◇	1 ◇	1 ◇	◇	1 ◇	1 ◇	1 ◇	◇	1 ◇	1 ◇	◇	1 ◇		1 ◇	1 ◇	1 ◇	1 ◇	◇	1 ◇	1 ◇	◇	1 ◇	1 ◇	1 ◇
			B				B				B							A								
		🍴	🛒	🍴	🍴	🛒	🛒	🍴	🍴		🛒	🍴	🛒	🍴		🍴	🍴	🛒	🍴		🛒	🍴	🛒	🍴	🍴	🍴
St Pancras International ⊖	d	15 00		15 30				16 00	16 25			16 30		16 55			17 00		17 25			17 30		17 55		18 00
Gatwick Airport 10 ✈	d																									
Luton Airport Parkway 7	d	15 29		*15 37*				16 29				*16 37*					17 21					*17 37*				18 21
Luton 10	d	*15 11*		16 01				*16 11*				16 52					*17 11*					17 52				*18 11*
Bedford 7	d	15 47		16 17				16 47				17 15					17 45					18 15				18 45
Wellingborough	d	16 01		16 31				17 00				17 28					17 58					18 28				18 58
Kettering	a	16 08		16 38				17 07				17 35					18 05					18 35				19 05
	d	16 09		16 39	16 45			17 08				17 36				17 50	18 06					18 36			18 50	19 06
Corby.	d				16a54											17a59									18a59	
Market Harborough	d	16 20		16 50				17 18				17 46					18 16					18 46				19 16
Leicester	a	16 41		17 11				17 37	17 47			18 08		18 21			18 35		18 44			19 09		19 20		19 35
	d	16 43		17 12				17 39	17 49			18 10		18 22			18 37		18 46			19 11		19 21		19 37
Syston	d																									
Sileby	d																									
Barrow Upon Soar	d																									
Loughborough	d	16 54		17 24				17 49				18 20					18 47					19 21				19 47
East Midlands Parkway	d	17 02		17 32				17 57	18 05			18 28		18 36			18 55		19 00			19 29		19 35		19 55
Beeston	a							18 06									19 00									20 02
Nottingham 8 🚌	a	17 14						18 14						18 50			19 07							19 53		20 08
	d					17 37				18 13			18 37							19 19			19 38			
Lincoln	a																									
Langley Mill	d					17 54				18 30			18 54							19 35						
Alfreton	d					18 02				18 38			19 02							19 43			20 00			
Long Eaton	a			17 36								18 31										19 32				
Derby 10	a			17 51					18 17			18 48							19 14			19 49				
	d		17 44	17 53			18 05		18 19		18 44							19 04	19 16		19 43					
Chesterfield	d		18 04			18 17			18 40	18 49	19 05		19 12						19 35	19 54	20 03		20 10			
Sheffield 7 🚌	a		18 19	18 29		18 34	18 46		18 57	19 15	19 20		19 31					19 39	19 49	20 15	20 18		20 31			
Doncaster 7	a		*18 54*				19 13		*19 39*		*20 07*							20 16	*20 30*		*21 05*					
Wakefield Kirkgate 4	a									19 52										20 52						
Wakefield Westgate 7	a		18 47	*19c29*							19 48										20 46		*21c29*			
Leeds 10	a		19 05							20 18	20 05									21 16	21 03					
York 8	a		19 32	*19 42*		*19 42*	19 42				20 32		*20 44*					20 44			21 37		*21 42*			

For general notes see front of timetable
For details of catering facilities see Directory of Train Operators

- **A** To Newcastle (Table 26)
- **B** To Edinburgh (Table 26)
- **C** To Liverpool Lime Street (Table 89)
- **D** To Glasgow Central (Table 26)
- **b** Change at Sheffield and Doncaster
- **c** Wakefield Kirkgate

Table 53

Sundays

19 July to 6 September

London → East Midlands → Sheffield

Route Diagram - See first page of Table 53

		XC 1◇ A	EM 1◇	NT ◇	XC 1◇	EM 1◇	EM 1◇	EM 1◇	EM 1◇	XC 1◇	EM 1◇	XC 1◇	NT ◇	EM 1◇	EM 1◇	EM 1◇	EM 1◇	XC 1◇	EM 1◇	EM 1◇	EM 1◇	EM 1◇	EM 1◇	EM 1◇	EM 1◇
St Pancras International ⊖	d		18 25			18 30	18 55		19 00		19 25			19 30	19 55		20 00		20 25	20 30		21 00	21 30	22 30	23 00
Gatwick Airport 10	d																								
Luton Airport Parkway 7	d					*18 37*			19 21					*19 37*			20 23			*20 37*		21 23	*21 37*	22 53	23 28
Luton 10	d					18 52			*19 11*					19 52			*20 11*			20 54		*21 11*	21 54	*22 36*	
Bedford 7	d					19 15			19 45					20 15			20 48			21 18		21 47	22 17	23 17	23 52
Wellingborough	d					19 28			19 58					20 28			21 00			21 31		22 00	22 30	23 31	00 06
Kettering	a					19 35			20 05					20 35			21 07			21 38		22 07	22 37	23 37	00 12
	d					19 36		19 45	20 06					20 36		20 46	21 08			21 39	21 55	22 08	22 38	23 38	00 13
Corby	d							19a54								20a55					22a04				
Market Harborough	d					19 46			20 16					20 46			21 18			21 50		22 18	22 48	23 48	00 23
Leicester	a		19 47			20 09	20 17		20 35		20 47			21 05	21 17		21 37		21 53	22 11		22 37	23 07	00 07	00 42
	d		19 49			20 11	20 20		20 37		20 49			21 07	21 25		21 46		21 55	22 13		22 56	23 18	00 09	00 44
Syston	d																								
Sileby	d																								
Barrow Upon Soar	d																								
Loughborough	d					20 21			20 47					21 27	21 44		22 03		22 11			23 15	23 37	00 27	01 03
East Midlands Parkway	d		20 08			20 29	20 34		20 55		21 05			21 34	21 52		22 15		22a24	22 40		23 26	23 48	00 38	01 14
Beeston	a								21 05								22 21					23 32		00 44	
Nottingham 8	a						20 48		21 13						22 03		22 29					23 40		00 51	
	d			20 13									21 20												
Lincoln	a																								
Langley Mill	d			20 29									21 41												
Alfreton	d			20 37									21 49												
Long Eaton	a					20 32								21 38											
Derby 10	a		20 20			20 55					21 17			21 49											
	d	20 05	20 22		20 43					21 11	21 19	21 44						22 46							
Chesterfield	d		20 43	20 48	21 03					21 30	21 40	22 03	22 08					23 06		23 26			00 17		02a15
Sheffield 7	a	20 38	20 58	21 14	21 16					21 44	21 55	22 18	22 32					23 21		23 41			00 31		
Doncaster 7	a	21 19	*21 39*		*22 03*							22 56						*00 19*							
Wakefield Kirkgate 4	a																								
Wakefield Westgate 7	a		21 32		21 44							22 46	23b28							00 12					
Leeds 10	a		21 50		22 03							23 08	*00 04*					00 37		00 49					
York 8	a	21 42								22 53		*00c39*													

Sundays

from 13 September

		EM	EM	EM	EM ◇	NT ◇	XC 1◇ B	EM 1◇	EM ◇ C	NT ◇	XC 1◇ B	EM ◇ C	EM	EM	EM 1◇	EM	EM 1◇	EM	NT ◇	XC 1◇ B	EM ◇	XC 1◇ A	EM	EM	EM 1◇	NT ◇
St Pancras International ⊖	d														09 00		09 30								10 00	
Gatwick Airport 10	d																									
Luton Airport Parkway 7	d														09 30										10 29	
Luton 10	d														*08 53*		09 59								*10 11*	
Bedford 7	d														09 49		10 18								10 49	
Wellingborough	d														10 03		10 32								11 03	
Kettering	a														10 13		10 41								11 13	
	d			00 05									10 24		10 14		10 42	10 51					11 23		11 14	
Corby	d														10 31										11 31	
Market Harborough	d	00 01	00 29	00a30									10a49	10 41		11 05		11a16					11a48	11 45		
Leicester	a	00 26	00 54											11 16	11 19	11 40	11 43							12 20	12 23	
	d							10 14							11 26		11 50								12 30	
Syston	d																									
Sileby	d																									
Barrow Upon Soar	d																									
Loughborough	d							10 25							11 37		12 01								12 41	
East Midlands Parkway	d														11 45		12 09								12 49	
Beeston	a														11 51											
Nottingham 8	a														12 00										13 01	
	d				09 31	10 10			10 40	11 15		11 46							12 19		12 39					13 11
Lincoln	a																									
Langley Mill	d					10 27				11 31									12 35		12 56					13 27
Alfreton	d				09 53	10 35			11 03	11 39		12 08							12 43		13 04					13 35
Long Eaton	a							10 33									12 12									
Derby 10	a							10 44									12 23									
	d						10 44	10 48			11 44						12 25			12 44		13 11				
Chesterfield	d				10 08	10 54	11 03	11 09	11 14	11 51	12 05	12 18					12 44		12 54	13 03	13 16	13 30				13e51
Sheffield 7	a				10 30	11 15	11 16	11 28	11 35	12 15	12 18	12 35					12 58		13 15	13 17	13 32	13 43				14 15
Doncaster 7	a							11 52	*12 39*		*12 54*						*13 35*			*14 02*		14 13				
Wakefield Kirkgate 4	a					11 52				12 52									13 52							14 52
Wakefield Westgate 7	a						11 44		*12 18*		12 44									13 44						
Leeds 10	a					12 18	12 02		*12 36*	13 18	13 02								14 18	14 02						15 18
York 8	a					*12f15*	12 32	12 15			13 32						*14c04*		*14c33*	14 32	*14 43*	14 43				*15c34*

For general notes see front of timetable
For details of catering facilities see Directory of Train Operators

- **A** To Newcastle (Table 26)
- **B** To Edinburgh (Table 26)
- **C** To Liverpool Lime Street (Table 89)
- **b** Wakefield Kirkgate
- **c** Change at Sheffield and Doncaster
- **e** Arr. 1346
- **f** Change at Sheffield

London → East Midlands → Sheffield

Route Diagram - See first page of Table 53

		XC	EM	EM	EM	EM	EM	EM	EM	XC	NT	XC	EM	EM	EM	EM	EM	EM	XC	NT	XC	EM	EM	EM	EM	XC
		1 ◇			1 ◇		◇	1 ◇		1 ◇	◇	1 ◇			1 ◇			◇	1 ◇	◇	1 ◇			1 ◇	◇	1 ◇
		A								B		C							B		D					B
		trolley	bus	bus	restaurant	bus	trolley	restaurant	bus	trolley		trolley	bus	bus	restaurant	bus	bus	trolley	trolley		trolley	bus	bus	restaurant	trolley	trolley
St Pancras International ⊖	d				10 30			11 00							11 30									12 30		
Gatwick Airport [10] ✈	d																									
Luton Airport Parkway [7]	d				*10 37*			11 29							11 57									12 57		
Luton [10]	d				11 00			11 33							12 00									13 00		
Bedford [7]	d				11 22			11 55							12 25									13 26		
Wellingborough	d				11 35			12 08							12 39									13 40		
Kettering	a				11 44			12 12							12 49									13 48		
	d		11 54		11 46			12 14	12 22				12 59		12 50		13 30					13 58		13 49		
Corby	d							12 30																		
Market Harborough	d		12a19	12 19		12 45			12a47				13a22	13 19		13 45	13a55					14a23	14 20			
Leicester	a			12 54	12 58	13 20		13 24						13 54	13 59	14 20							14 55	14 59		
	d				13 04			13 30							14 06									15 05		
Syston	d																									
Sileby	d																									
Barrow Upon Soar	d																									
Loughborough	d				13 16			13 41							14 17									15 17		
East Midlands Parkway	d				13 23			13 48							14 25									15 26		
Beeston	a							13 54																		
Nottingham [8] (tram)	a							14 02																		
	d						13 38				14 19							14 38		15 12					15 44	
Lincoln	a																									
Langley Mill	d						13 55				14 35							14 55		15 34						
Alfreton	d						14 03				14 43							15 03		15 42					16 04	
Long Eaton	a				13 27										14 29									15 29		
Derby [10]	a				13 41										14 41									15 46		
	d	13 44			13 49					14 11		14 44			14 48				15 05		15 44			15 51		16 11
Chesterfield	d	14 03			14 09		14 18			14 30	14 54	15 03			15 09			15 13		15 53	16 04			16 12	16 23	
Sheffield [7] (tram)	a	14 17			14 27		14 36			14 43	15 15	15 17			15 31			15 34	15 47	16 15	16 18			16 29	16 39	16 48
Doncaster [7]	a	*14 56*								15 13		*15 55*							16 15		*16 54*					17 13
Wakefield Kirkgate [4]	a										15 52									16 52						
Wakefield Westgate [7]	a	14 44			*15b29*							15 44									16 44			*17b29*		
Leeds [10]	a	15 02									16 18	16 02								17 18	17 02					
York [8]	a	15 32			*15 43*		*15 43*			15 43	*16c35*	16 32			*16 40*			*16 40*	16 40		17 32			*17 42*	*17 42*	17 42

		EM	EM	EM		NT	XC	EM	EM	EM	EM	EM	EM	EM	EM	XC	EM	EM	NT	XC	EM	XC	EM	EM	EM	EM
				1 ◇		◇	1 ◇	1 ◇			◇	◇	1 ◇			1 ◇	1 ◇		◇	1 ◇	◇	1 ◇			1 ◇	
							D				E	G				B				C		C				
		bus	bus	restaurant			trolley	restaurant	bus	bus	trolley	trolley	restaurant	bus	bus	trolley	restaurant	bus		trolley	trolley	trolley	bus	bus	restaurant	bus
St Pancras International ⊖	d			13 00				13 30					14 00				14 30								15 00	
Gatwick Airport [10] ✈	d																									
Luton Airport Parkway [7]	d			13 29				14 02					14 29				*14 37*								15 29	
Luton [10]	d			13 33				14 06					*14 11*				15 01								*15 11*	
Bedford [7]	d			13 56				14 20					14 47				15 17								15 46	
Wellingborough	d			14 10				14 34					15 00				15 31								15 59	
Kettering	a			14 17				14 43					15 05				15 39								16 07	
	d	14 27		14 18				14 46	14 53				15 09	15 15			15 41	15 48					16 17		16 08	
Corby	d			14 34									15 25												16 24	
Market Harborough	d	14a52	14 53						15a18	15 36				15a40	16 04			16a13					16a42	16 42		17 01
Leicester	a		15 28	15 32				16 04		16 11			16 14		16 29		16 42							17 17	17 20	17 36
	d			15 38				16 11					16 21				16 49								17 27	
Syston	d																									
Sileby	d																									
Barrow Upon Soar	d																									
Loughborough	d			15 50				16 23					16 32				17 01								17 38	
East Midlands Parkway	d			15 57				16 30					16 40				17 09								17 46	
Beeston	a			16 03									16 45													
Nottingham [8] (tram)	a			16 11									16 53												18 03	
	d					16 14					16 40	16 43							17 14		17 37					
Lincoln	a																									
Langley Mill	d					16 30					17 00	17 00							17 30		17 54					
Alfreton	d					16 38					17 08	17 08							17 38		18 02					
Long Eaton	a							16 34																		
Derby [10]	a							16 47									17 22									
	d						16 44	16 48								17 11	17 24			17 44		18 05				
Chesterfield	d					16 50	17 03	17 09			17 20	17 20					17 45		17 49	18 04	18 17					
Sheffield [7] (tram)	a					17 15	17 18	17 28			17 40	17 40				17 48	18 00		18 15	18 19	18 34	18 46				
Doncaster [7]	a						*17 57*									18 13	*18 39*			*18 54*		19 13				
Wakefield Kirkgate [4]	a					17 52													18 52							
Wakefield Westgate [7]	a						17 45	*18 28*			*18 33*	*18 33*				18 33	18 42			18 47						
Leeds [10]	a					18 18	18 02	*18 50*			*18 53*	*18 53*				18 53	19 00		19 18	19 05						
York [8]	a					*18c34*	18 32	*19c05*			*19c05*	*19c05*				19 21				19 32	*19 42*	19 42				

For general notes see front of timetable
For details of catering facilities see Directory of Train Operators

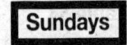

- **A** To Aberdeen (Table 51)
- **B** To Newcastle (Table 26)
- **C** To Edinburgh (Table 26)
- **D** To Glasgow Central (Table 26)
- **E** From 8 November
- **G** Until 1 November
- **b** Wakefield Kirkgate
- **c** Change at Sheffield and Doncaster

Sundays

from 13 September

London → East Midlands → Sheffield

Route Diagram - See first page of Table 53

		EM 1◇	EM 🚌	EM 🚌	NT ◇	XC 1◇ A	EM ◇	EM 1◇	EM 🚌	EM 🚌	XC 1◇ B	EM 1◇	EM 🚌	EM 🚌
St Pancras International	⊖ d	15 30						16 00				16 30		
Gatwick Airport 10	✈ d													
Luton Airport Parkway 7	d	*15 37*						16 29				*16 37*		
Luton 10	d	15 59						*16 11*				16 52		
Bedford 7	d	16 15						16 47				17 15		
Wellingborough	d	16 28						17 00				17 28		
Kettering	a	16 37						17 09				17 37		
	d	16 39	16 49					17 11	17 21			17 39	17 47	
Corby	d							17 27						
Market Harborough	d		17a12	17 36					17a46	18 00			18a12	18 35
Leicester	a	17 40		18 11				18 14		18 35		18 39		19 10
	d	17 46						18 21				18 45		
Syston	d													
Sileby	d													
Barrow Upon Soar	d													
Loughborough	d	17 57						18 32				18 57		
East Midlands Parkway	d	18 04						18 39				19 04		
Beeston	a							18 47						
Nottingham 8	a							18 54						
	d				18 14		18 37							
Lincoln	a													
Langley Mill	d				18 30		18 54							
Alfreton	d				18 38		19 02							
Long Eaton	a	18 08										19 08		
Derby 10	a	18 19										19 19		
	d	18 20				18 44					19 05	19 20		
Chesterfield	d	18 40			18 49	19 05	19 12					19 42		
Sheffield 7	a	18 56			19 15	19 20	19 31				19 39	19 55		
Doncaster 7	a	*19 39*				*20 07*					20 16	*20 30*		
Wakefield Kirkgate 4	a				19 52									
Wakefield Westgate 7	a					19 48								
Leeds 10	a				20 18	20 05								
York 8	a					20 32	*20 44*				20 44			

		NT ◇	XC 1◇ C	XC 1◇ D	EM ◇	EM 1◇	EM 🚌	EM 🚌	XC 1◇ B	NT ◇	XC 1◇	EM 1◇	EM 🚌
St Pancras International	⊖ d					17 00						17 30	
Gatwick Airport 10	✈ d												
Luton Airport Parkway 7	d					17 21						*17 37*	
Luton 10	d					*17 11*						17 54	
Bedford 7	d					17 45						18 17	
Wellingborough	d					17 58						18 31	
Kettering	a					18 07						18 40	
	d					18 08	18 15					18 42	18 50
Corby	d					18 24							
Market Harborough	d						18a40	19 09					19a15
Leicester	a					19 13		19 44				19 57	
	d					19 20						20 04	
Syston	d												
Sileby	d												
Barrow Upon Soar	d												
Loughborough	d					19 30						20 16	
East Midlands Parkway	d					19 38						20 24	
Beeston	a					19 44							
Nottingham 8	a					19 52							
	d	19 19			19 38					20 13			
Lincoln	a												
Langley Mill	d	19 35								20 29			
Alfreton	d	19 43			20 00					20 37			
Long Eaton	a											20 31	
Derby 10	a											20 45	
	d		19 44	19 45					20 05		20 44	20 47	
Chesterfield	d	19 54	20 06	20 06	20 10					20 48	21 03	21 09	
Sheffield 7	a	20 15	20 21	20 21	20 31				20 38	21 14	21 16	21 25	
Doncaster 7	a		*21 05*	*21 05*					21 19		*22 03*		
Wakefield Kirkgate 4	a	20 52											
Wakefield Westgate 7	a	*20b49*	20 49	20 49	*21c29*						21 44	*22 26*	
Leeds 10	a	21 16	21 05	21 05	*22 04*						22 06	*22 52*	
York 8	a		21 37	21 37	*21 42*				21 42				

		XC 1◇	EM 🚌	EM 🚌	EM 1◇	EM 🚌	EM 1◇	EM 🚌	XC 1◇	NT ◇	XC 1◇	EM 🚌	EM 🚌	EM 1◇	EM 🚌	EM 🚌	EM 🚌
St Pancras International	⊖ d				18 00		18 30							19 00			
Gatwick Airport 10	✈ d																
Luton Airport Parkway 7	d				18 21		*18 37*							19 21			
Luton 10	d				*18 11*		18 54							*19 11*			
Bedford 7	d				18 45		19 17							19 45			
Wellingborough	d				18 58		19 31							19 58			
Kettering	a				19 07		19 40							20 05			
	d		19 17		19 09		19 41	19 50				20 15		20 07		20 47	
Corby	d				19 25									20 22			
Market Harborough	d		19a42	19 36		20 17		20a15				20a40	20 36		21 01	21a12	21 46
Leicester	a			20 11	20 14	20 52	20 55						21 11	21 14	21 36		22 11
	d				20 21		21 02							21 21			
Syston	d																
Sileby	d																
Barrow Upon Soar	d																
Loughborough	d				20 32		21 14							21 31			
East Midlands Parkway	d				20 40		21 22							21 39			
Beeston	a				20 45									21 45			
Nottingham 8	a				20 53									21 51			
	d									21 20							
Lincoln	a																
Langley Mill	d									21 41							
Alfreton	d									21 52							
Long Eaton	a						21 26										
Derby 10	a						21 38										
	d	21 11					21 40		21 44		22 50						
Chesterfield	d	21 30					22 01		22 06	22 08	23 11						
Sheffield 7	a	21 44					22 16		22 19	22 32	23 27						
Doncaster 7	a								*22 56*		*00 19*						
Wakefield Kirkgate 4	a																
Wakefield Westgate 7	a						22 43		22 46	*23c28*							
Leeds 10	a						23 01		23 08	*00 04*	00 44						
York 8	a	22 53							*00e39*								

For general notes see front of timetable
For details of catering facilities see Directory of Train Operators

A To Edinburgh (Table 26)
B To Newcastle (Table 26)
C From 8 November
D Until 1 November

b Change at Sheffield
c Wakefield Kirkgate
e Change at Sheffield and Doncaster

Sheffield → East Midlands → London

Route Diagram - See first page of Table 53

Miles	Miles	Miles					EM 1◊	EM ◊		EM 1◊	EM 1◊	EM 1◊	EM		EM ◊	NT ◊	EM 1◊	EM 1◊	EM 1◊	EM 1◊	EM 1◊	EM 1◊	NT ◊		XC 1◊	EM
										D							G									
							☕			☕ Ħ	☕ Ħ	☕ Ħ					☕	⊠	☕	☕	☕	☕			Ħ	
—	—	—	York 8	d																						
—	—	—	Leeds 10	d																						
—	—	—	Wakefield Westgate 7	d																						
—	—	—	Wakefield Kirkgate 4	d																						
—	—	—	Doncaster 7	d																						
0	0	—	**Sheffield 7**	d												05 05		05 27			05 56		06 00		06 01	
12¼	12¼	—	Chesterfield	d												05 20		05 39			06 09		06 16		06 26	
—	36½	—	**Derby 10**	a														06 01			06 30				06 45	
—	—	—		d						04 55	05 17							06 03			06 32					
—	44	—	Long Eaton	d							05 27										06 42					
22½	—	—	Alfreton	d																			06 30			
34½	—	—	Langley Mill	d																			06 37			
—	—	—	Lincoln	d																						
40¾	—	—	**Nottingham 8**	a												06 12							07 08			
—	—	—		d				04 51				05 35			05 56					06 28		06 48				
44	—	—	Beeston	d																06 34		06 54				
—	—	—	East Midlands Parkway	d						05 06		05 46			06 15			06 16		06 40		07 01				
55½	53¼	—	Loughborough	d				05a07		05 14		05 54	06 05		06a25			06 24			06 52					06 53
59½	57¼	—	Barrow Upon Soar	d									06 09													06 57
61½	59¼	—	Sileby	d									06 14													07 03
64¼	62	—	Syston	d									06 19													07 08
68	65¾	—	**Leicester**	a						05 24	05 42	06 06	06 27					06 36		06 54	07 04	07 15				07 19
—	—	0		d			04 40			05 26	05 44	06 08						06 38		06 57	07 06	07 16				
84¼	82	—	Market Harborough	d						05 41	05 58	06 23						06 53		07 12		07 31				
—	—	41	Corby	d													06 37		07 08							
95¼	93	48½	Kettering	a			05 00			05 50	06 07	06 33					06 46	07 03	07 17	07 21	07 28	07 40				
—	—	—		d			05 01			05 51	06 09	06 34					06 47	07 05		07 22	07 29	07 41				
102¼	100	—	Wellingborough	d			05 09			05 59	06 17	06 42					06 56	07 13		07 30	07 38	07 49				
117½	115½	—	Bedford 7	d			05 32				06 32						07 13				07 55					
137	134¾	—	Luton 10	d			06 03			06 24	07 03						07 29			07 56	08 27	08 15				
138	135¾	—	Luton Airport Parkway 7	d			05 55			06 40	07 06	07 08					07 42	07 40		08 14	08 12	08 30				
—	—	—	Gatwick Airport 10	a			07 31			08 11	08 40	08 51					09 24	09 40		09 40	09 56	09 56				
167¼	165	—	**St Pancras International**	a			06 21			06 54	07 14	07 36					07 55	08 09		08 26	08 38	08 44				

		EM 1◊	EM 1◊	EM 1◊	EM 1◊	EM 1◊	EM 1◊	XC 1◊	EM 1◊	EM 1◊		EM	NT ◊	XC 1◊	EM 1◊	EM 1◊	EM 1◊	EM 1◊	EM 1◊	XC 1◊		EM	EM 1◊	NT ◊	XC 1◊	EM 1◊
					H J	J K	H		K	L					N			Q				U			V	
		⊠	☕	☕	☕	☕	☕	Ħ	☕	⊠				Ħ	⊠	☕	☕	⊠	☕	Ħ			☕		Ħ	☕
York 8	d	04 22			04b00	04b00		04c00					05 26	06e00	06f00					06 32				06g32	07 27	07 27
Leeds 10	d	05 25			06 00	06 00		06 00					06 05	06 15	06 15		06 34			07 05				07 05		
Wakefield Westgate 7	d	05 37			06 12	06 12		06 12						06 27	06 27		06 46			07 18					07h23	
Wakefield Kirkgate 4	d												06 21											07 23		
Doncaster 7	d	05 57			06 00	06 00								06 45						07 02					07 52	
Sheffield 7	d	06 27			06 47	06 47		06 50					07 03	07 18	07 27		07 32	07 41		07 53				08 05	08 20	08 27
Chesterfield	d	06 39			06 59	06 59		07 04					07 20	07 30	07 39		07 45	07 55		08 06				08 24	08 32	08 39
Derby 10	a	07 03			07 19	07 19		07 25						07 49	07 59			08 14		08 26					08 51	08 59
	d	07 03			07 21	07 22	07 24		07 26						08 01			08 16								09 01
Long Eaton	d						07 36		07 36									08 26	←							
Alfreton	d												07 33				07 56 →		07 56					08 35		
Langley Mill	d												07 40						08 04					08 42		
Lincoln	d															07 08						07 29				
Nottingham 8	a												08 02			07 57			08 21			08 30		09 02		
	d		07 10							07 50		07 31				08 02			08 28			08 32				
Beeston	d		07 17									07 37				08 08										
East Midlands Parkway	d		07 25		07 34	07 34				08 01		07 46						08 32	08 39			08 43				
Loughborough	d	07 22			07 42	07 42	07 47		07 47			07 56				08 22		08 40				08 54				
Barrow Upon Soar	d											08 01										08 58				
Sileby	d											08 05										09 02				
Syston	d											08 11										09 07				
Leicester	a	07 34	07 41		07 53	07 53	07 59		07 59	08 17		08 23			08 23	08 32		08 53	08 57			09 21				09 23
	d	07 35	07 42		07 55	07 55	08 01		08 01	08 18					08 25	08 34		08 53	08 57							09 25
Market Harborough	d		07 58				08 16		08 16							08 48			09 12							
Corby	d			08 03																			09 15			
Kettering	a	07 57	08 08	08 12	08 15	08 15	08 26		08 26							08 57							09 24			
	d	07 59	08 09		08 17	08 17	08 28		08 28							08 57							09 26			
Wellingborough	d	08 07			08 25	08 25	08 39		08 39							09 05							09 34			
Bedford 7	d		08 29				09 02		09 02							09 18							09 48			
Luton 10	d		09 03				09 19		09 19							09 47							10 04			
Luton Airport Parkway 7	d		09 06													09 34							10 16			
Gatwick Airport 10	a		10 26				10 55		10 55							11 10							11 40			
St Pancras International	a	08 57	09 08		09 13	09 13	09 47		09 47	09 30					09 37	10 00		10 06	10 19				10 30			10 34

For general notes see front of timetable
For details of catering facilities see Directory of Train Operators

- **A** From Liverpool Lime Street (Table 90)
- **B** From Liverpool Lime Street (Table 89)
- **C** From 14 September
- **D** MO until 31 August
- **G** From Melton Mowbray (Table 49)
- **H** Until 4 September
- **J** **The Sheffield Continental**
- **K** From 7 September
- **L** **The Robin Hood**
- **N** **The Master Cutler**
- **Q** **The South Yorkshireman**
- **U** From Sleaford (Table 18)
- **V** From Newcastle (Table 26)
- **b** Change at Leeds and Sheffield. Mondays dep. 0422
- **c** Mondays dep. 0422
- **e** Change at Doncaster
- **f** Change at Doncaster and Sheffield
- **g** Change at Sheffield
- **h** Wakefield Kirkgate. Change at Sheffield

From Monday 28 September a revised service will be in operation due to seasonal difficulties. Some trains will be retimed between 1 and 3 minutes. Passengers should check with National Rail Enquiries for precise times.

Sheffield → East Midlands → London

Route Diagram - See first page of Table 53

		EM	EM	EM	EM	EM	XC		NT	XC	EM	EM	EM	EM	EM	EM	EM		XC	NT	XC	EM	EM	EM	EM	EM
		1◇	1◇	1◇		◇	1◇		◇	1◇	1◇	1◇	1◇	1◇	1◇		◇		1◇	◇	1◇	1◇	1◇	1◇	1◇	1◇
							A			A									B		B					
		☕	☕	☕			🍴			🍴	☕	☕	☕	☕	☕				🍴		🍴	☕	☕	☕	☕	☕
York 8	d						07 44		*07b44*	08 27		*08 27*							08 44	*08b44*	09 27		*09 27*			
Leeds 10	d						08 11		08 02										09 11	09 05						
Wakefield Westgate 7	d						08 23												09 23							
Wakefield Kirkgate 4	d								08 23											09 23						
Doncaster 7	d								*08 16*	08 51							*08 56*		*09 01*		09 56					
Sheffield 7	d					08 38	08 54		09 05	09 23		09 27					09 38		09 54	10 05	10 23		10 27			
Chesterfield	d					08 53	09 06		09 22			09 39					09 53		10 06	10 22			10 39			
Derby 10	a						09 26			09 51		09 59							10 28		10 51		10 59			
	d		09 18									10 01		10 18									11 01		11 18	
Long Eaton	d		09 28											10 28											11 28	
Alfreton	d					09 03			09 33								10 03			10 33						
Langley Mill	d								09 40											10 40						
Lincoln	d				08 35											09 31										
Nottingham 8	a				09 30	09 30			10 01							10 30	10 30			11 01						
	d	09 02		09 28	09 32								10 02		10 28	10 32								11 02		11 28
Beeston	d	09 08											10 08											11 08		
East Midlands Parkway	d		09 32	09 39	09 43									10 32	10 39	10 43									11 32	11 39
Loughborough	d	09 20	09 40		09 54								10 20	10 40		10 54								11 20	11 40	
Barrow Upon Soar	d				09 58											10 58										
Sileby	d				10 02											11 02										
Syston	d				10 07											11 07										
Leicester	a	09 31	09 51	09 55	10 21							10 23	10 33	10 51	10 55	11 22							11 23	11 31	11 52	11 56
	d	09 33	09 53	09 57								10 25	10 33	10 53	10 57								11 25	11 33	11 53	11 57
Market Harborough	d	09 47		10 12									10 47		11 12									11 47		12 12
Corby	d																					11 14				
Kettering	a	09 56											10 55									11 23		11 56		
	d	09 56									10 24		10 56									11 25		11 56		
Wellingborough	d	10 04									10 32		11 04									11 33		12 04		
Bedford 7	d	10 18									10 49		11 18									11 49		12 19		
Luton 10	d	*10 47*									11 05		*11 47*									12 05		*13 03*		
Luton Airport Parkway 7	d	10 34									*11 16*		11 34									*12 16*		12 35		
Gatwick Airport 10 ✈	a	*12 10*									*12 40*		*13 10*									*13 40*		*14 10*		
St Pancras International ⊖	a	11 01	11 06	11 19							11 29	11 34	12 03	12 07	12 12							12 29	12 34	13 01	13 07	13 13

		EM	EM	XC		NT	XC	EM	EM	EM	EM	EM	EM	XC		EM	NT	XC	EM	EM	EM	EM	EM	EM		EM
			◇	1◇		◇	1◇	1◇	1◇	1◇	1◇	1◇	◇	1◇			◇	1◇	1◇	1◇	1◇	1◇	1◇			◇
				C			A							D				A								
				🍴			🍴	☕	☕	☕	☕	☕		🍴				🍴	☕	☕	☕	☕	☕			
York 8	d			09 44		*09b44*	10 34		*10 34*					10 44			*10b44*	11 27		*11 27*						
Leeds 10	d			10 11		10 05								11 11			11 05									
Wakefield Westgate 7	d			10 23										11 23												
Wakefield Kirkgate 4	d					10 23											11 23									
Doncaster 7	d			*10 02*			10 58							*11 02*				11 54								
Sheffield 7	d		10 38	10 54		11 05	11 23		11 27				11 38	11 54			12 05	12 23		12 27						12 38
Chesterfield	d		10 53	11 06		11 22			11 39				11 53	12 06			12 22			12 39						12 53
Derby 10	a			11 26			11 51		11 59					12 26				12 51		12 59						
	d								12 01		12 18									13 01		13 18				
Long Eaton	d										12 28											13 28				
Alfreton	d		11 03			11 33							12 03				12 33									13 03
Langley Mill	d					11 40											12 40									
Lincoln	d	10 36														11 42								12 30		
Nottingham 8	a	11 29	11 30			12 01							12 30			12 30	13 01							13 30		13 30
	d	11 32								12 02		12 28				12 32					13 02		13 28	13 32		
Beeston	d									12 08											13 08					
East Midlands Parkway	d	11 43									12 32	12 39				12 43						13 32	13 39	13 43		
Loughborough	d	11 54								12 20	12 40					12 54					13 20	13 40		13 54		
Barrow Upon Soar	d	11 58														12 58								13 58		
Sileby	d	12 02														13 02								14 02		
Syston	d	12 07														13 07								14 07		
Leicester	a	12 21							12 23	12 31	12 53	12 57				13 21				13 23	13 32	13 51	13 55	14 21		
	d								12 25	12 33	12 55	12 57								13 26	13 33	13 53	13 57			
Market Harborough	d									12 47		13 12									13 47		14 12			
Corby	d							12 15											13 15							
Kettering	a							12 24		12 56									13 24		13 56					
	d							12 26		12 56									13 26		13 56					
Wellingborough	d							12 34		13 04									13 34		14 04					
Bedford 7	d							12 49		13 18									13 49		14 19					
Luton 10	d							13 05		*13 47*									14 05		*15 03*					
Luton Airport Parkway 7	d							*13 16*		13 34									*14 16*		14 35					
Gatwick Airport 10 ✈	a							*14 40*		*15 10*									*15 40*		*16 10*					
St Pancras International ⊖	a							13 29	13 34	14 02	14 07	14 14							14 29	14 39	15 01	15 07	15 13			

For general notes see front of timetable
For details of catering facilities see Directory of Train Operators

- **A** From Newcastle (Table 26)
- **B** From Edinburgh (Table 26)
- **C** From Glasgow Central (Table 26)
- **D** From Dundee (Table 51)
- **b** Change at Sheffield

From Monday 28 September a revised service will be in operation due to seasonal difficulties. Some trains will be retimed between 1 and 3 minutes. Passengers should check with National Rail Enquiries for precise times.

Sheffield → East Midlands → London

Route Diagram - See first page of Table 53

		XC	XC	NT	XC	EM	EM	EM	EM	EM		EM	EM	XC	EM	NT	XC	EM	EM	EM		EM	EM	EM	XC	EM
		1 ◇	1 ◇	◇	1 ◇	1 ◇	1 ◇	1 ◇	1 ◇	1 ◇			◇	1 ◇	1 ◇	◇	1 ◇	1 ◇	1 ◇	1 ◇		1 ◇		◇	1 ◇	1 ◇
		A	B		C									D			C								E	
		🛒	🛒		🛒	☕	☕	☕	☕	☕				🛒	☕		🛒	☕	☕	☕		☕			🛒	☕
York 8	d	11 44	11 44	*11b44*	12 27		*12 27*							12 44		*12b44*	13 26	*13 26*							13 44	
Leeds 10	d	12 11	12 11	12 05										13 11		13 05									14 11	
Wakefield Westgate 7	d	12 23	12 23											13 23											14 23	
Wakefield Kirkgate 4	d			12 23												13 23										
Doncaster 7	d	*11 58*	*11 58*		12 55									*12 59*			13 55								*14 01*	
Sheffield 7	d	12 54	12 54	13 05	13 23		13 27						13 38	13 54		14 05	14 23	14 27						14 38	14 54	
Chesterfield	d	13 06	13 06	13 22			13 39						13 53	14 06		14 22		14 39						14 53	15 06	
Derby 10	a	13 25	13 26		13 51		13 59							14 26			14 51	14 59							15 26	
	d						14 01		14 18									15 01		15 18						
Long Eaton	d								14 28											15 28						
Alfreton	d			13 33									14 03			14 33								15 07		
Langley Mill	d			13 40												14 40										
Lincoln	d											13 40											14 35			
Nottingham 8	a			14 01								14 30	14 31			15 01							15 30	15 30		
	d							14 02		14 28		14 32							15 02			15 28	15 32			
Beeston	d							14 08											15 08							
East Midlands Parkway	d								14 32	14 39		14 43								15 32		15 39	15 43			
Loughborough	d							14 20	14 40			14 54							15 20	15 40			15 54			
Barrow Upon Soar	d											14 58											15 58			
Sileby	d											15 02											16 02			
Syston	d											15 07											16 07			
Leicester	a						14 23	14 31	14 51	14 55		15 21						15 23	15 31	15 52		15 56	16 21			
	d						14 25	14 33	14 53	14 57								15 25	15 33	15 53		15 57				
Market Harborough	d							14 47		15 12									15 47			16 12				
Corby	d					14 05									14 43											15 43
Kettering	a					14 14		14 56							14 52				15 56							15 52
	d					14 26		14 56							15 26				15 56							16 26
Wellingborough	d					14 34		15 04							15 34				16 04							16 34
Bedford 7	d					14 49		15 19							15 49				16 19							16 49
Luton 10	d					15 05		*16 03*							16 05				*16 55*							17 05
Luton Airport Parkway 7	d					*15 16*		15 35							*16 16*				16 35							*17 20*
Gatwick Airport 10	a					*16 40*		*17 15*							*18 12*				*18 24*							*18 56*
St Pancras International	a					15 29	15 34	16 01	16 06	16 13					16 29			16 34	17 00	17 07		17 20				17 29

		NT	XC	EM	EM	EM	EM		EM	EM	XC	EM	NT	XC	EM	EM	EM		EM	EM	EM	XC	EM	NT	XC	EM
																						FO				
		◇	1 ◇	1 ◇	1 ◇	1 ◇	1 ◇			◇	1 ◇	1 ◇	◇	1 ◇	1 ◇	1 ◇	1 ◇		1 ◇		◇	1 ◇	1 ◇	◇	1 ◇	1 ◇
			C								H			C								J			C	
			🛒	☕	☕	☕	☕				🛒	☕		🛒	☕	☕	☕		☕			🛒	☕		🛒	☕
York 8	d	*13b44*	14 32	*14 32*							14 44		*14b44*	15 29	*15 29*							15 44		*15b44*	16 25	*16 25*
Leeds 10	d	14 05									15 11		15 05									16 11		16 05		
Wakefield Westgate 7	d										15 23											16 23				
Wakefield Kirkgate 4	d	14 23											15 23											16 23		
Doncaster 7	d		14 57								*15 02*			15 55								*16 02*			16 53	
Sheffield 7	d	15 05	15 23	15 27						15 38	15 54		16 05	16 23	16 27						16 38	16 54		17 05	17 23	17 27
Chesterfield	d	15 22		15 39						15 53	16 06		16 22		16 39						16 56	17 06		17 22		17 39
Derby 10	a		15 51	15 59							16 26			16 51	16 59							17 27			17 51	17 59
	d			16 01		16 18									17 01		17 18									18 01
Long Eaton	d					16 28											17 28									
Alfreton	d	15 33								16 03			16 33								17 06			17 33		
Langley Mill	d	15 40											16 40											17 40		
Lincoln	d								15 30											16 35						
Nottingham 8	a	16 01							16 30	16 33			17 00							17 30	17 31			18 01		
	d				16 02		16 28		16 32							17 02			17 28	17 32						
Beeston	d				16 08											17 08										
East Midlands Parkway	d					16 32	16 39		16 46								17 32		17 39	17 46						
Loughborough	d				16 20	16 40			16 56							17 20	17 40			17 56						
Barrow Upon Soar	d								17 01											18 01						
Sileby	d								17 05											18 05						
Syston	d								17 10											18 10						
Leicester	a			16 23	16 31	16 51	16 55		17 23						17 23	17 31	17 52		17 55	18 24						18 23
	d			16 25	16 33	16 53	16 57								17 25	17 33	17 53		17 57							18 25
Market Harborough	d				16 47		17 12									17 47			18 12							
Corby	d											16 43											17 43			
Kettering	a				16 56	17 14						16 52				17 56	18 14						17 52			
	d				16 56	17 15						17 26				17 57	18 15						18 26			
Wellingborough	d				17 04							17 34				18 04							18 34			
Bedford 7	d				17 21							17 49				18 19							18 49			
Luton 10	d				*17 57*		17 50					18 05			18 15	*18 51*							19 05			
Luton Airport Parkway 7	d				17 34		*18 04*					*18 20*			*18 26*	18 35							*19 20*			
Gatwick Airport 10	a				*19 26*							*19 40*			*19 56*	*20 10*							*20 40*			
St Pancras International	a			17 34	18 06	18 13	18 19					18 29			18 39	19 01	19 08		19 19				19 29			19 34

For general notes see front of timetable
For details of catering facilities see Directory of Train Operators

- **A** Until 4 September. From Dundee (Table 51)
- **B** From 7 September. From Dundee (Table 51)
- **C** From Newcastle (Table 26)
- **D** From Glasgow Central (Table 26)
- **E** From Aberdeen (Table 51)
- **H** From Edinburgh (Table 26)
- **J** From 11 September
- **b** Change at Sheffield

From Monday 28 September a revised service will be in operation due to seasonal difficulties. Some trains will be retimed between 1 and 3 minutes. Passengers should check with National Rail Enquiries for precise times.

Table 53

Mondays to Fridays

Sheffield → East Midlands → London

Route Diagram - See first page of Table 53

		EM	EM	EM		EM	EM	XC	XC	EM	NT	XC	EM	EM		EM	EM	EM	EM	XC	EM	NT	XC	XC		EM
		1◇	1◇	1◇			◇	1◇	1◇	1◇	◇	1◇	1◇	1◇		1◇	1◇		◇	1◇	1◇	◇	1◇	1◇		1◇
								A	B			C								E			G C	H		
		☕	☕	☕				🛒	🛒	☕		🛒	☕	☕		☕	☕			🛒	☕		🛒	🛒		☕
York 8	d							16 44	16 44		16b44	17 34	17 34							17 44		17b44	18 24	18 24		17c55
Leeds 10	d						16 37	17 11	17 11		17 05								17 37	18 11		18 05				
Wakefield Westgate 7	d						16e55	17 23	17 23										17e55	18 23						
Wakefield Kirkgate 4	d										17 23											18 23				
Doncaster 7	d							17 01	17 01			17 58								18 02			18 52	18 52		18 47
Sheffield 7	d						17 44	17 54	17 54		18 05	18 23	18 27						18 45	18 54		19 05	19 23	19 23		19 27
Chesterfield	d						18 01	18 06	18 06		18 22		18 39						19 01	19 06		19 22				19 39
Derby 10	a							18 26	18 27			18 51	18 59							19 26			19 51	19 52		19 59
	d		18 18										19 01			19 18										20 01
Long Eaton	d		18 28													19 28										
Alfreton	d						18 11				18 33								19 11			19 33				
Langley Mill	d										18 40											19 40				
Lincoln	d					17 28												18 35								
Nottingham 8	a					18 31	18 33				19 00							19 29	19 38			20 00				
	d	18 02		18 28		18 32								19 02			19 28	19 32								
Beeston	d	18 08												19 08				19 38								
East Midlands Parkway	d		18 32	18 39		18 43										19 32	19 39	19 46								
Loughborough	d	18 20	18 40			18 54								19 20		19 40		19 56								
Barrow Upon Soar	d					18 58												20 01								
Sileby	d					19 02												20 05								
Syston	d					19 07												20 10								
Leicester	a	18 31	18 51	18 55		19 21							19 23	19 31		19 51	19 55	20 23								20 23
	d	18 33	18 53	18 57									19 25	19 33		19 53	19 57									20 25
Market Harborough	d	18 47		19 12										19 47			20 12									
Corby	d									18 43											19 43					
Kettering	a	18 56								18 52				19 56							19 52					
	d	18 56								19 26				19 56							20 26					
Wellingborough	d	19 04								19 34				20 04							20 34					
Bedford 7	d	19 19								19 48				20 18							20 53					
Luton 10	d									20 10											21 08					
Luton Airport Parkway 7	d	19 35												20 34							21 20					
Gatwick Airport 10	a	21 10								22 10				22 10												
St Pancras International	a	20 01	20 07	20 15						20 35			20 38	21 06		21 10	21 15				21 34					21 37

		EM	EM	XC	EM	EM	NT	XC	EM	EM		EM	EM	EM	EM	XC	XC	EM	EM	XC		EM	EM	EM		
		1◇	◇	1◇	1◇		◇	1◇	1◇	1◇		1◇	1◇		◇	1◇	1◇	◇	1◇	1◇			1◇	◇		
				J				C								J	C			K				D		
		☕		🛒	☕			🛒	☕	☕		☕	☕			🛒	🛒		☕	🛒			☕			
York 8	d		18 24	18 44			18b44	19 29				19 29				19 44	20 32	20 32		20 44			21c40			
Leeds 10	d			19 11			19 05									20 11		20 30		21 11			21 48			
Wakefield Westgate 7	d			19 23												20 23		20e46		21 23			22e07			
Wakefield Kirkgate 4	d						19 23																			
Doncaster 7	d			18 55				19 57								20 03	20 57			21 07			22 13			
Sheffield 7	d		19 38	19 54			20 05	20 23				20 39			20 41	20 54	21 26	21 38		22 00			23 21	23 38		
Chesterfield	d		19 53	20 06			20 22					20 53			20 58	21 06		21 54		22 24			23 45	00 02		
Derby 10	a			20 26				20 51				21 18				21 26	21 56			22 44			00 11			
	d											21 20														
Long Eaton	d																									
Alfreton	d		20 04				20 33								21 09			22 05								
Langley Mill	d						20 40											22 12								
Lincoln	d																									
Nottingham 8	a		20 31				21 01								21 38			22 38						00 41		
	d	20 02				20 32				21 02			21 28	21 32								23 10				
Beeston	d	20 08				20 38				21 08																
East Midlands Parkway	d	20 16				20 46				21 15		21 33		21 43								23 21				
Loughborough	d	20 24				20 56				21 22		21 41	21 47	21 54								23 29				
Barrow Upon Soar	d					21 01								21 58												
Sileby	d					21 05								22 02												
Syston	d					21 10								22 07												
Leicester	a	20 34				21 23				21 32		21 52	21 58	22 21								23 55				
	d	20 36								21 33		21 55	22 00													
Market Harborough	d	20 50								21 47			22 14													
Corby	d				20 43				21 43										22 43							
Kettering	a	20 59			20 52				21 52	21 56			22 23						22 52							
	d	20 59			21 17					21 57			22 24													
Wellingborough	d	21 07			21 26					22 05			22 32													
Bedford 7	d	21 22			21 53					22 19			22 46													
Luton 10	d				22 09					22 35			23 02													
Luton Airport Parkway 7	d	21 39			22 20					22 39																
Gatwick Airport 10	a																									
St Pancras International	a	22 06			22 35					23 04		23 07	23 33													

For general notes see front of timetable
For details of catering facilities see Directory of Train Operators

A Until 4 September. From Edinburgh (Table 26)

B From 7 September. From Edinburgh (Table 26)

C From Newcastle (Table 26)

D From Liverpool Lime Street (Table 89)

E From Edinburgh (Table 26)

G Until 4 September

H From 7 September. From Newcastle (Table 26)

J From Edinburgh (Table 26) to Bristol Temple Meads (Table 57)

K From Edinburgh (Table 26) to Birmingham New Street (Table 57)

b Change at Sheffield

c Change at Doncaster and Sheffield

e Wakefield Kirkgate

From Monday 28 September a revised service will be in operation due to seasonal difficulties. Some trains will be retimed between 1 and 3 minutes. Passengers should check with National Rail Enquiries for precise times.

Sheffield → East Midlands → London

Route Diagram - See first page of Table 53

Station																										
			EM	EM	EM	EM	EM	EM	EM	EM	EM	EM	NT	XC	EM	EM	EM	XC	EM	EM	EM	NT	XC	EM	EM	EM
			1◇	◇	1◇	◇	1◇	1◇	1◇	1◇		1◇	◇	1◇	1◇	1◇	1◇	1◇	1◇		1◇	◇	1◇	1◇	1◇	1◇
				B		C																				
			☕		☕		☕	☕	☕	☕		☕		🛒	☕	☕	☕	🛒	☕		☕		🛒	☒	☕	☕
York [8]	d																	*03 52*				*03b52*	*06c00*	*06e00*		
Leeds [10]	d																	06 00					06 15	*06 15*		
Wakefield Westgate [7]	d																	06 12					06 29	*06 29*		
Wakefield Kirkgate [4]	d																									
Doncaster [7]	d														*05 40*			*06 00*					06 47			
Sheffield [7]	d						05 27						05 54	06 01	06 25			06 50				07 03	07 18	07 27		
Chesterfield	d						05 39						06 19	06 26	06 37			07 03				07 20	07 30	07 39		
Derby [10]	a						05 59							06 45	06 59			07 24					07 49	07 59		
	d				05 25		06 01		06 18						07 01		07 18							08 01		08 18
Long Eaton	d				05 35				06 28								07 28									08 28
Alfreton	d												06 30									07 33				
Langley Mill	d												06 37									07 40				
Lincoln	d																								07 08	
Nottingham [8]	a												07 04									08 02			07 58	
	d			05⌇04		05⌇54		06 02		06 28						07 02			07 28	07 31					08 02	
Beeston	d							06 08								07 08				07 37					08 08	
East Midlands Parkway	d			⌇	05 39	06⌇15			06 32	06 39							07 32		07 39	07 46						08 32
Loughborough	d			05a19	05 47	06a25		06 20	06 40		06 50					07 20	07 40			07 56					08 20	08 40
Barrow Upon Soar	d										06 57									08 01						
Sileby	d										07 05									08 05						
Syston	d										07 10									08 10						
Leicester	a				05 57		06 23	06 31	06 51	06 55	07 21				07 23	07 31	07 51		07 55	08 23				08 23	08 31	08 51
	d		04 40		05 59		06 25	06 33	06 53	06 57					07 25	07 33	07 53		07 57					08 25	08 33	08 53
Market Harborough	d				06 14			06 47		07 12						07 47			08 12						08 47	
Corby	d											07 08									08 15					
Kettering	a		05 00		06 23			06 56	07 15			07 20				07 56					08 24				08 56	
	d		05 01		06 26			06 56	07 26							07 56					08 26				08 56	
Wellingborough	d		05 09		06 34			07 04	07 34							08 04					08 34				09 04	
Bedford [7]	d		05 32		06 49			07 19	07 49							08 19					08 49				09 19	
Luton [10]	d		*06 13*		07 05			*08 01*	08 05							*09 01*					09 05				*10 01*	
Luton Airport Parkway [7]	d		05 55		*07 20*			07 35	*08 20*							08 35					*09 20*				09 35	
Gatwick Airport [10] ✈	a																									
St Pancras International ⊖	a		06 21		07 31		07 34	08 00	08 31	08 12					08 34	09 01	09 06		09 12		09 29			09 34	10 00	10 06

Station																										
		EM		XC	XC	EM	EM	NT	XC	EM	EM	EM	EM	EM	EM	XC	NT	XC	EM	EM	EM	EM	EM	EM	EM	XC
		1◇		1◇	1◇		1◇	◇	1◇	1◇	1◇	1◇	1◇		◇	1◇	◇	1◇	1◇	1◇	1◇	1◇	1◇		◇	1◇
				E	G	H			J							J		J								K
		☒		🛒	🛒		☕		🛒	☕	☕	☕	☕			🛒		🛒	☕	☕	☕	☕	☕			🛒
York [8]	d			06⌇09	06⌇09			*06 28*	07 25	*07 25*						07 44	*07f44*	08 27		*08 27*						08 44
Leeds [10]	d	06 34		07⌇05	07⌇05			07 05					07 34			08 11	08 05									09 11
Wakefield Westgate [7]	d	06 46		07⌇18	07⌇18				*07g23*				07 46			08 23										09 23
Wakefield Kirkgate [4]	d							07 23									08 23									
Doncaster [7]	d			*07⌇02*	*07⌇02*				07 52								*08 17*	08 53							*08 59*	*09 01*
Sheffield [7]	d	07 32		07⌇54	07⌇54			08 05	08 20	08 27			08 32		08 38	08 54	09 05	09 23		09 27					09 38	09 54
Chesterfield	d	07 45		08⌇06	08⌇06			08 24	08 32	08 39			08 45		08 53	09 06	09 22			09 39					09 53	10 06
Derby [10]	a			08⌇25	08⌇26				08 51	08 59						09 26		09 51		09 59						10 26
	d									09 01		09 18								10 01		10 18				
Long Eaton	d											09 28										10 28				
Alfreton	d	07 56						08 35					08 56		09 03		09 33								10 03	
Langley Mill	d	08 04						08 42									09 40									
Lincoln	d					07 29								08 35										09 31		
Nottingham [8]	a	08 23				08 30		09 02					09 18	09 30	09 30		10 01							10 30	10 30	
	d	08 28				08 32					09 02		09 28	09 32							10 02		10 28	10 32		
Beeston	d										09 08										10 08					
East Midlands Parkway	d	08 39				08 43						09 32	09 39	09 43								10 32	10 39	10 43		
Loughborough	d					08 54					09 20	09 40		09 54							10 20	10 40		10 54		
Barrow Upon Soar	d					08 58								09 58										10 58		
Sileby	d					09 02								10 02										11 02		
Syston	d					09 07								10 07										11 07		
Leicester	a	08 55				09 21				09 23	09 31	09 51	09 55	10 21						10 23	10 31	10 51	10 55	11 21		
	d	08 57								09 25	09 33	09 53	09 57							10 25	10 33	10 53	10 57			
Market Harborough	d	09 12									09 47		10 12								10 47		11 12			
Corby	d						09 15																			
Kettering	a						09 24				09 56										10 56					
	d						09 26				09 56								10 26		10 56					
Wellingborough	d						09 34				10 04								10 34		11 04					
Bedford [7]	d						09 49				10 19								10 49		11 19					
Luton [10]	d						10 05				*11 01*								11 05		*12 01*					
Luton Airport Parkway [7]	d						*10 20*				10 35								*11 20*		11 35					
Gatwick Airport [10] ✈	a																									
St Pancras International ⊖	a	10 12					10 29			10 34	11 01	11 06	11 12						11 29	11 34	12 01	12 06	12 12			

For general notes see front of timetable
For details of catering facilities see Directory of Train Operators

- **A** From Liverpool Lime Street (Table 89)
- **B** Until 11 July and from 12 September
- **C** Until 11 July and from 12 September. To Norwich (Table 49)
- **E** From 12 September
- **G** Until 5 September
- **H** From Sleaford (Table 18)
- **J** From Newcastle (Table 26)
- **K** From Edinburgh (Table 26)
- **b** Change at Leeds and Sheffield
- **c** Change at Doncaster
- **e** Change at Doncaster and Sheffield
- **f** Change at Sheffield
- **g** Wakefield Kirkgate. Change at Sheffield

From Saturday 3 October a revised service will be in operation due to seasonal difficulties. Some trains will be retimed between 1 and 3 minutes. Passengers should check with National Rail Enquiries for precise times.

Table 53

Saturdays

Sheffield → East Midlands → London

Route Diagram - See first page of Table 53

		NT ◇	XC 1 ◇ A 🛒	EM 1 ◇ ☕		EM 1 ◇ ☕	EM 1 ◇ ☕	EM 1 ◇ ☕	EM 1 ◇ ☕	EM	EM ◇	XC 1 ◇ A 🛒	EM 1 ◇ ☕	NT ◇	XC 1 ◇ B 🛒	EM 1 ◇ ☕	EM 1 ◇ ☕	EM 1 ◇ ☕	EM 1 ◇ ☕	EM ◇	XC 1 ◇ C 🛒	EM	NT ◇	XC 1 ◇ B 🛒	EM 1 ◇ ☕	EM 1 ◇ ☕
York 8	d	*08b44*	09 28			*09 28*						09 44		*09b44*	10 25	*10 25*					10 44		*10b44*	11 27		*11 27*
Leeds 10	d	09 05										10 11		10 05							11 11		11 05			
Wakefield Westgate 7	d											10 23									11 23					
Wakefield Kirkgate 4	d	09 23												10 23									11 23			
Doncaster 7	d		09 53									*10 02*			10 53						*11 02*			11 55		
Sheffield 7	d	10 05	10 23			10 27					10 38	10 54		11 05	11 23	11 27				11 38	11 54		12 05	12 23		12 27
Chesterfield	d	10 22				10 39					10 53	11 06		11 22		11 39				11 53	12 06		12 22			12 39
Derby 10	a		10 51			10 59						11 26			11 51	11 59					12 26			12 51		12 59
	d					11 01		11 18								12 01		12 18								13 01
Long Eaton	d							11 28										12 28								
Alfreton	d	10 33									11 03			11 33						12 03			12 33			
Langley Mill	d	10 40												11 40									12 40			
Lincoln	d									10 36												11 42				
Nottingham 8	a	11 00								11 29	11 29			12 02						12 29		12 30	13 00			
	d						11 02		11 28	11 32							12 02		12 28			12 32				
Beeston	d						11 08										12 08									
East Midlands Parkway	d							11 32	11 39	11 43								12 32	12 39			12 43				
Loughborough	d						11 20	11 40		11 54							12 20	12 40				12 54				
Barrow Upon Soar	d									11 58												12 58				
Sileby	d									12 02												13 02				
Syston	d									12 07												13 07				
Leicester	a					11 23	11 31	11 51	11 55	12 21						12 23	12 31	12 51	12 55			13 21				13 23
	d					11 25	11 33	11 53	11 57							12 25	12 33	12 53	12 57							13 25
Market Harborough	d						11 47		12 12								12 47		13 12							
Corby	d			11 15									12 15												13 15	
Kettering	a			11 24			11 56						12 24				12 56								13 24	
	d			11 26			11 56						12 26				12 56								13 26	
Wellingborough	d			11 34			12 04						12 34				13 04								13 34	
Bedford 7	d			11 49			12 19						12 49				13 19								13 49	
Luton 10	d			12 05			*13 01*						13 05				*14 01*								14 05	
Luton Airport Parkway 7	d			*12 20*			12 35						*13 20*				13 35								*14 20*	
Gatwick Airport 10 ✈	a																									
St Pancras International ⊖	a			12 29		12 34	13 01	13 06	13 12				13 29			13 34	14 01	14 06	14 12						14 29	14 34

		EM 1 ◇ ☕	EM 1 ◇ ☕	EM 1 ◇ ☕	EM ◇	XC 1 ◇ D 🛒		EM	NT ◇	XC 1 ◇ B 🛒	EM 1 ◇ ☕	EM 1 ◇ ☕	EM 1 ◇ ☕	EM 1 ◇ ☕	EM 1 ◇ ☕	EM ◇	XC 1 ◇ C 🛒	EM 1 ◇ ☕	EM	NT ◇	XC 1 ◇ B 🛒	EM 1 ◇ ☕	EM 1 ◇ ☕	EM 1 ◇ ☕	EM 1 ◇ ☕	EM ◇
York 8	d					11 44			*11b44*	12 25		*12 25*					12 44			*12b44*	13 27	*13 27*				
Leeds 10	d					12 11			12 05								13 11			13 05						
Wakefield Westgate 7	d					12 23											13 23									
Wakefield Kirkgate 4	d								12 23											13 23						
Doncaster 7	d					*12 02*				12 52							*13 01*				13 54					
Sheffield 7	d				12 38	12 54			13 05	13 23		13 27				13 38	13 54			14 05	14 23	14 27				14 38
Chesterfield	d				12 53	13 06			13 22			13 39				13 53	14 06			14 22		14 39				14 53
Derby 10	a					13 26				13 51		13 59					14 27				14 51	14 59				
	d		13 18									14 01		14 18								15 01		15 18		
Long Eaton	d		13 28											14 28										15 28		
Alfreton	d				13 03				13 33							14 03				14 33						15 03
Langley Mill	d								13 40											14 40						
Lincoln	d							12 30											13 40							
Nottingham 8	a				13 29			13 30	14 00							14 29			14 30	15 00						15 29
	d	13 02		13 28				13 32					14 02		14 28				14 32				15 02		15 28	
Beeston	d	13 08											14 08										15 08			
East Midlands Parkway	d		13 32	13 39				13 43						14 32	14 39				14 43					15 32	15 39	
Loughborough	d	13 20	13 40					13 54					14 20	14 40					14 54				15 20	15 40		
Barrow Upon Soar	d							13 58											14 58							
Sileby	d							14 02											15 02							
Syston	d							14 07											15 07							
Leicester	a	13 31	13 51	13 55				14 21				14 23	14 31	14 51	14 55				15 21			15 23	15 31	15 51	15 55	
	d	13 33	13 53	13 57								14 25	14 33	14 53	14 57							15 25	15 33	15 53	15 57	
Market Harborough	d	13 47		14 12									14 47		15 12								15 47		16 12	
Corby	d										14 05							14 43								
Kettering	a	13 56									14 14		14 56					14 52					15 56			
	d	13 56									14 26		14 56					15 26					15 56			
Wellingborough	d	14 04									14 34		15 04					15 34					16 04			
Bedford 7	d	14 19									14 49		15 19					15 49					16 19			
Luton 10	d	*15 01*									15 05		*16 01*					16 05					*17 01*			
Luton Airport Parkway 7	d	14 35									*15 20*		15 35					*16 20*					16 35			
Gatwick Airport 10 ✈	a																									
St Pancras International ⊖	a	15 01	15 06	15 12							15 29	15 34	16 01	16 06	16 12			16 29				16 34	17 01	17 06	17 12	

For general notes see front of timetable
For details of catering facilities see Directory of Train Operators

- **A** From Edinburgh (Table 26)
- **B** From Newcastle (Table 26)
- **C** From Glasgow Central (Table 26)
- **D** From Dundee (Table 51)
- **b** Change at Sheffield

From Saturday 3 October a revised service will be in operation due to seasonal difficulties. Some trains will be retimed between 1 and 3 minutes. Passengers should check with National Rail Enquiries for precise times.

Table 53

Saturdays

Sheffield → East Midlands → London

Route Diagram - See first page of Table 53

		XC	EM	EM	NT	XC	EM	EM		EM	EM	EM	EM	XC	EM	NT	XC	EM	EM	EM	EM	EM	XC	EM	EM	NT
		1◇	1◇		◇	1◇	1◇	1◇		1◇	1◇		◇	1◇	1◇	◇	1◇	1◇	1◇	1◇	1◇	◇	1◇	1◇		◇
		A				B							C	D			B						D			
		🛒	☕			🛒	☕	☕		☕	☕			🛒	☕		🛒	☕	☕	☕	☕	🛒	🛒	☕		
York 8	d	13 44			13b44	14 27	*14 27*							14 44		14b44	15 26	*15 26*					15 44			15b44
Leeds 10	d	14 11			14 05									15 11		15 05							16 11			16 05
Wakefield Westgate 7	d	14 23												15 23									16 23			
Wakefield Kirkgate 4	d				14 23											15 23										16 23
Doncaster 7	d	*14 01*				14 56								*15 02*			15 55						*16 00*			
Sheffield 7	d	14 54			15 05	15 23	15 27						15 38	15 54		16 05	16 23	16 27				16 38	16 54			17 05
Chesterfield	d	15 06			15 22		15 39						15 53	16 06		16 22		16 39				16 53	17 06			17 22
Derby 10	a	15 26				15 51	15 59							16 26			16 51	16 59					17 26			
	d						16 01			16 18								17 01		17 18						
Long Eaton	d									16 28										17 28						
Alfreton	d				15 33								16 03			16 33						17 04				17 33
Langley Mill	d				15 40											16 40										17 40
Lincoln	d			14 35								15 30													16 35	
Nottingham 8	a			15 30	16 00							16 30	16 33			17 00						17 29			17 30	18 00
	d			15 32				16 02			16 28	16 32							17 02		17 28				17 32	
Beeston	d							16 08											17 08							
East Midlands Parkway	d			15 43						16 32	16 39	16 46								17 32	17 39				17 46	
Loughborough	d			15 54				16 20		16 40		16 56							17 20	17 40					17 56	
Barrow Upon Soar	d			15 58								17 01													18 01	
Sileby	d			16 02								17 05													18 05	
Syston	d			16 07								17 10													18 10	
Leicester	a			16 21			16 23	16 31		16 51	16 55	17 23						17 23	17 31	17 51	17 55				18 23	
	d						16 25	16 33		16 53	16 57							17 25	17 33	17 53	17 57					
Market Harborough	d							16 47			17 12								17 47		18 12					
Corby	d		15 43												16 43									17 43		
Kettering	a		15 52					16 56							16 52				17 56					17 52		
	d		16 26					16 56							17 26				17 56					18 26		
Wellingborough	d		16 34					17 04							17 34				18 04					18 34		
Bedford 7	d		16 49					17 19							17 49				18 19					18 51		
Luton 10	d		17 05					*18 01*							18 05									19 07		
Luton Airport Parkway 7	d		*17 20*					17 35							*18 20*				18 35					*19 24*		
Gatwick Airport 10	a																									
St Pancras International	a		17 29				17 34	18 01		18 06	18 12				18 29			18 34	18 59	19 09	19 12			19 34		

		XC	EM	EM	EM	EM	EM	EM	XC	EM		NT	XC	EM	EM	EM	EM	XC	EM	EM	EM	NT	XC	EM	EM	EM
		1◇	1◇	1◇	1◇	1◇		◇	1◇	1◇		◇	1◇	1◇	1◇	◇	1◇	1◇	1◇	1◇		◇	1◇	1◇	1◇	◇
		B							D				B			C	E	D					B			
		🛒	☕	☕	☕	☕			🛒	☕			🛒	☕	☕		☕	🛒	☕	☕			🛒	☕	☕	
York 8	d	16 25	*16 25*						16 44			16b44	17 25	*17 25*			17 49	17 44				17b49	18 25	*18 25*		
Leeds 10	d							*16 37*	17 11			17 05					*17 40*	18 11				18 05				
Wakefield Westgate 7	d							16c55	17 23								17e55	18 23								
Wakefield Kirkgate 4	d											17 23										18 23				
Doncaster 7	d	16 53							*17 01*				17 55				18 18						18 51			
Sheffield 7	d	17 23	17 27					17 44	17 54			18 05	18 23	18 27		18 38	18 47	18 54				19 05	19 23	19 27		19 38
Chesterfield	d		17 39					17 58	18 06			18 22		18 39		18 53		19 06				19 22		19 39		19 53
Derby 10	a	17 51	17 59						18 26				18 51	18 59			19 19	19 26					19 51	19 59		
	d		18 01		18 18									19 01			19 21							20 01		
Long Eaton	d				18 28												19 31									
Alfreton	d							18 08				18 33				19 03						19 33				20 04
Langley Mill	d											18 40										19 40				
Lincoln	d						17 28														18 35					
Nottingham 8	a						18 31	18 33				19 00				19 33					19 29	20 00				20 31
	d			18 02		18 28	18 32								19 02				19 28		19 32				20 02	
Beeston	d			18 08											19 08						19 38				20 08	
East Midlands Parkway	d				18 32	18 39	18 43										19 35		19 41		19 46				20 16	
Loughborough	d			18 20	18 40		18 54								19 20		19 41				19 56				20 24	
Barrow Upon Soar	d						18 58														20 01					
Sileby	d						19 02														20 05					
Syston	d						19 07														20 10					
Leicester	a		18 23	18 31	18 51	18 55	19 21							19 23	19 31		19 54		19 58		20 23			20 23	20 34	
	d		18 25	18 33	18 53	18 57								19 25	19 33		19 55		20 00					20 25	20 36	
Market Harborough	d			18 47		19 12									19 47				20 15						20 50	
Corby	d									18 43										19 43						
Kettering	a			18 56						18 52					19 56					19 52					20 59	
	d			18 56						19 26					19 56					20 26					20 59	
Wellingborough	d			19 04						19 34					20 04					20 34					21 07	
Bedford 7	d			19 21						19 53					20 21					20 53					21 21	
Luton 10	d									20 08										21 08						
Luton Airport Parkway 7	d			19 34						*20 24*					20 34					*21 22*					21 37	
Gatwick Airport 10	a																									
St Pancras International	a		19 38	20 06	20 09	20 12				20 34				20 37	21 06		21 08		21 15	21 34				21 41	22 06	

For general notes see front of timetable
For details of catering facilities see Directory of Train Operators

- **A** From Aberdeen (Table 51)
- **B** From Newcastle (Table 26)
- **C** From Liverpool Lime Street (Table 89)
- **D** From Edinburgh (Table 26)
- **E** Until 5 September from Scarborough (Table 39)
- **b** Change at Sheffield
- **c** Wakefield Kirkgate
- **e** Wakefield Kirkgate. Change at Sheffield

From Saturday 3 October a revised service will be in operation due to seasonal difficulties. Some trains will be retimed between 1 and 3 minutes. Passengers should check with National Rail Enquiries for precise times.

Sheffield → East Midlands → London

Saturdays

Route Diagram - See first page of Table 53

		XC 1◇ A	EM 1◇	EM	EM 1◇	NT ◇	XC 1◇ B	EM 1◇	EM 1◇	EM 1◇	EM C	EM D	EM ◇ E	XC 1◇ G	XC 1◇ B	EM ◇	XC 1◇ G	EM 1◇	EM C	EM D	EM ◇ H	EM ◇ J	EM 1◇ C	EM 1◇ D
York 8	d	18 44				18b44	19 25	19 25						19 44	20 23		20 44				20 44	20 44	21c52	21c52
Leeds 10	d	19 11				19 05								20 11		20 30	21 11						21 48	21 48
Wakefield Westgate 7	d	19 23												20 23		20e46	21 23						22e07	22e07
Wakefield Kirkgate 4	d					19 23																		
Doncaster 7	d	19 03					19 53							20 03		20 42	21 07				21 48	21 48	22 24	22 24
Sheffield 7	d	19 54				20 05	20 23	20 27					20 41	20 54	21 23	21 38	21 54				22 35	22 35	23 20	23 38
Chesterfield	d	20 06				20 22		20 39					20 59	21 06	21 35	21 54	22 06				22 51	22 51	23 33	23 51
Derby 10	a	20 26					20 51	21 00						21 26	21 54		22 25						23 53	00 11
	d							21 01																
Long Eaton	d																							
Alfreton	d					20 33							21 09			22 05								
Langley Mill	d					20 40										22 12								
Lincoln	d																							
Nottingham 8	a					21 01							21 33			22 33					23 29	23 33		
	d			20 32	20 43					21 18	21 32	21 32							23 10	23 10				
Beeston	d			20 38	20 49																			
East Midlands Parkway	d			20 46	20 55			21 14			21 43	21 43							23 21	23 21				
Loughborough	d			20 56	21 03			21 23		21 32	21 54	21a53							23 29	23 32				
Barrow Upon Soar	d			21 01							21 58													
Sileby	d			21 05							22 02													
Syston	d			21 10							22 07													
Leicester	a			21 23	21 13			21 39		21 43	22 20								23 54	23 54				
	d				21 15					21 45														
Market Harborough	d				21 29					21 59														
Corby	d		20 43						21 43									22 43						
Kettering	a		20 52		21 38				21 52	22 14								22 52						
	d		21 24		21 38					22 15														
Wellingborough	d		21 32		21 47					22 22														
Bedford 7	d		21 45		22 01					22 37														
Luton 10	d		22 07		22 18					23 00														
Luton Airport Parkway 7	d				22 21					23 36														
Gatwick Airport 10	a																							
St Pancras International	a		22 40		22 59					23 35														

Sundays

until 12 July

		EM 1◇	EM 1◇	EM 1◇	EM 1◇	EM 1◇	EM 1◇	EM 1◇	XC 1◇	NT ◇	EM 1◇	EM 1◇	EM 1◇	XC 1◇	NT ◇	EM 1◇	EM 1◇	EM 1◇	EM ◇	XC 1◇	NT ◇	EM 1◇	EM 1◇	EM 1◇	XC 1◇ B
York 8	d								07 12	07f12		07f12		09g00	08 10		09c00			09 28	09b28				10 28
Leeds 10	d								08 09					09 00	08 55		09 00	09 44		10 00	09 54		10 20		11 00
Wakefield Westgate 7	d								08 22					09 12			09e14	09 58		10 12	10b12		10 32		11 12
Wakefield Kirkgate 4	d														09 14						10 11				
Doncaster 7	d								08 03					09 32			09 39			10 30					11 30
Sheffield 7	d								08 55	09 00		09 17		09 57	10 07		10 17	10 28	10 49	10 57	11 03		11 06		11 57
Chesterfield	d								09 07	09 17		09 29		10 09	10 24		10 29	10 41	11 04	11 09	11 20		11 25		12 09
Derby 10	a								09 28			09 49		10 32			10 50			11 28			11 47		12 28
	d	06 50		07 52			08 47					09 51					10 52						11 48		
Long Eaton	d						08 58					10 01					11 02								
Alfreton	d									09 28					10 35				11 14		11 31				
Langley Mill	d									09 35					10 42						11 38				
Lincoln	d																								
Nottingham 8	a									09 55					11 02			11 12	11 38		11 58				
	d		07 28		08 19			09 15					10 15					11 19						12 15	
Beeston	d				08 25								10 22											12 22	
East Midlands Parkway	d	07 02	07 38	08 03	08 32		09 02	09 26				10 05	10 30				11 06	11 30					12 01	12 30	
Loughborough	d			08 11	08 39		09 10	09 34				10 13	10 38				11 14	11 38					12 09	12 38	
Barrow Upon Soar	d																								
Sileby	d																								
Syston	d																								
Leicester	a	07 18	07 52	08 22	08 50		09 21	09 47				10 23	10 51				11 24	11 51					12 21	12 52	
	d	07 20	07 54	08 23	08 52		09 22	09 49				10 25	10 53				11 26	11 53					12 23	12 53	
Market Harborough	d	07 38	08 11	08 40	09 09		09 39	10 07				10 39	11 08				11 40	12 08					12 38	13 08	
Corby	d					09 30					10 25					11 25						12 30			
Kettering	a	07 48	08 20	08 49	09 18	09 39	09 48	10 17			10 34	10 48	11 18			11 34	11 49	12 18				12 39	12 48	13 18	
	d	07 49	08 21	08 50	09 19		09 49	10 18				10 49	11 19				11 50	12 19					12 49	13 19	
Wellingborough	d	08 01	08 32	09 02	09 30		10 02	10 26				10 57	11 27				11 58	12 27					12 57	13 27	
Bedford 7	d	08 15	08 45	09 14	09 45		10 14	10 45				11 14	11 45				12 15	12 46					13 15	13 46	
Luton 10	d	08 34	09 31	09 39	10 31		10 39	11 31				11 39	12 31				12 40	13 31					13 39	14 31	
Luton Airport Parkway 7	d	08 46	09 07	09 50	10 10		10 50	11 10				11 50	12 09				13 04	13 10					13 50	14 10	
Gatwick Airport 10	a																								
St Pancras International	a	09 19	09 49	10 19	10 49		11 19	11 49				12 19	12 50				13 19	13 51					14 19	14 44	

For general notes see front of timetable
For details of catering facilities see Directory of Train Operators

A From Edinburgh (Table 26) to Bristol Temple Meads (Table 57)
B From Newcastle (Table 26)
C Until 11 July and from 12 September
D 18 July to 5 September
E From Liverpool Lime Street (Table 89)
G From Edinburgh (Table 26) to Birmingham New Street (Table 57)
H From 12 September. From Liverpool Lime Street (Table 89)
J Until 5 September. From Liverpool Lime Street (Table 89)
b Change at Sheffield
c Change at Doncaster and Sheffield
e Wakefield Kirkgate
f Change at Leeds and Sheffield
g Change at Doncaster

From Saturday 3 October a revised service will be in operation due to seasonal difficulties. Some trains will be retimed between 1 and 3 minutes. Passengers should check with National Rail Enquiries for precise times.

Sundays

until 12 July

Sheffield → East Midlands → London

Route Diagram - See first page of Table 53

		NT	EM	EM	EM	NT	EM	XC	EM	EM		NT	EM	EM	XC	EM	XC	XC	EM	EM	EM	EM	EM	EM	NT	XC
		◇	1 ◇	1 ◇	1 ◇	◇	◇	1 ◇	1 ◇	1 ◇		◇	1 ◇	◇	1 ◇	1 ◇	1 ◇	1 ◇	1 ◇	1 ◇	1 ◇	◇	1 ◇	1 ◇	◇	1 ◇
								A							A			A								B
York 8	d	10b28		10 28		10 45	10c45	11 28		11e29		11 45		11c45	12 28	12e57		13 28				13 28		13e37		14 19
Leeds 10	d	10 51		11 00		11 29		12 00		12 00		12 29			13 00	13 00		14 00						14 05	13 48	
Wakefield Westgate 7	d			11f13				12 12		12 12					13 12	13 12		14 12						14 18	14b18	
Wakefield Kirkgate 4	d	11 13				11 46						12 46													14 11	
Doncaster 7	d			11 42				12 30		12 42					13 30		13 42							14 13		14 50
Sheffield 7	d	12 00		12 24		12 31	12 49	12 57		13 20		13 31		13 49	13 57	14 07	14 20	14 50				14 53		15 02	15 07	15 20
Chesterfield	d	12 18		12 37		12 49	13 03	13 09		13 33		13 48		14 03	14 09	14 20	14 32	15 02				15 07		15 15	15 25	
Derby 10	a			12 57				13 30		13 52					14 28	14 42	14 51	15 22								15 49
	d			13 02						13 54						14 48										
Long Eaton	d			13 12						14 05						15 03										
Alfreton	d	12 29				12 59	13 14					13 59		14 14								15 18			15 36	
Langley Mill	d	12 36				13 07						14 06										15 25			15 43	
Lincoln	d																									
Nottingham 8	a	12 56				13 26	13 39					14 26		14 40								15 44			16 03	
	d				13 14								14 30							15 10	15 36					
Beeston	d				13 21								14 36							15 16						
East Midlands Parkway	d			13 16	13 30					14 09			14 43			15 08				15 23	15 46			15 52		
Loughborough	d			13 24	13 38					14 17			14 51			15 15				15 30				16 01		
Barrow Upon Soar	d																									
Sileby	d																									
Syston	d																									
Leicester	a			13 34	13 51					14 27			15 02			15 26				15 42	16 02			16 13		
	d			13 36	13 53					14 29			15 04			15 27				15 44	16 03			16 15		
Market Harborough	d			13 50	14 08					14 43			15 18							16 01				16 30		
Corby	d		13 30						14 25										15 25				16 25			
Kettering	a		13 39	13 59	14 18				14 34	14 52			15 27						15 34	16 10			16 34	16 40		
	d			14 00	14 19					14 53			15 28							16 11				16 41		
Wellingborough	d			14 07	14 29					15 00			15 35							16 18				16 49		
Bedford 7	d			14 25	14 52					15 25			15 55							16 35				17 07		
Luton 10	d			14 49	15 31					15 42			16 31			16 25				17 13				17 25		
Luton Airport Parkway 7	d			15 06	15 11					16 04			16 14			16 46				16 53				17 46		
Gatwick Airport 10	a																									
St Pancras International	a			15 22	15 45					16 15			16 45			16 55				17 27	17 31			17 59		

		EM	EM	EM	XC	EM	NT	EM	EM	EM	EM	EM	XC	XC	EM	NT	EM	EM	XC	EM	EM	EM	XC	EM	EM	NT
		1 ◇	1 ◇	◇	1 ◇	1 ◇	◇	1 ◇	1 ◇	1 ◇	1 ◇	◇	1 ◇	1 ◇	1 ◇	◇	1 ◇	1 ◇	1 ◇	1 ◇	1 ◇	◇	1 ◇	1 ◇	1 ◇	◇
					A								B	C					A				D			
York 8	d	14 19			14 28		14e36			14e36			15 20	15 28		15e34			16 20	16 20			16 28			16e29
Leeds 10	d				15 00		15 05			15 09				16 00		16 05			16b05				17 00			16 54
Wakefield Westgate 7	d				15 12					15 24				16 12					16g22				17 12			17b12
Wakefield Kirkgate 4	d						15 22									16 22										17 11
Doncaster 7	d						15 13			15 42			15 50			16 13			16 50							17 13
Sheffield 7	d	15 32		15 43	15 50		16 07			16 29		16 40	16 20	16 50		17 07			17 20	17 29		17 39	17 50			18 07
Chesterfield	d	15 44		15 57	16 02		16 25			16 43		16 56		17 02		17 24				17 43		17 54	18 02			18 25
Derby 10	a	16 09			16 22					17 04			16 49	17 22					17 49	18 04			18 22			
	d	16 14							16 47	17 09								17 47		18 07						
Long Eaton	d								16 57									17 57								
Alfreton	d			16 08			16 36					17 07				17 35						18 04				18 36
Langley Mill	d			16 15			16 43					17 14				17 43						18 12				18 43
Lincoln	d																									
Nottingham 8	a			16 33			17 03					17 32				18 03						18 29				19 03
	d		16 18			16 45					17 20				17 34						18 10				18 44	
Beeston	d		16 24								17 26										18 19					
East Midlands Parkway	d	16 25	16 31			16 55			17 01	17 21	17 32				17 49			18 01		18 20	18 25				18 54	
Loughborough	d		16 39						17 09		17 40							18 09			18 33				19 02	
Barrow Upon Soar	d																									
Sileby	d																									
Syston	d																									
Leicester	a	16 40	16 50			17 12			17 20	17 38	17 50				18 06			18 19		18 39	18 43				19 13	
	d	16 41	16 52			17 13			17 22	17 40	17 52				18 08			18 21		18 40	18 45				19 15	
Market Harborough	d		17 06						17 36		18 06							18 35			19 05				19 31	
Corby	d							17 20									18 20							19 20		
Kettering	a		17 15					17 29	17 45		18 15						18 29	18 44			19 14			19 29	19 40	
	d		17 16						17 46		18 16							18 45			19 15				19 41	
Wellingborough	d		17 23						17 53		18 23							18 52			19 22				19 48	
Bedford 7	d		17 40						18 12		18 40							19 10			19 40				20 07	
Luton 10	d		18 13						18 29		19 13							19 29			20 13				20 26	
Luton Airport Parkway 7	d		17 59						18 46		18 59							19 46			19 59					
Gatwick Airport 10	a																									
St Pancras International	a	18 04	18 29			18 34			18 59	19 04	19 29				19 34			19 59		20 04	20 29				20 57	

For general notes see front of timetable
For details of catering facilities see Directory of Train Operators

A From Edinburgh (Table 26)
B From Newcastle (Table 26)
C From Glasgow Central (Table 26)
D From Aberdeen (Table 51)
b Change at Sheffield
c Change at Leeds and Sheffield
e Change at Doncaster and Sheffield
f Wakefield Kirkgate
g Wakefield Kirkgate. Change at Sheffield

Sheffield → East Midlands → London

Sundays until 12 July

Route Diagram - See first page of Table 53

		XC 1◇ A	EM 1◇	EM ◇ B	XC 1◇ C	EM 1◇	EM 1◇	NT ◇	XC 1◇ A	EM 1◇	EM ◇ B	XC 1◇ D	EM 1◇	EM 1◇	NT ◇	XC 1◇ A	EM 1◇	EM ◇ B	XC 1◇ D	XC 1◇ A	EM ◇ B	XC 1◇ E	EM 1◇	EM ◇ B
York 8	d	17 20	17 40	*17 40*	17 28				18 20	*18 20*		18 28		*18b29*		19 20		*19 20*	19 28	20 20	*20b02*	20 28	*20 42*	*21b28*
Leeds 10	d	*17 05*	*17c09*		18 00			18 05	*18c05*			19 00			19 04	*19c04*		*19 09*	20 00			21 00		*21 40*
Wakefield Westgate 7	d	*17 18*	*17c24*		18 12				*18e22*			19 12				*19e20*		*19 24*	20 12			21 12		*21 55*
Wakefield Kirkgate 4	d							18 22							19 20									
Doncaster 7	d	17 50	18 06					*18 13*	18 50					*19 15*		19 50				20 50	*20 42*	*20 42*	*21 23*	22 20
Sheffield 7	d	18 20	18 32	18 41	18 50			19 07	19 20	19 31	19 40	19 50		20 03	20 06	20 20		20 40	20 50	21 20	21 40	21 50	22 13	23 29
Chesterfield	d		18 44	18 56	19 02			19 25		19 44	19 55	20 02		20 17	20 22			20 55	21 02	21 32	21 54	22 02	22 27	23 43
Derby 10	a	18 49	19 08		19 22				19 49	20 04		20 22		20 48		20 58			21 22	21 51		22 22	23 04	
	d		19 09							20 06				20 53										
Long Eaton	d		19 21							20 16														
Alfreton	d			19 06				19 36			20 06				20 33			21 06			22 05			23 54
Langley Mill	d			19 14				19 43			20 14				20 40			21 14			22 12			00 01
Lincoln	d																							
Nottingham 8	a			19 36				20 03			20 31				21 01			21 36			22 35			00 23
	d						19 46										21 13							
Beeston	d						19 52																	
East Midlands Parkway	d		19 26				19 58			20 21				21 05			21 23							
Loughborough	d		19 33				20 06			20 30							21 31							
Barrow Upon Soar	d																							
Sileby	d																							
Syston	d																							
Leicester	a		19 44				20 16			20 42				21 22			21 41							
	d		19 45				20 18			20 44				21 24			21 43							
Market Harborough	d		20 03				20 32			20 59				21 39			21 57							
Corby	d					20 20							21 25											
Kettering	a		20 12			20 29	20 41			21 09			21 34	21 49			22 06							
	d		20 13				20 42			21 10				21 50			22 07							
Wellingborough	d		20 21				20 49			21 18				21 58			22 14							
Bedford 7	d		20 40				21 08			21 37				22 18			22 32							
Luton 10	d						21 23			21 52				22 37			22 50							
Luton Airport Parkway 7	d		20 55				*21 36*			*22 06*							*23 06*							
Gatwick Airport 10	a																							
St Pancras International	a		21 27				21 57			22 27				23 12			23 28							

Sundays 19 July to 6 September

		EM 1◇	EM 1◇		EM 1◇	EM 1◇	EM 1◇	XC 1◇	EM 1◇	EM 1◇	NT ◇	XC 1◇	EM 1◇	EM 1◇	EM 1◇	EM 1◇	EM 1◇	NT ◇	EM 1◇	EM 1◇	EM ◇	XC 1◇ G	NT ◇	EM 1◇	XC 1◇ H	NT ◇
York 8	d							*07 12*			*07f12*						*08 10*	*08 10*		*09 15*	*09f15*	09 28			10 28	*10c28*
Leeds 10	d							08 09				08 30					09 15	09 05		09 54		10 00	10 02		11 00	10 57
Wakefield Westgate 7	d							08 22				08 43					09 27	*09c23*		10 06		10 12			11 12	
Wakefield Kirkgate 4	d																	09 21					10 18			11 13
Doncaster 7	d							*08 03*				09 02					*09 13*			*09 39*		10 31			11 30	
Sheffield 7	d							08 54			09 00	09 28				10 00	10 05	10 07		10 45	10 49	10 57	11 03		11 57	12 00
Chesterfield	d	06 19						09 08			09 17	09 41				10 12	10 18	10 24		10 59	11 04	11 09	11 20		12 09	12 18
Derby 10	a							09 29				10 02								11 20		11 28			12 28	
	d				06 56		07 51													11 26						
Long Eaton	d																									
Alfreton	d										09 28							10 35			11 14		11 31			12 29
Langley Mill	d										09 35							10 42					11 38			12 36
Lincoln	d																									
Nottingham 8	a										09 57						10 49	11 02			11 41		11 58			12 56
	d		07 13			08 07				09 02				10 01			11 08							12 01		
Beeston	d					08 13								10 08										12 08		
East Midlands Parkway	d	06 52	07 25		07 52	08 21	08 47			09 16				10 20		10 54	11 20			11 45				12 17		
Loughborough	d																									
Barrow Upon Soar	d																									
Sileby	d																									
Syston	d																									
Leicester	a	07 18	07 52		08 20	08 48	09 15			09 44				10 48		11 21	11 48			12 21				12 52		
	d	07 20	07 54		08 23	08 52	09 18			09 49				10 53		11 25	11 53			12 23				12 53		
Market Harborough	d	07 38	08 11		08 40	09 09	09 35			10 07				11 08		11 39	12 08			12 38				13 08		
Corby	d								09 30				10 25		11 25				12 30							
Kettering	a	07 48	08 20		08 49	09 18	09 44		09 39	10 17			10 34	11 18	11 34	11 48	12 18		12 39	12 48				13 18		
	d	07 49	08 21		08 50	09 19	09 45			10 18				11 19		11 49	12 19			12 49				13 19		
Wellingborough	d	08 01	08 32		09 02	09 30	09 57			10 26				11 27		11 57	12 27			12 57				13 27		
Bedford 7	d	08 15	08 45		09 14	09 45	10 14			10 45				11 45		12 14	12 46			13 15				13 46		
Luton 10	d	08 34	*09 31*		09 39	*10 31*	10 39			*11 31*				*12 31*		12 40	*13 31*			13 39				*14 31*		
Luton Airport Parkway 7	d	*08 46*	09 07			10 10				11 10				12 09			13 10			*13 50*				14 10		
Gatwick Airport 10	a																									
St Pancras International	a	09 19	09 49		10 19	10 49	11 19			11 49				12 50		13 19	13 51			14 19				14 44		

For general notes see front of timetable
For details of catering facilities see Directory of Train Operators

- **A** From Newcastle (Table 26)
- **B** From Liverpool Lime Street (Table 89)
- **C** From Glasgow Central (Table 26)
- **D** From Edinburgh (Table 26) to Bristol Temple Meads (Table 57)
- **E** From Edinburgh (Table 26) to Birmingham New Street (Table 57)
- **G** To Birmingham New Street (Table 57)
- **H** From Newcastle (Table 26) to Birmingham New Street (Table 57)
- **b** Change at Doncaster and Sheffield
- **c** Change at Sheffield
- **e** Wakefield Kirkgate. Change at Sheffield
- **f** Change at Leeds and Sheffield

Sheffield → East Midlands → London

Route Diagram - See first page of Table 53

		EM	EM	EM	NT	EM	XC	EM	EM	NT	EM	EM	XC	EM	XC	XC	EM	EM	EM	EM	EM	EM	NT	XC	EM	EM
		1 ◇	1 ◇	1 ◇	◇	◇	1 ◇	1 ◇	1 ◇	◇	1 ◇	◇	1 ◇	1 ◇	1 ◇	1 ◇	1 ◇	1 ◇	1 ◇	◇	1 ◇	1 ◇	◇	1 ◇	1 ◇	1 ◇
							A						A			A								B		
		☕	☕	☕			🛒	☕	☕		☕		🛒	☕	🛒	🛒	☕	☕	☕		☕	☕		🛒	☕	☕
York [8]	d		*10 28*		*10 45*	*10b45*	11 28		*11c29*	*11 45*		*11b45*	12 28	*12c57*		13 28				*13 28*		*13c37*		14 19	*14 19*	
Leeds [10]	d		*11 00*		11 29		12 00		*12 00*	12 29			13 00	*13 00*		14 00						14 05	14 05			
Wakefield Westgate [7]	d		*11e13*				12 12		*12 12*				13 12	*13 12*		14 12						14 18		*14f21*		
Wakefield Kirkgate [4]	d				11 46					12 46													14 21			
Doncaster [7]	d				*11 42*		12 30		*12 42*				13 30		*13 42*							*14 13*		14 50		
Sheffield [7]	d		12 07		12 31	12 49	12 57		13 20	13 31		13 49	13 57	14 07	14 20	14 50				14 53		15 02	15 07	15 20	15 32	
Chesterfield	d		12 23		12 49	13 03	13 09		13 33	13 48		14 03	14 09	14 20	14 32	15 02				15 07		15 15	15 25		15 44	
Derby [10]	a		12 47				13 31		13 53				14 28	14 42	14 51	15 22								15 49	16 09	
	d		12 49						13 55					14 48											16 14	
Long Eaton	d		12 59						14 05					15 03												
Alfreton	d				12 59	13 14				13 59		14 14								15 18			15 36			
Langley Mill	d				13 07					14 06										15 25			15 43			
Lincoln	d																									
Nottingham [8]	a				13 26	13 39				14 26		14 40								15 44			16 05			
	d			13 03							14 30							15 10	15 36							16 18
Beeston	d			13 10							14 36							15 16								16 24
East Midlands Parkway	d		13 05	13 20					14 09		14 43			15 08				15 23	15 46			15 52			16 25	16 31
Loughborough	d								14 17		14 51			15 15				15 30				16 01				16 39
Barrow Upon Soar	d																									
Sileby	d																									
Syston	d																									
Leicester	a		13 32	13 48					14 27		15 02			15 26				15 42	16 02			16 13			16 40	16 50
	d		13 36	13 53					14 29		15 04			15 27				15 44	16 03			16 15			16 41	16 52
Market Harborough	d		13 50	14 08					14 43		15 18							16 01				16 30				17 06
Corby	d	13 30						14 25									15 25				16 25					
Kettering	a	13 39	13 59	14 18				14 34	14 52		15 27						15 34	16 10			16 34	16 40				17 15
	d		14 00	14 19					14 53		15 28							16 11				16 41				17 16
Wellingborough	d		14 07	14 29					15 00		15 35							16 18				16 49				17 23
Bedford [7]	d		14 25	14 52					15 25		15 55							16 35				17 07				17 40
Luton [10]	d		14 49	*15 31*					15 42		*16 31*			16 25				*17 13*				17 25				*18 13*
Luton Airport Parkway [7]	d		*15 06*	15 11					*16 04*		16 14			*16 46*				16 53				*17 46*				17 59
Gatwick Airport [10] ✈	a																									
St Pancras International ⊖	a		15 22	15 45					16 15		16 45			16 55				17 27	17 31			17 59			18 04	18 29

		EM	XC	EM	NT	EM	EM	EM	XC	EM	EM	XC	EM	XC	NT	EM	EM	XC	EM	EM	EM	XC	EM	EM	NT	XC
		◇	1 ◇	1 ◇	◇	1 ◇	1 ◇	1 ◇	1 ◇	1 ◇	◇	1 ◇	1 ◇	1 ◇	◇	1 ◇	1 ◇	1 ◇	1 ◇	1 ◇	◇	1 ◇	1 ◇	1 ◇	◇	1 ◇
			A						B			C						A				D				B
			🛒	☕		☕	☕	☕	🛒	☕		🛒	☕	🛒		☕	☕	🛒	☕	☕		🛒	☕	☕		🛒
York [8]	d		14 28		*14c36*			*14c36*	15 20			15 28			*15c34*			16 20	*16 20*			16 28			*16c29*	17 20
Leeds [10]	d		15 00		15 05			*15 09*				16 00			16 05			*16g05*				17 00			17 05	*17 05*
Wakefield Westgate [7]	d		15 12					*15 24*				16 12						*16f22*				17 12				*17f21*
Wakefield Kirkgate [4]	d				15 22										16 22										17 21	
Doncaster [7]	d				*15 13*			*15 42*	15 50						*16 13*			16 50							*17 13*	17 50
Sheffield [7]	d	15 43	15 50		16 07			16 29	16 20		16 40	16 50			17 07			17 20	17 29		17 39	17 50			18 07	18 20
Chesterfield	d	15 57	16 03		16 25			16 43			16 56	17 02			17 24				17 43		17 54	18 02			18 25	
Derby [10]	a		16 22					17 04	16 49			17 22						17 49	18 04			18 22				18 49
	d						16 47	17 09									17 47		18 07							
Long Eaton	d						16 57										17 57									
Alfreton	d	16 08			16 36						17 07				17 35						18 04				18 36	
Langley Mill	d	16 15			16 43						17 14				17 43						18 12				18 43	
Lincoln	d																									
Nottingham [8]	a	16 33			17 03						17 32				18 03						18 29				19 03	
	d			16 41						17 20			17 34	17 47						18 10				18 44		
Beeston	d									17 26										18 19						
East Midlands Parkway	d			16 51			17 01	17 21		17 32			17 49				18 01		18 20	18 25				18 54		
Loughborough	d						17 09			17 40							18 09			18 33				19 02		
Barrow Upon Soar	d																									
Sileby	d																									
Syston	d																									
Leicester	a			17 12			17 20	17 38		17 50			18 06	18 12			18 19		18 37	18 43				19 13		
	d			17 13			17 22	17 40		17 52			18 08				18 21		18 38	18 45				19 15		
Market Harborough	d						17 36			18 06							18 35			19 05				19 31		
Corby	d					17 20										18 20							19 20			
Kettering	a					17 29	17 45			18 15						18 29	18 44			19 14			19 29	19 40		
	d						17 46			18 16							18 45			19 15				19 41		
Wellingborough	d						17 53			18 23							18 52			19 22				19 48		
Bedford [7]	d						18 12			18 40							19 10			19 40				20 07		
Luton [10]	d						18 29			*19 13*							19 29			*20 13*				20 26		
Luton Airport Parkway [7]	d						*18 46*			18 59							*19 46*			19 59						
Gatwick Airport [10] ✈	a																									
St Pancras International ⊖	a			18 34			18 59	19 04		19 29			19 34				19 59		20 04	20 29				20 57		

For general notes see front of timetable
For details of catering facilities see
Directory of Train Operators

- **A** From Edinburgh (Table 26)
- **B** From Newcastle (Table 26)
- **C** From Glasgow Central (Table 26)
- **D** From Aberdeen (Table 51)
- **b** Change at Leeds and Sheffield
- **c** Change at Doncaster and Sheffield
- **e** Wakefield Kirkgate
- **f** Wakefield Kirkgate. Change at Sheffield
- **g** Change at Sheffield

Sheffield → East Midlands → London

Sundays

19 July to 6 September

Route Diagram - See first page of Table 53

		EM	EM	XC	EM	EM	NT	XC	EM	EM	XC	EM	EM
		1◇	◇	1◇	1◇	1◇	◇	1◇	1◇	◇	1◇	1◇	1◇
			A	B				C		A	D		
York 8	d	17 40	17 40	17 28				18 20	18 20		18 28		18b29
Leeds 10	d	17c09		18 00			18 05	18c05			19 00		
Wakefield Westgate 7	d	17c24		18 12				18e22			19 12		
Wakefield Kirkgate 4	d						18 22						
Doncaster 7	d	18 06					18 13	18 50					19 15
Sheffield 7	d	18 32	18 41	18 50			19 07	19 20	19 31	19 40	19 50		20 03
Chesterfield	d	18 44	18 56	19 02			19 25		19 44	19 55	20 02		20 17
Derby 10	a	19 08		19 22				19 49	20 04		20 22		20 37
	d	19 09							20 06				20 48
Long Eaton	d	19 21							20 16				
Alfreton	d		19 06				19 36			20 06			
Langley Mill	d		19 14				19 43			20 14			
Lincoln	d												
Nottingham 8	a		19 36				20 03			20 31			
	d					19 46							
Beeston	d					19 52							
East Midlands Parkway	d	19 26				19 58			20 21				21 00
Loughborough	d	19 33				20 06			20 30				
Barrow Upon Soar	d												
Sileby	d												
Syston	d												
Leicester	a	19 44				20 16			20 42				21 19
	d	19 45				20 18			20 44				21 21
Market Harborough	d	20 03				20 32			20 59				21 36
Corby	d				20 20							21 25	
Kettering	a	20 12			20 29	20 41			21 09			21 34	21 51
	d	20 13				20 42			21 10				21 52
Wellingborough	d	20 21				20 49			21 18				22 00
Bedford 7	d	20 40				21 08			21 37				22 20
Luton 10	d					21 23			21 52				22 37
Luton Airport Parkway 7	d	20 55				21 36			22 06				
Gatwick Airport 10	a												
St Pancras International	a	21 27				21 57			22 27				23 12

		NT	XC	EM	EM	XC	XC	EM	XC	EM	EM	EM
		◇	1◇	1◇	◇	1◇	1◇	◇	1◇	1◇	1◇	◇
			C		A	D	C	A	E			A
York 8	d		19 20		19 20	19 28	20 20	20b02	20 28	20 42		21b28
Leeds 10	d	19 04	19c04		19 09	20 00			21 00			21 40
Wakefield Westgate 7	d		19e20		19 24	20 12			21 12			21 55
Wakefield Kirkgate 4	d	19 20										
Doncaster 7	d		19 50				20 50	20 42	20 42	21 23		22 20
Sheffield 7	d	20 06	20 20		20 40	20 50	21 32	21 40	21 50	22 13		23 29
Chesterfield	d	20 22			20 55	21 02	21 51	21 54	22 02	22 27	22 58	23 43
Derby 10	a		20 49			21 22	21 53		22 22	22 50	23 25	
	d											
Long Eaton	d											
Alfreton	d	20 33			21 06			22 05				23 54
Langley Mill	d	20 40			21 14			22 12				00 01
Lincoln	d											
Nottingham 8	a	21 01			21 36			22 35				00 23
	d			21 07								
Beeston	d											
East Midlands Parkway	d			21 17								
Loughborough	d			21 24								
Barrow Upon Soar	d											
Sileby	d											
Syston	d											
Leicester	a			21 44								
	d			21 46								
Market Harborough	d			22 00								
Corby	d											
Kettering	a			22 09								
	d			22 10								
Wellingborough	d			22 17								
Bedford 7	d			22 35								
Luton 10	d			22 51								
Luton Airport Parkway 7	d			23 06								
Gatwick Airport 10	a											
St Pancras International	a			23 28								

Sundays

from 13 September

		EM	EM	EM	EM	EM	EM	EM	EM		EM	EM	EM
							1◇				1◇		
		bus	bus	bus	bus	bus		bus	bus			bus	bus
York 8	d												
Leeds 10	d												
Wakefield Westgate 7	d												
Wakefield Kirkgate 4	d												
Doncaster 7	d												
Sheffield 7	d												
Chesterfield	d												
Derby 10	a												
	d						07 09						
Long Eaton	d						07 19						
Alfreton	d												
Langley Mill	d												
Lincoln	d												
Nottingham 8	a												
	d												
Beeston	d												
East Midlands Parkway	d						07 24				07 43		
Loughborough	d						07 31				07 52		
Barrow Upon Soar	d												
Sileby	d												
Syston	d												
Leicester	a						07 43				08 05		
	d		06 49		07 23		07 49	07 53			08 11	08 15	
Market Harborough	d	07 12	07a24	07 44	07a58	08 13		08a28	08 38			08a50	09 13
Corby	d												
Kettering	a	07 37		08 09		08 38	08 47		09 03		09 12		09 38
	d						08 48				09 13		
Wellingborough	d						09 02				09 27		
Bedford 7	d						09 14				09 43		
Luton 10	d						09 38				10 13		
Luton Airport Parkway 7	d						09 50				10 09		
Gatwick Airport 10	a												
St Pancras International	a						10 19				10 49		

		EM	EM	EM	EM	EM		XC	EM	NT	EM	XC	EM	EM
		1◇				1◇		1◇		◇		1◇		
								G						
			bus	bus	bus				bus		bus		bus	bus
York 8	d							06f15		06g15				
Leeds 10	d							08 09				07 45		
Wakefield Westgate 7	d							18 22				08 00		
Wakefield Kirkgate 4	d													
Doncaster 7	d							08 03		08 03				
Sheffield 7	d							08 54		09 00		08 31		
Chesterfield	d							09 08		09 17		08 46		
Derby 10	a							09 29				09 06		
	d	08 07				09 06								
Long Eaton	d	08 17				09 16								
Alfreton	d									09 28				
Langley Mill	d									09 35				
Lincoln	d													
Nottingham 8	a									09 57				
	d													
Beeston	d													
East Midlands Parkway	d	08 21				09 20								
Loughborough	d	08 29				09 28								
Barrow Upon Soar	d													
Sileby	d													
Syston	d													
Leicester	a	08 40				09 39								
	d	08 47	08 50	09 18		09 46			09 49				10 12	
Market Harborough	d		09a25	09a53	10 12				10a24		10 43		10a47	11 13
Corby	d	09 37				10 37								
Kettering	a	09 47			10 37	10 46					11 08			11 38
	d	09 48				10 47								
Wellingborough	d	10 02				10 57								
Bedford 7	d	10 14				11 14								
Luton 10	d	10 39				11 39								
Luton Airport Parkway 7	d	10 50				11 50								
Gatwick Airport 10	a													
St Pancras International	a	11 19				12 19								

For general notes see front of timetable
For details of catering facilities see Directory of Train Operators

A From Liverpool Lime Street (Table 89)
B From Glasgow Central (Table 26)
C From Newcastle (Table 26)
D From Edinburgh (Table 26) to Bristol Temple Meads (Table 57)
E From Edinburgh (Table 26) to Birmingham New Street (Table 57)
G Until 1 November
b Change at Doncaster and Sheffield
c Change at Sheffield
e Wakefield Kirkgate. Change at Sheffield
f By bus
g Until 1 November only. Change at Leeds and Sheffield. By bus to Leeds

Table 53

Sundays

from 13 September

Sheffield → East Midlands → London

Route Diagram - See first page of Table 53

Station		EM	XC	EM		EM	EM	XC	NT	EM	EM	EM	XC		EM	EM	EM	NT	EM	EM	EM	XC		EM		EM
		1◇	1◇				1◇	1◇	◇			1◇	1◇				1◇	◇			1◇	1◇				1◇
			A					B																		
				bus		bus				bus	bus				bus	bus			bus	bus				bus		
York 8	d	06b15	06c15				07 40	09e00	08f30			09g00	09 28								10g02	10 28				
Leeds 10	d		08 30				08 46	09 00	09 05			09 35	10 00					10 02			10 02	11 00				
Wakefield Westgate 7	d		08 43				08 58	09 12				09 47	10 12								10h18	11 12				
Wakefield Kirkgate 4	d								09 21									10 18								
Doncaster 7	d	08 03	09 01				08j03	09 32	09k32			09 39	10 31								10 42	11 30				
Sheffield 7	d	09 25	09 29				09 45	09 58	10 07			10 25	10 57					11 03			11 30	11 57				
Chesterfield	d	09 38	09 43				09 59	10 11	10 24			10 39	11 09					11 20			11 42	12 09				
Derby 10	a	09 58	10 03				10 19	10 32				11 00	11 28								12 03	12 28				
	d	10 00					10 30					11 01									12 07					
Long Eaton	d	10 13																			12 17					
Alfreton	d								10 35									11 31								
Langley Mill	d								10 42									11 38								
Lincoln	d																									
Nottingham 8	a								11 02									11 58								
	d																11 30									12 26
Beeston	d																11 37									12 33
East Midlands Parkway	d	10 17					10 46					11 14					11 43				12 24					12 41
Loughborough	d	10 25					10 55					11 22					11 51				12 31					12 49
Barrow Upon Soar	d																									
Sileby	d																									
Syston	d																									
Leicester	a	10 36					11 08					11 35					12 02				12 43					13 02
	d	10 43		10 46			11 14			11 18		11 42			11 45		12 09		12 12		12 49			12 53		13 09
Market Harborough	d			11a21		11 42				11a53	12 12				12a20	12 44			12a47	13 19				13a28		
Corby	d	11 38										12 36									13 43					
Kettering	a	11 47				12 07	12 15				12 37	12 45				13 09	13 17			13 44	13 52					14 17
	d	11 48					12 17					12 47					13 19				13 54					14 19
Wellingborough	d	11 58					12 27					12 57					13 28				14 04					14 29
Bedford 7	d	12 15					12 45					13 15					13 46				14 24					14 52
Luton 10	d	12 40					13 31					13 39					14 31				14 41					15 31
Luton Airport Parkway 7	d	13 04					13 10					13 50					14 12				15 06					15 11
Gatwick Airport 10	a																									
St Pancras International	a	13 19					13 49					14 19					14 44				15 15					15 45

Station		NT		EM	EM	NT	EM	EM		EM	EM	XC	EM	EM	EM	NT	EM		EM	EM	EM	XC	XC	EM	EM	EM
		◇			1◇	◇				1◇	◇	1◇			1◇	◇				1◇	◇	1◇	1◇			1◇
																						B	A			
				bus			bus	bus					bus	bus			bus		bus					bus	bus	
York 8	d	10m28			10 28	10 45					10n45	11 28			11g29	11 45					11n45	12 28	12 28			12g57
Leeds 10	d	10 57			11 09	11 29						12 00			12 00	12 29						13 00	13 00			13 05
Wakefield Westgate 7	d				11 24							12 12			12 12							13q12	13 12			13 17
Wakefield Kirkgate 4	d	11 13				11 46										12 46										
Doncaster 7	d				11 42							12 31			12 42							13 30	13 30			
Sheffield 7	d	12 00			12 28	12 31					12 49	12 57			13 18	13 31					13 49	13 57	13 57			14 07
Chesterfield	d	12 18			12 40	12 49					13 03	13 10			13 31	13 48					14 03	14 09	14 09			14 21
Derby 10	a				13 03							13 31			13 53							14 28	14 29			14 43
	d				13 09										13 56											14 46
Long Eaton	d				13 19										14 06											14 57
Alfreton	d	12 29				12 59					13 14					13 59					14 14					
Langley Mill	d	12 36				13 07										14 06										
Lincoln	d																									
Nottingham 8	a	12 56				13 26					13 39					14 26					14 38					
	d									13 31										14 31						
Beeston	d									13 37										14 38						
East Midlands Parkway	d				13 24					13 43					14 10					14 44						15 02
Loughborough	d				13 31					13 51					14 18					14 52						15 10
Barrow Upon Soar	d																									
Sileby	d																									
Syston	d																									
Leicester	a				13 43					14 02					14 29					15 03						15 23
	d				13 49		13 53			14 09			14 12		14 36		14 39			15 10				15 13		15 30
Market Harborough	d			14 16			14a28	14 39					14a47	15 07			15a14		15 35					15a48	16 05	
Corby	d				14 40										15 32											16 29
Kettering	a			14 41	14 49			15 04		15 13				15 32	15 41				16 00	16 08					16 30	16 39
	d				14 51					15 14					15 42					16 10						16 40
Wellingborough	d				15 00					15 26					15 52					16 19						16 49
Bedford 7	d				15 25					15 56					16 09					16 36						17 07
Luton 10	d				15 42										16 27					17 13						17 25
Luton Airport Parkway 7	d				16 04					16 13					16 46					16 54						17 46
Gatwick Airport 10	a																									
St Pancras International	a				16 15					16 45					16 55					17 27						17 59

For general notes see front of timetable
For details of catering facilities see Directory of Train Operators

A From 8 November
B Until 1 November
b Until 1 November only. Change at Leeds and Sheffield. By bus to Leeds
c By bus
e Change at Doncaster
f Until 1 November dep. 0900, change at Doncaster and Sheffield
g Change at Doncaster and Sheffield
h Wakefield Kirkgate
j From 8 November dep. 0901
k From 8 November dep. 0913
m Change at Sheffield
n Change at Leeds and Sheffield
q By changing at Sheffield, passengers may depart at 1317

Table 53

Sundays
from 13 September

Sheffield → East Midlands → London

Route Diagram - See first page of Table 53

		XC	XC		EM	EM	EM	EM	NT	XC	EM	EM		EM	EM	EM	EM	EM	XC	EM	EM		EM	NT	XC	EM
		1◇	1◇				1◇	◇	◇	1◇				1◇			1◇	◇	1◇				1◇	◇	1◇	
										A															A	
		🛒	🛒		🚌	🚌	☕			🛒	🚌	🚌		☕	🚌	🚌	☕		🛒	🚌	🚌		☕		🛒	🚌
York 8	d		13 28					*13 28*	13b37	14 19				*14 19*					14 28				14b36		15 20	
Leeds 10	d		14 00						14 05	14c05									15 00					15 05	15c05	
Wakefield Westgate 7	d		14 12							14e21									15 12						15e22	
Wakefield Kirkgate 4	d								14 21															15 22		
Doncaster 7	d	*13 42*							*14 13*	14 50													*15 13*		15 50	
Sheffield 7	d	14 22	14 50					14 53	15 07	15 20				15 27				15 43	15 50				16 03	16 07	16 20	
Chesterfield	d	14 34	15 02					15 07	15 25					15 40				15 57	16 03				16 17	16 25		
Derby 10	a	14 53	15 21							15 49				16 00					16 22				16 37		16 49	
	d													16 01									16 47			
Long Eaton	d													16 11									17 01			
Alfreton	d							15 18	15 36									16 08						16 36		
Langley Mill	d							15 25	15 43									16 15						16 43		
Lincoln	d																									
Nottingham 8	a							15 44	16 03									16 33						17 03		
	d						15 30										16 28									
Beeston	d						15 36										16 34									
East Midlands Parkway	d						15 42							16 16			16 40						17 06			
Loughborough	d						15 50							16 23			16 48						17 14			
Barrow Upon Soar	d																									
Sileby	d																									
Syston	d																									
Leicester	a						16 01							16 35			17 00						17 28			
	d				15 33		16 08				16 11			16 41	16 45		17 07			17 10			17 35			17 38
Market Harborough	d				16a08	16 38					16a46	17 08			17a20	17 37				17a45	18 05					18a13
Corby	d													17 32									18 30			
Kettering	a					17 03	17 11					17 33		17 41		18 02	18 10				18 30		18 40			
	d						17 13							17 43			18 12						18 41			
Wellingborough	d						17 22							17 52			18 22						18 51			
Bedford 7	d						17 40							18 11			18 40						19 09			
Luton 10	d						*18 13*							18 29			*19 13*						19 27			
Luton Airport Parkway 7	d						17 59							*18 46*			18 59						*19 46*			
Gatwick Airport 10 ✈	a																									
St Pancras International ⊖	a						18 29							18 59			19 29						19 59			

		EM	EM	EM	XC	NT	EM		XC	EM	XC	XC		EM	EM	EM		EM	EM	NT	XC	EM	EM	EM	EM	XC
			1◇	◇	1◇	◇			1◇	◇	1◇	1◇			1◇				1◇	◇	1◇	◇			1◇	1◇
											B	C									A					
		🚌	☕		🛒		🚌		🛒		🛒	🛒		🚌	☕	🚌		🚌	☕		🛒		🚌	🚌	☕	🛒
York 8	d			*15 20*	15 28	15b34			16 20	16b03	16 28	16 28			17 00					17c00	17 20	*17 20*			*17 20*	17 28
Leeds 10	d			*15 09*	16 00	16 05					17 00	17 00								17 05	*17 05*	*17 09*			*17 09*	18 00
Wakefield Westgate 7	d			*15 24*	16 12						17 12	17 12									17e21	*17 24*			*17 24*	18 12
Wakefield Kirkgate 4	d					16 22														17 21						
Doncaster 7	d					*16 13*			16 50	*16 42*	16 42	16 42			17 23						17 50					
Sheffield 7	d			16 40	16 50	17 07			17 20	17 39	17 50	17 50			17 54					18 07	18 20	18 41			18 46	18 50
Chesterfield	d			16 56	17 02	17 24				17 54	18 02	18 02			18 07					18 25		18 56			19 01	19 04
Derby 10	a				17 21				17 49		18 21	18 23			18 27						18 49				19 20	19 25
	d														18 29										19 22	
Long Eaton	d														18 39										19 35	
Alfreton	d			17 07		17 35				18 04										18 36		19 06				
Langley Mill	d			17 14		17 43				18 12										18 43		19 14				
Lincoln	d																									
Nottingham 8	a			17 32		18 03				18 29										19 03		19 36				
	d		17 30																18 46							
Beeston	d		17 36																18 53							
East Midlands Parkway	d		17 42												18 43				19 01						19 41	
Loughborough	d		17 50												18 51				19 09						19 48	
Barrow Upon Soar	d																									
Sileby	d																									
Syston	d																									
Leicester	a		18 01												19 02				19 22						20 01	
	d		18 08				18 11								19 08	19 12			19 29				19 32		20 08	
Market Harborough	d	18 38					18a46							19 36		19a44		20 01					20a07	20 37		
Corby	d																									
Kettering	a	19 03	19 11											20 01	20 10			20 26	20 35					21 02	21 10	
	d		19 13												20 11				20 36						21 12	
Wellingborough	d		19 22												20 21				20 46						21 21	
Bedford 7	d		19 40												20 40				21 08						21 45	
Luton 10	d		*20 13*																21 24						21 59	
Luton Airport Parkway 7	d		19 59												20 55				*21 36*						*22 36*	
Gatwick Airport 10 ✈	a																									
St Pancras International ⊖	a		20 29												21 27				21 57						22 27	

For general notes see front of timetable
For details of catering facilities see Directory of Train Operators

- **A** From Newcastle (Table 26)
- **B** From 8 November
- **C** Until 1 November
- **b** Change at Doncaster and Sheffield
- **c** Change at Sheffield
- **e** Wakefield Kirkgate. Change at Sheffield

Table 53

Sundays

from 13 September

Sheffield → East Midlands → London

Route Diagram - See first page of Table 53

		NT	XC	EM	EM	EM	EM	EM	EM	EM	XC	NT	XC	EM	EM	EM	XC	XC	EM	EM	XC	EM
		◇	1 ◇			1 ◇			1 ◇	◇	1 ◇	◇	1 ◇		◇	◇	1 ◇	1 ◇	◇	◇	1 ◇	◇
			A								B		A		C	B			B	C		D
				🚌	🚌		🚌	🚌						🚌								
			T			☕			☕		T		T				T	T			T	
York 8	d	17b36	18 20			18 20					18 28	18b29	19 20		19 20	19 20	19 28	20 20	20b02	20b02	20 28	21b28
Leeds 10	d	18 05	18c05								19 00	19 04	19c04		19 09	19 09	20 00				21 00	21 40
Wakefield Westgate 7	d		18e22								19 12		19e20		19 24	19 24	20 12				21 12	21 55
Wakefield Kirkgate 4	d	18 22										19 20										
Doncaster 7	d	18 13	18 50									19 15	19 50					20 50	20 42	20 42	20 42	22 20
Sheffield 7	d	19 07	19 20			19 31				19 40	19 50	20 06	20 20		20 40	20 40	20 50	21 20	21 40	21 40	21 50	23 29
Chesterfield	d	19 25				19 45				19 55	20 02	20 22			20 55	20 55	21 03	21 32	21 54	21 54	22 04	23 43
Derby 10	a		19 49			20 05					20 21		20 49				21 22	21 51			22 23	
	d					20 06																
Long Eaton	d																					
Alfreton	d	19 36								20 06		20 33			21 06	21 06			22 05	22 05		23 54
Langley Mill	d	19 43								20 14		20 40			21 13	21 14			22 12	22 12		00 01
Lincoln	d																					
Nottingham 8	a	20 03								20 31		21 01			21 35	21 36			22 35	22 36		00 23
	d								20 19													
Beeston	d																					
East Midlands Parkway	d					20 19			20 32													
Loughborough	d								20 39													
Barrow Upon Soar	d																					
Sileby	d																					
Syston	d																					
Leicester	a					20 36			20 51													
	d			20 11		20 43	20 46		20 57					21 01								
Market Harborough	d			20a46	21 12		21a12	21 36						21a36								
Corby	d					21 36																
Kettering	a				21 37	21 45		22 01	22 09													
	d					21 47			22 11													
Wellingborough	d					21 58			22 20													
Bedford 7	d					22 18			22 38													
Luton 10	d					22 37			22 56													
Luton Airport Parkway 7	d					23 06			23 36													
Gatwick Airport 10 ✈	a																					
St Pancras International ⊖	a					23 10			23 30													

For general notes see front of timetable
For details of catering facilities see Directory of Train Operators

A From Newcastle (Table 26)
B From 8 November
C Until 1 November
D Until 1 November from Liverpool Lime Street (Table 90). From 8 November from Liverpool Lime Street (Table 89)
b Change at Doncaster and Sheffield
c Change at Sheffield
e Wakefield Kirkgate. Change at Sheffield

Table 55

Mondays to Fridays
until 25 September

Nottingham → Mansfield → Worksop

Network Diagram - see first page of Table 50

Miles	Station		EM	EM	EM	EM	EM	EM	EM	EM	EM	EM	EM	EM	EM
0	**Nottingham** 8	d	05 40	06 05	07 00	08 25	08 53	09 25	09 55	10 25	10 55	11 25	11 55	12 25	12 55
5½	Bulwell	d	05 49	06 14	07 10	08 36	09 02		10 06		11 06		12 06		13 06
8¼	Hucknall	d	05 54	06 19	07 15	08 41	09 07	09 39	10 11	10 39	11 11	11 39	12 11	12 39	13 11
10¾	Newstead	d	05 59	06 24	07 21	08 46	09 12	09 44		10 44		11 44		12 44	
13¾	Kirkby In Ashfield	d	06 05	06 30	07 31	08 52	09 18	09 49	10 19	10 49	11 19	11 49	12 19	12 49	13 19
14½	Sutton Parkway	d	06 08	06 33	07 34	08 55	09 21	09 52	10 22	10 52	11 22	11 52	12 22	12 52	13 22
17¼	**Mansfield**	d	06 13	06 38	07 40	09 00	09 26	09 57	10 27	10 57	11 27	11 57	12 27	12 57	13 27
18¾	Mansfield Woodhouse	d	06 18	06 47	07 45	09 04	09a33	10 02	10a34	11 02	11a34	12 02	12a34	13 02	13a34
21½	Shirebrook	d	06 24	06 54	07 51	09 11		10 08		11 08		12 08		13 08	
22¼	Langwith - Whaley Thorns	d	06 28	06 58	07 55	09 15		10 12		11 12		12 12		13 12	
25½	Creswell (Derbys)	d	06 32	07 02	07 59	09 19		10 16		11 16		12 16		13 16	
26¾	Whitwell	d	06 36	07 05	08 03	09 22		10 20		11 20		12 20		13 20	
31½	**Worksop**	a	06 48	07 20	08 18	09 35		10 34		11 34		12 34		13 34	

Station		EM	EM	EM	EM	EM	EM	EM	EM	EM	EM	EM	EM	EM	EM
Nottingham 8	d	13 25	13 55	14 25	14 55	15 25	15 55	16 25	16 55	17 25	17 55	18 55	19 55	20 55	22 05
Bulwell	d		14 06		15 06		16 06		17 06	17 39	18 11	19 05	20 05	21 05	22 19
Hucknall	d	13 39	14 11	14 39	15 11	15 39	16 11	16 39	17 12	17 44	18 16	19 10	20 16	21 16	22 24
Newstead	d	13 44		14 44		15 44		16 44	17 17	17 49	18 21	19 15	20 21	21 21	22 29
Kirkby In Ashfield	d	13 49	14 19	14 49	15 19	15 49	16 19	16 49	17 23	17 55	18 27	19 21	20 27	21 27	22 34
Sutton Parkway	d	13 52	14 22	14 52	15 22	15 52	16 22	16 52	17 27	17 58	18 30	19 24	20 30	21 30	22 37
Mansfield	d	13 57	14 27	14 57	15 27	15 57	16 27	16 57	17 32	18 03	18 35	19 29	20 35	21 35	22 42
Mansfield Woodhouse	d	14 02	14a34	15 02	15a34	16 02	16a34	17 02	17a39	18 08	18 39	19 33	20 39	21 40	22 47
Shirebrook	d	14 08		15 08		16 08		17 08		18 14	18 46	19 40	20 46	21 46	22 53
Langwith - Whaley Thorns	d	14 12		15 12		16 12		17 12		18 18	18 50	19 44	20 50	21 50	22 57
Creswell (Derbys)	d	14 16		15 16		16 16		17 16		18 22	18 54	19 48	20 54	21 54	23 01
Whitwell	d	14 20		15 20		16 20		17 20		18 26	18 57	19 51	20 57	21 58	23 05
Worksop	a	14 34		15 34		16 34		17 34		18 37	19 09	20 04	21 09	22 08	23 16

Mondays to Fridays
from 28 September

Station		EM	EM	EM	EM	EM	EM	EM (bus)	EM	EM	EM (bus)	EM	EM	EM (bus)	EM	EM	EM (bus)	EM
Nottingham 8	d	05 40	06 05	07 00	08 25	08 52	09 25		09 55	10 25		10 55	11 25		11 55	12 25		12 55
Bulwell	d		06 14	07 10														
Hucknall	d	05 52	06 19	07 15	08 39	09 05	09 39	09 50	10 09	10 39	10 50	11 09	11 39	11 50	12 09	12 39	12 50	13 09
Newstead	d		06 24	07 21	08 44	09 10		10a10			11a10			12a10			13a10	
Kirkby In Ashfield	d		06 30	07 31	08 52	09 18	09 49		10 19	10 49		11 19	11 49		12 19	12 49		13 19
Sutton Parkway	d	06 05	06 33	07 34	08 55	09 22	09 52			10 52			11 52			12 52		
Mansfield	d	06 11	06 38	07 40	09 00	09 27	09 57		10 26	10 57		11 26	11 57		12 26	12 57		13 26
Mansfield Woodhouse	d	06 16	06 47	07 45	09 04	09a34	10 02		10a34	11 02		11a34	12 02		12a34	13 02		13a34
Shirebrook	d	06 23	06 54	07 51	09 11		10 08			11 08			12 08			13 08		
Langwith - Whaley Thorns	d	06 27	06 58	07 55	09 15		10 12			11 12			12 12			13 12		
Creswell (Derbys)	d	06 31	07 02	07 59	09 19		10 16			11 16			12 16			13 16		
Whitwell	d	06 34	07 05	08 03	09 22		10 20			11 20			12 20			13 20		
Worksop	a	06 48	07 20	08 18	09 35		10 36			11 36			12 36			13 36		

Station		EM	EM (bus)	EM	EM	EM (bus)	EM	EM	EM	EM	EM	EM	EM	EM	EM	EM	EM
Nottingham 8	d	13 25		13 55	14 25		14 55	15 25	15 55	16 25	16 55	17 25	17 55	18 55	19 55	20 55	22 05
Bulwell	d										17 05	17 39	18 06	19 05	20 05	21 05	22 19
Hucknall	d	13 39	13 50	14 09	14 39	14 50	15 09	15 39	16 09	16 39	17 11	17 44	18 16	19 10	20 16	21 16	22 24
Newstead	d		14a10			15a10			16 14		17 16		18 21	19 15	20 21	21 21	22 29
Kirkby In Ashfield	d	13 49		14 19	14 49		15 19	15 49	16 20	16 49	17 22	17 55	18 27	19 23	20 29	21 27	22 35
Sutton Parkway	d	13 52			14 52			15 52		16 52	17 25	17 58	18 30	19 26	20 32	21 30	22 38
Mansfield	d	13 57		14 26	14 57		15 26	15 57	16 27	16 57	17 31	18 03	18 35	19 31	20 37	21 35	22 43
Mansfield Woodhouse	d	14 02		14a34	15 02		15a34	16 02	16a35	17 02	17a38	18 08	18 39	19 36	20 42	21 39	22 48
Shirebrook	d	14 08			15 08			16 08		17 08		18 14	18 46	19 43	20 49	21 46	22 54
Langwith - Whaley Thorns	d	14 12			15 12			16 12		17 12		18 18	18 50	19 47	20 53	21 50	22 58
Creswell (Derbys)	d	14 16			15 16			16 16		17 16		18 22	18 54	19 51	20 57	21 54	23 02
Whitwell	d	14 20			15 20			16 20		17 20		18 26	18 57	19 54	21 00	21 57	23 06
Worksop	a	14 36			15 36			16 36		17 36		18 39	19 09	20 07	21 12	22 08	23 17

Saturdays
until 26 September

Station		EM	EM	EM	EM	EM	EM	EM	EM	EM	EM	EM	EM	EM
Nottingham 8	d	05 40	06 05	06 59	08 25	08 53	09 25	09 55	10 25	10 55	11 25	11 55	12 25	12 55
Bulwell	d	05 49	06 14	07 09	08 36	09 02		10 06		11 06		12 06		13 06
Hucknall	d	05 54	06 19	07 14	08 41	09 07	09 39	10 11	10 39	11 11	11 39	12 11	12 39	13 11
Newstead	d	05 59	06 24	07 20	08 46	09 12	09 44		10 44		11 44		12 44	
Kirkby In Ashfield	d	06 05	06 30	07 31	08 52	09 18	09 49	10 19	10 49	11 19	11 49	12 19	12 49	13 19
Sutton Parkway	d	06 08	06 33	07 34	08 55	09 21	09 52	10 22	10 52	11 22	11 52	12 22	12 52	13 22
Mansfield	d	06 13	06 38	07 40	09 00	09 26	09 57	10 27	10 57	11 27	11 57	12 27	12 57	13 27
Mansfield Woodhouse	d	06 18	06 47	07 45	09 04	09a33	10 02	10a34	11 02	11a34	12 02	12a34	13 02	13a34
Shirebrook	d	06 24	06 54	07 51	09 11		10 08		11 08		12 08		13 08	
Langwith - Whaley Thorns	d	06 28	06 58	07 55	09 15		10 12		11 12		12 12		13 12	
Creswell (Derbys)	d	06 32	07 02	07 59	09 19		10 16		11 16		12 16		13 16	
Whitwell	d	06 36	07 05	08 03	09 22		10 20		11 20		12 20		13 20	
Worksop	a	06 48	07 20	08 18	09 34		10 34		11 34		12 34		13 34	

For general notes see front of timetable
For details of catering facilities see
Directory of Train Operators

Saturdays

until 26 September

Nottingham → Mansfield → Worksop

Network Diagram - see first page of Table 50

		EM	EM	EM	EM	EM	EM	EM	EM	EM	EM	EM	EM	EM	EM	EM
Nottingham 8	d	13 25	13 55	14 25	14 55	15 25	15 55	16 25	16 55	17 25	17 55	18 55	19 55	20 55	22 05	23 05
Bulwell	d		14 06		15 06		16 06		17 06	17 39	18 11	19 05	20 05	21 05	22 19	23 18
Hucknall	d	13 39	14 11	14 39	15 11	15 39	16 11	16 39	17 12	17 44	18 16	19 10	20 16	21 16	22 24	23 23
Newstead	d	13 44		14 44		15 44		16 44	17 17	17 49	18 21	19 15	20 21	21 21	22 29	23 28
Kirkby In Ashfield	d	13 49	14 19	14 49	15 19	15 49	16 19	16 49	17 23	17 55	18 27	19 21	20 27	21 27	22 34	23 33
Sutton Parkway	d	13 52	14 22	14 52	15 22	15 52	16 22	16 52	17 27	17 58	18 30	19 24	20 30	21 30	22 37	23 36
Mansfield	d	13 57	14 27	14 57	15 27	15 57	16 27	16 57	17 32	18 03	18 35	19 29	20 35	21 35	22 42	23 41
Mansfield Woodhouse	d	14 02	14a34	15 02	15a34	16 02	16a34	17 02	17a39	18 08	18 39	19 33	20 39	21 40	22 47	23a46
Shirebrook	d	14 08		15 08		16 08		17 08		18 14	18 46	19 40	20 46	21 46	22 53	
Langwith - Whaley Thorns	d	14 12		15 12		16 12		17 12		18 18	18 50	19 44	20 50	21 50	22 57	
Creswell (Derbys)	d	14 16		15 16		16 16		17 16		18 22	18 54	19 48	20 54	21 54	23 01	
Whitwell	d	14 20		15 20		16 20		17 20		18 26	18 57	19 51	20 57	21 58	23 05	
Worksop	a	14 34		15 34		16 34		17 34		18 37	19 09	20 04	21 09	22 08	23 16	

Saturdays

from 3 October

		EM	EM	EM	EM	EM	EM	EM 🚌	EM	EM	EM 🚌	EM	EM	EM 🚌	EM	EM	EM 🚌	EM
Nottingham 8	d	05 40	06 05	06 59	08 23	08 50	09 25		09 55	10 25		10 55	11 25		11 55	12 25		12 55
Bulwell	d		06 14	07 09		08 59												
Hucknall	d	05 52	06 19	07 14	08 38	09 05	09 39	09 50	10 09	10 39	10 50	11 09	11 39	11 50	12 09	12 39	12 50	13 09
Newstead	d	05 57	06 24	07 20		09 10		10a10			11a10			12a10			13a10	
Kirkby In Ashfield	d	06 05	06 30	07 31	08 48	09 18	09 49		10 19	10 49		11 19	11 49		12 19	12 49		13 19
Sutton Parkway	d	06 08	06 33	07 34	08 51	09 22	09 52			10 52			11 52			12 52		
Mansfield	d	06 13	06 38	07 40	08 57	09 27	09 57		10 26	10 57		11 26	11 57		12 26	12 57		13 26
Mansfield Woodhouse	d	06 19	06 47	07 45	09 02	09a34	10 02		10a34	11 02		11a34	12 02		12a34	13 02		13a34
Shirebrook	d	06 25	06 54	07 51	09 09		10 08			11 08			12 08			13 08		
Langwith - Whaley Thorns	d	06 29	06 58	07 55	09 13		10 12			11 12			12 12			13 12		
Creswell (Derbys)	d	06 33	07 02	07 59	09 17		10 16			11 16			12 16			13 16		
Whitwell	d	06 37	07 05	08 03	09 20		10 20			11 20			12 20			13 20		
Worksop	a	06 50	07 20	08 18	09 33		10 36			11 36			12 34			13 36		

		EM	EM 🚌	EM	EM	EM 🚌	EM	EM	EM	EM	EM	EM	EM	EM	EM	EM	EM	EM
Nottingham 8	d	13 25		13 55	14 25		14 55	15 25	15 55	16 25	16 55	17 25	17 55	18 55	19 55	20 55	22 05	23 05
Bulwell	d										17 05	17 39	18 06	19 05	20 05	21 05	22 19	23 18
Hucknall	d	13 39	13 50	14 09	14 39	14 50	15 09	15 39	16 09	16 39	17 11	17 44	18 16	19 10	20 16	21 16	22 24	23 23
Newstead	d		14a10			15a10			16 14		17 16	17 49	18 21	19 15	20 21	21 21	22 29	23 28
Kirkby In Ashfield	d	13 49		14 19	14 49		15 19	15 49	16 20	16 49	17 22	17 55	18 27	19 23	20 29	21 27	22 35	23 33
Sutton Parkway	d	13 52			14 52			15 52		16 52	17 25	17 58	18 30	19 26	20 32	21 30	22 38	23 36
Mansfield	d	13 57		14 26	14 57		15 26	15 57	16 27	16 57	17 31	18 03	18 35	19 31	20 37	21 35	22 43	23 41
Mansfield Woodhouse	d	14 02		14a34	15 02		15a34	16 02	16a35	17 02	17a38	18 08	18 39	19 36	20 42	21 39	22 48	23a46
Shirebrook	d	14 08			15 08			16 08		17 08		18 14	18 46	19 43	20 49	21 46	22 54	
Langwith - Whaley Thorns	d	14 12			15 12			16 12		17 12		18 18	18 50	19 47	20 53	21 50	22 58	
Creswell (Derbys)	d	14 16			15 16			16 16		17 16		18 22	18 54	19 51	20 57	21 54	23 02	
Whitwell	d	14 20			15 20			16 20		17 20		18 26	18 57	19 54	21 00	21 57	23 06	
Worksop	a	14 36			15 36			16 34		17 36		18 39	19 09	20 07	21 12	22 08	23 17	

Sundays

		EM A	EM B	EM B	EM	EM	EM	EM	EM	EM	EM	EM
Nottingham 8	d	06 55	07 53	08 26	09 26	11 26	13 26	14 26	16 26	17 26	19 26	20 26
Bulwell	d											
Hucknall	d	07 26	08 09	08 39	09 39	11 39	13 39	14 39	16 39	17 39	19 39	20 39
Newstead	d	07 47	08 14	08 44	09 44	11 44	13 44	14 44	16 44	17 44	19 44	20 44
Kirkby In Ashfield	d	07 58	08 19	08 49	09 49	11 49	13 49	14 49	16 49	17 49	19 49	20 49
Sutton Parkway	d	08 09	08 22	08 52	09 52	11 52	13 52	14 52	16 52	17 52	19 52	20 52
Mansfield	d	08 25	08 27	08 57	09 57	11 57	13 57	14 57	16 57	17 57	19 57	20 57
Mansfield Woodhouse	d	08a27	08a34	09 02	10 02	12a04	14a04	15 02	17a04	18 02	20a04	21a04
Shirebrook	d			09 08	10 08			15 08		18 08		
Langwith - Whaley Thorns	d			09 12	10 12			15 12		18 12		
Creswell (Derbys)	d			09 16	10 16			15 16		18 16		
Whitwell	d			09 20	10 20			15 20		18 20		
Worksop	a			09 31	10 31			15 31		18 36		

For general notes see front of timetable
For details of catering facilities see Directory of Train Operators

A From 13 September
B Until 6 September

Table 55

Worksop → Mansfield → Nottingham

Mondays to Fridays
until 25 September

Network Diagram - see first page of Table 50

Miles			EM	EM ◇ A	EM B	EM	EM	EM	EM	EM	EM	EM	EM	EM	EM	EM	EM	EM	EM
0	**Worksop**	d	05 50		06 56		07 38	08 38		09 38		10 38		11 38		12 38		13 38	
4¾	Whitwell	d	05 59		07 05		07 47	08 47		09 47		10 47		11 47		12 47		13 47	
6	Creswell (Derbys)	d	06 02		07 08		07 50	08 50		09 50		10 50		11 50		12 50		13 50	
9¼	Langwith - Whaley Thorns	d	06 06		07 13		07 55	08 55		09 55		10 55		11 55		12 55		13 55	
10	Shirebrook	d	06 10		07 16		07 58	08 58		09 58		10 58		11 58		12 58		13 58	
12¾	Mansfield Woodhouse	d	06 17	07 07	07 25	07 39	08 06	09 06	09 37	10 07	10 37	11 07	11 37	12 07	12 37	13 07	13 37	14 07	14 37
14¼	**Mansfield**	d	06 22	07 11	07 29	07 43	08 10	09 10	09 40	10 10	10 40	11 10	11 40	12 10	12 40	13 10	13 40	14 10	14 40
17	Sutton Parkway	d	06 27	07 16	07 35	07 48	08 15	09 15	09 46	10 16	10 46	11 16	11 46	12 16	12 46	13 16	13 46	14 16	14 46
17¾	Kirkby In Ashfield	d	06 30	07 19	07 38	07 52	08 18	09 18	09 49	10 19	10 49	11 19	11 49	12 19	12 49	13 19	13 49	14 19	14 49
20¾	Newstead	d	06 35	07 26	07 43	07 57	08 23	09 23	09 54		10 54		11 54		12 54		13 54		14 54
23¼	Hucknall	d	06 39	07 31	07 48	08 02	08 28	09 27	09 58	10 26	10 58	11 26	11 58	12 26	12 58	13 26	13 58	14 26	14 58
26	Bulwell	d	06 43	07 35	07 53	08 06	08 32	09 31		10 30		11 30		12 30		13 30		14 30	
31½	**Nottingham** 3	a	06 58	07 48	08 04	08 18	08 44	09 44	10 15	10 44	11 14	11 44	12 14	12 44	13 19	13 44	14 14	14 44	15 14

		EM	EM	EM	EM	EM	EM	EM	EM	EM	EM	EM	EM
Worksop	d	14 38		15 38		16 42		17 45	18 41	19 21	20 15	21 20	22 20
Whitwell	d	14 47		15 47		16 51		17 54	18 50	19 30	20 24	21 29	22 29
Creswell (Derbys)	d	14 50		15 50		16 54		17 57	18 53	19 33	20 27	21 32	22 32
Langwith - Whaley Thorns	d	14 55		15 55		16 59		18 01	18 58	19 37	20 31	21 37	22 37
Shirebrook	d	14 58		15 58		17 02		18 07	19 01	19 41	20 35	21 40	22 40
Mansfield Woodhouse	d	15 07	15 37	16 07	16 37	17 10	17 43	18 14	19 09	19 48	20 43	21 48	22 48
Mansfield	d	15 10	15 40	16 10	16 40	17 14	17 46	18 18	19 13	19 52	20 50	21 53	22 52
Sutton Parkway	d	15 16	15 46	16 16	16 46	17 19	17 52	18 24	19 18	19 57	20 55	21 58	22 57
Kirkby In Ashfield	d	15 19	15 49	16 19	16 49	17 22	17 55	18 27	19 21	20 00	20 58	22 01	23 00
Newstead	d		15 54		16 54		17 59	18 31	19 26	20 05	21 03	22 06	23 05
Hucknall	d	15 26	15 58	16 26	16 58	17 30	18 04	18 36	19 30	20 09	21 07	22 10	23 09
Bulwell	d	15 30		16 30		17 34		18 40	19 34	20 14	21 14	22 14	23 13
Nottingham 8	a	15 44	16 14	16 44	17 14	17 48	18 20	18 51	19 47	20 36	21 26	22 28	23 26

Mondays to Fridays
from 28 September

		EM	EM ◇ A	EM B	EM	EM	EM	EM	EM	EM (bus)	EM	EM	EM (bus)	EM	EM	EM (bus)	EM	EM	EM (bus)	EM
Worksop	d	05 47		06 56		07 33	08 34		09 38			10 38			11 38			12 38		
Whitwell	d	05 56		07 05		07 42	08 43		09 47			10 47			11 47			12 47		
Creswell (Derbys)	d	05 59		07 08		07 45	08 46		09 50			10 50			11 50			12 50		
Langwith - Whaley Thorns	d	06 03		07 13		07 50	08 51		09 55			10 55			11 55			12 55		
Shirebrook	d	06 07		07 16		07 53	08 54		09 58			10 58			11 58			12 58		
Mansfield Woodhouse	d	06 15	07 07	07 25	07 36	08 01	09 03	09 37	10 06		10 37	11 06		11 37	12 06		12 37	13 06		13 37
Mansfield	d	06 20	07 11	07 29	07 40	08 05	09 07	09 41	10 10		10 41	11 10		11 41	12 10		12 40	13 10		13 41
Sutton Parkway	d	06 25	07 16	07 35	07 45	08 11	09 12		10 15			11 15			12 15			13 15		
Kirkby In Ashfield	d	06 28	07 19	07 38	07 49	08 14	09 15	09 48	10 18		10 48	11 18		11 48	12 18		12 48	13 18		13 48
Newstead	d	06 34	07 26	07 43	07 55	08 20	09 21	09 54		10 25			11 25			12 25			13 25	
Hucknall	d	06 39	07 31	07 48	08 00	08 25	09 26	09 58	10 27	10a45	10 56	11 27	11a45	11 56	12 27	12a45	12 56	13 27	13a45	13 56
Bulwell	d	06 43	07 35	07 53	08 05	08 29	09 30													
Nottingham 8	a	06 57	07 48	08 04	08 18	08 44	09 44	10 15	10 44		11 13	11 44		12 13	12 44		13 19	13 44		14 13

		EM	EM (bus)	EM	EM	EM (bus)	EM	EM	EM	EM (bus)	EM	EM	EM	EM	EM	EM	EM	EM
Worksop	d	13 38			14 38			15 38			16 42		17 45	18 41	19 21	20 15	21 20	22 20
Whitwell	d	13 47			14 47			15 47			16 51		17 54	18 50	19 30	20 24	21 29	22 29
Creswell (Derbys)	d	13 50			14 50			15 50			16 54		17 57	18 53	19 33	20 27	21 32	22 32
Langwith - Whaley Thorns	d	13 55			14 55			15 55			16 59		18 01	18 58	19 37	20 31	21 37	22 37
Shirebrook	d	13 58			14 58			15 58			17 02		18 05	19 01	19 41	20 35	21 40	22 40
Mansfield Woodhouse	d	14 06		14 37	15 06		15 37	16 06	16 37		17 10	17 43	18 12	19 09	19 48	20 43	21 48	22 48
Mansfield	d	14 10		14 41	15 10		15 41	16 10	16 41		17 14	17 46	18 16	19 13	19 52	20 47	21 53	22 52
Sutton Parkway	d	14 15			15 15			16 15			17 19	17 52	18 22	19 18	19 57	20 52	21 58	22 57
Kirkby In Ashfield	d	14 18		14 48	15 18		15 48	16 18	16 48		17 22	17 55	18 25	19 21	20 00	20 55	22 01	23 00
Newstead	d		14 25			15 25				17 00		18 01	18 31	19 26	20 05	21 02	22 06	23 05
Hucknall	d	14 27	14a45	14 56	15 27	15a45	15 56	16 27	16 56	17a20	17 30	18 05	18 36	19 30	20 09	21 06	22 10	23 09
Bulwell	d							16 31			17 34		18 40	19 34	20 14	21 12	22 14	23 13
Nottingham 8	a	14 44		15 13	15 44		16 13	16 44	17 13		17 48	18 26	18 51	19 47	20 36	21 24	22 28	23 26

For general notes see front of timetable
For details of catering facilities see Directory of Train Operators

A To Norwich (Table 49)
B To Lincoln (Table 27)

Table 55

Saturdays
until 26 September

Worksop → Mansfield → Nottingham

Network Diagram - see first page of Table 50

		EM	EM	EM	EM	EM	EM	EM	EM	EM	EM	EM	EM	EM
Worksop	d	05 50	06 56	07 38	08 38		09 38		10 38		11 38		12 38	
Whitwell	d	05 59	07 05	07 47	08 47		09 47		10 47		11 47		12 47	
Creswell (Derbys)	d	06 02	07 08	07 50	08 50		09 50		10 50		11 50		12 50	
Langwith - Whaley Thorns	d	06 06	07 13	07 55	08 55		09 55		10 55		11 55		12 55	
Shirebrook	d	06 10	07 16	07 58	08 58		09 58		10 58		11 58		12 58	
Mansfield Woodhouse	d	06 17	07 25	08 06	09 06	09 37	10 07	10 37	11 07	11 37	12 07	12 37	13 07	13 37
Mansfield	d	06 22	07 29	08 10	09 10	09 40	10 10	10 40	11 10	11 40	12 10	12 40	13 10	13 41
Sutton Parkway	d	06 27	07 35	08 15	09 15	09 46	10 16	10 46	11 16	11 46	12 16	12 46	13 16	
Kirkby In Ashfield	d	06 30	07 38	08 18	09 18	09 49	10 19	10 49	11 19	11 49	12 19	12 49	13 19	13 48
Newstead	d	06 35	07 43	08 23	09 23	09 54		10 54		11 54		12 54		
Hucknall (tram)	d	06 39	07 48	08 28	09 27	09 58	10 26	10 58	11 26	11 58	12 26	12 58	13 26	13 56
Bulwell (tram)	d	06 43	07 53	08 32	09 31		10 30		11 30		12 30		13 30	
Nottingham 8 (tram)	a	06 58	08 05	08 44	09 44	10 15	10 44	11 14	11 44	12 14	12 44	13 15	13 44	14 13

		EM	EM	EM	EM	EM	EM	EM	EM	EM	EM	EM	EM	EM	EM
Worksop	d	13 38		14 38		15 38		16 42		17 45	18 41	19 21	20 15	21 19	22 20
Whitwell	d	13 47		14 47		15 47		16 51		17 54	18 50	19 30	20 24	21 28	22 29
Creswell (Derbys)	d	13 50		14 50		15 50		16 54		17 57	18 53	19 33	20 27	21 31	22 32
Langwith - Whaley Thorns	d	13 55		14 55		15 55		16 59		18 01	18 58	19 37	20 31	21 36	22 37
Shirebrook	d	13 58		14 58		15 58		17 02		18 07	19 01	19 41	20 35	21 39	22 40
Mansfield Woodhouse	d	14 07	14 37	15 07	15 37	16 07	16 37	17 10	17 43	18 14	19 09	19 48	20 43	21 47	22 48
Mansfield	d	14 10	14 40	15 10	15 40	16 10	16 40	17 14	17 46	18 18	19 13	19 52	20 50	21 52	22 52
Sutton Parkway	d	14 16	14 46	15 16	15 46	16 16	16 46	17 19	17 52	18 24	19 18	19 57	20 55	21 57	22 57
Kirkby In Ashfield	d	14 19	14 49	15 19	15 49	16 19	16 49	17 22	17 55	18 27	19 21	20 00	20 58	22 00	23 00
Newstead	d		14 54		15 54		16 54		17 59	18 31	19 26	20 05	21 03	22 05	23 05
Hucknall (tram)	d	14 26	14 58	15 26	15 58	16 26	16 58	17 30	18 04	18 36	19 30	20 09	21 07	22 09	23 09
Bulwell (tram)	d	14 30		15 30		16 30		17 34		18 40	19 34	20 14	21 14	22 13	23 13
Nottingham 8 (tram)	a	14 44	15 14	15 44	16 15	16 44	17 14	17 48	18 20	18 51	19 47	20 32	21 26	22 25	23 26

Saturdays
from 3 October

		EM	EM	EM	EM	EM	EM	EM (bus)	EM	EM	EM (bus)	EM	EM	EM (bus)	EM	EM	EM (bus)	EM
Worksop	d	05 47	06 56	07 33	08 34		09 38			10 38			11 38			12 38		
Whitwell	d	05 56	07 05	07 42	08 43		09 47			10 47			11 47			12 47		
Creswell (Derbys)	d	05 59	07 08	07 45	08 46		09 50			10 50			11 50			12 50		
Langwith - Whaley Thorns	d	06 03	07 13	07 50	08 51		09 55			10 55			11 55			12 55		
Shirebrook	d	06 07	07 16	07 53	08 54		09 58			10 58			11 58			12 58		
Mansfield Woodhouse	d	06 15	07 25	08 01	09 03	09 37	10 06		10 37	11 06		11 37	12 06		12 37	13 06		13 37
Mansfield	d	06 20	07 29	08 05	09 07	09 40	10 10		10 41	11 10		11 41	12 10		12 40	13 10		13 40
Sutton Parkway	d	06 25	07 35	08 11	09 12	09 46	10 15			11 15			12 15		12 46	13 15		13 46
Kirkby In Ashfield	d	06 28	07 38	08 14	09 15	09 49	10 18		10 48	11 18		11 48	12 18		12 49	13 18		13 49
Newstead	d	06 34	07 43	08 20	09 21	09 54		10 25			11 25			12 25	12 54		13 25	13 54
Hucknall (tram)	d	06 39	07 48	08 25	09 26	09 58	10 27	10a45	10 56	11 27	11a45	11 56	12 27	12a45	12 58	13 27	13a45	13 58
Bulwell (tram)	d	06 43	07 53	08 29	09 30													
Nottingham 8 (tram)	a	06 58	08 05	08 44	09 44	10 15	10 44		11 14	11 44		12 14	12 44		13 15	13 44		14 14

		EM	EM (bus)	EM	EM	EM (bus)	EM	EM	EM	EM (bus)	EM	EM	EM	EM	EM	EM	EM	EM
Worksop	d	13 38			14 38			15 38			16 42		17 45	18 41	19 21	20 15	21 19	22 20
Whitwell	d	13 47			14 47			15 47			16 51		17 54	18 50	19 30	20 24	21 28	22 29
Creswell (Derbys)	d	13 50			14 50			15 50			16 54		17 57	18 53	19 33	20 27	21 31	22 32
Langwith - Whaley Thorns	d	13 55			14 55			15 55			16 59		18 01	18 58	19 37	20 31	21 36	22 37
Shirebrook	d	13 58			14 58			15 58			17 02		18 05	19 01	19 41	20 35	21 39	22 40
Mansfield Woodhouse	d	14 06		14 37	15 06		15 37	16 06	16 37		17 10	17 43	18 12	19 09	19 48	20 43	21 47	22 48
Mansfield	d	14 10		14 41	15 10		15 41	16 10	16 41		17 14	17 46	18 16	19 13	19 52	20 47	21 52	22 52
Sutton Parkway	d	14 15			15 15			16 15			17 19	17 52	18 22	19 18	19 57	20 52	21 57	22 57
Kirkby In Ashfield	d	14 18		14 48	15 18		15 48	16 18	16 48		17 22	17 55	18 25	19 21	20 00	20 55	22 00	23 00
Newstead	d		14 25			15 25				17 00		18 01	18 31	19 26	20 05	21 02	22 05	23 05
Hucknall (tram)	d	14 27	14a45	14 56	15 27	15a45	15 56	16 27	16 56	17a20	17 30	18 05	18 36	19 30	20 09	21 06	22 09	23 09
Bulwell (tram)	d							16 31			17 34		18 40	19 34	20 14	21 12	22 13	23 13
Nottingham 8 (tram)	a	14 44		15 14	15 44		16 15	16 44	17 14		17 48	18 26	18 51	19 47	20 32	21 24	22 25	23 26

For general notes see front of timetable
For details of catering facilities see
Directory of Train Operators

Sundays

Worksop → Mansfield → Nottingham

Network Diagram - see first page of Table 50

		EM A	EM A	EM B	EM B	EM	EM	EM	EM	EM	EM	EM	EM
				(bus)									
Worksop	d		09 38	09 14		10 38			15 38		18 40		
Whitwell	d		09 47	09 26		10 47			15 47		18 49		
Creswell (Derbys)	d		09 50	09 35		10 50			15 50		18 52		
Langwith - Whaley Thorns	d		09 55	09 44		10 55			15 55		18 57		
Shirebrook	d		09 58	09 53		10 58			15 58		19 00		
Mansfield Woodhouse	d	08 37	10 07	10a05	10 13	11 07	12 07	14 07	16 07	17 07	19 09	20 07	21 07
Mansfield	d	08 40	10 10		10 16	11 10	12 10	14 10	16 10	17 10	19 12	20 10	21 10
Sutton Parkway	d	08 46	10 16		10 22	11 16	12 16	14 16	16 16	17 16	19 18	20 16	21 16
Kirkby In Ashfield	d	08 49	10 19		10 25	11 19	12 19	14 19	16 19	17 19	19 21	20 19	21 19
Newstead	d	08 53	10 23		10 29	11 23	12 23	14 23	16 23	17 23	19 25	20 23	21 23
Hucknall (tram)	d	08 58	10 28		10 34	11 28	12 28	14 28	16 28	17 28	19 30	20 28	21 28
Bulwell (tram)	d												
Nottingham 8 (tram)	a	09 13	10 42		10 48	11 42	12 43	14 45	16 42	17 42	19 44	20 42	21 41

For general notes see front of timetable
For details of catering facilities see
Directory of Train Operators

A Until 6 September
B From 13 September

Table 56

Mondays to Fridays

until 4 September

Derby → Matlock

Network Diagram - see first page of Table 50

Miles			EM	EM	EM 1 ◇ A ☕	EM	EM	EM	EM	EM	EM	EM	EM	EM	EM	EM	EM	EM	EM	EM
—	**Nottingham**	d		06 18	06 37	07 18	08 15	09 18	10 18	11 18	12 18	13 18	14 18	15 18	16 18	17 18	18 18	19 18	20 11	21 37
—	Beeston	d		06 23	06 43	07 24	08 24	09 24	10 24	11 24	12 24	13 24	14 24	15 24	16 24	17 24	18 24	19 24	20 17	21 43
—	Attenborough	d		06 26	06 26	07 27	08 27	09 27	10 27	11 27	12 27	13 27	14 27	15 27	16 27	17 27	18 27	19 27	20 20	21 46
—	Long Eaton	d		06 34	06 34	07 35	08 34	09 35	10 35	11 35	12 35	13 36	14 35	15 35	16 35	17 35	18 36	19 35	20 28	21 53
—	St Pancras International 10 ⊖	d					06 37	07 55	08 55	09 55	10 55	11 55	12 55	13 55	14 55	15 55	16 55	17 55	18 55	19 55
0	**Derby 10**	d	05 38	06 50	07 20	07 50	08 50	09 50	10 50	11 53	12 54	13 54	14 54	15 53	16 50	17 54	18 54	19 50	20 56	22 16
5¼	Duffield	d	05 45	06 57		07 57	08 57	09 57	10 57	12 00	13 01	14 01	15 01	16 00	16 57	18 01	19 01	19 57	21 03	22 23
7¾	Belper	d	05 50	07 02	07a27	08 02	09 02	10 02	11 02	12 05	13 06	14 06	15 06	16 05	17 02	18 06	19 06	20 02	21 08	22 28
10½	Ambergate	d	05 58	07 08		08 08	09 08	10 08	11 08	12 11	13 13	14 13	15 13	16 12	17 08	18 13	19 13	20 08	21 14	22 34
12¾	Whatstandwell	d	06 02	07 12		08 12	09 12		11 12		13 17		15 17		17 12	18 17	19 17		21 18	22 38
15½	Cromford	d	06 07	07 17		08 17	09 17		11 17		13 22		15 22		17 17	18 22	19 22		21 23	22 43
16¼	Matlock Bath	d	06 10	07 20		08 20	09 20	10 17	11 22	12 20	13 24	14 22	15 24	16 21	17 20	18 24	19 24	20 17	21 26	22 46
17¼	**Matlock**	a	06 14	07 24		08 24	09 24	10 24	11 26	12 26	13 28	14 27	15 28	16 27	17 24	18 28	19 28	20 24	21 30	22 50

Mondays to Fridays

from 7 September

		EM	EM	EM 1 ◇ A ☕	EM	EM	EM	EM	EM	EM	EM	EM	EM	EM	EM	EM	EM	EM	EM
Nottingham	d		06 18	06 37	07 18	08 15	09 18	10 18	11 18	12 18	13 18	14 18	15 18	16 18	17 18	18 18	19 18	20 11	21 37
Beeston	d		06 23	06 43	07 24	08 24	09 24	10 24	11 24	12 24	13 24	14 24	15 24	16 24	17 24	18 24	19 24	20 17	21 43
Attenborough	d		06 27	06 27	07 27	08 27	09 27	10 27	11 27	12 27	13 27	14 27	15 27	16 27	17 27	18 27	19 27	20 20	21 46
Long Eaton	d		06 34	06 34	07 35	08 34	09 35	10 35	11 35	12 35	13 35	14 35	15 35	16 35	17 35	18 37	19 35	20 28	21 53
St Pancras International 10 ⊖	d					06 37	07 55	08 55	09 55	10 55	11 55	12 55	13 55	14 55	15 55	16 55	17 55	18 55	19 55
Derby 10	d	05 38	06 50	07 20	07 50	08 50	09 50	10 50	11 53	12 50	13 50	14 54	15 50	16 54	17 50	18 50	19 50	20 57	22 16
Duffield	d	05 45	06 57		07 57	08 58	09 57	10 57	12 00	12 57	13 57	15 01	15 57	17 01	17 57	18 57	19 57	21 04	22 23
Belper	d	05 50	07 02	07a27	08 02	09 03	10 02	11 02	12 05	13 02	14 02	15 06	16 02	17 06	18 02	19 02	20 02	21 09	22 28
Ambergate	d	05 58	07 08		08 08	09 09	10 08	11 08	12 11	13 08	14 08	15 12	16 08	17 12	18 08	19 08	20 08	21 15	22 34
Whatstandwell	d	06 02	07 12		08 12	09 13		11 12		13 12		15 16		17 16	18 12	19 12		21 19	22 38
Cromford	d	06 07	07 17		08 17	09 18		11 17		13 17		15 21		17 21	18 17	19 17		21 24	22 43
Matlock Bath	d	06 10	07 20		08 20	09 20	10 17	11 22	12 20	13 20	14 17	15 24	16 17	17 24	18 20	19 20	20 17	21 26	22 46
Matlock	a	06 14	07 24		08 24	09 24	10 24	11 26	12 26	13 24	14 23	15 28	16 24	17 28	18 24	19 24	20 24	21 30	22 50

Saturdays

		EM B	EM C	EM B	EM C	EM 1 ◇ A ☕	EM C	EM B	EM B	EM C	EM B	EM C	EM B	EM C	EM B	EM C	EM B	EM C
Nottingham	d			06 10	06 10	06 37	07 14	07 14	08 08	08 18	09 08	09 18	10 08	10 18	11 08	11 18	12 08	12 18
Beeston	d			06 17	06 17	06 43	07 21	07 21	07 41	08 24	08 42	09 24	09 26	10 24	10 26	11 24	11 26	12 24
Attenborough	d			06 21	06 20	06b21	07 25	07 25		08 27		09 27	09c29	10 27	10c29	11 27	11 29	12 27
Long Eaton	d			06 29	06 28	06e29	07 34	07 34	07 56	08 34	09 01	09 35	09 57	10 35	10 57	11 35	11 57	12 35
St Pancras International 10 ⊖	d								06 37		07 55		08 55		09 55		10 55	
Derby 10	d	05 40	05 40	06 48	06 48	07 20	07 51	07 52	08 47	08 50	09 47	09 50	10 47	10 50	11 47	11 48	12 47	12 49
Duffield	d	05 47	05 47	06 55	06 55		07 58	07 59	08 54	08 57	09 54	09 56	10 54	10 56	11 54	11 55	12 54	12 56
Belper	d	05 52	05 52	07 00	07 00	07a27	08 03	08 04	08 59	09 02	09 59	10 01	10 59	11 01	11 59	12 00	12 59	13 01
Ambergate	d	05 58	05 58	07 06	07 06		08 09	08 10	09 08	09 11	10 08	10 10	11 08	11 10	12 08	12 08	13 08	13 09
Whatstandwell	d	06 02	06 02	07 10	07 10		08 13	08 14	09 12	09 15			11 12	11 14			13 12	13 13
Cromford	d	06 07	06 07	07 15	07 15		08 18	08 19	09 17	09 20			11 17	11 19			13 17	13 18
Matlock Bath	d	06 10	06 10	07 19	07 19		08 21	08 22	09 19	09 21	10 17	10 19	11 20	11 22	12 17	12 17	13 20	13 20
Matlock	a	06 14	06 14	07 22	07 22		08 25	08 26	09 23	09 25	10 21	10 23	11 23	11 25	12 20	12 20	13 23	13 23

		EM B	EM C	EM B	EM C	EM B	EM C	EM B	EM C	EM B	EM C	EM B	EM C	EM B	EM C	EM B	EM C	EM	EM 🚌
Nottingham	d	13 08	13 18	14 08	14 18	15 08	15 18	16 08	16 18	17 08	17 18	18 08	18 18	19 08	19 18	19 20	20 09	20f20	23 15
Beeston	d	12 26	13 24	13 26	14 24	14 26	15 24	15 26	16 24	16 26	17 24	17 26	18 24	18 26	19 24	19 26	20 15	20g26	23 35
Attenborough	d	12 29	13 27	13 29	14 27	14 29	15 27	15 29	16 27	16 29	17 27	17 29	18 27	18 29	19 27	19c29	20 18	20c29	23 45
Long Eaton	d	12 57	13 35	13 57	14 35	14 57	15 35	15 57	16 35	16 56	17 35	17 57	18 37	18 57	19 35	20 02	20 28	20 57	23 56
St Pancras International 10 ⊖	d	11 55		12 55		13 55		14 55		15 55		16 55		17 55		18 55		19 55	
Derby 10	d	13 48	13 50	14 47	14 58	15 48	15 49	16 47	16 50	17 47	17 50	18 47	18 50	19 47	19 50	20 47	20 47	21 52	00a26
Duffield	d	13 55	13 56	14 54	15 06	15 55	15 57	16 54	16 56	17 54	17 56	18 54	18 56	19 54	19 59	20 54	20 53	21 59	
Belper	d	14 00	14 01	14 59	15 11	16 00	16 02	16 59	17 01	17 59	18 01	18 59	19 01	19 59	20 04	20 59	20 58	22 04	
Ambergate	d	14 08	14 10	15 06	15 17	16 07	16 09	17 08	17 08	18 08	18 10	19 08	19 10	20 08	20 13	21 08	21 07	22 11	
Whatstandwell	d			15 10	15 21			17 12	17 14	18 12	18 14	19 12	19 14			21 12	21 11	22 15	
Cromford	d			15 15	15 26			17 17	17 19	18 17	18 19	19 17	19 19			21 17	21 16	22 20	
Matlock Bath	d	14 17	14 19	15 18	15 29	16 16	16 18	17 20	17 22	18 20	18 22	19 20	19 22	20 17	20 22	21 20	21 19	22 23	
Matlock	a	14 20	14 23	15 21	15 32	16 19	16 21	17 23	17 25	18 23	18 25	19 23	19 25	20 21	20 26	21 23	21 22	22 26	

For general notes see front of timetable
For details of catering facilities see Directory of Train Operators

- **A** To Sheffield (Table 34)
- **B** Until 5 September
- **C** From 12 September
- **b** From 12 September dep. 0620
- **c** Until 5 September only
- **e** From 12 September dep. 0628
- **f** From 12 September dep. 2035
- **g** From 12 September dep. 2042

Table 56

Sundays

until 12 July

Derby → Matlock

Network Diagram - see first page of Table 50

		EM	EM	EM	EM	EM	EM	EM
Nottingham	d	09 23	11 23	13 29	14 52	17 23	18 52	21 23
Beeston	d	09 28	11 29	13 34	14 59	17 30	18 58	21 29
Attenborough	d	09 31	11 32	13 38	15 04	17 34	19 03	21 33
Long Eaton	d	09 39	11 43	13 47	15 12	17 41	19 11	21 41
St Pancras International [10] ⊖	d			*10 30*	*12 30*	*14 30*	*17 25*	*19 30*
Derby [10]	d	09 58	11 57	14 00	15 29	17 57	19 26	21 56
Duffield	d	10 05	12 04	14 07	15 36	18 05	19 33	22 04
Belper	d	10 10	12 09	14 12	15 41	18 10	19 38	22 09
Ambergate	d	10 16	12 15	14 18	15 47	18 16	19 44	22 15
Whatstandwell	d	10 20	12 19	14 22	15 51	18 20	19 48	22 19
Cromford	d	10 25	12 24	14 27	15 56	18 25	19 53	22 24
Matlock Bath	d	10 28	12 27	14 29	15 59	18 27	19 56	22 27
Matlock	a	10 32	12 31	14 33	16 03	18 31	20 00	22 31

Sundays

19 July to 6 September

		EM 🚌	EM	EM	EM	EM	EM	EM	EM
Nottingham	d	08 32		11 23	13 20	14 56	17 23	18 56	21 23
Beeston	d	08 53		11 29	13 25	15 01	17 30	19 01	21 29
Attenborough	d	09 04		11 32	13 29	15 06	17 34	19 06	21 33
Long Eaton	d	09 16		11 40	13 36	15 14	17 42	19 13	21 43
St Pancras International [10] ⊖	d				*10 30*	*12 30*	*14 30*	*17 25*	*19 25*
Derby [10]	d	09a46	09 56	11 53	13 49	15 29	17 57	19 26	21 58
Duffield	d		10 03	12 01	13 56	15 36	18 05	19 33	22 05
Belper	d		10 08	12 06	14 01	15 41	18 10	19 38	22 10
Ambergate	d		10 14	12 12	14 07	15 47	18 16	19 44	22 16
Whatstandwell	d		10 18	12 16	14 11	15 51	18 20	19 48	22 20
Cromford	d		10 23	12 21	14 16	15 56	18 25	19 53	22 25
Matlock Bath	d		10 26	12 23	14 19	15 59	18 27	19 56	22 28
Matlock	a		10 30	12 27	14 23	16 03	18 31	20 00	22 32

Sundays

from 13 September

		EM 🚌	EM	EM	EM	EM	EM	EM	EM
Nottingham	d	08 32		11 23	13 20	14 53	17 23	18 56	21 23
Beeston	d	08 53		11 29	13 25	14 59	17 29	19 01	21 29
Attenborough	d	09 04		11 32	13 28	15 02	17 32	19 04	21 32
Long Eaton	d	09 16		11 43	13 36	15 12	17 40	19 13	21 39
St Pancras International [10] ⊖	d				*10 30*	*11 30*	*14 30*	*15 30*	*18 30*
Derby [10]	d	09a46	09 56	11 57	13 56	15 32	17 54	19 26	21 55
Duffield	d		10 03	12 04	14 03	15 39	18 02	19 35	22 03
Belper	d		10 08	12 09	14 08	15 44	18 07	19 40	22 08
Ambergate	d		10 14	12 15	14 14	15 50	18 13	19 46	22 14
Whatstandwell	d		10 18	12 19	14 18	15 54	18 17	19 50	22 18
Cromford	d		10 23	12 24	14 23	15 59	18 22	19 55	22 23
Matlock Bath	d		10 26	12 27	14 26	16 02	18 24	19 57	22 25
Matlock	a		10 30	12 31	14 30	16 06	18 28	20 01	22 29

For general notes see front of timetable
For details of catering facilities see Directory of Train Operators

Table 56

Mondays to Fridays

until 4 September

Matlock → Derby

Network Diagram - see first page of Table 50

Miles			EM	EM	EM	EM	EM	EM	EM	EM	EM	EM	EM	EM	EM	EM	EM	EM	EM
0	**Matlock**	d	06 22	07 37	08 38	09 38	10 38	11 38	12 38	13 38	14 38	15 38	16 38	17 38	18 38	19 38	20 38	21 39	22 55
1	Matlock Bath	d	06 24	07 39	08 40	09 40	10 40	11 40	12 40	13 40	14 40	15 40	16 40	17 40	18 40	19 40	20 40	21 41	22 57
1¾	Cromford	d	06 27	07 42	08 43	09 43		11 43		13 43		15 43		17 43	18 43	19 43		21 44	23 00
4¾	Whatstandwell	d	06 32	07 47	08 48	09 48		11 48		13 48		15 48		17 48	18 48	19 48		21 49	23 05
6¾	Ambergate	d	06 37	07 52	08 53	09 53	10 53	11 53	12 53	13 53	14 53	15 53	16 53	17 53	18 53	19 53	20 53	21 54	23 10
9½	Belper	d	06 44	07 59	08 59	09 59	10 59	11 59	12 59	13 59	14 59	15 59	16 59	17 59	18 59	19 59	20 58	22 01	23 17
12	Duffield	d	06 48	08 04	09 03	10 03	11 03	12 03	13 03	14 03	15 03	16 03	17 03	18 03	19 03	20 03	21 02	22 05	23 21
17¼	**Derby** 10	a	06 56	08 12	09 15	10 15	11 14	12 14	13 14	14 14	15 14	16 14	17 14	18 14	19 14	20 14	21 12	22 14	23 30
—	St Pancras International	a	08b57	10 34	11 34	12 34	13 34	14 39	15 34	16 34	17 34	18 39	19 34	20 38	21 37	23 07			
—	Long Eaton	a	07 24	08 36	09 33	10 33	11 33	12 33	13 33	14 33	15 33	16 31	17 33	18 33	19 32	20 31	21 33	23 11	23 41
—	Attenborough	a	07 31	08 44	09 40	10 40	11 40	12 40	13 40	14 40	15 40	16 38	17 41	18 40	19 40	20 39	21 42	23 17	23 48
—	Beeston	a	07 34	08 47	09 43	10 43	11 43	12 43	13 43	14 43	15 43	16 41	17 44	18 43	19 43	20 42	21 45	23 20	23 51
—	**Nottingham**	a	07 41	08 59	09 54	10 54	11 54	12 54	13 54	14 54	15 54	16 51	17 54	18 54	19 54	20 54	21 57	23 27	00 03

Mondays to Fridays

from 7 September

		EM	EM	EM	EM	EM	EM	EM	EM	EM	EM	EM	EM	EM	EM	EM	EM	EM
Matlock	d	06 22	07 37	08 38	09 38	10 38	11 38	12 38	13 38	14 38	15 38	16 38	17 38	18 38	19 38	20 38	21 39	22 55
Matlock Bath	d	06 24	07 39	08 40	09 40	10 40	11 40	12 40	13 40	14 40	15 40	16 40	17 40	18 40	19 40	20 40	21 41	22 57
Cromford	d	06 27	07 42	08 43	09 43		11 43		13 43		15 43		17 43	18 43	19 43		21 44	23 00
Whatstandwell	d	06 32	07 47	08 48	09 48		11 48		13 48		15 48		17 48	18 48	19 48		21 49	23 05
Ambergate	d	06 37	07 52	08 53	09 53	10 53	11 53	12 53	13 53	14 53	15 53	16 53	17 53	18 53	19 53	20 53	21 54	23 10
Belper	d	06 44	07 59	08 59	09 59	10 59	11 59	12 59	13 59	14 59	15 59	16 59	17 59	18 59	19 59	20 58	22 01	23 17
Duffield	d	06 48	08 04	09 03	10 03	11 03	12 03	13 03	14 03	15 03	16 03	17 03	18 03	19 03	20 03	21 02	22 05	23 21
Derby 10	a	06 56	08 12	09 15	10 15	11 14	12 14	13 14	14 14	15 14	16 14	17 14	18 14	19 14	20 14	21 12	22 14	23 30
St Pancras International	a	08 57	10 34	11 34	12 34	13 34	14 39	15 34	16 34	17 34	18 39	19 34	20 38	21 37	23 07			
Long Eaton	a	07 24	08 36	09 33	10 33	11 33	12 33	13 33	14 33	15 33	16 33	17 33	18 33	19 32	20 31	21 33	23 11	
Attenborough	a	07 31	08 44	09 40	10 40	11 40	12 40	13 40	14 40	15 40	16 40	17 41	18 40	19 40	20 39	21 42	23 17	
Beeston	a	07 34	08 47	09 43	10 43	11 43	12 43	13 43	14 43	15 43	16 43	17 44	18 43	19 43	20 42	21 45	23 20	
Nottingham	a	07 41	08 59	09 54	10 54	11 54	12 54	13 54	14 54	15 54	16 54	17 54	18 54	19 54	20 54	21 57	23 27	

Saturdays

		EM A	EM B	EM A	EM B	EM A	EM B	EM A	EM B	EM A	EM B	EM A	EM B	EM A	EM B	EM A	EM B	EM A
Matlock	d	06 21	06 20	07 44	07 44	08 44	08 44	09 44	09 44	10 47	10 47	11 44	11 44	12 47	12 47	13 44	13 44	14 46
Matlock Bath	d	06 23	06 22	07 46	07 46	08 46	08 46	09 46	09 46	10 49	10 49	11 46	11 46	12 49	12 49	13 46	13 46	14 48
Cromford	d	06 26	06 25	07 49	07 49	08 49	08 49	09 49	09 49			11 49	11 49			13 49	13 49	
Whatstandwell	d	06 31	06 30	07 54	07 54	08 54	08 54	09 54	09 54			11 54	11 54			13 54	13 54	
Ambergate	d	06 36	06 35	08 00	08 00	09 00	09 00	10 00	10 00	11 01	11 01	12 00	12 00	13 01	13 01	14 00	14 00	14 59
Belper	d	06 43	06 42	08 06	08 06	09 06	09 06	10 06	10 06	11 07	11 07	12 06	12 06	13 07	13 07	14 06	14 06	15 07
Duffield	d	06 47	06 46	08 10	08 10	09 10	09 10	10 10	10 10	11 11	11 11	12 10	12 10	13 11	13 11	14 10	14 10	15 11
Derby 10	a	06 55	06 54	08 18	08 20	09 18	09 21	10 18	10 22	11 18	11 21	12 18	12 20	13 18	13 21	14 18	14 21	15 18
St Pancras International	a	09 06	09 06	10 34		11 34		12 34		13 34		14 34		15 34		16 34		17 34
Long Eaton	a	07 21	07 21	09 20	08 32	10 20	09 33	11 20	10 36	12 20	11 31	13 20	12 31	14 20	13 31	15 20	14 32	16 20
Attenborough	a	07 28	07 28		08 40		09 40		10 43		11 38		12 38		13 38		14 40	
Beeston	a	07 31	07 31	09 27	08 43	10 27	09 43	11 27	10 46	12 27	11 41	13 27	12 41	14 27	13 41	15 27	14 43	16 27
Nottingham	a	07 40	07 40	09 05	08 57	10 05	09 52	11 05	10 54	12 05	11 52	13 05	12 52	14 05	13 52	15 07	14 53	16 05

		EM B	EM A	EM B	EM A	EM B	EM A	EM B	EM A	EM B	EM A	EM B	EM	EM D	EM C
Matlock	d	14 46	15 44	15 44	16 47	16 47	17 44	17 44	18 41	18 41	19 41	19 41	20 43	20 43	21 41	22 55	22 55
Matlock Bath	d	14 48	15 46	15 46	16 49	16 49	17 46	17 46	18 43	18 43	19 43	19 43	20 45	20 45	21 43	22 57	22 57
Cromford	d		15 49	15 49			17 49	17 49	18 46	18 46	19 46	19 46			21 46	23 00	23 00
Whatstandwell	d		15 54	15 54			17 54	17 54	18 51	18 51	19 51	19 51			21 51	23 05	23 05
Ambergate	d	14 59	16 00	16 00	17 01	17 01	18 00	18 00	18 57	18 57	19 57	19 57	20 58	20 58	21 57	23 11	23 11
Belper	d	15 07	16 06	16 06	17 07	17 07	18 06	18 06	19 03	19 03	20 03	20 03	21 04	21 04	22 03	23 17	23 17
Duffield	d	15 11	16 10	16 10	17 11	17 11	18 10	18 10	19 07	19 07	20 07	20 07	21 08	21 08	22 07	23 21	23 21
Derby 10	a	15 21	16 18	16 21	17 18	17 21	18 18	18 21	19 15	19 16	20 15	20 15	21 15	21 15	22 20	23 30	23 30
St Pancras International	a		18 34		19 38		20 37		21 41								
Long Eaton	a	15 31	17 20	16 31	18 20	17 32	19 20	18 32	20 20	19 36	20 49	20 26	21 51	21 27	23c11	23 41	
Attenborough	a	15 39		16 38		17 40		18 39		19 43		20 33	21 58	21 35	23c18	23 48	
Beeston	a	15 42	17 27	16 41	18 27	17 43	19 27	18 42	20 27	19 46	20 56	20 36	22 01	21 38	23c21	23 51	
Nottingham	a	15 52	17 05	16 52	18 05	17 53	19 05	18 53	20 05	19 56	21 05	20 47	22 10	21 52	23c33	00 03	

For general notes see front of timetable
For details of catering facilities see Directory of Train Operators

A Until 5 September
B From 12 September
C From 18 July
D Until 11 July

b Mondays arr. 0913
c Until 5 September only

Table 56

Matlock → Derby

Sundays
until 12 July

Network Diagram - see first page of Table 50

		EM	EM	EM	EM 1	EM	EM	EM
Matlock	d	10 42	12 38	14 38	16 42	18 40	20 59	22 42
Matlock Bath	d	10 44	12 40	14 40	16 44	18 42	21 01	22 44
Cromford	d	10 47	12 43	14 43	16 47	18 45	21 04	22 47
Whatstandwell	d	10 52	12 48	14 48	16 52	18 50	21 09	22 52
Ambergate	d	10 57	12 53	14 52	16 57	18 55	21 13	23 00
Belper	d	11 04	13 00	14 59	17 04	19 02	21 20	23 07
Duffield	d	11 08	13 04	15 03	17 08	19 06	21 24	23 11
Derby 10	a	11 16	13 16	15 12	17 16	19 14	21 32	23 20
St Pancras International	a	14 19	16 15	18 04	19 59	22 27		
Long Eaton	a	11 29	13 31	15 24	17 29	20 15	21 45	
Attenborough	a	11 36	13 39	15 31	17 36		21 52	
Beeston	a	11 39	13 42	15 34	17 39		21 55	
Nottingham	a	11 46	13 49	15 41	17 47	20 02	22 02	23 58

Sundays
19 July to 6 September

		EM	EM	EM	EM 1	EM	EM	EM
Matlock	d	10 42	12 38	14 37	16 42	18 38	20 42	22 42
Matlock Bath	d	10 44	12 40	14 39	16 44	18 40	20 44	22 44
Cromford	d	10 47	12 43	14 42	16 47	18 43	20 47	22 47
Whatstandwell	d	10 52	12 48	14 47	16 52	18 48	20 52	22 52
Ambergate	d	10 57	12 53	14 51	16 57	18 53	20 56	23 00
Belper	d	11 04	13 00	14 58	17 04	19 02	21 03	23 07
Duffield	d	11 08	13 04	15 04	17 08	19 06	21 07	23 11
Derby 10	a	11 16	13 15	15 12	17 16	19 14	21 15	23 20
St Pancras International	a		16 15	18 04	19 59	22 27		
Long Eaton	a	11 31	13 30	15 25	17 29	20 15	21 28	
Attenborough	a	11 38	13 37	15 32	17 36		21 35	
Beeston	a	11 41	13 40	15 35	17 39		21 38	
Nottingham	a	11 49	13 48	15 42	17 47	20 07	21 45	

Sundays
from 13 September

		EM	EM	EM	EM 1	EM	EM	EM
Matlock	d	10 42	12 38	14 37	16 42	18 42	20 42	22 42
Matlock Bath	d	10 44	12 40	14 39	16 44	18 44	20 44	22 44
Cromford	d	10 47	12 43	14 42	16 47	18 47	20 47	22 47
Whatstandwell	d	10 52	12 48	14 47	16 52	18 52	20 52	22 52
Ambergate	d	10 57	12 53	14 51	16 57	18 57	20 56	22 57
Belper	d	11 04	13 00	14 58	17 04	19 04	21 03	23 07
Duffield	d	11 08	13 04	15 02	17 08	19 08	21 07	23 11
Derby 10	a	11 16	13 12	15 10	17 16	19 16	21 15	23 20
St Pancras International	a	15 15		18 59	21 27	23 10		
Long Eaton	a	11 29	13 27	15 23	17 29	19 30	21 28	
Attenborough	a	11 36	13 34	15 30	17 36	19 37	21 35	
Beeston	a	11 39	13 37	15 33	17 39	19 40	21 38	
Nottingham	a	11 46	13 48	15 40	17 47	19 47	21 45	

For general notes see front of timetable
For details of catering facilities see Directory of Train Operators

Table 57

Nottingham, Derby and Leicester → Birmingham → Cardiff and Bristol

Network Diagram - see first page of Table 50

Miles	Miles	Miles			AW	XC	XC	XC	EM	AW	GW	XC	GW	XC	GW	XC	GW	GW	AW	XC	XC	XC	XC	EM	EM
					MX	MX	MX	MO	MX																
						■1 ◇	■1 ◇	■1	■1 ◇		■1 ◇	■1 ◇	■1 ◇	■1 ◇		■1 ◇	■1 ◇	◇		■1 ◇	■1	■1 ◇	■1 ◇		■1 ◇
						A	B	C	D	E						G		H	E	J			K	L	
						🛒	🛒		☕		☕	🛒	☕	🛒		🛒	☕			🛒		🛒	🛒		⊠ 🛒
0	—	—	**Nottingham** ■8	d					01 51													06 00		06 18	06 28
3¼	—	—	Beeston	d																		06 06		06 23	06a33
4¾	—	—	Attenborough	d																		06 10		06 27	
7¾	—	—	Long Eaton	d																		06 17		06 34	
13½	—	—	Spondon	d																		06 24		06 41	
16	—	—	**Derby** ■10	a					02 08													06 31		06 50	
—	—	—		d		21p28	21p28													06 10		06 36	06 47		
22¼	—	—	Willington	d																					
27	—	—	Burton-on-Trent	d		21p38	21p38													06 20		06 48	06 57		
40	—	—	Tamworth	d		21p49	21p52													06 31		07 00	07 08		
41¾	—	—	Wilnecote	d																		07 04			
—	0	—	**Leicester**	d				23p19													06 16				
—	1¾	—	South Wigston	d				23p25													06 22				
—	4¾	—	Narborough	d				23p30													06 27				
—	13½	—	Hinckley	d				23p38													06 35				
—	18¾	—	Nuneaton	d				23p46													06 43				
—	29¼	—	Coleshill Parkway	d				00 02													06 59				
—	31	—	Water Orton	d																					
56¾	38¾	—	**Birmingham New Street** ■12	a		22p07	22p07	00 15												06 52	07 15	07 24	07 27		
—	—	0		d		22p16	22p16					05 00		05 42		06 42				07 12		07 30			
83¾	—	—	Worcester Shrub Hill ■7	d														07 09							
98½	—	39¼	Ashchurch for Tewkesbury	d										06 34				07 25							
105¾	—	46½	Cheltenham Spa	d	23p00	23p33	23p33			05 37	05 55	06 03	06 30	06 43	06 57	07 25	07 30	07 35	07 45	07 52		08 16			
112¼	—	—	Gloucester ■7	a	23p12					05 48	06 04	06 16	06 41	06 53	07 07		07 39	07 44	07 56			08 26			
—	—	87	Bristol Parkway ■7	a		00 04	00 04								07 48	07 56		08 25		08 27					
—	—	92¾	**Bristol Temple Meads** ■10	a		00 18	00 18								08 02	08 08		08 37		08 41					
157	—	—	Newport (South Wales)	a	00 13					06 41		07 09		07 52					08 50			09 11			
168¾	—	—	**Cardiff Central** ■7	a	00 35					07 00		07 31		08 13					09 09			09 31			

		XC	XC	XC	EM	XC	GW		AW	XC	XC	XC	XC	EM	EM	EM	XC	XC	XC	XC	EM	EM	EM	EM	GW
				R																					
		■1 ◇	■1	■1	■1 ◇	■1 ◇	■1 ◇			■1 ◇	■1	■1 ◇	■1 ◇	■1 ◇			■1 ◇	■1 ◇	■1 ◇	■1	■1 ◇			■1 ◇	
				N					E	Q		U	V				X		Y			V	U	Z	AA
		🛒		🛒	⊠ 🛒	🛒	☕			🛒		🛒	🛒	☕			🛒	🛒	🛒		☕			☕	
Nottingham ■8	d			06 37	06 48							07 00	07 00	07 10	07 18	07 31				07 37		07 40	07 40	08 02	
Beeston	d			06 43	06a53							07 06	07 06	07a16	07 24	07a37				07 43		07 46	07 46	08a07	
Attenborough	d											07 10	07 10		07 27							07 49	07 50		
Long Eaton	d											07 17	07 17		07 35					07 51	07 59	08 03	08 03		
Spondon	d																					08 10	08 10		
Derby ■10	a			07 00								07 31	07 31		07 47					08 01	08 11	08 20	08 20		
	d			07 06						07 26		07 36	07 36				07 50			08 06					
Willington	d											07 43	07 43												
Burton-on-Trent	d			07 18						07 37		07 49	07 49				08 00			08 18					
Tamworth	d			07 30						07 49		08 01	08 01				08 11			08 30					
Wilnecote	d											08 05	08 05							08 34					
Leicester	d		06 43			07 09					07 24								07 49						
South Wigston	d		06 49																07 55						
Narborough	d		06 54								07 33								08 00						
Hinckley	d		07 02								07 42								08 08						
Nuneaton	d		07 10			07 30					07 50								08 17						
Coleshill Parkway	d		07 26			07 46					08 05								08 32						
Water Orton	d		07 30								08 09														
Birmingham New Street ■12	a		07 44	07 55		08 03				08 09	08 19	08 24	08 24				08 29		08 50	08 56					
	d	07 42								08 12		08 30	08 30					08 42							
Worcester Shrub Hill ■7	d																								09 00
Ashchurch for Tewkesbury	d																								09 21
Cheltenham Spa	d	08 25					08 31		08 45	08 52		09 11	09 11					09 25							09 31
Gloucester ■7	a						08 40		08 56			09 21	09 21												09 41
Bristol Parkway ■7	a	08 56								09 25								09 56							10 18
Bristol Temple Meads ■10	a	09 13								09 41								10 16							10 38
Newport (South Wales)	a								09 50			10 11	10 11												
Cardiff Central ■7	a								10 09			10 30	10 31												

For general notes see front of timetable
For details of catering facilities see Directory of Train Operators

- **A** Until 4 September. From Edinburgh (Table 51)
- **B** From 8 September. From Edinburgh (Table 51)
- **C** Until 13 July
- **D** Also stops at Beeston dep 0137
- **E** To Maesteg (Table 128)
- **G** To Paignton (Table 51)
- **H** To Weymouth (Table 123)
- **J** To Plymouth (Table 51)
- **K** From Sheffield (Table 51)
- **L** To Matlock (Table 56)
- **N** To Bournemouth (Table 51)
- **Q** From Leeds to Plymouth (Table 51)
- **U** From 7 September
- **V** Until 4 September
- **X** From Leeds (Table 51)
- **Y** From Stansted Airport (Table 49)
- **Z** From Lincoln (Table 27)
- **AA** From Great Malvern (Table 71) to Westbury (Table 123)

From Monday 28 September a revised service will be in operation due to seasonal difficulties. Some East Midlands trains will be retimed between 1 and 3 minutes. Passengers should check with National Rail Enquiries for precise times.

Nottingham, Derby and Leicester → Birmingham → Cardiff and Bristol

Network Diagram - see first page of Table 50

		GW	XC 1◇ A	XC 1◇ B	XC 1 C	XC 1◇	EM D	XC 1◇	LM	XC 1◇ E	XC 1◇		XC 1	EM 1◇ G	EM 1◇ H	EM 1◇	GW 1◇	AW J	XC 1◇ K	XC 1	XC 1◇	EM G	EM H	XC 1◇	XC 1◇
Nottingham 8	d					08 08	08 15						08 37			09 02					09 08	09 18	09 18		
Beeston	d						08 24						08 43			09a07						09 24	09 24		
Attenborough	d						08 27															09 27	09 27		
Long Eaton	d						08 34						08 51	09 00	09 00							09 35	09 35		
Spondon	d						08 41						08 57												
Derby 10	a					08 32	08 50						09 03	09 10	09 15						09 32	09 48	09 49		
	d		08 26	08 28		08 37		08 53					09 07						09 28		09 37			09 53	
Willington	d																								
Burton-on-Trent	d		08 38	08 38		08 49							09 19						09 38		09 49				
Tamworth	d		08 49	08 49		09 01							09 30								10 01				
Wilnecote	d																								
Leicester	d				08 16						08 49									09 16					
South Wigston	d																								
Narborough	d				08 25															09 25					
Hinckley	d				08 34															09 34					
Nuneaton	d				08 41						09 10									09 42					
Coleshill Parkway	d				08 57						09 25									09 57					
Water Orton	d																			10 01					
Birmingham New Street 12	a		09 09	09 09	09 15	09 24		09 27			09 43		09 56						10 07	10 15	10 24			10 27	
	d		09 12	09 12		09 30				09 42									10 12		10 30				10 42
Worcester Shrub Hill 7	d								09 56																
Ashchurch for Tewkesbury	d								10 10																
Cheltenham Spa	d	09 40	09 52	09 52		10 11			10 19	10 25							10 31	10 45	10 52		11 11				11 25
Gloucester 7	a	09 51				10 21			10 29								10 40	10 56			11 21				
Bristol Parkway 7	a		10 26	10 26						10 56									11 26						11 56
Bristol Temple Meads 10	a		10 41	10 41						11 13									11 38						12 13
Newport (South Wales)	a					11 11												11 50			12 11				
Cardiff Central 7	a					11 31												12 10			12 31				

		XC 1◇	XC 1	EM 1◇ G	EM 1◇ H	EM 1◇	GW ◇ L	GW	AW J	XC 1◇ N	XC 1 C	XC 1◇	EM H	EM G	XC 1◇		XC 1◇	XC 1◇	XC 1	EM 1◇ G	EM 1◇ H	EM 1◇	GW 1◇	LM	XC 1◇ Q
Nottingham 8	d		09 37			10 02						10 08	10 18	10 18					10 37			11 02			
Beeston	d		09 43			10a07							10 24	10 24					10 43			11a07			
Attenborough	d												10 27	10 27											
Long Eaton	d		09 51	09 57	09 57								10 35	10 35					10 51	10 57	10 57				
Spondon	d																								
Derby 10	a		10 01	10 08	10 15							10 32	10 48	10 49					11 01	11 07	11 15				
	d		10 06							10 28		10 37			10 53				11 06						11 28
Willington	d																								
Burton-on-Trent	d		10 18									10 49							11 18						
Tamworth	d		10 30							10 48		11 01							11 30						
Wilnecote	d		10 34																						
Leicester	d	09 49									10 16							10 49							
South Wigston	d										10 22														
Narborough	d										10 27														
Hinckley	d										10 35														
Nuneaton	d	10 10									10 42							11 10							
Coleshill Parkway	d	10 25									10 59							11 25							
Water Orton	d																								
Birmingham New Street 12	a	10 43	10 56							11 09	11 15	11 24			11 27			11 43	11 56						12 04
	d									11 12		11 30					11 42								12 12
Worcester Shrub Hill 7	d						11 06																	12 15	
Ashchurch for Tewkesbury	d						11 21																	12 30	
Cheltenham Spa	d						11 32	11 40	11 45	11 52		12 11					12 25						12 31	12 40	12 52
Gloucester 7	a						11 42	11 50	11 57			12 21											12 40	12 53	
Bristol Parkway 7	a						12 19			12 26							12 56								13 24
Bristol Temple Meads 10	a						12 35			12 41							13 13								13 39
Newport (South Wales)	a								12 50			13 11													
Cardiff Central 7	a								13 10			13 31													

For general notes see front of timetable
For details of catering facilities see Directory of Train Operators

- **A** Until 4 September. From York to Plymouth (Table 51)
- **B** From 7 September. From York to Plymouth (Table 51)
- **C** From Cambridge (Table 49)
- **D** To Matlock (Table 56)
- **E** To Paignton (Table 51)
- **G** From 7 September
- **H** Until 4 September
- **J** To Maesteg (Table 128)
- **K** From Newcastle to Plymouth (Table 51)
- **L** From Great Malvern (Table 71) to Brighton (Table 123)
- **N** From Edinburgh to Plymouth (Table 51)
- **Q** To Plymouth (Table 51)

From Monday 28 September a revised service will be in operation due to seasonal difficulties. Some East Midlands trains will be retimed between 1 and 3 minutes. Passengers should check with National Rail Enquiries for precise times.

Nottingham, Derby and Leicester → Birmingham → Cardiff and Bristol

Network Diagram - see first page of Table 50

		XC 1	XC 1◇	EM A	EM B	XC 1◇	XC 1◇	XC 1◇	XC 1	EM 1◇ A	EM 1◇ B	EM 1◇	GW ◇ C	GW	AW D	XC 1◇ E	XC 1 G	XC 1◇	EM		XC 1◇	XC 1◇ H	XC 1◇	XC 1	EM 1◇ A
Nottingham 8	d		11 08	11 18	11 18				11 37			12 02						12 08	12 18					12 37	
Beeston	d			11 24	11 24				11 43			12a07							12 24					12 43	
Attenborough	d			11 27	11 27														12 27						
Long Eaton	d			11 35	11 35				11 51	11 57	11 57								12 35					12 51	12 57
Spondon	d																								
Derby 10	a		11 32	11 51	11 52				12 01	12 07	12 15							12 32	12 48					13 01	13 07
	d		11 37			11 53			12 06							12 28		12 37			12 53			13 06	
Willington	d																							13 14	
Burton-on-Trent	d		11 49						12 18									12 49						13 20	
Tamworth	d		12 01						12 30							12 48		13 01						13 33	
Wilnecote	d								12 34																
Leicester	d	11 16						11 49									12 16						12 49		
South Wigston	d																12 22								
Narborough	d	11 25															12 27								
Hinckley	d	11 34															12 35								
Nuneaton	d	11 42						12 10									12 42						13 10		
Coleshill Parkway	d	11 57						12 25									12 59						13 25		
Water Orton	d	12 01																							
Birmingham New Street 12	a	12 15	12 24			12 27		12 43	12 56							13 09	13 15	13 24			13 27		13 43	13 56	
	d		12 30				12 42									13 12		13 30				13 42			
Worcester Shrub Hill 7	d												13 06												
Ashchurch for Tewkesbury	d												13 21												
Cheltenham Spa	d		13 11				13 25						13 31	13 40	13 45	13 52		14 11				14 25			
Gloucester 7	a		13 21										13 41	13 50	13 57			14 21							
Bristol Parkway 7	a						13 56						14 18			14 27						14 56			
Bristol Temple Meads 10	a						14 13						14 40			14 41						15 13			
Newport (South Wales)	a		14 11												14 51			15 11							
Cardiff Central 7	a		14 31												15 10			15 31							

		EM 1◇ B	EM 1◇	GW 1◇	LM	AW D	XC 1◇ E	XC 1	XC 1◇	EM A	EM B	XC 1◇	XC 1◇	XC 1◇	XC 1	EM 1◇	EM 1◇ B	EM 1◇	GW ◇ C	GW	XC 1◇ J	XC 1	XC 1◇		EM
Nottingham 8	d		13 02						13 08	13 18	13 18				13 37			14 02					14 08		14 18
Beeston	d		13a07							13 24	13 24				13 43			14a07							14 24
Attenborough	d									13 27	13 27														14 27
Long Eaton	d	12 57								13 35	13 36				13 51	13 57	13 57								14 35
Spondon	d																								
Derby 10	a	13 15							13 32	13 48	13 48				14 01	14 07	14 15						14 32		14 48
	d						13 28		13 37			13 53			14 06						14 28		14 37		
Willington	d																								
Burton-on-Trent	d						13 38		13 49						14 18								14 49		
Tamworth	d								14 01						14 30						14 48		15 01		
Wilnecote	d														14 34										
Leicester	d							13 16						13 49								14 16			
South Wigston	d																					14 22			
Narborough	d							13 25														14 27			
Hinckley	d							13 34														14 35			
Nuneaton	d							13 42						14 10								14 42			
Coleshill Parkway	d							13 57						14 25								14 59			
Water Orton	d							14 01																	
Birmingham New Street 12	a						14 07	14 15	14 24			14 27		14 43	14 56						15 07	15 15	15 24		
	d						14 12		14 30				14 42								15 12		15 30		
Worcester Shrub Hill 7	d				14 13														15 06						
Ashchurch for Tewkesbury	d				14 27														15 21						
Cheltenham Spa	d			14 31	14 36	14 45	14 52		15 11				15 25						15 31	15 40	15 52		16 11		
Gloucester 7	a			14 40	14 53	14 56			15 21										15 41	15 51			16 21		
Bristol Parkway 7	a						15 24						15 56						16 18		16 26				
Bristol Temple Meads 10	a						15 41						16 13						16 38		16 41				
Newport (South Wales)	a					15 50			16 11														17 11		
Cardiff Central 7	a					16 10			16 31														17 31		

For general notes see front of timetable
For details of catering facilities see Directory of Train Operators

A From 7 September
B Until 4 September
C From Great Malvern (Table 71) to Weymouth (Table 123)
D To Maesteg (Table 128)
E From Dundee to Plymouth (Table 51)
G From Cambridge (Table 49)
H Fridays to Exeter St Davids (Table 51)
J From Glasgow Central to Penzance (Table 51)

From Monday 28 September a revised service will be in operation due to seasonal difficulties. Some East Midlands trains will be retimed between 1 and 3 minutes. Passengers should check with National Rail Enquiries for precise times.

Table 57

Mondays to Fridays

Nottingham, Derby and Leicester → Birmingham → Cardiff and Bristol

Network Diagram - see first page of Table 50

		XC 1◊	XC 1◊ A	XC 1◊	XC 1	EM 1◊ B	EM 1◊ C	EM 1◊	GW 1◊	LM	AW D	XC 1◊ E	XC 1	XC 1◊	EM B	EM C	XC 1◊	XC 1◊	XC 1◊	XC 1	EM 1◊ B	EM 1◊ C	EM 1◊	GW G	GW H
Nottingham 8	d				14 37			15 02						15 08	15 18	15 18				15 37			16 02		
Beeston	d				14 43			15a07							15 24	15 24				15 43			16a07		
Attenborough	d														15 27	15 27									
Long Eaton	d				14 51	14 57	14 57								15 35	15 35				15 51	15 57	15 57			
Spondon	d																								
Derby 10	a				15 01	15 07	15 15							15 32	15 50	15 51				16 01	16 07	16 15			
	d	14 53			15 06							15 28		15 37			15 53			16 06					
Willington	d																								
Burton-on-Trent	d				15 18							15 38		15 49						16 18					
Tamworth	d				15 30									16 01						16 30					
Wilnecote	d																			16 34					
Leicester	d			14 49									15 16						15 49						
South Wigston	d																								
Narborough	d												15 26												
Hinckley	d												15 34												
Nuneaton	d			15 10									15 42						16 10						
Coleshill Parkway	d			15 25									15 57						16 25						
Water Orton	d												16 01												
Birmingham New Street 12	a	15 27		15 43	15 56							16 08	16 15	16 24			16 27		16 43	16 56					
	d		15 42									16 12		16 30				16 42							
Worcester Shrub Hill 7	d									16 01															17 06
Ashchurch for Tewkesbury	d									16 23				17 05											17 21
Cheltenham Spa	d		16 25						16 31	16 36	16 45	16 52		17 15				17 25						17 31	17 40
Gloucester 7	a								16 40	16 53	16 56			17 25										17 39	17 50
Bristol Parkway 7	a		16 56									17 24						17 56						18 19	
Bristol Temple Meads 10	a		17 13									17 41						18 13						18 37	
Newport (South Wales)	a										17 50			18 11											
Cardiff Central 7	a										18 10			18 31											

		AW D	XC 1◊ J	XC 1 K		XC 1◊	EM	EM L	XC 1◊	XC 1◊	XC 1◊	XC 1	EM 1◊ B	EM 1◊ C	EM	EM 1◊	GW 1◊	LM	AW D	XC 1◊ N	XC 1	XC 1◊	EM U	EM V	EM L
Nottingham 8	d					16 08	16 18	16 32				16 37			16 50	17 02						17 08	17 18	17 18	17 32
Beeston	d						16 24					16 43			16 55	17a07							17 24	17 24	
Attenborough	d						16 27	16a39							16 58								17 27	17 27	17a39
Long Eaton	d						16 35					16 51	16 57	16 57	17 07								17 35	17 35	
Spondon	d																						17 42	17 42	
Derby 10	a					16 32	16 48					17 01	17 07	17 15	17 23							17 32	17 49	17 51	
	d		16 28			16 37			16 53			17 06								17 28		17 37			
Willington	d																								
Burton-on-Trent	d					16 49						17 18								17 38		17 49			
Tamworth	d		16 48			17 01						17 30										18 01			
Wilnecote	d																								
Leicester	d			16 16							16 49										17 16				
South Wigston	d			16 22																	17 22				
Narborough	d			16 27																	17 27				
Hinckley	d			16 35																	17 35				
Nuneaton	d			16 42							17 10										17 42				
Coleshill Parkway	d			16 59							17 25										17 59				
Water Orton	d																								
Birmingham New Street 12	a		17 07	17 15		17 24			17 27		17 43	17 56								18 07	18 15	18 24			
	d		17 12			17 30				17 42										18 12		18 30			
Worcester Shrub Hill 7	d																	18 14							
Ashchurch for Tewkesbury	d					18 08												18 29							
Cheltenham Spa	d	17 45	17 52			18 18				18 25							18 31	18a38	18 45	18 52		19 15			
Gloucester 7	a	17 57				18 28				18 35							18 45		18 56			19 25			
Bristol Parkway 7	a		18 24							19 08										19 26					
Bristol Temple Meads 10	a		18 41							19 25										19 39					
Newport (South Wales)	a	18 51				19 14													19 50			20 11			
Cardiff Central 7	a	19 09				19 35													20 12			20 31			

For general notes see front of timetable
For details of catering facilities see Directory of Train Operators

- **A** To Paignton (Table 51)
- **B** From 7 September
- **C** Until 4 September
- **D** To Maesteg (Table 128)
- **E** From Aberdeen to Penzance (Table 51)
- **G** To Westbury (Table 123)
- **H** From Worcester Foregate Street (Table 71) to Southampton Central (Table 123)
- **J** From Edinburgh to Penzance (Table 51)
- **K** From Cambridge (Table 49)
- **L** From Lincoln (Table 27)
- **N** From Edinburgh to Plymouth (Table 51). All Mondays to Thursdays and Fridays until 4 September
- **U** From 7 September. To Matlock (Table 56)
- **V** Until 4 September. To Matlock (Table 56)

From Monday 28 September a revised service will be in operation due to seasonal difficulties. Some East Midlands trains will be retimed between 1 and 3 minutes. Passengers should check with National Rail Enquiries for precise times.

Nottingham, Derby and Leicester → Birmingham → Cardiff and Bristol

Network Diagram - see first page of Table 50

Station		XC 1◇	XC 1◇	XC 1◇ A	XC 1	EM 1◇ B	EM 1◇ C	EM 1◇		GW ◇ D	AW E	XC 1◇ G	XC 1 H	GW	XC 1◇	EM C	EM B	XC 1◇	XC 1◇ J	XC 1◇	XC 1	EM 1◇ B	EM 1◇ C	EM 1◇	GW 1
Nottingham 8	d				17 37			18 02							18 08	18 18	18 18				18 37			19 02	
Beeston	d				17 43			18a07								18 24	18 24				18 43			19a07	
Attenborough	d															18 27	18 27								
Long Eaton	d				17 51	18 01	18 01									18 36	18 37				18 51	18 56	18 56		
Spondon	d				17 57																				
Derby 10	a				18 03	18 13	18 15								18 32	18 48	18 48				19 01	19 07	19 15		
	d	17 53			18 06							18 28			18 36			18 53			19 06				
Willington	d				18 14																				
Burton-on-Trent	d				18 20										18 49						19 18				
Tamworth	d				18 33							18 48			19 01						19 30				
Wilnecote	d				18 36																				
Leicester	d			17 49									18 19							18 49					
South Wigston	d			17 55									18 25												
Narborough	d			18 01									18 30												
Hinckley	d			18 09									18 38												
Nuneaton	d			18 17									18 46							19 10					
Coleshill Parkway	d			18 33									19 02							19 25					
Water Orton	d																								
Birmingham New Street 12	a	18 27		18 50	18 56							19 08	19 15		19 24			19 27		19 43	19 56				
	d		18 42									19 12			19 30				19 42						
Worcester Shrub Hill 7	d									19 06															
Ashchurch for Tewkesbury	d									19 21															
Cheltenham Spa	d		19 25							19 31	19 45	19 52		20 00	20 11				20 25						20 48
Gloucester 7	a									19 39	19 56			20 10	20 21										20 58
Bristol Parkway 7	a		19 56							20 18		20 27							20 56						
Bristol Temple Meads 10	a		20 13							20 38		20 41							21 13						
Newport (South Wales)	a		20 47								20 51				21 11										
Cardiff Central 7	a		21 07								21 10				21 31										

Station		XC 1◇ K	XC 1	GW	XC 1◇	EM	EM L	XC 1◇	XC 1◇	XC 1◇	XC 1	EM 1◇		EM 1◇	AW	XC 1◇ N	XC 1	EM 1◇ C	EM 1◇ B	EM B	EM C	EM	XC 1◇	XC 1◇	XC 1
Nottingham 8	d				19 08	19 18	19 32				19 37	20 02						20 07	20 07	20 11	20 11	20 32			20 37
Beeston	d					19 24	19a38				19 43	20a07								20 17	20 17	20a38			20 43
Attenborough	d					19 27					19 46									20 20	20 20				
Long Eaton	d					19 35					19 51			20 07				20 23	20 23	20 28	20 28				20 51
Spondon	d																								
Derby 10	a				19 32	19 48					20 01			20 19				20 34	20 35	20 44	20 46				21 01
	d	19 28			19 37			19 53			20 06					20 28							20 53		21 06
Willington	d																								21 14
Burton-on-Trent	d	19 38			19 49						20 18														21 20
Tamworth	d				20 01						20 30					20 48									21 33
Wilnecote	d										20 34														21 37
Leicester	d		19 16							19 49							20 16							20 49	
South Wigston	d		19 22														20 22								
Narborough	d		19 27														20 27								
Hinckley	d		19 35														20 35								
Nuneaton	d		19 42							20 10							20 42							21 10	
Coleshill Parkway	d		19 59							20 25							20 59							21 25	
Water Orton	d																								21 45
Birmingham New Street 12	a	20 09	20 15		20 24			20 27		20 43	20 56					21 07	21 15						21 40	21 43	21 57
	d	20 12			20 30				20 42							21 12									
Worcester Shrub Hill 7	d																								
Ashchurch for Tewkesbury	d																								
Cheltenham Spa	d	20 52		21 00	21 11				21 25						21 45	21 52									
Gloucester 7	a			21 11	21 21										21 58										
Bristol Parkway 7	a	21 25		21 52					22 00							22 23									
Bristol Temple Meads 10	a	21 38		22 10					22 19							22 41									
Newport (South Wales)	a				22 11										22 59										
Cardiff Central 7	a				22 31										23 21										

For general notes see front of timetable
For details of catering facilities see Directory of Train Operators

- **A** From Stansted Airport (Table 49)
- **B** From 7 September
- **C** Until 4 September
- **D** From Great Malvern (Table 71) to Weymouth (Table 123)
- **E** To Maesteg (Table 128)
- **G** From Edinburgh to Plymouth (Table 51)
- **H** From Cambridge (Table 49)
- **J** To Plymouth (Table 51)
- **K** From Edinburgh to Plymouth (Table51)
- **L** From Lincoln (Table 27)
- **N** From Edinburgh (Table 51)

From Monday 28 September a revised service will be in operation due to seasonal difficulties. Some East Midlands trains will be retimed between 1 and 3 minutes. Passengers should check with National Rail Enquiries for precise times.

Table 57

Mondays to Fridays

Nottingham, Derby and Leicester → Birmingham → Cardiff and Bristol

Network Diagram - see first page of Table 50

		NT	EM	EM	GW	GW	GW	AW	GW	XC	XC	XC	EM	XC	LM	XC	EM	XC	XC	EM	EM	EM	EM
															FO								
		◇	1 ◇	1 ◇			1 ◇			1 ◇	1	1 ◇		1 ◇		1	1 ◇	1 ◇	1 ◇				1 ◇
						A												B			C	D	
			⊏P	⊏P			⊏P			⚲		⚲					⊏P	⚲	⚲				⊏P
Nottingham 8	d	20 45		21 02									21 15			21 37				22 16	23 15	23 15	
Beeston	d			21a07									21 21			21 43				22 22	23 21	23 21	
Attenborough	d												21 25			21 46				22 25	23 24	23 24	
Long Eaton	d		21 05										21 33			21 53	21 59			22 33	23 32	23 33	23 38
Spondon	d															21 59							
Derby 10	a	21 05	21 15										21 50			22 05	22 12			22 52	23 48	23 49	23 50
	d									21 28				22 00		22 10		22 45					
Willington	d																						
Burton-on-Trent	d									21 38						22 21		22 56					
Tamworth	d									21 48						22 33		23 06					
Wilnecote	d															22 37							
Leicester	d										21 16	21 49							22 49				
South Wigston	d										21 22												
Narborough	d										21 27												
Hinckley	d										21 35												
Nuneaton	d										21 42	22 10							23 10				
Coleshill Parkway	d										21 59	22 25							23 25				
Water Orton	d																						
Birmingham New Street 12	a									22 07	22 15	22 43		22 54		23 05		23 34	23 43				
	d									22 16					23 00								
Worcester Shrub Hill 7	d					21 31			22 32						23 45								
Ashchurch for Tewkesbury	d					21 52			22 51						23 59								
Cheltenham Spa	d				22 00	22 05	22 31	23 00	23 05	23 33					00 08								
Gloucester 7	a				22 10	22 21	22 41	23 12	23 18						00 18								
Bristol Parkway 7	a						23 16			00 04													
Bristol Temple Meads 10	a						23 37			00 20													
Newport (South Wales)	a							00 13															
Cardiff Central 7	a							00 35															

Saturdays

until 5 September

		AW	XC	LM	EM	GW	XC	XC	GW	GW	XC	XC	GW	LM	AW	XC	XC	EM	EM	XC	XC	XC	XC	AW	XC
																							R		
			1 ◇		1 ◇		1 ◇	1 ◇		◇	1 ◇	1	1 ◇			1 ◇	1 ◇	1 ◇		1 ◇	1 ◇	1	1		1 ◇
			B						E	G	H				J	K			L	N			Q	J	U
			⚲		⊏P		⚲	⚲			⚲		⊏P			⚲	⚲	⊏P		⚲	⚲		⚲		⚲
Nottingham 8	d				01 51												05 57	06 02	06 10				06 37		
Beeston	d																06 03	06a07	06 17				06 43		
Attenborough	d																06 06		06 21						
Long Eaton	d																06 16		06 29						
Spondon	d																06 23		06 40						
Derby 10	a				02 08												06 30		06 46				07 00		
	d		21p28													06 10	06 36			06 47			07 06		07 25
Willington	d																								
Burton-on-Trent	d		21p38													06 20	06 48			06 57			07 18		07 36
Tamworth	d		21p49													06 31	07 00			07 08			07 30		07 48
Wilnecote	d																07 04								
Leicester	d											05 49										06 49			
South Wigston	d											05 55										06 55			
Narborough	d											06 00										07 00			
Hinckley	d											06 08										07 08			
Nuneaton	d											06 15										07 15			
Coleshill Parkway	d											06 31										07 31			
Water Orton	d																					07 36			
Birmingham New Street 12	a		22p07									06 45				06 50	07 24			07 27		07 47	07 50		08 08
	d		22p16	23p00			05 00	05 42			06 42					07 12	07 30				07 42				08 12
Worcester Shrub Hill 7	d			23p45						06 48				07 15											
Ashchurch for Tewkesbury	d			23p59				06 33		07 04				07 30											
Cheltenham Spa	d	23p00	23p33	00 08		05 30	06 04	06 43	06 48	07 14	07 25		07 29	07 39	07 45	07 52	08 11				08 25			08 45	08 52
Gloucester 7	a	23p12		00 18		05 40	06 13	06 54	06 58	07 25			07 38	07 50	07 56		08 21							08 56	
Bristol Parkway 7	a		00 04						07 39	08 18	07 56					08 24					08 56				09 25
Bristol Temple Meads 10	a		00 18						07 54	08 34	08 11					08 38					09 13				09 38
Newport (South Wales)	a	00 13					07 06	07 52							08 50		09 05							09 50	
Cardiff Central 7	a	00 35					07 25	08 13							09 10		09 25							10 10	

For general notes see front of timetable
For details of catering facilities see Directory of Train Operators

- **A** From Great Malvern (Table 71)
- **B** From Edinburgh (Table 51)
- **C** Until 4 September
- **D** From 7 September
- **E** To Weston-super-Mare (Table 134)
- **G** To Weymouth (Table 123)
- **H** To Paignton (Table 51)
- **J** To Maesteg (Table 128)
- **K** To Plymouth (Table 51)
- **L** To Matlock (Table 56)
- **N** From Sheffield (Table 51)
- **Q** To Bournemouth (Table 51)
- **U** From Leeds to Plymouth (Table 51)

From Monday 28 September a revised service will be in operation due to seasonal difficulties. Some East Midlands trains will be retimed between 1 and 3 minutes. Passengers should check with National Rail Enquiries for precise times.

Nottingham, Derby and Leicester → Birmingham → Cardiff and Bristol

Network Diagram - see first page of Table 50

		XC	GW	XC	EM	EM	EM	XC	XC	XC	XC	XC	EM	EM	GW	XC	XC	XC	GW	XC	XC		XC	XC	XC
		1 ◇	1 ◇	1 ◇	1 ◇			1 ◇	1 ◇	1 ◇	1 ◇	1	1 ◇	1 ◇		1 ◇	1	1 ◇		1 ◇	1 ◇		1 ◇	1 ◇	1
								A	B	C	D			E	G	H	J	D					K		
Nottingham 8	d			06 56	07 02	07 14	07 31				07 08	07 35		08 02						08 08					08 36
Beeston	d			07 03	07a07	07 21	07a37					07 41		08a07											08 42
Attenborough	d			07 06		07 25																			
Long Eaton	d			07 14		07 34						07 49	07 56												08 50
Spondon	d			07 24																					
Derby 10	a			07 29		07 49						07 59	08 16							08 32					09 01
	d			07 35				07 50				08 07				08 28				08 36	08 53				09 06
Willington	d			07 43																					
Burton-on-Trent	d			07 49				08 00				08 18				08 38				08 48					09 18
Tamworth	d			08 01				08 09				08 30				08 48				09 00					09 30
Wilnecote	d			08 05								08 34													
Leicester	d	07 16								07 49	07 49						08 16	08 21						08 49	
South Wigston	d																08 22	08 27							
Narborough	d																08 27	08 32							
Hinckley	d																08 35	08 40							
Nuneaton	d	07 36								08 10	08 10						08 43	08 48						09 10	
Coleshill Parkway	d	07 52								08 25	08 25						08 59	09 04						09 25	
Water Orton	d																								
Birmingham New Street 12	a	08 09		08 24				08 29		08 43	08 43	08 56				09 07	09 14	09 16		09 24	09 27			09 43	09 56
	d			08 30					08 42							09 12				09 30			09 42		
Worcester Shrub Hill 7	d														09 08										
Ashchurch for Tewkesbury	d														09 25										
Cheltenham Spa	d		09 00	09 11					09 25						09 35	09 52			10 01	10 11			10 26		
Gloucester 7	a		09 10	09 21											09 44				10 11	10 21					
Bristol Parkway 7	a								09 56						10 24	10 26							10 57		
Bristol Temple Meads 10	a								10 13						10 39	10 41							11 13		
Newport (South Wales)	a			10 05																11 05					
Cardiff Central 7	a			10 25																11 25					

		EM	EM	LM	AW	XC	XC	GW	XC	XC	XC	XC	XC	EM	EM	GW	AW	XC	XC	XC	GW	XC	XC	XC	XC
		1 ◇	1 ◇			1 ◇	1 ◇	1 ◇	1 ◇	1 ◇	1 ◇	1 ◇	1	1 ◇	1 ◇	◇		1 ◇	1	1 ◇		1 ◇	1 ◇	1 ◇	1 ◇
					L	N										Q	L	U	J	V					
Nottingham 8	d		09 02						09 08				09 20		10 02					09 51		10 08			
Beeston	d		09a07										09 26		10a07										
Attenborough	d												09 29												
Long Eaton	d	09 01											09 36	09 57											
Spondon	d												09 45												
Derby 10	a	09 20							09 32				09 50	10 16								10 32			
	d					09 28			09 36	09 53			09 57					10 28				10 36	10 53		
Willington	d																								
Burton-on-Trent	d					09 38			09 48				10b18					10 48				10 48			
Tamworth	d								10 00				10 30									11 00			
Wilnecote	d												10 34												
Leicester	d						09 16					09 49							10 16	10 16					10 49
South Wigston	d																		10 22	10 22					
Narborough	d						09 25												10 27	10 27					
Hinckley	d						09 34												10 35	10 35					
Nuneaton	d						09 42					10 10							10 43	10 43					11 10
Coleshill Parkway	d						09 57					10 25							10 59	10 59					11 25
Water Orton	d						10 01																		
Birmingham New Street 12	a					10 06	10 14		10 24	10 27		10 43	10 56					11 07	11 14	11 14		11 24	11 27		11 43
	d					10 12			10 30		10 42							11 12				11 30		11 42	
Worcester Shrub Hill 7	d			10 14												11 08									
Ashchurch for Tewkesbury	d			10 29												11 24									
Cheltenham Spa	d			10 40	10 45	10 52		11 00	11 11		11 25					11 34	11 45	11 52			12 01	12 11		12 25	
Gloucester 7	a			10 52	10 56			11 10	11 21							11 44	11 56				12 11	12 21			
Bristol Parkway 7	a					11 25					11 56					12 24		12 26						12 56	
Bristol Temple Meads 10	a					11 38					12 13					12 39		12 41						13 13	
Newport (South Wales)	a				11 50				12 05								12 50					13 06			
Cardiff Central 7	a				12 10				12 25								13 10					13 25			

For general notes see front of timetable
For details of catering facilities see Directory of Train Operators

- **A** From Leeds (Table 51)
- **B** To Newquay (Table 51)
- **C** Until 11 July
- **D** From 18 July
- **E** From Lincoln (Table 27)
- **G** To Westbury (Table 123)
- **H** From York to Plymouth (Table 51)
- **J** Until 11 July. From Cambridge (Table 49)
- **K** To Paignton (Table 51)
- **L** To Maesteg (Table 128)
- **N** From Newcastle to Penzance (Table 51)
- **Q** From Great Malvern (Table 71) to Brighton (Table 123)
- **U** From Edinburgh to Plymouth (Table 51)
- **V** From 18 July. From Stansted Airport (Table 49)
- **b** Arr. 1011

Table 57

Nottingham, Derby and Leicester → Birmingham → Cardiff and Bristol

Saturdays

until 5 September

Network Diagram - see first page of Table 50

		XC 1	EM 1◇	EM 1◇	LM A	XC 1◇ B	XC 1◇ C	GW 1◇	XC 1◇	XC 1◇	GW ◇ D	XC 1◇	XC 1◇	XC 1	EM 1◇	EM 1◇	AW E	XC 1◇ G	XC 1 H	XC 1◇ J		GW	XC 1◇	XC 1◇	XC 1◇ K
Nottingham 8	d	10 20		11 02					11 08					11 20		12 02				11 51			12 08		
Beeston	d	10 26		11a07										11 26		12a07									
Attenborough	d	10 29												11 29											
Long Eaton	d	10 36	10 57											11 36	11 57										
Spondon	d	10 45												11 45											
Derby 10	a	10 50	11 16						11 32					11 50	12 16								12 32		
	d	10 57				11 28			11 36	11 53				11 57				12 28					12 36	12 53	
Willington	d																								
Burton-on-Trent	d	11 18				11 38			11 48					12b18									12 48		
Tamworth	d	11 30							12 00					12 30				12 48					13 00		
Wilnecote	d													12 34											
Leicester	d						11 16						11 49						12 16	12 16					
South Wigston	d																		12 22	12 22					
Narborough	d						11 25												12 27	12 27					
Hinckley	d						11 34												12 35	12 35					
Nuneaton	d						11 42						12 10						12 43	12 43					
Coleshill Parkway	d						11 57						12 25						12 59	12 59					
Water Orton	d						12 01																		
Birmingham New Street 12	a	11 56				12 07	12 14		12 24	12 27			12 43	12 56				13 09	13 14	13 14			13 24	13 27	
	d					12 12			12 30			12 42						13 12					13 30		13 42
Worcester Shrub Hill 7	d				12 11						12 54														
Ashchurch for Tewkesbury	d				12 25						13 10														
Cheltenham Spa	d				12 36	12 52		13 00	13 11		13 20	13 25					13 45	13 52				14 01	14 11		14 25
Gloucester 7	a				12 51			13 10	13 21		13 32						13 56					14 11	14 21		
Bristol Parkway 7	a					13 24					14 21	13 58						14 26							14 56
Bristol Temple Meads 10	a					13 38					14 37	14 13						14 41							15 13
Newport (South Wales)	a								14 05								14 50						15 06		
Cardiff Central 7	a								14 25								15 09						15 25		

		XC 1◇	XC 1	EM 1◇	EM 1◇	LM	AW E	XC 1◇ L	XC 1 C	XC 1◇ J	GW 1◇	XC 1◇	XC 1◇	XC 1◇	XC 1◇	XC 1	EM 1◇	EM 1◇	GW ◇ N	XC 1◇ Q	XC 1◇	GW	XC 1◇	XC 1◇	XC 1◇
Nottingham 8	d		12 20		13 02					12 51		13 08				13 20		14 02					14 08		
Beeston	d		12 26		13a07											13 26		14a07							
Attenborough	d		12 29													13 29									
Long Eaton	d		12 37	12 57												13 36	13 57								
Spondon	d		12 45													13 45									
Derby 10	a		12 50	13 16								13 32				13 50	14 16						14 32		
	d		12 57					13 28				13 36	13 53			13 57				14 28			14 36	14 53	
Willington	d																								
Burton-on-Trent	d		13 18					13 38				13 48				14c18							14 48		
Tamworth	d		13 30									14 00				14 30				14 48			15 00		
Wilnecote	d															14 34									
Leicester	d	12 49							13 16	13 16					13 49						14 16				
South Wigston	d																				14 22				
Narborough	d								13 25	13 25											14 27				
Hinckley	d								13 34	13 34											14 35				
Nuneaton	d	13 10							13 42	13 42					14 10						14 43				
Coleshill Parkway	d	13 25							13 57	13 57					14 25						14 59				
Water Orton	d								14 01	14 01															
Birmingham New Street 12	a	13 43	13 56					14 07	14 14	14 14		14 24	14 27		14 43	14 56				15 08	15 14		15 24	15 27	
	d							14 12				14 30		14 42						15 12			15 30		15 42
Worcester Shrub Hill 7	d					14 10													15 08						
Ashchurch for Tewkesbury	d					14 25													15 24						
Cheltenham Spa	d					14 34	14 45	14 52			15 00	15 11		15 25					15 34	15 52		16 01	16 11		16 25
Gloucester 7	a					14 51	14 56				15 10	15 21							15 42			16 11	16 21		
Bristol Parkway 7	a							15 24						15 56					16 24	16 26					16 56
Bristol Temple Meads 10	a							15 41						16 13					16 39	16 41					17 13
Newport (South Wales)	a						15 50					16 05											17 05		
Cardiff Central 7	a						16 07					16 25											17 25		

For general notes see front of timetable
For details of catering facilities see Directory of Train Operators

- **A** From Worcester Foregate Street (Table 71)
- **B** From Edinburgh to Plymouth (Table 51)
- **C** Until 11 July
- **D** From Worcester Foregate Street (Table 71) to Weymouth (Table 123)
- **E** To Maesteg (Table 128)
- **G** From Glasgow Central to Newquay (Table 51)
- **H** Until 11 July. From Cambridge (Table 49)
- **J** From 18 July
- **K** To Paignton (Table 51)
- **L** From Dundee to Plymouth (Table 51)
- **N** From Great Malvern (Table 71) to Weymouth (Table 123)
- **Q** From Glasgow Central to Penzance (Table 51)
- **b** Arr. 1211
- **c** Arr. 1411

Table 57

Saturdays

until 5 September

Nottingham, Derby and Leicester → Birmingham → Cardiff and Bristol

Network Diagram - see first page of Table 50

		XC	XC	EM	EM	LM	AW	XC	XC	GW	XC	XC	XC	XC	XC	EM	EM	GW	AW		XC	XC	GW	XC	XC
		1 ◇	1	1 ◇	1 ◇			1 ◇	1 ◇	1 ◇	1 ◇	1 ◇	1 ◇	1 ◇	1	1 ◇	1 ◇				1 ◇	1 ◇		1 ◇	1 ◇
							A	B										C	A		D				
		⌶		⊡	⊡			⌶	⌶	⊡	⌶	⌶	⌶	⌶		⊡	⊡				⌶	⊡		⌶	⌶
Nottingham 8	d		14 20		15 02						15 08				15 20		16 02							16 08	
Beeston	d		14 26		15a07										15 26		16a07								
Attenborough	d		14 29												15 29										
Long Eaton	d		14 36	14 57											15 36	15 57									
Spondon	d		14 45												15 45										
Derby 10	a		14 50	15 16							15 32				15 50	16 16								16 32	
	d		14 57					15 28			15 36	15 53			15 57						16 28			16 36	16 53
Willington	d																							16 48	
Burton-on-Trent	d		15b18					15 38			15 48				16c18									17 00	
Tamworth	d		15 30								16 00				16 30						16 48				
Wilnecote	d														16 34										
Leicester	d	14 49							15 16					15 49								16 16			
South Wigston	d																					16 22			
Narborough	d								15 25													16 27			
Hinckley	d								15 34													16 35			
Nuneaton	d	15 10							15 42					16 10								16 43			
Coleshill Parkway	d	15 25							15 57					16 25								16 59			
Water Orton	d								16 01																
Birmingham New Street 12	a	15 43	15 56					16 07	16 14		16 24	16 27		16 43	16 56						17 07	17 14		17 24	17 27
	d							16 12			16 30		16 42								17 12			17 30	
Worcester Shrub Hill 7	d					16 11												17 08							
Ashchurch for Tewkesbury	d					16 26												17 24						18 08	
Cheltenham Spa	d					16 35	16 45	16 52		17 00	17 11		17 25					17 34	17 45		17 52		18 01	18 18	
Gloucester 7	a					16 51	16 56			17 10	17 21							17 44	17 56				18 11	18 28	
Bristol Parkway 7	a							17 24					17 56					18 24			18 26				
Bristol Temple Meads 10	a							17 38					18 13					18 39			18 41				
Newport (South Wales)	a						17 50				18 05								18 50					19 11	
Cardiff Central 7	a						18 10				18 25								19 10					19 32	

		XC	XC	XC	EM	EM	EM	LM	AW	XC	XC	GW	XC	XC	XC	XC	XC	EM	EM	EM	GW	AW	XC	XC	XC
																									SX
		1 ◇	1 ◇	1		1 ◇	1 ◇			1 ◇	1 ◇	1 ◇	1 ◇	1 ◇	1 ◇	1 ◇	1		1 ◇	1 ◇	◇		1 ◇	1	1 ◇
		E			G				A	H								G			J	A	H	K	L
		⌶	⌶			⊡	⊡			⌶	⌶	⊡	⌶	⌶	⌶	⌶			⊡	⊡			⌶		⌶
Nottingham 8	d			16 20	16 32		17 02						17 08				17 20	17 32		18 02					17 47
Beeston	d			16 26			17a07										17 26			18a07					
Attenborough	d			16 29	16a39												17 29	17a39							
Long Eaton	d			16 36		16 56											17 36		17 57						
Spondon	d			16 45													17 45								
Derby 10	a			16 50		17 16							17 32				17 50		18 16						
	d			16 57						17 28			17 36	17 53			17 57						18 28		
Willington	d																								
Burton-on-Trent	d			17 18						17 38			17 48				18e18								
Tamworth	d			17 30									18 00				18 30						18 48		
Wilnecote	d																18 34								
Leicester	d		16 49								17 16					17 49								18 16	18 16
South Wigston	d										17 22													18 22	18 22
Narborough	d										17 27													18 27	18 27
Hinckley	d										17 35													18 35	18 35
Nuneaton	d		17 10								17 43					18 10								18 43	18 43
Coleshill Parkway	d		17 25								17 59					18 25								18 59	18 59
Water Orton	d																								
Birmingham New Street 12	a		17 43	17 56						18 07	18 14		18 24	18 27		18 43	18 57						19 07	19 14	19 14
	d	17 42								18 12			18 30		18 42								19 12		
Worcester Shrub Hill 7	d							18 10													19 08				
Ashchurch for Tewkesbury	d							18 25													19 24				
Cheltenham Spa	d	18 25						18 34	18 45	18 52		19 00	19 11		19 25						19 34	19 45	19 52		
Gloucester 7	a	18 35						18 52	18 56			19 10	19 21								19 44	19 56			
Bristol Parkway 7	a	19 08								19 26					19 56						20 23		20 26		
Bristol Temple Meads 10	a	19 27								19 41					20 13						20 39		20 41		
Newport (South Wales)	a								19 50				20 05		20 54							20 50			
Cardiff Central 7	a								20 11				20 25		21 16							21 09			

For general notes see front of timetable
For details of catering facilities see Directory of Train Operators

A To Maesteg (Table 128)
B From Aberdeen to Penzance (Table 51)
C From Great Malvern (Table 71) to Westbury (Table 123)
D From Edinburgh to Penzance (Table 51)
E To Paignton (Table 51)
G From Lincoln (Table 27)
H From Edinburgh to Plymouth (Table 51)
J From Great Malvern (Table 71) to Weymouth (Table 123)
K Until 11 July. From Cambridge (Table 49)
L From 18 July. From Stansted Airport (Table 49)
b Arr. 1511
c Arr. 1611
e Arr. 1811

Table 57

Saturdays

Nottingham, Derby and Leicester → Birmingham → Cardiff and Bristol

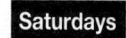

until 5 September

Network Diagram - see first page of Table 50

		GW	XC	XC	XC	XC	XC	EM	EM	XC	XC	GW	XC	XC	GW	XC	XC	XC	EM	EM	EM	AW	XC	XC	XC
			1◇	1◇	1◇	1◇	1	1◇	1◇	1◇	1◇		1◇	1◇		1◇	1◇	1		1◇	1◇		1◇	1◇	1◇
		A								B									C				D		
			✠	✠	✠	✠		⊡	⊡	✠	✠		✠	✠		✠	✠			⊡	⊡		✠	✠	✠
Nottingham 8	d		18 08				18 20		19 02				19 08					19 20	19 32	20 02					
Beeston	d						18 26		19a07									19 26	19a38	20a07					
Attenborough	d						18 29											19 29							
Long Eaton	d						18 36	18 57										19 36			20 02				
Spondon	d						18 45											19 45							
Derby 10	a		18 32				18 50	19 16					19 32					19 50			20 16				
	d		18 36	18 53			18 57			19 28			19 36	19 53				19 57					20 28		20 53
Willington	d																								
Burton-on-Trent	d		18 48				19b18			19 38			19 48					20c18							
Tamworth	d		19 00				19 30						20 00					20 30					20 48		
Wilnecote	d																	20 34							
Leicester	d					18 49					19 16						19 49							20 16	
South Wigston	d										19 22													20 22	
Narborough	d										19 27													20 27	
Hinckley	d										19 35													20 35	
Nuneaton	d					19 10					19 42						20 10							20 43	
Coleshill Parkway	d					19 25					19 59						20 25							20 59	
Water Orton	d																								
Birmingham New Street 12	a		19 24	19 27		19 43	19 56			20 07	20 14		20 24	20 27			20 43	20 56					21 07	21 14	21 31
	d		19 30		19 42					20 12			20 30			20 42							21 12		
Worcester Shrub Hill 7	d																								
Ashchurch for Tewkesbury	d																								
Cheltenham Spa	d	20 01	20 11		20 25					20 52		21 02	21 11		21 19	21 25						21 45	21 52		
Gloucester 7	a	20 11	20 21									21 12	21 21		21 29							21 56			
Bristol Parkway 7	a				20 56					21 23		21 53				21 57							22 23		
Bristol Temple Meads 10	a				21 13					21 35		22 04				22 13							22 41		
Newport (South Wales)	a		21 09										22 14									22 55			
Cardiff Central 7	a		21 32										22 39									23 18			

		XC	XC	EM	EM	EM	GW	XC	XC		XC	EM	XC	XC	XC	EM	EM	EM	XC	XC	XC	EM	EM		
		1◇	1		1◇	1◇		1◇	1		1◇		1◇	1◇	1	1◇			1◇	1	1◇		1◇		
							E	D			G		H				H	G	D	J	K	H	G		
																						bus			
		✠			⊡	⊡		✠			✠		✠	✠		⊡			✠		✠		⊡		
Nottingham 8	d		20 20	20 32	20 43							21 08			21 37		22 11	22 15				23 15			
Beeston	d		20 26	20a37	20a48							21 14			21 41		22 17	22 21				23 35			
Attenborough	d		20 29									21 17			21 45		22 20	22 24				23 45			
Long Eaton	d		20 36			20 57						21 26			21 52	21 57	22 29	22 32				23 56	23 27		
Spondon	d		20 45												21 59										
Derby 10	a		20 50			21 13						21 42			22 05	22 12	22 45	22 48				00 26	23 37		
	d		20 57					21 28						21 57	22 15				22 26						
Willington	d																								
Burton-on-Trent	d		21e18					21 38						22 07	22 26				22 37						
Tamworth	d		21 30					21 49						22 18	22 38				22 47						
Wilnecote	d														22 42										
Leicester	d	20 49							21 16		21 49		21 54							22 16	22 25				
South Wigston	d								21 22											22 22	22 31				
Narborough	d								21 27											22 27	22 36				
Hinckley	d								21 35											22 35	22 44				
Nuneaton	d	21 10							21 43		22 10		22 14							22 43	22 52				
Coleshill Parkway	d	21 25							21 59		22 25		22 30							22 59	23 08				
Water Orton	d																								
Birmingham New Street 12	a	21 43	22 00					22 12	22 14		22 43		22 42	22 48	23 05				23 11	23 14	23 25				
	d																								
Worcester Shrub Hill 7	d						21 31																		
Ashchurch for Tewkesbury	d						21 51																		
Cheltenham Spa	d						22 01																		
Gloucester 7	a						22 10																		
Bristol Parkway 7	a																								
Bristol Temple Meads 10	a																								
Newport (South Wales)	a																								
Cardiff Central 7	a																								

For general notes see front of timetable
For details of catering facilities see Directory of Train Operators

- **A** To Westbury (Table 123)
- **B** From Edinburgh to Plymouth (Table 51)
- **C** From Lincoln (Table 27)
- **D** From Edinburgh (Table 51)
- **E** From Great Malvern (Table 71)
- **G** Until 11 July
- **H** From 18 July
- **J** Until 11 July. From Cambridge (Table 49)
- **K** From 18 July. From Stansted Airport (Table 49)
- **b** Arr. 1911
- **c** Arr. 2011
- **e** Arr. 2111

Nottingham, Derby and Leicester → Birmingham → Cardiff and Bristol

Network Diagram - see first page of Table 50

		AW	XC	LM	EM	GW	XC	XC	GW	GW	XC	XC	GW	LM	AW	XC	XC	EM	EM	XC	XC	XC	XC	AW	XC
			1◇		1◇		1◇	1◇		◇	1◇	1	1◇			1◇	1◇	1◇		1◇	1◇	1	R 1		1◇
			A						B	C	D				E	G			H	J			K	E	L
Nottingham 8	d				01 51												05 57	06 02	06 10				06 37		
Beeston	d																06 03	06a07	06 17				06 43		
Attenborough	d																06 06		06 20						
Long Eaton	d																06 16		06 28						
Spondon	d																06 23		06 40						
Derby 10	a				02 08												06 30		06 46				07 00		
	d		21p28													06 10	06 36			06 47			07 06		07 25
Willington	d																								
Burton-on-Trent	d		21p38													06 20	06 48			06 57			07 18		07 36
Tamworth	d		21p52													06 31	07 00			07 08			07 30		07 48
Wilnecote	d																07 04								
Leicester	d											05 49										06 49			
South Wigston	d											05 55										06 55			
Narborough	d											06 00										07 00			
Hinckley	d											06 08										07 08			
Nuneaton	d											06 15										07 15			
Coleshill Parkway	d											06 31										07 31			
Water Orton	d																					07 36			
Birmingham New Street 12	a		22p07									06 45				06 50	07 24			07 27		07 47	07 50		08 08
	d		22p16	23p00			05 00	05 42			06 42					07 12	07 30				07 42				08 12
Worcester Shrub Hill 7	d			23p45						06 48				07 15											
Ashchurch for Tewkesbury	d			23p59				06 33		07 04				07 30											
Cheltenham Spa	d	23p00	23p33	00 08		05 30	06 04	06 43	06 48	07 14	07 25		07 29	07 39	07 45	07 52	08 11				08 25			08 45	08 52
Gloucester 7	a	23p12		00 18		05 40	06 13	06 54	06 58	07 25			07 38	07 50	07 56		08 21							08 56	
Bristol Parkway 7	a		00 04						07 39	08 18	07 56					08 24					08 56				09 25
Bristol Temple Meads 10	a		00 18						07 54	08 34	08 11					08 38					09 13				09 38
Newport (South Wales)	a	00 13					07 06	07 52							08 50		09 06							09 50	
Cardiff Central 7	a	00 35					07 25	08 13							09 10		09 25							10 10	

		XC	GW	XC	EM	EM	EM	XC	XC	XC	XC	EM	EM	GW	XC	XC	GW	XC	EM	XC	XC	XC	XC	EM	EM
		1◇	1◇	1◇	1◇			1◇	1◇	1◇	1	1◇	1◇		1◇	1		1◇		1◇	1◇	1◇	1	1◇	1◇
								N					Q	U	V	X			H		D				
Nottingham 8	d			06 56	07 02	07 14	07 31				07 37		08 02					08 08	08 18				08 37		09 02
Beeston	d			07 03	07a07	07 21	07a37				07 43		08a07						08 24				08 43		09a07
Attenborough	d			07 06		07 25													08 27						
Long Eaton	d			07 14		07 34					07 51	07 56							08 34				08 51	09 01	
Spondon	d			07 24															08 41						
Derby 10	a			07 29		07 49					08 01	08 16						08 32	08 50				09 01	09 20	
	d			07 36				07 50			08 06				08 28			08 36		08 53			09 06		
Willington	d			07 43																					
Burton-on-Trent	d			07 49				08 00			08 18				08 38			08 48					09 18		
Tamworth	d			08 01				08 11			08 30				08 50			09 00					09 30		
Wilnecote	d			08 05							08 34														
Leicester	d	07 16								07 49						08 16						08 49			
South Wigston	d															08 22									
Narborough	d															08 27									
Hinckley	d															08 35									
Nuneaton	d	07 36								08 10						08 43						09 10			
Coleshill Parkway	d	07 52								08 25						08 59						09 25			
Water Orton	d																								
Birmingham New Street 12	a	08 09		08 24				08 29		08 43	08 56				09 07	09 14		09 24		09 29		09 43	09 56		
	d			08 30					08 42						09 12			09 30			09 42				
Worcester Shrub Hill 7	d													09 08											
Ashchurch for Tewkesbury	d													09 25											
Cheltenham Spa	d		09 00	09 11					09 25					09 35	09 52		10 01	10 11			10 25				
Gloucester 7	a		09 10	09 21										09 44			10 11	10 21							
Bristol Parkway 7	a								09 56					10 24	10 26						10 56				
Bristol Temple Meads 10	a								10 13					10 39	10 41						11 13				
Newport (South Wales)	a			10 05														11 05							
Cardiff Central 7	a			10 25														11 25							

For general notes see front of timetable
For details of catering facilities see Directory of Train Operators

A From Edinburgh (Table 51)
B To Weston-super-Mare (Table 134)
C To Weymouth (Table 123)
D To Paignton (Table 51)
E To Maesteg (Table 128)
G To Plymouth (Table 51)
H To Matlock (Table 56)
J From Sheffield (Table 51)
K To Bournemouth (Table 51)
L From Leeds to Plymouth (Table 51)
N From Leeds (Table 51)
Q From Lincoln (Table 27)
U To Westbury (Table 123)
V From York to Plymouth (Table 51)
X From Cambridge (Table 49)

From Saturday 3 October a revised service will be in operation due to seasonal difficulties. Some East Midlands trains will be retimed between 1 and 3 minutes. Passengers should check with National Rail Enquiries for precise times.

Table 57

Nottingham, Derby and Leicester → Birmingham → Cardiff and Bristol

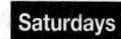

Saturdays

from 12 September

Network Diagram - see first page of Table 50

		LM	AW	XC	XC	GW	XC	EM	XC	XC	XC	XC	EM	EM	GW	AW	XC	XC	GW	XC	EM	XC	XC	XC	XC
				1◇	1	1◇	1◇		1◇	1◇	1◇	1	1◇	1◇	◇		1◇	1		1◇		1◇	1◇	1◇	1
			A	B				C							D	A	E	G							
				🛒		🍽	🛒		🛒	🛒	🛒		🍽	🍽			🛒			🛒		🛒	🛒	🛒	
Nottingham 8	d						09 08	09 18				09 37		10 02						10 08	10 18				10 37
Beeston	d							09 24				09 43		10a07							10 24				10 43
Attenborough	d							09 27													10 27				
Long Eaton	d							09 35				09 51	09 57								10 35				10 51
Spondon	d																								
Derby 10	a						09 32	09 48				10 01	10 16							10 32	10 49				11 01
	d			09 28			09 36		09 53			10 06					10 28			10 36		10 53			11 06
Willington	d																								
Burton-on-Trent	d			09 38			09 48					10 18								10 48					11 18
Tamworth	d						10 00					10 30					10 48			11 00					11 30
Wilnecote	d											10 34													
Leicester	d				09 16						09 49							10 16						10 49	
South Wigston	d																	10 22							
Narborough	d				09 25													10 27							
Hinckley	d				09 34													10 35							
Nuneaton	d				09 42						10 10							10 43						11 10	
Coleshill Parkway	d				09 57						10 25							10 59						11 25	
Water Orton	d				10 01																				
Birmingham New Street 12	a			10 07	10 14		10 24		10 27		10 43	10 56					11 07	11 14		11 24		11 27		11 43	11 56
	d			10 12			10 30			10 42							11 12			11 30			11 42		
Worcester Shrub Hill 7	d	10 14													11 08										
Ashchurch for Tewkesbury	d	10 29													11 24										
Cheltenham Spa	d	10 40	10 45	10 52		11 00	11 11			11 25					11 34	11 45	11 52		12 01	12 11			12 25		
Gloucester 7	a	10 52	10 56			11 10	11 21								11 44	11 56			12 11	12 21					
Bristol Parkway 7	a			11 24						11 56					12 24		12 26						12 56		
Bristol Temple Meads 10	a			11 38						12 13					12 39		12 41						13 13		
Newport (South Wales)	a		11 50				12 05									12 50				13 06					
Cardiff Central 7	a		12 10				12 25									13 10				13 25					

		EM	EM	LM	XC	XC	GW	XC	EM	XC	GW	XC	XC	XC	EM	EM	AW	XC	XC	GW	XC	EM	XC	XC	XC
		1◇	1◇		1◇	1	1◇	1◇		1◇	◇	1◇	1◇	1	1◇	1◇		1◇	1		1◇		1◇	1◇	1◇
				H	E						J						A	K	G						
		🍽	🍽		🛒		🍽	🛒		🛒	🛒	🛒	🛒		🍽	🍽		🛒			🛒		🛒	🛒	🛒
Nottingham 8	d		11 02					11 08	11 18					11 37		12 02					12 08	12 18			
Beeston	d		11a07						11 24					11 43		12a07						12 24			
Attenborough	d								11 27													12 27			
Long Eaton	d	10 57							11 35					11 51	11 57							12 35			
Spondon	d																								
Derby 10	a	11 07						11 32	11 49					12 01	12 16						12 32	12 49			
	d				11 28			11 36		11 53				12 06				12 28			12 36		12 53		
Willington	d																								
Burton-on-Trent	d				11 38			11 48						12 18							12 48				
Tamworth	d							12 00						12 30				12 48			13 00				
Wilnecote	d													12 34											
Leicester	d					11 16							11 49						12 16						12 49
South Wigston	d																		12 22						
Narborough	d					11 25													12 27						
Hinckley	d					11 34													12 35						
Nuneaton	d					11 42							12 10						12 43						13 10
Coleshill Parkway	d					11 57							12 25						12 59						13 25
Water Orton	d					12 01																			
Birmingham New Street 12	a				12 07	12 14		12 24		12 27			12 43	12 56				13 09	13 14		13 24		13 27		13 43
	d				12 12			12 30				12 42						13 12			13 30			13 42	
Worcester Shrub Hill 7	d			12 11							12 54														
Ashchurch for Tewkesbury	d			12 25							13 10														
Cheltenham Spa	d			12 36	12 52		13 00	13 11			13 20	13 25					13 45	13 52		14 01	14 11			14 25	
Gloucester 7	a			12 51			13 10	13 21			13 32						13 56			14 11	14 21				
Bristol Parkway 7	a				13 24						14 21	13 58						14 26						14 56	
Bristol Temple Meads 10	a				13 38						14 37	14 13						14 41						15 13	
Newport (South Wales)	a							14 05									14 50				15 06				
Cardiff Central 7	a							14 25									15 09				15 25				

For general notes see front of timetable
For details of catering facilities see Directory of Train Operators

A To Maesteg (Table 128)
B From Newcastle to Plymouth (Table 51)
C To Matlock (Table 56)
D From Great Malvern (Table 71) to Brighton (Table 123)
E From Edinburgh to Plymouth (Table 51)
G From Cambridge (Table 49)
H From Worcester Foregate Street (Table 71)
J From Worcester Foregate Street (Table 71) to Weymouth (Table 123)
K From Glasgow Central to Plymouth (Table 51)

From Saturday 3 October a revised service will be in operation due to seasonal difficulties. Some East Midlands trains will be retimed between 1 and 3 minutes. Passengers should check with National Rail Enquiries for precise times.

Nottingham, Derby and Leicester → Birmingham → Cardiff and Bristol

Network Diagram - see first page of Table 50

		XC	EM	EM	LM	AW	XC	XC	GW	XC	EM	XC	XC	XC	XC	EM	EM	GW	XC	XC	GW	XC	XC	XC	EM
		1	1 ◇	1 ◇			1 ◇	1	1 ◇	1 ◇		1 ◇	1 ◇	1 ◇	1	1 ◇	1 ◇	◇	1 ◇	1		1 ◇	1 ◇	1 ◇	
						A	B											C	D	E				G	
			☕	☕			🛒		☕	🛒		🛒	🛒	🛒		☕	☕		🛒			🛒	🛒	🛒	
Nottingham 8	🚌 d	12 37		13 02						13 08	13 18				13 37		14 02					14 08			14 18
Beeston	d	12 43		13a07							13 24				13 43		14a07								14 24
Attenborough	d										13 27														14 28
Long Eaton	d	12 51	12 57								13 35				13 51	13 57									14 36
Spondon	d																								
Derby 10	a	13 01	13 16							13 32	13 48				14 01	14 16						14 32			14 48
	d	13 06					13 28			13 36		13 53			14 06				14 29			14 36	14 53		
Willington	d	13 14																							
Burton-on-Trent	d	13 20					13 38			13 48					14 18							14 48			
Tamworth	d	13 33								14 00					14 30				14 49			15 00			
Wilnecote	d														14 34										
Leicester	d							13 16						13 49						14 16					
South Wigston	d																			14 22					
Narborough	d							13 25												14 27					
Hinckley	d							13 34												14 35					
Nuneaton	d							13 42						14 10						14 43					
Coleshill Parkway	d							13 57						14 25						14 59					
Water Orton	d							14 01																	
Birmingham New Street 12	a	13 56					14 07	14 14		14 24		14 27		14 43	14 56				15 09	15 14		15 24	15 27		
	d						14 12			14 30			14 42						15 12			15 30		15 42	
Worcester Shrub Hill 7	d				14 10													15 08							
Ashchurch for Tewkesbury	d				14 25													15 24							
Cheltenham Spa	d				14 34	14 45	14 52		15 00	15 11			15 25					15 34	15 52		16 01	16 11		16 25	
Gloucester 7	a				14 51	14 56			15 10	15 21								15 42			16 11	16 21			
Bristol Parkway 7	a						15 24						15 56					16 24	16 26					16 56	
Bristol Temple Meads 10	a						15 41						16 13					16 39	16 41					17 11	
Newport (South Wales)	a					15 50				16 05												17 05			
Cardiff Central 7	a					16 07				16 25												17 25			

		XC	XC	EM	EM	LM	AW	XC	XC	GW	XC	EM	XC	XC	XC	XC	EM	EM	GW	AW	XC	XC	GW	XC	EM
		1 ◇	1	1 ◇	1 ◇			1 ◇	1	1 ◇	1 ◇		1 ◇	1 ◇	1 ◇	1	1 ◇	1 ◇			1 ◇	1		1 ◇	
							A	H											J	A	K	E			L
		🛒		☕	☕			🛒		☕	🛒		🛒	🛒	🛒		☕	☕			🛒			🛒	
Nottingham 8	🚌 d		14 37		15 02						15 08	15 18				15 37		16 02						16 08	16 32
Beeston	d		14 43		15a07							15 24				15 43		16a07							
Attenborough	d											15 27													16a39
Long Eaton	d		14 51	14 57								15 35				15 51	15 57								
Spondon	d																								
Derby 10	a		15 01	15 16							15 32	15 48				16 01	16 16							16 32	
	d		15 06					15 28			15 36		15 53			16 06					16 28			16 36	
Willington	d																								
Burton-on-Trent	d		15 18					15 38			15 48					16 18								16 48	
Tamworth	d		15 30								16 00					16 30					16 48			17 00	
Wilnecote	d															16 34									
Leicester	d	14 49							15 16						15 49							16 16			
South Wigston	d																					16 22			
Narborough	d								15 25													16 27			
Hinckley	d								15 34													16 35			
Nuneaton	d	15 10							15 42						16 10							16 43			
Coleshill Parkway	d	15 25							15 57						16 25							16 59			
Water Orton	d								16 01																
Birmingham New Street 12	a	15 43	15 56					16 07	16 14		16 24		16 27		16 43	16 56					17 07	17 14		17 24	
	d							16 12			16 30			16 42							17 12			17 30	
Worcester Shrub Hill 7	d					16 11													17 08						
Ashchurch for Tewkesbury	d					16 26													17 24					18 08	
Cheltenham Spa	d					16 35	16 45	16 52		17 00	17 11			17 25					17 34	17 45	17 52		18 01	18 18	
Gloucester 7	a					16 51	16 56			17 10	17 21								17 44	17 56			18 11	18 28	
Bristol Parkway 7	a							17 24						17 56					18 24		18 26				
Bristol Temple Meads 10	a							17 38						18 13					18 39		18 41				
Newport (South Wales)	a						17 50				18 05									18 50				19 11	
Cardiff Central 7	a						18 10				18 25									19 10				19 32	

For general notes see front of timetable
For details of catering facilities see Directory of Train Operators

A To Maesteg (Table 128)
B From Dundee to Plymouth (Table 51)
C From Great Malvern (Table 71) to Weymouth (Table 123)
D From Glasgow Central to Penzance (Table 51)
E From Cambridge (Table 49)
G To Paignton (Table 51)
H From Aberdeen to Penzance (Table 51)
J From Great Malvern (Table 71) to Westbury (Table 123)
K From Edinburgh to Penzance (Table 51)
L From Lincoln (Table 27)

From Saturday 3 October a revised service will be in operation due to seasonal difficulties. Some East Midlands trains will be retimed between 1 and 3 minutes. Passengers should check with National Rail Enquiries for precise times.

Table 57

Saturdays

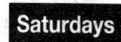

from 12 September

Nottingham, Derby and Leicester → Birmingham → Cardiff and Bristol

Network Diagram - see first page of Table 50

		XC	XC	EM	XC	XC	EM	EM	LM	AW	XC	XC	GW	XC	EM	XC	XC	EM	XC	XC	EM	EM	GW	AW	EM
		1 ◇	1 ◇		1 ◇	1	1 ◇	1 ◇			1 ◇	1	1 ◇	1 ◇		1 ◇	1 ◇		1 ◇	1	1 ◇	1 ◇	◇		
										A	B				C								D	A	
		trolley	trolley		trolley		buffet	buffet			trolley		buffet	trolley		trolley	trolley		trolley		buffet	buffet			
Nottingham [8]	d			16 18		16 37		17 02						17 08	17 32			17 18		17 37		18 02			18 18
Beeston	d			16 24		16 43		17a07										17 24		17 43		18a07			18 24
Attenborough	d			16 27											17a39			17 27							18 27
Long Eaton	d			16 35		16 51	16 56											17 35		17 51	17 57				18 37
Spondon	d																	17 42							
Derby [10]	a			16 48		17 01	17 16							17 32				17 49		18 01	18 16				18 48
	d	16 53				17 06					17 28			17 36		17 53				18 06					
Willington	d																			18 14					
Burton-on-Trent	d					17 18					17 38			17 48						18 20					
Tamworth	d					17 31								18 00						18 33					
Wilnecote	d																			18 37					
Leicester	d				16 49							17 16							17 49						
South Wigston	d											17 22													
Narborough	d											17 27													
Hinckley	d											17 35													
Nuneaton	d				17 10							17 43							18 10						
Coleshill Parkway	d				17 25							17 59							18 25						
Water Orton	d																								
Birmingham New Street [12]	a	17 27			17 43	17 56					18 07	18 14		18 24		18 27			18 43	19 00					
	d		17 42								18 12			18 30			18 42								
Worcester Shrub Hill [7]	d								18 10														19 08		
Ashchurch for Tewkesbury	d								18 25														19 24		
Cheltenham Spa	d		18 25						18 34	18 45	18 52		19 00	19 11			19 25						19 34	19 45	
Gloucester [7]	a		18 35						18 52	18 56			19 10	19 21									19 44	19 56	
Bristol Parkway [7]	a		19 08								19 26						19 56						20 23		
Bristol Temple Meads [10]	a		19 27								19 41						20 13						20 39		
Newport (South Wales)	a									19 50				20 05			20 54							20 50	
Cardiff Central [7]	a									20 11				20 25			21 16							21 09	

		XC	XC	GW	XC	XC	XC	XC	XC	EM	EM	XC	XC	GW	XC	EM	EM	XC	GW	XC	XC	XC	EM	EM	em
		1 ◇	1		1 ◇	1 ◇	1 ◇	1 ◇	1	1 ◇	1 ◇	1 ◇	1		1 ◇			1 ◇		1 ◇	1 ◇	1	1 ◇	1 ◇	
		B	E	G			H					B					C								
		trolley			trolley	trolley	trolley	trolley		buffet	buffet	trolley			trolley			trolley		trolley	trolley		buffet	buffet	
Nottingham [8]	d				18 08				18 37		19 02				19 08	19 18	19 32					19 37		20 02	20 09
Beeston	d								18 43		19a07					19 24	19a38					19 43		20a07	20 15
Attenborough	d															19 27									20 18
Long Eaton	d								18 51	18 57						19 35						19 51	19 57		20 28
Spondon	d																								
Derby [10]	a				18 32				19 01	19 16					19 32	19 48						20 01	20 16		20 44
	d	18 28			18 36	18 53			19 06			19 28			19 36			19 53				20 06			
Willington	d																								
Burton-on-Trent	d				18 48				19 18			19 38			19 48							20 18			
Tamworth	d	18 48			19 00				19 30						20 00							20 30			
Wilnecote	d																					20 34			
Leicester	d		18 16					18 49					19 16								19 49				
South Wigston	d		18 22										19 22												
Narborough	d		18 27										19 27												
Hinckley	d		18 35										19 35												
Nuneaton	d		18 43					19 10					19 42								20 10				
Coleshill Parkway	d		18 59					19 25					19 59								20 25				
Water Orton	d																								
Birmingham New Street [12]	a	19 07	19 14		19 24	19 27		19 43	19 56			20 07	20 14		20 24			20 27			20 43	20 56			
	d	19 12			19 30		19 42					20 12			20 30					20 42					
Worcester Shrub Hill [7]	d																								
Ashchurch for Tewkesbury	d																								
Cheltenham Spa	d	19 52		20 01	20 11		20 25					20 52		21 02	21 11				21 19	21 25					
Gloucester [7]	a			20 11	20 21									21 12	21 21				21 29						
Bristol Parkway [7]	a	20 29					20 56					21 23		21 53						21 57					
Bristol Temple Meads [10]	a	20 42					21 13					21 35		22 04						22 13					
Newport (South Wales)	a				21 09										22 14										
Cardiff Central [7]	a				21 32										22 39										

For general notes see front of timetable
For details of catering facilities see Directory of Train Operators

- **A** To Maesteg (Table 128)
- **B** From Edinburgh to Plymouth (Table 51)
- **C** From Lincoln (Table 27)
- **D** From Great Malvern (Table 71) to Weymouth (Table 123)
- **E** From Cambridge (Table 49)
- **G** To Westbury (Table 123)
- **H** To Plymouth (Table 51)

From Saturday 3 October a revised service will be in operation due to seasonal difficulties. Some East Midlands trains will be retimed between 1 and 3 minutes. Passengers should check with National Rail Enquiries for precise times.

Saturdays
from 12 September

Nottingham, Derby and Leicester → Birmingham → Cardiff and Bristol

Network Diagram - see first page of Table 50

		EM	AW	XC 1◇ A	XC 1	XC 1◇	XC 1◇	XC 1	EM 1◇	EM 1◇	GW B	EM	XC 1◇ A	XC 1	XC 1◇	XC 1◇	XC 1	EM 1◇	EM	XC 1◇ A	XC 1 C	EM 1◇	EM Bus	
Nottingham 8	d	20 32						20 35	20 43			21 08					21 35		22 15				23 15	
Beeston	d	20a37						20 42	20a48			21 14					21 41		22 21				23 35	
Attenborough	d											21 17					21 45		22 24				23 45	
Long Eaton	d							20 51		20 57		21 26					21 52	21 57	22 32			23 19	23 56	
Spondon	d																21 59							
Derby 10	a							21 01		21 13		21 42					22 05	22 12	22 48			23 29	00 26	
	d			20 28		20 53		21 06					21 28			21 57	22 15			22 28				
Willington	d							21 14																
Burton-on-Trent	d							21 20					21 38			22 07	22 26			22 38				
Tamworth	d			20 48				21 31					21 49			22 18	22 38			22 49				
Wilnecote	d																22 42							
Leicester	d				20 16		20 49							21 16	21 49						22 16			
South Wigston	d				20 22									21 22							22 22			
Narborough	d				20 27									21 27							22 27			
Hinckley	d				20 35									21 35							22 35			
Nuneaton	d				20 43		21 10							21 43	22 10						22 43			
Coleshill Parkway	d				20 59		21 25							21 59	22 25						22 59			
Water Orton	d																							
Birmingham New Street 12	a			21 07	21 14	21 31	21 43	22 00					22 12	22 14	22 43	22 48	23 05			23 12	23 14			
	d			21 12																				
Worcester Shrub Hill 7	d										21 31													
Ashchurch for Tewkesbury	d										21 51													
Cheltenham Spa	d		21 45	21 52							22 01													
Gloucester 7	a		21 56								22 10													
Bristol Parkway 7	a			22 23																				
Bristol Temple Meads 10	a			22 41																				
Newport (South Wales)	a		22 55																					
Cardiff Central 7	a		23 18																					

Sundays
until 12 July

		EM 1◇	GW	XC 1◇ D	GW E	XC 1◇		XC 1◇ G	EM	EM 1◇	GW 1◇	XC 1◇ G		EM 1◇ H	XC 1◇	GW	XC 1◇	AW		GW	XC 1◇ J	XC 1◇	EM 1◇ K	EM	GW 1◇
Nottingham 8	d	08 19							09 23	10 15												11 09		11 23	
Beeston	d	08a24							09 28	10a21														11 29	
Attenborough	d								09 31															11 32	
Long Eaton	d								09 39					10 29									11 38	11 43	
Spondon	d																								
Derby 10	a								09 56					10 44								11 28	11 49	11 54	
	d							09 30				10 33									11 30	11 36			
Willington	d																								
Burton-on-Trent	d											10 44									11 41	11 48			
Tamworth	d							09 48														12 00			
Wilnecote	d																								
Leicester	d														11 19										
South Wigston	d																								
Narborough	d														11 28										
Hinckley	d														11 37										
Nuneaton	d														11 45										
Coleshill Parkway	d														12 00										
Water Orton	d																								
Birmingham New Street 12	a							10 11				11 11			12 14						12 07	12 23			
	d			08 52		09 52		10 12				11 14					11 30				12 12	12 30			
Worcester Shrub Hill 7	d																								
Ashchurch for Tewkesbury	d																								
Cheltenham Spa	d		09 35	09 52	10 05	10 52		10 57			11 46	11 54				12 00	12 11	12 18		12 35	12 52	13 11			13 46
Gloucester 7	a		09 45		10 15	11 02					11 56					12 10	12 21	12 26		12 45		13 21			13 57
Bristol Parkway 7	a			10 23	10 55			11 28				12 26				12 51					13 23				
Bristol Temple Meads 10	a			10 35	11 08			11 41				12 39				13 09					13 35				
Newport (South Wales)	a					11 45											13 04	13 25				14 04			
Cardiff Central 7	a					12 06											13 25	13 45				14 25			

For general notes see front of timetable
For details of catering facilities see Directory of Train Operators

A From Edinburgh (Table 51)
B From Great Malvern (Table 71)
C From Cambridge (Table 49)
D To Penzance (Table 51)
E To Taunton (Table 134)
G From Leeds to Plymouth (Table 51)
H To York (Table 53)
J From York to Plymouth (Table 51)
K To Sheffield (Table 53)

From Saturday 3 October a revised service will be in operation due to seasonal difficulties. Some East Midlands trains will be retimed between 1 and 3 minutes. Passengers should check with National Rail Enquiries for precise times.

Table 57

Sundays

until 12 July

Nottingham, Derby and Leicester → Birmingham → Cardiff and Bristol

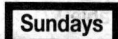

Network Diagram - see first page of Table 50

		XC		XC	XC	EM	EM	AW		XC	XC	XC	GW	XC		EM	XC	XC	EM	EM		XC	GW	XC	XC
		1 ◇		1	1 ◇	1 ◇	1 ◇			1 ◇	1 ◇	1		1 ◇		1 ◇	1 ◇	1 ◇	1 ◇			1 ◇	1 ◇	1 ◇	1
		A					B				C		D						B			E		G	
Nottingham 8	d				12 05	12 15								13 05		13 14				13 29					
Beeston	d					12a21										13a20				13 34					
Attenborough	d																			13 38					
Long Eaton	d						12 41												13 42	13 47					
Spondon	d																								
Derby 10	a				12 28		12 51							13 28					13 52	13 58					
	d	12 30			12 36						13 30			13 35			13 47							14 30	
Willington	d																								
Burton-on-Trent	d				12 48						13 41			13 49											
Tamworth	d	12 49			13 00									14 01										14 48	
Wilnecote	d																								
Leicester	d			12 19						12 49		13 19						13 49							14 19
South Wigston	d			12 24																					14 24
Narborough	d			12 29								13 28													14 29
Hinckley	d			12 38								13 36													14 38
Nuneaton	d			12 46						13 09		13 44						14 09							14 46
Coleshill Parkway	d			13 01						13 25		13 59						14 25							15 01
Water Orton	d																								
Birmingham New Street 12	a	13 07		13 15	13 21					13 42	14 10	14 15		14 21			14 27	14 42						15 07	15 15
	d	13 12			13 30						14 12			14 30								14 42		15 12	
Worcester Shrub Hill 7	d												14 36												
Ashchurch for Tewkesbury	d												14 51												
Cheltenham Spa	d	13 52			14 11			14 18			14 52		15 01	15 11								15 25	15 46	15 52	
Gloucester 7	a				14 21			14 29					15 10	15 21									15 57		
Bristol Parkway 7	a	14 23									15 25		15 49									16 00		16 23	
Bristol Temple Meads 10	a	14 35									15 38		16 09									16 13		16 35	
Newport (South Wales)	a				15 04			15 25						16 04											
Cardiff Central 7	a				15 25			15 45						16 25											

		XC	EM	XC		XC	EM	AW	XC	GW		XC	EM	XC	GW	XC		EM	XC	XC	EM	XC		GW	XC
		1 ◇	1 ◇	1 ◇		1 ◇	1 ◇		1 ◇			1 ◇		1		1 ◇		1 ◇	1 ◇	1 ◇	1 ◇	1 ◇		1 ◇	1 ◇
							B					C									B				G
Nottingham 8	d	14 05	14 30										14 52			15 05		15 10							
Beeston	d		14a35										14 59					15a15							
Attenborough	d												15 04												
Long Eaton	d						14 46						15 12								15 42				
Spondon	d																								
Derby 10	a	14 28					15 00						15 27			15 31					15 56				
	d	14 36		14 53								15 23				15 36			15 51						16 23
Willington	d																								
Burton-on-Trent	d	14 48										15 35				15 48									
Tamworth	d	15 00														16 00									16 43
Wilnecote	d															16 04									
Leicester	d					14 49								15 19						15 49					
South Wigston	d																								
Narborough	d													15 28											
Hinckley	d													15 36											
Nuneaton	d					15 09								15 44						16 09					
Coleshill Parkway	d					15 25								16 00						16 25					
Water Orton	d																								
Birmingham New Street 12	a	15 21		15 27		15 42						16 00		16 15		16 23			16 27	16 42					17 02
	d	15 30							15 42			16 12				16 30						16 42			17 12
Worcester Shrub Hill 7	d														16 40										
Ashchurch for Tewkesbury	d														16 58										
Cheltenham Spa	d	16 11						16 18	16 25	16 33		16 52			17 08	17 11						17 25		17 46	17 52
Gloucester 7	a	16 21						16 27		16 43					17 16	17 21								17 57	
Bristol Parkway 7	a								16 57			17 23			17 57							18 02			18 23
Bristol Temple Meads 10	a								17 13			17 35			18 10							18 14			18 37
Newport (South Wales)	a	17 04						17 31								18 04									
Cardiff Central 7	a	17 25						17 51								18 25									

For general notes see front of timetable
For details of catering facilities see Directory of Train Operators

- **A** From Newcastle to Plymouth (Table 51)
- **B** To Sheffield (Table 53)
- **C** From Edinburgh to Plymouth (Table 51)
- **D** To Weston-super-Mare (Table 134)
- **E** To Paignton (Table 51)
- **G** From Edinburgh to Penzance (Table 51)

Sundays

until 12 July

Nottingham, Derby and Leicester → Birmingham → Cardiff and Bristol

Network Diagram - see first page of Table 50

		XC 1	XC 1◇	EM 1◇	EM	XC 1◇		EM 1◇	AW	XC 1◇	XC 1◇	XC 1		GW	XC 1◇	EM 1◇	EM 1◇	XC 1◇		XC 1◇	EM	XC 1◇	GW 1◇	XC 1◇	XC 1
								A			B						C					D		E	
			🛒	🍴		🛒		🍴		🛒	🛒				🛒	🍴	🍴	🛒		🛒		🛒	🍴	🛒	
Nottingham 8 ⛴	d		16 05	16 18	16 21										17 00	17 20					17 23				
Beeston	d			16a23	16 26											17a25					17 30				
Attenborough	d				16 29																17 34				
Long Eaton	d				16 47			16 43									17 37				17 41				
Spondon	d																								
Derby 10	a		16 28		16 58			16 55							17 30		17 51				17 56				
	d		16 35								17 23				17 35			17 51						18 23	
Willington	d																								
Burton-on-Trent	d		16 48								17 35				17 48										
Tamworth	d		17 00												18 00									18 43	
Wilnecote	d																								
Leicester	d	16 19				16 48						17 16								17 48					18 16
South Wigston	d	16 24										17 22													
Narborough	d	16 29										17 27													18 25
Hinckley	d	16 38										17 36													18 33
Nuneaton	d	16 46				17 09						17 43								18 09					18 41
Coleshill Parkway	d	17 01				17 25						17 59								18 25					18 57
Water Orton	d																								
Birmingham New Street 12	a	17 15	17 21			17 42					18 00	18 15			18 21			18 25		18 42				19 02	19 15
	d		17 30							17 42	18 12				18 30							18 42		19 12	
Worcester Shrub Hill 7	d													18 40											
Ashchurch for Tewkesbury	d													18 55											
Cheltenham Spa	d		18 11						18 18	18 25	18 52			19 06	19 14							19 25	19 46	19 52	
Gloucester 7	a		18 21						18 29	18 35				19 15	19 24								19 56		
Bristol Parkway 7	a									19 08	19 23			19 55								20 00		20 23	
Bristol Temple Meads 10	a									19 25	19 35			20 08								20 14		20 35	
Newport (South Wales)	a		19 04						19 25						20 09										
Cardiff Central 7	a		19 25						19 47						20 30										

		XC 1◇		EM 1◇	EM 1◇	XC 1◇	XC 1◇	EM		EM	AW	XC 1◇	XC 1◇	XC 1		XC 1◇	EM 1◇	XC 1◇	EM 1◇	GW		XC 1◇	XC 1◇	GW	XC 1◇
								G					B												
		🛒		🍴	🍴	🛒	🛒					🛒	🛒			🛒	🍴	🛒	🍴			🛒	🛒		🛒
Nottingham 8 ⛴	d	18 05		18 10				18 17		18 52						19 10			19 46						20 10
Beeston	d			18a18				18 22		18 58									19a51						
Attenborough	d							18 25		19 03															
Long Eaton	d				18 32			18 37		19 11							19 33								
Spondon	d																								
Derby 10	a	18 31			18 48			18 57		19 22						19 31	19 49								20 30
	d	18 35				18 51							19 22			19 35		19 51							20 35
Willington	d																								
Burton-on-Trent	d	18 48											19 35			19 48									20 47
Tamworth	d	19 00														20 00									21 02
Wilnecote	d															20 04									
Leicester	d						18 49							19 19								19 49			
South Wigston	d													19 24											
Narborough	d													19 29											
Hinckley	d													19 38											
Nuneaton	d						19 09							19 46								20 09			
Coleshill Parkway	d						19 25							20 01								20 25			
Water Orton	d																								
Birmingham New Street 12	a	19 21				19 27	19 42						20 00	20 15		20 25		20 29				20 42			21 20
	d	19 30										19 42	20 12										20 42		
Worcester Shrub Hill 7	d																			20 36					
Ashchurch for Tewkesbury	d																			20 53					
Cheltenham Spa	d	20 11									20 18	20 25	20 52							21 03			21 25	21 46	
Gloucester 7	a	20 21									20 31									21 13				21 56	
Bristol Parkway 7	a											20 57	21 23							21 53			21 59		
Bristol Temple Meads 10	a											21 14	21 35							22 07			22 15		
Newport (South Wales)	a	21 04									21 25														
Cardiff Central 7	a	21 25									21 43														

For general notes see front of timetable
For details of catering facilities see Directory of Train Operators

A To Leeds (Table 53)
B From Glasgow Central to Plymouth (Table 51)
C To Sheffield (Table 53)
D To Paignton (Table 51)
E From Aberdeen to Plymouth (Table 51)
G From Skegness (Table 19)

Table 57

Sundays

until 12 July

Nottingham, Derby and Leicester → Birmingham → Cardiff and Bristol

Network Diagram - see first page of Table 50

		XC 1◇ A	XC 1	EM 1◇		EM	XC 1◇	XC 1◇	GW	XC 1◇		XC 1◇ A	XC 1	XC 1◇	EM 1◇	XC 1◇		XC 1◇	EM	XC 1	XC 1◇ A	EM 1◇ B			
Nottingham 8	d					20 23								21 05					21 23						
Beeston	d					20 28													21 29						
Attenborough	d					20 31													21 33						
Long Eaton	d			20 29		20 41									21 29				21 41			23 39			
Spondon	d																								
Derby 10	a			20 48		20 55								21 32	21 44				21 52			23 49			
	d	20 23					21 00					21 25		21 36				21 53			22 25				
Willington	d																								
Burton-on-Trent	d											21 35		21 48				22 04			22 35				
Tamworth	d	20 43										21 46		22 00				22 14			22 46				
Wilnecote	d													22 04											
Leicester	d		20 08					20 49					21 19			21 49				22 19					
South Wigston	d		20 15										21 25							22 25					
Narborough	d		20 20										21 29							22 29					
Hinckley	d		20 29										21 38							22 38					
Nuneaton	d		20 36					21 09					21 46			22 09				22 46					
Coleshill Parkway	d		20 52					21 25					22 01			22 25				23 01					
Water Orton	d																								
Birmingham New Street 12	a	21 01	21 06				21 37	21 42				22 04	22 15	22 27		22 47		22 43		23 19	23 09				
	d	21 12								21 42		22 12													
Worcester Shrub Hill 7	d																								
Ashchurch for Tewkesbury	d																								
Cheltenham Spa	d	21 53							22 01	22 25		22 52													
Gloucester 7	a								22 11																
Bristol Parkway 7	a	22 24								22 57		23 24													
Bristol Temple Meads 10	a	22 41								23 14		23 41													
Newport (South Wales)	a																								
Cardiff Central 7	a																								

Sundays

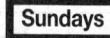

19 July to 6 September

		EM 1◇	GW	XC 1◇ C	GW D	XC 1◇	XC 1◇ E		GW 1◇	EM	XC 1◇ E	EM 1◇	XC 1◇	GW		XC 1◇	AW	GW	XC 1◇ G	XC 1◇ H	EM		GW 1◇	XC 1◇	XC 1◇ G
Nottingham 8	d	08 07								08 32		10 01									11 23				
Beeston	d	08a12								08 53		10a07									11 29				
Attenborough	d									09 04											11 32				
Long Eaton	d									09 16											11 40				
Spondon	d																								
Derby 10	a									09 46											11 52				
	d						09 30				10 03									11 30				11 06	
Willington	d																								
Burton-on-Trent	d						09 41				10 14									11 41				11 18	
Tamworth	d						09 53																	11 30	
Wilnecote	d																								
Leicester	d												11 19												
South Wigston	d																								
Narborough	d												11 28												
Hinckley	d												11 37												
Nuneaton	d												11 45												
Coleshill Parkway	d												12 00												
Water Orton	d																								
Birmingham New Street 12	a						10 13				10 41		12 14							12 07				11 51	
	d			08 52		10 12	10 16				10 45					11 12			11 45					12 12	12 42
Worcester Shrub Hill 7	d																								
Ashchurch for Tewkesbury	d																								
Cheltenham Spa	d		09 35	09 52	10 05	11 11	11 19		11 46		11 52			12 00		12 11	12 18	12 35	12 52				13 46	13 11	13 54
Gloucester 7	a		09 45		10 15	11 21			11 56					12 10		12 21	12 26	12 45					13 57	13 21	
Bristol Parkway 7	a			10 23	10 55		11 52				12 23			12 51					13 23						14 26
Bristol Temple Meads 10	a			10 35	11 08		12 07				12 36			13 09					13 35						14 38
Newport (South Wales)	a					12 04										13 04	13 25							14 04	
Cardiff Central 7	a					12 25										13 25	13 45							14 25	

For general notes see front of timetable
For details of catering facilities see Directory of Train Operators

- **A** From Edinburgh (Table 51)
- **B** To Sheffield (Table 53)
- **C** To Penzance (Table 51)
- **D** To Taunton (Table 134)
- **E** From Leeds to Plymouth (Table 51)
- **G** To Plymouth (Table 51)
- **H** From York (Table 51)

Sundays

19 July to 6 September

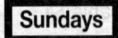

Nottingham, Derby and Leicester → Birmingham → Cardiff and Bristol

Network Diagram - see first page of Table 50

		XC	EM	EM	XC	EM		EM	AW		XC	XC	XC		XC	GW	XC	XC	XC	EM			EM	XC	GW
													$1												
		1◇	1◇	1◇	1◇	1◇		1◇			1	1			1◇		1◇	1◇	1◇				1◇	1◇	1◇
			A		B	A									C	D							A	E	
Nottingham 8	d	11 38		12 01				13 03									13 10			13 20					
Beeston	d			12a07				13a09												13 25					
Attenborough	d																			13 29					
Long Eaton	d		11 53			12 48														13 36			13 49		
Spondon	d																								
Derby 10	a	11 59	12 04			12 58											13 31			13 47			14 00		
	d	12 06			12 30										13 32		13 36	13 43							
Willington	d																								
Burton-on-Trent	d	12 18													13 43		13 48								
Tamworth	d	12 30			12 49												14 00								
Wilnecote	d																								
Leicester	d										12 19	12 49	13 19						13 42						
South Wigston	d										12 24														
Narborough	d										12 29		13 28												
Hinckley	d										12 38		13 37												
Nuneaton	d										12 46	13 09	13 45						14 04						
Coleshill Parkway	d										13 01	13 25	14 00						14 19						
Water Orton	d																								
Birmingham New Street 12	a	12 51			13 07						13 15	13 42	14 20		14 10		14 21	14 27	14 38						
	d	13 04													14 12		14 30							14 42	
Worcester Shrub Hill 7	d															14 36									
Ashchurch for Tewkesbury	d															14 51									
Cheltenham Spa	d	14 05							14 18						14 52	15 01	15 11							15 25	15 46
Gloucester 7	a	14 15							14 29							15 10	15 21								15 57
Bristol Parkway 7	a														15 25	15 49								16 00	
Bristol Temple Meads 10	a														15 38	16 09								16 13	
Newport (South Wales)	a	14 58							15 25								16 04								
Cardiff Central 7	a	15 19							15 45								16 25								

		XC	XC	XC	EM		XC	XC	EM	AW	XC	GW		XC	EM	XC	GW	XC	EM		XC	EM	XC	XC	GW
		1◇	1◇	1◇	1◇		1◇	1	1◇		1◇			1◇		1◇		1◇	1◇		1◇	1◇	1◇	1	1◇
		G	H						A					C		H						A			
Nottingham 8	d			14 05	14 30										14 56			15 05	15 10						
Beeston	d				14a35										15 01				15a15						
Attenborough	d														15 06										
Long Eaton	d								14 46						15 14							15 42			
Spondon	d																								
Derby 10	a			14 28					15 00						15 27			15 31				15 56			
	d	14 30		14 36			14 53							15 25				15 36			15 51				
Willington	d																								
Burton-on-Trent	d			14 48										15 35				15 48							
Tamworth	d	14 49		15 00														16 00							
Wilnecote	d																	16 04							
Leicester	d		14 18					14 49								15 19								15 49	
South Wigston	d		14 24																						
Narborough	d		14 29													15 28									
Hinckley	d		14 38													15 37									
Nuneaton	d		14 46					15 09								15 45								16 10	
Coleshill Parkway	d		15 01					15 25								16 00								16 26	
Water Orton	d																								
Birmingham New Street 12	a	15 07	15 15	15 21			15 27	15 42						16 00		16 15		16 23			16 27			16 42	
	d	15 12		15 30							15 42			16 12				16 30					16 42		
Worcester Shrub Hill 7	d																16 40								
Ashchurch for Tewkesbury	d																16 58								
Cheltenham Spa	d	15 52		16 11						16 18	16 25	16 33		16 52			17 08	17 11					17 25		17 46
Gloucester 7	a			16 21						16 27		16 43					17 16	17 21							17 57
Bristol Parkway 7	a	16 23									16 57			17 23			17 57						18 02		
Bristol Temple Meads 10	a	16 35									17 13			17 35			18 10						18 14		
Newport (South Wales)	a			17 04						17 31								18 04							
Cardiff Central 7	a			17 25						17 51								18 25							

For general notes see front of timetable
For details of catering facilities see Directory of Train Operators

- **A** To Sheffield (Table 53)
- **B** From Newcastle (Table 51)
- **C** From Edinburgh to Plymouth (Table 51)
- **D** To Weston-super-Mare (Table 134)
- **E** To Paignton (Table 51)
- **G** From Edinburgh to Penzance (Table 51)
- **H** From Stansted Airport (Table 49)

Table 57

Sundays

Nottingham, Derby and Leicester → Birmingham → Cardiff and Bristol

19 July to 6 September

Network Diagram - see first page of Table 50

	XC	XC	XC		EM	EM	XC	XC	EM	AW		XC	XC	XC	GW	XC	EM		EM	XC	XC	EM	XC	GW
	1 ◇	1 ◇	1 ◇		1 ◇		1	1 ◇	1 ◇			1 ◇	1 ◇	1 ◇		1 ◇	1 ◇		1 ◇	1 ◇	1		1 ◇	1 ◇
	A	B							C				D	B					E				G	
	[trolley]	[trolley]	[trolley]		[buffet]			[trolley]	[buffet]			[trolley]	[trolley]	[trolley]		[trolley]	[buffet]		[buffet]	[trolley]			[trolley]	[buffet]
Nottingham [8] d			16 10		16 18	16 21										17 10	17 20					17 23		
Beeston d					16a23	16 26											17a25					17 30		
Attenborough d						16 29																17 34		
Long Eaton d						16 47			16 43										17 37			17 42		
Spondon d																								
Derby [10] a			16 28			16 58			16 55							17 30			17 51			17 56		
d	16 23		16 36					16 51					17 25			17 36				17 51				
Willington d																								
Burton-on-Trent d			16 48										17 35			17 48								
Tamworth d	16 43		17 00													18 00								
Wilnecote d																								
Leicester d		16 19					16 48							17 24							17 48			
South Wigston d		16 24												17 31										
Narborough d		16 29												17 36										
Hinckley d		16 38												17 44										
Nuneaton d		16 46					17 09							17 52							18 09			
Coleshill Parkway d		17 01					17 25							18 07							18 25			
Water Orton d																								
Birmingham New Street [12] a	17 02	17 15	17 21				17 42	17 27					18 00	18 20		18 23				18 27	18 42			
d	17 12		17 30									17 42	18 12			18 30							18 42	
Worcester Shrub Hill [7] d															18 40									
Ashchurch for Tewkesbury d															18 55									
Cheltenham Spa d	17 52		18 11							18 18		18 25	18 52		19 06	19 14							19 25	19 46
Gloucester [7] a			18 21							18 29		18 35			19 15	19 24								19 56
Bristol Parkway [7] a	18 23											19 08	19 23		19 55								20 00	
Bristol Temple Meads [10] a	18 37											19 25	19 35		20 08								20 14	
Newport (South Wales) a			19 04							19 25						20 09								
Cardiff Central [7] a			19 25							19 47						20 30								

	XC	XC		XC	EM	EM	XC	XC	EM		EM	AW	XC	XC	XC	XC		EM	XC	EM	GW	XC	XC	GW
	1 ◇	1 ◇		1 ◇	1 ◇	1 ◇	1 ◇	1					1 ◇	1 ◇	1 ◇	1 ◇		1 ◇	1 ◇	1 ◇		1	1 ◇	
	H	B							J					D	B									
	[trolley]	[trolley]		[trolley]	[buffet]	[buffet]	[trolley]						[trolley]	[trolley]	[trolley]	[trolley]		[buffet]	[trolley]	[buffet]			[trolley]	
Nottingham [8] d				18 05	18 10				18 17		18 56					19 05				19 46				
Beeston d					18a18				18 22		19 01									19a51				
Attenborough d									18 25		19 06													
Long Eaton d						18 32			18 37		19 13							19 33						
Spondon d																								
Derby [10] a				18 31		18 48			18 54		19 24					19 31		19 49						
d	18 25			18 35			18 51							19 23		19 35			19 51					
Willington d																								
Burton-on-Trent d				18 48										19 35		19 48								
Tamworth d	18 43			19 00												20 00								
Wilnecote d																20 04								
Leicester d		18 19						18 49							19 19							19 49		
South Wigston d															19 24									
Narborough d		18 25													19 29									
Hinckley d		18 33													19 38									
Nuneaton d		18 41						19 09							19 46							20 09		
Coleshill Parkway d		18 57						19 25							20 01							20 25		
Water Orton d																								
Birmingham New Street [12] a	19 02	19 15		19 21			19 27	19 42						20 00	20 15	20 25			20 29			20 42		
d	19 12			19 30									19 42	20 12									20 42	
Worcester Shrub Hill [7] d																					20 36			
Ashchurch for Tewkesbury d																					20 53			
Cheltenham Spa d	19 52			20 11								20 18	20 25	20 52							21 03		21 25	21 46
Gloucester [7] a				20 21								20 31									21 13			21 56
Bristol Parkway [7] a	20 23												20 57	21 23							21 53		21 59	
Bristol Temple Meads [10] a	20 35												21 14	21 35							22 07		22 15	
Newport (South Wales) a				21 04								21 25												
Cardiff Central [7] a				21 25								21 43												

For general notes see front of timetable
For details of catering facilities see Directory of Train Operators

- **A** From Edinburgh to Penzance (Table 51)
- **B** From Stansted Airport (Table 49)
- **C** To Leeds (Table 53)
- **D** From Glasgow Central to Plymouth (Table 51)
- **E** To Sheffield (Table 53)
- **G** To Paignton (Table 51)
- **H** From Aberdeen to Plymouth (Table 51)
- **J** From Skegness (Table 19)

Sundays

Nottingham, Derby and Leicester → Birmingham → Cardiff and Bristol

19 July to 6 September

Network Diagram - see first page of Table 50

		XC		XC	XC	XC	XC	EM	EM		GW	XC	XC	XC	XC	XC		EM	XC	EM	XC	XC	XC		
		1 ◇		1 ◇	1 ◇	1 ◇	1	1 ◇				1 ◇	1 ◇	1 ◇	1 ◇	1		1 ◇	1 ◇		1 ◇	1 ◇	1		
				A	B									A							B	A			
		🛒		🛒	🛒	🛒		🍽				🛒	🛒	🛒	🛒			🍽	🛒		🛒	🛒			
Nottingham 8 🚊	d	20 10							20 23						21 10					21 23					
Beeston	d								20 28											21 29					
Attenborough	d								20 31											21 33					
Long Eaton	d							20 33	20 41									21 39		21 43					
Spondon	d																								
Derby 10	a	20 28						20 55	20 55						21 32			21 49		21 56					
	d	20 35		20 25		20 51								21 23	21 36				21 53			22 25			
Willington	d																								
Burton-on-Trent	d	20 48												21 35	21 48				22 04			22 35			
Tamworth	d	21 00		20 43										21 46	22 00				22 14			22 46			
Wilnecote	d														22 07										
Leicester	d				20 23		20 49						21 26			21 49					22 32		22 49		
South Wigston	d				20 31								21 32								22 38				
Narborough	d				20 36								21 37								22 43				
Hinckley	d				20 45								21 46								22 51				
Nuneaton	d				20 52		21 09						21 54			22 09					22 59		23 09		
Coleshill Parkway	d				21 08		21 25						22 09			22 25					23 15		23 25		
Water Orton	d																								
Birmingham New Street 12	a	21 24		21 02	21 25	21 29	21 42						22 23	22 04	22 27	22 46			22 43		23 28	23 05	23 42		
	d			21 12								21 42		22 12											
Worcester Shrub Hill 7	d																								
Ashchurch for Tewkesbury	d																								
Cheltenham Spa	d			21 52							22 01	22 25		22 52											
Gloucester 7	a										22 11														
Bristol Parkway 7	a			22 24								22 57		23 24											
Bristol Temple Meads 10	a			22 41								23 13		23 41											
Newport (South Wales)	a																								
Cardiff Central 7	a																								

Sundays

13 September to 1 November

		EM	GW	XC	GW	XC	EM	XC	XC	GW	XC	EM		XC	GW	XC	AW	GW		XC	XC	XC	XC	EM	EM
		1 ◇		1 ◇		1 ◇		1 ◇		1 ◇	1 ◇	1 ◇				1 ◇				1 ◇	1		1 ◇		1 ◇
				C	D	E					E	G								H					
							🚌		🚌					🚌								🚌			
		🍽		🛒		🛒		🛒		🍽	🛒	🍽				🛒				🛒			🛒		🍽
Nottingham 8 🚊	d	07 28					08 32							10 55										11 23	11 30
Beeston	d	07a35					08 53																	11 29	11a36
Attenborough	d						09 04																	11 32	
Long Eaton	d						09 16					10 33												11 43	
Spondon	d																								
Derby 10	a						09 46					10 44		11 25										11 54	
	d					09 30					10 33									11 30			11 38		
Willington	d																								
Burton-on-Trent	d										10 44									11 41			11 50		
Tamworth	d					09 50															11 58		12 03		
Wilnecote	d																								
Leicester	d								10 10													11 10			
South Wigston	d								10 25													11 25			
Narborough	d								10 35													11 35			
Hinckley	d								11 00													12 00			
Nuneaton	d								11 20													12 20			
Coleshill Parkway	d								12a10													13a10			
Water Orton	d																								
Birmingham New Street 12	a					10 10					11 11									12 07	12 19		12 26		
	d			09 12		10 12		10 30			11 12					11 30				12 12			12 30		
Worcester Shrub Hill 7	d																								
Ashchurch for Tewkesbury	d																								
Cheltenham Spa	d		09 35	09 52	10 05	10 52		11 11		11 46	11 52				12 00	12 11	12 18	12 35		12 52			13 11		
Gloucester 7	a		09 45		10 15			11 21		11 56					12 10	12 21	12 26	12 45					13 21		
Bristol Parkway 7	a			10 23	10 55	11 24					12 24				12 51					13 23					
Bristol Temple Meads 10	a			10 35	11 08	11 37					12 37				13 09					13 35					
Newport (South Wales)	a							12 04								13 04	13 25						14 04		
Cardiff Central 7	a							12 25								13 25	13 45						14 25		

For general notes see front of timetable
For details of catering facilities see Directory of Train Operators

A From Edinburgh (Table 51)
B From Stansted Airport (Table 49)
C To Penzance (Table 51)
D To Taunton (Table 134)
E From Leeds to Plymouth (Table 51)
G To York (Table 53)
H From York to Plymouth (Table 51)

Table 57

Sundays

Nottingham, Derby and Leicester → Birmingham → Cardiff and Bristol

13 September to 1 November

Network Diagram - see first page of Table 50

		XC 1		EM 1◇ A [P]	XC 🚌	GW 1◇ [P]	XC 1◇ B [trolley]	XC 1◇ [trolley]		EM 1◇ [P]	AW	XC 1◇ [trolley]	XC 1◇ [trolley]	XC 1◇ C [trolley]		XC 🚌	GW D	XC 1◇ [trolley]	EM 1◇ A [P]	XC 1◇ [trolley]		EM	EM 1◇ [P]	XC 1◇ E [trolley]	XC 1◇ [trolley]
Nottingham 8	d							12 10		12 26								13 08				13 20	13 31		
Beeston	d									12a32												13 25	13a36		
Attenborough	d																					13 28			
Long Eaton	d			12 13															13 28			13 36			
Spondon	d																								
Derby 10	a			12 23				12 30										13 28	13 41			13 48			
	d						12 30	12 36						13 32				13 36		13 43					
Willington	d																								
Burton-on-Trent	d							12 48						13 43				13 50							
Tamworth	d	12 42					12 49	13 00					13 44					14 02							14 45
Wilnecote	d																								
Leicester	d				12 10											13 10									
South Wigston	d				12 25											13 25									
Narborough	d				12 35											13 35									
Hinckley	d				13 00											14 00									
Nuneaton	d				13 20											14 20									
Coleshill Parkway	d				14a10											15a10									
Water Orton	d																								
Birmingham New Street 12	a	13 03					13 07	13 21					14 06	14 10				14 23		14 27					15 16
	d						13 12	13 30				13 42		14 12				14 30						14 43	
Worcester Shrub Hill 7	d																14 36								
Ashchurch for Tewkesbury	d																14 51								
Cheltenham Spa	d					13 46	13 52	14 12			14 18	14 25		14 53			15 01	15 11						15 25	
Gloucester 7	a					13 58		14 22			14 29						15 10	15 21							
Bristol Parkway 7	a						14 23					14 56		15 25			15 49							16 00	
Bristol Temple Meads 10	a						14 35					15 14		15 38			16 09							16 14	
Newport (South Wales)	a							15 05			15 25							16 04							
Cardiff Central 7	a							15 26			15 45							16 25							

		XC 🚌	GW 1◇ [P]	XC 1◇ G [trolley]		XC 1◇ [trolley]	EM 1◇ A [P]	EM 1◇ [P]	XC 1◇ [trolley]	EM		AW	XC 1◇ [trolley]	GW	XC 1◇ C [trolley]	XC 1◇ [trolley]		XC 🚌	GW	XC 1◇ [trolley]	EM 1◇ A [P]	EM 1◇ [P]		XC 1◇ [trolley]	XC 1◇ [trolley]
Nottingham 8	d					14 10		14 31		14 53										15 10		15 30			
Beeston	d							14a37		14 59												15a35			
Attenborough	d									15 02															
Long Eaton	d						14 27			15 12											15 30				
Spondon	d																								
Derby 10	a					14 29	14 42			15 23										15 29	15 46				
	d			14 30		14 35			14 54						15 25					15 35				15 51	
Willington	d																								
Burton-on-Trent	d					14 50									15 35					15 48					
Tamworth	d			14 49		15 02										15 52				16 00					
Wilnecote	d																			16 04					
Leicester	d	14 10																15 10							
South Wigston	d	14 25																15 25							
Narborough	d	14 35																15 35							
Hinckley	d	15 00																16 00							
Nuneaton	d	15 20																16 20							
Coleshill Parkway	d	16a10																17a10							
Water Orton	d																								
Birmingham New Street 12	a			15 07		15 23			15 27						16 00	16 14				16 23				16 27	
	d			15 12		15 30							15 42		16 12					16 30					16 42
Worcester Shrub Hill 7	d																		16 40						
Ashchurch for Tewkesbury	d																		16 58						
Cheltenham Spa	d		15 46	15 52		16 11						16 18	16 25	16 33	16 52				17 08	17 11					17 25
Gloucester 7	a		15 57			16 21						16 27		16 43					17 16	17 21					
Bristol Parkway 7	a			16 23									16 57		17 23				17 57						18 02
Bristol Temple Meads 10	a			16 35									17 13		17 35				18 10						18 14
Newport (South Wales)	a					17 04						17 31								18 04					
Cardiff Central 7	a					17 25						17 51								18 25					

For general notes see front of timetable
For details of catering facilities see Directory of Train Operators

A To Sheffield (Table 53)
B From Newcastle to Plymouth (Table 51)
C From Edinburgh to Plymouth (Table 51)
D To Weston-super-Mare (Table 134)
E To Paignton (Table 51)
G From Edinburgh to Penzance (Table 51)

Sundays

Nottingham, Derby and Leicester → Birmingham → Cardiff and Bristol

13 September to 1 November

Network Diagram - see first page of Table 50

Station		GW	XC A	XC	XC	XC	EM B	XC	EM	EM	AW	XC	XC C	XC	XC	GW	XC	XC	EM	EM	XC D	EM B
Nottingham 8	d				16 10				16 21	16 28							17 10		17 23	17 30		
Beeston	d								16 26	16a33									17 29	17a35		
Attenborough	d								16 29										17 32			
Long Eaton	d						16 35		16 40										17 40			18 09
Spondon	d																					
Derby 10	a				16 29		16 47		16 56								17 29		17 52			18 19
	d		16 25		16 35			16 51					17 25				17 36	17 51				
Willington	d																					
Burton-on-Trent	d				16 48								17 35				17 49					
Tamworth	d		16 43	16 52	17 00									17 55			18 01					
Wilnecote	d																					
Leicester	d					16 10									17 10							
South Wigston	d					16 25									17 25							
Narborough	d					16 35									17 35							
Hinckley	d					17 00									18 00							
Nuneaton	d					17 20									18 20							
Coleshill Parkway	d					18a10									19a10							
Water Orton	d																					
Birmingham New Street 12	a		17 02	17 13	17 20			17 27					18 00	18 16			18 23	18 26				
	d		17 12		17 30							17 42	18 12				18 30				18 42	
Worcester Shrub Hill 7	d															18 40						
Ashchurch for Tewkesbury	d															18 55						
Cheltenham Spa	d	17 46	17 52		18 11						18 18	18 25	18 52			19 06	19 14				19 25	
Gloucester 7	a	17 57			18 21						18 29	18 35				19 15	19 24					
Bristol Parkway 7	a		18 23									19 08	19 23			19 55					20 00	
Bristol Temple Meads 10	a		18 37									19 25	19 35			20 08					20 14	
Newport (South Wales)	a				19 04						19 25						20 09					
Cardiff Central 7	a				19 25						19 47						20 30					

Station		XC E	XC	XC	GW	XC	XC	EM	EM	EM B	EM	AW	XC	XC C	XC	XC	XC	GW	XC	XC	XC
Nottingham 8	d					18 10		18 23	18 46		18 56					19 10					
Beeston	d							18 29	18a52		19 01										
Attenborough	d							18 32			19 04										
Long Eaton	d							18 41		19 09	19 13										
Spondon	d																				
Derby 10	a					18 31		18 52		19 19	19 25					19 30					
	d	18 25				18 36	18 51							19 26		19 37	19 51				20 25
Willington	d																				
Burton-on-Trent	d					18 50								19 38		19 49					
Tamworth	d	18 44	18 56			19 02									19 54	20 01					20 43
Wilnecote	d															20 05					
Leicester	d			18 10																19 10	
South Wigston	d			18 25																19 25	
Narborough	d			18 35																19 35	
Hinckley	d			19 00																20 00	
Nuneaton	d			19 20																20 20	
Coleshill Parkway	d			20a10																21a10	
Water Orton	d																				
Birmingham New Street 12	a	19 03	19 18			19 23	19 26							20 03	20 16	20 24	20 29				21 02
	d	19 12				19 30							19 42	20 12					20 42		21 12
Worcester Shrub Hill 7	d																	20 36			
Ashchurch for Tewkesbury	d																	20 53			
Cheltenham Spa	d	19 52			20 05	20 11						20 18	20 25	20 52				21 03	21 25		21 53
Gloucester 7	a				20 17	20 21						20 31						21 13			
Bristol Parkway 7	a	20 23											20 57	21 23				21 53	21 59		22 24
Bristol Temple Meads 10	a	20 35											21 14	21 35				22 07	22 15		22 41
Newport (South Wales)	a					21 04						21 25									
Cardiff Central 7	a					21 25						21 43									

For general notes see front of timetable
For details of catering facilities see Directory of Train Operators

A From Edinburgh to Penzance (Table 51)
B To Sheffield (Table 53)
C From Glasgow Central to Plymouth (Table 51)
D To Paignton (Table 51)
E From Aberdeen to Plymouth (Table 51)

Table 57

Sundays

13 September to 1 November

Nottingham, Derby and Leicester → Birmingham → Cardiff and Bristol

Network Diagram - see first page of Table 50

		XC	XC	EM		XC	EM	GW	XC	GW		XC	XC	XC	XC	XC		EM	EM	XC	XC	XC	XC		
		1 ◇	1 ◇	1 ◇		1 ◇						1 ◇	1 ◇	1 ◇		1 ◇		1 ◇		1 ◇	1 ◇	1 ◇			
				A									B					C			B				
									Bus						Bus								Bus		
		Trolley	Trolley	Buffet		Trolley						Trolley	Trolley	Trolley		Trolley		Buffet		Trolley	Trolley	Trolley			
Nottingham [8]	d		20 10				20 23									21 05			21 23						
Beeston	d						20 28												21 29						
Attenborough	d						20 31												21 32						
Long Eaton	d			20 32			20 41											21 27	21 39						
Spondon	d																								
Derby [10]	a		20 29	20 45			20 55									21 34		21 38	21 51						
	d		20 35			20 51							21 23							21 53	22 25				
Willington	d																								
Burton-on-Trent	d		20 48										21 34							22 04	22 35				
Tamworth	d	20 50	21 00										21 44	21 51						22 14	22 46	22 53			
Wilnecote	d																								
Leicester	d								20 10						21 10								22 10		
South Wigston	d								20 25						21 25								22 25		
Narborough	d								20 35						21 35								22 35		
Hinckley	d								21 00						22 00								23 00		
Nuneaton	d								21 20						22 20								23 20		
Coleshill Parkway	d								22a10						23a10								23a55		
Water Orton	d																								
Birmingham New Street [12]	a	21 11	21 18			21 24							22 03	22 12						22 38	23 05	23 14			
	d											21 42	22 12												
Worcester Shrub Hill [7]	d																								
Ashchurch for Tewkesbury	d																								
Cheltenham Spa	d							21 46		22 01		22 25	22 53												
Gloucester [7]	a							21 56		22 11															
Bristol Parkway [7]	a											22 57	23 24												
Bristol Temple Meads [10]	a											23 14	23 41												
Newport (South Wales)	a																								
Cardiff Central [7]	a																								

Sundays

from 8 November

		EM	GW	XC	GW	XC	XC		XC	GW	XC	EM	XC	XC		GW	XC	GW	AW	XC	XC		XC	XC	XC
		1 ◇		1 ◇		1 ◇	◇ ◇		1 ◇	1 ◇	1 ◇	1 ◇					1 ◇			1 ◇	1 ◇		1		1 ◇
				D	E						G	H								J	K				
													Bus	Bus										Bus	
		Buffet		Trolley		Trolley	Trolley		Trolley	Buffet	Trolley	Buffet					Trolley			Trolley	Trolley				Buffet
Nottingham [8]	d	07 28												10 55											
Beeston	d	07a35																							
Attenborough	d																								
Long Eaton	d											10 33													
Spondon	d																								
Derby [10]	a											10 44		11 25											
	d						09 08				10 05										11 30				11 36
Willington	d																								
Burton-on-Trent	d										10 16										11 41				11 48
Tamworth	d						09 27																11 58		12 00
Wilnecote	d																								
Leicester	d												10 10											11 10	
South Wigston	d												10 25											11 25	
Narborough	d												10 35											11 35	
Hinckley	d												11 00											12 00	
Nuneaton	d												11 20											12 20	
Coleshill Parkway	d												12a10											13a10	
Water Orton	d																								
Birmingham New Street [12]	a						09 47				10 43										12 07		12 19		12 26
	d			08 42		09 30	09 52		10 30		10 46						11 30			11 45					12 30
Worcester Shrub Hill [7]	d																								
Ashchurch for Tewkesbury	d																								
Cheltenham Spa	d		09 35	09 52	10 05	10 29	10 52		11 29	11 46	11 52					12 00	12 29	12 35	12 40	12b52					13 29
Gloucester [7]	a		09 45		10 15	10 39			11 39	11 56						12 10	12 39	12 45	12 53						13 39
Bristol Parkway [7]	a			10 23	10 55		11 24				12 23					12 51				13 23					
Bristol Temple Meads [10]	a			10 35	11 08		11 37				12 36					13 09				13 35					
Newport (South Wales)	a					11 24			12 28								13 22		13 45						14 30
Cardiff Central [7]	a					11 47			12 49								13 44		14 05						14 52

For general notes see front of timetable
For details of catering facilities see Directory of Train Operators

A To Sheffield (Table 53)
B From Edinburgh (Table 51)
C To Leeds (Table 53)
D To Penzance (Table 51)
E To Taunton (Table 134)
G From Leeds to Plymouth (Table 51)
H To York (Table 53)
J To Plymouth (Table 51)
K From York (Table 51)
b Arr. 1242

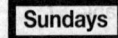

Nottingham, Derby and Leicester → Birmingham → Cardiff and Bristol

Network Diagram - see first page of Table 50

		EM	EM 1◇ ⊐P	EM 1◇ A ⊐P	GW 1◇ ⊐P	XC 1◇ B ⊼		XC 1	XC 🚌	XC 1◇ C ⊼	AW	XC 1◇ ⊼	EM 1◇ ⊐P		XC 1◇ B ⊼	XC 1◇ ⊼	XC 1◇ D ⊼	XC 🚌	GW E	XC 1◇ ⊼		EM 1◇ A ⊐P	XC 1◇ ⊼	EM	EM 1◇ ⊐P
Nottingham 8 🚊	d	11 23	11 30									12 10	12 26							13 08				13 20	13 31
Beeston	d	11 29	11a36										12a32											13 25	13a36
Attenborough	d	11 32																						13 28	
Long Eaton	d	11 43		12 13																		13 28		13 36	
Spondon	d																								
Derby 10	a	11 54		12 23								12 30								13 28		13 41		13 48	
	d									12 30		12 36					13 32			13 36			13 43		
Willington	d																								
Burton-on-Trent	d											12 48					13 43			13 49					
Tamworth	d							12 42		12 48		13 00				13 44				14 01					
Wilnecote	d																								
Leicester	d								12 10									13 10							
South Wigston	d								12 25									13 25							
Narborough	d								12 35									13 35							
Hinckley	d								13 00									14 00							
Nuneaton	d								13 20									14 20							
Coleshill Parkway	d								14a10									15a10							
Water Orton	d																								
Birmingham New Street 12	a							13 03		13 08		13 21				14 06	14 11			14 22			14 27		
	d					12 42						13 28			13 42					14 28					
Worcester Shrub Hill 7	d																		14 36						
Ashchurch for Tewkesbury	d																		14 51						
Cheltenham Spa	d				13 46	13 52					14 18	14 44			14b52				15 01	15 40					
Gloucester 7	a				13 58						14 29	14 54							15 10	15 50					
Bristol Parkway 7	a					14 25									15 23				15 49						
Bristol Temple Meads 10	a					14 37									15 36				16 09						
Newport (South Wales)	a										15 25	15 39								16 44					
Cardiff Central 7	a										15 45	16 00								17 07					

		GW 1◇ ⊐P	XC 1◇ G ⊼	XC 1◇ ⊼	XC 🚌		XC 1◇ D ⊼	XC 1◇ ⊼	EM 1◇ A ⊐P	EM 1◇ ⊐P	XC 1◇ ⊼	EM		GW	AW	XC 1◇ B ⊼	XC 1◇ D ⊼	XC 1◇ ⊼	XC 🚌		GW	XC 1◇ ⊼	EM 1◇ A ⊐P	EM 1◇ ⊐P	XC 1◇ ⊼
Nottingham 8 🚊	d							14 10		14 31		14 53										15 10		15 30	
Beeston	d									14a37		14 59												15a35	
Attenborough	d											15 02													
Long Eaton	d								14 27			15 12											15 30		
Spondon	d																								
Derby 10	a							14 29	14 42			15 23										15 30	15 46		
	d						14 30	14 35			14 54						15 25					15 35			15 51
Willington	d																								
Burton-on-Trent	d							14 48									15 35					15 48			
Tamworth	d			14 45			14 49	15 00										15 52				16 00			
Wilnecote	d																					16 04			
Leicester	d				14 10														15 10						
South Wigston	d				14 25														15 25						
Narborough	d				14 35														15 35						
Hinckley	d				15 00														16 00						
Nuneaton	d				15 20														16 20						
Coleshill Parkway	d				16a10														17a10						
Water Orton	d																								
Birmingham New Street 12	a			15 16			15 07	15 23			15 27						16 00	16 14				16 23			16 27
	d		14 42					15 28								15 42						16 28			
Worcester Shrub Hill 7	d																				16 40				
Ashchurch for Tewkesbury	d																				16 58				
Cheltenham Spa	d	15 46	15 52					16 27						16 33	16 40	16 52					17 08	17 37			
Gloucester 7	a	15 57						16 38						16 43	16 53						17 16	17 47			
Bristol Parkway 7	a		16 23													17 23					17 57				
Bristol Temple Meads 10	a		16 35													17 35					18 10				
Newport (South Wales)	a							17 28							17 45							18 42			
Cardiff Central 7	a							17 49							18 06							19 04			

For general notes see front of timetable
For details of catering facilities see Directory of Train Operators

A To Sheffield (Table 53)
B To Plymouth (Table 51)
C From Newcastle (Table 51)
D From Edinburgh (Table 51)
E To Weston-super-Mare (Table 134)
G To Penzance (Table 51)
b Arr. 1443

Table 57

Sundays

from 8 November

Nottingham, Derby and Leicester → Birmingham → Cardiff and Bristol

Network Diagram - see first page of Table 50

		GW	XC	XC		XC	XC	XC	AW	EM	XC		EM	XC	EM	XC	XC	XC		GW	XC	XC	EM	EM	XC
		1◇	1◇	1◇		1◇		1◇		1◇	1◇			1◇	1◇	1◇	1◇				1◇	1◇		1◇	1◇
			A	B						C						D									E
		⊡	⫟	⫟		⫟	🚌	⫟		⊡	⫟			⫟	⊡	⫟	⫟	🚌			⫟	⫟		⊡	⫟
Nottingham 8	d							16 10					16 21		16 28						17 10		17 23	17 30	
Beeston	d												16 26		16a33								17 29	17a35	
Attenborough	d												16 29										17 32		
Long Eaton	d									16 35			16 40										17 40		
Spondon	d																								
Derby 10	a							16 29		16 47			16 56								17 30		17 52		
	d			16 25				16 35			16 51					17 25					17 36	17 51			
Willington	d																								
Burton-on-Trent	d							16 47								17 35					17 48				
Tamworth	d			16 43		16 52		16 59									17 55				18 00				
Wilnecote	d																								
Leicester	d						16 10											17 10							
South Wigston	d						16 25											17 25							
Narborough	d						16 35											17 35							
Hinckley	d						17 00											18 00							
Nuneaton	d						17 20											18 20							
Coleshill Parkway	d						18a10											19a10							
Water Orton	d																								
Birmingham New Street 12	a			17 02		17 13		17 20			17 27					18 00	18 16				18 23	18 26			
	d		16 42					17 28						17 42							18 28				18 42
Worcester Shrub Hill 7	d																			18 40					
Ashchurch for Tewkesbury	d																			18 55					
Cheltenham Spa	d	17 46	17 52					18 27	18 35					18 52						19 06	19 41				19 55
Gloucester 7	a	17 57						18 38	18 46											19 15	19 51				
Bristol Parkway 7	a		18 23											19 23						19 55					20 27
Bristol Temple Meads 10	a		18 35											19 35						20 08					20 39
Newport (South Wales)	a							19 25	19 43												20 39				
Cardiff Central 7	a							19 46	20 05												21 00				

		EM	XC		XC	XC	GW	AW	XC	XC		EM	EM	EM	XC	EM	XC		XC	XC	XC	GW	XC	GW	XC
		1◇	1◇		1◇		1◇		1◇	1◇			1◇	1◇	1◇		1◇		1◇	1◇	1◇				1◇
		C	G											C	E		D								
		⊡	⫟		⫟	🚌	⊡		⫟	⫟			⊡	⊡	⫟		⫟		⫟	⫟	⫟		🚌		⫟
Nottingham 8	d								18 10			18 23	18 46			18 56				19 10					
Beeston	d											18 29	18a52			19 01									
Attenborough	d											18 32				19 04									
Long Eaton	d	18 09										18 41		19 09		19 13									
Spondon	d																								
Derby 10	a	18 19							18 31			18 52		19 19		19 25				19 30					
	d		18 25						18 36	18 51							19 26			19 37	19 51				
Willington	d																								
Burton-on-Trent	d								18 50								19 37			19 49					
Tamworth	d		18 43		18 56				19 03										19 54	20 01					
Wilnecote	d																			20 05					
Leicester	d					18 10																	19 10		
South Wigston	d					18 25																	19 25		
Narborough	d					18 35																	19 35		
Hinckley	d					19 00																	20 00		
Nuneaton	d					19 20																	20 20		
Coleshill Parkway	d					20a10																	21a10		
Water Orton	d																								
Birmingham New Street 12	a		19 02		19 19				19 23	19 26							20 02		20 16	20 24	20 29				
	d														19 42										20 42
Worcester Shrub Hill 7	d																					20 36			
Ashchurch for Tewkesbury	d																					20 53			
Cheltenham Spa	d						20 05	20 18							20b52							21 03		21 46	21 52
Gloucester 7	a						20 17	20 31														21 13		21 56	
Bristol Parkway 7	a														21 23							21 53			22 23
Bristol Temple Meads 10	a														21 36							22 07			22 40
Newport (South Wales)	a							21 25																	
Cardiff Central 7	a							21 43																	

For general notes see front of timetable
For details of catering facilities see Directory of Train Operators

- **A** To Penzance (Table 51)
- **B** From Edinburgh (Table 51)
- **C** To Sheffield (Table 53)
- **D** From Glasgow Central (Table 51)
- **E** To Plymouth (Table 51)
- **G** From Aberdeen (Table 51)
- **b** Arr. 2041

Sundays

from 8 November

Nottingham, Derby and Leicester → Birmingham → Cardiff and Bristol

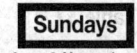

Network Diagram - see first page of Table 50

		XC		XC	EM	XC	XC	EM	GW		XC	XC	XC	XC	XC	EM		EM	XC	XC	XC	XC		
		1 ◇		1 ◇	1 ◇	1 ◇					1 ◇	1 ◇	1 ◇		1 ◇	1 ◇			1 ◇	1 ◇	1 ◇			
					A							B				C				B				
							🚌							🚌								🚌		
		🍴		🍴	⊡	🍴					🍴	🍴	🍴		🍴	⊡			🍴	🍴	🍴			
Nottingham 8 🚊	d			20 10				20 23							21 05			21 23						
Beeston	d							20 28										21 29						
Attenborough	d							20 31										21 32						
Long Eaton	d				20 32			20 41								21 27		21 39						
Spondon	d																							
Derby 10	a			20 29	20 45			20 55							21 34	21 38		21 51						
	d			20 35		20 51						21 23							21 53	22 25				
Willington	d																							
Burton-on-Trent	d			20 48								21 34							22 04	22 35				
Tamworth	d	20 50		21 00									21 51						22 14	22 46	22 53			
Wilnecote	d																							
Leicester	d						20 10							21 10								22 10		
South Wigston	d						20 25							21 25								22 25		
Narborough	d						20 35							21 35								22 35		
Hinckley	d						21 00							22 00								23 00		
Nuneaton	d						21 20							22 20								23 20		
Coleshill Parkway	d						22a10							23a10								23a55		
Water Orton	d																							
Birmingham New Street 12	a	21 12		21 18		21 24						21 59	22 12						22 38	23 05	23 14			
	d										21 44													
Worcester Shrub Hill 7	d																							
Ashchurch for Tewkesbury	d																							
Cheltenham Spa	d								22 01		22 52													
Gloucester 7	a								22 11															
Bristol Parkway 7	a										23 23													
Bristol Temple Meads 10	a										23 40													
Newport (South Wales)	a																							
Cardiff Central 7	a																							

For general notes see front of timetable
For details of catering facilities see Directory of Train Operators

A To Sheffield (Table 53)
B From Edinburgh (Table 51)
C To Leeds (Table 53)

Bristol and Cardiff → Birmingham → Leicester, Derby and Nottingham

Network Diagram - see first page of Table 50

Miles	Miles	Miles			EM MX 1◇	EM MO 1◇ A	EM MO 1◇ B	AW MX C	EM MX 1◇	EM 1◇	XC 1◇	EM	EM 1◇ D	XC 1		XC 1◇	EM	XC 1 E	XC 1 G	XC 1◇	XC 1◇	GW	EM 1◇ G	EM 1◇ E	EM
0	—	—	**Cardiff Central 7**	d				23p19																	
11¾	—	—	Newport (South Wales)	d				23p40																	
—	—	0	**Bristol Temple Meads 10**	d																					
—	—	5¾	Bristol Parkway 7	d																					
56½	—	—	Gloucester 7	d				00 40														06 01			
63	—	46¼	Cheltenham Spa	d				00a53														06 12			
70¼	—	53½	Ashchurch for Tewkesbury	d																		06 21			
85	—	—	Worcester Shrub Hill 7	a																		06 42			
112	—	92¾	**Birmingham New Street 12**	a																					
—	0	—		d							05 22			05 52		06 00		06 19	06 19	06 22	06 30				
119¾	7¾	—	Water Orton	d																					
—	9½	—	Coleshill Parkway	d										06 05						06 35					
—	20	—	Nuneaton	d							05 50			06 22						06 52					
—	25¼	—	Hinckley	d										06 29											
—	34	—	Narborough	d										06 37											
—	37	—	South Wigston	d										06 42											
—	38¾	—	**Leicester**	a							06 10			06 50						07 15					
127	—	—	Wilnecote	d														06 34	06 34						
128¾	—	—	Tamworth	d												06 15		06 39	06 39		06 46				
141¾	—	—	Burton-on-Trent	d														06 51	06 51		06 56				
146½	—	—	Willington	d																					
152¾	—	—	**Derby 10**	a												06 35		07 04	07 04		07 11				
—	—	—		d						05 17		06 24	06 32					07 10	07 13				07 24	07 26	07 33
155¼	—	—	Spondon	d								06 29						07 18	07 18						
161	—	—	Long Eaton	d						05a26		06 34	06a41					07 25	07 25				07a35	07a35	07 42
164	—	—	Attenborough	d								06 43					07 14	07 31	07 31						07 52
165½	—	—	Beeston	d	00 05	00 41	00 45		01 37			06 46					07 17	07 35	07 35						07 55
168¾	—	—	**Nottingham 8**	a	00 14	00 48	00 51		01 44			06 58					07 27	07 41	07 41						08 05

		XC 1 G	XC 1 E		XC 1 H	XC 1◇	EM	EM	XC 1 E	XC 1 G	EM 1◇	XC 1◇ J	XC 1◇	EM 1◇ D K		EM L	XC 1	XC 1	XC 1◇	EM 1◇	XC 1	GW N	AW	XC 1◇	XC 1◇
Cardiff Central 7	d																						06 12		
Newport (South Wales)	d																						06 28		
Bristol Temple Meads 10	d																		06 15						07 00
Bristol Parkway 7	d																		06 25						07 10
Gloucester 7	d																		07 02		07 10	07 15	07 21		
Cheltenham Spa	d																		07 12		07 21	07 25	07a34		07 42
Ashchurch for Tewkesbury	d																				07 29	07 34			
Worcester Shrub Hill 7	a																					07 54			
Birmingham New Street 12	a																		07 56		08 16				08 26
	d	06 49	06 49		06 52	07 03			07 19	07 19		07 22	07 30				07 49	07 52	08 03		08 19			08 22	
Water Orton	d																								
Coleshill Parkway	d				07 05							07 35						08 05						08 35	
Nuneaton	d				07 22							07 51						08 22						08 51	
Hinckley	d				07 29							07 58						08 29							
Narborough	d				07 37							08 06						08 37							
South Wigston	d				07 42							08 10						08 42							
Leicester	a				07 50							08 15						08 50						09 15	
Wilnecote	d								07 34	07 34															
Tamworth	d	07 07	07 07			07 19			07 38	07 38			07 46				08 07		08 19		08 37				
Burton-on-Trent	d	07 19	07 19			07 29			07 50	07 50			07 56				08 19		08 29		08 49				
Willington	d								07 55	07 56															
Derby 10	a	07 34	07 34			07 42			08 05	08 05			08 11				08 34		08 42		09 04				
	d	07 40	07 43					07 53	08 10	08 10				08 16		08 25	08 40				09 10				
Spondon	d	07 45	07 48													08 30									
Long Eaton	d	07 49	07 54					08 03	08 19	08 19				08a25		08 36					09 19				
Attenborough	d							08 13								08 44					09 26				
Beeston	d	07 58	08 02				08 06	08 16	08 27	08 27	08 31					08 47				09 17	09 29				
Nottingham 8	a	08 08	08 08				08 16	08 26	08 35	08 35	08 40					08 59	09 05			09 26	09 37				

For general notes see front of timetable
For details of catering facilities see Directory of Train Operators

A Until 13 July
B 20 July to 7 September
C From Maesteg (Table 128)
D From Sheffield (Table 53)
E From 7 September
G Until 4 September
H To Cambridge (Table 49)
J To Stansted Airport (Table 49)
K **The South Yorkshireman**
L From Matlock (Table 56)
N To Great Malvern (Table 71)

Bristol and Cardiff → Birmingham → Leicester, Derby and Nottingham

Network Diagram - see first page of Table 50

		XC	EM		EM		XC	XC	GW	XC	XC	AW	EM	XC		XC	XC	XC	EM	EM	XC		GW	XC	XC
		1 ◇	1 ◇				1 ◇	1 ◇	1 ◇	1	1 ◇		1 ◇	1		1 ◇	1 ◇	1 ◇	1 ◇		1 ◇			1	1 ◇
							A	B		C	D												E		D
		[trolley]	[buffet]						[buffet]		[trolley]		[buffet]			[trolley]	[trolley]	[trolley]	[buffet]						[trolley]
Cardiff Central 7	d						06 40	06 40				07 12					07 00				07 45				
Newport (South Wales)	d						06 55	06 55				07 27					07 15				08 00				
Bristol Temple Meads 10	d										07 30						08 00								08 30
Bristol Parkway 7	d										07 40						08 10								08 40
Gloucester 7	d						07 46	07 46	07 55			08 21									08 46		08 53		
Cheltenham Spa	d						07 56	07 56	08a04		08 12	08a34					08 42				08 56		09a03		09 12
Ashchurch for Tewkesbury	d						08 04	08 04																	
Worcester Shrub Hill 7	a																								
Birmingham New Street 12	a						08 45	08 45			08 56						09 26				09 39				09 56
Birmingham New Street 12	d	08 30					08 49	08 49		08 52	09 03			09 19		09 22		09 30			09 49			09 52	10 03
Water Orton	d									09 03															
Coleshill Parkway	d									09 07						09 35								10 05	
Nuneaton	d									09 22						09 52								10 22	
Hinckley	d									09 30														10 29	
Narborough	d									09 39														10 37	
South Wigston	d																							10 42	
Leicester	a									09 50						10 15								10 50	
Wilnecote	d													09 34											
Tamworth	d						09 07	09 07						09 39							10 07				10 19
Burton-on-Trent	d						09 19	09 19			09 26			09 51							10 19				
Willington	d																								
Derby 10	a	09 11					09 34	09 34			09 39			10 04				10 11			10 34				10 39
	d		09 18		09 21		09 40	09 40						10 10					10 18	10 22	10 40				
Spondon	d																								
Long Eaton	d		09a27		09 33									10 19					10a27	10 33					
Attenborough	d				09 40															10 40					
Beeston	d				09 43								10 17	10 27						10 43					
Nottingham 8	a				09 54		10 02	10 05					10 26	10 35						10 54	11 05				

		EM	XC		XC	XC	GW	XC	EM	EM	XC		GW	XC		XC	AW	EM	XC	XC	XC	XC	EM	EM	XC
		1 ◇	1		1 ◇	1 ◇		1 ◇	1 ◇		1 ◇		1 ◇	1		1 ◇		1 ◇	1	1 ◇	1 ◇	1 ◇	1 ◇		1 ◇
						G	H							C		D	J								
		[buffet]			[trolley]	[trolley]		[trolley]	[buffet]				[buffet]			[trolley]		[buffet]		[trolley]	[trolley]	[trolley]	[buffet]		
Cardiff Central 7	d										08 45						09 12								09 45
Newport (South Wales)	d										09 00						09 27								10 00
Bristol Temple Meads 10	d					09 00	08 41									09 30					10 00				
Bristol Parkway 7	d					09 10	08 52									09 40					10 10				
Gloucester 7	d						09 38				09 46		09 51				10 21								10 46
Cheltenham Spa	d					09 42	09 48				09 56		10a03			10 12	10a34				10 42				10 56
Ashchurch for Tewkesbury	d						09 55																		
Worcester Shrub Hill 7	a						10 14																		
Birmingham New Street 12	a					10 26					10 39					10 56					11 26				11 45
Birmingham New Street 12	d		10 19		10 22			10 30			10 49			10 52		11 03			11 19	11 22		11 30			11 49
Water Orton	d													11 03											
Coleshill Parkway	d				10 35									11 07						11 35					
Nuneaton	d				10 52									11 23						11 52					
Hinckley	d													11 30											
Narborough	d													11 39											
South Wigston	d																								
Leicester	a				11 15									11 50						12 15					
Wilnecote	d																		11 34						
Tamworth	d		10 37								11 07								11 39						12 07
Burton-on-Trent	d		10 49								11 19					11 26			11 51						12 19
Willington	d																								
Derby 10	a		11 04					11 11			11 34					11 39			12 04			12 11			12 34
	d		11 10						11 18	11 22	11 40								12 10				12 18	12 22	12 40
Spondon	d																								
Long Eaton	d		11 19						11a27	11 33									12 19				12a27	12 33	
Attenborough	d									11 40														12 40	
Beeston	d	11 17	11 27							11 43								12 17	12 27					12 43	
Nottingham 8	a	11 26	11 35							11 54	12 05							12 26	12 35					12 54	13 05

For general notes see front of timetable
For details of catering facilities see Directory of Train Operators

A From 7 September
B Until 4 September
C To Cambridge (Table 49)
D From Plymouth (Table 51)
E From Westbury (Table 123)
G From Paignton (Table 51)
H From Warminster (Table 123) to Great Malvern (Table 71)
J From Maesteg (Table 128)

Bristol and Cardiff → Birmingham → Leicester, Derby and Nottingham

Network Diagram - see first page of Table 50

		GW	XC 1		XC 1◇ A 🛒	LM	AW B	EM 1◇ ☕	XC 1	XC 1◇ 🛒	XC 1◇ 🛒	GW C	XC 1◇ 🛒
Cardiff Central 7	d						10 12						
Newport (South Wales)	d						10 27						
Bristol Temple Meads 10	d				10 30						11 00	10 41	
Bristol Parkway 7	d				10 40						11 10	10 52	
Gloucester 7	d	10 53				11 13	11 21					11 36	
Cheltenham Spa	d	11a03			11 12	11 23	11a34				11 42	11 48	
Ashchurch for Tewkesbury	d					11 31						11 55	
Worcester Shrub Hill 7	a					11 48						12 14	
Birmingham New Street 12	a				11 56						12 26		
	d		11 52		12 03				12 19	12 22			12 30
Water Orton	d												
Coleshill Parkway	d		12 05							12 35			
Nuneaton	d		12 22							12 52			
Hinckley	d		12 29										
Narborough	d		12 37										
South Wigston	d		12 42										
Leicester	a		12 50							13 15			
Wilnecote	d												
Tamworth	d				12 19				12 37				
Burton-on-Trent	d								12 49				
Willington	d								12 54				
Derby 10	a				12 39				13 04				13 11
	d								13 10				
Spondon	d												
Long Eaton	d								13 19				
Attenborough	d												
Beeston	d							13 17	13 27				
Nottingham 8 🚊	a							13 26	13 35				

		EM 1◇ ☕		EM	XC 1◇	GW 1◇ ☕	XC 1 D	XC 1◇ E 🛒	EM 1◇ ☕	XC 1	XC 1◇ 🛒	XC 1◇ G 🛒	XC 1◇ 🛒
Cardiff Central 7	d				10 45								
Newport (South Wales)	d				11 00								
Bristol Temple Meads 10	d							11 30				12 00	
Bristol Parkway 7	d							11 40				12 10	
Gloucester 7	d				11 46	11 51							
Cheltenham Spa	d				11 56	12a03		12 12				12 42	
Ashchurch for Tewkesbury	d												
Worcester Shrub Hill 7	a												
Birmingham New Street 12	a				12 45			12 56				13 26	
	d				12 49		12 52	13 03		13 19	13 22		13 30
Water Orton	d						13 03						
Coleshill Parkway	d						13 07				13 35		
Nuneaton	d						13 23				13 52		
Hinckley	d						13 30						
Narborough	d						13 39						
South Wigston	d												
Leicester	a						13 50				14 15		
Wilnecote	d									13 34			
Tamworth	d				13 07					13 39			
Burton-on-Trent	d				13 19			13 26		13 51			
Willington	d												
Derby 10	a				13 34			13 39		14 04			14 11
	d	13 18		13 22	13 40					14 10			
Spondon	d												
Long Eaton	d	13a27		13 33						14 19			
Attenborough	d			13 40									
Beeston	d			13 43					14 16	14 27			
Nottingham 8 🚊	a			13 54	14 05				14 26	14 35			

		EM 1◇ ☕			EM	XC 1◇	GW	XC 1	XC 1◇ A 🛒	LM	AW B	EM 1◇ ☕	XC 1
Cardiff Central 7	d					11 45					12 12		
Newport (South Wales)	d					12 00					12 28		
Bristol Temple Meads 10	d								12 30				
Bristol Parkway 7	d								12 40				
Gloucester 7	d					12 46	12 54			13 16	13 22		
Cheltenham Spa	d					12 56	13a03		13 12	13 27	13a34		
Ashchurch for Tewkesbury	d					13 04				13 34			
Worcester Shrub Hill 7	a									13 54			
Birmingham New Street 12	a					13 45			13 56				
	d					13 49		13 52	14 03				14 19
Water Orton	d												
Coleshill Parkway	d							14 05					
Nuneaton	d							14 22					
Hinckley	d							14 29					
Narborough	d							14 37					
South Wigston	d							14 42					
Leicester	a							14 50					
Wilnecote	d												
Tamworth	d					14 07			14 19				14 37
Burton-on-Trent	d					14 19							14 49
Willington	d												
Derby 10	a					14 34			14 39				15 04
	d	14 18			14 22	14 40							15 10
Spondon	d												
Long Eaton	d	14a27			14 33								15 19
Attenborough	d				14 40								
Beeston	d				14 43							15 17	15 27
Nottingham 8 🚊	a				14 54	15 05						15 26	15 35

		XC 1◇ 🛒		XC 1◇ 🛒	GW ◇ K	XC 1◇ 🛒	EM 1◇ ☕	EM	XC 1◇	GW 1◇ ☕	XC 1	XC 1◇ E 🛒	AW B
Cardiff Central 7	d								12 45				13 12
Newport (South Wales)	d								13 00				13 28
Bristol Temple Meads 10	d			13 00	12 41							13 30	
Bristol Parkway 7	d			13 10	12 52							13 40	
Gloucester 7	d				13 38				13 46	13 51			14 21
Cheltenham Spa	d			13 42	13 48				13 56	14a03		14 12	14a34
Ashchurch for Tewkesbury	d				13 55								
Worcester Shrub Hill 7	a				14 14								
Birmingham New Street 12	a			14 26					14 45			14 56	
	d	14 22				14 30			14 49		14 52	15 03	
Water Orton	d										15 03		
Coleshill Parkway	d	14 35									15 07		
Nuneaton	d	14 52									15 23		
Hinckley	d										15 30		
Narborough	d										15 39		
South Wigston	d												
Leicester	a	15 15									15 50		
Wilnecote	d												
Tamworth	d								15 07				
Burton-on-Trent	d								15 19			15 26	
Willington	d												
Derby 10	a					15 11			15 34			15 39	
	d						15 18	15 22	15 40				
Spondon	d												
Long Eaton	d						15a27	15 33					
Attenborough	d							15 40					
Beeston	d							15 43					
Nottingham 8 🚊	a							15 54	16 05				

For general notes see front of timetable
For details of catering facilities see Directory of Train Operators

- A From Penzance (Table 51)
- B From Maesteg (Table 128)
- C From Southampton Central (Table 123) to Great Malvern (Table 71)
- D To Cambridge (Table 49)
- E From Plymouth (Table 51)
- G From Paignton (Table 51)
- K From Brighton (Table 123) to Great Malvern (Table 71)

Bristol and Cardiff → Birmingham → Leicester, Derby and Nottingham

Network Diagram - see first page of Table 50

		EM	XC		XC	XC	XC	EM		EM	XC	GW	XC	XC		LM	XC	EM	XC	XC	XC	GW	XC	EM	EM
		1◇	1		1◇	1◇	1◇	1◇			1◇		1	1◇			1	1◇	1	1◇	1◇		1◇	1◇	
						A					C			D								E			G
Cardiff Central 7	d										13 45														
Newport (South Wales)	d										14 00														
Bristol Temple Meads 10	d					14 00								14 30							15 00	14 41			
Bristol Parkway 7	d					14 10								14 40							15 10	14 52			
Gloucester 7	d										14 46	14 53				15 13						15 37			
Cheltenham Spa	d					14 42					14 56	15a03		15 12		15 25					15 42	15 48			
Ashchurch for Tewkesbury	d															15 32						15 55			
Worcester Shrub Hill 7	a															15 52						16 22			
Birmingham New Street 12	a					15 26					15 45			15 56							16 26				
	d		15 19		15 22		15 30				15 49		15 52	16 03			16 09		16 19	16 22			16 30		
Water Orton	d																16 19								
Coleshill Parkway	d				15 35								16 05				16 23			16 35					
Nuneaton	d				15 52								16 21				16 39			16 52					
Hinckley	d												16 29				16 46								
Narborough	d												16 37				16 55								
South Wigston	d												16 42				16 59								
Leicester	a				16 15								16 50				17 06			17 15					
Wilnecote	d		15 34																						
Tamworth	d		15 39								16 07			16 21					16 38						
Burton-on-Trent	d		15 51								16 19								16 51						
Willington	d																								
Derby 10	a		16 04				16 11				16 34			16 39					17 04				17 11		
	d		16 10					16 18		16 22	16 40								17 10					17 18	17 22
Spondon	d																								17 27
Long Eaton	d		16 19					16a27		16 32									17 19					17a28	17 33
Attenborough	d									16 39															17 41
Beeston	d	16 17	16 27							16 42								17 17	17 27						17 44
Nottingham 8	a	16 26	16 35							16 54	17 05							17 26	17 35						17 54

		XC	GW		XC	XC	AW	XC	EM	EM	XC	XC	XC	XC		XC	EM		EM	XC	XC	GW	XC	XC	LM
		1◇	1◇		1◇	1◇		1		1◇	1	1	1◇	1◇		1◇	1◇			1	1◇		1	1◇	
						D	H				B	C		J										D	
Cardiff Central 7	d	14 45					15 12														15 45				
Newport (South Wales)	d	15 00					15 28														16 00				
Bristol Temple Meads 10	d					15 30								16 00										16 30	
Bristol Parkway 7	d					15 40								16 10										16 40	
Gloucester 7	d	15 46	15 51				16 22														16 46	16 53			17 10
Cheltenham Spa	d	15 56	16a03			16 12	16a34							16 42							16 56	17a03		17 12	17 24
Ashchurch for Tewkesbury	d																								17 31
Worcester Shrub Hill 7	a																								17 55
Birmingham New Street 12	a	16 45				16 56								17 26							17 45			17 56	
	d	16 49			16 52	17 03		17 09			17 19	17 19	17 22			17 30				17 39	17 49		17 52	18 03	
Water Orton	d							17 21												17 50			18 03		
Coleshill Parkway	d				17 05			17 25					17 35										18 07		
Nuneaton	d				17 22			17 42					17 52										18 23		
Hinckley	d				17 29			17 49															18 30		
Narborough	d				17 37																		18 39		
South Wigston	d																						18 44		
Leicester	a				17 50			18 09					18 15										18 50		
Wilnecote	d										17 34	17 35													
Tamworth	d	17 07									17 39	17 39								18 00	18 07			18 19	
Burton-on-Trent	d	17 19				17 28					17 51	17 51								18 12	18 19				
Willington	d																				18 25				
Derby 10	a	17 34				17 39					18 04	18 04				18 11				18 31	18 34			18 39	
	d	17 40							17 48		18 10	18 10					18 18		18 22		18 40				
Spondon	d								17 53																
Long Eaton	d								18 01		18 19	18 19					18a27		18 33						
Attenborough	d								18 09										18 40						
Beeston	d								18 12	18 18	18 27	18 27							18 43						
Nottingham 8	a	18 05							18 22	18 30	18 35	18 35							18 54		19 05				

For general notes see front of timetable
For details of catering facilities see Directory of Train Operators

A From Penzance (Table 51)
B Until 4 September
C From 7 September
D From Plymouth (Table 51)
E From Southampton Central (Table 123) to Worcester Foregate Street (Table 71)
G From Matlock (Table 56)
H From Maesteg (Table 128)
J From Paignton (Table 51)

Bristol and Cardiff → Birmingham → Leicester, Derby and Nottingham

Network Diagram - see first page of Table 50

		AW	EM	EM	XC	XC	XC	GW	XC	EM	EM	XC	GW	XC	XC	AW	EM	EM	XC	XC	XC	XC	XC
			1 ◇ ☕	1 ◇ ☕	1	1 ◇ 🛒	1 ◇ 🛒	A	1 ◇ B 🛒	1 ◇ ☕		1 ◇	1 ◇ ☕	1 C	1 ◇ 🛒	D		1 ◇ E ☕	1 B	1 G	1 ◇ 🛒	1 ◇ H 🛒	1 ◇ 🛒
Cardiff Central 7	d	16 05										16 45				17 12							
Newport (South Wales)	d	16 21										17 00				17 28							
Bristol Temple Meads 10	d						17 00	16 41							17 30							18 00	
Bristol Parkway 7	d						17 10	16 52							17 40							18 10	
Gloucester 7	d	17 22						17 38				17 46	17 51			18 22							
Cheltenham Spa	d	17a34					17 42	17 48				17 56	18a03		18 12	18a34						18 42	
Ashchurch for Tewkesbury	d							17 55															
Worcester Shrub Hill 7	a							18 19															
Birmingham New Street 12	a						18 26					18 45			18 56							19 26	
	d				18 19	18 22			18 30			18 49		18 52	19 03				19 19	19 19	19 22		19 30
Water Orton	d																						
Coleshill Parkway	d					18 35								19 05							19 35		
Nuneaton	d					18 52								19 22							19 52		
Hinckley	d													19 29									
Narborough	d													19 37									
South Wigston	d													19 42									
Leicester	a					19 15								19 50							20 15		
Wilnecote	d																		19 34	19 34			
Tamworth	d				18 37							19 07							19 39	19 39			
Burton-on-Trent	d				18 49							19 19			19 28				19 51	19 51			
Willington	d																						
Derby 10	a				19 04				19 11			19 34			19 41				20 04	20 04			20 11
	d				19 10					19 18	19 22	19 40							20 10	20 10			
Spondon	d																						
Long Eaton	d				19 19					19a27	19 32								20 19	20 19			
Attenborough	d										19 40												
Beeston	d		19 03	19 18	19 27						19 43						20 07	20 18	20 27	20 30			
Nottingham 8	a		19 10	19 27	19 35						19 54	20 05					20 20	20 28	20 35	20 36			

		EM	XC	GW	XC	XC	LM	AW	XC	XC	GW	XC	EM	EM	EM	XC	XC	GW	XC	XC	XC	GW	GW
			1 ◇		1	1 ◇ J 🛒	K	D	1 ◇ 🛒	1 ◇ 🛒	A	1 ◇		1 ◇ L ☕		1 ◇ B	1 ◇ G	1 ◇ ☕	1	1 ◇ J 🛒	1 ◇	N	1 ◇ ☕
Cardiff Central 7	d		17 45					18 12								18 45	18 45						
Newport (South Wales)	d		18 00					18 27								19 00	19 00						
Bristol Temple Meads 10	d					18 30				19 00	18 41									19 30	20 00	19 41	
Bristol Parkway 7	d					18 40				19 10	18 52									19 40	20 10	19 52	
Gloucester 7	d		18 46	18 53			19 10	19 21			19 38					19 46	19 46	19 53				20 36	20 51
Cheltenham Spa	d		18 56	19a03		19 12	19 22	19a34		19 42	19 48					19 56	19 57	20a03		20 12	20 42	20a48	21a03
Ashchurch for Tewkesbury	d						19 29				19 55					20 04	20 06						
Worcester Shrub Hill 7	a						19 52				20 15												
Birmingham New Street 12	a		19 45			19 56				20 28						20 45	20 45			20 56	21 45		
	d		19 49		19 52	20 03			20 22			20 30				20 49	20 49		20 52	21 03			
Water Orton	d				20 03																		
Coleshill Parkway	d				20 07				20 35										21 05				
Nuneaton	d				20 23				20 52										21 22				
Hinckley	d				20 30														21 29				
Narborough	d				20 39														21 37				
South Wigston	d				20 44														21 42				
Leicester	a				20 50				21 15										21 58				
Wilnecote	d															21 04	21 04						
Tamworth	d		20 07			20 19										21 09	21 09			21 21			
Burton-on-Trent	d		20 19													21 21	21 23			21 33			
Willington	d																						
Derby 10	a		20 34			20 39						21 11				21 34	21 34			21 46			
	d	20 22	20 40												21 25	21 40	21 40						
Spondon	d															21 45	21 45						
Long Eaton	d	20 33	20 49												21 36	21 52	21 52						
Attenborough	d	20 40													21 43	21 58	21 58						
Beeston	d	20 43	20 58										21 04	21 19	21 46	22 02	22 02						
Nottingham 8	a	20 54	21 10										21 16	21 29	21 57	22 10	22 10						

For general notes see front of timetable
For details of catering facilities see Directory of Train Operators

- **A** From Warminster (Table 123) to Great Malvern (Table 71)
- **B** Until 4 September
- **C** To Cambridge (Table 49)
- **D** From Maesteg (Table 128)
- **E** To Lincoln (Table 27)
- **G** From 7 September
- **H** Fridays from Exeter St Davids (Table 51)
- **J** From Plymouth (Table 51)
- **K** To Worcester Foregate Street (Table 71)
- **L** To Leeds (Table 53)
- **N** From Westbury (Table 123)

Bristol and Cardiff → Birmingham → Leicester, Derby and Nottingham

Network Diagram - see first page of Table 50

		XC	EM		EM	XC	XC	GW	AW	GW	GW	XC	EM	XC		XC	AW	XC	XC	GW	GW	AW FO	AW FX		
		1 ◇			**1** ◇	**1** ◇	**1** ◇			◇	**1** ◇	**1**		**1** ◇		**1** ◇		**1** ◇	**1** ◇						
							A	B	C	D							E	G		H	J	E	E		
					⊐P		⚭				⊐P														
Cardiff Central [7]	d	20 00							20 15							21 00	21 14		21 50			23 19	23 19		
Newport (South Wales)	d	20 15							20 30							21 15	21 29		22 05			23 37	23 40		
Bristol Temple Meads [10]	d						20 30			20 41								22 00							
Bristol Parkway [7]	d						20 40			20 52								22 10							
Gloucester [7]	d	20 57						21 17	21 23	21 34	21 54					22 06	22 23		22 47	22⟆54	22⟆54	00 39	00 40		
Cheltenham Spa	d	21 08					21 16	21a29	21a34	21 46	22a03					22 17	22a36	22 42	22 58	23a03	23⟆04	00a52	00a53		
Ashchurch for Tewkesbury	d									21 54						22 24									
Worcester Shrub Hill [7]	a									22 12											23⟆29				
Birmingham New Street [12]	a	21 57					22 06									23 35		23 44	00 04						
	d					22 10						22 19		23 09											
Water Orton	d																								
Coleshill Parkway	d											22 35													
Nuneaton	d											22 52													
Hinckley	d											22 59													
Narborough	d											23 07													
South Wigston	d											23 12													
Leicester	a											23 23													
Wilnecote	d													23 24											
Tamworth	d					22 28								23 28											
Burton-on-Trent	d					22 40								23 40											
Willington	d													23 45											
Derby [10]	a					22 54								23 55											
	d					22 59							23 31	23 59											
Spondon	d					23 04																			
Long Eaton	d					23 11							23 41												
Attenborough	d					23 17							23 48												
Beeston	d		22 07		22 17	23 20							23 51												
Nottingham [8] 🚢	a		22 16		22 27	23 30							00 03	00 20											

Saturdays
until 5 September

		EM	EM	EM	AW	EM	EM	XC	EM	EM	XC	XC	GW	EM	XC	XC	XC	EM	EM	XC	XC	XC	EM	XC	XC
		1 ◇	**1** ◇	**1** ◇		**1** ◇	**1** ◇	**1** ◇	**1** ◇		**1**	**1** ◇			**1**	**1** ◇	**1** ◇	**1** ◇		**1**	**1**	**1** ◇		**1**	**1** ◇
			K	L	E			K													N				K
		⊐P	⊐P	⊐P		⊐P	⊐P	⚭	⊐P			⚭				⚭	⚭	⊐P				⚭			⚭
Cardiff Central [7]	d				23p19																				
Newport (South Wales)	d				23p37																				
Bristol Temple Meads [10]	d																								
Bristol Parkway [7]	d																								
Gloucester [7]	d				00 39								05 50												
Cheltenham Spa	d				00a52								06 00												
Ashchurch for Tewkesbury	d												06 09												
Worcester Shrub Hill [7]	a												06 33												
Birmingham New Street [12]	a																								
	d							05⟆22			05 52	05 55			06 19	06 22	06 30			06 49	06 52	07 03		07 19	07⟆22
Water Orton	d																				07 02				
Coleshill Parkway	d							05⟆35			06 05					06 35					07 06				07⟆35
Nuneaton	d							05⟆52			06 22					06 52					07 22				07⟆52
Hinckley	d										06 29										07 29				
Narborough	d										06 37										07 37				
South Wigston	d										06 42										07 42				
Leicester	a							06⟆13			06 50					07 13					07 50				08⟆13
Wilnecote	d														06 34									07 34	
Tamworth	d											06 12			06 39		06 46			07 07		07 19		07 38	
Burton-on-Trent	d											06 22			06 51		06 56			07 19		07 29		07 50	
Willington	d																							07 55	
Derby [10]	a											06 35			07 05		07 09			07 35		07 43		08 05	
	d						05 25		06 18	06 24					07 10			07 18	07 33	07 38				08 10	
Spondon	d									06 29					07 15					07 44					
Long Eaton	d						05a34		06a27	06 34					07 22			07a27	07 43	07 52				08 20	
Attenborough	d									06 42				07 14	07 28				07 51	07 58					
Beeston	d	00 05	00⟆20	00⟆32		01 37				06 45				07 17	07 32				07 54	08 02			08 06	08 28	
Nottingham [8] 🚢	a	00 14	00⟆29	00⟆41		01 44				06 47				07 28	07 40				08 05	08 10			08 16	08 36	

For general notes see front of timetable
For details of catering facilities see Directory of Train Operators

A From Plymouth (Table 51)
B From Westbury (Table 123)
C From Swansea (Table 128)
D From Brighton (Table 123)
E From Maesteg (Table 128)
G From Paignton (Table 51)
H Until 4 September
J From 7 September
K Until 11 July
L From 18 July
N Until 11 July. To Cambridge (Table 49)

Table 57

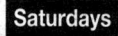

Saturdays
until 5 September

Bristol and Cardiff → Birmingham → Leicester, Derby and Nottingham

Network Diagram - see first page of Table 50

		XC	XC	EM	EM	XC	XC	XC	EM	XC	GW	AW	XC	XC	XC	XC	EM	XC	XC	XC	LM		GW	AW	EM
		1	1 ◇	1 ◇	1 ◇	1	1	1 ◇	1 ◇	1			1 ◇	1	1 ◇	1 ◇	1 ◇	1 ◇	1	1 ◇					1 ◇
		A											B	A							C				
			⊼	⊠	◫			⊼	◫				⊼		⊼	⊼	◫			⊼					◫
Cardiff Central 7	d											06 12						06 40						07 12	
Newport (South Wales)	d											06 28						06 55						07 27	
Bristol Temple Meads 10	d							06 15							07 00					07 30					
Bristol Parkway 7	d							06 25							07 10					07 40					
Gloucester 7	d							07 02		07 06	07 15	07 21						07 47			08 07		08 10	08 22	
Cheltenham Spa	d							07 12		07 18	07 25	07a34			07 42			07 58		08 12	08 18		08a24	08a32	
Ashchurch for Tewkesbury	d									07 25	07 34							08 05			08 25				
Worcester Shrub Hill 7	a										07 52										08 51				
Birmingham New Street 12	a							07 56		08 08					08 26			08 45		08 56					
	d	07 22	07 30			07 49	07 52	08 03		08 19			08 22	08 22		08 30		08 49	08 52	09 03					
Water Orton	d																		09 03						
Coleshill Parkway	d	07 35					08 05						08 35	08 35					09 07						
Nuneaton	d	07 52					08 22						08 52	08 52					09 23						
Hinckley	d						08 29												09 30						
Narborough	d						08 37												09 39						
South Wigston	d						08 42																		
Leicester	a	08 15					08 50						09 13	09 15					09 50						
Wilnecote	d																								
Tamworth	d		07 47			08 07		08 19		08 37								09 07							
Burton-on-Trent	d		07 58			08 19		08 29		08 49								09 19		09 26					
Willington	d																								
Derby 10	a		08 09			08 35		08 42		09 05						09 09		09 35		09 42					
	d			08 18		08 40				09 10							09 18	09 40							
Spondon	d																								
Long Eaton	d			08a27						09 20							09a27								
Attenborough	d																								
Beeston	d				08 31				09 17	09 28															10 17
Nottingham 8	a				08 42	09 05			09 26	09 36								10 05							10 26

		XC	XC	XC	XC	XC	EM	XC	XC	XC	EM	XC	XC	XC	XC	GW	XC	EM	XC	XC	XC	GW	AW	EM	XC
		1	1 ◇	1	1 ◇	1 ◇	1 ◇	1 ◇	1	1 ◇	1 ◇	1	1 ◇	1	1 ◇		1 ◇	1 ◇	1 ◇	1	1 ◇	1 ◇		1 ◇	1
			B	A									B	A		D							E		
			⊼		⊼	⊼	◫			⊼	◫		⊼		⊼		⊼	◫			⊼	◫		◫	
Cardiff Central 7	d				07 00			07 45											08 45				09 12		
Newport (South Wales)	d				07 14			08 00											09 00				09 27		
Bristol Temple Meads 10	d				08 00					08 30					09 00	08 41					09 30				
Bristol Parkway 7	d				08 10					08 40					09 10	08 52					09 40				
Gloucester 7	d							08 47								09 38			09 46			10 11	10 21		
Cheltenham Spa	d				08 42			08 58		09 12					09 42	09 48			09 58		10 12	10a23	10a34		
Ashchurch for Tewkesbury	d															09 57									
Worcester Shrub Hill 7	a															10 14									
Birmingham New Street 12	a				09 26			09 45		09 56					10 26				10 45		10 56				
	d	09 19	09 22	09 22		09 30		09 49	09 52	10 03		10 19	10 22	10 22			10 30		10 49	10 52	11 03				11 19
Water Orton	d																			11 03					
Coleshill Parkway	d		09 35	09 35					10 05				10 35	10 35						11 07					
Nuneaton	d		09 52	09 52					10 22				10 52	10 52						11 23					
Hinckley	d								10 29											11 30					
Narborough	d								10 37											11 39					
South Wigston	d								10 42																
Leicester	a		10 13	10 15					10 50				11 13	11 15						11 50					
Wilnecote	d	09 34																							11 34
Tamworth	d	09 39						10 07		10 19		10 37							11 07						11 39
Burton-on-Trent	d	09 51						10 19				10 49							11 19		11 26				11 51
Willington	d																								
Derby 10	a	10 05				10 09		10 35		10 42		11 05					11 09		11 35		11 42				12 05
	d	10 10					10 18	10 40				11 10						11 18	11 40						12 10
Spondon	d																								
Long Eaton	d	10 20					10a27					11 20						11a27							12 20
Attenborough	d																								
Beeston	d	10 28									11 17	11 28												12 16	12 28
Nottingham 8	a	10 36						11 05			11 26	11 36							12 05					12 26	12 36

For general notes see front of timetable
For details of catering facilities see Directory of Train Operators

- **A** From 18 July
- **B** Until 11 July
- **C** To Worcester Foregate Street (Table 71)
- **D** From Warminster (Table 123) to Great Malvern (Table 71)
- **E** From Maesteg (Table 128)

Table 57

Saturdays
until 5 September

Bristol and Cardiff → Birmingham → Leicester, Derby and Nottingham

Network Diagram - see first page of Table 50

		XC	XC	XC	XC	EM	XC	XC	XC	LM	GW	AW	EM	XC	XC	XC	XC	GW	XC	EM		XC	XC	XC	GW
		1 ◇	1	1 ◇	1 ◇	1 ◇	1 ◇	1	1 ◇				1 ◇	1	1 ◇	1	1 ◇		1 ◇	1 ◇		1 ◇	1	1 ◇	1 ◇
		A	B							C		D			A	B		E							
		trolley		trolley	trolley	buffet			trolley				buffet		trolley		trolley		trolley	buffet				trolley	buffet
Cardiff Central [7]	d						09 45					10 12										10 45			
Newport (South Wales)	d						10 00					10 27										11 00			
Bristol Temple Meads [10]	d			10 00					10 30								11 00	10 41						11 30	
Bristol Parkway [7]	d			10 10					10 40								11 10	10 52						11 40	
Gloucester [7]	d						10 47			11 01	11 11	11 22						11 38				11 47			12 11
Cheltenham Spa	d			10 42			10 58		11 12	11 18	11a22	11a34					11 42	11 49				11 58		12 12	12a23
Ashchurch for Tewkesbury	d									11 25								11 57							
Worcester Shrub Hill [7]	a									11 42								12 15							
Birmingham New Street [12]	a			11 26			11 45		11 56								12 26					12 45		12 56	
	d	11 22	11 22		11 30		11 49	11 52	12 03					12 19	12 22	12 22			12 30			12 49	12 52	13 03	
Water Orton	d																						13 03		
Coleshill Parkway	d	11 35	11 35					12 05							12 35	12 35							13 07		
Nuneaton	d	11 52	11 52					12 22							12 52	12 52							13 23		
Hinckley	d							12 29															13 30		
Narborough	d							12 37															13 39		
South Wigston	d							12 42																	
Leicester	a	12 13	12 15					12 50							13 13	13 15							13 50		
Wilnecote	d																								
Tamworth	d						12 07		12 19					12 37								13 07			
Burton-on-Trent	d						12 19							12 49								13 19		13 26	
Willington	d													12 54											
Derby [10]	a				12 09		12 35		12 42					13 05					13 09			13 35		13 42	
	d					12 18	12 40							13 10						13 18		13 40			
Spondon	d																								
Long Eaton	d					12a27								13 20						13a27					
Attenborough	d																								
Beeston	d												13 18	13 28											
Nottingham [8]	a						13 05						13 27	13 36								14 05			

		EM	XC	XC	XC	XC	XC	EM	XC	XC	XC	LM	GW	AW	EM	XC	XC	XC	XC	GW	XC	EM	XC	XC	XC
		1 ◇	1	1 ◇	1	1 ◇	1 ◇	1 ◇	1 ◇	1	1 ◇				1 ◇	1	1 ◇	1	1 ◇	◇	1 ◇	1 ◇	1 ◇	1	1 ◇
				A	B									D			A	B		G					
		buffet		trolley		trolley	trolley	buffet			trolley				buffet		trolley		trolley		trolley	buffet			trolley
Cardiff Central [7]	d								11 45					12 12									12 45		
Newport (South Wales)	d								12 00					12 27									13 00		
Bristol Temple Meads [10]	d					12 00					12 30								13 00	12 41					13 30
Bristol Parkway [7]	d					12 10					12 40								13 10	12 52					13 40
Gloucester [7]	d								12 47			13 01	13 11	13 22						13 38			13 47		
Cheltenham Spa	d					12 42			12 58		13 12	13 18	13a22	13a35					13 42	13 49			13 58		14 12
Ashchurch for Tewkesbury	d								13 05			13 25								13 57					
Worcester Shrub Hill [7]	a											13 52								14 15					
Birmingham New Street [12]	a					13 26			13 45		13 56								14 26				14 45		14 56
	d		13 19	13 22	13 22		13 30		13 49	13 52	14 03					14 19	14 22	14 22			14 30		14 49	14 52	15 03
Water Orton	d																							15 03	
Coleshill Parkway	d			13 35	13 35					14 05							14 35	14 35						15 07	
Nuneaton	d			13 52	13 52					14 22							14 52	14 52						15 23	
Hinckley	d									14 29														15 30	
Narborough	d									14 37														15 39	
South Wigston	d									14 42															
Leicester	a			14 13	14 15					14 50							15 13	15 15						15 50	
Wilnecote	d		13 34																						
Tamworth	d		13 39						14 07		14 19					14 37							15 07		
Burton-on-Trent	d		13 51						14 19							14 49							15 19		15 28
Willington	d																								
Derby [10]	a		14 05				14 09		14 35		14 42					15 05					15 09		15 35		15 42
	d		14 10					14 18	14 40							15 10						15 18	15 40		
Spondon	d																								
Long Eaton	d		14 20					14a27								15 20						15a27			
Attenborough	d																								
Beeston	d	14 17	14 28												15 17	15 28									
Nottingham [8]	a	14 26	14 36						15 05						15 26	15 36							16 05		

For general notes see front of timetable
For details of catering facilities see Directory of Train Operators

- **A** Until 11 July
- **B** From 18 July
- **C** To Worcester Foregate Street (Table 71)
- **D** From Maesteg (Table 128)
- **E** From Southampton Central (Table 123) to Worcester Foregate Street (Table 71)
- **G** From Brighton (Table 123) to Great Malvern (Table 71)

Table 57

Saturdays

until 5 September

Bristol and Cardiff → Birmingham → Leicester, Derby and Nottingham

Network Diagram - see first page of Table 50

		GW 1◇ ☕	AW A	EM 1◇ ☕	XC 1	XC 1◇ B 🛒	XC 1 C	XC 1◇ 🛒	XC 1◇ 🛒	EM 1◇ ☕	XC 1◇	XC 1	XC 1◇ 🛒	LM	GW	EM 1◇ ☕	XC 1	XC 1◇ B 🛒	XC 1 C		XC 1◇ 🛒	GW D	XC 1◇ 🛒	EM 1◇ ☕	XC 1◇
Cardiff Central 7	d		13 12								13 45														14 45
Newport (South Wales)	d		13 27								14 00														15 00
Bristol Temple Meads 10	d							14 00					14 30								15 00	14 41			
Bristol Parkway 7	d							14 10					14 40								15 10	14 52			
Gloucester 7	d	14 11	14 21								14 47			15 05	15 14							15 38			15 47
Cheltenham Spa	d	14a23	14a34					14 42			14 58		15 12	15 18	15a25						15 42	15 48			15 58
Ashchurch for Tewkesbury	d													15 25								15 57			
Worcester Shrub Hill 7	a													15 57								16 14			
Birmingham New Street 12	a							15 26			15 45		15 56								16 26				16 45
	d				15 19	15 22	15 22		15 30		15 49	15 52	16 03				16 19	16 22	16 22				16 30		16 49
Water Orton	d																								
Coleshill Parkway	d					15 35	15 35					16 05						16 35	16 35						
Nuneaton	d					15 52	15 52					16 22						16 52	16 52						
Hinckley	d											16 29													
Narborough	d											16 37													
South Wigston	d											16 42													
Leicester	a					16 13	16 15					16 50						17 13	17 15						
Wilnecote	d				15 34																				
Tamworth	d				15 39						16 07		16 21				16 37								17 07
Burton-on-Trent	d				15 51						16 19						16 49								17 19
Willington	d																								
Derby 10	a				16 05				16 09		16 35		16 42				17 05						17 09		17 35
	d				16 10					16 18	16 40						17 10							17 18	17 40
Spondon	d																								
Long Eaton	d				16 20					16a27							17 20							17a27	
Attenborough	d																								
Beeston	d			16 17	16 28											17 17	17 28								
Nottingham 8	a			16 26	16 36						17 05					17 26	17 36								18 05

		XC 1	XC 1◇ 🛒	GW 1◇ ☕	AW A	EM 1◇ ☕	XC 1	XC 1◇ B 🛒	XC 1 C	XC 1◇ 🛒	XC 1◇ 🛒	EM 1◇ ☕	XC 1◇	XC 1	XC 1◇ 🛒	LM	GW	AW A	EM 1◇ E ☕	XC 1	XC 1◇ B 🛒	XC 1 C	XC 1◇ 🛒	GW G	XC 1◇ 🛒
Cardiff Central 7	d				15 12								15 45					16 12							
Newport (South Wales)	d				15 27								16 00					16 27							
Bristol Temple Meads 10	d		15 30							16 00					16 30								17 00	16 41	
Bristol Parkway 7	d		15 40							16 10					16 40								17 10	16 52	
Gloucester 7	d			16 11	16 21								16 47			17 05	17 14	17 21						17 38	
Cheltenham Spa	d		16 12	16a23	16a34					16 42			16 58		17 12	17 18	17a25	17a34					17 42	17 48	
Ashchurch for Tewkesbury	d															17 25								17 57	
Worcester Shrub Hill 7	a															17 49								18 15	
Birmingham New Street 12	a		16 56							17 26			17 45		17 56								18 26		
	d	16 52	17 03				17 19	17 22	17 22		17 30		17 49	17 52	18 03					18 19	18 22	18 22			18 30
Water Orton	d	17 02																							
Coleshill Parkway	d	17 06						17 35	17 35					18 05							18 35	18 35			
Nuneaton	d	17 22						17 52	17 52					18 22							18 52	18 52			
Hinckley	d	17 29												18 29											
Narborough	d	17 38												18 37											
South Wigston	d													18 42											
Leicester	a	17 50						18 13	18 15					18 50							19 13	19 15			
Wilnecote	d						17 35																		
Tamworth	d						17 39						18 07		18 19					18 37					
Burton-on-Trent	d		17 26				17 51						18 19							18 49					
Willington	d																								
Derby 10	a		17 42				18 05				18 09		18 35		18 42					19 05					19 09
	d						18 10					18 18	18 40							19 10					
Spondon	d																								
Long Eaton	d						18 20					18a27								19 20					
Attenborough	d																								
Beeston	d					18 18	18 28												19 17	19 28					
Nottingham 8	a					18 26	18 36						19 05						19 26	19 36					

For general notes see front of timetable
For details of catering facilities see Directory of Train Operators

A From Maesteg (Table 128)
B Until 11 July
C From 18 July
D From Southampton Central (Table 123) to Great Malvern (Table 71)
E To Lincoln (Table 27)
G From Warminster (Table 123) to Great Malvern (Table 71)

Saturdays

until 5 September

Bristol and Cardiff → Birmingham → Leicester, Derby and Nottingham

Network Diagram - see first page of Table 50

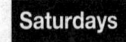

		EM	XC	EM	XC	XC	GW	AW	EM	XC	XC	XC	XC	XC	XC	XC	XC	LM	GW	AW	XC	XC	XC	GW	XC
		1◇	1◇		1◇	1◇	1◇		1◇	1	1◇	1	1◇	1◇	1◇	1	1◇				1◇	1	1◇	◇	1◇
		A		B							C	D				C				E	C	D		G	
		🍴			🛒	🛒	🍴		🍴		🛒		🛒	🛒			🛒				🛒		🛒		🛒
Cardiff Central 7	d		16 45					17 12							17 45					18 12					
Newport (South Wales)	d		17 00					17 27							18 00					18 27					
Bristol Temple Meads 10	d					17 30							18 00				18 30						19 00	18 41	
Bristol Parkway 7	d					17 40							18 10				18 40						19 10	18 52	
Gloucester 7	d		17 47				18 11	18 23							18 47			19 05	19 14	19 21				19 38	
Cheltenham Spa	d		17 58			18 12	18a23	18a33					18 42		18 58		19 12	19 18	19a25	19a34			19 42	19 48	
Ashchurch for Tewkesbury	d																	19 25						19 55	
Worcester Shrub Hill 7	a																	19 48						20 15	
Birmingham New Street 12	a		18 45			18 56							19 26		19 45		19 56						20 26		
	d		18 49		18 52	19 03				19 19	19 22	19 22		19 30	19 49	19 52	20 03				20 22	20 22			20 30
Water Orton	d															20 02									
Coleshill Parkway	d				19 05						19 35	19 35				20 06					20 35	20 35			
Nuneaton	d				19 22						19 52	19 52				20 22					20 52	20 52			
Hinckley	d				19 29											20 29									
Narborough	d				19 37											20 38									
South Wigston	d				19 42											20 42									
Leicester	a				19 50						20 13	20 15				20 50					21 13	21 15			
Wilnecote	d									19 34															
Tamworth	d		19 07							19 39					20 07		20 19								20 46
Burton-on-Trent	d		19 19			19 26				19 51					20 19										20 56
Willington	d																								
Derby 10	a		19 35			19 42				20 05				20 09	20 35		20 42								21 09
	d	19 21	19 40							20 10					20 40										
Spondon	d																								
Long Eaton	d	19a30								20 20					20 49										
Attenborough	d																								
Beeston	d			20 05					20 17	20 28					20 57										
Nottingham 8 🚢	a		20 05	20 16					20 26	20 36					21 05										

		EM	EM	XC	XC	XC	GW	XC	XC	GW	GW	EM	EM	EM	XC	AW	XC	XC	GW	XC	GW	EM	XC		
			1◇	1◇	1	1◇	1◇	1◇	1◇				1◇	1◇	1◇		1	1◇		1◇	1◇		1◇		
		B											C	D		H		J	K						
			🍴			🛒	🍴	🛒	🛒				🍴	🍴				🛒			🍴				
Cardiff Central 7	d			18 45											20 00	20 15				20 50					
Newport (South Wales)	d			19 00											20 15	20 30				21 05					
Bristol Temple Meads 10	d					19 30			20 00	19 41								21 00	20 41						
Bristol Parkway 7	d					19 40			20 10	19 52								21 10	20 52						
Gloucester 7	d			19 47			20 11			20 38	20 55				21 06	21 23			21 40	21 49	22 11				
Cheltenham Spa	d			19 58		20 12	20a23		20 42	20a46	21a05				21 18	21a34		21 42	21a49	22 00	22a23				
Ashchurch for Tewkesbury	d														21 25										
Worcester Shrub Hill 7	a																								
Birmingham New Street 12	a			20 40		20 56			21 41						22 07			22 27		22 42					
	d			20 49	20 52			21 03							22 10		22 22						22 49		
Water Orton	d																								
Coleshill Parkway	d				21 05												22 35								
Nuneaton	d				21 22												22 52								
Hinckley	d				21 29												22 59								
Narborough	d				21 37												23 07								
South Wigston	d				21 42												23 12								
Leicester	a				21 50												23 20								
Wilnecote	d			21 04																			23 04		
Tamworth	d			21 08				21 19							22 28								23 08		
Burton-on-Trent	d			21 20				21 29							22 39								23 20		
Willington	d														22 45										
Derby 10	a			21 35				21 42							22 55								23 38		
	d			21 40											23 00							23 31			
Spondon	d			21 45											23 05										
Long Eaton	d			21 52											23 12							23 41			
Attenborough	d			21 58											23 18							23 48			
Beeston	d	21 05	21 17	22 02								22 06	22 18	22 28	23 22							23 51			
Nottingham 8 🚢	a	21 16	21 26	22 10								22 16	22 27	22 36	23 33							00 03			

For general notes see front of timetable
For details of catering facilities see Directory of Train Operators

A From Scarborough (Table 26)
B To Lincoln (Table 27)
C Until 11 July
D From 18 July
E From Maesteg (Table 128)
G From Weymouth (Table 123) to Great Malvern (Table 71)
H From Swansea (Table 128)
J From Plymouth (Table 51)
K From Brighton (Table 123)

Table 57

Saturdays

from 12 September

Bristol and Cardiff → Birmingham → Leicester, Derby and Nottingham

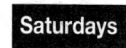

Network Diagram - see first page of Table 50

		EM 1◇	AW A	EM 1◇	EM 1◇	XC 1◇	EM 1◇	EM	XC 1	XC 1◇	GW	EM	XC 1	XC 1◇	XC 1◇	EM 1◇	EM	XC 1	XC 1 B	XC 1◇	EM	XC 1		XC 1◇	XC 1◇
Cardiff Central 7	d		23p19																						
Newport (South Wales)	d		23p37																						
Bristol Temple Meads 10	d																								
Bristol Parkway 7	d																								
Gloucester 7	d		00 39								05 50														
Cheltenham Spa	d		00a52								06 00														
Ashchurch for Tewkesbury	d										06 09														
Worcester Shrub Hill 7	a										06 33														
Birmingham New Street 12	a																								
	d					05 22			05 52	05 55			06 19	06 22	06 30			06 49	06 52	07 03		07 19		07 22	07 30
Water Orton	d																		07 02						
Coleshill Parkway	d					05 35			06 05					06 35					07 06					07 35	
Nuneaton	d					05 52			06 22					06 52					07 22					07 52	
Hinckley	d								06 29										07 29						
Narborough	d								06 37										07 37						
South Wigston	d								06 42										07 42						
Leicester	a					06 13			06 50					07 13					07 50					08 13	
Wilnecote	d												06 34									07 34			
Tamworth	d									06 12			06 39		06 46			07 07		07 19		07 38			07 47
Burton-on-Trent	d									06 22			06 51		06 56			07 19		07 29		07 50			07 58
Willington	d																					07 55			
Derby 10	a									06 35			07 05		07 09			07 35		07 42		08 05			08 09
	d				05 25		06 18	06 24					07 10			07 18	07 33	07 40				08 10			
Spondon	d							06 29					07 15					07 45							
Long Eaton	d				05a34		06a27	06 34					07 22			07a27	07 42	07 52				08 20			
Attenborough	d							06 42				07 14	07 28				07 51	07 58							
Beeston	d	00 05		01 37				06 45				07 17	07 32				07 54	08 02			08 06	08 28			
Nottingham 8	a	00 14		01 44				06 57				07 28	07 40				08 05	08 10			08 16	08 36			

		EM 1◇	EM	EM 1◇	XC 1	XC 1	XC 1◇	EM 1◇	XC 1	GW	AW	XC 1◇	XC 1◇	XC 1◇	EM 1◇	EM	XC 1◇	XC 1 B	XC 1◇	LM C	GW	AW		EM 1◇	XC 1
Cardiff Central 7	d										06 12						06 40					07 12			
Newport (South Wales)	d										06 28						06 55					07 27			
Bristol Temple Meads 10	d						06 15						07 00						07 30						
Bristol Parkway 7	d						06 25						07 10						07 40						
Gloucester 7	d						07 02		07 06	07 15	07 21						07 47			08 07	08 10	08 22			
Cheltenham Spa	d						07 12		07 18	07 25	07a34		07 42				07 58		08 12	08 18	08a24	08a32			
Ashchurch for Tewkesbury	d								07 25	07 34							08 05			08 25					
Worcester Shrub Hill 7	a									07 52										08 51					
Birmingham New Street 12	a						07 56		08 08				08 26				08 45		08 56						
	d				07 49	07 52	08 03		08 19			08 22		08 30			08 49	08 52	09 03						09 19
Water Orton	d																	09 03							
Coleshill Parkway	d					08 05						08 35						09 07							
Nuneaton	d					08 22						08 52						09 23							
Hinckley	d					08 29												09 30							
Narborough	d					08 37												09 39							
South Wigston	d					08 42																			
Leicester	a					08 50						09 13						09 50							
Wilnecote	d																								09 34
Tamworth	d				08 07		08 19		08 37								09 07								09 39
Burton-on-Trent	d				08 19		08 29		08 49								09 19		09 26						09 51
Willington	d																								
Derby 10	a				08 35		08 42		09 04					09 09			09 34		09 42						10 05
	d	08 18	08 21		08 39				09 10						09 18	09 23	09 34								10 10
Spondon	d		08 26																						
Long Eaton	d	08a27	08 32						09 20						09a27	09 33									10 20
Attenborough	d		08 40													09 40									
Beeston	d		08 43	08 31				09 17	09 28							09 43								10 17	10 28
Nottingham 8	a		08 57	08 42	09 05			09 26	09 36							09 52	10 03							10 26	10 36

For general notes see front of timetable
For details of catering facilities see Directory of Train Operators

A From Maesteg (Table 128)
B To Cambridge (Table 49)
C To Worcester Foregate Street (Table 71)

Table 57

Saturdays

from 12 September

Bristol and Cardiff → Birmingham → Leicester, Derby and Nottingham

Network Diagram - see first page of Table 50

		XC 1◇	XC 1◇	XC 1◇	EM 1◇	EM	XC 1◇	XC 1	XC 1◇	EM 1◇	XC 1	EM	XC 1◇	XC 1◇	GW A	XC 1◇	EM 1◇	XC 1◇	XC 1	XC 1◇	GW 1◇	AW B		EM 1◇	XC 1
Cardiff Central 7	d		07 00				07 45											08 45				09 12			
Newport (South Wales)	d		07 14				08 00											09 00				09 27			
Bristol Temple Meads 10	d		08 00						08 30					09 00	08 41					09 30					
Bristol Parkway 7	d		08 10						08 40					09 10	08 52					09 40					
Gloucester 7	d						08 47								09 38			09 47			10 11	10 21			
Cheltenham Spa	d		08 42				08 58		09 12					09 42	09 48			09 58		10 12	10a23	10a34			
Ashchurch for Tewkesbury	d														09 57										
Worcester Shrub Hill 7	a														10 14										
Birmingham New Street 12	a		09 26				09 45		09 56					10 26				10 45		10 56					
	d	09 22		09 30			09 49	09 52	10 03		10 19		10 22			10 30		10 49	10 52	11 03					11 19
Water Orton	d																		11 03						
Coleshill Parkway	d	09 35						10 05					10 35						11 07						
Nuneaton	d	09 52						10 22					10 52						11 23						
Hinckley	d							10 29											11 30						
Narborough	d							10 37											11 39						
South Wigston	d							10 42																	
Leicester	a	10 13						10 50					11 13						11 50						
Wilnecote	d																								11 34
Tamworth	d						10 07		10 19		10 37							11 07							11 39
Burton-on-Trent	d						10 19				10 49							11 19		11 26					11 51
Willington	d																								
Derby 10	a			10 09			10 35		10 42		11 05					11 09		11 35		11 41					12 05
	d				10 18	10 26	10 40				11 10	11 21					11 18	11 40							12 10
Spondon	d																								
Long Eaton	d				10a27	10 36					11 20	11 31					11a27								12 20
Attenborough	d					10 43						11 38													
Beeston	d					10 46				11 17	11 28	11 41												12 16	12 28
Nottingham 8	a					10 54	11 05			11 26	11 36	11 52						12 05						12 26	12 36

		XC 1◇	XC 1◇	XC 1◇	EM 1◇	EM	XC 1◇	XC 1	XC 1◇	LM C	GW	AW B	EM 1◇	XC 1	XC 1◇	XC 1◇	GW D	XC 1◇	EM 1◇	EM	XC 1◇	XC 1 E		XC 1◇	GW 1◇
Cardiff Central 7	d						09 45					10 12									10 45				
Newport (South Wales)	d						10 00					10 27									11 00				
Bristol Temple Meads 10	d		10 00						10 30							11 00	10 41							11 30	
Bristol Parkway 7	d		10 10						10 40							11 10	10 52							11 40	
Gloucester 7	d						10 47			11 01	11 11	11 22					11 38				11 47				12 11
Cheltenham Spa	d		10 42				10 58		11 12	11 18	11a22	11a34				11 42	11 49				11 58			12 12	12a23
Ashchurch for Tewkesbury	d									11 25							11 57								
Worcester Shrub Hill 7	a									11 42							12 15								
Birmingham New Street 12	a		11 26				11 45		11 56							12 26					12 45			12 56	
	d	11 22		11 30			11 49	11 52	12 03					12 19	12 22			12 30			12 49	12 52		13 03	
Water Orton	d																					13 03			
Coleshill Parkway	d	11 35						12 05							12 35							13 07			
Nuneaton	d	11 52						12 22							12 52							13 23			
Hinckley	d							12 29														13 30			
Narborough	d							12 37														13 39			
South Wigston	d							12 42																	
Leicester	a	12 13						12 50							13 13							13 50			
Wilnecote	d																								
Tamworth	d						12 07		12 19					12 37							13 07				
Burton-on-Trent	d						12 19							12 49							13 19			13 26	
Willington	d													12 54											
Derby 10	a			12 09			12 35		12 41					13 05				13 09			13 35			13 41	
	d				12 18	12 20	12 40							13 10					13 18	13 21	13 40				
Spondon	d																								
Long Eaton	d				12a27	12 31								13 20					13a27	13 31					
Attenborough	d					12 38														13 38					
Beeston	d					12 41							13 18	13 28						13 41					
Nottingham 8	a					12 52	13 05						13 27	13 36						13 52	14 05				

For general notes see front of timetable
For details of catering facilities see Directory of Train Operators

A From Warminster (Table 123) to Great Malvern (Table 71)
B From Maesteg (Table 128)
C To Worcester Foregate Street (Table 71)
D From Southampton Central (Table 123) to Worcester Foregate Street (Table 71)
E To Cambridge (Table 49)

Table 57

Saturdays

from 12 September

Bristol and Cardiff → Birmingham → Leicester, Derby and Nottingham

Network Diagram - see first page of Table 50

		EM	XC	XC	XC	XC	EM	EM	XC	XC	XC	LM	GW	AW	EM	XC	XC	XC	GW	XC	EM	EM		XC	XC
		1 ◇	1	1 ◇	1 ◇	1 ◇	1 ◇		1 ◇	1	1 ◇				1 ◇	1	1 ◇	1 ◇	◇	1 ◇	1 ◇			1 ◇	1
														A					B						
		☕		🛒	🛒	🛒	☕				🛒				☕		🛒	🛒		🛒	☕				
Cardiff Central 7	d								11 45					12 12										12 45	
Newport (South Wales)	d								12 00					12 27										13 00	
Bristol Temple Meads 10	d				12 00						12 30							13 00	12 41						
Bristol Parkway 7	d				12 10						12 40							13 10	12 52						
Gloucester 7	d								12 47			13 01	13 11	13 22					13 38					13 47	
Cheltenham Spa	d				12 42				12 58		13 12	13 18	13a22	13a35				13 42	13 49					13 58	
Ashchurch for Tewkesbury	d								13 05			13 25							13 57						
Worcester Shrub Hill 7	a											13 52							14 15						
Birmingham New Street 12	a				13 26				13 45		13 56							14 26						14 45	
	d		13 19	13 22		13 30			13 49	13 52	14 03					14 19	14 22			14 30				14 49	14 52
Water Orton	d																								15 03
Coleshill Parkway	d			13 35						14 05							14 35								15 07
Nuneaton	d			13 52						14 22							14 52								15 23
Hinckley	d									14 29															15 30
Narborough	d									14 37															15 39
South Wigston	d									14 42															
Leicester	a			14 13						14 50							15 13								15 50
Wilnecote	d		13 34																						
Tamworth	d		13 39						14 07		14 19					14 37								15 07	
Burton-on-Trent	d		13 51						14 19							14 49								15 19	
Willington	d																								
Derby 10	a		14 05			14 09			14 35		14 41					15 05				15 09				15 35	
	d		14 10				14 18	14 21	14 40							15 10					15 18	15 21		15 40	
Spondon	d																								
Long Eaton	d		14 20				14a27	14 32								15 20					15a27	15 31			
Attenborough	d							14 40														15 39			
Beeston	d	14 17	14 28					14 43							15 17	15 28						15 42			
Nottingham 8 🚌	a	14 26	14 36					14 53	15 05						15 26	15 36						15 52		16 05	

		XC	GW	AW	EM	XC	XC	XC	XC	EM	EM	XC	XC	XC	LM	GW	EM	XC	XC	XC	GW	XC		EM	EM
		1 ◇	1 ◇		1 ◇	1	1 ◇	1 ◇	1 ◇	1 ◇		1 ◇	1	1 ◇			1 ◇	1	1 ◇	1 ◇		1 ◇		1 ◇	
				A																	C				
		🛒	☕		☕		🛒	🛒	🛒	☕				🛒			☕		🛒	🛒		🛒		☕	
Cardiff Central 7	d			13 12								13 45													
Newport (South Wales)	d			13 27								14 00													
Bristol Temple Meads 10	d	13 30						14 00						14 30						15 00	14 41				
Bristol Parkway 7	d	13 40						14 10						14 40						15 10	14 52				
Gloucester 7	d		14 11	14 21								14 47			15 05	15 14					15 38				
Cheltenham Spa	d	14 12	14a23	14a34				14 42				14 58		15 12	15 18	15a25				15 42	15 48				
Ashchurch for Tewkesbury	d														15 25						15 57				
Worcester Shrub Hill 7	a														15 57						16 14				
Birmingham New Street 12	a	14 56						15 26				15 45		15 56						16 26					
	d	15 03				15 19	15 22		15 30			15 49	15 52	16 03				16 19	16 22			16 30			
Water Orton	d																								
Coleshill Parkway	d						15 35						16 05						16 35						
Nuneaton	d						15 52						16 22						16 52						
Hinckley	d												16 29												
Narborough	d												16 37												
South Wigston	d												16 42												
Leicester	a						16 13						16 50						17 13						
Wilnecote	d					15 34																			
Tamworth	d					15 39						16 07		16 21				16 37							
Burton-on-Trent	d	15 26				15 51						16 19						16 49							
Willington	d																								
Derby 10	a	15 41				16 05			16 09			16 35		16 42				17 05				17 09			
	d					16 10				16 18	16 21	16 40						17 10						17 18	17 21
Spondon	d																								17 26
Long Eaton	d					16 20				16a27	16 31							17 20						17a27	17 32
Attenborough	d										16 38														17 40
Beeston	d				16 17	16 28					16 41						17 17	17 28							17 43
Nottingham 8 🚌	a				16 26	16 36					16 52	17 05					17 26	17 36							17 53

For general notes see front of timetable
For details of catering facilities see Directory of Train Operators

A From Maesteg (Table 128)
B From Brighton (Table 123) to Great Malvern (Table 71)
C From Southampton Central (Table 123) to Great Malvern (Table 71)

Table 57

Saturdays

Bristol and Cardiff → Birmingham → Leicester, Derby and Nottingham

from 12 September

Network Diagram - see first page of Table 50

		XC	XC	XC	GW	AW	EM	XC	XC	XC	XC	EM	EM	XC	XC	XC	LM	GW	AW	EM	XC	XC		XC	GW
		1◇	1	1◇	1◇		1◇	1	1◇	1◇	1◇	1◇		1◇	1	1◇				1◇	1	1◇		1◇	
						A													A	B					C
				🛒	☕		☕		🛒	🛒	🛒	☕				🛒				☕		🛒		🛒	
Cardiff Central 7	d	14 45				15 12								15 45					16 12						
Newport (South Wales)	d	15 00				15 27								16 00					16 27						
Bristol Temple Meads 10	d			15 30						16 00						16 30								17 00	16 41
Bristol Parkway 7	d			15 40						16 10						16 40								17 10	16 52
Gloucester 7	d	15 47			16 11	16 21								16 47			17 05	17 14	17 21						17 38
Cheltenham Spa	d	15 58		16 12	16a23	16a34				16 42				16 58		17 12	17 18	17a25	17a34					17 42	17 48
Ashchurch for Tewkesbury	d																17 25								17 57
Worcester Shrub Hill 7	a																17 49								18 15
Birmingham New Street 12	a	16 45		16 56						17 26				17 45		17 56								18 26	
	d	16 49	16 52	17 03				17 19	17 22		17 30			17 49	17 52	18 03					18 19	18 22			
Water Orton	d		17 02																						
Coleshill Parkway	d		17 06						17 35						18 05							18 35			
Nuneaton	d		17 22						17 52						18 22							18 52			
Hinckley	d		17 29												18 29										
Narborough	d		17 38												18 37										
South Wigston	d														18 42										
Leicester	a		17 50						18 13						18 50							19 13			
Wilnecote	d							17 35																	
Tamworth	d	17 07						17 39						18 07		18 19					18 37				
Burton-on-Trent	d	17 19		17 26				17 51						18 19							18 49				
Willington	d																								
Derby 10	a	17 35		17 41				18 05			18 09			18 35		18 41					19 05				
	d	17 40						18 10				18 18	18 21	18 40							19 10				
Spondon	d																								
Long Eaton	d							18 20				18a27	18 32								19 20				
Attenborough	d												18 39												
Beeston	d						18 18	18 28					18 42							19 17	19 28				
Nottingham 8 🚊	a	18 05					18 26	18 36					18 53	19 05						19 26	19 36				

		XC	EM	XC	EM	XC	XC	GW	AW	EM	EM	XC	EM	XC	XC	XC	XC	XC	XC	LM	GW	AW		XC	XC
		1◇	1◇	1◇		1	1◇	1◇			1◇	1		1◇	1◇	1◇	1◇	1	1◇					1◇	1◇
			D			E			A	B												A			
		🛒	☕				🛒	☕			☕			🛒	🛒	🛒			🛒					🛒	🛒
Cardiff Central 7	d			16 45					17 12								17 45					18 12			
Newport (South Wales)	d			17 00					17 27								18 00					18 27			
Bristol Temple Meads 10	d						17 30								18 00				18 30						19 00
Bristol Parkway 7	d						17 40								18 10				18 40						19 10
Gloucester 7	d			17 47				18 11	18 23								18 47			19 05	19 14	19 21			
Cheltenham Spa	d			17 58			18 12	18a23	18a33						18 42		18 58		19 12	19 18	19a25	19a34			19 42
Ashchurch for Tewkesbury	d																			19 25					
Worcester Shrub Hill 7	a																			19 48					
Birmingham New Street 12	a			18 45			18 56								19 26		19 45		19 56						20 26
	d	18 30		18 49		18 52	19 03					19 19		19 22		19 30	19 49	19 52	20 03					20 22	
Water Orton	d																	20 02							
Coleshill Parkway	d					19 05								19 35				20 06						20 35	
Nuneaton	d					19 22								19 52				20 22						20 52	
Hinckley	d					19 29												20 29							
Narborough	d					19 37												20 38							
South Wigston	d					19 42												20 42							
Leicester	a					19 50								20 13				20 50						21 13	
Wilnecote	d											19 34													
Tamworth	d			19 07								19 39					20 07		20 19						
Burton-on-Trent	d			19 19			19 26					19 51					20 19								
Willington	d																								
Derby 10	a	19 09		19 35			19 42					20 05				20 09	20 35		20 42						
	d		19 21	19 40	19 26							20 10	20 15				20 40								
Spondon	d																								
Long Eaton	d		19a30		19 36							20 20	20 26				20 49								
Attenborough	d				19 43								20 33												
Beeston	d				19 46					20 05	20 17	20 28	20 36				20 57								
Nottingham 8 🚊	a			20 05	19 56					20 16	20 26	20 36	20 47				21 05								

For general notes see front of timetable
For details of catering facilities see Directory of Train Operators

- **A** From Maesteg (Table 128)
- **B** To Lincoln (Table 27)
- **C** From Warminster (Table 123) to Great Malvern (Table 71)
- **D** From York (Table 53)
- **E** To Cambridge (Table 49)

Table 57

Bristol and Cardiff → Birmingham → Leicester, Derby and Nottingham

Saturdays
from 12 September

Network Diagram - see first page of Table 50

		GW	XC	EM	EM	EM	XC	XC	XC	GW	XC	GW	GW	XC	AW	GW	EM	EM	XC	XC	GW	XC	EM
			1◇		1◇		1◇	1	1◇	1◇	1◇			1◇				1◇	1	1◇	1◇	1◇	
		A		B								C			D	E							
Cardiff Central 7	d						18 45								20 15					20 50			
Newport (South Wales)	d						19 00								20 30					21 05			
Bristol Temple Meads 10	d	18 41							19 30		20 00	19 41		20 30		20 41							
Bristol Parkway 7	d	18 52							19 40		20 10	19 52		20 40		20 52							
Gloucester 7	d	19 38					19 47			20 11		20 38	20 55		21 23	21 40				21 49	22 11		
Cheltenham Spa	d	19 48					19 58		20 12	20a23	20 42	20a46	21a05	21 12	21a34	21a49				22 00	22a23		
Ashchurch for Tewkesbury	d	19 55																					
Worcester Shrub Hill 7	a	20 15																					
Birmingham New Street 12	a						20 40		20 56		21 38			21 58						22 42			
	d		20 30				20 49	20 52	21 03										22 22			22 49	
Water Orton	d																						
Coleshill Parkway	d							21 05											22 35				
Nuneaton	d							21 22											22 52				
Hinckley	d							21 29											22 59				
Narborough	d							21 37											23 07				
South Wigston	d							21 42											23 12				
Leicester	a							21 50											23 20				
Wilnecote	d						21 04															23 04	
Tamworth	d		20 46				21 08		21 21													23 08	
Burton-on-Trent	d		20 56				21 20		21 33													23 20	
Willington	d																						
Derby 10	a		21 09				21 36		21 46													23 38	
	d					21 17	21 40																23 39
Spondon	d						21 45																
Long Eaton	d					21 28	21 52																00 10
Attenborough	d					21 35	21 58																00 22
Beeston	d			21 05	21 17	21 38	22 02										22 06	22 18					00 33
Nottingham 8	a			21 16	21 26	21 52	22 10										22 16	22 27					00 53

Sundays
until 12 July

		EM	EM	EM	EM	EM		XC	XC	EM	EM	XC		EM	XC	GW	XC	XC		XC	XC	GW	XC	EM	XC
		1◇		1◇		1◇		1	1◇	1◇	1◇	1			1◇		1◇	1◇		1	1◇	1◇	1◇	1◇	1◇
						G				G														G	
Cardiff Central 7	d																								
Newport (South Wales)	d																								
Bristol Temple Meads 10	d														09 00	09 44					10 10				
Bristol Parkway 7	d														09 10	09 55					10 23				
Gloucester 7	d														09 46	10 38						10 51			
Cheltenham Spa	d														09 57	10a49					10 56	11a02			
Ashchurch for Tewkesbury	d																								
Worcester Shrub Hill 7	a																								
Birmingham New Street 12	a														10 56						11 56				
	d							09 52	10 03			10 52			11 03		11 22	11 49		11 52	12 03		12 22		12 30
Water Orton	d																								
Coleshill Parkway	d							10 05				11 05					11 35			12 05			12 35		
Nuneaton	d							10 22				11 22					11 52			12 22			12 52		
Hinckley	d							10 29				11 29								12 29					
Narborough	d							10 38				11 37								12 37					
South Wigston	d							10 42												12 42					
Leicester	a							10 50				11 50					12 12			12 50			13 12		
Wilnecote	d																								
Tamworth	d								10 19									12 07			12 19				
Burton-on-Trent	d								10 29						11 26			12 19							
Willington	d																								
Derby 10	a								10 42						11 41			12 34			12 42				
	d		06 55	08 47	09 14	09 51				10 52				11 21				12 38						13 02	13 09
Spondon	d																								
Long Eaton	d		07a25	08a57	09 22	10a00				11a01				11 31										13a11	
Attenborough	d				09 31																				
Beeston	d	00 20			09 34						11 14			11 41											
Nottingham 8	a	00 29			09 45						11 22			11 49				13 08							

For general notes see front of timetable
For details of catering facilities see Directory of Train Operators

- **A** From Warminster (Table 123) to Great Malvern (Table 71)
- **B** To Lincoln (Table 27)
- **C** From Westbury (Table 123)
- **D** From Swansea (Table 128)
- **E** From Brighton (Table 123)
- **G** From Sheffield (Table 53)

Table 57

Sundays

until 12 July

Bristol and Cardiff → Birmingham → Leicester, Derby and Nottingham

Network Diagram - see first page of Table 50

		EM		EM	XC	XC	XC	GW		AW	EM	XC	XC	EM		XC	XC	XC	GW	XC		EM	XC	EM	EM
		1◇			1◇	1	1◇				1◇	1◇	1◇	1◇		1◇	1	1◇	1◇	1◇		1◇	1◇	1◇	
											A											A			
		☕					🛒				☕	🛒	🛒	☕				🛒	☕	🛒		☕	🛒	☕	
Cardiff Central 7	d				10 20					10 30						11 20									
Newport (South Wales)	d				10 34					10 45						11 34									
Bristol Temple Meads 10	d						11 00											12 00							
Bristol Parkway 7	d						11 10											12 10							
Gloucester 7	d				11 18			11 38		11 45						12 18			12 36						
Cheltenham Spa	d				11 29		11 42	11a48		11a57						12 29		12 42	12a46						
Ashchurch for Tewkesbury	d																								
Worcester Shrub Hill 7	a																								
Birmingham New Street 12	a				12 28		12 50									13 34		13 50							
	d				12 49	12 52	13 03					13 22	13 30			13 49	13 52	14 03		14 22			14 30		
Water Orton	d																								
Coleshill Parkway	d					13 05						13 35					14 05			14 35					
Nuneaton	d					13 22						13 52					14 22			14 52					
Hinckley	d					13 29											14 29								
Narborough	d					13 37											14 37								
South Wigston	d																14 42								
Leicester	a					13 50						14 12					14 50			15 12					
Wilnecote	d																								
Tamworth	d				13 07											14 07		14 19							
Burton-on-Trent	d				13 19		13 26									14 19									
Willington	d																								
Derby 10	a				13 31		13 42						14 09			14 34		14 42					15 05		
	d			13 19	13 37						13 54					14 38						14 48			15 14
Spondon	d																								
Long Eaton	d			13 31							14a04											15a02			15 24
Attenborough	d			13 39																					15 31
Beeston	d	13 11		13 42										14 14										15 13	15 34
Nottingham 8 🚊	a	13 19		13 49	14 08									14 22		15 08								15 20	15 41

		XC	GW	AW		XC	XC	XC	XC	GW		XC	EM	EM	XC	XC		XC	GW	XC	XC	AW		EM	XC
		1◇				1	1◇	1◇	1◇	1◇		1◇	1◇		1◇	1		1◇		1◇	1◇			1◇	1◇
			B																						
							🛒	🛒	🛒	☕		🛒	☕					🛒		🛒	🛒			☕	🛒
Cardiff Central 7	d	12 20		12 30											13 50							14 30			
Newport (South Wales)	d	12 34		12 45											14 04							14 45			
Bristol Temple Meads 10	d		12 44				13 30		14 00									14 30			15 00				
Bristol Parkway 7	d		12 55				13 40		14 10									14 40			15 10				
Gloucester 7	d	13 18	13 38	13 44						14 39					14 47				15 23			15 38			
Cheltenham Spa	d	13 29	13 50	13a57			14 12		14 42	14a48					14 58			15 12	15a33		15 42	15a51			
Ashchurch for Tewkesbury	d		13 59																						
Worcester Shrub Hill 7	a		14 24																						
Birmingham New Street 12	a	14 28					14 50		15 26						15 40			15 50			16 26				
	d	14 49				14 52	15 03	15 22				15 30			15 49	15 52		16 03		16 22					16 30
Water Orton	d																								
Coleshill Parkway	d					15 05		15 35								16 05				16 35					
Nuneaton	d					15 22		15 52								16 22				16 52					
Hinckley	d					15 29										16 29									
Narborough	d					15 37										16 37									
South Wigston	d															16 42									
Leicester	a					15 50		16 12								16 50				17 15					
Wilnecote	d	15 04																							
Tamworth	d	15 09													16 07			16 19							
Burton-on-Trent	d	15 21					15 26								16 19										
Willington	d																								
Derby 10	a	15 34					15 42					16 05			16 34			16 42							17 05
	d	15 38												16 18	16 38									16 47	
Spondon	d																								
Long Eaton	d													16 27										16a56	
Attenborough	d													16 35											
Beeston	d												16 06	16 38											
Nottingham 8 🚊	a	16 08											16 12	16 46	17 09										

For general notes see front of timetable
For details of catering facilities see Directory of Train Operators

A From Sheffield (Table 53)
B From Taunton (Table 134)

Table 57

Sundays

until 12 July

Bristol and Cardiff → Birmingham → Leicester, Derby and Nottingham

Network Diagram - see first page of Table 50

		EM	XC	GW	XC	XC		EM	XC	XC	GW	XC		EM	EM	XC	XC	XC		XC	XC	AW	XC	EM	EM
		1	1 ◇		1	1 ◇		1 ◇	1 ◇	1 ◇	1 ◇	1 ◇		1 ◇		1 ◇	1	1 ◇		1 ◇	1 ◇		1 ◇	1 ◇	1 ◇
				A																					B
Cardiff Central 7	d		14 50													15 50						16 30			
Newport (South Wales)	d		15 04													16 04						16 45			
Bristol Temple Meads 10	d			14 44		15 30				16 00								16 30			17 00				
Bristol Parkway 7	d			14 56		15 40				16 10								16 40			17 10				
Gloucester 7	d		15 47	15 52							16 36					16 47						17 38			
Cheltenham Spa	d		15 58	16 03		16 12				16 42	16a46					16 58		17 12			17 42	17a51			
Ashchurch for Tewkesbury	d			16 11																					
Worcester Shrub Hill 7	a			16 34																					
Birmingham New Street 12	a		16 40			16 50				17 26						17 40		17 50			18 27				
	d		16 49		16 52	17 03			17 22			17 30				17 49	17 52	18 03		18 22			18 30		
Water Orton	d																								
Coleshill Parkway	d				17 05				17 35								18 05			18 35					
Nuneaton	d				17 22				17 52								18 22			18 52					
Hinckley	d				17 29												18 29								
Narborough	d				17 37												18 37								
South Wigston	d				17 42												18 42								
Leicester	a				17 50				18 12								18 50			19 12					
Wilnecote	d																								
Tamworth	d		17 07													18 07		18 21							
Burton-on-Trent	d		17 19			17 28										18 19									
Willington	d																								
Derby 10	a		17 34			17 42						18 05				18 34		18 42					19 05		
	d	17 19	17 38					17 47							18 20	18 38									19 09
Spondon	d																								
Long Eaton	d	17 29						17a56							18 29										19a20
Attenborough	d	17 36													18 37										
Beeston	d	17 39												18 06	18 40									19 01	
Nottingham 8	a	17 47	18 08											18 14	18 46	19 02								19 07	

		XC		GW	XC	XC	XC	XC		GW	XC	EM	EM	XC		XC	XC	XC	XC	GW		AW	XC	EM	XC
		1 ◇			1	1 ◇	1 ◇	1 ◇		1 ◇	1 ◇	1 ◇	1 ◇	1 ◇		1	1 ◇	1 ◇	1 ◇				1 ◇	1 ◇	1
													C												
Cardiff Central 7	d	16 50												17 50								18 30			
Newport (South Wales)	d	17 04												18 04								18 45			
Bristol Temple Meads 10	d			16 43		17 30		18 00									18 30		19 00	18 40					
Bristol Parkway 7	d			16 55		17 40		18 10									18 40		19 10	18 51					
Gloucester 7	d	17 47		17 51						18 39				18 47						19 38		19 42			
Cheltenham Spa	d	17 58		18 03		18 12		18 42		18a48				18 58			19 12		19 42	19 48		19a52			
Ashchurch for Tewkesbury	d			18 11																19 57					
Worcester Shrub Hill 7	a			18 31																20 18					
Birmingham New Street 12	a	18 40				18 49		19 26						19 40			19 50		20 26						
	d	18 49			18 52	19 03	19 22				19 30			19 49		19 52	20 03	20 22					20 30		20 52
Water Orton	d																								
Coleshill Parkway	d				19 05		19 35									20 05		20 35							21 05
Nuneaton	d				19 22		19 52									20 22		20 51							21 22
Hinckley	d				19 29											20 29									21 29
Narborough	d				19 37											20 37									21 37
South Wigston	d				19 42											20 42									21 42
Leicester	a				19 50		20 12									20 50		21 12							21 53
Wilnecote	d	19 04																							
Tamworth	d	19 09												20 07			20 19						20 46		
Burton-on-Trent	d	19 21				19 28								20 19									20 56		
Willington	d																								
Derby 10	a	19 34				19 42					20 05			20 36			20 42						21 09		
	d	19 38											20 06	20 38											
Spondon	d																								
Long Eaton	d												20a15												
Attenborough	d																								
Beeston	d											20 02												21 03	
Nottingham 8	a	19 59										20 08		21 08										21 12	

For general notes see front of timetable
For details of catering facilities see Directory of Train Operators

A From Taunton (Table 134)
B From York (Table 53)
C From Sheffield (Table 53)

Table 57

Sundays

until 12 July

Bristol and Cardiff → Birmingham → Leicester, Derby and Nottingham

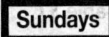

Network Diagram - see first page of Table 50

		AW	EM	XC	XC	GW	EM	EM	XC	XC	HL	GW	GW	XC	EM	XC	GW	XC	HL	GW
				1◇	1◇	1◇	1◇		1◇	1◇				1	1◇	1◇	1◇	1◇		
												A								
				🛒	🛒	☕	☕			🛒					☕		☕	🛒		
Cardiff Central 7	d								19 50		20 30					20 50			22 30	
Newport (South Wales)	d								20 04		20 45					21 04			22 49	
Bristol Temple Meads 10	d			19 30	20 00					20 30			20 43					22 10		
Bristol Parkway 7	d			19 40	20 10					20 40			20 55					22 20		
Gloucester 7	d					20 35			20 47		21a40	21 20	21 41			21 47	22 35		23a50	23 55
Cheltenham Spa	d			20 12	20 42	20a46			20 58	21 12		21a28	21a49			21 58	22a46	22 52		00a04
Ashchurch for Tewkesbury	d																			
Worcester Shrub Hill 7	a																			
Birmingham New Street 12	a			20 50	21 31				21 45	21 49						22 40		23 44		
	d			21 03					21 49	22 03				22 22		22 49				
Water Orton	d																			
Coleshill Parkway	d													22 35						
Nuneaton	d													22 52						
Hinckley	d													22 59						
Narborough	d													23 07						
South Wigston	d													23 12						
Leicester	a													23 20						
Wilnecote	d								22 04											
Tamworth	d								22 09	22 22						23 07				
Burton-on-Trent	d			21 26					22 21	22 35						23 19				
Willington	d																			
Derby 10	a			21 44					22 34	22 49						23 34				
	d	21 18	21 35					22 30	22 38							23 38				
Spondon	d																			
Long Eaton	d	21 28						22 39												
Attenborough	d	21 35						22 47												
Beeston	d	21 38	21 38				22 04	22 50							23 11					
Nottingham 8 🚊	a	21 45	21 45				22 11	22 57	23 08						23 18	23 59				

Sundays

19 July to 6 September

		EM	EM	XC	XC	EM	XC	XC	GW	GW	EM	XC	XC	XC	XC	GW	AW	XC	EM	XC	EM	EM	XC	XC	GW
		1◇		1	1◇		1◇	1◇		1◇	1◇	1	1◇	1◇	1◇			1	1◇	1◇	1◇		1◇	1◇	1◇
							B						B						C				B		
		☕	🚌		🛒		🛒	🛒		☕	☕		🛒		🛒				☕	🛒	☕		🛒	🛒	☕
Cardiff Central 7	d																10 30								
Newport (South Wales)	d																10 45								
Bristol Temple Meads 10	d							09 15	09 44						10 30									11 30	
Bristol Parkway 7	d							09 25	09 55						10 40									11 40	
Gloucester 7	d							10 01	10 38	10 51						11 38	11 45								12 36
Cheltenham Spa	d							10 12	10a49	11a02					11 12	11a48	11a57							12 12	12a46
Ashchurch for Tewkesbury	d																								
Worcester Shrub Hill 7	a																								
Birmingham New Street 12	a							10 50							11 50									12 50	
	d			09 52	10 03		10 33	11 03				11 22	11 39	11 49	12 03			12 22		12 30			12 39	13 03	
Water Orton	d																								
Coleshill Parkway	d			10 05			10 47					11 35	11 54					12 35					12 55		
Nuneaton	d			10 22			11 03					11 52	12 10					12 52					13 11		
Hinckley	d			10 29			11 10						12 17										13 18		
Narborough	d			10 37			11 19						12 26										13 27		
South Wigston	d			10 42									12 30												
Leicester	a			10 50			11 32					12 15	12 41					13 15					13 38		
Wilnecote	d																								
Tamworth	d				10 19									12 07	12 19										
Burton-on-Trent	d				10 29			11 26						12 19										13 26	
Willington	d																								
Derby 10	a				10 42			11 42						12 34	12 42					13 09				13 44	
	d		06 55			11 21								12 38					12 49			13 18			
Spondon	d																								
Long Eaton	d		07a25			11 31													12a58			13 30			
Attenborough	d					11 38																13 37			
Beeston	d	00 32				11 41					11 23										13 19	13 40			
Nottingham 8 🚊	a	00 41				11 49					11 35			13 08							13 26	13 48			

For general notes see front of timetable
For details of catering facilities see Directory of Train Operators

A From Westbury (Table 123)
B To Stansted Airport (Table 49)
C From Sheffield (Table 53)

Table 57

Sundays

19 July to 6 September

Bristol and Cardiff → Birmingham → Leicester, Derby and Nottingham

Network Diagram - see first page of Table 50

		EM 1◇ ☕	XC 1	XC 1◇ 🛒	EM 1◇ ☕	XC 1◇	XC 1◇ 🛒	XC 1◇ 🛒	XC 1	XC 1◇ 🛒	GW A	AW	EM 1◇ B ☕	XC 1◇ 🛒	EM 1◇ ☕	EM	XC 1◇ 🛒	XC 1◇		XC 1◇ 🛒	XC 1	XC 1◇ 🛒	GW 1◇ ☕	XC 1◇ 🛒	EM 1◇ ☕
Cardiff Central 7	d					11 50						12 30						12 50							
Newport (South Wales)	d					12 04						12 45						13 04							
Bristol Temple Meads 10	d						12 30			13 00	12 44									13 30		14 00			
Bristol Parkway 7	d						12 40			13 10	12 55									13 40		14 10			
Gloucester 7	d					12 47					13 38	13 44						13 51					14 39		
Cheltenham Spa	d					12 58	13 12			13 42	13 50	13a57						14 02		14 12		14 42	14a48		
Ashchurch for Tewkesbury	d										13 59														
Worcester Shrub Hill 7	a										14 24														
Birmingham New Street 12	a					13 40	13 50			14 26								14 44		14 50		15 26			
	d		13 22	13 30		13 49	14 03	13 56	14 22					14 30			14 44	14 49		15 03	15 22			15 30	
Water Orton	d																								
Coleshill Parkway	d		13 35					14 10	14 35								14 57				15 35				
Nuneaton	d		13 52					14 26	14 52								15 19				15 52				
Hinckley	d							14 33									15 26								
Narborough	d							14 42									15 34								
South Wigston	d							14 46																	
Leicester	a		14 15					14 55	15 15								15 48				16 15				
Wilnecote	d																	15 04							
Tamworth	d					14 07	14 19											15 09							
Burton-on-Trent	d					14 19												15 21		15 28					
Willington	d																								
Derby 10	a			14 09		14 34	14 42							15 05				15 34		15 42				16 05	
	d	13 55				14 40							14 48			15 15		15 38							
Spondon	d																								
Long Eaton	d	14a04											15a02			15 25									
Attenborough	d															15 32									
Beeston	d				14 20										15 12	15 35									16 06
Nottingham 8	a				14 29	15 08		15 23							15 18	15 42	16 15	16 08							16 12

		EM	XC 1◇	XC 1◇ C 🛒	XC 1◇ 🛒	GW	XC 1	XC 1◇ 🛒	AW	EM 1◇ ☕	XC 1◇ 🛒	EM 1	XC 1◇	XC 1◇ 🛒	GW A	XC 1◇ 🛒	EM 1◇ ☕	XC 1	XC 1◇ 🛒	GW 1◇ ☕	XC 1◇ 🛒	EM 1◇ ☕	EM	XC 1◇	EM 1◇ ☕
Cardiff Central 7	d		13 50						14 30				14 50											15 50	
Newport (South Wales)	d		14 04						14 45				15 04											16 04	
Bristol Temple Meads 10	d				14 30			15 00							14 44	15 30			16 00						
Bristol Parkway 7	d				14 40			15 10							14 56	15 40			16 10						
Gloucester 7	d		14 47			15 23			15 38				15 47		15 52					16 36				16 47	
Cheltenham Spa	d		14 58		15 12	15a33		15 42	15a51				15 58		16 03	16 12			16 42	16a46				16 58	
Ashchurch for Tewkesbury	d														16 11										
Worcester Shrub Hill 7	a														16 34										
Birmingham New Street 12	a		15 40		15 50			16 26					16 40			16 50			17 26					17 40	
	d		15 49	15 52	16 03		16 22				16 30		16 49	16 52		17 03		17 22			17 30			17 49	
Water Orton	d																								
Coleshill Parkway	d			16 05			16 35							17 05				17 35							
Nuneaton	d			16 22			16 52							17 22				17 52							
Hinckley	d			16 29										17 29											
Narborough	d			16 37										17 37											
South Wigston	d			16 42										17 42											
Leicester	a			16 50			17 15							17 50				18 15							
Wilnecote	d																								
Tamworth	d		16 07		16 19								17 07											18 07	
Burton-on-Trent	d		16 19										17 19			17 28								18 19	
Willington	d																								
Derby 10	a		16 34		16 42						17 05		17 34			17 42					18 05			18 34	
	d	16 18	16 38							16 47		17 19	17 38				17 47						18 20	18 40	
Spondon	d																								
Long Eaton	d	16 27								16a56		17 29					17a56						18 29		
Attenborough	d	16 35										17 36											18 37		
Beeston	d	16 38										17 39										18 06	18 40		19 01
Nottingham 8	a	16 46	17 09									17 47	18 02									18 14	18 46	19 08	19 07

For general notes see front of timetable
For details of catering facilities see Directory of Train Operators

A From Taunton (Table 134)
B From Sheffield (Table 53)
C To Stansted Airport (Table 49)

Table 57

Sundays

Bristol and Cardiff → Birmingham → Leicester, Derby and Nottingham

19 July to 6 September

Network Diagram - see first page of Table 50

		XC	XC	XC	XC	AW	XC	EM	EM	XC	GW	EM	XC	XC	XC	XC	GW	XC	EM	XC	EM	XC	XC	XC	XC
		1◇	1◇	1	1◇		1◇	1◇	1◇	1◇		1◇	1◇	1◇	1	1◇	1◇	1◇	1◇	1◇	1◇	1◇	1◇	1	1◇
		A						B					A						C			D			
		trolley	trolley		trolley		trolley	buffet	buffet			buffet	trolley	trolley		trolley	buffet	trolley	buffet		buffet	trolley	trolley		trolley
Cardiff Central 7	d					16 30				16 50										17 50					
Newport (South Wales)	d					16 45				17 04										18 04					
Bristol Temple Meads 10	d		16 30		17 00						16 43			17 30		18 00							18 30		19 00
Bristol Parkway 7	d		16 40		17 10						16 55			17 40		18 10							18 40		19 10
Gloucester 7	d					17 38				17 47	17 51						18 39			18 47					
Cheltenham Spa	d		17 12		17 42	17a51				17 58	18 03			18 12		18 42	18a48			18 58			19 12		19 42
Ashchurch for Tewkesbury	d										18 11														
Worcester Shrub Hill 7	a										18 31														
Birmingham New Street 12	a		17 50		18 27					18 40				18 56		19 26				19 40			19 50		20 26
	d	17 52	18 03	18 22			18 30			18 49			18 52	19 03	19 22			19 30		19 49		19 52	20 03	20 22	
Water Orton	d																								
Coleshill Parkway	d	18 05		18 35									19 05		19 35							20 05		20 35	
Nuneaton	d	18 22		18 52									19 22		19 52							20 22		20 51	
Hinckley	d	18 29											19 29									20 29			
Narborough	d	18 37											19 37									20 37			
South Wigston	d	18 42											19 43									20 42			
Leicester	a	18 50		19 15									19 50		20 15							20 50		21 15	
Wilnecote	d									19 04															
Tamworth	d		18 21							19 09										20 07			20 19		
Burton-on-Trent	d									19 21				19 28						20 19					
Willington	d																								
Derby 10	a		18 42				19 05			19 34				19 42				20 05		20 34			20 42		
	d							19 09		19 38									20 06	20 38					
Spondon	d																								
Long Eaton	d							19a20											20a15						
Attenborough	d																								
Beeston	d								19 45			20 02									21 06				
Nottingham 8	a								19 52	20 08		20 08								21 08	21 13				

		GW	AW	XC	XC	EM	XC	XC	XC	GW	XC	XC	EM	XC	GW	GW	XC	XC	XC	GW	EM	XC	GW		
				1◇	1		1◇	1◇	1◇	1◇	1◇		1◇	1◇			1◇		1	1◇	1◇	1◇			
															E										
				trolley			trolley		trolley	buffet		bus	buffet	trolley				bus		buffet	buffet	trolley			
Cardiff Central 7	d		18 30					18 50			19 50						20 50								
Newport (South Wales)	d		18 45					19 04			20 04						21 04								
Bristol Temple Meads 10	d	18 40					19 30		20 00					20 30		20 43						22 10			
Bristol Parkway 7	d	18 51					19 40		20 10					20 40		20 55						22 20			
Gloucester 7	d	19 38	19 42					19 50		20 35	20 50				21 20	21 41	21 47			22 35			23 55		
Cheltenham Spa	d	19 48	19a52				20 12	20 00	20 42	20a46	21 00			21 12	21a28	21a49	21 58			22a46		22 52	00a04		
Ashchurch for Tewkesbury	d	19 57																							
Worcester Shrub Hill 7	a	20 18																							
Birmingham New Street 12	a						20 50	20 42	21 31		21 45			21 56			22 45					23 44			
	d			20 30	20 52		21 03	20 49			21 49			22 03					22 22						
Water Orton	d																								
Coleshill Parkway	d				21 05														22 35						
Nuneaton	d				21 22														22 52						
Hinckley	d				21 29														22 59						
Narborough	d				21 37														23 07						
South Wigston	d				21 42														23 12						
Leicester	a				21 58														23 20						
Wilnecote	d										22 04														
Tamworth	d			20 46				21 07			22 09			22 21											
Burton-on-Trent	d			20 56			21 26	21 19			22 21														
Willington	d																								
Derby 10	a			21 09			21 43	21 35			22 34			22 44											
	d					21 18						21 45						22 45							
Spondon	d																								
Long Eaton	d					21 28																			
Attenborough	d					21 35																			
Beeston	d					21 38							22 22								23 33				
Nottingham 8	a					21 45						22 15	22 29					23 15			23 40				

For general notes see front of timetable
For details of catering facilities see Directory of Train Operators

A To Stansted Airport (Table 49)
B From York (Table 53)
C From Sheffield (Table 53)
D To Cambridge (Table 49)
E From Westbury (Table 123)

Sundays

Bristol and Cardiff → Birmingham → Leicester, Derby and Nottingham

13 September to 1 November

Network Diagram - see first page of Table 50

		EM 1◇	EM 1◇	EM	EM 1◇	EM 1◇		XC 1	XC 1◇	XC	EM	XC 1◇		XC 1◇	GW	GW 1◇	EM 1◇	XC		EM 1◇	XC 1◇	XC 1◇	XC 1◇	GW	AW
						A														A					
Cardiff Central 7	d																								10 30
Newport (South Wales)	d																								10 45
Bristol Temple Meads 10	d													09 15	09 44								10 30		
Bristol Parkway 7	d													09 25	09 55								10 40		
Gloucester 7	d													10 01	10 38	10 50								11 38	11 45
Cheltenham Spa	d													10 12	10a49	11a02							11 12	11a48	11a57
Ashchurch for Tewkesbury	d																								
Worcester Shrub Hill 7	a																								
Birmingham New Street 12	a													10 50									11 50		
	d							09 52	10 03			10 52		11 03							11 45	11 52	12 03		
Water Orton	d																								
Coleshill Parkway	d									10 05								10 50							
Nuneaton	d									10b45								11b45							
Hinckley	d									11 05								12 05							
Narborough	d									11 30								12 30							
South Wigston	d									11 40								12 40							
Leicester	a									12 00								13 00							
Wilnecote	d																								
Tamworth	d							10 10	10 19			11a10		11 19							12 03	12a09	12 19		
Burton-on-Trent	d								10 29					11 29							12 15				
Willington	d																								
Derby 10	a							10 34	10 43					11 42							12 28		12 40		
	d	07 09	08 07	18 20	09 06	10 00					11 19									12 07	12 33				
Spondon	d																								
Long Eaton	d	07a18	08a16	18 29	09a15	10a12					11 29									12a16					
Attenborough	d			18 37							11 36														
Beeston	d			18 40							11 39						11 52								
Nottingham 8	a			18 46							11 46						12 00				12 54				

		EM 1◇		XC 1◇	EM	XC 1◇	XC	EM 1◇		XC 1◇	XC 1◇	GW 1◇	EM 1◇	XC		XC 1◇	XC 1◇	XC 1◇	XC 1◇	XC 1◇		GW	AW	EM 1◇	XC
		A											A									B		C	
Cardiff Central 7	d					10 50											11 50						12 30		
Newport (South Wales)	d					11 04											12 04						12 45		
Bristol Temple Meads 10	d										11 30								12 30	13 00		12 44			
Bristol Parkway 7	d										11 40								12 40	13 10		12 55			
Gloucester 7	d					11 52						12 36					12 47					13 38	13 44		
Cheltenham Spa	d					12 03					12 12	12a46					12 58		13 12	13 42		13 50	13a57		
Ashchurch for Tewkesbury	d																					13 59			
Worcester Shrub Hill 7	a																					14 24			
Birmingham New Street 12	a					12 45					12 50						13 40		13 50	14 20					
	d			12 30		12 48				12 52	13 03					13 30	13 45	13 52	14 03						
Water Orton	d																								
Coleshill Parkway	d						11 50							12 50											13 50
Nuneaton	d						12b45							13b45											14b45
Hinckley	d						13 05							14 05											15 05
Narborough	d						13 30							14 30											15 30
South Wigston	d						13 40							14 40											15 40
Leicester	a						14 00							15 00											16 00
Wilnecote	d																								
Tamworth	d					13 06				13a11							14 03	14a10	14 19						
Burton-on-Trent	d					13 18					13 29						14 15								
Willington	d																								
Derby 10	a			13 09		13 31					13 42					14 09	14 28		14 41						
	d	13 09			13 17	13 36							13 56				14 32							14 46	
Spondon	d																								
Long Eaton	d	13a18			13 27								14a05											14a56	
Attenborough	d				13 34																				
Beeston	d				13 37			13 55																	
Nottingham 8	a				13 48	13 56		14 02									14 53								

For general notes see front of timetable
For details of catering facilities see Directory of Train Operators

A From Sheffield (Table 53)
B From Taunton (Table 134)
C From Leeds (Table 53)
b Arrives 5 minutes earlier

Table 57

Sundays

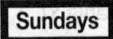

13 September to 1 November

Bristol and Cardiff → Birmingham → Leicester, Derby and Nottingham

Network Diagram - see first page of Table 50

		XC	EM	XC		XC	XC	XC	GW	EM		XC	EM	EM	XC	EM		XC	XC	XC	GW	XC		AW	XC
		1 ◊		1 ◊		1 ◊	1 ◊	1 ◊	1 ◊	1 ◊		1 ◊	1 ◊			1 ◊		1 ◊	1 ◊	1 ◊		1 ◊			
										A															
															(bus)										(bus)
		(trolley)				(trolley)	(trolley)	(trolley)	(buffet)	(buffet)		(trolley)	(buffet)			(buffet)			(trolley)	(trolley)		(trolley)			
Cardiff Central 7	d			12 50														13 50						14 30	
Newport (South Wales)	d			13 04														14 04						14 45	
Bristol Temple Meads 10	d						13 30	14 00												14 30		15 00			
Bristol Parkway 7	d						13 40	14 10												14 40		15 10			
Gloucester 7	d			13 51					14 39									14 47			15 23			15 38	
Cheltenham Spa	d			14 02			14 12	14 42	14a49									14 58		15 12	15a33	15 42		15a51	
Ashchurch for Tewkesbury	d																								
Worcester Shrub Hill 7	a																								
Birmingham New Street 12	a			14 44			14 50	15 26										15 40		15 50		16 26			
	d	14 30		14 47		14 52	15 03					15 30						15 45	15 52	16 03					
Water Orton	d																								
Coleshill Parkway	d														14 50										15 50
Nuneaton	d														15b45										16b45
Hinckley	d														16 05										17 05
Narborough	d														16 30										17 30
South Wigston	d														16 40										17 40
Leicester	a														17 00										18 00
Wilnecote	d			15 02																					
Tamworth	d			15 07		15a12												16 03	16a10	16 19					
Burton-on-Trent	d			15 19			15 30											16 15							
Willington	d																								
Derby 10	a	15 02		15 32			15 43					16 02						16 27		16 42					
	d		15 13	15 41						16 01				16 18				16 32							
Spondon	d																								
Long Eaton	d		15 23							16a10				16 27											
Attenborough	d		15 30											16 35											
Beeston	d		15 33										16 04	16 38		16 46									
Nottingham 8	a		15 40	16 01									16 11	16 46		16 53		16 56							

		EM	XC	EM	XC	GW		XC	XC	XC	GW	XC	EM	XC	EM	EM	XC	XC		XC	XC	AW	XC	EM	XC
		1 ◊	1 ◊	1	1 ◊			1 ◊	1 ◊	1 ◊	1 ◊	1 ◊			1 ◊	1 ◊	1 ◊	1 ◊		1 ◊	1 ◊		1 ◊		
		A				B									C										
														(bus)											(bus)
		(buffet)	(trolley)					(trolley)	(trolley)	(trolley)	(buffet)	(trolley)			(buffet)	(buffet)		(trolley)		(trolley)	(trolley)		(trolley)		
Cardiff Central 7	d				14 50												15 50					16 30			
Newport (South Wales)	d				15 04												16 04					16 45			
Bristol Temple Meads 10	d					14 44			15 30	16 00										16 30	17 00				
Bristol Parkway 7	d					14 56			15 40	16 10										16 40	17 10				
Gloucester 7	d				15 48	15 52					16 36						16 47					17 38			
Cheltenham Spa	d				15 58	16 03			16 12	16 42	16a46						16 59			17 12	17 42	17a51			
Ashchurch for Tewkesbury	d					16 11																			
Worcester Shrub Hill 7	a					16 34																			
Birmingham New Street 12	a				16 40				16 52	17 26							17 41			17 49	18 27				
	d		16 30		16 45			16 52	17 03			17 30					17 45	17 52		18 03			18 30		
Water Orton	d																								
Coleshill Parkway	d													16 50											17 50
Nuneaton	d													17b45											18b45
Hinckley	d													18 05											19 05
Narborough	d													18 30											19 30
South Wigston	d													18 40											19 40
Leicester	a													19 00											20 00
Wilnecote	d																								
Tamworth	d				17 03			17a10									18 03	18a10		18 21					
Burton-on-Trent	d				17 15				17 29								18 15								
Willington	d																								
Derby 10	a		17 02		17 28				17 42			18 02					18 28			18 43			19 02		
	d	16 47		17 19	17 33								18 20		18 29		18 33							19 18	
Spondon	d																								
Long Eaton	d	17a00		17 29									18 29		18a38									19 30	
Attenborough	d			17 36									18 37											19 37	
Beeston	d			17 39									18 40			18 47								19 40	
Nottingham 8	a			17 47	17 53								18 46			18 54	18 57							19 47	

For general notes see front of timetable
For details of catering facilities see Directory of Train Operators

A From Sheffield (Table 53)
B From Taunton (Table 134)
C From York (Table 53)

b Arrives 5 minutes earlier

Table 57

Sundays

Bristol and Cardiff → Birmingham → Leicester, Derby and Nottingham

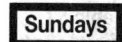

13 September to 1 November

Network Diagram - see first page of Table 50

		EM		EM	XC	GW	XC	XC		XC	GW	XC	XC	EM		XC	XC	XC	XC	GW		AW	XC	EM	XC
		1 ◊		1 ◊	1 ◊		1 ◊	1 ◊		1 ◊	1 ◊		1 ◊	1 ◊		1 ◊	1 ◊	1 ◊	1 ◊				1 ◊		
		A																							
												[bus]													[bus]
		[buffet]		[buffet]			[trolley]	[trolley]		[trolley]	[buffet]		[trolley]	[buffet]			[trolley]	[trolley]	[trolley]				[trolley]		
Cardiff Central 7	d				16 50											17 50						18 30			
Newport (South Wales)	d				17 04											18 04						18 45			
Bristol Temple Meads 10	d					16 43		17 30		18 00								18 30	19 00	18 40					
Bristol Parkway 7	d					16 55		17 40		18 10								18 40	19 10	18 51					
Gloucester 7	d				17 47	17 51					18 39					18 47				19 38		19 42			
Cheltenham Spa	d				17 58	18 03		18 12		18 42	18a48					18 58		19 12	19 42	19 48		19a52			
Ashchurch for Tewkesbury	d					18 11														19 57					
Worcester Shrub Hill 7	a					18 31														20 18					
Birmingham New Street 12	a				18 40			18 49		19 26						19 40		19 50	20 26						
	d				18 45		18 52	19 03					19 30			19 45	19 52	20 03					20 30		
Water Orton	d																								
Coleshill Parkway	d											18 50													19 50
Nuneaton	d											19b45													20b45
Hinckley	d											20 05													21 05
Narborough	d											20 30													21 30
South Wigston	d											20 40													21 40
Leicester	a											21 00													22 00
Wilnecote	d				19 00																				
Tamworth	d				19 04		19a10									20 03	20a10	20 19					20 46		
Burton-on-Trent	d				19 16			19 30								20 15							20 56		
Willington	d																								
Derby 10	a				19 29			19 43					20 02			20 28		20 42					21 09		
	d	19 22			19 34											20 33								21 18	
Spondon	d																								
Long Eaton	d	19a34																						21 28	
Attenborough	d																							21 35	
Beeston	d			19 45										20 46										21 38	
Nottingham 8	a			19 52	19 56									20 53		20 57								21 45	

		XC	XC	XC		GW	XC	XC	EM	XC		XC	XC	XC	GW	GW		XC	XC	GW	XC	GW			
		1	1 ◊	1 ◊		1 ◊	1 ◊	1	1 ◊					1 ◊					1 ◊	1 ◊	1 ◊				
															B										
										[bus]		[bus]	[bus]					[bus]							
			[trolley]	[trolley]		[buffet]			[buffet]					[trolley]						[buffet]	[trolley]				
Cardiff Central 7	d						19 50												20 50						
Newport (South Wales)	d						20 04												21 04						
Bristol Temple Meads 10	d		19 30	20 00										20 30		20 43					22 10				
Bristol Parkway 7	d		19 40	20 10										20 40		20 55					22 20				
Gloucester 7	d					20 35	20 50								21 25	21 41			21 47	22 35		23 55			
Cheltenham Spa	d		20 12	20 42		20a46	21 00							21 12	21a34	21a49			21 58	22a46	22 52	00a04			
Ashchurch for Tewkesbury	d																								
Worcester Shrub Hill 7	a																								
Birmingham New Street 12	a		20 55	21 31			21 45							21 49					22 40		23 44				
	d	20 52	21 03				21 49	21 52						22 03					22 49						
Water Orton	d																								
Coleshill Parkway	d											20 50						21 50							
Nuneaton	d											21b45						22b45							
Hinckley	d											22 05						23 05							
Narborough	d											22 30						23 30							
South Wigston	d											22 40						23 40							
Leicester	a											23 00						23 55							
Wilnecote	d						22 04																		
Tamworth	d	21a10	21 19				22 09	22a15						22 23					23 07						
Burton-on-Trent	d		21 29				22 21							22 35					23 19						
Willington	d																								
Derby 10	a		21 42				22 48							22 48					23 37						
	d									21 45			22 45												
Spondon	d																								
Long Eaton	d																								
Attenborough	d																								
Beeston	d								21 45																
Nottingham 8	a								21 51	22 15			23 15												

For general notes see front of timetable
For details of catering facilities see Directory of Train Operators

A From Sheffield (Table 53)
B From Westbury (Table 123)
b Arrives 5 minutes earlier

Table 57

Sundays

from 8 November

Bristol and Cardiff → Birmingham → Leicester, Derby and Nottingham

Network Diagram - see first page of Table 50

		EM	EM	EM	EM	XC	XC		XC	EM	XC	XC	XC	EM		EM	XC	XC	XC	GW	GW		EM	XC	XC
		■1 ◇	■1 ◇	■1 ◇	■1 ◇	■1	■1 ◇				■1 ◇	■1 ◇		■1 ◇		■1 ◇	■1 ◇	■1 ◇	■1 ◇		■1 ◇		■1 ◇	■1 ◇	
					A				🚌				🚌			A							A		🚌
		🛒	🛒	🛒	🛒		🍴				🍴	🍴		🛒		🛒		🍴	🍴		🛒		🛒	🍴	
Cardiff Central 7	d																								
Newport (South Wales)	d																								
Bristol Temple Meads 10	d											08 45							10 00	09 44					
Bristol Parkway 7	d											08 55							10 10	09 55					
Gloucester 7	d											09 31								10 38	10 50				
Cheltenham Spa	d											09 42							10 42	10a49	11a02				
Ashchurch for Tewkesbury	d																								
Worcester Shrub Hill 7	a																								
Birmingham New Street 12	a											10 56							11 56						
	d					09 52	10 03				10 52	11 03					11 45	11 52	12 03					12 30	
Water Orton	d																								
Coleshill Parkway	d								10 05				10 50												11 50
Nuneaton	d								10b45				11b45												12b45
Hinckley	d								11 05				12 05												13 05
Narborough	d								11 30				12 30												13 30
South Wigston	d								11 40				12 40												13 40
Leicester	a								12 00				13 00												14 00
Wilnecote	d																								
Tamworth	d					10 10	10 19				11a10	11 19					12 03	12a09	12 19						
Burton-on-Trent	d						10 29					11 29					12 15								
Willington	d																								
Derby 10	a					10 34	10 43					11 42					12 28		12 40					13 09	
	d	07 09	08 07	09 06	10 00					11 19						12 07	12 33						13 09		
Spondon	d																								
Long Eaton	d	07a18	08a16	09a15	10a12					11 29						12a16							13a18		
Attenborough	d									11 36															
Beeston	d									11 39				11 52											
Nottingham 8 🚋	a									11 46				12 00			12 54								

		EM	XC	GW	AW	XC		XC	XC	EM	EM	XC	XC		XC	GW	XC	XC	XC	XC		EM	XC	EM	XC
			■1 ◇			■1 ◇		■1 ◇	■1 ◇	■1 ◇	■1 ◇		■1 ◇		■1 ◇	■1 ◇	■1 ◇		■1 ◇	■1 ◇		■1 ◇	■1 ◇		■1 ◇
									B		A	🚌						🚌		B		C			
						🍴		🍴	🍴	🛒	🛒		🍴			🛒	🍴		🍴	🍴		🛒	🍴		
Cardiff Central 7	d		10 25		10 30										11 25										12 25
Newport (South Wales)	d		10 39		10 45										11 39										12 39
Bristol Temple Meads 10	d								11 30											12 30					
Bristol Parkway 7	d								11 40											12 40					
Gloucester 7	d		11 22	11 38	11 45										12 22	12 36									13 22
Cheltenham Spa	d		11 33	11a48	11a57				12 12						12 33	12a46				13 12					13 33
Ashchurch for Tewkesbury	d																								
Worcester Shrub Hill 7	a																								
Birmingham New Street 12	a		12 36						13 20						13 33					14 20					14 36
	d		12 45			12 52		13 03					13 30		13 45		13 52		14 03				14 30		14 45
Water Orton	d																								
Coleshill Parkway	d											12 50						13 50							
Nuneaton	d											13b45						14b45							
Hinckley	d											14 05						15 05							
Narborough	d											14 30						15 30							
South Wigston	d											14 40						15 40							
Leicester	a											15 00						16 00							
Wilnecote	d																								15 00
Tamworth	d		13 03			13a11									14 03		14a10		14 19						15 05
Burton-on-Trent	d		13 15					13 29							14 15										15 17
Willington	d																								
Derby 10	a		13 28					13 42					14 09		14 28				14 39				15 02		15 32
	d	13 17	13 33								13 56				14 32							14 46		15 13	15 40
Spondon	d																								
Long Eaton	d	13 27									14a05											14a56		15 23	
Attenborough	d	13 34																						15 30	
Beeston	d	13 37								13 55														15 33	
Nottingham 8 🚋	a	13 48	13 57							14 02					14 57									15 40	16 01

For general notes see front of timetable
For details of catering facilities see Directory of Train Operators

A From Sheffield (Table 53)
B From Plymouth (Table 51)
C From Leeds (Table 53)
b Arrives 5 minutes earlier

Table 57

Sundays

from 8 November

Bristol and Cardiff → Birmingham → Leicester, Derby and Nottingham

Network Diagram - see first page of Table 50

		GW	AW	XC	XC		XC	EM	XC	EM	EM	XC		EM	XC	GW	XC	XC	XC		XC	EM	XC	EM	XC
		A		1◇	1◇		1◇ B	1◇ C	1◇	1◇				1◇	1◇	1◇	1◇		1◇		1◇ D	1◇ C	1◇	1	1◇
				[trolley]	[trolley]		[trolley]	[buffet]	[trolley]	[buffet]		[bus]		[buffet]		[buffet]	[trolley]	[bus]	[trolley]		[trolley]	[buffet]	[trolley]		
Cardiff Central [7]	d		12 30												13 25										14 25
Newport (South Wales)	d		12 45												13 39										14 39
Bristol Temple Meads [10]	d	12 44					13 30														14 30				
Bristol Parkway [7]	d	12 55					13 40														14 40				
Gloucester [7]	d	13 38	13 44												14 22	14 39									15 22
Cheltenham Spa	d	13 50	13a57				14 12								14 33	14a49					15 12				15 33
Ashchurch for Tewkesbury	d	13 59																							
Worcester Shrub Hill [7]	a	14 24																							
Birmingham New Street [12]	a						15 20								15 36						16 19				16 40
	d			14 52	15 03				15 30						15 45		15 52		16 03				16 30		16 45
Water Orton	d																								
Coleshill Parkway	d											14 50						15 50							
Nuneaton	d											15 45						16b45							
Hinckley	d											16 05						17 05							
Narborough	d											16 30						17 30							
South Wigston	d											16 40						17 40							
Leicester	a											17 00						18 00							
Wilnecote	d																								
Tamworth	d			15a10											16 03		16a10		16 19						17 03
Burton-on-Trent	d				15 30										16 15										17 15
Willington	d																								
Derby [10]	a				15 43				16 02						16 27				16 42				17 02		17 28
	d							16 01			16 18				16 33							16 47		17 19	17 33
Spondon	d																								
Long Eaton	d							16a10			16 27											17a00		17 29	
Attenborough	d										16 35													17 36	
Beeston	d									16 04	16 38			16 46										17 39	
Nottingham [8] [tram]	a									16 11	16 46			16 53	16 57									17 47	17 53

		GW	AW	GW		XC	XC	XC	XC	EM	XC		EM	EM	XC	GW	XC	XC		XC	XC	XC	EM	EM	EM
				A		1◇	1◇	1◇ B	1◇				1◇ E	1◇	1◇	1◇	1◇	1◇		1◇ G	1◇			1◇ C	1◇
						[trolley]	[trolley]	[trolley]	[trolley]		[bus]		[buffet]	[buffet]		[buffet]	[trolley]	[trolley]		[trolley]	[trolley]	[bus]		[buffet]	[buffet]
Cardiff Central [7]	d		14 30												15 25										
Newport (South Wales)	d		14 45												15 39										
Bristol Temple Meads [10]	d			14 44				15 30												16 30					
Bristol Parkway [7]	d			14 56				15 40												16 40					
Gloucester [7]	d	15 27	15 38	15 52											16 22	16 36									
Cheltenham Spa	d	15a37	15a51	16 03				16 12							16 33	16a46				17 12					
Ashchurch for Tewkesbury	d			16 11																					
Worcester Shrub Hill [7]	a			16 34																					
Birmingham New Street [12]	a							17 25							17 39					18 20					
	d					16 52	17 02		17 30						17 45		17 52	18 02			18 30				
Water Orton	d																								
Coleshill Parkway	d										16 50											17 50			
Nuneaton	d										17b45											18b45			
Hinckley	d										18 05											19 05			
Narborough	d										18 30											19 30			
South Wigston	d										18 40											19 40			
Leicester	a										19 00											20 00			
Wilnecote	d																								
Tamworth	d					17a10									18 03		18a10	18 20							
Burton-on-Trent	d						17 28								18 15										
Willington	d																								
Derby [10]	a						17 42		18 02						18 29			18 43			19 02				
	d									18 20			18 29		18 33								19 18	19 22	
Spondon	d																								
Long Eaton	d									18 29			18a38										19 30	19a34	
Attenborough	d									18 37													19 37		
Beeston	d									18 40				18 47									19 40		19 45
Nottingham [8] [tram]	a									18 46				18 54	18 57								19 47		19 52

For general notes see front of timetable
For details of catering facilities see Directory of Train Operators

A From Taunton (Table 134)
B From Penzance (Table 51)
C From Sheffield (Table 53)
D From Paignton (Table 51)
E From York (Table 53)
G From Plymouth (Table 51)
b Arrives 5 minutes earlier

Table 57

Sundays

from 8 November

Bristol and Cardiff → Birmingham → Leicester, Derby and Nottingham

Network Diagram - see first page of Table 50

		XC 1◇ [trolley]	AW		GW	XC 1◇ [trolley]	XC [bus]	XC 1◇ [trolley]	XC 1◇ A [trolley]	XC 1◇ [trolley]		EM 1◇ [buffet]	XC 1◇	GW 1◇ [buffet]	XC 1◇ [trolley]	XC 1◇ [trolley]	XC 1◇ A [trolley]		XC [bus]	XC 1◇ [trolley]	EM	XC 1◇	GW	AW	XC 1
Cardiff Central 7	d	16 25	16 30										17 25									18 25		18 30	
Newport (South Wales)	d	16 39	16 45										17 39									18 39		18 45	
Bristol Temple Meads 10	d				16 43				17 30								18 30						18 40		
Bristol Parkway 7	d				16 55				17 40								18 40						18 51		
Gloucester 7	d	17 22	17 38		17 51								18 22	18 39								19 22	19 38	19 42	
Cheltenham Spa	d	17 33	17a51		18 03				18 12				18 33	18a48			19 12					19 34	19 48	19a52	
Ashchurch for Tewkesbury	d				18 11																		19 57		
Worcester Shrub Hill 7	a				18 31																		20 18		
Birmingham New Street 12	a	18 36							19 25				19 39				20 20					20 35			
	d	18 45				18 52		19 03		19 30			19 45		19 52	20 03				20 30		20 45			20 52
Water Orton	d																								
Coleshill Parkway	d						18 50												19 50						
Nuneaton	d						19b45												20b45						
Hinckley	d						20 05												21 05						
Narborough	d						20 30												21 30						
South Wigston	d						20 40												21 40						
Leicester	a						21 00												22 00						
Wilnecote	d	19 00																							
Tamworth	d	19 04				19a10							20 03		20a10	20 19				20 46		21 03			21a10
Burton-on-Trent	d	19 16						19 28					20 15							20 56		21 15			
Willington	d																								
Derby 10	a	19 29						19 42		20 02			20 28			20 42				21 09		21 31			
	d	19 33											20 32								21 18				
Spondon	d																								
Long Eaton	d																				21 28				
Attenborough	d																				21 35				
Beeston	d											20 46									21 38				
Nottingham 8 [ferry]	a	19 57										20 53	20 57								21 45				

		XC 1◇ [trolley]		XC 1◇ B [trolley]	EM 1◇ [buffet]	XC [bus]	XC 1◇	GW 1◇ [buffet]	XC 1		XC [bus]	XC [bus]	XC [bus]	XC 1◇ [trolley]	XC 1◇ A [trolley]	XC 1◇		GW C	GW	GW 1◇ [buffet]	XC 1◇ [trolley]	GW			
Cardiff Central 7	d						19 25									20 25									
Newport (South Wales)	d						19 39									20 39									
Bristol Temple Meads 10	d			19 30											20 30				20 43		22 10				
Bristol Parkway 7	d			19 40											20 40				20 55		22 20				
Gloucester 7	d						20 22	20 35								21 30		21 25	21 41	22 35		23 55			
Cheltenham Spa	d			20 12			20 33	20a46							21 11	21 41		21a34	21a49	22a46	22 52	00a04			
Ashchurch for Tewkesbury	d																								
Worcester Shrub Hill 7	a																								
Birmingham New Street 12	a			21 39			21 42								22 17	22 45					23 55				
	d	21 03					21 46		21 52					22 03		22 49									
Water Orton	d																								
Coleshill Parkway	d										20 50	21 50													
Nuneaton	d										21b45	22b45													
Hinckley	d										22 05	23 05													
Narborough	d										22 30	23 30													
South Wigston	d										22 40	23 40													
Leicester	a										23 00	23 55													
Wilnecote	d						22 01																		
Tamworth	d	21 19					22 06		22a10					22 23		23 07									
Burton-on-Trent	d	21 29					22 18							22 35		23 19									
Willington	d																								
Derby 10	a	21 42					22 33							22 48		23 37									
	d					21 45							22 45												
Spondon	d																								
Long Eaton	d																								
Attenborough	d																								
Beeston	d				21 45																				
Nottingham 8 [ferry]	a				21 51	22 15							23 15												

For general notes see front of timetable
For details of catering facilities see Directory of Train Operators

A From Plymouth (Table 51)
B From Penzance (Table 51)
C From Westbury (Table 123)

b Arrives 5 minutes earlier

Network Diagram for Tables 59, 60, 61, 62, 64, 66

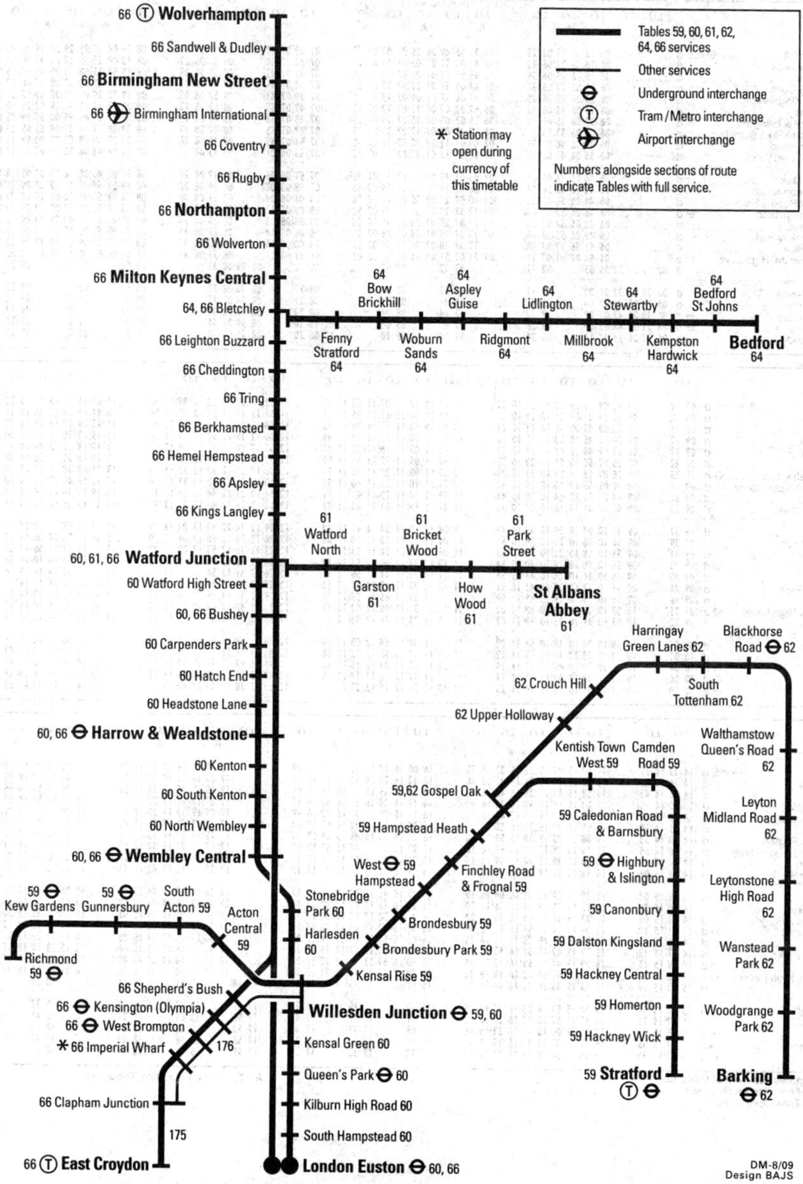

66 Wolverhampton
66 Sandwell & Dudley
66 Birmingham New Street
66 Birmingham International
66 Coventry
66 Rugby
66 Northampton
66 Wolverton
66 Milton Keynes Central
64, 66 Bletchley
66 Leighton Buzzard
66 Cheddington
66 Tring
66 Berkhamsted
66 Hemel Hempstead
66 Apsley
66 Kings Langley
60, 61, 66 Watford Junction
60 Watford High Street
60, 66 Bushey
60 Carpenders Park
60 Hatch End
60 Headstone Lane
60, 66 Harrow & Wealdstone
60 Kenton
60 South Kenton
60 North Wembley
60, 66 Wembley Central
Fenny Stratford 64
64 Bow Brickhill
Woburn Sands 64
64 Aspley Guise
Ridgmont 64
64 Lidlington
Millbrook 64
64 Stewartby
Kempston Hardwick 64
64 Bedford St Johns
Bedford 64
61 Watford North
Garston 61
61 Bricket Wood
How Wood 61
61 Park Street
St Albans Abbey 61
Harringay Green Lanes 62
Blackhorse Road 62
62 Crouch Hill
South Tottenham 62
62 Upper Holloway
Walthamstow Queen's Road 62
Kentish Town West 59
Camden Road 59
59,62 Gospel Oak
Leyton Midland Road 62
59 Caledonian Road & Barnsbury
59 Hampstead Heath
59 Highbury & Islington
West Hampstead 59
Finchley Road & Frognal 59
Leytonstone High Road 62
59 Canonbury
Brondesbury 59
Wanstead Park 62
59 Dalston Kingsland
Brondesbury Park 59
59 Hackney Central
Kensal Rise 59
59 Homerton
Woodgrange Park 62
59 Hackney Wick
59 Stratford
Barking 62
59 Kew Gardens
59 Gunnersbury
South Acton 59
Acton Central 59
Richmond 59
Stonebridge Park 60
Harlesden 60
66 Shepherd's Bush
66 Kensington (Olympia)
66 West Brompton
* 66 Imperial Wharf
176
Willesden Junction 59, 60
Kensal Green 60
Queen's Park 60
Kilburn High Road 60
South Hampstead 60
66 Clapham Junction
175
66 East Croydon
London Euston 60, 66
* Station may open during currency of this timetable
Tables 59, 60, 61, 62, 64, 66 services
Other services
Underground interchange
Tram / Metro interchange
Airport interchange
Numbers alongside sections of route indicate Tables with full service.
DM-8/09
Design BAJS

Stratford Low Level → Highbury and Islington West Hampstead, Willesden Junction and Richmond.

Network diagram - see first page of Table 59

Miles	Station		LO	LO	LO	LO A	LO		LO A	LO	LO A	LO	LO A		LO	LO A	LO	LO	LO A		LO	LO A	LO	LO A	LO	LO A
0	**Stratford 7** ⊖	d			06 13	06 19	06 29		06 39	06 49	06 59	07 09	07 19		07 29	07 37		07 49	07 59		08 09	08 19	08 29	08 39	08 49	08 59
1	Hackney Wick	d			06 16	06 22	06 32		06 42	06 52	07 02	07 12	07 22		07 32	07 40		07 52	08 02		08 12	08 22	08 32	08 42	08 52	09 02
1¾	Homerton	d			06 19	06 25	06 35		06 45	06 55	07 05	07 15	07 25		07 35	07 43		07 55	08 05		08 15	08 25	08 35	08 45	08 55	09 05
2½	Hackney Central	d			06 21	06 27	06 37		06 47	06 57	07 07	07 17	07 27		07 37	07 45		07 57	08 07		08 17	08 27	08 37	08 47	08 57	09 07
3¼	Dalston Kingsland	d			06 23	06 29	06 39		06 49	06 59	07 09	07 19	07 29		07 39	07 47		07 59	08 09		08 19	08 29	08 39	08 49	08 59	09 09
4¼	Canonbury	d			06 26	06 32	06 42		06 52	07 02	07 12	07 22	07 32		07 42	07 50		08 02	08 12		08 22	08 32	08 42	08 52	09 02	09 12
4¾	**Highbury & Islington** ⊖	d			06 29	06 35	06 45		06 55	07 05	07 15	07 25	07 35		07 45	07 53		08 05	08 15		08 25	08 35	08 45	08 55	09 05	09 15
5¼	Caledonian Rd & Barnsbury	d			06 31	06 37	06 47		06 57	07 07	07 17	07 27	07 37		07 47	07 55		08 07	08 17		08 27	08 37	08 47	08 57	09 07	09 17
6¼	Camden Road	d			06 34	06 40	06 51		07 00	07 11	07 20	07 31	07 40		07 51	07 59		08 11	08 20		08 31	08 40	08 50	09 00	09 11	09 20
6½	Kentish Town West	d			06 36	06 42	06 53		07 02	07 13	07 22	07 33	07 42		07 53	08 01		08 13	08 22		08 33	08 42	08 52	09 02	09 13	09 22
7½	**Gospel Oak**	d			06 40	06 46	06 57		07 06	07 17	07 26	07 37	07 46		07 57	08 05		08 17	08 26		08 37	08 46	08 56	09 06	09 18	09 26
8	Hampstead Heath	d			06 42	06 48	06 59		07 08	07 19	07 28	07 39	07 48		07 59	08 07		08 19	08 28		08 39	08 48	08 58	09 08	09 20	09 28
9	Finchley Road & Frognal	d			06 44	06 50	07 01		07 10	07 21	07 30	07 41	07 50		08 01	08 09		08 21	08 30		08 41	08 50	09 00	09 10	09 22	09 30
9½	West Hampstead ⊖	d			06 46	06 52	07 03		07 12	07 23	07 32	07 43	07 52		08 03	08 11		08 23	08 32		08 43	08 52	09 02	09 12	09 24	09 32
10	Brondesbury	d			06 48	06 54	07 05		07 14	07 25	07 34	07 45	07 54		08 05	08 13		08 25	08 34		08 45	08 54	09 04	09 14	09 26	09 34
10¼	Brondesbury Park	d			06 49	06 55	07 06		07 15	07 26	07 35	07 46	07 55		08 06	08 14		08 26	08 35		08 46	08 55	09 05	09 15	09 27	09 35
11	Kensal Rise	d			06 51	06 57	07 08		07 17	07 28	07 37	07 48	07 57		08 08	08 16		08 28	08 37		08 48	08 57	09 07	09 17	09 29	09 37
12	**Willesden Jn. High Level** ⊖	a			06 54	07 01	07 11		07 21	07 31	07 41	07 51	08 01		08 11	08 21		08 31	08 41		08 51	09 01	09 11	09 21	09 33	09 41
—		d	06 19	06 32	06 55		07 12			07 32		07 52			08 12		08 25	08 32			08 52		09 12		09 33	
13½	Acton Central	d	06 24	06 37	07 00		07 17			07 37		07 57			08 17		08 30	08 37			08 57		09 17		09 38	
14½	South Acton	d	06 28	06 41	07 04		07 21			07 41		08 01			08 21		08 34	08 41			09 01		09 21		09 42	
15¼	Gunnersbury ⊖	d	06 30	06 43	07 07		07 24			07 44		08 04			08 24		08 36	08 44			09 04		09 24		09 47	
16¼	Kew Gardens ⊖	d	06 33	06 46	07 09		07 26			07 46		08 06			08 26		08 39	08 46			09 06		09 26		09 50	
17½	**Richmond** ⊖	a	06 38	06 51	07 13		07 30			07 50		08 10			08 30		08 45	08 50			09 10		09 30		09 53	

Station		LO		LO	LO	LO	LO	LO		LO	LO	LO	LO	LO		LO	LO	LO	LO	LO		LO	LO	LO	LO	LO
Stratford 7 ⊖	d	09 09		09 22	09 37	09 52	10 07	10 22		10 37	10 52	11 07	11 22	11 37		11 52	12 07	12 22	12 37	12 52		13 07	13 22	13 37	13 52	14 07
Hackney Wick	d	09 12		09 26	09 41	09 56	10 11	10 26		10 41	10 56	11 11	11 26	11 41		11 56	12 11	12 26	12 41	12 56		13 11	13 25	13 41	13 56	14 11
Homerton	d	09 15		09 28	09 43	09 58	10 13	10 28		10 43	10 58	11 13	11 28	11 43		11 58	12 13	12 28	12 43	12 58		13 13	13 28	13 43	13 58	14 13
Hackney Central	d	09 17		09 30	09 45	10 00	10 15	10 30		10 45	11 00	11 15	11 30	11 45		12 00	12 15	12 30	12 45	13 00		13 15	13 30	13 45	14 00	14 15
Dalston Kingsland	d	09 19		09 33	09 48	10 03	10 18	10 33		10 48	11 03	11 18	11 33	11 48		12 03	12 18	12 33	12 48	13 03		13 18	13 33	13 48	14 03	14 18
Canonbury	d	09 22		09 35	09 50	10 05	10 20	10 35		10 50	11 05	11 20	11 35	11 50		12 05	12 20	12 35	12 50	13 05		13 20	13 35	13 50	14 05	14 20
Highbury & Islington ⊖	d	09 25		09 38	09 53	10 08	10 23	10 38		10 53	11 08	11 23	11 38	11 53		12 08	12 23	12 38	12 53	13 08		13 23	13 38	13 53	14 08	14 23
Caledonian Rd & Barnsbury	d	09 27		09 40	09 55	10 10	10 25	10 40		10 55	11 10	11 25	11 40	11 55		12 10	12 25	12 40	12 55	13 10		13 25	13 40	13 55	14 10	14 25
Camden Road	d	09 31		09 44	09 59	10 14	10 29	10 44		10 59	11 14	11 29	11 44	11 59		12 14	12 29	12 44	12 59	13 14		13 29	13 44	13 59	14 14	14 29
Kentish Town West	d	09 33		09 46	10 01	10 16	10 31	10 46		11 01	11 16	11 31	11 46	12 01		12 16	12 31	12 46	13 01	13 16		13 31	13 46	14 01	14 16	14 31
Gospel Oak	d	09 37		09 49	10 04	10 19	10 34	10 49		11 04	11 19	11 34	11 49	12 04		12 19	12 34	12 49	13 04	13 19		13 34	13 49	14 04	14 19	14 34
Hampstead Heath	d	09 39		09 50	10 06	10 20	10 36	10 50		11 06	11 20	11 36	11 50	12 06		12 20	12 36	12 50	13 06	13 20		13 36	13 50	14 06	14 20	14 36
Finchley Road & Frognal	d	09 41		09 53	10 08	10 23	10 38	10 53		11 08	11 23	11 38	11 53	12 08		12 23	12 38	12 53	13 08	13 23		13 38	13 53	14 08	14 23	14 38
West Hampstead ⊖	d	09 43		09 54	10 10	10 24	10 40	10 54		11 10	11 24	11 40	11 54	12 10		12 24	12 40	12 54	13 10	13 24		13 40	13 54	14 10	14 24	14 40
Brondesbury	d	09 45		09 56	10 11	10 26	10 41	10 56		11 11	11 26	11 41	11 56	12 11		12 26	12 41	12 56	13 11	13 26		13 41	13 56	14 11	14 26	14 41
Brondesbury Park	d	09 46		09 57	10 13	10 27	10 43	10 57		11 13	11 27	11 43	11 57	12 13		12 27	12 43	12 57	13 13	13 27		13 43	13 57	14 13	14 27	14 43
Kensal Rise	d	09 48		09 59	10 15	10 29	10 45	10 59		11 15	11 29	11 45	11 59	12 15		12 29	12 45	12 59	13 15	13 29		13 45	13 59	14 15	14 29	14 45
Willesden Jn. High Level ⊖	a	09 51		10 02	10 19	10 32	10 48	11 02		11 18	11 32	11 48	12 02	12 18		12 33	12 48	13 02	13 18	13 32		13 48	14 02	14 18	14 32	14 49
	d	09 52		10 03	10 19	10 33	10 49	11 03		11 19	11 33	11 49	12 03	12 19		12 33	12 49	13 03	13 19	13 33		13 49	14 03	14 19	14 33	14 49
Acton Central	d	09 57		10 08	10 24	10 38	10 54	11 08		11 24	11 38	11 54	12 08	12 24		12 38	12 54	13 08	13 24	13 38		13 54	14 08	14 24	14 38	14 54
South Acton	d	10 01		10 12	10 28	10 42	10 58	11 12		11 28	11 42	11 58	12 12	12 28		12 42	12 58	13 12	13 28	13 42		13 58	14 12	14 28	14 42	14 58
Gunnersbury ⊖	d	10 04		10 15	10 30	10 45	11 02	11 15		11 32	11 45	12 02	12 15	12 32		12 45	13 02	13 15	13 32	13 45		14 02	14 15	14 32	14 45	15 00
Kew Gardens ⊖	d	10 06		10 17	10 33	10 47	11 05	11 17		11 35	11 47	12 05	12 17	12 35		12 47	13 05	13 17	13 35	13 47		14 05	14 17	14 35	14 47	15 03
Richmond ⊖	a	10 10		10 23	10 41	10 53	11 10	11 23		11 40	11 53	12 10	12 23	12 40		12 54	13 10	13 23	13 40	13 53		14 10	14 23	14 40	14 53	15 10

Station		LO	LO		LO	LO	LO	LO	LO		LO	LO A	LO	LO A	LO		LO	LO A	LO	LO A	LO		LO A	LO	LO A	LO
Stratford 7 ⊖	d	14 22	14 37		14 52	15 07	15 22	15 37	15 52		16 09	16 19	16 29	16 39	16 49			16 59	17 09	17 19	17 29		17 39	17 49	17 59	18 09
Hackney Wick	d	14 26	14 41		14 56	15 11	15 26	15 41	15 56		16 12	16 22	16 32	16 42	16 52			17 02	17 12	17 22	17 32		17 42	17 52	18 02	18 12
Homerton	d	14 28	14 43		14 58	15 13	15 28	15 43	15 58		16 15	16 25	16 35	16 45	16 55			17 05	17 15	17 25	17 35		17 45	17 55	18 05	18 15
Hackney Central	d	14 30	14 45		15 00	15 15	15 30	15 45	16 00		16 17	16 27	16 37	16 47	16 57			17 07	17 17	17 27	17 37		17 47	17 57	18 07	18 17
Dalston Kingsland	d	14 33	14 48		15 03	15 18	15 33	15 48	16 03		16 19	16 29	16 39	16 49	16 59			17 09	17 19	17 29	17 39		17 49	17 59	18 09	18 19
Canonbury	d	14 35	14 50		15 05	15 20	15 35	15 50	16 05		16 22	16 32	16 42	16 52	17 02			17 12	17 22	17 32	17 42		17 52	18 02	18 12	18 22
Highbury & Islington ⊖	d	14 38	14 53		15 08	15 23	15 38	15 53	16 08		16 25	16 35	16 45	16 55	17 05			17 15	17 25	17 35	17 45		17 55	18 05	18 15	18 25
Caledonian Rd & Barnsbury	d	14 40	14 55		15 10	15 25	15 40	15 55	16 10		16 27	16 37	16 47	16 57	17 07			17 17	17 27	17 37	17 47		17 57	18 07	18 17	18 27
Camden Road	d	14 44	14 59		15 14	15 29	15 44	15 59	16 14		16 31	16 41	16 51	17 01	17 11			17 20	17 31	17 41	17 51		18 00	18 11	18 20	18 31
Kentish Town West	d	14 46	15 01		15 16	15 31	15 46	16 01	16 16		16 33	16 42	16 53	17 02	17 13			17 22	17 33	17 42	17 53		18 02	18 13	18 22	18 33
Gospel Oak	d	14 49	15 04		15 19	15 34	15 49	16 04	16 19		16 37	16 46	16 58	17 06	17 17			17 26	17 37	17 46	17 57		18 06	18 17	18 26	18 37
Hampstead Heath	d	14 50	15 06		15 20	15 35	15 51	16 06	16 20		16 39	16 48	17 00	17 08	17 19			17 28	17 39	17 48	17 59		18 08	18 19	18 28	18 39
Finchley Road & Frognal	d	14 53	15 08		15 23	15 38	15 53	16 08	16 22		16 41	16 50	17 02	17 10	17 21			17 30	17 41	17 50	18 01		18 10	18 21	18 30	18 41
West Hampstead ⊖	d	14 54	15 10		15 24	15 39	15 54	16 10	16 24		16 43	16 52	17 04	17 12	17 23			17 32	17 43	17 52	18 03		18 12	18 23	18 32	18 43
Brondesbury	d	14 56	15 11		15 26	15 41	15 56	16 11	16 25		16 45	16 54	17 06	17 14	17 25			17 34	17 45	17 54	18 05		18 14	18 25	18 34	18 45
Brondesbury Park	d	14 57	15 13		15 27	15 42	15 57	16 13	16 27		16 46	16 55	17 07	17 15	17 26			17 35	17 46	17 55	18 06		18 15	18 26	18 35	18 46
Kensal Rise	d	14 59	15 15		15 29	15 44	15 59	16 15	16 29		16 48	16 57	17 09	17 17	17 28			17 37	17 48	17 57	18 08		18 17	18 28	18 37	18 48
Willesden Jn. High Level ⊖	a	15 02	15 18		15 32	15 47	16 02	16 19	16 32		16 50	17 01	17 13	17 21	17 30			17 41	17 50	18 01	18 10		18 21	18 30	18 41	18 50
	d	15 03	15 19		15 33	15 48	16 03	16 19	16 33		16 51		17 13		17 31		17 38		17 51		18 11			18 31		18 51
Acton Central	d	15 08	15 24		15 38	15 53	16 08	16 24	16 38		16 57		17 18		17 37		17 43		17 57		18 17			18 37		18 57
South Acton	d	15 12	15 28		15 42	15 57	16 12	16 28	16 42		17 01		17 22		17 41		17 50		18 01		18 21			18 41		19 01
Gunnersbury ⊖	d	15 15	15 32		15 45	16 00	16 15	16 32	16 45		17 06		17 27		17 45		17 53		18 05		18 26			18 44		19 04
Kew Gardens ⊖	d	15 17	15 35		15 47	16 02	16 17	16 35	16 47		17 09		17 30		17 47		17 56		18 08		18 29			18 47		19 07
Richmond ⊖	a	15 23	15 39		15 53	16 08	16 24	16 40	16 53		17 12		17 33		17 51		17 59		18 11		18 32			18 50		19 10

For general notes see front of timetable
For details of catering facilities see
Directory of Train Operators

A To Clapham Junction (Table 176)

Stratford Low Level → Highbury and Islington West Hampstead, Willesden Junction and Richmond.

Network diagram - see first page of Table 59

Mondays to Fridays

	LO A	LO	LO A	LO	LO	LO	LO	LO	LO	LO	LO	LO	LO	LO	LO	LO	LO	LO	LO
Stratford 7 ⊖ d	18 19	18 29	18 39	18 49	19 06	19 23	19 33	19 52	20 12	20 32	20 52	21 12	21 32	21 52	22 12	22 32	22 52	23 12	23 32
Hackney Wick d	18 22	18 32	18 42	18 52	19 10	19 27	19 37	19 56	20 16	20 36	20 56	21 16	21 36	21 56	22 16	22 36	22 56	23 16	23 36
Homerton d	18 25	18 35	18 45	18 55	19 12	19 30	19 39	19 58	20 18	20 38	20 58	21 18	21 38	21 58	22 18	22 38	22 58	23 18	23 38
Hackney Central d	18 27	18 37	18 47	18 57	19 14	19 32	19 41	20 00	20 20	20 40	21 00	21 20	21 40	22 00	22 20	22 40	23 00	23 20	23 40
Dalston Kingsland d	18 29	18 39	18 49	18 59	19 17	19 34	19 44	20 03	20 23	20 43	21 03	21 23	21 43	22 03	22 23	22 43	23 03	23 23	23 43
Canonbury d	18 32	18 42	18 52	19 02	19 19	19 37	19 46	20 05	20 25	20 45	21 05	21 25	21 45	22 05	22 25	22 45	23 05	23 25	23 45
Highbury & Islington ⊖ d	18 35	18 45	18 55	19 05	19 22	19 40	19 49	20 08	20 28	20 48	21 08	21 28	21 48	22 08	22 28	22 48	23 08	23 28	23 48
Caledonian Rd & Barnsbury d	18 37	18 47	18 57	19 07	19 24	19 42	19 51	20 10	20 30	20 50	21 10	21 30	21 50	22 10	22 30	22 50	23 10	23 30	23 50
Camden Road d	18 41	18 51	19 01	19 11	19 27	19 45	19 54	20 13	20 33	20 53	21 13	21 33	21 53	22 13	22 33	22 53	23 13	23 33	23a55
Kentish Town West d	18 42	18 53	19 02	19 13	19 29	19 47	19 56	20 15	20 35	20 55	21 15	21 35	21 55	22 15	22 35	22 55	23 15	23 35	.
Gospel Oak d	18 46	18 57	19 06	19 17	19 32	19 51	19 59	20 18	20 38	20 58	21 18	21 38	21 58	22 18	22 38	22 58	23 18	23 38	.
Hampstead Heath d	18 48	18 59	19 08	19 19	19 33	19 53	20 00	20 19	20 39	20 59	21 19	21 39	21 59	22 19	22 39	22 59	23 19	23 39	.
Finchley Road & Frognal d	18 50	19 01	19 10	19 21	19 36	19 55	20 03	20 22	20 42	21 02	21 22	21 42	22 02	22 22	22 42	23 02	23 22	23 42	.
West Hampstead ⊖ d	18 52	19 03	19 12	19 23	19 37	19 57	20 04	20 23	20 43	21 03	21 23	21 43	22 03	22 23	22 43	23 03	23 23	23 43	.
Brondesbury d	18 54	19 05	19 14	19 25	19 39	19 58	20 06	20 25	20 45	21 05	21 25	21 45	22 05	22 25	22 45	23 05	23 25	23 45	.
Brondesbury Park d	18 55	19 06	19 15	19 26	19 40	20 00	20 07	20 26	20 46	21 06	21 26	21 46	22 06	22 26	22 46	23 06	23 26	23 46	.
Kensal Rise d	18 57	19 08	19 17	19 28	19 42	20 02	20 09	20 28	20 48	21 08	21 28	21 48	22 08	22 28	22 48	23 08	23 28	23 48	.
Willesden Jn. High Level ⊖ a	19 01	19 10	19 21	19 30	19 44	20 05	20 13	20 32	20 52	21 12	21 32	21 52	22 12	22 32	22 52	23 12	23 32	23b51	.
d	.	19 11	.	19 31	19 44	20 06	20 13	20 32	20 52	21 12	21 32	21 52	22 12	22 32	22 52	23 12	23 32	.	.
Acton Central d	.	19 17	.	19 37	19 49	20 14	20 18	20 37	20 57	21 17	21 37	21 57	22 17	22 37	22 57	23 17	23 37	.	.
South Acton d	.	19 21	.	19 41	19 53	20 16	20 22	20 41	21 01	21 21	21 41	22 01	22 21	22 41	23 01	23 21	23 41	.	.
Gunnersbury ⊖ d	.	19 26	.	19 44	19 57	20 18	20 25	20 44	21 04	21 24	21 44	22 04	22 24	22 44	23 04	23 24	23 44	.	.
Kew Gardens ⊖ d	.	19 29	.	19 46	19 58	20 21	20 27	20 46	21 06	21 26	21 46	22 06	22 26	22 46	23 06	23 26	23 46	.	.
Richmond ⊖ a	.	19 32	.	19 50	20 09	20 26	20 37	20 55	21 13	21 36	21 53	22 14	22 32	22 53	23 12	23 33	23 53	.	.

Saturdays

	LO	LO	LO	LO	LO	LO	LO	LO	LO	LO	LO	LO	LO	LO		LO	LO	LO	LO	LO
Stratford 7 ⊖ d	.	.	06 07	06 22	06 37	06 52	07 07	07 22	07 37	07 52	08 07	08 22	08 37	08 52		17 07	17 22	17 37	17 52	18 12
Hackney Wick d	.	.	06 11	06 26	06 41	06 56	07 11	07 26	07 41	07 56	08 11	08 26	08 41	08 56		17 11	17 26	17 41	17 56	18 16
Homerton d	.	.	06 13	06 28	06 43	06 58	07 13	07 28	07 43	07 58	08 13	08 28	08 43	08 58		17 13	17 28	17 43	17 58	18 18
Hackney Central d	.	.	06 15	06 30	06 45	07 00	07 15	07 30	07 45	08 00	08 15	08 30	08 45	09 00		17 15	17 30	17 45	18 00	18 20
Dalston Kingsland d	.	.	06 18	06 33	06 48	07 03	07 18	07 33	07 48	08 03	08 18	08 33	08 48	09 03		17 18	17 33	17 48	18 03	18 23
Canonbury d	.	.	06 20	06 35	06 50	07 05	07 20	07 35	07 50	08 05	08 20	08 35	08 50	09 05		17 20	17 35	17 50	18 05	18 25
Highbury & Islington ⊖ d	.	.	06 23	06 38	06 53	07 08	07 23	07 38	07 53	08 08	08 23	08 38	08 53	09 08	and at	17 23	17 38	17 53	18 08	18 28
Caledonian Rd & Barnsbury d	.	.	06 25	06 40	06 55	07 10	07 25	07 40	07 55	08 10	08 25	08 40	08 55	09 10		17 25	17 40	17 55	18 10	18 30
Camden Road d	.	.	06 29	06 44	06 59	07 14	07 29	07 44	07 59	08 14	08 29	08 44	08 59	09 14	the same	17 29	17 44	17 59	18 14	18 34
Kentish Town West d	.	.	06 31	06 46	07 01	07 16	07 31	07 46	08 01	08 16	08 31	08 46	09 01	09 16		17 31	17 46	18 01	18 16	18 36
Gospel Oak d	.	.	06 34	06 49	07 04	07 19	07 34	07 49	08 04	08 19	08 34	08 49	09 04	09 19	minutes	17 34	17 49	18 04	18 19	18 39
Hampstead Heath d	.	.	06 36	06 50	07 06	07 21	07 36	07 50	08 06	08 21	08 36	08 50	09 06	09 21		17 36	17 50	18 06	18 21	18 41
Finchley Road & Frognal d	.	.	06 38	06 53	07 08	07 23	07 38	07 53	08 08	08 23	08 38	08 53	09 08	09 23	past	17 38	17 53	18 08	18 23	18 43
West Hampstead ⊖ d	.	.	06 40	06 54	07 10	07 25	07 40	07 54	08 10	08 25	08 40	08 54	09 10	09 25		17 40	17 54	18 10	18 25	18 45
Brondesbury d	.	.	06 41	06 56	07 11	07 26	07 41	07 56	08 11	08 26	08 41	08 56	09 11	09 26	each	17 41	17 56	18 11	18 26	18 46
Brondesbury Park d	.	.	06 43	06 57	07 13	07 28	07 43	07 57	08 13	08 28	08 43	08 57	09 13	09 28		17 43	17 57	18 13	18 28	18 48
Kensal Rise d	.	.	06 45	06 59	07 15	07 30	07 45	07 59	08 15	08 30	08 45	08 59	09 15	09 30	hour until	17 45	17 59	18 15	18 30	18 50
Willesden Jn. High Level ⊖ a	.	.	06 48	07 02	07 18	07 33	07 48	08 03	08 18	08 33	08 49	09 02	09 18	09 33		17 48	18 02	18 18	18 33	18 53
d	06 17	06 33	06 49	07 03	07 19	07 34	07 49	08 03	08 19	08 34	08 49	09 03	09 19	09 34		17 49	18 03	18 19	18 34	18 54
Acton Central d	06 22	06 38	06 54	07 08	07 24	07 39	07 54	08 08	08 24	08 39	08 54	09 08	09 24	09 39		17 54	18 08	18 24	18 39	18 59
South Acton d	06 26	06 42	06 58	07 12	07 28	07 43	07 58	08 12	08 28	08 43	08 58	09 12	09 28	09 43		17 58	18 12	18 28	18 43	19 03
Gunnersbury ⊖ d	06 29	06 45	07 02	07 15	07 32	07 45	08 02	08 15	08 32	08 45	09 02	09 15	09 32	09 45		18 02	18 15	18 32	18 45	19 05
Kew Gardens ⊖ d	06 31	06 47	07 05	07 17	07 35	07 48	08 05	08 17	08 35	08 48	09 05	09 17	09 35	09 48		18 05	18 17	18 35	18 48	19 08
Richmond ⊖ a	06 37	06 53	07 10	07 23	07 40	07 53	08 10	08 24	08 40	08 53	09 10	09 23	09 40	09 53		18 10	18 23	18 41	18 53	19 13

	LO	LO	LO	LO	LO	LO	LO	LO	LO	LO	LO	LO	LO	LO	LO	LO	LO	LO
Stratford 7 ⊖ d	18 22	18 35	18 52	19 07	19 22	19 37	19 52	20 12	20 32	20 52	21 12	21 32	21 52	22 12	22 32	22 52	23 12	23 32
Hackney Wick d	18 26	18 38	18 56	19 11	19 26	19 41	19 56	20 16	20 36	20 56	21 16	21 36	21 56	22 16	22 36	22 56	23 16	23 36
Homerton d	18 28	18 41	18 58	19 13	19 28	19 43	19 58	20 18	20 38	20 58	21 18	21 38	21 58	22 18	22 38	22 58	23 18	23 38
Hackney Central d	18 30	18 43	19 00	19 15	19 30	19 45	20 00	20 20	20 40	21 00	21 20	21 40	22 00	22 20	22 40	23 00	23 20	23 40
Dalston Kingsland d	18 33	18 45	19 03	19 18	19 33	19 48	20 03	20 23	20 43	21 03	21 23	21 43	22 03	22 23	22 43	23 03	23 23	23 43
Canonbury d	18 35	18 48	19 05	19 20	19 35	19 50	20 05	20 25	20 45	21 05	21 25	21 45	22 05	22 25	22 45	23 05	23 25	23 45
Highbury & Islington ⊖ d	18 38	18 51	19 08	19 23	19 38	19 53	20 08	20 28	20 48	21 08	21 28	21 48	22 08	22 28	22 48	23 08	23 28	23 48
Caledonian Rd & Barnsbury d	18 40	18 53	19 10	19 25	19 40	19 55	20 10	20 30	20 50	21 10	21 30	21 50	22 10	22 30	22 50	23 10	23 30	23 50
Camden Road d	18 44	18 56	19 14	19 29	19 44	19 59	20 14	20 34	20 54	21 14	21 34	21 54	22 14	22 34	22 54	23 14	23 34	23a55
Kentish Town West d	18 46	18 58	19 16	19 31	19 46	20 01	20 16	20 36	20 56	21 16	21 36	21 56	22 16	22 36	22 56	23 16	23 36	.
Gospel Oak d	18 49	19 01	19 19	19 34	19 49	20 04	20 18	20 39	20 59	21 19	21 39	21 59	22 19	22 39	22 59	23 19	23 39	.
Hampstead Heath d	18 51	19 03	19 21	19 36	19 51	20 06	20 21	20 40	21 00	21 20	21 40	22 00	22 20	22 40	23 00	23 20	23 40	.
Finchley Road & Frognal d	18 53	19 06	19 23	19 38	19 53	20 08	20 23	20 43	21 03	21 23	21 43	22 03	22 23	22 43	23 03	23 23	23 43	.
West Hampstead ⊖ d	18 55	19 07	19 25	19 40	19 55	20 10	20 24	20 44	21 04	21 24	21 44	22 04	22 24	22 44	23 04	23 24	23 44	.
Brondesbury d	18 56	19 09	19 26	19 41	19 56	20 11	20 25	20 46	21 06	21 26	21 46	22 06	22 26	22 46	23 06	23 26	23 46	.
Brondesbury Park d	18 58	19 10	19 28	19 43	19 58	20 13	20 27	20 47	21 07	21 27	21 47	22 07	22 27	22 47	23 07	23 27	23 47	.
Kensal Rise d	19 00	19 12	19 30	19 45	20 00	20 15	20 29	20 49	21 09	21 29	21 49	22 09	22 29	22 49	23 09	23 29	23 49	.
Willesden Jn. High Level ⊖ a	19 05	19 15	19 33	19 48	20 03	20 18	20 32	20 52	21 13	21 33	21 52	22 12	22 33	22 52	23 13	23 33	23b52	.
d	.	19 16	19 34	19 49	20 05	20 19	20 33	20 53	21 13	21 33	21 53	22 13	22 33	22 53	23 13	23 33	.	.
Acton Central d	.	19 21	19 39	19 54	20 13	20 24	20 38	20 58	21 18	21 38	21 58	22 18	22 38	22 58	23 18	23 38	.	.
South Acton d	.	19 25	19 43	19 58	20 17	20 28	20 42	21 02	21 22	21 42	22 02	22 22	22 42	23 02	23 22	23 42	.	.
Gunnersbury ⊖ d	.	19 28	19 45	20 02	20 22	20 31	20 44	21 04	21 24	21 44	22 04	22 24	22 44	23 04	23 24	23 44	.	.
Kew Gardens ⊖ d	.	19 31	19 48	20 05	20 25	20 33	20 47	21 07	21 27	21 47	22 07	22 27	22 47	23 07	23 27	23 47	.	.
Richmond ⊖ a	.	19 36	19 53	20 10	20 30	20 40	20 53	21 13	21 36	21 53	22 12	22 32	22 53	23 13	23 33	23 53	.	.

For general notes see front of timetable
For details of catering facilities see Directory of Train Operators

A To Clapham Junction (Table 176)
b Willesden Jn Low Level

Sundays

Stratford Low Level → Highbury and Islington West Hampstead, Willesden Junction and Richmond.

Network diagram - see first page of Table 59

		LO			LO	LO			LO		LO		LO
Stratford 7 ⊖ ⛴	d				08 49	09 19			21 49		22 19		22 49
Hackney Wick	d				08 53	09 23			21 53		22 23		22 53
Homerton	d				08 55	09 25			21 55		22 25		22 55
Hackney Central	d				08 57	09 27			21 57		22 27		22 57
Dalston Kingsland	d				09 00	09 30			22 00		22 30		23 00
Canonbury	d				09 02	09 32			22 02		22 32		23 02
Highbury & Islington ⊖	d				09 05	09 35			22 05		22 35		23 05
Caledonian Rd & Barnsbury	d				09 07	09 37			22 07		22 37		23 07
Camden Road	d				09 11	09 41	and		22 11		22 41		23 11
Kentish Town West	d				09 13	09 43	every 30		22 13		22 43		23 13
Gospel Oak	d				09 16	09 46			22 16		22 46		23 16
Hampstead Heath	d				09 18	09 48	minutes		22 18		22 48		23 18
Finchley Road & Frognal	d				09 20	09 50			22 20		22 50		23 20
West Hampstead ⊖	d				09 22	09 52	until		22 22		22 52		23 22
Brondesbury	d				09 23	09 53			22 23		22 53		23 23
Brondesbury Park	d				09 25	09 55			22 25		22 55		23 25
Kensal Rise	d				09 27	09 57			22 27		22 57		23 27
Willesden Jn. High Level ⊖	a				09 30	10 00			22 30		23 00		23b30
	d	09 01			09 31	10 01			22 31		23 01		
Acton Central	d	09 06			09 36	10 06			22 36		23 06		
South Acton	d	09 10			09 40	10 10			22 40		23 10		
Gunnersbury ⊖	d	09 12			09 42	10 12			22 42		23 12		
Kew Gardens ⊖	d	09 15			09 45	10 15			22 45		23 15		
Richmond ⊖	a	09 20			09 50	10 20			22 50		23 20		

For general notes see front of timetable
For details of catering facilities see
Directory of Train Operators

b Willesden Jn Low Level

Richmond → Willesden Junction, West Hampstead Highbury and Islington and Stratford Low Level

Network diagram - see first page of Table 59

Miles		LO	LO	LO	LO 1 A	LO	LO 1 A	LO	LO 1 A	LO	LO 1 A	LO	LO 1 A	LO	LO	LO 1 A	LO	LO 1 A	LO	LO 1 A	LO	LO 1 A
0	**Richmond** ⊖ d			06 04		06 21		06 41		07 05		07 25		07 42	07 49		08 04		08 25		08 42	
1½	Kew Gardens ⊖ d			06 07		06 24		06 44		07 07		07 28		07 45	07 52		08 07		08 28		08 45	
2½	Gunnersbury ⊖ d			06 10		06 27		06 47		07 10		07 31		07 48	07 55		08 10		08 31		08 48	
3¼	South Acton d			06 12		06 29		06 49		07 12		07 33		07 50	07 57		08 12		08 33		08 50	
4	Acton Central d			06 15		06 35		06 54		07 15		07 36		07 53	08 00		08 15		08 36		08 53	
5¾	**Willesden Jn. High Level** ⊖ a			06 20		06 40		06 58		07 20		07 40		07 58	08 05		08 20		08 40		08 58	
—	d	05b58	06b11	06 23	06 31	06 43	06 51	07 01	07 11	07 23	07 31	07 43	07 51	08 00		08 11	08 23	08 31	08 43	08 51	09 00	09 11
6¾	Kensal Rise d	06 03	06 17	06 25	06 35	06 46	06 55	07 04	07 14	07 25	07 34	07 46	07 54	08 04		08 14	08 25	08 34	08 46	08 54	09 04	09 14
7½	Brondesbury Park d	06 05	06 19	06 27	06 37	06 48	06 57	07 06	07 16	07 27	07 36	07 48	07 56	08 06		08 16	08 27	08 36	08 48	08 56	09 06	09 16
7¾	Brondesbury d	06 07	06 21	06 29	06 39	06 50	06 59	07 08	07 18	07 29	07 38	07 50	07 58	08 08		08 18	08 29	08 38	08 50	08 58	09 08	09 18
8¼	West Hampstead ⊖ d	06 09	06 22	06 31	06 41	06 52	07 00	07 10	07 20	07 31	07 40	07 52	08 00	08 10		08 20	08 31	08 40	08 52	09 00	09 10	09 20
8¾	Finchley Road & Frognal d	06 10	06 24	06 32	06 42	06 53	07 02	07 11	07 21	07 32	07 41	07 53	08 01	08 11		08 21	08 32	08 41	08 53	09 01	09 11	09 21
9¾	Hampstead Heath d	06 13	06 27	06 35	06 45	06 56	07 05	07 14	07 24	07 35	07 44	07 56	08 04	08 14		08 24	08 35	08 44	08 56	09 04	09 14	09 24
10¼	**Gospel Oak** d	06 15	06 29	06 37	06 48	06 59	07 07	07 17	07 27	07 37	07 47	07 59	08 07	08 17		08 27	08 37	08 47	08 59	09 07	09 17	09 27
11	Kentish Town West d	06 17	06 31	06 39	06 50	07 01	07 09	07 19	07 29	07 39	07 49	08 01	08 09	08 19		08 29	08 39	08 49	09 01	09 09	09 19	09 29
11¼	Camden Road d	06 20	06 33	06 42	06 52	07 03	07 11	07 21	07 31	07 42	07 51	08 03	08 11	08 21		08 31	08 42	08 51	09 03	09 11	09 21	09 31
12½	Caledonian Rd & Barnsbury d	06 23	06 36	06 45	06 55	07 06	07 14	07 24	07 34	07 45	07 54	08 06	08 14	08 24		08 34	08 45	08 54	09 06	09 14	09 24	09 34
13	**Highbury & Islington** ⊖ d	06 25	06 39	06 47	06 58	07 09	07 17	07 27	07 37	07 47	07 57	08 09	08 17	08 27		08 37	08 47	08 57	09 09	09 17	09 27	09 37
13½	Canonbury ⊖ d	06 27	06 41	06 49	07 00	07 11	07 19	07 29	07 39	07 49	07 59	08 11	08 19	08 29		08 39	08 49	08 59	09 11	09 19	09 29	09 39
14½	Dalston Kingsland d	06 30	06 44	06 52	07 03	07 14	07 22	07 32	07 42	07 52	08 02	08 14	08 22	08 32		08 42	08 52	09 02	09 14	09 22	09 32	09 42
15¼	Hackney Central d	06 32	06 46	06 54	07 05	07 16	07 24	07 34	07 44	07 54	08 04	08 16	08 24	08 34		08 44	08 54	09 04	09 16	09 24	09 34	09 44
16	Homerton d	06 34	06 48	06 56	07 07	07 18	07 26	07 36	07 46	07 56	08 06	08 18	08 26	08 36		08 46	08 56	09 06	09 18	09 26	09 36	09 46
16¾	Hackney Wick d	06 37	06 51	06 59	07 09	07 20	07 28	07 38	07 48	07 59	08 08	08 20	08 28	08 38		08 48	08 59	09 08	09 20	09 28	09 38	09 48
17¾	**Stratford** 7 ⊖ a	06 44	06 58	07 05	07 15	07 26	07 34	07 44	07 54	08 05	08 14	08 26	08 34	08 44		08 54	09 06	09 14	09 26	09 35	09 44	09 57

	LO	LO 1 A	LO	LO	LO	LO	LO	LO	LO	LO	LO	LO	LO	LO	LO	LO	LO	LO	LO	LO	LO
Richmond ⊖ d	09 04		09 22	09 41	09 57	10 11	10 27	10 41	10 57	11 11	11 27	11 41	11 57	12 11	12 27	12 41	12 57	13 11	13 27	13 41	13 57
Kew Gardens ⊖ d	09 07		09 25	09 44	10 00	10 14	10 30	10 44	11 00	11 14	11 30	11 44	12 00	12 14	12 30	12 44	13 00	13 14	13 30	13 44	14 00
Gunnersbury ⊖ d	09 10		09 28	09 47	10 03	10 17	10 33	10 47	11 03	11 17	11 33	11 47	12 03	12 17	12 33	12 47	13 03	13 17	13 33	13 47	14 03
South Acton d	09 12		09 30	09 49	10 05	10 19	10 35	10 49	11 05	11 19	11 35	11 49	12 05	12 19	12 35	12 49	13 05	13 19	13 35	13 49	14 05
Acton Central d	09 15		09 36	09 53	10 08	10 23	10 38	10 53	11 08	11 23	11 38	11 53	12 08	12 23	12 38	12 53	13 08	13 23	13 38	13 53	14 08
Willesden Jn. High Level ⊖ a	09 20		09 41	10 00	10 14	10 29	10 43	11 00	11 13	11 29	11 43	11 59	12 13	12 30	12 43	12 58	13 13	13 29	13 43	13 59	14 13
d	09 23	09 31	09 44	10 00	10 14	10 30	10 44	11 00	11 14	11 30	11 44	12 00	12 14	12 30	12 44	13 00	13 14	13 30	13 44	14 00	14 14
Kensal Rise d	09 25	09 34	09 47	10 03	10 17	10 33	10 47	11 03	11 17	11 33	11 47	12 03	12 17	12 33	12 47	13 03	13 17	13 33	13 47	14 03	14 17
Brondesbury Park d	09 27	09 36	09 49	10 05	10 19	10 35	10 49	11 05	11 19	11 35	11 49	12 05	12 19	12 35	12 49	13 05	13 19	13 35	13 49	14 05	14 19
Brondesbury d	09 29	09 38	09 51	10 07	10 21	10 37	10 51	11 07	11 21	11 37	11 51	12 07	12 21	12 37	12 51	13 07	13 21	13 37	13 51	14 07	14 21
West Hampstead ⊖ d	09 31	09 40	09 53	10 08	10 22	10 38	10 52	11 08	11 22	11 38	11 52	12 08	12 22	12 38	12 52	13 08	13 22	13 38	13 52	14 08	14 22
Finchley Road & Frognal d	09 32	09 41	09 54	10 10	10 24	10 40	10 54	11 10	11 24	11 40	11 54	12 10	12 24	12 40	12 54	13 10	13 24	13 40	13 54	14 10	14 24
Hampstead Heath d	09 35	09 44	09 57	10 13	10 27	10 43	10 57	11 13	11 27	11 43	11 57	12 13	12 27	12 43	12 57	13 13	13 27	13 43	13 57	14 13	14 27
Gospel Oak d	09 37	09 47	10 00	10 15	10 29	10 45	10 59	11 15	11 29	11 45	11 59	12 15	12 29	12 45	12 59	13 15	13 29	13 45	13 59	14 15	14 29
Kentish Town West d	09 39	09 49	10 02	10 17	10 31	10 47	11 01	11 17	11 31	11 47	12 01	12 17	12 31	12 47	13 01	13 17	13 31	13 47	14 01	14 17	14 31
Camden Road d	09 42	09 51	10 04	10 19	10 33	10 49	11 03	11 19	11 33	11 49	12 03	12 19	12 33	12 49	13 03	13 19	13 33	13 49	14 03	14 19	14 33
Caledonian Rd & Barnsbury d	09 45	09 54	10 07	10 22	10 36	10 52	11 06	11 22	11 36	11 52	12 06	12 22	12 36	12 52	13 06	13 22	13 36	13 52	14 06	14 22	14 36
Highbury & Islington ⊖ d	09 47	09 57	10 08	10 25	10 39	10 55	11 09	11 25	11 39	11 55	12 09	12 25	12 39	12 55	13 09	13 25	13 39	13 55	14 09	14 25	14 39
Canonbury ⊖ d	09 49	09 59	10 10	10 27	10 41	10 57	11 11	11 27	11 41	11 57	12 11	12 27	12 41	12 57	13 11	13 27	13 41	13 57	14 11	14 27	14 41
Dalston Kingsland d	09 52	10 02	10 13	10 30	10 44	11 00	11 14	11 30	11 44	12 00	12 14	12 30	12 44	13 00	13 14	13 30	13 44	14 00	14 14	14 30	14 44
Hackney Central d	09 54	10 04	10 15	10 32	10 46	11 02	11 16	11 32	11 46	12 02	12 16	12 32	12 46	13 02	13 16	13 32	13 46	14 02	14 16	14 32	14 46
Homerton d	09 56	10 06	10 17	10 34	10 48	11 04	11 18	11 34	11 48	12 04	12 18	12 34	12 48	13 04	13 18	13 34	13 48	14 04	14 18	14 34	14 48
Hackney Wick d	09 59	10 08	10 19	10 37	10 51	11 07	11 21	11 37	11 51	12 07	12 21	12 37	12 51	13 07	13 21	13 37	13 51	14 07	14 21	14 37	14 51
Stratford 7 ⊖ a	10 08	10 15	10 25	10 45	10 59	11 14	11 28	11 45	11 58	12 14	12 29	12 44	12 58	13 15	13 28	13 44	13 58	14 14	14 28	14 44	14 58

	LO	LO	LO	LO	LO	LO	LO	LO	LO	LO	LO 1 A	LO	LO 1 A	LO	LO	LO 1 A	LO	LO 1 A	LO	LO 1 A	LO
Richmond ⊖ d	14 11	14 27	14 41	14 57	15 11	15 27	15 41	15 57	16 15	16 22		16 43		16 59	17 03		17 24		17 43		18 02
Kew Gardens ⊖ d	14 14	14 30	14 44	15 00	15 14	15 30	15 44	16 00	16 18	16 25		16 46		17 02	17 06		17 27		17 46		18 05
Gunnersbury ⊖ d	14 17	14 33	14 47	15 03	15 17	15 33	15 47	16 03	16 21	16 28		16 49		17 05	17 09		17 30		17 49		18 08
South Acton d	14 19	14 35	14 49	15 05	15 19	15 35	15 49	16 05	16 23	16 30		16 51		17 07	17 11		17 32		17 51		18 10
Acton Central d	14 23	14 38	14 53	15 08	15 23	15 38	15 53	16 08	16 26	16 35		16 54		17 10	17 14		17 37		17 54		18 15
Willesden Jn. High Level ⊖ a	14 29	14 44	14 59	15 13	15 30	15 43	15 59	16 13	16 31	16 38		16 58		17 15	17 18		17 40		17 58		18 18
d	14 30	14 44	15 00	15 14	15 30	15 44	16 00	16 14	16 32	16 41	16 51	17 01	17 11		17 21	17 31	17 41	17 51	18 01	18 11	18 21
Kensal Rise d	14 33	14 47	15 03	15 17	15 33	15 47	16 03	16 17	16 35	16 44	16 54	17 04	17 14		17 24	17 34	17 44	17 54	18 04	18 14	18 24
Brondesbury Park d	14 35	14 49	15 05	15 19	15 35	15 49	16 05	16 19	16 37	16 46	16 56	17 06	17 16		17 26	17 36	17 46	17 56	18 06	18 16	18 26
Brondesbury d	14 37	14 51	15 07	15 21	15 37	15 51	16 07	16 21	16 39	16 48	16 58	17 08	17 18		17 28	17 38	17 48	17 58	18 08	18 18	18 28
West Hampstead ⊖ d	14 38	14 52	15 08	15 22	15 38	15 52	16 08	16 22	16 40	16 50	17 00	17 10	17 20		17 30	17 40	17 50	18 00	18 10	18 20	18 30
Finchley Road & Frognal d	14 40	14 54	15 10	15 24	15 40	15 54	16 10	16 24	16 42	16 51	17 01	17 11	17 21		17 31	17 41	17 51	18 01	18 11	18 21	18 31
Hampstead Heath d	14 43	14 57	15 13	15 27	15 43	15 57	16 13	16 27	16 45	16 54	17 04	17 14	17 24		17 34	17 44	17 54	18 04	18 14	18 24	18 34
Gospel Oak d	14 45	14 59	15 15	15 29	15 45	15 59	16 15	16 29	16 47	16 57	17 07	17 17	17 27		17 37	17 47	17 57	18 07	18 17	18 27	18 37
Kentish Town West d	14 47	15 01	15 17	15 31	15 47	16 01	16 17	16 31	16 49	16 59	17 09	17 19	17 29		17 39	17 49	17 59	18 09	18 19	18 29	18 39
Camden Road d	14 49	15 03	15 19	15 33	15 49	16 03	16 19	16 33	16 51	17 01	17 11	17 21	17 31		17 41	17 51	18 01	18 11	18 21	18 31	18 41
Caledonian Rd & Barnsbury d	14 52	15 06	15 22	15 36	15 52	16 06	16 22	16 36	16 54	17 04	17 14	17 24	17 34		17 44	17 54	18 04	18 14	18 24	18 34	18 44
Highbury & Islington ⊖ d	14 55	15 09	15 25	15 39	15 55	16 09	16 24	16 39	16 57	17 07	17 17	17 27	17 37		17 47	17 57	18 07	18 17	18 27	18 37	18 47
Canonbury ⊖ d	14 57	15 11	15 27	15 41	15 57	16 11	16 26	16 41	16 59	17 09	17 19	17 29	17 39		17 49	17 59	18 09	18 19	18 29	18 39	18 49
Dalston Kingsland d	15 00	15 14	15 30	15 44	16 00	16 14	16 29	16 44	17 02	17 12	17 22	17 32	17 42		17 52	18 02	18 12	18 22	18 32	18 42	18 52
Hackney Central d	15 02	15 16	15 32	15 46	16 02	16 16	16 31	16 46	17 04	17 14	17 24	17 34	17 44		17 54	18 04	18 14	18 24	18 34	18 44	18 54
Homerton d	15 04	15 18	15 34	15 48	16 04	16 18	16 33	16 48	17 06	17 16	17 26	17 36	17 46		17 56	18 06	18 16	18 26	18 36	18 46	18 56
Hackney Wick d	15 07	15 21	15 37	15 51	16 07	16 21	16 35	16 51	17 08	17 18	17 28	17 38	17 48		17 58	18 08	18 18	18 28	18 38	18 48	18 58
Stratford 7 ⊖ a	15 14	15 30	15 44	15 59	16 14	16 28	16 42	16 58	17 15	17 24	17 36	17 44	17 54		18 04	18 14	18 26	18 34	18 44	18 56	19 04

For general notes see front of timetable
For details of catering facilities see Directory of Train Operators

A From Clapham Junction (Table 176)
b Willesden Jn Low Level

Richmond → Willesden Junction, West Hampstead Highbury and Islington and Stratford Low Level

Network diagram - see first page of Table 59

	LO 1 A	LO	LO 1 A		LO	LO 1 A	LO	LO	LO		LO	LO	LO	LO	LO		LO	LO	LO	LO	LO		LO		
Richmond ⊖ d		18 22			18 44		19 01	19 25	19 41		19 59	20 15	20 35	20 55	21 15		21 35	21 55	22 15	22 35	22 55		23 15		
Kew Gardens ⊖ d		18 25			18 47		19 04	19 28	19 44		20 02	20 18	20 38	20 58	21 18		21 38	21 58	22 18	22 38	22 58		23 18		
Gunnersbury ⊖ d		18 28			18 50		19 07	19 31	19 47		20 05	20 21	20 41	21 01	21 21		21 41	22 01	22 21	22 41	23 01		23 21		
South Acton d		18 30			18 52		19 09	19 33	19 49		20 07	20 23	20 43	21 03	21 23		21 43	22 03	22 23	22 43	23 03		23 23		
Acton Central d		18 35			18 55		19 14	19 36	19 52		20 10	20 26	20 46	21 06	21 26		21 46	22 06	22 26	22 46	23 06		23 26		
Willesden Jn. High Level ⊖ a		18 38			18 59		19 17	19 40	19 58		20 15	20 32	20 52	21 12	21 31		21 52	22 12	22 32	22 52	23 12		23 35		
d	18 31	18 41	18 51		19 01	19 11	19 21	19 42	19 58		20 16	20 32	20 52	21 12	21 32		21 52	22 12	22 32	22 52	23 12				
Kensal Rise d	18 34	18 44	18 54		19 04	19 14	19 24	19 45	20 01		20 19	20 35	20 55	21 15	21 35		21 55	22 15	22 35	22 55	23 15				
Brondesbury Park d	18 36	18 46	18 56		19 06	19 16	19 26	19 47	20 03		20 21	20 37	20 57	21 17	21 37		21 57	22 17	22 37	22 57	23 17				
Brondesbury d	18 38	18 48	18 58		19 08	19 18	19 28	19 49	20 05		20 23	20 39	20 59	21 19	21 39		21 59	22 19	22 39	22 59	23 19				
West Hampstead ⊖ d	18 40	18 50	19 00		19 10	19 20	19 30	19 50	20 06		20 24	20 40	21 00	21 20	21 40		22 00	22 20	22 40	23 00	23 20				
Finchley Road & Frognal d	18 41	18 51	19 01		19 11	19 21	19 31	19 52	20 08		20 26	20 42	21 02	21 22	21 42		22 02	22 22	22 42	23 02	23 22				
Hampstead Heath d	18 44	18 54	19 04		19 14	19 24	19 34	19 54	20 11		20 29	20 45	21 05	21 25	21 45		22 05	22 25	22 45	23 05	23 25				
Gospel Oak d	18 47	18 57	19 07		19 17	19 27	19 37	19 57	20 13		20 31	20 47	21 07	21 27	21 47		22 07	22 27	22 47	23 07	23 27				
Kentish Town West d	18 49	18 59	19 09		19 19	19 29	19 39	19 59	20 15		20 33	20 49	21 09	21 29	21 49		22 09	22 29	22 49	23 09	23 29				
Camden Road d	18 51	19 01	19 11		19 21	19 31	19 41	20 01	20 17		20 35	20 51	21 11	21 31	21 51		22 11	22 31	22 51	23 11	23 31				
Caledonian Rd & Barnsbury d	18 54	19 04	19 14		19 24	19 34	19 44	20 04	20 20		20 38	20 54	21 14	21 34	21 54		22 14	22 34	22 54	23 14	23 34				
Highbury & Islington ⊖ d	18 57	19 07	19 17		19 27	19 37	19 47	20 07	20 23		20 41	20 57	21 17	21 37	21 57		22 17	22 37	22 57	23 17	23 37				
Canonbury ⊖ d	18 59	19 09	19 19		19 29	19 39	19 49	20 09	20 25		20 43	20 59	21 19	21 39	21 59		22 19	22 39	22 59	23 19	23 39				
Dalston Kingsland d	19 02	19 12	19 22		19 32	19 42	19 52	20 12	20 28		20 46	21 02	21 22	21 42	22 02		22 22	22 42	23 02	23 22	23 42				
Hackney Central d	19 04	19 14	19 24		19 34	19 44	19 54	20 14	20 30		20 48	21 04	21 24	21 44	22 04		22 24	22 44	23 04	23 24	23 44				
Homerton d	19 06	19 16	19 26		19 36	19 46	19 56	20 16	20 32		20 50	21 06	21 26	21 46	22 06		22 26	22 46	23 06	23 26	23 46				
Hackney Wick d	19 08	19 18	19 28		19 38	19 48	19 58	20 18	20 35		20 53	21 09	21 29	21 49	22 09		22 29	22 49	23 09	23 29	23 49				
Stratford 7 ⊖ a	19 16	19 24	19 36		19 44	19 56	20 04	20 24	20 44		21 01	21 16	21 38	21 58	22 16		22 37	22 57	23 17	23 37	23 58				

Saturdays

	LO	LO		LO	LO		LO	LO			LO	LO	LO	LO			LO	LO		LO	LO		LO	LO
Richmond ⊖ d				06 11	06 27		06 41	06 57			07 11	07 27	07 41	07 57			18 11	18 26		18 41	18 56		19 16	19 26
Kew Gardens ⊖ d				06 14	06 30		06 44	07 00			07 14	07 30	07 44	08 00			18 14	18 29		18 44	18 59		19 19	19 29
Gunnersbury ⊖ d				06 17	06 33		06 47	07 03			07 17	07 33	07 47	08 03			18 17	18 32		18 47	19 02		19 22	19 32
South Acton d				06 19	06 35		06 49	07 05			07 19	07 35	07 49	08 05			18 19	18 34		18 49	19 04		19 24	19 34
Acton Central d				06 23	06 38		06 53	07 08			07 23	07 38	07 53	08 08			18 23	18 38		18 52	19 07		19 27	19 37
Willesden Jn. High Level ⊖ a				06 29	06 43		06 58	07 14			07 29	07 43	07 58	08 13	and at		18 29	18 43		18 57	19 12		19 32	19 43
d	05b58	06b11		06 29	06 44		06 59	07 14			07 29	07 44	07 59	08 14			18 29	18 44		18 58	19 13		19 33	19 43
Kensal Rise d	06 02	06 17		06 32	06 47		07 02	07 17			07 32	07 47	08 02	08 17	the same		18 32	18 47		19 01	19 16		19 36	19 46
Brondesbury Park d	06 04	06 19		06 34	06 49		07 04	07 19			07 34	07 49	08 04	08 19			18 34	18 49		19 03	19 18		19 38	19 48
Brondesbury d	06 06	06 21		06 36	06 51		07 06	07 21			07 36	07 51	08 06	08 21	minutes		18 36	18 51		19 05	19 20		19 40	19 50
West Hampstead ⊖ d	06 07	06 22		06 37	06 52		07 07	07 22			07 37	07 52	08 07	08 22			18 37	18 52		19 06	19 21		19 41	19 51
Finchley Road & Frognal d	06 09	06 24		06 39	06 54		07 09	07 24			07 39	07 54	08 09	08 24	past		18 39	18 54		19 08	19 23		19 43	19 53
Hampstead Heath d	06 12	06 27		06 42	06 57		07 12	07 27			07 42	07 57	08 12	08 27			18 42	18 57		19 11	19 26		19 46	19 56
Gospel Oak d	06 14	06 29		06 44	06 59		07 14	07 29			07 44	07 59	08 14	08 29	each		18 44	18 59		19 13	19 28		19 48	19 58
Kentish Town West d	06 16	06 31		06 46	07 01		07 16	07 31			07 46	08 01	08 16	08 31	hour until		18 46	19 01		19 15	19 30		19 50	20 00
Camden Road d	06 18	06 33		06 48	07 03		07 18	07 33			07 48	08 03	08 18	08 33			18 48	19 03		19 17	19 32		19 52	20 02
Caledonian Rd & Barnsbury d	06 21	06 36		06 51	07 06		07 21	07 36			07 51	08 06	08 21	08 36			18 51	19 06		19 20	19 35		19 55	20 05
Highbury & Islington ⊖ d	06 24	06 39		06 54	07 09		07 24	07 39			07 54	08 09	08 24	08 39			18 54	19 09		19 23	19 37		19 57	20 07
Canonbury ⊖ d	06 26	06 41		06 56	07 11		07 26	07 41			07 56	08 11	08 26	08 41			18 56	19 11		19 24	19 39		19 59	20 09
Dalston Kingsland d	06 29	06 44		06 59	07 14		07 29	07 44			07 59	08 14	08 29	08 44			18 59	19 14		19 27	19 42		20 02	20 12
Hackney Central d	06 31	06 46		07 01	07 16		07 31	07 46			08 01	08 16	08 31	08 46			19 01	19 16		19 29	19 44		20 04	20 14
Homerton d	06 33	06 48		07 03	07 18		07 33	07 48			08 03	08 18	08 33	08 48			19 03	19 18		19 31	19 46		20 06	20 16
Hackney Wick d	06 36	06 51		07 06	07 21		07 36	07 51			08 06	08 21	08 36	08 51			19 06	19 21		19 34	19 49		20 09	20 19
Stratford 7 ⊖ a	06 44	06 58		07 14	07 28		07 43	08 01			08 15	08 28	08 43	08 58			19 13	19 28		19 44	19 59		20 16	20 28

	LO	LO		LO	LO		LO	LO		LO	LO		LO	LO		LO	LO							
Richmond ⊖ d	19 40	19 56		20 16	20 36		20 56	21 16		21 36	21 56		22 16	22 36		22 56	23 16							
Kew Gardens ⊖ d	19 43	19 59		20 19	20 39		20 59	21 19		21 39	21 59		22 19	22 39		22 59	23 19							
Gunnersbury ⊖ d	19 46	20 02		20 22	20 42		21 02	21 22		21 42	22 02		22 22	22 42		23 02	23 22							
South Acton d	19 48	20 04		20 24	20 44		21 04	21 24		21 44	22 04		22 24	22 44		23 04	23 24							
Acton Central d	19 51	20 07		20 27	20 47		21 07	21 27		21 47	22 07		22 27	22 47		23 07	23 27							
Willesden Jn. High Level ⊖ a	19 59	20 13		20 32	20 52		21 12	21 32		21 52	22 12		22 32	22 52		23 13	23 35							
d	20 00	20 13		20 33	20 53		21 13	21 33		21 53	22 13		22 33	22 53		23 13								
Kensal Rise d	20 03	20 16		20 36	20 56		21 16	21 36		21 56	22 16		22 36	22 56		23 16								
Brondesbury Park d	20 05	20 18		20 38	20 58		21 18	21 38		21 58	22 18		22 38	22 58		23 18								
Brondesbury d	20 07	20 20		20 40	21 00		21 20	21 40		22 00	22 20		22 40	23 00		23 20								
West Hampstead ⊖ d	20 08	20 21		20 41	21 01		21 21	21 41		22 01	22 21		22 41	23 01		23 21								
Finchley Road & Frognal d	20 10	20 23		20 43	21 03		21 23	21 43		22 03	22 23		22 43	23 03		23 23								
Hampstead Heath d	20 13	20 26		20 46	21 06		21 26	21 46		22 06	22 26		22 46	23 06		23 26								
Gospel Oak d	20 15	20 28		20 48	21 08		21 28	21 48		22 08	22 28		22 48	23 08		23 28								
Kentish Town West d	20 17	20 30		20 50	21 10		21 30	21 50		22 10	22 30		22 50	23 10		23 30								
Camden Road d	20 19	20 32		20 52	21 12		21 32	21 52		22 12	22 32		22 52	23 12		23 32								
Caledonian Rd & Barnsbury d	20 22	20 35		20 55	21 15		21 35	21 55		22 15	22 35		22 55	23 15		23 35								
Highbury & Islington ⊖ d	20 24	20 37		20 57	21 17		21 37	21 57		22 17	22 37		22 57	23 17		23 37								
Canonbury ⊖ d	20 26	20 39		20 59	21 19		21 39	21 59		22 19	22 39		22 59	23 19		23 39								
Dalston Kingsland d	20 29	20 42		21 02	21 22		21 42	22 02		22 22	22 42		23 02	23 22		23 42								
Hackney Central d	20 31	20 44		21 04	21 24		21 44	22 04		22 24	22 44		23 04	23 24		23 44								
Homerton d	20 33	20 46		21 06	21 26		21 46	22 06		22 26	22 46		23 06	23 26		23 46								
Hackney Wick d	20 35	20 49		21 09	21 29		21 49	22 09		22 29	22 49		23 09	23 29		23 49								
Stratford 7 ⊖ a	20 42	20 57		21 19	21 39		21 59	22 16		22 36	22 56		23 17	23 36		23 58								

For general notes see front of timetable
For details of catering facilities see
Directory of Train Operators

A From Clapham Junction (Table 176)
b Willesden Jun Low Level

Table 59

Sundays

Richmond → Willesden Junction, West Hampstead Highbury and Islington and Stratford Low Level

Network diagram - see first page of Table 59

		LO			LO	LO			LO		LO		LO
Richmond	⊖ d				09 08	09 38			22 08		22 38		23 08
Kew Gardens	⊖ d				09 11	09 41			22 11		22 41		23 11
Gunnersbury	⊖ d				09 14	09 44			22 14		22 44		23 14
South Acton	d				09 16	09 46			22 16		22 46		23 16
Acton Central	d				09 19	09 49			22 19		22 49		23 19
Willesden Jn. High Level	⊖ a				09 24	09 54	and at		22 24		22 54		23 26
	d	08b55			09 25	09 55			22 25		22 55		
Kensal Rise	d	08 58			09 28	09 58	the same		22 28		22 58		
Brondesbury Park	d	09 00			09 30	10 00			22 30		23 00		
Brondesbury	d	09 02			09 32	10 02	minutes		22 32		23 02		
West Hampstead	⊖ d	09 03			09 33	10 03			22 33		23 03		
Finchley Road & Frognal	d	09 05			09 35	10 05	past		22 35		23 05		
Hampstead Heath	d	09 08			09 38	10 08			22 38		23 08		
Gospel Oak	d	09 10			09 40	10 10	each		22 40		23 10		
Kentish Town West	d	09 12			09 42	10 12	hour until		22 42		23 12		
Camden Road	d	09 14			09 44	10 14			22 44		23 14		
Caledonian Rd & Barnsbury	d	09 17			09 47	10 17			22 47		23 17		
Highbury & Islington	⊖ d	09 20			09 50	10 20			22 50		23 20		
Canonbury	⊖ d	09 22			09 52	10 22			22 52		23 22		
Dalston Kingsland	d	09 25			09 55	10 25			22 55		23 25		
Hackney Central	d	09 27			09 57	10 27			22 57		23 27		
Homerton	d	09 29			09 59	10 29			22 59		23 29		
Hackney Wick	d	09 32			10 02	10 32			23 02		23 32		
Stratford [7]	⊖ ⛴ a	09 39			10 09	10 39			23 09		23 39		

For general notes see front of timetable
For details of catering facilities see Directory of Train Operators

b Willesden Jn Low Level

London, Queens Park and Harrow & Wealdstone → Watford Junction

Network Diagram - See first page of Table 59

Miles			LO	LO MX	LO MO	LO MX	LO	LO	LO	LO	LO	LO	LO	LO	LO	LO	LO	LO	LO	LO	LO	LO
0	**London Euston** 15 ⊖	d	23p17	23p37	23p47	23p57	05 27	05 57	06 17	06 37	06 57	07 17	07 37	07 57	08 17	08 37	08 57	09 17	09 37	09 57	10 17	10 37
2½	South Hampstead	d	23p23	23p43	23p53	00 03	05 33	06 03	06 23	06 43	07 03	07 23	07 43	08 03	08 23	08 43	09 03	09 23	09 43	10 03	10 23	10 43
3	Kilburn High Road	d	23p24	23p44	23p54	00 04	05 34	06 04	06 24	06 44	07 04	07 24	07 44	08 04	08 24	08 44	09 04	09 24	09 44	10 04	10 24	10 44
3¾	**Queens Park (Dc)** ⊖	d	23p26	23p46	23p56	00 06	05 36	06 06	06 26	06 46	07 06	07 26	07 46	08 06	08 26	08 46	09 06	09 26	09 46	10 06	10 26	10 46
4½	Kensal Green	d	23p28	23p48	23p58	00 08	05 38	06 08	06 28	06 48	07 08	07 28	07 48	08 08	08 28	08 48	09 08	09 28	09 48	10 08	10 28	10 48
5½	**Willesden Jn Low Level**	d	23p31	23p51	00 01	00 11	05 41	06 11	06 31	06 51	07 11	07 31	07 51	08 11	08 31	08 51	09 11	09 31	09 51	10 11	10 31	10 51
6	Harlesden	d	23p33	23p53	00 03	00 13	05 43	06 13	06 33	06 53	07 13	07 33	07 53	08 13	08 33	08 53	09 13	09 33	09 53	10 13	10 33	10 53
7	Stonebridge Park	d	23p35	23p55	00 05	00 15	05 45	06 15	06 35	06 55	07 15	07 35	07 55	08 15	08 35	08 55	09 15	09 35	09 55	10 15	10 35	10 55
8	Wembley Central Dc	d	23p38	23p58	00 08	00 18	05 48	06 18	06 38	06 58	07 18	07 38	07 58	08 18	08 38	08 58	09 18	09 38	09 58	10 18	10 38	10 58
9	North Wembley	d	23p40	00 01	00 10	00 20	05 50	06 20	06 40	07 00	07 20	07 40	08 00	08 20	08 40	09 00	09 20	09 40	10 00	10 20	10 40	11 00
9½	South Kenton	d	23p42	00 02	00 12	00 22	05 52	06 22	06 42	07 02	07 22	07 42	08 02	08 22	08 42	09 02	09 22	09 42	10 02	10 22	10 42	11 02
10¼	Kenton	d	23p44	00 04	00 14	00 24	05 54	06 24	06 44	07 04	07 24	07 44	08 04	08 24	08 44	09 04	09 24	09 44	10 04	10 24	10 44	11 04
11¼	**Harrow & Wealdstone D.C.**	d	23p46	00 06	00 16	00 26	05 56	06 26	06 46	07 06	07 26	07 46	08 06	08 26	08 46	09 06	09 26	09 46	10 06	10 26	10 46	11 06
12½	Headstone Lane	d	23p49	00 09	00 19	00 29	05 59	06 29	06 49	07 09	07 29	07 49	08 09	08 29	08 49	09 09	09 29	09 49	10 09	10 29	10 49	11 09
13¼	Hatch End	d	23p51	00 11	00 21	00 31	06 01	06 31	06 51	07 11	07 31	07 51	08 11	08 31	08 51	09 11	09 31	09 51	10 11	10 31	10 51	11 11
14¾	Carpenders Park	d	23p54	00 14	00 24	00 34	06 04	06 34	06 54	07 14	07 34	07 54	08 14	08 34	08 54	09 14	09 34	09 54	10 14	10 34	10 54	11 14
16	Bushey Dc	d	23p57	00 17	00 27	00 37	06 07	06 37	06 57	07 17	07 37	07 57	08 17	08 37	08 57	09 17	09 37	09 57	10 17	10 37	10 57	11 17
16¾	Watford High Street	d	00 01	00 20	00 30	00 40	06 10	06 40	07 00	07 20	07 40	08 00	08 20	08 40	09 00	09 20	09 40	10 00	10 20	10 40	11 00	11 20
17¾	**Watford Junction Dc**	a	00 04	00 24	00 34	00 44	06 14	06 44	07 05	07 24	07 44	08 04	08 24	08 44	09 04	09 24	09 44	10 04	10 24	10 45	11 04	11 24

		LO	LO	LO	LO	LO	LO	LO	LO	LO	LO	LO	LO	LO	LO	LO	LO	LO	LO	LO	LO
London Euston 15 ⊖	d	10 57	11 17	11 37	11 57	12 17	12 37	12 57	13 17	13 37	13 57	14 17	14 37	14 57	15 17	15 37	15 57	16 17	16 37	16 57	17 17
South Hampstead	d	11 03	11 23	11 43	12 03	12 23	12 43	13 03	13 23	13 43	14 03	14 23	14 43	15 03	15 23	15 43	16 03	16 23	16 43	17 03	17 23
Kilburn High Road	d	11 04	11 24	11 44	12 04	12 24	12 44	13 04	13 24	13 44	14 04	14 24	14 44	15 04	15 24	15 44	16 04	16 24	16 44	17 04	17 24
Queens Park (Dc) ⊖	d	11 06	11 26	11 46	12 06	12 26	12 46	13 06	13 26	13 46	14 06	14 26	14 46	15 06	15 26	15 46	16 06	16 27	16 47	17 07	17 27
Kensal Green	d	11 08	11 28	11 48	12 08	12 28	12 48	13 08	13 28	13 48	14 08	14 28	14 48	15 08	15 28	15 48	16 08	16 29	16 49	17 09	17 29
Willesden Jn Low Level	d	11 11	11 31	11 51	12 11	12 31	12 51	13 11	13 31	13 51	14 11	14 31	14 51	15 11	15 31	15 51	16 11	16 32	16 52	17 12	17 32
Harlesden	d	11 13	11 33	11 53	12 13	12 33	12 53	13 13	13 33	13 53	14 13	14 33	14 53	15 13	15 33	15 53	16 13	16 34	16 54	17 14	17 34
Stonebridge Park	d	11 15	11 35	11 55	12 15	12 35	12 55	13 15	13 35	13 55	14 15	14 35	14 55	15 15	15 35	15 55	16 15	16 36	16 56	17 16	17 36
Wembley Central Dc	d	11 18	11 38	11 58	12 18	12 38	12 58	13 18	13 38	13 58	14 18	14 38	14 58	15 18	15 38	15 58	16 18	16 39	16 59	17 19	17 39
North Wembley	d	11 20	11 40	12 00	12 20	12 40	13 00	13 20	13 40	14 00	14 20	14 40	15 00	15 20	15 40	16 00	16 20	16 41	17 01	17 21	17 41
South Kenton	d	11 22	11 42	12 02	12 22	12 42	13 02	13 22	13 42	14 02	14 22	14 42	15 02	15 22	15 42	16 02	16 22	16 43	17 03	17 23	17 43
Kenton	d	11 24	11 44	12 04	12 24	12 44	13 04	13 24	13 44	14 04	14 24	14 44	15 04	15 24	15 44	16 04	16 24	16 45	17 05	17 25	17 45
Harrow & Wealdstone D.C.	d	11 26	11 46	12 06	12 26	12 46	13 06	13 26	13 46	14 06	14 26	14 46	15 06	15 26	15 46	16 06	16 26	16 48	17 08	17 28	17 48
Headstone Lane	d	11 29	11 49	12 09	12 29	12 49	13 09	13 29	13 49	14 09	14 29	14 49	15 09	15 29	15 49	16 09	16 29	16 51	17 11	17 31	17 51
Hatch End	d	11 31	11 51	12 11	12 31	12 51	13 11	13 31	13 51	14 11	14 31	14 51	15 11	15 31	15 51	16 11	16 31	16 53	17 13	17 33	17 53
Carpenders Park	d	11 34	11 54	12 14	12 34	12 54	13 14	13 34	13 54	14 14	14 34	14 54	15 14	15 34	15 54	16 14	16 34	16 56	17 16	17 36	17 56
Bushey Dc	d	11 37	11 57	12 17	12 37	12 57	13 17	13 37	13 57	14 17	14 37	14 57	15 17	15 37	15 57	16 17	16 37	16 59	17 19	17 39	17 59
Watford High Street	d	11 40	12 00	12 20	12 40	13 00	13 20	13 40	14 00	14 20	14 40	15 00	15 20	15 40	16 00	16 20	16 40	17 01	17 21	17 41	18 01
Watford Junction Dc	a	11 44	12 04	12 24	12 44	13 04	13 24	13 44	14 04	14 24	14 44	15 04	15 24	15 44	16 04	16 24	16 44	17 08	17 28	17 48	18 08

		LO	LO	LO	LO	LO	LO	LO	LO	LO	LO	LO	LO	LO	LO	LO	LO	LO	LO	LO	LO
London Euston 15 ⊖	d	17 37	17 57	18 17	18 37	18 57	19 17	19 37	19 57	20 17	20 37	20 57	21 17	21 37	21 57	22 17	22 37	22 57	23 17	23 37	23 57
South Hampstead	d	17 43	18 03	18 23	18 43	19 03	19 23	19 43	20 03	20 23	20 43	21 03	21 23	21 43	22 03	22 23	22 43	23 03	23 23	23 43	00 03
Kilburn High Road	d	17 44	18 04	18 24	18 44	19 04	19 24	19 44	20 04	20 24	20 44	21 04	21 24	21 44	22 04	22 24	22 44	23 04	23 24	23 44	00 04
Queens Park (Dc) ⊖	d	17 47	18 07	18 27	18 47	19 07	19 26	19 46	20 06	20 26	20 46	21 06	21 26	21 46	22 06	22 26	22 46	23 06	23 26	23 46	00 06
Kensal Green	d	17 49	18 09	18 29	18 49	19 09	19 28	19 48	20 08	20 28	20 48	21 08	21 28	21 48	22 08	22 28	22 48	23 08	23 28	23 48	00 08
Willesden Jn Low Level	d	17 52	18 12	18 32	18 52	19 12	19 31	19 51	20 11	20 31	20 51	21 11	21 31	21 51	22 11	22 31	22 51	23 11	23 31	23 51	00 11
Harlesden	d	17 54	18 14	18 34	18 54	19 14	19 33	19 53	20 13	20 33	20 53	21 13	21 33	21 53	22 13	22 33	22 53	23 13	23 33	23 53	00 13
Stonebridge Park	d	17 56	18 16	18 36	18 56	19 16	19 35	19 55	20 15	20 35	20 55	21 15	21 35	21 55	22 15	22 35	22 55	23 15	23 35	23 55	00 15
Wembley Central Dc	d	17 59	18 19	18 39	18 59	19 19	19 38	19 58	20 18	20 38	20 58	21 18	21 38	21 58	22 18	22 38	22 58	23 18	23 38	23 58	00 18
North Wembley	d	18 01	18 21	18 41	19 01	19 21	19 40	20 00	20 20	20 40	21 00	21 20	21 40	22 00	22 20	22 40	23 00	23 20	23 40	00 01	00 20
South Kenton	d	18 03	18 23	18 43	19 03	19 23	19 42	20 02	20 22	20 42	21 02	21 22	21 42	22 02	22 22	22 42	23 02	23 22	23 42	00 02	00 22
Kenton	d	18 05	18 25	18 45	19 05	19 25	19 44	20 04	20 24	20 44	21 04	21 24	21 44	22 04	22 24	22 44	23 04	23 24	23 44	00 04	00 24
Harrow & Wealdstone D.C.	d	18 08	18 28	18 48	19 08	19 28	19 46	20 06	20 26	20 46	21 06	21 26	21 46	22 06	22 26	22 46	23 06	23 26	23 46	00 06	00 26
Headstone Lane	d	18 11	18 31	18 51	19 11	19 31	19 49	20 09	20 29	20 49	21 09	21 29	21 49	22 09	22 29	22 49	23 09	23 29	23 49	00 09	00 29
Hatch End	d	18 13	18 33	18 53	19 13	19 33	19 51	20 11	20 31	20 51	21 11	21 31	21 51	22 11	22 31	22 51	23 11	23 31	23 51	00 11	00 31
Carpenders Park	d	18 16	18 36	18 56	19 16	19 36	19 54	20 14	20 34	20 54	21 14	21 34	21 54	22 14	22 34	22 54	23 14	23 34	23 54	00 14	00 34
Bushey Dc	d	18 19	18 39	18 59	19 19	19 39	19 57	20 17	20 37	20 57	21 17	21 37	21 57	22 17	22 37	22 57	23 17	23 37	23 57	00 17	00 37
Watford High Street	d	18 21	18 41	19 01	19 21	19 41	20 00	20 20	20 40	21 00	21 20	21 40	22 00	22 20	22 40	23 00	23 20	23 40	00 01	00 20	00 40
Watford Junction Dc	a	18 28	18 48	19 08	19 28	19 48	20 04	20 24	20 44	21 04	21 24	21 44	22 04	22 25	22 44	23 04	23 24	23 44	00 04	00 24	00 44

Saturdays

		LO	LO	LO	LO	LO	LO	LO	LO	LO	LO	LO	LO	LO	LO	LO	LO	LO	LO	LO	LO	LO
London Euston 15 ⊖	d	23p17	23p37	23p57	05 27	05 57	06 17	06 37	06 57	07 17	07 37	07 57	08 17	08 37	08 57	09 17	09 37	09 57	10 17	10 37	10 57	11 17
South Hampstead	d	23p23	23p43	00 03	05 33	06 03	06 23	06 43	07 03	07 23	07 43	08 03	08 23	08 43	09 03	09 23	09 43	10 03	10 23	10 43	11 03	11 23
Kilburn High Road	d	23p24	23p44	00 04	05 34	06 04	06 24	06 44	07 04	07 24	07 44	08 04	08 24	08 44	09 04	09 24	09 44	10 04	10 24	10 44	11 04	11 24
Queens Park (Dc) ⊖	d	23p26	23p46	00 06	05 36	06 06	06 26	06 46	07 06	07 26	07 46	08 06	08 26	08 46	09 06	09 26	09 46	10 06	10 26	10 46	11 06	11 26
Kensal Green	d	23p28	23p48	00 08	05 38	06 08	06 28	06 48	07 08	07 28	07 48	08 08	08 28	08 48	09 08	09 28	09 48	10 08	10 28	10 48	11 08	11 28
Willesden Jn Low Level	d	23p31	23p51	00 11	05 41	06 11	06 31	06 51	07 11	07 31	07 51	08 11	08 31	08 51	09 11	09 31	09 51	10 11	10 31	10 51	11 11	11 31
Harlesden	d	23p33	23p53	00 13	05 43	06 13	06 33	06 53	07 13	07 33	07 53	08 13	08 33	08 53	09 13	09 33	09 53	10 13	10 33	10 53	11 13	11 33
Stonebridge Park	d	23p35	23p55	00 15	05 45	06 15	06 35	06 55	07 15	07 35	07 55	08 15	08 35	08 55	09 15	09 35	09 55	10 15	10 35	10 55	11 15	11 35
Wembley Central Dc	d	23p38	23p58	00 18	05 48	06 18	06 38	06 58	07 18	07 38	07 58	08 18	08 38	08 58	09 18	09 38	09 58	10 18	10 38	10 58	11 18	11 38
North Wembley	d	23p40	00 01	00 20	05 50	06 20	06 40	07 00	07 20	07 40	08 00	08 20	08 40	09 00	09 20	09 40	10 00	10 20	10 40	11 00	11 20	11 40
South Kenton	d	23p42	00 02	00 22	05 52	06 22	06 42	07 02	07 22	07 42	08 02	08 22	08 42	09 02	09 22	09 42	10 02	10 22	10 42	11 02	11 22	11 42
Kenton	d	23p44	00 04	00 24	05 54	06 24	06 44	07 04	07 24	07 44	08 04	08 24	08 44	09 04	09 24	09 44	10 04	10 24	10 44	11 04	11 24	11 44
Harrow & Wealdstone D.C.	d	23p46	00 06	00 26	05 56	06 26	06 46	07 06	07 26	07 46	08 06	08 26	08 46	09 06	09 26	09 46	10 06	10 26	10 46	11 06	11 26	11 46
Headstone Lane	d	23p49	00 09	00 29	05 59	06 29	06 49	07 09	07 29	07 49	08 09	08 29	08 49	09 09	09 29	09 49	10 09	10 29	10 49	11 09	11 29	11 49
Hatch End	d	23p51	00 11	00 31	06 01	06 31	06 51	07 11	07 31	07 51	08 11	08 31	08 51	09 11	09 31	09 51	10 11	10 31	10 51	11 11	11 31	11 51
Carpenders Park	d	23p54	00 14	00 34	06 04	06 34	06 54	07 14	07 34	07 54	08 14	08 34	08 54	09 14	09 34	09 54	10 14	10 34	10 54	11 14	11 34	11 54
Bushey Dc	d	23p57	00 17	00 37	06 07	06 37	06 57	07 17	07 37	07 57	08 17	08 37	08 57	09 17	09 37	09 57	10 17	10 37	10 57	11 17	11 37	11 57
Watford High Street	d	00 01	00 20	00 40	06 10	06 40	07 00	07 20	07 40	08 00	08 20	08 40	09 00	09 20	09 40	10 00	10 20	10 40	11 00	11 20	11 40	12 00
Watford Junction Dc	a	00 04	00 24	00 44	06 14	06 44	07 05	07 24	07 44	08 04	08 24	08 44	09 04	09 24	09 44	10 04	10 24	10 44	11 04	11 24	11 44	12 04

For general notes see front of timetable
For details of catering facilities see
Directory of Train Operators

Stations Queen's Park to Harrow & Wealdstone inclusive are also served by London Underground Bakerloo line services

Saturdays

London, Queens Park and Harrow & Wealdstone → Watford Junction

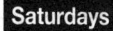

Network Diagram - See first page of Table 59

		LO		LO	LO	LO	LO		LO	LO	LO	LO		LO	LO	LO	LO		LO	LO	LO	LO		LO	LO	LO
London Euston 15 ⊖	d	11 37		11 57	12 17	12 37	12 57		13 17	13 37	13 57	14 17		14 37	14 57	15 17	15 37		15 57	16 17	16 37	16 57		17 17	17 37	17 57
South Hampstead	d	11 43		12 03	12 23	12 43	13 03		13 23	13 43	14 03	14 23		14 43	15 03	15 23	15 43		16 03	16 23	16 43	17 03		17 23	17 43	18 03
Kilburn High Road	d	11 44		12 04	12 24	12 44	13 04		13 24	13 44	14 04	14 24		14 44	15 04	15 24	15 44		16 04	16 24	16 44	17 04		17 24	17 44	18 04
Queens Park (Dc) ⊖	d	11 46		12 06	12 26	12 46	13 06		13 26	13 46	14 06	14 26		14 46	15 06	15 26	15 46		16 06	16 26	16 46	17 06		17 26	17 46	18 06
Kensal Green	d	11 48		12 08	12 28	12 48	13 08		13 28	13 48	14 08	14 28		14 48	15 08	15 28	15 48		16 08	16 28	16 48	17 08		17 28	17 48	18 08
Willesden Jn Low Level	d	11 51		12 11	12 31	12 51	13 11		13 31	13 51	14 11	14 31		14 51	15 11	15 31	15 51		16 11	16 31	16 51	17 11		17 31	17 51	18 11
Harlesden	d	11 53		12 13	12 33	12 53	13 13		13 33	13 53	14 13	14 33		14 53	15 13	15 33	15 53		16 13	16 33	16 53	17 13		17 33	17 53	18 13
Stonebridge Park	d	11 55		12 15	12 35	12 55	13 15		13 35	13 55	14 15	14 35		14 55	15 15	15 35	15 55		16 15	16 35	16 55	17 15		17 35	17 55	18 15
Wembley Central Dc	d	11 58		12 18	12 38	12 58	13 18		13 38	13 58	14 18	14 38		14 58	15 18	15 38	15 58		16 18	16 38	16 58	17 18		17 38	17 58	18 18
North Wembley	d	12 00		12 20	12 40	13 00	13 20		13 40	14 00	14 20	14 40		15 00	15 20	15 40	16 00		16 20	16 40	17 00	17 20		17 40	18 00	18 20
South Kenton	d	12 02		12 22	12 42	13 02	13 22		13 42	14 02	14 22	14 42		15 02	15 22	15 42	16 02		16 22	16 42	17 02	17 22		17 42	18 02	18 22
Kenton	d	12 04		12 24	12 44	13 04	13 24		13 44	14 04	14 24	14 44		15 04	15 24	15 44	16 04		16 24	16 44	17 04	17 24		17 44	18 04	18 24
Harrow & Wealdstone D.C.	d	12 06		12 26	12 46	13 06	13 26		13 46	14 06	14 26	14 46		15 06	15 26	15 46	16 06		16 26	16 46	17 06	17 26		17 46	18 06	18 26
Headstone Lane	d	12 09		12 29	12 49	13 09	13 29		13 49	14 09	14 29	14 49		15 09	15 29	15 49	16 09		16 29	16 49	17 09	17 29		17 49	18 09	18 29
Hatch End	d	12 11		12 31	12 51	13 11	13 31		13 51	14 11	14 31	14 51		15 11	15 31	15 51	16 11		16 31	16 51	17 11	17 31		17 51	18 11	18 31
Carpenders Park	d	12 14		12 34	12 54	13 14	13 34		13 54	14 14	14 34	14 54		15 14	15 34	15 54	16 14		16 34	16 54	17 14	17 34		17 54	18 14	18 34
Bushey Dc	d	12 17		12 37	12 57	13 17	13 37		13 57	14 17	14 37	14 57		15 17	15 37	15 57	16 17		16 37	16 57	17 17	17 37		17 57	18 17	18 37
Watford High Street	d	12 20		12 40	13 00	13 20	13 40		14 00	14 20	14 40	15 00		15 20	15 40	16 00	16 20		16 40	17 00	17 20	17 40		18 00	18 20	18 40
Watford Junction Dc	a	12 24		12 44	13 04	13 24	13 44		14 04	14 24	14 44	15 04		15 24	15 44	16 04	16 24		16 44	17 04	17 24	17 44		18 04	18 24	18 44

		LO	LO	LO		LO	LO	LO	LO		LO	LO	LO	LO		LO	LO	LO	LO		LO	LO	LO			
London Euston 15 ⊖	d	18 17	18 37	18 57		19 17	19 37	19 57	20 17		20 37	20 57	21 17	21 37		21 57	22 17	22 37	22 57		23 17	23 37	23 57			
South Hampstead	d	18 23	18 43	19 03		19 23	19 43	20 03	20 23		20 43	21 03	21 23	21 43		22 03	22 23	22 43	23 03		23 23	23 43	00 03			
Kilburn High Road	d	18 24	18 44	19 04		19 24	19 44	20 04	20 24		20 44	21 04	21 24	21 44		22 04	22 24	22 44	23 04		23 24	23 44	00 04			
Queens Park (Dc) ⊖	d	18 26	18 46	19 06		19 26	19 46	20 06	20 26		20 46	21 06	21 26	21 46		22 06	22 26	22 46	23 06		23 26	23 46	00 06			
Kensal Green	d	18 28	18 48	19 08		19 28	19 48	20 08	20 28		20 48	21 08	21 28	21 48		22 08	22 28	22 48	23 08		23 28	23 48	00 08			
Willesden Jn Low Level	d	18 31	18 51	19 11		19 31	19 51	20 11	20 31		20 51	21 11	21 31	21 51		22 11	22 31	22 51	23 11		23 31	23 51	00 11			
Harlesden	d	18 33	18 53	19 13		19 33	19 53	20 13	20 33		20 53	21 13	21 33	21 53		22 13	22 33	22 53	23 13		23 33	23 53	00 13			
Stonebridge Park	d	18 35	18 55	19 15		19 35	19 55	20 15	20 35		20 55	21 15	21 35	21 55		22 15	22 35	22 55	23 15		23 35	23 55	00 15			
Wembley Central Dc	d	18 38	18 58	19 18		19 38	19 58	20 18	20 38		20 58	21 18	21 38	21 58		22 18	22 38	22 58	23 18		23 38	23 58	00 18			
North Wembley	d	18 40	19 00	19 20		19 40	20 00	20 20	20 40		21 00	21 20	21 40	22 00		22 20	22 40	23 00	23 20		23 40	00 01	00 20			
South Kenton	d	18 42	19 02	19 22		19 42	20 02	20 22	20 42		21 02	21 22	21 42	22 02		22 22	22 42	23 02	23 22		23 42	00 02	00 22			
Kenton	d	18 44	19 04	19 24		19 44	20 04	20 24	20 44		21 04	21 24	21 44	22 04		22 24	22 44	23 04	23 24		23 44	00 04	00 24			
Harrow & Wealdstone D.C.	d	18 46	19 06	19 26		19 46	20 06	20 26	20 46		21 06	21 26	21 46	22 06		22 26	22 46	23 06	23 26		23 46	00 06	00 26			
Headstone Lane	d	18 49	19 09	19 29		19 49	20 09	20 29	20 49		21 09	21 29	21 49	22 09		22 29	22 49	23 09	23 29		23 49	00 09	00 29			
Hatch End	d	18 51	19 11	19 31		19 51	20 11	20 31	20 51		21 11	21 31	21 51	22 11		22 31	22 51	23 11	23 31		23 51	00 11	00 31			
Carpenders Park	d	18 54	19 14	19 34		19 54	20 14	20 34	20 54		21 14	21 34	21 54	22 14		22 34	22 54	23 14	23 34		23 54	00 14	00 34			
Bushey Dc	d	18 57	19 17	19 37		19 57	20 17	20 37	20 57		21 17	21 37	21 57	22 17		22 37	22 57	23 17	23 37		23 57	00 17	00 37			
Watford High Street	d	19 00	19 20	19 40		20 00	20 20	20 40	21 00		21 20	21 40	22 00	22 20		22 40	23 00	23 20	23 40		00 01	00 20	00 40			
Watford Junction Dc	a	19 04	19 24	19 44		20 04	20 24	20 44	21 04		21 24	21 44	22 06	22 24		22 44	23 04	23 24	23 44		00 04	00 24	00 44			

Sundays

		LO	LO	LO	LO		LO	LO	LO	LO		LO	LO	LO	LO		LO	LO	LO	LO		LO	LO	LO	LO	LO
London Euston 15 ⊖	d	23p17	23p37	23p57	00 22		02 00	06 47	07 17	07 47		08 17	08 47	09 17	09 47		10 17	10 47	11 17	11 47		12 17	12 47	13 17	13 47	14 17
South Hampstead	d	23p23	23p43	00 03				06 53	07 23	07 53		08 23	08 53	09 23	09 53		10 23	10 53	11 23	11 53		12 23	12 53	13 23	13 53	14 23
Kilburn High Road	d	23p24	23p44	00 04				06 54	07 24	07 54		08 24	08 54	09 24	09 54		10 24	10 54	11 24	11 54		12 24	12 54	13 24	13 54	14 24
Queens Park (Dc) ⊖	d	23p26	23p46	00 06	00 30			06 56	07 26	07 56		08 26	08 56	09 26	09 56		10 26	10 56	11 26	11 56		12 26	12 56	13 26	13 56	14 26
Kensal Green	d	23p28	23p48	00 08				06 58	07 28	07 58		08 28	08 58	09 28	09 58		10 28	10 58	11 28	11 58		12 28	12 58	13 28	13 58	14 28
Willesden Jn Low Level	d	23p31	23p51	00 11				07 01	07 31	08 01		08 31	09 01	09 31	10 01		10 31	11 01	11 31	12 01		12 31	13 01	13 31	14 01	14 31
Harlesden	d	23p33	23p53	00 13				07 03	07 33	08 03		08 33	09 03	09 33	10 03		10 33	11 03	11 33	12 03		12 33	13 03	13 33	14 03	14 33
Stonebridge Park	d	23p35	23p55	00 15				07 05	07 35	08 05		08 35	09 05	09 35	10 05		10 35	11 05	11 35	12 05		12 35	13 05	13 35	14 05	14 35
Wembley Central Dc	d	23p38	23p58	00 18	00 38		02 18	07 08	07 38	08 08		08 38	09 08	09 38	10 08		10 38	11 08	11 38	12 08		12 38	13 08	13 38	14 08	14 38
North Wembley	d	23p40	00 01	00 20				07 10	07 40	08 10		08 40	09 10	09 40	10 10		10 40	11 10	11 40	12 10		12 40	13 10	13 40	14 10	14 40
South Kenton	d	23p42	00 02	00 22				07 12	07 42	08 12		08 42	09 12	09 42	10 12		10 42	11 12	11 42	12 12		12 42	13 12	13 42	14 12	14 42
Kenton	d	23p44	00 04	00 24				07 14	07 44	08 14		08 44	09 14	09 44	10 14		10 44	11 14	11 44	12 14		12 44	13 14	13 44	14 14	14 44
Harrow & Wealdstone D.C.	d	23p46	00 06	00 26	00 45		02 27	07 16	07 46	08 16		08 46	09 16	09 46	10 16		10 46	11 16	11 46	12 16		12 46	13 16	13 46	14 16	14 46
Headstone Lane	d	23p49	00 09	00 29				07 19	07 49	08 19		08 49	09 19	09 49	10 19		10 49	11 19	11 49	12 19		12 49	13 19	13 49	14 19	14 49
Hatch End	d	23p51	00 11	00 31				07 21	07 51	08 21		08 51	09 21	09 51	10 21		10 51	11 21	11 51	12 21		12 51	13 21	13 51	14 21	14 51
Carpenders Park	d	23p54	00 14	00 34				07 24	07 54	08 24		08 54	09 24	09 54	10 24		10 54	11 24	11 54	12 24		12 54	13 24	13 54	14 24	14 54
Bushey Dc	d	23p57	00 17	00 37				07 27	07 57	08 27		08 57	09 27	09 57	10 27		10 57	11 27	11 57	12 27		12 57	13 27	13 57	14 27	14 57
Watford High Street	d	00 01	00 20	00 40				07 30	08 00	08 30		09 00	09 30	10 00	10 30		11 00	11 30	12 00	12 30		13 00	13 30	14 00	14 30	15 00
Watford Junction Dc	a	00 04	00 24	00 44	00 59		02 40	07 34	08 04	08 34		09 04	09 34	10 04	10 34		11 04	11 34	12 04	12 34		13 04	13 34	14 04	14 34	15 04

		LO		LO	LO	LO	LO		LO	LO	LO	LO		LO	LO	LO	LO		LO	LO	LO	LO	LO	LO		
London Euston 15 ⊖	d	14 47		15 17	15 47	16 17	16 47		17 17	17 47	18 17	18 47		19 17	19 47	20 17	20 47		21 17	21 47	22 17	22 47	23 17	23 47		
South Hampstead	d	14 53		15 23	15 53	16 23	16 53		17 23	17 53	18 23	18 53		19 23	19 53	20 23	20 53		21 23	21 53	22 23	22 53	23 23	23 53		
Kilburn High Road	d	14 54		15 24	15 54	16 24	16 54		17 24	17 54	18 24	18 54		19 24	19 54	20 24	20 54		21 24	21 54	22 24	22 54	23 24	23 54		
Queens Park (Dc) ⊖	d	14 56		15 26	15 56	16 26	16 56		17 26	17 56	18 26	18 56		19 26	19 56	20 26	20 56		21 26	21 56	22 26	22 56	23 26	23 56		
Kensal Green	d	14 58		15 28	15 58	16 28	16 58		17 28	17 58	18 28	18 58		19 28	19 58	20 28	20 58		21 28	21 58	22 28	22 58	23 28	23 58		
Willesden Jn Low Level	d	15 01		15 31	16 01	16 31	17 01		17 31	18 01	18 31	19 01		19 31	20 01	20 31	21 01		21 31	22 01	22 31	23 01	23 31	00 01		
Harlesden	d	15 03		15 33	16 03	16 33	17 03		17 33	18 03	18 33	19 03		19 33	20 03	20 33	21 03		21 33	22 03	22 33	23 03	23 33	00 03		
Stonebridge Park	d	15 05		15 35	16 05	16 35	17 05		17 35	18 05	18 35	19 05		19 35	20 05	20 35	21 05		21 35	22 05	22 35	23 05	23 35	00 05		
Wembley Central Dc	d	15 08		15 38	16 08	16 38	17 08		17 38	18 08	18 38	19 08		19 38	20 08	20 38	21 08		21 38	22 08	22 38	23 08	23 38	00 08		
North Wembley	d	15 10		15 40	16 10	16 40	17 10		17 40	18 10	18 40	19 10		19 40	20 10	20 40	21 10		21 40	22 10	22 40	23 10	23 40	00 10		
South Kenton	d	15 12		15 42	16 12	16 42	17 12		17 42	18 12	18 42	19 12		19 42	20 12	20 42	21 12		21 42	22 12	22 42	23 12	23 42	00 12		
Kenton	d	15 14		15 44	16 14	16 44	17 14		17 44	18 14	18 44	19 14		19 44	20 14	20 44	21 14		21 44	22 14	22 44	23 14	23 44	00 14		
Harrow & Wealdstone D.C.	d	15 16		15 46	16 16	16 46	17 16		17 46	18 16	18 46	19 16		19 46	20 16	20 46	21 16		21 46	22 16	22 46	23 16	23 46	00 16		
Headstone Lane	d	15 19		15 49	16 19	16 49	17 19		17 49	18 19	18 49	19 19		19 49	20 19	20 49	21 19		21 49	22 19	22 49	23 19	23 49	00 19		
Hatch End	d	15 21		15 51	16 21	16 51	17 21		17 51	18 21	18 51	19 21		19 51	20 21	20 51	21 21		21 51	22 21	22 51	23 21	23 51	00 21		
Carpenders Park	d	15 24		15 54	16 24	16 54	17 24		17 54	18 24	18 54	19 24		19 54	20 24	20 54	21 24		21 54	22 24	22 54	23 24	23 54	00 24		
Bushey Dc	d	15 27		15 57	16 27	16 57	17 27		17 57	18 27	18 57	19 27		19 57	20 27	20 57	21 27		21 57	22 27	22 57	23 27	23 57	00 27		
Watford High Street	d	15 30		16 00	16 30	17 00	17 30		18 00	18 30	19 00	19 30		20 00	20 30	21 00	21 30		22 00	22 30	23 00	23 30	00 01	00 30		
Watford Junction Dc	a	15 34		16 04	16 34	17 04	17 34		18 04	18 34	19 04	19 34		20 04	20 34	21 04	21 34		22 04	22 34	23 04	23 34	00 04	00 34		

For general notes see front of timetable
For details of catering facilities see Directory of Train Operators

Stations Queen's Park to Harrow & Wealdstone inclusive are also served by London Underground Bakerloo line services

Watford Junction → Harrow & Wealdstone, Queens Park and London

Network Diagram - See first page of Table 59

Miles		LO MO	LO	LO		LO	LO	LO		LO	LO	LO		LO	LO	LO		LO	LO	LO		LO	LO	LO	LO
0	**Watford Junction Dc** d	23p21	05 05	05 21		05 41	06 01	06 20		06 40	07 00	07 20		07 40	08 00	08 20		08 40	09 00	09 21		09 41	10 01	10 21	10 41
1	Watford High Street d	23p24	05 08	05 24		05 44	06 04	06 23		06 43	07 03	07 23		07 43	08 03	08 23		08 43	09 03	09 24		09 44	10 04	10 24	10 44
1¾	Bushey Dc d	23p26	05 10	05 26		05 46	06 06	06 25		06 45	07 05	07 25		07 45	08 05	08 25		08 45	09 05	09 26		09 46	10 06	10 26	10 46
3	Carpenders Park d	23p29	05 13	05 29		05 49	06 09	06 28		06 48	07 08	07 28		07 48	08 08	08 28		08 48	09 08	09 29		09 49	10 09	10 29	10 49
4½	Hatch End d	23p32	05 16	05 32		05 52	06 12	06 31		06 51	07 11	07 31		07 51	08 11	08 31		08 51	09 11	09 32		09 52	10 12	10 32	10 52
5¼	Headstone Lane d	23p34	05 18	05 34		05 54	06 14	06 33		06 53	07 13	07 33		07 53	08 13	08 33		08 53	09 13	09 34		09 54	10 14	10 34	10 54
6½	**Harrow & Wealdstone D.C.** d	23p37	05 21	05 37		05 57	06 17	06 36		06 56	07 16	07 36		07 56	08 16	08 36		08 56	09 16	09 37		09 57	10 17	10 37	10 57
7½	Kenton d	23p39	05 23	05 39		05 59	06 19	06 39		06 59	07 19	07 39		07 59	08 19	08 39		08 59	09 19	09 39		09 59	10 19	10 39	10 59
8¼	South Kenton d	23p41	05 25	05 41		06 01	06 21	06 41		07 01	07 21	07 41		08 01	08 21	08 41		09 01	09 21	09 41		10 01	10 21	10 41	11 01
8¾	North Wembley d	23p43	05 27	05 43		06 03	06 23	06 43		07 03	07 23	07 43		08 03	08 23	08 43		09 03	09 23	09 43		10 03	10 23	10 43	11 03
9¾	Wembley Central Dc d	23p45	05 29	05 45		06 05	06 25	06 45		07 05	07 25	07 45		08 05	08 25	08 45		09 05	09 25	09 45		10 05	10 25	10 45	11 05
10¾	Stonebridge Park d	23p48	05 32	05 48		06 08	06 28	06 48		07 08	07 28	07 48		08 08	08 28	08 48		09 08	09 28	09 48		10 08	10 28	10 48	11 08
11¾	Harlesden d	23p50	05 34	05 50		06 10	06 30	06 50		07 10	07 30	07 50		08 10	08 30	08 50		09 10	09 30	09 50		10 10	10 30	10 50	11 10
12½	**Willesden Jn Low Level** d	23p52	05 36	05 52		06 12	06 32	06 53		07 13	07 33	07 53		08 13	08 33	08 53		09 13	09 33	09 52		10 12	10 32	10 52	11 12
13¼	Kensal Green d	23p55	05 39	05 55		06 15	06 35	06 55		07 15	07 35	07 55		08 15	08 35	08 55		09 15	09 35	09 55		10 15	10 35	10 55	11 15
14	**Queens Park (Dc)** ⊖ d	23p57	05 41	05 57		06 17	06 37	06 58		07 18	07 38	07 58		08 18	08 38	08 58		09 18	09 38	09 57		10 17	10 37	10 57	11 17
14¾	Kilburn High Road d	23p59	05 43	05 59		06 19	06 39	07 00		07 20	07 40	08 00		08 20	08 40	09 00		09 20	09 40	09 59		10 19	10 39	10 59	11 19
15¼	South Hampstead d	00 01	05 45	06 01		06 21	06 41	07 02		07 22	07 42	08 02		08 22	08 42	09 02		09 22	09 42	10 01		10 21	10 41	11 01	11 21
17¾	**London Euston 15** ⊖ a	00 08	05 52	06 13		06 32	06 51	07 12		07 32	07 50	08 12		08 33	08 52	09 12		09 32	09 52	10 11		10 30	10 50	11 11	11 30

	LO		LO	LO	LO		LO	LO	LO		LO	LO	LO		LO	LO	LO		LO	LO	LO		LO	LO	LO
Watford Junction Dc d	11 01		11 21	11 41	12 01		12 21	12 41	13 01		13 21	13 41	14 01		14 21	14 41	15 01		15 21	15 41	16 01		16 21	16 41	17 01
Watford High Street d	11 04		11 24	11 44	12 04		12 24	12 44	13 04		13 24	13 44	14 04		14 24	14 44	15 04		15 24	15 44	16 04		16 24	16 44	17 04
Bushey Dc d	11 06		11 26	11 46	12 06		12 26	12 46	13 06		13 26	13 46	14 06		14 26	14 46	15 06		15 26	15 46	16 06		16 26	16 46	17 06
Carpenders Park d	11 09		11 29	11 49	12 09		12 29	12 49	13 09		13 29	13 49	14 09		14 29	14 49	15 09		15 29	15 49	16 09		16 29	16 49	17 09
Hatch End d	11 12		11 32	11 52	12 12		12 32	12 52	13 12		13 32	13 52	14 12		14 32	14 52	15 12		15 32	15 52	16 12		16 32	16 52	17 12
Headstone Lane d	11 14		11 34	11 54	12 14		12 34	12 54	13 14		13 34	13 54	14 14		14 34	14 54	15 14		15 34	15 54	16 14		16 34	16 54	17 14
Harrow & Wealdstone D.C. d	11 17		11 37	11 57	12 17		12 37	12 57	13 17		13 37	13 57	14 17		14 37	14 57	15 17		15 37	15 57	16 17		16 37	16 57	17 17
Kenton d	11 19		11 39	11 59	12 19		12 39	12 59	13 19		13 39	13 59	14 19		14 39	14 59	15 19		15 39	15 59	16 19		16 39	16 59	17 19
South Kenton d	11 21		11 41	12 01	12 21		12 41	13 01	13 21		13 41	14 01	14 21		14 41	15 01	15 21		15 41	16 01	16 21		16 41	17 01	17 21
North Wembley d	11 23		11 43	12 03	12 23		12 43	13 03	13 23		13 43	14 03	14 23		14 43	15 03	15 23		15 43	16 03	16 23		16 43	17 03	17 23
Wembley Central Dc d	11 25		11 45	12 05	12 25		12 45	13 05	13 25		13 45	14 05	14 25		14 45	15 05	15 25		15 45	16 05	16 25		16 45	17 05	17 25
Stonebridge Park d	11 28		11 48	12 08	12 28		12 48	13 08	13 28		13 48	14 08	14 28		14 48	15 08	15 28		15 48	16 08	16 28		16 48	17 08	17 28
Harlesden d	11 30		11 50	12 10	12 30		12 50	13 10	13 30		13 50	14 10	14 30		14 50	15 10	15 30		15 50	16 10	16 30		16 50	17 10	17 30
Willesden Jn Low Level d	11 32		11 52	12 12	12 32		12 52	13 12	13 32		13 52	14 12	14 32		14 52	15 12	15 32		15 52	16 12	16 32		16 52	17 12	17 32
Kensal Green d	11 35		11 55	12 15	12 35		12 55	13 15	13 35		13 55	14 15	14 35		14 55	15 15	15 35		15 55	16 15	16 35		16 55	17 15	17 35
Queens Park (Dc) ⊖ d	11 37		11 57	12 17	12 37		12 57	13 17	13 37		13 57	14 17	14 37		14 57	15 17	15 37		15 57	16 17	16 37		16 57	17 17	17 37
Kilburn High Road d	11 39		11 59	12 19	12 39		12 59	13 19	13 39		13 59	14 19	14 39		14 59	15 19	15 39		15 59	16 19	16 39		16 59	17 19	17 39
South Hampstead d	11 41		12 01	12 21	12 41		13 01	13 21	13 41		14 01	14 21	14 41		15 01	15 21	15 41		16 01	16 21	16 41		17 01	17 21	17 41
London Euston 15 ⊖ a	11 50		12 11	12 30	12 50		13 11	13 30	13 50		14 11	14 30	14 50		15 11	15 30	15 50		16 11	16 30	16 49		17 11	17 30	17 50

	LO	LO		LO	LO	LO		LO	LO	LO		LO	LO	LO		LO	LO	LO		LO	LO	LO	LO		
Watford Junction Dc d	17 21	17 41		18 01	18 21	18 41		19 01	19 21	19 41		20 01	20 21	20 41		21 01	21 21	21 41		22 01	22 21	22 41	23 01		
Watford High Street d	17 24	17 44		18 04	18 24	18 44		19 04	19 24	19 44		20 04	20 24	20 44		21 04	21 24	21 44		22 04	22 24	22 44	23 04		
Bushey Dc d	17 26	17 46		18 06	18 26	18 46		19 06	19 26	19 46		20 06	20 26	20 46		21 06	21 26	21 46		22 06	22 26	22 46	23 06		
Carpenders Park d	17 29	17 49		18 09	18 29	18 49		19 09	19 29	19 49		20 09	20 29	20 49		21 09	21 29	21 49		22 09	22 29	22 49	23 09		
Hatch End d	17 32	17 52		18 12	18 32	18 52		19 12	19 32	19 52		20 12	20 32	20 52		21 12	21 32	21 52		22 12	22 32	22 52	23 12		
Headstone Lane d	17 34	17 54		18 14	18 34	18 54		19 14	19 34	19 54		20 14	20 34	20 54		21 14	21 34	21 54		22 14	22 34	22 54	23 14		
Harrow & Wealdstone D.C. d	17 37	17 57		18 17	18 37	18 57		19 17	19 37	19 57		20 17	20 37	20 57		21 17	21 37	21 57		22 17	22 37	22 57	23 17		
Kenton d	17 39	17 59		18 19	18 39	18 59		19 19	19 39	19 59		20 19	20 39	20 59		21 19	21 39	21 59		22 19	22 39	22 59	23 19		
South Kenton d	17 41	18 01		18 21	18 41	19 01		19 21	19 41	20 01		20 21	20 41	21 01		21 21	21 41	22 01		22 21	22 41	23 01	23 21		
North Wembley d	17 43	18 03		18 23	18 43	19 03		19 23	19 43	20 03		20 23	20 43	21 03		21 23	21 43	22 03		22 23	22 43	23 03	23 23		
Wembley Central Dc d	17 45	18 05		18 25	18 45	19 05		19 25	19 45	20 05		20 25	20 45	21 05		21 25	21 45	22 05		22 25	22 45	23 05	23 25		
Stonebridge Park d	17 48	18 08		18 28	18 48	19 08		19 28	19 48	20 08		20 28	20 48	21 08		21 28	21 48	22 08		22 28	22 48	23 08	23 28		
Harlesden d	17 50	18 10		18 30	18 50	19 10		19 30	19 50	20 10		20 30	20 50	21 10		21 30	21 50	22 10		22 30	22 50	23 10	23 30		
Willesden Jn Low Level d	17 52	18 12		18 32	18 52	19 12		19 32	19 52	20 12		20 32	20 52	21 12		21 32	21 52	22 12		22 32	22 52	23 12	23 32		
Kensal Green d	17 55	18 15		18 35	18 55	19 15		19 35	19 55	20 15		20 35	20 55	21 15		21 35	21 55	22 15		22 35	22 55	23 15	23 35		
Queens Park (Dc) ⊖ d	17 57	18 17		18 37	18 57	19 17		19 37	19 57	20 17		20 37	20 57	21 17		21 37	21 57	22 17		22 37	22 57	23 17	23 37		
Kilburn High Road d	17 59	18 19		18 39	18 59	19 19		19 39	19 59	20 19		20 39	20 59	21 19		21 39	21 59	22 19		22 39	22 59	23 19	23 39		
South Hampstead d	18 01	18 21		18 41	19 01	19 21		19 41	20 01	20 21		20 41	21 01	21 21		21 41	22 01	22 21		22 41	23 01	23 21	23 41		
London Euston 15 ⊖ a	18 13	18 32		18 50	19 11	19 30		19 51	20 10	20 30		20 51	21 11	21 30		21 51	22 11	22 30		22 50	23 10	23 30	23 50		

Saturdays

	LO	LO	LO		LO	LO	LO		LO	LO	LO		LO	LO	LO		LO	LO	LO		LO	LO	LO		LO
Watford Junction Dc d	05 05	05 21	05 41		06 01	06 21	06 41		07 01	07 21	07 41		08 01	08 21	08 41		09 01	09 21	09 41		10 01	10 21	10 41		11 01
Watford High Street d	05 08	05 24	05 44		06 04	06 24	06 44		07 04	07 24	07 44		08 04	08 24	08 44		09 04	09 24	09 44		10 04	10 24	10 44		11 04
Bushey Dc d	05 10	05 26	05 46		06 06	06 26	06 46		07 06	07 26	07 46		08 06	08 26	08 46		09 06	09 26	09 46		10 06	10 26	10 46		11 06
Carpenders Park d	05 13	05 29	05 49		06 09	06 29	06 49		07 09	07 29	07 49		08 09	08 29	08 49		09 09	09 29	09 49		10 09	10 29	10 49		11 09
Hatch End d	05 16	05 32	05 52		06 12	06 32	06 52		07 12	07 32	07 52		08 12	08 32	08 52		09 12	09 32	09 52		10 12	10 32	10 52		11 12
Headstone Lane d	05 18	05 34	05 54		06 14	06 34	06 54		07 14	07 34	07 54		08 14	08 34	08 54		09 14	09 34	09 54		10 14	10 34	10 54		11 14
Harrow & Wealdstone D.C. d	05 21	05 37	05 57		06 17	06 37	06 57		07 17	07 37	07 57		08 17	08 37	08 57		09 17	09 37	09 57		10 17	10 37	10 57		11 17
Kenton d	05 23	05 39	05 59		06 19	06 39	06 59		07 19	07 39	07 59		08 19	08 39	08 59		09 19	09 39	09 59		10 19	10 39	10 59		11 19
South Kenton d	05 25	05 41	06 01		06 21	06 41	07 01		07 21	07 41	08 01		08 21	08 41	09 01		09 21	09 41	10 01		10 21	10 41	11 01		11 21
North Wembley d	05 27	05 43	06 03		06 23	06 43	07 03		07 23	07 43	08 03		08 23	08 43	09 03		09 23	09 43	10 03		10 23	10 43	11 03		11 23
Wembley Central Dc d	05 29	05 45	06 05		06 25	06 45	07 05		07 25	07 45	08 05		08 25	08 45	09 05		09 25	09 45	10 05		10 25	10 45	11 05		11 25
Stonebridge Park d	05 32	05 48	06 08		06 28	06 48	07 08		07 28	07 48	08 08		08 28	08 48	09 08		09 28	09 48	10 08		10 28	10 48	11 08		11 28
Harlesden d	05 34	05 50	06 10		06 30	06 50	07 10		07 30	07 50	08 10		08 30	08 50	09 10		09 30	09 50	10 10		10 30	10 50	11 10		11 30
Willesden Jn Low Level d	05 36	05 52	06 12		06 32	06 52	07 12		07 32	07 52	08 12		08 32	08 52	09 12		09 32	09 52	10 12		10 32	10 52	11 12		11 32
Kensal Green d	05 39	05 55	06 15		06 35	06 55	07 15		07 35	07 55	08 15		08 35	08 55	09 15		09 35	09 55	10 15		10 35	10 55	11 15		11 35
Queens Park (Dc) ⊖ d	05 41	05 57	06 17		06 37	06 57	07 17		07 37	07 57	08 17		08 37	08 57	09 17		09 37	09 57	10 17		10 37	10 57	11 17		11 37
Kilburn High Road d	05 43	05 59	06 19		06 39	06 59	07 19		07 39	07 59	08 19		08 39	08 59	09 19		09 39	09 59	10 19		10 39	10 59	11 19		11 39
South Hampstead d	05 45	06 01	06 21		06 41	07 01	07 21		07 41	08 01	08 21		08 41	09 01	09 21		09 41	10 01	10 21		10 41	11 01	11 21		11 41
London Euston 15 ⊖ a	05 54	06 10	06 30		06 50	07 10	07 30		07 51	08 12	08 30		08 51	09 11	09 30		09 51	10 11	10 30		10 51	11 11	11 30		11 51

For general notes see front of timetable
For details of catering facilities see
Directory of Train Operators

Stations Harrow & Wealdstone to Queen's Park inclusive are also served by London Underground Bakerloo Line services

Watford Junction → Harrow & Wealdstone, Queens Park and London

Saturdays

Network Diagram - See first page of Table 59

		LO	LO	LO	LO	LO	LO	LO	LO	LO	LO	LO	LO	LO	LO	LO	LO	LO	LO	LO
Watford Junction Dc	d	11 21	11 41	12 01	12 21	12 41	13 01	13 21	13 41	14 01	14 21	14 41	15 01	15 21	15 41	16 01	16 21	16 41	17 01	17 21
Watford High Street	d	11 24	11 44	12 04	12 24	12 44	13 04	13 24	13 44	14 04	14 24	14 44	15 04	15 24	15 44	16 04	16 24	16 44	17 04	17 24
Bushey Dc	d	11 26	11 46	12 06	12 26	12 46	13 06	13 26	13 46	14 06	14 26	14 46	15 06	15 26	15 46	16 06	16 26	16 46	17 06	17 26
Carpenders Park	d	11 29	11 49	12 09	12 29	12 49	13 09	13 29	13 49	14 09	14 29	14 49	15 09	15 29	15 49	16 09	16 29	16 49	17 09	17 29
Hatch End	d	11 32	11 52	12 12	12 32	12 52	13 12	13 32	13 52	14 12	14 32	14 52	15 12	15 32	15 52	16 12	16 32	16 52	17 12	17 32
Headstone Lane	d	11 34	11 54	12 14	12 34	12 54	13 14	13 34	13 54	14 14	14 34	14 54	15 14	15 34	15 54	16 14	16 34	16 54	17 14	17 34
Harrow & Wealdstone D.C.	d	11 37	11 57	12 17	12 37	12 57	13 17	13 37	13 57	14 17	14 37	14 57	15 17	15 37	15 57	16 17	16 37	16 57	17 17	17 37
Kenton	d	11 39	11 59	12 19	12 39	12 59	13 19	13 39	13 59	14 19	14 39	14 59	15 19	15 39	15 59	16 19	16 39	16 59	17 19	17 39
South Kenton	d	11 41	12 01	12 21	12 41	13 01	13 21	13 41	14 01	14 21	14 41	15 01	15 21	15 41	16 01	16 21	16 41	17 01	17 21	17 41
North Wembley	d	11 43	12 03	12 23	12 43	13 03	13 23	13 43	14 03	14 23	14 43	15 03	15 23	15 43	16 03	16 23	16 43	17 03	17 23	17 43
Wembley Central Dc	d	11 45	12 05	12 25	12 45	13 05	13 25	13 45	14 05	14 25	14 45	15 05	15 25	15 45	16 05	16 25	16 45	17 05	17 25	17 45
Stonebridge Park	d	11 48	12 08	12 28	12 48	13 08	13 28	13 48	14 08	14 28	14 48	15 08	15 28	15 48	16 08	16 28	16 48	17 08	17 28	17 48
Harlesden	d	11 50	12 10	12 30	12 50	13 10	13 30	13 50	14 10	14 30	14 50	15 10	15 30	15 50	16 10	16 30	16 50	17 10	17 30	17 50
Willesden Jn Low Level	d	11 52	12 12	12 32	12 52	13 12	13 32	13 52	14 12	14 32	14 52	15 12	15 32	15 52	16 12	16 32	16 52	17 12	17 32	17 52
Kensal Green	d	11 55	12 15	12 35	12 55	13 15	13 35	13 55	14 15	14 35	14 55	15 15	15 35	15 55	16 15	16 35	16 55	17 15	17 35	17 55
Queens Park (Dc) ⊖	d	11 57	12 17	12 37	12 57	13 17	13 37	13 57	14 17	14 37	14 57	15 17	15 37	15 57	16 17	16 37	16 57	17 17	17 37	17 57
Kilburn High Road	d	11 59	12 19	12 39	12 59	13 19	13 39	13 59	14 19	14 39	14 59	15 19	15 39	15 59	16 19	16 39	16 59	17 19	17 39	17 59
South Hampstead	d	12 01	12 21	12 41	13 01	13 21	13 41	14 01	14 21	14 41	15 01	15 21	15 41	16 01	16 21	16 41	17 01	17 21	17 41	18 01
London Euston 15 ⊖	a	12 11	12 30	12 49	13 13	13 31	13 50	14 11	14 30	14 51	15 11	15 30	15 51	16 11	16 30	16 51	17 11	17 30	17 51	18 11

		LO	LO	LO	LO	LO	LO	LO	LO	LO	LO	LO	LO	LO	LO	LO	LO A	LO B	LO
Watford Junction Dc	d	17 41	18 01	18 21	18 41	19 01	19 21	19 41	20 01	20 21	20 41	21 01	21 21	21 41	22 01	22 21	22 41	22 41	23 01
Watford High Street	d	17 44	18 04	18 24	18 44	19 04	19 24	19 44	20 04	20 24	20 44	21 04	21 24	21 44	22 04	22 24	22 44	22 44	23 04
Bushey Dc	d	17 46	18 06	18 26	18 46	19 06	19 26	19 46	20 06	20 26	20 46	21 06	21 26	21 46	22 06	22 26	22 46	22 46	23 06
Carpenders Park	d	17 49	18 09	18 29	18 49	19 09	19 29	19 49	20 09	20 29	20 49	21 09	21 29	21 49	22 09	22 29	22 49	22 49	23 09
Hatch End	d	17 52	18 12	18 32	18 52	19 12	19 32	19 52	20 12	20 32	20 52	21 12	21 32	21 52	22 12	22 32	22 52	22 52	23 12
Headstone Lane	d	17 54	18 14	18 34	18 54	19 14	19 34	19 54	20 14	20 34	20 54	21 14	21 34	21 54	22 14	22 34	22 54	22 54	23 14
Harrow & Wealdstone D.C.	d	17 57	18 17	18 37	18 57	19 17	19 37	19 57	20 17	20 37	20 57	21 17	21 37	21 57	22 17	22 37	22 57	22 57	23 17
Kenton	d	17 59	18 19	18 39	18 59	19 19	19 39	19 59	20 19	20 39	20 59	21 19	21 39	21 59	22 19	22 39	22 59	22 59	23 19
South Kenton	d	18 01	18 21	18 41	19 01	19 21	19 41	20 01	20 21	20 41	21 01	21 21	21 41	22 01	22 21	22 41	23 01	23 01	23 21
North Wembley	d	18 03	18 23	18 43	19 03	19 23	19 43	20 03	20 23	20 43	21 03	21 23	21 43	22 03	22 23	22 43	23 03	23 03	23 23
Wembley Central Dc	d	18 05	18 25	18 45	19 05	19 25	19 45	20 05	20 25	20 45	21 05	21 25	21 45	22 05	22 25	22 45	23 05	23 05	23 25
Stonebridge Park	d	18 08	18 28	18 48	19 08	19 28	19 48	20 08	20 28	20 48	21 08	21 28	21 48	22 08	22 28	22 48	23 08	23 08	23 28
Harlesden	d	18 10	18 30	18 50	19 10	19 30	19 50	20 10	20 30	20 50	21 10	21 30	21 50	22 10	22 30	22 50	23 10	23 10	23 30
Willesden Jn Low Level	d	18 12	18 32	18 52	19 12	19 32	19 52	20 12	20 32	20 52	21 12	21 32	21 52	22 12	22 32	22 52	23 12	23 12	23 32
Kensal Green	d	18 15	18 35	18 55	19 15	19 35	19 55	20 15	20 35	20 55	21 15	21 35	21 55	22 15	22 35	22 55	23 15	23 15	23 35
Queens Park (Dc) ⊖	d	18 17	18 37	18 57	19 17	19 37	19 57	20 17	20 37	20 57	21 17	21 37	21 57	22 17	22 37	22 57	23 17	23 17	23 37
Kilburn High Road	d	18 19	18 39	18 59	19 19	19 39	19 59	20 19	20 39	20 59	21 19	21 39	21 59	22 19	22 39	22 59	23 19	23 19	23 39
South Hampstead	d	18 21	18 41	19 01	19 21	19 41	20 01	20 21	20 41	21 01	21 21	21 41	22 01	22 21	22 41	23 01	23 21	23 21	23 41
London Euston 15 ⊖	a	18 30	18 51	19 11	19 30	19 51	20 11	20 30	20 50	21 10	21 30	21 50	22 10	22 30	22 50	23 10	23 30	23 32	23 50

Sundays

		LO	LO	LO	LO	LO	LO	LO	LO	LO	LO C	LO D	LO	LO	LO	LO	LO	LO	LO	LO
Watford Junction Dc	d	00 10	01 07	06 51	07 21	07 51	08 21	08 51	09 21	09 51	10 21	10 21	10 51	11 21	11 51	12 21	12 51	13 21	13 51	14 21
Watford High Street	d			06 54	07 24	07 54	08 24	08 54	09 24	09 54	10 24	10 24	10 54	11 24	11 54	12 24	12 54	13 24	13 54	14 24
Bushey Dc	d			06 56	07 26	07 56	08 26	08 56	09 26	09 56	10 26	10 26	10 56	11 26	11 56	12 26	12 56	13 26	13 56	14 26
Carpenders Park	d			06 59	07 29	07 59	08 29	08 59	09 29	09 59	10 29	10 29	10 59	11 29	11 59	12 29	12 59	13 29	13 59	14 29
Hatch End	d			07 02	07 32	08 02	08 32	09 02	09 32	10 02	10 32	10 32	11 02	11 32	12 02	12 32	13 02	13 32	14 02	14 32
Headstone Lane	d			07 04	07 34	08 04	08 34	09 04	09 34	10 04	10 34	10 34	11 04	11 34	12 04	12 34	13 04	13 34	14 04	14 34
Harrow & Wealdstone D.C.	d	00 22	01 19	07 07	07 37	08 07	08 37	09 07	09 37	10 07	10 37	10 37	11 07	11 37	12 07	12 37	13 07	13 37	14 07	14 37
Kenton	d			07 09	07 39	08 09	08 39	09 09	09 39	10 09	10 39	10 39	11 09	11 39	12 09	12 39	13 09	13 39	14 09	14 39
South Kenton	d			07 11	07 41	08 11	08 41	09 11	09 41	10 11	10 41	10 41	11 11	11 41	12 11	12 41	13 11	13 41	14 11	14 41
North Wembley	d			07 13	07 43	08 13	08 43	09 13	09 43	10 13	10 43	10 43	11 13	11 43	12 13	12 43	13 13	13 43	14 13	14 43
Wembley Central Dc	d	00 28	01 25	07 15	07 45	08 15	08 45	09 15	09 45	10 15	10 45	10 45	11 15	11 45	12 15	12 45	13 15	13 45	14 15	14 45
Stonebridge Park	d			07 18	07 48	08 18	08 48	09 18	09 48	10 18	10 48	10 48	11 18	11 48	12 18	12 48	13 18	13 48	14 18	14 48
Harlesden	d			07 20	07 50	08 20	08 50	09 20	09 50	10 20	10 50	10 50	11 20	11 50	12 20	12 50	13 20	13 50	14 20	14 50
Willesden Jn Low Level	d			07 22	07 52	08 22	08 52	09 22	09 52	10 22	10 52	10 52	11 22	11 52	12 22	12 52	13 22	13 52	14 22	14 52
Kensal Green	d			07 25	07 55	08 25	08 55	09 25	09 55	10 25	10 55	10 55	11 25	11 55	12 25	12 55	13 25	13 55	14 25	14 55
Queens Park (Dc) ⊖	d			07 27	07 57	08 27	08 57	09 27	09 57	10 27	10 57	10 57	11 27	11 57	12 27	12 57	13 27	13 57	14 27	14 57
Kilburn High Road	d			07 29	07 59	08 29	08 59	09 29	09 59	10 29	10 59	10 59	11 29	11 59	12 29	12 59	13 29	13 59	14 29	14 59
South Hampstead	d			07 31	08 01	08 31	09 01	09 31	10 01	10 31	11 01	11 01	11 31	12 01	12 31	13 01	13 31	14 01	14 31	15 01
London Euston 15 ⊖	a	00 44	01 41	07 38	08 08	08 38	09 08	09 38	10 08	10 38	11 08	11 09	11 38	12 08	12 40	13 08	13 40	14 08	14 40	15 08

For general notes see front of timetable
For details of catering facilities see Directory of Train Operators

A From 12 September
B Until 5 September
C 19 July to 6 September
D Until 12 July and from 13 September

Stations Harrow & Wealdstone to Queen's Park inclusive are also served by London Underground Bakerloo Line services

Table 60

Sundays

Watford Junction → Harrow & Wealdstone, Queens Park and London

Network Diagram - See first page of Table 59

		LO	LO	LO	LO	LO	LO	LO	LO	LO	LO	LO	LO	LO	LO	LO	LO	LO	LO
Watford Junction Dc	d	14 51	15 21	15 51	16 21	16 51	17 21	17 51	18 21	18 51	19 21	19 51	20 21	20 51	21 21	21 51	22 21	22 51	23 21
Watford High Street	d	14 54	15 24	15 54	16 24	16 54	17 24	17 54	18 24	18 54	19 24	19 54	20 24	20 54	21 24	21 54	22 24	22 54	23 24
Bushey Dc	d	14 56	15 26	15 56	16 26	16 56	17 26	17 56	18 26	18 56	19 26	19 56	20 26	20 56	21 26	21 56	22 26	22 56	23 26
Carpenders Park	d	14 59	15 29	15 59	16 29	16 59	17 29	17 59	18 29	18 59	19 29	19 59	20 29	20 59	21 29	21 59	22 29	22 59	23 29
Hatch End	d	15 02	15 32	16 02	16 32	17 02	17 32	18 02	18 32	19 02	19 32	20 02	20 32	21 02	21 32	22 02	22 32	23 02	23 32
Headstone Lane	d	15 04	15 34	16 04	16 34	17 04	17 34	18 04	18 34	19 04	19 34	20 04	20 34	21 04	21 34	22 04	22 34	23 04	23 34
Harrow & Wealdstone D.C.	d	15 07	15 37	16 07	16 37	17 07	17 37	18 07	18 37	19 07	19 37	20 07	20 37	21 07	21 37	22 07	22 37	23 07	23 37
Kenton	d	15 09	15 39	16 09	16 39	17 09	17 39	18 09	18 39	19 09	19 39	20 09	20 39	21 09	21 39	22 09	22 39	23 09	23 39
South Kenton	d	15 11	15 41	16 11	16 41	17 11	17 41	18 11	18 41	19 11	19 41	20 11	20 41	21 11	21 41	22 11	22 41	23 11	23 41
North Wembley	d	15 13	15 43	16 13	16 43	17 13	17 43	18 13	18 43	19 13	19 43	20 13	20 43	21 13	21 43	22 13	22 43	23 13	23 43
Wembley Central Dc	d	15 15	15 45	16 15	16 45	17 15	17 45	18 15	18 45	19 15	19 45	20 15	20 45	21 15	21 45	22 15	22 45	23 15	23 45
Stonebridge Park	d	15 18	15 48	16 18	16 48	17 18	17 48	18 18	18 48	19 18	19 48	20 18	20 48	21 18	21 48	22 18	22 48	23 18	23 48
Harlesden	d	15 20	15 50	16 20	16 50	17 20	17 50	18 20	18 50	19 20	19 50	20 20	20 50	21 20	21 50	22 20	22 50	23 20	23 50
Willesden Jn Low Level	d	15 22	15 52	16 22	16 52	17 22	17 52	18 22	18 52	19 22	19 52	20 22	20 52	21 22	21 52	22 22	22 52	23 22	23 52
Kensal Green	d	15 25	15 55	16 25	16 55	17 25	17 55	18 25	18 55	19 25	19 55	20 25	20 55	21 25	21 55	22 25	22 55	23 25	23 55
Queens Park (Dc) ⊖	d	15 27	15 57	16 27	16 57	17 27	17 57	18 27	18 57	19 27	19 57	20 27	20 57	21 27	21 57	22 27	22 57	23 27	23 57
Kilburn High Road	d	15 29	15 59	16 29	16 59	17 29	17 59	18 29	18 59	19 29	19 59	20 29	20 59	21 29	21 59	22 29	22 59	23 29	23 59
South Hampstead	d	15 31	16 01	16 31	17 01	17 31	18 01	18 31	19 01	19 31	20 01	20 31	21 01	21 31	22 01	22 31	23 01	23 31	00 01
London Euston 15 ⊖	a	15 40	16 08	16 40	17 08	17 40	18 08	18 40	19 08	19 40	20 08	20 40	21 08	21 38	22 08	22 38	23 08	23 38	00 08

For general notes see front of timetable
For details of catering facilities see Directory of Train Operators

Stations Harrow & Wealdstone to Queen's Park inclusive are also served by London Underground Bakerloo Line services

Table 61

Mondays to Fridays

Watford Junction → St. Albans

Network Diagram - See first page of Table 59

Miles			LM 1	LM 1	LM 1	LM 1	LM 1	LM 1	LM 1		LM 1	LM 1	LM 1	LM 1	LM 1	LM 1	LM 1	LM 1	LM 1	LM 1	LM 1	LM 1	LM 1	LM 1		
—	London Euston 15	⊖ d	05 30	06 04	06 53	07 46	08 34	09 24	10 05		10 54	11 34	12 24	13 04	13 54	14 34	15 24	16 04	16 54	17 40	18 24	19 04	20 04	21 04		
0	**Watford Junction**	d	06 00	06 42	07 24	08 09	09 01	09 46	10 31		11 16	12 01	12 46	13 31	14 16	15 01	15 46	16 31	17 21	18 10	18 55	19 38	20 31	21 31		
¾	Watford North	d	06 02	06 44	07 26	08 11	09 03	09 48	10 33		11 18	12 03	12 48	13 33	14 18	15 03	15 48	16 33	17 23	18 12	18 57	19 40	20 33	21 33		
1¾	Garston (Hertfordshire)	d	06 05	06 47	07 29	08 14	09 06	09 51	10 36		11 21	12 06	12 51	13 36	14 21	15 06	15 51	16 36	17 26	18 15	19 00	19 43	20 36	21 36		
3¼	Bricket Wood	d	06 08	06 50	07 32	08 17	09 09	09 54	10 39		11 24	12 09	12 54	13 39	14 24	15 09	15 54	16 39	17 29	18 18	19 03	19 46	20 39	21 39		
4½	How Wood	d	06 10	06 52	07 34	08 19	09 11	09 56	10 41		11 26	12 11	12 56	13 41	14 26	15 11	15 56	16 41	17 31	18 20	19 05	19 48	20 41	21 41		
5	Park Street	d	06 12	06 54	07 36	08 21	09 13	09 58	10 43		11 28	12 13	12 58	13 43	14 28	15 13	15 58	16 43	17 33	18 22	19 07	19 50	20 43	21 43		
6½	**St Albans Abbey**	a	06 16	06 58	07 40	08 25	09 17	10 02	10 47		11 32	12 17	13 02	13 47	14 32	15 17	16 02	16 47	17 37	18 26	19 11	19 54	20 47	21 47		

Saturdays

		LM 1	LM 1	LM 1	LM 1	LM 1		LM 1	LM 1	LM 1	LM 1	LM 1		LM 1	LM 1	LM 1	LM 1	LM 1	LM 1	LM 1	LM 1	LM 1	LM 1	LM 1		
London Euston 15	⊖ d	05 34	06 24	07 04	07 54	08 34		09 24	10 04	10 54	11 34	12 24		13 04	13 54	14 34	15 24	16 04	16 54	17 34	18 24	19 04	19 50	21 07		
Watford Junction	d	06 01	06 45	07 31	08 15	09 01		09 46	10 31	11 16	12 01	12 46		13 31	14 16	15 01	15 46	16 31	17 16	18 01	18 46	19 31	20 31	21 31		
Watford North	d	06 03	06 47	07 33	08 17	09 03		09 48	10 33	11 18	12 03	12 48		13 33	14 18	15 03	15 48	16 33	17 18	18 03	18 48	19 33	20 33	21 33		
Garston (Hertfordshire)	d	06 06	06 50	07 36	08 20	09 06		09 51	10 36	11 21	12 06	12 51		13 36	14 21	15 06	15 51	16 36	17 21	18 06	18 51	19 36	20 36	21 36		
Bricket Wood	d	06 09	06 53	07 39	08 23	09 09		09 54	10 39	11 24	12 09	12 54		13 39	14 24	15 09	15 54	16 39	17 24	18 09	18 54	19 39	20 39	21 39		
How Wood	d	06 11	06 55	07 41	08 25	09 11		09 56	10 41	11 26	12 11	12 56		13 41	14 26	15 11	15 56	16 41	17 26	18 11	18 56	19 41	20 41	21 41		
Park Street	d	06 13	06 57	07 43	08 27	09 13		09 58	10 43	11 28	12 13	12 58		13 43	14 28	15 13	15 58	16 43	17 28	18 13	18 58	19 43	20 43	21 43		
St Albans Abbey	a	06 17	07 01	07 47	08 31	09 17		10 02	10 47	11 32	12 17	13 02		13 47	14 32	15 17	16 02	16 47	17 32	18 17	19 02	19 47	20 47	21 47		

Sundays

		LM 1	LM 1		LM 1	LM 1		LM 1	LM 1		LM 1	LM 1		LM 1	LM 1		LM 1	LM 1		LM 1	LM 1		LM 1			
London Euston 15	⊖ d	07 23	08 23		09 53	10 53		11 23	12 34		13 34	14 34		15 34	16 34		17 34	18 34		19 34	20 34		21 28			
Watford Junction	d	08 07	09 07		10 20	11 20		12 07	13 07		14 07	15 07		16 07	17 07		18 07	19 07		20 07	21 02		22 04			
Watford North	d	08 09	09 09		10 22	11 22		12 09	13 09		14 09	15 09		16 09	17 09		18 09	19 09		20 09	21 04		22 06			
Garston (Hertfordshire)	d	08 12	09 12		10 25	11 25		12 12	13 12		14 12	15 12		16 12	17 12		18 12	19 12		20 12	21 07		22 09			
Bricket Wood	d	08 15	09 15		10 28	11 28		12 15	13 15		14 15	15 15		16 15	17 15		18 15	19 15		20 15	21 10		22 12			
How Wood	d	08 17	09 17		10 30	11 30		12 17	13 17		14 17	15 17		16 17	17 17		18 17	19 17		20 17	21 12		22 14			
Park Street	d	08 19	09 19		10 32	11 32		12 19	13 19		14 19	15 19		16 19	17 19		18 19	19 19		20 19	21 14		22 16			
St Albans Abbey	a	08 23	09 23		10 36	11 36		12 23	13 23		14 23	15 23		16 23	17 23		18 23	19 23		20 23	21 18		22 20			

For general notes see front of timetable
For details of catering facilities see
Directory of Train Operators

St. Albans → Watford Junction

Network Diagram - See first page of Table 59

Miles			LM 1	LM 1	LM 1	LM 1	LM 1	LM 1	LM 1	LM 1	LM 1	LM 1	LM 1	LM 1	LM 1	LM 1	LM 1	LM 1	LM 1	LM 1	LM 1	LM 1	LM 1	LM 1
0	**St Albans Abbey**	d	06 21	07 03	07 45	08 30	09 22	10 07	10 52	11 37	12 22	13 07	13 52	14 37	15 22	16 07	16 52	17 42	18 32	19 16	20 00	20 52	21 52
1½	Park Street	d	06 24	07 06	07 48	08 33	09 25	10 10	10 55	11 40	12 25	13 10	13 55	14 40	15 25	16 10	16 55	17 45	18 35	19 19	20 03	20 55	21 55
2¼	How Wood	d	06 26	07 08	07 50	08 35	09 27	10 12	10 57	11 42	12 27	13 12	13 57	14 42	15 27	16 12	16 57	17 47	18 37	19 21	20 05	20 57	21 57
3	Bricket Wood	d	06 29	07 11	07 53	08 38	09 30	10 15	11 00	11 45	12 30	13 15	14 00	14 45	15 30	16 15	17 00	17 50	18 40	19 24	20 08	21 00	22 00
4¾	Garston (Hertfordshire)	d	06 32	07 14	07 56	08 41	09 33	10 18	11 03	11 48	12 33	13 18	14 03	14 48	15 33	16 18	17 03	17 53	18 43	19 27	20 11	21 03	22 03
5½	Watford North	d	06 34	07 16	07 58	08 43	09 35	10 20	11 05	11 50	12 35	13 20	14 05	14 50	15 35	16 20	17 05	17 55	18 45	19 29	20 13	21 05	22 05
6½	**Watford Junction**	a	06 37	07 19	08 01	08 46	09 38	10 23	11 08	11 53	12 38	13 23	14 08	14 53	15 38	16 24	17 08	17 58	18 48	19 32	20 16	21 08	22 08
—	London Euston 15 ⊖	a	*07 06*	*07 52*	*08 29*	*09 26*	*10 08*	*10 49*	*11 38*	*12 38*	*13 08*	*13 49*	*14 38*	*15 38*	*16 08*	*16 48*	*17 38*	*18 40*	*19 18*	*20 10*	*20 47*	*21 38*	*22 51*

Saturdays

		LM 1	LM 1	LM 1	LM 1	LM 1	LM 1	LM 1	LM 1	LM 1	LM 1	LM 1	LM 1	LM 1	LM 1	LM 1	LM 1	LM 1	LM 1	LM 1	LM 1	LM 1
St Albans Abbey	d	06 22	07 06	07 52	08 36	09 22	10 07	10 52	11 37	12 22	13 07	13 52	14 37	15 22	16 07	16 52	17 37	18 22	19 07	19 52	20 52	21 52
Park Street	d	06 25	07 09	07 55	08 39	09 25	10 10	10 55	11 40	12 25	13 10	13 55	14 40	15 25	16 10	16 55	17 40	18 25	19 10	19 55	20 55	21 55
How Wood	d	06 27	07 11	07 57	08 41	09 27	10 12	10 57	11 42	12 27	13 12	13 57	14 42	15 27	16 12	16 57	17 42	18 27	19 12	19 57	20 57	21 57
Bricket Wood	d	06 30	07 14	08 00	08 44	09 30	10 15	11 00	11 45	12 30	13 15	14 00	14 45	15 30	16 15	17 00	17 45	18 30	19 15	20 00	21 00	22 00
Garston (Hertfordshire)	d	06 33	07 17	08 03	08 47	09 33	10 18	11 03	11 48	12 33	13 18	14 03	14 48	15 33	16 18	17 03	17 48	18 33	19 18	20 03	21 03	22 03
Watford North	d	06 35	07 19	08 05	08 49	09 35	10 20	11 05	11 50	12 35	13 20	14 05	14 50	15 35	16 20	17 05	17 50	18 35	19 20	20 05	21 05	22 05
Watford Junction	a	06 38	07 22	08 08	08 52	09 38	10 23	11 08	11 53	12 38	13 23	14 08	14 53	15 38	16 23	17 08	17 53	18 38	19 23	20 08	21 08	22 08
London Euston 15 ⊖	a	*07 11*	*07 46*	*08 38*	*09 18*	*10 08*	*10 48*	*11 38*	*12 38*	*13 08*	*13 48*	*14 38*	*15 38*	*16 08*	*16 46*	*17 38*	*18 38*	*19 08*	*19 48*	*20 39*	*21b43*	*22c36*

Sundays

		LM 1	LM 1	LM 1	LM 1	LM 1	LM 1	LM 1	LM 1	LM 1	LM 1	LM 1	LM 1	LM 1	LM 1	LM 1
St Albans Abbey	d	08 28	09 28	10 42	11 42	12 28	13 28	14 28	15 28	16 28	17 28	18 28	19 28	20 28	21 23	22 25
Park Street	d	08 31	09 31	10 45	11 45	12 31	13 31	14 31	15 31	16 31	17 31	18 31	19 31	20 31	21 26	22 28
How Wood	d	08 33	09 33	10 47	11 47	12 33	13 33	14 33	15 33	16 33	17 33	18 33	19 33	20 33	21 28	22 30
Bricket Wood	d	08 36	09 36	10 50	11 50	12 36	13 36	14 36	15 36	16 36	17 36	18 36	19 36	20 36	21 31	22 33
Garston (Hertfordshire)	d	08 39	09 39	10 53	11 53	12 39	13 39	14 39	15 39	16 39	17 39	18 39	19 39	20 39	21 34	22 36
Watford North	d	08 41	09 41	10 55	11 55	12 41	13 41	14 41	15 41	16 41	17 41	18 41	19 41	20 41	21 36	22 38
Watford Junction	a	08 44	09 44	10 58	11 58	12 44	13 44	14 44	15 44	16 44	17 44	18 44	19 44	20 44	21 39	22 41
London Euston 15 ⊖	a	*09 13*	*10 13*	*11 26*	*12 27*	*13 11*	*14 11*	*15 11*	*16 11*	*17 11*	*18 11*	*19 11*	*20 11*	*21 15*	*22 18*	*23 13*

For general notes see front of timetable
For details of catering facilities see
Directory of Train Operators

b From 12 September arr. 2137
c From 12 September arr. 2233

Table 62

Mondays to Fridays

Gospel Oak → Barking

Network diagram - see first page of Table 59

Miles			LO	LO	LO	LO	LO	LO	LO	LO	LO	LO	LO	LO	LO		LO	LO	LO	LO
0	**Gospel Oak**	d	06 25	06 55	07 15	07 40	08 00	08 20	08 40	09 00	09 20	09 40	10 00	10 25	10 55		14 25	14 55	15 12	15 35
1¼	Upper Holloway	d	06 29	06 59	07 19	07 44	08 04	08 24	08 44	09 04	09 24	09 44	10 04	10 29	10 59	and	14 29	14 59	15b19	15 39
2	Crouch Hill	d	06 32	07 02	07 22	07 47	08 07	08 27	08 47	09 07	09 27	09 47	10 07	10 32	11 02		14 32	15 02	15 22	15 42
3	Harringay Green Lanes	d	06 35	07 05	07 25	07 50	08 10	08 30	08 50	09 10	09 30	09 50	10 10	10 35	11 05	every 30	14 35	15 05	15 25	15 45
4½	South Tottenham	d	06 38	07 08	07 28	07 53	08 13	08 33	08 53	09 13	09 33	09 53	10 13	10 38	11 08		14 38	15 08	15 28	15 48
5¾	Blackhorse Road	⊖ d	06 41	07 11	07 31	07 56	08 16	08 36	08 56	09 16	09 36	09 56	10 16	10 41	11 11	minutes	14 41	15 11	15 31	15 51
6½	Walthamstow Queen's Road	d	06 44	07 14	07 34	07 59	08 19	08 39	08 59	09 19	09 39	09 59	10 19	10 44	11 14		14 44	15 14	15 34	15 54
7½	Leyton Midland Road	d	06 47	07 17	07 37	08 02	08 22	08 42	09 02	09 22	09 42	10 02	10 22	10 47	11 17	until	14 47	15 17	15 37	15 57
8¼	Leytonstone High Road	d	06 50	07 20	07 40	08 05	08 25	08 45	09 05	09 25	09 45	10 05	10 25	10 50	11 20		14 50	15 20	15 40	16 00
9½	Wanstead Park	d	06 53	07 23	07 43	08 08	08 28	08 48	09 08	09 28	09 48	10 08	10 28	10 53	11 23		14 53	15 23	15 43	16 03
10½	Woodgrange Park	d	06 55	07 25	07 45	08 10	08 30	08 50	09 10	09 30	09 50	10 10	10 30	10 55	11 25		14 55	15 25	15 45	16 05
12¼	**Barking**	⊖ a	06 59	07 31	07 51	08 16	08 36	08 56	09 16	09 36	09 56	10 16	10 36	10 59	11 29		14 59	15 29	15 49	16 09

		LO	LO	LO	LO	LO	LO	LO	LO	LO	LO	LO	LO	LO	LO	LO	LO	LO	LO	LO
Gospel Oak	d	15 55	16 15	16 35	16 55	17 15	17 35	17 55	18 15	18 35	18 55	19 25	19 55	20 25	20 55	21 25	21 55	22 25	22 55	23 25
Upper Holloway	d	15 59	16 19	16 39	16 59	17 19	17 39	17 59	18 19	18 39	18 59	19 29	19 59	20 29	20 59	21 29	21 59	22 29	22 59	23 29
Crouch Hill	d	16 02	16 22	16 42	17 02	17 22	17 42	18 02	18 22	18 42	19 02	19 32	20 02	20 32	21 02	21 32	22 02	22 32	23 02	23 32
Harringay Green Lanes	d	16 05	16 25	16 45	17 05	17 25	17 45	18 05	18 25	18 45	19 05	19 35	20 05	20 35	21 05	21 35	22 05	22 35	23 05	23 35
South Tottenham	d	16 08	16 28	16 48	17 08	17 28	17 48	18 08	18 28	18 48	19 08	19 38	20 08	20 38	21 08	21 38	22 08	22 38	23 08	23 38
Blackhorse Road	⊖ d	16 11	16 31	16 51	17 11	17 31	17 51	18 11	18 31	18 51	19 11	19 41	20 11	20 41	21 11	21 41	22 11	22 41	23 11	23 41
Walthamstow Queen's Road	d	16 14	16 34	16 54	17 14	17 34	17 54	18 14	18 34	18 54	19 14	19 44	20 14	20 44	21 14	21 44	22 14	22 44	23 14	23 44
Leyton Midland Road	d	16 17	16 37	16 57	17 17	17 37	17 57	18 17	18 37	18 57	19 17	19 47	20 17	20 47	21 17	21 47	22 17	22 47	23 17	23 47
Leytonstone High Road	d	16 20	16 40	17 00	17 20	17 40	18 00	18 20	18 40	19 00	19 20	19 50	20 20	20 50	21 20	21 50	22 20	22 50	23 20	23 50
Wanstead Park	d	16 23	16 43	17 03	17 23	17 43	18 03	18 23	18 43	19 03	19 23	19 53	20 23	20 53	21 23	21 53	22 23	22 53	23 23	23 53
Woodgrange Park	d	16 25	16 45	17 05	17 25	17 45	18 05	18 25	18 45	19 05	19 25	19 55	20 25	20 55	21 25	21 55	22 25	22 55	23 25	23 55
Barking	⊖ a	16 29	16 51	17 11	17 31	17 51	18 11	18 31	18 51	19 11	19 31	19 59	20 32	21 00	21 29	21 59	22 29	22 59	23 29	00 01

Saturdays

		LO	LO	LO	LO	LO	LO	LO	LO	LO	LO	LO	LO	LO		LO	LO	LO	LO	LO
Gospel Oak	d	06 25	06 55	07 15	07 40	08 00	08 20	08 40	09 00	09 20	09 40	10 00	10 25	10 55		14 25	14 55	15 12	15 35	15 55
Upper Holloway	d	06 29	06 59	07 19	07 44	08 04	08 24	08 44	09 04	09 24	09 44	10 04	10 29	10 59	and	14 29	14 59	15b19	15 39	15 59
Crouch Hill	d	06 32	07 02	07 22	07 47	08 07	08 27	08 47	09 07	09 27	09 47	10 07	10 32	11 02		14 32	15 02	15 22	15 42	16 02
Harringay Green Lanes	d	06 35	07 05	07 25	07 50	08 10	08 30	08 50	09 10	09 30	09 50	10 10	10 35	11 05	every 30	14 35	15 05	15 25	15 45	16 05
South Tottenham	d	06 38	07 08	07 28	07 53	08 13	08 33	08 53	09 13	09 33	09 53	10 13	10 38	11 08		14 38	15 08	15 28	15 48	16 08
Blackhorse Road	⊖ d	06 41	07 11	07 31	07 56	08 16	08 36	08 56	09 16	09 36	09 56	10 16	10 41	11 11	minutes	14 41	15 11	15 31	15 51	16 11
Walthamstow Queen's Road	d	06 44	07 14	07 34	07 59	08 19	08 39	08 59	09 19	09 39	09 59	10 19	10 44	11 14		14 44	15 14	15 34	15 54	16 14
Leyton Midland Road	d	06 47	07 17	07 37	08 02	08 22	08 42	09 02	09 22	09 42	10 02	10 22	10 47	11 17	until	14 47	15 17	15 37	15 57	16 17
Leytonstone High Road	d	06 50	07 20	07 40	08 05	08 25	08 45	09 05	09 25	09 45	10 05	10 25	10 50	11 20		14 50	15 20	15 40	16 00	16 20
Wanstead Park	d	06 53	07 23	07 43	08 08	08 28	08 48	09 08	09 28	09 48	10 08	10 28	10 53	11 23		14 53	15 23	15 43	16 03	16 23
Woodgrange Park	d	06 55	07 25	07 45	08 10	08 30	08 50	09 10	09 30	09 50	10 10	10 30	10 55	11 25		14 55	15 25	15 45	16 05	16 25
Barking	⊖ a	06 59	07 29	07 49	08 14	08 34	08 54	09 14	09 34	09 54	10 14	10 34	10 59	11 29		14 59	15 29	15 49	16 09	16 29

		LO	LO	LO	LO	LO	LO	LO	LO	LO	LO	LO	LO	LO	LO	LO	LO	LO	LO
Gospel Oak	d	16 15	16 35	16 55	17 15	17 35	17 55	18 15	18 35	18 55	19 25	19 55	20 25	20 55	21 25	21 55	22 25	22 55	23 25
Upper Holloway	d	16 19	16 39	16 59	17 19	17 39	17 59	18 19	18 39	18 59	19 29	19 59	20 29	20 59	21 29	21 59	22 29	22 59	23 29
Crouch Hill	d	16 22	16 42	17 02	17 22	17 42	18 02	18 22	18 42	19 02	19 32	20 02	20 32	21 02	21 32	22 02	22 32	23 02	23 32
Harringay Green Lanes	d	16 25	16 45	17 05	17 25	17 45	18 05	18 25	18 45	19 05	19 35	20 05	20 35	21 05	21 35	22 05	22 35	23 05	23 35
South Tottenham	d	16 28	16 48	17 08	17 28	17 48	18 08	18 28	18 48	19 08	19 38	20 08	20 38	21 08	21 38	22 08	22 38	23 08	23 38
Blackhorse Road	⊖ d	16 31	16 51	17 11	17 31	17 51	18 11	18 31	18 51	19 11	19 41	20 11	20 41	21 11	21 41	22 11	22 41	23 11	23 41
Walthamstow Queen's Road	d	16 34	16 54	17 14	17 34	17 54	18 14	18 34	18 54	19 14	19 44	20 14	20 44	21 14	21 44	22 14	22 44	23 14	23 44
Leyton Midland Road	d	16 37	16 57	17 17	17 37	17 57	18 17	18 37	18 57	19 17	19 47	20 17	20 47	21 17	21 47	22 17	22 47	23 17	23 47
Leytonstone High Road	d	16 40	17 00	17 20	17 40	18 00	18 20	18 40	19 00	19 20	19 50	20 20	20 50	21 20	21 50	22 20	22 50	23 20	23 50
Wanstead Park	d	16 43	17 03	17 23	17 43	18 03	18 23	18 43	19 03	19 23	19 53	20 23	20 53	21 23	21 53	22 23	22 53	23 23	23 53
Woodgrange Park	d	16 45	17 05	17 25	17 45	18 05	18 25	18 45	19 05	19 25	19 55	20 25	20 55	21 25	21 55	22 25	22 55	23 25	23 55
Barking	⊖ a	16 49	17 09	17 29	17 49	18 09	18 29	18 50	19 09	19 29	19 59	20 32	20 59	21 29	21 59	22 29	22 59	23 29	23 59

Sundays

		LO	LO		LO	LO
Gospel Oak	d	08 50	09 20		22 50	23 20
Upper Holloway	d	08 54	09 24	and	22 54	23 24
Crouch Hill	d	08 57	09 27		22 57	23 27
Harringay Green Lanes	d	09 00	09 30	every 30	23 00	23 30
South Tottenham	d	09 03	09 33		23 03	23 33
Blackhorse Road	⊖ d	09 06	09 36	minutes	23 06	23 36
Walthamstow Queen's Road	d	09 09	09 39		23 09	23 39
Leyton Midland Road	d	09 12	09 42	until	23 12	23 42
Leytonstone High Road	d	09 15	09 45		23 15	23 45
Wanstead Park	d	09 18	09 48		23 18	23 48
Woodgrange Park	d	09 20	09 50		23 20	23 50
Barking	⊖ a	09 24	09 54		23 24	23 54

For general notes see front of timetable
For details of catering facilities see Directory of Train Operators

b Arr. 1516

Barking → Gospel Oak

Network diagram - see first page of Table 59

Mondays to Fridays

Miles			LO	LO	LO	LO	LO	LO	LO	LO	LO	LO	LO	LO	LO	LO	LO		LO	LO
0	**Barking** ⊖	d	06 31	06 54	07 20	07 40	08 00	08 20	08 40	09 00	09 20	09 40	10 00	10 20	10 40	11 08	11 38		15 08	15 34
1¾	Woodgrange Park	d	06 34	06 57	07 23	07 43	08 03	08 23	08 43	09 03	09 23	09 43	10 03	10 23	10 43	11 11	11 41	and	15 11	15 37
2¾	Wanstead Park	d	06 37	07 00	07 26	07 46	08 06	08 26	08 46	09 06	09 26	09 46	10 06	10 26	10 46	11 14	11 44		15 14	15 40
4	Leytonstone High Road	d	06 41	07 04	07 30	07 50	08 10	08 30	08 50	09 10	09 30	09 50	10 10	10 30	10 50	11 18	11 48	every 30	15 18	15 44
4¾	Leyton Midland Road	d	06 43	07 06	07 32	07 52	08 12	08 32	08 52	09 12	09 32	09 52	10 12	10 32	10 52	11 20	11 50		15 20	15 46
5¾	Walthamstow Queen's Road	d	06 46	07 09	07 35	07 55	08 15	08 35	08 55	09 15	09 35	09 55	10 15	10 35	10 55	11 23	11 53	minutes	15 23	15 49
6½	Blackhorse Road ⊖	d	06 49	07 12	07 38	07 58	08 18	08 38	08 58	09 18	09 38	09 58	10 18	10 38	10 58	11 26	11 56		15 26	15 52
8¼	South Tottenham	d	06 53	07 16	07 42	08 02	08 22	08 42	09 02	09 22	09 42	10 02	10 22	10 42	11 02	11 30	12 00	until	15 30	15 56
9¼	Harringay Green Lanes	d	06 56	07 19	07 45	08 05	08 25	08 45	09 05	09 25	09 45	10 05	10 25	10 45	11 05	11 33	12 03		15 33	15 59
10¼	Crouch Hill	d	06 59	07 22	07 48	08 08	08 28	08 48	09 08	09 28	09 48	10 08	10 28	10 48	11 08	11 36	12 06		15 36	16 02
11	Upper Holloway	d	07 01	07 24	07 50	08 10	08 30	08 50	09 10	09 30	09 50	10 10	10 30	10 50	11 10	11 38	12 08		15 38	16 04
12¼	**Gospel Oak**	a	07 06	07 29	07 57	08 17	08 37	08 57	09 17	09 37	09 57	10 17	10 37	10 58	11 15	11 44	12 13		15 43	16 11

		LO	LO	LO	LO	LO	LO	LO	LO	LO	LO	LO	LO	LO	LO	LO	LO	LO	LO	LO
Barking ⊖	d	15 54	16 14	16 34	16 54	17 14	17 34	17 54	18 14	18 34	18 54	19 18	19 43	20 08	20 38	21 08	21 38	22 08	22 38	23 08
Woodgrange Park	d	15 57	16 17	16 37	16 57	17 17	17 37	17 57	18 17	18 37	18 57	19 21	19 46	20 11	20 41	21 11	21 41	22 11	22 41	23 11
Wanstead Park	d	16 00	16 20	16 40	17 00	17 20	17 40	18 00	18 20	18 40	19 00	19 24	19 49	20 14	20 44	21 14	21 44	22 14	22 44	23 14
Leytonstone High Road	d	16 04	16 24	16 44	17 04	17 24	17 44	18 04	18 24	18 44	19 04	19 28	19 53	20 18	20 48	21 18	21 48	22 18	22 48	23 18
Leyton Midland Road	d	16 06	16 26	16 46	17 06	17 26	17 46	18 06	18 26	18 46	19 06	19 30	19 55	20 20	20 50	21 20	21 50	22 20	22 50	23 20
Walthamstow Queen's Road	d	16 09	16 29	16 49	17 09	17 29	17 49	18 09	18 29	18 49	19 09	19 33	19 58	20 23	20 53	21 23	21 53	22 23	22 53	23 23
Blackhorse Road ⊖	d	16 12	16 32	16 52	17 12	17 32	17 52	18 12	18 32	18 52	19 12	19 36	20 01	20 26	20 56	21 26	21 56	22 26	22 56	23 26
South Tottenham	d	16 16	16 36	16 56	17 16	17 36	17 56	18 16	18 36	18 56	19 16	19 40	20 05	20 30	21 00	21 30	22 00	22 30	23 00	23 30
Harringay Green Lanes	d	16 19	16 39	16 59	17 19	17 39	17 59	18 19	18 39	18 59	19 19	19 43	20 08	20 33	21 03	21 33	22 03	22 33	23 03	23 33
Crouch Hill	d	16 22	16 42	17 02	17 22	17 42	18 02	18 22	18 42	19 02	19 22	19 46	20 11	20 36	21 06	21 36	22 06	22 36	23 06	23 36
Upper Holloway	d	16 24	16 44	17 04	17 24	17 44	18 04	18 24	18 44	19 04	19 24	19 48	20 13	20 38	21 08	21 38	22 08	22 38	23 08	23 38
Gospel Oak	a	16 31	16 51	17 11	17 31	17 51	18 11	18 31	18 51	19 11	19 31	19 53	20 19	20 43	21 13	21 43	22 13	22 43	23 14	23 43

Saturdays

		LO	LO	LO	LO	LO	LO	LO	LO	LO	LO	LO	LO	LO	LO	LO		LO	LO
Barking ⊖	d	06 32	06 54	07 20	07 40	08 00	08 20	08 40	09 00	09 20	09 40	10 00	10 20	10 40	11 08	11 38		15 08	15 34
Woodgrange Park	d	06 35	06 57	07 23	07 43	08 03	08 23	08 43	09 03	09 23	09 43	10 03	10 23	10 43	11 11	11 41	and	15 11	15 37
Wanstead Park	d	06 38	07 00	07 26	07 46	08 06	08 26	08 46	09 06	09 26	09 46	10 06	10 26	10 46	11 14	11 44		15 14	15 40
Leytonstone High Road	d	06 42	07 04	07 30	07 50	08 10	08 30	08 50	09 10	09 30	09 50	10 10	10 30	10 50	11 18	11 48	every 30	15 18	15 44
Leyton Midland Road	d	06 44	07 06	07 32	07 52	08 12	08 32	08 52	09 12	09 32	09 52	10 12	10 32	10 52	11 20	11 50		15 20	15 46
Walthamstow Queen's Road	d	06 47	07 09	07 35	07 55	08 15	08 35	08 55	09 15	09 35	09 55	10 15	10 35	10 55	11 23	11 53	minutes	15 23	15 49
Blackhorse Road ⊖	d	06 50	07 12	07 38	07 58	08 18	08 38	08 58	09 18	09 38	09 58	10 18	10 38	10 58	11 26	11 56		15 26	15 52
South Tottenham	d	06 54	07 16	07 42	08 02	08 22	08 42	09 02	09 22	09 42	10 02	10 22	10 42	11 02	11 30	12 00	until	15 30	15 56
Harringay Green Lanes	d	06 57	07 19	07 45	08 05	08 25	08 45	09 05	09 25	09 45	10 05	10 25	10 45	11 05	11 33	12 03		15 33	15 59
Crouch Hill	d	07 00	07 22	07 48	08 08	08 28	08 48	09 08	09 28	09 48	10 08	10 28	10 48	11 08	11 36	12 06		15 36	16 02
Upper Holloway	d	07 02	07 24	07 50	08 10	08 30	08 50	09 10	09 30	09 50	10 10	10 30	10 50	11 10	11 38	12 08		15 38	16 04
Gospel Oak	a	07 07	07 29	07 55	08 15	08 35	08 55	09 15	09 35	09 55	10 15	10 35	10 58	11 15	11 43	12 13		15 43	16 09

		LO	LO	LO	LO	LO	LO	LO	LO	LO	LO	LO	LO	LO	LO	LO	LO	LO	LO	LO
Barking ⊖	d	15 54	16 14	16 34	16 54	17 14	17 34	17 54	18 14	18 34	18 55	19 18	19 43	20 08	20 38	21 08	21 38	22 08	22 38	23 08
Woodgrange Park	d	15 57	16 17	16 37	16 57	17 17	17 37	17 57	18 17	18 37	18 58	19 21	19 46	20 11	20 41	21 11	21 41	22 11	22 41	23 11
Wanstead Park	d	16 00	16 20	16 40	17 00	17 20	17 40	18 00	18 20	18 40	19 01	19 24	19 49	20 14	20 44	21 14	21 44	22 14	22 44	23 14
Leytonstone High Road	d	16 04	16 24	16 44	17 04	17 24	17 44	18 04	18 24	18 44	19 05	19 28	19 53	20 18	20 48	21 18	21 48	22 18	22 48	23 18
Leyton Midland Road	d	16 06	16 26	16 46	17 06	17 26	17 46	18 06	18 26	18 46	19 07	19 30	19 55	20 20	20 50	21 20	21 50	22 20	22 50	23 20
Walthamstow Queen's Road	d	16 09	16 29	16 49	17 09	17 29	17 49	18 09	18 29	18 49	19 10	19 33	19 58	20 23	20 53	21 23	21 53	22 23	22 53	23 23
Blackhorse Road ⊖	d	16 12	16 32	16 52	17 12	17 32	17 52	18 12	18 32	18 52	19 13	19 36	20 01	20 26	20 56	21 26	21 56	22 26	22 56	23 26
South Tottenham	d	16 16	16 36	16 56	17 16	17 36	17 56	18 16	18 36	18 56	19 17	19 40	20 05	20 30	21 00	21 30	22 00	22 30	23 00	23 30
Harringay Green Lanes	d	16 19	16 39	16 59	17 19	17 39	17 59	18 19	18 39	18 59	19 20	19 43	20 08	20 33	21 03	21 33	22 03	22 33	23 03	23 33
Crouch Hill	d	16 22	16 42	17 02	17 22	17 42	18 02	18 22	18 42	19 02	19 23	19 46	20 11	20 36	21 06	21 36	22 06	22 36	23 06	23 36
Upper Holloway	d	16 24	16 44	17 04	17 24	17 44	18 04	18 24	18 44	19 04	19 25	19 48	20 13	20 38	21 08	21 38	22 08	22 38	23 08	23 38
Gospel Oak	a	16 29	16 49	17 09	17 29	17 49	18 11	18 29	18 49	19 09	19 30	19 53	20 18	20 43	21 13	21 43	22 13	22 43	23 13	23 43

Sundays

		LO	LO		LO	LO	LO
Barking ⊖	d	09 05	09 35		22 05	22 35	23 05
Woodgrange Park	d	09 08	09 38	and	22 08	22 38	23 08
Wanstead Park	d	09 11	09 41		22 11	22 41	23 11
Leytonstone High Road	d	09 15	09 45	every 30	22 15	22 45	23 15
Leyton Midland Road	d	09 17	09 47		22 17	22 47	23 17
Walthamstow Queen's Road	d	09 20	09 50	minutes	22 20	22 50	23 20
Blackhorse Road ⊖	d	09 23	09 53		22 23	22 53	23 23
South Tottenham	d	09 27	09 57	until	22 27	22 57	23 27
Harringay Green Lanes	d	09 30	10 00		22 30	23 00	23 30
Crouch Hill	d	09 33	10 03		22 33	23 03	23 33
Upper Holloway	d	09 35	10 05		22 35	23 05	23 35
Gospel Oak	a	09 40	10 10		22 40	23 10	23 40

For general notes see front of timetable
For details of catering facilities see
Directory of Train Operators

Mondays to Fridays

Bletchley — Bedford

Network Diagram - See first page of Table 59

Miles			LM	LM	LM	LM	LM	LM	LM	LM	LM	LM	LM	LM	LM	LM	LM	LM
—	Milton Keynes Central 3	d	05 21	06 20	07 14	08 21	09 47	10 47	11 47	12 47	13 47	14 47	15 21	16 21	17 21	18 21	19 47	20 47
0	**Bletchley**	d	05 41	06 37	07 39	08 39	10 01	11 01	12 01	13 01	14 01	15 01	15 47	16 47	17 31	18 31	20 01	21 01
1	Fenny Stratford	d	05 44	06 40	07 42	08 42	10 04	11 04	12 04	13 04	14 04	15 04	15 50	16 50	17 34	18 34	20 04	21 04
2	Bow Brickhill	d	05 48	06 44	07 46	08 46	10 08	11 08	12 08	13 08	14 08	15 08	15 54	16 54	17 38	18 38	20 08	21 08
4	Woburn Sands	d	05 52	06 48	07 50	08 50	10 12	11 12	12 12	13 12	14 12	15 12	15 58	16 58	17 42	18 42	20 12	21 12
5	Aspley Guise	d	05 55	06 51	07 53	08 53	10 15	11 15	12 15	13 15	14 15	15 15	16 01	17 01	17 45	18 45	20 15	21 15
6¾	Ridgmont	d	05 58	06 54	07 56	08 56	10 18	11 18	12 18	13 18	14 18	15 18	16 04	17 04	17 48	18 48	20 18	21 18
8½	Lidlington	d	06 02	06 58	08 00	09 00	10 22	11 22	12 22	13 22	14 22	15 22	16 08	17 08	17 52	18 52	20 22	21 22
10	Millbrook (Bedfordshire)	d	06 05	07 01	08 03	09 03	10 25	11 25	12 25	13 25	14 25	15 25	16 11	17 11	17 55	18 55	20 25	21 25
11¼	Stewartby	d	06 09	07 05	08 07	09 07	10 29	11 29	12 29	13 29	14 29	15 29	16 15	17 15	17 59	18 59	20 29	21 29
13	Kempston Hardwick	d	06 12	07 08	08 10	09 10	10 32	11 32	12 32	13 32	14 32	15 32	16 18	17 18	18 02	19 02	20 32	21 32
16	Bedford St Johns	d	06 19	07 15	08 17	09 17	10 39	11 39	12 39	13 39	14 39	15 39	16 25	17 25	18 09	19 09	20 39	21 39
16¾	**Bedford** 7	a	06 25	07 21	08 22	09 23	10 45	11 45	12 45	13 45	14 45	15 45	16 31	17 31	18 15	19 15	20 45	21 45

Saturdays

			LM	LM	LM	LM	LM	LM	LM	LM	LM	LM	LM	LM	LM	LM	LM	LM
	Milton Keynes Central 5	d	05 32	06 21	07 21	08 21	09 47	10 47	11 47	12 47	13 47	14 47	15 21	16 21	17 21	18 21	19 47	20 49
	Bletchley	d	05 41	06 37	07 39	08 39	10 01	11 01	12 01	13 01	14 01	15 01	15 47	16 47	17 31	18 31	20 01	21 01
	Fenny Stratford	d	05 44	06 40	07 42	08 42	10 04	11 04	12 04	13 04	14 04	15 04	15 50	16 50	17 34	18 34	20 04	21 04
	Bow Brickhill	d	05 48	06 44	07 46	08 46	10 08	11 08	12 08	13 08	14 08	15 08	15 54	16 54	17 38	18 38	20 08	21 08
	Woburn Sands	d	05 52	06 48	07 50	08 50	10 12	11 12	12 12	13 12	14 12	15 12	15 58	16 58	17 42	18 42	20 12	21 12
	Aspley Guise	d	05 55	06 51	07 53	08 53	10 15	11 15	12 15	13 15	14 15	15 15	16 01	17 01	17 45	18 45	20 15	21 15
	Ridgmont	d	05 58	06 54	07 56	08 56	10 18	11 18	12 18	13 18	14 18	15 18	16 04	17 04	17 48	18 48	20 18	21 18
	Lidlington	d	06 02	06 58	08 00	09 00	10 22	11 22	12 22	13 22	14 22	15 22	16 08	17 08	17 52	18 52	20 22	21 22
	Millbrook (Bedfordshire)	d	06 05	07 01	08 03	09 03	10 25	11 25	12 25	13 25	14 25	15 25	16 11	17 11	17 55	18 55	20 25	21 25
	Stewartby	d	06 09	07 05	08 07	09 07	10 29	11 29	12 29	13 29	14 29	15 29	16 15	17 15	17 59	18 59	20 29	21 29
	Kempston Hardwick	d	06 12	07 08	08 10	09 10	10 32	11 32	12 32	13 32	14 32	15 32	16 18	17 18	18 02	19 02	20 32	21 32
	Bedford St Johns	d	06 19	07 15	08 17	09 17	10 39	11 39	12 39	13 39	14 39	15 39	16 25	17 25	18 09	19 09	20 39	21 39
	Bedford 7	a	06 25	07 21	08 23	09 23	10 45	11 45	12 45	13 45	14 45	15 45	16 31	17 31	18 15	19 15	20 45	21 45

Mondays to Fridays

Miles			LM	LM	LM	LM	LM	LM	LM	LM	LM	LM	LM	LM	LM	LM	LM	LM
0	**Bedford** 7	d	06 31	07 31	08 31	09 33	10 55	11 55	12 55	13 55	14 55	15 55	16 37	17 37	18 25	19 35	20 55	21 56
¾	Bedford St Johns	d	06 34	07 34	08 34	09 36	10 58	11 58	12 58	13 58	14 58	15 58	16 40	17 40	18 28	19 38	20 58	21 59
3¾	Kempston Hardwick	d	06 41	07 41	08 41	09 43	11 05	12 05	13 05	14 05	15 05	16 05	16 47	17 47	18 35	19 45	21 05	22 06
5½	Stewartby	d	06 44	07 44	08 44	09 46	11 08	12 08	13 08	14 08	15 08	16 08	16 50	17 50	18 38	19 48	21 08	22 09
6¾	Millbrook (Bedfordshire)	d	06 48	07 48	08 48	09 50	11 12	12 12	13 12	14 12	15 12	16 12	16 54	17 54	18 42	19 52	21 12	22 13
8¼	Lidlington	d	06 51	07 51	08 51	09 53	11 15	12 15	13 15	14 15	15 15	16 15	16 57	17 57	18 45	19 55	21 15	22 16
10	Ridgmont	d	06 56	07 56	08 56	09 58	11 20	12 20	13 20	14 20	15 20	16 20	17 02	18 02	18 50	20 00	21 20	22 21
11¾	Aspley Guise	d	06 59	07 59	08 59	10 01	11 23	12 23	13 23	14 23	15 23	16 23	17 05	18 05	18 53	20 03	21 23	22 24
12¾	Woburn Sands	d	07 02	08 02	09 02	10 04	11 26	12 26	13 26	14 26	15 26	16 26	17 08	18 08	18 56	20 06	21 26	22 27
14¾	Bow Brickhill	d	07 06	08 06	09 06	10 08	11 30	12 30	13 30	14 30	15 30	16 30	17 12	18 12	19 00	20 10	21 30	22 31
15¾	Fenny Stratford	d	07 09	08 09	09 09	10 11	11 33	12 33	13 33	14 33	15 33	16 33	17 15	18 15	19 03	20 13	21 33	22 34
16¾	**Bletchley**	a	07 14	08 14	09 14	10 16	11 38	12 38	13 38	14 38	15 38	16 38	17 20	18 20	19 08	20 18	21 38	22 39
—	Milton Keynes Central 5	a	07 39	08 25	09 27	10 49	11 49	12 49	13 49	14 50	15 49	16 49	18 08	18 39	19 18	20 49	21 49	22 57

Saturdays

			LM	LM	LM	LM	LM	LM	LM	LM	LM	LM	LM	LM	LM	LM	LM	LM
	Bedford 7	d	06 31	07 31	08 31	09 33	10 55	11 55	12 55	13 55	14 55	15 55	16 37	17 37	18 25	19 35	20 55	21 56
	Bedford St Johns	d	06 34	07 34	08 34	09 36	10 58	11 58	12 58	13 58	14 58	15 58	16 40	17 40	18 28	19 38	20 58	21 59
	Kempston Hardwick	d	06 41	07 41	08 41	09 43	11 05	12 05	13 05	14 05	15 05	16 05	16 47	17 47	18 35	19 45	21 05	22 06
	Stewartby	d	06 44	07 44	08 44	09 46	11 08	12 08	13 08	14 08	15 08	16 08	16 50	17 50	18 38	19 48	21 08	22 09
	Millbrook (Bedfordshire)	d	06 48	07 48	08 48	09 50	11 12	12 12	13 12	14 12	15 12	16 12	16 54	17 54	18 42	19 52	21 12	22 13
	Lidlington	d	06 51	07 51	08 51	09 53	11 15	12 15	13 15	14 15	15 15	16 15	16 57	17 57	18 45	19 55	21 15	22 16
	Ridgmont	d	06 56	07 56	08 56	09 58	11 20	12 20	13 20	14 20	15 20	16 20	17 02	18 02	18 50	20 00	21 20	22 21
	Aspley Guise	d	06 59	07 59	08 59	10 01	11 23	12 23	13 23	14 23	15 23	16 23	17 05	18 05	18 53	20 03	21 23	22 24
	Woburn Sands	d	07 02	08 02	09 02	10 04	11 26	12 26	13 26	14 26	15 26	16 26	17 08	18 08	18 56	20 06	21 26	22 27
	Bow Brickhill	d	07 06	08 06	09 06	10 08	11 30	12 30	13 30	14 30	15 30	16 30	17 12	18 12	19 00	20 10	21 30	22 31
	Fenny Stratford	d	07 09	08 09	09 09	10 11	11 33	12 33	13 33	14 33	15 33	16 33	17 15	18 15	19 03	20 13	21 33	22 34
	Bletchley	a	07 14	08 14	09 14	10 16	11 38	12 38	13 38	14 38	15 38	16 38	17 20	18 20	19 08	20 18	21 38	22 39
	Milton Keynes Central 5	a	08 00	08 49	09 49	10 49	11 49	12 49	13 49	14 49	15 49	16 49	17 49	18 49	19 23	20 44	22 06	23 02

For general notes see front of timetable
For details of catering facilities see
Directory of Train Operators

No Sunday Service

Route Diagram for Table 65

London-Scotland
See Tables 400-404 for Sleeper trains.

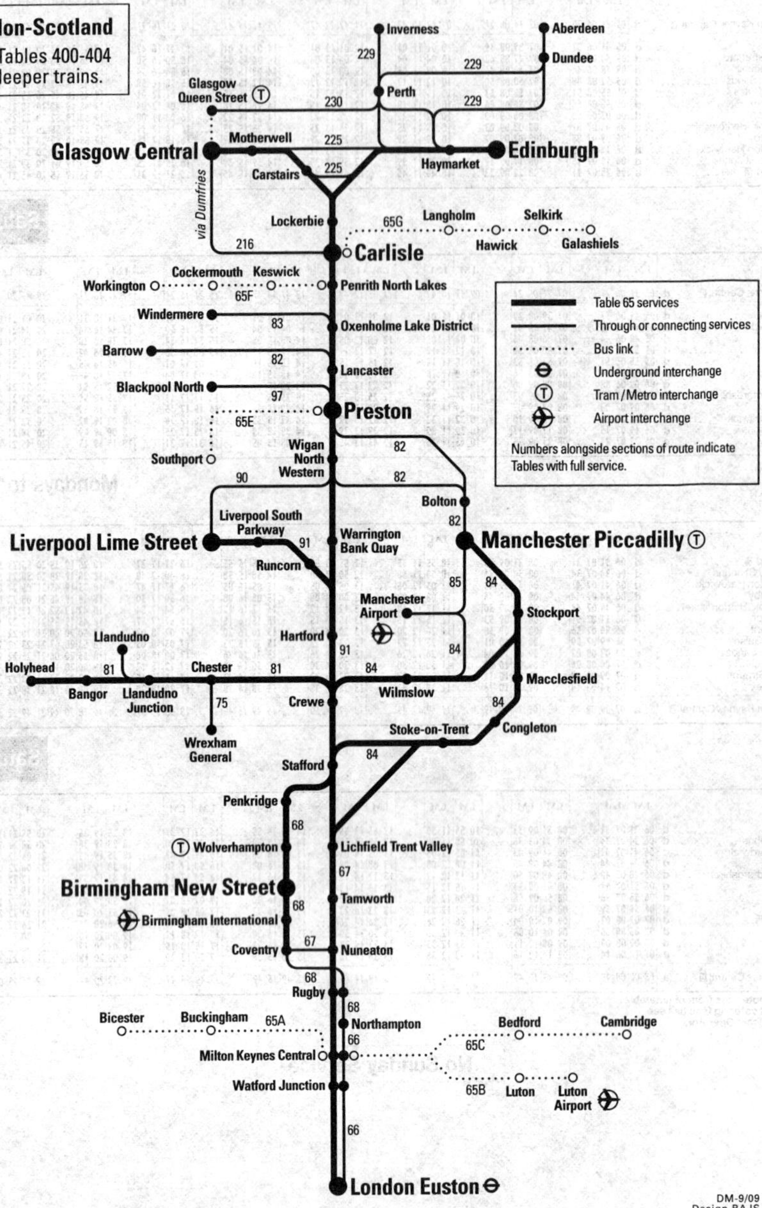

Inverness
Aberdeen
Dundee
229
Perth
Glasgow Queen Street
230
Glasgow Central
Motherwell
225
Edinburgh
Haymarket
Carstairs
via Dumfries
Lockerbie
65G
Langholm
Selkirk
Hawick
Galashiels
216
Carlisle
Cockermouth
Keswick
Workington
65F
Penrith North Lakes
Windermere
83
Oxenholme Lake District
Barrow
82
Lancaster
Blackpool North
97
Preston
65E
Southport
Wigan North Western
90
Bolton
Liverpool South Parkway
Liverpool Lime Street
91
Warrington Bank Quay
Runcorn
Manchester Piccadilly
85
84
Manchester Airport
Stockport
Hartford
Llandudno
Holyhead
81
Chester
Bangor
Llandudno Junction
75
Wrexham General
Crewe
Wilmslow
Macclesfield
Congleton
Stoke-on-Trent
Stafford
Penkridge
68
Wolverhampton
Lichfield Trent Valley
67
Birmingham New Street
Tamworth
Birmingham International
Coventry
Nuneaton
Rugby
66
Bicester
Buckingham
65A
Northampton
Bedford
Cambridge
65C
Milton Keynes Central
65B
Luton
Luton Airport
Watford Junction
London Euston
Table 65 services
Through or connecting services
Bus link
Underground interchange
Tram/Metro interchange
Airport interchange
Numbers alongside sections of route indicate Tables with full service.

DM-9/09
Design BAJS

London and West Midlands → North West England and Scotland

Route Diagram - see first page of Table 65

Miles	Miles	Miles	Miles	Miles			SR	NT	TP	VT	TP	LM	VT	TP		XC	LM	LM		NT	VT	NT	XC	VT	LM
									1	1 ◇	1 ◇	1 ◇	1 ◇	1 ◇		1 ◇	1 ◇	1 ◇			1 ◇		1 ◇	1 ◇	1 ◇
								A	B																
										⊠	🛒		⊠	🛒		🛒					⊠		☕	⊠	
0	—	—	—	—	**London Euston** 15 ⊖	d																		05 35	
—	—	—	—	—	Gatwick Airport 10 ✈	d																			
17½	—	—	—	—	Watford Junction	d																		05u50	
49¾	—	—	—	—	Milton Keynes Central	d																		06 10	
—	—	—	—	—	Northampton	d																			
82½	0	—	—	—	Rugby	d																		*06 02*	
97	—	—	—	—	Nuneaton	d																		06 39	
110	—	—	—	—	Tamworth Low Level	d																		*06 30*	
116¼	—	0	—	—	Lichfield Trent Valley	d																		*06 36*	
—	11½	—	—	—	Coventry	d																		06b12	
—	22	—	—	—	Birmingham International ✈	d																			*06 04*
—	30½	—	—	—	**Birmingham New Street** 12	d							05 30			05 57		06 01			06 17		06 20		06 36
—	43¼	—	—	—	Wolverhampton 7 ⛴	d							05 48			06 15		06 19			06 34		06 40		06 51
—	53¾	—	—	—	Penkridge	d												06 29							
133½	59½	—	—	—	**Stafford**	a							06 01			06 29		06 35					06 53	07 03	07 05
—	—	—	—	—		d							06 02			06 29		06 36					06 54	07 03	07 05
—	75¾	30¼	—	—	**Stoke-on-Trent**	a										06 50							07 12		
—	87¼	42	—	—	Congleton	a										07 02									
—	95¼	50¼	—	—	Macclesfield	a										07 11							07 30		
158	—	—	—	—	**Crewe** 10	a							06 21					06 56			07 07			07 22	07 29
—	—	—	0	—		d				05 57		06 02	06 24				06 31	06 57			07 09			07 24	07 31
—	—	—	—	—	Chester	a							06 44								*07 43*				
—	—	—	—	—	Wrexham General	a																			
—	—	—	—	—	Llandudno Junction	a							07 33								*08c48*				
—	—	—	—	—	Llandudno	a							*08 06*								*09c06*				
—	—	—	—	—	Bangor (Gwynedd)	a							07 49								*09c31*				
—	—	—	—	—	Holyhead	a							08 23								*10c05*				
—	—	—	—	—	Wilmslow	a							*06e56*								*07 44*				
—	—	—	—	—	Manchester Airport ✈	a							*07e04*								*08f04*				
—	107¼	62¼	—	—	Stockport	a										07 27							07 45		
—	113	68	—	—	**Manchester Piccadilly** 10 ⛴	a										07 40							08 01		
169¾	—	—	11¾	—	Hartford	a						06 13					06 46	07 09							07 46
182	—	—	—	—	Warrington Bank Quay	a				06 13											07 26				
—	—	—	—	—		d				06 14											07 27				
—	—	—	22½	—	Runcorn	a						06 26					06 57	07 22						07 40	07 59
—	—	—	30	—	Liverpool South Parkway 7 ✈	a						06 35					07 08	07 31							08 09
—	—	—	35½	—	**Liverpool Lime Street** 10	a						06 48					07 20	07 41						08 02	08 20
—	—	—	—	—		d														06 57					
—	—	—	—	—	Manchester Airport ✈	d				*05g29*	*05 37*			06 18											
—	—	—	—	—	**Manchester Piccadilly** 10 ⛴	d				*05g46*	06 03			06 33											
—	—	79¼	—	—	Bolton	d				*06g02*	06 19			06 50											
193¾	—	—	—	—	Wigan North Western	a				06 24										07 30	07 37	⟵			
—	—	—	—	—		d				06 25										07 31	07 38	07 31			
209	—	99¼	—	—	**Preston** 8	a				06 37	06 42			07 11						⟶	07 51	07 56			
—	—	—	—	—	Blackpool North	a					*07h41*										*08 29*	08h44			
—	—	—	—	—		d				*05 45*				*06 34*							*07 10*				
—	—	—	—	—	**Preston** 8	d		05 22		06 40	06 44			07 16	07 20						07 53				
230	—	—	—	—	**Lancaster** 6	a		05 42		06 54	06 59			07 31	07 36						08 08				
—	—	—	—	—		d		05 42	05 45	06 54	07 01			07 32	07 36						08 09				
—	—	—	—	—	Barrow-in-Furness	a		06 47							08 39										
249	—	—	—	—	Oxenholme Lake District	a			06 20	07 08	07 15										08 22				
—	—	—	—	—		d			06 21	07 10	07 15										08 23				
—	—	—	—	—	Windermere	a			06 41		*07 40*										*08 46*				
281¼	—	—	—	—	Penrith North Lakes	d				07 35				08 09											
299	—	—	—	—	**Carlisle** 8	a				07 50	07 55			08 25							09 01				
—	—	—	—	—		d	06 09			07 51	07 57			08 26							09 03				
324¼	—	—	0	—	Lockerbie	d				08 10	08 16														
372½	—	—	—	0	Carstairs	a																			
388¼	—	—	—	—	Motherwell	a								09s28											
401¼	—	—	—	—	**Glasgow Central** 15	a	08 37			09 14				09 45											
—	—	—	75	26¼	Haymarket	a					09s16										10s16				
—	—	—	76¼	27½	**Edinburgh** 10	a					09 22										10 22				
—	—	—	—	97¼	Perth	a	*10j34*				*10 52*			*11j34*							*11 54*				
—	—	—	135¼	—	Dundee	a	*10j57*				*10k32*			*11j59*							*11k43*				
—	—	—	206¾	—	Aberdeen	a	*12j33*				*11k45*			*13j14*							*13k07*				
—	—	—	—	215¼	Inverness	a					*13m37*														

For general notes see front of timetable
For details of catering facilities see Directory of Train Operators

A To Carlisle via Whitehaven (Table 100)
B Via Morecambe (Table 98)

b Change at Nuneaton
c Change at Crewe and Chester
e Change at Crewe
f Change at Crewe and Wilmslow
g Change at Preston
h From 5 October arr. 2 mins. later

j Via Glasgow Central and Glasgow Queen Street. Passengers make their own way from one station to the other
k Change at Haymarket
m Change at Edinburgh and Perth

OVERNIGHT SLEEPERS. For Sleeper trains, operated by First ScotRail, please refer to Tables 400 - 404

London and West Midlands → North West England and Scotland

Route Diagram - see first page of Table 65

Station		VT	TP	VT	NT	XC	LM	NT	VT		NT	VT	XC	VT	LM	VT	VT	TP	VT	VT	TP	XC		LM	NT
		1◇	1◇	1◇		1◇	1◇		1◇			1◇	1◇	1◇	1◇	1◇	1◇	1◇	1◇	1◇	1◇	1◇		1◇	
					A													B			B	C		D	
		⊠	⌶	⊠		⌶			⊠			⊠	⌶	⊠		⊠	⊠	⌶	⊠	⊠	⌶	⌶			
London Euston 15 ⊖	d	05 47		06 17								06 36		06 55		07 07	07 10		07 20	07 30					
Gatwick Airport 10 ✈	d																								
Watford Junction	d	06u02										06u51		*06 14*			*06 41*		*06 54*						
Milton Keynes Central	d	06 22		06 47										07 27			07u40		07 50						
Northampton	d	*06 17*																							
Rugby	d	06 44													*06b58*										
Nuneaton	d														*07b11*										
Tamworth Low Level	d														*07b28*										
Lichfield Trent Valley	d														*07b34*										
Coventry	d								*06 29*				*06 49*		*07 02*							07 27			
Birmingham International ✈	d					*06 28*			*06 45*				*07 09*		07 18							07 38			
Birmingham New Street 12	d					06 57	07 01		07 19				07 31		07 36							07 57		08 01	
Wolverhampton 7	d					07 15	07 19		07 36				07 49		07 53							08 15		08 19	
Penkridge	d						07 30								08 03									08 29	
Stafford	a					07 29	07 36								08 09	08 22						08 29		08 35	
	d					07 29	07 36								08 09	08 23						08 29		08 36	
Stoke-on-Trent	a			07 45									08 18	08 24					08 48			08 54			
Congleton	a																								
Macclesfield	a			08 01									08 35	08 41								09 11			
Crewe 10	a	07 30				07 50	07 56		08 07			08 10			08 30		08 47							08 56	
	d	07 32				07 52	07 58		08 09			08 11			08 31		08 49							08 58	
Chester	a											*08 45*					09 12								
Wrexham General	a																								
Llandudno Junction	a											*09c48*					*10 14*								
Llandudno	a											*10c06*					*10e36*								
Bangor (Gwynedd)	a																*10 36*								
Holyhead	a																*11 19*								
Wilmslow	a					08 08			*08 45*			08 27			*09 16*										
Manchester Airport ✈	a								*09 04*			*09 04*													
Stockport	a			08 16		08 20						08 37		08 55					09 16			09 27			
Manchester Piccadilly 10	a			08 28		08 40						08 49	09 00	09 07					09 28			09 40			
Hartford	a						08 09																	09 11	
Warrington Bank Quay	a	07 49							08 26											09 14					
	d	07 49							08 27											09 14					
Runcorn	a						08 22								08 48	08 54								09 21	
Liverpool South Parkway 7 ✈	a						08 31								08 59									09 31	
Liverpool Lime Street 10	a						08 43								09 09	09 15								09 42	
	d	*07 01*						07 57												*08 01*					08 57
Manchester Airport ✈	d	*07f00*	07 28															08 25							
Manchester Piccadilly 10	d	*07f15*	07 45															08 46							
Bolton	d	*07f31*	07 59															09 07							
Wigan North Western	a	08 00						08 30	08 37		←									09 25					09 30
	d	08 00						08 31	08 38		08 31									09 25					09 31
								→																	→
Preston 8	a	08 13	08 22						08 51		08 55							09 33		09 38					
Blackpool North	a								*09 25*		*09g51*														
	d	*07 36*																		*08 45*	←				
Preston 8	d	08 15	08 24		08 38				08 53									09 45		09 41	09 45				
																		→							
Lancaster 6	a	08 29	08 39		08 58				09 08											09 54	10 00				
	d	08 30	08 40		08 58				*09 08*											09 55	10 01				
Barrow-in-Furness	a				10 03				*10 47*																
Oxenholme Lake District	a	08 43	08 54																		10 17				
	d	08 43	08 54																		10 18				
Windermere	a		*09 33*																		10 39				
Penrith North Lakes	d		09 20						09 45											10 31					
Carlisle 8	a	09 21	09 35						09 59											10 46					
	d	09 22	09 37						10 01											10 47					
Lockerbie	d		09 56																						
Carstairs	a																								
Motherwell	a																								
Glasgow Central 15	a	10 36							11 16											12 01					
Haymarket	a		11s04																						
Edinburgh 10	a		11 10																						
Perth	a		*12 52*																	*13h36*					
Dundee	a		*12 36*																	*14h00*					
Aberdeen	a		*13 46*																	*15h13*					
Inverness	a		*15 06*																						

For general notes see front of timetable
For details of catering facilities see Directory of Train Operators

A To Carlisle via Whitehaven (Table 100)
B ⌶ to Preston
C From Southampton Central (Table 51)
D From Walsall (Table 70)
b Change at Stafford
c Change at Crewe and Chester
e Change at Chester and Llandudno Junction
f Change at Preston
g From 5 October arr. 2 mins. later
h Via Glasgow Central and Glasgow Queen Street. Passengers make their own way from one station to the other

OVERNIGHT SLEEPERS. For Sleeper trains, operated by First ScotRail, please refer to Tables 400 - 404

London and West Midlands → North West England and Scotland

Route Diagram - see first page of Table 65

		VT	NT	TP	VT	XC	VT	LM	VT	VT	VT	VT	XC		LM	NT	VT	NT	TP	VT	XC	TP	VT	LM	VT
		1 ◇		1 ◇	1 ◇	1 ◇	1 ◇	1 ◇	1 ◇	1 ◇	1 ◇	1 ◇	1 ◇		1 ◇		1 ◇		1 ◇	1 ◇	1 ◇	1 ◇	1 ◇	1 ◇	1 ◇
				A		B							C								D				
		⊠		⊥	⊠	⊥	⊠		⊠	⊠	⊠	⊠	⊥				⊠		⊥	⊠	⊥		⊠		⊠
London Euston 15 ⊖	d				07 35		08 00		08 07	08 10	08 20	08 30								08 40			09 00		09 07
Gatwick Airport 10 ✈	d																								
Watford Junction	d				07 10					08 01															
Milton Keynes Central	d				08 06					08u40	08 50														
Northampton	d																								
Rugby	d							08b03																09b03	
Nuneaton	d							08b16																09b16	
Tamworth Low Level	d							08b30																09b30	
Lichfield Trent Valley	d							08b36																09b36	
Coventry	d	07 42				07 49							08 27				08 42				08 49				
Birmingham International ✈	d	07 53				08 09							08 38				08 53				09 09				
Birmingham New Street 12	d	08 20				08 31		08 36					08 57		09 01		09 20				09 31			09 36	
Wolverhampton 7	d	08 37				08 49		08 53					09 15		09 19		09 37				09 49			09 53	
Penkridge	d							09 03																10 03	
Stafford	a							09 09	09 22				09 29		09 34									10 09	10 22
	d							09 09	09 23				09 29		09 35									10 09	10 23
Stoke-on-Trent	a					09 18	09 24				09 48		09 54								10 18		10 24		
Congleton	a																								
Macclesfield	a						09 41						10 11										10 41		
Crewe 10	a	09 07			09 10			09 30		09 47					09 56		10 07			10 10				10 30	
	d	09 09			09 11			09 31		09 49					09 57		10 09			10 11				10 31	
Chester	a				09 45					10 09										10 45					
Wrexham General	a																								
Llandudno Junction	a				10c48					11 04										11c48					
Llandudno	a				11c06					11 36										12c06					
Bangor (Gwynedd)	a									11 27															
Holyhead	a									12 13															
Wilmslow	a	09 45			09 27			10 16									10 45			10 27				11 16	
Manchester Airport ✈	a	10 04			10 04												11 04			11 04					
Stockport	a				09 36		09 55				10 16		10 27							10 36			10 55		
Manchester Piccadilly 10	a				09 49	10 00	10 07				10 28		10 40							10 49	11 00		11 07		
Hartford	a														10 10										
Warrington Bank Quay	a	09 26										10 14					10 26								
	d	09 27										10 14					10 27								
Runcorn	a							09 48	09 54						10 21									10 48	10 54
Liverpool South Parkway 7 ✈	a							09 59							10 31									10 59	
Liverpool Lime Street 10	a							10 09	10 15						10 43									11 09	11 15
	d											09 01				09 57									
Manchester Airport ✈	d			09 00								09e29							10 00						
Manchester Piccadilly 10	d			09 16								09e46							10 16						
Bolton	d			09 33								10e07							10 33						
Wigan North Western	a	09 37	←									10 25				10 30	10 37	←							
	d	09 38	09 31									10 25				10 31	10 38	10 31							
Preston 8	a	09 51	09 54	09 55								10 38				→	10 51	10 54	10 55						
Blackpool North	a		10 20	10 35														11 20							
	d			09 29								09 45							10 20			10 29			
Preston 8	d	09 53		10 00								10 41					10 53		10 58			11 04			
Lancaster 6	a	10 09		10 16								10 54					11 08		11 14			11 19			
	d	10 10		10 16								10 55					11 08		11 14			11 20			
Barrow-in-Furness	a			11 12																		12 39			
Oxenholme Lake District	a	10 24										11 08							11 28			11 36			
	d	10 25										11 08							11 28			11 37			
Windermere	a																					11 56			
Penrith North Lakes	d																11 45		11 53						
Carlisle 8	a	11 02										11 46					12 00		12 10						
	d	11 04										11 47					12 03		12 11						
Lockerbie	d																		12 30						
Carstairs	a																								
Motherwell	a																								
Glasgow Central 15	a											13 01					13 19		13 31						
Haymarket	a	12s16																							
Edinburgh 10	a	12 22																							
Perth	a	14 52										14f36													
Dundee	a	13g35										14f59													
Aberdeen	a	14g53										16f19													
Inverness	a	17 05										17h05													

For general notes see front of timetable
For details of catering facilities see Directory of Train Operators

A ⊥ to Preston
B From Bristol Temple Meads (Table 51)
C From Southampton Central (Table 51)
D From Cardiff Central (Table 51)
b Change at Stafford
c Change at Crewe and Chester
e Change at Preston
f Via Glasgow Central and Glasgow Queen Street. Passengers make their own way from one station to the other
g Change at Haymarket
h Change at Glasgow Central, Glasgow Queen Street and Perth. Passengers make their own way between Glasgow Central and Glasgow Queen Street

OVERNIGHT SLEEPERS. For Sleeper trains, operated by First ScotRail, please refer to Tables 400 - 404

London and West Midlands → North West England and Scotland

Route Diagram - see first page of Table 65

Station		VT	VT	VT		XC	LM	NT	VT	NT	TP	VT	XC	VT	LM	VT	VT		VT	VT	XC	LM	NT	VT	NT
		1◇	1◇	1◇		1◇	1◇		1◇		1◇	1◇	1◇	1◇	1◇	1◇	1◇		1◇	1◇	1◇	1◇		1◇	
						A					B		C								A				
		☒	☒	☒		🛒			☕		🛒	☒	🛒	☕		☕	☕		☕	☕	🛒			☕	
London Euston 15 ⊖	d	09 10	09 20	09 30								09 40		10 00		10 07	10 10		10 20	10 30					
Gatwick Airport 10 ✈	d																								
Watford Junction	d	*09 01*															*10 01*								
Milton Keynes Central	d	09u40	09 50														10u40		10 50						
Northampton	d																								
Rugby	d														*10b03*										
Nuneaton	d														*10b16*										
Tamworth Low Level	d														*10b30*										
Lichfield Trent Valley	d														*10b36*										
Coventry	d					09 27			*09 42*				*09 49*								10 27			*10 42*	
Birmingham International ✈	d					09 38			*09 53*				*10 09*								10 38			*10 53*	
Birmingham New Street 12	d					09 57	10 01		10 20				10 31		10 36						10 57	11 01		11 20	
Wolverhampton 7	d					10 15	10 19		10 37				10 49		10 53						11 15	11 19		11 37	
Penkridge	d														11 03										
Stafford	a					10 29	10 34								11 09	11 22					11 29	11 34			
	d					10 29	10 35								11 09	11 23					11 29	11 35			
Stoke-on-Trent	a		10 48			10 54							11 18	11 24					11 48		11 54				
Congleton	a																								
Macclesfield	a					11 11								11 41							12 11				
Crewe 10	a	10 47					10 56		11 07			11 10			11 30		11 47					11 56		12 07	
	d	10 49					10 57		11 09			11 11			11 31		11 49					11 57		12 09	
Chester	a	11 09										*11 45*					12 12								
Wrexham General	a																								
Llandudno Junction	a	12 00										*12c48*					*13 14*								
Llandudno	a	*12 36*										*13c06*					*13e36*								
Bangor (Gwynedd)	a	12 16															*13 31*								
Holyhead	a	12 50															*14 14*								
Wilmslow	a								*11 45*			11 27			*12 16*									*12 45*	
Manchester Airport ✈	a								*12 04*			*12 04*												*13 04*	
Stockport	a		11 16			11 27						11 36		11 55					12 16		12 27			*12 58*	
Manchester Piccadilly 10	a		11 28			11 40						11 49	12 00	12 07					12 28		12 40			*13 15*	
Hartford	a						11 11															12 10			
Warrington Bank Quay	a			11 14					11 26											12 14				12 26	
	d			11 14					11 27											12 14				12 27	
Runcorn	a						11 21								11 48	11 54						12 21			
Liverpool South Parkway 7 ✈	a						11 31								11 59							12 31			
Liverpool Lime Street 10	a						11 42								12 09	12 15						12 43			
	d			*10 01*				10 57												*11 01*			11 57		
Manchester Airport ✈	d			*10f29*							11 00									*11f29*					
Manchester Piccadilly 10	d			*10f46*							11 16									*11f46*					
Bolton	d			*11f07*							11 33									*12f07*					
Wigan North Western	a			11 25				11 30	11 37	←										12 25			12 30	12 37	←
	d			11 25				11 31	11 38	11 31										12 25			12 31	12 38	12 31
Preston 8	a			11 38				→	11 51	11 54	11 55									12 38			→	12 51	12 54
Blackpool North	a									12 20															13 21
	d			*10 45*							*11 20*									*11 45*					
Preston 8	d			11 41					11 53		11 58									12 41				12 53	
Lancaster 6	a			11 54					12 08		12 14									13 00				13 08	
	d			11 55					12 08		12 14													13 08	
Barrow-in-Furness	a										13 10														
Oxenholme Lake District	a								12 22															13 22	
	d								12 24															13 24	
Windermere	a								*12 47*																
Penrith North Lakes	d			12 30																					
Carlisle 8	a			12 45					13 01															14 01	
	d			12 47					13 03															14 03	
Lockerbie	d																								
Carstairs	a																								
Motherwell	a																								
Glasgow Central 15	a			14 01																				15 17	
Haymarket	a								14s16																
Edinburgh 10	a								14 22																
Perth	a								*15 53*															*17g18*	
Dundee	a								*15h37*																
Aberdeen	a								*16h50*															*19g34*	
Inverness	a								*19j34*																

For general notes see front of timetable
For details of catering facilities see Directory of Train Operators

- A From Bournemouth (Table 51)
- B 🛒 to Preston
- C From Paignton (Table 51)
- b Change at Stafford
- c Change at Crewe and Chester
- e Change at Chester and Llandudno Junction
- f Change at Preston
- g Via Glasgow Central and Glasgow Queen Street. Passengers make their own way from one station to the other
- h Change at Haymarket
- j Change at Edinburgh and Perth

OVERNIGHT SLEEPERS. For Sleeper trains, operated by First ScotRail, please refer to Tables 400 - 404

London and West Midlands → North West England and Scotland

Route Diagram - see first page of Table 65

		TP	VT	XC	TP	VT	LM	VT	VT	VT	VT	XC	LM	NT	VT	NT	TP	VT	XC	VT	LM	VT	VT
		1◇	1◇	1◇	1◇	1◇	1◇	1◇	1◇	1◇	1◇	1◇	1◇		1◇		1◇	1◇	1◇	1◇	1◇	1◇	1◇
				A								B					C		A				
		⊥	□	⊥		□		□	□	□	□	⊥			□		⊥	□	⊥	□		□	□
London Euston 15 ⊖	d		10 40			11 00		11 07	11 10	11 20	11 30							11 40		12 00		12 07	12 10
Gatwick Airport 10 ✈	d																						
Watford Junction	d								11 01														12 01
Milton Keynes Central	d								11u40	11 50													12u40
Northampton	d																						
Rugby	d						11b03														12b03		
Nuneaton	d						11b16														12b16		
Tamworth Low Level	d						11b31														12b31		
Lichfield Trent Valley	d						11b37														12b37		
Coventry	d			10 49								11 27			11 42				11 49				
Birmingham International ✈	d			11 09								11 38			11 53				12 09				
Birmingham New Street 12	d			11 31			11 36					11 57	12 01		12 20				12 31		12 36		
Wolverhampton 7 ⛴	d			11 49			11 53					12 15	12 19		12 37				12 49		12 53		
Penkridge	d						12 03														13 03		
Stafford	a						12 09	12 22				12 29	12 34								13 09	13 22	
	d						12 09	12 23				12 29	12 35								13 09	13 23	
Stoke-on-Trent	a			12 18		12 24				12 48		12 54							13 18	13 24			
Congleton	a																						
Macclesfield	a					12 41						13 11								13 41			
Crewe 10	a		12 10				12 30		12 47				12 56		13 07			13 10			13 30		13 47
	d		12 11				12 31		12 49				12 57		13 09			13 11			13 31		13 49
Chester	a		12 45						13 12									13 45					14 12
Wrexham General	a																						
Llandudno Junction	a		13c48						14 14									14c48					15 14
Llandudno	a		14c06						14e36									15c06					16 06
Bangor (Gwynedd)	a								14 36														15 31
Holyhead	a								15 11														16 14
Wilmslow	a		12 27				13 16								13 45			13 27			14 16		
Manchester Airport ✈	a		13 04												14 04			14 04					
Stockport	a		12 36			12 55				13 16		13 27						13 36		13 55			
Manchester Piccadilly 10 ⛴	a		12 49	13 00		13 07				13 28		13 40						13 49	14 00	14 07			
Hartford	a												13 11										
Warrington Bank Quay	a										13 14				13 26								
	d										13 14				13 27								
Runcorn	a						12 48	12 54					13 21								13 48	13 54	
Liverpool South Parkway 7 ✈	a						12 59						13 31								13 59		
Liverpool Lime Street 10	a						13 09	13 15					13 42								14 09	14 15	
	d										12 01			12 57									
Manchester Airport ✈	d	12 00									12f29						13 00						
Manchester Piccadilly 10 ⛴	d	12 16									12f46						13 16						
Bolton	d	12 33									13f07						13 33						
Wigan North Western	a										13 25			13 30	13 37	←							
	d										13 25			13 31	13 38	13 31							
Preston 8	a	12 55									13 38			→	13 51	13 54	13 55						
Blackpool North	a															14 20							
	d	12 20			12 29						12 45						13 20						
Preston 8	d	12 58			13 04						13 41				13 53		13 58						
Lancaster 6	a	13 14			13 19						13 54				14 08		14 14						
	d	13 14			13 20						13 55				14 08		14 14						
Barrow-in-Furness	a				14 38												15 10						
Oxenholme Lake District	a	13 28			13 36						14 08												
	d	13 28			13 37						14 08												
Windermere	a				13 56						14 44												
Penrith North Lakes	d	13 53													14 45								
Carlisle 8	a	14 10									14 46				15 00								
	d	14 11									14 47				15 03								
Lockerbie	d	14 30																					
Carstairs	a																						
Motherwell	a																						
Glasgow Central 15	a										16 01												
Haymarket	a														16s15								
Edinburgh 10	a	15 42													16 22								
Perth	a										17g36				17 52								
Dundee	a	17 20													17h38								
Aberdeen	a	19 00													19h00								
Inverness	a														20 08								

For general notes see front of timetable
For details of catering facilities see Directory of Train Operators

A From Bristol Temple Meads (Table 51)
B From Bournemouth (Table 51)
C ⊥ to Preston
b Change at Stafford
c Change at Crewe and Chester
e Change at Chester and Llandudno Junction
f Change at Preston
g Via Glasgow Central and Glasgow Queen Street. Passengers make their own way from one station to the other
h Change at Haymarket

OVERNIGHT SLEEPERS. For Sleeper trains, operated by First ScotRail, please refer to Tables 400 - 404

London and West Midlands → North West England and Scotland

Route Diagram - see first page of Table 65

		VT	VT	XC	LM	NT	VT	NT	TP		TP	TP	VT	XC	VT	LM	VT	VT	VT	XC	LM	NT	VT	NT
		1◇	1◇	1◇	1◇		1◇		1◇		1◇	1◇	1◇	1◇	1◇	1◇	1◇	1◇	1◇	1◇	1		1◇	
				A					B		C	C		D						A				
		🍽	🍽	🛒			🍽		🛒		🛒		🍽	🛒	🍽		🍽	🍽	⊠	🛒			🍽	
London Euston 15 ⊖	d	12 20	12 30										12 40		13 00		13 07	13 20	13 30					
Gatwick Airport 10 ✈	d																							
Watford Junction	d																	*13 01*						
Milton Keynes Central	d	12 50																13 50						
Northampton	d																							
Rugby	d															13b03								
Nuneaton	d															13b16								
Tamworth Low Level	d															13b30								
Lichfield Trent Valley	d															13b36								
Coventry	d			12 27			*12 42*							*12 49*						13 27			*13 42*	
Birmingham International ✈	d			12 38			*12 53*							*13 09*						13 38			*13 53*	
Birmingham New Street 12	d			12 57	13 01		13 20							13 31		13 36				13 57	14 01		14 20	
Wolverhampton 7 🚌	d			13 15	13 19		13 37							13 49		13 53				14 15	14 19		14 37	
Penkridge	d															14 03								
Stafford	a			13 29	13 34											14 09	14 22			14 29	14 34			
	d			13 29	13 35											14 09	14 23			14 29	14 35			
Stoke-on-Trent	a	13 48		13 54										14 18	14 24			14 48		14 54				
Congleton	a																							
Macclesfield	a			14 11											14 41					15 11				
Crewe 10	a				13 56		14 07						14 10			14 30					14 56		15 07	
	d				13 57		14 09						14 11			14 31					14 57		15 09	
Chester	a												*14 45*											
Wrexham General	a																							
Llandudno Junction	a												*15c48*											
Llandudno	a												*16c06*											
Bangor (Gwynedd)	a												*16c36*											
Holyhead	a												*17c11*											
Wilmslow	a						*14 45*						14 27			*15 16*							*15 45*	
Manchester Airport ✈	a						*15 04*						*15 04*										*16 04*	
Stockport	a	14 16		14 27									14 36		14 55			15 16		15 27				
Manchester Piccadilly 10 🚌	a	14 28		14 40									14 49	15 00	15 07			15 28		15 40				
Hartford	a				14 11																15 11			
Warrington Bank Quay	a		14 14				14 26												15 14				15 26	
	d		14 14				14 27												15 14				15 27	
Runcorn	a				14 21											14 48	14 54				15 21			
Liverpool South Parkway 7 ✈	a				14 31											14 59					15 31			
Liverpool Lime Street 10	a				14 42											15 09	15 15				15 42			
	d		*13 01*			13 57													*14 01*			14 57		
Manchester Airport ✈	d		*13e29*						14 00		14 00								*14e29*					
Manchester Piccadilly 10 🚌	d		*13e46*						14 16		14 16								*14e46*					
Bolton	d		*14e07*						14 33		14 33								*15e07*					
Wigan North Western	a		14 25			14 30	14 37	←											15 25			15 30	15 37	←
	d		14 25			14 31	14 38	14 31											15 25			15 31	15 38	15 31
Preston 8	a		14 38			→	14 51	14 54	14 55		14 55								15 38			→	15 51	15 54
Blackpool North	a							15 20																16 20
	d		*13 45*						*14 20*		*14 20*								*14 45*					
Preston 8	d		14 41				14 53		14 58	15 04	14 58	15 04							15 41				15 53	
Lancaster 6	a		15 00				15 08		15 14	15 20	15 14	15 20											16 08	
	d						15 09		15 14	15 20	15 14	15 20											16 08	
Barrow-in-Furness	a									*16 39*		*16 39*												
Oxenholme Lake District	a						15 22			15 37		15 37							16 04					
	d						15 24			15 38		15 38							16 06					
Windermere	a									16 00		16 00							*16 48*					
Penrith North Lakes	d								15 53		15 53								16 31				16 45	
Carlisle 8	a						16 01		16 09		16 09								16 46				17 00	
	d						16 03		16 10		16 10								16 47				17 02	
Lockerbie	d								16 29		16 29													
Carstairs	a																							
Motherwell	a																							
Glasgow Central 15	a						17 18												18 01					
Haymarket	a								17s30		17s30												18s14	
Edinburgh 10	a								17 39		17 39												18 22	
Perth	a								*18f58*		*18f58*								*19g42*				20 02	
Dundee	a								*19 27*		*19 27*												*19f52*	
Aberdeen	a								*20 57*		*20 57*												*21f12*	
Inverness	a								*21f03*		*21f03*												*23 14*	

For general notes see front of timetable
For details of catering facilities see Directory of Train Operators

A From Bournemouth (Table 51)

B Until 19 June and from 7 September. 🛒 to Edinburgh
C 22 June to 4 September
D From Paignton (Table 51)
b Change at Stafford
c Change at Crewe and Chester

e Change at Preston
f Change at Haymarket
g Via Glasgow Central and Glasgow Queen Street. Passengers make their own way from one station to the other

OVERNIGHT SLEEPERS. For Sleeper trains, operated by First ScotRail, please refer to Tables 400 - 404

London and West Midlands → North West England and Scotland

Route Diagram - see first page of Table 65

Station		TP	VT		XC	VT	LM	VT	VT	VT	VT	XC	LM	NT	VT	TP			NT	NT	VT	XC	VT	LM	VT
		1◇	1◇		1◇	1◇	1◇	1◇	1◇	1◇	1◇	1◇	1◇		1◇	1◇					1◇	1◇	1◇	1◇	1◇
		A			B							C								D		E			
		🛒	🍴		🛒	🍴		🍴	🍴	🍴	🍴	🛒			🍴	🛒					🍴	🛒	🍴		🍴
London Euston 15 ⊖	d		13 40			14 00		14 07	14 10	14 20	14 30										14 40		15 00		15 07
Gatwick Airport 10 ✈	d																								
Watford Junction	d								14 01																
Milton Keynes Central	d								14u40	14 50															
Northampton	d																								
Rugby	d						14b03																	15b03	
Nuneaton	d						14b16																	15b16	
Tamworth Low Level	d						14b30																	15b30	
Lichfield Trent Valley	d						14b36																	15b36	
Coventry	d				13 49							14 27			14 42							14 49			
Birmingham International ✈	d				14 09							14 38			14 53							15 09			
Birmingham New Street 12	d				14 31		14 36					14 57	15 01		15 20							15 31		15 36	
Wolverhampton 7 ⛴	d				14 49		14 53					15 15	15 19		15 37							15 49		15 53	
Penkridge	d						15 03																	16 03	
Stafford	a						15 09	15 22				15 29	15 34											16 09	16 22
	d						15 09	15 23				15 29	15 35											16 09	16 23
Stoke-on-Trent	a				15 18	15 24				15 48		15 54										16 18	16 24		
Congleton	a																								
Macclesfield	a					15 41						16 11											16 41		
Crewe 10	a		15 10				15 30		15 47				15 56		16 07						16 11			16 30	
	d		15 11				15 31		15 49				15 57		16 09						16 12			16 31	
Chester	a		15 45						16 12												16 45				
Wrexham General	a																								
Llandudno Junction	a		16c48						17 14												17c49				
Llandudno	a		17c06																		18c06				
Bangor (Gwynedd)	a								17 36																
Holyhead	a								18 19																
Wilmslow	a		15 27				16 16								16 45						16 27			17 16	
Manchester Airport ✈	a		16 04												17 04						17 04				
Stockport	a		15 36			15 55				16 16		16 27									16 36		16 54		
Manchester Piccadilly 10 ⛴	a		15 49		16 00	16 07				16 28		16 40									16 49	17 00	17 07		
Hartford	a												16 11												
Warrington Bank Quay	a										16 16				16 26										
	d										16 17				16 27										
Runcorn	a						15 48	15 54					16 24											16 48	16 54
Liverpool South Parkway 7 ✈	a						15 59						16 33											16 59	
Liverpool Lime Street 10	a						16 09	16 15					16 43											17 09	17 15
	d										15 31			15 57											
Manchester Airport ✈	d	15 00									15e29					16 00									
Manchester Piccadilly 10 ⛴	d	15 16									15e46					16 16				16 27					
Bolton	d	15 33									16e07					16 33				16 49					
Wigan North Western	a										16 28			16 29	16 37				←						
	d										16 29			16 31 →	16 38				16 31						
Preston 8	a	15 55									16 42				16 51	16 55			16 56	17 26					
Blackpool North	a																		17 23	18 06					
	d	15 20									15 45					16 29				16 41					
Preston 8	d	15 58									16 44				16 53	17 00	17 05			17 28					
Lancaster 6	a	16 14									17 00				17 09	17 15	17 23			17 48					
	d	16 14													17 10	17 16	17 25			17 48					
Barrow-in-Furness	a	17 18													18 25					18 59					
Oxenholme Lake District	a														17 24	17 30	17 42								
	d														17 25	17 30	17 42								
Windermere	a																18 04								
Penrith North Lakes	d														17 51										
Carlisle 8	a														18 06	18 10									
	d														18 07	18 11									
Lockerbie	d															18 30									
Carstairs	a																								
Motherwell	a																								
Glasgow Central 15	a														19 19										
Haymarket	a															19s31									
Edinburgh 10	a															19 39									
Perth	a																								
Dundee	a															21 30									
Aberdeen	a																								
Inverness	a																								

For general notes see front of timetable
For details of catering facilities see Directory of Train Operators

- **A** 🛒 to Preston
- **B** From Bristol Temple Meads (Table 51)
- **C** From Bournemouth (Table 51)
- **D** From Hazel Grove (Table 86)
- **E** From Penzance (Table 135)
- **b** Change at Stafford
- **c** Change at Crewe and Chester
- **e** Change at Preston

OVERNIGHT SLEEPERS. For Sleeper trains, operated by First ScotRail, please refer to Tables 400 - 404

London and West Midlands → North West England and Scotland

Route Diagram - see first page of Table 65

		VT	VT	VT	XC	LM	NT	VT	NT	TP		VT	XC	VT	TP	LM	VT	VT	VT	VT	NT	XC	LM
		1 ◇	1 ◇	1 ◇	1 ◇	1 ◇		1 ◇		1 ◇		1 ◇	1 ◇	1 ◇	1 ◇	1 ◇	1 ◇	1 ◇	1 ◇	1 ◇		1 ◇	1 ◇
					A								B		C							A	
		🍴	🍴	⊠	🛒			🍴		🛒		🍴	🛒	🍴			⊠	⊠	⊠	⊠		🛒	
London Euston 15 ⊖	d	15 10	15 20	15 30								15 40		16 00			16 07	16 10	16 20	16 30			
Gatwick Airport 10 ✈	d																						
Watford Junction	d	*15 01*																*16 01*					
Milton Keynes Central	d	15u40	15 50															16u40	16u50				
Northampton	d																						
Rugby	d															*16b03*							
Nuneaton	d															*16b16*							
Tamworth Low Level	d															*16b30*							
Lichfield Trent Valley	d															*16b36*							
Coventry	d				15 27			*15 42*					*15 49*									16 27	
Birmingham International ✈	d				15 38			*15 53*					*16 09*									16 38	
Birmingham New Street 12	d				15 57	16 01		16 20					16 31			16 36						16 57	17 01
Wolverhampton 7	d				16 15	16 19		16 37					16 49			16 53						17 15	17 19
Penkridge	d															17 03							17 29
Stafford	a				16 29	16 34										17 09	17 22					17 29	17 35
	d				16 29	16 35										17 09	17 23					17 29	17 36
Stoke-on-Trent	a		16 48		16 54								17 18	17 24					17 48			17 54	
Congleton	a																						
Macclesfield	a				17 11									17 41								18 11	
Crewe 10	a	16 47				16 56		17 07				17 10				17 30		17 47					17 56
	d	16 49				16 57		17 09				17 11				17 31		17 49					18 01
Chester	a	17 12										*17 45*						18 09					
Wrexham General	a																						
Llandudno Junction	a	*18 16*										*18c48*						18 59					
Llandudno	a	*18e36*										*19c06*						*19 36*					
Bangor (Gwynedd)	a	*18 38*																*19 22*					
Holyhead	a	*19 13*																*20 14*					
Wilmslow	a							*17 46*				17 27				*18 16*							
Manchester Airport ✈	a							*18 04*				*18 04*											
Stockport	a		17 16		17 27							17 36		17 55					18 16			18 27	
Manchester Piccadilly 10	a		17 28		17 40							17 49	18 00	18 07					18 28			18 40	
Hartford	a					17 11																	18 12
Warrington Bank Quay	a			17 14				17 26															
	d			17 14				17 27															
Runcorn	a					17 21										17 48	17 54						18 23
Liverpool South Parkway 7 ✈	a					17 31										17 59							18 33
Liverpool Lime Street 10	a					17 42										18 09	18 15						18 43
	d			*16 01*			16 57														17 27		
Manchester Airport ✈	d			*16f29*						17 00													
Manchester Piccadilly 10	d			*16f46*						17 15													
Bolton	d			*17f06*						17 32										*17g37*			
Wigan North Western	a			17 25			17 30	17 37	←												18 05		
	d			17 25			17 31	17 38	17 31												18 06		
Preston 8	a			17 38			→	17 51	17 54	17 55										18 30	18 31		
Blackpool North	a								18 20												*19 09*		
	d			*16 41*				*17 20*												*17 37*			
Preston 8	d			17 41				17 53		18 00	18 03									18 32			
Lancaster 6	a			17 54				18 08			18 23												
	d			17 55				18 08		18 18	18 25				18 29								
Barrow-in-Furness	a										19 30												
Oxenholme Lake District	a			18 08				18 22							18 45								
	d			18 08				18 23							18 46								
Windermere	a														19 08								
Penrith North Lakes	d							18 49		18 53													
Carlisle 8	a			18 47				19 04		19 10													
	d			18 47				19 04		19 11													
Lockerbie	d																						
Carstairs	a																						
Motherwell	a																						
Glasgow Central 15	a			20 01						20 30										20 40			
Haymarket	a							20s16															
Edinburgh 10	a							20 22															
Perth	a			21h42				*22 00*												22h36			
Dundee	a			22h07				*21 47*												23h03			
Aberdeen	a			23h20				*23 07*												00h25			
Inverness	a																						

For general notes see front of timetable
For details of catering facilities see Directory of Train Operators

A From Bournemouth (Table 51)
B From Bristol Temple Meads (Table 51)
C From Barrow-in-Furness (Table 82)
b Change at Stafford
c Change at Crewe and Chester
e Change at Chester and Llandudno Junction
f Change at Preston
g Until 2 October only
h Via Glasgow Central and Glasgow Queen Street. Passengers make their own way from one station to the other

OVERNIGHT SLEEPERS. For Sleeper trains, operated by First ScotRail, please refer to Tables 400 - 404

London and West Midlands → North West England and Scotland

Route Diagram - see first page of Table 65

Station		NT	VT	NT	VT	TP		VT	VT	XC	NT	VT		NT	LM	VT	VT	VT	VT	VT	XC	LM	VT	VT	TP
			1◇		1◇	1◇		1◇	1◇	1◇		1◇			1◇	1◇	1◇	1◇	1◇	1◇	1◇	1◇	1◇	1◇	1◇
										A											B				
London Euston 15	⊖ d				16 33			16 40				16 57				17 00	17 07	17 10	17 20	17 30				17 33	
Gatwick Airport 10	✈ d																								
Watford Junction	d																	16 42							
Milton Keynes Central	d																	17u40	17u50					17b31	
Northampton	d				16 56																			17 56	
Rugby	d				17 22							17 03						17 03						18 22	
Nuneaton	d											17 16			17c16			18 12							
Tamworth Low Level	d											18 00			17c30										
Lichfield Trent Valley	d											18 08			17c36										
Coventry	d		16 42							16 49											17 27		17 42		
Birmingham International	✈ d		16 53							17 09											17 38		17 53		
Birmingham New Street 12	d		17 20							17 31					17 36						17 57	18 01	18 20		
Wolverhampton 7	d		17 37							17 49					17 53						18 15	18 19	18 37		
Penkridge	d														18 03							18 29			
Stafford	a				17 52				←						18 09		18 24				18 29	18 35		18 52	
	d				17 56				17 56						18 09		18 25				18 29	18 35		18 56	
Stoke-on-Trent	a				↪					18 18						18 24			18 49		18 54			↪	
Congleton	a																								
Macclesfield	a															18 41					19 11				
Crewe 10	a		18 07					18 10	18 16						18 30		18 43	18 53				19 00	19 07		
	d		18 09					18 11	18 18						18 31		18 45	18 56				19 02	19 09		
Chester	a							18 45							19 09			19 16							
Wrexham General	a																								
Llandudno Junction	a							19e48							19 55			20 11							
Llandudno	a							20e06										20 34							
Bangor (Gwynedd)	a														20 12			20 27							
Holyhead	a														20 49			21 02							
Wilmslow	a							18 27	18 45						19 16										
Manchester Airport	✈ a								19 04																
Stockport	a							18 37								18 55			19 16		19 27				
Manchester Piccadilly 10	⛴ a							18 49		19 00						19 07			19 28		19 40				
Hartford	a														18 44										
Warrington Bank Quay	a		18 26						18 35			18 49								19 14			19 26		
	d		18 27						18 36			18 50								19 14			19 27		
Runcorn	a														18 57		19 02					19 22			
Liverpool South Parkway 7	✈ a														19 07							19 32			
Liverpool Lime Street 10	a														19 17		19 23					19 42			
	d	17 44									18 01												18 31		
Manchester Airport	✈ d		17f27			18 00														18f29					19 00
Manchester Piccadilly 10	⛴ d		17f46			18 16														18f46					19 16
Bolton	d		18f07			18 33														19f07					19 33
Wigan North Western	a	18 30	18 37	←					18 46		18 49	19 00		←						19 25			19 37		
	d	18 31	18 38	18 31					18 47		18 49	19 01		18 49						19 25			19 38		
Preston 8	a	↪	18 51	18 54		18 55			19 02		↪	19 14		19 15						19 38			19 51		19 55
Blackpool North	a			19 20					19g48					20 00											
	d					18 29						18 37								18 45					19 20
Preston 8	d		18 53			19 00	19 04					19 15								19 41			19 53		19 58
Lancaster 6	a		19 08			19 16	19 20					19 30								19 54			20 08		20 14
	d		19 09			19 16	19 20					19 30								19 55			20 08		20 14
Barrow-in-Furness	a						20 24																		21 17
Oxenholme Lake District	a		19 23			19 30						19 43								20 08					
	d		19 24			19 32						19 45								20 08					
Windermere	a					19 56														20 46					
Penrith North Lakes	d					19 56						20 10											20 45		
Carlisle 8	a		20 02			20 12						20 25								20 46			21 00		
	d		20 03			20 13						20 25								20 47			21 03		
Lockerbie	d											20 44													
Carstairs	a																								
Motherwell	a											21s26													
Glasgow Central 15	a		21 17									21 47								22 01					
Haymarket	a					21s30																	22s14		
Edinburgh 10	a					21 39																	22 22		
Perth	a					23 34																	00 07		
Dundee	a					22h48																	00 39		
Aberdeen	a					00h08																			
Inverness	a																								

For general notes see front of timetable
For details of catering facilities see Directory of Train Operators

- **A** From Paignton (Table 51)
- **B** From Bournemouth (Table 51)
- **b** Change at Northampton and Rugby
- **c** Change at Stafford
- **e** Change at Crewe and Chester
- **f** Change at Preston
- **g** From 5 October arr. 2 mins. later
- **h** Change at Haymarket

OVERNIGHT SLEEPERS. For Sleeper trains, operated by First ScotRail, please refer to Tables 400 - 404

London and West Midlands → North West England and Scotland

Route Diagram - see first page of Table 65

		VT	XC	VT	NT	VT	NT	LM	VT	VT	VT		VT	VT	XC	LM	VT	TP	VT	VT	VT	NT	XC
		1◇	1◇	1◇		1◇		1◇	1◇	1◇	1◇		1◇	1◇	1◇	1◇	1◇	1◇	1◇	1◇	1◇		1◇
			A												B								C
		⊠	⚲	⊠		⊠			⊠	⊠	⊠		⊠	⊠	⚲		⊓		⊠	⊠	⊠		⚲
London Euston 15 ⊖	d	17 40				17 57			18 00	18 07	18 10		18 20	18 30					18 33	18 40			
Gatwick Airport 10 ✈	d																						
Watford Junction	d										17 43		17 53										
Milton Keynes Central	d										18u40		18u50										
Northampton	d																		18 56				
Rugby	d																		19 22				
Nuneaton	d										19 13												
Tamworth Low Level	d					19 00																	
Lichfield Trent Valley	d					19 08																	
Coventry	d		17 49								18b45				18 27		18 42						18 49
Birmingham International ✈	d		18 09												18 38		18 53						19 09
Birmingham New Street 12	d		18 31					18 36							18 57	19 01	19 20						19 31
Wolverhampton 7	d		18 49					18 53							19 15	19 19	19 37						19 49
Penkridge	d							19 03								19 29							
Stafford	a			←				19 09		19 24					19 29	19 36			19 52		←		
	d			18 56				19 09		19 25					19 29	19 36			19 56		19 56		
Stoke-on-Trent	a		19 18						19 24				19 48		19 54				→				20 19
Congleton	a																						
Macclesfield	a								19 41						20 11								
Crewe 10	a	19 10		19 16				19 30		19 43	19 53					20 01	20 07			20 10	20 16		
	d	19 11		19 18				19 31		19 45	19 56						20 09			20 11	20 18		
Chester	a	19 45									20 16									20 45			
Wrexham General	a											20 44											
Llandudno Junction	a										21 05												
Llandudno	a										21c35												
Bangor (Gwynedd)	a										21 22												
Holyhead	a										21 56												
Wilmslow	a	19 27		19 45				20 16												20 27	20 45		
Manchester Airport ✈	a	20 04		20e04																21 04	21e04		
Stockport	a	19 36							19 55				20 16		20 27					20 36	20 58		
Manchester Piccadilly 10	a	19 49	20 00						20 07				20 28		20 40					20 49	21 15		21 00
Hartford	a							19 47															
Warrington Bank Quay	a					19 49								20 14			20 26						
	d					19 50								20 14			20 27						
Runcorn	a			19 34				19 55		20 01											20 34		
Liverpool South Parkway 7 ✈	a							20 08															
Liverpool Lime Street 10	a			19 55				20 23		20 22											20 55		
	d				19 23												19 42					20 25	
Manchester Airport ✈	d													19f29				20 00					
Manchester Piccadilly 10	d													19f46				20 16					
Bolton	d													20f07				20 33					
Wigan North Western	a				19 54	20 00	←							20 25			20 37					20 57	
	d				19 55	20 01	19 55							20 25			20 38					20 57	
Preston 8	a				→	20 14	20 18							20 38			20 51	20 55				21 22	
Blackpool North	a					20g54	20 44															21 53	
	d					19 37								19 45				20 20					
Preston 8	d					20 15								20 41			20 53	20 58					
Lancaster 6	a					20 30								20 54			21 08	21 14					
	d					20 30								20 55			21 08	21 14					
Barrow-in-Furness	a																	22 17					
Oxenholme Lake District	a													21 08			21 22						
	d													21 09			21 24						
Windermere	a													21 34									
Penrith North Lakes	d													21 34									
Carlisle 8	a					21 17								21 49			22 01						
	d					21 18								21 51			22 03						
Lockerbie	d					21 37																	
Carstairs	a																						
Motherwell	a					22s21																	
Glasgow Central 15	a					22 39								23 04			23 17						
Haymarket	a																						
Edinburgh 10	a																						
Perth	a																						
Dundee	a																						
Aberdeen	a																						
Inverness	a																						

For general notes see front of timetable
For details of catering facilities see Directory of Train Operators

- **A** From Bristol Temple Meads (Table 51)
- **B** From Bournemouth (Table 51)
- **C** From Bristol Temple Meads (Fridays from Exeter St Davids) (Table 51)
- **b** Change at Nuneaton
- **c** Change at Chester and Llandudno Junction
- **e** Change at Crewe and Wilmslow
- **f** Change at Preston
- **g** From 5 October arr. 2 mins. later

OVERNIGHT SLEEPERS. For Sleeper trains, operated by First ScotRail, please refer to Tables 400 - 404

London and West Midlands → North West England and Scotland

Route Diagram - see first page of Table 65

Station		LM	VT	VT	VT	VT	VT	XC	VT	NT	VT	VT	VT	XC	VT	LM	VT	VT	NT	VT	NT	XC	VT
			FO								FO												
		1 ◇	◇	1 ◇	1 ◇	1 ◇	1 ◇	1 ◇	1 ◇		◇	1 ◇	1 ◇	1 ◇	1 ◇	1 ◇	1 ◇	1 ◇		1 ◇		1 ◇	1 ◇
								A						B								A	
London Euston 15	d		18 46	19 00	19 07	19 10	19 20		19 30				19 40		20 00		20 07	20 10		20 30			20 40
Gatwick Airport 10	d																						
Watford Junction	d					18 44												19 41					
Milton Keynes Central	d					19u40	19 50											20u40					
Northampton	d																						
Rugby	d												20 03										
Nuneaton	d				20 03						←		20 16				21 03						
Tamworth Low Level	d		20s01								20s01		20 43							21 34			
Lichfield Trent Valley	d		→								20s09		20 50							21 42			
Coventry	d							19 27				19 42	19b45	19 49								20 27	
Birmingham International	d							19 38				19 53		20 09								20 38	
Birmingham New Street 12	d	19 36						19 57				20 20		20 31		20 36						20 57	
Wolverhampton 7	d	19 53						20 16				20 37		20 49		20 53						21 16	
Penkridge	d	20 03														21 03							
Stafford	a	20 09			20 26			20 29			20s35	20 51	21 02			21 09	21 27					21 29	
	d	20 09			20 27			20 29				20 53	21 04			21 09	21 27					21 29	
Stoke-on-Trent	a			20 24			20 48	20 54						21 18	21 23							21 54	
Congleton	a																						
Macclesfield	a			20 41				21 11							21 40							22 11	
Crewe 10	a	20 30				20 48			21 01			21 14				21 30		21 48					22 12
	d	20 31				20 50			21 03							21 31		21 50					22 13
Chester	a					21 10			21 45									22 15					
Wrexham General	a																						
Llandudno Junction	a					22 06												23 49					
Llandudno	a																						
Bangor (Gwynedd)	a					22 22												00 12					
Holyhead	a					22 56												00 55					
Wilmslow	a	21 16											21 36			22 16							22 29
Manchester Airport	a												22 04										23 04
Stockport	a			20 55			21 16	21 27					21 58		21 55							22 25	22 38
Manchester Piccadilly 10	a			21 07			21 28	21 40					21 55	22 00	22 07							22 40	22 51
Hartford	a	20 45														21 43							
Warrington Bank Quay	a								21 19		21s26									22 22			
	d								21 20											22 23			
Runcorn	a	20 55			21 00											21 53	21 58						
Liverpool South Parkway 7	a	21 05														22 04							
Liverpool Lime Street 10	a	21 15			21 21											22 14	22 20						
	d								20 25										21 42				
Manchester Airport	d								20c29														
Manchester Piccadilly 10	d								20c46														
Bolton	d								21c07														
Wigan North Western	a								21 30		21s38								22 28	22 33	←		
	d								21 31										22 28 →	22 34	22 28		
Preston 8	a								21 44		21 55									22 53	22 54		
Blackpool North	a										22e48										23 21		
	d								20 45														
Preston 8	d								21 45	21 51													
Lancaster 6	a								22 00	22 11													
	d								22 00	22 11													
Barrow-in-Furness	a								23 16	23 16													
Oxenholme Lake District	a								22 13														
	d								22 13														
Windermere	a								22 39														
Penrith North Lakes	d								22 39														
Carlisle 8	a								22 54														
	d								22 56														
Lockerbie	d																						
Carstairs	a																						
Motherwell	a																						
Glasgow Central 15	a								00 09														
Haymarket	a																						
Edinburgh 10	a																						
Perth	a																						
Dundee	a																						
Aberdeen	a																						
Inverness	a																						

For general notes see front of timetable
For details of catering facilities see Directory of Train Operators

A From Bournemouth (Table 51)
B From Bristol Temple Meads (Table 51)
b Change at Nuneaton and Tamworth Low Level
c Change at Preston
e From 9 October arr. 2250

OVERNIGHT SLEEPERS. For Sleeper trains, operated by First ScotRail, please refer to Tables 400 - 404

London and West Midlands → North West England and Scotland

Route Diagram - see first page of Table 65

		VT	TP	VT	LM	XC	VT	VT	NT	XC	LM		SR	VT	AW	LM	VT	SR FX	SR FO
		1 ◇	1 ◇	1 ◇	1 ◇	1 ◇	1 ◇	1 ◇		1 ◇	1 ◇		R	1 ◇	◇	1	1 ◇	R	R
						A							B						
		☕		☕			☕	☕					☕	☕			☕	☕	☕
London Euston 15 ⊖	d			21 00			21 07	21 10					21 15	21 40			22 00	23 50	23 50
Gatwick Airport 10 ✈	d																		
Watford Junction	d			20 41				21u25					21u33				21 58	00u10	00u10
Milton Keynes Central	d			21 31			21 38	21 34									22 39		
Northampton	d							21 17									22 17		
Rugby	d							22 03									23 19		
Nuneaton	d						22 07										23 30		
Tamworth Low Level	d																23s40		
Lichfield Trent Valley	d																23s47		
Coventry	d	20 42			20 49	21 27	21b44			21 49					22 11	22 24			
Birmingham International ✈	d	20 53			21 09	21 38				22 04					22 29	22 34			
Birmingham New Street 12	d	21 20			21 36	21 57				22 28	22 36				22 55	23 09			
Wolverhampton 7	d	21 41			21 53	22 16				22 46	22 57				23 13	23 35			
Penkridge	d				22 03						23 07					23 45			
Stafford	a	21 53			22 09	22 29		22 34		22 58	23 13				23 30	23 52	00s02		
	d	21 55			22 09	22 29		22 34		22 59	23 13				23 30	23 52			
Stoke-on-Trent	a			22 28		22 54				23 20				23s36					
Congleton	a																		
Macclesfield	a			22 44		23 11								23s52					
Crewe 10	a	22 18			22 30		22 46	22 54			23 43				23 55	00 16	00s28		
	d	22 19			22 31		22 48	22 55					23u54		23 57				
Chester	a							23 42							00 18				
Wrexham General	a																		
Llandudno Junction	a														01 28				
Llandudno	a																		
Bangor (Gwynedd)	a														01 45				
Holyhead	a														02 15				
Wilmslow	a							23 23											
Manchester Airport ✈	a														01c16		01 16		
Stockport	a			22 58		23 25		23 32						00s08			00s59		
Manchester Piccadilly 10	a			23 11		23 40		23 48		00e15				00 21	01c36		01 13		
Hartford	a				22 43														
Warrington Bank Quay	a	22 37						23 12											
	d	22 37						23 13											
Runcorn	a				22 56		23 07												
Liverpool South Parkway 7 ✈	a				23 08														
Liverpool Lime Street 10	a				23 21		23 35												
	d								23 02										
Manchester Airport ✈	d		22 00																
Manchester Piccadilly 10	d		22 16																
Bolton	d		22 33																
Wigan North Western	a	22 47						23 23	23 48										
	d	22 47						23 24	23 48										
Preston 8	a	23 05	23 09					23 43	00 13										
Blackpool North	a							00 20											
	d		22 20																
Preston 8	d		23 13										00u52						
Lancaster 6	a		23 28																
	d		23 29																
Barrow-in-Furness	a		00 32																
Oxenholme Lake District	a																		
	d																		
Windermere	a																		
Penrith North Lakes	d																		
Carlisle 8	a																	05s11	05s18
	d																		
Lockerbie	d																		
Carstairs	a																	06s20	06s25
Motherwell	a																	07s01	07s01
Glasgow Central 15	a																	07 18	07 21
Haymarket	a																		
Edinburgh 10	a																	07 20	07 13
Perth	a												05s39						
Dundee	a												06s08						
Aberdeen	a												07 35						
Inverness	a												08 30						

For general notes see front of timetable
For details of catering facilities see Directory of Train Operators

A From Bournemouth (Table 51)
B Also conveys portion to Fort William (Table 227)
b Change at Nuneaton
c Change at Crewe
e Tuesday and Wednesday mornings arr. 0037

OVERNIGHT SLEEPERS. For Sleeper trains, operated by First ScotRail, please refer to Tables 400 - 404

Table 65

London and West Midlands → North West England and Scotland

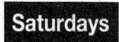

Saturdays

until 31 October

Route Diagram - see first page of Table 65

	SR	TP	VT	TP		VT	XC	LM	LM	NT	VT	NT	TP	XC	LM	XC	VT	NT	LM	NT	VT	NT	VT	XC
		1	1 ◇	1 ◇		1 ◇	1 ◇	1 ◇	1 ◇		1 ◇		1 ◇	1 ◇	1 ◇	1 ◇	1 ◇		1 ◇		1 ◇		1 ◇	1 ◇
		A																B						
London Euston 15 d																	06 05						06 36	
Gatwick Airport 10 d																								
Watford Junction d																	06u20						06u51	
Milton Keynes Central d																	06 41							
Northampton d																	06 38							
Rugby d														06b00			07 03							
Nuneaton d														06b16										
Tamworth Low Level d														06b31										
Lichfield Trent Valley d														06b37										
Coventry d																06 10					06 29			06 49
Birmingham International d																06 28					06 45			07 09
Birmingham New Street 12 d						05 30	05 57		06 01		06 20			06 31	06 36	06 57			07 01		07 20			07 31
Wolverhampton 7 d						05 48	06 14		06 18		06 37			06 49	06 54	07 14			07 18		07 37			07 49
Penkridge d									06 29										07 30					
Stafford a						06 00	06 29		06 35					07 00	07 08	07 29	07 33		07 36					
d						06 01	06 29		06 36					07 01	07 08	07 29	07 34		07 38					
Stoke-on-Trent a							06 50							07 18										08 18
Congleton a							07 02																	
Macclesfield a							07 11							07 36										08 35
Crewe 10 a						06 20			06 56		07 07				07 33	07 50	07 53		07 58		08 07		08 10	
d			05 57			06 23		06 31	06 58		07 09				07 34	07 53	07 55		08 00		08 09		08 11	
Chester a						06 43					07 44												08 45	
Wrexham General a																								
Llandudno Junction a						07 33					08c48												09c48	
Llandudno a						08 06					09c06												10c06	
Bangor (Gwynedd) a						07 49					09c31												10c36	
Holyhead a						08 23					10c05												11c19	
Wilmslow a						06e56					07 44					08 09					08 45		08 27	
Manchester Airport a						07e04					08 05												09 04	
Stockport a							07 27							07 49		08 20							08 37	08 49
Manchester Piccadilly 10 a							07 40							08 00		08 40							08 49	09 00
Hartford a								06 46	07 10						07 48				08 11					
Warrington Bank Quay a			06 13								07 26						08 11				08 27			
d			06 14								07 27						08 12				08 28			
Runcorn a								06 57	07 20						08 01				08 24					
Liverpool South Parkway 7 a								07 08	07 30						08 11				08 33					
Liverpool Lime Street 10 a								07 20	07 41						08 22				08 45					
d										06 57							07 01			07 57				
Manchester Airport d			05f29	06 18									07 28											
Manchester Piccadilly 10 d			05f46	06 33									07 45											
Bolton d			06f02	06 50									07 59											
Wigan North Western a			06 24							07 30	07 37	←					08 22			08 30	08 38	←		
d			06 25							07 31	07 38	07 31					08 23			08 31	08 39	08 31		
Preston 8 a			06 37	07 11						→	07 51	07 54	08 22				08 36			→	08 52	08 54		
Blackpool North a			07g41								08 29	08 18									09g48	09 20		
d			05 45	06 34							07 02		07 44											
Preston 8 d			06 40	07 16	07 20						07 53		08 24				08 37	08 42			08 54			
Lancaster 6 a			06 54	07 31	07 36						08 08		08 39				08 52	09 02			09 09			
d		05 45	06 54	07 32	07 36						08 09		08 40				08 52	09 02			09 09			
Barrow-in-Furness a					08 39													10 07						
Oxenholme Lake District a		06 20	07 08								08 22		08 54				09 05							
d		06 21	07 10								08 23		08 54				09 06							
Windermere a		06 41	07 40								08 46						09 33							
Penrith North Lakes d			07 37	08 09													09 32				09 46			
Carlisle 8 a			07 50	08 25							09 01		09 32				09 47				10 01			
d	06 12		07 51	08 26							09 03		09 34				09 48				10 04			
Lockerbie d			08 10										09 54											
Carstairs a																								
Motherwell a																								
Glasgow Central 15 a	08 37		09 13	09 45													11 03				11 17			
Haymarket a											10s16		11s04											
Edinburgh 10 a											10 22		11 10											
Perth a	10h34		11h19	11h34							11 54		12 52											
Dundee a	10h57										11j43		12 36											
Aberdeen a	12h14										13j07		13 46											
Inverness a			13h37										15 06											

For general notes see front of timetable
For details of catering facilities see Directory of Train Operators

A Via Morecambe (Table 98)

B To Carlisle via Whitehaven (Table 100)
b Change at Stafford
c Change at Crewe and Chester
e Change at Crewe
f Change at Preston

g From 10 October arr. 2 mins. later
h Via Glasgow Central and Glasgow Queen Street. Passengers make their own way from one station to the other
j Change at Haymarket

London and West Midlands → North West England and Scotland

Route Diagram - see first page of Table 65

		VT	LM	VT	VT	TP	VT	TP	XC	LM	NT	VT	NT	TP	TP	VT	XC	VT	LM	VT	VT	VT	VT	XC	LM
		1 ◇	1 ◇	1 ◇	1 ◇	1 ◇	1 ◇	1 ◇	1 ◇	1 ◇		1 ◇		1 ◇	1 ◇	1 ◇	1 ◇	1 ◇	1 ◇	1 ◇	1 ◇	1 ◇	1 ◇	1 ◇	1 ◇
						A		A	B								C							B	
		🍴		🍴	🍴	🛒	🍴	🛒	🛒			🍴		🛒		🍴	🍴 🛒	🍴		🍴	🍴	🍴	🍴	🛒	
London Euston 15 ⊖	d	06 55		07 07	07 20		07 30									07 35		08 00		08 07	08 10	08 20	08 30		
Gatwick Airport 10 ✈	d																								
Watford Junction	d				06 41											07 19					08 01				
Milton Keynes Central	d	07 27			07 50											08 06					08u40	08 50			
Northampton	d																								
Rugby	d																		08b04						
Nuneaton	d		07b10																08b17						
Tamworth Low Level	d		07b28																08b31						
Lichfield Trent Valley	d		07b34																08b37						
Coventry	d								07 27			07 29					07 49							08 27	
Birmingham International ✈	d								07 38			07 45					08 09							08 38	
Birmingham New Street 12	d		07 36						07 57	08 01		08 20					08 31		08 36					08 57	09 01
Wolverhampton 7	d		07 53						08 14	08 19		08 37					08 49		08 53					09 14	09 19
Penkridge	d		08 03							08 29									09 03						
Stafford	a		08 09	08 22					08 29	08 35									09 09	09 22				09 29	09 34
	d		08 09	08 23					08 29	08 36									09 09	09 23				09 29	09 35
Stoke-on-Trent	a	08 24			08 48				08 54								09 18	09 24				09 48		09 54	
Congleton	a																								
Macclesfield	a	08 41							09 11									09 41						10 11	
Crewe 10	a		08 30	08 41						08 57		09 07				09 10			09 30		09 48				09 56
	d		08 31	08 43						08 58		09 09				09 11			09 31		09 50				09 57
Chester	a															09 45					10 12				
Wrexham General	a																								
Llandudno Junction	a															10c48					11 14				
Llandudno	a															11c06					11e36				
Bangor (Gwynedd)	a																				11 36				
Holyhead	a																				12 11				
Wilmslow	a		09 16									09 45				09 27			10 16						
Manchester Airport ✈	a															10 04									
Stockport	a	08 55			09 16				09 27							09 36		09 55				10 16		10 27	
Manchester Piccadilly 10	a	09 07			09 28				09 40							09 49	10 00	10 07				10 28		10 40	
Hartford	a									09 11															10 10
Warrington Bank Quay	a						09 14					09 26											10 14		
	d						09 14					09 27											10 14		
Runcorn	a		08 48	08 59						09 22									09 48	09 54					10 21
Liverpool South Parkway 7 ✈	a		08 59							09 31									09 59						10 31
Liverpool Lime Street 10	a		09 09	09 21						09 42									10 09	10 15					10 43
	d						08 01				08 57												09 01		
Manchester Airport ✈	d					08 25								09 00									09f29		
Manchester Piccadilly 10	d					08 46								09 16									09f46		
Bolton	d					09 07								09 33									10f07		
Wigan North Western	a						09 25				09 30	09 37	←										10 25		
	d						09 25				09 31	09 38	09 31										10 25		
Preston 8	a					09 33	09 38				→	09 51	09 54	09 55									10 38		
Blackpool North	a												10 20												
	d						08 45	←				09 14		09 20	09g14								09 45		
Preston 8	d					09 45 →	09 41	09 45				09 53		09 58	10 04								10 41		
Lancaster 6	a						09 54	10 00				10 08		10 14	10 20								10 54		
	d						09 55	10 01				10 08		10 14	10 20								10 55		
Barrow-in-Furness	a														11 15										
Oxenholme Lake District	a							10 17				10 22		10 28									11 08		
	d							10 18				10 24		10 28									11 08		
Windermere	a							10 39																	
Penrith North Lakes	d						10 31							10 53											
Carlisle 8	a						10 46					11 01		11 10									11 46		
	d						10 47					11 03		11 11									11 47		
Lockerbie	d													11 31											
Carstairs	a																								
Motherwell	a																								
Glasgow Central 15	a						12 01							12 32									13 01		
Haymarket	a											12s16													
Edinburgh 10	a											12 22													
Perth	a						13h36					14 52											14h36		
Dundee	a						14h00					13j35											14h59		
Aberdeen	a											14j48											16h19		
Inverness	a											17 05											17k05		

For general notes see front of timetable
For details of catering facilities see Directory of Train Operators

A 🛒 to Preston
B From Southampton Central (Table 51)
C From Bristol Temple Meads (Table 51)
b Change at Stafford
c Change at Crewe and Chester
e Change at Chester and Llandudno Junction
f Change at Preston
g By changing at Preston, passengers may depart 0929
h Via Glasgow Central and Glasgow Queen Street. Passengers make their own way from one station to the other
j Change at Haymarket
k Change at Glasgow Central, Glasgow Queen Street and Perth. Passengers make their own way between Glasgow Central and Glasgow Queen Street

Table 65

Saturdays

until 31 October

London and West Midlands → North West England and Scotland

Route Diagram - see first page of Table 65

		NT	VT	NT	TP	VT	TP	XC	LM	VT	VT	VT	VT	VT	XC	LM	NT	VT	NT	TP	VT	XC	VT	LM	VT
			1 ◇		1 ◇	1 ◇	1 ◇	1 ◇	1 ◇	1 ◇	1 ◇	1 ◇	1 ◇	1 ◇	1 ◇	1 ◇		1 ◇		1 ◇	1 ◇	1 ◇	1 ◇	1 ◇	1 ◇
								A							B					C		D			
			☕		🛒	☕		☕ 🛒		⊠ ☕	☕	☕	☕	☕	🛒			☕		🛒	☕	☕ 🛒	☕		☕
London Euston 15 ⊖	d					08 40				08 50	09 00	09 07	09 20	09 30							09 40		10 00		10 07
Gatwick Airport 10 ✈	d																								
Watford Junction	d									09u05															
Milton Keynes Central	d									09 25			09 50												
Northampton	d																								
Rugby	d								09b03															10b03	
Nuneaton	d								09b16															10b16	
Tamworth Low Level	d								09b31															10b31	
Lichfield Trent Valley	d								09b37															10b37	
Coventry	d		08 42					08 49							09 27			09 42				09 49			
Birmingham International ✈	d		08 53					09 09							09 38			09 53				10 09			
Birmingham New Street 12	d		09 20					09 31	09 36						09 57	10 01		10 20				10 31		10 36	
Wolverhampton 7	d		09 37					09 49	09 53						10 14	10 19		10 37				10 49		10 53	
Penkridge	d								10 03															11 03	
Stafford	a								10 09			10 22			10 29	10 35								11 09	11 22
	d								10 09			10 23			10 29	10 35								11 09	11 23
Stoke-on-Trent	a							10 18			10 24		10 48		10 54							11 18	11 24		
Congleton	a																								
Macclesfield	a										10 41				11 11								11 41		
Crewe 10	a		10 07			10 10			10 30	10 34						10 56		11 07			11 10			11 30	
	d		10 09			10 11			10 31	10 45						10 57		11 09			11 11			11 31	
Chester	a					10 45				11 12											11 45				
Wrexham General	a																								
Llandudno Junction	a					11c48				12 04											12c48				
Llandudno	a					12c06				12 36											13c06				
Bangor (Gwynedd)	a									12 23															
Holyhead	a									12 56															
Wilmslow	a		10 45			10 27				11e16								11 45			11 27			12 16	
Manchester Airport ✈	a					11 04															12 04				
Stockport	a					10 36					10 55		11 16		11 27						11 36		11 55		
Manchester Piccadilly 10	a					10 49		11 00			11 07		11 28		11 40						11 49	12 00	12 07		
Hartford	a															11 10									
Warrington Bank Quay	a		10 26											11 14				11 26							
	d		10 27											11 14				11 27							
Runcorn	a								10 48			10 54				11 21								11 48	11 54
Liverpool South Parkway 7 ✈	a								10 59							11 31								11 59	
Liverpool Lime Street 10	a								11 09			11 15				11 42								12 09	12 15
	d	09 57												10 01			10 57								
Manchester Airport ✈	d				10 00									10f29						11 00					
Manchester Piccadilly 10	d				10 16									10f46						11 16					
Bolton	d				10 33									11f07						11 33					
Wigan North Western	a	10 30	10 37	←										11 25			11 30	11 37	←						
	d	10 31	10 38	10 31										11 25			11 31	11 38	11 31						
Preston 8	a	→	10 51	10 54	10 55									11 38			→	11 51	11 54	11 55					
Blackpool North	a			11 20															12 20						
	d				10 20		10 29							10 45				11 15							
Preston 8	d		10 53		10 58		11 04							11 41				11 53		11 58					
Lancaster 6	a		11 08		11 14		11 19							11 54				12 08		12 14					
	d		11 08		11 14		11 20							11 55				12 08		12 14					
Barrow-in-Furness	a						12 32													13 10					
Oxenholme Lake District	a				11 28		11 36											12 22							
	d				11 28		11 37											12 24							
Windermere	a						11 56											12 47							
Penrith North Lakes	d		11 45		11 53									12 30											
Carlisle 8	a		12 00		12 10									12 45				13 01							
	d		12 03		12 11									12 47				13 03							
Lockerbie	d				12 30																				
Carstairs	a																								
Motherwell	a																								
Glasgow Central 15	a		13 18											14 01											
Haymarket	a				13s33													14s16							
Edinburgh 10	a				13 40													14 22							
Perth	a													15g36				15 53							
Dundee	a				15 18													15h37							
Aberdeen	a				16 50													16h50							
Inverness	a																	19j34							

For general notes see front of timetable
For details of catering facilities see Directory of Train Operators

- **A** From Cardiff Central (Table 51)
- **B** From Bournemouth (Table 51)
- **C** 🛒 to Preston
- **D** From Paignton (Table 51)
- **b** Change at Stafford
- **c** Change at Crewe and Chester
- **e** Change at Crewe
- **f** Change at Preston
- **g** Via Glasgow Central and Glasgow Queen Street. Passengers make their own way from one station to the other
- **h** Change at Haymarket
- **j** Change at Edinburgh and Perth

Table 65

Saturdays

until 31 October

London and West Midlands → North West England and Scotland

Route Diagram - see first page of Table 65

Station		VT	VT	VT	XC	LM	NT	VT	NT	TP	VT	TP	XC	VT	LM	VT	VT	VT	VT	XC	LM	NT	VT	NT	TP
		1◇	1◇	1◇	1◇	1◇		1◇		1◇	1◇	1◇	1◇	1◇	1◇	1◇	1◇	1◇	1◇	1◇	1◇		1◇		1◇
					A								B							A					
London Euston 15 ⊖	d	10 10	10 20	10 30							10 40			11 00		11 07	11 10	11 20	11 30						
Gatwick Airport 10 ✈	d																								
Watford Junction	d	*10 01*															*11 01*								
Milton Keynes Central	d	10u40	10 50														11u40	11 50							
Northampton	d																								
Rugby	d														*11b03*										
Nuneaton	d														*11b16*										
Tamworth Low Level	d														*11b31*										
Lichfield Trent Valley	d														*11b37*										
Coventry	d				10 27			*10 42*					*10 49*							11 27			*11 42*		
Birmingham International ✈	d				10 38			*10 53*					*11 09*							11 38			*11 53*		
Birmingham New Street 12	d				10 57	11 01		11 20					11 31		11 36					11 57	12 01		12 20		
Wolverhampton 7	d				11 14	11 19		11 37					11 49		11 53					12 14	12 19		12 37		
Penkridge	d														12 03										
Stafford	a				11 29	11 35									12 09	12 22				12 29	12 35				
	d				11 29	11 35									12 09	12 23				12 29	12 35				
Stoke-on-Trent	a		11 48		11 54								12 18	12 24				12 48		12 54					
Congleton	a																								
Macclesfield	a				12 11									12 41						13 11					
Crewe 10	a	11 48				11 56		12 07			12 10				12 30		12 47				12 56		13 07		
	d	11 50				11 57		12 09			12 11				12 31		12 49				12 57		13 09		
Chester	a	12 12									*12 45*						13 12								
Wrexham General	a																								
Llandudno Junction	a	*13 14*									*13c48*						*14 14*								
Llandudno	a	*13e36*									*14c06*						*14e36*								
Bangor (Gwynedd)	a	*13 31*															*14 36*								
Holyhead	a	*14 14*															*15 11*								
Wilmslow	a							*12 45*			12 27				*13 16*								*13 45*		
Manchester Airport ✈	a										*13 04*														
Stockport	a		12 16		12 27						12 36			12 55				13 16		13 27					
Manchester Piccadilly 10	a		12 28		12 40						12 49		13 00	13 07				13 28		13 40					
Hartford	a					12 10															13 10				
Warrington Bank Quay	a			12 14				12 26											13 14				13 26		
	d			12 14				12 27											13 14				13 27		
Runcorn	a					12 21									12 48	12 54					13 21				
Liverpool South Parkway 7 ✈	a					12 31									12 59						13 31				
Liverpool Lime Street 10	a					12 43									13 09	13 15					13 42				
	d			*11 01*			11 57												*12 01*			12 57			
Manchester Airport ✈	d			*11f29*						12 00									*12f29*						13 00
Manchester Piccadilly 10	d			*11f46*						12 16									*12f46*						13 16
Bolton	d			*12f07*						12 33									*13f07*						13 33
Wigan North Western	a			12 25			12 30	12 37	←										13 25			13 30	13 37	←	
	d			12 25			12 31	12 38	12 31										13 25			13 31	13 38	13 31	
Preston 8	a			12 38			→	12 51	12 54	12 55									13 38			→	13 51	13 54	13 55
Blackpool North	a								13 21															14 20	
	d			*11 37*						*12 20*		*12 29*							*12 45*						*13 20*
Preston 8	d			12 41				12 53		12 58		13 04							13 41				13 53		13 58
Lancaster 6	a			12 54				13 08		13 14		13 19							13 54				14 08		14 14
	d			12 55				13 08		13 14		13 20							13 55				14 08		14 14
Barrow-in-Furness	a											*14g36*													*15g26*
Oxenholme Lake District	a			13 08				13 22		13 28		13 36							14 08						14 28
	d			13 09				13 24		13 28		13 37							14 08						14 28
Windermere	a											13 56													*14 52*
Penrith North Lakes	d									13 53													14 45		14 53
Carlisle 8	a			13 46				14 01		14 10									14 46				15 00		15 10
	d			13 47				14 03		14 11									14 47				15 02		15 11
Lockerbie	d									14 30															15 33
Carstairs	a																								
Motherwell	a																								16s23
Glasgow Central 15	a			15 01				15 17											16 01						16 42
Haymarket	a																						16s15		
Edinburgh 10	a									15 42													16 22		
Perth	a			*16h36*				*17h18*															*17 52*		
Dundee	a			*16h59*						*17 20*													*17j38*		
Aberdeen	a			*18h15*																			*19j00*		
Inverness	a							*19h34*															*20 08*		

For general notes see front of timetable
For details of catering facilities see Directory of Train Operators

A From Bournemouth (Table 51)

B From Bristol Temple Meads (Table 51)
b Change at Stafford
c Change at Crewe and Chester
e Change at Chester and Llandudno Junction
f Change at Preston

g Until 3 October only
h Via Glasgow Central and Glasgow Queen Street. Passengers make their own way from one station to the other
j Change at Haymarket

Table 65

London and West Midlands → North West England and Scotland

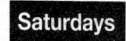

Saturdays

until 31 October

Route Diagram - see first page of Table 65

		VT	XC	VT	LM	VT	VT	VT	TP	VT	TP	XC	LM	NT	VT	NT	TP	VT	XC	VT	LM	VT	VT	VT	VT
		1 ◇	1 ◇	1 ◇	1 ◇	1 ◇	1 ◇	1 ◇	1 ◇	1 ◇	1 ◇	1 ◇	1 ◇		1 ◇		1 ◇	1 ◇	1 ◇	1 ◇	1 ◇	1 ◇	1 ◇	1 ◇	1 ◇
			A						B			C							D						
		☕	☕ 🛒	☕		☕	☕	☕	🛒	☕		🛒			☕		🛒	☕	☕ 🛒	☕		☕	☕	☕	☕
London Euston 15 ⊖	d	11 40		12 00		12 07	12 10	12 20		12 30								12 40		13 00		13 07	13 10	13 20	13 30
Gatwick Airport 10 ✈	d																								
Watford Junction	d						12 01																13 01		
Milton Keynes Central	d						12u40	12 50															13u40	13 50	
Northampton	d																								
Rugby	d				12b03																13b03				
Nuneaton	d				12b16																13b16				
Tamworth Low Level	d				12b31																13b31				
Lichfield Trent Valley	d				12b37																13b37				
Coventry	d		11 49									12 27			12 42				12 49						
Birmingham International ✈	d		12 09									12 38			12 53				13 09						
Birmingham New Street 12	d		12 31		12 36							12 57	13 01		13 20				13 31		13 36				
Wolverhampton 7	d		12 49		12 53							13 14	13 19		13 37				13 49		13 53				
Penkridge	d				13 03																14 03				
Stafford	a				13 09	13 22						13 29	13 35								14 09	14 22			
	d				13 09	13 23						13 29	13 35								14 09	14 23			
Stoke-on-Trent	a		13 18	13 24				13 48				13 54							14 18	14 24				14 48	
Congleton	a																								
Macclesfield	a			13 41								14 11								14 41					
Crewe 10	a	13 10			13 30		13 47						13 56		14 07			14 10			14 30		14 48		
	d	13 11			13 31		13 49						13 57		14 09			14 11			14 31		14 50		
Chester	a	13 45					14 12											14 45					15 12		
Wrexham General	a																								
Llandudno Junction	a	14c48					15 14											15c48					16 14		
Llandudno	a	15c06					15e36											16c06					16e36		
Bangor (Gwynedd)	a						15 31																16 36		
Holyhead	a						16 14																17 11		
Wilmslow	a	13 27			14 16										14 45			14 27			15 16				
Manchester Airport ✈	a	14 04																15 04							
Stockport	a	13 36		13 55				14 16				14 27						14 36		14 55				15 16	
Manchester Piccadilly 10	a	13 49	14 00	14 07				14 28				14 40						14 49	15 00	15 07				15 28	
Hartford	a												14 10												
Warrington Bank Quay	a									14 14					14 26										15 14
	d									14 14					14 27										15 14
Runcorn	a				13 48	13 54							14 21								14 48	14 54			
Liverpool South Parkway 7 ✈	a				13 59								14 31								14 59				
Liverpool Lime Street 10	a				14 09	14 15							14 42								15 09	15 15			
	d									13 01				13 57											14 01
Manchester Airport ✈	d								13 29								14 00								14f29
Manchester Piccadilly 10	d								13 46								14 16								14f46
Bolton	d								14 07								14 33								15f07
Wigan North Western	a									14 25				14 30	14 37	←									15 25
	d									14 25				14 31	14 38	14 31									15 25
Preston 8	a								14 33	14 38				→	14 51	14 54	14 55								15 38
Blackpool North	a															15 20									
	d									13 45	←						14 20								14 45
Preston 8	d								14 45 →	14 41	14 45				14 53		14 58								15 41
Lancaster 6	a									14 54	15 00				15 08		15 14								15 54
	d									14 55	15 01				15 09		15 14								15 56
Barrow-in-Furness	a										15 56														
Oxenholme Lake District	a														15 22		15 28								16 08
	d														15 24		15 28								16 09
Windermere	a																16 00								16 48
Penrith North Lakes	d									15 30							15 53								
Carlisle 8	a									15 45					16 01		16 09								16 46
	d									15 47					16 03		16 10								16 47
Lockerbie	d																16 29								
Carstairs	a																								
Motherwell	a																								
Glasgow Central 15	a									17 01					17 18										18 01
Haymarket	a																17s30								
Edinburgh 10	a																17 39								
Perth	a									18g43							18h58								19g42
Dundee	a									19g06							19 24								
Aberdeen	a									20g29							20 46								
Inverness	a																21h03								

For general notes see front of timetable
For details of catering facilities see Directory of Train Operators

A From Plymouth (from 12 September from Bristol Temple Meads) (Table 51)

B 🛒 to Preston

C From Bournemouth (Table 51)

D From Paignton (Table 51)

b Change at Stafford

c Change at Crewe and Chester

e Change at Chester and Llandudno Junction

f Change at Preston

g Via Glasgow Central and Glasgow Queen Street. Passengers make their own way from one station to the other

h Change at Haymarket

London and West Midlands → North West England and Scotland

Route Diagram - see first page of Table 65

		XC	LM	NT	VT	NT	TP	VT	XC	VT	LM	VT	VT	VT	VT	NT	SR	XC	LM	NT	VT	NT	TP		VT
		1◇	1◇		1◇		1◇	1◇	1◇	1◇	1◇	1◇	1◇	1◇	1◇			1◇	1◇		1◇		1◇		1◇
		A					B		C							D		A							
		✠			▭		✠	▭	▭ ✠	▭		▭	▭	▭	▭			✠			▭		✠		▭
London Euston 15 ⊖	d							13 40		14 00		14 07	14 10	14 20	14 30										14 40
Gatwick Airport 10 ✈	d																								
Watford Junction	d												14 01												
Milton Keynes Central	d												14u40	14 50											
Northampton	d																								
Rugby	d										14b03														
Nuneaton	d										14b16														
Tamworth Low Level	d										14b31														
Lichfield Trent Valley	d										14b37														
Coventry	d	13 27			13 42				13 49									14 27			14 42				
Birmingham International ✈	d	13 38			13 53				14 09									14 38			14 53				
Birmingham New Street 12	d	13 57	14 01		14 20				14 31		14 36							14 57	15 01		15 20				
Wolverhampton 7	d	14 14	14 19		14 37				14 49		14 53							15 14	15 19		15 37				
Penkridge	d										15 03														
Stafford	a	14 29	14 35								15 09	15 22						15 29	15 35						
	d	14 29	14 35								15 09	15 23						15 29	15 35						
Stoke-on-Trent	a	14 54							15 18	15 24				15 48				15 54							
Congleton	a																								
Macclesfield	a	15 11								15 41								16 11							
Crewe 10	a		14 56		15 07			15 10			15 30		15 47						15 56		16 08				16 11
	d		14 57		15 09			15 11			15 31		15 49						15 57		16 09				16 12
Chester	a							15 45					16 10												16 45
Wrexham General	a																								
Llandudno Junction	a							16c48					17 01												17c48
Llandudno	a							17c06					17 36												18c06
Bangor (Gwynedd)	a												17 17												
Holyhead	a												17 51												
Wilmslow	a				15 45			15 27			16 16										16 45				16 27
Manchester Airport ✈	a				16 04			16 04																	17 04
Stockport	a	15 27			15 58			15 36		15 55				16 16				16 27			16 58				16 36
Manchester Piccadilly 10	a	15 40			16 15			15 49	16 00	16 07				16 28				16 40			17 15				16 49
Hartford	a		15 10																16 10						
Warrington Bank Quay	a				15 26										16 14						16 26				
	d				15 27										16 14						16 27				
Runcorn	a		15 21								15 48	15 54							16 24						
Liverpool South Parkway 7 ✈	a		15 31								15 59								16 33						
Liverpool Lime Street 10	a		15 42								16 09	16 15							16 43						
	d			14 57											15 01					15 57					
Manchester Airport ✈	d						15 00								15e29								16 00		
Manchester Piccadilly 10	d						15 16								15e46								16 16		
Bolton	d						15 33								16e07								16 33		
Wigan North Western	a			15 30	15 37	←									16 25					16 30	16 37	←			
	d			15 31	15 38	15 31									16 25					16 31	16 38	16 31			
Preston 8	a			→	15 51	15 54	15 55								16 38					→	16 51	16 54	16 55		
Blackpool North	a					16 20																17 20			
	d						15 20								15 45								16 29		
Preston 8	d				15 53		15 58								16 41						16 53		17 00	17 04	
Lancaster 6	a				16 08		16 14								16 54						17 09		17 15	17 20	
	d				16 09		16 14								16 55	16 59					17 10		17 16	17 21	
Barrow-in-Furness	a						17 18									18 07								18f38	
Oxenholme Lake District	a																				17 24		17 30	17 38	
	d																				17 25		17 30	17 38	
Windermere	a																							18 00	
Penrith North Lakes	d				16 45										17 30										
Carlisle 8	a				17 00										17 45						18 03		18 10		
	d				17 03										17 47		17 58				18 04		18 11		
Lockerbie	d																						18 30		
Carstairs	a																								
Motherwell	a																								
Glasgow Central 15	a														19 01		20 27				19 17				
Haymarket	a				18s14																		19s31		
Edinburgh 10	a				18 22																		19 39		
Perth	a				20 02										20g36										
Dundee	a				19 52										20g59								21 30		
Aberdeen	a				21 12										22g13								23h20		
Inverness	a														23j14										

For general notes see front of timetable
For details of catering facilities see Directory of Train Operators

A From Bournemouth (Table 51)
B ✠ to Preston
C From Bristol Temple Meads (Table 51)
D To Millom (Table 100)
b Change at Stafford
c Change at Crewe and Chester
e Change at Preston
f Until 3 October only
g Via Glasgow Central and Glasgow Queen Street. Passengers make their own way from one station to the other
h Change at Haymarket and Dundee
j Change at Glasgow Central, Glasgow Queen Street and Perth. Passengers make their own way between Glasgow Central and Glasgow Queen Street

Saturdays until 31 October

London and West Midlands → North West England and Scotland

Route Diagram - see first page of Table 65

		XC	VT	LM	VT	VT	VT	VT	XC	LM	NT	VT	NT	TP	NT	VT	XC	VT	LM	VT	VT	VT	VT	XC	LM
		A							B					C			D							B	
London Euston 15	d		15 00		15 07	15 10	15 20	15 30								15 40		16 00		16 07	16 10	16 20	16 30		
Gatwick Airport 10	d																								
Watford Junction	d					15 01															16 01				
Milton Keynes Central	d					15u40	15 50														16u40	16 50			
Northampton	d																								
Rugby	d			15b03															16b03						
Nuneaton	d			15b16															16b16						
Tamworth Low Level	d			15b31															16b31						
Lichfield Trent Valley	d			15b37															16b37						
Coventry	d	14 49							15 27			15 42					15 49							16 27	
Birmingham International	d	15 09							15 38			15 53					16 09							16 38	
Birmingham New Street 12	d	15 31		15 36					15 57	16 01		16 20					16 31		16 36					16 57	17 01
Wolverhampton 7	d	15 49		15 53					16 14	16 19		16 37					16 49		16 53					17 14	17 19
Penkridge	d			16 03															17 03						17 29
Stafford	a			16 09	16 22				16 29	16 35									17 09	17 22				17 29	17 35
	d			16 09	16 23				16 29	16 35									17 09	17 23				17 29	17 36
Stoke-on-Trent	a	16 18	16 24				16 48		16 54								17 18	17 24				17 48		17 54	
Congleton	a																								
Macclesfield	a		16 41						17 11									17 41						18 11	
Crewe 10	a			16 30		16 47				16 56		17 07				17 10			17 30		17 47				17 56
	d			16 31		16 49				16 57		17 09				17 11			17 31		17 49				18 00
Chester	a					17 12										17 45					18 09				
Wrexham General	a																								
Llandudno Junction	a					18 16										18c48					19 05				
Llandudno	a					18e36										19c06					19 36				
Bangor (Gwynedd)	a					18 38															19 21				
Holyhead	a					19 13															19 55				
Wilmslow	a			17 16								17 45				17 27			18 16						
Manchester Airport	a															18 04									
Stockport	a		16 54				17 16		17 27			17 58				17 36		17 55				18 16		18 27	
Manchester Piccadilly 10	a	17 00	17 07				17 28		17 40			18 15				17 49	18 00	18 07				18 28		18 40	
Hartford	a									17 10															18 13
Warrington Bank Quay	a							17 14				17 26											18 14		
	d							17 14				17 27											18 14		
Runcorn	a			16 48	16 54					17 21									17 48	17 54					18 23
Liverpool South Parkway 7	a			16 59						17 31									17 59						18 33
Liverpool Lime Street 10	a			17 09	17 15					17 42									18 09	18 15					18 43
	d							16 01			16 57				17 27										
Manchester Airport	d							16f29						17 00											
Manchester Piccadilly 10	d							16f46						17 15											
Bolton	d							17f06						17 32									17f37		
Wigan North Western	a							17 25			17 30	17 37	←		18 05								18 25		
	d							17 25			17 31	17 38	17 31		18 05								18 25		
Preston 8	a							17 38			→	17 51	17 54	17 55	18 31								18 38		
Blackpool North	a												18 20		19 09								19g16		
	d							16 41				17 18											17 37		
Preston 8	d							17 41				17 53		17 58									18 41		
Lancaster 6	a							17 54				18 08		18 14									18 54		
	d							17 55				18 08		18 14									18 55		
Barrow-in-Furness	a													19 19											
Oxenholme Lake District	a							18 08				18 22											19 08		
	d							18 08				18 23											19 09		
Windermere	a											18 49													
Penrith North Lakes	d											18 49											19 34		
Carlisle 8	a							18 46				19 04											19 49		
	d							18 47				19 04											19 51		
Lockerbie	d																								
Carstairs	a																								
Motherwell	a																								
Glasgow Central 15	a							20 01															21 01		
Haymarket	a											20s19													
Edinburgh 10	a											20 24													
Perth	a							21h42				22 00											22h34		
Dundee	a							22h07				22 30											22h58		
Aberdeen	a							23h20				23 58											00h18		
Inverness	a																								

For general notes see front of timetable
For details of catering facilities see Directory of Train Operators

A From Bristol Temple Meads (from 12 September from Penzance) (Table 135)
B From Bournemouth (Table 51)
C to Preston
D From Bristol Temple Meads (Table 51)
b Change at Stafford
c Change at Crewe and Chester
e Change at Chester and Llandudno Junction
f Change at Preston
g From 10 October arr. 2 mins. later
h Via Glasgow Central and Glasgow Queen Street. Passengers make their own way from one station to the other

Table 65

Saturdays

until 31 October

London and West Midlands → North West England and Scotland

Route Diagram - see first page of Table 65

Station		NT	VT	NT	TP	TP	NT	VT	VT	XC	LM	VT	VT	VT	VT	VT	TP	XC	LM	VT	VT	NT	XC	VT	LM
			1 ◇		1 ◇	1 ◇		1 ◇	1 ◇	1 ◇	1 ◇	1 ◇	1 ◇	1 ◇	1 ◇	1 ◇	1 ◇	1 ◇	1 ◇	1 ◇	1 ◇		1 ◇	1 ◇	1 ◇
										A								B					C		
London Euston 15	⊖ d							16 33	16 40			17 00	17 07	17 10	17 20	17 30					17 40			18 00	
Gatwick Airport 10	✈ d																								
Watford Junction	d													17 01											
Milton Keynes Central	d													17u40	17 50										
Northampton	d																								
Rugby	d							17 03																	18b03
Nuneaton	d							17 16					18 03												18b16
Tamworth Low Level	d							17 38																	18b31
Lichfield Trent Valley	d							17 45																	18b37
Coventry	d		16 42							16 49								17 27		17 42			17 49		
Birmingham International	✈ d		16 53							17 09								17 38		17 53			18 09		
Birmingham New Street 12	d		17 20							17 31	17 36							17 57	18 01	18 20			18 31		18 36
Wolverhampton 7	d		17 37							17 49	17 53							18 14	18 19	18 37			18 49		18 53
Penkridge	d										18 03								18 29						19 03
Stafford	a							17 58			18 09		18 26					18 29	18 35						19 09
	d							17 58			18 09		18 27					18 29	18 35						19 09
Stoke-on-Trent	a									18 18		18 24			18 48			18 54					19 18	19 24	
Congleton	a																								
Macclesfield	a											18 41						19 11						19 41	
Crewe 10	a		18 07						18 10		18 30			18 48					18 59	19 07	19 10				19 30
	d		18 09						18 11		18 31			18 50						19 09	19 11				19 37
Chester	a								18 45					19 10							19 42				
Wrexham General	a																								
Llandudno Junction	a								19c48					20 06											
Llandudno	a								20c06					20 34											
Bangor (Gwynedd)	a													20 22											
Holyhead	a													20 56											
Wilmslow	a		18 45						18 27		19 16									19 45	19 27				20 16
Manchester Airport	✈ a								19 04												20 04				
Stockport	a		18 58						18 36			18 55			19 16			19 27		19 58	19 36			19 55	
Manchester Piccadilly 10	a		19 15						18 49	19 00		19 07			19 28			19 40		20 15	19 49		20 00	20 07	
Hartford	a										18 44														19 52
Warrington Bank Quay	a		18 26													19 14				19 26					
	d		18 27													19 14				19 27					
Runcorn	a							18 31			18 52		18 58												20 05
Liverpool South Parkway 7	✈ a										19 03														20 15
Liverpool Lime Street 10	a							18 54			19 13		19 19												20 26
	d	17 44					18 01													18 31		19 23			
Manchester Airport	✈ d		17e27		18 00											18e29	19 00								
Manchester Piccadilly 10	d		17e46		18 16											18e46	19 16								
Bolton	d		18e07		18 33											19e07	19 33								
Wigan North Western	a	18 30	18 37	←			18 49									19 25				19 37		19 54			
	d	18 31	18 38	18 31			18 49									19 25				19 38		19 55			
Preston 8	a	→	18 51	18 54	18 55		19 15									19 38	19 58			19 59		20 18			
Blackpool North	a			19 20			20 00															20 44			
	d				18 29											18 45	19 20								
Preston 8	d		18 53		19 00	19 04										19 41	20 02								
Lancaster 6	a		19 08		19 16	19 20										19 54	20 18								
	d		19 08		19 16	19 20										19 55	20 18								
Barrow-in-Furness	a					20 24											21 20								
Oxenholme Lake District	a		19 22		19 30											20 08									
	d		19 24		19 30											20 08									
Windermere	a				19 56											20 42									
Penrith North Lakes	d				19 55											20 34									
Carlisle 8	a		20 01		20 12											20 49									
	d		20 03		20 13											20 50									
Lockerbie	d				20 32																				
Carstairs	a																								
Motherwell	a																								
Glasgow Central 15	a		21 17		21 32											22 01									
Haymarket	a																								
Edinburgh 10	a																								
Perth	a															00f13									
Dundee	a																								
Aberdeen	a																								
Inverness	a																								

For general notes see front of timetable
For details of catering facilities see Directory of Train Operators

A From Paignton (Table 51)
B From Bournemouth (Table 51)
C From Bristol Temple Meads (Table 51)
b Change at Stafford
c Change at Crewe and Chester
e Change at Preston
f Via Glasgow Central and Glasgow Queen Street. Passengers make their own way from one station to the other

Table 65

London and West Midlands → North West England and Scotland

until 31 October

Route Diagram - see first page of Table 65

		VT	VT	VT	VT	TP	XC	LM	VT	NT	VT	VT	XC	VT	LM	VT	VT	VT	VT	XC	VT	VT	VT	XC	LM
							A						B			C	C	D	D	A				B	
London Euston 15	d	18 07	18 10	18 20	18 30						18 33	18 40		18b54		18 57	19 05	19 07	19 20		19 19		19c25		
Gatwick Airport 10	d																								
Watford Junction	d		18 01														19 01		19 01						
Milton Keynes Central	d		18u40	18 50													19 36		19 50						
Northampton	d																								
Rugby	d										19 03				19e03	19 03		19 03							20e03
Nuneaton	d										19 16				19e16	19 56		20 03		19f56					20e16
Tamworth Low Level	d										19 38				19e38										20e30
Lichfield Trent Valley	d										19 46														20e36
Coventry	d						18 27		18 42				18 49			18g45		18g45		19 27		19 42		19 49	
Birmingham International	d						18 38		18 53				19 09							19 38		19 53		20 09	
Birmingham New Street 12	d						18 57	19 01	19 20				19 31		19 36					19 57		20 20		20 31	20 36
Wolverhampton 7	d						19 14	19 19	19 37				19 49		19 53					20 14		20 37		20 49	20 53
Penkridge	d							19 29							20 03										21 03
Stafford	a	19 22					19 29	19 35			19 58				20 09	20 24		20 26		20 29		20 49			21 09
	d	19 23					19 29	19 36			19 59				20 09	20 24		20 27		20 29		20 50			21 09
Stoke-on-Trent	a			19 48			19 54						20 19	20 24			20 37		20 48	20 54				21 20	
Congleton	a																								
Macclesfield	a						20 11							20 41						21 11		22h20		21 38	
Crewe 10	a		19 48					20 01	20 07			20 10			20 30	20 46		20 45			21 02	21 09	21 18		21 30
	d		19 50						20 09			20 11			20 31	20 48		20 47			21 03		21 19		
Chester	a		20 12									20 45				21 21		21 21				21 45			
Wrexham General	a																								
Llandudno Junction	a		21 20													22 19		22 19				23j33			
Llandudno	a		21k35																						
Bangor (Gwynedd)	a		21 37													22 42		22 42				00m38			
Holyhead	a		22 19													23 15		23 15				02m02			
Wilmslow	a								20 45			20 27			21 16								21 34		22 16
Manchester Airport	a								21n05			21 05										22n04			23n23
Stockport	a			20 16			20 27		20 58			20 36		20 55	21 29		21 16		21 16	21 27		21 44	21 44	21 53	22 29
Manchester Piccadilly 10	a			20 28			20 40		21 15			20 49	21 00	21 07	21 43		21 28		21 28	21 40		21 56	21 56	22 05	22 43
Hartford	a														20 45										
Warrington Bank Quay	a				20 14				20 26												21 20				
	d				20 14				20 27												21 20				
Runcorn	a	19 54									20 32				20 55			21 04							
Liverpool South Parkway 7	a														21 05										
Liverpool Lime Street 10	a	20 15									20 53				21 15			21 25							
	d				19 23				19 42	20 25											20 25				
Manchester Airport	d				19q29	20 00																			
Manchester Piccadilly 10	d				19q46	20 16																			
Bolton	d				20q07	20 33																			
Wigan North Western	a				20 25				20 37	20 57											21 32				
	d				20 25				20 38	20 57											21 32				
Preston 8	a				20 38	20 58			20 59	21 22											21 49				
Blackpool North	a								21r48	21 53											22r48				
	d				19 45	20 29																			
Preston 8	d				20 41	21 02																			
Lancaster 6	a				20 54	21 18																			
	d				20 55	21 18																			
Barrow-in-Furness	a					22 20																			
Oxenholme Lake District	a				21 08																				
	d				21 09																				
Windermere	a				21 34																				
Penrith North Lakes	d				21 34																				
Carlisle 8	a				21 49																				
	d				21 50																				
Lockerbie	d																								
Carstairs	a																								
Motherwell	a				22s44																				
Glasgow Central 15	a				23 04																				
Haymarket	a																								
Edinburgh 10	a																								
Perth	a																								
Dundee	a																								
Aberdeen	a																								
Inverness	a																								

For general notes see front of timetable
For details of catering facilities see Directory of Train Operators

- **A** From Bournemouth (Table 51)
- **B** From Bristol Temple Meads (Table 51)
- **C** Until 5 September
- **D** From 12 September
- **b** From 12 September dep. 1900
- **c** From 12 September dep. 1940
- **e** Change at Stafford
- **f** Change at Stafford. From 12 September dep. 1916
- **g** Change at Nuneaton
- **h** Until 11 July only. Change at Crewe and Wilmslow. By bus from Wilmslow
- **j** Change at Crewe and Chester
- **k** Change at Chester and Llandudno Junction
- **m** Change at Crewe, Chester and Llandudno Junction. By bus from Llandudno Junction
- **n** Change at Crewe and Wilmslow
- **q** Change at Preston
- **r** From 10 October arr. 2 mins. later

Saturdays
until 31 October

London and West Midlands → North West England and Scotland

Route Diagram - see first page of Table 65

		NT	NT	TP	XC	XC	XC	VT	VT	VT	VT	VT	LM	VT	VT	XC	XC	VT	NT	VT	VT	XC	LM	AW
				1 ◇	1 ◇	1 ◇	1 ◇	1 ◇	1 ◇	1 ◇		1 ◇	1 ◇	1 ◇	1 ◇	1 ◇	1 ◇	1 ◇		1 ◇	1 ◇	1 ◇	1	
					A	B	C	D	E	G	G	H		D	H	J	K	H		D	H			
London Euston 15	d							19 41	19 47	19 47		20 11		20 14	20 20			20 30		20 26	21 00			
Gatwick Airport 10	d																							
Watford Junction	d							19b11	20 01	20 01		19b11		20u29	20 03			20u45		20 09	20 59			
Milton Keynes Central	d							19b48	20 51	20 51		19b48		19b54	21 05			19b54		21 22	21 45			
Northampton	d							20 17				20 17		20 56				20 56						
Rugby	d							20 52				21 14		21 35	20 03			21 35						
Nuneaton	d								21 33	21 33				20 16	21 33			20 16						
Tamworth Low Level	d													21 53				21 53						
Lichfield Trent Valley	d													22 00				22 00						
Coventry	d				20 27	20 22	20 22		20c15	20c15		20 27	20 49		20c15	21 27	21 27				21 27	21 49		22 11
Birmingham International	d				20 38	20 33	20 33						21 09			21 38	21 38					22 04		22 29
Birmingham New Street 12	d				20 57	20 57	20 57						21 36			21 57	21 57					22 31	22 36	22 55
Wolverhampton 7	d				21 15	21 14	21 14						21 53			22 14	22 14					22 49	22 56	23 13
Penkridge	d												22 03										23 06	
Stafford	a				21 28	21 30	21 30	21 36		21 58		21 47	22 09			22 29	22 29			22 35	22 35	23 02	23 13	
	d				21 28	21 30	21 30	21 37		22 00	22 10	21 47	22 09			22 29	22 29			22 36	22 36	23 03	23 13	
Stoke-on-Trent	a				21 48	21 49	22e10		22 05		22 40				22 05	23e10	22 50							
Congleton	a																							
Macclesfield	a				22 05	22 09	23e10		22 21		23 30				22 21	00e10	23 07							
Crewe 10	a							22 01		22 24		22 12	22 34	22 38				22 38		23 00	23 00	23 26	23 37	00 34
	d							22 03		22 27		22 13		22 40				22 40		23 01	23 01	23 28		
Chester	a																			23 42	23 42		00 19	
Wrexham General	a																							
Llandudno Junction	a																							
Llandudno	a																							
Bangor (Gwynedd)	a																							
Holyhead	a																							
Wilmslow	a						22 19	22f41		22 41						23 11				23 17	23 17	23 43		
Manchester Airport	a							23g23		23 23														
Stockport	a				22 19	22 24	22 35	22h51	22 35	22 51	23 59			23 26	22 35	23 21	23 21	23 26		23 26	23 26	23s53		
Manchester Piccadilly 10	a				22 40	22 40	22 48	23j04	22 51	23 04				23 39	22 51	23 35	23 35	23 39		23 39	23 39	00 09		
Hartford	a																							
Warrington Bank Quay	a													22 56				22 56						
	d													22 57				22 57						
Runcorn	a							22 20				22 30												
Liverpool South Parkway 7	a																							
Liverpool Lime Street 10	a							22 41				22 52												
	d		21 42											21 42				21 42	23 02					
Manchester Airport	d	20 29		22 00																				
Manchester Piccadilly 10	d	20 46		22 16																				
Bolton	d	21 07		22 33																				
Wigan North Western	a		22 28											23 07				23 07	23 48					
	d		22 28											23 08				23 08	23 48					
Preston 8	a		22 54	22 54										23 22				23 22	00 16					
Blackpool North	a		23 21											00 01				00 01						
	d	21 20		22 20																				
Preston 8	d	21 59		22 55																				
Lancaster 6	a	22 19		23 11																				
	d	22 19		23 11																				
Barrow-in-Furness	a	23 24		00 15																				
Oxenholme Lake District	a																							
	d																							
Windermere	a																							
Penrith North Lakes	d																							
Carlisle 8	a																							
	d																							
Lockerbie	d																							
Carstairs	a																							
Motherwell	a																							
Glasgow Central 15	a																							
Haymarket	a																							
Edinburgh 10	a																							
Perth	a																							
Dundee	a																							
Aberdeen	a																							
Inverness	a																							

For general notes see front of timetable
For details of catering facilities see Directory of Train Operators

A From 12 September. From Bournemouth (Table 51)
B 18 July to 5 September. From Newquay (Table 135)
C Until 11 July. From Newquay (Table 135)
D Until 5 September
E 18 July to 5 September
G Until 11 July
H From 12 September
J Until 11 July. From Bournemouth (Table 51)
K From 18 July. From Bournemouth (Table 51)
b Change at Northampton and Rugby
c Change at Nuneaton
e By bus
f 18 July to 5 September arr. 2317
g Until 11 July only. Change at Crewe and Wilmslow
h 18 July to 5 September arr. 2326
j 18 July to 5 September arr. 2339

Table 65

Saturdays

London and West Midlands → North West England and Scotland

from 7 November

Route Diagram - see first page of Table 65

		SR	TP	VT	TP	TP	VT	XC	LM	LM	NT	VT	NT	TP	XC	LM	XC	VT	NT	LM	NT	VT	NT	VT
			A																B					
London Euston 15	d																	06 05						06 36
Gatwick Airport 10	d																							
Watford Junction	d																	06u20						06u51
Milton Keynes Central	d																	06 41						
Northampton	d																	06 38						
Rugby	d														06b00			07 03						
Nuneaton	d														06b16									
Tamworth Low Level	d														06b31									
Lichfield Trent Valley	d														06b37									
Coventry	d																06 10					06 29		
Birmingham International	d																06 28					06 45		
Birmingham New Street 12	d						05 30	05 57		06 01		06 20			06 31	06 36	06 57			07 01		07 20		
Wolverhampton 7	d						05 48	06 14		06 18		06 37			06 49	06 54	07 14			07 18		07 37		
Penkridge	d									06 29										07 30				
Stafford	a						06 00	06 29		06 35					07 00	07 08	07 29	07 33		07 36				
	d						06 01	06 29		06 36					07 01	07 08	07 29	07 34		07 38				
Stoke-on-Trent	a							06 50							07 18									
Congleton	a							07 02																
Macclesfield	a							07 11							07 36									
Crewe 10	a						06 20			06 56		07 07				07 33	07 50	07 53		07 58		08 07		08 10
	d			05 57			06 23		06 31	06 58		07 09				07 34	07 53	07 55		08 00		08 09		08 11
Chester	a						06 43					07 44												08 45
Wrexham General	a																							
Llandudno Junction	a						07 33					08c48												09c48
Llandudno	a						08 06					09c06												10c06
Bangor (Gwynedd)	a						07 49					09c31												10c36
Holyhead	a						08 23					10c05												11c19
Wilmslow	a						06e56					07 44					08 09					08 45		08 27
Manchester Airport	a						07e04					08 05												09 04
Stockport	a							07 27							07 49		08 20							08 37
Manchester Piccadilly 10	a							07 40							08 00		08 40							08 49
Hartford	a								06 46	07 10						07 48				08 11				
Warrington Bank Quay	a			06 13								07 26						08 11				08 27		
	d			06 14								07 27						08 12				08 28		
Runcorn	a								06 57	07 20						08 01				08 24				
Liverpool South Parkway 7	a								07 08	07 30						08 11				08 33				
Liverpool Lime Street 10	a								07 20	07 41						08 22				08 45				
	d										06 57							07 01			07 57			
Manchester Airport	d			05f29	06 18									07 28										
Manchester Piccadilly 10	d			05f46	06 33									07 45										
Bolton	d			06f02	06 50									07 59										
Wigan North Western	a			06 24							07 30	07 37	←					08 22			08 30	08 38	←	
	d			06 25							07 31	07 38	07 31					08 23			08 31	08 39	08 31	
Preston 8	a			06 37	07 11						→	07 51	07 54	08 22				08 36			→	08 52	08 54	
Blackpool North	a			07 43								08 29	08 18									09 50	09 20	
	d			05 45	06 34							07 02		07 44										
Preston 8	d			06 40	07 16	07 20						07 53		08 24				08 37	08 42			08 54		
Lancaster 6	a			06 54	07 31	07 36						08 08		08 39				08 52	09 02			09 09		
	d		05 45	06 54	07 32	07 36						08 09		08 40				08 52	09 02			09 09		
Barrow-in-Furness	a					08 39													10 07					
Oxenholme Lake District	a		06 20	07 08								08 22		08 54				09 05						
	d		06 21	07 10								08 23		08 54				09 06						
Windermere	a		06 41	07 40								08 46						09 33						
Penrith North Lakes	d			07 37	08 09													09 32				09 46		
Carlisle 8	a			07 50	08 25							09 01		09 32				09 47				10 01		
	d	06 12		07 51	08 26							09 03		09 34				09 48				10 04		
Lockerbie	d			08 10										09 54										
Carstairs	a																							
Motherwell	a																							
Glasgow Central 15	a	08 37		09 13	09 45													11 03				11 17		
Haymarket	a											10s16		11s04										
Edinburgh 10	a											10 22		11 10										
Perth	a	10g34		11g19	11g34							11 54		12 52										
Dundee	a	10g57										11h43		12 36										
Aberdeen	a	12g14										13h07		13 46										
Inverness	a			13g37										15 06										

For general notes see front of timetable
For details of catering facilities see Directory of Train Operators

A Via Morecambe (Table 98)

B To Carlisle via Whitehaven (Table 100)
b Change at Stafford
c Change at Crewe and Chester
e Change at Crewe
f Change at Preston

g Via Glasgow Central and Glasgow Queen Street. Passengers make their own way from one station to the other
h Change at Haymarket

Table 65

Saturdays

from 7 November

London and West Midlands → North West England and Scotland

Route Diagram - see first page of Table 65

		XC	VT	LM		VT	VT	TP	VT	TP	XC	LM	NT	VT	NT	SR	TP		TP	VT	XC	VT	LM	VT	VT
		1◇	1◇	1◇		1◇	1◇	1◇	1◇	1◇	1◇	1◇		1◇			1◇		1◇	1◇	1◇	1◇	1◇	1◇	1◇
								A		A	B										C				
		⊼	⊡			⊡	⊡	⊼	⊡	⊼	⊼			⊡			⊼			⊡	⊡ ⊼	⊡		⊡	⊡
London Euston [15] ⊖	d		06 55			07 07	07 20		07 30											07 35		08 00		08 07	08 10
Gatwick Airport [10] ✈	d																								
Watford Junction	d						06 41													07 19					08 01
Milton Keynes Central	d		07 27				07 50													08 06					08u40
Northampton	d																								
Rugby	d																						08b04		
Nuneaton	d			07b10																			08b17		
Tamworth Low Level	d			07b28																			08b31		
Lichfield Trent Valley	d			07b34																			08b37		
Coventry	d	06 49									07 27			07 29							07 49				
Birmingham International ✈	d	07 09									07 38			07 45							08 09				
Birmingham New Street [12]	d	07 31		07 36							07 57	08 01		08 20							08 31		08 36		
Wolverhampton [7]	d	07 49		07 53							08 14	08 19		08 37							08 49		08 53		
Penkridge	d			08 03								08 29											09 03		
Stafford	a			08 09		08 22					08 29	08 35											09 09	09 22	
	d			08 09		08 23					08 29	08 36											09 09	09 23	
Stoke-on-Trent	a	08 18	08 24				08 48				08 54										09 18	09 24			
Congleton	a																								
Macclesfield	a	08 35	08 41								09 11											09 41			
Crewe [10]	a			08 30		08 41						08 57		09 07						09 10			09 30		09 48
	d			08 31		08 43						08 58		09 09						09 11			09 31		09 50
Chester	a																			09 45					10 12
Wrexham General	a																								
Llandudno Junction	a																			10c48					11 14
Llandudno	a																			11c06					11e36
Bangor (Gwynedd)	a																								11 36
Holyhead	a																								12 11
Wilmslow	a			09 16										09 45						09 27			10 16		
Manchester Airport ✈	a																			10 04					
Stockport	a	08 49	08 55				09 16				09 27									09 36		09 55			
Manchester Piccadilly [10]	a	09 00	09 07				09 28				09 40									09 49	10 00	10 07			
Hartford	a											09 11													
Warrington Bank Quay	a								09 14					09 26											
	d								09 14					09 27											
Runcorn	a			08 48		08 59						09 22											09 48	09 54	
Liverpool South Parkway [7] ✈	a			08 59								09 31											09 59		
Liverpool Lime Street [10]	a			09 09		09 21						09 42											10 09	10 15	
	d								08 01				08 57												
Manchester Airport ✈	d							08 25									09 00								
Manchester Piccadilly [10]	d							08 46									09 16								
Bolton	d							09 07									09 33								
Wigan North Western	a								09 25				09 30	09 37	←										
	d								09 25				09 31	09 38	09 31										
Preston [8]	a							09 33	09 38				→	09 51	09 54		09 55								
Blackpool North	a														10 20										
	d								08 45	←				09 14			09 20		09f14						
Preston [8]	d							09 45	09 41	09 45				09 53			09 58		10 04						
Lancaster [6]	a							→	09 54	10 00				10 08			10 14		10 20						
	d								09 55	10 01				10 08			10 14		10 20						
Barrow-in-Furness	a																		11 15						
Oxenholme Lake District	a									10 17				10 22			10 28								
	d									10 18				10 24			10 28								
Windermere	a									10 39															
Penrith North Lakes	d								10 31								10 53								
Carlisle [8]	a								10 46					11 01			11 10								
	d								10 47					11 03		11 07	11 11								
Lockerbie	d																11 31								
Carstairs	a																								
Motherwell	a																								
Glasgow Central [15]	a								12 01							13 29	12 32								
Haymarket	a													12s16											
Edinburgh [10]	a													12 22											
Perth	a								13g36					14 52											
Dundee	a													13h35											
Aberdeen	a													14h48											
Inverness	a													17 05											

For general notes see front of timetable
For details of catering facilities see Directory of Train Operators

A ⊼ to Preston

B From Southampton Central (Table 51)
C From Bristol Temple Meads (Table 51)
b Change at Stafford
c Change at Crewe and Chester
e Change at Chester and Llandudno Junction

f By changing at Preston, passengers may depart 0929
g Via Glasgow Central and Glasgow Queen Street. Passengers make their own way from one station to the other
h Change at Haymarket

Saturdays

London and West Midlands → North West England and Scotland

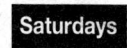

from 7 November

Route Diagram - see first page of Table 65

		VT	VT	XC	LM	NT	VT	NT		TP	VT	TP	XC	LM	VT	VT	VT	VT	VT	XC	LM		NT	VT	NT
		1 ◇	1 ◇	1 ◇	1 ◇		1 ◇			1 ◇	1 ◇	1 ◇	1 ◇	1 ◇	1 ◇	1 ◇	1 ◇	1 ◇	1 ◇	1 ◇	1 ◇			1 ◇	
				A									B							C					
London Euston 15 ⊖	d	08 20	08 30								08 40				08 50	09 00	09 07	09 20	09 30						
Gatwick Airport 10 ✈	d																								
Watford Junction	d														09u05										
Milton Keynes Central	d	08 50													09 25			09 50							
Northampton	d																								
Rugby	d													09b03											
Nuneaton	d													09b16											
Tamworth Low Level	d													09b31											
Lichfield Trent Valley	d													09b37											
Coventry	d			08 27			08 42						08 49							09 27				09 42	
Birmingham International ✈	d			08 38			08 53						09 09							09 38				09 53	
Birmingham New Street 12	d			08 57	09 01		09 20						09 31	09 36						09 57	10 01			10 20	
Wolverhampton 7	d			09 14	09 19		09 37						09 49	09 53						10 14	10 19			10 37	
Penkridge	d													10 03											
Stafford	a			09 29	09 34									10 09			10 22			10 29	10 35				
	d			09 29	09 35									10 09			10 23			10 29	10 35				
Stoke-on-Trent	a	09 48		09 54									10 18			10 24		10 48		10 54					
Congleton	a																								
Macclesfield	a			10 11												10 41				11 11					
Crewe 10	a				09 56		10 07				10 10			10 30	10 34						10 56			11 07	
	d				09 57		10 09				10 11			10 31	10 45						10 57			11 09	
Chester	a										10 45				11 12										
Wrexham General	a																								
Llandudno Junction	a										11c48				12 04										
Llandudno	a										12c06				12 36										
Bangor (Gwynedd)	a														12 23										
Holyhead	a														12 56										
Wilmslow	a						10 45				10 27				11e16									11 45	
Manchester Airport ✈	a										11 04														
Stockport	a	10 16		10 27							10 36					10 55		11 16		11 27					
Manchester Piccadilly 10	a	10 28		10 40							10 49		11 00			11 07		11 28		11 40					
Hartford	a				10 10																11 10				
Warrington Bank Quay	a		10 14				10 26												11 14					11 26	
	d		10 14				10 27												11 14					11 27	
Runcorn	a				10 21									10 48			10 54				11 21				
Liverpool South Parkway 7 ✈	a				10 31									10 59							11 31				
Liverpool Lime Street 10	a				10 43									11 09			11 15				11 42				
	d		09 01			09 57													10 01				10 57		
Manchester Airport ✈	d		09 29							10 00									10 29						
Manchester Piccadilly 10	d		09 46							10 16									10 46						
Bolton	d		10 07							10 33									11 07						
Wigan North Western	a		10 25			10 30	10 37	←											11 25				11 30	11 37	←
	d		10 25			10 31	10 38	10 31											11 25				11 31	11 38	11 31
Preston 8	a		10 38			→	10 51	10 54		10 55									11 38				→	11 51	11 54
Blackpool North	a							11 20																	12 20
	d		09 45							10 20		10 29							10 45					11 15	
Preston 8	d		10 41				10 53			10 58		11 04							11 41					11 53	
Lancaster 6	a		10 54				11 08			11 14		11 19							11 54					12 08	
	d		10 55				11 08			11 14		11 20							11 55					12 08	
Barrow-in-Furness	a																								
Oxenholme Lake District	a		11 08							11 28		11 36												12 22	
	d		11 08							11 28		11 37												12 24	
Windermere	a											11 56												12 47	
Penrith North Lakes	d						11 45			11 53									12 30						
Carlisle 8	a		11 46				12 00			12 10									12 45					13 01	
	d		11 47				12 03			12 11									12 47					13 03	
Lockerbie	d									12 30															
Carstairs	a																								
Motherwell	a																								
Glasgow Central 15	a		13 01				13 20												14 01						
Haymarket	a									13s33														14s16	
Edinburgh 10	a									13 40														14 22	
Perth	a		14f36																15f36					15 53	
Dundee	a		14f59							15 18														15g37	
Aberdeen	a		16f19							16 50														16g50	
Inverness	a		17h05																						

For general notes see front of timetable
For details of catering facilities see Directory of Train Operators

A From Southampton Central (Table 51)
B From Cardiff Central (Table 51)
C From Bournemouth (Table 51)
b Change at Stafford
c Change at Crewe and Chester
e Change at Crewe
f Via Glasgow Central and Glasgow Queen Street. Passengers make their own way from one station to the other
g Change at Haymarket
h Change at Glasgow Central, Glasgow Queen Street and Perth. Passengers make their own way between Glasgow Central and Glasgow Queen Street

London and West Midlands → North West England and Scotland

Route Diagram - see first page of Table 65

		TP	VT	XC	VT	LM	VT	VT	NT	TP	VT	XC		LM	VT	VT	VT	TP	XC	VT	VT	VT	VT	NT	VT
		1◇	1◇	1◇	1◇	1◇	1◇	1◇		1◇	1◇	1◇		1◇	1◇	1◇	1◇	1◇	1◇	1◇	1◇		1◇		
		A		B								C							D						
																						bus			bus
		trolley	catering	catering, trolley	catering		catering	catering		trolley	catering	trolley			catering	catering	catering		catering, trolley	catering	catering		catering		
London Euston 15 ⊖	d		09 40		10 00		10 07	10 10			10 20				10 30		10 40			11 00					
Gatwick Airport 10 ✈	d																								
Watford Junction	d										*10 01*														
Milton Keynes Central	d										10 50														
Northampton	d																								
Rugby	d					*10b03*																			
Nuneaton	d					*10b16*																			
Tamworth Low Level	d					*10b31*																			
Lichfield Trent Valley	d					*10b37*																			
Coventry	d			*09 49*								10 27				*10 42*			*10 49*						
Birmingham International ✈	d			*10 09*								10 38				*10 53*			*11 09*						
Birmingham New Street 12	d			10 31		10 36						10 57		11 01		11 20			11 31						
Wolverhampton 7	d			10 49		10 53						11 14		11 19		11 37			11 49						
Penkridge	d					11 03																			
Stafford	a					11 09	11 22					11 29		11 35											
	d					11 09	11 23					11 29		11 35											
Stoke-on-Trent	a			11 18	11 24						11 48	11 54							12 18	12 24					
Congleton	a																								
Macclesfield	a				11 41							12 11								12 41					
Crewe 10	a		11 10			11 30								11 56	12 03	12 07	12 10						←		
	d		11 11			11 31								11 57		12 14	12 11						12 14		12 20
Chester	a		*11 45*													→	*12 45*								
Wrexham General	a																								
Llandudno Junction	a		*12c48*														*13c48*								
Llandudno	a		*13c06*														*14c06*								
Bangor (Gwynedd)	a		*13c31*																						
Holyhead	a		*14c14*																						
Wilmslow	a		11 27			*12 16*											12 27						*12 45*		
Manchester Airport ✈	a		*12 04*														*13 04*								
Stockport	a		11 36		11 55						12 16	12 27					12 36			12 55					
Manchester Piccadilly 10	a		11 49	12 00	12 07						12 28	12 40					12 49		13 00	13 07					
Hartford	a													12 10											
Warrington Bank Quay	a							11 58																	13 05
	d							11 58														12 30			13 05
Runcorn	a					11 48	11 54							12 21											
Liverpool South Parkway 7 ✈	a					11 59								12 31											
Liverpool Lime Street 10	a					12 09	12 15							12 43											
	d							*11 01*	11 57															12 57	
Manchester Airport ✈	d	11 00								12 00											*12 29*				
Manchester Piccadilly 10	d	11 16								12 16											*12 46*				
Bolton	d	11 33								12 33											*13 07*				
Wigan North Western	a							12 09	12 30													13 00		13 30	13 35
	d							12 09	12 31													13 00		13 31	
Preston 8	a	11 55						12 23	12 54	12 55												13 40	13 48	13 54	
Blackpool North	a							*13 00*	13 21	*13 50*														14 20	
	d							*11 37*		*12 20*								*12 29*			*12 45*				
Preston 8	d	11 58						12 35		12 58								13 04			13 41		13 53		
Lancaster 6	a	12 14						12 49		13 14								13 19			13 54		14 08		
	d	12 14						12 49		13 14								13 20			13 55		14 08		
Barrow-in-Furness	a	13 10																							
Oxenholme Lake District	a							13 03		13 28								13 36			14 09				
	d							13 05		13 28								13 37			14 09				
Windermere	a																	13 56							
Penrith North Lakes	d									13 53											14 35		14 45		
Carlisle 8	a							13 42		14 10											14 50		15 00		
	d							13 45		14 11											14 51		15 02		
Lockerbie	d									14 30															
Carstairs	a																								
Motherwell	a																								
Glasgow Central 15	a							15 01													16 01				
Haymarket	a																						16s15		
Edinburgh 10	a									15 42													16 22		
Perth	a							*16e36*															*17 52*		
Dundee	a							*16e59*		*17 20*													*17f38*		
Aberdeen	a							*18e15*															*19f00*		
Inverness	a							*19e34*															*20 08*		

For general notes see front of timetable
For details of catering facilities see Directory of Train Operators

A trolley to Preston
B From Paignton (Table 51)
C From Bournemouth (Table 51)
D From Bristol Temple Meads (Table 51)
b Change at Stafford
c Change at Crewe and Chester
e Via Glasgow Central and Glasgow Queen Street. Passengers make their own way from one station to the other
f Change at Haymarket

Table 65

Saturdays

London and West Midlands → North West England and Scotland

from 7 November

Route Diagram - see first page of Table 65

		LM	VT		VT	VT	TP	VT	XC	LM	VT	VT	XC	VT	VT	VT		TP	NT	LM	VT	TP	VT	VT	VT
		1◇	1◇			1◇	1◇	1◇	1◇	1◇	1◇	1◇	1◇		1◇	1◇		1◇		1◇	1◇	1◇	1◇		1◇
									A				B					C							
					🚌									🚌										🚌	
			☕			☕	🍴	☕	🍴		☕	☕	☕ 🍴		☕	☕		🍴			☕	🍴	☕		☕
London Euston [15] ⊖	d		11 07			11 10		11 20			11 30	11 40			12 00						12 07		12 10		12 20
Gatwick Airport [10] ✈	d																								
Watford Junction	d					11 01																			12 01
Milton Keynes Central	d					11u40		11 50																	12 50
Northampton	d																								
Rugby	d	11b03																		12b03					
Nuneaton	d	11b16																		12b16					
Tamworth Low Level	d	11b31																		12b31					
Lichfield Trent Valley	d	11b37																		12b37					
Coventry	d								11 27				11 49												
Birmingham International ✈	d								11 38				12 09												
Birmingham New Street [12]	d	11 36							11 57	12 01			12 31							12 36					
Wolverhampton [7] ⛴	d	11 53							12 14	12 19			12 49							12 53					
Penkridge	d	12 03																		13 03					
Stafford	a	12 09	12 22						12 29	12 35										13 09	13 22				
	d	12 09	12 23						12 29	12 35										13 09	13 23				
Stoke-on-Trent	a							12 48	12 54				13 18		13 24										13 48
Congleton	a																								
Macclesfield	a								13 11						13 41										
Crewe [10]	a	12 30				12 47				12 56	13 04	13 10								13 30			13 45		
	d	12 31			12 35	12 49				12 57		13 11		13 15						13 31			13 47	13 55	
Chester	a					13 12						13 45													
Wrexham General	a																								
Llandudno Junction	a					14 14						14c48													
Llandudno	a					14e36						15c06													
Bangor (Gwynedd)	a					14 36						15c31													
Holyhead	a					15 11						16c14													
Wilmslow	a	13 16										13 27								14 16					
Manchester Airport ✈	a											14 04													
Stockport	a							13 16	13 27			13 36			13 55										14 16
Manchester Piccadilly [10] ⛴	a							13 28	13 40			13 49	14 00		14 07										14 28
Hartford	a									13 10															
Warrington Bank Quay	a				13 20									14 00										14 40	
	d				13 20									14 00										14 40	
Runcorn	a	12 48	12 54							13 21										13 48	13 54				
Liverpool South Parkway [7] ✈	a	12 59								13 31										13 59					
Liverpool Lime Street [10]	a	13 09	13 15							13 42										14 09	14 15				
	d																		13 57						
Manchester Airport ✈	d						13 00											13 29				14 00			
Manchester Piccadilly [10] ⛴	d						13 16											13 46				14 16			
Bolton	d						13 33											14 07				14 33			
Wigan North Western	a				13 50									14 30					14 30					15 10	
	d				13 50														14 31						
Preston [8]	a				14 30		13 55											14 33	14 54			14 55	15 17		
Blackpool North	a																		15 20				16 00		
	d						13 20									13 45						14 20	14 45		
Preston [8]	d						13 58									14 41		14 45				14 58	15 35		
Lancaster [6]	a						14 14									14 54		15 00				15 14	15 49		
	d						14 14									14 55		15 01				15 14	15 50		
Barrow-in-Furness	a																	15 56							
Oxenholme Lake District	a						14 28															15 28	16 03		
	d						14 28															15 28	16 05		
Windermere	a						14 52															16 00	16 48		
Penrith North Lakes	d						14 53									15 30						15 53			
Carlisle [8]	a						15 10									15 45						16 09	16 42		
	d						15 11									15 47						16 10	16 45		
Lockerbie	d						15 33															16 29			
Carstairs	a																								
Motherwell	a						16s23																		
Glasgow Central [15]	a						16 42									17 01							18 01		
Haymarket	a																					17s30			
Edinburgh [10]	a																					17 39			
Perth	a															18f43						18g58	19f42		
Dundee	a															19f06						19 24			
Aberdeen	a															20f29						20 46			
Inverness	a																					21g03			

For general notes see front of timetable
For details of catering facilities see Directory of Train Operators

A From Bournemouth (Table 51)

B From Bristol Temple Meads (Table 51)
C 🍴 to Preston
b Change at Stafford
c Change at Crewe and Chester
e Change at Chester and Llandudno Junction

f Via Glasgow Central and Glasgow Queen Street. Passengers make their own way from one station to the other
g Change at Haymarket

Table 65

Saturdays

from 7 November

London and West Midlands → North West England and Scotland

Route Diagram - see first page of Table 65

		XC	LM	VT	VT	VT	VT	NT	VT	XC	LM	VT	VT	TP	VT	VT	XC	LM	VT	VT	VT	XC	VT
		1◇	1◇	1◇	1◇		1◇			1◇	1◇	1◇	1◇	1◇	1◇	1◇	1◇	1◇	1◇		1◇	1◇	1◇
		A				🚌			🚌	B							A			🚌		C	
London Euston 15 ⊖	d			12 30	12 40							13 00	13 07		13 10	13 20			13 30		13 40		14 00
Gatwick Airport 10 ✈	d																						
Watford Junction	d														*13 01*								
Milton Keynes Central	d														13u40	13 50							
Northampton	d																						
Rugby	d										*13b03*												
Nuneaton	d										*13b16*												
Tamworth Low Level	d										*13b31*												
Lichfield Trent Valley	d										*13b37*												
Coventry	d	12 27					*12 42*			*12 49*							13 27					*13 49*	
Birmingham International ✈	d	12 38					*12 53*			*13 09*							13 38					*14 09*	
Birmingham New Street 12	d	12 57	13 01				13 20			13 31	13 36						13 57	14 01				14 31	
Wolverhampton 7	d	13 14	13 19				13 37			13 49	13 53						14 14	14 19				14 49	
Penkridge	d										14 03												
Stafford	a	13 29	13 35								14 09		14 22				14 29	14 35					
	d	13 29	13 35								14 09		14 23				14 29	14 35					
Stoke-on-Trent	a	13 54								14 18		14 24				14 48	14 54					15 18	15 24
Congleton	a																						
Macclesfield	a	14 11										14 41					15 11						15 41
Crewe 10	a		13 56	14 06	14 10		14 07				14 30				14 47		14 56	15 04			15 10		
	d		13 57		14 11		14 14		14 20		14 31				14 49		14 57				15 11		
Chester	a				*14 45*										15 10						*15 45*		
Wrexham General	a																						
Llandudno Junction	a				*15c48*										16 01						*16c48*		
Llandudno	a				*16c06*										*16 36*						*17c06*		
Bangor (Gwynedd)	a														16 17						*17c36*		
Holyhead	a														16 51						*18c19*		
Wilmslow	a				14 27		*14 45*				*15 16*										15 27		
Manchester Airport ✈	a				*15 04*																*16 04*		
Stockport	a	14 27			14 36							14 55				15 16	15 27				15 36		15 55
Manchester Piccadilly 10	a	14 40			14 49					15 00		15 07				15 28	15 40				15 49	16 00	16 07
Hartford	a		14 10															15 10					
Warrington Bank Quay	a								15 05														
	d					14 15			15 05											15 20			
Runcorn	a		14 21								14 48		14 54					15 21					
Liverpool South Parkway 7 ✈	a		14 31								14 59							15 31					
Liverpool Lime Street 10	a		14 42								15 09		15 15					15 42					
	d							14 57															
Manchester Airport ✈	d						*14 29*							15 00									
Manchester Piccadilly 10	d						*14 46*							15 16									
Bolton	d						*15 07*							15 33									
Wigan North Western	a					14 45		15 30	15 35											15 50			
	d					14 45		15 31												15 50			
Preston 8	a					15 25	15 48	15 54						15 55						16 30			
Blackpool North	a							16 20															
	d													*15 20*									
Preston 8	d						15 53							15 58									
Lancaster 6	a						16 08							16 14									
	d						16 09							16 14									
Barrow-in-Furness	a													17 18									
Oxenholme Lake District	a																						
	d																						
Windermere	a																						
Penrith North Lakes	d						16 45																
Carlisle 8	a						17 00																
	d						17 03																
Lockerbie	d																						
Carstairs	a																						
Motherwell	a																						
Glasgow Central 15	a																						
Haymarket	a						18s14																
Edinburgh 10	a						18 22																
Perth	a						*20 02*																
Dundee	a						*19 52*																
Aberdeen	a						*21 12*																
Inverness	a						*23 14*																

For general notes see front of timetable
For details of catering facilities see Directory of Train Operators

A From Bournemouth (Table 51)
B From Paignton (Table 51)
C From Bristol Temple Meads (Table 51)

b Change at Stafford
c Change at Crewe and Chester

Table 65

Saturdays
from 7 November

London and West Midlands → North West England and Scotland

Route Diagram - see first page of Table 65

		VT	NT	VT	LM	VT	TP	TP	VT	VT	VT	XC	LM	VT	VT	VT	VT	VT	NT	XC	VT	LM	VT	VT
		1 ◇			1 ◇	1 ◇	1 ◇		1 ◇		1 ◇	1 ◇	1 ◇	1 ◇	1 ◇	1 ◇		1 ◇		1 ◇		1 ◇	1 ◇	1 ◇
												A								B				
				🚌						🚌							🚌				🚌			
		☕				☕	🛒		☕		☕	🛒		☕	☕	☕		☕		☕ 🛒			☕	☕
London Euston 15 ⊖	d					14 07			14 10		14 20			14 30		14 40							15 00	15 07
Gatwick Airport 10 ✈	d																							
Watford Junction	d										*14 01*													
Milton Keynes Central	d										14 50													
Northampton	d																							
Rugby	d				*14b03*																	*15b03*		
Nuneaton	d				*14b16*																	*15b16*		
Tamworth Low Level	d				*14b31*																	*15b31*		
Lichfield Trent Valley	d				*14b37*																	*15b37*		
Coventry	d											14 27			*14 42*					*14 49*				
Birmingham International ✈	d											14 38			*14 53*					*15 09*				
Birmingham New Street 12	d				14 36							14 57	15 01		15 20					15 31		15 36		
Wolverhampton 7 ⛴	d				14 53							15 14	15 19		15 37					15 49		15 53		
Penkridge	d				15 03																	16 03		
Stafford	a				15 09	15 22						15 29	15 35									16 09		16 22
	d				15 09	15 23						15 29	15 35									16 09		16 23
Stoke-on-Trent	a										15 48	15 54								16 18			16 24	
Congleton	a																							
Macclesfield	a											16 11											16 41	
Crewe 10	a				15 30				15 45				15 56	16 06	16 07	16 11		←				16 30		
	d			15 20	15 31				15 47	16 00			15 57		16 15	16 12		16 15			16 20	16 31		
Chester	a														→	*16 45*								
Wrexham General	a																							
Llandudno Junction	a															*17c48*								
Llandudno	a															*18c06*								
Bangor (Gwynedd)	a																							
Holyhead	a																							
Wilmslow	a				*16 16*											16 27		*16 45*				*17 16*		
Manchester Airport ✈	a																	*17 04*						
Stockport	a										16 16	16 27				16 36		*16 58*					16 54	
Manchester Piccadilly 10 ⛴	a										16 28	16 40				16 49		*17 15*		17 00			17 07	
Hartford	a												16 10											
Warrington Bank Quay	a			16 05						16 45											17 05			
	d			16 05						16 45							16 15				17 05			
Runcorn	a				15 48	15 54							16 24									16 48		16 54
Liverpool South Parkway 7 ✈	a				15 59								16 33									16 59		
Liverpool Lime Street 10	a				16 09	16 15							16 43									17 09		17 15
	d		15 57																16 57					
Manchester Airport ✈	d	*15 29*					16 00		*16 29*															
Manchester Piccadilly 10 ⛴	d	*15 46*					16 16		*16 46*															
Bolton	d	*16 07*					16 33		*17 06*															
Wigan North Western	a		16 30	16 35						17 15							16 45		17 30		17 35			
	d		16 31														16 45		17 31					
Preston 8	a		16 54				16 55		17 17								17 25	17 48	17 54					
Blackpool North	a		17 20						*18 02*										18 20					
	d	*15 45*					*16 29*		*16 41*									*17 18*						
Preston 8	d	16 41					17 00	17 04	17 35									17 53						
Lancaster 6	a	16 54					17 15	17 20	17 49									18 08						
	d	16 55					17 16	17 21	17 50									18 08						
Barrow-in-Furness	a																							
Oxenholme Lake District	a						17 30	17 38										18 22						
	d						17 30	17 38										18 23						
Windermere	a							18 00										*18 49*						
Penrith North Lakes	d	17 30							18 26									18 49						
Carlisle 8	a	17 45					18 10		18 41									19 04						
	d	17 47					18 11		18 46									19 04						
Lockerbie	d						18 30																	
Carstairs	a																							
Motherwell	a																							
Glasgow Central 15	a	19 01							20 01															
Haymarket	a						19s31											20s19						
Edinburgh 10	a						19 39											20 24						
Perth	a	*20e36*							*21e42*									*22 00*						
Dundee	a	*20e59*					*21 30*		*22e07*									*22 30*						
Aberdeen	a	*22e13*							*23e20*									*23 58*						
Inverness	a	*23g14*																						

For general notes see front of timetable
For details of catering facilities see Directory of Train Operators

A From Bournemouth (Table 51)

B From Penzance (Table 135)
b Change at Stafford
c Change at Crewe and Chester

e Via Glasgow Central and Glasgow Queen Street. Passengers make their own way from one station to the other
g Change at Glasgow Central, Glasgow Queen Street and Perth. Passengers make their own way between Glasgow Central and Glasgow Queen Street

Table 65

Saturdays

from 7 November

London and West Midlands → North West England and Scotland

Route Diagram - see first page of Table 65

		TP	VT	NT	VT	XC	VT	LM	VT	VT	XC	VT	NT	TP	TP	VT	VT	NT	LM	VT	VT	VT	VT
		1◇	1◇		1◇	1◇		1◇	1◇	1◇	1◇	1◇		1◇	1◇	1◇			1◇	1◇		1◇	1◇
						A	Bus				B						Bus				Bus		
London Euston 15	d		15 10		15 20				15 30	15 40						16 00				16 07		16 10	16 20
Gatwick Airport 10	d																						
Watford Junction	d		15 01																				16 01
Milton Keynes Central	d		15u40		15 50																		16 50
Northampton	d																						
Rugby	d																		16b03				
Nuneaton	d																		16b16				
Tamworth Low Level	d																		16b31				
Lichfield Trent Valley	d																		16b37				
Coventry	d					15 27					15 49												
Birmingham International	d					15 38					16 09												
Birmingham New Street 12	d					15 57		16 01			16 31								16 36				
Wolverhampton 7	d					16 14		16 19			16 49								16 53				
Penkridge	d																		17 03				
Stafford	a					16 29		16 35											17 09	17 22			
	d					16 29		16 35											17 09	17 23			
Stoke-on-Trent	a				16 48	16 54					17 18					17 24							17 48
Congleton	a																						
Macclesfield	a					17 11										17 41							
Crewe 10	a		16 47					16 56	17 04	17 10									17 30			17 45	
	d		16 49					16 57		17 11							17 20		17 31			17 47	
Chester	a		17 12							17 45													
Wrexham General	a																						
Llandudno Junction	a		18 16							18c48													
Llandudno	a		18e36							19c06													
Bangor (Gwynedd)	a		18 38							19c31													
Holyhead	a		19 13							20c16													
Wilmslow	a									17 27									18 16				
Manchester Airport	a									18 04													
Stockport	a				17 16	17 27				17 36						17 55							18 16
Manchester Piccadilly 10	a				17 28	17 40				17 49	18 00					18 07							18 28
Hartford	a							17 10															
Warrington Bank Quay	a																18 05						
	d						17 20										18 05				18 15		
Runcorn	a							17 21											17 48	17 54			
Liverpool South Parkway 7	a							17 31											17 59				
Liverpool Lime Street 10	a							17 42											18 09	18 15			
	d			17 27									17 44					18 01					
Manchester Airport	d	17 00										17 27		18 00								18 29	
Manchester Piccadilly 10	d	17 15										17 46		18 16								18 46	
Bolton	d	17 32										18 07		18 33								19 07	
Wigan North Western	a			18 05			17 50						18 30				18 35	18 49			18 45		
	d			18 05			17 50						18 31					18 49			18 45		
Preston 8	a	17 55		18 31			18 30						18 54	18 55				19 15			19 25	19 20	
Blackpool North	a			19 09									19 20									20 00	
	d											17 37		18 29								18 45	
Preston 8	d	17 58										18 41		19 00	19 04							19 35	
Lancaster 6	a	18 14										18 54		19 16	19 20							19 49	
	d	18 14										18 55		19 16	19 20							19 49	
Barrow-in-Furness	a	19 19													20 24								
Oxenholme Lake District	a											19 08		19 30								20 03	
	d											19 09		19 30								20 04	
Windermere	a													19 56								20 42	
Penrith North Lakes	d											19 34		19 55								20 30	
Carlisle 8	a											19 49		20 12								20 45	
	d											19 51		20 13								20 48	
Lockerbie	d													20 32									
Carstairs	a																						
Motherwell	a																						
Glasgow Central 15	a											21 01		21 32								22 01	
Haymarket	a																						
Edinburgh 10	a																						
Perth	a											22f34										00f13	
Dundee	a											22f58											
Aberdeen	a											00f18											
Inverness	a																						

For general notes see front of timetable
For details of catering facilities see Directory of Train Operators

A From Bournemouth (Table 51)
B From Bristol Temple Meads (Table 51)
b Change at Stafford
c Change at Crewe and Chester
e Change at Chester and Llandudno Junction
f Via Glasgow Central and Glasgow Queen Street. Passengers make their own way from one station to the other

Table 65

Saturdays

London and West Midlands → North West England and Scotland

from 7 November

Route Diagram - see first page of Table 65

		XC	LM	VT	VT	VT		VT	XC	VT	TP	VT	VT	LM	VT	NT	VT	VT	XC		LM	VT	VT	VT	VT
		■1◇	■1◇	■1◇	■1◇	■1◇		■1◇	■1◇	■1◇	■1◇	■1◇		■1◇	■1◇		■1◇	■1◇	■1◇		■1◇	■1◇	■1◇		
		A							B										A						
		🛒		🍽	🍽	🍽		🍽	🛒	🍽		🍽	🚌		🍽		🍽	🍽	🛒			🍽	🍽	🚌	🚌
London Euston 15 ⊖	d			16 30		16 33		16 40		17 00					17 07		17 10	17 20				17 30	17 40		
Gatwick Airport 10 ✈	d																								
Watford Junction	d																*17 01*								
Milton Keynes Central	d																17u40	17 50							
Northampton	d																								
Rugby	d					*17 03*																			
Nuneaton	d					*17 16*									18 03										
Tamworth Low Level	d					17 38																			
Lichfield Trent Valley	d					17 45																			
Coventry	d	16 27			*16 42*				*16 49*										17 27						
Birmingham International ✈	d	16 38			*16 53*				*17 09*										17 38						
Birmingham New Street 12	d	16 57	17 01		17 20				17 31					17 36					17 57		18 01				
Wolverhampton 7	d	17 14	17 19		17 37				17 49					17 53					18 14		18 19				
Penkridge	d		17 29											18 03							18 29				
Stafford	a	17 29	17 35			17 58								18 09	18 26				18 29		18 35				
	d	17 29	17 36			17 58								18 09	18 27				18 29		18 35				
Stoke-on-Trent	a	17 54							18 18	18 24								18 48	18 54						
Congleton	a																								
Macclesfield	a	18 11								18 41									19 11						
Crewe 10	a		17 56	18 06	18 07			18 10				←		18 30			18 48				18 59	19 04	19 10		
	d		18 00		18 14			18 11				18 14	18 20	18 31			18 50						19 11		19 20
Chester	a				→			*18 45*									19 10						*19 42*		
Wrexham General	a																								
Llandudno Junction	a							*19b48*									20 06						*21b20*		
Llandudno	a							*20b06*									*20 34*						*21c35*		
Bangor (Gwynedd)	a																20 22						*21b37*		
Holyhead	a																20 56						*22b19*		
Wilmslow	a							18 27				*18 45*		*19 16*								*19 45*	19 27		
Manchester Airport ✈	a							*19 04*				*19 04*										*20e04*	*20 04*		
Stockport	a	18 27						18 36		18 55		*18 58*						19 16	19 27			*19 58*	19 36		
Manchester Piccadilly 10	a	18 40						18 49	19 00	19 07		*19 15*						19 28	19 40			*20 15*	19 49		
Hartford	a		18 13											18 44											
Warrington Bank Quay	a												19 05												20 05
	d												19 05											19 20	20 05
Runcorn	a		18 23			18 31								18 52	18 58										
Liverpool South Parkway 7 ✈	a		18 33											19 03											
Liverpool Lime Street 10	a		18 43			18 54								19 13	19 19										
	d															19 23									
Manchester Airport ✈	d										19 00														
Manchester Piccadilly 10	d										19 16														
Bolton	d										19 33														
Wigan North Western	a												19 35		19 54									19 50	20 35
	d														19 55									19 50	
Preston 8	a										19 58	19 59			20 18									20 30	
Blackpool North	a														20 44										
	d										*19 20*														
Preston 8	d										20 02														
Lancaster 6	a										20 18														
	d										20 18														
Barrow-in-Furness	a										21 20														
Oxenholme Lake District	a																								
	d																								
Windermere	a																								
Penrith North Lakes	d																								
Carlisle 8	a																								
	d																								
Lockerbie	d																								
Carstairs	a																								
Motherwell	a																								
Glasgow Central 15	a																								
Haymarket	a																								
Edinburgh 10	a																								
Perth	a																								
Dundee	a																								
Aberdeen	a																								
Inverness	a																								

For general notes see front of timetable
For details of catering facilities see Directory of Train Operators

A From Bournemouth (Table 51)
B From Paignton (Table 51)
b Change at Crewe and Chester
c Change at Crewe, Chester and Llandudno Junction
e Change at Crewe and Wilmslow

Saturdays
from 7 November

London and West Midlands → North West England and Scotland

Route Diagram - see first page of Table 65

		XC	VT	VT	TP	LM	VT	VT	VT	XC		LM	VT	NT	VT	VT	VT	VT	XC	LM	VT	VT	VT		XC
		A								B									A						B
London Euston 15	d		18 00				18 07	18 10	18 20				18 30		18 33	18 40					19 00	19 07	19 20		
Gatwick Airport 10	d																								
Watford Junction	d								18 01														19 01		
Milton Keynes Central	d								18 50														19 50		
Northampton	d																								
Rugby	d					18b03									19 03							20 03			
Nuneaton	d					18b16									19 16										
Tamworth Low Level	d					18b31									19 38										
Lichfield Trent Valley	d					18b37									19 46										
Coventry	d	17 49								18 27							18 42		18 49						19 27
Birmingham International	d	18 09								18 38							18 53		19 09						19 38
Birmingham New Street 12	d	18 31				18 36				18 57		19 01					19 20		19 31	19 36					19 57
Wolverhampton 7	d	18 49				18 53				19 14		19 19					19 37		19 49	19 53					20 14
Penkridge	d					19 03						19 29								20 03					
Stafford	a					19 09	19 22			19 29		19 35			19 58					20 09		20 26			20 29
	d					19 09	19 23			19 29		19 36			19 59					20 09		20 27			20 29
Stoke-on-Trent	a	19 18	19 24						19 48	19 54									20 19		20 24		20 48		20 54
Congleton	a																								
Macclesfield	a		19 41							20 11											20 41				21 11
Crewe 10	a					19 30		19 45				20 01	20 03			20 10	20 07			20 30		20 45			
	d					19 37		19 47					20 06			20 11	20 14	20 20		20 31		20 47			
Chester	a												20 28			20 45						21 21			
Wrexham General	a																								
Llandudno Junction	a																					22 19			
Llandudno	a																								
Bangor (Gwynedd)	a																					22 42			
Holyhead	a																					23 15			
Wilmslow	a					20 16										20 27	20 45			21 16					
Manchester Airport	a																21c05								
Stockport	a		19 55						20 16	20 27						20 36	20 58				20 55		21 16		21 27
Manchester Piccadilly 10	a	20 00	20 07						20 28	20 40						20 49	21 15		21 00		21 07		21 28		21 40
Hartford	a					19 52														20 45					
Warrington Bank Quay	a																	21 05							
	d																	21 05							
Runcorn	a					20 05	19 54								20 32					20 55		21 04			
Liverpool South Parkway 7	a					20 15														21 05					
Liverpool Lime Street 10	a					20 26	20 15								20 53					21 15		21 25			
	d													20 25											
Manchester Airport	d			19 29	20 00																				
Manchester Piccadilly 10	d			19 46	20 16																				
Bolton	d			20 07	20 33																				
Wigan North Western	a													20 57				21 35							
	d													20 57				21 35							
Preston 8	a				20 58			21 18						21 22			21 48	22 15							
Blackpool North	a							22 00						21 53			22 50								
	d			19 45	20 29																				
Preston 8	d			20 41	21 02																				
Lancaster 6	a			20 54	21 18																				
	d			20 55	21 18																				
Barrow-in-Furness	a				22 20																				
Oxenholme Lake District	a			21 08																					
	d			21 09																					
Windermere	a			21 34																					
Penrith North Lakes	d			21 34																					
Carlisle 8	a			21 49																					
	d			21 50																					
Lockerbie	d																								
Carstairs	a																								
Motherwell	a			22s44																					
Glasgow Central 15	a			23 04																					
Haymarket	a																								
Edinburgh 10	a																								
Perth	a																								
Dundee	a																								
Aberdeen	a																								
Inverness	a																								

For general notes see front of timetable
For details of catering facilities see Directory of Train Operators

- **A** From Bristol Temple Meads (Table 51)
- **B** From Bournemouth (Table 51)
- **b** Change at Stafford
- **c** Change at Crewe and Wilmslow

Saturdays
from 7 November

London and West Midlands → North West England and Scotland

Route Diagram - see first page of Table 65

		VT	VT	VT	VT	NT	XC	LM	NT	TP	XC	VT	VT		LM	VT	VT	NT	XC	VT	XC	LM	AW		
		1 ◇	1 ◇		1 ◇		1 ◇	1 ◇		1 ◇	1 ◇	1 ◇	1 ◇		1 ◇	1 ◇			1 ◇	1 ◇	1 ◇	1			
							A				B								B						
				bus													bus								
		☕	☕		☕		☕					☕	☕			☕				☕					
London Euston 15 ⊖	d		19 30		19 40							20 11	20 20			20 30				21 00					
Gatwick Airport 10 ✈	d																								
Watford Junction	d											19b11	20 03			20u46				20 59					
Milton Keynes Central	d											19b48	21 05			19b54				21 45					
Northampton	d											20 17				20 56									
Rugby	d							20c03				21 14				21 36									
Nuneaton	d							20c16					21 33			20 16									
Tamworth Low Level	d							20c30								21 55									
Lichfield Trent Valley	d							20c36								22 01									
Coventry	d	19 42					19 49				20 27				20 49				21 27		21 49		22 11		
Birmingham International ✈	d	19 53					20 09				20 38				21 09				21 38		22 04		22 29		
Birmingham New Street 12	d	20 20					20 31	20 36			20 57				21 36				21 57		22 31	22 36	22 55		
Wolverhampton 7	d	20 37					20 49	20 53			21 15				21 53				22 14		22 49	22 56	23 13		
Penkridge	d							21 03							22 03							23 06			
Stafford	a	20 49						21 09			21 28	21 47			22 09				22 29	22 35	23 02	23 13			
	d	20 50						21 09			21 28	21 47			22 09				22 29	22 36	23 03	23 13			
Stoke-on-Trent	a						21 20				21 48		22 05						22 50						
Congleton	a																								
Macclesfield	a						21 38				22 05		22 21						23 07						
Crewe 10	a	21 09	21 15		21 18			21 30				22 12			22 34	22 43				23 00	23 26	23 37	00 34		
	d			21 25	21 19							22 13					22 55			23 01	23 28				
Chester	a	21 45																		23 42		00 19			
Wrexham General	a																								
Llandudno Junction	a	23e33																							
Llandudno	a																								
Bangor (Gwynedd)	a	00f38																							
Holyhead	a	02f02																							
Wilmslow	a				21 34			22 16												23 17	23 43				
Manchester Airport ✈	a				22 04			23g23																	
Stockport	a				21 44		21 53	22 29			22 19		22 35						23 21	23 26	23s53				
Manchester Piccadilly 10	a				21 56		22 05	22 43			22 40		22 51						23 35	23 39	00 09				
Hartford	a																								
Warrington Bank Quay	a			22 10													23 40								
	d			22 10													23 40								
Runcorn	a											22 30													
Liverpool South Parkway 7 ✈	a																								
Liverpool Lime Street 10	a											22 52													
	d								21 42									23 02							
Manchester Airport ✈	d									22 00															
Manchester Piccadilly 10	d									22 16															
Bolton	d									22 33															
Wigan North Western	a			22 40					22 28								00s10	23 48							
	d			22 40					22 28									23 48							
Preston 8	a			23 20					22 54	22 54							00 50	00 16							
Blackpool North	a								23 21																
	d					21 20				22 20															
Preston 8	d					21 59				22 55															
Lancaster 6	a					22 19				23 11															
	d					22 19				23 11															
Barrow-in-Furness	a					23 24				00 15															
Oxenholme Lake District	a																								
	d																								
Windermere	a																								
Penrith North Lakes	d																								
Carlisle 8	a																								
	d																								
Lockerbie	d																								
Carstairs	a																								
Motherwell	a																								
Glasgow Central 15	a																								
Haymarket	a																								
Edinburgh 10	a																								
Perth	a																								
Dundee	a																								
Aberdeen	a																								
Inverness	a																								

For general notes see front of timetable
For details of catering facilities see Directory of Train Operators

A From Bristol Temple Meads (Table 51)
B From Bournemouth (Table 51)
b Change at Northampton and Rugby
c Change at Stafford
e Change at Crewe and Chester
f Change at Crewe, Chester and Llandudno Junction. By bus from Llandudno Junction
g Change at Crewe and Wilmslow

Table 65

Sundays
until 12 July

London and West Midlands → North West England and Scotland

Route Diagram - see first page of Table 65

		NT	TP	TP	VT	TP	NT	XC	VT	VT	VT	NT	VT		VT	LM	VT	XC	XC	VT	TP	NT	VT	VT	VT
			1 ◊	1 ◊	1 ◊	1 ◊		1 ◊	1 ◊	1 ◊	1 ◊		1 ◊		1 ◊	1 ◊	1 ◊	1 ◊	bus	1 ◊	1 ◊		1 ◊	1 ◊	1 ◊
London Euston 15 ⊖	d									08 10			08 15		08 20		08 45						09 15	09 20	
Gatwick Airport 10 ✈	d																								
Watford Junction	d									*08 09*							*08 42*							*09 12*	
Milton Keynes Central	d									08 55					09 05		09 33							10 07	
Northampton	d																08b50								
Rugby	d																09 56								←
Nuneaton	d												09 30										10 38 →		10 38
Tamworth Low Level	d																								
Lichfield Trent Valley	d																								
Coventry	d								*08 37*									*09 07*							
Birmingham International ✈	d								*08 55*							*09 03*		*09 25*		*09 51*					
Birmingham New Street 12	d				08 45			09 01	09 20							09 41		10 00		10 15					
Wolverhampton 7	d				09 04			09 19	09 37							09 57		10 18		10 32					
Penkridge	d															10 08									
Stafford	a				09 17			09 31					09 57		10 03	10 14		10 31						11 00	11 05
	d				09 19			09 32					09 58		10 05	10 14		10 32	10 40					11 02	11 05
Stoke-on-Trent	a														10b40				11 10						11b40
Congleton	a																								
Macclesfield	a												11c50		11b30			11e50	12 10						12b30
Crewe 10	a				09 43			09 56	10 12	10 17			10 22			10 38	10 52			11 07					11 30
	d				09 45			09 59	10 14	10 19	10 21		10 31			10 39	10 54			11 09					11 32
Chester	a				*10 22*								*11 00*			*11 22*				*11 48*					
Wrexham General	a																								
Llandudno Junction	a												*11 54*							*12 53*					
Llandudno	a												*12f10*							*13f08*					
Bangor (Gwynedd)	a												*12 10*							*13 10*					
Holyhead	a												*12 43*							*13 45*					
Wilmslow	a							10 14							10 42		*11 28*	11 11		*11 40*				11 45	
Manchester Airport ✈	a														*10 58*										
Stockport	a							10 24		10 40					10 52		*11 41*	11 21						11 55	
Manchester Piccadilly 10	a							10 40		10 54					11 04		*11 54*	11 38		*12 02*				12 09	
Hartford	a															10 51									
Warrington Bank Quay	a				10 01				10 31		10 37						11 13			11 26					
	d				10 02				10 32		10 37						11 13			11 27					
Runcorn	a												10 47			11 01									11 48
Liverpool South Parkway 7 ✈	a															11 11									
Liverpool Lime Street 10	a												11 08			11 21									12 09
	d	08 31					09 31					10 31										11 31			
Manchester Airport ✈	d		09 00			09 30														10g29	11 00				
Manchester Piccadilly 10	d		09 16			09 46														10g43	11 16				
Bolton	d		09 33			10 05											10g40			11g05	11 33				
Wigan North Western	a	09 13			10 12		10 13		10 42		10 48	11 13					11 24			11 37		12 13			
	d	09 14			10 13		10 16		10 43		10 48	11 14					11 24			11 38		12 14			
Preston 8	a	09 37	09 56		10 30	10 31	10 41		10 57		11 04	11 37					11 37			11 51	11 56	12 37			
Blackpool North	a	10 06					11 09				*11 39*	12 07										13 07			
	d		*09 20*			*09 50*											*10 50*			*11 13*	*11 20*				
Preston 8	d		10 00	10 05		10 39					11 06						11 38			11 53	12 02				
Lancaster 6	a		10 15	10 20		10 54					11 22						11 52			12 08	12 17				
	d		10 16	10 21		10 55											11 53			12 08	12 18				
Barrow-in-Furness	a		11 19																		13 21				
Oxenholme Lake District	a			10 37		11 09											12 06			12 22					
	d			10 38		11 09											12 06			12 24					
Windermere	a			11 00																*12 52*					
Penrith North Lakes	d					11 35											12 32								
Carlisle 8	a					11 50											12 47			13 01					
	d					11 52											12 47			13 03					
Lockerbie	d					12 11																			
Carstairs	a																								
Motherwell	a																								
Glasgow Central 15	a					13 15											13 59								
Haymarket	a																			14s13					
Edinburgh 10	a																			14 22					
Perth	a																*15h45*								
Dundee	a																			*16 48*					
Aberdeen	a																			*18j23*					
Inverness	a																								

For general notes see front of timetable
For details of catering facilities see Directory of Train Operators

- **b** By bus
- **c** Change at Crewe and Wilmslow. By bus from Wilmslow
- **e** Change at Wilmslow. By bus
- **f** Change at Crewe and Llandudno Junction
- **g** Change at Preston
- **h** Via Glasgow Central and Glasgow Queen Street. Passengers make their own way from one station to the other
- **j** Change at Edinburgh and Dundee

OVERNIGHT SLEEPERS. For Sleeper trains, operated by First ScotRail, please refer to Tables 400 - 404

Table 65

Sundays

until 12 July

London and West Midlands → North West England and Scotland

Route Diagram - see first page of Table 65

		LM	VT	XC		XC	VT	TP	VT	VT	LM	NT	VT	NT	XC	XC	VT		TP		NT	VT	VT	LM	VT
		1 ◇	1 ◇	1 ◇			1 ◇	1 ◇	1 ◇	1 ◇	1 ◇		1 ◇		1 ◇		1 ◇		1 ◇			1 ◇	1 ◇	1 ◇	1 ◇
				A											B				C						
			☕	🛒		🚌	☕	🛒	☕	☕			☕		🛒	🚌	☕		🛒			☕	☕		☕
London Euston 15 ⊖	d		09 45						10 15	10 20			10 45									11 15	11 20		12 02
Gatwick Airport 10 ✈	d																								
Watford Junction	d		*09 43*							*10 12*			*10 42*										*11 12*		
Milton Keynes Central	d		10 33							11 07			11 32									12 04	12 09		
Northampton	d		*09b55*										*10b55*												
Rugby	d		10 57										11 55										*11 56*		
Nuneaton	d								11 35														*12 10*		
Tamworth Low Level	d																						*12 25*		
Lichfield Trent Valley	d																						*12 31*		
Coventry	d	*10 04*		10 28		*10 28*	*10 34*								11 28		*11 34*								
Birmingham International ✈	d	*10 13*		10 40			*10 52*								11 40		*11 52*							*12 08*	
Birmingham New Street 12	d	10 42		10 59			11 20				11 42				12 01		12 20							12 35	
Wolverhampton 7 ⛴	d	10 59		11 17			11 37				11 59				12 19		12 36							12 52	
Penkridge	d	11 10									12 10													13 03	
Stafford	a	11 17		11 29					12 00	12 05	12 16				12 33							12 54		13 10	13 24
	d	11 17		11 30		11 40			12 01	12 07	12 16				12 34	12 40						12 55		13 10	13 25
Stoke-on-Trent	a					12 10				*12b40*						13 10							*13b40*		
Congleton	a																								
Macclesfield	a			*12c50*		13 10				*13b30*					*13c50*	14 10									
Crewe 10	a	11 37	11 54				12 07		12 19		12 37		12 49				13 07					13 16		13 30	13 43
	d	11 38	11 56				12 09		12 21		12 38		12 51				13 09					13 18		13 31	13 45
Chester	a	*12 20*					*12 48*				*13 18*											*13 47*			*14 18*
Wrexham General	a																								
Llandudno Junction	a						*13 55*															*14 55*			
Llandudno	a						*14e12*															*15e10*			
Bangor (Gwynedd)	a						*14 18*															*15 12*			
Holyhead	a						*14 55*															*15 55*			
Wilmslow	a			12 05						12 40					13 08								13 35		
Manchester Airport ✈	a									*13 05*															
Stockport	a			12 19						12 52					13 18								13 45		*14 38*
Manchester Piccadilly 10 ⛴	a			12 40						13 04					13 40								13 59		*14 51*
Hartford	a	11 50									12 50													13 43	
Warrington Bank Quay	a		12 13				12 26						13 08				13 26								
	d		12 13				12 27						13 08				13 27								
Runcorn	a	12 00							12 37		13 00											13 34		13 53	14 01
Liverpool South Parkway 7 ✈	a	12 10									13 10													14 03	
Liverpool Lime Street 10	a	12 20							13 03		13 20											13 56		14 13	14 23
	d											12 31									13 31				
Manchester Airport ✈	d						*11f30*	12 00									*12f30*		13 00						
Manchester Piccadilly 10 ⛴	d						*11f46*	12 16									*12f46*		13 16						
Bolton	d		*11f40*				*12f05*	12 33					*12f40*				*13f05*		13 33						
Wigan North Western	a		12 24				12 37					13 13	13 19	←			13 37				14 13				
	d		12 24				12 38					13 14	13 19	13 14			13 38				14 14				
Preston 8	a		12 37				12 51	12 56				→	13 35	13 37			13 51		13 56		14 37				
Blackpool North	a													14 07							15 07				
	d		*11 50*				*12 11*	*12 20*					*12 50*				*13 13*		*13 20*						
Preston 8	d		12 39				12 53	12 58					13 37				13 53		14 01	14 05					
Lancaster 6	a		12 53				13 08	13 14					13 51				14 08		14 16	14 21					
	d		12 54				13 08	13 14					13 52				14 08		14 16	14 21					
Barrow-in-Furness	a																			15 24					
Oxenholme Lake District	a		13 07				13 22	13 28					14 05						14 30						
	d		13 07				13 24	13 28					14 05						14 31						
Windermere	a							*13 52*					*14 52*												
Penrith North Lakes	d		13 33					13 54					14 31				14 45		14 56						
Carlisle 8	a		13 52				14 01	14 10					14 46				15 00		15 11						
	d		13 52				14 03	14 11					14 47				15 03		15 13						
Lockerbie	d							14 30																	
Carstairs	a																								
Motherwell	a																								
Glasgow Central 15	a		15 06				15 23						16 09						16 35						
Haymarket	a																16s14								
Edinburgh 10	a							15 35									16 22								
Perth	a																*18 28*								
Dundee	a							*17 24*									*18 14*								
Aberdeen	a							*18 46*									*19 30*								
Inverness	a																*20 44*								

For general notes see front of timetable
For details of catering facilities see Directory of Train Operators

A From Reading (Table 51)
B From Southampton Central (Table 51)
C 🛒 to Glasgow Central
b By bus
c Change at Wilmslow. By bus
e Change at Crewe and Llandudno Junction
f Change at Preston

OVERNIGHT SLEEPERS. For Sleeper trains, operated by First ScotRail, please refer to Tables 400 - 404

Table 65

Sundays

until 12 July

London and West Midlands → North West England and Scotland

Route Diagram - see first page of Table 65

Station		VT	VT	XC	VT	TP	VT	NT	XC	LM	VT	VT	VT	XC	VT	VT	TP	VT	NT	XC	LM	VT	VT
		1 ◇	1 ◇	1 ◇	1 ◇	1 ◇	1 ◇		1 ◇	1 ◇	1 ◇	1 ◇	1 ◇	1 ◇	1 ◇	1 ◇	1 ◇	1 ◇		1 ◇	1 ◇	1 ◇	1 ◇
				A										A									
London Euston 15 ⊖	d	12 15	12 25				12 35				12 55	13 02	13 15		13 25			13 35				13 55	14 02
Gatwick Airport 10 ✈	d																						
Watford Junction	d	12 01											13 07										
Milton Keynes Central	d	12 48											13 48										
Northampton	d																						
Rugby	d																						14 16
Nuneaton	d																						14 30
Tamworth Low Level	d																						14 45
Lichfield Trent Valley	d																						14 51
Coventry	d			12 28	12 34					12 57				13 26		13 40							13b46
Birmingham International ✈	d			12 40	12 52				13 05	13 08				13 38		13 51				14 07			
Birmingham New Street 12	d			13 01	13 20				13 31	13 35				14 01		14 20				14 31	14 35		
Wolverhampton 7	d			13 19	13 37				13 49	13 52				14 19		14 37				14 49	14 52		
Penkridge	d									14 03											15 03		
Stafford	a			13 33						14 10		14 20		14 33							15 10		15 24
	d			13 34						14 10		14 22		14 34							15 10		15 25
Stoke-on-Trent	a	13 50							14 19		14 26		14 50	14 56						15 19		15 25	
Congleton	a																						
Macclesfield	a			14c50							14 42			15 14								15 42	
Crewe 10	a				14 09		14 12			14 30		14 43				15 09		15 12			15 30		15 43
	d				14 11		14 13			14 31		14 45				15 11		15 13			15 31		15 45
Chester	a						14 47					15 18						15 47					16 18
Wrexham General	a																						
Llandudno Junction	a						15 55											16 55					
Llandudno	a						16e14																
Bangor (Gwynedd)	a						16 18											17 12					
Holyhead	a						16 55											17 55					
Wilmslow	a			14 09	14 46		14 29					15 22						15 29					
Manchester Airport ✈	a				15f05		15 05																
Stockport	a	14 18		14 22	14 58		14 38				14 56	15 37	15 18	15 28				15 38				15 56	
Manchester Piccadilly 10	a	14 30		14 40	15 15		14 51		15 00		15 09	15 51	15 30	15 40				15 51		16 00		16 09	
Hartford	a									14 43											15 43		
Warrington Bank Quay	a		14 16		14 28										15 16	15 28							
	d		14 16		14 29										15 16	15 29							
Runcorn	a									14 53		15 01									15 53		16 01
Liverpool South Parkway 7 ✈	a									15 03											16 03		
Liverpool Lime Street 10	a									15 13		15 23									16 13		16 22
	d							14 31											15 31				
Manchester Airport ✈	d		13g30			14 00									14g30		15 00						
Manchester Piccadilly 10	d		13g46			14 16									14g46		15 16						
Bolton	d		14g05			14 33									15g05		15 33						
Wigan North Western	a		14 27		14 39			15 13							15 27	15 39			16 13				
	d		14 27		14 40			15 14							15 27	15 40			16 14				
Preston 8	a		14 40		14 52	14 56		15 37							15 40	15 53	15 56		16 37				
Blackpool North	a							16 07											17 07				
	d		14 11		14 20										14 50	15 20							
Preston 8	d		14 42		14 55	15 00									15 42	15 55	16 00						
Lancaster 6	a		14 56		15 10	15 16									15 56	16 10	16 16						
	d		14 58		15 11	15 16									15 58	16 10	16 16						
Barrow-in-Furness	a																17 19						
Oxenholme Lake District	a				15 24	15 30									16 10								
	d				15 25	15 30									16 11								
Windermere	a					15 54									16 52								
Penrith North Lakes	d		15 32			15 54										16 47							
Carlisle 8	a		15 47		16 03	16 11									16 48	17 02							
	d		15 48		16 05	16 13									16 49	17 04							
Lockerbie	d					16 31																	
Carstairs	a																						
Motherwell	a																						
Glasgow Central 15	a		17 03		17 17										18 03								
Haymarket	a					17s30										18s13							
Edinburgh 10	a					17 37										18 22							
Perth	a		18h44		19h15																		
Dundee	a		19h08			19 28										19 57							
Aberdeen	a		20h29			20 47										21 17							
Inverness	a				21h34																		

For general notes see front of timetable
For details of catering facilities see Directory of Train Operators

- **A** From Bournemouth (Table 51)
- **b** Change at Nuneaton and Stafford
- **c** Change at Wilmslow. By bus
- **e** Change at Crewe and Llandudno Junction
- **f** Change at Crewe and Wilmslow
- **g** Change at Preston
- **h** Via Glasgow Central and Glasgow Queen Street. Passengers make their own way from one station to the other

OVERNIGHT SLEEPERS. For Sleeper trains, operated by First ScotRail, please refer to Tables 400 - 404

Table 65

Sundays

until 12 July

London and West Midlands → North West England and Scotland

Route Diagram - see first page of Table 65

		VT	VT	XC	VT	TP		VT	NT	XC	LM	VT		VT	VT	VT	VT	XC	VT	TP		VT	NT	XC	LM
		1 ◇	1 ◇	1 ◇	1 ◇	1 ◇		1 ◇		1 ◇	1 ◇	1 ◇		1 ◇	1 ◇	1 ◇	1 ◇	1 ◇	1 ◇	1 ◇		1 ◇		1 ◇	1 ◇
				A		B				C								A		D				E	
London Euston 15 ⊖	d	14 15	14 25					14 35				14 55		15 02	15 05	15 15	15 25					15 35			
Gatwick Airport 10 ✈	d																								
Watford Junction	d	*14 06*													*14 51*	*15 06*									
Milton Keynes Central	d	14 48													15u38	15 48									
Northampton	d																								
Rugby	d																								
Nuneaton	d																								
Tamworth Low Level	d																								
Lichfield Trent Valley	d																								
Coventry	d			14 26	*14 40*													15 26	*15 40*						
Birmingham International ✈	d			14 38	*14 51*					*15 07*								15 38	*15 51*					*16 07*	
Birmingham New Street 12	d			15 01	15 20					15 31	15 35							16 01	16 20					16 31	16 35
Wolverhampton 7	d			15 19	15 37					15 49	15 52							16 19	16u37					16 49	16 52
Penkridge	d										16 03														17 03
Stafford	a			15 33							16 10			16 20				16 35							17 10
	d			15 34							16 10			16 21				16 36							17 10
Stoke-on-Trent	a	15 50		15 56						16 19		16 24				16 50		16 56						17 19	
Congleton	a																								
Macclesfield	a			16 14								16 42						17 14							
Crewe 10	a				16 09			16 12			16 32				16 54				17 09			17 12			17 30
	d				16 11			16 13			16 34				16 57				17 11			17 13			17 31
Chester	a							*16 47*							17 19							*17 48*			
Wrexham General	a																								
Llandudno Junction	a							*17 55*							*18 25*										
Llandudno	a														*18b40*										
Bangor (Gwynedd)	a							*18 18*							*18 42*										
Holyhead	a							*18 55*							*19 25*										
Wilmslow	a				*16 49*			16 29			*17 22*								*17 46*			17 29			
Manchester Airport ✈	a							*17 05*																	
Stockport	a	16 18		16 28	*16 58*			16 38				16 56				17 18		17 30	*17 58*			17 38			
Manchester Piccadilly 10	a	16 30		16 40	*17 15*			16 51		17 00		17 09				17 30		17 40	*18 15*			17 51		18 00	
Hartford	a										16 45														17 43
Warrington Bank Quay	a		16 16		16 28												17 16		17 28						
	d		16 16		16 29												17 16		17 29						
Runcorn	a										16 55			16 58											17 53
Liverpool South Parkway 7 ✈	a										17 05														18 03
Liverpool Lime Street 10	a										17 16			17 22											18 13
	d								16 31														17 31		
Manchester Airport ✈	d		*15c30*			16 00											*16c30*			17 00					
Manchester Piccadilly 10	d		*15c46*			16 16											*16c46*			17 16					
Bolton	d		*16c05*			16 33											*17c05*			17 33					
Wigan North Western	a		16 27		16 39				17 13								17 27		17 39				18 13		
	d		16 27		16 40				17 14								17 27		17 40				18 14		
Preston 8	a		16 40		16 53	16 56			17 37								17 40		17 53	17 56			18 37		
Blackpool North	a								18 07														19 07		
	d		*16 11*		*16 20*												*17 11*		*17 20*						
Preston 8	d		16 42		16 55	17 02	17 06										17 42		17 55	18 02	18 06				
Lancaster 6	a		16 56		17 10	17 18	17 22										17 56		18 10	18 18	18 22				
	d		16 57		17 10	17 18	17 22										17 57		18 10	18 18	18 22				
Barrow-in-Furness	a		*18 09*																		19 26				
Oxenholme Lake District	a				17 24	17 32	17 39										18 10		18 24	18 32					
	d				17 25	17 32	17 39										18 10		18 25	18 32					
Windermere	a						18 02													*18 56*					
Penrith North Lakes	d		17 32			17 57													18 51	18 56					
Carlisle 8	a		17 47		18 03	18 13											18 48		19 06	19 13					
	d		17 48		18 05	18 15											18 49		19 06	19 15					
Lockerbie	d																			19 33					
Carstairs	a																								
Motherwell	a																			20s24					
Glasgow Central 15	a		19 00		19 17												20 03			20 45					
Haymarket	a																								
Edinburgh 10	a					19 37													20 24						
Perth	a		*20e46*																	*22e46*					
Dundee	a		*21e10*																*22 17*	*23e09*					
Aberdeen	a		*22e24*																*23 33*	*00e25*					
Inverness	a																								

For general notes see front of timetable
For details of catering facilities see Directory of Train Operators

A From Bournemouth (Table 51)
B 🍴 to Edinburgh
C From Plymouth (Table 51)
D 🍴 to Glasgow Central
E From Paignton (Table 51)
b Change at Chester and Llandudno Junction
c Change at Preston
e Via Glasgow Central and Glasgow Queen Street. Passengers make their own way from one station to the other

OVERNIGHT SLEEPERS. For Sleeper trains, operated by First ScotRail, please refer to Tables 400 - 404

Sundays

until 12 July

London and West Midlands → North West England and Scotland

Route Diagram - see first page of Table 65

		VT	VT	VT	VT	VT	XC	VT	TP	NT	VT	XC	LM	VT	VT	VT	VT	VT	TP	NT	XC	VT	XC
		1◇	1◇	1◇	1◇	1◇	1◇	1◇	1◇		1◇	1◇	1◇	1◇	1◇	1◇	1◇	1◇	1◇		1◇	1◇	1◇
							A					B									A		C
London Euston 15 ⊖	d	15 55	16 02	16 05	16 15	16 25					16 35			16 55	17 02	17 05	17 15	17 25				17 35	
Gatwick Airport 10 ✈	d																						
Watford Junction	d			*16 06*												*16 51*	*17 06*						
Milton Keynes Central	d			16u39	16 48											17u38	17 48						
Northampton	d																						
Rugby	d		*16 16*																				
Nuneaton	d		*16 30*													18 10							
Tamworth Low Level	d		*16 45*																				
Lichfield Trent Valley	d		*16 51*																				
Coventry	d		15b46				16 26	*16 40*													17 26		*17 40*
Birmingham International ✈	d						16 38	*16 51*				*17 07*									17 38		*18 07*
Birmingham New Street 12	d						17 01	17 20				17 31	17 35								18 01		18 31
Wolverhampton 7	d						17 19	17u37				17 49	17 52								18 19		18 49
Penkridge	d												18 03										
Stafford	a		17 24				17 35						18 10		18 24						18 37		
	d		17 25				17 36						18 10		18 25						18 39		
Stoke-on-Trent	a	17 25			17 50		17 56					18 19		18 25			18 50				18 58		19 19
Congleton	a																						
Macclesfield	a	17 42					18 14							18 42							19 16		
Crewe 10	a			17 54				18 09			18 12		18 30			18 53						19 12	
	d			17 57				18 11			18 13		18 31			18 56						19 13	
Chester	a			18 19							*18 47*					19 14						*19 48*	
Wrexham General	a																						
Llandudno Junction	a			*19 23*							*19 48*					20 07							
Llandudno	a																						
Bangor (Gwynedd)	a			*19 46*							*20 11*					20 29							
Holyhead	a			*20 20*							*20 47*					21 02							
Wilmslow	a							*18 46*			18 29		*19 22*									19 29	
Manchester Airport ✈	a										*19 05*												
Stockport	a	17 56			18 18		18 28				18 38		*19 37*	18 56			19 18				19 28	19 38	
Manchester Piccadilly 10	a	18 09			18 30		18 40				18 51	19 00		19 09			19 30				19 40	19 51	20 00
Hartford	a												18 43										
Warrington Bank Quay	a					18 16		18 28										19 16					
	d					18 17		18 29										19 16					
Runcorn	a		17 56										18 53		18 56								
Liverpool South Parkway 7 ✈	a												19 03										
Liverpool Lime Street 10	a		18 19										19 13		19 19								
	d									18 31										19 31			
Manchester Airport ✈	d					*17c30*			18 00									*18c30*	19 00				
Manchester Piccadilly 10	d					*17c46*			18 16									*18c46*	19 16				
Bolton	d					*18c05*			18 33									*19c05*	19 33				
Wigan North Western	a					18 27		18 39		19 13								19 27		20 13			
	d					18 28		18 40		19 14								19 27		20 14			
Preston 8	a					18 40		18 53	18 56	19 37								19 40	19 56	20 37			
Blackpool North	a									20 07										21 07			
	d					*18 11*		*18 20*										*18 50*	*19 20*				
Preston 8	d					18 42		18 55	19 00									19 42	20 00				
Lancaster 6	a					18 56		19 10	19 15									19 56	20 16				
	d					18 58		19 10	19 16									19 57	20 16				
Barrow-in-Furness	a																		21 19				
Oxenholme Lake District	a					19 10		19 24	19 30									20 10					
	d					19 11		19 26	19 30									20 10					
Windermere	a							*19 45*										*20 52*					
Penrith North Lakes	d					19 36			19 54									20 36					
Carlisle 8	a					19 51		20 03	20 11									20 51					
	d					19 53		20 05	20 13									20 52					
Lockerbie	d								20 31														
Carstairs	a																						
Motherwell	a																						
Glasgow Central 15	a					21 08		21 17										22 07					
Haymarket	a								21s30														
Edinburgh 10	a								21 37														
Perth	a								*00 07*									00e56					
Dundee	a								*23 56*														
Aberdeen	a																						
Inverness	a																						

For general notes see front of timetable
For details of catering facilities see Directory of Train Operators

A From Bournemouth (Table 51)
B From Bristol Temple Meads (Table 51)
C From Penzance (Table 135)
b Change at Nuneaton and Stafford
c Change at Preston
e Via Glasgow Central and Glasgow Queen Street. Passengers make their own way from one station to the other

OVERNIGHT SLEEPERS. For Sleeper trains, operated by First ScotRail, please refer to Tables 400 - 404

Table 65

Sundays

until 12 July

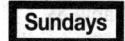

London and West Midlands → North West England and Scotland

Route Diagram - see first page of Table 65

Station		LM	VT	VT	VT	VT	VT		XC	VT	VT	NT	XC	LM	VT	VT	VT	VT	VT	XC		VT	VT	XC	NT
		1 ◇	1 ◇	1 ◇	1 ◇	1 ◇	1 ◇		1 ◇	R 1	1 ◇		1 ◇	1 ◇	1 ◇	1 ◇	1 ◇	1 ◇	1 ◇	1 ◇		1 ◇	1 ◇	1 ◇	
									A				B							A				B	
			☕	☕	☕	☕	☕		🍴	☕	☕		🍴		☕	☕	☕	☕	☕	🍴		☕	☕		
London Euston 15 ⊖	d		17 55	18 02	18 05	18 15	18 25				18 35				18 55	19 02	19 05	19 15	19 25				19 35		
Gatwick Airport 10 ✈	d																								
Watford Junction	d				17 51	18 06											18 51	19 06							
Milton Keynes Central	d				18u38	18 48											19u38	19 48							
Northampton	d																								
Rugby	d			18 16												18 16									
Nuneaton	d			18 30												20 01									
Tamworth Low Level	d			18 45																					
Lichfield Trent Valley	d			18 51																					
Coventry	d			17b46					18 26	18 40				19 00						19 26		19 40		19 54	
Birmingham International ✈	d								18 38	18 51			19 07	19 11						19 38		19 51		20 08	
Birmingham New Street 12	d	18 35							19 01	19 20			19 31	19 35						20 01		20 20		20 31	
Wolverhampton 7	d	18 52							19 19	19 37			19 49	19 52						20 19		20 38		20 49	
Penkridge	d	19 03												20 03											
Stafford	a	19 10		19 24					19 37					20 10		20 25				20 36		20 51			
	d	19 10		19 25					19 38					20 10		20 30				20 38		20 52			
Stoke-on-Trent	a		19 25			19 50			19 56				20 21		20 25			20 50		20 57				21 19	
Congleton	a																								
Macclesfield	a		19 42						20 14						20 42					21 15					
Crewe 10	a	19 30			19 54					20 09	20 12			20 30		20 48	20 55					21 10	21 13		
	d	19 31			19 57					20 11	20 13			20 31		20 50	20 58						21 14		
Chester	a				20 16						20 48						21 17						21 46		
Wrexham General	a																								
Llandudno Junction	a				21 11												22 08						22 53		
Llandudno	a																								
Bangor (Gwynedd)	a				21 28												22 25						23 10		
Holyhead	a				22 02												22 59						23 52		
Wilmslow	a									20 45	20 29			21 22								21 46	21 30		
Manchester Airport ✈	a										21 05														
Stockport	a		19 56			20 18			20 28	20 57	20 38			21 37	20 56		21c39	21 18		21 28		21 58	21 39		
Manchester Piccadilly 10	a		20 09			20 30			20 40	21 14	20 51		21 00		21 09		21c52	21 30		21 40		22 15	21 52	22 00	
Hartford	a	19 43												20 43											
Warrington Bank Quay	a						20 16			20 28									21 16						
	d						20 16			20 29									21 16						
Runcorn	a	19 53		19 57										20 53		21 06									
Liverpool South Parkway 7 ✈	a	20 03												21 03											
Liverpool Lime Street 10	a	20 13		20 19										21 13		21 27									
	d						19 31					20 31													21 31
Manchester Airport ✈	d						19e30												20e30						
Manchester Piccadilly 10	d						19e46												20e46						
Bolton	d						20e05												21e05						
Wigan North Western	a						20 27			20 39		21 13							21 27						22 13
	d						20 27			20 40		21 14							21 27						22 14
Preston 8	a						20 40			20 53		21 37							21 40						22 37
Blackpool North	a						21 16			21 38		22 07							22 38						23 07
	d						20 11			20 20									20 50						
Preston 8	d						20 42			20 55									21 42						
Lancaster 6	a						20 56			21 10									21 56						
	d						20 57			21 10									21 57						
Barrow-in-Furness	a																		23 10						
Oxenholme Lake District	a						21 10			21 24									22 10						
	d						21 11			21 26									22 11						
Windermere	a																								
Penrith North Lakes	d						21 36												22 36						
Carlisle 8	a						21 51			22 03									22 51						
	d						21 52			22 05									22 53						
Lockerbie	d									22 23															
Carstairs	a																								
Motherwell	a						22s48			23s13															
Glasgow Central 15	a						23 08			23 35									00 02						
Haymarket	a																								
Edinburgh 10	a																								
Perth	a																								
Dundee	a																								
Aberdeen	a																								
Inverness	a																								

For general notes see front of timetable
For details of catering facilities see Directory of Train Operators

- **A** From Bournemouth (Table 51)
- **B** From Bristol Temple Meads (Table 51)
- **b** Change at Nuneaton and Stafford
- **c** Change at Crewe
- **e** Change at Preston

OVERNIGHT SLEEPERS. For Sleeper trains, operated by First ScotRail, please refer to Tables 400 - 404

Sundays

until 12 July

London and West Midlands → North West England and Scotland

Route Diagram - see first page of Table 65

		VT	VT	VT	SR	VT	XC	VT	VT	VT	LM	VT	AW	XC	SR	VT	VT	AW	VT	SR	SR
		1 ◇	1 ◇	1 ◇	R	1 ◇	1 ◇	1 ◇	1 ◇	1 ◇	1	1 ◇	◇	1 ◇	R	1 ◇	1 ◇	◇	1 ◇	R	R
					A		B							B	C					D	E
		🛒	🛒	🛒	🛒	🛒		🛒	🛒	🛒		🛒			🛒	🛒	🛒		🛒	🛒	🛒
London Euston 15 ⊖	d	19 55	20 02	20 05	20 07	20 15	.	20 25	.	20 35	.	20 50	.	.	20 55	21 20	21 24	.	21 50	22 32	23 27
Gatwick Airport 10 ✈	d	.	.	.	.	.	.	.	.	.	.	.	.	.	.	.	.	.	.	.	.
Watford Junction	d	.	.	19 51	.	20 06	.	.	.	.	.	20 51	.	.	21u17	.	21 22	.	21 47	.	23u47
Milton Keynes Central	d	.	.	20 38	.	20 49	.	.	.	.	.	21 39	.	.	.	.	22 13	.	22 38	.	.
Northampton	d	.	.	.	.	.	.	.	.	.	.	20b55	.	.	.	.	.	.	21b55	.	.
Rugby	d	.	20 16	.	.	.	.	.	.	.	.	22 00	.	.	.	.	.	.	23 06	.	.
Nuneaton	d	.	21 01	20 30	.	.	.	.	.	.	.	.	.	.	.	22c53	.	.	23e26	.	.
Tamworth Low Level	d	.	.	20 45	.	.	.	21 32	.	.	.	.	.	.	.	.	.	.	.	.	.
Lichfield Trent Valley	d	.	.	20 51	.	.	.	21 39	.	.	.	.	.	.	.	.	.	.	.	.	.
Coventry	d	.	19f46	.	.	.	20 26	.	20 40	.	20 54	.	.	21 26	.	21f35	.	22 23	.	.	.
Birmingham International ✈	d	.	.	.	.	.	20 38	.	20 51	.	21 08	.	21 08	21 38	.	.	.	22 40	.	.	.
Birmingham New Street 12	d	.	.	.	.	.	21 01	.	21 20	.	21 35	.	21 24	22 01	.	.	.	22 55	.	.	.
Wolverhampton 7 ⛴	d	.	.	.	.	.	21 19	.	21 38	.	21 53	.	21 43	22 19	.	.	.	23 15	.	.	.
Penkridge	d	.	.	.	.	.	.	.	.	.	22 03	.	.	.	.	.	.	.	.	.	.
Stafford	a	.	.	21 32	.	.	21 37	.	21 58	22 03	22 13	.	.	22 37	.	23 18	.	23 30	23s53	.	.
	d	.	.	21 33	.	.	21 38	.	21 59	22 04	22 14	.	.	22 38	.	23 19	.	23 31	.	.	.
Stoke-on-Trent	a	21 25	.	.	.	21 50	21 56	.	.	.	.	.	.	22 55	.	.	23 30	.	.	.	.
Congleton	a	.	.	.	.	.	.	.	.	.	.	.	.	.	.	.	.	.	.	.	.
Macclesfield	a	21 42	.	.	.	.	22 14	.	.	.	.	.	.	23 13	.	.	23 49	.	.	.	.
Crewe 10	a	.	21 44	21 53	.	.	.	22 10	22 17	22 22	22 36	22 49	23 02	.	.	23 43	.	23 55	00s16	.	.
	d	.	21 46	21 55	.	.	.	22 13	22 18	22 23	.	22 51	23 05	.	23u42	23 47	.	00 10	.	.	.
Chester	a	.	22 18	.	.	.	.	.	22 50	.	.	.	23 26	.	.	.	.	00 31	.	.	.
Wrexham General	a	.	.	.	.	.	.	.	.	.	.	.	.	.	.	.	.	.	.	.	.
Llandudno Junction	a	.	.	.	.	.	.	.	23 50	.	.	.	.	.	.	.	.	01 24	.	.	.
Llandudno	a	.	.	.	.	.	.	.	.	.	.	.	.	.	.	.	.	.	.	.	.
Bangor (Gwynedd)	a	.	.	.	.	.	.	.	00 12	.	.	.	.	.	.	.	.	01 40	.	.	.
Holyhead	a	.	.	.	.	.	.	.	00 49	.	.	.	.	.	.	.	.	02 15	.	.	.
Wilmslow	a	.	.	.	.	.	.	.	.	22 38	23 22	.	.	.	.	.	.	.	.	.	.
Manchester Airport ✈	a	.	.	.	.	.	.	.	.	23 05	.	.	.	.	.	.	.	.	.	.	.
Stockport	a	21 56	.	.	.	22 18	22 28	.	.	22 48	.	.	.	23 27	.	.	00 05	.	00s45	.	.
Manchester Piccadilly 10 ⛴	a	22 09	.	.	.	22 30	22 40	.	.	23 00	.	.	.	23 41	.	.	00 17	.	00 58	.	.
Hartford	a	.	.	.	.	.	.	.	.	.	.	.	.	.	.	.	.	.	.	.	.
Warrington Bank Quay	a	.	.	.	.	.	.	22 29	22 36	.	.	23 08	.	.	.	.	.	.	.	.	.
	d	.	.	.	.	.	.	22 30	22 36	.	.	23 08	.	.	.	.	.	.	.	.	.
Runcorn	a	.	22 02	22 11	.	.	.	.	.	.	.	.	.	.	.	00 07	.	.	.	.	.
Liverpool South Parkway 7 ✈	a	.	.	.	.	.	.	.	.	.	.	.	.	.	.	.	.	.	.	.	.
Liverpool Lime Street 10	a	.	22 23	22 32	.	.	.	.	.	.	.	.	.	.	.	00 34	.	.	.	.	.
	d	.	.	.	.	.	.	.	.	.	.	22 31	.	.	.	.	.	.	.	.	.
Manchester Airport ✈	d	.	.	.	.	.	.	.	.	.	.	.	.	.	.	.	.	.	.	.	.
Manchester Piccadilly 10 ⛴	d	.	.	.	.	.	.	.	.	.	.	.	.	.	.	.	.	.	.	.	.
Bolton	d	.	.	.	.	.	.	.	.	.	.	.	.	.	.	.	.	.	.	.	.
Wigan North Western	a	.	.	.	.	.	.	22 40	22 47	.	.	23 19	.	.	.	.	.	.	.	.	.
	d	.	.	.	.	.	.	22 41	22 47	.	.	23 19	.	.	.	.	.	.	.	.	.
Preston 8	a	.	.	.	.	.	.	22 58	23 07	.	.	23 39	.	.	.	.	.	.	.	.	.
Blackpool North	a	.	.	.	.	.	.	.	00 04	.	.	00 14	.	.	.	.	.	.	.	.	.
	d	.	.	.	.	.	.	.	.	.	.	.	.	.	.	.	.	.	.	.	.
Preston 8	d	.	.	.	.	.	.	.	.	.	.	.	.	.	00u30	.	.	.	.	.	.
Lancaster 6	a	.	.	.	.	.	.	.	.	.	.	.	.	.	.	.	.	.	.	.	.
	d	.	.	.	.	.	.	.	.	.	.	.	.	.	.	.	.	.	.	.	.
Barrow-in-Furness	a	.	.	.	.	.	.	.	.	.	.	.	.	.	.	.	.	.	.	.	.
Oxenholme Lake District	a	.	.	.	.	.	.	.	.	.	.	.	.	.	.	.	.	.	.	.	.
	d	.	.	.	.	.	.	.	.	.	.	.	.	.	.	.	.	.	.	.	.
Windermere	a	.	.	.	.	.	.	.	.	.	.	.	.	.	.	.	.	.	.	.	.
Penrith North Lakes	d	.	.	.	.	.	.	.	.	.	.	.	.	.	.	.	.	.	.	.	.
Carlisle 8	a	.	.	.	.	.	.	.	.	.	.	.	.	.	.	.	.	.	.	.	05s04
	d	.	.	.	.	.	.	.	.	.	.	.	.	.	.	.	.	.	.	.	.
Lockerbie	d	.	.	.	.	.	.	.	.	.	.	.	.	.	.	.	.	.	.	.	.
Carstairs	a	.	.	.	.	.	.	.	.	.	.	.	.	.	.	.	.	.	.	07s13	06s24
Motherwell	a	.	.	.	.	.	.	.	.	.	.	.	.	.	.	.	.	.	.	07s39	07s01
Glasgow Central 15	a	.	.	.	.	.	.	.	.	.	.	.	.	.	.	.	.	.	.	07 57	07 18
Haymarket	a	.	.	.	.	.	.	.	.	.	.	.	.	.	.	.	.	.	.	.	.
Edinburgh 10	a	.	.	.	.	.	.	.	.	.	.	.	.	.	.	.	.	.	.	06s25	07 20
Perth	a	.	.	.	05s39	.	.	.	.	.	.	.	.	.	05s39	.	.	.	.	.	.
Dundee	a	.	.	.	06s08	.	.	.	.	.	.	.	.	.	06s08	.	.	.	.	.	.
Aberdeen	a	.	.	.	07 35	.	.	.	.	.	.	.	.	.	07 35	.	.	.	.	.	.
Inverness	a	.	.	.	08 30	.	.	.	.	.	.	.	.	.	08 30	.	.	.	.	.	.

For general notes see front of timetable
For details of catering facilities see Directory of Train Operators

A 24 May to 5 July. Also conveys portion to Fort William (Table 227)

B From Bournemouth (Table 51)

C 17 May and 12 July. Also conveys portion to Fort William (Table 227)

D 24 May to 5 July. Stops at Edinburgh before Carstairs, Motherwell and Glasgow Central

E 17 May and 12 July

b By bus

c Arr. 2246

e Arr. 2321

f Change at Nuneaton

OVERNIGHT SLEEPERS. For Sleeper trains, operated by First ScotRail, please refer to Tables 400 - 404

London and West Midlands → North West England and Scotland

19 July to 6 September

Route Diagram - see first page of Table 65

		NT	TP	TP	VT	TP	NT	XC	VT		VT	VT	NT	VT	VT	LM	VT	XC		VT	TP	NT	VT	LM	VT
			1 ◇	1 ◇	1 ◇	1 ◇		1 ◇	1 ◇		1 ◇	1 ◇		1 ◇	1 ◇	1 ◇	1 ◇	1 ◇		1 ◇	1 ◇		1 ◇	1 ◇	1 ◇
London Euston 15 ⊖	d										08 10			08 15	08 20		08 45						09 15		09 20
Gatwick Airport 10 ✈	d																								
Watford Junction	d										08 09						08 42								09 12
Milton Keynes Central	d										08 56				09 05		09 33								10 07
Northampton	d																09 30								
Rugby	d																10 09								
Nuneaton	d													09 42									10 45		
Tamworth Low Level	d																								
Lichfield Trent Valley	d																								
Coventry	d								08 37									09 07						10 04	
Birmingham International ✈	d								08 55							09 03		09 25		09 51				10 13	
Birmingham New Street 12	d				08 45			09 01	09 20							09 42		10 00		10 20				10 42	
Wolverhampton 7	d				09 04			09 19	09 37							09 59		10 18		10 37				10 59	
Penkridge	d															10 10								11 10	
Stafford	a				09 21			09 33						10 10		10 17		10 32					11 11	11 17	
	d				09 23			09 34						10 10		10 17		10 33					11 11	11 17	
Stoke-on-Trent	a														10 21			10 51							11 22
Congleton	a																								
Macclesfield	a														10 37			11 09							11 38
Crewe 10	a				09 40			09 54	10 07		10 15			10 29		10 37	10 58			11 07			11 30	11 37	
	d				09 42			09 56	10 09		10 17	10 21		10 31		10 38	11 00			11 09			11 32	11 38	
Chester	a				10 22									11 00		11 22				11 48				12 20	
Wrexham General	a																								
Llandudno Junction	a													11 54						12 53					
Llandudno	a													12b10						13b08					
Bangor (Gwynedd)	a													12 10						13 10					
Holyhead	a													12 43						13 45					
Wilmslow	a							10 12			10 31					11 22				11 40					
Manchester Airport ✈	a										10 55														
Stockport	a				10 21			10 21			10 40				10 52			11 22		12c37					11 53
Manchester Piccadilly 10	a				10 39			10 39			10 54				11 04			11 38		12 02					12 09
Hartford	a															10 50								11 50	
Warrington Bank Quay	a				09 59				10 26			10 37					11 16			11 26					
	d				09 59				10 27			10 37					11 17			11 27					
Runcorn	a													10 47		11 00							11 48	12 00	
Liverpool South Parkway 7 ✈	a															11 10								12 10	
Liverpool Lime Street 10	a													11 08		11 20							12 09	12 20	
	d	08 31					09 31						10 31									11 31			
Manchester Airport ✈	d		09 00			09 30											10e29				11 00				
Manchester Piccadilly 10	d		09 16			09 46											10e43				11 16				
Bolton	d		09 33			10 05											11e05				11 33				
Wigan North Western	a	09 13			10 10		10 13		10 37			10 48	11 13				11 27			11 37		12 13			
	d	09 14			10 10		10 14		10 38			10 48	11 14				11 28			11 38		12 14			
Preston 8	a	09 37	09 56		10 27	10 31	10 39		10 52			11 04	11 37				11 41			11 51	11 56	12 37			
Blackpool North	a	10 06					11 09					11 39	12 07									13 07			
	d		09 20			09 50						10 20					10 50			11 13	11 20				
Preston 8	d		10 00	10 05		10 39						11 06					11 42			11 53	12 02				
Lancaster 6	a		10 15	10 20		10 54						11 22					11 57			12 08	12 17				
	d		10 16	10 21		10 55											11 57			12 08	12 18				
Barrow-in-Furness	a		11 19																		13 21				
Oxenholme Lake District	a			10 37		11 09											12 10			12 22					
	d			10 38		11 09											12 11			12 24					
Windermere	a			11 00																12 52					
Penrith North Lakes	d					11 35											12 36								
Carlisle 8	a					11 50											12 54			13 01					
	d					11 52											12 55			13 03					
Lockerbie	d					12 11																			
Carstairs	a																								
Motherwell	a																								
Glasgow Central 15	a					13 15											14 10								
Haymarket	a																			14s13					
Edinburgh 10	a																			14 22					
Perth	a																16f45								
Dundee	a																			16 48					
Aberdeen	a																			18g23					
Inverness	a																								

For general notes see front of timetable
For details of catering facilities see Directory of Train Operators

b Change at Crewe and Llandudno Junction
c Change at Crewe and Wilmslow
e Change at Preston
f Via Glasgow Central and Glasgow Queen Street. Passengers make their own way from one station to the other
g Change at Edinburgh and Dundee

OVERNIGHT SLEEPERS. For Sleeper trains, operated by First ScotRail, please refer to Tables 400 - 404

Sundays

London and West Midlands → North West England and Scotland

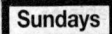

19 July to 6 September

Route Diagram - see first page of Table 65

Station		VT	XC	VT	TP	LM	NT	VT	LM	VT	VT	XC	VT	TP		NT	VT	LM	VT	VT	VT	VT
		1 ◇	1 ◇	1 ◇	1 ◇	1		1 ◇	1 ◇	1 ◇	1 ◇	1 ◇	1 ◇	1 ◇			1 ◇	1 ◇	1 ◇	1 ◇	1 ◇	1 ◇
			A									B		C								
		🍴	🛒	🍴	🛒			🍴		🍴	🍴	🛒	🍴	🛒			🍴		🍴	🍴	🍴	🍴
London Euston [15] ⊖	d	09 45						10 15		10 20	10 45						11 15		11 20	12 02	12 15	12 25
Gatwick Airport [10] ✈	d																					
Watford Junction	d									*10 12*	*10 42*								*11 12*		*12 01*	
Milton Keynes Central	d	10 31								11 07	11 32						12 04		12 09		12 48	
Northampton	d	*10 00*									*11 36*											
Rugby	d	11 07									12 07							*11b58*				
Nuneaton	d							11 45										*12b11*				
Tamworth Low Level	d																	*12b26*				
Lichfield Trent Valley	d																	*12b32*				
Coventry	d		10 28	*10 34*								11 28	*11 34*									
Birmingham International ✈	d		10 40	*10 52*								11 40	*11 52*					*12 08*				
Birmingham New Street [12]	d		11 01	11 20					11 42			12 01	12 20					12 35				
Wolverhampton [7] 🚊	d		11 19	11 37					11 59			12 20	12 36					12 52				
Penkridge	d								12 10									13 03				
Stafford	a		11 32					12 11	12 16			12 33					12 54	13 10		13 24		
	d		11 33			11 41		12 11	12 16			12 34					12 55	13 10		13 25		
Stoke-on-Trent	a		11 52			11 59				12 22		12 52							13 11		13 50	
Congleton	a																					
Macclesfield	a		12 10							12 38		13 10							13 28			
Crewe [10]	a	11 54		12 07		12 24		12 30	12 37		12 59		13 07				13 16	13 30		13 43		
	d	11 56		12 09				12 32	12 38		13 01		13 09				13 18	13 31		13 45		
Chester	a			*12 48*					*13 18*								*13 47*			*14 18*		
Wrexham General	a																					
Llandudno Junction	a			*13 55*													*14 55*					
Llandudno	a			*14c12*													*15c10*					
Bangor (Gwynedd)	a			*14 18*													*15 12*					
Holyhead	a			*14 55*													*15 55*					
Wilmslow	a			*12 46*					*13 22*								*13 47*					
Manchester Airport ✈	a			*13e05*																		
Stockport	a		12 26	*12 58*					*13 37*	12 52		13 26					*13 58*		13 42		14 18	
Manchester Piccadilly [10] 🚊	a		12 40	*13 15*					*13 52*	13 06		13 40					*14 15*		13 59		14 30	
Hartford	a								12 50									13 43				
Warrington Bank Quay	a	12 13		12 26							13 18		13 26									14 16
	d	12 13		12 27							13 18		13 27									14 16
Runcorn	a							12 48	13 00								13 34	13 53		14 01		
Liverpool South Parkway [7] ✈	a								13 10									14 03				
Liverpool Lime Street [10]	a							13 09	13 20								13 56	14 13		14 23		
	d						12 31									13 31						
Manchester Airport ✈	d			*11f30*	12 00						*12f30*			13 00								*13f30*
Manchester Piccadilly [10] 🚊	d			*11f46*	12 16						*12f46*			13 16								*13f46*
Bolton	d	*11f40*		*12f05*	12 33						*13f05*			13 33								*14f05*
Wigan North Western	a	12 24		12 37			13 13				13 29		13 37			14 13						14 27
	d	12 24		12 38			13 14				13 29		13 38			14 14						14 27
Preston [8]	a	12 37		12 51	12 56		13 37				13 42		13 51	13 56		14 37						14 40
Blackpool North	a						14 07									15 07						
	d	*11 50*		*12 11*	*12 20*						*13 13*			*13 20*								*14 11*
Preston [8]	d	12 39		12 53	12 58						13 44		13 53	14 01	14 05							14 42
Lancaster [6]	a	12 53		13 08	13 14						13 58		14 08	14 16	14 21							14 56
	d	12 54		13 08	13 14						13 59		14 08	14 16	14 21							14 58
Barrow-in-Furness	a														15 24							
Oxenholme Lake District	a	13 07		13 22	13 28						14 12			14 30								
	d	13 07		13 24	13 28						14 12			14 31								
Windermere	a				*13 52*						*14 52*											
Penrith North Lakes	d	13 33			13 54						14 38		14 45	14 56								15 32
Carlisle [8]	a	13 52		14 01	14 10						14 53		15 00	15 11								15 47
	d	13 52		14 03	14 11						14 54		15 03	15 13								15 48
Lockerbie	d				14 30																	
Carstairs	a																					
Motherwell	a																					
Glasgow Central [15]	a	15 06		15 23							16 10			16 35								17 03
Haymarket	a												16s14									
Edinburgh [10]	a				15 35								16 22									
Perth	a												*18 28*									*18g44*
Dundee	a				*17 24*								*18 14*									*19g08*
Aberdeen	a				*18 46*								*19 30*									*20g29*
Inverness	a												*20 44*									

For general notes see front of timetable
For details of catering facilities see Directory of Train Operators

A From Reading (Table 51)
B From Southampton Central (Table 51)
C 🛒 to Glasgow Central
b Change at Stafford
c Change at Crewe and Llandudno Junction
e Change at Crewe and Wilmslow
f Change at Preston
g Via Glasgow Central and Glasgow Queen Street. Passengers make their own way from one station to the other

OVERNIGHT SLEEPERS. For Sleeper trains, operated by First ScotRail, please refer to Tables 400 - 404

Table 65

Sundays

London and West Midlands → North West England and Scotland

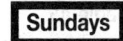

19 July to 6 September

Route Diagram - see first page of Table 65

	XC	VT	TP	NT	VT	XC	LM	VT		VT	VT	XC	VT	VT	TP	VT	NT		XC	LM	VT	VT	VT	VT
	1◇	1◇	1◇		1◇	1◇	1◇	1◇		1◇	1◇	1◇	1◇	1◇	1◇	1◇			1◇	1◇	1◇	1◇	1◇	1◇
	A											A							B					
	🛒	🍴	🛒		🍴	🛒		🍴		🍴	🍴	🛒	🍴	🍴		🍴			🛒		🍴	🍴	🍴	🍴
London Euston [15] ⊖ d					12 35			12 55		13 02	13 15		13 25			13 35					13 55	14 02	14 15	14 25
Gatwick Airport [10] ✈ d																								
Watford Junction d											13 07												14 06	
Milton Keynes Central d											13 48												14 48	
Northampton d																								
Rugby d																						14 16		
Nuneaton d																						14 30		
Tamworth Low Level d																						14 45		
Lichfield Trent Valley d																						14 51		
Coventry d	12 28	12 34					12 57					13 26		13 40								13b46		
Birmingham International ✈ d	12 40	12 52				13 05	13 08					13 38		13 51					14 07					
Birmingham New Street [12] d	13 01	13 20				13 31	13 35					14 01		14 20					14 31	14 35				
Wolverhampton [7] 🚌 d	13 19	13 37				13 49	13 52					14 19		14 37					14 49	14 52				
Penkridge d							14 03													15 03				
Stafford a	13 33						14 10			14 20		14 33								15 10		15 24		
d	13 34						14 10			14 22		14 34								15 10		15 25		
Stoke-on-Trent a	13 56					14 19		14 26			14 50	14 56							15 19		15 25		15 50	
Congleton a																								
Macclesfield a	14 14							14 42				15 14									15 42			
Crewe [10] a		14 09			14 12		14 30			14 43				15 09		15 12				15 30		15 43		
d		14 11			14 13		14 31			14 45				15 11		15 13				15 31		15 45		
Chester a					14 47					15 18						15 47						16 18		
Wrexham General a																								
Llandudno Junction a					15 55											16 55								
Llandudno a					16c14																			
Bangor (Gwynedd) a					16 18											17 12								
Holyhead a					16 55											17 55								
Wilmslow a		14 46			14 29					15 22				15 46		15 29								
Manchester Airport ✈ a					15 05																			
Stockport a	14 28	14 58			14 38			14 56			15 18	15 28		15 58		15 38					15 56		16 18	
Manchester Piccadilly [10] 🚌 a	14 40	15 15			14 51	15 00		15 09			15 30	15 40		16 15		15 51			16 00		16 09		16 30	
Hartford a							14 43													15 43				
Warrington Bank Quay a		14 28											15 16	15 28										16 16
d		14 29											15 16	15 29										16 16
Runcorn a							14 53			15 01										15 53		16 01		
Liverpool South Parkway [7] ✈ a							15 03													16 03				
Liverpool Lime Street [10] a							15 13			15 23										16 13		16 22		
d				14 31													15 31							
Manchester Airport ✈ d			14 00										14e30		15 00									15e30
Manchester Piccadilly [10] 🚌 d			14 16										14e46		15 16									15e46
Bolton d			14 33										15e05		15 33									16e05
Wigan North Western a		14 39		15 13									15 27	15 39			16 13							16 27
d		14 40		15 14									15 27	15 40			16 14							16 27
Preston [8] a		14 52	14 56	15 37									15 40	15 53	15 56		16 37							16 40
Blackpool North a				16 07													17 07							
d		14 20											14 50	15 20										16 11
Preston [8] d		14 55	15 00										15 42	15 55	16 00									16 42
Lancaster [6] a		15 10	15 16										15 56	16 10	16 16									16 56
d		15 11	15 16										15 58	16 10	16 16									16 57
Barrow-in-Furness a															17 19									18 09
Oxenholme Lake District a		15 24	15 30										16 10											
d		15 25	15 30										16 11											
Windermere a			15 54										16 52											
Penrith North Lakes d			15 54											16 47										17 32
Carlisle [8] a		16 03	16 11										16 48	17 02										17 47
d		16 05	16 13										16 49	17 04										17 48
Lockerbie d			16 31																					
Carstairs a																								
Motherwell a																								
Glasgow Central [15] a		17 17											18 03											19 00
Haymarket a			17s30											18s13										
Edinburgh [10] a			17 37											18 22										
Perth a		19f15																						20f46
Dundee a			19 28											19 57										21f10
Aberdeen a			20 47											21 17										22f24
Inverness a		21f34																						

For general notes see front of timetable
For details of catering facilities see Directory of Train Operators

A From Bournemouth (Table 51)
B From Paignton (Table 51)
b Change at Nuneaton and Stafford
c Change at Crewe and Llandudno Junction
e Change at Preston
f Via Glasgow Central and Glasgow Queen Street. Passengers make their own way from one station to the other

OVERNIGHT SLEEPERS. For Sleeper trains, operated by First ScotRail, please refer to Tables 400 - 404

Sundays

London and West Midlands → North West England and Scotland

19 July to 6 September

Route Diagram - see first page of Table 65

		XC	VT	TP		VT	NT	XC	LM	VT	VT	VT	VT	VT	XC	VT	TP		VT	NT	XC	LM
		1◇	1◇	1◇		1◇		1◇	1◇	1◇	1◇	1◇	1◇	1◇	1◇	1◇	1◇		1◇		1◇	1◇
		A		B				C							A		D				E	
		trolley	buffet	trolley		buffet		trolley		buffet	buffet	buffet	buffet	buffet	trolley	buffet	trolley		buffet		trolley	
London Euston 15 ⊖	d					14 35				14 55	15 02	15 05	15 15	15 25					15 35			
Gatwick Airport 10 ✈	d																					
Watford Junction	d											14 51	15 06									
Milton Keynes Central	d											15u38	15 48									
Northampton	d																					
Rugby	d																					
Nuneaton	d																					
Tamworth Low Level	d																					
Lichfield Trent Valley	d																					
Coventry	d	14 26	14 40												15 26	15 40						
Birmingham International ✈	d	14 38	14 51					15 07							15 38	15 51					16 07	
Birmingham New Street 12	d	15 01	15 20					15 31	15 35						16 01	16 20					16 31	16 35
Wolverhampton 7	d	15 19	15 37					15 49	15 52						16 19	16u37					16 49	16 52
Penkridge	d								16 03													17 03
Stafford	a	15 33							16 10		16 20				16 35							17 10
	d	15 34							16 10		16 21				16 36							17 10
Stoke-on-Trent	a	15 56						16 19		16 24			16 50		16 56						17 19	
Congleton	a																					
Macclesfield	a	16 14								16 42					17 14							
Crewe 10	a		16 09			16 12			16 32			16 54				17 09			17 12			17 30
	d		16 11			16 13			16 34			16 57				17 11			17 13			17 31
Chester	a					16 47						17 19							17 48			
Wrexham General	a																					
Llandudno Junction	a					17 55						18 25										
Llandudno	a											18b40										
Bangor (Gwynedd)	a					18 18						18 42										
Holyhead	a					18 55						19 25										
Wilmslow	a		16 49			16 29			17 22							17 46			17 29			
Manchester Airport ✈	a		17c05			17 05																
Stockport	a	16 28	16 58			16 38			17 37	16 56			17 18		17 30	17 58			17 38			
Manchester Piccadilly 10	a	16 40	17 15			16 51		17 00		17 09			17 30		17 40	18 15			17 51		18 00	
Hartford	a								16 45													17 43
Warrington Bank Quay	a		16 28											17 16		17 28						
	d		16 29											17 16		17 29						
Runcorn	a								16 55		16 58											17 53
Liverpool South Parkway 7 ✈	a								17 05													18 03
Liverpool Lime Street 10	a								17 16		17 22											18 13
	d						16 31													17 31		
Manchester Airport ✈	d			16 00										16e30			17 00					
Manchester Piccadilly 10	d			16 16										16e46			17 16					
Bolton	d			16 33										17e05			17 33					
Wigan North Western	a		16 39				17 13							17 27		17 39				18 13		
	d		16 40				17 14							17 27		17 40				18 14		
Preston 8	a		16 53	16 56			17 37							17 40		17 53	17 56			18 37		
Blackpool North	a						18 07													19 07		
	d		16 20											17 11		17 20						
Preston 8	d		16 55	17 02	17 06									17 42		17 55	18 02	18 06				
Lancaster 6	a		17 10	17 18	17 22									17 56		18 10	18 18	18 22				
	d		17 10	17 18	17 22									17 57		18 10	18 18	18 22				
Barrow-in-Furness	a																	19 26				
Oxenholme Lake District	a		17 24	17 32	17 39									18 10		18 24	18 32					
	d		17 25	17 32	17 39									18 10		18 25	18 32					
Windermere	a				18 02												18 56					
Penrith North Lakes	d			17 57												18 51	18 56					
Carlisle 8	a		18 03	18 13										18 48		19 06	19 13					
	d		18 05	18 15										18 49		19 06	19 15					
Lockerbie	d																19 33					
Carstairs	a																					
Motherwell	a																20s24					
Glasgow Central 15	a		19 17											20 03			20 45					
Haymarket	a																					
Edinburgh 10	a			19 37												20 24						
Perth	a																22f46					
Dundee	a															22 17	23f09					
Aberdeen	a															23 33	00f25					
Inverness	a																					

For general notes see front of timetable
For details of catering facilities see Directory of Train Operators

A From Bournemouth (Table 51)
B trolley to Edinburgh
C From Plymouth (Table 51)
D trolley to Glasgow Central
E From Paignton (Table 51)
b Change at Chester and Llandudno Junction
c Change at Crewe and Wilmslow
e Change at Preston
f Via Glasgow Central and Glasgow Queen Street. Passengers make their own way from one station to the other

OVERNIGHT SLEEPERS. For Sleeper trains, operated by First ScotRail, please refer to Tables 400 - 404

Table 65

Sundays

London and West Midlands → North West England and Scotland

19 July to 6 September

Route Diagram - see first page of Table 65

		VT	VT	VT	SR	VT	VT	XC	VT		TP	NT	VT	XC	LM	VT	VT	VT		VT	VT	TP	NT	XC	VT
		1 ◇	1 ◇	1 ◇		1 ◇	1 ◇	1 ◇	1 ◇		1 ◇		1 ◇	1 ◇	1 ◇	1 ◇	1 ◇	1 ◇		1 ◇	1 ◇	1 ◇		1 ◇	1 ◇
								A						B										A	
London Euston 15 ⊖	d	15 55	16 02	16 05		16 15	16 25						16 35			16 55	17 02	17 05		17 15	17 25				17 35
Gatwick Airport 10	d																								
Watford Junction	d			16 06														16 51		17 06					
Milton Keynes Central	d			16u39		16 48												17u38		17 48					
Northampton	d																								
Rugby	d		16 16																						
Nuneaton	d		16 30															18 10							
Tamworth Low Level	d		16 45																						
Lichfield Trent Valley	d		16 51																						
Coventry	d		15b46					16 26	16 40															17 26	
Birmingham International	d							16 38	16 51					17 07										17 38	
Birmingham New Street 12	d							17 01	17 20					17 31	17 35									18 01	
Wolverhampton 7	d							17 19	17u37					17 49	17 52									18 19	
Penkridge	d														18 03										
Stafford	a		17 24					17 35							18 10		18 24							18 37	
	d		17 25					17 36							18 10		18 25							18 39	
Stoke-on-Trent	a	17 25				17 50		17 56						18 19		18 25				18 50				18 58	
Congleton	a																								
Macclesfield	a	17 42						18 14								18 42								19 16	
Crewe 10	a			17 54					18 09				18 12		18 30			18 53							19 12
	d			17 57					18 11				18 13		18 31			18 56							19 13
Chester	a			18 19									18 47					19 14							19 48
Wrexham General	a																								
Llandudno Junction	a			19 23									19 48					20 07							
Llandudno	a																								
Bangor (Gwynedd)	a			19 46									20 11					20 29							
Holyhead	a			20 20									20 47					21 02							
Wilmslow	a								18 46				18 29		19 22										19 29
Manchester Airport	a												19 05												
Stockport	a	17 56				18 18		18 28	18 58				18 38			18 56				19 18				19 28	19 38
Manchester Piccadilly 10	a	18 09				18 30		18 40	19 15				18 51	19 00		19 09				19 30				19 40	19 51
Hartford	a														18 43										
Warrington Bank Quay	a						18 16		18 28												19 16				
	d						18 17		18 29												19 16				
Runcorn	a		17 56												18 53		18 56								
Liverpool South Parkway 7	a														19 03										
Liverpool Lime Street 10	a		18 19												19 13		19 19								
	d											18 31											19 31		
Manchester Airport	d						17c30				18 00										18c30	19 00			
Manchester Piccadilly 10	d						17c46				18 16										18c46	19 16			
Bolton	d						18c05				18 33										19c05	19 33			
Wigan North Western	a						18 27		18 39			19 13									19 27		20 13		
	d						18 28		18 40			19 14									19 27		20 14		
Preston 8	a						18 40		18 53		18 56	19 37									19 40	19 56	20 37		
Blackpool North	a										19 38	20 07										20 39	21 07		
	d						18 11		18 20												18 50	19 20			
Preston 8	d						18 42		18 55		19 00										19 42	20 00			
Lancaster 6	a						18 56		19 10		19 15										19 56	20 16			
	d						18 58		19 10		19 16										19 57	20 16			
Barrow-in-Furness	a																					21 19			
Oxenholme Lake District	a						19 10		19 24		19 30										20 10				
	d						19 11		19 26		19 30										20 10				
Windermere	a								19 45												20 52				
Penrith North Lakes	d						19 36				19 54										20 36				
Carlisle 8	a						19 51		20 03		20 11										20 51				
	d				19 35		19 53		20 05		20 13										20 52				
Lockerbie	d										20 31														
Carstairs	a																								
Motherwell	a																								
Glasgow Central 15	a				21 55		21 08		21 17												22 07				
Haymarket	a										21s30														
Edinburgh 10	a										21 37														
Perth	a										00 07										00e56				
Dundee	a										23 56														
Aberdeen	a																								
Inverness	a																								

For general notes see front of timetable
For details of catering facilities see Directory of Train Operators

- **A** From Bournemouth (Table 51)
- **B** From Bristol Temple Meads (Table 51)
- **b** Change at Nuneaton and Stafford
- **c** Change at Preston
- **e** Via Glasgow Central and Glasgow Queen Street. Passengers make their own way from one station to the other

OVERNIGHT SLEEPERS. For Sleeper trains, operated by First ScotRail, please refer to Tables 400 - 404

Sundays

London and West Midlands → North West England and Scotland

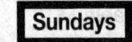

19 July to 6 September

Route Diagram - see first page of Table 65

	XC	LM	VT	VT	VT	VT	VT	XC	VT	VT	NT	XC	LM	VT	VT	VT	VT	VT	XC	VT	VT
	A							B	R			C							B		
London Euston 15 d			17 55	18 02	18 05	18 15	18 25			18 35				18 55	19 02	19 05	19 15	19 25			19 35
Gatwick Airport 10 d																					
Watford Junction d					17 51	18 06										18 51	19 06				
Milton Keynes Central d					18u38	18 48										19u38	19 48				
Northampton d																					
Rugby d				18 16											18 16						
Nuneaton d				18 30											20 01						
Tamworth Low Level d				18 45																	
Lichfield Trent Valley d				18 51																	
Coventry d	17 40							18 26	18 40				19 00						19 26	19 40	
Birmingham International d	18 07							18 38	18 51			19 07	19 11						19 38	19 51	
Birmingham New Street 12 d	18 31	18 35						19 01	19 20			19 31	19 35						20 01	20 20	
Wolverhampton 7 d	18 49	18 52						19 19	19 37			19 49	19 52						20 19	20 38	
Penkridge d		19 03											20 03								
Stafford a		19 10		19 24				19 37					20 10		20 25				20 37	20 51	
d		19 10		19 25				19 38					20 10		20 30				20 38	20 52	
Stoke-on-Trent a	19 19		19 25			19 50		19 56				20 21		20 25			20 50		20 57		
Congleton a																					
Macclesfield a			19 42					20 14						20 42					21 15		
Crewe 10 a		19 30			19 54				20 09	20 12			20 30		20 48	20 55				21 10	21 13
d		19 31			19 57				20 11	20 13			20 31		20 50	20 58					21 14
Chester a					20 16					20 48						21 17					21 46
Wrexham General a																					
Llandudno Junction a					21 11											22 08					22 53
Llandudno a																					
Bangor (Gwynedd) a					21 28											22 25					23 10
Holyhead a					22 02											22 59					23 52
Wilmslow a									20 45	20 29			21 22							21 46	21 30
Manchester Airport a										21 05											
Stockport a			19 56			20 18		20 28	20 57	20 38				20 56			21 18		21 28	21 58	21 39
Manchester Piccadilly 10 a	20 00		20 09			20 30		20 40	21 14	20 51		21 00		21 09			21 30		21 40	22 15	21 52
Hartford a		19 43											20 43								
Warrington Bank Quay a							20 16		20 28									21 16			
d							20 16		20 29									21 16			
Runcorn a		19 53		19 57									20 53		21 06						
Liverpool South Parkway 7 a		20 03											21 03								
Liverpool Lime Street 10 a		20 13		20 19									21 13		21 27						
d											20 31										
Manchester Airport d							19b30											20b30			
Manchester Piccadilly 10 d							19b46											20b46			
Bolton d							20b05											21b05			
Wigan North Western a							20 27		20 39		21 13							21 27			
d							20 27		20 40		21 14							21 27			
Preston 8 a							20 40		20 53		21 37							21 40			
Blackpool North a							21 16		21 38		22 07							22 38			
d							20 11		20 20									20 50			
Preston 8 d							20 42		20 55									21 42			
Lancaster 6 a							20 56		21 10									21 56			
d							20 57		21 10									21 57			
Barrow-in-Furness a																		23 10			
Oxenholme Lake District a							21 10		21 24									22 10			
d							21 11		21 26									22 11			
Windermere a																					
Penrith North Lakes d							21 36											22 36			
Carlisle 8 a							21 51		22 03									22 51			
d							21 52		22 05									22 53			
Lockerbie d									22 23												
Carstairs a																					
Motherwell a							22s48		23s13												
Glasgow Central 15 a							23 08		23 35									00 02			
Haymarket a																					
Edinburgh 10 a																					
Perth a																					
Dundee a																					
Aberdeen a																					
Inverness a																					

For general notes see front of timetable
For details of catering facilities see Directory of Train Operators

A From Penzance (Table 135)
B From Bournemouth (Table 51)
C From Bristol Temple Meads (Table 51)
b Change at Preston

OVERNIGHT SLEEPERS. For Sleeper trains, operated by First ScotRail, please refer to Tables 400 - 404

Table 65

Sundays

London and West Midlands → North West England and Scotland

19 July to 6 September

Route Diagram - see first page of Table 65

		XC	NT	VT	VT	VT	VT	XC	VT		VT	VT	LM	VT	AW	XC	SR	VT	VT	AW	VT	SR		
		1 ◇		1 ◇	1 ◇	1 ◇	1 ◇	1 ◇	1 ◇		1 ◇	1 ◇	1	1 ◇	◇	1 ◇	R	1 ◇	1 ◇	◇	1 ◇	R		
		A						B								B	C							
				☕	☕	☕	☕		☕		☕	☕		☕			☕	☕	☕		☕	☕		
London Euston 15 ⊖	d			19 55	20 02	20 05	20 15		20 25			20 35		20 50			20 55	21 20	21 24		21 50	23 27		
Gatwick Airport 10 ✈	d																							
Watford Junction	d					19 51	20 06							20 51			21u17		21 22		21 47	23u47		
Milton Keynes Central	d					20 38	20 48							21 39					22 13		22 38			
Northampton	d													20 58							22 53			
Rugby	d				20 16									22 00							23 19			
Nuneaton	d				21 01	20 30												22 54			23 30			
Tamworth Low Level	d					20 45			21 32															
Lichfield Trent Valley	d					20 51			21 39															
Coventry	d	19 54			19b46			20 26			20 40		20 54			21 26		21b35		22 23				
Birmingham International ✈	d	20 08						20 38			20 51		21 08		21 08	21 38				22 40				
Birmingham New Street 12	d	20 31						21 01			21 20		21 35		21 24	22 01				22 55				
Wolverhampton 7	d	20 49						21 19			21 38		21 53		21 43	22 19				23 13				
Penkridge	d												22 03											
Stafford	a					21 32		21 37			21 58	22 03	22 13			22 37		23 21		23 31	23s54			
	d					21 33		21 38			21 59	22 04	22 14			22 38		23 22		23 32				
Stoke-on-Trent	a	21 19		21 25			21 50	21 56								22 55			23 33					
Congleton	a																							
Macclesfield	a			21 42				22 14								23 13			23 49					
Crewe 10	a				21 44	21 53			22 10		22 17	22 22	22 36	22 49	23 02			23 43		23 55	00s16			
	d				21 46	21 55			22 13		22 18	22 23		22 51	23 05		23u42	23 47		00 10				
Chester	a				22 18						22 50				23 26					00 31				
Wrexham General	a																							
Llandudno Junction	a										23 50									01 24				
Llandudno	a																							
Bangor (Gwynedd)	a										00 12									01 40				
Holyhead	a										00 49									02 15				
Wilmslow	a											22 38	23 22											
Manchester Airport ✈	a											23 05												
Stockport	a			21 56			22 18	22 28				22 48				23 27			00 05		00s46			
Manchester Piccadilly 10	a	22 00		22 09			22 30	22 40				23 00				23 41			00 17		00 58			
Hartford	a																							
Warrington Bank Quay	a								22 29		22 36			23 08										
	d								22 30		22 36			23 08										
Runcorn	a				22 02	22 11												00 07						
Liverpool South Parkway 7 ✈	a																							
Liverpool Lime Street 10	a				22 23	22 32												00 34						
	d		21 31											22 31										
Manchester Airport ✈	d																							
Manchester Piccadilly 10	d																							
Bolton	d																							
Wigan North Western	a		22 13						22 40		22 47			23 19										
	d		22 14						22 41		22 47			23 19										
Preston 8	a		22 37						22 58		23 07			23 39										
Blackpool North	a		23 07								00 04			00 14										
	d																							
Preston 8	d																00u30							
Lancaster 6	a																							
	d																							
Barrow-in-Furness	a																							
Oxenholme Lake District	a																							
	d																							
Windermere	a																							
Penrith North Lakes	d																							
Carlisle 8	a																					05s04		
	d																							
Lockerbie	d																							
Carstairs	a																					06s24		
Motherwell	a																					07s01		
Glasgow Central 15	a																					07 18		
Haymarket	a																							
Edinburgh 10	a																					07 20		
Perth	a																05s39							
Dundee	a																06s08							
Aberdeen	a																07 35							
Inverness	a																08 30							

For general notes see front of timetable
For details of catering facilities see Directory of Train Operators

A From Bristol Temple Meads (Table 51)
B From Bournemouth (Table 51)
C Also conveys portion to Fort William (Table 227)

b Change at Nuneaton

OVERNIGHT SLEEPERS. For Sleeper trains, operated by First ScotRail, please refer to Tables 400 - 404

Table 65

Sundays

London and West Midlands → North West England and Scotland

13 September to 1 November

Route Diagram - see first page of Table 65

		NT	VT	NT	XC	TP	VT	VT	VT	NT	VT	LM	VT	VT	XC	VT	TP	NT	VT	LM	VT	VT	XC
			1 ◇		1 ◇	1 ◇	1 ◇	1 ◇	1 ◇		1 ◇	1 ◇	1 ◇	1 ◇	1 ◇	1 ◇	1 ◇		1 ◇	1 ◇	1 ◇	1 ◇	1 ◇
																							A
London Euston 15	d							08 10			08 15		08 20	08 45					09 15		09 20	09 45	
Gatwick Airport 10	d																						
Watford Junction	d							08 09													09 12	09 43	
Milton Keynes Central	d							08 56					09 05	09 33							10 07	10 33	
Northampton	d																					10 00	
Rugby	d													09 56								10 57	
Nuneaton	d										09 30								10 38				
Tamworth Low Level	d																						
Lichfield Trent Valley	d																						
Coventry	d						08 37								09 07					10 04			10 28
Birmingham International	d						08 55					09 03			09 25	09 51				10 13			10 40
Birmingham New Street 12	d		08 45		09 01		09 20					09 41			10 00	10 15				10 42			11 01
Wolverhampton 7	d		09 04		09 19		09 37					09 57			10 18	10 32				10 59			11 19
Penkridge	d											10 08								11 10			
Stafford	a		09 17		09 31						09 57	10 14			10 30				11 05	11 17			11 31
	d		09 19		09 32						09 58	10 14			10 31				11 05	11 17			11 32
Stoke-on-Trent	a												10 18		10 51						11 17		11 51
Congleton	a																						
Macclesfield	a												10 36		11 09						11 37		12 09
Crewe 10	a		09 43		09 55		10 12	10 18			10 22	10 38		10 52		11 07			11 30	11 37		11 54	
	d		09 45		09 58		10 14	10 20	10 21		10 31	10 39		10 54		11 09			11 32	11 38		11 56	
Chester	a		10 25								11 00	11 26				11 48				12 18			
Wrexham General	a																						
Llandudno Junction	a										11 54					12 53							
Llandudno	a															13b20							
Bangor (Gwynedd)	a										12 10					13 10							
Holyhead	a										12 43					13 45							
Wilmslow	a				10 13			10 46				11 22				11 40							
Manchester Airport	a							11c04															
Stockport	a				10 23		10 58	10 41					10 51		11 21						11 52		12 21
Manchester Piccadilly 10	a				10 37		11 15	10 54					11 04		11 40						12 06		12 40
Hartford	a											10 51								11 50			
Warrington Bank Quay	a		10 01				10 31		10 37					11 13		11 26						12 13	
	d		10 02				10 32		10 37					11 13		11 27						12 13	
Runcorn	a										10 47	11 01							11 48	12 00			
Liverpool South Parkway 7	a											11 11								12 10			
Liverpool Lime Street 10	a										11 08	11 21							12 09	12 20			
	d	08 31		09 31						10 31								11 31					
Manchester Airport	d					09 30										10e25	10 58						
Manchester Piccadilly 10	d					09 46										10e43	11 16						
Bolton	d					10 05										11e05	11 33					11e40	
Wigan North Western	a	09 13	10 12	10 13			10 42		10 48	11 13				11 24		11 37		12 13				12 24	
	d	09 14	10 13	10 16			10 43		10 48	11 14				11 24		11 38		12 14				12 24	
Preston 8	a	09 37	10 30	10 41			10 56		11 04	11 37				11 37		11 51	11 56	12 37				12 37	
Blackpool North	a	10 06		11 09					11 39	12 07								13 07					
	d					10 11			10 20							11 13	11 20					11 50	
Preston 8	d					10 45			11 06					11 38		11 53	11 58					12 39	
Lancaster 6	a					11 00			11 23					11 52		12 08	12 14					12 53	
	d					11 01								11 53		12 08	12 14					12 54	
Barrow-in-Furness	a																						
Oxenholme Lake District	a					11 17								12 06		12 22	12 28					13 07	
	d					11 18								12 06		12 24	12 28					13 07	
Windermere	a					11 40											12 52						
Penrith North Lakes	d													12 32			12 54					13 33	
Carlisle 8	a													12 47		13 01	13 09					13 52	
	d													12 47		13 03	13 11					13 52	
Lockerbie	d																13 30						
Carstairs	a																						
Motherwell	a																						
Glasgow Central 15	a													13 59			14 36					15 06	
Haymarket	a															14s13							
Edinburgh 10	a															14 22							
Perth	a																16f45						
Dundee	a															16 48	17f09						
Aberdeen	a																18f23						
Inverness	a																						

For general notes see front of timetable
For details of catering facilities see Directory of Train Operators

A From Reading (Table 51)
b Change at Crewe and Llandudno Junction. By bus from Llandudno Junction
c Change at Crewe and Wilmslow
e Change at Preston
f Via Glasgow Central and Glasgow Queen Street. Passengers make their own way from one station to the other

OVERNIGHT SLEEPERS. For Sleeper trains, operated by First ScotRail, please refer to Tables 400 - 404

Table 65

Sundays

London and West Midlands → North West England and Scotland

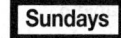

13 September to 1 November

Route Diagram - see first page of Table 65

		VT 1◇	TP 1◇	LM 1	VT 1◇	VT 1◇	LM 1◇	NT	VT 1◇	NT	XC 1◇ A	VT 1◇	TP 1◇ B		NT	VT 1◇	VT 1◇	LM 1◇	VT 1◇	VT 1◇	VT 1◇	XC 1◇ C	VT 1◇
London Euston 15 ⊖	d				10 15	10 20			10 45							11 15	11 20		12 02	12 15	12 25		
Gatwick Airport 10 ✈	d																						
Watford Junction	d					10 12			10 42								11 12			12 01			
Milton Keynes Central	d					11 07			11 32							12 04	12 07			12 48			
Northampton	d								11 00														
Rugby	d								11 56									11b58					
Nuneaton	d				11 35													12b11					
Tamworth Low Level	d																	12b26					
Lichfield Trent Valley	d																	12b32					
Coventry	d	10 34									11 28	11 34										12 28	12 34
Birmingham International ✈	d	10 52									11 40	11 52						12 08				12 40	12 52
Birmingham New Street 12	d	11 20					11 42				12 01	12 20						12 35				13 01	13 20
Wolverhampton 7	d	11 37					11 59				12 20	12 36						12 52				13 19	13 37
Penkridge	d						12 10											13 03					
Stafford	a				12 00		12 16				12 33					12 54		13 10	13 24			13 33	
	d			11 41	12 01		12 16				12 34					12 55		13 10	13 25			13 34	
Stoke-on-Trent	a			11 59		12 17					12 52						13 09			13 50		13 56	
Congleton	a																						
Macclesfield	a					12 37					13 10						13 27					14 14	
Crewe 10	a	12 07		12 24	12 30		12 37		12 49			13 07				13 16		13 30	13 43				14 09
	d	12 09			12 32		12 38		12 51			13 09				13 18		13 31	13 45				14 11
Chester	a	12 48					13 15									13 47			14 18				
Wrexham General	a																						
Llandudno Junction	a	13 55														14 55							
Llandudno	a																						
Bangor (Gwynedd)	a	14 18														15 12							
Holyhead	a	14 55														15 55							
Wilmslow	a	12 46					13 22									13 47							14 46
Manchester Airport ✈	a	13c05																					
Stockport	a	12 58				12 52					13 28					13 58	13 41			14 18		14 28	14 58
Manchester Piccadilly 10	a	13 15				13 06					13 40					14 15	13 59			14 30		14 40	15 15
Hartford	a						12 50											13 43					
Warrington Bank Quay	a	12 26							13 08			13 26									14 16		14 28
	d	12 27							13 08			13 27									14 16		14 29
Runcorn	a				12 48		13 00									13 34		13 53	14 01				
Liverpool South Parkway 7 ✈	a						13 10											14 03					
Liverpool Lime Street 10	a				13 09		13 20									13 56		14 13	14 23				
	d							12 31							13 31								
Manchester Airport ✈	d	11e30	11 58									12e30	12 58								13e30		
Manchester Piccadilly 10	d	11e46	12 16									12e46	13 16								13e46		
Bolton	d	12e05	12 33						12e40			13e05	13 33								14e05		
Wigan North Western	a	12 37						13 13	13 19	←		13 37			14 13						14 27		14 39
	d	12 38						13 14	13 19	13 14		13 38			14 14						14 27		14 40
Preston 8	a	12 51	12 56					→	13 35	13 37		13 51	13 56		14 37						14 40		14 52
Blackpool North	a		13 38							14 07					15 07								
	d	12 11	12 20						12 50			13 13	13 20								14 11		14 20
Preston 8	d	12 53	12 58						13 37			13 53	14 01	14 05							14 42		14 55
Lancaster 6	a	13 08	13 14						13 51			14 08	14 16	14 21							14 56		15 10
	d	13 08	13 14						13 52			14 08	14 16	14 21							14 58		15 11
Barrow-in-Furness	a													15 24									
Oxenholme Lake District	a	13 22	13 28						14 05				14 30										15 24
	d	13 24	13 28						14 05				14 31										15 25
Windermere	a		13 52						14 52														
Penrith North Lakes	d		13 54						14 31			14 45	14 56								15 32		
Carlisle 8	a	14 01	14 10						14 46			15 00	15 11								15 47		16 03
	d	14 03	14 11						14 47			15 03	15 13								15 48		16 05
Lockerbie	d		14 30																				
Carstairs	a																						
Motherwell	a																						
Glasgow Central 15	a	15 23							16 10				16 35								17 03		17 17
Haymarket	a											16s14											
Edinburgh 10	a		15 35									16 22											
Perth	a											18 28									18f44		19f15
Dundee	a		17 24									18 14									19f08		
Aberdeen	a		18 46									19 30									20f29		
Inverness	a											20 44											21f34

For general notes see front of timetable
For details of catering facilities see Directory of Train Operators

- **A** From Southampton Central (Table 51)
- **B** Trolley service to Glasgow Central
- **C** From Bournemouth (Table 51)
- **b** Change at Stafford
- **c** Change at Crewe and Wilmslow
- **e** Change at Preston
- **f** Via Glasgow Central and Glasgow Queen Street. Passengers make their own way from one station to the other

OVERNIGHT SLEEPERS. For Sleeper trains, operated by First ScotRail, please refer to Tables 400 - 404

Table 65

Sundays

London and West Midlands → North West England and Scotland

13 September to 1 November

Route Diagram - see first page of Table 65

		TP	NT	VT	XC	LM	VT	VT	VT	VT	XC	VT	TP	VT	NT	XC	LM	VT	VT	VT	VT	XC
		1◇		1◇	1◇	1◇	1◇	1◇	1◇	1◇	1◇	1◇	1◇	1◇		1◇	1◇	1◇	1◇	1◇	1◇	1◇
											A					B						A
London Euston 15 ⊖	d			12 35			12 55	13 02	13 15	13 25				13 35				13 55	14 02	14 15	14 25	
Gatwick Airport 10 ✈	d																					
Watford Junction	d								13 07											14 06		
Milton Keynes Central	d								13 48											14 48		
Northampton	d																					
Rugby	d																		14 16			
Nuneaton	d																		14 30			
Tamworth Low Level	d																		14 45			
Lichfield Trent Valley	d																		14 51			
Coventry	d					12 57					13 26	13 40							13b46			14 26
Birmingham International ✈	d				13 05	13 08					13 38	13 51				14 07						14 38
Birmingham New Street 12	d				13 31	13 35					14 01	14 20				14 31	14 35					15 01
Wolverhampton 7	d				13 49	13 52					14 19	14 37				14 49	14 52					15 19
Penkridge	d					14 03											15 03					
Stafford	a					14 10		14 20			14 33						15 10		15 24			15 33
	d					14 10		14 22			14 34						15 10		15 25			15 34
Stoke-on-Trent	a				14 19		14 26		14 50		14 56					15 19		15 25		15 50		15 56
Congleton	a																					
Macclesfield	a						14 42				15 14							15 42				16 14
Crewe 10	a			14 12		14 30		14 43				15 09		15 12			15 30		15 43			
	d			14 13		14 31		14 45				15 11		15 13			15 31		15 45			
Chester	a			14 47				15 18						15 47								
Wrexham General	a																					
Llandudno Junction	a			15 55										16 55								
Llandudno	a			16c30																		
Bangor (Gwynedd)	a			16 18										17 12								
Holyhead	a			16 54										17 55								
Wilmslow	a			14 29				15 22				15 46		15 29								
Manchester Airport ✈	a			15 05																		
Stockport	a			14 38			14 56		15 18		15 28	15 58		15 38				15 56		16 18		16 28
Manchester Piccadilly 10	a			14 51	15 00		15 09		15 30		15 40	16 15		15 51		16 00		16 09		16 30		16 40
Hartford	a					14 43											15 43					
Warrington Bank Quay	a									15 16		15 28									16 16	
	d									15 16		15 29									16 16	
Runcorn	a					14 53		15 01									15 53		16 01			
Liverpool South Parkway 7 ✈	a					15 03											16 03					
Liverpool Lime Street 10	a					15 13		15 23									16 13		16 22			
	d		14 31												15 31							
Manchester Airport ✈	d	13 58								14e30			14 58								15e30	
Manchester Piccadilly 10	d	14 16								14e46			15 16								15e46	
Bolton	d	14 33								15e05			15 33								16e05	
Wigan North Western	a		15 13							15 27		15 39			16 13						16 27	
	d		15 14							15 27		15 40			16 14						16 27	
Preston 8	a	14 56	15 37							15 40		15 53	15 56		16 37						16 40	
Blackpool North	a		16 07												17 07							
	d									14 50		15 20									16 11	
Preston 8	d	15 00								15 42		15 55	16 00								16 42	
Lancaster 6	a	15 16								15 56		16 10	16 16								16 56	
	d	15 16								15 58		16 10	16 16								16 57	
Barrow-in-Furness	a												17 19								18 09	
Oxenholme Lake District	a	15 30								16 10												
	d	15 30								16 11												
Windermere	a	15 54								16 52												
Penrith North Lakes	d	15 54										16 47									17 32	
Carlisle 8	a	16 11								16 48		17 02									17 47	
	d	16 13								16 49		17 04									17 48	
Lockerbie	d	16 31																				
Carstairs	a																					
Motherwell	a																					
Glasgow Central 15	a									18 03											19 00	
Haymarket	a	17s30										18s13										
Edinburgh 10	a	17 37										18 22										
Perth	a																				20f46	
Dundee	a	19 28										19 57									21f10	
Aberdeen	a	20 47										21 17									22f24	
Inverness	a																					

For general notes see front of timetable
For details of catering facilities see Directory of Train Operators

A From Bournemouth (Table 51)
B From Paignton (Table 51)
b Change at Nuneaton and Stafford
c Change at Crewe and Llandudno Junction. By bus from Llandudno Junction
e Change at Preston
f Via Glasgow Central and Glasgow Queen Street. Passengers make their own way from one station to the other

OVERNIGHT SLEEPERS. For Sleeper trains, operated by First ScotRail, please refer to Tables 400 - 404

Table 65

Sundays

London and West Midlands → North West England and Scotland

13 September to 1 November

Route Diagram - see first page of Table 65

		VT	TP	NT	VT	XC	LM	VT	VT	VT	VT	VT	XC	VT	VT	TP		NT	XC	LM	VT	VT	VT
		1 ◇	1 ◇		1 ◇	1 ◇ A	1 ◇	1 ◇	1 ◇	1 ◇	1 ◇	1 ◇	1 ◇ B	1 ◇	1 ◇	1 ◇ C			1 ◇ D	1 ◇	1 ◇	1 ◇	1 ◇
London Euston 15 ⊖	d				14 35			14 55	15 02	15 05	15 15	15 25			15 35						15 55	16 02	16 05
Gatwick Airport 10 ✈	d																						
Watford Junction	d									14 51	15 06												16 06
Milton Keynes Central	d									15u38	15 48												16u39
Northampton	d																						
Rugby	d																					16 16	
Nuneaton	d																					16 30	
Tamworth Low Level	d																					16 45	
Lichfield Trent Valley	d																					16 51	
Coventry	d	14 40											15 26	15 40								15b46	
Birmingham International ✈	d	14 51				15 07							15 38	15 51					16 07				
Birmingham New Street 12	d	15 20				15 31	15 35						16 01	16 20					16 31	16 35			
Wolverhampton 7	d	15 37				15 49	15 52						16 19	16u37					16 49	16 52			
Penkridge	d						16 03													17 03			
Stafford	a						16 10		16 20				16 35							17 10		17 24	
	d						16 10		16 21				16 36							17 10		17 25	
Stoke-on-Trent	a					16 19		16 24			16 50		16 56						17 19		17 25		
Congleton	a																						
Macclesfield	a							16 42					17 14								17 42		
Crewe 10	a	16 09			16 12		16 32			16 54				17 09	17 12					17 30			17 54
	d	16 11			16 13		16 34			16 57				17 11	17 13					17 31			17 57
Chester	a				16 47					17 19					17 47								18 19
Wrexham General	a																						
Llandudno Junction	a				17 55										18 55								19 23
Llandudno	a														19c20								
Bangor (Gwynedd)	a				18 18										19 12								19 46
Holyhead	a				18 55										19 55								20 20
Wilmslow	a	16 49			16 29		17 22							17 46	17 29								
Manchester Airport ✈	a				17 05																		
Stockport	a	16 58			16 38			16 56			17 18		17 30	17 58	17 38						17 56		
Manchester Piccadilly 10	a	17 15			16 51	17 00		17 09			17 30		17 40	18 15	17 51				18 00		18 09		
Hartford	a						16 45													17 43			
Warrington Bank Quay	a	16 28										17 16		17 28									
	d	16 29										17 16		17 29									
Runcorn	a						16 55		16 58											17 53		17 56	
Liverpool South Parkway 7 ✈	a						17 05													18 03			
Liverpool Lime Street 10	a						17 16		17 22											18 13		18 19	
	d			16 31														17 31					
Manchester Airport ✈	d		15 58									16e30				16 58							
Manchester Piccadilly 10	d		16 16									16e46				17 16							
Bolton	d		16 33									17e05				17 33							
Wigan North Western	a	16 39		17 13								17 27		17 39				18 13					
	d	16 40		17 14								17 27		17 40				18 14					
Preston 8	a	16 53	16 56	17 37								17 40		17 53		17 57		18 37					
Blackpool North	a			18 07														19 07					
	d	16 20										17 11		17 20									
Preston 8	d	16 55	17 02									17 42		17 55		18 02	18 06						
Lancaster 6	a	17 10	17 18									17 56		18 10		18 18	18 22						
	d	17 10	17 18									17 57		18 10		18 18	18 22						
Barrow-in-Furness	a																19 26						
Oxenholme Lake District	a	17 24	17 32									18 10		18 24		18 32							
	d	17 25	17 32									18 10		18 25		18 32							
Windermere	a		18 02													18 56							
Penrith North Lakes	d		17 57											18 51		18 56							
Carlisle 8	a	18 03	18 13									18 48		19 06		19 13							
	d	18 05	18 15									18 49		19 06		19 15							
Lockerbie	d															19 33							
Carstairs	a																						
Motherwell	a															20s24							
Glasgow Central 15	a	19 17										20 03				20 45							
Haymarket	a																						
Edinburgh 10	a		19 37											20 24									
Perth	a															22f46							
Dundee	a													22 17		23f09							
Aberdeen	a													23 33		00f25							
Inverness	a																						

For general notes see front of timetable
For details of catering facilities see Directory of Train Operators

A From Plymouth (Table 51)
B From Bournemouth (Table 51)
C ⚲ to Glasgow Central
D From Paignton (Table 51)
b Change at Nuneaton and Stafford
c Change at Crewe and Llandudno Junction. By bus from Llandudno Junction
e Change at Preston
f Via Glasgow Central and Glasgow Queen Street. Passengers make their own way from one station to the other

OVERNIGHT SLEEPERS. For Sleeper trains, operated by First ScotRail, please refer to Tables 400 - 404

Table 65

Sundays

London and West Midlands → North West England and Scotland

13 September to 1 November

Route Diagram - see first page of Table 65

		SR	VT		VT	XC	VT	TP	NT	VT	XC	LM		VT	VT	VT	VT	VT	TP	NT	XC		VT	XC	LM
			1 ◇		1 ◇	1 ◇	1 ◇	1 ◇		1 ◇	1 ◇	1 ◇		1 ◇	1 ◇	1 ◇	1 ◇	1 ◇	1 ◇		1 ◇		1 ◇	1 ◇	1 ◇
						A					B										A			C	
			🍴		🍴	🛒	🍴	🛒		🍴	🛒			🍴	🍴	🍴	🍴	🍴			🛒		🍴	🛒	
London Euston 15 ⊖	d		16 15		16 25					16 35				16 55	17 02	17 05	17 15	17 25					17 35		
Gatwick Airport 10 ✈	d																								
Watford Junction	d															16 51	17 06								
Milton Keynes Central	d		16 48													17u38	17 48								
Northampton	d																								
Rugby	d																								
Nuneaton	d															18 10									
Tamworth Low Level	d																								
Lichfield Trent Valley	d																								
Coventry	d					16 26	16 40									17b46					17 26			17 40	
Birmingham International ✈	d					16 38	16 51				17 07										17 38			18 07	
Birmingham New Street 12	d					17 01	17 20				17 31	17 35									18 01			18 31	18 35
Wolverhampton 7 ⛴	d					17 19	17u37				17 49	17 52									18 19			18 49	18 52
Penkridge	d											18 03													19 03
Stafford	a					17 35						18 10			18 24						18 37				19 10
	d					17 36						18 10			18 25						18 39				19 10
Stoke-on-Trent	a		17 50			17 56					18 19			18 25			18 50				18 58			19 19	
Congleton	a																								
Macclesfield	a					18 14								18 42							19 16				
Crewe 10	a						18 09			18 12		18 30				18 53							19 12		19 30
	d						18 11			18 13		18 31				18 56							19 13		19 31
Chester	a									18 47						19 14							19 48		
Wrexham General	a																								
Llandudno Junction	a									19 48						20 07									
Llandudno	a																								
Bangor (Gwynedd)	a									20 11						20 29									
Holyhead	a									20 47						21 02									
Wilmslow	a						18 46			18 29		19 22											19 29		
Manchester Airport ✈	a						19c05			19 05															
Stockport	a		18 18			18 28	18 58			18 38		19 37		18 56			19 18				19 28		19 38		
Manchester Piccadilly 10 ⛴	a		18 30			18 40	19 15			18 51	19 00			19 09			19 30				19 40		19 51	20 00	
Hartford	a											18 43													19 43
Warrington Bank Quay	a				18 16		18 28											19 16							
	d				18 17		18 29											19 16							
Runcorn	a											18 53			18 56										19 53
Liverpool South Parkway 7 ✈	a											19 03													20 03
Liverpool Lime Street 10	a											19 13			19 19										20 13
	d								18 31											19 31					
Manchester Airport ✈	d				17e30			17 58										18e30	18 58						
Manchester Piccadilly 10 ⛴	d				17e46			18 16										18e46	19 16						
Bolton	d				18e05			18 33										19e05	19 33						
Wigan North Western	a				18 27		18 39		19 13									19 27		20 13					
	d				18 28		18 40		19 14									19 27		20 14					
Preston 8	a				18 40		18 53	18 56	19 37									19 40	19 56	20 37					
Blackpool North	a								20 07										20 39	21 07					
	d				18 11		18 20											18 50	19 20						
Preston 8	d				18 42		18 55	19 00										19 42	20 00						
Lancaster 6	a				18 56		19 10	19 16										19 56	20 16						
	d				18 58		19 10	19 16										19 57	20 16						
Barrow-in-Furness	a																		21 19						
Oxenholme Lake District	a				19 10		19 24	19 30										20 10							
	d				19 11		19 26	19 30										20 10							
Windermere	a						19 45											20 52							
Penrith North Lakes	d				19 36			19 54										20 36							
Carlisle 8	a				19 51		20 03	20 11										20 51							
	d	19 35			19 53		20 05	20 13										20 52							
Lockerbie	d							20 31																	
Carstairs	a																								
Motherwell	a																								
Glasgow Central 15	a	21 55			21 08		21 17											22 07							
Haymarket	a							21s30																	
Edinburgh 10	a							21 37																	
Perth	a							00 07										00f56							
Dundee	a							23 56																	
Aberdeen	a																								
Inverness	a																								

For general notes see front of timetable
For details of catering facilities see Directory of Train Operators

- **A** From Bournemouth (Table 51)
- **B** From Bristol Temple Meads (Table 51)
- **C** From Penzance (Table 135)
- **b** Change at Nuneaton
- **c** Change at Crewe and Wilmslow
- **e** Change at Preston
- **f** Via Glasgow Central and Glasgow Queen Street. Passengers make their own way from one station to the other

OVERNIGHT SLEEPERS. For Sleeper trains, operated by First ScotRail, please refer to Tables 400 - 404

Table 65

Sundays

London and West Midlands → North West England and Scotland

13 September to 1 November

Route Diagram - see first page of Table 65

		VT	VT	VT	VT	VT	XC	VT	VT	NT	XC	LM	VT	VT	VT	VT	VT	XC	VT	VT	XC	NT	VT
		1◇	1◇	1◇	1◇	1◇	1◇	R 1	1◇		1◇	1◇	1◇	1◇	1◇	1◇	1◇	1◇	1◇	1◇	1◇		1◇
							A				B							A			B		
		🚂	🚂	🚂	🚂	🚂	⚲	🚂	🚂		⚲		🚂	🚂	🚂	🚂	🚂	⚲	🚂	🚂			🚂
London Euston 15 ⊖	d	17 55	18 02	18 05	18 15	18 25			18 35				18 55	19 02	19 05	19 15	19 25			19 35			19 55
Gatwick Airport 10 ✈	d																						
Watford Junction	d			17 51	18 06										18 51	19 06							
Milton Keynes Central	d			18u38	18 48										19u38	19 48							
Northampton	d																						
Rugby	d		18 16											18 16									
Nuneaton	d		18 30											20 01									
Tamworth Low Level	d		18 45																				
Lichfield Trent Valley	d		18 51																				
Coventry	d						18 26	18 40				19 00						19 26	19 40		19 54		
Birmingham International ✈	d						18 38	18 51			19 07	19 11						19 38	19 51		20 08		
Birmingham New Street 12	d						19 01	19 20			19 31	19 35						20 01	20 20		20 31		
Wolverhampton 7	d						19 19	19 37			19 49	19 52						20 19	20 38		20 49		
Penkridge	d											20 03											
Stafford	a		19 24				19 37					20 10		20 25				20 36	20 51				
	d		19 25				19 38					20 10		20 30				20 38	20 52				
Stoke-on-Trent	a	19 25			19 50		19 56				20 21		20 25			20 50		20 57			21 19		21 25
Congleton	a																						
Macclesfield	a	19 42					20 14						20 42					21 15					21 42
Crewe 10	a			19 54				20 09	20 12			20 30		20 48	20 55				21 10	21 13			
	d			19 57				20 11	20 13			20 31		20 50	20 58					21 14			
Chester	a			20 16					20 48						21 17					21 46			
Wrexham General	a																						
Llandudno Junction	a			21 11											22 08					22 53			
Llandudno	a																						
Bangor (Gwynedd)	a			21 28											22 25					23 10			
Holyhead	a			22 02											22 59					23 52			
Wilmslow	a							20 45	20 29			21 22							21 46	21 30			
Manchester Airport ✈	a			21b05					21 05														
Stockport	a	19 56			20 18		20 28	20 57	20 38				20 56			21 18		21 28	21 58	21 39			21 56
Manchester Piccadilly 10	a	20 09			20 30		20 40	21 14	20 51		21 00		21 09			21 30		21 40	22 15	21 52	22 00		22 09
Hartford	a											20 43											
Warrington Bank Quay	a					20 16		20 28									21 16						
	d					20 16		20 29									21 16						
Runcorn	a		19 57									20 53		21 06									
Liverpool South Parkway 7 ✈	a											21 03											
Liverpool Lime Street 10	a		20 19									21 13		21 27									
	d									20 31												21 31	
Manchester Airport ✈	d					19c30											20c30						
Manchester Piccadilly 10	d					19c46											20c46						
Bolton	d					20c05											21c05						
Wigan North Western	a					20 27		20 39		21 13							21 27					22 13	
	d					20 27		20 40		21 14							21 27					22 14	
Preston 8	a					20 40		20 53		21 37							21 40					22 37	
Blackpool North	a							21 38		22 07							22 38					23 07	
	d					20 11		20 20									20 50						
Preston 8	d					20 42		20 55									21 42						
Lancaster 6	a					20 56		21 10									21 56						
	d					20 57		21 10									21 57						
Barrow-in-Furness	a																23 10						
Oxenholme Lake District	a					21 10		21 24									22 10						
	d					21 11		21 26									22 11						
Windermere	a																						
Penrith North Lakes	d					21 36											22 36						
Carlisle 8	a					21 51		22 03									22 51						
	d					21 52		22 05									22 53						
Lockerbie	d							22 23															
Carstairs	a																						
Motherwell	a					22s48		23s13															
Glasgow Central 15	a					23 08		23 35									00 02						
Haymarket	a																						
Edinburgh 10	a																						
Perth	a																						
Dundee	a																						
Aberdeen	a																						
Inverness	a																						

For general notes see front of timetable
For details of catering facilities see Directory of Train Operators

A From Bournemouth (Table 51)
B From Bristol Temple Meads (Table 51)
b Change at Crewe and Wilmslow
c Change at Preston

OVERNIGHT SLEEPERS. For Sleeper trains, operated by First ScotRail, please refer to Tables 400 - 404

London and West Midlands → North West England and Scotland

Sundays

13 September to 1 November

Route Diagram - see first page of Table 65

		VT	VT	VT		XC	VT	VT	VT	LM	VT	AW	XC		XC	SR	VT	VT	AW	VT	SR			
		1 ◇	1 ◇	1 ◇		1 ◇	1 ◇	1 ◇	1 ◇	1	1 ◇	◇	1 ◇		1 ◇	R	1 ◇	1 ◇	◇	1 ◇	R			
						A							A			B								
		🍴	🍴	🍴			🍴	🍴	🍴		🍴					🍴	🍴	🍴		🍴	🍴			
London Euston 15 ⊖	d	20 02	20 05	20 15			20 25		20 35		20 50					20 57	21 20	21 24		21 50	23 27			
Gatwick Airport 10 ✈	d																							
Watford Junction	d		19 51	20 06							20 51					21u17		21 22		21 47	23u47			
Milton Keynes Central	d		20 38	20 48							21 39							22 13		22 38				
Northampton	d										20 58									22 53				
Rugby	d	20 16									22 00									23 19				
Nuneaton	d	21 01	20 30														22 54			23 30				
Tamworth Low Level	d		20 45				21 32																	
Lichfield Trent Valley	d		20 51				21 39																	
Coventry	d	19b46				20 26		20 40		20 54			21 26		21 46				22 23					
Birmingham International ✈	d					20 38		20 51		21 08		21 08	21 38		21 57				22 40					
Birmingham New Street 12	d					21 01		21 20		21 35		21 24	22 01		22 28				22 55					
Wolverhampton 7	d					21 19		21 38		21 53		21 43	22 19		22 46				23 13					
Penkridge	d									22 03														
Stafford	a		21 32			21 37		21 58	22 03	22 13			22 37		22 58		23 18		23 30	23s54				
	d		21 33			21 38		21 59	22 04	22 14			22 38		22 59		23 19		23 31					
Stoke-on-Trent	a			21 50		21 56							22 55					23 33						
Congleton	a																							
Macclesfield	a					22 14							23 13					23 49						
Crewe 10	a	21 44	21 53				22 10	22 17	22 22	22 36	22 49	23 02			23 24		23 43		23 55	00s16				
	d	21 46	21 55				22 13	22 18	22 23		22 51	23 05			23 26	23u42	23 47		00 10					
Chester	a	22 21						22 50			23 26	23 26			23 59				00 31					
Wrexham General	a																							
Llandudno Junction	a							23 50											01 24					
Llandudno	a																							
Bangor (Gwynedd)	a							00 12											01 40					
Holyhead	a							00 49											02 15					
Wilmslow	a								22 38						23 42									
Manchester Airport ✈	a								23 05															
Stockport	a			22 18		22 28			22 48				23 27		23s51			00 05		00s46				
Manchester Piccadilly 10	a			22 30		22 40			23 00				23 40		00 05			00 17		00 58				
Hartford	a																							
Warrington Bank Quay	a						22 29	22 36			23 08													
	d						22 30	22 36			23 08													
Runcorn	a	22 02	22 11														00 07							
Liverpool South Parkway 7 ✈	a																							
Liverpool Lime Street 10	a	22 23	22 32														00 34							
	d						21 31				22 31													
Manchester Airport ✈	d																							
Manchester Piccadilly 10	d																							
Bolton	d																							
Wigan North Western	a						22 40	22 47			23 19													
	d						22 41	22 47			23 19													
Preston 8	a						22 58	23 07			23 39													
Blackpool North	a							00 04			00 14													
	d																							
Preston 8	d															00u30								
Lancaster 6	a																							
	d																							
Barrow-in-Furness	a																							
Oxenholme Lake District	a																							
	d																							
Windermere	a																							
Penrith North Lakes	d																							
Carlisle 8	a																				05s04			
	d																							
Lockerbie	d																							
Carstairs	a																				06s24			
Motherwell	a																				07s01			
Glasgow Central 15	a																				07 18			
Haymarket	a																							
Edinburgh 10	a																					07 20		
Perth	a															05s39								
Dundee	a															06s08								
Aberdeen	a															07 35								
Inverness	a															08 30								

For general notes see front of timetable
For details of catering facilities see Directory of Train Operators

A From Bournemouth (Table 51)
B Also conveys portion to Fort William (Table 227)
b Change at Nuneaton

OVERNIGHT SLEEPERS. For Sleeper trains, operated by First ScotRail, please refer to Tables 400 - 404

Sundays

from 8 November

London and West Midlands → North West England and Scotland

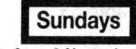

Route Diagram - see first page of Table 65

		NT	NT	VT	TP	VT	XC	VT	NT	VT	VT	VT	VT	VT	LM		VT	VT	TP	VT	NT	VT	XC	VT	VT
					1◇	1◇	1◇	1◇			1◇	1◇		1◇	1◇		1◇	1◇	1◇				1◇	1◇	1◇
				🚌						🚌			🚌							🚌		🚌			
						☕	🛒	☕			☕	☕		☕			☕	☕	🛒				🛒	☕	☕
London Euston 15 ⊖	d											08 10		08 15			08 20	08 44							
Gatwick Airport 10 ✈	d																								
Watford Junction	d											08 09						08 42							
Milton Keynes Central	d											08 56					09 05	09 33							
Northampton	d																	09 30							
Rugby	d																	09 56							
Nuneaton	d													09 30											
Tamworth Low Level	d																								
Lichfield Trent Valley	d																								
Coventry	d										08 37												09 07		
Birmingham International ✈	d										08 55				09 03								09 25		09 51
Birmingham New Street 12	d						09 01				09 20				09 41								10 00		10 20
Wolverhampton 7 ⛴	d						09 19				09 37				09 57								10 18		10 37
Penkridge	d														10 08										
Stafford	a						09 31							09 57	10 14								10 30		
	d						09 32							09 58	10 14								10 31		
Stoke-on-Trent	a																10 18						10 51		
Congleton	a																								
Macclesfield	a																10 36						11 09		
Crewe 10	a						09 55				10 12	10 17		10 22	10 38			10 55							11 12
	d					09 21	09 58				10 16	10 20	10 25	10 31	10 39							11 05			11 27
Chester	a													11 00				11 26							11 48
Wrexham General	a																								
Llandudno Junction	a													11 54											12 53
Llandudno	a																								13b20
Bangor (Gwynedd)	a													12 10											13 10
Holyhead	a													12 43											13 45
Wilmslow	a						10 13					10 46			11 22										11 40
Manchester Airport ✈	a											11c04													
Stockport	a						10 23					10 41					10 51						11 21		
Manchester Piccadilly 10 ⛴	a						10 37					10 54					11 04						11 40		12 02
Hartford	a														10 51										
Warrington Bank Quay	a												11 10									11 50			
	d			09 30						10 30			11 10							11 15		11 50			
Runcorn	a													10 47	11 01										
Liverpool South Parkway 7 ✈	a														11 11										
Liverpool Lime Street 10	a													11 08	11 21										
	d	08 31	09 31						10 31												11 31				
Manchester Airport ✈	d				09 30						10 25								10 58						11 30
Manchester Piccadilly 10 ⛴	d				09 46						10 43								11 16						11 46
Bolton	d				10 05						11 05								11 33					11 40	12 05
Wigan North Western	a	09 13	10 13	10 00					11 13	11 00			11 40							11 45	12 13	12 20			
	d	09 14	10 14	10 00					11 14	11 00										11 45	12 14				
Preston 8	a	09 37	10 39	10 40		10 42			11 37	11 40	11 42								11 56	12 25	12 37				12 44
Blackpool North	a	10 06	11 09			11 39			12 07												13 07				
	d				10 11			10 20			11 13								11 20					11 50	12 11
Preston 8	d				10 45	10 51		11 06			11 53								11 58					12 39	12 47
Lancaster 6	a				11 00	11 06		11 23			12 08								12 14					12 53	13 02
	d				11 01	11 06					12 08								12 14					12 54	13 02
Barrow-in-Furness	a																								
Oxenholme Lake District	a				11 17	11 21					12 22								12 28					13 07	13 16
	d				11 18	11 21					12 24								12 28					13 07	13 18
Windermere	a				11 40														12 52						
Penrith North Lakes	d					11 47													12 54					13 33	13 44
Carlisle 8	a					12 02					13 01								13 09					13 52	13 59
	d										13 03								13 11					13 52	14 03
Lockerbie	d																		13 30						
Carstairs	a																								
Motherwell	a																								
Glasgow Central 15	a																		14 36					15 06	15 23
Haymarket	a										14s13														
Edinburgh 10	a										14 22														
Perth	a																		16e45						
Dundee	a										16 48								17e09						
Aberdeen	a										18f23								18e23						
Inverness	a																								

For general notes see front of timetable
For details of catering facilities see Directory of Train Operators

b Change at Crewe and Llandudno Junction. By bus from Llandudno Junction
c Change at Crewe and Wilmslow
e Via Glasgow Central and Glasgow Queen Street. Passengers make their own way from one station to the other
f Change at Edinburgh and Dundee

OVERNIGHT SLEEPERS. For Sleeper trains, operated by First ScotRail, please refer to Tables 400 - 404

Table 65

London and West Midlands → North West England and Scotland

Sundays

from 8 November

Route Diagram - see first page of Table 65

		VT	LM	VT	VT	TP	XC	VT		NT	VT	VT	LM	VT	LM	VT	VT	TP		VT	NT	VT	XC		VT
		1 ◇	1 ◇	1 ◇	1 ◇	1 ◇	1 ◇					1 ◇	1	1 ◇	1 ◇	1 ◇	1 ◇	1 ◇					1 ◇		1 ◇
							A											B					C		
								🚌			🚌									🚌		🚌			
		🍴		🍴	🍴	🛒	🛒					🍴		🍴		🍴	🍴	🛒					🛒		🍴
London Euston 15 ⊖	d	09 15		09 20	09 45									10 15		10 20	10 45								11 15
Gatwick Airport 10 ✈	d																								
Watford Junction	d			*09 12*	*09 43*											*10 12*	*10 42*								
Milton Keynes Central	d			10 07	10 33											11 07	11 32								12 04
Northampton	d				*10 00*												*11 00*								
Rugby	d				10 57												11 56								
Nuneaton	d	10 38												11 35											
Tamworth Low Level	d																								
Lichfield Trent Valley	d																								
Coventry	d		*10 04*				10 28					*10 34*											11 28		
Birmingham International ✈	d		*10 13*				10 40					*10 52*											11 40		
Birmingham New Street 12	d		10 42				11 01					11 20			11 42								12 01		
Wolverhampton 7	d		10 59				11 19					11 37			11 59								12 20		
Penkridge	d		11 10												12 10										
Stafford	a	11 05	11 17				11 31							12 00	12 16								12 33		12 54
	d	11 05	11 17				11 32						11 41	12 01	12 16								12 34		12 55
Stoke-on-Trent	a			11 17			11 51						11 59			12 17							12 52		
Congleton	a																								
Macclesfield	a			11 37			12 09									12 37							13 10		
Crewe 10	a	11 30	11 37		11 57							12 07	12 24	12 30	12 37		12 48								13 16
	d	11 32	11 38								12 10	12 09		12 32	12 38							13 00			13 18
Chester	a		*12 18*									*12 48*			*13 15*										*13 47*
Wrexham General	a																								
Llandudno Junction	a											*13 55*													*14 55*
Llandudno	a																								
Bangor (Gwynedd)	a											*14 18*													*15 12*
Holyhead	a											*14 55*													*15 55*
Wilmslow	a											*12 46*			*13 22*										*13 47*
Manchester Airport ✈	a																								
Stockport	a			11 52			12 21									12 52							13 28		*13 58*
Manchester Piccadilly 10 ⛴	a			12 06			12 40									13 06							13 40		*14 15*
Hartford	a		11 50												12 50										
Warrington Bank Quay	a										12 55											13 45			
	d							12 20			12 55									13 20		13 45			
Runcorn	a	11 48	12 00											12 48	13 00										13 34
Liverpool South Parkway 7 ✈	a		12 10												13 10										
Liverpool Lime Street 10	a	12 09	12 20											13 09	13 20										13 56
	d									12 31											13 31				
Manchester Airport ✈	d					11 58						*12 30*						12 58							
Manchester Piccadilly 10 ⛴	d					12 16						*12 46*						13 16							
Bolton	d					12 33						*13 05*						13 33							
Wigan North Western	a							12 50		13 13	13 25									13 50	14 13	14 15			
	d							12 50		13 14										13 50	14 14				
Preston 8	a					12 56		13 30		13 37		13 42						13 56		14 30	14 37				
Blackpool North	a									14 07											15 07				
	d					*12 20*						*13 13*						*13 20*							
Preston 8	d					12 58						13 53						14 01	14 05						
Lancaster 6	a					13 14						14 08						14 16	14 21						
	d					13 14						14 08						14 16	14 21						
Barrow-in-Furness	a																		15 24						
Oxenholme Lake District	a					13 28												14 30							
	d					13 28												14 31							
Windermere	a					*13 52*																			
Penrith North Lakes	d					13 54						14 45						14 56							
Carlisle 8	a					14 10						15 00						15 11							
	d					14 11						15 03						15 13							
Lockerbie	d					14 30																			
Carstairs	a																								
Motherwell	a																								
Glasgow Central 15	a																	16 35							
Haymarket	a											16s14													
Edinburgh 10	a					15 35						16 22													
Perth	a											*18 28*													
Dundee	a					*17 24*						*18 14*													
Aberdeen	a					*18 46*						*19 30*													
Inverness	a											*20 44*													

For general notes see front of timetable
For details of catering facilities see Directory of Train Operators

A From Reading (Table 51)
B 🛒 to Glasgow Central
C From Southampton Central (Table 51)

OVERNIGHT SLEEPERS. For Sleeper trains, operated by First ScotRail, please refer to Tables 400 - 404

Sundays

from 8 November

London and West Midlands → North West England and Scotland

Route Diagram - see first page of Table 65

		VT	LM	VT	VT	TP	VT	NT	VT	XC	VT	VT	VT	XC	LM		VT	VT	TP	VT	XC	VT	NT	XC	LM
		1 ◇	1 ◇	1 ◇	1 ◇	1 ◇	1 ◇		1 ◇	1 ◇	1 ◇	1 ◇		1 ◇	1 ◇		1 ◇	1 ◇	1 ◇	1 ◇	1 ◇	1 ◇		1 ◇	1 ◇
										A				B							A			B	
													🚌												
		[P]		[P]	[P]	[T]	[P]		[P]	[T]	[P]	[P]		[T]			[P]	[P]		[P]	[T]	[P]		[T]	
London Euston 15 ⊖	d	11 20		12 02			12 15		12 25		12 35						12 55	13 02		13 15		13 35			
Gatwick Airport 10 ✈	d																								
Watford Junction	d	11 12					12 01													13 07					
Milton Keynes Central	d	12 07					12 48													13 48					
Northampton	d																								
Rugby	d		11b58																						
Nuneaton	d		12b11																						
Tamworth Low Level	d		12b26																						
Lichfield Trent Valley	d		12b32																						
Coventry	d		11 34							12 28		12 34			12 57						13 26			13 40	
Birmingham International ✈	d		12 08							12 40		12 52		13 05	13 08						13 38			14 07	
Birmingham New Street 12	d		12 35							13 01		13 20		13 31	13 35						14 01			14 31	14 35
Wolverhampton 7	d		12 52							13 19		13 37		13 49	13 52						14 19			14 49	14 52
Penkridge	d		13 03												14 03										15 03
Stafford	a		13 10	13 24						13 33					14 10			14 20			14 33				15 10
	d		13 10	13 25						13 34					14 10			14 22			14 34				15 10
Stoke-on-Trent	a	13 09					13 50			13 56				14 19			14 26			14 50	14 56			15 19	
Congleton	a																								
Macclesfield	a	13 27								14 14							14 42				15 14				
Crewe 10	a		13 30	13 43							14 12				14 30			14 43				15 12			15 30
	d		13 31	13 45							14 13	14 17	14 20		14 31			14 45				15 13			15 31
Chester	a			14 18							14 47							15 18				15 47			
Wrexham General	a																								
Llandudno Junction	a										15 55											16 55			
Llandudno	a										16c30														
Bangor (Gwynedd)	a										16 18											17 12			
Holyhead	a										16 54											17 55			
Wilmslow	a										14 29	14 46						15 22				15 29			
Manchester Airport ✈	a											15e05													
Stockport	a	13 41					14 18			14 28	14 38	14 58					14 56			15 18	15 28	15 38			
Manchester Piccadilly 10	a	13 59					14 30			14 40	14 51	15 15		15 00			15 09			15 30	15 40	15 51		16 00	
Hartford	a		13 43												14 43										15 43
Warrington Bank Quay	a												15 05												
	d												15 05												
Runcorn	a		13 53	14 01											14 53			15 01							15 53
Liverpool South Parkway 7 ✈	a		14 03												15 03										16 03
Liverpool Lime Street 10	a		14 13	14 23											15 13			15 23							16 13
	d							14 31															15 31		
Manchester Airport ✈	d				13 30	13 58			14 30										14 58						
Manchester Piccadilly 10	d				13 46	14 16			14 46										15 16						
Bolton	d				14 05	14 33			15 05										15 33						
Wigan North Western	a							15 13					15 35										16 13		
	d							15 14															16 14		
Preston 8	a					14 56		15 37	15 42			15 48							15 56				16 37		
Blackpool North	a							16 07															17 07		
	d				14 11	14 20			14 50			15 13							15 20						
Preston 8	d				14 42	15 00			15 43			15 53							16 00						
Lancaster 6	a				14 56	15 16			15 58			16 08							16 16						
	d				14 58	15 16			15 59			16 08							16 16						
Barrow-in-Furness	a																		17 19						
Oxenholme Lake District	a					15 30			16 12																
	d					15 30			16 13																
Windermere	a					15 54			16 52																
Penrith North Lakes	d				15 32	15 54						16 46													
Carlisle 8	a				15 47	16 11			16 51			17 01													
	d				15 48	16 13			16 51			17 04													
Lockerbie	d					16 31																			
Carstairs	a																								
Motherwell	a																								
Glasgow Central 15	a				17 03				18 03																
Haymarket	a					17s30						18s13													
Edinburgh 10	a					17 37						18 22													
Perth	a				18f44																				
Dundee	a				19f08	19 28						19 57													
Aberdeen	a				20f29	20 47						21 17													
Inverness	a				21f34																				

For general notes see front of timetable
For details of catering facilities see Directory of Train Operators

A From Bournemouth (Table 51)
B From Plymouth (Table 51)
b Change at Stafford
c Change at Crewe and Llandudno Junction. By bus from Llandudno Junction
e Change at Crewe and Wilmslow
f Via Glasgow Central and Glasgow Queen Street. Passengers make their own way from one station to the other

OVERNIGHT SLEEPERS. For Sleeper trains, operated by First ScotRail, please refer to Tables 400 - 404

Table 65

Sundays

from 8 November

London and West Midlands → North West England and Scotland

Route Diagram - see first page of Table 65

		VT	VT	VT	VT	XC	VT	TP		NT	VT	XC	LM	VT	VT	VT	VT	VT	XC	VT	VT	TP			NT
		1◇	1◇	1◇	1◇	1◇	1◇	1◇			1◇	1◇	1◇	1◇	1◇	1◇	1◇	1◇	1◇	1◇	1◇	1◇			
						A						B							A			C			
London Euston 15 ⊖	d	13 55	14 02	14 15	14 25						14 35			14 55	15 02	15 05	15 15	15 25			15 35				
Gatwick Airport 10 ✈	d																								
Watford Junction	d			14 06												14 51	15 06								
Milton Keynes Central	d			14 48												15u38	15 48								
Northampton	d																								
Rugby	d		14 16																						
Nuneaton	d		14 30																						
Tamworth Low Level	d		14 45																						
Lichfield Trent Valley	d		14 51																						
Coventry	d		13b46			14 26	14 40												15 26	15 40					
Birmingham International ✈	d					14 38	14 51					15 07							15 38	15 51					
Birmingham New Street 12	d					15 01	15 20					15 31	15 35						16 01	16 20					
Wolverhampton 7	d					15 19	15 37					15 49	15 52						16 19	16u37					
Penkridge	d												16 03												
Stafford	a		15 24			15 33							16 10		16 20				16 35						
	d		15 25			15 34							16 10		16 21				16 36						
Stoke-on-Trent	a	15 25		15 50		15 56						16 19		16 24			16 50		16 56						
Congleton	a																								
Macclesfield	a	15 42				16 14								16 42					17 14						
Crewe 10	a		15 43				16 09				16 12		16 32			16 54				17 09	17 12				
	d		15 45				16 11				16 13		16 34			16 57				17 11	17 13				
Chester	a										16 47					17 19					17 47				
Wrexham General	a																								
Llandudno Junction	a										17 55					18 55					18 55				
Llandudno	a															19c20					19e20				
Bangor (Gwynedd)	a										18 18					19 12					19 12				
Holyhead	a										18 55					19 55					19 55				
Wilmslow	a						16 49				16 29		17 22							17 46	17 29				
Manchester Airport ✈	a										17 05														
Stockport	a	15 56		16 18		16 28	16 58				16 38		17 37	16 56			17 18		17 30	17 58	17 38				
Manchester Piccadilly 10	a	16 09		16 30		16 40	17 15				16 51	17 00		17 09			17 30		17 40	18 15	17 51				
Hartford	a												16 45												
Warrington Bank Quay	a				16 16		16 28											17 16		17 28					
	d				16 16		16 29											17 16		17 29					
Runcorn	a		16 01										16 55		16 58										
Liverpool South Parkway 7 ✈	a												17 05												
Liverpool Lime Street 10	a		16 22										17 16		17 22										
	d									16 31															17 31
Manchester Airport ✈	d				15f30			15 58										16f30				16 58			
Manchester Piccadilly 10	d				15f46			16 16										16f46				17 16			
Bolton	d				16f05			16 33										17f05				17 33			
Wigan North Western	a				16 27		16 39			17 13								17 27		17 39					18 13
	d				16 27		16 40			17 14								17 27		17 40					18 14
Preston 8	a				16 40		16 53	16 56		17 37								17 40		17 53		17 56			18 37
Blackpool North	a							17 38		18 07															19 07
	d				16 11		16 20											17 11		17 20					
Preston 8	d				16 42		16 55	17 02										17 42		17 55		18 02	18 06		
Lancaster 6	a				16 56		17 10	17 18										17 56		18 10		18 18	18 22		
	d				16 57		17 10	17 18										17 57		18 10		18 18	18 22		
Barrow-in-Furness	a				18 09																		19 26		
Oxenholme Lake District	a						17 24	17 32										18 10		18 24		18 32			
	d						17 25	17 32										18 10		18 25		18 32			
Windermere	a							18 02														18 56			
Penrith North Lakes	d				17 32			17 57												18 51		18 56			
Carlisle 8	a				17 47		18 03	18 13										18 48		19 06		19 13			
	d				17 48		18 05	18 15										18 49		19 06		19 15			
Lockerbie	d																					19 33			
Carstairs	a																								
Motherwell	a																					20s24			
Glasgow Central 15	a				19 00		19 17											20 03				20 45			
Haymarket	a																								
Edinburgh 10	a							19 37												20 24					
Perth	a				20g46																	22g46			
Dundee	a				21g10															22 17		23g09			
Aberdeen	a				22g24															23 33		00g25			
Inverness	a																								

For general notes see front of timetable
For details of catering facilities see Directory of Train Operators

A From Bournemouth (Table 51)
B From Penzance (Table 135)
C to Glasgow Central
b Change at Nuneaton and Stafford
c Change at Chester and Llandudno Junction. By bus from Llandudno Junction
e Change at Crewe and Llandudno Junction. By bus from Llandudno Junction
f Change at Preston
g Via Glasgow Central and Glasgow Queen Street. Passengers make their own way from one station to the other

OVERNIGHT SLEEPERS. For Sleeper trains, operated by First ScotRail, please refer to Tables 400 - 404

Table 65

Sundays

from 8 November

London and West Midlands → North West England and Scotland

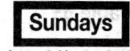

Route Diagram - see first page of Table 65

		XC	LM	VT	VT	VT	SR	VT	VT	VT	TP	NT	XC	VT	XC		LM	VT	VT	VT	VT	VT	TP	NT	XC
		1◇	1◇	1◇	1◇	1◇		1◇	1◇	1◇	1◇		1◇	1◇	1◇		1◇	1◇	1◇	1◇	1◇	1◇	1◇		1◇
		A											B		C										B
London Euston 15	d			15 55	16 02	16 05		16 15	16 25					16 35				16 55	17 02	17 05	17 15	17 25			
Gatwick Airport 10	d																								
Watford Junction	d					16 06														16 51	17 06				
Milton Keynes Central	d					16u39		16 48												17u38	17 48				
Northampton	d																								
Rugby	d				16 16																				
Nuneaton	d				16 30															18 10					
Tamworth Low Level	d				16 45																				
Lichfield Trent Valley	d				16 51																				
Coventry	d				15b46					16 40			16 26							17c46					17 26
Birmingham International	d	16 07								16 51			16 38		17 07										17 38
Birmingham New Street 12	d	16 31	16 35							17 20			17 01		17 31		17 35								18 01
Wolverhampton 7	d	16 49	16 52							17u37			17 19		17 49		17 52								18 19
Penkridge	d		17 03														18 03								
Stafford	a		17 10		17 24								17 35				18 10		18 24						18 37
	d		17 10		17 25								17 36				18 10		18 25						18 39
Stoke-on-Trent	a	17 19		17 25				17 50					17 56		18 19			18 25			18 50				18 58
Congleton	a																								
Macclesfield	a			17 42									18 14					18 42							19 16
Crewe 10	a		17 30			17 54				18 09				18 12			18 30			18 53					
	d		17 31			17 57				18 11				18 13			18 31			18 56					
Chester	a					18 19								18 47						19 14					
Wrexham General	a																								
Llandudno Junction	a					19 23								19 48						20 07					
Llandudno	a																								
Bangor (Gwynedd)	a					19 46								20 11						20 29					
Holyhead	a					20 20								20 47						21 02					
Wilmslow	a									18 46				18 29			19 22								
Manchester Airport	a									19e05				19 05											
Stockport	a			17 56				18 18		18 58			18 28	18 38			19 37	18 56			19 18				19 28
Manchester Piccadilly 10	a	18 00		18 09				18 30		19 15			18 40	18 51	19 00			19 09			19 30				19 40
Hartford	a		17 43														18 43								
Warrington Bank Quay	a								18 16	18 28												19 16			
	d								18 17	18 29												19 16			
Runcorn	a		17 53		17 56												18 53		18 56						
Liverpool South Parkway 7	a		18 03														19 03								
Liverpool Lime Street 10	a		18 13		18 19												19 13		19 19						
	d											18 31												19 31	
Manchester Airport	d								17f30		17 58											18f30	18 58		
Manchester Piccadilly 10	d								17f46		18 16											18f46	19 16		
Bolton	d								18f05		18 33											19f05	19 33		
Wigan North Western	a								18 27	18 39		19 13										19 27		20 13	
	d								18 28	18 40		19 14										19 27		20 14	
Preston 8	a								18 40	18 53	18 56	19 37										19 40	19 56	20 37	
Blackpool North	a											20 07												21 07	
	d								18 11	18 20												18 50	19 20		
Preston 8	d								18 42	18 55	19 00											19 42	20 00		
Lancaster 6	a								18 56	19 10	19 16											19 56	20 16		
	d								18 58	19 10	19 16											19 57	20 16		
Barrow-in-Furness	a																						21 19		
Oxenholme Lake District	a								19 10	19 24	19 30											20 10			
	d								19 11	19 26	19 30											20 10			
Windermere	a									19 45												20 52			
Penrith North Lakes	d								19 36		19 54											20 36			
Carlisle 8	a								19 51	20 03	20 11											20 51			
	d						19 35		19 53	20 05	20 13											20 52			
Lockerbie	d										20 31														
Carstairs	a																								
Motherwell	a																								
Glasgow Central 15	a						21 55		21 08	21 17												22 07			
Haymarket	a										21s30														
Edinburgh 10	a										21 37														
Perth	a										00 07											00g56			
Dundee	a										23 56														
Aberdeen	a																								
Inverness	a																								

For general notes see front of timetable
For details of catering facilities see Directory of Train Operators

A From Paignton (Table 51)
B From Bournemouth (Table 51)
C From Penzance (Table 135)
b Change at Nuneaton and Stafford
c Change at Nuneaton
e Change at Crewe and Wilmslow
f Change at Preston
g Via Glasgow Central and Glasgow Queen Street. Passengers make their own way from one station to the other

OVERNIGHT SLEEPERS. For Sleeper trains, operated by First ScotRail, please refer to Tables 400 - 404

Table 65

Sundays

from 8 November

London and West Midlands → North West England and Scotland

Route Diagram - see first page of Table 65

		VT	XC	LM	VT	VT	VT	VT	VT	XC	VT	VT	NT	XC	LM	VT	VT	VT	VT	VT	XC	VT	VT
											R												
		1 ◇	1 ◇	1 ◇	1 ◇	1 ◇	1 ◇	1 ◇	1 ◇	1 ◇	1	1 ◇		1 ◇	1 ◇	1 ◇	1 ◇	1 ◇	1 ◇	1 ◇	1 ◇	1 ◇	1 ◇
			A							B				A							B		
London Euston 15 ⊖	d	17 35			17 55	18 02	18 05	18 15	18 25			18 35				18 55	19 02	19 05	19 15	19 25			19 35
Gatwick Airport 10 ✈	d																						
Watford Junction	d						17 51	18 06										18 51	19 06				
Milton Keynes Central	d						18u38	18 48										19u38	19 48				
Northampton	d																						
Rugby	d					18 16											18 16						
Nuneaton	d					18 30											20 01						
Tamworth Low Level	d					18 45																	
Lichfield Trent Valley	d					18 51																	
Coventry	d		17 40							18 26	18 40				19 00						19 26	19 40	
Birmingham International ✈	d		18 07							18 38	18 51			19 07	19 11						19 38	19 51	
Birmingham New Street 12	d		18 31	18 35						19 01	19 20			19 31	19 35						20 01	20 20	
Wolverhampton 7	d		18 49	18 52						19 19	19 37			19 49	19 52						20 19	20 38	
Penkridge	d			19 03											20 03								
Stafford	a			19 10		19 24				19 37					20 10		20 25				20 36	20 51	
	d			19 10		19 25				19 38					20 10		20 30				20 38	20 52	
Stoke-on-Trent	a		19 19		19 25			19 50		19 56				20 21		20 25			20 50		20 57		
Congleton	a																						
Macclesfield	a				19 42					20 14						20 42					21 15		
Crewe 10	a	19 12		19 30			19 54				20 09	20 12			20 30		20 48	20 55				21 10	21 13
	d	19 13		19 31			19 57				20 11	20 13			20 31		20 50	20 58					21 14
Chester	a	19 48					20 16					20 48						21 17					21 46
Wrexham General	a																						
Llandudno Junction	a						21 11											22 19					22 53
Llandudno	a																						
Bangor (Gwynedd)	a						21 28											22 35					23 10
Holyhead	a						22 02											23 09					23 52
Wilmslow	a	19 29									20 45	20 29			21 22							21 46	21 30
Manchester Airport ✈	a											21 05											
Stockport	a	19 38			19 56			20 18		20 28	20 57	20 38			21 37	20 56			21 18		21 28	21 58	21 39
Manchester Piccadilly 10	a	19 51	20 00		20 09			20 30		20 40	21 14	20 51		21 00		21 09			21 30		21 40	22 15	21 52
Hartford	a			19 43											20 43								
Warrington Bank Quay	a								20 16		20 28									21 16			
	d								20 16		20 29									21 16			
Runcorn	a			19 53		19 57									20 53		21 06						
Liverpool South Parkway 7 ✈	a			20 03											21 03								
Liverpool Lime Street 10	a			20 13		20 19									21 13		21 27						
	d												20 31										
Manchester Airport ✈	d								19b30											20b30			
Manchester Piccadilly 10	d								19b46											20b46			
Bolton	d								20b05											21b05			
Wigan North Western	a								20 27		20 39		21 13							21 27			
	d								20 27		20 40		21 14							21 27			
Preston 8	a								20 40		20 53		21 37							21 40			
Blackpool North	a										21 38		22 07							22 38			
	d								20 11		20 20									20 50			
Preston 8	d								20 42		20 55									21 42			
Lancaster 6	a								20 56		21 10									21 56			
	d								20 57		21 10									21 57			
Barrow-in-Furness	a																			23 10			
Oxenholme Lake District	a								21 10		21 24									22 10			
	d								21 11		21 26									22 11			
Windermere	a																						
Penrith North Lakes	d								21 36											22 36			
Carlisle 8	a								21 51		22 03									22 51			
	d								21 52		22 05									22 53			
Lockerbie	d										22 23												
Carstairs	a																						
Motherwell	a								22s48		23s13												
Glasgow Central 15	a								23 08		23 35									00 02			
Haymarket	a																						
Edinburgh 10	a																						
Perth	a																						
Dundee	a																						
Aberdeen	a																						
Inverness	a																						

For general notes see front of timetable
For details of catering facilities see Directory of Train Operators

A From Plymouth (Table 51)
B From Bournemouth (Table 51)
b Change at Preston

OVERNIGHT SLEEPERS. For Sleeper trains, operated by First ScotRail, please refer to Tables 400 - 404

Sundays

from 8 November

London and West Midlands → North West England and Scotland

Route Diagram - see first page of Table 65

		XC	NT	VT	VT	VT	VT	XC	VT	VT	VT	LM	VT	AW	XC	XC	SR	VT	VT	AW	VT	SR
		1 ◇		1 ◇	1 ◇	1 ◇	1 ◇	1 ◇	1 ◇	1 ◇	1 ◇	1	1 ◇	◇	1 ◇	1 ◇	R	1 ◇	1 ◇	◇	1 ◇	R
		A						B							B	A	C					
		✕		☕	☕	☕	☕		☕	☕	☕		☕				☕	☕	☕		☕	☕
London Euston 15 ⊖	d			19 55	20 02	20 05	20 15		20 25		20 35		20 50				20 57	21 20	21 24		21 50	23 27
Gatwick Airport 10 ✈	d																					
Watford Junction	d					19 51	20 06						20 51				21u17		21 22		21 47	23u47
Milton Keynes Central	d					20 38	20 48						21 39						22 13		22 38	
Northampton	d												20 58								22 53	
Rugby	d				20 16								22 00								23 19	
Nuneaton	d				21 01	20 30												22 54			23 30	
Tamworth Low Level	d					20 45			21 32													
Lichfield Trent Valley	d					20 51			21 39													
Coventry	d	19 54			19b46			20 26		20 40		20 54		20 54	21 26	21 46				22 23		
Birmingham International ✈	d	20 08						20 38		20 51		21 08		21 08	21 38	21 57				22 40		
Birmingham New Street 12	d	20 31						21 01		21 20		21 35		21 24	22 01	22 28				22 55		
Wolverhampton 7	d	20 49						21 19		21 38		21 53		21 43	22 19	22 46				23 13		
Penkridge	d											22 03										
Stafford	a					21 32		21 37		21 58	22 03	22 13			22 37	22 58		23 18		23 30	23s54	
	d					21 33		21 38		21 59	22 04	22 14			22 38	22 59		23 19		23 31		
Stoke-on-Trent	a	21 19		21 25			21 50	21 56							22 55				23 33			
Congleton	a																					
Macclesfield	a			21 42				22 14							23 13				23 49			
Crewe 10	a				21 44	21 53			22 10	22 17	22 22	22 36	22 49	23 02		23 24		23 43		23 55	00s16	
	d				21 46	21 55			22 13	22 18	22 23		22 51	23 05		23 26	23u42	23 47		00 10		
Chester	a				22 21					22 50				23 26		23 59				00 31		
Wrexham General	a																					
Llandudno Junction	a									23 50										01 24		
Llandudno	a																					
Bangor (Gwynedd)	a									00 12										01 40		
Holyhead	a									00 49										02 15		
Wilmslow	a										22 38	23 22				23 42						
Manchester Airport ✈	a										23 05											
Stockport	a			21 56			22 18	22 28			22 48				23 27	23s51			00 05		00s46	
Manchester Piccadilly 10	a	22 00		22 09			22 30	22 40			23 00				23 40	00 05			00 17		00 58	
Hartford	a																					
Warrington Bank Quay	a								22 29	22 36			23 08									
	d								22 30	22 36			23 08									
Runcorn	a				22 02	22 11												00 07				
Liverpool South Parkway 7 ✈	a																					
Liverpool Lime Street 10	a				22 23	22 32												00 34				
	d		21 31										22 31									
Manchester Airport ✈	d																					
Manchester Piccadilly 10	d																					
Bolton	d																					
Wigan North Western	a		22 13						22 40	22 47			23 19									
	d		22 14						22 41	22 47			23 19									
Preston 8	a		22 37						22 58	23 07			23 39									
Blackpool North	a		23 07							00 04			00 14									
	d																					
Preston 8	d																00u30					
Lancaster 6	a																					
	d																					
Barrow-in-Furness	a																					
Oxenholme Lake District	a																					
	d																					
Windermere	a																					
Penrith North Lakes	d																					
Carlisle 8	a																					05s04
	d																					
Lockerbie	d																					
Carstairs	a																					06s24
Motherwell	a																					07s01
Glasgow Central 15	a																					07 18
Haymarket	a																					
Edinburgh 10	a																					07 20
Perth	a																05s39					
Dundee	a																06s08					
Aberdeen	a																07 35					
Inverness	a																08 30					

For general notes see front of timetable
For details of catering facilities see Directory of Train Operators

A From Plymouth (Table 51)
B From Bournemouth (Table 51)
C Also conveys portion to Fort William (Table 227)
b Change at Nuneaton

OVERNIGHT SLEEPERS. For Sleeper trains, operated by First ScotRail, please refer to Tables 400 - 404

Scotland and North West England → West Midlands and London

Route Diagram - see first page of Table 65

Miles	Miles	Miles	Miles	Miles	Station		AW	VT 1◇ ⊠	XC 1◇ A	VT 1◇ ⊠	XC 1◇ A	VT 1◇ ⊠	LM 1◇	VT 1◇ ⊠	XC 1◇ B	VT 1◇ ⊠	VT 1◇ ⊠	XC 1◇ B	LM 1◇	VT 1◇ ⊠	VT 1◇ ⊠	VT 1◇ ⊠	VT 1◇ ⊠	VT 1◇ ⊠	LM 1◇
—	0	—	—	—	Inverness	d																			
—	—	0	—	—	Aberdeen	d																			
—	—	71¼	—	—	Dundee	d																			
—	118	—	—	—	Perth	d																			
—	130¼	187¼	—	—	**Edinburgh** 10	d																			
—	131½	188½	—	—	Haymarket	d																			
0	—	—	—	—	**Glasgow Central** 15	d																			
12¾	—	—	—	—	Motherwell	d																			
28¾	158	—	—	—	Carstairs	d																			
77	—	263½	—	—	Lockerbie	d																			
102¼	—	—	—	—	**Carlisle** 8	a																			
—	—	—	—	—		d																			
120	—	—	—	—	Penrith North Lakes	d																			
—	—	—	—	—	Windermere	d																			
152¼	—	—	—	—	Oxenholme Lake District	a																			
—	—	—	—	—		d																			
—	—	—	—	—	Barrow-in-Furness	d														04 35					
171¼	—	—	—	—	Lancaster 6	a																			
—	—	—	—	—		d														05 35					
192¼	—	—	—	—	**Preston** 8	a														05 52					
—	—	—	—	—	Blackpool North	a														07 03					
—	—	—	—	—		d						04 57								05 29		05 45			
—	—	—	0	—	**Preston** 8	d						05 30								06 00		06 16			
207½	—	—	—	—	Wigan North Western	a						05 44								06 11		06 27			
—	—	—	—	—		d						05 45								06 11		06 27			
—	—	—	20	—	Bolton	a														06b34					
—	—	—	31¼	—	**Manchester Piccadilly** 10	a														06b56					
—	—	—	—	—	Manchester Airport	a														07b17					
—	—	—	—	—	**Liverpool Lime Street** 10	a						06 58										07 28			
—	0	—	—	—		d				05 27							06 05								06 31
—	5½	—	—	—	Liverpool South Parkway 7	d																			06 41
—	13	—	—	—	Runcorn	d				05 43							06 21								06 49
219¼	—	—	—	—	Warrington Bank Quay	a						05 55								06 22		06 38			
—	—	—	—	—		d						05 56								06 22		06 38			
231½	23¾	—	—	—	Hartford	d																			07 02
—	—	—	—	0	**Manchester Piccadilly** 10	d		05 05	05 00					05 55	06 00	06 10							06 27	06 35	06 30
—	—	—	37	5¾	Stockport	d		05 13						06 03	06 08	06 18							06 35	06 43	06 39
—	—	—	—	—	Manchester Airport	d																06 05			
—	—	—	—	—	Wilmslow	d								06 11								06 17			06 47
—	—	—	—	—	Holyhead	d															04 50				
—	—	—	—	—	Bangor (Gwynedd)	d															05 16				
—	—	—	—	—	Llandudno	d																			
—	—	—	—	—	Llandudno Junction	d							04 38								05 34				05 46
—	—	—	—	—	Wrexham General	d																			
—	—	—	—	—	Chester	d	04 23	04 55					05 37	05 51							06 26				06 43
243¼	35½	—	—	—	**Crewe** 10	a	04 44	05 34	05 44	06 00				06 27	06 32			←		06 42	06 47	06 59			07 14
—	—	—	—	—		d	05 00	05 36	05 47	06 02			06 20	06 29	06 38			06 38	06 47	06 53		07 01			07 16
—	—	—	49	17¾	Macclesfield	d									→	06 31							06 48	06 55	
—	—	—	57	25¾	Congleton	d					←														
—	—	—	68¾	37¼	**Stoke-on-Trent**	d			06 07		06 07					06 48							07 06	07 12	
267¾	—	—	—	53½	**Stafford**	a	05 24	05 53	→	06 20	06 25		06 40				06 52	06 57	07 10				07 27		07 40
—	—	—	—	—		d	05 24	05 55		06 21	06 25		06 41				06 53	06 58	07 12				07 28		07 41
—	—	—	—	59¼	Penkridge	a							06 46						07 17						07 46
—	—	—	—	69¾	Wolverhampton 7	a	05 38				06 39		06 57					07 12	07 28			07 31	07 43		07 57
—	—	—	—	82½	**Birmingham New Street** 12	a	05 55				06 58		07 18					07 31	07 48			07 55	08 05		08 17
—	—	—	—	91	Birmingham International	a	06 19				07 13		07 45					07 59	08 13				08 19		08 38
—	—	—	—	101½	Coventry	a	06 30				07 24		08 02					08 10	08 24				08 30		08 49
285	—	—	99¼	—	Lichfield Trent Valley	a						06 40					07 07		07c39				→		
291¼	—	—	—	—	Tamworth Low Level	a						06 46					07 14		07c46						
304¼	—	—	—	—	Nuneaton	a		06 17						07 06					08c02	07 32					
318¾	—	—	—	113	Rugby	a	07 12	06 30		06 52		07 06				07 28		08 21						07 52	09 12
—	—	—	—	—	Northampton	a				07 26		07 34				07 54								08 37	
351½	—	—	—	—	Milton Keynes Central	a		06 51		07 12						08 21									
383½	—	—	—	—	Watford Junction	a		07 38		08 25						09e26									
—	—	—	—	—	Gatwick Airport 10	a																			
401¼	—	—	—	—	**London Euston** 15	a		07 28		07 50		08 00		08 11		08 22	08 26			08 36				08 49	

For general notes see front of timetable
For details of catering facilities see Directory of Train Operators

A To Bournemouth (Table 51)
B To Bristol Temple Meads (Table 51)
b Change at Preston
c Change at Stafford
e Change at Rugby and Milton Keynes Central

OVERNIGHT SLEEPERS. For Sleeper trains, operated by First ScotRail, please refer to Tables 400 - 404

Scotland and North West England → West Midlands and London

Route Diagram - see first page of Table 65

		VT		VT	VT	XC	LM	TP	VT	VT	VT	VT	VT	VT	XC	VT	LM	VT	LM	VT	XC		LM	NT	TP
		1 ◇		1 ◇	1 ◇	1 ◇	1 ◇	1 ◇	1 ◇	1 ◇	1 ◇	1 ◇	1 ◇	1 ◇	1 ◇	1 ◇	1 ◇	1 ◇	1 ◇	1 ◇	1 ◇		1 ◇		1 ◇
						A									B						C				D
		⊠		⊠	⊠	⌶		⌶	⊠	⊠	⊠	⊠	⊠	⊠	⌶	⊠		⊠		⊠	⌶				⌶
Inverness	d																								
Aberdeen	d																								
Dundee	d																								
Perth	d																								
Edinburgh 10	d																								
Haymarket	d																								
Glasgow Central 15	d								04 25																
Motherwell	d																								
Carstairs	d																								
Lockerbie	d																								
Carlisle 8	a								05 42																
	d								05 43																
Penrith North Lakes	d								05 57																
Windermere	d																								
Oxenholme Lake District	a								06 20																
	d								06 20																
Barrow-in-Furness	d							05 31																	06 19
Lancaster 6	a							06 23	06 35																07 21
	d							06 26	06 35					06 58											07 22
Preston 8	a							06 45	06 53					07 15											07 41
Blackpool North	a								*07b41*					*08 05*											*08 29*
	d								*06 19*					*06 34*										07 02	
Preston 8	d							06 47	06 56					07 17										07 30	07 47
Wigan North Western	a								07 06					07 28										07 50	
	d								07 08					07 28										07 50	
Bolton	a							07 08	*07c34*																08 08
Manchester Piccadilly 10	a							07 27	*07c56*																08 27
Manchester Airport ✈	a							07 47	*08c17*																08 47
Liverpool Lime Street 10	a													*08 28*										08 35	
	d				07 00		07 05										07 34	07 48					08 04		
Liverpool South Parkway 7 ✈	d						07 15										07 44						08 15		
Runcorn	d				07u15		07 23										07 52	08 04					08 25		
Warrington Bank Quay	a								07 17					07 39											
	d								07 18					07 39											
Hartford	d						07 36										08 04								
Manchester Piccadilly 10	d	06 43		07 00		07 06				07 15					07 26	07 35				07 55	08 07				
Stockport	d	06 51		07u07						07 23					07 35	07 43				08 04					
Manchester Airport ✈	d											*07e11*													
Wilmslow	d	06 59										*07e21*					*07 47*			08 11					
Holyhead	d						*05 32*					05 53													
Bangor (Gwynedd)	d						*06 02*					06 20													
Llandudno	d																			*06f34*					
Llandudno Junction	d						*06 21*					06 38								*06f44*					
Wrexham General	d												07 00												
Chester	d						*07 08*					07 35								*07 55*					
Crewe 10	a	07 15					07 48					07 54		07 59			08 19		←	08 27			08 47		
	d	07 17					07 49					07 57		08 01			08 22		08 22	08 29			08 49		
Macclesfield	d														07 49	07 56	→								
Congleton	d																								
Stoke-on-Trent	d					07 44				07 50					08 07	08 12					08 44				
Stafford	a	07 34					08 10								08 24			08 35	08 42				09 09		
	d	07 35					08 10								08 25			08 36	08 43				09 10		
Penkridge	a						08 16												08 48				09 15		
Wolverhampton 7	a					08 13	08 26							08 31	08 39				08 58		09 13		09 27		
Birmingham New Street 12	a					08 31	08 47							08 56	08 58				09 18		09 31		09 47		
Birmingham International ✈	a					*08 59*					←			*09 19*	09 13				*09 38*		*09 59*				
Coventry	a					*09 10*	*09 24*				08 30			*09 30*	09 24				*09 49*		*10 10*				
Lichfield Trent Valley	a						*08g40*																*09g39*		
Tamworth Low Level	a						*08g47*																*09g46*		
Nuneaton	a						*09g02*									08 44							*10g02*		
Rugby	a					*09 21*						08 45							*10 12*		*10 22*				
Northampton	a											*09 34*													
Milton Keynes Central	a									08s46		*10 05*													
Watford Junction	a									*09 27*	09s15	*10 30*				09s31									
Gatwick Airport 10 ✈	a																								
London Euston 15 ⊖	a	08 55		08 58	09 01				09 09	09 23	09 34	09 38				09 52		09 56		10 04					

For general notes see front of timetable
For details of catering facilities see Directory of Train Operators

A To Bristol Temple Meads (Table 51)
B To Bournemouth (Table 51)
C To Paignton (Table 51)
D ⌶ from Preston
b From 5 October arr. 2 mins. later
c Change at Preston
e Change at Crewe
f Change at Chester and Crewe
g Change at Stafford

OVERNIGHT SLEEPERS. For Sleeper trains, operated by First ScotRail, please refer to Tables 400 - 404

Scotland and North West England → West Midlands and London

Route Diagram - see first page of Table 65

		VT	VT	VT	XC	VT	LM	VT	TP	VT	LM	NT	VT	XC	LM	TP	VT	VT	VT	NT	VT	XC	VT	LM
		1 ◇	1 ◇	1 ◇	1 ◇	1 ◇	1 ◇	1 ◇	1 ◇	1 ◇	1 ◇		1 ◇	1 ◇	1 ◇	1 ◇	1 ◇	1 ◇	1 ◇		1 ◇	1 ◇	1 ◇	1 ◇
					A							B		C		D						A		
		⊠	⊠	⊠	🛒	⊠		⊠	🛒	⊠			⊠	🛒		🛒	⊠	⊠	⊠		⊠	🛒	⊠	
Inverness	d																							
Aberdeen	d																							
Dundee	d																							
Perth	d																				05b10			
Edinburgh 10	d								05 36												06 52			
Haymarket	d								05u40												06u56			
Glasgow Central 15	d	05 40								05 50							06 30							
Motherwell	d									06 05							06u45							
Carstairs	d																							
Lockerbie	d																07 26							
Carlisle 8	a	06 46								07 02							07 43				08 05			
	d	06 49								07 04							07 46				08 07			
Penrith North Lakes	d									07 19							08 00				08 22			
Windermere	d	06 50															07 57							
Oxenholme Lake District	a	07 22								07 42							08 22							
	d	07 24								07 42							08 23							
Barrow-in-Furness	d											07 00				07 28								
Lancaster 6	a	07 37							07 46	07 56		08 03				08 26	08 37				08 56			
	d	07 38							07 47	07 57		08 04				08 26	08 38				08 57			
Preston 8	a	07 56							08 06	08 15		08 29				08 45	08 56				09 15			
Blackpool North	a								08c44			09 05				09 25	09c51				10 00			
	d	07 18															08 20			08 29	08 45			
Preston 8	d	07 58							08 12	08 17						08 47	08 58			09 04	09 17			
Wigan North Western	a	08 09								08 28							09 09			09 24	09 28			
	d	08 09								08 28							09 09			09 24	09 28			
Bolton	a								08 34	08e55						09 08	09e34				09e55			
Manchester Piccadilly 10 🚌	a								08 56	09e18						09 27	09e56				10e18			
Manchester Airport ✈	a								09 19							09 47	10e17							
Liverpool Lime Street 10	a	09 18								09 58										10 02	10 28			
	d						08 34	08 48							09 04									09 34
Liverpool South Parkway 7 ✈	d						08 44								09 15									09 44
Runcorn	d						08 52	09 04							09 25									09 52
Warrington Bank Quay	a	08 20								08 39							09 20				09 39			
	d	08 20								08 39							09 20				09 39			
Hartford	d						09 06																	10 04
Manchester Piccadilly 10 🚌	d		08 15		08 27	08 35							08 55	09 07	08 55			09 15				09 27	09 35	09 30
Stockport	d		08 23		08 35	08 42							09 04		09 04			09 23				09 35	09 42	09 39
Manchester Airport ✈	d																		09f11					
Wilmslow	d									08 22			09 11						09f21					09 47
Holyhead	d			06 55															07 15					
Bangor (Gwynedd)	d			07 22															08 02					
Llandudno	d			07 10									07g45						08h10					
Llandudno Junction	d			07 40									07g54						08 25					
Wrexham General	d			08 02															09 02					
Chester	d			08 35									08 55						09 35					
Crewe 10	a			08 54			09 20			08 59			09 27		09 44				09 54		09 59			10 19
	d			08 56			09 22			09 01			09 29		09 49				09 56		10 01			10 22
Macclesfield	d				08 49	08 55																09 49	09 55	
Congleton	d																							
Stoke-on-Trent	d		08 50		09 07	09 12								09 44				09 50				10 07	10 11	
Stafford	a				09 24		09 42 →	09 35			←				10 09							10 24		10 42
	d				09 25		→	09 36			09 43				10 10							10 25		10 43
Penkridge	a														10 15									→
Wolverhampton 7 🚌	a				09 39					09 31	09 56			10 13	10 27						10 31	10 39		
Birmingham New Street 12	a				09 58					09 56	10 17			10 31	10 47						10 55	10 58		
Birmingham International ✈	a				10 13					10 19	10 38			10 59							11 19	11 13		
Coventry	a				10 24					10 30	10 49			11 10	11 24						11 30	11 24		
Lichfield Trent Valley	a														10j39									
Tamworth Low Level	a														10j46									
Nuneaton	a														11j01									
Rugby	a										11 12			11 22										
Northampton	a																							
Milton Keynes Central	a		09 46	10s01														10 46	11s01					
Watford Junction	a		10 30	10 51														11 29	11 51					
Gatwick Airport 10 ✈	a																							
London Euston 15 ⊖	a	10 12	10 23	10 38		10 42		10 56					11 04				11 12	11 23	11 38				11 42	

For general notes see front of timetable
For details of catering facilities see Directory of Train Operators

A To Bournemouth (Table 51)
B From Millom (Table 100)
C To Bristol Temple Meads (Table 51)
D 🛒 from Preston
b Change at Haymarket
c From 5 October arr. 2 mins. later
e Change at Preston
f Change at Crewe
g Change at Chester and Crewe
h Change at Llandudno Junction and Chester
j Change at Stafford

OVERNIGHT SLEEPERS. For Sleeper trains, operated by First ScotRail, please refer to Tables 400 - 404

Scotland and North West England → West Midlands and London

Route Diagram - see first page of Table 65

		VT	LM	VT	XC	LM	TP	VT	VT	NT	VT	VT	XC	VT	LM		VT	LM	TP	VT	XC	LM	TP	VT	NT
		1 ◇	1 ◇	1 ◇	1 ◇	1 ◇	1 ◇	1 ◇	1 ◇		1 ◇	1 ◇	1 ◇	1 ◇	1 ◇		1 ◇	1 ◇	1 ◇	1 ◇	1 ◇	1 ◇	1 ◇	1 ◇	
					A								B								A		C		
		⊠		⊠	☕		☕	⊠	🍽		⊠	⊠	☕	🍽			🍽			🍽	☕		☕	⊠	
Inverness	d																								
Aberdeen	d																								
Dundee	d																								
Perth	d							05b16																06b09	
Edinburgh 10	d																								
Haymarket	d																								
Glasgow Central 15	d						07 10	07 35				08 00												08 40	
Motherwell	d							07u53																	
Carstairs	d																								
Lockerbie	d						08 06																		
Carlisle 8	a						08 28	08 46				09 08												09 46	
	d						08 30	08 49				09 09												09 49	
Penrith North Lakes	d						08 44																	10 03	
Windermere	d						08 50												09 41						
Oxenholme Lake District	a						09 08	09 22											10 00						
	d						09 11	09 23											10 01						
Barrow-in-Furness	d						08 00																09 23		
Lancaster 6	a						09 26	09 37				09 56							10 18				10 26	10 37	
	d						09 26	09 38				09 57							10 18				10 26	10 38	
Preston 8	a						09 45	09 56				10 15							10 37				10 45	10 56	
Blackpool North	a						10 20	10 35				11 00											11 20	11c48	
	d							09 20		09 37		09 45												10 20	10 37
Preston 8	d						09 47	09 58		10 04		10 17											10 47	10 58	11 04
Wigan North Western	a							10 09		10 24		10 28												11 09	11 24
	d							10 09		10 24		10 28												11 09	11 24
Bolton	a						10 08	10e34				10e55											11 08	11e34	
Manchester Piccadilly 10	a						10 27	10e56				11e18											11 27	11e56	
Manchester Airport ✈	a						10 47	11e17															11 47	12e17	
Liverpool Lime Street 10	a									11 02		11 28													12 02
	d	09 48				10 04									10 34		10 48					11 04			
Liverpool South Parkway 7 ✈	d					10 15									10 44							11 15			
Runcorn	d	10 04				10 25									10 52		11 04					11 25			
Warrington Bank Quay	a							10 20				10 39												11 20	
	d							10 20				10 39												11 20	
Hartford	d														11 04										
Manchester Piccadilly 10	d			09 55	10 07				10 15				10 27	10 35	10 30					10 55	11 07				
Stockport	d			10 04					10 23				10 35	10 42	10 39					11 04					
Manchester Airport ✈	d										10f11														
Wilmslow	d			10 11							10f21				10 47					11 11					
Holyhead	d										08 55														
Bangor (Gwynedd)	d										09 22														
Llandudno	d			08g45							09 10									09g45					
Llandudno Junction	d			08g54							09 40									09g54					
Wrexham General	d										10 02														
Chester	d			09 55							10 35									10 55					
Crewe 10	a			10 27		10 45					10 54	10 59			11 19			←		11 27		11 45			
	d			10 29		10 49					10 56	11 01			11 22			11 22		11 29		11 49			
Macclesfield	d												10 49	10 55	→										
Congleton	d																								
Stoke-on-Trent	d				10 44				10 50				11 07	11 11							11 44				
Stafford	a	10 35	←			11 09							11 24				11 35	11 42				12 09			
	d	10 36	10 43			11 10							11 25				11 36	11 43				12 10			
Penkridge	a					11 15																12 15			
Wolverhampton 7	a		10 56		11 13	11 27						11 31	11 39					11 56			12 13	12 27			
Birmingham New Street 12	a		11 18		11 31	11 47						11 56	11 58					12 17			12 31	12 47			
Birmingham International ✈	a		11 38		11 59							12 19	12 13					12 38			12 59				
Coventry	a		11 49		12 10	12 24						12 30	12 24					12 49			13 10				
Lichfield Trent Valley	a					11h39																12h39			
Tamworth Low Level	a					11h46																12h46			
Nuneaton	a					12h01																13h01			
Rugby	a		12 12		12 22													13 12			13 22				
Northampton	a																								
Milton Keynes Central	a								11 46		12s01														
Watford Junction	a								12 29		12 51														
Gatwick Airport 10 ✈	a																								
London Euston 15 ⊖	a	11 56		12 04				12 12	12 23		12 38			12 42			12 56			13 04				13 12	

For general notes see front of timetable
For details of catering facilities see Directory of Train Operators

A To Bristol Temple Meads (Table 51)

B To Bournemouth (Table 51)

C ☕ from Preston

b Via Glasgow Queen Street and Glasgow Central. Passengers make their own way from one station to the other

c From 5 October arr. 2 mins. later

e Change at Preston

f Change at Crewe

g Change at Chester and Crewe

h Change at Stafford

OVERNIGHT SLEEPERS. For Sleeper trains, operated by First ScotRail, please refer to Tables 400 - 404

Scotland and North West England → West Midlands and London

Route Diagram - see first page of Table 65

		VT	VT	VT	XC	VT	LM	VT	LM	VT	XC	LM	TP	VT	NT	VT	VT	VT	XC	VT	LM	VT	LM	TP
		1 ◇	1 ◇	1 ◇	1 ◇	1 ◇	1 ◇	1 ◇	1 ◇	1 ◇	1 ◇	1 ◇	1 ◇	1 ◇		1 ◇	1 ◇	1 ◇	1 ◇	1 ◇	1 ◇	1 ◇	1 ◇	1 ◇
					A						B		C						A					
		[P]	[P]	[X]	[T]	[P]		[P]		[P]	[T]		[T]	[X]		[P]	[P]	[P]	[T]	[P]		[P]		
Inverness	d																							
Aberdeen	d													05b33				06b33						
Dundee	d			07c20										06b52				07b52						
Perth	d			06c55										07b15				08b12						
Edinburgh 10	d			08 52																				
Haymarket	d			08u57																				
Glasgow Central 15	d													09 40				10 00						
Motherwell	d																							
Carstairs	d																							
Lockerbie	d																							
Carlisle 8	a			10 05										10 47				11 08						
	d			10 07										10 49				11 09						
Penrith North Lakes	d																	11 24						
Windermere	d												10 49											
Oxenholme Lake District	a			10 41									11 08	11 22										
	d			10 42									11 10	11 23										
Barrow-in-Furness	d												10 16											11 25
Lancaster 6	a			10 56									11 26	11 37										12 18
	d			10 57									11 26	11 38										12 18
Preston 8	a			11 15									11 45	11 56				12 15						12 37
Blackpool North	a			12 00									12 20	12e48				13 00						
	d			10 45										11 20	11 37			11 45						
Preston 8	d			11 17									11 47	11 58	12 04			12 17						
Wigan North Western	a			11 28										12 09	12 24			12 28						
	d			11 28										12 09	12 24			12 28						
Bolton	a			11f55									12 08	12f34				12f55						
Manchester Piccadilly 10	a			12f18									12 27	12f56				13f18						
Manchester Airport	a												12 47	13f17										
Liverpool Lime Street 10	a			12 28											13 02			13 28						
	d						11 34	11 48				12 04									12 34	12 48		
Liverpool South Parkway 7	d						11 44					12 15									12 44			
Runcorn	d						11 52	12 04				12 25									12 52	13 04		
Warrington Bank Quay	a			11 39										12 20				12 39						
	d			11 39										12 20				12 39						
Hartford	d						12 04														13 06			
Manchester Piccadilly 10	d	11 15			11 27	11 35	11 30			11 55	12 07					12 15			12 27	12 35	12 30			
Stockport	d	11 23			11 35	11 42	11 39			12 04						12 23			12 35	12 42	12 39			
Manchester Airport	d		11g11														12g11							
Wilmslow	d		11g21				11 47			12 11							12g21				12 47			
Holyhead	d		09 23														10 33							
Bangor (Gwynedd)	d		10 02														11 06							
Llandudno	d		10h10							10j44							11h10							
Llandudno Junction	d		10 25							10j53							11 25							
Wrexham General	d		11 04														12 02							
Chester	d		11 35							11 55							12 35							
Crewe 10	a		11 54	11 59			12 19			12 27		12 45					12 54	12 59			13 20			
	d		11 56	12 01			12 22			12 29		12 49					12 56	13 01			13 22			
Macclesfield	d				11 49	11 55													12 49	12 55				
Congleton	d																							
Stoke-on-Trent	d	11 50			12 07	12 11					12 44					12 50			13 07	13 11				
Stafford	a				12 24		12 42	12 35	←			13 09							13 24		13 42	13 35	←	
	d				12 25		12 43	12 36	12 43			13 10							13 25		13 43	13 36	13 43	
Penkridge	a						→					13 15									→			
Wolverhampton 7	a			12 31	12 39				12 56		13 13	13 27						13 31	13 39				13 56	
Birmingham New Street 12	a			12 55	12 58				13 17		13 31	13 47						13 56	13 58				14 17	
Birmingham International	a			13 19	13 13				13 38		13 59							14 19	14 13				14 38	
Coventry	a			13 30	13 24				13 49		14 10							14 30	14 24				14 49	
Lichfield Trent Valley	a											13k39												
Tamworth Low Level	a											13k46												
Nuneaton	a											14k01												
Rugby	a								14 12		14 22												15 12	
Northampton	a																							
Milton Keynes Central	a	12 46	13s01													13 46	14s01							
Watford Junction	a	13 29	13 51													14 29	14 51							
Gatwick Airport 10	a																							
London Euston 15	a	13 23	13 38			13 42		13 56		14 04				14 12		14 24	14 38			14 42		14 58		

For general notes see front of timetable
For details of catering facilities see Directory of Train Operators

A To Bournemouth (Table 51)
B To Bristol Temple Meads (Fridays to Exeter St Davids) (Table 51)
C [T] from Preston
b Via Glasgow Queen Street and Glasgow Central. Passengers make their own way from one station to the other
c Change at Haymarket
e From 5 October arr. 2 mins. later
f Change at Preston
g Change at Crewe
h Change at Llandudno Junction and Chester
j Change at Chester and Crewe
k Change at Stafford

OVERNIGHT SLEEPERS. For Sleeper trains, operated by First ScotRail, please refer to Tables 400 - 404

Scotland and North West England → West Midlands and London

Route Diagram - see first page of Table 65

		VT	XC	LM	TP	TP	VT	VT	NT	VT	VT	XC	VT	LM	VT	LM	XC	TP	VT	VT	LM	VT	NT	VT
		1◇	1◇	1◇	1◇	1◇	1◇	1◇		1◇	1◇	1◇	1◇	1◇	1◇	1◇	1◇	1◇	1◇	1◇	1◇	1◇		1◇
			A									B					C	D						
Inverness	d				04b57						06b46													
Aberdeen	d										07b52													
Dundee	d				08b27						09b06													
Perth	d				07b59		08c41				08b47								09c15					
Edinburgh 10	d				09 55						10 52													
Haymarket	d				09u58						10u57													
Glasgow Central 15	d					10 10	10 40												11 40					
Motherwell	d																							
Carstairs	d																							
Lockerbie	d				11 00																			
Carlisle 8	a				11 22	11 27	11 47				12 05								12 46					
	d				11 33		11 49				12 07								12 49					
Penrith North Lakes	d				11 47														13 03					
Windermere	d						11 59											12 51						
Oxenholme Lake District	a				12 11		12 22				12 41							13 07						
	d				12 11		12 23				12 43							13 09						
Barrow-in-Furness	d																	12 11						
Lancaster 6	a				12 26		12 37				12 56							13 26						
	d				12 26		12 38				12 57							13 26				13 39		
Preston 8	a				12 45		12 56				13 15							13 45	13 50			13 56		
Blackpool North	a				13 21		13e48				14 00							14 20				14e48		
	d						12 20		12 37		12 45											13 20	13 37	
Preston 8	d				12 47		12 58		13 04		13 17							13 47	13 53			13 59	14 04	
Wigan North Western	a						13 09		13 24		13 28											14 09	14 24	
	d						13 09		13 24		13 28											14 10	14 24	
Bolton	a				13 08		13f34				13f55							14 08				14f34		
Manchester Piccadilly 10	a				13 27		13f56				14f18							14 27				14f56		
Manchester Airport	a				13 47		14f17											14 47				15f17		
Liverpool Lime Street 10	a								14 02		14 28												15 02	
	d			13 04										13 34	13 48						14 04			
Liverpool South Parkway 7	d			13 15										13 44							14 15			
Runcorn	d			13 25										13 52	14 04						14 25			
Warrington Bank Quay	a						13 20				13 39											14 20		
	d						13 20				13 39											14 21		
Hartford	d													14 04										
Manchester Piccadilly 10	d	12 55	13 07					13 15				13 27	13 35	13 30			14 07		13 55					14 15
Stockport	d	13 04						13 23				13 35	13 42	13 39					14 04					14 23
Manchester Airport	d													13 11					13 11					
Wilmslow	d	13 11									13 22			13 47					14 11					
Holyhead	d									11 23														
Bangor (Gwynedd)	d									12 24														
Llandudno	d	11g44								12 10									12g44					
Llandudno Junction	d	11g53								12 42									12g53					
Wrexham General	d									13 00														
Chester	d	12 55								13 35									13 55					
Crewe 10	a	13 27		13 44						13 54	13 59			14 19		←			14 27	14 44				
	d	13 29		13 49						13 56	14 01			14 22		14 22			14 29	14 49				
Macclesfield	d											13 49	13 55	→										
Congleton	d																							
Stoke-on-Trent	d		13 44					13 50				14 07	14 11				14 44							14 50
Stafford	a			14 09								14 24			14 35	14 46				15 09				
	d			14 10								14 25			14 36	14 46				15 10				
Penkridge	a			14 15																15 15				
Wolverhampton 7	a		14 13	14 27							14 31	14 39				14 59	15 13			15 27				
Birmingham New Street 12	a		14 31	14 47							14 55	14 58				15 20	15 31			15 47				
Birmingham International	a		14 59								15 19	15 13				15 45	15 59							
Coventry	a		15 10	15 24							15 30	15 24				16 00	16 10							
Lichfield Trent Valley	a			14h39																15h39				
Tamworth Low Level	a			14h46																15h46				
Nuneaton	a			15h01																16h01				
Rugby	a		15 22													16 12	16 22							
Northampton	a																							
Milton Keynes Central	a							14 46		15s01														15 46
Watford Junction	a							15 29		15 51														16 29
Gatwick Airport 10	a																							
London Euston 15 ⊖	a	15 04					15 12	15 23		15 38			15 42		15 56				16 03	16 04		16 11		16 23

For general notes see front of timetable
For details of catering facilities see Directory of Train Operators

A To Bristol Temple Meads (Table 51)
B To Bournemouth (Table 51)
C To Paignton (Table 51)
D [trolley] from Preston
b Change at Haymarket
c Via Glasgow Queen Street and Glasgow Central. Passengers make their own way from one station to the other
e From 5 October arr. 2 mins. later
f Change at Preston
g Change at Chester and Crewe
h Change at Stafford

OVERNIGHT SLEEPERS. For Sleeper trains, operated by First ScotRail, please refer to Tables 400 - 404

Scotland and North West England → West Midlands and London

Route Diagram - see first page of Table 65

Station		VT	VT	XC	VT	LM		VT	LM	VT	XC	LM	TP	TP	TP	TP	VT	VT	VT	NT	VT	XC	VT	LM	VT
		1 ◇	1 ◇	1 ◇	1 ◇	1 ◇		1 ◇	1 ◇	1 ◇	1 ◇	1 ◇	1 ◇	1 ◇	1 ◇	1 ◇	1 ◇	1 ◇	1 ◇		1 ◇	1 ◇	1 ◇	1 ◇	1 ◇
				A							B		C	C	D	D						A			
Inverness	d		07b55																						
Aberdeen	d		08c42											09 07		09 07									
Dundee	d		09c52											10 17		10 17					11e30				
Perth	d		10c14																		10e57				
Edinburgh 10	d													12 08		12 08					12 52				
Haymarket	d																				12u57				
Glasgow Central 15	d		12 00														12 40								
Motherwell	d																								
Carstairs	d																								
Lockerbie	d													13 06		13 06									
Carlisle 8	a		13 08											13 28		13 28	13 47				14 05				
	d		13 09											13 30		13 30	13 49				14 07				
Penrith North Lakes	d																				14 22				
Windermere	d																14 00								
Oxenholme Lake District	a													14 10		14 10	14 22								
	d													14 10		14 10	14 24								
Barrow-in-Furness	d												13 25		13 25										
Lancaster 6	a		13 56										14 18		14 18		14 37				14 56				
	d		13 58										14 18		14 18		14 38				14 57				
Preston 8	a		14 15										14 37	14 41	14 37	14 41	14 56				15 15				
Blackpool North	a		15 00											15 20		15 20	15f48				16 00				
	d		13 45														14 20			14 37	14 45				
Preston 8	d		14 17											14 47		14 47	14 58			15 04	15 17				
Wigan North Western	a		14 28														15 09			15 24	15 28				
	d		14 28														15 09			15 24	15 28				
Bolton	a		14g55											15 08		15 08	15g34				15g55				
Manchester Piccadilly 10	a		15g18											15 27		15 27	15g56				16g18				
Manchester Airport	a													15 47		15 47	16g17								
Liverpool Lime Street 10	a		15 28																	16 02	16 28				
	d					14 34		14 48				15 04												15 34	15 48
Liverpool South Parkway 7	d					14 44						15 15												15 44	
Runcorn	d					14 52		15 04				15 25												15 52	16 04
Warrington Bank Quay	a		14 39														15 20				15 39				
	d		14 39														15 20				15 39				
Hartford	d					15 04																		16 04	
Manchester Piccadilly 10	d			14 27	14 35	14 30				14 55	15 07							15 15				15 27	15 35	15 30	
Stockport	d			14 35	14 42	14 39				15 04								15 23				15 35	15 42	15 39	
Manchester Airport	d	14h11																	15h11					15 47	
Wilmslow	d	14h21				14 47				15 11									15h21						
Holyhead	d	12 38																	13 58						
Bangor (Gwynedd)	d	13 07																	14 25						
Llandudno	d	13j10								13k44									14 10						
Llandudno Junction	d	13 25								13k53									14 43						
Wrexham General	d	14 02																							
Chester	d	14 35								14 55															
Crewe 10	a	14 54	14 59			15 19				15 27		15 44							15 54		15 59			16 19	
	d	14 56	15 01			15 22				15 29		15 49							15 57		16 01			16 22	
Macclesfield	d			14 49	14 55																	15 49	15 55	→	
Congleton	d																								
Stoke-on-Trent	d			15 07	15 11						15 44							15 50				16 07	16 11		
Stafford	a			15 24		15 42		15 35	←			16 09										16 24			16 35
	d			15 25		15 43		15 36	15 43			16 10										16 25			16 36
Penkridge	a					→						16 15													
Wolverhampton 7	a		15 31	15 39					15 56		16 13	16 26									16 31	16 39			
Birmingham New Street 12	a		15 56	15 58					16 17		16 31	16 47									16 55	16 58			
Birmingham International	a		16 19	16 13					16 38		16 59										17 19	17 13			
Coventry	a		16 30	16 24					16 49		17 10										17 30	17 24			
Lichfield Trent Valley	a											16m39													
Tamworth Low Level	a											16m46													
Nuneaton	a											17m01													
Rugby	a								17 12		17 22										17 55				
Northampton	a																								
Milton Keynes Central	a	16s01																16 46	17s01						
Watford Junction	a	16 51																17 29	17 51						
Gatwick Airport 10	a																								
London Euston 15	⊖ a	16 38			16 42			16 56		17 04							17 12	17 23	17 38				17 42		17 56

For general notes see front of timetable
For details of catering facilities see Directory of Train Operators

- **A** To Bournemouth (Table 51)
- **B** To Bristol Temple Meads (Table 51)
- **C** Until 19 June and from 7 September
- **D** 22 June to 4 September
- **b** Change at Perth, Glasgow Queen Street and Glasgow Central. Passengers make their own way between Glasgow Queen Street and Glasgow Central
- **c** Via Glasgow Queen Street and Glasgow Central. Passengers make their own way from one station to the other
- **e** Change at Haymarket
- **f** From 5 October arr. 2 mins. later
- **g** Change at Preston
- **h** Change at Crewe
- **j** Change at Llandudno Junction and Chester
- **k** Change at Chester and Crewe
- **m** Change at Stafford

OVERNIGHT SLEEPERS. For Sleeper trains, operated by First ScotRail, please refer to Tables 400 - 404

Scotland and North West England → West Midlands and London

Route Diagram - see first page of Table 65

		LM	TP	VT	VT	XC	LM	VT	VT	VT	NT	VT	XC	VT	LM	VT	LM	VT	XC	LM	TP	TP	VT
		1 ◇	1 ◇	1 ◇	1 ◇	1 ◇	1 ◇	1 ◇	1 ◇	1 ◇		1 ◇	1 ◇	1 ◇	1 ◇	1 ◇	1 ◇	1 ◇	1 ◇	1 ◇	1 ◇	1 ◇	1 ◇
			A			B							C						D				
			🛒	⊠	☕	🛒		☕	⊠	⊠		☕	🛒	⊠		⊠		⊠	🛒			🛒	⊠
Inverness	d			09b18																			
Aberdeen	d			09b37								10b38											
Dundee	d			10b52								11b49											
Perth	d			11b37								12b11											
Edinburgh 10	d																						
Haymarket	d																						
Glasgow Central 15	d			13 40								14 00										14 10	14 40
Motherwell	d																						
Carstairs	d																						
Lockerbie	d																					15 06	
Carlisle 8	a			14 46								15 08										15 28	15 47
	d			14 49								15 09										15 30	15 49
Penrith North Lakes	d																					15 44	
Windermere	d		14 48																				16 02
Oxenholme Lake District	a		15 07	15 22								15 44										16 08	16 22
	d		15 09	15 24								15 44										16 08	16 24
Barrow-in-Furness	d		14 16																		15 25		
Lancaster 6	a		15 26																		16 18	16 23	16 37
	d		15 26					15 39													16 18	16 23	16 38
Preston 8	a		15 45	15 50				15 56				16 15									16 37	16 42	16 56
Blackpool North	a		16 20									17 00									17 23		17c48
	d							15 20			15 37	15 45											16 20
Preston 8	d		15 47	15 53				15 59			16 04	16 17									16 47		16 58
Wigan North Western	a							16 09			16 24	16 28											17 09
	d							16 10			16 24	16 28											17 09
Bolton	a		16 08					16e34				16e55									17 08		17e34
Manchester Piccadilly 10	a		16 27					16e56				17e21									17 27		17e56
Manchester Airport ✈	a		16 47					17e17													17 48		18e17
Liverpool Lime Street 10	a										17 05	17 28											
	d						16 04								16 34	16 48				17 04			
Liverpool South Parkway 7 ✈	d						16 15								16 44					17 15			
Runcorn	d						16 25								16 53	17 04				17 25			
Warrington Bank Quay	a							16 20				16 39											17 20
	d							16 21				16 39											17 20
Hartford	d														17 06								
Manchester Piccadilly 10	d				15 55	16 07			16 15				16 27	16 35	16 30			16 55	17 06				
Stockport	d				16 04				16 23				16 35	16 42	16 39			17 04					
Manchester Airport ✈	d									16f11													
Wilmslow	d				16 11					16f21					16 49			17 11					
Holyhead	d									14 32													
Bangor (Gwynedd)	d									15 02													
Llandudno	d				14g40					15 08													
Llandudno Junction	d				14g49					15 25													
Wrexham General	d									16 02													
Chester	d				15 55					16 35								16 55					
Crewe 10	a	←			16 27		16 44			16 54		16 59			17 19		←	17 27		17 46			
	d	16 22			16 29		16 49			16 56		17 01			17 22		17 22	17 29		17 49			
Macclesfield	d												16 49	16 56	→				17 27				
Congleton	d																						
Stoke-on-Trent	d					16 44			16 50				17 08	17 12					17 44				
Stafford	a	16 46					17 10						17 24			17 35	17 42			18 09			
	d	16 46					17 10						17 25			17 36	17 43			18 10			
Penkridge	a						17 15													18 15			
Wolverhampton 7	a	16 59				17 13	17 27					17 31	17 39				17 56		18 13	18 27			
Birmingham New Street 12	a	17 20				17 31	17 47					17 56	17 58				18 17		18 31	18 48			
Birmingham International ✈	a	17 45				17 59						18 19	18 13				18 38		18 59				
Coventry	a	18 00				18 10						18 30	18 24				18 49		19 10				
Lichfield Trent Valley	a						17h39													18h39			
Tamworth Low Level	a						17h46													18h46			
Nuneaton	a						18h01													19h02			
Rugby	a	18 12				18 22											19 12		19 22				
Northampton	a																						
Milton Keynes Central	a								17 46	18s01						18 23							
Watford Junction	a								18 29	18 51								18s48					
Gatwick Airport 10 ✈	a																						
London Euston 15 ⊖	a			18 01	18 06			18 11	18 23	18 38				18 42		18 59		19 08					19 13

For general notes see front of timetable
For details of catering facilities see Directory of Train Operators

A 🛒 from Preston

B To Bristol Temple Meads (Table 51)
C To Bournemouth (Table 51)
D To Cardiff Central (Table 51)
b Via Glasgow Queen Street and Glasgow Central. Passengers make their own way from one station to the other
c From 5 October arr. 2 mins. later
e Change at Preston
f Change at Crewe
g Change at Chester and Crewe
h Change at Stafford

OVERNIGHT SLEEPERS. For Sleeper trains, operated by First ScotRail, please refer to Tables 400 - 404

Scotland and North West England → West Midlands and London

Route Diagram - see first page of Table 65

		NT	VT	VT	VT	XC	VT	LM	VT	LM	VT	XC	LM	VT	NT	VT	TP	VT	XC	VT	LM	VT	VT	XC
			[1] ◇	[1] ◇	[1] ◇	[1] ◇	[1] ◇	[1] ◇	[1] ◇	[1] ◇	[1] ◇	[1] ◇	[1] ◇	[1] ◇		[1] ◇	[1] ◇	[1] ◇	[1] ◇	[1] ◇	[1] ◇	[1] ◇	[1] ◇	[1] ◇
						A						B					C		A					D
			⊠	🍽	⊠	🛒	⊠		⊠		⊠	🛒		⊠		⊠	🛒	🍽	🛒	⊠		⊠	⊠	🛒
Inverness	d			10b47																				
Aberdeen	d			15c55																				
Dundee	d			13b34														13e50						
Perth	d			13b01														14e11						
Edinburgh [10]	d			14 52																				
Haymarket	d			14u57																				
Glasgow Central [15]	d																	16 00						
Motherwell	d																							
Carstairs	d																							
Lockerbie	d																							
Carlisle [8]	a			16 05														17 08						
	d			16 07														17 09						
Penrith North Lakes	d			16 22																				
Windermere	d																17 06							
Oxenholme Lake District	a																17 25	17 44						
	d																17 30	17 44						
Barrow-in-Furness	d													16 20										
Lancaster [6]	a			16 56													17 47							
	d			16 57										17 36			17 48							
Preston [8]	a			17 15										17 54			18 06	18 15						
Blackpool North	a			18 02													18f46	18f53						
	d	16 35		16 41										17 20	17 37									
Preston [8]	d	17 04		17 17										17 56	18 04		18 08	18 17						
Wigan North Western	a	17 24		17 28										18 07	18 24			18 28						
	d	17 24		17 28										18 08	18 24			18 28						
Bolton	a			18g08													18 34							
Manchester Piccadilly [10]	a			18g27													18 56							
Manchester Airport	a			18g47													19 17							
Liverpool Lime Street [10]	a	18 02		18 28											19 03			19 28						
	d							17 34	17 48				18 04								18 34	18 48		
Liverpool South Parkway [7]	d							17 44					18 15								18 44			
Runcorn	d							17 52	18 04				18 25								18 52	19 04		
Warrington Bank Quay	a			17 39										18 19				18 39						
	d			17 39										18 19				18 39						
Hartford	d							18 06													19 04			
Manchester Piccadilly [10]	d		17 15			17 27	17 35	17 30			17 55	18 05				18 15			18 27	18 35	18 30		18 55	19 07
Stockport	d		17 23			17 35	17 43	17 40			18 04					18 23			18 35	18 42	18 39		19 04	
Manchester Airport	d				17h11													18 11						
Wilmslow	d				17h21	17 44		17 48			18 11							18 22					19 11	
Holyhead	d				15 23																		16j36	
Bangor (Gwynedd)	d				16 02																		17j04	
Llandudno	d				16 08																		17j07	
Llandudno Junction	d				16 25																		17j22	
Wrexham General	d				17 02																			
Chester	d				17 35						17 55												18 55	
Crewe [10]	a			17 59	17 54			18 20		←	18 27		18 47					18 59			19 16	19 21	19 27	
	d			18 01	17 56			18 22		18 22	18 29		18 49					19 01			19 18	19 23	19 29	
Macclesfield	d						17 55	→				18 25								18 55				
Congleton	d																		18 54					
Stoke-on-Trent	d		17 50				18 12					18 44				18 50			19 07	19 12				19 44
Stafford	a					18 25			18 35	18 42			19 09						19 24		19 41	19 41		
	d					18 25			18 36	18 43			19 10						19 25		19 42	19 43		
Penkridge	a												19 15								19 47			
Wolverhampton [7]	a			18 31		18 39				18 56		19 13	19 27					19 31	19 39		19 57			20 13
Birmingham New Street [12]	a			18 55		18 58				19 17		19 31	19 47					19 56	19 58		20 17			20 31
Birmingham International	a			19 19		19 13				19 38		19 59						20 19	20 13		20 45			20 59
Coventry	a			19 30		19 24				19 49		20 10						20 30	20 24		21 00			21 10
Lichfield Trent Valley	a												19k39											
Tamworth Low Level	a												19k46											
Nuneaton	a												20k02											
Rugby	a									20 12		20 21									21 13			21 21
Northampton	a																							
Milton Keynes Central	a		18 46		19s01						19 31					19 46							20 32	
Watford Junction	a		19 29		19 53				19s42		20 26					20 29						20s46		
Gatwick Airport [10]	a																							
London Euston [15]	a		19 23		19 38		19 42		20 02		20 08			20 13		20 23				20 42		21 06	21 10	

For general notes see front of timetable
For details of catering facilities see Directory of Train Operators

- **A** To Bournemouth (Table 51)
- **B** To Plymouth (Table 51)
- **C** 🛒 from Preston
- **D** To Bristol Temple Meads (Table 51)
- **b** Change at Haymarket
- **c** Mondays to Fridays. Change at Haymarket
- **e** Via Glasgow Queen Street and Glasgow Central. Passengers make their own way from one station to the other
- **f** From 5 October arr. 2 mins. later
- **g** Change at Preston
- **h** Change at Crewe
- **j** Change at Chester and Crewe
- **k** Change at Stafford

OVERNIGHT SLEEPERS. For Sleeper trains, operated by First ScotRail, please refer to Tables 400 - 404

Table 65

Mondays to Fridays

Scotland and North West England → West Midlands and London

Route Diagram - see first page of Table 65

		LM	TP	VT	VT	VT	XC	LM	NT	VT	VT	TP	VT	XC	VT	LM		VT	NT	VT	NT	XC	LM	TP	VT
		1 ◇	**1** ◇	**1** ◇	**1** ◇	**1** ◇	**1** ◇	**1** ◇		**1** ◇	**1** ◇	**1** ◇	**1** ◇	**1** ◇	**1** ◇	**1** ◇		**1** ◇		**1** ◇		**1** ◇	**1** ◇	**1** ◇	**1** ◇
							A																		
			🛒	⊠	☕	☕	🛒			☕	☕		☕		☕			☕		☕				🛒	☕
Inverness	d												12b54												
Aberdeen	d																			13c42					14c39
Dundee	d		14b34										15b17												15c49
Perth	d		13b58										15b00							15c14					16c11
Edinburgh 10	d		16 11										16 52											18 11	
Haymarket	d		16u14										16u57											18u14	
Glasgow Central 15	d			16 40																17 40					18 40
Motherwell	d			16u54																					
Carstairs	d																								
Lockerbie	d		17 10																	18 32				19 10	
Carlisle 8	a		17 32	17 49									18 05							18 52				19 32	19 47
	d		17 33	17 51									18 07							18 54				19 33	19 49
Penrith North Lakes	d		17 48	18 05																19 09				19 48	
Windermere	d											18 12								19 10					20 00
Oxenholme Lake District	a			18 27								18 31	18 41							19 32				20 12	20 22
	d			18 29								18 33	18 42							19 32				20 12	20 24
Barrow-in-Furness	d		17 21	17 43																18 03					
Lancaster 6	a		18 26	18 43								18 49	18 56							19 47				20 26	20 37
	d		18 26	18 44								18 50	18 57							19 47				20 26	20 38
Preston 8	a		18 45	19 02								19 10	19 15							20 05				20 45	20 56
Blackpool North	a		19 20									19e48	20 00							20 44					21e48
	d			18 29					18 37				18 45		19 20				19 37						20 20
Preston 8	d		18 47	19 04					19 04			19 13	19 17		19 58				20 04	20 08				20 47	20 58
Wigan North Western	a			19 16					19 24				19 28		20 09				20 24	20 19	←				21 09
	d			19 16					19 24				19 28		20 09				→	20 19	20 24				21 09
Bolton	a		19 08	19f34								19 39	20f25											21 08	21f34
Manchester Piccadilly 10	a		19 27	19f56								20 02	20f56											21 27	21f56
Manchester Airport ✈	a		19 47	20f17								20 24	21f17											21 47	22f17
Liverpool Lime Street 10	a								20 02				20 58								21 02				
	d	19 11						19 34		19 48						20 04							20 34		
Liverpool South Parkway 7 ✈	d	19 21						19 44								20 15							20 44		
Runcorn	d	19 29						19 52		20 04						20 25							20 52		
Warrington Bank Quay	a			19 27									19 39		20 20					20 30					21 20
	d			19 27									19 39		20 20					20 31					21 20
Hartford	d							20 04															21 04		
Manchester Piccadilly 10	d				19 15		19 27			19 30	19 55			20 07				20 15				20 27			
Stockport	d				19 23		19 35			19 39	20 04							20 23				20 35	20 17		
Manchester Airport ✈	d							19g14															20g14		
Wilmslow	d							19 31		19 47	20 11												20 31		
Holyhead	d					17 21														18 23					
Bangor (Gwynedd)	d					18 00														19 02					
Llandudno	d					18h08					18j44									19k10					
Llandudno Junction	d					18 23					18j53									19 25					
Wrexham General	d					19 02																			
Chester	d					19 35					19 55									20 17					
Crewe 10	a	19 53				19 54		20 16		20 21	20 27		19 59		20 39	20 45				20 51			21 16		
	d	19 55				19 56		20 18		20 23	20 29		20 01		20 41	20 47				20 54			21 18		
Macclesfield	d				19 36		19 49											20 36				20 49			
Congleton	d																								
Stoke-on-Trent	d				19 52		20 07							20 44				20 53				21 07			
Stafford	a	20 15					20 24	20 38			20 47					21 09				21 12		21 24	21 38		
	d	20 16					20 25	20 42			20 48					21 10				21 14		21 25	21 41		
Penkridge	a							20 47								21 15							21 46		
Wolverhampton 7	a	20 29					20 39	20 57					20 33	21 13		21 26				21 30		21 39	21 57		
Birmingham New Street 12	a	20 47					20 58	21 18					20 55	21 36		21 47				21 51		22 00	22 17		
Birmingham International ✈	a						21 13	21 45					21 19	22 05						22 13		22 29	22 45		
Coventry	a	21 24					21 24	22 00					21 30	22 20						22 24		22 47	23 00		
Lichfield Trent Valley	a																								
Tamworth Low Level	a																								
Nuneaton	a									21 02															
Rugby	a							22 12					22 12	22 33	21 27					22 42					
Northampton	a														21 54										
Milton Keynes Central	a			20 45	20 48	21s03					21 35				21 47			21 50							22 37
Watford Junction	a				21 19	21 51				21s48								22s11							22s58
Gatwick Airport 10 ✈	a																								
London Euston 15 ⊖	a			21 24	21 25	21 42				22 09	22 12				22 46			22 51							23 38

For general notes see front of timetable
For details of catering facilities see Directory of Train Operators

A To Southampton Central (Table 51)

b Change at Haymarket
c Via Glasgow Queen Street and Glasgow Central. Passengers make their own way from one station to the other
e From 5 October arr. 2 mins. later
f Change at Preston
g Change at Wilmslow and Crewe
h Change at Llandudno Junction and Chester
j Change at Chester and Crewe
k Change at Llandudno Junction and Crewe

OVERNIGHT SLEEPERS. For Sleeper trains, operated by First ScotRail, please refer to Tables 400 - 404

Scotland and North West England → West Midlands and London

Route Diagram - see first page of Table 65

		VT	VT	VT	XC	NT	VT	LM	XC	TP	LM	VT	LM	NT	TP	NT	NT	TP	SR	SR	SR	SR
																				Ⓡ	Ⓡ	Ⓡ
		1◇	1◇	1◇	1◇		1◇	1◇	1◇	1◇	1◇	1◇	1		1◇			1◇				
																	A					B
		🍴	🍴	🍴			🍴					🍴			🍴					🍴	🍴	🍴
Inverness	d						14b51												16c56			20 38
Aberdeen	d						16e01					16f37							18f33			21 40
Dundee	d						17e26					17f51			18e19				19f46			23u06
Perth	d						17e00								18e00				20f11			23u21
Edinburgh 10	d						18 52								20 11						23 40	
Haymarket	d						18u57								20u14							
Glasgow Central 15	d											20 10							22 03	23 40		
Motherwell	d																			23u56		
Carstairs	d																			01u16		
Lockerbie	d											21 07			21 12							
Carlisle 8	a						20 06					21 24			21 34				00 26			
	d						20 08					21 26			21 36					01u40		
Penrith North Lakes	d											21 41										
Windermere	d											21 40						22 45				
Oxenholme Lake District	a						20 42					22 04			22 11			23 04				
	d						20 42					22 05			22 12			23 06				
Barrow-in-Furness	d									20 07						21 43		21 43				
Lancaster 6	a						20 57			21 11		22 19			22 26	22 44		23 23				
	d						20 57			21 11		22 20			22 26	22 45	23 07	23 24				
Preston 8	a						21 15			21 29		22 37			22 45	23 10	23 28	23 45				04s32
Blackpool North	a						21 53			22 06					23 21	23g48		00 20				
	d					20 38	20 45					21 45		22 14								
Preston 8	d					21 04	21 17			21 31		22 40		22 43	22 47							
Wigan North Western	a					21 23	21 28					22 51		23 02								
	d					21 23	21 28					22 52		23 03								
Bolton	a									22 25		23h25			23h34		00 18					
Manchester Piccadilly 10	a									22 30					23 44							
Manchester Airport ✈	a									22 47					00 22							
Liverpool Lime Street 10	a					22 14	23 15							23 54								
	d			20 48				21 34			22 34		23 34									
Liverpool South Parkway 7 ✈	d							21 44			22 44		23 45									
Runcorn	d			21 04				21 52			22 52		23 53									
Warrington Bank Quay	a						21 39					23 02										
	d						21 39					23 03										
Hartford	d							22 04			23 07		00 07									
Manchester Piccadilly 10	d		21 15	20 30	21 27				22 07													
Stockport	d		21 23	20 39	21 35			21 17	22 16													
Manchester Airport ✈	d							21j14														
Wilmslow	d			20 47				21 31														
Holyhead	d	19 21																				
Bangor (Gwynedd)	d	20 20																				
Llandudno	d	20 08					19k42															
Llandudno Junction	d	20 38					19k51															
Wrexham General	d	21 02																				
Chester	d	21 35					20 55															
Crewe 10	a	21 54		21 22			21 59	22 16			23 22	23 26	00 22									05m32
	d	21 56		21 24			22 01	22 20														
Macclesfield	d		21 36		21 49				22 29													
Congleton	d																					
Stoke-on-Trent	d		21 53		22 07				22 47													
Stafford	a			21 43	22 25			22 40	23 06													
	d			21 44	22 25			22 41	23 07													
Penkridge	a							22 46														
Wolverhampton 7	a	22 27			22 39		22 32	22 57	23 19													
Birmingham New Street 12	a	22 50			23 03		22 55	23 18	23 40													
Birmingham International ✈	a						23 19		00 04													
Coventry	a						23 30		00 13													
Lichfield Trent Valley	a			21 57																		
Tamworth Low Level	a			22 04																		
Nuneaton	a			22 16																		
Rugby	a			22 30			23 43															
Northampton	a			23 54																		
Milton Keynes Central	a		22 49	22 54																		
Watford Junction	a		23s10	23s15																06n14		
Gatwick Airport 10 ✈	a																					
London Euston 15 ⊖	a		23 50	23 53																06q37		07r47

For general notes see front of timetable
For details of catering facilities see Directory of Train Operators

- **A** From Morecambe (Table 98)
- **B** Also conveys portion from Fort William (Table 227)
- **b** Change at Perth and Haymarket
- **c** Change at Perth, Glasgow Queen Street and Glasgow Central. Passengers make their own way between Glasgow Queen Street and Glasgow Central
- **e** Change at Haymarket
- **f** Via Glasgow Queen Street and Glasgow Central. Passengers make their own way from one station to the other
- **g** From 5 October arr. 2 mins. later
- **h** Change at Preston
- **j** Change at Wilmslow and Crewe
- **k** Change at Chester and Crewe
- **m** Stops to set down only. Saturday mornings arr. 0534
- **n** Stops to set down only. Saturday mornings arr. 0627
- **q** Saturday mornings arr. 0650
- **r** Saturday mornings arr. 0748

OVERNIGHT SLEEPERS. For Sleeper trains, operated by First ScotRail, please refer to Tables 400 - 404

Table 65

Scotland and North West England → West Midlands and London

Saturdays

until 31 October

Route Diagram - see first page of Table 65

		AW	XC	VT	XC	VT	LM	VT	XC	VT	VT	VT	LM	VT	LM	VT	VT	XC	XC	LM	TP	VT	VT	VT	VT
			1 ◇	1 ◇	1 ◇	1 ◇	1 ◇	1 ◇	1 ◇	1 ◇	1 ◇	1 ◇	1 ◇	1 ◇	1 ◇	1 ◇	1 ◇	1 ◇	1 ◇	1 ◇	1 ◇	1 ◇	1 ◇	1 ◇	1 ◇
			A		A				B									C	D						
			🛒	☕	🛒	☕		☕	🛒	☕	☕	☕		☕		☕	☕	🛒	🛒			☕	☕	☕	☕
Inverness	d																								
Aberdeen	d																								
Dundee	d																								
Perth	d																								
Edinburgh [10]	d																								
Haymarket	d																								
Glasgow Central [15]	d																					04 25			
Motherwell	d																								
Carstairs	d																								
Lockerbie	d																								
Carlisle [8]	a																					05 42			
	d																					05 43			
Penrith North Lakes	d																					05 58			
Windermere	d																								
Oxenholme Lake District	a																					06 20			
	d																					06 21			
Barrow-in-Furness	d									*04 35*											05 31				
Lancaster [6]	a																				06 23	06 35			
	d									05 40											06 26	06 36			06 58
Preston [8]	a									05 55											06 45	06 54			07 15
Blackpool North	a									*07 03*												*07b41*			*08 05*
	d									*04 57*				*05 45*								*06 19*			*06 34*
Preston [8]	d									05 58				06 17							06 47	06 58			07 17
Wigan North Western	a									06 09				06 28								07 09			07 28
	d									06 09				06 28								07 10			07 28
Bolton	a									*06c34*											07 08	*07c34*			
Manchester Piccadilly [10]	a									*06c56*											07 27	*07c56*			
Manchester Airport	a									*07c17*											07 47	*08c17*			
Liverpool Lime Street [10]	a													*07 28*											*08 28*
	d					05 47									06 33	06 45				07 05					
Liverpool South Parkway [7]	d														06 43					07 15					
Runcorn	d					06 03									06 51	07 01				07 23					
Warrington Bank Quay	a									06 20				06 39								07 20			07 39
	d									06 20				06 39								07 20			07 39
Hartford	d														07 02					07 36					
Manchester Piccadilly [10]	d		05 11	05 25				05 55	06 00		06 10	06 35			*06 30*		06 55	07 07	07 00	*06 55*			07 15		
Stockport	d			05 34				06 03	06 08		06 18	06 43			*06 39*		07 04		07 09	*07 04*			07 23		
Manchester Airport	d													*06 05*											*07 11*
Wilmslow	d			05 41				06 11						*06 14*	06 47		07 11								*07 21*
Holyhead	d														*04e25*										
Bangor (Gwynedd)	d														*04e57*										
Llandudno	d																								
Llandudno Junction	d						*04 38*								*05 46*										
Wrexham General	d																							*06 49*	
Chester	d	04 23	*04 55*				*05 37*	*05 51*							*06 43*					*07 17*				07 17	
Crewe [10]	a	04 44	05 45	05 57				06 27						06 59	07 14	07 18	07 27			07 47				07 36	07 59
	d	05 00	05 47	06 00			06 20	06 29					06 47	07 01	07 16	07 20	07 29			07 49				07 38	08 01
Macclesfield	d								06 21		06 31	06 55							07 25						
Congleton	d				⟵																				
Stoke-on-Trent	d		06 07		06 07				06 39		06 48	07 12						07 44	07 44				07 50		
Stafford	a	05 24	⟶	06 17	06 25	06 34	06 41		06 57				07 10		07 40	07 38				08 10					
	d	05 24		06 19	06 25	06 35	06 41		06 58				07 12		07 41	07 39				08 10					
Penkridge	a						06 47						07 17		07 46					08 16					
Wolverhampton [7]	a	05 38			06 39		06 57		07 12				07 28	07 32	07 57			08 13	08 16	08 28					08 31
Birmingham New Street [12]	a	05 55			06 58		07 17		07 31				07 47	07 55	08 17			08 31	08 37	08 47					08 55
Birmingham International	a	*06 19*			07 13		*07 39*		*07 59*				*08 13*	*08 19*	*08 38*			*08 59*	*08 59*						*09 19*
Coventry	a	*06 30*			07 24		*07 50*		*08 10*				*08 24*	*08 30*	*08 49*			*09 10*	*09 10*						*09 30*
Lichfield Trent Valley	a										07 11		*07f41*												
Tamworth Low Level	a										07 17		*07f48*												
Nuneaton	a					06 57							*08f03*												
Rugby	a	*07 12*		06 49			*08 12*		*08 21*			07 52			*09 12*			*09 21*	*09 21*						
Northampton	a			*07 34*								*08 34*													
Milton Keynes Central	a			07 11				07 31		07 37													08 46		
Watford Junction	a			07s34		07s44				*08 20*													*09 34*		
Gatwick Airport [10]	a																								
London Euston [15]	a			07 54		08 05		08 10		08 14	08 27	08 46				08 59	09 04					09 12	09 23	09 30	

For general notes see front of timetable
For details of catering facilities see Directory of Train Operators

A To Bournemouth (Table 51)

B To Bristol Temple Meads (Table 51)

C From 12 September. To Bristol Temple Meads (Table 51)

D Until 5 September. To Newquay (Table 135)

b From 10 October arr. 2 mins. later

c Change at Preston

e Change at Llandudno Junction and Crewe

f Change at Stafford

Scotland and North West England → West Midlands and London

Route Diagram - see first page of Table 65

		VT		VT	XC	LM	VT	LM	VT	XC	XC	LM	NT	TP	VT	VT	VT	VT	XC	VT	LM	VT	LM	VT	XC
		1◇		1◇	1◇	1◇	1◇	1◇	1◇	1◇	1◇	1◇		1◇	1◇	1◇	1◇	1◇	1◇	1◇	1◇	1◇	1◇	1◇	1◇
					A					B	C			D					A						E
Inverness	d																								
Aberdeen	d																								
Dundee	d																								
Perth	d																								
Edinburgh 10	d																								
Haymarket	d																								
Glasgow Central 15	d														05 40			05 50							
Motherwell	d																	06u05							
Carstairs	d																								
Lockerbie	d																								
Carlisle 8	a														06 46			07 02							
	d														06 49			07 03							
Penrith North Lakes	d																	07 18							
Windermere	d														*06 50*										
Oxenholme Lake District	a														07 22			07 41							
	d														07 24			07 42							
Barrow-in-Furness	d													06 19											
Lancaster 6	a													07 21	07 37			07 56							
	d													07 22	07 38			07 57							
Preston 8	a													07 41	07 56			08 15							
Blackpool North	a													*08 18*	08b44			*09 05*							
	d												07 02		*07 18*			*07 29*							
Preston 8	d												07 30	07 47	07 58			08 17							
Wigan North Western	a												07 50		08 09			08 28							
	d												07 50		08 09			08 28							
Bolton	a													08 08	*08c34*			*08c55*							
Manchester Piccadilly 10	a													08 27	*08c56*			*09c18*							
Manchester Airport	a													08 47	*09c19*										
Liverpool Lime Street 10	a												08 34		*09 18*			*09 58*							
	d			07 19		07 34	07 48					08 04									08 34	08 48			
Liverpool South Parkway 7	d					07 44						08 15									08 44				
Runcorn	d			07 36		07 52	08 04					08 25									08 52	09 04			
Warrington Bank Quay	a														08 20			08 39							
	d														08 20			08 39							
Hartford	d					08 04															09 06				
Manchester Piccadilly 10	d	07 35			07 27	*07 30*			07 55	08 07	08 00					08 15			08 27	08 35	*08 30*			08 55	09 07
Stockport	d	07 43			07 35	*07 39*			08 04		08 09					08 23			08 35	08 42	*08 39*			09 04	
Manchester Airport	d																	*08 11*							
Wilmslow	d					*07 47*			08 11									*08 22*			*08 47*			09 11	
Holyhead	d								*05e22*								06 50								
Bangor (Gwynedd)	d								*06e01*								07 17								
Llandudno	d								*06e34*								*07 10*							*07e45*	
Llandudno Junction	d								*06e44*								07 35							*07e54*	
Wrexham General	d																*08 01*								
Chester	d								*07 55*								08 35							*08 55*	
Crewe 10	a			07 52		08 19		←	08 27			08 47					08 54	08 59			09 20		←	09 27	
	d			07 55		08 22		08 22	08 29			08 49					08 56	09 01			09 22		09 22	09 29	
Macclesfield	d	07 56			07 49	→					08 25								08 49	08 55	→				
Congleton	d																								
Stoke-on-Trent	d	08 12			08 07					08 44	08 45					08 50			09 07	09 13					09 44
Stafford	a			08 14	08 25		08 35	08 42				09 09							09 25			09 35	09 42		
	d			08 16	08 25		08 36	08 43				09 10							09 25			09 36	09 43		
Penkridge	a							08 48				09 15													
Wolverhampton 7	a				08 39			08 58		09 13	09 17	09 27						09 31	09 39				09 56		10 13
Birmingham New Street 12	a				08 58			09 18		09 31	09 38	09 47						09 55	09 58				10 17		10 31
Birmingham International	a				09 13			*09 38*		*09 59*	*09 59*							*10 19*	10 13				*10 38*		*10 59*
Coventry	a				09 24			*09 49*		*10 10*	*10 10*							*10 30*	10 24				*10 49*		*11 10*
Lichfield Trent Valley	a			08 30								*09f39*													
Tamworth Low Level	a			08 36								*09f46*													
Nuneaton	a						08 58															09 58			
Rugby	a							*10 12*		*10 21*	*10 21*												*11 12*		*11 21*
Northampton	a																								
Milton Keynes Central	a															09 46	10s01								
Watford Junction	a															*10 29*	*10 51*								
Gatwick Airport 10	a																								
London Euston 15	a	09 42		09 46			10 01		10 04						10 12	10 23	10 38			10 42		11 01		11 04	

For general notes see front of timetable
For details of catering facilities see Directory of Train Operators

- **A** To Bournemouth (Table 51)
- **B** From 12 September. To Paignton (Table 51)
- **C** Until 5 September. To Paignton (Table 51)
- **D** Trolley service from Preston
- **E** To Bristol Temple Meads (Table 51)
- **b** From 10 October arr. 2 mins. later
- **c** Change at Preston
- **e** Change at Chester and Crewe
- **f** Change at Stafford

Table 65

Scotland and North West England → West Midlands and London

Saturdays
until 31 October

Route Diagram - see first page of Table 65

		LM	TP	VT		NT	VT	VT	VT	XC	VT	LM	VT	LM	VT	XC	LM	TP	VT	NT	VT	VT	VT	XC	VT
		1◇	1◇	1◇			1◇	1◇	1◇	1◇	1◇	1◇	1◇	1◇	1◇	1◇	1◇	1◇	1◇		1◇	1◇	1◇	1◇	1◇
			A							B						C								B	
			🛒	☕			☕	☕	☕	🛒	☕		☕		☕	🛒		🛒	☕		☕	☕	☕	🛒	☕
Inverness	d																								
Aberdeen	d																								
Dundee	d																								
Perth	d																		05b16						
Edinburgh 10	d								06 52																
Haymarket	d								06u56																
Glasgow Central 15	d			06 30														07 10	07 35				08 00		
Motherwell	d			06u45															07u53						
Carstairs	d																								
Lockerbie	d			07 25														08 08							
Carlisle 8	a			07 43					08 05									08 28	08 46				09 08		
	d			07 46					08 07									08 30	08 49				09 09		
Penrith North Lakes	d			08 00					08 22									08 44							
Windermere	d			07 57														08 50							
Oxenholme Lake District	a			08 22														09 08	09 22						
	d			08 23														09 11	09 23						
Barrow-in-Furness	d		07 28																				08 25		
Lancaster 6	a		08 26	08 37					08 56									09 26	09 37				09 56		
	d		08 26	08 38					08 57									09 26	09 38				09 57		
Preston 8	a		08 45	08 56					09 15									09 45	09 56				10 15		
Blackpool North	a		09 20	09c48					10 00									10 20	10 35				11 00		
	d			08 20		08 38			08 45										09 20	09 37			09 45		
Preston 8	d		08 47	08 58		09 04			09 17									09 47	09 58	10 04			10 17		
Wigan North Western	a			09 09		09 24			09 28										10 09	10 24			10 28		
	d			09 09		09 24			09 28										10 09	10 24			10 28		
Bolton	a		09 08	09e34					09e55									10 08	10e34				10e55		
Manchester Piccadilly 10	a		09 27	09e56					10e18									10 27	10e56				11e18		
Manchester Airport ✈	a		09 47	10e17														10 47	11e17						
Liverpool Lime Street 10	a					10 02			10 29											11 02			11 28		
	d	09 04										09 34	09 48				10 04								
Liverpool South Parkway 7 ✈	d	09 15										09 44					10 15								
Runcorn	d	09 25										09 52	10 04				10 25								
Warrington Bank Quay	a			09 20					09 39										10 20				10 39		
	d			09 20					09 39										10 20				10 39		
Hartford	d											10 04													
Manchester Piccadilly 10	d						09 15			09 27	09 35	09 30			09 55	10 07					10 15			10 27	10 35
Stockport	d						09 23			09 35	09 42	09 39			10 04						10 23			10 35	10 42
Manchester Airport ✈	d							09f11							09 11							10f11			
Wilmslow	d							09f21				09 47			10 11							10f21			
Holyhead	d							07 55														08 55			
Bangor (Gwynedd)	d							08 22														09 22			
Llandudno	d							08 10							08g45							09 10			
Llandudno Junction	d							08 40							08g54							09 40			
Wrexham General	d							09 02														10 02			
Chester	d							09 35							09 55							10 35			
Crewe 10	a	09 44						09 54	09 59			10 19		←	10 27		10 45					10 54	10 59		
	d	09 49						09 56	10 01			10 22		10 22	10 29		10 49					10 56	11 01		
Macclesfield	d									09 49	09 55	→												10 49	10 55
Congleton	d																								
Stoke-on-Trent	d						09 50			10 07	10 12					10 44					10 50			11 07	11 12
Stafford	a	10 09								10 25			10 35	10 42			11 09							11 25	
	d	10 10								10 25			10 36	10 43			11 10							11 25	
Penkridge	a	10 15															11 15								
Wolverhampton 7	a	10 27							10 31	10 39				10 56		11 13	11 27						11 31	11 39	
Birmingham New Street 12	a	10 47							10 55	10 58				11 17		11 31	11 47						11 55	11 58	
Birmingham International ✈	a								11 19	11 13				11 38		11 59							12 19	12 13	
Coventry	a								11 30	11 24				11 49		12 10							12 30	12 24	
Lichfield Trent Valley	a	10h39															11h39								
Tamworth Low Level	a	10h46															11h46								
Nuneaton	a	11h01															12h01								
Rugby	a													12 12		12 21									
Northampton	a																								
Milton Keynes Central	a						10 46	11s01													11 46	12s01			
Watford Junction	a						11 29	11 51													12 29	12 50			
Gatwick Airport 10 ✈	a																								
London Euston 15 ⊖	a			11 12			11 23	11 38			11 42		11 56		12 04				12 12		12 23	12 38			12 42

For general notes see front of timetable
For details of catering facilities see Directory of Train Operators

A 🛒 from Preston

B To Bournemouth (Table 51)
C To Bristol Temple Meads (Table 51)
b Via Glasgow Queen Street and Glasgow Central. Passengers make their own way from one station to the other

c From 10 October arr. 2 mins. later
e Change at Preston
f Change at Crewe
g Change at Chester and Crewe
h Change at Stafford

Saturdays

until 31 October

Scotland and North West England → West Midlands and London

Route Diagram - see first page of Table 65

	LM	VT	LM	TP	VT		XC	LM	TP	VT	NT	VT	VT	VT	XC	VT	LM	VT	LM	VT	XC	LM	TP	TP
	1◇	1◇	1◇	1◇	1◇		1◇	1◇	1◇	1◇		1◇	1◇	1◇	1◇	1◇	1◇	1◇	1◇	1◇	1◇	1◇	1◇	1◇
							A		B						C						D		B	
		⊡			⊡		ᴛ		ᴛ	⊡		⊡	⊡	⊡	ᴛ	⊡		⊡		⊡	ᴛ		ᴛ	ᴛ
Inverness d																								
Aberdeen d																								
Dundee d														07b20										07b35
Perth d														06b55										07b59
Edinburgh 10 d														08 52										09 22
Haymarket d														08u57										09u26
Glasgow Central 15 d										08 40														
Motherwell d																								
Carstairs d																								
Lockerbie d																								10 24
Carlisle 8 a										09 46				10 05										10 44
d										09 49				10 07										10 52 →
Penrith North Lakes d										10 03														
Windermere d				09 41																			10 49	
Oxenholme Lake District a				10 00										10 41									11 08	
d				10 01										10 42									11 10	
Barrow-in-Furness d									09 23														10 16	
Lancaster 6 a				10 18					10 26	10 37				10 56									11 26	
d				10 18					10 26	10 38				10 57									11 26	
Preston 8 a				10 37					10 45	10 56				11 15									11 45	
Blackpool North a									11 20	11c49				12 00									12 20	
d										10 20	10 37			10 45										
Preston 8 d									10 47	10 58	11 04			11 17									11 47	
Wigan North Western a										11 09	11 24			11 28										
d										11 09	11 24			11 28										
Bolton a									11 08	11e34				11e55									12 08	
Manchester Piccadilly 10 a									11 27	11e56				12e18									12 27	
Manchester Airport ✈ a									11 47	12e17													12 47	
Liverpool Lime Street 10 a											12 02			12 28										
d	10 34	10 48						11 04									11 34	11 48				12 04		
Liverpool South Parkway 7 ✈ d	10 44							11 15									11 44					12 15		
Runcorn d	10 52	11 04						11 25									11 52	12 04				12 25		
Warrington Bank Quay a										11 20				11 39										
d										11 20				11 39										
Hartford d	11 04																12 04							
Manchester Piccadilly 10 d	10 30				10 55		11 07					11 15			11 27	11 35	11 30			11 55	12 07			
Stockport d	10 39				11 04							11 23			11 35	11 42	11 39			12 04				
Manchester Airport ✈ d													11f11											
Wilmslow d	10 47				11 11								11f21				11 47			12 11				
Holyhead d													09 23											
Bangor (Gwynedd) d													10 02											
Llandudno d					09g45								10h10							10g44				
Llandudno Junction d					09g54								10 25							10g53				
Wrexham General d													11 00											
Chester d					10 55								11 35							11 55				
Crewe 10 a	11 19		←		11 27			11 44					11 54	11 59			12 19		←	12 27		12 44		
d	11 22		11 22		11 29			11 49					11 56	12 01			12 22		12 22	12 29		12 49		
Macclesfield d	→														11 49	11 55	→							
Congleton d																								
Stoke-on-Trent d							11 44					11 50			12 07	12 12					12 44			
Stafford a		11 35	11 42					12 09							12 24			12 35	12 42			13 09		
d		11 36	11 43					12 10							12 25			12 36	12 43			13 10		
Penkridge a								12 15														13 15		
Wolverhampton 7 a			11 56				12 13	12 27						12 31	12 39				12 56		13 13	13 27		
Birmingham New Street 12 a			12 17				12 31	12 47						12 55	12 58				13 17		13 31	13 47		
Birmingham International ✈ a			12 38				12 59							13 19	13 13				13 38		13 59			
Coventry a			12 49				13 10	13 24						13 30	13 24				13 49		14 10			
Lichfield Trent Valley a								12j39														13j39		
Tamworth Low Level a								12j46														13j46		
Nuneaton a								13j01														14j01		
Rugby a			13 12				13 21												14 12		14 21			
Northampton a																								
Milton Keynes Central a												12 46	13s01											
Watford Junction a												13 29	13 50											
Gatwick Airport 10 ✈ a																								
London Euston 15 ⊖ a		12 56			13 04					13 12		13 23	13 38			13 42		13 56		14 04				

For general notes see front of timetable
For details of catering facilities see Directory of Train Operators

A To Bristol Temple Meads (Table 51)
B ᴛ from Preston
C To Bournemouth (Table 51)
D To Paignton (from 12 September to Bristol Temple Meads) (Table 51)
b Change at Haymarket
c From 10 October arr. 2 mins. later
e Change at Preston
f Change at Crewe
g Change at Chester and Crewe
h Change at Llandudno Junction and Chester
j Change at Stafford

Table 65

Saturdays

Scotland and North West England → West Midlands and London

until 31 October

Route Diagram - see first page of Table 65

		VT	NT	TP	VT	VT	VT	XC	VT	LM	VT	LM	TP	VT	XC	LM	TP	VT	NT	VT	VT	VT	XC	VT
		1◇		1◇	1◇	1◇	1◇	1◇	1◇	1◇	1◇	1◇	1◇	1◇	1◇	1◇	1◇	1◇		1◇	1◇	1◇	1◇	1◇
								A							B								A	
Inverness	d																					06b46		
Aberdeen	d	05c33					06c33															07b52		
Dundee	d	06c52					07c52											08c18				09b06		
Perth	d	07c15					08c12											08c41				08b47		
Edinburgh 10	d																					10 52		
Haymarket	d																					10u57		
Glasgow Central 15	d	09 40					10 00										10 10	10 40						
Motherwell	d																							
Carstairs	d																							
Lockerbie	d																							
Carlisle 8	a	10 47		←			11 08										11 27	11 46				12 05		
	d	10 49		10 52			11 09										11 28	11 49				12 07		
Penrith North Lakes	d			11 07			11 24										11 42							
Windermere	d																	11 59						
Oxenholme Lake District	a	11 22		11 31													12 06	12 22				12 41		
	d	11 23		11 31													12 07	12 23				12 43		
Barrow-in-Furness	d												11 25											
Lancaster 6	a	11 37		11 46									12 18				12 22	12 37				12 56		
	d	11 38		11 46									12 18				12 23	12 38				12 57		
Preston 8	a	11 56		12 05			12 15						12 37				12 41	12 56				13 15		
Blackpool North	a			12e48			13 00										13 21	13e48				14 00		
	d	11 15	11 37																12 37			12 45		
Preston 8	d	11 58	12 04	12 10			12 17										12 47	12 58	13 04			13 17		
Wigan North Western	a	12 09	12 24				12 28											13 09	13 24			13 28		
	d	12 09	12 24				12 28											13 09	13 24			13 28		
Bolton	a			12 34			12f55										13 08	13f34				13f55		
Manchester Piccadilly 10	a			12 56			13f18										13 27	13f56				14f18		
Manchester Airport	a			13 17													13 47	14f17						
Liverpool Lime Street 10	a		13 02				13 28												14 02			14 28		
	d									12 34	12 48					13 04								
Liverpool South Parkway 7	d									12 44						13 15								
Runcorn	d									12 52	13 04					13 25								
Warrington Bank Quay	a	12 20					12 39											13 20				13 39		
	d	12 20					12 39											13 20				13 39		
Hartford	d									13 06														
Manchester Piccadilly 10	d				12 15			12 27	12 35	12 30				12 55	13 07					13 15			13 27	13 35
Stockport	d				12 23			12 35	12 42	12 39				13 04						13 23			13 35	13 42
Manchester Airport	d					12g11																13 11		
Wilmslow	d					12g21				12 47				13 11								13 22		
Holyhead	d					10 33															11 23			
Bangor (Gwynedd)	d					11 06															12 02			
Llandudno	d					11h10								11j44							12h10			
Llandudno Junction	d					11 25								11j53							12 25			
Wrexham General	d					12 02															13 00			
Chester	d					12 35								12 55							13 35			
Crewe 10	a					12 54	12 59			13 20		←		13 27		13 44					13 54	13 59		
	d					12 57	13 01			13 22		13 22		13 29		13 49					13 56	14 01		
Macclesfield	d							12 49	12 55	→													13 49	13 55
Congleton	d																							
Stoke-on-Trent	d				12 50			13 07	13 12						13 44					13 50			14 07	14 12
Stafford	a							13 25			13 35	13 42				14 09							14 25	
	d							13 25			13 36	13 43				14 10							14 25	
Penkridge	a															14 15								
Wolverhampton 7	a						13 31	13 39				13 56			14 13	14 27						14 31	14 39	
Birmingham New Street 12	a						13 55	13 58				14 17			14 31	14 47						14 55	14 58	
Birmingham International	a						14 19	14 13				14 38			14 59							15 19	15 13	
Coventry	a						14 30	14 24				14 49			15 10							15 30	15 24	
Lichfield Trent Valley	a															14k39								
Tamworth Low Level	a															14k46								
Nuneaton	a															15k01								
Rugby	a											15 12			15 21									
Northampton	a																							
Milton Keynes Central	a				13 46	14s01														14 46	15s01			
Watford Junction	a				14 29	14 50														15 29	15 50			
Gatwick Airport 10	a																							
London Euston 15	a	14 12			14 23	14 38			14 42		14 56			15 04				15 12		15 23	15 38			15 42

For general notes see front of timetable
For details of catering facilities see Directory of Train Operators

A To Bournemouth (Table 51)

B To Bristol Temple Meads (Table 51)

b Change at Haymarket

c Via Glasgow Queen Street and Glasgow Central. Passengers make their own way from one station to the other

e From 10 October arr. 2 mins. later

f Change at Preston

g Change at Crewe

h Change at Llandudno Junction and Chester

j Change at Chester and Crewe

k Change at Stafford

Scotland and North West England → West Midlands and London

Route Diagram - see first page of Table 65

		LM	VT	LM	VT	XC	LM	TP	VT	NT		VT	VT	VT	XC	VT	LM	VT	LM	VT	XC	LM	TP	TP	TP
		1 ◇	1 ◇	1 ◇	1 ◇	1 ◇	1 ◇	1 ◇	1 ◇			1 ◇	1 ◇	1 ◇	1 ◇	1 ◇	1 ◇	1 ◇	1 ◇	1 ◇	1 ◇	1 ◇	1 ◇	1 ◇	1 ◇
						A		B							C						D		E	E	G
Inverness	d													07b55											
Aberdeen	d													08c42										09e07	
Dundee	d													09c52										10e34	
Perth	d								09c15					10c14										09e55	
Edinburgh 10	d																							12 08	
Haymarket	d																							12u11	
Glasgow Central 15	d								11 40					12 00											
Motherwell	d																								
Carstairs	d																								
Lockerbie	d																							13 06	
Carlisle 8	a								12 46					13 08										13 28	
	d								12 49					13 09										13 30	
Penrith North Lakes	d								13 03																
Windermere	d							12 51																	
Oxenholme Lake District	a							13 07																14 05	
	d							13 09																14 06	
Barrow-in-Furness	d							12 11															13 25		13 25
Lancaster 6	a							13 26	13 37					13 56									14 18	14 22	14 18
	d							13 26	13 38					13 58									14 18	14 22	14 18
Preston 8	a							13 45	13 56					14 15									14 37	14 41	14 37
Blackpool North	a							14 20	14f48					15 00										15 20	
	d								13 20	13 37				13 45											
Preston 8	d							13 47	13 58	14 04				14 17										14 47	
Wigan North Western	a								14 09	14 24				14 28											
	d								14 09	14 24				14 28											
Bolton	a							14 08	14g34					14g55										15 08	
Manchester Piccadilly 10	a							14 27	14g56					15g18										15 27	
Manchester Airport	a							14 47	15g17															15 47	
Liverpool Lime Street 10	a									15 02				15 28											
	d	13 34	13 48				14 04										14 34	14 48				15 04			
Liverpool South Parkway 7	d	13 44					14 15										14 44					15 15			
Runcorn	d	13 52	14 04				14 25										14 52	15 04				15 25			
Warrington Bank Quay	a								14 20					14 39											
	d								14 20					14 39											
Hartford	d	14 04															15 04								
Manchester Piccadilly 10	d	13 30			13 55	14 07						14 15			14 27	14 35	14 30			14 55	15 07				
Stockport	d	13 39			14 04							14 23			14 35	14 42	14 39			15 04					
Manchester Airport	d												14h11												
Wilmslow	d	13 47			14 11								14h21				14 47			15 11					
Holyhead	d												12 38												
Bangor (Gwynedd)	d												13 07												
Llandudno	d				12j44								13k10							13j44					
Llandudno Junction	d				12j53								13 25							13j53					
Wrexham General	d												14 02												
Chester	d				13 55								14 35							14 55					
Crewe 10	a	14 19		←	14 27		14 44						14 54	14 59			15 19		←	15 27		15 44			
	d	14 22		14 22	14 29		14 49						14 56	15 01			15 22		15 22	15 29		15 49			
Macclesfield	d	→													14 49	14 55	→								
Congleton	d																								
Stoke-on-Trent	d					14 44						14 50			15 07	15 12					15 44				
Stafford	a		14 35	14 46			15 09								15 25			15 35	15 42			16 09			
	d		14 36	14 46			15 10								15 25			15 36	15 43			16 10			
Penkridge	a						15 15															16 15			
Wolverhampton 7	a			14 59		15 13	15 27							15 31	15 39				15 56		16 13	16 27			
Birmingham New Street 12	a			15 18		15 31	15 47							15 55	15 58				16 17		16 31	16 47			
Birmingham International	a			15 38		15 59								16 19	16 13				16 38		16 59				
Coventry	a			15 49		16 10								16 30	16 24				16 49		17 10				
Lichfield Trent Valley	a						15m39															16m39			
Tamworth Low Level	a						15m46															16m46			
Nuneaton	a						16m01															17m01			
Rugby	a			16 12		16 21													17 12		17 21				
Northampton	a																								
Milton Keynes Central	a											15 46	16s01												
Watford Junction	a											16 29	16 50												
Gatwick Airport 10	a																								
London Euston 15	⊖ a		15 56		16 04				16 12			16 23	16 38			16 42		16 56		17 04					

For general notes see front of timetable
For details of catering facilities see Directory of Train Operators

- **A** To Bristol Temple Meads (from 12 September to Paignton) (Table 51)
- **B** 🍴 from Preston
- **C** To Bournemouth (Table 51)
- **D** To Bristol Temple Meads (Table 51)
- **E** Until 20 June and from 13 September
- **G** 27 June to 5 September
- **b** Change at Perth, Glasgow Queen Street and Glasgow Central. Passengers make their own way between Glasgow Queen Street and Glasgow Central
- **c** Via Glasgow Queen Street and Glasgow Central. Passengers make their own way from one station to the other
- **e** Change at Haymarket
- **f** From 10 October arr. 2 mins. later
- **g** Change at Preston
- **h** Change at Crewe
- **j** Change at Chester and Crewe
- **k** Change at Llandudno Junction and Chester
- **m** Change at Stafford

Table 65

Saturdays

until 31 October

Scotland and North West England → West Midlands and London

Route Diagram - see first page of Table 65

		TP	VT	NT	VT	VT	VT	XC	VT	LM	VT	LM		VT	XC	LM	TP	VT	VT	NT	VT	VT	XC	VT	LM
		1 ◇	1 ◇		1 ◇	1 ◇	1 ◇	1 ◇	1 ◇	1 ◇	1 ◇	1 ◇		1 ◇	1 ◇	1 ◇	1 ◇	1 ◇	1 ◇		1 ◇	1 ◇	1 ◇	1 ◇	1 ◇
		A						B							C								B		
		🛒	ꟷP		ꟷP	ꟷP	ꟷP	🛒	ꟷP		ꟷP			ꟷP	🛒		🛒	ꟷP	ꟷP		ꟷP	ꟷP	🛒	ꟷP	
Inverness	d																	09b18							
Aberdeen	d	09c07															09b37					10b38			
Dundee	d	10c34															10b52					11b49			
Perth	d	09c55					10c57										11b14	11b37				12b11			
Edinburgh 10	d	12 08					12 52																		
Haymarket	d	12u11					12u57																		
Glasgow Central 15	d		12 40														13 00	13 40				14 00			
Motherwell	d																								
Carstairs	d																								
Lockerbie	d	13 06															13 58								
Carlisle 8	a	13 28	13 47				14 05										14 21	14 46				15 09			
	d	13 30	13 49				14 07										14 30	14 49				15 11			
Penrith North Lakes	d						14 22										14 45								
Windermere	d		14 00															14 59							
Oxenholme Lake District	a	14 05	14 22														15 08	15 22				15 45			
	d	14 06	14 24														15 09	15 23				15 46			
Barrow-in-Furness	d																	14 16							
Lancaster 6	a	14 22	14 37				14 56										15 26	15 37							
	d	14 22	14 38				14 57										15 26	15 38							
Preston 8	a	14 41	14 56				15 15										15 45	15 56				16 15			
Blackpool North	a	15 20	15e48				16 00										16 20					17 00			
	d		14 20	14 37			14 45											15 20		15 37		15 45			
Preston 8	d	14 47	14 58	15 04			15 17										15 47	15 58		16 04		16 17			
Wigan North Western	a		15 09	15 24			15 28											16 09		16 24		16 28			
	d		15 09	15 24			15 28											16 09		16 24		16 28			
Bolton	a	15 08	15f34				15f55										16 08	16f34				16f55			
Manchester Piccadilly 10	a	15 27	15f56				16f18										16 27	16f56				17f18			
Manchester Airport	a	15 47	16f17														16 47	17f17							
Liverpool Lime Street 10	a			16 02			16 28													17 05		17 28			
	d									15 34	15 48					16 04									16 34
Liverpool South Parkway 7	d									15 44						16 15									16 44
Runcorn	d									15 52	16 04					16 25									16 52
Warrington Bank Quay	a		15 20				15 39											16 20				16 39			
	d		15 20				15 39											16 20				16 39			
Hartford	d									16 04															17 06
Manchester Piccadilly 10	d				15 15			15 27	15 35	15 30				15 55	16 07				16 15				16 27	16 35	16 30
Stockport	d				15 23			15 35	15 42	15 39				16 04					16 23				16 35	16 42	16 39
Manchester Airport	d					15g11															16g11				
Wilmslow	d					15g21				15 47				16 11							16g21				16 49
Holyhead	d					13 23															14 36				
Bangor (Gwynedd)	d					14 02															15 06				
Llandudno	d					14h10								14j42							15 10				
Llandudno Junction	d					14 25								14j51							15 25				
Wrexham General	d					15 00																			
Chester	d					15 35								15 55							16 20				
Crewe 10	a					15 54	15 59			16 19		←		16 27		16 44					16 44	16 59			17 20
	d					15 56	16 01			16 22		16 22		16 29		16 49					16 56	17 01			17 22
Macclesfield	d							15 49	15 55	→													16 49	16 56	→
Congleton	d																								
Stoke-on-Trent	d				15 50			16 07	16 12						16 44				16 50				17 07	17 13	
Stafford	a							16 24			16 35	16 46				17 09							17 25		
	d							16 25			16 36	16 46				17 10							17 25		
Penkridge	a															17 15									
Wolverhampton 7	a						16 31	16 39				16 59			17 13	17 27						17 31	17 39		
Birmingham New Street 12	a						16 55	16 58				17 18			17 31	17 47						17 55	17 58		
Birmingham International	a						17 19	17 13				17 38			17 59							18 19	18 13		
Coventry	a						17 30	17 24				17 49			18 10							18 30	18 24		
Lichfield Trent Valley	a															17k39									
Tamworth Low Level	a															17k46									
Nuneaton	a															18k01									
Rugby	a											18 12			18 21										
Northampton	a																								
Milton Keynes Central	a				16 46	17s01													17 46		18 01				
Watford Junction	a				17 29	17 50													18 29		18 50				
Gatwick Airport 10	a																								
London Euston 15	⊖ a		17 12		17 23	17 38			17 42		17 57			18 04				18 12	18 23		18 38			18 42	

For general notes see front of timetable
For details of catering facilities see Directory of Train Operators

A 27 June to 5 September
B To Bournemouth (Table 51)
C To Paignton (from 12 September to Bristol Temple Meads) (Table 51)
b Via Glasgow Queen Street and Glasgow Central. Passengers make their own way from one station to the other
c Change at Haymarket
e From 10 October arr. 2 mins. later
f Change at Preston
g Change at Crewe
h Change at Llandudno Junction and Chester
j Change at Chester and Crewe
k Change at Stafford

Scotland and North West England → West Midlands and London

Route Diagram - see first page of Table 65

		VT	LM	VT	XC	LM	XC	TP	VT	VT	VT	VT	NT	VT		LM	TP	VT	XC	LM	VT	NT	VT	TP	VT
		1◇	1◇	1◇	1◇	1◇	1◇	1◇	1◇	1◇	1◇	1◇		1◇		1◇	1◇	1◇	1◇	1◇	1◇		1◇	1◇	1◇
					A		B										C		D					C	
Inverness	d													10b47											
Aberdeen	d							11 05													11c42				12c42
Dundee	d							12 34						13b34											13c50
Perth	d													13b01							13c14				14c11
Edinburgh 10	d							14 11						14 52											
Haymarket	d													14u57											
Glasgow Central 15	d								14 40												15 40				16 00
Motherwell	d																								
Carstairs	d																								
Lockerbie	d																								
Carlisle 8	a							15 28	15 46					16 05							16 46				17 08
	d							15 30	15 49					16 07							16 49				17 09
Penrith North Lakes	d							15 44						16 22							17 03				
Windermere	d								16 02															17 06	
Oxenholme Lake District	a							16 08	16 22															17 25	17 44
	d							16 08	16 24															17 30	17 44
Barrow-in-Furness	d								15 18								16 22								
Lancaster 6	a							16 26	16 37					16 56			17 15				17 37			17 47	
	d							16 26	16 38					16 57			17 15				17 38			17 48	
Preston 8	a							16 45	16 56					17 15			17 34				17 56			18 06	18 15
Blackpool North	a							17 20	17e48					18 02			18 20							18e48	19 00
	d								16 20				16 35	16 41							17 18	17 37			17 37
Preston 8	d							16 47	16 58				17 04	17 17			17 47				17 58	18 04		18 08	18 17
Wigan North Western	a								17 09				17 24	17 28							18 09	18 24			18 28
	d								17 09				17 24	17 28							18 09	18 24			18 28
Bolton	a							17 08	17f34					17f55			18 08							18 34	
Manchester Piccadilly 10	a							17 27	17f56					18f18			18 27							18 56	
Manchester Airport	a							17 48	18f17								18 47							19 17	
Liverpool Lime Street 10	a												18 02	18 28								19 02			19 28
	d	16 48				17 04						17 48				17 34				18 04					
Liverpool South Parkway 7	d					17 15										17 44				18 15					
Runcorn	d	17 04				17 25						18 04				17 52				18 25					
Warrington Bank Quay	a								17 20					17 39							18 20				18 39
	d								17 20					17 39							18 20				18 39
Hartford	d															18 05									
Manchester Piccadilly 10	d			16 55	17 06		17 27			17 15	17 35					17 30		17 55	18 05				18 15		
Stockport	d			17 04			17 35			17 23	17 43					17 40		18 04					18 23		
Manchester Airport	d													17 11											18 11
Wilmslow	d			17 11										17 21		17 48		18 11							18 22
Holyhead	d															15g23									
Bangor (Gwynedd)	d															16g02									
Llandudno	d			15g44												16h10		16g44							
Llandudno Junction	d			15g53												16g25		16g53							
Wrexham General	d																								
Chester	d			16 55												17 35		17 55							
Crewe 10	a		⟵	17 27		17 46								17 59		18 19		18 27		18 46					18 59
	d		17 22	17 29		17 49								18 01		18 22		18 29		18 49					19 01
Macclesfield	d				17 27						17 55								18 25						
Congleton	d						17 54																		
Stoke-on-Trent	d				17 44		18 07			17 50	18 13								18 44				18 50		
Stafford	a	17 35	17 42			18 09	18 25					18 34				18 42				19 09					
	d	17 36	17 43			18 10	18 25					18 36				18 43				19 10					
Penkridge	a					18 15														19 15					
Wolverhampton 7	a		17 56		18 13	18 27	18 39							18 31		18 56			19 13	19 27					19 31
Birmingham New Street 12	a		18 17		18 31	18 47	18 58							18 55		19 17			19 31	19 47					19 55
Birmingham International	a		18 38		18 59		19 13							19 19		19 45			20 05						20 19
Coventry	a		18 49		19 10		19 24							19 30		20 00			20 20	20 24					20 30
Lichfield Trent Valley	a					18j39														19j39					
Tamworth Low Level	a					18j46														19j46					
Nuneaton	a					19j01														20j01					
Rugby	a		19 12		19 21		19 42							19 42		20 12			20 32						20k41
Northampton	a																								
Milton Keynes Central	a									18 46													19 46		
Watford Junction	a									19 29													20 34		
Gatwick Airport 10	a																								
London Euston 15	⊖ a	18 56		19 04					19 12	19 23	19 42	19 56						20 04			20 15		20 28		

For general notes see front of timetable
For details of catering facilities see Directory of Train Operators

A To Cardiff Central (Table 51)
B To Bournemouth (Table 51)
C trolley service from Preston
D To Bristol Temple Meads (from 12 September to Plymouth) (Table 51)
b Change at Haymarket
c Via Glasgow Queen Street and Glasgow Central. Passengers make their own way from one station to the other
e From 10 October arr. 2 mins. later
f Change at Preston
g Change at Chester and Crewe
h Change at Llandudno Junction, Chester and Crewe
j Change at Stafford
k From 12 September arr. 2042

Table 65

Saturdays

until 31 October

Scotland and North West England → West Midlands and London

Route Diagram - see first page of Table 65

		XC	VT	LM	VT	LM	TP	XC	LM	VT	TP	VT	VT	NT	VT	XC		VT	VT	LM	VT	NT	LM	XC	TP
		A						B		C		D	C			E		D	C			G			
Inverness	d														12b54										
Aberdeen	d																								13c42
Dundee	d										14b34				15b17										
Perth	d										13b58				15b00										15c14
Edinburgh 10	d										16 11				16 52										
Haymarket	d										16u14				16u57										
Glasgow Central 15	d											16 40	16 40												17 07
Motherwell	d											16u54	16u54												
Carstairs	d																								
Lockerbie	d										17 10														18 05
Carlisle 8	a										17 32	17 49	17 49		18 05										18 27
	d										17 33	17 52	17 52		18 07										18 29
Penrith North Lakes	d										17 48														18 44
Windermere	d											18 02	18 02												
Oxenholme Lake District	a											18 25	18 25		18 41										19 08
	d											18 26	18 26		18 42										19 08
Barrow-in-Furness	d						17 21															18 03			
Lancaster 6	a						18 17				18 26	18 40	18 40		18 56							19 04			19 26
	d						18 17				18 26	18 41	18 41		18 57							19 05			19 26
Preston 8	a						18 36				18 45	18 59	18 59		19 15							19 30			19 45
Blackpool North	a						19e16				19 20	19e48	19 48		20 00										
	d											18 29	18 29	18 37	18 45										
Preston 8	d										18 47	19 01	19 01	19 04	19 17										19 47
Wigan North Western	a											19 12	19 12	19 24	19 28										
	d											19 12	19 12	19 24	19 28										
Bolton	a										19 08	19f34	19f34												20 08
Manchester Piccadilly 10	a										19 27	19f56	19f56												20 27
Manchester Airport	a										19 50	20f17	20f17												20 47
Liverpool Lime Street 10	a													20 02	20 58										
	d			18 34	18 48				19 04											19 34	19 48				
Liverpool South Parkway 7	d			18 44					19 14											19 44					
Runcorn	d			18 52	19 04				19 23											19 52	20 04				
Warrington Bank Quay	a											19 23	19 23		19 39										
	d											19 23	19 23		19 39										
Hartford	d			19 04																20 04					
Manchester Piccadilly 10	d	18 27	18 35	18 30				19 07		18 55						19 27		19 35	19 35	19 30				20 07	
Stockport	d	18 35	18 42	18 39				19 16		19 04						19 35		19 42	19 42	19 39				20 16	
Manchester Airport	d																			19g14					
Wilmslow	d			18 47						19 11										19 47					
Holyhead	d									16h38															
Bangor (Gwynedd)	d									17h07															
Llandudno	d									17h44															
Llandudno Junction	d									17h53															
Wrexham General	d																								
Chester	d									18 55															
Crewe 10	a			19 19		←			19 49	19 27					19 59					20 16			←		
	d			19 22		19 22			19 51	19 29					20 01					20 22			20 22		
Macclesfield	d		18 55	→												19 49		19 55	19 55	→					
Congleton	d	18 54																							
Stoke-on-Trent	d	19 07	19 12					19 44								20 07		20 12	20 12					20 44	
Stafford	a	19 25			19 35	19 42			20 11							20 25					20 35		20 42		
	d	19 25			19 36	19 43			20 12							20 25					20 36		20 43		
Penkridge	a					19 48																	20 48		
Wolverhampton 7	a	19 39				19 57		20 13	20 28						20 31	20 39							20 57	21 13	
Birmingham New Street 12	a	19 58				20 17		20 31	20 47						20 56	20 58							21 17	21 36	
Birmingham International	a	20 13				20 45		21 05							21 19	21 13							21 45	22 05	
Coventry	a	20 24				21 00		21 20							21 30	21 24							22 00	22 20	
Lichfield Trent Valley	a																								
Tamworth Low Level	a																								
Nuneaton	a																								
Rugby	a	20j41				21 12		21 32								21k41							22 12	22 32	
Northampton	a																								
Milton Keynes Central	a											20 43	20 59					21 10	21 26						
Watford Junction	a											21s23	21s38					21 50	22 16						
Gatwick Airport 10	a																								
London Euston 15	a		21m16		21n25					21q58		21 47	22 03					22 02	22 21		22r43				

For general notes see front of timetable
For details of catering facilities see Directory of Train Operators

- **A** To Bournemouth (Table 51)
- **B** To Bristol Temple Meads (Table 51)
- **C** Until 5 September
- **D** From 12 September
- **E** To Southampton Central (Table 51)
- **G** From Carlisle via Whitehaven (Table 100)
- **b** Change at Haymarket
- **c** Via Glasgow Queen Street and Glasgow Central. Passengers make their own way from one station to the other
- **e** From 10 October arr. 2 mins. later
- **f** Change at Preston
- **g** Change at Wilmslow and Crewe
- **h** Change at Chester and Crewe
- **j** From 12 September arr. 2042
- **k** From 12 September arr. 2142
- **m** From 12 September arr. 2101
- **n** From 12 September arr. 2115
- **q** From 12 September arr. 2119
- **r** From 12 September arr. 2217

Table 65

Saturdays

until 31 October

Scotland and North West England → West Midlands and London

Route Diagram - see first page of Table 65

		VT	VT	NT	VT	XC	VT	VT	LM	XC	TP	VT	NT	TP	VT	XC	XC	SR	LM	TP	NT	NT	SR
		1 ◇	1 ◇		1 ◇	1 ◇	1 ◇	1 ◇	1 ◇	1 ◇	1 ◇	1 ◇		1 ◇	1 ◇	1 ◇	1 ◇		1 ◇	1 ◇			
		A	B				A	B								C	D						
Inverness	d														14b51								16c56
Aberdeen	d				14e39						14f49				16f01			16e37					18e33
Dundee	d				15e49						16f03				17f26			17e51					19e46
Perth	d				16e11						15f59				17f00			18e12					20e11
Edinburgh 10	d										18 11				18 52								
Haymarket	d										18u14				18u57								
Glasgow Central 15	d	17 40	17 40		18 00							18 40						20 03					22 03
Motherwell	d																						
Carstairs	d																						
Lockerbie	d	18 32	18 32								19 10												
Carlisle 8	a	18 50	18 50		19 08						19 32	19 47			20 05			22 24					00 34
	d	18 52	18 52		19 09						19 33	19 49			20 07								
Penrith North Lakes	d	19 06	19 06								19 48	20 03			20 22								
Windermere	d	19 00	19 00									20 00								21 40			
Oxenholme Lake District	a	19 28	19 28								20 12	20 25			20 45					21 59			
	d	19 29	19 29								20 12	20 26			20 45					22 01			
Barrow-in-Furness	d													19 42								21 43	
Lancaster 6	a	19 43	19 43		19 55						20 26	20 40		20 45	20 59					22 17		22 44	
	d	19 44	19 44		19 56						20 26	20 41		20 45	21 00					22 17		22 45	
Preston 8	a	20 02	20 02		20 15						20 45	20 59		21 03	21 18					22 38		23 08	
Blackpool North	a	20 44	20 44		20g54									21g48	22 00					23 21		23g48	
	d	19 20	19 20	19 37	19 45							20 29	20 38		20 45						22 14		
Preston 8	d	20 04	20 04	20 04	20 17						20 47	21 01	21 04	21 15	21 20						22 43		
Wigan North Western	a	20 15	20 15	20 24	20 28							21 12	21 24		21 31						23 02		
	d	20 15	20 15	20 24	20 28							21 12	21 24		21 31						23 03		
Bolton	a	20h34	20h34								21 08	21h34		21 39	22h25					23j25		00 07	
Manchester Piccadilly 10	a	20h56	20h56								21 27	21h56		22 02	22h56					23 53			
Manchester Airport	a	21h17	21h17								21 47	22h17		22k57	23h17					00 22			
Liverpool Lime Street 10	a			21 02	21 28								22 14		23 15						23 54		
	d								20 34										21 34				
Liverpool South Parkway 7	d								20 44										21 44				
Runcorn	d								20 52										21 52				
Warrington Bank Quay	a	20 26	20 26		20 39							21 23			21 42								
	d	20 26	20 26		20 39							21 23			21 42								
Hartford	d								21 03										22 04				
Manchester Piccadilly 10	d					20 27	20 35	20 35	20 30	21 06						21 27	21 27		21 30				
Stockport	d					20 35	20 43	20 43	20 39							21 35	21 35		21 39				
Manchester Airport	d								20m14							21 14							
Wilmslow	d								20 47							21 45			21 47				
Holyhead	d	17n21	17n21		18 23																		
Bangor (Gwynedd)	d	18n00	18n00		19 02																		
Llandudno	d	18n44	18n44		19q10							19n42											
Llandudno Junction	d	18n53	18n53		19 25							19n51											
Wrexham General	d																						
Chester	d	19 55	19 55		20 17				20 35			20 55											
Crewe 10	a	20 45	20 45		20 59				21 15			21 42			22 02				22 18				
	d	20 47	20 47		21 01				21 17			21 44			22 04				22 20				
Macclesfield	d					20 49	20 56	20 56									21 49						
Congleton	d																						
Stoke-on-Trent	d					21 07	21 13	21 13		21 44							22 07						
Stafford	a					21 25			21 41			22 08			22 28	22 32	22 33		22 45				
	d					21 25			21 41			22 09			22 29	22 33	22 33		22 45				
Penkridge	a								21 47										22 51				
Wolverhampton 7	a				21 31	21 39			21 57	22 13		22 23			22 42	22 50	22 50		23 01				
Birmingham New Street 12	a				21 55	22 03			22 19	22 37		22 47			23 01	23 22	23 22		23 20				
Birmingham International	a				22 19				22 45	23 05					23 30								
Coventry	a				22 30				23 00	23 20					23 48								
Lichfield Trent Valley	a																						
Tamworth Low Level	a																						
Nuneaton	a																						
Rugby	a				22 41					23r32													
Northampton	a																						
Milton Keynes Central	a	21 51	22 11				22 12	22 28															
Watford Junction	a	22 34	22 44				22s42	23s11															
Gatwick Airport 10	a																						
London Euston 15	⊖ a	22 43	23 03				23 04	23 36															

For general notes see front of timetable
For details of catering facilities see Directory of Train Operators

- **A** From 12 September
- **B** Until 5 September
- **C** Until 11 July
- **D** From 18 July
- **b** Change at Perth and Haymarket
- **c** Change at Perth, Glasgow Queen Street and Glasgow Central. Passengers make their own way between Glasgow Queen Street and Glasgow Central
- **e** Via Glasgow Queen Street and Glasgow Central. Passengers make their own way from one station to the other
- **f** Change at Haymarket
- **g** From 10 October arr. 2 mins. later
- **h** Change at Preston
- **j** From 10 October arr. 2334
- **k** Until 3 October arr. 2217, change at Preston
- **m** Change at Wilmslow and Crewe
- **n** Change at Chester and Crewe
- **q** Change at Llandudno Junction and Crewe
- **r** Until 11 July arr. 0008 Sunday mornings, change at Birmingham New Street and Coventry. By bus from Coventry

Table 65

Saturdays

from 7 November

Scotland and North West England → West Midlands and London

Route Diagram - see first page of Table 65

	AW	XC	VT	XC	VT	LM	VT	XC	VT	VT	VT	LM	VT	LM	VT	VT	XC	LM	TP	VT	VT	VT	VT	VT
		1◇	1◇	1◇	1◇	1◇	1◇	1◇	1◇	1◇	1◇	1◇	1◇	1◇	1◇	1◇	1◇	1◇	1◇	1◇	1◇	1◇	1◇	1◇
		A		A				B									B							
		⊼	⊡	⊼	⊡		⊡	⊼	⊡	⊡	⊡		⊡		⊡	⊡	⊼			⊡	⊡	⊡	⊡	⊡
Inverness d																								
Aberdeen d																								
Dundee d																								
Perth d																								
Edinburgh 10 d																								
Haymarket d																								
Glasgow Central 15 d																				04 25				
Motherwell d																								
Carstairs d																								
Lockerbie d																								
Carlisle 8 a																				05 42				
d																				05 43				
Penrith North Lakes d																				05 58				
Windermere d																								
Oxenholme Lake District a																				06 20				
d																				06 21				
Barrow-in-Furness d																			05 31					
Lancaster 6 a																			06 23	06 35				
d									05 40										06 26	06 36			06 58	
Preston 8 a									05 55										06 45	06 54			07 15	
Blackpool North a									07 03											07 43			08 05	
d									04 57				05 45							06 19			06 34	
Preston 8 d									05 58				06 17						06 47	06 58			07 17	
Wigan North Western a									06 09				06 28							07 09			07 28	
d									06 09				06 28							07 10			07 28	
Bolton a									06b34										07 08	07b34				
Manchester Piccadilly 10 a									06b56										07 27	07b56				
Manchester Airport ✈ a									07b17										07 47	08b17				
Liverpool Lime Street 10 a													07 28										08 28	
d					05 47									06 33	06 45			07 05						
Liverpool South Parkway 7 ✈ d														06 43				07 15						
Runcorn d					06 03									06 51	07 01			07 23						
Warrington Bank Quay a									06 20				06 39							07 20			07 39	
d									06 20				06 39							07 20			07 39	
Hartford d														07 02				07 36						
Manchester Piccadilly 10 d		05 11	05 25				05 55	06 00		06 10	06 35			06 30		06 55	07 07				07 15			07 35
Stockport d			05 34				06 03	06 08		06 18	06 43			06 39		07 04					07 23			07 43
Manchester Airport ✈ d													06 05			06 05							07 11	
Wilmslow d			05 41				06 11						06 14	06 47		07 11							07 21	
Holyhead d														04c25										
Bangor (Gwynedd) d														04c57										
Llandudno d																								
Llandudno Junction d						04 38								05 46										
Wrexham General d																						06 49		
Chester d	04 23	04 55				05 37	05 51							06 43				07 17				07 17		
Crewe 10 a	04 44	05 45	05 57				06 27						06 59	07 14	07 18	07 27		07 47				07 36	07 59	
d	05 00	05 47	06 00			06 20	06 29					06 47	07 01	07 16	07 20	07 29		07 49				07 38	08 01	
Macclesfield d								06 21		06 31	06 55													07 56
Congleton d				←																				
Stoke-on-Trent d		06 07		06 07				06 39		06 48	07 12						07 44				07 50			08 12
Stafford a	05 24	→	06 17	06 25	06 34	06 41		06 57				07 10		07 40	07 38			08 10						
d	05 24		06 19	06 25	06 35	06 41		06 58				07 12		07 41	07 39			08 10						
Penkridge a						06 47						07 17		07 46				08 16						
Wolverhampton 7 a	05 38			06 39		06 57		07 12				07 28	07 32	07 57			08 13	08 28					08 31	
Birmingham New Street 12 a	05 55			06 58		07 17		07 31				07 47	07 55	08 17			08 31	08 47					08 55	
Birmingham International ✈ a	06 19			07 13		07 39		07 59				08 13	08 19	08 38			08 59						09 19	
Coventry a	06 30			07 24		07 50		08 10				08 24	08 30	08 49			09 10						09 30	
Lichfield Trent Valley a										07 11		07e41												
Tamworth Low Level a										07 17		07e48												
Nuneaton a					06 57							08e03												
Rugby a	07 12		06 49			08 12		08 21			07 52			09 12			09 21							
Northampton a			07 34								08 34													
Milton Keynes Central a			07 11				07 31		07 37		09 03										08 46			
Watford Junction a			07s34		07s44				08 20												09 34			
Gatwick Airport 10 ✈ a																								
London Euston 15 ⊖ a			07 54		08 05		08 10		08 14	08 27	08 46				08 59	09 04				09 12	09 23	09 30		09 42

For general notes see front of timetable
For details of catering facilities see Directory of Train Operators

A To Bournemouth (Table 51)
B To Bristol Temple Meads (Table 51)
b Change at Preston
c Change at Llandudno Junction and Crewe
e Change at Stafford

Table 65

Saturdays

from 7 November

Scotland and North West England → West Midlands and London

Route Diagram - see first page of Table 65

Station		VT	XC	LM	VT	LM	VT	XC	LM	NT	TP	VT	VT	VT	VT	XC	VT	LM		VT	LM	VT	XC	LM	TP
		1◇	1◇	1◇	1◇	1◇	1◇	1◇	1◇		1◇	1◇	1◇	1◇	1◇	1◇	1◇	1◇		1◇	1◇	1◇	1◇	1◇	1◇
			A					B			C					A							D		C
		☕	🛒		☕		☕	🛒			🛒	☕	☕	☕	☕	🛒	☕			☕		☕	🛒		🛒
Inverness	d																								
Aberdeen	d																								
Dundee	d																								
Perth	d																								
Edinburgh 10	d																								
Haymarket	d																								
Glasgow Central 15	d											05 40			05 50										
Motherwell	d														06u05										
Carstairs	d																								
Lockerbie	d																								
Carlisle 8	a											06 46			07 02										
	d											06 49			07 03										
Penrith North Lakes	d														07 18										
Windermere	d											*06 50*													
Oxenholme Lake District	a											07 22			07 41										
	d											07 24			07 42										
Barrow-in-Furness	d										06 19														07 28
Lancaster 6	a										07 21	07 37			07 56										08 26
	d										07 22	07 38			07 57										08 26
Preston 8	a										07 41	07 56			08 15										08 45
Blackpool North	a										*08 18*	08 46			09 05										*09 20*
	d									07 02		*07 18*			*07 29*										
Preston 8	d									07 30	07 47	07 58			08 17										08 47
Wigan North Western	a									07 50		08 09			08 28										
	d									07 50		08 09			08 28										
Bolton	a										08 08	*08b34*			*08b55*										09 08
Manchester Piccadilly 10	a										08 27	*08b56*			*09b18*										09 27
Manchester Airport ✈	a										08 47	*09b19*													09 47
Liverpool Lime Street 10	a									08 34		*09 18*			*09 58*										
	d	07 19		07 34	07 48				08 04									08 34		08 48				09 04	
Liverpool South Parkway 7 ✈	d			07 44					08 15									08 44						09 15	
Runcorn	d	07 36		07 52	08 04				08 25									08 52		09 04				09 25	
Warrington Bank Quay	a											08 20			08 39										
	d											08 20			08 39										
Hartford	d			08 04														09 06							
Manchester Piccadilly 10	d		07 27	07 30			07 55	08 07					08 15			08 27	08 35	*08 30*				08 55	09 07		
Stockport	d		07 35	07 39			08 04						08 23			08 35	08 42	*08 39*				09 04			
Manchester Airport ✈	d														*08 11*										
Wilmslow	d			*07 47*			08 11								*08 22*			*08 47*				09 11			
Holyhead	d						*05c22*							06 50											
Bangor (Gwynedd)	d						*06c01*							07 17											
Llandudno	d						*06c34*							*07 10*								*07c45*			
Llandudno Junction	d						*06c44*							07 35								*07c54*			
Wrexham General	d													*08 01*											
Chester	d						*07 55*							08 35								*08 55*			
Crewe 10	a	07 52		08 19		←	08 27		08 47					08 54	08 59			09 20			←	09 27		09 44	
	d	07 55		08 22		08 22	08 29		08 49					08 56	09 01			09 22			09 22	09 29		09 49	
Macclesfield	d		07 49	→												08 49	08 55	→							
Congleton	d																								
Stoke-on-Trent	d		08 07					08 44					08 50			09 07	09 13						09 44		
Stafford	a	08 14	08 25		08 35	08 42			09 09							09 25				09 35	09 42			10 09	
	d	08 16	08 25		08 36	08 43			09 10							09 25				09 36	09 43			10 10	
Penkridge	a					08 48			09 15															10 15	
Wolverhampton 7	a		08 39			08 58		09 13	09 27						09 31	09 39					09 56		10 13	10 27	
Birmingham New Street 12	a		08 58			09 18		09 31	09 47						09 55	09 58					10 17		10 31	10 47	
Birmingham International ✈	a		09 13			*09 38*		*09 59*							*10 19*	10 13					*10 38*		*10 59*		
Coventry	a		09 24			*09 49*		*10 10*	*10 24*						*10 30*	10 24					*10 49*		*11 10*		
Lichfield Trent Valley	a	08 30							*09e39*															*10e39*	
Tamworth Low Level	a	08 36							*09e46*															*10e46*	
Nuneaton	a				08 58															09 58				*11e01*	
Rugby	a					*10 12*		*10 21*													*11 12*		*11 21*		
Northampton	a																								
Milton Keynes Central	a												09 46	10s01											
Watford Junction	a												*10 29*	*10 51*											
Gatwick Airport 10 ✈	a																								
London Euston 15 ⊖	a	09 46			10 01		10 04					10 12	10 23	10 38			10 42			11 01		11 04			

For general notes see front of timetable
For details of catering facilities see Directory of Train Operators

A To Bournemouth (Table 51)
B To Paignton (Table 51)
C 🛒 from Preston
D To Bristol Temple Meads (Table 51)

b Change at Preston
c Change at Chester and Crewe
e Change at Stafford

Table 65

Saturdays

from 7 November

Scotland and North West England → West Midlands and London

Route Diagram - see first page of Table 65

		VT	NT	VT	VT	VT	XC	VT	LM	VT	LM	VT	XC	LM	TP	VT	NT	VT	VT	VT	XC	VT	LM	VT	LM
		1◇		1◇	1◇	1◇	1◇	1◇	1◇	1◇	1◇	1◇	1◇	1◇	1◇	1◇		1◇	1◇	1◇	1◇	1◇	1◇	1◇	1◇
							A						B								A				
		☕		☕	☕	☕	🛒	☕		☕		☕	🛒		🛒	☕		☕	☕	☕	🛒	☕		☕	
Inverness	d																								
Aberdeen	d																								
Dundee	d																								
Perth	d															05b16									
Edinburgh 10	d					06 52																			
Haymarket	d					06u56																			
Glasgow Central 15	d	06 30													07 10	07 35				08 00					
Motherwell	d	06u45														07u53									
Carstairs	d																								
Lockerbie	d	07 25													08 08										
Carlisle 8	a	07 43				08 05									08 28	08 46				09 08					
	d	07 46				08 07									08 30	08 49				09 09					
Penrith North Lakes	d	08 00				08 22									08 44										
Windermere	d	07 57													08 50										
Oxenholme Lake District	a	08 22													09 08	09 22									
	d	08 23													09 11	09 23									
Barrow-in-Furness	d																								
Lancaster 6	a	08 37				08 56									09 26	09 37				09 56					
	d	08 38				08 57									09 26	09 38				09 57					
Preston 8	a	08 56				09 15									09 45	09 56				10 15					
Blackpool North	a	09 50				10 00									10 20	10 35				11 00					
	d	08 20	08 38			08 45										09 20	09 37			09 45					
Preston 8	d	08 58	09 04			09 17									09 47	09 58	10 04			10 17					
Wigan North Western	a	09 09	09 24			09 28										10 09	10 24			10 28					
	d	09 09	09 24			09 28										10 09	10 24			10 28					
Bolton	a	09c34				09c55									10 08	10c34				10c55					
Manchester Piccadilly 10	a	09c56				10c18									10 27	10c56				11c18					
Manchester Airport ✈	a	10c17													10 47	11c17									
Liverpool Lime Street 10	a		10 02			10 29											11 02			11 28					
	d								09 34	09 48				10 04									10 34	10 48	
Liverpool South Parkway 7 ✈	d								09 44					10 15									10 44		
Runcorn	d								09 52	10 04				10 25									10 52	11 04	
Warrington Bank Quay	a	09 20				09 39										10 20				10 39					
	d	09 20				09 39										10 20				10 39					
Hartford	d								10 04														11 04		
Manchester Piccadilly 10	d			09 15			09 27	09 35	09 30			09 55	10 07					10 15			10 27	10 35	10 30		
Stockport	d			09 23			09 35	09 42	09 39			10 04						10 23			10 35	10 42	10 39		
Manchester Airport ✈	d				09e11														10e11						
Wilmslow	d				09e21				09 47			10 11							10e21				10 47		
Holyhead	d				07 52														08 55						
Bangor (Gwynedd)	d				08 19														09 22						
Llandudno	d				08 10							08f45							09 10						
Llandudno Junction	d				08 37							08f54							09 40						
Wrexham General	d				09 02														10 02						
Chester	d				09 35							09 55							10 35						
Crewe 10	a				09 54	09 59			10 19		←	10 27		10 45					10 54	10 59			11 19		←
	d				09 56	10 01			10 22		10 22	10 29		10 49					10 56	11 01			11 22		11 22
Macclesfield	d						09 49	09 55	→												10 49	10 55	→		
Congleton	d																								
Stoke-on-Trent	d			09 50			10 07	10 12					10 44					10 50			11 07	11 12			
Stafford	a						10 25			10 35	10 42			11 09							11 25			11 35	11 42
	d						10 25			10 36	10 43			11 10							11 25			11 36	11 43
Penkridge	a													11 15											
Wolverhampton 7	a					10 31	10 39				10 56		11 13	11 27						11 31	11 39				11 56
Birmingham New Street 12	a					10 55	10 58				11 17		11 31	11 47						11 55	11 58				12 17
Birmingham International ✈	a					11 19	11 13				11 38		11 59							12 19	12 13				12 38
Coventry	a					11 30	11 24				11 49		12 10							12 30	12 24				12 49
Lichfield Trent Valley	a													11g39											
Tamworth Low Level	a													11g46											
Nuneaton	a													12g01											
Rugby	a										12 12		12 21												
Northampton	a																								13 12
Milton Keynes Central	a			10 46	11s01													11 46	12s01						
Watford Junction	a			11 29	11 51													12 29	12 50						
Gatwick Airport 10 ✈	a																								
London Euston 15 ⊖	a	11 12		11 23	11 38			11 42		11 56		12 04				12 12		12 23	12 38			12 42		12 56	

For general notes see front of timetable
For details of catering facilities see Directory of Train Operators

A To Bournemouth (Table 51)
B To Bristol Temple Meads (Table 51)
b Via Glasgow Queen Street and Glasgow Central. Passengers make their own way from one station to the other
c Change at Preston
e Change at Crewe
f Change at Chester and Crewe
g Change at Stafford

Table 65

Saturdays

from 7 November

Scotland and North West England → West Midlands and London

Route Diagram - see first page of Table 65

		TP	VT	XC	LM	TP	VT	VT	NT	VT	VT	XC	VT	LM		VT	LM	VT	XC	LM	VT	XC	TP	VT	VT
		1 ◇	1 ◇	1 ◇	1 ◇	1 ◇	1 ◇	1 ◇		1 ◇	1 ◇	1 ◇	1 ◇	1 ◇		1 ◇	1 ◇	1 ◇	1 ◇	1 ◇	1 ◇	1 ◇	1 ◇	1 ◇	1 ◇
				A		B						C							A			C	B		
			🛒	🍴		🍴	🛒	🛒		🛒	🛒	🍴	🛒			🛒		🛒	🍴		🛒	🍴	🍴	🛒	🛒
Inverness	d										11b04														
Aberdeen	d										07c20														
Dundee	d										06c55														
Perth	d																								
Edinburgh 10	d										08 52														
Haymarket	d										08u57														
Glasgow Central 15	d						08 40																		
Motherwell	d																								
Carstairs	d																								
Lockerbie	d																								
Carlisle 8	a						09 46				10 05														
	d						09 49				10 07														
Penrith North Lakes	d						10 03																		
Windermere	d	09 41																					10 49		
Oxenholme Lake District	a	10 00									10 41												11 08		
	d	10 01									10 42												11 10		
Barrow-in-Furness	d					09 23																			
Lancaster 6	a	10 18				10 26	10 37				10 56												11 26		
	d	10 18				10 26	10 38				10 57												11 26		
Preston 8	a	10 37				10 45	10 56				11 15												11 45		
Blackpool North	a					11 20	11 51				12 00												12 20		
	d						10 20		10 37		10 45														
Preston 8	d					10 47	10 58		11 04		11 17												11 47		
Wigan North Western	a						11 09		11 24		11 28														
	d						11 09		11 24		11 28														
Bolton	a					11 08	11e34				11e55												12 08		
Manchester Piccadilly 10	a					11 27	11e56				12e18												12 27		
Manchester Airport ✈	a					11 47	12e17																12 47		
Liverpool Lime Street 10	a								12 02		12 28														
	d				11 04									11 34		11 48				12 04					
Liverpool South Parkway 7 ✈	d				11 15									11 44						12 15					
Runcorn	d				11 25									11 52		12 04				12 25					
Warrington Bank Quay	a						11 20				11 39														
	d						11 20				11 39														
Hartford	d													12 04											
Manchester Piccadilly 10	d		10 55	11 07				11 15				11 27	11 35	11 30				11 55	12 07		12 15	12 27			12 35
Stockport	d		11 04					11 23				11 35	11 42	11 39				12 04			12 23	12 35			12 42
Manchester Airport ✈	d									11f11														12 11	
Wilmslow	d		11 11							11f21				11 47				12 11						12 21	
Holyhead	d									09 23															
Bangor (Gwynedd)	d									10 02															
Llandudno	d		09g45							10h10								10g44							
Llandudno Junction	d		09g54							10 25								10g53							
Wrexham General	d									11 00															
Chester	d		10 55							11 35								11 55							
Crewe 10	a		11 27		11 44					11 54	11 59			12 19			⟵	12 27		12 44					
	d		11 29		11 49					11 56	12 01			12 22			12 22	12 29		12 49				12 57	
Macclesfield	d											11 49	11 55	⟶								12 49			12 55
Congleton	d																								
Stoke-on-Trent	d			11 44				11 50				12 07	12 12						12 44		12 50	13 07			13 12
Stafford	a				12 09							12 24				12 35	12 42			13 09		13 25			
	d				12 10							12 25				12 36	12 43			13 10		13 25			
Penkridge	a				12 15															13 15					
Wolverhampton 7	a			12 13	12 27						12 31	12 39					12 56		13 13	13 27		13 39			
Birmingham New Street 12	a			12 31	12 47						12 50	12 58					13 17		13 31	13 47		13 58			
Birmingham International ✈	a			12 59								13 13					13 38		13 59			14 13			
Coventry	a			13 10								13 24					13 49		14 10			14 24			
Lichfield Trent Valley	a				12j39															13j39					
Tamworth Low Level	a				12j46															13j46					
Nuneaton	a				13j01															14j01					
Rugby	a			13 21													14 12		14 21						
Northampton	a																								
Milton Keynes Central	a							12 46		13s01											13 46			14s01	
Watford Junction	a							13 29		13 50											14 29			14 50	
Gatwick Airport 10 ✈	a																								
London Euston 15 ⊖	a		13 04				13 12	13 23		13 38			13 42			13 56		14 04			14 23			14 38	14 42

For general notes see front of timetable
For details of catering facilities see Directory of Train Operators

A To Bristol Temple Meads (Table 51)
B 🍴 from Preston
C To Bournemouth (Table 51)
b Saturdays. Change at Haymarket
c Change at Haymarket
e Change at Preston
f Change at Crewe
g Change at Chester and Crewe
h Change at Llandudno Junction and Chester
j Change at Stafford

Table 65

Scotland and North West England → West Midlands and London

Saturdays

from 7 November

Route Diagram - see first page of Table 65

		LM	VT	LM	NT	VT	TP	XC	VT	VT	LM	VT	VT	VT	TP	XC	TP	VT	VT	LM	VT	LM	NT	VT	XC
		1 ◇	1 ◇	1 ◇		1 ◇	1 ◇	1 ◇		1 ◇	1 ◇	1 ◇		1 ◇	1 ◇	1 ◇	1 ◇	1 ◇	1 ◇	1 ◇	1 ◇	1 ◇		1 ◇	1 ◇
								A								B									C
									🚌				🚌												
			🍽			🍽	🛒	🛒		🍽		🍽		🍽		🛒	🛒	🍽	🍽		🍽			🍽	🛒
Inverness	d																								
Aberdeen	d													06b33											
Dundee	d						07c35							07b52				08b18							
Perth	d						07c59							08b12				08b41							
Edinburgh 10	d						09 22																		
Haymarket	d						09u26																		
Glasgow Central 15	d													10 00			10 10	10 40							
Motherwell	d																								
Carstairs	d																								
Lockerbie	d						10 24																		
Carlisle 8	a						10 44							11 08			11 27	11 46							
	d						10 52							11 09			11 28	11 49							
Penrith North Lakes	d						11 07							11 24			11 42	12 03							
Windermere	d																	11 59							
Oxenholme Lake District	a						11 31										12 06	12 26							
	d						11 31										12 07	12 26							
Barrow-in-Furness	d														11 25										
Lancaster 6	a						11 46							11 59	12 18		12 22	12 41							
	d						11 46							11 59	12 18		12 23	12 41							
Preston 8	a						12 05							12 17	12 37		12 41	13 01							
Blackpool North	a						12 50							13 00			13 21	13 50							
	d				11 37		11 37																12 37		
Preston 8	d				12 04		12 10							12 19			12 47						13 04		
Wigan North Western	a				12 24																		13 24		
	d				12 24				12 05				12 30										13 24		
Bolton	a						12 34										13 08								
Manchester Piccadilly 10	a						12 56										13 27								
Manchester Airport	a						13 17										13 47								
Liverpool Lime Street 10	a				13 02																		14 02		
	d	12 34	12 48								13 04									13 34	13 48				
Liverpool South Parkway 7	d	12 44									13 15									13 44					
Runcorn	d	12 52	13 04								13 25									13 52	14 04				
Warrington Bank Quay	a								12 35				13 00												
	d								12 35				13 00												
Hartford	d	13 06																		14 04					
Manchester Piccadilly 10	d	12 30				12 55		13 07				13 15				13 27			13 35	13 30				13 55	14 07
Stockport	d	12 39				13 04						13 23				13 35			13 42	13 39				14 04	
Manchester Airport	d																			13 11					
Wilmslow	d	12 47				13 11														13 47				14 11	
Holyhead	d					10e33																		11e23	
Bangor (Gwynedd)	d					11e06																		12e02	
Llandudno	d					11e44																		12e44	
Llandudno Junction	d					11e53																		12e53	
Wrexham General	d																								
Chester	d					12 55																		13 55	
Crewe 10	a	13 20		←		13 27			13 20		13 44		13 45	13 54						14 19		←		14 27	
	d	13 22		13 22		13 29				13 32	13 49			13 56						14 22		14 22		14 29	
Macclesfield	d	→														13 49			13 55	→					
Congleton	d																								
Stoke-on-Trent	d							13 44				13 50				14 07			14 12						14 44
Stafford	a		13 35	13 42							14 09					14 25					14 35	14 46			
	d		13 36	13 43							14 10					14 25					14 36	14 46			
Penkridge	a										14 15														
Wolverhampton 7	a			13 56				14 13			14 27					14 39						14 59			15 13
Birmingham New Street 12	a			14 17				14 31			14 47					14 58						15 18			15 31
Birmingham International	a			14 38				14 59								15 13						15 38			15 59
Coventry	a			14 49				15 10			15 24					15 24						15 49			16 10
Lichfield Trent Valley	a										14f39														
Tamworth Low Level	a										14f46														
Nuneaton	a										15f01														
Rugby	a			15 12				15 21														16 12			16 21
Northampton	a																								
Milton Keynes Central	a											14 46													
Watford Junction	a											15 29													
Gatwick Airport 10	a																								
London Euston 15	⊖ a		14 56			15 04				15 08		15 23		15 38					15 42		15 56			16 04	

For general notes see front of timetable
For details of catering facilities see Directory of Train Operators

A To Bristol Temple Meads (Table 51)
B To Bournemouth (Table 51)
C To Paignton (Table 51)

b Via Glasgow Queen Street and Glasgow Central. Passengers make their own way from one station to the other
c Change at Haymarket
e Change at Chester and Crewe
f Change at Stafford

Scotland and North West England → West Midlands and London

Route Diagram - see first page of Table 65

		VT	VT	LM	VT	VT	VT	VT	XC	TP		VT	LM	VT	LM	NT	VT	XC	VT	VT	LM	VT	VT	VT	XC
			1 ◇	1 ◇	1 ◇		1 ◇	1 ◇	1 ◇	1 ◇		1 ◇	1 ◇	1 ◇	1 ◇		1 ◇	1 ◇		1 ◇	1 ◇	1 ◇		1 ◇	1 ◇
									A	B								C							A
		bus				bus													bus				bus		
			catering		catering		catering	catering	trolley	trolley		catering		catering			catering	trolley		catering		catering		catering	trolley
Inverness	d						06b46																	07c55	
Aberdeen	d						07b52																	08e42	
Dundee	d						09b06																	09e52	
Perth	d						08b47																	10e14	
Edinburgh 10	d						10 52																		
Haymarket	d						10u57																		
Glasgow Central 15	d																							12 00	
Motherwell	d																								
Carstairs	d																								
Lockerbie	d																								
Carlisle 8	a						12 05																	13 08	
	d						12 07																	13 09	
Penrith North Lakes	d																							13 24	
Windermere	d									12 51															
Oxenholme Lake District	a						12 41			13 07															
	d						12 43			13 09															
Barrow-in-Furness	d																								
Lancaster 6	a						12 56			13 26														13 59	
	d						12 57			13 26														13 59	
Preston 8	a						13 15			13 45														14 17	
Blackpool North	a						14 00			14 20														15 00	
	d						12 45									13 37								13 45	
Preston 8	d	12 30					13 19			13 47						14 04			13 25					14 19	
Wigan North Western	a	13 10														14 24			14 05						
	d	13 10				13 35										14 24			14 05				14 30		
Bolton	a						13 55			14 08														14 55	
Manchester Piccadilly 10	a						14 18			14 27														15 18	
Manchester Airport	a									14 47															
Liverpool Lime Street 10	a															15 02									
	d			14 04									14 34	14 48							15 04				
Liverpool South Parkway 7	d			14 15									14 44								15 15				
Runcorn	d			14 25									14 52	15 04							15 25				
Warrington Bank Quay	a	13 40				14 05													14 35				15 00		
	d	13 40				14 05													14 35				15 00		
Hartford	d												15 04												
Manchester Piccadilly 10	d				14 15				14 27			14 35	14 30				14 55	15 07				15 15			15 27
Stockport	d				14 23				14 35			14 42	14 39				15 04					15 23			15 35
Manchester Airport	d						14 11																	15 11	
Wilmslow	d						14 21						14 47				15 11							15 21	
Holyhead	d							12 38																	
Bangor (Gwynedd)	d							13 07																	
Llandudno	d							13f10									13g44								
Llandudno Junction	d							13 25									13g53								
Wrexham General	d							14 02																	
Chester	d							14 35									14 55								
Crewe 10	a	14 25		14 44		14 50	14 53	14 54					15 19		←		15 27		15 20		15 44		15 45	15 54	
	d		14 35	14 49			15 01	14 56					15 22		15 22		15 29			15 33	15 49			15 56	
Macclesfield	d								14 49			14 55	→												15 49
Congleton	d																								
Stoke-on-Trent	d				14 50				15 07			15 12						15 44				15 50			16 07
Stafford	a			15 09					15 25					15 35	15 42						16 09				16 24
	d			15 10					15 25					15 36	15 43						16 10				16 25
Penkridge	a			15 15																	16 15				
Wolverhampton 7	a			15 27			15 31		15 39						15 56			16 13			16 27				16 39
Birmingham New Street 12	a			15 47			15 50		15 58						16 17			16 31			16 47				16 58
Birmingham International	a								16 13						16 38			16 59							17 13
Coventry	a								16 24						16 49			17 10							17 24
Lichfield Trent Valley	a			15h39																	16h39				
Tamworth Low Level	a			15h46																	16h46				
Nuneaton	a			16h01																	17h01				
Rugby	a														17 12			17 21							18 12
Northampton	a																								
Milton Keynes Central	a				15 46			16s01														16 46			
Watford Junction	a				16 29			16 50														17 29			
Gatwick Airport 10	a																								
London Euston 15	a		16 12		16 23			16 38				16 42		16 56			17 04			17 08		17 23		17 37	

For general notes see front of timetable
For details of catering facilities see Directory of Train Operators

- **A** To Bournemouth (Table 51)
- **B** trolley from Preston
- **C** To Bristol Temple Meads (Table 51)
- **b** Change at Haymarket
- **c** Change at Perth, Glasgow Queen Street and Glasgow Central. Passengers make their own way between Glasgow Queen Street and Glasgow Central
- **e** Via Glasgow Queen Street and Glasgow Central. Passengers make their own way from one station to the other
- **f** Change at Llandudno Junction and Chester
- **g** Change at Chester and Crewe
- **h** Change at Stafford

Scotland and North West England → West Midlands and London

Saturdays

from 7 November

Route Diagram - see first page of Table 65

		TP	TP	VT	VT	VT	LM	VT	LM	NT	VT	XC	VT	VT	LM	VT	VT	VT	XC	TP	VT	LM	VT	LM	VT
		1 ◇	1 ◇	1 ◇		1 ◇	1 ◇	1 ◇	1 ◇		1 ◇	1 ◇		1 ◇	1 ◇	1 ◇	1 ◇	1 ◇	1 ◇	1 ◇	1 ◇	1 ◇	1 ◇	1 ◇	1 ◇
												A							B						
					🚌								🚌												
			⊼	☕		☕		☕			☕	⊼		☕		☕	☕	☕	⊼	⊼	☕		☕		☕
Inverness	d																								
Aberdeen	d		09b07																	09c37					
Dundee	d		10b34															11b30							
Perth	d		09b55															10b57		11c14					
Edinburgh 10	d		12 08															12 52							
Haymarket	d		12u11															12u57							
Glasgow Central 15	d			12 40																13 00					
Motherwell	d																								
Carstairs	d																								
Lockerbie	d		13 06																	13 58					
Carlisle 8	a		13 28	13 47														14 05		14 21					
	d		13 30	13 49														14 07		14 30					
Penrith North Lakes	d																	14 22		14 45					
Windermere	d			14 00																					
Oxenholme Lake District	a		14 05	14 22																15 08					
	d		14 06	14 24																15 09					
Barrow-in-Furness	d	13 25																							
Lancaster 6	a	14 18	14 22	14 37														14 56		15 26					
	d	14 18	14 22	14 38														14 57		15 26					
Preston 8	a	14 37	14 41	14 58														15 15		15 45					
Blackpool North	a		15 20	15 50														16 00		16 20					
	d									14 37								14 45							
Preston 8	d	14 47			15 10					15 04			14 30					15 19		15 47					
Wigan North Western	a				15 50					15 24			15 10												
	d				15 50					15 24			15 10												
Bolton	a	15 08																15 55		16 08					
Manchester Piccadilly 10	a	15 27																16 18		16 27					
Manchester Airport	a	15 47																		16 47					
Liverpool Lime Street 10	a									16 02															
	d						15 34	15 48							16 04							16 34	16 48		
Liverpool South Parkway 7	d						15 44								16 15							16 44			
Runcorn	d						15 52	16 04							16 25							16 52	17 04		
Warrington Bank Quay	a				16 20								15 40												
	d												15 40												
Hartford	d						16 04															17 06			
Manchester Piccadilly 10	d					15 35	15 30				15 55	16 07				16 15			16 27		16 35	16 30			16 55
Stockport	d					15 42	15 39				16 04					16 23			16 35		16 42	16 39			17 04
Manchester Airport	d																16e11								
Wilmslow	d						15 47				16 11						16e21					16 49			17 11
Holyhead	d										13f23						14 36								
Bangor (Gwynedd)	d										14f02						15 06								
Llandudno	d										14f42						15 10								15f44
Llandudno Junction	d										14f51						15 25								15f53
Wrexham General	d																15 00								
Chester	d										15 55						16 20								16 55
Crewe 10	a						16 19		←		16 27		16 25		16 44		16 44	16 53				17 20		←	17 27
	d						16 22		16 22		16 29			16 35	16 49		16 56	17 01				17 22		17 22	17 29
Macclesfield	d					15 55	→												16 49		16 56	→			
Congleton	d																								
Stoke-on-Trent	d					16 12						16 44				16 50			17 07		17 13				
Stafford	a							16 35	16 46						17 09				17 25				17 35	17 42	
	d							16 36	16 46						17 10				17 25				17 36	17 43	
Penkridge	a														17 15										
Wolverhampton 7	a								16 59			17 13			17 27			17 31	17 39					17 56	
Birmingham New Street 12	a								17 18			17 31			17 47			17 50	17 58					18 17	
Birmingham International	a								17 38			17 59							18 13					18 38	
Coventry	a								17 49			18 10							18 24					18 49	
Lichfield Trent Valley	a														17g39										
Tamworth Low Level	a														17g46										
Nuneaton	a														18g01										
Rugby	a								18 12			18 21							19 12					19 12	
Northampton	a																								
Milton Keynes Central	a															17 46	18 01								
Watford Junction	a															18 29	18 50								
Gatwick Airport 10	a																								
London Euston 15	a					17 42		17 57			18 04			18 13		18 23	18 38				18 42		18 56		19 04

For general notes see front of timetable
For details of catering facilities see Directory of Train Operators

- **A** To Bristol Temple Meads (Table 51)
- **B** To Bournemouth (Table 51)
- **b** Change at Haymarket
- **c** Via Glasgow Queen Street and Glasgow Central. Passengers make their own way from one station to the other
- **e** Change at Crewe
- **f** Change at Chester and Crewe
- **g** Change at Stafford

Table 65

Saturdays

from 7 November

Scotland and North West England → West Midlands and London

Route Diagram - see first page of Table 65

		XC	VT	VT	LM	NT		VT	VT	VT	VT	XC	TP	VT	VT	LM	VT	LM	NT	VT	XC	LM	VT	VT	VT
		1 ◇		1 ◇	1 ◇			1 ◇		1 ◇		1 ◇	1 ◇	1 ◇	1 ◇	1 ◇	1 ◇	1 ◇		1 ◇	1 ◇	1 ◇	1 ◇		1 ◇
		A										B									C				
		(trolley)	(bus)	(restaurant)				(restaurant)	(bus)	(restaurant)	(bus)	(trolley)	(trolley)	(restaurant)	(restaurant)		(restaurant)			(restaurant)	(trolley)		(restaurant)	(bus)	(restaurant)
Inverness	d									09b18															10c47
Aberdeen	d									10b38			11 05												
Dundee	d									11b49			12 34												13c34
Perth	d									12b11															13c01
Edinburgh 10	d												14 11												14 52
Haymarket	d																								14u57
Glasgow Central 15	d									14 00				14 40											
Motherwell	d																								
Carstairs	d																								
Lockerbie	d																								
Carlisle 8	a									15 08			15 28	15 46											16 05
	d									15 09			15 30	15 49											16 07
Penrith North Lakes	d												15 44	16 03											
Windermere	d									14 59				16 02											
Oxenholme Lake District	a									15 44			16 08	16 26											16 41
	d									15 44			16 08	16 27											16 42
Barrow-in-Furness	d																								
Lancaster 6	a									15 58			16 26	16 41											16 56
	d									15 58			16 26	16 41											16 57
Preston 8	a									16 16			16 45	17 01											17 14
Blackpool North	a									17 00			17 20	17 50											18 02
	d					15 37				15 45									16 35						16 41
Preston 8	d		15 25			16 04				16 19	16 30		16 47						17 04						17 19
Wigan North Western	a		16 05			16 24					17 10								17 24						
	d		16 05			16 24			16 30		17 10								17 24					17 35	
Bolton	a									16 55			17 08												17 55
Manchester Piccadilly 10	a									17 18			17 27												18 18
Manchester Airport	a												17 48												
Liverpool Lime Street 10	a					17 05													18 02						
	d				17 04											17 34	17 48					18 04			
Liverpool South Parkway 7	d				17 15											17 44						18 15			
Runcorn	d				17 25											17 52	18 04					18 25			
Warrington Bank Quay	a		16 35						17 00		17 40													18 05	
	d		16 35						17 00															18 05	
Hartford	d															18 05									
Manchester Piccadilly 10	d	17 06						17 15				17 27			17 35	17 30				17 55	18 05		18 15		
Stockport	d							17 23				17 35			17 43	17 40				18 04			18 23		
Manchester Airport	d									17 11															18 11
Wilmslow	d									17 21						17 48				18 11					18 22
Holyhead	d															15e23									
Bangor (Gwynedd)	d															16e02									
Llandudno	d															16f10				16e44					
Llandudno Junction	d															16e25				16e53					
Wrexham General	d																								
Chester	d															17 35				17 55					
Crewe 10	a		17 20		17 46				17 45	17 54						18 19		←		18 27		18 46		18 50	18 53
	d			17 32	17 49					17 56						18 22		18 22		18 29		18 49			19 01
Macclesfield	d	17 27													17 55	→					18 25				
Congleton	d											17 54													
Stoke-on-Trent	d	17 44						17 50				18 07			18 13						18 44		18 50		
Stafford	a				18 09							18 25					18 34	18 42				19 09			
	d				18 10							18 25					18 36	18 43				19 10			
Penkridge	a				18 15																	19 15			
Wolverhampton 7	a	18 13			18 27							18 39						18 56			19 13	19 27			19 31
Birmingham New Street 12	a	18 31			18 47							18 58						19 17			19 31	19 47			19 56
Birmingham International	a	18 59										19 13						19 45			20 05				20 19
Coventry	a	19 10										19 24						20 00			20 20				20 30
Lichfield Trent Valley	a				18g39																	19g39			
Tamworth Low Level	a				18g46																	19g46			
Nuneaton	a				19g01																	20g01			
Rugby	a	19 21										19 42						20 12			20 32				
Northampton	a																								
Milton Keynes Central	a							18 46															19 46		
Watford Junction	a							19 29															20 34		
Gatwick Airport 10	a																								
London Euston 15	⊖ a			19 08				19 23		19 37					19 42		19 56			20 04			20 28		

For general notes see front of timetable
For details of catering facilities see Directory of Train Operators

A To Cardiff Central (Table 51)

B To Bournemouth (Table 51)

C To Plymouth (Table 51)

b Via Glasgow Queen Street and Glasgow Central. Passengers make their own way from one station to the other

c Change at Haymarket

e Change at Chester and Crewe

f Change at Llandudno Junction, Chester and Crewe

g Change at Stafford

Table 65

Saturdays

from 7 November

Scotland and North West England → West Midlands and London

Route Diagram - see first page of Table 65

	VT	TP	XC	VT	LM	VT	LM	NT	VT	TP	XC	LM	VT	TP	XC	TP	VT	LM	VT	LM	VT	NT	VT	XC
		1◇	1◇	1◇	1◇	1◇	1◇		1◇	1◇	1◇	1◇	1◇	1◇	1◇	1◇	1◇	1◇	1◇	1◇			1◇	1◇
		A	B							A	C				D									
	bus																				bus			
		trolley	trolley	catering		catering			catering	trolley	trolley		catering		trolley	trolley	catering		catering				catering	
Inverness d																								
Aberdeen d													12b42											
Dundee d													13b50			14c34								
Perth d													14b11											
Edinburgh 10 d																16 11								
Haymarket d																16u14								
Glasgow Central 15 d													16 00										16 40	
Motherwell d																							16u54	
Carstairs d																								
Lockerbie d																17 10								
Carlisle 8 a													17 08			17 32							17 49	
d													17 09			17 33							17 52	
Penrith North Lakes d													17 24			17 48							18 06	
Windermere d										17 06													18 02	
Oxenholme Lake District a										17 25			17 47										18 29	
d										17 30			17 48										18 29	
Barrow-in-Furness d		16 22												17 21										
Lancaster 6 a		17 15								17 47			18 02	18 17		18 26							18 44	
d		17 15								17 48			18 02	18 17		18 26							18 44	
Preston 8 a		17 34								18 06			18 20	18 36		18 45							19 04	
Blackpool North a		18 20								18 50			19 00	19 18		19 20							19 50	
d								17 37														18 37		
Preston 8 d	17 25	17 47						18 04		18 08			18 23			18 47					18 30	19 04		
Wigan North Western a	18 05							18 24													19 10	19 24		
d	18 05							18 24													19 10	19 24		
Bolton a		18 08								18 34						19 08								
Manchester Piccadilly 10 a		18 27								18 56						19 27								
Manchester Airport a		18 47								19 17						19 50								
Liverpool Lime Street 10 a								19 02														20 02		
d					18 34	18 48						19 04						19 34	19 48					
Liverpool South Parkway 7 d					18 44							19 14						19 44						
Runcorn d					18 52	19 04						19 23						19 52	20 04					
Warrington Bank Quay a	18 35																				19 40			
d																					19 40			
Hartford d					19 04													20 04						
Manchester Piccadilly 10 d			18 27	18 35	18 30				18 55		19 07				19 27		19 35	19 30						20 07
Stockport d			18 35	18 42	18 39				19 04		19 16				19 35		19 42	19 39						20 16
Manchester Airport d																		19e14						
Wilmslow d					18 47				19 11									19 47						
Holyhead d									16f38															
Bangor (Gwynedd) d									17f07															
Llandudno d									17f44															
Llandudno Junction d									17f53															
Wrexham General d																								
Chester d									18 55															
Crewe 10 a					19 19		←		19 27			19 49	19 55					20 16		←	20 25			
d					19 22		19 22		19 29			19 51	19 56					20 22		20 22				
Macclesfield d				18 55	→										19 49		19 55	→						
Congleton d			18 54																					
Stoke-on-Trent d			19 07	19 12							19 44				20 07		20 12							20 44
Stafford a			19 25			19 35	19 42					20 11			20 25				20 35	20 42				
d			19 25			19 36	19 43					20 12			20 25				20 36	20 43				
Penkridge a							19 48													20 48				
Wolverhampton 7 a			19 39				19 57				20 13	20 28			20 39					20 57				21 13
Birmingham New Street 12 a			19 58				20 17				20 31	20 47			20 58					21 17				21 36
Birmingham International a			20 13				20 45				21 05				21 13					21 45				22 05
Coventry a			20 24				21 00				21 20				21 24					22 00				22 20
Lichfield Trent Valley a																								
Tamworth Low Level a																								
Nuneaton a																								
Rugby a			20 42								21 32		20 51		21 42					22 12				22 32
Northampton a													21 34											
Milton Keynes Central a													22 04				21 10							
Watford Junction a													22 34				21 50							
Gatwick Airport 10 a																								
London Euston 15 a				21 01		21 15			21 19				22 55				22 02		22 17					

For general notes see front of timetable
For details of catering facilities see Directory of Train Operators

A trolley from Preston

B To Bournemouth (Table 51)
C To Bristol Temple Meads (Table 51)
D To Southampton Central (Table 51)

b Via Glasgow Queen Street and Glasgow Central. Passengers make their own way from one station to the other
c Change at Haymarket
e Change at Wilmslow and Crewe
f Change at Chester and Crewe

Scotland and North West England → West Midlands and London

Route Diagram - see first page of Table 65

		VT	XC	NT	LM	TP	VT	VT	NT	XC	VT	XC	TP	VT	LM	NT	TP	VT	SR	TP	NT	NT	SR
		1 ◇	1 ◇		1 ◇	1 ◇	1 ◇			1 ◇	1 ◇	1 ◇	1 ◇	1 ◇	1 ◇		1 ◇	1 ◇		1 ◇			
				A																			
Inverness	d	12b54																14c51					16e56
Aberdeen	d					13f42					14f39		14b49					16b01	16f37				18f33
Dundee	d	15b17									15f49		16b03					17b26	17f51				19f46
Perth	d	15b00				15f14					16f11							17b00	18f12				20f11
Edinburgh 10	d	16 52											18 11					18 52					
Haymarket	d	16u57											18u14					18u57					
Glasgow Central 15	d					17 07					18 00			18 40					20 03				22 03
Motherwell	d																						
Carstairs	d																						
Lockerbie	d					18 05					18 52		19 10										
Carlisle 8	a	18 05				18 27					19 11		19 32	19 47				20 05	22 24				00 34
	d	18 07				18 29					19 13		19 33	19 49				20 07					
Penrith North Lakes	d					18 44					19 28		19 48	20 03				20 22					
Windermere	d										19 00			20 00						21 40			
Oxenholme Lake District	a	18 41				19 08					19 51		20 12	20 25				20 45		21 59			
	d	18 42				19 08					19 51		20 12	20 26				20 45		22 01			
Barrow-in-Furness	d			18 03													19 42					21 43	
Lancaster 6	a	18 56		19 04		19 26					20 06		20 26	20 40			20 45	20 59		22 17		22 44	
	d	18 57		19 05		19 26					20 06		20 26	20 41			20 45	21 00		22 17		22 45	
Preston 8	a	19 15		19 30		19 45					20 24		20 45	21 01			21 03	21 19		22 38		23 08	
Blackpool North	a	20 00				20 44					21 00						21 50	22 00		23 21		23 50	
	d	18 45							19 37		19 45					20 38		20 45			22 14		
Preston 8	d	19 19				19 47		19 25	20 04		20 27		20 47			21 04	21 15	21 22			22 43		
Wigan North Western	a							20 05	20 24							21 24					23 02		
	d							20 05	20 24							21 24					23 03		
Bolton	a					20 08					20 34		21 08				21 39			23 34		00 07	
Manchester Piccadilly 10	a					20 27					20 56		21 27				22 02			23 53			
Manchester Airport	a					20 47					21 17		21 47				22 57			00 22			
Liverpool Lime Street 10	a								21 02							22 14					23 54		
	d				20 34										21 34								
Liverpool South Parkway 7	d				20 44										21 44								
Runcorn	d				20 52										21 52								
Warrington Bank Quay	a							20 35															
	d							20 35															
Hartford	d				21 03										22 04								
Manchester Piccadilly 10	d		20 27		20 30		20 35			21 07		21 27			21 30								
Stockport	d		20 35		20 39		20 43					21 35			21 39								
Manchester Airport	d				20g14										21g14								
Wilmslow	d				20 47										21 47								
Holyhead	d	18 23																					
Bangor (Gwynedd)	d	19 02																					
Llandudno	d	19h10									19j42												
Llandudno Junction	d	19 25									19j51												
Wrexham General	d																						
Chester	d	20 17			20 35						20 55												
Crewe 10	a	20 45			21 15			21 20			22 02				22 18			22 43					
	d	21 01			21 17						22 04				22 20								
Macclesfield	d		20 49				20 56					21 49											
Congleton	d																						
Stoke-on-Trent	d		21 07				21 13			21 44		22 07											
Stafford	a		21 25		21 41						22 28	22 33			22 45								
	d		21 25		21 41						22 29	22 33			22 45								
Penkridge	a				21 47										22 51								
Wolverhampton 7	a	21 31	21 39		21 57					22 13	22 42	22 50			23 01								
Birmingham New Street 12	a	21 56	22 03		22 19					22 37	23 00	23 22			23 20								
Birmingham International	a	22 19			22 45					23 05	23 30												
Coventry	a	22 30			23 00					23 20	23 48												
Lichfield Trent Valley	a																						
Tamworth Low Level	a																						
Nuneaton	a																						
Rugby	a	22 41								23 32													
Northampton	a																						
Milton Keynes Central	a						22 12																
Watford Junction	a						22s42																
Gatwick Airport 10	a																						
London Euston 15	a						23 04																

For general notes see front of timetable
For details of catering facilities see Directory of Train Operators

A From Carlisle via Whitehaven (Table 100)

b Change at Haymarket
c Change at Perth and Haymarket
e Change at Perth, Glasgow Queen Street and Glasgow Central. Passengers make their own way between Glasgow Queen Street and Glasgow Central
f Via Glasgow Queen Street and Glasgow Central. Passengers make their own way from one station to the other
g Change at Wilmslow and Crewe
h Change at Llandudno Junction and Crewe
j Change at Chester and Crewe

Table 65

Sundays until 12 July

Scotland and North West England → West Midlands and London

Route Diagram - see first page of Table 65

Station		VT	VT	VT	XC	VT	VT	VT	XC	VT	LM		NT	LM	VT	XC	XC	VT	VT	VT	NT	VT		NT	TP
		1 ◇	1 ◇	1 ◇	1 ◇	1 ◇	1 ◇	1 ◇	1 ◇	1 ◇	1 ◇			1	1 ◇		1 ◇	1 ◇	1 ◇	1 ◇		1 ◇			1 ◇
					A				A							▪	A								
		⊡	⊡	⊡	⚒	⊡	⊡	⊡	⚒	⊡					⊡		⚒	⊡	⊡	⊡		⊡			
Inverness	d																								
Aberdeen	d																								
Dundee	d																								
Perth	d																								
Edinburgh 10	d																								
Haymarket	d																								
Glasgow Central 15	d																								
Motherwell	d																								
Carstairs	d																								
Lockerbie	d																								
Carlisle 8	a																								
	d																								
Penrith North Lakes	d																								
Windermere	d																								
Oxenholme Lake District	a																								
	d																								
Barrow-in-Furness	d																								09 23
Lancaster 6	a																								10 26
	d																								10 26
Preston 8	a																								10 45
Blackpool North	a																								*11 39*
	d						*08 20*						08 50		*09 20*						09 50	*09 44*			*10 11*
Preston 8	d						09 00						09 15		10 00						10 15	10 17		⟵	10 47
Wigan North Western	a						09 10						09 35		10 10						10 38	10 28			
	d						09 11						09 36		10 11						10 38	10 28		10 38	
Bolton	a																				⟶				11 08
Manchester Piccadilly 10 ▪	a																								11 27
Manchester Airport ✈	a																								11 47
Liverpool Lime Street 10	a						*10 22*						10 22											11 24	
	d		08 15			08 38				09 36										10 38					
Liverpool South Parkway 7 ✈	d																								
Runcorn	d		08 34			08 54				09 52										10 54					
Warrington Bank Quay	a						09 21								10 21							10 39			
	d						09 22								10 22							10 39			
Hartford	d																								
Manchester Piccadilly 10 ▪	d	08 05		08 20	08 27			09 20	09 27	*08 42*	09 30						10 26	10 20	10 35						
Stockport	d	08 14		08 28	08 36			09 27	09 36		09 39						10 35	10 29	10 43						
Manchester Airport ✈	d							*09 09*																	
Wilmslow	d	08 22		08 38	08 43			09 36	09 43	*09 17*	09 47						10 43	10 37	10 53						
Holyhead	d														*07b50*					*08 40*					
Bangor (Gwynedd)	d						*07 43*								*08b28*					*09 08*					
Llandudno	d																								
Llandudno Junction	d						*08 01*								*08b51*					*09 26*					
Wrexham General	d																								
Chester	d				*08 27*		*08 57*			*09 27*					*09 57*					*10 27*					
Crewe 10	a	08 39		08 54	09 01	09 11	09 41			10 10					10 41			10 53		11 12		10 59			
	d	08 43		08 57	09 04	09 13	09 43			10 12	10 20			10 47	10 43			10 55		11 14		11 03			
Macclesfield	d	*07c30*						*09e00*								09 45	*10e00*		*10c10*						
Congleton	d																								
Stoke-on-Trent	d	*08c20*						*09c35*								10 45			*11c00*						
Stafford	a	09 07			09 28	09 38		10 16	10 24	10 38	10 45			11 12		11 15	11 24		11 36	11 41					
	d	09 09			09 29	09 39		10 17	10 26	10 40	10 45						11 25		11 38	11 42					
Penkridge	a										10 51														
Wolverhampton 7 ▪	a				09 41				10 40		11 01						11 37					11 41			
Birmingham New Street 12	a				09 58				10 59		11 18						11 57					12 05			
Birmingham International ✈	a				10 13				11 13		*11 39*						12 13					*12 38*			
Coventry	a				10 24				11 24		*11 50*						12 24					*12 49*			
Lichfield Trent Valley	a																								
Tamworth Low Level	a																								
Nuneaton	a					10 01				11 02										12 04					
Rugby	a				*11 00*		10 38		*12 00*		*12 03*				11 38		*13 00*					*13 23*			
Northampton	a						*12c01*								*13c01*										
Milton Keynes Central	a		10 13				11 04	11 18		11 48					12 04				12 29						
Watford Junction	a	10s35	*11 05*	10s47		11s20	11s42	*12 06*										12s35	*13 17*	12s54					
Gatwick Airport 10 ✈	a																								
London Euston 15 ⊖	a	10 58	11 03	11 08		11 44	12 04	12 08		12 38					12 51			12 58	13 09	13 15					

For general notes see front of timetable
For details of catering facilities see Directory of Train Operators

A To Bournemouth (Table 51)
b Change at Chester and Crewe
c By bus
e Change at Wilmslow. By bus

OVERNIGHT SLEEPERS. For Sleeper trains, operated by First ScotRail, please refer to Tables 400 - 404

Table 65

Sundays

until 12 July

Scotland and North West England → West Midlands and London

Route Diagram - see first page of Table 65

		VT	VT	VT	XC	NT	VT	NT	XC	VT	LM		VT	LM	VT	VT	VT	VT	XC	XC	NT	VT		VT	NT
		1◇	1◇	1◇			1◇		1◇	1◇	1◇		1◇	1◇	1◇	1◇	1◇	1◇		1◇		1◇		1◇	
									A											A					
Inverness	d																								
Aberdeen	d																								
Dundee	d																								
Perth	d																								
Edinburgh 10	d																								
Haymarket	d																								
Glasgow Central 15	d																								
Motherwell	d																								
Carstairs	d																								
Lockerbie	d																								
Carlisle 8	a																								
	d															10 46									
Penrith North Lakes	d															11 00									
Windermere	d																								
Oxenholme Lake District	a															11 22									
	d															11 23									
Barrow-in-Furness	d																								
Lancaster 6	a															11 37									
	d															11 38								12 00	
Preston 8	a															11 56								12 15	
Blackpool North	a															*12 38*								*13 00*	
	d	*10 20*				10 50	*10 44*									*11 20*					11 50			*11 44*	
Preston 8	d	10 58				11 15	11 17									11 58					12 15			12 17	
Wigan North Western	a	11 09				11 35	11 28	←								12 09					12 35			12 28	←
	d	11 09				11 36	11 28	11 36								12 09					12 36			12 28	12 36
Bolton	a					→										*12b34*					→				
Manchester Piccadilly 10	a															*12b57*									
Manchester Airport	a															*13b17*									
Liverpool Lime Street 10	a							12 22																	13 22
	d										11 34		11 48												
Liverpool South Parkway 7	d										11 44														
Runcorn	d										11 52		12 04												
Warrington Bank Quay	a	11 20					11 39									12 20								12 39	
	d	11 20					11 39							←		12 20								12 39	
Hartford	d										12 04			12 04											
Manchester Piccadilly 10	d		11 09						11 27	11 35	→				11 55		12 15			12 26		12 35			
Stockport	d		11 17						11 37	11 43				*11 40*	12 05		12 23			12 36		12 44			
Manchester Airport	d								*11 08*					*11 08*											
Wilmslow	d								11 44	11 53				*11 48*	12 12					12 43		12 53			
Holyhead	d																	10 55							
Bangor (Gwynedd)	d																	11 22							
Llandudno	d																	*11 07*							
Llandudno Junction	d																	11 40							
Wrexham General	d			*10 53*																					
Chester	d			11 28														12 33						*12 24*	
Crewe 10	a			11 47			11 59							12 19	12 28			12 52						12 59	
	d			11 49			12 01							12 22	12 30			12 54						13 01	
Macclesfield	d				10 45				*11c00*										11 45	*12e00*					
Congleton	d																								
Stoke-on-Trent	d				11 45					*11c50*							*12c30*		12 45			*12c50*			
Stafford	a		11 58		12 15				12 26	12 27			12 35	12 41			13 04		13 15	13 26		13 27			
	d		12 00						12 27	12 28			12 36	12 42			13 06			13 27		13 29			
Penkridge	a													12 48											
Wolverhampton 7	a						12 34		12 40					12 59						13 40				13 31	
Birmingham New Street 12	a						12 55		12 58					13 16						13 58				13 55	
Birmingham International	a						*13 19*		13 13					*13 38*						14 13				*14 19*	
Coventry	a						*13 30*		13 24					*13 49*						14 24				*14 30*	
Lichfield Trent Valley	a		*12 34*																						
Tamworth Low Level	a		*12 41*																						
Nuneaton	a		*12 58*	12 30																					
Rugby	a						*14 00*							*14 23*										*15 00*	
Northampton	a																								
Milton Keynes Central	a		12 50	13s03													13 54	14s02							
Watford Junction	a		*13 34*	*13 51*													*14 35*	*14 51*							
Gatwick Airport 10	a																								
London Euston 15	⊖ a	13 23	13 31	13 44						13 53			14 03		14 12	14 18	14 40	14 43				14 52			

For general notes see front of timetable
For details of catering facilities see Directory of Train Operators

- **A** To Bournemouth (Table 51)
- **b** Change at Preston
- **c** By bus
- **e** Change at Wilmslow. By bus

OVERNIGHT SLEEPERS. For Sleeper trains, operated by First ScotRail, please refer to Tables 400 - 404

Scotland and North West England → West Midlands and London

Route Diagram - see first page of Table 65

		LM	VT	LM	VT	TP	VT	VT	NT	VT	VT		NT	XC	VT	LM	VT	LM	VT	XC	TP	VT		VT	VT
		1 ◇	1 ◇	1 ◇	1 ◇	1 ◇	1 ◇	1 ◇		1 ◇	1 ◇			1 ◇	1 ◇	1 ◇	1 ◇	1 ◇	1 ◇	1 ◇	1 ◇	1 ◇		1 ◇	1 ◇
														A						B					
			☕		☕		☕	☕		☕	☕			🍴	☕		☕		☕	🍴		☕		☕	☕
Inverness	d																								
Aberdeen	d																								
Dundee	d																				09b25				
Perth	d																				09b27				
Edinburgh 10	d										10 52										11 10				
Haymarket	d										10u57										11u13				
Glasgow Central 15	d						10 32															11 32			
Motherwell	d						10u49																		
Carstairs	d																								
Lockerbie	d																				12 08				
Carlisle 8	a						11 44				12 05										12 30	12 47			
	d						11 46				12 07										12 32	12 49			
Penrith North Lakes	d						12 00														12 46				
Windermere	d						*11 58*															*12 58*			
Oxenholme Lake District	a						12 22				12 41										13 10	13 22			
	d						12 24				12 43										13 10	13 23			
Barrow-in-Furness	d					11 15																			
Lancaster 6	a					12 17	12 37				12 56										13 26	13 37			
	d					12 19	12 38				12 57										13 26	13 38			
Preston 8	a					12 37	12 56				13 15										13 45	13 56			
Blackpool North	a						*13 38*				*14 00*											*14 38*			
	d					*12 11*	*12 20*		12 50		*12 44*										*13 13*	*13 20*			
Preston 8	d					12 47	12 58		13 15		13 17										13 47	13 58			
Wigan North Western	a						13 09		13 35		13 28		←									14 09			
	d						13 09		13 36		13 28		13 36									14 09			
Bolton	a					13 08	*13c34*		↪												14 08	*14c34*			
Manchester Piccadilly 10 ⛴	a					13 27	*13c57*														14 27	*14c57*			
Manchester Airport ✈	a					13 47	*14c17*														14 47	*15c17*			
Liverpool Lime Street 10	a												14 22												
	d	12 34	12 48													13 34	13 48								
Liverpool South Parkway 7 ✈	d	12 44														13 44									
Runcorn	d	12 52	13 04													13 52	14 04								
Warrington Bank Quay	a						13 20				13 39											14 20			
	d			←			13 20				13 39							←				14 20			
Hartford	d	13 03		13 03												14 03		14 03							
Manchester Piccadilly 10 ⛴	d	↪			12 55			13 15						13 27	13 35	↪		*13 30*	13 55	14 07				14 15	
Stockport	d				13 05			13 22						13 36	13 42			*13 39*	14 04					14 22	
Manchester Airport ✈	d																	*13e06*							
Wilmslow	d				13 12													*13 47*	14 11						
Holyhead	d									11 48															12 47
Bangor (Gwynedd)	d									12 15															13 14
Llandudno	d									*12 18*															
Llandudno Junction	d									12 33															13 32
Wrexham General	d									*12 55*															
Chester	d				*12 57*					13 28									*13 57*						14 33
Crewe 10	a			13 18	13 28					13 47	13 59							14 18	14 27						14 52
	d			13 22	13 30					13 49	14 01							14 22	14 29						14 54
Macclesfield	d			*12f00*										13 49	13 55										
Congleton	d																								
Stoke-on-Trent	d							13 50						14 07	14 12					14 43				14 50	
Stafford	a		13 35	13 42										14 24			14 35	14 42							
	d		13 36	13 43										14 25			14 36	14 43							
Penkridge	a			13 48														14 48							
Wolverhampton 7 ⛴	a			13 58							14 33			14 40				14 58		15 13					
Birmingham New Street 12	a			14 15							14 55			14 58				15 15		15 31					
Birmingham International ✈	a			*14 38*							*15 19*			15 13				*15 38*		*15 59*					
Coventry	a			*14 49*							*15 30*			15 24				*15 49*		*16 11*					
Lichfield Trent Valley	a			*14g35*																					
Tamworth Low Level	a			*14g42*																					
Nuneaton	a			*14g58*						14 31															
Rugby	a			*15 23*							*16 00*									*16 23*					
Northampton	a																								
Milton Keynes Central	a							14 49		15s04														15 49	16s04
Watford Junction	a							*15 33*		*15 51*														*16 33*	*16 51*
Gatwick Airport 10 ✈	a																								
London Euston 15 ⊖	a		15 03		15 12		15 18	15 30		15 45					15 48		16 03		16 11			16 18		16 30	16 44

For general notes see front of timetable
For details of catering facilities see Directory of Train Operators

A To Bournemouth (Table 51)
B To Bristol Temple Meads (Table 51)
b Change at Haymarket
c Change at Preston
e Change at Wilmslow and Crewe
f By bus
g Change at Stafford

OVERNIGHT SLEEPERS. For Sleeper trains, operated by First ScotRail, please refer to Tables 400 - 404

Sundays

until 12 July

Scotland and North West England → West Midlands and London

Route Diagram - see first page of Table 65

		NT	VT	NT	XC	VT	LM	VT	LM	VT	XC		TP	VT	VT	VT	VT	XC	NT	NT	VT	LM		VT	LM
			1 ◇		1 ◇	1 ◇	1 ◇	1 ◇	1 ◇	1 ◇	1 ◇		1 ◇	1 ◇	1 ◇	1 ◇	1 ◇	1 ◇			1 ◇	1 ◇		1 ◇	1 ◇
					A						B							A							
			⊡		⊼	⊡		⊡		⊡	⊼			⊡	⊡	⊡	⊡	⊼			⊡			⊡	
Inverness	d																								
Aberdeen	d																09b48								
Dundee	d																11b02								
Perth	d																								
Edinburgh 10	d																12 52								
Haymarket	d																12u56								
Glasgow Central 15	d		11 51											12 40											
Motherwell	d																								
Carstairs	d																								
Lockerbie	d																								
Carlisle 8	a		13 08											13 51			14 05								
	d		13 09											13 54			14 07								
Penrith North Lakes	d																14 22								
Windermere	d													13 58											
Oxenholme Lake District	a													14 27											
	d													14 28											
Barrow-in-Furness	d		12 45										13 22												
Lancaster 6	a		13 56										14 25	14 42			14 56								
	d		13 58										14 25	14 43			14 57								
Preston 8	a		14 15										14 45	15 01			15 15								
Blackpool North	a		15 00											15 40			16 00								
	d	13 50	13 44										14 11	14 20			14 44		14 50						
Preston 8	d	14 15	14 17										14 47	15 03			15 17		15 15						
Wigan North Western	a	14 35	14 28	←										15 14			15 28		15 35	←					
	d	14 36	14 28	14 36										15 14			15 28		15 36	15 36					
Bolton	a	↪											15 08	15c34					↪						
Manchester Piccadilly 10 🚊	a												15 27	15c57											
Manchester Airport ✈	a												15 47	16c17											
Liverpool Lime Street 10	a			15 22																16 22					
	d						14 34	14 48														15 34		15 48	
Liverpool South Parkway 7 ✈	d						14 44															15 44			
Runcorn	d						14 52	15 04														15 52		16 04	
Warrington Bank Quay	a		14 39											15 25			15 39								
	d		14 39						←					15 25			15 39								←
Hartford	d						15 03		15 03													16 03			16 03
Manchester Piccadilly 10 🚊	d				14 27	14 35	↪		14 30	14 55	15 07				15 15			15 27			15 35	↪			15 30
Stockport	d				14 36	14 42			14 39	15 04					15 22			15 36			15 42				15 39
Manchester Airport ✈	d																								15e06
Wilmslow	d								14 47	15 11															15 47
Holyhead	d															13 55									
Bangor (Gwynedd)	d															14 22									
Llandudno	d															14 20									
Llandudno Junction	d															14 40									
Wrexham General	d																								
Chester	d									14 57						15 33									
Crewe 10	a		14 59						15 19	15 27						15 52	15 59								16 18
	d		15 01						15 22	15 29						15 54	16 01								16 22
Macclesfield	d				14 49	14 55												15 49			15 55				
Congleton	d																								
Stoke-on-Trent	d				15 07	15 12					15 43				15 50			16 07			16 12				
Stafford	a				15 24			15 35	15 42									16 24						16 36	16 42
	d				15 25			15 36	15 43									16 25						16 37	16 43
Penkridge	a								15 48																16 48
Wolverhampton 7 🚊	a		15 31		15 40				15 58		16 13						16 34	16 40							16 58
Birmingham New Street 12	a		15 55		15 58				16 15		16 31						16 55	16 58							17 15
Birmingham International ✈	a		16 19		16 13				16 38		16 59						17 19	17 13							17 38
Coventry	a		16 30		16 24				16 49		17 11						17 30	17 24							17 49
Lichfield Trent Valley	a								16f34																
Tamworth Low Level	a								16f41																
Nuneaton	a								16f58																
Rugby	a		17 00								17 23						18 00								
Northampton	a																								
Milton Keynes Central	a														16 49	17s03									
Watford Junction	a														17 33	17 51									
Gatwick Airport 10 ✈	a																								
London Euston 15 ⊖	a					16 48		17 03		17 11				17 23	17 30	17 44					17 48			18 04	

For general notes see front of timetable
For details of catering facilities see Directory of Train Operators

A To Bournemouth (Table 51)
B To Bristol Temple Meads (Table 51)
b Change at Haymarket
c Change at Preston
e Change at Wilmslow and Crewe
f Change at Stafford

OVERNIGHT SLEEPERS. For Sleeper trains, operated by First ScotRail, please refer to Tables 400 - 404

Table 65

Sundays

Scotland and North West England → West Midlands and London

until 12 July

Route Diagram - see first page of Table 65

		VT	XC	TP	VT	VT	NT	VT	VT	NT	XC		VT	LM	VT	LM	VT	XC	TP	VT	VT	VT		NT	VT
		1 ◇	1 ◇	1 ◇	1 ◇	1 ◇		1 ◇	1 ◇		1 ◇		1 ◇	1 ◇	1 ◇	1 ◇	1 ◇	1 ◇	1 ◇	1 ◇	1 ◇	1 ◇			1 ◇
			A								B							C							
		☕	✕	✕	☕	☕		☕	☕		✕		☕		☕		☕	✕		☕	☕	☕			☕
Inverness	d																								09 38
Aberdeen	d																								11b47
Dundee	d			11b25																					13b01
Perth	d				11c05																				11 56
Edinburgh 10	d			13 09																					14 52
Haymarket	d			13u12																					14u57
Glasgow Central 15	d				13 35				13 56											14 36					
Motherwell	d																								
Carstairs	d																								
Lockerbie	d			14 07																					
Carlisle 8	a			14 30	14 46				15 09											15 46					16 05
	d			14 31	14 49				15 09											15 49					16 07
Penrith North Lakes	d			14 46																					16 22
Windermere	d				14 58															15 58					
Oxenholme Lake District	a			15 10	15 22				15 44											16 22					
	d			15 10	15 23				15 44											16 23					
Barrow-in-Furness	d																		15 22						
Lancaster 6	a			15 25	15 37														16 25	16 37					16 56
	d			15 25	15 38														16 25	16 38					16 57
Preston 8	a			15 45	15 56				16 15										16 45	16 56					17 15
Blackpool North	a				16 38				17 00											17 38					18 00
	d				15 20		15 50		15 44										16 11	16 20				16 50	16 44
Preston 8	d			15 47	15 58		16 15		16 17										16 47	16 58				17 15	17 17
Wigan North Western	a				16 09		16 35		16 28	←										17 09				17 35	17 28
	d				16 09		16 36		16 28	16 36										17 09				17 36	17 28
Bolton	a			16 08	16e34		↪												17 08	17e34				↪	
Manchester Piccadilly 10	a			16 27	16e57														17 27	17e57					
Manchester Airport	a			16 47	17e17														17 47	18e17					
Liverpool Lime Street 10	a									17 22															
	d							16 18						16 34	16 48										
Liverpool South Parkway 7	d													16 44											
Runcorn	d							16 34						16 52	17 04										
Warrington Bank Quay	a				16 20				16 39											17 20					17 39
	d				16 20				16 39							←				17 20					17 39
Hartford	d													17 03		17 03									
Manchester Piccadilly 10	d	15 55	16 07			16 15					16 27		16 35	↪		16 30	16 55	17 07			17 15				
Stockport	d	16 04				16 23					16 36		16 42			16 39	17 04				17 22				
Manchester Airport	d																								
Wilmslow	d	16 11														16 47	17 11								
Holyhead	d															14f30									
Bangor (Gwynedd)	d															15f08									
Llandudno	d															15g11									
Llandudno Junction	d															15f26									
Wrexham General	d																					17 10			
Chester	d	15 57														16 27	16 57					17 35			
Crewe 10	a	16 27						16 50	16 59							17 18	17 27					17 53			17 59
	d	16 29						16 53	17 01							17 22	17 29					17 55			18 01
Macclesfield	d										16 49		16 55												
Congleton	d																								
Stoke-on-Trent	d		16 43			16 50					17 07		17 12					17 43			17 50				
Stafford	a										17 24				17 35	17 42									
	d										17 25				17 36	17 43									
Penkridge	a															17 48									
Wolverhampton 7	a		17 13						17 31		17 40					17 58		18 13							18 32
Birmingham New Street 12	a		17 31						17 55		17 58					18 15		18 31							18 55
Birmingham International	a		17 59						18 19		18 13					18 38		18 59							19 19
Coventry	a		18 11						18 30		18 24					18 49		19 11							19 30
Lichfield Trent Valley	a															18h34									
Tamworth Low Level	a															18h41									
Nuneaton	a															18h58									
Rugby	a		18 23						19 00									19 23							20 00
Northampton	a																								
Milton Keynes Central	a					17 49		18s03													18 49	19s03			
Watford Junction	a					18 33		18 51													19 33	19 51			
Gatwick Airport 10	a																								
London Euston 15	a	18 11			18 18	18 30		18 44					18 48		19 03		19 11			19 18	19 30	19 44			

For general notes see front of timetable
For details of catering facilities see Directory of Train Operators

A To Bristol Temple Meads (Table 51)

B To Bournemouth (Table 51)
C To Paignton (Table 51)
b Change at Haymarket
c Via Glasgow Queen Street and Glasgow Central. Passengers make their own way from one station to the other
e Change at Preston
f Change at Chester and Crewe
g Change at Llandudno Junction, Chester and Crewe
h Change at Stafford

OVERNIGHT SLEEPERS. For Sleeper trains, operated by First ScotRail, please refer to Tables 400 - 404

Scotland and North West England → West Midlands and London

Route Diagram - see first page of Table 65

		NT	XC	VT	LM	VT	LM	VT	XC	TP	TP		TP	VT	TP	VT	NT	VT	NT	VT	XC	VT		LM	VT
			[1] ◇	[1] ◇	[1] ◇	[1] ◇	[1] ◇	[1] ◇	[1] ◇	[1] ◇	[1] ◇		[1] ◇	[1] ◇	[1] ◇	[1] ◇		[1] ◇		[1] ◇	[1] ◇	[1] ◇		[1] ◇	[1] ◇
			A						B												C				
			✕	◫		◫		◫	✕		✕			◫		◫		◫		◫	✕	◫			◫
Inverness	d																								
Aberdeen	d																								
Dundee	d																								
Perth	d										13b05														
Edinburgh [10]	d																								
Haymarket	d																								
Glasgow Central [15]	d										15 06			15 35				15 55							
Motherwell	d																								
Carstairs	d																								
Lockerbie	d										16 07														
Carlisle [8]	a										16 28			16 46				17 08							
	d										16 30			16 49				17 09							
Penrith North Lakes	d										16 44			17 03											
Windermere	d												16 58												
Oxenholme Lake District	a										17 08		17 15					17 44							
	d										17 08		17 16					17 44							
Barrow-in-Furness	d									16 25															
Lancaster [6]	a									17 18	17 23		17 32	17 37											
	d									17 18	17 23		17 33	17 38											
Preston [8]	a									17 37	17 42		17 51	17 56				18 15							
Blackpool North	a													18 38				19 00							
	d										17 11			17 20	←		17 50	17 40							
Preston [8]	d										17 47		18 10	17 58	18 10		18 15	18 17							
Wigan North Western	a	←											→	18 09			18 35	18 28	←						
	d	17 36												18 09			18 36	18 28	18 36						
Bolton	a										18 08				18 34		→								
Manchester Piccadilly [10]	a										18 27				18 57										
Manchester Airport	a										18 47				19 17										
Liverpool Lime Street [10]	a	18 22																	19 22						
	d				17 34	17 48																		18 34	18 48
Liverpool South Parkway [7]	d				17 44																			18 44	
Runcorn	d				17 52	18 04																		18 52	19 04
Warrington Bank Quay	a													18 20				18 39							
	d						←							18 20				18 39							
Hartford	d				18 03		18 03																	19 03	
Manchester Piccadilly [10]	d		17 27	17 35	→		17 30	17 55	18 07							18 15					18 27	18 35		→	
Stockport	d		17 36	17 42			17 39	18 04								18 22					18 36	18 42			
Manchester Airport	d						17c06																		
Wilmslow	d						17 47	18 11																	
Holyhead	d							15e40												16 25					
Bangor (Gwynedd)	d							16e08												17 04					
Llandudno	d							16f16												16g16					
Llandudno Junction	d							16e35												17 25					
Wrexham General	d																			18 08					
Chester	d							17 57												18 35					
Crewe [10]	a						18 19	18 27										18 59		18 53					
	d						18 22	18 29										19 01		18 55					
Macclesfield	d		17 49	17 55																	18 49	18 55			
Congleton	d																								
Stoke-on-Trent	d		18 07	18 12					18 43							18 50					19 07	19 12			
Stafford	a		18 24			18 35	18 42														19 24				19 35
	d		18 25			18 36	18 43														19 25				19 36
Penkridge	a						18 48																		
Wolverhampton [7]	a		18 40				18 58		19 13									19 31			19 40				
Birmingham New Street [12]	a		18 58				19 15		19 31									19 55			19 58				
Birmingham International	a		19 13				19 38											20 19			20 13				
Coventry	a		19 24				19 49											20 30			20 24				
Lichfield Trent Valley	a																								
Tamworth Low Level	a																								
Nuneaton	a																								
Rugby	a																	21 00							
Northampton	a																								
Milton Keynes Central	a															19 49				20s03					
Watford Junction	a															20 33				20 52					
Gatwick Airport [10]	a																								
London Euston [15]	a			19 48		20 03		20 11						20 18		20 30				20 44		20 48			21 06

For general notes see front of timetable
For details of catering facilities see Directory of Train Operators

A To Bournemouth (Table 51)
B To Bristol Temple Meads (Table 51)
C To Southampton Central (Table 51)
b Via Glasgow Queen Street and Glasgow Central. Passengers make their own way from one station to the other
c Change at Wilmslow and Crewe
e Change at Chester and Crewe
f Change at Llandudno Junction, Chester and Crewe
g Change at Llandudno Junction and Chester

OVERNIGHT SLEEPERS. For Sleeper trains, operated by First ScotRail, please refer to Tables 400 - 404

Sundays

until 12 July

Scotland and North West England → West Midlands and London

Route Diagram - see first page of Table 65

		LM 1◇	SR	VT 1◇	XC 1◇ A	TP 1◇	VT 1◇	VT 1◇	NT	VT 1◇	NT		XC 1◇ B	VT 1◇	LM 1◇	VT 1◇	XC 1◇ A	AW ◇	TP 1◇	TP 1◇	VT 1◇	VT 1◇		LM 1◇	VT 1◇
Inverness	d						12b30			13c25															
Aberdeen	d									13c50											13b27				
Dundee	d					13c25															14b43				
Perth	d						14b50														15b05				
Edinburgh 10	d					16 10				16 52															
Haymarket	d					16u13				16u56															
Glasgow Central 15	d		14 48				16 36													17 06	17 36				
Motherwell	d						16u54																		
Carstairs	d																								
Lockerbie	d					17 08															18 32				
Carlisle 8	a		17 18			17 30	17 49			18 05										18 21	18 50				
	d					17 32	17 51			18 07										18 28	18 52				
Penrith North Lakes	d					17 46	18 05													18 42	19 06				
Windermere	d						18 04														19 00				
Oxenholme Lake District	a					18 10	18 27			18 41										19 06	19 28				
	d					18 10	18 28			18 42										19 07	19 29				
Barrow-in-Furness	d																		18 15						
Lancaster 6	a					18 26	18 42			18 56									19 17	19 21	19 43				
	d					18 26	18 43			18 57									19 17	19 22	19 44				
Preston 8	a					18 45	19 01			19 15									19 36	19 41	20 02				
Blackpool North	a						19 38			20 00											20 39				
	d						18 20		18 50	18 44											19 20				
Preston 8	d					18 47	19 03		19 15	19 17									19 47		20 04				
Wigan North Western	a						19 14		19 35	19 28	←										20 15				
	d						19 14		19 36	19 28	19 36										20 15				
Bolton	a					19 08	19e34		→										20 08		20e34				
Manchester Piccadilly 10	a					19 27	19e57												20 27		20e57				
Manchester Airport ✈	a					19 47	20e17												20 47		21e17				
Liverpool Lime Street 10	a										20 22										21 22				
	d														19 34	19 48								20 34	
Liverpool South Parkway 7 ✈	d														19 44									20 44	
Runcorn	d														19 52	20 04								20 52	
Warrington Bank Quay	a						19 25			19 39											20 26				
	d	←					19 25			19 39											20 26				
Hartford	d	19 03													20 03									21 03	
Manchester Piccadilly 10	d	18 30		18 55	19 07			19 15					19 27	19 35	19 30		20 07					20 20		20 30	20 55
Stockport	d	18 39		19 04				19 22					19 35	19 42	19 39		20 16					20 27		20 39	21 03
Manchester Airport ✈	d														19f06										
Wilmslow	d	18 47		19 11											19 47									20 47	
Holyhead	d														17 30			18 25							
Bangor (Gwynedd)	d														17 59			19 04							
Llandudno	d																	18 55							
Llandudno Junction	d														18 24			19 24							
Wrexham General	d																	19 08							
Chester	d			18 57											19 22			20 27			19 57				
Crewe 10	a	19 19		19 27						19 59					20 15	20 22		20 48			20 45			21 15	
	d	19 22		19 29						20 01					20 18	20 24		20 52			20 47			21 17	
Macclesfield	d												19 48	19 55			20 29					20 40			21 15
Congleton	d																								
Stoke-on-Trent	d				19 43			19 50					20 07	20 12			20 47					20 57			21 33
Stafford	a	19 42											20 24		20 37	20 42	21 08	21 16						21 36	
	d	19 43											20 25		20 38	20 44	21 09	21 16						21 38	
Penkridge	a	19 48													20 44									21 44	
Wolverhampton 7	a	19 58			20 13					20 34			20 39		20 55		21 21	21 34						21 55	
Birmingham New Street 12	a	20 15			20 31					20 57			21 00		21 15		21 39	21 52						22 15	
Birmingham International ✈	a	20 39								21 25			21 13		21 39			22 08						22 39	
Coventry	a	20 50								21 44			21 23		21 50			22 44						22 50	
Lichfield Trent Valley	a	20g34																							
Tamworth Low Level	a	20g41																							
Nuneaton	a	20g58																							
Rugby	a	21 03								21 57					22 03			22 57							
Northampton	a																								
Milton Keynes Central	a							20 48								21 38					21 55	22 03			22 37
Watford Junction	a							21 36								22 26					22 31	22 52			23s07
Gatwick Airport 10 ✈	a																								
London Euston 15 ⊖	a			21 14			21 27		21 34					22 04		22 29					22 53	22 57			23 32

For general notes see front of timetable
For details of catering facilities see Directory of Train Operators

- **A** To Bristol Temple Meads (Table 51)
- **B** To Reading (Table 51)
- **b** Via Glasgow Queen Street and Glasgow Central. Passengers make their own way from one station to the other
- **c** Change at Haymarket
- **e** Change at Preston
- **f** Change at Wilmslow and Crewe
- **g** Change at Stafford

OVERNIGHT SLEEPERS. For Sleeper trains, operated by First ScotRail, please refer to Tables 400 - 404

Table 65

Sundays

until 12 July

Scotland and North West England → West Midlands and London

Route Diagram - see first page of Table 65

		VT	NT	TP	VT	XC	NT	VT	NT	LM	TP		XC	NT	TP	VT	NT	SR	SR	SR	SR	SR	SR	
																			[R]	[R]	[R]	[R]	[R]	
		1 ◊		1 ◊	1 ◊	1 ◊		1 ◊		1	1 ◊		1 ◊		1 ◊	1 ◊								
																			A	A	B	C	D	
		☕		🍴	☕			☕							🍴	☕			☕	☕	☕	☕	☕	
Inverness	d																	16b15				20 25	20 25	
Aberdeen	d			15c10											17c10			17e47				21 42	21 42	
Dundee	d			16c25											18c19			19e02				23u06	23u06	
Perth	d															17e05		19e24				23u00	23u00	
Edinburgh 10	d			18 10				18 52							19 57					23 15	23u15			
Haymarket	d			18u13				18u57							20u00									
Glasgow Central 15	d				18 35											20 06		22 28	23 15		21 40			
Motherwell	d																		23u31		22u01			
Carstairs	d																		23u47		22u22			
Lockerbie	d			19 08												21 02								
Carlisle 8	a			19 30	19 43			20 05							21 14	21 21		00 49						
	d			19 32	19 44			20 07							21 15	21 24			01u08					
Penrith North Lakes	d			19 46				20 22								21 39								
Windermere	d				19 50						21 00													
Oxenholme Lake District	a			20 10	20 19						21 19					22 02								
	d			20 10	20 19						21 21					22 03								
Barrow-in-Furness	d										20 02													
Lancaster 6	a			20 26	20 34			20 56			21 37				22 02	22 17								
	d			20 26	20 34			20 57			21 38				22 03	22 18								
Preston 8	a			20 45	20 52			21 15			21 58				22 23	22 35						04s33		
Blackpool North	a				21 38			22 00			22 38				23 00	00 04								
	d		19 50		20 20		20 50	20 44						21 50			22 44							
Preston 8	d		20 15	20 47	20 55		21 15	21 17						22 15	22 29	22 38	23 09							
Wigan North Western	a		20 35		21 06		21 35	21 28	←					22 35		22 49	23 29							
	d		20 36		21 07		21 36	21 28	21 36					22 36		22 50	23 30							
Bolton	a			21 08	21f34		→	22f25							22 50	23f59						05 42		
Manchester Piccadilly 10	a			21 27	21f57										23 14	00f15						06 01		
Manchester Airport	a			21 47	22f17										23 30	01g00						06 18		
Liverpool Lime Street 10	a		21 22						22 22					23 23			00 16							
	d	20 48								21 34														
Liverpool South Parkway 7	d									21 44														
Runcorn	d	21 04								21 52														
Warrington Bank Quay	a				21 18			21 39								23 00								
	d				21 18			21 39								23 01								
Hartford	d									22 03														
Manchester Piccadilly 10	d					21 07				21 34			22 07											
Stockport	d					21 16				21 17			22 16											
Manchester Airport	d									21h06														
Wilmslow	d									21 52														
Holyhead	d									19j15														
Bangor (Gwynedd)	d									19j54														
Llandudno	d																							
Llandudno Junction	d									20j17														
Wrexham General	d																							
Chester	d				20 57					21 27														
Crewe 10	a	21 22			21 38			21 59		22 17						23 20						05s37		
	d	21 24			21 40			22 01		22 22														
Macclesfield	d					21 29							22 29											
Congleton	d																							
Stoke-on-Trent	d					21 47							22 47											
Stafford	a	21 42			22 01	22 06				22 41			23 05											
	d	21 44			22 02	22 07				22 44			23 06											
Penkridge	a									22 50														
Wolverhampton 7	a				22 17	22 20		22 31		23 00			23 18											
Birmingham New Street 12	a				22 40	22 45		22 55		23 17			23 41											
Birmingham International	a					23 09		23 31																
Coventry	a					23 20		23 50																
Lichfield Trent Valley	a	21 58																						
Tamworth Low Level	a	22 04																						
Nuneaton	a	22 15																						
Rugby	a	22 29				23 33																		
Northampton	a	00k01																						
Milton Keynes Central	a	22 53																						
Watford Junction	a	23s33																	06s23					
Gatwick Airport 10	a																							
London Euston 15	⊖ a	23 54																	06 46		07 05	07 47	09 21	

For general notes see front of timetable
For details of catering facilities see Directory of Train Operators

A 17 May and 12 July

B 24 May to 5 July. Stops at Edinburgh after Glasgow Central, Motherwell and Carstairs

C 17 May and 12 July. Also conveys portion from Fort William (Table 227)

D 24 May to 5 July. Also conveys portion from Fort William (Table 227)

b Change at Perth, Glasgow Queen Street and Glasgow Central. Passengers make their own way between Glasgow Queen Street and Glasgow Central

c Change at Haymarket

e Via Glasgow Queen Street and Glasgow Central. Passengers make their own way from one station to the other

f Change at Preston

g Change at Preston and Manchester Piccadilly

h Change at Wilmslow and Crewe

j Change at Chester and Crewe

k By bus

OVERNIGHT SLEEPERS. For Sleeper trains, operated by First ScotRail, please refer to Tables 400 - 404

Table 65

Sundays

Scotland and North West England → West Midlands and London

19 July to 6 September

Route Diagram - see first page of Table 65

		VT	VT	VT	XC	VT	VT	VT	XC	VT		LM	NT	VT	NT	VT	XC	VT	VT	NT		VT	NT	XC	TP
		1 ◇	1 ◇	1 ◇	1 ◇	1 ◇	1 ◇	1 ◇	1 ◇	1 ◇		1 ◇		1 ◇		1 ◇	1 ◇	1 ◇	1 ◇			1 ◇		1 ◇	1 ◇
					A				A								A							A	
		⊡	⊡	⊡	✕	⊡	⊡	⊡	✕	⊡				⊡		⊡	✕	⊡	⊡			⊡		✕	
Inverness	d																								
Aberdeen	d																								
Dundee	d																								
Perth	d																								
Edinburgh 10	d																								
Haymarket	d																								
Glasgow Central 15	d																								
Motherwell	d																								
Carstairs	d																								
Lockerbie	d																								
Carlisle 8	a																								
	d																								
Penrith North Lakes	d																								
Windermere	d																								
Oxenholme Lake District	a																								
	d																								
Barrow-in-Furness	d																								09 23
Lancaster 6	a																								10 26
	d																								10 26
Preston 8	a																								10 45
Blackpool North	a																								11 39
	d						08 20						08 50	09 20						09 50		09 44			
Preston 8	d						09 00						09 15	10 00						10 15		10 17			10 47
Wigan North Western	a						09 10						09 35	10 10	←					10 35		10 28	←		
	d						09 11						09 36	10 11	09 36					10 36		10 28	10 36		
Bolton	a												↪							↪					11 08
Manchester Piccadilly 10	a																								11 27
Manchester Airport	a																								11 47
Liverpool Lime Street 10	a						10 22								10 22								11 22		
	d			08 15		08 38				09 36									10 38						
Liverpool South Parkway 7	d																								
Runcorn	d			08 34		08 54				09 52									10 54						
Warrington Bank Quay	a						09 21							10 21								10 39			
	d						09 22							10 22								10 39			
Hartford	d																								
Manchester Piccadilly 10	d	08 05	08 20		08 27			09 20	09 27	09 04		09 30				10 20	10 24	10 35							
Stockport	d	08 14	08 28		08 36			09 27	09 36	09 17		09 39				10 29	10 34	10 43							
Manchester Airport	d									09b09															
Wilmslow	d	08 22			08 43					09 28		09 47				10 37									
Holyhead	d													07c50					08 40						
Bangor (Gwynedd)	d						07 43							08c28					09 08						
Llandudno	d																								
Llandudno Junction	d						08 01							08c51					09 26						
Wrexham General	d																								
Chester	d				08 27		08 57			09 27				09 57					10 27						
Crewe 10	a	08 39		08 54	09 01	09 11	09 41			10 12				10 41		10 53			11 12			10 59			
	d	08 43		08 55	09 04	09 13	09 43			10 14		10 20		10 43		10 55			11 14			11 01			
Macclesfield	d		08 42					09 40	09 49								10 47	10 56							
Congleton	d																								
Stoke-on-Trent	d		08 59					09 57	10 07								11 07	11 12							
Stafford	a	09 00			09 24	09 31			10 25	10 31		10 41					11 24		11 31					←	
	d	09 02			09 25	09 32			10 26	10 33		10 42					11 25		11 33					11 25	
Penkridge	a											10 48					↪								
Wolverhampton 7	a				09 40				10 40			11 00										11 31		11 40	
Birmingham New Street 12	a				09 58				10 58			11 17										11 55		11 58	
Birmingham International	a				10 13				11 13			11 39										12 19		12 13	
Coventry	a				10 24				11 24			11 50										12 30		12 24	
Lichfield Trent Valley	a																		12 34						
Tamworth Low Level	a																		12 41						
Nuneaton	a					09 54				10 55									11 55						
Rugby	a				10 56		10 31		11 56			12 03		11 31										12 56	
Northampton	a						11 17							12 17											
Milton Keynes Central	a			10 18			11 04	11 13		11 48				12 04				12 20							
Watford Junction	a	10s35	10s41	11 05		11s20	11s42	12 06								12s35		13 17	12s53						
Gatwick Airport 10	a																								
London Euston 15	⊖ a	10 58	11 03	11 07		11 44	12 04	12 08		12 38				12 51		12 58		13 01	13 15						

For general notes see front of timetable
For details of catering facilities see Directory of Train Operators

A To Bournemouth (Table 51)
b Change at Wilmslow and Crewe
c Change at Chester and Crewe

OVERNIGHT SLEEPERS. For Sleeper trains, operated by First ScotRail, please refer to Tables 400 - 404

Sundays

Scotland and North West England → West Midlands and London

19 July to 6 September

Route Diagram - see first page of Table 65

		VT	VT	NT	VT	VT	NT	XC		VT	LM	VT	LM	VT	VT	VT	NT	VT		VT	NT	XC	VT	LM	VT
		1◇	1◇		1◇	1◇		1◇		1◇	1◇	1◇	1◇	1◇	1◇	1◇		1◇		1◇		1◇	1◇	1◇	1◇
								A														A			
Inverness	d																								
Aberdeen	d																								
Dundee	d																								
Perth	d																								
Edinburgh 10	d																								
Haymarket	d																								
Glasgow Central 15	d																								
Motherwell	d																								
Carstairs	d																								
Lockerbie	d																								
Carlisle 8	a																								
	d														10 46										
Penrith North Lakes	d														11 00										
Windermere	d																								
Oxenholme Lake District	a														11 22										
	d														11 23										
Barrow-in-Furness	d																								
Lancaster 6	a														11 37										
	d														11 38					12 00					
Preston 8	a														11 56					12 15					
Blackpool North	a														*12 38*					*13 00*					
	d	*10 20*		10 50		*10 44*									*11 20*		11 50			*11 44*					
Preston 8	d	10 58		11 15		11 17									11 58		12 15			12 17					
Wigan North Western	a	11 09		11 35		11 28	←								12 09		12 35			12 28	←				
	d	11 09		11 36		11 28	11 36								12 09		12 36			12 28	12 36				
Bolton	a			↳											*12b34*		↳								
Manchester Piccadilly 10	a														*12b57*					*13b27*					
Manchester Airport	a														*13b17*					*13b47*					
Liverpool Lime Street 10	a						12 22														13 22				
	d										11 34	11 48												12 34	12 48
Liverpool South Parkway 7	d										11 44													12 44	
Runcorn	d										11 52	12 04												12 52	13 04
Warrington Bank Quay	a	11 20				11 39									12 20					12 39					
	d	11 20				11 39							←		12 20					12 39					
Hartford	d										12 04		12 04											13 03	
Manchester Piccadilly 10	d		11 15		*10c30*			11 27		11 35	→		*11 24*	11 55		12 15						12 26	12 35	→	
Stockport	d		11 23		*10c41*			11 37		11 43			*11 40*	12 05		12 23						12 36	12 44		
Manchester Airport	d												*11e08*												
Wilmslow	d				*10c47*								*11 48*	12 12											
Holyhead	d				*08 40*													10 55							
Bangor (Gwynedd)	d				*09 08*													11 22							
Llandudno	d																	*11 07*							
Llandudno Junction	d				*09 26*													11 40							
Wrexham General	d				*10 53*																				
Chester	d				11 28													12 33							
Crewe 10	a				11 47	11 59							12 19	12 28				12 52		12 59					
	d				11 49	12 01							12 22	12 30				12 54		13 01					
Macclesfield	d							11 50		11 56												12 49	12 57		
Congleton	d																								
Stoke-on-Trent	d		11 51					12 08		12 13						12 51						13 07	13 14		
Stafford	a							12 25				12 35	12 41									13 24			13 35
	d							12 26				12 36	12 42									13 25			13 36
Penkridge	a												12 48												
Wolverhampton 7	a					12 34		12 40					12 59							13 31		13 40			
Birmingham New Street 12	a					12 55		12 58					13 16							13 55		13 58			
Birmingham International	a					*13 19*		13 13					*13 38*							*14 19*		14 13			
Coventry	a					*13 30*		13 24					*13 49*							*14 30*		14 24			
Lichfield Trent Valley	a																								
Tamworth Low Level	a																								
Nuneaton	a				12 30																				
Rugby	a							*13 56*					*14 23*									*14 56*			
Northampton	a																								
Milton Keynes Central	a		12 50		13s03											13 50		14s02							
Watford Junction	a		*13 33*		*13 51*											*14 34*		*14 51*							
Gatwick Airport 10	a																								
London Euston 15	a	13 23	13 31		13 44					13 49		14 03		14 12	14 18	14 31		14 43					14 50		15 03

For general notes see front of timetable
For details of catering facilities see
Directory of Train Operators

A To Bournemouth (Table 51)
b Change at Preston
c Change at Crewe
e Change at Wilmslow and Crewe

OVERNIGHT SLEEPERS. For Sleeper trains, operated by First ScotRail, please refer to Tables 400 - 404

Table 65

Scotland and North West England → West Midlands and London

19 July to 6 September

Route Diagram - see first page of Table 65

Station		LM	VT	XC	TP	VT		VT	NT	VT	VT	XC	VT	LM	VT	LM		VT	NT	XC	TP	VT	VT	NT	VT
		1 ◇	1 ◇	1 ◇	1 ◇	1 ◇		1 ◇		1 ◇	1 ◇	1 ◇	1 ◇	1 ◇	1 ◇	1 ◇		1 ◇		1 ◇	1 ◇	1 ◇	1 ◇		1 ◇
				A								B								C					
			☕	🛒		☕		☕		☕	☕	🛒	☕		☕			☕		🛒		☕	☕		☕
Inverness	d																								
Aberdeen	d																								
Dundee	d																				09b25				
Perth	d																				09b27				
Edinburgh [10]	d										10 52										11 10				
Haymarket	d										10u57										11u13				
Glasgow Central [15]	d					10 32																11 32			
Motherwell	d					10u49																			
Carstairs	d																								
Lockerbie	d																				12 08				
Carlisle [8]	a					11 44					12 05										12 30	12 47			
	d					11 46					12 07										12 32	12 49			
Penrith North Lakes	d					12 00															12 46				
Windermere	d					*11 58*																*12 58*			
Oxenholme Lake District	a					12 22					12 41										13 10	13 22			
	d					12 24					12 43										13 10	13 23			
Barrow-in-Furness	d				11 15																				
Lancaster [6]	a				12 17	12 37					12 56										13 26	13 37			
	d				12 19	12 38					12 57										13 26	13 38			
Preston [8]	a				12 37	12 56					13 15										13 45	13 56			
Blackpool North	a					*13 38*					*14 00*											*14 38*			
	d					*12 20*			12 50		*12 44*											*13 20*		13 50	
Preston [8]	d				12 47	12 58			13 15		13 17										13 47	13 58		14 15	
Wigan North Western	a					13 09			13 35		13 28								←			14 09		14 35	
	d					13 09			13 36		13 28								13 36			14 09		14 36	
Bolton	a				13 08	*13c34*			→												14 08	*14c34*		→	
Manchester Piccadilly [10] ⛴	a				13 27	*13c57*															14 27	*14c57*			
Manchester Airport ✈	a				13 47	*14c17*															14 47	*15c17*			
Liverpool Lime Street [10]	a																		14 22						
	d													13 34	13 48										
Liverpool South Parkway [7] ✈	d													13 44											
Runcorn	d													13 52	14 04										
Warrington Bank Quay	a					13 20					13 39											14 20			
	d	←				13 20					13 39					←						14 20			
Hartford	d	13 03												14 03		14 03									
Manchester Piccadilly [10] ⛴	d	*12 30*	12 55	13 07				13 15				13 27	13 35	→		*13 30*		13 55		14 07			14 15		
Stockport	d	*12 40*	13 05					13 22				13 36	13 42			*13 39*		14 04					14 22		
Manchester Airport ✈	d															*13e06*									
Wilmslow	d	*12 48*	13 12													*13 47*		14 11							
Holyhead	d									11 48															12 47
Bangor (Gwynedd)	d									12 15															13 14
Llandudno	d									*12 18*															
Llandudno Junction	d									12 33															13 32
Wrexham General	d									*12 55*															
Chester	d		*12 57*							13 28								*13 57*							14 33
Crewe [10]	a	13 18	13 28							13 47	13 59					14 18		14 27							14 52
	d	13 22	13 30							13 49	14 01					14 22		14 29							14 54
Macclesfield	d											13 49	13 55												
Congleton	d																								
Stoke-on-Trent	d			13 43				13 50				14 07	14 12							14 43			14 50		
Stafford	a	13 42										14 24			14 35	14 42									
	d	13 43										14 25			14 36	14 43									
Penkridge	a	13 48														14 48									
Wolverhampton [7] ⛴	a	13 58		14 13							14 33	14 40				14 58				15 13					
Birmingham New Street [12]	a	14 15		14 31							14 55	14 58				15 15				15 31					
Birmingham International ✈	a	*14 38*		*14 59*							*15 19*	15 13				*15 38*				*15 59*					
Coventry	a	*14 49*		*15 11*							*15 30*	15 24				*15 49*				*16 11*					
Lichfield Trent Valley	a	*14f35*																							
Tamworth Low Level	a	*14f42*																							
Nuneaton	a	*14f58*								14 31															
Rugby	a			*15 23*								*15 56*								*16 23*					
Northampton	a																								
Milton Keynes Central	a							14 49		15s04													15 49		16s04
Watford Junction	a							*15 33*		*15 51*													*16 33*		*16 51*
Gatwick Airport [10] ✈	a																								
London Euston [15] ⊖	a		15 12			15 18		15 30		15 45			15 48		16 03			16 11				16 18	16 30		16 44

For general notes see front of timetable
For details of catering facilities see Directory of Train Operators

- **A** To Paignton (Table 51)
- **B** To Bournemouth (Table 51)
- **C** To Bristol Temple Meads (Table 51)
- **b** Change at Haymarket
- **c** Change at Preston
- **e** Change at Wilmslow and Crewe
- **f** Change at Stafford

OVERNIGHT SLEEPERS. For Sleeper trains, operated by First ScotRail, please refer to Tables 400 - 404

Table 65

Sundays

Scotland and North West England → West Midlands and London

19 July to 6 September

Route Diagram - see first page of Table 65

		VT	NT	XC		VT	LM	VT	LM	VT	XC	TP	VT	VT		NT	VT	VT	NT	XC	VT	LM	VT	LM	VT
		1 ◇		1 ◇		1 ◇	1 ◇	1 ◇	1 ◇	1 ◇	1 ◇	1 ◇	1 ◇	1 ◇			1 ◇	1 ◇		1 ◇	1 ◇	1 ◇	1 ◇	1 ◇	1 ◇
				A							B									A					
		🍽		🛒		🍽		🍽		🍽	🛒		🍽	🍽			🍽	🍽		🛒	🍽		🍽		🍽
Inverness	d																								
Aberdeen	d																	09b48							
Dundee	d																	11b02							
Perth	d																								
Edinburgh [10]	d																	12 52							
Haymarket	d																	12u56							
Glasgow Central [15]	d	11 51											12 40												
Motherwell	d																								
Carstairs	d																								
Lockerbie	d																								
Carlisle [8]	a	13 08											13 51					14 05							
	d	13 09											13 54					14 07							
Penrith North Lakes	d																	14 22							
Windermere	d												13 58												
Oxenholme Lake District	a												14 27												
	d												14 28												
Barrow-in-Furness	d	12 45										13 22													
Lancaster [6]	a	13 56										14 25	14 42					14 56							
	d	13 58										14 25	14 43					14 57							
Preston [8]	a	14 15										14 45	15 01					15 15							
Blackpool North	a	15 00											15 39					16 00							
	d	13 44											14 20			14 50		14 44							
Preston [8]	d	14 17										14 47	15 03			15 15		15 17							
Wigan North Western	a	14 28	←										15 14			15 35		15 28	←						
	d	14 28	14 36										15 14			15 36		15 28	15 36						
Bolton	a											15 08	15c34			→									
Manchester Piccadilly [10]	a											15 27	15c57												
Manchester Airport	a											15 47	16c17												
Liverpool Lime Street [10]	a		15 22																16 22						
	d						14 34	14 48														15 34	15 48		
Liverpool South Parkway [7]	d						14 44															15 44			
Runcorn	d						14 52	15 04														15 52	16 04		
Warrington Bank Quay	a	14 39											15 25					15 39							
	d	14 39							←				15 25					15 39						←	
Hartford	d						15 03		15 03													16 03		16 03	
Manchester Piccadilly [10]	d			14 27		14 35	→		14 30	14 55	15 07			15 15						15 27	15 35	→		15 30	15 55
Stockport	d			14 36		14 42			14 39	15 04				15 22						15 36	15 42			15 39	16 04
Manchester Airport	d																							15e06	
Wilmslow	d								14 47	15 11														15 47	16 11
Holyhead	d																13 55								
Bangor (Gwynedd)	d																14 22								
Llandudno	d																14 20								
Llandudno Junction	d																14 40								
Wrexham General	d																								
Chester	d									14 57							15 33								15 57
Crewe [10]	a	14 59							15 19	15 27							15 52	15 59						16 18	16 27
	d	15 01							15 22	15 29							15 54	16 01						16 22	16 29
Macclesfield	d			14 49		14 55														15 49	15 55				
Congleton	d																								
Stoke-on-Trent	d			15 07		15 12					15 43			15 50						16 07	16 12				
Stafford	a			15 24				15 35	15 42											16 24			16 36	16 42	
	d			15 25				15 36	15 43											16 25			16 37	16 43	
Penkridge	a								15 48															16 48	
Wolverhampton [7]	a	15 31		15 40					15 58		16 13							16 34		16 40				16 58	
Birmingham New Street [12]	a	15 55		15 58					16 15		16 31							16 55		16 58				17 15	
Birmingham International	a	16 19		16 13					16 38		16 59							17 19		17 13				17 38	
Coventry	a	16 30		16 24					16 49		17 11							17 30		17 24				17 49	
Lichfield Trent Valley	a								16f34																
Tamworth Low Level	a								16f41																
Nuneaton	a								16f58																
Rugby	a			16 56							17 23									17 56					
Northampton	a																								
Milton Keynes Central	a													16 49			17s03								
Watford Junction	a													17 33			17 51								
Gatwick Airport [10]	a																								
London Euston [15]	⊖ a					16 48		17 03		17 11			17 23	17 30			17 44				17 48		18 04		18 11

For general notes see front of timetable
For details of catering facilities see Directory of Train Operators

- **A** To Bournemouth (Table 51)
- **B** To Bristol Temple Meads (Table 51)
- **b** Change at Haymarket
- **c** Change at Preston
- **e** Change at Wilmslow and Crewe
- **f** Change at Stafford

OVERNIGHT SLEEPERS. For Sleeper trains, operated by First ScotRail, please refer to Tables 400 - 404

Table 65

Sundays

Scotland and North West England → West Midlands and London

19 July to 6 September

Route Diagram - see first page of Table 65

		XC		TP	VT	VT	NT	VT	VT	NT	XC	VT		LM	VT	LM	VT	XC	TP	VT	VT	NT		VT	VT
		1 ◇		1 ◇	1 ◇	1 ◇		1 ◇	1 ◇		1 ◇	1 ◇		1 ◇	1 ◇	1 ◇	1 ◇	1 ◇	1 ◇	1 ◇	1 ◇			1 ◇	1 ◇
		A									B							C							
		🍴		🍴	🍽	🍽		🍽	🍽		🍴	🍽			🍽		🍽	🍴		🍽	🍽			🍽	🍽
Inverness	d																								09 38
Aberdeen	d				09b27																				11c47
Dundee	d			11c25																					13c01
Perth	d				11b05																				11 56
Edinburgh 10	d			13 09																					14 52
Haymarket	d			13u12																					14u57
Glasgow Central 15	d				13 35				13 56											14 36					
Motherwell	d																								
Carstairs	d																								
Lockerbie	d			14 07																					
Carlisle 8	a			14 30	14 46				15 09											15 46					16 05
	d			14 31	14 49				15 09											15 49					16 07
Penrith North Lakes	d			14 46																					16 22
Windermere	d				14 58															15 58					
Oxenholme Lake District	a			15 10	15 22				15 44											16 22					
	d			15 10	15 23				15 44											16 23					
Barrow-in-Furness	d																		15 22						
Lancaster 6	a			15 25	15 37														16 25	16 37					16 56
	d			15 25	15 38														16 25	16 38					16 57
Preston 8	a			15 45	15 56				16 15										16 45	16 56					17 15
Blackpool North	a				16 38				17 00											17 38					18 00
	d			15 13	15 20		15 50		15 44										16 11	16 20		16 50			16 44
Preston 8	d			15 47	15 58		16 15		16 17										16 47	16 58		17 15			17 17
Wigan North Western	a				16 09		16 35		16 28	←										17 09		17 35			17 28
	d				16 09		16 36		16 28	16 36										17 09		17 36			17 28
Bolton	a			16 08	16e34		→												17 08	17e34		→			
Manchester Piccadilly 10	a			16 27	16e57														17 27	17e57					
Manchester Airport ✈	a			16 47	17e17														17 47	18e17					
Liverpool Lime Street 10	a									17 22															
	d							16 18						16 34	16 48										
Liverpool South Parkway 7 ✈	d													16 44											
Runcorn	d							16 34						16 52	17 04										
Warrington Bank Quay	a				16 20				16 39											17 20					17 39
	d				16 20				16 39							←				17 20					17 39
Hartford	d													17 03		17 03									
Manchester Piccadilly 10	d	16 07				16 15					16 27	16 35		→		16 30	16 55	17 07			17 15				
Stockport	d					16 23					16 36	16 42				16 39	17 04				17 22				
Manchester Airport ✈	d																								
Wilmslow	d															16 47	17 11								
Holyhead	d															14f30									
Bangor (Gwynedd)	d															15f08									
Llandudno	d															15g11									
Llandudno Junction	d															15f26									
Wrexham General	d																							17 10	
Chester	d															16 27	16 57							17 35	
Crewe 10	a							16 50	16 59							17 18	17 27							17 53	17 59
	d							16 53	17 01							17 22	17 29							17 55	18 01
Macclesfield	d										16 49	16 55													
Congleton	d																								
Stoke-on-Trent	d	16 43				16 50					17 07	17 12						17 43			17 50				
Stafford	a										17 24				17 35	17 42									
	d										17 25				17 36	17 43									
Penkridge	a															17 48									
Wolverhampton 7	a	17 13							17 31		17 40					17 58		18 13							18 32
Birmingham New Street 12	a	17 31							17 55		17 58					18 15		18 31							18 55
Birmingham International ✈	a	17 59							18 19		18 13					18 38		18 59							19 19
Coventry	a	18 11							18 30		18 24					18 49		19 11							19 30
Lichfield Trent Valley	a															18h34									
Tamworth Low Level	a															18h41									
Nuneaton	a															18h58									
Rugby	a	18 23									18 56							19 23							
Northampton	a																								
Milton Keynes Central	a					17 49		18s03													18 49			19s03	
Watford Junction	a					18 33		18 51													19 33			19 51	
Gatwick Airport 10 ✈	a																								
London Euston 15 ⊖	a				18 18	18 30		18 44				18 48			19 03		19 11			19 18	19 30			19 44	

For general notes see front of timetable
For details of catering facilities see Directory of Train Operators

A To Bristol Temple Meads (Table 51)

B To Bournemouth (Table 51)

C To Paignton (Table 51)

b Via Glasgow Queen Street and Glasgow Central. Passengers make their own way from one station to the other

c Change at Haymarket

e Change at Preston

f Change at Chester and Crewe

g Change at Llandudno Junction, Chester and Crewe

h Change at Stafford

OVERNIGHT SLEEPERS. For Sleeper trains, operated by First ScotRail, please refer to Tables 400 - 404

Scotland and North West England → West Midlands and London

19 July to 6 September

Route Diagram - see first page of Table 65

		NT	XC	VT	LM	VT	LM	VT	XC	TP	TP	TP	VT	TP	VT	NT	VT	VT	NT	XC	VT	LM	VT
			1◇	1◇	1◇	1◇	1◇	1◇	1◇	1◇	1◇	1◇	1◇	1◇	1◇		1◇	1◇		1◇	1◇	1◇	1◇
			A						B											C			
Inverness	d																						
Aberdeen	d										11b29												
Dundee	d																						
Perth	d										13b05												
Edinburgh 10	d																						
Haymarket	d																						
Glasgow Central 15	d										15 06		15 35					15 55					
Motherwell	d																						
Carstairs	d																						
Lockerbie	d										16 07												
Carlisle 8	a										16 28		16 46					17 08					
	d										16 30		16 49					17 09					
Penrith North Lakes	d										16 44		17 03										
Windermere	d											16 58											
Oxenholme Lake District	a										17 08	17 15						17 44					
	d										17 08	17 16						17 44					
Barrow-in-Furness	d									16 25													
Lancaster 6	a									17 18	17 23	17 32	17 37										
	d									17 18	17 23	17 33	17 38										
Preston 8	a									17 37	17 42	17 51	17 56					18 15					
Blackpool North	a												18 38					19 00					
	d												17 20	←		17 50		17 40					
Preston 8	d									17 47		18 10 →	17 58	18 10		18 15		18 17					
Wigan North Western	a	←											18 09			18 35		18 28	←				
	d	17 36											18 09			18 36		18 28	18 36				
Bolton	a									18 08				18 34		→							
Manchester Piccadilly 10	a									18 27				18 57									
Manchester Airport	a									18 47				19 17									
Liverpool Lime Street 10	a	18 22																	19 22				
	d				17 34	17 48																18 34	18 48
Liverpool South Parkway 7	d				17 44																	18 44	
Runcorn	d				17 52	18 04																18 52	19 04
Warrington Bank Quay	a												18 20					18 39					
	d						←						18 20					18 39					
Hartford	d				18 03		18 03															19 03	
Manchester Piccadilly 10	d		17 27	17 35	→		17 30	17 55	18 07						18 15					18 27	18 35	→	
Stockport	d		17 36	17 42			17 39	18 04							18 22					18 36	18 42		
Manchester Airport	d							17 06															
Wilmslow	d						17 47	18 11															
Holyhead	d							15c40									16 25						
Bangor (Gwynedd)	d							16c08									17 04						
Llandudno	d							16e16									16f16						
Llandudno Junction	d							16c35									17 25						
Wrexham General	d																18 08						
Chester	d							17 57									18 35						
Crewe 10	a						18 19	18 27									18 53	18 59					
	d						18 22	18 29									18 55	19 01					
Macclesfield	d		17 49	17 55																18 49	18 55		
Congleton	d																						
Stoke-on-Trent	d		18 07	18 12					18 43						18 50					19 07	19 12		
Stafford	a		18 24			18 35	18 42													19 24			19 35
	d		18 25			18 36	18 43													19 25			19 36
Penkridge	a						18 48																
Wolverhampton 7	a		18 40				18 58		19 13									19 31		19 40			
Birmingham New Street 12	a		18 58				19 15		19 31									19 55		19 58			
Birmingham International	a		19 13				19 38											20 19		20 13			
Coventry	a		19 24				19 49											20 30		20 24			
Lichfield Trent Valley	a																						
Tamworth Low Level	a																						
Nuneaton	a																						
Rugby	a		19 56																	20 56			
Northampton	a																						
Milton Keynes Central	a														19 49		20s03						
Watford Junction	a														20 33		20 52						
Gatwick Airport 10	a																						
London Euston 15	a			19 48		20 03		20 11					20 18		20 30		20 44				20 48		21 06

For general notes see front of timetable
For details of catering facilities see Directory of Train Operators

A To Bournemouth (Table 51)
B To Bristol Temple Meads (Table 51)
C To Southampton Central (Table 51)

b Via Glasgow Queen Street and Glasgow Central. Passengers make their own way from one station to the other
c Change at Chester and Crewe
e Change at Llandudno Junction, Chester and Crewe
f Change at Llandudno Junction and Chester

OVERNIGHT SLEEPERS. For Sleeper trains, operated by First ScotRail, please refer to Tables 400 - 404

Sundays

Scotland and North West England → West Midlands and London

19 July to 6 September

Route Diagram - see first page of Table 65

		LM	SR	VT	XC	TP	VT	VT	NT		VT	NT	XC	VT	LM	VT	XC	TP	TP		VT	AW	VT	LM	VT
		1 ◇		1 ◇	1 ◇	1 ◇	1 ◇	1 ◇			1 ◇		1 ◇	1 ◇	1 ◇	1 ◇	1 ◇	1 ◇	1 ◇		1 ◇	◇	1 ◇	1 ◇	1 ◇
					A								B				A								
Inverness	d						12b30				13c25														
Aberdeen	d										13c50														
Dundee	d					13c25					15c04										14b43				
Perth	d						14b50				15c25										15b05				
Edinburgh 10	d					16 10					16 52														
Haymarket	d					16u13					16u56														
Glasgow Central 15	d		14 48				16 36												17 06		17 36				
Motherwell	d						16u54																		
Carstairs	d																								
Lockerbie	d					17 08															18 32				
Carlisle 8	a		17 18			17 30	17 49				18 05								18 21		18 50				
	d					17 32	17 51				18 07								18 28		18 52				
Penrith North Lakes	d					17 46	18 05												18 42		19 06				
Windermere	d						18 04														19 00				
Oxenholme Lake District	a					18 10	18 27				18 41								19 06		19 28				
	d					18 10	18 28				18 42								19 07		19 29				
Barrow-in-Furness	d																	18 15							
Lancaster 6	a					18 26	18 42				18 56							19 17	19 21		19 43				
	d					18 26	18 43				18 57							19 17	19 22		19 44				
Preston 8	a					18 45	19 01				19 15							19 36	19 41		20 02				
Blackpool North	a						19 38				20 00										20 39				
	d						18 20		18 50		18 44										19 20				
Preston 8	d					18 47	19 03		19 15		19 17							19 47			20 04				
Wigan North Western	a						19 14		19 35		19 28	←									20 15				
	d						19 14		19 36		19 28	19 36									20 15				
Bolton	a					19 08	19e34		→									20 08			20e34				
Manchester Piccadilly 10	a					19 27	19e57											20 27			20e57				
Manchester Airport	a					19 47	20e17											20 47			21e17				
Liverpool Lime Street 10	a											20 22									21 22				
	d														19 34	19 48								20 34	
Liverpool South Parkway 7	d														19 44									20 44	
Runcorn	d														19 52	20 04								20 52	
Warrington Bank Quay	a						19 25				19 39										20 26				
	d	←					19 25				19 39										20 26				
Hartford	d	19 03													20 03									21 03	
Manchester Piccadilly 10	d	18 30		18 55	19 07			19 15					19 27	19 35	19 30		20 07						20 20	20 30	20 55
Stockport	d	18 39		19 04				19 22					19 35	19 42	19 39		20 16						20 27	20 39	21 03
Manchester Airport	d														19f06										
Wilmslow	d	18 47		19 11											19 47									20 47	
Holyhead	d														17 30							18 25			
Bangor (Gwynedd)	d														17 59							19 04			
Llandudno	d																					18 55			
Llandudno Junction	d														18 24							19 24			
Wrexham General	d																					19 08			
Chester	d			18 57											19 22						19 57	20 27			
Crewe 10	a	19 19		19 27							19 59				20 15	20 22					20 45	20 48		21 15	
	d	19 22		19 29							20 01				20 18	20 24					20 47	20 52		21 17	
Macclesfield	d												19 48	19 55			20 29						20 40		21 15
Congleton	d																								
Stoke-on-Trent	d				19 43			19 50					20 07	20 12			20 47						20 57		21 33
Stafford	a	19 42											20 24		20 37	20 42	21 07					21 16		21 36	
	d	19 43											20 25		20 38	20 44	21 08					21 16		21 38	
Penkridge	a	19 48													20 44									21 44	
Wolverhampton 7	a	19 58			20 13						20 34		20 39		20 55		21 21					21 34		21 55	
Birmingham New Street 12	a	20 15			20 31						20 57		21 00		21 15		21 39					21 52		22 15	
Birmingham International	a	20 39									21 25		21 13		21 39		22 08					22 08		22 39	
Coventry	a	20 50			21 23						21 44		21 23		21 50		22 44					22 44		22 50	
Lichfield Trent Valley	a	20g34																							
Tamworth Low Level	a	20g41																							
Nuneaton	a	20g58																							
Rugby	a	21 03											21 56		22 03		22 56								
Northampton	a																								
Milton Keynes Central	a							20 48								21 38					21 55		22 03		22 50
Watford Junction	a							21 36								22 26					22 31		22 52		23s31
Gatwick Airport 10	a																								
London Euston 15	⊖ a			21 14			21 27	21 34						22 04		22 29					22 53		22 57		23 53

For general notes see front of timetable
For details of catering facilities see Directory of Train Operators

- **A** To Bristol Temple Meads (Table 51)
- **B** To Reading (Table 51)
- **b** Via Glasgow Queen Street and Glasgow Central. Passengers make their own way from one station to the other
- **c** Change at Haymarket
- **e** Change at Preston
- **f** Change at Wilmslow and Crewe
- **g** Change at Stafford

OVERNIGHT SLEEPERS. For Sleeper trains, operated by First ScotRail, please refer to Tables 400 - 404

Scotland and North West England → West Midlands and London

19 July to 6 September

Route Diagram - see first page of Table 65

		VT	NT	TP	VT	XC	LM	NT	VT	NT	TP	XC	NT	TP	VT	NT	SR	SR	SR	SR
																		[R]	[R]	[R]
		1 ◇		1 ◇	1 ◇	1 ◇	1		1 ◇		1 ◇	1 ◇		1 ◇	1 ◇					A
		☕		🍴	☕				☕					🍴	☕			☕	☕	☕
Inverness	d																16b15			20 25
Aberdeen	d			15c10										17c10			17e47			21 42
Dundee	d			16c25										18c19			19e02			23u06
Perth	d														17e05		19e24			23u00
Edinburgh 10	d			18 10					18 52					19 57					23 15	
Haymarket	d			18u13					18u57					20u00						
Glasgow Central 15	d				18 35										20 06		22 28	23 15		
Motherwell	d																	23u31		
Carstairs	d																	23u47		
Lockerbie	d			19 08											21 02					
Carlisle 8	a			19 30	19 43				20 05					21 14	21 21		00 49			
	d			19 32	19 44				20 07					21 15	21 24			01u08		
Penrith North Lakes	d			19 46					20 22						21 39					
Windermere	d				19 50						21 00									
Oxenholme Lake District	a			20 10	20 19						21 19				22 02					
	d			20 10	20 19						21 21				22 03					
Barrow-in-Furness	d										20 02									
Lancaster 6	a			20 26	20 34				20 56		21 37			22 02	22 17					
	d			20 26	20 34				20 57		21 38			22 03	22 18					
Preston 8	a			20 45	20 52				21 15		21 58			22 23	22 35					04s33
Blackpool North	a				21 38				22 00		22 38			23 00	00 04					
	d		19 50		20 20			20 50	20 44				21 50			22 44				
Preston 8	d		20 15	20 47	20 55			21 15	21 17	←			22 15	22 29	22 38	23 09				
Wigan North Western	a		20 35		21 06			21 35	21 28				22 35		22 49	23 29				
	d		20 36		21 07			21 36	21 28	21 36			22 36		22 50	23 30				
Bolton	a			21 08	21f34			→	22f25					22 50	23f59					05 42
Manchester Piccadilly 10	a			21 27	21f57									23 14	00f15					06 01
Manchester Airport ✈	a			21 47	22f17									23 30	01g00					06 18
Liverpool Lime Street 10	a		21 22							22 22			23 23			00 16				
	d	20 48					21 34													
Liverpool South Parkway 7 ✈	d						21 44													
Runcorn	d	21 04					21 52													
Warrington Bank Quay	a				21 18				21 39						23 00					
	d				21 18				21 39						23 01					
Hartford	d						22 03													
Manchester Piccadilly 10	d					21 07	21 34					22 07								
Stockport	d					21 16	21 17					22 16								
Manchester Airport ✈	d						21h06													
Wilmslow	d						21 52													
Holyhead	d						19j15													
Bangor (Gwynedd)	d						19j54													
Llandudno	d																			
Llandudno Junction	d						20j17													
Wrexham General	d																			
Chester	d				20 57		21 27													
Crewe 10	a	21 22			21 38		22 17		21 59						23 20					05s37
	d	21 24			21 40		22 22		22 01											
Macclesfield	d					21 29						22 29								
Congleton	d																			
Stoke-on-Trent	d					21 47						22 47								
Stafford	a	21 42			22 01	22 06	22 41					23 04								
	d	21 44			22 02	22 07	22 44					23 05								
Penkridge	a						22 50													
Wolverhampton 7	a				22 17	22 20	23 00		22 31			23 18								
Birmingham New Street 12	a				22 40	22 45	23 17		22 55			23 41								
Birmingham International ✈	a					23 09			23 31											
Coventry	a					23 20			23 50											
Lichfield Trent Valley	a	21 58																		
Tamworth Low Level	a	22 04																		
Nuneaton	a	22 15																		
Rugby	a	22 29				23 33														
Northampton	a	23 17																		
Milton Keynes Central	a	23 08																		
Watford Junction	a	23s38																06s23		
Gatwick Airport 10 ✈	a																			
London Euston 15	⊖ a	23 59																06 46		07 47

For general notes see front of timetable
For details of catering facilities see Directory of Train Operators

A Also conveys portion from Fort William (Table 227)

b Change at Perth, Glasgow Queen Street and Glasgow Central. Passengers make their own way between Glasgow Queen Street and Glasgow Central

c Change at Haymarket

e Via Glasgow Queen Street and Glasgow Central. Passengers make their own way from one station to the other

f Change at Preston

g Change at Preston and Manchester Piccadilly

h Change at Wilmslow and Crewe

j Change at Chester and Crewe

OVERNIGHT SLEEPERS. For Sleeper trains, operated by First ScotRail, please refer to Tables 400 - 404

Table 65

Sundays

Scotland and North West England → West Midlands and London

13 September to 1 November

Route Diagram - see first page of Table 65

		VT	VT	VT	XC	VT	VT	VT	XC	VT	LM	NT	VT	VT	XC	VT	VT	NT	VT	NT	VT	VT	NT	VT	VT
		1◇	1◇	1◇	1◇	1◇	1◇	1◇	1◇	1◇	1◇		1◇	1◇	1◇	1◇	1◇		1◇		1◇	1◇		1◇	1◇
					A				A						A										
		⊡	⊡	⊡	✕	⊡	⊡	⊡	✕	⊡			⊡	⊡	✕	⊡	⊡		⊡		⊡	⊡		⊡	⊡
Inverness	d																								
Aberdeen	d																								
Dundee	d																								
Perth	d																								
Edinburgh 10	d																								
Haymarket	d																								
Glasgow Central 15	d																								
Motherwell	d																								
Carstairs	d																								
Lockerbie	d																								
Carlisle 8	a																								
	d																								
Penrith North Lakes	d																								
Windermere	d																								
Oxenholme Lake District	a																								
	d																								
Barrow-in-Furness	d																								
Lancaster 6	a																								
	d																								
Preston 8	a																								
Blackpool North	a																								
	d						08 20					08 50	09 20					09 50	09 44		10 20		10 50		10 44
Preston 8	d						09 00					09 15	10 00					10 15	10 17		10 58		11 15		11 17
Wigan North Western	a						09 10					09 35	10 10					10 38	10 28	←	11 09		11 35		11 28
	d						09 11					09 36	10 11					10 38	10 28	10 38	11 09		11 36		11 28
Bolton	a																	→					→		
Manchester Piccadilly 10	a																								
Manchester Airport	a																								
Liverpool Lime Street 10	a											10 22								11 24					
	d		08 15			08 38				09 36							10 38								
Liverpool South Parkway 7	d																								
Runcorn	d		08 34			08 54				09 52							10 54								
Warrington Bank Quay	a						09 21						10 21						10 39		11 20				11 39
	d						09 22						10 22						10 39		11 20				11 39
Hartford	d																								
Manchester Piccadilly 10	d	08 05		08 20	08 27			09 20	09 27		09 30			10 20	10 27	10 35						11 15			
Stockport	d	08 14		08 28	08 36			09 27	09 36		09 39			10 29	10 36	10 42						11 23			
Manchester Airport	d									09b09															
Wilmslow	d	08 22			08 43					09 28	09 47			10 36										10c47	
Holyhead	d																08 50								
Bangor (Gwynedd)	d																09 18								
Llandudno	d																								
Llandudno Junction	d																09 36								
Wrexham General	d																							10 53	
Chester	d					08 40				09 40							10 35							11 28	
Crewe 10	a	08 39	08 54		09 01	09 11	09 41			10 10			10 41	10 52			11 12		10 59					11 47	11 59
	d	08 43	08 55		09 04	09 13	09 43			10 12	10 20		10 43	10 55			11 14		11 03					11 49	12 01
Macclesfield	d			08 42				09 40	09 49						10 49	10 55									
Congleton	d																								
Stoke-on-Trent	d			09 07				09 57	10 07						11 07	11 12						11 51			
Stafford	a	09 07			09 27	09 38			10 26	10 38	10 45				11 24		11 41								
	d	09 09			09 28	09 39			10 27	10 40	10 45				11 25		11 42								
Penkridge	a										10 51														
Wolverhampton 7	a				09 40				10 40		11 01				11 38				11 42						12 34
Birmingham New Street 12	a				09 58				10 58		11 18				11 57				12 05						12 55
Birmingham International	a				10 13				11 13		11 39				12 13				12 38						13 19
Coventry	a				10 24				11 24		11 50				12 24				12 49						13 30
Lichfield Trent Valley	a																12 34								
Tamworth Low Level	a																12 41								
Nuneaton	a					10 01				11 02							12 04							12 30	
Rugby	a				10 56		10 38		11 56		12 03		11 38		12 56				13 23						
Northampton	a						11 17						12 17												
Milton Keynes Central	a		10 13				11 04	11 18		11 48			12 04			12 29						12 50		13s03	
Watford Junction	a	10s35	11 05	10s47		11s20	11s42	12 06						12s35		13 17	12s54					13 33		13 51	
Gatwick Airport 10	a																								
London Euston 15 ⊖	a	10 58	11 03	11 08		11 44	12 04	12 08		12 38			12 51	12 58		13 09	13 15				13 23	13 31		13 44	

For general notes see front of timetable
For details of catering facilities see Directory of Train Operators

A To Bournemouth (Table 51)
b Change at Wilmslow and Crewe
c Change at Crewe

OVERNIGHT SLEEPERS. For Sleeper trains, operated by First ScotRail, please refer to Tables 400 - 404

Table 65

Sundays

Scotland and North West England → West Midlands and London

13 September to 1 November

Route Diagram - see first page of Table 65

		NT	XC	VT	LM	VT	LM	VT	VT	VT	NT	VT	VT	NT	XC	VT	LM	VT	LM	VT	XC	TP	VT	VT	NT
			1 ◇	1 ◇	1 ◇	1 ◇	1 ◇	1 ◇	1 ◇	1 ◇		1 ◇	1 ◇		1 ◇	1 ◇	1 ◇	1 ◇	1 ◇	1 ◇	1 ◇	1 ◇	1 ◇	1 ◇	
			A												A						B				
			🛒	☕		☕		☕	☕	☕		☕	☕		🛒	☕		☕		☕	🛒		☕	☕	
Inverness	d																								
Aberdeen	d																								
Dundee	d																								
Perth	d																								
Edinburgh 10	d																								
Haymarket	d																								
Glasgow Central 15	d																						10 32		
Motherwell	d																						10u49		
Carstairs	d																								
Lockerbie	d																								
Carlisle 8	a																						11 44		
	d								10 46														11 46		
Penrith North Lakes	d								11 00														12 00		
Windermere	d																						11 58		
Oxenholme Lake District	a								11 22														12 22		
	d								11 23														12 24		
Barrow-in-Furness	d																					11 15			
Lancaster 6	a								11 37													12 17	12 37		
	d								11 38				12 00									12 19	12 38		
Preston 8	a								11 56				12 15									12 37	12 56		
Blackpool North	a								12 38				13 00										13 38		
	d								11 20		11 50		11 44										12 20		12 50
Preston 8	d								11 58		12 15		12 17									12 47	12 58		13 15
Wigan North Western	a	←							12 09		12 35		12 28	←									13 09		13 35
	d	11 36							12 09		12 36		12 28	12 36									13 09		13 36
Bolton	a								12b34		→											13 08	13b34		→
Manchester Piccadilly 10	a								12b57													13 27	13b57		
Manchester Airport	a								13b17													13 47	14b17		
Liverpool Lime Street 10	a	12 22												13 22											
	d				11 34	11 48											12 34	12 48							
Liverpool South Parkway 7	d				11 44												12 44								
Runcorn	d				11 52	12 04											12 52	13 04							
Warrington Bank Quay	a								12 20				12 39										13 20		
	d						←		12 20				12 39						←				13 20		
Hartford	d				12 04		12 04										13 03		13 03						
Manchester Piccadilly 10	d		11 27	11 35	→		11 30	11 55		12 15					12 26	12 35	→		12 30	12 55	13 07			13 15	
Stockport	d		11 36	11 43			11 40	12 05		12 23					12 36	12 44			12 40	13 05				13 22	
Manchester Airport	d						11c10																		
Wilmslow	d						11 47	12 12											12 48	13 12					
Holyhead	d											10 55													
Bangor (Gwynedd)	d											11 22													
Llandudno	d											10e15													
Llandudno Junction	d											11 40													
Wrexham General	d																								
Chester	d											12 33													
Crewe 10	a						12 19	12 28				12 52	12 59						13 18	13 28					
	d						12 22	12 30				12 54	13 01						13 22	13 30					
Macclesfield	d		11 49	11 56											12 49	12 57									
Congleton	d																								
Stoke-on-Trent	d		12 07	12 13						12 51					13 07	13 14					13 43			13 50	
Stafford	a		12 25			12 35	12 41								13 24			13 35	13 42						
	d		12 26			12 36	12 42								13 25			13 36	13 43						
Penkridge	a						12 48												13 48						
Wolverhampton 7	a		12 40				12 59						13 31		13 40				13 58		14 13				
Birmingham New Street 12	a		12 58				13 16						13 55		13 58				14 15		14 31				
Birmingham International	a		13 13				13 38						14 19		14 13				14 38		14 59				
Coventry	a		13 24				13 49						14 30		14 24				14 49		15 11				
Lichfield Trent Valley	a																		14f35						
Tamworth Low Level	a																		14f42						
Nuneaton	a																		14f58						
Rugby	a		13 56				14 23								14 56						15 23				
Northampton	a																								
Milton Keynes Central	a									13 50		14s02												14 49	
Watford Junction	a									14 34		14 51												15 33	
Gatwick Airport 10	a																								
London Euston 15	⊖ a			13 49		14 03		14 12	14 18	14 31		14 43				14 50		15 03		15 12			15 18	15 30	

For general notes see front of timetable
For details of catering facilities see Directory of Train Operators

A To Bournemouth (Table 51)
B To Paignton (Table 51)
b Change at Preston
c Change at Wilmslow and Crewe
e By bus
f Change at Stafford

OVERNIGHT SLEEPERS. For Sleeper trains, operated by First ScotRail, please refer to Tables 400 - 404

Table 65

Sundays

Scotland and North West England → West Midlands and London

13 September to 1 November

Route Diagram - see first page of Table 65

		VT	VT	XC	VT	LM	VT	LM	VT	XC	NT	TP	VT	VT	NT	VT	VT	NT	XC	VT	LM	VT	LM	VT
		1◇	1◇	1◇	1◇	1◇	1◇	1◇	1◇	1◇		1◇	1◇	1◇		1◇	1◇		1◇	1◇	1◇	1◇	1◇	1◇
				A						B									A					
Inverness	d																							
Aberdeen	d																							
Dundee	d											09b25												
Perth	d											09b27												
Edinburgh 10	d		10 52									11 10												
Haymarket	d		10u57									11u13												
Glasgow Central 15	d												11 32				11 51							
Motherwell	d																							
Carstairs	d																							
Lockerbie	d											12 08												
Carlisle 8	a		12 05									12 30	12 47				13 08							
	d		12 07									12 32	12 49				13 09							
Penrith North Lakes	d											12 46												
Windermere	d												12 58											
Oxenholme Lake District	a		12 41									13 10	13 22											
	d		12 43									13 10	13 23											
Barrow-in-Furness	d																12 45							
Lancaster 6	a		12 56									13 26	13 37				13 56							
	d		12 57									13 26	13 38				13 58							
Preston 8	a		13 15									13 45	13 56				14 15							
Blackpool North	a		14 00										14 38				15 00							
	d		12 44										13 20		13 50		13 44							
Preston 8	d		13 17									13 47	13 58		14 15		14 17							
Wigan North Western	a		13 28								←		14 09		14 35		14 28	←						
	d		13 28								13 36		14 09		14 36		14 28	14 36						
Bolton	a											14 08	14c34		→									
Manchester Piccadilly 10	a											14 27	14c57											
Manchester Airport	a											14 47	15c17											
Liverpool Lime Street 10	a										14 22							15 22						
	d					13 34	13 48														14 34	14 48		
Liverpool South Parkway 7	d					13 44															14 44			
Runcorn	d					13 52	14 04														14 52	15 04		
Warrington Bank Quay	a		13 39										14 20				14 39							
	d		13 39					←					14 20				14 39						←	
Hartford	d					14 03		14 03													15 03		15 03	
Manchester Piccadilly 10	d			13 27	13 35	→		13 30	13 55	14 07				14 15					14 27	14 35	→		14 30	14 55
Stockport	d			13 36	13 42			13 39	14 04					14 22					14 36	14 42			14 39	15 04
Manchester Airport	d							13e06																
Wilmslow	d							13 47	14 11														14 47	15 11
Holyhead	d	11 48														12 47								
Bangor (Gwynedd)	d	12 15														13 14								
Llandudno	d	10f15														13g15								
Llandudno Junction	d	12 33														13 32								
Wrexham General	d	12 55																						
Chester	d	13 28														14 33	14 20							
Crewe 10	a	13 47	13 59					14 18	14 27							14 52	14 59						15 19	15 27
	d	13 49	14 01					14 22	14 29							14 54	15 01						15 22	15 29
Macclesfield	d			13 49	13 55														14 49	14 55				
Congleton	d																							
Stoke-on-Trent	d			14 07	14 12					14 43				14 50					15 07	15 12				
Stafford	a			14 24			14 35	14 42											15 24			15 35	15 42	
	d			14 25			14 36	14 43											15 25			15 36	15 43	
Penkridge	a							14 48															15 48	
Wolverhampton 7	a		14 33	14 40				14 58		15 13							15 31		15 40				15 58	
Birmingham New Street 12	a		14 55	14 58				15 15		15 31							15 55		15 58				16 15	
Birmingham International	a		15 19	15 13				15 38		15 59							16 19		16 13				16 38	
Coventry	a		15 30	15 24				15 49		16 11							16 30		16 24				16 49	
Lichfield Trent Valley	a																						16h34	
Tamworth Low Level	a																						16h41	
Nuneaton	a	14 31																					16h58	
Rugby	a			15 56						16 23									16 56					
Northampton	a																							
Milton Keynes Central	a	15s04												15 49		16s04								
Watford Junction	a	15 51												16 33		16 51								
Gatwick Airport 10	a																							
London Euston 15	a	15 45			15 48		16 03		16 11				16 18	16 30		16 44				16 48		17 03		17 11

For general notes see front of timetable
For details of catering facilities see Directory of Train Operators

- **A** To Bournemouth (Table 51)
- **B** To Bristol Temple Meads (Table 51)
- **b** Change at Haymarket
- **c** Change at Preston
- **e** Change at Wilmslow and Crewe
- **f** Change at Llandudno Junction and Chester. By bus to Llandudno Junction
- **g** By bus
- **h** Change at Stafford

OVERNIGHT SLEEPERS. For Sleeper trains, operated by First ScotRail, please refer to Tables 400 - 404

Table 65

Sundays

Scotland and North West England → West Midlands and London

13 September to 1 November

Route Diagram - see first page of Table 65

		XC	TP	VT	VT	NT	VT	VT	NT	XC	VT	LM	VT	LM	VT	XC	TP	VT	VT	NT	VT	VT	NT	XC	VT
		1 ◇	1 ◇	1 ◇	1 ◇		1 ◇	1 ◇		1 ◇	1 ◇	1 ◇	1 ◇	1 ◇	1 ◇	1 ◇	1 ◇	1 ◇	1 ◇		1 ◇	1 ◇		1 ◇	1 ◇
		A								B						A								B	
		🛒		🍽	🍽		🍽	🍽		🛒	🍽		🍽		🍽	🛒	🛒	🍽	🍽		🍽	🍽		🛒	🍽
Inverness	d																								
Aberdeen	d							09b48																	
Dundee	d							11b02									11b25								
Perth	d																	11c05							
Edinburgh 10	d							12 52									13 09								
Haymarket	d							12u56									13u12								
Glasgow Central 15	d			12 40														13 35				13 56			
Motherwell	d																								
Carstairs	d																								
Lockerbie	d																14 08								
Carlisle 8	a			13 51				14 05									14 30	14 46				15 09			
	d			13 54				14 07									14 31	14 49				15 09			
Penrith North Lakes	d							14 22									14 46								
Windermere	d			13 58														14 58							
Oxenholme Lake District	a			14 27													15 10	15 22				15 44			
	d			14 28													15 10	15 23				15 44			
Barrow-in-Furness	d		13 22																						
Lancaster 6	a		14 25	14 42				14 56									15 25	15 37							
	d		14 25	14 43				14 57									15 25	15 38							
Preston 8	a		14 45	15 01				15 15									15 45	15 56				16 15			
Blackpool North	a			15 39				16 00										16 38				17 00			
	d			14 20		14 50		14 44									15 13	15 20		15 50		15 44			
Preston 8	d		14 47	15 03		15 15		15 17									15 47	15 58		16 15		16 17			
Wigan North Western	a			15 14		15 35		15 28	←									16 09		16 35		16 28	←		
	d			15 14		15 36		15 28	15 36									16 09		16 36		16 28	16 36		
Bolton	a		15 08	15e34		→											16 08	16e34		→					
Manchester Piccadilly 10	a		15 27	15e57													16 27	16e57							
Manchester Airport ✈	a		15 47	16e17													16 47	17e17							
Liverpool Lime Street 10	a								16 22														17 22		
	d											15 34	15 48								16 18				
Liverpool South Parkway 7 ✈	d											15 44													
Runcorn	d											15 52	16 04								16 34				
Warrington Bank Quay	a			15 25				15 39										16 20				16 39			
	d			15 25				15 39						←				16 20				16 39			
Hartford	d											16 03		16 03											
Manchester Piccadilly 10	d	15 07			15 15					15 27	15 35	→		15 30	15 55	16 07			16 15					16 27	16 35
Stockport	d				15 22					15 36	15 42			15 39	16 04				16 23					16 36	16 42
Manchester Airport ✈	d													15f06											
Wilmslow	d													15 47	16 11										
Holyhead	d						13 55																		
Bangor (Gwynedd)	d						14 22																		
Llandudno	d																								
Llandudno Junction	d						14 40																		
Wrexham General	d																								
Chester	d						15 33																		
Crewe 10	a						15 52	15 59						16 18	16 27						16 50	16 59			
	d						15 54	16 01						16 22	16 29						16 53	17 01			
Macclesfield	d									15 49	15 55													16 49	16 55
Congleton	d																								
Stoke-on-Trent	d	15 43			15 50					16 07	16 12					16 43			16 50					17 07	17 12
Stafford	a									16 24			16 36	16 42										17 24	
	d									16 25			16 37	16 43										17 25	
Penkridge	a													16 48											
Wolverhampton 7	a	16 13						16 34		16 40				16 58		17 13						17 31		17 40	
Birmingham New Street 12	a	16 31						16 55		16 58				17 15		17 31						17 55		17 58	
Birmingham International ✈	a	16 59						17 19		17 13				17 38		17 59						18 19		18 13	
Coventry	a	17 11						17 30		17 24				17 49		18 11						18 30		18 24	
Lichfield Trent Valley	a																								
Tamworth Low Level	a																								
Nuneaton	a																								
Rugby	a	17 23								17 56						18 23								18 56	
Northampton	a																								
Milton Keynes Central	a				16 49		17s03												17 49		18s03				
Watford Junction	a				17 33		17 51												18 33		18 51				
Gatwick Airport 10 ✈	a																								
London Euston 15 ⊖	a			17 23	17 30		17 44				17 48		18 04		18 11			18 18	18 30		18 44				18 48

For general notes see front of timetable
For details of catering facilities see Directory of Train Operators

A To Bristol Temple Meads (Table 51)
B To Bournemouth (Table 51)
b Change at Haymarket
c Via Glasgow Queen Street and Glasgow Central. Passengers make their own way from one station to the other
e Change at Preston
f Change at Wilmslow and Crewe

OVERNIGHT SLEEPERS. For Sleeper trains, operated by First ScotRail, please refer to Tables 400 - 404

Sundays

Scotland and North West England → West Midlands and London

13 September to 1 November

Route Diagram - see first page of Table 65

		LM	VT	LM	VT	XC	TP	VT	VT	NT	VT	VT	NT	XC	VT	LM	VT	LM	VT	XC	TP	VT	VT	NT	VT
		1 ◇	1 ◇	1 ◇	1 ◇	1 ◇	1 ◇	1 ◇	1 ◇		1 ◇	1 ◇		1 ◇	1 ◇	1 ◇	1 ◇	1 ◇	1 ◇	1 ◇	1 ◇	1 ◇	1 ◇		1 ◇
						A								B						C					
			🍽		🍽	🛒		🍽	🍽		🍽	🍽		🛒	🍽		🍽		🍽	🛒	🛒	🍽	🍽		🍽
Inverness	d											09 38													
Aberdeen	d											11b47													
Dundee	d											13b01													
Perth	d											11 56									13c05				
Edinburgh 10	d											14 52													
Haymarket	d											14u57													
Glasgow Central 15	d							14 36													15 06	15 35			
Motherwell	d																								
Carstairs	d																								
Lockerbie	d																				16 07				
Carlisle 8	a							15 46				16 05									16 28	16 46			
	d							15 49				16 07									16 30	16 49			
Penrith North Lakes	d											16 22									16 44	17 03			
Windermere	d							15 58																	
Oxenholme Lake District	a							16 22													17 08				
	d							16 23													17 08				
Barrow-in-Furness	d						15 30																		
Lancaster 6	a						16 25	16 37				16 56									17 23	17 37			
	d						16 25	16 38				16 57									17 23	17 38			
Preston 8	a						16 45	16 56				17 15									17 42	17 56			
Blackpool North	a							17 38				18 00										18 38			
	d							16 20		16 50		16 44										17 20		17 50	
Preston 8	d						16 47	16 58		17 15		17 17	←								17 47	17 58		18 15	
Wigan North Western	a							17 09		17 35		17 28										18 09		18 35	
	d							17 09		17 36		17 28	17 36									18 09		18 36	
Bolton	a						17 08	17e34		→											18 08	18e34		→	
Manchester Piccadilly 10 ⇌	a						17 27	17e57													18 27	18e57			
Manchester Airport ✈	a						17 47	18e17													18 47	19e17			
Liverpool Lime Street 10	a												18 22												
	d	16 34	16 48													17 34	17 48								
Liverpool South Parkway 7 ✈	d	16 44														17 44									
Runcorn	d	16 52	17 04													17 52	18 04								
Warrington Bank Quay	a							17 20				17 39										18 20			
	d			←				17 20				17 39						←				18 20			
Hartford	d	17 03		17 03												18 03		18 03							
Manchester Piccadilly 10 ⇌	d	→		16 30	16 55	17 07			17 15					17 27	17 35	→		17 30	17 55	18 07			18 15		
Stockport	d			16 39	17 04				17 22					17 36	17 42			17 39	18 04				18 22		
Manchester Airport ✈	d																	17f06							
Wilmslow	d			16 47	17 11													17 48	18 11						
Holyhead	d			14g30							15 30														16 25
Bangor (Gwynedd)	d			15g08							15 59														17 04
Llandudno	d										16h00														
Llandudno Junction	d			15g26							16 25														17 25
Wrexham General	d										17 10														18 08
Chester	d			16 27							17 35	17 22													18 35
Crewe 10	a			17 18	17 27						17 53	17 59						18 19	18 27						18 53
	d			17 22	17 29						17 55	18 01						18 22	18 29						18 55
Macclesfield	d													17 49	17 55										
Congleton	d																								
Stoke-on-Trent	d					17 43			17 50					18 07	18 12					18 43			18 50		
Stafford	a		17 35	17 42										18 24			18 35	18 42							
	d		17 36	17 43										18 25			18 36	18 43							
Penkridge	a			17 48														18 48							
Wolverhampton 7 ⇌	a			17 58		18 13						18 32		18 40				18 58		19 13					
Birmingham New Street 12	a			18 15		18 31						18 55		18 58				19 15		19 31					
Birmingham International ✈	a			18 38		18 59						19 19		19 13				19 38							
Coventry	a			18 49		19 11						19 30		19 24				19 49							
Lichfield Trent Valley	a			18j34																					
Tamworth Low Level	a			18j41																					
Nuneaton	a			18j58																					
Rugby	a					19 23								19 56											
Northampton	a																								
Milton Keynes Central	a								18 49		19s03												19 49		20s03
Watford Junction	a								19 33		19 51												20 33		20 52
Gatwick Airport 10 ✈	a																								
London Euston 15 ⊖	a		19 03		19 11			19 18	19 30		19 44				19 48		20 03		20 11			20 18	20 30		20 44

For general notes see front of timetable
For details of catering facilities see Directory of Train Operators

A To Paignton (Table 51)
B To Bournemouth (Table 51)
C To Bristol Temple Meads (Table 51)
b Change at Haymarket
c Via Glasgow Queen Street and Glasgow Central. Passengers make their own way from one station to the other
e Change at Preston
f Change at Wilmslow and Crewe
g Change at Chester and Crewe
h Change at Llandudno Junction and Chester. By bus to Llandudno Junction
j Change at Stafford

OVERNIGHT SLEEPERS. For Sleeper trains, operated by First ScotRail, please refer to Tables 400 - 404

Sundays

Scotland and North West England → West Midlands and London

13 September to 1 November

Route Diagram - see first page of Table 65

		VT	NT	XC	VT	LM	VT	LM	VT	XC	NT	VT	NT	XC	TP	VT	VT	VT	LM	VT	XC	AW	TP	TP	VT
		1◇		1◇	1◇	1◇	1◇	1◇	1◇	1◇		1◇		1◇	1◇	1◇	1◇	1◇	1◇	1◇	1◇	◇	1◇	1◇	1◇
				A						B				C							B				
		☕		🛒	☕		☕		☕	🛒		☕		🛒	🛒	☕	☕	☕		☕				🛒	☕
Inverness	d											13b25													
Aberdeen	d											13b50													
Dundee	d														13b25										14c43
Perth	d															14c50									15c05
Edinburgh 10	d											16 52			16 10										
Haymarket	d											16u56			16u13										
Glasgow Central 15	d	15 55														16 36								17 06	17 36
Motherwell	d															16u54									
Carstairs	d																								
Lockerbie	d														17 08										18 32
Carlisle 8	a	17 08										18 05			17 30	17 49								18 21	18 50
	d	17 09										18 07			17 32	17 51								18 28	18 52
Penrith North Lakes	d														17 46	18 05								18 42	19 06
Windermere	d	*16 58*														*18 04*									*19 00*
Oxenholme Lake District	a	17 44										18 41			18 10	18 27								19 06	19 28
	d	17 44										18 42			18 10	18 28								19 07	19 29
Barrow-in-Furness	d																						18 15		
Lancaster 6	a											18 56			18 26	18 42							19 17	19 21	19 43
	d											18 57			18 26	18 43							19 17	19 22	19 44
Preston 8	a	18 15										19 15			18 45	19 01							19 36	19 41	20 02
Blackpool North	a	*19 00*										*20 00*				*19 38*									*20 39*
	d	*17 44*									18 50	*18 44*				*18 20*									*19 20*
Preston 8	d	18 17									19 15	19 17			18 47	19 03								19 47	20 04
Wigan North Western	a	18 28	←								19 35	19 28	←			19 14									20 15
	d	18 28	18 36								19 36	19 28	19 36			19 14									20 15
Bolton	a										→				19 08	19e34								20 08	20e34
Manchester Piccadilly 10	a														19 27	19e57								20 27	20e57
Manchester Airport ✈	a														19 47	20e17								20 47	21e17
Liverpool Lime Street 10	a		19 22										20 22												21 22
	d					18 34	18 48												19 34	19 48					
Liverpool South Parkway 7 ✈	d					18 44													19 44						
Runcorn	d					18 52	19 04												19 52	20 04					
Warrington Bank Quay	a	18 39										19 39				19 25									20 26
	d	18 39						←				19 39				19 25									20 26
Hartford	d					19 03		19 03											20 03						
Manchester Piccadilly 10	d			18 27	18 35	→		*18 30*	18 55	19 07				19 27			19 15	19 35	*19 30*		20 07				
Stockport	d			18 36	18 42			*18 39*	19 04					19 35			19 22	19 42	*19 39*		20 16				
Manchester Airport ✈	d																		*19f06*						
Wilmslow	d							*18 47*	19 11										*19 47*						
Holyhead	d																		*17 30*			18 25			
Bangor (Gwynedd)	d																		*17 59*			19 04			
Llandudno	d																								
Llandudno Junction	d																		*18 24*			19 24			
Wrexham General	d																					*19 08*			
Chester	d								*18 57*										*19 22*	*19 50*		20 27			
Crewe 10	a	18 59						19 19	19 27			19 59							20 15	20 22		20 48			20 45
	d	19 01						19 22	19 29			20 01							20 18	20 24		20 52			20 47
Macclesfield	d			18 49	18 55									19 48				19 55			20 29				
Congleton	d																								
Stoke-on-Trent	d			19 07	19 12					19 43				20 07			19 50	20 12			20 47				
Stafford	a			19 24			19 35	19 42						20 24					20 37	20 42	21 08	21 16			
	d			19 25			19 36	19 43						20 25					20 38	20 44	21 09	21 16			
Penkridge	a							19 48											20 44						
Wolverhampton 7	a	19 31		19 40				19 58		20 13		20 34		20 39					20 55		21 21	21 34			
Birmingham New Street 12	a	19 55		19 58				20 15		20 31		20 57		21 00					21 15		21 39	21 52			
Birmingham International ✈	a	*20 19*		20 13				*20 39*				*21 25*		21 13					*21 39*			22 08			
Coventry	a	*20 30*		20 24				*20 50*				*21 44*		21 23					*21 50*			22 44			
Lichfield Trent Valley	a							20g34																	
Tamworth Low Level	a							20g41																	
Nuneaton	a							20g58																	
Rugby	a			*20 56*				*21 03*						*21 56*					*22 03*			*22 56*			
Northampton	a																								
Milton Keynes Central	a																20 48			21 38					21 55
Watford Junction	a																*21 36*			*22 26*					22 31
Gatwick Airport 10 ✈	a																								
London Euston 15 ⊖	a				20 48		21 06		21 14							21 27	21 34	22 04		22 29					22 53

For general notes see front of timetable
For details of catering facilities see
Directory of Train Operators

A To Southampton Central (Table 51)

B To Bristol Temple Meads (Table 51)

C To Reading (Table 51)

b Change at Haymarket

c Via Glasgow Queen Street and Glasgow Central. Passengers make their own way from one station to the other

e Change at Preston

f Change at Wilmslow and Crewe

g Change at Stafford

OVERNIGHT SLEEPERS. For Sleeper trains, operated by First ScotRail, please refer to Tables 400 - 404

Table 65

Sundays

Scotland and North West England → West Midlands and London

13 September to 1 November

Route Diagram - see first page of Table 65

		VT	LM	VT	VT	NT	TP	VT	XC	LM	NT	VT	NT	TP	XC	NT	TP	VT	NT	SR	SR	SR	SR
		1◇	1◇	1◇	1◇		1◇	1◇	1◇	1		1◇		1◇	1◇		1◇	1◇			R	R	R
																							A
		☕		☕	☕		🛒	☕				☕					🛒	☕			☕	☕	☕
Inverness	d																			16b15			20 25
Aberdeen	d						15c10										17c10			17e47			21 42
Dundee	d						16c25										18c19			19e02			23u06
Perth	d																	17e05		19e24			23u00
Edinburgh 10	d						18 10					18 52					19 57					23 15	
Haymarket	d						18u13					18u57					20u00						
Glasgow Central 15	d							18 35										20 06		22 28	23 15		
Motherwell	d																				23u31		
Carstairs	d																				23u47		
Lockerbie	d						19 08											21 02					
Carlisle 8	a						19 30	19 43				20 05					21 14	21 21		00 49			
	d						19 32	19 44				20 07					21 15	21 24			01u08		
Penrith North Lakes	d						19 46					20 22						21 39					
Windermere	d							19 50						21 00									
Oxenholme Lake District	a						20 10	20 19						21 19				22 02					
	d						20 10	20 19						21 21				22 03					
Barrow-in-Furness	d													20 02									
Lancaster 6	a						20 26	20 34				20 56		21 37			22 02	22 17					
	d						20 26	20 34				20 57		21 38			22 03	22 18					
Preston 8	a						20 45	20 52				21 15		21 58			22 23	22 35					04s33
Blackpool North	a							21 38				22 00		22 38			23 00	00 04					
	d					19 50		20 20			20 50	20 44				21 50			22 44				
Preston 8	d					20 15	20 47	20 55			21 15	21 17	←			22 15	22 29	22 38	23 09				
Wigan North Western	a					20 35		21 06			21 35	21 28				22 35		22 49	23 29				
	d					20 36		21 07			21 36	21 28	21 36			22 36		22 50	23 30				
Bolton	a						21 08	21f34			→	22f25					22 50	23f59					05 42
Manchester Piccadilly 10	a						21 27	21f57									23 14	00f15					06 01
Manchester Airport	a						21 47	22f17									23 30	01g31					06 18
Liverpool Lime Street 10	a					21 22							22 22			23 23			00 16				
	d		20 34		20 48					21 34													
Liverpool South Parkway 7	d		20 44							21 44													
Runcorn	d		20 52		21 04					21 52													
Warrington Bank Quay	a							21 18				21 39						23 00					
	d							21 18				21 39						23 01					
Hartford	d		21 03							22 03													
Manchester Piccadilly 10	d	20 20	20 30	20 55					21 07	21 34					22 07								
Stockport	d	20 27	20 39	21 03					21 16	21 17					22 16								
Manchester Airport	d									21h06													
Wilmslow	d		20 47							21 52													
Holyhead	d									19 40													
Bangor (Gwynedd)	d									20 09													
Llandudno	d																						
Llandudno Junction	d									20 37													
Wrexham General	d																						
Chester	d				20 50					21 50													
Crewe 10	a		21 15		21 22			21 38		22 17		21 59						23 20					05s37
	d		21 17		21 24			21 40		22 22		22 01											
Macclesfield	d	20 40		21 15					21 29						22 29								
Congleton	d																						
Stoke-on-Trent	d	20 57		21 33					21 47						22 47								
Stafford	a		21 36		21 42			22 01	22 06	22 41					23 05								
	d		21 38		21 44			22 02	22 07	22 44					23 06								
Penkridge	a		21 44							22 50													
Wolverhampton 7	a		21 55					22 17	22 20	23 00		22 31			23 18								
Birmingham New Street 12	a		22 15					22 40	22 45	23 17		22 55			23 41								
Birmingham International	a		22 39						23 09			23 31											
Coventry	a		22 50						23 20			23 50											
Lichfield Trent Valley	a				21 58																		
Tamworth Low Level	a				22 04																		
Nuneaton	a				22 15																		
Rugby	a				22 29				23 33														
Northampton	a				23 17																		
Milton Keynes Central	a	22 03		22 50	23 08																		
Watford Junction	a	22 52		23s31	23s38																06s23		
Gatwick Airport 10	a																						
London Euston 15	⊖ a	22 57		23 53	23 59																06 46		07 47

For general notes see front of timetable
For details of catering facilities see Directory of Train Operators

A Also conveys portion from Fort William (Table 227)

b Change at Perth, Glasgow Queen Street and Glasgow Central. Passengers make their own way between Glasgow Queen Street and Glasgow Central

c Change at Haymarket

e Via Glasgow Queen Street and Glasgow Central. Passengers make their own way from one station to the other

f Change at Preston

g Change at Preston and Manchester Piccadilly

h Change at Wilmslow and Crewe

OVERNIGHT SLEEPERS. For Sleeper trains, operated by First ScotRail, please refer to Tables 400 - 404

Table 65

Sundays

from 8 November

Scotland and North West England → West Midlands and London

Route Diagram - see first page of Table 65

		VT	VT	VT	XC	VT	VT	VT	VT	XC	VT	LM	NT	VT	VT	VT	XC	VT	VT	NT	VT	VT	VT	VT	VT
		1◇	1◇	1◇	1◇	1◇		1◇	1◇	1◇	1◇	1◇			1◇	1◇	1◇	1◇	1◇			1◇	1◇	1◇	1◇
					A					A							A								
							🚌							🚌							🚌				
Inverness	d																								
Aberdeen	d																								
Dundee	d																								
Perth	d																								
Edinburgh 10	d																								
Haymarket	d																								
Glasgow Central 15	d																								
Motherwell	d																								
Carstairs	d																								
Lockerbie	d																								
Carlisle 8	a																								
	d																								
Penrith North Lakes	d																								
Windermere	d																								
Oxenholme Lake District	a																								
	d																								
Barrow-in-Furness	d																								
Lancaster 6	a																								
	d																								
Preston 8	a																								
Blackpool North	a																								
	d												08 50							09 50					
Preston 8	d						07 35						09 15	08 35						10 15	09 30				
Wigan North Western	a						08 15						09 35	09 15						10 35	10 10				
	d						08 15						09 36	09 15						10 36	10 10				
Bolton	a																								
Manchester Piccadilly 10	a																								
Manchester Airport	a																								
Liverpool Lime Street 10	a												10 22							11 22					
	d		08 15			08 38					09 36								10 38						
Liverpool South Parkway 7	d																								
Runcorn	d		08 34			08 54					09 52								10 54						
Warrington Bank Quay	a						08 45							09 45							10 40				
	d						08 45							09 45							10 40				
Hartford	d																								
Manchester Piccadilly 10	d	08 05		08 20	08 27				09 20	09 27		*09 30*				10 20	10 27	10 35				*10 30*	11 15		
Stockport	d	08 14		08 28	08 36				09 27	09 36		*09 39*				10 29	10 36	10 42				*10 39*	11 23		
Manchester Airport	d										09b09														
Wilmslow	d	08 22			08 43						*09 28*	*09 47*				10 36						*10 47*			
Holyhead	d																		*08 50*						
Bangor (Gwynedd)	d																		*09 18*						
Llandudno	d																								
Llandudno Junction	d																		*09 36*						
Wrexham General	d																							*10 53*	
Chester	d					*08 40*					*09 40*								*10 35*					11 28	
Crewe 10	a	08 39	08 54		09 01	09 11	09 30				10 10			10 30		10 52			11 12		11 25			11 47	
	d	08 43	08 55		09 04	09 13		09 43			10 12	10 20			10 43	10 55			11 14			11 33		11 49	12 01
Macclesfield	d			08 42					09 40	09 49							10 49	10 55							
Congleton	d																								
Stoke-on-Trent	d			09 07					09 57	10 07							11 07	11 12					11 51		
Stafford	a	09 07			09 27	09 38				10 26	10 38	10 45					11 24		11 41						
	d	09 09			09 28	09 39				10 27	10 40	10 45					11 25		11 42						
Penkridge	a											10 51													
Wolverhampton 7	a				09 40					10 40		11 01					11 40								12 34
Birmingham New Street 12	a				09 58					10 58		11 18					11 58								12 55
Birmingham International	a				10 13					11 13		*11 39*					12 13								*13 19*
Coventry	a				10 24					11 24		*11 50*					12 24								*13 30*
Lichfield Trent Valley	a																		*12 34*						
Tamworth Low Level	a																		*12 41*						
Nuneaton	a					10 01					11 02								12 04					12 30	
Rugby	a				*10 56*			10 38		*11 56*		*12 03*			11 38		*12 56*								
Northampton	a							*11 17*							*12 17*										
Milton Keynes Central	a		10 13					11 04	11 18		11 48				12 04			12 29					12 50	13s03	
Watford Junction	a	10s35	*11 05*	10s47		11s20		11s42	*12 06*							12s35		*13 17*	12s54				*13 33*	*13 51*	
Gatwick Airport 10	a																								
London Euston 15	⊖ a	10 58	11 03	11 08		11 44		12 04	12 08		12 38				12 51	12 58		13 09	13 15			13 23	13 31	13 44	

For general notes see front of timetable
For details of catering facilities see Directory of Train Operators

A To Bournemouth (Table 51)
b Change at Wilmslow and Crewe

OVERNIGHT SLEEPERS. For Sleeper trains, operated by First ScotRail, please refer to Tables 400 - 404

Table 65

Sundays

from 8 November

Scotland and North West England → West Midlands and London

Route Diagram - see first page of Table 65

		XC	VT	LM	VT	LM	VT	VT	VT	VT	NT	VT	VT	XC	VT	LM	VT	LM	VT	NT	XC	VT	VT	VT	XC
		1◇	1◇	1◇	1◇	1◇	1◇		1◇	1◇		1◇	1◇	1◇	1◇	1◇	1◇	1◇	1◇		1◇	1◇	1◇	1◇	1◇
		A												A							B				A
								🚌																	
		⚲	☕		☕		☕		☕	☕		☕	☕	⚲	☕		☕		☕		⚲	☕	☕	☕	⚲
Inverness	d																								
Aberdeen	d																								
Dundee	d																								
Perth	d																								
Edinburgh 10	d																								
Haymarket	d																								
Glasgow Central 15	d																								
Motherwell	d																								
Carstairs	d																								
Lockerbie	d																								
Carlisle 8	a																								
	d											10 46													
Penrith North Lakes	d											11 00													
Windermere	d																								
Oxenholme Lake District	a											11 22													
	d											11 23													
Barrow-in-Furness	d																								
Lancaster 6	a											11 37													
	d											11 38												12 10	
Preston 8	a											11 58												12 27	
Blackpool North	a											*12 38*												*13 07*	
	d										10 50									11 50				*11 50*	
Preston 8	d							10 30			11 15									12 15				12 30	
Wigan North Western	a							11 10			11 35									12 35					
	d							11 10			11 36									12 36					
Bolton	a											*12 34*													
Manchester Piccadilly 10	a											*12 57*													
Manchester Airport	a											*13 17*													
Liverpool Lime Street 10	a										12 22									13 22					
	d			11 34	11 48											12 34	12 48								
Liverpool South Parkway 7	d			11 44												12 44									
Runcorn	d			11 52	12 04											12 52	13 04								
Warrington Bank Quay	a							11 40																	
	d					←		11 40										←							
Hartford	d			12 04		12 04										13 03		13 03							
Manchester Piccadilly 10	d	11 27	11 35	→		*11 30*	11 55			12 15				12 26	12 35	→		*12 30*	12 55		13 07	13 15			13 27
Stockport	d	11 36	11 43			*11 40*	12 05			12 23				12 36	12 44			*12 40*	13 05			13 22			13 36
Manchester Airport	d					*11b10*																			
Wilmslow	d					*11 47*	12 12											*12 48*	13 12						
Holyhead	d												10 55												
Bangor (Gwynedd)	d												11 22												
Llandudno	d												*10c15*												
Llandudno Junction	d												11 40												
Wrexham General	d																								
Chester	d												12 33										*13 18*		
Crewe 10	a					12 19	12 28	12 25					12 52					13 18	13 28					13 48	
	d					12 22	12 30		12 33				12 54					13 22	13 30				13 55	14 01	
Macclesfield	d	11 49	11 56											12 49	12 57										13 49
Congleton	d																								
Stoke-on-Trent	d	12 07	12 13							12 51				13 07	13 14						13 43	13 50			14 07
Stafford	a	12 25			12 35	12 41								13 24			13 35	13 42							14 24
	d	12 26			12 36	12 42								13 25			13 36	13 43							14 25
Penkridge	a					12 48												13 48							
Wolverhampton 7	a	12 40				12 59								13 40				13 58			14 13			14 33	14 40
Birmingham New Street 12	a	12 58				13 16								13 58				14 15			14 31			14 55	14 58
Birmingham International	a	13 13				*13 38*								14 13				*14 38*			*14 59*			*15 19*	15 13
Coventry	a	13 24				*13 49*								14 24				*14 49*			*15 11*			*15 30*	15 24
Lichfield Trent Valley	a																	*14e35*							
Tamworth Low Level	a																	*14e42*							
Nuneaton	a																	*14e58*							
Rugby	a	*13 56*				*14 23*								*14 56*							*15 23*				*15 56*
Northampton	a																								
Milton Keynes Central	a									13 50			14s02									14 49	15s03		
Watford Junction	a									*14 34*			*14 51*									*15 33*	*15 51*		
Gatwick Airport 10	a																								
London Euston 15 ⊖	a		13 49		14 03		14 12		14 18	14 31			14 43		14 50		15 03		15 12			15 30	15 43		

For general notes see front of timetable
For details of catering facilities see Directory of Train Operators

A To Bournemouth (Table 51)
B To Penzance (Table 135)
b Change at Wilmslow and Crewe
c By bus
e Change at Stafford

OVERNIGHT SLEEPERS. For Sleeper trains, operated by First ScotRail, please refer to Tables 400 - 404

Sundays

Scotland and North West England → West Midlands and London

from 8 November

Route Diagram - see first page of Table 65

Station		TP	VT	LM	VT	LM	VT	VT	VT	NT	XC	VT		VT	VT	XC	TP	VT	VT	LM	VT	LM	VT	NT	VT
		1 ◇	1 ◇	1 ◇	1 ◇	1 ◇	1 ◇	1 ◇			1 ◇	1 ◇		1 ◇	1 ◇	1 ◇	1 ◇	1 ◇	1 ◇	1 ◇	1 ◇	1 ◇	1 ◇		1 ◇
											A					B									
									bus																
Inverness	d																								
Aberdeen	d																								
Dundee	d																09b25								
Perth	d																09b27								
Edinburgh 10	d														10 52		11 10								
Haymarket	d														10u57		11u13								
Glasgow Central 15	d							10 31										11 32							11 51
Motherwell	d							10u49																	
Carstairs	d																								
Lockerbie	d																12 08								
Carlisle 8	a							11 46							12 05		12 30	12 48							13 08
	d							11 48							12 07		12 32	12 50							13 09
Penrith North Lakes	d							12 03									12 46								
Windermere	d							*11 58*										*12 58*							
Oxenholme Lake District	a							12 26							12 41		13 10	13 23							13 44
	d							12 27							12 43		13 10	13 25							13 44
Barrow-in-Furness	d	11 15																							*12 45*
Lancaster 6	a	12 17						12 41							12 56		13 26	13 38							13 59
	d	12 19						12 41							12 57		13 26	13 39							13 59
Preston 8	a	12 37						12 59							13 15		13 45	13 59							14 17
Blackpool North	a							*13 38*							*14 00*			*14 38*							*15 00*
	d							*12 20*		12 50														13 50	*13 44*
Preston 8	d	12 47						13 06	13 10	13 15					13 30		13 47							14 15	14 20
Wigan North Western	a								13 50	13 35														14 35	
	d								13 50	13 36														14 36	
Bolton	a	13 08						*13 34*									14 08	*14 34*							
Manchester Piccadilly 10	a	13 27						*13 57*									14 27	*15 00*							
Manchester Airport ✈	a	13 47						*14 17*									14 47	*15 17*							
Liverpool Lime Street 10	a									14 22														15 22	
	d			13 34	13 48															14 34	14 48				
Liverpool South Parkway 7 ✈	d			13 44																14 44					
Runcorn	d			13 52	14 04															14 52	15 04				
Warrington Bank Quay	a								14 20																
	d					⟵			14 20													⟵			
Hartford	d			14 03		14 03														15 03		15 03			
Manchester Piccadilly 10	d		13 35	⟶		*13 30*	13 55				14 07	14 15				14 27			14 35	⟶		*14 30*	14 55		
Stockport	d		13 42			*13 39*	14 04					14 22				14 36			14 42			*14 39*	15 04		
Manchester Airport ✈	d					*13c06*																			
Wilmslow	d					*13 47*	14 11															*14 47*	15 11		
Holyhead	d													12 47											
Bangor (Gwynedd)	d													13 14											
Llandudno	d													*13e15*											
Llandudno Junction	d													13 32											
Wrexham General	d													*12 55*											
Chester	d													14 33	*14 20*										
Crewe 10	a					14 20	14 27		15 05					14 52	14 52							15 19	15 27		
	d					14 22	14 29							14 54	15 01							15 22	15 29		
Macclesfield	d		13 55													14 49			14 55						
Congleton	d																								
Stoke-on-Trent	d		14 12								14 43	14 50				15 07			15 12						
Stafford	a				14 35	14 42										15 24					15 35	15 42			
	d				14 36	14 43										15 25					15 36	15 43			
Penkridge	a					14 48																15 48			
Wolverhampton 7	a					14 58					15 13				15 31	15 40						15 58			
Birmingham New Street 12	a					15 15					15 31				15 55	15 58						16 15			
Birmingham International ✈	a					*15 38*					*15 59*				*16 19*	16 13						*16 38*			
Coventry	a					*15 49*					*16 11*				*16 30*	16 24						*16 49*			
Lichfield Trent Valley	a																					*16f34*			
Tamworth Low Level	a																					*16f41*			
Nuneaton	a																					*16f58*			
Rugby	a										*16 23*					*16 56*									
Northampton	a																								
Milton Keynes Central	a											15 49		16s04											
Watford Junction	a											*16 33*		*16 51*											
Gatwick Airport 10 ✈	a																								
London Euston 15 ⊖	a		15 48		16 03		16 11	16 18				16 30		16 44					16 48		17 03		17 11		17 16

For general notes see front of timetable
For details of catering facilities see Directory of Train Operators

- **A** To Plymouth (Table 51)
- **B** To Bournemouth (Table 51)
- **b** Change at Haymarket
- **c** Change at Wilmslow and Crewe
- **e** By bus
- **f** Change at Stafford

OVERNIGHT SLEEPERS. For Sleeper trains, operated by First ScotRail, please refer to Tables 400 - 404

Table 65

Sundays

from 8 November

Scotland and North West England → West Midlands and London

Route Diagram - see first page of Table 65

Station		VT	XC	VT	VT	VT	XC	TP	VT	LM	VT	LM	VT	NT	VT	TP	VT	VT	NT	VT	VT	NT	XC	VT	LM
			1◇	1◇	1◇	1◇	1◇	1◇	1◇	1◇	1◇	1◇	1◇		1◇	1◇	1◇	1◇		1◇	1◇		1◇	1◇	1◇
			A				B																B		
		🚌	🛒	🍴	🍴	🍴	🛒		🍴		🍴		🍴		🍴	🛒	🍴	🍴		🍴	🍴		🛒	🍴	
Inverness	d																								
Aberdeen	d														09b48										
Dundee	d														11b02	11b25									
Perth	d																11c05								
Edinburgh 10	d														12 52	13 09									
Haymarket	d														12u56	13u12									
Glasgow Central 15	d																13 35				13 56				
Motherwell	d																								
Carstairs	d																								
Lockerbie	d															14 08									
Carlisle 8	a														14 05	14 30	14 46				15 09				
	d														14 07	14 31	14 49				15 09				
Penrith North Lakes	d														14 22	14 46									
Windermere	d															13 58	14 58								
Oxenholme Lake District	a															15 10	15 22				15 44				
	d															15 10	15 23				15 44				
Barrow-in-Furness	d							13 22																	
Lancaster 6	a							14 25							14 56	15 25	15 37								
	d							14 25							14 57	15 25	15 38								
Preston 8	a							14 45							15 18	15 45	15 56				16 15				
Blackpool North	a							15 39							16 00		16 38				17 00				
	d													14 50			15 20		15 50		15 44				
Preston 8	d	14 30						14 47						15 15		15 47	15 58		16 15		16 17				
Wigan North Western	a	15 10												15 35			16 09		16 35		16 28	←			
	d	15 10												15 36			16 09		16 36		16 28	16 36			
Bolton	a							15 08								16 08	16e34		→						
Manchester Piccadilly 10	a							15 27								16 27	16e57								
Manchester Airport	a							15 47								16 47	17e17								
Liverpool Lime Street 10	a													16 22								17 22			
	d									15 34	15 48									16 18					16 34
Liverpool South Parkway 7	d									15 44															16 44
Runcorn	d									15 52	16 04									16 34					16 52
Warrington Bank Quay	a	15 40															16 20				16 39				
	d											←					16 20				16 39				
Hartford	d									16 03		16 03													17 03
Manchester Piccadilly 10	d		15 07	15 15			15 27		15 35	→		15 30	15 55					16 15					16 27	16 35	→
Stockport	d			15 22			15 36		15 42			15 39	16 04					16 23					16 36	16 42	
Manchester Airport	d											15f06													
Wilmslow	d											15 47	16 11												
Holyhead	d				13 55																				
Bangor (Gwynedd)	d				14 22																				
Llandudno	d																								
Llandudno Junction	d				14 40																				
Wrexham General	d																								
Chester	d				15 33																				
Crewe 10	a				15 52							16 18	16 27							16 50	16 59				
	d				15 54	16 01						16 22	16 29							16 53	17 01				
Macclesfield	d						15 49		15 55														16 49	16 55	
Congleton	d																								
Stoke-on-Trent	d		15 43	15 50			16 07		16 12									16 50					17 07	17 12	
Stafford	a						16 24				16 36	16 42											17 24		
	d						16 25				16 37	16 43											17 25		
Penkridge	a											16 48													
Wolverhampton 7	a		16 13			16 34	16 40					16 58									17 31		17 40		
Birmingham New Street 12	a		16 31			16 55	16 58					17 15									17 55		17 58		
Birmingham International	a		16 59			17 19	17 13					17 38									18 19		18 13		
Coventry	a		17 11			17 30	17 24					17 49									18 30		18 24		
Lichfield Trent Valley	a																								
Tamworth Low Level	a																								
Nuneaton	a																								
Rugby	a		17 23				17 56					18 23											18 56		
Northampton	a																								
Milton Keynes Central	a			16 49	17s03													17 49		18s03					
Watford Junction	a			17 33	17 51													18 33		18 51					
Gatwick Airport 10	a																								
London Euston 15 ⊖	a			17 30	17 44				17 48		18 04		18 11				18 18	18 30		18 44				18 48	

For general notes see front of timetable
For details of catering facilities see Directory of Train Operators

A To Penzance (Table 135)
B To Bournemouth (Table 51)
b Change at Haymarket
c Via Glasgow Queen Street and Glasgow Central. Passengers make their own way from one station to the other
e Change at Preston
f Change at Wilmslow and Crewe

OVERNIGHT SLEEPERS. For Sleeper trains, operated by First ScotRail, please refer to Tables 400 - 404

Scotland and North West England → West Midlands and London

Sundays from 8 November

Route Diagram - see first page of Table 65

		VT	LM	VT	XC	TP	VT	VT	VT	XC	VT	LM	VT	NT	VT	XC	NT	LM	VT	XC	TP	VT	VT	NT	VT
		1◇	1◇	1◇	1◇	1◇	1◇	1◇	1◇	1◇	1◇	1◇	1◇		1◇	1◇		1◇	1◇	1◇	1◇	1◇	1◇		1◇
					A					B						B				A					
		🍴		🍴	🛒		🍴	🍴	🍴	🛒	🍴		🍴		🍴	🛒			🍴	🛒	🛒	🍴	🍴		🍴
Inverness	d														09 38										
Aberdeen	d														11b47										
Dundee	d														13b01										
Perth	d														11 56						13c05				
Edinburgh 10	d														14 52										
Haymarket	d														14u57										
Glasgow Central 15	d						14 36														15 06	15 35			
Motherwell	d																								
Carstairs	d																								
Lockerbie	d																				16 07				
Carlisle 8	a						15 46								16 05						16 28	16 46			
	d						15 49								16 07						16 30	16 49			
Penrith North Lakes	d														16 22						16 44	17 03			
Windermere	d						15 58																		
Oxenholme Lake District	a						16 22														17 08				
	d						16 23														17 08				
Barrow-in-Furness	d					15 30																			
Lancaster 6	a					16 25	16 37								16 56						17 23	17 37			
	d					16 25	16 38								16 57						17 23	17 38			
Preston 8	a					16 45	16 56								17 15						17 42	17 56			
Blackpool North	a						17 38								18 00							18 38			
	d						16 20							16 50	16 44							17 20		17 50	
Preston 8	d					16 47	16 58							17 15	17 17						17 47	17 58		18 15	
Wigan North Western	a						17 09							17 35	17 28		←					18 09		18 35	
	d						17 09							17 36	17 28		17 36					18 09		18 36	
Bolton	a					17 08	17e34							→							18 08	18e34		→	
Manchester Piccadilly 10 🚊	a					17 27	17e57														18 27	18e57			
Manchester Airport ✈	a					17 47	18e17														18 47	19e17			
Liverpool Lime Street 10	a																18 22								
	d	16 48										17 34	17 48												
Liverpool South Parkway 7 ✈	d											17 44													
Runcorn	d	17 04										17 52	18 04												
Warrington Bank Quay	a						17 20								17 39							18 20			
	d		←				17 20								17 39			←				18 20			
Hartford	d		17 03									18 03						18 03							
Manchester Piccadilly 10 🚊	d		16 30	16 55	17 07			17 15		17 27	17 35	→						17 30	17 55	18 07			18 15		
Stockport	d		16 39	17 04				17 22		17 36	17 42							17 39	18 04				18 22		
Manchester Airport ✈	d																	17f06							
Wilmslow	d		16 47	17 11														17 48	18 11						
Holyhead	d		14g30						15 30																16 25
Bangor (Gwynedd)	d		15g08						15 59																17 04
Llandudno	d								16h00																
Llandudno Junction	d		15g26						16 25																17 25
Wrexham General	d								17 10																18 08
Chester	d		16 27						17 35						17 22										18 35
Crewe 10	a		17 18	17 27					17 53						17 59			18 19	18 27						18 53
	d		17 22	17 29					17 55						18 01			18 22	18 29						18 55
Macclesfield	d									17 49	17 55														
Congleton	d																								
Stoke-on-Trent	d				17 43			17 50		18 07	18 12									18 43			18 50		
Stafford	a	17 35	17 42							18 24			18 35					18 42							
	d	17 36	17 43							18 25			18 36			18 25		18 43							
Penkridge	a		17 48							→								18 48							
Wolverhampton 7 🚊	a		17 58		18 13										18 32	18 40		18 58		19 13					
Birmingham New Street 12	a		18 15		18 31										18 55	18 58		19 15		19 31					
Birmingham International ✈	a		18 38		18 59										19 19	19 13		19 38							
Coventry	a		18 49		19 11										19 30	19 24		19 49							
Lichfield Trent Valley	a		18j34																						
Tamworth Low Level	a		18j41																						
Nuneaton	a		18j58																						
Rugby	a				19 23											19 56									
Northampton	a																								
Milton Keynes Central	a							18 49	19s03														19 49		20s03
Watford Junction	a							19 33	19 51														20 33		20 52
Gatwick Airport 10 ✈	a																								
London Euston 15 ⊖	a	19 03		19 11			19 18	19 30	19 44		19 48		20 03						20 11			20 18	20 30		20 44

For general notes see front of timetable
For details of catering facilities see Directory of Train Operators

A To Plymouth (Table 51)
B To Bournemouth (Table 51)
b Change at Haymarket
c Via Glasgow Queen Street and Glasgow Central. Passengers make their own way from one station to the other
e Change at Preston
f Change at Wilmslow and Crewe
g Change at Chester and Crewe
h Change at Llandudno Junction and Chester. By bus to Llandudno Junction
j Change at Stafford

OVERNIGHT SLEEPERS. For Sleeper trains, operated by First ScotRail, please refer to Tables 400 - 404

Table 65

Scotland and North West England → West Midlands and London

Sundays from 8 November

Route Diagram - see first page of Table 65

		VT	NT	XC	VT	LM	VT	LM		VT	NT	XC	VT	NT	XC	TP	VT	VT	VT	LM	VT	XC	AW	TP	TP
		1 ◇		1 ◇	1 ◇	1 ◇	1 ◇	1 ◇		1 ◇		1 ◇	1 ◇		1 ◇	1 ◇	1 ◇	1 ◇	1 ◇	1 ◇	1 ◇	1 ◇	◇	1 ◇	1 ◇
				A								B			C							B			
		🍴		☕	🍴		🍴			🍴		☕	🍴		☕	☕	🍴	🍴	🍴		🍴				☕
Inverness	d												13b25				12c30								
Aberdeen	d												13b50												
Dundee	d												15b04												
Perth	d												15b25				14c50								
Edinburgh 10	d												16 52			16 10									
Haymarket	d												16u56			16u13									
Glasgow Central 15	d	15 55															16 36								17 06
Motherwell	d																16u54								
Carstairs	d																								
Lockerbie	d															17 08									
Carlisle 8	a	17 08											18 05			17 30	17 49								18 21
	d	17 09											18 07			17 32	17 51								18 28
Penrith North Lakes	d															17 46	18 05								18 42
Windermere	d	16 58															18 04								
Oxenholme Lake District	a	17 44											18 41			18 10	18 27								19 06
	d	17 44											18 42			18 10	18 28								19 07
Barrow-in-Furness	d																							18 15	
Lancaster 6	a												18 56			18 26	18 42							19 17	19 21
	d												18 57			18 26	18 43							19 17	19 22
Preston 8	a	18 15											19 15			18 45	19 01							19 36	19 41
Blackpool North	a	19 00											20 00				19 38								
	d	17 44									18 50		18 44				18 20								
Preston 8	d	18 17									19 15		19 17			18 47	19 03							19 47	
Wigan North Western	a	18 28	←								19 35		19 28	←			19 14								
	d	18 28	18 36								19 36		19 28	19 36			19 14								
Bolton	a										→					19 08	19e34							20 08	
Manchester Piccadilly 10	a															19 27	19e57							20 27	
Manchester Airport	a															19 47	20e17							20 47	
Liverpool Lime Street 10	a		19 22											20 22											
	d					18 34	18 48													19 34	19 48				
Liverpool South Parkway 7	d					18 44														19 44					
Runcorn	d					18 52	19 04													19 52	20 04				
Warrington Bank Quay	a	18 39											19 39				19 25								
	d	18 39						←					19 39				19 25								
Hartford	d					19 03		19 03												20 03					
Manchester Piccadilly 10	d			18 27	18 35	→		18 30		18 55		19 07			19 27			19 15	19 35	19 30		20 07			
Stockport	d			18 36	18 42			18 39		19 04					19 35			19 22	19 42	19 39		20 16			
Manchester Airport	d																			19f06					
Wilmslow	d							18 47		19 11										19 47					
Holyhead	d																			17 30			18 25		
Bangor (Gwynedd)	d																			17 59			19 04		
Llandudno	d																								
Llandudno Junction	d																			18 24			19 24		
Wrexham General	d																						19 08		
Chester	d									18 57										19 22	19 50		20 27		
Crewe 10	a	18 59						19 19		19 27			19 59							20 15	20 22		20 48		
	d	19 01						19 22		19 29			20 01							20 18	20 24		20 52		
Macclesfield	d			18 49	18 55										19 48				19 55			20 29			
Congleton	d																								
Stoke-on-Trent	d			19 07	19 12							19 43			20 07			19 50	20 12			20 47			
Stafford	a			19 24			19 35	19 42							20 24					20 37	20 42	21 08	21 16		
	d			19 25			19 36	19 43							20 25					20 38	20 44	21 09	21 16		
Penkridge	a							19 48												20 44					
Wolverhampton 7	a	19 31		19 40				19 58				20 13	20 34		20 39					20 55		21 21	21 34		
Birmingham New Street 12	a	19 55		19 58				20 15				20 31	20 57		21 00					21 15		21 39	21 52		
Birmingham International	a	20 19		20 13				20 39					21 25		21 13					21 39			22 08		
Coventry	a	20 30		20 24				20 50					21 44		21 23					21 50			22 44		
Lichfield Trent Valley	a							20g34																	
Tamworth Low Level	a							20g41																	
Nuneaton	a							20g58																	
Rugby	a			20 56				21 03							21 56					22 03			22 56		
Northampton	a																								
Milton Keynes Central	a																	20 48			21 38				
Watford Junction	a																	21 36			22 26				
Gatwick Airport 10	a																								
London Euston 15	⊖ a				20 48		21 06			21 14							21 27	21 34	22 04		22 29				

For general notes see front of timetable
For details of catering facilities see Directory of Train Operators

A To Southampton Central (Table 51)
B To Bristol Temple Meads (Table 51)
C To Reading (Table 51)
b Change at Haymarket
c Via Glasgow Queen Street and Glasgow Central. Passengers make their own way from one station to the other
e Change at Preston
f Change at Wilmslow and Crewe
g Change at Stafford

OVERNIGHT SLEEPERS. For Sleeper trains, operated by First ScotRail, please refer to Tables 400 - 404

Table 65

Sundays

from 8 November

Scotland and North West England → West Midlands and London

Route Diagram - see first page of Table 65

		VT	VT	LM	VT	VT	NT	TP	VT	XC	LM	NT	VT	TP	XC	NT	TP	VT	NT	SR	SR	SR	SR
																					R	R	R
		1◇	1◇	1◇	1◇	1◇		1◇	1◇	1◇	1		1◇	1◇	1◇		1◇	1◇					
																							A
		[buffet]	[buffet]		[buffet]	[buffet]		[trolley]	[buffet]				[buffet]				[trolley]	[buffet]			[buffet]	[buffet]	[buffet]
Inverness	d																			16b15			20 25
Aberdeen	d							15c10									17c10			17e47			21 42
Dundee	d							16c25									18c19			19e02			23u06
Perth	d																	17e05		19e24			23u00
Edinburgh 10	d							18 10					18 52				19 57					23 15	
Haymarket	d							18u13					18u57				20u00						
Glasgow Central 15	d	17 36							18 35									20 06		22 28	23 15		
Motherwell	d																				23u31		
Carstairs	d																				23u47		
Lockerbie	d	18 32						19 08										21 02					
Carlisle 8	a	18 50						19 30	19 43				20 05				21 14	21 21		00 49			
	d	18 52						19 32	19 44				20 07				21 15	21 24			01u08		
Penrith North Lakes	d	19 06						19 46					20 22					21 39					
Windermere	d	*19 00*							*19 50*					21 00									
Oxenholme Lake District	a	19 28						20 10	20 19					21 19				22 02					
	d	19 29						20 10	20 19					21 21				22 03					
Barrow-in-Furness	d													*20 02*									
Lancaster 6	a	19 43						20 26	20 34				20 56	21 37			22 02	22 17					
	d	19 44						20 26	20 34				20 57	21 38			22 03	22 18					
Preston 8	a	20 02						20 45	20 52				21 15	21 58			22 23	22 35					04s33
Blackpool North	a	*20 39*							*21 38*				*22 00*	*22 38*			*23 00*	*00 04*					
	d	*19 20*					19 50		*20 20*			20 50	*20 44*			21 50			22 44				
Preston 8	d	20 04					20 15	20 47	20 55			21 15	21 17			22 15	22 29	22 38	23 09				
Wigan North Western	a	20 15					20 35		21 06			21 35	21 28			22 35		22 49	23 29				
	d	20 15					20 36		21 07			21 36	21 28			22 36		22 50	23 30				
Bolton	a	*20f34*						21 08	*21f34*				*22f25*				22 50	*23f59*					
Manchester Piccadilly 10	a	*20f57*						21 27	*21f57*								23 14	*00f15*					
Manchester Airport ✈	a	*21f17*						21 47	*22f17*								23 30	*01g31*					
Liverpool Lime Street 10	a						21 22					22 22	22 22			23 23			00 16				
	d			20 34		20 48					21 34												
Liverpool South Parkway 7 ✈	d			20 44							21 44												
Runcorn	d			20 52		21 04					21 52												
Warrington Bank Quay	a	20 26							21 18				21 39					23 00					
	d	20 26							21 18				21 39					23 01					
Hartford	d			21 03							22 03												
Manchester Piccadilly 10	d		20 20	*20 30*	20 55					21 07	*21 34*				22 07								
Stockport	d		20 27	*20 39*	21 03					21 16	*21 17*				22 16								
Manchester Airport ✈	d										*21h06*												
Wilmslow	d			*20 47*							*21 52*												
Holyhead	d										*19 40*												
Bangor (Gwynedd)	d										*20 09*												
Llandudno	d																						
Llandudno Junction	d										*20 37*												
Wrexham General	d																						
Chester	d					*20 50*					*21 50*												
Crewe 10	a	20 45		21 15		21 22			21 38		22 17		21 59					23 20					05s37
	d	20 47		21 17		21 24			21 40		22 22		22 01										
Macclesfield	d		20 40		21 15					21 29					22 29								
Congleton	d																						
Stoke-on-Trent	d		20 57		21 33					21 47					22 47								
Stafford	a			21 36		21 42			22 01	22 06	22 41				23 05								
	d			21 38		21 44			22 02	22 07	22 44				23 06								
Penkridge	a			21 44							22 50												
Wolverhampton 7	a			21 55					22 17	22 20	23 00		22 31		23 18								
Birmingham New Street 12	a			22 15					22 40	22 45	23 17		22 55		23 41								
Birmingham International ✈	a			*22 39*						*23 09*			*23 31*										
Coventry	a			*22 50*						*23 20*			*23 50*										
Lichfield Trent Valley	a					21 58																	
Tamworth Low Level	a					22 04																	
Nuneaton	a					22 15																	
Rugby	a			*23 03*		22 29				*23 33*													
Northampton	a					*23 17*																	
Milton Keynes Central	a	21 55	22 03		22 50	23 08																	
Watford Junction	a	22 31	*22 52*		23s31	23s38															06s23		
Gatwick Airport 10 ✈	a																						
London Euston 15 ⊖	a	22 53	22 57		23 53	23 59															06 46		07 47

For general notes see front of timetable
For details of catering facilities see Directory of Train Operators

A Also conveys portion from Fort William (Table 227)

b Change at Perth, Glasgow Queen Street and Glasgow Central. Passengers make their own way between Glasgow Queen Street and Glasgow Central

c Change at Haymarket

e Via Glasgow Queen Street and Glasgow Central. Passengers make their own way from one station to the other

f Change at Preston

g Change at Preston and Manchester Piccadilly

h Change at Wilmslow and Crewe

OVERNIGHT SLEEPERS. For Sleeper trains, operated by First ScotRail, please refer to Tables 400 - 404

Milton Keynes Central → Buckingham and Bicester

Bus Service

Mondays to Fridays

		VT	VT	VT	VT	VT	VT	VT	VT	VT	VT	VT	VT	VT
Milton Keynes Central	d	05 45	06 15	06 45	07 15	07 35	08 05	08 45	09 15	09 45	10 15	10 45	11 15	11 45
Buckingham Tesco	d	06 05	06 35	07 05	07 35	07 55	08 25	09 05	09 35	10 05	10 35	11 05	11 35	12 05
Bicester Bure Place	a	06 25	06 55	07 25	07 55	08 15	08 45	09 25	09 55	10 25	10 55	11 25	11 55	12 25

		VT	VT	VT	VT	VT	VT	VT	VT	VT	VT	VT	VT	VT	VT	VT	VT
Milton Keynes Central	d	12 15	12 45	13 15	13 45	14 15	14 45	15 15	15 45	16 15	16 45	17 15	17 45	18 15	18 45	19 45	20 45
Buckingham Tesco	d	12 35	13 05	13 35	14 05	14 35	15 05	15 35	16 05	16 35	17 05	17 35	18 05	18 35	19 05	20 05	21 05
Bicester Bure Place	a	12 55	13 25	13 55	14 25	14 55	15 25	15 55	16 25	16 55	17 25	17 55	18 25	18 55	19 25	20 25	21 25

Saturdays

		VT	VT	VT	VT	VT	VT	VT	VT	VT	VT	VT	VT	VT
Milton Keynes Central	d	05 50	06 20	06 50	07 20	07 45	08 15	08 45	09 15	09 45	10 15	10 45	11 15	11 45
Buckingham Tesco	d	06 10	06 40	07 10	07 40	08 05	08 35	09 05	09 35	10 05	10 35	11 05	11 35	12 05
Bicester Bure Place	a	06 30	07 00	07 30	08 00	08 25	08 55	09 25	09 55	10 25	10 55	11 25	11 55	12 25

		VT	VT	VT	VT	VT	VT	VT	VT	VT	VT	VT	VT	VT	VT	VT	VT
Milton Keynes Central	d	12 15	12 45	13 15	13 45	14 15	14 45	15 15	15 45	16 15	16 45	17 15	17 45	18 15	18 45	19 45	20 45
Buckingham Tesco	d	12 35	13 05	13 35	14 05	14 35	15 05	15 35	16 05	16 35	17 05	17 35	18 05	18 35	19 05	20 05	21 05
Bicester Bure Place	a	12 55	13 25	13 55	14 25	14 55	15 25	15 55	16 25	16 55	17 25	17 55	18 25	18 55	19 25	20 25	21 25

Sundays

		VT	VT	VT	VT	VT	VT	VT	VT	VT	VT	VT	VT	VT	VT	VT	VT	VT	VT	VT	VT	VT	VT	VT	VT	VT
Milton Keynes Central	d	06 45	07 45	08 45	09 45	10 15	10 45	11 15	11 45	12 15	12 45	13 15	13 45	14 15	14 45	15 15	15 45	16 15	16 45	17 15	17 45	18 15	18 45	19 45	20 40	21 35
Buckingham Tesco	d	07 05	08 05	09 05	10 05	10 35	11 05	11 35	12 05	12 35	13 05	13 35	14 05	14 35	15 05	15 35	16 05	16 35	17 05	17 35	18 05	18 35	19 05	20 05	21 00	21 55
Bicester Bure Place	a	07 25	08 25	09 25	10 25	10 55	11 25	11 55	12 25	12 55	13 25	13 55	14 25	14 55	15 25	15 55	16 25	16 55	17 25	17 55	18 25	18 55	19 25	20 25	21 20	22 15

For general notes see front of timetable
For details of catering facilities see
Directory of Train Operators

This is the X5 service operated by Stagecoach East

Bicester and Buckingham → Milton Keynes Central

Bus Service

Mondays to Fridays

		VT	VT	VT	VT	VT	VT	VT	VT	VT	VT	VT	VT	VT
Bicester Bure Place	d	07 35	08 05	08 35	09 05	09 35	10 05	10 35	11 05	11 35	12 05	12 35	13 05	13 35
Buckingham Tesco	d	07 55	08 25	08 55	09 25	09 55	10 25	10 55	11 25	11 55	12 25	12 55	13 25	13 55
Milton Keynes Central	a	08 15	08 45	09 15	09 45	10 15	10 45	11 15	11 45	12 15	12 45	13 15	13 45	14 15

		VT	VT	VT	VT	VT	VT	VT	VT	VT	VT	VT	VT	VT	VT	VT	VT
Bicester Bure Place	d	14 05	14 35	15 05	15 35	16 05	16 35	17 05	17 35	18 05	18 35	19 05	19 30	20 00	20 30	21 30	22 30
Buckingham Tesco	d	14 25	14 55	15 25	15 55	16 25	16 55	17 25	17 55	18 25	18 55	19 25	19 50	20 20	20 50	21 50	22 50
Milton Keynes Central	a	14 45	15 15	15 45	16 15	16 45	17 15	17 45	18 15	18 45	19 15	19 45	20 10	20 40	21 10	22 10	23 10

Saturdays

		VT	VT	VT	VT	VT	VT	VT	VT	VT	VT	VT	VT	VT
Bicester Bure Place	d	07 35	08 05	08 35	09 05	09 35	10 05	10 35	11 05	11 35	12 05	12 35	13 05	13 35
Buckingham Tesco	d	07 55	08 25	08 55	09 25	09 55	10 25	10 55	11 25	11 55	12 25	12 55	13 25	13 55
Milton Keynes Central	a	08 15	08 45	09 15	09 45	10 15	10 45	11 15	11 45	12 15	12 45	13 15	13 45	14 15

		VT	VT	VT	VT	VT	VT	VT	VT	VT	VT	VT	VT	VT	VT	VT	VT
Bicester Bure Place	d	14 05	14 35	15 05	15 35	16 05	16 35	17 05	17 35	18 05	18 35	19 05	19 30	20 00	20 30	21 30	22 30
Buckingham Tesco	d	14 25	14 55	15 25	15 55	16 25	16 55	17 25	17 55	18 25	18 55	19 25	19 50	20 20	20 50	21 50	22 50
Milton Keynes Central	a	14 45	15 15	15 45	16 15	16 45	17 15	17 45	18 15	18 45	19 15	19 45	20 10	20 40	21 10	22 10	23 10

Sundays

		VT	VT	VT	VT	VT	VT	VT	VT	VT	VT	VT	VT
Bicester Bure Place	d	08 35	09 35	10 35	11 35	12 05	12 35	13 05	13 35	14 05	14 35	15 05	15 35
Buckingham Tesco	d	08 55	09 55	10 55	11 55	12 25	12 55	13 25	13 55	14 25	14 55	15 25	15 55
Milton Keynes Central	a	09 15	10 15	11 15	12 15	12 45	13 15	13 45	14 15	14 45	15 15	15 45	16 15

		VT	VT	VT	VT	VT	VT	VT	VT	VT	VT	VT	VT
Bicester Bure Place	d	16 05	16 35	17 05	17 35	18 05	18 35	19 05	19 30	20 00	20 30	21 30	22 30
Buckingham Tesco	d	16 25	16 55	17 25	17 55	18 25	18 55	19 25	19 50	20 20	20 50	21 50	22 50
Milton Keynes Central	a	16 45	17 15	17 45	18 15	18 45	19 15	19 45	20 10	20 40	21 10	22 10	23 10

For general notes see front of timetable
For details of catering facilities see
Directory of Train Operators

This is the X5 service operated by Stagecoach East

Table 65B

Mondays to Fridays

Milton Keynes Central — London Luton Airport
Bus Service

		VT	VT	VT	VT	VT	VT	VT	VT	VT	VT	VT	VT	VT	VT	VT	VT	VT
Milton Keynes Central	d	06 40	07 50	08 55	09 55	10 55	11 55	12 55	13 55	14 55	15 55	16 55	17 25	17 55	18 55	19 55	20 55	21 55
Milton Keynes The Point	d	06 45	07 55	09 00	10 00	11 00	12 00	13 00	14 00	15 00	16 00	17 00	17 30	18 00	19 00	20 00	21 00	22 00
Luton	d	07 25	08 40	09 40	10 40	11 40	12 40	13 40	14 40	15 40	16 40	17 40	18 10	18 40	19 40	20 40	21 40	22 40
London Luton Airport	a	07 35	08 55	09 50	10 50	11 50	12 50	13 50	14 50	15 50	16 50	17 50	18 20	18 50	19 50	20 50	21 50	22 50

Saturdays

		VT	VT	VT	VT	VT	VT	VT	VT	VT	VT	VT	VT	VT	VT	VT
Milton Keynes Central	d	06 40	07 50	08 55	09 55	10 55	11 55	12 55	13 55	14 55	15 55	16 55	17 55	18 55	19 55	20 55
Milton Keynes The Point	d	06 45	07 55	09 00	10 00	11 00	12 00	13 00	14 00	15 00	16 00	17 00	18 00	19 00	20 00	21 00
Luton	d	07 25	08 45	09 40	10 40	11 40	12 40	13 40	14 40	15 40	16 40	17 40	18 40	19 40	20 40	21 40
London Luton Airport	a	07 35	08 55	09 50	10 50	11 50	12 50	13 50	14 50	15 50	16 50	17 50	18 50	19 50	20 50	21 50

Sundays

		VT	VT	VT	VT	VT	VT	VT	VT	VT	VT	VT	VT	VT
Milton Keynes Central	d	09 20	10 20	11 20	12 20	13 20	14 20	15 20	16 20	17 20	18 20	19 20	20 20	21 20
Milton Keynes The Point	d	09 25	10 25	11 25	12 25	13 25	14 25	15 25	16 25	17 25	18 25	19 25	20 25	21 25
Luton	d	10 05	11 05	12 05	13 05	14 05	15 05	16 05	17 05	18 05	19 05	20 05	21 05	22 05
London Luton Airport	a	10 15	11 15	12 15	13 15	14 15	15 15	16 15	17 15	18 15	19 15	20 15	21 15	22 15

Mondays to Fridays

		VT	VT	VT	VT	VT	VT	VT	VT	VT	VT	VT	VT	VT	VT	VT	VT
London Luton Airport	d	05 50	06 50	07 50	09 05	10 05	11 05	12 05	13 05	14 05	15 05	16 05	17 05	18 05	19 05	20 05	21 05
Luton	d	06 00	07 00	08 00	09 15	10 15	11 15	12 15	13 15	14 15	15 15	16 15	17 15	18 15	19 15	20 15	21 15
Luton Galaxy Centre	d	06 02	07 02	08 02	09 17	10 17	11 17	12 17	13 17	14 17	15 17	16 17	17 17	18 17	19 17	20 17	21 17
Milton Keynes The Point	d	06 40	07 45	08 48	09 55	10 55	11 55	12 55	13 55	14 55	15 55	16 55	17 55	18 55	19 55	.	.
Milton Keynes Central	a	06 45	07 50	09 00	10 00	11 00	12 00	13 00	14 00	15 00	16 00	17 00	18 00	19 00	20 00	20 55	21 55

Saturdays

		VT	VT	VT	VT	VT	VT	VT	VT	VT	VT	VT	VT	VT	VT	VT
London Luton Airport	d	05 50	06 50	07 50	09 05	10 05	11 05	12 05	13 05	14 05	15 05	16 05	17 05	18 05	19 05	20 05
Luton	d	06 00	07 00	08 00	09 15	10 15	11 15	12 15	13 15	14 15	15 15	16 15	17 15	18 15	19 15	20 15
Luton Galaxy Centre	d	06 02	07 02	08 02	09 17	10 17	11 17	12 17	13 17	14 17	15 17	16 17	17 17	18 17	19 17	20 17
Milton Keynes The Point	d	.	07 45	08 55	09 55	10 55	11 55	12 55	13 55	14 55	15 55	16 55	17 55	18 55	.	.
Milton Keynes Central	a	06 40	07 50	09 00	10 00	11 00	12 00	13 00	14 00	15 00	16 00	17 00	18 00	19 00	19 50	20 50

Sundays

		VT	VT	VT	VT	VT	VT	VT	VT	VT	VT	VT	VT	VT
London Luton Airport	d	08 20	09 20	10 20	11 20	12 20	13 20	14 20	15 20	16 20	17 20	18 20	19 20	20 20
Luton	d	08 30	09 30	10 30	11 30	12 30	13 30	14 30	15 30	16 30	17 30	18 30	19 30	20 30
Luton Galaxy Centre	d	08 32	09 32	10 32	11 32	12 32	13 32	14 32	15 32	16 32	17 32	18 32	19 32	20 32
Milton Keynes The Point	d	09 10	10 10	11 10	12 10	13 10	14 10	15 10	16 10	17 10	18 10	19 10	20 10	21 10
Milton Keynes Central	a	09 15	10 15	11 15	12 15	13 15	14 15	15 15	16 15	17 15	18 15	19 15	20 15	21 15

For general notes see front of timetable
For details of catering facilities see
Directory of Train Operators

Table 65C

Mondays to Fridays

Milton Keynes Central → Bedford and Cambridge
Bus Service

		VT 🚌	VT 🚌	VT 🚌	VT 🚌	VT 🚌	VT 🚌	VT 🚌	VT 🚌	VT 🚌	VT 🚌	VT 🚌	VT 🚌	VT 🚌	VT 🚌	VT 🚌	VT 🚌	VT 🚌
Milton Keynes Central	d	07 00	07 45	08 15	08 45	09 15	09 45	10 15	10 45	11 15	11 45	12 15	12 45	13 15	13 45	14 15	14 45	15 15
Bedford Bus Station	a	08 10	08 40	09 05	09 35	10 05	10 35	11 05	11 35	12 05	12 35	13 05	13 35	14 05	14 35	15 05	15 35	16 05
St Neots Cross Keys	a	08 47	09 17	09 47	10 17	10 47	11 17	11 47	12 17	12 47	13 17	13 47	14 17	14 47	15 17	15 47	16 17	16 47
Cambridge Parkside Bay 16	a	09 25	09 55	10 25	10 55	11 25	11 55	12 25	12 55	13 25	13 55	14 25	14 55	15 25	15 55	16 25	16 55	17 25

		VT 🚌	VT 🚌	VT 🚌	VT 🚌	VT 🚌	VT 🚌	VT 🚌	VT 🚌	VT 🚌	VT 🚌	VT 🚌	VT 🚌	VT 🚌	VT 🚌
Milton Keynes Central	d	15 45	16 15	16 45	17 15	17 45	18 15	18 45	19 15	19 45	20 10	20 40	21 10	22 10	23 10
Bedford Bus Station	a	16 35	17 05	17 35	18 05	18 40	19 10	19 40	20 05	20 30	20 50	21 20	21 50	22 50	23 50
St Neots Cross Keys	a	17 17	17 47	18 17	18 47	19 15	.....	20 15	.....	21 10	.....	22 00	.....	.....	.....
Cambridge Parkside Bay 16	a	17 55	18 25	18 55	19 25	19 48	.	20 48	.	21 43	.	22 33	.	.	.

Saturdays

		VT 🚌	VT 🚌	VT 🚌	VT 🚌	VT 🚌	VT 🚌	VT 🚌	VT 🚌	VT 🚌	VT 🚌	VT 🚌	VT 🚌	VT 🚌	VT 🚌	VT 🚌	VT 🚌	VT 🚌
Milton Keynes Central	d	07 15	07 50	08 15	08 45	09 15	09 45	10 15	10 45	11 15	11 45	12 15	12 45	13 15	13 45	14 15	14 45	15 15
Bedford Bus Station	a	08 05	08 40	09 05	09 35	10 05	10 35	11 05	11 35	12 05	12 35	13 05	13 35	14 05	14 35	15 05	15 35	16 05
St Neots Cross Keys	a	08 47	09 17	09 47	10 17	10 47	11 17	11 47	12 17	12 47	13 17	13 47	14 17	14 47	15 17	15 47	16 17	16 47
Cambridge Parkside Bay 16	a	09 25	09 55	10 25	10 55	11 25	11 55	12 25	12 55	13 25	13 55	14 25	14 55	15 25	15 55	16 25	16 55	17 25

		VT 🚌	VT 🚌	VT 🚌	VT 🚌	VT 🚌	VT 🚌	VT 🚌	VT 🚌	VT 🚌	VT 🚌	VT 🚌	VT 🚌	VT 🚌	VT 🚌
Milton Keynes Central	d	15 45	16 15	16 45	17 15	17 45	18 15	18 45	19 15	19 45	20 10	20 40	21 10	22 10	23 10
Bedford Bus Station	a	16 35	17 05	17 35	18 05	18 40	19 10	19 40	20 05	20 30	20 50	21 20	21 50	22 50	23 50
St Neots Cross Keys	a	17 17	17 47	18 17	18 47	19 15	.....	20 15	.....	21 10	.....	22 00	.....	.....	.....
Cambridge Parkside Bay 16	a	17 55	18 25	18 55	19 25	19 48	.	20 48	.	21 43	.	22 33	.	.	.

Sundays

		VT 🚌	VT 🚌	VT 🚌	VT 🚌	VT 🚌	VT 🚌	VT 🚌	VT 🚌	VT 🚌	VT 🚌	VT 🚌	VT 🚌	VT 🚌	VT 🚌	VT 🚌	VT 🚌	VT 🚌	VT 🚌	VT 🚌	VT 🚌	VT 🚌	VT 🚌	VT 🚌	VT 🚌
Milton Keynes Central	d	09 15	10 15	11 15	12 15	12 45	13 15	13 45	14 15	14 45	15 15	15 45	16 15	16 45	17 15	17 45	18 15	18 45	19 15	19 45	20 10	20 40	21 10	22 10	23 10
Bedford Bus Station	a	10 05	11 05	12 05	13 05	13 35	14 05	14 35	15 05	15 35	16 05	16 35	17 05	17 35	18 05	18 35	19 05	19 35	20 00	20 30	20 50	21 20	21 50	22 50	23 50
St Neots Cross Keys	a	10 47	11 47	12 47	13 47	14 17	14 47	15 17	15 47	16 17	16 45	17 15	17 45	18 15	18 45	19 15	.....	20 15	.....	21 10	.....	22 00	.....	.....	.....
Cambridge Parkside Bay 16	a	11 25	12 25	13 25	14 25	14 55	15 25	15 55	16 25	16 55	17 18	17 48	18 18	18 48	19 18	19 48	.	20 48	.	21 43	.	22 33	.	.	.

For general notes see front of timetable
For details of catering facilities see
Directory of Train Operators

This is the X5 service operated by Stagecoach East

Cambridge and Bedford → Milton Keynes Central

Bus Service

		VT	VT		VT	VT		VT	VT		VT	VT		VT	VT		VT	VT		VT	VT		VT	VT		VT
Cambridge Parkside Bay 16	d							05 30			06 30	07 00		07 30	08 10		08 40	09 10		09 40	10 10		10 40	11 10		11 40
St Neots Sq (Bus)	d							06 05			07 05	07 35		08 05	08 45		09 15	09 45		10 15	10 45		11 15	11 45		12 15
Bedford Bus Station	d	05 00	05 30		06 00	06 30		06 45	07 15		07 45	08 15		09 00	09 30		10 00	10 30		11 00	11 30		12 00	12 30		13 00
Milton Keynes Central	a	05 45	06 15		06 45	07 15		07 35	08 05		08 45	09 15		09 45	10 15		10 45	11 15		11 45	12 15		12 45	13 15		13 45

		VT	VT		VT	VT		VT	VT		VT	VT		VT	VT		VT	VT		VT	VT					
Cambridge Parkside Bay 16	d	12 10	12 40		13 10	13 40		14 10	14 40		15 10	15 40		16 10	16 40		17 10	17 40		18 10	18 40					
St Neots Sq (Bus)	d	12 45	13 15		13 45	14 15		14 45	15 15		15 45	16 15		16 45	17 15		17 45	18 15		18 45	19 15					
Bedford Bus Station	d	13 30	14 00		14 30	15 00		15 30	16 00		16 30	17 00		17 30	18 00		18 30	19 00		19 30	20 00					
Milton Keynes Central	a	14 15	14 45		15 15	15 45		16 15	16 45		17 15	17 45		18 15	18 45		19 10	19 45		20 10	20 45					

Saturdays

		VT	VT		VT	VT		VT	VT		VT	VT		VT	VT		VT	VT		VT	VT		VT	VT		VT
Cambridge Parkside Bay 16	d										06 40	07 10		07 40	08 10		08 40	09 10		09 40	10 10		10 40	11 10		11 40
St Neots Sq (Bus)	d										07 15	07 45		08 15	08 45		09 15	09 45		10 15	10 45		11 15	11 45		12 15
Bedford Bus Station	d	05 05	05 35		06 05	06 35		07 00	07 30		08 00	08 30		09 00	09 30		10 00	10 30		11 00	11 30		12 00	12 30		13 00
Milton Keynes Central	a	05 50	06 20		06 50	07 20		07 45	08 15		08 45	09 15		09 45	10 15		10 45	11 15		11 45	12 15		12 45	13 15		13 45

		VT	VT		VT	VT		VT	VT		VT	VT		VT	VT		VT	VT		VT	VT					
Cambridge Parkside Bay 16	d	12 10	12 40		13 10	13 40		14 10	14 40		15 10	15 40		16 10	16 40		17 10	17 40		18 10	18 40					
St Neots Sq (Bus)	d	12 45	13 15		13 45	14 15		14 45	15 15		15 45	16 15		16 45	17 15		17 45	18 15		18 45	19 15					
Bedford Bus Station	d	13 30	14 00		14 30	15 00		15 30	16 00		16 30	17 00		17 30	18 00		18 30	19 00		19 30	20 00					
Milton Keynes Central	a	14 15	14 45		15 15	15 45		16 15	16 45		17 15	17 45		18 15	18 45		19 15	19 45		20 10	20 45					

Sundays

		VT	VT	VT	VT	VT	VT	VT	VT	VT	VT	VT	VT	VT	VT	VT	VT	VT	VT	VT	VT	VT	VT	VT	VT	VT
Cambridge Parkside Bay 16	d					08 10		09 10		10 10		11 10	11 40	12 10	12 40	13 10	13 40	14 10	14 40	15 10	15 40	16 10	16 40	17 10	17 40	18 40
St Neots Sq (Bus)	d					08 45		09 45		10 45		11 45	12 15	12 45	13 15	13 45	14 15	14 45	15 15	15 45	16 15	16 45	17 15	17 45	18 15	19 15
Bedford Bus Station	d	06 00	07 00	08 00	09 00	09 30	10 00	10 30	11 00	11 30	12 00	12 30	13 00	13 30	14 00	14 30	15 00	15 30	16 00	16 30	17 00	17 30	18 00	18 30	19 00	20 00
Milton Keynes Central	a	06 45	07 45	08 45	09 45	10 15	10 45	11 15	11 45	12 15	12 45	13 15	13 45	14 15	14 45	15 15	15 45	16 15	16 45	17 15	17 45	18 15	18 45	19 10	19 45	20 40

For general notes see front of timetable
For details of catering facilities see Directory of Train Operators

This is the X5 service operated by Stagecoach East

Table 65E **Mondays to Fridays**

Preston — Southport
Bus Service

Mondays to Fridays

		VT	VT	VT	VT	VT	VT	VT	VT	VT	VT	VT	VT	VT	VT	VT	VT	VT	VT	VT	VT	VT	VT	VT	VT	VT	VT
Preston 8	d	05 04	05 36	06 06	06 25	06 55	07 25	08 09	08 39	09 09	09 39	10 09	10 39	11 09	11 39	12 09	12 39	13 09	13 39	14 09	14 39	15 09	15 39	16 19	16 49	17 19	18 24
Southport (Lord Street)	a	05 33	06 05	06 35	06 55	07 28	07 58	08 46	09 16	09 46	10 16	10 46	11 16	11 46	12 16	12 46	13 16	13 46	14 16	14 46	15 16	15 46	16 16	16 56	17 26	17 56	19 01

Saturdays

		VT	VT	VT	VT	VT	VT	VT	VT	VT	VT	VT	VT	VT	VT	VT	VT	VT	VT	VT	VT	VT	VT
Preston 8	d	06 13	07 05	08 09	08 39	09 09	09 39	10 09	10 39	11 09	11 39	12 09	12 39	13 09	13 39	14 09	14 39	15 09	15 39	16 09	16 39	17 19	18 19
Southport (Lord Street)	a	06 45	07 38	08 46	09 16	09 46	10 16	10 46	11 16	11 46	12 16	12 46	13 16	13 46	14 16	14 46	15 16	15 46	16 16	16 46	17 16	17 56	19 24

Sundays

		VT	VT	VT	VT	VT	VT	VT	VT	VT	VT	VT
Preston 8	d	06 33	08 09	09 09	10 09	11 09	12 09	13 09	14 09	15 09	16 09	18 09
Southport (Lord Street)	a	07 02	08 46	09 46	10 46	11 46	12 46	13 46	14 46	15 46	16 46	18 46

Mondays to Fridays

		VT	VT	VT	VT	VT	VT	VT	VT	VT	VT	VT	VT	VT	VT	VT	VT	VT	VT	VT	VT	VT	VT	VT	VT	VT	VT	VT	VT
Southport (Lord Street)	d	06 55	07 21	07 41	08 38	09 08	09 38	10 08	10 38	11 08	11 38	12 08	12 38	13 08	13 38	14 08	14 38	15 08	15 38	16 08	16 43	17 30	18 00	18 20	18 50	19 20	19 50	20 20	21 20
Preston 8	a	07 31	08 06	08 41	09 20	09 50	10 20	10 50	11 20	11 50	12 20	12 50	13 20	13 50	14 20	14 50	15 20	15 50	16 20	16 50	17 24	18 11	18 41	18 52	19 22	19 52	20 22	20 52	21 52

Saturdays

		VT	VT	VT	VT	VT	VT	VT	VT	VT	VT	VT	VT	VT	VT	VT	VT	VT	VT	VT	VT	VT	VT	VT	VT	VT	VT
Southport (Lord Street)	d	08 08	08 38	09 08	09 38	10 08	10 38	11 08	11 38	12 08	12 38	13 08	13 38	14 08	14 38	15 08	15 38	16 08	16 38	17 03	17 41	18 20	18 50	19 20	19 50	20 20	21 20
Preston 8	a	08 50	09 20	09 50	10 20	10 50	11 20	11 50	12 20	12 50	13 20	13 50	14 20	14 50	15 20	15 50	16 20	16 50	17 20	17 45	18 23	19 02	19 32	20 02	20 32	20 52	21 52

Sundays

		VT	VT	VT	VT	VT	VT	VT	VT	VT	VT	VT
Southport (Lord Street)	d	09 06	11 05	12 05	13 05	14 05	15 05	16 05	17 05	18 05	19 05	21 05
Preston 8	a	09 45	11 45	12 45	13 45	14 45	15 45	16 45	17 45	18 45	19 45	21 45

For general notes see front of timetable
For details of catering facilities see
Directory of Train Operators

This is the X2 service operated jointly by Stagecoach in Lancashire and Stagecoach in Merseyside

Table 65F

Mondays to Fridays

Penrith — Keswick, Cockermouth and Workington
Bus Service

		VT	VT	VT	VT	VT	VT	VT	VT	VT	VT	VT	VT	VT	VT	VT	VT
Penrith North Lakes	d	07 22	08 22	09 22	10 22	11 22	12 22	13 22	14 22	15 22	16 22	17 22	18 30	19 30	20 35	21 40	22 45
Keswick (Bus Station)	a	07 53	09 00	10 00	11 00	12 00	13 00	14 00	15 00	16 00	17 08	18 00	19 00	20 00	21 05	22 10	23 15
Cockermouth (Main Street)	a	08 32	09 39	10 39	11 39	12 39	13 39	14 39	15 39	16 39	17 39	18 39	19 39	20 39	21 40	22 40	23 45
Workington (Bus Station)	a	08 57	10 04	11 04	12 04	13 04	14 04	15 04	16 04	17 04	18 04	19 04	20 04	20 58	21 58	22 58	00 03

Saturdays

		VT	VT	VT	VT	VT	VT	VT	VT	VT	VT	VT	VT	VT	VT	VT	VT
Penrith North Lakes	d	07 22	08 22	09 22	10 22	11 22	12 22	13 22	14 22	15 22	16 22	17 22	18 30	19 30	20 35	21 40	22 45
Keswick (Bus Station)	a	07 53	09 00	10 00	11 00	12 00	13 00	14 00	15 00	16 00	17 00	18 00	19 00	20 00	21 05	22 10	23 15
Cockermouth (Main Street)	a	08 32	09 39	10 39	11 39	12 39	13 39	14 39	15 39	16 39	17 39	18 39	19 39	20 39	21 40	22 40	23 45
Workington (Bus Station)	a	08 57	10 04	11 04	12 04	13 04	14 04	15 04	16 04	17 04	18 04	19 04	20 04	20 58	21 58	22 58	00 03

Sundays

		VT	VT	VT	VT	VT	VT	VT
Penrith North Lakes	d	08 45	09 20	11 20	13 20	15 20	17 20	19 20
Keswick (Bus Station)	a	09 22	09 55	11 55	13 55	15 55	17 55	19 55
Cockermouth (Main Street)	a	—	10 31	12 31	14 31	16 31	18 31	20 31
Workington (Bus Station)	a	—	10 52	12 52	14 52	16 52	18 52	20 52

Mondays to Fridays

		VT	VT	VT	VT	VT	VT	VT	VT	VT	VT	VT	VT	VT	VT	VT	VT	VT
Workington (Bus Station)	d	05 20	06 20	06 55	07 55	09 20	10 20	11 20	12 20	13 20	14 20	15 20	16 20	17 20	—	18 20	19 15	21 15
Cockermouth (Main Street)	d	05 41	06 41	07 16	08 16	09 41	10 41	11 41	12 41	13 41	14 41	15 41	16 41	17 41	—	18 41	19 37	22 37
Keswick (Bus Station)	d	06 20	07 20	07 55	08 55	10 20	11 20	12 20	13 20	14 20	15 20	16 20	17 20	18 20	18 40	19 20	20 10	22 06
Penrith North Lakes	a	06 50	07 59	08 36	09 36	11 01	12 01	13 01	14 01	15 01	16 01	17 01	18 01	19 01	19 15	19 55	20 45	22 33

Saturdays

		VT	VT	VT	VT	VT	VT	VT	VT	VT	VT	VT	VT	VT	VT	VT	VT	VT
Workington (Bus Station)	d	05 20	06 20	06 55	07 55	09 20	10 20	11 20	12 20	13 20	14 20	15 20	16 20	17 20	—	18 20	19 15	21 15
Cockermouth (Main Street)	d	05 41	06 41	07 16	08 16	09 41	10 41	11 41	12 41	13 41	14 41	15 41	16 41	17 41	—	18 41	19 37	22 37
Keswick (Bus Station)	d	06 20	07 20	07 55	08 55	10 20	11 20	12 20	13 20	14 20	15 20	16 20	17 20	18 20	18 40	19 20	20 10	22 06
Penrith North Lakes	a	06 50	07 59	08 36	09 36	11 01	12 01	13 01	14 01	15 01	16 01	17 01	18 01	19 01	19 15	19 55	20 45	22 33

Sundays

		VT	VT	VT	VT	VT	VT	VT
Workington (Bus Station)	d	07 15	09 15	10 15	13 15	15 15	17 15	—
Cockermouth (Main Street)	d	07 36	09 36	10 36	13 36	15 36	17 36	—
Keswick (Bus Station)	d	08 15	10 15	11 15	14 15	16 15	18 12	18 40
Penrith North Lakes	a	08 50	10 50	11 50	14 50	16 50	18 47	19 15

For general notes see front of timetable
For details of catering facilities see
Directory of Train Operators

This is an amalgamation of the X4/X5/X50 services operated by Stagecoach in Cumbria

Table 65G

Mondays to Fridays

Carlisle — Scottish Border Towns
Bus Service

		VT	VT	VT	VT	VT	VT	VT	VT	VT	VT	VT	VT FO
Carlisle	d	09 10	10 10	11 10	12 10	13 10	14 10	15 10	16 10	17 10	18 50	20 50	22 50
Langholm	a	09 57	10 57	11 57	12 57	13 57	14 57	15 57	16 57	17 57	19 37	21 37	23 32
Hawick	a	10 32	11 32	12 32	13 32	14 32	15 32	16 32	17 32	18 32	20 12	22 12	00 07
Selkirk	a	10 55	11 55	12 55	13 55	14 55	15 55	16 55	17 55	18 55	20 35	22 35	00 30
Galashiels	a	11 15	12 15	13 15	14 15	15 15	16 15	17 15	18 15	19 15	20 50	22 50	00 45

Saturdays

		VT	VT	VT	VT	VT	VT	VT	VT	VT	VT	VT	VT
Carlisle	d	09 10	10 10	11 10	12 10	13 10	14 10	15 10	16 10	17 10	18 50	20 50	22 50
Langholm	a	09 57	10 57	11 57	12 57	13 57	14 57	15 57	16 57	17 57	19 37	21 37	23 32
Hawick	a	10 32	11 32	12 32	13 32	14 32	15 32	16 32	17 32	18 32	20 12	22 12	00 07
Selkirk	a	10 55	11 55	12 55	13 55	14 55	15 55	16 55	17 55	18 55	20 35	22 35	00 30
Galashiels	a	11 15	12 15	13 15	14 15	15 15	16 15	17 15	18 15	19 15	20 50	22 50	00 45

Sundays

		VT	VT	VT
Carlisle	d	14 05	18 05	21 20
Langholm	a	14 50	18 50	22 05
Hawick	a	15 25	19 25	22 40
Selkirk	a	15 45	19 45	23 00
Galashiels	a	16 00	20 00	23 15

Mondays to Fridays

		VT	VT	VT	VT	VT	VT	VT	VT	VT	VT	VT	VT FO
Galashiels	d	06 20	07 15	08 10	09 25	10 25	11 25	12 25	13 25	14 25	16 30	17 35	19 25
Selkirk	d	06 35	07 30	08 25	09 40	10 40	11 40	12 40	13 40	14 40	16 45	17 50	19 40
Hawick	d	06 55	07 50	08 45	10 00	11 00	12 00	13 00	14 00	15 00	17 05	18 10	19 58
Langholm	d	07 35	08 30	09 25	10 40	11 40	12 40	13 40	14 40	15 40	17 45	18 50	20 38
Carlisle	a	08 27	09 17	10 12	11 27	12 27	13 27	14 27	15 27	16 27	18 32	19 37	21 25

Saturdays

		VT	VT	VT	VT	VT	VT	VT	VT	VT	VT
Galashiels	d	06 20	07 15	08 10	09 25	10 25	11 25	12 25	13 25	14 25	19 25
Selkirk	d	06 35	07 30	08 25	09 40	10 40	11 40	12 40	13 40	14 40	19 40
Hawick	d	06 55	07 50	08 45	10 00	11 00	12 00	13 00	14 00	15 00	19 58
Langholm	d	07 35	08 30	09 25	10 40	11 40	12 40	13 40	14 40	15 40	20 38
Carlisle	a	08 27	09 17	10 12	11 27	12 27	13 27	14 27	15 27	16 27	21 25

Sundays

		VT	VT	VT	VT
Galashiels	d	09 30	11 30	15 30	17 30
Selkirk	d	09 45	11 45	15 45	17 45
Hawick	d	10 05	12 05	16 05	18 05
Langholm	d	10 38	12 38	16 38	18 38
Carlisle	a	11 27	13 27	17 27	19 27

For general notes see front of timetable
For details of catering facilities see
Directory of Train Operators

London → Watford Junction, Milton Keynes, Northampton and West Midlands

Network Diagram - See first page of Table 59

Miles	Miles	Miles		LM	VT	VT	LM	VT	LM	LM	LM	LM	LM	LM	LM	SN	LM	VT	VT	VT	LM	VT	SN	LM	SN
				MO	MO	MO	MX	MX	MO	MX		MO	MX												
				1	1 ◇	1 ◇	1	1 ◇	1	1	1	1	1	1	1	1	1 ◇	1 ◇	1 ◇	1 ◇	1 ◇	1 ◇	1	1	1
					A	B									C										
					☕	☕		⊠										⊠	⊠	⊠		⊠			
0	0	—	**London Euston** [15] ⊖ d	22p58	23p24	23p24	23p24	23p43	23p34	23p34	00 04	00 34	00 34	01 34			05 30	05 35	05 47	06 03		06 17		06 04	
—	—	0	East Croydon d																						
—	—	7¾	Clapham Junction [10] d													05 03							05 30		05 55
—	—	8¾	Imperial Wharf § d																						
—	—	9¼	West Brompton ⊖ d													05 10							05 40		06 03
—	—	11¼	Kensington (Olympia) ⊖ d													05 14							05 44		06 07
—	—	12½	Shepherd's Bush d													05 17							05 47		06 10
8	—	16¾	Wembley Central d									00 44	00 46	01 45									06s02		
11½	11½	—	Harrow & Wealdstone ⊖ d	23p10					23p46	23p46	00 16	00 48	00 51	01 50		05 34	05 42						06 07	06 16	06 27
16	—	—	Bushey d							23p51			00 56												
—	—	—	**Watford Junction** a	23p17			23p40		23p53	23p54	00 23	00 55	00 59	01 56		05 41	05 49						06 14	06 23	06 35
17½	17½	—	d	23p17			23p41		23p53	23p55	00 23	00 59	00 59	01 57			05 49	05u50	06u02				06 14	06 23	
21	—	—	Kings Langley d	23p22					23p58	23p59		01 04	01 04				05 54							06 28	
23	—	—	Apsley d	23p25					00 01	00 03		01 07	01 07				05 57							06 31	
—	—	—	Hemel Hempstead a	23p28			23p48		00 04	00 06	00 31	01 10	01 10	02 04			06 00						06 22	06 34	
24½	—	—	d	23p28			23p48		00 04	00 06	00 31	01 10	01 10	02 04			06 00				⟵		06 22	06 34	
28	—	—	Berkhamsted d	23p33			23p53		00 09	00 11	00 35	01 15	01 15	02 09			06 05				06 05		06 26	06 39	
31¾	—	—	Tring d	23p38					00 14	00 16	00 40	01 20	01 20	02 14			⟶				06 12		06 33	06a46	
36	—	—	Cheddington d	23p43					00 19	00 21		01 25	01 25								06 18				
40¼	—	—	Leighton Buzzard d	23p50			00 06		00 26	00 28	00 50	01 32	01 32	02 24							06 23		06 42		
46¾	—	—	Bletchley d	23p57			00 13		00 33	00 35	00 58	01 39	01 39	02 31	05 17						06 31		06 49		
—	—	—	**Milton Keynes Central** [10] a	00 06	00 10	00 10	00 22	00 26	00 42	00 44	01 06	01 48	01 48	02 40	05 21			06 09	06 22		06 36	06 47	06 55		
49¾	49¾	—	d	00 06	00 11	00 11	00 22	00 26	00 42		01 07	01 48	01 48		05 21			06 10	06 22		06 37				
52½	52½	—	Wolverton d	00 10			00 26		00 46		01 10	01 52	01 52		05 25						06 40				
65¾	—	—	**Northampton** a	00 24			00 40		01 00		01 25	02 06	02 06		05 37						06 54				
—	—	—	**Rugby** a		00s47	00s47		01s00							06 02				06 44	06 50	07 16				
84½	82½	—	d												06 02					06 51	07 16				
—	—	—	Nuneaton a												06 14			06 38							
96	—	—	Coventry a		00s57	00s57		01s13												07 01	07 28				
106¾	—	—	Birmingham International ✈ a		01s08	01s08		01s23												07 12	07 45				
115¼	—	—	**Birmingham New Street** [12] a		01s21	01s21		01s35												07 27	08 03				
120½	—	—	Sandwell & Dudley a																						
128	—	—	Wolverhampton [7] a		01 53	01 59		02 05																	

	VT	VT	LM	VT	LM	VT	LM	VT	LM	SN	LM	VT	LM	LM	VT	VT	LM	VT	LM	LM	VT	LM	SN	LM	VT
	1 ◇	1 ◇	1 ◇	1 ◇	1	1 ◇	1 ◇	1 ◇	1	1	1	1 ◇	1	1	1 ◇	1 ◇	1 ◇	1 ◇	1	1 ◇	1 ◇	1	1	1	1 ◇
			C																						
	⊠	⊠		⊠		⊠		⊠				⊠			⊠	⊠		⊠			⊠				⊠
London Euston [15] ⊖ d	06 23	06 43	06 24	06 55	06 34	07 03	06 53	07 20	07 13		07 04	07 23	07 24	07 34	07 35	07 43	07 46	08 03		07 54	08 20	08 13		08 05	08 23
East Croydon d																									
Clapham Junction [10] d										06 38													07 38		
Imperial Wharf § d																									
West Brompton ⊖ d										06 45													07 47		
Kensington (Olympia) ⊖ d										06 49													07 50		
Shepherd's Bush d										06 52													07 53		
Wembley Central d										07s07													08s08		
Harrow & Wealdstone ⊖ d					06 47					07 12	07 16			07 46									08 13	08 17	
Bushey d																								08 22	
Watford Junction a			06 40		06 53		07 09			07 19	07 23		07 41	07 53			08 00			08 10			08 20	08 25	
d	06u37		06 41		06 54		07 10			07 19	07 23	07u37	07 42	07 53			08 01			08 11			08 20	08 26	08u37
Kings Langley d					06 58						07 28			07 58										08 30	
Apsley d					07 02						07 31			08 01										08 34	
Hemel Hempstead a			06 48		07 05		07 17			07 27	07 34		07 49	08 04						08 18			08 28	08 37	
d			06 48		07 05		07 17			07 27	07 34		07 50	08 04						08 18			08 28	08 37	
Berkhamsted d			06 53		07 09		07 22			07 32	07 39		07 55	08 09						08 23			08 32	08 41	
Tring d			07 00		07 16					07 39	07a46		08 02	08a16					⟵				08 39	08a48	
Cheddington d			07 05		07 21								08 07						08 07						
Leighton Buzzard d			07 10		07 26		07 35		07 42	07 51			⟶						08 12	08 36		08 42	08 48		
Bletchley d			07 17		07 34		07 43		07 50	07 58									08 19	08 43		08 50	08 55		
Milton Keynes Central [10] a		07 13	07 23	07 25	07 39		07 49	07 50	07 54	08 03					08 05	08 13	08 24		08 25	08 49	08 50	08 54	09 01		
d		07 13	07 23				07 49		07 55							08 13	08 25			08 49		08 55			
Wolverton d			07 27				07 53		07 59											08 53		08 59			
Northampton a			07 40				08 06		08 13								08 40			09 06		09 13			
Rugby a			08 03			07 50	08 37										09 03	08 50		09 37					
d			08 03			07 51	08 37										09 03	08 51		09 37					
Nuneaton a			08 16														09 16								
Coventry a	07 22	07 42				08 01	08 49					08 22				08 42		09 01		09 49					09 22
Birmingham International ✈ a	07 33	07 53				08 12	09 04					08 33				08 53		09 12		10 04					09 33
Birmingham New Street [12] a	07 45	08 08				08 27	09 16					08 45				09 08		09 27		10 16					09 45
Sandwell & Dudley a	07 57											08 57													09 57
Wolverhampton [7] a	08 11											09 11													10 11

For general notes see front of timetable
For details of catering facilities see Directory of Train Operators

§ It is unknown , at the time of going to press, when this station will open. For further details contact National rail Enquiries 08457-484950 or see local publicity

A Until 13 July and from 14 September
B 20 July to 7 September
C To Crewe (Table 67)

London → Watford Junction, Milton Keynes, Northampton and West Midlands

Network Diagram - See first page of Table 59

		LM 1	LM 1	VT 1◇ ⊠	LM 1◇	VT 1◇ ⊠	LM 1	LM 1◇	VT 1◇ ⊠	LM 1	SN 1	LM 1	VT 1◇ ⊠		VT 1◇ ⊠	LM 1	LM 1	LM 1◇	VT 1◇ ☕	LM 1◇	VT 1◇ ☕	LM 1	SN 1	LM 1	VT 1◇ ☕	VT 1◇ ☕
London Euston 15	⊖ d	08 24	08 34	08 43	08 46	09 03		08 54	09 20	09 13		09 05	09 23		09 43	09 24	09 34	09 46	10 03	09 54	10 20	10 13		10 05	10 23	10 43
East Croydon	d																									
Clapham Junction 10	d										08 38												09 38			
Imperial Wharf §	d																									
West Brompton	⊖ d										08 47												09 47			
Kensington (Olympia)	⊖ d										08 50												09 50			
Shepherd's Bush	d										08 53												09 53			
Wembley Central	d										09s08												10s08			
Harrow & Wealdstone	⊖ d	08 36	08 46								09 13	09 17					09 47						10 13	10 17		
Bushey	d		08 51									09 22					09 52							10 22		
Watford Junction	a	08 43	08 54		09 00			09 10			09 20	09 25				09 40	09 55	10 00		10 10			10 20	10 25		
	d	08 44	08 55		09 01			09 11			09 20	09 26	09u37			09 41	09 56	10 01		10 11			10 20	10 26	10u37	
Kings Langley	d		08 59									09 30					10 00							10 30		
Apsley	d		09 03									09 34					10 04							10 34		
Hemel Hempstead	a	08 51	09 06					09 18			09 28	09 37				09 48	10 07			10 18			10 28	10 37		
	d	08 52	09 06					09 18			09 28	09 37				09 48	10 07			10 18			10 28	10 37		
Berkhamsted	d	08 57	09 10					09 23			09 32	09 41				09 53	10 11			10 23			10 32	10 41		
Tring	d	09 04	09a17				←				09 39	09a48				10 00	10a18						10 39	10a48		
Cheddington	d	09 09 →					09 09									10 05										
Leighton Buzzard	d						09 14	09 36		09 42	09 48					10 10				10 36		10 42	10 48			
Bletchley	d						09 21	09 43		09 50	09 55					10 17				10 43		10 50	10 55			
Milton Keynes Central 10	a			09 13	09 24		09 27	09 49	09 50	09 54	10 01				10 13	10 23		10 24		10 49	10 50	10 54	11 01			11 13
	d			09 13	09 25			09 49		09 55					10 13			10 25		10 49		10 55				11 13
Wolverton	d							09 53		09 59										10 53		10 59				
Northampton	a				09 40			10 06		10 13								10 40		11 07		11 13				
Rugby	a				10 03	09 50		10 37										11 03	10 50	11 37						
	d				10 03	09 51		10 37										11 03	10 51	11 37						
Nuneaton	a				10 16													11 16								
Coventry	a			09 42		10 01		10 49					10 22		10 42				11 01	11 49					11 22	11 42
Birmingham International	✈ a			09 53		10 12		11 04					10 33		10 53				11 12	12 04					11 33	11 53
Birmingham New Street 12	a			10 08		10 27		11 16					10 45		11 08				11 27	12 16					11 45	12 08
Sandwell & Dudley	a												10 57												11 57	
Wolverhampton 7	⛴ a												11 11												12 11	

		LM 1	LM 1	LM 1◇	VT 1◇ ☕	LM 1◇	VT 1◇ ☕	LM 1	SN 1	LM 1	VT 1◇ ☕	VT 1◇ ☕	LM 1	LM 1	LM 1◇	VT 1◇ ☕	LM 1◇	VT 1◇ ☕	LM 1	SN 1	LM 1	VT 1◇ ☕	VT 1◇ ☕	LM 1	LM 1	LM 1◇
London Euston 15	⊖ d	10 24	10 34	10 46	11 03	10 54	11 20	11 13		11 04	11 23	11 43	11 24	11 34	11 46	12 03	11 54	12 20	12 13		12 04	12 23	12 43	12 24	12 34	12 46
East Croydon	⛴ d								10 10											11 10						
Clapham Junction 10	d								10 38											11 38						
Imperial Wharf §	d																									
West Brompton	⊖ d								10 47											11 47						
Kensington (Olympia)	⊖ d								10 50											11 50						
Shepherd's Bush	d								10 53											11 53						
Wembley Central	d								11s07											12s07						
Harrow & Wealdstone	⊖ d		10 47						11 12	11 16				11 46						12 12	12 16				12 46	
Bushey	d		10 52							11 21				11 51							12 21				12 51	
Watford Junction	a	10 40	10 55	11 00		11 10			11 19	11 24			11 40	11 54	12 00		12 10			12 19	12 24			12 40	12 54	13 00
	d	10 41	10 56	11 01		11 11			11 19	11 25	11u37		11 41	11 55	12 01		12 11			12 19	12 25	12u37		12 41	12 55	13 01
Kings Langley	d		11 00							11 29				11 59							12 29				12 59	
Apsley	d		11 04							11 33				12 03							12 33				13 03	
Hemel Hempstead	a	10 48	11 07			11 18			11 27	11 36			11 48	12 06			12 18			12 27	12 36			12 48	13 06	
	d	10 48	11 07			11 18			11 27	11 36			11 48	12 06			12 18			12 27	12 36			12 48	13 06	
Berkhamsted	d	10 53	11 11			11 23			11 31	11 40			11 53	12 10			12 23			12 31	12 40			12 53	13 10	
Tring	d	11 00	11a18						11 38	11a47			12 00	12a17						12 38	12a47			13 00	13a17	
Cheddington	d	11 05											12 05											13 05		
Leighton Buzzard	d	11 10				11 36		11 42	11 48				12 10				12 36		12 42	12 48				13 10		
Bletchley	d	11 17				11 43		11 50	11 55				12 17				12 43		12 50	12 55				13 17		
Milton Keynes Central 10	a	11 23		11 24		11 49	11 50	11 54	12 01			12 13	12 23		12 24		12 49	12 50	12 54	13 01			13 13	13 23		13 24
	d			11 25		11 49		11 55				12 13			12 25		12 49		12 55				13 13			13 25
Wolverton	d					11 53		11 59									12 53		12 59							
Northampton	a			11 40		12 06		12 13							12 40		13 06		13 13							13 40
Rugby	a			12 03	11 50	12 37									13 03	12 50	13 37									14 03
	d			12 03	11 51	12 37									13 03	12 51	13 37									14 03
Nuneaton	a			12 16											13 16											14 16
Coventry	a				12 01	12 49					12 22	12 42				13 01	13 49					13 22	13 42			
Birmingham International	✈ a				12 12	13 04					12 33	12 53				13 12	14 04					13 33	13 53			
Birmingham New Street 12	a				12 27	13 16					12 45	13 08				13 27	14 16					13 45	14 08			
Sandwell & Dudley	a										12 57											13 57				
Wolverhampton 7	⛴ a										13 11											14 11				

For general notes see front of timetable
For details of catering facilities see
Directory of Train Operators

§ It is unknown , at the time of going to press, when this station will open. For further details contact National rail Enquiries 08457-484950 or see local publicity

London → Watford Junction, Milton Keynes, Northampton and West Midlands

Network Diagram - See first page of Table 59

		VT	LM	VT	LM	SN	LM	VT	VT	LM	LM	LM	VT	LM	VT	LM	SN	LM	VT	VT	LM	LM	LM		VT	LM
		1◇	1◇	1◇	1	1	1	1◇	1◇	1	1	1◇	1◇	1◇	1◇	1	1	1	1◇	1◇	1	1	1◇		1◇	1◇
		☕		☕				☕	☕				☕		☕				☕	☕					☕	
London Euston 15	⊖ d	13 03	12 54	13 20	13 13		13 04	13 23	13 43	13 24	13 34	13 46	14 03	13 54	14 20	14 13		14 04	14 23	14 43	14 24	14 34	14 46		15 03	14 54
East Croydon	d					12 10											13 10									
Clapham Junction 10	d					12 38											13 38									
Imperial Wharf §	d																									
West Brompton	⊖ d					12 47											13 47									
Kensington (Olympia)	⊖ d					12 50											13 50									
Shepherd's Bush	d					12 53											13 53									
Wembley Central	d					13s07											14s07									
Harrow & Wealdstone	⊖ d					13 12	13 16				13 46						14 12	14 16				14 46				
Bushey	d						13 21				13 51							14 21				14 51				
Watford Junction	a		13 10			13 19	13 24			13 40	13 54	14 00		14 10			14 19	14 24			14 40	14 54	15 00			15 10
	d		13 11			13 19	13 25	13u37		13 41	13 55	14 01		14 11			14 19	14 25	14u37		14 41	14 55	15 01			15 11
Kings Langley	d						13 29				13 59							14 29				14 59				
Apsley	d						13 33				14 03							14 33				15 03				
Hemel Hempstead	a		13 18			13 27	13 36			13 48	14 06			14 18			14 27	14 36			14 48	15 06				15 18
	d		13 18			13 27	13 36			13 48	14 06			14 18			14 27	14 36			14 48	15 06				15 18
Berkhamsted	d		13 23			13 31	13 40			13 53	14 10			14 23			14 31	14 40			14 53	15 10				15 23
Tring	d					13 38	13a47			14 00	14a17						14 38	14a47			15 00	15a17				
Cheddington	d									14 05											15 05					
Leighton Buzzard	d		13 36		13 42	13 48				14 10				14 37		14 42	14 48				15 10					15 36
Bletchley	d		13 43		13 50	13 55				14 17				14 44		14 50	14 55				15 17					15 43
Milton Keynes Central 10	a		13 49	13 50	13 54	14 01			14 13	14 23		14 24		14 50	14 50	14 55	15 01			15 13	15 23		15 24			15 49
	d		13 49		13 55				14 13			14 25		14 50		14 55				15 13			15 25			15 49
Wolverton	d		13 53		13 59									14 54		14 59										15 53
Northampton	a		14 06		14 13							14 40		15 08		15 13							15 40			16 06
Rugby	a	13 50	14 37									15 03	14 50	15 37									16 03		15 50	16 37
	d	13 51	14 37									15 03	14 51	15 37									16 03		15 51	16 37
Nuneaton	a											15 16											16 16			
Coventry	a	14 01	14 49					14 22	14 42				15 01	15 49					15 22	15 42					16 01	16 49
Birmingham International	✈ a	14 12	15 04					14 33	14 53				15 12	16 04					15 33	15 53					16 12	17 04
Birmingham New Street 12	a	14 27	15 16					14 45	15 08				15 27	16 16					15 45	16 08					16 27	17 16
Sandwell & Dudley	a							14 57											15 57							
Wolverhampton 7	a							15 11											16 11							

		VT	LM	SN	LM	VT	VT	LM	LM	LM	VT	LM	LM	SN	LM	VT	VT	VT	LM	LM	LM	LM	VT	VT	LM	SN
		1◇	1	1	1	1◇	1◇	1	1	1◇	1◇	1◇	1	1	1	1◇	1◇	1◇	1	1	1	1	1◇	1◇	1	1
		☕				☕	☕				⊠					⊠	⊠	⊠					⊠	⊠		
London Euston 15	⊖ d	15 20	15 13		15 04	15 23	15 43	15 24	15 34	15 46	16 03	15 54	16 13		16 04	16 23	16 33	16 43	16 24	16 34	16 48	16 54	17 03	17 10	17 13	
East Croydon	d			14 10										15 10												16 10
Clapham Junction 10	d			14 38										15 38												16 38
Imperial Wharf §	d																									
West Brompton	⊖ d			14 47										15 47												16 47
Kensington (Olympia)	⊖ d			14 50										15 50												16 50
Shepherd's Bush	d			14 53										15 53												16 53
Wembley Central	d			15s07										16s08												17s08
Harrow & Wealdstone	⊖ d			15 12	15 16				15 46					16 13	16 17					16 46						17 13
Bushey	d				15 21				15 51						16 22					16 51						
Watford Junction	a			15 19	15 24			15 40	15 54	16 00		16 10		16 20	16 25				16 41	16 54		17 10				17 20
	d			15 19	15 25	15u37		15 41	15 55	16 01		16 11		16 20	16 26	16u37			16 42	16 55		17 11				17 21
Kings Langley	d				15 29				15 59						16 30					16 59						
Apsley	d				15 33				16 03						16 34					17 03						
Hemel Hempstead	a			15 27	15 36			15 48	16 06			16 18		16 28	16 37				16 49	17 06		17 18				17 28
	d			15 27	15 36			15 48	16 06			16 18		16 28	16 37				16 49	17 06		17 18				17 28
Berkhamsted	d			15 31	15 40			15 53	16 10			16 23		16 32	16 41				16 54	17 10		17 23				17 33
Tring	d			15 38	15a47			16 00	16a17					16 39	16a48				17 01	17a19		17a32				
Cheddington	d							16 05											17 06							
Leighton Buzzard	d		15 42	15 48				16 10				16 36	16 42	16 48					17 11		17 20				17 42	17 47
Bletchley	d		15 50	15 55				16 17				16 43	16 50	16 56					17 18							17 54
Milton Keynes Central 10	a	15 50	15 54	16 01			16 13	16 23		16 24		16 49	16 54	17 00					17 25		17 30				17 52	17 59
	d		15 55				16 13			16 25		16 49	16 54					17u13			17 31			17u40	17 52	
Wolverton	d		15 59									16 53	16 58								17 35				17 56	
Northampton	a		16 13							16 40		17 06	17 13								17 49				18 11	
Rugby	a									17 03	16 50	17 37					17 20						17 50			
	d									17 03	16 51	17 37											17 51			
Nuneaton	a									17 16														18 11		
Coventry	a					16 22	16 42				17 01	17 49				17 22		17 42					18 01			
Birmingham International	✈ a					16 33	16 53				17 12	18 04				17 33		17 53					18 12			
Birmingham New Street 12	a					16 45	17 08				17 27	18 16				17 45		18 08					18 27			
Sandwell & Dudley	a					16 57										17 57										
Wolverhampton 7	a					17 11										18 11										

For general notes see front of timetable
For details of catering facilities see
Directory of Train Operators

§ It is unknown , at the time of going to press, when this station will open. For further details contact National rail Enquiries 08457-484950 or see local publicity

London → Watford Junction, Milton Keynes, Northampton and West Midlands

Network Diagram - See first page of Table 59

	LM	LM	VT	VT	VT	LM	LM	LM	LM	VT	VT	LM	LM	SN	LM	LM	VT	VT	VT	LM	LM	LM	VT	LM	VT
	1	1	1 ◇	1 ◇	1 ◇	1	1	1	1	1 ◇	1 ◇	1 ◇	1	1	1	1	1 ◇	1 ◇	1 ◇	1 ◇	1	1	1 ◇	1 ◇	1 ◇
																				A					
			⊠	⊠	⊠					⊠	⊠						⊠	⊠	⊠				☕		☕
London Euston 15 ⊖ d	17 04	17 09	17 23	17 33	17 43	17 24	17 46	17 34	17 40	18 03	18 10	17 54	18 13		18 04	18 09	18 23	18 33	18 43	18 24	18 34	18 40	19 03	18 49	19 20
East Croydon d														17 10											
Clapham Junction 10 d														17 38											
Imperial Wharf § d																									
West Brompton ⊖ d														17 47											
Kensington (Olympia) ⊖ d														17 50											
Shepherd's Bush d														17 53											
Wembley Central d														18s08											
Harrow & Wealdstone ⊖ d	17 18					17 36			17 52					18 13	18 18					18 37	18 46				
Bushey d		17 25							17 57							18 25						18 56			
Watford Junction a	17 25	17 30				17 43		17 52	18 00			18 10		18 20	18 25	18 30				18 44	18 53	18 59			
d	17 26	17 31	17u37			17 43		17 53	18 01			18 11		18 20	18 25	18 30	18u37			18 44	18 53	18 59			
Kings Langley d		17 35						17 57								18 35						19 04			
Apsley d		17 39						18 01								18 38						19 07			
Hemel Hempstead a		17 42				17 51		18 04				18 18		18 28		18 41				18 52		19 10			
d		17 42				17 51		18 04				18 18		18 28		18 41				18 52		19 10			
Berkhamsted d		17 46				17 55			18 11			18 23		18 32		18 46					19 05	19 15			
Tring d	17 43	17a55						18 13	18a21						18 43	18a55					19 12	19a24			
Cheddington d	17 48							18 18							18 48						19 18				
Leighton Buzzard d	17 54						18 20	18 25					18 42	18 47	18 53						19 27			19 22	
Bletchley d	18 01					18 14		18 32				18 41		18 54	19 00					19 13	19a34			19 29	
Milton Keynes Central 10 a	18 08					18 20	18 30	18 39				18 46	18 52	18 59	19 07					19 18				19 34	19 50
d					18u13	18 20	18 31				18u40	18 47	18 52						19u13	19 19				19 34	
Wolverton d							18 35					18 50	18 56							19 22				19 38	
Northampton a						18 36	18 49					19 07	19 11							19 36				19 53	
Rugby a				18 21		19 03				18 50		19 37						19 21		20 03			19 50	20 16	
d										18 51		19 37								20 03			19 51	20 16	
Nuneaton a											19 12									20 16					
Coventry a			18 22		18 42					19 01		19 49					19 22		19 42				20 01	20 28	
Birmingham International ✈ a			18 33		18 53					19 12		20 04					19 33		19 53				20 12	20 45	
Birmingham New Street 12 a			18 45		19 08					19 27		20 16					19 45		20 08				20 27	21 01	
Sandwell & Dudley a			18 57														19 58								
Wolverhampton 7 a			19 11														20 12								

	LM	LM	SN	LM	VT	VT	VT	LM	LM	LM	VT	LM	VT	LM	SN	LM	VT	VT	LM	LM	LM	VT	VT	VT	LM
	1	1	1	1	1 ◇	1 ◇	1 ◇	1	1	1	1 ◇	1 ◇	1 ◇	1	1	1	1 ◇	1 ◇	1	1	◇	1 ◇	1 ◇	1 ◇	1
					☕	☕	☕				☕		☕				☕	☕				☕	☕	☕	
London Euston 15 ⊖ d	19 13	18 54		19 04	19 07	19 23	19 43	19 24	19 34	19 46	20 03	19 54	20 07	20 13		20 04	20 23	20 43	20 24	20 34	20 46	21 00	21 03	21 07	20 54
East Croydon d			18 08												19 07										
Clapham Junction 10 d			18 38												19 38										
Imperial Wharf § d																									
West Brompton ⊖ d			18 47												19 47										
Kensington (Olympia) ⊖ d			18 50												19 50										
Shepherd's Bush d			18 53												19 53										
Wembley Central d			19s08												20s07										
Harrow & Wealdstone ⊖ d		19 06	19 13	19 18					19 46						20 12	20 16				20 46					
Bushey d				19 23					19 51							20 21				20 51					
Watford Junction a		19 13	19 20	19 26				19 40	19 54			20 10			20 19	20 24			20 40	20 54					21 10
d		19 13	19 21	19 26		19u37		19 41	19 55			20 11			20 19	20 25	20u37		20 41	20 55					21 11
Kings Langley d				19 31					19 59							20 29				20 59					
Apsley d				19 34					20 03							20 33				21 03					
Hemel Hempstead a		19 21	19 28	19 37				19 48	20 06			20 18			20 27	20 36			20 48	21 06					21 18
d		19 21	19 28	19 37				19 48	20 06			20 18			20 27	20 36			20 48	21 06					21 18
Berkhamsted d		19 25	19 33	19 42				19 53	20 10			20 23			20 31	20 40			20 53	21 10					21 23
Tring d		19 32	19 40	19a49				20 00	20a17						20 38	20a47			21 00	21a17					
Cheddington d								20 05											21 05						
Leighton Buzzard d	19 42	19 47	19 52					20 10		20 20		20 36		20 42	20 47				21 10		21 20				21 36
Bletchley d	19 50	19 56	20 01					20 17				20 43		20 50	20 55				21 17						21 43
Milton Keynes Central 10 a	19 54	20 02	20 06				20 13	20 23		20 30		20 49		20 54	21 01			21 13	21 23		21 30	21 30	21 33	21 37	21 49
d	19 55						20 13			20 31		20 49		20 55				21 13			21 31		21 34	21 38	21 49
Wolverton d	19 59									20 35		20 53		20 59							21 35				21 53
Northampton a	20 13									20 49		21 06		21 13							21 49				22 06
Rugby a											20 50	21 37									22 16		21 55		
d											20 51	21 37									22 16		21 56		
Nuneaton a					20 02								21 02											22 06	
Coventry a						20 22	20 42				21 01	21 49					21 22	21 42			22 29		22 06		
Birmingham International ✈ a						20 33	20 53				21 12	22 04					21 33	21 53			22 45		22 17		
Birmingham New Street 12 a						20 45	21 06				21 25	22 16					21 46	22 06			23 03		22 29		
Sandwell & Dudley a						20 58	21 23										21 58	22 23					22 40		
Wolverhampton 7 a						21 12	21 38				21 55						22 12	22 38					22 55		

For general notes see front of timetable
For details of catering facilities see Directory of Train Operators

§ It is unknown , at the time of going to press, when this station will open. For further details contact National rail Enquiries 08457-484950 or see local publicity

A To Crewe (Table 67)

London → Watford Junction, Milton Keynes, Northampton and West Midlands

Network Diagram - See first page of Table 59

		LM	SN	LM	VT	LM	LM	VT	LM	VT	LM	LM	SN	LM	LM	LM	VT	LM	LM	SN	LM	VT FX	VT FO	LM
		1 ◇	1	1	1 ◇	1	1	1 ◇	1	1 ◇	1	1	1	1	1	1	1 ◇	1	1	1	1	1 ◇	1 ◇	1
					☕			☕		☕							☕					⊠	☕	
London Euston [15] ⊖	d	21 13		21 04	21 10	21 24	21 34	21 43	21 46	22 00		21 54		22 04	22 24	22 34	22 43		22 54		23 24	23 43	23 43	23 34
East Croydon	d																							
Clapham Junction [10]	d		20 38										21 38							22 38				
Imperial Wharf §	d																							
West Brompton ⊖	d		20 47										21 47							22 47				
Kensington (Olympia) ⊖	d		20 50										21 50							22 50				
Shepherd's Bush	d		20 53										21 53							22 53				
Wembley Central	d		21s07																					
Harrow & Wealdstone ⊖	d		21 12	21 16			21 46						22 16	22 20		22 46				23 16				23 46
Bushey	d			21 21			21 51							22 25		22 51								23 51
Watford Junction	a		21 19	21 24		21 40	21 54					22 10	22 23	22 28	22 40	22 54			23 11	23 23	23 40			23 54
	d		21 19	21 25	21u25	21 41	21 55	21u58				22 11		22 29	22 41	22 55	22u57		23 12		23 41			23 55
Kings Langley	d			21 29			21 59							22 33		22 59								23 59
Apsley	d			21 33			22 03							22 37		23 03								00 03
Hemel Hempstead	a		21 27	21 36		21 48	22 06					22 18		22 40	22 48	23 06			23 19		23 48			00 06
	d		21 27	21 36		21 48	22 06				←	22 18		22 40	22 48	23 06		←	23 19		23 48			00 06
Berkhamsted	d		21 31	21 40		21 53	22 10				22 10	22 23		22 44	22 53	23 10		23 10	23 24		23 53			00 11
Tring	d		21 38	21 48			→				22 17	22 30		22 49		→		23 15	23 31					00 16
Cheddington	d			21 53							22 22							23 20						00 21
Leighton Buzzard	d	21 45	21 50	21 58		22 06			22 23		22 27	22 41		22 57	23 06			23 27	23 39		00 06			00 28
Bletchley	d	21 53	21 58	22a05		22 15					22 35	22 48		23a06	23 18			23 35	23 46		00 13			00 35
Milton Keynes Central [10]	a	21 57	22 04			22 21		22 23	22 36	22 37	22 40	22 57			23 23		23 23	23 43	23 55		00 22	00 26	00 26	00 44
	d	21 58						22 24	22 36	22 39		22 57			23 24		23 24		23 55		00 22	00 26	00 26	
Wolverton	d	22 02							22 40			23 01			23 27				23 59		00 26			
Northampton	a	22 15							22 59			23 16			23 42				00 13		00 40			
Rugby	a	22 37			22 02					23 18							00s05					01s00	01s05	
	d	22 37								23 19														
Nuneaton	a									23 29														
Coventry	a	22 49						23 11									00s17					01s13	01s18	
Birmingham International ✈	a	23 04						23 22									00s28					01s23	01s29	
Birmingham New Street [12]	a	23 16						23 35									00s40					01s35	01s41	
Sandwell & Dudley	a							23 46																
Wolverhampton [7] ⛴	a							23 59									01 10					02 05	02 17	

Saturdays

		LM	VT	LM	LM	LM	LM	LM	SN	LM	SN	VT		VT	SN	LM	SN	VT	VT	VT	SN	VT	LM	VT		VT
		1	1 ◇	1	1	1	1	1	1	1	1	1 ◇		1 ◇	1	1 ◇	1	1 ◇	1 ◇	1 ◇	1	1 ◇	1	1 ◇		1 ◇
								A								A										
			☕									☕		☕				☕	☕	☕		☕		☕		☕
London Euston [15] ⊖	d	23p24	23p43	23p34	00 04	00 34	01 34			05 34		06 05		06 23		06 24		06 55	07 03	07 20		07 35	07 04	07 23		07 43
East Croydon ⛴	d																				06 10					
Clapham Junction [10]	d								05 08		05 38						06 08				06 38					
Imperial Wharf §	d																									
West Brompton ⊖	d								05 15		05 45						06 18				06 47					
Kensington (Olympia) ⊖	d								05 19		05 49						06 22				06 50					
Shepherd's Bush	d								05 22		05 52						06 25				06 53					
Wembley Central	d					00 45	01 45				06s07										07s07					
Harrow & Wealdstone ⊖	d			23p46	00 16	00 50	01 50		05 40	05 46	06 12						06 41				07 12		07 16			
Bushey	d			23p51		00 55																				
Watford Junction	a	23p40		23p54	00 23	00 58	01 56		05 47	05 53	06 19					06 40	06 50				07 19		07 23			
	d	23p41		23p55	00 23	00 58	01 57			05 53	06 19	06u20		06u37		06 41					07 19		07 23	07u37		
Kings Langley	d			23p59		01 03				05 58													07 28			
Apsley	d			00 03		01 06				06 01													07 31			
Hemel Hempstead	a	23p48		00 06	00 31	01 09	02 04			06 04	06 27					06 48					07 27		07 34			
	d	23p48		00 06	00 31	01 09	02 04			06 04	06 27					06 48					07 27		07 34			
Berkhamsted	d	23p53		00 11	00 35	01 14	02 09			06 09	06 31				←	06 53					07 32		07 39			
Tring	d			00 16	00 40	01 21	02 16			06 14	06 37				06 37	07 00					07 39		07 46			
Cheddington	d			00 21		01 26				06 19	→					07 05							07 51			
Leighton Buzzard	d	00 06		00 28	00 50	01 31	02 24			06 25					06 47	07 10					07 48		07 56			
Bletchley	d	00 13		00 35	00 58	01 38	02 31	05 17		06 34					06 55	07 17					07 55		08 03			
Milton Keynes Central [10]	a	00 22	00 26	00 44	01 06	01 45	02 37	05 21		06 39		06 39			07 00	07 23		07 25		07 50	08 00	08 05	08 09			08 13
	d	00 22	00 26		01 07	01 45		05 21		06 40		06 41				07 23							08 09			08 13
Wolverton	d	00 26			01 10	01 49		05 25		06 43						07 27							08 13			
Northampton	a	00 40			01 25	02 05		05 37		06 57						07 40							08 29			
Rugby	a		01s05					06 00				07 01				08 04			07 50							
	d							06 00								08 04			07 51							
Nuneaton	a							06 16								08 16										
Coventry	a		01s18											07 22					08 01					08 22		08 42
Birmingham International ✈	a		01s29											07 33					08 12					08 33		08 53
Birmingham New Street [12]	a		01s41											07 45					08 27					08 45		09 08
Sandwell & Dudley	a													07 57										08 57		
Wolverhampton [7] ⛴	a		02 17											08 11										09 11		

For general notes see front of timetable
For details of catering facilities see Directory of Train Operators

§ It is unknown , at the time of going to press, when this station will open. For further details contact National rail Enquiries 08457-484950 or see local publicity

A To Crewe (Table 67)

London → Watford Junction, Milton Keynes, Northampton and West Midlands

Network Diagram - See first page of Table 59

	LM 1	LM 1	LM 1◇	LM 1	VT 1◇ ☕	VT 1◇ ☕	SN 1	LM 1	VT 1◇ ☕	VT 1◇ ☕	LM 1◇			LM 1	LM 1	VT 1◇ A ☕	LM 1	VT 1◇ ☕	VT 1◇ ☕	LM 1	SN 1	LM 1	VT 1◇ ☕	VT 1◇ ☕	LM 1
London Euston 15 ⊖ d	07 24	07 34	07 46	07 54	08 03	08 20		08 04	08 23	08 43	08 46			08 24	08 34	08 50	08 54	09 03	09 20	09 13		09 04	09 23	09 43	09 24
East Croydon d							07 10														08 10				
Clapham Junction 10 d							07 38														08 38				
Imperial Wharf § d																									
West Brompton ⊖ d							07 47														08 47				
Kensington (Olympia) ⊖ d							07 50														08 50				
Shepherd's Bush d							07 53														08 53				
Wembley Central d							08s07														09s07				
Harrow & Wealdstone ⊖ d		07 46					08 12	08 16							08 46						09 12	09 16			
Bushey d								08 21							08 51							09 21			
Watford Junction a	07 40	07 53	08 00	08 10			08 19	08 24						08 40	08 54		09 10				09 19	09 24			09 40
d	07 41	07 53	08 01	08 11			08 19	08 25	08u37					08 41	08 55	09u05	09 11				09 19	09 25	09u37		09 41
Kings Langley d		07 58						08 29							08 59							09 29			
Apsley d		08 01						08 33							09 03							09 33			
Hemel Hempstead a	07 48	08 04		08 18			08 27	08 36						08 48	09 06		09 18				09 27	09 36			09 48
d	07 48	08 04		08 18			08 27	08 36						08 48	09 06		09 18				09 27	09 36			09 48
Berkhamsted d	07 53	08 09		08 23			08 31	08 40						08 53	09 10		09 23				09 33	09 40			09 53
Tring d	08 00	08a16					08 37	08a47						09 00	09a17						09 38	09a47			10 00
Cheddington d	08 05													09 05											10 05
Leighton Buzzard d	08 10			08 36			08 47							09 10			09 36			09 42	09 47				10 10
Bletchley d	08 18			08 43			08 55							09 17			09 43			09 50	09 55				10 17
Milton Keynes Central 10 a	08 23		08 24	08 49		08 50	09 00			09 13	09 21			09 23		09 24	09 49		09 50	09 54	10 00			10 13	10 23
d			08 25	08 49						09 13	09 23						09 49			09 54				10 13	
Wolverton d				08 53													09 53			09 58					
Northampton a			08 41	09 09							09 39						10 09			10 13					
Rugby a			09 03		08 50						10 03	10 16						09 51							
d			09 03		08 51						10 03	10 16						09 52							
Nuneaton a			09 16								10 16														
Coventry a					09 01				09 22	09 42		10 28						10 02					10 22	10 42	
Birmingham International ✈ a					09 12				09 33	09 53		10 45						10 13					10 33	10 53	
Birmingham New Street 12 a					09 27				09 45	10 08		11 01						10 27					10 45	11 08	
Sandwell & Dudley a									09 57														10 57		
Wolverhampton 7 a									10 11														11 11		

	LM 1		LM 1◇		LM 1	VT 1◇ ☕	VT 1◇ ☕	LM 1	SN 1	LM 1	VT 1◇ ☕	VT 1◇ ☕	LM 1		LM 1	LM 1◇		LM 1	VT 1◇ ☕	VT 1◇ ☕	LM 1	SN 1	LM 1	VT 1◇ ☕	VT 1◇ ☕
London Euston 15 ⊖ d	09 34		09 46		09 54	10 03	10 20	10 13		10 04	10 23	10 43	10 24		10 34	10 46		10 54	11 03	11 20	11 13		11 04	11 23	11 43
East Croydon d									09 10													10 10			
Clapham Junction 10 d									09 38													10 38			
Imperial Wharf § d																									
West Brompton ⊖ d									09 47													10 47			
Kensington (Olympia) ⊖ d									09 50													10 50			
Shepherd's Bush d									09 53													10 53			
Wembley Central d									10s07													11s08			
Harrow & Wealdstone ⊖ d	09 46								10 12	10 16					10 46							11 13	11 16		
Bushey d	09 51									10 21					10 51								11 21		
Watford Junction a	09 54		10 00		10 10				10 19	10 24			10 40		10 54	11 00		11 10				11 20	11 24		
d	09 55		10 01		10 11				10 19	10 25	10u37		10 41		10 55	11 01		11 11				11 20	11 25	11u37	
Kings Langley d	09 59									10 29					10 59								11 29		
Apsley d	10 03									10 33					11 03								11 33		
Hemel Hempstead a	10 06				10 18				10 27	10 36			10 48		11 06			11 18				11 28	11 36		
d	10 06				10 18				10 27	10 36			10 48		11 06			11 18				11 28	11 36		
Berkhamsted d	10 10				10 23				10 31	10 40			10 53		11 10			11 23				11 32	11 40		
Tring d	10a17								10 37	10a47			11 00		11a17							11 37	11a47		
Cheddington d													11 05												
Leighton Buzzard d					10 36			10 42	10 47				11 10					11 36			11 42	11 47			
Bletchley d					10 43			10 50	10 55				11 17					11 43			11 50	11 55			
Milton Keynes Central 10 a			10 23		10 49		10 50	10 54	11 00			11 13	11 23			11 24		11 49		11 50	11 54	12 00			12 13
d			10 24		10 49			10 54				11 13				11 25		11 49			11 54				12 13
Wolverton d					10 53			10 58										11 53			11 58				
Northampton a			10 40		11 09			11 13								11 41		12 09			12 13				
Rugby a			11 03	11 16		10 50										12 03	12 16		11 50						
d			11 03	11 16		10 51										12 03	12 16		11 51						
Nuneaton a			11 16													12 16									
Coventry a				11 28		11 01					11 22	11 42					12 28		12 01					12 22	12 42
Birmingham International ✈ a				11 45		11 12					11 33	11 53					12 45		12 12					12 33	12 53
Birmingham New Street 12 a				12 01		11 27					11 45	12 08					13 01		12 27					12 45	13 08
Sandwell & Dudley a											11 57													12 57	
Wolverhampton 7 a											12 11													13 11	

For general notes see front of timetable
For details of catering facilities see Directory of Train Operators

§ It is unknown , at the time of going to press, when this station will open. For further details contact National rail Enquiries 08457-484950 or see local publicity

A To Holyhead (Table 81)

London → Watford Junction, Milton Keynes, Northampton and West Midlands

Network Diagram - See first page of Table 59

	LM 1	LM 1		LM 1◇		LM 1	VT 1◇ ⊡	VT 1◇ ⊡	LM 1	SN 1	LM 1	VT 1◇ ⊡	VT 1◇ ⊡	LM 1		LM 1	LM 1◇		LM 1	VT 1◇ ⊡	VT 1◇ ⊡	LM 1	SN 1	LM 1	VT 1◇ ⊡
London Euston 15 ⊖ d	11 24	11 34		11 46		11 54	12 03	12 20	12 13		12 04	12 23	12 43	12 24		12 34	12 46		12 54	13 03	13 20	13 13		13 04	13 23
East Croydon d										11 10													12 10		
Clapham Junction 10 d										11 38													12 38		
Imperial Wharf § d																									
West Brompton ⊖ d										11 47													12 47		
Kensington (Olympia) ⊖ d										11 50													12 50		
Shepherd's Bush d										11 53													12 53		
Wembley Central d										12s07													13s07		
Harrow & Wealdstone ⊖ d		11 46								12 12	12 16					12 46							13 12	13 16	
Bushey d		11 51									12 21					12 51								13 21	
Watford Junction a	11 40	11 54		12 00		12 10				12 19	12 24			12 40		12 54	13 00		13 10				13 19	13 24	
d	11 41	11 55		12 01		12 11				12 19	12 25	12u37		12 41		12 55	13 01		13 11				13 19	13 25	13u37
Kings Langley d		11 59									12 29					12 59								13 29	
Apsley d		12 03									12 33					13 03								13 33	
Hemel Hempstead a	11 48	12 06				12 18				12 27	12 36			12 48		13 06			13 18				13 27	13 36	
d	11 48	12 06				12 18				12 27	12 36			12 48		13 06			13 18				13 27	13 36	
Berkhamsted d	11 53	12 10				12 23				12 31	12 40			12 53		13 10			13 23				13 31	13 40	
Tring d	12 00	12a17								12 37	12a47			13 00		13a17							13 37	13a47	
Cheddington d	12 05													13 05											
Leighton Buzzard d	12 10					12 36			12 42	12 47				13 10					13 36			13 42	13 47		
Bletchley d	12 17					12 43			12 50	12 55				13 17					13 43			13 50	13 55		
Milton Keynes Central 10 a	12 23			12 24		12 49		12 50	12 54	13 00			13 13	13 23			13 24		13 49		13 50	13 54	14 00		
d				12 25		12 49			12 54				13 13				13 25		13 49			13 54			
Wolverton d						12 53			12 58										13 53			13 58			
Northampton a				12 41		13 09			13 13								13 41		14 09			14 13			
Rugby a				13 03	13 16		12 50										14 03	14 16		13 50					
d				13 03	13 16		12 51										14 03	14 16		13 51					
Nuneaton a				13 16													14 16								
Coventry a					13 28		13 01					13 22	13 42					14 28		14 01					14 22
Birmingham International ✈ a					13 45		13 12					13 33	13 53					14 45		14 12					14 33
Birmingham New Street 12 a					14 01		13 27					13 45	14 08					15 01		14 27					14 45
Sandwell & Dudley a												13 57													14 57
Wolverhampton 7 a												14 11													15 11

	VT 1◇ ⊡	LM 1	LM 1		LM 1◇		LM 1	VT 1◇ ⊡	VT 1◇ ⊡	LM 1	SN 1	LM 1	VT 1◇ ⊡	VT 1◇ ⊡	LM 1		LM 1	LM 1◇		LM 1	VT 1◇ ⊡	VT 1◇ ⊡	LM 1	SN 1	LM 1
London Euston 15 ⊖ d	13 43	13 24	13 34		13 46		13 54	14 03	14 20	14 13		14 04	14 23	14 43	14 24		14 34	14 46		14 54	15 03	15 20	15 13		15 04
East Croydon d											13 10													14 10	
Clapham Junction 10 d											13 38													14 38	
Imperial Wharf § d																									
West Brompton ⊖ d											13 47													14 47	
Kensington (Olympia) ⊖ d											13 50													14 50	
Shepherd's Bush d											13 53													14 53	
Wembley Central d											14s08													15s07	
Harrow & Wealdstone ⊖ d			13 46								14 13	14 16					14 46							15 12	15 16
Bushey d			13 51									14 21					14 51								15 21
Watford Junction a		13 40	13 54		14 00		14 10				14 20	14 24			14 40		14 54	15 00		15 10				15 19	15 24
d		13 41	13 55		14 01		14 11				14 21	14 25	14u37		14 41		14 55	15 01		15 11				15 19	15 25
Kings Langley d			13 59									14 29					14 59								15 29
Apsley d			14 03									14 33					15 03								15 33
Hemel Hempstead a		13 48	14 06				14 18				14 28	14 36			14 48		15 06			15 18				15 27	15 36
d		13 48	14 06				14 18				14 28	14 36			14 48		15 06			15 18				15 27	15 36
Berkhamsted d		13 53	14 10				14 23				14 33	14 40			14 53		15 10			15 23				15 31	15 40
Tring d		14 00	14a17								14 38	14a47			15 00		15a17							15 37	15a47
Cheddington d		14 05													15 05										
Leighton Buzzard d		14 10					14 36			14 42	14 47				15 10					15 36			15 42	15 47	
Bletchley d		14 17					14 43			14 50	14 55				15 17					15 43			15 50	15 55	
Milton Keynes Central 10 a	14 13	14 23			14 24		14 49		14 50	14 54	15 00			15 13	15 23			15 24		15 49		15 50	15 54	16 00	
d	14 13				14 25		14 49			14 54				15 13				15 25		15 49			15 54		
Wolverton d							14 53			14 58										15 53			15 58		
Northampton a					14 41		15 09			15 13								15 41		16 09			16 13		
Rugby a					15 03	15 16		14 50										16 03	16 16		15 50				
d					15 03	15 16		14 51										16 03	16 16		15 51				
Nuneaton a					15 16													16 16							
Coventry a	14 42					15 28		15 01					15 22	15 42					16 28		16 01				
Birmingham International ✈ a	14 53					15 45		15 12					15 33	15 53					16 45		16 12				
Birmingham New Street 12 a	15 08					16 01		15 27					15 45	16 08					17 01		16 27				
Sandwell & Dudley a													15 57												
Wolverhampton 7 a													16 11												

For general notes see front of timetable
For details of catering facilities see Directory of Train Operators

§ It is unknown , at the time of going to press, when this station will open. For further details contact National rail Enquiries 08457-484950 or see local publicity

London → Watford Junction, Milton Keynes, Northampton and West Midlands

Network Diagram - See first page of Table 59

	VT	VT	LM	LM	LM		LM	VT	VT	LM	SN	LM	VT	VT	LM	LM	LM		LM	VT	VT	VT	LM
	1 ◇ ☕	1 ◇ ☕	1	1	1 ◇		1	1 ◇ ☕	1 ◇ ☕	1	1	1	1 ◇ ☕	1 ◇ ☕	1	1	1 ◇		1	1 ◇ ☕	1 ◇ ☕	1 ◇ ☕	1
London Euston 15 ⊖ d	15 23	15 43	15 24	15 34	15 46		15 54	16 03	16 20	16 13		16 04	16 23	16 43	16 24	16 34	16 46		16 54	17 03	17 07	17 20	17 13
East Croydon d											15 10												
Clapham Junction 10 d											15 38												
Imperial Wharf § d																							
West Brompton ⊖ d											15 47												
Kensington (Olympia) ⊖ d											15 50												
Shepherd's Bush d											15 53												
Wembley Central d											16s07												
Harrow & Wealdstone ⊖ d				15 46							16 12	16 16				16 46							
Bushey d				15 51								16 21				16 51							
Watford Junction a			15 40	15 54	16 00		16 10				16 19	16 24			16 41	16 54	17 00		17 10				
d	15u37		15 41	15 55	16 01		16 11				16 19	16 25	16u37		16 42	16 55	17 01		17 11				
Kings Langley d				15 59								16 29				16 59							
Apsley d				16 03								16 33				17 03							
Hemel Hempstead a			15 48	16 06			16 18				16 27	16 36			16 49	17 06			17 18				
d			15 48	16 06			16 18				16 27	16 36			16 49	17 06			17 18				
Berkhamsted d			15 53	16 10			16 23				16 31	16 40			16 54	17 10			17 23				
Tring d			16 00	16a17							16 37	16a47			17 01	17a19							
Cheddington d			16 05												17 06								
Leighton Buzzard d			16 10				16 36			16 42	16 47				17 11				17 36				17 42
Bletchley d			16 17				16 43			16 50	16 55				17 18				17 43				17 50
Milton Keynes Central 10 a		16 13	16 23		16 24		16 49		16 50	16 54	17 00			17 13	17 25		17 24		17 49			17 50	17 54
d		16 13			16 25		16 49			16 54				17 13			17 25		17 49				17 54
Wolverton d							16 53			16 58									17 53				17 58
Northampton a					16 41		17 09			17 13							17 41		18 09				18 13
Rugby a					17 03	17 16		16 50									18 03	18 16		17 50			
d					17 03	17 16		16 51									18 03	18 16		17 51			
Nuneaton a					17 16												18 16				18 02		
Coventry a	16 22	16 42				17 28		17 01					17 22	17 42				18 28		18 01			
Birmingham International ✈ a	16 33	16 53				17 45		17 12					17 33	17 53				18 45		18 12			
Birmingham New Street 12 a	16 45	17 08				18 01		17 27					17 45	18 08				19 01		18 27			
Sandwell & Dudley a	16 57												17 57										
Wolverhampton 7 a	17 11												18 11										

	SN	LM	VT	VT	LM	LM	LM	LM	VT	VT	LM	SN	LM	VT	VT	LM	LM	LM	LM	VT	VT	VT	VT
	1	1	1 ◇ ☕	1 ◇ ☕	1	1	1	1	1 ◇ ☕	1 ◇ ☕	1	1	1	1 ◇ ☕	1 ◇ ☕	1	1	1 A	1 B	1 ◇ B ☕	1 ◇ A ☕	1 ◇ B ☕	1 ◇ B ☕
London Euston 15 ⊖ d		17 04	17 23	17 43	17 24	17 34	17 46	17 54	18 03	18 20	18 13		18 04	18 23	18 43	18 24	18 34	18 46	18 46	18 57	19 03	19 02	19 05
East Croydon d	16 10											17 10											
Clapham Junction 10 d	16 38											17 38											
Imperial Wharf § d																							
West Brompton ⊖ d	16 47											17 47											
Kensington (Olympia) ⊖ d	16 50											17 50											
Shepherd's Bush d	16 53											17 53											
Wembley Central d	17s07											18s07											
Harrow & Wealdstone ⊖ d	17 12	17 16				17 46						18 12	18 16				18 46						
Bushey d		17 21				17 51							18 21				18 51						
Watford Junction a	17 19	17 24			17 41	17 54	18 00	18 10				18 19	18 24			18 40	18 54	19 00	19 00				
d	17 19	17 25	17u37		17 42	17 55	18 01	18 11				18 19	18 25	18u37		18 41	18 55	19 01	19 01				
Kings Langley d		17 29				17 59							18 29				18 59						
Apsley d		17 33				18 03							18 33				19 03						
Hemel Hempstead a	17 27	17 36			17 49	18 06		18 18				18 27	18 36			18 48	19 06						
d	17 27	17 36			17 49	18 06		18 18				18 27	18 36			18 48	19 06						
Berkhamsted d	17 31	17 40			17 54	18 10		18 23				18 31	18 40			18 53	19 10						
Tring d	17 37	17a49			18 01	18a17						18 37	18a47			19 00	19a17						
Cheddington d					18 06											19 05							
Leighton Buzzard d	17 47				18 11			18 36			18 42	18 47				19 10							
Bletchley d	17 55				18 18			18 43			18 50	18 55				19 17							
Milton Keynes Central 10 a	18 00			18 13	18 24		18 24	18 49		18 50	18 54	19 00			19 13	19 23		19 24	19 26				19 35
d				18 13			18 25	18 49			18 54				19 13			19 25	19 27				
Wolverton d								18 53			18 58												
Northampton a							18 40	19 09			19 13							19 40	19 41				
Rugby a									18 50												19 50	19 52	
d									18 51												19 51	19 53	
Nuneaton a																				19 55			
Coventry a			18 22	18 42					19 01					19 22	19 42						20 01	20 03	
Birmingham International ✈ a			18 33	18 53					19 12					19 33	19 53						20 12	20 14	
Birmingham New Street 12 a			18 45	19 08					19 25					19 45	20 08						20 25	20 30	
Sandwell & Dudley a			18 57						19 53					19 58							20 53	20 53	
Wolverhampton 7 a			19 11						20 08					20 12							21 08	21 08	

For general notes see front of timetable
For details of catering facilities see Directory of Train Operators

§ It is unknown , at the time of going to press, when this station will open. For further details contact National rail Enquiries 08457-484950 or see local publicity

A From 12 September
B Until 5 September

London → Watford Junction, Milton Keynes, Northampton and West Midlands

Network Diagram - See first page of Table 59

	LM	SN	VT	LM	VT	VT		LM	VT	LM	VT	LM	LM	VT	VT	LM	LM	VT		LM	LM	SN	VT	VT	VT
	1	1	1 ◇	1	1 ◇	1 ◇		1	1 ◇	1	1 ◇	1	1	1 ◇	1 ◇	1	1	1 ◇		1	1	1	1 ◇	1 ◇	1 ◇
			A		B	B			A		B	A	B	A	B	A	B	A		A	B		A	B	A
			☕		☕	☕			☕		☕			☕	☕			☕					☕	☕	☕
London Euston 15 ⊖ d	18 54		19 08	19 04	19 07	19 20		19 13	19 30	19 14	19 23	19 30	19 30	19 41	19 43	19 44	19 46	19 47		19 50	19 50		20 07	20 11	20 14
East Croydon d		18 10																				19 07			
Clapham Junction 10 d		18 38																				19 38			
Imperial Wharf § d																									
West Brompton ⊖ d		18 47																				19 45			
Kensington (Olympia) ⊖ d		18 50																				19 48			
Shepherd's Bush d		18 52																				19 50			
Wembley Central d																									
Harrow & Wealdstone ⊖ d		19 12		19 16								19 42	19 42							20 02	20 03	20 08			
Bushey d				19 21								19 47	19 47												
Watford Junction a	19 10	19 21		19 24						19 30		19 50	19 50			20 01	20 02			20 09	20 10	20 15			
d	19 11		19u22	19 25						19 31	19u37	19 51	19 51			20 01	20 03			20 09	20 10		20u23		20u29
Kings Langley d				19 29								19 55	19 55							20 14	20 15				
Apsley d				19 33								19 59	19 59							20 17	20 18				
Hemel Hempstead a	19 18									19 38		20 02	20 02			20 09	20 10			20 20	20 21				
d	19 18									19 38		20 02	20 02			20 09	20 10			20 20	20 21				
Berkhamsted d	19 23			19 39								20 06	20 06			20 15	20 15			20 25	20 26				
Tring d				19a45						19 48		20 12	20 12			20 20	20 20			20 32	20 32				
Cheddington d										19 53						20 25	20 25								
Leighton Buzzard d	19 36							19 42		19 58		20 22	20 22			20 31	20 31			20 40	20 40				
Bletchley d	19 43							19 50		20 06		20a28	20a29			20 38	20 38			20 47	20a47				
Milton Keynes Central 10 a	19 48					19 50		19 54	20 05	20 11					20 20	20 44	20 44	20 49		20 52					
d	19 48							19 54	20 06						20 20	20 44	20 44	20 51							
Wolverton d	19 52							19 58								20 48	20 48								
Northampton a	20 06							20 13								21 03	21 03								
Rugby a														20 52										21 13	21 34
d																									
Nuneaton a					20 02													21 32							
Coventry a			20 22						20 49		20 22				20 49								21 35		
Birmingham International ✈ a			20 33						21 00		20 33				21 00								21 53		
Birmingham New Street 12 a			20 45						21 13		20 45				21 13								22 05		
Sandwell & Dudley a			20 58								20 58												22 24		
Wolverhampton 7 a			21 12						21 49		21 12				21 49								22 38		

	VT	VT	VT	VT	VT	VT	LM		LM	SN	VT	VT	LM	VT	LM	VT	LM	SN	LM		SN	LM	LM		
	1 ◇	1 ◇	1 ◇	1 ◇	1 ◇	1 ◇	1		1	1	1 ◇	1 ◇	1	1 ◇	1	1 ◇	1	1	1		1	1	1		
	B	B	A	A	C	D					B	B		A		B									
	☕	☕	☕	☕	☕	☕					☕	☕		☕		☕									
London Euston 15 ⊖ d	20 20	20 23	20 26	20 29	20 30	20 30	20 34		20 40		21 00	21 03	21 07	21 24	21 28	21 43	21 54		22 34			23 04	23 48		
East Croydon d																									
Clapham Junction 10 d										20 25								21 38			22 38				
Imperial Wharf § d																									
West Brompton ⊖ d										20 32								21 53			22 47				
Kensington (Olympia) ⊖ d										20 36								21 57			22 50				
Shepherd's Bush d										20 39								22 00			22 53				
Wembley Central d																									
Harrow & Wealdstone ⊖ d									20 52	20 59							22 06	22 20			23 12	23 16	00 01		
Bushey d																									
Watford Junction a							20 50		20 59	21 06			21 24		21 44		22 13	22 27	22 50		23 19	23 23	00 07		
d		20u38		20u45	20u45	20u46	20 51		20 59			21u18	21 24	21u40	21 45	21u58	22 13		22 51			23 23	00 07		
Kings Langley d									21 04								22 18					23 28	00 12		
Apsley d									21 07								22 21					23 31	00 15		
Hemel Hempstead a							20 58						21 32		21 52		22 24		22 58			23 34	00 18		
d							20 58						21 32		21 52		22 24		22 58			23 34	00 18		
Berkhamsted d							21 03						21 37		21 57		22 29		23 03			23 39	00 23		
Tring d									21 18								22 34					23 44	00 30		
Cheddington d							21 11										22 41					23 51	00 35		
Leighton Buzzard d							21 16						21 50		22 08		22 46		23 14			23 56	00 40		
Bletchley d							21 24		21 31				21 57		22 15		22 53		23 21			00 03	00 47		
Milton Keynes Central 10 a	21 03		21 20	21 26			21 32		21 40		21 43	21 50	22 06	22 17	22 24	22 29	23 02		23 30			00 12	00 56		
d	21 05			21 27			21 33					21 50	22 06	22 18	22 25	22 30	23 02		23 30			00 12	00 56		
Wolverton d							21 36						22 10		22 28		23 06		23 34			00 16	01 00		
Northampton a							21 59						22 29		22 47		23 20		23 52			00 30	01 18		
Rugby a				22 11	21 34	21 35						22 11		22 51		22 51									
d				22 11								22 11		22 52		22 52									
Nuneaton a	21 32																								
Coventry a		21 35		22 22								22 22		23 02		23 02									
Birmingham International ✈ a		21 53		22 33								22 33		23 13		23 13									
Birmingham New Street 12 a		22 05		22 45								22 45		23 25		23 25									
Sandwell & Dudley a		22 24		22 56								22 56		23 37		23 37									
Wolverhampton 7 a		22 38		23 10								23 10		23 51		23 51									

For general notes see front of timetable
For details of catering facilities see Directory of Train Operators

§ It is unknown, at the time of going to press, when this station will open. For further details contact National rail Enquiries 08457-484950 or see local publicity

A Until 5 September
B From 12 September
C 12 September to 31 October
D From 7 November

Sundays

London → Watford Junction, Milton Keynes Northampton and West Midlands

Network Diagram - See first page of Table 59

		LM 1	LM 1	LM 1	LM 🚌	LM 🚌	LM 🚌	LM 🚌	LM 1	LM 1	LM 1	VT 1◇ ☕	VT 1◇ A ☕		VT 1◇ B ☕	VT 1◇ ☕	LM 1	SN 1	VT 1◇ C ☕	VT 1◇ D ☕	VT 1◇ B ☕	VT 1◇ A ☕	VT 1◇ B ☕	LM 1	VT 1◇ A ☕	VT 1◇ B ☕
London Euston 15 ⊖	d	23p04	23p48	00 10					07 07	07 23	07 50	08 10	08 15		08 15	08 20	08 23		08 44	08 45	08 45	08 50	08 50	08 53	09 15	09 15
East Croydon 🚊	d																									
Clapham Junction 10	d																	08 15								
Imperial Wharf §	d																									
West Brompton ⊖	d																	08 22								
Kensington (Olympia) ⊖	d																	08 26								
Shepherd's Bush	d																	08 29								
Wembley Central	d																									
Harrow & Wealdstone ⊖	d	23p16	00 01	00 22					07 19	07 35	08 02						08 35	08 48						09 05		
Bushey	d																									
Watford Junction	a	23p23	00 07	00 29					07 26	07 42	08 09						08 42	08 58						09 12		
	d	23p23	00 07	00 29	01 10	01 15	02 50	02 55	07 26	07 42	08 09						08 42					09u05	09u05	09 12		
Kings Langley	d	23p28	00 12	00 34		01 31		03 11	07 31	07 47							08 47									
Apsley	d	23p31	00 15	00 37		01 42		03 22	07 34	07 50							08 50									
Hemel Hempstead	a	23p34	00 18	00 40		01 47		03 27	07 37	07 53	08 17						08 53							09 20		
	d	23p34	00 18	00 40		01 48		03 28	07 37	07 53	08 17						08 53							09 20		
Berkhamsted	d	23p39	00 23	00 45		01 59		03 39	07 42	07 58	08 21						08 58							09 24		
Tring	d	23p44	00 30	00 50		02 15		03 55	07a50	08 03														09 29		
Cheddington	d	23p51	00 35	00 55		02 36		04 16		08 12														09 34		
Leighton Buzzard	d	23p56	00 40	01 02	01 56	02 57	03 36	04 37		08 17	08 34						09 11							09 41		
Bletchley	d	00 03	00 47	01 09	02 22	03 23	04 02	05 03		08 23	08 41						09 18							09 49		
Milton Keynes Central 10	a	00 12	00 56	01 18	02 37	03 38	04 17	05 18		08 32	08 50	08 55				09 05	09 27		09 32	09 32	09 32	09 38	09 38	09 57		
	d	00 12	00 56	01 18						08 32	08 50						09 27		09 33	09 33	09 33	09 39	09 39	09 58		
Wolverton	d	00 16	01 00	01 22						08 36	08 54						09 31							10 01		
Northampton	a	00 30	01 18	01 40						08 50	09 08						09 45							10 16		
Rugby	a																		09 55	09 55	10 08	10 01	10 12			
	d																					10 02	10 14			
Nuneaton	a												09 29		09 41										10 34	10 44
Coventry	a																					10 23	10 23			
Birmingham International ✈	a																					10 34	10 34			
Birmingham New Street 12	a																					10 47	10 47			
Sandwell & Dudley	a																					10 59	10 59			
Wolverhampton 7 🚊	a																					11 13	11 13			

		VT 1◇ ☕	LM 1		SN 1	VT 1◇ B ☕	VT 1◇ A ☕	VT 1◇ B ☕	VT 1◇ A ☕	LM 1	VT 1◇ A ☕	VT 1◇ B ☕	VT 1◇ ☕	LM 1	SN 1	VT 1◇ D ☕		VT 1◇ E ☕	VT 1◇ B ☕	VT 1◇ A ☕	VT 1◇ B ☕	LM 1	VT 1◇ ☕	VT 1◇ ☕	LM 1	SN 1
London Euston 15 ⊖	d	09 20	09 23			09 45	09 45	09 50	09 50	09 53	10 15	10 15	10 20	10 23		10 45		10 45	10 45	10 50	10 50	10 53	11 15	11 20	11 23	
East Croydon 🚊	d																									
Clapham Junction 10	d				09 15										10 15											11 15
Imperial Wharf §	d																									
West Brompton ⊖	d				09 22										10 22											11 22
Kensington (Olympia) ⊖	d				09 26										10 26											11 26
Shepherd's Bush	d				09 29										10 29											11 29
Wembley Central	d																									
Harrow & Wealdstone ⊖	d		09 36		09 48					10 05				10 35	10 48							11 05			11 35	11 48
Bushey	d																									
Watford Junction	a		09 42		09 58					10 12				10 42	10 58							11 12			11 42	11 58
	d		09 43					10u03	10u03	10 12				10 42						11u05	11u05	11 12			11 42	
Kings Langley	d		09 47											10 47											11 47	
Apsley	d		09 51											10 50											11 50	
Hemel Hempstead	a		09 54							10 20				10 53								11 20			11 53	
	d		09 54							10 20				10 53								11 20			11 53	
Berkhamsted	d		09 58							10 24				10 58								11 24			11 58	
Tring	d									10 29												11 29				
Cheddington	d									10 34												11 34				
Leighton Buzzard	d		10 11							10 41				11 11								11 41			12 12	
Bletchley	d		10 19							10 49				11 18								11 49			12 19	
Milton Keynes Central 10	a	10 06	10 27			10 30	10 31	10 36	10 37	10 57			11 06	11 27		11 31		11 31	11 31	11 38	11 38	11 57	12 02	12 08	12 27	
	d		10 28			10 31	10 33	10 38	10 39	10 58				11 27		11 32		11 32	11 32	11 39	11 39	11 58			12 27	
Wolverton	d		10 31							11 01				11 31								12 01			12 31	
Northampton	a		10 46							11 16				11 45								12 16			12 45	
Rugby	a					11 05	10 55	11 11	11 01							11 54		11 55	12 06	12 01	12 12					
	d							11 12	11 02											12 02	12 14					
Nuneaton	a										11 33	11 44														
Coventry	a							11 22	11 22											12 23	12 23					
Birmingham International ✈	a							11 33	11 33											12 34	12 34					
Birmingham New Street 12	a							11 45	11 45											12 47	12 47					
Sandwell & Dudley	a							11 58	11 58											12 59	12 59					
Wolverhampton 7 🚊	a							12 15	12 17											13 13	13 13					

For general notes see front of timetable
For details of catering facilities see Directory of Train Operators

§ It is unknown , at the time of going to press, when this station will open. For further details contact National rail Enquiries 08457-484950 or see local publicity

A Until 12 July and from 13 September
B 19 July to 6 September
C From 8 November
D Until 12 July
E From 13 September

London → Watford Junction, Milton Keynes Northampton and West Midlands

Network Diagram - See first page of Table 59

	VT 1◇ ☕	VT 1◇ ☕	LM 1	VT 1◇ ☕	LM 1		SN 1	VT 1◇ ☕	LM 1	LM 1◇ A	LM 1◇ B	VT 1◇ ☕	VT 1◇ ☕	LM 1	VT 1◇ ☕	LM 1	SN 1	VT 1◇ ☕		LM 1	LM 1 B	LM 1 A	VT 1◇ ☕	VT 1◇ ☕	LM 1
London Euston 15 ⊖ d	11 45	12 15	11 53	12 18	12 14			12 38	12 34	12 50	12 50	12 58	13 15	12 54	13 18	13 14		13 38		13 34	13 50	13 50	13 58	14 15	13 54
East Croydon d																									
Clapham Junction 10 d							12 05										13 05								
Imperial Wharf § d																									
West Brompton ⊖ d							12 12										13 12								
Kensington (Olympia) ⊖ d							12 16										13 16								
Shepherd's Bush d							12 19										13 19								
Wembley Central d																									
Harrow & Wealdstone ⊖ d			12 05		12 26		12 36							13 06		13 26	13 36								14 06
Bushey d					12 31											13 31									
Watford Junction a			12 12		12 34		12 46		12 50	13 06	13 06			13 13		13 34	13 46			13 50	14 05	14 05			14 13
d	12u01		12 12	12u32	12 35				12 51	13 07	13 07			13 13	13u32	13 35				13 51	14 06	14 06			14 13
Kings Langley d					12 39											13 39									
Apsley d					12 43											13 43									
Hemel Hempstead a			12 20		12 46				12 58					13 21		13 46				13 58					14 21
d			12 20		12 46				12 58					13 21		13 46				13 58					14 21
Berkhamsted d			12 24		12 50				13 03					13 25		13 50				14 03					14 25
Tring d			12 29		12a57									13 30		13a57									14 30
Cheddington d			12 34											13 35											14 35
Leighton Buzzard d			12 41						13 16					13 42						14 16					14 42
Bletchley d			12 49						13 23					13 50						14 23					14 50
Milton Keynes Central 10 a	12 26	12 48	12 57					13 11	13 29	13 35	13 35		13 48	13 56				14 11		14 29	14 34	14 34		14 48	14 56
d	12 27		12 58					13 11	13 29	13 36	13 36							14 11		14 29	14 34	14 42			
Wolverton d			13 01						13 33											14 33					
Northampton a			13 16						13 46		13 51									14 46	14 51				
Rugby a	12 46									14 01	14 16	13 48									15 19	15 08	14 48		
d	12 47									14 16	14 16	13 49											14 49		
Nuneaton a										14 29	14 29														
Coventry a	12 56			13 20				13 40				14 00			14 20			14 40					15 00		
Birmingham International ✈ a	13 07			13 31				13 51				14 11			14 31			14 51					15 11		
Birmingham New Street 12 a	13 22			13 44				14 06				14 25			14 44			15 06					15 25		
Sandwell & Dudley a				13 56											14 56										
Wolverhampton 7 a				14 10											15 10										

	VT 1◇ ☕	LM 1	SN 1	VT 1◇ ☕	LM 1	LM 1◇ B	LM 1◇ A	VT 1◇ ☕		VT 1◇ ☕	LM 1	VT 1◇ ☕	LM 1	SN 1	VT 1◇ ☕	LM 1	LM 1 B	LM 1 A	VT 1◇ ☕	VT 1◇ ☕	LM 1		VT 1◇ ☕	LM 1	SN 1
London Euston 15 ⊖ d	14 18	14 14		14 38	14 34	14 50	14 50	14 58		15 15	14 54	15 18	15 14		15 38	15 34	15 50	15 50	15 58	16 15	15 54		16 18	16 14	
East Croydon d																									
Clapham Junction 10 d			14 05											15 05											16 05
Imperial Wharf § d																									
West Brompton ⊖ d			14 12											15 12											16 12
Kensington (Olympia) ⊖ d			14 16											15 16											16 16
Shepherd's Bush d			14 19											15 19											16 19
Wembley Central d																									
Harrow & Wealdstone ⊖ d		14 26	14 36								15 06		15 26	15 36							16 06			16 26	16 36
Bushey d		14 31											15 31											16 31	
Watford Junction a		14 34	14 46		14 50	15 06	15 06				15 13		15 34	15 46		15 50	16 05	16 05			16 13			16 34	16 46
d	14u32	14 35			14 51	15 06	15 06				15 13	15u32	15 35			15 51	16 06	16 06			16 13		16u32	16 35	
Kings Langley d		14 39											15 39											16 39	
Apsley d		14 43											15 43											16 43	
Hemel Hempstead a		14 46			14 58						15 21		15 46			15 58					16 21			16 46	
d		14 46			14 58						15 21		15 46			15 58					16 21			16 46	
Berkhamsted d		14 50			15 03						15 25		15 50			16 03					16 25			16 50	
Tring d		14a57									15 30		15a57								16 30			16a57	
Cheddington d											15 35										16 35				
Leighton Buzzard d					15 16						15 42					16 16					16 42				
Bletchley d					15 23						15 50					16 23					16 50				
Milton Keynes Central 10 a				15 11	15 29	15 35	15 35			15 48	15 56				16 11	16 29	16 34	16 34		16 48	16 56				
d				15 11	15 29	15 36	15 42								16 11	16 29	16 34	16 42							
Wolverton d					15 33											16 33									
Northampton a					15 46	15 51										16 46	16 51								
Rugby a						16 16	16 07	15 48									17 19	17 08	16 48						
d						16 16	16 16	15 49											16 49						
Nuneaton a						16 29	16 29																		
Coventry a	15 20			15 40				16 00				16 20			16 40				17 00				17 20		
Birmingham International ✈ a	15 31			15 51				16 11				16 31			16 51				17 11				17 31		
Birmingham New Street 12 a	15 44			16 06				16 25				16 44			17 06				17 25				17 44		
Sandwell & Dudley a	15 56											16 56											17 56		
Wolverhampton 7 a	16 10											17 10											18 10		

For general notes see front of timetable
For details of catering facilities see Directory of Train Operators

§ It is unknown , at the time of going to press, when this station will open. For further details contact National rail Enquiries 08457-484950 or see local publicity

A Until 12 July
B From 19 July

Table 66

Sundays

London → Watford Junction, Milton Keynes Northampton and West Midlands

Network Diagram - See first page of Table 59

		VT	LM	LM	VT	LM	VT	VT	LM	VT	LM	SN		VT	LM	LM	LM	VT	VT	LM	VT	LM	SN	VT	LM	LM
		1 ◇	1	1 ◇	1 ◇	1 ◇	1 ◇	1 ◇	1	1 ◇	1	1		1 ◇	1	1	1	1 ◇	1 ◇	1	1 ◇	1	1	1 ◇	1	1 ◇
				A		B										A	B									A
		☕			☕		☕	☕		☕				☕				☕	☕		☕			☕		
London Euston 15 ⊖	d	16 38	16 34	16 50	17 05	16 50	16 58	17 15	16 54	17 18	17 14			17 38	17 34	17 50	17 50	17 58	18 15	17 54	18 18	18 14		18 38	18 34	18 50
East Croydon	d																									
Clapham Junction 10	d											17 05											18 05			
Imperial Wharf §	d																									
West Brompton ⊖	d											17 12											18 12			
Kensington (Olympia) ⊖	d											17 16											18 16			
Shepherd's Bush	d											17 19											18 19			
Wembley Central	d																									
Harrow & Wealdstone ⊖	d								17 06		17 26	17 36								18 06		18 26	18 36			
Bushey	d										17 31											18 31				
Watford Junction	a		16 50	17 06		17 06			17 13		17 34	17 46			17 50	18 05	18 05			18 13		18 34	18 46		18 50	19 06
	d		16 51	17 06		17 06			17 13	17u32	17 35				17 51	18 06	18 06			18 13	18u32	18 35			18 51	19 06
Kings Langley	d										17 39											18 39				
Apsley	d										17 43											18 43				
Hemel Hempstead	a		16 58						17 21		17 46				17 58					18 21		18 46			18 58	
	d		16 58						17 21		17 46				17 58					18 21		18 46			18 58	
Berkhamsted	d		17 03						17 25		17 50				18 03					18 25		18 50			19 03	
Tring	d								17 30		17a57									18 30		18a57				
Cheddington	d								17 35											18 35						
Leighton Buzzard	d		17 16						17 42						18 16					18 42					19 16	
Bletchley	d		17 23						17 50						18 23					18 50					19 23	
Milton Keynes Central 10	a	17 11	17 29	17 35		17 35		17 48	17 56					18 11	18 29	18 34	18 34		18 48	18 56				19 11	19 28	19 35
	d	17 11	17 29	17 36	17u38	17 42								18 11	18 29	18 34	18 42							19 11	19 28	19 36
Wolverton	d		17 33												18 33										19 33	
Northampton	a		17 46	17 51											18 46	18 51									19 46	19 51
Rugby	a			18 16		18 07	17 48									19 19	19 08	18 48								20 16
	d			18 16		18 16	17 49											18 49								20 16
Nuneaton	a			18 29	18 09	18 29																				20 29
Coventry	a	17 40					18 00			18 20				18 40				19 00			19 20			19 40		
Birmingham International ✈	a	17 51					18 11			18 31				18 51				19 11			19 31			19 51		
Birmingham New Street 12	a	18 06					18 25			18 44				19 06				19 23			19 44			20 06		
Sandwell & Dudley	a									18 56											19 56					
Wolverhampton 7	a									19 10								19 58			20 10					

		LM		VT	VT	VT	LM	VT	LM	SN	VT	LM	LM	LM	VT		VT	VT	VT	LM	VT	LM	SN	VT	LM	VT
		1 ◇		1 ◇	1 ◇	1 ◇	1	1 ◇	1	1	1 ◇	1	1	1	1 ◇		1 ◇	1 ◇	1 ◇	1	1 ◇	1	1	1 ◇	1	1 ◇
		B											A	B												
				☕	☕	☕		☕			☕				☕		☕	☕	☕		☕			☕		☕
London Euston 15 ⊖	d	18 50		18 58	19 02	19 15	18 54	19 18	19 14		19 38	19 34	19 50	19 50	19 58		20 02	20 05	20 15	19 54	20 18	20 14		20 38	20 34	20 50
East Croydon	d																									
Clapham Junction 10	d									19 05													20 05			
Imperial Wharf §	d																									
West Brompton ⊖	d									19 12													20 12			
Kensington (Olympia) ⊖	d									19 16													20 16			
Shepherd's Bush	d									19 19													20 19			
Wembley Central	d																									
Harrow & Wealdstone ⊖	d						19 06		19 26	19 36										20 06		20 26	20 36			
Bushey	d								19 31													20 31				
Watford Junction	a	19 06					19 13		19 34	19 46		19 50	20 05	20 05						20 13		20 34	20 46		20 50	
	d	19 06					19 13	19u32	19 35			19 51	20 06	20 06						20 13	20u32	20 35			20 51	
Kings Langley	d								19 39													20 39				
Apsley	d								19 43													20 43				
Hemel Hempstead	a						19 21		19 46			19 58								20 21		20 46			20 58	
	d						19 21		19 46			19 58								20 21		20 46			20 58	
Berkhamsted	d						19 25		19 50			20 03								20 25		20 50			21 03	
Tring	d						19 30		19a57											20 30		20a57				
Cheddington	d						19 35													20 35						
Leighton Buzzard	d						19 42					20 16								20 42					21 16	
Bletchley	d						19 50					20 23								20 50					21 23	
Milton Keynes Central 10	a	19 35				19 48	19 56				20 11	20 29	20 34	20 34				20 38	20 48	20 56				21 16	21 29	21 38
	d	19 42									20 11	20 29	20 34	20 41										21 16	21 29	21 39
Wolverton	d											20 33													21 33	
Northampton	a											20 46	20 51												21 46	
Rugby	a	20 07		19 48									21 19	21 06	20 48											21 59
	d	20 16		19 49											20 49											
Nuneaton	a	20 29			20 00												21 00									
Coventry	a			20 00				20 20			20 40				21 00						21 20			21 46		
Birmingham International ✈	a			20 11				20 31			20 51				21 11						21 31			21 57		
Birmingham New Street 12	a			20 23				20 44			21 04				21 24						21 44			22 09		
Sandwell & Dudley	a			20 46				20 56			21 15				21 36						21 56			22 24		
Wolverhampton 7	a			20 57				21 10			21 31				21 51						22 10			22 39		

For general notes see front of timetable
For details of catering facilities see
Directory of Train Operators

§ It is unknown , at the time of going to press, when this station will open. For further details contact National rail Enquiries 08457-484950 or see local publicity

A From 19 July

B Until 12 July

London → Watford Junction, Milton Keynes Northampton and West Midlands

Network Diagram - See first page of Table 59

		VT	LM	VT	VT	VT	LM	SN	SN	VT	VT	VT	VT	LM	VT	VT	LM	SN	LM	VT	VT	LM
		1 ◇	1	1 ◇	1 ◇	1 ◇	1	1	1	1 ◇	1 ◇	1 ◇	1 ◇	1	1 ◇	1 ◇	1	1	1	1 ◇	1 ◇	1
				A	B			B	A	A	B	A	B		A	B				C	D	
		☕		☕	☕	☕				☕	☕	☕	☕		☕	☕				☕	☕	
London Euston 15 ⊖	d	20 54	21 02	21 20	21 20	21 24	21 28			21 50	21 50	21 54	21 54	21 58	22 24	22 24	22 28		22 58	23 24	23 24	23 34
East Croydon	d																					
Clapham Junction 10	d							21 15	21 15									22 15				
Imperial Wharf §	d																					
West Brompton ⊖	d							21 22	21 22									22 22				
Kensington (Olympia) ⊖	d							21 26	21 26									22 26				
Shepherd's Bush	d							21 29	21 29									22 29				
Wembley Central	d																					
Harrow & Wealdstone ⊖	d						21 40	21 48	21 49					22 10			22 40	22 48	23 10			23 46
Bushey	d																					
Watford Junction	a		21 22				21 47	21 57	21 58					22 17			22 47	22 58	23 17			23 53
	d	21u11	21 22				21 47					22u08	22u08	22 17	22u38	22u38	22 47		23 17	23u39	23u39	23 53
Kings Langley	d						21 52										22 52		23 22			23 58
Apsley	d						21 55										22 55		23 25			00 01
Hemel Hempstead	a		21 30				21 58							22 25			22 58		23 28			00 04
	d		21 30				21 58							22 25			22 58		23 28			00 04
Berkhamsted	d		21 34				22 03							22 29			23 03		23 33			00 09
Tring	d													22 34					23 38			00 14
Cheddington	d													22 39					23 43			00 19
Leighton Buzzard	d		21 47				22 16							22 46			23 16		23 50			00 26
Bletchley	d		21 55				22 23							22 54			23 23		23 57			00 33
Milton Keynes Central 10	a	21 44	22 03			22 12	22 32			22 36	22 36	22 42	22 42	23 02	23 10	23 10	23 32		00 06	00 10	00 10	00 42
	d	21 45	22 04				22 32			22 38	22 38	22 44	22 44	23 03	23 11	23 11	23 32		00 06	00 11	00 11	00 42
Wolverton	d		22 07				22 36							23 06			23 36		00 10			00 46
Northampton	a		22 22				22 50							23 21			23 50		00 24			01 00
Rugby	a	22 05								23 02	23 18	23 09	23 22		23 39	23 46				00s47	00s47	
	d	22 06								23 06	23 19	23 20	23 24		23 43	23 48						
Nuneaton	a			22 46	22 53					23 21	23 29											
Coventry	a	22 15										23 33	23 33		23 54	23 57				00s57	00s57	
Birmingham International ✈	a	22 26										23 51	23 51		00 08	00 08				01s08	01s08	
Birmingham New Street 12	a	22 39										00 04	00 04		00 22	00 22				01s21	01s21	
Sandwell & Dudley	a	22 52																				
Wolverhampton 7	a	23 06										00 28	00 28		00 55	00 55				01 53	01 59	

For general notes see front of timetable
For details of catering facilities see Directory of Train Operators

§ It is unknown , at the time of going to press, when this station will open. For further details contact National rail Enquiries 08457-484950 or see local publicity

A Until 12 July
B From 19 July
C Until 12 July and from 13 September
D 19 July to 6 September

West Midlands, Northampton, Milton Keynes and Watford Junction → London

Network Diagram - See first page of Table 59

Miles	Miles	Miles			LM MX 1 ◇	LM MO 1	LM TO 1	LM MTX 1	LM 1	LM 1	LM 1	SN 1	LM 1	LM 1	LM 1	LM 1	LM 1		VT 1 ◇ ⊠	LM 1	SN 1	LM 1	LM	VT 1 ◇ ⊠	VT 1 ◇ ⊠
0	—	—	Wolverhampton 7	d															05 00					05 20	
7½	—	—	Sandwell & Dudley	d																				05 30	
12¾	—	—	**Birmingham New Street 12**	d	21p33														05 29					05 50	
21¼	—	—	Birmingham International	d	21p45														05 39					06 00	
32	—	—	Coventry	d	22p01														05 50					06 11	
—	—	—	Nuneaton	d																					
43½	0	—	**Rugby**	a	22p12														06 01						
—	—	—		d	22p13											05 20			06 03						06 20
62¼	—	—	**Northampton**	d	22p52	22p55	23p30	23p46		04 15	04 48		05 05			05 45							06 17		06 42
75¼	30	—	Wolverton	d	23p04	23p11	23p42	23p58		04 27	05 00		05 17			05 57							06 29		
—	—	—	**Milton Keynes Central 10**	a	23p09	23p14	23p47	00 03		04 30	05 03		05 20			06 01			06 22				06 33	06 38	
78¼	32¾	—		d	23p10	23p15	23p48	00 04	03 30	04 31	05 04		05 21		05 54	06 02	06 20		06 23				06 34	06 38	
81¼	—	—	Bletchley	d	23p15	23p20	23p55	00 09	03 35	04 36	05 09		05 26	05 38	05 59	06 07	06 25						06 39		
87¾	—	—	Leighton Buzzard	d	23p21	23p26	00 01	00 15	03 41	04 42	05 15		05 32	05 44	06 05	06 14	06 32					←	06 46		
92	—	—	Cheddington	d	23p26	23p31	00 06	00 20			05 20			05 50			06 38 →					06 38			
96¼	—	—	Tring	d	23p35	23p40	00 13	00 29	03 53	04 54	05 29			05 56						06 24		06 43			
100	—	—	Berkhamsted	d	23p40	23p45	00 18	00 34	03 58	04 59	05 34		05 47	06 01	06 17					06 28		06 47			
—	—	—	Hemel Hempstead	a	23p44	23p49	00 22	00 38	04 02	05 03	05 38		05 52	06 05	06 22					06 33		06 52			
103½	—	—		d	23p44	23p49	00 22	00 38	04 02	05 03	05 38		05 52	06 05	06 22					06 33		06 52			
105	—	—	Apsley	d	23p47						05 41			06 08						06 36					
107	—	—	Kings Langley	d	23p51						05 45			06 12						06 39					
—	—	—	**Watford Junction**	a	23p55	23p56	00 29	00 45	04 09	05 10	05 49		05 59	06 16	06 29	06 32			06s43	06 44		06 59	07 04		
110½	65	—		d	23p56	23p57	00 30	00 46	04 10	05 11	05 50	05 54	05 59	06 17	06 29	06 33				06 44	06 53	06 59	07 05		
112	—	—	Bushey	d	23p59															06 47					
116½	71	—	Harrow & Wealdstone	⊖ d	00 04	00 03	00 36	00 52	04 16	05 17	05 56	06 00		06 23						06 52	06 59	07 05			
119¾	—	0	Wembley Central	d			00 40	00 56	04 20	05 21		06 05									07 04				
—	—	4¼	Shepherd's Bush	a								06 19									07 19				
—	—	5½	Kensington (Olympia)	⊖ a								06 21									07 21				
—	—	7½	West Brompton	⊖ a								06 24									07 24				
—	—	8	Imperial Wharf §	a																					
—	—	9	Clapham Junction 10	a								06 32									07 32				
—	—	16¾	East Croydon	a																					
128	82½	—	**London Euston 15**	⊖ a	00 18	00 17	00 52	01 08	04 34	05 35	06 10		06 19	06 37	06 49	06 50			07 02	07 06		07 20	07 22	07 15	07 30

		LM 1	LM 1	VT 1 ◇ ⊠	LM 1	VT 1 ◇ ⊠	VT 1 ◇ ⊠	SN 1	VT 1 ◇ ⊠		VT 1 ◇ ⊠	LM 1	VT 1 ◇ ⊠	LM 1	LM 1 ◇	LM 1	VT 1 ◇ ⊠	VT 1 ◇ ⊠	LM 1	VT 1 ◇ ⊠	VT 1 ◇ ⊠	LM 1	LM 1		LM 1
Wolverhampton 7	d					05 45	06 04										06 27			06 45					
Sandwell & Dudley	d					05 56	06 15										06 37			06 56					
Birmingham New Street 12	d					06 10	06 30								05 53		06 50			07 10					
Birmingham International	d					06 20	06 39								06 05		07 00			07 20					
Coventry	d					06 31	06 51								06 21		07 11			07 31					
Nuneaton	d			06 18									07 07								07 34				
Rugby	a			06 30											06 32										
	d			06 32	06 08				06 53		07 08				06 33			07 29					07 04		
Northampton	d				06 37										07 03	07 13							07 32		07 38
Wolverton	d				06 49										07 15	07 25									07 50
Milton Keynes Central 10	a			06 51	06 53	06 59			07 12						07 18	07 29	07s40						07 46		07 54
	d		06 50	06 52	06 55	07 00		07 01	07 14					07 14	07 19	07 30							07 47		07 54
Bletchley	d		06 55		07 00			07 05				07 12		07 19					07 37				07 52		
Leighton Buzzard	d		07 01		07 07			07 13						07 25	07 31	07 39			07 44				07 58		08 06
Cheddington	d		07 07											07 31									08 04		
Tring	d	06 56	07 13					07 22				07 26		07 36								07 59	08 10		
Berkhamsted	d	07 00	07 18					07 26				07 30		07 41								08 03	08 15		
Hemel Hempstead	a	07 05	07 22					07 31				07 35							08 01			08 08			
	d	07 05	07 22					07 31				07 35							08 02			08 08			
Apsley	d	07 08										07 38										08 11			
Kings Langley	d	07 11										07 41										08 14			
Watford Junction	a	07 16	07 29				07s36	07 38				07 46		07 51					08 09			08 19	08 25		
	d	07 16	07 30					07 38				07 46		07 51					08 09			08 19	08 25		
Bushey	d	07 19										07 49										08 22			
Harrow & Wealdstone	⊖ d	07 24	07 36					07 45						07 57					08 15				08 31		
Wembley Central	d							07u49																	
Shepherd's Bush	a							08 04																	
Kensington (Olympia)	⊖ a							08 06																	
West Brompton	⊖ a							08 09																	
Imperial Wharf §	a																								
Clapham Junction 10	a							08 17																	
East Croydon	a																								
London Euston 15	⊖ a	07 38	07 52	07 28	07 43	07 36	07 55		07 50		08 00	08 07	08 11	08 13	08 06	08 16	08 17	08 22	08 29	08 34	08 36	08 40	08 45		08 39

For general notes see front of timetable
For details of catering facilities see
Directory of Train Operators

§ It is unknown , at the time of going to press, when this station will open. For further details contact National rail Enquiries 08457-484950 or see local publicity

West Midlands, Northampton, Milton Keynes and Watford Junction → London

Network Diagram - See first page of Table 59

	VT 1◇ ⊠	VT 1◇ ⊠	VT 1◇ ⊠	LM 1	LM 1	SN 1	LM 1◇	VT 1◇ ⊠	LM 1	LM 1	VT 1◇ ⊠	LM 1	LM 1		LM 1◇	VT 1◇ ⊠	VT 1◇ ⊠	LM 1	SN 1	VT 1◇ ⊠	LM 1◇	VT 1◇ ⊠	LM 1	VT 1◇ ⊠
Wolverhampton 7 d	07 04										07 45													
Sandwell & Dudley d	07 15										07 56													
Birmingham New Street 12 d	07 30						06 53	07 50			08 10									08 30	07 53	08 50		
Birmingham International d		07 41					07 05	08 00			08 20									08 39	08 05	09 00		
Coventry d		07 52					07 21	08 11			08 31									08 51	08 21	09 11		
Nuneaton d															08 02		08 46							
Rugby a							07 33	08 21							08 18						08 32	09 21		
d			07 55				07 33	08 23							08 18	08 46					08 33	09 23		
Northampton d							08 05			08 25					08 47						09 05		09 25	
Wolverton d							08 17			08 37											09 17		09 37	
Milton Keynes Central 10 a							08 21			08 41					09 00					09 18	09 20		09 41	
d				08 00		08 13	08 21			08 41			08 47		09 00				09 13	09 19	09 21		09 41	09 47
Bletchley d				08 05		08 17	08 27		08 32	08 46			08 52						09 17		09 26		09 46	
Leighton Buzzard d				08 12		08 24	08 34		08 38	08 53			08 58						09 24		09 32		09 53	
Cheddington d													09 04											
Tring d					08 26	08 34			08 48			08 56	09 10					09 26	09 34					
Berkhamsted d					08 30	08 39			08 53			09 00	09 15					09 30	09 39		09 45			
Hemel Hempstead a				08 28	08 35	08 43			08 57			09 05	09 19					09 35	09 43		09 50			
d				08 28	08 35	08 43			08 57			09 05	09 19					09 35	09 43		09 50			
Apsley d					08 38							09 08						09 38						
Kings Langley d					08 41							09 11						09 41						
Watford Junction a				08 35	08 46	08 51			09 04		09s15	09 16	09 26		09 27		09s31	09 46	09 51		09 57			
d				08 35	08 46	08 51			09 05			09 16	09 27		09 28			09 46	09 51		09 57			
Bushey d					08 49							09 19						09 49						
Harrow & Wealdstone ⊖ d				08 41		08 58			09 11			09 24						09 54	09 58					
Wembley Central d						09u05													10u05					
Shepherd's Bush a						09 22													10 23					
Kensington (Olympia) ⊖ a						09 25													10 25					
West Brompton ⊖ a						09 28													10 27					
Imperial Wharf § a																								
Clapham Junction 10 a						09 35													10 33					
East Croydon a						09 57													10 57					
London Euston 15 ⊖ a	08 42	08 49	08 49	08 55	09 08		09 11	09 14	09 26	09 27	09 34	09 38	09 46		09 44	09 38	09 52	10 08		09 54	10 20	10 14	10 27	10 23

	VT 1◇ ⊠	LM 1	LM 1	LM 1◇	LM 1		SN 1	VT 1◇ ⊠	LM 1◇	VT 1◇ ⊠	LM 1	VT 1◇ ⊠	VT 1◇ ⊠	LM 1	LM 1	LM 1◇	LM 1	SN 1	VT 1◇ ☕		LM 1◇	VT 1◇ ☕	LM 1	VT 1◇ ☕
Wolverhampton 7 d	08 45												09 45											
Sandwell & Dudley d	08 56												09 56											
Birmingham New Street 12 d	09 10							09 30	08 53	09 50			10 10						10 30		09 53	10 50		
Birmingham International d	09 20							09 39	09 05	10 00			10 20						10 39		10 05	11 00		
Coventry d	09 31							09 51	09 21	10 11			10 31						10 51		10 21	11 11		
Nuneaton d				09 03												10 02								
Rugby a				09 18					09 32	10 22						10 18					10 32	11 22		
d				09 20					09 33	10 24						10 19					10 33	11 24		
Northampton d				09 50					10 05		10 25					10 50					11 05		11 25	
Wolverton d									10 17		10 37										11 17		11 37	
Milton Keynes Central 10 a				10 05				10 18	10 20		10 41					11 04			11 18		11 20		11 41	
d			09 47	10 05			10 13	10 19	10 21		10 41	10 47			10 47	11 04		11 13	11 19		11 21		11 41	11 47
Bletchley d			09 52				10 17		10 26		10 46				10 52			11 17			11 26		11 46	
Leighton Buzzard d			09 58				10 24		10 32		10 53				10 58			11 24			11 32		11 53	
Cheddington d			10 04												11 04									
Tring d		09 56	10 10		10 26		10 34							10 56	11 10		11 26	11 34						
Berkhamsted d		10 00	10 15		10 30		10 39		10 45					11 00	11 15		11 30	11 39			11 45			
Hemel Hempstead a		10 05	10 19		10 35		10 43		10 50					11 05	11 19		11 35	11 43			11 50			
d		10 05	10 19		10 35		10 43		10 50					11 05	11 19		11 35	11 43			11 50			
Apsley d		10 08			10 38									11 08			11 38							
Kings Langley d		10 11			10 41									11 11			11 41							
Watford Junction a	10s15	10 16	10 26	10 30	10 46		10 51		10 57				11s15	11 16	11 26	11 29	11 46	11 51			11 57			
d		10 16	10 27	10 30	10 46		10 51		10 57					11 16	11 27	11 29	11 46	11 51			11 57			
Bushey d		10 19			10 49									11 19			11 49							
Harrow & Wealdstone ⊖ d		10 24			10 54		10 59							11 24			11 54	11 59						
Wembley Central d							11u04											12u04						
Shepherd's Bush a							11 18											12 19						
Kensington (Olympia) ⊖ a							11 20											12 21						
West Brompton ⊖ a							11 23											12 24						
Imperial Wharf § a																								
Clapham Junction 10 a							11 30											12 32						
East Croydon a							11 57											12 57						
London Euston 15 ⊖ a	10 34	10 38	10 46	10 49	11 08			10 54	11 18	11 14	11 27	11 23	11 34	11 38	11 46	11 49	12 08		11 54		12 18	12 14	12 27	12 23

For general notes see front of timetable
For details of catering facilities see Directory of Train Operators

§ It is unknown , at the time of going to press, when this station will open. For further details contact National rail Enquiries 08457-484950 or see local publicity

West Midlands, Northampton, Milton Keynes and Watford Junction → London

Network Diagram - See first page of Table 59

		VT 1◇ ☕	LM 1	LM 1	LM 1◇	LM 1	SN 1	VT 1◇ ☕	LM 1◇	VT 1◇ ☕	LM 1	VT 1◇ ☕		VT 1◇ ☕	LM 1	LM 1	LM 1◇	LM 1	SN 1	VT 1◇ ☕	LM 1◇	VT 1◇ ☕	LM 1	VT 1◇ ☕	VT 1◇ ☕
Wolverhampton 7 🚌	d	10 45												11 45											12 45
Sandwell & Dudley	d	10 56												11 56											12 56
Birmingham New Street 12	d	11 10						11 30	10 53	11 50				12 10						12 30	11 53	12 50			13 10
Birmingham International ✈	d	11 20						11 39	11 05	12 00				12 20						12 39	12 05	13 00			13 20
Coventry	d	11 31						11 51	11 21	12 11				12 31						12 51	12 21	13 11			13 31
Nuneaton	d				11 02												12 02								
Rugby	a				11 17				11 32	12 22							12 17				12 32	13 22			
	d				11 19				11 33	12 24							12 19				12 33	13 24			
Northampton	d				11 50				12 05		12 25						12 50				13 05		13 25		
Wolverton	d								12 17		12 37										13 17		13 37		
Milton Keynes Central 10	a				12 04			12 18	12 20		12 41						13 04			13 18	13 20		13 41		
	d			11 47	12 04		12 13	12 19	12 21		12 41	12 46				12 47	13 04		13 13	13 19	13 21		13 41	13 47	
Bletchley	d			11 52			12 17		12 26		12 46					12 52			13 17		13 26		13 46		
Leighton Buzzard	d			11 58			12 24		12 32		12 53					12 58			13 24		13 32		13 53		
Cheddington	d			12 04												13 04									
Tring	d		11 56	12 10		12 26	12 34								12 56	13 10		13 26	13 34						
Berkhamsted	d		12 00	12 15		12 30	12 39		12 45						13 00	13 15		13 30	13 39		13 45				
Hemel Hempstead	a		12 05	12 19		12 35	12 43		12 50						13 05	13 19		13 35	13 43		13 50				
	d		12 05	12 19		12 35	12 43		12 50						13 05	13 19		13 35	13 43		13 50				
Apsley	d		12 08			12 38									13 08			13 38							
Kings Langley	d		12 11			12 41									13 11			13 41							
Watford Junction	a	12s15	12 16	12 26	12 29	12 46	12 51		12 57					13s15	13 16	13 26	13 29	13 46	13 51		13 57				14s15
	d		12 16	12 27	12 29	12 46	12 51		12 57						13 16	13 27	13 29	13 46	13 51		13 57				
Bushey	d		12 19			12 49									13 19			13 49							
Harrow & Wealdstone ⊖	d		12 24			12 54	12 59								13 24			13 54	13 59						
Wembley Central	d						13u04												14u04						
Shepherd's Bush	a						13 19												14 19						
Kensington (Olympia) ⊖	a						13 21												14 21						
West Brompton ⊖	a						13 24												14 24						
Imperial Wharf §	a																								
Clapham Junction 10	a						13 32												14 32						
East Croydon 🚌	a						13 57												14 57						
London Euston 15 ⊖	a	12 34	12 38	12 46	12 49	13 08		12 54	13 18	13 14	13 27	13 23		13 34	13 38	13 46	13 49	14 08		13 54	14 18	14 14	14 27	14 24	14 35

		LM 1	LM 1	LM 1◇		LM 1	SN 1	VT 1◇ ☕	LM 1◇	VT 1◇ ☕	LM 1	VT 1◇ ☕	VT 1◇ ☕	LM 1	LM 1	LM 1◇	LM 1	SN 1		VT 1◇ ☕	LM 1◇	VT 1◇ ☕	LM 1	VT 1◇ ☕	VT 1◇ ☕
Wolverhampton 7 🚌	d												13 45												14 45
Sandwell & Dudley	d												13 56												14 56
Birmingham New Street 12	d							13 30	12 53	13 50			14 10							14 30	13 53	14 50			15 10
Birmingham International ✈	d							13 39	13 05	14 00			14 20							14 39	14 05	15 00			15 20
Coventry	d							13 51	13 21	14 11			14 31							14 51	14 21	15 11			15 31
Nuneaton	d			13 02												14 02									
Rugby	a			13 17					13 32	14 22						14 17					14 32	15 22			
	d			13 24					13 33	14 24						14 19					14 33	15 24			
Northampton	d			13 50					14 05		14 25					14 50					15 05		15 25		
Wolverton	d								14 17		14 37										15 17		15 37		
Milton Keynes Central 10	a			14 04				14 18	14 20		14 41					15 04				15 18	15 20		15 41		
	d		13 47	14 04			14 13	14 19	14 21		14 41	14 47			14 47	15 04		15 13		15 19	15 21		15 41	15 47	
Bletchley	d		13 52				14 17		14 26		14 46				14 52			15 17			15 26		15 46		
Leighton Buzzard	d		13 58				14 24		14 32		14 53				14 58			15 24			15 32		15 53		
Cheddington	d		14 04												15 05										
Tring	d	13 56	14 10			14 26	14 34							14 56	15 11		15 26	15 34							
Berkhamsted	d	14 00	14 15			14 30	14 39		14 45					15 00	15 15		15 30	15 39			15 45				
Hemel Hempstead	a	14 05	14 19			14 35	14 43		14 50					15 05	15 20		15 35	15 43			15 50				
	d	14 05	14 19			14 35	14 43		14 50					15 05	15 20		15 35	15 43			15 50				
Apsley	d	14 08				14 38								15 08			15 38								
Kings Langley	d	14 11				14 41								15 11			15 41								
Watford Junction	a	14 16	14 26	14 29		14 46	14 51		14 57				15s15	15 16	15 27	15 29	15 46	15 51			15 57				16s15
	d	14 16	14 27	14 29		14 46	14 51		14 57					15 16	15 27	15 29	15 46	15 51			15 57				
Bushey	d	14 19				14 49								15 19			15 49								
Harrow & Wealdstone ⊖	d	14 24				14 54	14 59							15 24			15 54	15 59							
Wembley Central	d						15u04											16u05							
Shepherd's Bush	a						15 23											16 19							
Kensington (Olympia) ⊖	a						15 25											16 21							
West Brompton ⊖	a						15 27											16 24							
Imperial Wharf §	a																								
Clapham Junction 10	a						15 33											16 32							
East Croydon 🚌	a						15 57											16 59							
London Euston 15 ⊖	a	14 38	14 46	14 49		15 08		14 54	15 18	15 14	15 27	15 23	15 35	15 38	15 46	15 49	16 08			15 54	16 18	16 14	16 27	16 23	16 34

For general notes see front of timetable
For details of catering facilities see
Directory of Train Operators

§ It is unknown , at the time of going to press, when this station will open. For further details contact National rail Enquiries 08457-484950 or see local publicity

West Midlands, Northampton, Milton Keynes and Watford Junction → London

Network Diagram - See first page of Table 59

Station		LM 1	LM 1	LM 1 ◇	LM 1	SN 1	VT 1 ◇ ☕	LM 1 ◇	VT 1 ◇ ☕	LM 1		VT 1 ◇ ☕	VT 1 ◇ ☕	LM 1	LM 1	LM 1 ◇	LM 1	SN 1	VT 1 ◇ ⊠	LM 1 ◇	VT 1 ◇ ⊠	LM 1	VT 1 ◇ ⊠	VT 1 ◇ ⊠	LM 1
Wolverhampton 7	d												15 45											16 45	
Sandwell & Dudley	d												15 56											16 56	
Birmingham New Street 12	d						15 30	14 53	15 50				16 10						16 30	15 53	16 50			17 10	
Birmingham International	d						15 39	15 05	16 00				16 20						16 39	16 05	17 00			17 20	
Coventry	d						15 51	15 21	16 11				16 31						16 51	16 21	17 11			17 31	
Nuneaton	d			15 02												16 02									
Rugby	a			15 17				15 32	16 22							16 17				16 32	17 22				
	d			15 19				15 33	16 24							16 19				16 33	17 24				
Northampton	d			15 50				16 05		16 25						16 50				17 05		17 25			
Wolverton	d							16 17		16 37										17 17		17 37			
Milton Keynes Central 10	a			16 04			16 18	16 20		16 41						17 04			17 18	17 20		17 41			
	d		15 47	16 04		16 13	16 19	16 21		16 41		16 47			16 47	17 04		17 13	17 19	17 21		17 41	17 47		
Bletchley	d		15 52			16 17		16 26		16 46					16 52			17 17		17 26		17 46			
Leighton Buzzard	d		15 58			16 24		16 32		16 53					16 58			17 24		17 32		17 53			
Cheddington	d		16 04												17 04										
Tring	d	15 56	16 10		16 26	16 34								16 56	17 10		17 26	17 34							17 58
Berkhamsted	d	16 00	16 15		16 30	16 39		16 45						17 00	17 15		17 30	17 39		17 45					18 02
Hemel Hempstead	a	16 05	16 19		16 35	16 43		16 50						17 05	17 19		17 35	17 43		17 50					18 07
	d	16 05	16 19		16 35	16 43		16 50						17 05	17 19		17 35	17 43		17 50					18 07
Apsley	d	16 08			16 38									17 08			17 38								18 10
Kings Langley	d	16 11			16 41									17 11			17 41								18 13
Watford Junction	a	16 16	16 26	16 29	16 46	16 51		16 57					17s15	17 16	17 26	17 29	17 46	17 51		17 57				18s15	18 18
	d	16 16	16 27	16 29	16 46	16 51		16 57						17 16	17 27	17 29	17 46	17 51		17 57					18 18
Bushey	d	16 19			16 49									17 19			17 49								18 21
Harrow & Wealdstone ⊖	d	16 24			16 54	16 59								17 24			17 54	17 59							18 26
Wembley Central	d					17u05												18u05							
Shepherd's Bush	a					17 19												18 19							
Kensington (Olympia) ⊖	a					17 21												18 21							
West Brompton ⊖	a					17 24												18 24							
Imperial Wharf §	a																								
Clapham Junction 10	a					17 32												18 32							
East Croydon	a					17 59												19 02							
London Euston 15 ⊖	a	16 38	16 46	16 48	17 08		16 54	17 18	17 14	17 27		17 23	17 34	17 38	17 46	17 49	18 08		17 54	18 18	18 14	18 27	18 23	18 34	18 40

Station		LM 1		LM 1 ◇	LM 1	SN 1	VT 1 ◇ ⊠	LM 1 ◇	VT 1 ◇ ⊠	VT 1 ◇ ⊠	LM 1	VT 1 ◇ ⊠	LM 1	LM 1	VT 1 ◇ ⊠	LM 1 ◇		LM 1	SN 1	VT 1 ◇ ⊠	LM 1 ◇	VT 1 ◇ ⊠	VT 1 ◇ ⊠	LM 1	VT 1 ◇ ⊠
Wolverhampton 7	d											17 45													
Sandwell & Dudley	d											17 56													
Birmingham New Street 12	d						17 30	16 53		17 50		18 10								18 30	17 53		18 50		
Birmingham International	d						17 39	17 05		18 00		18 20								18 39	18 05		19 00		
Coventry	d						17 51	17 21		18 11		18 31								18 51	18 21		19 11		
Nuneaton	d			17 02												18 02									
Rugby	a			17 17				17 32		18 22						18 17					18 32		19 22		
	d			17 19				17 33		18 24						18 19					18 33		19 24		
Northampton	d			17 50				18 05			18 25					18 50					19 05			19 25	
Wolverton	d							18 17			18 37										19 17			19 37	
Milton Keynes Central 10	a			18 04			18 18	18 20			18 41					19 04				19 18	19 20			19 41	
	d	17 47		18 04		18 13	18 19	18 21	18 24		18 41			18 47	18 48	19 04			19 13	19 19	19 21	19 32		19 41	19 47
Bletchley	d	17 52				18 17		18 26			18 46			18 52					19 17		19 26			19 46	
Leighton Buzzard	d	17 58				18 24		18 32			18 53			18 58					19 24		19 32			19 53	
Cheddington	d	18 04												19 05											
Tring	d	18 10			18 26	18 34							18 58	19 11				19 28	19 34						
Berkhamsted	d	18 15			18 30	18 39		18 45					19 02	19 15				19 32	19 39		19 45				
Hemel Hempstead	a	18 19			18 35	18 43		18 50					19 07	19 20				19 37	19 44		19 50				
	d	18 19			18 35	18 43		18 50					19 07	19 20				19 37	19 44		19 50				
Apsley	d				18 38								19 10					19 40							
Kings Langley	d				18 41								19 13					19 43							
Watford Junction	a	18 26		18 29	18 46	18 51		18 57				19s15	19 18	19 29		19 29		19 48	19 53		19 58				
	d	18 27		18 29	18 46	18 51		18 57					19 18	19 29		19 29		19 48	19 53		19 58				
Bushey	d				18 49								19 21					19 51							
Harrow & Wealdstone ⊖	d				18 54	18 59							19 26					19 56	20 01						
Wembley Central	d					19u05													20u06						
Shepherd's Bush	a					19 18													20 21						
Kensington (Olympia) ⊖	a					19 20													20 23						
West Brompton ⊖	a					19 23													20 25						
Imperial Wharf §	a																								
Clapham Junction 10	a					19 30													20 32						
East Croydon	a																								
London Euston 15 ⊖	a	18 46		18 49	19 08		18 54	19 18	18 59	19 14	19 27	19 35	19 40	19 46	19 23	19 49		20 10		19 54	20 20	20 08	20 14	20 27	20 23

For general notes see front of timetable
For details of catering facilities see Directory of Train Operators

§ It is unknown , at the time of going to press, when this station will open. For further details contact National rail Enquiries 08457-484950 or see local publicity

West Midlands, Northampton, Milton Keynes and Watford Junction → London

Network Diagram - See first page of Table 59

Station		VT	LM	LM	LM	LM	SN	VT		LM	VT	VT	LM	VT	LM	VT	LM	VT	LM	LM	VT	SN		LM	VT
		1 ◇	1	1	1 ◇	1	1	1 ◇		1 ◇	1 ◇	1 ◇	1	1 ◇	1	1 ◇	1	1 ◇	1	1	1 ◇	1		1 ◇	1 ◇
		⊠						☕			⊠	☕		⊠		☕		☕			☕				☕
Wolverhampton 7	d	18 45																19 45							
Sandwell & Dudley	d	18 56																19 56							
Birmingham New Street 12	d	19 10						19 30		18 53		19 50						20 10						19 53	
Birmingham International	d	19 20						19 39		19 05		20 00						20 20						20 05	
Coventry	d	19 31						19 51		19 21		20 11						20 31						20 21	
Nuneaton	d				19 02																21 03				
Rugby	a				19 18					19 32		20 21												20 32	
	d				19 21					19 33		20 23												20 33	
Northampton	d				19 50					20 05			20 25											21 05	
Wolverton	d									20 17			20 38											21 17	
Milton Keynes Central 10	a				20 04			20 18		20 20			20 41					20 58						21 20	
	d			19 47	20 04		20 13	20 19		20 21	20 34		20 42	20 46	20 47	20 49		20 59				21 13		21 21	21 36
Bletchley	d			19 52			20 17			20 26			20 47		20 52							21 17		21 26	
Leighton Buzzard	d			19 58			20 24			20 32			20 54		20 59				←			21 24		21 32	
Cheddington	d			20 04											21 06				21 06						
Tring	d		19 56	20 10		20 26	20 34								→		20 56		21 12	21 26		21 34			
Berkhamsted	d		20 00	20 15		20 30	20 39			20 45							21 00		21 17	21 30		21 39		21 45	
Hemel Hempstead	a		20 05	20 19		20 35	20 43			20 50							21 05		21 21	21 35		21 43		21 50	
	d		20 05	20 19		20 35	20 43			20 50							21 05		21 21	21 35		21 43		21 50	
Apsley	d		20 08			20 38											21 08			21 38					
Kings Langley	d		20 11			20 41											21 11			21 41					
Watford Junction	a	20s15	20 16	20 26	20 29	20 46	20 51			20 57							21 16	21s19	21 28	21 46	21s48	21 51		21 57	
	d		20 16	20 27	20 29	20 46	20 51			20 57							21 16		21 29	21 46		21 51		21 57	
Bushey	d		20 19			20 49											21 19			21 49					
Harrow & Wealdstone	⊖ d		20 24			20 54	20 59										21 24			21 54		21 59			
Wembley Central	d						21u04																		
Shepherd's Bush	a						21 23															22 23			
Kensington (Olympia)	⊖ a						21 25															22 25			
West Brompton	⊖ a						21 27															22 27			
Imperial Wharf §	a																								
Clapham Junction 10	a						21 34															22 34			
East Croydon	a																								
London Euston 15	⊖ a	20 34	20 38	20 47	20 49	21 08		20 54		21 18	21 10	21 14	21 29	21 24		21 25	21 38	21 38	21 48	22 08	22 09			22 20	22 12

Station		VT	LM	VT	VT	VT	SN	LM	LM	SN	LM	VT	LM	VT		VT	VT	SN	LM	LM MO	LM MX	VT FO	VT FX		
		1 ◇	1	1 ◇	1 ◇	1 ◇	1	1	1	1	1 ◇	1 ◇	1 ◇	1 ◇		1 ◇	1 ◇	1	1 ◇	1	1	1 ◇	1 ◇		
		☕		☕	☕	☕						☕		☕		☕	☕					☕	☕		
Wolverhampton 7	d					20 47											21 45					22 45	22 45		
Sandwell & Dudley	d					20 57											21 56					22 55	22 55		
Birmingham New Street 12	d	20 50				21 10					20 53						22 10		21 33			23 10	23 10		
Birmingham International	d	21 00				21 20					21 05						22 20		21 45			23 20	23 20		
Coventry	d	21 11				21 31					21 21						22 31		22 01			23 31	23 31		
Nuneaton	d															22 17									
Rugby	a	21 21									21 32					22 30	22 42		22 12			23 43	23 43		
	d	21 23		21 28							21 33					22 34	22 43		22 13			23 44	23 44		
Northampton	d		21 32								22 05								22 52	23 30	23 46				
Wolverton	d		21 44								22 18								23 04	23 42	23 58				
Milton Keynes Central 10	a		21 47	21 47		21 58					22 22					22 54	23s03		23 09	23 47	00 03	00s22	00s23		
	d		21 48	21 49	21 52	21 59			22 02	22 11	22 22	22 38		22 51		22 56			23 10	23 48	00 04				
Bletchley	d		21 53						22 09	22 15	22 27		←						23 15	23 55	00 09				
Leighton Buzzard	d		21 59					←	22 16	22 22	22 34		22 34						23 21	00 01	00 15				
Cheddington	d		22 05					22 05	22 22		→								23 26	00 06	00 20				
Tring	d		→					22 11	22 27	22 34									23 35	00 13	00 29				
Berkhamsted	d							22 16	22 32	22 39			22 49						23 40	00 18	00 34				
Hemel Hempstead	a							22 20	22 36	22 43			22 53						23 44	00 22	00 38				
	d							22 20	22 36	22 43			22 53						23 44	00 22	00 38				
Apsley	d								22 39										23 47						
Kings Langley	d								22 43										23 51						
Watford Junction	a				22s11	22s20		22 28	22 47	22 52		22s58	23 01	23s10		23s15	23s24		23 55	00 29	00 45	00s52	00s52		
	d						22 27	22 31	22 48	22 53			23 02					23 29	23 56	00 30	00 46				
Bushey	d								22 51										23 59						
Harrow & Wealdstone	⊖ d						22 33		22 56	23 00								23 35	00 04	00 36	00 52				
Wembley Central	d																			00 40	00 56				
Shepherd's Bush	a						22 49			23 21								23 53							
Kensington (Olympia)	⊖ a						22 51			23 23								23 56							
West Brompton	⊖ a						22 54			23 26								23 59							
Imperial Wharf §	a																								
Clapham Junction 10	a						23 01			23 33								00 07							
East Croydon	a																								
London Euston 15	⊖ a	22 33		22 46	22 51	22 58		22 51	23 11			23 38	23 25	23 50		23 53	00 03		00 18	00 52	01 08	01 13	01 13		

For general notes see front of timetable
For details of catering facilities see
Directory of Train Operators

§ It is unknown , at the time of going to press, when this station will open. For further details contact National rail Enquiries 08457-484950 or see local publicity

Table 66

Saturdays

West Midlands, Northampton, Milton Keynes and Watford Junction → London

Network Diagram - See first page of Table 59

		LM	LM	LM	LM	SN	LM	LM	VT	SN	LM	LM	LM	VT	LM		VT	VT	VT	LM	SN	VT	LM	VT	VT
		1◇	1	1	1	1	1	1	1◇	1	1	1	1	1◇	1		1◇	1◇	1◇	1	1	1◇	1	1◇	1◇
									☕					☕			☕	☕	☕			☕		☕	☕
Wolverhampton 7	d													05 45				06 06				06 27			
Sandwell & Dudley	d													05 56				06 17				06 37			
Birmingham New Street 12	d	21p33							05 50					06 10				06 30				06 50			
Birmingham International	d	21p45							06 00					06 20				06 40				07 00			
Coventry	d	22p01							06 10					06 31				06 51				07 11			
Nuneaton	d																		06 59						
Rugby	a	22p12							06 23													07 21			
	d	22p13							06 24								06 51					07 23			
Northampton	d	22p52	23p46				05 16				06 05												07 05		
Wolverton	d	23p04	23p58				05 28				06 17												07 17		
Milton Keynes Central 10	a	23p09	00 03				05 32				06 20			06 58			07 11						07 20		
	d	23p10	00 04	03 40	04 35		05 32				06 21		06 47	06 59			07 12				07 13		07 21	07 32	07 38
Bletchley	d	23p15	00 09	03 45	04 40		05 37	06 10			06 26	06 40	06 52							07 10	07 17		07 26		
Leighton Buzzard	d	23p21	00 15	03 51	04 46		05 44	06 16			06 32	06 46	06 58		←					07 16	07 24		07 32		
Cheddington	d	23p26	00 20				05 50						07 04		07 04										
Tring	d	23p35	00 29	04 03	04 58		05 56	06 26				06 56	→		07 10					07 26	07 34				
Berkhamsted	d	23p40	00 34	04 08	05 03		06 00	06 31			06 45	07 01			07 15					07 31	07 39		07 45		
Hemel Hempstead	a	23p44	00 38	04 12	05 07		06 05	06 35			06 50	07 05			07 19					07 35	07 43		07 50		
	d	23p44	00 38	04 12	05 07		06 05	06 35			06 50	07 05			07 19					07 35	07 43		07 50		
Apsley	d	23p47					06 08	06 38				07 08								07 38					
Kings Langley	d	23p51					06 11	06 42				07 12								07 42					
Watford Junction	a	23p55	00 45	04 19	05 14		06 16	06 46			06 59	07 16		07s19	07 26		07s34	07s38	07s44	07 46	07 51		07 57		
	d	23p56	00 46	04 20	05 15	05 51	06 16	06 47		06 55	07 00	07 17			07 27					07 47	07 52		07 57		
Bushey	d	23p59					06 19	06 50				07 20								07 50					
Harrow & Wealdstone	⊖ d	00 04	00 52	04 26	05 21	05 58	06 24	06 55		07 01		07 25								07 55	07 59				
Wembley Central	d		00 56	04 34	05 25					07 06											08u04				
Shepherd's Bush	a					06 19				07 19											08 19				
Kensington (Olympia)	⊖ a					06 22				07 22											08 22				
West Brompton	⊖ a					06 25				07 25											08 25				
Imperial Wharf §	a																								
Clapham Junction 10	a					06 33				07 33											08 33				
East Croydon	a					06 57				07 57											08 57				
London Euston 15	⊖ a	00 18	01 08	04 46	05 41		06 38	07 11	07 16		07 20	07 39		07 38	07 46		07 54	07 56	08 05	08 09		08 14	08 19	08 10	08 14

		VT	LM	LM	LM	LM	VT	LM		SN	VT	VT	LM	LM	VT	LM	VT	LM	LM	LM	VT	LM	SN		VT
		1◇	1	1	1	1	1◇	1		1	1◇	1◇	1	1	1◇	1	1◇	1	1◇	1◇	1◇	1	1		1◇
		☕					☕				☕	☕			☕		☕				☕				☕
Wolverhampton 7	d	06 45									07 04						07 44								08 06
Sandwell & Dudley	d	06 56									07 15						07 56								
Birmingham New Street 12	d	07 10									07 30	07 50					08 10		07 33						08 30
Birmingham International	d	07 20									07 40	08 00					08 20		07 45						08 39
Coventry	d	07 31									07 52	08 11					08 31		08 01						08 51
Nuneaton	d																			08 04	08 59				
Rugby	a											08 21							08 12	08 19					
	d						07 54					08 23							08 13	08 20					
Northampton	d				07 33								08 05	08 25					08 50	08 50					
Wolverton	d				07 45								08 17	08 37											
Milton Keynes Central 10	a				07 49						08 18		08 20	08 41					09 03						09 18
	d			07 44	07 49					08 13	08 19		08 21	08 41	08 47			08 47	09 03				09 13		09 19
Bletchley	d			07 49	07 54					08 17			08 26	08 46				08 52					09 17		
Leighton Buzzard	d			07 55	08 03					08 24			08 32	08 53				08 58					09 24		
Cheddington	d			08 01		←												09 04							
Tring	d		07 56	08 07		08 07		08 26		08 34						08 56		09 10				09 26	09 34		
Berkhamsted	d		08 00	→		08 12		08 30		08 39			08 45			09 00		09 15				09 30	09 39		
Hemel Hempstead	a		08 05			08 16		08 35		08 43			08 50			09 05		09 19				09 35	09 43		
	d		08 05			08 16		08 35		08 43			08 50			09 05		09 19				09 35	09 43		
Apsley	d		08 08					08 38								09 08						09 38			
Kings Langley	d		08 11					08 41								09 11						09 41			
Watford Junction	a	08s15	08 16		08 20	08 23		08 46		08 50			08 57			09 16	09s17	09 26	09 34			09 46	09 51		
	d		08 16		08 20	08 24		08 46		08 51			08 57			09 16		09 27	09 34			09 46	09 52		
Bushey	d		08 19					08 49								09 19						09 49			
Harrow & Wealdstone	⊖ d		08 24					08 54		08 58						09 24						09 54	09 59		
Wembley Central	d									09u03													10u04		
Shepherd's Bush	a									09 19													10 19		
Kensington (Olympia)	⊖ a									09 22													10 22		
West Brompton	⊖ a									09 25													10 25		
Imperial Wharf §	a																								
Clapham Junction 10	a									09 33													10 33		
East Croydon	a									09 57													10 57		
London Euston 15	⊖ a	08 34	08 38		08 38	08 43	08 46	09 08			08 54	09 14	09 18	09 27	09 23	09 38	09 35	09 46	09 51		10 01	10 08			09 55

For general notes see front of timetable
For details of catering facilities see
Directory of Train Operators

§ It is unknown , at the time of going to press, when this station will open. For further details contact National rail Enquiries 08457-484950 or see local publicity

West Midlands, Northampton, Milton Keynes and Watford Junction → London

Network Diagram - See first page of Table 59

		VT	LM	LM	VT	VT	LM	LM	LM	LM	VT	LM	SN	VT	VT		LM	LM	VT	VT	LM	LM	LM	LM	LM
		1 ◊ ☕	1	1	1 ◊ ☕	1 ◊ ☕	1	1	1 ◊	1 ◊	1 ◊ ☕	1	1	1 ◊ ☕	1 ◊ ☕		1	1	1 ◊ ☕	1 ◊ ☕	1	1	1 ◊	1 ◊	1
Wolverhampton 7	d					08 45														09 45					
Sandwell & Dudley	d					08 56														09 56					
Birmingham New Street 12	d	08 50				09 10			08 33					09 30	09 50					10 10			09 33		
Birmingham International	d	09 00				09 20			08 45					09 39	10 00					10 20			09 45		
Coventry	d	09 11				09 31			09 01					09 51	10 11					10 31			10 01		
Nuneaton	d									09 04	09 59													10 02	
Rugby	a	09 21							09 12	09 20					10 21								10 12	10 17	
	d	09 23							09 13	09 20					10 23								10 13	10 18	
Northampton	d		09 05	09 25					09 50	09 50							10 05	10 25					10 50	10 50	
Wolverton	d		09 17	09 37													10 17	10 37							
Milton Keynes Central 10	a		09 20	09 41					10 04					10 18			10 20	10 41					11 04		
	d		09 21	09 41	09 47			09 47	10 04				10 13	10 19			10 21	10 41	10 47			10 47	11 04		
Bletchley	d		09 26	09 46				09 52					10 17				10 26	10 46				10 52			
Leighton Buzzard	d		09 32	09 53				09 58					10 24				10 32	10 53				10 58			
Cheddington	d							10 04														11 04			
Tring	d						09 56	10 10				10 26	10 34								10 56	11 10			11 26
Berkhamsted	d		09 45				10 00	10 15				10 30	10 39				10 45				11 00	11 15			11 30
Hemel Hempstead	a		09 50				10 05	10 19				10 35	10 43				10 50				11 05	11 19			11 35
	d		09 50				10 05	10 19				10 35	10 43				10 50				11 05	11 19			11 35
Apsley	d						10 08					10 38									11 08				11 38
Kings Langley	d						10 11					10 41									11 11				11 41
Watford Junction	a		09 57			10s15	10 16	10 26	10 29			10 46	10 51				10 57			11s15	11 16	11 26	11 29		11 46
	d		09 57				10 16	10 27	10 29			10 46	10 52				10 57				11 16	11 27	11 29		11 46
Bushey	d						10 19					10 49									11 19				11 49
Harrow & Wealdstone ⊖	d						10 24					10 54	10 59								11 24				11 54
Wembley Central	d												11u04												
Shepherd's Bush	a												11 19												
Kensington (Olympia) ⊖	a												11 22												
West Brompton ⊖	a												11 25												
Imperial Wharf §	a																								
Clapham Junction 10	a												11 33												
East Croydon	a												11 57												
London Euston 15 ⊖	a	10 14	10 19	10 27	10 23	10 34	10 38	10 46	10 48		11 01	11 08		10 54	11 14		11 19	11 27	11 23	11 34	11 38	11 46	11 48		12 08

		SN	VT	LM	LM	VT	VT	LM		LM	LM	LM	VT	LM	SN	VT	VT	LM	LM	VT	VT	LM	LM		
		1	1 ◊ ☕	1	1	1 ◊ ☕	1 ◊ ☕	1		1	1 ◊	1 ◊	1 ◊ ☕	1	1	1 ◊ ☕	1 ◊ ☕	1	1	1 ◊ ☕	1 ◊ ☕	1	1		
Wolverhampton 7	d						10 45														11 45				
Sandwell & Dudley	d						10 56														11 56				
Birmingham New Street 12	d		10 30				11 10				10 33		10 50			11 30	11 50				12 10				
Birmingham International	d		10 39				11 20				10 45		11 00			11 39	12 00				12 20				
Coventry	d		10 51				11 31				11 01		11 11			11 51	12 11				12 31				
Nuneaton	d											11 03													
Rugby	a										11 12	11 19	11 21				12 21								
	d										11 13	11 19	11 23				12 23								
Northampton	d			11 05	11 25						11 50	11 50						12 05	12 25						
Wolverton	d			11 17	11 37													12 17	12 37						
Milton Keynes Central 10	a		11 18	11 20	11 41						12 04					12 18		12 20	12 41						
	d	11 13	11 19	11 21	11 41	11 47				11 47	12 04				12 13	12 19		12 21	12 41	12 47			12 47		
Bletchley	d	11 17		11 26	11 46					11 52					12 17			12 26	12 46				12 52		
Leighton Buzzard	d	11 24		11 32	11 53					11 58					12 24			12 32	12 53				12 58		
Cheddington	d									12 04													13 04		
Tring	d	11 34						11 56		12 10				12 26	12 34							12 56	13 10		
Berkhamsted	d	11 39		11 45				12 00		12 15				12 30	12 39			12 45				13 00	13 15		
Hemel Hempstead	a	11 43		11 50				12 05		12 19				12 35	12 43			12 50				13 05	13 19		
	d	11 43		11 50				12 05		12 19				12 35	12 43			12 50				13 05	13 19		
Apsley	d							12 08						12 38								13 08			
Kings Langley	d							12 11						12 41								13 11			
Watford Junction	a	11 51		11 57			12s15	12 16		12 26	12 29			12 46	12 50			12 57			13s15	13 16	13 26		
	d	11 52		11 57				12 16		12 27	12 29			12 46	12 51			12 57				13 16	13 27		
Bushey	d							12 19						12 49								13 19			
Harrow & Wealdstone ⊖	d	11 58						12 24						12 54	12 58							13 24			
Wembley Central	d	12u03													13u03										
Shepherd's Bush	a	12 19													13 19										
Kensington (Olympia) ⊖	a	12 22													13 22										
West Brompton ⊖	a	12 25													13 25										
Imperial Wharf §	a																								
Clapham Junction 10	a	12 33													13 33										
East Croydon	a	12 57													13 57										
London Euston 15 ⊖	a		11 54	12 18	12 27	12 23	12 34	12 38		12 46	12 48		12 14	13 08		12 54	13 14	13 18	13 27	13 23	13 32	13 38	13 46		

For general notes see front of timetable
For details of catering facilities see Directory of Train Operators

§ It is unknown , at the time of going to press, when this station will open. For further details contact National rail Enquiries 08457-484950 or see local publicity

Table 66

Saturdays

West Midlands, Northampton, Milton Keynes and Watford Junction → London

Network Diagram - See first page of Table 59

		LM 1◇	LM 1◇	LM 1	SN 1	VT 1◇☕	VT 1◇☕	LM 1	LM 1	VT 1◇☕	VT 1◇☕	LM 1	LM 1	LM 1◇	LM 1◇		LM 1	SN 1	VT 1◇☕	VT 1◇☕	LM 1	LM 1	VT 1◇☕	VT 1◇☕	LM 1
Wolverhampton 7	d										12 45													13 45	
Sandwell & Dudley	d										12 56													13 56	
Birmingham New Street 12	d	11 33				12 30	12 50				13 10			12 33					13 30	13 50				14 10	
Birmingham International	d	11 45				12 39	13 00				13 20			12 45					13 39	14 00				14 20	
Coventry	d	12 01				12 51	13 11				13 31			13 01					13 51	14 11				14 31	
Nuneaton	d		12 02												13 03										
Rugby	a	12 12	12 17				13 21							13 12	13 19					14 21					
	d	12 13	12 18				13 23							13 13	13 19					14 23					
Northampton	d	12 50	12 50					13 05	13 25					13 50	13 50						14 05	14 25			
Wolverton	d							13 17	13 37												14 17	14 37			
Milton Keynes Central 10	a	13 04				13 18		13 20	13 41					14 04					14 18		14 20	14 41			
	d	13 04			13 13	13 19		13 21	13 41	13 47			13 47	14 04				14 13	14 19		14 21	14 41	14 47		
Bletchley	d				13 17			13 26	13 46				13 52					14 17			14 26	14 46			
Leighton Buzzard	d				13 24			13 32	13 53				13 58					14 24			14 32	14 53			
Cheddington	d												14 04												
Tring	d			13 26	13 34							13 56	14 10				14 26	14 34							14 56
Berkhamsted	d			13 30	13 39			13 45				14 00	14 15				14 30	14 39			14 45				15 00
Hemel Hempstead	a			13 35	13 43			13 50				14 05	14 19				14 35	14 43			14 50				15 05
	d			13 35	13 43			13 50				14 05	14 19				14 35	14 43			14 50				15 05
Apsley	d			13 38								14 08					14 38								15 08
Kings Langley	d			13 41								14 11					14 41								15 11
Watford Junction	a	13 29		13 46	13 50			13 57			14s15	14 16	14 26	14 29			14 46	14 50			14 57			15s15	15 16
	d	13 29		13 46	13 51			13 57				14 16	14 27	14 29			14 46	14 51			14 57				15 16
Bushey	d			13 49								14 19					14 49								15 19
Harrow & Wealdstone ⊖	d			13 54	13 58							14 24					14 54	14 58							15 24
Wembley Central	d				14u03													15u03							
Shepherd's Bush	a				14 19													15 19							
Kensington (Olympia) ⊖	a				14 22													15 22							
West Brompton ⊖	a				14 25													15 25							
Imperial Wharf §	a																								
Clapham Junction 10	a				14 33													15 33							
East Croydon	a				14 57													15 57							
London Euston 15 ⊖	a	13 48		14 08		13 54	14 14	14 18	14 27	14 23	14 34	14 38	14 46	14 48			15 08		14 54	15 14	15 18	15 27	15 23	15 34	15 38

		LM 1	LM 1◇	LM 1◇	LM 1	SN 1	VT 1◇☕	VT 1◇☕		LM 1	LM 1	VT 1◇☕	VT 1◇☕	LM 1	LM 1	LM 1◇	LM 1◇	LM 1	SN 1	VT 1◇☕	VT 1◇☕	LM 1	LM 1		VT 1◇☕
Wolverhampton 7	d												14 45												
Sandwell & Dudley	d												14 56												
Birmingham New Street 12	d		13 33				14 30	14 50					15 10			14 33				15 30	15 50				
Birmingham International	d		13 45				14 39	15 00					15 20			14 45				15 39	16 00				
Coventry	d		14 01				14 51	15 11					15 31			15 01				15 51	16 11				
Nuneaton	d			14 02													15 02								
Rugby	a		14 12	14 17				15 21								15 12	15 17				16 21				
	d		14 13	14 18				15 23								15 13	15 19				16 23				
Northampton	d		14 50	14 50						15 05	15 25					15 50	15 50					16 05	16 25		
Wolverton	d									15 17	15 37											16 17	16 37		
Milton Keynes Central 10	a		15 04				15 18			15 20	15 41					16 04				16 18		16 20	16 41		
	d	14 47	15 04			15 13	15 19			15 21	15 41	15 47			15 47	16 04			16 13	16 19		16 21	16 41		16 47
Bletchley	d	14 52				15 17				15 26	15 46				15 52				16 17			16 26	16 46		
Leighton Buzzard	d	14 58				15 24				15 32	15 53				15 58				16 24			16 32	16 53		
Cheddington	d	15 04													16 04										
Tring	d	15 10			15 26	15 34								15 56	16 10			16 26	16 34						
Berkhamsted	d	15 15			15 30	15 39				15 45				16 00	16 15			16 30	16 39			16 45			
Hemel Hempstead	a	15 19			15 35	15 43				15 50				16 05	16 19			16 35	16 43			16 50			
	d	15 19			15 35	15 43				15 50				16 05	16 19			16 35	16 43			16 50			
Apsley	d				15 38									16 08				16 38							
Kings Langley	d				15 41									16 11				16 41							
Watford Junction	a	15 28	15 29		15 46	15 50				15 57			16s15	16 16	16 28	16 29		16 46	16 50			16 57			
	d	15 29	15 29		15 46	15 51				15 57				16 16	16 29	16 29		16 46	16 51			16 57			
Bushey	d				15 49									16 19				16 49							
Harrow & Wealdstone ⊖	d				15 54	15 58								16 24				16 54	16 58						
Wembley Central	d					16u03													17u03						
Shepherd's Bush	a					16 19													17 19						
Kensington (Olympia) ⊖	a					16 22													17 22						
West Brompton ⊖	a					16 25													17 25						
Imperial Wharf §	a																								
Clapham Junction 10	a					16 33													17 33						
East Croydon	a					16 57													17 57						
London Euston 15 ⊖	a	15 46	15 48		16 08		15 54	16 14		16 18	16 27	16 23	16 34	16 38	16 46	16 48		17 08		16 54	17 14	17 18	17 27		17 23

For general notes see front of timetable
For details of catering facilities see Directory of Train Operators

§ It is unknown , at the time of going to press, when this station will open. For further details contact National rail Enquiries 08457-484950 or see local publicity

West Midlands, Northampton, Milton Keynes and Watford Junction → London

Network Diagram - See first page of Table 59

Station		VT 1◇ ☕	LM 1	LM 1	LM 1◇	LM 1◇	LM 1	SN 1	VT 1◇ ☕	VT 1◇ ☕	LM 1	LM 1	VT 1◇ ☕	VT 1◇ ☕	LM 1		LM 1	VT 1◇ ☕	LM 1◇	LM 1◇	LM 1	SN 1	VT 1◇ ☕	VT 1◇ ☕	LM 1
Wolverhampton [7] ⛴	d	15 45												16 45											
Sandwell & Dudley	d	15 56												16 56											
Birmingham New Street [12]	d	16 10			15 33				16 30	16 50				17 10					16 33				17 30	17 50	
Birmingham International ✈	d	16 20			15 45				16 39	17 00				17 20					16 45				17 39	18 00	
Coventry	d	16 31			16 01				16 51	17 11				17 31					17 01				17 51	18 11	
Nuneaton	d					16 02														17 03					
Rugby	a				16 12	16 17				17 21									17 12	17 19				18 21	
	d				16 13	16 18				17 23									17 13	17 19				18 23	
Northampton	d				16 50	16 50					17 05	17 25							17 50	17 50					18 05
Wolverton	d										17 17	17 37													18 17
Milton Keynes Central [10]	a				17 04				17 18		17 20	17 41							18 04				18 18		18 20
	d			16 47	17 04			17 13	17 19		17 21	17 41	17 47				17 47	18 02	18 04			18 13	18 19		18 21
Bletchley	d			16 52				17 17			17 26	17 46					17 52					18 17			18 26
Leighton Buzzard	d			16 58				17 24			17 32	17 53					17 58					18 24			18 32
Cheddington	d			17 04													18 04								
Tring	d		16 56	17 10			17 26	17 34							17 56		18 10				18 26	18 34			
Berkhamsted	d		17 00	17 15			17 30	17 39			17 45				18 00		18 15				18 30	18 39			18 45
Hemel Hempstead	a		17 05	17 19			17 35	17 43			17 50				18 05		18 19				18 35	18 43			18 50
	d		17 05	17 19			17 35	17 43			17 50				18 05		18 19				18 35	18 43			18 50
Apsley	d		17 08				17 38								18 08						18 38				
Kings Langley	d		17 11				17 41								18 11						18 41				
Watford Junction	a	17s15	17 16	17 28	17 29		17 46	17 50			17 57			18s15	18 16		18 28		18 29		18 46	18 50			18 57
	d		17 16	17 29	17 29		17 46	17 51			17 57				18 16		18 29		18 29		18 46	18 51			18 57
Bushey	d		17 19				17 49								18 19						18 49				
Harrow & Wealdstone ⊖	d		17 24				17 54	17 58							18 24						18 54	18 58			
Wembley Central	d							18u03														19u03			
Shepherd's Bush	a							18 19														19 19			
Kensington (Olympia) ⊖	a							18 22														19 22			
West Brompton ⊖	a							18 25														19 25			
Imperial Wharf §	a																								
Clapham Junction [10]	a							18 33														19 33			
East Croydon ⛴	a							18 57														19 57			
London Euston [15] ⊖	a	17 34	17 38	17 46	17 49		18 08	....	17 54	18 14	18 18	18 27	18 23	18 34	18 38	....	18 46	18 38	18 48		19 08	....	18 54	19 14	19 18

Station		VT 1◇ ☕	VT 1◇ ☕	LM 1	LM 1	LM 1◇	LM 1◇	SN 1		LM 1	SN 1	VT 1◇ ☕	VT 1◇ ☕	LM 1	VT 1◇ ☕	LM 1	LM 1	VT 1◇ ☕	SN 1	LM 1	LM 1 A	LM 1 B	VT 1◇ C ☕		LM 1
Wolverhampton [7] ⛴	d		17 45															18 45							
Sandwell & Dudley	d		17 56															18 56							
Birmingham New Street [12]	d		18 10			17 33						18 30	18 50					19 10							
Birmingham International ✈	d		18 20			17 45						18 39	19 00					19 20							
Coventry	d		18 31			18 01						18 51	19 11					19 31							
Nuneaton	d						18 02																		
Rugby	a					18 12	18 17						19 21					19 42							
	d					18 13	18 18						19 23					19 44							
Northampton	d				18 31	18 50	18 50							19 05			19 31			19 59	20 21	20 27			
Wolverton	d				18 43									19 17			19 43			20 12					
Milton Keynes Central [10]	a				18 46	19 04						19 18		19 20			19 46	20 05		20 15	20 36	20 42			
	d	18 47			18 47	19 04					19 13	19 19		19 21	19 47		19 47	20 07		20 16	20 36	20 43	20 45		20 49
Bletchley	d				18 52						19 17			19 26			19 52								20 55
Leighton Buzzard	d				18 58						19 24			19 32			19 58			20 25	20 46	20 55			
Cheddington	d				19 04												20 05				20 55	21 00			
Tring	d			18 56	19 10					19 24	19 34					19 56	20 10				21 00	21 05			21 13
Berkhamsted	d			19 00	19 15					19 28	19 39			19 45		20 00	20 15								21 18
Hemel Hempstead	a			19 05	19 19					19 33	19 43			19 50		20 05	20 19				21 07	21 12			21 22
	d			19 05	19 19					19 33	19 43			19 50		20 05	20 19				21 07	21 12			21 22
Apsley	d			19 08						19 36						20 08					21 10	21 15			
Kings Langley	d			19 11						19 39						20 12					21 13	21 19			
Watford Junction	a		19s15	19 16	19 26	19 29				19 44	19 50			19 57		20 18	20 26	20s34		20 49	21 18	21 23	21s23		21 29
	d			19 16	19 27	19 29		19 31		19 44	19 51			19 59		20 19	20 27		20 43	20 49	21 18	21 24			21 30
Bushey	d			19 19						19 47															
Harrow & Wealdstone ⊖	d			19 24				19 38		19 52	19 58					20 25			20 50						21 36
Wembley Central	d							19 43																	
Shepherd's Bush	a							19 57			20 19								21 08						
Kensington (Olympia) ⊖	a							19 59			20 22								21 10						
West Brompton ⊖	a							20 02			20 25								21 13						
Imperial Wharf §	a																								
Clapham Junction [10]	a							20 10			20 33								21 21						
East Croydon ⛴	a										20 57														
London Euston [15] ⊖	a	19 23	19 34	19 38	19 46	19 48		....	....	20 06	....	19 54	20 17	20 19	20 28	20 39	20 46	20 56	....	21 08	21 37	21 43	21 47	....	21 52

For general notes see front of timetable
For details of catering facilities see Directory of Train Operators

§ It is unknown , at the time of going to press, when this station will open. For further details contact National rail Enquiries 08457-484950 or see local publicity

A From 12 September
B Until 5 September
C 12 September to 31 October

West Midlands, Northampton, Milton Keynes and Watford Junction → London

Saturdays

Network Diagram - See first page of Table 59

Station		VT	VT	VT	SN	LM	VT	VT	LM	LM	VT	VT	VT	VT	VT	SN	LM	LM	VT	SN	VT	LM	VT	LM
		1◇	1◇	1◇	1	1	1◇	1◇	1	1	1◇	1◇	1◇	1◇	1◇	1	1	1	1◇	1	1◇	1	1◇	1
		A	B	B			A	A	B	A	C	B	A	B	A		B	A	A		B		A	
Wolverhampton 7	d		19 45				19 45					20 45			20 45						21 45		21 45	
Sandwell & Dudley	d		19 56				19 56					20 56			20 56						21 57		21 57	
Birmingham New Street 12	d		20 10				20 10					21 10			21 10						22 10		22 10	
Birmingham International	d		20 20				20 20					21 20			21 20						22 20		22 20	
Coventry	d		20 31				20 31					21 31			21 31						22 31		22 31	
Nuneaton	d																							
Rugby	a		20 42				20 41					21 42			21 41						22 41		22 41	
	d		20 43				20 43					21 43			21 43						22 43		22 43	
Northampton	d					21 00			21 12	21 14							22 00	22 05				22 55		23 30
Wolverton	d					21 12											22 12	22 16				23 07		23 42
Milton Keynes Central 10	a		21 04			21 15	21 20		21 28	21 32		22 04			22 17		22 18	22 23			23s05	23 10	23s16	23 45
	d	21 01	21 05	21 11		21 16	21 22	21 28	21 28	21 33	21 53	22 05	22 13	22 13	22 19		22 18	22 24	22 30			23 11		23 46
Bletchley	d								21 33	21 38							22 23	22 29				23 16		23 51
Leighton Buzzard	d								21 40	21 44							22 29	22 34				23 22		23 57
Cheddington	d								21 45	21 49							22 34	22 39				23 27		
Tring	d								21 54	21 56							22 43	22 45				23 36		
Berkhamsted	d					21 38			21 58	22 01							22 48	22 51				23 41		
Hemel Hempstead	a					21 43			22 03	22 05							22 52	22 54				23 45		
	d					21 43			22 03	22 05							22 52	22 54				23 45		
Apsley	d								22 06	22 08							22 55	22 57				23 48		
Kings Langley	d								22 09	22 12							22 59	23 02				23 52		
Watford Junction	a	21s38	21s34			21 50	21s55		22 14	22 16		22s34		22s42	22s44		23 04	23 06	23s11		23s34	23 56	00s01	00 18
	d				21 43	21 50			22 14	22 17						22 48	23 04	23 07		23 25		23 57		00 18
Bushey	d																							
Harrow & Wealdstone ⊖	d				21 50											22 55	23 10	23 13		23 31		00 03		
Wembley Central	d																							
Shepherd's Bush	a				22 08											23 13				23 48				
Kensington (Olympia) ⊖	a				22 10											23 15				23 51				
West Brompton ⊖	a				22 13											23 18				23 54				
Imperial Wharf §	a																							
Clapham Junction 10	a				22 21											23 26				00 02				
East Croydon	a																							
London Euston 15 ⊖	a	22 03	21 57	22 02		22 11	22 16	22 21	22 33	22 36	22 43	22 55	23 03	23 04	23 06		23 24	23 27	23 36		23 57	00 17	00 22	00 42

Sundays

Station		LM	LM	LM	LM	LM	LM	LM	LM	LM	SN	LM	LM	VT	SN	LM	VT	VT	LM		VT	SN	VT	VT	LM
		1	1	1		1		1		1	1	1	1	1◇	1	1	1◇	1◇	1		1◇	1	1◇	1◇	1
					bus		bus		bus								D	E					E	D	
Wolverhampton 7	d													08 05							09 05				
Sandwell & Dudley	d													08 15							09 16				
Birmingham New Street 12	d													08 30							09 30				
Birmingham International	d													08 40							09 40				
Coventry	d													08 51							09 51				
Nuneaton	d																						09 55	10 02	
Rugby	a													09 02							10 02				
	d													09 04							10 04				
Northampton	d	22p55	23p30				06 15					08 23	08 53			09 30			10 07						10 37
Wolverton	d	23p07	23p42				06 48					08 37	09 07			09 44			10 20						10 51
Milton Keynes Central 10	a	23p10	23p45				06 57					08 40	09 10	09 37		09 47			10 24		10 37				10 54
	d	23p11	23p46		06 20		06 58		07 55			08 41	09 11	09 39		09 48	10 15	10 19	10 24		10 39				10 55
Bletchley	d	23p16	23p51		06 33		07 11		08a07	08 16		08 46	09 16			09 53			10 29						11 00
Leighton Buzzard	d	23p22	23p57		06 58		07 36			08 22		08 52	09 22			09 59			10 36						11 06
Cheddington	d	23p27			07 12					08 27			09 27						10 41						
Tring	d	23p36		07 03	07a27	07 33	07a56	08 03		08 36			09 36						10 46						
Berkhamsted	d	23p41		07 07		07 38		08 07		08 41		09 07	09 41			10 14			10 50						11 21
Hemel Hempstead	a	23p45		07 12		07 42		08 12		08 45		09 12	09 45			10 19			10 55						11 26
	d	23p45		07 12		07 43		08 12		08 45		09 12	09 45			10 19			10 55						11 26
Apsley	d	23p48				07 46		08 15				09 15				10 22									11 29
Kings Langley	d	23p52				07 49		08 18				09 18				10 25									11 32
Watford Junction	a	23p56	00 18	07 19		07 54		08 23		08 52		09 23	09 52	10s07		10 30			11 05		11s10		11s20	11s20	11 37
	d	23p57	00 18	07 20		07 55		08 23		08 53	09 17	09 23	09 53		10 17	10 30			11 05			11 17			11 37
Bushey	d																								
Harrow & Wealdstone ⊖	d	00 03		07 26		08 01		08 29		08 59	09 23	09 29	09 59		10 23	10 36			11 11			11 23			11 43
Wembley Central	d																								
Shepherd's Bush	a										09 45				10 45							11 45			
Kensington (Olympia) ⊖	a										09 47				10 47							11 47			
West Brompton ⊖	a										09 50				10 50							11 50			
Imperial Wharf §	a																								
Clapham Junction 10	a										09 58				10 58							11 58			
East Croydon	a																								
London Euston 15 ⊖	a	00 17	00 42	07 41		08 15		08 43		09 13		09 43	10 13	10 28		10 50	11 03	11 07	11 26		11 31		11 44	11 44	11 57

For general notes see front of timetable
For details of catering facilities see Directory of Train Operators

§ It is unknown , at the time of going to press, when this station will open. For further details contact National rail Enquiries 08457-484950 or see local publicity

A Until 5 September
B From 12 September
C 12 September to 31 October
D Until 12 July and from 13 September
E 19 July to 6 September

West Midlands, Northampton, Milton Keynes and Watford Junction → London

Network Diagram - See first page of Table 59

		VT 1◇ A	VT 1◇ B	VT 1◇ A	VT 1◇ B	LM 1	VT 1◇	LM 1	VT 1◇ A	VT 1◇ B	VT 1◇ A	VT 1◇ B	SN 1	LM 1	LM 1	VT 1◇ A		VT 1◇	VT 1◇ B	VT 1◇ A	VT 1◇ B	VT 1◇	LM 1	VT 1◇	VT 1◇
Wolverhampton 7	d						10 05											11 05							11 45
Sandwell & Dudley	d						10 15											11 15							11 57
Birmingham New Street 12	d						10 30											11 30				11 50			12 10
Birmingham International	d						10 40											11 40				12 00			12 20
Coventry	d						10 51											11 51				12 11			12 31
Nuneaton	d								10⌇56	11⌇03										11⌇56	12⌇05				
Rugby	a						11 02											12 03				12 23			
	d	10⌇33	10⌇39				11 04				11⌇33	11⌇39						12 05				12 25			
Northampton	d					11 07		11 25															12 25		
Wolverton	d					11 21		11 37															12 37		
Milton Keynes Central 10	a	11⌇04	11⌇04			11 24	11 35	11 41	11⌇48	11⌇48	12⌇04	12⌇04						12 25					12 40		
	d	11⌇06	11⌇06	11⌇15	11⌇20	11 25	11 37	11 42	11⌇50	11⌇50	12⌇06	12⌇06			12 11	12⌇21		12 26	12⌇30				12 41	12 52	
Bletchley	d					11 30		11 47						11 54	12 16								12 46		
Leighton Buzzard	d					11 36		11 54						12 00	12 22								12 52		
Cheddington	d					11 41								12 05	12 30										
Tring	d					11 50								12 15	12 35										
Berkhamsted	d					11 55		12 06						12 19	12 40								13 05		
Hemel Hempstead	a					11 59		12 11						12 24	12 44								13 10		
	d					11 59		12 11						12 24	12 44								13 10		
Apsley	d													12 27											
Kings Langley	d													12 30											
Watford Junction	a	11s42	11s42			12 06	12s07	12 18						12 35	12 51					12s53	12s54		13 17		13s18
	d					12 07		12 18					12 22	12 35	12 52								13 17		
Bushey	d													12 38											
Harrow & Wealdstone ⊖	d					12 13		12 24					12 29	12 43	12 58								13 23		
Wembley Central	d																								
Shepherd's Bush	a												12 45												
Kensington (Olympia) ⊖	a												12 47												
West Brompton ⊖	a												12 50												
Imperial Wharf §	a																								
Clapham Junction 10	a												12 58												
East Croydon	a																								
London Euston 15 ⊖	a	12⌇04	12⌇04	12⌇08	12⌇08	12 27	12 27	12 37	12⌇38	12⌇38	12⌇51	12⌇51		12 57	13 11	13⌇01		13 04	13⌇09	13⌇15	13⌇15	13 19	13 37	13 31	13 39

		VT 1◇	SN 1	LM 1 C	LM 1 D	LM 1	LM 1	VT 1◇ C	VT 1◇ D	VT 1◇	VT 1◇ E	VT 1◇ G	LM 1		VT 1◇ C	VT 1◇ D	SN 1	LM 1◇ C	LM 1◇ D	LM 1	LM 1	VT 1◇ C	VT 1◇ D	VT 1◇	VT 1◇
Wolverhampton 7	d										12⌇45	12⌇45													13 45
Sandwell & Dudley	d										12⌇55	12⌇56													13 56
Birmingham New Street 12	d							12⌇30	12⌇30	12 50	13⌇10	13⌇10										13⌇30	13⌇30	13 50	14 10
Birmingham International	d							12⌇39	12⌇39	13 01	13⌇20	13⌇20										13⌇39	13⌇39	14 01	14 20
Coventry	d							12⌇51	12⌇51	13 11	13⌇31	13⌇31										13⌇51	13⌇51	14 11	14 31
Nuneaton	d	12 31																12⌇58	12⌇58						
Rugby	a									13 23								13⌇17	13⌇18					14 23	
	d			12⌇26	12⌇31					13 26								13⌇17	13⌇27					14 26	
Northampton	d			12⌇50									13 25					13⌇50							
Wolverton	d												13 37												
Milton Keynes Central 10	a	13s03		13⌇04	12⌇58			13⌇18	13⌇19				13 40					14⌇04	13⌇52			14⌇18	14⌇18		
	d			13⌇05	13⌇05		13 11	13⌇19	13⌇20				13 41		13⌇52	13⌇58		14⌇05	14⌇05		14 11	14⌇19	14⌇20		
Bletchley	d						13 16						13 46								14 16				
Leighton Buzzard	d						13 22						13 52								14 22				
Cheddington	d						13 30														14 30				
Tring	d					13 15	13 35													14 15	14 35				
Berkhamsted	d					13 19	13 40						14 05							14 19	14 40				
Hemel Hempstead	a					13 24	13 44						14 10							14 24	14 44				
	d					13 24	13 44						14 10							14 24	14 44				
Apsley	d					13 27														14 27					
Kings Langley	d					13 30														14 30					
Watford Junction	a			13⌇33	13⌇34	13 35	13 51				14s16	14s16	14 17					14⌇34	14⌇35	14 35	14 51				15s16
	d		13 22	13⌇33	13⌇34	13 35	13 52						14 17				14 22	14⌇34	14⌇35	14 35	14 52				
Bushey	d					13 38														14 38					
Harrow & Wealdstone ⊖	d		13 28			13 43	13 58						14 23				14 28			14 43	14 58				
Wembley Central	d																								
Shepherd's Bush	a		13 45														14 45								
Kensington (Olympia) ⊖	a		13 47														14 47								
West Brompton ⊖	a		13 50														14 50								
Imperial Wharf §	a																								
Clapham Junction 10	a		13 58														14 58								
East Croydon	a																								
London Euston 15 ⊖	a	13 44		13⌇53	13⌇54	13 57	14 11	13⌇59	13⌇59	14 20	14⌇36	14⌇35	14 37		14⌇31	14⌇40		14⌇53	14⌇54	14 57	15 11	14⌇59	14⌇59	15 20	15 36

For general notes see front of timetable
For details of catering facilities see Directory of Train Operators

§ It is unknown, at the time of going to press, when this station will open. For further details contact National rail Enquiries 08457-484950 or see local publicity

A 19 July to 6 September
B Until 12 July and from 13 September
C From 19 July
D Until 12 July
E From 13 September
G Until 6 September

Sundays

West Midlands, Northampton, Milton Keynes and Watford Junction → London

Network Diagram - See first page of Table 59

		LM 1	VT 1◇ ☕	SN 1	LM 1 A	VT 1◇ B ☕	LM 1 C	LM 1	LM 1	VT 1◇ ☕		VT 1◇ ☕	VT 1◇ ☕	LM 1	VT 1◇ ☕	SN 1	LM 1◇ A	LM 1◇ C	LM 1	LM 1	VT 1◇ ☕	VT 1◇ ☕	VT 1◇ C ☕	VT 1◇ A ☕	LM 1
Wolverhampton 7	d												14 45										15 45	15 45	
Sandwell & Dudley	d												14 56										15 56	15 56	
Birmingham New Street 12	d									14 30		14 50	15 10								15 30	15 50	16 10	16 10	
Birmingham International	d									14 39		15 01	15 20								15 39	16 01	16 20	16 20	
Coventry	d									14 51		15 11	15 31								15 51	16 11	16 31	16 31	
Nuneaton	d					14 32											14 58	14 58							
Rugby	a											15 23					15 18	15 17				16 23			
	d				14 29		14 26					15 26					15 30	15 17				16 24			
Northampton	d	14 25					14 50							15 25				15 50							16 25
Wolverton	d	14 37												15 37											16 37
Milton Keynes Central 10	a	14 40			14 56	15s04	15 04			15 18				15 40			15 56	16 04			16 18				16 40
	d	14 41	14 51		15 05		15 05		15 11	15 19				15 41	15 51		16 05	16 05		16 11	16 19				16 41
Bletchley	d	14 46							15 16					15 46						16 16					16 46
Leighton Buzzard	d	14 52							15 22					15 52						16 22					16 52
Cheddington	d								15 30											16 30					
Tring	d							15 15	15 35										16 15	16 35					
Berkhamsted	d	15 05						15 19	15 40					16 05					16 19	16 40					17 05
Hemel Hempstead	a	15 10						15 24	15 44					16 10					16 24	16 44					17 10
	d	15 10						15 24	15 44					16 10					16 24	16 44					17 10
Apsley	d							15 27											16 27						
Kings Langley	d							15 30											16 30						
Watford Junction	a	15 17			15 33		15 33	15 35	15 51				16s16	16 17			16 33	16 33	16 35	16 51			17s16	17s17	17 17
	d	15 17		15 22	15 33		15 33	15 35	15 52					16 17		16 22	16 33	16 33	16 35	16 52					17 17
Bushey	d							15 38											16 38						
Harrow & Wealdstone ⊖	d	15 23		15 28				15 43	15 58					16 23		16 28			16 43	16 58					17 23
Wembley Central	d																								
Shepherd's Bush	a			15 45												16 45									
Kensington (Olympia) ⊖	a			15 47												16 47									
West Brompton ⊖	a			15 50												16 50									
Imperial Wharf §	a																								
Clapham Junction 10	a			15 58												16 58									
East Croydon	a																								
London Euston 15 ⊖	a	15 37	15 30		15 53	15 45	15 53	15 57	16 11	15 59		16 20	16 36	16 37	16 30		16 53	16 53	16 57	17 11	16 59	17 19	17 36	17 36	17 37

		VT 1◇ ☕	SN 1	LM 1 A	LM 1 C	LM 1	LM 1		VT 1◇ ☕	VT 1◇ ☕	VT 1◇ ☕	LM 1	VT 1◇ ☕	SN 1	LM 1◇ A	LM 1◇ C	LM 1	LM 1	VT 1◇ ☕	VT 1◇ ☕	VT 1◇ ☕	LM 1	VT 1◇ ☕	SN 1	LM 1 A
Wolverhampton 7	d										16 45										17 45				
Sandwell & Dudley	d										16 56										17 56				
Birmingham New Street 12	d								16 30	16 50	17 10								17 30	17 50	18 10				
Birmingham International	d								16 39	17 01	17 20								17 39	18 01	18 20				
Coventry	d								16 51	17 11	17 31								17 51	18 11	18 31				
Nuneaton	d														16 58	16 58									
Rugby	a									17 23					17 18	17 17				18 23					
	d			16 30	16 25					17 26					17 29	17 17				18 26					18 29
Northampton	d				16 50							17 25				17 50						18 25			
Wolverton	d											17 37										18 37			
Milton Keynes Central 10	a			16 57	17 04				17 18			17 40			17 56	18 04			18 18			18 40			18 56
	d	16 51		17 05	17 05		17 11		17 19			17 41	17 51		18 05	18 05		18 11	18 19			18 41	18 51		19 05
Bletchley	d						17 16					17 46						18 16				18 46			
Leighton Buzzard	d						17 22					17 52						18 22				18 52			
Cheddington	d						17 30											18 30							
Tring	d					17 15	17 35										18 15	18 35							
Berkhamsted	d					17 19	17 40					18 05					18 19	18 40				19 05			
Hemel Hempstead	a					17 24	17 44					18 10					18 24	18 44				19 10			
	d					17 24	17 44					18 10					18 24	18 44				19 10			
Apsley	d					17 27											18 27								
Kings Langley	d					17 30											18 30								
Watford Junction	a			17 33	17 33	17 35	17 51				18s16	18 17			18 33	18 33	18 35	18 51			19s16	19 17			19 33
	d		17 22	17 33	17 33	17 35	17 52					18 17		18 22	18 33	18 33	18 35	18 52				19 17		19 22	19 33
Bushey	d					17 38											18 38								
Harrow & Wealdstone ⊖	d		17 28			17 43	17 58					18 23		18 28			18 43	18 58				19 23		19 28	
Wembley Central	d																								
Shepherd's Bush	a		17 45											18 45										19 45	
Kensington (Olympia) ⊖	a		17 47											18 47										19 47	
West Brompton ⊖	a		17 50											18 50										19 50	
Imperial Wharf §	a																								
Clapham Junction 10	a		17 58											18 58										19 58	
East Croydon	a																								
London Euston 15 ⊖	a	17 30		17 53	17 53	17 57	18 11		17 59	18 20	18 36	18 37	18 30		18 53	18 53	18 57	19 11	18 59	19 20	19 36	19 37	19 30		19 53

For general notes see front of timetable
For details of catering facilities see Directory of Train Operators

§ It is unknown , at the time of going to press, when this station will open. For further details contact National rail Enquiries 08457-484950 or see local publicity

A Until 12 July
B Until 1 November
C From 19 July

West Midlands, Northampton, Milton Keynes and Watford Junction → London

Network Diagram - See first page of Table 59

		LM	LM	LM		VT	VT	VT	LM	VT	SN	LM	LM	LM	LM	LM	VT	SN	LM	VT	VT	LM	LM		LM
		1	1	1		1◇	1◇	1◇	1	1◇	1	1◇	1◇	1	1	1	1◇	1	1	1◇	1◇	1	1		1
		A										B	C	A	D							A	D		
						⊡	⊡	⊡		⊡							⊡			⊡	⊡				
Wolverhampton 7	d							18 45													19 45				
Sandwell & Dudley	d							18 56													19 56				
Birmingham New Street 12	d					18 30	18 50	19 10									19 30				20 10				
Birmingham International	d					18 39	19 01	19 20									19 39				20 20				
Coventry	d					18 51	19 11	19 31									19 51				20 31				
Nuneaton	d											18 58	18 58												
Rugby	a						19 23					19 18	19 17												
	d	18 24					19 26					19 30	19 17									20 20	20 40		
Northampton	d	18 50							19 25				19 50						20 25			20 45			
Wolverton	d								19 37			19 55	20 02						20 37			21 02	21 04		
Milton Keynes Central 10	a	19 04				19 18			19 40			19 58	20 06				20 18		20 40			21 05	21 07		
	d	19 05		19 11		19 19			19 41	19 51		20 06	20 06			20 11	20 19		20 41	20 50		21 05	21 07		21 16
Bletchley	d			19 16					19 46							20 16			20 46						21 21
Leighton Buzzard	d			19 22					19 52							20 22			20 52						21 27
Cheddington	d			19 30												20 27									21 32
Tring	d		19 15	19 35										20 15	20 15	20 36									21 41
Berkhamsted	d		19 19	19 40					20 05					20 19	20 19	20 41			21 12						21 46
Hemel Hempstead	a		19 24	19 44					20 10					20 24	20 24	20 45			21 16						21 50
	d		19 24	19 44					20 10					20 24	20 24	20 45			21 16						21 50
Apsley	d		19 27											20 27	20 27				21 19						
Kings Langley	d		19 30											20 30	20 30				21 23						
Watford Junction	a	19 33	19 35	19 51				20s16	20 17			20 33	20 33	20 35	20 35	20 52			21 27		21s32	21 36	21 36		21 58
	d	19 33	19 35	19 52					20 17		20 22	20 33	20 33	20 35	20 35	20 53		21 17	21 28			21 36	21 36		21 59
Bushey	d		19 38											20 38	20 38										
Harrow & Wealdstone	d		19 43	19 58					20 23		20 28			20 43	20 43	20 59		21 23	21 34						22 05
Wembley Central	d																								
Shepherd's Bush	a										20 45							21 45							
Kensington (Olympia)	a										20 47							21 47							
West Brompton	a										20 50							21 50							
Imperial Wharf §	a																								
Clapham Junction 10	a										20 58							21 58							
East Croydon	a																								
London Euston 15	a	19 53	19 57	20 11		19 59	20 20	20 36	20 37	20 30		20 52	20 52	20 57	20 59	21 15	21 02		21 48	21 34	21 54	21 57	21 57		22 18

		VT	VT	SN	LM	VT	VT	LM	LM	VT	VT	VT	SN	LM	LM	VT	VT	VT	LM	VT	VT	VT	VT
		1◇	1◇	1	1	1◇	1◇	1◇	1◇	1◇	1◇	1◇	1	1	1	1◇	1◇	1◇	1	1◇	1◇	1◇	1◇
								B	C	D	D	A		A	D	A	D	A		D	A	D	A
		⊡	⊡			⊡	⊡			⊡	⊡	⊡				⊡	⊡	⊡		⊡	⊡	⊡	⊡
Wolverhampton 7	d									21 05		21 05								22 05	22 05	22 37	22 37
Sandwell & Dudley	d									21 15		21 15								22 15	22 15	22 47	22 47
Birmingham New Street 12	d	20 30								21 30		21 30								22 30	22 30	23 00	23 00
Birmingham International	d	20 40								21 40		21 40								22 40	22 40	23 10	23 10
Coventry	d	20 51								21 51		21 51								22 51	22 51	23 21	23 21
Nuneaton	d							20 58	20 58								22 16	22 16					
Rugby	a	21 03						21 18	21 17	22 03		22 03					22 29	22 29		23 03	23 03	23 33	23 33
	d	21 05						21 21	21 17	22 05		22 04					22 31	22 31		23 05	23 04	23 35	23 35
Northampton	d				21 25				21 53					22 25	22 25				22 55				
Wolverton	d				21 39			21 46	22 07					22 38	22 40				23 11				
Milton Keynes Central 10	a	21 26			21 44			21 50	22 10	22 27		22 38		22 41	22 43		22 53	23 08	23 14	23 27	23 38	23s57	00s12
	d	21 28	21 39		21 44	21 57	22 04	22 11	22 11	22 29	22 39	22 39		22 42	22 44	22 52	22 55	23 10	23 15	23 29	23 40		
Bletchley	d				21 49			22 16	22 16					22 47	22 49				23 20				
Leighton Buzzard	d				21 56			22 22	22 22					22 53	22 55				23 26				
Cheddington	d							22 27	22 27										23 31				
Tring	d							22 36	22 36										23 40				
Berkhamsted	d				22 11			22 41	22 41					23 08	23 10				23 45				
Hemel Hempstead	a				22 15			22 45	22 45					23 13	23 15				23 49				
	d				22 15			22 45	22 45					23 13	23 15				23 49				
Apsley	d				22 18									23 16	23 18								
Kings Langley	d				22 22									23 19	23 21								
Watford Junction	a	22s03			22 26	22 31		22 52	22 52	22s58	23s07	23s09		23 24	23 26	23s31	23s33	23s38	23 56	00s01	00s08	00s35	00s42
	d			22 17	22 27	22 32		22 53	22 53				23 17	23 24	23 26				23 57				
Bushey	d																						
Harrow & Wealdstone	d			22 23	22 33			22 59	22 59				23 23	23 30	23 32				00 03				
Wembley Central	d																						
Shepherd's Bush	a			22 45									23 45										
Kensington (Olympia)	a			22 47									23 47										
West Brompton	a			22 50									23 50										
Imperial Wharf §	a																						
Clapham Junction 10	a			22 58									23 58										
East Croydon	a												00 22										
London Euston 15	a	22 24	22 29		22 47	22 53	22 57	23 13	23 13	23 18	23 32	23 29		23 46	23 46	23 53	23 54	23 59	00 17	00 22	00 29	01 02	01 09

For general notes see front of timetable
For details of catering facilities see Directory of Train Operators

§ It is unknown , at the time of going to press, when this station will open. For further details contact National rail Enquiries 08457-484950 or see local publicity

A From 19 July
B Until 12 July. From Crewe (Table 67)
C From 19 July. From Crewe (Table 67)
D Until 12 July

Network Diagram for Tables 67, 68, 69, 70

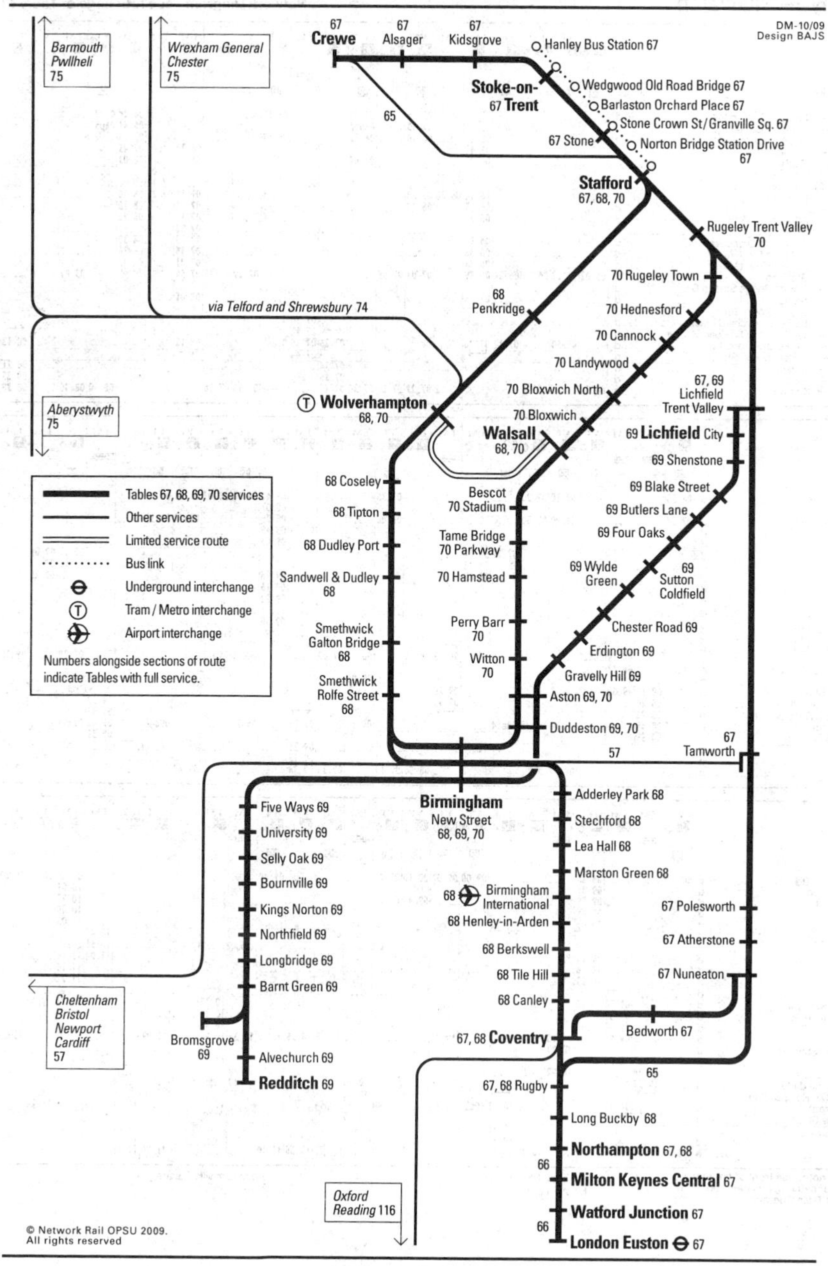

London → Stoke-on-Trent and Crewe
Coventry → Nuneaton

Network Diagram - see first page of Table 67

Miles	Miles	Miles			VT 1◇ ⊠	XC 1◇ 🛒	LM 1◇	XC 1◇ ☕	LM 1 A	LM	VT 1◇ ⊠	LM 1◇	VT 1◇ ⊠	LM 1 A	LM 🚌	VT 1◇ ⊠	XC 1◇ 🛒	LM 1◇	LM 1	LM	LM 1◇	VT 1◇ ⊠	LM 1◇		LM 1
0	—	—	**London Euston** 15 ⊖	d							05 35		05 47			06 17					06 24	06 36			
17½	—	—	Watford Junction	d							05u50		06u02								06 41	06u51			
49¾	—	—	Milton Keynes Central	d					05 21		06 10		06 22			06 47					07 23				
65¾	—	—	Northampton	d					05 42										06 38		07 45				
84½	—	—	Rugby	d					06 02				06 44						06 58		08 03				
—	—	0	**Coventry**	d						06 12										07 06					
—	—	6¼	Bedworth	d						06 23										07 17					
99	—	10	Nuneaton	a					06 14	06 30	06 38								07 11	07 27	08 16				
—	—	—		d					06 15		06 39								07 11		08 16				
104	—	—	Atherstone	d					06 21										07 17		08 22				
108	—	—	Polesworth	d															07 22						
111½	—	—	Tamworth Low Level	d					06 30										07 28		08 30				
117¾	—	—	Lichfield Trent Valley	d					06 36										07 34		08 36				
125¾	—	—	Rugeley Trent Valley	d					06 43										07 41		08 42				
135½	0	—	**Stafford**	d	06 02	06 29	06 36	06 54	06b59		07 03	07 05					07 29	07 36	07 54		→		08 09		
—	—	—	Norton Bridge Station Drv	d																					
144½	—	—	Stone	d					07 15										08 05						
—	—	—	Stone Crown Street	d											07 00										
—	—	—	Barlaston Orchard Place	d											07 10										
—	—	—	Wedgwood Old Road Bridge	d										←	07 12										←
151¾	—	—	**Stoke-on-Trent**	d		06a50		07a12	07 26					07 26	07 35	07a45			08 13						08 13
—	—	—	Hanley Bus Station	a					→						07 44				→						
159	—	—	Kidsgrove	d										07 34											08 21
161¼	—	—	Alsager	d										07 38											08 25
167¾	24½	—	**Crewe**	a	06 21		06 56				07 22	07 29	07 30	07 48			07 50	07 56				08 10	08 30		08 38

		VT 1◇ ⊠	LM 🚌	LM 🚌	VT 1◇ ⊠	VT 1◇ ⊠	VT 1◇ ⊠	XC 1◇ 🛒	LM	LM 🚌	LM 1◇	VT 1◇ ⊠	LM 1◇	LM 1◇	LM 1◇	LM 1◇	VT 1◇ ⊠	VT 1◇ ⊠	VT 1◇ ⊠	VT 1◇ ⊠		LM 🚌	XC 1◇ 🛒	LM	LM 1◇
London Euston 15 ⊖	d	06 55			07 07	07 10	07 20					07 35				07 46	08 00	08 07	08 10	08 20					
Watford Junction	d															08 01									
Milton Keynes Central	d	07 27				07u40	07 50					08 06				08 25			08u40	08 50					
Northampton	d															08 45									
Rugby	d															09 03									
Coventry	d							07 27	08 04														08 27	09 06	
Bedworth	d								08 15															09 17	
Nuneaton	a								08 23							09 16								09 25	
	d															09 16									
Atherstone	d															09 22									
Polesworth	d																								
Tamworth Low Level	d															09 30									
Lichfield Trent Valley	d												←			→									
Rugeley Trent Valley	d												08 42												
Stafford	d			08 15	08a22			08 29		08 35	08 36		08 54	09 09				09a22					09 29		09 35
Norton Bridge Station Drv	d			08 37																					
Stone	d												09 05									←			
Stone Crown Street	d		08 10	09c00						09 20												09 30			
Barlaston Orchard Place	d		08 20							09 30												09 32			
Wedgwood Old Road Bridge	d		08 22							→					←										
Stoke-on-Trent	d	08a24	08 48				08a48	08a54					09 13		09 13		09a24			09a48		09 48	09a54		
Hanley Bus Station	a		08 55										→									09 55			
Kidsgrove	d														09 21										
Alsager	d														09 25										
Crewe	a					08 47					08 56	09 10		09 30	09 38				09 47						09 56

		VT 1◇ ⊠	LM 🚌	LM 1◇	LM 1◇	LM 🚌	LM 1◇	LM 1◇	VT 1◇ ⊠	VT 1◇ ⊠	VT 1◇ ⊠	VT 1◇ ⊠	LM 🚌	XC 1◇ 🛒	LM 1◇	VT 1◇ ⊠	LM 🚌	LM 1◇		LM 1◇	LM 1◇	LM	LM 1◇	VT 1◇ ☕	VT 1◇ ☕
London Euston 15 ⊖	d	08 40			08 46				09 00	09 07	09 10	09 20				09 40							09 46	10 00	10 07
Watford Junction	d				09 01																		10 01		
Milton Keynes Central	d				09 25						09u40	09 50											10 25		
Northampton	d				09 45																		10 45		
Rugby	d				10 03																		11 03		
Coventry	d													09 27								10 45			
Bedworth	d																					10 56			
Nuneaton	a				10 16																	11 04	11 16		
	d				10 16																		11 16		
Atherstone	d				10 22																		11 22		
Polesworth	d			←														←							
Tamworth Low Level	d			09 30	10 30													10 30					11 31		
Lichfield Trent Valley	d			09 36	→													10 36					→		
Rugeley Trent Valley	d			09 42														10 42							
Stafford	d		09 35	09 54		10 05	10 09			10a22				10 29	10 35		10 35	10 54		11 09					11a22
Norton Bridge Station Drv	d					10 27																			
Stone	d			10 05														11 05							
Stone Crown Street	d		10 20			10c52							←				11 20								
Barlaston Orchard Place	d		10 30										10 30				11 30								
Wedgwood Old Road Bridge	d		→					←					10 32				→				←				
Stoke-on-Trent	d			10 13				10 13	10a24			10a48	10 48	10a54				11 13			11 13			11a24	
Hanley Bus Station	a			→									10 55					→							
Kidsgrove	d							10 21													11 21				
Alsager	d							10 25													11 25				
Crewe	a	10 10					10 30	10 38			10 47				10 56	11 10				11 30	11 38				

For general notes see front of timetable
For details of catering facilities see Directory of Train Operators

A From Bletchley (Table 66)
b Arr. 0652
c Stone Granville Square. Arrival time

London → Stoke-on-Trent and Crewe
Coventry → Nuneaton

Network Diagram - see first page of Table 67

		VT	VT	LM	XC	LM	VT	LM	LM	LM	LM	LM	LM	VT	VT	VT		VT	LM	LM	XC	LM	VT	LM	LM
		1 ◇	1 ◇		1 ◇	1 ◇	1 ◇		1 ◇	1 ◇	1 ◇		1 ◇	1 ◇	1 ◇	1 ◇		1 ◇			1 ◇	1 ◇	1 ◇		1 ◇
		☕	☕	🚌	🛒		☕	🚌						☕	☕	☕		☕	🚌	🚌	🛒		☕	🚌	
London Euston 15 ⊖	d	10 10	10 20				10 40						10 46	11 00	11 07	11 10		11 20					11 40		
Watford Junction	d												11 01												
Milton Keynes Central	d	10u40	10 50										11 25			11u40		11 50							
Northampton	d												11 45												
Rugby	d												12 03												
Coventry	d				10 27							11 45									11 27				
Bedworth	d											11 56													
Nuneaton	a											12 03	12 16												
	d												12 16												
Atherstone	d												12 22												
Polesworth	d								←																←
Tamworth Low Level	d								11 31				12 31												12 31
Lichfield Trent Valley	d								11 37				→												12 37
Rugeley Trent Valley	d								11 43																12 43
Stafford	d				11 29	11 35		11 35	11 54	12 09					12a22					12 25	12 29	12 35		12 35	12 54
Norton Bridge Station Drv	d																			12 45					
Stone	d								12 05																13 05
Stone Crown Street	d			←				12 20											←	13b29				13 20	
Barlaston Orchard Place	d			11 30				12 30											12 30					13 30	
Wedgwood Old Road Bridge	d			11 32				→			←								12 32					→	
Stoke-on-Trent	d		11a48	11 48	11a54				12 13		12 13			12a24				12a48	12 48		12a54				13 13
Hanley Bus Station	a			11 55					→										12 55						→
Kidsgrove	d										12 21														
Alsager	d										12 25														
Crewe	a	11 47				11 56	12 10			12 30	12 38					12 47						12 56	13 10		

		LM	LM	LM	LM	VT	VT	VT	VT	LM	XC	LM	VT	LM		LM	LM	LM	LM	LM	LM	VT	VT	VT	VT
		1 ◇	1 ◇		1 ◇	1 ◇	1 ◇	1 ◇	1 ◇		1 ◇	1 ◇	1 ◇			1 ◇	1 ◇	1 ◇			1 ◇	1 ◇	1 ◇	1 ◇	1 ◇
						☕	☕	☕	☕	🚌	🛒		☕	🚌					🚌			☕	☕	☕	☕
London Euston 15 ⊖	d				11 46	12 00	12 07	12 10	12 20				12 40								12 46	13 00	13 07	13 10	13 20
Watford Junction	d				12 01																13 01				
Milton Keynes Central	d				12 25			12u40	12 50												13 25			13u40	13 50
Northampton	d				12 45																13 45				
Rugby	d				13 03																14 03				
Coventry	d			12 45							12 27									13 45					
Bedworth	d			12 56																13 56					
Nuneaton	a			13 03	13 16															14 03	14 16				
	d				13 16																14 16				
Atherstone	d				13 22																14 22				
Polesworth	d															←									
Tamworth Low Level	d				13 30											13 30					14 30				
Lichfield Trent Valley	d				→											13 36					→				
Rugeley Trent Valley	d															13 42									
Stafford	d	13 09					13a22				13 29	13 35		13 35		13 54	14 09		14 15				14a22		
Norton Bridge Station Drv	d																		14 37						
Stone	d															14 05									
Stone Crown Street	d									←				14 20					14b51						
Barlaston Orchard Place	d									13 30				14 30											
Wedgwood Old Road Bridge	d		←							13 32				→				←							
Stoke-on-Trent	d		13 13			13a24			13a48	13 48	13a54					14 13		14 13				14a24			14a48
Hanley Bus Station	a									13 55						→									
Kidsgrove	d		13 21															14 21							
Alsager	d		13 25															14 25							
Crewe	a	13 30	13 38					13 47				13 56	14 10				14 30	14 38						14 47	

		LM	XC	LM	VT	LM	LM	LM	LM	LM	LM	VT		VT	VT	VT	LM	XC	LM	VT	LM	LM	LM	LM	LM
			1 ◇	1 ◇	1 ◇		1 ◇	1 ◇	1 ◇		1 ◇	1 ◇		1 ◇	1 ◇	1 ◇		1 ◇	1 ◇	1 ◇		1 ◇	1 ◇	1 ◇	
		🚌	🛒		☕	🚌						☕		☕	☕	☕	🚌	🛒		☕	🚌				
London Euston 15 ⊖	d				13 40						13 46	14 00		14 07	14 10	14 20				14 40					
Watford Junction	d										14 01														
Milton Keynes Central	d										14 25				14u40	14 50									
Northampton	d										14 45														
Rugby	d										15 03														
Coventry	d		13 27							14 45								14 27							15 45
Bedworth	d									14 56															15 56
Nuneaton	a									15 03	15 16														16 03
	d										15 16														
Atherstone	d										15 22														
Polesworth	d						←															←			
Tamworth Low Level	d						14 30				15 30											15 30			
Lichfield Trent Valley	d						14 36				→											15 36			
Rugeley Trent Valley	d						14 43															15 43			
Stafford	d		14 29	14 35		14 35	14 54	15 09						15a22				15 29	15 35		15 35	15 54	16 09		
Norton Bridge Station Drv	d																								
Stone	d						15 05															16 05			
Stone Crown Street	d	←				15 20											←				16 20				
Barlaston Orchard Place	d	14 30				15 30											15 30				16 30				
Wedgwood Old Road Bridge	d	14 32				→			←								15 32				→			←	
Stoke-on-Trent	d	14 48	14a54				15 13		15 13			15a24				15a48	15 48	15a54				16 13		16 13	
Hanley Bus Station	a	14 55					→										15 55					→			
Kidsgrove	d								15 21															16 21	
Alsager	d								15 25															16 25	
Crewe	a			14 56	15 10			15 30	15 38						15 47				15 56	16 11			16 30	16 38	

For general notes see front of timetable
For details of catering facilities see Directory of Train Operators

b Stone Granville Square. Arrival time

London → Stoke-on-Trent and Crewe
Coventry → Nuneaton

Network Diagram - see first page of Table 67

Station		LM	VT	VT	VT	VT	LM	XC	LM	LM		VT	LM	LM	LM	LM	LM	LM	VT	VT	VT	VT	LM	LM	XC
		1◇	1◇ ☕	1◇ ☕	1◇ ☕	1◇ ☕	🚌	1◇ 🛒	🚌	1◇		1◇ ☕	🚌	1◇	1◇	1◇		1◇	1◇ ☕	1◇ ⊠	1◇ ⊠	1◇ ⊠	🚌	🚌	1◇ 🛒
London Euston [15] ⊖	d	14 46	15 00	15 07	15 10	15 20						15 40						15 46	16 00	16 07	16 10	16 20			
Watford Junction	d	15 01																16 01							
Milton Keynes Central	d	15 25			15u40	15 50												16 25			16u40	16u50			
Northampton	d	15 45																16 45							
Rugby	d	16 03																17 03							
Coventry	d							15 27									16 45								16 27
Bedworth	d																16 56								
Nuneaton	a	16 16															17 03	17 16							
	d	16 16																17 16							
Atherstone	d	16 22																17 22							
Polesworth	d																								
Tamworth Low Level	d	16 30 →												← 16 30				17 30							
Lichfield Trent Valley	d													16 36				17 36							
Rugeley Trent Valley	d													16 43				17 43							
Stafford	d			16a22				16 29	16 30	16 35			16 35	16 54	17 09			18b20 →		17a22				17 25	17 29
Norton Bridge Station Drv	d								16a52															17a52	
Stone	d													17 05											
Stone Crown Street	d												17 20												
Barlaston Orchard Place	d						← 16 30						17 30 →										← 17 30		
Wedgwood Old Road Bridge	d						16 32																17 32		
Stoke-on-Trent	d		16a24			16a48	16 48	16a54						17 13 →		← 17 13			17a24			17a48	17 48		17a54
Hanley Bus Station	a						16 55																17 55		
Kidsgrove	d															17 21									
Alsager	d															17 25									
Crewe	a				16 47					16 56		17 10			17 30	17 38					17 47				

Station		LM	LM	VT	VT	VT	LM	VT		VT	LM	VT	LM	LM	VT	VT	XC	LM	LM	VT	VT	VT	VT	VT	LM
		🚌	1◇	1◇ ⊠	1◇ ⊠	1◇ ⊠	1◇	1◇ ⊠		1◇ ⊠	1◇	1◇ ⊠	🚌		1◇ ⊠	1◇ ⊠	1◇ 🛒	1◇	1◇	1◇ ⊠	1◇ ⊠	1◇ ⊠	1◇ ⊠	1◇ ⊠	1◇
London Euston [15] ⊖	d			16 33	16 40			16 57		17 00		17 07			17 10	17 20				17 33	17 40	17 57	18 00		
Watford Junction	d																								
Milton Keynes Central	d														17u40	17u50									
Northampton	d																								
Rugby	d			17 22																18 22					
Coventry	d													17 45			17 27								
Bedworth	d													17 56											
Nuneaton	a													18 03	18 11										
	d														18 12										
Atherstone	d																								
Polesworth	d																								
Tamworth Low Level	d							18 00														19 00			
Lichfield Trent Valley	d							18a06														19a06			
Rugeley Trent Valley	d																								
Stafford	d	17 35	17 36	17 56 →		← 17 56	18 09				← 18 20	18 25					18 29	18 35		18 56 →				← 18 56	19 09
Norton Bridge Station Drv	d																								
Stone	d										18 31														
Stone Crown Street	d	18 20																							
Barlaston Orchard Place	d	18 30 →											← 18 30												
Wedgwood Old Road Bridge	d												18 32												
Stoke-on-Trent	d									18a24	18 41		18 48			18a49	18a54						19a24		
Hanley Bus Station	a												19 00												
Kidsgrove	d										18 49 →								← 18 49						
Alsager	d																		18 53						
Crewe	a		17 56		18 10	18 16	18 30					18 43			18 53			19 00	19 05		19 10			19 16	19 30

Station		VT	LM	VT	VT	XC		LM	LM	VT	VT	VT FO	VT	VT	LM	VT	VT	VT	XC	VT	LM	VT FO	VT	LM	VT
		1◇ ⊠		1◇ ⊠	1◇ ⊠	1◇ 🛒		1◇	1◇	1◇ ⊠	1◇ ⊠	◇ ☕	1◇ ⊠	1◇ ⊠	1◇	1◇ ☕	1◇ ☕	1◇ ☕	1◇ 🛒	1◇ ☕		◇ ☕	1◇ ☕	1◇	1◇ ☕
London Euston [15] ⊖	d	18 07		18 10	18 20			18 24		18 33	18 40	18 46	19 00			19 07	19 10	19 20		19 30					19 40
Watford Junction	d							18 44																	
Milton Keynes Central	d			18u40	18u50			19 19									19u40	19 50							
Northampton	d							19 42 →																← 19 42	
Rugby	d									19 22														20 03	
Coventry	d		18 45			18 27													19 27		19 45				
Bedworth	d		18 56																		19 56				
Nuneaton	a		19 03	19 12												20 02					20 03			20 16	
	d			19 13												20 03								20 16	
Atherstone	d																							20 22	
Polesworth	d																								
Tamworth Low Level	d											20s01 →										← 20s01		20 31	20 43
Lichfield Trent Valley	d																					20s09		20 37	20 50
Rugeley Trent Valley	d																							20 44	
Stafford	d	19 25				19 29			19 36	19 56 →				← 19 56	20 09	20a26			20 29			20s35	20 53		21a02
Norton Bridge Station Drv	d																								
Stone	d																								
Stone Crown Street	d																								
Barlaston Orchard Place	d																								
Wedgwood Old Road Bridge	d																								
Stoke-on-Trent	d				19a48	19a54							20a24					20a48	20a54					21 05	
Hanley Bus Station	a																								
Kidsgrove	d																							21 14	
Alsager	d																							21 18	
Crewe	a	19 43		19 53					20 01		20 10			20 16	20 30		20 48			21 01			21 14	21 27	

For general notes see front of timetable
For details of catering facilities see Directory of Train Operators

b Arr. 1800

London → Stoke-on-Trent and Crewe
Coventry → Nuneaton

Network Diagram - see first page of Table 67

		VT	LM	VT		XC	VT	VT	VT	LM	VT	VT	LM	XC	LM	VT	VT	XC	VT	LM	AW	LM	VT		
		1◇ ☕	1◇	1◇ ☕		1◇	1◇ ☕	1◇ ☕	1◇ ☕		1◇ ☕	1◇ ☕	1◇	1◇		1◇ ☕	1◇ ☕	1◇	1◇ ☕	1◇	◇	1	1◇ ☕		
London Euston 15	⊖ d	20 00		20 07			20 10	20 30	20 40			21 00				21 07	21 10		21 40				22 00		
Watford Junction	d																21u25								
Milton Keynes Central	d						20u40					21 31				21 38							22 39		
Northampton	d																								
Rugby	d																22 03						23 19		
Coventry	d					20 27				20 45				21 27	21 44										
Bedworth	d									20 56					21 55										
Nuneaton	a			21 02						21 03					22 02	22 06							23 29		
	d			21 03												22 07							23 30		
Atherstone	d																								
Polesworth	d																								
Tamworth Low Level	d							21 34																	
Lichfield Trent Valley	d							21a40															23s40		
Rugeley Trent Valley	d																						23s47		
Stafford	d		21 09	21a27		21 29					21 55		22 09	22 29			22 34	22 59		23 13	23 30	23 52	00s02		
Norton Bridge Station Drv	d																								
Stone	d																								
Stone Crown Street	d																								
Barlaston Orchard Place	d																								
Wedgwood Old Road Bridge	d																								
Stoke-on-Trent	d	21a23				21a54						22a28		22a54				23a20	23s36						
Hanley Bus Station	a																								
Kidsgrove	d																								
Alsager	d																								
Crewe	a		21 30				21 48		22 12		22 18		22 30			22 46	22 54			23 43	23 55	00 16	00s28		

Saturdays

		VT	XC	LM	LM	LM	XC	LM	LM	LM	LM	XC	VT	LM	LM	LM	LM	VT	VT	LM	LM	LM	VT	VT	LM
		1◇ ☕	1◇ 🍴	1◇	1 A		1◇ 🍴	1◇	1 A	1	🚌	1◇ 🍴	1◇ ☕	1◇	1		1◇	1◇ ☕	1◇ ☕	1◇	1	🚌	1◇ ☕	1◇ ☕	🚌
London Euston 15	⊖ d												06 05				06 24	06 36	06 55				07 07	07 20	
Watford Junction	d												06u20				06 41	06u51							
Milton Keynes Central	d				05 21								06 41				07 23		07 27					07 50	
Northampton	d				05 42					06 38							07 45								
Rugby	d				06 00					06 56			07 03				08 04								
Coventry	d					06 16										07 16									
Bedworth	d					06 27										07 27									
Nuneaton	a				06 16	06 34				07 09						07 35	08 16								
	d				06 16					07 10							08 17								
Atherstone	d				06 22					07 16					←		08 22								
Polesworth	d									07 21					07 21										
Tamworth Low Level	d				06 31					→					07 28		08 31								
Lichfield Trent Valley	d				06 37										07 34		08 37								
Rugeley Trent Valley	d				06 44										07 41		08 43								
Stafford	d	06 01	06 29	06 36	06 54		07 01	07 08				07 29	07 34	07 38	07 54		→			08 09		08 15	08 23		
Norton Bridge Station Drv	d																					08 37			
Stone	d				07 05										08 05										
Stone Crown Street	d										07 00											09b00			08 30
Barlaston Orchard Place	d										07 08														08 38
Wedgwood Old Road Bridge	d										07 10														08 40
Stoke-on-Trent	d		06a50		07 13		07a18				07 21				08 13				08a24					08a48	08 51
Hanley Bus Station	a								←		07 27										←				08 57
Kidsgrove	d				07 21				07 21						08 21						08 21				
Alsager	d				→				07 25						→						08 25				
Crewe	a	06 20		06 56				07 33	07 38			07 50	07 53	07 58				08 10		08 30	08 37		08 41		

For general notes see front of timetable
For details of catering facilities see Directory of Train Operators

A From Bletchley (Table 66)

b Stone Granville Square. Arrival time

London → Stoke-on-Trent and Crewe
Coventry → Nuneaton

Network Diagram - see first page of Table 67

		XC	LM	VT	LM	LM	LM	LM	LM	VT	VT	VT	VT	LM	XC	LM	VT	LM	LM	LM	LM	LM	VT	LM
		1 ◇	1 ◇	1 ◇	1 ◇	1 ◇	1 ◇		1 ◇	1 ◇	1 ◇	1 ◇	1 ◇	(bus)	1 ◇	1 ◇	1 ◇	1 ◇	(bus)	1 ◇		1 ◇	1 ◇	1 ◇
		(trolley)		(catering)						(catering)	(catering)	(catering)	(catering)		(trolley)		(catering)						(catering)	
London Euston 15 ⊖	d			07 35					07 46	08 00	08 07	08 10	08 20				08 40					08 46	08 50	
Watford Junction	d								08 01														09u05	
Milton Keynes Central	d			08 06					08 25			08u40	08 50									09 23	09 25	
Northampton	d								08 45													09 45		
Rugby	d								09 03													10 03		
Coventry	d	07 27						08 45							08 27						09 45			
Bedworth	d							08 56													09 56			
Nuneaton	a							09 03	09 16												10 03	10 16		
	d								09 16													10 16		
Atherstone	d								09 22													10 22		
Polesworth	d																	←						
Tamworth Low Level	d								09 31 →									09 31				10 31		
Lichfield Trent Valley	d				←													09 37				10 37		
Rugeley Trent Valley	d				08 43													09 43				10 43 →		
Stafford	d	08 29	08 36		08 54	09 09					09a22				09 29	09 35		09 54	10 05	10 09				
Norton Bridge Station Drv	d																		10 27					
Stone	d				09 05													10 05						
Stone Crown Street	d													09 30					10b52					
Barlaston Orchard Place	d													09 38										
Wedgwood Old Road Bridge	d						←							09 40										←
Stoke-on-Trent	d	08a54			09 13 →		09 13			09a24			09a48	09 51	09a54			10 13 →						10 13
Hanley Bus Station	a													09 57										
Kidsgrove	d						09 21																	10 21
Alsager	d						09 25																	10 25
Crewe	a		08 56	09 10		09 30	09 37					09 48				09 56	10 10			10 30			10 34	10 37

		VT	VT	VT	LM	XC	LM	VT	LM	LM	LM	LM	LM	VT	VT	VT	VT	LM	XC	LM	LM	VT	VT	LM	LM
		1 ◇	1 ◇	1 ◇	(bus)	1 ◇	1 ◇	1 ◇	1 ◇	1 ◇	1 ◇		1 ◇	1 ◇	1 ◇	1 ◇	1 ◇	(bus)	1 ◇	1 ◇	(bus)	1 ◇	1 ◇	1 ◇	1 ◇
																A						B			
		(catering)	(catering)	(catering)		(trolley)		(catering)						(catering)	(catering)	(catering)	(catering)		(trolley)			(catering)	(catering)		
London Euston 15 ⊖	d	09 00	09 07	09 20				09 40					09 46	10 00	10 07	10 10	10 20					10 30	10 40		
Watford Junction	d												10 01												
Milton Keynes Central	d			09 50									10 24			10u40	10 50								
Northampton	d												10 45												
Rugby	d												11 03												
Coventry	d					09 27						10 45							10 27						
Bedworth	d											10 56													
Nuneaton	a											11 04	11 16												
	d												11 16												
Atherstone	d												11 22												
Polesworth	d																							←	
Tamworth Low Level	d												11 31 →											11 31	
Lichfield Trent Valley	d								←															11 37	
Rugeley Trent Valley	d								10 43															11 43	
Stafford	d		10a22			10 29	10 35		10 54	11 09					11a22				11 29	11 35	11 35			11 54	12 09
Norton Bridge Station Drv	d																								
Stone	d								11 05															12 05	
Stone Crown Street	d				10 30													11 30			12 30 →				
Barlaston Orchard Place	d				10 38													11 38							
Wedgwood Old Road Bridge	d				10 40						←							11 40							
Stoke-on-Trent	d	10a24		10a48	10 51	10a54			11 13 →		11 13			11a24			11a48	11 51	11a54					12 13 →	
Hanley Bus Station	a				10 57													11 57							
Kidsgrove	d										11 21														
Alsager	d										11 25														
Crewe	a						10 56	11 10		11 30	11 37					11 48				11 56		12 03	12 10		12 30

		LM	LM	LM	VT	VT	VT	VT	LM	LM	XC	LM	VT	VT	LM	LM	LM	LM	LM	VT	VT	VT	VT	VT
		1 ◇		1 ◇	1 ◇	1 ◇	1 ◇	1 ◇	(bus)	(bus)	1 ◇	1 ◇	1 ◇	1 ◇	1 ◇	1 ◇	1 ◇		1 ◇	1 ◇	1 ◇	1 ◇	1 ◇	1 ◇
													B									B	A	
					(catering)	(catering)	(catering)	(catering)			(trolley)		(catering)	(catering)						(catering)	(catering)	(catering)	(catering)	(catering)
London Euston 15 ⊖	d			10 46	11 00	11 07	11 10	11 20					11 30	11 40					11 46	12 00	12 07	12 10	12 10	12 20
Watford Junction	d			11 01															12 01					
Milton Keynes Central	d			11 25			11u40	11 50											12 25				12u40	12 50
Northampton	d			11 45															12 45					
Rugby	d			12 03															13 03					
Coventry	d		11 45								11 27							12 45						
Bedworth	d		11 56															12 56						
Nuneaton	a		12 03	12 16														13 03	13 16					
	d			12 16															13 16					
Atherstone	d			12 22															13 22					
Polesworth	d														←									
Tamworth Low Level	d			12 31 →											12 31				13 31 →					
Lichfield Trent Valley	d														12 37									
Rugeley Trent Valley	d														12 43									
Stafford	d					12a22				12 25	12 29	12 35			12 54	13 09					13a22			
Norton Bridge Station Drv	d									12 45														
Stone	d								←						13 05									
Stone Crown Street	d								12 30	13b29														
Barlaston Orchard Place	d								12 38															
Wedgwood Old Road Bridge	d	←							12 40								←							
Stoke-on-Trent	d	12 13			12a24			12a48	12 51		12a54				13 13 →		13 13			13a24				13a48
Hanley Bus Station	a								12 57															
Kidsgrove	d	12 21															13 21							
Alsager	d	12 25															13 25							
Crewe	a	12 37					12 47					12 56	13 04	13 10		13 30	13 37					13 45	13 47	

For general notes see front of timetable
For details of catering facilities see Directory of Train Operators

A Until 31 October
B From 7 November

b Stone Granville Square. Arrival time

Table 67

Saturdays

London → Stoke-on-Trent and Crewe
Coventry → Nuneaton

Network Diagram - see first page of Table 67

		LM	XC	LM	LM	VT	VT	LM	LM	LM	LM	LM	LM	VT	VT	VT	VT	VT	LM	XC	LM	VT	VT	LM	LM
			1 ◇	1 ◇		1 ◇	1 ◇	1 ◇	1 ◇	1 ◇			1 ◇	1 ◇	1 ◇	1 ◇	1 ◇	1 ◇		1 ◇	1 ◇	1 ◇	1 ◇	1 ◇	1 ◇
						A										A	B					A			
		🚌			🚌						🚌								🚌						
			🛒			☕	☕							☕	☕	☕	☕	☕		🛒		☕	☕		
London Euston 15	⊖ d					12 30	12 40						12 46	13 00	13 07	13 10	13 10	13 20				13 30	13 40		
Watford Junction	d												13 01												
Milton Keynes Central	d												13 25			13u40	13u40	13 50							
Northampton	d												13 45												
Rugby	d												14 03												
Coventry	d		12 27									13 45								13 27					
Bedworth	d											13 56													
Nuneaton	a											14 03	14 16												
	d												14 16												
Atherstone	d												14 22												
Polesworth	d							←																←	
Tamworth Low Level	d							13 31					14 31 →											14 31	
Lichfield Trent Valley	d							13 37																14 37	
Rugeley Trent Valley	d							13 43																14 43	
Stafford	d		13 29	13 35	13 35			13 54	14 09		14 15				14a22					14 29	14 35			14 54	15 09
Norton Bridge Station Drv	d										14 37														
Stone	d							14 05																15 05	
Stone Crown Street	d	13 30			14 30						14b51								←						
Barlaston Orchard Place	d	13 38			14 38 →														14 38						
Wedgwood Old Road Bridge	d	13 40								←									14 40						
Stoke-on-Trent	d	13 51	13a54					14 13		14 13				14a24				14a48	14 51	14a54				15 13	
Hanley Bus Station	a	13 57						→											14 57					→	
Kidsgrove	d									14 21															
Alsager	d									14 25															
Crewe	a			13 56		14 06	14 10		14 30	14 37						14 47	14 48				14 56	15 04	15 10		15 30

		LM	LM	LM	VT	VT	VT	VT	VT	LM		XC	LM	LM	VT	VT	LM	LM	LM	LM	LM	VT	VT	VT	VT
		1 ◇		1 ◇	1 ◇	1 ◇	1 ◇	1 ◇	1 ◇			1 ◇	1 ◇		1 ◇	1 ◇	1 ◇	1 ◇	1 ◇		1 ◇	1 ◇	1 ◇	1 ◇	1 ◇
							A	B							A										
										🚌				🚌											
					☕	☕	☕	☕	☕			🛒			☕	☕						☕	☕	☕	☕
London Euston 15	⊖ d			13 46	14 00	14 07	14 10	14 10	14 20						14 30	14 40					14 46	15 00	15 07	15 10	15 20
Watford Junction	d			14 01																	15 01				
Milton Keynes Central	d			14 25				14u40	14 50												15 25			15u40	15 50
Northampton	d			14 45																	15 45				
Rugby	d			15 03																	16 03				
Coventry	d		14 45									14 27								15 45					
Bedworth	d		14 56																	15 56					
Nuneaton	a		15 03	15 16																16 03	16 16				
	d			15 16																	16 16				
Atherstone	d			15 22																	16 22				
Polesworth	d																←								
Tamworth Low Level	d			15 31 →													15 31				16 31 →				
Lichfield Trent Valley	d																15 37								
Rugeley Trent Valley	d																15 43								
Stafford	d					15a22						15 29	15 35	15 35			15 54	16 09					16a22		
Norton Bridge Station Drv	d																								
Stone	d																16 05								
Stone Crown Street	d									15 30				16 30											
Barlaston Orchard Place	d									15 38				16 38 →											
Wedgwood Old Road Bridge	d	←								15 40									←						
Stoke-on-Trent	d	15 13			15a24				15a48	15 51		15a54					16 13		16 13			16a24			16a48
Hanley Bus Station	a									15 57							→								
Kidsgrove	d	15 21																	16 21						
Alsager	d	15 25																	16 25						
Crewe	a	15 37					15 45	15 47					15 56		16 06	16 11		16 30	16 37					16 47	

		LM	XC	LM	LM	VT	VT	LM	LM	LM	LM	LM	VT	VT	VT	VT	VT	LM	LM	XC	LM	VT	VT	VT	LM
			1 ◇		1 ◇	1 ◇	1 ◇	1 ◇	1 ◇	1 ◇		1 ◇	1 ◇	1 ◇	1 ◇	1 ◇	1 ◇			1 ◇	1 ◇	1 ◇	1 ◇	1 ◇	1 ◇
						A									A	B						A			
		🚌		🚌														🚌	🚌						
			🛒			☕	☕						☕	☕	☕	☕	☕			🛒		☕	☕	☕	
London Euston 15	⊖ d					15 30	15 40					15 46	16 00	16 07	16 10	16 10	16 20					16 30	16 33	16 40	16 46
Watford Junction	d											16 01													17 01
Milton Keynes Central	d											16 25				16u40	16 50								17 25
Northampton	d											16 45													17 45
Rugby	d											17 03													→
Coventry	d		15 27								16 45									16 27					
Bedworth	d										16 56														
Nuneaton	a										17 03	17 16													
	d											17 16													
Atherstone	d											17 22													
Polesworth	d							←																	
Tamworth Low Level	d							16 31				17 31											17 38		
Lichfield Trent Valley	d							16 37				17 37											17 45		
Rugeley Trent Valley	d							16 43				17 43 →													
Stafford	d		16 29	16 30	16 35			16 54	17 09					17a22				17 25		17 29	17 36		17a58		
Norton Bridge Station Drv	d			16a52														17a52							
Stone	d							17 05																	
Stone Crown Street	d	←																	17 30						
Barlaston Orchard Place	d	16 38																	17 38						
Wedgwood Old Road Bridge	d	16 40								←									17 40						
Stoke-on-Trent	d	16 51	16a54					17 13		17 13			17a24				17a48		17 51	17a54					
Hanley Bus Station	a	16 57						→											17 57						
Kidsgrove	d									17 21															
Alsager	d									17 25															
Crewe	a				16 56	17 04	17 10		17 30	17 37					17 45	17 47					17 56	18 06		18 10	

For general notes see front of timetable
For details of catering facilities see Directory of Train Operators

A From 7 November
B Until 31 October

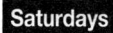

b Stone Granville Square. Arrival time

Table 67

Saturdays

London → Stoke-on-Trent and Crewe
Coventry → Nuneaton

Network Diagram - see first page of Table 67

Station		VT	LM	LM	VT	VT		VT	LM	XC	LM	LM	VT	LM	LM	VT	LM	VT	LM	VT	LM	VT	VT	VT	XC
		1◇	1◇	1◇	1◇	1◇		1◇		1◇		1◇	1◇	1◇	1◇	1◇	1◇	1◇	1◇	1◇	1◇	1◇	1◇	1◇	1◇
													A									A	B		
									🚌																
		☕			☕	☕		☕		🛒			☕			☕		☕		☕		☕	☕	☕	🛒
London Euston 15 ⊖	d	17 00			17 07	17 10		17 20					17 30			17 40		18 00		18 07		18 10	18 10	18 20	
Watford Junction	d																								
Milton Keynes Central	d					17u40		17 50						←									18u40	18 50	
Northampton	d													17 45											
Rugby	d													18 03											
Coventry	d									17 27	17 45														18 27
Bedworth	d										17 56														
Nuneaton	a				18 02						18 03			18 16											
	d				18 03									18 16											
Atherstone	d													18 22											
Polesworth	d																←								
Tamworth Low Level	d													18 31 →			18 31								
Lichfield Trent Valley	d			←													18 37								
Rugeley Trent Valley	d			17 43													18 43								
Stafford	d		18 09	18b20	18a26					18 29		18 35					18 54		19 09	19a22					19 29
Norton Bridge Station Drv	d																								
Stone	d			18 31													19 05								
Stone Crown Street	d								18 30																
Barlaston Orchard Place	d								18 38																
Wedgwood Old Road Bridge	d								18 40																
Stoke-on-Trent	d	18a24		18 41				18a48	18 51	18a54							19 13	19a24						19a48	19a54
Hanley Bus Station	a								18 57						←						←				
Kidsgrove	d			18 49 →											18 49		19 21 →				19 21				
Alsager	d														18 53						19 25				
Crewe	a		18 30			18 48						18 59	19 04		19 05	19 10			19 30		19 35	19 45	19 48		

Station		LM	LM	VT	LM	VT	VT	VT	LM	LM	VT	VT	VT	VT	VT	XC	VT	VT	VT	VT	VT	LM	LM	VT	LM
			1◇	1◇	1	1◇	1◇	1◇	1◇	1	1◇	1◇	1◇	1◇	1◇	1◇	1◇	1◇	1◇	1◇	1◇	1		1◇	1◇
				A				C			C	D	C	D	D		E	C		A	D			C	
				☕		☕	☕	☕			☕	☕	☕	☕	☕	🛒	☕	☕	☕	☕	☕			☕	
London Euston 15 ⊖	d			18 30		18 33	18 40	18 54			18 57	19 00	19 05	19 07	19 20		19 30	19 19		19 30	19 40			19 25	
Watford Junction	d																								
Milton Keynes Central	d												19 36		19 50										
Northampton	d				18 45																	19 45			
Rugby	d				19 03																	20 03			
Coventry	d	18 45														19 27							20 15		
Bedworth	d	18 56																					20 26		
Nuneaton	a	19 03			19 16						19 55			20 02								20 16	20 34		
	d				19 16						19 56			20 03								20 16			
Atherstone	d				19 22																	20 22			
Polesworth	d																								
Tamworth Low Level	d				19 30	19 38																20 30			
Lichfield Trent Valley	d				19 36	19 46																20 36			
Rugeley Trent Valley	d				19 43																	20 43			
Stafford	d		19 36		19 53	19a58			20 09		20 24			20 27		20 29			20 50			20 55			21 09
Norton Bridge Station Drv	d																								
Stone	d				20 05																	21 08			
Stone Crown Street	d																								
Barlaston Orchard Place	d																								
Wedgwood Old Road Bridge	d																								
Stoke-on-Trent	d				20 13			20a24				20a24	20a37		20a48	20a54						21 16 →			
Hanley Bus Station	a									←															
Kidsgrove	d				20 21 →					20 21															
Alsager	d									20 25															
Crewe	a		20 01	20 03			20 10		20 30	20 35	20 46			20 45			21 01	21 02	21 09	21 15	21 18			21 18	21 30

Station		LM	XC	XC	VT	VT	VT	XC	VT	LM	VT	VT	VT	XC	XC	VT	VT	VT	LM	VT	XC	XC	LM		
		1	1◇	1◇	1◇	1◇	1◇		1◇	1◇		1◇	1◇	1◇	1◇	1◇	1◇	1◇		1◇		1◇	1		
			D	G	C	H	G	H	D		H	C	D	H	J	C	E	A		D	H				
								🚌			🚌										🚌				
			🛒	🛒	☕	☕	☕		☕			☕	☕	🛒	🛒	☕	☕	☕		☕		🛒			
London Euston 15 ⊖	d				19 41	19 47	19 47		20 11			20 14	20 20			20 26	20 30	20 30		21 00					
Watford Junction	d											20u29					20u45	20u46							
Milton Keynes Central	d					20 51	20 51						21 05			21 22				21 45					
Northampton	d																								
Rugby	d				20 52				21 14			21 35					21 35	21 36							
Coventry	d		20 27											21 27	21 27				21 45						
Bedworth	d																		21 56						
Nuneaton	a					21 32	21 32						21 32						22 03						
	d					21 33	21 33						21 33												
Atherstone	d																								
Polesworth	d																								
Tamworth Low Level	d											21 53					21 53	21 55							
Lichfield Trent Valley	d											22 00					22 00	22 01							
Rugeley Trent Valley	d																								
Stafford	d		21 29	21 29	21 37	22 00		21 40	21 47	22 09	22 10			22a29	22 29	22 36				22 36	22 40	23 03	23 13		
Norton Bridge Station Drv	d																								
Stone	d																								
Stone Crown Street	d																								
Barlaston Orchard Place	d																								
Wedgwood Old Road Bridge	d	←																							
Stoke-on-Trent	d	21 16	21a48	21a49			22a05	22a10			22a40		22a05		22a50						23a10				
Hanley Bus Station	a																								
Kidsgrove	d	21 24																							
Alsager	d	21 28																							
Crewe	a	21 38			22 01	22 24			22 12	22 34		22 38				23 00	22 38	22 43		23 00		23 26	23 37		

For general notes see front of timetable
For details of catering facilities see Directory of Train Operators

A From 7 November
B Until 31 October
C Until 5 September
D From 12 September
E 12 September to 31 October
G 18 July to 5 September
H Until 11 July
J From 18 July
b Arr. 1804

Table 67

Sundays

until 12 July

London → Stoke-on-Trent and Crewe
Coventry → Nuneaton

Network Diagram - see first page of Table 67

		VT	XC	VT	VT	VT		VT	LM	VT	XC	VT		VT	VT	LM	XC	VT		XC	LM	LM	VT	VT	VT
		1◇	1◇	1◇	1◇	1◇		🚌	1◇	1◇	🚌	1◇		1◇	🚌	1◇	1◇	1◇		🚌	🚌	1	1◇	1◇	🚌
		☕	trolley	☕	☕	☕				☕		☕		☕			trolley	☕					☕	☕	
London Euston 15 ⊖	d			08 10	08 15	08 20				08 45		09 20		09 15				09 45					10 15	10 20	
Watford Junction	d																								
Milton Keynes Central	d			08 55		09 05				09 33		10 07						10 33						11 07	
Northampton	d																								
Rugby	d									09 56								10 57							
Coventry	d																10 28								
Bedworth	d																								
Nuneaton	a				09 29									10 34									11 33		
	d				09 30									10 38									11 35		
Atherstone	d																								
Polesworth	d																								
Tamworth Low Level	d																								
Lichfield Trent Valley	d																								
Rugeley Trent Valley	d																								
Stafford	d	09 19	09 32		09 58	10a03		10 10	10 14		10 40	11a00		11 05	11 10	11 17	11a29			11 40	11 41	11 54	12 01	12a05	12 10
Norton Bridge Station Drv	d																								
Stone	d																								
Stone Crown Street	d																				12b02				
Barlaston Orchard Place	d																								
Wedgwood Old Road Bridge	d																								
Stoke-on-Trent	d							10a40			11a10				11a40					12a10	12 20				12a40
Hanley Bus Station	a																								
Kidsgrove	d																				12 38 →				
Alsager	d																								
Crewe	a	09 43	09 56	10 17	10 22				10 38	10 52				11 30		11 37		11 54				12 16	12 19		

		LM		XC	VT	LM	XC	LM		VT	LM	LM	LM	VT		LM	VT	XC	VT	VT		LM	LM	LM	LM
		1◇		1◇	1◇	🚌	🚌	1◇		1◇		🚌	1◇	🚌		1◇	1◇	1◇	1◇	1◇		🚌	1◇		1◇
				trolley	☕					☕							☕	trolley	☕	☕					
London Euston 15 ⊖	d				10 45					11 15							12 02		12 15	12 35					12 50
Watford Junction	d																								13 07
Milton Keynes Central	d				11 32					12 04									12 48						13 36
Northampton	d																								
Rugby	d				11 55			11 56																	14 16
Coventry	d			11 28							11 55							12 28						13 46	
Bedworth	d										12 06													13 57	
Nuneaton	a							12 10			12 13													14 04	14 29
	d							12 10																	14 30
Atherstone	d							12 17																	14 37
Polesworth	d																								
Tamworth Low Level	d							12 25																	14 45 →
Lichfield Trent Valley	d							12 31																	
Rugeley Trent Valley	d							12 38								←									
Stafford	d	12 16		12a33			12 40	13c00 →		12 55		13 01	13 10	13 10		13 00	13 25	13a33					14 10		
Norton Bridge Station Drv	d																								
Stone	d																								
Stone Crown Street	d											13b22													
Barlaston Orchard Place	d																								
Wedgwood Old Road Bridge	d																								
Stoke-on-Trent	d						13a10					13 40		13a40					13a50						
Hanley Bus Station	a					←																←			
Kidsgrove	d					12 38						13 58 →										13 58			
Alsager	d					12 52																14 12			
Crewe	a	12 37			12 49	13 07				13 16			13 30			13 34	13 43			14 12		14 27	14 30		

		VT	VT	VT		XC	VT	VT	LM	LM		VT	VT	XC	LM	LM		VT	LM	LM	LM	VT		VT	VT
		1◇	1◇	1◇		1◇	1◇	1◇	1◇	1◇		1◇	1◇	1◇		1◇		1◇	1◇		1◇	1◇		1◇	1◇
		☕	☕	☕		trolley	☕	☕				☕	☕	trolley				☕				☕		☕	☕
London Euston 15 ⊖	d	12 55	13 02	13 15			13 35	13 55				14 02	14 15					14 35			14 50	14 55		15 02	15 05
Watford Junction	d																				15 06				
Milton Keynes Central	d			13 48									14 48								15 42				15u38
Northampton	d																								
Rugby	d																				16 16				
Coventry	d					13 26								14 26	14 46					15 46					
Bedworth	d														14 57					15 57					
Nuneaton	a														15 04					16 04	16 29				
	d																				16 30				
Atherstone	d																				16 37				
Polesworth	d									←															
Tamworth Low Level	d									14 45											16 45 →				
Lichfield Trent Valley	d									14 51															
Rugeley Trent Valley	d									14 58															
Stafford	d		14 22			14 34			15 10	15 16		15 25		15 34					16 10					16a20	
Norton Bridge Station Drv	d																								
Stone	d									15 32															
Stone Crown Street	d																								
Barlaston Orchard Place	d																								
Wedgwood Old Road Bridge	d																								
Stoke-on-Trent	d	14a26		14a50		14a56		15a25		15 41			15a50	15a56								16a24			
Hanley Bus Station	a															←									
Kidsgrove	d									15 53 →						15 53									
Alsager	d															15 58									
Crewe	a		14 43				15 12		15 30			15 43				16 07		16 12	16 32						16 54

For general notes see front of timetable
For details of catering facilities see
Directory of Train Operators

b Stone Granville Square
c Arr. 1254

Table 67

Sundays

until 12 July

London → Stoke-on-Trent and Crewe
Coventry → Nuneaton

Network Diagram - see first page of Table 67

		VT 1◇	XC 1◇	VT 1◇	VT 1◇	LM 1◇			LM 1◇	VT 1◇	VT 1◇	VT 1◇		XC 1◇	LM	LM 1◇	VT 1◇	LM 1◇	LM	VT 1◇	LM 1◇	VT 1◇	VT 1◇	LM 1◇	VT 1◇
London Euston 15 ⊖	d	15 15		15 35	15 55					16 02	16 05	16 15					16 35	16 50		16 55		17 02	17 05	←	17 15
Watford Junction	d																	17 06 →						17 06	
Milton Keynes Central	d	15 48									16u39	16 48											17u38	17 42	17 48
Northampton	d																								
Rugby	d																							18 16	
Coventry	d		15 26											16 26	16 46				17 46						
Bedworth	d														16 57				17 57						
Nuneaton	a														17 04				18 04				18 09	18 29	
	d																						18 10	18 30	
Atherstone	d																							18 37	
Polesworth	d								←															18 45 →	
Tamworth Low Level	d								16 45																
Lichfield Trent Valley	d								16 51																
Rugeley Trent Valley	d								16 58																
Stafford	d		16 34			17 10			17 16	17a24				17 34							18 10	18a24			
Norton Bridge Station Drv	d																								
Stone	d								17 32																
Stone Crown Street	d																								
Barlaston Orchard Place	d																								
Wedgwood Old Road Bridge	d																								
Stoke-on-Trent	d	16a50	16a56		17a25				17 41			17a50		17a56						18a25					18a50
Hanley Bus Station	a																								
Kidsgrove	d								17 55							←									
Alsager	d								17 58 →							17 58									
Crewe	a			17 12		17 30					17 54					18 07	18 12				18 30		18 53		

		XC 1◇		VT 1◇	VT 1◇	LM 1◇	LM 1◇	VT 1◇		VT 1◇	VT 1◇	XC 1◇	LM 1◇	VT 1◇		LM 1◇	VT 1◇	LM 1◇	VT 1◇	VT 1◇		VT 1◇	XC 1◇	LM	VT 1◇
London Euston 15 ⊖	d			17 35	17 55			18 02		18 05	18 15			18 35		18 50	18 55		19 02	19 05		19 15			
Watford Junction	d															19 06									
Milton Keynes Central	d									18u38	18 48					19 42				19u38		19 48			
Northampton	d																								
Rugby	d															20 16									
Coventry	d	17 26										18 26				→							19 26	19 46	
Bedworth	d																							19 57	
Nuneaton	a																		20 00					20 04	
	d																		20 01						
Atherstone	d																								
Polesworth	d						←																		
Tamworth Low Level	d						18 45																		
Lichfield Trent Valley	d						18 51																		
Rugeley Trent Valley	d						18 58																		
Stafford	d	18 36				19 10	19 16	19a24				19 34						20 10	20b30				20 38		20 52
Norton Bridge Station Drv	d																								
Stone	d						19 32																		
Stone Crown Street	d																								
Barlaston Orchard Place	d																								
Wedgwood Old Road Bridge	d																								
Stoke-on-Trent	d	18a56			19a25		19 41				19a50	19a56					20a25					20a50	20a57		
Hanley Bus Station	a																								
Kidsgrove	d						19 55						←												
Alsager	d						19 59 →						19 59												
Crewe	a			19 12		19 30				19 54			20 08	20 12				20 30	20 48	20 55					21 10

		VT 1◇	VT 1◇	LM 1◇		VT 1◇	VT 1◇	VT 1◇	VT 1◇	XC 1◇		LM 1◇	VT 1◇	VT 1◇	LM 1	XC 1◇		LM	VT 1◇	VT 1◇	VT 1◇	AW ◇	VT 1◇		
London Euston 15 ⊖	d	19 35	19 55			20 02	20 05	20 15	20 25					20 35					20 50	21 20	21 24		21 50		
Watford Junction	d																								
Milton Keynes Central	d						20 38	20 49											21 39		22 13		22 38		
Northampton	d			←																					
Rugby	d			20 16															22 00				23 06		
Coventry	d									20 26						21 26		21 35							
Bedworth	d																	21 46							
Nuneaton	a			20 29		21 00												21 53		22 46			23 21		
	d			20 30		21 01														22 53			23 26		
Atherstone	d			20 37																					
Polesworth	d																								
Tamworth Low Level	d			20 45					21 32																
Lichfield Trent Valley	d			20 51					21 39																
Rugeley Trent Valley	d			20 58																					
Stafford	d			21 16			21 33			21 34			21 59	22 04	22 14	22 34				23 19		23 31	23s53		
Norton Bridge Station Drv	d																								
Stone	d			21 32																					
Stone Crown Street	d																								
Barlaston Orchard Place	d																								
Wedgwood Old Road Bridge	d																								
Stoke-on-Trent	d		21a25	21 43				21a50		21a56						22a56					23a30				
Hanley Bus Station	a											←													
Kidsgrove	d			21 54 →								21 54													
Alsager	d											22 00													
Crewe	a	21 13				21 44	21 53		22 10			22 11	22 17	22 22	22 36				22 49	23 43		23 55	00s16		

For general notes see front of timetable
For details of catering facilities see Directory of Train Operators

b Arr. 2025

Table 67

Sundays

from 19 July

London → Stoke-on-Trent and Crewe
Coventry → Nuneaton

Network Diagram - see first page of Table 67

		VT	VT	XC	XC	VT	VT	VT	VT	VT	VT	LM	LM	VT	VT	VT	XC	XC	VT	VT	VT	LM	XC	XC	VT
		1 ◇	1 ◇	1 ◇	1 ◇	1 ◇	1 ◇	1 ◇	1 ◇	1 ◇	1 ◇	1 ◇	1 ◇	1 ◇	1 ◇	1 ◇	1 ◇	1 ◇	1 ◇	1 ◇	1 ◇	1 ◇	1 ◇	1 ◇	1 ◇
		A	B	A	C	A	D	B	C	A		A		B	D	A	C	A	C	A			C	A	B
		🍴	🍴	🛒	🛒	🍴	🍴	🍴	🍴	🍴	🍴			🍴	🍴	🍴	🛒	🛒	🍴	🍴	🍴		🛒	🛒	🍴
London Euston 15 ⊖	d					08 10	08 10	08 10	08 15	08 15	08 20			08 45	08 44	08 45			09 15	09 15	09 20				09 45
Watford Junction	d																								
Milton Keynes Central	d					08 56	08 56	08 56			09 05			09 33	09 33	09 33					10 07				10 33
Northampton	d																								
Rugby	d													09 56	09 56	10 09									10 57
Coventry	d																						10 28	10 28	
Bedworth	d																								
Nuneaton	a								09 29	09 41									10 34	10 44					
	d								09 30	09 42									10 38	10 45					
Atherstone	d																								
Polesworth	d																								
Tamworth Low Level	d																								
Lichfield Trent Valley	d																								
Rugeley Trent Valley	d																								
Stafford	d	09 23	09 19	09 34	09 32				09 58	10 10		10 17	10 14				10 31	10 33	11 05	11 11		11 17	11 31	11 33	
Norton Bridge Station Drv	d																								
Stone	d																								
Stone Crown Street	d																								
Barlaston Orchard Place	d																								
Wedgwood Old Road Bridge	d																								
Stoke-on-Trent	d										10a21						10a51	10a51			11a22		11a51	11a52	
Hanley Bus Station	a																								
Kidsgrove	d																								
Alsager	d																								
Crewe	a	09 40	09 43	09 54	09 55	10 15	10 17	10 18	10 22	10 29		10 37	10 38	10 52	10 55	10 58			11 30	11 30		11 37			11 54

		VT	VT	LM	XC	VT	VT	VT	LM	XC	VT	VT	LM	VT	LM	XC	VT	VT	LM	LM	LM	VT	VT	XC	VT
		1 ◇	1 ◇	1		1 ◇	1 ◇	1 ◇	1 ◇	1 ◇	1 ◇	1 ◇	1 ◇	1 ◇			1 ◇	1 ◇	1 ◇	1 ◇	1 ◇	1 ◇	1 ◇	1 ◇	1 ◇
		D	A		E 🚌	C	A				D	B		A		E 🚌									
		🍴	🍴			🍴	🍴	🍴		🛒	🍴	🍴		🍴			🍴	🍴				🍴	🍴	🛒	🍴
London Euston 15 ⊖	d	09 45	09 45			10 15	10 15	10 20			10 45	10 45		10 45			11 15	11 20				12 02	12 15		12 35
Watford Junction	d																								
Milton Keynes Central	d	10 33	10 31					11 07			11 32	11 32		11 32			12 04	12 09					12 48		
Northampton	d												11 36												
Rugby	d	10 57	11 07								11 56	11 56	11 58	12 07											
Coventry	d									11 28					11 55									12 28	
Bedworth	d														12 06										
Nuneaton	a					11 33	11 44						12 11		12 13										
	d				11 20	11 35	11 45						12 11			12 20									
Atherstone	d												12 18												
Polesworth	d																								
Tamworth Low Level	d				11a40								12 26			12a40									
Lichfield Trent Valley	d												12 32												
Rugeley Trent Valley	d												12 39						←						
Stafford	d			11 41		12 01	12 11		12 16	12 34			13b00 →				12 55		13 00	13 10		13 25		13 34	
Norton Bridge Station Drv	d																								
Stone	d			11 51															13 12						
Stone Crown Street	d																								
Barlaston Orchard Place	d																								
Wedgwood Old Road Bridge	d																				←				
Stoke-on-Trent	d			11 59				12a22		12a52								13a11	13 20 →		13 20		13a50	13a56	
Hanley Bus Station	a																								
Kidsgrove	d			12 08																	13 28				
Alsager	d			12 12																	13 31				
Crewe	a	11 57	11 54	12 24		12 30	12 30		12 37		12 48	12 49		12 59			13 16			13 30	13 42	13 43			14 12

		XC	LM	LM	XC	LM	VT	VT	VT	XC	VT	VT	LM	LM	VT	VT	XC	LM	LM	VT	XC	LM	LM	XC	LM
			1 ◇			1 ◇	1 ◇	1 ◇	1 ◇	1 ◇	1 ◇	1 ◇	1 ◇	1 ◇	1 ◇	1 ◇	1 ◇		1 ◇	1 ◇		1 ◇			1 ◇
		E 🚌			E 🚌																E 🚌			E 🚌	
							🍴	🍴	🍴	🛒	🍴	🍴			🍴	🍴	🛒			🍴					
London Euston 15 ⊖	d					12 50	12 55	13 02	13 15		13 35	13 55			14 02	14 15				14 35					14 50
Watford Junction	d					13 07																			15 06
Milton Keynes Central	d					13 36			13 48							14 48									15 36
Northampton	d					13 56																			15 56
Rugby	d					14 16																			16 16
Coventry	d			13 46						13 26							14 26	14 46					15 46		
Bedworth	d			13 57														14 57					15 57		
Nuneaton	a			14 04		14 29												15 04					16 04		16 29
	d	13 20			14 20	14 30															15 20			16 20	16 30
Atherstone	d					14 37																			16 37
Polesworth	d													←											
Tamworth Low Level	d	13a40			14a40	14 45 →								14 45							15a40			16a40	16 45 →
Lichfield Trent Valley	d													14 51											
Rugeley Trent Valley	d													14 58											
Stafford	d		14 10					14 22		14 34			15 10	15 16	15 25		15 34					16 10			
Norton Bridge Station Drv	d																								
Stone	d													15 32											
Stone Crown Street	d																								
Barlaston Orchard Place	d																								
Wedgwood Old Road Bridge	d																								
Stoke-on-Trent	d						14a26		14a50	14a56		15a25		15 41		15a50	15a56								
Hanley Bus Station	a																		←						
Kidsgrove	d													15 52 →					15 52						
Alsager	d																		15 58						
Crewe	a		14 30					14 43			15 12		15 30		15 43				16 08	16 12		16 32			

For general notes see front of timetable
For details of catering facilities see Directory of Train Operators

A Until 6 September
B 13 September to 1 November
C From 13 September
D From 8 November
E From 13 September. From Leicester (Table 57)
b Arr. 1253

Table 67

Sundays
from 19 July

London → Stoke-on-Trent and Crewe
Coventry → Nuneaton

Network Diagram - see first page of Table 67

		VT	VT	VT	VT	XC	VT	VT	LM	LM	LM	XC	VT	VT	VT	XC	LM	VT	LM	VT	LM	VT	LM	VT	VT
		1◇	1◇	1◇	1◇	1◇	1◇	1◇	1◇	1◇			1◇	1◇	1◇	1◇	1◇	1◇	1◇	1◇	1◇	1◇		1◇	1◇
												A 🚌													
		☕	☕	☕	☕	🛒	☕	☕					☕	☕	☕	🛒		☕		☕		☕		☕	☕
London Euston 15 ⊖	d	14 55	15 02	15 05	15 15		15 35	15 55					16 02	16 05	16 15			16 35	16 50	16 55		17 02		17 05	17 15
Watford Junction	d																		17 06						
Milton Keynes Central	d			15u38	15 48									16u39	16 48				17 36					17u38	17 48
Northampton	d																		17 56						
Rugby	d																		→						
Coventry	d					15 26					16 46					16 26							17 46		
Bedworth	d										16 57												17 57		
Nuneaton	a										17 04												18 04	18 09	
	d											17 20												18 10	
Atherstone	d																								
Polesworth	d									←															
Tamworth Low Level	d									16 45		17a40													
Lichfield Trent Valley	d									16 51															
Rugeley Trent Valley	d									16 58															
Stafford	d		16a20			16 36			17 10	17 16			17a24			17 34					18 10	18a24			
Norton Bridge Station Drv	d																								
Stone	d									17 32															
Stone Crown Street	d																								
Barlaston Orchard Place	d																								
Wedgwood Old Road Bridge	d																								
Stoke-on-Trent	d	16a24			16a50	16a56		17a25		17 41					17a50	17a56				18a25					18a50
Hanley Bus Station	a																								
Kidsgrove	d									17 52							←								
Alsager	d									17 59							17 59								
Crewe	a			16 54			17 12		17 30	→				17 54			18 08	18 12			18 30			18 53	

		XC	VT	VT	XC	LM	LM	XC	VT	VT	VT	XC	LM	VT	LM	VT	LM	VT	VT	VT	XC	LM	XC	VT	VT
		1◇	1◇	1◇		1◇	1◇		1◇	1◇	1◇	1◇	1◇	1◇	1◇	1◇	1◇	1◇	1◇	1◇	1◇			1◇	1◇
					A 🚌			A 🚌															A 🚌		
		🛒	☕	☕					☕	☕	☕	🛒		☕		☕		☕	☕	☕	🛒			☕	☕
London Euston 15 ⊖	d		17 35	17 55					18 02	18 05	18 15			18 35	18 50	18 55		19 02	19 05	19 15					19 35
Watford Junction	d														19 06										
Milton Keynes Central	d						←			18u38	18 48				19 36				19u38	19 48					
Northampton	d						17 56								19 56										
Rugby	d						18 16								→										
Coventry	d	17 26										18 26									19 26	19 46			
Bedworth	d																					19 57			
Nuneaton	a						18 29											20 00				20 04			
	d				18 20		18 30	19 20										20 01					20 20		
Atherstone	d						18 37																		
Polesworth	d																								
Tamworth Low Level	d				18a40		18 45	19a40															20a40		
Lichfield Trent Valley	d						18 51																		
Rugeley Trent Valley	d						18 58																		
Stafford	d	18 36				19 10	19 16		19a24			19 34					20 10	20b30			20 38			20 52	
Norton Bridge Station Drv	d																								
Stone	d						19 32																		
Stone Crown Street	d																								
Barlaston Orchard Place	d																								
Wedgwood Old Road Bridge	d																								
Stoke-on-Trent	d	18a58		19a25			19 41				19a50	19a56				20a25				20a50	20a57				
Hanley Bus Station	a																								
Kidsgrove	d						19 52						←												
Alsager	d						19 58						19 58												
Crewe	a		19 12			19 30	→			19 54			20 07	20 12			20 30	20 48	20 55					21 10	21 13

		VT	LM	VT	VT	VT	VT	XC	XC	LM	VT	VT	LM	XC	LM	VT	XC	XC	VT	VT	VT	AW	AW	VT
		1◇	1◇	1◇	1◇	1◇	1◇	1◇		1◇	1◇	1◇	1	1◇		1◇		1◇	1◇	1◇	1◇	◇	◇	1◇
									A 🚌								A 🚌	B	B	C		B	C	
		☕		☕	☕	☕	☕	🛒			☕	☕		🛒		☕		🛒	☕	☕	☕			☕
London Euston 15 ⊖	d	19 55		20 02	20 05	20 15	20 25					20 35				20 50			21 20	21 20	21 24			21 50
Watford Junction	d																							
Milton Keynes Central	d		←		20 38	20 48										21 39					22 13			22 38
Northampton	d		19 56																					
Rugby	d		20 16													22 00								23 19
Coventry	d							20 26						21 26	21 35									
Bedworth	d														21 46									
Nuneaton	a		20 29	21 00											21 53				22 53	22 53				23 29
	d		20 30	21 01					21 20								22 20		22 54	22 54				23 30
Atherstone	d		20 37																					
Polesworth	d																							
Tamworth Low Level	d		20 45				21 32		21a40								22a40							
Lichfield Trent Valley	d		20 51				21 39																	
Rugeley Trent Valley	d		20 58																					
Stafford	d		21 16		21 33			21 34			21 59	22 04	22 14	22 34				22 59	23 19	23 22		23 31	23 32	23s54
Norton Bridge Station Drv	d																							
Stone	d		21 32																					
Stone Crown Street	d																							
Barlaston Orchard Place	d																							
Wedgwood Old Road Bridge	d																							
Stoke-on-Trent	d	21a25	21 43			21a50		21a56						22a55							23a33			
Hanley Bus Station	a									←														
Kidsgrove	d		21 54							21 54														
Alsager	d		→							22 00														
Crewe	a			21 44	21 53		22 10			22 11	22 17	22 22	22 36			22 49		23 24	23 43	23 43		23 55	23 55	00s16

For general notes see front of timetable
For details of catering facilities see Directory of Train Operators

A From 13 September. From Leicester (Table 57)
B From 13 September
C Until 6 September
b Arr. 2025

Crewe and Stoke-on-Trent → London
Nuneaton → Coventry

Network Diagram - see first page of Table 67

Miles	Miles	Miles			AW	VT	LM	XC	VT	LM	VT	XC	LM	VT	LM	VT	VT	XC	LM	LM	LM	VT	LM	LM	VT
						1◇	1	1◇	1◇		1◇	1◇	1◇	1◇	1◇	1◇	1◇	1◇		1◇		1◇		1◇	1◇
																						A			
																			🚌		🚌				
						⊠		🛒	⊠		⊠	🛒		⊠		⊠	⊠	🛒				⊠			⊠
0	0	—	**Crewe**	d	05 00	05 36		05 47	06 02				06 20	06 29	06 35			06 38		06 47		06 53			
6½	—	—	Alsager	d											06 44									←	
8¾	—	—	Kidsgrove	d											06 48									06 48	
—	—	—	Hanley Bus Station	d								←			→						06 50				
16	—	—	**Stoke-on-Trent**	d				06 07				06 07				06 48					06 56			06 58	07 06
—	—	—	Wedgwood Old Road Bridge	d				→													07 08				
—	—	—	Barlaston Orchard Place	d																	07 11				
—	—	—	Stone Granville Square	d															06 40		→				
23¼	—	—	Stone	d																				07 06	
—	—	—	Norton Bridge Station Drv	d																					
32¼	24½	—	**Stafford**	d	05a24	05 55			06 21			06 25	06a40				06 53	06a57	06a58	07a10				07b22	07 28
42	—	—	Rugeley Trent Valley	d			06 00																	07 33	
50	—	—	Lichfield Trent Valley	d			06 07				06 41						07 08							07 40	
56¼	—	—	Tamworth Low Level	d			06 14				06 47						07 15							→	
59¾	—	—	Polesworth	d																					
63¾	—	—	Atherstone	d			06 23																		
—	—	—	Nuneaton	a		06 17	06 29							07 06								07 32			
68¾	—	0		d		06 18	06 30			06 37				07 07								07 34	07 37		
—	—	3¾	Bedworth	d						06 44													07 44		
—	—	10	**Coventry**	a						06 56		07 24											07 57		08 30 →
83¼	—	—	Rugby	a		06 30	06 47		06 52		07 06					07 28									
102	—	—	Northampton	a																					
118	—	—	Milton Keynes Central	a		06 51			07 12																
150¼	—	—	Watford Junction	a																					
167¾	—	—	**London Euston**	a		07 28			07 50		08 00			08 11		08 22	08 26					08 36			

		VT	VT	LM	LM	LM	LM	VT	LM	VT	LM	LM	LM	VT	LM	XC	LM	VT	VT	LM	VT	LM	LM	LM	VT
		1◇	1◇	1◇	1◇		1◇	1◇	1◇	1◇	1◇			1◇		1◇	1◇	1◇	1◇	1◇	1◇		1◇	1◇	1◇
						🚌						🚌	🚌									🚌			
		⊠	⊠					⊠		⊠				⊠		🛒		⊠	⊠		⊠				⊠
Crewe	d		07 17	07 16	07 33		07 49							07 57						08 22	08 29		08 33	08 49	
Alsager	d				07 41						←												08 41		
Kidsgrove	d				07 46						07 46												08 46		
Hanley Bus Station	d				→								07 50										→		
Stoke-on-Trent	d	07 12						07 50			07 54		08 01			08 07		08 12							08 50
Wedgwood Old Road Bridge	d					←							08 10									←			
Barlaston Orchard Place	d					07 11							08 11									08 11			
Stone Granville Square	d					07 25							→									08 25			
Stone	d										08 02														
Norton Bridge Station Drv	d											07 56													
Stafford	d		07 35	07a40		08a08	08a10				08c21	08a15				08 25			08 36	08a42		09a08		09a09	
Rugeley Trent Valley	d								←		08 33														
Lichfield Trent Valley	d								07 40		→														
Tamworth Low Level	d								07 47																
Polesworth	d																								
Atherstone	d								07 56																
Nuneaton	a								08 02									08 44							
	d								08 02						08 28			08 46							
Bedworth	d									←					08 35										
Coventry	a									08 30					08 47	09 24									
Rugby	a	07 52							08 18					08 45											
Northampton	a								08 41								←								
Milton Keynes Central	a							08s46	09 00								09 00								09 46
Watford Junction	a								→	09s15							09 27	09s31							
London Euston	a	08 49	08 55					09 23		09 34				09 38			09 44	09 52	09 56		10 04				10 23

		VT	LM	LM	LM	XC	LM	VT	LM	VT	LM	VT	LM	LM	LM	LM	VT	VT	LM	XC	VT	LM	VT	LM	LM
		1◇	1◇	1◇		1◇		1◇	1◇	1◇	1◇	1◇		1◇		1◇	1◇	1◇	1◇	1◇	1◇	1◇	1◇	1◇	
							🚌						🚌		🚌										🚌
		⊠				🛒		⊠		⊠		⊠					⊠	⊠		🛒	⊠		⊠		
Crewe	d	08 56									09 22	09 29		09 33		09 49		09 56						10 22	
Alsager	d			←										09 41					←						
Kidsgrove	d			08 46										09 47					09 47						
Hanley Bus Station	d						09 00							→											10 00
Stoke-on-Trent	d			08 54		09 07	09 11	09 12									09 50		09 55	10 07	10 11				10 11
Wedgwood Old Road Bridge	d						09 20								←										10 20
Barlaston Orchard Place	d						09 21								09 21										10 21
Stone Granville Square	d						→						08 56		09 30										10 30
Stone	d			09 02															10 03						
Norton Bridge Station Drv	d												09 46												
Stafford	d		←	09e21		09 25				09 36	09a42		10a05		10a08	10a09			10f21	10 25			10 36	10a42	11a08
Rugeley Trent Valley	d		08 33	09 33															10 32						
Lichfield Trent Valley	d		08 40	09 40															10 39						
Tamworth Low Level	d		08 47	09 47															10 46						
Polesworth	d																		→			←			
Atherstone	d		08 56	09 56																		09 56			
Nuneaton	a		09 02	→																		10 02			
	d		09 03		09 30																	10 02			
Bedworth	d				09 37																				
Coventry	a				09 53	10 24														11 24					
Rugby	a		09 18																			10 18			
Northampton	a		09 42																			10 42			
Milton Keynes Central	a	10s01	10 05						←								10 46	11s01				11 04			
Watford Junction	a		10 30						10 30													11 29			
London Euston	a	10 38	→					10 42	10 49	10 56		11 04					11 23	11 38			11 42	11 49	11 56		

For general notes see front of timetable
For details of catering facilities see Directory of Train Operators

A From Holyhead (Table 81)
b Arr. 0716
c Arr. 0812
e Arr. 0912
f Arr. 1013

Crewe and Stoke-on-Trent → London
Nuneaton → Coventry

Network Diagram - see first page of Table 67

		VT	LM	LM	VT	VT	LM	XC	VT	LM	LM	VT	LM	LM	VT	LM	LM	VT	VT	LM	XC	LM	VT	LM	LM
		1◇	1◇	1◇	1◇	1◇	1◇	1◇	1◇	1◇		1◇	1◇		1◇	1◇	1◇	1◇	1◇	1◇	1◇		1◇	1◇	
		⊠			☕	⊠		🛒	☕			☕		🚌	☕			☕	☕		🛒	🚌	☕		
Crewe	d	10 29	10 33	10 49		10 56							11 22		11 29	11 33	11 49		11 56						
Alsager	d		10 41													11 41									
Kidsgrove	d		10 46 →				← 10 46									11 47 →				← 11 47					
Hanley Bus Station	d													11 00											
Stoke-on-Trent	d				10 50		10 54	11 07	11 11					11 11				11 50		11 55	12 07		12 11		
Wedgwood Old Road Bridge	d													11 20											
Barlaston Orchard Place	d													11 21											
Stone Granville Square	d													11 30								11 39			
Stone	d						11 02													12 03					
Norton Bridge Station Drv	d																					12 06			
Stafford	d			11a09			11b21	11 25				11 36	11a42	12a08			12a09			12c21	12 25	12a25			
Rugeley Trent Valley	d						11 32													12 32					
Lichfield Trent Valley	d						11 39													12 39					
Tamworth Low Level	d						11 46 →			← 10 46										12 46 →				← 11 46	
Polesworth	d																								
Atherstone	d									10 55														11 55	
Nuneaton	a									11 01														12 01	
	d									11 02	11 10													12 02	12 10
Bedworth	d										11 17														12 17
Coventry	a							12 24			11 34										13 24				12 34
Rugby	a									11 17														12 17	
Northampton	a									11 42														12 42	
Milton Keynes Central	a				11 46	12s01				12 04								12 46	13s01					13 04	
Watford Junction	a									12 29														13 29	
London Euston	a	12 04			12 23	12 38			12 42	12 49		12 56			13 04			13 23	13 38				13 42	13 49	

		VT	LM	LM	VT	LM	LM	VT	VT	LM	XC	VT	LM	LM	VT	LM	LM	VT	LM	LM	VT	VT	LM	LM	XC
		1◇	1◇		1◇	1◇	1◇	1◇	1◇	1◇	1◇	1◇	1◇		1◇	1◇		1◇	1◇	1◇	1◇	1◇	1◇		1◇
		☕		🚌	☕			☕	☕		🛒	☕			☕		🚌	☕			☕	☕		🚌	🛒
Crewe	d		12 22		12 29	12 33	12 49		12 56							13 22		13 29	13 33	13 49		13 56			
Alsager	d					12 41													13 41						
Kidsgrove	d					12 46 →				← 12 46									13 46 →				← 13 46		
Hanley Bus Station	d			12 00													13 00								
Stoke-on-Trent	d			12 11				12 50		12 54	13 07	13 11					13 11				13 50		13 54		14 07
Wedgwood Old Road Bridge	d			12 20													13 20								
Barlaston Orchard Place	d			12 21													13 21								
Stone Granville Square	d			12 30													13 30							13 29	
Stone	d									13 02													14 02		
Norton Bridge Station Drv	d																							13 56	
Stafford	d	12 36	12a42	13a08			13a09			13e21	13 25				13 36	13a42	14a08			14a09			14f21	14a15	14 25
Rugeley Trent Valley	d									13 32													14 32		
Lichfield Trent Valley	d									13 39													14 39		
Tamworth Low Level	d									13 46 →			← 12 46										14 46 →		
Polesworth	d																								
Atherstone	d												12 55												
Nuneaton	a												13 01												
	d												13 02	13 10											
Bedworth	d													13 17											
Coventry	a										14 24			13 38											15 24
Rugby	a												13 17												
Northampton	a												13 48												
Milton Keynes Central	a							13 46	14s01				14 04								14 46	15s01			
Watford Junction	a												14 29												
London Euston	a	13 56			14 04			14 24	14 38			14 42	14 49		14 58			15 04			15 23	15 38			

		VT	LM	LM	VT	LM	LM	VT	LM	LM	VT	VT	LM	XC	VT	LM	LM	VT	LM	LM	VT	LM	LM	VT	VT
		1◇	1◇		1◇	1◇		1◇	1◇	1◇	1◇	1◇	1◇	1◇	1◇	1◇		1◇	1◇		1◇	1◇	1◇	1◇	1◇
		☕			☕		🚌	☕			☕	☕		🛒	☕			☕		🚌	☕			☕	☕
Crewe	d					14 22		14 29	14 33	14 49		14 56							15 22		15 29	15 33	15 49		15 57
Alsager	d								14 41													15 41			
Kidsgrove	d								14 46 →				← 14 46									15 46 →			
Hanley Bus Station	d						14 00													15 00					
Stoke-on-Trent	d	14 11					14 11				14 50		14 54	15 07	15 11					15 11				15 50	
Wedgwood Old Road Bridge	d						14 20													15 20					
Barlaston Orchard Place	d						14 21													15 21					
Stone Granville Square	d						14 30													15 30					
Stone	d												15 02												
Norton Bridge Station Drv	d																								
Stafford	d				14 36	14a46	15a08			15a09			15g21	15 25				15 36	15a42	16a08			16a09		
Rugeley Trent Valley	d												15 32												
Lichfield Trent Valley	d												15 39												
Tamworth Low Level	d		← 13 46										15 46 →			← 14 46									
Polesworth	d																								
Atherstone	d		13 55													14 55									
Nuneaton	a		14 01													15 01									
	d		14 02	14 10												15 02	15 10								
Bedworth	d			14 17													15 17								
Coventry	a			14 34										16 24			15 34								
Rugby	a		14 17													15 17									
Northampton	a		14 42													15 42									
Milton Keynes Central	a		15 04								15 46	16s01				16 04								16 46	17s01
Watford Junction	a		15 29													16 29									
London Euston	a	15 42	15 49		15 56			16 04			16 23	16 38			16 42	16 48		16 56			17 04			17 23	17 38

For general notes see front of timetable
For details of catering facilities see
Directory of Train Operators

b Arr. 1112
c Arr. 1213
e Arr. 1312
f Arr. 1412
g Arr. 1512

Crewe and Stoke-on-Trent → London
Nuneaton → Coventry

Network Diagram - see first page of Table 67

		LM	XC	LM	VT	LM	LM	VT	LM	LM	VT	LM	VT	LM	VT	LM	XC	LM	LM	VT	LM	LM	VT	LM	VT
		1◇	1◇	🚌	1◇	1◇		1◇	1◇	🚌	1◇	1◇	1◇	1◇	1◇	1◇	1◇	🚌	🚌	1◇	1◇		1◇	1◇	1◇
			🛒		☕			☕			☕		⊠		⊠		🛒			⊠			⊠		⊠
Crewe	d								16 22		16 29	16 33		16 49	16 56									17 22	17 29
Alsager	d	←										16 41				←									
Kidsgrove	d	15 46										16 46				16 46									
Hanley Bus Station	d									16 00		→							17 00						
Stoke-on-Trent	d	15 54	16 07		16 11					16 11			16 50			16 54	17 07		17 11	17 12					
Wedgwood Old Road Bridge	d									16 20									17 20						
Barlaston Orchard Place	d									16 21									17 21						
Stone Granville Square	d			15 41						16 30									→						
Stone	d	16 02														17 02									
Norton Bridge Station Drv	d			16 11														17 06							
Stafford	d	16b21	16 25	16a30				16 36	16a46	17a08				17a10		17c21	17 25	17a25					17 36	17a42	
Rugeley Trent Valley	d	16 32														17 32									
Lichfield Trent Valley	d	16 39				←										17 39					←				
Tamworth Low Level	d	16 46				15 46										17 46					16 46				
Polesworth	d	→														→									
Atherstone	d					15 55															16 55				
Nuneaton	a					16 01															17 01				
	d					16 02	16 10														17 02	17 10			
Bedworth	d						16 17															17 17			
Coventry	a		17 24				16 34										18 24					17 38			
Rugby	a					16 17															17 17				
Northampton	a					16 40															17 42				
Milton Keynes Central	a					17 04							17 46		18s01						18 04		18 23		
Watford Junction	a					17 29															18 29				18s48
London Euston	a				17 42	17 49		17 56			18 06		18 23		18 38					18 42	18 49		18 59		19 08

		LM	LM	LM	VT	VT	LM	LM	VT	LM	LM	XC	VT	LM	VT	LM	LM	VT	LM	LM	LM	XC	VT	LM	LM
		1◇	🚌	1◇	1◇	1◇	1◇	🚌	1◇	1◇		1◇	1◇	1◇	1◇	1◇	1◇	1◇	1◇		1◇	1◇	1◇	1◇	1◇
																						A			
					⊠	⊠			⊠			🛒	⊠		⊠			⊠				🛒	⊠		
Crewe	d	17 33		17 49		17 56								18 22	18 29	18 33	18 49							19 18	
Alsager	d	17 41					←									18 41					←				
Kidsgrove	d	17 46					17 46									18 46					18 46				
Hanley Bus Station	d	→						18 00								→									
Stoke-on-Trent	d				17 50		17 54	18 11	18 12									18 50			18 54	19 07	19 12		
Wedgwood Old Road Bridge	d		←					18 20																	
Barlaston Orchard Place	d		17 21					18 21																	
Stone Granville Square	d		17 30					18a30																	
Stone	d						18 02														19 02				
Norton Bridge Station Drv	d																								
Stafford	d		18a08	18a09			18e21					18 25	18 36	18a42			19a09				19f21	19 25		19a41	
Rugeley Trent Valley	d						18 33														19 33				
Lichfield Trent Valley	d						18 40			←									←		19 40				
Tamworth Low Level	d						18 47			17 46									18 47		19 47				
Polesworth	d						→																		
Atherstone	d									17 55									18 56		19 56				
Nuneaton	a									18 01									19 02		20 02				
	d									18 02	18 10								19 02	19 10	20 02				
Bedworth	d										18 17									19 17					
Coventry	a										18 34	19 24								19 38		20 24			
Rugby	a									18 17									19 18		20 18				
Northampton	a									18 42									19 44		20 44				
Milton Keynes Central	a				18 46	19s01				19 04					19 31			19 46	20 04						←
Watford Junction	a									19 29			19s42						20 29						20 29
London Euston	a				19 23	19 38			19 42	19 49			20 02		20 08			20 23	→				20 42		20 49

		VT	VT	VT	LM	VT	LM	XC	LM	VT	VT	VT	LM	VT	LM	VT	XC	LM	VT	VT	LM	XC	LM	XC
		1◇	1◇	1◇	1◇	1◇		1◇	1◇	1◇	1◇	1◇	1◇	1◇		1◇	1◇	1◇	1◇	1◇		1◇	1◇	1◇
								A																
		⊠	⊠	☕		☕		🛒		☕	☕	☕		☕		☕			☕	☕				
Crewe	d	19 23	19 29		19 55	19 56			20 18	20 23	20 29	20 41	20 47			20 54		21 18		21 24			22 20	
Alsager	d																							
Kidsgrove	d																							
Hanley Bus Station	d																							
Stoke-on-Trent	d			19 52				20 07						20 53			21 07		21 53			22 07		22 47
Wedgwood Old Road Bridge	d																							
Barlaston Orchard Place	d																							
Stone Granville Square	d																							
Stone	d																							
Norton Bridge Station Drv	d																							
Stafford	d	19 43			20a15			20 25	20a38		20 48		21a09			21a12	21a24	21a38		21 44		22a25	22a40	23a06
Rugeley Trent Valley	d																							
Lichfield Trent Valley	d																			21 58				
Tamworth Low Level	d																			22 05				
Polesworth	d																							
Atherstone	d																							
Nuneaton	a									21 02										22 16				
	d						20 10			21 03					21 10					22 17	22 20			
Bedworth	d						20 17								21 17						22 27			
Coventry	a						20 34	21 24							21 34						22 39			
Rugby	a											21 27								22 30				
Northampton	a																							
Milton Keynes Central	a		20 32	20 48		21s03					21 35	21 47		21 50					22 49	22 54				
Watford Junction	a	20s46								21s48				22s11					23s10	23s15				
London Euston	a	21 06	21 10	21 25		21 42				22 09	22 12	22 46		22 51					23 50	23 53				

For general notes see front of timetable
For details of catering facilities see Directory of Train Operators

A 🛒 to Birmingham New Street
b Arr. 1612
c Arr. 1713
e Arr. 1812
f Arr. 1912

Crewe and Stoke-on-Trent → London
Nuneaton → Coventry

Network Diagram - see first page of Table 67

		AW	XC	VT	LM	XC	VT	LM	VT	XC	LM	LM	VT	LM	VT	VT	VT	LM	LM	LM	VT	VT	LM	LM	VT
			1◇	1◇		1◇	1◇	1◇	1◇	1◇	1◇	1◇	1◇	1◇	1◇	1◇	1◇	1◇	1◇	1◇	1◇	1◇	1◇		1◇
			[trolley]	[restaurant]		[trolley]	[restaurant]		[restaurant]	[trolley]			[restaurant]		[restaurant]	[restaurant]	[restaurant]				[restaurant]	[restaurant]			[restaurant]
Crewe	d	05 00	05 47	06 00				06 20	06 29		06 38	06 47		←		07 20	07 29	07 33	07 16			07 38	07 49		07 55
Alsager	d										06 47							07 41							
Kidsgrove	d										06 51			06 51				07 46							
Hanley Bus Station	d					←					→							→							
Stoke-on-Trent	d		06 07 →			06 07				06 39			06 48	07 00	07 12						07 50				
Wedgwood Old Road Bridge	d																								
Barlaston Orchard Place	d																								
Stone Granville Square	d																								
Stone	d													07 08											
Norton Bridge Station Drv	d																								
Stafford	d	05a24		06 19		06 25	06 35	06a41		06a57		07a10		07 26		07 39			07a40	←			08a10		08 16
Rugeley Trent Valley	d													07 34											
Lichfield Trent Valley	d												07 12	07 41 →						07 41					08 31
Tamworth Low Level	d												07 18							07 48					08 37
Polesworth	d																								
Atherstone	d																			07 57					
Nuneaton	a						06 57													08 03					
	d				06 47		06 59													08 04 →				08 14	
Bedworth	d				06 54																			08 21	
Coventry	a				07 06	07 24																		08 33	
Rugby	a			06 49											07 52										
Northampton	a																								
Milton Keynes Central	a			07 11					07 31												08 46				
Watford Junction	a			07s34			07s44																		
London Euston	a			07 54			08 05		08 10				08 27		08 46	08 59	09 04				09 23	09 30			09 46

		LM	LM	XC	LM	VT	LM	VT	LM	VT	LM	LM	VT	VT	LM	LM	LM	XC	LM	VT	LM	VT	LM	LM	VT
			1◇	1◇		1◇	1◇	1◇	1◇	1◇	1◇	1◇	1◇	1◇	1◇		1◇	1◇		1◇	1◇	1◇	1◇		1◇
		[bus]		[trolley]	[bus]	[restaurant]		[restaurant]		[restaurant]			[restaurant]	[restaurant]				[trolley]	[bus]	[restaurant]		[restaurant]		[bus]	[restaurant]
Crewe	d		←						08 22	08 29	08 33	08 49		08 56			←						09 22		09 29
Alsager	d										08 41														
Kidsgrove	d		07 46								08 46						08 46								
Hanley Bus Station	d				08 00						→								09 00						
Stoke-on-Trent	d		07 54	08 07	08 11	08 12							08 50				08 54	09 07	09 11	09 13					
Wedgwood Old Road Bridge	d				08 20														09 20						
Barlaston Orchard Place	d				08 21														09 21						
Stone Granville Square	d				08a27														09a27					08 56	
Stone	d		08 02														09 02								
Norton Bridge Station Drv	d	07 56																						09 46	
Stafford	d	08a15	08 23	08 25				08 36	08a42			09a09			←		09b21	09 25				09 36	09a42	10a05	
Rugeley Trent Valley	d		08 33												08 33		09 32								
Lichfield Trent Valley	d		→												08 40		09 39								
Tamworth Low Level	d														08 47		09 46 →								
Polesworth	d																								
Atherstone	d														08 56										
Nuneaton	a						←	08 58							09 02							09 58			
	d						08 04	08 59							09 04	09 15						09 59			
Bedworth	d															09 22									
Coventry	a			09 24												09 34		10 24							
Rugby	a						08 19								09 20										
Northampton	a						08 40								09 41										
Milton Keynes Central	a						09 03						09 46	10s01	10 04						←				
Watford Junction	a						09 34								10 29						10 29				
London Euston	a					09 42	09 51	10 01		10 04			10 23	10 38	→					10 42	10 48	11 01			11 04

For general notes see front of timetable
For details of catering facilities see
Directory of Train Operators

b Arr. 0912

Table 67

Saturdays

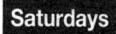

Crewe and Stoke-on-Trent → London
Nuneaton → Coventry

Network Diagram - see first page of Table 67

Station		LM	LM	VT	VT	LM	XC	LM	VT	LM		LM	VT	LM	VT	LM	LM	VT	VT	LM	XC	LM	VT	LM	LM
		1◇	1◇	1◇	1◇	1◇	1◇	🚌	1◇	1◇			1◇	1◇	1◇	1◇	1◇	1◇	1◇	1◇	1◇	🚌	1◇	1◇	
				☕	☕		🛒		☕				☕		☕			☕	☕		🛒		☕		
Crewe	d	09 33	09 49		09 56									10 22	10 29	10 33	10 49		10 56						
Alsager	d	09 41				←										10 41				←					
Kidsgrove	d	09 46				09 46										10 46				10 46					
Hanley Bus Station	d	→						10 00								→						11 00			
Stoke-on-Trent	d			09 50		09 54	10 07	10 11	10 12									10 50		10 54	11 07	11 11	11 12		
Wedgwood Old Road Bridge	d							10 20														11 20			
Barlaston Orchard Place	d							10 21														11 21			
Stone Granville Square	d							10 35														11a27			
Stone	d					10 02														11 02					
Norton Bridge Station Drv	d																								
Stafford	d		10a09			10b21	10 25	11a18					10 36	10a42			11a09			11c21	11 25				
Rugeley Trent Valley	d					10 32														11 32					
Lichfield Trent Valley	d					10 39				←										11 39				←	
Tamworth Low Level	d					10 46				09 46										11 46				10 46	
Polesworth	d					→														→					
Atherstone	d									09 55														10 55	
Nuneaton	a									10 01														11 01	
	d									10 02		10 15												11 03	11 15
Bedworth	d											10 22													11 22
Coventry	a						11 24					10 34									12 24				11 34
Rugby	a									10 17														11 19	
Northampton	a									10 38														11 40	
Milton Keynes Central	a			10 46	11s01					11 04								11 46	12s01					12 04	
Watford Junction	a									11 29														12 29	
London Euston	a			11 23	11 38				11 42	11 48			11 56		12 04			12 23	12 38				12 42	12 48	

Station		VT	LM	VT	LM	LM	VT	VT	LM	XC	LM	LM	VT	LM	LM	VT	LM	VT	LM	LM	VT	VT	LM	XC	LM
		1◇	1◇	1◇	1◇	1◇	1◇	1◇	1◇	1◇	🚌	🚌	1◇	1◇		1◇	1◇	1◇	1◇	1◇	1◇	1◇	1◇	1◇	🚌
		☕		☕			☕	☕		🛒			☕			☕		☕			☕	☕		🛒	
Crewe	d		11 22	11 29	11 33	11 49		11 56									12 22	12 29	12 33	12 49		12 57			
Alsager	d				11 41				←										12 41				←		
Kidsgrove	d				11 46				11 46										12 46				12 46		
Hanley Bus Station	d				→							12 00							→						13 00
Stoke-on-Trent	d						11 50		11 54	12 07		12 11	12 12								12 50		12 54	13 07	13 11
Wedgwood Old Road Bridge	d											12 20													13 20
Barlaston Orchard Place	d											12 21													13 21
Stone Granville Square	d										11 39	12 35													13a27
Stone	d								12 02														13 02		
Norton Bridge Station Drv	d										12 06														
Stafford	d	11 36	11a42			12a09			12e21	12 25	12a25	13a18				12 36	12a42			13a09			13f21	13 25	
Rugeley Trent Valley	d								12 32														13 32		
Lichfield Trent Valley	d								12 39					←									13 39		
Tamworth Low Level	d								12 46					11 46									13 46		
Polesworth	d								→														→		
Atherstone	d													11 55											
Nuneaton	a													12 01											
	d													12 02	12 15										
Bedworth	d														12 22										
Coventry	a									13 24					12 34									14 24	
Rugby	a													12 17											
Northampton	a													12 38											
Milton Keynes Central	a						12 46	13s01						13 04							13 46	14s01			
Watford Junction	a													13 29											
London Euston	a	12 56		13 04			13 23	13 38					13 42	13 48		13 56		14 04			14 23	14 38			

Station		VT	LM	LM	VT	LM	VT	VT	LM	LM	VT	VT	VT	LM	LM	XC	LM	VT	LM	LM		VT	LM	VT	LM
		1◇	1◇		1◇	1◇	1◇	1◇	1◇	1◇	1◇	1◇	1◇	1◇		1◇		1◇	1◇			1◇	1◇	1◇	1◇
								A				B	A												
															🚌		🚌								
		☕			☕		☕	☕			☕	☕	☕			🛒		☕				☕		☕	
Crewe	d					13 22	13 29	13 32	13 33	13 49		13 56	13 56										14 22	14 29	14 33
Alsager	d								13 41					←											14 41
Kidsgrove	d								13 46					13 46											14 46
Hanley Bus Station	d								→								14 00								→
Stoke-on-Trent	d	13 12									13 50			13 54		14 07	14 11	14 12							
Wedgwood Old Road Bridge	d																14 20								
Barlaston Orchard Place	d																14 21								
Stone Granville Square	d														13 29		14 35								
Stone	d													14 02											
Norton Bridge Station Drv	d														13 56										
Stafford	d				13 36	13a42				14a09				14g21	14a15	14 25	15a18					14 36	14a46		
Rugeley Trent Valley	d													14 32											
Lichfield Trent Valley	d		←											14 39					←						
Tamworth Low Level	d		12 46											14 46					13 46						
Polesworth	d													→											
Atherstone	d		12 55																13 55						
Nuneaton	a		13 01																14 01						
	d		13 03	13 15															14 02	14 15					
Bedworth	d			13 22																14 22					
Coventry	a			13 34												15 24				14 34					
Rugby	a		13 19																14 17						
Northampton	a		13 40																14 38						
Milton Keynes Central	a		14 04								14 46	15s01							15 04						
Watford Junction	a		14 29																15 29						
London Euston	a	14 42	14 48		14 56		15 04	15 08			15 23	15 38	15 38					15 42	15 48			15 56		16 04	

For general notes see front of timetable
For details of catering facilities see Directory of Train Operators

A From 7 November
B Until 31 October
b Arr. 1012
c Arr. 1112
e Arr. 1212
f Arr. 1312
g Arr. 1412

Crewe and Stoke-on-Trent → London
Nuneaton → Coventry

Network Diagram - see first page of Table 67

		VT	LM	VT	VT	LM	XC	LM	VT	LM	LM	VT	LM	VT	VT	LM	LM	VT	VT	VT	LM	LM	LM	XC	LM
		A													A				A	B					
Crewe	d	14 35	14 49		14 56								15 22	15 29	15 33	15 33	15 49		15 56	15 56					
Alsager	d					←										15 41							←		
Kidsgrove	d					14 46										15 46							15 46		
Hanley Bus Station	d							15 00								→									
Stoke-on-Trent	d			14 50		14 54	15 07	15 11	15 12									15 50					15 54	16 07	
Wedgwood Old Road Bridge	d							15 20																	
Barlaston Orchard Place	d							15 21																	
Stone Granville Square	d							15a27																	15 41
Stone	d					15 02																	16 02		
Norton Bridge Station Drv	d																								16 11
Stafford	d		15a09			15b21	15 25					15 36	15a42				16a09				←		16c21	16 25	16a30
Rugeley Trent Valley	d					15 32				←											15 32		16 32		
Lichfield Trent Valley	d					→															15 39		16 39		
Tamworth Low Level	d									14 46											15 46		16 46		
Polesworth	d																						→		
Atherstone	d									14 55											15 55				
Nuneaton	a									15 01											16 01				
	d									15 02	15 15										16 02	16 15			
Bedworth	d										15 22											16 22			
Coventry	a						16 24				15 34											16 34		17 24	
Rugby	a									15 17											16 17				
Northampton	a									15 39											16 38				
Milton Keynes Central	a			15 46	16s01					16 04								16 46		17s01	17 04				
Watford Junction	a									16 29											17 29				
London Euston	a	16 12		16 23	16 38				16 42	16 48		16 56		17 04	17 08			17 23	17 37	17 38	→				

		LM	VT	LM	VT	LM	VT	LM	VT	LM	VT	VT	LM	LM	XC	LM	VT	LM	LM	VT	LM	VT	VT	LM	LM
									A														A		
Crewe	d					16 22	16 29	16 33	16 35	16 49		16 56									17 22	17 29	17 32	17 33	17 49
Alsager	d							16 41					←											17 41	
Kidsgrove	d							16 46					16 46											17 46	
Hanley Bus Station	d	16 00						→								17 00								→	
Stoke-on-Trent	d	16 11	16 12								16 50		16 54		17 07	17 11	17 13								
Wedgwood Old Road Bridge	d	16 20														17 20									
Barlaston Orchard Place	d	16 21														17 21									
Stone Granville Square	d	16a27														17a27									
Stone	d												17 02												
Norton Bridge Station Drv	d													17 06											
Stafford	d				16 36	16a46				17a09			17e21	17a25	17 25					17 36	17a42				18a09
Rugeley Trent Valley	d												17 32												
Lichfield Trent Valley	d												→					←							
Tamworth Low Level	d																	16 46							
Polesworth	d																								
Atherstone	d																	16 55							
Nuneaton	a																	17 01							
	d																	17 03	17 15						
Bedworth	d																		17 22						
Coventry	a														18 24				17 34						
Rugby	a																	17 19							
Northampton	a																	17 40							
Milton Keynes Central	a			←							17 46	18 01						18 04							
Watford Junction	a			17 29														18 29							
London Euston	a		17 42	17 49	17 57		18 04		18 13		18 23	18 38					18 42	18 48		18 56		19 04	19 08		

		VT	VT	LM	LM	LM	XC	LM	VT	LM	VT	LM	VT	LM	LM	VT	LM	LM	XC	VT	VT	VT	LM	VT	LM
			A																	C	C	D		D	
Crewe	d		17 56									18 22	18 29	18 33	18 49										19 22
Alsager	d					←								18 41				←							
Kidsgrove	d					17 46								18 46				18 46							
Hanley Bus Station	d							18 00						→											
Stoke-on-Trent	d	17 50				17 54	18 07	18 11	18 13							18 50		18 54	19 07	19 12		19 12			
Wedgwood Old Road Bridge	d							18 20																	
Barlaston Orchard Place	d							18 21																	
Stone Granville Square	d							18a30																	
Stone	d					18 02												19 02							
Norton Bridge Station Drv	d																								
Stafford	d			←		18f21	18 25				18 36	18a42			19a09			19g21	19 25		19 36			19 36	19a42
Rugeley Trent Valley	d			17 32		18 32												19 32							
Lichfield Trent Valley	d			17 39		18 39												19 39							
Tamworth Low Level	d			17 46		18 46												19 46							
Polesworth	d																								
Atherstone	d			17 55		18 55												19 55							
Nuneaton	a			18 01		19 01												20 01							
	d			18 02	18 15	19 02											19 46	20 02					21 15		
Bedworth	d				18 22												19 53						21 22		
Coventry	a				18 34		19 24										20 05		20 24				21 34		
Rugby	a			18 17		19 18												20 17							
Northampton	a			18 38		19 38												20 38							
Milton Keynes Central	a	18 46		19 04						←						19 46									
Watford Junction	a			19 29						19 29															
London Euston	a	19 23	19 37	→					19 42	19 48	19 56		20 04			20 28				21 01	21 15	21 16		21 25	

For general notes see front of timetable
For details of catering facilities see Directory of Train Operators

- **A** From 7 November
- **B** Until 31 October
- **C** From 12 September
- **D** Until 5 September
- **b** Arr. 1512
- **c** Arr. 1612
- **e** Arr. 1712
- **f** Arr. 1812
- **g** Arr. 1912

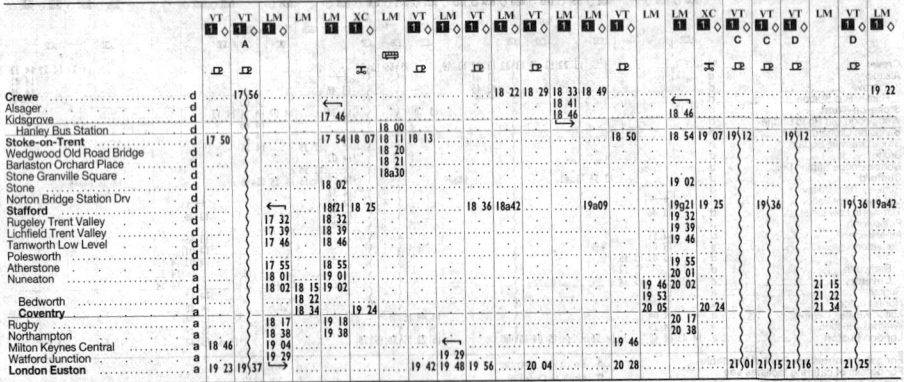

Table 67

Crewe and Stoke-on-Trent → London
Nuneaton → Coventry

Saturdays

Network Diagram - see first page of Table 67

		VT	VT	LM	VT	XC	VT	VT	VT	VT	LM	VT	VT	XC	VT	VT	LM	LM	VT	XC	VT	XC	LM		
		1◇	1◇	1◇	1◇	1◇	1◇	1◇	1◇	1◇	1◇	1◇	1◇	1◇	1◇	1◇	1◇		1◇		1◇	1◇	1◇		
		A	B		C		A	A	B	B		D	B		A	B			E	G 🚌		H			
		☕	☕		☕	trolley	☕	☕	☕	☕		☕	☕	trolley	☕	☕			☕		☕	trolley			
Crewe	d	19 29	19 29	19 51	19 56						20 22	20 47	20 47				21 17		21 44		22 04		22 20		
Alsager	d																								
Kidsgrove	d																								
Hanley Bus Station	d																								
Stoke-on-Trent	d					20 07	20 12		20 12					21 07	21 13	21 13				21 50		22 07			
Wedgwood Old Road Bridge	d																								
Barlaston Orchard Place	d																								
Stone Granville Square	d																								
Stone	d																								
Norton Bridge Station Drv	d																								
Stafford	d			20a11		20 25		20 36		20 36	20a42			21a25			21a41		22a08	22a20	22a28	22a33	22a45		
Rugeley Trent Valley	d																								
Lichfield Trent Valley	d																								
Tamworth Low Level	d																								
Polesworth	d																								
Atherstone	d																								
Nuneaton	a																								
	d																	22 15							
Bedworth	d																	22 22							
Coventry	a					21 24												22 34							
Rugby	a				20 51																				
Northampton	a																								
Milton Keynes Central	a						21 10		21 26			21 51	22 11		22 12	22 28									
Watford Junction	a														22s42	23s11									
London Euston	a	21 19	21 58				22 02	22 17	22 21	22 43		22 43	23 03		23 04	23 36									

Sundays

until 12 July

		VT	VT	VT	XC	VT	VT	VT	XC	VT	XC	VT	LM	LM	LM	VT	LM	XC	VT	LM	XC	VT	VT	VT	VT
			1◇	1◇	1◇	1◇		1◇		1◇	1◇	1◇	1◇			1◇	1		1◇		1◇		1◇	1◇	1◇
		🚌					🚌		🚌					🚌	🚌			🚌		🚌		🚌			
			☕	☕	trolley	☕		☕		☕	trolley	☕				☕			☕		trolley		☕	☕	☕
Crewe	d		08 43	08 57	09 04	09 13		09 43				10 12	10 20		10 35	10 43	10 47		10 55					11 14	
Alsager	d														10 52										
Kidsgrove	d														11 06										
Hanley Bus Station	d														→										
Stoke-on-Trent	d	08 20					09 35		09 45					10 40				10 45				11 00			
Wedgwood Old Road Bridge	d																								
Barlaston Orchard Place	d																			←					
Stone Granville Square	d													10 56 →						10 56					
Stone	d																								
Norton Bridge Station Drv	d																								
Stafford	d	08a50	09 09		09 28	09 39	10a05		10a15	10 17	10 25	10 40	10a45				11a12	11a15		11a16	11 25	11a30	11 38	11 42	12 00
Rugeley Trent Valley	d																								
Lichfield Trent Valley	d																								
Tamworth Low Level	d																								
Polesworth	d																								
Atherstone	d																								
Nuneaton	a					10 01						11 02												12 04	
	d					10 02						11 03												12 05	
Bedworth	d																								
Coventry	a				10 24						11 24										12 24				
Rugby	a							10 38								11 38									
Northampton	a																								
Milton Keynes Central	a							11 04		11 18		11 48				12 04							12 29		12 50
Watford Junction	a		10s35	10s47		11s20		11s42											12s35					12s54	
London Euston	a		10 58	11 08		11 44		12 04		12 08		12 38				12 51			12 58				13 09	13 15	13 31

For general notes see front of timetable
For details of catering facilities see
Directory of Train Operators

- **A** From 12 September
- **B** Until 5 September
- **C** From 7 November
- **D** 12 September to 31 October
- **E** Until 31 October
- **G** Until 11 July
- **H** From 18 July

Sundays

until 12 July

Crewe and Stoke-on-Trent → London
Nuneaton → Coventry

Network Diagram - see first page of Table 67

		LM 🚌	LM 1◇	XC 🚌	LM	VT 🚌	VT 1◇ 🍽	XC 1◇ 🛒	VT 1◇ 🍽	VT 1◇ 🍽	LM 1◇	VT 1◇ 🍽	VT 🚌	VT 1◇ 🍽	XC 🚌	VT 1◇ 🍽	VT 🚌	XC 1◇ 🛒	VT 1◇ 🍽	LM 1◇	VT 1◇ 🍽	LM 1◇	VT 1◇ 🍽	VT 1◇ 🍽	LM
Crewe	d		11 38				11 49				12 22	12 30				12 54						13 22	13 30		
Alsager	d	←																							
Kidsgrove	d	11 06																							
Hanley Bus Station	d																								
Stoke-on-Trent	d	11 25		11 45		11 50							12 30		12 45		12 50							13 50	
Wedgwood Old Road Bridge	d																								
Barlaston Orchard Place	d																								
Stone Granville Square	d	11 41																							
Stone	d																								
Norton Bridge Station Drv	d																								
Stafford	d	12a01	12 10	12a15		12a20		12 25	12 28	12 36	12a41		13a00	13 06	13a15		13a20	13 25	13 29		13 36	13a42			
Rugeley Trent Valley	d		12 28																	←					
Lichfield Trent Valley	d		12 35																	12 35					
Tamworth Low Level	d		→																	12 42					
Polesworth	d																								
Atherstone	d																			12 51					
Nuneaton	a						12 30													12 58					
	d				12 30		12 31													12 58					14 11
Bedworth	d				12 36																				14 17
Coventry	a				12 54			13 24										14 24							14 34
Rugby	a																			13 18					
Northampton	a																								
Milton Keynes Central	a						13s03							13 54		14s02				13 52				14 49	
Watford Junction	a																			14 35					
London Euston	a						13 44		13 53	14 03		14 12		14 40		14 43			14 52	14 54	15 03		15 12	15 30	

		LM 1◇	VT 1◇ A 🍽	XC 1◇ 🛒	VT 1◇ 🍽	VT 1◇ 🍽	LM 1◇	VT 1◇ 🍽	VT 1◇ 🍽	VT 1◇ 🍽	XC 1◇ 🛒	VT 1◇ 🍽	LM 1◇	LM	VT 1◇ 🍽	LM 1◇	VT 1◇ 🍽	VT 1◇ 🍽	LM 1◇	VT 1◇ 🍽	LM	XC 1◇ 🛒	VT 1◇ 🍽	VT 1◇ 🍽	LM 1◇
Crewe	d	13 38	13 49				14 22	14 29		14 54						15 22	15 29		15 38	15 54					16 22
Alsager	d	13 46																	15 46						
Kidsgrove	d	13 51																	15 52						
Hanley Bus Station	d																								
Stoke-on-Trent	d	13 59		14 07	14 12				14 50		15 07	15 12						15 50	15 59			16 07	16 12		
Wedgwood Old Road Bridge	d																								
Barlaston Orchard Place	d																								
Stone Granville Square	d																								
Stone	d	14 07																	16 08						
Norton Bridge Station Drv	d																								
Stafford	d	14 19		14 25		14 36	14a42				15 25		←		15 36	15a42			16 18			16 25		16 37	16a42
Rugeley Trent Valley	d	14 29											14 29						16 28						
Lichfield Trent Valley	d	→											14 36						→						
Tamworth Low Level	d												14 43												
Polesworth	d																								
Atherstone	d												14 52												
Nuneaton	a		14 31										14 58												
	d		14 32										14 58	15 11							16 11				
Bedworth	d													15 17							16 17				
Coventry	a			15 24							16 24			15 34							16 34	17 24			
Rugby	a												15 18												
Northampton	a																								
Milton Keynes Central	a		15s04						15 49	16s04			15 56					16 49		17s03					
Watford Junction	a												16 33												
London Euston	a		15 45		15 48	16 03		16 11	16 30	16 44		16 48	16 53		17 03		17 11	17 30		17 44			17 48	18 04	

		VT 1◇ 🍽	VT 1◇ 🍽	VT 1◇ 🍽	XC 1◇ 🛒	VT 1◇ 🍽	LM 1◇	LM	VT 1◇ 🍽	LM 1◇	VT 1◇ 🍽	VT 1◇ 🍽	LM 1◇	VT 1◇ 🍽	LM	XC 1◇ 🛒	VT 1◇ 🍽	VT 1◇ 🍽	LM 1◇	VT 1◇ 🍽	VT 1◇ 🍽	VT 1◇ 🍽	XC 1◇ 🛒	VT 1◇ 🍽	LM 1◇
Crewe	d	16 29		16 53						17 22	17 29		17 38	17 55					18 22	18 29		18 55			
Alsager	d												17 46												
Kidsgrove	d												17 51												
Hanley Bus Station	d																								
Stoke-on-Trent	d		16 50		17 07	17 12						17 50	17 59			18 07	18 12				18 50		19 07	19 12	
Wedgwood Old Road Bridge	d																								
Barlaston Orchard Place	d																								
Stone Granville Square	d																								
Stone	d												18 07												
Norton Bridge Station Drv	d																								
Stafford	d				17 25		←		17 36	17a42			18 18			18 25		18 36	18a42				19 25		←
Rugeley Trent Valley	d						16 28						18 27												18 27
Lichfield Trent Valley	d						16 35						→												18 35
Tamworth Low Level	d						16 42																		18 42
Polesworth	d																								
Atherstone	d						16 51																		18 51
Nuneaton	a						16 58																		18 58
	d						16 58	17 11							18 11										18 58
Bedworth	d							17 17							18 17										
Coventry	a				18 24			17 34							18 34	19 24							20 24		
Rugby	a						17 18																		19 18
Northampton	a																								
Milton Keynes Central	a		17 49	18s03			17 56					18 49		19s03							19 49	20s03			19 58
Watford Junction	a						18 33																		20 33
London Euston	a	18 11	18 30	18 44		18 48	18 53		19 03		19 11	19 30		19 44			19 48	20 03		20 11	20 30	20 44		20 48	20 52

For general notes see front of timetable
For details of catering facilities see
Directory of Train Operators

A From Holyhead (Table 81)

Table 67

Sundays
until 12 July

Crewe and Stoke-on-Trent → London
Nuneaton → Coventry

Network Diagram - see first page of Table 67

		VT	LM	VT	VT	LM	LM	XC	VT	LM	VT	XC	VT	AW	VT	LM	LM	VT	LM	VT	VT	XC	LM	XC
		1 ◇	1 ◇	1 ◇	1 ◇		1 ◇	1 ◇	1 ◇	1 ◇	1 ◇	1 ◇	1 ◇	◇	1 ◇	1 ◇	1 ◇	1 ◇		1 ◇	1 ◇	1 ◇	1	1 ◇
		☕		☕	☕			🍴	☕		☕	🍴	☕		☕			☕		☕	☕	🍴		🍴
Crewe	d		19 22	19 29			19 36			20 18	20 24		20 47	20 52			21 17			21 24	21 40		22 22	
Alsager	d						19 44																	
Kidsgrove	d						19 50																	
Hanley Bus Station	d																							
Stoke-on-Trent	d				19 50		19 57	20 07	20 12			20 47			20 57			21 33				21 47		22 47
Wedgwood Old Road Bridge	d																							
Barlaston Orchard Place	d																							
Stone Granville Square	d																							
Stone	d						20 06																	
Norton Bridge Station Drv	d																							
Stafford	d	19 36	19a42				20 16	20 25		20a37	20 44	21a08		21a16			21a36			21 44	22a01	22a06	22a41	23a05
Rugeley Trent Valley	d						20 28									←								
Lichfield Trent Valley	d						20 35									20 35				21 59				
Tamworth Low Level	d						→									20 42				22 05				
Polesworth	d																							
Atherstone	d															20 51								
Nuneaton	a															20 58				22 15				
	d					20 11										20 58			22 00	22 16				
Bedworth	d					20 17													22 06					
Coventry	a					20 34		21 23											22 21					
Rugby	a															21 18				22 29				
Northampton	a																							
Milton Keynes Central	a				20 48						21 38		21 55		22 03	21 50		22 37		22 53				
Watford Junction	a												22 31			22 52		23s07		23s33				
London Euston	a	21 06		21 14	21 34				22 04		22 29		22 53		22 57	23 13		23 32		23 54				

Sundays
from 19 July

		VT	VT	VT	VT	VT	XC	XC	VT	VT	VT	VT	VT	VT	VT	XC	XC	VT	VT	LM	LM	LM	LM	VT	VT
		1 ◇	1 ◇	1 ◇	1 ◇	1 ◇	1 ◇	1 ◇	1 ◇	1 ◇	1 ◇	1 ◇	1 ◇	1 ◇	1 ◇	1 ◇	1 ◇	1 ◇	1 ◇	1 ◇	1 ◇	1	1	1 ◇	1 ◇
		A	B	A	B	A	A	B	B	A	B	A	B	A	B	A	B	A	B	A	B	A	B	A	B
		☕	☕	☕	☕	☕	🍴	🍴	☕	☕	☕	☕	☕	☕	☕	🍴	🍴	☕	☕					☕	☕
Crewe	d	08⌇43	08⌇43		08⌇55	08⌇55	09⌇04	09⌇04		09⌇13	09⌇13	09⌇43	09⌇43					10⌇14	10⌇12	10⌇20	10⌇20	10⌇37	10⌇38	10⌇43	10⌇43
Alsager	d																					10⌇46	10⌇47		
Kidsgrove	d																					10⌇50	10⌇51		
Hanley Bus Station	d																								
Stoke-on-Trent	d			08⌇59					09⌇07					09⌇57	09⌇57	10⌇07	10⌇07					10⌇58	10⌇59		
Wedgwood Old Road Bridge	d																								
Barlaston Orchard Place	d																								
Stone Granville Square	d																								
Stone	d																					11⌇06	11⌇07		
Norton Bridge Station Drv	d																								
Stafford	d	09⌇02	09⌇09				09⌇25	09⌇28		09⌇32	09⌇39					10⌇25	10⌇27	10⌇33	10⌇40	10a41	10a45	11a17	11a19		
Rugeley Trent Valley	d																								
Lichfield Trent Valley	d																								
Tamworth Low Level	d																								
Polesworth	d																								
Atherstone	d																								
Nuneaton	a									09⌇54	10⌇01							10⌇55	11⌇02						
	d									09⌇55	10⌇02							10⌇56	11⌇03						
Bedworth	d																								
Coventry	a						10⌇24	10⌇24								11⌇24	11⌇24								
Rugby	a											10⌇31	10⌇38											11⌇31	11⌇38
Northampton	a																								
Milton Keynes Central	a				10⌇13	10⌇18						11⌇04	11⌇04	11⌇13	11⌇18			11⌇48	11⌇48					12⌇04	12⌇04
Watford Junction	a	10s35	10s35	10s41					10s47	11s20	11s20	11s42	11s42												
London Euston	a	10⌇58	10⌇58	11⌇03	11⌇03	11⌇07			11⌇08	11⌇44	11⌇44	12⌇04	12⌇04	12⌇08	12⌇08			12⌇38	12⌇38					12⌇51	12⌇51

For general notes see front of timetable
For details of catering facilities see Directory of Train Operators

A Until 6 September
B From 13 September

Sundays

from 19 July

Crewe and Stoke-on-Trent → London
Nuneaton → Coventry

Network Diagram - see first page of Table 67

		VT		XC	VT	VT	XC	VT	VT	VT	VT	LM	LM	VT	XC	XC	XC	VT	VT	LM	VT	VT	VT	VT	XC
		1◇		1◇	1◇	1◇		1◇	1◇	1◇	1◇	1◇		1◇		1◇	1◇	1◇	1◇	1◇	1◇	1◇	1◇	1◇	1◇
					A	B	C 🚌	A	B	D					C 🚌	B	A					D			
		☕		🛒	☕	☕		☕	☕	☕	☕			☕		🛒	🛒	☕	☕		☕	☕	☕	☕	🛒
Crewe	d	10 55						11 14	11 14	11 33		11 38		11 49						12 22	12 30	12 33		12 54	
Alsager	d											11 46													
Kidsgrove	d											11 52													
Hanley Bus Station	d																								
Stoke-on-Trent	d			11 07	11 12	11 12					11 51	11 59				12 07	12 07	12 13					12 51		13 07
Wedgwood Old Road Bridge	d																								
Barlaston Orchard Place	d																								
Stone Granville Square	d																								
Stone	d											12 08													
Norton Bridge Station Drv	d																								
Stafford	d			11 25				11 33	11 42			12 18				12 26	12 25		12 36	12a41					13 25
Rugeley Trent Valley	d											12 28 →													
Lichfield Trent Valley	d																								
Tamworth Low Level	d						11 20								12 20										
Polesworth	d																								
Atherstone	d																								
Nuneaton	a						11 40	11 55	12 04					12 30	12 40										
	d							11 56	12 05				12 30	12 31											
Bedworth	d												12 36												
Coventry	a			12 24									12 54			13 24	13 24								14 24
Rugby	a																								
Northampton	a																								
Milton Keynes Central	a				12 20	12 29					12 50			13s03									13 50	14s02	
Watford Junction	a	12s35						12s53	12s54																
London Euston	a	12 58			13 01	13 09		13 15	13 15	13 23	13 31			13 44				13 49	14 03		14 12	14 18	14 31	14 43	

		VT	LM	XC		VT	LM	VT	VT	LM	LM	VT	VT	XC	XC	VT	VT	LM	VT	VT	VT	XC	VT	LM	LM
		1◇	1◇			1◇	1◇	1◇	1◇	1◇		1◇	1◇		1◇	1◇	1◇	1◇	1◇	1◇	1◇	1◇	1◇	1◇	
				C 🚌								E	D	C 🚌											
		☕				☕		☕	☕			☕	☕		🛒	☕	☕		☕	☕	☕	🛒	☕		
Crewe	d						13 22	13 30		13 38		13 49	13 55					14 22	14 29		14 54				
Alsager	d									13 46															
Kidsgrove	d									13 51															
Hanley Bus Station	d																								
Stoke-on-Trent	d	13 14							13 50	13 59					14 07	14 12				14 50		15 07	15 12		
Wedgwood Old Road Bridge	d																								
Barlaston Orchard Place	d																								
Stone Granville Square	d																								
Stone	d									14 07															
Norton Bridge Station Drv	d																								
Stafford	d		←			13 36	13a42			14 19					14 25		14 36	14a42				15 25		←	
Rugeley Trent Valley	d		12 28							14 29 →														14 29	
Lichfield Trent Valley	d		12 35																					14 36	
Tamworth Low Level	d		12 42	13 20										14 20										14 43	
Polesworth	d																								
Atherstone	d		12 51																					14 52	
Nuneaton	a		12 58	13 40								14 31		14 40										14 58	
	d		12 58								14 11	14 32												14 58	15 11
Bedworth	d										14 17														15 17
Coventry	a										14 34				15 24							16 24			15 34
Rugby	a		13 17																					15 17	
Northampton	a		13 39																					15 39	
Milton Keynes Central	a		14 04						14 49			15s04	15s03							15 49	16s04			16 04	
Watford Junction	a		14 34																					16 33	
London Euston	a	14 50	14 53			15 03		15 12	15 30			15 45	15 43			15 48	16 03		16 11	16 30	16 44		16 48	16 53	

		XC	VT	LM	VT	VT		LM	LM	VT	XC	XC	VT	VT	LM	VT	VT	VT	XC	VT	LM	LM	XC	VT	LM
			1◇	1◇	1◇	1◇			1◇	1◇		1◇	1◇	1◇	1◇	1◇	1◇	1◇	1◇	1◇	1◇			1◇	1◇
		C 🚌									C 🚌												C 🚌		
			☕		☕	☕				☕		🛒	☕	☕		☕	☕	☕	🛒	☕				☕	
Crewe	d			15 22	15 29				15 38	15 54					16 22	16 29		16 53							17 22
Alsager	d								15 46																
Kidsgrove	d								15 52																
Hanley Bus Station	d																								
Stoke-on-Trent	d					15 50			15 59			16 07	16 12				16 50		17 07	17 12					
Wedgwood Old Road Bridge	d																								
Barlaston Orchard Place	d																								
Stone Granville Square	d																								
Stone	d								16 08																
Norton Bridge Station Drv	d																								
Stafford	d		15 36	15a42					16 18			16 25		16 37	16a42				17 25		←			17 36	17a42
Rugeley Trent Valley	d								16 28 →												16 28				
Lichfield Trent Valley	d																				16 35				
Tamworth Low Level	d	15 20									16 20										16 42		17 20		
Polesworth	d																								
Atherstone	d																				16 51				
Nuneaton	a	15 40									16 40										16 58		17 40		
	d							16 11													16 58	17 11			
Bedworth	d							16 17														17 17			
Coventry	a							16 34				17 24							18 24			17 34			
Rugby	a																				17 17				
Northampton	a																				17 39				
Milton Keynes Central	a					16 49				17s03							17 49	18s03			18 04				
Watford Junction	a																				18 33				
London Euston	a		17 03		17 11	17 30				17 44			17 48	18 04		18 11	18 30	18 44		18 48	18 53			19 03	

For general notes see front of timetable
For details of catering facilities see Directory of Train Operators

- **A** Until 6 September
- **B** From 13 September
- **C** From 13 September. To Leicester (Table 57)
- **D** From 8 November
- **E** Until 1 November. From Holyhead (Table 81)

Table 67

Sundays

from 19 July

Crewe and Stoke-on-Trent → London
Nuneaton → Coventry

Network Diagram - see first page of Table 67

		VT	VT	LM	LM	VT	XC	XC		VT	VT	LM	VT
		1◇	1◇		1◇	1◇		1◇		1◇	1◇	1◇	1◇
							A						
		☕	☕			☕	🚌	🛒		☕	☕		☕
Crewe	d	17 29			17 38	17 55						18 22	18 29
Alsager	d				17 46								
Kidsgrove	d				17 51								
Hanley Bus Station	d												
Stoke-on-Trent	d		17 50		17 59			18 07		18 12			
Wedgwood Old Road Bridge	d												
Barlaston Orchard Place	d												
Stone Granville Square	d												
Stone	d				18 07								
Norton Bridge Station Drv	d												
Stafford	d				18 18			18 25			18 36	18a42	
Rugeley Trent Valley	d				18 27								
Lichfield Trent Valley	d				→								
Tamworth Low Level	d						18 20						
Polesworth	d												
Atherstone	d												
Nuneaton	a						18 40						
	d			18 11									
Bedworth	d			18 17									
Coventry	a			18 34				19 24					
Rugby	a												
Northampton	a												
Milton Keynes Central	a		18 49			19s03							
Watford Junction	a												
London Euston	a	19 11	19 30			19 44				19 48	20 03		20 11

		VT	VT	XC	VT	LM	XC	VT	LM	VT	VT	LM	XC
		1◇	1◇	1◇	1◇	1◇		1◇	1◇	1◇	1◇		
							A						A
		☕	☕	🛒	☕		🚌	☕		☕	☕		🚌
Crewe	d		18 55						19 22	19 29			
Alsager	d												
Kidsgrove	d												
Hanley Bus Station	d												
Stoke-on-Trent	d	18 50		19 07	19 12						19 50		
Wedgwood Old Road Bridge	d												
Barlaston Orchard Place	d												
Stone Granville Square	d												
Stone	d												
Norton Bridge Station Drv	d												
Stafford	d			19 25		←		19 36	19a42				
Rugeley Trent Valley	d					18 27							
Lichfield Trent Valley	d					18 35							
Tamworth Low Level	d					18 42	19 20						20 20
Polesworth	d												
Atherstone	d					18 51							
Nuneaton	a					18 58	19 40						20 40
	d					18 58						20 11	
Bedworth	d											20 17	
Coventry	a			20 24								20 34	
Rugby	a					19 17							
Northampton	a					19 39							
Milton Keynes Central	a	19 49	20s03			20 06					20 48		
Watford Junction	a					20 33							
London Euston	a	20 30	20 44		20 48	20 52		21 06		21 14	21 34		

		LM	XC	VT	LM	VT	XC	XC	VT	AW	VT	LM
		1◇	1◇	1◇	1◇	1◇	1◇	1◇	1◇	◇	1◇	1◇
							B	C				
			🛒	☕		☕	🛒	🛒	☕		☕	
Crewe	d	19 36			20 18	20 24			20 47	20 52		
Alsager	d	19 44										
Kidsgrove	d	19 50										
Hanley Bus Station	d											
Stoke-on-Trent	d	19 57	20 07	20 12			20 47	20 47			20 57	
Wedgwood Old Road Bridge	d											
Barlaston Orchard Place	d											
Stone Granville Square	d											
Stone	d	20 06										
Norton Bridge Station Drv	d											
Stafford	d	20 16	20 25		20a37	20 44	21a07	21a08		21a16		
Rugeley Trent Valley	d	20 28										
Lichfield Trent Valley	d	20 35										←
Tamworth Low Level	d	20 42										20 42
Polesworth	d	→										
Atherstone	d											20 51
Nuneaton	a											20 58
	d											20 58
Bedworth	d											
Coventry	a		21 23									
Rugby	a											21 17
Northampton	a											21 39
Milton Keynes Central	a					21 38			21 55		22 03	22 10
Watford Junction	a								22 31			22 52
London Euston	a			22 04		22 29			22 53		22 57	23 13

		XC	LM	VT	LM	VT	VT	XC	XC	LM	XC	XC		
			1◇	1◇		1◇	1◇	1◇		1	1◇	1◇		
		A							A		D	E		
		🚌		☕		☕	☕	🛒	🚌		🛒	🛒		
Crewe	d		21 17			21 24	21 40			22 22				
Alsager	d													
Kidsgrove	d													
Hanley Bus Station	d													
Stoke-on-Trent	d			21 33				21 47			22 47	22 47		
Wedgwood Old Road Bridge	d													
Barlaston Orchard Place	d													
Stone Granville Square	d													
Stone	d													
Norton Bridge Station Drv	d													
Stafford	d		21a36			21 44	22a01	22a06		22a41	23a04	23a05		
Rugeley Trent Valley	d													
Lichfield Trent Valley	d					21 59								
Tamworth Low Level	d	21 20				22 05			22 20					
Polesworth	d													
Atherstone	d													
Nuneaton	a	21 40				22 15			22 40					
	d				22 00	22 16								
Bedworth	d				22 06									
Coventry	a				22 21									
Rugby	a					22 29								
Northampton	a													
Milton Keynes Central	a			22 50		23 08								
Watford Junction	a			23s31		23s38								
London Euston	a			23 53		23 59								

For general notes see front of timetable
For details of catering facilities see Directory of Train Operators

- **A** From 13 September. To Leicester (Table 57)
- **B** Until 1 November
- **C** From 8 November
- **D** Until 6 September
- **E** From 13 September

Northampton → Coventry → Birmingham → Wolverhampton → Stafford

Network Diagram - see first page of Table 67

Miles			VT	VT	VT	VT	LM	VT	LM	XC	LM	LM	LM	LM	VT	XC		AW	LM	LM	LM	LM	XC	LM	LM
			MO	MO	MO	MO	MO																		
			1◊	1◊	1◊	1◊		1◊		1◊	1◊		1	1	1◊	1◊		◊		1◊		1	1◊	1◊	1
			A	B	A	B	A	C			D			E						D	G			D	
			☕	☕	☕	☕	🚌	⊠		ℸ					⊠	☕		ℸ					ℸ		
—	London Euston [15] ⊖	d	21p54	21p54	22p24	22p24																			
0	**Northampton**	d					23p32						05 17	05 42											05 56
9½	Long Buckby	d					23p53						05 27												06 06
18¾	Rugby	d	23b20	23p24	23c43	23p48	00 24						05 37	06 02											06 16
32¼	**Coventry**	a	23p33	23p33	23p54	23p57	01 04						05 49												06 28
—		d	23p34	23p34	23p58	23p58							05 49									06 10			06 29
34	Canley	d																				06 13			06 32
36	Tile Hill	d											05 54									06 17			06 36
38	Berkswell	d																				06 20			06 39
41¼	Hampton-in-Arden	d											06 00									06 24			
43	**Birmingham International** ✈	a	23p51	23p51	00 08	00 08							06 04									06 27			06 45
—		d	23p52	23p52	00 09	00 09							06 04						06 18			06 28			06 45
45	Marston Green	d											06 07									06 31			06 48
46½	Lea Hall	d																	06 22						06 51
47¾	Stechford	d																	06 24						06 54
49½	Adderley Park	d																	06 27						
51½	**Birmingham New Street** [12]	a	00 04	00 04	00 22	00 22							06 16						06 32			06 39			07 01
—		d	00 08	00 08	00 25	00 25		05 30	05 51	05 57	06 01	06 07			06 17	06 20		06 24		06 36	06 39		06 57	07 01	
54¾	Smethwick Rolfe Street	d										06 13									06 45				
55½	Smethwick Galton Bdg L.L. [7]	d									06 08	06 15						06 31			06 47			07 08	
56¾	Sandwell & Dudley	d							05 59			06 17									06 49				
57¾	Dudley Port	d										06 20									06 52				
58½	Tipton	d										06 22									06 54				
60	Coseley	d										06 25									06 57				
64¼	**Wolverhampton** [7]	a	00 28	00 28	00 55	00 55		05 47	06 09	06 14	06 19	06 30			06 34	06 38		06 42		06 51	07 03		07 14	07 19	
—		d						05 48		06 15	06 19					06 40				06 51			07 15	07 19	
74¼	Penkridge	d									06 29													07 30	
79½	**Stafford**	a						06 01		06 29	06 35			06 52		06 53				07 05			07 29	07 36	

		LM	LM	VT	AW	LM	VT	LM	XC		LM	LM	VT	XC	LM	LM	LM	VT	LM	LM	VT	AW	VT	LM	XC
			1	1◊	◊		1◊	1	1◊		1◊		1◊	1◊	1◊	1◊		1◊		1	1◊	◊	1◊	1◊	1◊
					C						D				H										
				⊠	ℸ		⊠		ℸ				⊠	ℸ				⊠			⊠	ℸ	⊠		ℸ
London Euston [15] ⊖	d						06 03						06 23			05 30		06 43					07 03	06 24	
Northampton	d		06 17					06 38								06 56				07 17				07 45	
Long Buckby	d		06 27													07 06				07 27					
Rugby	d		06 37				06 51	06 58								07 16				07 37			07 51	08 03	
Coventry	a		06 49				07 01						07 22			07 28		07 42		07 49			08 01		
	d		06 49				07 02					07 07	07 22	07 27		07 29		07 42		07 49			08 02		
Canley	d											07 09				07 32									
Tile Hill	d		06 54									07 13				07 36				07 54					
Berkswell	d											07 16				07 39									
Hampton-in-Arden	d		07 00									07 20								08 00					
Birmingham International ✈	a		07 04				07 12					07 23	07 33	07 37		07 45		07 53		08 04			08 12		
	d		07 04		07 09		07 13				07 18	07 24	07 33	07 38		07 45		07 53		08 04		08 09	08 13		
Marston Green	d		07 07									07 27				07 48				08 07					
Lea Hall	d										07 22					07 51									
Stechford	d										07 24					07 54									
Adderley Park	d										07 27					07 57									
Birmingham New Street [12]	a		07 16		07 19		07 27				07 32	07 36	07 45	07 49		08 03		08 08		08 16		08 19	08 27		
	d	07 09		07 19	07 22	07 27			07 31		07 36	07 39	07 49	07 57	08 01		08 05		08 09		08 20	08 24			08 31
Smethwick Rolfe Street	d	07 15										07 45							08 15						
Smethwick Galton Bdg L.L. [7]	d	07 17			07 28							07 47			08 08				08 17			08 30			
Sandwell & Dudley	d	07 19										07 49	07 58				08 13		08 19						
Dudley Port	d	07 22										07 52							08 22						
Tipton	d	07 24										07 54							08 24						
Coseley	d	07 27									07 46	07 57							08 27						
Wolverhampton [7]	a	07 33		07 35	07 39	07 44			07 48		07 53	08 03	08 11	08 14	08 19		08 24		08 33		08 37	08 42			08 48
	d										07 53			08 15	08 19										
Penkridge	d										08 03				08 29										
Stafford	a							07 53			08 09			08 29	08 35									08 53	

For general notes see front of timetable
For details of catering facilities see Directory of Train Operators

A Until 13 July
B From 20 July
C To Holyhead (Table 81)
D To Liverpool Lime Street (Table 91)
E From Bletchley (Table 66)
G From Walsall (Table 70)
H From Walsall (Table 70) to Liverpool Lime Street (Table 91)
b Previous night. Arr. 2309
c Previous night. Arr. 2339

Northampton → Coventry → Birmingham → Wolverhampton → Stafford

Network Diagram - see first page of Table 67

	LM		LM	LM	LM	VT	XC	LM	LM	LM	VT	LM	LM	VT	AW	VT		LM	XC	LM	LM	LM	LM	VT
			■1◇		■1	■1◇	■1◇	■1◇	■1		■1◇		■1◇	■1◇	◇	■1◇		■1◇	■1◇		■1◇		■1	■1◇
			A	B				A							C						A	D		
						⊠	🛒				⊠			⊠	🛒	⊠			🛒					⊠
London Euston 15 ⊖ d						07 23					07 43		06 53			08 03		07 46						08 23
Northampton d									07 56				08 17					08 45						
Long Buckby d									08 06				08 27											
Rugby d									08 16				08 37			08 51		09 03						
Coventry a						08 22			08 28		08 42		08 49			09 01								09 22
d					08 11	08 22	08 27		08 29		08 42		08 49			09 02							09 11	09 22
Canley d					08 14				08 32														09 14	
Tile Hill d					08 18				08 36				08 54										09 18	
Berkswell d					08 21				08 39														09 21	
Hampton-in-Arden d					08 25								09 00										09 25	
Birmingham International ✈ a					08 28	08 33	08 37		08 45		08 53		09 04			09 12							09 28	09 33
d	08 18				08 29	08 33	08 38		08 45		08 53		09 04		09 09	09 13				09 18			09 29	09 33
Marston Green d					08 32				08 48				09 07										09 32	
Lea Hall d	08 22								08 51											09 22				
Stechford d	08 24								08 54											09 24				
Adderley Park d	08 27																			09 27				
Birmingham New Street 12 a	08 32				08 42	08 45	08 49		09 01		09 08		09 16		09 19	09 27				09 32			09 42	09 45
d			08 36	08 39		08 49	08 57	09 01		09 05		09 09		09 20	09 24				09 31		09 36	09 39		09 49
Smethwick Rolfe Street d				08 45								09 15										09 45		
Smethwick Galton Bdg L.L. 7 d				08 47				09 08				09 17			09 30							09 47		
Sandwell & Dudley d				08 49		08 58				09 13		09 19										09 49		09 58
Dudley Port d				08 52								09 22										09 52		
Tipton d				08 54								09 24										09 54		
Coseley d			08 46	08 57								09 27									09 46	09 57		
Wolverhampton 7 ⛴ a			08 53	09 03		09 11	09 14	09 19		09 28		09 33		09 37	09 43				09 48		09 53	10 03		10 11
d			08 53				09 15	09 19													09 53			
Penkridge d			09 03																		10 03			
Stafford a			09 09				09 29	09 34										09 53			10 09			

	XC	LM	LM	LM	VT	LM	LM	VT	AW		VT	LM	XC	LM	LM	LM	LM	VT	XC	LM	LM	LM	VT	LM
	■1◇	■1◇	■1		■1◇		■1◇	■1◇	◇		■1◇	■1◇	■1◇		■1◇		■1	■1◇	■1◇	■1◇	■1		■1◇	
		A													A	D				A				D
	🛒				⊠			⊡	🛒		⊠		🛒					⊠	🛒				⊠	
London Euston 15 ⊖ d					08 43		07 54				09 03	08 46						09 23					09 43	
Northampton d			08 56				09 17					09 45									09 56			
Long Buckby d			09 06				09 27														10 06			
Rugby d			09 16				09 37				09 51	10 03									10 16			
Coventry a			09 28		09 42		09 49				10 01							10 22			10 28		10 42	
d	09 27		09 29		09 42		09 49				10 02						10 11	10 22	10 27		10 29		10 42	
Canley d			09 32														10 14				10 32			
Tile Hill d			09 36				09 54										10 18				10 36			
Berkswell d			09 39														10 21				10 39			
Hampton-in-Arden d							10 00										10 25							
Birmingham International ✈ a	09 37		09 45		09 53		10 04				10 12						10 28	10 33	10 37		10 45		10 53	
d	09 38		09 45		09 53		10 04		10 09		10 13			10 18			10 29	10 33	10 38		10 45		10 53	
Marston Green d			09 48				10 07										10 32				10 48			
Lea Hall d			09 51											10 23							10 51			
Stechford d			09 54											10 25							10 54			
Adderley Park d														10 29										
Birmingham New Street 12 a	09 49		10 01		10 08		10 16		10 19		10 27			10 34			10 42	10 45	10 49		11 01		11 08	
d	09 57	10 01		10 05		10 09		10 20	10 24				10 31		10 36	10 39		10 49	10 57	11 01		11 05		11 09
Smethwick Rolfe Street d						10 15										10 45								11 15
Smethwick Galton Bdg L.L. 7 d		10 08				10 17			10 30							10 47				11 08				11 17
Sandwell & Dudley d				10 13		10 19										10 49		10 58				11 13		11 19
Dudley Port d						10 22										10 52								11 22
Tipton d						10 24										10 54								11 24
Coseley d						10 27									10 46	10 57								11 27
Wolverhampton 7 ⛴ a	10 14	10 19		10 24		10 33		10 37	10 42				10 48		10 53	11 03		11 11	11 14	11 19		11 24		11 33
d	10 15	10 19													10 53				11 15	11 19				
Penkridge d															11 03									
Stafford a	10 29	10 34										10 53			11 09				11 29	11 34				

For general notes see front of timetable
For details of catering facilities see Directory of Train Operators

A To Liverpool Lime Street (Table 91)
B From Four Oaks (Table 69)
C To Holyhead (Table 81)
D From Walsall (Table 70)

Northampton → Coventry → Birmingham → Wolverhampton → Stafford

Network Diagram - see first page of Table 67

		LM	VT		AW	VT	LM	XC	LM	LM	LM	LM	VT	XC	LM	LM	LM	VT		LM	LM	VT	AW	VT	LM
		1 ◇	1 ◇		◇	1 ◇	1 ◇	1 ◇		1 ◇		1	1 ◇	1 ◇	1 ◇	1		1 ◇			1 ◇	1 ◇	◇	1 ◇	1 ◇
					A					B	C				B					C					
London Euston 15 ⊖	d	08 54				10 03	09 46						10 23					10 43			09 54			11 03	10 46
Northampton	d	10 17					10 45									10 56					11 17				11 45
Long Buckby	d	10 27														11 06					11 27				
Rugby	d	10 37				10 51	11 03									11 16					11 37			11 51	12 03
Coventry	a	10 49				11 01							11 22			11 28		11 42			11 49			12 01	
	d	10 49				11 02						11 11	11 22	11 27		11 29		11 42			11 49			12 02	
Canley	d											11 14				11 32									
Tile Hill	d	10 54										11 18				11 36					11 54				
Berkswell	d											11 21				11 39									
Hampton-in-Arden	d	11 00										11 25									12 00				
Birmingham International ✈	a	11 04				11 12						11 28	11 33	11 37		11 45		11 53			12 04			12 12	
	d	11 04			11 09	11 13			11 18			11 29	11 33	11 38		11 45		11 53			12 04		12 09	12 13	
Marston Green	d	11 07										11 32				11 48					12 07				
Lea Hall	d								11 22							11 51									
Stechford	d								11 24							11 54									
Adderley Park	d								11 27																
Birmingham New Street 12	a	11 16			11 19	11 27			11 32			11 42	11 45	11 49		12 01		12 08			12 16		12 19	12 27	
	d		11 20		11 24			11 31		11 36	11 39		11 49	11 57	12 01		12 05			12 09		12 20	12 24		
Smethwick Rolfe Street	d										11 45									12 15					
Smethwick Galton Bdg L.L. 7	d				11 30						11 47				12 08					12 17			12 30		
Sandwell & Dudley	d										11 49		11 58				12 13			12 19					
Dudley Port	d										11 52									12 22					
Tipton	d										11 54									12 24					
Coseley	d									11 46	11 57									12 27					
Wolverhampton 7	a		11 37		11 42			11 48		11 53	12 03		12 11	12 14	12 19		12 24			12 33		12 37	12 42		
	d									11 53				12 15	12 19										
Penkridge	d									12 03															
Stafford	a						11 53			12 09				12 29	12 34										12 53

		XC	LM	LM	LM	LM	VT	XC	LM	LM	LM		VT	LM	LM	VT	AW	VT	LM	XC	LM	LM	LM	LM	VT
		1 ◇		1 ◇		1	1 ◇	1 ◇	1 ◇	1			1 ◇		1 ◇	1 ◇	◇	1 ◇	1 ◇	1 ◇		1 ◇		1	1 ◇
				B	C				B					C			A					B	C		
London Euston 15 ⊖	d						11 23						11 43		10 54			12 03	11 46						12 23
Northampton	d									11 56					12 17				12 45						
Long Buckby	d									12 06					12 27										
Rugby	d									12 16					12 37			12 51	13 03						
Coventry	a						12 22			12 28			12 42		12 49			13 01							13 22
	d					12 11	12 22	12 27		12 29			12 42		12 49			13 02						13 11	13 22
Canley	d					12 14				12 32														13 14	
Tile Hill	d					12 18				12 36					12 54									13 18	
Berkswell	d					12 21				12 39														13 21	
Hampton-in-Arden	d					12 25									13 00									13 25	
Birmingham International ✈	a					12 28	12 33	12 37		12 45			12 53		13 04			13 12						13 28	13 33
	d		12 18			12 29	12 33	12 38		12 45			12 53		13 04		13 09	13 13			13 18			13 29	13 33
Marston Green	d					12 32				12 48					13 07									13 32	
Lea Hall	d		12 22							12 51											13 22				
Stechford	d		12 24							12 54											13 24				
Adderley Park	d		12 27																		13 27				
Birmingham New Street 12	a		12 32			12 42	12 45	12 49		13 01			13 08		13 16		13 19	13 27			13 32			13 42	13 45
	d	12 31		12 36	12 39		12 49	12 57	13 01		13 05			13 09		13 20	13 24			13 31		13 36	13 39		13 49
Smethwick Rolfe Street	d				12 45									13 15									13 45		
Smethwick Galton Bdg L.L. 7	d				12 47				13 08					13 17			13 30						13 47		
Sandwell & Dudley	d				12 49		12 58				13 13			13 19									13 49		13 58
Dudley Port	d				12 52									13 22									13 52		
Tipton	d				12 54									13 24									13 54		
Coseley	d			12 46	12 57									13 27								13 46	13 57		
Wolverhampton 7	a	12 48		12 53	13 03		13 11	13 14	13 19		13 24			13 33		13 37	13 42			13 48		13 53	14 03		14 11
	d			12 53				13 15	13 19													13 53			
Penkridge	d			13 03																		14 03			
Stafford	a			13 09				13 29	13 34										13 53			14 09			

For general notes see front of timetable
For details of catering facilities see Directory of Train Operators

A To Holyhead (Table 81)
B To Liverpool Lime Street (Table 91)
C From Walsall (Table 70)

Northampton → Coventry → Birmingham → Wolverhampton → Stafford

Network Diagram - see first page of Table 67

		XC 1◇ [trolley]	LM 1◇ A	LM 1		LM	VT 1◇ [restaurant]	LM B	LM 1◇	VT 1◇ [restaurant]	AW ◇ [trolley]	VT 1◇ [restaurant]	LM 1◇	XC 1◇ [trolley]	LM	LM 1◇ A	LM B	LM 1	VT 1◇ [restaurant]		XC 1◇ [trolley]	LM 1◇ A	LM 1	LM	VT 1◇ [restaurant]
London Euston [15] ⊖	d						12 43		11 54			13 03	12 46						13 23						13 43
Northampton	d			12 56					13 17				13 45										13 56		
Long Buckby	d			13 06					13 27														14 06		
Rugby	d			13 16					13 37			13 51	14 03										14 16		
Coventry	a			13 28			13 42		13 49			14 01							14 22				14 28		14 42
	d	13 27		13 29			13 42		13 49			14 02						14 11	14 22		14 27		14 29		14 42
Canley	d			13 32														14 14					14 32		
Tile Hill	d			13 36					13 54									14 18					14 36		
Berkswell	d			13 39														14 21					14 39		
Hampton-in-Arden	d								14 00									14 25							
Birmingham International ✈	a	13 37		13 45			13 53		14 04			14 12						14 28	14 33		14 37		14 45		14 53
	d	13 38		13 45			13 53		14 04		14 09	14 13			14 18			14 29	14 33		14 38		14 45		14 53
Marston Green	d			13 48					14 07									14 32					14 48		
Lea Hall	d			13 51											14 22								14 51		
Stechford	d			13 54											14 24								14 54		
Adderley Park	d														14 27										
Birmingham New Street [12]	a	13 49		14 01			14 08		14 16		14 19	14 27			14 32			14 42	14 45		14 49		15 01		15 08
	d	13 57	14 01			14 05		14 09		14 20	14 24			14 31		14 36	14 39		14 49		14 57	15 01		15 05	
Smethwick Rolfe Street	d							14 15									14 45								
Smethwick Galton Bdg L.L. [7]	d		14 08					14 17			14 30						14 47					15 08			
Sandwell & Dudley	d					14 13		14 19									14 49		14 58					15 13	
Dudley Port	d							14 22									14 52								
Tipton	d							14 24									14 54								
Coseley	d							14 27								14 46	14 57								
Wolverhampton [7]	a	14 14	14 19			14 24		14 33		14 37	14 42			14 48		14 53	15 03		15 11		15 14	15 19		15 24	
	d	14 15	14 19													14 53					15 15	15 19			
Penkridge	d															15 03									
Stafford	a	14 29	14 34										14 53			15 09					15 29	15 34			

		LM B	LM 1◇	VT 1◇ [restaurant]	AW ◇ C [trolley]	VT 1◇ [restaurant]	LM 1◇	XC 1◇ [trolley]	LM	LM 1◇ A	LM B	LM 1		VT 1◇ [restaurant]	XC 1◇ [trolley]	LM 1◇ A	LM 1	LM	VT 1◇ [restaurant]	LM B	LM 1◇	VT 1◇ [restaurant]	AW R [trolley]	VT 1◇ [restaurant]	LM 1◇
London Euston [15] ⊖	d		12 54			14 03	13 46							14 23					14 43		13 54			15 03	14 46
Northampton	d		14 17				14 45										14 56				15 17				15 45
Long Buckby	d		14 27														15 06				15 27				
Rugby	d		14 37			14 51	15 03										15 16				15 37			15 51	16 03
Coventry	a		14 49			15 01								15 22			15 28		15 42		15 49			16 01	
	d		14 49			15 02						15 11		15 22	15 27		15 29		15 42		15 49			16 02	
Canley	d											15 14					15 32								
Tile Hill	d		14 54									15 18					15 36				15 54				
Berkswell	d											15 21					15 39								
Hampton-in-Arden	d		15 00									15 25									16 00				
Birmingham International ✈	a		15 04			15 12						15 28		15 33	15 37		15 45		15 53		16 04			16 12	
	d		15 04		15 09	15 13			15 18			15 29		15 33	15 38		15 45		15 53		16 04		16 09	16 13	
Marston Green	d		15 07									15 32					15 48				16 07				
Lea Hall	d								15 22								15 51								
Stechford	d								15 24								15 54								
Adderley Park	d								15 27																
Birmingham New Street [12]	a		15 16		15 19	15 27			15 32			15 42		15 45	15 49		16 01		16 08		16 16		16 19	16 27	
	d	15 09		15 20	15 24			15 31		15 36	15 39			15 49	15 57	16 01		16 05		16 09		16 20	16 24		
Smethwick Rolfe Street	d	15 15									15 45									16 15					
Smethwick Galton Bdg L.L. [7]	d	15 17			15 30						15 47					16 08				16 17			16 30		
Sandwell & Dudley	d	15 19									15 49			15 58				16 13		16 19					
Dudley Port	d	15 22									15 52									16 22					
Tipton	d	15 24									15 54									16 24					
Coseley	d	15 27								15 46	15 57									16 27					
Wolverhampton [7]	a	15 33		15 37	15 42			15 48		15 53	16 03			16 11	16 14	16 19		16 24		16 33		16 37	16 42		
	d									15 53					16 15	16 19									
Penkridge	d									16 03															
Stafford	a						15 53			16 09					16 29	16 34									16 53

For general notes see front of timetable
For details of catering facilities see Directory of Train Operators

A To Liverpool Lime Street (Table 91)
B From Walsall (Table 70)
C To Holyhead (Table 81)

Northampton → Coventry → Birmingham → Wolverhampton → Stafford

Network Diagram - see first page of Table 67

		XC	LM	LM	LM		LM	VT	XC	LM	LM	LM	VT	LM	LM	VT	AW	VT	XC	LM		VT	LM	LM	LM
		1 ◇		1 ◇			1	1 ◇	1 ◇	1 ◇	1		1 ◇		1 ◇	1 ◇	◇	1 ◇	1 ◇			1 ◇	1 ◇	1 ◇	
				A	B					A				B			C							A	B
		🛒						🍴	🛒				🍴			🍴	🛒	⊠	🛒			⊠			
London Euston 15 ⊖	d							15 23					15 43		14 54			16 03				16 33	15 46		
Northampton	d										15 56				16 17								16 45		
Long Buckby	d										16 06				16 27										
Rugby	d										16 16				16 37			16 51				17 22	17 03		
Coventry	a							16 22			16 28		16 42		16 49			17 01							
	d						16 11	16 22	16 27		16 29		16 42		16 49			17 02							
Canley	d						16 14				16 32														
Tile Hill	d						16 18				16 36				16 54										
Berkswell	d						16 21				16 39														
Hampton-in-Arden	d						16 25								17 00										
Birmingham International ✈	a						16 28	16 33	16 37		16 45		16 53		17 04			17 12							
	d		16 18				16 29	16 33	16 38		16 45		16 53		17 04		17 09	17 13		17 18					
Marston Green	d						16 32				16 48				17 07										
Lea Hall	d		16 22								16 51									17 22					
Stechford	d		16 24								16 54									17 24					
Adderley Park	d		16 27																	17 27					
Birmingham New Street 12	a		16 32				16 42	16 45	16 49		17 01		17 08		17 16		17 19	17 27		17 32					
	d	16 31		16 36	16 39			16 49	16 57	17 01		17 05		17 09		17 20	17 24		17 31					17 36	17 39
Smethwick Rolfe Street	d				16 45									17 15											17 45
Smethwick Galton Bdg L.L. 7	d				16 47					17 08				17 17			17 31								17 47
Sandwell & Dudley	d				16 49			16 58				17 13		17 19											17 49
Dudley Port	d				16 52									17 22											17 52
Tipton	d				16 54									17 24											17 54
Coseley	d			16 46	16 57									17 27										17 46	17 57
Wolverhampton 7 🚌	a	16 48		16 53	17 03			17 11	17 14	17 19		17 24		17 33		17 37	17 42		17 48					17 53	18 03
	d			16 53					17 15	17 19														17 53	
Penkridge	d			17 03						17 29														18 03	
Stafford	a			17 09					17 29	17 35												17 52	18 00	18 09	

		LM	VT	XC	LM	LM	LM	VT	LM	LM	VT	AW	VT		XC	LM	LM	LM	LM	VT	XC	LM	LM	LM	VT
		1	1 ◇	1 ◇	1 ◇	1		1 ◇		1 ◇	1 ◇	◇	1 ◇		1 ◇		1 ◇		1	1 ◇	1 ◇	1 ◇	1		1 ◇
					A				B								A	B				D			
			⊠	🛒				⊠			🍴	🛒	⊠		🛒					⊠	🛒				⊠
London Euston 15 ⊖	d		16 23					16 43		15 54			17 03							17 23					17 43
Northampton	d					16 56				17 17													17 56		
Long Buckby	d					17 06				17 27													18 06		
Rugby	d					17 16				17 37			17 51										18 16		
Coventry	a		17 22			17 28		17 42		17 49			18 01							18 22			18 28		18 42
	d	17 11	17 22	17 27		17 29		17 42		17 49			18 02						18 11	18 22	18 27		18 29		18 42
Canley	d	17 14				17 32													18 14				18 32		
Tile Hill	d	17 18				17 36				17 54									18 18				18 36		
Berkswell	d	17 21				17 39													18 21				18 39		
Hampton-in-Arden	d	17 25								18 00									18 25						
Birmingham International ✈	a	17 28	17 33	17 37		17 45		17 53		18 04			18 12						18 28	18 33	18 37		18 45		18 53
	d	17 29	17 33	17 38		17 45		17 53		18 04		18 09	18 13			18 18			18 29	18 33	18 38		18 45		18 53
Marston Green	d	17 32				17 48				18 07									18 32				18 48		
Lea Hall	d					17 51										18 22							18 51		
Stechford	d					17 54										18 24							18 54		
Adderley Park	d															18 27									
Birmingham New Street 12	a	17 42	17 45	17 49		18 01		18 08		18 16		18 19	18 27			18 32			18 42	18 45	18 49		19 01		19 08
	d		17 49	17 57	18 01		18 05		18 09		18 20	18 24			18 31		18 36	18 39		18 49	18 57	19 01		19 05	
Smethwick Rolfe Street	d								18 15									18 45							
Smethwick Galton Bdg L.L. 7	d				18 08				18 17			18 30						18 47				19 08			
Sandwell & Dudley	d		17 58				18 13		18 19									18 49		18 58				19 13	
Dudley Port	d								18 22									18 52							
Tipton	d								18 24									18 54							
Coseley	d								18 27								18 46	18 57							
Wolverhampton 7 🚌	a		18 11	18 14	18 19		18 24		18 33		18 37	18 42			18 48		18 53	19 03		19 11	19 14	19 19		19 24	
	d			18 15	18 19												18 53				19 15	19 19			
Penkridge	d				18 29												19 03					19 29			
Stafford	a			18 29	18 35												19 09				19 29	19 36			

For general notes see front of timetable
For details of catering facilities see Directory of Train Operators

A To Liverpool Lime Street (Table 91)
B From Walsall (Table 70)
C To Holyhead (Table 81)
D To Crewe (Table 67)

Northampton → Coventry → Birmingham → Wolverhampton → Stafford

Network Diagram - see first page of Table 67

		LM	LM	VT	AW	VT		LM	XC	LM	LM	LM	LM	VT	XC	LM	LM	VT	LM	LM	VT		AW	VT	LM
			1	1◇	◇	1◇		1	1◇		1◇		1	1◇	1◇	1		1◇		1◇	1◇		◇	1◇	1◇
		A									B	A													C
				☕	⌶	⊠			⌶					⊠	⌶			⊠			☕			☕	
London Euston 15 ⊖	d					18 03		17 24						18 23				18 43		17 54				19 03	18 24
Northampton	d		18 17					18 41								18 56				19 17					19 42
Long Buckby	d		18 27					18 51								19 06				19 27					19 53
Rugby	d		18 37			18 51		19a03								19 16				19 37				19 51	20a03
Coventry	a		18 49			19 01								19 22		19 28		19 42		19 49				20 01	
	d		18 49			19 02							19 11	19 22	19 27	19 29		19 42		19 49				20 02	
Canley	d												19 14			19 32									
Tile Hill	d		18 54										19 18			19 36				19 54					
Berkswell	d												19 21			19 39									
Hampton-in-Arden	d		19 00										19 25							20 00					
Birmingham International ✈	a		19 04			19 12							19 28	19 33	19 37	19 45		19 53		20 04				20 12	
	d		19 04		19 09	19 13				19 18			19 29	19 33	19 38	19 45		19 53		20 04			20 09	20 13	
Marston Green	d		19 07										19 32			19 48				20 07					
Lea Hall	d									19 22						19 51									
Stechford	d									19 24						19 54									
Adderley Park	d									19 27															
Birmingham New Street 12	a		19 16		19 19	19 27				19 32			19 42	19 45	19 49	20 01		20 08		20 16			20 19	20 27	
	d	19 09		19 20	19 24				19 31		19 36	19 39		19 50	19 57		20 05		20 09		20 20		20 24		
Smethwick Rolfe Street	d	19 15										19 45							20 15						
Smethwick Galton Bdg L.L. 7	d	19 17			19 30							19 47							20 17				20 30		
Sandwell & Dudley	d	19 19										19 49		19 59			20 13		20 19						
Dudley Port	d	19 22										19 52							20 22						
Tipton	d	19 24										19 54							20 24						
Coseley	d	19 27									19 46	19 57							20 27						
Wolverhampton 7 🚢	a	19 33		19 37	19 42				19 48		19 53	20 03		20 12	20 14		20 24		20 33		20 37		20 42		
	d										19 53				20 15						20 37				
Penkridge	d										20 03														
Stafford	a										20 09				20 29						20 51				

		XC	LM	LM	LM	LM	VT	XC	LM	LM	LM	VT	LM	VT		AW	VT	LM	LM	LM	LM	VT	XC	LM	LM
		1◇		1◇		1	1◇	1◇	1◇			1◇	1	1◇		◇	1◇		1◇		1	1◇	1◇	1	
				B				D											B						
							☕	⌶				☕		☕			☕					☕	⌶		
London Euston 15 ⊖	d						19 23		18 49			19 43					20 03					20 23			
Northampton	d								19 56				20 17											20 56	
Long Buckby	d								20 06				20 27											21 06	
Rugby	d								20 16				20 37				20 51							21 16	
Coventry	a						20 22		20 28			20 42	20 49				21 01					21 22		21 28	
	d					20 11	20 22	20 27	20 29			20 42	20 49				21 02				21 11	21 22	21 27	21 29	
Canley	d					20 14			20 32												21 14			21 32	
Tile Hill	d					20 18			20 36				20 54								21 18			21 36	
Berkswell	d					20 21			20 39												21 21			21 39	
Hampton-in-Arden	d					20 25							21 00								21 25				
Birmingham International ✈	a					20 28	20 33	20 37	20 45			20 53	21 04				21 12				21 28	21 33	21 37	21 44	
	d		20 18			20 29	20 33	20 38	20 45			20 53	21 04			21 09	21 13	21 18			21 29	21 33	21 38	21 45	
Marston Green	d					20 32			20 48				21 07								21 32			21 48	
Lea Hall	d		20 22						20 51									21 22						21 51	
Stechford	d		20 24						20 54									21 24						21 54	
Adderley Park	d		20 27															21 27							
Birmingham New Street 12	a		20 32			20 42	20 45	20 49	21 01			21 06	21 16			21 19	21 25	21 32			21 42	21 46	21 49	22 01	
	d	20 31		20 36	20 39		20 50	20 57		21 05	21 09	21 13		21 20		21 24	21 28		21 36	21 39		21 50	21 57		22 09
Smethwick Rolfe Street	d				20 45						21 15									21 45					22 15
Smethwick Galton Bdg L.L. 7	d				20 47						21 17					21 30				21 47					22 17
Sandwell & Dudley	d				20 49		20 59			21 13	21 19	21 24								21 49		21 59			22 19
Dudley Port	d				20 52						21 22									21 52					22 22
Tipton	d				20 54						21 24									21 54					22 24
Coseley	d			20 46	20 57						21 27								21 46	21 57					22 27
Wolverhampton 7 🚢	a	20 48		20 53	21 03		21 12	21 14		21 24	21 33	21 38		21 40		21 42	21 55		21 53	22 03		22 12	22 14		22 33
	d			20 53				21 15						21 41					21 53				22 15		
Penkridge	d			21 03															22 03						
Stafford	a			21 09				21 29						21 53					22 09				22 29		

For general notes see front of timetable
For details of catering facilities see Directory of Train Operators

A From Walsall (Table 70)
B To Liverpool Lime Street (Table 91)
C To Crewe (Table 67)
D ⌶ to Birmingham New Street

Northampton → Coventry → Birmingham → Wolverhampton → Stafford

Network Diagram - see first page of Table 67

		VT	LM	LM	XC	VT	LM		LM	LM	LM	XC	AW	LM	LM	LM	AW	VT	LM	VT	VT	VT			
																					FX	FO			
		1 ◇	1 ◇		1 ◇	1 ◇			1 ◇		1	1 ◇	◇	◇	1	1 ◇		1 ◇	1	1 ◇	1 ◇	1 ◇			
									A				B		C										
		☕				☕												☕		☕	⊠	☕			
London Euston 15 ⊖	d	20 43	19 54			21 03								20 46		21 13		21 43		22 43	23 43	23 43			
Northampton	d		21 17											21 56		22 17			22 56						
Long Buckby	d		21 27											22 06		22 27			23 06						
Rugby	d		21 37			21 56								22 16		22 37			23 16	00s05	01s00	01s05			
Coventry	a	21 42	21 49			22 06								22 29		22 49		23 11	23 29	00s17	01s13	01s18			
	d	21 42	21 49			22 07					22 11	22 24		22 29		22 49		23 12	23 29						
Canley	d										22 14			22 32					23 32						
Tile Hill	d		21 54								22 18			22 36		22 54			23 36						
Berkswell	d										22 21			22 39					23 39						
Hampton-in-Arden	d		22 00								22 25					23 00			23 44						
Birmingham International ✈	a	21 53	22 04			22 17					22 28	22 33		22 45		23 04		23 22	23 47	00s28	01s23	01s29			
	d	21 53	22 04			22 18	22 21				22 29	22 34		22 45		23 04		23 23	23 47						
Marston Green	d		22 07								22 32			22 48		23 07			23 50						
Lea Hall	d						22 25							22 51					23 54						
Stechford	d						22 27							22 54					23 56						
Adderley Park	d						22 30																		
Birmingham New Street 12	a	22 06	22 16			22 29	22 35				22 42	22 50		23 03		23 16		23 35	00 04	00s40	01s35	01s41			
	d	22 13		22 21	22 28	22 32			22 36	22 39			22 55		23 09		23 32	23 38							
Smethwick Rolfe Street	d									22 45					23 15										
Smethwick Galton Bdg L.L. 7	d								22 43	22 47					23 17										
Sandwell & Dudley	d	22 24		22 29		22 41				22 49					23 19			23 47							
Dudley Port	d									22 52					23 22										
Tipton	d									22 54					23 24										
Coseley	d								22 50	22 57					23 27										
Wolverhampton 7 🚢	a	22 38		22 41	22 45	22 55			22 57	23 03			23 11		23 35		00 02	23 59		01 10	02 05	02 17			
	d				22 46				22 57				23 13		23 35										
Penkridge	d								23 07						23 45										
Stafford	a				22 58				23 13				23 30		23 52										

Saturdays

		VT	XC	LM	LM	LM	VT	AW	XC	LM	LM	LM	LM	XC	LM	LM	LM	LM	LM	LM	VT	AW	XC	LM	LM
		1 ◇	1 ◇	1 ◇	1		1 ◇	◇	1 ◇		1 ◇		1	1 ◇	1 ◇	1			1	1	1 ◇	◇	1 ◇		1 ◇
		B		D	E						D	G			D			G				B			D
		☕	🛒				☕	🛒	🛒					🛒							☕	🛒	🛒		
London Euston 15 ⊖	d																								
Northampton	d				05 42											05 56			06 17	06 38					
Long Buckby	d															06 06			06 27						
Rugby	d				06 00											06 16			06 37	06 56					
Coventry	a															06 28			06 49						
	d												06 10			06 29			06 49						
Canley	d												06 13			06 32									
Tile Hill	d												06 17			06 36			06 54						
Berkswell	d												06 20			06 39									
Hampton-in-Arden	d												06 24						07 00						
Birmingham International ✈	a												06 27			06 45			07 04						
	d									06 18			06 28			06 45			07 04			07 09		07 18	
Marston Green	d												06 31			06 48			07 07						
Lea Hall	d									06 22						06 51								07 22	
Stechford	d									06 24						06 54								07 24	
Adderley Park	d									06 27														07 27	
Birmingham New Street 12	a									06 32			06 39			07 01			07 16			07 19		07 32	
	d	05 30	05 57	06 01		06 09	06 20	06 24	06 31		06 36	06 39		06 57	07 01		07 05	07 09			07 20	07 24	07 31		07 36
Smethwick Rolfe Street	d					06 15						06 45						07 15							
Smethwick Galton Bdg L.L. 7	d			06 07		06 17		06 30				06 47			07 07			07 17				07 30			
Sandwell & Dudley	d					06 19						06 49					07 13	07 19							
Dudley Port	d					06 22						06 52						07 22							
Tipton	d					06 24						06 54						07 24							
Coseley	d					06 27						06 57						07 27							07 46
Wolverhampton 7 🚢	a	05 47	06 14	06 18		06 33	06 37	06 42	06 48		06 54	07 03		07 14	07 18		07 24	07 33			07 37	07 42	07 48		07 53
	d	05 48	06 14	06 18					06 49		06 54			07 14	07 18										07 53
Penkridge	d			06 29											07 30										08 03
Stafford	a	06 00	06 29	06 35	06 54				07 00		07 08			07 29	07 36					07 53					08 09

For general notes see front of timetable
For details of catering facilities see Directory of Train Operators

- **A** To Crewe (Table 67)
- **B** To Holyhead (Table 81)
- **C** To Crewe (Table 91)
- **D** To Liverpool Lime Street (Table 91)
- **E** From Bletchley (Table 66)
- **G** From Walsall (Table 70)

Northampton → Coventry → Birmingham → Wolverhampton → Stafford

Network Diagram - see first page of Table 67

		LM	LM	VT	XC	LM	LM	LM	LM		LM	VT	AW	VT	LM	XC	LM	LM	LM	LM	VT	XC	LM	LM	LM
			1	1 ◇	1 ◇	1 ◇	1				1	1 ◇	◇	1 ◇	1 ◇	1 ◇		1 ◇		1	1 ◇	1 ◇	1 ◇	1	
						A			B									A	B				A		
London Euston 15 ⊖	d			06 23										07 03	06 24						07 23				
Northampton	d						06 56				07 17				07 45									07 56	
Long Buckby	d						07 06				07 27													08 06	
Rugby	d						07 16				07 37			07 51	08 04									08 16	
Coventry	a			07 22			07 28				07 49			08 01							08 22			08 28	
	d		07 10	07 22	07 27		07 29				07 49			08 02						08 11	08 22	08 27		08 29	
Canley	d		07 13				07 32													08 14				08 32	
Tile Hill	d		07 17				07 36				07 54									08 18				08 36	
Berkswell	d		07 20				07 39													08 21				08 39	
Hampton-in-Arden	d		07 24								08 00									08 25					
Birmingham International ✈	a		07 27	07 33	07 37		07 45				08 04			08 12						08 28	08 33	08 37		08 45	
	d		07 28	07 33	07 38		07 45				08 04		08 09	08 13			08 18			08 29	08 33	08 38		08 45	
Marston Green	d		07 31				07 48				08 07									08 32				08 48	
Lea Hall	d						07 51										08 22							08 51	
Stechford	d						07 54										08 24							08 54	
Adderley Park	d																08 27								
Birmingham New Street 12	a		07 42	07 45	07 49		08 01				08 16		08 19	08 27			08 32			08 42	08 45	08 49		09 01	
	d	07 39		07 49	07 57	08 01		08 05	08 09			08 20	08 24			08 31		08 36	08 39		08 49	08 57	09 01		09 05
Smethwick Rolfe Street	d	07 45							08 15										08 45						
Smethwick Galton Bdg L.L. 7	d	07 47				08 08			08 17				08 30						08 47				09 08		
Sandwell & Dudley	d	07 49		07 58				08 13	08 19										08 49		08 58				09 13
Dudley Port	d	07 52							08 22										08 52						
Tipton	d	07 54							08 24										08 54						
Coseley	d	07 57							08 27									08 46	08 57						
Wolverhampton 7	a	08 03		08 11	08 14	08 19		08 24	08 33			08 37	08 42			08 48		08 53	09 03		09 11	09 14	09 19		09 24
	d				08 14	08 19												08 53				09 14	09 19		
Penkridge	d					08 29												09 03							
Stafford	a				08 29	08 35									08 53			09 09				09 29	09 34		

		VT	LM	LM	VT	AW	VT	LM	XC	LM	LM	LM	LM	VT	XC	LM	LM	LM		VT	LM	LM	VT	AW	VT
		1 ◇		1	1 ◇	◇	1 ◇	1 ◇	1 ◇		1 ◇		1	1 ◇	1 ◇	1 ◇	1			1 ◇		1	1 ◇	◇	1 ◇
			B			C					A	B				A					B				
London Euston 15 ⊖	d	07 43					08 03	07 46						08 23						08 43					09 03
Northampton	d			08 17				08 45									08 56					09 17			
Long Buckby	d			08 27													09 06					09 27			
Rugby	d			08 37			08 51	09 03									09 16					09 37			09 52
Coventry	a	08 42		08 49			09 01							09 22			09 28			09 42		09 49			10 02
	d	08 42		08 49			09 02						09 11	09 22	09 27		09 29			09 42		09 49			10 03
Canley	d												09 14				09 32								
Tile Hill	d			08 54									09 18				09 36					09 54			
Berkswell	d												09 21				09 39								
Hampton-in-Arden	d			09 00									09 25									10 00			
Birmingham International ✈	a	08 53		09 04			09 12						09 28	09 33	09 37		09 45			09 53		10 04			10 13
	d	08 53		09 04		09 09	09 13			09 18			09 29	09 33	09 38		09 45			09 53		10 04		10 09	10 14
Marston Green	d			09 07									09 32				09 48					10 07			
Lea Hall	d									09 22							09 51								
Stechford	d									09 24							09 54								
Adderley Park	d									09 27															
Birmingham New Street 12	a	09 08		09 16		09 19	09 27			09 32			09 42	09 45	09 49		10 01			10 08		10 16		10 19	10 27
	d		09 09		09 20	09 24			09 31		09 36	09 39		09 49	09 57	10 01		10 05			10 09		10 20	10 24	
Smethwick Rolfe Street	d		09 15									09 45									10 15				
Smethwick Galton Bdg L.L. 7	d		09 17			09 30						09 47				10 08					10 17			10 30	
Sandwell & Dudley	d		09 19									09 49		09 58				10 13			10 19				
Dudley Port	d		09 22									09 52									10 22				
Tipton	d		09 24									09 54									10 24				
Coseley	d		09 27								09 46	09 57									10 27				
Wolverhampton 7	a		09 33		09 37	09 42			09 48		09 53	10 03		10 11	10 14	10 19		10 24			10 33		10 37	10 42	
	d										09 53				10 14	10 19									
Penkridge	d										10 03														
Stafford	a							09 53			10 09				10 29	10 35									

For general notes see front of timetable
For details of catering facilities see Directory of Train Operators

A To Liverpool Lime Street (Table 91)
B From Walsall (Table 70)
C To Holyhead (Table 81)

Northampton → Coventry → Birmingham → Wolverhampton → Stafford

Network Diagram - see first page of Table 67

		LM		XC	LM	LM	LM	LM	VT	XC	LM	LM	LM	VT	LM	LM	VT	AW	VT	LM		XC	LM	LM	LM
		1◇		1◇		1◇		1	1◇	1◇	1◇	1		1◇		1	1◇	◇	1◇	1◇		1◇		1◇	
						A	B				A				B			C						A	B
				🛒					🍽	🛒				🍽			🍽	🛒	🍽			🛒			
London Euston 15 ⊖	d	08 46							09 23					09 43					10 03	09 46					
Northampton	d	09 45	09 56 →									← 09 56				10 17				10 45	10 56 →				
Long Buckby	d											10 06				10 27									
Rugby	d	10 03										10 16				10 37			10 51	11 03					
Coventry	a								10 22			10 28		10 42		10 49			11 01						
	d							10 11	10 22	10 27		10 29		10 42		10 49			11 02						
Canley	d							10 14				10 32													
Tile Hill	d							10 18				10 36				10 54									
Berkswell	d							10 21				10 39													
Hampton-in-Arden	d							10 25								11 00									
Birmingham International ✈	a							10 28	10 33	10 37		10 45		10 53		11 04			11 12						
	d				10 18			10 29	10 33	10 38		10 45		10 53		11 04		11 09	11 13				11 18		
Marston Green	d							10 32				10 48				11 07									
Lea Hall	d				10 22							10 51											11 22		
Stechford	d				10 24							10 54											11 24		
Adderley Park	d				10 27																		11 27		
Birmingham New Street 12	a				10 33			10 42	10 45	10 49		11 01		11 08		11 16		11 19	11 27				11 32		
	d			10 31		10 36	10 39		10 49	10 57	11 01		11 05		11 09		11 20	11 24				11 31		11 36	11 39
Smethwick Rolfe Street	d						10 45								11 15										11 45
Smethwick Galton Bdg L.L. 7	d						10 47				11 08				11 17			11 30							11 47
Sandwell & Dudley	d						10 49		10 58				11 13		11 19										11 49
Dudley Port	d						10 52								11 22										11 52
Tipton	d						10 54								11 24										11 54
Coseley	d					10 46	10 57								11 27									11 46	11 57
Wolverhampton 7 ⛴	a			10 48		10 53	11 03		11 11	11 14	11 19		11 24		11 33		11 37	11 42				11 48		11 53	12 03
	d					10 53				11 14	11 19													11 53	
Penkridge	d					11 03																		12 03	
Stafford	a	10 53				11 09				11 29	11 35									11 53				12 09	

		LM	VT	XC	LM		LM	LM	VT	LM	LM	VT	AW	VT	LM		XC	LM	LM	LM	LM	VT	XC	LM	LM
		1	1◇	1◇	1◇		1		1◇		1	1◇	◇	1◇	1◇		1◇		1◇		1	1◇	1◇	1◇	1
					A					B		D							A	B				A	
			🍽	🛒					🍽			🍽	🛒	🍽			🛒					🍽	🛒		
London Euston 15 ⊖	d		10 23						10 43					11 03	10 46							11 23			
Northampton	d						← 10 56				11 17				11 45	11 56 →									← 11 56
Long Buckby	d						11 06				11 27														12 06
Rugby	d						11 16				11 37			11 51	12 03										12 16
Coventry	a		11 22				11 28		11 42		11 49			12 01								12 22			12 28
	d	11 11	11 22	11 27			11 29		11 42		11 49			12 02							12 11	12 22	12 27		12 29
Canley	d	11 14					11 32														12 14				12 32
Tile Hill	d	11 18					11 36				11 54										12 18				12 36
Berkswell	d	11 21					11 39														12 21				12 39
Hampton-in-Arden	d	11 25									12 00										12 25				
Birmingham International ✈	a	11 28	11 33	11 37			11 45		11 53		12 04			12 12							12 28	12 33	12 37		12 45
	d	11 29	11 33	11 38			11 45		11 53		12 04		12 09	12 13				12 18			12 29	12 33	12 38		12 45
Marston Green	d	11 32					11 48				12 07										12 32				12 48
Lea Hall	d						11 51											12 22							12 51
Stechford	d						11 54											12 24							12 54
Adderley Park	d																	12 27							
Birmingham New Street 12	a	11 42	11 45	11 49			12 01		12 08		12 16		12 19	12 27				12 32			12 42	12 45	12 49		13 01
	d		11 49	11 57	12 01			12 05		12 09		12 20	12 24				12 31		12 36	12 39		12 49	12 57	13 01	
Smethwick Rolfe Street	d									12 15										12 45					
Smethwick Galton Bdg L.L. 7	d				12 08					12 17			12 30							12 47				13 08	
Sandwell & Dudley	d		11 58					12 13		12 19										12 49		12 58			
Dudley Port	d									12 22										12 52					
Tipton	d									12 24										12 54					
Coseley	d									12 27									12 46	12 57					
Wolverhampton 7 ⛴	a		12 11	12 14	12 19			12 24		12 33		12 37	12 42				12 48		12 53	13 03		13 11	13 14	13 19	
	d			12 14	12 19														12 53				13 14	13 19	
Penkridge	d																		13 03						
Stafford	a			12 29	12 35										12 53				13 09				13 29	13 35	

For general notes see front of timetable
For details of catering facilities see Directory of Train Operators

A To Liverpool Lime Street (Table 91)
B From Walsall (Table 70)
C To Holyhead (Table 81)
D Until 31 October

Northampton → Coventry → Birmingham → Wolverhampton → Stafford

Network Diagram - see first page of Table 67

		LM	VT [1]◇ ☕	LM A	LM [1]	VT [1]◇ ☕	AW ◇ B 🛒	VT [1]◇ ☕	LM [1]◇		XC [1]◇ 🛒	LM	LM [1]◇ C	LM A	LM [1]	VT [1]◇ ☕	XC [1]◇ 🛒	LM [1]◇ C	LM [1]	LM	VT [1]◇ ☕	LM A	LM [1]
London Euston [15] ⊖	d		11 43					12 03	11 46							12 23					12 43		
Northampton	d				12 17				12 45	12 56 →									← 12 56				13 17
Long Buckby	d				12 27														13 06				13 27
Rugby	d				12 37			12 51	13 03										13 16				13 37
Coventry	a		12 42		12 49			13 01								13 22			13 28		13 42		13 49
	d		12 42		12 49			13 02							13 11	13 22	13 27		13 29		13 42		13 49
Canley	d														13 14				13 32				
Tile Hill	d				12 54										13 18				13 36				13 54
Berkswell	d														13 21				13 39				
Hampton-in-Arden	d				13 00										13 25								14 00
Birmingham International ✈	a		12 53		13 04			13 12							13 28	13 33	13 37		13 45		13 53		14 04
	d		12 53		13 04		13 09	13 13				13 18			13 29	13 33	13 38		13 45		13 53		14 04
Marston Green	d				13 07										13 32				13 48				14 07
Lea Hall	d											13 22							13 51				
Stechford	d											13 24							13 54				
Adderley Park	d											13 27											
Birmingham New Street [12]	a		13 08		13 16		13 19	13 27				13 32			13 42	13 45	13 49		14 01		14 08		14 16
	d	13 05		13 09		13 20	13 23				13 31		13 36	13 39		13 49	13 57	14 01		14 05		14 09	
Smethwick Rolfe Street	d			13 15										13 45								14 15	
Smethwick Galton Bdg L.L. [7]	d			13 17			13 29							13 47				14 08				14 17	
Sandwell & Dudley	d	13 13		13 19										13 49		13 58				14 13		14 19	
Dudley Port	d			13 22										13 52								14 22	
Tipton	d			13 24										13 54								14 24	
Coseley	d			13 27									13 46	13 57								14 27	
Wolverhampton [7] ⛴	a	13 24		13 33		13 37	13 42				13 48		13 53	14 03		14 11	14 14	14 19		14 24		14 33	
	d												13 53				14 14	14 19					
Penkridge	d												14 03										
Stafford	a								13 53				14 09				14 29	14 35					

		LM [1]◇		VT [1]◇ D ☕	AW ◇ 🛒	VT [1]◇ ☕	XC [1]◇ 🛒	LM	LM [1]◇ C	LM A	LM [1]	VT [1]◇ ☕	XC [1]◇ 🛒	LM [1]◇ E	LM [1]	LM	VT [1]◇ ☕	LM A	LM [1]	VT [1]◇ ☕	AW ◇ B 🛒	VT [1]◇ ☕	LM [1]◇		XC [1]◇ 🛒
London Euston [15] ⊖	d	12 46				13 03						13 23					13 43					14 03	13 46		
Northampton	d	13 45	13 56 →												← 13 56				14 17				14 45	14 56 →	
Long Buckby	d														14 06				14 27						
Rugby	d	14 03				13 51									14 16				14 37			14 51	15 03		
Coventry	a					14 01						14 22			14 28		14 42		14 49			15 01			
	d					14 02					14 11	14 22	14 27		14 29		14 42		14 49			15 02			
Canley	d										14 14				14 32										
Tile Hill	d										14 18				14 36				14 54						
Berkswell	d										14 21				14 39										
Hampton-in-Arden	d										14 25								15 00						
Birmingham International ✈	a					14 12					14 28	14 33	14 37		14 45		14 53		15 04			15 12			
	d				14 09	14 13		14 18			14 29	14 33	14 38		14 45		14 53		15 04		15 09	15 13			
Marston Green	d										14 32				14 48				15 07						
Lea Hall	d							14 22							14 51										
Stechford	d							14 24							14 54										
Adderley Park	d							14 27																	
Birmingham New Street [12]	a				14 19	14 27		14 32			14 42	14 45	14 49		15 01		15 08		15 16		15 19	15 27			
	d			14 20	14 24		14 31		14 36	14 39		14 49	14 57	15 01		15 05		15 09		15 20	15 24				15 31
Smethwick Rolfe Street	d									14 45								15 15							
Smethwick Galton Bdg L.L. [7]	d				14 30					14 47				15 08				15 17			15 30				
Sandwell & Dudley	d									14 49		14 58				15 13		15 19							
Dudley Port	d									14 52								15 22							
Tipton	d									14 54								15 24							
Coseley	d								14 46	14 57								15 27							
Wolverhampton [7] ⛴	a			14 37	14 42		14 48		14 53	15 03		15 11	15 14	15 19		15 24		15 33		15 37	15 42				15 48
	d								14 53				15 14	15 19											
Penkridge	d								15 03																
Stafford	a	14 53							15 09				15 29	15 35									15 53		

For general notes see front of timetable
For details of catering facilities see Directory of Train Operators

A From Walsall (Table 70)
B To Holyhead (Table 81)
C To Liverpool Lime Street (Table 91)
D Until 31 October
E To Liverpool Lime Street (Table 65)

Northampton → Coventry → Birmingham → Wolverhampton → Stafford

Network Diagram - see first page of Table 67

		LM		LM	LM	LM	VT	XC	LM	LM	LM	VT	LM	LM	VT	AW	VT	LM		XC	LM	LM	LM	LM	VT
				1 ◇		1	1 ◇	1 ◇	1 ◇	1		1 ◇		1	1 ◇	R	1 ◇	1 ◇		1 ◇		1 ◇		1	1 ◇
				A	B				A				B		C							A	B		
							☕	🛒				☕			☕	🛒	☕			🛒					☕
London Euston 15 ⊖	d						14 23					14 43					15 03	14 46							15 23
Northampton	d									← 14 56				15 17				15 45	15 56 →						
Long Buckby	d									15 06				15 27											
Rugby	d									15 16				15 37			15 51	16 03							
Coventry	a						15 22			15 28		15 42		15 49			16 01								16 22
	d					15 11	15 22	15 27		15 29		15 42		15 49			16 02							16 11	16 22
Canley	d					15 14				15 32														16 14	
Tile Hill	d					15 18				15 36				15 54										16 18	
Berkswell	d					15 21				15 39														16 21	
Hampton-in-Arden	d					15 25								16 00										16 25	
Birmingham International ✈	a					15 28	15 33	15 37		15 45		15 53		16 04			16 12							16 28	16 33
	d	15 18				15 29	15 33	15 38		15 45		15 53		16 04		16 09	16 13				16 18			16 29	16 33
Marston Green	d					15 32				15 48				16 07										16 32	
Lea Hall	d	15 22								15 51											16 22				
Stechford	d	15 24								15 54											16 24				
Adderley Park	d	15 27																			16 27				
Birmingham New Street 12	a	15 32				15 42	15 45	15 49		16 01		16 08		16 16		16 19	16 27				16 32			16 42	16 45
	d			15 36	15 39		15 49	15 57	16 01		16 05		16 09		16 20	16 24				16 31		16 36	16 39		16 49
Smethwick Rolfe Street	d				15 45								16 15										16 45		
Smethwick Galton Bdg L.L. 7	d				15 47				16 08				16 17			16 30							16 47		
Sandwell & Dudley	d				15 49		15 58				16 13		16 19										16 49		16 58
Dudley Port	d				15 52								16 22										16 52		
Tipton	d				15 54								16 24										16 54		
Coseley	d			15 46	15 57								16 27									16 46	16 57		
Wolverhampton 7 ⛴	a			15 53	16 03		16 11	16 14	16 19		16 24		16 33		16 37	16 42				16 48		16 53	17 03		17 11
	d			15 53				16 14	16 19													16 53			
Penkridge	d			16 03																		17 03			
Stafford	a			16 09				16 29	16 35									16 53				17 09			

		XC	LM	LM	LM	VT	LM	LM	VT	AW	VT		LM		XC	XC	LM	LM	LM	LM	VT	XC	LM	LM	LM
		1 ◇	1 ◇	1		1 ◇		1	1 ◇	◇	1 ◇		1 ◇		1 ◇	1 ◇		1 ◇		1	1 ◇	1 ◇	1 ◇	1	
			A				B			D					E	G		A	B				H		
		🛒				☕			☕	🛒	☕				🛒	🛒					☕	🛒			
London Euston 15 ⊖	d					15 43					16 03		15 46								16 23				
Northampton	d			← 15 56				16 17					16 45	16 56 →										← 16 56	
Long Buckby	d			16 06				16 27																17 06	
Rugby	d			16 16				16 37			16 51		17 03											17 16	
Coventry	a			16 28		16 42		16 49			17 01										17 22			17 28	
	d	16 27		16 29		16 42		16 49			17 02									17 11	17 22	17 27		17 29	
Canley	d			16 32																17 14				17 32	
Tile Hill	d			16 36				16 54												17 18				17 36	
Berkswell	d			16 39																17 21				17 39	
Hampton-in-Arden	d							17 00												17 25					
Birmingham International ✈	a	16 37		16 45		16 53		17 04			17 12									17 28	17 33	17 37		17 45	
	d	16 38		16 45		16 53		17 04		17 09	17 13						17 18			17 29	17 33	17 38		17 45	
Marston Green	d			16 48				17 07												17 32				17 48	
Lea Hall	d			16 51													17 22							17 51	
Stechford	d			16 54													17 24							17 54	
Adderley Park	d																17 27								
Birmingham New Street 12	a	16 49		17 01		17 08		17 16		17 19	17 27						17 32			17 42	17 45	17 49		18 01	
	d	16 57	17 01		17 05		17 09		17 20	17 24					17 31	17 31		17 36	17 39		17 49	17 57	18 01		18 05
Smethwick Rolfe Street	d						17 15												17 45						
Smethwick Galton Bdg L.L. 7	d		17 08				17 17			17 31									17 47				18 08		
Sandwell & Dudley	d				17 13		17 19												17 49		17 58				18 13
Dudley Port	d						17 22												17 52						
Tipton	d						17 24												17 54						
Coseley	d						17 27											17 46	17 57						
Wolverhampton 7 ⛴	a	17 14	17 19		17 24		17 33		17 37	17 42					17 47	17 48		17 53	18 03		18 11	18 14	18 19		18 24
	d	17 14	17 19															17 53				18 14	18 19		
Penkridge	d		17 29															18 03					18 29		
Stafford	a	17 29	17 35										18 04					18 09				18 29	18 35		

For general notes see front of timetable
For details of catering facilities see Directory of Train Operators

- A To Liverpool Lime Street (Table 91)
- B From Walsall (Table 70)
- C Until 31 October
- D To Holyhead (Table 81)
- E Until 5 September
- G From 12 September
- H To Crewe (Table 67)

Table 68

Northampton → Coventry → Birmingham → Wolverhampton → Stafford

Network Diagram - see first page of Table 67

		VT 1◇	LM	LM 1	VT 1◇	AW ◇	VT 1◇	LM 1◇		XC 1◇	LM	LM 1◇	LM	LM 1	VT 1◇	XC 1◇	LM 1◇	LM 1	LM	VT 1◇		LM	LM 1	VT 1◇	AW ◇
			A		B							C	A				D					A			
London Euston 15 ⊖	d	16 43					17 03	16 46							17 23					17 43					
Northampton	d			17 17				17 45	17 56 →									← 17 56					18 17		
Long Buckby	d			17 27														18 06					18 27		
Rugby	d			17 37			17 51	18 03										18 16					18 37		
Coventry	a	17 42		17 49			18 01								18 22			18 28		18 42			18 49		
	d	17 42		17 49			18 02							18 11	18 22	18 27		18 29		18 42			18 49		
Canley	d													18 14				18 32							
Tile Hill	d			17 54										18 18				18 36					18 54		
Berkswell	d													18 21				18 39							
Hampton-in-Arden	d			18 00										18 25									19 00		
Birmingham International ✈	a	17 53		18 04			18 12							18 28	18 33	18 37		18 45		18 53			19 04		
	d	17 53		18 04		18 09	18 13				18 18			18 29	18 33	18 38		18 45		18 53			19 04		19 09
Marston Green	d			18 07										18 32				18 48					19 07		
Lea Hall	d										18 22							18 51							
Stechford	d										18 24							18 54							
Adderley Park	d										18 27														
Birmingham New Street 12	a	18 08		18 16		18 19	18 27				18 32			18 42	18 45	18 49		19 01		19 08			19 16		19 19
	d		18 09		18 20	18 24				18 31		18 36	18 39		18 49	18 57	19 01		19 05			19 09		19 20	19 24
Smethwick Rolfe Street	d		18 15										18 45									19 15			
Smethwick Galton Bdg L.L. 7	d		18 17			18 30							18 47				19 08					19 17			19 30
Sandwell & Dudley	d		18 19										18 49		18 58				19 13			19 19			
Dudley Port	d		18 22										18 52									19 22			
Tipton	d		18 24										18 54									19 24			
Coseley	d		18 27									18 46	18 57									19 27			
Wolverhampton 7	a		18 33		18 37	18 42				18 48		18 53	19 03		19 11	19 14	19 19		19 24			19 33		19 37	19 42
	d											18 53				19 14	19 19								
Penkridge	d											19 03					19 29								
Stafford	a							18 53				19 09				19 29	19 35								

		XC 1◇	VT 1◇	LM 1	LM	LM 1◇	LM	VT 1◇	LM 1	VT 1◇	XC 1◇	LM 1	LM	VT 1◇	LM	LM 1	VT 1◇	AW ◇	XC 1◇	VT 1◇	VT 1◇	LM 1	LM	LM	LM 1◇
						C	A													E	G		E	G	D
London Euston 15 ⊖	d		18 03							18 23				18 43						19 03	19 02				
Northampton	d			18 45								18 56				19 17						19 45			
Long Buckby	d											19 06				19 27									
Rugby	d		18 51	19 03								19 16				19 37				19 51	19 53	20 03			
Coventry	a		19 01							19 22		19 28		19 42		19 49				20 01	20 03				
	d		19 02						19 11	19 22	19 27	19 29		19 42		19 49				20 02	20 04				
Canley	d								19 14			19 32													
Tile Hill	d								19 18			19 36				19 54									
Berkswell	d								19 21			19 39													
Hampton-in-Arden	d								19 25							20 00									
Birmingham International ✈	a		19 12						19 28	19 33	19 37	19 45		19 53		20 04				20 12	20 14				
	d		19 13		19 18				19 29	19 33	19 38	19 45		19 53		20 04		20 09		20 13	20 15		20 18	20 18	
Marston Green	d								19 32			19 48				20 07									
Lea Hall	d				19 22							19 51											20 22	20 22	
Stechford	d				19 24							19 54											20 24	20 24	
Adderley Park	d				19 27																		20 27	20 27	
Birmingham New Street 12	a		19 25		19 32			←	19 42	19 45	19 49	20 01		20 08		20 16		20 19		20 25	20 30		20 32	20 34	
	d	19 31	19 42 →			19 36	19 39	19 42		19 50	19 57		20 05		20 09		20 20	20 24	20 31	20 42 →	20 42 →				20 36
Smethwick Rolfe Street	d						19 45								20 15										
Smethwick Galton Bdg L.L. 7	d						19 47								20 17			20 30							
Sandwell & Dudley	d						19 49	19 54		19 59			20 13		20 19										
Dudley Port	d						19 52								20 22										
Tipton	d						19 54								20 24										
Coseley	d					19 46	19 57								20 27										20 46
Wolverhampton 7	a	19 48				19 53	20 03	20 08		20 12	20 14		20 24		20 33		20 37	20 42	20 48						20 53
	d					19 53					20 14						20 37								20 53
Penkridge	d					20 03																			21 03
Stafford	a			19 53		20 09					20 29						20 49					20 55			21 09

For general notes see front of timetable
For details of catering facilities see Directory of Train Operators

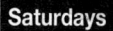

- **A** From Walsall (Table 70)
- **B** Until 31 October
- **C** To Liverpool Lime Street (Table 91)
- **D** To Crewe (Table 67)
- **E** From 12 September
- **G** Until 5 September

Northampton → Coventry → Birmingham → Wolverhampton → Stafford

Network Diagram - see first page of Table 67

Station		LM	VT 1◊ A	VT 1◊ B	LM 1	VT 1◊ A	VT 1◊ B		XC 1◊ A	XC 1◊ A	XC 1◊ B	LM 1	LM	LM	VT 1◊ A	VT 1◊ B	AW ◊	LM 1	VT 1◊ A	VT 1◊ B	LM	LM 1◊ C	LM	LM 1	XC 1◊
London Euston 15 ⊖	d					19 08	19 23								19 30	19 43									
Northampton	d											19 56						20 17							
Long Buckby	d											20 06						20 27							
Rugby	d											20 16						20b43							
Coventry	a					20 22	20 22					20 28			20 49	20 49		20 54							
	d				20 11	20 22	20 22		20 27		20 27	20 29			20 49	20 49		20 54						21 11	21 27
Canley	d				20 14							20 32						20 57						21 14	
Tile Hill	d				20 18							20 36						21 01						21 18	
Berkswell	d				20 21							20 39						21 04						21 21	
Hampton-in-Arden	d				20 25													21 09						21 25	
Birmingham International ✈	a				20 28	20 33	20 33		20 37		20 37	20 45			21 00	21 00		21 12						21 28	21 37
	d				20 29	20 33	20 33		20 38		20 38	20 45			21 00	21 00	21 09	21 12			21 18			21 29	21 38
Marston Green	d				20 32							20 48						21 15						21 32	
Lea Hall	d											20 51									21 22				
Stechford	d											20 54									21 24				
Adderley Park	d																				21 27				
Birmingham New Street 12	a		←	←	20 42	20 45	20 45		20 49		20 49	21 01			21 13	21 13	21 19	21 25	←	←	21 32			21 42	21 49
	d	20 39	20 42	20 42		20 50	20 50			20 57	20 57		21 05	21 09	21 27 →	21 27 →	21 24		21 27	21 27		21 36	21 39		21 57
Smethwick Rolfe Street	d	20 45												21 15									21 45		
Smethwick Galton Bdg L.L. 7	d	20 47												21 17			21 30						21 47		
Sandwell & Dudley	d	20 49	20 54	20 54		20 59	20 59						21 13	21 19									21 49		
Dudley Port	d	20 52												21 22									21 52		
Tipton	d	20 54												21 24									21 54		
Coseley	d	20 57												21 27								21 46	21 57		
Wolverhampton 7	a	21 03	21 08	21 08		21 12	21 12			21 14	21 13		21 24	21 33			21 42		21 49	21 49		21 53	22 03		22 14
	d									21 14	21 14											21 53			22 14
Penkridge	d																					22 03			
Stafford	a									21 29	21 29											22 09			22 29

Station		LM 1	LM	LM	VT 1◊ A	VT 1◊ B	LM 1	XC 1◊	XC 1◊	LM	LM 1 D	LM	LM 1	VT 1◊ A	VT 1◊ B	XC 1◊	AW E	LM 1	LM	LM 1	VT 1◊ A	VT 1◊ B	AW	LM 1	
London Euston 15 ⊖	d				20 07	20 23								20 29	21 03						21 24	21 43			
Northampton	d	20 56					21 17											21 56		22 17				22 56	
Long Buckby	d	21 06					21 27											22 06		22 27				23 06	
Rugby	d	21 17					21 37							22 11	22 11			22 16		22 37	22 52	22 52		23 16	
Coventry	a	21 29			21 35	21 35	21 49							22 22	22 22			22 28		22 49	23 02	23 02		23 28	
	d	21 29			21 35	21 35	21 49	21 56					22 11	22 22	22 22	22 27		22 29		22 49	23 02	23 02		23 29	
Canley	d	21 32											22 14					22 32						23 32	
Tile Hill	d	21 36					21 54						22 18					22 36		22 54				23 36	
Berkswell	d	21 39											22 21					22 39						23 39	
Hampton-in-Arden	d						22 00						22 25							23 00				23 44	
Birmingham International ✈	a	21 45			21 53	21 53	22 04	22 12					22 28	22 33	22 33	22 37		22 45		23 04	23 13	23 13		23 47	
	d	21 45			21 53	21 53	22 04	22 13		22 21			22 29	22 33	22 33	22 38		22 45		23 04	23 13	23 13		23 47	
Marston Green	d	21 48					22 07						22 32					22 48		23 07				23 50	
Lea Hall	d	21 52								22 25								22 51						23 54	
Stechford	d	21 54								22 27								22 54						23 56	
Adderley Park	d									22 30															
Birmingham New Street 12	a	22 01			22 05	22 05	22 16	22 25		22 35			22 42	22 45	22 45	22 54		23 01		23 16	23 25	23 25		00 04	
	d		22 05	22 09	22 16	22 16			22 31		22 36	22 39		22 48	22 48		22 55		23 09		23 29	23 29	23 35		
Smethwick Rolfe Street	d			22 15								22 45							23 15						
Smethwick Galton Bdg L.L. 7	d			22 17							22 42	22 47							23 17						
Sandwell & Dudley	d		22 13	22 19	22 25	22 25						22 49		22 57	22 57				23 19		23 38	23 38			
Dudley Port	d			22 22								22 52							23 22						
Tipton	d			22 24								22 54							23 24						
Coseley	d			22 27							22 48	22 57							23 27						
Wolverhampton 7	a		22 24	22 33	22 38	22 38			22 48		22 55	23 03		23 10	23 10		23 12		23 33		23 51	23 51	23 53		
	d								22 49		22 56														
Penkridge	d										23 06														
Stafford	a								23 02		23 13														

For general notes see front of timetable
For details of catering facilities see Directory of Train Operators

A Until 5 September
B From 12 September
C To Crewe (Table 67)
D To Crewe (Table 65)
E To Crewe (Table 131)
b Arr. 2038

Table 68

Sundays

until 12 July

Northampton → Coventry → Birmingham → Wolverhampton → Stafford

Network Diagram - see first page of Table 67

		VT	XC	LM	LM	VT	LM	LM	LM	LM	XC	AW	VT		LM	LM	LM	LM	VT	LM	XC	AW	LM	LM	LM
		1 ◇	1 ◇	1		1 ◇	1	1	1 ◇	bus	1 ◇	A	1 ◇			1	1	1 ◇	1 ◇	bus	1 ◇	◇	1	bus	
London Euston 15 ⊖	d																		08 50						
Northampton	d									08 50										09 15				09 55	
Long Buckby	d									09 11										09 36				10 16	
Rugby	d									09a41						09 50			10 02	10a06			10 20	10a46	
Coventry	a															10 03			10 23				10 32		
	d			08 37				09 07								10 04	10 08		10 24		10 28		10 34		
Canley	d			08 40				09 10									10 11						10 37		
Tile Hill	d			08 44				09 14									10 15						10 41		
Berkswell	d			08 47				09 17									10 18						10 44		
Hampton-in-Arden	d			08 51				09 21									10 22						10 48		
Birmingham International ✈	a			08 54				09 24								10 13	10 26		10 34		10 38		10 51		
	d			08 55			09 03	09 25				09 51				10 13	10 26		10 35		10 40	10 48	10 52		
Marston Green	d			08 58			09 06	09 28								10 16	10 29						10 55		
Lea Hall	d						09 09									10 20									
Stechford	d						09 12									10 22									
Adderley Park	d						09 15									10 26									
Birmingham New Street 12	a			09 06			09 20	09 36				10 02				10 30	10 38		10 47		10 51	10 58	11 03		
	d	08 45	09 01		09 09	09 20			09 41		10 00	10 05	10 15		10 23			10 42	10 51		10 59	11 05			11 09
Smethwick Rolfe Street	d				09 15										10 29										11 15
Smethwick Galton Bdg L.L. 7	d				09 17										10 31										11 17
Sandwell & Dudley	d				09 19										10 33				11 00						11 19
Dudley Port	d				09 22										10 36										11 22
Tipton	d				09 24										10 38										11 24
Coseley	d				09 27										10 41										11 27
Wolverhampton 7	a	09 03	09 18		09 32	09 37			09 57		10 17	10 21	10 32		10 46			10 59	11 13		11 16	11 26			11 32
	d	09 04	09 19						09 57		10 18							10 59			11 17				
Penkridge	d								10 08									11 10							
Stafford	a	09 17	09 31						10 14		10 31							11 17			11 29				

		VT	LM	LM		VT	LM	XC	LM	LM	LM	VT	AW	LM	LM	VT	LM		XC	LM	LM	LM	VT	AW	VT
		1 ◇	1	1 ◇		1 ◇	bus	1 ◇	1	bus		1 ◇	◇	1 ◇	1	1 ◇	bus		1 ◇	1	bus		1 ◇	◇	1 ◇
London Euston 15 ⊖	d					09 50										10 50									11 45
Northampton	d						10 15			10 55							11 15				11 55				
Long Buckby	d						10 36			11 16							11 36				12 16				
Rugby	d					11 02	11a06		11 21	11a46						12 02	12a06			12 21	12a46				12 47
Coventry	a					11 22			11 32							12 23				12 32					12 56
	d		11 08			11 22		11 28	11 34						12 08	12 24			12 28	12 34					12 57
Canley	d								11 37											12 37					
Tile Hill	d								11 41											12 41					
Berkswell	d								11 44											12 44					
Hampton-in-Arden	d								11 48											12 48					
Birmingham International ✈	a		11 17			11 33		11 38	11 51						12 17	12 34			12 38	12 51					13 07
	d		11 18			11 33		11 40	11 52				12 08		12 18	12 35			12 40	12 52				13 05	13 08
Marston Green	d		11 21						11 55						12 21					12 55					
Lea Hall	d		11 24												12 24										
Stechford	d		11 27												12 27										
Adderley Park	d		11 30												12 30										
Birmingham New Street 12	a		11 36			11 46		11 51	12 03				12 18		12 36	12 47			12 51	13 03				13 15	13 22
	d	11 20		11 42		11 49		12 01			12 09	12 20	12 24	12 35		12 51			13 01			13 09	13 20	13 24	
Smethwick Rolfe Street	d										12 15											13 15			
Smethwick Galton Bdg L.L. 7	d										12 17											13 17			
Sandwell & Dudley	d					11 59					12 19					13 00						13 19			
Dudley Port	d										12 22											13 22			
Tipton	d										12 24											13 24			
Coseley	d										12 27											13 27			
Wolverhampton 7	a	11 37		11 59		12 17		12 18			12 32	12 36	12 40	12 52		13 13			13 18			13 32	13 37	13 41	
	d			11 59				12 19						12 52					13 19						
Penkridge	d			12 10										13 03											
Stafford	a			12 16				12 33						13 10					13 33						

For general notes see front of timetable
For details of catering facilities see Directory of Train Operators

A To Shrewsbury (Table 74)

Table 68

Sundays

until 12 July

Northampton → Coventry → Birmingham → Wolverhampton → Stafford

Network Diagram - see first page of Table 67

		LM	XC	LM	LM	VT	XC	LM		VT	LM	LM	VT	AW	VT	XC	LM	LM	LM	VT	XC		LM	VT	LM
			1 ◇	1 ◇	1	1 ◇	1 ◇	1		1 ◇			1 ◇	◇	1 ◇	1 ◇	1 ◇	1		1 ◇	1 ◇		1	1 ◇	
		bus									bus								bus						bus
			trolley			shop	trolley			shop			shop	trolley	shop	trolley				shop	trolley			shop	
London Euston 15 ⊖	d					12 18				12 38					12 58					13 18				13 38	
Northampton	d	12 15									12 55								13 15						13 55
Long Buckby	d	12 36									13 16								13 36						14 16
Rugby	d	13a06						13 15			13a46				13 49				14a06				14 15		14a46
Coventry	a					13 20		13 28		13 40					14 00					14 20			14 28	14 40	
	d				13 10	13 21	13 26	13 29		13 40					14 00			14 10		14 20	14 26		14 29	14 40	
Canley	d							13 32															14 32		
Tile Hill	d				13 15			13 36										14 15					14 36		
Berkswell	d							13 39															14 39		
Hampton-in-Arden	d							13 43															14 43		
Birmingham International ✈	a				13 22	13 31	13 37	13 46		13 51					14 11			14 22		14 31	14 35		14 46	14 51	
	d				13 22	13 32	13 38	13 47		13 51				14 07	14 11			14 22		14 31	14 38		14 47	14 51	
Marston Green	d				13 25			13 50										14 25					14 50		
Lea Hall	d				13 29													14 29							
Stechford	d				13 31													14 31							
Adderley Park	d				13 35													14 35							
Birmingham New Street 12	a				13 40	13 44	13 49	13 58		14 06				14 18	14 25			14 40		14 44	14 49		14 58	15 06	
	d		13 31	13 35		13 48	14 01					14 09	14 20	14 24		14 31	14 35			14 48	15 01				
Smethwick Rolfe Street	d											14 15													
Smethwick Galton Bdg L.L. 7	d											14 17													
Sandwell & Dudley	d					13 57						14 19								14 57					
Dudley Port	d											14 22													
Tipton	d											14 24													
Coseley	d											14 27													
Wolverhampton 7 ⛴	a		13 48	13 52		14 10	14 18					14 32	14 37	14 42		14 48	14 52			15 10	15 18				
	d			13 52			14 19										14 52				15 19				
Penkridge	d			14 03													15 03								
Stafford	a			14 10			14 33										15 10				15 33				

		LM	VT	AW	VT	LM	XC	LM	LM	VT	XC	LM		VT	LM	LM	VT	AW	VT	LM	XC	LM	LM	VT	XC
			1 ◇	◇ A	1 ◇		1 ◇	1 ◇	1	1 ◇	1 ◇	1		1 ◇			1 ◇	◇	1 ◇		1 ◇	1 ◇	1	1 ◇	1 ◇
						bus									bus					bus					
			shop	trolley	shop		trolley			shop	trolley			shop			shop	trolley	shop		trolley			shop	trolley
London Euston 15 ⊖	d				13 58					14 18				14 38					14 58					15 18	
Northampton	d					14 15									14 55					15 15					
Long Buckby	d					14 36									15 16					15 36					
Rugby	d				14 49	15a06						15 15			15a46				15 49	16a06					
Coventry	a				15 00					15 20		15 28		15 40					16 00					16 20	
	d				15 00				15 10	15 20	15 26	15 29		15 40					16 00				16 10	16 20	16 26
Canley	d											15 32													
Tile Hill	d								15 15			15 36											16 15		
Berkswell	d											15 39													
Hampton-in-Arden	d											15 43													
Birmingham International ✈	a				15 11				15 22	15 31	15 35	15 46		15 51					16 11				16 22	16 31	16 35
	d			15 07	15 11				15 22	15 31	15 38	15 47		15 51				16 07	16 11				16 22	16 31	16 38
Marston Green	d								15 25			15 50											16 25		
Lea Hall	d								15 29														16 29		
Stechford	d								15 31														16 31		
Adderley Park	d								15 35														16 35		
Birmingham New Street 12	a			15 18	15 25				15 40	15 44	15 49	15 58		16 06				16 18	16 25				16 40	16 44	16 49
	d	15 09	15 20	15 24			15 31	15 35		15 48	16 01					16 09	16 20	16 24			16 31	16 35		16 48	17 01
Smethwick Rolfe Street	d	15 15														16 15									
Smethwick Galton Bdg L.L. 7	d	15 17														16 17									
Sandwell & Dudley	d	15 19								15 57						16 19								16 57	
Dudley Port	d	15 22														16 22									
Tipton	d	15 24														16 24									
Coseley	d	15 27														16 27									
Wolverhampton 7 ⛴	a	15 32	15 37	15 42			15 48	15 52		16 10	16 18					16 32	16 37	16 42			16 48	16 52		17 10	17 18
	d							15 52			16 19											16 52			17 19
Penkridge	d							16 03														17 03			
Stafford	a							16 10			16 34											17 10			17 34

For general notes see front of timetable
For details of catering facilities see Directory of Train Operators

A To Holyhead (Table 81)

Table 68

Sundays

until 12 July

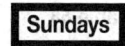

Northampton → Coventry → Birmingham → Wolverhampton → Stafford

Network Diagram - see first page of Table 67

		LM	VT		LM	LM		AW	VT	LM	XC	LM	LM	VT	XC	LM		VT	LM	LM	AW	VT	LM	XC	LM
		1	1 ◇				1 ◇	◇ A	1 ◇		1 ◇	1 ◇	1	1 ◇	1 ◇	1		1 ◇			◇	1 ◇		1 ◇	1 ◇
			🍽		🚌		🍽	trolley	🍽	🚌	trolley			🍽	trolley			🍽	🚌		trolley	🍽	🚌	trolley	
London Euston 15 ⊖	d		15 38						15 58					16 18				16 38				16 58			
Northampton	d				15 55					16 15									16 55				17 15		
Long Buckby	d				16 16					16 36									17 16				17 36		
Rugby	d	16 15			16a46				16 49	17a06						17 15			17a46			17 49	18a06		
Coventry	a	16 28	16 40						17 00					17 20		17 28		17 40				18 00			
	d	16 29	16 40						17 00				17 10	17 20	17 26	17 29		17 40				18 00			
Canley	d	16 32														17 32									
Tile Hill	d	16 36											17 15			17 36									
Berkswell	d	16 39														17 39									
Hampton-in-Arden	d	16 43														17 43									
Birmingham International ✈	a	16 46	16 51						17 11				17 22	17 31	17 35	17 46		17 51				18 11			
	d	16 47	16 51					17 07	17 11				17 22	17 31	17 38	17 47		17 51			18 07	18 11			
Marston Green	d	16 50											17 25			17 50									
Lea Hall	d												17 29												
Stechford	d												17 31												
Adderley Park	d												17 35												
Birmingham New Street 12	a	16 58	17 06					17 18	17 25				17 40	17 44	17 49	17 58		18 06			18 18	18 25			
	d					17 09	17 20	17 24			17 31	17 35		17 48	18 01					18 09	18 24			18 31	18 35
Smethwick Rolfe Street	d					17 15														18 15					
Smethwick Galton Bdg L.L. 7	d					17 17														18 17					
Sandwell & Dudley	d					17 19								17 57						18 19					
Dudley Port	d					17 22														18 22					
Tipton	d					17 24														18 24					
Coseley	d					17 27														18 27					
Wolverhampton 7 ⛴	a					17 32	17 37	17 42			17 48	17 52		18 10	18 18					18 32	18 42			18 48	18 52
	d											17 52			18 19										18 52
Penkridge	d											18 03													19 03
Stafford	a											18 10			18 35										19 10

		LM	VT	XC	LM	VT	LM		LM	VT	AW	VT	LM	XC	LM	LM	VT	XC	LM	VT		LM	LM	XC	VT
		1	1 ◇	1 ◇	1	1 ◇				R 1	◇	1 ◇		1 ◇	1 ◇	1	1 ◇	1 ◇	1	1 ◇				1 ◇	1 ◇
			🍽	trolley		🍽	🚌			🍽	trolley	🍽	🚌	trolley			🍽	trolley		🍽		🚌		trolley	🍽
London Euston 15 ⊖	d		17 18			17 38						17 58					18 18			18 38					
Northampton	d						17 55						18 15									18 55			
Long Buckby	d						18 16						18 36									19 16			
Rugby	d				18 15		18a46					18 49	19a06						19 15			19a46			
Coventry	a		18 20		18 28	18 40						19 00					19 20		19 28	19 40					
	d	18 10	18 20	18 26	18 29	18 40						19 00				19 10	19 20	19 26	19 29	19 40				19 54	
Canley	d				18 32														19 32						
Tile Hill	d	18 15			18 36											19 15			19 36						
Berkswell	d				18 39														19 39						
Hampton-in-Arden	d				18 43														19 43						
Birmingham International ✈	a	18 22	18 31	18 35	18 46	18 51						19 11				19 22	19 31	19 35	19 46	19 51				20 03	
	d	18 22	18 31	18 38	18 47	18 51					19 07	19 11				19 22	19 31	19 38	19 47	19 51				20 04	
Marston Green	d	18 25			18 50											19 25			19 50						
Lea Hall	d	18 29														19 29									
Stechford	d	18 31														19 31									
Adderley Park	d	18 35														19 35									
Birmingham New Street 12	a	18 40	18 44	18 49	18 58	19 06					19 18	19 23				19 40	19 44	19 49	19 58	20 06				20 15	
	d		18 48	19 01					19 09	19 20	19 24	19 27		19 31	19 35		19 48	20 01					20 09		20 20
Smethwick Rolfe Street	d								19 15														20 15		
Smethwick Galton Bdg L.L. 7	d								19 17														20 17		
Sandwell & Dudley	d		18 57						19 19								19 57						20 19		
Dudley Port	d								19 22														20 22		
Tipton	d								19 24														20 24		
Coseley	d								19 27														20 27		
Wolverhampton 7 ⛴	a		19 10	19 18					19 32	19 37	19 42	19 58		19 48	19 52		20 10	20 18					20 32		20 36
	d			19 19											19 52			20 19							20 38
Penkridge	d														20 03										
Stafford	a			19 37											20 10			20 37							20 51

For general notes see front of timetable
For details of catering facilities see Directory of Train Operators

A To Holyhead (Table 81)

Table 68

Sundays

until 12 July

Northampton → Coventry → Birmingham → Wolverhampton → Stafford

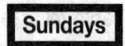

Network Diagram - see first page of Table 67

		AW	XC	VT	LM	LM	VT	XC	LM	VT	LM		LM	VT	AW	XC	VT	LM	LM	LM	VT	XC	LM	LM	LM
		◇	1 ◇	1 ◇		1	1 ◇	1 ◇	1	1 ◇				1 ◇	◇	1 ◇	1 ◇		1	1	1 ◇	1 ◇	1		
					🚌						🚌							🚌						🚌	
			🛒	🍴			🍴	🛒		🍴				🍴		🛒	🍴				🍴	🛒			
London Euston 15 ⊖	d			18 58			19 18			19 38							19 58				20 18				
Northampton	d				19 15						19 55							20 15						20 55	
Long Buckby	d				19 36						20 16							20 36						21 16	
Rugby	d			19 49	20a06				20 15		20a46						20 49	21a06					21 15	21a46	
Coventry	a			20 00			20 20		20 28	20 40							21 00				21 20		21 27		
	d			20 00		20 10	20 20	20 26	20 29	20 40						20 54	21 00			21 10	21 21	21 26	21 29		
Canley	d								20 32														21 32		
Tile Hill	d					20 15			20 36											21 15			21 36		
Berkswell	d								20 39														21 39		
Hampton-in-Arden	d								20 43														21 43		
Birmingham International ✈	a			20 11		20 22	20 31	20 37	20 46	20 51						21 03	21 11			21 22	21 31	21 35	21 46		
	d	20 08		20 11		20 22	20 31	20 38	20 47	20 51					21 08	21 04	21 11			21 22	21 32	21 38	21 47		
Marston Green	d					20 25			20 50											21 25			21 50		
Lea Hall	d					20 29														21 29					
Stechford	d					20 31														21 31					
Adderley Park	d					20 35														21 35					
Birmingham New Street 12	a	20 18		20 23		20 40	20 44	20 49	20 58	21 04					21 18	21 20	21 24			21 40	21 44	21 49	21 58		
	d	20 24	20 31	20 37			20 48	21 01		21 07			21 09	21 20	21 24		21 28		21 35		21 48	22 01			22 09
Smethwick Rolfe Street	d												21 15												22 15
Smethwick Galton Bdg L.L. 7	d												21 17												22 17
Sandwell & Dudley	d			20 47			20 57			21 16			21 19				21 37				21 57				22 19
Dudley Port	d												21 22												22 22
Tipton	d												21 24												22 24
Coseley	d												21 27												22 27
Wolverhampton 7 ⛴	a	20 42	20 48	20 57			21 10	21 18		21 31			21 33	21 38	21 42		21 51		21 52		22 10	22 18			22 32
	d							21 19						21 38					21 53			22 19			
Penkridge	d																		22 03						
Stafford	a							21 34						21 58					22 13			22 34			

		VT		XC	AW	LM	VT	LM	XC	AW	LM	LM	LM	LM	AW		XC	LM	LM	VT	VT	VT	LM		
		1 ◇		1 ◇		1	1 ◇		1 ◇	◇	1						1 ◇	1	1	1 ◇	1 ◇	1 ◇			
					A					B					A										
								🚌				🚌	🚌										🚌		
		🍴		🛒			🍴		🛒								🛒			🍴	🍴	🍴			
London Euston 15 ⊖	d	20 38					20 54													21 54	22 24	23 24			
Northampton	d							21 15				21 55	22 15										23 32		
Long Buckby	d							21 36				22 16	22 36										23 53		
Rugby	d						22 06	22a06			22 15	22a46	23a06						23 15	23b20	23 43	00s47	00 24		
Coventry	a	21 46					22 15				22 27								23 27	23 33	23 54	00s57	01 04		
	d	21 46		21 54		22 08	22 16		22 23		22 29						22 54	23 08	23 29	23 34	23 58				
Canley	d										22 32								23 32						
Tile Hill	d										22 36								23 36						
Berkswell	d										22 39								23 39						
Hampton-in-Arden	d										22 43								23 43						
Birmingham International ✈	a	21 57		22 03		22 17	22 26		22 32		22 46						23 03	23 17	23 46	23 51	00 08	01s08			
	d	21 57		22 04	22 11	22 18	22 27		22 33	22 40	22 47				23 08		23 04	23 18	23 47	23 52	00 09				
Marston Green	d					22 21					22 50							23 21	23 50						
Lea Hall	d					22 24												23 24							
Stechford	d					22 27												23 27							
Adderley Park	d					22 30												23 30							
Birmingham New Street 12	a	22 09		22 20	22 21	22 36	22 39		23 06	22 50	22 58				23 19		23 35	23 36	23 58	00 04	00 22	01s21			
	d	22 13			22 24		22 44			22 55				23 09	23 24					00 08	00 25				
Smethwick Rolfe Street	d													23 15											
Smethwick Galton Bdg L.L. 7	d													23 17											
Sandwell & Dudley	d	22 25					22 53							23 19											
Dudley Port	d													23 22											
Tipton	d													23 24											
Coseley	d													23 27											
Wolverhampton 7 ⛴	a	22 39			22 41		23 06			23 13				23 32	23 40					00 28	00 55	01 53			
	d									23 15															
Penkridge	d																								
Stafford	a									23 30															

For general notes see front of timetable
For details of catering facilities see Directory of Train Operators

A To Shrewsbury (Table 74)
B To Holyhead (Table 81)
b Arr. 2309

Sundays from 19 July

Northampton → Coventry → Birmingham → Wolverhampton → Stafford

Network Diagram - see first page of Table 67

Station	VT 1◇ A	VT 1◇ B	XC 1◇ C	XC 1◇ B	LM 1	LM	VT 1◇	LM 1	LM 1		LM 1◇ C	LM 1◇ B	XC 1◇ C	XC 1◇ B	AW D	VT 1◇ A	VT 1◇ E	LM	LM 1		LM 1	LM 1◇	VT 1◇ C	VT 1◇ B
London Euston 15 ⊖ d																							08 50	08 50
Northampton d																			09 30					
Long Buckby d																			09 40					
Rugby d																			09 50				10 02	10 14
Coventry a																			10 03				10 23	10 23
d					08 37				09 07										10 04		10 08		10 24	10 24
Canley d					08 40				09 10												10 11			
Tile Hill d					08 44				09 14												10 15			
Berkswell d					08 47				09 17												10 18			
Hampton-in-Arden d					08 51				09 21												10 22			
Birmingham International ✈ a					08 54				09 24										10 13		10 26		10 34	10 34
d					08 55			09 03	09 25						09 51				10 13		10 26		10 35	10 35
Marston Green d					08 58			09 06	09 28										10 16		10 29			
Lea Hall d								09 09											10 20					
Stechford d								09 12											10 22					
Adderley Park d								09 15											10 26					
Birmingham New Street 12 a					09 06			09 20	09 36						10 02				10 30		10 38		10 47	10 47
d	08 45	08 45	09 01	09 01		09 09	09 20				09 41	09 42	10 00	10 00	10 05	10 15	10 20	10 23				10 42	10 51	10 51
Smethwick Rolfe Street d						09 15												10 29						
Smethwick Galton Bdg L.L. 7 d						09 17												10 31						
Sandwell & Dudley d						09 19												10 33					11 00	11 00
Dudley Port d						09 22												10 36						
Tipton d						09 24												10 38						
Coseley d						09 27												10 41						
Wolverhampton 7 a	09 03	09 03	09 18	09 18		09 32	09 37				09 57	09 59	10 17	10 17	10 21	10 32	10 37	10 46				10 59	11 13	11 13
d	09 04	09 04	09 19	09 19							09 57	09 59	10 18	10 18								10 59		
Penkridge d											10 08	10 10										11 10		
Stafford a	09 17	09 21	09 31	09 33							10 14	10 17	10 30	10 32								11 17		

Station	XC 1◇ C	XC 1◇ B	AW ◇	LM 1	LM	VT 1◇	LM 1		LM 1◇	VT 1◇ B	VT 1◇ C	XC 1◇	LM 1	LM 1◇ G	LM	VT 1◇ H	AW ◇		LM 1◇	LM 1	VT 1◇ C	VT 1◇ B	XC 1◇	LM 1
London Euston 15 ⊖ d										09 50	09 50										10 50	10 50		
Northampton d				10 00									11 00	11 36										12 00
Long Buckby d				10 10									11 10	11 46										12 10
Rugby d				10 20						11 12	11 02		11 20	11 58							12 02	12 14		12 21
Coventry a				10 32						11 22	11 22		11 32								12 23	12 23		12 32
d	10 28	10 28		10 34			11 08			11 22	11 22	11 28	11 34							12 08	12 24	12 24	12 28	12 34
Canley d				10 37									11 37											12 37
Tile Hill d				10 41									11 41											12 41
Berkswell d				10 44									11 44											12 44
Hampton-in-Arden d				10 48									11 48											12 48
Birmingham International ✈ a	10 38	10 38		10 51			11 17			11 33	11 33	11 38	11 51							12 17	12 34	12 34	12 38	12 51
d	10 40	10 40	10 48	10 52			11 18			11 33	11 33	11 40	11 52				12 08			12 18	12 35	12 35	12 40	12 52
Marston Green d				10 55			11 21						11 55							12 21				12 55
Lea Hall d							11 24													12 24				
Stechford d							11 27													12 27				
Adderley Park d							11 30													12 30				
Birmingham New Street 12 a	10 51	10 51	10 58	11 03			11 36			11 45	11 45	11 51	12 03				12 18			12 36	12 47	12 47	12 51	13 03
d	11 01	11 01	11 05		11 09	11 20			11 42	11 49	11 49	12 01			12 09	12 20	12 24		12 35		12 51	12 51	13 01	
Smethwick Rolfe Street d					11 15										12 15									
Smethwick Galton Bdg L.L. 7 d					11 17										12 17									
Sandwell & Dudley d					11 19					11 59	11 59				12 19						13 00	13 00		
Dudley Port d					11 22										12 22									
Tipton d					11 24										12 24									
Coseley d					11 27										12 27									
Wolverhampton 7 a	11 18	11 18	11 26		11 32	11 37			11 59	12 15	12 17	12 19			12 32	12 36	12 40		12 52		13 13	13 13	13 18	
d	11 19	11 19							11 59			12 19							12 52				13 19	
Penkridge d									12 10										13 03					
Stafford a	11 31	11 32							12 16			12 32		12 53					13 10				13 33	

For general notes see front of timetable
For details of catering facilities see Directory of Train Operators

A 13 September to 1 November
B Until 6 September
C From 13 September
D To Shrewsbury (Table 74)
E Until 6 September and from 8 November
G To Crewe (Table 67)
H Until 1 November

Table 68

Sundays

from 19 July

Northampton → Coventry → Birmingham → Wolverhampton → Stafford

Network Diagram - see first page of Table 67

		LM	VT 1 ◇ 🍽	AW ◇ 🛒	VT 1 ◇ 🍽	XC 1 ◇ 🛒		LM 1 ◇	LM 1	VT 1 ◇ 🍽	XC 1 ◇ 🛒	LM 1	VT 1 ◇ 🍽	LM	VT 1 ◇ A 🍽	AW ◇ 🛒		VT 1 ◇ 🍽	XC 1 ◇ 🛒	LM 1 ◇	LM 1	VT 1 ◇ 🍽	XC 1 ◇ 🛒	LM 1	LM 1 ◇ B
London Euston 15 ⊖	d				11 45					12 18			12 38					12 58				13 18			12 50
Northampton	d											12 53												13 51	13 56
Long Buckby	d											13 03												14 01	14 06
Rugby	d				12 47							13 15						13 49						14b15	14 16
Coventry	a				12 56					13 20		13 28	13 40					14 00				14 20		14 28	
	d				12 57				13 10	13 21	13 26	13 29	13 40					14 00			14 10	14 20	14 26	14 29	
Canley	d											13 32												14 32	
Tile Hill	d								13 15			13 36									14 15			14 36	
Berkswell	d											13 39												14 39	
Hampton-in-Arden	d											13 43												14 43	
Birmingham International ✈	a				13 07				13 22	13 31	13 37	13 46	13 51					14 11			14 22	14 31	14 35	14 46	
	d			13 05	13 08				13 22	13 32	13 38	13 47	13 51			14 07		14 11			14 22	14 31	14 38	14 47	
Marston Green	d								13 25			13 50									14 25			14 50	
Lea Hall	d								13 29												14 29				
Stechford	d								13 31												14 31				
Adderley Park	d								13 35												14 35				
Birmingham New Street 12	a			13 15	13 22				13 40	13 44	13 49	13 58	14 06			14 18		14 25			14 40	14 44	14 49	14 58	
	d	13 09	13 20	13 24		13 31		13 35		13 48	14 01			14 09	14 20	14 24			14 31	14 35		14 48	15 01		
Smethwick Rolfe Street	d	13 15												14 15											
Smethwick Galton Bdg L.L. 7	d	13 17												14 17											
Sandwell & Dudley	d	13 19								13 57				14 19								14 57			
Dudley Port	d	13 22												14 22											
Tipton	d	13 24												14 24											
Coseley	d	13 27												14 27											
Wolverhampton 7 🚌	a	13 32	13 37	13 41		13 48		13 52		14 10	14 18			14 32	14 37	14 42			14 48	14 52		15 10	15 18		
	d							13 52			14 19									14 52			15 19		
Penkridge	d							14 03												15 03					
Stafford	a							14 10			14 33									15 10			15 33		15 14

		VT 1 ◇ 🍽	LM	VT 1 ◇ 🍽		AW ◇ C 🛒	VT 1 ◇ 🍽	XC 1 ◇ 🛒	LM 1 ◇	LM 1	VT 1 ◇ 🍽	XC 1 ◇ 🛒	LM 1	LM 1		VT 1 ◇ 🍽	LM	VT 1 ◇ 🍽	AW ◇ 🛒	VT 1 ◇ 🍽	XC 1 ◇ 🛒	LM 1 ◇	LM 1	VT 1 ◇ 🍽	XC 1 ◇ 🛒
London Euston 15 ⊖	d	13 38					13 58				14 18			13 50		14 38				14 58				15 18	
Northampton	d												14 53	14 58											
Long Buckby	d												15 03	15 08											
Rugby	d						14 49						15 15	15a19						15 49					
Coventry	a	14 40					15 00				15 20		15 28			15 40				16 00				16 20	
	d	14 40					15 00			15 10	15 20	15 26	15 29			15 40				16 00			16 10	16 20	16 26
Canley	d												15 32												
Tile Hill	d									15 15			15 36										16 15		
Berkswell	d												15 39												
Hampton-in-Arden	d												15 43												
Birmingham International ✈	a	14 51					15 11			15 22	15 31	15 35	15 46			15 51				16 11			16 22	16 31	16 35
	d	14 51				15 07	15 11			15 22	15 31	15 38	15 47			15 51			16 07	16 11			16 22	16 31	16 38
Marston Green	d									15 25			15 50										16 25		
Lea Hall	d									15 29													16 29		
Stechford	d									15 31													16 31		
Adderley Park	d									15 35													16 35		
Birmingham New Street 12	a	15 06				15 18	15 25			15 40	15 44	15 49	15 58			16 06			16 18	16 25			16 40	16 44	16 49
	d		15 09	15 20		15 24		15 31	15 35		15 48	16 01					16 09	16 20	16 24		16 31	16 35		16 48	17 01
Smethwick Rolfe Street	d		15 15														16 15								
Smethwick Galton Bdg L.L. 7	d		15 17														16 17								
Sandwell & Dudley	d		15 19								15 57						16 19							16 57	
Dudley Port	d		15 22														16 22								
Tipton	d		15 24														16 24								
Coseley	d		15 27														16 27								
Wolverhampton 7 🚌	a		15 32	15 37		15 42		15 48	15 52		16 10	16 18					16 32	16 37	16 42		16 48	16 52		17 10	17 18
	d								15 52			16 19										16 52			17 19
Penkridge	d								16 03													17 03			
Stafford	a								16 10			16 35										17 10			17 34

For general notes see front of timetable
For details of catering facilities see Directory of Train Operators

A Until 1 November
B To Crewe (Table 67)
C Until 6 September to Holyhead (Table 81)
b Arr. 1412

Table 68

Sundays

from 19 July

Northampton → Coventry → Birmingham → Wolverhampton → Stafford

Network Diagram - see first page of Table 67

		LM		LM	VT	LM	VT	AW	VT	XC	LM	LM		VT	XC	LM	LM	VT	LM	AW	VT	XC		LM	LM
		1		1◇	1◇		1◇	◇	1◇	1◇	1◇	1		1◇	1◇	1	1	1◇		◇	1◇	1◇		1◇	1
				A				B																	
					☕		☕	🛒	☕	🛒				☕	🛒			☕		🛒	☕	🛒			
London Euston 15 ⊖	d			14 50	15 38				15 58					16 18			15 50	16 38			16 58				
Northampton	d	15 51		15 56												16 53	16 58								
Long Buckby	d	16 01		16 06												17 03	17 08								
Rugby	d	16 15		16 16					16 49							17 15	17a19				17 49				
Coventry	a	16 28			16 40				17 00					17 20		17 28		17 40			18 00				
	d	16 29			16 40				17 00			17 10		17 20	17 26	17 29		17 40			18 00				18 10
Canley	d	16 32														17 32									
Tile Hill	d	16 36										17 15				17 36									18 15
Berkswell	d	16 39														17 39									
Hampton-in-Arden	d	16 43														17 43									
Birmingham International ✈	a	16 46			16 51				17 11			17 22		17 31	17 35	17 46		17 51			18 11				18 22
	d	16 47			16 51			17 07	17 11			17 22		17 31	17 38	17 47		17 51		18 07	18 11				18 22
Marston Green	d	16 50										17 25				17 50									18 25
Lea Hall	d											17 29													18 29
Stechford	d											17 31													18 31
Adderley Park	d											17 35													18 35
Birmingham New Street 12	a	16 58			17 06			17 18	17 25			17 40		17 44	17 49	17 58		18 06		18 18	18 25				18 40
	d					17 09	17 20	17 24		17 31	17 35			17 48	18 01				18 09	18 24		18 31		18 35	
Smethwick Rolfe Street	d					17 15													18 15						
Smethwick Galton Bdg L.L. 7	d					17 17													18 17						
Sandwell & Dudley	d					17 19								17 57					18 19						
Dudley Port	d					17 22													18 22						
Tipton	d					17 24													18 24						
Coseley	d					17 27													18 27						
Wolverhampton 7	a					17 32	17 37	17 42		17 48	17 52			18 10	18 18				18 32	18 42		18 48		18 52	
	d										17 52				18 19									18 52	
Penkridge	d										18 03													19 03	
Stafford	a			17 14							18 10				18 35									19 10	

		VT	XC	LM	LM	VT	LM	VT	AW	VT		XC	LM	VT	LM	VT	XC	LM	LM	VT		LM	XC	VT	AW
								R																	
		1◇	1◇	1	1◇	1◇		1	◇	1◇		1◇	1◇	1◇	1	1◇	1◇	1	1	1◇			1◇	1◇	◇
					A					C				D											
		☕	🛒			☕		☕	🛒	☒		🛒		☕		☕	🛒			☕			🛒	☕	
London Euston 15 ⊖	d	17 18			16 50	17 38				17 58				17 58		18 18			17 50	18 38					
Northampton	d			17 51	17 56													18 53	18 58						
Long Buckby	d			18 01	18 06													19 03	19 08						
Rugby	d			18 15	18 16					18 49				18 49				19 15	19a19						
Coventry	a	18 20		18 28		18 40				19 00				19 00		19 20		19 28		19 40					
	d	18 20	18 26	18 29		18 40				19 00				19 00	19 10	19 20	19 26	19 29		19 40			19 54		
Canley	d			18 32														19 32							
Tile Hill	d			18 36											19 15			19 36							
Berkswell	d			18 39														19 39							
Hampton-in-Arden	d			18 43														19 43							
Birmingham International ✈	a	18 31	18 35	18 46		18 51				19 11				19 11	19 22	19 31	19 35	19 46		19 51			20 03		
	d	18 31	18 38	18 47		18 51			19 07	19 11				19 11	19 22	19 31	19 38	19 47		19 51			20 04		20 08
Marston Green	d			18 50											19 25			19 50							
Lea Hall	d														19 29										
Stechford	d														19 31										
Adderley Park	d														19 35										
Birmingham New Street 12	a	18 44	18 49	18 58		19 06			19 18	19 23				19 23	19 40	19 44	19 49	19 58		20 06			20 15		20 18
	d	18 48	19 01				19 09	19 20	19 24	19 27		19 31	19 35	19 38		19 48	20 01					20 09		20 20	20 24
Smethwick Rolfe Street	d						19 15															20 15			
Smethwick Galton Bdg L.L. 7	d						19 17															20 17			
Sandwell & Dudley	d	18 57					19 19									19 57						20 19			
Dudley Port	d						19 22															20 22			
Tipton	d						19 24															20 24			
Coseley	d						19 27															20 27			
Wolverhampton 7	a	19 10	19 18				19 32	19 37	19 42	19 58		19 48	19 52	19 58		20 10	20 18					20 32		20 36	20 42
	d		19 19										19 52				20 19							20 38	
Penkridge	d												20 03												
Stafford	a		19 37		19 14								20 10				20 37							20 51	

For general notes see front of timetable
For details of catering facilities see Directory of Train Operators

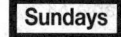

A To Crewe (Table 67)
B To Holyhead (Table 81)
C From 13 September
D Until 6 September

Table 68

Sundays

from 19 July

Northampton → Coventry → Birmingham → Wolverhampton → Stafford

Network Diagram - see first page of Table 67

Station		XC	VT	LM	VT	XC	LM	LM	VT	LM	VT	AW	XC	VT	LM	LM	VT	XC	LM	LM	LM	VT	AW
		1 ◇	1 ◇	1	1 ◇	1 ◇	1	1 ◇	1 ◇	1 ◇	1 ◇	◇	1 ◇	1 ◇	1	1	1 ◇	1 ◇	1	1		1 ◇	
								A															B
London Euston 15 ⊖	d		18 58		19 18			18 50	19 38					19 58			20 18			19 50		20 38	
Northampton	d						19 51	19 56											20 53	20 58			
Long Buckby	d						20 01	20 06											21 03	21 08			
Rugby	d		19 49				20 15	20 16						20 49					21 15	21a19			
Coventry	a		20 00		20 20		20 28		20 40					21 00			21 20		21 27			21 46	
	d		20 00	20 10	20 20	20 26	20 29		20 40				20 54	21 00		21 10	21 20	21 26	21 29			21 46	
Canley	d						20 32												21 32				
Tile Hill	d			20 15			20 36									21 15			21 36				
Berkswell	d						20 39												21 39				
Hampton-in-Arden	d						20 43												21 43				
Birmingham International ✈	a		20 11	20 22	20 31	20 37	20 46		20 51				21 03	21 11		21 22	21 31	21 35	21 46			21 57	
	d		20 11	20 22	20 31	20 38	20 47		20 51			21 08	21 04	21 11		21 22	21 31	21 38	21 47			21 57	22 11
Marston Green	d			20 25			20 50									21 25			21 50				
Lea Hall	d			20 29												21 29							
Stechford	d			20 31												21 31							
Adderley Park	d			20 35												21 35							
Birmingham New Street 12	a		20 23	20 40	20 44	20 49	20 58		21 04			21 18	21 20	21 24		21 40	21 44	21 49	21 58			22 09	22 21
	d	20 31	20 37		20 48	21 01			21 07	21 09	21 20	21 24		21 28	21 35		21 48	22 01			22 09	22 13	22 24
Smethwick Rolfe Street	d									21 15											22 15		
Smethwick Galton Bdg L.L. 7	d									21 17											22 17		
Sandwell & Dudley	d		20 47		20 57				21 16	21 19				21 37			21 57				22 19	22 25	
Dudley Port	d									21 22											22 22		
Tipton	d									21 24											22 24		
Coseley	d									21 27											22 27		
Wolverhampton 7	a	20 48	20 57		21 10	21 18			21 31	21 33	21 38	21 42		21 51	21 52		22 10	22 18			22 32	22 39	22 41
	d					21 19					21 38				21 53			22 19					
Penkridge	d														22 03								
Stafford	a					21 34		21 14			21 58				22 13			22 34					

Station		XC	XC	LM	VT	XC	XC	AW	AW	LM	LM	AW	XC	XC	LM	LM	VT	VT	LM	VT	VT
		1 ◇	1 ◇	1	1 ◇	1 ◇	1 ◇	◇	◇	1			1 ◇	1 ◇	1	1	1 ◇	1 ◇	1	1 ◇	1 ◇
			C			D	C	E	G			B	D	C						C	D
London Euston 15 ⊖	d				20 54												21 54	22 24		23 24	23 24
Northampton	d									21 53						22 53			23 32		
Long Buckby	d									22 03						23 03			23 42		
Rugby	d				22 06					22 15						23 15	23 24	23 48	23 52	00s47	00s47
Coventry	a				22 15					22 27						23 27	23 33	23 57	00 06	00s57	00s57
	d	21 54		22 08	22 16	22 23	22 23			22 29			22 54	22 54	23 08	23 29	23 34	23 58			
Canley	d									22 32						23 32					
Tile Hill	d									22 36						23 36					
Berkswell	d									22 39						23 39					
Hampton-in-Arden	d									22 43						23 43					
Birmingham International ✈	a	22 03		22 17	22 26	22 32	22 32			22 46			23 03	23 03	23 17	23 46	23 51	00 08		01s08	01s08
	d	22 04		22 18	22 27	22 33	22 33	22 40	22 40	22 47		23 08	23 04	23 04	23 18	23 47	23 52	00 09			
Marston Green	d			22 21						22 50					23 21	23 50					
Lea Hall	d			22 24											23 24						
Stechford	d			22 27											23 27						
Adderley Park	d			22 30											23 30						
Birmingham New Street 12	a	22 20		22 36	22 39	22 47	23 06	22 50	22 50	22 58		23 19	23 20	23 35	23 36	23 58	00 04	00 22		01s21	01s21
	d		22 28		22 44			22 55	22 55		23 09	23 24					00 08	00 25			
Smethwick Rolfe Street	d										23 15										
Smethwick Galton Bdg L.L. 7	d										23 17										
Sandwell & Dudley	d				22 53						23 19										
Dudley Port	d										23 22										
Tipton	d										23 24										
Coseley	d										23 27										
Wolverhampton 7	a		22 45		23 06			23 11	23 11		23 32	23 40					00 28	00 55		01 53	01 59
	d		22 46					23 13	23 13												
Penkridge	d																				
Stafford	a		22 58					23 30	23 31												

For general notes see front of timetable
For details of catering facilities see Directory of Train Operators

A To Crewe (Table 67)
B To Shrewsbury (Table 74)
C From 13 September
D Until 6 September
E From 13 September. To Holyhead (Table 81)
G Until 6 September. To Holyhead (Table 81)

Stafford → Wolverhampton → Birmingham → Coventry → Northampton

Network Diagram - see first page of Table 67

Miles	Station		LM	LM	VT	VT	LM	VT	LM	AW	XC	VT	LM	AW	VT	LM	LM	AW	LM	LM	VT	LM	XC	VT	LM
			MX																						
			■1	■1	■1◇	■1◇	■1	■1◇	■1◇		■1◇	■1◇	■1		■1◇	■1	■1				■1◇	■1◇	■1◇	■1◇	■1
														A				A		A					
					⊠	⊠		⊠			⊤	⊠			⊠						⊠		⊤	⊠	
0	**Stafford**	d								05 24													06 25		
5¾	Penkridge	d																							
10¼	**Wolverhampton** 7	a								05 38													06 39		
—		d			05 00	05 20				05 40		05 45		06 00	06 04					06 17	06 27		06 41	06 45	
18½	Coseley	d																		06 22					
20	Tipton	d																		06 25					
20¾	Dudley Port	d																		06 27					
22¾	Sandwell & Dudley	d				05 30						05 56			06 15					06 31	06 37			06 56	
24	Smethwick Galton Bdg L.L. 7	d												06 11						06 34					
24¾	Smethwick Rolfe Street	d																		06 36					
28	**Birmingham New Street** 12	a			05 26	05 39				05 55		06 05		06 17	06 24			←		06 43	06 46		06 58	07 05	
—		d	23p53		05 29	05 50			05 53		06 04	06 10	06 13	06 36 →	06 30		06 33	06 36	06 39		06 50	06 53	07 04	07 10	07 13
30	Adderley Park	d																	06 44						
32	Stechford	d											06 20						06 47						07 20
33	Lea Hall	d											06 23						06 50						07 23
34½	Marston Green	d	00 01						06 01				06 26				06 41					07 01			07 26
36¼	**Birmingham International** ✈	a	00 04		05 37	05 59			06 05		06 13	06 19	06 29		06 38		06 45	06 50	06 54		06 59	07 05	07 13	07 19	07 29
—		d	00 05		05 39	06 00			06 05		06 14	06 20	06 29		06 39		06 45				07 00	07 05	07 14	07 20	07 29
38¼	Hampton-in-Arden	d											06 32				06 48					07 08			
41½	Berkswell	d							06 11				06 37									07 13			07 35
43½	Tile Hill	d							06 14				06 40				06 55								07 38
45½	Canley	d							06 17				06 44									07 18			
47¼	**Coventry**	a	00 13		05 49	06 10			06 20		06 24	06 30	06 47		06 49		07 00				07 10	07 21	07 24	07 30	07 43
—		d			05 50	06 11			06 21			06 31			06 51		07 01				07 11	07 21		07 31	
60¾	Rugby	d		05 20	06 03		06 08	06 20	06 33							07 04	07 13					07 33			
70	Long Buckby	d		05 30			06 18		06 43							07 14	07 23					07 43			
79½	**Northampton**	a		05 41			06 33	06 39	06 54							07 26	07 34					07 54			
—	London Euston 15 ⊖	a		06 50	07 02	07 15	07 43	07 30	08 06			07 36			07 55	08 45					08 17	09 11		08 34	

Station		LM	LM	VT	VT	AW	XC	LM	AW	LM	LM	LM	LM	VT	LM	VT	LM	LM	XC	VT	LM	LM	LM	LM	VT
																			R						
			■1◇	■1◇	■1◇		■1◇	■1				■1◇	■1◇	■1◇	■1◇	■1◇			■1	■1◇	■1		■1◇		■1◇
		A	B			A			A			C							D	E		G	H		
				⊠	⊠		⊤							⊠		⊠			⊤	⊠					⊠
Stafford	d		06 41				06 58					07 12	07 22							07 28			07 41		
Penkridge	d		06 47									07 18											07 47		
Wolverhampton 7	a		06 57				07 12					07 28								07 43			07 57		
	d	06 49	06 57	07 04		07 10	07 15				07 19	07 28				07 32	07 37	07 40		07 45		07 49	07 57	08 03	
Coseley	d	06 54	07 03								07 24							07 45				07 54	08 03		
Tipton	d	06 57									07 26							07 47				07 56			
Dudley Port	d	06 59									07 28							07 49				07 58			
Sandwell & Dudley	d	07 03		07 15							07 32						07 46			07 56		08 02			
Smethwick Galton Bdg L.L. 7	d	07 06				07 21					07 34	07 40						07 53				08 04			
Smethwick Rolfe Street	d	07 09									07 36							07 55				08 06			
Birmingham New Street 12	a	07 14	07 18	07 24		07 27	07 31		←		07 44	07 48				07 55	07 55	08 03		08 05		08 14	08 17	08 20	
	d			07 30		07 36 →		07 33	07 36	07 39				07 50	07 53				08 04	08 10	08 13				08 30
Adderley Park	d									07 44															
Stechford	d									07 47											08 20				
Lea Hall	d									07 50											08 23				
Marston Green	d							07 41							08 01						08 26				
Birmingham International ✈	a							07 45	07 50	07 54				07 59	08 05				08 13	08 19	08 29				08 38
	d				07 41			07 45						08 00	08 05				08 14	08 20	08 29				08 39
Hampton-in-Arden	d							07 48													08 32				
Berkswell	d														08 11						08 37				
Tile Hill	d							07 55							08 14						08 40				
Canley	d							07 58							08 17						08 44				
Coventry	a				07 51			08 02						08 10	08 20				08 24	08 30	08 47				08 49
	d				07 52			08 03						08 11	08 21					08 31					08 51
Rugby	d							08 15					08 18	08 23	08 33										
Long Buckby	d							08 25							08 43										
Northampton	a							08 37					08 41		08 55										
London Euston 15 ⊖	a			08 42	08 49								09 44	09 14	10 20					09 34					09 54

For general notes see front of timetable
For details of catering facilities see Directory of Train Operators

A From Shrewsbury (Table 74)
B From Crewe (Table 67)
C From Crewe (Table 65)
D From Nottingham (Table 57)
E From Manchester Piccadilly (Table 65)
G To Walsall (Table 70)
H From Liverpool Lime Street (Table 91)

Table 68 — Mondays to Fridays

Stafford → Wolverhampton → Birmingham → Coventry → Northampton

Network Diagram - see first page of Table 67

		AW ◇ 🛒	XC 1◇ 🛒	LM 1	AW ◇ 🛒	LM	LM	LM 1◇ A	LM 1◇	VT 1◇ ⊠	LM 1◇	LM	VT 1◇ ⊠	XC 1◇ 🛒	VT 1◇ ⊠	LM 1	LM B	LM 1◇ A	VT 1◇ ⊠	AW ◇ C 🛒	LM 1	AW ◇ C 🛒	LM	LM B	LM 1◇ A
Stafford	d							08 10	08 21					08 25				08 43							09 10
Penkridge	d							08 16										08 48							09 16
Wolverhampton 7	a							08 26						08 39				08 58							09 27
	d	08 09	08 15				08 19	08 28				08 36	08 32	08 41	08 45		08 49	08 59		09 09				09 19	09 28
Coseley	d						08 24										08 54	09 05						09 24	
Tipton	d						08 26										08 56							09 26	
Dudley Port	d						08 28										08 58							09 28	
Sandwell & Dudley	d						08 32					08 46			08 56		09 02							09 32	
Smethwick Galton Bdg L.L. 7	d	08 21					08 34	08 40									09 04			09 20				09 34	09 40
Smethwick Rolfe Street	d						08 36										09 06							09 36	
Birmingham New Street 12	a	08 27	08 31		←		08 44	08 47				08 55	08 56	08 58	09 06		09 14	09 18		09 26		←		09 44	09 47
	d	08 36 →		08 33	08 36	08 39				08 50	08 53			09 04	09 10	09 13			09 30	09 36 →	09 33	09 36	09 39		
Adderley Park	d					08 44																	09 44		
Stechford	d					08 47										09 20							09 48		
Lea Hall	d					08 50										09 23							09 50		
Marston Green	d			08 41							09 01					09 26					09 41				
Birmingham International ✈	a			08 45	08 50	08 54				08 59	09 05			09 13	09 19	09 29			09 38		09 45	09 50	09 55		
	d			08 45						09 00	09 05			09 14	09 20	09 29			09 39		09 45				
Hampton-in-Arden	d			08 48												09 32					09 48				
Berkswell	d										09 11					09 37									
Tile Hill	d			08 55							09 14					09 40					09 55				
Canley	d										09 17					09 44									
Coventry	a			09 00						09 10	09 20			09 24	09 30	09 47			09 49		10 00				
	d			09 01						09 11	09 21				09 31				09 51		10 01				
Rugby	d			09 13					09 20	09 23	09 33										10 13				
Long Buckby	d			09 23							09 43										10 23				
Northampton	a			09 34					09 42		09 54										10 34				
London Euston 15 ⊖	a								10 49	10 14	11 18				10 34				10 54						

		VT 1◇ ⊠	LM 1◇	VT 1◇ ⊠	LM 1◇	LM	VT 1◇ ⊠	XC 1◇ 🛒	VT 1◇ ⊠	LM 1	LM B	LM 1◇ A	VT 1◇ ☕	AW ◇ 🛒	XC 1◇ 🛒	LM 1	AW ◇ 🛒	LM	LM B	LM 1◇ A	LM 1◇	VT 1◇ ☕	LM 1◇	VT 1◇ ⊠	LM
Stafford	d		09 21					09 25				09 43								10 10	10 21				
Penkridge	d																			10 16					
Wolverhampton 7	a							09 39				09 56								10 27					
	d	09 32 →				09 36	09 32	09 41	09 45		09 49	09 57		10 09	10 15				10 19	10 28				10 32	10 36
Coseley	d										09 54	10 03							10 24						
Tipton	d										09 56								10 26						
Dudley Port	d										09 58								10 28						
Sandwell & Dudley	d					09 46			09 56		10 02								10 32						10 46
Smethwick Galton Bdg L.L. 7	d										10 04			10 20					10 34	10 40					
Smethwick Rolfe Street	d										10 06								10 36						
Birmingham New Street 12	a					09 55	09 56	09 58	10 05		10 14	10 17		10 26	10 31		←		10 44	10 47				10 55	10 55
	d			09 50	09 53			10 04	10 10	10 13			10 30	10 36 →		10 33	10 36	10 39				10 50	10 53		
Adderley Park	d																	10 44							
Stechford	d									10 20								10 47							
Lea Hall	d									10 23								10 50							
Marston Green	d				10 01					10 26						10 41							11 01		
Birmingham International ✈	a			09 59	10 05			10 13	10 19	10 29			10 38			10 45	10 50	10 54				10 59	11 05		
	d			10 00	10 05			10 14	10 20	10 29			10 39			10 45						11 00	11 05		
Hampton-in-Arden	d									10 32						10 48									
Berkswell	d				10 11					10 37													11 11		
Tile Hill	d				10 14					10 40						10 55							11 14		
Canley	d				10 17					10 44													11 17		
Coventry	a			10 10	10 20			10 24	10 30	10 47			10 49			11 00						11 10	11 20		
	d			10 11	10 21				10 31				10 51			11 01						11 11	11 21		
Rugby	d		10 19	10 24	10 33											11 13					11 19	11 24	11 33		
Long Buckby	d				10 43											11 23							11 43		
Northampton	a		10 42		10 54											11 34					11 42		11 54		
London Euston 15 ⊖	a		11 49	11 14	12 18				11 34				11 54								12 49	12 14	13 18		

For general notes see front of timetable
For details of catering facilities see Directory of Train Operators

A From Liverpool Lime Street (Table 91)
B To Walsall (Table 70)
C From Holyhead (Table 81)

Stafford → Wolverhampton → Birmingham → Coventry → Northampton

Network Diagram - see first page of Table 67

		XC	VT	LM	LM	LM	VT	AW	XC	LM	AW	LM	LM	LM	LM	VT	LM		LM	VT	XC	VT	LM	LM	VT
		1 ◇	1 ◇	1		1 ◇	1 ◇	◇	1 ◇	1	◇			1 ◇	1 ◇	1 ◇	1 ◇			1 ◇	1 ◇	1 ◇		1 ◇	1 ◇
					A	B		C			C		A	B									A	B	
		🛒	🍴				🍴	🛒	🛒		🛒					🍴				⊠	🛒	🍴			🍴
Stafford	d	10 25				10 43								11 10	11 21						11 25			11 43	
Penkridge	d													11 16											
Wolverhampton 7	a	10 39				10 56								11 27							11 39			11 56	
	d	10 41	10 45		10 49	10 57		11 13	11 15				11 19	11 28					11 36	11 32	11 41	11 45	11 49	11 57	
Coseley	d				10 54	11 03							11 24										11 54	12 03	
Tipton	d				10 56								11 26										11 56		
Dudley Port	d				10 58								11 28										11 58		
Sandwell & Dudley	d		10 56		11 02								11 32						11 46			11 56	12 02		
Smethwick Galton Bdg L.L. 7	d				11 04			11 24					11 34	11 40									12 04		
Smethwick Rolfe Street	d				11 06								11 36										12 06		
Birmingham New Street 12	a	10 58	11 05		11 14	11 18		11 30	11 31		←		11 44	11 47					11 55	11 56	11 58	12 05	12 14	12 17	
	d	11 04	11 10	11 13			11 30	11 36 →		11 33	11 36	11 39				11 50	11 53				12 04	12 10			12 30
Adderley Park	d											11 44													
Stechford	d			11 20								11 47													
Lea Hall	d			11 23								11 50													
Marston Green	d			11 26						11 41							12 01								
Birmingham International ✈	a	11 13	11 19	11 29			11 38			11 45	11 50	11 54				11 59	12 05				12 13	12 19			12 38
	d	11 14	11 20	11 29			11 39			11 45						12 00	12 05				12 14	12 20			12 39
Hampton-in-Arden	d			11 32						11 48															
Berkswell	d			11 37													12 11								
Tile Hill	d			11 40						11 55							12 14								
Canley	d			11 44													12 17								
Coventry	a	11 24	11 30	11 47			11 49			12 00						12 10	12 20				12 24	12 30			12 49
	d		11 31				11 51			12 01						12 11	12 21					12 31			12 51
Rugby	d									12 13					12 19	12 24	12 33								
Long Buckby	d									12 23							12 43								
Northampton	a									12 34					12 42		12 54								
London Euston 15 ⊖	a		12 34				12 54								13 49	13 14	14 18					13 34			13 54

		AW	LM	XC	LM	AW	LM	LM	LM	LM	VT	LM	VT	LM	XC	VT	LM	LM	LM	VT	AW	XC	LM	AW	LM
		◇	1	1 ◇	1	◇			1 ◇	1 ◇	1 ◇	1 ◇	1 ◇		1 ◇	1 ◇	1		1 ◇	1 ◇	◇	1 ◇	1	◇	
								A	B									A	B		C			C	
		🛒		🛒		🛒					🍴		⊠		🛒	🍴				🍴	🛒	🛒		🛒	
Stafford	d								12 10	12 21					12 25				12 43						
Penkridge	d								12 16																
Wolverhampton 7	a								12 27						12 39				12 56						
	d	12 09		12 15				12 19	12 28				12 32	12 36	12 41	12 45		12 49	12 57		13 09	13 15			
Coseley	d							12 24										12 54	13 03						
Tipton	d							12 26										12 56							
Dudley Port	d							12 28										12 58							
Sandwell & Dudley	d							12 32						12 46		12 56		13 02							
Smethwick Galton Bdg L.L. 7	d	12 20						12 34	12 40									13 04			13 20				
Smethwick Rolfe Street	d							12 36										13 06							
Birmingham New Street 12	a	12 26		12 31		←		12 44	12 47				12 55	12 55	12 58	13 05		13 14	13 17		13 26	13 31		←	
	d	12 36 →	12 13		12 33	12 36	12 39				12 50	12 53			13 04	13 10	13 13			13 30	13 36 →		13 33	13 36	13 39
Adderley Park	d						12 44																		13 44
Stechford	d		12 20				12 47										13 20								13 47
Lea Hall	d		12 23				12 50										13 23								13 50
Marston Green	d		12 26		12 41							13 01					13 26						13 41		
Birmingham International ✈	a		12 29		12 45	12 50	12 54				12 59	13 05			13 13	13 19	13 29			13 38			13 45	13 50	13 54
	d		12 29		12 45						13 00	13 05			13 14	13 20	13 29			13 39			13 45		
Hampton-in-Arden	d		12 32		12 48												13 32						13 48		
Berkswell	d		12 37									13 11					13 37								
Tile Hill	d		12 40		12 55							13 14					13 40						13 55		
Canley	d		12 44									13 17					13 44								
Coventry	a		12 47		13 00						13 10	13 20			13 24	13 30	13 47			13 49			14 00		
	d				13 01						13 11	13 21				13 31				13 51			14 01		
Rugby	d				13 13					13b24	13 24	13 33											14 13		
Long Buckby	d				13 23							13 43											14 23		
Northampton	a				13 34					13 48		13 54											14 34		
London Euston 15 ⊖	a									14 49	14 14	15 18				14 35				14 54					

For general notes see front of timetable
For details of catering facilities see Directory of Train Operators

A To Walsall (Table 70)
B From Liverpool Lime Street (Table 91)
C From Holyhead (Table 81)

b Arr. 1317

Stafford → Wolverhampton → Birmingham → Coventry → Northampton

Network Diagram - see first page of Table 67

	LM A	LM 1◇ B	LM 1◇	VT 1◇ 🍽	LM 1◇	LM	VT 1◇ 🍽	XC 1◇ 🛒	VT 1◇ 🍽	LM 1	LM A	LM 1◇ B	VT 1◇ 🍽	AW ◇ 🛒	XC 1◇ 🛒	LM 1	AW ◇ 🛒	LM	LM A	LM 1◇ B	LM 1◇	VT 1◇ 🍽	LM 1◇	VT 1◇ 🍽
Stafford d		13 10	13 21					13 25				13 43								14 10	14 21			
Penkridge d		13 16																		14 16				
Wolverhampton 7 a		13 27						13 39				13 56								14 27				
d	13 19	13 28				13 36	13 32	13 41	13 45		13 49	13 57		14 09	14 15				14 19	14 28				14 32
Coseley d	13 24										13 54	14 03							14 24					
Tipton d	13 26										13 56								14 26					
Dudley Port d	13 28										13 58								14 28					
Sandwell & Dudley d	13 32					13 46			13 56		14 02								14 32					
Smethwick Galton Bdg L.L. 7 d	13 34	13 40									14 04			14 20					14 34	14 40				
Smethwick Rolfe Street d	13 36										14 06								14 36					
Birmingham New Street 12 a	13 44	13 47				13 55	13 56	13 58	14 05		14 14	14 17		14 26	14 31		←		14 44	14 47				14 55
d				13 50	13 53			14 04	14 10	14 13			14 30	14 36 →		14 33	14 36	14 39				14 50	14 53	
Adderley Park d																		14 44						
Stechford d										14 20								14 47						
Lea Hall d										14 23								14 50						
Marston Green d					14 01					14 26						14 41							15 01	
Birmingham International ✈ a				13 59	14 05			14 13	14 19	14 29			14 38			14 45	14 50	14 54				14 59	15 05	
d				14 00	14 05			14 14	14 20	14 29			14 39			14 45						15 00	15 05	
Hampton-in-Arden d										14 32						14 48								
Berkswell d					14 11					14 37													15 11	
Tile Hill d					14 14					14 40						14 55							15 14	
Canley d					14 17					14 44													15 17	
Coventry a				14 10	14 20			14 24	14 30	14 47			14 49			15 00						15 10	15 20	
d				14 11	14 21				14 31				14 51			15 01						15 11	15 21	
Rugby d			14 19	14 24	14 33											15 13					15 19	15 24	15 33	
Long Buckby d					14 43											15 23							15 43	
Northampton a			14 42		14 54											15 34					15 42		15 54	
London Euston 15 ⊖ a			15 49	15 14	16 18				15 35				15 54								16 48	16 14	17 18	

	LM	XC 1◇ 🛒	VT 1◇ 🍽	LM 1	LM A	LM 1◇ B	VT 1◇ 🍽	AW ◇ C 🛒	XC 1◇ 🛒	LM 1	AW ◇ C 🛒	LM	LM A	LM 1◇ D	LM 1◇	VT 1◇ 🍽	LM 1◇	LM	VT 1◇ 🍽	XC 1◇ 🛒	VT 1◇ 🍽	LM 1	LM A	LM 1◇ B
Stafford d		14 25				14 46								15 10	15 21					15 25				15 43
Penkridge d														15 16										
Wolverhampton 7 a		14 39				14 59								15 27						15 39				15 56
d	14 36	14 41	14 45		14 49	14 59		15 09	15 15				15 19	15 28				15 36	15 32	15 41	15 45		15 49	15 57
Coseley d					14 54	15 05							15 24										15 54	16 03
Tipton d					14 56								15 26										15 56	
Dudley Port d					14 58								15 28										15 58	
Sandwell & Dudley d	14 46		14 56		15 02								15 32					15 46			15 56		16 02	
Smethwick Galton Bdg L.L. 7 d					15 04			15 20					15 34	15 40									16 04	
Smethwick Rolfe Street d					15 06								15 36										16 06	
Birmingham New Street 12 a	14 55	14 58	15 05		15 14	15 20		15 26	15 31		←		15 44	15 47				15 55	15 56	15 58	16 05		16 14	16 17
d		15 04	15 10	15 13			15 30	15 36 →		15 33	15 36	15 39				15 50	15 53			16 04	16 10	16 13		
Adderley Park d												15 44												
Stechford d				15 20								15 47										16 20		
Lea Hall d				15 23								15 50										16 23		
Marston Green d				15 26						15 41							16 01					16 26		
Birmingham International ✈ a		15 13	15 19	15 29			15 38			15 45	15 50	15 54				15 59	16 05			16 13	16 19	16 29		
d		15 14	15 20	15 29			15 39			15 45						16 00	16 05			16 14	16 20	16 29		
Hampton-in-Arden d				15 32						15 48												16 32		
Berkswell d				15 37													16 11					16 37		
Tile Hill d				15 40						15 55							16 14					16 40		
Canley d				15 44													16 17					16 44		
Coventry a		15 24	15 30	15 47			15 49			16 00						16 10	16 20			16 24	16 30	16 47		
d			15 31				15 51			16 01						16 11	16 21				16 31			
Rugby d										16 13					16 19	16 24	16 33							
Long Buckby d										16 23							16 43							
Northampton a										16 34					16 40		16 54							
London Euston 15 ⊖ a			16 34				16 54								17 49	17 14	18 18				17 34			

For general notes see front of timetable
For details of catering facilities see Directory of Train Operators

A To Walsall (Table 70)
B From Liverpool Lime Street (Table 91)
C From Holyhead (Table 81)
D From Liverpool Lime Street (Table 65)

Stafford → Wolverhampton → Birmingham → Coventry → Northampton

Network Diagram - see first page of Table 67

		VT	AW	XC	LM	AW	LM	LM	LM	LM	VT	LM	VT	LM	XC	VT	LM	LM	LM	LM	VT	AW	XC	LM	AW
		1 ◇	◇	1 ◇	1	◇			1 ◇	1 ◇	1 ◇	1 ◇	1 ◇		1 ◇	1 ◇	1		1	1 ◇	1 ◇	◇	1 ◇	1	◇
								A	B									A		B		C			C
		⊠	🛒	🛒		🛒					⊠		🍽		🛒	⊠					⊠	🛒	🛒		🛒
Stafford	d								16 10	16 21					16 25					16 46					
Penkridge	d								16 16																
Wolverhampton 7	a								16 26						16 39					16 59					
	d		16 09	16 15				16 19	16 28				16 32	16 36	16 41	16 45		16 49		16 59		17 09	17 15		
Coseley	d							16 24										16 54		17 05					
Tipton	d							16 26										16 56							
Dudley Port	d							16 28										16 58							
Sandwell & Dudley	d							16 32						16 46		16 56		17 02							
Smethwick Galton Bdg L.L. 7	d		16 20					16 34	16 40									17 04				17 20			
Smethwick Rolfe Street	d							16 36										17 06							
Birmingham New Street 12	a		16 26	16 31		⟵		16 44	16 47				16 55	16 55	16 58	17 05		17 14		17 20		17 26	17 31		⟵
	d	16 30	16 36 ⟶		16 33	16 36	16 39				16 50	16 53			17 04	17 10	17 13		17 16		17 30	17 36 ⟶		17 33	17 36
Adderley Park	d						16 44												17 21						
Stechford	d						16 47										17 20								
Lea Hall	d						16 50												17 25						
Marston Green	d				16 41							17 01							17 28					17 41	
Birmingham International ✈	a	16 38			16 45	16 50	16 54				16 59	17 05			17 13	17 19	17 27		17 32		17 38			17 45	17 50
	d	16 39			16 45						17 00	17 05			17 14	17 20	17 27		17 33		17 39			17 45	
Hampton-in-Arden	d				16 48														17 36					17 48	
Berkswell	d											17 11							17 40						
Tile Hill	d				16 55							17 14					17 35							17 55	
Canley	d											17 17					17 39								
Coventry	a	16 49			17 00						17 10	17 20			17 24	17 30	17 43		17 47		17 49			18 00	
	d	16 51			17 01						17 11	17 21				17 31	17 43				17 51			18 01	
Rugby	d				17 13					17 19	17 24	17 33					17 55							18 13	
Long Buckby	d				17 23							17 43					18 05							18 23	
Northampton	a				17 34					17 42		17 54					18 17							18 34	
London Euston 15 ⊖	a	17 54								18 49	18 14	19 18				18 34					18 54				

		LM	LM	LM	LM	VT	LM	LM	VT	XC	VT	LM	LM	LM	VT	AW	XC	LM	AW	LM	LM	LM	LM	VT	LM
				1 ◇	1 ◇	1 ◇	1 ◇		1 ◇	1 ◇	1 ◇	1		1 ◇	1 ◇	◇	1 ◇	1	◇			1 ◇	1 ◇	1 ◇	1 ◇
			A	B									A	D							A	B			
						⊠			🍽	🛒	⊠				⊠	🛒	🛒		🛒					⊠	
Stafford	d			17 10	17 21					17 25				17 43								18 10	18 21		
Penkridge	d			17 16																		18 16			
Wolverhampton 7	a			17 27						17 39				17 56								18 27			
	d		17 19	17 28				17 36	17 32	17 41	17 45		17 49	17 57		18 09	18 15				18 19	18 28			
Coseley	d		17 24										17 54	18 03							18 24				
Tipton	d		17 26										17 56								18 26				
Dudley Port	d		17 28										17 58								18 28				
Sandwell & Dudley	d		17 32					17 46			17 56		18 02								18 32				
Smethwick Galton Bdg L.L. 7	d		17 34	17 40									18 04			18 20					18 34	18 40			
Smethwick Rolfe Street	d		17 36										18 06								18 36				
Birmingham New Street 12	a		17 44	17 47				17 55	17 56	17 58	18 05		18 14	18 17		18 26	18 31		⟵		18 44	18 48			
	d	17 39				17 50	17 53			18 04	18 10	18 13			18 30	18 36 ⟶		18 33	18 36	18 39				18 50	18 53
Adderley Park	d	17 44																		18 44					
Stechford	d	17 47										18 20								18 47					
Lea Hall	d	17 50										18 23								18 50					
Marston Green	d						18 01					18 26						18 41							19 01
Birmingham International ✈	a	17 54				17 59	18 05			18 13	18 19	18 29			18 38			18 45	18 50	18 54				18 59	19 05
	d					18 00	18 05			18 14	18 20	18 29			18 39			18 45						19 00	19 05
Hampton-in-Arden	d											18 32						18 48							
Berkswell	d						18 11					18 37													19 11
Tile Hill	d						18 14					18 40						18 55							19 14
Canley	d						18 17					18 44													19 17
Coventry	a					18 10	18 20			18 24	18 30	18 47			18 49			19 00						19 10	19 20
	d					18 11	18 21				18 31				18 51			19 01						19 11	19 21
Rugby	d				18 19	18 24	18 33											19 13					19 21	19 24	19 33
Long Buckby	d						18 43											19 23							19 43
Northampton	a				18 42		18 54											19 34					19 44		19 54
London Euston 15 ⊖	a				19 49	19 14	20 20				19 35				19 54								20 49	20 14	21 18

For general notes see front of timetable
For details of catering facilities see Directory of Train Operators

A To Walsall (Table 70)
B From Liverpool Lime Street (Table 91)
C From Holyhead (Table 81)
D From Liverpool Lime Street (Table 65)

Stafford → Wolverhampton → Birmingham → Coventry → Northampton

Network Diagram - see first page of Table 67

		VT	LM	XC	VT	LM	LM	LM	VT	AW	XC	LM	AW	LM	LM	LM	LM	VT	LM	LM	VT	XC	VT	LM	LM
		1 ◇		1 ◇	1 ◇	1		1 ◇	1 ◇	◇	1 ◇	1	◇			1 ◇	1 ◇	1 ◇	1 ◇		1 ◇	1 ◇	1 ◇	1	
								A		B			B		C	A						D			
		☕		trolley	⊠				☕	trolley	trolley		trolley					☕			☕	trolley	☕		
Stafford	d			18 25				18 43								19 10	19 21					19 25			
Penkridge	d															19 16									
Wolverhampton 7 ⇌	a			18 39				18 56								19 27						19 39			
	d	18 32	18 36	18 41	18 45		18 49	18 57		19 09	19 15				19 19	19 28				19 36	19 32	19 41	19 45		19 49
Coseley	d						18 54	19 03							19 24										19 54
Tipton	d						18 56								19 26										19 56
Dudley Port	d						18 58								19 28										19 58
Sandwell & Dudley	d		18 46		18 56		19 02								19 32					19 46			19 56		20 02
Smethwick Galton Bdg L.L. 7	d						19 04			19 20					19 34	19 40									20 04
Smethwick Rolfe Street	d						19 06								19 36										20 06
Birmingham New Street 12	a	18 55	18 55	18 58	19 05		19 14	19 17		19 26	19 31		←		19 44	19 47				19 55	19 56	19 58	20 05		20 14
	d			19 04	19 10	19 13			19 30	19 36 →		19 33	19 36	19 39				19 50	19 53			20 04	20 10	20 13	
Adderley Park	d													19 44											
Stechford	d					19 20								19 47										20 20	
Lea Hall	d					19 23								19 50										20 23	
Marston Green	d					19 26						19 41							20 01					20 26	
Birmingham International ✈	a			19 13	19 19	19 29			19 38			19 45	19 50	19 54				19 59	20 05			20 13	20 19	20 29	
	d			19 14	19 20	19 29			19 39			19 45						20 00	20 05			20 14	20 20	20 29	
Hampton-in-Arden	d					19 32						19 48												20 32	
Berkswell	d					19 37													20 11					20 37	
Tile Hill	d					19 40						19 55							20 14					20 40	
Canley	d					19 44													20 17					20 44	
Coventry	a			19 24	19 30	19 47			19 49			20 00						20 10	20 20			20 24	20 30	20 47	
	d				19 31				19 51			20 01						20 11	20 21				20 31		
Rugby	d											20 13					20 19	20 23	20 33						
Long Buckby	d											20 23							20 43						
Northampton	a											20 34					20 44		20 54						
London Euston 15 ⊖	a				20 34				20 54									21 14	22 20				21 38		

		LM	AW	XC	LM	AW	LM	LM	LM	VT	LM	VT	LM	XC	VT	LM	LM	LM	LM	XC	LM	LM	LM	VT	LM
		1 ◇	◇	1 ◇	1	◇			1 ◇	1 ◇	1 ◇	1 ◇		1 ◇	1 ◇	1		1 ◇	1 ◇	1 ◇			1 ◇	1 ◇	1
		A							E					D				A					A		
			trolley	trolley		trolley				☕		☕		trolley	☕									☕	
Stafford	d	19 42							20 16					20 25				20 42					21 10	21 14	
Penkridge	d	19 47																20 47					21 16		
Wolverhampton 7 ⇌	a	19 57							20 29					20 39				20 57					21 26	21 30	
	d	19 57	20 09	20 15				20 19	20 29			20 34	20 36	20 41	20 47		20 49	20 57		21 15		21 19	21 28	21 33	
Coseley	d	20 03						20 24									20 54	21 03				21 24			
Tipton	d							20 26									20 56					21 26			
Dudley Port	d							20 28									20 58					21 28			
Sandwell & Dudley	d							20 32					20 46		20 57		21 02					21 32			
Smethwick Galton Bdg L.L. 7	d		20 20					20 34	20 41								21 04					21 34	21 40		
Smethwick Rolfe Street	d							20 36									21 06					21 36			
Birmingham New Street 12	a	20 17	20 27	20 31		←		20 44	20 47			20 55	20 57	20 58	21 06		21 14	21 18		21 36		21 44	21 47	21 51	
	d		20 36 →		20 33	20 36	20 39			20 50	20 53			21 04	21 10	21 13			21 33		21 39				21 53
Adderley Park	d						20 44														21 44				
Stechford	d						20 47									21 20					21 47				
Lea Hall	d						20 50									21 23					21 50				
Marston Green	d				20 41						21 01					21 26			21 41						22 01
Birmingham International ✈	a				20 45	20 50	20 54			20 59	21 05			21 13	21 19	21 29			21 45		21 54				22 05
	d				20 45					21 00	21 05			21 14	21 20	21 29			21 45						22 05
Hampton-in-Arden	d				20 48											21 32			21 48						
Berkswell	d										21 11					21 37									22 11
Tile Hill	d				20 55						21 14					21 40			21 55						22 14
Canley	d										21 17					21 44									22 17
Coventry	a				21 00					21 10	21 20			21 24	21 30	21 53			22 00						22 20
	d				21 01					21 11	21 21				21 31				22 01						22 21
Rugby	d				21 13					21 23	21 33								22 13						22 33
Long Buckby	d				21 23						21 43								22 23						22 43
Northampton	a				21 34						21 54								22 34						22 55
London Euston 15 ⊖	a									22 33	23 25				22 58				00 18						

For general notes see front of timetable
For details of catering facilities see Directory of Train Operators

A From Liverpool Lime Street (Table 91)
B From Holyhead (Table 81)
C To Walsall (Table 70)
D trolley to Birmingham New Street
E From Liverpool Lime Street (Table 65)

Table 68

Mondays to Fridays

Stafford → Wolverhampton → Birmingham → Coventry → Northampton

Network Diagram - see first page of Table 67

		LM	XC	XC	VT	LM	LM	LM	AW	LM	LM	VT	LM	VT	LM	XC	VT	LM	LM	LM	AW	XC	LM
			1 ◇	1 ◇	1 ◇	1		1 ◇	◇	1		1 ◇	1	1 ◇		1 ◇	1 ◇	1		1 ◇	◇	1 ◇	1
								A												A			
				⊼	⊡							⊡		⊡			⊡						
Stafford	d		21 25					21 41								22 25				22 41		23 07	
Penkridge	d							21 47												22 47			
Wolverhampton 7	a		21 39					21 57								22 39				22 57		23 19	
	d	21 36	21 41		21 45		21 49	21 57	22 13		22 19	22 28		22 32	22 36	22 41	22 45		22 49	22 57	22 55	23 21	
Coseley	d						21 54	22 03			22 24								22 54	23 03			
Tipton	d						21 56				22 26								22 56				
Dudley Port	d						21 58				22 28								22 58				
Sandwell & Dudley	d	21 46			21 56		22 02				22 32				22 46		22 55		23 02				
Smethwick Galton Bdg L.L. 7	d						22 04		22 24		22 34								23 04				
Smethwick Rolfe Street	d						22 06				22 36								23 06				
Birmingham New Street 12	a	21 55	22 00		22 05		22 14	22 17	22 30		22 44	22 50		22 55	22 55	23 03	23 04		23 14	23 18	23 26	23 40	
	d			22 04	22 10	22 13				22 33			22 53				23 10	23 13					23 53
Adderley Park	d																	23 18					
Stechford	d					22 20												23 21					
Lea Hall	d					22 23												23 24					
Marston Green	d					22 26				22 41			23 01					23 27					00 01
Birmingham International ✈	a			22 13	22 19	22 29				22 45			23 05				23 19	23 30					00 04
	d			22 14	22 20	22 29				22 45			23 05				23 20	23 30					00 05
Hampton-in-Arden	d					22 32				22 48								23 33					
Berkswell	d					22 37							23 11					23 38					
Tile Hill	d					22 40				22 55			23 14					23 41					
Canley	d					22 44							23 17					23 45					
Coventry	a			22 24	22 30	22 47				23 00			23 20				23 30	23 48					00 13
	d				22 31								23 21				23 31						
Rugby	d				22 43								23 33				23 44						
Long Buckby	d												23 43										
Northampton	a												23 54				00s05						
London Euston 15	⊖ a				00 03												01 13						

Saturdays

		LM	VT	AW	XC	VT	LM	AW	VT	LM	AW	LM	LM	VT	LM		XC	VT	LM	LM	LM	VT	AW	XC	LM
		1	1 ◇		1 ◇	1 ◇	1		1 ◇	1				1 ◇	1		1 ◇	1 ◇	1		1 ◇	1 ◇		1 ◇	1
								B			B									C	D		B		
			⊡		⊼	⊡			⊡					⊡			⊼	⊡				⊡		⊼	
Stafford	d			05 24													06 25				06 41			06 58	
Penkridge	d																				06 47				
Wolverhampton 7	a			05 38													06 39				06 57			07 13	
	d			05 40		05 45		06 03	06 06				06 19	06 27			06 41	06 45		06 49	06 57	07 04	07 10	07 15	
Coseley	d												06 24							06 54	07 03				
Tipton	d												06 26							06 56					
Dudley Port	d												06 28							06 58					
Sandwell & Dudley	d					05 56			06 17				06 32	06 37				06 56		07 02		07 15			
Smethwick Galton Bdg L.L. 7	d							06 14					06 34							07 04			07 21		
Smethwick Rolfe Street	d												06 36							07 06					
Birmingham New Street 12	a			05 55		06 05		06 20	06 26		←		06 44	06 47			06 58	07 05		07 14	07 17	07 24	07 27	07 31	
	d	23p53	05 50		06 04	06 10	06 13	06 36 →	06 30	06 33	06 36	06 39		06 50	06 53		07 04	07 10	07 13			07 30	07 36 →		07 33
Adderley Park	d											06 44													
Stechford	d						06 20					06 47							07 20						
Lea Hall	d						06 23					06 50							07 23						
Marston Green	d	00 01					06 26			06 41					07 01				07 26						07 41
Birmingham International ✈	a	00 04	05 59		06 13	06 19	06 29		06 39	06 45	06 50	06 54		06 59	07 05		07 13	07 19	07 29			07 39			07 45
	d	00 05	06 00		06 14	06 20	06 29		06 40	06 45				07 00	07 05		07 14	07 20	07 29			07 40			07 45
Hampton-in-Arden	d						06 32			06 48									07 32						07 48
Berkswell	d						06 37								07 11				07 37						
Tile Hill	d						06 40			06 55					07 14				07 40						07 55
Canley	d						06 44								07 17				07 44						
Coventry	a	00 13	06 10		06 24	06 30	06 47		06 50	07 00				07 10	07 20		07 24	07 30	07 47			07 50			08 00
	d		06 10			06 31			06 51	07 01				07 11	07 21			07 31				07 52			08 01
Rugby	d		06 24							07 13				07 23	07 33										08 13
Long Buckby	d									07 23					07 43										08 23
Northampton	a									07 34					07 54										08 34
London Euston 15	⊖ a		07 16			07 38			07 56					08 14				08 34				08 54			→

For general notes see front of timetable
For details of catering facilities see Directory of Train Operators

A From Liverpool Lime Street (Table 91)
B From Shrewsbury (Table 74)
C To Walsall (Table 70)
D From Crewe (Table 67)

Stafford → Wolverhampton → Birmingham → Coventry → Northampton

Network Diagram - see first page of Table 67

		AW	LM	LM	LM	LM	LM	VT		LM	VT	LM	XC	VT	LM	LM	LM	VT	AW	XC	LM	AW	XC		LM
					1 ◇	1 ◇	1 ◇	1 ◇		1	1 ◇		R 1	1 ◇	1		1 ◇	1 ◇	◇	1 ◇	1	◇	1 ◇		
		A		B	C								D			B	E			G			H		
								⊏P			⊏P		ꝏ	⊏P				⊏P	ꝏ	ꝏ		ꝏ	ꝏ		
Stafford	d				07 12		07 26										07 41								
Penkridge	d				07 18												07 47								
Wolverhampton 7	a				07 28												07 57								
	d			07 19	07 28						07 32	07 37		07 44		07 49	07 57	08 06	08 11	08 15			08 18		
Coseley	d			07 24												07 54	08 03								
Tipton	d			07 26												07 56									
Dudley Port	d			07 28												07 58									
Sandwell & Dudley	d			07 32								07 46		07 56		08 02									
Smethwick Galton Bdg L.L. 7	d			07 34	07 40											08 04			08 21						
Smethwick Rolfe Street	d			07 36												08 06									
Birmingham New Street 12	a	←		07 44	07 47						07 55	07 55		08 05		08 14	08 17	08 24	08 28	08 31		←	08 37		
	d	07 36	07 39					07 50		07 53			08 04	08 10	08 13			08 30	08 36 →		08 33	08 36			08 39
Adderley Park	d		07 44																						08 44
Stechford	d		07 47												08 20										08 47
Lea Hall	d		07 50												08 23										08 50
Marston Green	d									08 01					08 26						08 41				
Birmingham International ✈	a	07 50	07 54					07 59		08 05			08 13	08 19	08 29			08 38			08 45	08 50			08 54
	d							08 00		08 05			08 14	08 20	08 29			08 39			08 45				
Hampton-in-Arden	d														08 32						08 48				
Berkswell	d									08 11					08 37										
Tile Hill	d									08 14					08 40						08 55				
Canley	d									08 17					08 44										
Coventry	a							08 10		08 20			08 24	08 30	08 47			08 49			09 00				
	d							08 11		08 21				08 31				08 51			09 01				
Rugby	d						08 20	08 23		08 33											09 13				
Long Buckby	d					←				08 43											09 23				
Northampton	a					08 34	08 40			08 54											09 34				
																					→				
London Euston 15	⊖ a					09 51		09 14						09 35				09 55							

		LM	LM	LM	LM	VT	LM	VT	LM	XC	VT	LM	LM	LM	VT		AW	XC	LM	AW	XC	LM	LM	LM	
			1 ◇	1 ◇	1 ◇	1 ◇	1	1 ◇		1 ◇	1 ◇	1		1 ◇	1 ◇		◇	1 ◇	1	◇	1 ◇			1 ◇	
		B	E										B	E			J	G		J	H		B	E	
						⊏P		⊏P		ꝏ	⊏P				⊏P		ꝏ	ꝏ		ꝏ	ꝏ				
Stafford	d		08 10		08 23					08 25				08 43										09 10	
Penkridge	d		08 16											08 48										09 16	
Wolverhampton 7	a		08 28							08 39				08 58										09 27	
	d	08 19	08 28					08 32	08 36	08 41	08 45		08 49	08 59			09 09	09 15			09 18		09 19	09 28	
Coseley	d	08 24											08 54	09 05									09 24		
Tipton	d	08 26											08 56										09 26		
Dudley Port	d	08 28											08 58										09 28		
Sandwell & Dudley	d	08 32							08 46		08 56		09 02										09 32		
Smethwick Galton Bdg L.L. 7	d	08 34	08 40										09 04				09 20						09 34	09 40	
Smethwick Rolfe Street	d	08 36											09 06										09 36		
Birmingham New Street 12	a	08 44	08 47					08 55	08 55	08 58	09 05		09 14	09 18			09 26	09 31		←	09 38		09 44	09 47	
	d					08 50	08 53			09 04	09 10	09 13			09 30		09 36 →		09 33	09 36		09 39			
Adderley Park	d																					09 44			
Stechford	d											09 20										09 47			
Lea Hall	d											09 23										09 50			
Marston Green	d						09 01					09 26							09 41						
Birmingham International ✈	a					08 59	09 05			09 13	09 19	09 29			09 38				09 45	09 50		09 54			
	d					09 00	09 05			09 14	09 20	09 29			09 39				09 45						
Hampton-in-Arden	d											09 32							09 48						
Berkswell	d						09 11					09 37													
Tile Hill	d						09 14					09 40							09 55						
Canley	d						09 17					09 44													
Coventry	a					09 10	09 20			09 24	09 30	09 47			09 49				10 00						
	d					09 11	09 21				09 31				09 51				10 01						
Rugby	d				09 20	09 23	09 33												10 13						
Long Buckby	d			←			09 43												10 23						
Northampton	a			09 34	09 41		09 54												10 34						
																			→						
London Euston 15	⊖ a			10 48		10 14					10 34				10 54										

For general notes see front of timetable
For details of catering facilities see Directory of Train Operators

- **A** From Shrewsbury (Table 74)
- **B** To Walsall (Table 70)
- **C** From Crewe (Table 67)
- **D** From Nottingham (Table 57)
- **E** From Liverpool Lime Street (Table 91)
- **G** From 12 September
- **H** Until 5 September
- **J** From Holyhead (Table 81)

Table 68

Saturdays

Stafford → Wolverhampton → Birmingham → Coventry → Northampton

Network Diagram - see first page of Table 67

		LM	LM	VT	LM	VT	LM	XC		VT	LM	LM	LM	VT	AW	XC	LM	AW	LM	LM	LM	LM	LM		VT
		1 ◇	1 ◇	1 ◇	1	1 ◇		1 ◇		1 ◇	1		1 ◇	1 ◇	◇	1 ◇	1	◇			1 ◇	1 ◇	1 ◇		1 ◇
												A	B							A	B				
				☕		☕		🛒		☕				☕	🛒	🛒		🛒							☕
Stafford	d		09 21					09 25					09 43								10 10		10 21		
Penkridge	d																				10 16				
Wolverhampton 7	a							09 39					09 56								10 27				
	d					09 32	09 36	09 41		09 45		09 49	09 57		10 09	10 15				10 19	10 28				
Coseley	d											09 54	10 03							10 24					
Tipton	d											09 56								10 26					
Dudley Port	d											09 58								10 28					
Sandwell & Dudley	d						09 46			09 56		10 02								10 32					
Smethwick Galton Bdg L.L. 7	d											10 04			10 20					10 34	10 40				
Smethwick Rolfe Street	d											10 06								10 36					
Birmingham New Street 12	a					09 55	09 55	09 58		10 05		10 14	10 17		10 26	10 31		←		10 44	10 47				
	d			09 50	09 53			10 04		10 10	10 13			10 30	10 36 →		10 33	10 36	10 39						10 50
Adderley Park	d																		10 44						
Stechford	d										10 20								10 47						
Lea Hall	d										10 23								10 50						
Marston Green	d				10 01						10 26						10 41								
Birmingham International ✈	a			09 59	10 05			10 13		10 19	10 29			10 38			10 45	10 50	10 54						10 59
	d			10 00	10 05			10 14		10 20	10 29			10 39			10 45								11 00
Hampton-in-Arden	d										10 32						10 48								
Berkswell	d				10 11						10 37														
Tile Hill	d				10 14						10 40						10 55								
Canley	d				10 17						10 44														
Coventry	a			10 10	10 20			10 24		10 30	10 47			10 49			11 00								11 10
	d			10 11	10 21					10 31				10 51			11 01								11 11
Rugby	d		10 18	10 23	10 33												11 13						11 19		11 23
Long Buckby	d	←			10 43												11 23					←			
Northampton	a	10 34	10 38		10 54												11 34					11 34	11 40		
																	→								
London Euston 15 ⊖	a	11 48		11 14						11 34				11 54								12 48			12 14

		LM	VT	LM	XC	VT	LM	LM	LM	VT	AW	XC	LM	AW	LM			LM	LM	LM	LM	VT	LM	VT	LM
		1	1 ◇		1 ◇	1 ◇	1		1 ◇	1 ◇	◇	1 ◇	1	◇					1 ◇	1 ◇	1 ◇	1 ◇	1	1 ◇	
								A	B		C			C				D	E						
			☕		🛒	☕				☕	🛒	🛒		🛒								☕		☕	
Stafford	d				10 25				10 43										11 10		11 21				
Penkridge	d																		11 16						
Wolverhampton 7	a				10 39				10 56										11 27						
	d		10 32	10 36	10 41	10 45		10 49	10 57		11 09	11 15						11 19	11 28					11 32	11 36
Coseley	d							10 54	11 03									11 24							
Tipton	d							10 56										11 26							
Dudley Port	d							10 58										11 28							
Sandwell & Dudley	d			10 46		10 56		11 02										11 32							11 46
Smethwick Galton Bdg L.L. 7	d							11 04			11 20							11 34	11 40						
Smethwick Rolfe Street	d							11 06										11 36							
Birmingham New Street 12	a		10 55	10 55	10 58	11 05		11 14	11 17		11 26	11 31		←				11 44	11 47					11 55	11 55
	d	10 53			11 04	11 10	11 13			11 30	11 36 →		11 33	11 36	11 39							11 50	11 53		
Adderley Park	d														11 44										
Stechford	d						11 20								11 47										
Lea Hall	d						11 23								11 50										
Marston Green	d	11 01					11 26						11 41										12 01		
Birmingham International ✈	a	11 05			11 13	11 19	11 29			11 38			11 45	11 50	11 54							11 59	12 05		
	d	11 05			11 14	11 20	11 29			11 39			11 45									12 00	12 05		
Hampton-in-Arden	d						11 32						11 48												
Berkswell	d	11 11					11 37																12 11		
Tile Hill	d	11 14					11 40						11 55										12 14		
Canley	d	11 17					11 44																12 17		
Coventry	a	11 20			11 24	11 30	11 48			11 49			12 00									12 10	12 20		
	d	11 21				11 31				11 51			12 01									12 11	12 21		
Rugby	d	11 33											12 13								12 18	12 23	12 33		
Long Buckby	d	11 43											12 23							←			12 43		
Northampton	a	11 54											12 34							12 34	12 38		12 54		
													→												
London Euston 15 ⊖	a					12 34				12 54										13 48		13 14			

For general notes see front of timetable
For details of catering facilities see
Directory of Train Operators

A To Walsall (Table 70)
B From Liverpool Lime Street (Table 91)
C From Holyhead (Table 81)
D To Walsall (Table 70)
E From Liverpool Lime Street (Table 91)

Table 68

Stafford → Wolverhampton → Birmingham → Coventry → Northampton

Network Diagram - see first page of Table 67

		XC	VT	LM	LM	LM	VT	AW		XC	LM	AW	LM	LM	LM	LM	LM	VT	VT	LM	VT	LM	XC		VT
		1 ◇	1 ◇	1		1 ◇	1 ◇	◇		1 ◇	1	◇			1 ◇	1 ◇	1 ◇	1 ◇	1 ◇	1	1 ◇		1 ◇		1 ◇
					A	B								A	B				C		D				
		⊥	⊏				⊏	⊥		⊥		⊥						⊏	⊏		⊏		⊥		⊏
Stafford	d	11 25				11 43									12 10		12 21						12 25		
Penkridge	d														12 16										
Wolverhampton 7	a	11 39				11 56									12 27								12 39		
	d	11 41	11 45		11 49	11 57		12 09		12 15				12 19	12 28				12⟨32		12⟨32	12 36	12 41		12 45
Coseley	d				11 54	12 03								12 24											
Tipton	d				11 56									12 26											
Dudley Port	d				11 58									12 28											
Sandwell & Dudley	d		11 56		12 02									12 32								12 46			12 56
Smethwick Galton Bdg L.L. 7	d				12 04			12 20						12 34	12 40										
Smethwick Rolfe Street	d				12 06									12 36											
Birmingham New Street 12	a	11 58	12 05		12 14	12 17		12 26		12 31		←		12 44	12 47				12⟨50		12⟨55	12 55	12 58		13 05
	d	12 04	12 10	12 13			12 30	12 36 →			12 33	12 36	12 39					12 50		12 53			13 04		13 10
Adderley Park	d												12 44												
Stechford	d			12 20									12 47												
Lea Hall	d			12 23									12 50												
Marston Green	d			12 26							12 41									13 01					
Birmingham International ✈	a	12 13	12 19	12 29			12 38				12 45	12 50	12 54					12 59		13 05			13 13		13 19
	d	12 14	12 20	12 29			12 39				12 45							13 00		13 05			13 14		13 20
Hampton-in-Arden	d			12 32							12 48														
Berkswell	d			12 37																13 11					
Tile Hill	d			12 40							12 55									13 14					
Canley	d			12 44																13 17					
Coventry	a	12 24	12 30	12 47			12 49				13 00							13 10		13 20			13 24		13 30
	d		12 31				12 51				13 01							13 11		13 21					13 31
Rugby	d										13 13						13 19	13 23		13 33					
Long Buckby	d										13 23					←				13 43					
Northampton	a										13 34 →					13 34	13 40			13 54					
London Euston 15	⊖ a		13 32				13 54									14 48		14 14							14 34

		LM	LM	LM	VT	AW	XC	LM	AW	LM	LM	LM	LM	LM	VT		LM	VT	LM	XC	VT	LM	LM	LM	VT
		1		1 ◇	1 ◇	◇	1 ◇	1	◇			1 ◇	1 ◇	1 ◇	1 ◇		1	1 ◇		1 ◇	1 ◇	1		1 ◇	1 ◇
			A	B		E			E		A	B						D					A	B	
					⊏	⊥	⊥		⊥						⊏			⊏		⊥	⊏				⊏
Stafford	d			12 43								13 10		13 21						13 25				13 43	
Penkridge	d											13 16													
Wolverhampton 7	a			12 56								13 27								13 39				13 56	
	d		12 49	12 57		13 09	13 15				13 19	13 28						13⟨32	13 36	13 41	13 45		13 49	13 57	
Coseley	d		12 54	13 03							13 24												13 54	14 03	
Tipton	d		12 56								13 26												13 56		
Dudley Port	d		12 58								13 28												13 58		
Sandwell & Dudley	d		13 02								13 32								13 46		13 56		14 02		
Smethwick Galton Bdg L.L. 7	d		13 04			13 20					13 34	13 40											14 04		
Smethwick Rolfe Street	d		13 06								13 36												14 06		
Birmingham New Street 12	a		13 14	13 17		13 26	13 31		←		13 44	13 47						13⟨55	13 55	13 58	14 05		14 14	14 17	
	d	13 13			13 30	13 36 →		13 33	13 36	13 39					13 50		13 53			14 04	14 10	14 13			14 30
Adderley Park	d									13 44															
Stechford	d	13 20								13 47												14 20			
Lea Hall	d	13 23								13 50												14 23			
Marston Green	d	13 26						13 41									14 01					14 26			
Birmingham International ✈	a	13 29			13 38			13 45	13 50	13 54					13 59		14 05			14 13	14 19	14 29			14 38
	d	13 29			13 39			13 45							14 00		14 05			14 14	14 20	14 29			14 39
Hampton-in-Arden	d	13 32						13 48														14 32			
Berkswell	d	13 37															14 11					14 37			
Tile Hill	d	13 40						13 55									14 14					14 40			
Canley	d	13 44															14 17					14 44			
Coventry	a	13 47			13 49			14 00							14 10		14 20			14 24	14 30	14 47			14 49
	d				13 51			14 01							14 11		14 21				14 31				14 51
Rugby	d							14 13						14 18	14 23		14 33								
Long Buckby	d							14 23					←				14 43								
Northampton	a							14 34 →					14 34	14 38			14 54								
London Euston 15	⊖ a				14 54								15 48		15 14						15 34				15 54

For general notes see front of timetable
For details of catering facilities see Directory of Train Operators

- **A** To Walsall (Table 70)
- **B** From Liverpool Lime Street (Table 91)
- **C** From 7 November
- **D** Until 31 October
- **E** From Holyhead (Table 81)

Stafford → Wolverhampton → Birmingham → Coventry → Northampton

Network Diagram - see first page of Table 67

		AW	XC	LM	AW	LM	LM	LM		LM	LM	VT	LM	VT	LM	XC	VT	LM	LM	LM	VT	AW	XC		LM
		◇	[1] ◇	[1]	◇			[1] ◇		[1] ◇	[1] ◇	[1] ◇	[1]	[1] ◇		[1] ◇	[1] ◇	[1]		[1] ◇	[1] ◇	◇	[1] ◇		[1]
							A	B						C					A	B		D			
		🛒	🛒		🛒							🍽		🍽		🛒	🍽				🍽	🛒	🛒		
Stafford	d							14 10			14 21					14 25				14 46					
Penkridge	d							14 16																	
Wolverhampton [7] 🚊	a							14 27								14 39				14 59					
	d	14 09	14 15				14 19	14 28						14 32	14 36	14 41	14 45		14 49	14 59		15 09	15 15		
Coseley	d						14 24												14 54	15 05					
Tipton	d						14 26												14 56						
Dudley Port	d						14 28												14 58						
Sandwell & Dudley	d						14 32								14 46		14 56		15 02						
Smethwick Galton Bdg L.L. [7]	d	14 20					14 34	14 40											15 04			15 20			
Smethwick Rolfe Street	d						14 36												15 06						
Birmingham New Street [12]	a	14 26	14 31		←		14 44	14 47						14 55	14 55	14 58	15 05		15 14	15 18		15 26	15 31		
	d	14 36 →		14 33	14 36	14 39						14 50	14 53			15 04	15 10	15 13			15 30	15 36 →			15 33
Adderley Park	d					14 44																			
Stechford	d					14 47												15 20							
Lea Hall	d					14 50												15 23							
Marston Green	d			14 41									15 01					15 26							15 41
Birmingham International ✈	a			14 45	14 50	14 54						14 59	15 05			15 13	15 19	15 29			15 38				15 45
	d			14 45								15 00	15 05			15 14	15 20	15 29			15 39				15 45
Hampton-in-Arden	d			14 48														15 32							15 48
Berkswell	d												15 11					15 37							
Tile Hill	d			14 55									15 14					15 40							15 55
Canley	d												15 17					15 44							
Coventry	a			15 00								15 10	15 20			15 24	15 30	15 47			15 49				16 00
	d			15 01								15 11	15 21				15 31				15 51				16 01
Rugby	d			15 13							15 19	15 23	15 33												16 13
Long Buckby	d			15 23						←			15 43												16 23
Northampton	a			15 34						15 34	15 39		15 54												16 34
				→						⏟	⏟														→
London Euston [15] ⊖	a									16 48		16 14					16 34				16 54				

		AW	LM	LM	LM	LM	LM	VT	VT	LM	VT	LM	XC	VT	LM		LM	LM	VT	AW	XC	LM	AW	LM	LM
		◇			[1] ◇	[1] ◇	[1] ◇	[1] ◇	[1] ◇	[1]	[1] ◇		[1] ◇	[1] ◇	[1]			[1] ◇	[1] ◇	◇	[1] ◇	[1]	◇		
		D		A	B				E		C						A	B							A
		🛒						🍽	🍽		🍽		🛒	🍽					🍽	🛒	🛒		🛒		
Stafford	d				15 10		15 21						15 25					15 43							
Penkridge	d				15 16																				
Wolverhampton [7] 🚊	a				15 27								15 39					15 56							
	d			15 19	15 28				15 32		15 32	15 36	15 41	15 45			15 49	15 57		16 09	16 15				16 19
Coseley	d			15 24													15 54	16 03							16 24
Tipton	d			15 26													15 56								16 26
Dudley Port	d			15 28													15 58								16 28
Sandwell & Dudley	d			15 32								15 46		15 56			16 02								16 32
Smethwick Galton Bdg L.L. [7]	d			15 34	15 40												16 04			16 20					16 34
Smethwick Rolfe Street	d			15 36													16 06								16 36
Birmingham New Street [12]	a	←		15 44	15 47				15 50		15 55	15 55	15 58	16 05			16 14	16 17		16 26	16 31		←		16 44
	d	15 36	15 39					15 50		15 53			16 04	16 10	16 13				16 30	16 36 →		16 33	16 36	16 39	
Adderley Park	d		15 44																					16 44	
Stechford	d		15 47												16 20									16 47	
Lea Hall	d		15 50												16 23									16 50	
Marston Green	d									16 01					16 26							16 41			
Birmingham International ✈	a	15 50	15 54					15 59		16 05			16 13	16 19	16 29				16 38			16 45	16 50	16 54	
	d							16 00		16 05			16 14	16 20	16 29				16 39			16 45			
Hampton-in-Arden	d														16 32							16 48			
Berkswell	d									16 11					16 37										
Tile Hill	d									16 14					16 40							16 55			
Canley	d									16 17					16 44										
Coventry	a							16 10		16 20			16 24	16 30	16 47				16 49			17 00			
	d							16 11		16 21				16 31					16 51			17 01			
Rugby	d						16 18	16 23		16 33												17 13			
Long Buckby	d					←				16 43												17 23			
Northampton	a					16 34	16 38			16 54												17 34			
						⏟	⏟															→			
London Euston [15] ⊖	a					17 49		17 14						17 34					17 54						

For general notes see front of timetable
For details of catering facilities see Directory of Train Operators

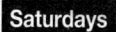

A To Walsall (Table 70)
B From Liverpool Lime Street (Table 91)
C Until 31 October
D From Holyhead (Table 81)
E From 7 November

Table 68

Saturdays

Stafford → Wolverhampton → Birmingham → Coventry → Northampton

Network Diagram - see first page of Table 67

		LM	LM	LM	VT	LM	VT	LM		XC	VT	LM	LM	LM	VT	AW	XC	LM	AW	LM	LM	LM	LM	LM	VT
		1 ◇	1 ◇	1 ◇	1 ◇	1	1 ◇			1 ◇	1 ◇	1		1 ◇	1 ◇	◇	1 ◇	1	◇			1 ◇	1 ◇	1 ◇	1 ◇
		A					B						C	A		D			D		C	A			
					☕		☕			🛒	☕				☕	🛒	🛒		🛒						☕
Stafford	d	16 10		16 21						16 25				16 46								17 10		17 21	
Penkridge	d	16 16																				17 16			
Wolverhampton 7	🚋 a	16 27								16 39				16 59								17 27			
	d	16 28					16 32	16 36		16 41	16 45		16 49	16 59		17 09	17 15				17 19	17 28			
Coseley	d												16 54	17 05							17 24				
Tipton	d												16 56								17 26				
Dudley Port	d												16 58								17 28				
Sandwell & Dudley	d							16 46			16 56		17 02								17 32				
Smethwick Galton Bdg L.L. 7	d	16 40											17 04			17 20					17 34	17 40			
Smethwick Rolfe Street	d												17 06								17 36				
Birmingham New Street 12	a	16 47					16 55	16 55		16 58	17 05		17 14	17 18		17 26	17 31		←		17 44	17 47			
	d				16 50	16 53				17 04	17 10	17 13			17 30	17 36 →		17 33	17 36	17 39					17 50
Adderley Park	d											17 17								17 44					
Stechford	d											17 21								17 47					
Lea Hall	d											17 23								17 50					
Marston Green	d					17 01						17 26						17 41							
Birmingham International	✈ a				16 59	17 05				17 13	17 19	17 29			17 38			17 45	17 50	17 54					17 59
	d				17 00	17 05				17 14	17 20	17 30			17 39			17 45							18 00
Hampton-in-Arden	d											17 33						17 48							
Berkswell	d					17 11						17 38													
Tile Hill	d					17 14						17 41						17 55							
Canley	d					17 17						17 44													
Coventry	a				17 10	17 20				17 24	17 30	17 47			17 49			18 00							18 10
	d				17 11	17 21					17 31				17 51			18 01							18 11
Rugby	d			17 19	17 23	17 33												18 13						18 18	18 23
Long Buckby	d		←			17 43												18 23					←		
Northampton	a		17 34	17 40		17 54												18 34					18 34	18 38	
																		→							
London Euston 15	⊖ a		18 48		18 14						18 34				18 54								19 48		19 14

		VT		LM	VT	LM	XC	VT	LM	LM	LM	VT	AW	XC	LM	AW	LM		LM	LM	LM	VT	LM	VT	LM
		1 ◇		1	1 ◇		1 ◇	1 ◇	1		1 ◇	1 ◇	◇	1 ◇	1	◇				1 ◇	1	1 ◇	1	1 ◇	
		E			B					C	A								C	A				B	
		☕			☕		🛒	☕				☕	🛒	🛒		🛒						☕		☕	
Stafford	d						17 25				17 43									18 10	18 21				
Penkridge	d																			18 16					
Wolverhampton 7	🚋 a						17 39				17 56									18 27					
	d	17 32			17 32	17 36	17 41	17 45		17 49	17 57		18 09	18 15					18 19	18 28				18 32	18 36
Coseley	d									17 54	18 03								18 24						
Tipton	d									17 56									18 26						
Dudley Port	d									17 58									18 28						
Sandwell & Dudley	d					17 46		17 56		18 02									18 32						18 46
Smethwick Galton Bdg L.L. 7	d									18 04			18 20						18 34	18 40					
Smethwick Rolfe Street	d									18 06									18 36						
Birmingham New Street 12	a	17 50			17 55	17 55	17 58	18 05		18 14	18 17		18 26	18 31		←			18 44	18 47				18 55	18 55
	d			17 53			18 04	18 10	18 13			18 30	18 36 →		18 33	18 36	18 39					18 50	18 53		
Adderley Park	d																18 44								
Stechford	d								18 20								18 47								
Lea Hall	d								18 23								18 50								
Marston Green	d			18 01					18 26						18 41								19 01		
Birmingham International	✈ a			18 05			18 13	18 19	18 29			18 38			18 45	18 50	18 54					18 59	19 05		
	d			18 05			18 14	18 20	18 29			18 39			18 45							19 00	19 05		
Hampton-in-Arden	d								18 32						18 48										
Berkswell	d			18 11					18 37														19 11		
Tile Hill	d			18 14					18 40						18 55								19 14		
Canley	d			18 17					18 44														19 17		
Coventry	a			18 20			18 24	18 30	18 47			18 49			19 00							19 10	19 20		
	d			18 21				18 31				18 51			19 01							19 11	19 21		
Rugby	d			18 33											19 13						19 18	19 23	19 33		
Long Buckby	d			18 43											19 23								19 43		
Northampton	a			18 54											19 34						19 38		19 54		
London Euston 15	⊖ a							19 34				19 54										20 17			

For general notes see front of timetable
For details of catering facilities see Directory of Train Operators

A From Liverpool Lime Street (Table 91)
B Until 31 October
C To Walsall (Table 70)
D From Holyhead (Table 81)
E From 7 November

Table 68

Saturdays

Stafford → Wolverhampton → Birmingham → Coventry → Northampton

Network Diagram - see first page of Table 67

		XC	VT	LM	LM	LM	AW	XC	LM	AW		LM	LM	LM	LM	LM	VT	LM	VT	XC	VT	VT	LM	LM	LM
		1 ◇	1 ◇	1		1 ◇	◇	1 ◇	1	◇				1 ◇	1	1	1 ◇		1 ◇	1 ◇	1 ◇	1 ◇	1		1 ◇
						A	B			B			C	A			D		E		G	H			A
		⊤	⊏P				⊤	⊤		⊤							⊏P		⊏P	⊤	⊏P	⊏P			
Stafford	d	18 25				18 43								19 10	19 21					19 25					19 43
Penkridge	d													19 16											19 49
Wolverhampton 7	a	18 39				18 56								19 27						19 39					19 57
	d	18 41	18 45		18 49	18 57	19 09	19 15					19 19	19 28			19 32	19 36	19 32	19 41	19 45	19 45		19 49	19 57
Coseley	d				18 54	19 03							19 24											19 54	20 03
Tipton	d				18 56								19 26											19 56	
Dudley Port	d				18 58								19 28											19 58	
Sandwell & Dudley	d		18 56		19 02								19 32					19 46			19 56	19 56		20 02	
Smethwick Galton Bdg L.L. 7	d				19 04		19 20						19 34	19 40										20 04	
Smethwick Rolfe Street	d				19 06								19 36											20 06	
Birmingham New Street 12	a	18 58	19 05		19 14	19 17	19 26	19 31		⟵			19 44	19 47			19 55	19 55	19 56	19 58	20 05	20 05		20 14	20 17
	d	19 04	19 10	19 13			19 36 ⟶		19 33	19 36		19 39				19 53				20 04	20 10	20 10	20 13		
Adderley Park	d											19 44													
Stechford	d			19 20								19 47											20 20		
Lea Hall	d			19 23								19 50											20 23		
Marston Green	d			19 26					19 41							20 01							20 26		
Birmingham International ✈	a	19 13	19 19	19 29					19 45	19 50		19 54				20 05				20 13	20 19	20 19	20 29		
	d	19 14	19 20	19 29					19 45							20 05				20 14	20 20	20 20	20 29		
Hampton-in-Arden	d			19 32					19 48														20 32		
Berkswell	d			19 37												20 11							20 37		
Tile Hill	d			19 40					19 55							20 14							20 40		
Canley	d			19 44												20 17							20 44		
Coventry	a	19 24	19 30	19 47					20 00							20 20				20 24	20 30	20 30	20 47		
	d		19 31						20 01							20 21					20 31	20 31			
Rugby	d		19 44						20 13						20 18	20 33					20 43	20 43			
Long Buckby	d								20 23							20 43									
Northampton	a								20 34						20 38	20 54									
London Euston 15 ⊖	a		20 56																		22 16	21 57			

		AW	XC		LM	AW	LM	LM	LM	LM	VT	LM	XC	VT	VT	LM	LM	LM		LM	XC	LM	LM	LM	VT
		◇	1 ◇		1	◇			1 ◇	1	1 ◇		1 ◇	1 ◇	1 ◇	1		1 ◇		1	1 ◇			1	1 ◇
									A		D			G	H			A							D
		⊤	⊤			⊤					⊏P		⊤	⊏P	⊏P						⊤				⊏P
Stafford	d								20 12				20 25					20 43							
Penkridge	d																	20 49							
Wolverhampton 7	a								20 28				20 39					20 57							
	d	20 09	20 15					20 19	20 28		20 32	20 36	20 41	20 45	20 45		20 49	20 57			21 15		21 19		21 33
Coseley	d							20 24									20 54	21 03					21 24		
Tipton	d							20 26									20 56						21 26		
Dudley Port	d							20 28									20 58						21 28		
Sandwell & Dudley	d							20 32				20 46		20 56	20 56		21 02						21 32		
Smethwick Galton Bdg L.L. 7	d	20 20						20 34	20 40								21 04						21 34		
Smethwick Rolfe Street	d							20 36									21 06						21 36		
Birmingham New Street 12	a	20 26	20 31			⟵		20 44	20 47		20 56	20 57	20 58	21 05	21 05		21 14	21 17			21 36		21 44		21 55
	d	20 36 ⟶			20 33	20 36	20 39			20 53			21 04	21 10	21 10	21 13				21 33		21 39		21 53	
Adderley Park	d						20 44															21 44			
Stechford	d						20 47									21 20						21 47			
Lea Hall	d						20 50									21 23						21 50			
Marston Green	d				20 41					21 01						21 26				21 41				22 01	
Birmingham International ✈	a				20 45	20 50	20 54			21 05			21 13	21 19	21 19	21 29				21 45		21 54		22 05	
	d				20 45					21 05			21 14	21 20	21 20	21 29				21 45				22 05	
Hampton-in-Arden	d				20 48											21 32				21 48					
Berkswell	d									21 11						21 37								22 11	
Tile Hill	d				20 55					21 14						21 40				21 55				22 14	
Canley	d									21 17						21 44								22 17	
Coventry	a				21 00					21 20			21 24	21 30	21 30	21 47				22 00				22 20	
	d				21 01					21 21				21 31	21 31					22 01				22 21	
Rugby	d				21 13					21 33				21 43	21 43					22 13				22 33	
Long Buckby	d				21 23					21 43										22 23				22 43	
Northampton	a				21 34					21 54										22 34				22 54	
London Euston 15 ⊖	a													23 06	22 55										

For general notes see front of timetable
For details of catering facilities see Directory of Train Operators

A From Liverpool Lime Street (Table 91)
B From Holyhead (Table 81)
C To Walsall (Table 70)
D Until 31 October
E From 7 November
G Until 5 September
H From 12 September

Saturdays

Stafford → Wolverhampton → Birmingham → Coventry → Northampton

Network Diagram - see first page of Table 67

		LM	VT 1◇ A	XC 1◇	VT 1◇ B	VT 1◇ C	LM 1	LM	LM 1◇ D	AW ◇	LM 1	XC 1◇
Stafford	d			21 25					21 41			
Penkridge	d								21 47			
Wolverhampton 7	a			21 39					21 57			
	d	21 36	21 32	21 41	21 45	21 45		21 49	21 57	22 09		22 15
Coseley	d							21 54	22 03			
Tipton	d							21 56				
Dudley Port	d							21 58				
Sandwell & Dudley	d	21 46			21 57	21 57		22 02				
Smethwick Galton Bdg L.L. 7	d							22 04		22 20		
Smethwick Rolfe Street	d							22 06				
Birmingham New Street 12	a	21 55	21 56	22 03	22 06	22 06		22 14	22 19	22 26		22 37
	d				22 10	22 10	22 13				22 33	
Adderley Park	d											
Stechford	d						22 20					
Lea Hall	d						22 23					
Marston Green	d						22 26				22 41	
Birmingham International	a				22 19	22 19	22 29				22 45	
	d				22 20	22 20	22 29				22 45	
Hampton-in-Arden	d						22 32				22 48	
Berkswell	d						22 37					
Tile Hill	d						22 40				22 55	
Canley	d						22 44					
Coventry	a				22 30	22 30	22 47				23 00	
	d				22 31	22 31						
Rugby	d				22 43	22 43						
Long Buckby	d											
Northampton	a											
London Euston 15 ⊖	a				23 57	00 22						

		LM	VT 1◇ E	LM 1	LM	VT 1◇ A	VT 1◇ E	LM 1	LM	XC 1◇	LM 1◇ D	AW ◇
Stafford	d		22 09			22 29	22 29			22 33	22 45	
Penkridge	d										22 51	
Wolverhampton 7	a		22 23			22 42	22 42			22 50	23 01	
	d	22 19	22 24		22 36	22 42	22 42		22 49	22 52	23 01	23 09
Coseley	d	22 24							22 54		23 07	
Tipton	d	22 26							22 56			
Dudley Port	d	22 28							22 58			
Sandwell & Dudley	d	22 32			22 46				23 02			
Smethwick Galton Bdg L.L. 7	d	22 34							23 04			
Smethwick Rolfe Street	d	22 36							23 06			
Birmingham New Street 12	a	22 44	22 47		22 55	23 00	23 01		23 14	23 22	23 20	23 24
	d			22 53				23 13				
Adderley Park	d							23 18				
Stechford	d							23 21				
Lea Hall	d							23 24				
Marston Green	d			23 01				23 27				
Birmingham International	a			23 05				23 30				
	d			23 05				23 30				
Hampton-in-Arden	d							23 33				
Berkswell	d			23 11				23 38				
Tile Hill	d			23 14				23 41				
Canley	d			23 17				23 45				
Coventry	a			23 20				23 48				
	d			23 21								
Rugby	d			23 33								
Long Buckby	d			23 43								
Northampton	a			23 54								
London Euston 15 ⊖	a											

Sundays

until 12 July

		VT 1◇	LM 1	LM 1	LM	XC 1◇	LM (bus)	LM 1	AW G	VT 1◇	LM 1	LM
Stafford	d											
Penkridge	d											
Wolverhampton 7	a											
	d	08 05			08 22				09 00	09 05		09 22
Coseley	d				08 27							09 27
Tipton	d				08 29							09 29
Dudley Port	d				08 31							09 31
Sandwell & Dudley	d	08 15			08 35					09 16		09 35
Smethwick Galton Bdg L.L. 7	d				08 37							09 37
Smethwick Rolfe Street	d				08 39							09 39
Birmingham New Street 12	a	08 24			08 46				09 15	09 24		09 46
	d	08 30	08 34	08 38		09 04		09 14	09 20	09 30	09 34	
Adderley Park	d			08 42							09 38	
Stechford	d			08 46							09 42	
Lea Hall	d			08 48							09 44	
Marston Green	d		08 42	08 52				09 22			09 48	
Birmingham International	a	08 39	08 45	08 55		09 13		09 25	09 31	09 39	09 51	
	d	08 40	08 45			09 14		09 25		09 40	09 51	
Hampton-in-Arden	d							09 28				
Berkswell	d		08 51					09 33				
Tile Hill	d		08 54					09 36				
Canley	d		08 57					09 40				
Coventry	a	08 50	09 00			09 24		09 44		09 50	10 01	
	d	08 51						09 44		09 51		
Rugby	d	09 04					09 27	10a01		10 04		
Long Buckby	d						09 53					
Northampton	a						10 18					
London Euston 15 ⊖	a	10 28								11 31		

		LM (bus)	XC 1◇	LM (bus)	LM 1	AW G	VT 1◇	LM 1	LM	LM (bus)	XC 1◇	LM (bus)
Stafford	d		09 28								10 25	
Penkridge	d											
Wolverhampton 7	a		09 41								10 40	
	d		09 41			09 59	10 05		10 22		10 41	
Coseley	d								10 27			
Tipton	d								10 29			
Dudley Port	d								10 31			
Sandwell & Dudley	d						10 15		10 35			
Smethwick Galton Bdg L.L. 7	d								10 37			
Smethwick Rolfe Street	d								10 39			
Birmingham New Street 12	a		09 58			10 14	10 24		10 46		10 59	
	d		10 04		10 14	10 20	10 30	10 34			11 04	
Adderley Park	d							10 38				
Stechford	d							10 42				
Lea Hall	d							10 44				
Marston Green	d				10 22			10 48				
Birmingham International	a		10 13		10 25	10 32	10 39	10 51			11 13	
	d		10 14		10 25		10 40	10 51			11 14	
Hampton-in-Arden	d				10 28							
Berkswell	d				10 33							
Tile Hill	d				10 36							
Canley	d				10 40							
Coventry	a		10 24		10 44		10 50	11 01			11 24	
	d				10 44		10 51					
Rugby	d	10 10		10 27	11a00		11 04			11 10		11 27
Long Buckby	d	10 36		10 53						11 36		11 53
Northampton	a	11 01		11 18						12 01		12 18
London Euston 15 ⊖	a						12 27					

For general notes see front of timetable
For details of catering facilities see Directory of Train Operators

- **A** From 7 November
- **B** From 12 September
- **C** Until 5 September
- **D** From Liverpool Lime Street (Table 91)
- **E** Until 31 October
- **G** From Shrewsbury (Table 74)

Table 68

Sundays

until 12 July

Stafford → Wolverhampton → Birmingham → Coventry → Northampton

Network Diagram - see first page of Table 67

	LM	AW	LM	VT	LM	LM	LM	VT	XC	VT		LM	VT	LM	VT	LM	AW	LM	LM	VT	VT		LM	XC
	[1]	◇	[1] ◇	[1] ◇	[1]		bus	[1] ◇	[1] ◇	[1] ◇		bus	[1] ◇	[1]	[1] ◇	[1]	◇		bus	[1] ◇	[1] ◇		bus	[1] ◇
				☕				☕	🛒	☕			☕		☕		🛒			☕	☕			🛒
Stafford d			10 45						11 25															12 25
Penkridge d			10 51																					
Wolverhampton [7] a			11 01						11 37															12 40
d		10 58	11 01	11 05		11 22			11 41	11 41			11 45				12 18	12 22			12 34			12 41
Coseley d						11 27												12 27						
Tipton d						11 29												12 29						
Dudley Port d						11 31												12 31						
Sandwell & Dudley d				11 15		11 35							11 57					12 35						
Smethwick Galton Bdg L.L. [7] d						11 37												12 37						
Smethwick Rolfe Street d						11 39												12 39						
Birmingham New Street [12] a		11 14	11 18	11 26		11 46			11 58	12 05			12 06				12 34	12 46			12 55			12 58
d	11 14	11 20		11 30	11 34			11 50	12 04				12 10	12 14	12 30	12 34	12 38			12 50				13 04
Adderley Park d					11 38											12 38								
Stechford d					11 42											12 42								
Lea Hall d					11 44											12 44								
Marston Green d	11 22				11 48									12 22		12 48								
Birmingham International ✈ a	11 25	11 32		11 39	11 51			11 59	12 13				12 19	12 25	12 38	12 51	12 56			12 59				13 13
d	11 25			11 40	11 51			12 00	12 14				12 20	12 25	12 39	12 51				13 01				13 14
Hampton-in-Arden d	11 28													12 28										
Berkswell d	11 33													12 33										
Tile Hill d	11 36													12 36		12 58								
Canley d	11 40													12 40										
Coventry a	11 44			11 50	12 01			12 10	12 24				12 30	12 44	12 49	13 04				13 11				13 24
d	11 44			11 51				12 11					12 31	12 44	12 51					13 11				
Rugby d	12a00			12 05			12 10	12 25				12 27		13a00					13 10	13 26			13 27	
Long Buckby d							12 36					12 53							13 36				13 53	
Northampton a							13 01					13 18							14 01				14 18	
London Euston [15] ⊖ a				13 04				13 19					13 39		13 59					14 20				

	VT	LM	LM	VT	LM	AW	LM	LM	VT	VT		XC	VT	LM	LM	LM	VT	LM	AW	XC	LM		AW	LM
	[1] ◇	[1]	[1] ◇	[1] ◇	[1]	◇		bus	[1] ◇	[1] ◇		[1] ◇	[1] ◇	bus	[1]	[1] ◇	[1] ◇	bus	◇	[1] ◇	[1]		◇	
	☕			☕		🛒			☕	☕		🛒	☕				☕		🛒	🛒			🛒	
Stafford d			12 42									13 25				13 43								
Penkridge d			12 49													13 49								
Wolverhampton [7] a			12 59									13 40				13 58								
d	12 45		12 59			13 09	13 22			13 32		13 41	13 45			13 58			14 09	14 15				14 22
Coseley d							13 27																	14 27
Tipton d							13 29																	14 29
Dudley Port d							13 31																	14 31
Sandwell & Dudley d	12 56						13 35						13 56											14 35
Smethwick Galton Bdg L.L. [7] d							13 37																	14 37
Smethwick Rolfe Street d							13 39																	14 39
Birmingham New Street [12] a	13 05		13 16			13 24	13 46			13 55		13 58	14 05			14 15			14 24	14 31			←	14 46
d	13 10	13 14		13 30	13 34	13 37			13 50			14 04	14 10		14 14		14 30		14 37 →		14 34		14 37	
Adderley Park d					13 38																14 38			
Stechford d					13 42																14 42			
Lea Hall d					13 44																14 44			
Marston Green d		13 22			13 48										14 22						14 48			
Birmingham International ✈ a	13 19	13 25		13 38	13 51	13 56			13 59			14 13	14 19		14 25		14 38				14 51		14 56	
d	13 20	13 25		13 39	13 51				14 01			14 14	14 20		14 25		14 39				14 51			
Hampton-in-Arden d		13 28													14 28									
Berkswell d		13 33													14 33									
Tile Hill d		13 36			13 58										14 36						14 58			
Canley d		13 40													14 40									
Coventry a	13 30	13 44		13 49	14 05				14 11			14 24	14 30		14 44		14 49				15 04			
d	13 31	13 44		13 51					14 11				14 31		14 44		14 51							
Rugby d		14a00						14 10	14 26					14 27	15a00			15 10						
Long Buckby d								14 36						14 53				15 36						
Northampton a								15 01						15 18				16 01						
London Euston [15] ⊖ a	14 35			14 59					15 20				15 36				15 59							

For general notes see front of timetable
For details of catering facilities see
Directory of Train Operators

Stafford → Wolverhampton → Birmingham → Coventry → Northampton

Sundays

until 12 July

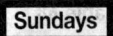

Network Diagram - see first page of Table 67

		VT	LM	VT	XC	VT	LM	LM	VT	AW	XC		LM	AW	LM	LM	VT	LM	VT	XC	VT	LM		LM	LM
		1 ◇	🚌	1 ◇	1 ◇	1 ◇	1	1 ◇	1 ◇	◇	1 ◇		1	◇		🚌	1 ◇	🚌	1 ◇	1 ◇	1 ◇	1		🚌	1 ◇
		🍽		🍽	🛒	🍽			🍽	🛒	🛒			🛒			🍽		🍽	🛒	🍽				
Stafford	d				14 25			14 43												15 25					15 43
Penkridge	d							14 49																	15 49
Wolverhampton 7	a				14 40			14 58												15 40					15 58
	d			14 34	14 41	14 45		14 58		15 09	15 15				15 22				15 32	15 41	15 45				15 58
Coseley	d														15 27										
Tipton	d														15 29										
Dudley Port	d														15 31										
Sandwell & Dudley	d					14 56									15 35						15 56				
Smethwick Galton Bdg L.L. 7	d														15 37										
Smethwick Rolfe Street	d														15 39										
Birmingham New Street 12	a			14 55	14 58	15 05		15 15		15 24	15 31			←	15 46				15 55	15 58	16 05				16 15
	d	14 50			15 04	15 10	15 14		15 30	15 37 →			15 34	15 37			15 50			16 04	16 10	16 14			
Adderley Park	d												15 38												
Stechford	d												15 42												
Lea Hall	d												15 44												
Marston Green	d						15 22						15 48									16 22			
Birmingham International ✈	a	14 59			15 13	15 19	15 25		15 38				15 51	15 56			15 59			16 13	16 19	16 25			
	d	15 01			15 14	15 20	15 25		15 39				15 51				16 01			16 14	16 20	16 25			
Hampton-in-Arden	d						15 28															16 28			
Berkswell	d						15 33															16 33			
Tile Hill	d						15 36						15 58									16 36			
Canley	d						15 40															16 40			
Coventry	a	15 11			15 24	15 30	15 44		15 49				16 05				16 11			16 24	16 30	16 44			
	d	15 11				15 31	15 44		15 51								16 11				16 31	16 44			
Rugby	d	15 26	15 27				16a00									16 10	16 24	16 27				17a00		17 10	
Long Buckby	d		15 53													16 36		16 53						17 36	
Northampton	a		16 18													17 01		17 18						18 01	
London Euston 15 ⊖	a	16 20				16 36			16 59								17 19				17 36				

		VT	AW	XC	LM	AW	LM	VT	LM	VT	XC		VT	LM	LM	LM	VT	XC	LM	AW	LM	VT		LM	VT
		1 ◇		1 ◇	1			1 ◇	🚌	1 ◇	1 ◇		1 ◇	1	🚌	1 ◇	1 ◇	1 ◇	1	◇		1 ◇		🚌	1 ◇
		🍽	🛒	🛒		🛒		🍽		🍽	🛒		🍽				🍽	🛒		🛒		🍽			🍽
Stafford	d										16 25					16 43									
Penkridge	d															16 49									
Wolverhampton 7	a										16 40					16 58									
	d		16 10	16 15			16 22			16 34	16 41		16 45			16 58		17 15		17 19	17 22				17 32
Coseley	d						16 27														17 27				
Tipton	d						16 29														17 29				
Dudley Port	d						16 31														17 31				
Sandwell & Dudley	d						16 35						16 56								17 35				
Smethwick Galton Bdg L.L. 7	d						16 37														17 37				
Smethwick Rolfe Street	d						16 39														17 39				
Birmingham New Street 12	a		16 26	16 31		←	16 46			16 55	16 58		17 05			17 15		17 31		17 35	17 46				17 55
	d	16 30	16 36 →		16 34	16 36		16 50			17 04		17 10	17 14			17 30		17 34	17 38		17 50			
Adderley Park	d				16 38														17 38						
Stechford	d				16 42														17 42						
Lea Hall	d				16 44														17 44						
Marston Green	d				16 48									17 22					17 48						
Birmingham International ✈	a	16 38			16 51	16 56		16 59			17 13		17 19	17 25			17 38		17 51	17 56		17 59			
	d	16 39			16 51			17 01			17 14		17 20	17 25			17 39		17 51			18 01			
Hampton-in-Arden	d													17 28											
Berkswell	d													17 33											
Tile Hill	d				16 58									17 36					17 58						
Canley	d													17 40											
Coventry	a	16 49			17 05			17 11			17 24		17 30	17 44			17 49		18 05			18 11			
	d	16 51						17 11					17 31	17 44			17 51					18 11			
Rugby	d							17 26	17 27					18a00	18 10							18 26		18 27	
Long Buckby	d								17 53						18 36									18 53	
Northampton	a								18 18						19 01									19 18	
London Euston 15 ⊖	a	17 59						18 20					18 36				18 59					19 20			

For general notes see front of timetable
For details of catering facilities see
Directory of Train Operators

Stafford → Wolverhampton → Birmingham → Coventry → Northampton

Sundays

until 12 July

Network Diagram - see first page of Table 67

		XC	VT	LM	LM	LM	VT	AW	XC	LM	AW	LM	VT	LM	VT	XC	VT	LM	LM	LM	VT	AW	XC
		1 ◇	1 ◇	1		1 ◇	1 ◇	◇	1 ◇	1	◇		1 ◇		1 ◇	1 ◇	1 ◇	1		1 ◇	1 ◇	◇	1 ◇
		⊼	☕		🚌		☕	⊼	⊼		⊼		☕	🚌	☕	⊼	☕		🚌		☕		⊼
Stafford	d	17 25				17 43										18 25				18 43			
Penkridge	d					17 49														18 49			
Wolverhampton 7	a	17 40				17 58										18 40				18 58			
	d	17 41	17 45			17 58		18 10	18 15			18 22			18 32	18 41	18 45			18 58		19 09	19 15
Coseley	d											18 27											
Tipton	d											18 29											
Dudley Port	d											18 31											
Sandwell & Dudley	d		17 56									18 35					18 56						
Smethwick Galton Bdg L.L. 7	d											18 37											
Smethwick Rolfe Street	d											18 39											
Birmingham New Street 12	a	17 58	18 05			18 15		18 28	18 31		←	18 46			18 55	18 58	19 05			19 15		19 24	19 31
	d	18 04	18 10	18 14			18 30	18 37 →		18 34	18 37		18 50			19 04	19 10	19 14			19 30	19 37 →	
Adderley Park	d									18 38													
Stechford	d									18 42													
Lea Hall	d									18 44													
Marston Green	d			18 22						18 48								19 22					
Birmingham International ✈	a	18 13	18 19	18 25			18 38			18 51	18 56		18 59			19 13	19 19	19 25			19 38		
	d	18 14	18 20	18 25			18 39			18 51			19 01			19 14	19 20	19 25			19 39		
Hampton-in-Arden	d			18 28														19 28					
Berkswell	d			18 33														19 33					
Tile Hill	d			18 36						18 58								19 36					
Canley	d			18 40														19 40					
Coventry	a	18 24	18 30	18 44			18 49			19 05			19 11			19 24	19 30	19 44			19 49		
	d		18 31	18 44			18 51						19 11				19 31	19 44			19 51		
Rugby	d			19a00	19 10								19 26	19 27				20a00	20 10				
Long Buckby	d				19 36									19 53					20 36				
Northampton	a				20 01									20 18					21 01				
London Euston 15 ⊖	a		19 36				19 59						20 20				20 36				21 02		

		LM	AW	LM	VT	LM	XC	VT	LM	LM	VT	LM	AW	XC	LM	AW	LM	VT	LM	XC	LM	LM	VT
		1	◇		1 ◇		1 ◇	1 ◇	1	1 ◇	1 ◇		◇	1 ◇	1	◇		1 ◇		1 ◇	1	1 ◇	1 ◇
					☕	🚌	⊼	☕			☕	🚌	⊼	⊼		⊼		☕	🚌	⊼			☕
Stafford	d						19 25			19 43										20 25		20 38	
Penkridge	d									19 49												20 45	
Wolverhampton 7	a						19 40			19 58										20 39		20 55	
	d			19 22	19 32		19 41	19 45		19 58			20 09	20 15			20 22	20 34		20 41		20 58	21 05
Coseley	d			19 27													20 27						
Tipton	d			19 29													20 29						
Dudley Port	d			19 31													20 31						
Sandwell & Dudley	d			19 35				19 56									20 35						21 15
Smethwick Galton Bdg L.L. 7	d			19 37													20 37						
Smethwick Rolfe Street	d			19 39													20 39						
Birmingham New Street 12	a		←	19 46	19 55		19 58	20 05		20 15			20 24	20 31		←	20 47	20 57		20 58		21 15	21 25
	d	19 34	19 37				20 04	20 10	20 14		20 30		20 37 →		20 34	20 37				21 04	21 14		21 30
Adderley Park	d	19 38													20 38								
Stechford	d	19 42													20 42								
Lea Hall	d	19 44													20 44								
Marston Green	d	19 48							20 22						20 48						21 22		
Birmingham International ✈	a	19 51	19 56				20 13	20 19	20 25		20 39				20 51	20 56				21 13	21 25		21 39
	d	19 51					20 14	20 20	20 25		20 40				20 51					21 14	21 25		21 40
Hampton-in-Arden	d								20 28												21 28		
Berkswell	d								20 33												21 33		
Tile Hill	d	19 58							20 36						20 58						21 36		
Canley	d								20 40												21 40		
Coventry	a	20 05					20 24	20 30	20 44		20 50				21 04					21 23	21 44		21 50
	d							20 31	20 44		20 51										21 44		21 51
Rugby	d					20 27			21a00		21 05	21 10							21 27		21a57		22 05
Long Buckby	d					20 53						21 36							21 53				
Northampton	a					21 18						22 01							22 18				
London Euston 15 ⊖	a							21 54			22 24												23 18

For general notes see front of timetable
For details of catering facilities see
Directory of Train Operators

Table 68

Sundays
until 12 July

Stafford → Wolverhampton → Birmingham → Coventry → Northampton

Network Diagram - see first page of Table 67

		LM	LM 1	AW ◇	XC 1 ◇	LM	AW ◇ A	LM 1	LM 1 ◇	VT 1 ◇	LM		LM 1	AW ◇	VT 1 ◇	XC 1 ◇	LM	VT 1 ◇	VT 1 ◇	LM 1	LM 1	XC 1 ◇			
		🚌			🛒					🍴	🚌			🛒	🍴	🛒		🍴	🍴			🛒			
Stafford	d				21 08		21 16		21 38						22 02	22 06					22 44	23 06			
Penkridge	d								21 45												22 51				
Wolverhampton 7	a				21 21		21 34		21 55						22 17	22 20					23 00	23 18			
	d			21 12	21 22	21 25	21 35		21 58	22 05				22 09	22 18	22 22	22 25	22 32	22 37		23 00	23 19			
Coseley	d					21 30											22 30								
Tipton	d					21 32											22 32								
Dudley Port	d					21 34											22 34								
Sandwell & Dudley	d					21 38				22 15							22 38		22 47						
Smethwick Galton Bdg L.L. 7	d					21 40											22 40								
Smethwick Rolfe Street	d					21 42											22 42								
Birmingham New Street 12	a			21 28	21 39	21 49	21 52		22 15	22 24				22 28	22 40	22 45	22 49	22 55	22 56		23 17	23 41			
	d		21 34	21 37			21 55	22 14		22 30			22 34	22 41					23 00	23 14					
Adderley Park	d		21 38										22 38							23 19					
Stechford	d		21 42										22 42							23 22					
Lea Hall	d		21 44										22 45							23 25					
Marston Green	d		21 48					22 22					22 48							23 28					
Birmingham International ✈	a		21 51	21 56			22 08	22 25		22 39			22 51	22 55					23 09	23 31					
	d		21 51					22 25		22 40			22 52						23 10	23 32					
Hampton-in-Arden	d							22 28												23 35					
Berkswell	d							22 33												23 40					
Tile Hill	d							22 36												23 43					
Canley	d							22 40												23 46					
Coventry	a		22 01					22 44		22 50			23 01						23 20	23 50					
	d							22 44		22 51									23 21						
Rugby	d	22 10						22a57		23 05	23 10								23 35						
Long Buckby	d	22 36									23 36														
Northampton	a	23 01									00 01														
London Euston 15 ⊖	a									00 22									01 02						

Sundays
from 19 July

		VT 1 ◇	LM 1	LM 1	LM	XC 1 ◇	LM 1	AW	VT 1 ◇		LM 1	LM	XC 1 ◇	XC 1 ◇	LM 1	AW	VT 1 ◇	LM 1		LM	XC 1 ◇	XC 1 ◇	LM 1	AW ◇	LM 1 ◇
		🍴				🛒			🍴				🛒	🛒			🍴				🛒	🛒			
Stafford	d												09 25	09 28							10 25	10 27			10 42
Penkridge	d																								10 49
Wolverhampton 7	a												09 40	09 40							10 40	10 40			11 00
	d	08 05			08 22			09 00	09 05			09 22	09 41	09 41		09 59	10 05			10 22	10 41	10 41		10 58	11 01
Coseley	d				08 27							09 27								10 27					
Tipton	d				08 29							09 29								10 29					
Dudley Port	d				08 31							09 31								10 31					
Sandwell & Dudley	d	08 15			08 35				09 16			09 35					10 15			10 35					
Smethwick Galton Bdg L.L. 7	d				08 37							09 37								10 37					
Smethwick Rolfe Street	d				08 39							09 39								10 39					
Birmingham New Street 12	a	08 24			08 46			09 15	09 24			09 46	09 58	09 58		10 14	10 24			10 46	10 58	10 58		11 14	11 17
	d	08 30	08 34	08 38		09 04	09 14	09 20	09 30		09 34		10 04	10 04	10 14	10 20	10 30	10 34			11 04	11 04	11 14	11 20	
Adderley Park	d			08 42							09 38							10 38							
Stechford	d			08 46							09 42							10 42							
Lea Hall	d			08 48							09 44							10 44							
Marston Green	d		08 42	08 52			09 22				09 48				10 22			10 48					11 22		
Birmingham International ✈	a	08 39	08 45	08 55		09 13	09 25	09 31	09 39		09 51		10 13	10 13	10 25	10 32	10 39	10 51			11 13	11 13	11 25	11 32	
	d	08 40	08 45			09 14	09 25		09 40		09 51		10 14	10 14	10 25		10 40	10 51			11 14	11 14	11 25		
Hampton-in-Arden	d						09 28								10 28								11 28		
Berkswell	d		08 51				09 33								10 33								11 33		
Tile Hill	d		08 54				09 36								10 36								11 36		
Canley	d		08 57				09 40								10 40								11 40		
Coventry	a	08 50	09 00			09 24	09 44		09 50		10 01		10 24	10 24	10 44		10 50	11 01			11 24	11 24	11 44		
	d	08 51					09 44		09 51						10 44		10 51						11 44		
Rugby	d	09 04					09 56		10 04						10 56		11 04						11 56		
Long Buckby	d						10 06								11 06								12 06		
Northampton	a						10 17								11 17								12 17		
London Euston 15 ⊖	a	10 28							11 31								12 27								

For general notes see front of timetable
For details of catering facilities see
Directory of Train Operators

A From Holyhead (Table 81)

Table 68

Sundays

Stafford → Wolverhampton → Birmingham → Coventry → Northampton

from 19 July

Network Diagram - see first page of Table 67

		LM	VT	LM	LM		VT	VT	XC	XC	VT	VT	LM	LM		VT	LM	AW	AW	LM		VT	VT		LM
		1 ◇	1 ◇	1			1 ◇	1 ◇	1 ◇	1 ◇	1 ◇	1 ◇	1	1		1 ◇	1	◇	◇			1 ◇	1 ◇		1 ◇
			☕				☕	☕	🍴	🍴	☕	☕				☕		🍴	🍴			☕	☕		
Stafford	d	10 45							11 25	11 25															12 18
Penkridge	d	10 51																							
Wolverhampton 7	a	11 01							11 38	11 40															
	d	11 01	11 05		11 22			11 32	11 41	11 41	11 42	11 45						12 18	12 18	12 22			12 34		
Coseley	d				11 27															12 27					
Tipton	d				11 29															12 29					
Dudley Port	d				11 31															12 31					
Sandwell & Dudley	d		11 15		11 35							11 57								12 35					
Smethwick Galton Bdg L.L. 7	d				11 37															12 37					
Smethwick Rolfe Street	d				11 39															12 39					
Birmingham New Street 12	a	11 18	11 26		11 46			11 55	11 58	11 58	12 05	12 06						12 33	12 34	12 46			12 55		
	d		11 30	11 34			11 50		12 04	12 04		12 10		12 14		12 30	12 34	12 38	12 38			12 50			
Adderley Park	d			11 38													12 38								
Stechford	d			11 42													12 42								
Lea Hall	d			11 44													12 44								
Marston Green	d			11 48										12 22			12 48								
Birmingham International ✈	a		11 39	11 51			11 59		12 13	12 13		12 19		12 25		12 38	12 51	12 56	12 56			12 59			
	d		11 40	11 51			12 00		12 14	12 14		12 20		12 25		12 39	12 51					13 01			
Hampton-in-Arden	d													12 28											
Berkswell	d													12 33											
Tile Hill	d													12 36			12 58								
Canley	d													12 40											
Coventry	a		11 50	12 01			12 10		12 24	12 24		12 30		12 44		12 49	13 04					13 11			
	d		11 51				12 11					12 31		12 44		12 51						13 11			
Rugby	d		12 05				12 25						12 26	12 56								13 26			13 17
Long Buckby	d												12 37	13 06											13 28
Northampton	a												12 48	13 17											13 39
London Euston 15 ⊖	a		13 04				13 19					13 39	13 53			13 59						14 20			14 53

		XC	VT	VT	LM	LM	VT	LM	AW		LM	VT	VT	XC	VT	LM	LM	LM		VT	LM	AW	XC	LM	AW
		1 ◇	1 ◇	1 ◇	1	1 ◇	1 ◇	1	◇			1 ◇	1 ◇	1 ◇	1 ◇	1	1	1 ◇		1 ◇	1 ◇	◇	1 ◇	1	◇
		🍴	☕	☕			☕		🍴			☕	☕	🍴	☕					☕		🍴	🍴		🍴
Stafford	d	12 25				12 42								13 25				13 43			14 19				
Penkridge	d					12 49												13 49							
Wolverhampton 7	a	12 40				12 59								13 40				13 58							
	d	12 41	12 45	12 45		12 59			13 09		13 22		13 32	13 41	13 45			13 58				14 09	14 15		
Coseley	d										13 27														
Tipton	d										13 29														
Dudley Port	d										13 31														
Sandwell & Dudley	d		12 56	12 55							13 35				13 56										
Smethwick Galton Bdg L.L. 7	d										13 37														
Smethwick Rolfe Street	d										13 39														
Birmingham New Street 12	a	12 58	13 05	13 06		13 16			13 24		13 46		13 55	13 58	14 05			14 15				14 24	14 31		←
	d	13 04	13 10	13 10	13 14		13 30	13 34	13 37			13 50		14 04	14 10		14 14			14 30		14 37 →		14 34	14 37
Adderley Park	d							13 38																14 38	
Stechford	d							13 42																14 42	
Lea Hall	d							13 44																14 44	
Marston Green	d				13 22			13 48									14 22							14 48	
Birmingham International ✈	a	13 13	13 19	13 19	13 25		13 38	13 51	13 56			13 59		14 13	14 19		14 25			14 38				14 51	14 56
	d	13 14	13 20	13 20	13 25		13 39	13 51				14 01		14 14	14 20		14 25			14 39				14 51	
Hampton-in-Arden	d				13 28												14 28								
Berkswell	d				13 33												14 33								
Tile Hill	d				13 36			13 58									14 36							14 58	
Canley	d				13 40												14 40								
Coventry	a	13 24	13 30	13 30	13 44		13 49	14 05				14 11		14 24	14 30		14 44			14 49				15 04	
	d		13 31	13 31	13 44		13 51					14 11			14 31		14 44			14 51					
Rugby	d				13 56							14 26				14 26	14 56				15 17				
Long Buckby	d				14 06											14 37	15 06				15 28				
Northampton	a				14 17											14 48	15 17				15 39				
London Euston 15 ⊖	a		14 35	14 36			14 59					15 20			15 36	15 53				15 59	16 53				

		LM	VT	VT	VT		XC	VT	LM	LM	VT	AW	XC	LM		AW	LM	VT	LM	VT	XC	VT	LM		LM
			1 ◇	1 ◇	1 ◇		1 ◇	1 ◇	1	1 ◇	1 ◇	◇	1 ◇	1		◇		1 ◇	1	1 ◇	1 ◇	1 ◇	1		1 ◇
			☕	☕	☕		🍴	☕			☕	🍴	🍴			🍴		☕		☕	🍴	☕			
Stafford	d						14 25			14 43											15 25				15 43
Penkridge	d									14 49															15 49
Wolverhampton 7	a						14 40			14 58											15 40				15 58
	d	14 22		14 33	14 34		14 41	14 45		14 58		15 09	15 15				15 22			15 32	15 41	15 45			15 58
Coseley	d	14 27															15 27								
Tipton	d	14 29															15 29								
Dudley Port	d	14 31															15 31								
Sandwell & Dudley	d	14 35						14 56									15 35					15 56			
Smethwick Galton Bdg L.L. 7	d	14 37															15 37								
Smethwick Rolfe Street	d	14 39															15 39								
Birmingham New Street 12	a	14 46		14 55	14 55		14 58	15 05		15 15		15 24	15 31			←	15 46			15 55	15 58	16 05			16 15
	d		14 50				15 04	15 10	15 14		15 30	15 37 →		15 34		15 37		15 50			16 04	16 10	16 14		
Adderley Park	d													15 38											
Stechford	d													15 42											
Lea Hall	d													15 44											
Marston Green	d								15 22					15 48									16 22		
Birmingham International ✈	a		14 59				15 13	15 19	15 25		15 38			15 51		15 56		15 59			16 13	16 19	16 25		
	d		15 01				15 14	15 20	15 25		15 39			15 51				16 01			16 14	16 20	16 25		
Hampton-in-Arden	d								15 28														16 28		
Berkswell	d								15 33														16 33		
Tile Hill	d								15 36					15 58									16 36		
Canley	d								15 40														16 40		
Coventry	a		15 11				15 24	15 30	15 44		15 49			16 05				16 11			16 24	16 30	16 44		
	d		15 11					15 31	15 44		15 51							16 11				16 31	16 44		
Rugby	d		15 26						15 56									16 24	16 25				16 56		
Long Buckby	d								16 06										16 37				17 06		
Northampton	a								16 17										16 48				17 17		
London Euston 15 ⊖	a		16 20					16 36			16 59							17 19	17 53			17 36			

For general notes see front of timetable
For details of catering facilities see
Directory of Train Operators

Stafford → Wolverhampton → Birmingham → Coventry → Northampton

Network Diagram - see first page of Table 67

Station		VT	LM	AW	XC	LM	AW	LM	VT	VT	XC	VT	LM	LM	VT	XC	LM	AW	LM	LM	VT	VT	XC
		1 ◇	1 ◇		1 ◇	1			1 ◇	1 ◇	1 ◇	1 ◇	1	1 ◇	1 ◇	1 ◇	1	◇		1	1 ◇	1 ◇	1 ◇
Stafford	d		16 18								16 25			16 43									17 25
Penkridge	d													16 49									
Wolverhampton 7	a										16 40			16 58									17 40
	d			16 10	16 15			16 22		16 34	16 41	16 45		16 58		17 15		17 19	17 22			17 32	17 41
Coseley	d							16 27											17 27				
Tipton	d							16 29											17 29				
Dudley Port	d							16 31											17 31				
Sandwell & Dudley	d							16 35				16 56							17 35				
Smethwick Galton Bdg L.L. 7	d							16 37											17 37				
Smethwick Rolfe Street	d							16 39											17 39				
Birmingham New Street 12	a			16 26	16 31		←	16 46		16 55	16 58	17 05		17 15		17 31		17 35	17 46			17 55	17 58
	d	16 30		16 36 →		16 34	16 36		16 50		17 04	17 10	17 14		17 30		17 34	17 38			17 50		18 04
Adderley Park	d					16 38											17 38						
Stechford	d					16 42											17 42						
Lea Hall	d					16 44											17 44						
Marston Green	d					16 48							17 22				17 48						
Birmingham International	a	16 38				16 51	16 56		16 59		17 13	17 19	17 25		17 38		17 51	17 56			17 59		18 13
	d	16 39				16 51			17 01		17 14	17 20	17 25		17 39		17 51				18 01		18 14
Hampton-in-Arden	d												17 28										
Berkswell	d												17 33										
Tile Hill	d					16 58							17 36				17 58						
Canley	d												17 40										
Coventry	a	16 49				17 05			17 11		17 24	17 30	17 44		17 49		18 05				18 11		18 24
	d	16 51							17 11			17 31	17 44		17 51						18 11		
Rugby	d		17 17						17 26				17 56							18 24	18 26		
Long Buckby	d		17 28										18 06							18 37			
Northampton	a		17 39										18 17							18 48			
London Euston 15	⊖ a	17 59	18 53						18 20			18 36			18 59					19 53	19 20		

Station		VT	LM	LM	VT	LM	AW	XC	LM	AW	LM	VT	VT	XC	VT	LM	LM	VT	AW	AW	XC	LM
		1 ◇	1	1 ◇	1 ◇	1 ◇	◇	1 ◇	1	◇		1 ◇	1 ◇	1 ◇	1 ◇	1	1 ◇	1 ◇	◇ A	◇ A	1 ◇	1
Stafford	d			17 43		18 18								18 25			18 43					
Penkridge	d			17 49													18 49					
Wolverhampton 7	a			17 58										18 40			18 58					
	d	17 45		17 58			18 10	18 15			18 22		18 32	18 41	18 45		18 58		19 09	19 09	19 15	
Coseley	d										18 27											
Tipton	d										18 29											
Dudley Port	d										18 31											
Sandwell & Dudley	d	17 56									18 35				18 56							
Smethwick Galton Bdg L.L. 7	d										18 37											
Smethwick Rolfe Street	d										18 39											
Birmingham New Street 12	a	18 05		18 15			18 28	18 31		←	18 46		18 55	18 58	19 05		19 15		19 24	19 28	19 31	
	d	18 10	18 14		18 30		18 37 →		18 34	18 37		18 50		19 04	19 10	19 14		19 30	19 37 →	19 37 →		19 34
Adderley Park	d								18 38													19 38
Stechford	d								18 42													19 42
Lea Hall	d								18 44													19 44
Marston Green	d		18 22						18 48							19 22						19 48
Birmingham International	a	18 19	18 25		18 38				18 51	18 56		18 59		19 13	19 19	19 25		19 38				19 51
	d	18 20	18 25		18 39				18 51			19 01		19 14	19 20	19 25		19 39				19 51
Hampton-in-Arden	d		18 28													19 28						
Berkswell	d		18 33													19 33						
Tile Hill	d		18 36						18 58							19 36						19 58
Canley	d		18 40													19 40						
Coventry	a	18 30	18 44		18 49				19 05			19 11		19 24	19 30	19 44		19 49				20 05
	d	18 31	18 44		18 51							19 11			19 31	19 44		19 51				
Rugby	d		18 56			19 17						19 26				19 56						
Long Buckby	d		19 06			19 28										20 06						
Northampton	a		19 17			19 39										20 17						
London Euston 15	⊖ a	19 36			19 59	20 52						20 20			20 36			21 02				

Station		AW	AW	LM	VT	LM	XC	VT	LM	LM	VT	LM	AW	XC	LM	AW	LM	VT	XC	LM	LM	VT	VT
		◇ A	◇ A		1 ◇	1	1 ◇	1 ◇	1	1 ◇	1 ◇	1 ◇	◇	1 ◇	1	◇		1 ◇	1 ◇	1	1 ◇	1 ◇	1 ◇
Stafford	d						19 25			19 43		20 16							20 25		20 38		
Penkridge	d									19 49											20 45		
Wolverhampton 7	a						19 40			19 58									20 39		20 55		
	d			19 22	19 32		19 41	19 45		19 58			20 09	20 15			20 22	20 34	20 41		20 58	21 05	21 05
Coseley	d			19 27													20 27						
Tipton	d			19 29													20 29						
Dudley Port	d			19 31													20 31						
Sandwell & Dudley	d			19 35				19 56									20 35					21 15	21 15
Smethwick Galton Bdg L.L. 7	d			19 37													20 37						
Smethwick Rolfe Street	d			19 39													20 39						
Birmingham New Street 12	a	←	←	19 46	19 55		19 58	20 05		20 15			20 24	20 31		←	20 47	20 57	20 58		21 15	21 25	21 26
	d	19 37	19 37				20 04	20 10	20 14		20 30		20 37 →		20 34	20 37			21 04	21 14		21 30	21 30
Adderley Park	d														20 38								
Stechford	d														20 42								
Lea Hall	d														20 44								
Marston Green	d								20 22						20 48					21 22			
Birmingham International	a	19 56	19 56				20 13	20 19	20 25		20 39				20 51	20 56			21 13	21 25		21 39	21 39
	d						20 14	20 20	20 25		20 40				20 51				21 14	21 25		21 40	21 40
Hampton-in-Arden	d								20 28											21 28			
Berkswell	d								20 33											21 33			
Tile Hill	d								20 36						20 58					21 36			
Canley	d								20 40											21 40			
Coventry	a						20 24	20 30	20 44		20 50				21 04				21 23	21 44		21 50	21 50
	d							20 31	20 44		20 51									21 44		21 51	21 51
Rugby	d					20 20			20 56		21 05	21 17								21 56		22 04	22 04
Long Buckby	d					20 32			21 06			21 28								22 06			
Northampton	a					20 43			21 17			21 39								22 17			
London Euston 15	⊖ a					21 57		21 54			22 24	23 13										23 29	23 29

For general notes see front of timetable
For details of catering facilities see Directory of Train Operators

A Until 1 November

Table 68

Sundays

from 19 July

Stafford → Wolverhampton → Birmingham → Coventry → Northampton

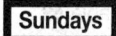

Network Diagram - see first page of Table 67

		LM	AW	AW	XC		LM	AW	LM	LM	VT	LM	AW	VT		XC	LM	VT	VT	LM	LM	XC	XC		
		1	◇	◇	1 ◇			◇	1	1 ◇	1 ◇	1	◇	1 ◇		1 ◇		1 ◇	1 ◇	1	1	1 ◇	1 ◇		
					trolley						first class		trolley	first class		trolley		first class	first class			trolley	trolley		
Stafford	d				21 08			21 16		21 38				22 02		22 07					22 44	23 05	23 06		
Penkridge	d									21 45											22 51				
Wolverhampton 7	a				21 21			21 34		21 55				22 17		22 20					23 00	23 18	23 18		
	d		21 12	21 12	21 22		21 25	21 35		21 58	22 05		22 09	22 18		22 22	22 25	22 32	22 37		23 00	23 19	23 19		
Coseley	d						21 30										22 30								
Tipton	d						21 32										22 32								
Dudley Port	d						21 34										22 34								
Sandwell & Dudley	d						21 38				22 15						22 38		22 47						
Smethwick Galton Bdg L.L. 7	d						21 40										22 40								
Smethwick Rolfe Street	d						21 42										22 42								
Birmingham New Street 12	a		21 28	21 29	21 39		21 49	21 52		22 15	22 24		22 28	22 40		22 45	22 49	22 55	22 56		23 17	23 41	23 41		
	d	21 34	21 37	21 37				21 55	22 14		22 30	22 34	22 41						23 00	23 14					
Adderley Park	d	21 38										22 38								23 19					
Stechford	d	21 42										22 42								23 22					
Lea Hall	d	21 44										22 45								23 25					
Marston Green	d	21 48							22 22			22 48								23 28					
Birmingham International ✈	a	21 51	21 56	21 56				22 08	22 25		22 39	22 51	22 55						23 09	23 31					
	d	21 51							22 25		22 40	22 52							23 10	23 32					
Hampton-in-Arden	d								22 28											23 35					
Berkswell	d								22 33											23 40					
Tile Hill	d								22 36											23 43					
Canley	d								22 40											23 46					
Coventry	a	22 01							22 44		22 50	23 01							23 20	23 50					
	d								22 44		22 51								23 21						
Rugby	d								22 56		23 04								23 35						
Long Buckby	d								23 06																
Northampton	a								23 17										23s54						
London Euston 15 ⊖	a										00 29								01 09						

For general notes see front of timetable
For details of catering facilities see Directory of Train Operators

Lichfield → Birmingham → Longbridge and Redditch

Network Diagram - see first page of Table 67

Miles	Miles			LM	LM	LM	LM	LM	LM	LM	LM	LM	LM	LM	LM	LM	XC	LM	LM	LM	LM		LM	LM	LM	XC
				MO A 🚌													1 ◇ B 🍴									1 ◇ B 🍴
0	—	**Lichfield Trent Valley**	d								06 10		06 22					06 52		07 10			07 22		07 40	
1¼	—	**Lichfield City**	d								06 13		06 25			06 45		06 55		07 15			07 25		07 45	
4¼	—	Shenstone	d								06 18					06 50				07 20					07 50	
6¾	—	Blake Street	d						06 04		06 22		06 33			06 53		07 03		07 24			07 33		07 54	
8½	—	Butlers Lane	d						06 06		06 24		06 35			06 55		07 05		07 26			07 35		07 56	
9½	—	Four Oaks	d						06 09	06 18	06 27		06 38	06 48		06 58		07 08	07 18	07 29			07 38	07 48	07 59	
11	—	Sutton Coldfield	d						06 12	06 21	06 30		06 41	06 51		07 02		07 11	07 21	07 32			07 41	07 51	08 02	
12	—	Wylde Green	d						06 15	06 24	06 33		06 44	06 54		07 04		07 14	07 24	07 35			07 44	07 54	08 05	
12¾	—	Chester Road	d						06 17	06 26	06 35		06 46	06 56		07 06		07 16	07 26	07 37			07 46	07 56	08 07	
13¾	—	Erdington	d						06 18	06 28	06 36		06 47	06 58		07 08		07 17	07 28	07 38			07 47	07 58	08 08	
14½	—	Gravelly Hill	d						06 21	06 30	06 39		06 50	07 00		07 10		07 20	07 30	07 41			07 50	08 00	08 11	
15¾	—	Aston	d						06 24	06 34	06 42		06 53	07 04		07 14		07 23	07 34	07 44			07 53	08 04	08 14	
17	—	Duddeston	d						06 27	06 36	06 45			07 06					07 36	07 47				08 06	08 17	
18½	—	**Birmingham New Street 12**	a						06 31	06 41	06 49		07 00	07 12		07 20		07 30	07 41	07 51			08 01	08 12	08 21	
—	0		d		05 54	06 04	06 14	06 24	06 34	06 44	06 54	06 59	07 04	07 14	07 20	07 24	07 30	07 34	07 44	07 54	07 59		08 04	08 14	08 24	08 30
19½	—	Five Ways	d		05 57	06 07	06 17	06 27	06 37	06 47	06 57		07 07	07 17		07 27		07 37	07 47	07 57			08 07	08 17	08 27	
20	1½	University	d		06 01	06 11	06 21	06 31	06 41	06 51	07 01	07 05	07 11	07 21	07 27	07 31	07a36	07 41	07 51	08 01	08 06		08 11	08 21	08 31	08a36
20¾	—	Selly Oak	d	23p32	06 03	06 13	06 23	06 33	06 43	06 53	07 03		07 13	07 23		07 33		07 43	07 53	08 03			08 13	08 23	08 33	
21¾	—	Bournville	d	23p40	06 05	06 15	06 25	06 35	06 45	06 55	07 05		07 15	07 25		07 35		07 45	07 55	08 05			08 15	08 25	08 35	
22¾	—	Kings Norton	d	23p50	06 07	06 17	06 27	06 37	06 47	06 57	07 07		07 17	07 27		07 37		07 47	07 57	08 07			08 17	08 27	08 37	
24¼	—	Northfield	d	23p57	06 10	06 20	06 30	06 40	06 50	07 00	07 10		07 20	07 30		07 40		07 50	08 00	08 10			08 20	08 30	08 40	
25¼	—	Longbridge	d	00∫07	06a14	06a24	06 34	06a44	06a54	07 04	07a14		07a24	07 34		07a44		07a54	08 04	08a14			08a24	08 34	08a44	
28	9½	Barnt Green	d	00∫17			06 39			07 09				07 39	07 43				08 09					08 39		
29¾	—	Alvechurch	d	00b24			06 43			07 13				07 43					08 13					08 43		
33	—	**Redditch**	a	00∫34			06 53			07 23				07 53					08 23					08 53		
—	13	Bromsgrove	a									07 22			07 48						08 21					

		LM	LM	LM	LM	LM	LM	LM	LM	XC	LM	LM	LM	LM	LM	LM	LM		XC	LM	LM	LM	LM	LM	LM	LM
			C							1 ◇ B 🍴									1 ◇ B 🍴							
Lichfield Trent Valley	d	07 54				08 10			08 40		08 52				09 22					09 52				10 22		
Lichfield City	d	07 57		08 10		08 15	08 26		08 45		08 55			09 14	09 25		09 44			09 55			10 14	10 25		10 44
Shenstone	d					08 20			08 50					09 19			09 49						10 19			10 49
Blake Street	d	08 05				08 24	08 33		08 54		09 03			09 23	09 33		09 53			10 03			10 23	10 33		10 53
Butlers Lane	d	08 07				08 26	08 35		08 56		09 05			09 25	09 35		09 55			10 05			10 25	10 35		10 55
Four Oaks	d	08 10	08 15	08 20		08 29	08 38	08 48	08 59		09 08	09 18		09 28	09 38	09 48	09 58			10 08	10 18		10 28	10 38	10 48	10 58
Sutton Coldfield	d	08 13	08 18	08 23		08 32	08 42	08 51	09 02		09 11	09 21		09 31	09 41	09 51	10 01			10 11	10 21		10 31	10 41	10 51	11 01
Wylde Green	d	08 16	08 21	08 26		08 35	08 45	08 54	09 05		09 14	09 24		09 34	09 44	09 54	10 04			10 14	10 24		10 34	10 44	10 54	11 04
Chester Road	d	08 18	08 23	08 28		08 37	08 47	08 56	09 07		09 16	09 26		09 36	09 46	09 56	10 06			10 16	10 26		10 36	10 46	10 56	11 06
Erdington	d	08 19	08 25	08 29		08 38	08 48	08 58	09 08		09 18	09 28		09 38	09 48	09 58	10 08			10 18	10 28		10 38	10 48	10 58	11 08
Gravelly Hill	d	08 22		08 32		08 41	08 51	09 00	09 11		09 20	09 30		09 40	09 50	10 00	10 10			10 20	10 30		10 40	10 50	11 00	11 10
Aston	d	08 25		08 35		08 44	08 54	09 04	09 14		09 24	09 34		09 44	09 54	10 04	10 14			10 24	10 34		10 44	10 54	11 04	11 14
Duddeston	d			08 37		08 47	08 57	09 06				09 36				10 06					10 36				11 06	
Birmingham New Street 12	a	08 31	08 35	08 42		08 51	09 01	09 11	09 21		09 31	09 41		09 51	10 01	10 11	10 21			10 31	10 41		10 51	11 01	11 11	11 21
	d	08 34		08 44	08 49	08 54	09 04	09 14	09 24	09 30	09 34	09 44	09 49	09 54	10 04	10 14	10 24		10 30	10 34	10 44	10 49	10 54	11 04	11 14	11 24
Five Ways	d	08 37		08 47		08 57	09 07	09 17	09 27		09 37	09 47		09 57	10 07	10 17	10 27			10 37	10 47		10 57	11 07	11 17	11 27
University	d	08 41		08 51	08 55	09 01	09 11	09 21	09 31	09a36	09 41	09 51	09 55	10 01	10 11	10 21	10 31		10a36	10 41	10 51	10 55	11 01	11 11	11 21	11 31
Selly Oak	d	08 43		08 53		09 03	09 13	09 23	09 33		09 43	09 53		10 03	10 13	10 23	10 33			10 43	10 53		11 03	11 13	11 23	11 33
Bournville	d	08 45		08 55		09 05	09 15	09 25	09 35		09 45	09 55		10 05	10 15	10 25	10 35			10 45	10 55		11 05	11 15	11 25	11 35
Kings Norton	d	08 47		08 57		09 07	09 17	09 27	09 37		09 47	09 57		10 07	10 17	10 27	10 37			10 47	10 57		11 07	11 17	11 27	11 37
Northfield	d	08 50		09 00		09 10	09 20	09 30	09 40		09 50	10 00		10 10	10 20	10 30	10 40			10 50	11 00		11 10	11 20	11 30	11 40
Longbridge	d	08a54		09 06		09a14	09a24	09 34	09a44		09a54	10 06		10a14	10a24	10 34	10a44			10a54	11 06		11a14	11a24	11 34	11a44
Barnt Green	d			09 10				09 39				10 10				10 39					11 10				11 39	
Alvechurch	d			09 15				09 43				10 15				10 43					11 15				11 43	
Redditch	a			09 23				09 53				10 23				10 53					11 23				11 53	
Bromsgrove	a				09 11								10 11									11 10				

		XC	LM	LM	LM	LM	LM	LM	LM	XC	LM	LM	LM		LM	LM	LM	LM	XC	LM	LM	LM	LM	LM	LM	LM
		1 ◇ B 🍴								1 ◇ B 🍴									1 ◇ B 🍴							
Lichfield Trent Valley	d		10 52				11 22				11 52					12 22				12 52				13 22		
Lichfield City	d		10 55			11 14	11 25		11 44		11 55				12 14	12 25		12 44		12 55			13 14	13 25		13 44
Shenstone	d					11 19			11 49						12 19			12 49					13 19			13 49
Blake Street	d		11 03			11 23	11 33		11 53		12 03				12 23	12 33		12 53		13 03			13 23	13 33		13 53
Butlers Lane	d		11 05			11 25	11 35		11 55		12 05				12 25	12 35		12 55		13 05			13 25	13 35		13 55
Four Oaks	d		11 08	11 18		11 28	11 38	11 48	11 58		12 08	12 18			12 28	12 38	12 48	12 58		13 08	13 18		13 28	13 38	13 48	13 58
Sutton Coldfield	d		11 11	11 21		11 31	11 41	11 51	12 01		12 11	12 21			12 31	12 41	12 51	13 01		13 11	13 21		13 31	13 41	13 51	14 01
Wylde Green	d		11 14	11 24		11 34	11 44	11 54	12 04		12 14	12 24			12 34	12 44	12 54	13 04		13 14	13 24		13 34	13 44	13 54	14 04
Chester Road	d		11 16	11 26		11 36	11 46	11 56	12 06		12 16	12 26			12 36	12 46	12 56	13 06		13 16	13 26		13 36	13 46	13 56	14 06
Erdington	d		11 18	11 28		11 38	11 48	11 58	12 08		12 18	12 28			12 38	12 48	12 58	13 08		13 18	13 28		13 38	13 48	13 58	14 08
Gravelly Hill	d		11 20	11 30		11 40	11 50	12 00	12 10		12 20	12 30			12 40	12 50	13 00	13 10		13 20	13 30		13 40	13 50	14 00	14 10
Aston	d		11 24	11 34		11 44	11 54	12 04	12 14		12 24	12 34			12 44	12 54	13 04	13 14		13 24	13 34		13 44	13 54	14 04	14 14
Duddeston	d			11 36				12 06				12 36					13 06				13 36				14 06	
Birmingham New Street 12	a		11 31	11 41		11 51	12 01	12 11	12 21		12 31	12 41			12 51	13 01	13 11	13 21		13 31	13 41		13 51	14 01	14 11	14 21
	d	11 30	11 34	11 44	11 49	11 54	12 04	12 14	12 24	12 30	12 34	12 44	12 49		12 54	13 04	13 14	13 24	13 30	13 34	13 44	13 49	13 54	14 04	14 14	14 24
Five Ways	d		11 37	11 47		11 57	12 07	12 17	12 27		12 37	12 47			12 57	13 07	13 17	13 27		13 37	13 47		13 57	14 07	14 17	14 27
University	d	11a36	11 41	11 51	11 55	12 01	12 11	12 21	12 31	12a36	12 41	12 51	12 55		13 01	13 11	13 21	13 31	13a36	13 41	13 51	13 55	14 01	14 11	14 21	14 31
Selly Oak	d		11 43	11 53		12 03	12 13	12 23	12 33		12 43	12 53			13 03	13 13	13 23	13 33		13 43	13 53		14 03	14 13	14 23	14 33
Bournville	d		11 45	11 55		12 05	12 15	12 25	12 35		12 45	12 55			13 05	13 15	13 25	13 35		13 45	13 55		14 05	14 15	14 25	14 35
Kings Norton	d		11 47	11 57		12 07	12 17	12 27	12 37		12 47	12 57			13 07	13 17	13 27	13 37		13 47	13 57		14 07	14 17	14 27	14 37
Northfield	d		11 50	12 00		12 10	12 20	12 30	12 40		12 50	13 00			13 10	13 20	13 30	13 40		13 50	14 00		14 10	14 20	14 30	14 40
Longbridge	d		11a54	12 06		12a14	12a24	12 34	12a44		12a54	13 06			13a14	13a24	13 34	13a44		13a54	14 06		14a14	14a24	14 34	14a44
Barnt Green	d			12 10				12 39				13 10					13 39				14 10				14 39	
Alvechurch	d			12 15				12 43				13 15					13 43				14 15				14 43	
Redditch	a			12 23				12 53				13 23					13 53				14 23				14 53	
Bromsgrove	a				12 10								13 11									14 12				

For general notes see front of timetable
For details of catering facilities see
Directory of Train Operators

A From 9 November
B From Nottingham (Table 57)
C To Wolverhampton (Table 68)

b Alvechurch Red Lion Pub

Lichfield → Birmingham → Longbridge and Redditch

Network Diagram - see first page of Table 67

		XC 1 ◇ A	LM	LM	LM	LM	LM	LM	LM	XC 1 ◇ A	LM	LM	LM	LM	LM	LM	LM	LM	XC 1 ◇ A	LM	LM	LM	LM	LM	LM
Lichfield Trent Valley	d		13 52				14 22				14 52				15 22					15 51				16 22	
Lichfield City	d		13 55			14 14	14 25		14 44		14 55			15 14	15 25			15 44		15 54			16 14	16 25	
Shenstone	d					14 19			14 49					15 19				15 49		15 59			16 19		
Blake Street	d		14 03			14 23	14 33		14 53		15 03			15 23	15 33			15 53		16 03			16 23	16 33	
Butlers Lane	d		14 05			14 25	14 35		14 55		15 05			15 25	15 35			15 55		16 05			16 25	16 35	
Four Oaks	d		14 08	14 18		14 28	14 38	14 48	14 58		15 08	15 18		15 28	15 38	15 48		15 58		16 08	16 18		16 28	16 38	16 48
Sutton Coldfield	d		14 11	14 21		14 31	14 41	14 51	15 01		15 11	15 21		15 31	15 41	15 51		16 01		16 11	16 21		16 31	16 41	16 51
Wylde Green	d		14 14	14 24		14 34	14 44	14 54	15 04		15 14	15 24		15 34	15 44	15 54		16 04		16 14	16 24		16 34	16 44	16 54
Chester Road	d		14 16	14 26		14 36	14 46	14 56	15 06		15 16	15 26		15 36	15 46	15 56		16 06		16 16	16 26		16 36	16 46	16 56
Erdington	d		14 18	14 28		14 38	14 48	14 58	15 08		15 18	15 28		15 38	15 48	15 58		16 08		16 18	16 28		16 38	16 48	16 58
Gravelly Hill	d		14 20	14 30		14 40	14 50	15 00	15 10		15 20	15 30		15 40	15 50	16 00		16 10		16 20	16 30		16 40	16 50	17 00
Aston	d		14 24	14 34		14 44	14 54	15 04	15 14		15 24	15 34		15 44	15 54	16 04		16 14		16 24	16 34		16 44	16 54	17 04
Duddeston	d			14 36				15 06				15 36				16 06					16 36				17 06
Birmingham New Street 12	a		14 31	14 41		14 51	15 01	15 11	15 21		15 31	15 41		15 51	16 01	16 11		16 21		16 31	16 41		16 51	17 01	17 11
	d	14 30	14 34	14 44	14 49	14 54	15 04	15 14	15 24	15 30	15 34	15 44	15 49	15 54	16 04	16 14	16 20	16 24	16 30	16 34	16 44	16 49	16 54	17 04	17 14
Five Ways	d		14 37	14 47		14 57	15 07	15 17	15 27		15 37	15 47		15 57	16 07	16 17		16 27		16 37	16 47		16 57	17 07	17 17
University	d	14a36	14 41	14 51	14 55	15 01	15 11	15 21	15 31	15a36	15 41	15 51	15 55	16 01	16 11	16 21	16 26	16 31	16a36	16 41	16 51	16 55	17 01	17 11	17 21
Selly Oak	d		14 43	14 53		15 03	15 13	15 23	15 33		15 43	15 53		16 04	16 14	16 24		16 34		16 44	16 54		17 04	17 14	17 24
Bournville	d		14 45	14 55		15 05	15 15	15 25	15 35		15 45	15 55		16 06	16 16	16 26		16 36		16 46	16 56		17 06	17 16	17 26
Kings Norton	d		14 47	14 57		15 07	15 17	15 27	15 37		15 47	15 57		16 09	16 19	16 29		16 39		16 49	16 59		17 09	17 19	17 29
Northfield	d		14 50	15 00		15 10	15 20	15 30	15 40		15 50	16 00		16 11	16 21	16 31		16 41		16 51	17 01		17 11	17 21	17 31
Longbridge	d		14a54	15 06		15a14	15a24	15 34	15a44		15a54	16 06		16a15	16a25	16 37		16a45		16a55	17 06		17a15	17a25	17 34
Barnt Green	d			15 10				15 39				16 10				16 41					17 10				17 39
Alvechurch	d			15 15				15 43				16 15				16 45					17 15				17 43
Redditch	a			15 23				15 53				16 23				16 54					17 23				17 53
Bromsgrove	a				15 10								16 11				16 41					17 10			

		LM	LM	XC 1 ◇ B	LM	LM	LM	LM	LM	LM	LM	LM	LM	XC 1 ◇ B	LM	LM	LM	LM	LM	LM	LM	XC 1 ◇ A	LM	LM
Lichfield Trent Valley	d				16 52					17 21			17 40		17 52		18 10	18 22					18 52	
Lichfield City	d		16 44		16 55	17 05				17 24			17 44		17 55		18 14	18 25			18 44		18 55	
Shenstone	d		16 49							17 29			17 49				18 19				18 49			
Blake Street	d		16 53		17 03	17 13				17 33			17 53		18 03		18 23	18 33			18 53		19 03	
Butlers Lane	d		16 55		17 05	17 15				17 35			17 55		18 05		18 25	18 35			18 55		19 05	
Four Oaks	d		16 58		17 08	17 18		17 28		17 38	17 48		17 58		18 08	18 18	18 28	18 38	18 48		18 58		19 08	19 18
Sutton Coldfield	d		17 01		17 11	17 21		17 31		17 41	17 51		18 01		18 11	18 21	18 31	18 41	18 51		19 01		19 11	19 21
Wylde Green	d		17 04		17 14	17 24		17 34		17 44	17 54		18 04		18 14	18 24	18 34	18 44	18 54		19 04		19 14	19 24
Chester Road	d		17 06		17 16	17 26		17 36		17 46	17 56		18 06		18 16	18 26	18 36	18 46	18 56		19 06		19 16	19 26
Erdington	d		17 08		17 18	17 28		17 38		17 48	17 58		18 08		18 18	18 28	18 38	18 48	18 58		19 08		19 18	19 28
Gravelly Hill	d		17 10		17 20	17 30		17 40		17 50	18 00		18 10		18 20	18 30	18 40	18 50	19 00		19 10		19 20	19 30
Aston	d		17 14		17 24	17 34		17 44		17 54	18 04		18 14		18 24	18 34	18 44	18 54	19 04		19 14		19 24	19 34
Duddeston	d					17 36					18 06					18 36			19 06					19 36
Birmingham New Street 12	a		17 21		17 31	17 41		17 51		18 01	18 11		18 21		18 31	18 41	18 51	19 01	19 11		19 21		19 31	19 41
	d	17 19	17 24	17 30	17 34	17 44	17 49	17 54	17 59	18 04	18 14	18 19	18 24	18 30	18 34	18 44	18 54	19 04	19 14	19 19	19 24	19 30	19 34	19 44
Five Ways	d		17 27		17 37	17 47		17 57		18 07	18 17		18 27		18 37	18 47	18 57	19 07	19 17		19 27		19 37	19 47
University	d	17 25	17 31	17 36	17 41	17 51	17a55	18 01	18 05	18 11	18 21		18 31	18 36	18 41	18 51	19 01	19 11	19 21	19 25	19 31	19a36	19 41	19 51
Selly Oak	d		17 34		17 44	17 54		18 04		18 14	18 24		18 34		18 44	18 54	19 03	19 13	19 23		19 33		19 43	19 53
Bournville	d		17 36		17 46	17 56		18 06		18 16	18 26		18 36		18 46	18 56	19 05	19 15	19 25		19 35		19 45	19 55
Kings Norton	d		17 39		17 49	17 59		18 09		18 19	18 29		18 39		18 49	18 59	19 07	19 17	19 27		19 37		19 47	19 57
Northfield	d		17 41		17 51	18 01		18 11		18 21	18 31		18 41		18 51	19 01	19 10	19 20	19 30		19 40		19 50	20 00
Longbridge	d		17a45		17a55	18 06		18a15		18a25	18 34		18a45		18a55	19 04	19a14	19a24	19 36		19a44		19a54	20 06
Barnt Green	d					18 10					18 39					19 09			19 40					20 10
Alvechurch	d					18 15					18 43					19 13			19 44					20 14
Redditch	a					18 23					18 53					19 23			19 53					20 23
Bromsgrove	a	17 45		17 49					18 21			18 45		18 49						19 40				

		LM	LM	LM	LM	LM	XC 1 ◇ A	LM	LM	LM	LM	LM	LM	LM	LM	LM C	LM	LM	LM	LM	LM C	LM	LM	LM
Lichfield Trent Valley	d			19 22					20 00			20 30		21 00			21 30		22 00			22 30	22 57	
Lichfield City	d		19 14	19 25		19 44			20 04			20 34		21 04			21 34		22 04			22 34	23 00	
Shenstone	d		19 19			19 49			20 09			20 39		21 09			21 39		22 09			22 39	23 05	
Blake Street	d		19 23	19 33		19 53		20 03	20 13			20 43		21 13			21 43		22 13			22 43	23 09	23 36
Butlers Lane	d		19 25	19 35		19 55		20 05	20 15			20 45		21 15			21 45		22 15			22 45	23 11	23 38
Four Oaks	d		19 28	19 38	19 50	19 58		20 08	20 18	20 28		20 48	20 58	21 18	21 28		21 48	21 58	22 18	22 28		22 48	23 14	23 41
Sutton Coldfield	d		19 31	19 41	19 53	20 01		20 11	20 21	20 31		20 51	21 01	21 21	21 31		21 51	22 01	22 21	22 31		22 51	23 17	23 44
Wylde Green	d		19 34	19 44	19 56	20 04		20 14	20 24	20 34		20 54	21 04	21 24	21 34		21 54	22 04	22 24	22 34		22 54	23 20	
Chester Road	d		19 36	19 46	19 58	20 06		20 16	20 26	20 36		20 56	21 06	21 26	21 36		21 56	22 06	22 26	22 36		22 56		
Erdington	d		19 38	19 48	20 00	20 08		20 18	20 28	20 38		20 58	21 08	21 28	21 38		21 58	22 08	22 28	22 38		22 58		
Gravelly Hill	d		19 40	19 50	20 02	20 10		20 20	20 30	20 40		21 00	21 10	21 30	21 40		22 00	22 10	22 30	22 40		23 00		
Aston	d		19 44	19 54	20 06	20 14		20 24	20 34	20 44		21 04	21 14	21 34	21 44		22 04	22 14	22 34	22 44		23 04		
Duddeston	d			19 56				20 26	20 36			21 06		21 36			22 06		22 36			23 06		
Birmingham New Street 12	a		19 51	20 03	20 13	20 21		20 33	20 41	20 51		21 12	21 21	21 42	21 51		22 12	22 21	22 42	22 51		23 12	23 31	23 59
	d	19 49	19 54		20 14	20 24	20 30		20 44	20 54	20 59	21 14	21 24	21 44	21 54	22 00	22 14	22 24	22 44	22 54	23 00	23 14	23 34	
Five Ways	d		19 57		20 17	20 27			20 47	20 57		21 17	21 27	21 47	21 57		22 17	22 27	22 47	22 57		23 17	23 37	
University	d	19 55	20 01		20 21	20 31	20a36		20 51	21 01	21 06	21 21	21 31	21 51	22 01	22 06	22 21	22 31	22 51	23 01	23 06	23 21	23 41	
Selly Oak	d		20 03		20 23	20 33			20 53	21 03		21 23	21 33	21 53	22 03		22 23	22 33	22 53	23 03		23 23	23 43	
Bournville	d		20 05		20 25	20 35			20 55	21 05		21 25	21 35	21 55	22 05		22 25	22 35	22 55	23 05		23 25	23 45	
Kings Norton	d		20 07		20 27	20 37			20 57	21 07		21 27	21 37	21 57	22 07		22 27	22 37	22 57	23 07		23 27	23 47	
Northfield	d		20 10		20 30	20 40			21 00	21 10		21 30	21 40	22 00	22 10		22 30	22 40	23 00	23 10		23 30	23 50	
Longbridge	d		20a14		20 34	20a44			21 04	21a14		21 34	21a44	22 04	22a14		22 34	22a44	23 04	23a14		23 34	23a54	
Barnt Green	d				20 39				21 09			21 39		22 09			22 39		23 09			23 39		
Alvechurch	d				20 43				21 13			21 43		22 13			22 43		23 13			23 43		
Redditch	a				20 53				21 23			21 53		22 23			22 53		23 23			23 53		
Bromsgrove	a	20 09									21 22					22 22					23 20			

For general notes see front of timetable
For details of catering facilities see Directory of Train Operators

A From Nottingham (Table 57)
B From Nottingham to Cardiff Central (Table 57)
C Until 4 September

Table 69

Saturdays

Lichfield → Birmingham → Longbridge and Redditch

Network Diagram - see first page of Table 67

		XC	LM	LM	LM	LM	LM	LM	LM		LM	LM	LM	LM	XC	LM	LM	LM		LM	LM	LM	LM	XC	LM	LM
		1 ◇ A													1 ◇ B									1 ◇ B		
Lichfield Trent Valley	d											06 21				06 52					07 22				07 52	
Lichfield City	d											06 24	06 38			06 55	07 08				07 25		07 46		07 55	
Shenstone	d											06 29				07 00					07 30		07 51			
Blake Street	d						06 04					06 33				07 04					07 34		07 54		08 03	
Butlers Lane	d						06 06					06 35				07 06					07 36		07 56		08 05	
Four Oaks	d						06 09					06 38	06 48			07 09	07 18				07 39	07 48	07 59		08 08	08 18
Sutton Coldfield	d						06 12					06 41	06 51			07 12	07 21				07 42	07 51	08 03		08 11	08 21
Wylde Green	d						06 15					06 44	06 54			07 15	07 24				07 45	07 54	08 05		08 14	08 24
Chester Road	d						06 17					06 46	06 56			07 17	07 26				07 47	07 56	08 08		08 16	08 26
Erdington	d						06 18					06 47	06 58			07 18	07 28				07 48	07 58	08 09		08 18	08 28
Gravelly Hill	d						06 21					06 50	07 00			07 21	07 30				07 51	08 00	08 12		08 20	08 30
Aston	d						06 24					06 53	07 04			07 24	07 34				07 54	08 04	08 15		08 24	08 34
Duddeston	d						06 27					06 56	07 06			07 27	07 36					08 06				08 36
Birmingham New Street 12	a						06 31					07 01	07 12			07 31	07 42				08 01	08 11	08 21		08 31	08 41
	d	05 42	05 54	06 04	06 14	06 24	06 34	06 44	06 49		06 54	07 04	07 14	07 24	07 30	07 34	07 44	07 49		07 54	08 04	08 14	08 24	08 30	08 34	08 44
Five Ways	d		05 57	06 07	06 17	06 27	06 37	06 47			06 57	07 07	07 17	07 27		07 37	07 47			07 57	08 07	08 17	08 27		08 37	08 47
University	d		06 01	06 11	06 21	06 31	06 41	06 51	06 57		07 01	07 11	07 21	07 31	07a36	07 41	07 51	07 57		08 01	08 11	08 21	08 31	08a36	08 41	08 51
Selly Oak	d		06 03	06 13	06 23	06 33	06 43	06 53			07 03	07 13	07 23	07 33		07 43	07 53			08 03	08 13	08 23	08 33		08 43	08 53
Bournville	d		06 05	06 15	06 25	06 35	06 45	06 55			07 05	07 15	07 25	07 35		07 45	07 55			08 05	08 15	08 25	08 35		08 45	08 55
Kings Norton	d		06 07	06 17	06 27	06 37	06 47	06 57			07 07	07 17	07 27	07 37		07 47	07 57			08 07	08 17	08 27	08 37		08 47	08 57
Northfield	d		06 10	06 20	06 30	06 40	06 50	07 00			07 10	07 20	07 30	07 40		07 50	08 00			08 10	08 20	08 30	08 40		08 50	09 00
Longbridge	d		06a14	06a24	06 34	06a44	06a54	07 06			07a14	07a24	07 34	07a44		07a54	08 06			08a14	08a24	08 34	08a44		08a54	09 06
Barnt Green	d				06 39			07 10					07 39				08 10					08 39				09 10
Alvechurch	d				06 43			07 15					07 43				08 15					08 43				09 15
Redditch	a				06 53			07 23					07 53				08 23					08 53				09 23
Bromsgrove	a	06 03							07 11									08 11								

		LM	LM	LM		LM	LM	XC	LM	LM	LM	LM	LM		LM	LM	XC	LM	LM	LM	LM	LM		LM	LM	XC
								1 ◇ B									1 ◇ B									1 ◇ B
Lichfield Trent Valley	d			08 22					08 52				09 22					09 52				10 22				
Lichfield City	d		08 14	08 25			08 44		08 55			09 14	09 25			09 44		09 55			10 14	10 25			10 44	
Shenstone	d		08 19				08 49					09 19				09 49					10 19				10 49	
Blake Street	d		08 22	08 33			08 52		09 03			09 23	09 33			09 53		10 03			10 23	10 33			10 53	
Butlers Lane	d		08 24	08 35			08 54		09 05			09 25	09 35			09 55		10 05			10 25	10 35			10 55	
Four Oaks	d		08 28	08 38		08 48	08 58		09 08	09 18		09 28	09 38		09 48	09 58		10 08	10 18		10 28	10 38		10 48	10 58	
Sutton Coldfield	d		08 31	08 41		08 51	09 01		09 11	09 21		09 31	09 41		09 51	10 01		10 11	10 21		10 31	10 41		10 51	11 01	
Wylde Green	d		08 34	08 44		08 54	09 04		09 14	09 24		09 34	09 44		09 54	10 04		10 14	10 24		10 34	10 44		10 54	11 04	
Chester Road	d		08 36	08 46		08 56	09 06		09 16	09 26		09 36	09 46		09 56	10 06		10 16	10 26		10 36	10 46		10 56	11 06	
Erdington	d		08 38	08 48		08 58	09 08		09 18	09 28		09 38	09 48		09 58	10 08		10 18	10 28		10 38	10 48		10 58	11 08	
Gravelly Hill	d		08 40	08 50		09 00	09 10		09 20	09 30		09 40	09 50		10 00	10 10		10 20	10 30		10 40	10 50		11 00	11 10	
Aston	d		08 44	08 54		09 04	09 14		09 24	09 34		09 44	09 54		10 04	10 14		10 24	10 34		10 44	10 54		11 04	11 14	
Duddeston	d					09 06				09 36					10 06				10 36					11 06		
Birmingham New Street 12	a		08 51	09 01		09 11	09 21		09 32	09 41		09 51	10 01		10 11	10 21		10 31	10 41		10 51	11 01		11 11	11 21	
	d	08 49	08 54	09 04		09 14	09 24	09 30	09 34	09 44	09 49	09 54	10 04		10 14	10 24	10 30	10 34	10 44	10 49	10 54	11 04		11 14	11 24	11 30
Five Ways	d		08 57	09 07		09 17	09 27		09 37	09 47		09 57	10 07		10 17	10 27		10 37	10 47		10 57	11 07		11 17	11 27	
University	d	08 57	09 01	09 11		09 21	09 31	09a36	09 41	09 51	09 57	10 01	10 11		10 21	10 31	10a36	10 41	10 51	10 57	11 01	11 11		11 21	11 31	11a36
Selly Oak	d		09 03	09 13		09 23	09 33		09 43	09 53		10 03	10 13		10 23	10 33		10 43	10 53		11 03	11 13		11 23	11 33	
Bournville	d		09 05	09 15		09 25	09 35		09 45	09 55		10 05	10 15		10 25	10 35		10 45	10 55		11 05	11 15		11 25	11 35	
Kings Norton	d		09 07	09 17		09 27	09 37		09 47	09 57		10 07	10 17		10 27	10 37		10 47	10 57		11 07	11 17		11 27	11 37	
Northfield	d		09 10	09 20		09 30	09 40		09 50	10 00		10 10	10 20		10 30	10 40		10 50	11 00		11 10	11 20		11 30	11 40	
Longbridge	d		09a14	09a24		09 34	09a44		09a54	10 06		10a14	10a24		10 34	10a44		10a54	11 06		11a14	11a24		11 34	11a44	
Barnt Green	d					09 39				10 10					10 39				11 10					11 39		
Alvechurch	d					09 43				10 15					10 43				11 15					11 43		
Redditch	a					09 53				10 23					10 53				11 23					11 53		
Bromsgrove	a	09 11									10 11									11 11						

		LM	LM	LM	LM	LM	LM	LM		XC	LM	LM	LM	LM	LM	LM	LM		XC	LM	LM	LM	LM	LM	LM	LM
										1 ◇ B									1 ◇ B							
Lichfield Trent Valley	d	10 52				11 22					11 52				12 22					12 52				13 22		
Lichfield City	d	10 55			11 14	11 25		11 44			11 55			12 14	12 25		12 44			12 55			13 14	13 25		13 44
Shenstone	d				11 19			11 49						12 19			12 49						13 19			13 49
Blake Street	d	11 03			11 23	11 33		11 53			12 03			12 23	12 33		12 53			13 03			13 23	13 33		13 53
Butlers Lane	d	11 05			11 25	11 35		11 55			12 05			12 25	12 35		12 55			13 05			13 25	13 35		13 55
Four Oaks	d	11 08	11 18		11 28	11 38	11 48	11 58			12 08	12 18		12 28	12 38	12 48	12 58			13 08	13 18		13 28	13 38	13 48	13 58
Sutton Coldfield	d	11 11	11 21		11 31	11 41	11 51	12 01			12 11	12 21		12 31	12 41	12 51	13 01			13 11	13 21		13 31	13 41	13 51	14 01
Wylde Green	d	11 14	11 24		11 34	11 44	11 54	12 04			12 14	12 24		12 34	12 44	12 54	13 04			13 14	13 24		13 34	13 44	13 54	14 04
Chester Road	d	11 16	11 26		11 36	11 46	11 56	12 06			12 16	12 26		12 36	12 46	12 56	13 06			13 16	13 26		13 36	13 46	13 56	14 06
Erdington	d	11 18	11 28		11 38	11 48	11 58	12 08			12 18	12 28		12 38	12 48	12 58	13 08			13 18	13 28		13 38	13 48	13 58	14 08
Gravelly Hill	d	11 20	11 30		11 40	11 50	12 00	12 10			12 20	12 30		12 40	12 50	13 00	13 10			13 20	13 30		13 40	13 50	14 00	14 10
Aston	d	11 24	11 34		11 44	11 54	12 04	12 14			12 24	12 34		12 44	12 54	13 04	13 14			13 24	13 34		13 44	13 54	14 04	14 14
Duddeston	d		11 36				12 06					12 36				13 06					13 36				14 06	
Birmingham New Street 12	a	11 31	11 41		11 51	12 01	12 11	12 21			12 31	12 41		12 51	13 01	13 11	13 21			13 31	13 41		13 51	14 01	14 11	14 21
	d	11 34	11 44	11 49	11 54	12 04	12 14	12 24		12 30	12 34	12 44	12 49	12 54	13 04	13 14	13 24		13 30	13 34	13 44	13 49	13 54	14 04	14 14	14 24
Five Ways	d	11 37	11 47		11 57	12 07	12 17	12 27			12 37	12 47		12 57	13 07	13 17	13 27			13 37	13 47		13 57	14 07	14 17	14 27
University	d	11 41	11 51	11 57	12 01	12 11	12 21	12 31		12a36	12 41	12 51	12 57	13 01	13 11	13 21	13 31		13a36	13 41	13 51	13 57	14 01	14 11	14 21	14 31
Selly Oak	d	11 43	11 53		12 03	12 13	12 23	12 33			12 43	12 53		13 03	13 13	13 23	13 33			13 43	13 53		14 03	14 13	14 23	14 33
Bournville	d	11 45	11 55		12 05	12 15	12 25	12 35			12 45	12 55		13 05	13 15	13 25	13 35			13 45	13 55		14 05	14 15	14 25	14 35
Kings Norton	d	11 47	11 57		12 07	12 17	12 27	12 37			12 47	12 57		13 07	13 17	13 27	13 37			13 47	13 57		14 07	14 17	14 27	14 37
Northfield	d	11 50	12 00		12 10	12 20	12 30	12 40			12 50	13 00		13 10	13 20	13 30	13 40			13 50	14 00		14 10	14 20	14 30	14 40
Longbridge	d	11a54	12 06		12a14	12a24	12 34	12a44			12a54	13 06		13a14	13a24	13 34	13a44			13a54	14 06		14a14	14a24	14 34	14a44
Barnt Green	d		12 10				12 39					13 10				13 39					14 10				14 39	
Alvechurch	d		12 15				12 43					13 15				13 43					14 15				14 43	
Redditch	a		12 23				12 53					13 23				13 53					14 23				14 53	
Bromsgrove	a			12 11									13 11									14 11				

For general notes see front of timetable
For details of catering facilities see Directory of Train Operators

A To Cardiff Central (Table 132)
B From Nottingham (Table 57)

Table 69

Lichfield → Birmingham → Longbridge and Redditch

Saturdays

Network Diagram - see first page of Table 67

		XC 1 ◇ A	LM		LM	LM	LM	LM	LM	LM	XC 1 ◇ A	LM		LM	LM	LM	LM	LM	LM	LM	XC 1 ◇ A		LM	LM	LM	LM
Lichfield Trent Valley	d		13 52					14 22				14 52					15 22						15 52			
Lichfield City	d		13 55				14 14	14 25		14 44		14 55				15 14	15 25			15 44			15 55			16 14
Shenstone	d						14 19			14 49						15 19				15 49						16 19
Blake Street	d		14 03				14 23	14 33		14 53		15 03				15 23	15 33			15 53			16 03			16 23
Butlers Lane	d		14 05				14 25	14 35		14 55		15 05				15 25	15 35			15 55			16 05			16 25
Four Oaks	d		14 08		14 18		14 28	14 38	14 48	14 58		15 08		15 18		15 28	15 38	15 48		15 58			16 08	16 18		16 28
Sutton Coldfield	d		14 11		14 21		14 31	14 41	14 51	15 01		15 11		15 21		15 31	15 41	15 51		16 01			16 11	16 21		16 31
Wylde Green	d		14 14		14 24		14 34	14 44	14 54	15 04		15 14		15 24		15 34	15 44	15 54		16 04			16 14	16 24		16 34
Chester Road	d		14 16		14 26		14 36	14 46	14 56	15 06		15 16		15 26		15 36	15 46	15 56		16 06			16 16	16 26		16 36
Erdington	d		14 18		14 28		14 38	14 48	14 58	15 08		15 18		15 28		15 38	15 48	15 58		16 08			16 18	16 28		16 38
Gravelly Hill	d		14 20		14 30		14 40	14 50	15 00	15 10		15 20		15 30		15 40	15 50	16 00		16 10			16 20	16 30		16 40
Aston	d		14 24		14 34		14 44	14 54	15 04	15 14		15 24		15 34		15 44	15 54	16 04		16 14			16 24	16 34		16 44
Duddeston	d				14 36				15 06					15 36				16 06						16 36		
Birmingham New Street 12	a		14 31		14 41		14 51	15 01	15 11	15 21		15 31		15 41		15 51	16 01	16 11		16 21			16 31	16 41		16 51
	d	14 30	14 34		14 44	14 49	14 54	15 04	15 14	15 24	15 30	15 34		15 44	15 49	15 54	16 04	16 14	16 19	16 24	16 30		16 34	16 44	16 49	16 54
Five Ways	d		14 37		14 47		14 57	15 07	15 17	15 27		15 37		15 47		15 57	16 07	16 17		16 27			16 37	16 47		16 57
University	d	14a36	14 41		14 51	14 57	15 01	15 11	15 21	15 31	15a36	15 41		15 51	15 57	16 01	16 11	16 21		16 31	16a36		16 41	16 51	16 57	17 01
Selly Oak	d		14 43		14 53		15 03	15 13	15 23	15 33		15 43		15 53		16 04	16 14	16 24		16 34			16 44	16 54		17 04
Bournville	d		14 45		14 55		15 05	15 15	15 25	15 35		15 45		15 55		16 06	16 16	16 26		16 36			16 46	16 56		17 06
Kings Norton	d		14 47		14 57		15 07	15 17	15 27	15 37		15 47		15 57		16 09	16 19	16 29		16 39			16 49	16 59		17 09
Northfield	d		14 50		15 00		15 10	15 20	15 30	15 40		15 50		16 00		16 11	16 21	16 31		16 41			16 51	17 01		17 11
Longbridge	d		14a54		15 06		15a14	15a24	15 34	15a44		15a54		16 06		16a15	16a25	16 37		16a45			16a55	17 06		17a15
Barnt Green	d				15 10				15 39					16 10				16 41						17 10		
Alvechurch	d				15 15				15 43					16 15				16 45						17 15		
Redditch	a				15 23				15 53					16 23				16 54						17 23		
Bromsgrove	a					15 11									16 11				16 43						17 11	

		LM	LM	LM	LM	XC 1 ◇ B	LM		LM	LM	LM	LM	LM	LM	XC 1 ◇ A	LM		LM	LM	LM	LM	LM	LM	LM	XC 1 ◇ A	LM
Lichfield Trent Valley	d	16 22					16 52					17 22				17 52					18 22					18 52
Lichfield City	d	16 25			16 44		16 55				17 14	17 25		17 44		17 55				18 14	18 25			18 44		18 55
Shenstone	d				16 49						17 19			17 49						18 19				18 49		
Blake Street	d	16 33			16 53		17 03				17 23	17 33		17 53		18 03				18 23	18 33			18 53		19 03
Butlers Lane	d	16 35			16 55		17 05				17 25	17 35		17 55		18 05				18 25	18 35			18 55		19 05
Four Oaks	d	16 38	16 48		16 58		17 08		17 18		17 28	17 38	17 48	17 58		18 08		18 18		18 28	18 38	18 48		18 58		19 08
Sutton Coldfield	d	16 41	16 51		17 01		17 11		17 21		17 31	17 41	17 51	18 01		18 11		18 21		18 31	18 41	18 51		19 01		19 11
Wylde Green	d	16 44	16 54		17 04		17 14		17 24		17 34	17 44	17 54	18 04		18 14		18 24		18 34	18 44	18 54		19 04		19 14
Chester Road	d	16 46	16 56		17 06		17 16		17 26		17 36	17 46	17 56	18 06		18 16		18 26		18 36	18 46	18 56		19 06		19 16
Erdington	d	16 48	16 58		17 08		17 18		17 28		17 38	17 48	17 58	18 08		18 18		18 28		18 38	18 48	18 58		19 08		19 18
Gravelly Hill	d	16 50	17 00		17 10		17 20		17 30		17 40	17 50	18 00	18 10		18 20		18 30		18 40	18 50	19 00		19 10		19 20
Aston	d	16 54	17 04		17 14		17 24		17 34		17 44	17 54	18 04	18 14		18 24		18 34		18 44	18 54	19 04		19 14		19 24
Duddeston	d		17 06						17 36				18 06					18 36				19 06				
Birmingham New Street 12	a	17 01	17 11		17 21		17 31		17 41		17 51	18 01	18 11	18 21		18 31		18 41		18 51	19 01	19 11		19 21		19 31
	d	17 04	17 14	17 19	17 24	17 30	17 34		17 44	17 49	17 54	18 04	18 14	18 24	18 30	18 34		18 44	18 49	18 54	19 04	19 14	19 19	19 24	19 30	19 34
Five Ways	d	17 07	17 17		17 27		17 37		17 47		17 57	18 07	18 17	18 27		18 37		18 47		18 57	19 07	19 17		19 27		19 37
University	d	17 11	17 21		17 31	17 36	17 41		17 51	17 57	18 01	18 11	18 21	18 31	18a36	18 41		18 51	18 57	19 01	19 11	19 21	19 27	19 31	19a36	19 41
Selly Oak	d	17 14	17 24		17 34		17 44		17 54		18 04	18 14	18 24	18 34		18 44		18 54		19 03	19 13	19 23		19 33		19 43
Bournville	d	17 16	17 26		17 36		17 46		17 56		18 06	18 16	18 26	18 36		18 46		18 56		19 05	19 15	19 25		19 35		19 45
Kings Norton	d	17 19	17 29		17 39		17 49		17 59		18 09	18 19	18 29	18 39		18 49		18 59		19 07	19 17	19 27		19 37		19 47
Northfield	d	17 21	17 31		17 41		17 51		18 01		18 11	18 21	18 31	18 41		18 51		19 01		19 10	19 20	19 30		19 40		19 50
Longbridge	d	17a25	17 36		17a45		17a55		18 06		18a15	18a25	18 34	18a45		18a55		19 06		19a14	19a24	19 36		19a44		19a54
Barnt Green	d		17 40						18 10				18 39					19 10				19 40				
Alvechurch	d		17 45						18 15				18 43					19 15				19 45				
Redditch	a		17 53						18 23				18 53					19 23				19 53				
Bromsgrove	a			17 41		17 49				18 10									19 10				19 41			

		LM		LM	LM	LM	LM	XC 1 ◇ A	LM	LM	LM		LM	LM	LM	LM	LM	LM	LM	LM	LM	LM	LM	LM		
Lichfield Trent Valley	d				19 22					20 00				20 30		21 00		21 30		22 00		22 30	22 57			
Lichfield City	d			19 14	19 25		19 44			20 04				20 34		21 04		21 34		22 04		22 34	23 00			
Shenstone	d			19 19			19 49			20 09				20 39		21 09		21 39		22 09		22 39	23 05			
Blake Street	d			19 23	19 33		19 53		20 03	20 13				20 43		21 13		21 43		22 13		22 43	23 09	23 36		
Butlers Lane	d			19 25	19 35		19 55		20 05	20 15				20 45		21 15		21 45		22 15		22 45	23 11	23 38		
Four Oaks	d	19 18		19 28	19 38	19 50	19 58		20 08	20 18	20 28			20 48	20 58	21 18	21 28	21 48	21 58	22 18	22 28	22 48	23 14	23 41		
Sutton Coldfield	d	19 21		19 31	19 41	19 53	20 01		20 11	20 21	20 31			20 51	21 01	21 21	21 31	21 51	22 01	22 21	22 31	22 51	23 17	23 44		
Wylde Green	d	19 24		19 34	19 44	19 56	20 04		20 14	20 24	20 34			20 54	21 04	21 24	21 34	21 54	22 04	22 24	22 34	22 54	23 20			
Chester Road	d	19 26		19 36	19 46	19 58	20 06		20 16	20 26	20 36			20 56	21 06	21 26	21 36	21 56	22 06	22 26	22 36	22 56				
Erdington	d	19 28		19 38	19 48	20 00	20 08		20 18	20 28	20 38			20 58	21 08	21 28	21 38	21 58	22 08	22 28	22 38	22 58				
Gravelly Hill	d	19 30		19 40	19 50	20 02	20 10		20 20	20 30	20 40			21 00	21 10	21 30	21 40	22 00	22 10	22 30	22 40	23 00				
Aston	d	19 34		19 44	19 54	20 06	20 14		20 24	20 34	20 44			21 04	21 14	21 34	21 44	22 04	22 14	22 34	22 44	23 04				
Duddeston	d	19 36			19 56				20 26	20 36				21 06		21 36		22 06		22 36		23 06				
Birmingham New Street 12	a	19 41		19 51	20 03	20 13	20 21		20 33	20 41	20 51			21 12	21 21	21 42	21 51	22 12	22 21	22 42	22 51	23 12	23 31	23 59		
	d	19 44		19 54		20 14	20 24	20 30		20 44	20 54		20 59	21 14	21 24	21 44	21 54	22 14	22 24	22 44	22 54	23 14	23 34			
Five Ways	d	19 47		19 57		20 17	20 27			20 47	20 57			21 17	21 27	21 47	21 57	22 17	22 27	22 47	22 57	23 17	23 37			
University	d	19 51		20 01		20 21	20 31	20a36		20 51	21 01		21 05	21 21	21 31	21 51	22 01	22 21	22 31	22 51	23 01	23 21	23 41			
Selly Oak	d	19 53		20 03		20 23	20 33			20 53	21 03			21 23	21 33	21 53	22 03	22 23	22 33	22 53	23 03	23 23	23 44			
Bournville	d	19 55		20 05		20 25	20 35			20 55	21 05			21 25	21 35	21 55	22 05	22 25	22 35	22 55	23 05	23 25	23 46			
Kings Norton	d	19 57		20 07		20 27	20 37			20 57	21 07			21 27	21 37	21 57	22 07	22 27	22 37	22 57	23 07	23 27	23 48			
Northfield	d	20 00		20 10		20 30	20 40			21 00	21 10			21 30	21 40	22 00	22 10	22 30	22 40	23 00	23 10	23 30	23 51			
Longbridge	d	20 04		20a14		20 34	20a44			21 04	21a14			21 34	21a44	22 04	22a14	22 34	22a44	23 04	23a14	23 34	23a54			
Barnt Green	d	20 09				20 39				21 09				21 39		22 09		22 39		23 09		23 39				
Alvechurch	d	20 13				20 43				21 13				21 43		22 13		22 43		23 13		23 43				
Redditch	a	20 23				20 53				21 23				21 53		22 23		22 53		23 23		23 53				
Bromsgrove	a												21 21													

For general notes see front of timetable
For details of catering facilities see Directory of Train Operators

A From Nottingham (Table 57)
B From Nottingham to Cardiff Central (Table 57)

Lichfield → Birmingham → Longbridge and Redditch

Network Diagram - see first page of Table 67

		LM	LM	LM	XC 1◇ A	LM	LM	XC 1◇ B	LM	LM		XC 1◇ C	LM	LM	LM	XC 1◇ D	LM	LM	XC 1◇ E	LM		LM	XC 1◇ E	LM	LM	LM
Lichfield Trent Valley	d			09 33		10 03	10 33		11 03	11 33			12 03	12 33			13 03	13 33		14 03		14 33		15 03		15 33
Lichfield City	d			09 36		10 06	10 36		11 06	11 36			12 06	12 36			13 06	13 36		14 06		14 36		15 06		15 36
Shenstone	d			09 41		10 11	10 41		11 11	11 41			12 11	12 41			13 11	13 41		14 11		14 41		15 11		15 41
Blake Street	d			09 45		10 15	10 45		11 15	11 45			12 15	12 45			13 15	13 45		14 15		14 45		15 15		15 45
Butlers Lane	d			09 47		10 17	10 47		11 17	11 47			12 17	12 47			13 17	13 47		14 17		14 47		15 17		15 47
Four Oaks	d		09 20	09 50		10 20	10 50		11 20	11 50			12 20	12 50			13 20	13 50		14 20		14 50		15 20		15 50
Sutton Coldfield	d		09 23	09 53		10 23	10 53		11 23	11 53			12 23	12 53			13 23	13 53		14 23		14 53		15 23		15 53
Wylde Green	d		09 26	09 56		10 26	10 56		11 26	11 56			12 26	12 56			13 26	13 56		14 26		14 56		15 26		15 56
Chester Road	d		09 28	09 58		10 28	10 58		11 28	11 58			12 28	12 58			13 28	13 58		14 28		14 58		15 28		15 58
Erdington	d		09 29	09 59		10 29	10 59		11 29	11 59			12 29	12 59			13 29	13 59		14 29		14 59		15 29		15 59
Gravelly Hill	d		09 32	10 02		10 32	11 02		11 32	12 02			12 32	13 02			13 32	14 02		14 32		15 02		15 32		16 02
Aston	d		09 35	10 05		10 35	11 05		11 35	12 05			12 35	13 05			13 35	14 05		14 35		15 05		15 35		16 05
Duddeston	d		09 37	10 07		10 37	11 07		11 37	12 07			12 37	13 07			13 37	14 07		14 37		15 07		15 37		16 07
Birmingham New Street 12	a		09 42	10 12		10 42	11 12		11 42	12 12			12 42	13 12			13 42	14 12		14 42		15 12		15 42		16 12
	d	09 15	09 45	10 15	10 30	10 45	11 15	11 30	11 45	12 15		12 30	12 45	13 15	13 20	13 30	13 45	14 15	14 30	14 45		15 15	15 30	15 45	16 00	16 15
Five Ways	d	09 18	09 48	10 18		10 48	11 18		11 48	12 18			12 48	13 18			13 48	14 18		14 48		15 18		15 48		16 18
University	d	09 22	09 52	10 22	10a36	10 52	11 22	11a36	11 52	12 22		12a36	12 52	13 22		13a36	13 52	14 22	14a36	14 52		15 22	15a36	15 52		16 22
Selly Oak	d	09 25	09 55	10 25		10 55	11 25		11 55	12 25			12 55	13 25			13 55	14 25		14 55		15 25		15 55		16 25
Bournville	d	09 27	09 57	10 27		10 57	11 27		11 57	12 27			12 57	13 27			13 57	14 27		14 57		15 27		15 57		16 27
Kings Norton	d	09 29	09 59	10 29		10 59	11 29		11 59	12 29			12 59	13 29			13 59	14 29		14 59		15 29		15 59		16 29
Northfield	d	09 32	10 02	10 32		11 02	11 32		12 02	12 32			13 02	13 32			14 02	14 32		15 02		15 32		16 02		16 32
Longbridge	d	09 35	10 05	10 35		11 05	11 35		12 05	12 35			13 05	13 35			14 05	14 35		15 05		15 35		16 05		16 35
Barnt Green	d	09 39	10 09	10 39		11 09	11 39		12 09	12 39			13 09	13 39			14 09	14 39		15 09		15 39		16 09		16 39
Alvechurch	d	09 44	10 14	10 44		11 14	11 44		12 14	12 44			13 14	13 44			14 14	14 44		15 14		15 44		16 14		16 44
Redditch	a	09 53	10 23	10 53		11 23	11 53		12 23	12 53			13 23	13 53			14 23	14 53		15 23		15 53		16 23		16 53
Bromsgrove	a														13 43										16 20	

		XC 1◇ E	LM	LM	XC 1◇ E	LM	LM		LM	XC 1◇ E	LM	LM	LM	XC 1◇ E	LM	LM	LM	LM	LM	LM	LM	LM	LM	LM		
Lichfield Trent Valley	d		16 03	16 33		17 03			17 33		18 03		18 33		19 03	19 33	20 03		20 33	21 03	21 33	22 03	22 33	23 03		
Lichfield City	d		16 06	16 36		17 06			17 36		18 06		18 36		19 06	19 36	20 06		20 36	21 06	21 36	22 06	22 36	23 06		
Shenstone	d		16 11	16 41		17 11			17 41		18 11		18 41		19 11	19 41	20 11		20 41	21 11	21 41	22 11	22 41	23 11		
Blake Street	d		16 15	16 45		17 15			17 45		18 15		18 45		19 15	19 45	20 15		20 45	21 15	21 45	22 15	22 45	23 15		
Butlers Lane	d		16 17	16 47		17 17			17 47		18 17		18 47		19 17	19 47	20 17		20 47	21 17	21 47	22 17	22 47	23 17		
Four Oaks	d		16 20	16 50		17 20			17 50		18 20		18 50		19 20	19 50	20 20		20 50	21 20	21 50	22 20	22 50	23 20		
Sutton Coldfield	d		16 23	16 53		17 23			17 53		18 23		18 53		19 23	19 53	20 23		20 53	21 23	21 53	22 23	22 53	23 23		
Wylde Green	d		16 26	16 56		17 26			17 56		18 26		18 56		19 26	19 56	20 26		20 56	21 26	21 56	22 26	22 56	23 26		
Chester Road	d		16 28	16 58		17 28			17 58		18 28		18 58		19 28	19 58	20 28		20 58	21 28	21 58	22 28	22 58			
Erdington	d		16 29	16 59		17 29			17 59		18 29		18 59		19 29	19 59	20 29		20 59	21 29	21 59	22 29	22 59			
Gravelly Hill	d		16 32	17 02		17 32			18 02		18 32		19 02		19 32	20 02	20 32		21 02	21 32	22 02	22 32	23 02			
Aston	d		16 35	17 05		17 35			18 05		18 35		19 05		19 35	20 05	20 35		21 05	21 35	22 05	22 35	23 05			
Duddeston	d		16 37	17 07		17 37			18 07		18 37		19 07		19 37	20 07	20 37		21 07	21 37	22 07	22 37	23 07			
Birmingham New Street 12	a		16 42	17 12		17 42			18 12		18 42		19 12		19 42	20 12	20 42		21 12	21 42	22 12	22 42	23 12	23 39		
	d	16 30	16 45	17 15	17 30	17 45	18 00		18 15	18 30	18 45	19 00	19 15	19 30	19 45	20 15	20 45	21 00	21 15	21 45	22 15	22 45	23 15			
Five Ways	d		16 48	17 18		17 48			18 18		18 48		19 18		19 48	20 18	20 48		21 18	21 48	22 18	22 48	23 18			
University	d	16a36	16 52	17 22	17a36	17 52			18 22	18a36	18 52		19 22	19a36	19 52	20 22	20 52		21 22	21 52	22 22	22 52	23 22			
Selly Oak	d		16 55	17 25		17 55			18 25		18 55		19 25		19 55	20 25	20 55		21 25	21 55	22 25	22 55	23 25			
Bournville	d		16 57	17 27		17 57			18 27		18 57		19 27		19 57	20 27	20 57		21 27	21 57	22 27	22 57	23 27			
Kings Norton	d		16 59	17 29		17 59			18 29		18 59		19 29		19 59	20 29	20 59		21 29	21 59	22 29	22 59	23 29			
Northfield	d		17 02	17 32		18 02			18 32		19 02		19 32		20 02	20 32	21 02		21 32	22 02	22 32	23 02	23 32			
Longbridge	d		17 05	17 35		18 05			18 35		19 05		19 35		20 05	20 35	21 05		21 35	22 05	22 35	23 05	23 35			
Barnt Green	d		17 09	17 39		18 09			18 39		19 09		19 39		20 09	20 39	21 09		21 39	22 09	22 39	23 09	23 39			
Alvechurch	d		17 14	17 44		18 14			18 44		19 14		19 44		20 14	20 44	21 14		21 44	22 14	22 44	23 14	23 44			
Redditch	a		17 23	17 53		18 23			18 53		19 23		19 53		20 23	20 53	21 23		21 53	22 23	22 53	23 23	23 53			
Bromsgrove	a						18 20					19 21						21 21								

For general notes see front of timetable
For details of catering facilities see Directory of Train Operators

A From 13 September
B Until 12 July and from 13 September
C Until 12 July and from 13 September.
Until 12 July from Nottingham, from 13 September from Derby (Table 57)
D Until 12 July and from 13 September.
From 13 September from Nottingham (Table 57)
E From Nottingham (Table 57)

Table 69

Sundays

from 8 November

Lichfield → Birmingham → Longbridge and Redditch

Network Diagram - see first page of Table 67

		LM	LM (bus)	LM	LM (bus)	LM	LM (bus)	LM		LM (bus)	LM	LM (bus)	LM	LM (bus)	LM	LM (bus)		LM (bus)	LM	LM (bus)	LM (bus)	LM	LM (bus)	LM		LM (bus)
Lichfield Trent Valley	d					09 33		10 03			10 33		11 03		11 33				12 03			12 33		13 03		
Lichfield City	d					09 36		10 06			10 36		11 06		11 36				12 06			12 36		13 06		
Shenstone	d					09 41		10 11			10 41		11 11		11 41				12 11			12 41		13 11		
Blake Street	d					09 45		10 15			10 45		11 15		11 45				12 15			12 45		13 15		
Butlers Lane	d					09 47		10 17			10 47		11 17		11 47				12 17			12 47		13 17		
Four Oaks	d			09 20		09 50		10 20			10 50		11 20		11 50				12 20			12 50		13 20		
Sutton Coldfield	d			09 23		09 53		10 23			10 53		11 23		11 53				12 23			12 53		13 23		
Wylde Green	d			09 26		09 56		10 26			10 56		11 26		11 56				12 26			12 56		13 26		
Chester Road	d			09 28		09 58		10 28			10 58		11 28		11 58				12 28			12 58		13 28		
Erdington	d			09 29		09 59		10 29			10 59		11 29		11 59				12 29			12 59		13 29		
Gravelly Hill	d			09 32		10 02		10 32			11 02		11 32		12 02				12 32			13 02		13 32		
Aston	d			09 35		10 05		10 35			11 05		11 35		12 05				12 35			13 05		13 35		
Duddeston	d			09 37		10 07		10 37			11 07		11 37		12 07				12 37			13 07		13 37		
Birmingham New Street 12	a			09 42		10 12		10 42			11 12		11 42		12 12				12 42			13 12		13 42		
	d	09 15		09 45		10 15		10 45			11 15		11 45		12 15	12 40			12 45	13 00		13 15		13 45		
Five Ways	d	09 18		09 48		10 18		10 48			11 18		11 48		12 18				12 48			13 18		13 48		
University	d	09 22		09 52		10 22		10 52			11 22		11 52		12 22				12 52			13 22		13 52		
Selly Oak	d	09 25	09 32	09 55	10 02	10 25	10 32	10 55		11 02	11 25	11 32	11 55	12 02	12 25			12 32	12 55		13 02	13 25	13 32	13 55		14 02
Bournville	d	09 27	09 40	09 57	10 10	10 27	10 40	10 57		11 10	11 27	11 40	11 57	12 10	12 27			12 40	12 57		13 10	13 27	13 40	13 57		14 10
Kings Norton	d	09a32	09 50	10a02	10 20	10a32	10 50	11a02		11 20	11a32	11 50	12a02	12 20	12a32			12 50	13a02		13 20	13a32	13 50	14a02		14 20
Northfield	d		09 57		10 27		10 57			11 27		11 57		12 27				12 57			13 27		13 57			14 27
Longbridge	d		10 07		10 37		11 07			11 37		12 07		12 37				13 07			13 37		14 07			14 37
Barnt Green	d		10 17		10 47		11 17			11 47		12 17		12 47				13 17			13 47		14 17			14 47
Alvechurch	d		10b24		10b54		11b24			11b54		12b24		12b54				13b24			13b54		14b24			14b54
Redditch	a		10 34		11 04		11 34			12 04		12 34		13 04				13 34			14 04		14 34			15 04
Bromsgrove	a															13 20				13 35						

		LM	LM (bus)	LM	LM (bus)	LM (bus)	LM	LM (bus)		LM	LM (bus)	LM	LM (bus)	LM	LM (bus)	LM (bus)		LM	LM (bus)	LM	LM (bus)	LM	LM (bus)	LM		LM (bus)
Lichfield Trent Valley	d	13 33		14 03			14 33			15 03		15 33		16 03				16 33		17 03		17 33		18 03		
Lichfield City	d	13 36		14 06			14 36			15 06		15 36		16 06				16 36		17 06		17 36		18 06		
Shenstone	d	13 41		14 11			14 41			15 11		15 41		16 11				16 41		17 11		17 41		18 11		
Blake Street	d	13 45		14 15			14 45			15 15		15 45		16 15				16 45		17 15		17 45		18 15		
Butlers Lane	d	13 47		14 17			14 47			15 17		15 47		16 17				16 47		17 17		17 47		18 17		
Four Oaks	d	13 50		14 20			14 50			15 20		15 50		16 20				16 50		17 20		17 50		18 20		
Sutton Coldfield	d	13 53		14 23			14 53			15 23		15 53		16 23				16 53		17 23		17 53		18 23		
Wylde Green	d	13 56		14 26			14 56			15 26		15 56		16 26				16 56		17 26		17 56		18 26		
Chester Road	d	13 58		14 28			14 58			15 28		15 58		16 28				16 58		17 28		17 58		18 28		
Erdington	d	13 59		14 29			14 59			15 29		15 59		16 29				16 59		17 29		17 59		18 29		
Gravelly Hill	d	14 02		14 32			15 02			15 32		16 02		16 32				17 02		17 32		18 02		18 32		
Aston	d	14 05		14 35			15 05			15 35		16 05		16 35				17 05		17 35		18 05		18 35		
Duddeston	d	14 07		14 37			15 07			15 37		16 07		16 37				17 07		17 37		18 07		18 37		
Birmingham New Street 12	a	14 12		14 42			15 12			15 42		16 12		16 42				17 12		17 42		18 12		18 42		
	d	14 15		14 45	14 55		15 15			15 45		16 15		16 45	17 00			17 15		17 45		18 15		18 45		
Five Ways	d	14 18		14 48			15 18			15 48		16 18		16 48				17 18		17 48		18 18		18 48		
University	d	14 22		14 52			15 22			15 52		16 22		16 52				17 22		17 52		18 22		18 52		
Selly Oak	d	14 25	14 32	14 55		15 02	15 25	15 32		15 55	16 02	16 25	16 32	16 55		17 02		17 25	17 32	17 55	18 02	18 25	18 32	18 55		19 02
Bournville	d	14 27	14 40	14 57		15 10	15 27	15 40		15 57	16 10	16 27	16 40	16 57		17 10		17 27	17 40	17 57	18 10	18 27	18 40	18 57		19 10
Kings Norton	d	14a32	14 50	15a02		15 20	15a32	15 50		16a02	16 20	16a32	16 50	17a02		17 20		17a32	17 50	18a02	18 20	18a32	18 50	19a02		19 20
Northfield	d		14 57			15 27		15 57			16 27		16 57			17 27			17 57		18 27		18 57			19 27
Longbridge	d		15 07			15 37		16 07			16 37		17 07			17 37			18 07		18 37		19 07			19 37
Barnt Green	d		15 17			15 47		16 17			16 47		17 17			17 47			18 17		18 47		19 17			19 47
Alvechurch	d		15b24			15b54		16b24			16b54		17b24			17b54			18b24		18b54		19b24			19b54
Redditch	a		15 34			16 04		16 34			17 04		17 34			18 04			18 34		19 04		19 34			20 04
Bromsgrove	a				15 30										17 35											

		LM	LM (bus)	LM	LM (bus)	LM (bus)	LM	LM (bus)		LM	LM (bus)	LM	LM (bus)	LM (bus)	LM	LM (bus)		LM	LM (bus)	LM	LM (bus)	LM	LM	LM (bus)		
Lichfield Trent Valley	d	18 33		19 03			19 33			20 03		20 33			21 03			21 33		22 03		22 33	23 03			
Lichfield City	d	18 36		19 06			19 36			20 06		20 36			21 06			21 36		22 06		22 36	23 06			
Shenstone	d	18 41		19 11			19 41			20 11		20 41			21 11			21 41		22 11		22 41	23 11			
Blake Street	d	18 45		19 15			19 45			20 15		20 45			21 15			21 45		22 15		22 45	23 15			
Butlers Lane	d	18 47		19 17			19 47			20 17		20 47			21 17			21 47		22 17		22 47	23 17			
Four Oaks	d	18 50		19 20			19 50			20 20		20 50			21 20			21 50		22 20		22 50	23 20			
Sutton Coldfield	d	18 53		19 23			19 53			20 23		20 53			21 23			21 53		22 23		22 53	23 23			
Wylde Green	d	18 56		19 26			19 56			20 26		20 56			21 26			21 56		22 26		22 56	23 26			
Chester Road	d	18 58		19 28			19 58			20 28		20 58			21 28			21 58		22 28		22 58				
Erdington	d	18 59		19 29			19 59			20 29		20 59			21 29			21 59		22 29		22 59				
Gravelly Hill	d	19 02		19 32			20 02			20 32		21 02			21 32			22 02		22 32		23 02				
Aston	d	19 05		19 35			20 05			20 35		21 05			21 35			22 05		22 35		23 05				
Duddeston	d	19 07		19 37			20 07			20 37		21 07			21 37			22 07		22 37		23 07				
Birmingham New Street 12	a	19 12		19 42			20 12			20 42		21 12			21 42			22 12		22 42		23 12	23 39			
	d	19 15		19 45	20 00		20 15			20 45		21 15	21 25		21 45			22 15		22 45		23 15				
Five Ways	d	19 18		19 48			20 18			20 48		21 18			21 48			22 18		22 48		23 18				
University	d	19 22		19 52			20 22			20 52		21 22			21 52			22 22		22 52		23 22				
Selly Oak	d	19 25	19 32	19 55		20 02	20 25	20 32		20 55	21 02	21 25		21 32	21 55	22 02		22 25	22 32	22 55	23 02	23 25		23 32		
Bournville	d	19 27	19 40	19 57		20 10	20 27	20 40		20 57	21 10	21 27		21 40	21 57	22 10		22 27	22 40	22 57	23 10	23 27		23 40		
Kings Norton	d	19a32	19 50	20a02		20 20	20a32	20 50		21a02	21 20	21a32		21 50	22a02	22 20		22a32	22 50	23a02	23 20	23a32		23 50		
Northfield	d		19 57			20 27		20 57			21 27			21 57		22 27			22 57		23 27			23 57		
Longbridge	d		20 07			20 37		21 07			21 37			22 07		22 37			23 07		23 37			00 07		
Barnt Green	d		20 17			20 47		21 17			21 47			22 17		22 47			23 17		23 47			00 17		
Alvechurch	d		20b24			20b54		21b24			21b54			22b24		22b54			23b24		23b54			00b24		
Redditch	a		20 34			21 04		21 34			22 04			22 34		23 04			23 34		00 04			00 34		
Bromsgrove	a				20 35								22 00													

For general notes see front of timetable
For details of catering facilities see
Directory of Train Operators

b Alvechurch Red Lion Pub

Redditch and Longbridge → Birmingham → Lichfield

Network Diagram - see first page of Table 67

Miles	Miles			LM	LM	LM	LM	LM	LM	LM	LM	LM	LM	LM	LM	LM		LM	LM	LM	LM	LM	XC 1 A	LM	LM	LM
—	0	Bromsgrove	d					06 21			06 42					07 25							07 49			
0	—	**Redditch**	d							06 27				06 57						07 27					07 57	
3¼	—	Alvechurch	d							06 32				07 02						07 32					08 02	
5	3½	Barnt Green	d							06 38				07 08						07 38					08 08	
7¾	—	Longbridge	d			06 13	06 23		06 33	06 43		06 53	07 03	07 13	07 23				07 33	07 43		07 53		08 03	08 13	
8¾	—	Northfield	d			06 15	06 25		06 35	06 45		06 55	07 05	07 15	07 25				07 35	07 45		07 55		08 05	08 15	
10¼	—	Kings Norton	d			06 17	06 27		06 37	06 47		06 57	07 07	07 17	07 27				07 38	07 47		07 57		08 07	08 17	
11¼	—	Bournville	d			06 20	06 30		06 40	06 50		07 00	07 10	07 20	07 30				07 40	07 50		08 00		08 10	08 20	
12¼	—	Selly Oak	d			06 22	06 32		06 42	06 52		07 02	07 12	07 22	07 32				07 43	07 52		08 02		08 12	08 22	
13	11½	University	d			06 24	06 34	06 39	06 44	06 54	07 00	07 04	07 14	07 24	07 34				07 45	07 54	08 00	08 04	08 09	08 14	08 24	08 30
13½	—	Five Ways	d			06 27	06 37		06 47	06 57		07 07	07 17	07 27	07 37				07 49	07 57		08 07		08 17	08 27	
14½	13	**Birmingham New Street 12**	a			06 34	06 42	06 45	06 52	07 02	07 07	07 14	07 22	07 34	07 42	07 45			07 52	08 03	08 09	08 12	08 16	08 22	08 34	08 37
—	—		d	06 05	06 25	06 35	06 45		06 55	07 05		07 15	07 25	07 35	07 45			07 56	07 58	08 05		08 15		08 25	08 35	
16	—	Duddeston	d	06 09	06 29				06 59				07 29						08 03					08 29		
17¼	—	Aston	d	06 12	06 32	06 41	06 51		07 02	07 11		07 21	07 32	07 41	07 51				08 06	08 11		08 21		08 32	08 41	
18¾	—	Gravelly Hill	d	06 15	06 35	06 44	06 54		07 05	07 14		07 24	07 35	07 44	07 54				08 09	08 14		08 24		08 35	08 44	
19¾	—	Erdington	d	06 18	06 37	06 46	06 56		07 08	07 16		07 26	07 38	07 46	07 56				08 11	08 16		08 26		08 37	08 46	
20¼	—	Chester Road	d	06 19	06 39	06 48	06 58		07 10	07 18		07 28	07 40	07 48	07 58				08 13	08 18		08 28		08 39	08 48	
21	—	Wylde Green	d	06 21	06 41	06 50	07 00		07 12	07 21		07 30	07 42	07 50	08 00				08 15	08 20		08 30		08 41	08 50	
22	—	Sutton Coldfield	d	06 24	06 44	06 54	07 04		07 15	07 24		07 34	07 45	07 54	08 03			08 08	08 18	08 24		08 34		08 44	08 54	
23½	—	Four Oaks	d	06 28	06 47	06 57	07a11		07 18	07 28		07a41	07 48		08a09			08 12	08 21	08 28		08a41		08 48	08 58	
24½	—	Butlers Lane	d	06 30	06 49	06 59			07 20	07 30			07 50							08 30				08 50	09 00	
26½	—	Blake Street	d	06 32	06 51	07 01			07 22	07 32			07 52							08 32				08 52	09 02	
28¾	—	Shenstone	d	06 36	06 55				07 26				07 56						08 27	08 36				08 56		
31¾	—	**Lichfield City**	d	06a41	07 00	07 12			07 31	07 42			08 01	08a08				08a22	08 32	08 42				09a01	09 10	
33	—	**Lichfield Trent Valley**	a		07 06	07 16			07 36	07 46			08 06						08 35	08 46					09 15	

		LM	XC 1 ◇ B	LM	LM	LM	LM		LM	LM	LM	LM	XC 1 ◇ C	LM	LM	LM	LM	LM	LM	LM	XC 1 ◇ C		LM	LM	LM	LM
Bromsgrove	d		08 23			08 41					09 09						09 54								10 42	
Redditch	d				08 27					08 57					09 27				09 57					10 27		
Alvechurch	d				08 32					09 02					09 32				10 02					10 32		
Barnt Green	d				08 38					09 08					09 38				10 08					10 38		
Longbridge	d	08 23		08 33	08 43		08 53		09 03	09 13		09 23		09 33	09 43	09 53		10 03	10 13	10 23			10 33	10 43		10 53
Northfield	d	08 25		08 35	08 45		08 55		09 05	09 15		09 25		09 35	09 45	09 55		10 05	10 15	10 25			10 35	10 45		10 55
Kings Norton	d	08 27		08 37	08 47		08 57		09 07	09 17		09 27		09 37	09 47	09 57		10 07	10 17	10 27			10 37	10 47		10 57
Bournville	d	08 30		08 40	08 50		09 00		09 10	09 20		09 30		09 40	09 50	10 00		10 10	10 20	10 30			10 40	10 50		11 00
Selly Oak	d	08 32		08 42	08 52		09 02		09 12	09 22		09 32		09 42	09 52	10 02		10 12	10 22	10 32			10 42	10 52		11 02
University	d	08 34	08 39	08 44	08 54	09 00	09 04		09 14	09 25	09 30	09 34	09 39	09 44	09 54	10 04	10 09	10 14	10 24	10 34	10 39		10 44	10 54	10 59	11 04
Five Ways	d	08 37		08 47	08 57		09 07		09 17	09 27		09 37		09 47	09 57	10 07		10 17	10 27	10 37			10 47	10 57		11 07
Birmingham New Street 12	a	08 42	08 45	08 53	09 03	09 07	09 12		09 22	09 33	09 42	09 42	09 45	09 53	10 03	10 12	10 24	10 22	10 34	10 42	10 45		10 53	11 02	11 13	11 12
	d	08 45		08 55	09 05		09 15		09 25	09 35		09 45		09 55	10 05	10 15		10 25	10 35	10 45			10 55	11 05		11 15
Duddeston	d			08 59					09 29					09 59				10 29					10 59			
Aston	d	08 51		09 02	09 11		09 21		09 32	09 41		09 51		10 02	10 11	10 21		10 32	10 41	10 51			11 02	11 11		11 21
Gravelly Hill	d	08 54		09 05	09 14		09 24		09 35	09 44		09 54		10 05	10 14	10 24		10 35	10 44	10 54			11 05	11 14		11 24
Erdington	d	08 56		09 08	09 16		09 26		09 38	09 46		09 56		10 08	10 16	10 26		10 38	10 46	10 56			11 08	11 16		11 26
Chester Road	d	08 58		09 09	09 18		09 28		09 39	09 48		09 58		10 09	10 18	10 28		10 39	10 48	10 58			11 09	11 18		11 28
Wylde Green	d	09 00		09 11	09 20		09 30		09 41	09 50		10 00		10 11	10 20	10 30		10 41	10 50	11 00			11 11	11 20		11 30
Sutton Coldfield	d	09 04		09 14	09 24		09 34		09 44	09 54		10 04		10 14	10 24	10 34		10 44	10 54	11 04			11 14	11 24		11 34
Four Oaks	d	09a11		09 18	09 28		09a41		09 48	09 58		10a11		10 18	10 28	10a41		10 48	10 58	11a11			11 18	11 28		11a41
Butlers Lane	d			09 20	09 30				09 50	10 00				10 20	10 30			10 50	11 00				11 20	11 30		
Blake Street	d			09 22	09 32				09 52	10 02				10 22	10 32			10 52	11 02				11 22	11 32		
Shenstone	d			09 26					09 56					10 26				10 56					11 26			
Lichfield City	d			09a34	09 40				10a01	10 10				10a31	10 40			11a01	11 10				11a31	11 40		
Lichfield Trent Valley	a				09 45					10 15					10 45				11 15					11 45		

		LM	LM	LM	XC 1 ◇ C	LM	LM	LM	LM	LM	LM	LM		XC 1 ◇ C	LM	LM	LM	LM	LM	LM	LM	XC 1 ◇ C	LM	LM	LM	LM
Bromsgrove	d							11 42									12 42								13 42	
Redditch	d		10 57				11 27				11 57					12 27				12 57				13 27		
Alvechurch	d		11 02				11 32				12 02					12 32				13 02				13 32		
Barnt Green	d		11 08				11 38				12 08					12 38				13 08				13 38		
Longbridge	d	11 03	11 13	11 23		11 33	11 43		11 53	12 03	12 13	12 23			12 33	12 43		12 53	13 03	13 13	13 23		13 33	13 43		13 53
Northfield	d	11 05	11 15	11 25		11 35	11 45		11 55	12 05	12 15	12 25			12 35	12 45		12 55	13 05	13 15	13 25		13 35	13 45		13 55
Kings Norton	d	11 07	11 17	11 27		11 37	11 47		11 57	12 07	12 17	12 27			12 37	12 47		12 57	13 07	13 17	13 27		13 37	13 47		13 57
Bournville	d	11 10	11 20	11 30		11 40	11 50		12 00	12 10	12 20	12 30			12 40	12 50		13 00	13 10	13 20	13 30		13 40	13 50		14 00
Selly Oak	d	11 12	11 22	11 32		11 42	11 52		12 02	12 12	12 22	12 32			12 42	12 52		13 02	13 12	13 22	13 32		13 42	13 52		14 02
University	d	11 14	11 24	11 34	11 39	11 44	11 54	11 59	12 04	12 14	12 24	12 34		12 39	12 44	12 54	12 59	13 04	13 14	13 24	13 34	13 39	13 44	13 54	13 59	14 04
Five Ways	d	11 17	11 27	11 37		11 47	11 57		12 07	12 17	12 27	12 37			12 47	12 57		13 07	13 17	13 27	13 37		13 47	13 57		14 07
Birmingham New Street 12	a	11 22	11 33	11 42	11 45	11 53	12 03	12 13	12 12	12 22	12 33	12 42		12 45	12 53	13 03	13 13	13 12	13 22	13 33	13 42	13 45	13 53	14 03	14 13	14 12
	d	11 25	11 35	11 45		11 55	12 05		12 15	12 25	12 35	12 45			12 55	13 05		13 15	13 25	13 35	13 45		13 55	14 05		14 15
Duddeston	d	11 29				11 59				12 29					12 59				13 29				13 59			
Aston	d	11 32	11 41	11 51		12 02	12 11		12 21	12 32	12 41	12 51			13 02	13 11		13 21	13 32	13 41	13 51		14 02	14 11		14 21
Gravelly Hill	d	11 35	11 44	11 54		12 05	12 14		12 24	12 35	12 44	12 54			13 05	13 14		13 24	13 35	13 44	13 54		14 05	14 14		14 24
Erdington	d	11 38	11 46	11 56		12 08	12 16		12 26	12 38	12 46	12 56			13 08	13 16		13 26	13 38	13 46	13 56		14 08	14 16		14 26
Chester Road	d	11 39	11 48	11 58		12 09	12 18		12 28	12 39	12 48	12 58			13 09	13 18		13 28	13 39	13 48	13 58		14 09	14 18		14 28
Wylde Green	d	11 41	11 50	12 00		12 11	12 20		12 30	12 41	12 50	13 00			13 11	13 20		13 30	13 41	13 50	14 00		14 11	14 20		14 30
Sutton Coldfield	d	11 44	11 54	12 04		12 14	12 24		12 34	12 44	12 54	13 04			13 14	13 24		13 34	13 44	13 54	14 04		14 14	14 24		14 34
Four Oaks	d	11 48	11 58	12a11		12 18	12 28		12a41	12 48	12 58	13a11			13 18	13 28		13a41	13 48	13 58	14a11		14 18	14 28		14a41
Butlers Lane	d	11 50	12 00			12 20	12 30			12 50	13 00				13 20	13 30			13 50	14 00			14 20	14 30		
Blake Street	d	11 52	12 02			12 22	12 32			12 52	13 02				13 22	13 32			13 52	14 02			14 22	14 32		
Shenstone	d	11 56				12 26				12 56					13 26				13 56				14 26			
Lichfield City	d	12a01	12 10			12a31	12 40			13a01	13 10				13a31	13 40			14a01	14 10			14a31	14 40		
Lichfield Trent Valley	a		12 15				12 45				13 15					13 45				14 15				14 45		

For general notes see front of timetable
For details of catering facilities see Directory of Train Operators

A From Gloucester to Nottingham (Table 57)
B From Cardiff Central (Table 132) to Nottingham (Table 57)
C To Nottingham (Table 57)

Redditch and Longbridge → Birmingham → Lichfield

Network Diagram - see first page of Table 67

		LM	LM		LM	XC 1 ◊ A	LM	LM	LM	LM	LM	LM	LM	XC 1 ◊ A	LM	LM	LM		LM	LM	LM	LM	XC 1 ◊ A	LM	LM	LM
Bromsgrove	d								14 42								15 42									16 42
Redditch	d		13 57					14 27				14 57				15 27					15 57				16 27	
Alvechurch	d		14 02					14 32				15 02				15 32					16 02				16 32	
Barnt Green	d		14 08					14 38				15 08				15 38					16 08				16 38	16 49
Longbridge	d	14 03	14 13		14 23		14 33	14 43		14 53	15 03	15 13	15 23		15 33	15 43			15 53	16 03	16 13	16 23		16 33	16 43	
Northfield	d	14 05	14 15		14 25		14 35	14 45		14 55	15 05	15 15	15 25		15 35	15 45			15 55	16 05	16 15	16 25		16 35	16 45	
Kings Norton	d	14 07	14 17		14 27		14 37	14 47		14 57	15 07	15 17	15 27		15 37	15 47			15 57	16 07	16 17	16 27		16 37	16 47	
Bournville	d	14 10	14 20		14 30		14 40	14 50		15 00	15 10	15 20	15 30		15 40	15 50			16 00	16 10	16 20	16 30		16 40	16 50	
Selly Oak	d	14 12	14 22		14 32		14 42	14 52		15 02	15 12	15 22	15 32		15 42	15 52			16 02	16 12	16 22	16 32		16 42	16 52	
University	d	14 14	14 24		14 34	14 39	14 44	14 54	14 59	15 04	15 14	15 24	15 34	15 39	15 44	15 54	15 59		16 04	16 14	16 24	16 34	16 39	16 44	16 54	16 59
Five Ways	d	14 17	14 27		14 37		14 47	14 57		15 07	15 17	15 27	15 37		15 47	15 57			16 07	16 17	16 27	16 37		16 47	16 57	
Birmingham New Street 12	a	14 22	14 33		14 42	14 45	14 53	15 03	15 13	15 12	15 22	15 33	15 42	15 45	15 53	16 03	16 13		16 12	16 22	16 34	16 42	16 45	16 53	17 03	17 13
	d	14 25	14 35		14 45		14 55	15 05		15 15	15 25	15 35	15 45		15 55	16 05			16 15	16 25	16 35	16 45		16 55	17 05	
Duddeston	d	14 29					14 59				15 29				15 59					16 29				16 59		
Aston	d	14 32	14 41		14 51		15 02	15 11		15 21	15 32	15 41	15 51		16 02	16 11			16 21	16 32	16 41	16 51		17 02	17 11	
Gravelly Hill	d	14 35	14 44		14 54		15 05	15 14		15 24	15 35	15 44	15 54		16 05	16 14			16 24	16 35	16 44	16 54		17 05	17 14	
Erdington	d	14 38	14 46		14 56		15 08	15 16		15 26	15 38	15 46	15 56		16 08	16 16			16 26	16 38	16 46	16 56		17 08	17 16	
Chester Road	d	14 39	14 48		14 58		15 09	15 18		15 28	15 39	15 48	15 58		16 09	16 18			16 28	16 39	16 48	16 58		17 09	17 18	
Wylde Green	d	14 41	14 50		15 00		15 11	15 20		15 30	15 41	15 50	16 00		16 11	16 20			16 30	16 41	16 50	17 00		17 11	17 20	
Sutton Coldfield	d	14 44	14 54		15 04		15 14	15 24		15 34	15 44	15 54	16 04		16 14	16 24			16 34	16 44	16 54	17 04		17 14	17 24	
Four Oaks	d	14 48	14 58		15a11		15 18	15 28		15a41	15 48	15 58	16a11		16 18	16 28			16a41	16 48	16 58	17a11		17 18	17 28	
Butlers Lane	d	14 50	15 00				15 20	15 30			15 50	16 00			16 20	16 30				16 50	17 00			17 20	17 30	
Blake Street	d	14 52	15 02				15 22	15 32			15 52	16 02			16 22	16 32				16 52	17 02			17 22	17 32	
Shenstone	d	14 56					15 26				15 56				16 26					16 56				17 26	17 36	
Lichfield City	d	15a01	15 10				15a31	15 40			16a01	16 10			16a31	16 40				17a01	17 10			17 31	17 41	
Lichfield Trent Valley	a		15 15					15 45				16 15				16 45					17 15			17 35	17 46	

		LM	LM	LM	LM	XC 1 ◊ A	LM	LM		LM	LM	LM	LM	LM	XC 1 ◊ A	LM	LM	LM	LM	LM	LM	LM		XC 1 ◊ A	LM	LM
Bromsgrove	d									17 43								18 42								
Redditch	d			16 57				17 27					17 57				18 27				18 57					19 27
Alvechurch	d			17 02				17 32					18 02				18 32				19 02					19 32
Barnt Green	d			17 08				17 38					18 08				18 38	18 49			19 08					19 38
Longbridge	d	16 53	17 03	17 13	17 23		17 33	17 43			17 53	18 03	18 13	18 23		18 33	18 43		18 53	19 03	19 13	19 23			19 33	19 43
Northfield	d	16 55	17 05	17 15	17 25		17 35	17 45			17 55	18 05	18 15	18 25		18 35	18 45		18 55	19 05	19 15	19 25			19 35	19 45
Kings Norton	d	16 57	17 07	17 17	17 27		17 37	17 47			17 57	18 07	18 17	18 27		18 37	18 47		18 57	19 07	19 17	19 27			19 37	19 47
Bournville	d	17 00	17 10	17 20	17 30		17 40	17 50			18 00	18 10	18 20	18 30		18 40	18 50		19 00	19 10	19 20	19 30			19 40	19 50
Selly Oak	d	17 02	17 12	17 22	17 32		17 42	17 52			18 02	18 12	18 22	18 32		18 42	18 52		19 02	19 12	19 22	19 32			19 42	19 52
University	d	17 04	17 14	17 24	17 34	17 39	17 44	17 54		17 59	18 04	18 14	18 24	18 34	18 39	18 44	18 54	18 59	19 04	19 14	19 24	19 34		19 39	19 44	19 54
Five Ways	d	17 07	17 17	17 27	17 37		17 47	17 57			18 07	18 17	18 27	18 37		18 47	18 57		19 07	19 17	19 27	19 37			19 47	19 57
Birmingham New Street 12	a	17 12	17 23	17 33	17 42	17 45	17 53	18 03		18 13	18 12	18 23	18 33	18 42	18 45	18 53	19 03	19 12	19 12	19 23	19 33	19 43		19 45	19 53	20 03
	d	17 15	17 25	17 35	17 45		17 55	18 05			18 15	18 25	18 35	18 45		18 55	19 05		19 15	19 25	19 35				19 55	20 05
Duddeston	d		17 29				17 59					18 29				18 59					19 39					20 09
Aston	d	17 21	17 32	17 41	17 51		18 02	18 11			18 21	18 32	18 41	18 51		19 02	19 11		19 21	19 31	19 42				20 01	20 12
Gravelly Hill	d	17 24	17 35	17 44	17 54		18 05	18 14			18 24	18 35	18 44	18 54		19 05	19 14		19 24	19 34	19 45				20 04	20 15
Erdington	d	17 26	17 38	17 46	17 56		18 08	18 16			18 26	18 38	18 46	18 56		19 07	19 16		19 26	19 36	19 48				20 06	20 18
Chester Road	d	17 28	17 39	17 48	17 58		18 09	18 18			18 28	18 39	18 48	18 58		19 09	19 18		19 28	19 38	19 50				20 08	20 20
Wylde Green	d	17 30	17 41	17 50	18 00		18 11	18 20			18 30	18 41	18 50	19 00		19 11	19 20		19 30	19 40	19 52				20 10	20 22
Sutton Coldfield	d	17 34	17 44	17 54	18 04		18 14	18 24			18 34	18 44	18 54	19 04		19 14	19 24		19 34	19 44	19 55				20 14	20 25
Four Oaks	d	17a41	17 48	17 58	18a11		18 18	18 28			18a41	18 48	18 58	19a11		19 18	19 28		19a41	19 51	19 58				20a21	20 28
Butlers Lane	d		17 50	18 00			18 20	18 30				18 50	19 00			19 20	19 30			19 53	20 00					20 30
Blake Street	d		17 52	18 02			18 22	18 32				18 52	19 02			19 22	19 32			19a58	20 02					20 32
Shenstone	d		17 56	18 06			18 26					18 56				19 26					20 06					20 36
Lichfield City	d		18 01	18 11			18a31	18 40				19a01	19 10			19a31	19 40				20 11					20 41
Lichfield Trent Valley	a		18 05	18 16				18 45					19 15				19 45				20 16					20 46

		LM	LM	LM	LM	XC 1 ◊ A	LM	LM	LM	LM	LM	LM	XC 1 ◊		LM	LM	LM	LM	LM B	LM	LM C	LM	LM	LM
Bromsgrove	d		19 46						20 59										22 27		22 29			
Redditch	d				19 57			20 27			20 57				21 27		21 57		↓	22 27	↓		22 57	
Alvechurch	d				20 02			20 32			21 02				21 32		22 02		↓	22 32	↓		23 02	
Barnt Green	d				20 08			20 38			21 08				21 38		22 08		↓	22 38	↓		23 08	
Longbridge	d	19 53		20 03	20 13		20 30	20 43		21 00	21 13	21 30			21 43	22 00	22 13	22 30	↓	22 43	↓	22 52	23 13	23 30
Northfield	d	19 55		20 05	20 15		20 32	20 45		21 02	21 15	21 32			21 45	22 02	22 15	22 32	↓	22 45	↓	22 54	23 15	23 32
Kings Norton	d	19 57		20 07	20 17		20 34	20 47		21 04	21 17	21 34			21 47	22 04	22 17	22 34	↓	22 47	↓	22 56	23 17	23 34
Bournville	d	20 00		20 10	20 20		20 37	20 50		21 07	21 20	21 37			21 50	22 07	22 20	22 37	↓	22 50	↓	22 59	23 20	23 37
Selly Oak	d	20 02		20 12	20 22		20 39	20 52		21 09	21 22	21 39			21 52	22 09	22 22	22 39	↓	22 52	↓	23 01	23 22	23 39
University	d	20 04	20 09	20 14	20 24	20 39	20 42	20 54	21 16	21 12	21 24	21 42	21 46		21 54	22 12	22 24	22 42	22 45	22 54	23 00	23 03	23 24	23 41
Five Ways	d	20 07		20 17	20 27		20 45	20 57		21 15	21 27	21 45			21 57	22 15	22 27	22 45	↓	22 57	↓	23 06	23 27	23 44
Birmingham New Street 12	a	20 13	20 20	20 23	20 34	20 45	20 50	21 02	21 23	21 20	21 33	21 50	21 57		22 02	22 20	22 33	22 49	22 52	23 03	23 07	23 12	23 34	23 50
	d			20 25	20 35		20 55	21 05		21 25	21 35	21 55			22 05	22 25	22 35	22 55				23 15		
Duddeston	d				20 39			21 09			21 39				22 09		22 39	22 59				23 19		
Aston	d			20 31	20 42		21 01	21 12		21 31	21 42	22 01			22 12	22 31	22 42	23 02				23 22		
Gravelly Hill	d			20 34	20 45		21 04	21 15		21 34	21 45	22 04			22 15	22 34	22 45	23 05				23 25		
Erdington	d			20 36	20 48		21 06	21 18		21 36	21 48	22 06			22 18	22 36	22 48	23 08				23 28		
Chester Road	d			20 38	20 50		21 08	21 20		21 38	21 50	22 08			22 20	22 38	22 50	23 10				23 30		
Wylde Green	d			20 40	20 52		21 10	21 22		21 40	21 52	22 10			22 22	22 40	22 52	23 12				23 32		
Sutton Coldfield	d			20 44	20 55		21 14	21 25		21 44	21 55	22 14			22 25	22 44	22 55	23 15				23 35		
Four Oaks	d			20a51	20 58		21a21	21 28		21a51	21 58	22a21			22 28	22a51	22 58	23 18				23 38		
Butlers Lane	d				21 00			21 30			22 00				22 30		23 00	23 20				23 40		
Blake Street	d				21 02			21 32			22 02				22 32		23 02	23a23				23 42		
Shenstone	d				21 06			21 36			22 06				22 36		23 06					23 46		
Lichfield City	d				21 11			21 41			22 11				22 41		23 11					23a51		
Lichfield Trent Valley	a				21 16			21 46			22 16				22 46		23 16							

For general notes see front of timetable
For details of catering facilities see Directory of Train Operators

A To Nottingham (Table 57)
B Until 4 September
C From 7 September

Table 69

Redditch and Longbridge → Birmingham → Lichfield

Network Diagram - see first page of Table 67

		LM	LM	LM	LM	LM	LM	LM	LM	LM	LM	LM	LM	LM	XC 1 A	LM	LM	LM	LM	LM	XC 1 ◇ B	LM	LM	LM
Bromsgrove	d								06 50						07 44		07 50							08 40
Redditch	d						06 27				06 57			07 27					07 57				08 27	
Alvechurch	d						06 32				07 02			07 32					08 02				08 32	
Barnt Green	d						06 38				07 08			07 38					08 08				08 38	
Longbridge	d			06 13	06 23	06 33	06 43	06 53		07 03	07 13	07 23	07 33	07 43		07 53		08 03	08 13	08 23		08 33	08 43	
Northfield	d			06 15	06 25	06 35	06 45	06 55		07 05	07 15	07 25	07 35	07 45		07 55		08 05	08 15	08 25		08 35	08 45	
Kings Norton	d			06 17	06 27	06 37	06 47	06 57		07 07	07 17	07 27	07 37	07 47		07 57		08 07	08 17	08 27		08 37	08 47	
Bournville	d			06 20	06 30	06 40	06 50	07 00		07 10	07 20	07 30	07 40	07 49		08 00		08 10	08 20	08 30		08 40	08 50	
Selly Oak	d			06 22	06 32	06 42	06 52	07 02		07 12	07 22	07 32	07 42	07 52		08 02		08 12	08 22	08 32		08 42	08 52	
University	d			06 24	06 34	06 44	06 54	07 04	07 09	07 14	07 24	07 34	07 44	07 54	07 59	08 04	08 09	08 14	08 24	08 34	08 39	08 44	08 54	08 59
Five Ways	d			06 27	06 37	06 48	06 57	07 07		07 17	07 27	07 37	07 47	07 57		08 07		08 17	08 27	08 37		08 47	08 57	
Birmingham New Street 12	a			06 34	06 44	06 52	07 02	07 12	07 16	07 22	07 34	07 42	07 52	08 03	08 08	08 12	08 16	08 22	08 34	08 42	08 45	08 53	09 03	09 11
	d	05 57	06 25	06 35		06 55	07 05	07 15		07 25	07 35	07 45	07 55	08 05		08 15		08 25	08 35	08 45		08 55	09 05	
Duddeston	d	06 01	06 29			06 59				07 29			07 59					08 29				08 59		
Aston	d	06 04	06 32			07 02	07 11	07 21		07 32	07 41	07 51	08 02	08 11		08 21		08 32	08 41	08 51		09 02	09 11	
Gravelly Hill	d	06 07	06 35			07 05	07 14	07 24		07 35	07 44	07 54	08 05	08 14		08 24		08 35	08 44	08 54		09 05	09 14	
Erdington	d	06 10	06 38	06 45		07 08	07 16	07 26		07 38	07 46	07 56	08 08	08 16		08 26		08 38	08 46	08 56		09 08	09 16	
Chester Road	d	06 12	06 40	06 47		07 10	07 18	07 28		07 40	07 48	07 58	08 09	08 18		08 28		08 39	08 48	08 58		09 09	09 18	
Wylde Green	d	06 14	06 42	06 49		07 12	07 20	07 30		07 42	07 50	08 00	08 11	08 20		08 30		08 41	08 50	09 00		09 11	09 20	
Sutton Coldfield	d	06 17	06 45	06 52		07 15	07 24	07 34		07 45	07 54	08 04	08 14	08 24		08 34		08 44	08 54	09 04		09 14	09 24	
Four Oaks	d	06 20	06 48	06 56		07 18	07 28	07a41		07 48	07 58	08a11	08 18	08 28		08a41		08 48	08 58	09a11		09 18	09 28	
Butlers Lane	d	06 22	06 50	06 58		07 20	07 30			07 50	08 00		08 20	08 30				08 50	09 00			09 20	09 30	
Blake Street	d	06 24	06 52	07 00		07 22	07 32			07 52	08 02		08 22	08 32				08 52	09 02			09 22	09 32	
Shenstone	d	06 28	06 56			07 26				07 56			08 26	08 36				08 56				09 26		
Lichfield City	d	06a34	07a02	07 08		07a31	07 40			08a01	08 10		08a31	08 41				09a01	09 10			09a31	09 40	
Lichfield Trent Valley	a			07 13			07 45				08 15			08 46					09 15				09 45	

		LM	LM	LM	LM	XC 1 ◇ C	LM	LM	LM	LM	LM	LM	LM	LM	XC 1 ◇ C	LM	LM	LM	LM	LM	LM	LM	LM
Bromsgrove	d								09 40				10 14					10 42				11 13	
Redditch	d			08 57				09 27				09 57					10 27				10 57		
Alvechurch	d			09 02				09 32				10 02					10 32				11 02		
Barnt Green	d			09 08				09 38				10 08					10 38				11 08		
Longbridge	d	08 53	09 03	09 13	09 23		09 33	09 43		09 53	10 03	10 13		10 23		10 33	10 43		10 53	11 03	11 13		11 23
Northfield	d	08 55	09 05	09 15	09 25		09 35	09 45		09 55	10 05	10 15		10 25		10 35	10 45		10 55	11 05	11 15		11 25
Kings Norton	d	08 57	09 07	09 17	09 27		09 37	09 47		09 57	10 07	10 17		10 27		10 37	10 47		10 57	11 07	11 17		11 27
Bournville	d	09 00	09 10	09 20	09 30		09 40	09 50		10 00	10 10	10 20		10 30		10 40	10 50		11 00	11 10	11 20		11 30
Selly Oak	d	09 02	09 12	09 22	09 32		09 42	09 52		10 02	10 12	10 22		10 32		10 42	10 52		11 02	11 12	11 22		11 32
University	d	09 04	09 14	09 24	09 34	09 39	09 44	09 54	09 59	10 04	10 14	10 24		10 34	10 39	10 44	10 54	10 59	11 04	11 14	11 24		11 34
Five Ways	d	09 07	09 17	09 27	09 37		09 47	09 57		10 07	10 17	10 27		10 37		10 47	10 57		11 07	11 17	11 27		11 37
Birmingham New Street 12	a	09 12	09 22	09 33	09 42	09 45	09 53	10 03	10 11	10 12	10 22	10 34	10 41	10 42	10 45	10 53	11 02	11 11	11 12	11 22	11 33	11 38	11 42
	d	09 15	09 25	09 35	09 45		09 55	10 05		10 15	10 25	10 35		10 45		10 55	11 05		11 15	11 25	11 35		11 45
Duddeston	d		09 29				09 59				10 29					10 59				11 29			
Aston	d	09 21	09 32	09 41	09 51		10 02	10 11		10 21	10 32	10 41		10 51		11 02	11 11		11 21	11 32	11 41		11 51
Gravelly Hill	d	09 24	09 35	09 44	09 54		10 05	10 14		10 24	10 35	10 44		10 54		11 05	11 14		11 24	11 35	11 44		11 54
Erdington	d	09 26	09 38	09 46	09 56		10 08	10 16		10 26	10 38	10 46		10 56		11 08	11 16		11 26	11 38	11 46		11 56
Chester Road	d	09 28	09 39	09 48	09 58		10 09	10 18		10 28	10 39	10 48		10 58		11 09	11 18		11 28	11 39	11 48		11 58
Wylde Green	d	09 30	09 41	09 50	10 00		10 11	10 20		10 30	10 41	10 50		11 00		11 11	11 20		11 30	11 41	11 50		12 00
Sutton Coldfield	d	09 34	09 44	09 54	10 04		10 14	10 24		10 34	10 44	10 54		11 04		11 14	11 24		11 34	11 44	11 54		12 04
Four Oaks	d	09a41	09 48	09 58	10a11		10 18	10 28		10a41	10 48	10 58		11a11		11 18	11 28		11a41	11 48	11 58		12a11
Butlers Lane	d		09 50	10 00			10 20	10 30			10 50	11 00				11 20	11 30			11 50	12 00		
Blake Street	d		09 52	10 02			10 22	10 32			10 52	11 02				11 22	11 32			11 52	12 02		
Shenstone	d		09 56				10 26				10 56					11 26				11 56			
Lichfield City	d		10a01	10 10			10a31	10 40			11a01	11 10				11a31	11 40			12a01	12 10		
Lichfield Trent Valley	a			10 15				10 45				11 15					11 45				12 15		

		XC 1 ◇ C	LM	LM	LM	LM	LM	LM	LM	XC 1 ◇ C	LM	LM	LM	LM	LM	LM	LM	XC 1 ◇ C	LM	LM	LM	LM	LM	LM
Bromsgrove	d				11 42								12 42								13 42			
Redditch	d			11 27				11 57				12 27				12 57				13 27				13 57
Alvechurch	d			11 32				12 02				12 32				13 02				13 32				14 02
Barnt Green	d			11 38				12 08				12 38				13 08				13 38				14 08
Longbridge	d		11 33	11 43		11 53	12 03	12 13	12 23		12 33	12 43		12 53	13 03	13 13	13 23		13 33	13 43		13 53	14 03	14 13
Northfield	d		11 35	11 45		11 55	12 05	12 15	12 25		12 35	12 45		12 55	13 05	13 15	13 25		13 35	13 45		13 55	14 05	14 15
Kings Norton	d		11 37	11 47		11 57	12 07	12 17	12 27		12 37	12 47		12 57	13 07	13 17	13 27		13 37	13 47		13 57	14 07	14 17
Bournville	d		11 40	11 50		12 00	12 10	12 20	12 30		12 40	12 50		13 00	13 10	13 20	13 30		13 40	13 50		14 00	14 10	14 20
Selly Oak	d		11 42	11 52		12 02	12 12	12 22	12 32		12 42	12 52		13 02	13 12	13 22	13 32		13 42	13 52		14 02	14 12	14 22
University	d	11 39	11 44	11 54	11 59	12 04	12 14	12 24	12 34	12 39	12 44	12 54	12 59	13 04	13 14	13 24	13 34	13 39	13 44	13 54	13 59	14 04	14 14	14 24
Five Ways	d		11 47	11 57		12 07	12 17	12 27	12 37		12 47	12 57		13 07	13 17	13 27	13 37		13 47	13 57		14 07	14 17	14 27
Birmingham New Street 12	a	11 45	11 53	12 03	12 11	12 12	12 22	12 33	12 42	12 45	12 53	13 03	13 11	13 12	13 22	13 33	13 42	13 45	13 53	14 03	14 11	14 12	14 22	14 33
	d		11 55	12 05		12 15	12 25	12 35	12 45		12 55	13 05		13 15	13 25	13 35	13 45		13 55	14 05		14 15	14 25	14 35
Duddeston	d		11 59				12 29				12 59				13 29				13 59				14 29	
Aston	d		12 02	12 11		12 21	12 32	12 41	12 51		13 02	13 11		13 21	13 32	13 41	13 51		14 02	14 11		14 21	14 32	14 41
Gravelly Hill	d		12 05	12 14		12 24	12 35	12 44	12 54		13 05	13 14		13 24	13 35	13 44	13 54		14 05	14 14		14 24	14 35	14 44
Erdington	d		12 08	12 16		12 26	12 38	12 46	12 56		13 08	13 16		13 26	13 38	13 46	13 56		14 08	14 16		14 26	14 38	14 46
Chester Road	d		12 09	12 18		12 28	12 39	12 48	12 58		13 09	13 18		13 28	13 39	13 48	13 58		14 09	14 18		14 28	14 39	14 48
Wylde Green	d		12 11	12 20		12 30	12 41	12 50	13 00		13 11	13 20		13 30	13 41	13 50	14 00		14 11	14 20		14 30	14 41	14 50
Sutton Coldfield	d		12 14	12 24		12 34	12 44	12 54	13 04		13 14	13 24		13 34	13 44	13 54	14 04		14 14	14 24		14 34	14 44	14 54
Four Oaks	d		12 18	12 28		12a41	12 48	12 58	13a11		13 18	13 28		13a41	13 48	13 58	14a11		14 18	14 28		14a41	14 48	14 58
Butlers Lane	d		12 20	12 30			12 50	13 00			13 20	13 30			13 50	14 00			14 20	14 30			14 50	15 00
Blake Street	d		12 22	12 32			12 52	13 02			13 22	13 32			13 52	14 02			14 22	14 32			14 52	15 02
Shenstone	d		12 26				12 56				13 26				13 56				14 26				14 56	
Lichfield City	d		12a31	12 40			13a01	13 10			13a31	13 40			14a01	14 10			14a31	14 40			15a01	15 10
Lichfield Trent Valley	a			12 45				13 15				13 45				14 15				14 45				15 15

For general notes see front of timetable
For details of catering facilities see Directory of Train Operators

A From Gloucester to Nottingham (Table 57)
B From Cardiff Central (Table 132) to Nottingham (Table 57)
C To Nottingham (Table 57)

Table 69

Saturdays

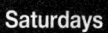

Redditch and Longbridge → Birmingham → Lichfield

Network Diagram - see first page of Table 67

		LM	XC 1◇ A		LM	LM	LM	LM	LM	LM	LM	XC 1◇ A		LM	LM	LM	LM	LM	LM	LM	LM		XC 1◇ A	LM	LM	LM
Bromsgrove	d						14 42									15 42				16 13						16 42
Redditch	d					14 27				14 57					15 27				15 57						16 27	
Alvechurch	d					14 32				15 02					15 32				16 02						16 32	
Barnt Green	d					14 39				15 08					15 38				16 08						16 38	
Longbridge	d	14 23			14 33	14 44		14 53	15 03	15 13	15 23			15 33	15 43		15 53	16 03	16 13		16 23			16 33	16 43	
Northfield	d	14 25			14 35	14 46		14 55	15 05	15 15	15 25			15 35	15 45		15 55	16 05	16 15		16 25			16 35	16 45	
Kings Norton	d	14 27			14 37	14 48		14 57	15 07	15 17	15 27			15 37	15 47		15 57	16 07	16 17		16 27			16 37	16 47	
Bournville	d	14 30			14 40	14 51		15 00	15 10	15 20	15 30			15 40	15 50		16 00	16 10	16 20		16 30			16 40	16 50	
Selly Oak	d	14 32			14 42	14 53		15 02	15 12	15 22	15 32			15 42	15 52		16 02	16 12	16 22		16 32			16 42	16 52	
University	d	14 34	14 39		14 44	14 55	14 59	15 04	15 14	15 24	15 34	15 39		15 44	15 54	15 59	16 04	16 14	16 24		16 34		16 39	16 44	16 54	16 59
Five Ways	d	14 37			14 47	14 58		15 07	15 17	15 27	15 37			15 47	15 57		16 07	16 17	16 27		16 37			16 47	16 57	
Birmingham New Street [12]	a	14 42	14 45		14 53	15 03	15 11	15 12	15 22	15 33	15 42	15 45		15 53	16 03	16 11	16 12	16 22	16 34	16 41	16 42		16 45	16 53	17 03	17 11
	d	14 45			14 55	15 05		15 15	15 25	15 35	15 45			15 55	16 05		16 15	16 25	16 35		16 45			16 55	17 05	
Duddeston	d				14 59				15 29					15 59				16 29						16 59		
Aston	d	14 51			15 02	15 11		15 21	15 32	15 41	15 51			16 02	16 11		16 21	16 32	16 41		16 51			17 02	17 11	
Gravelly Hill	d	14 54			15 05	15 14		15 24	15 35	15 44	15 54			16 05	16 14		16 24	16 35	16 44		16 54			17 05	17 14	
Erdington	d	14 56			15 08	15 16		15 26	15 38	15 46	15 56			16 08	16 16		16 26	16 38	16 46		16 56			17 08	17 16	
Chester Road	d	14 58			15 09	15 18		15 28	15 39	15 48	15 58			16 09	16 18		16 28	16 39	16 48		16 58			17 09	17 18	
Wylde Green	d	15 00			15 11	15 20		15 30	15 41	15 50	16 00			16 11	16 20		16 30	16 41	16 50		17 00			17 11	17 20	
Sutton Coldfield	d	15 04			15 14	15 24		15 34	15 44	15 54	16 04			16 14	16 24		16 34	16 44	16 54		17 04			17 14	17 24	
Four Oaks	d	15a11			15 18	15 28		15a41	15 48	15 58	16a11			16 18	16 28		16a41	16 48	16 58		17a11			17 18	17 28	
Butlers Lane	d				15 20	15 30			15 50	16 00				16 20	16 30			16 50	17 00					17 20	17 30	
Blake Street	d				15 22	15 32			15 52	16 02				16 22	16 32			16 52	17 02					17 22	17 32	
Shenstone	d				15 26				15 56					16 26				16 56						17 26		
Lichfield City	d				15a31	15 40			16a01	16 10				16a31	16 40			17a01	17 10					17a31	17 40	
Lichfield Trent Valley	a					15 45				16 15					16 45				17 15						17 45	

		LM	LM	LM	LM	XC 1◇ A	LM		LM	LM	LM	LM	LM	LM	XC 1◇ A	LM		LM	LM	LM	LM	LM	LM	XC 1◇ A	LM	LM
Bromsgrove	d									17 43									18 44							
Redditch	d			16 57					17 27				17 57					18 27				18 57				19 27
Alvechurch	d			17 02					17 32				18 02					18 32				19 02				19 32
Barnt Green	d			17 08					17 38				18 08					18 38				19 08				19 38
Longbridge	d	16 53	17 03	17 13	17 23		17 33		17 43		17 53	18 03	18 13	18 23		18 33		18 43		18 53	19 03	19 13	19 23		19 33	19 43
Northfield	d	16 55	17 05	17 15	17 25		17 35		17 45		17 55	18 05	18 15	18 25		18 35		18 45		18 55	19 05	19 15	19 25		19 35	19 45
Kings Norton	d	16 57	17 07	17 17	17 27		17 37		17 47		17 57	18 07	18 17	18 27		18 37		18 47		18 57	19 07	19 17	19 27		19 37	19 47
Bournville	d	17 00	17 10	17 20	17 30		17 40		17 50		18 00	18 10	18 20	18 30		18 40		18 50		19 00	19 10	19 20	19 30		19 40	19 50
Selly Oak	d	17 02	17 12	17 22	17 32		17 42		17 52		18 02	18 12	18 22	18 32		18 42		18 52		19 02	19 12	19 22	19 32		19 42	19 52
University	d	17 04	17 14	17 24	17 34	17 39	17 44		17 54	17 59	18 04	18 14	18 24	18 34	18 39	18 44		18 54	18 59	19 04	19 14	19 24	19 34	19 39	19 44	19 54
Five Ways	d	17 07	17 17	17 27	17 37		17 47		17 57		18 07	18 17	18 27	18 37		18 47		18 57		19 07	19 17	19 27	19 37		19 47	19 57
Birmingham New Street [12]	a	17 12	17 23	17 33	17 42	17 45	17 53		18 03	18 11	18 12	18 23	18 33	18 42	18 45	18 53		19 03	19 11	19 12	19 23	19 33	19 43	19 45	19 53	20 03
	d	17 15	17 25	17 35	17 45		17 55		18 05		18 15	18 25	18 35	18 45		18 55		19 05		19 15	19 25	19 35			19 55	20 05
Duddeston	d		17 29				17 59					18 29				18 59						19 39				20 09
Aston	d	17 21	17 32	17 41	17 51		18 02		18 11		18 21	18 32	18 41	18 51		19 02		19 11		19 21	19 31	19 42			20 01	20 12
Gravelly Hill	d	17 24	17 35	17 44	17 54		18 05		18 14		18 24	18 35	18 44	18 54		19 05		19 14		19 24	19 34	19 45			20 04	20 15
Erdington	d	17 26	17 38	17 46	17 56		18 08		18 16		18 26	18 38	18 46	18 56		19 08		19 16		19 26	19 36	19 48			20 06	20 18
Chester Road	d	17 28	17 39	17 48	17 58		18 10		18 18		18 28	18 39	18 48	18 58		19 09		19 18		19 28	19 38	19 50			20 08	20 20
Wylde Green	d	17 30	17 41	17 50	18 00		18 12		18 20		18 30	18 41	18 50	19 00		19 11		19 20		19 30	19 40	19 52			20 10	20 22
Sutton Coldfield	d	17 34	17 44	17 54	18 04		18 15		18 24		18 34	18 44	18 54	19 04		19 14		19 24		19 34	19 44	19 55			20 14	20 25
Four Oaks	d	17a41	17 48	17 58	18a11		18 18		18 28		18a41	18 48	18 58	19a11		19 18		19 28		19a41	19 51	19 58			20a21	20 28
Butlers Lane	d		17 50	18 00			18 20		18 30			18 50	19 00			19 20		19 30			19 53	20 00				20 30
Blake Street	d		17 52	18 02			18 22		18 32			18 52	19 02			19 22		19 32			19a58	20 02				20 32
Shenstone	d		17 56				18 26					18 56				19 26						20 06				20 36
Lichfield City	d		18a01	18 10			18a31		18 40			19a01	19 10			19a31		19 40				20 11				20 41
Lichfield Trent Valley	a			18 15					18 45				19 15					19 45				20 16				20 46

		LM		LM	LM	XC 1◇ A	LM	LM	LM	LM	LM		LM	LM	XC 1◇ B	LM	LM	XC 1◇	LM	LM		LM	LM	LM		
Bromsgrove	d									20 59					21 44											
Redditch	d				19 57			20 27			20 57			21 27			21 57			22 27			22 57			
Alvechurch	d				20 02			20 32			21 02			21 32			22 02			22 32			23 02			
Barnt Green	d				20 08			20 38			21 08			21 38			22 08			22 38			23 08			
Longbridge	d	19 53		20 03	20 13		20 30	20 43	21 00		21 13		21 30	21 43		22 00	22 13		22 30	22 43		22 52	23 13	23 30		
Northfield	d	19 55		20 05	20 15		20 32	20 45	21 02		21 15		21 32	21 45		22 02	22 15		22 32	22 45		22 54	23 15	23 32		
Kings Norton	d	19 57		20 07	20 17		20 34	20 47	21 04		21 17		21 34	21 47		22 04	22 17		22 34	22 47		22 56	23 17	23 34		
Bournville	d	20 00		20 10	20 20		20 37	20 50	21 07		21 20		21 37	21 50		22 07	22 20		22 37	22 50		22 59	23 20	23 37		
Selly Oak	d	20 02		20 12	20 22		20 39	20 52	21 09		21 22		21 39	21 52		22 09	22 22		22 39	22 52		23 01	23 22	23 39		
University	d	20 04		20 14	20 24	20 34	20 42	20 54	21 12	21 16	21 24		21 42	21 54	22 01	22 12	22 24	22 36	22 42	22 54		23 03	23 24	23 41		
Five Ways	d	20 07		20 17	20 27		20 45	20 57	21 15		21 27		21 45	21 57		22 15	22 27		22 45	22 57		23 06	23 27	23 44		
Birmingham New Street [12]	a	20 13		20 23	20 34	20 40	20 50	21 03	21 20	21 22	21 33		21 50	22 03	22 07	22 20	22 33	22 42	22 49	23 03		23 12	23 33	23 50		
	d			20 25	20 35		20 55	21 05	21 25		21 35		21 55	22 05		22 25	22 35		22 55			23 15				
Duddeston	d				20 39			21 09			21 39			22 09			22 39		22 59			23 19				
Aston	d			20 31	20 42		21 01	21 12	21 31		21 42		22 01	22 12		22 31	22 42		23 02			23 22				
Gravelly Hill	d			20 34	20 45		21 04	21 15	21 34		21 45		22 04	22 15		22 34	22 45		23 05			23 25				
Erdington	d			20 36	20 48		21 06	21 18	21 36		21 48		22 06	22 18		22 36	22 48		23 08			23 28				
Chester Road	d			20 38	20 50		21 08	21 20	21 38		21 50		22 08	22 20		22 38	22 50		23 10			23 30				
Wylde Green	d			20 40	20 52		21 10	21 22	21 40		21 52		22 10	22 22		22 40	22 52		23 12			23 32				
Sutton Coldfield	d			20 44	20 55		21 14	21 25	21 44		21 55		22 14	22 25		22 44	22 55		23 15			23 35				
Four Oaks	d			20a51	20 58		21a21	21 28	21a51		21 58		22a21	22 28		22a51	22 58		23 18			23 38				
Butlers Lane	d				21 00			21 30			22 00			22 30			23 00		23 20			23 40				
Blake Street	d				21 02			21 32			22 02			22 32			23 02		23a23			23 42				
Shenstone	d				21 06			21 36			22 06			22 36			23 06					23 46				
Lichfield City	d				21 11			21 41			22 11			22 41			23 11					23a51				
Lichfield Trent Valley	a				21 16			21 46			22 16			22 46			23 16									

For general notes see front of timetable
For details of catering facilities see
Directory of Train Operators

A To Nottingham (Table 57)

B Until 5 September.
From Cardiff Central (Table 132) to Nottingham (Table 57)

Table 69

Sundays
until 1 November

Redditch and Longbridge → Birmingham → Lichfield

Network Diagram - see first page of Table 67

		LM	LM	LM	LM	LM	LM	LM	LM	XC 1 ◇ A	LM	LM	XC 1 ◇ B	LM	LM	XC 1 ◇ B	LM	LM	LM	XC 1 ◇ B	LM	LM	XC 1 ◇ B	LM	LM	LM
Bromsgrove	d																		15 09						16 51	
Redditch	d			09 27	09 57	10 27	10 57	11 27	11 57		12 27	12 57		13 27	13 57		14 27	14 57			15 27	15 57		16 27		16 57
Alvechurch	d			09 32	10 02	10 32	11 02	11 32	12 02		12 32	13 02		13 32	14 02		14 32	15 02			15 32	16 02		16 32		17 02
Barnt Green	d			09 38	10 08	10 38	11 08	11 38	12 08		12 38	13 08		13 38	14 08		14 38	15 08			15 38	16 08		16 38		17 08
Longbridge	d			09 43	10 13	10 43	11 13	11 43	12 13		12 43	13 13		13 43	14 13		14 43	15 13			15 43	16 13		16 43		17 13
Northfield	d			09 45	10 15	10 45	11 15	11 45	12 15		12 45	13 15		13 45	14 15		14 45	15 15			15 45	16 15		16 45		17 15
Kings Norton	d			09 48	10 18	10 48	11 18	11 48	12 18		12 48	13 18		13 48	14 18		14 48	15 18			15 48	16 18		16 48		17 18
Bournville	d			09 50	10 20	10 50	11 20	11 50	12 20		12 50	13 20		13 50	14 20		14 50	15 20			15 50	16 20		16 50		17 20
Selly Oak	d			09 53	10 23	10 53	11 23	11 53	12 23		12 53	13 23		13 53	14 23		14 53	15 23			15 53	16 23		16 53		17 23
University	d			09 55	10 25	10 55	11 25	11 55	12 25	12 39	12 55	13 25	13 34	13 55	14 25	14 38	14 55	15 25		15 34	15 55	16 25	16 34	16 55		17 25
Five Ways	d			09 59	10 29	10 59	11 29	11 59	12 29		12 59	13 29		13 59	14 29		14 59	15 29			15 59	16 29		16 59		17 29
Birmingham New Street 12	a			10 02	10 33	11 02	11 33	12 02	12 33	12 45	13 02	13 33	13 40	14 02	14 33	14 44	15 02	15 33	15 37	15 40	16 03	16 33	16 40	17 03	17 17	17 33
	d	09 05	09 35	10 05	10 35	11 05	11 35	12 05	12 35		13 05	13 35		14 05	14 35		15 05	15 35			16 05	16 35		17 05		17 35
Duddeston	d	09 09	09 39	10 09	10 39	11 09	11 39	12 09	12 39		13 09	13 39		14 09	14 39		15 09	15 39			16 09	16 39		17 09		17 39
Aston	d	09 12	09 42	10 12	10 42	11 12	11 42	12 12	12 42		13 12	13 42		14 12	14 42		15 12	15 42			16 12	16 42		17 12		17 42
Gravelly Hill	d	09 15	09 45	10 15	10 45	11 15	11 45	12 15	12 45		13 15	13 45		14 15	14 45		15 15	15 45			16 15	16 45		17 15		17 45
Erdington	d	09 17	09 47	10 17	10 47	11 17	11 47	12 17	12 47		13 17	13 47		14 17	14 47		15 17	15 47			16 17	16 47		17 17		17 47
Chester Road	d	09 19	09 49	10 19	10 49	11 19	11 49	12 19	12 49		13 19	13 49		14 19	14 49		15 19	15 49			16 19	16 49		17 19		17 49
Wylde Green	d	09 21	09 51	10 21	10 51	11 21	11 51	12 21	12 51		13 21	13 51		14 21	14 51		15 21	15 51			16 21	16 51		17 21		17 51
Sutton Coldfield	d	09 24	09 54	10 24	10 54	11 24	11 54	12 24	12 54		13 24	13 54		14 24	14 54		15 24	15 54			16 24	16 54		17 24		17 54
Four Oaks	d	09 27	09 57	10 27	10 57	11 27	11 57	12 27	12 57		13 27	13 57		14 27	14 57		15 27	15 57			16 27	16 57		17 27		17 57
Butlers Lane	d	09 29	09 59	10 29	10 59	11 29	11 59	12 29	12 59		13 29	13 59		14 29	14 59		15 29	15 59			16 29	16 59		17 29		17 59
Blake Street	d	09 31	10 01	10 31	11 01	11 31	12 01	12 31	13 01		13 31	14 01		14 31	15 01		15 31	16 01			16 31	17 01		17 31		18 01
Shenstone	d	09 35	10 05	10 35	11 05	11 35	12 05	12 35	13 05		13 35	14 05		14 35	15 05		15 35	16 05			16 35	17 05		17 35		18 05
Lichfield City	d	09 40	10 10	10 40	11 10	11 40	12 10	12 40	13 10		13 40	14 10		14 40	15 10		15 40	16 10			16 40	17 10		17 40		18 10
Lichfield Trent Valley	a	09 45	10 16	10 45	11 15	11 45	12 15	12 45	13 15		13 45	14 15		14 45	15 15		15 45	16 15			16 45	17 15		17 45		18 15

		XC 1 ◇ B	LM	LM	LM	XC 1 ◇ B	LM	LM	XC 1 ◇ B	LM	LM	LM	XC 1 ◇ C	XC 1 ◇ D	LM	LM	LM	XC 1 ◇ E	LM	LM	XC 1 ◇ G	XC 1 ◇ D	LM	LM
Bromsgrove	d			17 52								20 10					21 08							
Redditch	d		17 27		17 57		18 27	18 57		19 27	19 57				20 27	20 57			21 27	21 57			22 27	22 57
Alvechurch	d		17 32		18 02		18 32	19 02		19 32	20 02				20 32	21 02			21 32	22 02			22 32	23 02
Barnt Green	d		17 38		18 08		18 38	19 08		19 38	20 08				20 38	21 08			21 38	22 08			22 38	23 08
Longbridge	d		17 43		18 13		18 43	19 13		19 43	20 13				20 43	21 13			21 43	22 13			22 43	23 13
Northfield	d		17 45		18 15		18 45	19 15		19 45	20 15				20 45	21 15			21 45	22 15			22 45	23 15
Kings Norton	d		17 48		18 18		18 48	19 18		19 48	20 18				20 48	21 18			21 48	22 18			22 48	23 18
Bournville	d		17 50		18 20		18 50	19 20		19 50	20 20				20 50	21 20			21 50	22 20			22 50	23 20
Selly Oak	d		17 53		18 23		18 53	19 23		19 53	20 23				20 53	21 23			21 53	22 23			22 53	23 23
University	d	17 34	17 55		18 25	18 34	18 55	19 25	19 34	19 55	20 25		20 34	20 36	20 55	21 25		21 39	21 55	22 25	22 34	22 34	22 55	23 25
Five Ways	d		17 59		18 29		19 00	19 29		19 59	20 29				20 59	21 29			21 59	22 29			22 59	23 29
Birmingham New Street 12	a	17 40	18 03	18 13	18 33	18 40	19 03	19 33	19 40	20 02	20 33	20 36	20 40	20 42	21 03	21 33	21 42	21 45	22 03	22 33	22 40	22 45	23 02	23 33
	d		18 05		18 35		19 05	19 35		20 05	20 35				21 05	21 35			22 05	22 35			23 05	
Duddeston	d		18 09		18 39		19 09	19 39		20 09	20 39				21 09	21 39			22 09	22 39			23 09	
Aston	d		18 12		18 42		19 12	19 42		20 12	20 42				21 12	21 42			22 12	22 42			23 12	
Gravelly Hill	d		18 15		18 45		19 15	19 45		20 15	20 45				21 15	21 45			22 15	22 45			23 15	
Erdington	d		18 17		18 47		19 17	19 47		20 17	20 47				21 17	21 47			22 17	22 47			23 17	
Chester Road	d		18 19		18 49		19 19	19 49		20 19	20 49				21 19	21 49			22 19	22 49			23 19	
Wylde Green	d		18 21		18 51		19 21	19 51		20 21	20 51				21 21	21 51			22 21	22 51			23 21	
Sutton Coldfield	d		18 24		18 54		19 24	19 54		20 24	20 54				21 24	21 54			22 24	22 54			23 24	
Four Oaks	d		18 27		18 57		19 27	19 57		20 27	20 57				21 27	21 57			22 27	22 57			23 27	
Butlers Lane	d		18 29		18 59		19 29	19 59		20 29	20 59				21 29	21 59			22 29	22 59			23 29	
Blake Street	d		18 31		19 01		19 31	20 01		20 31	21 01				21 31	22 01			22 31	23 01			23 31	
Shenstone	d		18 35		19 05		19 35	20 05		20 35	21 05				21 35	22 05			22 35	23 05			23 35	
Lichfield City	d		18 40		19 10		19 40	20 10		20 40	21 10				21 40	22 10			22 40	23 10			23 40	
Lichfield Trent Valley	a		18 45		19 15		19 45	20 15		20 45	21 15				21 45	22 15			22 45	23 15			23 45	

Sundays
from 8 November

		LM	LM	LM bus	LM	LM bus	LM	LM bus	LM	LM bus	LM	LM bus	LM	LM bus	LM	LM bus	LM	LM bus	LM	LM bus	LM	LM bus
Bromsgrove	d																					
Redditch	d			08 43		09 13		09 43		10 13		10 43		11 13		11 43		12 13		12 43		13 13
Alvechurch	d			08b54		09b24		09b54		10b24		10b54		11b24		11b54		12b24		12b54		13b24
Barnt Green	d			09 01		09 31		10 01		10 31		11 01		11 31		12 01		12 31		13 01		13 31
Longbridge	d			09 11		09 41		10 11		10 41		11 11		11 41		12 11		12 41		13 11		13 41
Northfield	d			09 21		09 51		10 21		10 51		11 21		11 51		12 21		12 51		13 21		13 51
Kings Norton	d			09 28	09 45	09 58	10 15	10 28	10 45	10 58	11 15	11 28	11 45	11 58	12 15	12 28	12 45	12 58	13 15	13 28	13 45	13 58
Bournville	d			09 38	09 50	10 08	10 20	10 38	10 50	11 08	11 20	11 38	11 50	12 08	12 20	12 38	12 50	13 08	13 20	13 38	13 50	14 08
Selly Oak	d			09a45	09 53	10a15	10 23	10a45	10 53	11a15	11 23	11a45	11 53	12a15	12 23	12a45	12 53	13a15	13 23	13a45	13 53	14a15
University	d				09 55		10 25		10 55		11 25		11 55		12 25		12 55		13 25		13 55	
Five Ways	d				09 59		10 29		10 59		11 29		11 59		12 29		12 59		13 29		13 59	
Birmingham New Street 12	a				10 02		10 33		11 02		11 33		12 02		12 33		13 02		13 33		14 02	
	d	09 05	09 35		10 05		10 35		11 05		11 35		12 05		12 35		13 05		13 35		14 05	
Duddeston	d	09 09	09 39		10 09		10 39		11 09		11 39		12 09		12 39		13 09		13 39		14 09	
Aston	d	09 12	09 42		10 12		10 42		11 12		11 42		12 12		12 42		13 12		13 42		14 12	
Gravelly Hill	d	09 15	09 45		10 15		10 45		11 15		11 45		12 15		12 45		13 15		13 45		14 15	
Erdington	d	09 17	09 47		10 17		10 47		11 17		11 47		12 17		12 47		13 17		13 47		14 17	
Chester Road	d	09 19	09 49		10 19		10 49		11 19		11 49		12 19		12 49		13 19		13 49		14 19	
Wylde Green	d	09 21	09 51		10 21		10 51		11 21		11 51		12 21		12 51		13 21		13 51		14 21	
Sutton Coldfield	d	09 24	09 54		10 24		10 54		11 24		11 54		12 24		12 54		13 24		13 54		14 24	
Four Oaks	d	09 27	09 57		10 27		10 57		11 27		11 57		12 27		12 57		13 27		13 57		14 27	
Butlers Lane	d	09 29	09 59		10 29		10 59		11 29		11 59		12 29		12 59		13 29		13 59		14 29	
Blake Street	d	09 31	10 01		10 31		11 01		11 31		12 01		12 31		13 01		13 31		14 01		14 31	
Shenstone	d	09 35	10 05		10 35		11 05		11 35		12 05		12 35		13 05		13 35		14 05		14 35	
Lichfield City	d	09 40	10 10		10 40		11 10		11 40		12 10		12 40		13 10		13 40		14 10		14 40	
Lichfield Trent Valley	a	09 45	10 16		10 45		11 15		11 45		12 15		12 45		13 15		13 45		14 15		14 45	

For general notes see front of timetable
For details of catering facilities see Directory of Train Operators

A From 13 September. To Nottingham (Table 57)

B To Nottingham (Table 57)

C Until 12 July. To Nottingham (Table 57)

D 19 July to 6 September. To Derby (Table 57)

E Until 12 July and from 13 September to Nottingham, 19 July to 6 September to Derby (Table 57)

G Until 12 July and from 13 September. Until 12 July to Nottingham, from 13 September to Derby (Table 57)

b Alvechurch Red Lion Pub

Sundays

from 8 November

Redditch and Longbridge → Birmingham → Lichfield

Network Diagram - see first page of Table 67

		LM	LM (bus)	LM	LM (bus)	LM		LM (bus)	LM (bus)	LM	LM (bus)	LM		LM (bus)	LM	LM (bus)	LM	LM (bus)		LM (bus)	LM	LM (bus)	LM	LM (bus)		LM
Bromsgrove	d							15 00										16 55								
Redditch	d		13 43		14 13				14 43		15 13			15 43		16 13				16 43		17 13		17 43		
Alvechurch	d		13b54		14b24				14b54		15b24			15b54		16b24				16b54		17b24		17b54		
Barnt Green	d		14 01		14 31				15 01		15 31			16 01		16 31				17 01		17 31		18 01		
Longbridge	d		14 11		14 41				15 11		15 41			16 11		16 41				17 11		17 41		18 11		
Northfield	d		14 21		14 51				15 21		15 51			16 21		16 51				17 21		17 51		18 21		
Kings Norton	d	14 15	14 28	14 45	14 58	15 15			15 28	15 45	15 58	16 15		16 28	16 45	16 58	17 15			17 28	17 45	17 58	18 15	18 28		18 45
Bournville	d	14 20	14 38	14 50	15 08	15 20			15 38	15 50	16 08	16 20		16 38	16 50	17 08	17 20			17 38	17 50	18 08	18 20	18 38		18 50
Selly Oak	d	14 23	14a45	14 53	15a15	15 23			15a45	15 53	16a15	16 23		16a45	16 53	17a15	17 23			17a45	17 53	18a15	18 23	18a45		18 53
University	d	14 25		14 55		15 25				15 55		16 25			16 55		17 25				17 55		18 25			18 55
Five Ways	d	14 29		14 59		15 29				15 59		16 29			16 59		17 29				17 59		18 29			19 00
Birmingham New Street 12	a	14 33		15 02		15 33		15 40		16 03		16 33			17 03		17 33	17 35			18 03		18 33			19 03
	d	14 35		15 05		15 35				16 05		16 35			17 05		17 35				18 05		18 35			19 05
Duddeston	d	14 39		15 09		15 39				16 09		16 39			17 09		17 39				18 09		18 39			19 09
Aston	d	14 42		15 12		15 42				16 12		16 42			17 12		17 42				18 12		18 42			19 12
Gravelly Hill	d	14 45		15 15		15 45				16 15		16 45			17 15		17 45				18 15		18 45			19 15
Erdington	d	14 47		15 17		15 47				16 17		16 47			17 17		17 47				18 17		18 47			19 17
Chester Road	d	14 49		15 19		15 49				16 19		16 49			17 19		17 49				18 19		18 49			19 19
Wylde Green	d	14 51		15 21		15 51				16 21		16 51			17 21		17 51				18 21		18 51			19 21
Sutton Coldfield	d	14 54		15 24		15 54				16 24		16 54			17 24		17 54				18 24		18 54			19 24
Four Oaks	d	14 57		15 27		15 57				16 27		16 57			17 27		17 57				18 27		18 57			19 27
Butlers Lane	d	14 59		15 29		15 59				16 29		16 59			17 29		17 59				18 29		18 59			19 29
Blake Street	d	15 01		15 31		16 01				16 31		17 01			17 31		18 01				18 31		19 01			19 31
Shenstone	d	15 05		15 35		16 05				16 35		17 05			17 35		18 05				18 35		19 05			19 35
Lichfield City	d	15 10		15 40		16 10				16 40		17 10			17 40		18 10				18 40		19 10			19 40
Lichfield Trent Valley	a	15 15		15 45		16 15				16 45		17 15			17 45		18 15				18 45		19 15			19 45

		LM (bus)	LM	LM (bus)	LM (bus)	LM		LM (bus)	LM	LM (bus)	LM	LM (bus)		LM (bus)	LM	LM (bus)	LM	LM (bus)	LM	LM (bus)	LM (bus)	LM	LM (bus)	LM		
Bromsgrove	d			18 55								20 30								21 55						
Redditch	d	18 13			18 43			19 13		19 43				20 13		20 43		21 13			21 43		22 13			
Alvechurch	d	18b24			18b54			19b24		19b54				20b24		20b54		21b24			21b54		22b24			
Barnt Green	d	18 31			19 01			19 31		20 01				20 31		21 01		21 31			22 01		22 31			
Longbridge	d	18 41			19 11			19 41		20 11				20 41		21 11		21 41			22 11		22 41			
Northfield	d	18 51			19 21			19 51		20 21				20 51		21 21		21 51			22 21		22 51			
Kings Norton	d	18 58	19 15		19 28	19 45		19 58	20 15	20 28	20 45			20 58	21 15	21 28	21 45	21 58	22 15		22 28	22 45	22 58	23 15		
Bournville	d	19 08	19 20		19 38	19 50		20 08	20 20	20 38	20 50			21 08	21 20	21 38	21 50	22 08	22 20		22 38	22 50	23 08	23 20		
Selly Oak	d	19a15	19 23		19a45	19 53		20a15	20 23	20a45	20 53			21a15	21 23	21a45	21 53	22a15	22 23		22a45	22 53	23a15	23 23		
University	d		19 25			19 55			20 25		20 55				21 25		21 55		22 25			22 55		23 25		
Five Ways	d		19 29			19 59			20 29		20 59				21 29		21 59		22 29			22 59		23 29		
Birmingham New Street 12	a		19 33	19 35		20 02			20 33		21 03	21 10			21 33		22 03		22 33	22 35		23 02		23 33		
	d		19 35			20 05			20 35		21 05				21 35		22 05		22 35			23 05				
Duddeston	d		19 39			20 09			20 39		21 09				21 39		22 09		22 39			23 09				
Aston	d		19 42			20 12			20 42		21 12				21 42		22 12		22 42			23 12				
Gravelly Hill	d		19 45			20 15			20 45		21 15				21 45		22 15		22 45			23 15				
Erdington	d		19 47			20 17			20 47		21 17				21 47		22 17		22 47			23 17				
Chester Road	d		19 49			20 19			20 49		21 19				21 49		22 19		22 49			23 19				
Wylde Green	d		19 51			20 21			20 51		21 21				21 51		22 21		22 51			23 21				
Sutton Coldfield	d		19 54			20 24			20 54		21 24				21 54		22 24		22 54			23 24				
Four Oaks	d		19 57			20 27			20 57		21 27				21 57		22 27		22 57			23 27				
Butlers Lane	d		19 59			20 29			20 59		21 29				21 59		22 29		22 59			23 29				
Blake Street	d		20 01			20 31			21 01		21 31				22 01		22 31		23 01			23 31				
Shenstone	d		20 05			20 35			21 05		21 35				22 05		22 35		23 05			23 35				
Lichfield City	d		20 10			20 40			21 10		21 40				22 10		22 40		23 10			23 40				
Lichfield Trent Valley	a		20 15			20 45			21 15		21 45				22 15		22 45		23 15			23 45				

For general notes see front of timetable
For details of catering facilities see
Directory of Train Operators

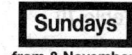

b Alvechurch Red Lion Pub

Table 70

Mondays to Fridays

Birmingham → Walsall, Rugeley and Stafford

Network Diagram - see first page of Table 67

Miles	Station		LM MX	LM MO A (bus)	LM	LM	LM	LM [1]	LM		LM	LM	LM	LM	LM	LM	LM		LM	LM	LM	LM	LM	LM	LM
—	Wolverhampton [7] (train)	d												07 49					08 49		09 19		09 49		10 19
0	**Birmingham New Street [12]**	d	23p18	23p30	05 33	05 56	06 27	06 47	07 17		07 39	07 47	08 07	08 17	08 39	08 47	09 07		09 17	09 39	09 47	10 07	10 17	10 39	10 47
1½	Duddeston	d	23p22	23p40		06 00	06 32	06 52	07 22			07 52		08 22		08 52			09 22		09 52		10 22		10 52
2¾	Aston	d	23p26	23p45		06 03	06 35	06 55	07 25			07 55		08 25		08 55			09 25		09 55		10 25		10 55
3½	Witton	d	23p28	23p52		06 05	06 37	06 57	07 27			07 57		08 27		08 57			09 27		09 57		10 27		10 57
4¼	Perry Barr	d	23p30	23p59		06 07	06 39	06 59	07 29			07 59		08 29		08 59			09 29		09 59		10 29		10 59
5¾	Hamstead	d	23p33	00 09	05 41	06 10	06 42	07 01	07 32			08 02		08 31		09 01			09 31		10 01		10 31		11 01
8½	Tame Bridge Parkway	d	23p38	00 20	05 45	06 15	06 47	07 05	07 37		07 50	08 07	08 20	08 35	08 50	09 05	09 20		09 35	09 50	10 05	10 20	10 35	10 50	11 05
9½	Bescot Stadium	d	23p41	00 29	05 48	06 18	06 50	07 08	07 40			08 10		08 38		09 08			09 38		10 08		10 38		11 08
10¾	**Walsall**	a	23p46	00 37	05 55	06 23	06 55	07 14	07 44		07 59	08 14	08 29	08 44	08 59	09 14	09 29		09 44	09 59	10 14	10 29	10 46	10 59	11 14
—		d	23p47			06 24	06 56		07 45		08 00		08 30		09 00		09 30			10 00		10 30		11 00	
14	Bloxwich	d	23p54			06 31	07 03		07 52		08 07				09 07					10 07				11 07	
14½	Bloxwich North	d	23p56			06 33	07 05		07 54		08 09				09 09					10 09				11 09	
16¾	Landywood	d	00 01			06 37	07 09		07 58		08 13				09 13					10 13				11 13	
18¾	Cannock	d	00 05			06 42	07 14		08 03		08 18		08 44		09 18		09 44			10 18		10 44		11 18	
20¾	Hednesford	d	00a10			06 47	07 19		08a09		08 23		08 49		09 23		09 49			10 23		10 49		11 23	
24¾	Rugeley Town	d				06 55	07 27				08 31		08 57		09 31		09 57			10 31		10 57		11 31	
26¼	**Rugeley Trent Valley**	a				07 00	07 32				08 36		09 04		09 36		10 04			10 36		11 04		11 36	
—	Stafford	a					*07 53*				*08 53*				*09 53*					*10 53*				*11 53*	

Station		LM	LM		LM	LM	LM	LM	LM	LM	LM		LM	LM	LM	LM	LM	LM	LM		LM	LM	LM	LM	LM
Wolverhampton [7] (train)	d		10 49			11 19		11 49		12 19			12 49		13 19		13 49		14 19			14 49		15 19	
Birmingham New Street [12]	d	11 07	11 17		11 39	11 47	12 07	12 17	12 39	12 47	13 07		13 17	13 39	13 47	14 07	14 17	14 39	14 47		15 07	15 17	15 39	15 47	16 07
Duddeston	d		11 22			11 52		12 22		12 52			13 22		13 52		14 22		14 52			15 22		15 52	
Aston	d		11 25			11 55		12 25		12 55			13 25		13 55		14 25		14 55			15 25		15 55	
Witton	d		11 27			11 57		12 27		12 57			13 27		13 57		14 27		14 57			15 27		15 57	
Perry Barr	d		11 29			11 59		12 29		12 59			13 29		13 59		14 29		14 59			15 29		15 59	
Hamstead	d		11 31			12 01		12 31		13 01			13 31		14 01		14 31		15 01			15 31		16 01	
Tame Bridge Parkway	d	11 20	11 35		11 50	12 05	12 20	12 35	12 50	13 05	13 20		13 35	13 50	14 05	14 20	14 35	14 50	15 05		15 20	15 35	15 50	16 05	16 20
Bescot Stadium	d		11 38			12 08		12 38		13 08			13 38		14 08		14 38		15 08			15 38		16 08	
Walsall	a	11 29	11 44		11 59	12 14	12 29	12 46	12 59	13 14	13 29		13 44	13 59	14 14	14 29	14 44	14 59	15 14		15 29	15 46	15 59	16 14	16 29
	d	11 30			12 00		12 30		13 00		13 33			14 00		14 33		15 00			15 30		16 00		16 31
Bloxwich	d				12 07				13 07					14 07				15 07					16 07		16 38
Bloxwich North	d				12 09				13 09					14 09				15 09					16 09		16 40
Landywood	d				12 13				13 13					14 13				15 13					16 13		16 45
Cannock	d	11 44			12 18		12 44		13 18		13 48			14 18		14 48		15 18			15 44		16 18		16 49
Hednesford	d	11 49			12 23		12 49		13 23		13a59			14 23		14a59		15 23			15 49		16 23		16 54
Rugeley Town	d	11 57			12 31		12 57		13 31					14 31				15 31			15 57		16 31		17 02
Rugeley Trent Valley	a	12 04			12 36		13 04		13 36					14 36				15 36			16 04		16 36		17 08
Stafford	a				*12 53*				*13 53*					*14 53*				*15 53*					*16 53*		

Station		LM	LM	LM	LM		LM	LM	LM	LM	LM	LM	LM		LM	LM	LM	LM	LM	LM	LM	LM	LM		
Wolverhampton [7] (train)	d	15 49		16 19			16 49		17 19		17 49		18 19			19 19									
Birmingham New Street [12]	d	16 17	16 39	16 47	17 07		17 17	17 42	17 47	18 07	18 17	18 39	18 47		19 17	19 47	20 17	20 47	21 17	21 47	22 17	22 47	23 18		
Duddeston	d	16 22		16 52			17 22		17 52		18 22		18 52		19 22	19 52		20 52		21 52		22 52	23 22		
Aston	d	16 25		16 55			17 25		17 55		18 25		18 55		19 25	19 55		20 55		21 55		22 55	23 26		
Witton	d	16 27		16 57			17 27		17 57		18 27		18 57		19 27	19 57		20 57		21 57		22 57	23 28		
Perry Barr	d	16 29		16 59			17 29		17 59		18 29		18 59		19 29	19 59		20 59		21 59		22 59	23 30		
Hamstead	d	16 31		17 01			17 31		18 01		18 31		19 01		19 32	20 01		21 01		22 01		23 01	23 33		
Tame Bridge Parkway	d	16 35	16 50	17 05	17 20		17 35	17 54	18 05	18 20	18 35	18 50	19 05		19 37	20 05	20 30	21 05	21 30	22 05	22 30	23 05	23 38		
Bescot Stadium	d	16 38		17 08			17 38		18 08		18 38		19 08		19 40	20 08		21 08		22 08		23 08	23 41		
Walsall	a	16 44	16 59	17 14	17 29		17 44	18 01	18 14	18 29	18 44	18 59	19 15		19 45	20 14	20 38	21 14	21 38	22 14	22 38	23 16	23 46		
	d		17 00		17 30			18 02		18 30		19 00			19 46		20 39		21 39		22 39		23 47		
Bloxwich	d		17 07		17 37			18 09		18 37		19 07			19 53		20 46		21 46		22 46		23 54		
Bloxwich North	d		17 09		17 39			18 11		18 39		19 09			19 55		20 49		21 49		22 49		23 56		
Landywood	d		17 13		17 43			18 15		18 43		19 13			19 59		20 53		21 53		22 53		00 01		
Cannock	d		17 18		17 48			18 20		18 48		19 18			20 04		20 57		21 57		22 57		00 05		
Hednesford	d		17 23		17 53			18 25		18 53		19 23			20 09		21 02		22 02		23 02		00a10		
Rugeley Town	d		17 31		18 01			18 33		19 01		19 31			20 17		21 10		22 10		23 10				
Rugeley Trent Valley	a		17 36		18 06			18 38		19 06		19 36			20 22		21 15		22 15		23 15				
Stafford	a		*18 00*																						

For general notes see front of timetable
For details of catering facilities see
Directory of Train Operators

A 20 July to 7 September

Table 70

Saturdays

Birmingham → Walsall, Rugeley and Stafford

Network Diagram - see first page of Table 67

		LM	LM	LM	LM	LM	LM	LM	LM	LM	LM	LM	LM	LM	LM	LM	LM	LM	LM	LM	LM	LM
Wolverhampton [7] ⇌	d					06 49		07 19		07 49		08 19		08 49		09 19		09 49		10 19		10 49
Birmingham New Street [12]	d	23p18	06 02	06 27	07 07	07 17	07 39	07 47	08 07	08 17	08 39	08 47	09 07	09 17	09 39	09 47	10 07	10 17	10 39	10 47	11 07	11 17
Duddeston	d	23p22	06 06	06 32		07 22		07 52		08 22		08 52		09 22		09 52		10 22		10 52		11 22
Aston	d	23p26	06 09	06 35		07 25		07 55		08 25		08 55		09 25		09 55		10 25		10 55		11 25
Witton	d	23p28	06 11	06 37		07 27		07 57		08 27		08 57		09 27		09 57		10 27		10 57		11 27
Perry Barr	d	23p30	06 13	06 40		07 29		07 59		08 29		08 59		09 29		09 59		10 29		10 59		11 29
Hamstead	d	23p33	06 16	06 43		07 31		08 01		08 31		09 01		09 31		10 01		10 31		11 01		11 31
Tame Bridge Parkway	d	23p38	06 21	06 48	07 20	07 35	07 50	08 05	08 20	08 35	08 50	09 05	09 20	09 35	09 50	10 05	10 20	10 35	10 50	11 05	11 20	11 35
Bescot Stadium	d	23p41	06 24	06 50		07 38		08 08		08 38		09 08		09 38		10 08		10 38		11 08		11 38
Walsall	a	23p46	06 29	06 56	07 29	07 44	07 57	08 14	08 29	08 44	08 59	09 14	09 29	09 44	09 59	10 14	10 29	10 44	10 59	11 14	11 29	11 44
	d	23p47	06 30	06 57	07 30		07 57		08 30		09 00		09 30		10 00		10 30		11 00		11 30	
Bloxwich	d	23p54	06 37	07 04			08 04				09 07				10 07				11 07			
Bloxwich North	d	23p56	06 39	07 06			08 06				09 09				10 09				11 09			
Landywood	d	00 01	06 43	07 10			08 10				09 13				10 13				11 13			
Cannock	d	00 05	06 48	07 15	07 44		08 15		08 44		09 18		09 44		10 18		10 44		11 18		11 44	
Hednesford	d	00a10	06a53	07 20	07 49		08 20		08 49		09 23		09 49		10 23		10 49		11 23		11 49	
Rugeley Town	d			07 28	07 57		08 28		08 57		09 31		09 57		10 31		10 57		11 31		11 57	
Rugeley Trent Valley	a			07 32	08 04		08 35		09 01		09 36		10 04		10 36		11 04		11 36		12 04	
Stafford	a			*07 53*			*08 53*				*09 53*				*10 53*				*11 53*			

		LM	LM	LM	LM	LM	LM	LM	LM	LM	LM	LM	LM	LM	LM	LM	LM	LM	LM	LM	LM
Wolverhampton [7] ⇌	d		11 19		11 49		12 19		12 49		13 19		13 49		14 19		14 49		15 19		15 49
Birmingham New Street [12]	d	11 39	11 47	12 07	12 17	12 39	12 47	13 07	13 17	13 39	13 47	14 07	14 17	14 39	14 47	15 07	15 17	15 39	15 47	16 07	16 17
Duddeston	d		11 52		12 22		12 52		13 22		13 52		14 22		14 52		15 22		15 52		16 22
Aston	d		11 55		12 25		12 55		13 25		13 55		14 25		14 55		15 25		15 55		16 25
Witton	d		11 57		12 27		12 57		13 27		13 57		14 27		14 57		15 27		15 57		16 27
Perry Barr	d		11 59		12 29		12 59		13 29		13 59		14 29		14 59		15 29		15 59		16 29
Hamstead	d		12 01		12 31		13 01		13 31		14 01		14 31		15 01		15 31		16 01		16 31
Tame Bridge Parkway	d	11 50	12 05	12 20	12 35	12 50	13 05	13 20	13 35	13 50	14 05	14 20	14 35	14 50	15 05	15 20	15 35	15 50	16 05	16 20	16 35
Bescot Stadium	d		12 08		12 38		13 08		13 38		14 08		14 38		15 08		15 38		16 08		16 38
Walsall	a	11 59	12 14	12 29	12 44	12 59	13 14	13 29	13 44	13 59	14 14	14 29	14 44	14 59	15 14	15 29	15 46	15 59	16 14	16 29	16 44
	d	12 00		12 30		13 00		13 30		14 00		14 30		15 00		15 30		16 00		16 30	
Bloxwich	d	12 07				13 07				14 07				15 07				16 07			
Bloxwich North	d	12 09				13 09				14 09				15 09				16 09			
Landywood	d	12 13				13 13				14 13				15 13				16 13			
Cannock	d	12 18		12 44		13 18		13 44		14 18		14 44		15 18		15 44		16 18		16 44	
Hednesford	d	12 23		12 49		13 23		13 49		14 23		14 49		15 23		15 49		16 23		16 49	
Rugeley Town	d	12 31		12 57		13 31		13 57		14 31		14 57		15 31		15 57		16 31		16 57	
Rugeley Trent Valley	a	12 36		13 04		13 36		14 04		14 36		15 04		15 36		16 04		16 36		17 04	
Stafford	a	*12 53*				*13 53*				*14 53*				*15 53*				*16 53*			

		LM	LM	LM	LM	LM	LM	LM	LM	LM	LM	LM	LM	LM	LM	LM	LM	LM	LM	LM
Wolverhampton [7] ⇌	d		16 19		16 49		17 19		17 49		18 19		19 19							
Birmingham New Street [12]	d	16 39	16 47	17 07	17 17	17 39	17 47	18 07	18 17	18 39	18 47	19 17	19 47	20 17	20 47	21 17	21 47	22 19	22 47	23 18
Duddeston	d		16 52		17 22		17 52		18 22		18 52	19 22	19 52		20 52		21 52		22 52	23 22
Aston	d		16 55		17 25		17 55		18 25		18 55	19 25	19 55		20 55		21 55		22 55	23 26
Witton	d		16 57		17 27		17 57		18 27		18 57	19 27	19 57		20 57		21 57		22 57	23 28
Perry Barr	d		16 59		17 29		17 59		18 29		18 59	19 29	19 59		20 59		21 59		22 59	23 30
Hamstead	d		17 01		17 31		18 01		18 31		19 01	19 32	20 01		21 01		22 01		23 01	23 33
Tame Bridge Parkway	d	16 50	17 05	17 20	17 35	17 50	18 05	18 20	18 35	18 50	19 05	19 37	20 05	20 30	21 05	21 30	22 05	22 30	23 05	23 38
Bescot Stadium	d		17 08		17 38		18 08		18 38		19 08	19 40	20 08		21 08		22 08		23 08	23 41
Walsall	a	16 59	17 14	17 29	17 44	17 59	18 14	18 29	18 44	18 59	19 14	19 45	20 14	20 38	21 14	21 38	22 14	22 38	23 14	23 46
	d	17 00		17 30		18 00		18 30		19 00		19 46		20 39		21 39		22 39		23 47
Bloxwich	d	17 07		17 37		18 07		18 37		19 07		19 53		20 46		21 46		22 46		23 54
Bloxwich North	d	17 09		17 39		18 09		18 39		19 09		19 55		20 49		21 49		22 49		23 56
Landywood	d	17 13		17 43		18 13		18 43		19 13		19 59		20 53		21 53		22 53		00 01
Cannock	d	17 18		17 48		18 18		18 48		19 18		20 04		20 57		21 57		22 57		00 05
Hednesford	d	17 23		17 53		18 23		18 53		19 23		20 09		21 02		22 02		23 02		00a10
Rugeley Town	d	17 31		18 01		18 31		19 01		19 31		20 17		21 10		22 10		23 10		
Rugeley Trent Valley	a	17 36		18 06		18 36		19 06		19 36		20 22		21 15		22 15		23 15		
Stafford	a	*18 04*				*18 53*				*19 53*		*20 55*								

Sundays

until 12 July and from 13 September

		LM	LM	LM	LM	LM	LM	LM	LM	LM	LM	LM	LM	LM	LM	LM	LM	LM
Wolverhampton [7] ⇌	d																	
Birmingham New Street [12]	d	23p18	09 17	09 40	10 17	10 40	11 17	11 40	12 17	12 40	13 17	13 40	14 17	14 40	15 17	15 40	16 17	16 40
Duddeston	d	23p22	09 21		10 21		11 21		12 21		13 21		14 21		15 21		16 21	
Aston	d	23p26	09 24		10 24		11 24		12 24		13 24		14 24		15 24		16 24	
Witton	d	23p28	09 26		10 26		11 26		12 26		13 26		14 26		15 26		16 26	
Perry Barr	d	23p30	09 29		10 29		11 29		12 29		13 29		14 29		15 29		16 29	
Hamstead	d	23p33	09 32		10 32		11 32		12 32		13 32		14 32		15 32		16 32	
Tame Bridge Parkway	d	23p38	09 37	09 52	10 37	10 52	11 37	11 52	12 37	12 52	13 37	13 52	14 37	14 52	15 37	15 52	16 37	16 52
Bescot Stadium	d	23p41	09 39		10 39		11 39		12 39		13 39		14 40		15 39		16 39	
Walsall	a	23p46	09 44	10 00	10 44	11 00	11 44	12 00	12 44	13 00	13 44	14 00	14 44	15 00	15 44	16 00	16 44	17 00
	d	23p47		10 01		11 01		12 01		13 01		14 01		15 01		16 01		17 01
Bloxwich	d	23p54		10 08		11 08		12 08		13 08		14 08		15 08		16 08		17 08
Bloxwich North	d	23p56		10 10		11 10		12 10		13 10		14 10		15 10		16 10		17 10
Landywood	d	00 01		10 15		11 15		12 15		13 15		14 15		15 15		16 15		17 15
Cannock	d	00 05		10 19		11 19		12 19		13 19		14 19		15 19		16 19		17 19
Hednesford	d	00a10		10 24		11 24		12 24		13 24		14 24		15 24		16 24		17 24
Rugeley Town	d			10 32		11 32		12 32		13 32		14 32		15 32		16 32		17 32
Rugeley Trent Valley	a			10 37		11 37		12 37		13 37		14 37		15 37		16 37		17 37
Stafford	a					*12b53*						*15 14*				*17 14*		

For general notes see front of timetable
For details of catering facilities see
Directory of Train Operators

b Until 12 July arr. 1254

Table 70

Sundays

until 12 July and from 13 September

Birmingham → Walsall, Rugeley and Stafford

Network Diagram - see first page of Table 67

		LM	LM	LM	LM	LM	LM	LM	LM	LM	LM	LM	LM	LM
Wolverhampton 7 🚢	d													
Birmingham New Street 12	d	17 17	17 40	18 17	18 40	19 17	19 40	20 17	20 40	21 17	21 40	22 17	22 40	23 17
Duddeston	d	17 21		18 21		19 21		20 21		21 21		22 21		23 21
Aston	d	17 24		18 24		19 24		20 24		21 24		22 24		23 24
Witton	d	17 26		18 26		19 26		20 26		21 26		22 26		23 26
Perry Barr	d	17 29		18 29		19 29		20 29		21 29		22 29		23 29
Hamstead	d	17 32		18 32		19 32		20 32		21 32		22 32		23 32
Tame Bridge Parkway	d	17 37	17 52	18 37	18 52	19 37	19 52	20 37	20 52	21 37	21 52	22 37	22 52	23 37
Bescot Stadium	d	17 39		18 40		19 39		20 39		21 39		22 39		23 39
Walsall	a	17 44	18 00	18 44	19 00	19 44	20 00	20 44	21 00	21 46	22 00	22 44	23 00	23 44
	d		18 01		19 01		20 01		21 01		22 01		23 01	
Bloxwich	d		18 08		19 08		20 08		21 08		22 08		23 08	
Bloxwich North	d		18 10		19 10		20 10		21 10		22 10		23 10	
Landywood	d		18 15		19 15		20 15		21 15		22 15		23 15	
Cannock	d		18 19		19 19		20 19		21 19		22 19		23 19	
Hednesford	d		18 24		19 24		20 24		21 24		22 24		23 24	
Rugeley Town	d		18 32		19 32		20 32		21 32		22 32		23 32	
Rugeley Trent Valley	a		18 37		19 37		20 37		21 37		22 37		23 37	
Stafford	a		*19 14*				*21 14*							

Sundays

19 July to 6 September

		LM	LM 🚌	LM 🚌	LM	LM 🚌	LM 🚌	LM	LM 🚌	LM 🚌	LM	LM 🚌	LM 🚌	LM	LM 🚌	LM 🚌	LM	LM 🚌	LM 🚌	LM	LM 🚌	LM 🚌	LM	LM 🚌
Wolverhampton 7 🚢	d																							
Birmingham New Street 12	d	23p18	08 30	09 10		09 30	10 10		10 30	11 10		11 30	12 10		12 30	13 10		13 30	14 10		14 30	15 10		15 30
Duddeston	d	23p22	08 40			09 40			10 40			11 40			12 40			13 40			14 40			15 40
Aston	d	23p26	08 45			09 45			10 45			11 45			12 45			13 45			14 45			15 45
Witton	d	23p28	08 52			09 52			10 52			11 52			12 52			13 52			14 52			15 52
Perry Barr	d	23p30	09 00			10 00			11 00			12 00			13 00			14 00			15 00			16 00
Hamstead	d	23p33	09 09			10 09			11 09			12 09			13 09			14 09			15 09			16 09
Tame Bridge Parkway	d	23p38	09 20	09 36		10 20	10 36		11 20	11 36		12 20	12 36		13 20	13 36		14 20	14 36		15 20	15 36		16 20
Bescot Stadium	d	23p41	09 29			10 29			11 29			12 29			13 29			14 29			15 29			16 29
Walsall	a	23p46	09 37	09 51		10 37	10 51		11 37	11 51		12 37	12 51		13 37	13 51		14 37	14 51		15 37	15 51		16 37
	d	23p47			10 01			11 01			12 01			13 01			14 01			15 01			16 01	
Bloxwich	d	23p54			10 08			11 08			12 08			13 08			14 08			15 08			16 08	
Bloxwich North	d	23p56			10 10			11 10			12 10			13 10			14 10			15 10			16 10	
Landywood	d	00 01			10 15			11 15			12 15			13 15			14 15			15 15			16 15	
Cannock	d	00 05			10 19			11 19			12 19			13 19			14 19			15 19			16 19	
Hednesford	d	00a10			10 24			11 24			12 24			13 24			14 24			15 24			16 24	
Rugeley Town	d				10 32			11 32			12 32			13 32			14 32			15 32			16 32	
Rugeley Trent Valley	a				10 37			11 37			12 37			13 37			14 37			15 37			16 37	
Stafford	a							*12 53*									*15 14*						*17 14*	

		LM 🚌	LM	LM 🚌	LM 🚌	LM	LM 🚌	LM 🚌	LM	LM 🚌	LM 🚌	LM	LM 🚌	LM 🚌	LM	LM 🚌	LM 🚌	LM	LM 🚌	LM 🚌	LM	LM 🚌	LM 🚌
Wolverhampton 7 🚢	d																						
Birmingham New Street 12	d	16 10		16 30	17 10		17 30	18 10		18 30	19 10		19 30	20 10		20 30	21 10		21 30	22 10		22 30	23 30
Duddeston	d			16 40			17 40			18 40			19 40			20 40			21 40			22 40	23 40
Aston	d			16 45			17 45			18 45			19 45			20 45			21 45			22 45	23 45
Witton	d			16 52			17 52			18 52			19 52			20 52			21 52			22 52	23 52
Perry Barr	d			17 00			18 00			19 00			20 00			21 00			22 00			23 00	23 59
Hamstead	d			17 09			18 09			19 09			20 09			21 09			22 09			23 09	00 09
Tame Bridge Parkway	d	16 36		17 20	17 36		18 20	18 36		19 20	19 36		20 20	20 36		21 20	21 36		22 20	22 36		23 20	00 20
Bescot Stadium	d			17 29			18 29			19 29			20 29			21 29			22 29			23 29	00 29
Walsall	a	16 51		17 37	17 51		18 37	18 51		19 37	19 51		20 37	20 51		21 37	21 51		22 37	22 51		23 37	00 37
	d		17 01			18 01			19 01			20 01			21 01			22 01			23 01		
Bloxwich	d		17 08			18 08			19 08			20 08			21 08			22 08			23 08		
Bloxwich North	d		17 10			18 10			19 10			20 10			21 10			22 10			23 10		
Landywood	d		17 15			18 15			19 15			20 15			21 15			22 15			23 15		
Cannock	d		17 19			18 19			19 19			20 19			21 19			22 19			23 19		
Hednesford	d		17 24			18 24			19 24			20 24			21 24			22 24			23 24		
Rugeley Town	d		17 32			18 32			19 32			20 32			21 32			22 32			23 32		
Rugeley Trent Valley	a		17 37			18 37			19 37			20 37			21 37			22 37			23 37		
Stafford	a					*19 14*						*21 14*											

For general notes see front of timetable
For details of catering facilities see
Directory of Train Operators

Stafford, Rugeley and Walsall → Birmingham

Network Diagram - see first page of Table 67

Miles	Station		LM	LM	LM	LM	LM	LM	LM	LM	LM	LM	LM	LM	LM	LM	LM	LM	LM	LM	LM	LM	LM
			MX					1 ◇ A															
—	Stafford	d									07 22				08 21				09 21				10 21
0	**Rugeley Trent Valley**	d				06 21	06 39		07 04		07 40				08 42		09 06		09 42		10 06		10 42
1½	Rugeley Town	d				06 25	06 43		07 08		07 44				08 46		09 10		09 46		10 10		10 46
5¼	Hednesford	d			06 07	06 33	06 51		07 16	07 38	07 52		08 17		08 54		09 18		09 54		10 18		10 54
7¼	Cannock	d			06 11	06 37	06 55		07 20	07 42	07 56		08 21		08 58		09 22		09 58		10 22		10 58
9¼	Landywood	d			06 14	06 40	06 58		07 23		07 59		08 24				09 25				10 25		
11¾	Bloxwich North	d			06 19	06 45	07 03		07 27		08 04		08 29				09 30				10 30		
12¼	Bloxwich	d			06 21	06 47	07 05		07 29		08 06		08 31				09 32				10 32		
15½	**Walsall**	a			06 28	06 54	07 12		07 37	07 56	08 13		08 38		09 12		09 39		10 12		10 39		11 12
—		d	23p40	06 01	06 29	07 00	07 13	07 30	07 37	08 00	08 14	08 30	08 39	09 01	09 13	09 30	09 40	10 01	10 13	10 31	10 40	11 01	11 13
16¾	Bescot Stadium	d	23p44	06 04	06 34	07 04		07 34		08 04		08 34		09 04		09 34		10 04		10 34		11 04	
17¾	Tame Bridge Parkway	d	23p47	06 07	06 37	07 07	07 19	07 37	07 43	08 07	08 20	08 37	08 46	09 07	09 19	09 37	09 46	10 07	10 19	10 37	10 46	11 07	11 19
20½	Hamstead	d	23p51	06 11	06 41	07 12		07 41		08 11		08 41		09 11		09 41		10 11		10 41		11 11	
22	Perry Barr	d	23p54	06 14	06 44	07 15		07 44		08 14		08 44		09 14		09 44		10 14		10 44		11 14	
22¾	Witton	d	23p57	06 16	06 46	07 17		07 47		08 17		08 47		09 16		09 47		10 16		10 46		11 16	
23½	Aston	d	23p59	06 18	06 49	07 20		07 50		08 20		08 50		09 19		09 50		10 19		10 49		11 19	
24¾	Duddeston	d	00 02	06 21	06 52	07 23		07 53		08 23		08 53		09 21		09 53		10 21		10 51		11 21	
26¼	**Birmingham New Street 12**	a	00 09	06 28	06 57	07 28	07 36	07 57	08 00	08 29	08 37	08 57	09 02	09 28	09 36	09 57	10 03	10 28	10 36	10 58	11 03	11 28	11 37
—	Wolverhampton 7	a		07 03				08 19						10 03				11 03		11 33		12 03	

Station		LM	LM	LM	LM	LM	LM	LM	LM	LM	LM	LM	LM	LM	LM	LM	LM	LM	LM	LM	LM	LM	LM
Stafford	d				11 21				12 21				13 21				14 21				15 21		
Rugeley Trent Valley	d		11 06		11 42		12 06		12 42		13 06		13 42				14 42				15 42		16 06
Rugeley Town	d		11 10		11 46		12 10		12 46		13 10		13 46				14 46				15 46		16 10
Hednesford	d		11 18		11 54		12 18		12 54		13 18		13 54		14 18		14 54		15 18		15 54		16 18
Cannock	d		11 22		11 58		12 22		12 58		13 22		13 58		14 22		14 58		15 22		15 58		16 22
Landywood	d		11 25				12 25				13 25				14 25				15 25				16 25
Bloxwich North	d		11 30				12 30				13 30				14 30				15 30				16 30
Bloxwich	d		11 32				12 32				13 32				14 32				15 32				16 32
Walsall	a		11 39		12 12		12 39		13 12		13 39		14 12		14 39		15 12		15 39		16 12		16 39
	d	11 31	11 40	12 01	12 13	12 31	12 40	13 01	13 13	13 31	13 40	14 01	14 13	14 31	14 40	15 01	15 13	15 31	15 40	16 01	16 13	16 31	16 40
Bescot Stadium	d	11 34		12 04		12 34		13 04		13 34		14 04		14 34		15 04		15 34		16 04		16 34	
Tame Bridge Parkway	d	11 37	11 46	12 07	12 19	12 37	12 46	13 07	13 19	13 37	13 46	14 07	14 19	14 37	14 46	15 07	15 19	15 37	15 46	16 07	16 19	16 37	16 46
Hamstead	d	11 41		12 11		12 41		13 11		13 41		14 11		14 41		15 11		15 41		16 11		16 41	
Perry Barr	d	11 44		12 14		12 44		13 14		13 44		14 14		14 44		15 14		15 44		16 14		16 44	
Witton	d	11 46		12 16		12 46		13 16		13 46		14 16		14 46		15 16		15 46		16 16		16 46	
Aston	d	11 49		12 19		12 49		13 19		13 49		14 19		14 49		15 19		15 49		16 19		16 49	
Duddeston	d	11 51		12 21		12 51		13 21		13 51		14 21		14 51		15 21		15 51		16 21		16 51	
Birmingham New Street 12	a	11 58	12 03	12 28	12 36	12 58	13 03	13 28	13 36	13 58	14 03	14 28	14 36	14 58	15 03	15 28	15 36	15 58	16 03	16 28	16 36	16 58	17 03
Wolverhampton 7	a	12 33		13 03		13 33		14 03		14 33		15 03		15 33		16 03		16 33		17 03		17 33	

Station		LM	LM	LM	LM	LM	LM	LM	LM	LM	LM	LM	LM	LM	LM	LM	LM	LM	LM	LM	LM
Stafford	d		16 21				17 21				18 21			19 21							
Rugeley Trent Valley	d		16 42		17 13		17 42		18 12		18 46		19 10	19 42		20 35		21 40		22 35	
Rugeley Town	d		16 46		17 17		17 46		18 16		18 50		19 14	19 46		20 39		21 44		22 39	
Hednesford	d		16 54		17 25		17 54		18 24		18 58		19 21	19 54		20 47		21 52		22 47	
Cannock	d		16 58		17 29		17 58		18 28		19 02		19 25	19 58		20 51		21 56		22 51	
Landywood	d				17 32				18 31				19 29	20 01		20 54		21 59		22 54	
Bloxwich North	d				17 37				18 36				19 33	20 06		20 59		22 04		22 59	
Bloxwich	d				17 39				18 38				19 35	20 08		21 01		22 06		23 01	
Walsall	a		17 12		17 46		18 12		18 45		19 16		19 43	20 15		21 08		22 16		23 08	
	d	17 01	17 13	17 31	17 47	18 01	18 13	18 31	18 46	19 01	19 18	19 36	19 43	20 16	20 40	21 10	21 40	22 17	22 40	23 10	23 40
Bescot Stadium	d	17 04		17 34		18 04		18 34		19 04	19 23		19 48		20 44		21 44		22 44		23 44
Tame Bridge Parkway	d	17 07	17 19	17 37	17 53	18 07	18 19	18 37	18 52	19 07	19 26		19 51	20 22	20 47	21 16	21 47	22 23	22 47	23 16	23 47
Hamstead	d	17 11		17 41		18 11		18 41		19 11	19 30		19 55		20 51		21 51		22 51		23 51
Perry Barr	d	17 14		17 44		18 14		18 44		19 14	19 33		19 58		20 54		21 54		22 54		23 54
Witton	d	17 16		17 46		18 16		18 46		19 16	19 36		20 01		20 57		21 57		22 57		23 57
Aston	d	17 19		17 49		18 19		18 49		19 19	19 39		20 03		21 00		22 00		23 00		23 59
Duddeston	d	17 21		17 51		18 21		18 51		19 21	19 42		20 06		21 03		22 03		23 03		00 02
Birmingham New Street 12	a	17 28	17 36	17 58	18 10	18 28	18 36	18 58	19 09	19 28	19 46		20 11	20 39	21 09	21 35	22 09	22 40	23 09	23 33	00 09
Wolverhampton 7	a	18 03		18 33		19 03		19 33		20 03		19 50									

Saturdays

Station		LM	LM	LM	LM	LM	LM	LM	LM	LM	LM	LM	LM	LM	LM	LM	LM	LM	LM	LM	LM	LM
Stafford	d								07 26				08 23				09 21				10 21	
Rugeley Trent Valley	d				06 26				07 39		08 06		08 42		09 06		09 42		10 06		10 42	
Rugeley Town	d				06 30				07 43		08 10		08 46		09 10		09 46		10 10		10 46	
Hednesford	d				06 38	06 58			07 51		08 18		08 54		09 18		09 54		10 18		10 54	
Cannock	d				06 42	07 02			07 55		08 22		08 58		09 22		09 58		10 22		10 58	
Landywood	d				06 45	07 05			07 58		08 25				09 25				10 25			
Bloxwich North	d				06 50	07 10			08 03		08 30				09 30				10 30			
Bloxwich	d				06 52	07 12			08 05		08 32				09 32				10 32			
Walsall	a				06 59	07 19			08 12		08 39		09 12		09 39		10 12		10 39		11 12	
	d	23p40	06 01	06 31	07 00	07 20	07 31	08 01	08 13	08 31	08 40	09 01	09 13	09 31	09 40	10 01	10 13	10 31	10 40	11 01	11 13	11 31
Bescot Stadium	d	23p44	06 04	06 34	07 04		07 34	08 04		08 34		09 04		09 34		10 04		10 34		11 04		11 34
Tame Bridge Parkway	d	23p47	06 07	06 37	07 07	07 26	07 37	08 07	08 19	08 37	08 46	09 07	09 19	09 37	09 46	10 07	10 19	10 37	10 46	11 07	11 19	11 37
Hamstead	d	23p51	06 11	06 41	07 12		07 41	08 11		08 41		09 11		09 41		10 11		10 41		11 11		11 41
Perry Barr	d	23p54	06 14	06 44	07 15		07 44	08 14		08 44		09 14		09 44		10 14		10 44		11 14		11 44
Witton	d	23p57	06 16	06 46	07 17		07 46	08 16		08 46		09 16		09 46		10 16		10 46		11 16		11 46
Aston	d	23p59	06 18	06 48	07 20		07 48	08 18		08 48		09 19		09 49		10 19		10 49		11 19		11 49
Duddeston	d	00 02	06 21	06 51	07 23		07 51	08 21		08 51		09 21		09 51		10 21		10 51		11 21		11 51
Birmingham New Street 12	a	00 09	06 28	06 58	07 28	07 44	07 58	08 28	08 36	08 58	09 02	09 29	09 36	09 58	10 03	10 28	10 36	10 58	11 03	11 28	11 36	11 58
Wolverhampton 7	a		07 03	07 33			08 33	09 03		09 33		10 03		10 33		11 03		11 33		12 03		12 33

For general notes see front of timetable
For details of catering facilities see
Directory of Train Operators

A To Liverpool Lime Street (Table 65)

Table 70

Saturdays

Stafford, Rugeley and Walsall → Birmingham

Network Diagram - see first page of Table 67

		LM		LM	LM	LM	LM		LM	LM	LM	LM		LM	LM	LM	LM		LM	LM	LM	LM		LM	LM	LM
Stafford	d				11 21					12 21					13 21					14 21					15 21	
Rugeley Trent Valley	d	11 06			11 42		12 06			12 42		13 06			13 42		14 06			14 42		15 06			15 42	
Rugeley Town	d	11 10			11 46		12 10			12 46		13 10			13 46		14 10			14 46		15 10			15 46	
Hednesford	d	11 18			11 54		12 18			12 54		13 18			13 54		14 18			14 54		15 18			15 54	
Cannock	d	11 22			11 58		12 22			12 58		13 22			13 58		14 22			14 58		15 22			15 58	
Landywood	d	11 25					12 25					13 25					14 25					15 25				
Bloxwich North	d	11 30					12 30					13 30					14 30					15 30				
Bloxwich	d	11 32					12 32					13 32					14 32					15 32				
Walsall	a	11 39			12 12		12 39			13 12		13 39			14 12		14 39			15 12		15 39			16 12	
	d	11 40		12 01	12 13	12 31	12 40		13 01	13 13	13 31	13 40		14 01	14 13	14 31	14 40		15 01	15 13	15 31	15 40		16 01	16 13	16 31
Bescot Stadium	d			12 04		12 34			13 04		13 34			14 04		14 34			15 04		15 34			16 04		16 34
Tame Bridge Parkway	d	11 46		12 07	12 19	12 37	12 46		13 07	13 19	13 37	13 46		14 07	14 19	14 37	14 46		15 07	15 19	15 37	15 46		16 07	16 19	16 37
Hamstead	d			12 11		12 41			13 11		13 41			14 11		14 41			15 11		15 41			16 11		16 41
Perry Barr	d			12 14		12 44			13 14		13 44			14 14		14 44			15 14		15 44			16 14		16 44
Witton	d			12 16		12 46			13 16		13 46			14 16		14 46			15 16		15 46			16 16		16 46
Aston	d			12 19		12 49			13 19		13 49			14 19		14 49			15 19		15 49			16 19		16 49
Duddeston	d			12 21		12 51			13 21		13 51			14 21		14 51			15 21		15 51			16 21		16 51
Birmingham New Street 12	a	12 03		12 28	12 36	12 58	13 03		13 28	13 36	13 58	14 03		14 28	14 36	14 58	15 03		15 28	15 36	15 58	16 03		16 28	16 36	16 58
Wolverhampton 7	a			13 03		13 33			14 03		14 33			15 03		15 33			16 03		16 33			17 03		17 33

		LM	LM	LM		LM	LM	LM	LM		LM	LM	LM	LM		LM	LM	LM	LM	LM	LM	LM	LM	LM A		
Stafford	d			16 21					17 21					18 21			19 21									
Rugeley Trent Valley	d	16 06		16 42			17 06		17 42			18 12		18 45		19 10	19 42		20 35		21 35		22 35			
Rugeley Town	d	16 10		16 46			17 10		17 46			18 16		18 49		19 14	19 46		20 39		21 39		22 39			
Hednesford	d	16 18		16 54			17 18		17 54			18 24		18 57		19 21	19 54		20 47		21 47		22 47			
Cannock	d	16 22		16 58			17 22		17 58			18 28		19 01		19 25	19 58		20 51		21 51		22 51			
Landywood	d	16 25					17 25					18 31				19 29	20 01		20 54		21 54		22 54			
Bloxwich North	d	16 30					17 30					18 36				19 33	20 06		20 59		21 59		22 59			
Bloxwich	d	16 32					17 32					18 38				19 35	20 08		21 01		22 01		23 01			
Walsall	a	16 39		17 12			17 39		18 12			18 45		19 15		19 43	20 15		21 08		22 08		23 08			
	d	16 40	17 01	17 13		17 31	17 40	18 01	18 13		18 31	18 46	19 01	19 18		19 43	20 16	20 40	21 10	21 40	22 10	22 40	23 10	23 40		
Bescot Stadium	d		17 04			17 34		18 04			18 34		19 04	19 23		19 48		20 44		21 44		22 44		23 44		
Tame Bridge Parkway	d	16 46	17 07	17 19		17 37	17 46	18 07	18 19		18 37	18 52	19 07	19 26		19 51	20 22	20 47	21 16	21 47	22 16	22 47	23 16	23 47		
Hamstead	d		17 11			17 41		18 11			18 41		19 11	19 30		19 55		20 51		21 51		22 51		23 51		
Perry Barr	d		17 14			17 44		18 14			18 44		19 14	19 33		19 58		20 54		21 54		22 54		23 54		
Witton	d		17 16			17 46		18 16			18 46		19 16	19 36		20 01		20 57		21 57		22 57		23 57		
Aston	d		17 19			17 49		18 19			18 49		19 19	19 39		20 03		21 00		22 00		23 00		23 59		
Duddeston	d		17 21			17 51		18 21			18 51		19 21	19 42		20 06		21 03		22 03		23 03		00 02		
Birmingham New Street 12	a	17 03	17 28	17 36		17 58	18 03	18 28	18 36		18 58	19 09	19 28	19 46		20 11	20 39	21 09	21 33	22 09	22 33	23 09	23 34	00 09		
Wolverhampton 7	a		18 03			18 33		19 03			19 33		20 03													

Sundays

until 12 July and from 13 September

		LM		LM		LM		LM		LM		LM		LM		LM		LM		LM		LM		LM		LM
Stafford	d																	12b18								14 19
Rugeley Trent Valley	d					09 48				10 48				11 48				12 48				13 48				14 48
Rugeley Town	d					09 52				10 52				11 52				12 52				13 52				14 52
Hednesford	d					10 00				11 00				12 00				13 00				14 00				15 00
Cannock	d					10 04				11 04				12 04				13 04				14 04				15 04
Landywood	d					10 07				11 07				12 07				13 07				14 07				15 07
Bloxwich North	d					10 12				11 12				12 12				13 12				14 12				15 12
Bloxwich	d					10 14				11 14				12 14				13 14				14 14				15 14
Walsall	a					10 21				11 21				12 21				13 21				14 21				15 21
	d	23p40		10 00		10 23		11 00		11 23		12 00		12 23		13 00		13 23		14 00		14 23		15 00		15 23
Bescot Stadium	d	23p44		10 04				11 04				12 04				13 04				14 04				15 04		
Tame Bridge Parkway	d	23p47		10 07		10 29		11 07		11 29		12 07		12 29		13 07		13 29		14 07		14 29		15 07		15 29
Hamstead	d	23p51		10 11				11 11				12 11				13 11				14 11				15 11		
Perry Barr	d	23p54		10 14				11 14				12 14				13 14				14 14				15 14		
Witton	d	23p57		10 17				11 17				12 17				13 17				14 17				15 17		
Aston	d	23p59		10 20				11 20				12 20				13 20				14 20				15 20		
Duddeston	d	00 02		10 23				11 23				12 23				13 23				14 23				15 23		
Birmingham New Street 12	a	00 09		10 27		10 45		11 27		11 45		12 27		12 46		13 27		13 45		14 27		14 45		15 27		15 45
Wolverhampton 7	a																									

		LM		LM		LM		LM		LM		LM		LM		LM	LM	LM	LM	LM	LM	LM	LM	LM		
Stafford	d							16 18								18 18				20 16						
Rugeley Trent Valley	d			15 48				16 48				17 48				18 48		19 48		20 48		21 48		22 48		
Rugeley Town	d			15 52				16 52				17 52				18 52		19 52		20 52		21 52		22 52		
Hednesford	d			16 00				17 00				18 00				19 00		20 00		21 00		22 00		23 00		
Cannock	d			16 04				17 04				18 04				19 04		20 04		21 04		22 04		23 04		
Landywood	d			16 07				17 07				18 07				19 07		20 07		21 07		22 07		23 07		
Bloxwich North	d			16 12				17 12				18 12				19 12		20 12		21 12		22 12		23 12		
Bloxwich	d			16 14				17 14				18 14				19 14		20 14		21 14		22 14		23 14		
Walsall	a			16 21				17 21				18 21				19 21		20 21		21 21		22 21		23 21		
	d	16 00		16 23		17 00		17 23		18 00		18 23		19 00		19 23	20 00	20 23	21 00	21 23	22 00	22 23	23 00	23 23		
Bescot Stadium	d	16 04				17 04				18 04				19 04			20 04		21 04		22 04		23 04			
Tame Bridge Parkway	d	16 07		16 29		17 07		17 29		18 07		18 29		19 07		19 29	20 07	20 29	21 07	21 29	22 07	22 29	23 07	23 29		
Hamstead	d	16 11				17 11				18 11				19 11			20 11		21 11		22 11		23 11			
Perry Barr	d	16 14				17 14				18 14				19 14			20 14		21 14		22 14		23 14			
Witton	d	16 17				17 17				18 17				19 17			20 17		21 17		22 17		23 17			
Aston	d	16 20				17 20				18 20				19 20			20 20		21 20		22 20		23 20			
Duddeston	d	16 23				17 23				18 23				19 23			20 23		21 23		22 23		23 23			
Birmingham New Street 12	a	16 27		16 45		17 27		17 45		18 27		18 45		19 27		19 45	20 27	20 45	21 27	21 45	22 27	22 45	23 27	23 45		
Wolverhampton 7	a																									

For general notes see front of timetable
For details of catering facilities see
Directory of Train Operators

A Until 11 July and from 12 September
b Until 12 July dep. 1210

Sundays

19 July to 6 September

Stafford, Rugeley and Walsall → Birmingham

Network Diagram - see first page of Table 67

	LM (bus)	LM	LM (bus)	LM (bus)	LM		LM (bus)	LM (bus)	LM	LM (bus)	LM (bus)		LM	LM (bus)	LM (bus)	LM	LM (bus)		LM (bus)	LM	LM (bus)	LM (bus)	LM		LM (bus)
Stafford d													12 18							14 19					
Rugeley Trent Valley d		09 48			10 48				11 48				12 48			13 48				14 48			15 48		
Rugeley Town d		09 52			10 52				11 52				12 52			13 52				14 52			15 52		
Hednesford d		10 00			11 00				12 00				13 00			14 00				15 00			16 00		
Cannock d		10 04			11 04				12 04				13 04			14 04				15 04			16 04		
Landywood d		10 07			11 07				12 07				13 07			14 07				15 07			16 07		
Bloxwich North d		10 12			11 12				12 12				13 12			14 12				15 12			16 12		
Bloxwich d		10 14			11 14				12 14				13 14			14 14				15 14			16 14		
Walsall a		10 21			11 21				12 21				13 21			14 21				15 21			16 21		
d	10 00		10 30	11 00			11 30	12 00		12 30	13 00			13 30	14 00		14 30		15 00		15 30	16 00			16 30
Bescot Stadium d	10 09			11 09				12 09			13 09				14 09				15 09			16 09			
Tame Bridge Parkway d	10 18		10 46	11 18			11 46	12 18		12 46	13 18			13 46	14 18		14 46		15 18		15 46	16 18			16 46
Hamstead d	10 28			11 28				12 28			13 28				14 28				15 28			16 28			
Perry Barr d	10 38			11 38				12 38			13 38				14 38				15 38			16 38			
Witton d	10 45			11 45				12 45			13 45				14 45				15 45			16 45			
Aston d	10 49			11 49				12 49			13 49				14 49				15 49			16 49			
Duddeston d	10 54			11 54				12 54			13 54				14 54				15 54			16 54			
Birmingham New Street 12 a	11 03		11 11	12 03			12 11	13 03		13 11	14 03			14 11	15 03		15 11		16 03		16 11	17 03			17 11
Wolverhampton 7 (ship) a																									

	LM (bus)	LM	LM (bus)	LM (bus)	LM		LM (bus)	LM (bus)	LM	LM (bus)	LM (bus)		LM	LM (bus)	LM (bus)	LM	LM (bus)	LM (bus)	LM	LM (bus)	LM (bus)	LM	LM (bus)		
Stafford d		16 18							18 18							20 16									
Rugeley Trent Valley d		16 48			17 48				18 48				19 48			20 48			21 48			22 48			
Rugeley Town d		16 52			17 52				18 52				19 52			20 52			21 52			22 52			
Hednesford d		17 00			18 00				19 00				20 00			21 00			22 00			23 00			
Cannock d		17 04			18 04				19 04				20 04			21 04			22 04			23 04			
Landywood d		17 07			18 07				19 07				20 07			21 07			22 07			23 07			
Bloxwich North d		17 12			18 12				19 12				20 12			21 12			22 12			23 12			
Bloxwich d		17 14			18 14				19 14				20 14			21 14			22 14			23 14			
Walsall a		17 21			18 21				19 21				20 21			21 21			22 21			23 21			
d	17 00		17 30	18 00			18 30	19 00		19 30	20 00			20 30	21 00		21 30	22 00		22 30	23 00		23 30		
Bescot Stadium d	17 09			18 09				19 09			20 09				21 09			22 09			23 09				
Tame Bridge Parkway d	17 18		17 46	18 18			18 46	19 18		19 46	20 18			20 46	21 18		21 46	22 18		22 46	23 18		23 46		
Hamstead d	17 28			18 28				19 28			20 28				21 28			22 28			23 28				
Perry Barr d	17 38			18 38				19 38			20 38				21 38			22 38			23 38				
Witton d	17 45			18 45				19 45			20 45				21 45			22 45			23 45				
Aston d	17 49			18 49				19 49			20 49				21 49			22 49			23 49				
Duddeston d	17 54			18 54				19 54			20 54				21 54			22 54			23 54				
Birmingham New Street 12 a	18 03		18 11	19 03			19 11	20 03		20 11	21 03			21 11	22 03		22 11	23 03		23 11	00 03		00 11		
Wolverhampton 7 (ship) a																									

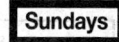

For general notes see front of timetable
For details of catering facilities see
Directory of Train Operators

Network Diagram for Tables 71, 72

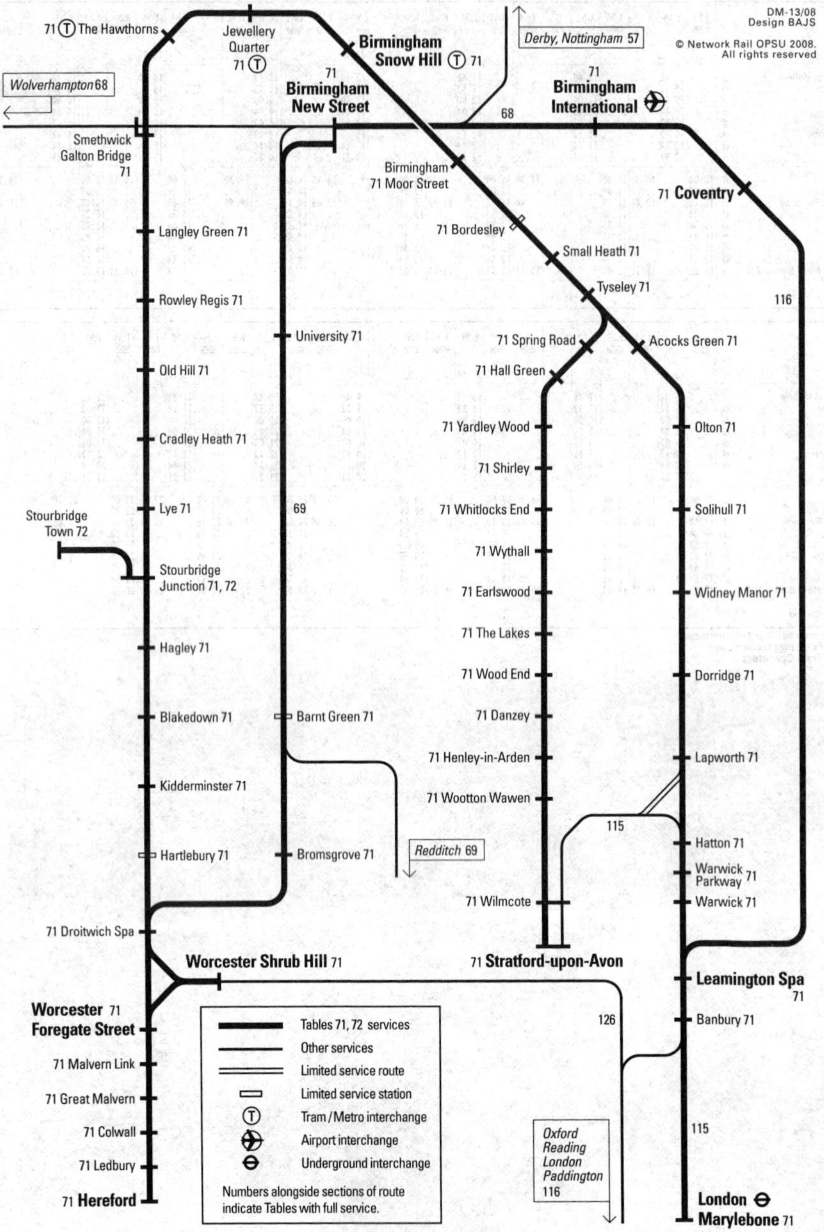
DM-13/08
Design BAJS
© Network Rail OPSU 2008.
All rights reserved
71 The Hawthorns
Jewellery Quarter 71
Birmingham Snow Hill 71
Derby, Nottingham 57
Wolverhampton 68
71 Birmingham New Street
71 Birmingham International
68
Smethwick Galton Bridge 71
Birmingham Moor Street 71
71 Coventry
Langley Green 71
71 Bordesley
Small Heath 71
Tyseley 71
Rowley Regis 71
116
University 71
71 Spring Road
Acocks Green 71
Old Hill 71
71 Hall Green
71 Yardley Wood
Olton 71
Cradley Heath 71
71 Shirley
Lye 71
69
71 Whitlocks End
Solihull 71
Stourbridge Town 72
Stourbridge Junction 71, 72
71 Wythall
71 Earlswood
Widney Manor 71
71 The Lakes
Hagley 71
71 Wood End
Dorridge 71
Blakedown 71
Barnt Green 71
71 Danzey
71 Henley-in-Arden
Lapworth 71
Kidderminster 71
71 Wootton Wawen
115
Hatton 71
Hartlebury 71
Bromsgrove 71
Redditch 69
Warwick Parkway 71
71 Wilmcote
Warwick 71
71 Droitwich Spa
Worcester Shrub Hill 71
71 Stratford-upon-Avon
Leamington Spa 71
Worcester Foregate Street 71
126
Banbury 71
71 Malvern Link
71 Great Malvern
71 Colwall
71 Ledbury
71 Hereford
115
Oxford
Reading
London
Paddington
116
London Marylebone 71
Tables 71, 72 services
Other services
Limited service route
Limited service station
Tram/Metro interchange
Airport interchange
Underground interchange
Numbers alongside sections of route indicate Tables with full service.

Table 71

Mondays to Fridays

Hereford, Worcester and Stourbridge → Birmingham → Leamington Spa, Marylebone and Stratford-upon-Avon

Network Diagram - See first page of Table 71

Miles	Miles	Miles			CH MX	CH	CH	LM	XC	CH	CH	LM	GW	LM	LM	XC	LM	CH	CH	XC	LM	CH	LM	LM	GW
							◇		[1] ◇				[1] ◇			[1] ◇			◇	[1] ◇					[1] ◇
						⊤	⊤		⊤		⊤		⊓			⊤			⊤	⊤		⊤			⊘
0	—	—	**Hereford [7]**	d																					05 35
13¾	—	—	Ledbury	a																					05 51
—	—	—		d																					05 52
18	—	—	Colwall	d																					05 59
20¾	—	—	**Great Malvern**	a																					06 05
—	—	—		d									05 17				05 50								06 05
22	—	—	Malvern Link	d									05 20				05 53								06 09
28¾	0	—	**Worcester Foregate Street [7]**	a									05 30				06 01								06 19
—	—	—		d									05 31				06 02								06 20
29½	—	—	**Worcester Shrub Hill [7]**	a									05 35												06 24
—	—	—		d								05 30												06 15	
34¼	5½	—	Droitwich Spa	d								05 38					06 12							06 23	
40½	—	—	Bromsgrove	d													06 21								
44	—	—	Barnt Green	d																					
52	—	—	University	d													06 39								
—	11	—	Hartlebury	d																				06 31	
—	14¾	—	**Kidderminster**	d								05 48							06 10			06 30		06 38	
—	17¾	—	Blakedown	d																				06 43	
—	19½	—	Hagley	d																				06 46	
—	21½	—	**Stourbridge Junction [2]**	d								05 57							06 18		06 24	06 39		06 51	
—	22¾	—	Lye	d								06 01									06 27			06 54	
—	24	—	Cradley Heath	d								06 04							06 24		06 31	06 44		06 58	
—	25¼	—	Old Hill	d								06 08									06 35			07 02	
—	26¾	—	Rowley Regis	d								06 12							06 30		06 38	06 50		07 05	
—	28¼	0	Langley Green	d								06 15									06 41			07 08	
—	29½	—	Smethwick Galton Bdg H.L. [7]	d								06 18							06 35		06 45	06 56		07 12	
54½	—	6½	**Birmingham New Street [12]**	a													06 45								
—	—	—		d					06 04							06 33				07 04					
—	—	—	**Birmingham International** ✈	d					06 14											07 14					
—	—	—	**Coventry**	d					06 25											07 25					
—	30¼	—	The Hawthorns	d								06 21							06 38		06 47	06 58		07 14	
—	32¾	—	Jewellery Quarter	d								06 24									06 51			07 18	
—	33½	—	**Birmingham Snow Hill**	a								06 28							06 46		06 54	07 04		07 20	
—	—	—		d	23p30		05 43	05 55			06 14	06 29		06 33	06 43				06 50		07 00	07 14	07 19	07 25	
—	34	—	**Birmingham Moor Street**	d	23p33		05 46	05 58			06 17	06 32		06 36	06 46				06 53		07 05	07 17	07 22	07 28	
—	34¾	—	Bordesley	d																					
—	35¾	9¼	Small Heath	d				06 02						06 41	06 50						07 09			07 32	
—	36¾	10¼	Tyseley	d	23p38			06 04				06 36		06 42	06 52						07 11			07 34	
—	—	11¼	Acocks Green	d	23p40			06 07						06 45							07 14		07 28		
—	—	12¼	Olton	d	23p43			06 10						06 48							07 17		07 30		
—	—	14	Solihull	d	23p47		05 56	06 13			06 27			06 50					07 03		07 20	07 28	07 34		
—	—	15½	Widney Manor	d	23p50			06 17						06 55							07 23		07 37		
—	—	17½	Dorridge	d	23p54		06 01	06 21			06 32			07a04					07 08		07 27	07 33	07a42		
—	—	20	Lapworth	d	23p58			06 25													07 31				
—	—	24¼	Hatton	d	00 04					06 31								07 03			07 37				
—	—	27	Warwick Parkway	d	00 08	05 40	06 12				06 44							07 09	07 19			07 45			
—	—	28¼	Warwick	d	00 11		06 15			06 38								07 13			07 43	07 48			
—	—	30¼	**Leamington Spa [8]**	a	00 14	05 45	06 20		06 37	06 45	06 49					06 59		07 17	07 24	07 37	07 49	07 52			
—	—	—		d	00 15	05 45	06 20		06 38		06 49					07 00		07 18	07 24	07 38		07 52			
—	—	—	Banbury	d	00a38	06 03	06 38		06a54		07 07					07a18		07 36	07 42	07a54		08 10			
—	—	—	**London Marylebone [10]** ⊖	a		07 18	07 53				08 16							08 51	08 54			09 25			
—	37¾	—	Spring Road	d								06 39			06 55									07 37	
—	38¾	—	Hall Green	d								06 42			06 58									07 40	
—	39¾	—	Yardley Wood	d								06 45			07 01									07 43	
—	40¾	—	Shirley	d								06 48			07 06									07 46	
—	41¾	—	Whitlocks End	d								06 51			07 09									07 49	
—	42¾	—	Wythall	d								06 53			07 11									07 51	
—	43¾	—	Earlswood (West Midlands)	d											07 14									07 54	
—	44½	—	The Lakes	d											07x16									07x56	
—	45¾	—	Wood End	d											07x18									07x58	
—	47½	—	Danzey	d											07x21									08x01	
—	50¼	—	Henley-in-Arden	d								07 03			07 26									08 06	
—	52¼	—	Wootton Wawen	d											07x28									08x09	
—	56	—	Wilmcote	d				06 42							07 34									08 14	
—	58¾	—	**Stratford-upon-Avon**	a				06 46				07 15			07 39									08 20	

For general notes see front of timetable
For details of catering facilities see Directory of Train Operators

From 5 October a revised Chiltern Railways service will be in operation due to seasonal difficulties. Trains will arrive at their destination 3 minutes later than shown

Hereford, Worcester and Stourbridge → Birmingham → Leamington Spa, Marylebone and Stratford-upon-Avon

Network Diagram - See first page of Table 71

		LM	XC	LM	CH	CH	LM	GW	LM	LM	XC	CH	LM	LM	GW	LM	LM	XC	LM	XC	CH	LM	XC	LM	LM
			1 ◇			◇		1			R 1				1 ◇			1		1 ◇	◇		1 ◇		
																		A B					B C		
			⊼		⊼	⊼					⊼	⊼			⊘					⊼	⊼				
Hereford 7	d														06 43							07 08			
Ledbury	a														06 59							07 23			
	d														06 59							07 24			
Colwall	d														07 07							07 30			
Great Malvern	a														07 14							07 35			
	d									06 48				07 05	07 14							07 39			
Malvern Link	d									06 50				07 08	07 18							07 42			
Worcester Foregate Street 7	a									06 59				07 16	07 30							07 50			
	d						06 47	06 50		06 59				07 17	07 30		07 33					07 51			08 04
Worcester Shrub Hill 7	a							06 52		07 02				07 19	07 34							07 53			
	d	06 26								07 06			07 15	07 24								07 57			
Droitwich Spa	d	06 32					06 55			07 14			07 23	07 32			07 42					08 05			08 11
Bromsgrove	d	06 42								07 25								07 49					08 23		
Barnt Green	d																								
University	d	07 00												08 00				08 09				08 30	08 39		
Hartlebury	d						07 02						07 31												
Kidderminster	d					06 56	07 09		07 18			07 30	07 37				07 53				08 10				08 22
Blakedown	d						07 14		07 24				07 42				07 58				08 15				08 27
Hagley	d						07 18		07 28				07 46				08 02				08 18				08 30
Stourbridge Junction 2	d					07 07	07 23		07 32			07 40	07 50			07 56	08 08		08 14		08 23				08 35
Lye	d					07 11			07 35							07 59			08 17						08 38
Cradley Heath	d					07 14	07 29		07 39			07 45	07 56			08 02	08 14		08 21		08 28				08 41
Old Hill	d					07 18			07 43							08 06			08 25						08 45
Rowley Regis	d					07 22	07 35		07 47			07 53	08 01			08 10	08 20		08 29		08 34				08 49
Langley Green	d					07 25			07 50							08 13			08 32						08 52
Smethwick Galton Bdg H.L. 7	d					07 29	07 40		07 53			07 59	08 06			08 16	08 25		08 35		08 40				08 55
Birmingham New Street 12	a	07 07								07 45				08 09				08 16				08 37	08 45		
	d		07 33								08 04									08 33					
Birmingham International ✈	d										08 14														
Coventry	d										08 25														
The Hawthorns 🚊	d					07 32	07 42		07 56			08 02	08 09			08 19	08 28		08 38		08 42				08 58
Jewellery Quarter 🚊	d					07 36	07 46		07 59			08 06	08 12			08 22	08 31		08 41		08 47				09 01
Birmingham Snow Hill 🚊	a					07 40	07 49		08 03			08 11	08 16			08 25	08 35		08 45		08 51				09 05
	d			07 39		07 45	07 50		08 05			08 12	08 17			08 27	08 37		08 47		08 52			08 57	09 07
Birmingham Moor Street	d			07 42		07 48	07 53		08 08			08 15	08 20			08 30	08 40		08 50		08 55			09 00	09 10
Bordesley	d																								
Small Heath	d			07 46					08 12								08 44								09 14
Tyseley	d			07 48			07 58		08 14								08 46								09 16
Acocks Green	d						08 01						08 26				08 49							09 06	
Olton	d						08 03						08 28				08 52							09 08	
Solihull	d					07 58	08 07					08 25	08 32				08 55				09 05			09 12	
Widney Manor	d						08 10						08 35				08 58							09 15	
Dorridge	d					08 03	08a16					08 30	08a41				09a03				09 10			09a22	
Lapworth	d					08 07																			
Hatton	d				07 56	08 13																			
Warwick Parkway	d					08 19						08 41									09 21				
Warwick	d				08 05	08 23						08 44									09 24				
Leamington Spa 8	a		07 59		08 09	08 26					08 37	08 49								08 59	09 29				
	d		08 00		08 09	08 27					08 38	08 49								09 00	09 29				
Banbury	d		08a18		08 28	08 45					08a54	09 09								09a18	09 47				
London Marylebone 10 ⊖	a				09 55	10 01						10 25									10 58				
Spring Road	d			07 51					08 17							08 36			08 56						09 19
Hall Green	d			07 54					08 20							08 39			08 59						09 22
Yardley Wood	d			07 57					08 23							08 42			09 02						09 25
Shirley	d			08a00					08a26							08 45			09a05						09a28
Whitlocks End	d															08 48									
Wythall	d															08 50									
Earlswood (West Midlands)	d															08 53									
The Lakes	d															08x55									
Wood End	d															08x57									
Danzey	d															09x00									
Henley-in-Arden	d															09 05									
Wootton Wawen	d															09x08									
Wilmcote	d															09 13									
Stratford-upon-Avon	a															09 19									

For general notes see front of timetable
For details of catering facilities see Directory of Train Operators

A From Gloucester to Nottingham (Table 57)
B To Nottingham (Table 57)
C From Cardiff Central (Table 132)

From 5 October a revised Chiltern Railways service will be in operation due to seasonal difficulties. Trains will arrive at their destination 3 minutes later than shown

Hereford, Worcester and Stourbridge → Birmingham → Leamington Spa, Marylebone and Stratford-upon-Avon

Network Diagram - See first page of Table 71

Station		XC	LM	CH	LM	LM	LM	LM	GW	XC	LM	GW	GW	CH	CH	LM	LM	XC	CH	LM	LM	LM	LM	LM	GW
		[1] ◇		◇						[1] ◇			[1] ◇		◇			[1] ◇	◇						[1] ◇
									A			A													
		[trolley]								[trolley]			[restaurant]					[trolley]							[trolley]
Hereford [7]	d		07 34																				08 49		
Ledbury	a		07 51																				09 05		
	d		07 51																				09 08		
Colwall	d		07 57																				09 14		
Great Malvern	a		08 02																				09 19		
	d		08 03						08 25		08 38		08 58										09 19		09 54
Malvern Link	d		08 06						08 28		08 41		09 00										09 22		09 56
Worcester Foregate Street [7]	a		08 15						08 41		08 50	←	09 09										09 31		10 05
	d		08 19					08 35	08 54		08 51	08 54	09 09				09 06						09 31		10 05
Worcester Shrub Hill [7]	a							08 37	→			08 56	09 12										09 34		10 08
	d							08 41															09 37	09 47	
Droitwich Spa	d		08 30					08 49			09 00						09 15						09 45	09 55	
Bromsgrove	d		08 41								09 09												09 54		
Barnt Green	d																								
University	d		09 00								09 30												10 09		
Hartlebury	d																								
Kidderminster	d						08 58	09 06									09 26			09 36		09 56		10 06	
Blakedown	d						09 03	09 11									09 31			09 41				10 11	
Hagley	d						09 06	09 15									09 35			09 45				10 15	
Stourbridge Junction [2]	d				08 45	08 55	09 11	09 18								09 25	09 38			09 49	09 55	10 09		10 19	
Lye	d					08 58										09 28					09 58				
Cradley Heath	d				08 51	09 01	09 16	09 24								09 31	09 43			09 54	10 01	10 14		10 24	
Old Hill	d					09 05										09 35					10 05				
Rowley Regis	d				08 57	09 09	09 22	09 30								09 39	09 49			10 00	10 09	10 20		10 30	
Langley Green	d					09 12										09 42					10 12				
Smethwick Galton Bdg H.L. [7]	d				09 02	09 15	09 27	09 35								09 45	09 54			10 05	10 15	10 25		10 35	
Birmingham New Street [12]	a		09 07								09 42												10 24		
	d	09 04								09 33								10 04							
Birmingham International ✈	d	09 14																10 14							
Coventry	d	09 25																10 25							
The Hawthorns 🚋	d				09 05	09 18	09 30	09 38								09 48	09 57			10 08	10 18	10 28		10 38	
Jewellery Quarter 🚋	d				09 09	09 21	09 33	09 41								09 51	10 00			10 11	10 21	10 31		10 41	
Birmingham Snow Hill 🚋	a				09 15	09 25	09 36	09 45								09 55	10 05			10 15	10 25	10 35		10 45	
	d			09 12	09 17	09 27	09 37	09 47							09 52	09 57	10 07		10 12	10 17	10 27	10 37		10 47	
Birmingham Moor Street	d			09 15	09 20	09 30	09 40	09 50							09 55	10 00	10 10		10 15	10 20	10 30	10 40		10 50	
Bordesley	d																								
Small Heath	d						09 44										10 14					10 44			
Tyseley	d						09 46										10 16					10 46			
Acocks Green	d				09 26		09 49									10 06				10 26		10 49			
Olton	d				09 28		09 52									10 08				10 28		10 52			
Solihull	d			09 25	09 32		09 55								10 05	10 12			10 25	10 32		10 55			
Widney Manor	d				09 35		09 58									10 15				10 35		10 58			
Dorridge	d			09 30	09a41		10a04								10 10	10a22			10 30	10a41		11a04			
Lapworth	d			09 34															10 34						
Hatton	d			09 40										10 01					10 40						
Warwick Parkway	d			09 45										10 06	10 21				10 45						
Warwick	d			09 49										10 10	10 24				10 49						
Leamington Spa [8]	a	09 37		09 53						09 59				10 13	10 29			10 37	10 53						
	d	09 38		09 54						10 00				10 14	10 29			10 38	10 54						
Banbury	d	09a54		10 12						10a18				10 32	10 47			10a54	11 12						
London Marylebone [10] ⊖	a			11 30										11 57	12 02				12 30						
Spring Road	d					09 36		09 56									10 19				10 36			10 56	
Hall Green	d					09 39		09 59									10 22				10 39			10 59	
Yardley Wood	d					09 42		10 02									10 25				10 42			11 02	
Shirley	d					09 45		10a05									10a28				10 45			11a05	
Whitlocks End	d					09 48															10 48				
Wythall	d					09 50															10 50				
Earlswood (West Midlands)	d					09 53															10 53				
The Lakes	d					09x55															10x55				
Wood End	d					09x57															10x57				
Danzey	d					10x00															11x00				
Henley-in-Arden	d					10 05															11 05				
Wootton Wawen	d					10x08															11x08				
Wilmcote	d					10 13															11 13				
Stratford-upon-Avon	a					10 21															11 21				

For general notes see front of timetable
For details of catering facilities see
Directory of Train Operators

A To Westbury (Table 123)

From 5 October a revised Chiltern Railways service will be in operation due to seasonal difficulties. Trains will arrive at their destination 3 minutes later than shown

Hereford, Worcester and Stourbridge → Birmingham → Leamington Spa, Marylebone and Stratford-upon-Avon

Network Diagram - See first page of Table 71

Station		XC	CH	LM	LM	XC	CH	LM	LM	LM	LM	LM	GW
		1 ◇	◇			1 ◇	◇						◇ A
Hereford [7]	d									09 40			
Ledbury	a									09 57			
	d									09 58			
Colwall	d									10 04			
Great Malvern	a									10 09			
	d									10 10			10 51
Malvern Link	d									10 13			10 53
Worcester Foregate Street [7]	a									10 22			11 02
	d							10 15		10 23			11 02
Worcester Shrub Hill [7]	a												11 06
	d											10 47	
Droitwich Spa	d							10 24		10 33		10 55	
Bromsgrove	d									10 42			
Barnt Green	d												
University	d									10 59			
Hartlebury	d												
Kidderminster	d				10 26			10 36			10 56	11 06	
Blakedown	d							10 41				11 11	
Hagley	d							10 44				11 14	
Stourbridge Junction [2]	d			10 25	10 39			10 49	10 55		11 09	11 19	
Lye	d			10 28					10 58				
Cradley Heath	d			10 31	10 44			10 54	11 01		11 14	11 24	
Old Hill	d			10 35					11 05				
Rowley Regis	d			10 39	10 50			11 00	11 09		11 20	11 30	
Langley Green	d			10 42					11 12				
Smethwick Galton Bdg H.L. [7]	d			10 45	10 55			11 05	11 15		11 25	11 35	
Birmingham New Street [12]	a									11 13			
	d	10 33				11 04							
Birmingham International ✈	d					11 14							
Coventry	d					11 25							
The Hawthorns	d			10 48	10 58			11 08	11 18		11 28	11 38	
Jewellery Quarter	d			10 51	11 01			11 11	11 21		11 31	11 41	
Birmingham Snow Hill	a			10 55	11 05			11 15	11 25		11 35	11 45	
	d		10 52	10 57	11 07		11 12	11 17	11 27		11 37	11 47	
Birmingham Moor Street	d		10 55	11 00	11 10		11 15	11 20	11 30		11 40	11 50	
Bordesley	d												
Small Heath	d				11 14						11 44		
Tyseley	d				11 16						11 46		
Acocks Green	d			11 06				11 26			11 49		
Olton	d			11 08				11 28			11 52		
Solihull	d		11 05	11 12			11 25	11 32			11 55		
Widney Manor	d			11 15				11 35			11 58		
Dorridge	d		11 10	11a21			11 30	11a41			12a04		
Lapworth	d												
Hatton	d												
Warwick Parkway	d		11 21				11 41						
Warwick	d		11 24				11 45						
Leamington Spa [8]	a	10 59	11 29			11 37	11 51						
	d	11 00	11 29			11 38	11 52						
Banbury	d	11a18	11 47			11a54	12 09						
London Marylebone [10] ⊖	a		12 59				13 29						
Spring Road	d				11 19				11 36			11 56	
Hall Green	d				11 22				11 39			11 59	
Yardley Wood	d				11 25				11 42			12 02	
Shirley	d				11a28				11 45			12a05	
Whitlocks End	d								11 48				
Wythall	d								11 50				
Earlswood (West Midlands)	d								11 53				
The Lakes	d								11x55				
Wood End	d								11x57				
Danzey	d								12x00				
Henley-in-Arden	d								12 05				
Wootton Wawen	d								12x08				
Wilmcote	d								12 13				
Stratford-upon-Avon	a								12 21				

Station		XC	CH	CH	LM	LM	XC	CH	LM	LM	LM	LM	LM
		1 ◇					1 ◇	◇					
Hereford [7]	d									10 40			
Ledbury	a									10 56			
	d									10 59			
Colwall	d									11 05			
Great Malvern	a									11 10			
	d									11 10			11 38
Malvern Link	d									11 13			11 40
Worcester Foregate Street [7]	a									11 22			11 49
	d								11 15	11 23			11 50
Worcester Shrub Hill [7]	a												
	d												
Droitwich Spa	d								11 24	11 33			11 58
Bromsgrove	d									11 42			
Barnt Green	d												
University	d									11 59			
Hartlebury	d												
Kidderminster	d					11 26			11 36			11 56	12 10
Blakedown	d								11 41				
Hagley	d								11 44				
Stourbridge Junction [2]	d				11 25	11 39			11 49		11 55	12 09	12 19
Lye	d				11 28						11 58		
Cradley Heath	d				11 31	11 44			11 54		12 01	12 14	12 24
Old Hill	d				11 35						12 05		
Rowley Regis	d				11 39	11 50			12 00		12 09	12 20	12 30
Langley Green	d				11 42						12 12		
Smethwick Galton Bdg H.L. [7]	d				11 45	11 55			12 05		12 15	12 25	12 35
Birmingham New Street [12]	a									12 13			
	d	11 33					12 04						
Birmingham International ✈	d						12 14						
Coventry	d						12 25						
The Hawthorns	d				11 48	11 58			12 08		12 18	12 28	12 38
Jewellery Quarter	d				11 51	12 01			12 11		12 21	12 31	12 41
Birmingham Snow Hill	a				11 55	12 05			12 15		12 25	12 35	12 45
	d			11 52	11 57	12 07		12 12	12 17		12 27	12 37	12 47
Birmingham Moor Street	d			11 55	12 00	12 10		12 15	12 20		12 30	12 40	12 50
Bordesley	d												
Small Heath	d					12 14						12 44	
Tyseley	d					12 16						12 46	
Acocks Green	d				12 06				12 26			12 49	
Olton	d				12 08				12 28			12 52	
Solihull	d			12 05	12 12			12 25	12 32			12 55	
Widney Manor	d				12 15				12 35			12 58	
Dorridge	d			12 10	12a22			12 30	12a41			13a04	
Lapworth	d							12 34					
Hatton	d		11 57					12 40					
Warwick Parkway	d			12 21				12 45					
Warwick	d		12 03	12 24				12 49					
Leamington Spa [8]	a	11 59	12 07	12 29			12 37	12 53					
	d	12 00	12 08	12 29			12 38	12 54					
Banbury	d	12a18	12 27	12 47			12a54	13 12					
London Marylebone [10] ⊖	a		13 56	13 59				14 30					
Spring Road	d					12 19					12 36		12 56
Hall Green	d					12 22					12 39		12 59
Yardley Wood	d					12 25					12 42		13 02
Shirley	d					12a28					12 45		13a05
Whitlocks End	d										12 48		
Wythall	d										12 50		
Earlswood (West Midlands)	d										12 53		
The Lakes	d										12x55		
Wood End	d										12x57		
Danzey	d										13x00		
Henley-in-Arden	d										13 05		
Wootton Wawen	d										13x08		
Wilmcote	d										13 13		
Stratford-upon-Avon	a										13 21		

For general notes see front of timetable
For details of catering facilities see Directory of Train Operators

A To Brighton (Table 123)

From 5 October a revised Chiltern Railways service will be in operation due to seasonal difficulties. Trains will arrive at their destination 3 minutes later than shown

Hereford, Worcester and Stourbridge → Birmingham → Leamington Spa, Marylebone and Stratford-upon-Avon

Network Diagram - See first page of Table 71

Station		GW	XC	CH	LM	LM	XC	CH	LM	LM	LM	LM	LM	GW	XC	CH	CH	LM	LM	XC	CH	LM	LM	LM	LM
		1 ◇	1 ◇				1 ◇	◇						◇ A	1 ◇					1 ◇	◇				
		trolley	trolley				trolley								trolley					trolley					
Hereford 7	d										11 40												12 39		
Ledbury	a										11 57												12 55		
	d										11 57												13 00		
Colwall	d										12 04												13 06		
Great Malvern	a										12 09												13 11		
	d										12 11			12 51									13 11		
Malvern Link	d										12 14			12 53									13 14		
Worcester Foregate Street 7	a										12 23			13 03									13 23		
	d	12 06							12 15		12 23		12 46	13 03									13 23		
Worcester Shrub Hill 7	a	12 08												13 06											
	d																					13 16			
Droitwich Spa	d								12 24		12 33		12 55									13 24	13 32		
Bromsgrove	d										12 42												13 42		
Barnt Green	d																								
University	d										12 59												13 59		
Hartlebury	d																								
Kidderminster	d					12 26			12 36			12 56	13 06									13 36			13 56
Blakedown	d								12 41				13 11									13 41			
Hagley	d								12 44				13 14									13 44			
Stourbridge Junction 2	d				12 25	12 39			12 49	12 55		13 09	13 19					13 25	13 37			13 49		13 55	14 09
Lye	d				12 28					12 58								13 28						13 58	
Cradley Heath	d				12 31	12 44			12 54	13 01		13 14	13 24					13 31	13 43			13 54		14 01	14 14
Old Hill	d				12 35					13 05								13 35						14 05	
Rowley Regis	d				12 39	12 50			13 00	13 09		13 20	13 30					13 39	13 49			14 00		14 09	14 20
Langley Green	d				12 42					13 12								13 42						14 12	
Smethwick Galton Bdg H.L. 7	d				12 45	12 55			13 05	13 15		13 25	13 35					13 45	13 53			14 05		14 15	14 25
Birmingham New Street 12	a										13 13												14 13		
	d		12 33				13 04								13 33					14 04					
Birmingham International ✈	d						13 14													14 14					
Coventry	d						13 25													14 25					
The Hawthorns 🚋	d				12 48	12 58			13 08	13 18		13 28	13 38					13 48	13 56			14 08		14 18	14 28
Jewellery Quarter 🚋	d				12 51	13 01			13 11	13 21		13 31	13 41					13 51	13 59			14 11		14 21	14 31
Birmingham Snow Hill 🚋	a				12 55	13 05			13 15	13 25		13 35	13 45					13 55	14 03			14 15		14 25	14 35
	d			12 52	12 57	13 07		13 12	13 17	13 27		13 37	13 47				13 52	13 57	14 07		14 12	14 17		14 27	14 37
Birmingham Moor Street	d			12 55	13 00	13 10		13 15	13 20	13 30		13 40	13 50				13 55	14 00	14 10		14 15	14 20		14 30	14 40
Bordesley	d																								
Small Heath	d					13 14						13 44							14 14						14 44
Tyseley	d					13 16						13 46							14 16						14 46
Acocks Green	d				13 06				13 26			13 49						14 06				14 26			14 49
Olton	d				13 08				13 28			13 52						14 08				14 28			14 52
Solihull	d			13 05	13 12			13 25	13 32			13 55					14 05	14 12			14 25	14 32			14 55
Widney Manor	d				13 15				13 35			13 58						14 15				14 35			14 58
Dorridge	d			13 10	13a21			13 30	13a41			14a04					14 10	14a22			14 30	14a41			15a04
Lapworth	d																				14 34				
Hatton	d															13 57					14 40				
Warwick Parkway	d			13 21				13 41									14 21				14 45				
Warwick	d			13 24				13 45								14 03	14 24				14 49				
Leamington Spa 8	a		12 59	13 29			13 37	13 51							13 59	14 07	14 29			14 37	14 53				
	d		13 00	13 29			13 38	13 52							14 00	14 08	14 29			14 38	14 54				
Banbury	d		13a18	13 47			13a54	14 09							14a18	14 27	14 47			14a54	15 12				
London Marylebone 10 ⊖	a			14 59				15 28								15 53	16 00				16 31				
Spring Road	d					13 19				13 36			13 56						14 19					14 36	
Hall Green	d					13 22				13 39			13 59						14 22					14 39	
Yardley Wood	d					13 25				13 42			14 02						14 25					14 42	
Shirley	d					13a28				13 45			14a05						14a28					14 45	
Whitlocks End	d									13 48														14 48	
Wythall	d									13 50														14 50	
Earlswood (West Midlands)	d									13 53														14 53	
The Lakes	d									13x55														14x55	
Wood End	d									13x57														14x57	
Danzey	d									14x00														15x00	
Henley-in-Arden	d									14 05														15 05	
Wootton Wawen	d									14x08														15x08	
Wilmcote	d									14 13														15 13	
Stratford-upon-Avon	a									14 21														15 21	

For general notes see front of timetable
For details of catering facilities see Directory of Train Operators

A To Weymouth (Table 123)

From 5 October a revised Chiltern Railways service will be in operation due to seasonal difficulties. Trains will arrive at their destination 3 minutes later than shown

Hereford, Worcester and Stourbridge → Birmingham → Leamington Spa, Marylebone and Stratford-upon-Avon

Network Diagram - See first page of Table 71

		LM	GW	XC	CH	LM	LM	XC	CH	LM	LM	LM	LM	LM	GW	GW	XC	CH	CH	LM	LM	XC	CH	LM	LM
			1 ◇	1 ◇				1 ◇	◇						1 ◇	◇	1 ◇	◇				1 ◇			
																A									
			🍴	🍴				🍴							🍴		🍴					🍴			
Hereford 7	d		13 11									13 41													14 40
Ledbury	a		13 27									13 58													14 56
	d		13 28									13 59													14 59
Colwall	d		13 35									14 05													15 05
Great Malvern	a		13 41									14 10													15 10
	d		13 47							14 00		14 11			14 34	14 51									15 10
Malvern Link	d		13 51							14 02		14 14			14 37	14 53									15 13
Worcester Foregate Street 7	a		14 01							14 10		14 23			14 51	15 02									15 22
	d		14 02							14 15		14 23			14 52	15 02								15 15	15 23
Worcester Shrub Hill 7	a		14 06												14 56	15 06									
	d	13 47												14 47											
Droitwich Spa	d	13 55								14 24		14 32		14 55										15 24	15 33
Bromsgrove	d											14 42													15 42
Barnt Green	d																								
University	d											14 59													15 59
Hartlebury	d																								
Kidderminster	d	14 06					14 26			14 36			14 56	15 06							15 26			15 36	
Blakedown	d	14 11								14 41				15 11							15 31			15 41	
Hagley	d	14 14								14 44				15 14							15 34			15 44	
Stourbridge Junction 2	d	14 19				14 25	14 39			14 49	14 55		15 09	15 19						15 25	15 39			15 49	
Lye	d					14 28					14 58									15 28					
Cradley Heath	d	14 24				14 31	14 44			14 54	15 01		15 14	15 24						15 31	15 44			15 54	
Old Hill	d					14 35					15 05									15 35					
Rowley Regis	d	14 30				14 39	14 50			15 00	15 09		15 20	15 30						15 39	15 50			16 00	
Langley Green	d					14 42					15 12									15 42					
Smethwick Galton Bdg H.L. 7	d	14 35				14 45	14 55			15 05	15 15		15 25	15 35						15 45	15 55			16 05	
Birmingham New Street 12	a											15 13													16 13
	d			14 33				15 04									15 33					16 04			
Birmingham International ✈	d							15 14														16 14			
Coventry	d							15 25														16 25			
The Hawthorns 🚊	d	14 38				14 48	14 58			15 08	15 18		15 28	15 38						15 48	15 58			16 08	
Jewellery Quarter 🚊	d	14 41				14 51	15 01			15 11	15 21		15 31	15 41						15 51	16 01			16 11	
Birmingham Snow Hill 🚊	a	14 45				14 55	15 05			15 15	15 24		15 35	15 45						15 55	16 05			16 15	
	d	14 47			14 52	14 57	15 07		15 12	15 17	15 25		15 37	15 47					15 52	15 57	16 07		16 12	16 17	
Birmingham Moor Street	d	14 50			14 55	15 00	15 10		15 15	15 20	15 28		15 40	15 50					15 55	16 00	16 10		16 15	16 20	
Bordesley	d																								
Small Heath	d						15 14						15 44								16 14				
Tyseley	d						15 16						15 46								16 16				
Acocks Green	d					15 06				15 26			15 49							16 06				16 26	
Olton	d					15 08				15 28			15 52							16 08				16 28	
Solihull	d				15 05	15 12			15 25	15 32			15 55						16 05	16 12			16 25	16 32	
Widney Manor	d					15 15				15 35			15 58							16 15				16 35	
Dorridge	d				15 10	15a21			15 30	15a41			16a04						16 10	16a22			16 30	16a41	
Lapworth	d																						16 34		
Hatton	d																	15 57					16 40		
Warwick Parkway	d				15 21				15 41										16 21				16 45		
Warwick	d				15 24				15 44									16 03	16 24				16 49		
Leamington Spa 8	a			14 59	15 29			15 37	15 49								15 59	16 07	16 29			16 37	16 53		
	d			15 00	15 29			15 38	15 49								16 00	16 08	16 29			16 38	16 54		
Banbury	d			15a18	15 47			15a54	16 07								16a18	16 27	16 47			16a54	17 12		
London Marylebone 10 ⊖	a				17 01				17 31									17 56	18 05				18 33		
Spring Road	d	14 56					15 19				15 35			15 56							16 19				
Hall Green	d	14 59					15 22				15 37			15 59							16 22				
Yardley Wood	d	15 02					15 25				15 40			16 02							16 25				
Shirley	d	15a05					15a28				15 44			16a05							16a28				
Whitlocks End	d										15 46														
Wythall	d										15 49														
Earlswood (West Midlands)	d										15 51														
The Lakes	d										15x53														
Wood End	d										15x55														
Danzey	d										15x59														
Henley-in-Arden	d										16 04														
Wootton Wawen	d										16x06														
Wilmcote	d										16 12														
Stratford-upon-Avon	a										16 21														

For general notes see front of timetable
For details of catering facilities see Directory of Train Operators

A To Weymouth (Table 123)

From 5 October a revised Chiltern Railways service will be in operation due to seasonal difficulties. Trains will arrive at their destination 3 minutes later than shown

Hereford, Worcester and Stourbridge → Birmingham → Leamington Spa, Marylebone and Stratford-upon-Avon

Network Diagram - See first page of Table 71

		LM	LM	LM	GW	XC	CH	LM	LM	XC	CH	LM	LM	LM	LM	XC	CH	LM	LM	LM	GW	CH	XC	LM	LM
					1 ◇	1 ◇				1 ◇	◇					1 ◇							1 ◇		
																					A				
					☕	🛒				🛒						🛒							🛒		
Hereford 7	d				15 11										15 40										
Ledbury	a				15 27										15 57										
	d				15 27										16 00										
Colwall	d				15 35										16 06										
Great Malvern	a				15 40										16 11										
	d			15 29	15 40										16 11										
Malvern Link	d			15 31	15 44										16 14										
Worcester Foregate Street 7	a			15 39	15 57										16 23										
	d			15 40	16 01							16 05			16 23				16 34	16 47	17 02				
Worcester Shrub Hill 7	a			15 42	16 05														16 36		17 04				
	d			15 47									16 15						16 40						
Droitwich Spa	d			15 55								16 14	16 23		16 33				16 48	16 56					
Bromsgrove	d														16 42										
Barnt Green	d														16 49										
University	d														16 59										
Hartlebury	d											16 21													
Kidderminster	d		15 56	16 06					16 23			16 30	16 37					16 53	16 59	17 06					17 28
Blakedown	d			16 11					16 28			16 35	16 43						17 04	17 11					17 33
Hagley	d			16 14					16 31			16 39	16 47						17 08	17 15					17 36
Stourbridge Junction 2	d	15 55	16 09	16 19				16 25	16 35			16 44	16 51	16 55				17 06	17 13	17 19				17 25	17 40
Lye	d	15 58						16 28						16 58										17 28	
Cradley Heath	d	16 01	16 14	16 24				16 31	16 41			16 50	16 57	17 01				17 12	17 19	17 24				17 31	17 46
Old Hill	d	16 05						16 35						17 05										17 35	
Rowley Regis	d	16 09	16 20	16 30				16 39	16 47			16 55	17 03	17 09				17 17	17 24	17 30				17 39	17 52
Langley Green	d	16 12						16 42						17 12										17 42	
Smethwick Galton Bdg H.L. 7	d	16 15	16 25	16 35				16 45	16 52			17 00	17 08	17 15				17 22	17 29	17 35				17 45	17 56
Birmingham New Street 12	a														17 13										
	d					16 33				17 04						17 33							18 04		
Birmingham International ✈	d									17 14													18 14		
Coventry	d									17 25													18 25		
The Hawthorns 🚋	d	16 18	16 28	16 38				16 48	16 54			17 03	17 10	17 18				17 25	17 32	17 38				17 48	17 59
Jewellery Quarter 🚋	d	16 21	16 31	16 41				16 51	16 58			17 06	17 14	17 21				17 28	17 35	17 41				17 51	18 02
Birmingham Snow Hill 🚋	a	16 25	16 35	16 45				16 55	17 01			17 12	17 17	17 25				17 32	17 38	17 45				17 55	18 05
	d	16 27	16 37	16 47			16 52	16 57	17 02		17 10	17 15	17 22	17 27				17 34	17 42	17 47		17 52		17 57	18 07
Birmingham Moor Street	d	16 30	16 40	16 50			16 55	17 00	17 05		17 13	17 18	17 25	17 30				17 37	17 45	17 50		17 55		18 00	18 10
Bordesley	d																								
Small Heath	d		16 44	16 54								17 22						17 41	17 49	17 54				18 04	18 14
Tyseley	d	16 34	16 46	16 56				17 04				17 24		17 34				17 45	17 51	17 56				18 06	18 16
Acocks Green	d		16 49					17 07					17 31					17 48	17 54					18 09	
Olton	d		16 52					17 10					17 33					17 50	17 57					18 12	
Solihull	d		16 55				17 05	17 12			17 23		17 37					17 54	18 00			18 05		18 15	
Widney Manor	d		16 58					17 16			17 26		17 40					17 57	18 03					18 19	
Dorridge	d		17a04				17 10	17a22			17 30		17a46					18 01	18a08			18 12		18 23	
Lapworth	d										17 34							18 05						18 27	
Hatton	d										17 40						18 01	18 11						18 33	
Warwick Parkway	d						17 20				17 45							18 15				18 23		18 37	
Warwick	d						17 23				17 49						18 08	18 19				18 26		18 40	
Leamington Spa 8	a					16 59	17 28			17 37	17 53					17 59	18 12	18 24				18 30	18 37	18 47	
	d					17 00	17 28			17 38	17 54					18 00	18 12					18 30	18 38		
Banbury	d					17a18	17 46			17a54	18 12					18a18	18 32					18 48	18a54		
London Marylebone 10 ⊖	a						19 08				19 33						19 58					20 06			
Spring Road	d	16 37		16 59					17 11			17 27		17 37						17 59					18 19
Hall Green	d	16 40		17 02					17 14			17 30		17 40						18 02					18 22
Yardley Wood	d	16 43		17 05					17 17			17 33		17 43						18 05					18 25
Shirley	d	16 46		17a08					17 20			17a37		17 46						18 08					18a28
Whitlocks End	d	16 49							17 23					17 49						18 11					
Wythall	d	16 51							17 25					17 51						18 13					
Earlswood (West Midlands)	d	16 54												17 54						18 16					
The Lakes	d	16x56												17x56						18x18					
Wood End	d	16x58												17x58						18x20					
Danzey	d	17x01												18x01						18x23					
Henley-in-Arden	d	17 06							17 35					18 06						18 28					
Wootton Wawen	d	17x09												18x09						18x30					
Wilmcote	d	17 14												18 14						18 38					
Stratford-upon-Avon	a	17 22							17 49					18 22						18 45					

For general notes see front of timetable
For details of catering facilities see
Directory of Train Operators

A To Southampton Central (Table 123)

From 5 October a revised Chiltern Railways service will be in operation due to seasonal difficulties. Trains will arrive at their destination 3 minutes later than shown

Hereford, Worcester and Stourbridge → Birmingham → Leamington Spa, Marylebone and Stratford-upon-Avon

Network Diagram - See first page of Table 71

		CH	LM	GW	LM	LM	LM	LM	XC	LM	XC	LM	CH	LM	LM	LM	GW	XC	LM	GW	GW	CH	CH	XC	CH
		◇		[1] ◇					[1] ◇		[1] ◇						[1] ◇	[1] ◇		◇	[1]	◇		[1] ◇	◇
																				A					
				(buffet)					(trolley)		(trolley)						(buffet)	(trolley)							
Hereford [7]	d				16 40							17 40													
Ledbury	a				16 56							17 56													
	d				16 59							18 01													
Colwall	d				17 05							18 08													
Great Malvern	a				17 10							18 12													
	d			17 00	17 10	17 41						18 13								18 51					
Malvern Link	d			17 03	17 13	17 44						18 16								18 53					
Worcester Foregate Street [7]	a			17 17	17 23	17 52						18 24								19 02					
	d		17 16	17 20	17 24	17 53				17 55		18 25					18 47		18 47	19 02	19 27				
Worcester Shrub Hill [7]	a			17 24		17 55											18 50			19 06	19 29				
	d															18 37									
Droitwich Spa	d		17 25		17 33					18 04		18 34				18 45			18 56						
Bromsgrove	d				17 43							18 42													
Barnt Green	d											18 49													
University	d				17 59							18 59													
Hartlebury	d		17 32																19 03						
Kidderminster	d		17 38					18 00		18 17				18 37		18 55			19 10						
Blakedown	d		17 43					18 05						18 42		19 00			19 15						
Hagley	d		17 46					18 09						18 46		19 04			19 19						
Stourbridge Junction [2]	d		17 50				17 57	18 13		18 25				18 51		19 09			19 24						
Lye	d						18 00			18 28				18 54					19 27						
Cradley Heath	d		17 56				18 03	18 19		18 31				18 57		19 15			19 30						
Old Hill	d						18 07			18 35				19 01					19 34						
Rowley Regis	d		18 02				18 11	18 25		18 39				19 05		19 21			19 38						
Langley Green	d						18 14			18 42				19 08					19 41						
Smethwick Galton Bdg H.L. [7]	d		18 07				18 17	18 30		18 45				19 11		19 26			19 44						
Birmingham New Street [12]	a				18 13							19 12													
	d								18 33		19 04							19 33						20 04	
Birmingham International ✈	d										19 14													20 14	
Coventry	d										19 25													20 25	
The Hawthorns (tram)	d		18 10				18 20	18 33		18 48				19 14		19 29			19 47						
Jewellery Quarter (tram)	d		18 13				18 23	18 36		18 51				19 17		19 32			19 50						
Birmingham Snow Hill (tram)	a		18 17				18 26	18 41		18 55				19 20		19 35			19 53						
	d	18 12	18 22				18 27	18 45		18 57			19 12	19 22	19 27	19 37			19 55						20 12
Birmingham Moor Street	d	18 15	18 25				18 30	18 48		19 00			19 15	19 25	19 30	19a39			19 58						20 15
Bordesley	d																								
Small Heath	d						18 34	18 52		19 04					19 34				20 02						
Tyseley	d						18 36	18 54		19 06					19 36				20 04						
Acocks Green	d		18 31					18 57						19 31					20 07						
Olton	d		18 33					19 00						19 33					20 10						
Solihull	d	18 25	18 37					19 03					19 25	19 37					20 13						20 25
Widney Manor	d		18 40					19 07					19 28	19 40					20 17						20 28
Dorridge	d	18 30	18a45					19 11					19 32	19a47					20a23						20 32
Lapworth	d	18 34						19 15					19 36												20 36
Hatton	d	18 40						19 21					19 42									19 59	20 17		20 42
Warwick Parkway	d	18 45											19 47									20 06			20 47
Warwick	d	18 49						19 27					19 50									20 09	20 23		20 50
Leamington Spa [8]	a	18 53						19 32	18 59		19 37		19 54					19 59				20 14	20 33	20 37	20 54
	d	18 54							19 00		19 38		19 54					20 00				20 14		20 38	20 54
Banbury	d	19 12							19a18		19a54		20 12					20a18				20 32		20a54	21 12
London Marylebone [10] ⊖	a	20 35											21 32									21 57			22 32
Spring Road	d						18 39			19 09					19 39										
Hall Green	d						18 42			19 12					19 42										
Yardley Wood	d						18 45			19 15					19 45										
Shirley	d						18 48			19a18					19 48										
Whitlocks End	d						18 51								19 51										
Wythall	d						18 53								19 53										
Earlswood (West Midlands)	d						18 56								19 56										
The Lakes	d						18x58								19x58										
Wood End	d						19x00								20x00										
Danzey	d						19x03								20x03										
Henley-in-Arden	d						19 08								20 08										
Wootton Wawen	d						19x10								20x10										
Wilmcote	d						19 16								20 16										
Stratford-upon-Avon	a						19 23								20 23										

For general notes see front of timetable
For details of catering facilities see Directory of Train Operators

A To Weymouth (Table 123)

From 5 October a revised Chiltern Railways service will be in operation due to seasonal difficulties. Trains will arrive at their destination 3 minutes later than shown

Hereford, Worcester and Stourbridge → Birmingham → Leamington Spa, Marylebone and Stratford-upon-Avon

Network Diagram - See first page of Table 71

		LM	LM	XC	LM	XC	CH	LM	LM	LM	GW	GW	XC	CH	LM	LM	LM	LM	LM	GW	GW	CH	CH	LM
				1 ◇		1 ◇	◇				1 ◇		1 ◇							1 ◇	1			
												A					B	C		B	C			
											(catering)		(trolley)							(catering)				
Hereford 7	d		18 48						19 50								21 30	21 30		21 53	21 53			22 55
Ledbury	a		19 03						20 07								21 46	21 46		22 09	22 09			23 10
	d		19 04						20 18								21 47	21 47		22 11	22 11			23 13
Colwall	d		19 10						20 24								21 53	21 53		22 18	22 18			23 19
Great Malvern	a		19 15						20 29								21 58	21 58		22 24	22 24			23 24
	d		19 15						20 29			21 15					21 58	21 58		22 24	22 34			23 24
Malvern Link	d		19 18						20 32			21 18					22 01	22 01		22 28	22 38			23 27
Worcester Foregate Street 7	a		19 27						20 41			21 26					22 10	22 10		22 38	22 48			23 34
	d		19 27		19 45				20 42		20 59	21 27					22 10	22 10	22 17	22 39	22 49			23 34
Worcester Shrub Hill 7	a										21 02	21 29							22 19	22 43	22 53			23 39
	d									20 53						21 52			22 27					
Droitwich Spa	d		19 36		19 54				20 49	21 01						22 00	22 17	22 17	22 35					
Bromsgrove	d		19 46						20 59								22 27	22 29						
Barnt Green	d																							
University	d		20 09						21 16								22 45	22 46						
Hartlebury	d																							
Kidderminster	d				20 10					21 11						22 10			22 45					
Blakedown	d				20 15					21 16						22 15								
Hagley	d				20 19					21 20						22 19								
Stourbridge Junction 2	d	19 54			20 24			20 54		21 24					21 54	22 24			22 54					
Lye	d	19 57			20 27			20 57		21 27					21 57	22 27			22 57					
Cradley Heath	d	20 00			20 30			21 00		21 30					22 00	22 30			23 00					
Old Hill	d	20 04			20 34			21 04		21 34					22 04	22 34			23 04					
Rowley Regis	d	20 08			20 38			21 08		21 38					22 08	22 38			23 08					
Langley Green	d	20 11			20 41			21 11		21 41					22 11	22 41			23 11					
Smethwick Galton Bdg H.L. 7	d	20 14			20 44			21 14		21 44					22 14	22 44			23 14					
Birmingham New Street 12	a		20 20						21 23								22 52	22 57						
	d			20 33		21 04							22 04											
Birmingham International ✈	d					21 14							22 14											
Coventry	d					21 25							22 25											
The Hawthorns 🚊	d	20 17			20 47			21 17		21 47					22 17	22 47			23 17					
Jewellery Quarter 🚊	d	20 20			20 50			21 20		21 50					22 20	22 50			23 20					
Birmingham Snow Hill 🚊	a	20 23			20 53			21 23		21 53					22 23	22 53			23 24					
	d	20 27			20 55		21 15	21 25		21 55				22 15	22 25	22 57			23 25				23 30	
Birmingham Moor Street	d	20 30			20 58		21 18	21 28		21 58				22 18	22 28	23 00			23 28				23 33	
Bordesley	d																							
Small Heath	d	20 34			21 02			21 32		22 02					22 32	23 04			23 32					
Tyseley	d	20 36			21 04			21 34		22 04				22 23	22 34	23 06			23 34				23 38	
Acocks Green	d				21 07					22 07				22 25		23 09							23 40	
Olton	d				21 10					22 10				22 28		23 11							23 43	
Solihull	d				21 13		21 27			22 13				22 32		23 15							23 47	
Widney Manor	d				21 17					22 17				22 35		23 18							23 50	
Dorridge	d				21a22		21 33			22a22				22 39		23a24							23 54	
Lapworth	d						21 37							22 43									23 58	
Hatton	d						21 42							22 49									00 04	
Warwick Parkway	d						21 47							22 53									00 08	
Warwick	d						21 51							22 56								23 21	00 11	
Leamington Spa 8	a			20 59		21 37	21 54						22 37	23 00								23 24	00 14	
	d			21 00		21 38	21 55						22 38	23 01								23 25	00 15	
Banbury	d			21a18		21a54	22 14						22a54	23a23								23a43	00a38	
London Marylebone 10 ⊖	a						23 33																	
Spring Road	d	20 39						21 37							22 37				23 37					
Hall Green	d	20 42						21 40							22 40				23 40					
Yardley Wood	d	20 45						21 43							22 43				23 43					
Shirley	d	20 48						21a46							22a46				23a46					
Whitlocks End	d	20 51																						
Wythall	d	20 53																						
Earlswood (West Midlands)	d	20 56																						
The Lakes	d	20x58																						
Wood End	d	21x00																						
Danzey	d	21x03																						
Henley-in-Arden	d	21 08																						
Wootton Wawen	d	21x10																						
Wilmcote	d	21 16																						
Stratford-upon-Avon	a	21 23																						

For general notes see front of timetable
For details of catering facilities see Directory of Train Operators

A To Gloucester (Table 57)
B Until 4 September
C From 7 September

From 5 October a revised Chiltern Railways service will be in operation due to seasonal difficulties. Trains will arrive at their destination 3 minutes later than shown

Table 71

Saturdays

Hereford, Worcester and Stourbridge → Birmingham → Leamington Spa, Marylebone and Stratford-upon-Avon

Network Diagram - See first page of Table 71

		CH	XC	CH	XC	CH	LM	GW	XC	CH	LM	LM	LM	GW	LM	XC	CH	CH	LM	XC	CH	LM	LM	LM	LM
			1 ◇		1 ◇			1 ◇	1 ◇					1 ◇		1 ◇				R 1					
Hereford 7	d																								
Ledbury	a																								
	d																								
Colwall	d																								
Great Malvern	a																								
	d							05 39					06 20	06 35											
Malvern Link	d							05 43					06 23	06 39											
Worcester Foregate Street 7	a							05 52					06 30	06 48											
	d							05 54					06 31	06 50											
Worcester Shrub Hill 7	a							05 57						06 53											
	d						05 44					06 24							06 58			07 33			
Droitwich Spa	d						05 52					06 32	06 40						07 06			07 40			
Bromsgrove	d												06 50									07 50			
Barnt Green	d																								
University	d												07 09									08 09			
Hartlebury	d											06 39							07 16						
Kidderminster	d						06 02			06 37		06 45						07 14	07 22					07 46	
Blakedown	d						06 07					06 50							07 27					07 51	
Hagley	d						06 11					06 54							07 30					07 54	
Stourbridge Junction 2	d						06 15			06 45		07 02						07 22	07 35					07 59	08 05
Lye	d						06 18					07 05							07 38						08 08
Cradley Heath	d						06 22			06 50		07 09						07 27	07 41					08 04	08 11
Old Hill	d						06 26					07 13							07 45						08 15
Rowley Regis	d						06 29			06 56		07 16						07 33	07 49					08 10	08 19
Langley Green	d						06 32					07 19							07 52						08 22
Smethwick Galton Bdg H.L. 7	d						06 36			07 02		07 23						07 39	07 55					08 15	08 25
Birmingham New Street 12	a												07 16									08 16			
	d		06 04		06 33				07 04							07 33				08 04					
Birmingham International ✈	d		06 14						07 14											08 14					
Coventry	d		06 25						07 25											08 25					
The Hawthorns	d						06 38			07 04		07 25						07 41	07 58					08 18	08 28
Jewellery Quarter	d						06 42					07 29							08 01					08 21	08 31
Birmingham Snow Hill	a						06 46			07 10		07 32						07 48	08 05					08 25	08 35
	d	23p30		06 12		06 37	06 51			07 12	07 20	07 35			07 47			07 52	08 07		08 12		08 17	08 27	08 37
Birmingham Moor Street	d	23p33		06 15		06 40	06 54			07 15	07 23	07 38			07 50			07 55	08 10		08 15		08 20	08 30	08 40
Bordesley	d																								
Small Heath	d						06 58				07 27								08 14						08 44
Tyseley	d	23p38					07 00				07 29								08 16						08 46
Acocks Green	d	23p40					07 03					07 47											08 26		08 49
Olton	d	23p43					07 06					07 49											08 28		08 52
Solihull	d	23p47		06 25		06 50	07 09			07 25		07 53						08 05			08 25		08 32		08 55
Widney Manor	d	23p50					07 12					07 56									08 28		08 35		08 58
Dorridge	d	23p54		06 31		06 55	07a17			07 31		08a01						08 11			08 32		08a41		09a04
Lapworth	d	23p58								07 35											08 36				
Hatton	d	00 04								07 41							07 57				08 42				
Warwick Parkway	d	00 08		06 41		07 06				07 45								08 22			08 46				
Warwick	d	00 11		06 45		07 09				07 48							08 04	08 25			08 49				
Leamington Spa 8	a	00 14	06 37	06 49	06 58	07 13			07 37	07 52						07 58	08 08	08 29		08 37	08 51				
	d	00 15	06 38	06 49	07 00	07 14			07 38	07 53						08 00	08 09	08 30		08 38	08 53				
Banbury	d	00a38	06a54	07 07	07a17	07 34			07a54	08 13						08a17	08 29	08 49		08a54	09 13				
London Marylebone 10 ⊖	a			08 29		08 47				09 30							09 55	10 01			10 34				
Spring Road	d										07 32				07 56				08 19					08 36	
Hall Green	d										07 35				07 59				08 22					08 39	
Yardley Wood	d										07 38				08 02				08 25					08 42	
Shirley	d										07 41				08 11				08a28					08 45	
Whitlocks End	d										07 44				08 14										
Wythall	d										07 46				08 16									08 49	
Earlswood (West Midlands)	d										07 49				08 19										
The Lakes	d										07x51				08x21										
Wood End	d										07x53				08x23										
Danzey	d										07x56				08x26										
Henley-in-Arden	d										08 01				08 31									08 59	
Wootton Wawen	d										08x04				08x34										
Wilmcote	d										08 09				08 39										
Stratford-upon-Avon	a										08 17				08 47									09 14	

For general notes see front of timetable
For details of catering facilities see Directory of Train Operators

From 10 October a revised Chiltern Railways service will be in operation due to seasonal difficulties. Trains will arrive at their destination 3 minutes later than shown

Hereford, Worcester and Stourbridge → Birmingham → Leamington Spa, Marylebone and Stratford-upon-Avon

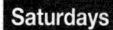

Network Diagram - See first page of Table 71

	LM	GW	XC	CH	LM	LM	XC	CH	LM	LM	LM	GW	LM	LM	XC	CH	CH	LM	LM	XC	CH	LM	LM	LM
		1 ◇	1 ◇	◇			1 ◇	◇				1 ◇			1 ◇		◇			1 ◇	◇			
		🍽	🛒				🛒					🍽			🛒					🛒				
Hereford 7 d		07 10									07 40												08 40	
Ledbury a		07 28									07 57												08 57	
d		07 30									07 58												08 58	
Colwall d		07 38									08 04												09 04	
Great Malvern a		07 42									08 09												09 09	
d	07 30	07 43									08 10	08 43										09 00	09 10	
Malvern Link d	07 32	07 47									08 13	08 47										09 03	09 13	
Worcester Foregate Street 7 a	07 40	07 57									08 22	08 56										09 11	09 22	
d	07 43	07 58									08 22	08 56						08 56				09 15	09 22	
Worcester Shrub Hill 7 a		08 01										09 01												
d									08 14															
Droitwich Spa d	07 52								08 22		08 31							09 05				09 24	09 31	
Bromsgrove d											08 40												09 40	
Barnt Green d																								
University d											08 59												09 59	
Hartlebury d									08 29															
Kidderminster d	08 06			08 13					08 36								09 03	09 16	09 26			09 36		
Blakedown d	08 11								08 41								09 08		09 31			09 42		
Hagley d	08 14								08 44								09 12		09 34			09 45		
Stourbridge Junction 2 d	08 19			08 26		08 35			08 49	08 55			09 09				09 15	09 25	09 39			09 50		09 55
Lye d						08 38				08 58								09 28						09 58
Cradley Heath d	08 24			08 32		08 41			08 54	09 01			09 14				09 21	09 31	09 44			09 55		10 01
Old Hill d						08 45				09 05								09 35						10 05
Rowley Regis d	08 30			08 37		08 49			09 00	09 09			09 20				09 26	09 39	09 51			10 01		10 09
Langley Green d						08 52				09 12								09 42						10 12
Smethwick Galton Bdg H.L. 7 d	08 35			08 43		08 55			09 05	09 15			09 25				09 33	09 45	09 55			10 06		10 15
Birmingham New Street 12 a											09 11												10 11	
d			08 33				09 04								09 33					10 04				
Birmingham International ✈ d							09 14													10 14				
Coventry d							09 25													10 25				
The Hawthorns 🚋 d	08 38			08 45		08 58			09 08	09 18			09 28				09 34	09 48	09 58			10 09		10 18
Jewellery Quarter 🚋 d	08 41					09 01			09 11	09 21			09 31					09 51	10 01			10 12		10 21
Birmingham Snow Hill 🚋 a	08 45			08 51		09 05			09 16	09 25			09 35				09 42	09 55	10 06			10 17		10 25
d	08 47			08 52	08 57	09 07		09 12	09 17	09 27			09 37	09 47			09 52	09 57	10 07		10 12	10 17		10 27
Birmingham Moor Street d	08 50			08 55	09 00	09 10		09 15	09 20	09 30			09 40	09 50			09 55	10 00	10 10		10 15	10 20		10 30
Bordesley d																								
Small Heath d						09 14							09 44						10 14					
Tyseley d						09 16							09 46						10 16					
Acocks Green d					09 06				09 25				09 49					10 06				10 26		
Olton d					09 08				09 27				09 52					10 08				10 28		
Solihull d				09 05	09 12			09 25	09 31				09 55				10 05	10 12			10 25	10 32		
Widney Manor d					09 15				09 34				09 58					10 15				10 35		
Dorridge d				09 11	09a21			09 31	09a41				10a04				10 11	10a23			10 31	10a41		
Lapworth d								09 35													10 35			
Hatton d																09 57					10 41			
Warwick Parkway d				09 22				09 44									10 22				10 45			
Warwick d				09 25				09 47								10 04	10 25				10 48			
Leamington Spa 8 a			08 58	09 29			09 37	09 50							09 58	10 09	10 29			10 37	10 52			
d			09 00	09 30			09 38	09 52							10 00	10 09	10 30			10 38	10 53			
Banbury d			09a17	09 49			09a54	10 13							10a17	10 29	10 49			10a54	11 13			
London Marylebone 10 ⊖ a				11 02				11 32								11 56	11 59				12 30			
Spring Road d	08 56					09 19				09 36				09 56					10 19					10 36
Hall Green d	08 59					09 22				09 39				09 59					10 22					10 39
Yardley Wood d	09 02					09 25				09 42				10 02					10 25					10 42
Shirley d	09 07					09a28				09 45				10 07					10a28					10 45
Whitlocks End d	09 10													10 10										
Wythall d	09 12									09 49				10 12										10 49
Earlswood (West Midlands) d	09 15													10 15										
The Lakes d	09x17													10x17										
Wood End d	09x19													10x19										
Danzey d	09x22													10x22										
Henley-in-Arden d	09 27									09 59				10 27										10 59
Wootton Wawen d	09x30													10x30										
Wilmcote d	09 35													10 35										
Stratford-upon-Avon a	09 43									10 14				10 43										11 16

For general notes see front of timetable
For details of catering facilities see Directory of Train Operators

From 10 October a revised Chiltern Railways service will be in operation due to seasonal difficulties. Trains will arrive at their destination 3 minutes later than shown

Hereford, Worcester and Stourbridge → Birmingham → Leamington Spa, Marylebone and Stratford-upon-Avon

Network Diagram - See first page of Table 71

		LM	LM	XC 1 ◇	LM	GW 1 ◇	CH ◇	LM	LM	XC 1 ◇	CH ◇	LM	LM	LM	LM	LM	GW 1 ◇	GW ◇ A	XC 1 ◇	CH	CH	LM	LM	XC 1 ◇
Hereford 7	d													09 36										
Ledbury	a													09 52										
	d													09 58										
Colwall	d													10 04										
Great Malvern	a													10 09										
	d					09 43								10 10			10 32	10 51						
Malvern Link	d					09 47								10 13			10 36	10 54						
Worcester Foregate Street 7	a					09 57								10 22			10 56	11 04						
	d					09 58						10 15		10 22			10 58	11 04						
Worcester Shrub Hill 7	a					10 01											11 01	11 07						
	d		09 47		09 56											10 47								
Droitwich Spa	d		09 55		10 04							10 24		10 33		10 55								
Bromsgrove	d				10 14									10 42										
Barnt Green	d																							
University	d													10 59										
Hartlebury	d																							
Kidderminster	d	09 56	10 06						10 26			10 36			10 56	11 06							11 26	
Blakedown	d		10 11									10 41				11 11								
Hagley	d		10 14									10 45				11 14								
Stourbridge Junction 2	d	10 09	10 19					10 25	10 39			10 49	10 55		11 08	11 19						11 25	11 39	
Lye	d							10 28					10 58									11 28		
Cradley Heath	d	10 14	10 24					10 31	10 44			10 55	11 01		11 14	11 24						11 31	11 44	
Old Hill	d							10 35					11 05									11 35		
Rowley Regis	d	10 20	10 30					10 39	10 50			11 01	11 09		11 20	11 30						11 39	11 50	
Langley Green	d							10 42					11 12									11 42		
Smethwick Galton Bdg H.L. 7	d	10 25	10 35					10 45	10 55			11 06	11 15		11 25	11 35						11 45	11 55	
Birmingham New Street 12	a				10 41									11 11										
	d			10 33						11 04									11 33					12 04
Birmingham International ✈	d									11 14														12 14
Coventry	d									11 25														12 25
The Hawthorns	d	10 28	10 38					10 48	10 58			11 08	11 18		11 28	11 38						11 48	11 58	
Jewellery Quarter	d	10 31	10 41					10 51	11 01			11 12	11 21		11 31	11 41						11 51	12 01	
Birmingham Snow Hill	a	10 35	10 45					10 56	11 05			11 17	11 25		11 35	11 45						11 56	12 05	
	d	10 37	10 47				10 52	10 57	11 07		11 12	11 17	11 27		11 37	11 47					11 52	11 57	12 07	
Birmingham Moor Street	d	10 40	10 50				10 55	11 00	11 10		11 15	11 20	11 30		11 40	11 50					11 55	12 00	12 10	
Bordesley	d																							
Small Heath	d	10 44							11 14						11 44								12 14	
Tyseley	d	10 46							11 16						11 46								12 16	
Acocks Green	d	10 49						11 06				11 26			11 49							12 06		
Olton	d	10 52						11 08				11 28			11 52							12 08		
Solihull	d	10 55					11 05	11 12			11 25	11 32			11 55						12 05	12 12		
Widney Manor	d	10 58						11 15				11 35			11 58							12 15		
Dorridge	d	11a04					11 11	11a23			11 31	11a41			12a04						12 11	12a23		
Lapworth	d																							
Hatton	d																			11 57				
Warwick Parkway	d						11 22				11 41										12 22			
Warwick	d						11 25				11 45									12 04	12 25			
Leamington Spa 8	a			10 58			11 29			11 37	11 49								11 58	12 08	12 29			12 37
	d			11 00			11 30			11 38	11 49								12 00	12 09	12 30			12 38
Banbury	d			11a17			11 49			11a54	12 07								12a17	12 29	12 49			12a54
London Marylebone 10 ⊖	a						13 01				13 26									13 58	14 01			
Spring Road	d		10 56						11 19				11 36			11 56							12 19	
Hall Green	d		10 59						11 22				11 39			11 59							12 22	
Yardley Wood	d		11 02						11 25				11 42			12 02							12 25	
Shirley	d		11 12						11a28				11 45			12 07							12a28	
Whitlocks End	d		11 15													12 10								
Wythall	d		11 17										11 49			12 12								
Earlswood (West Midlands)	d		11 20													12 15								
The Lakes	d		11x22													12x17								
Wood End	d		11x24													12x19								
Danzey	d		11x27													12x22								
Henley-in-Arden	d		11 32										11 59			12 27								
Wootton Wawen	d		11x35													12x30								
Wilmcote	d		11 40													12 35								
Stratford-upon-Avon	a		11 48										12 14			12 43								

For general notes see front of timetable
For details of catering facilities see
Directory of Train Operators

A To Brighton (Table 123)

From 10 October a revised Chiltern Railways service will be in operation due to seasonal difficulties. Trains will arrive at their destination 3 minutes later than shown

Table 71

Saturdays

Hereford, Worcester and Stourbridge → Birmingham → Leamington Spa, Marylebone and Stratford-upon-Avon

Network Diagram - See first page of Table 71

		CH	LM	LM	LM	LM	LM	LM	XC	CH	LM	LM	XC	CH	LM	LM	LM	GW	LM	LM	GW	XC	CH	CH	LM
								A	1 ◇				1 ◇					◇ B			1 ◇	1 ◇			
Hereford 7	d			10 40													11 40				12 13				
Ledbury	a			10 56													11 57				12 30				
	d			10 58													11 58				12 32				
Colwall	d			11 04													12 04				12 40				
Great Malvern	a			11 09													12 09				12 44				
	d			11 10			11 36										12 10				12 45				
Malvern Link	d			11 13			11 38										12 13				12 49				
Worcester Foregate Street 7	a			11 22			11 46										12 22				12 59				
	d			11 22			11 47	12 07							12 15		12 22	12 40		12 46	13 00				
Worcester Shrub Hill 7	a							12 09										12 42			13 03				
	d		11 15																						
Droitwich Spa	d		11 23	11 33			11 56								12 24		12 33			12 55					
Bromsgrove	d			11 42													12 42								
Barnt Green	d																								
University	d			11 59													12 59								
Hartlebury	d																								
Kidderminster	d		11 36			11 56	12 06					12 26			12 36				12 56	13 06					
Blakedown	d		11 41				12 11								12 41					13 11					
Hagley	d		11 44				12 15								12 44					13 14					
Stourbridge Junction 2	d		11 49		11 55	12 09	12 19				12 25	12 39			12 49	12 55			13 09	13 19					13 25
Lye	d				11 58						12 28					12 58									13 28
Cradley Heath	d		11 54		12 01	12 14	12 24				12 31	12 44			12 54	13 01			13 14	13 24					13 31
Old Hill	d				12 05						12 35					13 05									13 35
Rowley Regis	d		12 00		12 09	12 20	12 30				12 39	12 50			13 00	13 09			13 20	13 30					13 39
Langley Green	d				12 12						12 42					13 12									13 42
Smethwick Galton Bdg H.L. 7	d		12 05		12 15	12 25	12 35				12 45	12 55			13 05	13 15			13 25	13 35					13 45
Birmingham New Street 12	a			12 11													13 11								
	d								12 33				13 04									13 33			
Birmingham International ✈	d												13 14												
Coventry	d												13 25												
The Hawthorns	d		12 08		12 18	12 28	12 38				12 48	12 58			13 08	13 18			13 28	13 38					13 48
Jewellery Quarter	d		12 11		12 21	12 31	12 41				12 51	13 01			13 11	13 21			13 31	13 41					13 51
Birmingham Snow Hill	a		12 16		12 25	12 35	12 45				12 56	13 05			13 16	13 25			13 35	13 45					13 56
	d	12 12	12 17		12 27	12 37	12 47			12 52	12 57	13 07		13 12	13 17	13 27			13 37	13 47				13 52	13 57
Birmingham Moor Street	d	12 15	12 20		12 30	12 40	12 50			12 55	13 00	13 10		13 15	13 20	13 30			13 40	13 50				13 55	14 00
Bordesley	d																								
Small Heath	d					12 44						13 14							13 44						
Tyseley	d					12 46						13 16							13 46						
Acocks Green	d		12 26			12 49					13 06				13 26				13 49						14 06
Olton	d		12 28			12 52					13 08				13 28				13 52						14 08
Solihull	d	12 25	12 32			12 55				13 05	13 12			13 25	13 32				13 55					14 05	14 12
Widney Manor	d		12 35			12 58					13 15				13 35				13 58						14 15
Dorridge	d	12 31	12a41			13a04				13 11	13a21			13 31	13a41				14a04					14 11	14a23
Lapworth	d	12 35																							
Hatton	d	12 41																					13 57		
Warwick Parkway	d	12 45								13 22				13 41										14 22	
Warwick	d	12 48								13 25				13 45									14 04	14 25	
Leamington Spa 8	a	12 51							12 58	13 29			13 37	13 49								13 58	14 08	14 29	
	d	12 53							13 00	13 30			13 38	13 49								14 00	14 09	14 30	
Banbury	d	13 13							13a17	13 49			13a54	14 07								14a17	14 29	14 49	
London Marylebone 10 ⊖	a	14 32								15 01				15 30									15 58	16 01	
Spring Road	d				12 36		12 56					13 19				13 36				13 58					
Hall Green	d				12 39		12 59					13 22				13 39				14 01					
Yardley Wood	d				12 42		13 02					13 25				13 42				14 04					
Shirley	d				12 45		13 10					13a28				13 45				14 09					
Whitlocks End	d						13 13													14 12					
Wythall	d				12 49		13 15									13 49				14 14					
Earlswood (West Midlands)	d						13 18													14 17					
The Lakes	d						13x20													14x19					
Wood End	d						13x22													14x21					
Danzey	d						13x25													14x24					
Henley-in-Arden	d				12 59		13 30									13 59				14 29					
Wootton Wawen	d						13x33													14x32					
Wilmcote	d						13 38													14 37					
Stratford-upon-Avon	a				13 14		13 46									14 14				14 45					

For general notes see front of timetable
For details of catering facilities see Directory of Train Operators

A To Gloucester (Table 57)
B To Weymouth (Table 123)

From 10 October a revised Chiltern Railways service will be in operation due to seasonal difficulties. Trains will arrive at their destination 3 minutes later than shown

Hereford, Worcester and Stourbridge → Birmingham → Leamington Spa, Marylebone and Stratford-upon-Avon

Network Diagram - See first page of Table 71

		LM	XC	CH	LM	LM	LM	LM		XC	LM	CH	LM	LM	XC	CH	LM	LM	LM	LM	LM	GW	GW	XC	CH
			1 ◇							1 ◇					1 ◇							1 ◇	◇ A	1 ◇	
			⚲							⚲					⚲							⚲		⚲	
Hereford 7	d							12 40											13 40						
Ledbury	a							12 57											13 57						
	d							12 58											13 58						
Colwall	d							13 04											14 04						
Great Malvern	a							13 09											14 09						
	d							13 10			13 36								14 10			14 32	14 51		
Malvern Link	d							13 13			13 38								14 13			14 36	14 54		
Worcester Foregate Street 7	a							13 22			13 46								14 22			14 55	15 03		
	d							13 22			13 47						14 15		14 22			14 57	15 03		
Worcester Shrub Hill 7	a																					15 00	15 06		
	d				13 15																14 43				
Droitwich Spa	d				13 23			13 33			13 56						14 24		14 33		14 55				
Bromsgrove	d							13 42											14 42						
Barnt Green	d																								
University	d							13 59											14 59						
Hartlebury	d																								
Kidderminster	d	13 26			13 36		13 56				14 06			14 26			14 36			14 56	15 06				
Blakedown	d				13 41						14 11						14 41				15 11				
Hagley	d				13 44						14 15						14 44				15 14				
Stourbridge Junction 2	d	13 38			13 49	13 55	14 09				14 19		14 25	14 38			14 49	14 55		15 08	15 19				
Lye	d					13 58							14 28					14 58							
Cradley Heath	d	13 44			13 54	14 01	14 14				14 24		14 31	14 44			14 54	15 01		15 14	15 24				
Old Hill	d					14 05							14 35					15 05							
Rowley Regis	d	13 50			14 00	14 09	14 20				14 30		14 39	14 50			15 00	15 09		15 20	15 30				
Langley Green	d					14 12							14 42					15 12							
Smethwick Galton Bdg H.L. 7	d	13 55			14 05	14 15	14 25				14 35		14 45	14 55			15 05	15 15		15 25	15 35				
Birmingham New Street 12	a							14 11											15 11						
	d		14 04							14 33					15 04									15 33	
Birmingham International ✈	d		14 14												15 14										
Coventry	d		14 25												15 25										
The Hawthorns 🚋	d	13 58			14 08	14 18	14 28				14 38		14 48	14 58			15 08	15 18		15 28	15 38				
Jewellery Quarter 🚋	d	14 01			14 11	14 21	14 31				14 41		14 51	15 01			15 11	15 21		15 31	15 41				
Birmingham Snow Hill 🚋	a	14 05			14 16	14 25	14 35				14 45		14 56	15 05			15 16	15 25		15 35	15 45				
	d	14 07		14 12	14 17	14 27	14 37				14 47	14 52	14 57	15 07		15 12	15 17	15 27		15 37	15 47				
Birmingham Moor Street	d	14 10		14 15	14 20	14 30	14 40				14 50	14 55	15 00	15 10		15 15	15 20	15 30		15 40	15 50				
Bordesley	d																								
Small Heath	d	14 14					14 44							15 14						15 44					
Tyseley	d	14 16					14 46							15 16						15 46					
Acocks Green	d				14 26		14 49						15 06				15 26			15 49					
Olton	d				14 28		14 52						15 08				15 28			15 52					
Solihull	d			14 25	14 32		14 55					15 05	15 12			15 25	15 32			15 55					
Widney Manor	d				14 35		14 58						15 15				15 35			15 58					
Dorridge	d			14 31	14a41		15a04					15 11	15a21			15 31	15a41			16a04					
Lapworth	d			14 35																					
Hatton	d			14 41																					15 57
Warwick Parkway	d			14 45								15 22				15 41									
Warwick	d			14 48								15 25				15 45									16 04
Leamington Spa 8	a		14 37	14 51						14 58		15 29			15 37	15 49								15 58	16 08
	d		14 38	14 53						15 00		15 30			15 38	15 49								16 00	16 09
Banbury	d		14a54	15 13						15a17		15 49			15a54	16 07								16a17	16 29
London Marylebone 10 ⊖	a			16 37								16 59				17 29									17 58
Spring Road	d	14 19				14 36					14 56			15 19				15 36			15 56				
Hall Green	d	14 22				14 39					14 59			15 22				15 39			15 59				
Yardley Wood	d	14 25				14 42					15 02			15 25				15 42			16 02				
Shirley	d	14a28				14 45					15 10			15a28				15 45			16 07				
Whitlocks End	d										15 13										16 10				
Wythall	d					14 49					15 15							15 49			16 12				
Earlswood (West Midlands)	d										15 18										16 15				
The Lakes	d										15x20										16x17				
Wood End	d										15x22										16x19				
Danzey	d										15x25										16x22				
Henley-in-Arden	d					14 59					15 30							15 59			16 27				
Wootton Wawen	d										15x33										16x30				
Wilmcote	d										15 38										16 35				
Stratford-upon-Avon	a					15 14					15 46							16 14			16 43				

For general notes see front of timetable
For details of catering facilities see
Directory of Train Operators

A To Weymouth (Table 123)

From 10 October a revised Chiltern Railways service will be in operation due to seasonal difficulties. Trains will arrive at their destination 3 minutes later than shown

Table 71

Saturdays

Hereford, Worcester and Stourbridge → Birmingham → Leamington Spa, Marylebone and Stratford-upon-Avon

Network Diagram - See first page of Table 71

		CH	LM	LM	XC	CH	LM	LM	LM	LM	LM	XC	LM	GW	CH	LM	LM	XC	CH	LM	LM	LM	LM	LM	GW
					1 ◇							1 ◇		1 ◇				1 ◇							1 ◇
Hereford 7	d							14 40						15 10								15 40			
Ledbury	a							14 56						15 27								15 57			
	d							14 57						15 29								15 58			
Colwall	d							15 03						15 37								16 04			
Great Malvern	a							15 08						15 41								16 09			
	d							15 10			15 30			15 43								16 10			16 32
Malvern Link	d							15 13			15 32			15 47								16 13			16 36
Worcester Foregate Street 7	a							15 22			15 40			15 59								16 22			16 56
	d						15 15	15 22			15 46			15 59						16 13		16 22			16 58
Worcester Shrub Hill 7	a													16 03											17 01
	d												15 54											16 47	
Droitwich Spa	d						15 24	15 33			15 55		16 03							16 22		16 33		16 55	
Bromsgrove	d							15 42					16 13									16 42			
Barnt Green	d																								
University	d							15 59														16 59			
Hartlebury	d																			16 29					
Kidderminster	d			15 26			15 36			15 56	16 06						16 26			16 36			16 56	17 06	
Blakedown	d			15 31			15 41				16 11						16 31			16 41				17 11	
Hagley	d			15 34			15 44				16 14						16 34			16 44				17 14	
Stourbridge Junction 2	d		15 25	15 38			15 49		15 55	16 08	16 19					16 25	16 39			16 49	16 55		17 08	17 19	
Lye	d		15 28						15 58							16 28					16 58				
Cradley Heath	d		15 31	15 44			15 54		16 01	16 14	16 24					16 31	16 44			16 54	17 01		17 14	17 24	
Old Hill	d		15 35						16 05							16 35					17 05				
Rowley Regis	d		15 39	15 50			16 00		16 09	16 20	16 30					16 39	16 50			17 00	17 09		17 20	17 30	
Langley Green	d		15 42						16 12							16 42					17 12				
Smethwick Galton Bdg H.L. 7	d		15 45	15 55			16 05		16 15	16 25	16 35					16 45	16 55			17 05	17 15		17 25	17 35	
Birmingham New Street 12	a							16 11					16 41									17 11			
	d				16 04							16 33						17 04							
Birmingham International ✈	d				16 14													17 14							
Coventry	d				16 25													17 25							
The Hawthorns 🚋	d		15 48	15 58			16 08		16 18	16 28	16 38					16 48	16 58			17 08	17 18		17 28	17 38	
Jewellery Quarter 🚋	d		15 51	16 01			16 11		16 21	16 31	16 41					16 51	17 01			17 11	17 21		17 31	17 41	
Birmingham Snow Hill 🚋	a		15 56	16 05			16 16		16 25	16 35	16 45					16 56	17 05			17 16	17 25		17 35	17 45	
	d	15 52	15 57	16 05		16 12	16 17		16 27	16 37	16 47				16 52	16 57	17 07		17 12	17 17	17 27		17 37	17 47	
Birmingham Moor Street	d	15 55	16 00	16 08		16 15	16 20		16 30	16 40	16 50				16 55	17 00	17 10		17 15	17 20	17 30		17 40	17 50	
Bordesley	d																								
Small Heath	d			16 12						16 44	16 54						17 14						17 44	17 54	
Tyseley	d			16 14					16 34	16 46	16 56					17 04	17 16				17 34		17 46	17 56	
Acocks Green	d		16 06				16 26			16 49						17 07				17 26			17 49		
Olton	d		16 08				16 28			16 52						17 10				17 28			17 52		
Solihull	d	16 05	16 12			16 25	16 32			16 55					17 05	17 13			17 25	17 32			17 55		
Widney Manor	d		16 15				16 35			16 58						17 16				17 35			17 58		
Dorridge	d	16 11	16a22			16 31	16a41			17a04					17 11	17a22			17 31	17a41			18a04		
Lapworth	d					16 35													17 35						
Hatton	d					16 41													17 41						
Warwick Parkway	d	16 22				16 45									17 22				17 45						
Warwick	d	16 25				16 48									17 25				17 48						
Leamington Spa 8	a	16 29			16 37	16 52						16 58			17 29			17 37	17 52						
	d	16 30			16 38	16 53						17 00			17 30			17 38	17 53						
Banbury	d	16 49			16a54	17 13						17a17			17 49			17a54	18 13						
London Marylebone 10 ⊖	a	18 01				18 32									19 02				19 30						
Spring Road	d			16 17					16 37		16 59						17 19				17 37			17 59	
Hall Green	d			16 20					16 40		17 02						17 22				17 40			18 02	
Yardley Wood	d			16 23					16 43		17 05						17 25				17 43			18 05	
Shirley	d			16a26					16 46		17 10						17a28				17 46			18 08	
Whitlocks End	d										17 13													18 11	
Wythall	d								16 50		17 15										17 50			18 13	
Earlswood (West Midlands)	d										17 18													18 16	
The Lakes	d										17x20													18x18	
Wood End	d										17x22													18x20	
Danzey	d										17x25													18x23	
Henley-in-Arden	d								17 00		17 30										18 00			18 28	
Wootton Wawen	d										17x33													18x30	
Wilmcote	d										17 38													18 36	
Stratford-upon-Avon	a								17 15		17 46										18 14			18 43	

For general notes see front of timetable
For details of catering facilities see Directory of Train Operators

From 10 October a revised Chiltern Railways service will be in operation due to seasonal difficulties. Trains will arrive at their destination 3 minutes later than shown

Table 71

Saturdays

Hereford, Worcester and Stourbridge → Birmingham → Leamington Spa, Marylebone and Stratford-upon-Avon

Network Diagram - See first page of Table 71

		GW	XC	CH	CH	LM	LM	XC	CH	LM	LM	LM	LM	GW	XC	LM	XC	CH	LM	LM	GW	LM	XC	LM	GW
			1 ◇					1 ◇						1 ◇	1 ◇		1 ◇	◇			1 ◇		1 ◇		◇
		A																							B
			trolley					trolley						restaurant	trolley		trolley				restaurant		trolley		
Hereford 7	d										16 40									17 40					
Ledbury	a										16 57									17 56					
	d										16 58									17 58					
Colwall	d										17 04									18 04					
Great Malvern	a										17 09									18 09					
	d	16 51									17 10			17 43					18 00	18 10	18 29				18 51
Malvern Link	d	16 54									17 13			17 47					18 02	18 13	18 32				18 54
Worcester Foregate Street 7	a	17 04									17 22			17 57					18 10	18 22	18 42				19 04
	d	17 04									17 22		17 48	17 58					18 11	18 24	18 44			18 49	19 05
Worcester Shrub Hill 7	a	17 07												18 01					18 13		18 47				19 07
	d									17 15									18 17						
Droitwich Spa	d									17 23	17 34		17 57						18 25	18 35				18 58	
Bromsgrove	d										17 43									18 44					
Barnt Green	d																								
University	d										17 59									18 59					
Hartlebury	d									17 30														19 05	
Kidderminster	d						17 26			17 36			18 07						18 36					19 11	
Blakedown	d						17 31			17 41			18 12											19 16	
Hagley	d						17 34			17 44			18 16											19 19	
Stourbridge Junction 2	d					17 25	17 39			17 49		17 55	18 20			18 27			18 49			18 55		19 24	
Lye	d					17 28						17 58				18 30						18 58		19 27	
Cradley Heath	d					17 31	17 44			17 54		18 01	18 25			18 33			18 54			19 01		19 30	
Old Hill	d					17 35						18 05				18 37						19 05		19 34	
Rowley Regis	d					17 39	17 50			18 00		18 09	18 31			18 41			19 00			19 09		19 38	
Langley Green	d					17 42						18 12				18 44						19 12		19 41	
Smethwick Galton Bdg H.L. 7	d					17 45	17 55			18 05		18 15	18 36			18 47			19 05			19 15		19 44	
Birmingham New Street 12	a										18 11									19 11					
	d		17 33					18 04							18 33		19 04						19 33		
Birmingham International ✈	d							18 14									19 14								
Coventry	d							18 25									19 25								
The Hawthorns 🚊	d					17 48	17 58			18 08		18 18	18 39			18 50			19 08			19 18		19 47	
Jewellery Quarter 🚊	d					17 51	18 01			18 11		18 21	18 42			18 53			19 11			19 21		19 50	
Birmingham Snow Hill 🚊	a					17 56	18 05			18 16		18 25	18 45			18 56			19 15			19 25		19 55	
	d				17 52	17 57	18 07		18 12	18 17		18 27	18 47			18 57		19 10	19 17			19 27		19 55	
Birmingham Moor Street	d				17 55	18 00	18 10		18 15	18 20		18 30	18 50			19 00		19 13	19 20			19 30		19 58	
Bordesley	d																								
Small Heath	d						18 14			18 24			18 54			19 04			19 24			19 34		20 02	
Tyseley	d						18 16			18 26			18 56			19 06			19 26			19 36		20 04	
Acocks Green	d					18 06				18 29			18 59						19 29					20 07	
Olton	d					18 08				18 32			19 02						19 32					20 10	
Solihull	d				18 05	18 12			18 25	18 35			19 05					19 23	19 35					20 13	
Widney Manor	d					18 15			18 28	18 38			19 08					19 26	19 39					20 17	
Dorridge	d				18 11	18a23			18 32	18a44			19a14					19 30	19a43					20a23	
Lapworth	d								18 36									19 34							
Hatton	d			17 57					18 42									19 40							
Warwick Parkway	d				18 22				18 46									19 44							
Warwick	d			18 04	18 25				18 49									19 47							
Leamington Spa 8	a		17 58	18 08	18 29			18 37	18 53						18 58		19 37	19 51					19 58		
	d		18 00	18 09	18 30			18 38	18 53						19 00		19 38	19 52					20 00		
Banbury	d		18a17	18 29	18 49			18a54	19 13						19a17		19a54	20 13					20a17		
London Marylebone 10 ⊖	a			19 56	20 02				20 37									21 37							
Spring Road	d						18 19					18 36				19 09						19 39			
Hall Green	d						18 22					18 39				19 12						19 42			
Yardley Wood	d						18 25					18 42				19 15						19 45			
Shirley	d						18a28					18 45				19a18						19 48			
Whitlocks End	d											18 48										19 51			
Wythall	d											18 50										19 53			
Earlswood (West Midlands)	d											18 53										19 56			
The Lakes	d											18x55										19x58			
Wood End	d											18x57										20x00			
Danzey	d											19x00										20x03			
Henley-in-Arden	d											19 05										20 08			
Wootton Wawen	d											19x08										20x10			
Wilmcote	d											19 13										20 16			
Stratford-upon-Avon	a											19 21										20 23			

For general notes see front of timetable
For details of catering facilities see Directory of Train Operators

A To Westbury (Table 123)
B To Weymouth (Table 123)

From 10 October a revised Chiltern Railways service will be in operation due to seasonal difficulties. Trains will arrive at their destination 3 minutes later than shown

Table 71

Saturdays

Hereford, Worcester and Stourbridge → Birmingham → Leamington Spa, Marylebone and Stratford-upon-Avon

Network Diagram - See first page of Table 71

		CH	XC	CH	LM	LM	GW	XC	XC	CH	LM	LM	LM	GW	GW	CH	LM	LM	LM	LM	LM	GW	LM
		◇	1 ◇	◇			1 ◇	1 ◇	1 ◇	◇				1 ◇								1	
															A								
			⚲				⊡	⚲	⚲					⊡									
Hereford 7	d					19 11						20 00		20 20					21 33				22 43
Ledbury	a					19 28						20 15		20 36					21 48				23 00
	d					19 28						20 16		20 40					21 49				23 02
Colwall	d					19 35						20 22		20 48					21 55				23 09
Great Malvern	a					19 39						20 27		20 52					22 00				23 13
	d					19 40						20 28		20 53	21 14			21 30	22 00			22 40	23 14
Malvern Link	d					19 42						20 31		20 57	21 17			21 32	22 03			22 43	23 16
Worcester Foregate Street 7	a					19 51						20 39		21 09	21 27			21 41	22 17			22 50	23 24
	d					19 52	20 02					20 42		21 10	21 27			21 42	22 18			22 51	23 25
Worcester Shrub Hill 7	a						20 05							21 13	21 30			21 44	22 20			22 53	23 31
	d												20 52					21 52			22 48		
Droitwich Spa	d					20 01						20 49	21 00					22 00			22 56		
Bromsgrove	d											20 59											
Barnt Green	d																						
University	d											21 16											
Hartlebury	d																						
Kidderminster	d				19 40	20 11							21 11					22 10			23 06		
Blakedown	d				19 45	20 16							21 16					22 15			23 11		
Hagley	d				19 49	20 20							21 20					22 19			23 15		
Stourbridge Junction 2	d				19 54	20 24					20 54		21 24				21 54	22 24		22 54	23 19		
Lye	d				19 57	20 27					20 57		21 27				21 57	22 27		22 57			
Cradley Heath	d				20 00	20 30					21 00		21 30				22 00	22 30		23 00			
Old Hill	d				20 04	20 34					21 04		21 34				22 04	22 34		23 04			
Rowley Regis	d				20 08	20 38					21 08		21 38				22 08	22 38		23 08			
Langley Green	d				20 11	20 41					21 11		21 41				22 11	22 41		23 11			
Smethwick Galton Bdg H.L. 7	d				20 14	20 44					21 14		21 44				22 14	22 44		23 14			
Birmingham New Street 12	a											21 22											
	d		20 04					20 33	21 04														
Birmingham International ✈	d		20 14						21 14														
Coventry	d		20 25						21 25														
The Hawthorns 🚊	d				20 17	20 47					21 17		21 47				22 17	22 47		23 17			
Jewellery Quarter 🚊	d				20 20	20 50					21 20		21 50				22 20	22 50		23 20			
Birmingham Snow Hill 🚊	a				20 23	20 54					21 23		21 53				22 23	22 53		23 24	23 37		
	d			20 10	20 27	20 55				21 11	21 25		21 55			22 15	22 25	22 55		23 25	23 38		
Birmingham Moor Street	d			20 13	20 30	20 58				21 14	21 28		21 58			22 18	22 28	22 58		23 28	23 41		
Bordesley	d																						
Small Heath	d				20 34	21 02					21 32		22 02				22 32	23 02		23 32	23 45		
Tyseley	d				20 36	21 04					21 34		22 04			22 23	22 34	23 04		23 34	23 47		
Acocks Green	d					21 07							22 07			22 25		23 07			23 50		
Olton	d					21 10							22 10			22 28		23 10			23 53		
Solihull	d			20 23		21 13				21 23			22 13			22 32		23 13			23 56		
Widney Manor	d			20 26		21 17				21 26			22 17			22 35		23 17			23 59		
Dorridge	d			20 30		21a22				21 30			22a22			22 39		23a22			00 04		
Lapworth	d			20 34						21 34						22 43					00 08		
Hatton	d	20 10		20 40						21 40						22 49					00 14		
Warwick Parkway	d	20 16		20 44						21 44						22 53							
Warwick	d	20 19		20 47						21 47						22 56					00 19		
Leamington Spa 8	a	20 21	20 37	20 51				20 58	21 37	21 51						23 00					00 26		
	d	20 23	20 38	20 52				21 00	21 38	21 52						23 01							
Banbury	d	20 42	20a54	21 15				21a17	21a54	22 15						23a23							
London Marylebone 10 ⊖	a	22 21		22 40						23 40													
Spring Road	d				20 39						21 37						22 37			23 37			
Hall Green	d				20 42						21 40						22 40			23 40			
Yardley Wood	d				20 45						21 43						22 43			23 43			
Shirley	d				20 48						21a46						22a46			23a46			
Whitlocks End	d				20 51																		
Wythall	d				20 53																		
Earlswood (West Midlands)	d				20 56																		
The Lakes	d				20x58																		
Wood End	d				21x00																		
Danzey	d				21x03																		
Henley-in-Arden	d				21 08																		
Wootton Wawen	d				21x10																		
Wilmcote	d				21 16																		
Stratford-upon-Avon	a				21 23																		

For general notes see front of timetable
For details of catering facilities see Directory of Train Operators

A To Gloucester (Table 57)

From 10 October a revised Chiltern Railways service will be in operation due to seasonal difficulties. Trains will arrive at their destination 3 minutes later than shown

Sundays

until 1 November

Hereford, Worcester and Stourbridge → Birmingham → Leamington Spa, Marylebone and Stratford-upon-Avon

Network Diagram - See first page of Table 71

		LM	CH	XC 1◇	CH	GW 1◇	LM	CH	CH	XC 1◇	CH	LM	CH	LM	XC 1◇	CH	LM	LM	GW 1◇	XC 1◇	CH
Hereford 7	d																				
Ledbury	a																				
	d																				
Colwall	d																				
Great Malvern	a																				
	d					09 00											10 02	10 56	11 07		
Malvern Link	d					09 03											10 04	10 58	11 10		
Worcester Foregate Street 7	a					09 10											10 12	11 06	11 18		
	d					09 12											10 16	11 20 →	11 19		
Worcester Shrub Hill 7	a					09 14											10 18		11 22		
	d	22p48										09 21					10 22				
Droitwich Spa	d	22p56										09 32					10 30				
Bromsgrove	d																				
Barnt Green	d																				
University	d																				
Hartlebury	d																				
Kidderminster	d	23p06										09 42		10 08			10 40				
Blakedown	d	23p11										09 47		10 13							
Hagley	d	23p15										09 51		10 17			10 47				
Stourbridge Junction 2	d	23p19										09 55		10 22			10 52				
Lye	d													10 25							
Cradley Heath	d											10 01		10 29			10 58				
Old Hill	d													10 33							
Rowley Regis	d											10 06		10 36			11 03				
Langley Green	d													10 39							
Smethwick Galton Bdg H.L. 7	d											10 12		10 43			11 09				
Birmingham New Street 12	a																				
	d			09 04						10 04					11 04					11 33	
Birmingham International ✈	d			09 14						10 14					11 14						
Coventry	d			09 25						10 25					11 25						
The Hawthorns 🚋	d											10 15		10 45			11 12				
Jewellery Quarter 🚋	d											10 18		10 49			11 15				
Birmingham Snow Hill 🚋	a	23p37										10 20		10 52			11 17				
	d	23p38	08 40		09 10		09 19	09 40			10 10	10 22	10 40	10 53		11 10	11 19				11 40
Birmingham Moor Street	d	23p41	08 43		09 13		09 22	09 43			10 13	10 25	10 43	10 56		11 13	11 22				11 43
Bordesley	d																				
Small Heath	d	23p45																			
Tyseley	d	23p47					09 26					10 29					11 26				
Acocks Green	d	23p50												11 02							
Olton	d	23p53												11 04							
Solihull	d	23p56	08 52		09 22			09 52			10 22		10 52	11 08		11 22					11 52
Widney Manor	d	23p59												11 11							
Dorridge	d	00 04	08 58		09 28			09 58			10 28		10 58	11a16		11 28					11 58
Lapworth	d	00 08											11 02								
Hatton	d	00 14							10 17				11 07								
Warwick Parkway	d		09 10		09 38			10 10			10 39		11 12			11 39					12 10
Warwick	d	00 19	09 12		09 41				10 25		10 41					11 42					
Leamington Spa 8	a	00 26	09 16	09 36	09 46			10 15	10 28	10 36	10 46		11 16		11 36	11 46				11 59	12 15
	d		09 17	09 38	09 47			10 16	10 29	10 38	10 47		11 18		11 38	11 47				12 00	12 16
Banbury	d		09 36	09a54	10 06			10 36	10 48	10a54	11 06		11 37		11a54	12 06				12a18	12 36
London Marylebone 10 ⊖	a		10 51		11 23			11 58	12 17		12 22		13 01			13 22					13 58
Spring Road	d						09 29					10 32					11 29				
Hall Green	d						09 32					10 35					11 32				
Yardley Wood	d						09 35					10 38					11 35				
Shirley	d						09 38					10 41					11 38				
Whitlocks End	d																				
Wythall	d						09 42					10 45					11 42				
Earlswood (West Midlands)	d																				
The Lakes	d						09x45					10x48					11x45				
Wood End	d																				
Danzey	d																				
Henley-in-Arden	d						09 53					10 56					11 53				
Wootton Wawen	d																				
Wilmcote	d						10 03					11 04					12 01				
Stratford-upon-Avon	a						10 08					11 11					12 08				

For general notes see front of timetable
For details of catering facilities see
Directory of Train Operators

From 4 October a revised Chiltern Railways service will be in operation due to seasonal difficulties. Trains will arrive at their destination 3 minutes later than shown

Table 71

Sundays

until 1 November

Hereford, Worcester and Stourbridge → Birmingham → Leamington Spa, Marylebone and Stratford-upon-Avon

Network Diagram - See first page of Table 71

Station		LM	CH	XC 1 ◇	CH	LM	XC 1 ◇	CH	LM	XC 1 ◇	CH	LM A	LM B	XC 1 ◇	CH	LM	CH	XC 1 ◇	CH	LM C
Hereford 7	d																			
Ledbury	a																			
	d																			
Colwall	d																			
Great Malvern	a																			
	d											12 04	12 04							
Malvern Link	d											12 06	12 06							
Worcester Foregate Street 7	a					←						12 15	12 18							
	d					11 20						12 16	12 19							13 20
Worcester Shrub Hill 7	a											12 18	12 21							
	d											12 21	12 24							
Droitwich Spa	d					11 29						12 29	12 32							13 29
Bromsgrove	d											(wavy line)	(wavy line)							(wavy line)
Barnt Green	d											(wavy line)	(wavy line)							(wavy line)
University	d											(wavy line)	(wavy line)							(wavy line)
Hartlebury	d																			
Kidderminster	d					11 39						12 39	12 42							13 39
Blakedown	d											12 44	12 47							
Hagley	d					11 46						12 48	12 51							13 46
Stourbridge Junction 2	d	11 22				11 52			12 22			12 52	12 55			13 22				13 52
Lye	d	11 25							12 25							13 25				
Cradley Heath	d	11 29				11 58			12 29			12 58	13 01			13 29				13 58
Old Hill	d	11 33							12 33							13 33				
Rowley Regis	d	11 36				12 03			12 36			13 03	13 06			13 36				14 03
Langley Green	d	11 39							12 39							13 39				
Smethwick Galton Bdg H.L. 7	d	11 43				12 08			12 43			13 08	13 11			13 43				14 08
Birmingham New Street 12	a																			
	d			12 04			12 33			13 04				13 33				14 04		
Birmingham International ✈	d			12 14						13 14								14 14		
Coventry	d			12 25						13 25								14 25		
The Hawthorns 🚋	d	11 45				12 11			12 45			13 11	13 14			13 45				14 11
Jewellery Quarter 🚋	d	11 49				12 14			12 49			13 14	13 17			13 49				14 14
Birmingham Snow Hill 🚋	a	11 52				12 17			12 52			13 17	13 20			13 52				14 17
	d	11 53			12 10	12 19		12 40	12 53		13 10	13 19	13 22		13 40	13 53			14 10	14 19
Birmingham Moor Street	d	11 56			12 13	12 22		12 43	12 56		13 13	13 22	13 25		13 43	13 56			14 13	14 22
Bordesley	d																			
Small Heath	d																			
Tyseley	d					12 26						13 26	13 29							14 26
Acocks Green	d	12 02							13 04							14 02				
Olton	d	12 04							13 06							14 04				
Solihull	d	12 08			12 22			12 52	13 10		13 22				13 52	14 08			14 22	
Widney Manor	d	12 11							13 13							14 11				
Dorridge	d	12a16			12 28			12 58	13a18		13 28				13 58	14a17			14 28	
Lapworth	d														14 02					
Hatton	d		12 17												14 07		14 17			
Warwick Parkway	d				12 38			13 09			13 38				14 12				14 39	
Warwick	d		12 25		12 41						13 41						14 25		14 41	
Leamington Spa 8	a		12 28	12 36	12 46		12 59	13 15		13 36	13 46			13 59	14 17		14 28	14 36	14 46	
	d		12 29	12 38	12 47		13 00	13 16		13 38	13 47			14 00	14 18		14 29	14 38	14 47	
Banbury	d		12 48	12a54	13 06		13a18	13 35		13a54	14 06			14a18	14 37		14 48	14a54	15 06	
London Marylebone 10 ⊖	a		14 16		14 22			15 00			15 23				16 01		16 16		16 22	
Spring Road	d					12 29						13 29	13 32							14 29
Hall Green	d					12 32						13 32	13 35							14 32
Yardley Wood	d					12 35						13 35	13 38							14 35
Shirley	d					12 38						13 38	13 41							14 38
Whitlocks End	d																			
Wythall	d					12 42						13 42	13 45							14 42
Earlswood (West Midlands)	d																			
The Lakes	d					12x45						13x45	13x48							14x45
Wood End	d																			
Danzey	d																			
Henley-in-Arden	d					12 53						13 53	13 56							14 52
Wootton Wawen	d																			
Wilmcote	d					13 01						14 01	14 04							15 00
Stratford-upon-Avon	a					13 08						14 08	14 11							15 06

For general notes see front of timetable
For details of catering facilities see Directory of Train Operators

A From 13 September
B Until 6 September
C Until 28 June, and from 20 September

From 4 October a revised Chiltern Railways service will be in operation due to seasonal difficulties. Trains will arrive at their destination 3 minutes later than shown

Table 71I

Sundays

until 1 November

Hereford, Worcester and Stourbridge → Birmingham → Leamington Spa, Marylebone and Stratford-upon-Avon

Network Diagram - See first page of Table 71I

		LM	GW	GW	XC	CH	LM	XC	CH	LM	XC	LM	CH	LM	CH	XC	CH	LM	GW	XC	CH
			1 ◇	1 ◇	1 ◇			1 ◇			1 ◇					1 ◇			1 ◇	1 ◇	
		A																			
				🍴	⊼			⊼			⊼					⊼			🍴	⊼	
Hereford 7	d			13 28															14 30		
Ledbury	a			13 44															14 46		
	d			13 46															14 55		
Colwall	d			13 53															15 02		
Great Malvern	a			13 58															15 07		
	d		13 10	13 59								14 35							15 08		
Malvern Link	d		13 13	14 03								14 37							15 12		
Worcester Foregate Street 7	a		13 22	14 13								14 45							15 21		
	d	13 20	13 23	14 14						14 20		14 45						15 20	15 23		
Worcester Shrub Hill 7	a		13 27	14 17								14 48							15 26		
	d											14 51									
Droitwich Spa	d	13 29								14 29		14 59						15 29			
Bromsgrove	d											15 09									
Barnt Green	d																				
University	d																				
Hartlebury	d																				
Kidderminster	d	13 39								14 39								15 39			
Blakedown	d									14 44											
Hagley	d	13 46								14 48								15 46			
Stourbridge Junction 2	d	13 52					14 22			14 52				15 22				15 52			
Lye	d						14 25							15 25							
Cradley Heath	d	13 58					14 29			14 58				15 29				15 58			
Old Hill	d						14 33							15 33							
Rowley Regis	d	14 03					14 36			15 03				15 36				16 03			
Langley Green	d						14 39							15 39							
Smethwick Galton Bdg H.L. 7	d	14 08					14 43			15 08				15 43				16 08			
Birmingham New Street 12	a											15 37									
	d				14 33			15 04			15 33					16 04				16 33	
Birmingham International ✈	d							15 14								16 14					
Coventry	d							15 25								16 25					
The Hawthorns 🚋	d	14 11					14 45			15 11				15 45				16 11			
Jewellery Quarter 🚋	d	14 14					14 49			15 14				15 49				16 14			
Birmingham Snow Hill 🚋	a	14 17					14 52			15 17				15 52				16 17			
	d	14 19				14 40	14 53		15 10	15 19			15 40	15 53			16 10	16 19			16 40
Birmingham Moor Street	d	14 22				14 43	14 56		15 13	15 22			15 43	15 56			16 13	16 22			16 43
Bordesley	d																				
Small Heath	d																				
Tyseley	d	14 26								15 26								16 26			
Acocks Green	d						15 02							16 02							
Olton	d						15 04							16 04							
Solihull	d					14 52	15 08		15 22				15 52	16 08			16 22				16 52
Widney Manor	d						15 11							16 11							
Dorridge	d					14 58	15a17		15 27				15 58	16a16			16 28				16 58
Lapworth	d												16 02								
Hatton	d												16 07		16 17						
Warwick Parkway	d					15 10			15 38				16 12				16 38				17 09
Warwick	d								15 41						16 25		16 41				
Leamington Spa 8	a				14 59	15 15		15 36	15 45		15 59		16 17		16 28	16 36	16 46			16 59	17 15
	d				15 00	15 16		15 38	15 47		16 00		16 18		16 29	16 38	16 47			17 00	17 16
Banbury	d				15a18	15 36		15a54	16 06		16a18		16 37		16 48	16a54	17 06			17a18	17 35
London Marylebone 10 ⊖	a					16 58			17 23				18 02		18 16		18 21				18 58
Spring Road	d	14 29								15 29								16 29			
Hall Green	d	14 32								15 32								16 32			
Yardley Wood	d	14 35								15 35								16 35			
Shirley	d	14b54								15 38								16 38			
Whitlocks End	d																				
Wythall	d	14 58								15 42								16 42			
Earlswood (West Midlands)	d																				
The Lakes	d	15x01								15x45								16x45			
Wood End	d																				
Danzey	d																				
Henley-in-Arden	d	15 08								15 53								16 53			
Wootton Wawen	d																				
Wilmcote	d	15 16								16 01								17 01			
Stratford-upon-Avon	a	15 22								16 08								17 08			

For general notes see front of timetable
For details of catering facilities see Directory of Train Operators

A 5 July to 13 September
b Arr. 1438

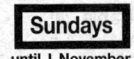

From 4 October a revised Chiltern Railways service will be in operation due to seasonal difficulties. Trains will arrive at their destination 3 minutes later than shown

Table 71

Sundays

until 1 November

Hereford, Worcester and Stourbridge → Birmingham → Leamington Spa, Marylebone and Stratford-upon-Avon

Network Diagram - See first page of Table 71

		LM	LM	LM	XC 1◇	CH	LM	LM	XC 1◇	CH	LM	CH	XC 1◇	CH	LM	GW 1◇	LM	XC 1◇	CH	XC 1◇
Hereford 7	d			15 30												16 30				
Ledbury	a			15 47												16 46				
	d			15 51												16 47				
Colwall	d			15 58												16 55				
Great Malvern	a			16 02												17 00				
	d			16 03												17 00	17 16			
Malvern Link	d			16 05												17 04	17 19			
Worcester Foregate Street 7	a			16 14												17 21	17 28			
	d			16 15			16 20								17 20	17 22	17 28			
Worcester Shrub Hill 7	a			16 18				←								17 25	17 31			
	d	15 46		16 33				16 33									17 34			
Droitwich Spa	d	15 54		→			16 29	16 41							17 29		17 42			
Bromsgrove	d							16 51									17 52			
Barnt Green	d																			
University	d																			
Hartlebury	d																			
Kidderminster	d	16 04					16 39								17 39					
Blakedown	d														17 44					
Hagley	d	16 11					16 46								17 48					
Stourbridge Junction 2	d	16 16	16 22				16 52				17 22				17 52					
Lye	d		16 25								17 25									
Cradley Heath	d		16 29				16 58				17 29				17 58					
Old Hill	d		16 33								17 33									
Rowley Regis	d		16 36				17 03				17 36				18 03					
Langley Green	d		16 39								17 39									
Smethwick Galton Bdg H.L. 7	d	16 29	16 43				17 08				17 43				18 08					
Birmingham New Street 12	a							17 17									18 13			
	d				17 04				17 33				18 04					18 33		19 04
Birmingham International ✈	d				17 14								18 14							19 14
Coventry	d				17 25								18 25							19 25
The Hawthorns	d		16 45				17 11				17 45				18 11					
Jewellery Quarter	d		16 49				17 14				17 49				18 14					
Birmingham Snow Hill	a	16 35	16 52				17 17				17 53				18 17					
	d	16 45	16 53			17 10	17 19			17 40	17 53			18 10	18 19				18 40	
Birmingham Moor Street	d	16a47	16 56			17 13	17 22			17 43	17 56			18 13	18 22				18 43	
Bordesley	d																			
Small Heath	d																			
Tyseley	d						17 26								18 26					
Acocks Green	d		17 02								18 02									
Olton	d		17 04								18 04									
Solihull	d		17 08			17 22				17 52	18 08			18 22					18 52	
Widney Manor	d		17 11								18 11									
Dorridge	d		17a17			17 28				17 58	18a17			18 28					18 58	
Lapworth	d									18 02										
Hatton	d									18 07		18 17								
Warwick Parkway	d					17 38				18 12				18 38					19 09	
Warwick	d					17 41						18 25		18 41						
Leamington Spa 8	a				17 36	17 46			17 59	18 17		18 28	18 36	18 46				18 59	19 15	19 36
	d				17 38	17 47			18 00	18 18		18 29	18 38	18 47				19 00	19 16	19 38
Banbury	d				17a54	18 06			18a18	18 37		18 48	18a54	19 06				19a18	19 35	19a54
London Marylebone 10 ⊖	a					19 22				20 02		20 16		20 21					20 58	
Spring Road	d						17 29								18 29					
Hall Green	d						17 32								18 32					
Yardley Wood	d						17 35								18 35					
Shirley	d						17 38								18 38					
Whitlocks End	d																			
Wythall	d						17 42								18 42					
Earlswood (West Midlands)	d																			
The Lakes	d						17x45								18x45					
Wood End	d																			
Danzey	d																			
Henley-in-Arden	d						17 53								18 53					
Wootton Wawen	d																			
Wilmcote	d						18 01								19 01					
Stratford-upon-Avon	a						18 08								19 08					

For general notes see front of timetable
For details of catering facilities see
Directory of Train Operators

From 4 October a revised Chiltern Railways service will be in operation due to seasonal difficulties. Trains will arrive at their destination 3 minutes later than shown

Table 71

Sundays

until 1 November

Hereford, Worcester and Stourbridge → Birmingham → Leamington Spa, Marylebone and Stratford-upon-Avon

Network Diagram - See first page of Table 71

Station		CH	LM	GW	XC		CH	XC	CH	LM		XC	LM	BW	XC		CH	LM	LM	GW	LM	LM	LM		
				1 ◇	1 ◇			1 ◇				1 ◇		1 ◇	1 ◇					1 ◇					
Hereford 7	d			18 30															20 05				22 40		
Ledbury	a			18 46															20 20				22 56		
	d			18 48															20 21				22 56		
Colwall	d			18 55															20 27				23 03		
Great Malvern	a			19 00															20 32				23 07		
	d			19 08										20 08					20 32	20 55		22 02	23 08		
Malvern Link	d			19 12										20 12					20 35	20 59		22 05	23 10		
Worcester Foregate Street 7	a			19 23										20 24					20 44	21 08		22 13	23 19		
	d		18 20	19 24										20 24					20 44	21 10		22 17	23 22		
Worcester Shrub Hill 7	a			19 27										20 27					20 47	21 12		22 19	23 24		
	d									19 38			19 53					20 34	20 50		21 22	22 26			
Droitwich Spa	d		18 29							19 46			20 01					20 42	20 58		21 30	22 34			
Bromsgrove	d												20 10						21 08						
Barnt Green	d																								
University	d																								
Hartlebury	d																								
Kidderminster	d		18 39							19 56								20 52			21 41	22 44			
Blakedown	d																								
Hagley	d		18 46							20 03								20 59			21 48	22 51			
Stourbridge Junction 2	d		18 52							20 07								21 03			21 52	22 55			
Lye	d																								
Cradley Heath	d		18 58							20 13								21 08			21 58	23 01			
Old Hill	d																								
Rowley Regis	d		19 03							20 19								21 14			22 03	23 06			
Langley Green	d																								
Smethwick Galton Bdg H.L. 7	d		19 08							20 24								21 19			22 08	23 11			
Birmingham New Street 12	a												20 36						21 42						
	d				19 33			20 04				20 33			21 04										
Birmingham International ✈	d							20 14							21 14										
Coventry	d							20 25							21 24										
The Hawthorns 🚋	d		19 11							20 26								21 21				22 11	23 14		
Jewellery Quarter 🚋	d		19 14							20 30								21 25				22 14	23 17		
Birmingham Snow Hill 🚋	a		19 19							20 33								21 28				22 18	23 21		
	d	19 10	19 21						20 15	20 33							21 15	21 28				22 18			
Birmingham Moor Street	d	19 13	19a23						20 18	20a36							21 18	21a31				22a21			
Bordesley	d																								
Small Heath	d																								
Tyseley	d																								
Acocks Green	d																								
Olton	d																								
Solihull	d	19 21							20 28								21 28								
Widney Manor	d	19 24							20 31								21 31								
Dorridge	d	19 29							20 35								21 35								
Lapworth	d	19 33																							
Hatton	d	19 38					20 14																		
Warwick Parkway	d	19 43							20 46								21 46								
Warwick	d	19 46					20 22		20 49								21 49								
Leamington Spa 8	a	19 49			19 59		20 25	20 36	20 53			20 59			21 34		21 53								
	d	19 52			20 00		20 26	20 38	20 54			21 00					21 54								
Banbury	d	20 13			20a18		20 48	20a54	21 13			21a18					22 15								
London Marylebone 10	⊖ a	21 52					22 16		22 52								23 53								
Spring Road	d																								
Hall Green	d																								
Yardley Wood	d																								
Shirley	d																								
Whitlocks End	d																								
Wythall	d																								
Earlswood (West Midlands)	d																								
The Lakes	d																								
Wood End	d																								
Danzey	d																								
Henley-in-Arden	d																								
Wootton Wawen	d																								
Wilmcote	d																								
Stratford-upon-Avon	a																								

For general notes see front of timetable
For details of catering facilities see Directory of Train Operators

From 4 October a revised Chiltern Railways service will be in operation due to seasonal difficulties. Trains will arrive at their destination 3 minutes later than shown

Table 71

Sundays
from 8 November

Hereford, Worcester and Stourbridge → Birmingham → Leamington Spa, Marylebone and Stratford-upon-Avon

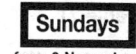

Network Diagram - See first page of Table 71

		LM	CH	XC 1 ◇	CH	GW 1 ◇	LM	CH	CH	XC 1 ◇	CH	LM	CH	LM	XC 1 ◇	CH	LM	LM	GW 1 ◇	XC 1 ◇	CH
Hereford 7	d																				
Ledbury	a																				
	d																				
Colwall	d																				
Great Malvern	a																				
	d					09 00											10 02	10 56	11 07		
Malvern Link	d					09 03											10 04	10 58	11 10		
Worcester Foregate Street 7	a					09 10											10 12	11 06	11 18		
	d					09 12											10 16	11 20	11 19		
Worcester Shrub Hill 7	a					09 14											10 18	→	11 22		
	d	22p48										09 21					10 22				
Droitwich Spa	d	22p56										09 32					10 30				
Bromsgrove	d																				
Barnt Green	d																				
University	d																				
Hartlebury	d																				
Kidderminster	d	23p06										09 42		10 08			10 40				
Blakedown	d	23p11										09 47		10 13							
Hagley	d	23p15										09 51		10 17			10 47				
Stourbridge Junction 2	d	23p19										09 55		10 22			10 52				
Lye	d													10 25							
Cradley Heath	d											10 01		10 29			10 58				
Old Hill	d													10 33							
Rowley Regis	d											10 06		10 36			11 03				
Langley Green	d													10 39							
Smethwick Galton Bdg H.L. 7	d											10 12		10 43			11 09				
Birmingham New Street 12	a																				
	d			09 04						10 04					11 04					11 33	
Birmingham International ✈	d			09 14						10 14					11 14						
Coventry	d			09 25						10 25					11 25						
The Hawthorns 🚋	d											10 15		10 45			11 12				
Jewellery Quarter 🚋	d											10 18		10 49			11 15				
Birmingham Snow Hill 🚋	a	23p37										10 20		10 52			11 17				
	d	23p38	08 40		09 10		09 19	09 40			10 10	10 22	10 40	10 53		11 10	11 19				11 40
Birmingham Moor Street	d	23p41	08 43		09 13		09 22	09 43			10 13	10 25	10 43	10 56		11 13	11 22				11 43
Bordesley	d																				
Small Heath	d	23p45																			
Tyseley	d	23p47					09 26					10 29					11 26				
Acocks Green	d	23p50												11 02							
Olton	d	23p53												11 04							
Solihull	d	23p56	08 52		09 22			09 52			10 22		10 52	11 08		11 22					11 52
Widney Manor	d	23p59												11 11							
Dorridge	d	00 04	08 58		09 28			09 58			10 28		10 58	11a16		11 28					11 58
Lapworth	d	00 08											11 02								
Hatton	d	00 14							10 17				11 07								
Warwick Parkway	d		09 10		09 38			10 09			10 38		11 12			11 38					12 09
Warwick	d	00 19	09 12		09 41				10 25		10 41					11 41					
Leamington Spa 8	a	00 26	09 16	09 36	09 46			10 15	10 28	10 36	10 46		11 16		11 36	11 46				11 59	12 15
	d		09 17	09 38	09 47			10 16	10 29	10 38	10 47		11 18		11 38	11 47				12 00	12 16
Banbury	d		09 36	09a54	10 06			10 35	10 48	10a54	11 06		11 37		11a54	12 06				12a18	12 35
London Marylebone 10 ⊖	a		10 54		11 26			12 01	12 20		12 25		13 04			13 25					14 01
Spring Road	d						09 29					10 32					11 29				
Hall Green	d						09 32					10 35					11 32				
Yardley Wood	d						09 35					10 38					11 35				
Shirley	d						09 38					10 41					11 38				
Whitlocks End	d																				
Wythall	d						09 42					10 45					11 42				
Earlswood (West Midlands)	d																				
The Lakes	d						09x45					10x48					11x45				
Wood End	d																				
Danzey	d																				
Henley-in-Arden	d						09 53					10 56					11 53				
Wootton Wawen	d																				
Wilmcote	d						10 03					11 04					12 01				
Stratford-upon-Avon	a						10 08					11 11					12 08				

For general notes see front of timetable
For details of catering facilities see Directory of Train Operators

Sundays

from 8 November

Hereford, Worcester and Stourbridge → Birmingham → Leamington Spa, Marylebone and Stratford-upon-Avon

Network Diagram - See first page of Table 71

		LM	CH	XC	CH	LM	XC	CH	LM	XC	CH	LM	XC	CH	LM	CH	XC	CH	LM	GW
				1 ◇			1 ◇			1 ◇			1 ◇				1 ◇			1 ◇
Hereford 7	d																			
Ledbury	a																			
	d																			
Colwall	d																			
Great Malvern	a																			
	d											12 04								13 10
Malvern Link	d											12 06								13 13
Worcester Foregate Street 7	a					←						12 15								13 22
	d					11 20						12 16							13 20	13 23
Worcester Shrub Hill 7	a											12 18								13 27
	d											12 21								
Droitwich Spa	d					11 29						12 29							13 29	
Bromsgrove	d																			
Barnt Green	d																			
University	d																			
Hartlebury	d																			
Kidderminster	d					11 39						12 39							13 39	
Blakedown	d											12 44								
Hagley	d					11 46						12 48							13 46	
Stourbridge Junction 2	d	11 22				11 52			12 22			12 52			13 22				13 52	
Lye	d	11 25							12 25						13 25					
Cradley Heath	d	11 29				11 58			12 29			12 58			13 29				13 58	
Old Hill	d	11 33							12 33						13 33					
Rowley Regis	d	11 36				12 03			12 36			13 03			13 36				14 03	
Langley Green	d	11 39							12 39						13 39					
Smethwick Galton Bdg H.L. 7	d	11 43				12 08			12 43			13 08			13 43				14 08	
Birmingham New Street 12	a																			
	d			12 04			12 33			13 04			13 33				14 04			
Birmingham International ✈	d			12 14						13 14							14 14			
Coventry	d			12 25						13 25							14 25			
The Hawthorns 🚊	d	11 45				12 11			12 45			13 11			13 45				14 11	
Jewellery Quarter 🚊	d	11 49				12 14			12 49			13 14			13 49				14 14	
Birmingham Snow Hill 🚊	a	11 52				12 17			12 52			13 17			13 52				14 17	
	d	11 53			12 10	12 19		12 40	12 53		13 10	13 19		13 40	13 53			14 10	14 19	
Birmingham Moor Street	d	11 56			12 13	12 22		12 43	12 56		13 13	13 22		13 43	13 56			14 13	14 22	
Bordesley	d																			
Small Heath	d																			
Tyseley	d					12 26						13 26							14 26	
Acocks Green	d	12 02							13 04						14 02					
Olton	d	12 04							13 06						14 04					
Solihull	d	12 08			12 22			12 52	13 10		13 22			13 52	14 08			14 22		
Widney Manor	d	12 11							13 13						14 11					
Dorridge	d	12a16			12 28			12 58	13a18		13 28			13 58	14a17			14 28		
Lapworth	d													14 02						
Hatton	d		12 17											14 07		14 17				
Warwick Parkway	d				12 38			13 09			13 38			14 12				14 38		
Warwick	d		12 25		12 41						13 41					14 25		14 41		
Leamington Spa 8	a		12 28	12 36	12 46		12 59	13 15		13 36	13 46		13 59	14 17		14 28	14 36	14 46		
	d		12 29	12 38	12 47		13 00	13 16		13 38	13 47		14 00	14 18		14 29	14 38	14 47		
Banbury	d		12 48	12a54	13 06		13a18	13 35		13a54	14 06		14a18	14 37		14 48	14a54	15 06		
London Marylebone 10 ⊖	a		14 19		14 25			15 03			15 26			16 04		16 19		16 25		
Spring Road	d					12 29						13 29							14 29	
Hall Green	d					12 32						13 32							14 32	
Yardley Wood	d					12 35						13 35							14 35	
Shirley	d					12 38						13 38							14 38	
Whitlocks End	d																			
Wythall	d					12 42						13 42							14 42	
Earlswood (West Midlands)	d																			
The Lakes	d					12x45						13x45							14x45	
Wood End	d																			
Danzey	d																			
Henley-in-Arden	d					12 53						13 53							14 52	
Wootton Wawen	d																			
Wilmcote	d					13 01						14 01							15 00	
Stratford-upon-Avon	a					13 08						14 08							15 06	

For general notes see front of timetable
For details of catering facilities see Directory of Train Operators

Table 71

Sundays
from 8 November

Hereford, Worcester and Stourbridge → Birmingham → Leamington Spa, Marylebone and Stratford-upon-Avon

Network Diagram - See first page of Table 71

		GW	XC	CH	LM	XC	CH	LM	XC	LM	CH	LM	CH	XC	CH	LM	GW	XC	CH	LM	LM
		1 ◇	1 ◇			1 ◇			1 ◇	bus				1 ◇			1 ◇	1 ◇			
Hereford 7	d	13 28															14 30				
Ledbury	a	13 44															14 46				
	d	13 46															14 55				
Colwall	d	13 53															15 02				
Great Malvern	a	13 58															15 07				
	d	13 59						14 11									15 08				
Malvern Link	d	14 03						14 13									15 12				
Worcester Foregate Street 7	a	14 13						14 21									15 21				
	d	14 14						14 22								15 20	15 23				
Worcester Shrub Hill 7	a	14 17															15 26				
	d																			15 46	
Droitwich Spa	d							14 31		14u40						15 29				15 54	
Bromsgrove	d									15 00											
Barnt Green	d																				
University	d																				
Hartlebury	d																				
Kidderminster	d							14 41								15 39				16 04	
Blakedown	d							14 46													
Hagley	d							14 50								15 46				16 11	
Stourbridge Junction 2	d				14 22			14 54				15 22				15 52				16 16	16 22
Lye	d				14 25							15 25									16 25
Cradley Heath	d				14 29			15 00				15 29				15 58					16 29
Old Hill	d				14 33							15 33									16 33
Rowley Regis	d				14 36			15 05				15 36				16 03					16 36
Langley Green	d				14 39							15 39									16 39
Smethwick Galton Bdg H.L. 7	d				14 43			15 10				15 43				16 08				16 29	16 43
Birmingham New Street 12	a									15 40											
	d		14 33			15 04			15 33					16 04				16 33			
Birmingham International ✈	d					15 14								16 14							
Coventry	d					15 25								16 25							
The Hawthorns 🚊	d				14 45			15 13				15 45				16 11					16 45
Jewellery Quarter 🚊	d				14 49			15 16				15 49				16 14					16 49
Birmingham Snow Hill 🚊	a				14 52			15 19				15 52				16 17				16 35	16 52
	d			14 40	14 53		15 10	15 21			15 40	15 53			16 10	16 19			16 40	16 45	16 53
Birmingham Moor Street	d			14 43	14 56		15 13	15 24			15 43	15 56			16 13	16 22			16 43	16a47	16 56
Bordesley	d																				
Small Heath	d																				
Tyseley	d							15 28								16 26					
Acocks Green	d				15 02							16 02									17 02
Olton	d				15 04							16 04									17 04
Solihull	d			14 52	15 08		15 22				15 52	16 08			16 22				16 52		17 08
Widney Manor	d				15 11							16 11									17 11
Dorridge	d			14 58	15a17		15 28				15 58	16a16			16 28				16 58		17a17
Lapworth	d										16 02										
Hatton	d										16 07		16 17								
Warwick Parkway	d			15 09			15 38				16 12				16 38				17 09		
Warwick	d						15 40						16 25		16 41						
Leamington Spa 8	a		14 59	15 15		15 36	15 45		15 59		16 17		16 28	16 36	16 46			16 59	17 15		
	d		15 00	15 16		15 38	15 47		16 00		16 18		16 29	16 38	16 47			17 00	17 16		
Banbury	d		15a18	15 35		15a54	16 06		16a18		16 37		16 48	16a54	17 06			17a18	17 35		
London Marylebone 10	⊖ a			17 01			17 26				18 05		18 19		18 24				19 01		
Spring Road	d							15 31								16 29					
Hall Green	d							15 34								16 32					
Yardley Wood	d							15 37								16 35					
Shirley	d							15 40								16 38					
Whitlocks End	d																				
Wythall	d							15 44								16 42					
Earlswood (West Midlands)	d																				
The Lakes	d							15x47								16x45					
Wood End	d																				
Danzey	d																				
Henley-in-Arden	d							15 55								16 53					
Wootton Wawen	d																				
Wilmcote	d							16 03								17 01					
Stratford-upon-Avon	a							16 10								17 08					

For general notes see front of timetable
For details of catering facilities see Directory of Train Operators

Table 71

Sundays

from 8 November

Hereford, Worcester and Stourbridge → Birmingham → Leamington Spa, Marylebone and Stratford-upon-Avon

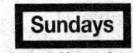

Network Diagram - See first page of Table 71

Station		XC 1◇	CH		LM	XC 1◇	LM 🚌	CH		LM	CH	XC 1◇	CH		LM	GW 1◇	XC 1◇	CH		XC 1◇	CH	LM	GW 1◇		XC 1◇
Hereford 7	d				15 20											16 30							18 30		
Ledbury	a				15 37											16 46							18 46		
	d				15 42											16 47							18 48		
Colwall	d				15 49											16 55							18 55		
Great Malvern	a				15 54											17 00							19 00		
	d				15 54											17 00						17 57	19 08		
Malvern Link	d				15 57											17 04						17 59	19 12		
Worcester Foregate Street 7	a				16 06											17 22						18 08	19 23		
	d				16 09										17 20	17 23						18 09	19 24		
Worcester Shrub Hill 7	a				16 12											17 25						18 11	19 27		
	d				16 15																	18 15			
Droitwich Spa	d				16 23		16 35								17 29							18 23			
Bromsgrove	d						16 55																		
Barnt Green	d																								
University	d																								
Hartlebury	d																								
Kidderminster	d				16 34										17 39							18 39			
Blakedown	d														17 44										
Hagley	d				16 41										17 48							18 46			
Stourbridge Junction 2	d				16 52					17 22					17 52							18 52			
Lye	d									17 25															
Cradley Heath	d				16 58					17 29					17 58							18 58			
Old Hill	d									17 33															
Rowley Regis	d				17 03					17 36					18 03							19 03			
Langley Green	d									17 39															
Smethwick Galton Bdg H.L. 7	d				17 08					17 43					18 08							19 08			
Birmingham New Street 12	a						17 35																		
	d	17 04				17 33						18 04					18 33			19 04					19 33
Birmingham International ✈	d	17 14										18 14								19 14					
Coventry	d	17 25										18 25								19 25					
The Hawthorns 🚊	d				17 11					17 45					18 11							19 11			
Jewellery Quarter 🚊	d				17 14					17 49					18 14							19 14			
Birmingham Snow Hill 🚊	a				17 17					17 53					18 17							19 19			
	d		17 10		17 19			17 40		17 53			18 10		18 19			18 40			19 10	19 21			
Birmingham Moor Street	d		17 13		17 22			17 43		17 56			18 13		18 22			18 43			19 13	19a23			
Bordesley	d																								
Small Heath	d																								
Tyseley	d				17 26										18 26										
Acocks Green	d									18 02															
Olton	d									18 04															
Solihull	d		17 22					17 52		18 08			18 22					18 52			19 21				
Widney Manor	d									18 11											19 24				
Dorridge	d		17 28					17 58		18a17			18 28					18 58			19 29				
Lapworth	d							18 02													19 33				
Hatton	d							18 07			18 17										19 38				
Warwick Parkway	d		17 38					18 12					18 38					19 09			19 43				
Warwick	d		17 41								18 25		18 41								19 46				
Leamington Spa 8	a	17 36	17 46			17 59		18 17			18 28	18 36	18 46				18 59	19 15		19 36	19 49				19 59
	d	17 38	17 47			18 00		18 18			18 29	18 38	18 47				19 00	19 16		19 38	19 52				20 00
Banbury	d	17a54	18 06			18a18		18 37			18 48	18a54	19 06				19a18	19 35		19a54	20 13				20a19
London Marylebone 10 ⊖	a		19 25					20 05			20 19		20 24					21 01			21 55				
Spring Road	d				17 29										18 29										
Hall Green	d				17 32										18 32										
Yardley Wood	d				17 35										18 35										
Shirley	d				17 38										18 38										
Whitlocks End	d																								
Wythall	d				17 42										18 42										
Earlswood (West Midlands)	d																								
The Lakes	d				17x45										18x45										
Wood End	d																								
Danzey	d																								
Henley-in-Arden	d				17 53										18 53										
Wootton Wawen	d																								
Wilmcote	d				18 01										19 01										
Stratford-upon-Avon	a				18 08										19 08										

For general notes see front of timetable
For details of catering facilities see
Directory of Train Operators

Sundays

from 8 November

Hereford, Worcester and Stourbridge → Birmingham → Leamington Spa, Marylebone and Stratford-upon-Avon

Network Diagram - See first page of Table 71

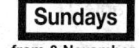

		LM	CH	XC	CH	LM	XC	XC	LM	GW	LM	CH	LM	GW	LM	LM	LM	LM	LM
		🚌		1 ◇			1 ◇	1 ◇	🚌	1 ◇				1 ◇		🚌			🚌
Hereford 7	d										20 05								22 50
Ledbury	a										20 22								23 13
	d										20 22								23 13
Colwall	d										20 29								23 25
Great Malvern	a										20 33								23s40
	d									20 08	20 38			20 55			22 02	23 04	
Malvern Link	d									20 12	20 40			20 59			22 05	23 16	23s48
Worcester Foregate Street 7	a									20 23	20 49			21 08	←		22 13	23 25	00s05
	d									20 24	21 20			21 10	21 20		22 17	23 26	
Worcester Shrub Hill 7	a									20 27	→			21 12			22 19	23 28	00 12
	d					19 38			19 55				20 34				22 26		
Droitwich Spa	d	18u35				19 46			20 10				20 42		21 29	21u35	22 34		
Bromsgrove	d	18 55							20 30							21 55			
Barnt Green	d																		
University	d																		
Hartlebury	d																		
Kidderminster	d					19 56							20 52		21 41		22 44		
Blakedown	d																		
Hagley	d					20 03							20 59		21 48		22 51		
Stourbridge Junction 2	d					20 07							21 03		21 52		22 55		
Lye	d																		
Cradley Heath	d					20 13							21 08		22 02		23 01		
Old Hill	d																		
Rowley Regis	d					20 19							21 14		22 11		23 06		
Langley Green	d																		
Smethwick Galton Bdg H.L. 7	d					20 24							21 19		22 16		23 11		
Birmingham New Street 12	a	19 35							21 10							22 35			
	d			20 04			20 33	21 04											
Birmingham International ✈	d			20 14				21 14											
Coventry	d			20 25				21 24											
The Hawthorns 🚋	d					20 26							21 21		22 19		23 14		
Jewellery Quarter 🚋	d					20 30							21 25		22 22		23 17		
Birmingham Snow Hill 🚋	a					20 33							21 28		22 26		23 21		
	d				20 15	20 33						21 15	21 28		22 26				
Birmingham Moor Street	d				20 18	20a36						21 18	21a31		22a29				
Bordesley	d																		
Small Heath	d																		
Tyseley	d																		
Acocks Green	d																		
Olton	d																		
Solihull	d				20 28							21 28							
Widney Manor	d				20 31							21 31							
Dorridge	d				20 35							21 35							
Lapworth	d																		
Hatton	d		20 14																
Warwick Parkway	d				20 46							21 46							
Warwick	d		20 22		20 49							21 49							
Leamington Spa 8	a		20 25	20 36	20 53		20 59	21 34				21 53							
	d		20 26	20 38	20 54		21 00					21 54							
Banbury	d		20 48	20a54	21 13		21a18					22 15							
London Marylebone 10 ⊖	a		22 19		22 55							23 56							
Spring Road	d																		
Hall Green	d																		
Yardley Wood	d																		
Shirley	d																		
Whitlocks End	d																		
Wythall	d																		
Earlswood (West Midlands)	d																		
The Lakes	d																		
Wood End	d																		
Danzey	d																		
Henley-in-Arden	d																		
Wootton Wawen	d																		
Wilmcote	d																		
Stratford-upon-Avon	a																		

For general notes see front of timetable
For details of catering facilities see Directory of Train Operators

Stratford -upon-Avon, Marylebone and Leamington Spa → Birmingham → Stourbridge, Worcester and Hereford

Network Diagram - See first page of Table 71

Miles	Miles	Miles			CH	LM	GW	LM	LM	LM	LM	LM	GW	LM	GW	LM	LM	LM	CH	XC	LM	LM	LM	CH	XC
					MX ◇		1						A		1 ◇					1 ◇ B				C	1 ◇ D
—	0	—	**Stratford-upon-Avon**	d													06 31					06 54			
—	2¾	—	Wilmcote	d													06 36					06 59			
—	6½	—	Wootton Wawen	d													06x41					07x04			
—	8¼	—	Henley-in-Arden	d													06 45					07 09			
—	11¼	—	Danzey	d													06x49					07x13			
—	13	—	Wood End	d													06x53					07x17			
—	14½	—	The Lakes	d													06x55					07x19			
—	15	—	Earlswood (West Midlands)	d													06 57					07 22			
—	16	—	Wythall	d													07 00					07 24			
—	17	—	Whitlocks End	d													07 02					07 27			
—	18	—	Shirley	d							06 31	06 52					07 05					07 30			
—	19¼	—	Yardley Wood	d							06 34	06 55					07 08					07 33			
—	20½	—	Hall Green	d							06 37	06 58					07 11					07 36			
—	21	—	Spring Road	d							06 39	07 00					07 13					07 38			
—	—	—	**London Marylebone** 10 ⊖	d	22p20																				
—	—	—	Banbury	d	23p30															06 54				07 02	07 25
—	—	—	**Leamington Spa** 8	a	23p48															07 10				07 22	07 41
—	—	0		d	23p48				05 48							06 30			06 55	07 12			07 07	07 22	07 43
—	—	2	Warwick	d	23p53				05 52							06 34			06 59				07 11	07 26	
—	—	3¼	Warwick Parkway	d	23p56				05 55							06 37			07 02				07 15	07 30	
—	—	6	Hatton	d					06 00							06 42			07a07				07 20	07 34	
—	—	10½	Lapworth	d					06 06							06 48							07 27		
—	—	12¾	Dorridge	d	00 07			05 53	06 11							06 53		07 12					07 33	07 43	
—	—	14¾	Widney Manor	d				05 57	06 15							06 57		07 16					07 37	07 47	
—	—	16¼	Solihull	d	00 13			06 01	06 18							07 00		07 20					07 41	07 51	
—	—	18	Olton	d				06 04	06 22							07 04		07 23					07 44	07 55	
—	—	19	Acocks Green	d				06 07	06 24							07 06		07 26					07 47		
—	22	20	Tyseley	d				06 10	06 27		06 42	07 03				07 10	07 17	07 29				07 42	07 50		
—	23	21	Small Heath	d				06 12	06 30		06 44	07 05				07 13	07 19	07 32				07 44	07 53		
—	24	—	Bordesley	d																					
—	24¾	—	**Birmingham Moor Street**	d	00 23			06 16	06 35		06 48	07 09				07 19	07 23	07 36				07 48	07 57	08 04	
—	25¼	—	**Birmingham Snow Hill** 🚋	a	00 32			06 19	06 37		06 51	07 12				07 21	07 27	07 38				07 52	07 59	08 11	
—	—	—		d				06 20			06 53	07 15				07 23		07 39				07 53	08 03		
—	26	—	Jewellery Quarter 🚋	d				06 22			06 55	07 17				07 25		07 42				07 55	08 05		
—	28½	—	The Hawthorns 🚋	d				06 27			07 00	07 22				07 30		07 46				08 00	08 10		
—	—	—	**Coventry**	a																07 22					
—	—	—	**Birmingham International** ✈	a																07 37					
—	—	24	**Birmingham New Street** 12	a																07 49					08 17
0	—	—		d						06 59				07 20							07 59				
—	29¼	29	Smethwick Galton Bdg H.L. 7	d				06 29			07 03	07 24				07 32		07 49				08 02	08 12		
—	30¼	30½	Langley Green	d				06 32			07 06					07 35		07 52					08 15		
—	32¼	—	Rowley Regis	d				06 36			07 09	07 29				07 39		07 56				08 07	08 19		
—	33¼	—	Old Hill	d				06 39			07 12					07 42		07 59					08 22		
—	34¾	—	Cradley Heath	d				06 42			07 16	07 33				07 45		08 02				08 12	08 25		
—	36¼	—	Lye	d				06 45			07 19					07 48		08 05					08 28		
—	37¼	—	**Stourbridge Junction** 2	d				06 49			07 23	07a39				07 52		08a09				08 19	08 32		
—	39¼	—	Hagley	d				06 52			07 26					07 55						08 23	08 36		
—	41	—	Blakedown	d				06 55			07 29					07 58						08 26	08 39		
—	44¼	—	**Kidderminster**	d				07 00			07 35					08 03						08 31	08a45		
—	47¾	—	Hartlebury	d							07 40					08 08						08 36			
2½	—	—	University	d						07 05				07 27							08 06				
10½	—	—	Barnt Green	d										07 43											
13	—	—	Bromsgrove	d						07 23				07 48							08 21				
19¼	53½	—	Droitwich Spa	d				07 12		07 33	07 47			07 58		08 17					08 31	08 44			
25	—	—	**Worcester Shrub Hill** 7	a										08 05		08 24									
—	—	—		d		06 00	06 30						07 55	08 09	08 18	08 28									
25¾	58¾	—	**Worcester Foregate Street** 7	a		06 02	06 36	07 22		07 41	07 57		07 58	08 11	08 21	08 30					08 39	08 59			
—	—	—		d		06 03				07 42			07 58	08 12	08 22						08 40				
32½	—	—	Malvern Link	d		06 12				07 52			08 07	08 20							08 50				
33¾	—	—	**Great Malvern**	a		06 15				07 54			08 12	08 23	08 37						08 52				
—	—	—		d		06 15				08 01											08 53				
36½	—	—	Colwall	d		06 20				08 06											08 58				
40¾	—	—	Ledbury	a		06 27				08 13											09 06				
—	—	—		d		06 29				08 14											09 10				
54½	—	—	**Hereford** 7	a		06 50				08 34											09 30				

For general notes see front of timetable
For details of catering facilities see Directory of Train Operators

A From Gloucester (Table 57)
B From Southampton Central (Table 51)
C From High Wycombe (Table 115)
D From Guildford (Table 51)

From 5 October a revised Chiltern Railways service will be in operation due to seasonal difficulties. Trains will arrive at their destination 3 minutes later than shown

Stratford -upon-Avon, Marylebone and Leamington Spa → Birmingham → Stourbridge, Worcester and Hereford

Network Diagram - See first page of Table 71

Station		LM	LM	LM	GW	LM	LM	XC	LM	LM	LM	LM	CH	XC	LM	LM	LM	CH	CH	GW	LM	XC	LM	LM	CH
					[1]			[1] ◇ A					◇	[1] ◇						B		[1] ◇ C			
Stratford-upon-Avon	d	07 23							07 45							08 27									
Wilmcote	d								07 50							08 32									
Wootton Wawen	d								07x55							08x37									
Henley-in-Arden	d	07 34							07 59							08 41									
Danzey	d								08x04							08x45									
Wood End	d								08x08							08x49									
The Lakes	d								08x10							08x51									
Earlswood (West Midlands)	d	07 43							08 13							08 54									
Wythall	d	07 45							08 15							08 56									
Whitlocks End	d	07 48							08 18							08 59									
Shirley	d	07 52		08 09					08 22			08 38				09 02							09 22		
Yardley Wood	d	07 55		08 12					08 25			08 41				09 05							09 25		
Hall Green	d	07 58		08 15					08 28			08 44				09 08							09 28		
Spring Road	d	08 00		08 17					08 30			08 46				09 10							09 30		
London Marylebone [10] ⊖	d												06 50					07 20	07 23						07 50
Banbury	d							07 54					08 05	08 25				08 35	08 45			08 54			08 57
Leamington Spa [8]	a							08 10					08 23	08 41				08 53	09 03			09 10			09 15
	d						07 47	08 12			08 00		08 24	08 43				08 53	09 03			09 12			09 15
Warwick	d						07 51				08 04		08 28					08 57	09 08						09 19
Warwick Parkway	d						07 55				08 08		08 32					09 01	09 11						09 22
Hatton	d						08 00				08 13							09 07	09a17						
Lapworth	d						08 06				08 19							09 12							
Dorridge	d		07 58				08 11			08 20	08 25		08 43		08 46		09 09	09 16						09 28	09 33
Widney Manor	d		08 01				08 14			08 24	08 29				08 50		09 13							09 32	
Solihull	d		08 04				08 18			08 28	08 32		08 48		08 53		09 16	09 21						09 35	09 39
Olton	d		08 08				08 21			08 31	08 36				08 57		09 20							09 39	
Acocks Green	d		08 11				08 24			08 34	08 38				08 59		09 22							09 41	
Tyseley	d		08 14	08 20			08 28		08 33	08 37		08 49			09 02								09 33		
Small Heath	d			08 23			08 31		08 35	08 39		08 51			09 05								09 35		
Bordesley	d																								
Birmingham Moor Street	d	08 07	08 19	08 27			08 35		08 39	08 43	08 48	08 55	09 00		09 09	09 17	09 29	09 33					09 39	09 48	09 51
Birmingham Snow Hill	a	08 11	08 21	08 29			08 37		08 42	08 46	08 51	08 58	09 07		09 11	09 20	09 31	09 41					09 42	09 50	10 01
	d	08 13	08 23	08 33					08 43		08 53	09 03			09 13	09 23	09 33						09 43	09 53	
Jewellery Quarter	d	08 15	08 25	08 35					08 45		08 55	09 05			09 15	09 25	09 35						09 45	09 55	
The Hawthorns	d	08 20	08 30	08 40					08 50		09 00	09 10			09 20	09 30	09 40						09 50	10 00	
Coventry	a							08 22														09 22			
Birmingham International ✈	a							08 37														09 37			
Birmingham New Street [12]	a							08 49						09 17								09 49			
	d					08 49															09 49				
Smethwick Galton Bdg H.L. [7]	d	08 22	08 32	08 42					08 52		09 02	09 12			09 22	09 32	09 42						09 52	10 02	
Langley Green	d			08 45								09 15					09 45								
Rowley Regis	d	08 27	08 37	08 49					08 57		09 07	09 19			09 27	09 37	09 49						09 57	10 07	
Old Hill	d			08 52								09 22					09 52								
Cradley Heath	d	08 32	08 42	08 55					09 02		09 12	09 25			09 32	09 42	09 55						10 02	10 12	
Lye	d			08 58								09 28					09 58								
Stourbridge Junction [2]	d	08a38	08a49	09 02					09 08		09a18	09 32			09 37	09a48	10 02						10 07	10a18	
Hagley	d								09 12						09 41								10 11		
Blakedown	d								09 15						09 44								10 14		
Kidderminster	d			09a12					09 20			09a42			09 49		10a12						10 19		
Hartlebury	d																								
University	d					08 55															09 55				
Barnt Green	d																								
Bromsgrove	d					09 11															10 11				
Droitwich Spa	d					09 21			09 32						10 01						10 23		10 31		
Worcester Shrub Hill [7]	a								09 42																
	d				09 16															10 15					
Worcester Foregate Street [7]	a				09 19	09 29									10 09					10 17	10 31		10 39		
	d				09 19	09 30														10 18	10 32		10 41		
Malvern Link	d				09 28	09 40														10 27	10 42		10 51		
Great Malvern	a				09 34	09 42														10 31	10 45		10 54		
	d					09 43															10 45				
Colwall	d					09 48															10 50				
Ledbury	a					09 56															10 58				
	d					10 00															11 00				
Hereford [7]	a					10 19															11 20				

For general notes see front of timetable
For details of catering facilities see Directory of Train Operators

A From Southampton Central (Table 51)
B From Warminster (Table 123)
C From Bournemouth (Table 51)

From 5 October a revised Chiltern Railways service will be in operation due to seasonal difficulties. Trains will arrive at their destination 3 minutes later than shown

Stratford -upon-Avon, Marylebone and Leamington Spa → Birmingham → Stourbridge, Worcester and Hereford

Network Diagram - See first page of Table 71

		XC	LM	GW	LM	LM	LM	CH	LM	XC	GW	LM	LM	CH	CH	XC	LM	LM	LM	LM	CH	GW	LM	XC	LM
		1 ◇		1 ◇						1 ◇	1 ◇					1 ◇					◇			1 ◇	
										A												B		A	
		☕		🍽						☕	☕			☕	☕	☕					☕			☕	
Stratford-upon-Avon	d					09 27													10 27						
Wilmcote	d					09 32													10 32						
Wootton Wawen	d					09x37													10x37						
Henley-in-Arden	d					09 41													10 41						
Danzey	d					09x45													10x45						
Wood End	d					09x49													10x49						
The Lakes	d					09x51													10x51						
Earlswood (West Midlands)	d					09 54													10 54						
Wythall	d					09 56													10 56						
Whitlocks End	d					09 59													10 59						
Shirley	d		09 42			10 02						10 22					10 42		11 02						11 22
Yardley Wood	d		09 45			10 05						10 25					10 45		11 05						11 25
Hall Green	d		09 48			10 08						10 28					10 48		11 08						11 28
Spring Road	d		09 50			10 10						10 30					10 50		11 10						11 30
London Marylebone 10 ⊖	d							08 20						08 50	08 54						09 20				
Banbury	d	09 25						09 35		09 54				09 57	10 14	10 25					10 35			10 54	
Leamington Spa 8	a	09 41						09 53		10 10				10 15	10 33	10 41					10 54			11 10	
	d	09 43						09 54		10 12				10 15	10 34	10 43					10 54			11 12	
Warwick	d							09 58						10 19	10 38						10 59				
Warwick Parkway	d							10 02						10 22							11 02				
Hatton	d							10 07							10a45										
Lapworth	d							10 12																	
Dorridge	d				09 46		10 09	10 17					10 28	10 33				10 46		11 09	11 13				
Widney Manor	d				09 50		10 13						10 32					10 50		11 13					
Solihull	d				09 53		10 16	10 23					10 35	10 39				10 53		11 16	11 19				
Olton	d				09 57		10 20						10 39					10 57		11 20					
Acocks Green	d				09 59		10 22						10 41					10 59		11 22					
Tyseley	d				10 02							10 33						11 02							11 33
Small Heath	d				10 05							10 35						11 05							11 35
Bordesley	d																								
Birmingham Moor Street	d		09 58		10 09	10 17	10 29	10 34				10 39	10 48	10 51			10 57	11 09	11 17	11 29	11 31				11 39
Birmingham Snow Hill 🚋	a		10 01		10 11	10 20	10 31	10 41				10 42	10 50	11 01			11 01	11 11	11 20	11 31	11 41				11 42
	d		10 03		10 13	10 23	10 33					10 43	10 53				11 03	11 13	11 23	11 33					11 43
Jewellery Quarter 🚋	d		10 05		10 15	10 25	10 35					10 45	10 55				11 05	11 15	11 25	11 35					11 45
The Hawthorns 🚋	d		10 10		10 20	10 30	10 40					10 50	11 00				11 10	11 20	11 30	11 40					11 50
Coventry	a									10 22														11 22	
Birmingham International ✈	a									10 37														11 37	
Birmingham New Street 12	a	10 17								10 49						11 17								11 49	
	d								10 49														11 49		
Smethwick Galton Bdg H.L. 7	d		10 12		10 22	10 32	10 42					10 52	11 02				11 12	11 22	11 32	11 42					11 52
Langley Green	d		10 15				10 45										11 15			11 45					
Rowley Regis	d		10 19		10 27	10 37	10 49					10 57	11 07				11 19	11 27	11 37	11 49					11 57
Old Hill	d		10 22				10 52										11 22			11 52					
Cradley Heath	d		10 25		10 32	10 42	10 55					11 02	11 12				11 25	11 32	11 42	11 55					12 02
Lye	d		10 28				10 58										11 28			11 58					
Stourbridge Junction 2	d		10 32		10 37	10a48	11 02					11 07	11a18				11 32	11 37	11a48	12 02					12 07
Hagley	d				10 41							11 11						11 41							12 11
Blakedown	d				10 44							11 14						11 44							12 14
Kidderminster	d		10a42		10 49		11a12					11 19					11a42	11 49		12a12					12 19
Hartlebury	d																								
University	d								10 55														11 55		
Barnt Green	d																								
Bromsgrove	d								11 11														12 11		
Droitwich Spa	d				11 01				11 21			11 31						12 01					12 21		12 31
Worcester Shrub Hill 7	a											11 38													
	d			10 52							11 36											12 15			
Worcester Foregate Street 7	a			10 55	11 09				11 31		11 42							12 09				12 17	12 30		12 39
	d			10 56					11 32													12 18	12 31		
Malvern Link	d			11 05					11 42													12 27	12 40		
Great Malvern	a			11 09					11 44													12 33	12 42		
	d			11 09					11 45														12 43		
Colwall	d			11 15					11 50														12 48		
Ledbury	a			11 23					11 58														12 56		
	d			11 24					12 00														12 58		
Hereford 7	a			11 47					12 22														13 18		

For general notes see front of timetable
For details of catering facilities see Directory of Train Operators

A From Bournemouth (Table 51)
B From Southampton Central (Table 123)

From 5 October a revised Chiltern Railways service will be in operation due to seasonal difficulties. Trains will arrive at their destination 3 minutes later than shown

Stratford -upon-Avon, Marylebone and Leamington Spa → Birmingham → Stourbridge, Worcester and Hereford

Network Diagram - See first page of Table 71

		LM	CH	XC	LM	GW	LM	LM	LM	CH	LM	XC	LM	LM	CH	CH	XC	LM	GW	LM	LM	LM	CH	GW	LM
			◇	1 ◇		1 ◇				◇		1 ◇			◇	◇	1 ◇		1 ◇					◇	
												A												B	
			⌶	⌶		⊐				⌶		⌶			⌶	⌶	⌶		⊐				⌶		
Stratford-upon-Avon	d							11 27													12 27				
Wilmcote	d							11 32													12 32				
Wootton Wawen	d							11x37													12x37				
Henley-in-Arden	d							11 41													12 41				
Danzey	d							11x45													12x45				
Wood End	d							11x49													12x49				
The Lakes	d							11x51													12x51				
Earlswood (West Midlands)	d							11 54													12 54				
Wythall	d							11 56													12 56				
Whitlocks End	d							11 59													12 59				
Shirley	d				11 42			12 02					12 22					12 42			13 02				
Yardley Wood	d				11 45			12 05					12 25					12 45			13 05				
Hall Green	d				11 48			12 08					12 28					12 48			13 08				
Spring Road	d				11 50			12 10					12 30					12 50			13 10				
London Marylebone 10 ⊖	d		09 50							10 20					10 50	10 54							11 20		
Banbury	d		10 57	11 25						11 35		11 54			11 57	12 17	12 25						12 35		
Leamington Spa 8	a		11 15	11 41						11 54		12 10			12 15	12 37	12 41						12 54		
	d		11 15	11 43						11 54		12 12			12 15	12 38	12 43						12 54		
Warwick	d		11 19							11 59					12 19	12 42							12 59		
Warwick Parkway	d		11 22							12 02					12 22								13 02		
Hatton	d									12 07						12a49									
Lapworth	d									12 13															
Dorridge	d	11 28	11 33				11 46		12 09	12 17				12 28	12 33					12 46		13 09	13 13		
Widney Manor	d	11 32					11 50		12 13					12 32						12 50		13 13			
Solihull	d	11 35	11 39				11 53		12 16	12 23				12 35	12 39					12 53		13 16	13 19		
Olton	d	11 39					11 57		12 20					12 39						12 57		13 20			
Acocks Green	d	11 41					11 59		12 22					12 41						12 59		13 22			
Tyseley	d						12 02						12 33							13 02					
Small Heath	d						12 05						12 35							13 05					
Bordesley	d																								
Birmingham Moor Street	d	11 48	11 51		11 58		12 10	12 17	12 29	12 35			12 39	12 48	12 51			12 58		13 09	13 17	13 29	13 32		
Birmingham Snow Hill	a	11 50	12 01		12 00		12 12	12 20	12 31	12 42			12 42	12 51	13 02			13 01		13 11	13 20	13 31	13 41		
	d	11 53			12 03		12 13	12 23	12 33				12 43	12 53				13 03		13 13	13 23	13 33			
Jewellery Quarter	d	11 55			12 05		12 15	12 25	12 35				12 45	12 55				13 05		13 15	13 25	13 35			
The Hawthorns	d	12 00			12 10		12 20	12 30	12 40				12 50	13 00				13 10		13 20	13 30	13 40			
Coventry	a											12 22													
Birmingham International ✈	a											12 37													
Birmingham New Street 12	a			12 17								12 49					13 17								
	d										12 49														13 49
Smethwick Galton Bdg H.L. 7	d	12 02			12 12		12 22	12 32	12 42				12 52	13 02				13 12		13 22	13 32	13 42			
Langley Green	d				12 15				12 45									13 15				13 45			
Rowley Regis	d	12 07			12 19		12 27	12 37	12 49				12 57	13 07				13 19		13 27	13 37	13 49			
Old Hill	d				12 22				12 52									13 22				13 52			
Cradley Heath	d	12 12			12 25		12 32	12 42	12 55				13 02	13 12				13 25		13 32	13 42	13 55			
Lye	d				12 28				12 58									13 28				13 58			
Stourbridge Junction 2	d	12a18			12 32		12 37	12a48	13 02				13 07	13a18				13a32		13 40	13a50	14 02			
Hagley	d						12 41						13 11							13 43					
Blakedown	d						12 44						13 14							13 46					
Kidderminster	d				12a42		12 49		13a12				13 19							13 51		14a12			
Hartlebury	d																								
University	d										12 55														13 55
Barnt Green	d																								
Bromsgrove	d										13 11														14 13
Droitwich Spa	d						13 01				13 22		13 31							14 03					14 23
Worcester Shrub Hill 7	a												13 38							14 11					
	d					12 50													13 40					14 15	
Worcester Foregate Street 7	a					12 54	13 10				13 30								13 43					14 18	14 31
	d					12 54	13 10				13 31								13 44					14 18	14 32
Malvern Link	d					13 03	13 20				13 41								13 53					14 27	14 42
Great Malvern	a					13 07	13 24				13 43								14 00					14 37	14 45
	d					13 09					13 44														14 45
Colwall	d					13 15					13 49														14 50
Ledbury	a					13 23					13 57														14 57
	d					13 28					14 00														14 58
Hereford 7	a					13 48					14 22														15 19

For general notes see front of timetable
For details of catering facilities see Directory of Train Operators

A From Bournemouth (Table 51)
B From Brighton (Table 123)

From 5 October a revised Chiltern Railways service will be in operation due to seasonal difficulties. Trains will arrive at their destination 3 minutes later than shown

Stratford -upon-Avon, Marylebone and Leamington Spa → Birmingham → Stourbridge, Worcester and Hereford

Network Diagram - See first page of Table 71

		XC	LM	LM	CH	XC	LM	LM	LM	LM	CH	LM	XC	LM	LM	CH	CH	XC	LM	GW	LM	LM	LM	CH	LM
		1 ◇			◇	1 ◇							1 ◇			◇		1 ◇		1 ◇					
		A											A												
		🛒			🛒	🛒							🛒					🛒		🍽					
Stratford-upon-Avon	d								13 27													14 27			
Wilmcote	d								13 32													14 32			
Wootton Wawen	d								13x37													14x37			
Henley-in-Arden	d								13 41													14 41			
Danzey	d								13x45													14x45			
Wood End	d								13x49													14x49			
The Lakes	d								13x51													14x51			
Earlswood (West Midlands)	d								13 54													14 54			
Wythall	d								13 56													14 56			
Whitlocks End	d								13 59													14 59			
Shirley	d		13 22				13 42		14 02					14 22					14 42			15 02			
Yardley Wood	d		13 25				13 45		14 05					14 25					14 45			15 05			
Hall Green	d		13 28				13 48		14 08					14 28					14 48			15 08			
Spring Road	d		13 30				13 50		14 10					14 30					14 50			15 10			
London Marylebone 10 ⊖	d				11 50						12 20					12 50	12 54							13 20	
Banbury	d	12 54			12 57	13 25					13 35		13 54			13 57	14 17	14 25						14 35	
Leamington Spa 8	a	13 10			13 15	13 41					13 54		14 10			14 14	14 37	14 41						14 54	
	d	13 12			13 15	13 43					13 54		14 12			14 15	14 38	14 43						14 54	
Warwick	d				13 19						13 59					14 19	14 42							14 59	
Warwick Parkway	d				13 22						14 02					14 22								15 02	
Hatton	d										14 07						14a49								
Lapworth	d										14 13														
Dorridge	d			13 28	13 33			13 46		14 09	14 17				14 28	14 33					14 46		15 09	15 13	
Widney Manor	d			13 32				13 50		14 13					14 32						14 50		15 13		
Solihull	d			13 35	13 39			13 53		14 16	14 23				14 35	14 39					14 53		15 16	15 19	
Olton	d			13 39				13 57		14 20					14 39						14 57		15 20		
Acocks Green	d			13 41				13 59		14 22					14 41						14 59		15 22		
Tyseley	d		13 33					14 02						14 33							15 02				
Small Heath	d		13 35					14 05						14 35							15 05				
Bordesley	d																								
Birmingham Moor Street	d		13 39	13 48	13 51		13 59	14 09	14 17	14 29	14 35			14 39	14 48	14 51			14 58		15 09	15 17	15 29	15 33	
Birmingham Snow Hill 🚊	a		13 42	13 51	14 01		14 01	14 11	14 21	14 31	14 42			14 42	14 51	15 02			15 01		15 11	15 21	15 31	15 41	
	d		13 43	13 53			14 03	14 13	14 23	14 33				14 43	14 53				15 03		15 13	15 23	15 33		
Jewellery Quarter 🚊	d		13 45	13 55			14 05	14 15	14 25	14 35				14 45	14 55				15 05		15 15	15 25	15 35		
The Hawthorns 🚊	d		13 50	14 00			14 10	14 20	14 30	14 40				14 50	15 00				15 10		15 20	15 30	15 40		
Coventry	a	13 22											14 22												
Birmingham International ✈	a	13 37											14 37												
Birmingham New Street 12	a	13 49				14 17							14 49					15 17							
	d											14 49													15 49
Smethwick Galton Bdg H.L. 7	d		13 52	14 02			14 12	14 22	14 32	14 42				14 52	15 02				15 12		15 22	15 32	15 42		
Langley Green	d						14 15			14 45									15 15				15 45		
Rowley Regis	d		13 57	14 07			14 19	14 27	14 37	14 49				14 57	15 07				15 19		15 27	15 37	15 49		
Old Hill	d						14 22			14 52									15 22				15 52		
Cradley Heath	d		14 02	14 12			14 25	14 32	14 42	14 55				15 02	15 12				15 25		15 32	15 42	15 55		
Lye	d						14 28			14 58									15 28				15 58		
Stourbridge Junction 2	d		14 07	14a18			14 32	14 37	14a49	15 02				15 07	15a18				15 32		15 37	15a48	16 02		
Hagley	d		14 11					14 41						15 11							15 41		16 05		
Blakedown	d		14 14					14 44						15 14							15 44				
Kidderminster	d		14 19				14a42	14 49		15a12				15 19					15a42		15 49		16a13		
Hartlebury	d																								
University	d											14 55													15 55
Barnt Green	d																								
Bromsgrove	d											15 11													16 11
Droitwich Spa	d		14 31					15 01				15 21		15 31							16 01				16 21
Worcester Shrub Hill 7	a		14 39																		16 10				
	d		14 43																	15 44					
Worcester Foregate Street 7	a		14 45					15 09				15 31		15 39						15 47					16 31
	d		14 46									15 32								15 48					16 32
Malvern Link	d		14 54									15 42								15 57					16 42
Great Malvern	a		14 58									15 44								16 04					16 44
	d											15 45													16 45
Colwall	d											15 50													16 50
Ledbury	a											15 58													16 58
	d											16 01													17 00
Hereford 7	a											16 22													17 20

For general notes see front of timetable
For details of catering facilities see Directory of Train Operators

A From Bournemouth (Table 51)

From 5 October a revised Chiltern Railways service will be in operation due to seasonal difficulties. Trains will arrive at their destination 3 minutes later than shown

Stratford -upon-Avon, Marylebone and Leamington Spa → Birmingham → Stourbridge, Worcester and Hereford

Network Diagram - See first page of Table 71

		XC	LM	LM	CH	XC	GW	LM	LM	LM	LM	LM	CH	LM	XC	LM	LM	CH	CH	XC	LM	LM	LM	XC	LM
		1 ◇			◇	1 ◇									1 ◇				◇	1 ◇				1 ◇	
		A					B								A										
		🛒				🛒									🛒					🛒				🛒	
Stratford-upon-Avon	d										15 27														16 23
Wilmcote	d										15 32														16 28
Wootton Wawen	d										15x37														16x33
Henley-in-Arden	d										15 41														16 38
Danzey	d										15x45														16x43
Wood End	d										15x49														16x47
The Lakes	d										15x51														16x49
Earlswood (West Midlands)	d										15 54														16 52
Wythall	d										15 56														16 55
Whitlocks End	d										15 59														16 58
Shirley	d		15 22					15 42			16 02					16 22					16 42				17 02
Yardley Wood	d		15 25					15 45			16 05					16 25					16 45				17 05
Hall Green	d		15 28					15 48			16 08					16 28					16 48				17 08
Spring Road	d		15 30					15 50			16 10					16 30					16 50				17 10
London Marylebone 10 ⊖	d				13 50								14 20					14 50	14 54						
Banbury	d	14 54			14 57	15 25							15 35		15 54			15 57	16 17	16 25					
Leamington Spa 8	a	15 10			15 15	15 41							15 54		16 10			16 15	16 37	16 41					
	d	15 12			15 15	15 43							15 54		16 12			16 15	16 38	16 43					
Warwick	d				15 19								15 59					16 19	16 42						
Warwick Parkway	d				15 22								16 02					16 22							
Hatton	d												16 07						16a49						
Lapworth	d												16 13												
Dorridge	d			15 28	15 33					15 46		16 09	16 17				16 27	16 33					16 46		
Widney Manor	d			15 32						15 50		16 13					16 31						16 50		
Solihull	d			15 35	15 39					15 53		16 16	16 23				16 34	16 39					16 53		
Olton	d			15 39						15 57		16 20					16 38						16 57		
Acocks Green	d			15 41						15 59		16 22					16 40						16 59		
Tyseley	d		15 33							16 02						16 33	16 43				16 53		17 02		
Small Heath	d		15 35							16 05						16 35							17 05		
Bordesley	d																								
Birmingham Moor Street	d		15 39	15 48	15 51			15 58		16 09	16 17	16 29	16 35			16 39	16 48	16 51			16 58		17 09		17 17
Birmingham Snow Hill 🚊	a		15 42	15 51	16 01			16 01		16 11	16 21	16 31	16 42			16 42	16 51	17 01			17 01		17 12		17 21
	d		15 43	15 53				16 03		16 13	16 23	16 33				16 43	16 53				17 03		17 13		17 23
Jewellery Quarter 🚊	d		15 45	15 55				16 05		16 15	16 25	16 35				16 45	16 55				17 05		17 15		17 25
The Hawthorns 🚊	d		15 50	16 00				16 10		16 20	16 30	16 40				16 50	17 00				17 10		17 20		17 30
Coventry	a	15 22													16 22										
Birmingham International ✈	a	15 37													16 37										
Birmingham New Street 12	a	15 49				16 17									16 49					17 17					
	d								16 20					16 49								17 19		17 30	
Smethwick Galton Bdg H.L. 7	d		15 52	16 02				16 12		16 21	16 32	16 43				16 52	17 02				17 13		17 22		17 32
Langley Green	d							16 15				16 46									17 16				17 35
Rowley Regis	d		15 57	16 07				16 19		16 27	16 38	16 49				16 58	17 07				17 19		17 28		17 39
Old Hill	d							16 22				16 52									17 22				17 42
Cradley Heath	d		16 02	16 12				16 25		16 32	16 43	16 56				17 03	17 12				17 26		17 33		17 45
Lye	d							16 28				16 59									17 29				17 48
Stourbridge Junction 2	d		16 07	16a18				16 32		16 39	16a49	17 02				17 10	17a18				17 33		17 42		17a53
Hagley	d		16 11							16 42		17 06				17 14					17 37		17 46		
Blakedown	d		16 14							16 45		17 09				17 17					17 40		17 49		
Kidderminster	d		16 19					16a42		16 50		17a15				17 22					17a45		17 54		
Hartlebury	d															17 27									
University	d								16 26					16 55								17 25		17 36	
Barnt Green	d																								
Bromsgrove	d								16 42					17 11								17 45		17a49	
Droitwich Spa	d		16 31						16 52	17 02				17 22		17 38						17 55	18 06		
Worcester Shrub Hill 7	a								16 59					17 29								18 04	18 18		
	d						16 40		17 07					17 33								18 09			
Worcester Foregate Street 7	a		16 40				16 42		17 09	17 12				17 35		17 47						18 11			
	d								17 10					17 36								18 12			
Malvern Link	d								17 19					17 45								18 21			
Great Malvern	a								17 22					17 47								18 24			
	d													17 48								18 24			
Colwall	d													17 53								18 28			
Ledbury	a													18 01								18 36			
	d													18 03								18 37			
Hereford 7	a													18 23								18 57			

For general notes see front of timetable
For details of catering facilities see Directory of Train Operators

A From Bournemouth (Table 51)
B From Southampton Central (Table 123)

From 5 October a revised Chiltern Railways service will be in operation due to seasonal difficulties. Trains will arrive at their destination 3 minutes later than shown

Stratford -upon-Avon, Marylebone and Leamington Spa → Birmingham → Stourbridge, Worcester and Hereford

Network Diagram - See first page of Table 71

	GW	CH	XC	LM	LM	LM	LM	LM	CH	XC	LM	LM	LM	CH	CH	GW	LM	XC	XC	XC	LM	LM	LM	CH
	A		1 ◇ B 🛒						◇ 🛒	1 ◇ 🛒				🛒		1		1 ◇ C 🛒	1 ◇ B 🛒	1 ◇ 🛒				◇ D 🛒
Stratford-upon-Avon d												17 27									17 58			
Wilmcote d												17 32												
Wootton Wawen d												17x37												
Henley-in-Arden d												17 41									18 08			
Danzey d												17x45												
Wood End d												17x49												
The Lakes d												17x51												
Earlswood (West Midlands) d												17 54												
Wythall d												17 56												
Whitlocks End d												17 59												
Shirley d							17 22				17 45	18 02									18 22		18 37	
Yardley Wood d							17 25				17 48	18 05									18 25		18 40	
Hall Green d							17 28				17 51	18 08									18 28		18 43	
Spring Road d							17 30				17 53	18 10									18 30		18 45	
London Marylebone 10 ⊖ d		15 20							16 00					16 30	16 36									17 00
Banbury d		16 35	16 54						17 03	17 25				17 33	17 49				17 54	18 25				18 03
Leamington Spa 8 a		16 53	17 10						17 22	17 41				17 50	18 07				18 10	18 41				18 23
d		16 54	17 12						17 22	17 43				17 50	18 07				18 12	18 43				18 23
Warwick d		16 59							17 27					17 56										
Warwick Parkway d		17 02							17 30					17 59	18 14									18 29
Hatton d															18a20									
Lapworth d		17 10												18 08										
Dorridge d		17 14			17 09			17 27	17 43				18 02	18 12								18 23		18 40
Widney Manor d					17 13			17 31					18 06									18 27		
Solihull d		17 21			17 16			17 34	17 48				18 09	18 18								18 30		18 45
Olton d					17 20			17 38					18 13									18 34		
Acocks Green d					17 22			17 40					18 15									18 36		
Tyseley d							17 33	17 43					18 20								18 33	18 39	18 48	
Small Heath d							17 35	17 46					18 22								18 35	18 42		
Bordesley d																								
Birmingham Moor Street d		17 33			17 29		17 39	17 50	17 59		18 00	18 17	18 26	18 30							18 39	18 46	18 53	18 56
Birmingham Snow Hill 🚊 a		17 41			17 31		17 42	17 52	18 12		18 02	18 20	18 29	18 41							18 42	18 48	18 55	19 01
d					17 33		17 43	17 53			18 03	18 23									18 43		18 57	19 10
Jewellery Quarter 🚊 d					17 35		17 45	17 55			18 05	18 25									18 45		18 59	
The Hawthorns 🚊 d					17 40		17 50	18 00			18 10	18 30									18 50		19 04	19 16
Coventry a			17 22																18 22					
Birmingham International ✈ a			17 37																18 37					
Birmingham New Street 12 a			17 49							18 17									18 49	19 17				
d				17 49		17 59											18 19	18 30						
Smethwick Galton Bdg H.L. 7 d					17 42		17 53	18 02			18 13	18 33									18 53		19 07	19 19
Langley Green d							17 56				18 16	18 36											19 10	
Rowley Regis d					17 48		17 59	18 08			18 19	18 39									18 58		19 13	19 24
Old Hill d							18 02				18 22	18 42											19 16	
Cradley Heath d					17 53		18 06	18 13			18 26	18 46									19 03		19 20	19 29
Lye d							18 09				18 29	18 49											19 23	
Stourbridge Junction 2 d					18 03		18 13	18 20			18 33	18 54									19 08		19a27	19 36
Hagley d					18 07		18 17	18 24			18 37	18 58									19 12			
Blakedown d					18 10		18 20	18 27			18 40	19 01									19 15			
Kidderminster d					18 15		18a26	18 32			18a46	19a06									19 20			19a48
Hartlebury d					18 20			18 37																
University d				17 55		18 05												18 36						
Barnt Green d																								
Bromsgrove d						18 22											18 46	18a49						
Droitwich Spa d				18 19	18 29	18b40		18 46									18 56				19 32			
Worcester Shrub Hill 7 a				18 28		18 48		18 58									19 11							
d	18 20			18 32		18 54										19 11								
Worcester Foregate Street 7 a	18 22			18 34	18 38	18 56										19 17					19 41			
d	18 23			18 35		18 57																		
Malvern Link d	18 31			18 45		19 06																		
Great Malvern a	18 36			18 47		19 09																		
d				18 48																				
Colwall d				18 53																				
Ledbury a				19 01																				
d				19 06																				
Hereford 7 a				19 26																				

For general notes see front of timetable
For details of catering facilities see Directory of Train Operators

A From Warminster (Table 123)
B From Bournemouth (Table 51)
C From Nottingham to Cardiff Central (Table 51)
D 🛒 to Birmingham Snow Hill
b Arr. 1832

From 5 October a revised Chiltern Railways service will be in operation due to seasonal difficulties. Trains will arrive at their destination 3 minutes later than shown

Stratford -upon-Avon, Marylebone and Leamington Spa → Birmingham → Stourbridge, Worcester and Hereford

Network Diagram - See first page of Table 71

Station		GW 1 ◇	LM	LM A	LM	GW B	LM	LM	CH	LM	XC 1 ◇ C	CH	LM	GW 1 ◇	LM	CH ◇ D	XC 1 ◇	LM	CH	XC 1 ◇ C	LM	GW 1 ◇	LM	CH D	GW 1 ◇
Stratford-upon-Avon	d		18 26					18 50										19 27							
Wilmcote	d		18 31					18 55										19 32							
Wootton Wawen	d		18x36					19x00										19x37							
Henley-in-Arden	d		18 40					19 04										19 41							
Danzey	d		18x44															19x45							
Wood End	d		18x48															19x49							
The Lakes	d		18x50															19x51							
Earlswood (West Midlands)	d		18 53															19 54							
Wythall	d		18 55															19 56							
Whitlocks End	d		18 58															19 59							
Shirley	d		19 02					19 16					19 30					20 02							
Yardley Wood	d		19 05					19 19					19 33					20 05							
Hall Green	d		19 08					19 22					19 36					20 08							
Spring Road	d		19 10					19 24					19 38					20 10							
London Marylebone 10 ⊖	d								17 30			17 41				18 00			18 30					19 00	
Banbury	d								18 39		18 54	18 58				19 03	19 25		19 36	19 54				20 03	
Leamington Spa 8	a								18 58		19 10	19 15				19 22	19 41		19 54	20 10				20 23	
	d								18 58		19 12	19 16				19 22	19 43		19 54	20 12				20 23	
Warwick	d								19 03			19 20							19 59						
Warwick Parkway	d								19 06							19 28			20 02					20 29	
Hatton	d								19 11			19a27							20 07						
Lapworth	d								19 17										20 13						
Dorridge	d						18 58		19 21						19 31	19 39			20 17				20 28	20 40	
Widney Manor	d						19 02								19 35								20 32		
Solihull	d						19 06		19 27						19 38	19 44			20 23				20 35	20 45	
Olton	d						19 09								19 41								20 39		
Acocks Green	d						19 12								19 44								20 41		
Tyseley	d						19 16						19 41		19 47								20 44		
Small Heath	d						19 19						19 43		19 49								20 47		
Bordesley	d																								
Birmingham Moor Street	d		19 17				19 23	19 32	19 38				19 48		19 53	19 57		20 17	20 34				20 51	20 57	
Birmingham Snow Hill	a		19 19				19 25	19 35	19 47				19 50		19 56	20 01		20 20	20 44				20 54	21 03	
	d						19 27	19 36							19 57	20 10		20 21					20 55	21 05	
Jewellery Quarter	d						19 29	19 38							19 59			20 24					20 57		
The Hawthorns	d						19 34	19 43							20 04	20 16		20 28					21 02	21 11	
Coventry	a										19 22									20 22					
Birmingham International ✈	a										19 37									20 37					
Birmingham New Street 12	a										19 50						20 17			20 49					
	d				19 19					19 49											20 59				
Smethwick Galton Bdg H.L. 7	d						19 36	19 45							20 06	20 19		20 31					21 05	21 14	
Langley Green	d						19 39								20 09			20 34					21 08		
Rowley Regis	d						19 43	19 50							20 13	20 24		20 37					21 11	21 20	
Old Hill	d						19 46								20 16			20 40					21 14		
Cradley Heath	d						19 49	19 55							20 19	20 29		20 43					21 17	21 25	
Lye	d						19 52								20 22			20 46					21 20		
Stourbridge Junction 2	d						19 56	20a01							20 26	20 36		20a51					21 24	21 33	
Hagley	d						19 59								20 29								21 28		
Blakedown	d						20 02								20 32								21 31		
Kidderminster	d						20 07								20 37	20a50							21 36	21a49	
Hartlebury	d																								
University	d				19 25					19 55											21 06				
Barnt Green	d																								
Bromsgrove	d				19 40					20 09											21 23				
Droitwich Spa	d				19 50		20 19			20 25					20 50						21 33		21 47		
Worcester Shrub Hill 7	a				20 01		20 26			20 34					21 00								21 58		
	d	19 45		19 54	20 12	20 20								20 41								21 49	22 02		22 43
Worcester Foregate Street 7	a	19 48		19 56	20 14	20 22								20 45							21 41	21 52	22 04		22 47
	d	19 49			20 15	20 25								20 45							21 42	21 53			22 47
Malvern Link	d	19 58			20 24	20 34								20 54							21 52	22 05			22 56
Great Malvern	a	20 02			20 26	20 38								20 58							21 54	22 09			23 03
	d	20 02			20 27									20 58							21 56	22 19			
Colwall	d	20 08			20 32									21 04							22 02	22 27			
Ledbury	a	20 16			20 39									21 12							22 10	22 35			
	d	20 17			20 40									21 14							22 12	22 37			
Hereford 7	a	20 37			21 00									21 36							22 32	22 57			

For general notes see front of timetable
For details of catering facilities see Directory of Train Operators

A From Gloucester (Table 57)
B From Warminster (Table 123)
C From Bournemouth (Table 51)
D to Birmingham Snow Hill

From 5 October a revised Chiltern Railways service will be in operation due to seasonal difficulties. Trains will arrive at their destination 3 minutes later than shown

Stratford -upon-Avon, Marylebone and Leamington Spa → Birmingham → Stourbridge, Worcester and Hereford

Network Diagram - See first page of Table 7l

		XC	LM	CH	CH	XC	LM	LM	LM	CH	XC	LM	CH	XC	LM	LM	LM	CH	LM	CH	XC	CH	CH FO	CH FO
		1 ◇			◇	1 ◇ A	B	C			1 ◇		◇	1 ◇ A	B	C		◇		◇	1 ◇	◇		◇
Stratford-upon-Avon	d		20 27																					
Wilmcote	d		20 32																					
Wootton Wawen	d		20x37																					
Henley-in-Arden	d		20 41																					
Danzey	d		20x45																					
Wood End	d		20x49																					
The Lakes	d		20x51																					
Earlswood (West Midlands)	d		20 54																					
Wythall	d		20 56																					
Whitlocks End	d		20 59																					
Shirley	d		21 02									21 56							22 54					
Yardley Wood	d		21 05									21 59							22 57					
Hall Green	d		21 08									22 02							23 00					
Spring Road	d		21 10									22 04							23 02					
London Marylebone 10 ⊖	d			19 30	19 33					20 00			20 30					21 00		21 33		22 20	23 10	23 54
Banbury	d	20 25		20 38	20 49	20 54				21 06	21 41		21 47	21 54				22 08		22 42	22 53	23 30	00 33	01 18
Leamington Spa 8	a	20 41		20 55	21 06	21 10				21 25	21 59		22 04	22 10				22 28		23 00	23 10	23 48	00 51	01 39
	d	20 43		20 56	21 07	21 12				21 25	22 00		22 05	22 12				22 30		23 00	23 12	23 48	00 52	
Warwick	d			21 00	21 12								22 10							23 05		23 53	00 56	
Warwick Parkway	d			21 04						21 31			22 14					22 35		23 07		23 56	01a06	
Hatton	d			21 09	21a19								22 19											
Lapworth	d			21 14									22 24											
Dorridge	d			21 19					21 31	21 42			22 29				22 33	22 46		23 18		00 07		
Widney Manor	d								21 35				22 32				22 37							
Solihull	d			21 25					21 38	21 47			22 36				22 40	22 51		23 24		00 13		
Olton	d								21 42				22 40				22 43							
Acocks Green	d								21 44				22 43				22 46							
Tyseley	d								21 47			22 07					22 50		23 05					
Small Heath	d								21 50			22 09					22 52		23 07					
Bordesley	d																							
Birmingham Moor Street	d		21 17	21 37					21 54	21 59		22 13	22 50				22 56	23 00	23 12	23 34		00 23		
Birmingham Snow Hill ⛴	a		21 20	21 47					21 56	22 04		22 16	22 58				22 59	23 05	23 15	23 45		00 32		
	d		21 21						21 57	22 10		22 17					23 00	23 15						
Jewellery Quarter ⛴	d		21 23						22 00			22 19					23 03	23 17						
The Hawthorns ⛴	d		21 28						22 04	22 16		22 24					23 07	23 22						
Coventry	a					21 22								22 22										
Birmingham International ✈	a					21 37								22 33										
Birmingham New Street 12	a	21 22				21 49					22 35			22 50							23 55			
	d						22 00	21 42							23 00	23 00								
Smethwick Galton Bdg H.L. 7	d		21 30						22 07	22 19		22 27					23 10	23 25						
Langley Green	d		21 33						22 10			22 30					23 13	23 28						
Rowley Regis	d		21 36						22 13	22 24		22 33					23 17	23 31						
Old Hill	d		21 39						22 16			22 36					23 20	23 34						
Cradley Heath	d		21 42						22 19	22 29		22 40					23 23	23 38						
Lye	d		21 45						22 22			22 43					23 26	23 41						
Stourbridge Junction 2	d		21a50						22 26	22 36		22a47					23 28	23a50						
Hagley	d								22 30								23 32							
Blakedown	d								22 33								23 35							
Kidderminster	d								22 38	22a50							23 40							
Hartlebury	d																							
University	d						22 06								23 06									
Barnt Green	d																							
Bromsgrove	d						22 23								23 20									
Droitwich Spa	d						22 34	22 16	22 49						23 30	23 30	23 52							
Worcester Shrub Hill 7	a						22 48	22 25	22 57						23 39	23 39	00 01							
	d								23 05															
Worcester Foregate Street 7	a								23 07															
	d								23 08															
Malvern Link	d								23 16															
Great Malvern	a								23 19															
	d																							
Colwall	d																							
Ledbury	a																							
	d																							
Hereford 7	a																							

For general notes see front of timetable
For details of catering facilities see Directory of Train Operators

A From Bournemouth (Table 51)
B Until 4 September
C From 7 September

From 5 October a revised Chiltern Railways service will be in operation due to seasonal difficulties. Trains will arrive at their destination 3 minutes later than shown

Table 71

Saturdays

Stratford -upon-Avon, Marylebone and Leamington Spa → Birmingham → Stourbridge, Worcester and Hereford

Network Diagram - See first page of Table 71

		CH	CH	CH	XC	LM	LM	LM	GW	LM	LM	LM	LM	XC	GW	LM	LM	CH	XC	LM	LM	LM	GW	XC	LM
		◇		◇	1 ◇				1 ◇					1 ◇	1 ◇				1 ◇				1 ◇	1 ◇	
					A									B					C		D			B	
Stratford-upon-Avon	d																07 00								07 45
Wilmcote	d																07 05								07 50
Wootton Wawen	d																07x10								07x55
Henley-in-Arden	d																07 14								07 59
Danzey	d																07x19								08x04
Wood End	d																07x22								08x08
The Lakes	d																07x24								08x10
Earlswood (West Midlands)	d																07 27								08 13
Wythall	d																07 29								08 15
Whitlocks End	d																07 32								08 18
Shirley	d											07 05					07 35								08 21
Yardley Wood	d											07 08					07 38								08 24
Hall Green	d											07 11					07 41								08 27
Spring Road	d											07 13					07 43								08 29
London Marylebone 10 ⊖	d	22p20	23p10	23p54																					
Banbury	d	23p30	00 33	01 18										06 53				07 02	07 31					07 53	
Leamington Spa 8	a	23p48	00 51	01 39										07 10				07 21	07 48					08 10	
	d	23p48	00 52								06 28			07 11				07 21	07 49					08 11	
Warwick	d	23p53	00 56								06 32							07 25							
Warwick Parkway	d	23p56	01a06															07 29							
Hatton	d										06 39														
Lapworth	d										06 45														
Dorridge	d	00 07									06 50					07 27		07 40		08 05					
Widney Manor	d										06 53					07 31				08 08					
Solihull	d	00 13									06 56					07 34		07 46		08 12					
Olton	d										07 00					07 38				08 15					
Acocks Green	d										07 02					07 40				08 18					
Tyseley	d										07 05	07 17				07 43	07 46			08 21					08 32
Small Heath	d										07 08	07 20				07 46	07 49								08 34
Bordesley	d																								
Birmingham Moor Street	d	00 23						06 31		07 01	07 12	07 24				07 50	07 55	07 59		08 26					08 38
Birmingham Snow Hill	a	00 32						06 33		07 03	07 15	07 26				07 52	07 57	08 08		08 29					08 42
	d							06 35		07 05		07 30				07 53	08 03			08 30					08 43
Jewellery Quarter	d							06 37		07 07		07 32				07 55	08 05			08 32					08 45
The Hawthorns	d							06 42		07 12		07 37				08 00	08 10			08 37					08 50
Coventry	a													07 24										08 22	
Birmingham International	a													07 37										08 37	
Birmingham New Street 12	a													07 49					08 17					08 49	
	d				05 42		06 49						07 49									08 49			
Smethwick Galton Bdg H.L. 7	d							06 45		07 15		07 39				08 02	08 12			08 39					08 52
Langley Green	d							06 48		07 18		07 42					08 15			08 42					
Rowley Regis	d							06 51		07 21		07 46				08 07	08 19			08 46					08 57
Old Hill	d							06 54		07 24		07 49					08 22			08 49					
Cradley Heath	d							06 57		07 27		07 52				08 12	08 25			08 52					09 02
Lye	d							07 00		07 30		07 55					08 28			08 55					
Stourbridge Junction 2	d							07 04		07 35		07a59				08 17	08a32			08a59					09a08
Hagley	d							07 08		07 38						08 21									
Blakedown	d							07 11		07 41						08 24									
Kidderminster	d							07 16		07 46						08 29									
Hartlebury	d							07 21																	
University	d						06 57						07 57									08 57			
Barnt Green	d																								
Bromsgrove	d				06a03		07 11						08 11									09 11			
Droitwich Spa	d						07 21	07 29		07 58			08 21			08 40						09 21			
Worcester Shrub Hill 7	a							07 39		08 06															
	d					06 30			07 44	08 10					08 45						09 05		09 45		
Worcester Foregate Street 7	a					06 32	07 29		07 46	08 12			08 29		08 48	08 49					09 07	09 29	09 48		
	d					06 33	07 30		07 48	08 13			08 30		08 49							09 30	09 49		
Malvern Link	d					06 42	07 39		07 57	08 22			08 40		09 00							09 40	09 58		
Great Malvern	a					06 44	07 41		08 04	08 26			08 42		09 07							09 42	10 05		
	d					06 45	07 42						08 43									09 43			
Colwall	d					06 50	07 47						08 48									09 48			
Ledbury	a					06 57	07 55						08 56									09 56			
	d					06 58	08 00						09 00									10 00			
Hereford 7	a					07 14	08 21						09 20									10 21			

For general notes see front of timetable
For details of catering facilities see Directory of Train Operators

A To Cardiff Central (Table 132)
B From Southampton Central (Table 51)
C From Guildford (Table 51)
D From Gloucester (Table 57)

From 10 October a revised Chiltern Railways service will be in operation due to seasonal difficulties. Trains will arrive at their destination 3 minutes later than shown

Table 71

Saturdays

Stratford -upon-Avon, Marylebone and Leamington Spa → Birmingham → Stourbridge, Worcester and Hereford

Network Diagram - See first page of Table 71

		LM	LM	CH	LM	XC 1 ◇ (cutlery)	CH	LM	LM	GW A	LM	XC 1 ◇ B (cutlery)	LM	LM	CH ◇	XC 1 ◇ (cutlery)	LM	GW 1 ◇ (trolley)	LM	LM	LM	CH	LM	XC 1 ◇ B (cutlery)	LM
Stratford-upon-Avon	d							08 27					08 59							09 27					
Wilmcote	d							08 32												09 32					
Wootton Wawen	d							08x37												09x37					
Henley-in-Arden	d							08 41					09 09							09 41					
Danzey	d							08x45												09x45					
Wood End	d							08x49												09x49					
The Lakes	d							08x51												09x51					
Earlswood (West Midlands)	d							08 54												09 54					
Wythall	d							08 56					09 20							09 56					
Whitlocks End	d							08 59												09 59					
Shirley	d		08 38					09 02					09 24				09 42			10 02					
Yardley Wood	d		08 41					09 05					09 27				09 45			10 05					
Hall Green	d		08 44					09 08					09 30				09 48			10 08					
Spring Road	d		08 46					09 10					09 32				09 50			10 10					
London Marylebone 10	⊖ d			06 27											07 24							08 18			
Banbury	d			08 01		08 35	08 40					08 53			08 58	09 25						09 39		09 53	
Leamington Spa 8	a			08 19		08 52	08 58					09 10			09 16	09 42						09 57		10 10	
	d	07 56		08 20		08 53	09 00					09 11			09 17	09 43						09 58		10 11	
Warwick	d	08 00		08 24			09 04								09 21							10 02			
Warwick Parkway	d	08 04		08 28			09 08								09 25							10 06			
Hatton	d	08 09		08 33			09a12																		
Lapworth	d	08 15		08 38																					
Dorridge	d	08 21		08 43	08 46				09 09					09 28	09 36				09 46		10 09	10 17			10 28
Widney Manor	d	08 25		08 47	08 50				09 13					09 32					09 50		10 13				10 32
Solihull	d	08 28		08 51	08 53				09 16					09 35	09 42				09 53		10 16	10 23			10 35
Olton	d	08 31			08 57				09 20					09 39					09 57		10 20				10 39
Acocks Green	d	08 34			08 59				09 22					09 41					09 59		10 22				10 41
Tyseley	d	08 37	08 49		09 02								09 35						10 02						
Small Heath	d	08 40	08 51		09 05								09 37						10 05						
Bordesley	d																								
Birmingham Moor Street	d	08 44	08 55	09 01	09 09			09 17	09 29				09 41	09 48	09 52		10 01		10 09	10 17	10 29	10 34			10 49
Birmingham Snow Hill	⛴ a	08 48	08 58	09 11	09 11			09 20	09 31				09 44	09 50	10 02		10 03		10 11	10 20	10 31	10 41			10 51
	d	08 53	09 03		09 13			09 23	09 33				09 45	09 53			10 03		10 13	10 23	10 33				10 53
Jewellery Quarter	⛴ d	08 55	09 05		09 15			09 25	09 35				09 47	09 55			10 05		10 15	10 25	10 35				10 55
The Hawthorns	⛴ d	09 00	09 10		09 20			09 30	09 40				09 52	10 00			10 10		10 20	10 30	10 40				11 00
Coventry	a											09 22												10 22	
Birmingham International	✈ a											09 37												10 37	
Birmingham New Street 12	a					09 17						09 49				10 17								10 49	
	d										09 49												10 49		
Smethwick Galton Bdg H.L. 7	d	09 02	09 12		09 22			09 32	09 42				09 54	10 02			10 12		10 22	10 32	10 42				11 02
Langley Green	d		09 15						09 45								10 15				10 45				
Rowley Regis	d	09 07	09 19		09 27			09 37	09 49				09 59	10 07			10 19		10 27	10 37	10 49				11 07
Old Hill	d		09 22						09 52								10 22				10 52				
Cradley Heath	d	09 12	09 25		09 32			09 42	09 55				10 04	10 12			10 25		10 32	10 42	10 55				11 12
Lye	d		09 28						09 58								10 28				10 58				
Stourbridge Junction 2	d	09 17	09 32		09 37			09a48	10 02				10 09	10a18			10 32		10 37	10a48	11 02				11a18
Hagley	d	09 21			09 41								10 13						10 41						
Blakedown	d	09 24			09 44								10 16						10 44						
Kidderminster	d	09 29	09a42		09 49				10a12				10 21				10a42		10 49		11a12				
Hartlebury	d																								
University	d										09 57												10 57		
Barnt Green	d																								
Bromsgrove	d										10 11												11 11		
Droitwich Spa	d	09 40			10 01						10 21		10 32						11 01				11 21		
Worcester Shrub Hill 7	a	09 49											10 40												
	d									10 15								10 45							
Worcester Foregate Street 7	a				10 09					10 17	10 29							10 48	11 10				11 29		
	d									10 18	10 30							10 49	11 11				11 30		
Malvern Link	d									10 27	10 40							10 58	11 19				11 40		
Great Malvern	a									10 30	10 42							11 01	11 22				11 42		
	d										10 43							11 08					11 43		
Colwall	d										10 48							11 14					11 48		
Ledbury	a										10 56							11 21					11 56		
	d										11 00							11 23					12 00		
Hereford 7	a										11 20							11 40					12 21		

For general notes see front of timetable
For details of catering facilities see
Directory of Train Operators

A From Warminster (Table 123)
B From Bournemouth (Table 51)

From 10 October a revised Chiltern Railways service will be in operation due to seasonal difficulties. Trains will arrive at their destination 3 minutes later than shown

Table 71

Saturdays

Stratford -upon-Avon, Marylebone and Leamington Spa → Birmingham → Stourbridge, Worcester and Hereford

Network Diagram - See first page of Table 71

		CH	CH	XC	LM	LM	LM	LM	LM	LM	CH	GW	LM	XC	LM	LM	CH	XC	LM	GW	LM	LM	LM	CH	LM
				1 ◇			A					B		1 ◇ C			◇	1 ◇		1 ◇				◇	
Stratford-upon-Avon	d				09 59				10 27						10 59							11 27			
Wilmcote	d								10 32													11 32			
Wootton Wawen	d								10x37													11x37			
Henley-in-Arden	d				10 09				10 41						11 09							11 41			
Danzey	d								10x45													11x45			
Wood End	d								10x49													11x49			
The Lakes	d								10x51													11x51			
Earlswood (West Midlands)	d								10 54													11 54			
Wythall	d				10 20				10 56						11 20							11 56			
Whitlocks End	d								10 59													11 59			
Shirley	d				10 24	10 42			11 02						11 24				11 42			12 02			
Yardley Wood	d				10 27	10 45			11 05						11 27				11 45			12 05			
Hall Green	d				10 30	10 48			11 08						11 30				11 48			12 08			
Spring Road	d				10 32	10 50			11 10						11 32				11 50			12 10			
London Marylebone 10 ⊖	d	08 45	08 54								09 18						09 45							10 18	
Banbury	d	09 58	10 19	10 25							10 39			10 53			10 58	11 25						11 35	
Leamington Spa 8	a	10 17	10 37	10 42							10 57			11 10			11 16	11 42						11 54	
	d	10 17	10 38	10 43							10 58			11 11			11 17	11 43						11 54	
Warwick	d	10 21	10 42								11 02						11 21							11 59	
Warwick Parkway	d	10 25									11 06						11 25							12 02	
Hatton	d	10 30	10a49																					12 07	
Lapworth	d	10 35																						12 13	
Dorridge	d	10 40						10 46		11 09	11 17					11 28	11 36				11 46		12 09	12 17	
Widney Manor	d							10 50		11 13						11 32					11 50		12 13		
Solihull	d	10 45						10 53		11 16	11 23					11 35	11 42				11 53		12 16	12 23	
Olton	d							10 57		11 20						11 39					11 57		12 20		
Acocks Green	d							10 59		11 22						11 41					11 59		12 22		
Tyseley	d				10 35			11 02							11 35						12 02				
Small Heath	d				10 37			11 05							11 37						12 05				
Bordesley	d																								
Birmingham Moor Street	d	10 55			10 41	10 58		11 09	11 17	11 29	11 34				11 41	11 48	11 52		11 59		12 09	12 17	12 29	12 35	
Birmingham Snow Hill	a	11 04			10 44	11 01		11 11	11 20	11 31	11 41				11 44	11 50	12 01		12 02		12 11	12 20	12 31	12 42	
	d				10 45	11 03		11 13	11 23	11 33					11 45	11 53			12 03		12 13	12 23	12 33		
Jewellery Quarter	d				10 47	11 05		11 15	11 25	11 35					11 47	11 55			12 05		12 15	12 25	12 35		
The Hawthorns	d				10 52	11 10		11 20	11 30	11 40					11 52	12 00			12 10		12 20	12 30	12 40		
Coventry	a													11 22											
Birmingham International ✈	a													11 37											
Birmingham New Street 12	a			11 17										11 49				12 17							
	d												11 49												12 49
Smethwick Galton Bdg H.L. 7	d				10 54	11 12		11 22	11 32	11 42					11 54	12 02			12 12		12 22	12 32	12 42		
Langley Green	d					11 15				11 45									12 15				12 45		
Rowley Regis	d				10 59	11 19		11 27	11 37	11 49					11 59	12 07			12 19		12 27	12 37	12 49		
Old Hill	d					11 22				11 52									12 22				12 52		
Cradley Heath	d				11 04	11 25		11 32	11 42	11 55					12 04	12 12			12 25		12 32	12 42	12 55		
Lye	d					11 28				11 58									12 28				12 58		
Stourbridge Junction 2	d				11 09	11 32		11 38	11a48	12 02					12 09	12a18			12 32		12 37	12a48	13 02		
Hagley	d				11 13			11 42							12 13						12 41				
Blakedown	d				11 16			11 45							12 16						12 44				
Kidderminster	d				11 21	11a43		11 50		12a12					12 21				12a42		12 49		13a12		
Hartlebury	d																								
University	d												11 57												12 57
Barnt Green	d																								
Bromsgrove	d												12 11												13 11
Droitwich Spa	d				11 32			12 02					12 21		12 32						13 01				13 21
Worcester Shrub Hill 7	a				11 40																				
	d						11 43					12 16								12 45					
Worcester Foregate Street 7	a						11 45	12 11				12 17	12 29		12 41					12 48	13 09				13 29
	d												12 30							12 49	13 10				13 30
Malvern Link	d												12 40							12 58	13 19				13 40
Great Malvern	a												12 42							13 01	13 22				13 42
	d												12 43							13 07					13 43
Colwall	d												12 49							13 14					13 48
Ledbury	a												12 56							13 21					13 56
	d												13 00							13 23					14 00
Hereford 7	a												13 20							13 40					14 21

For general notes see front of timetable
For details of catering facilities see
Directory of Train Operators

A From Gloucester (Table 57)
B From Southampton Central (Table 123)
C From Bournemouth (Table 51)

From 10 October a revised Chiltern Railways service will be in operation due to seasonal difficulties. Trains will arrive at their destination 3 minutes later than shown

Table 71

Saturdays

Stratford -upon-Avon, Marylebone and Leamington Spa → Birmingham → Stourbridge, Worcester and Hereford

Network Diagram - See first page of Table 71

Station		XC	LM	CH	CH	XC	LM	LM	GW	LM	LM	LM	CH	GW	LM	XC	LM	LM	CH	XC	LM	LM	LM	LM	CH
		1 ◇ A		◇	◇	1 ◇			1 ◇					◇ B		1 ◇ A			◇	1 ◇					
Stratford-upon-Avon	d						11 59				12 27						12 59						13 27		
Wilmcote	d										12 32												13 32		
Wootton Wawen	d										12x37												13x37		
Henley-in-Arden	d						12 09				12 41						13 09						13 41		
Danzey	d										12x45												13x45		
Wood End	d										12x49												13x49		
The Lakes	d										12x51												13x51		
Earlswood (West Midlands)	d										12 54												13 54		
Wythall	d						12 20				12 56						13 20						13 56		
Whitlocks End	d										12 59												13 59		
Shirley	d						12 24	12 42			13 02						13 24				13 42		14 02		
Yardley Wood	d						12 27	12 45			13 05						13 27				13 45		14 05		
Hall Green	d						12 30	12 48			13 08						13 30				13 48		14 08		
Spring Road	d						12 32	12 50			13 10						13 32				13 50		14 10		
London Marylebone 10 ⊖	d			10 50	10 53								11 20						11 50						12 20
Banbury	d	11 53		11 58	12 19	12 25							12 34			12 53			12 58	13 25					13 35
Leamington Spa 8	a	12 10		12 16	12 36	12 42							12 52			13 10			13 17	13 42					13 54
	d	12 11		12 17	12 38	12 43							12 53			13 11			13 17	13 43					13 54
Warwick	d			12 21	12 42								12 59						13 21						13 59
Warwick Parkway	d			12 26									13 02						13 25						14 02
Hatton	d				12a48																				14 07
Lapworth	d																								14 13
Dorridge	d		12 28	12 36						12 46		13 09	13 13					13 28	13 36			13 46		14 09	14 17
Widney Manor	d		12 32							12 50		13 13						13 32				13 50		14 13	
Solihull	d		12 35	12 42						12 53		13 16	13 20					13 35	13 42			13 53		14 16	14 23
Olton	d		12 39							12 57		13 20						13 39				13 57		14 20	
Acocks Green	d		12 41							12 59		13 22						13 41				13 59		14 22	
Tyseley	d						12 35			13 02							13 35					14 02			
Small Heath	d						12 37			13 05							13 37					14 05			
Bordesley	d																13 40								
Birmingham Moor Street	d		12 48	12 53			12 41	12 57		13 09	13 17	13 29	13 32				13 43	13 48	13 53		13 58	14 09	14 17	14 29	14 34
Birmingham Snow Hill 🚊	a		12 50	13 01			12 44	13 01		13 11	13 20	13 31	13 41				13 45	13 50	14 01		14 01	14 11	14 21	14 31	14 42
	d		12 53				12 45	13 03		13 13	13 23	13 33					13 45	13 53			14 03	14 13	14 23	14 33	
Jewellery Quarter 🚊	d		12 55				12 47	13 05		13 15	13 25	13 35					13 47	13 55			14 05	14 15	14 25	14 35	
The Hawthorns 🚊	d		13 00				12 52	13 10		13 20	13 30	13 40					13 52	14 00			14 10	14 20	14 30	14 40	
Coventry	a	12 22														13 22									
Birmingham International ✈	a	12 37														13 37									
Birmingham New Street 12	a	12 49				13 17										13 49				14 17					
	d														13 49										
Smethwick Galton Bdg H.L. 7	d		13 02				12 54	13 12		13 22	13 32	13 42					13 54	14 02			14 12	14 22	14 32	14 42	
Langley Green	d							13 15				13 45									14 15			14 45	
Rowley Regis	d		13 07				12 59	13 19		13 27	13 37	13 49					13 59	14 07			14 19	14 27	14 37	14 49	
Old Hill	d							13 22				13 52									14 22			14 52	
Cradley Heath	d		13 12				13 04	13 25		13 32	13 42	13 55					14 04	14 12			14 25	14 32	14 42	14 55	
Lye	d							13 28				13 58									14 28			14 58	
Stourbridge Junction 2	d		13a18				13 09	13 32		13 37	13a48	14 02					14 09	14a18			14 32	14 37	14a48	15 02	
Hagley	d						13 13			13 41							14 13					14 41			
Blakedown	d						13 16			13 44							14 16					14 44			
Kidderminster	d						13 21	13a42		13 49		14a12					14 21				14a42	14 49		15a12	
Hartlebury	d																								
University	d														13 57										
Barnt Green	d																								
Bromsgrove	d														14 11										
Droitwich Spa	d						13 32			14 01					14 21		14 32					15 01			
Worcester Shrub Hill 7	a						13 40										14 41								
	d								13 49					14 15			14 46								
Worcester Foregate Street 7	a								13 52	14 09				14 18	14 29		14 48					15 09			
	d								13 53					14 18	14 30		14 49								
Malvern Link	d								14 02					14 27	14 40		14 57								
Great Malvern	a								14 09					14 30	14 42		15 00								
	d														14 43										
Colwall	d														14 48										
Ledbury	a														14 56										
	d														14 58										
Hereford 7	a														15 18										

For general notes see front of timetable
For details of catering facilities see
Directory of Train Operators

A From Bournemouth (Table 51)
B From Brighton (Table 123)

From 10 October a revised Chiltern Railways service will be in operation due to seasonal difficulties. Trains will arrive at their destination 3 minutes later than shown

Table 71

Saturdays

Stratford -upon-Avon, Marylebone and Leamington Spa → Birmingham → Stourbridge, Worcester and Hereford

Network Diagram - See first page of Table 71

Station		LM	XC	LM	CH	CH	XC	LM	LM	GW	LM	LM	LM	CH	GW	LM	XC	LM	LM	CH	XC	LM	GW	LM	LM
			1 ◇		◇		1 ◇			1 ◇				◇			1 ◇			◇	1 ◇		1 ◇		
			A												B		A								
Stratford-upon-Avon	d							13 59				14 27						14 59							15 27
Wilmcote	d											14 32													15 32
Wootton Wawen	d											14x37													15x37
Henley-in-Arden	d							14 09				14 41						15 09							15 41
Danzey	d											14x45													15x45
Wood End	d											14x49													15x49
The Lakes	d											14x51													15x51
Earlswood (West Midlands)	d											14 54													15 54
Wythall	d							14 20				14 56						15 20							15 56
Whitlocks End	d											14 59													15 59
Shirley	d							14 23	14 42			15 02						15 24				15 42			16 02
Yardley Wood	d							14 26	14 45			15 05						15 27				15 45			16 05
Hall Green	d							14 29	14 48			15 08						15 30				15 48			16 08
Spring Road	d							14 31	14 50			15 10						15 32				15 50			16 10
London Marylebone 10 ⊖	d				12 50	12 53								13 20						13 50					
Banbury	d		13 53		13 58	14 19	14 25							14 35			14 53			14 58	15 25				
Leamington Spa 8	a		14 10		14 17	14 37	14 42							14 54			15 10			15 17	15 42				
	d		14 11		14 17	14 38	14 43							14 54			15 11			15 17	15 43				
Warwick	d				14 21	14 42								14 59						15 21					
Warwick Parkway	d				14 25									15 02						15 25					
Hatton	d					14a48																			
Lapworth	d																								
Dorridge	d			14 28	14 36						14 46		15 09	15 13					15 28	15 36				15 46	
Widney Manor	d			14 32							14 50		15 13						15 32					15 50	
Solihull	d			14 35	14 42						14 53		15 16	15 20					15 35	15 42				15 53	
Olton	d			14 39							14 57		15 20						15 39					15 57	
Acocks Green	d			14 41							14 59		15 22						15 41					15 59	
Tyseley	d							14 34			15 02							15 35						16 02	
Small Heath	d							14 37			15 05							15 37						16 05	
Bordesley	d																								
Birmingham Moor Street	d			14 48	14 53			14 41	14 57		15 09	15 17	15 29	15 33				15 41	15 48	15 53		15 57		16 09	16 17
Birmingham Snow Hill	a			14 50	15 01			14 43	15 01		15 11	15 21	15 31	15 41				15 44	15 51	16 01		16 01		16 12	16 21
	d			14 53				14 44	15 03		15 13	15 23	15 33					15 45	15 53			16 03		16 13	16 23
Jewellery Quarter	d			14 55				14 46	15 05		15 15	15 25	15 35					15 47	15 55			16 05		16 15	16 25
The Hawthorns	d			15 00				14 51	15 10		15 20	15 30	15 40					15 52	16 00			16 10		16 20	16 30
Coventry	a		14 22														15 22								
Birmingham International ✈	a		14 37														15 37								
Birmingham New Street 12	a		14 49				15 17										15 49				16 17				
	d	14 49														15 49									
Smethwick Galton Bdg H.L. 7	d			15 02				14 53	15 12		15 22	15 32	15 42					15 54	16 02			16 12		16 22	16 32
Langley Green	d								15 15				15 45									16 15			
Rowley Regis	d			15 07				14 58	15 19		15 27	15 37	15 49					15 59	16 07			16 19		16 27	16 37
Old Hill	d								15 22				15 52									16 22			
Cradley Heath	d			15 12				15 03	15 25		15 32	15 42	15 55					16 04	16 12			16 25		16 32	16 42
Lye	d								15 28				15 58									16 28			
Stourbridge Junction 2	d			15a18				15 09	15 32		15 37	15a48	16 02					16 09	16a18			16 32		16 37	16a48
Hagley	d							15 13			15 41							16 13						16 41	
Blakedown	d							15 16			15 44							16 16						16 44	
Kidderminster	d							15 21	15a42		15 49		16a12					16 21				16a42		16 49	
Hartlebury	d																								
University	d	14 57														15 57									
Barnt Green	d																								
Bromsgrove	d	15 11														16 11									
Droitwich Spa	d	15 21						15 32			16 01					16 21		16 32						17 01	
Worcester Shrub Hill 7	a							15 40										16 40							
	d									15 50					16 15								16 46		
Worcester Foregate Street 7	a	15 29								15 52	16 09				16 17	16 29							16 48	17 09	
	d	15 30								15 54					16 18	16 30							16 50	17 10	
Malvern Link	d	15 40								16 03					16 26	16 40							16 59	17 19	
Great Malvern	a	15 42								16 09					16 29	16 42							17 06	17 22	
	d	15 43														16 43									
Colwall	d	15 48														16 48									
Ledbury	a	15 56														16 56									
	d	15 58														17 00									
Hereford 7	a	16 19														17 20									

For general notes see front of timetable
For details of catering facilities see Directory of Train Operators

A From Bournemouth (Table 51)
B From Southampton Central (Table 123)

From 10 October a revised Chiltern Railways service will be in operation due to seasonal difficulties. Trains will arrive at their destination 3 minutes later than shown

Stratford -upon-Avon, Marylebone and Leamington Spa → Birmingham → Stourbridge, Worcester and Hereford

Network Diagram - See first page of Table 71

		LM	CH	LM	XC	CH	XC	LM	LM	CH	LM	GW	LM	LM	XC	LM	LM	CH	GW	LM	XC	LM	LM	CH	XC
					1 ◇	◇	1 ◇					1 ◇			1 ◇						1 ◇				1 ◇
					A										B				C		A				
					⚲		⚲					☕			⚲						⚲				⚲
Stratford-upon-Avon	d							15 59								16 27						16 59			
Wilmcote	d															16 32									
Wootton Wawen	d															16x37									
Henley-in-Arden	d							16 09								16 41						17 09			
Danzey	d															16x45									
Wood End	d															16x49									
The Lakes	d															16x51									
Earlswood (West Midlands)	d															16 54									
Wythall	d							16 20								16 56						17 20			
Whitlocks End	d															16 59									
Shirley	d							16 24			16 42					17 02						17 24			
Yardley Wood	d							16 27			16 45					17 05						17 27			
Hall Green	d							16 30			16 48					17 08						17 30			
Spring Road	d							16 32			16 50					17 10						17 32			
London Marylebone 10 ⊖	d		14 20			14 53				14 50								15 20						15 50	
Banbury	d		15 35		15 53	16 19	16 25			15 58								16 34			16 53			16 58	17 25
Leamington Spa 8	a		15 54		16 10	16 37	16 42			16 16								16 52			17 10			17 16	17 42
	d		15 54		16 11	16 38	16 43			16 17								16 53			17 11			17 17	17 43
Warwick	d		15 59			16 42				16 21								16 59						17 21	
Warwick Parkway	d		16 02							16 25								17 02						17 25	
Hatton	d		16 07			16a48												17 07							
Lapworth	d		16 13															17 13							
Dorridge	d	16 09	16 17						16 27	16 36				16 46			17 09	17 17					17 28	17 36	
Widney Manor	d	16 13							16 31					16 50			17 13						17 32		
Solihull	d	16 16	16 23						16 34	16 42				16 53			17 16	17 23					17 35	17 42	
Olton	d	16 20							16 38					16 57			17 20						17 39		
Acocks Green	d	16 22							16 40					16 59			17 22						17 41		
Tyseley	d							16 35	16 43		16 53			17 02								17 35	17 44		
Small Heath	d							16 37						17 05								17 37			
Bordesley	d																								
Birmingham Moor Street	d	16 29	16 34					16 41	16 48	16 53	16 58			17 09		17 17	17 29	17 34				17 41	17 49	17 53	
Birmingham Snow Hill ⛴	a	16 32	16 41					16 44	16 51	17 02	17 01			17 12		17 21	17 31	17 41				17 44	17 52	18 02	
	d	16 33						16 45	16 53		17 03			17 13		17 23	17 33					17 45	17 53		
Jewellery Quarter ⛴	d	16 35						16 47	16 55		17 05			17 15		17 25	17 35					17 47	17 55		
The Hawthorns ⛴	d	16 40						16 52	17 00		17 10			17 20		17 30	17 40					17 52	18 00		
Coventry	a				16 22																17 22				
Birmingham International ✈	a				16 37																17 37				
Birmingham New Street 12	a				16 49		17 17														17 49				18 17
	d			16 49									17 19		17 30					17 49					
Smethwick Galton Bdg H.L. 7	d	16 42						16 54	17 02		17 12			17 22		17 32	17 42					17 54	18 02		
Langley Green	d	16 45									17 15						17 45						18 05		
Rowley Regis	d	16 49						16 59	17 07		17 19			17 27		17 37	17 49					17 59	18 09		
Old Hill	d	16 52									17 22						17 52						18 12		
Cradley Heath	d	16 55						17 04	17 12		17 25			17 32		17 42	17 55					18 04	18 15		
Lye	d	16 58									17 28						17 58						18 18		
Stourbridge Junction 2	d	17 02						17 11	17a18		17 32			17 37		17a48	18 02					18 11	18a22		
Hagley	d	17 06						17 14						17 41			18 06					18 14			
Blakedown	d	17 09						17 17						17 44			18 09					18 17			
Kidderminster	d	17a15						17 22			17a42			17 49			18a15					18 22			
Hartlebury	d							17 27						17 54								18 27			
University	d			16 57											17 36					17 57					
Barnt Green	d																								
Bromsgrove	d			17 11									17 42		17a49					18 11					
Droitwich Spa	d			17 21				17 35					17 52	18 03						18 19		18 35			
Worcester Shrub Hill 7	a												18 06	18 14						18 27					
	d											17 45							18 19	18 31					
Worcester Foregate Street 7	a			17 29				17 43				17 48							18 21	18 33		18 43			
	d			17 30								17 49							18 22	18 34					
Malvern Link	d			17 39								17 58							18 30	18 44					
Great Malvern	a			17 41								18 05							18 33	18 46					
	d			17 42																18 47					
Colwall	d			17 47																18 52					
Ledbury	a			17 55																18 59					
	d			18 00																19 00					
Hereford 7	a			18 21																19 20					

For general notes see front of timetable
For details of catering facilities see Directory of Train Operators

A From Bournemouth (Table 51)
B From Nottingham to Cardiff Central (Table 57)
C From Warminster (Table 123)

From 10 October a revised Chiltern Railways service will be in operation due to seasonal difficulties. Trains will arrive at their destination 3 minutes later than shown

Table 71

Saturdays

Stratford -upon-Avon, Marylebone and Leamington Spa → Birmingham → Stourbridge, Worcester and Hereford

Network Diagram - See first page of Table 71

		LM	LM	GW	LM	LM	CH	LM	XC	GW	CH	XC	LM	LM	CH	LM	LM	GW	LM	CH	XC	LM	GW	LM	CH
				1 ◇					1 ◇	1 ◇		1 ◇									1 ◇		1 ◇		
									A												A				
Stratford-upon-Avon	d				17 27								17 59				18 19					18 46			
Wilmcote	d				17 32												18 24					18 51			
Wootton Wawen	d				17x37												18x29					18x56			
Henley-in-Arden	d				17 41								18 09				18 33					19 00			
Danzey	d				17x45												18x37					19x04			
Wood End	d				17x49												18x41					19x08			
The Lakes	d				17x51												18x43					19x10			
Earlswood (West Midlands)	d				17 54												18 46					19 12			
Wythall	d				17 56								18 20				18 48					19 15			
Whitlocks End	d				17 59												18 51					19 17			
Shirley	d	17 42			18 02								18 23				18 54					19 21			
Yardley Wood	d	17 46			18 05								18 26				18 58					19 24			
Hall Green	d	17 49			18 08								18 29				19 01					19 27			
Spring Road	d	17 51			18 10								18 31				19 03					19 29			
London Marylebone 10 ⊖	d						16 20				16 53				16 50					17 20					17 50
Banbury	d						17 35		17 53		18 19	18 25			17 58					18 35	18 53				19 03
Leamington Spa 8	a						17 54		18 10		18 37	18 42			18 17					18 54	19 10				19 22
	d						17 54		18 11		18 38	18 43			18 17					18 54	19 11				19 23
Warwick	d						17 59				18 42				18 21					18 59					19 27
Warwick Parkway	d						18 02								18 25					19 02					19 30
Hatton	d						18 07				18a48									19 07					
Lapworth	d						18 13													19 13					
Dorridge	d		17 46			18 09	18 17							18 28	18 36				19 00	19 17				19 28	19 42
Widney Manor	d		17 50			18 13								18 32					19 06					19 32	
Solihull	d		17 53			18 16	18 23							18 35	18 42				19 09	19 23				19 35	19 48
Olton	d		17 57			18 20								18 39					19 12					19 39	
Acocks Green	d		17 59			18 22								18 41					19 15					19 41	
Tyseley	d		18 02										18 34	18 45			19 06		19 18			19 32		19 44	
Small Heath	d		18 04										18 36	18 47			19 08		19 20			19 34		19 47	
Bordesley	d																								
Birmingham Moor Street	d	18 01	18 08		18 17	18 28	18 34						18 40	18 51	18 55		19 12		19 24	19 34		19 38		19 51	19 59
Birmingham Snow Hill 🚊	a	18 04	18 11		18 20	18 31	18 41						18 43	18 54	19 04		19 15		19 27	19 41		19 41		19 53	20 06
	d		18 13		18 23	18 33								18 57					19 28					19 55	
Jewellery Quarter 🚊	d		18 15		18 25	18 35								18 59					19 30					19 57	
The Hawthorns 🚊	d		18 20		18 30	18 40								19 04					19 35					20 02	
Coventry	a								18 22												19 22				
Birmingham International ✈	a								18 37												19 37				
Birmingham New Street 12	a								18 49			19 17									19 49				
	d							18 49								19 19									
Smethwick Galton Bdg H.L. 7	d		18 22		18 32	18 42								19 06					19 37					20 04	
Langley Green	d		18 25			18 45								19 09					19 40					20 07	
Rowley Regis	d		18 29		18 37	18 49								19 13					19 44					20 11	
Old Hill	d		18 32			18 52								19 16					19 47					20 14	
Cradley Heath	d		18 35		18 42	18 55								19 19					19 50					20 17	
Lye	d		18 38			18 58								19 22					19 53					20 20	
Stourbridge Junction 2	d		18a42		18 48	19 02								19 26					19 57					20 24	
Hagley	d				18 51	19 06								19 29					20 00					20 27	
Blakedown	d				18 54	19 09								19 32					20 03					20 30	
Kidderminster	d				18 59	19a15								19 37					20 08					20 35	
Hartlebury	d				19 04																				
University	d							18 57								19 27									
Barnt Green	d																								
Bromsgrove	d							19 11								19 42									
Droitwich Spa	d				19 13			19 21						19 49		19 57			20 20					20 47	
Worcester Shrub Hill 7	a							19 28						19 57					20 29					20 54	
	d			18 51				19 33		19 43								20 20					20 48	20 58	
Worcester Foregate Street 7	a			18 54	19 21			19 35		19 45						20 05		20 22					20 50	21 00	
	d			18 55	19 22			19 36								20 06		20 25					20 52	21 01	
Malvern Link	d			19 04	19 31			19 45								20 16		20 34					21 01	21 09	
Great Malvern	a			19 07	19 34			19 50								20 18		20 38					21 04	21 12	
	d			19 08												20 25							21 05		
Colwall	d			19 14												20 30							21 11		
Ledbury	a			19 21												20 38							21 18		
	d			19 29												20 39							21 20		
Hereford 7	a			19 45												20 59							21 37		

For general notes see front of timetable
For details of catering facilities see
Directory of Train Operators

A From Bournemouth (Table 51)

From 10 October a revised Chiltern Railways service will be in operation due to seasonal difficulties. Trains will arrive at their destination 3 minutes later than shown

Table 71

Saturdays

Stratford -upon-Avon, Marylebone and Leamington Spa → Birmingham → Stourbridge, Worcester and Hereford

Network Diagram - See first page of Table 71

		XC 1◇ trolley	LM	CH	XC 1◇ A trolley	LM	LM	CH	CH	XC 1◇ trolley	GW 1◇ trolley	CH	XC 1◇ A trolley	LM	LM	LM	CH ◇	XC 1◇ trolley	XC 1◇ A trolley	LM	CH ◇	XC 1◇ trolley	LM	CH ◇
Stratford-upon-Avon	d		19 27											20 27										
Wilmcote	d		19 32											20 32										
Wootton Wawen	d		19x37											20x37										
Henley-in-Arden	d		19 41											20 41										
Danzey	d		19x45											20x45										
Wood End	d		19x49											20x49										
The Lakes	d		19x51											20x51										
Earlswood (West Midlands)	d		19 54											20 54										
Wythall	d		19 56											20 56										
Whitlocks End	d		19 59											20 59										
Shirley	d		20 02											21 02		21 56							23 00	
Yardley Wood	d		20 05											21 05		21 59							23 03	
Hall Green	d		20 08											21 08		22 02							23 06	
Spring Road	d		20 10											21 10		22 04							23 08	
London Marylebone 10 ⊖	d			18 20				18 50	18 53			19 20					20 00				20 50			22 00
Banbury	d	19 25		19 35	19 53			20 03	20 19	20 25		20 35	20 53				21 19	21 25	21 53		22 07	22 25		23 06
Leamington Spa 8	a	19 42		19 52	20 10			20 22	20 37	20 42		20 54	21 10				21 37	21 42	22 10		22 27	22 42		23 23
	d	19 43		19 53	20 11			20 23	20 38	20 43		20 54	21 11				21 38	21 43	22 11		22 27	22 43		23 24
Warwick	d			19 59				20 27	20 42			20 59					21 42				22 31			23 28
Warwick Parkway	d			20 02				20 30				21 02					21 46				22 35			23 34
Hatton	d			20 07					20a49			21 07												
Lapworth	d			20 13								21 13												
Dorridge	d			20 17			20 28	20 42				21 17			21 28		21 58			22 28	22 46			23 43
Widney Manor	d						20 32								21 32					22 32				23 46
Solihull	d			20 23			20 35	20 47				21 23			21 35		22 03			22 35	22 52			23 50
Olton	d						20 39								21 39					22 39				
Acocks Green	d						20 41								21 41					22 41				
Tyseley	d						20 44								21 44	22 07				22 44			23 11	
Small Heath	d						20 47								21 47	22 09				22 47			23 13	
Bordesley	d																							
Birmingham Moor Street	d		20 17	20 35			20 51	20 58				21 34		21 17	21 51	22 13	22 16			22 51	23 03		23 17	23 59
Birmingham Snow Hill 🚋	a		20 20	20 42			20 53	21 06				21 41		21 20	21 53	22 16	22 26			22 53	23 10		23 20	00 08
	d		20 21				20 55							21 21	21 55	22 18				22 56			23 22	
Jewellery Quarter 🚋	d		20 24				20 57							21 23	21 57	22 20				22 59			23 24	
The Hawthorns 🚋	d		20 28				21 02							21 28	22 02	22 25				23 03			23 29	
Coventry	a				20 22								21 22					21 55	22 22					
Birmingham International ✈	a				20 37								21 37					22 12	22 37					
Birmingham New Street 12	a	20 17			20 49					21 17			21 49					22 25	22 54			23 17		
	d					20 59																		
Smethwick Galton Bdg H.L. 7	d		20 31				21 05							21 30	22 04	22 27				23 06			23 23	
Langley Green	d		20 34				21 08							21 33	22 07	22 30				23 09			23 31	
Rowley Regis	d		20 37				21 11							21 36	22 11	22 34				23 12			23 38	
Old Hill	d		20 40				21 14							21 39	22 14	22 37				23 15			23 41	
Cradley Heath	d		20 43				21 17							21 42	22 17	22 40				23 18			23 44	
Lye	d		20 46				21 20							21 45	22 20	22 43				23 21			23 47	
Stourbridge Junction 2	d		20a50				21 24							21a50	22 24	22a47				23 26			23a51	
Hagley	d						21 28								22 27					23 29				
Blakedown	d						21 31								22 30					23 32				
Kidderminster	d						21 36								22 35					23 37				
Hartlebury	d																							
University	d					21 05																		
Barnt Green	d																							
Bromsgrove	d					21 21																		
Droitwich Spa	d					21 31	21 47								22 46					23 48				
Worcester Shrub Hill 7	a						21 55								22 55					23 56				
	d										22 08				22 57									
Worcester Foregate Street 7	a					21 39					22 11				23 00									
	d					21 42					22 11				23 00									
Malvern Link	d					21 52					22 20				23 09									
Great Malvern	a					21 54					22 27				23 12									
	d					22 00																		
Colwall	d					22 05																		
Ledbury	a					22 13																		
	d					22 14																		
Hereford 7	a					22 34																		

For general notes see front of timetable
For details of catering facilities see
Directory of Train Operators

A From Bournemouth (Table 51)

From 10 October a revised Chiltern Railways service will be in operation due to seasonal difficulties. Trains will arrive at their destination 3 minutes later than shown

Table 71

Sundays

until 1 November

Stratford -upon-Avon, Marylebone and Leamington Spa → Birmingham → Stourbridge, Worcester and Hereford

Network Diagram - See first page of Table 71

		CH	LM	GW	LM	CH	XC	LM	GW	CH	XC	LM	LM	CH	GW	LM	CH	XC	LM	CH	LM	CH	XC	LM	LM
		◇		1◇			1◇		1◇		1◇				1◇			1◇					1◇		
											A							B					B		
				🛒			🛒		☕		🛒				☕			🛒					🛒		
Stratford-upon-Avon	d				09 28							10 28				11 28								12 30	
Wilmcote	d				09 33							10 33				11 33								12 35	
Wootton Wawen	d																								
Henley-in-Arden	d				09 40							10 40				11 40								12 42	
Danzey	d																								
Wood End	d																								
The Lakes	d				09x48							10x48				11x48								12x50	
Earlswood (West Midlands)	d																								
Wythall	d				09 52							10 52				11 52								12 54	
Whitlocks End	d																								
Shirley	d				09 57							10 57				11 57								12 59	
Yardley Wood	d				10 00							11 00				12 00								13 02	
Hall Green	d				10 03							11 03				12 03								13 05	
Spring Road	d				10 05							11 05				12 05								13 07	
London Marylebone 10 ⊖	d	22p00				08 10				09 15				09 33			10 17			10 50		11 20			
Banbury	d	23p06				09 27	09 53			10 36	10 53			11 01			11 38	11 53		12 02		12 41	12 53		
Leamington Spa 8	a	23p23				09 46	10 10			10 55	11 10			11 20			11 57	12 10		12 21		13 00	13 10		
	d	23p24				09 46	10 11			10 58	11 11			11 21			11 58	12 11		12 22		13 01	13 11		
Warwick	d	23p28				09 51				11 02				11 25			12 02					13 05			
Warwick Parkway	d	23p34				09 54				11 06							12 06			12 27		13 09			
Hatton	d					09 59								11a31			12 11								
Lapworth	d					10 05											12 16								
Dorridge	d	23p43				10 09		10 25		11 18			11 25				12 20		12 25	12 39		13 20			13 25
Widney Manor	d	23p46						10 29					11 29						12 29						13 29
Solihull	d	23p50				10 15		10 32		11 24			11 32				12 26		12 32	12 44		13 26			13 32
Olton	d							10 36					11 36						12 36						13 36
Acocks Green	d							10 38					11 38						12 38						13 38
Tyseley	d				10 08							11 08				12 08								13 10	
Small Heath	d																								
Bordesley	d																								
Birmingham Moor Street	d	23 59	09 26		10 13	10 26		10 45		11 34		11 13	11 45			12 13	12 36		12 45	12 56		13 39		13 15	13 45
Birmingham Snow Hill 🚋	a	00 08	09 28		10 15	10 39		10 47		11 45		11 15	11 47			12 15	12 44		12 47	13 03		13 46		13 17	13 48
	d		09 30		10 18			10 48				11 18	11 48			12 18			12 48					13 20	13 48
Jewellery Quarter 🚋	d		09 32		10 20			10 51				11 20	11 51			12 20			12 51					13 22	13 51
The Hawthorns 🚋	d		09 37		10 25			10 55				11 25	11 55			12 25			12 55					13 27	13 55
Coventry	a						10 22				11 22							12 22					13 22		
Birmingham International ✈	a						10 38				11 38							12 38					13 37		
Birmingham New Street 12	a						10 51				11 51							12 51					13 49		
	d																				13 20				
Smethwick Galton Bdg H.L. 7	d		09 39		10 27			10 58				11 27	11 58			12 27			12 58					13 29	13 58
Langley Green	d							11 01					12 01						13 01						14 01
Rowley Regis	d		09 44		10 32			11 04				11 32	12 04			12 32			13 04					13 34	14 04
Old Hill	d							11 07					12 07						13 07						14 07
Cradley Heath	d		09 49		10 37			11 10				11 37	12 10			12 37			13 10					13 39	14 10
Lye	d							11 13					12 13						13 13						14 13
Stourbridge Junction 2	d		09 54		10 43			11a17				11 43	12a17			12 43			13a17					13 46	14a18
Hagley	d		09 58		10 46							11 47				12 46								13 49	
Blakedown	d											11 50				12 49									
Kidderminster	d		10 04		10 52							11 55				12 54								13 55	
Hartlebury	d																								
University	d																								
Barnt Green	d																								
Bromsgrove	d																				13 43				
Droitwich Spa	d		10 15		11 04							12 06				13 06					13 54			14 07	
Worcester Shrub Hill 7	a		10 23		11 11							12 14				13 13					14 01				
	d		10 26	10 37	11 25				12 05						13 13	13 29					14 21 →				
Worcester Foregate Street 7	a		10 29	10 39	11 27				12 07						13 15	13 31								14 20	
	d		10 29	10 41	11 28				12 09						13 17	13 32									
Malvern Link	d		10 38	10 50	11 36				12 18						13 26	13 40									
Great Malvern	a		10 41	10 54	11 39				12 21						13 29	13 43									
	d								12 22						13 30										
Colwall	d								12 28						13 36										
Ledbury	a								12 35						13 43										
	d								12 38						13 49										
Hereford 7	a								12 55						14 05										

For general notes see front of timetable
For details of catering facilities see
Directory of Train Operators

A From Southampton Central (Table 51)
B From Bournemouth (Table 51)

From 4 October a revised Chiltern Railways service will be in operation due to seasonal difficulties. Trains will arrive at their destination 3 minutes later than shown

Table 71

Sundays

until 1 November

Stratford -upon-Avon, Marylebone and Leamington Spa → Birmingham → Stourbridge, Worcester and Hereford

Network Diagram - See first page of Table 71

		CH	CH	XC	LM	GW	LM	CH	XC	LM	CH	XC	CH	XC	CH	LM	LM	LM	CH	XC	LM	CH	XC	LM	CH
				1 ◇		1 ◇			1 ◇			1 ◇		1 ◇						1 ◇			1 ◇		
									B					B									B		
				✠		⊡			✠			✠		✠						✠			✠		
Stratford-upon-Avon	d						13 28									14 28					15 28				
Wilmcote	d						13 33									14 33					15 33				
Wootton Wawen	d																								
Henley-in-Arden	d						13 40									14 40					15 40				
Danzey	d																								
Wood End	d																								
The Lakes	d						13x48									14x48					15x48				
Earlswood (West Midlands)	d																								
Wythall	d						13 52									14 52					15 52				
Whitlocks End	d																								
Shirley	d						13 57									14 57					15 57				
Yardley Wood	d						14 00									15 00					16 00				
Hall Green	d						14 03									15 03					16 03				
Spring Road	d						14 05									15 05					16 05				
London Marylebone 10 ⊖	d	11 33	11 50					12 20			12 50		13 20		13 33				13 50			14 20			14 50
Banbury	d	13 01	13 05	13 35				13 41	13 53		14 02	14 25	14 41	14 53	15 01				15 06	15 25		15 41	15 53		16 02
Leamington Spa 8	a	13 20	13 25	13 51				14 01	14 10		14 21	14 41	15 00	15 10	15 20				15 24	15 41		15 58	16 10		16 21
	d	13 21	13 25	13 53				14 01	14 11		14 22	14 43	15 01	15 11	15 21				15 25	15 43		15 59	16 11		16 22
Warwick	d	13 25						14 05					15 05		15 25							16 03			
Warwick Parkway	d		13 31					14 09			14 27		15 09						15 31			16 06			16 27
Hatton	d	13a31													15a31							16 11			
Lapworth	d							14 16														16 16			
Dorridge	d		13 42					14 21		14 25	14 39		15 20				15 25		15 42			16 21		16 25	16 39
Widney Manor	d									14 29							15 29							16 29	
Solihull	d		13 48					14 26		14 32	14 44		15 26				15 32		15 48			16 26		16 32	16 44
Olton	d									14 36							15 36							16 36	
Acocks Green	d									14 38							15 38							16 38	
Tyseley	d						14 08									15 08					16 08				
Small Heath	d																								
Bordesley	d																								
Birmingham Moor Street	d		13 59				14 13	14 37		14 45	14 56		15 37			15 13	15 45		15 59		16 13	16 37		16 45	16 56
Birmingham Snow Hill ⛴	a		14 08				14 15	14 45		14 47	15 03		15 49			15 15	15 48		16 06		16 15	16 49		16 48	17 03
	d						14 18			14 48						15 18	15 48				16 18			16 48	
Jewellery Quarter ⛴	d						14 20			14 51						15 20	15 51				16 20			16 51	
The Hawthorns ⛴	d						14 25			14 55						15 25	15 55				16 25			16 55	
Coventry	a								14 22					15 22									16 22		
Birmingham International ✈	a								14 35					15 35									16 35		
Birmingham New Street 12	a			14 19					14 49			15 09		15 49						16 09			16 49		
	d																	16 00							
Smethwick Galton Bdg H.L. 7	d						14 27			14 58						15 27	15 58				16 27			16 58	
Langley Green	d									15 01							16 01							17 01	
Rowley Regis	d						14 32			15 04						15 32	16 04				16 32			17 04	
Old Hill	d									15 07							16 07							17 07	
Cradley Heath	d						14 37			15 10						15 37	16 10				16 37			17 10	
Lye	d									15 13							16 13							17 13	
Stourbridge Junction 2	d						14 43			15a17						15 43	16a18				16 43			17a18	
Hagley	d						14 46									15 46					16 46				
Blakedown	d						14 49																		
Kidderminster	d						14 54									15 52					16 52				
Hartlebury	d																								
University	d																								
Barnt Green	d																								
Bromsgrove	d																	16 21							
Droitwich Spa	d						15 06									16 04		16 30			17 04				
Worcester Shrub Hill 7	a				⟵													16 41							
	d				14 21	15 10												16 44							
Worcester Foregate Street 7	a				14 23	15 13	15 14									16 12		16 46			17 12				
	d				14 24	15 14												16 47							
Malvern Link	d				14 32	15 23												16 56							
Great Malvern	a				14 35	15 26												17 01							
	d				14 36	15 28																			
Colwall	d				14 41	15 34																			
Ledbury	a				14 48	15 41																			
	d				14 49	15 49																			
Hereford 7	a				15 10	16 06																			

For general notes see front of timetable
For details of catering facilities see
Directory of Train Operators

B From Bournemouth (Table 51)

From 4 October a revised Chiltern Railways service will be in operation due to seasonal difficulties. Trains will arrive at their destination 3 minutes later than shown

Table 71

Sundays

until 1 November

Stratford -upon-Avon, Marylebone and Leamington Spa → Birmingham → Stourbridge, Worcester and Hereford

Network Diagram - See first page of Table 71

		XC	GW	LM	CH		XC	CH	LM	LM	LM	CH	XC	GW	LM	CH	XC	CH	LM	XC	GW	CH	XC	CH	LM
		1 ◇	1 ◇				1 ◇						1 ◇	1 ◇			1 ◇			1 ◇	1 ◇		1 ◇		
							A										A						A		
		🍴	🍴				🍴						🍴	☕			🍴			🍴	🍴		🍴		
Stratford-upon-Avon	d								16 28						17 28										18 28
Wilmcote	d								16 33						17 33										18 33
Wootton Wawen	d																								
Henley-in-Arden	d								16 40						17 40										18 40
Danzey	d								16x45																
Wood End	d																								
The Lakes	d								16x48						17x48										18x48
Earlswood (West Midlands)	d																								
Wythall	d								16 52						17 52										18 52
Whitlocks End	d																								
Shirley	d								16 57						17 57										18 57
Yardley Wood	d								17 00						18 00										19 00
Hall Green	d								17 03						18 03										19 03
Spring Road	d								17 05						18 05										19 05
London Marylebone 10 ⊖	d				15 20			15 33				15 50				16 20		16 57				17 20		17 35	
Banbury	d	16 25			16 41		16 53	17 01				17 05	17 25			17 41	17 53	18 09		18 25		18 41	18 53	19 01	
Leamington Spa 8	a	16 41			17 00		17 10	17 20				17 25	17 41			18 00	18 10	18 28		18 41		19 00	19 10	19 21	
	d	16 43			17 01		17 11	17 21				17 25	17 43			18 01	18 11	18 29		18 43		19 01	19 11	19 21	
Warwick	d				17 05			17 25								18 05						19 05		19 25	
Warwick Parkway	d				17 09							17 31				18 09		18 34				19 09			
Hatton	d							17a31								18 13								19a31	
Lapworth	d															18 18									
Dorridge	d				17 20					17 25		17 42				18 23		18 46				19 20			
Widney Manor	d									17 29						18 26						19 24			
Solihull	d				17 26					17 32		17 48				18 30		18 51				19 27			
Olton	d									17 36															
Acocks Green	d									17 38															
Tyseley	d								17 09						18 08										19 08
Small Heath	d																								
Bordesley	d																								
Birmingham Moor Street	d			17 02	17 39				17 13	17 45		17 59			18 13	18 42		19 02				19 38			19 13
Birmingham Snow Hill 🚋	a			17 04	17 46				17 18	17 48		18 07			18 15	18 49		19 10				19 46			19 15
	d			17 06					17 20	17 48					18 18										19 18
Jewellery Quarter 🚋	d								17 22	17 51					18 20										19 20
The Hawthorns 🚋	d								17 27	17 55					18 25										19 25
Coventry	a						17 22										18 22						19 22		
Birmingham International ✈	a						17 35										18 35						19 35		
Birmingham New Street 12	a	17 09					17 49						18 09				18 49			19 09			19 49		
	d										18 00								19 00						
Smethwick Galton Bdg H.L. 7	d								17 29	17 58					18 27										19 27
Langley Green	d									18 01															
Rowley Regis	d								17 34	18 04					18 32										19 32
Old Hill	d									18 07															
Cradley Heath	d								17 39	18 10					18 37										19 37
Lye	d									18 13															
Stourbridge Junction 2	d			17 27					17 45	18a19					18 43										19 43
Hagley	d			17 30					17 48						18 47										19 46
Blakedown	d														18 50										
Kidderminster	d			17 36					17 54						18 55										19 52
Hartlebury	d																								
University	d																								
Barnt Green	d																								
Bromsgrove	d										18 21								19 21						
Droitwich Spa	d			17 48					18 06		18 30				19 06				19 31						20 08
Worcester Shrub Hill 7	a								18 13		18 38				19 14				19 41						20 15
	d		17 11								18 41			19 13							20 09				
Worcester Foregate Street 7	a		17 14	18 01							18 44			19 15							20 15				
	d		17 15								18 44			19 17							20 16				
Malvern Link	d		17 25								18 53			19 25							20 25				
Great Malvern	a		17 27								18 56			19 29							20 29				
	d		17 29								18 57														
Colwall	d		17 35								19 03														
Ledbury	a		17 42								19 10														
	d		17 45								19 10														
Hereford 7	a		18 01								19 31														

For general notes see front of timetable
For details of catering facilities see
Directory of Train Operators

A From Bournemouth (Table 51)

From 4 October a revised Chiltern Railways service will be in operation due to seasonal difficulties. Trains will arrive at their destination 3 minutes later than shown

Table 71

Sundays

until 1 November

Stratford -upon-Avon, Marylebone and Leamington Spa → Birmingham → Stourbridge, Worcester and Hereford

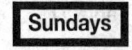

Network Diagram - See first page of Table 71

		CH	XC	GW	LM	CH	XC	CH	LM	XC	LM	CH	XC	CH	XC	CH	XC	XC	LM	CH	XC	XC	CH
			1 ◇	1 ◇			1 ◇			1 ◇			1 ◇		1 ◇		1 ◇	1 ◇			1 ◇	1 ◇	
							A						A				B	C			B	C	
Stratford-upon-Avon	d				19 28																		
Wilmcote	d				19 33																		
Wootton Wawen	d																						
Henley-in-Arden	d				19 40																		
Danzey	d																						
Wood End	d																						
The Lakes	d				19x48																		
Earlswood (West Midlands)	d																						
Wythall	d				19 52																		
Whitlocks End	d																						
Shirley	d				19 57																		
Yardley Wood	d				20 00																		
Hall Green	d				20 03																		
Spring Road	d				20 05																		
London Marylebone 10	⊖ d	17 57				18 20		18 57				19 22		19 57		20 20				20 50			22 00
Banbury	d	19 09	19 25			19 41	19 53	20 09		20 25		20 44	20 53	21 09	21 25	21 41	21 53	21 53		22 10	22 25	22 25	23 06
Leamington Spa 8	a	19 28	19 41			19 58	20 10	20 28		20 41		21 02	21 10	21 28	21 41	22 01	22 10	22 10		22 30	22 41	22 41	23 23
	d	19 29	19 43			20 03	20 11	20 29		20 43		21 03	21 11	21 29	21 43	22 01	22 11	22 11		22 30	22 43	22 43	23 24
Warwick	d					20 08						21 08				22 05				22 35			23 28
Warwick Parkway	d	19 34				20 11		20 34				21 11		21 34		22 09				22 39			23 32
Hatton	d																			22 43			
Lapworth	d					20 20														22 48			
Dorridge	d	19 46				20 24		20 46				21 22		21 46		22 20				22 53			23 43
Widney Manor	d					20 28						21 26								22 56			
Solihull	d	19 51				20 31		20 51				21 29		21 51		22 26				23 00			23 48
Olton	d																						
Acocks Green	d																						
Tyseley	d				20 08																		
Small Heath	d																						
Bordesley	d																						
Birmingham Moor Street	d	20 02			20 13	20 42		21 02			21 35	21 41		22 02		22 38			22 52	23 11			23 58
Birmingham Snow Hill	⛴ a	20 10			20 15	20 53		21 10			21 37	21 48		22 10		22 45			22 54	23 18			00 08
	d				20 18						21 45								22 55				
Jewellery Quarter	⛴ d				20 20						21 47								22 57				
The Hawthorns	⛴ d				20 25						21 52								23 02				
Coventry	a		19 53				20 22			20 53			21 22		21 53		22 22	22 22			22 53	22 53	
Birmingham International	✈ a		20 03				20 37			21 03			21 35		22 03		22 32	22 32			23 03	23 03	
Birmingham New Street 12	a		20 15				20 49			21 20			21 49		22 20		22 47	23 06			23 20	23 35	
	d								21 00														
Smethwick Galton Bdg H.L. 7	d				20 27						21 54								23 04				
Langley Green	d																						
Rowley Regis	d				20 32						21 59								23 09				
Old Hill	d																						
Cradley Heath	d				20 37						22 03								23 14				
Lye	d																						
Stourbridge Junction 2	d				20 43						22 09								23 19				
Hagley	d				20 46						22 12								23 23				
Blakedown	d																						
Kidderminster	d				20 53						22 18								23 29				
Hartlebury	d																						
University	d																						
Barnt Green	d																						
Bromsgrove	d								21 21														
Droitwich Spa	d				21 05				21 31		22 30								23 40				
Worcester Shrub Hill 7	a				21 25				21 38		22 37								23 48				
	d			21 16	21 28				21 42		22 41												
Worcester Foregate Street 7	a			21 18	21 31				21 44		22 43												
	d			21 20	21 31				21 45		22 44												
Malvern Link	d			21 29	21 40				21 54		22 52												
Great Malvern	a			21 32	21 43				21 57		22 55												
	d			21 33					21 57														
Colwall	d			21 39					22 02														
Ledbury	a			21 46					22 09														
	d			21 49					22 10														
Hereford 7	a			22 05					22 30														

For general notes see front of timetable
For details of catering facilities see Directory of Train Operators

A From Bournemouth (Table 51)
B 19 July to 6 September
C Until 12 July, and from 13 September

From 4 October a revised Chiltern Railways service will be in operation due to seasonal difficulties. Trains will arrive at their destination 3 minutes later than shown

Table 71

Sundays

from 8 November

Stratford -upon-Avon, Marylebone and Leamington Spa → Birmingham → Stourbridge, Worcester and Hereford

Network Diagram - See first page of Table 71

		CH	LM	GW	LM	CH	XC	LM	GW	CH	XC	LM	LM	CH	GW	LM	LM	CH	XC	LM	CH	LM	CH	XC	LM
		◇		1 ◇			1 ◇		1 ◇		1 ◇				1 ◇		bus		1 ◇			bus		1 ◇	
				trolley			trolley		catering		trolley				catering				trolley					trolley	
Stratford-upon-Avon	d				09 28							10 28				11 28									12 30
Wilmcote	d				09 33							10 33				11 33									12 35
Wootton Wawen	d																								
Henley-in-Arden	d				09 40							10 40				11 40									12 42
Danzey	d																								
Wood End	d																								
The Lakes	d				09x48							10x48				11x48									12x50
Earlswood (West Midlands)	d																								
Wythall	d				09 52							10 52				11 52									12 54
Whitlocks End	d																								
Shirley	d				09 57							10 57				11 57									12 59
Yardley Wood	d				10 00							11 00				12 00									13 02
Hall Green	d				10 03							11 03				12 03									13 05
Spring Road	d				10 05							11 05				12 05									13 07
London Marylebone 10 ⊖	d	22p00				08 10				09 15				09 33				10 17			10 50		11 20		
Banbury	d	23p06				09 27	09 53			10 36	10 53			11 01				11 38	11 53		12 02		12 41	12 53	
Leamington Spa 8	a	23p23				09 46	10 10			10 55	11 10			11 20				11 57	12 10		12 21		13 00	13 10	
	d	23p24				09 46	10 11			10 58	11 11			11 21				11 58	12 11		12 22		13 01	13 11	
Warwick	d	23p28				09 51				11 02				11 25				12 02					13 05		
Warwick Parkway	d	23p34				09 54				11 06								12 06			12 27		13 09		
Hatton	d					09 59								11a31				12 11							
Lapworth	d					10 05												12 16							
Dorridge	d	23p43				10 09		10 25		11 18			11 25					12 20		12 25	12 39		13 20		
Widney Manor	d	23p46						10 29					11 29							12 29					
Solihull	d	23p50				10 15		10 32		11 24			11 32					12 26		12 32	12 44		13 26		
Olton	d							10 36					11 36							12 36					
Acocks Green	d							10 38					11 38							12 38					
Tyseley	d				10 08							11 08				12 08									13 10
Small Heath	d																								
Bordesley	d																								
Birmingham Moor Street	d	23 59	09 26		10 13	10 26		10 45		11 34		11 13	11 45			12 13		12 36		12 45	12 56		13 39		13 15
Birmingham Snow Hill 🚊	a	00 13	09 28		10 15	10 42		10 47		11 48		11 15	11 47			12 15		12 47		12 47	13 06		13 49		13 17
	d		09 30		10 30			10 48				11 30	11 48			12 30				12 48					13 20
Jewellery Quarter 🚊	d		09 32		10 32			10 51				11 32	11 51			12 32				12 51					13 22
The Hawthorns 🚊	d		09 37		10 37			10 55				11 37	11 55			12 37				12 55					13 27
Coventry	a						10 22				11 22								12 22					13 22	
Birmingham International ✈	a						10 38				11 38								12 38					13 37	
Birmingham New Street 12	a						10 51				11 51								12 51					13 49	
	d																12 40					13 00			
Smethwick Galton Bdg H.L. 7	d		09 39		10 39			10 58				11 39	11 58			12 39				12 58					13 29
Langley Green	d							11 01					12 01							13 01					
Rowley Regis	d		09 44		10 44			11 04				11 44	12 04			12 44				13 04					13 34
Old Hill	d							11 07					12 07							13 07					
Cradley Heath	d		09 49		10 49			11 10				11 49	12 10			12 49				13 10					13 39
Lye	d							11 13					12 13							13 13					
Stourbridge Junction 2	d		09 54		10 55			11a17				11 55	12a17			12 55				13a17					13 46
Hagley	d		09 58		10 58							11 59				12 58									13 49
Blakedown	d											12 02				13 01									
Kidderminster	d		10 04		11 04							12 07				13 06									13 55
Hartlebury	d																								
University	d																								
Barnt Green	d																								
Bromsgrove	d																13 20					13 35			
Droitwich Spa	d		10 15		11 06							12 18				13 18	13s40					14a00			14 07
Worcester Shrub Hill 7	a		10 23		11 23							12 26				13 25									14 14
	d		10 26	10 37	11 27				12 05						13 13	13 29									14 21
Worcester Foregate Street 7	a		10 29	10 39	11 29				12 07						13 15	13 31	14 00								14 23
	d		10 29	10 41	11 30				12 09						13 17	13 32									14 24
Malvern Link	d		10 38	10 50	11 38				12 18						13 26	13 40									14 32
Great Malvern	a		10 41	10 54	11 41				12 21						13 29	13 43									14 35
	d								12 22						13 30										14 36
Colwall	d								12 28						13 36										14 41
Ledbury	a								12 35						13 43										14 48
	d								12 38						13 49										14 49
Hereford 7	a								12 55						14 05										15 10

For general notes see front of timetable
For details of catering facilities see Directory of Train Operators

Table 71

Sundays
from 8 November

Stratford -upon-Avon, Marylebone and Leamington Spa → Birmingham → Stourbridge, Worcester and Hereford

Network Diagram - See first page of Table 71

		LM	CH	CH	XC 1 ◇	GW 1 ◇	LM	CH	XC 1 ◇	LM		CH	LM (bus)	XC 1 ◇	CH	XC 1 ◇	CH	LM	LM	CH	XC 1 ◇	LM	CH	XC 1 ◇	LM
Stratford-upon-Avon	d						13 28											14 28				15 28			
Wilmcote	d						13 33											14 33				15 33			
Wootton Wawen	d																								
Henley-in-Arden	d						13 40											14 40				15 40			
Danzey	d																								
Wood End	d																								
The Lakes	d						13x48											14x48				15x48			
Earlswood (West Midlands)	d																								
Wythall	d						13 52											14 52				15 52			
Whitlocks End	d																								
Shirley	d						13 57											14 57				15 57			
Yardley Wood	d						14 00											15 00				16 00			
Hall Green	d						14 03											15 03				16 03			
Spring Road	d						14 05											15 05				16 05			
London Marylebone 10 ⊖	d		11 33	11 50				12 20				12 50			13 20		13 33			13 50			14 20		
Banbury	d		13 01	13 05	13 36			13 41	13 53			14 02		14 25	14 41	14 53	15 01			15 05	15 25		15 40	15 53	
Leamington Spa 8	a		13 20	13 25	13 52			14 01	14 10			14 21		14 41	15 00	15 10	15 20			15 24	15 41		15 58	16 10	
	d		13 21	13 25	13 54			14 01	14 11			14 22		14 43	15 01	15 11	15 21			15 25	15 43		15 59	16 11	
Warwick	d		13 25					14 05							15 05		15 25						16 03		
Warwick Parkway	d			13 31				14 09				14 27			15 09					15 31			16 06		
Hatton	d		13a31														15a31						16 11		
Lapworth	d							14 16															16 16		
Dorridge	d	13 25		13 42				14 21		14 25		14 39			15 20				15 25	15 42			16 21		16 25
Widney Manor	d	13 29								14 29									15 29						16 29
Solihull	d	13 32		13 48				14 26		14 32		14 44			15 26				15 32	15 48			16 26		16 32
Olton	d	13 36								14 36									15 36						16 36
Acocks Green	d	13 38								14 38									15 38						16 38
Tyseley	d						14 08											15 08				16 08			
Small Heath	d																								
Bordesley	d																								
Birmingham Moor Street	d	13 45		13 59			14 13	14 37		14 45		14 56			15 37			15 13	15 45	15 59		16 13	16 37		16 45
Birmingham Snow Hill (tram)	a	13 48		14 11			14 15	14 38		14 47		15 06			15 52			15 15	15 48	16 09		16 15	16 52		16 48
	d	13 48					14 18			14 48								15 28	15 48			16 18			16 48
Jewellery Quarter (tram)	d	13 51					14 20			14 51								15 30	15 51			16 20			16 51
The Hawthorns (tram)	d	13 55					14 25			14 55								15 35	15 55			16 25			16 55
Coventry	a								14 22							15 22								16 22	
Birmingham International ✈	a								14 35							15 35								16 35	
Birmingham New Street 12	a				14 20				14 49					15 09		15 49					16 09			16 49	
	d												14 55												
Smethwick Galton Bdg H.L. 7	d	13 58					14 27			14 58								15 37	15 58			16 27			16 58
Langley Green	d	14 01								15 01									16 01						17 01
Rowley Regis	d	14 04					14 32			15 04								15 42	16 04			16 32			17 04
Old Hill	d	14 07								15 07									16 07						17 07
Cradley Heath	d	14 10					14 37			15 10								15 47	16 10			16 37			17 10
Lye	d	14 13								15 13									16 13						17 13
Stourbridge Junction 2	d	14a18					14 43			15a17								15 53	16a18			16 43			17a18
Hagley	d						14 46											15 56				16 46			
Blakedown	d						14 49																		
Kidderminster	d						14 54											16 02				16 52			
Hartlebury	d																								
University	d																								
Barnt Green	d																								
Bromsgrove	d												15 30												
Droitwich Spa	d						15 06						15s55					16 14				17 04			
Worcester Shrub Hill 7	a																	16 21							
	d					15 10												16 25							
Worcester Foregate Street 7	a					15 13	15 14											16 27				17 12			
	d					15 14												16 28							
Malvern Link	d					15 23												16 37							
Great Malvern	a					15 26												16 40							
	d					15 28																			
Colwall	d					15 34																			
Ledbury	a					15 41																			
	d					15 49																			
Hereford 7	a					16 06																			

For general notes see front of timetable
For details of catering facilities see Directory of Train Operators

Stratford -upon-Avon, Marylebone and Leamington Spa → Birmingham → Stourbridge, Worcester and Hereford

from 8 November

Network Diagram - See first page of Table 71

		CH	GW 1 ◇	LM	LM	XC 1 ◇	CH	XC 1 ◇	CH	LM	LM	CH	XC 1 ◇	GW 1 ◇	LM	CH	XC 1 ◇	CH	XC 1 ◇	GW 1 ◇	CH	XC 1 ◇	CH	LM	LM
Stratford-upon-Avon	d									16 28					17 28									18 28	
Wilmcote	d									16 33					17 33									18 33	
Wootton Wawen	d																								
Henley-in-Arden	d									16 40					17 40									18 40	
Danzey	d									16x45															
Wood End	d																								
The Lakes	d									16x48					17x48									18x48	
Earlswood (West Midlands)	d																								
Wythall	d									16 52					17 52									18 52	
Whitlocks End	d																								
Shirley	d									16 57					17 57									18 57	
Yardley Wood	d									17 00					18 00									19 00	
Hall Green	d									17 03					18 03									19 03	
Spring Road	d									17 05					18 05									19 05	
London Marylebone 10	⊖ d	14 50					15 20		15 33			15 50				16 20		16 57			17 20		17 35		
Banbury	d	16 02				16 25	16 41	16 53	17 01			17 05	17 25			17 41	17 53	18 09	18 25		18 41	18 53	19 01		
Leamington Spa 8	a	16 21				16 41	17 00	17 10	17 20			17 25	17 41			18 00	18 10	18 28	18 41		19 00	19 10	19 20		
	d	16 22				16 43	17 01	17 11	17 21			17 25	17 43			18 01	18 11	18 29	18 43		19 01	19 11	19 21		
Warwick	d						17 05		17 25							18 05					19 05		19 25		
Warwick Parkway	d	16 27					17 09					17 31				18 09		18 34			19 09				
Hatton	d								17a31							18 13							19a31		
Lapworth	d															18 18									
Dorridge	d	16 39					17 20				17 25	17 42				18 23		18 46			19 20				
Widney Manor	d										17 29					18 26					19 24				
Solihull	d	16 44					17 26				17 32	17 48				18 30		18 51			19 27				
Olton	d										17 36														
Acocks Green	d										17 38														
Tyseley	d									17 09					18 08									19 08	
Small Heath	d																								
Bordesley	d																								
Birmingham Moor Street	d	16 56		17 02			17 39			17 13	17 45	17 59			18 13	18 42		19 02			19 38			19 13	
Birmingham Snow Hill	⇌ a	17 06		17 04			17 49			17 18	17 48	18 10			18 15	18 52		19 13			19 49			19 15	
	d			17 06						17 28	17 48				18 18									19 18	
Jewellery Quarter	⇌ d									17 30	17 51				18 20									19 20	
The Hawthorns	⇌ d									17 35	17 55				18 25									19 25	
Coventry	a							17 22									18 22					19 22			
Birmingham International	✈ a							17 35									18 35					19 35			
Birmingham New Street 12	a					17 09		17 49					18 09				18 49		19 09			19 49			
	d				17 00																				20 00
Smethwick Galton Bdg H.L. 7	d									17 37	17 58				18 27									19 27	
Langley Green	d										18 01														
Rowley Regis	d									17 42	18 04				18 32									19 32	
Old Hill	d										18 07														
Cradley Heath	d									17 47	18 10				18 37									19 37	
Lye	d										18 13														
Stourbridge Junction 2	d			17 27						17 53	18a19				18 43									19 43	
Hagley	d			17 30						17 56					18 47									19 46	
Blakedown	d														18 50										
Kidderminster	d			17 36						18 02					18 55									19 52	
Hartlebury	d																								
University	d																								
Barnt Green	d																								
Bromsgrove	d				17 35																				20 35
Droitwich Spa	d			17 48	18s00					18 14					19 06									20 08	21s00
Worcester Shrub Hill 7	a									18 20					19 14									20 15	
	d		17 11							18 25				19 13						20 09					
Worcester Foregate Street 7	a		17 14	18 01						18 27				19 15						20 15					
	d		17 15							18 28				19 17						20 16					
Malvern Link	d		17 25							18 37				19 25						20 25					
Great Malvern	a		17 27							18 40				19 29						20 29					
	d		17 27							18 57															
Colwall	d		17 35							19 04															
Ledbury	a		17 42							19 11															
	d		17 45							19 11															
Hereford 7	a		18 01							19 31															

For general notes see front of timetable
For details of catering facilities see Directory of Train Operators

Table 71

Sundays

from 8 November

Stratford -upon-Avon, Marylebone and Leamington Spa → Birmingham → Stourbridge, Worcester and Hereford

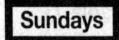

Network Diagram - See first page of Table 71

		CH	XC 1 ◇	GW 1 ◇	LM	CH	XC 1 ◇	CH	XC 1 ◇	LM	LM	GW 1 ◇	LM	CH	XC 1 ◇	CH	XC 1 ◇	CH	XC 1 ◇	LM	CH	XC 1 ◇	CH
Stratford-upon-Avon	d				19 28																		
Wilmcote	d				19 33																		
Wootton Wawen	d																						
Henley-in-Arden	d				19 40																		
Danzey	d																						
Wood End	d																						
The Lakes	d				19x48																		
Earlswood (West Midlands)	d																						
Wythall	d				19 52																		
Whitlocks End	d																						
Shirley	d				19 57																		
Yardley Wood	d				20 00																		
Hall Green	d				20 03																		
Spring Road	d				20 05																		
London Marylebone 10 ⊖	d	17 57				18 20		18 57						19 22		19 57		20 20			20 50		22 00
Banbury	d	19 09	19 25			19 41	19 53	20 09	20 25					20 44	20 53	21 09	21 25	21 41	21 53		22 10	22 25	23 06
Leamington Spa 8	a	19 28	19 41			19 58	20 10	20 28	20 41					21 02	21 10	21 28	21 41	22 01	22 10		22 30	22 41	23 23
	d	19 29	19 43			20 03	20 11	20 29	20 43					21 03	21 11	21 29	21 43	22 01	22 11		22 31	22 43	23 24
Warwick	d					20 08								21 08				22 05			22 35		23 28
Warwick Parkway	d	19 34				20 11		20 34						21 11		21 34		22 09			22 39		23 32
Hatton	d																				22 43		
Lapworth	d					20 20															22 48		
Dorridge	d	19 46				20 24		20 46						21 22		21 46		22 20			22 53		23 43
Widney Manor	d					20 28								21 26							22 56		
Solihull	d	19 51				20 31		20 51						21 29		21 51		22 26			23 00		23 48
Olton	d																						
Acocks Green	d																						
Tyseley	d				20 08																		
Small Heath	d																						
Bordesley	d																						
Birmingham Moor Street	d	20 02			20 13	20 42		21 02					21 35	21 41		22 02		22 38		22 52	23 10		23 58
Birmingham Snow Hill 🚊	a	20 13			20 15	20 56		21 13					21 37	21 51		22 13		22 48		22 54	23 21		00 13
	d				20 18								21 47							22 55			
Jewellery Quarter 🚊	d				20 20								21 49							22 57			
The Hawthorns 🚊	d				20 25								21 54							23 02			
Coventry	a		19 53				20 22		20 53						21 22		21 53		22 22			22 53	
Birmingham International ✈	a		20 03				20 37		21 03						21 35		22 03		22 32			23 03	
Birmingham New Street 12	a		20 15				20 49		21 20						21 49		22 20		23 06			23 35	
	d										21 25												
Smethwick Galton Bdg H.L. 7	d				20 27								21 56							23 04			
Langley Green	d																						
Rowley Regis	d				20 32								22 01							23 09			
Old Hill	d																						
Cradley Heath	d				20 37								22 05							23 14			
Lye	d																						
Stourbridge Junction 2	d				20 43								22 11							23 19			
Hagley	d				20 46								22 14							23 23			
Blakedown	d																						
Kidderminster	d				20 53								22 22							23 29			
Hartlebury	d																						
University	d																						
Barnt Green	d																						
Bromsgrove	d										22 00												
Droitwich Spa	d				21 05						22s25		22 33							23 40			
Worcester Shrub Hill 7	a				21 25								22 41							23 48			
	d			21 16	21 28							22 21	22 45										
Worcester Foregate Street 7	a			21 18	21 31							22 24	22 47										
	d			21 20	21 31							22 24	22 48										
Malvern Link	d			21 29	21 40							22 33	22 56										
Great Malvern	a			21 32	21 43							22 40	22 59										
	d			21 33						21 50													
Colwall	d			21 39						22 02													
Ledbury	a			21 46						22 19													
	d			21 49						22 20													
Hereford 7	a			22 05						22 45													

For general notes see front of timetable
For details of catering facilities see
Directory of Train Operators

Table 72

Mondays to Saturdays

Stourbridge Junction → Stourbridge Town

Network Diagram - See first page of Table 71

Miles			LM SX	LM	LM SX	LM	LM SX	LM SX		LM	LM SX	LM	LM	LM	LM		LM	LM	LM	LM	LM	LM		LM	LM	LM
0	Stourbridge Junction 2	d	05 47	05 58	06 08	06 19	06 29	06 39		06 49	06 59	07 09	07 19	07 29	07 39		07 49	07 59	08 09	08 19	08 29	08 39		08 49	08 59	09 09
¾	Stourbridge Town	a	05 50	06 01	06 11	06 22	06 32	06 42		06 52	07 02	07 12	07 22	07 32	07 42		07 52	08 02	08 12	08 22	08 32	08 42		08 52	09 02	09 12

		LM	LM	LM	LM	LM		LM	LM	LM	LM	LM	LM		LM	LM	LM	LM	LM	LM		LM	LM	LM	LM	LM
Stourbridge Junction 2	d	09 19	09 29	09 39	09 49	09 59		10 09	10 19	10 29	10 39	10 49	10 59		11 09	11 19	11 29	11 39	11 49	11 59		12 09	12 19	12 29	12 39	12 49
Stourbridge Town	a	09 22	09 32	09 42	09 52	10 02		10 12	10 22	10 32	10 42	10 52	11 02		11 12	11 22	11 32	11 42	11 52	12 02		12 12	12 22	12 32	12 42	12 52

		LM	LM	LM		LM	LM	LM	LM	LM	LM		LM	LM	LM	LM	LM	LM		LM	LM	LM	LM	LM	LM	LM
Stourbridge Junction 2	d	12 59	13 09	13 19		13 29	13 39	13 49	13 59	14 09	14 19		14 29	14 39	14 49	14 59	15 09	15 19		15 29	15 39	15 49	15 59	16 09	16 19	16 29
Stourbridge Town	a	13 02	13 12	13 22		13 32	13 42	13 52	14 02	14 12	14 22		14 32	14 42	14 52	15 02	15 12	15 22		15 32	15 42	15 52	16 02	16 12	16 22	16 32

		LM		LM	LM	LM	LM	LM	LM		LM	LM	LM	LM	LM	LM		LM	LM	LM	LM	LM	LM		LM	LM
Stourbridge Junction 2	d	16 39		16 49	16 59	17 09	17 19	17 29	17 39		17 49	17 59	18 09	18 19	18 29	18 39		18 49	18 59	19 09	19 19	19 29	19 39		19 49	19 59
Stourbridge Town	a	16 42		16 52	17 02	17 12	17 22	17 32	17 42		17 52	18 02	18 12	18 22	18 32	18 42		18 52	19 02	19 12	19 22	19 32	19 42		19 52	20 02

		LM	LM	LM	LM	LM	LM		LM	LM	LM	LM	LM	LM		LM	LM	LM	LM	LM	LM		LM	LM	LM	
Stourbridge Junction 2	d	20 09	20 19	20 29	20 39	20 49	20 59		21 09	21 19	21 29	21 39	21 49	21 59		22 09	22 19	22 29	22 39	22 50	23 00		23 15	23 30	23 54	
Stourbridge Town	a	20 12	20 22	20 32	20 42	20 52	21 02		21 12	21 22	21 32	21 42	21 52	22 02		22 12	22 22	22 32	22 42	22 53	23 03		23 18	23 33	23 57	

Sundays

		LM	LM	LM	LM	LM		LM	LM	LM	LM	LM		LM	LM	LM	LM	LM		LM	LM	LM	LM	LM		LM
Stourbridge Junction 2	d	09 43	10 00	10 11	10 21	10 41		10 54	11 11	11 21	11 41	11 54		12 11	12 21	12 41	12 54	13 11		13 21	13 41	13 54	14 11	14 21		14 41
Stourbridge Town	a	09 46	10 03	10 14	10 24	10 44		10 57	11 14	11 24	11 44	11 57		12 14	12 24	12 44	12 57	13 14		13 24	13 44	13 57	14 14	14 24		14 44

		LM	LM	LM	LM	LM		LM	LM	LM	LM	LM		LM	LM	LM	LM	LM		LM	LM	LM	LM	LM		
Stourbridge Junction 2	d	14 54	15 11	15 21	15 41	15 54		16 11	16 21	16 41	16 54	17 11		17 21	17 41	17 54	18 11	18 21		18 41	18 54	19 11	19 21	19 47		
Stourbridge Town	a	14 57	15 14	15 24	15 44	15 57		16 14	16 24	16 44	16 57	17 14		17 24	17 44	17 57	18 14	18 24		18 44	18 57	19 14	19 24	19 50		

For general notes see front of timetable
For details of catering facilities see
Directory of Train Operators

Stourbridge Town → Stourbridge Junction

Network Diagram - See first page of Table 71

Miles																										
			LM SX	LM SX	LM SO	LM SX	LM SX	LM SX	LM SO		LM SX	LM	LM SX	LM	LM	LM	LM		LM	LM	LM	LM	LM	LM	LM	LM
0	Stourbridge Town	d	05 52	06 03	06 10	06 13	06 24	06 34	06 40	.....	06 44	06 54	07 04	07 14	07 24	07 34	07 44	.....	07 54	08 04	08 14	08 24	08 34	08 44	08 54	09 04
¾	Stourbridge Junction 2	a	05 55	06 06	06 13	06 16	06 27	06 37	06 43	.	06 47	06 57	07 07	07 17	07 27	07 37	07 47	.	07 57	08 07	08 17	08 27	08 37	08 47	08 57	09 07

		LM		LM	LM	LM	LM	LM	LM	LM		LM	LM	LM	LM	LM	LM	LM		LM	LM	LM	LM	LM	LM	LM
Stourbridge Town	d	09 14	.....	09 24	09 34	09 44	09 54	10 04	10 14	10 24	.....	10 34	10 44	10 54	11 04	11 14	11 24	11 34	.....	11 44	11 54	12 04	12 14	12 24	12 34	12 44
Stourbridge Junction 2	a	09 17	.	09 27	09 37	09 47	09 57	10 07	10 17	10 27	.	10 37	10 47	10 57	11 07	11 17	11 27	11 37	.	11 47	11 57	12 07	12 17	12 27	12 37	12 47

		LM	LM		LM	LM	LM	LM	LM	LM	LM		LM	LM	LM	LM	LM	LM	LM		LM	LM	LM	LM	LM	LM
Stourbridge Town	d	12 54	13 04	.....	13 14	13 24	13 34	13 44	13 54	14 04	14 14	.....	14 24	14 34	14 44	14 54	15 04	15 14	15 24	.....	15 34	15 44	15 54	16 04	16 14	16 24
Stourbridge Junction 2	a	12 57	13 07	.	13 17	13 27	13 37	13 47	13 57	14 07	14 17	.	14 27	14 37	14 47	14 57	15 07	15 17	15 27	.	15 37	15 47	15 57	16 07	16 17	16 27

		LM	LM	LM		LM	LM	LM	LM	LM	LM	LM		LM	LM	LM	LM	LM	LM	LM		LM	LM	LM	LM	LM
Stourbridge Town	d	16 34	16 44	16 54	.....	17 04	17 14	17 24	17 34	17 44	17 54	18 04	.....	18 14	18 24	18 34	18 44	18 54	19 04	19 14	.....	19 24	19 34	19 44	19 54	20 04
Stourbridge Junction 2	a	16 37	16 47	16 57	.	17 07	17 17	17 27	17 37	17 47	17 57	18 07	.	18 17	18 27	18 37	18 47	18 57	19 07	19 17	.	19 27	19 37	19 47	19 57	20 07

		LM	LM	LM	LM		LM	LM	LM	LM	LM	LM	LM		LM	LM	LM	LM	LM	LM	LM		LM	LM	LM	
Stourbridge Town	d	20 14	20 24	20 34	20 44	.....	20 54	21 04	21 14	21 24	21 34	21 44	21 54	.....	22 04	22 14	22 24	22 34	22 44	22 55	23 05	.....	23 20	23 35	23 59	.....
Stourbridge Junction 2	a	20 17	20 27	20 37	20 47	.	20 57	21 07	21 17	21 27	21 37	21 47	21 57	.	22 07	22 17	22 27	22 37	22 47	22 58	23 08	.	23 23	23 38	00 02	.

Sundays

		LM	LM	LM	LM	LM		LM	LM	LM	LM	LM		LM	LM	LM	LM	LM		LM	LM	LM	LM	LM		LM
Stourbridge Town	d	09 49	10 05	10 16	10 36	10 46	.....	11 00	11 16	11 36	11 46	12 00	.....	12 16	12 36	12 46	13 00	13 16	.....	13 36	13 46	14 00	14 16	14 36	.....	14 46
Stourbridge Junction 2	a	09 52	10 08	10 19	10 39	10 49	.	11 03	11 19	11 39	11 49	12 03	.	12 19	12 39	12 49	13 03	13 19	.	13 39	13 49	14 03	14 19	14 39	.	14 49

		LM	LM	LM	LM	LM		LM	LM	LM	LM	LM		LM	LM	LM	LM	LM		LM	LM	LM	LM	LM		
Stourbridge Town	d	15 00	15 16	15 36	15 46	16 00	.....	16 16	16 36	16 46	17 00	17 16	.....	17 36	17 46	18 00	18 16	18 36	.....	18 46	19 00	19 16	19 36	19 55	.....	.....
Stourbridge Junction 2	a	15 03	15 19	15 39	15 49	16 03	.	16 19	16 39	16 49	17 03	17 19	.	17 39	17 49	18 03	18 19	18 39	.	18 49	19 03	19 19	19 39	19 58	.	.

For general notes see front of timetable
For details of catering facilities see
Directory of Train Operators

Network Diagram for Tables 74, 75

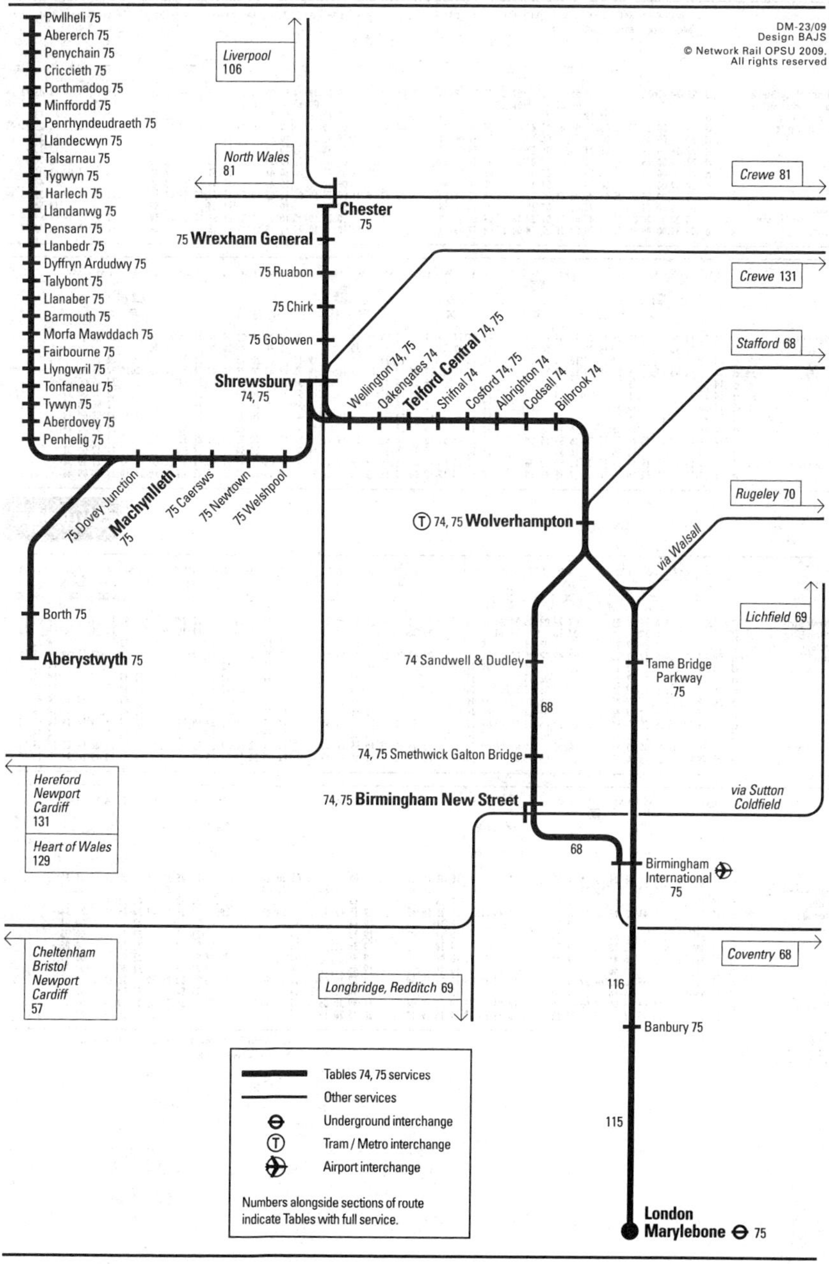

DM-23/09
Design BAJS
Pwllheli 75
Abererch 75
Penychain 75
Criccieth 75
Porthmadog 75
Minffordd 75
Penrhyndeudraeth 75
Llandecwyn 75
Talsarnau 75
Tygwyn 75
Harlech 75
Llandanwg 75
Pensarn 75
Llanbedr 75
Dyffryn Ardudwy 75
Talybont 75
Llanaber 75
Barmouth 75
Morfa Mawddach 75
Fairbourne 75
Llyngwril 75
Tonfaneau 75
Tywyn 75
Aberdovey 75
Penhelig 75
75 Dovey Junction
Machynlleth 75
75 Caersws
75 Newtown
75 Welshpool
Borth 75
Aberystwyth 75
Liverpool 106
North Wales 81
Crewe 81
Chester 75
75 Wrexham General
75 Ruabon
75 Chirk
75 Gobowen
Shrewsbury 74, 75
Crewe 131
Wellington 74, 75
Oakengates 74
Telford Central 74, 75
Shifnal 74
Cosford 74, 75
Albrighton 74
Codsall 74
Bilbrook 74
Stafford 68
Rugeley 70
74, 75 Wolverhampton
via Walsall
Lichfield 69
74 Sandwell & Dudley
Tame Bridge Parkway 75
68
74, 75 Smethwick Galton Bridge
74, 75 Birmingham New Street
via Sutton Coldfield
Hereford
Newport
Cardiff
131
Heart of Wales
129
68
Birmingham International 75
Cheltenham
Bristol
Newport
Cardiff
57
Coventry 68
Longbridge, Redditch 69
116
Banbury 75
115
London Marylebone 75
Tables 74, 75 services
Other services
Underground interchange
Tram / Metro interchange
Airport interchange
Numbers alongside sections of route indicate Tables with full service.

Birmingham → Shrewsbury

Network Diagram - see first page of Table 74

Miles			AW MO	AW MX	AW MX	LM	AW	LM	AW	LM	LM		AW	WS	LM	AW	LM	AW	LM	AW	LM		AW	WS	LM	AW
			A				◇		◇				◇	1 ◇		◇		◇		◇			◇	1 ◇		◇
0	**Birmingham New Street**	d	23p24	23p32		05 51	06 24		07 22	07 27	08 05		08 24		09 05	09 24	10 05	10 24	11 05	11 24	12 05		12 24		13 05	13 24
4	Smethwick Galton Bdg L.L.	d					06 31		07 28				08 30			09 30		10 30		11 30			12 30			13 30
5¼	Sandwell & Dudley	d				05 59					08 13				09 13		10 13		11 13		12 13				13 13	
13	**Wolverhampton 7**	d	23p46	00 02	00 20	06 13	06 43	06 48	07 41	07 46	08 25		08 43		09 29	09 43	10 25	10 43	11 25	11 43	12 25		12 43	12u53	13 25	13 43
17	Bilbrook	d	23p52	00 08		06 19		06 54		07 51	08 31				09 35		10 31		11 31		12 31				13 31	
17½	Codsall	d	23p54	00 11		06 21		06 57		07 54	08 33				09 37		10 33		11 33		12 33				13 33	
20¾	Albrighton	d	23p59	00 15		06 26		07 01		07 58	08 38				09 42		10 38		11 38		12 38				13 38	
22¼	Cosford	d	00 02	00 19		06 29		07 05		08 02	08 41			09 32	09 45		10 41		11 41		12 41			13 04	13 41	
25½	Shifnal	d	00 07	00 24		06 34		07 10		08 06	08 46				09 50		10 46		11 46		12 46				13 46	
28½	Telford Central	d	00 13	00 29	00 36	06 40	06 59	07 16	07 58	08 13	08 52		08 59	09 41	09 56	10 03	10 52	10 59	11 52	11 59	12 52		12 59	13 13	13 52	13 59
29½	Oakengates	d	00 15	00 31		06 42		07 18		08 16	08 54				09 58		10 54		11 54		12 54				13 54	
32½	Wellington (Shropshire)	d	00 20	00 36	00 43	06 47	07 06	07 24	08 04	08 22	08 59		09 06		10 02	10 10	10 59	11 06	11 59	12 06	12 59		13 06	13 19	13 59	14 06
43	**Shrewsbury**	a	00 35	00 49	00 59	07 00	07 18	07 38	08 17	08 37	09 15		09 19	09 58	10 16	10 23	11 15	11 19	12 15	12 19	13 15		13 19	13 32	14 15	14 19

		LM	AW	WS	LM	AW	LM	AW		LM	AW	LM	LM	AW	WS	LM	AW	LM	AW	LM	AW	WS	LM	AW
			◇	1 ◇		◇		R			◇			◇	1 ◇		◇		◇		◇	1 ◇		
Birmingham New Street	d	14 05	14 24		15 05	15 24	16 05	16 24		17 05	17 24	17 46	18 05	18 24		19 05	19 24	20 05	20 24	21 05	21 24		22 21	23 32
Smethwick Galton Bdg L.L.	d		14 30			15 30		16 30			17 31			18 30			19 30		20 30		21 30			
Sandwell & Dudley	d	14 13			15 13		16 13			17 13			18 13			19 13		20 13		21 13			22 29	
Wolverhampton 7	d	14 25	14 43	14u53	15 25	15 43	16 25	16 43		17 25	17 43	18 07	18 25	18 43	18u58	19 25	19 43	20 25	20 43	21 25	21 43	22u30	22 43	00 02
Bilbrook	d	14 31			15 31		16 31			17 31		18 13	18 31			19 31		20 31		21 31			22 49	00 08
Codsall	d	14 33			15 33		16 33			17 33		18 15	18 33			19 33		20 33		21 33			22 51	00 11
Albrighton	d	14 38			15 38		16 38			17 38		18 20	18 38			19 38		20 38		21 38			22 56	00 15
Cosford	d	14 41		15 04	15 41		16 41			17 41		18 23	18 41		19 06	19 41		20 41		21 41		22 41	22 59	00 19
Shifnal	d	14 46			15 46		16 46			17 46		18 28	18 46			19 46		20 46		21 46			23 04	00 24
Telford Central	d	14 52	14 59	15 13	15 52	15 59	16 52	16 59		17 52	17 59	18 33	18 52	18 59	19 15	19 52	19 59	20 52	20 59	21 52	21 59	22 50	23 10	00 29
Oakengates	d	14 54			15 54		16 54			17 54		18 35	18 54			19 54		20 54		21 54			23 12	00 31
Wellington (Shropshire)	d	14 59	15 06	15 19	15 59	16 06	16 59	17 06		17 59	18 06	18 41	18 59	19 06	19 21	19 59	20 06	20 59	21 06	21 59	22 06	22 57	23 17	00 36
Shrewsbury	a	15 15	15 19	15 32	16 15	16 19	17 15	17 19		18 15	18 19	18 56	19 15	19 20	19 34	20 15	20 19	21 15	21 19	22 14	22 19	23 10	23 30	00 49

Saturdays

		AW	AW	AW	LM		AW	LM	AW	LM		AW	WS	LM	AW		LM	AW	LM	AW		LM	AW	WS	LM	AW
				◇			◇		◇			◇	1 ◇		◇			◇		◇			◇	1 ◇		◇
Birmingham New Street	d	23p32		06 24	07 05		07 24	08 05	08 24	09 05		09 24		10 05	10 24		11 05	11 24	12 05	12 24		13 05	13 23		14 05	14 24
Smethwick Galton Bdg L.L.	d			06 30			07 30		08 30			09 30			10 30			11 30		12 30			13 29			14 30
Sandwell & Dudley	d				07 13			08 13		09 13				10 13			11 13		12 13			13 13			14 13	
Wolverhampton 7	d	00 02	00 20	06 42	07 25		07 42	08 25	08 43	09 25		09 43	09u59	10 25	10 43		11 25	11 43	12 25	12 43		13 25	13 43	13u59	14 25	14 43
Bilbrook	d	00 08			07 31			08 31		09 31				10 31			11 31		12 31			13 31			14 31	
Codsall	d	00 11			07 33			08 33		09 33				10 33			11 33		12 33			13 33			14 33	
Albrighton	d	00 15			07 38			08 38		09 38				10 38			11 38		12 38			13 38			14 38	
Cosford	d	00 19			07 41			08 41		09 41			10 10	10 41			11 41		12 41			13 41		14 10	14 41	
Shifnal	d	00 24			07 46			08 46		09 46				10 46			11 46		12 46			13 46			14 46	
Telford Central	d	00 29	00 36	06 59	07 51		07 59	08 52	08 59	09 52		09 59	10 19	10 52	10 59		11 52	11 59	12 52	12 59		13 52	13 59	14 19	14 52	14 59
Oakengates	d	00 31			07 53			08 54		09 54				10 54			11 54		12 54			13 54			14 54	
Wellington (Shropshire)	d	00 36	00 43	07 05	07 59		08a05	08 59	09 06	09 59		10 06	10 25	10 59	11 06		11 59	12 06	12 59	13 06		13 59	14 06	14 25	14 59	15 06
Shrewsbury	a	00 49	00 59	07 18	08 15			09 15	09 19	10 15		10 19	10 38	11 15	11 19		12 15	12 19	13 15	13 19		14 15	14 19	14 38	15 15	15 19

		LM		AW	LM	AW	LM		AW	WS	LM	AW		LM	AW	LM	AW		WS	LM	AW	LM	AW	AW
				◇		R			◇	1 ◇		◇			◇		◇		1 ◇		◇		B	
Birmingham New Street	d	15 05		15 24	16 05	16 24	17 05		17 24		18 05	18 24		19 05	19 24	20 05	20 24			21 05	21 24	22 05	22 55	23 35
Smethwick Galton Bdg L.L.	d			15 30		16 30			17 31			18 30			19 30		20 30				21 30			
Sandwell & Dudley	d	15 13			16 13		17 13				18 13			19 13		20 13				21 13		22 13		
Wolverhampton 7	d	15 25		15 43	16 25	16 43	17 25		17 43	17u59	18 25	18 43		19 25	19 43	20 25	20 43		20u55	21 25	21 42	22 25	23 13	23 54
Bilbrook	d	15 31			16 31		17 31				18 31			19 31		20 31				21 31		22 31		00 01
Codsall	d	15 33			16 33		17 33				18 33			19 33		20 33				21 33		22 33		00 03
Albrighton	d	15 38			16 38		17 38				18 38			19 38		20 38				21 38		22 38		00 08
Cosford	d	15 41			16 41		17 41			18 10	18 41			19 41		20 41			21 06	21 41		22 41		00 11
Shifnal	d	15 46			16 46		17 46				18 46			19 46		20 46				21 46		22 46		00 16
Telford Central	d	15 52		15 59	16 52	16 59	17 52		17 59	18 19	18 52	18 59		19 52	19 59	20 52	20 59		21 15	21 52	21 59	22 52	23 29	00 22
Oakengates	d	15 54			16 54		17 54				18 54			19 54		20 54				21 54		22 54		00 24
Wellington (Shropshire)	d	15 59		16 06	16 59	17 06	17 59		18 06	18 25	18 59	19 06		19 59	20 06	20 59	21 06		21 21	21 59	22 05	22 59	23 36	00 29
Shrewsbury	a	16 15		16 19	17 15	17 19	18 15		18 19	18 38	19 15	19 19		20 15	20 19	21 15	21 19		21 36	22 14	22 21	23 15	23 49	00 42

For general notes see front of timetable
For details of catering facilities see Directory of Train Operators

A From Birmingham International (Table 68)
B To Crewe (Table 131)

Birmingham → Shrewsbury

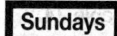

Network Diagram - see first page of Table 74

		AW	AW	AW	AW	WS		WS	AW	AW	AW	AW
					◇	1 ◇		1 ◇	◇	◇	◇	◇
				A	B	C		D		B		G
Birmingham New Street	d	23p35		10 05	11 05				12 24	13 24	14 24	15 24
Smethwick Galton Bdg L.L.	d											
Sandwell & Dudley	d											
Wolverhampton 7	d	23p54	00 20	10 22	11 27	12u03		12u06	12 41	13 42	14 43	15 43
Bilbrook	d	00 01		10 28	11 33					13 48		15 49
Codsall	d	00 03		10 31	11 35					13 50		15 51
Albrighton	d	00 08		10 35	11 40					13 55		15 56
Cosford	d	00 11		10 39	11 43	12 15		12 18		13 58		15 59
Shifnal	d	00 16		10 44	11 48					14 03		16 04
Telford Central	d	00 22	00 36	10 49	11 54	12 23		12 26	12 57	14 09	14 59	16 09
Oakengates	d	00 24		10 52	11 57					14 11		16 12
Wellington (Shropshire)	d	00 29	00 43	10 57	12 01	12 29		12 32	13 04	14 15	15 06	16 17
Shrewsbury	a	00 42	00 59	11 10	12 15	12 44		12 47	13 17	14 28	15 19	16 30

			AW	AW	AW	WS	WS	AW	AW	WS	AW	AW	AW		
			◇	◇	◇	1 ◇	1 ◇	◇	◇	1 ◇	◇				
				H		C	D	B			J	A	A		
Birmingham New Street	d		16 24	17 24	18 24			19 24	20 24		21 24	22 24	23 24		
Smethwick Galton Bdg L.L.	d						18 48								
Sandwell & Dudley	d														
Wolverhampton 7	d		16 43	17 43	18 43	18u54	18u57	19 43	20 43	21u01	21 43	22 42	23 46		
Bilbrook	d			17 49				19 49			21 49	22 48	23 52		
Codsall	d			17 51				19 51			21 51	22 50	23 54		
Albrighton	d			17 56				19 56			21 56	22 55	23 59		
Cosford	d			17 59		19 08	19 08	19 59		21 12	21 59	22 58	00 02		
Shifnal	d			18 04				20 04			22 04	23 03	00 07		
Telford Central	d		16 59	18 09	18 59	19 17	19 17	20 09	20 59	21 21	22 10	23 09	00 13		
Oakengates	d			18 11				20 12			22 13	23 12	00 15		
Wellington (Shropshire)	d		17 06	18 16	19 06	19 23	19 23	20 17	21 06	21 27	22 17	23 16	00 20		
Shrewsbury	a		17 19	18 29	19 20	19 39	19 39	20 30	21 19	21 40	22 30	23 33	00 35		

For general notes see front of timetable
For details of catering facilities see Directory of Train Operators

A From Birmingham International (Table 68)

B From Birmingham International (Table 68) to Chester (Table 75)

C Until 12 July and from 13 September

D 19 July to 6 September.

G From Birmingham International (Table 68) to Holyhead (Table 81) until 6 September, Chester (Table 75) from 13 September

H From Birmingham International (Table 68) to Holyhead (Table 81)

J From Birmingham International (Table 51) to Chester (Table 131)

Shrewsbury → Birmingham

Network Diagram - see first page of Table 74

Mondays to Fridays

Miles			AW	AW	LM	WS	LM	AW	LM		LM	AW	LM	WS	AW	LM	AW		LM	AW	LM	AW	LM	WS	AW	LM
			MX																							
			◇			[1] ◇						◇		[1] ◇	◇		◇			◇		◇		[1] ◇	◇	
			A	B				B																		
						🍴						🛒		🍴	🛒		🛒					🛒		🍴	🛒	
0	**Shrewsbury**	d	23p26	05 21	05 28	05 52	05 58	06 31	06 55		07 14	07 31	07 47	08 07	08 31	08 47	09 31		09 47	10 35	10 47	11 31	11 47	12 07	12 31	12 47
10½	Wellington (Shropshire)	d	23p40	05 35	05 41		06 11	06 45	07 08		07 27	07 45	08 00	08 21	08 45	09 00	09 45		10 00	10 49	11 00	11 45	12 00	12 21	12 45	13 00
13¼	Oakengates	d	23p44		05 46		06 16				07 32		08 05			09 05			10 05		11 05		12 05			13 05
14½	Telford Central	d	23p47	05 41	05 49	06 09	06 19	06 51	07 14		07 35	07 51	08 08	08 27	08 51	09 08	09 51		10 08	10 55	11 08	11 51	12 08	12 27	12 51	13 08
17½	Shifnal	d	23p52		05 54		06 24				07 40		08 13			09 13			10 13		11 13		12 13			13 13
20¾	Cosford	d	23p57		05 59	06a17	06 29				07 45		08 18	08a35		09 18			10 18		11 18		12 18	12 36		13 18
22¼	Albrighton	d	00 01		06 02		06 32				07 48		08 21			09 21			10 21		11 21		12 21			13 21
25½	Codsall	d	00 06		06 07		06 38				07 54		08 27			09 27			10 27		11 27		12 27			13 27
26	Bilbrook	d	00 08		06 09		06 40				07 56		08 29			09 29			10 29		11 29		12 29			13 29
30	**Wolverhampton** [7] 🚋	a	00 17	05 58	06 16		06 47	07 08	07 34		08 02	08 08	08 36		09 08	09 36	10 08		10 36	11 12	11 36	12 08	12 36	12s47	13 08	13 36
37¾	Sandwell & Dudley	a			06 31		07 03		07 46				08 46			09 46			10 46		11 46		12 46			13 46
39	Smethwick Galton Bdg L.L.	a		06 11	06 34		07 06	07 21				08 20			09 20		10 20			11 24		12 20			13 20	
43	**Birmingham New Street** [12]	a		06 17	06 43		07 14	07 27	07 55		08 20	08 27	08 55		09 26	09 55	10 26		10 55	11 30	11 55	12 26	12 55		13 26	13 55

		AW		LM	AW	LM	AW	LM	WS	AW		LM	AW	LM	WS	AW	LM	AW	LM	LM	AW	LM	AW	AW		
		◇			◇		◇		[1] ◇	◇			◇		[1] ◇	◇		◇			◇		◇	◇		
																								A		
		🛒			🛒		🛒		🍴	🛒			🛒		🍴	🛒		🛒								
Shrewsbury	d	13 31		13 47	14 31	14 47	15 31	15 47	16 07	16 31		16 47	17 31	17 47	18 07	18 31	18 47	19 32	19 47	20 47	21 33	21 47	22 18	23 26		
Wellington (Shropshire)	d	13 45		14 00	14 45	15 00	15 45	16 00		16 45		17 00	17 45	18 00	18 21	18 45	19 00	19 46	20 00	21 00	21 47	22 00	22 32	23 40		
Oakengates	d			14 05		15 05		16 05				17 05		18 05			19 05		20 05	21 05		22 05		23 44		
Telford Central	d	13 51		14 08	14 51	15 08	15 51	16 08	16 24	16 51		17 08	17 51	18 08	18 27	18 51	19 08	19 52	20 08	21 08	21 53	22 08	22 38	23 47		
Shifnal	d			14 13		15 13		16 13				17 13		18 13			19 13		20 13	21 13		22 13		23 52		
Cosford	d			14 18		15 18		16 18	16 33			17 18		18 18	18 36		19 18		20 18	21 18		22 18		23 57		
Albrighton	d			14 21		15 21		16 21				17 21		18 21			19 21		20 21	21 21		22 21		00 01		
Codsall	d			14 27		15 27		16 27				17 27		18 27			19 27		20 27	21 27		22 27		00 06		
Bilbrook	d			14 29		15 29		16 29				17 29		18 29			19 29		20 29	21 29		22 29		00 08		
Wolverhampton [7] 🚋	a	14 08		14 36	15 08	15 36	16 08	16 36	16s47	17 08		17 36	18 08	18 36	18s47	19 08	19 36	20 09	20 36	21 36	22 10	22 36	22 55	00 17		
Sandwell & Dudley	a			14 46		15 46		16 46				17 46		18 46			19 46		20 46	21 46		22 46				
Smethwick Galton Bdg L.L.	a	14 20			15 20		16 20			17 20			18 20			19 20		20 20			22 24					
Birmingham New Street [12]	a	14 26		14 55	15 26	15 55	16 26	16 55		17 26		17 55	18 26	18 55		19 26	19 55	20 27	20 57	21 55	22 30	22 55	23 26			

Saturdays

		AW	AW	AW	LM		WS	AW	LM	AW		LM	AW	LM	WS		AW	LM	AW	LM		AW	LM	WS	AW	LM
		◇					[1] ◇	◇		◇			◇		[1] ◇		◇		◇			◇		[1] ◇	◇	
		A	B	B																						
							🍴	🛒		🛒			🛒		🍴		🛒		🛒			🛒		🍴	🛒	
Shrewsbury	d	23p26	05 24	06 31	06 47		07 05	07 32	07 47	08 31		08 47	09 31	09 47	10 08		10 31	10 47	11 31	11 47		12 31	12 47	13 03	13 31	13 47
Wellington (Shropshire)	d	23p40	05 38	06 45	07 00		07 18	07 46	08 00	08 45		09 00	09 45	10 00	10 21		10 45	11 00	11 45	12 00		12 45	13 00	13 16	13 45	14 00
Oakengates	d	23p44			07 05				08 05			09 05		10 05				11 05		12 05			13 05			14 05
Telford Central	d	23p47	05 44	06 51	07 08		07 24	07 52	08 08	08 51		09 08	09 51	10 08	10 27		10 51	11 08	11 51	12 08		12 51	13 08	13 22	13 51	14 08
Shifnal	d	23p52			07 13				08 13			09 13		10 13				11 13		12 13			13 13			14 13
Cosford	d	23p57			07 18		07 32		08 18			09 18		10 18	10 36			11 18		12 18			13 18	13 30		14 18
Albrighton	d	00 01			07 21				08 21			09 21		10 21				11 21		12 21			13 21			14 21
Codsall	d	00 06			07 27				08 27			09 27		10 27				11 27		12 27			13 27			14 27
Bilbrook	d	00 08			07 29				08 29			09 29		10 29				11 29		12 29			13 29			14 29
Wolverhampton [7] 🚋	a	00 17	06 01	07 08	07 36		07s47	08 09	08 36	09 08		09 36	10 08	10 36	10s47		11 08	11 36	12 08	12 36		13 08	13 36	13s47	14 08	14 36
Sandwell & Dudley	a				07 46				08 46			09 46		10 46				11 46		12 46			13 46			14 46
Smethwick Galton Bdg L.L.	a		06 14	07 21				08 21		09 20			10 20				11 20		12 20			13 20			14 20	
Birmingham New Street [12]	a		06 20	07 27	07 55			08 28	08 55	09 26		09 55	10 26	10 55			11 26	11 55	12 26	12 55		13 26	13 55		14 26	14 55

		AW		LM	AW	LM	AW		LM	AW	LM	AW		LM	WS	AW	LM		LM	AW	LM	AW		AW		
		◇			◇		◇			◇		◇			[1] ◇	◇				◇		◇		◇		
																								A		
		🛒			🛒		🛒			🛒		🛒			🍴	🛒										
Shrewsbury	d	14 31		14 47	15 31	15 47	16 31		16 47	17 31	17 47	18 31		18 47	19 05	19 32	19 47		20 47	21 31	21 47	22 31		23 26		
Wellington (Shropshire)	d	14 45		15 00	15 45	16 00	16 45		17 00	17 45	18 00	18 45		19 00	19 18	19 46	20 00		21 00	21 45	22 00	22 45		23 40		
Oakengates	d			15 05		16 05			17 05		18 05			19 05			20 05		21 05		22 05			23 44		
Telford Central	d	14 51		15 08	15 51	16 08	16 51		17 08	17 51	18 08	18 51		19 08	19 24	19 52	20 08		21 08	21 51	22 08	22 51		23 47		
Shifnal	d			15 13		16 13			17 13		18 13			19 13			20 13		21 13		22 13			23 52		
Cosford	d			15 18		16 18			17 18		18 18			19 18	19 32		20 18		21 18		22 18			23 57		
Albrighton	d			15 21		16 21			17 21		18 21			19 21			20 21		21 21		22 21			00 01		
Codsall	d			15 27		16 27			17 27		18 27			19 27			20 27		21 27		22 27			00 06		
Bilbrook	d			15 29		16 29			17 29		18 29			19 29			20 29		21 29		22 29			00 08		
Wolverhampton [7] 🚋	a	15 08		15 36	16 08	16 36	17 08		17 36	18 08	18 36	19 08		19 36	19s49	20 09	20 36		21 36	22 08	22 36	23 08		00 15		
Sandwell & Dudley	a			15 46		16 46			17 46		18 46			19 46			20 46		21 46		22 45					
Smethwick Galton Bdg L.L.	a	15 20			16 20		17 20			18 20		19 20				20 20				22 20						
Birmingham New Street [12]	a	15 26		15 55	16 26	16 55	17 26		17 55	18 26	18 55	19 26		19 55		20 26	20 57		21 55	22 26	22 55	23 24				

For general notes see front of timetable
For details of catering facilities see Directory of Train Operators

A From Chester (Table 75)
B To Birmingham International (Table 68)

Sundays

Shrewsbury → Birmingham

Network Diagram - see first page of Table 74

		AW	AW	AW	AW	WS	AW	AW		AW	AW	WS	AW	AW	AW	AW	WS	AW	AW	AW	AW	AW	AW	AW		
		◇			◇	1 ◇	◇	◇		◇	◇	1 ◇	◇		◇	◇	1 ◇	◇	◇	◇	◇	◇	◇	◇		
		A	B	B	C		D	E		C			C		C			G	H		J	K		L		
						🍴	🛒	🛒		🛒	🛒	🍴	🛒	🛒	🛒	🛒	🍴			🛒			🛒			
Shrewsbury	d	23p26	08 10	09 09	10 10	11 31	11 40	11 40		12 20	13 31	13 56	14 20	15 33	16 29	17 33	17 56	18 20	18 20	19 31	20 23	20 23	21 31	22 23		
Wellington (Shropshire)	d	23p40	08 24	09 23	10 23	11 44	11 54	11 54		12 34	13 45	14 09	14 34	15 47	16 43	17 47	18 09	18 34	18 34	19 45	20 37	20 37	21 45	22 37		
Oakengates	d	23p44	08 28	09 27	10 28					12 38			14 38		16 47			18 38	18 38		20 41	20 41		22 42		
Telford Central	d	23p47	08 31	09 30	10 31	11 50	12 00	12 00		12 41	13 51	14 15	14 41	15 53	16 50	17 53	18 15	18 41	18 41	19 51	20 44	20 44	21 51	22 45		
Shifnal	d	23p52	08 36	09 35	10 35					12 46			14 46		16 55			18 46	18 46		20 49	20 49		22 50		
Cosford	d	23p57	08 41	09 40	10 40	11 59				12 51		14 23	14 51		17 00		18 24	18 51	18 51		20 54	20 54		22 55		
Albrighton	d	00 01	08 44	09 43	10 43					12 54			14 54		17 03			18 54	18 54		20 57	20 57		22 58		
Codsall	d	00 06	08 50	09 48	10 49					12 59			14 59		17 08			18 59	18 59		21 02	21 02		23 04		
Bilbrook	d	00 08	08 52	09 50	10 51					13 01			15 01		17 10			19 01	19 01		21 04	21 04		23 06		
Wolverhampton 7	a	00 15	08 59	09 57	10 57	12s10	12 17	12 17		13 08	14 08	14s36	15 08	16 10	17 17	18 10	18s35	19 08	19 08	20 08	21 11	21 11	22 08	23 16		
Sandwell & Dudley	a																									
Smethwick Galton Bdg L.L.	a																									
Birmingham New Street 12	a		09 15	10 14	11 14		12 33	12 34		13 24	14 24		15 24	16 26	17 35	18 28		19 24	19 28	20 24	21 28	21 29	22 28			

For general notes see front of timetable
For details of catering facilities see Directory of Train Operators

A From Chester (Table 75)
B To Birmingham International (Table 68)
C From Chester (Table 75) to Birmingham International (Table 68)
D From 13 September
E Until 6 September
G Until 1 November. From Chester (Table 75) to Birmingham International (Table 68)
H From 8 November. From Chester (Table 75) to Birmingham International (Table 68)
J Until 6 September. From Chester (Table 75) to Birmingham International (Table 68)
K From 13 September. From Chester (Table 75) to Birmingham International (Table 68)
L Until 6 September from Holyhead (Table 81). From 13 September from Chester (Table 75)

Birmingham and Shrewsbury → Chester, Aberystwyth, Barmouth and Pwllheli

Network Diagram - see first page of Table 74

Miles	Miles	Miles			AW MX	AW	AW ◇	AW	AW	AW ◇	AW	VT 1 ◇	AW	AW ◇ A	AW ◇	AW ◇	AW ◇ A	AW ◇ A	AW ◇	WS 1 ◇
—	—	—	London Euston 15 ⊖	d															*06 43*	
—	—	—	London Marylebone 10 ⊖	d																06 45
—	—	—	Banbury	d																07u59
—	—	—	Birmingham International ✈	d													07 09		08 09	
0	—	—	**Birmingham New Street 12**	d											06 24		07 22		08 24	
—	—	—	Tame Bridge Parkway	d																
4	—	—	Smethwick Galton Bdg L.L.	d											06 31		07 28		08 30	
12¾	—	—	**Wolverhampton 7**	d											06 43		07 41		08 43	
22	—	—	Cosford	d																09 32
28¼	—	—	Telford Central	d											06 59		07 58		08 59	09 41
32¼	—	—	Wellington (Shropshire)	d											07 06		08 04		09 06	
42¾	—	—	**Shrewsbury**	a											07 18		08 17		09 19	09 58
—	—	—	Cardiff Central 7	d										05 10			*05 40*	07 20		*07 50*
—	—	—	Manchester Piccadilly 10	d															*07 30*	
—	—	—	Crewe 10	d											*05 55*				*08 08*	
—	—	0	**Shrewsbury**	d	23p37			05 20			06 10			07 24	07 27		08 24	09 24	09 27	10 03
—	—	17¾	Gobowen	d	23p56			05 39			06 30			07 43			08 43	09 43		10 24
—	—	20¾	Chirk	d	00 02			05 45			06 35			07 48			08 49	09 48		10 29
—	—	25	Ruabon	d	00 08			05 51			06 42			07 54			08 55	09 54		10 36
—	—	30	Wrexham General	a	00 14			05 57			06 49			08 01			09 01	10 01		10 44
—	—	—		d	00 14			06 04				07 00		08 02			09 02	10 02		
—	—	42	**Chester**	a	00 34			06 25				07 19		08 20			09 19	10 20		
62½	—	—	Welshpool	d											07 49				09 49	
76½	—	—	Newtown (Powys)	d											08 05				10 05	
82	—	—	Caersws	d											08 14				10 14	
103¾	—	—	**Machynlleth 4**	a											08 47				10 47	
—	0	—		d		04 35	05 15		06 30	06 49			08 07		08 49	09 05			10 49	
107¾	4	—	Dovey Junction 4	d		04 42	05 22		06 37	06 56			08 14		08 56	09 12			10 56	
116	—	—	Borth	d		04 53			06 48				08 25		09 07				11 07	
124¼	—	—	**Aberystwyth**	a		05 12			07 07				08 44		09 26				11 26	
—	9	—	Penhelig	d			05x30			07x04						09x20				
—	10	—	Aberdovey	d			05 34			07 07						09 23				
—	13½	—	Tywyn	a			05 40			07 13						09 29				
—	—	—		d			05 40			07 15						09 30				
—	16	—	Tonfanau	d			05x44			07x19						09x34				
—	20	—	Llwyngwril	d			05x50			07x25						09x40				
—	22¾	—	Fairbourne	d			05 57			07 33						09 48				
—	23¾	—	Morfa Mawddach	d			05x59			07x35						09 50				
—	25½	—	**Barmouth**	a			06 08			07 40						09 56				
—	—	—		d			06 09			07 50						09 57				
—	26¾	—	Llanaber	d			06x13			07x53						10x00				
—	29¼	—	Talybont	d						07x57						10x04				
—	30¼	—	Dyffryn Ardudwy	d						07x59						10x06				
—	32½	—	Llanbedr	d						08x02						10x09				
—	33¼	—	Pensarn	d						08x04						10x11				
—	34	—	Llandanwg	d						08x05						10x12				
—	35¾	—	Harlech	a			06 29			08 11						10 18				
—	—	—		d			06 29			08 32						10 21				
—	38½	—	Tygwyn	d						08x36						10x25				
—	39¼	—	Talsarnau	d						08x37						10x27				
—	40½	—	Llandecwyn	d						08x40						10x29				
—	41¼	—	Penrhyndeudraeth	d						08 43						10 32				
—	42½	—	Minffordd	d						08 46						10 36				
—	44½	—	Porthmadog	a			06 45			08 51						10 41				
—	—	—		d			06 45			08 52						10 42				
—	49½	—	Criccieth	d						08 59						10 50				
—	54	—	Penychain	d			06x58			09x05						10x55				
—	55½	—	Abererch	d						09x08						10x58				
—	57½	—	**Pwllheli**	a			07 05			09 13						11 09				

For general notes see front of timetable
For details of catering facilities see
Directory of Train Operators

A To Holyhead (Table 81)

Birmingham and Shrewsbury → Chester, Aberystwyth, Barmouth and Pwllheli

Network Diagram - see first page of Table 74

		AW ◇ A	AW ◇ B	AW ◇ C 🛒	AW ◇ C 🛒	AW ◇ D 🛒		AW ◇ C 🛒	AW ◇ C 🛒	AW ◇ D 🛒		WS 1 ◇ 🍽	AW ◇ C 🛒	AW ◇ C 🛒	AW ◇ E 🛒		AW ◇ G 🛒		WS 1 ◇ 🍽	AW ◇ C 🛒
London Euston 15 ⊖	d			07 43		08 43		09 43		10 43			11 43		12 43		12 43			13 43
London Marylebone 10 ⊖	d											10 17							12 17	
Banbury	d											11u30							13u30	
Birmingham International ✈	d			09 09		10 09		11 09		12 09			13 09		14 09		14 09			15 09
Birmingham New Street 12	d			09 24		10 24		11 24		12 24			13 24		14 24		14 24			15 24
Tame Bridge Parkway	d											12 39							14 38	
Smethwick Galton Bdg L.L.	d			09 30		10 30		11 30		12 30			13 30		14 30		14 30			15 30
Wolverhampton 7	d			09 43		10 43		11 43		12 43		12u53	13 43		14 43		14 43		14u53	15 43
Cosford	d											13 04							15 04	
Telford Central	d			10 03		10 59		11 59		12 59		13 13	13 59		14 59		14 59		15 13	15 59
Wellington (Shropshire)	d			10 10		11 06		12 06		13 06		13 19	14 06		15 06		15 06		15 19	16 06
Shrewsbury	a			10 23		11 19		12 19		13 19		13 32	14 19		15 19		15 19		15 32	16 19
Cardiff Central 7	d				09 20			09 50	11 20				11 50	13 20						13 50
Manchester Piccadilly 10	d					09 30				11 30					13 30		13 30			
Crewe 10	d					10 12				12 12					14 12		14 12			
Shrewsbury	d			10 26	11 24	11 27		12 22	13 24	13 27		13 37	14 22	15 24	15 27		15 27		15 37	16 22
Gobowen	d			10 46	11 43			12 42	13 43			14 01	14 42	15 43					16 01	16 42
Chirk	d			10 51	11 48			12 47	13 48			14 06	14 47	15 48					16 06	16 47
Ruabon	d			10 57	11 54			12 54	13 54			14 13	14 54	15 54					16 13	16 54
Wrexham General	a			11 03	12 01			13 00	14 01			14 23	15 00	16 01					16 23	17 00
	d			11 04	12 02			13 00	14 02				15 00	16 02						17 02
Chester	a			11 21	12 19			13 19	14 20				15 21	16 20						17 22
Welshpool	d					11 49				13 49					15 49		15 49			
Newtown (Powys)	d					12 05				14 05					16 05		16 05			
Caersws	d					12 14				14 14					16 14		16 14			
Machynlleth 4	a					12 47				14 47					16 47		16 47			
	d	11 00	11 00			12 49	12 56			14 49	14 56				16 49	17 00	16 49	17 06		
Dovey Junction 4	d	11 07	11 07			12 56	13 03			14 56	15 03				16 56	17 07	16 56	17 13		
Borth	d					13 07				15 07					17 07		17 07			
Aberystwyth	a					13 26				15 26					17 26		17 26			
Penhelig	d	11x15	11x15				13x11				15x11					17x15		17x21		
Aberdovey	d	11 19	11 19				13 14				15 14					17 18		17 24		
Tywyn	a	11 25	11 25				13 20				15 20					17 24		17 30		
	d	11 26	11 30				13 22				15 22					17 26		17 31		
Tonfanau	d	11x30	11x34				13x26				15x26					17x30		17x35		
Llwyngwril	d	11x36	11x40				13x32				15x32					17x36		17x41		
Fairbourne	d	11 44	11 48				13 40				15 40					17 44		17 48		
Morfa Mawddach	d	11x46	11x50				13x42				15x42					17x46		17x50		
Barmouth	a	11 52	11 55				13 48				15 47					17 52		17 55		
	d	11 56	11 56				13 52				15 52					17 56		17 56		
Llanaber	d	11x59	11x59				13x55				15x55					17x59		17x59		
Talybont	d	12x03	12x03				13x59				15x58					18x03		18x03		
Dyffryn Ardudwy	d	12x05	12x05				14x01				16x00					18x05		18x05		
Llanbedr	d	12x08	12x08				14x04				16x04					18x08		18x08		
Pensarn	d	12x10	12x10				14x06				16x05					18x10		18x10		
Llandanwg	d	12x11	12x11				14x07				16x07					18x11		18x11		
Harlech	a	12 17	12 17				14 13				16 12					18 17		18 17		
	d	12 25	12 25				14 31				16 21					18 26		18 26		
Tygwyn	d	12x29	12x29				14x35				16x25					18x30		18x30		
Talsarnau	d	12x31	12x31				14x36				16x26					18x31		18x31		
Llandecwyn	d	12x33	12x33				14x39				16x29					18x34		18x34		
Penrhyndeudraeth	d	12 36	12 36				14 42				16 32					18 37		18 37		
Minffordd	d	12 40	12 40				14 45				16 35					18 40		18 40		
Porthmadog	a	12 45	12 45				14 50				16 40					18 44		18 44		
	d	12 47	12 47				14 53				16 42					18 46		18 46		
Criccieth	d	12 55	12 55				15 01				16 50					18 54		18 54		
Penychain	d	13x00	13x00				15x06				16x55					18x59		18x59		
Abererch	d	13x03	13x03				15x09				16x58					19x03		19x03		
Pwllheli	a	13 14	13 14				15 18				17 09					19 13		19 13		

For general notes see front of timetable
For details of catering facilities see Directory of Train Operators

A From 7 September
B Until 4 September
C To Holyhead (Table 81)
D 🛒 to Aberystwyth
E From 7 September. 🛒 to Aberystwyth
G Until 4 September. 🛒 to Aberystwyth

Table 75 — Mondays to Fridays

Birmingham and Shrewsbury → Chester, Aberystwyth, Barmouth and Pwllheli

Network Diagram - see first page of Table 74

		AW	AW	AW		AW	AW	AW		WS	AW	AW		AW	AW	AW		WS	AW
				FO															
		R	**R**				**R**												
						◇		◇		**1** ◇	◇	◇		◇	◇	◇		**1** ◇	
		A				A	A							A					
		🍴	🍴			🍴	🍴	🍴		☕		🍴						☕	
London Euston 15 ⊖	d		14 43			15 43		16 43				17 43			18 43	19 43			
London Marylebone 10 ⊖	d									16 33								20 03	
Banbury	d																	21u16	
Birmingham International ✈	d		16 09			17 09		18 09				19 09			20 09	21 09			
Birmingham New Street 12	d		16 24			17 24		18 24				19 24			20 24	21 24			
Tame Bridge Parkway	d									18 40								22 14	
Smethwick Galton Bdg L.L.	d		16 30			17 31		18 30				19 30			20 30	21 30			
Wolverhampton 7	d		16 43			17 43		18 43		18u58		19 43			20 43	21 43		22u30	
Cosford	d									19 06								22 41	
Telford Central	d		16 59			17 59		18 59		19 15		19 59			20 59	21 59		22 50	
Wellington (Shropshire)	d		17 06			18 06		19 06		19 21		20 06			21 06	22 06		22 57	
Shrewsbury	a		17 19			18 19		19 20		19 34		20 19			21 19	22 19		23 10	
Cardiff Central 7	d	15 20				16 15	17 20					17 50		19 34		20 10		20 53	
Manchester Piccadilly 10	d		15 30					17 30							19 30				
Crewe 10	d		16 12					18 12							20 12				
Shrewsbury	d	17 24	17 27			18 24	19 24	19 29		19 39		20 24		21 39	21 42	22 23		23 15	23 37
Gobowen	d	17 43				18 43	19 43			20 03		20 43		21 58		22 43		23 36	23 56
Chirk	d	17 48				18 49	19 48			20 08		20 49		22 03		22 48		23 41	00 02
Ruabon	d	17 54				18 55	19 54			20 15		20 55		22 09		22 54		23 48	00 08
Wrexham General	a	18 01				19 01	20 01			20 23		21 01		22 15		23 00		23 57	00 14
	d	18 02				19 02	20 02					21 02		22 15		23 01			00 14
Chester	a	18 21				19 20	20 20					21 19		22 34		23 18			00 34
Welshpool	d		17 49					19 51							22 04				
Newtown (Powys)	d		18 05					20 07							22 20				
Caersws	d		18 14					20 16							22 29				
Machynlleth 4	a		18 47					20 47							23 00				
	d		18 49	19 00				20 49			21 17				23 05				
Dovey Junction 4	d		18 56	19 07				20 56			21 24				23 12				
Borth	d		19 07					21 07							23 23				
Aberystwyth	a		19 26					21 26							23 42				
Penhelig	d			19x16							21x32								
Aberdovey	d			19 19							21 35								
Tywyn	a			19 25							21 41								
	d			19 25							21 42								
Tonfanau	d			19x30							21x46								
Llwyngwril	d			19x36							21x52								
Fairbourne	d			19 44							21 59								
Morfa Mawddach	d			19x46							22x02								
Barmouth	a			19 55							22 08								
	d										22 08								
Llanaber	d										22x11								
Talybont	d										22x15								
Dyffryn Ardudwy	d										22x17								
Llanbedr	d										22x20								
Pensarn	d										22x22								
Llandanwg	d										22x23								
Harlech	a										22 29								
	d										22 29								
Tygwyn	d										22x33								
Talsarnau	d										22x35								
Llandecwyn	d										22x37								
Penrhyndeudraeth	d										22 40								
Minffordd	d										22 44								
Porthmadog	a										22 48								
	d										22 48								
Criccieth	d										22 56								
Penychain	d										23x01								
Abererch	d										23x04								
Pwllheli	a										23 13								

For general notes see front of timetable
For details of catering facilities see Directory of Train Operators

A To Holyhead (Table 81)

Saturdays

Birmingham and Shrewsbury → Chester, Aberystwyth, Barmouth and Pwllheli

Network Diagram - see first page of Table 74

	AW	AW	AW ◇	AW	AW	AW ◇	AW ◇	AW ◇ A 🛒	AW ◇ 🛒	AW ◇	AW ◇ A 🛒	AW A 🛒	AW ◇ 🛒	AW ◇	AW ◇ A 🛒		WS 1 ◇ 🍽	AW ◇ A 🛒	AW ◇ B 🛒		AW ◇ A 🛒	AW ◇ A 🛒	AW ◇ B 🛒	
London Euston 15 ⊖ d													06 23		07 43				08 43		09 43		10 43	
London Marylebone 10 ⊖ d																	07 20							
Banbury d																	08u31							
Birmingham International ✈ d											07 09		08 09		09 09				10 09		11 09		12 09	
Birmingham New Street 12 d									06 24		07 24		08 24		09 24				10 24		11 24		12 24	
Tame Bridge Parkway d																	09 40							
Smethwick Galton Bdg L.L. d									06 30		07 30		08 30		09 30				10 30		11 30		12 30	
Wolverhampton 7 d									06 42		07 42		08 43		09 43		09u59		10 43		11 43		12 43	
Cosford d																	10 10							
Telford Central d									06 59		07 59		08 59		09 59		10 19		10 59		11 59		12 59	
Wellington (Shropshire) d									07 05		08 05		09 06		10 06		10 25		11 06		12 06		13 06	
Shrewsbury a									07 18		08 18		09 19		10 19		10 38		11 19		12 19		13 19	
Cardiff Central 7 d								05 21			05 40	07 20			07 50			09 20				11 20		
Manchester Piccadilly 10 d													07 30						09 30				11 30	
Crewe 10 d									05 55				08 08						10 13				12 12	
Shrewsbury d	23p37			05 20			06 10	07 24	07 27		08 24	09 24	09 27		10 22		10 42	11 24	11 27		12 22	13 24	13 27	
Gobowen d	23p56			05 39			06 30	07 43			08 43	09 43			10 42		11 03	11 43			12 42	13 43		
Chirk d	00 02			05 45			06 35	07 48			08 49	09 48			10 47		11 08	11 48			12 47	13 48		
Ruabon d	00 08			05 51			06 42	07 54			08 55	09 54			10 54		11 15	11 54			12 54	13 54		
Wrexham General a	00 14			05 57			06 48	08 00			09 01	10 01			11 00		11 24	12 01			13 00	14 01		
d	00 14			05 58			06 49	08 01			09 02	10 02			11 00			12 02			13 00	14 02		
Chester a	00 34			06 16			07 07	08 19			09 19	10 19			11 20			12 19			13 19	14 20		
Welshpool d									07 49				09 49						11 49				13 49	
Newtown (Powys) d									08 05				10 05						12 05				14 05	
Caersws d									08 14				10 14						12 14				14 14	
Machynlleth 4 a									08 47				10 47						12 47				14 47	
d		04 35	05 15		06 30	06 49			08 49	09 05			10 49	11 00					12 49	12 56			14 49	14 56
Dovey Junction 4 d		04 42	05 22		06 37	06 56			08 56	09 12			10 56	11 07					12 56	13 03			14 56	15 03
Borth d		04 53			06 48				09 07				11 07						13 07				15 07	
Aberystwyth a		05 12			07 07				09 26				11 26						13 26				15 26	
Penhelig d			05x30			07x04				09x20				11x15						13x11				15x11
Aberdovey d			05 34			07 07				09 23				11 19						13 14				15 14
Tywyn a			05 40			07 13				09 29				11 25						13 20				15 20
d			05 40			07 15				09 30				11 26						13 22				15 22
Tonfanau d			05x44			07x19				09x34				11x30						13x26				15x26
Llwyngwril d			05x50			07x25				09x40				11x36						13x32				15x32
Fairbourne d			05 57			07 33				09 48				11 44						13 40				15 40
Morfa Mawddach d			05x59			07x35				09 50				11x46						13x42				15x42
Barmouth a			06 08			07 40				09 56				11 52						13 48				15 47
d			06 09			07 50				09 57				11 56						13 52				15 52
Llanaber d			06x13			07x53				10x00				11x59						13x55				15x55
Talybont d						07x57				10x04				12x03						13x59				15x58
Dyffryn Ardudwy d						07x59				10x06				12x05						14x01				16x00
Llanbedr d						08x02				10x09				12x08						14x04				16x04
Pensarn d						08x04				10x11				12x10						14x06				16x05
Llandanwg d						08x05				10x12				12x11						14x07				16x07
Harlech a			06 29			08 11				10 18				12 17						14 13				16 12
d			06 29			08 32				10 21				12 25						14 31				16 21
Tygwyn d						08x36				10x25				12x29						14x35				16x25
Talsarnau d						08x37				10x27				12x31						14x36				16x26
Llandecwyn d						08x40				10x29				12x33						14x39				16x29
Penrhyndeudraeth d						08 43				10 32				12 36						14 42				16 32
Minffordd d						08 46				10 36				12 40						14 45				16 35
Porthmadog a			06 45			08 51				10 41				12 45						14 50				16 40
d			06 45			08 52				10 42				12 47						14 53				16 42
Criccieth d						08 59				10 50				12 55						15 01				16 50
Penychain d			06x58			09x05				10x55				13x00						15x06				16x55
Abererch d						09x08				10x58				13x03						15x09				16x58
Pwllheli a			07 05			09 13				11 09				13 14						15 18				17 09

For general notes see front of timetable
For details of catering facilities see Directory of Train Operators

A To Holyhead (Table 81)
B 🛒 to Aberystwyth

Birmingham and Shrewsbury → Chester, Aberystwyth, Barmouth and Pwllheli

Network Diagram - see first page of Table 74

		AW ◇ A 🍴	WS 1 ◇ 🍽		AW ◇ A 🍴	AW ◇ B 🍴		AW ◇ A 🍴	AW ◇ A 🍴	AW R 🍴	AW ◇ A 🍴		WS 1 ◇ 🍽	AW	AW ◇ A 🍴	AW ◇ 🍴	AW ◇	AW ◇ 🍴	AW ◇ C	AW ◇	WS 1 ◇ 🍽	AW ◇	AW		
London Euston 15 ⊖	d	11 43				12 43		13 43		14 43	15 43					16 43		17 43		18 43		19b30			
London Marylebone 10 ⊖	d		11 24										15 24								18 24				
Banbury	d		12u38										16u38								19u38				
Birmingham International ✈	d	13 09				14 09		15 09		16 09	17 09					18 09		19 09		20 09		21 09			
Birmingham New Street 12	d	13 23				14 24		15 24		16 24	17 24					18 24		19 24		20 24		21 24			
Tame Bridge Parkway	d		13 40										17 42								20 40				
Smethwick Galton Bdg L.L.	d	13 29				14 30		15 30		16 30	17 31					18 30		19 30		20 30		21 30			
Wolverhampton 7 🚌	d	13 43	13u59			14 43		15 43		16 43	17 43		17u59			18 43		19 43		20 43	20u55	21 42			
Cosford	d		14 10										18 10								21 06				
Telford Central	d	13 59	14 19			14 59		15 59		16 59	17 59		18 19			18 59		19 59		20 59	21 15	21 59			
Wellington (Shropshire)	d	14 06	14 25			15 06		16 06		17 06	18 06		18 25			19 06		20 06		21 06	21 21	22 05			
Shrewsbury	a	14 19	14 38			15 19		16 19		17 19	18 19		18 38			19 19		20 19		21 19	21 36	22 21			
Cardiff Central 7	d	*11 50*	*11 50*		13 20			*13 50*	15 20		*15 50*				17 20			*17 50*	19 34			*20 10*	*20 53*		
Manchester Piccadilly 10 🚌	d					*13 30*				*15 30*						*17 30*				*19 30*					
Crewe 10	d					*14 12*				*16 12*						*18 12*				*20 12*					
Shrewsbury	d	14 22	14 42		15 24	15 27		16 22	17 24	17 27	18 24		18 42		19 24	19 27		20 24	21 37	21 42	21 47	22 23	23 33		
Gobowen	d	14 42	15 03		15 43			16 42	17 43		18 43		19 03		19 44			20 43	21 56		22 14	22 42	23 52		
Chirk	d	14 47	15 08		15 48			16 47	17 48		18 49		19 08		19 49			20 49	22 01		22 19	22 48	23 58		
Ruabon	d	14 54	15 15		15 54			16 54	17 54		18 55		19 15		19 55			20 55	22 07		22 26	22 54	00 04		
Wrexham General	a	15 00	15 24		16 01			17 00	18 01		19 01		19 24		20 01			21 01	22 13		22 35	23 00	00 10		
	d	15 00			16 02			17 02	18 01		19 02			19 46	20 02			21 02	22 13			23 01	00 14		
Chester	a	15 21			16 21			17 20	18 20		19 20			20 04	20 20			21 19	22 31			23 18	00 31		
Welshpool	d					15 49				17 49						19 49				22 04					
Newtown (Powys)	d					16 05				18 05						20 05				22 20					
Caersws	d					16 14				18 14						20 14				22 29					
Machynlleth 4	a					16 47				18 47						20 47				23 00					
	d					16 49	17 00			18 49						20 49	21 17			23 05					
Dovey Junction 4	d					16 56	17 07			18 56						20 56	21 24			23 12					
Borth	d					17 07				19 07						21 07				23 23					
Aberystwyth	a					17 26				19 26						21 26				23 42					
Penhelig	d						17x15										21x32								
Aberdovey	d						17 18										21 35								
Tywyn	a						17 24										21 41								
	d						17 26										21 42								
Tonfanau	d						17x30										21x46								
Llwyngwril	d						17x36										21x52								
Fairbourne	d						17 44										21 59								
Morfa Mawddach	d						17x46										22x02								
Barmouth	a						17 52										22 08								
	d						17 56										22 08								
Llanaber	d						17x59										22x11								
Talybont	d						18x03										22x15								
Dyffryn Ardudwy	d						18x05										22x17								
Llanbedr	d						18x08										22x20								
Pensarn	d						18x10										22x22								
Llandanwg	d						18x11										22x23								
Harlech	a						18 17										22 29								
	d						18 26										22 29								
Tygwyn	d						18x30										22x33								
Talsarnau	d						18x31										22x35								
Llandecwyn	d						18x34										22x37								
Penrhyndeudraeth	d						18 37										22 40								
Minffordd	d						18 40										22 44								
Porthmadog	a						18 44										22 48								
	d						18 46										22 48								
Criccieth	d						18 54										22 56								
Penychain	d						18x59										23x01								
Abererch	d						19x03										23x04								
Pwllheli	a						19 13										23 13								

For general notes see front of timetable
For details of catering facilities see Directory of Train Operators

A To Holyhead (Table 81)
B 🍴 to Aberystwyth
C To Llandudno Junction (Table 81)

b From 12 September dep. 1943

Table 75

Sundays

until 12 July

Birmingham and Shrewsbury → Chester, Aberystwyth, Barmouth and Pwllheli

Network Diagram - see first page of Table 74

		AW	AW	AW ◇	AW ◇	AW	AW 🛒	AW	AW ◇ 🛒	WS [1] ◇	AW ◇ 🛒	AW ◇	AW ◇ 🛒	AW ◇ 🛒
London Euston [15] ⊖	d								*08 50*		*09 50*		*10 50*	*12 38*
London Marylebone [10] ⊖	d									09 30				
Banbury	d									10u42				
Birmingham International ✈	d								10 48		12 08		13 05	14 07
Birmingham New Street [12]	d								11 05		12 24		13 24	14 24
Tame Bridge Parkway	d									11 46				
Smethwick Galton Bdg L.L.	d													
Wolverhampton [7] ⛴	d								11 27	12u03	12 41		13 42	14 43
Cosford	d								11 43	12 15			13 58	
Telford Central	d								11 54	12 23	12 57		14 09	14 59
Wellington (Shropshire)	d								12 01	12 29	13 04		14 15	15 06
Shrewsbury	a								12 15	12 44	13 17		14 28	15 19
Cardiff Central [7]	d								*09 35*		*10 40*		*11 45*	*12 45*
Manchester Piccadilly [10] ⛴	d										*11 24*			*13 30*
Crewe [10]	d										*12 13*			*14 13*
Shrewsbury	d	23p30		08 33			10 16		12 16	12 47	13 25		14 30	15 26
Gobowen	d	23p49					10 35		12 36	13 08			14 50	
Chirk	d	23p55					10 40		12 41	13 13			14 55	
Ruabon	d	00 01					10 46		12 48	13 20			15 02	
Wrexham General	a	00 07					10 52		12 54	13 30			15 08	
	d	00 08					10 53		12 55				15 08	
Chester	a	00 25					11 11		13 19				15 29	
Welshpool	d			08 56							13 47			15 49
Newtown (Powys)	d			09 12							14 03			16 05
Caersws	d			09 21							14 12			16 14
Machynlleth [4]	a			09 52							14 47			16 47
	d		08 30	09 55	09 56	10 50		12 35			14 49	15 00		16 49
Dovey Junction [4]	d		08 37	10 02	10 03	10 57		12 42			14 56	15 07		16 56
Borth	d		08 48	10 12		11 08		12 53			15 07			17 07
Aberystwyth	a		09 05	10 29		11 25		13 10			15 26			17 26
Penhelig	d				10x11							15x15		
Aberdovey	d				10 14							15 19		
Tywyn	a				10 20							15 25		
	d				10 21							15 30		
Tonfanau	d				10x25							15x34		
Llwyngwril	d				10x31							15x41		
Fairbourne	d				10 39							15 48		
Morfa Mawddach	d				10x41							15x51		
Barmouth	a				10 46							15 56		
	d				10 47							15 57		
Llanaber	d				10x50							16x01		
Talybont	d				10x54							16x05		
Dyffryn Ardudwy	d				10x56							16x07		
Llanbedr	d				11x00							16x11		
Pensarn	d				11x02							16x13		
Llandanwg	d				11x03							16x14		
Harlech	a				11 10							16 21		
	d				11 10							16 21		
Tygwyn	d				11x14							16x25		
Talsarnau	d				11x16							16x27		
Llandecwyn	d				11x19							16x30		
Penrhyndeudraeth	d				11 22							16 33		
Minffordd	d				11 24							16 36		
Porthmadog	a				11 29							16 40		
	d				11 30							16 41		
Criccieth	d				11 37							16 48		
Penychain	d				11x42							16x55		
Abererch	d				11x46							16x58		
Pwllheli	a				11 54							17 06		

For general notes see front of timetable
For details of catering facilities see Directory of Train Operators

Sundays until 12 July

Birmingham and Shrewsbury → Chester, Aberystwyth, Barmouth and Pwllheli

Network Diagram - see first page of Table 74

		AW ◇ A 🍴	AW ◇ B 🍴		AW [R] A	AW ◇ A 🍴	AW ◇ 🍴	AW [R] A	WS [1] ◇ 🍵	AW ◇ 🍴	AW ◇	WS [1] ◇ 🍵	AW
London Euston [15] ⊖	d	13 38	14 38			15 38	16 38			17 38	18 38		
London Marylebone [10] ⊖	d								16 15			18 32	
Banbury	d								17u29			19u46	
Birmingham International ✈	d	15 07	16 07			17 07	18 07			19 07	20 08		
Birmingham New Street [12]	d	15 24	16 24			17 24	18 24			19 24	20 24		
Tame Bridge Parkway	d								18 30			20 47	
Smethwick Galton Bdg L.L.	d												
Wolverhampton [7] ⛴	d	15 43	16 43			17 43	18 43		18u54	19 43	20 43	21u01	
Cosford	d	15 59				17 59			19 08	19 59		21 12	
Telford Central	d	16 09	16 59			18 09	18 59		19 17	20 09	20 59	21 21	
Wellington (Shropshire)	d	16 17	17 06			18 16	19 06		19 23	20 17	21 06	21 27	
Shrewsbury	a	16 30	17 19			18 29	19 20		19 39	20 30	21 19	21 40	
Cardiff Central [7]	d	*13 45*	*15 00*		15 20	*16 00*	*17 20*	17 20	*17 40*		*18 45*		
Manchester Piccadilly [10] ⛴	d		*15 30*				*17 30*				*19 30*		
Crewe [10]	d		*16 13*				*18 13*				*20 13*		
Shrewsbury	d	16 32	17 26		17 30	18 30	19 27	19 32	19 50	20 34	21 26	21 43	
Gobowen	d	16 51			17 49	18 50		19 51	20 11	20 53		22 04	
Chirk	d	16 57			17 55	18 55		19 57	20 16	20 59		22 09	
Ruabon	d	17 03			18 01	19 02		20 03	20 23	21 05		22 16	
Wrexham General	a	17 09			18 07	19 08		20 09	20 31	21 11		22 26	
	d	17 10			18 08	19 08		20 10		21 12			22 35
Chester	a	17 28			18 25	19 26	21 30	20 31		21 30			22a53
Welshpool	d		17 48				19 49				21 48		
Newtown (Powys)	d		18 04				20 05				22 04		
Caersws	d		18 13				20 14				22 13		
Machynlleth [4]	a		18 47				20 47				22 43		
	d		18 49	18 55			20 49				22 46		
Dovey Junction [4]	d		18 56	19 02			20 56				22 53		
Borth	d		19 07				21 07				23 04		
Aberystwyth	a		19 26				21 26				23 23		
Penhelig	d			19x10									
Aberdovey	d			19 14									
Tywyn	a			19 20									
	d			19 20									
Tonfanau	d			19x24									
Llwyngwril	d			19x31									
Fairbourne	d			19 38									
Morfa Mawddach	d			19x41									
Barmouth	a			19 46									
	d			19 47									
Llanaber	d			19x51									
Talybont	d			19x55									
Dyffryn Ardudwy	d			19x57									
Llanbedr	d			20x01									
Pensarn	d			20x03									
Llandanwg	d			20x04									
Harlech	a			20 11									
	d			20 11									
Tygwyn	d			20x15									
Talsarnau	d			20x17									
Llandecwyn	d			20x20									
Penrhyndeudraeth	d			20 23									
Minffordd	d			20 26									
Porthmadog	a			20 30									
	d			20 31									
Criccieth	d			20 38									
Penychain	d			20x45									
Abererch	d			20x48									
Pwllheli	a			20 56									

For general notes see front of timetable
For details of catering facilities see Directory of Train Operators

A To Holyhead (Table 81)
B 🍴 to Aberystwyth

Table 75

Sundays

Birmingham and Shrewsbury → Chester, Aberystwyth, Barmouth and Pwllheli

19 July to 6 September

Network Diagram - see first page of Table 74

		AW	AW	AW ◇	AW ◇	AW	AW	AW	AW ◇	WS 1 ◇	AW ◇	AW ◇	AW ◇	AW ◇
London Euston 15	⊖ d								*08 50*		*09 50*		*10 50*	*12 38*
London Marylebone 10	⊖ d									09 30				
Banbury	d									10u42				
Birmingham International	✈ d								10 48		12 08		13 05	14 07
Birmingham New Street 12	d								11 05		12 24		13 24	14 24
Tame Bridge Parkway	d													
Smethwick Galton Bdg L.L.	d													
Wolverhampton 7	d								11 27	12u06	12 41		13 42	14 43
Cosford	d								11 43	12 18			13 58	
Telford Central	d								11 54	12 26	12 57		14 09	14 59
Wellington (Shropshire)	d								12 01	12 32	13 04		14 15	15 06
Shrewsbury	a								12 15	12 47	13 17		14 28	15 19
Cardiff Central 7	d								*09 35*		*10 40*		*11 45*	*12 45*
Manchester Piccadilly 10	d										*11 24*			*13 30*
Crewe 10	d										*12 13*			*14 13*
Shrewsbury	d	23p30		08 33			10 16		12 16	12 49	13 25		14 30	15 26
Gobowen	d	23p49					10 35		12 36	13 10			14 50	
Chirk	d	23p55					10 40		12 41	13 15			14 55	
Ruabon	d	00 01					10 46		12 48	13 22			15 02	
Wrexham General	a	00 07					10 52		12 54	13 30			15 08	
	d	00 08					10 53		12 55				15 08	
Chester	a	00 25					11 11		13 19				15 29	
Welshpool	d			08 56							13 47			15 49
Newtown (Powys)	d			09 12							14 03			16 05
Caersws	d			09 21							14 12			16 14
Machynlleth 4	a			09 52							14 47			16 47
	d		08 30	09 55	09 56	10 50		12 35			14 49	15 00		16 49
Dovey Junction 4	d		08 37	10 02	10 03	10 57		12 42			14 56	15 07		16 56
Borth	d		08 48	10 12		11 08		12 53			15 07			17 07
Aberystwyth	a		09 05	10 29		11 25		13 10			15 26			17 26
Penhelig	d				10x11							15x15		
Aberdovey	d				10 14							15 19		
Tywyn	a				10 20							15 25		
	d				10 21							15 30		
Tonfanau	d				10x25							15x34		
Llwyngwril	d				10x31							15x41		
Fairbourne	d				10 39							15 48		
Morfa Mawddach	d				10x41							15x51		
Barmouth	a				10 46							15 56		
	d				10 47							15 57		
Llanaber	d				10x50							16x01		
Talybont	d				10x54							16x05		
Dyffryn Ardudwy	d				10x56							16x07		
Llanbedr	d				11x00							16x11		
Pensarn	d				11x02							16x13		
Llandanwg	d				11x03							16x14		
Harlech	a				11 10							16 21		
	d				11 10							16 21		
Tygwyn	d				11x14							16x25		
Talsarnau	d				11x16							16x27		
Llandecwyn	d				11x19							16x30		
Penrhyndeudraeth	d				11 22							16 33		
Minffordd	d				11 24							16 36		
Porthmadog	a				11 29							16 40		
	d				11 30							16 41		
Criccieth	d				11 37							16 48		
Penychain	d				11x42							16x55		
Abererch	d				11x46							16x58		
Pwllheli	a				11 54							17 06		

For general notes see front of timetable
For details of catering facilities see Directory of Train Operators

Sundays

Birmingham and Shrewsbury → Chester, Aberystwyth, Barmouth and Pwllheli

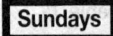

19 July to 6 September

Network Diagram - see first page of Table 74

		AW	AW		AW	AW	AW	AW	WS	AW	AW	WS	AW
		◇ A ✠	◇ B ✠		R A	◇ A ✠	◇ ✠	R A	1 ◇ ☕	◇ ✠	◇	1 ◇ ☕	
London Euston 15 ⊖	d	13 38	14 38			15 38	16 38			17 38	18 38		
London Marylebone 10 ⊖	d								16 15			18 32	
Banbury	d								17u29			19u46	
Birmingham International ✈	d	15 07	16 07			17 07	18 07			19 07	20 08		
Birmingham New Street 12	d	15 24	16 24			17 24	18 24			19 24	20 24		
Tame Bridge Parkway	d												
Smethwick Galton Bdg L.L.	d								18 48				
Wolverhampton 7 🚌	d	15 43	16 43			17 43	18 43		18u57	19 43	20 43	21u01	
Cosford	d	15 59				17 59			19 08	19 59		21 12	
Telford Central	d	16 09	16 59			18 09	18 59		19 17	20 09	20 59	21 21	
Wellington (Shropshire)	d	16 17	17 06			18 16	19 06		19 23	20 17	21 06	21 27	
Shrewsbury	a	16 30	17 19			18 29	19 20		19 39	20 30	21 19	21 40	
Cardiff Central 7	d	13 45	15 00		15 20	16 00	17 20	17 20	17 40		18 45		
Manchester Piccadilly 10 🚌	d		15 30				17 30				19 30		
Crewe 10	d		16 13				18 13				20 13		
Shrewsbury	d	16 32	17 26		17 30	18 30	19 27	19 32	19 50	20 34	21 26	21 42	
Gobowen	d	16 51			17 49	18 50		19 51	20 11	20 53		22 04	
Chirk	d	16 57			17 55	18 55		19 57	20 16	20 59		22 09	
Ruabon	d	17 03			18 01	19 02		20 03	20 23	21 05		22 16	
Wrexham General	a	17 09			18 07	19 08		20 09	20 31	21 11		22 26	
	d	17 10			18 08	19 08		20 10		21 12			22 35
Chester	a	17 28			18 25	19 26		20 31		21 30			22a53
Welshpool	d		17 48				19 49				21 48		
Newtown (Powys)	d		18 04				20 05				22 04		
Caersws	d		18 13				20 14				22 13		
Machynlleth 4	a		18 47				20 47				22 43		
	d		18 49	18 55			20 49				22 46		
Dovey Junction 4	d		18 56	19 02			20 56				22 53		
Borth	d		19 07				21 07				23 04		
Aberystwyth	a		19 26				21 26				23 23		
Penhelig	d			19x10									
Aberdovey	d			19 14									
Tywyn	a			19 20									
	d			19 20									
Tonfanau	d			19x24									
Llwyngwril	d			19x31									
Fairbourne	d			19 38									
Morfa Mawddach	d			19x41									
Barmouth	a			19 46									
	d			19 47									
Llanaber	d			19x51									
Talybont	d			19x55									
Dyffryn Ardudwy	d			19x57									
Llanbedr	d			20x01									
Pensarn	d			20x03									
Llandanwg	d			20x04									
Harlech	a			20 11									
	d			20 11									
Tygwyn	d			20x15									
Talsarnau	d			20x17									
Llandecwyn	d			20x20									
Penrhyndeudraeth	d			20 23									
Minffordd	d			20 26									
Porthmadog	a			20 30									
	d			20 31									
Criccieth	d			20 38									
Penychain	d			20x45									
Abererch	d			20x48									
Pwllheli	a			20 56									

For general notes see front of timetable
For details of catering facilities see Directory of Train Operators

A To Holyhead (Table 81)
B ✠ to Aberystwyth

Table 75

Sundays

Birmingham and Shrewsbury → Chester, Aberystwyth, Barmouth and Pwllheli

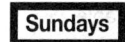

from 13 September

Network Diagram - see first page of Table 74

	AW	AW	AW	AW	AW	AW	WS	AW	AW	AW	AW	AW		AW	AW	AW	AW	WS	AW	AW	WS	AW
														R			R					
					◇	◇	1 ◇	◇	◇	◇	◇	◇			◇	◇		1 ◇	◇	◇	1 ◇	
												A		B	B		B					
				[trolley]		[trolley]	[buffet]	[trolley]	[trolley]	[trolley]	[trolley]	[trolley]			[trolley]	[trolley]		[buffet]	[trolley]		[buffet]	
London Euston 15 ⊖ d						08 50		09 50	10 50	12 38	13 38	14 38			15 38	16 38			17 38	18 38		
London Marylebone 10 ⊖ d							09 30											16 15			18 32	
Banbury d							10u42											17u29			19u46	
Birmingham International ✈ d						10 48		12 08	13 05	14 07	15 07	16 07			17 07	18 07			19 07	20 08		
Birmingham New Street 12 d						11 05		12 24	13 24	14 24	15 24	16 24			18 04	18 24			19 24	20 24		
Tame Bridge Parkway d							11 46											18 30			20 47	
Smethwick Galton Bdg L.L. d																						
Wolverhampton 7 🚌 d						11 27	12u03	12 41	13 42	14 43	15 43	16 43			17 43	18 43		18u54	19 43	20 43	21u01	
Cosford d						11 43	12 15		13 58		15 59				17 59			19 08	19 59		21 12	
Telford Central d						11 54	12 23	12 57	14 09	14 59	16 09	16 59			18 09	18 59		19 17	20 09	20 59	21 21	
Wellington (Shropshire) d						12 01	12 29	13 04	14 15	15 06	16 17	17 06			18 16	19 06		19 23	20 17	21 06	21 27	
Shrewsbury a						12 15	12 44	13 17	14 28	15 19	16 30	17 19			18 29	19 20		19 39	20 30	21 19	21 40	
Cardiff Central 7 d					08 30	09 35		10 40	11 45	12 45	13 45	15 00		15 20	16 00	17 20	17 20	17 40		18 45		
Manchester Piccadilly 10 🚌 d					09 30			11 30		13 30		15 30				17 30				19 30		
Crewe 10 d					10 13			12 13		14 13		16 13				18 13				20 13		
Shrewsbury d	23p30			10 16	11 23	12 16	12 47	13 25	14 30	15 26	16 32	17 26		17 30	18 30	19 27	19 32	19 50	20 34	21 26	21 43	
Gobowen d	23p49			10 35		12 36	13 08		14 50		16 51			17 49	18 50		19 51	20 11	20 53		22 04	
Chirk d	23p55			10 40		12 41	13 13		14 55		16 57			17 55	18 55		19 57	20 16	20 59		22 09	
Ruabon d	00 01			10 46		12 48	13 20		15 02		17 03			18 01	19 02		20 03	20 23	21 05		22 16	
Wrexham General a	00 07			10 52		12 54	13 30		15 08		17 09			18 07	19 08		20 09	20 31	21 11		22 26	
d	00 08			10 53		12 55			15 08		17 10			18 08	19 08		20 10		21 12			22 35
Chester a	00 25			11 11		13 19			15 29		17 30			18 25	19 26		20 31		21 30			22 53
Welshpool d					11 45			13 47		15 49		17 48				19 49				21 48		
Newtown (Powys) d					12 01			14 03		16 05		18 04				20 05				22 04		
Caersws d					12 10			14 12		16 14		18 13				20 14				22 13		
Machynlleth 4 a					12 45			14 47		16 47		18 47				20 47				22 43		
d		08 50	10 50		12 46			14 49		16 49		18 49	18 55			20 49				22 46		
Dovey Junction 4 d		08 57	10 57		12 53			14 56		16 56		18 56	19 02			20 56				22 53		
Borth d		09 08	11 08		13 04			15 07		17 07		19 07				21 07				23 04		
Aberystwyth a		09 25	11 25		13 21			15 26		17 26		19 26				21 26				23 23		
Penhelig d													19x10									
Aberdovey d													19 14									
Tywyn a													19 20									
d													19 20									
Tonfanau d													19x24									
Llwyngwril d													19x31									
Fairbourne d													19 38									
Morfa Mawddach d													19x41									
Barmouth a													19 46									
d													19 47									
Llanaber d													19x51									
Talybont d													19x55									
Dyffryn Ardudwy d													19x57									
Llanbedr d													20x01									
Pensarn d													20x03									
Llandanwg d													20x04									
Harlech a													20 11									
d													20 11									
Tygwyn d													20x15									
Talsarnau d													20x17									
Llandecwyn d													20x20									
Penrhyndeudraeth d													20 23									
Minffordd d													20 26									
Porthmadog a													20 30									
d													20 31									
Criccieth d													20 38									
Penychain d													20x45									
Abererch d													20x48									
Pwllheli a													20 56									

For general notes see front of timetable
For details of catering facilities see Directory of Train Operators

A [trolley] to Aberystwyth
B To Holyhead (Table 81)

Pwllheli, Barmouth, Aberystwyth and Chester → Shrewsbury and Birmingham

Network Diagram - see first page of Table 74

Miles	Miles	Miles	Station		AW MX	WS 1 ◇ 🍽	AW ◇ A	AW	AW ◇ B 🛒	AW ◇ 🛒	AW ◇ C 🛒	WS 1 ◇ 🍽	AW ◇ C 🛒	AW ◇	AW ◇ 🛒	AW ◇	AW ◇ C 🛒	AW ◇ C 🛒
—	0	—	**Pwllheli**	d												06 21		
—	1¾	—	Abererch	d												06x25		
—	3¼	—	Penychain	d												06x27		
—	7¾	—	Criccieth	d												06 35		
—	12¾	—	Porthmadog	a												06 42		
—	—	—		d												06 47		
—	15	—	Minffordd	d												06 51		
—	16¼	—	Penrhyndeudraeth	d												06 54		
—	17	—	Llandecwyn	d												06x57		
—	18¼	—	Talsarnau	d												06x59		
—	19	—	Tygwyn	d												07x01		
—	21½	—	Harlech	a												07 05		
—	—	—		d												07 20		
—	23½	—	Llandanwg	d												07x25		
—	24¼	—	Pensarn	d												07x26		
—	25	—	Llanbedr	d												07x28		
—	27	—	Dyffryn Ardudwy	d												07x32		
—	28½	—	Talybont	d												07x34		
—	30½	—	Llanaber	d												07x37		
—	32	—	**Barmouth**	a												07 42		
—	—	—		d										06 46		07 48		
—	33¾	—	Morfa Mawddach	d										06x50		07x53		
—	34¾	—	Fairbourne	d										06 53		07 56		
—	37¼	—	Llwyngwril	d										07x00		08x03		
—	41½	—	Tonfanau	d										07x06		08x09		
—	44¼	—	Tywyn	a										07 10		08 13		
—	—	—		d										07 16		08 16		
—	47½	—	Aberdovey	d										07 22		08 22		
—	48½	—	Penhelig	d										07x24		08x24		
0	—	—	**Aberystwyth**	d	23p53					05 30					07 30			
8¼	—	—	Borth	d	00 06					05 43					07 43			
16½	53½	—	Dovey Junction [4]	d	00 17					05 54				07 35	07 54	08 35		
20½	57½	—	**Machynlleth** [4]	a	00 24					06 03				07 44	08 03	08 44		
—	—	—		d						06 07				08 07				
42¼	—	—	Caersws	d						06 37				08 37				
47¾	—	—	Newtown (Powys)	d						06 46				08 46				
61¾	—	—	Welshpool	d						07 01				09 01				
—	—	0	**Chester**	d			05 15	05 45	06 22		07 22		08 22				09 30	10 22
—	—	12	Wrexham General	a			05 31	06 03	06 38		07 38		08 38				09 46	10 38
—	—	—		d		05 12	05 31		06 39		07 44	07 23	08 38				09 46	10 38
—	—	17	Ruabon	d			05 38		06 46		07 51	07 31	08 45				09 53	10 45
—	—	21¼	Chirk	d			05 44		06 52		07 57	07 38	08 51				09 59	10 51
—	—	24¼	Gobowen	d		05 27	05 50		06 58		08 03	07 43	08 57				10 05	10 57
81½	—	42	**Shrewsbury**	a		05 50	06 10		07 18	07 25	08 25	08 05	09 17	09 25			10 31	11 17
—	—	—	Crewe [10]	a						08 26				10 26				
—	—	—	Manchester Piccadilly [10] ⛴	a						09 15				11 15				
—	—	—	Cardiff Central [7]	a	12 54		08 17		09 22	09 52	10 55	09 58	11 19	11 55			12 54	13 20
—	—	—	**Shrewsbury**	d		05 52				07 31	08 31	08 07		09 31			10 35	
92	—	—	Wellington (Shropshire)	d						07 45	08 45	08 21		09 45			10 49	
96	—	—	Telford Central	d		06 09				07 51	08 51	08 27		09 51			10 55	
122¾	—	—	Cosford	d		06 17						08 36						
111½	—	—	**Wolverhampton** [7] ⛴	a						08 08	09 08			10 08			11 12	
120¾	—	—	Smethwick Galton Bdg L.L.	a						08 20	09 20			10 20			11 24	
—	—	—	Tame Bridge Parkway	d		06 41						09 02						
124¾	—	—	**Birmingham New Street** [12]	a						08 27	09 26			10 26			11 30	
—	—	—	Birmingham International ✈	a						08 50	09 50			10 50			11 50	
—	—	—	Banbury	a		07s46						10s06						
—	—	—	London Marylebone [10] ⊖	a		08 57						11 23						
—	—	—	London Euston [15] ⊖	a						10 14	11 14			12 14			13 14	

For general notes see front of timetable
For details of catering facilities see Directory of Train Operators

A To Maesteg (Table 128)
B From Holyhead (Table 81)
C From Holyhead (Table 81)

Pwllheli, Barmouth, Aberystwyth and Chester → Shrewsbury and Birmingham

Network Diagram - see first page of Table 74

		AW	AW	WS	AW	AW	AW	AW	AW	AW	AW	AW	AW	AW	WS	AW	AW	AW	AW	WS
		◇	◇	[1] ◇	◇	[R]	◇	◇	◇	◇	◇	◇	◇	◇	[1] ◇	◇	◇	◇	◇	[1] ◇
					A	A	B	B	C	C	A	D				A	A			
			🛒	☕	🛒	🛒		🛒		🛒	🛒	🛒		🛒	☕	🛒	🛒		🛒	☕
Pwllheli	d	07 28					09§36		09§36				11 38					13 42		
Abererch	d	07x32					09x40		09x40				11x42					13x46		
Penychain	d						09x42		09x42				11x44					13x48		
Criccieth	d	07 42					09§49		09§49				11 51					13 55		
Porthmadog	a	07 49					09§56		09§56				11 58					14 02		
	d	07 51					09§58		09§58				12 02					14 06		
Minffordd	d	07 55					10§02		10§02				12 06					14 10		
Penrhyndeudraeth	d	07 58					10§05		10§05				12 09					14 13		
Llandecwyn	d						10x08		10x08				12x12					14x16		
Talsarnau	d	08x03					10x10		10x10				12x14					14x18		
Tygwyn	d	08 05					10x12		10x12				12x16					14x20		
Harlech	a	08 09					10§16		10§16				12 20					14 24		
	d	08 33					10§22		10§22				12 25					14 30		
Llandanwg	d	08x38					10x27		10x27				12x30					14x35		
Pensarn	d	08x39					10x29		10x29				12x31					14x36		
Llanbedr	d	08x41					10x31		10x31				12x33					14x38		
Dyffryn Ardudwy	d	08x45					10x34		10x34				12x37					14x42		
Talybont	d	08x47					10x36		10x36				12x39					14x44		
Llanaber	d	08x50					10x40		10x40				12x42					14x47		
Barmouth	a	08 54					10§43		10§43				12 46					14 51		
	d	08 59					11§04		10§49				12 49					14 52		
Morfa Mawddach	d	09x04					11x09		10x54				12x54					14x57		
Fairbourne	d	09 06					11§11		10§56				12 56					14 59		
Llwyngwril	d	09x13					11x18		11x03				13x03					15x06		
Tonfanau	d	09x19					11x24		11x09				13x09					15x12		
Tywyn	a	09 25					11§29		11§14				13 16					15 17		
	d	09 31					11§29		11§27				13 23					15 23		
Aberdovey	d	09 37					11§35		11§33				13 29					15 29		
Penhelig	d	09x40					11x38		11x35				13x32					15x32		
Aberystwyth	d		09 30					11§30		11§30				13 30					15 30	
Borth	d		09 43					11§43		11§43				13 43					15 43	
Dovey Junction [4]	d	09 50	09 54				11§48	11§54	11§46	11§54			13 41	13 54				15 41	15 54	
Machynlleth [4]	a	09 57	10 03				11§59	12§03	11§56	12§03			13 53	14 03				15 49	16 03	
	d	10 07					12§07		12§07				14 07					16 07		
Caersws	d	10 37					12§37		12§37				14 37					16 37		
Newtown (Powys)	d	10 46					12§46		12§46				14 46					16 46		
Welshpool	d	11 01					13§01		13§01				15 01					17 01		
Chester	d				11 22	12 22					13 22	14 22				15 22	16 22			
Wrexham General	a				11 38	12 38					13 38	14 38				15 38	16 38			
	d			11 23	11 44	12 38					13 44	14 38			15 23	15 44	16 38			17 23
Ruabon	d			11 31	11 51	12 45					13 51	14 45			15 31	15 51	16 45			17 31
Chirk	d			11 38	11 57	12 51					13 57	14 51			15 38	15 57	16 51			17 38
Gobowen	d			11 43	12 03	12 57					14 03	14 57			15 43	16 03	16 57			17 43
Shrewsbury	a	11 25		12 06	12 27	13 17	13§25		13§25		14 27	15 17	15 25		16 06	16 27	17 17	17 25		18 06
Crewe [10]	a	*12 25*					*14§26*		*14§26*				*16 26*					*18 25*		
Manchester Piccadilly [10] 🚌	a	*13 15*					*15§15*		*15§15*				*17 15*					*19 15*		
Cardiff Central [7]	a	*13 54*			*14 54*	15 20	*15§53*		*15§53*		*16 54*	17 17	*17 52*			*18 59*	19 20	*19 49*		
Shrewsbury	d	11 31		12 07	12 31		13§31		13§31		14 31		15 31		16 07	16 31		17 31		18 07
Wellington (Shropshire)	d	11 45		12 21	12 45		13§45		13§45		14 45		15 45			16 45		17 45		18 21
Telford Central	d	11 51		12 27	12 51		13§51		13§51		14 51		15 51		16 24	16 51		17 51		18 27
Cosford	d			12 36											16 33					18 36
Wolverhampton [7] 🚌	a	12 08		12s47	13 08		14§08		14§08		15 08		16 08		16s47	17 08		18 08		18s47
Smethwick Galton Bdg L.L.	a	12 20			13 20		14§20		14§20		15 20		16 20			17 20		18 20		
Tame Bridge Parkway	d			13 02											17 02					19 02
Birmingham New Street [12]	a	12 26			13 26		14§26		14§26		15 26		16 26			17 26		18 26		
Birmingham International ✈	a	12 50			13 50		14§50		14§50		15 50		16 50			17 50		18 50		
Banbury	a			14s06											18s03					20s07
London Marylebone [10] ⊖	a			15 23											19 22					21 20
London Euston [15] ⊖	a	*14 14*			*15 14*		*16§14*		*16§14*		*17 14*		*18 14*			*19 14*		*20 14*		

For general notes see front of timetable
For details of catering facilities see Directory of Train Operators

A From Holyhead (Table 81)
B Until 4 September
C From 7 September
D From Holyhead (Table 81) to Maesteg (Table 128)

Pwllheli, Barmouth, Aberystwyth and Chester → Shrewsbury and Birmingham

Network Diagram - see first page of Table 74

		AW	AW		AW	AW	AW		AW	AW	VT		AW	AW	AW		AW	AW	AW		AW	AW			
																					FO				
		◇	◇		◇	◇	◇		◇	◇	1 ◇		◇		◇			◇	◇						
		A	B		C	A			A						A										
		🛒				🛒	🛒		🛒																
Pwllheli	d		15ʃ32		15ʃ32					17 38								20 00							
Abererch	d		15x36		15x36					17x42								20x04							
Penychain	d		15x38		15x38					17x44								20x06							
Criccieth	d		15ʃ45		15ʃ45					17 51								20 13							
Porthmadog	a		15ʃ52		15ʃ52					17 58								20 20							
	d		15ʃ56		15ʃ56					18 02								20 23							
Minffordd	d		16ʃ00		16ʃ00					18 06								20 27							
Penrhyndeudraeth	d		16ʃ03		16ʃ03					18 09								20 30							
Llandecwyn	d		16x06		16x06					18x12								20x33							
Talsarnau	d		16x08		16x08					18x14								20x35							
Tygwyn	d		16x11		16x11					18x16								20x37							
Harlech	a		16ʃ15		16ʃ15					18 20								20 41							
	d		16ʃ20		16ʃ20					18 25								20 46							
Llandanwg	d		16x25		16x25					18x30								20x51							
Pensarn	d		16x26		16x26					18x31								20x52							
Llanbedr	d		16x28		16x28					18x33								20x54							
Dyffryn Ardudwy	d		16x32		16x32					18x37								20x58							
Talybont	d		16x34		16x34					18x39								21x00							
Llanaber	d		16x37		16x37					18x42								21x03							
Barmouth	a		16ʃ41		16ʃ41					18 46								21 07							
	d		16ʃ50		16ʃ50					18 49								21 14			22 12				
Morfa Mawddach	d		16x55		16x55					18x54								21x19			22x17				
Fairbourne	d		16ʃ57		16ʃ57					18 56								21 21			22 19				
Llwyngwril	d		17x04		17x04					19x03								21x28			22x27				
Tonfanau	d		17x10		17x10					19x09								21x34			22x33				
Tywyn	a		17ʃ15		17ʃ15					19 14								21 39			22 37				
	d		17ʃ27		17ʃ32					19 26								21 46			22 38				
Aberdovey	d		17ʃ33		17ʃ38					19 32								21 52			22 44				
Penhelig	d		17x36		17x40					19x35								21x55			22x46				
Aberystwyth	d		ʃ		ʃ		17 30						19 30				21 36					23 53			
Borth	d		ʃ		ʃ		17 43						19 43				21 49					00 06			
Dovey Junction 4	d		17ʃ46		17ʃ51		17 54			19 46			19 54				22 00	22 06			22 57	00 17			
Machynlleth 4	a		17ʃ58		18ʃ02		18 03			19 58			20 03				22 07	22 16			23 03	00 24			
	d						18 07						20 07												
Caersws	d						18 37						20 39												
Newtown (Powys)	d						18 46						20 48												
Welshpool	d						19 01						21 03												
Chester	d	17 22				18 20			19 27		20 27				21 21				22 28						
Wrexham General	a	17 38				18 36			19 43		20 44				21 37				22 44						
	d	17 44				18 36			19 43					20 49	21 37				22 44						
Ruabon	d	17 51				18 43			19 50					20 57	21 44				22 51						
Chirk	d	17 57				18 49			19 56					21 03	21 50				22 57						
Gobowen	d	18 03				18 55			20 02					21 08	21 56				23 03						
Shrewsbury	a	18 24				19 15	19 28		20 22				21 27	21 28	22 16				23 23						
Crewe 10	a						*20 26*						*23 03*												
Manchester Piccadilly 10	⛴ a						*21 15*						*23 48*												
Cardiff Central 7	a	*20 58*				21 19	*22 09*		23 04					*00 11*	*01 10*										
Shrewsbury	d	18 31					19 32						21 33		22 18				23 26						
Wellington (Shropshire)	d	18 45					19 46						21 47		22 32				23 40						
Telford Central	d	18 51					19 52						21 53		22 38				23 47						
Cosford	d																		23 57						
Wolverhampton 7	⛴ a	19 08					20 09						22 10		22 55				00 17						
Smethwick Galton Bdg L.L.	a	19 20					20 20						22 24												
Tame Bridge Parkway	d																								
Birmingham New Street 12	a	19 26					20 27						22 30		23 26										
Birmingham International	✈ a	19 50					20 50						*23 05*		*00 04*										
Banbury	a																								
London Marylebone 10	⊖ a																								
London Euston 15	⊖ a	*21 14*					*22 33*						*01 13*												

For general notes see front of timetable
For details of catering facilities see Directory of Train Operators

A From Holyhead (Table 81)
B From 7 September
C Until 4 September

Table 75

Saturdays

Pwllheli, Barmouth, Aberystwyth and Chester → Shrewsbury and Birmingham

Network Diagram - see first page of Table 74

		AW	AW	WS	AW	AW	AW	AW	AW	AW	AW	WS	AW	AW	AW	AW	AW	WS	AW	AW	AW	AW
				1 ◇	◇	◇	◇	◇	◇	◇	◇	1 ◇	◇	◇	◇	◇	◇	1 ◇	◇	◇	◇	◇
					A		A	A					A	A			A		A			A
				ꟷP	⌶	⌶	⌶	⌶		⌶		ꟷP	⌶	⌶		⌶	⌶	ꟷP	⌶		⌶	⌶
Pwllheli	d										06 21				07 28					09 36		
Abererch	d										06x25				07x32					09x40		
Penychain	d										06x27				07x34					09x42		
Criccieth	d										06 35				07 42					09 49		
Porthmadog	a										06 42				07 49					09 56		
	d										06 47				07 51					09 58		
Minffordd	d										06 51				07 55					10 02		
Penrhyndeudraeth	d										06 54				07 58					10 05		
Llandecwyn	d										06x57									10x08		
Talsarnau	d										06x59				08x03					10x10		
Tygwyn	d										07x01				08 05					10x12		
Harlech	a										07 05				08 09					10 16		
	d										07 20				08 33					10 22		
Llandanwg	d										07x25				08x38					10x27		
Pensarn	d										07x26				08x39					10x29		
Llanbedr	d										07x28				08x41					10x31		
Dyffryn Ardudwy	d										07x32				08x45					10x34		
Talybont	d										07x34				08x47					10x36		
Llanaber	d										07x37				08x50					10x40		
Barmouth	a										07 42				08 54					10 43		
	d								06 46		07 48				08 59					10 49		
Morfa Mawddach	d								06x50		07x53				09x04					10x54		
Fairbourne	d								06 53		07 56				09 06					10 56		
Llwyngwril	d								07x00		08x03				09x13					11x03		
Tonfanau	d								07x06		08x09				09x19					11x09		
Tywyn	a								07 10		08 13				09 25					11 14		
	d								07 16		08 16				09 31					11 27		
Aberdovey	d								07 22		08 22				09 37					11 33		
Penhelig	d								07x24		08x24				09x40					11x35		
Aberystwyth	d	23p53				05 30				07 30						09 30					11 30	
Borth	d	00 06				05 43				07 43						09 43					11 43	
Dovey Junction 4	d	00 17				05 54			07 35	07 54	08 35				09 50	09 54				11 46	11 54	
Machynlleth 4	a	00 24				06 03			07 44	08 03	08 44				10 00	10 03				11 56	12 03	
	d					06 07				08 07						10 07					12 07	
Caersws	d					06 37				08 37						10 37					12 37	
Newtown (Powys)	d					06 46				08 46						10 46					12 46	
Welshpool	d					07 01				09 01						11 01					13 01	
Chester	d		05 37		06 12		07 22	08 22					09 30	10 22			11 22		12 22			13 22
Wrexham General	a		05 55		06 28		07 38	08 38					09 46	10 38			11 38		12 38			13 38
	d			06 18	06 38		07 44	08 38				09 26	09 46	10 38			11 44	12 20	12 38			13 44
Ruabon	d			06 26	06 45		07 51	08 45				09 34	09 53	10 45			11 51	12 28	12 45			13 51
Chirk	d			06 32	06 51		07 57	08 51					09 59	10 51			11 57		12 51			13 57
Gobowen	d			06 37	06 57		08 03	08 57				09 44	10 05	10 57			12 03	12 37	12 57			14 03
Shrewsbury	a			07 00	07 17	07 28	08 23	09 17		09 25		10 07	10 27	11 17		11 25	12 27	13 00	13 17		13 25	14 27
Crewe 10	a					*08 25*				*10 25*						*12 25*					*14 26*	
Manchester Piccadilly 10	a					*09 14*				*11 15*						*13 15*					*15 15*	
Cardiff Central 7	a				09 23	*09 54*	*10 53*	11 20		*11 54*			*12 54*	13 20		*13 54*	*14 54*		15 21		*15 54*	*16 54*
Shrewsbury	d			07 05		07 32	08 31			09 31		10 08	10 31			11 31	12 31	13 03			13 31	14 31
Wellington (Shropshire)	d			07 18		07 46	08 45			09 45		10 21	10 45			11 45	12 45	13 16			13 45	14 45
Telford Central	d			07 24		07 52	08 51			09 51		10 27	10 51			11 51	12 51	13 22			13 51	14 51
Cosford	d			07 32								10 36						13 30				
Wolverhampton 7	a			07s47		08 09	09 08			10 08		10s47	11 08			12 08	13 08	13s47			14 08	15 08
Smethwick Galton Bdg L.L.	a					08 21	09 20			10 20			11 20			12 20	13 20				14 20	15 20
Tame Bridge Parkway	d			08 01								11 01						14 01				
Birmingham New Street 12	a					08 28	09 26			10 26			11 26			12 26	13 26				14 26	15 26
Birmingham International ✈	a					08 50	09 50			10 50			11 50			12 50	13 50				14 50	15 50
Banbury	a			09s06								12s12						15s07				
London Marylebone 10 ⊖	a			10 24								13 27						16 23				
London Euston 15 ⊖	a					*10 14*	*11 14*			*12 14*			*13 14*			*14 14*	*15 14*				*16 14*	*17 14*

For general notes see front of timetable
For details of catering facilities see Directory of Train Operators

A From Holyhead (Table 81)

Table 75

Saturdays

Pwllheli, Barmouth, Aberystwyth and Chester → Shrewsbury and Birmingham

Network Diagram - see first page of Table 74

		AW	AW	AW	AW	AW	AW	AW	AW		AW	WS	AW	AW	AW	AW	AW	AW	AW	AW	AW	AW	AW
		R	◇	◇	◇	◇	◇	◇	◇		◇	1 ◇	◇	◇	◇	◇		◇	◇		◇	◇	
		A			B	B			B				B		B				B				
		🛒		🛒	🛒	🛒		🛒	🛒			🍴	🛒	🛒	🛒								
Pwllheli	d		11 38				13 42				15 32					17 38					20 00		
Abererch	d		11x42				13x46				15x36					17x42					20x04		
Penychain	d		11x44				13x48				15x38					17x44					20x06		
Criccieth	d		11 51				13 55				15 45					17 51					20 13		
Porthmadog	a		11 58				14 02				15 52					17 58					20 20		
	d		12 02				14 06				15 56					18 02					20 23		
Minffordd	d		12 06				14 10				16 00					18 06					20 27		
Penrhyndeudraeth	d		12 09				14 13				16 03					18 09					20 30		
Llandecwyn	d		12x12				14x16				16x06					18x12					20x33		
Talsarnau	d		12x14				14x18				16x08					18x14					20x35		
Tygwyn	d		12x16				14x20				16x11					18x16					20x37		
Harlech	a		12 20				14 24				16 15					18 20					20 41		
	d		12 25				14 30				16 20					18 25					20 46		
Llandanwg	d		12x30				14x35				16x25					18x30					20x51		
Pensarn	d		12x31				14x36				16x26					18x31					20x52		
Llanbedr	d		12x33				14x38				16x28					18x33					20x54		
Dyffryn Ardudwy	d		12x37				14x42				16x32					18x37					20x58		
Talybont	d		12x39				14x44				16x34					18x39					21x00		
Llanaber	d		12x42				14x47				16x37					18x42					21x03		
Barmouth	a		12 46				14 51				16 41					18 46					21 07		
	d		12 49				14 52				16 50					18 49					21 14		
Morfa Mawddach	d		12x54				14x57				16x55					18x54					21x19		
Fairbourne	d		12 56				14 59				16 57					18 56					21 21		
Llwyngwril	d		13x03				15x06				17x04					19x03					21x28		
Tonfanau	d		13x09				15x12				17x10					19x09					21x34		
Tywyn	a		13 16				15 17				17 15					19 14					21 39		
	d		13 23				15 23				17 27					19 26					21 46		
Aberdovey	d		13 29				15 29				17 33					19 32					21 52		
Penhelig	d		13x32				15x32				17x36					19x35					21x55		
Aberystwyth	d			13 30				15 30						17 30				19 30		21 36			23 46
Borth	d			13 43				15 43						17 43				19 43		21 49			23 59
Dovey Junction 4	d		13 41	13 54			15 41	15 54			17 46			17 54		19 46		19 54		22 00	22 06		00 10
Machynlleth 4	a		13 53	14 03			15 49	16 03			17 58			18 03		19 58		20 03		22 07	22 16		00 17
	d			14 07				16 07						18 07				20 07					
Caersws	d			14 37				16 37						18 37				20 37					
Newtown (Powys)	d			14 46				16 46						18 46				20 46					
Welshpool	d			15 01				17 01						19 01				21 01					
Chester	d	14 22			15 22	16 22			17 22				18 22		19 27		20 27		21 22			22 28	
Wrexham General	a	14 38			15 38	16 38			17 38				18 38		19 43		20 43		21 38			22 44	
	d	14 38			15 44	16 38			17 44			18 18	18 38		19 43		20 43		21 39			22 44	
Ruabon	d	14 45			15 51	16 45			17 51			18 26	18 45		19 50		20 51		21 47			22 51	
Chirk	d	14 51			15 57	16 51			17 57			18 32	18 51		19 56		20 57		21 54			22 57	
Gobowen	d	14 57			16 03	16 57			18 03			18 37	18 57		20 02		21 02		22 01			23 03	
Shrewsbury	a	15 17		15 25	16 27	17 17		17 25	18 23			19 00	19 18	19 28	20 23		21 22	21 25	22 23			23 23	
Crewe 10	a			*16 25*				*18 25*						*20 26*				*23 04*					
Manchester Piccadilly 10	a			*17 15*				*19 15*						*21 15*				*23 48*					
Cardiff Central 7	a	17 18		*17 54*	*18 54*	19 26		*19 48*	20 54				21 20	22 09	23 05								
Shrewsbury	d			15 31	16 31			17 31	18 31			19 05		19 32				21 31	22 31			23 26	
Wellington (Shropshire)	d			15 45	16 45			17 45	18 45			19 18		19 46				21 45	22 45			23 40	
Telford Central	d			15 51	16 51			17 51	18 51			19 24		19 52				21 51	22 51			23 47	
Cosford	d											19 32										23 57	
Wolverhampton 7	a			16 08	17 08			18 08	19 08			19s49		20 09				22 08	23 08			00 15	
Smethwick Galton Bdg L.L.	a			16 20	17 20			18 20	19 20					20 20				22 20					
Tame Bridge Parkway	d											20 02											
Birmingham New Street 12	a			16 26	17 26			18 26	19 26					20 26				22 26	23 24				
Birmingham International ✈	a			16 50	17 50			18 50	19 50					20 50				*23 05*					
Banbury	a											21s08											
London Marylebone 10 ⊖	a											22 22											
London Euston 15 ⊖	a			*18 14*	*19 14*			*20 17*	22b16					23c06									

For general notes see front of timetable
For details of catering facilities see Directory of Train Operators

A From Holyhead (Table 81) to Maesteg (Table 128)
B From Holyhead (Table 81)
b From 12 September arr. 2157
c From 12 September arr. 2255

Table 75

Sundays

until 12 July

Pwllheli, Barmouth, Aberystwyth and Chester → Shrewsbury and Birmingham

Network Diagram - see first page of Table 74

		AW	AW	AW ◇	AW ◇	WS 1 ◇	AW	AW ◇	AW ◇ A	AW ◇	WS 1 ◇	AW ◇	AW ◇	AW
					trolley	dining	trolley	trolley		trolley	dining	trolley		trolley
Pwllheli	d												11 55	
Abererch	d												11x59	
Penychain	d												12x01	
Criccieth	d												12 08	
Porthmadog	a												12 17	
	d												12 18	
Minffordd	d												12 23	
Penrhyndeudraeth	d												12 26	
Llandecwyn	d												12x29	
Talsarnau	d												12x31	
Tygwyn	d												12x33	
Harlech	a												12 37	
	d												12 38	
Llandanwg	d												12x43	
Pensarn	d												12x44	
Llanbedr	d												12x46	
Dyffryn Ardudwy	d												12x50	
Talybont	d												12x52	
Llanaber	d												12x56	
Barmouth	a												13 00	
	d												13 02	
Morfa Mawddach	d												13x07	
Fairbourne	d												13 09	
Llwyngwril	d												13x17	
Tonfanau	d												13x23	
Tywyn	a												13 28	
	d												13 28	
Aberdovey	d												13 34	
Penhelig	d												13x37	
Aberystwyth	d	23p46			09 10					11 30				13 30
Borth	d	23p59			09 23					11 43				13 43
Dovey Junction 4	d	00 10			09 34					11 54			13 47	13 54
Machynlleth 4	a	00 17			09 43					12 03			13 56	14 03
	d				10 05					12 05			14 07	
Caersws	d				10 35					12 35			14 37	
Newtown (Powys)	d				10 44					12 44			14 46	
Welshpool	d				11 02					12 59			15 01	
Chester	d		08 08	09 12				11 22	12 22			13 22		
Wrexham General	a		08 26	09 28				11 38	12 38			13 38		
	d			09 30		10 47		11 39	12 38		13 11	13 39		
Ruabon	d			09 36		10 55		11 46	12 45		13 19	13 46		
Chirk	d			09 43		11 02		11 52	12 51		13 26	13 52		
Gobowen	d			09 48		11 07		11 58	12 57		13 31	13 58		
Shrewsbury	a			10 09	11 25	11 30		12 18	13 17	13 23	13 54	14 18	15 25	
Crewe 10	a	*18 25*			*12 25*					*14 25*			*16 29*	
Manchester Piccadilly 10	a	*19 15*			*13 15*					*15 15*			*17 15*	
Cardiff Central 7	a			*13 12*		*13 50*	←	*14 46*	15 30		*16 00*	*16 56*	*17 43*	
Shrewsbury	d			10 10	11 40 →	11 31	11 40	12 20		13 31	13 56	14 20	15 33	
Wellington (Shropshire)	d			10 23		11 44	11 54	12 34		13 45	14 09	14 34	15 47	
Telford Central	d			10 31		11 50	12 00	12 41		13 51	14 15	14 41	15 53	
Cosford	d			10 40		11 59		12 51			14 23	14 51		
Wolverhampton 7	a			10 57		12s10	12 17	13 08		14 08	14s36	15 08	16 10	
Smethwick Galton Bdg L.L.	a													
Tame Bridge Parkway	d					12 26					14 51			
Birmingham New Street 12	a			11 14			12 34	13 24		14 24		15 24	16 26	
Birmingham International	a			11 32			12 56	13 56		14 56		15 56	16 56	
Banbury	a					13s34					16s05			
London Marylebone 10	a					14 48					17 15			
London Euston 15	a			*13 04*			*14 20*	*15 20*		*16 20*		*17 19*	*18 20*	

For general notes see front of timetable
For details of catering facilities see Directory of Train Operators

A From Holyhead (Table 81)

Table 75

Sundays

until 12 July

Pwllheli, Barmouth, Aberystwyth and Chester → Shrewsbury and Birmingham

Network Diagram - see first page of Table 74

		AW	AW	AW	WS	AW	AW	AW	AW	AW	AW	AW	AW	AW	AW
		◇	◇	◇	1 ◇	◇	R	◇	◇	◇	◇	◇			
							A					A			
		🚲		🚲	🍴		🚲	🚲			🚲				
Pwllheli	d		13 55							17 45					
Abererch	d		13x59							17x49					
Penychain	d		14x01							17x52					
Criccieth	d		14 08							17 59					
Porthmadog	a		14 16							18 07					
	d		14 20							18 08					
Minffordd	d		14 24							18 13					
Penrhyndeudraeth	d		14 27							18 16					
Llandecwyn	d		14x30							18x19					
Talsarnau	d		14x32							18x21					
Tygwyn	d		14x34							18x23					
Harlech	a		14 39							18 27					
	d		14 39							18 28					
Llandanwg	d		14x44							18x33					
Pensarn	d		14x45							18x34					
Llanbedr	d		14x47							18x36					
Dyffryn Ardudwy	d		14x51							18x40					
Talybont	d		14x53							18x42					
Llanaber	d		14x57							18x47					
Barmouth	a		15 01							18 50					
	d		15 02							18 52					
Morfa Mawddach	d		15x07							18x57					
Fairbourne	d		15 09							18 59					
Llwyngwril	d		15x16							19x07					
Tonfanau	d		15x22							19x13					
Tywyn	a		15 27							19 18					
	d		15 27							19 22					
Aberdovey	d		15 33							19 28					
Penhelig	d		15x36							19x31					
Aberystwyth	d			15 30				17 30			19 30		21 30		23 30
Borth	d			15 43				17 43			19 43		21 43		23 43
Dovey Junction 4	d		15 46	15 54				17 54		19 41	19 54		21 54		23 54
Machynlleth 4	a		15 54	16 03				18 03		19 54	20 03		22 04		00 04
	d		16 07					18 07			20 07				
Caersws	d		16 37					18 37			20 37				
Newtown (Powys)	d		16 46					18 46			20 46				
Welshpool	d		17 01					19 01			21 01				
Chester	d	15 31				17 22	18 24		19 25			21 24		22 04	
Wrexham General	a	15 47				17 38	18 40		19 41			21 41		22 22	
	d	15 48			17 03	17 39	18 40		19 42			21 43			
Ruabon	d	15 55			17 11	17 46	18 47		19 49			21 50			
Chirk	d	16 01			17 18	17 52	18 53		19 55			21 56			
Gobowen	d	16 07			17 23	17 58	18 59		20 01			22 01			
Shrewsbury	a	16 27	17 27		17 46	18 18	19 19	19 25	20 21		21 25	22 22			
Crewe 10	a		*18 25*					*20 27*			*23 02*				
Manchester Piccadilly 10	a		*19 15*					*21 14*							
Cardiff Central 7	a	*18 55*			*20 05*	*20 49*	*21 30*	*22 05*	*22 57*		*00 19*				
Shrewsbury	d	16 29	17 33		17 56	18 20		19 31	20 23		21 31	22 23			
Wellington (Shropshire)	d	16 43	17 47		18 09	18 34		19 45	20 37		21 45	22 37			
Telford Central	d	16 50	17 53		18 15	18 41		19 51	20 44		21 51	22 45			
Cosford	d	17 00			18 24	18 51			20 54			22 55			
Wolverhampton 7	a	17 17	18 10		18s35	19 08		20 08	21 11		22 08	23 16			
Smethwick Galton Bdg L.L.	a														
Tame Bridge Parkway	d				18 50										
Birmingham New Street 12	a	17 35	18 28			19 24		20 24	21 28		22 28				
Birmingham International	a	17 56	18 56			19 56		20 56	21 56		22 55				
Banbury	a				19s58										
London Marylebone 10	a				21 10										
London Euston 15	a	*19 20*	*20 20*			*21 54*		*23 18*	*00 22*		*01 02*				

For general notes see front of timetable
For details of catering facilities see Directory of Train Operators

A From Holyhead (Table 81)

Sundays

Pwllheli, Barmouth, Aberystwyth and Chester → Shrewsbury and Birmingham

19 July to 6 September

Network Diagram - see first page of Table 74

		AW	AW	AW ◇	AW ◇ ✕	WS 1 ◇ ☕	AW ◇ ✕	AW ◇ ✕	AW ◇ A	AW ◇ ✕	WS 1 ◇ ☕	AW ◇ ✕	AW ◇	AW ✕
Pwllheli	d												11 55	
Abererch	d												11x59	
Penychain	d												12x01	
Criccieth	d												12 08	
Porthmadog	a												12 17	
	d												12 18	
Minffordd	d												12 23	
Penrhyndeudraeth	d												12 26	
Llandecwyn	d												12x29	
Talsarnau	d												12x31	
Tygwyn	d												12x33	
Harlech	a												12 37	
	d												12 38	
Llandanwg	d												12x43	
Pensarn	d												12x44	
Llanbedr	d												12x46	
Dyffryn Ardudwy	d												12x50	
Talybont	d												12x52	
Llanaber	d												12x56	
Barmouth	a												13 00	
	d												13 02	
Morfa Mawddach	d												13x07	
Fairbourne	d												13 09	
Llwyngwril	d												13x17	
Tonfanau	d												13x23	
Tywyn	a												13 28	
	d												13 28	
Aberdovey	d												13 34	
Penhelig	d												13x37	
Aberystwyth	d	23p46			09 10					11 30				13 30
Borth	d	23p59			09 23					11 43				13 43
Dovey Junction 4	d	00 10			09 34					11 54			13 47	13 54
Machynlleth 4	a	00 17			09 43					12 03			13 56	14 03
	d				10 05					12 05			14 07	
Caersws	d				10 35					12 35			14 37	
Newtown (Powys)	d				10 44					12 44			14 46	
Welshpool	d				11 02					12 59			15 51	
Chester	d		08 08	09 12				11 22	12 22			13 22		
Wrexham General	a		08 26	09 28				11 38	12 38			13 38		
	d			09 30		10 47		11 39	12 38		13 11	13 39		
Ruabon	d			09 36		10 55		11 46	12 45		13 19	13 46		
Chirk	d			09 43		11 02		11 52	12 51		13 26	13 52		
Gobowen	d			09 48		11 07		11 58	12 57		13 31	13 58		
Shrewsbury	a			10 09	11 25	11 30		12 18	13 17	13 23	13 54	14 18	15 25	
Crewe 10	a				12 25					14 25			16 29	
Manchester Piccadilly 10	a				13 15					15 15			17 15	
Cardiff Central 7	a			13 12		13 50	←	14 46	15 30		16 00	16 56	17 43	
Shrewsbury	d			10 10	11 40 →	11 31	11 40	12 20		13 31	13 56	14 20	15 33	
Wellington (Shropshire)	d			10 23		11 44	11 54	12 34		13 45	14 09	14 34	15 47	
Telford Central	d			10 31		11 50	12 00	12 41		13 51	14 15	14 41	15 33	
Cosford	d			10 40		11 59		12 51			14 23	14 51		
Wolverhampton 7	a			10 57		12s10	12 17	13 08		14 08	14s36	15 08	16 10	
Smethwick Galton Bdg L.L.	a													
Tame Bridge Parkway	d													
Birmingham New Street 12	a			11 14			12 34	13 24		14 24		15 24	16 26	
Birmingham International	a			11 32			12 56	13 56		14 56		15 56	16 56	
Banbury	a					13s34					16s05			
London Marylebone 10 ⊖	a					14 48					17 15			
London Euston 15 ⊖	a			13 04			14 20	15 20		16 20		17 19	18 20	

For general notes see front of timetable
For details of catering facilities see Directory of Train Operators

A From Holyhead (Table 81)

Table 75

Sundays

Pwllheli, Barmouth, Aberystwyth and Chester → Shrewsbury and Birmingham

19 July to 6 September

Network Diagram - see first page of Table 74

		AW	AW	AW	WS	AW	AW	AW	AW	AW	AW	AW	AW	AW	AW
		◇	◇	◇	1 ◇	◇	R	◇	◇	◇	◇	◇			
							A					A			
		🍴		🍴	🍴		🍴	🍴			🍴				
Pwllheli	d		13 55							17 45					
Abererch	d		13x59							17x49					
Penychain	d		14x01							17x52					
Criccieth	d		14 08							17 59					
Porthmadog	a		14 16							18 07					
	d		14 20							18 08					
Minffordd	d		14 24							18 13					
Penrhyndeudraeth	d		14 27							18 16					
Llandecwyn	d		14x30							18x19					
Talsarnau	d		14x32							18x21					
Tygwyn	d		14x34							18x23					
Harlech	a		14 39							18 27					
	d		14 39							18 28					
Llandanwg	d		14x44							18x33					
Pensarn	d		14x45							18x34					
Llanbedr	d		14x47							18x36					
Dyffryn Ardudwy	d		14x51							18x40					
Talybont	d		14x53							18x42					
Llanaber	d		14x57							18x47					
Barmouth	a		15 01							18 50					
	d		15 02							18 52					
Morfa Mawddach	d		15x07							18x57					
Fairbourne	d		15 09							18 59					
Llwyngwril	d		15x16							19x07					
Tonfanau	d		15x22							19x13					
Tywyn	a		15 27							19 18					
	d		15 27							19 22					
Aberdovey	d		15 33							19 28					
Penhelig	d		15x36							19x31					
Aberystwyth	d			15 30				17 30			19 30		21 30		23 30
Borth	d			15 43				17 43			19 43		21 43		23 43
Dovey Junction 4	d		15 46	15 54				17 54		19 41	19 54		21 54		23 54
Machynlleth 4	a		15 54	16 03				18 03		19 54	20 03		22 04		00 04
	d			16 07				18 07			20 07				
Caersws	d			16 37				18 37			20 37				
Newtown (Powys)	d			16 46				18 46			20 46				
Welshpool	d			17 01				19 01			21 01				
Chester	d	15 31				17 22	18 24		19 25			21 24		22 04	
Wrexham General	a	15 47				17 38	18 40		19 41			21 41		22 22	
	d	15 48			17 03	17 39	18 40		19 42			21 43			
Ruabon	d	15 55			17 11	17 46	18 47		19 49			21 50			
Chirk	d	16 01			17 18	17 52	18 53		19 55			21 56			
Gobowen	d	16 07			17 23	17 58	18 59		20 01			22 01			
Shrewsbury	a	16 27		17 27	17 46	18 18	19 19	19 25	20 21		21 25	22 22			
Crewe 10	a			18 25				20 27			23 02				
Manchester Piccadilly 10	a			19 15				21 14							
Cardiff Central 7	a	18 55			20 05	20 49	21 30	22 05	22 57		00 19				
Shrewsbury	d	16 29		17 33	17 56	18 20		19 31	20 23		21 31	22 23			
Wellington (Shropshire)	d	16 43		17 47	18 09	18 34		19 45	20 37		21 45	22 37			
Telford Central	d	16 50		17 53	18 15	18 41		19 51	20 44		21 51	22 45			
Cosford	d	17 00			18 24	18 51			20 54			22 55			
Wolverhampton 7	a	17 17		18 10	18s35	19 08		20 08	21 11		22 08	23 16			
Smethwick Galton Bdg L.L.	a														
Tame Bridge Parkway	d														
Birmingham New Street 12	a	17 35		18 28		19 24		20 24	21 28		22 28				
Birmingham International	a	17 56		18 56		19 56		20 56	21 56		22 55				
Banbury	a				19s58										
London Marylebone 10	a				21 10										
London Euston 15	a	19 20				21 54		23 29	00 29		01 09				

For general notes see front of timetable
For details of catering facilities see
Directory of Train Operators

A From Holyhead (Table 81)

Table 75

Sundays

Pwllheli, Barmouth, Aberystwyth and Chester → Shrewsbury and Birmingham

from 13 September

Network Diagram - see first page of Table 74

		AW	AW	AW	AW	WS	AW	AW	AW	AW	WS	AW	AW	AW
				◇	◇	1 ◇	◇	◇	◇	◇	1 ◇	◇		◇
									A					
					🍴	🍽	🍴	🍴		🍴	🍽	🍴	🍴	🍴
Pwllheli	d													
Abererch	d													
Penychain	d													
Criccieth	d													
Porthmadog	a													
	d													
Minffordd	d													
Penrhyndeudraeth	d													
Llandecwyn	d													
Talsarnau	d													
Tygwyn	d													
Harlech	a													
	d													
Llandanwg	d													
Pensarn	d													
Llanbedr	d													
Dyffryn Ardudwy	d													
Talybont	d													
Llanaber	d													
Barmouth	a													
	d													
Morfa Mawddach	d													
Fairbourne	d													
Llwyngwril	d													
Tonfanau	d													
Tywyn	a													
	d													
Aberdovey	d													
Penhelig	d													
Aberystwyth	d	23p46					09 29			11 30			13 30	
Borth	d	23p59					09 42			11 43			13 43	
Dovey Junction 4	d	00 10					09 53			11 54			13 54	
Machynlleth 4	a	00 17					10 02			12 03			14 03	
	d				10 05					12 05			14 07	
Caersws	d				10 35					12 35			14 37	
Newtown (Powys)	d				10 44					12 44			14 46	
Welshpool	d				11 02					12 59			15 01	
Chester	d		08 08	09 12				11 22	12 22			13 22		15 31
Wrexham General	a		08 26	09 28				11 38	12 38			13 38		15 47
	d			09 30		10 47		11 39	12 38		13 11	13 39		15 48
Ruabon	d			09 36		10 55		11 46	12 45		13 19	13 46		15 55
Chirk	d			09 43		11 02		11 52	12 51		13 26	13 52		16 01
Gobowen	d			09 48		11 07		11 58	12 57		13 31	13 58		16 07
Shrewsbury	a			10 09	11 25	11 30		12 18	13 17	13 23	13 54	14 18	15 25	16 27
Crewe 10	a			*11 21*	*12 25*					*14 25*			*16 29*	
Manchester Piccadilly 10 ⛴	a			*12 02*	*13 15*					*15 15*			*17 15*	
Cardiff Central 7	a	*13 12*		*13 07*		*13 57*		*14 46*	15 30		*16 00*	*16 56*	*17 43*	*18 55*
Shrewsbury	d			10 10	*11 40* ⟶	11 31	11 40	12 20		13 31	13 56	14 20	15 33	16 29
Wellington (Shropshire)	d			10 23		11 44	11 54	12 34		13 45	14 09	14 34	15 47	16 43
Telford Central	d			10 31		11 50	12 00	12 41		13 51	14 15	14 41	15 53	16 50
Cosford	d			10 40		11 59		12 51			14 23	14 51		17 00
Wolverhampton 7 ⛴	a			10 57		12s10	12 17	13 08		14 08	14s36	15 08	16 10	17 17
Smethwick Galton Bdg L.L.	a													
Tame Bridge Parkway	d					12 25					14 51			
Birmingham New Street 12	a			11 14			12 33	13 24		14 24		15 24	16 26	17 35
Birmingham International ✈	a			11 32			12 56	13 56		14 56		15 56	16 56	17 56
Banbury	a					13s34					16s05			
London Marylebone 10 ⊖	a					14 48					17 15			
London Euston 15 ⊖	a			*13 04*			*14 20*	*15 20*		*16 20*		*17 19*	*18 20*	*19 20*

For general notes see front of timetable
For details of catering facilities see Directory of Train Operators

A From Holyhead (Table 81)

Table 75

Sundays

from 13 September

Pwllheli, Barmouth, Aberystwyth and Chester → Shrewsbury and Birmingham

Network Diagram - see first page of Table 74

		AW	AW	WS	AW	AW	AW	AW	AW	AW	AW	AW	AW	AW
		◇	◇	[1] ◇	◇	◇	[R]	◇	◇	◇				
					A	B	C							
			[catering]	[catering]			[catering]	[catering]		[catering]				
Pwllheli	d	13 55												
Abererch	d	13x59												
Penychain	d	14x01												
Criccieth	d	14 08												
Porthmadog	a	14 16												
	d	14 20												
Minffordd	d	14 24												
Penrhyndeudraeth	d	14 27												
Llandecwyn	d	14x30												
Talsarnau	d	14x32												
Tygwyn	d	14x34												
Harlech	a	14 39												
	d	14 39												
Llandanwg	d	14x44												
Pensarn	d	14x45												
Llanbedr	d	14x47												
Dyffryn Ardudwy	d	14x51												
Talybont	d	14x53												
Llanaber	d	14x57												
Barmouth	a	15 01												
	d	15 02												
Morfa Mawddach	d	15x07												
Fairbourne	d	15 09												
Llwyngwril	d	15x16												
Tonfanau	d	15x22												
Tywyn	a	15 27												
	d	15 27												
Aberdovey	d	15 33												
Penhelig	d	15x36												
Aberystwyth	d		15 30					17 30		19 30		21 30		23 30
Borth	d		15 43					17 43		19 43		21 43		23 43
Dovey Junction [4]	d	15 46	15 54					17 54		19 54		21 54		23 54
Machynlleth [4]	a	15 54	16 03					18 03		20 03		22 04		00 04
	d		16 07					18 07		20 07				
Caersws	d		16 37					18 37		20 37				
Newtown (Powys)	d		16 46					18 46		20 46				
Welshpool	d		17 01					19 01		21 01				
Chester	d				17 22	17 22	18 24		19 25		21 24		22 04	
Wrexham General	a				17 38	17 38	18 40		19 41		21 41		22 22	
	d			17 03	17 39	17 39	18 40		19 42		21 43			
Ruabon	d			17 11	17 46	17 46	18 47		19 49		21 50			
Chirk	d			17 18	17 52	17 52	18 53		19 55		21 56			
Gobowen	d			17 23	17 58	17 58	18 59		20 01		22 01			
Shrewsbury	a		17 27	17 46	18 18	18 18	19 19	19 25	20 21	21 25	22 22			
Crewe [10]	a		18 25					20 27		23 02				
Manchester Piccadilly [10]	a		19 15					21 14						
Cardiff Central [7]	a			20 05	20 49	20 49	21 30	22 05	22 57	00 19				
Shrewsbury	d		17 33	17 56	18 20	18 20		19 31	20 23	21 31	22 23			
Wellington (Shropshire)	d		17 47	18 09	18 34	18 34		19 45	20 37	21 45	22 37			
Telford Central	d		17 53	18 15	18 41	18 41		19 51	20 44	21 51	22 45			
Cosford	d			18 24	18 51	18 51			20 54		22 55			
Wolverhampton [7]	a		18 10	18s35	19 08	19 08		20 08	21 11	22 08	23 16			
Smethwick Galton Bdg L.L.	a													
Tame Bridge Parkway	d			18 50										
Birmingham New Street [12]	a		18 28		19 24	19 28		20 24	21 29	22 28				
Birmingham International	a		18 56		19 56	19 56		20 56	21 56	22 55				
Banbury	a			19s58										
London Marylebone [10]	a			21 10										
London Euston [15]	a		20 20		21 54	21 54		23 29	00 29	01 09				

For general notes see front of timetable
For details of catering facilities see Directory of Train Operators

A Until 1 November
B From 8 November
C From Holyhead (Table 81)

Network Diagram for Tables 78, 79, 84, 85, 86

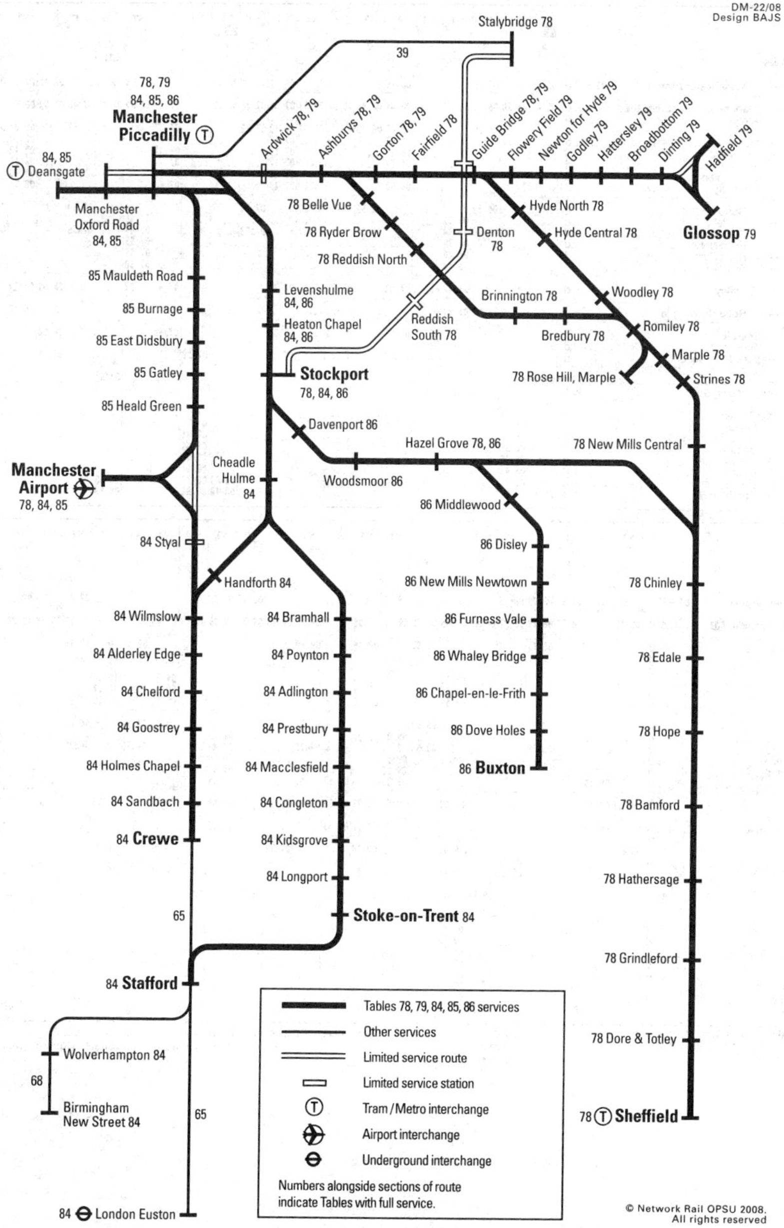

DM-22/08
Design BAJS
Stalybridge 78
39
78, 79
84, 85, 86
Manchester Piccadilly
84, 85
Deansgate
Manchester Oxford Road 84, 85
Ardwick 78, 79
Ashburys 78, 79
Gorton 78, 79
Fairfield 78
Guide Bridge 78, 79
Flowery Field 79
Newton for Hyde 79
Godley 79
Hattersley 79
Broadbottom 79
Dinting 79
Hadfield 79
Glossop 79
78 Belle Vue
78 Ryder Brow
78 Reddish North
Hyde North 78
Hyde Central 78
Denton 78
Reddish South 78
Brinnington 78
Bredbury 78
Woodley 78
Romiley 78
Marple 78
78 Rose Hill, Marple
Strines 78
85 Mauldeth Road
85 Burnage
85 East Didsbury
85 Gatley
85 Heald Green
Levenshulme 84, 86
Heaton Chapel 84, 86
Stockport 78, 84, 86
Davenport 86
Hazel Grove 78, 86
78 New Mills Central
Manchester Airport 78, 84, 85
Cheadle Hulme 84
Woodsmoor 86
86 Middlewood
84 Styal
86 Disley
Handforth 84
86 New Mills Newtown
78 Chinley
84 Wilmslow
84 Bramhall
86 Furness Vale
84 Alderley Edge
84 Poynton
86 Whaley Bridge
78 Edale
84 Chelford
84 Adlington
86 Chapel-en-le-Frith
84 Goostrey
84 Prestbury
86 Dove Holes
78 Hope
84 Holmes Chapel
84 Macclesfield
86 Buxton
84 Sandbach
84 Congleton
78 Bamford
84 Crewe
84 Kidsgrove
84 Longport
78 Hathersage
65
Stoke-on-Trent 84
78 Grindleford
84 Stafford
Tables 78, 79, 84, 85, 86 services
Other services
Limited service route
Limited service station
Tram / Metro interchange
Airport interchange
Underground interchange
Numbers alongside sections of route indicate Tables with full service.
Wolverhampton 84
78 Dore & Totley
68
Birmingham New Street 84
65
78 Sheffield
84 London Euston

Manchester Airport and Manchester → Romiley, Marple, Chinley and Sheffield

Network Diagram - see first page of Table 78

Miles	Miles	Miles			TP 1◇ A	NT	NT B	NT	NT	NT	NT C	NT	NT C	NT	NT C	TP 1◇ A 🍴	NT	NT	NT	EM ◇ D 🍴	NT C	NT	NT	NT C	NT
—	—	—	**Manchester Airport**	85 ✈ d	05 15		*05 37*			*06 18*		*06 23*		*06 41*		06 55			*07 05*			*07 17*	*07 35*	*07 41*	
0	0	—	**Manchester Piccadilly 10**	⇌ d	05 44	05 50	06 16	06 24	06 30	06 41	06 46	06 57	07 03	07 06	07 18	07 20		07 23	07 39	07 42	07 48	07 52	08 04	08 07	08 12
½	½	—	Ardwick	d																					
1½	1½	—	Ashburys	d			06 20			06 45	06 50		07 07	07 10	07 22			07 27			07 52		08 08	08 11	
2½	—	—	Belle Vue	d						06 47				07 12				07 29					08 10		
2¾	—	—	Ryder Brow	d						06 49				07 14				07 31					08 12		
3¾	—	—	Reddish North	d						06 52				07 17				07 34					08 15		
5½	—	—	Brinnington	d						06 55				07 20				07 37					08 18		
6½	—	—	Bredbury	d						06 58				07 23				07 40					08 21		
—	2½	—	Gorton	d			06 22				06 52		07 09		07 24						07 54			08 13	
—	3½	—	Fairfield	d				06 31											07 46						08 20
—	4¾	—	Guide Bridge	d			06a26	06 34			06a56		07a13		07a28				07 49		07a58			08a17	08 23
—	6½	—	Hyde North	d				06 38											07 53						08 28
—	7¾	—	Hyde Central	d				06 40											07 55						08 30
—	9¼	—	Woodley	d				06 43											07 58						08 33
7½	10½	—	**Romiley**	d				06 47	06 44	07 02		07 09		07 26				07 43	08 02			08 05	08 24		→
—	12½	—	**Rose Hill Marple**	a				06 53											08 08				08 30		
9	—	—	**Marple**	d					06 47	07 05		07 13		07 30			←	07a48				08 08			
11¼	—	—	Strines	d																					
12¾	—	—	New Mills Central	d					06a55	07a12		07a20		07 39			07 39					08a15			
—	—	—	Stockport	86 d	05 52	06 00								→		07 28				07 54					
—	—	0	Hazel Grove	86 d		06 07																			
16½	—	8½	**Chinley**	d		06 18											07 47								
22	—	—	Edale	d		06 26											07 55								
27¼	—	—	Hope (Derbyshire)	d		06 32											08 01								
29	—	—	Bamford	d		06 35											08 04								
30¾	—	—	Hathersage	d		06 39											08 09								
32¼	—	—	Grindleford	d		06 42											08 11								
37¾	—	—	Dore & Totley	d		06 51										08 03	08 23			08 28					
42	—	—	**Sheffield 7**	⇌ a	06 49	07 01										08 10	08 32			08 34					

		NT	NT	TP 1◇ A 🍴	NT C	NT	EM ◇ D 🍴	NT	NT B	NT	NT	NT	NT B	NT	TP 1◇ A 🍴	NT	EM ◇ D 🍴	NT	NT B	NT	NT B	NT	TP 1◇ A 🍴	NT	EM ◇ D 🍴
Manchester Airport	85 ✈ d			07 54	*08 00*	*08 05*				*08 35*			*08 41*		08 55	*09 05*				*09 35*	*09 41*		09 55	*10 05*	
Manchester Piccadilly 10	⇌ d	08 15		08 20	08 29	08 37	08 43	08 45	08 48	09 00	09 05		09 15	09 18	09 20	09 36	09 43	09 45	09 48	10 03	10 15	10 18	10 20	10 36	10 43
Ardwick	d																								
Ashburys	d				08 33				08 52		09 09		09 19	09 23					09 52	10 07	10 19				
Belle Vue	d													09 26						10 09					
Ryder Brow	d													09 28						10 11					
Reddish North	d							08 52			09 14							09 52		10 14					
Brinnington	d							08 56			09 17							09 56		10 17					
Bredbury	d							08 59			09 20							09 59		10 20					
Gorton	d				08 35				08 54				09 21						09 54		10 21				
Fairfield	d									09 07						09 43								10 43	
Guide Bridge	d				08a39				08a58	09 11			09a25			09 46			09a58		10a25			10 46	
Hyde North	d									09 17						09 50								10 50	
Hyde Central	d		←							09 20		←				09 52								10 52	
Woodley	d		08 33							09 23		09 23				09 55								10 55	
Romiley	d	08 29	08 37					09 02		→	09 23	09 26		09 35		09 59		10 02		10 23		10 30		10 59	
Rose Hill Marple	a		08 45									09 33				10 05								11 05	
Marple	d	08a32				08 52		09 06			09a28			09a39				10 06		10 27		10a35			
Strines	d					08 56												10 10							
New Mills Central	d					09a01		09 11										10a15		10a34					
Stockport	86 d			08 28			08 54								09 28		09 54						10 28		10 54
Hazel Grove	86 d																								
Chinley	d							09 19																	
Edale	d							09 28																	
Hope (Derbyshire)	d							09 34																	
Bamford	d							09 37																	
Hathersage	d							09 40																	
Grindleford	d							09 44																	
Dore & Totley	d							09 53																	
Sheffield 7	⇌ a			09 08			09 35	10 03							10 08		10 35						11 08		11 35

For general notes see front of timetable
For details of catering facilities see Directory of Train Operators

A To Cleethorpes (22 June to 4 September to Doncaster) (Table 29)
B To Hadfield (Table 79)
C To Manchester Piccadilly (Table 79)
D From Liverpool Lime Street to Norwich (Table 49)

Manchester Airport and Manchester → Romiley, Marple, Chinley and Sheffield

Network Diagram - see first page of Table 78

	NT	NT A	NT	NT A	TP 1◇ B ⚒	NT	NT	EM ◇ C ⚒	NT	NT A	NT	NT A	TP 1◇ B ⚒	NT	NT	EM ◇ C ⚒	NT	NT A	NT	NT A	TP 1◇ B ⚒	NT	NT	EM ◇ C ⚒
Manchester Airport 85 ✈ d			10 35	10 41	10 55		11 05				11 35	11 41	11 55		12 05				12 35	12 41	12 55		13 05	
Manchester Piccadilly 10 d	10 45	10 48	11 03	11 18	11 20	11 23	11 36	11 43	11 45	11 48	12 03	12 18	12 20	12 23	12 36	12 43	12 45	12 48	13 03	13 18	13 20	13 23	13 36	13 43
Ardwick d																								
Ashburys d		10 52	11 07	11 22						11 52	12 07	12 22						12 52	13 07	13 22				
Belle Vue d			11 09								12 09								13 09					
Ryder Brow d			11 11								12 11								13 11					
Reddish North d	10 52		11 14						11 52		12 14						12 52		13 14					
Brinnington d	10 56		11 17						11 56		12 17						12 56		13 17					
Bredbury d	10 59		11 20						11 59		12 20						12 59		13 20					
Gorton d		10 54		11 24						11 54		12 24						12 54		13 24				
Fairfield d							11 43								12 43								13 43	
Guide Bridge d		10a58		11a28			11 46			11a58		12a28			12 46			12a58		13a28			13 46	
Hyde North d							11 50								12 50								13 50	
Hyde Central d							11 52								12 52								13 52	
Woodley d							11 55								12 55								13 55	
Romiley d	11 02		11 23			11 37	11 59		12 02		12 23			12 37	12 59		13 02		13 23			13 37	13 59	
Rose Hill Marple a							12 05								13 05								14 05	
Marple d	11 06		11 27			11a43			12 06		12 27			12a43			13 06		13 27			13a43		
Strines d									12 10															
New Mills Central d	11 11		11a34						12a15		12a34						13 11		13a34					
Stockport 86 d					11 28			11 54					12 28			12 54					13 28			13 54
Hazel Grove 86 d																								
Chinley d	11 19																13 19							
Edale d	11 28																13 28							
Hope (Derbyshire) d	11 34																13 34							
Bamford d	11 37																13 37							
Hathersage d	11 40																13 40							
Grindleford d	11 44																13 44							
Dore & Totley d	11 53																13 53							
Sheffield 7 a	12 03				12 08			12 35					13 08			13 35	14 03				14 08			14 35

	NT	NT A	NT	NT A	TP 1◇ B ⚒	NT	NT	EM ◇ D ⚒	NT	NT A	NT	NT A	TP 1◇ B ⚒	NT	NT	EM ◇ C ⚒	NT	NT E	NT	NT	NT E	TP 1◇ B ⚒	NT	NT E
Manchester Airport 85 ✈ d			13 35	13 41	13 55		14 05				14 35	14 41	14 55		15 05				15 35		15 41	15 55		16 05
Manchester Piccadilly 10 d	13 45	13 48	14 03	14 18	14 20	14 23	14 36	14 43	14 45	14 48	15 03	15 18	15 20	15 23	15 36	15 43	15 45	15 48	16 03	16 06	16 15	16 20	16 23	16 36
Ardwick d																								
Ashburys d		13 52	14 07	14 22						14 52	15 07	15 22						15 52	16 07		16 19			16 40
Belle Vue d			14 09								15 09								16 09					
Ryder Brow d			14 11								15 11								16 11					
Reddish North d	13 52		14 14						14 52		15 14						15 52		16 14				16 30	
Brinnington d	13 56		14 17						14 56		15 17						15 56		16 17				16 34	
Bredbury d	13 59		14 20						14 59		15 20						15 59		16 20				16 37	
Gorton d		13 54		14 24						14 54		15 24						15 54			16 21			16 42
Fairfield d							14 43								15 43					16 13				
Guide Bridge d		13a58		14a28			14 46			14a58		15a28			15 46			15a58		16 16	16a25			16a46
Hyde North d							14 50								15 50					16 20				
Hyde Central d							14 52								15 52					16 22				
Woodley d							14 55								15 55					16 25				
Romiley d	14 02		14 23			14 37	14 59		15 02		15 23			15 37	15 59		16 02		16 23	16 29			16 40	
Rose Hill Marple a							15 05								16 05					16 36				
Marple d	14 06		14 27			14a43			15 06		15 27			15a43			16 06		16 27				16a44	
Strines d	14 10																16 10							
New Mills Central d	14a15		14a34						15 11		15a34						16 13		16a34					
Stockport 86 d					14 28			14 54					15 28			15 54						16 28		
Hazel Grove 86 d																								
Chinley d									15 19								16 21							
Edale d									15 28								16 30							
Hope (Derbyshire) d									15 34								16 36							
Bamford d									15 37								16 39							
Hathersage d									15 40								16 42							
Grindleford d									15 44								16 46							
Dore & Totley d									15 53								16 54							
Sheffield 7 a					15 08			15 34	16 03				16 08			16 35	17 03					17 08		

For general notes see front of timetable
For details of catering facilities see Directory of Train Operators

A To Hadfield (Table 79)
B To Cleethorpes (22 June to 4 September to Doncaster) (Table 29)
C From Liverpool Lime Street to Norwich (Table 49)
D From Liverpool Lime Street to Nottingham (Table 49)
E To Manchester Piccadilly (Table 79)

Manchester Airport and Manchester → Romiley, Marple, Chinley and Sheffield

Network Diagram - see first page of Table 78

	EM	NT	NT	NT	NT	NT	NT	TP	NT	NT	NT	NT	EM	NT	NT	NT	NT	NT	TP	NT	NT	EM	NT	NT
	◇							1 ◇					◇						1 ◇			◇		
	A			B		B		C				B	D		B			E	C			A		E
	🛒							🛒					🛒						🛒			🛒		
Manchester Airport 85 ✈ d				16 29	16 35	16 41		16 55			17 05				17 27	17 35		17 41	17 55	17 46	18 03			
Manchester Piccadilly 10 d	16 43	16 45	16 48	16 59	17 03	17 15	17 18	17 20		17 23	17 32	17 37	17 43	17 48	17 59	18 03	18 06	18 15	18 20	18 22	18 36	18 43	18 45	18 48
Ardwick d					17 07												18 09							
Ashburys d		16 49	16 52	17 03	17 09	17 19					17 36	17 41		17 52	18 03	18 07	18 11	18 19						18 52
Belle Vue d		16 51			17 12						17 38					18 09								
Ryder Brow d		16 53			17 14						17 40					18 11								
Reddish North d		16 56			17 16						17 43			17 57		18 14							18 52	
Brinnington d		16 59			17 20						17 46			18 00		18 17							18 56	
Bredbury d		17 02			17 23		17 30				17 49			18 04		18 20							18 59	
Gorton d				17 05		17 21						17 43			18 05			18 21						18 54
Fairfield d			16 56														18 15				18 43			
Guide Bridge d			16 59	17a09		17a25						17a47			18a09		18 18	18a25			18 46			18a58
Hyde North d			17 03							17 34							18 22				18 50			
Hyde Central d			17 05							17 36							18 25				18 52			
Woodley d			17 08							17 39							18 28				18 55			
Romiley d		17 05	17 13		17 27		17 33			17 43	17 53			18 07		18 23	18 31			18 35	18 59		19 02	
Rose Hill Marple a			17 20							17 49							18 37				19 05			
Marple d		17 09			17a31		17 37				17 57			18 11		18a28				18 39			19 06	
Strines d							17 41		←		18 01			18 15						18 43				
New Mills Central d		17a16					17 45		17 45		18a04			18 19						18a48			19 11	
Stockport 86 d	16 54						→	17 28					17 54						18 28			18 54		
Hazel Grove 86 d																								
Chinley d	17 09							17 43	17 51					18a27									19 19	
Edale d									18 00														19 28	
Hope (Derbyshire) d									18 06														19 34	
Bamford d									18 09														19 37	
Hathersage d									18 13														19 40	
Grindleford d									18 16														19 44	
Dore & Totley d	17 30							18 05	18 25				18 32						19 03				19 53	
Sheffield 7 a	17 37							18 15	18 36				18 41						19 10			19 33	20 03	

	NT	TP	NT	NT	EM	NT	NT	TP	NT	EM	NT	NT	TP	NT	NT	TP	EM	NT	NT	NT	NT	TP
		1 ◇			◇			1 ◇		◇			1 ◇			1 ◇	◇					1 ◇
		C	E		D		E	C		D		E	C		E		D		E		G	
					🛒					🛒												
Manchester Airport 85 ✈ d	18 29	18 55	18 41		19 09		19 20	19 55	20 03	20 09		20 20	20 47	21 09	21 20	21 47	22 00	22 19	22 22	22 29		23 52
Manchester Piccadilly 10 d	19 00	19 18	19 18	19 23	19 43	19 45	19 48	20 20	20 36	20 43	20 45	20 48	21 20	21 45	21 48	22 20	22 28	22 45	22 48	23 24	23 27	00 15
Ardwick d																						
Ashburys d	19 04		19 22			19 49	19 52					20 52		21 49	21 52			22 49	22 52	23 28	23 31	
Belle Vue d	19 06					19 51								21 51				22 51		23 30		
Ryder Brow d	19 08					19 53								21 53				22 53		23 32		
Reddish North d	19 11					19 56					20 52			21 56				22 56		23 35		
Brinnington d	19 14					19 59					20 56			21 59				22 59		23 38		
Bredbury d	19 17					20 02					20 59			22 02				23 02		23 41		
Gorton d			19 24				19 54					20 54			21 54				22 54		23 33	
Fairfield d									20 43													
Guide Bridge d			19a28				19a58		20 46			20a58			21a58				22a58		23a37	
Hyde North d									20 50													
Hyde Central d									20 52													
Woodley d									20 55													
Romiley d	19 20			19 39		20 05			20 59		21 02			22 05				23 05		23 44		
Rose Hill Marple a									21 05													
Marple d	19a25			19a42		20 09					21 06			22 09				23 09		23 48		
Strines d						20 13								22 13				23 13		23 52		
New Mills Central d						20a18					21 11			22a18				23a18		23a57		
Stockport 86 d		19 26			19 54			20 28		20 54			21 28			22 28	22 37					
Hazel Grove 86 d																						
Chinley d											21 19						22 53					
Edale d											21 28						23 02					
Hope (Derbyshire) d											21 34						23 08					
Bamford d											21 37						23 11					
Hathersage d											21 40						23 15					
Grindleford d											21 44						23 19					
Dore & Totley d											21 53						23 28					
Sheffield 7 a		20 08			20 36			21 08		21 35	22 03		22 08			23 13	23 35					01 08

For general notes see front of timetable
For details of catering facilities see Directory of Train Operators

- **A** From Liverpool Lime Street to Norwich (Table 49)
- **B** To Manchester Piccadilly (Table 79)
- **C** To Cleethorpes (22 June to 4 September to Doncaster) (Table 29)
- **D** From Liverpool Lime Street to Nottingham (Table 49)
- **E** To Hadfield (Table 79)
- **G** To Glossop (Table 79)

Table 78

Saturdays

Manchester Airport and Manchester → Romiley, Marple, Chinley and Sheffield

Network Diagram - see first page of Table 78

		TP	NT	NT	NT	NT	NT	NT	TP	NT	EM	NT	NT	NT	NT	TP	NT	NT	EM	NT	NT	NT	NT	TP	NT
		1 ◇ A		B		B		B	1 ◇ A		◇ C		B		B	1 ◇ A			◇ C		B		B	1 ◇ A	
Manchester Airport	85 d	05 15		05 37	06 01	06 18	06 23	06 41	06 55	07 05				07 33	07 41	07 54		08 05				08 35	08 41	08 55	
Manchester Piccadilly 10	d	05 44	05 50	06 16	06 35	06 48	07 03	07 18	07 20	07 39	07 42	07 44	07 48	08 03	08 15	08 20	08 23	08 36	08 43	08 45	08 48	09 03	09 18	09 20	09 23
Ardwick	d																								
Ashburys	d			06 20	06 39	06 52	07 07	07 22					07 52	08 07	08 19						08 52	09 07	09 22		
Belle Vue	d				06 41		07 09							08 09								09 09			
Ryder Brow	d				06 43		07 11							08 11								09 11			
Reddish North	d				06 46		07 14					07 52		08 14						08 52		09 14			
Brinnington	d				06 49		07 17					07 56		08 17						08 56		09 17			
Bredbury	d				06 52		07 20					07 59		08 20						08 59		09 20			
Gorton	d			06 22		06 54		07 24					07 54		08 21						08 54		09 24		
Fairfield	d									07 46								08 43							
Guide Bridge	d			06a26		06a58		07a28		07 49			07a58		08a25			08 46			08a58		09a28		
Hyde North	d									07 53								08 50							
Hyde Central	d									07 55								08 52							
Woodley	d									07 58								08 55							
Romiley	d				06 55		07 23			08 02		08 02		08 23			08 37	08 59		09 02		09 23			09 37
Rose Hill Marple	a									08 08								09 05							
Marple	d				06 59		07a28					08 06		08a28			08a43			09 06		09a28			09a43
Strines	d																			09 10					
New Mills Central	d				07 04							08 11								09 13					
Stockport	86 d	05 52	06 00						07 28		07 54					08 28			08 54					09 28	
Hazel Grove	86 d		06 07																						
Chinley	d		06 18		07 12							08 19								09 21					
Edale	d		06 26		07 21							08 28								09 30					
Hope (Derbyshire)	d		06 32		07 27							08 34								09 36					
Bamford	d		06 35		07 30							08 37								09 39					
Hathersage	d		06 39		07 33							08 40								09 42					
Grindleford	d		06 42		07 37							08 44								09 46					
Dore & Totley	d		06 51		07 47				08 03		08 28	08 53								09 54					
Sheffield 7	a	06 49	07 01		07 57				08 10		08 34	09 03				09 08			09 35	10 03				10 08	

		NT	EM	NT	NT	NT	NT	TP	NT	NT	EM	NT	NT	NT	NT	TP	NT	NT	EM	NT	NT	NT	NT	TP	NT
			◇ C		B		B	1 ◇ A			◇ C		B		B	1 ◇ A			◇ C		B		B	1 ◇ A	
Manchester Airport	85 d	09 05				09 35	09 41	09 55		10 05				10 35	10 41	10 55		11 05				11 35	11 41	11 55	
Manchester Piccadilly 10	d	09 36	09 43	09 45	09 48	10 03	10 18	10 20	10 23	10 36	10 43	10 45	10 48	11 03	11 18	11 20	11 23	11 36	11 43	11 45	11 48	12 03	12 18	12 20	12 23
Ardwick	d																								
Ashburys	d				09 52	10 07	10 22						10 52	11 07	11 22						11 52	12 07	12 22		
Belle Vue	d					10 09								11 09								12 09			
Ryder Brow	d					10 11								11 11								12 11			
Reddish North	d			09 52		10 14						10 52		11 14						11 52		12 14			
Brinnington	d			09 56		10 17						10 56		11 17						11 56		12 17			
Bredbury	d			09 59		10 20						10 59		11 20						11 59		12 20			
Gorton	d				09 54		10 24						10 54		11 24						11 54		12 24		
Fairfield	d	09 43								10 43								11 43							
Guide Bridge	d	09 46			09a58		10a28			10 46			10a58		11a28			11 46			11a58		12a28		
Hyde North	d	09 50								10 50								11 50							
Hyde Central	d	09 52								10 52								11 52							
Woodley	d	09 55								10 55								11 55							
Romiley	d	09 59		10 02		10 23			10 37	10 59		11 02		11 23			11 37	11 59		12 02		12 23			12 37
Rose Hill Marple	a	10 05								11 05								12 05							
Marple	d			10 06		10a28			10a43			11 06		11a28			11a43			12 06		12a28			12a43
Strines	d			10 10																12 10					
New Mills Central	d			10 13								11 11								12 13					
Stockport	86 d		09 54					10 28			10 54					11 28			11 54					12 28	
Hazel Grove	86 d																								
Chinley	d			10 21								11 19								12 21					
Edale	d			10 30								11 28								12 30					
Hope (Derbyshire)	d			10 36								11 34								12 36					
Bamford	d			10 39								11 37								12 39					
Hathersage	d			10 42								11 40								12 42					
Grindleford	d			10 46								11 44								12 46					
Dore & Totley	d			10 54								11 53								12 54					
Sheffield 7	a		10 35	11 03				11 08			11 35	12 03				12 08			12 35	13 03				13 08	

For general notes see front of timetable
For details of catering facilities see Directory of Train Operators

A To Cleethorpes (27 June to 5 September to Doncaster) (Table 29)
B To Hadfield (Table 79)
C From Liverpool Lime Street to Norwich (Table 49)

Manchester Airport and Manchester → Romiley, Marple, Chinley and Sheffield

Network Diagram - see first page of Table 78

		NT	EM	NT	NT	NT	NT	TP	NT	NT	EM	NT	NT	NT	NT	TP	NT	NT	EM	NT	NT	NT	NT	TP	NT
			◇ A		B		B	1 ◇ C			◇ A		B		B	1 ◇ C			◇ D		B		B	1 ◇ C	
Manchester Airport	85 d	12 05				12 35	12 41	12b47		13 05				13 35	13 41	13b47		14 05				14 35	14 41	14b47	
Manchester Piccadilly 10	d	12 36	12 43	12 45	12 48	13 03	13 18	13 20	13 23	13 36	13 43	13 45	13 48	14 03	14 18	14 20	14 23	14 36	14 43	14 45	14 48	15 03	15 18	15 20	15 23
Ardwick	d																								
Ashburys	d				12 52	13 07	13 22						13 52	14 07	14 22						14 52	15 07	15 22		
Belle Vue	d					13 09								14 09								15 09			
Ryder Brow	d					13 11								14 11								15 11			
Reddish North	d			12 52		13 14						13 52		14 14						14 52		15 14			
Brinnington	d			12 56		13 17						13 56		14 17						14 56		15 17			
Bredbury	d			12 59		13 20						13 59		14 20						14 59		15 20			
Gorton	d				12 54		13 24						13 54		14 24						14 54		15 24		
Fairfield	d	12 43								13 43								14 43							
Guide Bridge	d	12 46			12a58		13a28			13 46			13a58		14a28			14 46			14a58		15a28		
Hyde North	d	12 50								13 50								14 50							
Hyde Central	d	12 52								13 52								14 52							
Woodley	d	12 55								13 55								14 55							
Romiley	d	12 59		13 02		13 23			13 37	13 59		14 02		14 23			14 37	14 59		15 02		15 23			15 37
Rose Hill Marple	a	13 05								14 05								15 05							
Marple	d			13 06		13a28			13a43			14 06		14a28			14a43			15 06		15a28			15a43
Strines	d											14 10													
New Mills Central	d			13 11								14 13								15 11					
Stockport	86 d		12 54					13 28			13 54					14 28			14 54					15 28	
Hazel Grove	86 d																								
Chinley	d			13 19								14 21								15 19					
Edale	d			13 28								14 30								15 28					
Hope (Derbyshire)	d			13 34								14 36								15 34					
Bamford	d			13 37								14 39								15 37					
Hathersage	d			13 40								14 42								15 40					
Grindleford	d			13 44								14 46								15 44					
Dore & Totley	d			13 53								14 54								15 53					
Sheffield 7	a		13 35	14 03				14 08			14 35	15 03				15 08			15 35	16 03				16 08	

		NT	EM	NT	NT	NT	NT	TP	NT	NT	EM	NT	NT	NT	NT	TP	NT	NT	EM	NT	NT	NT	NT	TP	NT
			◇ A		B		B	1 ◇ C			◇ A		B		B	1 ◇ C			◇ D		B		B	1 ◇ C	
Manchester Airport	85 d	15 05				15 35	15 41	15b47		16 05				16 35	16 41	16b47		17 05				17 35	17 41	17b47	
Manchester Piccadilly 10	d	15 36	15 43	15 45	15 48	16 02	16 18	16 20	16 23	16 36	16 43	16 45	16 48	17 02	17 18	17 20	17 23	17 36	17 43	17 45	17 48	18 03	18 18	18 20	18 23
Ardwick	d																								
Ashburys	d				15 52	16 06	16 22						16 52	17 06	17 22						17 52	18 07	18 22		
Belle Vue	d					16 08								17 08								18 09			
Ryder Brow	d					16 10								17 10								18 11			
Reddish North	d			15 52		16 13						16 52		17 13						17 52		18 14			
Brinnington	d			15 56		16 16						16 56		17 16						17 56		18 17			
Bredbury	d			15 59		16 19						16 59		17 19						17 59		18 20			
Gorton	d				15 54		16 24						16 54		17 24						17 54		18 24		
Fairfield	d	15 43								16 43								17 43							
Guide Bridge	d	15 46			15a58		16a28			16 46			16a58		17a28			17 46			17a58		18a28		
Hyde North	d	15 50								16 50								17 50							
Hyde Central	d	15 52								16 52								17 52							
Woodley	d	15 55								16 55								17 55							
Romiley	d	15 59		16 02		16 22			16 37	16 59		17 02		17 22			17 37	17 59		18 02		18 23			18 37
Rose Hill Marple	a	16 05								17 05								18 06							
Marple	d			16 06		16a27			16a43			17 06		17a27			17a43			18 06		18a28			18a43
Strines	d			16 10																18 10					
New Mills Central	d			16 13								17 11								18 13					
Stockport	86 d		15 54					16 28			16 54					17 28			17 54					18 28	
Hazel Grove	86 d																								
Chinley	d			16 21							17 09	17 19				17 43				18 21					
Edale	d			16 30								17 28								18 30					
Hope (Derbyshire)	d			16 36								17 34								18 36					
Bamford	d			16 39								17 37								18 39					
Hathersage	d			16 42								17 40								18 42					
Grindleford	d			16 46								17 44								18 46					
Dore & Totley	d			16 54							17 30	17 52				18 05				18 54				19 03	
Sheffield 7	a		16 35	17 03				17 08			17 37	18 01				18 15			18 34	19 03				19 10	

For general notes see front of timetable
For details of catering facilities see Directory of Train Operators

A From Liverpool Lime Street to Norwich (Table 49)
B To Hadfield (Table 79)
C To Cleethorpes (Table 29)
D From Liverpool Lime Street to Nottingham (Table 49)
b Until 31 October dep. 8 mins. later

Table 78

Saturdays

Manchester Airport and Manchester → Romiley, Marple, Chinley and Sheffield

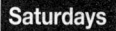

Network Diagram - see first page of Table 78

		NT	EM ◇ A	NT	NT B	TP 1◇ C	NT	EM ◇ D	NT	NT B	TP 1◇ C	NT	EM ◇ D	NT	NT B	TP 1◇ E	EM ◇ D	NT	NT B	TP 1◇	NT	NT B	NT	NT G
Manchester Airport	85 d	18 03				18b47		19 09		19 19	19b47	20 03	20 09		20 20	20 47	21 09		21 20	21 47	22 19	22 22	22 29	
Manchester Piccadilly 10	d	18 36	18 43	18 45	18 48	19 18	19 23	19 43	19 45	19 48	20 20	20 36	20 43	20 45	20 48	21 20	21 43	21 45	21 48	22 20	22 45	22 48	23 24	23 27
Ardwick	d																							
Ashburys	d				18 52		19 28		19 49	19 52					20 52			21 49	21 52		22 49	22 52	23 28	23 31
Belle Vue	d						19 31		19 51									21 51			22 51		23 30	
Ryder Brow	d						19 33		19 53									21 53			22 53		23 32	
Reddish North	d			18 52			19 35		19 56					20 52				21 56			22 56		23 35	
Brinnington	d			18 56			19 39		19 59					20 56				21 59			22 59		23 38	
Bredbury	d			18 59			19 42		20 02					20 59				22 02			23 02		23 41	
Gorton	d				18 54					19 54					20 54				21 54			22 54		23 33
Fairfield	d	18 43										20 43												
Guide Bridge	d	18 46			18a58					19a58		20 46			20a58				21a58			22a58		23a37
Hyde North	d	18 50										20 50												
Hyde Central	d	18 52										20 52												
Woodley	d	18 55										20 55												
Romiley	d	18 59		19 02			19 45		20 05			20 59		21 02				22 05			23 05		23 44	
Rose Hill Marple	a	19 05										21 05												
Marple	d			19 06			19a49		20 09					21 06				22 09			23 09		23 48	
Strines	d								20 13									22 13			23 13		23 52	
New Mills Central	d			19 11					20a18					21 11				22a18			23a18		23a57	
Stockport	86 d		18 54			19 26		19 54			20 28		20 54			21 28	21 52			22 28				
Hazel Grove	86 d																							
Chinley	d			19 19										21 19						22 45				
Edale	d			19 28										21 28						22 53				
Hope (Derbyshire)	d			19 34										21 34						22 58				
Bamford	d			19 37										21 37						23 01				
Hathersage	d			19 40										21 40						23 04				
Grindleford	d			19 44										21 44						23 08				
Dore & Totley	d			19 53										21 53						23 15				
Sheffield 7	a		19 35	20 03		20 08		20 35			21 08		21 34	22 03		22 08	22 31			23 27				

Sundays

until 6 September

		NT	NT	TP 1◇	NT B	NT	NT B	NT B	NT	NT B	TP 1◇ H	NT B	NT	NT B	TP 1◇ J	NT B	EM ◇ K	NT B	NT B	TP 1◇ H	EM ◇ A	NT
Manchester Airport	85 d			08 39							10 44									12 55		
Manchester Piccadilly 10	d	07 45	08 22	08 58	09 18	09 45	09 48	10 18	10 45	10 48	11 18	11 18	11 45	11 48	12 18	12 18	12 44	12 48	13 18	13 20	13 44	13 45
Ashburys	d				09 22		09 52	10 22		10 52		11 22		11 52		12 22		12 52	13 22			
Belle Vue	d																					
Ryder Brow	d																					
Reddish North	d	07 52	08 29			09 52			10 52				11 52									13 52
Brinnington	d	07 56	08 33			09 56			10 56				11 56									13 56
Bredbury	d	07 59	08 36			09 59			10 59				11 59									13 59
Gorton	d				09 24		09 54	10 24		10 54		11 24		11 54		12 24		12 54	13 24			
Guide Bridge	d				09a28		09a58	10a28		10a58		11a28		11a58		12a28		12a58	13a28			
Romiley	d	08 02	08 39			10 02			11 02				12 02									14 02
Marple	d	08 06	08 43			10 06			11 06				12 06									14 06
Strines	d	08 10	08 47			10 10			11 10				12 10									14 10
New Mills Central	d	08 14	08 51			10 14			11 14				12 14									14 14
Stockport	86 d			09 06							11 27				12 28		12 54			13 28	13 54	
Hazel Grove	86 d																					
Chinley	d	08 23	09 00			10 23			11 23				12 23									14 23
Edale	d	08 32	09 09			10 32			11 32				12 32									14 32
Hope (Derbyshire)	d	08 38	09 15			10 38			11 38				12 38									14 38
Bamford	d	08 41	09 18			10 41			11 41				12 41									14 41
Hathersage	d	08 45	09 22			10 45			11 45				12 45									14 45
Grindleford	d	08 48	09 25			10 48			11 48				12 48									14 48
Dore & Totley	d	08 57	09 34			10 57			11 57				12 57									14 58
Sheffield 7	a	09 06	09 42	09 45		11 06			12 06		12 08		13 06		13 08		13e42			14 08	14f43	15 07

For general notes see front of timetable
For details of catering facilities see Directory of Train Operators

- **A** From Liverpool Lime Street to Norwich (Table 49)
- **B** To Hadfield (Table 79)
- **C** To Cleethorpes (Table 29)
- **D** From Liverpool Lime Street to Nottingham (Table 49)
- **E** To Cleethorpes (27 June to 5 September to Doncaster) (Table 29)
- **G** To Glossop (Table 79)
- **H** To Cleethorpes (from 28 June to Doncaster) (Table 29)
- **J** To Doncaster (Table 29)
- **K** To Norwich (Table 49)
- **b** Until 31 October dep. 8 mins. later
- **e** Until 12 July arr. 5 mins. earlier
- **f** Until 12 July arr. 4 mins. earlier

Table 78

Sundays until 6 September

Manchester Airport and Manchester → Romiley, Marple, Chinley and Sheffield

Network Diagram - see first page of Table 78

	NT A		NT A	TP 1◇ B	EM ◇ C trolley	NT	NT A		NT A	TP 1◇ B	EM ◇ C trolley	NT	NT A		NT A	TP 1◇ B	EM ◇ C trolley	NT	NT A		NT A	TP 1◇ B	EM ◇ D trolley	NT
Manchester Airport 85 ✈ d				13 55						14 55						15 55						16 55		
Manchester Piccadilly [10] d	13 48		14 18	14 20	14 44	14 45	14 48		15 18	15 20	15 44	15 45	15 48		16 18	16 20	16 44	16 45	16 48		17 18	17 20	17 44	17 45
Ashburys d	13 52		14 22				14 52		15 22				15 52		16 22				16 52		17 22			
Belle Vue d																								
Ryder Brow d																								
Reddish North d						14 52						15 52						16 52						17 52
Brinnington d						14 56						15 56						16 56						17 56
Bredbury d						14 59						15 59						16 59						17 59
Gorton d	13 54		14 24				14 54		15 24				15 54		16 24				16 54		17 24			
Guide Bridge d	13a58		14a28				14a58		15a28				15a58		16a28				16a58		17a28			
Romiley d						15 02						16 02						17 02						18 02
Marple d						15 06						16 06						17 06						18 06
Strines d						15 10						16 10						17 10						18 10
New Mills Central d						15 14						16 14						17 14						18 14
Stockport 86 d				14 28	14 54					15 28	15 54					16 28	16 54					17 28	17 54	
Hazel Grove 86 d																								
Chinley d						15 23						16 23						17 23						18 23
Edale d						15 32						16 32						17 32						18 32
Hope (Derbyshire) d						15 38						16 38						17 38						18 38
Bamford d						15 41						16 41						17 41						18 41
Hathersage d						15 45						16 45						17 45						18 45
Grindleford d						15 48						16 48						17 48						18 48
Dore & Totley d						15 57						16 57						17 57						18 57
Sheffield [7] a				15 08	15 33	16 06				16 08	16 36	17 06				17 08	17 36	18 06				18 08	18 37	19 06

	NT A	NT A	TP 1◇ B		EM ◇ D trolley	NT A	NT A	TP 1◇ B	EM ◇ D trolley		NT	NT A	TP 1◇ B	EM ◇ D trolley	NT A		TP 1◇	EM ◇ D	TP 1◇	EM ◇ D	NT	TP 1◇		
Manchester Airport 85 ✈ d			17 55					18 55					19 55				20 55		21 55			22 55		
Manchester Piccadilly [10] d	17 48	18 18	18 20		18 44	18 48	19 18	19 20	19 44		19 45	19 48	20 18	20 44	20 48		21 20	22 11	22 16		22 20	23 20		
Ashburys d	17 52	18 22				18 52	19 22					19 52			20 52									
Belle Vue d																								
Ryder Brow d																								
Reddish North d											19 52										22 27			
Brinnington d											19 56										22 31			
Bredbury d											19 59										22 34			
Gorton d	17 54	18 24				18 54	19 24					19 54			20 54									
Guide Bridge d	17a58	18a28				18a58	19a28					19a58			20a58									
Romiley d											20 02										22 37			
Marple d											20 06										22 40			
Strines d											20 10										22 44			
New Mills Central d											20 14									←	22a48			
Stockport 86 d			18 28		18 54			19 28	19 54				20 27	20 54			21 28	22 28 →	22 24	22 28		23 28		
Hazel Grove 86 d																								
Chinley d											20 23									22 43				
Edale d											20 32									22 51				
Hope (Derbyshire) d											20 38									22 57				
Bamford d											20 41									23 00				
Hathersage d											20 45									23 03				
Grindleford d											20 48									23 07				
Dore & Totley d											20 57									23 17				
Sheffield [7] a			19 08		19 34			20 08	20 34		21 06		21 08	21 36			22 11		23 06	23b25		00 15		

Sundays from 13 September

	NT 🚌	NT	TP 1◇	NT E	NT A	NT		NT A	NT A	NT E	NT A	TP 1◇ G	NT A		NT	NT A	TP 1◇ H	NT A	EM ◇ J trolley	NT A		NT A	TP 1◇ G	EM ◇ C trolley
Manchester Airport 85 ✈ d			08 39									10 44											12 55	
Manchester Piccadilly [10] d	06 45	07 57	08 58	09 00	09 18	09 22		09 32	10 18	10 45	10 48	11 18	11 18		11 45	11 48	12 18	12 18	12 44	12 48		13 18	13 20	13 44
Ashburys d					09 22			09 36	10 22		10 52		11 22			11 52		12 22		12 52		13 22		
Belle Vue d																								
Ryder Brow d																								
Reddish North d	07 00					09 29				10 52					11 52									
Brinnington d	07 20					09 33				10 56					11 56									
Bredbury d	07 28					09 36				10 59					11 59									
Gorton d					09 24			09 38	10 24		10 54		11 24			11 54		12 24		12 54		13 24		
Guide Bridge d					09a28			09a42	10a28		10a58		11a28			11a58		12a28		12a58		13a28		
Romiley d	07 36					09 39				11 02					12 02									
Marple d	07 45					09 43				11 06					12 06									
Strines d	07 51					09 47				11 10					12 10									
New Mills Central d	07 57			09 21		09 51				11 14					12 14									
Stockport 86 d		08 11	09 06									11 27					12 28		12 55				13 28	13 54
Hazel Grove 86 d																								
Chinley d	08a17	08 27		09 28		09 59				11 23					12 23									
Edale d		08 35		09 37		10 08				11 32					12 32									
Hope (Derbyshire) d		08 41		09 43		10 14				11 38					12 38									
Bamford d		08 44		09 46		10 17				11 41					12 41									
Hathersage d		08 48		09 50		10 20				11 45					12 45									
Grindleford d		08 51		09 53		10 24				11 48					12 48									
Dore & Totley d		09 00		10 02		10 34				11 57					12 57									
Sheffield [7] a		09 08	09 45	10 10		10 43				12 06		12 08			13 06		13 08		13 37				14 08	14 39

For general notes see front of timetable
For details of catering facilities see Directory of Train Operators

- **A** To Hadfield (Table 79)
- **B** To Cleethorpes (from 28 June to Doncaster) (Table 29)
- **C** From Liverpool Lime Street to Norwich (Table 49)
- **D** From Liverpool Lime Street to Nottingham (Table 49)
- **E** 13 September
- **G** To Cleethorpes (Table 29)
- **H** To Doncaster (Table 29)
- **J** To Norwich (Table 49)
- **b** Until 12 July arr. 2 mins. earlier

Sundays

from 13 September

Manchester Airport and Manchester → Romiley, Marple, Chinley and Sheffield

Network Diagram - see first page of Table 78

	NT	NT A	NT A	TP 1 ◇ B	EM ◇ C	NT D	NT A	NT A	TP 1 ◇ B	EM ◇ C	NT	NT A	NT A	TP 1 ◇ B	EM ◇ C	NT D	NT A	NT A	TP 1 ◇ B	EM ◇ E	NT
Manchester Airport 85 d				13 55					14 55					15 55					16 55		
Manchester Piccadilly 10 d	13 45	13 48	14 18	14 20	14 44	14 45	14 48	15 18	15 20	15 44	15 45	15 48	16 18	16 20	16 44	16 45	16 48	17 18	17 20	17 44	17 45
Ashburys d		13 52	14 22				14 52	15 22				15 52	16 22				16 52	17 22			
Belle Vue d																					
Ryder Brow d																					
Reddish North d	13 52					14 52					15 52					16 52					17 52
Brinnington d	13 56					14 56					15 56					16 56					17 56
Bredbury d	13 59					14 59					15 59					16 59					17 59
Gorton d		13 54	14 24				14 54	15 24				15 54	16 24				16 54	17 24			
Guide Bridge d		13a58	14a28				14a58	15a28				15a58	16a28				16a58	17a28			
Romiley d	14 02					15 02					16 02					17 02					18 02
Marple d	14 06					15 06					16 06					17 06					18 06
Strines d	14 10					15 10					16 10					17 10					18 10
New Mills Central d	14 14					15 14					16 14					17 14					18 14
Stockport 86 d				14 28	14 54				15 28	15 54				16 28	16 54				17 28	17 54	
Hazel Grove 86 d																					
Chinley d	14 23					15 23					16 23					17 23					18 23
Edale d	14 32					15 32					16 32					17 32					18 32
Hope (Derbyshire) d	14 38					15 38					16 38					17 38					18 38
Bamford d	14 41					15 41					16 41					17 41					18 41
Hathersage d	14 45					15 45					16 45					17 45					18 45
Grindleford d	14 48					15 48					16 48					17 48					18 48
Dore & Totley d	14 58					15 57					16 57					17 57					18 57
Sheffield 7 a	15 07			15 08	15 37	16 06			16 08	16 36	17 06			17 08	17 36	18 06			18 08	18 37	19 06

	NT A	NT A	TP 1 ◇ B	EM ◇ E	NT A	NT A	TP 1 ◇ B	EM ◇ E	NT	NT A	TP 1 ◇ B	EM ◇ E	NT A	TP 1 ◇	EM ◇ E	TP 1 ◇	EM ◇ E	NT	TP 1 ◇
Manchester Airport 85 d			17 55				18 55				19 55			20 55		21 55			22 55
Manchester Piccadilly 10 d	17 48	18 18	18 20	18 44	18 48	19 18	19 20	19 44	19 45	19 48	20 18	20 44	20 48	21 20		22 16		22 20	23 20
Ashburys d	17 52	18 22			18 52	19 22				19 52			20 52						
Belle Vue d																			
Ryder Brow d																			
Reddish North d									19 52									22 27	
Brinnington d									19 56									22 31	
Bredbury d									19 59									22 34	
Gorton d	17 54	18 24			18 54	19 24				19 54			20 54						
Guide Bridge d	17a58	18a28			18a58	19a28				19a58			20a58						
Romiley d									20 02									22 37	
Marple d									20 06									22 40	
Strines d									20 10									22 44	
New Mills Central d									20 14								←	22a48	
Stockport 86 d			18 28	18 54			19 28	19 54			20 27	20 54		21 28	22 28 →	22 24	22 28		23 28
Hazel Grove 86 d																			
Chinley d									20 23								22 43		
Edale d									20 32								22 51		
Hope (Derbyshire) d									20 38								22 57		
Bamford d									20 41								23 00		
Hathersage d									20 45								23 03		
Grindleford d									20 48								23 07		
Dore & Totley d									20 57								23 17		
Sheffield 7 a			19 08	19 34			20 08	20 34	21 06		21 08	21 36		22 11		23 06	23 23		00 15

For general notes see front of timetable
For details of catering facilities see Directory of Train Operators

A To Hadfield (Table 79)
B To Cleethorpes (Table 29)
C From Liverpool Lime Street to Norwich (Table 49)
D 13 September
E From Liverpool Lime Street to Nottingham (Table 49)

Sheffield, Chinley, Marple and Romiley → Manchester and Manchester Airport

Network Diagram - see first page of Table 78

Miles	Miles	Miles		TP 1◇	TP 1◇	NT A	NT B	NT C	TP 1◇ D	NT	NT B		NT C	NT A	EM ◇ E 🍴	NT B	NT C	NT A	NT	NT B		NT C	TP 1◇ G 🍴	NT A
0	—	—	**Sheffield 7** d	03 45	05 11				06 11						06 20								07 09	
4¾	—	—	Dore & Totley d												06 27								07 14	
9¾	—	—	Grindleford d												06 35									
11¼	—	—	Hathersage d												06 39									
13	—	—	Bamford d												06 43									
14¾	—	—	Hope (Derbyshire) d												06 47									
20	—	—	Edale d												06 55									
25½	—	0	**Chinley** d												07 03									
—	—	8½	Hazel Grove 86 a																					
—	—	—	Stockport 86 a		05 53				06 53						07 22								07 53	
29¼	—	—	New Mills Central d				06 10	06 13			06 33		06 36			06 58	07 01			07 20		07 23		
30¾	—	—	Strines d				06 13	06 16			06 36		06 39			07 01	07 04			07 23		07 26		
33	—	—	**Marple** d				06 16	06 19			06 39		06 42			07 04	07 07			07 26		07 29		
—	0	—	**Rose Hill Marple** d							06b30									07 16					
34¼	2	—	**Romiley** d				06 20	06 23		06 37	06 43		06 46			07 09	07 12		07 21	07 30		07 33		
—	3¼	—	Woodley d							06 40									07 24					
—	4¾	—	Hyde Central d							06 43									07 27					
—	6	—	Hyde North d							06 46									07 30					
—	7¾	—	Guide Bridge d			06 27				06 50				06 57				07 27	07 34					07 47
—	9	—	Fairfield d							06 53									07 37					
—	10	—	Gorton d			06 30								07 00				07 30						07 50
35½	—	—	Bredbury d				06 23	06 26			06 46		06 49			07 12	07 15			07 33		07 36		
36½	—	—	Brinnington d				06 25	06 28			06 49		06 52			07 14	07 17			07 36		07 39		
38¼	—	—	Reddish North d				06 28	06 31			06 52		06 55			07 17	07 20			07 40		07 43		
39¼	—	—	Ryder Brow d				06 31	06 34			06 55		06 58			07 21	07 24			07 42		07 45		
39½	—	—	Belle Vue d				06 33	06 36			06 57		07 00			07 23	07 26			07 44		07 47		
40½	11	—	Ashburys d			06 33	06 39	06 39			07 03		07 03	07 06		07 29	07 29	07 33		07 50		07 50		07 53
41½	12	—	Ardwick d															07 36						
42	12½	8¾	**Manchester Piccadilly 10** a	04 40	06 05	06 42	06 47	06 47	07 02	07 03	07 12		07 12	07 15	07 34	07 36	07 36	07 43	07 47	07 56		07 56	08 02	08 03
—	—	—	**Manchester Airport** 85 ✈ a	05 00	06 29	*07 12*	*07 17*	*07 17*	07c26	*07 38*	*07 42*		*07 42*	*07 47*		*08 07*	*08 07*	*08 12*	*08 17*				08 29	*08 39*

	NT	NT	NT	NT A	NT	NT	EM ◇ E 🍴		NT A	NT	NT	NT	TP 1◇ G 🍴	NT A	NT	NT A		NT	NT	EM ◇ E 🍴	NT A	NT	TP 1◇ G 🍴	NT A
Sheffield 7 d						07 12	07 35						08 05							08 42			09 11	
Dore & Totley d						07 19	07 42						08 10											
Grindleford d						07 29																		
Hathersage d						07 32																		
Bamford d						07 36																		
Hope (Derbyshire) d						07 39																		
Edale d						07 47																		
Chinley d						07 55	08 03						08 32											
Hazel Grove 86 a							08 16																	
Stockport 86 a							08 24						08 53							09 25			09 53	
New Mills Central d		07e36				08 02					08 24								09 04					
Strines d		07 39				08 05													09 07					
Marple d		07 42			07 59	08 09					08 29				08 48				09 10			09 35		
Rose Hill Marple d	07 41									08 15		08 35						08 59						
Romiley d	07 46	07 49	⟵		08 02	08 13				08 20	08 33	08 40			08 51			09 04	09 14			09 38		
Woodley d	07 49		07 49							08 23								09 07						
Hyde Central d	⟶		07 52							08 26								09 10						
Hyde North d			07 55							08 29								09 13						
Guide Bridge d			07 59	08 10					08 27	08 33				08 49		09 12		09 17			09 28			09 58
Fairfield d			08 02							08 36								09 20						
Gorton d				08 13					08 31					08 52		09 15					09 31			10 01
Bredbury d		07 52			08 06						08 36	08 43			08 54				09 17			09 41		
Brinnington d		07 55			08 09						08 39	08 45			08 57				09 19			09 44		
Reddish North d		07 58			08 12						08 43	08 48			09 00				09 22			09 47		
Ryder Brow d					08 15										09 03									
Belle Vue d					08 16										09 04									
Ashburys d				08 16	08 20				08 34		08 48			08 56	09 07	09 18					09 34			10 04
Ardwick d					08 22							08 54												
Manchester Piccadilly 10 a		08 09	08 12	08 25	08 30	08 33	08 36		08 43	08 47	08 55	09 00	09 02	09 04	09 15	09 27		09 30	09 34	09 36	09 42	09 57	10 02	10 12
Manchester Airport 85 ✈ a			*08 42*	*08 53*			*09 07*		*09 12*	*09 19*			09 33	*09 38*	*09 47*	*09 53*				*10 07*	*10 12*	*10 38*	10 26	*10 42*

For general notes see front of timetable
For details of catering facilities see Directory of Train Operators

A From Hadfield (Table 79)
B From 5 October
C Until 2 October
D From Doncaster (Table 29)
E From Nottingham to Liverpool Lime Street (Table 49)
G From Cleethorpes (22 June to 4 September from Doncaster) (Table 29)
b Until 2 October dep. 2 mins. later
c 22 June to 4 September arr. 0732
e Until 2 October dep. 3 mins. later

Sheffield, Chinley, Marple and Romiley → Manchester and Manchester Airport

Network Diagram - see first page of Table 78

	NT	NT	NT	EM ◇ A	NT B	NT	NT	TP 1 ◇ C	NT	NT B	NT	NT	EM ◇ A	NT B	NT	NT	TP 1 ◇ C	NT	NT B	NT	NT
Sheffield 7 d			09 14	09 42				10 11				10 14	10 42				11 11				
Dore & Totley d			09 21									10 21									
Grindleford d			09 29									10 29									
Hathersage d			09 32									10 32									
Bamford d			09 36									10 36									
Hope (Derbyshire) d			09 39									10 39									
Edale d			09 47									10 47									
Chinley d			09 55									10 55									
Hazel Grove 86 a																					
Stockport 86 a				10 25				10 53					11 25				11 53				
New Mills Central d			10 01				10 30					11 01				11 30					12 01
Strines d			10 04																		12 04
Marple d	09 52		10 06				10 35				10 52	11 07				11 35				11 52	12 07
Rose Hill Marple d		09 55				10 30									11 30						
Romiley d	09 55	10 00	10 11			10 35	10 38		←		10 55	11 11			11 35	11 38		←		11 55	12 11
Woodley d		10 03				10 38 →			10 38						11 38 →			11 38			
Hyde Central d		10 06							10 41									11 41			
Hyde North d		10 09							10 44									11 44			
Guide Bridge d		10 13			10 28				10 48	10 58				11 28				11 48	11 58		
Fairfield d		10 16							10 51									11 51			
Gorton d					10 31					11 01				11 31					12 01		
Bredbury d			10 14				10 41					11 14				11 41					12 14
Brinnington d			10 16				10 44					11 16				11 44					12 16
Reddish North d			10 19				10 47					11 19				11 47					12 19
Ryder Brow d	10 03										11 03									12 03	
Belle Vue d	10 04										11 04									12 04	
Ashburys d	10 07				10 34					11 04	11 07			11 34					12 04	12 07	
Ardwick d																					
Manchester Piccadilly 10 a	10 15	10 26	10 32	10 36	10 42		10 57	11 02	11 02	11 12	11 15	11 32	11 36	11 42		11 57	12 02	12 02	12 12	12 15	12 32
Manchester Airport 85 ✈ a	*10 47*	*10 53*		*11 07*	*11 12*			11 26	*11 38*	*11 42*	*11 47*		*12 07*	*12 12*			12 26	*12 38*	*12 42*	*12 47*	

	EM ◇ A	NT B	NT	NT	TP 1 ◇ C	NT	NT B	NT	NT	EM ◇ A	NT B	NT	NT	TP 1 ◇ C	NT	NT B	NT	NT	EM ◇ A	NT B	NT	NT
Sheffield 7 d	11 42				12 11				12 14	12 42				13 11					13 42			
Dore & Totley d									12 21													
Grindleford d									12 29													
Hathersage d									12 32													
Bamford d									12 36													
Hope (Derbyshire) d									12 39													
Edale d									12 47													
Chinley d									12 55													
Hazel Grove 86 a																						
Stockport 86 a	12 25				12 53					13 25				13 53					14 25			
New Mills Central d				12 30					13 01				13 30					14 01				14 30
Strines d																		14 04				
Marple d				12 35				12 52	13 07				13 35				13 52	14 06				14 35
Rose Hill Marple d			12 30									13 30									14 30	
Romiley d			12 35	12 38		←		12 55	13 11			13 35	13 38		←		13 55	14 11			14 35	14 38
Woodley d			12 38 →			12 38						13 38 →			13 38						14 38 →	
Hyde Central d						12 41									13 41							
Hyde North d						12 44									13 44							
Guide Bridge d		12 28				12 48	12 58				13 28				13 48	13 58				14 28		
Fairfield d						12 51									13 51							
Gorton d		12 31					13 01				13 31					14 01				14 31		
Bredbury d				12 41					13 14				13 41					14 14				14 41
Brinnington d				12 44					13 16				13 44					14 16				14 44
Reddish North d				12 47					13 19				13 47					14 19				14 47
Ryder Brow d								13 03									14 03					
Belle Vue d								13 04									14 04					
Ashburys d		12 34					13 04	13 07			13 34					14 04	14 07			14 34		
Ardwick d																						
Manchester Piccadilly 10 a	12 36	12 42		12 57	13 02	13 02	13 12	13 15	13 32	13 36	13 42		13 57	14 02	14 02	14 12	14 15	14 32	14 36	14 42		14 57
Manchester Airport 85 ✈ a	*13 07*	*13 12*			13 26	*13 38*	*13 42*	*13 47*		*14 07*	*14 12*			14 26	*14 38*	*14 42*	*14 47*		*15 07*	*15 12*		

For general notes see front of timetable
For details of catering facilities see Directory of Train Operators

A From Norwich to Liverpool Lime Street (Table 49)
B From Hadfield (Table 79)
C From Cleethorpes (22 June to 4 September from Doncaster) (Table 29)

Sheffield, Chinley, Marple and Romiley → Manchester and Manchester Airport

Network Diagram - see first page of Table 78

		TP 1 ◇ A ⌶	NT	NT B	NT	NT	EM ◇ C ⌶	NT B	NT	NT	TP 1 ◇ A ⌶	NT	NT B	NT	NT	EM ◇ C ⌶	NT B	NT	TP 1 ◇ A ⌶	NT B	NT	NT
Sheffield 7	d	14 11				14 14	14 42				15 11					15 42			16 10			
Dore & Totley	d					14 21																
Grindleford	d					14 29																
Hathersage	d					14 32																
Bamford	d					14 36																
Hope (Derbyshire)	d					14 39																
Edale	d					14 47																
Chinley	d					14 55																
Hazel Grove	86 a																					
Stockport	86 a	14 53					15 25				15 53					16 25			16 52			
New Mills Central	d					15 01				15 30					16 01						16 37	
Strines	d														16 04							
Marple	d				14 52	15 07				15 35				15 52	16 07						16 42	16 52
Rose Hill Marple	d								15 30									16 26				
Romiley	d		←		14 55	15 11			15 35	15 38		←		15 55	16 11			16 31			16 45	16 55
Woodley	d		14 38						15 38 →			15 38									16 49	
Hyde Central	d		14 41									15 41									16 52	
Hyde North	d		14 44									15 44									16 54	
Guide Bridge	d		14 48	14 58				15 28				15 48	15 58				16 28			16 49	16 58	
Fairfield	d		14 51									15 51										
Gorton	d			15 01				15 31					16 01				16 31			16 52		
Bredbury	d					15 14				15 41					16 14			16 34				
Brinnington	d					15 16				15 44					16 16			16 37				
Reddish North	d					15 19				15 47					16 19			16 40				
Ryder Brow	d				15 03									16 03				16 42				17 03
Belle Vue	d				15 04									16 04				16 44				17 04
Ashburys	d			15 04	15 07			15 34					16 04	16 07			16 34	16 47		16 55	17 03	17 07
Ardwick	d																					
Manchester Piccadilly 10	a	15 02	15 02	15 12	15 15	15 32	15 36	15 42		15 57	16 02	16 02	16 12	16 15	16 32	16 36	16 42	16 56	17 02	17 05	17 09	17 15
Manchester Airport	85 a	15 26	15 38	15 42	15 47		16 07	16 12			16 26	16 38	16 42	16 47		17 07	17 12		17 32			17 48

		NT	NT B	EM ◇ C ⌶	NT	NT	NT B	NT	TP 1 ◇ A ⌶	NT B	NT	NT	NT B	EM ◇ C ⌶	NT	NT	TP 1 ◇ A ⌶	NT B	NT	NT B	NT	EM ◇ C ⌶	NT B
Sheffield 7	d	16 14		16 42					17 11			17 14		17 40			18 10					18 42	
Dore & Totley	d	16 21										17 21											
Grindleford	d	16 29										17 29											
Hathersage	d	16 32										17 32											
Bamford	d	16 36										17 36											
Hope (Derbyshire)	d	16 39										17 39											
Edale	d	16 47										17 47											
Chinley	d	16 55										17 55					18 34				18 54		
Hazel Grove	86 a																						
Stockport	86 a			17 25					17 53					18 25			18 53					19 25	
New Mills Central	d	17 01				17 23						18 01									19 01		
Strines	d											18 04									19 04		
Marple	d	17 05				17 27					17 52	18 07				18 35					19 06		
Rose Hill Marple	d				17 10			17 36							18 11				18 44				
Romiley	d	17 10			17 15	17 32		17 41			17 55	18 11			18 16	18 38			18 49		19 11		
Woodley	d				17 18										18 19								
Hyde Central	d				17 21										18 22								
Hyde North	d				17 24										18 25								
Guide Bridge	d		17 15		17 28		17 42			17 57			18 17		18 29			18 46		19 01			19 28
Fairfield	d				17 31										18 32								
Gorton	d		17 18				17 45			18 01			18 20					18 49		19 04			19 31
Bredbury	d	17 13						17 44				18 14				18 41			18 52		19 14		
Brinnington	d							17 46								18 44			18 54		19 16		
Reddish North	d							17 49								18 47			18 58		19 19		
Ryder Brow	d										18 03								19 00				
Belle Vue	d										18 04								19 02				
Ashburys	d		17 24				17 48	17 55		18 03	18 07		18 23					18 54	19 05	19 08			19 34
Ardwick	d																						
Manchester Piccadilly 10	a	17 29	17 33	17 37	17 42	17 46	17 57	18 01	18 02	18 12	18 15	18 31	18 32	18 36	18 41	18 57	19 02	19 03	19 12	19 15	19 32	19 36	19 42
Manchester Airport	85 a		18 07		18 12	18 17		18 38	18 26	18 42	18 47			19 08	19 13		19 28	19 38		19 47		20 07	20 17

For general notes see front of timetable
For details of catering facilities see Directory of Train Operators

A From Cleethorpes (22 June to 4 September from Doncaster) (Table 29)
B From Hadfield (Table 79)
C From Norwich to Liverpool Lime Street (Table 49)

Sheffield, Chinley, Marple and Romiley → Manchester and Manchester Airport

Network Diagram - see first page of Table 78

	TP 1◇ A ⚲	NT	NT	NT B		NT	EM ◇ C ⚲	NT B	TP 1◇ A ⚲	NT	NT B	EM ◇ D ⚲	NT		NT	NT B	TP 1◇ A	NT	NT B	NT	NT
Sheffield 7 ⇌ d	19 11					19 14	19 42		20 11			20 32			20 35		22 11			22 47	
Dore & Totley d						19 21									20 43					22 54	
Grindleford d						19 29									20 50					23 01	
Hathersage d						19 32									20 53					23 05	
Bamford d						19 36									20 57					23 08	
Hope (Derbyshire) d						19 39									21 00					23 12	
Edale d						19 47									21 08					23 19	
Chinley d						19 55									21 16					23 27	
Hazel Grove 86 a																					
Stockport 86 a	19 53						20 25		20 53			21 20					22 53			23 47	
New Mills Central d						20 01				20 30					21b30			22 30			23 30
Strines d										20 33								22 33			23 33
Marple d			19 37			20 07				20 36					21 36			22 36			23 36
Rose Hill Marple d		19 30											21 12								
Romiley d		19 35	19 40			20 11				20 40			21 17		21 40			22 40			23 40
Woodley d		19 38											21 20								
Hyde Central d		19 41											21 23								
Hyde North d		19 44											21 26								
Guide Bridge d		19 48		19 58				20 28			20 58		21 30			21 58			22 58		
Fairfield d		19 51											21 33								
Gorton d				20 01				20 31			21 01					22 01			23 01		
Bredbury d			19 43			20 14				20 43					21 43			22 43			23 43
Brinnington d			19 46			20 16				20 45					21 45			22 45			23 45
Reddish North d			19 49			20 19				20 48					21 48			22 48			23 48
Ryder Brow d			19 51							20 51					21 51			22 51			23 51
Belle Vue d			19 53							20 52					21 52			22 52			23 52
Ashburys d			19 56	20 04				20 34		20 55	21 04				21 55	22 04		22 55	23 04		23 55
Ardwick d																					
Manchester Piccadilly 10 ⇌ a	20 02	20 02	20 05	20 12		20 32	20 36	20 42	21 02	21 03	21 12	21 32	21 42		22 05	22 12	23 02	23 03	23 12	00 02	00 03
Manchester Airport 85 ✈ a	20 35			*20 53*			*21 07*	*21 17*	21 35		*21 47*	*22 10*	*22 17*			*22 47*	23 26		*00 22*		*01 10*

Saturdays

	TP 1◇	TP 1◇	TP 1◇ E	NT B	EM ◇ G ⚲	NT H	NT J	NT B	NT	TP 1◇ K ⚲		NT	NT B	NT	EM ◇ G ⚲	NT B	NT	NT	TP 1◇ K ⚲	NT	NT B		NT	NT
Sheffield 7 ⇌ d	03 45	05 11	06 11		06 20					07 09				07 12	07 35				08 05					08 14
Dore & Totley d					06 27					07 14				07 19	07 42				08 10					08 21
Grindleford d					06 35									07 29										08 29
Hathersage d					06 39									07 32										08 32
Bamford d					06 43									07 36										08 36
Hope (Derbyshire) d					06 47									07 39										08 39
Edale d					06 55									07 47										08 47
Chinley d					07 03									07 55	08 03				08 32					08 55
Hazel Grove 86 a															08 16									
Stockport 86 a		05 53	06 53		07 22					07 53					08 24				08 53					
New Mills Central d						06 58	07 01							08 01										09 01
Strines d						07 01	07 04							08 04										09 04
Marple d						07 04	07 07		07 35					08 07				08 35					08 52	09 07
Rose Hill Marple d												07 30					08 30							
Romiley d						07 09	07 12		07 38			07 35		08 12			08 35	08 38		←			08 55	09 11
Woodley d												07 38					08 38 →			08 38				
Hyde Central d												07 41								08 41				
Hyde North d												07 44								08 44				
Guide Bridge d				06 57				07 28				07 48	07 58			08 28				08 48	08 58			
Fairfield d												07 51								08 51				
Gorton d				07 00				07 31					08 01			08 31					09 01			
Bredbury d						07 12	07 15		07 41					08 15				08 41						09 14
Brinnington d						07 14	07 17		07 44					08 16				08 44						09 16
Reddish North d						07 17	07 20		07 47					08 19				08 47						09 19
Ryder Brow d						07 21	07 24																09 03	
Belle Vue d						07 23	07 26																09 04	
Ashburys d				07 03		07 29	07 29	07 34					08 04			08 34					09 04		09 07	
Ardwick d																								
Manchester Piccadilly 10 ⇌ a	04 40	06 05	07 02	07 12	07 34	07 36	07 36	07 42	07 59	08 02		08 02	08 12	08 32	08 36	08 42		08 57	09 02	09 02	09 12		09 15	09 32
Manchester Airport 85 ✈ a	05 00	06 29	07c26	*07 42*		*08 07*	*08 07*	*08 12*		08 29		*08 37*	*08 42*		*09 08*	*09 12*			09 26	*09 38*	*09 42*		*09 47*	

For general notes see front of timetable
For details of catering facilities see Directory of Train Operators

- **A** From Cleethorpes (22 June to 4 September from Doncaster) (Table 29)
- **B** From Hadfield (Table 79)
- **C** From Norwich to Liverpool Lime Street (Table 49)
- **D** From Norwich (Table 49)
- **E** From Doncaster (Table 29)
- **G** From Nottingham to Liverpool Lime Street (Table 49)
- **H** From 10 October
- **J** Until 3 October
- **K** From Cleethorpes (27 June to 5 September from Doncaster) (Table 29)
- **b** Arr. 2122
- **c** 27 June to 5 September arr. 0732

Table 78

Saturdays

Sheffield, Chinley, Marple and Romiley → Manchester and Manchester Airport

Network Diagram - see first page of Table 78

	EM ◇ A	NT B	NT	NT	TP 1 ◇ C	NT	NT B	NT	NT	EM ◇ D	NT B	NT	NT	TP 1 ◇ C	NT	NT B	NT	NT	EM ◇ D	NT B	NT	NT
Sheffield 7 d	08 42				09 11				09 14	09 42				10 11				10 14	10 42			
Dore & Totley d									09 21									10 21				
Grindleford d									09 29									10 29				
Hathersage d									09 32									10 32				
Bamford d									09 36									10 36				
Hope (Derbyshire) d									09 39									10 39				
Edale d									09 47									10 47				
Chinley d									09 55									10 55				
Hazel Grove 86 a																						
Stockport 86 a	09 25				09 53					10 25				10 53					11 25			
New Mills Central d									10 01									11 01				
Strines d									10 04													
Marple d				09 35				09 52	10 07				10 35				10 52	11 07				11 35
Rose Hill Marple d			09 30									10 30									11 30	
Romiley d			09 35	09 38		←		09 55	10 11			10 35	10 38		←		10 55	11 11			11 35	11 38
Woodley d			09 38 →			09 38						10 38 →			10 38						11 38 →	
Hyde Central d						09 41									10 41							
Hyde North d						09 44									10 44							
Guide Bridge d		09 28				09 48	09 58				10 28				10 48	10 58				11 28		
Fairfield d						09 51									10 51							
Gorton d		09 31					10 01				10 31					11 01				11 31		
Bredbury d				09 41					10 14				10 41					11 14				11 41
Brinnington d				09 44					10 16				10 44					11 16				11 44
Reddish North d				09 47					10 19				10 47					11 19				11 47
Ryder Brow d								10 03									11 03					
Belle Vue d								10 04									11 04					
Ashburys d		09 34					10 04	10 07			10 34					11 04	11 07			11 34		
Ardwick d																						
Manchester Piccadilly 10 a	09 36	09 42		09 57	10 02	10 02	10 12	10 15	10 32	10 36	10 42		10 57	11 02	11 02	11 12	11 15	11 32	11 36	11 42		11 57
Manchester Airport 85 a	*10 07*	*10 12*			10 26	*10 38*	*10 42*	*10 47*		*11 07*	*11 12*			11 26	*11 38*	*11 42*	*11 47*		*12 07*	*12 12*		

	TP 1 ◇ C	NT	NT B	NT	NT	EM ◇ D	NT B	NT	NT	TP 1 ◇ C	NT	NT B	NT	NT	EM ◇ D	NT B	NT	NT	TP 1 ◇ C	NT	NT B	NT
Sheffield 7 d	11 11				11 14	11 42				12 11				12 14	12 42				13 11			
Dore & Totley d					11 21									12 21								
Grindleford d					11 29									12 29								
Hathersage d					11 32									12 32								
Bamford d					11 36									12 36								
Hope (Derbyshire) d					11 39									12 39								
Edale d					11 47									12 47								
Chinley d					11 55									12 55								
Hazel Grove 86 a																						
Stockport 86 a	11 53					12 25				12 53					13 25				13 53			
New Mills Central d					12 01									13 01								
Strines d					12 04																	
Marple d				11 52	12 07				12 35				12 52	13 07				13 35				13 52
Rose Hill Marple d								12 30									13 30					
Romiley d		←		11 55	12 11			12 35	12 38		←		12 55	13 11			13 35	13 38		←		13 55
Woodley d		11 38						12 38 →			12 38						13 38 →			13 38		
Hyde Central d		11 41									12 41									13 41		
Hyde North d		11 44									12 44									13 44		
Guide Bridge d		11 48	11 58				12 28				12 48	12 58				13 28				13 48	13 58	
Fairfield d		11 51									12 51									13 51		
Gorton d			12 01				12 31					13 01				13 31					14 01	
Bredbury d					12 14				12 41					13 14				13 41				
Brinnington d					12 16				12 44					13 16				13 44				
Reddish North d					12 19				12 47					13 19				13 47				
Ryder Brow d				12 03									13 03									14 03
Belle Vue d				12 04									13 04									14 04
Ashburys d			12 04	12 07			12 34					13 04	13 07			13 34					14 04	14 07
Ardwick d																						
Manchester Piccadilly 10 a	12 02	12 02	12 12	12 15	12 32	12 36	12 42		12 57	13 02	13 02	13 12	13 15	13 32	13 36	13 42		13 57	14 02	14 02	14 12	14 15
Manchester Airport 85 a	12b26	*12c38*	*12 42*	*12 47*		*13 07*	*13 12*			13 33	*13c38*	*13 42*	*13 47*		*14 07*	*14 12*			14b26	*14c38*	*14 42*	*14 47*

For general notes see front of timetable
For details of catering facilities see Directory of Train Operators

- **A** From Nottingham to Liverpool Lime Street (Table 49)
- **B** From Hadfield (Table 79)
- **C** From Cleethorpes (27 June to 5 September from Doncaster) (Table 29)
- **D** From Norwich to Liverpool Lime Street (Table 49)
- **b** From 7 November arr. 7 mins. later
- **c** From 7 November arr. 4 mins. later

Table 78

Saturdays

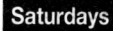

Sheffield, Chinley, Marple and Romiley → Manchester and Manchester Airport

Network Diagram - see first page of Table 78

		NT	EM ◇ A 🛒	NT B	NT	NT	TP **1** ◇ C 🛒	NT	NT B	NT	NT		EM ◇ A 🛒	NT B	NT	NT	TP **1** ◇ C 🛒	NT	NT B	NT	NT	EM ◇ A 🛒		NT B	NT
Sheffield 7	d	13 14	13 42				14 11				14 14		14 42				15 11				15 14	15 42			
Dore & Totley	d	13 21									14 21										15 21				
Grindleford	d	13 29									14 29										15 29				
Hathersage	d	13 32									14 32										15 32				
Bamford	d	13 36									14 36										15 36				
Hope (Derbyshire)	d	13 39									14 39										15 39				
Edale	d	13 47									14 47										15 47				
Chinley	d	13 55									14 55										15 55				
Hazel Grove 86	a																								
Stockport 86	a		14 25				14 53						15 25				15 53					16 25			
New Mills Central	d	14 01									15 01										16 01				
Strines	d	14 04																			16 04				
Marple	d	14 07				14 35				14 52	15 07					15 35				15 52	16 07				
Rose Hill Marple	d				14 30										15 30										16 30
Romiley	d	14 11			14 35	14 38		←		14 55	15 11				15 35	15 38		←		15 55	16 11				16 35
Woodley	d				14 38 →			14 38							15 38 →			15 38							16 38 →
Hyde Central	d							14 41										15 41							
Hyde North	d							14 44										15 44							
Guide Bridge	d			14 28				14 48	14 58					15 28				15 48	15 58					16 28	
Fairfield	d							14 51										15 51							
Gorton	d			14 31					15 01					15 31					16 01					16 31	
Bredbury	d	14 14				14 41					15 14					15 41					16 14				
Brinnington	d	14 16				14 44					15 16					15 44					16 16				
Reddish North	d	14 19				14 47					15 19					15 47					16 19				
Ryder Brow	d									15 03										16 03					
Belle Vue	d									15 04										16 04					
Ashburys	d			14 34					15 04	15 07				15 34					16 04	16 07				16 34	
Ardwick	d																								
Manchester Piccadilly 10	a	14 32	14 36	14 42		14 57	15 02	15 02	15 12	15 15	15 32		15 36	15 42		15 57	16 02	16 02	16 12	16 15	16 33	16 36		16 42	
Manchester Airport 85 ✈	a		15 07	15 12			15b26	15c38	15 42	15 47			16 07	16 12			16b26	16c38	16 42	16 47		17 07		17 12	

		NT	TP **1** ◇ C 🛒	NT	NT B	NT	NT	EM ◇ A 🛒	NT B	NT	NT		TP **1** ◇ C 🛒	NT	NT B	NT	NT	EM ◇ A 🛒	NT B	NT	NT	TP **1** ◇ C 🛒		NT	NT B
Sheffield 7	d		16 10				16 14	16 42					17 11				17 14	17 40				18 10			
Dore & Totley	d						16 21										17 21								
Grindleford	d						16 29										17 29								
Hathersage	d						16 32										17 32								
Bamford	d						16 36										17 36								
Hope (Derbyshire)	d						16 39										17 39								
Edale	d						16 47										17 47								
Chinley	d						16 55										17 55					18 34			
Hazel Grove 86	a																								
Stockport 86	a		16 52					17 25					17 53					18 25				18 53			
New Mills Central	d						17 01										18 01								
Strines	d																18 04								
Marple	d	16 34				16 52	17 07				17 34					17 52	18 07				18 35				
Rose Hill Marple	d									17 30										18 30					
Romiley	d	16 38		←		16 55	17 11			17 35	17 38			←		17 55	18 11			18 35	18 38			←	
Woodley	d			16 38						17 38 →				17 38						18 38 →				18 38	
Hyde Central	d			16 41										17 41										18 41	
Hyde North	d			16 44										17 44										18 44	
Guide Bridge	d			16 48	16 58				17 28					17 48	17 58				18 28					18 48	18 58
Fairfield	d			16 51										17 51										18 51	
Gorton	d				17 01				17 31						18 01				18 31						19 01
Bredbury	d	16 41					17 14				17 41						18 14				18 41				
Brinnington	d	16 43					17 16				17 43						18 16				18 44				
Reddish North	d	16 46					17 19				17 46						18 19				18 47				
Ryder Brow	d					17 03										18 03									
Belle Vue	d					17 04										18 04									
Ashburys	d				17 04	17 07			17 34						18 04	18 07			18 34						19 04
Ardwick	d																								
Manchester Piccadilly 10	a	16 56	17 02	17 02	17 12	17 15	17 32	17 37	17 42		17 56		18 02	18 02	18 12	18 15	18 32	18 36	18 42		18 57	19 02		19 02	19 12
Manchester Airport 85 ✈	a		17f32	17g36		17 48	18 07		18 12				18b26	18j38	18 42	18 47		19 08	19 13			19b28		19k38	

For general notes see front of timetable
For details of catering facilities see Directory of Train Operators

- **A** From Norwich to Liverpool Lime Street (Table 49)
- **B** From Hadfield (Table 79)
- **C** From Cleethorpes (27 June to 5 September from Doncaster) (Table 29)
- **b** From 7 November arr. 7 mins. later
- **c** From 7 November arr. 4 mins. later
- **f** From 7 November arr. 1 min. later
- **g** From 7 November arr. 1748
- **j** From 7 November arr. 1842
- **k** From 7 November arr. 1950

Table 78

Saturdays

Sheffield, Chinley, Marple and Romiley → Manchester and Manchester Airport

Network Diagram - see first page of Table 78

		NT	NT	EM ◇ A	NT B	TP ■1 ◇ C	NT	NT B	NT	NT	EM ◇ D	TP ■1 ◇ C	NT	NT B	EM ◇ D	NT	NT	NT B	NT	NT B	NT	NT
Sheffield 7	d		18 14	18 42		19 11				19 14	19 42	20 11			20 31		20 35				22 24	
Dore & Totley	d		18 21							19 21							20 42				22 31	
Grindleford	d		18 28							19 29							20 50				22 38	
Hathersage	d		18 32							19 32							20 53				22 41	
Bamford	d		18 35							19 36							20 57				22 45	
Hope (Derbyshire)	d		18 39							19 39							21 00				22 48	
Edale	d		18 46							19 47							21 08				22 56	
Chinley	d		18 54							19 55							21 16				23 04	
Hazel Grove	86 a																					
Stockport	86 a			19 25		19 53					20 25	20 53			21 20						23 21	
New Mills Central	d		19 01							20 01			20 30				21b30		22 30			23 30
Strines	d		19 04										20 33						22 33			23 33
Marple	d	18 52	19 07						19 56	20 07			20 36				21 36		22 36			23 36
Rose Hill Marple	d						19 30									21 12						
Romiley	d	18 55	19 11				19 35		19 59	20 11			20 40			21 17	21 40		22 40			23 40
Woodley	d						19 38									21 20						
Hyde Central	d						19 41									21 23						
Hyde North	d						19 44									21 26						
Guide Bridge	d				19 28		19 48	19 58						20 58		21 30		21 58		22 58		
Fairfield	d						19 51									21 33						
Gorton	d				19 31			20 01						21 01				22 01		23 01		
Bredbury	d		19 14						20 02	20 14			20 43				21 43		22 43			23 43
Brinnington	d		19 16						20 05	20 16			20 45				21 45		22 45			23 45
Reddish North	d		19 19						20 08	20 19			20 48				21 48		22 48			23 48
Ryder Brow	d	19 03							20 10				20 51				21 51		22 51			23 51
Belle Vue	d	19 04							20 12				20 52				21 52		22 52			23 52
Ashburys	d	19 07			19 34			20 04	20 15				20 55	21 04			21 55	22 04	22 55	23 04		23 55
Ardwick	d																					
Manchester Piccadilly 10	a	19 15	19 32	19 36	19 42	20 02	20 02	20 12	20 22	20 32	20 37	21 02	21 02	21 12	21 32	21 42	22 05	22 12	23 03	23 12	23 43	00 03
Manchester Airport	85 ✈ a	19 50		20 07	20 17	20 35			20 47	21 07	21 17	21 35		21 47	22 08	22 17		22 57			00 22	01 00

Sundays

until 6 September

		TP ■1 ◇	TP ■1 ◇ E	NT	NT B	TP ■1 ◇	NT B	NT	EM ◇ G	NT B	TP ■1 ◇ H	NT B	NT	EM ◇ J	NT B	TP ■1 ◇ H	NT B	NT	EM ◇ J	NT B	TP ■1 ◇ H	NT B
Sheffield 7	d	07 50	09 10	09 20		10 10		10 19	10 41		11 10		11 14	11 38		12 10		12 13	12 41		13 10	
Dore & Totley	d			09 27				10 26	10 48				11 21					12 21				
Grindleford	d			09 35				10 34					11 29					12 28				
Hathersage	d			09 38				10 38					11 32					12 32				
Bamford	d			09 42				10 41					11 36					12 35				
Hope (Derbyshire)	d			09 45				10 45					11 39					12 39				
Edale	d			09 53				10 52					11 47					12 46				
Chinley	d			10 01				11 00					11 55					12 54				
Hazel Grove	86 a																					
Stockport	86 a	08 31	09 52			10 52			11 26		11 52			12 25		12 52			13 25		13 52	
New Mills Central	d			10 07				11 07					12 01					13 01				
Strines	d			10 10				11 10					12 04					13 04				
Marple	d			10 13				11 12					12 07					13 06				
Romiley	d			10 17				11 17					12 11					13 11				
Guide Bridge	d				10 28		10 58			11 28		11 58			12 28		12 58			13 28		13 58
Gorton	d				10 31		11 01			11 31		12 01			12 31		13 01			13 31		14 01
Bredbury	d			10 20				11 20					12 14					13 14				
Brinnington	d			10 22				11 21					12 16					13 15				
Reddish North	d			10 25				11 24					12 19					13 18				
Ryder Brow	d																					
Belle Vue	d																					
Ashburys	d				10 34		11 04			11 34		12 04			12 34		13 04			13 34		14 04
Manchester Piccadilly 10	a	08 43	10 06	10 36	10 42	11 06	11 12	11 38	11 38	11 42	12 06	12 12	12 31	12 37	12 42	13 06	13 12	13 31	13 37	13 42	14 06	14 12
Manchester Airport	85 ✈ a	09 07	10 30								12 29					13 29					14 29	

For general notes see front of timetable
For details of catering facilities see Directory of Train Operators

- **A** From Norwich to Liverpool Lime Street (Table 49)
- **B** From Hadfield (Table 79)
- **C** From Cleethorpes (27 June to 5 September from Doncaster) (Table 29)
- **D** From Norwich (Table 49)
- **E** From Meadowhall (Table 34)
- **G** From 19 July. From Nottingham to Liverpool Lime Street (Table 49)
- **H** From Cleethorpes (from 28 June from Doncaster) (Table 29)
- **J** From Nottingham to Liverpool Lime Street (Table 49)
- **b** Arr. 2122

Table 78

Sundays until 6 September

Sheffield, Chinley, Marple and Romiley → Manchester and Manchester Airport

Network Diagram - see first page of Table 78

		NT	EM ◇ A	NT B	TP 1 ◇ C	NT B	EM ◇ A	NT B	TP 1 ◇ D	NT B	NT	EM ◇ E	NT B	TP 1 ◇ D	NT B	NT	EM ◇ E	NT B	TP 1 ◇ D	NT B	NT
Sheffield 7	d	13 13	13 38		14 11		14 39		15 11		15 14	15 37		16 11		16 15	16 44		17 11		17 14
Dore & Totley	d	13 20									15 21					16 22					17 21
Grindleford	d	13 28									15 29					16 30					17 29
Hathersage	d	13 31									15 32					16 33					17 32
Bamford	d	13 35									15 36					16 37					17 36
Hope (Derbyshire)	d	13 38									15 39					16 40					17 39
Edale	d	13 46									15 47					16 48					17 47
Chinley	d	13 54									15 55					16 56					17 55
Hazel Grove 86	a																				
Stockport 86	a		14 25		14 52		15 25		15 53			16 25		16 53			17 27		17 53		
New Mills Central	d	14 00									16 01					17 02					18 01
Strines	d	14 03									16 04					17 05					18 04
Marple	d	14 06									16 07					17 08					18 07
Romiley	d	14 10									16 11					17 12					18 11
Guide Bridge	d			14 28		14 58		15 28		15 58			16 28		16 58			17 28		17 58	
Gorton	d			14 31		15 01		15 31		16 01			16 31		17 01			17 31		18 01	
Bredbury	d	14 13									16 14					17 15					18 14
Brinnington	d	14 15									16 16					17 17					18 16
Reddish North	d	14 18									16 19					17 20					18 19
Ryder Brow	d																				
Belle Vue	d																				
Ashburys	d			14 34		15 04		15 34		16 04			16 34		17 04			17 34		18 04	
Manchester Piccadilly 10	a	14 30	14 37	14 42	15 06	15 12	15 37	15 42	16 06	16 12	16 30	16 37	16 42	17 06	17 12	17 31	17 37	17 42	18 06	18 12	18 31
Manchester Airport 85	a				15 29				16 29					17 29					18 29		

		EM ◇ A	NT B	TP 1 ◇ D	NT B	NT	EM ◇ A	NT B	TP 1 ◇ D	NT B	NT	EM ◇ G	NT B	TP 1 ◇ D	NT B	EM ◇ G	TP 1 ◇ D	NT B	NT	NT
Sheffield 7	d	17 44		18 11		18 15	18 37		19 11		19 14	19 35		20 11		20 35	21 11		22 17	
Dore & Totley	d					18 22					19 22								22 24	
Grindleford	d					18 30					19 29								22 32	
Hathersage	d					18 33					19 33								22 35	
Bamford	d					18 37					19 36								22 39	
Hope (Derbyshire)	d					18 40					19 40								22 42	
Edale	d					18 48					19 47								22 50	
Chinley	d					18 56					19 55								22 58	
Hazel Grove 86	a																			
Stockport 86	a	18 25		18 53			19 25		19 53			20 25		20 53		21 24	21 53		23 16	
New Mills Central	d					19 02					20 02									23 01
Strines	d					19 05					20 05									23 04
Marple	d					19 08					20 07									23 07
Romiley	d					19 12					20 12									23 11
Guide Bridge	d		18 28		18 58			19 28		19 58			20 28		20 58			21 58		
Gorton	d		18 31		19 01			19 31		20 01			20 31		21 01			22 01		
Bredbury	d					19 15					20 15									23 14
Brinnington	d					19 17					20 16									23 16
Reddish North	d					19 20					20 19									23 19
Ryder Brow	d																			
Belle Vue	d																			
Ashburys	d		18 34		19 04			19 34		20 04			20 34		21 04			22 04		
Manchester Piccadilly 10	a	18 37	18 42	19 06	19 12	19 36	19 37	19 42	20 06	20 12	20 31	20 38	20 42	21 06	21 12	21 36	22 06	22 12	23 29	23 31
Manchester Airport 85	a			19 29					20 29					21 29			22 29			

Sundays from 13 September

		TP 1 ◇	TP 1 ◇ H	NT	NT B	NT B	NT J	NT B	TP 1 ◇ K	NT B	NT	EM ◇ E	NT B	TP 1 ◇ K	NT B	NT J	EM ◇ E	NT B	TP 1 ◇ K	NT B	NT
Sheffield 7	d	07 50	09 10	09 20			10 19		11 10		11 14	11 38		12 10		12 13	12 41		13 10		13 13
Dore & Totley	d			09 27			10 26				11 21					12 21					13 20
Grindleford	d			09 35			10 34				11 29					12 28					13 28
Hathersage	d			09 38			10 38				11 32					12 32					13 31
Bamford	d			09 42			10 41				11 36					12 35					13 35
Hope (Derbyshire)	d			09 45			10 45				11 39					12 39					13 38
Edale	d			09 53			10 52				11 47					12 46					13 46
Chinley	d			10 01			11 00				11 55					12 54					13 54
Hazel Grove 86	a																				
Stockport 86	a	08 31	09 52						11 52			12 25		12 52			13 25		13 52		
New Mills Central	d			10 07			11 07				12 01					13 01					14 00
Strines	d			10 10			11 10				12 04					13 04					14 03
Marple	d			10 13			11 12				12 07					13 06					14 06
Romiley	d			10 17			11 17				12 11					13 11					14 10
Guide Bridge	d				10 28	10 58		11 28		11 58			12 28		12 58			13 28		13 58	
Gorton	d				10 31	11 01		11 31		12 01			12 31		13 01			13 31		14 01	
Bredbury	d			10 20			11 20				12 14					13 14					14 13
Brinnington	d			10 22			11 21				12 16					13 15					14 15
Reddish North	d			10 25			11 24				12 19					13 18					14 18
Ryder Brow	d																				
Belle Vue	d																				
Ashburys	d				10 34	11 04		11 34		12 04			12 34		13 04			13 34		14 04	
Manchester Piccadilly 10	a	08 43	10 06	10 36	10 42	11 12	11 36	11 42	12 06	12 12	12 31	12 37	12 42	13 06	13 12	13 31	13 37	13 42	14 06	14 12	14 30
Manchester Airport 85	a	09 07	10 30						12 29					13 29					14 34		

For general notes see front of timetable
For details of catering facilities see Directory of Train Operators

A From Norwich to Liverpool Lime Street (Table 49)
B From Hadfield (Table 79)
C From Doncaster (Table 29)
D From Cleethorpes (from 28 June from Doncaster) (Table 29)
E From Nottingham to Liverpool Lime Street (Table 49)
G From Norwich (Table 49)
H From Meadowhall (Table 34)
J 13 September
K From Cleethorpes (Table 29)

Table 78

Sundays

from 13 September

Sheffield, Chinley, Marple and Romiley → Manchester and Manchester Airport

Network Diagram - see first page of Table 78

		EM	NT		TP	NT	EM	NT		TP	NT	NT	EM		NT	TP	NT	NT		EM	NT	TP	NT		NT
		◇			[1] ◇		◇			[1] ◇			◇			[1] ◇				◇		[1] ◇			
		A	B		C	B	D	B		E	B		A		B	E	B	G		A	B	E	B		
Sheffield [7]	d	13 38			14 11		14 39			15 11		15 14	15 37			16 11		16 15		16 44		17 11			17 14
Dore & Totley	d											15 21						16 22							17 21
Grindleford	d											15 29						16 30							17 29
Hathersage	d											15 32						16 33							17 32
Bamford	d											15 36						16 37							17 36
Hope (Derbyshire)	d											15 39						16 40							17 39
Edale	d											15 47						16 48							17 47
Chinley	d											15 55						16 56							17 55
Hazel Grove	86 a																								
Stockport	86 a	14 25			14 52		15 25			15 53			16 25			16 53				17 27		17 53			
New Mills Central	d											16 01						17 02							18 01
Strines	d											16 04						17 05							18 04
Marple	d											16 07						17 08							18 07
Romiley	d											16 11						17 12							18 11
Guide Bridge	d		14 28			14 58		15 28			15 58				16 28		16 58				17 28		17 58		
Gorton	d		14 31			15 01		15 31			16 01				16 31		17 01				17 31		18 01		
Bredbury	d											16 14						17 15							18 14
Brinnington	d											16 16						17 17							18 16
Reddish North	d											16 19						17 20							18 19
Ryder Brow	d																								
Belle Vue	d																								
Ashburys	d		14 34			15 04		15 34			16 04				16 34		17 04				17 34		18 04		
Manchester Piccadilly [10]	a	14 37	14 42		15 06	15 12	15 37	15 42		16 06	16 12	16 30	16 37		16 42	17 06	17 12	17 31		17 37	17 42	18 06	18 12		18 31
Manchester Airport	85 a				15 34					16 34						17 29						18 29			

		EM	NT	TP	NT		NT	EM	NT	TP		NT	NT	EM	NT		TP	NT	EM	TP	NT	NT	NT		
		◇		[1] ◇				◇		[1] ◇				◇			[1] ◇		◇	[1] ◇					
		D	B	E	B		G	D	B	E		B		H	B		E	B	H	E	B				
Sheffield [7]	d	17 44		18 11			18 15	18 37		19 11			19 14	19 35			20 11		20 35	21 11		22 17			
Dore & Totley	d						18 22						19 22									22 24			
Grindleford	d						18 30						19 29									22 32			
Hathersage	d						18 33						19 33									22 35			
Bamford	d						18 37						19 36									22 39			
Hope (Derbyshire)	d						18 40						19 40									22 42			
Edale	d						18 48						19 47									22 50			
Chinley	d						18 56						19 55									22 58			
Hazel Grove	86 a																								
Stockport	86 a	18 25		18 53				19 25		19 53				20 25			20 53		21 24	21 53		23 16			
New Mills Central	d						19 02						20 02										23 01		
Strines	d						19 05						20 05										23 04		
Marple	d						19 08						20 07										23 07		
Romiley	d						19 12						20 12										23 11		
Guide Bridge	d		18 28		18 58				19 28			19 58			20 28			20 58			21 58				
Gorton	d		18 31		19 01				19 31			20 01			20 31			21 01			22 01				
Bredbury	d						19 15						20 15										23 14		
Brinnington	d						19 17						20 16										23 16		
Reddish North	d						19 20						20 19										23 19		
Ryder Brow	d																								
Belle Vue	d																								
Ashburys	d		18 34		19 04				19 34			20 04			20 34			21 04			22 04				
Manchester Piccadilly [10]	a	18 37	18 42	19 06	19 12		19 36	19 37	19 42	20 06		20 12	20 31	20 38	20 42		21 06	21 12	21 36	22 06	22 12	23 29	23 31		
Manchester Airport	85 a			19 29						20 34							21 30			22 29					

For general notes see front of timetable
For details of catering facilities see Directory of Train Operators

A From Nottingham to Liverpool Lime Street (Table 49)
B From Hadfield (Table 79)
C From Doncaster (Table 29)
D From Norwich to Liverpool Lime Street (Table 49)
E From Cleethorpes (Table 29)
G 13 September
H From Norwich (Table 49)

Manchester → Glossop and Hadfield

Network Diagram - see first page of Table 78

Miles	Miles			NT	NT	NT	NT	NT	NT	NT	NT	NT	NT	NT	NT	NT		NT
0	—	**Manchester Piccadilly 10**	78 ⛴ d	06 16	06 46	07 03	07 18	07 48	08 07	08 29	08 48	09 15	09 48	10 15	10 48	11 18	and at	15 18
½	—	Ardwick	78 d															
1½	—	Ashburys	78 d	06 20	06 50	07 07	07 22	07 52	08 11	08 33	08 52	09 19	09 52	10 19	10 52	11 22	the same	15 22
2½	—	Gorton	78 d	06 22	06 52	07 09	07 24	07 54	08 13	08 35	08 54	09 21	09 54	10 21	10 54	11 24		15 24
4¾	—	Guide Bridge	78 d	06 26	06 56	07 13	07 28	07 58	08 17	08 39	08 58	09 25	09 58	10 25	10 58	11 28	minutes	15 28
6¾	—	Flowery Field	d	06 29	06 59	07 16	07 31	08 01	08 20	08 42	09 01	09 28	10 01	10 28	11 01	11 31		15 31
7½	—	Newton for Hyde	d	06 31	07 01	07 18	07 33	08 03	08 22	08 44	09 03	09 30	10 03	10 30	11 03	11 33	past	15 33
8½	—	Godley	d	06 33	07 03	07 20	07 35	08 05	08 24	08 46	09 05	09 32	10 05	10 32	11 05	11 35		15 35
9	—	Hattersley	d	06 35	07 05	07 22	07 37	08 07	08 26	08 48	09 07	09 34	10 07	10 34	11 07	11 37	each	15 37
10	—	Broadbottom	d	06 37	07 07	07 24	07 39	08 09	08 28	08 50	09 09	09 36	10 09	10 36	11 09	11 39		15 39
12¼	0	Dinting 3	d	06 45	07 15	07 35	07 45	08 14	08 34	08 56	09 16	09 46	10 16	10 46	11 16	11 46	hour until	15 46
13¼	—	**Glossop**	a	06 48	07 25	07 45	08 03	08 26	08 46	09 06	09 19	09 49	10 19	10 49	11 19	11 49		15 49
—	—		d	06 51							09 22	09 52	10 22	10 52	11 22	11 52		15 52
15	¾	**Hadfield**	a	06 59	07 17	07 37	07 47	08 17	08 38	08 58	09 29	09 59	10 29	10 59	11 29	11 59		15 59

		NT	NT	NT	NT	NT	NT	NT	NT	NT	NT	NT	NT	NT	NT	NT
Manchester Piccadilly 10	78 ⛴ d	15 48	16 15	16 36	16 59	17 15	17 37	17 59	18 15	18 48	19 18	19 48	20 48	21 48	22 48	23 27
Ardwick	78 d															
Ashburys	78 d	15 52	16 19	16 40	17 03	17 19	17 41	18 03	18 19	18 52	19 22	19 52	20 52	21 52	22 52	23 31
Gorton	78 d	15 54	16 21	16 42	17 05	17 21	17 43	18 05	18 21	18 54	19 24	19 54	20 54	21 54	22 54	23 33
Guide Bridge	78 d	15 58	16 25	16 46	17 10	17 25	17 47	18 10	18 25	18 58	19 28	19 58	20 58	21 58	22 58	23 37
Flowery Field	d	16 01	16 28	16 49	17 13	17 28	17 50	18 13	18 28	19 01	19 31	20 01	21 01	22 01	23 01	23 40
Newton for Hyde	d	16 03	16 30	16 51	17 15	17 30	17 52	18 15	18 30	19 03	19 33	20 03	21 03	22 03	23 03	23 42
Godley	d	16 05	16 32	16 53	17 17	17 32	17 54	18 17	18 32	19 05	19 35	20 05	21 05	22 05	23 05	23 44
Hattersley	d	16 07	16 34	16 55	17 19	17 34	17 56	18 19	18 34	19 07	19 37	20 07	21 07	22 07	23 07	23 46
Broadbottom	d	16 09	16 36	16 57	17 22	17 36	17 59	18 21	18 36	19 09	19 39	20 09	21 09	22 09	23 09	23 48
Dinting 3	d	16 16	16 42	17 03	17 28	17 42	18 05	18 27	18 42	19 16	19 46	20 16	21 15	22 15	23 16	23 54
Glossop	a	16 19	16 45	17 06	17 31	17 45	18 08	18 30	18 45	19 19	19 49	20 19	21 18	22 18	23 19	00 05
	d	16 22	16 48	17 09	17 34	17 48	18 11	18 33	18 48	19 22	19 52	20 22	21 21	22 21	23 22	
Hadfield	a	16 29	16 54	17 15	17 40	17 54	18 17	18 39	18 54	19 29	19 59	20 29	21 28	22 28	23 29	23 56

Saturdays

		NT	NT	NT	NT	NT	NT	NT		NT	NT	NT	NT	NT	NT	NT
Manchester Piccadilly 10	78 ⛴ d	06 16	06 48	07 18	07 48	08 15	08 48	09 18	and at	18 18	18 48	19 48	20 48	21 48	22 48	23 27
Ashburys	78 d	06 20	06 52	07 22	07 52	08 19	08 52	09 22	the same	18 22	18 52	19 52	20 52	21 52	22 52	23 31
Gorton	78 d	06 22	06 54	07 24	07 54	08 21	08 54	09 24		18 24	18 54	19 54	20 54	21 54	22 54	23 33
Guide Bridge	78 d	06 26	06 58	07 28	07 58	08 25	08 58	09 28	minutes	18 28	18 58	19 58	20 58	21 58	22 58	23 37
Flowery Field	d	06 29	07 01	07 31	08 01	08 28	09 01	09 31		18 31	19 01	20 01	21 01	22 01	23 01	23 40
Newton for Hyde	d	06 31	07 03	07 33	08 03	08 30	09 03	09 33	past	18 33	19 03	20 03	21 03	22 03	23 03	23 42
Godley	d	06 33	07 05	07 35	08 05	08 32	09 05	09 35		18 35	19 05	20 05	21 05	22 05	23 05	23 44
Hattersley	d	06 35	07 07	07 37	08 07	08 34	09 07	09 37	each	18 37	19 07	20 07	21 07	22 07	23 07	23 46
Broadbottom	d	06 37	07 09	07 39	08 09	08 36	09 09	09 39		18 39	19 09	20 09	21 09	22 09	23 09	23 48
Dinting 3	d	06 45	07 16	07 46	08 16	08 46	09 16	09 46	hour until	18 46	19 16	20 16	21 16	22 16	23 16	23 54
Glossop	a	06 48	07 19	07 49	08 19	08 49	09 19	09 49		18 49	19 19	20 19	21 19	22 19	23 19	00 05
	d	06 51	07 22	07 52	08 22	08 52	09 22	09 52		18 52	19 22	20 22	21 22	22 22	23 22	
Hadfield	a	06 59	07 29	07 59	08 29	08 59	09 29	09 59		18 59	19 29	20 29	21 29	22 29	23 29	23 56

Sundays

		NT	NT A	NT B	NT	NT		NT	NT	NT
Manchester Piccadilly 10	78 ⛴ d	09 18	09 32	09 48	10 18	10 48	and at	19 18	19 48	20 48
Ashburys	78 d	09 22	09 36	09 52	10 22	10 52	the same	19 22	19 52	20 52
Gorton	78 d	09 24	09 38	09 54	10 24	10 54		19 24	19 54	20 54
Guide Bridge	78 d	09 28	09b58	09 58	10 28	10 58	minutes	19 28	19 58	20 58
Flowery Field	d	09 32	10 01	10 01	10 31	11 01		19 31	20 01	21 01
Newton for Hyde	d	09 34	10 03	10 03	10 33	11 03	past	19 33	20 03	21 03
Godley	d	09 36	10 05	10 05	10 35	11 05		19 35	20 05	21 05
Hattersley	d	09 38	10 07	10 07	10 37	11 07	each	19 37	20 07	21 07
Broadbottom	d	09 40	10 09	10 09	10 39	11 09		19 39	20 09	21 09
Dinting 3	d	09 46	10 16	10 16	10 46	11 16	hour until	19 46	20 16	21 16
Glossop	a	09 49	10 19	10 19	10 49	11 19		19 49	20 19	21 19
	d	09 52	10 22	10 22	10 52	11 22		19 52	20 22	21 22
Hadfield	a	09 58	10 28	10 28	10 58	11 28		19 58	20 28	21 28

For general notes see front of timetable
For details of catering facilities see Directory of Train Operators

A From 13 September
B Until 6 September
b Arr. 0942

From 5 October a revised Northern service will be in operation due to seasonal difficulties. Customers should check with NRES for precise times

Hadfield and Glossop → Manchester

Network Diagram - see first page of Table 78

Mondays to Fridays

Miles	Miles			NT	NT	NT	NT	NT	NT	NT	NT	NT	NT	NT		NT	NT	NT
0	0	**Hadfield**	d	06 00	06 30	07 00	07 20	07 40	07 58	08 21	08 41	09 01	09 31	10 01	and at	16 01	16 31	16 57
1¾	—	**Glossop**	a	06 05	06 35	07 05	07 25	07 45	08 03	08 26	08 46	09 06	09 36	10 06		16 06		
—	—		d	06 08	06 38	07 08	07 28	07 48	08 06	08 29	08 49	09 09	09 39	10 09	the same	16 09	16 22	16 48
2¾	¾	Dinting 3	d	06 11	06 41	07 11	07 31	07 51	08 09	08 32	08 52	09 12	09 42	10 12		16 12	16 33	16 59
5	—	Broadbottom	d	06 15	06 45	07 15	07 35	07 56	08 13	08 37	08 57	09 16	09 46	10 16	minutes	16 16	16 37	17 03
6	—	Hattersley	d	06 18	06 48	07 18	07 38	07 59	08 16	08 40	08 59	09 19	09 49	10 19		16 19	16 40	17 06
6½	—	Godley	d	06 20	06 50	07 20	07 40	08 01	08 18	08 42	09 02	09 21	09 51	10 21	past	16 21	16 42	17 08
7½	—	Newton for Hyde	d	06 22	06 52	07 22	07 42	08 03	08 21	08 44	09 04	09 23	09 53	10 23		16 23	16 44	17 10
8¼	—	Flowery Field	d	06 24	06 54	07 25	07 44	08 06	08 23	08 46	09 07	09 25	09 55	10 25	each	16 25	16 46	17 12
10¼	—	Guide Bridge	78 a	06 27	06 57	07 27	07 47	08 10	08 27	08 49	09 12	09 28	09 58	10 28		16 28	16 49	17 15
12½	—	Gorton	78 a	06 30	07 00	07 30	07 50	08 13	08 30	08 52	09 15	09 31	10 01	10 31	hour until	16 31	16 52	17 18
13½	—	Ashburys	78 a	06 33	07 06	07 33	07 53	08 16	08 34	08 56	09 18	09 34	10 04	10 34		16 34	16 55	17 24
14½	—	Ardwick	78 a			07 35												
15	—	**Manchester Piccadilly 10**	78 ⛴ a	06 42	07 15	07 43	08 03	08 25	08 43	09 04	09 27	09 42	10 12	10 42		16 42	17 05	17 33

		NT	NT	NT	NT	NT	NT	NT	NT	NT	NT	NT	NT
Hadfield	d	17 22	17 44	17 59	18 28	18 43	19 01	19 31	20 01	20 31	21 31	22 31	23 59
Glossop	a						19 06	19 36	20 06	20 36	21 36	22 36	00 05
	d	17 09	17 34	17 48	18 11	18 33	19 09	19 39	20 09	20 39	21 39	22 39	
Dinting 3	d	17 24	17 46	18 01	18 30	18 45	19 12	19 42	20 12	20 42	21 42	22 42	
Broadbottom	d	17 28	17 50	18 05	18 34	18 49	19 16	19 46	20 16	20 46	21 46	22 46	
Hattersley	d	17 31		18 08	18 37	18 52	19 19	19 49	20 19	20 49	21 49	22 49	
Godley	d	17 33		18 10	18 39	18 54	19 21	19 51	20 21	20 51	21 51	22 51	
Newton for Hyde	d	17 36	17 54	18 12	18 41	18 56	19 23	19 53	20 23	20 53	21 53	22 53	
Flowery Field	d	17 38		18 14	18 43	18 58	19 25	19 55	20 25	20 55	21 55	22 55	
Guide Bridge	78 a	17 42	17 57	18 17	18 46	19 01	19 28	19 58	20 28	20 58	21 58	22 58	
Gorton	78 a	17 45		18 20	18 49	19 04	19 31	20 01	20 31	21 01	22 01	23 01	
Ashburys	78 a	17 48	18 03	18 23	18 54	19 08	19 34	20 04	20 34	21 04	22 04	23 04	
Ardwick	78 a												
Manchester Piccadilly 10	78 ⛴ a	17 57	18 12	18 32	19 03	19 15	19 42	20 12	20 42	21 12	22 12	23 12	

Saturdays

		NT	NT	NT		NT	NT	NT	NT	NT	NT
Hadfield	d	06 30	07 01	07 31	and at	19 01	19 31	20 31	21 31	22 31	23 59
Glossop	a	06 35	07 06	07 36		19 06	19 36	20 36	21 36	22 36	00 05
	d	06 38	07 09	07 39	the same	19 09	19 39	20 39	21 39	22 39	
Dinting 3	d	06 41	07 12	07 42		19 12	19 42	20 42	21 42	22 42	
Broadbottom	d	06 45	07 16	07 46	minutes	19 16	19 46	20 46	21 46	22 46	
Hattersley	d	06 48	07 19	07 49		19 19	19 49	20 49	21 49	22 49	
Godley	d	06 50	07 21	07 51	past	19 21	19 51	20 51	21 51	22 51	
Newton for Hyde	d	06 52	07 23	07 53		19 23	19 53	20 53	21 53	22 53	
Flowery Field	d	06 54	07 25	07 55	each	19 25	19 55	20 55	21 55	22 55	
Guide Bridge	78 a	06 57	07 28	07 58		19 28	19 58	20 58	21 58	22 58	
Gorton	78 a	07 00	07 31	08 01	hour until	19 31	20 01	21 01	22 01	23 01	
Ashburys	78 a	07 03	07 34	08 04		19 34	20 04	21 04	22 04	23 04	
Manchester Piccadilly 10	78 ⛴ a	07 12	07 42	08 12		19 42	20 12	21 12	22 12	23 12	

Sundays

		NT	NT		NT	NT	NT
Hadfield	d	10 01	10 31	and at	20 01	20 31	21 31
Glossop	a	10 06	10 36		20 06	20 36	21 36
	d	10 09	10 39	the same	20 09	20 39	21 39
Dinting 3	d	10 12	10 42		20 12	20 42	21 42
Broadbottom	d	10 16	10 46	minutes	20 16	20 46	21 46
Hattersley	d	10 19	10 49		20 19	20 49	21 49
Godley	d	10 21	10 51	past	20 21	20 51	21 51
Newton for Hyde	d	10 23	10 53		20 23	20 53	21 53
Flowery Field	d	10 25	10 55	each	20 25	20 55	21 55
Guide Bridge	78 a	10 28	10 58		20 28	20 58	21 58
Gorton	78 a	10 31	11 01	hour until	20 31	21 01	22 01
Ashburys	78 a	10 34	11 04		20 34	21 04	22 04
Manchester Piccadilly 10	78 ⛴ a	10 42	11 12		20 42	21 12	22 12

For general notes see front of timetable
For details of catering facilities see
Directory of Train Operators

From 5 October a revised Northern service will be in operation due to seasonal difficulties. Customers should check with NRES for precise times

Network Diagram for Tables 81, 102

DM-35/08
Design BAJS

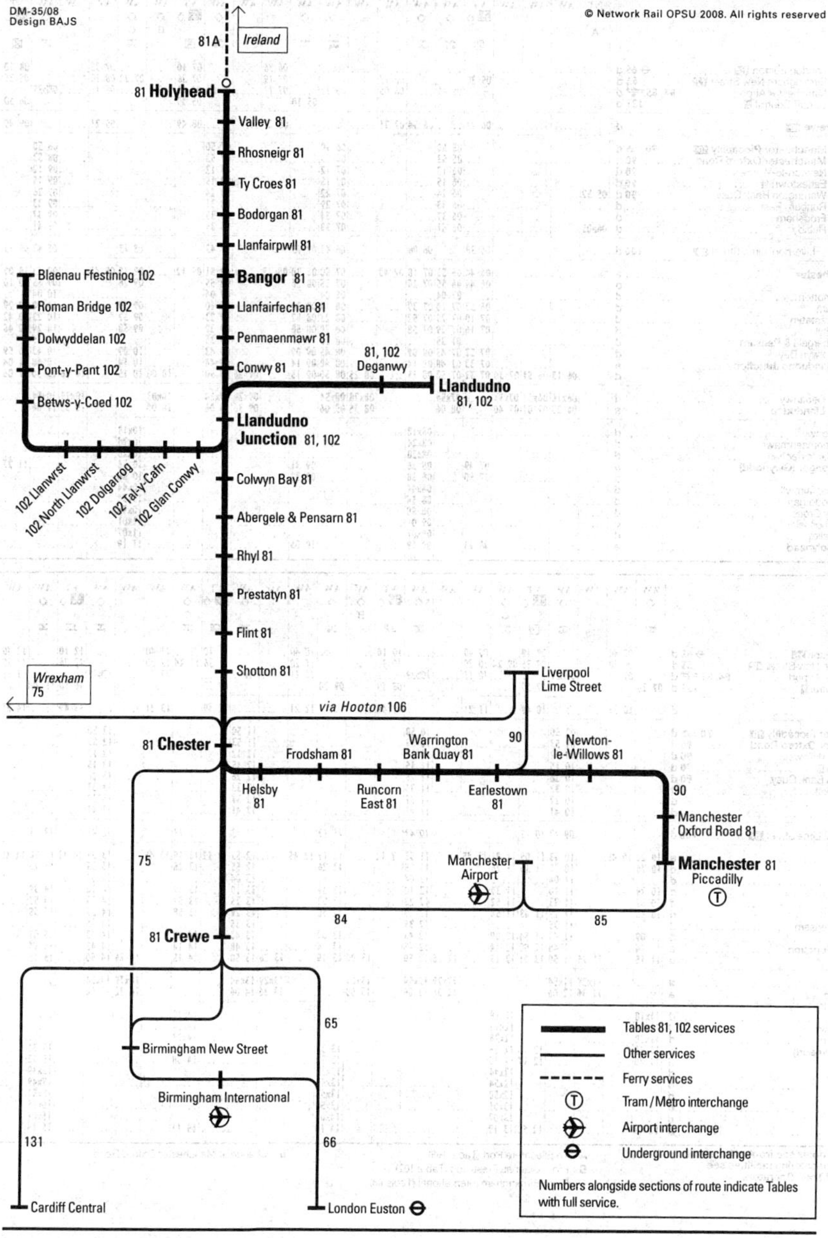

Crewe and Manchester → Chester and North Wales

Network Diagram - see first page of Table 81

Miles	Miles			NT	AW	AW	AW	VT	AW	AW	AW	AW	AW	AW	AW	AW	AW	VT	AW	AW	AW	AW	AW	VT
				A				1 ◇ ⊠	◇ ⊥	◇ ⊥			◇ ⊥	◇ ⊥			◇ ⊥	1 ◇ ⊠	◇ B	◇ C ⊥			◇ ⊥	1 ◇ ⊠
—	—	London Euston 15 ⊖ 65	d												06 36			07 10			07 35			08 10
—	—	Birmingham New Street 12 65	d					05 30			06 17				07 19			07 36		07 22	08 20			08 36
—	—	Manchester Airport 84, 85 ✈	d						05 15		06 05		06 23		07 11		07 05	07 11			08 11		08b25	
—	—	Cardiff Central 7 131	d											05 10				05 40						06 50
0	—	**Crewe** 10	d					06 24		06 54	07 21				08 21			08 49			09 21			09 49
—	0	**Manchester Piccadilly** 10 90	d						05 50				06 50				07 50						08 50	
—	½	**Manchester Oxford Road** 90	d						05 53				06 53				07 53						08 53	
—	16¼	Newton-le-Willows 90	d						06 12				07 12				08 12						09 12	
—	18	Earlestown 8 90	d						06 15				07 15				08 15						09 15	
—	22	Warrington Bank Quay 90	d	05 52					06 26				07 22				08 24						09 26	
—	27	Runcorn East	d						06 33				07 29				08 31						09 33	
—	30¼	Frodsham	d						06 37				07 34				08 35						09 37	
—	32¾	Helsby	d	06a05					06 41				07 38				08 39						09 41	
—	—	Liverpool Lime Street 10 106	d					05 38		06 08			06 43	07 13			07 43			08 13			08 43	09 13
21	40¼	**Chester**	a					06 44	06 53	07 18	07 43		07 50	08 20	08 45		08 51	09 12		09 19	09 45		09 53	10 09
—	—		d					06 44	06 55	07 26			07 55	08 26			08 55			09 26			09 55	10 16
29	—	Shotton	d						07 04				08 04				09 04						10 04	
33½	—	Flint	d					06 57	07 10	07 39			08 10	08 39			09 10			09 39			10 10	10 29
47½	—	Prestatyn	d					07 10	07 23	07 52			08 23	08 52			09 23			09 52			10 23	10 42
51	—	Rhyl	d					07 16	07 29	07 58			08 29	08 58			09 29			09 58			10 29	10 48
55¼	—	Abergele & Pensarn	d						07 35				08 35				09 35						10 35	
61½	—	Colwyn Bay	d					07 27	07 43	08 09			08 43	09 09			09 43			10 09			10 43	10 59
65½	—	**Llandudno Junction**	a					07 33	07 48	08 14			08 48	09 14			09 48			10 14			10 48	11 04
—	0		d		06 13	06 51	07 30	07 33	07 50	08 15		08 25	08 50	09 15		09 26	09 50		10 00	10 15		10 26	10 50	11 06
—	1¼	Deganwy	d		06x16	06x54	07x33		07x54			08x28	08x54			09x29	09x54		10x03			10x29	10x54	
—	3	**Llandudno**	a		06 23	07 01	07 40		08 06			08 35	09 06			09 36	10 06		10 08			10 36	11 06	
66½	—	Conwy	d							08x18										10x18				
70¾	—	Penmaenmawr	d							08x24										10x24				
73¼	—	Llanfairfechan	d							08x28										10x28				
80¾	—	**Bangor (Gwynedd)**	a					07 49		08 36				09 31						10 36				11 27
—	—		d					07 50		08 38				09 32						10 38				
84½	—	Llanfairpwll	d							08x44										10x44				
93½	—	Bodorgan	d							08 54										10x54				
96¼	—	Ty Croes	d							08 58										10x58				
98	—	Rhosneigr	d							09 01										11x01				
102	—	Valley	d							09x07										11x07				
105½	—	**Holyhead**	a					08 23		09 19				10 05						11 19				

		AW	AW	AW	AW	VT	AW	AW	AW	AW	VT	AW	AW	AW	AW	AW	VT	AW	AW	AW	AW	VT	AW	AW
		◇ ⊥			◇ ⊥	1 ◇ ⊠	◇ C ⊥			◇ ⊥	1 ◇ ⊐	◇ B	◇ ⊥			◇ ⊥	1 ◇ ⊐	◇ C ⊥			◇ ⊥	1 ◇ ⊐	◇ ⊥	
London Euston 15 ⊖ 65	d		08 40			09 10		09 40			10 10			10 40			11 10		11 40			12 10		12 40
Birmingham New Street 12 65	d		09 20			09 36	09 24	10 20			10 36			11 20			11 36	11 24	12 20			12 36		13 20
Manchester Airport 84, 85 ✈	d		09 11		09b29			10 11		10b29				11 11		11b29			12 11		12b29			13 11
Cardiff Central 7 131	d	07 20				07 50					08 50		09 20				09 50					10 50	11 20	
Crewe 10	d		10 21			10 49		11 21			11 49			12 21			12 49		13 21			13 49		14 21
Manchester Piccadilly 10 90	d				09 50					10 50						11 50					12 50			
Manchester Oxford Road 90	d				09 53					10 53						11 53					12 53			
Newton-le-Willows 90	d				10 12					11 12						12 12					13 12			
Earlestown 8 90	d				10 15					11 15						12 15					13 15			
Warrington Bank Quay 90	d				10 26					11 26						12 26					13 26			
Runcorn East	d				10 33					11 33						12 33					13 33			
Frodsham	d				10 37					11 37						12 37					13 37			
Helsby	d				10 41					11 41						12 41					13 41			
Liverpool Lime Street 10 106	d				09 43	10 13				10 43			11 13			11 43		12 13			12 43		13 13	
Chester	a	10 20	10 45		10 53	11 09	11 21	11 45		11 53	12 12		12 19	12 45		12 53	13 12	13 19	13 45		13 53	14 12	14 20	14 45
	d	10 26			10 55	11 16	11 26			11 55			12 26			12 55		13 26			13 55		14 26	
Shotton	d				11 04					12 04						13 04					14 04			
Flint	d	10 39			11 10		11 39			12 10			12 39			13 10		13 39			14 10		14 39	
Prestatyn	d	10 52			11 23		11 52			12 23			12 52			13 23		13 52			14 23		14 52	
Rhyl	d	10 58			11 29	11 43	11 58			12 29			12 58			13 29		13 58			14 29		14 58	
Abergele & Pensarn	d				11 35					12 35						13 35					14 35			
Colwyn Bay	d	11 09			11 43	11 54	12 09			12 43			13 09			13 43		14 09			14 43		15 09	
Llandudno Junction	a	11 14			11 48	12 00	12 14			12 48			13 14			13 48		14 14			14 48		15 14	
	d	11 15		11 26	11 50	12 01	12 15		12 26	12 50		13 00	13 15		13 26	13 50		14 15		14 26	14 50		15 15	
Deganwy	d			11x29	11x54				12x29	12x54		13x03			13x29	13x54				14x29	14x54			
Llandudno	a			11 36	12 06				12 36	13 06		13 09			13 36	14 06				14 36	15 06			
Conwy	d	11x18					12x18											14x18						
Penmaenmawr	d	11x24					12x24											14x24						
Llanfairfechan	d	11x28					12x28											14x28						
Bangor (Gwynedd)	a	11 38				12 16	12 36						13 31					14 36					15 31	
	d	11 40				12 17	12 38						13 32					14 38					15 32	
Llanfairpwll	d						12x44						13x39										15x39	
Bodorgan	d						12x54						13x49										15x49	
Ty Croes	d						12x58						13x53										15x53	
Rhosneigr	d						13x01						13x56										15x56	
Valley	d						13x07						14x01										16x01	
Holyhead	a	12 13				12 50	13 19						14 14					15 11					16 14	

For general notes see front of timetable
For details of catering facilities see Directory of Train Operators

A To Ellesmere Port (Table 109)
B From Blaenau Ffestiniog (Table 102)
C From Birmingham International (Table 68)

b Change at Manchester Oxford Road

Crewe and Manchester → Chester and North Wales

Network Diagram - see first page of Table 81

	AW ◇ 🛒	AW ◇ A	AW ◇ B 🛒	AW	AW ◇ 🛒	VT [1] ◇ ☕	AW ◇ 🛒	AW	AW ◇ 🛒	VT [1] ◇ ☕	AW ◇ B 🛒	AW	AW	AW ◇ A	AW ◇ 🛒	VT [1] ◇ ⊠	AW [R] 🛒	AW 🛒	AW	AW	AW ◇ 🛒	AW [R] [1] ⊠	VT [1] ◇ ⊠
London Euston [15] ⊖ 65 d				13 40		14 10		14 40		15 10		15 40				16 10			16 40			16b40	17 10
Birmingham New Street [12] 65 d			13 24	14 20		14 36		15 20		15 36	15 24	16 20				16 36			17 20			17b36	
Manchester Airport 84, 85 ✈ d	13c29			14 11	14c29			15 11	15c29			16 11			16c29			17c00	17 11		17c27		
Cardiff Central [7] 131 d				11 50		12 50	13 20			13 50						14 50	15 20					16 15	
Crewe [10] d				15 21		15 49		16 21		16 49		17 21				17 49			18 21			18 46	18 56
Manchester Piccadilly [10] 90 ⛴ d	13 50				14 50				15 50						16 50			17 19			17 50		
Manchester Oxford Road 90 d	13 53				14 53				15 53						16 53			17 22			17 53		
Newton-le-Willows 90 d	14 12				15 12				16 12						17 12			17 40			18 12		
Earlestown [8] 90 d	14 15				15 15				16 15						17 15			17 44			18 15		
Warrington Bank Quay 90 d	14 26				15 26				16 26						17 26			17 53			18 24		
Runcorn East d	14 33				15 33				16 33						17 33			18 00			18 31		
Frodsham d	14 37				15 37				16 37						17 37			18 05			18 36		
Helsby d	14 41				15 41				16 41						17 41			18 09			18 40		
Liverpool Lime Street [10] 106 d	13 43		14 13		14 43		15 13		15 43		16 35				17 05	17 20	17 35				17 50	18 13	
Chester a	14 53		15 21	15 45	15 53	16 12	16 20	16 45	16 54	17 12	17 22	17 45			17 53	18 09	18 21	18 22	18 45		18 52	19 09	19 16
d	14 55		15 26		15 55		16 26		16 55		17 26				17 55	18 11	18 27				18 55	19 10	19 22
Shotton d	15 04				16 04				17 04		17 35				18 04						19 04		
Flint d	15 10		15 39		16 10		16 39		17 10		17 41				18 10	18 24	18 40				19 10	19 24	19 35
Prestatyn d	15 23		15 52		16 23		16 52		17 23		17 54				18 23	18 37	18 53				19 23		19 48
Rhyl d	15 29		15 58		16 29		16 58		17 29		18 00				18 29	18 43	18 59				19 29	19 42	19 55
Abergele & Pensarn d	15 35				16 35				17 35		18 06				18 35						19 35		
Colwyn Bay d	15 43		16 09		16 43		17 09		17 43		18 14				18 43	18 54	19 10				19 43		20 06
Llandudno Junction a	15 48		16 14		16 48		17 14		17 49		18 19				18 48	18 59	19 15				19 48	19 55	20 11
d	15 50	16 04	16 15		16 50		17 15		17 50		18 21		18 26	18 41	18 50	19 01	19 16			19 26	19 50	19 56	20 12
Deganwy d	15x54	16x07			16x54				17x54				18x29	18x44	18x54					19x29	19x54		
Llandudno a	16 06	16 13			17 06				18 06				18 36	18 49	19 06					19 36	20 06		
Conwy d			16x18				17x18				18x24												
Penmaenmawr d			16x24				17x24				18x30												
Llanfairfechan d			16x28				17x28				18x34												
Bangor (Gwynedd) a			16 36				17 36				18 42					19 22	19 33					20 12	20 27
d			16 38				17 38				18 43						19 34					20 14	20 29
Llanfairpwll d							17x44										19x41						
Bodorgan d							17x54										19x51						
Ty Croes d							17x58										19x55						
Rhosneigr d							18x01										19x58						
Valley d							18x07										20x04						
Holyhead a			17 11				18 19				19 16						20 14					20 49	21 02

	AW	AW ◇ B 🛒	AW	AW 🛒	VT [1] ◇ C ⊠	AW [R] 🛒	ME D	AW	AW	AW ◇ A	VT [1] ◇ ☕	AW ◇	AW	AW	VT [1] ◇ ☕	AW ◇	AW	AW	AW	AW	AW ◇	AW ◇ E
London Euston [15] ⊖ 65 d			17 40		18 10			18 40			19 10		19 30		20 10				21 10		21e10	
Birmingham New Street [12] 65 d		17 24	18 20		18 36			19 20			19 36				20 36				21f57		22 55	22b36
Manchester Airport 84, 85 ✈ d			18 11	18c29					19c29					20c29			21c29	22c00		22 29		
Cardiff Central [7] 131 d					16 50	17 20					17 50				18 50	19 34			20 10			20 53
Crewe [10] d			19 21		19 56			20 21			20 50	21 00	21 21		21 50				23 21		23 57	00 02
Manchester Piccadilly [10] 90 ⛴ d				18 50					19 50					20 50			21 50	22 12		23 14		
Manchester Oxford Road 90 d				18 53					19 53					20 53			21 53	22 29		23 17		
Newton-le-Willows 90 d				19 12					20 12					21 12			22 12	22 47		23 36		
Earlestown [8] 90 d				19 16					20 15					21 15			22 15	22 50		23 39		
Warrington Bank Quay 90 d				19 26					20 26					21 26			22 24	22 59		23 48		
Runcorn East d				19 33					20 33					21 33			22 31	23 06		23 55		
Frodsham d				19 37					20 37					21 37			22 35	23 10		23 59		
Helsby d				19 41					20 41					21 41			22 39	23 14		00 03		
Liverpool Lime Street [10] 106 d		18 43			19 13	19 43	19 43				20 13					21 43					23 43	
Chester a		19 20	19 45	19 53	20 16	20 20	20 26	20 45	20 53		21 10	21 21	21 45	21 53	22 15	22 34	22 51	23 26	23 42	00 15	00 18	00 27
d		19 31			20 22	20 31					21 17	21 30				22 56					00 40	
Shotton d		19 40										21 39				23 05						
Flint d		19 46				20 44					21 30	21 45				23 11					00 53	
Prestatyn d		19 59				20 58					21 43	21 59				23 24					01 06	
Rhyl d		20 05			20 49	21 04					21 50	22 05				23 30					01 12	
Abergele & Pensarn d		20 11										22 11				23 36						
Colwyn Bay d		20 19			21 00	21 15					22 01	22 19				23 44					01 23	
Llandudno Junction a		20 24			21 05	21 20					22 06	22 24				23 49					01 28	
d	20 24	20 26			21 07	21 21				21 25	22 07	22 26				23 51					01 29	
Deganwy d	20x27									21x28												
Llandudno a	20 34									21 35												
Conwy d		20x29										22x29				23x54						
Penmaenmawr d		20x35										22x35				23x59						
Llanfairfechan d		20x39										22x39				00x04						
Bangor (Gwynedd) a		20 47			21 22	21 37					22 22	22 47				00 12					01 45	
d		20 48			21 23	21 38					22 24	22 48				00 13					01 45	
Llanfairpwll d						21x45										00x20						
Bodorgan d						21x55										00x30						
Ty Croes d						21x59										00x34						
Rhosneigr d						22x02										00x37						
Valley d						22x07										00x42						
Holyhead a		21 21			21 56	22 19					22 56	23 21				00 55					02 15	

For general notes see front of timetable
For details of catering facilities see Directory of Train Operators

A From Blaenau Ffestiniog (Table 102)
B From Birmingham International (Table 68)
C Also conveys portion to Wrexham General (Table 75)
D From Chester (Table 106)
E From Carmarthen (Table 128)

b Change at Crewe
c Change at Manchester Oxford Road
e Change at Stafford
f Change at Stafford and Crewe

Crewe and Manchester → Chester and North Wales

Network Diagram - see first page of Table 81

		NT	AW	AW	AW	VT	AW	AW	AW	AW	AW	AW	AW	AW	AW	AW	AW	AW	AW	AW	VT	AW	AW	AW
						1 ◇	◇	◇			◇	◇			◇	◇	◇			◇	1 ◇	◇		
		A														B	C							
						⊡	⌶	⌶			⌶	⌶			⌶		⌶			⌶	⊡	⌶		
London Euston 15	⊖ 65 d												06 36					07 35			08 10		08 40	
Birmingham New Street 12	65 d					05 30			06 20				07 20				07 24	08 20			08 36		09 20	
Manchester Airport	84, 85 ✈ d						05 15	06 05			06 23		07 11		07 05			08 11		08b25			09 11	
Cardiff Central 7	131 d											05 21	04 40					05 40			06 50	07 20		
Crewe 10	d					06 23		07 03	07 21				08 21					09 21			09 50		10 21	
Manchester Piccadilly 10	90 d						05 50				06 50				07 50					08 50				
Manchester Oxford Road	90 d						05 53				06 53				07 53					08 53				
Newton-le-Willows	90 d						06 12				07 12				08 12					09 12				
Earlestown 8	90 d						06 15				07 15				08 15					09 15				
Warrington Bank Quay	90 d	05 52					06 26				07 24				08 24					09 26				
Runcorn East	d						06 33				07 31				08 31					09 33				
Frodsham	d						06 37				07 35				08 35					09 37				
Helsby	d	06a05					06 41				07 39				08 39					09 41				
Liverpool Lime Street 10	106 d					05 38		06 08			06 43	07 13			07 43		08 13			08 43		09 13		
Chester	a					06 43	06 53	07 23	07 44		07 51	08 19	08 45		08 51		09 19	09 45		09 53	10 12	10 19	10 45	
	d					06 44	06 55	07 26			07 55	08 26			08 55		09 26			09 55		10 26		
Shotton	d						07 04				08 04				09 04					10 04				
Flint	d					06 57	07 10	07 39			08 10	08 39			09 10		09 39			10 10		10 39		
Prestatyn	d					07 10	07 23	07 52			08 23	08 52			09 23		09 52			10 23		10 52		
Rhyl	d					07 16	07 29	07 58			08 29	08 58			09 29		09 58			10 29		10 58		
Abergele & Pensarn	d						07 35				08 35				09 35					10 35				
Colwyn Bay	d					07 27	07 43	08 09			08 43	09 09			09 43		10 09			10 43		11 09		
Llandudno Junction	a					07 33	07 48	08 14			08 48	09 14			09 48		10 14			10 48		11 14		
	d		06 13	06 51	07 30	07 33	07 50	08 15		08 25	08 50	09 15		09 26	09 50	10 00	10 15		10 26	10 50		11 15		11 26
Deganwy	d		06x16	06x54	07x33		07x54			08x28	08x54			09x29	09x54	10x03			10x29	10x54				11x29
Llandudno	a		06 23	07 01	07 40		08 06			08 35	09 06			09 36	10 06	10 08			10 36	11 06				11 36
Conwy	d							08x18									10x18					11x18		
Penmaenmawr	d							08x24									10x24					11x24		
Llanfairfechan	d							08x28									10x28					11x28		
Bangor (Gwynedd)	a					07 49		08 36				09 31					10 36					11 36		
	d					07 50		08 38				09 32					10 38					11 38		
Llanfairpwll	d							08x44									10x44							
Bodorgan	d							08 54									10x54							
Ty Croes	d							08 58									10x58							
Rhosneigr	d							09 01									11x01							
Valley	d							09x07									11x07							
Holyhead	a					08 23		09 19				10 05					11 19					12 11		

		AW	VT	AW	AW	AW	AW	VT	AW	AW		AW	AW	AW	VT	AW	AW	AW	AW	VT	AW	AW	AW	AW
		◇	1 ◇	◇			◇	1 ◇	◇	◇				◇	1 ◇	◇			◇	1 ◇	◇			◇
				C				D	B							C				D				
		⌶	⊠ ⊡	⌶			⌶	⊡		⌶				⌶	⊡	⌶			⌶	⊡	⌶			⌶
London Euston 15	⊖ 65 d		08 50		09 40			10 10				10 40			11 10		11 40			12 10			12 40	
Birmingham New Street 12	65 d		09 36	09 24	10 20			10 36				11 20			11 36	11 24	12c20			12 36			13 20	
Manchester Airport	84, 85 ✈ d	09b29			10 11		10b29					11 11		11b29			12 11		12b29				13 11	13b29
Cardiff Central 7	131 d		07 50					08 50		09 20		08 50			09 50					10 50	11 20		10 50	
Crewe 10	d		10 45		11 21			11 50				12 21			12 49		13 21			13 49			14 21	
Manchester Piccadilly 10	90 d	09 50					10 50							11 50					12 50					13 50
Manchester Oxford Road	90 d	09 53					10 53							11 53					12 53					13 53
Newton-le-Willows	90 d	10 12					11 12							12 12					13 12					14 12
Earlestown 8	90 d	10 15					11 15							12 15					13 15					14 15
Warrington Bank Quay	90 d	10 26					11 26							12 26					13 26					14 26
Runcorn East	d	10 33					11 33							12 33					13 33					14 33
Frodsham	d	10 37					11 37							12 37					13 37					14 37
Helsby	d	10 41					11 41							12 41					13 41					14 41
Liverpool Lime Street 10	106 d	09 43	10 13				10 43			11 13				11 43		12 13			12 43		13 13			13 43
Chester	a	10 53	11 12	11 20	11 45		11 53	12 12		12 19		12 45		12 53	13 12	13 19	13 45		13 53	14 12	14 20	14 45		14 53
	d	10 55	11 16	11 26			11 55			12 26				12 55		13 26			13 55		14 26			14 55
Shotton	d	11 04					12 04							13 04					14 04					15 04
Flint	d	11 10		11 39			12 10			12 39				13 10		13 39			14 10		14 39			15 10
Prestatyn	d	11 23		11 52			12 23			12 52				13 23		13 52			14 23		14 52			15 23
Rhyl	d	11 29	11 45	11 58			12 29			12 58				13 29		13 58			14 29		14 58			15 29
Abergele & Pensarn	d	11 35					12 35							13 35					14 35					15 35
Colwyn Bay	d	11 43	11 58	12 09			12 43			13 09				13 43		14 09			14 43		15 09			15 43
Llandudno Junction	a	11 48	12 04	12 14			12 48			13 14				13 48		14 14			14 48		15 14			15 48
	d	11 50	12 05	12 15		12 26	12 50		13 00	13 15			13 26	13 50		14 15		14 26	14 50		15 15		15 26	15 50
Deganwy	d	11x54				12x29	12x54		13x03				13x29	13x54				14x29	14x54				15x29	15x54
Llandudno	a	12 06				12 36	13 06		13 09				13 36	14 06				14 36	15 06				15 36	16 06
Conwy	d			12x18												14x18								
Penmaenmawr	d			12x24												14x24								
Llanfairfechan	d			12x28												14x28								
Bangor (Gwynedd)	a		12 23	12 36						13 31						14 36					15 31			
	d		12 24	12 38						13 32						14 38					15 32			
Llanfairpwll	d			12x44						13x39											15x39			
Bodorgan	d			12 54						13x49											15x49			
Ty Croes	d			12 58						13x53											15x53			
Rhosneigr	d			13 01						13x56											15x56			
Valley	d			13x07						14x01											16x01			
Holyhead	a		12 56	13 19						14 14						15 11					16 14			

For general notes see front of timetable
For details of catering facilities see Directory of Train Operators

- **A** To Ellesmere Port (Table 109)
- **B** From Blaenau Ffestiniog (Table 102)
- **C** From Birmingham International (Table 68)
- **D** Until 31 October
- **b** Change at Manchester Oxford Road
- **c** From 7 November dep. 1201

Table 81

Saturdays

Crewe and Manchester → Chester and North Wales

Network Diagram - see first page of Table 81

	AW	VT	VT	AW	AW	AW	AW	VT	AW	AW	AW	AW	VT	AW	AW	AW	AW	AW	VT	AW	AW	AW	AW
	◇	1 ◇	1 ◇	◇			◇	1 ◇	◇			◇	1 ◇	◇			◇	◇	1 ◇	◇			◇
	A	B	C	D				C						D			A		C				
		🍴	🍴	🛒			🛒	🍴	🛒			🛒	🍴	🛒				🛒	🍴	🛒			🛒
London Euston 15 ⊖ 65 d		13 10	13 10		13 40			14 10		14 40			15 10		15 40				16 10		16 40		
Birmingham New Street 12 65 d		13 36	13 36	13 23	14b20			14 36		15 20			15 36	15 24	16c20				16 36		17 20		
Manchester Airport 84, 85 ✈ d					14 11		14e29			15 11		15e29			16 11			16e29			17 11		17e27
Cardiff Central 7 131 d		11 50	11 50					12 50	13 20	12 50			13 50						14 50	15 20	14 50		
Crewe 10 d		14 49	14 50		15 21			15 49		16 21			16 49		17 21				17 49		18 21		
Manchester Piccadilly 10 90 ⛴ d							14 50					15 50						16 50					17 50
Manchester Oxford Road 90 d							14 53					15 53						16 53					17 53
Newton-le-Willows 90 d							15 12					16 12						17 12					18 12
Earlestown 8 90 d							15 15					16 15						17 15					18 15
Warrington Bank Quay 90 d							15 26					16 26						17 26					18 25
Runcorn East d							15 33					16 33						17 33					18 32
Frodsham d							15 37					16 37						17 37					18 36
Helsby d							15 41					16 41						17 41					18 40
Liverpool Lime Street 10 106 d		14 13		14 13			14 43	15 13	15 13			15 43		16 13				16 43	17 13	17 13			17 43
Chester a		15 10	15 12	15 21	15 45		15 53	16 10	16 21	16 45		16 53	17 12	17 20	17 45			17 53	18 09	18 20	18 45		18 52
d		15 12		15 26			15 55	16 12	16 26			16 55		17 26				17 55	18 16	18 26			18 55
Shotton d							16 04					17 04		17 35				18 04					19 04
Flint d		15 25		15 39			16 10	16 25	16 39			17 10		17 41				18 10	18 29	18 39			19 10
Prestatyn d		15 38		15 52			16 23	16 38	16 52			17 23		17 54				18 23	18 42	18 52			19 23
Rhyl d		15 45		15 58			16 29	16 45	16 58			17 29		18 00				18 29	18 49	18 58			19 29
Abergele & Pensarn d							16 35					17 35		18 06				18 35					19 35
Colwyn Bay d		15 56		16 09			16 43	16 56	17 09			17 43		18 14				18 43	19 00	19 09			19 43
Llandudno Junction a		16 01		16 14			16 48	17 01	17 14			17 48		18 19				18 48	19 05	19 14			19 48
d	16 00	16 02		16 15		16 26	16 50	17 02	17 15		17 26	17 50		18 21		18 26	18 41	18 50	19 06	19 15		19 26	19 50
Deganwy d	16x03					16x29	16x54				17x29	17x54				18x29	18x44	18x54				19x29	19x54
Llandudno a	16 09					16 36	17 06				17 36	18 06				18 36	18 49	19 06				19 36	20 06
Conwy d				16x18					17x18					18x24									
Penmaenmawr d				16x24					17x24					18x30									
Llanfairfechan d				16x28					17x28					18x34									
Bangor (Gwynedd) a		16 17		16 36				17 17	17 36					18 42					19 21	19 31			
d		16 19		16 38				17 19	17 38					18 43					19 23	19 32			
Llanfairpwll d									17x44											19x39			
Bodorgan d									17x54											19x51			
Ty Croes d									17x58											19x55			
Rhosneigr d									18x01											19x58			
Valley d									18x07											20x04			
Holyhead a		16 51		17 11				17 51	18 19					19 16					19 55	20 16			

	VT	AW	AW	AW	AW	VT	AW	VT	AW	AW	AW	AW	AW	AW	AW	AW	AW	AW	AW	AW	AW
	1 ◇		◇			1 ◇	◇	1 ◇			◇	◇			◇						◇
			D			C		B			A										E
	🍴		🛒		🛒	🍴	🛒	🍴											🚌		
London Euston 15 ⊖ 65 d	17 10			17 40		18 10		18 30	18 40			18f57	19g19					20h26			
Birmingham New Street 12 65 d	17 36		17 24	18j20		18 36		18 36	19 20			19 36	20 20					21k57			22m36
Manchester Airport 84, 85 ✈ d				18 11	18e29					19e29				20e29		21e29	22 00			22 29	
Cardiff Central 7 131 d	15 50					16 50	17 20	16 50				17 50			19 34			20 10			20 53
Crewe 10 d	18 50			19 21		19 50		20 06	20 21			21 00	21 21					23 21			23 58
Manchester Piccadilly 10 90 ⛴ d					18 50					19 50				20 50		21 50	22 26			23 14	
Manchester Oxford Road 90 d					18 53					19 53				20 53		21 53	22 29			23 17	
Newton-le-Willows 90 d					19 12					20 12				21 12		22 12	22 47			23 36	
Earlestown 8 90 d					19 16					20 15				21 15		22 15	22 50			23 39	
Warrington Bank Quay 90 d					19 26					20 30				21 27		22 24	22 59			23 48	
Runcorn East d					19 33					20 37				21 34		22 31	23 06			23 55	
Frodsham d					19 37					20 41				21 38		22 35	23 10			23 59	
Helsby d					19 41					20 45				21 42		22 39	23 14			00 03	
Liverpool Lime Street 10 106 d	18 13		18 43				19 43					20 13			21 43						
Chester a	19 10		19 20	19 42	19 55	20 12	20 20	20 28	20 45	20 57		21 21	21 45	21 54	22 31	22 51	23 26	23 42		00 15	00 19
d	19 17		19 31				20 31					21 26			22 36						
Shotton d			19 40									21 35			22 45						
Flint d	19 30		19 46				20 44					21 41			22 51						
Prestatyn d	19 43		19 59				20 58					21 54			23 05						
Rhyl d	19 50		20 05				21 04					22 00			23 11						
Abergele & Pensarn d			20 11									22 06			23 17						
Colwyn Bay d	20 01		20 19				21 15					22 14			23 25						
Llandudno Junction a	20 06		20 24				21 20					22 19			23 33						
d	20 07	20 24	20 26				21 21				21 25	22 21							23 50		
Deganwy d		20x27									21x28										
Llandudno a		20 34									21 35										
Conwy d			20x29									22x24							23 56		
Penmaenmawr d			20x35									22x30							00 08		
Llanfairfechan d			20x39									22x34							00 23		
Bangor (Gwynedd) a	20 22		20 47				21 37					22 42							00 38		
d	20 24		20 48				21 38					22 43							00 38		
Llanfairpwll d							21x45												00 47		
Bodorgan d							21x55												00 57		
Ty Croes d							21x59												01 07		
Rhosneigr d							22x02												01 27		
Valley d							22x07												01 52		
Holyhead a	20 56		21 21				22 19					23 15							02 02		

For general notes see front of timetable
For details of catering facilities see Directory of Train Operators

A From Blaenau Ffestiniog (Table 102)
B From 7 November
C Until 31 October
D From Birmingham International (Table 68)
E From Carmarthen (Table 128)
b From 7 November dep. 1401
c From 7 November dep. 1601
e Change at Manchester Oxford Road
f From 12 September dep. 1907
g 12 September to 31 October dep. 1930. From 7 November dep. 1907
h From 12 September dep. 2100
j From 7 November dep. 1801
k Change at Stafford and Crewe
m Change at Crewe

Table 81

Sundays

until 6 September

Crewe and Manchester → Chester and North Wales

Network Diagram - see first page of Table 81

			AW ◇	AW ◇	AW 🚌	AW	AW ◇	ME A	AW	NT B	AW	AW	AW	VT 1 ◇ ⊡	AW	AW	AW ◇ C	AW ◇	AW	AW	NT D	AW
London Euston 15	⊖ 65	d												08 15	08b20			08 45		09b20		
Birmingham New Street 12	65	d							08 45					09 20	09e41			10f15		10 42		
Manchester Airport	84, 85 ✈	d			06 40					08 39		09h35		09g09					10h32		10 44	
Cardiff Central 7	131	d																		08 30		
Crewe 10		d		08 27			09 27		09 57					10 40	10 57			11 27		11 57		
Manchester Piccadilly 10	90	d			07 44					09 23		09 56							10 55		11 22	
Manchester Oxford Road	90	d			07 54					09 18		09 59							10 59		11 17	
Newton-le-Willows	90	d			08 19							10 18							11 20			
Earlestown 8	90	d			08 27							10 21							11 23			
Warrington Bank Quay	90	d			08 42							10 28							11 30			
Runcorn East		d			08 57							10 35							11 37			
Frodsham		d			09 15							10 40							11 41			
Helsby		d			09 23							10 44							11 45			
Liverpool Lime Street 10	106	d		08 13			08 43	09 13						10 13				11 13				
Chester		a		08 46	09 38		09 45	09 56	10 22	10 47		10 59		11 00	11 22			11 48	11 57	12 20	12 46	
		d	06 20	09 02			09 48							11 08				12 03				
Shotton		d					09 57											12 12				
Flint		d	06 33	09 15			10 03											12 18				
Prestatyn		d	06 46	09 28			10 16							11 31				12 31				
Rhyl		d	06 52	09 34			10 22							11 38				12 37				
Abergele & Pensarn		d					10 28															
Colwyn Bay		d	07 03	09 45			10 36							11 49				12 48				
Llandudno Junction		a	07 08	09 50			10 41							11 54				12 53				
		d	07 09	09 54		10 00	10 43				10 50		11 25	11 55		12 00	12 42	12 54				12 58
Deganwy		d				10x03					10x53		11x28			12x03	12x45					13x01
Llandudno		a				10 10					11 00		11 35			12 10	12 51					13 08
Conwy		d					10x46															
Penmaenmawr		d					10x52															
Llanfairfechan		d					10x56															
Bangor (Gwynedd)		a	07 25	10 10			11 04							12 10				13 10				
		d	07 29	10 11			11 05							12 12				13 11				
Llanfairpwll		d					11x12															
Bodorgan		d					11x22															
Ty Croes		d					11x26															
Rhosneigr		d					11x29															
Valley		d					11x34															
Holyhead		a	08 00	10 48			11 48							12 43				13 45				

			AW	AW ◇ 🍴	AW 🍴	AW	AW	AW ◇ 🍴	AW 🍴	AW	NT D	AW	AW	AW ◇ 🍴	AW 🍴	AW	AW	AW ◇ 🍴	AW 🍴	AW	NT D
London Euston 15	⊖ 65	d		09 45		10b20		11 15		12 02				12 35		13 02		13 35		14 02	
Birmingham New Street 12	65	d		11 20		11 42		12 20		12 35				13 20		13 35		14 20		14 35	
Manchester Airport	84, 85 ✈	d		11g08	11h35				12h35		12 55				13h35				14h35		14 55
Cardiff Central 7	131	d				09 35				10 40						11 45				12 45	
Crewe 10		d		12 27		12 57		13 27		13 57				14 27		14 57		15 27		15 57	
Manchester Piccadilly 10	90	d			11 56				12 56		13 22				13 56				14 56		15 22
Manchester Oxford Road	90	d			11 59				12 59		13 17				13 59				14 59		15 17
Newton-le-Willows	90	d			12 18				13 18						14 18				15 18		
Earlestown 8	90	d			12 21				13 21						14 21				15 21		
Warrington Bank Quay	90	d			12 28				13 29						14 28				15 29		
Runcorn East		d			12 35				13 36						14 35				15 36		
Frodsham		d			12 39				13 40						14 39				15 40		
Helsby		d			12 43				13 44						14 43				15 44		
Liverpool Lime Street 10	106	d		12 13				13 13						14 13				15 13			
Chester		a		12 48	12 55	13 18		13 47	13 56	14 18	14 46			14 47	14 55	15 18		15 47	15 56	16 18	16 46
		d		13 02				14 02						15 02				16 02			
Shotton		d		13 11				14 11						15 11				16 11			
Flint		d		13 17				14 17						15 17				16 17			
Prestatyn		d		13 30				14 30						15 30				16 30			
Rhyl		d		13 36				14 36						15 36				16 36			
Abergele & Pensarn		d		13 42				14 42						15 42				16 42			
Colwyn Bay		d		13 50				14 50						15 50				16 50			
Llandudno Junction		a		13 55				14 55						15 55				16 55			
		d	13 35	13 57			14 02	14 57				15 00	15 30	15 57			16 04	16 57			
Deganwy		d	13x38				14x05					15x03	15x33				16x07				
Llandudno		a	13 45				14 12					15 10	15 40				16 14				
Conwy		d		14x00										16x00							
Penmaenmawr		d		14x06										16x06							
Llanfairfechan		d		14x10										16x10							
Bangor (Gwynedd)		a		14 18				15 12						16 18				17 12			
		d		14 19				15 14						16 19				17 14			
Llanfairpwll		d						15x20										17x20			
Bodorgan		d						15x30										17x30			
Ty Croes		d						15x34										17x34			
Rhosneigr		d						15x37										17x37			
Valley		d						15x43										17x43			
Holyhead		a		14 55				15 55						16 55				17 55			

For general notes see front of timetable
For details of catering facilities see Directory of Train Operators

- **A** From Chester (Table 106)
- **B** From Wigan Wallgate (Table 82)
- **C** From Blaenau Ffestiniog (Table 102)
- **D** From Southport (Table 82)
- **b** From 19 July dep. 5 mins earlier
- **e** From 19 July dep. 0942
- **f** From 19 July dep. 1020
- **g** Until 12 July only
- **h** Change at Manchester Oxford Road

Table 81

Sundays

until 6 September

Crewe and Manchester → Chester and North Wales

Network Diagram - see first page of Table 81

	AW ◇ [trolley]	AW [trolley]	VT [1] ◇ [buffet]	AW ◇ A [trolley]	AW		AW [trolley]	VT [1] ◇ [buffet]	AW ◇ B	AW [R]	NT C		AW ◇	AW [trolley]	VT [1] ◇ [buffet]	AW ◇ A [trolley]	AW		AW	VT [1] ◇ [buffet]	AW [R]	NT C	AW
London Euston [15] ⊖ 65 d	14 35		15 05		15 35			16 05					16 35		17 05		17 35			18 05			18 35
Birmingham New Street [12] 65 d	15 20		15 35	15 24	16 20			16 35					17 20		17 35	17 24				18 35			19 20
Manchester Airport 84, 85 ✈ d		15b35					16b35				16 55			17b35					18b35			18 55	
Cardiff Central [7] 131 d			13 45					15 00		15 20					16 00					16 45	17 20		
Crewe [10] d	16 27		16 57		17 27			17 57					18 27		18 56		19 27			19 57			20 27
Manchester Piccadilly [10] 90 ⛴ d		15 56					16 56				17 22			17 56					18 56			19 22	
Manchester Oxford Road 90 d		15 59					16 59				17 17			17 59					18 59			19 17	
Newton-le-Willows 90 d		16 18					17 18							18 18					19 18				
Earlestown [8] 90 d		16 21					17 21							18 21					19 21				
Warrington Bank Quay 90 d		16 28					17 28							18 28					19 29				
Runcorn East d		16 35					17 35							18 35					19 36				
Frodsham d		16 39					17 39							18 39					19 40				
Helsby d		16 43					17 43							18 43					19 44				
Liverpool Lime Street [10] 106 d	16 13			16 43						17 13			17 43		18 13	18 43				19 13	19 43		
Chester a	16 47	16 55	17 19	17 28	17 48		17 55	18 19		18 25	18 46		18 47	18 55	19 14	19 26	19 48		19 56	20 16	20 31	20 46	20 48
d	17 02			17 32						18 30			18 55		19 21	19 38				20 22	20 36		
Shotton d	17 11			17 41						18 39			19 04			19 47					20 45		
Flint d	17 17			17 47						18 45			19 10			19 53				20 35	20 51		
Prestatyn d	17 30			18 00						18 58			19 23		19 44	20 06				20 49	21 04		
Rhyl d	17 36			18 06						19 04			19 29		19 51	20 12				20 55	21 10		
Abergele & Pensarn d	17 42			18 12						19 10			19 35			20 18					21 16		
Colwyn Bay d	17 50			18 20						19 18			19 43		20 02	20 26				21 06	21 24		
Llandudno Junction a	17 55			18 25						19 23			19 48		20 07	20 31				21 11	21 29		
d	17 57			18 27					18 30	19 25			19 50		20 14	20 33				21 13	21 31		
Deganwy d									18x34														
Llandudno a									18 40														
Conwy d	18x00									19x28			19x53			20x36					21x34		
Penmaenmawr d	18x06									19x34			19x59			20x42					21x40		
Llanfairfechan d	18x10									19x38			20x03			20x46					21x44		
Bangor (Gwynedd) a	18 18			18 42						19 46			20 11		20 29	20 54				21 28	21 52		
d	18 19			18 44						19 47			20 12		20 31	20 55				21 29	21 54		
Llanfairpwll d				18x50																	22x00		
Bodorgan d				19x00																	22x10		
Ty Croes d				19x04																	22x14		
Rhosneigr d				19x07																	22x17		
Valley d				19x13																	22x23		
Holyhead a	18 55			19 25						20 20			20 47		21 02	21 30				22 02	22 38		

	AW	VT [1] ◇ [buffet]		AW ◇	AW	AW	NT C	AW ◇		AW	ME D	AW ◇ E	ME D	AW		ME D	AW	AW	ME D	AW ◇ G			
London Euston [15] ⊖ 65 d		19 05		19 35		20 02		20 25				20c50								21e20			
Birmingham New Street [12] 65 d		19 35		20 20				21 20				21f24					21 35			22 55			
Manchester Airport 84, 85 ✈ d	19b35				20b35		20 55			21b35				22b35				22 55					
Cardiff Central [7] 131 d		17 40				18 45														20 40			
Crewe [10] d		20 58		21 27		21 57		22 29				23 05					23 38			00 10			
Manchester Piccadilly [10] 90 ⛴ d	19 56				20 56		21 22			21 56				22 56				23 25					
Manchester Oxford Road 90 d	19 59				20 59		21 17			21 59				22 59				23 28					
Newton-le-Willows 90 d	20 18				21 18					22 18				23 18				23 46					
Earlestown [8] 90 d	20 21				21 21					22 21				23 21				23 49					
Warrington Bank Quay 90 d	20 30				21 28					22 28				23 28				23 56					
Runcorn East d	20 37				21 35					22 35				23 35				00 03					
Frodsham d	20 41				21 39					22 39				23 39				00 07					
Helsby d	20 45				21 43					22 43				23 43				00 11					
Liverpool Lime Street [10] 106 d		20 13		20 43				21 43			22 13		22 43			23 13			23 43				
Chester a	20 57	21 17		21 46	21 55	22 18	22 46	22 50		22 55	22 56	23 26	23 26	23 55		23 56	23 59	00 24	00 26	00 31			
d		21 19		22 00				23 00												00 35			
Shotton d				22 09				23 09															
Flint d		21 32		22 15				23 15												00 48			
Prestatyn d		21 46		22 28				23 28												01 01			
Rhyl d		21 52		22 34				23 34												01 07			
Abergele & Pensarn d				22 40																			
Colwyn Bay d		22 03		22 48				23 45												01 18			
Llandudno Junction a		22 08		22 53				23 50												01 24			
d		22 10		22 55				23 51												01 25			
Deganwy d																							
Llandudno a																							
Conwy d								23x54															
Penmaenmawr d								00x01															
Llanfairfechan d								00x04															
Bangor (Gwynedd) a		22 25		23 10				00 12												01 40			
d		22 26		23 12				00 14												01 41			
Llanfairpwll d				23x18																			
Bodorgan d				23x28																			
Ty Croes d				23x32																			
Rhosneigr d				23x35																			
Valley d				23x41																			
Holyhead a		22 59		23 52				00 49												02 15			

For general notes see front of timetable
For details of catering facilities see Directory of Train Operators

A From Birmingham International (Table 68)
B From Blaenau Ffestiniog (Table 102)
C From Southport (Table 82)
D From Chester (Table 106)
E From Birmingham International (Table 51)
G From Birmingham International (Table 65)

b Change at Manchester Oxford Road
c Change at Crewe
e Change at Stafford
f By changing at Crewe, passengers may depart at 2135

Table 81

Sundays

from 13 September

Crewe and Manchester → Chester and North Wales

Network Diagram - see first page of Table 81

		AW 🚌	AW ◇	AW	NT A	AW	VT ■1 ◇ buffet	AW	AW ◇	AW	AW	NT B	AW C 🚌	AW ◇ trolley	AW trolley	AW	AW ◇ trolley	AW trolley	AW	NT B	AW ◇ trolley
London Euston 15	⊖ 65 d						08 15	08b15			09 15			09 45		10 15	11 15		12 02		12 35
Birmingham New Street 12	65 d			08c45			09 20	09 41	10e15		10 42			11 20		11 42	12f20		12 35		13 20
Manchester Airport	84, 85 ✈ d	07g30			08 47	09g30				10 31		10 44			11g33			12g35		12 55	
Cardiff Central 7	131 d										08 30					09 35			10 40		
Crewe 10	d		09 24	10 04			10 40	11 05	11 27		11 57			12 27		12 54	13 27		13 57		14 27
Manchester Piccadilly 10	90 ⛴ d	07h44			09 23	09 53				10 55		11 22			11 56			12 56		13 22	
Manchester Oxford Road	90 d	07 54			09 18	09 59				10 59		11 17			11 59			12 59		13 17	
Newton-le-Willows	90 d	08 19				10 18				11 20					12 18			13 18			
Earlestown 8	90 d	08 27				10 21				11 23					12 21			13 21			
Warrington Bank Quay	90 d	08 42				10 28				11 30					12 28			13 29			
Runcorn East	d	08 57				10 35				11 37					12 35			13 36			
Frodsham	d	09 15				10 40				11 41					12 39			13 40			
Helsby	d	09 23				10 44				11 45					12 43			13 44			
Liverpool Lime Street 10	106 d		08 43				10 13		11 13					12 13			13 13				14 13
Chester	a	09 38	09 45	10 25	10 47	10 57	11 00	11 26	11 48	11 57	12 18	12 46		12 48	12 55	13 15	13 47	13 56	14 18	14 46	14 47
	d		09 48				11 08		12 03					13 02			14 02				15 02
Shotton	d		09 57						12 12					13 11			14 11				15 11
Flint	d		10 03						12 18					13 17			14 17				15 17
Prestatyn	d		10 16				11 31		12 31					13 30			14 30				15 30
Rhyl	d		10 22				11 38		12 37					13 36			14 36				15 36
Abergele & Pensarn	d		10 28											13 42			14 42				15 42
Colwyn Bay	d		10 36				11 49		12 48					13 50			14 50				15 50
Llandudno Junction	a		10 41				11 54		12 53					13 55			14 55				15 55
	d		10 43				11 55		12 54				13 00	13 57			14 57				15 57
Deganwy	d												13 05								
Llandudno	a												13 20								
Conwy	d		10x46											14x00							16x00
Penmaenmawr	d		10x52											14x06							16x06
Llanfairfechan	d		10x56											14x10							16x10
Bangor (Gwynedd)	a		11 04				12 10		13 10					14 18			15 12				16 18
	d		11 05				12 12		13 11					14 19			15 14				16 19
Llanfairpwll	d		11x11														15x20				
Bodorgan	d		11x21														15x30				
Ty Croes	d		11x26														15x34				
Rhosneigr	d		11x29														15x37				
Valley	d		11x34														15x43				
Holyhead	a		11 44				12 43		13 45					14 55			15 55				16 54

		AW trolley	AW	AW C 🚌	AW ◇ trolley	AW trolley	NT B	AW ◇ trolley	AW trolley	VT ■1 ◇ buffet	AW ◇	AW trolley	VT ■1 ◇ buffet	AW C 🚌	AW R	NT B	AW ◇	AW trolley	VT ■1 ◇ buffet	AW ◇ D trolley	AW
London Euston 15	⊖ 65 d		13 02		13 35			14 35		15 05	15 35		16 05				16 35		17 05		17 35
Birmingham New Street 12	65 d		13 35		14j20			15 20		15 35	16 20		16 35				17 20		17 35	17 24	
Manchester Airport	84, 85 ✈ d	13g35				14g35	14 55		15g35			16g35				16 55		17g35			
Cardiff Central 7	131 d		11 45					12 45		13 45			15 00		15 20				16 00		
Crewe 10	d		14 57		15 27			16 27		16 57	17 27		17 57				18 27		18 56		19 27
Manchester Piccadilly 10	90 ⛴ d	13 56				14 56	15 22		15 56			16 56				17 22		17 56			
Manchester Oxford Road	90 d	13 59				14 59	15 17		15 59			16 59				17 17		17 59			
Newton-le-Willows	90 d	14 18				15 18			16 18			17 18						18 18			
Earlestown 8	90 d	14 21				15 21			16 21			17 21						18 21			
Warrington Bank Quay	90 d	14 28				15 29			16 28			17 28						18 28			
Runcorn East	d	14 35				15 36			16 35			17 35						18 35			
Frodsham	d	14 39				15 40			16 39			17 39						18 39			
Helsby	d	14 43				15 44			16 43			17 43						18 43			
Liverpool Lime Street 10	106 d				15 13			16 13			17 13						17 43		18 13	18 43	
Chester	a	14 55	15 18		15 47	15 56	16 46	16 47	16 55	17 19	17 47	17 55	18 19		18 25	18 46	18 47	18 55	19 14	19 26	19 48
	d				16 02			17 02			18 02				18 30		18 55		19 21	19 38	
Shotton	d				16 11			17 11			18 11				18 39		19 04			19 47	
Flint	d				16 17			17 17			18 17				18 45		19 10			19 53	
Prestatyn	d				16 30			17 30			18 30				18 58		19 23		19 44	20 06	
Rhyl	d				16 36			17 36			18 36				19 04		19 29		19 51	20 12	
Abergele & Pensarn	d				16 42			17 42			18 42				19 10		19 35			20 18	
Colwyn Bay	d				16 50			17 50			18 50				19 18		19 43		20 02	20 26	
Llandudno Junction	a				16 55			17 55			18 55				19 23		19 48		20 07	20 31	
	d			16 10	16 57			17 57			18 57			19 00	19 25		19 50		20 14	20 33	
Deganwy	d			16 15										19 05							
Llandudno	a			16 30										19 20							
Conwy	d							18x00							19x28		19x53			20x36	
Penmaenmawr	d							18x06							19x34		19x59			20x42	
Llanfairfechan	d							18x10							19x38		20x03			20x46	
Bangor (Gwynedd)	a				17 12			18 18			19 12				19 46		20 11		20 29	20 54	
	d				17 14			18 19			19 14				19 47		20 12		20 31	20 55	
Llanfairpwll	d				17x20						19x20										
Bodorgan	d				17x30						19x30										
Ty Croes	d				17x34						19x34										
Rhosneigr	d				17x37						19x37										
Valley	d				17x43						19x43										
Holyhead	a				17 55			18 55			19 55				20 20		20 47		21 02	21 30	

For general notes see front of timetable
For details of catering facilities see Directory of Train Operators

- **A** From Wigan Wallgate (Table 82)
- **B** From Southport (Table 82)
- **C** From Blaenau Ffestiniog (Table 102)
- **D** From Birmingham International (Table 68)
- **b** From 8 November dep. 0844
- **c** Until 1 November only
- **e** From 8 November dep. 1020
- **f** From 8 November dep. 1201
- **g** Change at Manchester Oxford Road
- **h** By changing at Manchester Oxford Road, passengers may depart at 0746
- **j** From 8 November dep. 1335

Sundays

from 13 September

Crewe and Manchester → Chester and North Wales

Network Diagram - see first page of Table 81

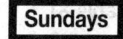

	AW	VT	AW	NT	AW	AW	VT	VT	AW	AW	AW	NT	AW	AW	AW	AW	AW	AW	AW
		1 ◊	R	A			1 ◊ B	1 ◊ C	◊			A	◊		◊ E				◊ E
London Euston 15 ⊖ 65 d		18 05			18 35		19 05	19 05	19 35		20 02		20 25		20b50				21c20
Birmingham New Street 12 65 d		18 35			19 20		19 35	19 35	20 20				21 20		21e24		22 28		22 55
Manchester Airport 84, 85 (rail-link) d	18f35			18 55		19f35				20f35		20 55		21f35		22f35		22 55	
Cardiff Central 7 131 d		16 45	17 20				17 40	17 40			18 45								20 40
Crewe 10 d		19 57			20 27		20 58	20 58	21 27		22 00		22 29		23 05		23 38		00 10
Manchester Piccadilly 10 90 d	18 56			19 22		19 56				20 56		21 22		21 56		22 56		23 25	
Manchester Oxford Road 90 d	18 59			19 17		19 59				20 59		21 17		21 59		22 59		23 28	
Newton-le-Willows 90 d	19 18					20 18				21 18				22 18		23 18		23 46	
Earlestown 8 90 d	19 21					20 21				21 21				22 21		23 21		23 49	
Warrington Bank Quay 90 d	19 29					20 30				21 28				22 28		23 28		23 56	
Runcorn East d	19 36					20 37				21 35				22 35		23 35		00 03	
Frodsham d	19 40					20 41				21 39				22 39		23 39		00 07	
Helsby d	19 44					20 45				21 43				22 43		23 43		00 11	
Liverpool Lime Street 10 106 d		19 13	19 43				20 13	20 13	20 43										
Chester a	19 56	20 16	20 31	20 46	20 48	20 57	21 17	21 17	21 46	21 55	22 21	22 46	22 50	22 55	23 26	23 55	23 59	00 24	00 31
d		20 22	20 36				21 19	21 30	22 00				23 00						00 35
Shotton d			20 45						22 09				23 09						
Flint d		20 35	20 51				21 32	21 43	22 15				23 15						00 48
Prestatyn d		20 49	21 04				21 46	21 56	22 28				23 28						01 01
Rhyl d		20 55	21 10				21 52	22 03	22 34				23 34						01 07
Abergele & Pensarn d			21 16						22 40										
Colwyn Bay d		21 06	21 24				22 03	22 14	22 48				23 45						01 18
Llandudno Junction a		21 11	21 29				22 08	22 19	22 53				23 50						01 24
d		21 13	21 31				22 10	22 20	22 55				23 51						01 25
Deganwy d																			
Llandudno a																			
Conwy d			21x34										23x54						
Penmaenmawr d			21x40										00x01						
Llanfairfechan d			21x44										00x04						
Bangor (Gwynedd) a		21 28	21 52				22 25	22 35	23 10				00 12						01 40
d		21 29	21 54				22 26	22 37	23 12				00 14						01 41
Llanfairpwll d			22x00						23x18										
Bodorgan d			22x10						23x28										
Ty Croes d			22x14						23x32										
Rhosneigr d			22x17						23x35										
Valley d			22x23						23x41										
Holyhead a		22 02	22 38				22 59	23 09	23 52				00 49						02 15

For general notes see front of timetable
For details of catering facilities see Directory of Train Operators

A From Southport (Table 82)
B Until 1 November
C From 8 November
E From Birmingham International (Table 68)

b Change at Crewe
c Change at Stafford
e By changing at Crewe, passengers may depart at 2135
f Change at Manchester Oxford Road

Table 81

North Wales and Chester → Manchester and Crewe

Network Diagram - see first page of Table 81

Miles	Miles			AW	AW	AW	AW	AW	AW	AW	VT	AW	AW	NT	AW	AW	AW	VT	AW	AW
										◇ ⌶	1 ◇ ⊠		◇ A ⌶	B	1 ◇ ⊠ ⊡	⌶	◇ A ⌶	1 ◇ C ⊠	◇ ⌶	
0	—	**Holyhead**	d							04 25	04 50		05 11		05 32			05 53		
3½	—	Valley	d							04x31										
7½	—	Rhosneigr	d																	
9¼	—	Ty Croes	d																	
12	—	Bodorgan	d																	
21	—	Llanfairpwll	d							04x48										
24¾	—	**Bangor (Gwynedd)**	a							04 55	05 16		05 38		06 00			06 19		
—	—		d							04 57	05 16		05 40		06 02			06 20		
32¼	—	Llanfairfechan	d										05x48							
34¾	—	Penmaenmawr	d										05x52							
39	—	Conwy	d										05x58							
—	0	**Llandudno**	d																06 34	07 10
—	1¾	Deganwy	d																06x38	07x14
40	3	**Llandudno Junction**	a							05 13	05 34		06 01		06 19			06 37	06 42	07 20
—	—		d			04 38				05 15	05 34	05 46	06 07		06 21			06 38	06 44	
44	—	Colwyn Bay	d			04 44				05 21	05 40	05 52	06 13					06 44	06 50	
50¼	—	Abergele & Pensarn	d			04 51						05 59							06 57	
54½	—	Rhyl	d			04 57				05 31	05 51	06 05	06 23		06 36			06 55	07 03	
58	—	Prestatyn	d			05 02				05 37		06 10	06 29					07 00	07 08	
72	—	Flint	d			05 16				05 50		06 24	06 42		06 52				07 21	
76¼	—	Shotton	d			05 22						06 30							07 27	
84¼	—	**Chester**	a			05 33				06 05	06 19	06 41	06 59		07 07		⟵	07 25	07 38	
—	0		d	04 23	04 55	05 37	05 38	05 51	06 13	06 22	06 26	06 43	07 22		07 08	07 12	07 22	07 35	07 40	
—	—	Liverpool Lime Street 10	106 a			*06 43*					*07 13*	*07 43*	⟶		*08 05*			*08 20*	*08 35*	
—	7½	Helsby	d				05 47		06 22					07 06		07 21			07 49	
—	10	Frodsham	d				05 51		06 26							07 25			07 53	
—	13¼	Runcorn East	d				05 56		06 32							07 31			07 59	
—	18¼	Warrington Bank Quay	90 a				06 05		06 39					07 23		07 38			08 06	
—	22¼	Earlestown 8	90 a				06 12		06 47							07 46			08 15	
—	24	Newton-le-Willows	90 a				06 15		06 50							07 49			08 18	
—	39¾	**Manchester Oxford Road**	90 a				06 35		07 09							08 09			08 41	
—	40¼	**Manchester Piccadilly** 10	90 a				06 46		07 18							08 18			08 50	
105½	—	**Crewe** 10	a	04 44	05 20	05 58		06 15			06 47	07 03			07 32			07 54		
—	—	Cardiff Central 7	131 a	*07 51*	*08 55*					09 22	*09 52*				09 58			*10 55*		
—	—	Manchester Airport	84, 85 ✈ a				*07 17*	*07 04*	*07 47*							*08 47*		*09 04*	*09c19*	
—	—	Birmingham New Street 12	65 a	05 55	*06 58*	*07 18*		*07 31*			*07 55*	*08 17*			*08e47*		09 26	*09 18*		
—	—	London Euston 15	⊖ 65 a		*07 28*			*08 11*			08 36	*08 55*						09 38		

		AW	AW	VT	AW	AW	AW	AW	VT	AW	AW	AW	AW	VT	AW	AW	AW	AW	AW	VT
			◇ ⌶	1 ◇ ⊠	◇ ⌶			◇ A ⌶	1 ◇ ⊠	◇ ⌶			◇ ⌶	1 ◇ ⊠	◇ ⌶			◇ A ⌶	◇ D	1 ◇ ⊡
Holyhead	d		06 27	06 55				07 15					08 05	08 55				09 23		
Valley	d		06x33					07x21					08x11					09x29		
Rhosneigr	d		06x39					07x26					08x17					09x34		
Ty Croes	d		06x42					07x30					08x20					09x38		
Bodorgan	d		06x47					07x34					08x25					09x42		
Llanfairpwll	d		06x56					07x44					08x34					09x52		
Bangor (Gwynedd)	a		07 04	07 21				07 52					08 42	09 21				10 00		
	d		07 08	07 22				08 02					09 02	09 22				10 02		
Llanfairfechan	d							08x10					09x10					10x10		
Penmaenmawr	d							08x14					09x14					10x14		
Conwy	d							08x20					09x20					10x20		
Llandudno	d				07 45	08 10				08 45	09 10				09 45	10 10			10 20	
Deganwy	d				07x49	08x14				08x49	09x14				09x49	10x14			10x24	
Llandudno Junction	a		07 24	07 39	07 53	08 20		08 23		08 53	09 20		09 23	09 39	09 53	10 20		10 23	10 30	
	d		07 25	07 40	07 54			08 25		08 54			09 25	09 40	09 54			10 25		
Colwyn Bay	d		07 31	07 47	08 00			08 31		09 00			09 31	09 47	10 00			10 31		
Abergele & Pensarn	d				08 07					09 07					10 07					
Rhyl	d		07 42	07 58	08 13			08 41		09 13			09 41	09 58	10 13			10 41		
Prestatyn	d		07 47	08 04	08 19			08 47		09 19			09 47	10 04	10 19			10 47		
Flint	d		08 01	08 17	08 32			09 00		09 32			10 00	10 17	10 32			11 00		
Shotton	d				08 38					09 38					10 38					
Chester	a		08 15	08 31	08 50			09 15		09 50			10 15	10 31	10 50			11 15		
	d	07 55	08 22	08 35	08 52		08 55	09 30	09 35	09 52		09 55	10 22	10 35	10 52		10 55	11 22		11 35
Liverpool Lime Street 10	106 a		*09 13*		*09 43*			*10 13*		*10 43*			*11 13*		*11 43*			*12 13*		
Helsby	d				09 01					10 01					11 01					
Frodsham	d				09 05					10 05					11 05					
Runcorn East	d				09 11					10 11					11 11					
Warrington Bank Quay	90 a				09 18					10 18					11 18					
Earlestown 8	90 a				09 26					10 26					11 26					
Newton-le-Willows	90 a				09 29					10 29					11 29					
Manchester Oxford Road	90 a				09 48					10 48					11 48					
Manchester Piccadilly 10	90 a				09 57					10 57					11 57					
Crewe 10	a	08 17		08 54			09 17		09 54			10 17		10 54			11 17			11 54
Cardiff Central 7	131 a		11 15	*11 55*					*12 54*				13 20	*13 54*						*14 54*
Manchester Airport	84, 85 ✈ a	*09 04*			*10c17*		*10 04*			*11c17*		*11 04*			*12c17*		*12 04*			
Birmingham New Street 12	65 a	*09 47*		*10 17*			*10 47*	11 30	*11 18*			*11 47*		*12 17*			*12 47*	13 26		*13 17*
London Euston 15	⊖ 65 a	*10 04*		10 38			*11 04*		11 38			*12 04*		12 38			*13 04*			13 38

For general notes see front of timetable
For details of catering facilities see Directory of Train Operators

- **A** To Birmingham International (Table 68)
- **B** From Ellesmere Port (Table 109)
- **C** Also conveys portion from Wrexham General (Table 75)
- **D** To Blaenau Ffestiniog (Table 102)
- **c** Change at Manchester Oxford Road
- **e** Change at Crewe

North Wales and Chester → Manchester and Crewe

Network Diagram - see first page of Table 81

		AW	AW	AW		AW	VT	AW	AW		AW	AW	VT	AW		AW	AW	AW	AW		VT	AW	AW	AW
		◇				R	1 ◇	◇				◇	1 ◇	◇				◇	◇		1 ◇	◇		
												A						B	C					
		🛒				🛒	☕	🛒				🛒	☕	🛒				🛒			☕	🛒		
Holyhead	d					10 33						11 23						12 38						
Valley	d					10x40						11x29												
Rhosneigr	d											11x34												
Ty Croes	d											11x38												
Bodorgan	d											11x42												
Llanfairpwll	d					10x56						11x50												
Bangor (Gwynedd)	a					11 04						12 00						13 05						
	d					11 06						12 02	12 24					13 07						
Llanfairfechan	d											12x10												
Penmaenmawr	d											12x14												
Conwy	d											12x20												
Llandudno	d	10 44	11 10					11 44	12 10					12 44		13 10			13 20			13 44	14 10	
Deganwy	d	10x48	11x14					11x48	12x14					12x48		13x14			13x24			13x48	14x14	
Llandudno Junction	a	10 52	11 20			11 22		11 52	12 20			12 23	12 40	12 52		13 20		13 23	13 30			13 52	14 20	
	d	10 53				11 25		11 53				12 25	12 42	12 53				13 25				13 53		
Colwyn Bay	d	10 59				11 31		11 59				12 31	12 48	12 59				13 31				13 59		
Abergele & Pensarn	d	11 06						12 06						13 06								14 06		
Rhyl	d	11 12				11 41		12 12				12 41	12 59	13 12				13 41				14 12		
Prestatyn	d	11 18				11 47		12 18				12 47	13 05	13 18				13 47				14 18		
Flint	d	11 31				12 00		12 31				13 00	13 18	13 31				14 00				14 31		
Shotton	d	11 37						12 37						13 37								14 37		
Chester	a	11 49				12 15		12 49				13 15	13 32	13 49				14 15				14 49		
	d	11 50		11 55		12 22	12 35	12 50			12 55	13 22	13 35	13 50			13 55	14 22			14 35	14 50		14 55
Liverpool Lime Street 10	106 a	12 43				13 13		13 43				14 13	14 43	14 43				15 13				15 43		
Helsby	d	12 00						13 00						14 00								15 00		
Frodsham	d	12 04						13 04						14 04								15 04		
Runcorn East	d	12 09						13 09						14 09								15 09		
Warrington Bank Quay	90 a	12 18						13 18						14 18								15 18		
Earlestown 8	90 a	12 26						13 26						14 26								15 26		
Newton-le-Willows	90 a	12 29						13 29						14 29								15 29		
Manchester Oxford Road	90 a	12 48						13 48						14 48								15 48		
Manchester Piccadilly 10	90 ⛴ a	12 57						13 57						14 57								15 57		
Crewe 10	a			12 17			12 54				13 17		13 54				14 17				14 54			15 17
Cardiff Central 7	131 a					15 20	15 53						16 54					17 17			17 52			
Manchester Airport	84, 85 ✈ a	13b17		13 04				14b17			14 04			15b17			15 04					16b17		16 04
Birmingham New Street 12	65 a			13 47			14 17				14 47	15 26	15 20				15 47				16 17			16 47
London Euston 15	⊖ 65 a			14 04			14 38				15 04		15 38				16 04				16 38			17 04

		AW	VT		AW	AW	NT	AW		AW	VT	AW	AW		AW	AW	VT	AW		AW	AW	AW	AW	AW
		◇	1 ◇		◇			◇		◇	1 ◇		◇		◇	◇	1 ◇			◇	◇			
		A					D								A	C								
		🛒	☕		🛒			🛒		🛒	⊠		🛒		🛒		⊠			🛒	🛒			
Holyhead	d	13 23	13 58							14 32					15 23						16 36			
Valley	d	13x29													15x29									
Rhosneigr	d	13x34													15x34									
Ty Croes	d	13x38													15x38									
Bodorgan	d	13x42													15x42									
Llanfairpwll	d	13x52													15x52									
Bangor (Gwynedd)	a	14 00	14 24							14 58					16 00						17 02			
	d	14 02	14 25							15 02					16 02						17 04			
Llanfairfechan	d	14x10								15x10					16x10									
Penmaenmawr	d	14x14								15x14					16x14									
Conwy	d	14x20								15x20					16x20									
Llandudno	d				14 40			15 08					16 08			16 20				17 07		18 08		
Deganwy	d				14x44			15x12					16x12			16x24				17x11		18x12		
Llandudno Junction	a	14 23	14 42		14 48			15 16		15 23			16 16		16 23	16 28				17 15	17 21	18 18		
	d	14 25	14 43		14 49			15 17		15 25			16 17		16 25					17 16	17 22			
Colwyn Bay	d	14 31	14 50		14 55			15 23		15 31			16 23		16 31					17 22	17 28			
Abergele & Pensarn	d				15 02					15 38					16 38						17 35			
Rhyl	d	14 41	15 00		15 08			15 34		15 44			16 34		16 44					17 33	17 41			
Prestatyn	d	14 47			15 14			15 39		15 49			16 39		16 50					17 38	17 47			
Flint	d	15 00			15 27			15 53		16 03			16 53		17 03					17 52	18 02			
Shotton	d				15 33			15 59					16 59							17 58				
Chester	a	15 17			15 44			16 10		16 16			17 10		17 17					18 11	18 16			
	d	15 22			15 46	15 55		16 22		16 22	16 35	16 55	17 19		17 22		17 35	17 55		18 16	18 20		18 50	18 55
Liverpool Lime Street 10	106 a	16 13			16 43					17 13					18 13						19 13			
Helsby	d				15 55		16 11	16 31					17 28							18 25			19 00	
Frodsham	d				15 59		16 16	16 35					17 33							18 30			19 04	
Runcorn East	d				16 04		16 22	16 41					17 38							18 35			19 09	
Warrington Bank Quay	90 a				16 12		16 34	16 51					17 49							18 45			19 18	
Earlestown 8	90 a				16 26			16 59					17 57							18 57			19 26	
Newton-le-Willows	90 a				16 29			17 01					17 59							18 59			19 29	
Manchester Oxford Road	90 a				16 48			17 21					18 19							19 21			19 48	
Manchester Piccadilly 10	90 ⛴ a				16 57			17 30					18 28							19 29			19 57	
Crewe 10	a		15 54			16 17					16 54	17 17					17 54	18 17						19 17
Cardiff Central 7	131 a		18 59							19 20	19 49						20 58	22 09			21 19			
Manchester Airport	84, 85 ✈ a				17b17	17 04		17b53				18 04	18b47					19 04		19b53			20b17	
Birmingham New Street 12	65 a	17 26	17 20			17 47					18 17	18 48			19 26		19 17	19 47						20 47
London Euston 15	⊖ 65 a		17 38			18 06					18 38	19 08					19 38	20 08						21 10

For general notes see front of timetable
For details of catering facilities see Directory of Train Operators

A To Birmingham International (Table 68)
B To Maesteg (Table 128)
C To Blaenau Ffestiniog (Table 102)
D From Ellesmere Port (Table 109)
b Change at Manchester Oxford Road

North Wales and Chester → Manchester and Crewe

Network Diagram - see first page of Table 81

	AW		VT	AW	AW	AW		AW	AW	AW	AW		AW	AW	VT	AW		AW	AW	AW	AW		
	◇		[1] ◇	◇	◇				◇	◇				◇	[1] ◇				◇				
	A				B																		
	⊤		⊑	⊤					⊤						⊑								
Holyhead d	17 21								18 23					19 21					20 37				
Valley d	17x27								18x29					19x27									
Rhosneigr d	17x32								18x34					19x32									
Ty Croes d	17x36								18x38					19x36									
Bodorgan d	17x40								18x42					19x40									
Llanfairpwll d	17x50								18x52					19x50									
Bangor (Gwynedd) a	17 58								19 00					19 58					21 04				
d	18 00								19 02					20 00	20 20				21 06				
Llanfairfechan d	18x08								19x10					20x08					21x14				
Penmaenmawr d	18x12								19x14					20x12					21x18				
Conwy d	18x18								19x20					20x18					21x24				
Llandudno d				18 44	19 03	19 10				19 42	20 08					20 42				21 45			
Deganwy d				18x48	19x07	19x14				19x46	20x12					20x46				21x49			
Llandudno Junction a	18 21			18 52	19 11	19 20			19 23	19 50	20 18			20 21	20 36	20 50			21 27	21 53			
d	18 23			18 53					19 25	19 51				20 23	20 38	20 51			21 29	21 55			
Colwyn Bay d	18 29			18 59					19 31	19 57				20 29	20 44	20 57			21 35	22 01			
Abergele & Pensarn d				19 06						20 04						21 04			21 42	22 09			
Rhyl d	18 39			19 12					19 41	20 10				20 39	20 55	21 10			21 48	22 16			
Prestatyn d	18 45			19 18					19 47	20 16				20 45	21 00	21 16			21 53	22 22			
Flint d	18 58			19 31					20 00	20 29				20 58	21 14	21 29			22 07	22 37			
Shotton d				19 37						20 35						21 35			22 13	22 44			
Chester a	19 15			19 49					20 15	20 47				21 15	21 28	21 47			22 23	22 55			
d			19 35	19 50				19 55	20 17	20 50			20 55	21 21	21 35			21 52	22 25	23 01	23 22		
Liverpool Lime Street [10] 106 a	20 13			20 43					21 13	21 43				22 13		22 43			23 13				
Helsby d				20 00						20 59								22 01			23 31		
Frodsham d				20 04						21 03								22 05			23 35		
Runcorn East d				20 09						21 09								22 11			23 41		
Warrington Bank Quay 90 a				20 18						21 16								22 18			23 49		
Earlestown [8] 90 a				20 26						21 26								22 26			23 56		
Newton-le-Willows 90 a				20 29						21 29								22 29			23 59		
Manchester Oxford Road 90 a				20 48						21 48								22 50					
Manchester Piccadilly [10] 90 ⛴ a				20 57						21 57								22 58			00 28		
Crewe [10] a			19 54					20 17	20 41				21 17		21 54				22 46	23 26			
Cardiff Central [7] 131 a			23 04						00 11						01 10								
Manchester Airport 84, 85 ✈ a				21b17						22b17								00 22		01 16	01 10		
Birmingham New Street [12] 65 a			21 18					21 47	21 51					23 26	22 50								
London Euston [15] ⊖ 65 a			21 42					22 12	23 53														

Saturdays

	AW	AW	AW	AW	AW	AW	AW	AW	AW	VT	AW	AW	AW	NT	AW	AW	VT	AW	AW	AW	AW	VT	VT
							◇			[1] ◇	◇	◇				◇	[1] ◇	◇			◇	[1] ◇	[1] ◇
											C			D							C	E	G
							⊤		⊤	⊑	⊤	⊤				⊤	⊑	⊤			⊤	⊑	⊑
Holyhead d							04 25				05 22					06 33	06 50				07 15	07 52	07 55
Valley d							04x31				05x28					06x39					07x21		
Rhosneigr d											05x33										07x26		
Ty Croes d											05x37										07x30		
Bodorgan d											05x41										07x34		
Llanfairpwll d							04x48				05x51					06x56					07x44		
Bangor (Gwynedd) a							04 55				05 59					07 03	07 16				07 52	08 18	08 21
d							04 57				06 01					07 08	07 17				08 02	08 19	08 22
Llanfairfechan d											06x09										08x10		
Penmaenmawr d											06x13										08x14		
Conwy d											06x19										08x20		
Llandudno d												06 34	07 10					07 45	08 10				
Deganwy d												06x38	07x14					07x49	08x14				
Llandudno Junction a							05 13				06 22	06 42	07 20			07 24	07 34	07 53	08 20		08 23	08 36	08 39
d			04 38				05 15	05 46			06 24	06 44				07 25	07 35	07 54			08 25	08 37	08 40
Colwyn Bay d			04 44				05 21	05 52			06 30	06 50				07 31	07 42	08 00			08 31	08 44	08 47
Abergele & Pensarn d			04 51					05 59				06 57						08 07					
Rhyl d			04 57				05 31	06 05			06 40	07 03				07 42	07 53	08 13			08 41	08 55	08 58
Prestatyn d			05 02				05 37	06 10			06 46	07 08				07 47	07 59	08 19			08 47	09 01	09 04
Flint d			05 16				05 50	06 24			06 59	07 21				08 01	08 12	08 32			09 00	09 15	09 18
Shotton d			05 22					06 30				07 27						08 38					
Chester a			05 33				06 05	06 41			07 15	07 38				08 15	08 26	08 50			09 15	09 28	09 31
d	04 23	04 55	05 37	05 38	05 51	06 13	06 12	06 43	07 12	07 17	07 22	07 40		07 53	07 55	08 22	08 35	08 52		08 55	09 30	09 35	09 35
Liverpool Lime Street [10] 106 a			06 43				07 13	07 43			08 13	08 43				09 13		09 43			10 13		
Helsby d				05 47		06 22			07 21			07 49						09 01					
Frodsham d				05 51		06 26			07 25			07 53						09 05					
Runcorn East d				05 56		06 32			07 31			07 59		08c15				09 11					
Warrington Bank Quay 90 a				06 05		06 39			07 38			08 06						09 18					
Earlestown [8] 90 a				06 12		06 47			07 46			08 15						09 26					
Newton-le-Willows 90 a				06 15		06 50			07 49			08 18						09 29					
Manchester Oxford Road 90 a				06 35		07 09			08 09			08 41						09 48					
Manchester Piccadilly [10] 90 ⛴ a				06 46		07 18			08 18			08 50						09 57					
Crewe [10] a	04 44	05 20	05 58		06 15			07 03		07 36					08 17		08 54			09 17		09 54	09 54
Cardiff Central [7] 131 a	07 55	08 52					09 23	09 54		10 53						11 20	11 54					12 54	12 54
Manchester Airport 84, 85 ✈ a				07 17	07 04	07 47		08 05	08 47			09b19			09 04			10b17		10 04			
Birmingham New Street [12] 65 a	05 55	06 58	07 17		07 47			08 17		08 47	09 26				09 47		10 17			10 47	11 26	11 17	11 17
London Euston [15] ⊖ 65 a		07 54			08 10			08 59		09 30					10 04		10 38			11 04		11 38	11 38

For general notes see front of timetable
For details of catering facilities see Directory of Train Operators

- **A** To Shrewsbury (Table 75)
- **B** To Blaenau Ffestiniog (Table 102)
- **C** To Birmingham International (Table 68)
- **D** Until 5 September
- **E** From 7 November
- **G** Until 31 October
- **b** Change at Manchester Oxford Road
- **c** Runcorn (Main Line). Arrival time

Table 81

Saturdays

North Wales and Chester → Manchester and Crewe

Network Diagram - see first page of Table 81

		AW ◇ (trolley)	AW	AW	AW ◇ (trolley)	VT [1] ◇ (buffet)	AW ◇ (trolley)	AW	AW	AW ◇ A (trolley)	AW ◇ B	VT [1] ◇ (buffet)	AW ◇ (trolley)	AW	AW	AW ◇ (trolley)	VT [1] ◇ C (buffet)	AW ◇ (trolley)	AW	AW	AW ◇ A (trolley)	VT [1] ◇ C (buffet)	AW ◇ (trolley)	AW
Holyhead	d				08 20	08 55				09 23						10 33					11 23			
Valley	d				08x26					09x29						10x40					11x29			
Rhosneigr	d				08x32					09x34											11x34			
Ty Croes	d				08x35					09x38											11x38			
Bodorgan	d				08x40					09x42											11x42			
Llanfairpwll	d				08x49					09x52						10x56					11x52			
Bangor (Gwynedd)	a				08 57	09 21				10 00						11 04					12 00			
	d				09 02	09 22				10 02						11 06					12 02			
Llanfairfechan	d				09x10					10x10											12x10			
Penmaenmawr	d				09x14					10x14											12x14			
Conwy	d				09x20					10x20											12x20			
Llandudno	d	08 45	09 10				09 45	10 10			10 20		10 44	11 10				11 44	12 10				12 44	13 10
Deganwy	d	08x49	09x14				09x49	10x14			10x24		10x48	11x14				11x48	12x14				12x48	13x14
Llandudno Junction	a	08 53	09 20		09 23	09 39	09 53	10 20		10 23	10 30		10 52	11 20		11 22		11 52	12 20		12 23		12 52	13 20
	d	08 54			09 25	09 40	09 54			10 25			10 53			11 25		11 53			12 25		12 53	
Colwyn Bay	d	09 00			09 31	09 47	10 00			10 31			10 59			11 31		11 59			12 31		12 59	
Abergele & Pensarn	d	09 07					10 07						11 06					12 06					13 06	
Rhyl	d	09 13			09 41	09 58	10 13			10 41			11 12			11 41		12 12			12 41		13 12	
Prestatyn	d	09 19			09 47	10 03	10 19			10 47			11 18			11 47		12 18			12 47		13 18	
Flint	d	09 32			10 00		10 32			11 00			11 31			12 00		12 31			13 00		13 31	
Shotton	d	09 38					10 38						11 37					12 37					13 37	
Chester	a	09 50			10 15	10 28	10 50			11 15			11 49			12 15		12 49			13 15		13 49	
	d	09 52		09 55	10 22	10 35	10 52		10 55	11 22		11 35	11 50		11 55	12 22	12 35	12 50		12 55	13 22	13 35	13 50	
Liverpool Lime Street [10] 106	a	10 43			11 13		11 43			12 13			12 43			13 13		13 43			14 13		14 43	
Helsby	d	10 01					11 01						12 00					13 00					14 00	
Frodsham	d	10 05					11 05						12 04					13 04					14 04	
Runcorn East	d	10 11					11 11						12 09					13 09					14 09	
Warrington Bank Quay 90	a	10 18					11 18						12 18					13 18					14 18	
Earlestown [8] 90	a	10 26					11 26						12 26					13 26					14 26	
Newton-le-Willows 90	a	10 29					11 29						12 29					13 29					14 29	
Manchester Oxford Road 90	a	10 48					11 48						12 48					13 48					14 48	
Manchester Piccadilly [10] 90	a	10 57					11 57						12 57					13 57					14 57	
Crewe [10]	a			10 17		10 54			11 17			11 54			12 17		12 54			13 17		13 54		
Cardiff Central [7] 131	a				13 20	13 54						14 54			15 54	15 21	15 54			16 54		16 54		
Manchester Airport 84, 85 ✈	a	11b17		11 04			12b17		12 04				13b17		13 04			14b17		14 04			15b17	
Birmingham New Street [12] 65	a			11 47		12 17			12 47	13 26		13 17			13 47		14 17			14 47	15 26	15 18		
London Euston [15] ⊖ 65	a			12 04		12 38			13 04			13 38			14 04		14 38			15 04		15 38		

		AW	AW [R] D (trolley)	AW ◇ B	VT [1] ◇ (buffet)	AW ◇ (trolley)	AW	AW	AW ◇ A (trolley)	VT [1] ◇ C (buffet)	AW ◇ (trolley)	AW	AW ◇ (trolley)	AW	NT E	VT [1] ◇ (buffet)	AW ◇ (trolley)	AW ◇ (trolley)	AW	AW	AW ◇ A (trolley)	AW ◇ B	VT [1] ◇ (buffet)	AW ◇ (trolley)
Holyhead	d		12 38						13 23				14 23			14 36					15 23			
Valley	d								13x29												15x29			
Rhosneigr	d								13x34												15x34			
Ty Croes	d								13x38												15x38			
Bodorgan	d								13x42												15x42			
Llanfairpwll	d								13x52												15x52			
Bangor (Gwynedd)	a		13 05						14 00				14 53			15 04					16 00			
	d		13 07						14 02				14 54			15 06					16 02			
Llanfairfechan	d								14x10				15x02								16x10			
Penmaenmawr	d								14x14				15x06								16x14			
Conwy	d								14x20				15x12								16x20			
Llandudno	d			13 20		13 44	14 10				14 42			15 10				15 44	16 10			16 20		16 44
Deganwy	d			13x24		13x48	14x14				14x46			15x14				15x48	16x14			16x24		16x48
Llandudno Junction	a		13 23	13 30		13 52	14 20		14 23		14 50		15 16	15 20		15 24		15 52	16 20		16 23	16 30		16 52
	d		13 25			13 53			14 25		14 51		15 17			15 25		15 53			16 25			16 53
Colwyn Bay	d		13 31			13 59			14 31		14 57		15 23			15 33		15 59			16 31			16 59
Abergele & Pensarn	d					14 06					15 04							16 06						17 06
Rhyl	d		13 41			14 12			14 41		15 10		15 34			15 46		16 12			16 41			17 12
Prestatyn	d		13 47			14 18			14 47		15 16		15 39					16 18			16 47			17 18
Flint	d		14 00			14 31			15 00		15 29		15 53					16 31			17 00			17 31
Shotton	d					14 37					15 35							16 37						17 37
Chester	a		14 15			14 49			15 17		15 46		16 07			16 17	←	16 49			17 14			17 49
	d	13 55	14 22		14 35	14 50		14 55	15 22	15 35	15 48	15 55	16 22			16 20	16 22	16 50		16 55	17 22		17 35	17 50
Liverpool Lime Street [10] 106	a		15 13			15 43			16 13		16 43		↪			17 13		17 43			18 13			18 43
Helsby	d					15 00					15 57				16 11			17 00						18 00
Frodsham	d					15 04					16 02				16 16			17 04						18 04
Runcorn East	d					15 09					16 07				16 22			17 09						18 09
Warrington Bank Quay 90	a					15 18					16 16				16 34			17 18						18 18
Earlestown [8] 90	a					15 26					16 26							17 26						18 26
Newton-le-Willows 90	a					15 29					16 29							17 29						18 29
Manchester Oxford Road 90	a					15 48					16 48							17 48						18 48
Manchester Piccadilly [10] 90	a					15 57					16 57							17 57						18 57
Crewe [10]	a	14 17			14 54			15 17		15 54		16 17				16 44				17 17			17 54	
Cardiff Central [7] 131	a		17 18		17 54			18 54		18 54						19 48	19 26						20 54	
Manchester Airport 84, 85 ✈	a	15 04				16b17		16 04			17b17	17 04						18b17		18 04				19b17
Birmingham New Street [12] 65	a	15 47			16 17			16 47	17 26	17 18		17 47				17c55				18 47	19 26		19 17	
London Euston [15] ⊖ 65	a	16 04			16 38			17 04		17 38		18 04				18 38				19 04				

For general notes see front of timetable
For details of catering facilities see Directory of Train Operators

- **A** To Birmingham International (Table 68)
- **B** To Blaenau Ffestiniog (Table 102)
- **C** Until 31 October
- **D** To Maesteg (Table 128)
- **E** From Ellesmere Port (Table 109)
- **b** Change at Manchester Oxford Road
- **c** From 7 November arr. 1750

Table 81

Saturdays

North Wales and Chester → Manchester and Crewe

Network Diagram - see first page of Table 81

		AW	AW	AW ◇	AW ◇	AW	AW	AW ◇ A	AW ◇	AW ◇ B	AW	AW	AW ◇	VT ◇	AW ◇	AW	AW	AW ◇	AW	AW	AW ◇	AW	AW
Holyhead	d			16 38				17 21					18 23					19 21			20 37		
Valley	d							17x27					18x29					19x27					
Rhosneigr	d							17x32					18x34					19x32					
Ty Croes	d							17x36					18x38					19x36					
Bodorgan	d							17x40					18x42					19x40					
Llanfairpwll	d							17x50					18x52					19x50					
Bangor (Gwynedd)	a			17 05				17 58					19 00					19 58			21 04		
	d			17 07				18 00					19 02					20 00			21 06		
Llanfairfechan	d							18x08					19x10					20x08			21x14		
Penmaenmawr	d							18x12					19x14					20x12			21x18		
Conwy	d							18x18					19x20					20x18			21x24		
Llandudno	d	17 10			17 44	18 08			18 44	19 03	19 10				19 42	20 08			20 42			21 45	
Deganwy	d	17x14			17x48	18x12			18x48	19x07	19x14				19x46	20x12			20x46			21x49	
Llandudno Junction	a	17 20		17 23	17 52	18 18		18 21	18 52	19 11	19 20		19 23		19 50	20 18		20 21	20 50		21 27	21 53	
	d			17 25	17 53			18 23	18 53				19 25		19 51			20 23	20 51		21 29	21 55	
Colwyn Bay	d			17 31	17 59			18 29	18 59				19 31		19 57			20 29	20 57		21 35	22 01	
Abergele & Pensarn	d				18 06				19 06						20 04				21 04		21 42	22 09	
Rhyl	d			17 41	18 12			18 39	19 12				19 41		20 10			20 39	21 10		21 48	22 16	
Prestatyn	d			17 47	18 18			18 45	19 18				19 47		20 16			20 45	21 16		21 53	22 22	
Flint	d			18 00	18 31			18 58	19 31				20 00		20 29			20 58	21 29		22 07	22 37	
Shotton	d				18 37				19 37						20 35				21 35		22 13	22 44	
Chester	a			18 15	18 49			19 15	19 49				20 15		20 47			21 15	21 47		22 23	22 59	
	d		17 55	18 22	18 50		18 55		19 50			19 55	20 17	20 35	20 50		20 55	21 22		21 52	22 25	23 01	23 22
Liverpool Lime Street 10	106 a			*19 13*	*19 43*			*20 13*	*20 43*				*21 13*		*21 43*			*22 13*	*22 43*		*23 13*		
Helsby	d				19 00				20 00						20 59					22 01			23 31
Frodsham	d				19 04				20 04						21 03					22 05			23 35
Runcorn East	d				19 09				20 09						21 09					22 11			23 41
Warrington Bank Quay	90 a				19 18				20 18						21 16					22 19			23 49
Earlestown 8	90 a				19 26				20 26						21 26					22 26			23 56
Newton-le-Willows	90 a				19 29				20 29						21 29					22 30			23 59
Manchester Oxford Road	90 a				19 48				20 48						21 48					22 50			
Manchester Piccadilly 10	90 a				19 57				20 57						21 57					22 58			00 26
Crewe 10	a		18 17				19 17					20 17	20 41	20 54			21 17				22 46	23 26	
Cardiff Central 7	131 a		*22 09*	21 20			*23 01*							*00 03*									
Manchester Airport	84, 85 a		*19 04*		*20b17*				*21b17*						*22b17*					*00 22*			*01 00*
Birmingham New Street 12	65 a		*19 47*				*20 47*						*21c55*	*22 19*			*22e47*	23 24					
London Euston 15	⊖ 65 a		*20 04*				*21f58*					*23g03*											

Sundays

until 6 September

		AW	AW	AW		AW	NT C	AW		AW ◇	AW	AW ◇		AW ◇ B	AW	AW		NT C	AW	VT 1 ◇		AW	AW	AW ◇
Holyhead	d									07 50		08 40												10 20
Valley	d									07x56														10x26
Rhosneigr	d									08x02														10x31
Ty Croes	d									08x05														10x35
Bodorgan	d									08x10														10x39
Llanfairpwll	d									08x19														10x49
Bangor (Gwynedd)	a									08 27		09 07												10 57
	d					07 43				08 28		09 08												10 59
Llanfairfechan	d									08x36														11x07
Penmaenmawr	d									08x40														11x11
Conwy	d									08x46														11x17
Llandudno	d													10 22					11 07					
Deganwy	d													10x26					11x11					
Llandudno Junction	a					07 59				08 50		09 24		10 30					11 17					11 20
	d					08 01				08 51		09 26												11 22
Colwyn Bay	d					08 07				08 57		09 32												11 28
Abergele & Pensarn	d					08 14						09 39												11 35
Rhyl	d					08 20				09 08		09 45												11 41
Prestatyn	d					08 25						09 50												11 46
Flint	d					08 39						10 04												12 00
Shotton	d					08 45				09 28		10 10												12 06
Chester	a					08 56				09 39		10 21												12 18
	d	07 57	08 27	08 41		08 57	08 59	09 27		09 42	09 57	10 27			10 36	10 57		11 08		11 28		11 36	11 57	12 22
Liverpool Lime Street 10	106 a					*10 13*				*10 43*		*11 13*												*13 13*
Helsby	d			08 50						09 51					10 45							11 45		
Frodsham	d			08 54						09 55					10 49							11 49		
Runcorn East	d			08 59						10 00					10 54							11 54		
Warrington Bank Quay	90 a			09 08						10 07					11 03							12 03		
Earlestown 8	90 a			09 17						10 19					11 10							12 10		
Newton-le-Willows	90 a			09 20						10 22					11 13							12 13		
Manchester Oxford Road	90 a			09 39			10 28			10 41					11 32			12 37				12 32		
Manchester Piccadilly 10	90 a			09 48			10 23			10 50					11 41			12 33				12 41		
Crewe 10	a	08 22	08 52			09 22		09 52			10 22	10 52				11 22				11 47			12 22	
Cardiff Central 7	131 a							*13 07*				*13 50*								*14 41*				15 30
Manchester Airport	84, 85 a			*10 13*			*10 55*			*11b17*					*12b02*			*13b17*				*13 17*		
Birmingham New Street 12	65 a		*09 58*					*11h18*			*11j55*	*12k05*								*12 55*				
London Euston 15	⊖ 65 a		*11 44*			*12 04*		*12 38*			*12 51*	*13 15*								13 44				

For general notes see front of timetable
For details of catering facilities see Directory of Train Operators

A To Shrewsbury (Table 75)

B To Blaenau Ffestiniog (Table 102)
C To Southport (Table 82)
b Change at Manchester Oxford Road
c From 7 November arr. 2156
e From 7 November arr. 2300
f From 12 September arr. 2119

g Until 31 October only. From 12 September arr. 2243
h From 19 July arr. 1117
j Until 12 July arr. 1157, change at Crewe and Stafford
k Until 12 July only

Table 81

Sundays
until 6 September

North Wales and Chester → Manchester and Crewe

Network Diagram - see first page of Table 81

	AW	VT		AW	AW	AW		AW	NT	VT		AW	AW	AW		VT	AW	AW		AW	AW	NT	AW
		1 ◊							A	1 ◊						1 ◊	◊ B					A	
Holyhead d		10 55								11 48						12 47							
Valley d																							
Rhosneigr d																							
Ty Croes d																							
Bodorgan d																							
Llanfairpwll d																							
Bangor (Gwynedd) a		11 21								12 14						13 13							
d		11 22								12 15						13 14							
Llanfairfechan d																							
Penmaenmawr d																							
Conwy d																							
Llandudno d				11 40				12 18				13 19					13 30			13 50			14 20
Deganwy d				11x44				12x22				13x23					13x34			13x54			14x24
Llandudno Junction a		11 39		11 50				12 28		12 32		13 29				13 31	13 38			14 00			14 30
d		11 40								12 33						13 32							
Colwyn Bay d		11 47								12 40						13 39							
Abergele & Pensarn d																							
Rhyl d		11 58								12 51						13 50							
Prestatyn d		12 03								12 57						13 56							
Flint d		12 17														14 09							
Shotton d																							
Chester a		12 30								13 21						14 23							
d	12 24	12 33			12 36	12 57			13 08	13 28			13 36	13 57		14 33		14 36			14 57	15 08	
Liverpool Lime Street 10 106 a		13 43								14 13						15 13							
Helsby d					12 45								13 45					14 45					
Frodsham d					12 49								13 49					14 49					
Runcorn East d					12 54								13 54					14 54					
Warrington Bank Quay 90 a					13 03								14 03					15 03					
Earlestown 8 90 a					13 10								14 10					15 10					
Newton-le-Willows 90 a					13 13								14 13					15 13					
Manchester Oxford Road 90 a					13 32				14 37				14 32					15 32				16 37	
Manchester Piccadilly 10 90 a					13 41				14 33				14 41					15 41				16 33	
Crewe 10 a	12 45	12 52				13 18				13 47				14 18		14 52					15 18		
Cardiff Central 7 131 a		16 00								16 51						17 43							
Manchester Airport 84, 85 a					14 17				15b17				15 17					16 17				17b17	
Birmingham New Street 12 65 a	13 55	14 15								14 55				15 55		16 15					16 55		
London Euston 15 ⊖ 65 a		14 43				15 12				15 45				16 11		16 44					17 11		

	VT		AW	AW	AW		AW	AW	AW		AW	NT	VT		AW	AW	AW		AW	VT	AW		AW
	1 ◊							◊				A	1 ◊			◊			R	1 ◊			
Holyhead d	13 55							14 30								15 40			16 25				
Valley d								14x36											16x31				
Rhosneigr d								14x42											16x36				
Ty Croes d								14x45											16x40				
Bodorgan d								14x50											16x44				
Llanfairpwll d								14x59											16x54				
Bangor (Gwynedd) a	14 21							15 07								16 06			17 02				
d	14 22							15 08								16 08			17 04				
Llanfairfechan d																16x16							
Penmaenmawr d																16x20							
Conwy d																16x26							
Llandudno d			15 11						15 45						16 16								
Deganwy d			15x15						15x49						16x20								
Llandudno Junction a	14 39		15 21					15 25	15 55						16 26	16 29			17 20				
d	14 40							15 26								16 35			17 25				
Colwyn Bay d	14 46							15 32								16 41			17 31				
Abergele & Pensarn d								15 39								16 48			17 38				
Rhyl d	14 57							15 45								16 54			17 44				
Prestatyn d	15 03							15 51								16 59			17 49				
Flint d								16 04								17 13			18 03				
Shotton d								16 10								17 19			18 11				
Chester a	15 31							16 21								17 32			18 20				
d	15 33			15 36	15 57		16 27	16 36			16 57	17 08	17 35			17 36	17 57		18 24	18 35	18 36		18 57
Liverpool Lime Street 10 106 a	16 43							17 13								18 43			19 13				
Helsby d				15 45				16 45								17 45					18 45		
Frodsham d				15 49				16 49								17 49					18 49		
Runcorn East d				15 54				16 54								17 54					18 54		
Warrington Bank Quay 90 a				16 03				17 03								18 03					19 03		
Earlestown 8 90 a				16 10				17 10								18 10					19 10		
Newton-le-Willows 90 a				16 13				17 13								18 13					19 13		
Manchester Oxford Road 90 a				16 32				17 32				18 37				18 32					19 32		
Manchester Piccadilly 10 90 a				16 41				17 41				18 33				18 41					19 41		
Crewe 10 a	15 52				16 18		16 48				17 18		17 53				18 18			18 53			19 18
Cardiff Central 7 131 a	18 51						20 00						20 44						21 30	22 00			
Manchester Airport 84, 85 a				17 17				18 17								19 17					20 17		
Birmingham New Street 12 65 a	17 15						17 55				18 55		19 15				19 55			20 15			
London Euston 15 ⊖ 65 a	17 44				18 11						19 11		19 44				20 11			20 44			21 14

For general notes see front of timetable
For details of catering facilities see Directory of Train Operators

A To Southport (Table 82)
B To Blaenau Ffestiniog (Table 102)
b Change at Manchester Oxford Road

Table 81

Sundays
until 6 September

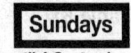

North Wales and Chester → Manchester and Crewe

Network Diagram - see first page of Table 81

		NT	AW	AW	AW	AW	AW	AW	AW	NT	AW	AW	AW	AW	AW	AW	AW	AW
			◇				◇				◇					◇		◇
		A	🚲				B			C	D							
Holyhead	d		17 30				18 25				19 15					20 35		21 40
Valley	d						18x31				19x21					20x41		
Rhosneigr	d						18x36				19x26					20x46		
Ty Croes	d						18x40				19x30					20x50		
Bodorgan	d						18x44				19x34					20x54		
Llanfairpwll	d						18x54				19x44					21x04		
Bangor (Gwynedd)	a		17 57				19 02				19 52					21 12		22 09
	d		17 59				19 04				19 54					21 14		22 11
Llanfairfechan	d		18x07								20x02					21x22		
Penmaenmawr	d		18x11								20x06					21x26		
Conwy	d		18x17								20x12					21x32		
Llandudno	d			18 55														
Deganwy	d			18x59														
Llandudno Junction	a		18 20	19 05			19 20				20 15					21 35		22 27
	d		18 24				19 24				20 17					21 37		22 29
Colwyn Bay	d		18 30				19 30				20 23					21 43		22 35
Abergele & Pensarn	d		18 37				19 37				20 30					21 50		
Rhyl	d		18 43				19 43				20 36					21 56		22 45
Prestatyn	d		18 48				19 48				20 41					22 01		22 51
Flint	d		19 02				20 02				20 55					22 15		23 04
Shotton	d		19 08				20 10				21 01					22 21		
Chester	a		19 19				20 19				21 13					22 32		23 18
	d	19 08	19 22		19 36	19 57	20 27	20 36	20 57	21 08		21 27	21 36	21 57	22 09	22 35	22 57	
Liverpool Lime Street 10	106 a		*20 13*				*21 13*				*22 13*					*23 43*		
Helsby	d				19 45			20 45					21 45		22 18			
Frodsham	d				19 49			20 49					21 49		22 22			
Runcorn East	d				19 54			20 54					21 54		22 27			
Warrington Bank Quay	90 a				20 03			21 03					22 03		22 36			
Earlestown 8	90 a				20 10			21 10					22 10		22 44			
Newton-le-Willows	90 a				20 13			21 13					22 13		22 47			
Manchester Oxford Road	90 a	20 37			20 32			21 32		22 37			22 32		23 06			
Manchester Piccadilly 10	90 ⛴ a	20 33			20 41			21 41		22 33			22 41		23 15			
Crewe 10	a		19 44			20 18	20 48		21 18			21 48		22 18		22 59	23 18	
Cardiff Central 7	131 a		*22 52*				*00 14*											
Manchester Airport	84, 85 ✈ a	*21b17*			*21 17*			*22 17*		*23 08*			*23 20*		*23b30*			
Birmingham New Street 12	65 a		*20 57*			*21 52*	*21 52*		*22 40*			*22 55*						
London Euston 15	⊖ 65 a		*22 29*			*22 53*	*23c54*											

Sundays
from 13 September

		AW	AW	NT	AW	AW	AW	AW	AW	NT	VT	AW	AW	AW	VT	AW	NT	AW	VT
							◇				1 ◇		◇		1 ◇				1 ◇
				A				E		A							A		G
								🚌	🚲		🍴	🚲			🍴	🚲			🍴
Holyhead	d						08 50						10 20		10 55				11 48
Valley	d												10x26						
Rhosneigr	d												10x31						
Ty Croes	d												10x35						
Bodorgan	d												10x39						
Llanfairpwll	d												10x49						
Bangor (Gwynedd)	a						09 17						10 57		11 21				12 14
	d						09 18						10 59		11 22				12 15
Llanfairfechan	d												11x07						
Penmaenmawr	d												11x11						
Conwy	d												11x17						
Llandudno	d							10 15											
Deganwy	d							10 30											
Llandudno Junction	a						09 34	10 35					11 20		11 39				12 32
	d						09 36						11 22		11 40				12 33
Colwyn Bay	d						09 42						11 28		11 47				12 40
Abergele & Pensarn	d						09 49						11 35						
Rhyl	d						09 55						11 41		11 58				12 51
Prestatyn	d						10 00						11 46		12 03				12 57
Flint	d						10 14						12 00		12 17				
Shotton	d						10 20						12 06						
Chester	a						10 31						12 18		12 30				13 21
	d	08 40	08 41	09 06	09 40	09 42	10 35		10 36	11 03	11 28	11 36	12 22	12 24	12 33	12 36	13 08	13 18	13 28
Liverpool Lime Street 10	106 a						*11 43*						*13 13*		*13 43*				*14 13*
Helsby	d		08 50			09 51			10 45			11 45				12 45			
Frodsham	d		08 54			09 55			10 49			11 49				12 49			
Runcorn East	d		08 59			10 00			10 54			11 54				12 54			
Warrington Bank Quay	90 a		09 08			10 07			11 03			12 03				13 03			
Earlestown 8	90 a		09 17			10 19			11 10			12 10				13 10			
Newton-le-Willows	90 a		09 20			10 22			11 13			12 13				13 13			
Manchester Oxford Road	90 a		09 39	10 37		10 41			11 32	12 32		12 32				13 32	14 37		
Manchester Piccadilly 10	90 ⛴ a		09 49	10 33		10 50			11 41	12 28		12 41				13 41	14 33		
Crewe 10	a	09 01			10 01		10 57				11 47			12 45	12 52			13 39	13 47
Cardiff Central 7	131 a				*13 07*		*13 57*				*14 41*		15 30		*16 00*			*16 51*	*16 51*
Manchester Airport	84, 85 ✈ a		*10b13*	*11 06*		*11b17*			*12b04*	*13 02*		*13 17*				*14 17*	*15b17*		
Birmingham New Street 12	65 a	*10e58*			*11 18*						*12 55*			*13f55*	*14 15*			*14 55*	*14 55*
London Euston 15	⊖ 65 a	*11 44*			*12 38*		*13 15*				13 44			*15 12*	14 43			*15g45*	15 45

For general notes see front of timetable
For details of catering facilities see Directory of Train Operators

- **A** To Southport (Table 82)
- **B** To Birmingham International (Table 65)
- **C** To Wigan Wallgate (Table 82)
- **D** To Wolverhampton (Table 74)
- **E** To Blaenau Ffestiniog (Table 102)
- **G** Until 1 November
- **b** Change at Manchester Oxford Road
- **c** Change at Stafford
- **e** Change at Crewe and Stafford
- **f** From 8 November arr. 1415
- **g** From 8 November arr. 1543

Table 81

Sundays
from 13 September

North Wales and Chester → Manchester and Crewe

Network Diagram - see first page of Table 81

		AW	AW		AW	VT	AW		NT	VT	AW		AW	AW	AW		NT	AW	VT		AW	AW	VT	AW
		A 🚌	trolley			1 ◇ restaurant	trolley		B	1 ◇ restaurant	trolley			◇ trolley	A 🚌		B	◇ trolley	1 ◇ restaurant			R trolley	1 ◇ restaurant	
Holyhead	d					12 47				13 55				14 30				15 30				16 25		
Valley	d													14x36								16x31		
Rhosneigr	d													14x42								16x36		
Ty Croes	d													14x45								16x40		
Bodorgan	d													14x50								16x44		
Llanfairpwll	d													14x59								16x54		
Bangor (Gwynedd)	a					13 13				14 21				15 07				15 57				17 02		
	d					13 14				14 22				15 08				15 59				17 04		
Llanfairfechan	d																	16x07						
Penmaenmawr	d																	16x11						
Conwy	d																	16x17						
Llandudno	d	13 15													16 00									
Deganwy	d	13 20													16 15									
Llandudno Junction	a	13 25				13 31				14 39				15 25	16 20			16 20				17 20		
	d					13 32				14 40				15 26				16 25				17 25		
Colwyn Bay	d					13 39				14 46				15 32				16 31				17 31		
Abergele & Pensarn	d													15 39				16 38				17 38		
Rhyl	d					13 50				14 57				15 45				16 44				17 44		
Prestatyn	d					13 56				15 03				15 51				16 49				17 49		
Flint	d					14 09								16 04				17 03				18 03		
Shotton	d													16 10				17 09				18 11		
Chester	a					14 23				15 31				16 21				17 20				18 20		
	d		13 36		14 20	14 33	14 36		15 08	15 33	15 36		16 27	16 36			17 08	17 22	17 35		17 36	18 24	18 35	18 36
Liverpool Lime Street 10	106 a					15 13				16 43				17 13				18 13				19 13		
Helsby	d		13 45				14 45				15 45			16 45							17 45			18 45
Frodsham	d		13 49				14 49				15 49			16 49							17 49			18 49
Runcorn East	d		13 54				14 54				15 54			16 54							17 54			18 54
Warrington Bank Quay	90 a		14 03				15 03				16 03			17 03							18 03			19 03
Earlestown 8	90 a		14 10				15 10				16 10			17 10							18 10			19 10
Newton-le-Willows	90 a		14 13				15 13				16 13			17 13							18 13			19 13
Manchester Oxford Road	90 a		14 32				15 32		16 37		16 32			17 32			18 37				18 32			19 32
Manchester Piccadilly 10	90 ⛴ a		14 41				15 41		16 33		16 41			17 41			18 33				18 41			19 41
Crewe 10	a				14 41	14 52				15 52			16 48					17 43	17 53				18 53	
Cardiff Central 7	131 a					17 43				18 51			20 00						20 44			21 30		
Manchester Airport	84, 85 ✈ a		15 17				16 17				17 17			18 17							19 17		21 59	20 17
Birmingham New Street 12	65 a				15 55	16 15				17 15			17 55					18 55	19 15				20 15	
London Euston 15	⊖ 65 a					16 44				17 44			19 11						19 44				20 44	

		AW		NT	AW	AW		AW	AW	AW		AW	NT	AW		AW	AW	AW		AW	AW	AW		
				B	◇ trolley				◇ C				D	◇						◇		◇		
Holyhead	d				17 30				18 25					19 40						20 35		21 40		
Valley	d								18x31											20x41				
Rhosneigr	d								18x36											20x46				
Ty Croes	d								18x40											20x50				
Bodorgan	d								18x44											20x54				
Llanfairpwll	d								18x54											21x04				
Bangor (Gwynedd)	a				17 57				19 02					20 07						21 12		22 09		
	d				17 59				19 04					20 09						21 14		22 11		
Llanfairfechan	d				18x07									20x17						21x22				
Penmaenmawr	d				18x11									20x21						21x26				
Conwy	d				18x17									20x27						21x32				
Llandudno	d																							
Deganwy	d																							
Llandudno Junction	a				18 20				19 20					20 30						21 35		22 27		
	d				18 24				19 24					20 37						21 37		22 29		
Colwyn Bay	d				18 30				19 30					20 43						21 43		22 35		
Abergele & Pensarn	d				18 37				19 37					20 50						21 50				
Rhyl	d				18 43				19 43					20 56						21 56		22 45		
Prestatyn	d				18 48				19 48					21 01						22 01		22 51		
Flint	d				19 02				20 02					21 15						22 15		23 04		
Shotton	d				19 08				20 10					21 21						22 21				
Chester	a				19 19				20 19					21 32						22 32		23 18		
	d	18 57		19 08	19 22	19 36		19 50	20 27	20 36		20 50	21 08	21 35		21 36	21 50	22 09		22 35	23 00			
Liverpool Lime Street 10	106 a				20 13				21 13					22 43						23 43				
Helsby	d					19 45				20 45						21 45		22 18						
Frodsham	d					19 49				20 49						21 49		22 22						
Runcorn East	d					19 54				20 54						21 54		22 27						
Warrington Bank Quay	90 a					20 03				21 03						22 03		22 36						
Earlestown 8	90 a					20 10				21 10						22 10		22 44						
Newton-le-Willows	90 a					20 13				21 13						22 13		22 47						
Manchester Oxford Road	90 a			20 37		20 32				21 32			22 37			22 32		23 06						
Manchester Piccadilly 10	90 ⛴ a			20 33		20 41				21 41			22 33			22 41		23 15						
Crewe 10	a	19 18			19 44			20 11	20 48			21 11		21 59			22 11			22 59	23 21			
Cardiff Central 7	131 a				22 52				00 14															
Manchester Airport	84, 85 ✈ a					21 17				22 17			23 08			23 20		23b30						
Birmingham New Street 12	65 a				20 57			21c39	21 52			22 40					23 17							
London Euston 15	⊖ 65 a	21 14						22 29				23 59												

For general notes see front of timetable
For details of catering facilities see Directory of Train Operators

A To Blaenau Ffestiniog (Table 102)
B To Southport (Table 82)
C To Birmingham International (Table 65)
D To Wigan Wallgate (Table 82)

b Change at Manchester Oxford Road
c Change at Crewe and Stafford

Holyhead — Dublin

		AW R A	AW R B	AW R A	AW R B	AW R C
Holyhead	d	02 40	10 25	14 10	15 00	17 15
Dun Laoghaire	a		12 24		16 59	
Dublin Ferryport §	a	05 55		17 25		19 15

Daily

		AW R A	AW R B	AW R C	AW R B	AW R A
Dublin Ferryport §	d	08 05		14 30		20 55
Dun Laoghaire	d		13 30		17 45	
Holyhead	a	11 30	15 29	16 30	19 44	00 20

For general notes see front of timetable
For details of catering facilities see Directory of Train Operators

§ Bus connections to/from city centre and railway stations

A Irish Ferries Cruise Ferry
B Stena Line High-Speed Sea Service
C Irish Ferries Fast Ferry

Network Diagram for Tables 82, 83

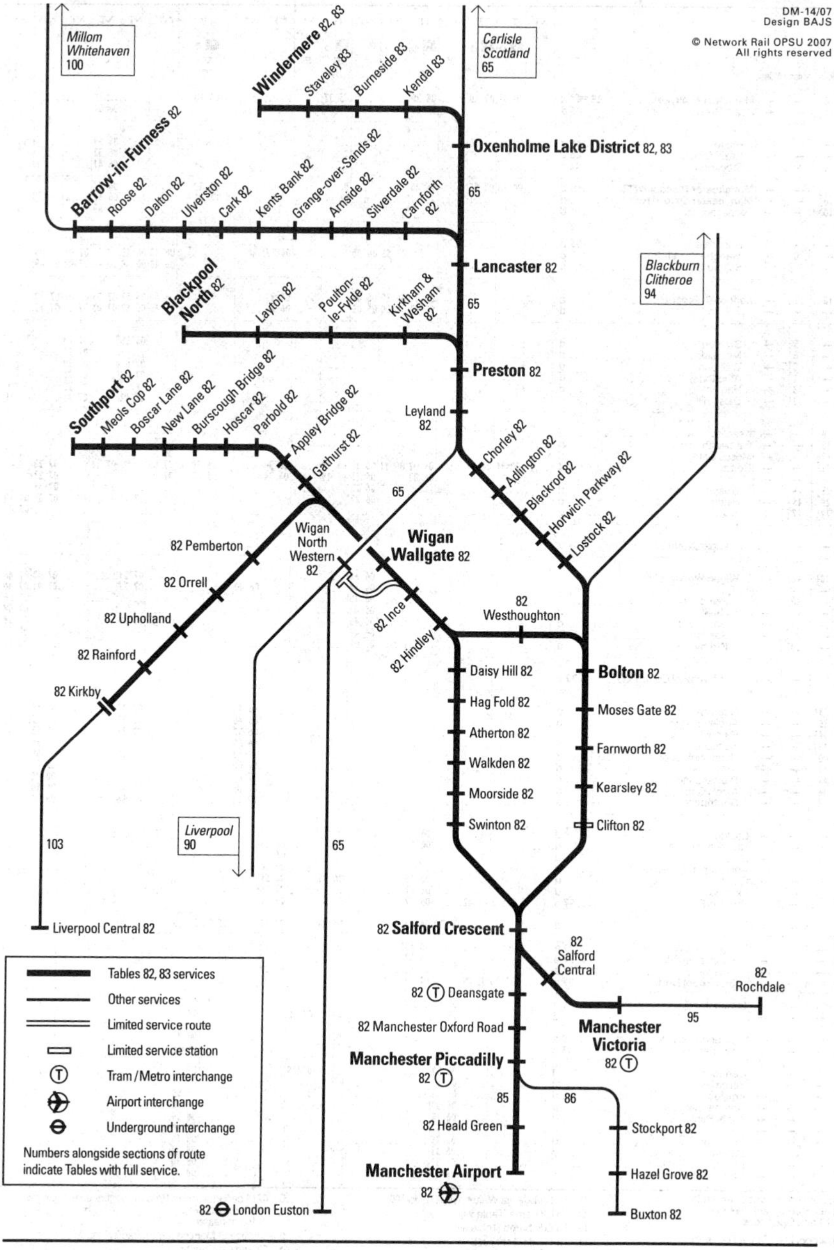

DM-14/07
Design BAJS
© Network Rail OPSU 2007
All rights reserved
Millom
Whitehaven
100
Carlisle
Scotland
65
Windermere 82, 83
Staveley 83
Burneside 83
Kendal 83
Oxenholme Lake District 82, 83
Barrow-in-Furness 82
Roose 82
Dalton 82
Ulverston 82
Cark 82
Kents Bank 82
Grange-over-Sands 82
Arnside 82
Silverdale 82
Carnforth 82
65
Lancaster 82
Blackburn
Clitheroe
94
Blackpool North 82
Layton 82
Poulton-le-Fylde 82
Kirkham & Wesham 82
65
Preston 82
Southport 82
Meols Cop 82
Boscar Lane 82
New Lane 82
Burscough Bridge 82
Hoscar 82
Parbold 82
Appley Bridge 82
Gathurst 82
Leyland 82
Chorley 82
Adlington 82
Blackrod 82
Horwich Parkway 82
Lostock 82
65
Wigan North Western 82
Wigan Wallgate 82
82 Pemberton
82 Orrell
82 Upholland
82 Rainford
82 Kirkby
82 Ince
82 Hindley
82 Westhoughton
Daisy Hill 82
Hag Fold 82
Atherton 82
Walkden 82
Moorside 82
Swinton 82
Bolton 82
Moses Gate 82
Farnworth 82
Kearsley 82
Clifton 82
103
Liverpool
90
65
Liverpool Central 82
82 Salford Crescent
82 Salford Central
82 Rochdale
82 Deansgate
95
82 Manchester Oxford Road
Manchester Victoria 82
Manchester Piccadilly 82
85
86
82 Heald Green
Stockport 82
Hazel Grove 82
Manchester Airport 82
Buxton 82
82 London Euston
Tables 82, 83 services
Other services
Limited service route
Limited service station
Tram / Metro interchange
Airport interchange
Underground interchange
Numbers alongside sections of route indicate Tables with full service.

Manchester → Bolton → Wigan, Kirkby, Southport, Preston, Blackpool North and Barrow-in-Furness

Network Diagram - see first page of Table 82

Miles	Miles	Miles	Miles	Miles			NT MX A	TP [1] ◇	TP [1] ◇	NT B	TP [1] ◇ 🍴	NT C	NT	TP [1] ◇ D 🍴	NT E	NT	NT	TP [1] ◇ G 🍴		NT	NT	NT C	NT	NT	NT
0	0	0	—	—	**Manchester Airport**	85 ✈ d		00 01	03 40		05 29			*05 37*				06 18				*06b23*			
1½	1½	1½	—	—	Heald Green	85 d					05 33											*06b04*			
—	—	—	—	—	Buxton	86 d																05 59			
—	—	—	—	—	Hazel Grove	86 d																06 33			
—	—	—	—	—	Stockport	84 d												*05 53*				06 41			
9¾	9¾	9¾	—	—	**Manchester Piccadilly** [10]	🚊 d		00 16	03 55		05 46			06 03				06 33				06 54			
10¼	10¼	10¼	—	—	**Manchester Oxford Road**	d								06 06				06 36				06 57			
10½	10½	10½	—	—	Deansgate	🚊 d																06 59			
—	—	—	—	—	Rochdale	95 d																	*06 24*		
—	—	—	0	—	**Manchester Victoria**	🚊 d						05 55	06 00			06 17				06 38	06 45		07 01	07 06	
—	—	—	¾	—	Salford Central	d														06 40	06 48		07 04	07 09	
12	12	12	1¾	—	**Salford Crescent**	a					05 51	05 59	06 04			06 23				06 44	06 51	07 03	07 07	07 12	
—	—	—	—	—		d					05 52	06 00	06 05			06 24				06 45	06 52	07 03	07 08	07 13	
—	—	—	5¾	—	Swinton	d															06 58		07 14		
—	—	—	6½	—	Moorside	d																	07 17		
—	—	—	8¼	—	Walkden	d															07 03		07 20		
—	—	—	11¾	—	Atherton	d															07 08		07 26		
—	—	—	13	—	Hag Fold	d																	07 28		←
—	—	—	13¼	—	Daisy Hill	d															07 12		07 31		07 31
18	18	18	—	—	Kearsley	d														06 52			→		
18¾	18	18¾	—	—	Farnworth	d														06 54					
19¾	19¾	19¾	—	—	Moses Gate	d														06 57					
21	21	21	—	—	**Bolton**	a		00s31	04s09		06 02	06 11	06 15	06 19		06 34		06 50		07 00		07 16		07 23	
—	—	—	—	—		d					06 02		06 15	06 19		06 34		06 50		07 01				07 23	
—	—	25½	—	—	Westhoughton	d							06 23											07 31	
—	—	28	15¾	—	Hindley	d							06 27								07 16			07 35	07 39
—	—	29½	17¼	0	Ince	d																			07 42
—	—	—	—	¾	Wigan North Western	a														07 19					
—	—	30½	18¼	—	**Wigan Wallgate**	a							06 32								07 21			07 40	07 45
—	—	—	—	—		d							06 34				06 40				07 23			07 41	07 46
—	—	—	20	—	Pemberton	d							06 38												07 50
—	—	—	22	—	Orrell	d							06 42												07 54
—	—	—	23¼	—	Upholland	d							06 45												07 58
—	—	—	25¼	—	Rainford	d							06 49												08 01
—	—	—	30½	—	**Kirkby**	a							07 01												08 13
—	—	—	—	—	Liverpool Central [10]	103 a							*07 31*												*08 46*
—	—	33¼	—	—	Gathurst	d											06 44				07 27			07 46	
—	—	35	—	—	Appley Bridge	d											06 48				07 31			07 49	
—	—	37¼	—	—	Parbold	d											06 52				07 35			07 53	
—	—	38¾	—	—	Hoscar	d											06 55							07 56	
—	—	40¼	—	—	Burscough Bridge	d											06 58				07 39			07 59	
—	—	41½	—	—	New Lane	d											07 00							08 02	
—	—	43½	—	—	Bescar Lane	d											07 04							08 05	
—	—	46¾	—	—	Meols Cop	d											07 09				07 47			08 10	
—	—	48	—	—	**Southport**	a											07 18				07 56			08 20	
24	24	—	—	—	Lostock	d					06 07					06 39									
26	26	—	—	—	Horwich Parkway	d					06 11					06 43									
27½	27½	—	—	—	Blackrod	d										06 46									
29½	29½	—	—	—	Adlington (Lancashire)	d										06 50									
33½	33½	—	—	—	Chorley	d					06 18			06 31		06 55									
37	37	—	—	—	Leyland	d	00 04				06 27					07 06									
41	41	—	—	—	**Preston** [8]	65, 97 a	00 13	01s03	04s42		06 32			06 42		07 11		07 11							
—	—	—	—	—		d				05 22	06 34			06 44		07 13		07 16	07 20						
48¾	—	—	—	—	Kirkham & Wesham	97 a					06 43			*07 11*		07 22									
55¼	—	—	—	—	Poulton-le-Fylde	97 a					06 53					07 30		*07 54*							
57¼	—	—	—	—	Layton	97 a					06 56					07 34									
58½	—	—	—	—	**Blackpool North**	97 a		01 30	05 09		07 03					07 41		*08 05*							
—	62	—	—	—	**Lancaster** [6]	65 a				05 42	*06c54*			06 59				07 31	07 36						
—	—	—	—	—		d				05 42				07 01	07 10				07 36						
—	81	—	—	—	Oxenholme Lake District	65 a					*07c08*			07 15					*08 22*						
—	91	—	—	—	Windermere	83 a								*07 40*					*08e46*						
—	68	—	—	—	Carnforth	d				05 52					07a19				07 45						
—	71¾	—	—	—	Silverdale	d				05 58									07 51						
—	74	—	—	—	Arnside	d				06 03									07 55						
—	77¼	—	—	—	Grange-over-Sands	d				06 09									08 00						
—	79½	—	—	—	Kents Bank	d				06 12									08 04						
—	81½	—	—	—	Cark	d				06 17									08 08						
—	87½	—	—	—	Ulverston	d				06 25									08 16						
—	90¾	—	—	—	Dalton	d				06 33									08 24						
—	95	—	—	—	Roose	d				06 39									08 30						
—	96¾	—	—	—	**Barrow-in-Furness**	a				06 47									08 39						

For general notes see front of timetable
For details of catering facilities see Directory of Train Operators

A From Liverpool Lime Street (Table 90)
B To Carlisle via Whitehaven (Table 100)
C To Clitheroe (Table 94)
D To Edinburgh (Table 65)
E To Leeds (Table 36)
G 0716 departure from Preston continues to Glasgow Central (Table 65). 🍴 to Lancaster
b Change at Manchester Piccadilly
c Change at Preston
e Change at Lancaster and Oxenholme Lake District

From 5 October a revised Northern service will be in operation due to seasonal difficulties. Customers should check with NRES for precise times

Manchester → Bolton → Wigan, Kirkby, Southport, Preston, Blackpool North and Barrow-in-Furness

Network Diagram - see first page of Table 82

		NT	TP	NT	NT	NT	NT	TP	NT	NT		NT	NT	NT	NT	NT	TP	NT	NT	NT	NT	NT	NT	NT	TP
			1 ◇					1 ◇									1 ◇								1 ◇
		A			B			C	D	E			G		A						B	H			J
			🛒					🛒									🛒								🛒
Manchester Airport	85 ✈ d		07 00					07 28									08 00			08 03					08 25
Heald Green	85 d						*06b49*	07 32												*07 49*					08 29
Buxton	86 d						06 23					06 50													*07 24*
Hazel Grove	86 d						07 00					07 27								*07 48*					*08 17*
Stockport	84 d		*06 53*				07 10	*07 22*				07 37					*07 53*			*07 57*					*08 24*
Manchester Piccadilly 10	🚇 d		07 15				07 27	07 45				07 54					08 15			08 22					08 46
Manchester Oxford Road	d		07 18				07 30					07 57					08 19			08 26					08 49
Deansgate	🚇 d						07 32					07 59								08 28					08 51
Rochdale	95 d								*07 16*				*07 30*					*07 52*			*08 00*	08 00		*08 14*	
Manchester Victoria	🚇 d			07 16	07 23	07 27			07 47				08 00	08 03		08 11		08 22			08 29	08 33		08 46	
Salford Central	d			07 19	07 26	07 30			07 50				08 03	08 08		08 13		08 25			08 32	08 36		08 49	
Salford Crescent	a			07 24	07 29	07 33	07 37		07 53			08 04	08 07	08 12		08 17		08 29		08 33	08 37	08 39		08 52	08 56
	d			07 25	07 30	07 33	07 37		07 53			08 04	08 08	08 13		08 17		08 30		08 34	08 37	08 40		08 53	08 56
Swinton	d								08 00					08 19										08 59	
Moorside	d								08 02					08 22											
Walkden	d					07 42			08 06					08 25										09 04	
Atherton	d					07 48			08 11					08 31										09 09	
Hag Fold	d								08 14					08 33					←						
Daisy Hill	d					07 51			08 17					08 36					08 36					09 13	
Kearsley	d						07 45							→								08 47			
Farnworth	d						07 47															08 49			
Moses Gate	d						07 49															08 52			
Bolton	a		07 31	07 35	07 41		07 53	07 59				08 14	08 19			08 27	08 32	08 40		08 44	08 49	08 55			09 06
	d		07 31	07 35			07 53	07 59				08 15				08 28	08 32	08 40		08 45		08 56			09 07
Westhoughton	d						08 01									08 35				08 53					
Hindley	d								08 21							08 39			08 43					09 17	
Ince	d															08 42			08 46						
Wigan North Western	a						08 16																		
Wigan Wallgate	a					08 03			08 26							08 45			08 49			09 14		09 22	
	d								08 28							08 47			08 51					09 24	
Pemberton	d																		08 55						
Orrell	d																		08 59						
Upholland	d																		09 02						
Rainford	d																		09 06						
Kirkby	a																		09 18						
Liverpool Central 10	103 a																		*09 46*						
Gathurst	d															08 51								09 28	
Appley Bridge	d															08 55				09 11				09 32	
Parbold	d															08 59				09 15				09 36	
Hoscar	d																								
Burscough Bridge	d															09 03				09 20				09 40	
New Lane	d																								
Bescar Lane	d																								
Meols Cop	d															09 11								09 48	
Southport	a								08 54							09 20				09 36				09 57	
Lostock	d			07 42								08 20						08 45							
Horwich Parkway	d		07 38	07 46								08 24					08 39	08 49							09 13
Blackrod	d			07 49														08 52							
Adlington (Lancashire)	d			07 53														08 56							
Chorley	d		07 46	07 58				08 11				08 32					08 47	09 01							09 21
Leyland	d	07 46		08 08								08 43			08 46			09 12							
Preston 8	65, 97 a	07 56	07 57	08 14				08 22				08 49			08 55		08 58	09 17							09 33
	d		07 59	08 15				08 24		08 38		08 51					08 59	09 19							09 45
Kirkham & Wesham	97 a		08 08	08 25								*09 11*						09 28							
Poulton-le-Fylde	97 a		08 18	08 33				*08 56*									09 16	09 36							
Layton	97 a		08 22	08 37														09 43							
Blackpool North	97 a		08 29	08 44				*09 05*				09 16					09 25	09 51							
Lancaster 6	65 a		*08c29*					08 39		08 58								*09c54*							10 00
	d							08 40		08 58													09 39		10 01
Oxenholme Lake District	65 a		*08c43*					08 54																	10 17
Windermere	83 a							*09 33*																	10 39
Carnforth	d									09 08													09 49		
Silverdale	d									09 14													09 56		
Arnside	d									09 19													10 00		
Grange-over-Sands	d									09 25													10 06		
Kents Bank	d									09 28													10 10		
Cark	d									09 33													10 14		
Ulverston	d									09 41													10 23		
Dalton	d									09 49													10 32		
Roose	d									09 55													10 38		
Barrow-in-Furness	a									10 03													10 47		

For general notes see front of timetable
For details of catering facilities see Directory of Train Operators

A From Liverpool Lime Street (Table 90)
B To Blackburn (Table 94)
C To Edinburgh (Table 65)
D From Huddersfield (Table 39)
E To Carlisle via Whitehaven (Table 100)
G To Clitheroe (Table 94)
H From Todmorden (Table 41)
J 🛒 to Preston
b Change at Manchester Piccadilly
c Change at Preston

From 5 October a revised Northern service will be in operation due to seasonal difficulties. Customers should check with NRES for precise times

Manchester → Bolton → Wigan, Kirkby, Southport, Preston, Blackpool North and Barrow-in-Furness

Network Diagram - see first page of Table 82

Station		NT	NT A	NT	NT B	NT	TP 1 ◇ C ⊼		NT	NT	NT	NT	TP 1 ◇ ⊼	NT	NT A		NT	NT D	NT B	NT	TP 1 ◇ E ⊼	NT	NT	NT	NT
Manchester Airport	85 ✈ d						09 00			09 03			09 29								10 00		10 03		
Heald Green	85 d									*08 49*			09 33										*09 49*		
Buxton	86 d	*07b48*											*08 27*												
Hazel Grove	86 d	08 32											*09 04*	09 33											
Stockport	84 d	08 41					*08 53*			*08 56*			*09 25*	09 41							*09 53*		*09 56*		
Manchester Piccadilly [10]	🚊 d	08 54					09 16			09 22			09 46	09 54							10 16		10 22		
Manchester Oxford Road	d	08 58					09 19			09 26			09 49	09 58							10 19		10 26		
Deansgate	🚊 d	09 00								09 28			09 51	10 00									10 28		
Rochdale	95 d		*08 30*						*08 51*		09 00	*09 14*			*09 30*							*09 51*		10 00	
Manchester Victoria	🚊 d		09 00	09 07		09 10			09 22		09 33	09 46			10 00		10 07			10 10		10 22		10 33	
Salford Central	d		09 03	09 10		09 13			09 25		09 35	09 49			10 03		10 10			10 13		10 25		10 36	
Salford Crescent	a	09 04	09 07	09 13		09 16			09 29	09 33	09 39	09 52	09 56	10 04	10 07		10 13			10 16		10 29	10 33	10 39	
	d	09 04	09 08	09 13		09 17			09 30	09 34	09 40	09 53	09 56	10 04	10 08		10 13			10 17		10 30	10 34	10 40	
Swinton	d					09 23						09 59								10 23					
Moorside	d					09 26														10 26					
Walkden	d					09 29						10 04								10 29					
Atherton	d					09 35						10 09								10 35					
Hag Fold	d					09 37														10 37					
Daisy Hill	d					09 40						10 13								10 40					
Kearsley	d										09 47													10 47	
Farnworth	d										09 49													10 49	
Moses Gate	d										09 52													10 52	
Bolton	a	09 14	09 19	09 23			09 32		09 40	09 45	09 55		10 06	10 14	10 19		10 23				10 32	10 40	10 45	10 55	
	d	09 15		09 24			09 33		09 40	09 45	09 56		10 07	10 15			10 24				10 33	10 40	10 45	10 56	
Westhoughton	d			09 31						09 53							10 31						10 53		
Hindley	d			09 35		09 45				09 57		10 17					10 35			10 45			10 57		
Ince	d					09 48														10 48					
Wigan North Western	a																								
Wigan Wallgate	a			09 44		09 51				10 02	10 13	10 22					10 44			10 51			11 02	11 13	
	d					09 52				10 03		10 24								10 52			11 03		
Pemberton	d					09 56														10 56					
Orrell	d					10 00														11 00					
Upholland	d					10 04														11 04					
Rainford	d					10 07														11 07					
Kirkby	a					10 19														11 19					
Liverpool Central [10]	103 a					*10 46*														*11 46*					
Gathurst	d											10 28													
Appley Bridge	d									10 10		10 32											11 10		
Parbold	d									10 14		10 36											11 14		
Hoscar	d											10 39													
Burscough Bridge	d									10 18		10 42											11 18		
New Lane	d											10 44													
Bescar Lane	d											10 48													
Meols Cop	d											10 53													
Southport	a									10 35		11 02											11 35		
Lostock	d	09 20							09 45					10 20								10 45			
Horwich Parkway	d	09 24							09 49				10 13	10 24								10 49			
Blackrod	d								09 52													10 52			
Adlington (Lancashire)	d								09 56													10 56			
Chorley	d	09 32					09 44		10 01				10 21	10 32							10 44	11 01			
Leyland	d	09 42			09 46				10 12					10 42					10 46			11 12			
Preston [8]	65, 97 a	09 50			09 54		09 55		10 17				10 33	10 50					10 54		10 55	11 17			
	d				09 55		10 00	10 08	10 19				10 38						10 55		10 58	11 19			
Kirkham & Wesham	97 a	*10 11*			10 05				10 28					*11 11*					11 05			11 28			
Poulton-le-Fylde	97 a							10 25	10 36				10 56									11 36			
Layton	97 a								10 43													11 43			
Blackpool North	97 a				10 20			10 35	10 48				11 05						11 20			11 48			
Lancaster [6]	65 a						10 16						*10c54*						*11c19*		11 14				
	d						10 16											11 00			11 14				11 31
Oxenholme Lake District	65 a												*11c08*						*11c36*		11 28				
Windermere	83 a																				*11 56*				
Carnforth	d						10 25											11a09							11 41
Silverdale	d																								11 48
Arnside	d						10 34																		11 52
Grange-over-Sands	d						10 39																		11 58
Kents Bank	d																								12 02
Cark	d																								12 06
Ulverston	d						10 52																		12 15
Dalton	d																								12 24
Roose	d																								12 30
Barrow-in-Furness	a						11 12																		12 39

For general notes see front of timetable
For details of catering facilities see Directory of Train Operators

A To Clitheroe (Table 94)
B From Liverpool Lime Street (Table 90)
C ⊼ to Preston
D From Morecambe to Leeds (Table 36)
E To Glasgow Central (Table 65)
b Change at Manchester Piccadilly
c Change at Preston

From 5 October a revised Northern service will be in operation due to seasonal difficulties. Customers should check with NRES for precise times

Manchester → Bolton → Wigan, Kirkby, Southport, Preston, Blackpool North and Barrow-in-Furness

Network Diagram - see first page of Table 82

		NT	TP	NT	NT	NT	NT	NT	TP	NT	NT	NT	NT	TP	NT	NT	NT	NT	NT	TP		NT	NT	NT	NT
			[1] ◇						[1] ◇					[1] ◇						[1] ◇					
					A		B		C							A		B		D					
			🛒						🛒					🛒						🛒					
Manchester Airport	85 ✈ d		10 29						11 00		11 03			11 29						12 00			12 03		
Heald Green	85 d		10 33								10 49			11 33									11 49		
Buxton	86 d		09 27											10 30											
Hazel Grove	86 d		10 04	10 33										11 04	11 33										
Stockport	84 d		10 26	10 41					10 53		10 56			11 26	11 41					11 53			11 56		
Manchester Piccadilly [10]	d		10 46	10 54					11 16		11 22			11 46	11 54					12 16			12 22		
Manchester Oxford Road	d		10 49	10 58					11 19		11 26			11 49	11 58					12 19			12 26		
Deansgate	d		10 51	11 00							11 28			11 51	12 00								12 28		
Rochdale	95 d	10 14			10 30					10 51		11 00	11 14			11 30						11 51		12 00	
Manchester Victoria	d	10 46			11 00	11 07		11 10		11 22		11 33	11 46			12 00	12 07		12 10			12 22		12 33	
Salford Central	d	10 49			11 03	11 10		11 13		11 25		11 36	11 49			12 03	12 10		12 13			12 25		12 35	
Salford Crescent	a	10 52	10 56	11 04	11 07	11 13		11 16		11 29	11 33	11 39	11 52	11 56	12 04	12 07	12 13		12 16			12 29	12 33	12 39	
	d	10 53	10 56	11 04	11 08	11 13		11 17		11 30	11 34	11 40	11 53	11 56	12 04	12 08	12 13		12 17			12 30	12 34	12 40	
Swinton	d	10 59						11 23					11 59						12 23						
Moorside	d							11 26											12 26						
Walkden	d	11 04						11 29					12 04						12 29						
Atherton	d	11 09						11 35					12 09						12 35						
Hag Fold	d							11 37											12 37						
Daisy Hill	d	11 13						11 40					12 13						12 40						
Kearsley	d											11 47												12 47	
Farnworth	d											11 49												12 49	
Moses Gate	d											11 52												12 52	
Bolton	a		11 06	11 14	11 19	11 23			11 32	11 40	11 45	11 55		12 06	12 14	12 19	12 23			12 32		12 40	12 45	12 55	
	d		11 07	11 15		11 24			11 33	11 40	11 45	11 56		12 07	12 15		12 24			12 33		12 40	12 45	12 56	
Westhoughton	d					11 31					11 53						12 31						12 53		
Hindley	d	11 17				11 35		11 45			11 57		12 17				12 35		12 45				12 57		
Ince	d							11 48											12 48						
Wigan North Western	a																								
Wigan Wallgate	a	11 22				11 44		11 51			12 02	12 13	12 22				12 44		12 51				13 02	13 11	
	d	11 24						11 52			12 03		12 24						12 52				13 03		
Pemberton	d							11 56											12 56						
Orrell	d							12 00											13 00						
Upholland	d							12 04											13 04						
Rainford	d							12 07											13 07						
Kirkby	a							12 19											13 19						
Liverpool Central [10]	103 a							12 46											13 46						
Gathurst	d	11 28											12 28												
Appley Bridge	d	11 32									12 10		12 32										13 10		
Parbold	d	11 36									12 14		12 36										13 14		
Hoscar	d	11 39																							
Burscough Bridge	d	11 42									12 18		12 41										13 18		
New Lane	d	11 44																							
Bescar Lane	d	11 48																							
Meols Cop	d	11 53											12 49												
Southport	a	12 02									12 35		12 59										13 35		
Lostock	d			11 20						11 45					12 20							12 45			
Horwich Parkway	d		11 13	11 24						11 49				12 13	12 24							12 49			
Blackrod	d									11 52												12 52			
Adlington (Lancashire)	d									11 56												12 56			
Chorley	d		11 21	11 32					11 44	12 01				12 21	12 32					12 44		13 01			
Leyland	d			11 42			11 46			12 12					12 42			12 46				13 12			
Preston [8]	65, 97 a		11 33	11 49			11 54		11 55	12 17				12 33	12 49			12 54		12 55		13 17			
	d		11 38				11 55		11 58	12 19				12 38				12 55		12 58		13 19			
Kirkham & Wesham	97 a			12 13			12 05			12 28					13 11			13 05				13 28			
Poulton-le-Fylde	97 a		11 56							12 36				12 56								13 36			
Layton	97 a									12 43								13 43				13 43			
Blackpool North	97 a		12 05				12 20			12 48				13 05				13 21				13 48			
Lancaster [6]	65 a		11b54						12 14					13b00				13b19		13 14					
	d								12 14											13 14					13 32
Oxenholme Lake District	65 a		12b22						13 22					13b22				13b36		13 28					
Windermere	83 a		12c47																	13 56					
Carnforth	d								12 23																13 42
Silverdale	d																								13 48
Arnside	d								12 31																13 52
Grange-over-Sands	d								12 37																13 58
Kents Bank	d																								14 02
Cark	d																								14 06
Ulverston	d								12 49																14 15
Dalton	d																								14 23
Roose	d																								14 29
Barrow-in-Furness	a								13 10																14 38

For general notes see front of timetable
For details of catering facilities see Directory of Train Operators

A To Clitheroe (Table 94)
B From Liverpool Lime Street (Table 90)
C 🛒 to Preston
D To Edinburgh (Table 65)

b Change at Preston
c Change at Preston and Oxenholme Lake District

From 5 October a revised Northern service will be in operation due to seasonal difficulties. Customers should check with NRES for precise times

Manchester → Bolton → Wigan, Kirkby, Southport, Preston, Blackpool North and Barrow-in-Furness

Network Diagram - see first page of Table 82

Station		NT	TP 1 ◇ 🛒	NT	NT A	NT	NT B	NT C	NT	TP 1 ◇ D 🛒	NT	NT	NT	NT	TP 1 ◇ 🛒	NT	NT A	NT	NT C	NT	TP 1 ◇ E 🛒		TP 1 ◇ G 🛒	NT	NT
Manchester Airport	85 ✈ d		12 29							13 00		13 03			13 29						14 00		14 00		14 03
Heald Green	85 d		12 33									*12 49*			13 33										*13 49*
Buxton	86 d		*11 27*												*12 30*										
Hazel Grove	86 d		*12 04*	12 33											*13 04*	13 33									
Stockport	84 d		*12 26*	12 41						*12 53*		*12 56*			*13 26*	13 41					*13 53*		*13 53*		*13 56*
Manchester Piccadilly 10	🚇 d		12 46	12 54						13 16		13 22			13 46	13 54					14 16		14 16		14 22
Manchester Oxford Road	d		12 49	12 58						13 19		13 26			13 49	13 58					14 19		14 19		14 26
Deansgate	🚇 d		12 51	13 00								13 28			13 51	14 00									14 28
Rochdale	95 d	*12 14*			*12 30*						*12 51*		13 00	*13 14*			*13 30*							*13 51*	
Manchester Victoria	🚇 d	12 46			13 00	13 07			13 10		13 22		13 33	13 46			14 00	14 07		14 10				14 22	
Salford Central	d	12 49			13 03	13 10			13 13		13 25		13 36	13 49			14 03	14 10		14 13				14 25	
Salford Crescent	a	12 52	12 56	13 04	13 07	13 13			13 16		13 29	13 33	13 39	13 52	13 56	14 04	14 07	14 13		14 16				14 29	14 33
	d	12 53	12 56	13 04	13 08	13 13			13 17		13 30	13 34	13 40	13 53	13 56	14 04	14 08	14 13		14 17				14 30	14 34
Swinton	d	12 59							13 23					13 59						14 23					
Moorside	d								13 26											14 26					
Walkden	d	13 04							13 29					14 04						14 29					
Atherton	d	13 09							13 35					14 09						14 35					
Hag Fold	d								13 37											14 37					
Daisy Hill	d	13 13							13 40					14 13						14 40					
Kearsley	d												13 47												
Farnworth	d												13 49												
Moses Gate	d												13 52												
Bolton	a		13 06	13 14	13 19	13 23				13 32	13 40	13 45	13 55		14 06	14 14	14 19	14 23			14 32		14 32	14 40	14 45
	d		13 07	13 15		13 24				13 33	13 40	13 45	13 56		14 07	14 15		14 24			14 33		14 33	14 40	14 45
Westhoughton	d					13 31						13 53						14 31							14 53
Hindley	d	13 17				13 35			13 45			13 57		14 17				14 35		14 45					14 57
Ince	d								13 48											14 48					
Wigan North Western	a																								
Wigan Wallgate	a	13 22				13 44			13 51			14 02	14 13	14 22				14 44		14 51					15 02
	d	13 24							13 52			14 03		14 24						14 52					15 03
Pemberton	d								13 56											14 56					
Orrell	d								14 00											15 00					
Upholland	d								14 04											15 04					
Rainford	d								14 07											15 07					
Kirkby	a								14 19											15 19					
Liverpool Central 10	103 a								*14 46*											*15 46*					
Gathurst	d	13 28												14 28											
Appley Bridge	d	13 32										14 10		14 32											15 10
Parbold	d	13 36										14 14		14 36											15 14
Hoscar	d	13 39																							
Burscough Bridge	d	13 42										14 18		14 41											15 18
New Lane	d	13 44																							
Bescar Lane	d	13 48																							
Meols Cop	d	13 53												14 49											
Southport	a	14 02										14 35		14 59											15 35
Lostock	d			13 20							13 45					14 20								14 45	
Horwich Parkway	d		13 13	13 24							13 49				14 13	14 24								14 49	
Blackrod	d										13 52													14 52	
Adlington (Lancashire)	d										13 56													14 56	
Chorley	d		13 21	13 32						13 44	14 01				14 21	14 32					14 44		14 44	15 01	
Leyland	d			13 42				13 46			14 12					14 42			14 46					15 12	
Preston 8	65, 97 a		13 33	13 50				13 54		13 55	14 17				14 33	14 50			14 54		14 55		14 55	15 17	
	d		13 38					13 55		13 58	14 19				14 38				14 55		14 58	15 04	14 58	15 19	
Kirkham & Wesham	97 a		*14 05*	*14 11*				14 05			14 28					*15 11*			15 05					15 28	
Poulton-le-Fylde	97 a		13 56								14 36				14 56									15 36	
Layton	97 a										14 43													15 43	
Blackpool North	97 a		14 05					14 20			14 48				15 05				15 20					15 48	
Lancaster 6	65 a		*13b54*							14 14					*15b00*						15 14	15 20	15 14		
	d						13 48			14 14												15 20			
Oxenholme Lake District	65 a		*14b08*												*15b22*							15 37	15 37		
Windermere	83 a		*14c44*																			16 00	*16 00*		
Carnforth	d						13a58			14 23															
Silverdale	d																								
Arnside	d									14 31															
Grange-over-Sands	d									14 37															
Kents Bank	d																								
Cark	d																								
Ulverston	d									14 49															
Dalton	d																								
Roose	d																								
Barrow-in-Furness	a									15 10															

For general notes see front of timetable
For details of catering facilities see Directory of Train Operators

A To Clitheroe (Table 94)
B From Heysham Port (Table 98) to Leeds (Table 36)
C From Liverpool Lime Street (Table 90)
D 🛒 to Preston
E Until 19 June and from 7 September. 1458 departure from Preston continues to Edinburgh (Table 65). 🛒 to Lancaster
G 22 June to 4 September. To Edinburgh (Table 65)
b Change at Preston
c Change at Preston and Oxenholme Lake District

From 5 October a revised Northern service will be in operation due to seasonal difficulties. Customers should check with NRES for precise times

Manchester → Bolton → Wigan, Kirkby, Southport, Preston, Blackpool North and Barrow-in-Furness

Network Diagram - see first page of Table 82

	NT	NT A		NT	TP 1 ◇ ⚒	NT	NT B	NT	NT C	NT	TP 1 ◇ D ⚒	NT	NT	NT	NT B	NT	TP 1 ◇ ⚒	NT	NT	NT E	NT C	TP 1 ◇ G ⚒		NT
Manchester Airport 85 ✈ d					14 29						15 00		15 03				15 29					16 00		
Heald Green 85 d					14 33								*14 49*				15 33							
Buxton 86 d					*13 25*												*14 30*							
Hazel Grove 86 d					*14 01*	14 33											*15 04*	15 33						
Stockport 84 d					*14 26*	14 41					*14 53*		*14 56*				*15 26*	15 41				*15 53*		
Manchester Piccadilly 10 ⛴ d					14 46	14 54					15 16		15 22				15 46	15 54				16 16		
Manchester Oxford Road d					14 49	14 58					15 19		15 26				15 49	15 58				16 19		
Deansgate ⛴ d					14 51	15 00							15 28				15 51	16 00						
Rochdale 95 d	14 00			*14 14*			*14 30*					*14 51*		15 00	*15 14*				*15 30*					
Manchester Victoria ⛴ d	14 33			14 46			15 00	15 07		15 10		15 22		15 33	15 40	15 46			16 07					16 10
Salford Central d	14 36			14 49			15 03	15 10		15 13		15 25		15 35	15 43	15 49			16 10					16 13
Salford Crescent a	14 39			14 52	14 56	15 04	15 07	15 13		15 16		15 29	15 33	15 39	15 46	15 52	15 56	16 04	16 13					16 16
d	14 40			14 53	14 56	15 04	15 08	15 13		15 17		15 30	15 34	15 40	15 47	15 53	15 56	16 04	16 13					16 17
Swinton d				14 59						15 23						15 59								16 23
Moorside d										15 26														16 26
Walkden d				15 04						15 29						16 04								16 29
Atherton d				15 09						15 35						16 09								16 35
Hag Fold d										15 37														16 37
Daisy Hill d				15 13						15 40						16 13								16 40
Kearsley d	14 47													15 47										
Farnworth d	14 49													15 49										
Moses Gate d	14 52													15 52										
Bolton a	14 55				15 06	15 14	15 19	15 23			15 32	15 40	15 45	15 55	15 59		16 06	16 19	16 23			16 32		
d	14 56				15 07	15 15		15 24			15 33	15 40	15 45	15 56			16 07		16 24			16 33		
Westhoughton d								15 31					15 53						16 31					
Hindley d				15 17				15 35		15 45			15 57			16 17			16 35					16 45
Ince d										15 48														16 48
Wigan North Western a																								
Wigan Wallgate a	15 13			15 22				15 44		15 51			16 02	16 11		16 22			16 44					16 51
d				15 24						15 52			16 03			16 24								16 52
Pemberton d										15 56														16 56
Orrell d										16 00														17 00
Upholland d										16 04														17 04
Rainford d										16 07														17 07
Kirkby a										16 19														17 19
Liverpool Central 10 103 a										*16 46*														*17 46*
Gathurst d				15 28									16 08			16 28								
Appley Bridge d				15 32									16 11			16 32								
Parbold d				15 36									16 15			16 36								
Hoscar d													16 18											
Burscough Bridge d				15 40									16 21			16 40								
New Lane d													16 24											
Bescar Lane d													16 27											
Meols Cop d				15 48									16 32			16 48								
Southport a				15 57									16 42			16 57								
Lostock d						15 20						15 45					16 12							
Horwich Parkway d					15 13	15 24						15 49					16 15							
Blackrod d												15 52												
Adlington (Lancashire) d												15 56												
Chorley d					15 21	15 32					15 44	16 01					16 23					16 44		
Leyland d						15 42			15 46			16 12									16 48			
Preston 8 65, 97 a					15 33	15 50			15 54		15 55	16 19					16 35				16 56	16 55		
d					15 38				15 55		15 58						16 38				16 58	17 00	17 05	
Kirkham & Wesham 97 a						*16 13*			16 05								16 47				17 07			
Poulton-le-Fylde 97 a					15 56							*16 50*					16 57							
Layton 97 a																	17 00							
Blackpool North 97 a					16 05				16 20			*17 00*					17 07				17 23			
Lancaster 6 65 a					*16b08*						16 14						*17b00*					17 15	17 23	
d		15 33									16 14									16 54		17 16	17 25	
Oxenholme Lake District 65 a					*16b04*																	17 30	17 41	
Windermere 83 a					*16c48*																		18 04	
Carnforth d		15 43									16 22									17 05				
Silverdale d		15 50									16 28									17 12				
Arnside d		15 54									16 32									17 16				
Grange-over-Sands d		16 00									16 38									17 22				
Kents Bank d		16 04									16 41									17 26				
Cark d		16 08									16 46									17 30				
Ulverston d		16 17									16 54									17 39				
Dalton d		16 26									17 02									17 48				
Roose d		16 32									17 08									17 54				
Barrow-in-Furness a		16 39									17 18									18 02				

For general notes see front of timetable
For details of catering facilities see Directory of Train Operators

A To Carlisle via Whitehaven (Table 100)
B To Clitheroe (Table 94)
C From Liverpool Lime Street (Table 90)
D ⚒ to Preston
E To Millom (Table 100)
G 1700 departure from Preston continues to Edinburgh (Table 65). ⚒ to Oxenholme Lake District
b Change at Preston
c Change at Preston and Oxenholme Lake District

From 5 October a revised Northern service will be in operation due to seasonal difficulties. Customers should check with NRES for precise times

Manchester → Bolton → Wigan, Kirkby, Southport, Preston, Blackpool North and Barrow-in-Furness

Network Diagram - see first page of Table 82

	NT	NT	NT	NT	NT	NT	NT		TP	NT	NT	NT	NT	TP	NT	NT	NT	NT	NT	NT	NT	NT	NT	TP
									1 ◇					1 ◇										1 ◇
		A	B								A	C	D	E					G	C		G		
									🛒					🛒										🛒
Manchester Airport 85 ✈ d				16 03					16 29					17 00			17 03							17 27
Heald Green 85 d				15 49					16 33								16 49							17 31
Buxton 86 d																		16 30						16 30
Hazel Grove 86 d					16 04					16 33								17 04						
Stockport 84 d				15 56	16 12				16 26	16 41				16 52			16 55	17 12						17b26
Manchester Piccadilly 10 ⇌ d				16 22	16 27				16 46	16 54				17 15			17 22	17 27						17 46
Manchester Oxford Road d				16 26	16 30				16 49	16 58				17 18			17 26	17 30						17 49
Deansgate ⇌ d				16 28	16 33					17 00								17 33						17 51
Rochdale 95 d	15 51					16 00	16 14				16 30					16 51			17 00		17 14			
Manchester Victoria ⇌ d	16 20	16 23				16 36	16 46				17 00		17 06		17 10	17 19			17 36		17 40		17 45	
Salford Central d	16 23	16 26				16 39	16 49				17 03		17 09		17 12	17 22			17 39		17 43		17 48	
Salford Crescent a	16 26	16 30		16 34	16 38	16 42	16 52			17 04	17 07		17 13		17 16	17 25	17 34	17 38	17 42		17 46		17 51	17 55
d	16 27	16 31		16 34	16 38	16 43	16 53			17 04	17 08		17 14		17 17	17 27	17 34	17 38	17 43		17 47		17 52	17 55
Swinton d							16 59								17 23								17 58	
Moorside d							17 02								17 26								18 01	
Walkden d							17 05								17 31								18 05	
Atherton d							17 11						17 26		17 37						17 59		18 11	
Hag Fold d							17 14								17 39								18 13	
Daisy Hill d							17 17						17 30		17 43						18 03		18 17	
Kearsley d						16 50													17 53					
Farnworth d						16 52													17 55			←		
Moses Gate d						16 55													17 57 →			17 57		
Bolton a	16 37	16 42		16 45	16 48	16 58			17 05	17 14	17 19			17 31		17 37	17 45	17 48				18 01		18 05
d	16 37			16 45	16 49	16 59			17 06	17 15				17 32		17 37	17 45	17 49				18 01		18 07
Westhoughton d				16 53		17 06											17 53					18 09		
Hindley d				16 57		17 10	17 21								17 48							18 13	18 22	
Ince d							17 24								17 51									
Wigan North Western a																								
Wigan Wallgate a				17 02		17 19	17 31						17 38		17 54		18 01				18 11	18 22	18 27	
d				17 03									17 40		17 55		18 02				18 15		18 28	
Pemberton d															17 59								18 32	
Orrell d															18 03								18 36	
Upholland d															18 07								18 40	
Rainford d															18 10								18 43	
Kirkby a															18 22								18 54	
Liverpool Central 10 103 a															18 46								19 31	
Gathurst d				17 08									17 44								18 19			
Appley Bridge d				17 11									17 48				18 09				18 23			
Parbold d				17 15									17 52				18 13				18 28			
Hoscar d																								
Burscough Bridge d				17 20									17 57				18 17				18 33			
New Lane d																								
Bescar Lane d																								
Meols Cop d				17 27									18 05								18 41			
Southport a				17 37									18 14				18 35				18 50			
Lostock d	16 43				16 54					17 20						17 43		17 54						18 11
Horwich Parkway d	16 47				16 58					17 24						17 47		17 58						18 15
Blackrod d	16 51				17 01											17 51		18 01						18 18
Adlington (Lancashire) d	16 55				17 05											17 55		18 05						
Chorley d	17 00				17 10				17 19	17 32				17 44		18 00		18 10						18 25
Leyland d	17 12				17 21					17 42		17 46				18 11				18 22				18 33
Preston 8 65, 97 a	17 19				17 26				17 30	17 50		17 54		17 55		18 16		18 25		18 31				18 38
d	17 21				17 28				17 32			17 55		17 58		18 18		18 26						18 40
Kirkham & Wesham 97 a	17 30								17 41	18 11		18 05				18 27								18 49
Poulton-le-Fylde 97 a	17 38				17 56				17 51							18 35		18 43						18 59
Layton 97 a	17 43								17 54							18 39								19 02
Blackpool North 97 a	17 48				18 06				18 02			18 20				18 46		18 53						19 09
Lancaster 6 65 a					17 48				17c54					18 13										19c08
d			17 19		17 48									18 25										
Oxenholme Lake District 65 a									18c08					18 45										19c23
Windermere 83 a														19 08										
Carnforth d			17 28		18 00									18 35										
Silverdale d			17 35		18 06									18 41										
Arnside d			17 40		18 11									18 45										
Grange-over-Sands d			17 46		18 19									18 51										
Kents Bank d			17 49		18 23									18 54										
Cark d			17 54		18 27									18 59										
Ulverston d			18 02		18 36									19 07										
Dalton d			18 10		18 44									19 15										
Roose d			18 17		18 50									19 21										
Barrow-in-Furness a			18 25		18 59									19 30										

For general notes see front of timetable
For details of catering facilities see Directory of Train Operators

A To Clitheroe (Table 94)
B From Morecambe (Table 98)
C From Liverpool Lime Street (Table 90)
D From Stalybridge (Table 39)
E Also conveys portion to Glasgow Central, detached at Preston (Table 65). 🛒 to Preston
G Also stops at Clifton 1748
b Change at Manchester Oxford Road
c Change at Preston

From 5 October a revised Northern service will be in operation due to seasonal difficulties. Customers should check with NRES for precise times

Manchester → Bolton → Wigan, Kirkby, Southport, Preston, Blackpool North and Barrow-in-Furness

Network Diagram - see first page of Table 82

	NT	NT A	NT	NT B	TP 1◇ C		NT B	NT	NT D	NT	NT	NT		TP 1◇	NT	NT A	NT E	NT	TP 1◇	NT B	NT	NT	TP 1◇	NT A
Manchester Airport 85 d					18 00					18 03				18 29					19 00		19 03		19 29	
Heald Green 85 d										17 49				18 33									19 33	
Buxton 86 d	16 59													17 27	17 59								18 27	
Hazel Grove 86 d	17 33													18 04	18 33								19 04	
Stockport 84 d	17 41				17 53					17 56				18 26	18 41				18 53		18 56		19 26	
Manchester Piccadilly 10 d	17 54				18 16					18 22				18 46	18 54				19 16		19 20		19 46	
Manchester Oxford Road d	17 58				18 19					18 26				18 49	18 58				19 19		19 24		19 49	
Deansgate d	18 00									18 28				18 51	19 00						19 26		19 51	
Rochdale 95 d		17 30						17 51	18 00			18 14				18 32						19 00		19 32
Manchester Victoria d		18 00	18 10					18 20	18 23		18 33	18 45				19 00		19 10				19 28		20 00
Salford Central d		18 03	18 13					18 23	18 26		18 36	18 48				19 03		19 13				19 31		20 03
Salford Crescent a	18 04	18 07	18 16					18 26	18 30	18 34	18 39	18 51		18 56	19 04	19 07		19 16			19 29	19 34	19 56	20 07
d	18 04	18 08	18 17					18 27	18 31	18 34	18 40	18 52		18 56	19 04	19 08		19 17			19 30	19 35	19 56	20 08
Swinton d			18 23									18 58						19 23						
Moorside d			18 26									19 01						19 26						
Walkden d			18 29									19 04						19 29						
Atherton d			18 35									19 10						19 35						
Hag Fold d			18 37									19 12						19 37						
Daisy Hill d			18 40									19 15						19 40						
Kearsley d											18 47													
Farnworth d											18 49													
Moses Gate d											18 52													
Bolton a	18 14	18 19			18 32			18 37	18 42	18 45	18 55			19 06	19 19	19 20			19 32		19 40	19 45	20 06	20 19
d	18 15				18 33			18 37		18 45	18 56			19 07					19 33		19 40	19 45	20 07	
Westhoughton d										18 53	19 03										19 48			
Hindley d			18 45							18 57	19 09	19 20						19 45			19 52			
Ince d			18 48									19 23						19 48						
Wigan North Western a			18 56																					
Wigan Wallgate a										19 02	19 18	19 30						19 55			19 57			
d										19 03											19 59			
Pemberton d																								
Orrell d																								
Upholland d																								
Rainford d																								
Kirkby a																								
Liverpool Central 10 103 a																								
Gathurst d										19 08											20 03			
Appley Bridge d										19 11											20 07			
Parbold d										19 15											20 11			
Hoscar d										19 18														
Burscough Bridge d										19 21											20 15			
New Lane d										19 23														
Bescar Lane d										19 27														
Meols Cop d										19 32											20 23			
Southport a										19 42											20 32			
Lostock d	18 20							18 42						19 12								19 50		
Horwich Parkway d	18 24							18 46						19 15								19 54	20 13	
Blackrod d								18 49														19 57		
Adlington (Lancashire) d								18 53														20 01		
Chorley d	18 32				18 44			18 58						19 23					19 44			20 06	20 21	
Leyland d	18 42			18 46			19 06	19 10												20 10		20 18		
Preston 8 65, 97 a	18 48			18 54	18 55		19 15	19 18						19 33					19 55	20 18		20 24	20 33	
d	18 49			18 55	19 00	19 04		19 20						19 38					19 58	20 19		20 25	20 38	
Kirkham & Wesham 97 a	19 11			19 05				19 29						20 11								20 35	21 11	
Poulton-le-Fylde 97 a							19 50	19 37						19 56						20 50		20 43	20 56	
Layton 97 a								19 43														20 47		
Blackpool North 97 a	19 14			19 20	19 33		20 00	19 48						20 05						20 44		20 54	21 06	
Lancaster 6 65 a					19 16	19 20								19b54					20 14				20b54	
d					19 16	19 20											19 24		20 14					
Oxenholme Lake District 65 a					19 30	19 43								20b08									21b08	
Windermere 83 a					19 56									20c46									21c34	
Carnforth d						19 29											19a34		20 22					
Silverdale d						19 35													20 28					
Arnside d						19 39													20 32					
Grange-over-Sands d						19 44													20 38					
Kents Bank d						19 48													20 41					
Cark d						19 52													20 46					
Ulverston d						20 00													20 54					
Dalton d						20 08													21 02					
Roose d						20 14													21 08					
Barrow-in-Furness a						20 24													21 17					

For general notes see front of timetable
For details of catering facilities see Directory of Train Operators

A To Clitheroe (Table 94)
B From Liverpool Lime Street (Table 90)
C 1900 departure from Preston continues to Edinburgh (Table 65)
D To Blackburn (Table 94)
E From Morecambe to Leeds (Table 36)
b Change at Preston
c Change at Preston and Oxenholme Lake District

From 5 October a revised Northern service will be in operation due to seasonal difficulties. Customers should check with NRES for precise times

Manchester → Bolton → Wigan, Kirkby, Southport, Preston, Blackpool North and Barrow-in-Furness

Network Diagram - see first page of Table 82

	NT	TP 1 ◇	NT	NT	NT	TP 1 ◇	NT	NT	NT	NT	NT	TP 1 ◇	NT	NT	NT	TP 1 ◇	NT	NT	TP 1 ◇	NT	NT	NT	NT
				A			B						B	A							C		
Manchester Airport 85 ✈ d		20 00			20 03	20 29					21 03	21 29				22 00		22 19	22 29	22b22			
Heald Green 85 d						20 33						21 33						21 51	22 33	22b12			
Buxton 86 d						19 27						20 27							21 27				
Hazel Grove 86 d						20 04						21 04							22 04				
Stockport 84 d		19 53			19 56	20 26					20 56	21 21				21 42		21 58	22 21	22 34			
Manchester Piccadilly 10 ⇌ d		20 16			20 20	20 46					21 20	21 46				22 16		22 36	22 46	22 50			
Manchester Oxford Road d		20 19			20 24	20 49					21 24	21 49				22 19		22 39	22 49	22 53			
Deansgate ⇌ d					20 26	20 51					21 26	21 51						22 41	22 51	22 55			
Rochdale 95 d			19 52				20 14			20 52			20 56				21 52				21 56	22 52	
Manchester Victoria ⇌ d	20 10		20 22				21 00		21 10	21 22			22 01		22 10		22 22				23 00	23 20	23 23
Salford Central d	20 13		20 25				21 03		21 13	21 25			22c04		22c13		22c25				23c03	23c23	23c26
Salford Crescent a	20 16		20 29		20 33	20 56	21 07		21 16	21 29	21 33	21 56	22 07		22 17		22 29	22 46	22 54	22 59	23 07	23 26	23 29
d	20 17		20 30		20 34	20 56	21 08		21 17	21 30	21 34	21 56	22 08		22 17		22 30	22 46	22 56	22 59	23 08	23 26	23 30
Swinton d	20 23								21 23						22 23							23 33	
Moorside d	20 26								21 26						22 26							23 35	
Walkden d	20 29								21 29						22 29							23 39	
Atherton d	20 35								21 35						22 35							23 44	
Hag Fold d	20 37								21 37						22 37							23 47	
Daisy Hill d	20 40								21 40						22 40							23 50	
Kearsley d																				23 07			
Farnworth d																				23 09			
Moses Gate d																				23 11			
Bolton a		20 32	20 40		20 45	21 06	21 19			21 40	21 45	22 06	22 19			22 32	22 40	22 56	23 06	23 15	23 19		23 40
d		20 33	20 40		20 45	21 07				21 40	21 45	22 07				22 33	22 40	22 57	23 07	23 15			23 40
Westhoughton d					20 53						21 53							23 04		23 23			
Hindley d	20 45				20 57				21 45		21 57				22 45			23 08		23 27		23 54	
Ince d	20 48								21 48						22 48							23 57	
Wigan North Western a																							
Wigan Wallgate a	20 55				21 02				21 55		22 02				22 55			23 13		23 38		00 04	
d					21 03						22 03							23 15					
Pemberton d																							
Orrell d																							
Upholland d																							
Rainford d																							
Kirkby a																							
Liverpool Central 10 103 a																							
Gathurst d					21 08						22 08							23 19					
Appley Bridge d					21 11						22 11							23 23					
Parbold d					21 15						22 15							23 27					
Hoscar d					21 18																		
Burscough Bridge d					21 21						22 20							23 31					
New Lane d					21 24																		
Bescar Lane d					21 27																		
Meols Cop d					21 32						22 27							23 39					
Southport a					21 42						22 37							23 48					
Lostock d			20 45							21 45							22 45						23 45
Horwich Parkway d			20 49			21 13				21 49		22 13					22 49		23 13				23 49
Blackrod d			20 52							21 52							22 52						23 52
Adlington (Lancashire) d			20 56							21 56							22 56						23 56
Chorley d		20 44	21 01			21 21				22 01		22 21					23 01		23 21				00 01
Leyland d			21 12	21 16						22 11				22 44			23 12						00 12
Preston 8 65, 97 a		20 55	21 17	21 22		21 33				22 17		22 33		22 54		23 09	23 17		23 33				00 17
d		20 58	21 19	21 24		21 38		21 51		22 19		22 35		22 56		23 13	23 19		23 35				00 19
Kirkham & Wesham 97 a			21 28			22 28				22 28		23 00					23 28						00 28
Poulton-le-Fylde 97 a			21 36	21 50		21 56				22 36		22 52					23 36		23 52				00 36
Layton 97 a			21 40			22 43				22 43							23 40						00 41
Blackpool North 97 a			21 48	21 53		22 06				22 48		23 01		23 21			23 48		00 01				00 48
Lancaster 6 65 a		21 14				22e00		22 11								23 28							
d		21 14						22 11								23 29							
Oxenholme Lake District 65 a						22e13																	
Windermere 83 a						22f39																	
Carnforth d		21 22						22 21								23 37							
Silverdale d		21 28						22 27								23 43							
Arnside d		21 32						22 32								23 47							
Grange-over-Sands d		21 38						22 38								23 53							
Kents Bank d		21 41						22 41								23 56							
Cark d		21 46						22 46								00 01							
Ulverston d		21 54						22 54								00 09							
Dalton d		22 02						23 02								00 17							
Roose d		22 08						23 08								00 23							
Barrow-in-Furness a		22 17						23 16								00 32							

For general notes see front of timetable
For details of catering facilities see Directory of Train Operators

A From Liverpool Lime Street (Table 90)
B To Clitheroe (Table 94)
C To Blackburn (Table 94)
b Change at Manchester Piccadilly
c Fridays only
e Change at Preston
f Change at Preston and Oxenholme Lake District

From 5 October a revised Northern service will be in operation due to seasonal difficulties. Customers should check with NRES for precise times

Table 82

Saturdays

Manchester → Bolton → Wigan, Kirkby, Southport, Preston, Blackpool North and Barrow-in-Furness

Network Diagram - see first page of Table 82

	NT A	TP 1◇	TP 1◇	TP 1◇	NT B	NT	NT	NT	TP 1◇ C 🍴		NT		NT	NT B	NT	NT	NT A	TP 1◇ 🍴	NT	NT D	NT	NT	NT E	TP 1◇ G 🍴
Manchester Airport 85 ✈ d		00 01	03 40	05 29					06 18					06b23				07 00						07 28
Heald Green 85 d				05 33										06b04				*06 04*						07 32
Buxton 86 d														05 59										*06 27*
Hazel Grove 86 d														06 33										*07 03*
Stockport 84 d									*05 53*					06 41				*06 53*						*07 22*
Manchester Piccadilly 10 d		00 16	03 55	05 46					06 33					06 54				07 15						07 45
Manchester Oxford Road d									06 36					06 57				07 18						
Deansgate d														06 59										
Rochdale 95 d															*06 18*					*06 55*				
Manchester Victoria d					05 55	06 00	06 17				06 38		06 45		07 06	07 10			07 16	07 23		07 27		
Salford Central d											06 40		06 48		07 09	07 13			07 19	07 26		07 30		
Salford Crescent a				05 51	05 59	06 04	06 23				06 44		06 51	07 03	07 12	07 16			07 24	07 29		07 33		
d				05 52	06 00	06 05	06 24				06 45		06 52	07 03	07 13	07 16			07 25	07 30		07 33		
Swinton d													06 58		07 19									
Moorside d															07 22									
Walkden d													07 03		07 25							07 42		
Atherton d													07 08		07 31							07 48		
Hag Fold d															07 33						←			
Daisy Hill d													07 12		07 36						07 36	07 51		
Kearsley d											06 52				→									
Farnworth d											06 54													
Moses Gate d											06 57													
Bolton a		00s31	04s09	06 02	06 11	06 15	06 34		06 50		07 00			07 16		07 26		07 31	07 35	07 41				07 59
d				06 02		06 15	06 34		06 50		07 01					07 27		07 31	07 35					07 59
Westhoughton d						06 23										07 34								
Hindley d						06 27							07 16			07 38					07 42			
Ince d																					07 45			
Wigan North Western a											07 19													
Wigan Wallgate a						06 32							07 21			07 43					07 48	08 03		
d						06 34		06 40					07 23			07 45					07 50			
Pemberton d						06 38															07 54			
Orrell d						06 42															07 58			
Upholland d						06 45															08 01			
Rainford d						06 49															08 05			
Kirkby a						07 01															08 17			
Liverpool Central 10 103 a						*07 31*															*08 46*			
Gathurst d								06 44					07 27			07 49								
Appley Bridge d								06 48					07 31			07 53								
Parbold d								06 52					07 35			07 57								
Hoscar d								06 55								08 00								
Burscough Bridge d								06 58					07 39			08 03								
New Lane d								07 00								08 05								
Bescar Lane d								07 04								08 09								
Meols Cop d								07 09					07 47			08 14								
Southport a								07 18					07 56			08 23								
Lostock d				06 07			06 39												07 42					
Horwich Parkway d				06 11			06 43											07 38	07 46					
Blackrod d							06 46												07 49					
Adlington (Lancashire) d							06 50												07 53					
Chorley d				06 18			06 55											07 46	07 58					08 11
Leyland d	00 04			06 27			07 06										07 46		08 08					
Preston 8 65, 97 a	00 13	01s03	04s42	06 32			07 11		07 11								07 54	07 57	08 14					08 22
d				06 34			07 13		07 16	07 20							07 55	07 59	08 15					08 24
Kirkham & Wesham 97 a				06 43			07 22										*08 13*	08 08	08 25					
Poulton-le-Fylde 97 a				06 53			07 30		*07 54*									08 18	08 33					
Layton 97 a				06 56			07 34											08 22	08 37					
Blackpool North 97 a		01 30	05 09	07 03			07 41		*08 05*								08 18	08 29	08 44					*09 05*
Lancaster 6 65 a				*06c54*					07 31	07 36														08 39
d										07 36													08 24	08 40
Oxenholme Lake District 65 a				*07c08*						*08 22*														08 54
Windermere 83 a				*07e40*						*08f46*														*09 33*
Carnforth d										07 45													08a33	
Silverdale d										07 51														
Arnside d										07 55														
Grange-over-Sands d										08 00														
Kents Bank d										08 04														
Cark d										08 08														
Ulverston d										08 16														
Dalton d										08 24														
Roose d										08 30														
Barrow-in-Furness a										08 39														

For general notes see front of timetable
For details of catering facilities see Directory of Train Operators

A From Liverpool Lime Street (Table 90)

B To Clitheroe (Table 94)

C 0716 departure from Preston continues to Glasgow Central (Table 65). 🍴 to Lancaster

D To Blackburn (Table 94)

E To Leeds (Table 36)

G To Edinburgh (Table 65)

b Change at Manchester Piccadilly

c Change at Preston

e Change at Preston and Oxenholme Lake District

f Change at Lancaster and Oxenholme Lake District

From 10 October a revised Northern service will be in operation due to seasonal difficulties. Customers should check with NRES for precise times

Manchester → Bolton → Wigan, Kirkby, Southport, Preston, Blackpool North and Barrow-in-Furness

Network Diagram - see first page of Table 82

		NT A	NT	NT B	NT	NT C	NT	TP 1◇ [trolley]	NT	NT	NT D	NT E	NT	TP 1◇ G [trolley]	NT	NT B	NT	NT C	TP 1◇ H [trolley]		TP 1◇ J	NT	NT
Manchester Airport	85 ✈ d							08 00		08 03				08 25					09 00				
Heald Green	85 d									*07 49*				08 29									
Buxton	86 d													*07 27*	07 56								
Hazel Grove	86 d		07 32							*07 48*				*08 17*	08 33								
Stockport	84 d		07 40					*07 53*		*07 57*				*08 24*	08 41				*08 53*				
Manchester Piccadilly 10	⇌ d		07 54					08 15		08 22				08 46	08 54				09 16				
Manchester Oxford Road	d		07 58					08 19		08 25				08 49	08 58				09 19				
Deansgate	⇌ d		08 00							08 28				08 51	09 00								
Rochdale	95 d			*07 30*					*07 52*		*08 00*	08 00	*08 14*			*08 30*							*08 51*
Manchester Victoria	⇌ d			08 00	08 07		08 10		08 22		08 29	08 33	08 46			09 00	09 07					09 10	09 22
Salford Central	d			08 03	08 10		08 13		08 25		08 32	08 36	08 49			09 03	09 10					09 13	09 25
Salford Crescent	a		08 04	08 07	08 13		08 16		08 29	08 33	08 37	08 39	08 52	08 56	09 04	09 07	09 13					09 16	09 29
	d		08 04	08 08	08 13		08 17		08 30	08 34	08 37	08 40	08 53	08 56	09 04	09 08	09 13					09 17	09 30
Swinton	d						08 23						08 59									09 23	
Moorside	d						08 26															09 26	
Walkden	d						08 29						09 04									09 29	
Atherton	d						08 35						09 09									09 35	
Hag Fold	d						08 37															09 37	
Daisy Hill	d						08 40						09 13									09 40	
Kearsley	d											08 47											
Farnworth	d											08 49											
Moses Gate	d											08 52											
Bolton	a		08 14	08 19	08 23			08 32	08 40	08 44	08 49	08 55		09 06	09 14	09 19	09 23		09 32				09 40
	d		08 15		08 24			08 32	08 40	08 45		08 56		09 07	09 15		09 24		09 33				09 40
Westhoughton	d				08 31					08 53							09 31						
Hindley	d				08 35		08 45						09 17				09 35					09 45	
Ince	d						08 48															09 48	
Wigan North Western	a																						
Wigan Wallgate	a				08 44		08 51			09 00		09 14	09 22				09 44					09 51	
	d						08 52			09 05			09 24									09 52	
Pemberton	d						08 56															09 56	
Orrell	d						09 00															10 00	
Upholland	d						09 04															10 04	
Rainford	d						09 07															10 07	
Kirkby	a						09 19															10 19	
Liverpool Central 10	103 a						*09 46*															*10 46*	
Gathurst	d												09 28										
Appley Bridge	d									09 11			09 32										
Parbold	d									09 15			09 36										
Hoscar	d																						
Burscough Bridge	d									09 20			09 40										
New Lane	d																						
Bescar Lane	d																						
Meols Cop	d												09 48										
Southport	a									09 36			09 57										
Lostock	d		08 20						08 45						09 20								09 45
Horwich Parkway	d		08 24					08 39	08 49					09 13	09 24								09 49
Blackrod	d								08 52														09 52
Adlington (Lancashire)	d								08 56														09 56
Chorley	d		08 32					08 47	09 01					09 21	09 32				09 44				10 01
Leyland	d		08 42			08 46			09 12						09 42			09 46					10 12
Preston 8	65, 97 a		08 50			08 54		08 58	09 17					09 33	09 50			09 54	09 55				10 17
	d	08 42				08 55		08 59	09 19					09 45				09 55	09 58	10 08	10 04		10 19
Kirkham & Wesham	97 a					*09 11*			09 28									*10 11*					10 28
Poulton-le-Fylde	97 a							09 16	09 36											10 25			10 36
Layton	97 a								09 43														10 43
Blackpool North	97 a					09 20		09 25	09 48									10 20		10 35			10 48
Lancaster 6	65 a	09 02							*09b54*					10 00					10 14		10 20		
	d	09 02												10 01					10 14		10 20		
Oxenholme Lake District	65 a													10 17					10 28				
Windermere	83 a	*10 39*												10 39									
Carnforth	d	09 12																			10 29		
Silverdale	d	09 18																					
Arnside	d	09 23																			10 37		
Grange-over-Sands	d	09 29																			10 43		
Kents Bank	d	09 32																					
Cark	d	09 37																					
Ulverston	d	09 45																			10 55		
Dalton	d	09 53																					
Roose	d	09 59																					
Barrow-in-Furness	a	10 07																			11 15		

For general notes see front of timetable
For details of catering facilities see Directory of Train Operators

A To Carlisle via Whitehaven (Table 100)
B To Clitheroe (Table 94)
C From Liverpool Lime Street (Table 90)
D To Blackburn (Table 94)
E From Hebden Bridge (from 18 July from Todmorden) (Table 41)
G [trolley] to Preston
H Oxenholme Lake District portion continues to Glasgow Central (Table 65)
J From Blackpool North (Table 97)
b Change at Preston

From 10 October a revised Northern service will be in operation due to seasonal difficulties. Customers should check with NRES for precise times

Table 82

Saturdays

Manchester → Bolton → Wigan, Kirkby, Southport, Preston, Blackpool North and Barrow-in-Furness

Network Diagram - see first page of Table 82

	NT	NT	NT		TP	NT	NT	NT	NT	NT	NT	TP	NT	NT	NT		NT	NT	TP	NT	NT	NT	NT	NT
					1 ◇		A		B	C		1 ◇ D					E		1 ◇		A		C	
					🍴							🍴							🍴					
Manchester Airport 85 ✈ d	09 03				09 29							10 00		10 03					10 29					
Heald Green 85 d	08 49				09 33									09 49					10 33					
Buxton 86 d					08 27														09 27					
Hazel Grove 86 d					09 04	09 33													10 04	10 33				
Stockport 84 d	08 56				09 25	09 41						09 53		09 56					10 26	10 40				
Manchester Piccadilly 10 d	09 22				09 46	09 54						10 16		10 22					10 46	10 54				
Manchester Oxford Road d	09 26				09 49	09 58						10 19		10 26					10 49	10 58				
Deansgate d	09 28				09 51	10 00								10 28					10 51	11 00				
Rochdale 95 d		09 00	09 14				09 30						09 51		10 00			10b14			10 30			
Manchester Victoria d		09 33	09 46				10 00	10 07			10 10		10 22		10 33			10 46			11 00	11 07		11 10
Salford Central d		09 35	09 49				10 03	10 10			10 13		10 25		10 36			10 49			11 03	11 10		11 13
Salford Crescent a	09 33	09 39	09 52		09 56	10 04	10 07	10 13			10 16		10 29	10 33	10 39			10 52	10 56	11 04	11 07	11 13		11 16
d	09 34	09 40	09 53		09 56	10 04	10 08	10 13			10 17		10 30	10 34	10 40			10 53	10 56	11 04	11 08	11 13		11 17
Swinton d			09 59								10 23							10 59						11 23
Moorside d											10 26													11 26
Walkden d			10 04								10 29							11 04						11 29
Atherton d			10 09								10 35							11 09						11 35
Hag Fold d											10 37													11 37
Daisy Hill d			10 13								10 40							11 13						11 40
Kearsley d		09 47													10 47									
Farnworth d		09 49													10 49									
Moses Gate d		09 52													10 52									
Bolton a	09 45	09 55			10 06	10 14	10 19	10 23				10 32	10 40	10 45	10 55				11 06	11 14	11 19	11 23		
d	09 45	09 56			10 07	10 15		10 24				10 33	10 40	10 45	10 56				11 07	11 15		11 24		
Westhoughton d	09 53							10 31						10 53								11 31		
Hindley d	09 57		10 17					10 35			10 45			10 57				11 17				11 35		11 45
Ince d											10 48													11 48
Wigan North Western a																								
Wigan Wallgate a	10 02	10 13	10 22					10 44			10 51			11 02	11 13			11 22				11 44		11 51
d	10 03		10 24								10 52			11 03				11 24						11 52
Pemberton d											10 56													11 56
Orrell d											11 00													12 00
Upholland d											11 04													12 04
Rainford d											11 07													12 07
Kirkby a											11 19													12 19
Liverpool Central 10 103 a											11 46													12 46
Gathurst d			10 28															11 28						
Appley Bridge d	10 10		10 32											11 10				11 32						
Parbold d	10 14		10 36											11 14				11 36						
Hoscar d			10 39															11 39						
Burscough Bridge d	10 18		10 42											11 18				11 42						
New Lane d			10 44															11 44						
Bescar Lane d			10 48															11 48						
Meols Cop d			10 53															11 53						
Southport a	10 35		11 02											11 35				12 02						
Lostock d						10 20							10 45							11 20				
Horwich Parkway d					10 13	10 24							10 49						11 13	11 24				
Blackrod d													10 52											
Adlington (Lancashire) d													10 56											
Chorley d					10 21	10 32						10 44	11 01						11 21	11 32				
Leyland d						10 42				10 46			11 12							11 42			11 46	
Preston 8 65, 97 a					10 33	10 50				10 54		10 55	11 17						11 33	11 49			11 54	
d					10 38					10 55		10 58	11 19						11 38				11 55	
Kirkham & Wesham 97 a										11 11			11 28										12 13	
Poulton-le-Fylde 97 a					10 56								11 36						11 56					
Layton 97 a													11 44											
Blackpool North 97 a					11 05					11 20			11 49						12 05				12 20	
Lancaster 6 65 a					10c54					11c19		11 14							11c54					
d									11 00			11 14					11 28							
Oxenholme Lake District 65 a					11c08					11c36		11 28							12c22					
Windermere 83 a												11 56							12e47					
Carnforth d									11a09								11 37							
Silverdale d																	11 43							
Arnside d																	11 48							
Grange-over-Sands d																	11 54							
Kents Bank d																	11 57							
Cark d																	12 02							
Ulverston d																	12 10							
Dalton d																	12 18							
Roose d																	12 24							
Barrow-in-Furness a																	12 32							

For general notes see front of timetable
For details of catering facilities see Directory of Train Operators

A To Clitheroe (Table 94)
B From Morecambe to Leeds (Table 36)
C From Liverpool Lime Street (Table 90)
D To Edinburgh (Table 65)
E To Carlisle via Whitehaven (Table 100)
b Until 11 July dep. 1015
c Change at Preston
e Change at Preston and Oxenholme Lake District

From 10 October a revised Northern service will be in operation due to seasonal difficulties. Customers should check with NRES for precise times

Table 82

Saturdays

Manchester → Bolton → Wigan, Kirkby, Southport, Preston, Blackpool North and Barrow-in-Furness

Network Diagram - see first page of Table 82

		TP 1◇ A ⚲	NT	NT	NT	NT		TP 1◇ ⚲	NT	NT B	NT	NT C	NT	TP 1◇ D ⚲	NT	NT	NT	NT E		NT	TP 1◇ ⚲	NT	NT B	NT	NT G
Manchester Airport 85 ✈	d	11 00		11 03				11 29						12 00		12 03					12 29				
Heald Green 85	d			*10 49*				11 33								*11 49*					12 33				
Buxton 86	d							*10 30*													*11 27*				
Hazel Grove 86	d							*11 04*	11 33												*12 04*	12 33			
Stockport 84	d	*10 53*		*10 56*				*11 26*	11 41					*11 53*		*11 56*					*12 26*	12 41			
Manchester Piccadilly 10 ⛴	d	11 16		11 22				11 46	11 54					12 16		12 22					12 46	12 54			
Manchester Oxford Road ⛴	d	11 19		11 26				11 49	11 58					12 19		12 26					12 49	12 58			
Deansgate ⛴	d			11 28				11 51	12 00							12 28					12 51	13 00			
Rochdale 95	d		*10 51*		11 00	*11 14*				*11 30*					*11 51*		12 00			*12 14*			*12 30*		
Manchester Victoria ⛴	d		11 22		11 33	11 46				12 00	12 07		12 10		12 22		12 33			12 46			13 00	13 07	
Salford Central	d		11 25		11 36	11 49				12 03	12 10		12 13		12 25		12 35			12 49			13 03	13 10	
Salford Crescent	a		11 29	11 33	11 39	11 52		11 56	12 04	12 07	12 13		12 16		12 29	12 33	12 39			12 52	12 56	13 04	13 07	13 13	
	d		11 30	11 34	11 40	11 53		11 56	12 04	12 08	12 13		12 17		12 30	12 34	12 40			12 53	12 56	13 04	13 08	13 13	
Swinton	d					11 59							12 23							12 59					
Moorside	d												12 26												
Walkden	d					12 04							12 29							13 04					
Atherton	d					12 09							12 35							13 09					
Hag Fold	d												12 37												
Daisy Hill	d					12 13							12 40							13 13					
Kearsley	d				11 47												12 47								
Farnworth	d				11 49												12 49								
Moses Gate	d				11 52												12 52								
Bolton	a	11 32	11 40	11 45	11 55			12 06	12 14	12 19	12 23			12 32	12 40	12 45	12 55				13 06	13 14	13 19	13 23	
	d	11 33	11 40	11 45	11 56			12 07	12 15		12 24			12 33	12 40	12 45	12 56				13 07	13 15		13 24	
Westhoughton	d			11 53							12 31					12 53								13 31	
Hindley	d			11 57		12 17					12 35		12 45			12 57				13 17				13 35	
Ince	d												12 48												
Wigan North Western	a																								
Wigan Wallgate	a			12 02	12 13	12 22					12 44		12 51			13 02	13 11			13 22				13 44	
	d			12 03		12 24							12 52			13 03				13 24					
Pemberton	d												12 56												
Orrell	d												13 00												
Upholland	d												13 04												
Rainford	d												13 07												
Kirkby	a												13 19												
Liverpool Central 10 103	a												*13 46*												
Gathurst	d					12 28														13 28					
Appley Bridge	d			12 10		12 32										13 10				13 32					
Parbold	d			12 14		12 36										13 14				13 36					
Hoscar	d																			13 39					
Burscough Bridge	d			12 18		12 41										13 18				13 42					
New Lane	d																			13 44					
Bescar Lane	d																			13 48					
Meols Cop	d					12 49														13 53					
Southport	a			12 35		12 59										13 35				14 02					
Lostock	d		11 45						12 20						12 45							13 20			
Horwich Parkway	d		11 49					12 13	12 24						12 49						13 13	13 24			
Blackrod	d		11 52												12 52										
Adlington (Lancashire)	d		11 56												12 56										
Chorley	d	11 44	12 01					12 21	12 32					12 44	13 01						13 21	13 32			
Leyland	d		12 12						12 42			12 46			13 12							13 42			
Preston 8 65, 97	a	11 55	12 17					12 33	12 49			12 54		12 55	13 17						13 33	13 50			
	d	11 58	12 19					12 38				12 55		12 58	13 19						13 38				
Kirkham & Wesham 97	a		12 28					*13 11*				*13 11*			13 28										
Poulton-le-Fylde 97	a		12 36					12 56							13 36						13 56				
Layton 97	a		12 43					*13 43*							13 43										
Blackpool North 97	a		12 48					13 05				13 21			13 48						14 05				
Lancaster 6 65	a	12 14						*12b54*				*13b19*		13 14							*13b54*				
	d	12 14												13 14				13 32							13 48
Oxenholme Lake District 65	a							*13b08*	*13 28*			*13b36*		13 28							*14b08*				
Windermere 83	a													*13 56*											
Carnforth	d	12 23																13 41							13a58
Silverdale	d																	13 47							
Arnside	d	12 31																13 52							
Grange-over-Sands	d	12 37																13 58							
Kents Bank	d																	14 01							
Cark	d																	14 06							
Ulverston	d	12 49																14 14							
Dalton	d																	14 22							
Roose	d																	14 28							
Barrow-in-Furness	a	13 10																14 36							

For general notes see front of timetable
For details of catering facilities see Directory of Train Operators

A ⚲ to Preston
B To Clitheroe (Table 94)
C From Liverpool Lime Street (Table 90)
D To Edinburgh (Table 65)
E To Carlisle via Whitehaven (Table 100)
G From Heysham Port (Table 98) to Leeds (Table 36)
b Change at Preston

From 10 October a revised Northern service will be in operation due to seasonal difficulties. Customers should check with NRES for precise times

Table 82

Saturdays

Manchester → Bolton → Wigan, Kirkby, Southport, Preston, Blackpool North and Barrow-in-Furness

Network Diagram - see first page of Table 82

	NT	NT	TP	NT	NT	NT	NT		NT	TP		NT	NT	NT	NT	NT	TP	NT	NT		NT	NT	TP	NT
			1 ◇							1 ◇							1 ◇						1 ◇	
	A		B				C			D			E		A		G							
Manchester Airport 85 ✈ d			13 00		13 03					13 29							14 00		14 03				14 29	
Heald Green 85 d					12 49					13 33									13 49				14 33	
Buxton 86 d										12 30													13 27	
Hazel Grove 86 d										13 04		13 33											14 04	14 33
Stockport 84 d			12 53		12 56					13 26		13 41					13 53		13 56				14 26	14 41
Manchester Piccadilly 10 d			13 16		13 22					13 46		13 54					14 16		14 22				14 46	14 54
Manchester Oxford Road d			13 19		13 26					13 49		13 58					14 19		14 26				14 49	14 58
Deansgate d					13 28					13 51		14 00							14 28				14 51	15 00
Rochdale 95 d				12 51		13 00			13 14				13 30					13 51			14 00	14 14		
Manchester Victoria d		13 10		13 22		13 33			13 46				14 00	14 07		14 10		14 22			14 33	14 46		
Salford Central d		13 13		13 25		13 36			13 49				14 03	14 10		14 13		14 25			14 36	14 49		
Salford Crescent a		13 16		13 29	13 33	13 39			13 52	13 56		14 04	14 07	14 13		14 16		14 29	14 33		14 39	14 52	14 56	15 04
d		13 17		13 30	13 34	13 40			13 53	13 56		14 04	14 08	14 13		14 17		14 30	14 34		14 40	14 53	14 56	15 04
Swinton d		13 23							13 59							14 23						14 59		
Moorside d		13 26														14 26								
Walkden d		13 29							14 04							14 29						15 04		
Atherton d		13 35							14 09							14 35						15 09		
Hag Fold d		13 37														14 37								
Daisy Hill d		13 40							14 13							14 40						15 13		
Kearsley d						13 47															14 47			
Farnworth d						13 49															14 49			
Moses Gate d						13 52															14 52			
Bolton a			13 32	13 40	13 45	13 55				14 06		14 14	14 19	14 23			14 32	14 40	14 45		14 55		15 06	15 14
d			13 33	13 40	13 45	13 56				14 07		14 15		14 24			14 33	14 40	14 45		14 56		15 07	15 15
Westhoughton d					13 53									14 31					14 53					
Hindley d		13 45			13 57				14 17					14 35		14 45			14 57			15 17		
Ince d		13 48														14 48								
Wigan North Western a																								
Wigan Wallgate a		13 51			14 02	14 13			14 22					14 44		14 51			15 02		15 13	15 22		
d		13 52			14 03				14 24							14 52			15 03			15 24		
Pemberton d		13 56														14 56								
Orrell d		14 00														15 00								
Upholland d		14 04														15 04								
Rainford d		14 07														15 07								
Kirkby a		14 19														15 19								
Liverpool Central 10 103 a		14 46														15 46								
Gathurst d									14 28													15 28		
Appley Bridge d					14 10				14 32										15 10			15 32		
Parbold d					14 14				14 36										15 14			15 36		
Hoscar d																								
Burscough Bridge d					14 18				14 41										15 18			15 40		
New Lane d																								
Bescar Lane d																								
Meols Cop d									14 49													15 48		
Southport a					14 35				14 59										15 35			15 57		
Lostock d				13 45								14 20						14 45						15 20
Horwich Parkway d				13 49						14 13		14 24						14 49					15 13	15 24
Blackrod d				13 52														14 52						
Adlington (Lancashire) d				13 56														14 56						
Chorley d			13 44	14 01						14 21		14 32					14 44	15 01					15 21	15 32
Leyland d	13 46			14 12								14 42			14 46			15 12						15 42
Preston 8 65, 97 a	13 54		13 55	14 17						14 33		14 50			14 54		14 55	15 17					15 33	15 50
d	13 55		13 58	14 19						14 38	14 45				14 55		14 58	15 19					15 38	
Kirkham & Wesham 97 a	14 11			14 28											15 11			15 28						
Poulton-le-Fylde 97 a				14 36						14 56								15 36					15 56	
Layton 97 a				14 43														15 43						
Blackpool North 97 a	14 20			14 48						15 05					15 20			15 48					16 05	
Lancaster 6 65 a			14 14							14b54	15 00						15 14						15b54	
d			14 14				14 22				15 01						15 14							
Oxenholme Lake District 65 a			14 28								15 22						15 28						16b08	
Windermere 83 a			14 52														16 00						16c48	
Carnforth d							14 32				15 09													
Silverdale d							14 38																	
Arnside d							14 42				15 18													
Grange-over-Sands d							14 48				15 23													
Kents Bank d							14 52																	
Cark d							14 56																	
Ulverston d							15 05				15 36													
Dalton d							15 13																	
Roose d							15 19																	
Barrow-in-Furness a							15 26				15 56													

For general notes see front of timetable
For details of catering facilities see Directory of Train Operators

A From Liverpool Lime Street (Table 90)
B To Glasgow Central (Table 65)
C To Carlisle via Whitehaven (Table 100)
D to Preston
E To Clitheroe (Table 94)
G To Edinburgh (Table 65)
b Change at Preston
c Change at Preston and Oxenholme Lake District

From 10 October a revised Northern service will be in operation due to seasonal difficulties. Customers should check with NRES for precise times

Manchester → Bolton → Wigan, Kirkby, Southport, Preston, Blackpool North and Barrow-in-Furness

Network Diagram - see first page of Table 82

	NT	NT	NT	NT	TP	NT	NT	NT	NT		NT	NT	TP	NT	NT	NT	NT	NT	TP	NT		NT	NT
					1 ◇								1 ◇						1 ◇				
	A		B		C				A		D					E		B	G			A	
					🛒								🛒						🛒				
Manchester Airport 85 ✈ d					15 00		15 03						15 29						16 00				16 03
Heald Green 85 d							*14 49*						15 33										*15 49*
Buxton 86 d													*14 30*										
Hazel Grove 86 d													*15 04*	15 33									
Stockport 84 d					*14 53*		*14 56*						*15 26*	15 41					*15 53*				*15 56*
Manchester Piccadilly 10 ⇌ d					15 16		15 22						15 46	15 54					16 16				16 22
Manchester Oxford Road d					15 19		15 26						15 49	15 58					16 19				16 26
Deansgate ⇌ d							15 28						15 51	16 00									16 28
Rochdale 95 d	*14 30*					*14 51*		15 00	*15 14*						*15 30*					*15 51*			
Manchester Victoria ⇌ d	15 00	15 07		15 10		15 22		15 33	15 40			15 46			16 07		16 10			16 20		16 23	
Salford Central d	15 03	15 10		15 13		15 25		15 35	15 43			15 49			16 10		16 13			16 23		16 26	
Salford Crescent a	15 07	15 13		15 16		15 29	15 33	15 39	15 46			15 52	15 56	16 04	16 13		16 16			16 26		16 30	16 34
d	15 08	15 13		15 17		15 30	15 34	15 40	15 47			15 53	15 56	16 04	16 13		16 17			16 27		16 31	16 34
Swinton d				15 23								15 59					16 23						
Moorside d				15 26													16 26						
Walkden d				15 29								16 04					16 29						
Atherton d				15 35								16 09					16 35						
Hag Fold d				15 37													16 37						
Daisy Hill d				15 40								16 13					16 40						
Kearsley d								15 47															
Farnworth d								15 49															
Moses Gate d								15 52															
Bolton a	15 19	15 23			15 32	15 40	15 45	15 55	15 59				16 06	16 14	16 23				16 32	16 37		16 42	16 45
d		15 24			15 33	15 40	15 45	15 56					16 07	16 15	16 24				16 33	16 37			16 45
Westhoughton d		15 31					15 53								16 31								16 53
Hindley d		15 35		15 45			15 57					16 17			16 35		16 45						16 57
Ince d				15 48													16 48						
Wigan North Western a																							
Wigan Wallgate a		15 44		15 51			16 02	16 11				16 22			16 44		16 51						17 02
d				15 52			16 03					16 24					16 52						17 03
Pemberton d				15 56													16 56						
Orrell d				16 00													17 00						
Upholland d				16 04													17 04						
Rainford d				16 07													17 07						
Kirkby a				16 19													17 19						
Liverpool Central 10 103 a				*16 46*													*17 46*						
Gathurst d							16 08					16 28											17 08
Appley Bridge d							16 11					16 32											17 11
Parbold d							16 15					16 36											17 15
Hoscar d							16 18																
Burscough Bridge d							16 21					16 40											17 20
New Lane d							16 24																
Bescar Lane d							16 27																
Meols Cop d							16 32					16 48											17 27
Southport a							16 42					16 57											17 37
Lostock d						15 45								16 20						16 43			
Horwich Parkway d						15 49							16 13	16 24						16 47			
Blackrod d						15 52														16 51			
Adlington (Lancashire) d						15 56														16 55			
Chorley d					15 44	16 01							16 21	16 32					16 44	17 00			
Leyland d			15 46			16 12								16 42				16 46		17 12			
Preston 8 65, 97 a			15 54		15 55	16 19							16 33	16 50				16 54	16 55	17 19			
d			15 55		15 58								16 38					16 55	17 00 17 04	17 21			
Kirkham & Wesham 97 a			*16 13*										16 47					*17 11*		17 30			
Poulton-le-Fylde 97 a						*16 50*							16 57							17 38			
Layton 97 a													17 00							17 43			
Blackpool North 97 a			16 20			*17 00*							17 07					17 20		17 48			
Lancaster 6 65 a					16 14								*16b54*						17 15 17 20				
d					16 14						16 40					16 59			17 16 17 21				
Oxenholme Lake District 65 a													*17b24*						17 30 17 38				
Windermere 83 a																			18 00				
Carnforth d					16 22						16a49					17 10							
Silverdale d					16 28											17 17							
Arnside d					16 32											17 21							
Grange-over-Sands d					16 38											17 27							
Kents Bank d					16 41											17 31							
Cark d					16 46											17 35							
Ulverston d					16 54											17 44							
Dalton d					17 02											17 53							
Roose d					17 08											17 59							
Barrow-in-Furness a					17 18											18 07							

For general notes see front of timetable
For details of catering facilities see Directory of Train Operators

A To Clitheroe (Table 94)
B From Liverpool Lime Street (Table 90)
C 🛒 to Preston
D From Morecambe to Leeds (Table 36)
E To Millom (Table 100)
G 1700 departure from Preston continues to Edinburgh (Table 65). 🛒 to Oxenholme Lake District
b Change at Preston

From 10 October a revised Northern service will be in operation due to seasonal difficulties. Customers should check with NRES for precise times

Manchester → Bolton → Wigan, Kirkby, Southport, Preston, Blackpool North and Barrow-in-Furness

Network Diagram - see first page of Table 82

	NT	NT	TP	NT	NT	NT	NT	NT	NT	TP	NT	
			1 ◇							1 ◇		
						A			B	C		
			🛒							🛒		
Manchester Airport 85 ✈ d			16 29							17 00		
Heald Green 85 d			16 33									
Buxton 86 d			*15 27*									
Hazel Grove 86 d			*16 04*		16 33							
Stockport 84 d			*16 26*		16 41					*16 52*		
Manchester Piccadilly 10 d			16 46		16 54					17 15		
Manchester Oxford Road d			16 49		16 58					17 18		
Deansgate d					17 00							
Rochdale 95 d	16 00			*16 14*		*16 30*					*16 51*	
Manchester Victoria d	16 36			16 46		17 00	17 07	17 10			17 19	
Salford Central d	16 39			16 49		17 03	17 10	17 13			17 22	
Salford Crescent a	16 42			16 52	17 04	17 07	17 13	17 17			17 25	
d	16 43			16 53	17 04	17 08	17 13	17 18			17 27	
Swinton d				16 59				17 24				
Moorside d				17 02				17 26				
Walkden d				17 05				17 29				
Atherton d				17 11				17 35				
Hag Fold d				17 14				17 37				
Daisy Hill d				17 17				17 40				
Kearsley d	16 50											
Farnworth d	16 52											
Moses Gate d	16 55											
Bolton a	16 58		17 05		17 14	17 19	17 23			17 31	17 37	
d	16 59		17 06		17 15		17 24			17 32	17 37	
Westhoughton d	17 06						17 31					
Hindley d	17 10			17 21			17 35	17 45				
Ince d				17 24				17 48				
Wigan North Western a												
Wigan Wallgate a	17 19			17 27			17 44	17 51				
d				17 29				17 52				
Pemberton d								17 56				
Orrell d								18 00				
Upholland d								18 04				
Rainford d								18 07				
Kirkby a								18 19				
Liverpool Central 10 103 a								*18 46*				
Gathurst d				17 33								
Appley Bridge d				17 37								
Parbold d				17 41								
Hoscar d												
Burscough Bridge d				17 45								
New Lane d												
Bescar Lane d												
Meols Cop d				17 53								
Southport a				18 02								
Lostock d					17 20						17 43	
Horwich Parkway d					17 24						17 47	
Blackrod d											17 51	
Adlington (Lancashire) d											17 55	
Chorley d			17 19		17 32					17 44	18 00	
Leyland d					17 42				17 46		18 11	
Preston 8 65, 97 a			17 30		17 50				17 54	17 55	18 16	
d			17 32						17 55	17 58	18 18	
Kirkham & Wesham 97 a			17 41						*18 11*		18 27	
Poulton-le-Fylde 97 a			17 51								18 35	
Layton 97 a			17 54								18 43	
Blackpool North 97 a			18 02						18 20		18 48	
Lancaster 6 65 a			*17c54*							18 14		
d		17 32								18 14		
Oxenholme Lake District 65 a			*18c08*									
Windermere 83 a			*18e49*									
Carnforth d		17 43								18 24		
Silverdale d		17 49								18 30		
Arnside d		17 53								18 34		
Grange-over-Sands d		17 59								18 40		
Kents Bank d		18 03								18 43		
Cark d		18 07								18 48		
Ulverston d		18 16								18 56		
Dalton d		18 24								19 04		
Roose d		18 30								19 10		
Barrow-in-Furness a		18 38								19 19		

	NT	NT	NT	NT	NT	NT	TP	NT	NT	NT	NT	NT
							1 ◇					
	D		E	B		E				A		B
							🛒					
Manchester Airport 85 ✈ d		17 03					17 27					
Heald Green 85 d		*16 49*					17 31					
Buxton 86 d							*16 30*					
Hazel Grove 86 d							*17 04*		17 33			
Stockport 84 d		*16 55*					*17b26*		17 41			
Manchester Piccadilly 10 d		17 22					17 46		17 54			
Manchester Oxford Road d		17 26					17 49		17 58			
Deansgate d							17 51		18 00			
Rochdale 95 d	17 00				*17 14*					*17 30*		
Manchester Victoria d	17 23		17 36		17 40			17 50		18 00	18 08	
Salford Central d	17 26		17 39		17 43			17 53		18 03	18 12	
Salford Crescent a	17 30	17 34	17 42		17 46		17 55	17 58	18 04	18 07	18 16	
d	17 31	17 34	17 43		17 47		17 55	17 59	18 04	18 08	18 17	
Swinton d								18 05			18 23	
Moorside d								18 08			18 26	
Walkden d								18 11			18 29	
Atherton d					17 59			18 17			18 35	
Hag Fold d								18 19			18 37	
Daisy Hill d					18 03			18 22			18 40	
Kearsley d			17 53									
Farnworth d			17 55			←						
Moses Gate d			17 57			17 57						
Bolton a	17 42	17 45	→			18 01	18 05		18 14	18 19		
d		17 45				18 01	18 07		18 15			
Westhoughton d		17 53				18 09						
Hindley d						18 13		18 27			18 45	
Ince d											18 48	
Wigan North Western a											18 56	
Wigan Wallgate a		18 01			18 11	18 22		18 32				
d		18 02			18 15			18 33				
Pemberton d								18 37				
Orrell d								18 41				
Upholland d								18 45				
Rainford d								18 48				
Kirkby a								19 00				
Liverpool Central 10 103 a								*19 31*				
Gathurst d					18 19							
Appley Bridge d		18 09			18 23							
Parbold d		18 13			18 28							
Hoscar d												
Burscough Bridge d		18 17			18 33							
New Lane d												
Bescar Lane d												
Meols Cop d					18 41							
Southport a		18 35			18 50							
Lostock d							18 11		18 20			
Horwich Parkway d							18 15		18 24			
Blackrod d							18 18					
Adlington (Lancashire) d												
Chorley d							18 25		18 32			
Leyland d				18 21			18 33		18 42			18 46
Preston 8 65, 97 a				18 31			18 38		18 48			18 54
d							18 40		18 50			18 55
Kirkham & Wesham 97 a							18 49					*19 11*
Poulton-le-Fylde 97 a							18 59					
Layton 97 a							19 02					
Blackpool North 97 a							19 09		19 16			19 20
Lancaster 6 65 a				*18 54*			*19c08*					*19c20*
d												
Oxenholme Lake District 65 a				*19 08*			*19c22*					
Windermere 83 a												
Carnforth d												
Silverdale d												
Arnside d												
Grange-over-Sands d												
Kents Bank d												
Cark d												
Ulverston d												
Dalton d												
Roose d												
Barrow-in-Furness a												

For general notes see front of timetable
For details of catering facilities see Directory of Train Operators

- **A** To Clitheroe (Table 94)
- **B** From Liverpool Lime Street (Table 90)
- **C** 🛒 to Preston
- **D** To Blackburn (Table 94)
- **E** Also stops at Clifton 1748
- **b** Change at Manchester Oxford Road
- **c** Change at Preston
- **e** Change at Preston and Oxenholme Lake District

From 10 October a revised Northern service will be in operation due to seasonal difficulties. Customers should check with NRES for precise times

Manchester → Bolton → Wigan, Kirkby, Southport, Preston, Blackpool North and Barrow-in-Furness

Network Diagram - see first page of Table 82

		TP		TP	NT	NT	NT	NT	NT	NT	TP	NT	NT	NT		NT	TP	NT	NT	NT	TP	NT	NT	TP	NT
		1 ◇		1 ◇							1 ◇						1 ◇				1 ◇			1 ◇	
		A			B		C						D	E				B				D			
		🍴									🍴														
Manchester Airport	85 ✈ d	18 00						18 03			18 29						19 00		19 03		19 29			20 00	
Heald Green	85 d							*17 49*			18 33										19 33				
Buxton	86 d										*17 27*										*18 27*				
Hazel Grove	86 d										*18 04*	18 33									*19 04*				
Stockport	84 d	*17 53*						*17 56*			*18 26*	18 41					*18 53*		*18 56*		*19 26*			*19 53*	
Manchester Piccadilly 10	🚇 d	18 16						18 22			18 46	18 54					19 16		19 20		19 46			20 16	
Manchester Oxford Road	d	18 19						18 26			18 49	18 58					19 19		19 24		19 49			20 19	
Deansgate	🚇 d							18 28			18 51	19 00							19 26		19 51				
Rochdale	95 d					*17 51*	18 00			*18b14*			*18 32*							*19 00*		*19 32*			*19c53*
Manchester Victoria	🚇 d					18 20	18 23		18 33	18 45			19 00			19 10				19 28		20 00	20 10		20 22
Salford Central	d					18 23	18 26		18 36	18 48			19 03			19 13				19 31		20 03	20 13		20 25
Salford Crescent	a					18 26	18 30	18 34	18 39	18 51	18 56	19 04	19 07			19 16			19 29	19 34	19 56	20 07	20 16		20 29
	d					18 27	18 31	18 34	18 40	18 52	18 56	19 04	19 08			19 17			19 30	19 35	19 56	20 08	20 17		20 30
Swinton	d									18 58						19 23							20 23		
Moorside	d									19 01						19 26							20 26		
Walkden	d									19 04						19 29							20 29		
Atherton	d									19 10						19 35							20 35		
Hag Fold	d									19 12						19 37							20 37		
Daisy Hill	d									19 15						19 40							20 40		
Kearsley	d								18 47																
Farnworth	d								18 49																
Moses Gate	d								18 52																
Bolton	a	18 32				18 37	18 42	18 45	18 55		19 06	19 19	19 20				19 32		19 40	19 45	20 06	20 19		20 32	20 40
	d	18 33				18 37		18 45	18 56		19 07						19 33		19 40	19 45	20 07			20 33	20 40
Westhoughton	d							18 53	19 03										19 48						
Hindley	d							18 57	19 09	19 20						19 45			19 52				20 45		
Ince	d									19 23						19 48							20 48		
Wigan North Western	a																								
Wigan Wallgate	a							19 02	19 18	19 30						19 55			19 57				20 55		
	d							19 03											19 59						
Pemberton	d																								
Orrell	d																								
Upholland	d																								
Rainford	d																								
Kirkby	a																								
Liverpool Central 10	103 a																								
Gathurst	d							19 07											20 03						
Appley Bridge	d							19 11											20 07						
Parbold	d							19 15											20 11						
Hoscar	d							19 18																	
Burscough Bridge	d							19 21											20 15						
New Lane	d							19 23																	
Bescar Lane	d							19 27																	
Meols Cop	d							19 32											20 23						
Southport	a							19 42											20 32						
Lostock	d					18 42					19 12									19 50					20 45
Horwich Parkway	d					18 46					19 15									19 54	20 13				20 49
Blackrod	d					18 49														19 57					20 52
Adlington (Lancashire)	d					18 53														20 01					20 56
Chorley	d	18 44				18 58					19 23						19 44			20 06	20 21			20 44	21 01
Leyland	d				19 06	19 11												20 10		20 18					21 12
Preston 8	65, 97 a	18 55			19 15	19 18					19 33						19 58	20 18		20 24	20 33			20 58	21 17
	d	19 00		19 04		19 20					19 38						20 02	20 19		20 25	20 38			21 02	21 19
Kirkham & Wesham	97 a					19 29					*20 11*									20 35	*21 11*				21 28
Poulton-le-Fylde	97 a					19 37					19 56									20 43	20 56				21 36
Layton	97 a					19 43														20 47					21 40
Blackpool North	97 a					19 48					20 05							20 44		20 54	21 06				21 48
Lancaster 6	65 a	19 16		19 20							*19e54*						20 18				*20e54*			21 18	
	d	19 16		19 20										19 24			20 18							21 18	
Oxenholme Lake District	65 a	19 30									*20e08*						*21 08*				*21e08*				
Windermere	83 a	*19 56*									*20f42*						*21g34*				*21f34*				
Carnforth	d			19 29										19a33			20 26							21 26	
Silverdale	d			19 35													20 32							21 32	
Arnside	d			19 39													20 36							21 36	
Grange-over-Sands	d			19 44													20 42							21 42	
Kents Bank	d			19 48													20 45							21 45	
Cark	d			19 52													20 50							21 50	
Ulverston	d			20 00													20 58							21 58	
Dalton	d			20 08													21 06							22 06	
Roose	d			20 14													21 12							22 12	
Barrow-in-Furness	a			20 24													21 20							22 20	

For general notes see front of timetable
For details of catering facilities see Directory of Train Operators

- **A** To Glasgow Central (Table 65)
- **B** From Liverpool Lime Street (Table 90)
- **C** To Blackburn (Table 94)
- **D** To Clitheroe (Table 94)
- **E** From Morecambe to Leeds (Table 36)
- **b** Until 11 July dep. 1816
- **c** Until 11 July dep. 1952
- **e** Change at Preston
- **f** Change at Preston and Oxenholme Lake District
- **g** Change at Lancaster and Oxenholme Lake District

From 10 October a revised Northern service will be in operation due to seasonal difficulties. Customers should check with NRES for precise times

Table 82

Saturdays

Manchester → Bolton → Wigan, Kirkby, Southport, Preston, Blackpool North and Barrow-in-Furness

Network Diagram - see first page of Table 82

		NT	NT	TP 1◇		NT	NT	NT	NT	NT	TP 1◇	NT	TP 1◇	NT	NT	NT		NT	TP 1◇	NT	NT	NT	NT		
		A				B						B		A							C				
Manchester Airport	85 ✈ d		20 03	20 29						21 03	21 29		22 00			22 19			22 29						
Heald Green	85 d			20 33							21 33					21 51			22 33						
Buxton	86 d			19 27							20 27								21 27						
Hazel Grove	86 d			20 04							21 04								22 04						
Stockport	84 d		19 56	20 21						20 56	21 21		21b54			21 58			22 12	22 40					
Manchester Piccadilly 10	⇌ d		20 20	20 46						21 20	21 46		22 16			22 36			22 46	22 54					
Manchester Oxford Road	d		20 24	20 49						21 24	21 49		22 19			22 39			22 49	22 58					
Deansgate	⇌ d		20 26	20 51						21 26	21 51					22 41			22 51	23 00					
Rochdale	95 d					20c14			20 52			20 56			21 52			21 56				22 52			
Manchester Victoria	⇌ d					21 00	21 10		21 22			22 00			22 22			22 45			23 05	23 16	23 20		
Salford Central	d					21 03	21 13		21 25			22 03			22 25			22 48			23 08	23 19	23 23		
Salford Crescent	a		20 33	20 56		21 07	21 16		21 29	21 33	21 56	22 07			22 29	22 46		22 51	22 54	23 02	23 11	23 22	23 26		
	d		20 34	20 56		21 08	21 17		21 30	21 34	21 56	22 08			22 30	22 46		22 52	22 56	23 04	23 12	23 22	23 26		
Swinton	d						21 23											22 58					23 33		
Moorside	d						21 26											23 01					23 35		
Walkden	d						21 29											23 04					23 39		
Atherton	d						21 35											23 10					23 44		
Hag Fold	d						21 37											23 12					23 47		
Daisy Hill	d						21 40											23 15					23 50		
Kearsley	d																			23 11					
Farnworth	d																			23 13					
Moses Gate	d																			23 16					
Bolton	a		20 45	21 06		21 19			21 40	21 45	22 06	22 19	22 32		22 40	22 56			23 06	23 19	23 23	23 32			
	d		20 45	21 07					21 40	21 45	22 07		22 33		22 40	22 57			23 07	23 20		23 33			
Westhoughton	d		20 53							21 53						23 04				23 27					
Hindley	d		20 57				21 45			21 57						23 08		23 20		23 31			23 54		
Ince	d						21 48											23 23					23 57		
Wigan North Western	a																								
Wigan Wallgate	a		21 02				21 55			22 02						23 13		23 30		23 41			00 04		
	d		21 03							22 03						23 15									
Pemberton	d																								
Orrell	d																								
Upholland	d																								
Rainford	d																								
Kirkby	a																								
Liverpool Central 10	103 a																								
Gathurst	d		21 08							22 08						23 19									
Appley Bridge	d		21 11							22 11						23 23									
Parbold	d		21 15							22 15						23 27									
Hoscar	d		21 18																						
Burscough Bridge	d		21 21							22 20						23 31									
New Lane	d		21 24																						
Bescar Lane	d		21 27																						
Meols Cop	d		21 32							22 27						23 39									
Southport	a		21 42							22 37						23 48									
Lostock	d								21 45						22 45							23 38			
Horwich Parkway	d			21 13					21 49		22 13				22 49				23 13			23 42			
Blackrod	d								21 52						22 52							23 45			
Adlington (Lancashire)	d								21 56						22 56							23 49			
Chorley	d			21 21					22 01		22 21				23 01				23 21			23 54			
Leyland	d	21 16							22 11					22 44	23 12							00 04			
Preston 8	65, 97 a	21 22		21 33					22 17		22 33		22 54	22 54	23 17				23 33			00 10			
	d	21 24		21 38				21 59	22 19		22 35		22 55	22 56	23 19				23 35			00 11			
Kirkham & Wesham	97 a								22 28		23 00				23 28							00 21			
Poulton-le-Fylde	97 a	21 50		21 56					22 36		22 52				23 36				23 52			00 29			
Layton	97 a								22 40						23 40							00 33			
Blackpool North	97 a	21 53		22 06					22 48		23 01			23 21	23 48				00 01			00 40			
Lancaster 6	65 a							22 19					23 11												
	d							22 19					23 11												
Oxenholme Lake District	65 a																								
Windermere	83 a																								
Carnforth	d							22 29					23 20												
Silverdale	d							22 35					23 26												
Arnside	d							22 40					23 30												
Grange-over-Sands	d							22 46					23 35												
Kents Bank	d							22 49					23 39												
Cark	d							22 54					23 43												
Ulverston	d							23 02					23 51												
Dalton	d							23 10					23 59												
Roose	d							23 16					00 05												
Barrow-in-Furness	a							23 24					00 15												

For general notes see front of timetable
For details of catering facilities see Directory of Train Operators

A From Liverpool Lime Street (Table 90)
B To Clitheroe (Table 94)
C To Blackburn (Table 94)

b Until 11 July dep. 2151
c Until 11 July dep. 2020

From 10 October a revised Northern service will be in operation due to seasonal difficulties. Customers should check with NRES for precise times

Table 82

Sundays
until 6 September

Manchester → Bolton → Wigan, Southport, Preston, Blackpool North and Barrow-in-Furness

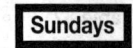

Network Diagram - see first page of Table 82

		NT	TP	TP	NT	TP		NT	NT	TP	NT	NT		TP	NT	NT	TP			NT	NT	NT	NT	NT	TP
						1 ◇				1 ◇				1 ◇			1 ◇								1 ◇
		A			B						B	A					C			B	D	E		G	
			🚌	🚌													✠								
Manchester Airport	85 ⇌ d		00 10	05 30		07 55			08b06	08 30				09 00			09 30							09b35	10 29
Heald Green	85 d					07 33				08 12							09 09								10 11
Buxton	86 d															08b23									09 19
Hazel Grove	86 d															09b00									09 55
Stockport	84 d		00 02						08 22					08 31		09 22								10 12	
Manchester Piccadilly 10	⇌ d		00 35	05 55		08 11			08 35	08 46				09 16		09 35	09 46							10 26	10 43
Manchester Oxford Road	d					08 14			08 37	08 49				09 19		09 38	09 49							10 37	10 49
Deansgate	⇌ d					08 16			08 40	08 51						09 40	09 51							10 40	10 51
Rochdale	95 d																						09 41		
Manchester Victoria	⇌ d				08 01			08 25			09 00				09 25					10 00			10 25		
Salford Crescent	a				08 07	08 19		08 29	08 44	08 54	09 06				09 29	09 44	09 54			10 06			10 29	10 44	10 54
	d				08 08	08 20		08 30	08 44	08 55	09 08				09 30	09 44	09 55			10 08			10 30	10 44	10 55
Bolton	a		01s00	06s20	08 19	08 30		08 40	08 54	09 05	09 19			09 32	09 40	09 54	10 05			10 19			10 40	10 54	11 05
	d					08 30		08 40	08 55	09 05				09 33	09 40	09 55	10 05						10 40	10 55	11 05
Westhoughton	d								09 02							10 02								11 02	
Hindley	d								09 06							10 06								11 06	
Wigan North Western	a																								
Wigan Wallgate	a								09 11							10 11								11 11	
	d								09 13							10 13								11 13	
Gathurst	d								09 17							10 17								11 17	
Appley Bridge	d								09 21							10 21								11 21	
Parbold	d								09 25							10 25								11 25	
Burscough Bridge	d								09 29							10 29								11 29	
Meols Cop	d								09 37							10 37								11 37	
Southport	a								09 46							10 46								11 46	
Lostock	d							08 45							09 45								10 45		
Horwich Parkway	d					08 37		08 49		09 12					09 49		10 12						10 49		11 12
Blackrod	d							08 52							09 52								10 52		
Adlington (Lancashire)	d							08 56							09 56								10 56		
Chorley	d					08 45		09 01		09 20				09 44	10 01		10 20						11 01		11 20
Leyland	d	00 07		06s45				09 12				09 29			10 12						10 31	10 33	11 12		
Preston 8	65 a	00 16	01s35	07s00		08 56		09 17		09 32		09 37		09 56	10 17		10 31				10 39	10 41	11 20		11 32
	d					08 57		09 19		09 34		09 39		10 00	10 19		10 34	10 39			10 40	10 42	11 21		11 34
Kirkham & Wesham	97 a			07s20				09 28							10 28		11 31						11 31		11 53
Poulton-le-Fylde	97 a			07s40		09 14		09 36		09 51		09 56			10 36		10 51				10 59	10 59	11 39		11 51
Layton	97 a							09 41							10 41								11 44		
Blackpool North	97 a		02 15	07 55		09 25		09 46		10 00		10 06			10 46		11 00				11 09	11 09	11 49		12 00
Lancaster 6	65 a													10 15			10c54	10 54			11c08	11c13	11e52		
	d													10 16				10 55							
Oxenholme Lake District	65 a													10 37				11 09			11c22	11c27	12e06		
Windermere	83 a													11 00							11f52	11f52			
Carnforth	d													10 24											
Silverdale	d													10 30											
Arnside	d													10 34											
Grange-over-Sands	d													10 40											
Kents Bank	d													10 44											
Cark	d													10 48											
Ulverston	d													10 56											
Dalton	d													11 04											
Roose	d													11 10											
Barrow-in-Furness	a													11 19											

For general notes see front of timetable
For details of catering facilities see Directory of Train Operators

A From Liverpool Lime Street (Table 90)
B To Clitheroe (Table 94)
C 1039 departure from Preston continues to Glasgow Central (Table 65)
D From 19 July. From Liverpool Lime Street (Table 90)
E Until 12 July. From Liverpool Lime Street (Table 90)
G From Chester (Table 88)

b Change at Manchester Piccadilly
c Change at Preston
e Change at Preston. From 19 July arr. Lancaster 1157, Oxenholme Lake District 1210
f Change at Preston and Oxenholme Lake District

Table 82

Sundays

until 6 September

Manchester → Bolton → Wigan, Southport, Preston, Blackpool North and Barrow-in-Furness

Network Diagram - see first page of Table 82

Station		NT A	NT B	TP 1 ◇	NT	NT	TP 1 ◇	NT A	NT C	NT B	TP 1 ◇ D	NT	NT E	TP 1 ◇	NT A	NT B	TP 1 ◇ G		NT	NT	TP 1 ◇
Manchester Airport	85 d			11 00		*11 03*	11 30				12 00			12 30			13 00				13 30
Heald Green	85 d					*11 07*								*12 12*							*13 12*
Buxton	86 d					*10 23*								*11 27*							*12 27*
Hazel Grove	86 d					*10 59*								*12 04*							*13 04*
Stockport	84 d			*10 53*		*11 07*					*11 53*		12 21	*12b26*			*12 53*			13 22	*13b26*
Manchester Piccadilly 10	d			11 16		11 35	11 46				12 16		12 35	12 46			13 16			13 35	13 46
Manchester Oxford Road	d			11 19		11 37	11 49				12 19		12 37	12 49			13 19			13 37	13 49
Deansgate	d					11 40	11 51						12 40	12 51						13 40	13 51
Rochdale	95 d	*10 17*			*10 23*			*11 09*				*11 23*			*12 09*				*12 23*		
Manchester Victoria	d	11 00			11 25			12 00				12 25			13 00				13 25		
Salford Crescent	a	11 06			11 29	11 44	11 54	12 06				12 29	12 44	12 54	13 06				13 29	13 44	13 54
	d	11 08			11 30	11 44	11 55	12 08				12 30	12 44	12 55	13 08				13 30	13 44	13 55
Bolton	a	11 19		11 32	11 40	11 54	12 05	12 19			12 32	12 40	12 54	13 05	13 19		13 32		13 40	13 54	14 05
	d			11 33	11 40	11 55	12 05				12 33	12 40	12 55	13 05			13 33		13 40	13 55	14 05
Westhoughton	d					12 02							13 02							14 02	
Hindley	d					12 06							13 06							14 06	
Wigan North Western	a																				
Wigan Wallgate	a					12 11							13 11							14 11	
	d					12 13							13 13							14 13	
Gathurst	d					12 17							13 17							14 17	
Appley Bridge	d					12 21							13 21							14 21	
Parbold	d					12 25							13 25							14 25	
Burscough Bridge	d					12 29							13 29							14 29	
Meols Cop	d					12 37							13 37							14 37	
Southport	a					12 46							13 46							14 46	
Lostock	d				11 45							12 45							13 45		
Horwich Parkway	d				11 49		12 12					12 49		13 12					13 49		14 12
Blackrod	d				11 52							12 52							13 52		
Adlington (Lancashire)	d				11 56							12 56							13 56		
Chorley	d			11 44	12 01		12 20				12 44	13 01		13 20			13 44		14 01		14 20
Leyland	d		11 29		12 12					12 29		13 12				13 29			14 12		
Preston 8	65 a		11 37	11 56	12 18		12 32			12 37	12 56	13 18		13 32		13 37	13 56		14 18		14 32
	d		11 39	12 02	12 20		12 34			12 39	12 58	13 20		13 34		13 39	14 01	14 05	14 20		14 34
Kirkham & Wesham	97 a				12 29		*12 53*					13 29		*13 53*					14 29		*14 53*
Poulton-le-Fylde	97 a		11 57	*12 31*	12 37		12 51			12 57	*13 31*	13 37		13 51		13 57	*14c31*		14 37		14 51
Layton	97 a				12 42							13 42							14 42		
Blackpool North	97 a		12 07	*12 38*	12 47		13 00			13 07	*13 38*	13 47		14 00		14 07	*14 38*		14 47		15 00
Lancaster 6	65 a		*12e08*	12 17	*12e53*					*13e08*	13 14	*13f51*				*14e08*	14 16	14 21			*14e56*
	d			12 18					12 48		13 14						14 16	14 21			
Oxenholme Lake District	65 a		*12e22*		*13e07*					*13e22*	13 28	*14f05*					14 30				
Windermere	83 a		*12g52*								*13 52*						*14 54*				
Carnforth	d			12 26					12a57									14 30			
Silverdale	d			12 32														14 35			
Arnside	d			12 36														14 40			
Grange-over-Sands	d			12 42														14 45			
Kents Bank	d			12 46														14 49			
Cark	d			12 50														14 53			
Ulverston	d			12 58														15 01			
Dalton	d			13 06														15 10			
Roose	d			13 12														15 15			
Barrow-in-Furness	a			13 21														15 24			

For general notes see front of timetable
For details of catering facilities see Directory of Train Operators

A To Clitheroe (Table 94)
B From Liverpool Lime Street (Table 90)
C From Morecambe to Leeds (Table 36)
D To Edinburgh (Table 65)
E From Chester (Table 88)
G To Glasgow Central (Table 65)
b Change at Manchester Oxford Road
c From 19 July arr. 1430
e Change at Preston
f Change at Preston. From 19 July arr. Lancaster 1358, Oxenholme Lake District 1412
g Change at Preston and Oxenholme Lake District

Table 82

Sundays
until 6 September

Manchester → Bolton → Wigan, Southport, Preston, Blackpool North and Barrow-in-Furness

Network Diagram - see first page of Table 82

Station			NT	NT	NT	TP	NT	NT	TP	NT	NT	TP	NT	NT	TP	NT	NT	NT	TP		NT	NT
						1 ◇			1 ◇			1 ◇			1 ◇				1 ◇			
			A	B	C	D		E		A	C					A		C	G			E
						🍴													🍴			
Manchester Airport	85 ✈	d				14 00			14 30			15 00			15 30				16 00			
Heald Green	85	d							14 12						15 12							
Buxton	86	d							13 27						14 27							
Hazel Grove	86	d							14 04						15 04							
Stockport	84	d				13 53		14 21	14b26			14 53		15 22	15b26				15 54			16 21
Manchester Piccadilly 10	✈	d				14 16		14 35	14 46			15 16		15 35	15 46				16 16			16 35
Manchester Oxford Road		d				14 19		14 37	14 49			15 19		15 37	15 49				16 19			16 37
Deansgate	✈	d						14 40	14 51					15 40	15 51							16 40
Rochdale	95	d	13 09				13 23			14 09			14 23			15 09					15 23	
Manchester Victoria	✈	d	14 00				14 25			15 00			15 25			16 00					16 25	
Salford Crescent		a	14 06				14 29	14 44	14 54	15 06			15 29	15 44	15 54	16 06					16 29	16 44
		d	14 08				14 30	14 44	14 55	15 08			15 30	15 44	15 55	16 08					16 30	16 44
Bolton		a	14 19			14 32	14 40	14 54	15 05	15 19		15 32	15 40	15 54	16 05	16 19			16 32		16 40	16 54
		d				14 33	14 40	14 55	15 05			15 33	15 40	15 55	16 05				16 33		16 40	16 55
Westhoughton		d						15 02						16 02								17 02
Hindley		d						15 06						16 06								17 06
Wigan North Western		a																				
Wigan Wallgate		a						15 11						16 11								17 11
		d						15 13						16 13								17 13
Gathurst		d						15 17						16 17								17 17
Appley Bridge		d						15 21						16 21								17 21
Parbold		d						15 25						16 25								17 25
Burscough Bridge		d						15 29						16 29								17 29
Meols Cop		d						15 37						16 37								17 37
Southport		a						15 46						16 46								17 46
Lostock		d					14 45						15 45								16 45	
Horwich Parkway		d					14 49		15 12				15 49		16 12						16 49	
Blackrod		d					14 52						15 52								16 52	
Adlington (Lancashire)		d					14 56						15 56								16 56	
Chorley		d				14 44	15 01		15 20			15 44	16 01		16 20				16 44		17 01	
Leyland		d			14 29		15 13				15 29		16 12					16 29			17 12	
Preston 8	65	a			14 37	14 56	15 18		15 32		15 37	15 56	16 18		16 32			16 37	16 56		17 18	
		d			14 39	15 00	15 20		15 34		15 39	16 00	16 20		16 34			16 39	17 02	17 06	17 20	
Kirkham & Wesham	97	a					15 29		15 53				16 29		16 53						17 29	
Poulton-le-Fylde	97	a			14 57	15 32	15 37		15 51		15 57	16 31	16 37		16 51			16 57	17 31		17 37	
Layton	97	a					15 43						16 42								17 42	
Blackpool North	97	a			15 07	15c40	15 48		16 00		16 07	16 38	16 47		17 00			17 07	17 38		17 47	
Lancaster 6	65	a			15e10	15 16			15e56		16e10	16 16			16e56			17e10	17 18	17 21		
		d		14 50		15 16						16 16					17 04		17 18	17 22		
Oxenholme Lake District	65	a			15e24	15 30			16e10									17e24	17 32	17 38		
Windermere	83	a				15 54			16f52											18 02		
Carnforth		d		14a59								16 24					17 14					
Silverdale		d										16 30					17 20					
Arnside		d										16 34					17 25					
Grange-over-Sands		d										16 40					17 31					
Kents Bank		d										16 44					17 34					
Cark		d										16 48					17 38					
Ulverston		d										16 56					17 47					
Dalton		d										17 04					17 56					
Roose		d										17 10					18 02					
Barrow-in-Furness		a										17 19					18 09					

For general notes see front of timetable
For details of catering facilities see Directory of Train Operators

A To Clitheroe (Table 94)
B From Morecambe to Leeds (Table 36)
C From Liverpool Lime Street (Table 90)
D To Edinburgh (Table 65)
E From Chester (Table 88)
G 1702 departure from Preston continues to Edinburgh (Table 65)
b Change at Manchester Oxford Road
c From 19 July arr. 1539
e Change at Preston
f Change at Preston and Oxenholme Lake District

Table 82

Sundays

until 6 September

Manchester → Bolton → Wigan, Southport, Preston, Blackpool North and Barrow-in-Furness

Network Diagram - see first page of Table 82

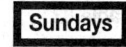

	TP 1 ◇	NT A	NT B	NT C	TP 1 ◇ D (18 02)	TP 1 ◇ D (18 06)	NT	NT	TP 1 ◇	NT A	NT C	TP 1 ◇ E	NT	NT G	TP 1 ◇	NT A	NT C	TP 1 ◇	NT	NT B	NT
Manchester Airport 85 d	16 30				17 00				17 30			18 00			18 30			19 00			
Heald Green 85 d	*16 12*								*17 12*						*18 12*						
Buxton 86 d	*15 27*								*16 27*						*17 27*						
Hazel Grove 86 d	*16 04*								*17 04*						*18 04*						
Stockport 84 d	*16b26*				*16 54*			17 22	*17b27*			*17 54*		18 21	*18b26*			*18 54*			19 22
Manchester Piccadilly 10 d	16 46				17 16			17 35	17 46			18 16		18 35	18 46			19 16			19 35
Manchester Oxford Road d	16 49				17 19			17 37	17 49			18 19		18 37	18 49			19 19			19 37
Deansgate d	16 51							17 40	17 51					18 40	18 51						19 40
Rochdale 95 d		*16 09*					*16 23*			*17 09*			*17 23*			*18 09*			*18 23*		
Manchester Victoria d		17 00					17 25			18 00			18 25			19 00			19 25		
Salford Crescent a	16 54	17 06					17 29	17 44	17 54	18 06			18 29	18 44	18 54	19 06			19 29		19 44
d	16 55	17 08					17 30	17 44	17 55	18 08			18 30	18 44	18 55	19 08			19 30		19 44
Bolton a	17 05	17 19			17 32		17 40	17 54	18 05	18 19		18 32	18 40	18 54	19 05	19 19		19 32	19 40		19 54
d	17 05				17 33		17 40	17 55	18 05			18 33	18 40	18 55	19 05			19 33	19 40		19 55
Westhoughton d								18 02						19 02							20 02
Hindley d								18 06						19 06							20 06
Wigan North Western a																					
Wigan Wallgate a								18 11						19 11							20 11
d								18 13						19 13							20 13
Gathurst d								18 17						19 17							20 17
Appley Bridge d								18 21						19 21							20 21
Parbold d								18 25						19 25							20 25
Burscough Bridge d								18 29						19 29							20 29
Meols Cop d								18 37						19 37							20 37
Southport a								18 46						19 46							20 46
Lostock d							17 45						18 45						19 45		
Horwich Parkway d	17 12						17 49		18 12				18 49		19 12				19 49		
Blackrod d							17 52						18 52						19 52		
Adlington (Lancashire) d							17 56						18 56						19 56		
Chorley d	17 20				17 44		18 01		18 20			18 44	19 01		19 20			19 44	20 01		
Leyland d				17 29			18 12				18 29		19 13				19 29		20 12		
Preston 8 65 a	17 32			17 37	17 56		18 18		18 32		18 37	18 56	19 18		19 32		19 37	19 56	20 18		
d	17 34			17 39	18 02	18 06	18 20		18 34		18 39	19 00	19 20		19 34		19 39	20 00	20 20		
Kirkham & Wesham 97 a	*17 53*						18 29		*18 53*				19 29		*19 53*				20 29		
Poulton-le-Fylde 97 a	17 51			17 57	*18 31*		18 37		18 51		18 57	*19 31*	19 37		19 51		19 57	*20 32*	20 37		
Layton 97 a							18 42						19 42						20 43		
Blackpool North 97 a	18 00			18 07	*18 38*		18 47		19 00		19 07	*19 38*	19 47		20 00		20 07	*20 39*	20 48		
Lancaster 6 65 a	*17c56*			*18c10*	18 18	18 22			*18c56*		*19c10*	19 15			*19c56*			20 16			
d			18 04		18 18	18 22						19 16						20 16		20 20	
Oxenholme Lake District 65 a	*18c10*			*18c24*	18 32				*19c10*		*19c24*	19 30			*20c10*						
Windermere 83 a					*18 56*						*19e45*				*20e52*						
Carnforth d			18a13			18 31												20 24		20a29	
Silverdale d						18 36												20 30			
Arnside d						18 41												20 34			
Grange-over-Sands d						18 46												20 40			
Kents Bank d						18 50												20 44			
Cark d						18 54												20 48			
Ulverston d						19 02												20 56			
Dalton d						19 11												21 04			
Roose d						19 16												21 10			
Barrow-in-Furness a						19 26												21 19			

For general notes see front of timetable
For details of catering facilities see Directory of Train Operators

A To Clitheroe (Table 94)
B From Morecambe to Leeds (Table 36)
C From Liverpool Lime Street (Table 90)
D 1802 departure from Preston continues to Glasgow Central (Table 65)
E To Edinburgh (Table 65)
G From Chester (Table 88)
b Change at Manchester Oxford Road
c Change at Preston
e Change at Preston and Oxenholme Lake District

Manchester → Bolton → Wigan, Southport, Preston, Blackpool North and Barrow-in-Furness

Network Diagram - see first page of Table 82

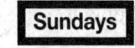

Station		TP	NT	NT	NT	NT	TP	NT	NT	NT	NT	NT	TP	NT	NT	NT	NT	TP
		1 ◇					1 ◇						1 ◇					1 ◇
			A	B		C		A		B				D	B	C	B	
Manchester Airport	85 d	19 30				19b55	20 30					20b55	21 30			21b55		22 30
Heald Green	85 d	19 12					20 12						21 12					22 12
Buxton	86 d	18 27					19 27						20 27					21 27
Hazel Grove	86 d	19 04					20 04						21 04					22 04
Stockport	84 d	19c26				20 21	20 21					21 22	21 24			22 21		
Manchester Piccadilly 10	d	19 46				20 35	20 46					21 35	21 46			22 35		22 46
Manchester Oxford Road	d	19 49				20 37	20 49					21 37	21 49			22 37		22 49
Deansgate	d	19 51				20 40	20 51					21 40	21 51			22 40		22 51
Rochdale	95 d		19 09		19 23			20e20			20 23			21f20				
Manchester Victoria	d		20 00		20 25			21 00			21 25			22 00				
Salford Crescent	a	19 54	20 06		20 29	20 44	20 54	21 06			21 29	21 44	21 54	22 06		22 44		22 54
	d	19 55	20 08		20 30	20 44	20 55	21 08			21 30	21 44	21 55	22 08		22 44		22 55
Bolton	a	20 05	20 19		20 40	20 54	21 05	21 19			21 40	21 54	22 05	22 19		22 54		23 05
	d	20 05			20 40	20 55	21 05				21 40	21 55	22 05			22 55		23 05
Westhoughton	d					21 02						22 02				23 02		
Hindley	d					21 06						22 06				23 06		
Wigan North Western	a																	
Wigan Wallgate	a					21 11						22 13				23 13		
	d					21 13												
Gathurst	d					21 17												
Appley Bridge	d					21 21												
Parbold	d					21 25												
Burscough Bridge	d					21 29												
Meols Cop	d					21 37												
Southport	a					21 46												
Lostock	d				20 45						21 45							23 10
Horwich Parkway	d	20 12			20 49		21 12				21 49		22 12					23 14
Blackrod	d				20 52						21 52							23 17
Adlington (Lancashire)	d				20 56						21 56							23 20
Chorley	d	20 20			21 01		21 20				22 01		22 20					23 24
Leyland	d			20 29	21 12					21 29	22 11				22 29		23 27	23 40
Preston 8	65 a	20 32		20 37	21 18		21 32			21 37	22 18		22 32		22 37		23 35	23 45
	d	20 34		20 39	21 20		21 34			21 39	22 20		22 34		22 38		23 38	23 47
Kirkham & Wesham	97 a	20 53		20 58	21 29						22 29							23 56
Poulton-le-Fylde	97 a	20 51		20 57	21 37		21 51			21 57	22 37		22 51		22 57		23 55	00 05
Layton	97 a				21 42						22 42							
Blackpool North	97 a	21 00		21 07	21 47		22 00			22 07	22 47		23 00		23 07		00 04	00 14
Lancaster 6	65 a	20g56		21g10			21g56											
	d								22 05									
Oxenholme Lake District	65 a	21g10		21g24			22g10											
Windermere	83 a																	
Carnforth	d								22 15									
Silverdale	d								22 21									
Arnside	d								22 26									
Grange-over-Sands	d								22 32									
Kents Bank	d								22 35									
Cark	d								22 39									
Ulverston	d								22 48									
Dalton	d								22 57									
Roose	d								23 03									
Barrow-in-Furness	a								23 10									

For general notes see front of timetable
For details of catering facilities see Directory of Train Operators

A To Clitheroe (Table 94)
B From Liverpool Lime Street (Table 90)
C From Chester (Table 88)
D To Blackburn (Table 94)
b Change at Manchester Piccadilly
c Change at Manchester Oxford Road
e From 19 July dep. 2019
f From 19 July dep. 2111
g Change at Preston

Table 82

Sundays

from 13 September

Manchester → Bolton → Wigan, Southport, Preston, Blackpool North and Barrow-in-Furness

Network Diagram - see first page of Table 82

		NT	TP	TP	TP	NT	NT	NT	NT	NT	TP	NT	NT	TP	NT	NT	NT	NT	NT	TP	NT
		A	(bus)	(bus)	1 ◇	B			B	A	1 ◇			1 ◇	B	C	D		E	1 ◇	B
Manchester Airport	85 d		00 10	05 30	07 30						08 47		09b03	09 30					10b03	10 25	
Heald Green	85 d				*07 12*						*08 27*			*09 09*						*10 10*	
Buxton	86 d												08b23						09b23		
Hazel Grove	86 d												09b00						09b59		
Stockport	84 d		*00 02*								*08 31*		09 22						10 19		
Manchester Piccadilly 10	d		00 35	05 55	07 46						09 03		09 35	09 46					10 35	10 43	
Manchester Oxford Road	d				07 49						09 06		09 37	09 49					10 38	10 49	
Deansgate	d				07 51						09 08		09 40	09 51					10 40	10 51	
Rochdale	95 d																	*09 41*			*10 17*
Manchester Victoria	d					08 01	08 25	08 39	09 00			09 25			10 00			10 25			11 00
Salford Crescent	a				07 54	08 08	08 29	08 44	09 07		09 11	09 29	09 44	09 54	10 07			10 29	10 44	10 54	11 06
	d				07 55	08 09	08 30	08 44	09 08		09 12	09 30	09 44	09 55	10 08			10 30	10 44	10 55	11 08
Bolton	a		01s00	06s20	08 05	08 20	08 40	08 54	09 19		09 22	09 40	09 54	10 05	10 19			10 40	10 54	11 05	11 19
	d				08 06		08 40	08 55			09 23	09 40	09 55	10 05				10 40	10 55	11 05	
Westhoughton	d							09 02					10 02						11 02		
Hindley	d							09 06					10 06						11 06		
Wigan North Western	a																				
Wigan Wallgate	a							09 11					10 11						11 11		
	d							09 13					10 13						11 13		
Gathurst	d							09 17					10 17						11 17		
Appley Bridge	d							09 21					10 21						11 21		
Parbold	d							09 25					10 25						11 25		
Burscough Bridge	d							09 29					10 29						11 29		
Meols Cop	d							09 37					10 37						11 37		
Southport	a							09 46					10 46						11 46		
Lostock	d						08 45					09 45						10 45			
Horwich Parkway	d				08 12		08 49				09 30	09 49		10 12				10 49		11 12	
Blackrod	d						08 52					09 52						10 52			
Adlington (Lancashire)	d						08 56					09 56						10 56			
Chorley	d				08 20		09 01				09 37	10 01		10 20				11 01		11 20	
Leyland	d	00 07		06s45			09 12			09 29		10 12				10 31	10 33	11 12			
Preston 8	65 a	00 16	01s35	07s00	08 31		09 17			09 37	09 49	10 17		10 32		10 39	10 41	11 20		11 32	
	d				08 32		09 19			09 39	09 51	10 19		10 34		10 40	10 42	11 21		11 34	
Kirkham & Wesham	97 a			07s20	*08c58*		09 28					10 28						11 31		*11c53*	
Poulton-le-Fylde	97 a			07s40	08 49		09 36			09 56	10 08	10 36		10 51		10 59	10 59	11 39		11 51	
Layton	97 a						09 41					10 41						11 44			
Blackpool North	97 a		02 15	07 55	08 58		09 46			10 06	10 17	10 46		11 00		11 09	11 09	11 49		12 00	
Lancaster 6	65 a													*11e00*		*11e06*	*11e23*				
	d																				
Oxenholme Lake District	65 a													*11e17*		*11e21*					
Windermere	83 a													*11e40*							
Carnforth	d																				
Silverdale	d																				
Arnside	d																				
Grange-over-Sands	d																				
Kents Bank	d																				
Cark	d																				
Ulverston	d																				
Dalton	d																				
Roose	d																				
Barrow-in-Furness	a																				

For general notes see front of timetable
For details of catering facilities see Directory of Train Operators

A From Liverpool Lime Street (Table 90)

B To Blackburn (Table 94)

C From 8 November. From Liverpool Lime Street (Table 90)

D Until 1 November. From Liverpool Lime Street (Table 90)

E From Chester (Table 88)

b Change at Manchester Piccadilly

c Until 1 November only

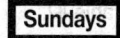

e Change at Preston

Table 82

Sundays

from 13 September

Manchester → Bolton → Wigan, Southport, Preston, Blackpool North and Barrow-in-Furness

Network Diagram - see first page of Table 82

		NT	TP		NT	NT	TP	NT		NT	NT	TP	NT		NT	TP	NT	NT		TP		NT	NT		TP
			1 ◇				1 ◇					1 ◇				1 ◇				1 ◇					1 ◇
		A	B					C		D	A	E			G		C	A		B					
			⚮									⚮								⚮					
Manchester Airport	85 ✈ d		10 58				11 30					11 58			12b03	12 30				12 58			13b03		13 30
Heald Green	85 d						11 11									12 12									13 12
Buxton	86 d						10 27									11 26									12 27
Hazel Grove	86 d						11 03									12 02									13 04
Stockport	84 d		10 52			11 12	11 12					11 54			12 16	12c26				12 53			13 22		13c26
Manchester Piccadilly 10	✈ d		11 16			11 27	11 46					12 16			12 30	12 46				13 16			13 35		13 46
Manchester Oxford Road	d		11 19			11 37	11 49					12 19			12 37	12 49				13 19			13 37		13 49
Deansgate	✈ d					11 40	11 51								12 40	12 51							13 40		13 51
Rochdale	95 d							11 12									12 11								
Manchester Victoria	✈ d				11 25			12 00					12 25				13 00					13 25			
Salford Crescent	a				11 29	11 44	11 54	12 06					12 29		12 44	12 54	13 06					13 29	13 44		13 54
	d				11 30	11 44	11 55	12 08					12 30		12 44	12 55	13 08					13 30	13 44		13 55
Bolton	a		11 32		11 40	11 54	12 05	12 19				12 32	12 40		12 54	13 05	13 19			13 32		13 40	13 54		14 05
	d		11 33		11 40	11 55	12 05					12 33	12 40		12 55	13 05				13 33		13 40	13 55		14 05
Westhoughton	d					12 02									13 02								14 02		
Hindley	d					12 06									13 06								14 06		
Wigan North Western	a																								
Wigan Wallgate	a					12 11									13 11								14 11		
	d					12 13									13 13								14 13		
Gathurst	d					12 17									13 17								14 17		
Appley Bridge	d					12 21									13 21								14 21		
Parbold	d					12 25									13 25								14 25		
Burscough Bridge	d					12 29									13 29								14 29		
Meols Cop	d					12 37									13 37								14 37		
Southport	a					12 46									13 46								14 46		
Lostock	d				11 45								12 45									13 45			
Horwich Parkway	d				11 49		12 12						12 49			13 12						13 49			14 12
Blackrod	d				11 52								12 52									13 52			
Adlington (Lancashire)	d				11 56								12 56									13 56			
Chorley	d		11 44		12 01		12 20					12 44	13 01			13 20				13 44		14 01			14 20
Leyland	d	11 29			12 12						12 29		13 12					13 29				14 12			
Preston 8	65 a	11 37	11 56		12 18		12 32				12 37	12 56	13 18			13 32		13 37		13 56		14 18			14 32
	d	11 39	11 58		12 20		12 34				12 39	12 58	13 20			13 34		13 39		14 01	14 05	14 20			14 34
Kirkham & Wesham	97 a				12 29		12e53						13 29			13e53						14 29			14e53
Poulton-le-Fylde	97 a	11 57	12 31		12 37		12 51				12 57	13 31	13 37			13 51		13 57		14 30		14 37			14 51
Layton	97 a				12 42								13 42									14 42			
Blackpool North	97 a	12 07	12 38		12 47		13 00				13 07	13 38	13 47			14 00		14 07		14 38		14 47			15 00
Lancaster 6	65 a	12f08	12 14		12f53						13g08	13 14	13h51					14f08		14 16	14 21				14f56
	d		12 14							12 48		13 14								14 16	14 21				
Oxenholme Lake District	65 a	12f22	12 28		13f07						13g22	13 28	14j05							14 30					
Windermere	83 a		12 52									13 52								14 54					
Carnforth	d									12a57											14 30				
Silverdale	d																				14 35				
Arnside	d																				14 40				
Grange-over-Sands	d																				14 45				
Kents Bank	d																				14 49				
Cark	d																				14 53				
Ulverston	d																				15 01				
Dalton	d																				15 10				
Roose	d																				15 15				
Barrow-in-Furness	a																				15 24				

For general notes see front of timetable
For details of catering facilities see Directory of Train Operators

A From Liverpool Lime Street (Table 90)
B To Glasgow Central (Table 65)
C To Blackburn (Table 94)
D 13 September. From Morecambe to Leeds (Table 36)
E To Edinburgh (Table 65)
G From Chester (Table 88)
b Change at Manchester Piccadilly
c Change at Manchester Oxford Road
e Until 1 November only
f Change at Preston
g Change at Preston. From 8 November arr. Lancaster 1302, Oxenholme Lake District 1316
h Change at Preston. From 8 November arr. 1408
j Until 1 November change at Preston. From 8 November arr. 1530, change at Preston and Lancaster

Table 82

Sundays

from 13 September

Manchester → Bolton → Wigan, Southport, Preston, Blackpool North and Barrow-in-Furness

Network Diagram - see first page of Table 82

	NT	NT	NT	TP	NT	NT	TP	NT	NT	TP	NT	NT	TP	NT	NT	NT	TP	NT	NT	TP
				1 ◇			1 ◇			1 ◇			1 ◇				1 ◇			1 ◇
	A	B	C	D		E		A	C					A		C	D		E	
Manchester Airport 85 d				13 58		14b03	14 30			14 58		15b03	15 30				15 58		16b03	16 30
Heald Green 85 d							14 12						15 12							16 12
Buxton 86 d							13 27						14 27							15 27
Hazel Grove 86 d							14 04						15 04							16 04
Stockport 84 d				13 53		14 21	14c26			14 53		15 22	15c26				15 54		16 21	16c26
Manchester Piccadilly 10 d				14 16		14 35	14 46			15 16		15 35	15 46				16 16		16 35	16 46
Manchester Oxford Road d				14 19		14 37	14 49			15 19		15 37	15 49				16 19		16 37	16 49
Deansgate d						14 40	14 51					15 40	15 51						16 40	16 51
Rochdale 95 d	13 11							14 11						15 11						
Manchester Victoria d	14 00				14 25			15 00			15 25			16 00				16 25		
Salford Crescent a	14 07				14 29	14 44	14 54	15 06			15 29	15 44	15 54	16 06				16 29	16 44	16 54
d	14 08				14 30	14 44	14 55	15 08			15 30	15 44	15 55	16 08				16 30	16 44	16 55
Bolton a	14 19			14 32	14 40	14 54	15 05	15 19		15 32	15 40	15 54	16 05	16 19			16 32	16 40	16 54	17 05
d				14 33	14 40	14 55	15 05			15 33	15 40	15 55	16 05				16 33	16 40	16 55	17 05
Westhoughton d						15 02						16 02							17 02	
Hindley d						15 06						16 06							17 06	
Wigan North Western a																				
Wigan Wallgate a						15 11						16 11							17 11	
d						15 13						16 13							17 13	
Gathurst d						15 17						16 17							17 17	
Appley Bridge d						15 21						16 21							17 21	
Parbold d						15 25						16 25							17 25	
Burscough Bridge d						15 29						16 29							17 29	
Meols Cop d						15 37						16 37							17 37	
Southport a						15 46						16 46							17 46	
Lostock d					14 45						15 45							16 45		
Horwich Parkway d					14 49		15 12				15 49		16 12					16 49		17 12
Blackrod d					14 52						15 52							16 52		
Adlington (Lancashire) d					14 56						15 56							16 56		
Chorley d				14 44	15 01		15 20			15 44	16 01		16 20				16 44	17 01		17 20
Leyland d			14 29		15 13				15 29		16 12					16 29		17 12		
Preston 8 65 a			14 37	14 56	15 18		15 32		15 37	15 56	16 18		16 32			16 37	16 56	17 18		17 32
d			14 39	15 00	15 20		15 34		15 39	16 00	16 20		16 34			16 39	17 02	17 20		17 34
Kirkham & Wesham 97 a					15 29		15e53				16 29		16e53					17 29		17e53
Poulton-le-Fylde 97 a			14 57	15 32	15 37		15 51		15 57	16 31	16 37		16 51			16 57	17 31	17 37		17 51
Layton 97 a					15 43						16 42							17 42		
Blackpool North 97 a			15 07	15 39	15 48		16 00		16 07	16 38	16 47		17 00			17 07	17 38	17 47		18 00
Lancaster 6 65 a			15f10	15 16			15g56		16h10	16 16			16j56			17j10	17 18			17j56
d		14 50		15 16						16 16					17 04		17 18			
Oxenholme Lake District 65 a			15f24	15 30			16g10						17j24			17j24	17 32			18j10
Windermere 83 a				15 54			16k52										18 02			
Carnforth d		14a59								16 24					17 14					
Silverdale d										16 30					17 20					
Arnside d										16 34					17 25					
Grange-over-Sands d										16 40					17 31					
Kents Bank d										16 44					17 34					
Cark d										16 48					17 38					
Ulverston d										16 56					17 47					
Dalton d										17 04					17 56					
Roose d										17 10					18 02					
Barrow-in-Furness a										17 19					18 09					

For general notes see front of timetable
For details of catering facilities see Directory of Train Operators

- **A** To Blackburn (Table 94)
- **B** 13 September. From Morecambe to Leeds (Table 36)
- **C** From Liverpool Lime Street (Table 90)
- **D** To Edinburgh (Table 65)
- **E** From Chester (Table 88)
- **b** Change at Manchester Piccadilly
- **c** Change at Manchester Oxford Road
- **e** Until 1 November only
- **f** Change at Preston. From 8 November arr. Lancaster 1516, Oxenholme Lake District 1530
- **g** Change at Preston. From 8 November arr. 2 mins. later
- **h** Change at Preston. From 8 November arr. 1608
- **j** Change at Preston
- **k** Change at Preston and Oxenholme Lake District

Table 82

Sundays

from 13 September

Manchester → Bolton → Wigan, Southport, Preston, Blackpool North and Barrow-in-Furness

Network Diagram - see first page of Table 82

		NT	NT	NT	TP		NT	NT	TP	NT	NT	TP	NT	NT	TP	NT	NT	TP	NT	NT
					1 ◇				1 ◇			1 ◇			1 ◇			1 ◇		
		A	B	C	D					A	C	E		G		A	C			B
Manchester Airport	85 d				16 58			17b03	17 30			17 58		18b03	18 30			18 58		
Heald Green	85 d								17 12						18 12					
Buxton	86 d								16 27						17 27					
Hazel Grove	86 d								17 04						18 04					
Stockport	84 d				16 54			17 22	17c27			17 54		18 21	18c26			18 54		
Manchester Piccadilly 10	d				17 16			17 35	17 46			18 16		18 35	18 46			19 16		
Manchester Oxford Road	d				17 19			17 37	17 49			18 19		18 37	18 49			19 19		
Deansgate	d							17 40	17 51					18 40	18 51					
Rochdale	95 d	16 11								17 11						18 11				
Manchester Victoria	d	17 00					17 25			18 00			18 25			19 00			19 25	
Salford Crescent	a	17 06					17 29	17 44	17 54	18 07			18 29	18 44	18 54	19 06			19 29	
	d	17 08					17 30	17 44	17 55	18 08			18 30	18 44	18 55	19 08			19 30	
Bolton	a	17 19			17 32		17 40	17 54	18 05	18 19		18 32	18 40	18 54	19 05	19 19		19 32	19 40	
	d				17 33		17 40	17 55	18 05			18 33	18 40	18 55	19 05			19 33	19 40	
Westhoughton	d							18 02						19 02						
Hindley	d							18 06						19 06						
Wigan North Western	a																			
Wigan Wallgate	a							18 11						19 11						
	d							18 13						19 13						
Gathurst	d							18 17						19 17						
Appley Bridge	d							18 21						19 21						
Parbold	d							18 25						19 25						
Burscough Bridge	d							18 29						19 29						
Meols Cop	d							18 37						19 37						
Southport	a							18 46						19 46						
Lostock	d						17 45						18 45						19 45	
Horwich Parkway	d						17 49		18 12				18 49		19 12				19 49	
Blackrod	d						17 52						18 52						19 52	
Adlington (Lancashire)	d						17 56						18 56						19 56	
Chorley	d				17 44		18 01		18 20			18 44	19 01		19 20			19 44	20 01	
Leyland	d			17 29			18 12				18 29		19 13				19 29		20 12	
Preston 8	65 a			17 37	17 56		18 18		18 32		18 37	18 56	19 18		19 32		19 37	19 56	20 18	
	d			17 39	18 02	18 06	18 20		18 34		18 39	19 00	19 20		19 34		19 39	20 00	20 20	
Kirkham & Wesham	97 a						18 29		18e53				19 29		19e53				20 29	
Poulton-le-Fylde	97 a			17 57			18 37		18 51		18 57	19 31	19 37		19 51		19 57	20 32	20 37	
Layton	97 a						18 42						19 42						20 43	
Blackpool North	97 a			18 07			18 47		19 00		19 07	19 38	19 47		20 00		20 07	20 39	20 48	
Lancaster 6	65 a			18f10	18 18	18 22			18f56		19f10	19 16			19f56			20 16		
	d		18 04		18 18	18 22						19 16						20 16		20 20
Oxenholme Lake District	65 a			18f24	18 32				19f10		19f24	19 30			20f10					
Windermere	83 a				18 56						19g45				20g52					
Carnforth	d		18a13			18 31												20 24		20a29
Silverdale	d					18 36												20 30		
Arnside	d					18 41												20 34		
Grange-over-Sands	d					18 46												20 40		
Kents Bank	d					18 50												20 44		
Cark	d					18 54												20 48		
Ulverston	d					19 02												20 56		
Dalton	d					19 11												21 04		
Roose	d					19 16												21 10		
Barrow-in-Furness	a					19 26												21 19		

For general notes see front of timetable
For details of catering facilities see Directory of Train Operators

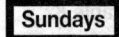

A To Blackburn (Table 94)
B From Morecambe to Leeds (Table 36)
C From Liverpool Lime Street (Table 90)
D 1802 departure from Preston continues to Glasgow Central (Table 65)
E To Edinburgh (Table 65)
G From Chester (Table 88)
b Change at Manchester Piccadilly
c Change at Manchester Oxford Road
e Until 1 November only
f Change at Preston
g Change at Preston and Oxenholme Lake District

Table 82

Sundays

from 13 September

Manchester → Bolton → Wigan, Southport, Preston, Blackpool North and Barrow-in-Furness

Network Diagram - see first page of Table 82

	NT	TP 1 ◇	NT A	NT B	NT	NT C	TP 1 ◇	NT A	NT	NT B	NT	NT	TP 1 ◇	NT A	NT B	NT C	NT B	TP 1 ◇
Manchester Airport 85 ⇌ d	19b03	19 30				20b03	20 30					21b03	21 30			22b03		22 30
Heald Green 85 d		19 12					20 12						21 12					22 12
Buxton 86 d		18 27					19 27						20 27					21 27
Hazel Grove 86 d		19 04					20 04						21 04					22 04
Stockport 84 d	19 22	19c26				20 21						21 22	21 24			22 21		
Manchester Piccadilly 10 ⇌ d	19 35	19 46				20 35	20 46					21 35	21 46			22 35		22 46
Manchester Oxford Road d	19 37	19 49				20 37	20 49					21 37	21 49			22 37		22 49
Deansgate ⇌ d	19 40	19 51				20 40	20 51					21 40	21 51			22 40		22 51
Rochdale 95 d			19 11					20 19						21 11				
Manchester Victoria ⇌ d			20 00		20 25			21 00			21 25			22 00				
Salford Crescent a	19 44	19 54	20 06		20 29	20 44	20 54	21 06			21 29	21 44	21 54	22 06		22 44		22 54
d	19 44	19 55	20 08		20 30	20 44	20 55	21 08			21 30	21 44	21 55	22 08		22 44		22 55
Bolton a	19 54	20 05	20 19		20 40	20 54	21 05	21 19			21 40	21 54	22 05	22 19		22 54		23 05
d	19 55	20 05			20 40	20 55	21 05				21 40	21 55	22 05			22 55		23 05
Westhoughton d	20 02					21 02						22 02				23 02		
Hindley d	20 06					21 06						22 06				23 06		
Wigan North Western a																		
Wigan Wallgate a	20 11					21 11						22 13				23 13		
d	20 13					21 13												
Gathurst d	20 17					21 17												
Appley Bridge d	20 21					21 21												
Parbold d	20 25					21 25												
Burscough Bridge d	20 29					21 29												
Meols Cop d	20 37					21 37												
Southport a	20 46					21 46												
Lostock d					20 45						21 45							23 10
Horwich Parkway d		20 12			20 49		21 12				21 49		22 12					23 14
Blackrod d					20 52						21 52							23 17
Adlington (Lancashire) d					20 56						21 56							23 20
Chorley d		20 20			21 01		21 20				22 01		22 20					23 24
Leyland d				20 29	21 12					21 29	22 11				22 29		23 27	23 40
Preston 8 65 a		20 32		20 37	21 18		21 32			21 37	22 18		22 32		22 37		23 35	23 45
d		20 34		20 39	21 20		21 34			21 39	22 20		22 34		22 38		23 38	23 47
Kirkham & Wesham 97 a		20e53			21 29						22 29							23 56
Poulton-le-Fylde 97 a		20 51		20 57	21 37		21 51			21 57	22 37		22 51		22 57		23 55	00 05
Layton 97 a					21 42						22 42							
Blackpool North 97 a		21 00		21 07	21 47		22 00			22 07	22 47		23 00		23 07		00 04	00 14
Lancaster 6 65 a		20f56		21f10			21f56											
d									22 05									
Oxenholme Lake District 65 a		21f10		21f24			22f10											
Windermere 83 a																		
Carnforth d									22 15									
Silverdale d									22 21									
Arnside d									22 26									
Grange-over-Sands d									22 32									
Kents Bank d									22 35									
Cark d									22 39									
Ulverston d									22 48									
Dalton d									22 57									
Roose d									23 03									
Barrow-in-Furness a									23 10									

For general notes see front of timetable
For details of catering facilities see Directory of Train Operators

A To Blackburn (Table 94)
B From Liverpool Lime Street (Table 90)
C From Chester (Table 88)
b Change at Manchester Piccadilly
c Change at Manchester Oxford Road
e Until 1 November only
f Change at Preston

Barrow-in-Furness, Blackpool North, Preston, Southport, Kirkby and Wigan → Bolton → Manchester

Network Diagram - see first page of Table 82

Miles	Miles	Miles	Miles	Miles			TP [1] ◇	TP [1] ◇	TP [1] ◇	NT	TP [1] ◇ 🛒	NT	NT	NT A	TP [1] ◇ B 🛒	NT	NT	TP [1] ◇ 🛒	NT C	NT	NT D	NT	NT	NT
—	0	—	—	—	**Barrow-in-Furness**	d			04 35						05 31									
—	1¾	—	—	—	Roose	d																		
—	6	—	—	—	Dalton	d																		
—	9¼	—	—	—	Ulverston	d			04 50						05 46									
—	15¼	—	—	—	Cark	d																		
—	17¼	—	—	—	Kents Bank	d																		
—	19½	—	—	—	Grange-over-Sands	d			05 03						05 59									
—	22¾	—	—	—	Arnside	d			05 10						06 06									
—	25	—	—	—	Silverdale	d																		
—	28¾	—	—	—	Carnforth	d			05 20						06 16						06 44			
—	—	—	—	—	Windermere	83 d																		
—	—	—	—	—	Oxenholme Lake District	65 d												06b20						
—	34¾	—	—	—	**Lancaster [6]**	65 a			05 28						06 23						06 53			
—	—	—	—	—		d					05b35				06 26			06b35						
0	—	—	—	—	**Blackpool North**	97 d	03 36	04 50			05 45						06 19	06 34					06 53	
1¼	—	—	—	—	Layton	97 d											06 22	06 37						
3¼	—	—	—	—	Poulton-le-Fylde	97 d					05 51						06 27	06 41						
9¾	—	—	—	—	Kirkham & Wesham	97 d									06 08		06 36	06 50						
—	55¾	—	—	—	**Preston [8]**	65, 97 a		05 14			06 08				06 45		06 46	07 01					07 15	
—	—	—	—	—		d	04u01	05 16			06 10				06 47		06 48	07 03					07 17	
21½	59¾	—	—	—	Leyland	d											06 53	07 08					07 22	
26	64¼	—	—	—	Chorley	d		05 26			06 19				06 56		07 01	07 15					07 31	
29	67¼	—	—	—	Adlington (Lancashire)	d											07 06						07 36	
31	69¼	—	—	—	Blackrod	d											07 10	07 21					07 40	
32½	70¾	—	—	—	Horwich Parkway	d					06 27						07 14	07 27					07 44	
34½	72¾	—	—	—	Lostock	d		05 34			06 30						07 20	07 30					07 49	
—	—	0	—	—	**Southport**	d										06 23				06 53				
—	—	1¼	—	—	Meols Cop	d										06 28				06 58				
—	—	4½	—	—	Bescar Lane	d														07 03				
—	—	6½	—	—	New Lane	d														07 07				
—	—	7¾	—	—	Burscough Bridge	d										06 36				07 09				
—	—	9¼	—	—	Hoscar	d														07 13				
—	—	10¾	—	—	Parbold	d										06 41				07 16				
—	—	13	—	—	Appley Bridge	d										06 45				07 20				
—	—	14¾	—	—	Gathurst	d										06 49				07 23				
—	—	—	—	—	Liverpool Central [10]	103 d																		06 25
—	—	—	0	—	**Kirkby**	d																		07 11
—	—	—	5¼	—	Rainford	d																		07 19
—	—	—	7¼	—	Upholland	d																		07 23
—	—	—	8½	—	Orrell	d																		07 27
—	—	—	10½	—	Pemberton	d																		07 30
—	—	17½	12¼	—	**Wigan Wallgate**	a										06 54				07 29				07 35
—	—	—	—	—		d				06 03		06 32	06 36			06 55			07 15	07 29				07 37
—	—	—	—	0	Wigan North Western	d																07 22		
—	—	18½	13¼	¾	Ince	d				06 06			06 39						07 18			07 25		07 40
—	—	20	14¾	—	Hindley	d				06 09		06 37	06 42						07 21			07 29		07 43
—	—	22½	—	—	Westhoughton	d						06 42				07 03						07 33		
37½	75¾	27	—	—	**Bolton**	a		05 42			06 34	06 52			07 08	07 11	07 25	07 34				07 42	07 54	
—	—	—	—	—		d	04u30	05 43			06 35	06 53		06 56	07 08	07 12	07 25	07 35				07 43	07 55	
38¼	76½	27¾	—	—	Moses Gate	d								06 59								07 46		
39¾	78	29¼	—	—	Farnworth	d								07 01								07 48		
40½	78¾	30	—	—	Kearsley	d								07 03								07 50		
—	—	—	17¼	—	Daisy Hill	d				06 13			06 46						07 26	07 39				07 47
—	—	—	17½	—	Hag Fold	d				06 16			06 49						07 29					07 50
—	—	—	18¾	—	Atherton	d				06 19			06 52						07 32	07 43				07 53
—	—	—	22¼	—	Walkden	d				06 24			06 58						07 38					07 59
—	—	—	24	—	Moorside	d				06 28			07 01						07 41					08 03
—	—	—	24¾	—	Swinton	d				06 30			07 04						07 44					08 06
46½	84¾	36	28¾	—	**Salford Crescent**	a		05 55		06 38	06 47	07 05	07 11	07 15		07 24	07 38	07 47	07 51	07 59		08 02	08 07	08 13
—	—	—	—	—		d		05 55		06 38	06 47	07 08	07 11	07 15		07 25	07 38	07 47	07 51	07 59		08 02	08 08	08 13
—	—	—	29¾	—	Salford Central	d				06 41			07 14	07 19			07 41		07 55	08 02		08 05		08 16
—	—	—	30½	—	**Manchester Victoria** 🚊	a				06 46			07 20	07 26			07 46		08 00	08 08		08 12		08 20
—	—	—	—	—	Rochdale	95 a				07 17				08 01			08 19					08 34		08 51
48	86¼	37¼	—	—	Deansgate 🚊	a					06 51	07 11				07 28		07 51					08 11	
48¼	86½	37¾	—	—	**Manchester Oxford Road**	a					06 52	07 13			07 23	07 30		07 52					08 14	
48¾	87	38¼	—	—	**Manchester Piccadilly [10]** 🚊	a		06 01			06 56	07 17			07 27	07 34		07 56					08 18	
—	—	—	—	—	Stockport	84 a		06 27			07 22	07 34			07 50	07c53		08 22					08 34	
—	—	—	—	—	Hazel Grove	86 a		06 45				07 45				08 09		08 45					08 45	
—	—	—	—	—	Buxton	86 a		07 50								08 44								
57	95¼	46½	—	—	Heald Green	85 a		06 32			07 10					08 02		08 10						
58½	96¾	48	—	—	**Manchester Airport**	85 ✈ a	05 06	06 18			07 17				07 47	07 53		08 17						

For general notes see front of timetable
For details of catering facilities see Directory of Train Operators

A From Blackburn (Table 94). Also stops at Clifton 0707
B 🛒 from Preston
C To Stalybridge (Table 39)
D From Skipton (Table 36)
b Change at Preston
c Change at Manchester Oxford Road

From 5 October a revised Northern service will be in operation due to seasonal difficulties. Customers should check with NRES for precise times

Barrow-in-Furness, Blackpool North, Preston, Southport, Kirkby and Wigan → Bolton → Manchester

Network Diagram - see first page of Table 82

	NT	NT	TP	TP	NT	NT	NT	NT	TP	TP	NT	NT	NT	NT	NT	NT	NT		TP	NT	NT	NT	NT	NT
	A	B	1◇ C ⊤	1◇ C ⊤				B	1◇	1◇ D ⊤						E	G		1◇ C ⊤				A	B
Barrow-in-Furness d				06 19												07 00			07 28					
Roose d				06 23												07 04								
Dalton d				06 29												07 10			07 37					
Ulverston d				06 38												07 19			07 45					
Cark d				06 46												07 27			07 53					
Kents Bank d				06 50												07 32								
Grange-over-Sands d				06 54												07 36			08 00					
Arnside d				07 00												07 43			08 06					
Silverdale d				07 04												07 48			08 10					
Carnforth d				07 12												07 54			08 18					
Windermere 83 d										06b50														
Oxenholme Lake District 65 d				06 20						07 24					07 42									
Lancaster 6 65 a				07 21												08 03			08 26					
d	06c58			07 22						07 47					07 57	08 04			08 26					
Blackpool North 97 d	07 02		07 10				07 18		07 36													08 20	08 29	
Layton 97 d			07 13				07 21		07 39													08 23		
Poulton-le-Fylde 97 d	07 08		07 17				07 26		07 43													08 28		
Kirkham & Wesham 97 d	07 09		07 26				07 35		07 52										08 09			08 37		
Preston 8 65, 97 a	07 28		07 37	07 41			07 46		08 03	08 06						08 29			08 45			08 47		
d	07 30		07 47				07 47		08 12						08 23				08 47			08 49	09 04	
Leyland d	07a35						07 53								08 29							08 54	09a09	
Chorley d			07 56				08 01		08 22						08 36				08 56			09 02		
Adlington (Lancashire) d							08 06															09 07		
Blackrod d							08 10															09 10		
Horwich Parkway d							08 14								08 45							09 14		
Lostock d							08 20								08 50							09 20		
Southport d					07 22								07 58							08 24				
Meols Cop d					07 27								08 03							08 30				
Bescar Lane d																								
New Lane d																								
Burscough Bridge d					07 35								08 11							08 36				
Hoscar d																								
Parbold d					07 40								08 16							08 41				
Appley Bridge d					07 44								08 20							08 45				
Gathurst d					07 48								08 23							08 50				
Liverpool Central 10 103 d														07 50										
Kirkby d														08 21										
Rainford d														08 29										
Upholland d														08 33										
Orrell d														08 36										
Pemberton d														08 39										
Wigan Wallgate a					07 53								08 28	08 45						08 55				
d					07 54	08 00					08 13		08 29	08 50						08 56				
Wigan North Western d												08 20												
Ince d											08 16			08 53										
Hindley d											08 19	08 25	08 34	08 57										
Westhoughton d					08 03							08 29								09 04				
Bolton a			08 08		08 11		08 25		08 34			08 38			08 55				09 08	09 12		09 25		
d		07 59	08 08		08 12		08 25	08 31	08 35			08 39			08 56		09 02		09 08	09 13		09 25		09 31
Moses Gate d		08 02										08 42												
Farnworth d		08 04										08 44												
Kearsley d		08 06										08 46									←			
Daisy Hill d						08 07					08 23		08 39	09 01							09 01			
Hag Fold d											08 26			→							09 04			
Atherton d						08 12					08 29		08 43								09 06			
Walkden d						08 18					08 35		08 49								09 12			
Moorside d											08 39										09 15			
Swinton d											08 42		08 54								09 18			
Salford Crescent a		08 17			08 24	08 29	08 38	08 43	08 47		08 50	08 56	09 02		09 08		09 15			09 25	09 27	09 38		09 43
d		08 17			08 25	08 30	08 38	08 44	08 47		08 50	08 56	09 02		09 09		09 16			09 26	09 27	09 38		09 44
Salford Central d		08 20				08 32	08 41	08 46			08 53	08 59	09 04				09 18				09 31	09 41		09 46
Manchester Victoria a		08 25				08 38	08 46	08 51			08 59	09 06	09 11				09 26				09 38	09 46		09 51
Rochdale 95 a		08 51				09 02		09 19					09 35				09 54				10 02			10 19
Deansgate a					08 28										09 12					09 29				
Manchester Oxford Road a			08 23		08 31				08 52						09 14				09 23	09 31				
Manchester Piccadilly 10 a			08 27		08 35				08 56						09 18				09 27	09 35				
Stockport 84 a			08 50		08e53				09 22						09 34				09 50	09e53				
Hazel Grove 86 a					09 13										09 45					10 13				
Buxton 86 a					09 53															10 53				
Heald Green 85 a					09 02				09 12											10 02				
Manchester Airport 85 a			08 47		08 53				09 19										09 47	09 53				

For general notes see front of timetable
For details of catering facilities see Directory of Train Operators

- **A** To Liverpool Lime Street (Table 90)
- **B** From Clitheroe (Table 94)
- **C** ⊤ from Preston
- **D** From Edinburgh (Table 65)
- **E** From Millom (Table 100)
- **G** From Blackburn (Table 94)
- **b** Change at Oxenholme Lake District and Lancaster
- **c** Change at Preston
- **e** Change at Manchester Oxford Road

From 5 October a revised Northern service will be in operation due to seasonal difficulties. Customers should check with NRES for precise times

Barrow-in-Furness, Blackpool North, Preston, Southport, Kirkby and Wigan → Bolton → Manchester

Network Diagram - see first page of Table 82

Station	Table		TP 1◇	NT A	NT	NT	NT	NT B	NT	TP 1◇ C	NT	NT	NT	NT D	NT E	TP 1◇	NT G	NT	NT	NT	NT	TP 1◇ H	NT	NT	NT
Barrow-in-Furness		d		08 00																		09 23			
Roose		d		08 04																		09 27			
Dalton		d		08 10																		09 33			
Ulverston		d		08 19																		09 42			
Cark		d		08 27																		09 50			
Kents Bank		d		08 32																		09 54			
Grange-over-Sands		d		08 36																		09 58			
Arnside		d		08 43																		10 04			
Silverdale		d		08 48																		10 08			
Carnforth		d		08 54													10 02					10 16			
Windermere	83	d	07b57							08 50												09 41			
Oxenholme Lake District	65	d	08c23							09 11				09c23								10 01			
Lancaster 6	65	a		09 07						09 26							10 12					10 26			
		d	08c38				08 57			09 26				09c38						09 57		10 26			10c18
Blackpool North	97	d	08 45										09 20	09 37		09 45									10 20
Layton	97	d											09 23												10 23
Poulton-le-Fylde	97	d	08 51										09 28	09c35		09 51									10 28
Kirkham & Wesham	97	d								09 10			09 37	09 52								10 10			10 37
Preston 8	65, 97	a	09 09							09 45			09 47	10 02		10 09						10 45			10 47
		d	09 10				09 23			09 47			09 49	10 04		10 10				10 23		10 47			10 49
Leyland		d					09 29						09 54	10a09						10 29					10 54
Chorley		d	09 20				09 36			09 56			10 02			10 20				10 36		10 56			11 02
Adlington (Lancashire)		d											10 07												11 07
Blackrod		d											10 10												11 10
Horwich Parkway		d	09 27				09 45						10 14			10 27				10 45					11 14
Lostock		d					09 50						10 20							10 50					11 20
Southport		d				08 57					09 24								10 00				10 24		
Meols Cop		d				09 02													10 05						
Bescar Lane		d				09 07																			
New Lane		d				09 11																			
Burscough Bridge		d				09 13					09 36								10 13				10 36		
Hoscar		d				09 17																			
Parbold		d				09 20					09 41								10 18				10 41		
Appley Bridge		d				09 24					09 45								10 22				10 45		
Gathurst		d				09 27													10 25						
Liverpool Central 10	103	d										09 05												10 05	
Kirkby		d										09 32												10 32	
Rainford		d										09 40												10 40	
Upholland		d										09 44												10 44	
Orrell		d										09 47												10 47	
Pemberton		d										09 50												10 50	
Wigan Wallgate		a				09 32					09 51	09 56							10 30				10 51	10 56	
		d			09 20	09 32			09 48		09 53	09 58						10 20	10 32		10 48		10 53	10 58	
Wigan North Western		d																							
Ince		d										10 01												11 01	
Hindley		d			09 25	09 37					09 58	10 04						10 25	10 37				10 58	11 04	
Westhoughton		d			09 29						10 02							10 29					11 02		
Bolton		a	09 34		09 38		09 55		10 02	10 08	10 12		10 25			10 34		10 38		10 55	11 02	11 08	11 12		11 25
		d	09 35		09 39		09 56	10 00	10 03	10 08	10 13		10 25		10 31	10 35		10 39		10 56	11 03	11 08	11 13		11 25
Moses Gate		d			09 42													10 42							
Farnworth		d			09 44													10 44							
Kearsley		d			09 46													10 46							
Daisy Hill		d				09 41						10 09							10 41					11 09	
Hag Fold		d										10 12												11 12	
Atherton		d				09 45						10 15							10 45					11 15	
Walkden		d				09 50						10 20							10 50					11 20	
Moorside		d										10 24												11 24	
Swinton		d				09 55						10 26							10 55					11 26	
Salford Crescent		a	09 47		09 56	10 03	10 08	10 13	10 15		10 25	10 34	10 38		10 43	10 47		10 56	11 02	11 08	11 15		11 25	11 34	11 38
		d	09 47		09 56	10 03	10 09	10 13	10 15		10 26	10 34	10 38		10 44	10 47		10 56	11 03	11 09	11 15		11 26	11 34	11 38
Salford Central		d			09 59	10 05		10 16	10 17			10 36	10 41		10 46			10 59	11 05		11 17			11 36	11 41
Manchester Victoria	⛴	a			10 06	10 11		10 21	10 25			10 43	10 46		10 51			11 06	11 11		11 25			11 43	11 46
Rochdale	95	a				10 34			10 51			11 02			11 19				11 34		11 51			12 02	
Deansgate	⛴	a	09 51				10 12				10 29					10 51				11 12			11 29		
Manchester Oxford Road		a	09 52				10 14			10 23	10 31					10 52				11 14		11 23	11 31		
Manchester Piccadilly 10	⛴	a	09 56				10 18			10 27	10 35					10 56				11 18		11 27	11 35		
Stockport	84	a	10 22				10 34			10 50	10e53					11 22				11 34		11 50	11e53		
Hazel Grove	86	a					10 45				11 13					11 45				11 45			12 13		
Buxton	86	a									11 50												12 53		
Heald Green	85	a	10 10								11 02					11 10							12 02		
Manchester Airport	85 ✈	a	10 17							10 47	10 53					11 17						11 47	11 53		

For general notes see front of timetable
For details of catering facilities see Directory of Train Operators

A From Maryport (Table 100)
B From Blackburn (Table 94)
C From Glasgow Central (Table 65)
D To Liverpool Lime Street (Table 90)
E From Clitheroe (Table 94)
G From Leeds to Morecambe (Table 36)
H from Preston
b Change at Oxenholme Lake District and Preston
c Change at Preston
e Change at Manchester Oxford Road

From 5 October a revised Northern service will be in operation due to seasonal difficulties. Customers should check with NRES for precise times

Barrow-in-Furness, Blackpool North, Preston, Southport, Kirkby and Wigan → Bolton → Manchester

Network Diagram - see first page of Table 82

	NT	NT	TP	NT	NT	NT	NT	NT	TP		NT	NT	NT	NT	NT	TP	NT	NT	NT	NT	NT	TP	TP	NT
			1◇						1◇							1◇						1◇	1◇	
	A	B				C			D					A	B		E						G	
			⌶						⌶							⌶							⌶	
Barrow-in-Furness d						10 16																11 25		
Roose d						10 20																		
Dalton d						10 26																		
Ulverston d						10 35																11 40		
Cark d						10 43																		
Kents Bank d						10 47																		
Grange-over-Sands d						10 51																11 53		
Arnside d						10 57																12 00		
Silverdale d						11 02																		
Carnforth d						11 08											12 02					12 09		
Windermere 83 d									10 49															
Oxenholme Lake District 65 d							*10 42*		11 10					*11b23*									12 11	
Lancaster 6 65 a						11 20			11 26								12 11					12 18	12 26	
d	*10b38*						*10 57*		11 26					*11b38*								12 18	12 26	
Blackpool North 97 d	10 37		10 45										11 20	11 37		11 45								
Layton 97 d													11 23											
Poulton-le-Fylde 97 d	*10b35*		10 51										11 28	*11b35*		11 51								
Kirkham & Wesham 97 d	10 52								*11 10*				11 37	11 52									*12 10*	
Preston 8 65, 97 a	11 02		11 09						11 45				11 47	12 02		12 09						12 37	12 45	
d	11 04		11 10				11 23		11 47				11 49	12 04		12 10				12 23			12 47	
Leyland d	11a09						11 29						11 54	12a09						12 29				
Chorley d			11 20				11 36		11 56				12 02			12 20				12 36			12 56	
Adlington (Lancashire) d													12 07											
Blackrod d													12 10											
Horwich Parkway d			11 27				11 45						12 14			12 27				12 45				
Lostock d							11 50						12 20							12 50				
Southport d					10 54						11 24								12 00					12 24
Meols Cop d					10 59														12 05					
Bescar Lane d					11 04																			
New Lane d					11 08																			
Burscough Bridge d					11 11						11 36								12 13					12 36
Hoscar d					11 15																			
Parbold d					11 18						11 41								12 18					12 41
Appley Bridge d					11 22						11 45								12 22					12 45
Gathurst d					11 25														12 25					
Liverpool Central 10 103 d												*11 05*												
Kirkby d												11 32												
Rainford d												11 40												
Upholland d												11 44												
Orrell d												11 47												
Pemberton d												11 50												
Wigan Wallgate a					11 30						11 51	11 56							12 30					12 51
d				11 20	11 32			11 48			11 53	11 58						12 20	12 32		12 48			12 53
Wigan North Western d																								
Ince d												12 01												
Hindley d				11 25	11 37						11 58	12 04						12 25	12 37					12 58
Westhoughton d				11 29							12 02							12 29						13 02
Bolton a			11 34	11 38			11 55	12 02	12 08		12 12		12 25			12 34		12 38		12 55	13 02		13 08	13 12
d		11 31	11 35	11 39			11 56	12 03	12 08		12 13		12 25		12 31	12 35		12 39		12 56	13 03		13 08	13 13
Moses Gate d				11 42														12 42						
Farnworth d				11 44														12 44						
Kearsley d				11 46														12 46						
Daisy Hill d					11 41							12 09							12 41					
Hag Fold d												12 12												
Atherton d					11 45							12 15							12 45					
Walkden d					11 50							12 20							12 50					
Moorside d												12 24												
Swinton d					11 55							12 26							12 55					
Salford Crescent a		11 43	11 47	11 56	12 02		12 08	12 15			12 25	12 34	12 38		12 43	12 47		12 56	13 02	13 08	13 15			13 25
d		11 44	11 47	11 56	12 03		12 09	12 15			12 26	12 34	12 38		12 44	12 47		12 56	13 03	13 09	13 15			13 26
Salford Central d		11 46		11 59	12 05			12 17				12 36	12 41		12 46			12 59	13 05		13 17			
Manchester Victoria 🚊 a		11 51		12 06	12 11			12 25				12 43	12 46		12 51			13 06	13 11		13 25			
Rochdale 95 a		*12 19*			*12 34*			12 51				*13 02*			*13 19*				*13 34*		13 51			
Deansgate 🚊 a			11 51				12 12				12 29					12 51				13 12				13 29
Manchester Oxford Road a			11 52				12 14		12 23		12 31					12 52				13 14			13 23	13 31
Manchester Piccadilly 10 🚊 a			11 56				12 18		12 27		12 35					12 56				13 18			13 27	13 35
Stockport 84 a			*12 22*				12 34		*12 50*		*12c53*					*13 22*				13 34			*13 50*	*13c53*
Hazel Grove 86 a							12 45				*13 13*									13 45				*14 13*
Buxton 86 a											*13 50*													*14 53*
Heald Green 85 a			12 10								*13 02*					13 10								*14 02*
Manchester Airport 85 ✈ a			12 17						12 47		12 53					13 17							13 47	13 53

For general notes see front of timetable
For details of catering facilities see Directory of Train Operators

A To Liverpool Lime Street (Table 90)
B From Clitheroe (Table 94)
C From Sellafield (Table 100)
D ⌶ from Preston
E From Leeds (Table 36) to Heysham Port (Table 98)
G From Glasgow Central and Edinburgh (Table 65)
b Change at Preston
c Change at Manchester Oxford Road

From 5 October a revised Northern service will be in operation due to seasonal difficulties. Customers should check with NRES for precise times

Barrow-in-Furness, Blackpool North, Preston, Southport, Kirkby and Wigan → Bolton → Manchester

Network Diagram - see first page of Table 82

	NT	NT	NT	NT	TP		NT	NT	NT	NT	NT	TP	NT	NT	NT	NT	NT	TP	NT	NT	NT	NT	TP	TP
					1 ◇							1 ◇						1 ◇					1 ◇	1 ◇
			A	B			C					D				A	B						E	G E
					🛒							🛒						🛒						🛒
Barrow-in-Furness d							12 11																13 25	
Roose d							12 15																	
Dalton d							12 21																	
Ulverston d							12 29																13 40	
Cark d							12 37																	
Kents Bank d							12 41																	
Grange-over-Sands d							12 45																13 53	
Arnside d							12 51																14 00	
Silverdale d							12 56																	
Carnforth d							13 02																14 09	
Windermere 83 d			11b59									12 51												
Oxenholme Lake District 65 d			12c23							12 43		13 09												14 10
Lancaster 6 65 a							13 15					13 26											14 18	
d			12c38							12 57		13 26				13c39					13 58		14 18	
Blackpool North 97 d		12 20	12 37		12 45										13 20	13 37		13 45						
Layton 97 d		12 23													13 23									
Poulton-le-Fylde 97 d		12 28	12c35		12 51										13 28	13c35		13 51						
Kirkham & Wesham 97 d		12 37	12 52									13 10			13 37	13 52								14 10
Preston 8 65, 97 a		12 47	13 02		13 09							13 45			13 47	14 02		14 09					14 37	14 41
d		12 49	13 04		13 10					13 23		13 47			13 49	14 04		14 10			14 23			14 47
Leyland d		12 54	13a09							13 29					13 54	14a09					14 29			
Chorley d		13 02			13 20					13 36		13 56			14 02			14 20			14 36			14 56
Adlington (Lancashire) d		13 07													14 07									
Blackrod d		13 10													14 10									
Horwich Parkway d		13 14			13 27					13 45					14 14			14 27			14 45			
Lostock d		13 20								13 50					14 20						14 50			
Southport d									12 54				13 24							14 00				
Meols Cop d									12 59											14 05				
Bescar Lane d									13 04															
New Lane d									13 08															
Burscough Bridge d									13 11				13 36							14 13				
Hoscar d									13 15															
Parbold d									13 18				13 41							14 18				
Appley Bridge d									13 22				13 45							14 22				
Gathurst d									13 25											14 25				
Liverpool Central 10 103 d	12 05													13 05										
Kirkby d	12 32													13 32										
Rainford d	12 40													13 40										
Upholland d	12 44													13 44										
Orrell d	12 47													13 47										
Pemberton d	12 50													13 50										
Wigan Wallgate a	12 56								13 30				13 51	13 56						14 30				
d	12 58							13 20	13 32		13 48		13 53	13 58					14 20	14 32		14 48		
Wigan North Western d																								
Ince d	13 01													14 01										
Hindley d	13 04							13 25	13 37				13 58	14 04					14 25	14 37				
Westhoughton d								13 29					14 02						14 29					
Bolton a		13 25			13 34			13 38		13 55	14 02	14 08	14 12		14 25			14 34	14 38		14 55	15 02		15 08
d		13 25		13 31	13 35			13 39		13 56	14 03	14 08	14 13		14 25		14 31	14 35	14 39		14 56	15 03		15 08
Moses Gate d								13 42											14 42					
Farnworth d								13 44											14 44					
Kearsley d								13 46											14 46					
Daisy Hill d	13 09								13 41					14 09						14 41				
Hag Fold d	13 12													14 12										
Atherton d	13 15								13 45					14 15						14 45				
Walkden d	13 20								13 50					14 20						14 50				
Moorside d	13 24													14 24										
Swinton d	13 26								13 55					14 26						14 55				
Salford Crescent a	13 34	13 38		13 43	13 47			13 56	14 02	14 08	14 15		14 25	14 34	14 38		14 43	14 47	14 56	15 02	15 08	15 15		
d	13 34	13 38		13 44	13 47			13 56	14 03	14 09	14 15		14 26	14 34	14 38		14 44	14 47	14 56	15 03	15 09	15 15		
Salford Central d	13 36	13 41		13 46				13 59	14 05		14 17			14 36	14 41		14 46		14 59	15 05		15 17		
Manchester Victoria 🚢 a	13 43	13 46		13 51				14 06	14 11		14 25			14 43	14 46		14 51		15 06	15 11		15 25		
Rochdale 95 a	14 02			14 19					14 34		14 51			15 02			15 19			15 34		15 51		
Deansgate 🚢 a					13 51					14 12			14 29					14 51			15 12			
Manchester Oxford Road a					13 52					14 14		14 23	14 31					14 52			15 14			15 23
Manchester Piccadilly 10 🚢 a					13 56					14 18		14 27	14 35					14 56			15 18			15 27
Stockport 84 a					14 22					14 34		14 50	14e53					15 22			15 34			15 50
Hazel Grove 86 a					14 45					14 45			15 13								15 45			
Buxton 86 a													15 50											
Heald Green 85 a					14 10								15 02					15 10						
Manchester Airport 85 ✈ a					14 17							14 47	14 53					15 17						15 47

For general notes see front of timetable
For details of catering facilities see Directory of Train Operators

- **A** To Liverpool Lime Street (Table 90)
- **B** From Clitheroe (Table 94)
- **C** From Carlisle via Whitehaven (Table 100)
- **D** 🛒 from Preston
- **E** Until 19 June and from 7 September
- **G** From Edinburgh (Table 65)
- **b** Change at Oxenholme Lake District and Preston
- **c** Change at Preston
- **e** Change at Manchester Oxford Road

From 5 October a revised Northern service will be in operation due to seasonal difficulties. Customers should check with NRES for precise times

Barrow-in-Furness, Blackpool North, Preston, Southport, Kirkby and Wigan → Bolton → Manchester

Network Diagram - see first page of Table 82

Station		TP 1◊ A	TP 1◊ B A (trolley)		NT	NT	NT	NT C	NT D	TP 1◊ (trolley)	NT	NT	NT	NT	NT	TP 1◊ E (trolley)	NT	NT D	NT	NT	NT C		TP 1◊ (trolley)	NT G	NT
Barrow-in-Furness	d	13 25											14 16												
Roose	d												14 20												
Dalton	d												14 26												
Ulverston	d	13 40											14 35												
Cark	d												14 43												
Kents Bank	d												14 47												
Grange-over-Sands	d	13 53											14 51												
Arnside	d	14 00											14 57												
Silverdale	d												15 02												
Carnforth	d	14 09											15 08											15 38	
Windermere	83 d							*14b00*								14 48									
Oxenholme Lake District	65 d		14 10					*14c24*								15 09					*15c24*				
Lancaster [6]	65 a	14 18											15 20			15 26								15 47	
	d	14 18						*14c38*						*14 57*		15 26					*15c39*				
Blackpool North	97 d						14 20	14 37		14 45										15 20	15 37		15 45		
Layton	97 d						14 23													15 23					
Poulton-le-Fylde	97 d						14 28	*14c35*		14 51										15 28	*15c35*		15 51		
Kirkham & Wesham	97 d		*14 10*				14 37	14 52								*15 10*				15 37	15 52				
Preston [8]	65, 97 a	14 37	14 41				14 47	15 02		15 09						15 45				15 47	16 02		16 09		
	d		14 47				14 49	15 04		15 10				15 23		15 47				15 49	16 04		16 10		
Leyland	d						14 54	15a09						15 29						15 54	16a09				
Chorley	d		14 56				15 02			15 20				15 36		15 56				16 02			16 20		
Adlington (Lancashire)	d						15 07													16 07					
Blackrod	d						15 10													16 10					
Horwich Parkway	d						15 14			15 27				15 45						16 14			16 27		
Lostock	d						15 20							15 50						16 20					
Southport	d				14 24							14 54					15 24								
Meols Cop	d											14 59													
Bescar Lane	d											15 04													
New Lane	d											15 08													
Burscough Bridge	d				14 36							15 11					15 36								
Hoscar	d											15 15													
Parbold	d				14 41							15 18					15 41								
Appley Bridge	d				14 45							15 22					15 45								
Gathurst	d											15 25													
Liverpool Central [10]	103 d					*14 05*													*15 05*						
Kirkby	d					14 32													15 32						
Rainford	d					14 40													15 40						
Upholland	d					14 44													15 44						
Orrell	d					14 47													15 47						
Pemberton	d					14 50													15 50						
Wigan Wallgate	a				14 51	14 56						15 30					15 51		15 56						
	d				14 53	14 58					15 20	15 32			15 48		15 53		15 58						16 20
Wigan North Western	d																								
Ince	d					15 01													16 01						
Hindley	d				14 58	15 04					15 25	15 37					15 58		16 04						16 25
Westhoughton	d				15 02						15 29						16 02								16 29
Bolton	a		15 08		15 12		15 25			15 34	15 38			15 55	16 02	16 08	16 12			16 25			16 34		16 38
	d		15 08		15 13		15 25		15 31	15 35	15 39			15 56	16 03	16 08	16 13	16 17		16 25			16 35		16 39
Moses Gate	d										15 42														16 42
Farnworth	d										15 44														16 44
Kearsley	d										15 46														16 46
Daisy Hill	d					15 09						15 41							16 09						
Hag Fold	d					15 12													16 12						
Atherton	d					15 15						15 45							16 15						
Walkden	d					15 20						15 50							16 20						
Moorside	d					15 24													16 24						
Swinton	d					15 26						15 55							16 26						
Salford Crescent	a				15 25	15 33	15 38		15 43	15 47	15 56	16 02		16 08	16 15		16 25	16 30	16 34	16 38			16 47		16 56
	d				15 26	15 34	15 38		15 44	15 47	15 56	16 03		16 09	16 15		16 26	16 30	16 34	16 38			16 47		16 56
Salford Central	d					15 36	15 41		15 46		15 59	16 05			16 17			16 33	16 36	16 42					16 59
Manchester Victoria (tram)	a					15 43	15 46		15 53		16 06	16 11			16 23			16 40	16 43	16 46					17 06
Rochdale	95 a					*16 02*			*16 19*			*16 35*			16 51				*17 02*	*17 19*					
Deansgate (tram)	a				15 29					15 51				16 12									16 51		
Manchester Oxford Road	a		15 23		15 31					15 52				16 14		16 23	16 31						16 52		
Manchester Piccadilly [10] (tram)	a		15 27		15 35					15 56				16 18		16 27	16 35						16 56		
Stockport	84 a		*15 50*		*15e53*					*16 22*				16 34		*16 50*	16e53						*17 17*		
Hazel Grove	86 a				*16 13*									16 43			*17 09*						*17 45*		
Buxton	86 a				*16 53*									17 22			*17 50*								
Heald Green	85 a				*16 02*					16 10						16 40	*17 02*						17 10		
Manchester Airport	85 ✈ a		15 47		15 53					16 17						16 47	16 53						17 17		

For general notes see front of timetable
For details of catering facilities see Directory of Train Operators

- **A** 22 June to 4 September
- **B** From Edinburgh (Table 65)
- **C** To Liverpool Lime Street (Table 90)
- **D** From Clitheroe (Table 94)
- **E** (trolley) from Preston
- **G** From Leeds to Morecambe (Table 36)
- **b** Change at Oxenholme Lake District and Preston
- **c** Change at Preston
- **e** Change at Manchester Oxford Road

From 5 October a revised Northern service will be in operation due to seasonal difficulties. Customers should check with NRES for precise times

Barrow-in-Furness, Blackpool North, Preston, Southport, Kirkby and Wigan → Bolton → Manchester

Network Diagram - see first page of Table 82

	NT A	NT	NT	TP 1◇	TP 1◇ B 🛒	NT	NT	NT	NT C	NT D	TP 1◇ 🛒	NT
Barrow-in-Furness d				15 25								
Roose d												
Dalton d												
Ulverston d				15 40								
Cark d												
Kents Bank d												
Grange-over-Sands d				15 53								
Arnside d				16 00								
Silverdale d												
Carnforth d				16 09								
Windermere 83 d									*16b02*			
Oxenholme Lake District 65 d		*15 44*			16 08				*16c24*			
Lancaster 6 65 a				16 18	16 23							
d				16 18	16 23				*16c38*			
Blackpool North 97 d								16 20	16 35		16 41	
Layton 97 d								16 23			16 44	
Poulton-le-Fylde 97 d								16 28	*16c35*		16 48	
Kirkham & Wesham 97 d					*16 10*			16 37	16 52		16 58	
Preston 8 65, 97 a				16 37	16 42			16 47	17 02		17 09	
d		16 23		16 47				16 49	17 04		17 10	
Leyland d		16 29						16 54	17a09			
Chorley d		16 36		16 56				17 02			17 20	
Adlington (Lancashire) d								17 07				
Blackrod d								17 10				
Horwich Parkway d		16 45						17 14			17 27	
Lostock d		16 50						17 20				
Southport d	16 00					16 24						
Meols Cop d	16 05											
Bescar Lane d												
New Lane d												
Burscough Bridge d	16 13					16 36						
Hoscar d												
Parbold d	16 18					16 41						
Appley Bridge d	16 22					16 45						
Gathurst d	16 25											
Liverpool Central 10 103 d							*16 05*					
Kirkby d							16 32					
Rainford d							16 40					
Upholland d							16 44					
Orrell d							16 47					
Pemberton d							16 50					
Wigan Wallgate a	16 30					16 51	16 56					
d	16 32		16 48			16 53	16 58					17 20
Wigan North Western d												
Ince d							17 01					
Hindley d	16 37					16 58	17 04					17 25
Westhoughton d						17 02						17 29
Bolton a		16 55	17 02	17 08		17 12		17 25			17 34	17 38
d		16 56	17 03	17 08		17 13		17 25		17 31	17 35	17 39
Moses Gate d												17 42
Farnworth d												17 44
Kearsley d												17 46
Daisy Hill d	16 41						17 08					
Hag Fold d							17 11					
Atherton d	16 45						17 14					
Walkden d	16 50						17 19					
Moorside d							17 23					
Swinton d	16 55						17 25					
Salford Crescent a	17 02	17 08	17 15			17 25	17 33	17 38		17 43	17 47	17 56
d	17 03	17 09	17 15			17 26	17 33	17 38		17 44	17 47	17 56
Salford Central d	17 05		17 17				17 36	17 41		17 46		17 59
Manchester Victoria 🚊 a	17 13		17 23				17 43	17 45		17 52		18 06
Rochdale 95 a	*17 37*		17 51							*18 18*		
Deansgate 🚊 a		17 15									17 51	
Manchester Oxford Road a		17 17		17 23		17 30					17 52	
Manchester Piccadilly 10 🚊 a		17 21		17 27		17 35					17 56	
Stockport 84 a		17 32		*17 50*		*17e53*					*18 20*	
Hazel Grove 86 a		17 39				*18 13*						
Buxton 86 a		18 14				*18 53*						
Heald Green 85 a				17 40		*18 02*					18 10	
Manchester Airport 85 ✈ a				17 48		17 53					18 17	

	NT	NT	NT D	TP 1◇ 🛒		NT	NT	NT	NT	NT C	TP 1◇ E 🛒	NT
Barrow-in-Furness d							16 20					
Roose d							16 24					
Dalton d							16 30					
Ulverston d							16 38					
Cark d							16 46					
Kents Bank d							16 50					
Grange-over-Sands d							16 54					
Arnside d							17 00					
Silverdale d							17 05					
Carnforth d							17 11					
Windermere 83 d											17 06	
Oxenholme Lake District 65 d											17 30	
Lancaster 6 65 a							17 25				17 47	
d				*16c57*						*17c36*	17 48	
Blackpool North 97 d				17 20						17 37		
Layton 97 d				17 23								
Poulton-le-Fylde 97 d				17 27								
Kirkham & Wesham 97 d				*17 10*					*17 29*	17 52		
Preston 8 65, 97 a				17 45						18 02	18 06	
d				17 47					17 56	18 04	18 08	
Leyland d									18 01	18a09		
Chorley d				17 56					18 08		18 17	
Adlington (Lancashire) d									18 13			
Blackrod d									18 17			
Horwich Parkway d									18 20		18 27	
Lostock d											18 30	
Southport d	16 54					17 24						
Meols Cop d	16 59					17 29						
Bescar Lane d	17 04											
New Lane d	17 08											
Burscough Bridge d	17 11					17 37						
Hoscar d	17 15											
Parbold d	17 18					17 42						
Appley Bridge d	17 22					17 46						
Gathurst d	17 25											
Liverpool Central 10 103 d								*17 05*				
Kirkby d								17 32				
Rainford d								17 40				
Upholland d								17 44				
Orrell d								17 47				
Pemberton d								17 50				
Wigan Wallgate a	17 30					17 52		17 56				
d	17 32	17 39				17 54		17 58				18 20
Wigan North Western d												
Ince d								18 01				
Hindley d	17 37							18 04				18 25
Westhoughton d		17 47				18 02						18 29
Bolton a		17 55		18 08		18 12			18 30		18 34	18 38
d		17 56	18 02	18 08		18 13			18 30		18 35	18 39
Moses Gate d												18 42
Farnworth d												18 44
Kearsley d												18 46
Daisy Hill d	17 41							18 08				
Hag Fold d								18 11				
Atherton d	17 45							18 14				
Walkden d	17 50							18 19				
Moorside d								18 23				
Swinton d	17 55							18 25				
Salford Crescent a	18 02	18 08	18 15			18 25		18 33	18 43		18 47	18 56
d	18 03	18 09	18 15			18 26		18 33	18 43		18 47	18 56
Salford Central d	18 05		18 17					18 36	18 46			18 59
Manchester Victoria 🚊 a	18 11		18 24					18 43	18 50			19 06
Rochdale 95 a	*18 35*		18 47					*19 01*	*19 19*			
Deansgate 🚊 a		18 12									18 51	
Manchester Oxford Road a		18 14		18 23		18 31					18 52	
Manchester Piccadilly 10 🚊 a		18 18		18 27		18 35					18 56	
Stockport 84 a		18 34		*18 50*		*18e53*					*19 22*	
Hazel Grove 86 a		18 43				*19 13*					*19 45*	
Buxton 86 a		19 22				*19 53*						
Heald Green 85 a				18 40		*19 02*					19 10	
Manchester Airport 85 ✈ a				18 47		18 53					19 17	

For general notes see front of timetable
For details of catering facilities see Directory of Train Operators

A To Huddersfield (Table 39)
B From Glasgow Central (Table 65)
C To Liverpool Lime Street (Table 90)
D From Clitheroe (Table 94)
E 🛒 from Preston
b Change at Oxenholme Lake District and Preston
c Change at Preston
e Change at Manchester Oxford Road

From 5 October a revised Northern service will be in operation due to seasonal difficulties. Customers should check with NRES for precise times

Barrow-in-Furness, Blackpool North, Preston, Southport, Kirkby and Wigan → Bolton → Manchester

Network Diagram - see first page of Table 82

	NT	TP 1 ◇ A	NT B	TP 1 ◇ C	NT	NT	NT	NT	NT D	NT	NT E	NT B		TP 1 ◇	NT	TP 1 ◇	NT G	NT H	NT	NT	NT E	NT B	TP 1 ◇	NT
Barrow-in-Furness d		17 21						17 43									18 03							
Roose d																	18 07							
Dalton d		17 30															18 13							
Ulverston d		17 38						17 59									18 21							
Cark d		17 46															18 29							
Kents Bank d																	18 33							
Grange-over-Sands d		17 53															18 37							
Arnside d		17 59															18 43							
Silverdale d																	18 48							
Carnforth d		18 09						18 23	18 29								18 54							
Windermere 83 d																18 12								
Oxenholme Lake District 65 d				17b44										18b29		18 33	18 42			18b42				
Lancaster 6 65 a		18 20						18 38	18 42							18 49	19 04							
d				18 26										18b44		18 50	19 05			18b57				
Blackpool North 97 d							18 20				18 37			18 45						19 20	19 37		19 45	
Layton 97 d							18 23													19 23				
Poulton-le-Fylde 97 d							18 28				18b35			18 51						19 28			19 51	
Kirkham & Wesham 97 d				18 10			18 37				18 52									19 37			19 37	
Preston 8 65, 97 a				18 45			18 47				19 02			19 09		19 10	19 30			19 47	20 02		20 09	
d				18 47			18 49				19 04			19 10		19 13				19 49	20 04		20 10	
Leyland d							18 54				19a09									19 54	20a09			
Chorley d				18 56			19 02							19 20		19 25				20 02			20 20	
Adlington (Lancashire) d							19 07													20 07				
Blackrod d							19 10													20 10				
Horwich Parkway d							19 14							19 27						20 14			20 27	
Lostock d							19 20													20 20				
Southport d					18 17										19 00				19 23					
Meols Cop d					18 22										19 05				19 28					
Bescar Lane d					18 27																			
New Lane d					18 31																			
Burscough Bridge d					18 33										19 13				19 36					
Hoscar d					18 37																			
Parbold d					18 40										19 18				19 41					
Appley Bridge d					18 44										19 22				19 45					
Gathurst d					18 47										19 25				19 48					
Liverpool Central 10 103 d						18 05				18 35														
Kirkby d						18 32				19 02														
Rainford d						18 40				19 10														
Upholland d						18 44				19 14														
Orrell d						18 47				19 17														
Pemberton d						18 50				19 20														
Wigan Wallgate a					18 52	18 56				19 27					19 30				19 53					
d	18 32				18 53	18 58									19 32				19 55					20 27
Wigan North Western d																								
Ince d						19 01																		20 30
Hindley d	18 37				18 58	19 04									19 37				20 00					20 33
Westhoughton d					19 02														20 04					
Bolton a				19 08	19 12		19 25							19 34		19 39			20 12	20 25			20 34	
d			19 02	19 08	19 13		19 25					19 31		19 35		19 40		20 02	20 13	20 25		20 31	20 35	
Moses Gate d																								
Farnworth d																								
Kearsley d																								
Daisy Hill d	18 41					19 08									19 41									20 37
Hag Fold d						19 11																		20 40
Atherton d	18 45					19 14									19 45									20 43
Walkden d	18 50					19 19									19 50									20 49
Moorside d						19 23																		20 52
Swinton d	18 55					19 25									19 55									20 55
Salford Crescent a	19 02		19 14		19 25	19 33	19 38					19 44		19 47	20 02			20 15	20 25	20 38		20 43	20 47	21 02
d	19 03		19 15		19 26	19 33	19 38					19 44		19 47	20 03			20 15	20 26	20 38		20 44	20 47	21 03
Salford Central d	19 05		19 17			19 36	19 41					19 46			20 05			20 18		20 41		20 46		21 05
Manchester Victoria ⛴ a	19 11		19 22			19 43	19 46					19 52			20 11			20 23		20 46		20 51		21 11
Rochdale 95 a	19 40														20 40							21 39		21 40
Deansgate ⛴ a					19 29									19 51					20 29				20 51	
Manchester Oxford Road a				19 23	19 31									19 52		19 58			20 31				20 52	
Manchester Piccadilly 10 ⛴ a				19 27	19 35									19 56		20 02			20 35				20 56	
Stockport 84 a					19c53											20 22			20c53				21 22	
Hazel Grove 86 a					20 13														21 13					
Buxton 86 a					20 53														21 53					
Heald Green 85 a					20 02									20 10		20 15			21 02				21 10	
Manchester Airport 85 ✈ a				19 47	19 53									20 17		20 24			20 53				21 17	

For general notes see front of timetable
For details of catering facilities see Directory of Train Operators

- **A** To Windermere (Table 83)
- **B** From Clitheroe (Table 94)
- **C** From Edinburgh (Table 65)
- **D** From Leeds to Morecambe (Table 36)
- **E** To Liverpool Lime Street (Table 90)
- **G** From Carlisle via Whitehaven (Table 100)
- **H** From Blackburn (Table 94)
- **b** Change at Preston
- **c** Change at Manchester Oxford Road

From 5 October a revised Northern service will be in operation due to seasonal difficulties. Customers should check with NRES for precise times

Barrow-in-Furness, Blackpool North, Preston, Southport, Kirkby and Wigan → Bolton → Manchester

Network Diagram - see first page of Table 82

		TP 1 ◇ A 🍴	NT	NT	NT B	NT C	TP 1 ◇	NT	NT		TP 1 ◇	NT	NT C	TP 1 ◇	NT	NT	NT B	TP 1 ◇ A 🍴	NT	NT	NT C	TP 1 ◇	NT	NT	
Barrow-in-Furness	d										20 07												21 43		
Roose	d										20 11												21 47		
Dalton	d										20 17												21 53		
Ulverston	d										20 26												22 01		
Cark	d										20 34												22 09		
Kents Bank	d										20 38												22 13		
Grange-over-Sands	d										20 42												22 17		
Arnside	d										20 48												22 23		
Silverdale	d										20 52												22 28		
Carnforth	d										21 01												22 34		
Windermere	83 d	19 10			20b00														21b40						
Oxenholme Lake District	65 d	20 12		19c32	20c24						20 42							22 12	22c05						
Lancaster 6	65 a	20 26									21 11							22 26					22 44		
	d	20 26		19c47	20c38						21 11							22 26	22c20				22 45	23c07	
Blackpool North	97 d			20 20	20 38		20 45					21 20		21 45			22 14		22 20			22 45		23 13	
Layton	97 d			20 23								21 23							22 23					23 16	
Poulton-le-Fylde	97 d			20 28	20 35		20 51					21 28		21 51					22 28			22 51		23 21	
Kirkham & Wesham	97 d	20 10		20 37							21 10	21 37							22 37					23 30	
Preston 8	65, 97 a	20 45		20 46	21 02		21 09				21 29	21 47		22 09			22 41	22 45	22 47			23 09	23 10	23 40	
	d	20 47		20 49	21 04		21 11				21 31	21 49		22 10			22 43	22 47	22 49			23 10		23 42	
Leyland	d			20 54	21a09							21 54					22a48		22 54					23 48	
Chorley	d	20 56		21 02			21 20					22 02		22 20					23 02			23 20		23 55	
Adlington (Lancashire)	d			21 07								22 07							23 07					00 01	
Blackrod	d			21 10								22 10							23 10					00 04	
Horwich Parkway	d			21 14			21 27					22 14		22 27					23 14			23 27		00 08	
Lostock	d			21 20								22 20							23 20					00 13	
Southport	d		20 23						21 23							22 18				23 10					
Meols Cop	d		20 28						21 28							22 23				23 15					
Bescar Lane	d															22 28									
New Lane	d															22 32									
Burscough Bridge	d		20 36						21 36							22 34				23 23					
Hoscar	d															22 38									
Parbold	d		20 41						21 41							22 41				23 28					
Appley Bridge	d		20 45						21 45							22 45				23 32					
Gathurst	d		20 48						21 48							22 48				23 35					
Liverpool Central 10	103 d																								
Kirkby	d																								
Rainford	d																								
Upholland	d																								
Orrell	d																								
Pemberton	d																								
Wigan Wallgate	a		20 53						21 53							22 53				23 44					
	d		20 55					21 27	21 55						22 27	22 55									
Wigan North Western	d																								
Ince	d							21 30							22 30										
Hindley	d		21 00					21 33	22 00						22 33	23 00									
Westhoughton	d		21 04						22 04							23 04									
Bolton	a	21 08	21 12	21 25			21 34		22 12			22 25		22 34		23 12			23 25			23 34		00 18	
	d	21 08	21 13	21 25		21 31	21 35		22 13			22 25	22 31	22 35		23 13			23 25		23 31	23 35		00 19	
Moses Gate	d																								
Farnworth	d																								
Kearsley	d																								
Daisy Hill	d							21 37							22 37										
Hag Fold	d							21 40							22 40										
Atherton	d							21 43							22 43										
Walkden	d							21 49							22 49										
Moorside	d							21 52							22 52										
Swinton	d							21 55							22 55										
Salford Crescent	a		21 25	21 38		21 43	21 47	22 02	22 25			22 38	22 43	22 47	23 02	23 25			23 38		23 43	23 47			
	d		21 26	21 38		21 44	21 47	22 03	22 26			22 38	22 44	22 47	23 03	23 26			23 38		23 44	23 47			
Salford Central	d			21 41		21 46		22e05	22e28			22e41	22e46		23e05										
Manchester Victoria	⇌ a			21 46		21 51		22 11	22 34			22 46	22 51		23 13				23 46		23 50			00 35	
Rochdale	95 a					22 39		22 40							23 40										
Deansgate	⇌ a		21 29				21 51							22 51		23 29									
Manchester Oxford Road	a	21 23	21 31				21 52				22 26			22 52		23 31									
Manchester Piccadilly 10	⇌ a	21 27	21 35				21 56				22 30			22 56		23 37		23 44				23 53			
Stockport	84 a		21 57				22 15				22 57			23 19											
Hazel Grove	86 a		22 13											23 27											
Buxton	86 a		22 53											00 07											
Heald Green	85 a		22 02				22 09				23 02			23 09								00 15			
Manchester Airport	85 ✈ a	21 47	21 53				22 17				22 47			23 17								00 22			

For general notes see front of timetable
For details of catering facilities see Directory of Train Operators

- **A** From Edinburgh (Table 65)
- **B** To Liverpool Lime Street (Table 90)
- **C** From Clitheroe (Table 94)
- **b** Change at Oxenholme Lake District and Preston
- **c** Change at Preston
- **e** Fridays only

From 5 October a revised Northern service will be in operation due to seasonal difficulties. Customers should check with NRES for precise times

Table 82

Saturdays

Barrow-in-Furness, Blackpool North, Preston, Southport, Kirkby and Wigan → Bolton → Manchester

Network Diagram - see first page of Table 82

	TP 1 ◇	TP 1 ◇	TP 1 ◇	TP 1 ◇	NT	NT	NT A	TP 1 ◇	NT	NT		NT B	TP 1 ◇ 🛒	NT	NT	NT	NT	NT C	NT D	TP 1 ◇ E 🛒	NT		NT	NT G
Barrow-in-Furness d			04 35					05 31												06 19				
Roose d																				06 23				
Dalton d																				06 29				
Ulverston d			04 50					05 46												06 38				
Cark d																				06 46				
Kents Bank d																				06 50				
Grange-over-Sands d			05 03					05 59												06 54				
Arnside d			05 10					06 06												07 00				
Silverdale d																				07 04				
Carnforth d			05 20					06 16												07 12				07 43
Windermere 83 d																								
Oxenholme Lake District 65 d													06b21											
Lancaster 6 65 a			05 28					06 23												07 21				07 52
d				05b40				06 26					06b36					06b58		07 22				
Blackpool North 97 d	03 36	04 50		05 45						06 19			06 34			06 53		07 02					07 18	
Layton 97 d										06 22			06 37										07 21	
Poulton-le-Fylde 97 d				05 51						06 27			06 41					07 08					07 26	
Kirkham & Wesham 97 d								06 08		06 36			06 50					07 09					07 35	
Preston 8 65, 97 a		05 14		06 08				06 45		06 46			07 01			07 15		07 28		07 41			07 46	
d	04u01	05 16		06 10				06 47		06 48			07 03			07 17		07 30		07 47			07 47	
Leyland d										06 53			07 08			07 22		07a35					07 53	
Chorley d		05 26		06 19				06 56		07 01			07 15			07 31				07 56			08 01	
Adlington (Lancashire) d										07 06						07 36							08 06	
Blackrod d										07 10			07 21			07 40							08 10	
Horwich Parkway d				06 27						07 14			07 27			07 44							08 14	
Lostock d		05 34		06 30						07 20			07 30			07 49							08 20	
Southport d									06 23												07 22			
Meols Cop d									06 28												07 27			
Bescar Lane d																								
New Lane d																								
Burscough Bridge d									06 36												07 35			
Hoscar d																								
Parbold d									06 41												07 40			
Appley Bridge d									06 45												07 44			
Gathurst d									06 49												07 48			
Liverpool Central 10 103 d																	06 25							
Kirkby d																	07 11							
Rainford d																	07 19							
Upholland d																	07 23							
Orrell d																	07 27							
Pemberton d																	07 30							
Wigan Wallgate a									06 54								07 35				07 53			
d					06 32	06 36			06 55					07 15			07 37				07 54			
Wigan North Western d															07 22									
Ince d						06 39								07 18	07 25		07 40							
Hindley d					06 37	06 42								07 21	07 29		07 43							
Westhoughton d					06 42				07 03						07 33						08 03			
Bolton a		05 42		06 34	06 52			07 08	07 11	07 25			07 34		07 42	07 54				08 08	08 11		08 25	
d	04u30	05 43		06 35	06 53		06 56	07 08	07 12	07 25		07 30	07 35		07 43	07 55			07 59	08 08	08 12		08 25	
Moses Gate d							06 59								07 46				08 02					
Farnworth d							07 01								07 48				08 04					
Kearsley d							07 03								07 50				08 06					
Daisy Hill d						06 46								07 26			07 47							
Hag Fold d						06 49								07 29			07 50							
Atherton d						06 52								07 32			07 53							
Walkden d						06 58								07 38			07 59							
Moorside d						07 01								07 41			08 03							
Swinton d						07 04								07 44			08 05							
Salford Crescent a		05 55		06 47	07 05	07 11	07 15		07 24	07 38		07 43	07 47	07 51	08 02	08 07	08 13		08 17		08 24		08 38	
d		05 55		06 47	07 08	07 11	07 15		07 25	07 38		07 43	07 47	07 51	08 02	08 08	08 13		08 17		08 25		08 38	
Salford Central d						07 14	07 19			07 41		07 46		07 55	08 05		08 16		08 20				08 41	
Manchester Victoria 🚋 a						07 20	07 22			07 46		07 51		08 01	08 12		08 20		08 25				08 46	
Rochdale 95 a							08c01					08 19			08 34		08 51		08 51					
Deansgate 🚋 a				06 51	07 11				07 28				07 51			08 11					08 28			
Manchester Oxford Road a				06 52	07 13			07 23	07 30				07 52			08 14				08 23	08 31			
Manchester Piccadilly 10 🚋 a		06 01		06 56	07 17			07 27	07 34				07 56			08 18				08 27	08 35			
Stockport 84 a		06 27		07 22	07 34			07 50	07e53				08 22			08 34				08 50	08e53			
Hazel Grove 86 a		07 10			07 45				08 11												09 13			
Buxton 86 a		07 50							08 46												09 53			
Heald Green 85 a		06 32		07 10					08 02				08 10								09 02			
Manchester Airport 85 ✈ a	05 06	06 18		07 17				07 47	07 53				08 17							08 47	08 53			

For general notes see front of timetable
For details of catering facilities see Directory of Train Operators

A From Blackburn (Table 94). Also stops at Clifton 0707
B From Blackburn (Table 94)
C To Liverpool Lime Street (Table 90)
D From Clitheroe (Table 94)
E 🛒 from Preston
G From Leeds (Table 36)
b Change at Preston
c Until 11 July arr. 0800
e Change at Manchester Oxford Road

From 10 October a revised Northern service will be in operation due to seasonal difficulties. Customers should check with NRES for precise times

Barrow-in-Furness, Blackpool North, Preston, Southport, Kirkby and Wigan → Bolton → Manchester

Network Diagram - see first page of Table 82

Station	NT A	TP 1◇ 🚲	NT	NT	NT	NT	NT	NT B	TP 1◇ C 🚲	NT		NT	NT	NT D	NT A	TP 1◇ 🚲	NT	NT	NT	NT B	NT		TP 1◇ E 🚲	NT
Barrow-in-Furness d									07 28															
Roose d																								
Dalton d									07 37															
Ulverston d									07 45															
Cark d									07 53															
Kents Bank d																								
Grange-over-Sands d									08 00															
Arnside d									08 06															
Silverdale d									08 10															
Carnforth d									08 18															
Windermere 83 d		06b50												07b57									08 50	
Oxenholme Lake District 65 d		07c24					07 42							08c23									09 11	
Lancaster 6 65 a									08 26														09 26	
d		07c38					07 57		08 26					08c38					08 57				09 26	
Blackpool North 97 d		07 44											08 20	08 38		08 45							09 14	
Layton 97 d		07 47											08 23											
Poulton-le-Fylde 97 d		07 51											08 28	08 35		08 51							09 20	
Kirkham & Wesham 97 d		08 00							08 09				08 37										09 10	
Preston 8 65, 97 a		08 11							08 45				08 47	09 02		09 09							09 45	
d		08 12					08 23		08 47				08 49	09 04		09 10			09 23				09 47	
Leyland d							08 29						08 54	09a09					09 29					
Chorley d		08 22					08 36		08 56				09 02			09 20			09 36				09 56	
Adlington (Lancashire) d													09 07											
Blackrod d													09 10											
Horwich Parkway d							08 45						09 14			09 27			09 45					
Lostock d							08 50						09 20						09 50					
Southport d					07 53					08 25								08 57						09 24
Meols Cop d					07 58					08 30								09 02						
Bescar Lane d					08 03													09 07						
New Lane d					08 07													09 11						
Burscough Bridge d					08 09					08 38								09 13						09 36
Hoscar d					08 13													09 17						
Parbold d					08 16					08 43								09 20						09 41
Appley Bridge d					08 20					08 47								09 24						09 45
Gathurst d					08 23					08 50								09 27						
Liverpool Central 10 103 d						07 50																		
Kirkby d						08 21																		
Rainford d						08 29																		
Upholland d						08 33																		
Orrell d						08 36																		
Pemberton d						08 39																		
Wigan Wallgate a					08 28	08 45				08 55								09 32						09 51
d			08 13		08 29	08 50				08 56							09 20	09 32			09 48			09 53
Wigan North Western d				08 20																				
Ince d			08 16			08 53																		
Hindley d			08 19	08 25	08 34	08 57											09 25	09 37						09 58
Westhoughton d				08 30						09 04							09 29							10 02
Bolton a		08 34		08 38			08 55		09 08	09 12			09 25			09 34	09 38		09 55		10 02		10 08	10 12
d	08 31	08 35		08 39			08 56	09 03	09 08	09 13			09 25		09 31	09 35	09 39		09 56	10 00	10 03		10 08	10 13
Moses Gate d				08 42													09 42							
Farnworth d				08 44													09 44							
Kearsley d				08 46								←					09 46							
Daisy Hill d			08 23		08 39	09 01 →						09 01						09 41						
Hag Fold d			08 26									09 04												
Atherton d			08 29		08 43							09 06						09 45						
Walkden d			08 35		08 49							09 12						09 50						
Moorside d			08 39									09 15												
Swinton d			08 42		08 54							09 18						09 55						
Salford Crescent a	08 43	08 47	08 50	08 56	09 03		09 08	09 15		09 25		09 27	09 38		09 43	09 47	09 56	10 03	10 08	10 13	10 15			10 25
d	08 44	08 47	08 50	08 56	09 03		09 09	09 16		09 26		09 27	09 38		09 44	09 47	09 56	10 03	10 09	10 13	10 15			10 26
Salford Central d	08 46		08 53	08 59	09 06			09 18				09 31	09 41		09 46		09 59	10 05		10 16	10 17			
Manchester Victoria ⇌ a	08 51		08 59	09 06	09 11			09 26				09 38	09 46		09 51		10 06	10 11		10 23	10 25			
Rochdale 95 a	09 19				09 35			09 52				10 02			10 19			10 34			10 51			
Deansgate ⇌ a							09 12			09 29						09 51			10 12					10 29
Manchester Oxford Road a		08 52					09 14		09 23	09 31						09 52			10 14				10 23	10 31
Manchester Piccadilly 10 ⇌ a		08 56					09 18		09 27	09 35						09 56			10 18				10 27	10 35
Stockport 84 a		09 22					09 34		09 50	09e53						10 22			10 34				10 50	10e53
Hazel Grove 86 a		09 45					09 45			10 13									10 45					11 13
Buxton 86 a										10 53														11 50
Heald Green 85 a		09 12								10 02						10 10								11 02
Manchester Airport 85 ✈ a		09 19							09 47	09 53						10 17							10 47	10 53

For general notes see front of timetable
For details of catering facilities see Directory of Train Operators

A From Clitheroe (Table 94)
B From Blackburn (Table 94)
C 🚲 from Preston
D To Liverpool Lime Street (Table 90)
E From Glasgow Central (Table 65)
b Change at Oxenholme Lake District and Preston
c Change at Preston
e Change at Manchester Oxford Road

From 10 October a revised Northern service will be in operation due to seasonal difficulties. Customers should check with NRES for precise times

Table 82

Saturdays

Barrow-in-Furness, Blackpool North, Preston, Southport, Kirkby and Wigan → Bolton → Manchester

Network Diagram - see first page of Table 82

		NT	NT	NT	NT	NT	TP	NT	NT	NT	NT	NT	TP	NT	NT	NT	NT	NT	TP	NT	NT	NT	NT
							1 ◇						1 ◇						1 ◇				
				A	B	C		D					E				B	C				G	
							🍴						🍴						🍴				
Barrow-in-Furness	d			08 25									09 23									10 16	
Roose	d			08 29									09 27									10 20	
Dalton	d			08 36									09 33									10 26	
Ulverston	d			08 44									09 42									10 34	
Cark	d			08 53									09 50									10 43	
Kents Bank	d			08 58									09 54									10 47	
Grange-over-Sands	d			09 02									09 58									10 51	
Arnside	d			09 08									10 04									10 57	
Silverdale	d			09 13									10 08									11 02	
Carnforth	d			09 20				10 02					10 16									11 08	
Windermere	83 d												*09 41*										
Oxenholme Lake District	65 d				*09b23*								*10 01*										*10 42*
Lancaster 6	65 a			09 33				10 12					10 26									11 20	
	d						*09b38*				*09 57*		10 26			*10b18*	*10b38*						*10 57*
Blackpool North	97 d		09 20		09 37		09 45									10 20	10 37		10 45				
Layton	97 d		09 23													10 23							
Poulton-le-Fylde	97 d		09 28		*09 35*		09 51									10 28	*10 35*		10 51				
Kirkham & Wesham	97 d		09 37				*09 37*						*10 10*			10 37							
Preston 8	65, 97 a		09 47		10 02		10 09						10 45			10 47	11 02		11 09				
	d		09 49		10 04		10 10				10 23		10 47			10 49	11 04		11 10				11 23
Leyland	d		09 54		10a09						10 29					10 54	11a09						11 29
Chorley	d		10 02				10 20				10 36		10 56			11 02			11 20				11 36
Adlington (Lancashire)	d		10 07													11 07							
Blackrod	d		10 10													11 10							
Horwich Parkway	d		10 14				10 27				10 45					11 14			11 27				11 45
Lostock	d		10 20								10 50					11 20							11 50
Southport	d									10 00				10 24							10 54		
Meols Cop	d									10 05											10 59		
Bescar Lane	d																				11 04		
New Lane	d																				11 08		
Burscough Bridge	d									10 13				10 36							11 11		
Hoscar	d																				11 15		
Parbold	d									10 18				10 41							11 18		
Appley Bridge	d									10 22				10 45							11 22		
Gathurst	d									10 25											11 25		
Liverpool Central 10	103 d	*09 05*													*10 05*								
Kirkby	d	09 32													10 32								
Rainford	d	09 40													10 40								
Upholland	d	09 44													10 44								
Orrell	d	09 47													10 47								
Pemberton	d	09 50													10 50								
Wigan Wallgate	a	09 56								10 30				10 51	10 56						11 30		
	d	09 58							10 20	10 32		10 48		10 53	10 58					11 20	11 32		
Wigan North Western	d																						
Ince	d	10 01													11 01								
Hindley	d	10 04							10 25	10 37				10 58	11 04					11 25	11 37		
Westhoughton	d								10 29					11 02						11 29			
Bolton	a		10 25				10 34		10 38		10 55	11 02	11 08	11 12		11 25			11 34	11 38			11 55
	d		10 25			10 31	10 35		10 39		10 56	11 03	11 08	11 13		11 25		11 31	11 35	11 39			11 56
Moses Gate	d								10 42											11 42			
Farnworth	d								10 44											11 44			
Kearsley	d								10 46											11 46			
Daisy Hill	d	10 09								10 41					11 09						11 41		
Hag Fold	d	10 12													11 12								
Atherton	d	10 15								10 45					11 15						11 45		
Walkden	d	10 20								10 50					11 20						11 50		
Moorside	d	10 24													11 24								
Swinton	d	10 26								10 55					11 26						11 55		
Salford Crescent	a	10 34	10 38			10 43	10 47		10 56	11 02	11 08	11 15		11 25	11 34	11 38		11 43	11 47	11 56	12 02		12 08
	d	10 34	10 38			10 44	10 47		10 56	11 03	11 09	11 15		11 26	11 34	11 38		11 44	11 47	11 56	12 03		12 09
Salford Central	d	10 36	10 41			10 46			10 59	11 05		11 17			11 36	11 41		11 46		11 59	12 05		
Manchester Victoria	🚋 a	10 43	10 46			10 51			11 06	11 11		11 25			11 43	11 46		11 51		12 06	12 11		
Rochdale	95 a	*11 02*				*11 19*				*11 34*		11 51			*12 02*			*12 19*			*12 34*		
Deansgate	🚋 a						10 51				11 12			11 29					11 51				12 12
Manchester Oxford Road	a						10 52				11 14		11 23	11 31					11 52				12 14
Manchester Piccadilly 10	🚋 a						10 56				11 18		11 27	11 35					11 56				12 18
Stockport	84 a						*11 22*				11 34		*11 50*	*11c53*					*12 22*				12 34
Hazel Grove	86 a										11 45			*12 13*									12 45
Buxton	86 a													*12 53*									
Heald Green	85 a						11 10							*12 02*					12 10				
Manchester Airport	85 ✈ a						11 17						11 47	11 53					12 17				

For general notes see front of timetable
For details of catering facilities see Directory of Train Operators

- **A** From Maryport (Table 100)
- **B** To Liverpool Lime Street (Table 90)
- **C** From Clitheroe (Table 94)
- **D** From Leeds to Morecambe (Table 36)
- **E** 🍴 from Preston
- **G** From Sellafield (Table 100)
- **b** Change at Preston
- **c** Change at Manchester Oxford Road

From 10 October a revised Northern service will be in operation due to seasonal difficulties. Customers should check with NRES for precise times

Barrow-in-Furness, Blackpool North, Preston, Southport, Kirkby and Wigan → Bolton → Manchester

Network Diagram - see first page of Table 82

		NT	NT	TP	NT	NT	NT	NT	NT	TP	TP		NT	NT	NT	NT	NT	TP	TP	NT	NT	NT		NT	NT
				1 ◇ A				B	C	1 ◇ D	1 ◇		E					1 ◇	1 ◇ G					B	C
Barrow-in-Furness	d																	11 25							
Roose	d																								
Dalton	d																								
Ulverston	d																	11 40							
Cark	d																								
Kents Bank	d																								
Grange-over-Sands	d																	11 53							
Arnside	d																	12 00							
Silverdale	d																								
Carnforth	d												12 02					12 09							
Windermere	83 d			10 49																				11b59	
Oxenholme Lake District	65 d			11 10				11c23		11 31									12 07					12c23	
Lancaster 6	65 a			11 26						11 46			12 11					12 18	12 22						
	d			11 26				11c38		11 46								12 18	12 23					12c38	
Blackpool North	97 d		11 15					11 37			11 32											12 20		12 37	
Layton	97 d		11 18																			12 23			
Poulton-le-Fylde	97 d		11 23					*11 31*		*11 38*	11 38											12 28		*12 35*	
Kirkham & Wesham	97 d		11 32	*11 10*															*12 10*			12 37			
Preston 8	65, 97 a		11 42	11 45			←	12 02		12 05	11 58							12 37	12 41			12 47		13 02	
	d		11 49 →	11 47			11 49	12 04		12 10						12 23			12 47			12 49		13 04	
Leyland	d						11 54	12a09								12 29						12 54		13a09	
Chorley	d			11 56			12 02			12 20						12 36			12 56			13 02			
Adlington (Lancashire)	d						12 07															13 07			
Blackrod	d						12 10															13 10			
Horwich Parkway	d						12 14			12 27						12 45						13 14			
Lostock	d						12 20									12 50						13 20			
Southport	d				11 24										12 00					12 24					
Meols Cop	d														12 05										
Bescar Lane	d																								
New Lane	d																								
Burscough Bridge	d				11 36										12 13					12 36					
Hoscar	d																								
Parbold	d				11 41										12 18					12 41					
Appley Bridge	d				11 45										12 22					12 45					
Gathurst	d														12 25										
Liverpool Central 10	103 d					*11 05*															*12 05*				
Kirkby	d					11 32															12 32				
Rainford	d					11 40															12 40				
Upholland	d					11 44															12 44				
Orrell	d					11 47															12 47				
Pemberton	d					11 50															12 50				
Wigan Wallgate	a				11 51	11 56									12 30					12 51	12 56				
	d	11 48			11 53	11 58								12 20	12 32		12 48			12 53	12 58				
Wigan North Western	d																								
Ince	d					12 01															13 01				
Hindley	d				11 58	12 04								12 25	12 37					12 58	13 04				
Westhoughton	d				12 02									12 29						13 02					
Bolton	a	12 02		12 08	12 12		12 25			12 34				12 38		12 55	13 02		13 08	13 12		13 25			
	d	12 03		12 08	12 13		12 25		12 31	12 35				12 39		12 56	13 03		13 08	13 13		13 25			13 31
Moses Gate	d													12 42											
Farnworth	d													12 44											
Kearsley	d													12 46											
Daisy Hill	d					12 09									12 41						13 09				
Hag Fold	d					12 12															13 12				
Atherton	d					12 15									12 45						13 15				
Walkden	d					12 20									12 50						13 20				
Moorside	d					12 24															13 24				
Swinton	d					12 26									12 55						13 26				
Salford Crescent	a	12 15			12 25	12 34	12 38		12 43	12 47				12 56	13 02	13 08	13 15			13 25	13 34	13 38			13 43
	d	12 15			12 26	12 34	12 38		12 44	12 47				12 56	13 03	13 09	13 15			13 26	13 34	13 38			13 44
Salford Central	d	12 17				12 36	12 41		12 46					12 59	13 05		13 17				13 36	13 41			13 46
Manchester Victoria	a	12 25				12 43	12 46		12 51					13 06	13 11		13 25				13 43	13 46			13 51
Rochdale	95 a	12 51				*13 02*			*13 19*						*13 34*		13 51				*14 02*				*14 19*
Deansgate	a				12 29					12 51						13 12				13 29					
Manchester Oxford Road	a			12 23	12 31					12 52						13 14			13 23	13 31					
Manchester Piccadilly 10	a			12 27	12 35					12 56						13 18			13 27	13 35					
Stockport	84 a			*12 50*	12e53					*13 22*						13 34			*13 50*	13e53					
Hazel Grove	86 a				*13 13*					*13 45*						13 45				*14 13*					
Buxton	86 a				*13 50*															*14 53*					
Heald Green	85 a				*13 02*					13 10										*14 02*					
Manchester Airport	85 a			12 47	12 53					13 17									13 47	13 53					

For general notes see front of timetable
For details of catering facilities see Directory of Train Operators

- **A** from Preston
- **B** To Liverpool Lime Street (Table 90)
- **C** From Clitheroe (Table 94)
- **D** From Edinburgh (Table 65)
- **E** From Leeds (Table 36) to Heysham Port (Table 98)
- **G** From Glasgow Central (Table 65)
- **b** Change at Oxenholme Lake District and Preston
- **c** Change at Preston
- **e** Change at Manchester Oxford Road

From 10 October a revised Northern service will be in operation due to seasonal difficulties. Customers should check with NRES for precise times

Table 82

Saturdays

Barrow-in-Furness, Blackpool North, Preston, Southport, Kirkby and Wigan → Bolton → Manchester

Network Diagram - see first page of Table 82

	TP 1 ◇ ⌶	NT A	NT	NT	NT	NT	TP 1 ◇ B ⌶	NT	NT	NT	NT C	NT D	TP 1 ◇ ⌶	NT	NT	NT	NT	TP 1 ◇ E	TP 1 ◇ E G ⌶	TP 1 ◇ H	TP 1 ◇ G H ⌶	NT
Barrow-in-Furness d		12 11																13 25		13 25		
Roose d		12 15																				
Dalton d		12 21																				
Ulverston d		12 29																13 40		13 40		
Cark d		12 37																				
Kents Bank d		12 41																				
Grange-over-Sands d		12 45																13 53		13 53		
Arnside d		12 51																14 00		14 00		
Silverdale d		12 56																				
Carnforth d		13 02																14 09		14 09		
Windermere 83 d							12 51															
Oxenholme Lake District 65 d					12 43		13 09												14 06		14 06	
Lancaster 6 65 a		13 15					13 26											14 18	14 22	14 18		
d					12 57		13 26				13b38					13 58		14 18	14 22	14 18		
Blackpool North 97 d	12 45									13 20	13 37		13 45									
Layton 97 d										13 23												
Poulton-le-Fylde 97 d	12 51									13 28	13 35		13 51									
Kirkham & Wesham 97 d							13 10			13 37									14 10		14 10	
Preston 8 65, 97 a	13 09						13 45			13 47	14 02		14 09					14 37	14 41	14 37	14 41	
d	13 10				13 23		13 47			13 49	14 04		14 10			14 23		14 47			14 47	
Leyland d					13 29					13 54	14a09					14 29						
Chorley d	13 20				13 36		13 56			14 02			14 20			14 36		14 56			14 56	
Adlington (Lancashire) d										14 07												
Blackrod d										14 10												
Horwich Parkway d	13 27				13 45					14 14			14 27			14 45						
Lostock d					13 50					14 20						14 50						
Southport d				12 54				13 24							14 00							14 24
Meols Cop d				12 59											14 05							
Bescar Lane d				13 04																		
New Lane d				13 08																		
Burscough Bridge d				13 11				13 36							14 13							14 36
Hoscar d				13 15																		
Parbold d				13 18				13 41							14 18							14 41
Appley Bridge d				13 22				13 45							14 22							14 45
Gathurst d				13 25											14 25							
Liverpool Central 10 103 d									13 05													
Kirkby d									13 32													
Rainford d									13 40													
Upholland d									13 44													
Orrell d									13 47													
Pemberton d									13 50													
Wigan Wallgate a				13 30				13 51	13 56						14 30							14 51
d			13 20	13 32		13 48		13 53	13 58					14 20	14 32		14 48					14 53
Wigan North Western d																						
Ince d									14 01													
Hindley d			13 25	13 37				13 58	14 04					14 25	14 37							14 58
Westhoughton d			13 29					14 02						14 29								15 02
Bolton a	13 34		13 38		13 55	14 02	14 08	14 12		14 25			14 34	14 38		14 55	15 02	15 08			15 08	15 12
d	13 35		13 39		13 56	14 03	14 08	14 13		14 25		14 31	14 35	14 39		14 56	15 03	15 08			15 08	15 13
Moses Gate d			13 42											14 42								
Farnworth d			13 44											14 44								
Kearsley d			13 46											14 46								
Daisy Hill d				13 41					14 09						14 41							
Hag Fold d									14 12													
Atherton d				13 45					14 15						14 45							
Walkden d				13 50					14 20						14 50							
Moorside d									14 24													
Swinton d				13 55					14 26						14 55							
Salford Crescent a	13 47		13 56	14 02	14 08	14 15		14 25	14 34	14 38		14 43	14 47	14 56	15 02	15 08	15 15					15 25
d	13 47		13 56	14 03	14 09	14 15		14 26	14 34	14 38		14 44	14 47	14 56	15 03	15 09	15 15					15 26
Salford Central d			13 59	14 05		14 17			14 36	14 41		14 46		14 59	15 05		15 17					
Manchester Victoria a			14 06	14 11		14 25			14 43	14 46		14 51		15 06	15 11		15 25					
Rochdale 95 a				14 34		14 51			15 02			15 19			15 34		15 51					
Deansgate a	13 51				14 12			14 29					14 51			15 12						15 29
Manchester Oxford Road a	13 52				14 14		14 23	14 31					14 52			15 14		15 23			15 23	15 31
Manchester Piccadilly 10 a	13 56				14 18		14 27	14 35					14 56			15 18		15 27			15 27	15 35
Stockport 84 a	14 22				14 34		14 50	14c53					15 22			15 34		15 50			15 50	15c53
Hazel Grove 86 a					14 45			15 13								15 45						16 13
Buxton 86 a								15 50														16 53
Heald Green 85 a	14 10							15 02					15 10									16 02
Manchester Airport 85 ✈ a	14 17						14 47	14 53					15 17					15 47			15 47	15 53

For general notes see front of timetable
For details of catering facilities see Directory of Train Operators

- **A** From Carlisle via Whitehaven (Table 100)
- **B** ⌶ from Preston
- **C** To Liverpool Lime Street (Table 90)
- **D** From Clitheroe (Table 94)
- **E** Until 20 June and from 12 September
- **G** From Edinburgh (Table 65)
- **H** 27 June to 5 September
- **b** Change at Preston
- **c** Change at Manchester Oxford Road

From 10 October a revised Northern service will be in operation due to seasonal difficulties. Customers should check with NRES for precise times

Barrow-in-Furness, Blackpool North, Preston, Southport, Kirkby and Wigan → Bolton → Manchester

Network Diagram - see first page of Table 82

	NT	NT	NT	NT	TP	NT	NT	NT	NT	NT		TP	NT	NT	NT	NT	NT	TP	NT	NT	NT		NT	NT
					1 ◇							1 ◇						1 ◇						
			A	B				C				D		B			A		E					G
Barrow-in-Furness d								14 16																15 18
Roose d								14 20																15 22
Dalton d								14 26																15 28
Ulverston d								14 35																15 36
Cark d								14 43																15 45
Kents Bank d								14 47																15 49
Grange-over-Sands d								14 51																15 53
Arnside d								14 57																15 59
Silverdale d								15 02																16 04
Carnforth d								15 08											15 36					16 10
Windermere 83 d			14b00														14b59							
Oxenholme Lake District 65 d			14c24									15 09					15c23						15 46	
Lancaster 6 65 a								15 21				15 26							15 45					16 23
d			14c38						14 57			15 26					15c38							
Blackpool North 97 d		14 20	14 37		14 45											15 20	15 37	15 45						
Layton 97 d		14 23														15 23								
Poulton-le-Fylde 97 d		14 28	14 35		14 51											15 28	15 35	15 51						
Kirkham & Wesham 97 d		14 37										15 10				15 37								
Preston 8 65, 97 a		14 47	15 02		15 09							15 45				15 47	16 02	16 09						
d		14 49	15 04		15 10				15 23			15 47				15 49	16 04	16 10					16 23	
Leyland d		14 54	15a09						15 29							15 54	16a09						16 29	
Chorley d		15 02			15 20				15 36			15 56				16 02		16 20					16 36	
Adlington (Lancashire) d		15 07														16 07								
Blackrod d		15 10														16 10								
Horwich Parkway d		15 14			15 27				15 45							16 14		16 27					16 45	
Lostock d		15 20							15 50							16 20							16 50	
Southport d							14 54						15 24								16 00			
Meols Cop d							14 59														16 05			
Bescar Lane d							15 04																	
New Lane d							15 08																	
Burscough Bridge d							15 11						15 36								16 13			
Hoscar d							15 15																	
Parbold d							15 18						15 41								16 18			
Appley Bridge d							15 22						15 45								16 22			
Gathurst d							15 25														16 25			
Liverpool Central 10 103 d	14 05														15 05									
Kirkby d	14 32														15 32									
Rainford d	14 40														15 40									
Upholland d	14 44														15 44									
Orrell d	14 47														15 47									
Pemberton d	14 50														15 50									
Wigan Wallgate a	14 56						15 30						15 51		15 56						16 30			
d	14 58					15 20	15 32			15 48			15 53		15 58					16 20	16 32			
Wigan North Western d																								
Ince d	15 01														16 01									
Hindley d	15 04					15 25	15 37						15 58		16 04					16 25	16 37			
Westhoughton d						15 29							16 02							16 29				
Bolton a		15 25			15 34	15 38			15 55	16 02		16 08	16 12			16 25		16 34		16 38			16 55	
d		15 25		15 31	15 35	15 39			15 56	16 03		16 08	16 13	16 17		16 25		16 35		16 39			16 56	
Moses Gate d						15 42														16 42				
Farnworth d						15 44														16 44				
Kearsley d						15 46														16 46				
Daisy Hill d	15 09						15 41								16 09						16 41			
Hag Fold d	15 12														16 12									
Atherton d	15 15						15 45								16 15						16 45			
Walkden d	15 20						15 50								16 20						16 50			
Moorside d	15 24														16 24									
Swinton d	15 26						15 55								16 26						16 55			
Salford Crescent a	15 34	15 38		15 43	15 47	15 56	16 02		16 08	16 15			16 25	16 30	16 33	16 38		16 47		16 56	17 02		17 08	
d	15 34	15 38		15 44	15 47	15 56	16 03		16 09	16 15			16 26	16 30	16 34	16 38		16 47		16 56	17 03		17 09	
Salford Central d	15 36	15 41		15 46		15 59	16 05			16 17				16 33	16 37	16 41				16 59	17 05			
Manchester Victoria a	15 43	15 46		15 53		16 06	16 11			16 23				16 40	16 43	16 46				17 06	17 11			
Rochdale 95 a	16 02			16 19			16 34			16 51					17 02	17 19					17 37			
Deansgate a					15 51				16 12									16 51					17 12	
Manchester Oxford Road a					15 52				16 14			16 23	16 31					16 52					17 14	
Manchester Piccadilly 10 a					15 56				16 18			16 27	16 35					16 56					17 18	
Stockport 84 a					16 22				16 34			16 50	16e53					17 21					17 34	
Hazel Grove 86 a					16 45				16 45				17 13					17 39					17 43	
Buxton 86 a													17 50										18 25	
Heald Green 85 a					16 10							16 40	17 02					17 10						
Manchester Airport 85 a					16 17							16 47	16 53					17 17						

For general notes see front of timetable
For details of catering facilities see Directory of Train Operators

- **A** To Liverpool Lime Street (Table 90)
- **B** From Clitheroe (Table 94)
- **C** From Whitehaven (Table 100)
- **D** From Glasgow Central (Table 65)
- **E** From Leeds to Morecambe (Table 36)
- **G** From Carlisle via Whitehaven (Table 100)
- **b** Change at Oxenholme Lake District and Preston
- **c** Change at Preston
- **e** Change at Manchester Oxford Road

From 10 October a revised Northern service will be in operation due to seasonal difficulties. Customers should check with NRES for precise times

Table 82

Saturdays

Barrow-in-Furness, Blackpool North, Preston, Southport, Kirkby and Wigan → Bolton → Manchester

Network Diagram - see first page of Table 82

Station		NT	TP	NT	NT	NT	NT	NT	TP	NT	NT		NT	NT	TP	TP	NT	NT	NT	NT	TP	NT		NT	TP
			1 ◇						1 ◇						1 ◇	1 ◇					1 ◇				1 ◇
			A				B	C						C						B	D				
			🛒						🛒							🛒					🛒				
Barrow-in-Furness	d														16 22										17 21
Roose	d																								
Dalton	d																								17 30
Ulverston	d														16 37										17 38
Cark	d																								17 46
Kents Bank	d																								
Grange-over-Sands	d														16 50										17 53
Arnside	d														16 57										17 59
Silverdale	d																								
Carnforth	d														17 06										18 09
Windermere	83 d						16b02														17 06				
Oxenholme Lake District	65 d		16 08				16c24														17 30				
Lancaster 6	65 a		16 26												17 15						17 47				18 17
	d		16 26				16c38						16 57		17 15					17c38	17 48				18 17
Blackpool North	97 d					16 20	16 35		16 41							17 11			17 18	17 37					
Layton	97 d					16 23			16 44							17 14									
Poulton-le-Fylde	97 d					16 28	16 35		16 48							17 18			17 24						
Kirkham & Wesham	97 d		16 10			16 37			16 58							17 10			17 33						
Preston 8	65, 97 a		16 45			16 47	17 02		17 09						17 34	17 39				18 02	18 06				18 36
	d		16 47			16 49	17 04		17 10				17 23		17 47				17 56	18 04	18 08				
Leyland	d					16 54	17a09						17 29						18 01	18a09					
Chorley	d		16 56			17 02			17 20				17 36		17 56				18 08		18 17				
Adlington (Lancashire)	d					17 07													18 13						
Blackrod	d					17 10													18 17						
Horwich Parkway	d					17 14			17 27				17 45						18 20		18 27				
Lostock	d					17 20							17 50								18 30				
Southport	d			16 24							16 55						17 24							17 54	
Meols Cop	d										17 00						17 29							17 59	
Bescar Lane	d										17 05													18 04	
New Lane	d										17 09													18 08	
Burscough Bridge	d			16 36							17 11						17 37							18 11	
Hoscar	d										17 15													18 15	
Parbold	d			16 41							17 18						17 42							18 18	
Appley Bridge	d			16 45							17 22						17 46							18 22	
Gathurst	d										17 25													18 25	
Liverpool Central 10	103 d				16 05													17 05							
Kirkby	d				16 32													17 32							
Rainford	d				16 40													17 40							
Upholland	d				16 44													17 44							
Orrell	d				16 47													17 47							
Pemberton	d				16 50													17 50							
Wigan Wallgate	a			16 51	16 56						17 30						17 52	17 56						18 30	
	d	16 48		16 53	16 58					17 20	17 32						17 54	17 58				18 20		18 32	
Wigan North Western	d																								
Ince	d				17 01													18 01							
Hindley	d			16 58	17 04					17 25	17 37							18 04				18 25		18 37	
Westhoughton	d			17 02						17 29							18 02					18 29			
Bolton	a	17 02	17 08	17 12		17 25			17 34	17 38			17 55		18 08		18 12		18 30		18 34	18 38			
	d	17 03	17 08	17 13		17 25		17 31	17 35	17 39			17 56	18 02	18 08		18 13		18 30		18 35	18 39			
Moses Gate	d									17 42												18 42			
Farnworth	d									17 44												18 44			
Kearsley	d									17 46												18 46			
Daisy Hill	d				17 08						17 41							18 08						18 41	
Hag Fold	d				17 11													18 11							
Atherton	d				17 14						17 45							18 14						18 45	
Walkden	d				17 19						17 50							18 19						18 50	
Moorside	d				17 23													18 23							
Swinton	d				17 25						17 55							18 25						18 55	
Salford Crescent	a	17 15		17 25	17 33	17 38		17 43	17 47	17 56	18 02		18 08	18 14			18 25	18 33	18 43		18 47	18 56		19 02	
	d	17 15		17 26	17 33	17 38		17 44	17 47	17 56	18 03		18 09	18 15			18 26	18 33	18 43		18 47	18 56		19 03	
Salford Central	d	17 17			17 36	17 41		17 46		17 59	18 05			18 17				18 36	18 46			18 59		19 05	
Manchester Victoria	⇌ a	17 23			17 43	17 46		17 54		18 06	18 11			18 26				18 43	18 50			19 06		19 11	
Rochdale	95 a	17 51						18 18			18 35			18 49				19 01	19 19					19 40	
Deansgate	⇌ a			17 29					17 51				18 12								18 51				
Manchester Oxford Road	a		17 23	17 31					17 52				18 14		18 23		18 31				18 52				
Manchester Piccadilly 10	⇌ a		17 27	17 35					17 56				18 18		18 27		18 35				18 56				
Stockport	84 a		17 50	17e53					18 20				18 34		18 50		18e53				19 15				
Hazel Grove	86 a			18 13									18 45				19 13				19 45				
Buxton	86 a			18 50													19 53								
Heald Green	85 a		17 40	18 02					18 10						18 40		19 02				19 10				
Manchester Airport	85 ✈ a		17 48	17 53					18 17						18 47		18 53				19 17				

For general notes see front of timetable
For details of catering facilities see Directory of Train Operators

- **A** From Edinburgh (Table 65)
- **B** To Liverpool Lime Street (Table 90)
- **C** From Clitheroe (Table 94)
- **D** 🛒 from Preston
- **b** Change at Oxenholme Lake District and Preston
- **c** Change at Preston
- **e** Change at Manchester Oxford Road

From 10 October a revised Northern service will be in operation due to seasonal difficulties. Customers should check with NRES for precise times

Barrow-in-Furness, Blackpool North, Preston, Southport, Kirkby and Wigan → Bolton → Manchester

Network Diagram - see first page of Table 82

		NT	TP	NT	NT	NT	NT	NT	NT	NT	TP		NT	NT	NT	TP	NT	NT	NT	NT	TP	NT		TP	NT
			1 ◇								1 ◇					1 ◇					1 ◇			1 ◇	
		A	B				C		D	A				E	G	H			D	A				B	
			🍴													🍴								🍴	
Barrow-in-Furness	d													18 03											
Roose	d													18 07											
Dalton	d													18 13											
Ulverston	d													18 21											
Cark	d													18 29											
Kents Bank	d													18 33											
Grange-over-Sands	d													18 37											
Arnside	d													18 43											
Silverdale	d													18 48											
Carnforth	d						18 26							18 55											
Windermere	83 d										18b02										19b00				
Oxenholme Lake District	65 d		17c44								18c26			18 42		19 08					19c29			20 12	
Lancaster 6	65 a						18 38							19 04		19 26								20 26	
	d		18 26			18c17					18c41			19 05		19 26		18c57			19c44			20 26	
Blackpool North	97 d					18 20			18 37		18 45							19 20	19 37		19 45				
Layton	97 d					18 23												19 23							
Poulton-le-Fylde	97 d					18 28			18 35		18 51							19 28			19 51				
Kirkham & Wesham	97 d		18 10			18 37										19 10		19 37						20 10	
Preston 8	65, 97 a		18 45			18 47			19 02		19 09			19 30		19 45		19 47	20 02		20 09			20 45	
	d		18 47			18 49			19 04		19 10					19 47		19 49	20 04		20 10			20 47	
Leyland	d					18 54			19a09									19 54	20a09						
Chorley	d		18 56			19 02					19 20					19 56		20 02			20 20			20 56	
Adlington (Lancashire)	d					19 07												20 07							
Blackrod	d					19 10												20 10							
Horwich Parkway	d					19 14					19 27							20 14			20 27				
Lostock	d					19 20												20 20							
Southport	d			18 17									19 00				19 23								20 23
Meols Cop	d			18 22									19 05				19 28								20 28
Bescar Lane	d			18 27																					
New Lane	d			18 31																					
Burscough Bridge	d			18 33									19 13				19 36								20 36
Hoscar	d			18 37																					
Parbold	d			18 40									19 18				19 41								20 41
Appley Bridge	d			18 44									19 22				19 45								20 45
Gathurst	d			18 47									19 25				19 48								20 48
Liverpool Central 10	103 d				18 05			18 35																	
Kirkby	d				18 32			19 02																	
Rainford	d				18 40			19 10																	
Upholland	d				18 44			19 14																	
Orrell	d				18 47			19 17																	
Pemberton	d				18 50			19 20																	
Wigan Wallgate	a			18 52	18 56			19 27					19 30				19 53								20 53
	d			18 53	18 58								19 32				19 55					20 27			20 55
Wigan North Western	d																								
Ince	d				19 01																	20 30			
Hindley	d			18 58	19 04								19 37				20 00					20 33			21 00
Westhoughton	d			19 02													20 04								21 04
Bolton	a		19 08	19 12		19 25					19 34					20 08	20 12	20 25			20 34			21 08	21 12
	d	19 02	19 08	19 13		19 25				19 31	19 35				20 02	20 08	20 13	20 25		20 31	20 35			21 08	21 13
Moses Gate	d																								
Farnworth	d																								
Kearsley	d																								
Daisy Hill	d				19 08								19 41									20 37			
Hag Fold	d				19 11																	20 40			
Atherton	d				19 14								19 45									20 43			
Walkden	d				19 19								19 50									20 49			
Moorside	d				19 23																	20 52			
Swinton	d				19 25								19 55									20 55			
Salford Crescent	a	19 14		19 25	19 33	19 38				19 44	19 47		20 02		20 15		20 25	20 38		20 43	20 47	21 02			21 25
	d	19 15		19 26	19 33	19 38				19 44	19 47		20 03		20 15		20 26	20 38		20 44	20 47	21 03			21 26
Salford Central	d	19 17			19 36	19 41				19 46			20 05		20 17			20 41		20 46		21 05			
Manchester Victoria	⇌ a	19 22			19 43	19 46				19 52			20 11		20 23			20 46		20 51		21 11			
Rochdale	95 a												20 40							21 39		21 40			
Deansgate	⇌ a			19 29							19 51						20 29				20 51				21 29
Manchester Oxford Road	a		19 23	19 31							19 52					20 23	20 31				20 52			21 23	21 31
Manchester Piccadilly 10	⇌ a		19 27	19 35							19 56					20 27	20 35				20 56			21 27	21 35
Stockport	84 a		19 53	19e53							20 15					20 53	20e53				21 27				21e52
Hazel Grove	86 a			20 13													21 13								22 13
Buxton	86 a			20 53													21 53								22 53
Heald Green	85 a			20 02							20 10						21 02				21 10				22 02
Manchester Airport	85 ✈ a		19 50	19 53							20 17					20 47	20 53				21 17			21 47	21 53

For general notes see front of timetable
For details of catering facilities see Directory of Train Operators

A From Clitheroe (Table 94)
B From Edinburgh (Table 65)
C From Leeds to Morecambe (Table 36)
D To Liverpool Lime Street (Table 90)
E From Carlisle via Whitehaven (Table 100)
G From Blackburn (Table 94)
H From Glasgow Central (Table 65)
b Change at Oxenholme Lake District and Preston
c Change at Preston
e Change at Manchester Oxford Road

From 10 October a revised Northern service will be in operation due to seasonal difficulties. Customers should check with NRES for precise times

Saturdays

Barrow-in-Furness, Blackpool North, Preston, Southport, Kirkby and Wigan → Bolton → Manchester

Network Diagram - see first page of Table 82

Station	NT	NT A	TP [1] ◊	NT B	TP [1] ◊	NT	TP [1] ◊	NT	NT	NT B	TP [1] ◊	NT	NT	NT A	NT	NT	TP [1] ◊	NT B	NT	NT
Barrow-in-Furness d			19 42													21 43				
Roose d			19 46													21 47				
Dalton d			19 52													21 53				
Ulverston d			20 01													22 01				
Cark d			20 09													22 09				
Kents Bank d			20 13													22 13				
Grange-over-Sands d			20 17													22 17				
Arnside d			20 23													22 23				
Silverdale d			20 27													22 28				
Carnforth d			20 37													22 35				
Windermere 83 d					20b00										21c40					
Oxenholme Lake District 65 d					20c26				20c45						22c01					
Lancaster [6] 65 a			20 45													22 44				
d	19c56		20 45		20c45				21c00						22c17	22 45				
Blackpool North 97 d	20 20	20 38			20 45				21 20		21 45			22 14	22 20		22 45			23 02
Layton 97 d	20 23								21 23						22 23					23 05
Poulton-le-Fylde 97 d	20 28	20 35			20 51				21 28		21 51				22 28		22 51			23 10
Kirkham & Wesham 97 d	20 37								21 37						22 37					23 19
Preston [8] 65, 97 a	20 47	21 02	21 03		21 09		←		21 47		22 09			22 41	22 47	23 08	23 09			23 29
d	20 49	21 04	21 15		21 11		21 15		21 49		22 10			22 43	22 49		23 10			23 31
Leyland d	20 54	21a09	→						21 54					22a48	22 54					23 36
Chorley d	21 02				21 20		21 24		22 02		22 20				23 02		23 20			23 44
Adlington (Lancashire) d	21 07								22 07						23 07					23 49
Blackrod d	21 10								22 10						23 10					23 52
Horwich Parkway d	21 14				21 27				22 14		22 27				23 14		23 27			23 56
Lostock d	21 20								22 20						23 20					00 02
Southport d								21 23					22 18						23 10	
Meols Cop d								21 28					22 23						23 15	
Bescar Lane d													22 28							
New Lane d													22 32							
Burscough Bridge d								21 36					22 34						23 23	
Hoscar d													22 38							
Parbold d								21 41					22 41						23 28	
Appley Bridge d								21 45					22 45						23 32	
Gathurst d								21 48					22 48						23 35	
Liverpool Central [10] 103 d																				
Kirkby d																				
Rainford d																				
Upholland d																				
Orrell d																				
Pemberton d																				
Wigan Wallgate a								21 53					22 53						23 44	
d						21 27		21 55				22 27	22 55							
Wigan North Western d																				
Ince d						21 30						22 30								
Hindley d						21 33		22 00				22 33	23 00							
Westhoughton d								22 04					23 04							
Bolton a	21 25				21 34		21 39	22 12	22 25		22 34		23 12		23 25		23 34			00 07
d	21 25			21 31	21 35		21 39	22 13	22 25	22 31	22 35		23 13		23 25		23 35	23 38		00 07
Moses Gate d																				
Farnworth d																				
Kearsley d																				
Daisy Hill d						21 37						22 37								
Hag Fold d						21 40						22 40								
Atherton d						21 43						22 43								
Walkden d						21 49						22 49								
Moorside d						21 52						22 52								
Swinton d						21 55						22 55								
Salford Crescent a	21 38			21 43	21 47	22 02		22 25	22 38	22 43	22 47	23 02	23 25		23 38		23 47	23 50		
d	21 38			21 44	21 47	22 03		22 26	22 38	22 44	22 47	23 03	23 26		23 38		23 47	23 53		
Salford Central d	21 41			21 46		22 05		22 28	22 41	22 46		23 05								
Manchester Victoria a	21 46			21 51		22 11		22 34	22 46	22 51		23 13			23 47			23 59		00 25
Rochdale 95 a				22 39		22 42			23 07			23 41								
Deansgate a					21 51						22 51		23 29							
Manchester Oxford Road a					21 52		21 56				22 52		23 31							
Manchester Piccadilly [10] a					21 56		22 02				22 56		23 37				23 53			
Stockport 84 a							22 27				23 19									
Hazel Grove 86 a											23 27									
Buxton 86 a											00 07									
Heald Green 85 a					22 09		23 02				23 09						00 15			
Manchester Airport 85 a					22 17		22 57				23 17						00 22			

For general notes see front of timetable
For details of catering facilities see Directory of Train Operators

A To Liverpool Lime Street (Table 90)
B From Clitheroe (Table 94)
b Change at Oxenholme Lake District and Preston
c Change at Preston

From 10 October a revised Northern service will be in operation due to seasonal difficulties. Customers should check with NRES for precise times

Table 82

Sundays

until 6 September

Barrow-in-Furness, Blackpool North, Preston, Southport and Wigan → Bolton → Manchester

Network Diagram - see first page of Table 82

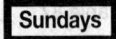

		TP 🚌	TP 🚌	TP 1◇	NT A		NT	NT B	TP 1◇	NT		NT C	NT	NT D	TP 1◇		NT A	NT C	TP 1◇	NT		NT E	NT D	TP 1◇	NT
Barrow-in-Furness	d																		09 23						
Roose	d																		09 27						
Dalton	d																		09 33						
Ulverston	d																		09 42						
Cark	d																		09 50						
Kents Bank	d																		09 54						
Grange-over-Sands	d																		09 58						
Arnside	d																		10 04						
Silverdale	d																		10 08						
Carnforth	d																		10 16			10 30			
Windermere	83 d																								
Oxenholme Lake District	65 d																								
Lancaster 6	65 a																		10 26			10 39			
	d																		10 26						
Blackpool North	97 d	03 20	05 20	07 48			08 20		08 44			08 50	09 20		09 44			09 50	*10 11*	10 20				10 44	
Layton	97 d						08 23						09 23							10 23					
Poulton-le-Fylde	97 d			07 54			08 28		08 50			08 56	09 28		09 50			09 56	*10 17*	10 28				10 50	
Kirkham & Wesham	97 d						08 37		*08 51*				09 37					*09 54*		10 37					
Preston 8	65 a			08 12			08 47		09 08			09 14	09 47		10 08			10 14	10 45	10 47				11 08	
	d	04u00	06u00	08 14			08 49		09 10			09 15	09 49		10 10			10 15	10 47	10 49				11 10	
Leyland	d						08 54					09a21	09 54					10a21		10 54					
Chorley	d			08 23			09 02		09 20				10 02		10 20				10 56	11 02				11 20	
Adlington (Lancashire)	d						09 07						10 07							11 07					
Blackrod	d						09 10						10 10							11 10					
Horwich Parkway	d			08 30			09 14		09 27				10 14		10 27					11 14				11 27	
Lostock	d						09 20						10 20							11 20					
Southport	d									09 09							10 05								11 05
Meols Cop	d									09 14							10 10								11 10
Burscough Bridge	d									09 22							10 18								11 18
Parbold	d									09 27							10 23								11 23
Appley Bridge	d									09 31							10 27								11 27
Gathurst	d									09 34							10 30								11 30
Wigan Wallgate	a									09 39							10 35								11 35
	d				08 40					09 40							10 36								11 36
Wigan North Western	d																								
Hindley	d				08 45					09 45							10 41								11 41
Westhoughton	d				08 49					09 50							10 46								11 46
Bolton	a			08 37	08 57		09 25		09 34	09 58			10 25		10 34		10 54		11 08	11 25				11 34	11 54
	d	04u35	06u35	08 37	08 58		09 25	09 31	09 35	09 58			10 25	10 31	10 35		10 54		11 08	11 25			11 31	11 35	11 54
Salford Crescent	a			08 49	09 10		09 38	09 43	09 47	10 11			10 38	10 43	10 47		11 07			11 38			11 43	11 47	12 07
	d			08 50	09 11		09 38	09 44	09 47	10 11			10 38	10 44	10 47		11 07			11 38			11 44	11 47	12 07
Manchester Victoria 🚊	a						09 43	09 51					10 43	10 51						11 43			11 51		
Rochdale	a							*10 28*						*11 28*									*12 28*		
Deansgate 🚊	a			08 53	09 14				09 51	10 15					10 51		11 11							11 51	12 11
Manchester Oxford Road	a			08 55	09 17				09 53	10 17					10 53		11 13		11 23					11 53	12 13
Manchester Piccadilly 10 🚊	a			08 59	09 21				09 57	10 21					10 57		11 19		11 27					11 57	12 19
Stockport	84 a			*09 27*	09 31				*10 28*	10 43					*11b17*		11 30		*12 03*					*12 22*	12 32
Hazel Grove	86 a				*10c13*					*11 13*									*12 13*						*13c13*
Buxton	86 a				*10c51*					*11 51*									*12 51*						*13c51*
Heald Green	85 a				*09c57*					*11 00*									*11 57*						*12c57*
Manchester Airport	85 ✈ a	05 25	07 25	09 19	*09c55*				10 13	*10 55*					11 17				11 47					12 17	*12c55*

For general notes see front of timetable
For details of catering facilities see Directory of Train Operators

- **A** To Chester (Table 88)
- **B** From Blackburn (Table 94)
- **C** To Liverpool Lime Street (Table 90)
- **D** From Clitheroe (Table 94)
- **E** From Leeds to Morecambe (Table 36)
- **b** From 19 July arr. 1123
- **c** Change at Manchester Piccadilly

Table 82

Sundays

until 6 September

Barrow-in-Furness, Blackpool North, Preston, Southport and Wigan → Bolton → Manchester

Network Diagram - see first page of Table 82

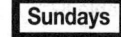

		NT	NT	NT	TP	NT	NT	TP	NT	NT	NT	TP	NT	NT	TP	NT	NT	TP	NT	NT
					1 ◇			1 ◇				1 ◇			1 ◇			1 ◇		
		A		B		C	A			D	B			A	E		B		C	A
Barrow-in-Furness	d							11 15												
Roose	d							11 19												
Dalton	d							11 25												
Ulverston	d							11 34												
Cark	d							11 42												
Kents Bank	d							11 46												
Grange-over-Sands	d							11 50												
Arnside	d							11 56												
Silverdale	d							12 00												
Carnforth	d							12 08		12 35										
Windermere	83 d											*11b58*						*12b58*		
Oxenholme Lake District	65 d				*11c23*							*12c24*			13 10	*12c43*		*13c23*		
Lancaster 6	65 a							12 17		12 44					13 26					
	d				*11c38*			12 19				*12c38*			13 26	*12c57*		*13c38*		
Blackpool North	97 d	10 50	11 20		11 44		11 50	*12 11*	12 20			12 44		12 50	*13 13*	13 20		13 44		13 50
Layton	97 d		11 23						12 23							13 23				
Poulton-le-Fylde	97 d	10 56	11 28		11 50		11 56	*12 17*	12 28			12 50		12 56	*13 19*	13 28		13 50		13 56
Kirkham & Wesham	97 d		11 37				*11 53*		12 37					*12 53*		13 37				*13 53*
Preston 8	65 a	11 14	11 47		12 08		12 14	12 37	12 47			13 08		13 14	13 45	13 47		14 08		14 14
	d	11 15	11 49		12 10		12 15	12 47	12 49			13 10		13 15	13 47	13 49		14 10		14 15
Leyland	d	11a21	11 54				12a21		12 54					13a21		13 54				14a21
Chorley	d		12 02		12 20			12 56	13 02			13 20			13 56	14 02		14 20		
Adlington (Lancashire)	d		12 07						13 07							14 07				
Blackrod	d		12 10						13 10							14 10				
Horwich Parkway	d		12 14		12 27				13 14			13 27				14 14		14 27		
Lostock	d		12 20						13 20							14 20				
Southport	d					12 05							13 05						14 05	
Meols Cop	d					12 10							13 10						14 10	
Burscough Bridge	d					12 18							13 18						14 18	
Parbold	d					12 23							13 23						14 23	
Appley Bridge	d					12 27							13 27						14 27	
Gathurst	d					12 30							13 30						14 30	
Wigan Wallgate	a					12 35							13 35						14 35	
	d					12 36							13 36						14 36	
Wigan North Western	d																			
Hindley	d					12 41							13 41						14 41	
Westhoughton	d					12 46							13 46						14 46	
Bolton	a		12 25		12 34	12 54		13 08	13 25			13 34	13 54		14 08	14 25		14 34	14 54	
	d		12 25	12 31	12 35	12 54		13 08	13 25		13 31	13 35	13 54		14 08	14 25	14 31	14 35	14 54	
Salford Crescent	a		12 38	12 43	12 47	13 07			13 38		13 43	13 47	14 07			14 38	14 43	14 47	15 07	
	d		12 38	12 44	12 47	13 07			13 38		13 44	13 47	14 07			14 38	14 44	14 47	15 07	
Manchester Victoria	⇌ a		12 43	12 51					13 43		13 51					14 43	14 51			
Rochdale	a			*13 28*							*14 28*						*15 28*			
Deansgate	⇌ a				12 51	13 11						13 51	14 11					14 51	15 11	
Manchester Oxford Road	a				12 53	13 13		13 23				13 53	14 13		14 23			14 53	15 13	
Manchester Piccadilly 10	⇌ a				12 57	13 19		13 27				13 57	14 19		14 27			14 57	15 19	
Stockport	84 a				*13 22*	13 30		*13 53*				*14 22*	14 33		*14 49*			*15 22*	15 30	
Hazel Grove	86 a							*14 13*							*15 13*					
Buxton	86 a							*14 51*							*15 51*					
Heald Green	85 a							*13 57*							*14 57*					
Manchester Airport	85 ✈ a				13 17			13 47				14 17			14 47			15 17		

For general notes see front of timetable
For details of catering facilities see Directory of Train Operators

A To Liverpool Lime Street (Table 90)
B From Clitheroe (Table 94)
C To Chester (Table 88)
D From Leeds to Morecambe (Table 36)
E From Edinburgh (Table 65)
b Change at Oxenholme Lake District and Preston
c Change at Preston

Table 82

Sundays

until 6 September

Barrow-in-Furness, Blackpool North, Preston, Southport and Wigan → Bolton → Manchester

Network Diagram - see first page of Table 82

		TP	NT	NT	TP	NT	NT	TP	NT	NT	TP	NT	NT	TP	NT	NT	NT	TP	NT	NT
		1 ◇		A	1 ◇		B	1 ◇ C		A	1 ◇	D	B	1 ◇		E	A	1 ◇		B
Barrow-in-Furness	d	13 22												15 22						
Roose	d	13 26												15 26						
Dalton	d	13 32												15 32						
Ulverston	d	13 41												15 41						
Cark	d	13 49												15 49						
Kents Bank	d	13 53												15 53						
Grange-over-Sands	d	13 57												15 57						
Arnside	d	14 03												16 03						
Silverdale	d	14 07												16 07						
Carnforth	d	14 15												16 15		16 37				
Windermere	83 d				*13b58*						*14b58*							*15b58*		
Oxenholme Lake District	65 d				*14c28*			15 10			*15c23*			*15c44*				*16c23*		
Lancaster 6	65 a	14 25						15 25						16 25		16 46				
	d	14 25	*13c58*		*14c43*			15 25	*14c57*		*15c38*			16 25				*16c38*		
Blackpool North	97 d	*14 11*	14 20		14 44		14 50	*15 13*	15 20		15 44		15 50	*16 11*	16 20			16 44		16 50
Layton	97 d		14 23						15 23						16 23					
Poulton-le-Fylde	97 d	*14 17*	14 28		14 50		14 56	*15 19*	15 28		15 50		15 56	*16 17*	16 28			16 50		16 56
Kirkham & Wesham	97 d		14 37				*14 53*		15 37				*15 53*		16 37					*16 53*
Preston 8	65 a	14 45	14 47		15 08		15 14	15 45	15 47		16 08		16 14	16 45	16 47			17 08		17 14
	d	14 47	14 49		15 10		15 15	15 47	15 49		16 10		16 15	16 47	16 49			17 10		17 15
Leyland	d		14 54				15a21		15 54				16a21		16 54					17a21
Chorley	d	14 56	15 02		15 20			15 56	16 02		16 20			16 56	17 02			17 20		
Adlington (Lancashire)	d		15 07						16 07						17 07					
Blackrod	d		15 10						16 10						17 10					
Horwich Parkway	d		15 14		15 27				16 14		16 27				17 14			17 27		
Lostock	d		15 20						16 20						17 20					
Southport	d					15 05						16 05							17 05	
Meols Cop	d					15 10						16 10							17 10	
Burscough Bridge	d					15 18						16 18							17 18	
Parbold	d					15 23						16 23							17 23	
Appley Bridge	d					15 27						16 27							17 27	
Gathurst	d					15 30						16 30							17 30	
Wigan Wallgate	a					15 35						16 35							17 35	
	d					15 36						16 36							17 36	
Wigan North Western	d																			
Hindley	d					15 41						16 41							17 41	
Westhoughton	d					15 46						16 46							17 46	
Bolton	a	15 08	15 25		15 34	15 54		16 08	16 25		16 34	16 54		17 08	17 25			17 34	17 54	
	d	15 08	15 25	15 31	15 35	15 54		16 08	16 25	16 31	16 35	16 54		17 08	17 25		17 31	17 35	17 54	
Salford Crescent	a		15 38	15 43	15 47	16 07			16 38	16 43	16 47	17 07			17 38		17 43	17 47	18 07	
	d		15 38	15 44	15 47	16 07			16 38	16 44	16 47	17 07			17 38		17 44	17 47	18 07	
Manchester Victoria	a		15 43	15 51					16 43	16 51					17 43		17 51			
Rochdale	a			*16 28*						*17 28*							*18 28*			
Deansgate	a				15 51	16 11					16 51	17 11						17 51	18 11	
Manchester Oxford Road	a	15 23			15 53	16 13		16 23			16 53	17 13		17 23				17 53	18 13	
Manchester Piccadilly 10	a	15 27			15 57	16 19		16 27			16 57	17 19		17 27				17 57	18 19	
Stockport	84 a	*15 53*			*16 22*	16 31		*16 53*			*17 22*	17 30		*17 53*				*18 22*	18 33	
Hazel Grove	86 a	*16 13*						*17 13*						*18 13*						
Buxton	86 a	*16 51*						*17 51*						*18 51*						
Heald Green	85 a	*15 57*						*16 57*						*17 57*						
Manchester Airport	85 ✈ a	15 47			16 17			16 47			17 17			17 47				18 17		

For general notes see front of timetable
For details of catering facilities see Directory of Train Operators

- **A** From Clitheroe (Table 94)
- **B** To Liverpool Lime Street (Table 90)
- **C** From Edinburgh (Table 65)
- **D** To Chester (Table 88)
- **E** From Leeds to Morecambe (Table 36)
- **b** Change at Oxenholme Lake District and Preston
- **c** Change at Preston

Table 82

Sundays
until 6 September

Barrow-in-Furness, Blackpool North, Preston, Southport and Wigan → Bolton → Manchester

Network Diagram - see first page of Table 82

	TP 1◇	TP 1◇ A ✠	NT		NT B	TP 1◇	TP 1◇	NT C		NT D	TP 1◇ E ✠	NT	NT B		TP 1◇	NT	NT D	NT G		TP 1◇	TP 1◇ A ✠	NT	NT B	TP 1◇
Barrow-in-Furness d	16 25																			18 15				
Roose d																				18 19				
Dalton d																				18 25				
Ulverston d	16 40																			18 34				
Cark d																				18 42				
Kents Bank d																				18 46				
Grange-over-Sands d	16 53																			18 50				
Arnside d	17 00																			18 56				
Silverdale d																				19 00				
Carnforth d	17 09																	19 05		19 07				
Windermere 83 d						16 58									18b04									19b00
Oxenholme Lake District 65 d		17 08				17 16					18 10	17c44			18c28						19 07			19c29
Lancaster 6 65 a	17 18	17 23				17 32					18 26							19 14		19 17	19 21			
d	17 18	17 23				17 33	17c38				18 26				18c43					19 17	19 22			19c44
Blackpool North 97 d		17 11	17 20				17 40			17 50	18 11	18 20			18 44		18 50				19 13	19 20		19 44
Layton 97 d			17 23									18 23										19 23		
Poulton-le-Fylde 97 d		17 17	17 28				17 46			17 56	18 17	18 28			18 50		18 56				19 19	19 28		19 50
Kirkham & Wesham 97 d			17 37				17 50					18 37					18 53					19 37		19 37
Preston 8 65 a	17 37	17 42	17 47			17 51	18 04			18 14	18 45	18 47			19 08		19 14			19 36	19 41	19 47		20 08
d	17 47		17 49			18 10				18 15	18 47	18 49			19 10		19 15			19 47		19 49		20 10
Leyland d			17 54							18a21		18 54					19a21					19 54		
Chorley d	17 56		18 02			18 20					18 56	19 02			19 20					19 56		20 02		20 20
Adlington (Lancashire) d			18 07									19 07										20 07		
Blackrod d			18 10									19 10										20 10		
Horwich Parkway d			18 14			18 27						19 14			19 27							20 14		20 27
Lostock d			18 20									19 20										20 20		
Southport d								18 05								19 05								
Meols Cop d								18 10								19 10								
Burscough Bridge d								18 18								19 18								
Parbold d								18 23								19 23								
Appley Bridge d								18 27								19 27								
Gathurst d								18 30								19 30								
Wigan Wallgate a								18 35								19 35								
d								18 36								19 36								
Wigan North Western d																								
Hindley d								18 41								19 41								
Westhoughton d								18 46								19 46								
Bolton a	18 08		18 25			18 34		18 54			19 08	19 25			19 34	19 54				20 08		20 25		20 34
d	18 08		18 25		18 31	18 35		18 54			19 08	19 25	19 31		19 35	19 54				20 08		20 25	20 31	20 35
Salford Crescent a			18 38		18 43	18 47		19 07				19 38	19 43		19 47	20 07						20 38	20 43	20 47
d			18 38		18 44	18 47		19 07				19 38	19 44		19 47	20 07						20 38	20 44	20 47
Manchester Victoria ⇌ a			18 43		18 51							19 43	19 51									20 43	20 51	
Rochdale a					19 28								20 28										21 28	
Deansgate ⇌ a						18 51		19 11							19 51	20 11								20 51
Manchester Oxford Road a	18 23					18 53		19 13			19 23				19 53	20 13				20 23				20 53
Manchester Piccadilly 10 ⇌ a	18 27					18 57		19 19			19 27				19 57	20 19				20 27				20 57
Stockport 84 a	18 50					19 22		19 30			19 53				20 15	20 32				20 53				21 15
Hazel Grove 86 a	19 13										20 13									21 13				
Buxton 86 a	19 51										20 51									21 51				
Heald Green 85 a	18 57										19 57									20 57				
Manchester Airport 85 ✈ a	18 47					19 17					19 47				20 17					20 47				21 17

For general notes see front of timetable
For details of catering facilities see Directory of Train Operators

- **A** From Glasgow Central (Table 65)
- **B** From Clitheroe (Table 94)
- **C** To Chester (Table 88)
- **D** To Liverpool Lime Street (Table 90)
- **E** From Edinburgh (Table 65)
- **G** From Leeds to Morecambe (Table 36)
- **b** Change at Oxenholme Lake District and Preston
- **c** Change at Preston

Table 82

Sundays

until 6 September

Barrow-in-Furness, Blackpool North, Preston, Southport and Wigan → Bolton → Manchester

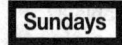

Network Diagram - see first page of Table 82

		NT		NT	TP	NT	NT		TP	NT	NT	NT		NT	NT	NT	TP	TP		NT	NT	NT	TP		
					1 ◇				1 ◇								1 ◇	1 ◇					1 ◇		
		A		B	C		D				B				B	D		C			B	D			
					✕													✕							
Barrow-in-Furness	d											20 02													
Roose	d											20 06													
Dalton	d											20 12													
Ulverston	d											20 21													
Cark	d											20 29													
Kents Bank	d											20 33													
Grange-over-Sands	d											20 37													
Arnside	d											20 43													
Silverdale	d											20 48													
Carnforth	d											20 54													
Windermere	83 d								19b50						21c00										
Oxenholme Lake District	65 d				20 10				20c19						21c21						22c03				
Lancaster 6	65 a				20 26							21 07													
	d				20 26				20c34					20c57	21c38			22 03			22c18				
Blackpool North	97 d			19 50	*20 11*	20 20			20 44		20 50			21 20	21 50		21 56				22 44		23 00		
Layton	97 d					20 23								21 23									23 03		
Poulton-le-Fylde	97 d			19 56	*20 17*	20 28			20 50		20 56			21 28	21 56		22 02				22 50		23 07		
Kirkham & Wesham	97 d			*19 53*		20 37					*20 53*			21 37	*21 53*								23 16		
Preston 8	65 a			20 14	20 45	20 47			21 08		21 14			21 47	22 14		22 20	22 23			23 08		23 26		
	d			20 15	20 47	20 49			21 10		21 15			21 49	22 15			22 29			23 09		23 28		
Leyland	d			20a21		20 54					21a21			21 54	22a21						23a15		23 33		
Chorley	d				20 56	21 02			21 20					22 02				22 38					23 39		
Adlington (Lancashire)	d					21 07								22 07									23 43		
Blackrod	d					21 10								22 10									23 47		
Horwich Parkway	d					21 14			21 27					22 14									23 50		
Lostock	d					21 20								22 20									23 54		
Southport	d	20 05								21 05										22 05					
Meols Cop	d	20 10								21 10										22 10					
Burscough Bridge	d	20 18								21 18										22 18					
Parbold	d	20 23								21 23										22 23					
Appley Bridge	d	20 27								21 27										22 27					
Gathurst	d	20 30								21 30										22 30					
Wigan Wallgate	a	20 35								21 35										22 35					
	d	20 36								21 36										22 36					
Wigan North Western	d																								
Hindley	d	20 41								21 41										22 41					
Westhoughton	d	20 46								21 46										22 46					
Bolton	a	20 54			21 08	21 25			21 34	21 54				22 25				22 50		22 54			23 59		
	d	20 54			21 08	21 25	21 31		21 35	21 54				22 25		22 31		22 51		22 54		23 31	23 59		
Salford Crescent	a	21 07				21 38	21 43		21 47	22 07				22 38		22 43		23 03		23 07		23 43			
	d	21 07				21 38	21 44		21 47	22 07				22 38		22 44		23 03		23 07		23 44			
Manchester Victoria	⇌ a					21 43	21 51							22 43		22 51						23 51			
Rochdale	a						*22 28*									*23 58*									
Deansgate	⇌ a	21 11							21 51	22 11								23 08		23 11					
Manchester Oxford Road	a	21 13			21 23				21 53	22 13								23 10		23 13					
Manchester Piccadilly 10	⇌ a	21 19			21 27				21 57	22 19								23 14		23 19			00 15		
Stockport	84 a	21 30			*21 49*				*22 15*	22 31								*23e32*		23 32					
Hazel Grove	86 a				*22 13*					*23f13*															
Buxton	86 a				*22 51*					*23f51*															
Heald Green	85 a				*21 57*					*23f02*															
Manchester Airport	85 ✈ a				21 47				22 17	*22f55*								23 30		*00f17*			00 30		

For general notes see front of timetable
For details of catering facilities see Directory of Train Operators

- **A** To Chester (Table 88)
- **B** To Liverpool Lime Street (Table 90)
- **C** From Edinburgh (Table 65)
- **D** From Clitheroe (Table 94)
- **b** Change at Oxenholme Lake District and Preston
- **c** Change at Preston
- **e** Change at Manchester Oxford Road
- **f** Change at Manchester Piccadilly

Table 82

Sundays

from 13 September

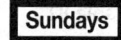

Barrow-in-Furness, Blackpool North, Preston, Southport and Wigan → Bolton → Manchester

Network Diagram - see first page of Table 82

	TP	TP	NT	TP	NT	NT	TP	NT	NT	NT	NT	TP	NT	NT	NT	NT	NT	TP	NT	NT	NT	NT	TP	NT
				1 ◇			1 ◇					1 ◇						1 ◇					1 ◇	
			A			B			C		B		A	C		D	B			C		B		A
	🚌	🚌																						
Barrow-in-Furness d																								
Roose d																								
Dalton d																								
Ulverston d																								
Cark d																								
Kents Bank d																								
Grange-over-Sands d																								
Arnside d																								
Silverdale d																								
Carnforth d																10 30								
Windermere 83 d																								
Oxenholme Lake District 65 d																							11b23	
Lancaster 6 65 a																10 39								
d																							11b38	
Blackpool North 97 d	03 20	05 20		08 14	08 20		08 44		08 50	09 20		09 44		09 50	10 20			10 44		10 50	11 20		11 44	
Layton 97 d					08 23					09 23					10 23						11 23			
Poulton-le-Fylde 97 d				08 20	08 28		08 50		08 56	09 28		09 50		09 56	10 28			10 50		10 56	11 28		11 50	
Kirkham & Wesham 97 d					08 37					09 37				09c54	10 37						11 37			
Preston 8 65 a				08 38	08 47		09 08		09 14	09 47		10 08		10 14	10 47			11 08		11 14	11 47		12 08	
d	04u00	06u00		08 42	08 49		09 10		09 15	09 49		10 10		10 15	10 49			11 10		11 15	11 49		12 10	
Leyland d					08 54				09a21	09 54				10a21	10 54					11a21	11 54			
Chorley d				08 51	09 02		09 20			10 02		10 20			11 02			11 20			12 02		12 20	
Adlington (Lancashire) d					09 07					10 07					11 07						12 07			
Blackrod d					09 10					10 10					11 10						12 10			
Horwich Parkway d				08 59	09 14		09 27			10 14		10 27			11 14			11 27			12 14		12 27	
Lostock d					09 20					10 20					11 20						12 20			
Southport d								09 09					10 05						11 05					12 05
Meols Cop d								09 14					10 10						11 10					12 10
Burscough Bridge d								09 22					10 18						11 18					12 18
Parbold d								09 27					10 23						11 23					12 23
Appley Bridge d								09 31					10 27						11 27					12 27
Gathurst d								09 34					10 30						11 30					12 30
Wigan Wallgate a								09 39					10 35						11 35					12 35
d			08 40					09 40					10 36						11 36					12 36
Wigan North Western d																								
Hindley d			08 45					09 45					10 41						11 41					12 41
Westhoughton d			08 49					09 50					10 46						11 46					12 46
Bolton a			08 57	09 05	09 25		09 34	09 58		10 25		10 34	10 54		11 25			11 34	11 54		12 25		12 34	12 54
d	04u35	06u35	08 58	09 06	09 25	09 31	09 35	09 58		10 25	10 31	10 35	10 54		11 25		11 31	11 35	11 54		12 25	12 31	12 35	12 54
Salford Crescent a			09 10	09 18	09 38	09 43	09 47	10 11		10 38	10 43	10 47	11 07		11 38		11 43	11 47	12 07		12 38	12 43	12 47	13 07
d			09 11	09 19	09 38	09 44	09 47	10 11		10 38	10 44	10 47	11 07		11 38		11 44	11 47	12 07		12 38	12 44	12 47	13 07
Manchester Victoria 🚊 a					09 43	09 51				10 43	10 51				11 43		11 51				12 43	12 51		
Rochdale a						*10 28*					*11 28*						*12 28*					*13 28*		
Deansgate 🚊 a			09 14	09 22			09 51	10 15				10 51	11 11					11 51	12 11				12 51	13 11
Manchester Oxford Road a			09 17	09 24			09 53	10 17				10 53	11 13					11 53	12 13				12 53	13 13
Manchester Piccadilly 10 🚊 a			09 21	09 28			09 57	10 21				10 57	11 19					11 57	12 19				12 57	13 19
Stockport 84 a			09 31	*10 04*			*10 28*	10 32				*11 23*	11 30					*12 23*	12 32				*13 22*	13 30
Hazel Grove 86 a				*10 13*				*11e13*					*12e13*						*13e13*					
Buxton 86 a				*10 51*				*11e51*					*12e51*						*13e51*					
Heald Green 85 a				*09 57*				*11e00*					*11e59*						*12e57*					
Manchester Airport 85 ✈ a	05 25	07 25		09 53			10 13	*10e53*				11 17	*12e04*					12 17	*13e02*				13 17	

For general notes see front of timetable
For details of catering facilities see Directory of Train Operators

- A To Chester (Table 88)
- B From Blackburn (Table 94)
- C To Liverpool Lime Street (Table 90)
- D 13 September. From Leeds to Morecambe (Table 36)
- b Change at Preston
- c From 8 November dep. 0937
- e Change at Manchester Piccadilly

Table 82

Sundays

from 13 September

Barrow-in-Furness, Blackpool North, Preston, Southport and Wigan → Bolton → Manchester

Network Diagram - see first page of Table 82

		NT	TP	NT	NT	NT	TP	NT	NT	TP	NT	NT	TP	NT	NT	NT	TP	NT	NT	TP	NT	NT	TP	NT	NT
			1 ◇				1 ◇			1 ◇			1 ◇				1 ◇			1 ◇			1 ◇		
		A			B	C			A	D		C			E	A			C			A	D 🚲		C
Barrow-in-Furness	d		11 15											12 45			13 22								
Roose	d		11 19											12 49			13 26								
Dalton	d		11 25											12 55			13 32								
Ulverston	d		11 34											13 04			13 41								
Cark	d		11 42											13 12			13 49								
Kents Bank	d		11 46											13 16			13 53								
Grange-over-Sands	d		11 50											13 20			13 57								
Arnside	d		11 56											13 26			14 03								
Silverdale	d		12 00											13 31			14 07								
Carnforth	d		12 08		12 35									13 37			14 15								
Windermere	83 d						11b58						12b58							13c58					
Oxenholme Lake District	65 d						12e24			13 10	12f43		13f23							14g28			15 10		
Lancaster 6	65 a		12 17		12 44					13 26				13 50			14 25						15 25		
	d		12 19				12e38			13 26	12f57		13f38				14 25	13h58		14g43			15 25	14f57	
Blackpool North	97 d	11 50	12 11	12 20			12 44		12 50	13 13	13 20		13 44			13 50	14 11	14 20		14 44		14 50	15 13	15 20	
Layton	97 d			12 23							13 23							14 23						15 23	
Poulton-le-Fylde	97 d	11 56	12 17	12 28			12 50		12 56	13 19	13 28		13 50			13 56	14 17	14 28		14 50		14 56	15 19	15 28	
Kirkham & Wesham	97 d	11j53		12 37					12j53		13 37					13j53		14 37				14j53		15 37	
Preston 8	65 a	12 14	12 37	12 47			13 08		13 14	13 45	13 47		14 08			14 14	14 45	14 47		15 08		15 14	15 45	15 47	
	d	12 15	12 47	12 49			13 10		13 15	13 47	13 49		14 10			14 15	14 47	14 49		15 10		15 15	15 47	15 49	
Leyland	d	12a21		12 54					13a21		13 54					14a21		14 54				15a21		15 54	
Chorley	d		12 56	13 02			13 20			13 56	14 02		14 20				14 56	15 02		15 20			15 56	16 02	
Adlington (Lancashire)	d			13 07							14 07							15 07						16 07	
Blackrod	d			13 10							14 10							15 10						16 10	
Horwich Parkway	d			13 14			13 27				14 14		14 27					15 14		15 27				16 14	
Lostock	d			13 20							14 20							15 20						16 20	
Southport	d							13 05							14 05						15 05				
Meols Cop	d							13 10							14 10						15 10				
Burscough Bridge	d							13 18							14 18						15 18				
Parbold	d							13 23							14 23						15 23				
Appley Bridge	d							13 27							14 27						15 27				
Gathurst	d							13 30							14 30						15 30				
Wigan Wallgate	a							13 35							14 35						15 35				
	d							13 36							14 36						15 36				
Wigan North Western	d																								
Hindley	d							13 41							14 41						15 41				
Westhoughton	d							13 46							14 46						15 46				
Bolton	a		13 08	13 25			13 34	13 54		14 08	14 25		14 34		14 54		15 08	15 25		15 34	15 54		16 08	16 25	
	d		13 08	13 25		13 31	13 35	13 54		14 08	14 25	14 31	14 35		14 54		15 08	15 25	15 31	15 35	15 54		16 08	16 25	16 31
Salford Crescent	a			13 38		13 43	13 47	14 07			14 38	14 43	14 47		15 07			15 38	15 43	15 47	16 07			16 38	16 43
	d			13 38		13 44	13 47	14 07			14 38	14 44	14 47		15 07			15 38	15 44	15 47	16 07			16 38	16 44
Manchester Victoria 🚊	a			13 43		13 51					14 43	14 51						15 43	15 51					16 43	16 51
Rochdale	a					14 28						15 28							16 28						17 28
Deansgate 🚊	a						13 51	14 11					14 51		15 11					15 51	16 11				
Manchester Oxford Road	a		13 23				13 53	14 13		14 23			14 53		15 13		15 23			15 53	16 13		16 23		
Manchester Piccadilly 10 🚊	a		13 27				13 57	14 19		14 27			14 57		15 19		15 27			15 57	16 19		16 27		
Stockport	84 a		13 53				14 22	14 33		14 49			15 22		15 30		15 53			16 22	16 31		16 53		
Hazel Grove	86 a		14 13							15 13							16 13						17 13		
Buxton	86 a		14 51							15 51							16 51						17 51		
Heald Green	85 a		13 57							14 57							15 57						16 57		
Manchester Airport	85 ✈ a		13 47				14 17			14 47			15 17				15 47			16 17			16 47		

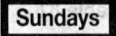

For general notes see front of timetable
For details of catering facilities see Directory of Train Operators

- A To Liverpool Lime Street (Table 90)
- B 13 September. From Leeds to Morecambe (Table 36)
- C From Blackburn (Table 94)
- D From Edinburgh (Table 65)
- E To Chester (Table 88)
- b Change at Oxenholme Lake District and Preston
- c Change at Oxenholme Lake District and Preston. From 8 November dep. 1258
- e Change at Preston. From 8 November dep. Oxenholme Lake District 1227, Lancaster 1241
- f Change at Preston
- g Change at Preston. From 8 November dep. Oxenholme Lake District 1344, Lancaster 1425
- h Change at Preston. From 8 November dep. 1359
- j Until 1 November only

Table 82

Sundays

Barrow-in-Furness, Blackpool North, Preston, Southport and Wigan → Bolton → Manchester

from 13 September

Network Diagram - see first page of Table 82

	TP 1◇	NT A	NT B	TP 1◇	NT	NT C	NT D	TP 1◇	NT	NT B	TP 1◇ E	NT	NT D	TP 1◇	NT A	NT B	TP 1◇ G	NT	NT D	TP 1◇	NT	NT B	NT C
Barrow-in-Furness d				15 30																			
Roose d																							
Dalton d																							
Ulverston d				15 45																			
Cark d																							
Kents Bank d																							
Grange-over-Sands d				15 58																			
Arnside d				16 05																			
Silverdale d																							
Carnforth d				16 15		16 37																	19 05
Windermere 83 d	14b58							15b58									16 58			18b04			
Oxenholme Lake District 65 d	15c23			15c44				16c23			17 08						18 10	17c44		18c28			
Lancaster 6 65 a				16 25		16 46					17 23						18 26						19 14
d	15c38			16 25				16c38			17 23	16c57		17c38			18 26			18c43			
Blackpool North 97 d	15 44		15 50	16 11	16 20			16 44		16 50	17 11	17 20		17 44		17 50	18 11	18 20		18 44		18 50	
Layton 97 d					16 23							17 23						18 23					
Poulton-le-Fylde 97 d	15 50		15 56	16 17	16 28			16 50		16 56	17 17	17 28		17 50		17 56	18 17	18 28		18 50		18 56	
Kirkham & Wesham 97 d			15e53		16 37					16e53		17 37		17e50				18 37				18e53	
Preston 8 65 a	16 08		16 14	16 45	16 47			17 08		17 14	17 42	17 47		18 08		18 14	18 45	18 47		19 08		19 14	
d	16 10		16 15	16 47	16 49			17 10		17 15	17 47	17 49		18 10		18 15	18 47	18 49		19 10		19 15	
Leyland d			16a21		16 54					17a21		17 54				18a21		18 54				19a21	
Chorley d	16 20			16 56	17 02			17 20			17 56	18 02		18 20			18 56	19 02		19 20			
Adlington (Lancashire) d					17 07							18 07						19 07					
Blackrod d					17 10							18 10						19 10					
Horwich Parkway d	16 27				17 14			17 27				18 14		18 27				19 14		19 27			
Lostock d					17 20							18 20						19 20					
Southport d		16 05							17 05						18 05						19 05		
Meols Cop d		16 10							17 10						18 10						19 10		
Burscough Bridge d		16 18							17 18						18 18						19 18		
Parbold d		16 23							17 23						18 23						19 23		
Appley Bridge d		16 27							17 27						18 27						19 27		
Gathurst d		16 30							17 30						18 30						19 30		
Wigan Wallgate a		16 35							17 35						18 35						19 35		
d		16 36							17 36						18 36						19 36		
Wigan North Western d																							
Hindley d		16 41							17 41						18 41						19 41		
Westhoughton d		16 46							17 46						18 46						19 46		
Bolton a	16 34	16 54		17 08	17 25			17 34	17 54		18 08	18 25		18 34	18 54		19 08	19 25		19 34	19 54		
d	16 35	16 54		17 08	17 25		17 31	17 35	17 54		18 08	18 25	18 31	18 35	18 54		19 08	19 25	19 31	19 35	19 54		
Salford Crescent a	16 47	17 07			17 38		17 43	17 47	18 07			18 38	18 43	18 47	19 07			19 38	19 43	19 47	20 07		
d	16 47	17 07			17 38		17 44	17 47	18 07			18 38	18 44	18 47	19 07			19 38	19 44	19 47	20 07		
Manchester Victoria a					17 43		17 51					18 43	18 51					19 43	19 51				
Rochdale a							18 28						19 28						20 28				
Deansgate a	16 51	17 11						17 51	18 11					18 51	19 11					19 51	20 11		
Manchester Oxford Road a	16 53	17 13		17 23				17 53	18 13		18 23			18 53	19 13		19 23			19 53	20 13		
Manchester Piccadilly 10 a	16 57	17 19		17 27				17 57	18 19		18 27			18 57	19 19		19 27			19 57	20 19		
Stockport 84 a	17 22	17 30		17 53				18 22	18 33		18 50			19 22	19 30		19 53			20 15	20 32		
Hazel Grove 86 a				18 13							19 13						20 13						
Buxton 86 a				18 51							19 51						20 51						
Heald Green 85 a				17 57							18 57						19 57						
Manchester Airport 85 a	17 17			17 47				18 17			18 47			19 17			19 47			20 17			

For general notes see front of timetable
For details of catering facilities see Directory of Train Operators

- **A** To Chester (Table 88)
- **B** To Liverpool Lime Street (Table 90)
- **C** From Leeds to Morecambe (Table 36)
- **D** From Blackburn (Table 94)
- **E** From Glasgow Central (Table 65)
- **G** From Edinburgh (Table 65)
- **b** Change at Oxenholme Lake District and Preston
- **c** Change at Preston
- **e** Until 1 November only

Table 82

Sundays
from 13 September

Barrow-in-Furness, Blackpool North, Preston, Southport and Wigan → Bolton → Manchester

Network Diagram - see first page of Table 82

		TP	TP	NT	NT	TP	NT	NT	TP	NT	NT	TP	NT	NT	NT	NT	NT	NT	TP	TP	NT	NT	NT	TP
		1 ◇	1 ◇			1 ◇			1 ◇			1 ◇							1 ◇	1 ◇				1 ◇
			A		B		C	D	E		B			D			D	B		E		D	B	
Barrow-in-Furness	d	18 15													20 02									
Roose	d	18 19													20 06									
Dalton	d	18 25													20 12									
Ulverston	d	18 34													20 21									
Cark	d	18 42													20 29									
Kents Bank	d	18 46													20 33									
Grange-over-Sands	d	18 50													20 37									
Arnside	d	18 56													20 43									
Silverdale	d	19 00													20 48									
Carnforth	d	19 07													20 54									
Windermere 83	d					*19b00*						*19b50*					*21c00*							
Oxenholme Lake District 65	d		19 07			*19c29*			20 10			*20c19*					*21c21*					*22c03*		
Lancaster 6 65	a	19 17	19 21						20 26						21 07									
	d	19 17	19 22			*19c44*			20 26			*20c34*				*20c57*	*21c38*			22 03		*22c18*		
Blackpool North 97	d	*19 13*		19 20		19 44		19 50	*20 11*	20 20		20 44		20 50		21 20	21 50		21 56			22 44		23 00
Layton 97	d			19 23						20 23						21 23								23 03
Poulton-le-Fylde 97	d	*19 19*		19 28		19 50		19 56	*20 17*	20 28		20 50		20 56		21 28	21 56		22 02			22 50		23 07
Kirkham & Wesham 97	d			19 37				*19e53*		20 37				*20e53*		21 37	*21e53*							23 16
Preston 8 65	a	19 36	19 41	19 47		20 08		20 14	20 45	20 47		21 08		21 14		21 47	22 14		22 20	22 23		23 08		23 26
	d		19 47	19 49		20 10		20 15	20 47	20 49		21 10		21 15		21 49	22 15			22 29		23 09		23 28
Leyland	d			19 54				20a21		20 54				21a21		21 54	22a21					23a15		23 33
Chorley	d		19 56	20 02		20 20			20 56	21 02		21 20				22 02				22 38				23 39
Adlington (Lancashire)	d			20 07						21 07						22 07								23 43
Blackrod	d			20 10						21 10						22 10								23 47
Horwich Parkway	d			20 14		20 27				21 14		21 27				22 14								23 50
Lostock	d			20 20						21 20						22 20								23 54
Southport	d						20 05						21 05								22 05			
Meols Cop	d						20 10						21 10								22 10			
Burscough Bridge	d						20 18						21 18								22 18			
Parbold	d						20 23						21 23								22 23			
Appley Bridge	d						20 27						21 27								22 27			
Gathurst	d						20 30						21 30								22 30			
Wigan Wallgate	a						20 35						21 35								22 35			
	d						20 36						21 36								22 36			
Wigan North Western	d																							
Hindley	d						20 41						21 41								22 41			
Westhoughton	d						20 46						21 46								22 46			
Bolton	a		20 08	20 25		20 34	20 54		21 08	21 25		21 34	21 54			22 25				22 50	22 54			23 59
	d		20 08	20 25	20 31	20 35	20 54		21 08	21 25	21 31	21 35	21 54			22 25		22 31		22 51	22 54		23 31	23 59
Salford Crescent	a			20 38	20 43	20 47	21 07			21 38	21 43	21 47	22 07			22 38		22 43		23 03	23 07		23 43	
	d			20 38	20 44	20 47	21 07			21 38	21 44	21 47	22 07			22 38		22 44		23 03	23 08		23 44	
Manchester Victoria ⇌	a			20 43	20 51					21 43	21 51					22 43		22 51					23 51	
Rochdale	a				*21 28*						*22 28*							*23f58*						
Deansgate ⇌	a					20 51	21 11					21 51	22 11							23 08	23 11			
Manchester Oxford Road	a		20 23			20 53	21 13		21 23			21 53	22 13							23 10	23 14			
Manchester Piccadilly 10 ⇌	a		20 27			20 57	21 19		21 27			21 57	22 19							23 14	23 19			00 15
Stockport 84	a		*20 53*			*21 15*	21 30		*21 49*			*22 15*	22 31								23 32			
Hazel Grove 86	a		*21 13*						*22 13*				*23g13*											
Buxton 86	a		*21 51*						*22 51*				*23g51*											
Heald Green 85	a		*20 57*						*21 57*				*23g02*											
Manchester Airport 85 ✈	a		20 47			21 17			21 47			22 17	*23g08*							23 30	*00g17*			00 30

For general notes see front of timetable
For details of catering facilities see Directory of Train Operators

A From Glasgow Central (Table 65)
B From Blackburn (Table 94)
C To Chester (Table 88)
D To Liverpool Lime Street (Table 90)
E From Edinburgh (Table 65)
b Change at Oxenholme Lake District and Preston
c Change at Preston
e Until 1 November only
f 13, 20 and 27 September only
g Change at Manchester Piccadilly

Table 83

Mondays to Fridays

Oxenholme: Lake District — Windermere

Network Diagram - see first page of Table 82

Miles			TP 1 A	TP 1	TP 1	TP 1	TP 1◇ B	TP 1◇ C	TP 1	TP 1◇ C	TP 1	TP 1◇ D	TP 1	TP 1◇ B	TP 1◇ E	TP 1	TP 1	TP 1	TP 1
0	**Oxenholme Lake District**	d	06 21	07 21	08 27	09 14	10 18	11 37	12 28	13 37	14 24	15 38	16 28	17 42	18 46	19 37	20 27	21 15	22 20
2¼	Kendal	d	06 25	07 25	08 31	09 18	10 22	11 41	12 32	13 41	14 28	15 43	16 32	17 47	18 50	19 41	20 31	21 19	22 24
4	Burneside	d		07x29	08x35	09x22	10x26		12x36		14x32	15x46	16x36	17x50	18x54	19x45	20x35	21x23	22x28
6½	Staveley	d		07x34	08x40	09x27	10x31		12x41		14x37	15x51	16x41	17x55	18x59	19x50	20x40	21x28	22x33
10	**Windermere**	a	06 41	07 40	08 46	09 33	10 39	11 56	12 47	13 56	14 44	16 00	16 48	18 04	19 08	19 56	20 46	21 34	22 39

Saturdays

		TP 1 A	TP 1	TP 1	TP 1	TP 1◇ B	TP 1◇ C	TP 1	TP 1◇ C	TP 1	TP 1	TP 1	TP 1◇ B	TP 1	TP 1	TP 1	TP 1
Oxenholme Lake District	d	06 21	07 21	08 27	09 14	10 18	11 37	12 28	13 37	14 33	15 38	16 28	17 38	18 30	19 37	20 23	21 15
Kendal	d	06 25	07 25	08 31	09 18	10 22	11 41	12 32	13 41	14 37	15 43	16 32	17 42	18 34	19 41	20 27	21 19
Burneside	d		07x29	08x35	09x22	10x26		12x36		14x41	15x46	16x36	17x46	18x38	19x45	20x31	21x23
Staveley	d		07x34	08x40	09x27	10x31		12x41		14x46	15x51	16x41	17x51	18x43	19x50	20x36	21x28
Windermere	a	06 41	07 40	08 46	09 33	10 39	11 56	12 47	13 56	14 52	16 00	16 48	18 00	18 49	19 56	20 42	21 34

Sundays

		TP 1◇ G	TP 1◇ H	TP 1 J	TP 1	TP 1	TP 1	TP 1	TP 1	TP 1◇ K	TP 1	TP 1	TP 1
Oxenholme Lake District	d	10§38	11§18	11§33	12 33	13 33	14 35	15 35	16 33	17 39	18 37	19 29	20 33
Kendal	d	10§42	11§22	11§37	12 37	13 37	14 39	15 39	16 37	17 44	18 41	19 33	20 37
Burneside	d	10x46	11x26	11x41	12x41	13x41	14x43	15x43	16x41	17x47	18x45		20x41
Staveley	d	10x51	11x31	11x46	12x46	13x46	14x48	15x48	16x46	17x52	18x50		20x46
Windermere	a	11§00	11§40	11§52	12 52	13 52	14 54	15 54	16 52	18 02	18 56	19 45	20 52

Mondays to Fridays

Miles	Miles			TP 1	TP 1	TP 1	TP 1◇ L	TP 1◇ N	TP 1	TP 1◇ N	TP 1	TP 1◇ N	TP 1	TP 1◇ N	TP 1◇ N	TP 1	TP 1	TP 1	TP 1	TP 1◇ Q
—	0	**Windermere**	d	06 50	07 57	08 50	09 41	10 49	11 59	12 51	14 00	14 48	16 02	17 06	18 12	19 10	20 00	20 50	21 40	22 45
—	3½	Staveley	d	06x55	08x02		09x46	10x54	12x04		14x05	14x53		17x11	18x17		20x05	20x55	21x45	22x50
—	6	Burneside	d	07x00	08x07		09x51	10x59	12x09		14x10	14x58		17x16	18x22		20x10	21x00	21x50	22x55
—	7¾	Kendal	d	07 04	08 11	09 01	09 55	11 03	12 13	13 02	14 14	15 02	16 14	17 20	18 26	19 21	20 14	21 04	21 54	22 59
—	10	**Oxenholme Lake District**	a	07 09	08 16	09 06	10 00	11 08	12 18	13 07	14 19	15 07	16 19	17 25	18 31	19 27	20 19	21 09	21 59	23 04

Saturdays

		TP 1	TP 1	TP 1	TP 1◇ L	TP 1◇ N	TP 1	TP 1◇ N	TP 1	TP 1	TP 1	TP 1◇ N	TP 1	TP 1	TP 1	TP 1	TP 1◇ L
Windermere	d	06 50	07 57	08 50	09 41	10 49	11 59	12 51	14 00	14 59	16 02	17 06	18 02	19 00	20 00	20 47	21 40
Staveley	d	06x55	08x02		09x46	10x54	12x04		14x05	15x04		17x11	18x07	19x05	20x05		21x45
Burneside	d	07x00	08x07		09x51	10x59	12x09		14x10	15x09		17x16	18x12	19x10	20x10		21x50
Kendal	d	07 04	08 11	09 01	09 55	11 03	12 13	13 02	14 14	15 13	16 14	17 20	18 16	19 14	20 14	20 58	21 54
Oxenholme Lake District	a	07 09	08 16	09 06	10 00	11 08	12 18	13 07	14 19	15 18	16 19	17 25	18 21	19 19	20 19	21 04	21 59

For general notes see front of timetable
For details of catering facilities see Directory of Train Operators

A From Lancaster (Table 98)
B From Manchester Airport (Table 82)
C From Preston (Table 65)
D From Manchester Airport (Table 82). 22 June to 4 September from Preston (Table 65)
E From Barrow-in-Furness (Table 82)
G Until 6 September. From Preston (Table 65)
H From 13 September. From Preston (Table 65)
J Until 6 September
K Until 6 September from Manchester Airport (Table 82)
L To Preston (Table 65)
N To Manchester Airport (Table 82)
Q To Blackpool North (Table 65)

Table 83

Sundays

Windermere → Oxenholme: Lake District

Network Diagram - see first page of Table 82

		TP 1 A	TP 1	TP 1	TP 1	TP 1	TP 1	TP 1 ◊ B	TP 1 C	TP 1	TP 1	TP 1	TP 1 ◊ D
Windermere	d	11§02	11 58	12 58	13 58	14 58	15 58	16§58	16§58	18 04	19 00	19 50	21 00
Staveley	d	11x07	12x03	13x03	14x03	15x03	16x03	§	17x03	18x09	19x05		21x05
Burneside	d	11x12	12x08	13x08	14x08	15x08	16x08	§	17x08	18x14	19x10		21x10
Kendal	d	11§16	12 12	13 12	14 12	15 12	16 12	17§09	17§12	18 18	19 14	20 01	21 14
Oxenholme Lake District	a	11§21	12 18	13 17	14 17	15 17	16 17	17§15	17§17	18 23	19 19	20 06	21 19

For general notes see front of timetable
For details of catering facilities see Directory of Train Operators

A Until 6 September

B Until 6 September.
To Manchester Airport (Table 82)

C From 13 September

D To Preston (Table 65)

Stoke-on-Trent and Crewe → Manchester Airport, Stockport and Manchester

Network Diagram - see first page of Table 78

Miles	Miles	Miles		NT	NT	TP	NT	NT	VT	NT	NT	TP	AW	NT	NT	NT	NT	NT	EM	XC	NT	NT	NT	NT
				MX	MX																			
						1 ◇			1			1 ◇							◇	1 ◇				
				A		B				C		D		E		G		A	H				E	J
																			⊤	⊤				
—	—	—	London Euston 15 ⊖ 65 d																					
—	—	—	Birmingham New Street 12 68 d																	05 57	*05 30*			
—	—	—	Wolverhampton 7 68 ⛴ d																	06 15	*05 48*			
—	—	—	Stafford 65, 68 d																	06 29	*06 02*			
0	—	—	**Stoke-on-Trent** 50, 68 d														06 30			06 51				
3	—	—	Longport 50 d														06 34							
6¼	—	—	Kidsgrove 50 d														06 38							
—	0	—	**Crewe 10** 65 d		00 44			05 48	06 12				06 27								06 33	06 49		
—	4¾	—	Sandbach d					05 55													06 40	06 56		
—	8½	—	Holmes Chapel d					06 00													06 45	07 00		
—	10½	—	Goostrey d					06 03														07 03		
—	14¼	—	Chelford d					06 07														07 08		
—	17¼	—	Alderley Edge d					06 11							06 49						06 53	07 12		
—	19	0	**Wilmslow** d				05 46	06 15	06 28				06 45		06 52						06 57	07 16		
—	—	2	Styal d																					
—	—	4¼	**Manchester Airport** ✈ a		01 16		05 53														07 04			
—	20½	—	Handforth d					06 18							06 55							07 19		
11¾	—	—	Congleton d														06 45			07 03				
19¾	—	—	**Macclesfield** a														06 52			07 11				
—	—	—	d								06 22						06 53			07 12				
22½	—	—	Prestbury d								06 26						06 57							
24½	—	—	Adlington (Cheshire) d								06 29						07 00							
26½	—	—	Poynton d								06 33						07 04							
28	—	—	Bramhall d								06 35						07 07							
29½	22¾	—	Cheadle Hulme d					06 22			06 38				06 59		07 11					07 24		
31¾	25	—	**Stockport** a					06 27	06 37		06 43		06 54		07 04		07 15			07 27		07 29		
—	—	—	d	00 02		05 53		06 27	06 38	06 41	06 43	06 53	06 54	06 58	07 04	07 10	07 16	07 19	07 22	07 27		07 29	07 31	07 37
31¾	26½	—	Heaton Chapel d					06 31			06 46				07 08	07 15						07 33		07 41
34¾	28	—	Levenshulme d					06 34			06 49				07 11	07 18						07 36		07 44
37¾	31	—	**Manchester Piccadilly 10** ⛴ a	00 18	01 36	06 05	06 25	06 42	06 49	06 52	06 58	07 02	07 09	07 10	07 21	07 26	07 27	07 31	07 34	07 40	07 42	07 44	07 45	07 52
—	—	—	d							06 54						07 27			07 34					07 54
38¼	31½	—	**Manchester Oxford Road** a							06 56						07 29			07 37					07 56
38¾	32	—	Deansgate ⛴ a							06 59						07 32								07 59

	NT	NT	XC	NT	TP	AW	NT	NT	NT	NT	NT	VT	NT	EM	XC	NT	NT	NT		VT	NT	NT	XC	TP
			1 ◇		1 ◇	◇						1 ◇		◇	1 ◇					1 ◇			1 ◇	1 ◇
					K	L	E			N			A	H							Q			K
			⊓		⊤							⊠		⊤	⊤					⊠			⊤	⊤
London Euston 15 ⊖ 65 d												06 17			05b47					06 36				
Birmingham New Street 12 68 d			06 20	*06 17*											06 57			*06 36*		*07 01*			07 31	
Wolverhampton 7 68 ⛴ d			06 40	*06 19*											07 15			*06 51*		*07 19*			07 49	
Stafford 65, 68 d			06 54	*06 36*											07 29			*07 05*		*07 36*				
Stoke-on-Trent 50, 68 d			07 13					07 17				07 45										07 57	08 19	
Longport 50 d								07 21																
Kidsgrove 50 d								07 25														08 04		
Crewe 10 65 d				07 22		07 27									07 52			07 55		08 11				
Sandbach d				07c35														08 02						
Holmes Chapel d				07 41							←							08 07						
Goostrey d				07 45 →							07 45													
Chelford d											07 51													
Alderley Edge d		07 31							07 53		07 56							08 15						
Wilmslow d		07 34				07 44			07 56		08 00				08 09		←	08 19		08 27				
Styal d									07 59 →								07 59							
Manchester Airport ✈ a																	08 04							
Handforth d		07 37									08 03							08 22						
Congleton d								07 32														08 11		
Macclesfield a			07 30					07 39				08 01										08 18	08 35	
d	07 15		07 30					07 40				08 02				08 06						08 19	08 37	
Prestbury d	07 21							07 44								08 10						08 23		
Adlington (Cheshire) d	07 25							07 47														08 26		
Poynton d	07 29							07 51								08 15						08 30		
Bramhall d	07 33							07 54								08 17						08 33		
Cheadle Hulme d	07 36	07 42						07 59			08 09					08 20		08 26				08 37		
Stockport a	07 41	07 47	07 45			07 54		08 03			08 14	08 16			08 20	08 27		08 31		08 37		08 41		
d	07 42	07 48	07 49		07 53	07 54	07 57	08 04		08 10	08 14	08 17	08 19	08 24	08 20	08 28		08 31		08 38	08 41	08 42		08 53
Heaton Chapel d								08 07			08 18							08 35				08 45		
Levenshulme d								08 10			08 21					08 32						08 48		
Manchester Piccadilly 10 ⛴ a	07 56	07 59	08 01		08 02	08 08	08 09	08 21		08 25	08 27	08 28	08 32	08 36	08 40	08 42	08 42	08 45		08 49	08 52	08 56	09 00	09 02
d											08 29			08 37							08 54			
Manchester Oxford Road a											08 33			08 40							08 56			
Deansgate ⛴ a																					09 00			

For general notes see front of timetable
For details of catering facilities see Directory of Train Operators

- **A** From Chester (Table 88)
- **B** From Sheffield to Manchester Airport (Table 78)
- **C** From Buxton (Table 86) to Clitheroe (Table 94)
- **D** From Doncaster to Manchester Airport (Table 29)
- **E** From Hazel Grove (Table 86)
- **G** From Buxton (Table 86) to Wigan North Western (Table 82)
- **H** From Nottingham to Liverpool Lime Street (Table 49)
- **J** From Buxton (Table 86) to Blackpool North (Table 82)
- **K** From Cleethorpes to Manchester Airport (22 June to 4 September from Doncaster) (Table 29)
- **L** From Cardiff Central (Table 131)
- **N** From Buxton (Table 86)
- **Q** From Hazel Grove (Table 86) to Preston (Table 82)
- **b** Change at Crewe
- **c** Arr. 0730

Stoke-on-Trent and Crewe → Manchester Airport, Stockport and Manchester

Network Diagram - see first page of Table 78

		VT	AW	NT	NT	VT	NT	EM	XC	NT	NT	VT	NT	NT	XC	TP	VT	AW	NT	NT	VT	NT	EM	XC	NT
		[1] ◇	◇			[1] ◇		◇	[1] ◇			[1] ◇			[1] ◇	[1] ◇	[1] ◇	◇			[1] ◇		◇	[1] ◇	
			A		B		C	D	E				G		H	J		K		B		C	L	E	
		⊠	⚲			⊠		⚲	⚲			⊠			⚲	⚲	⊠	⚲			⊠		⚲	⚲	
London Euston [15]	⊖ 65 d	06 55				07 20			07b07			07 35					08 00				08 20			08b07	
Birmingham New Street [12]	68 d		*07 19*						07 57		*07 36*	*08 01*			08 31			*08 20*						08 57	
Wolverhampton [7]	68 ⇌ d								08 15		*07 53*	*08 19*			08 49									09 15	
Stafford	65, 68 d								08 29		*08 09*	*08 36*												09 29	
Stoke-on-Trent	50, 68 d	08 25				08 48			08 55					08 58	09 18		09 25				09 48			09 55	
Longport	50 d																								
Kidsgrove	50 d													09 05											
Crewe [10]	65 d		08 28							08 31	08 50	09 11						09 28							09 33
Sandbach	d									08 38	08 57														09 40
Holmes Chapel	d									08 42	09 02														09 44
Goostrey	d									08 45	09 05														
Chelford	d									08 50	09 09														
Alderley Edge	d			08 49						08 54	09 13								09 49						09 53
Wilmslow	d		08 46	08 52						08 57	09 17	09 27						09 46	09 52						09 57
Styal	d																								
Manchester Airport	✈ a									09 04															10 04
Handforth	d			08 55							09 20								09 55						
Congleton	d													09 12											
Macclesfield	a	08 41							09 11					09 19			09 41							10 11	
	d	08 41							09 12					09 20			09 41							10 12	
Prestbury	d													09 24											
Adlington (Cheshire)	d													09 27											
Poynton	d													09 30											
Bramhall	d													09 33											
Cheadle Hulme	d			08 59							09 24			09 37					09 59						
Stockport	a	08 55	08 58	09 04		09 16			09 27		09 29	09 36		09 41			09 55	09 58	10 04		10 16			10 27	
	d	08 56	08 58	09 04	09 12	09 17	09 21	09 25	09 27		09 29	09 37	09 41	09 42		09 53	09 56	09 58	10 04	10 12	10 17	10 21	10 26	10 27	
Heaton Chapel	d			09 08	09 16						09 33			09 45					10 08	10 16					
Levenshulme	d			09 11	09 19						09 36			09 48					10 11	10 19					
Manchester Piccadilly [10]	⇌ a	09 07	09 15	09 20	09 28	09 28	09 36	09 36	09 40	09 42	09 44	09 49	09 52	09 56	10 00	10 02	10 07	10 15	10 20	10 28	10 28	10 36	10 36	10 40	10 42
	d							09 37					09 54										10 37		
Manchester Oxford Road	a							09 40					09 56										10 40		
Deansgate	⇌ a												10 00												

		NT	VT	NT	NT	XC	TP	VT	AW	NT	NT	VT	NT		EM	XC	NT	NT	VT	NT	NT	XC	TP	VT	AW
			[1] ◇			[1] ◇	[1] ◇	[1] ◇	◇			[1] ◇			◇	[1] ◇			[1] ◇			[1] ◇	[1] ◇	[1] ◇	◇
				G		N	J		K		B		C		L	Q				G		U	J		V
			⊠			⚲	⚲	⊠	⚲			⊠			⚲	⚲			⊠			⚲	⚲	⊓	⚲
London Euston [15]	⊖ 65 d		08 40					09 00				09 20				09b07			09 40					10 00	
Birmingham New Street [12]	68 d	*08 36*	*09 01*			09 31			*09 20*							09 57		*09 36*	*10 01*			10 31			*10 20*
Wolverhampton [7]	68 ⇌ d	*08 53*	*09 19*			09 49										10 15		*09 53*	*10 19*			10 49			
Stafford	65, 68 d	*09 09*	*09 35*													10 29		*10 09*	*10 35*						
Stoke-on-Trent	50, 68 d				09 58	10 18		10 25				10 48				10 55					10 58	11 18		11 25	
Longport	50 d																								
Kidsgrove	50 d				10 05																11 05				
Crewe [10]	65 d	09 50	10 11						10 28								10 33	10 50	11 11						11 28
Sandbach	d	09 57															10 40	10 57							
Holmes Chapel	d	10 02															10 44	11 02							
Goostrey	d	10 05																11 05							
Chelford	d	10 09																11 09							
Alderley Edge	d	10 13								10 49							10 53	11 13							
Wilmslow	d	10 17	10 27						10 46	10 52							10 57	11 17	11 27						11 46
Styal	d																								
Manchester Airport	✈ a																11 04								
Handforth	d	10 20								10 55								11 20							
Congleton	d				10 12																11 12				
Macclesfield	a				10 19			10 41								11 11					11 19			11 41	
	d				10 20			10 41								11 12					11 20			11 41	
Prestbury	d				10 24																11 24				
Adlington (Cheshire)	d				10 27																11 27				
Poynton	d				10 30																11 30				
Bramhall	d				10 33																11 33				
Cheadle Hulme	d	10 24			10 37					10 59								11 24			11 37				
Stockport	a	10 29	10 36		10 41			10 55	10 58	11 04		11 16				11 27		11 29	11 36		11 41			11 55	11 58
	d	10 29	10 37	10 41	10 42		10 53	10 56	10 58	11 04	11 12	11 17	11 21		11 26	11 27		11 29	11 37	11 41	11 42		11 53	11 56	11 58
Heaton Chapel	d	10 33			10 45					11 08	11 16							11 33			11 45				
Levenshulme	d	10 36			10 48					11 11	11 19							11 36			11 48				
Manchester Piccadilly [10]	⇌ a	10 44	10 49	10 52	10 56	11 00	11 02	11 07	11 15	11 20	11 28	11 28	11 36		11 36	11 40	11 42	11 44	11 49	11 52	11 56	12 00	12 02	12 07	12 15
	d			10 54											11 37					11 54					
Manchester Oxford Road	a			10 56											11 40					11 56					
Deansgate	⇌ a			11 00																12 00					

For general notes see front of timetable
For details of catering facilities see Directory of Train Operators

- **A** From Cardiff Central (Table 131)
- **B** From Buxton (Table 86)
- **C** From Chester (Table 88)
- **D** From Nottingham to Liverpool Lime Street (Table 49)
- **E** From Southampton Central (Table 51)
- **G** From Hazel Grove (Table 86) to Preston (Table 82)
- **H** From Bristol Temple Meads (Table 51)
- **J** From Cleethorpes to Manchester Airport (22 June to 4 September from Doncaster) (Table 29)
- **K** From Carmarthen (Table 128)
- **L** From Norwich to Liverpool Lime Street (Table 49)
- **N** From Cardiff Central (Table 51)
- **Q** From Bournemouth (Table 51)
- **U** From Paignton (Table 51)
- **V** From Milford Haven (Table 128)
- **b** Change at Stafford

Stoke-on-Trent and Crewe → Manchester Airport, Stockport and Manchester

Network Diagram - see first page of Table 78

	NT	NT	VT	NT	EM	XC	NT	NT	VT	NT	NT	XC	TP	VT	AW	NT	NT	VT	NT	EM	XC	NT	NT	VT
			1 ◇		◇	1 ◇			1 ◇			1 ◇	1 ◇	1 ◇	◇			1 ◇		◇	1 ◇			1 ◇
		A		B	C	D				E		G	H		J		A		B	C	D			
London Euston 15 ⊖ 65 d			10 20			10b07			10 40					11 00				11 20			11b07			11 40
Birmingham New Street 12 68 d						10 57		10 36	11 01			11 31			11 20						11 57		11 36	12 01
Wolverhampton 7 68 d						11 15		10 53	11 19			11 49									12 15		11 53	12 19
Stafford 65, 68 d						11 29		11 09	11 35												12 29		12 09	12 35
Stoke-on-Trent 50, 68 d			11 48			11 55					11 58	12 18		12 25				12 48			12 55			
Longport 50 d																								
Kidsgrove 50 d											12 05													
Crewe 10 65 d							11 33	11 50	12 11						12 28							12 33	12 50	13 11
Sandbach d							11 40	11 57														12 40	12 57	
Holmes Chapel d							11 44	12 02														12 44	13 02	
Goostrey d								12 05															13 05	
Chelford d								12 09															13 09	
Alderley Edge d	11 49						11 53	12 13								12 49						12 53	13 13	
Wilmslow d	11 52						11 57	12 17	12 27						12 46	12 52						12 57	13 17	13 27
Styal d																								
Manchester Airport ✈ a							12 04															13 04		
Handforth d	11 55							12 20								12 55							13 20	
Congleton d											12 12													
Macclesfield a						12 11					12 19			12 41							13 11			
d						12 12					12 20			12 41							13 12			
Prestbury d											12 24													
Adlington (Cheshire) d											12 27													
Poynton d											12 30													
Bramhall d											12 33													
Cheadle Hulme d	11 59							12 24			12 37					12 59							13 24	
Stockport a	12 04		12 16			12 27		12 29	12 36		12 41			12 55	12 58	13 04		13 16			13 27		13 29	13 36
d	12 04	12 12	12 17	12 21	12 26	12 27		12 29	12 37	12 41	12 42		12 53	12 56	12 58	13 04	13 12	13 17	13 21	13 26	13 27		13 29	13 37
Heaton Chapel d	12 08	12 16						12 33			12 45					13 08	13 16						13 33	
Levenshulme d	12 11	12 19						12 36			12 48					13 11	13 19						13 36	
Manchester Piccadilly 10 a	12 20	12 28	12 28	12 36	12 36	12 40	12 42	12 44	12 49	12 52	12 56	13 00	13 02	13 07	13 15	13 20	13 28	13 28	13 36	13 36	13 40	13 42	13 44	13 49
d					12 37					12 54										13 37				
Manchester Oxford Road a					12 40					12 56										13 40				
Deansgate a										13 00														

	NT	NT	XC	TP	VT	AW		NT	NT	VT	NT	EM	XC	NT	NT	VT	NT	NT	XC	TP	VT	AW	NT	NT
			1 ◇	1 ◇	1 ◇	◇				1 ◇		◇	1 ◇			1 ◇			1 ◇	1 ◇	1 ◇	◇		
	E		G	H		K			A		B	C	D				E		L	H		J		A
London Euston 15 ⊖ 65 d					12 00					12 20			12b07			12 40					13 00			
Birmingham New Street 12 68 d			12 31			12 20							12 57		12 36	13 01			13 31			13 20		
Wolverhampton 7 68 d			12 49										13 15		12 53	13 19			13 49					
Stafford 65, 68 d													13 29		13 09	13 35								
Stoke-on-Trent 50, 68 d		12 58	13 18		13 25					13 48			13 55					13 58	14 18		14 25			
Longport 50 d																								
Kidsgrove 50 d		13 05																14 05						
Crewe 10 65 d						13 28								13 33	13 50	14 11						14 28		
Sandbach d														13 40	13 57									
Holmes Chapel d														13 44	14 02									
Goostrey d															14 05									
Chelford d															14 09									
Alderley Edge d								13 49						13 53	14 13								14 49	
Wilmslow d						13 46		13 52						13 57	14 17	14 27						14 46	14 52	
Styal d																								
Manchester Airport ✈ a														14 04										
Handforth d								13 55							14 20								14 55	
Congleton d		13 12																14 12						
Macclesfield a		13 19			13 41								14 11					14 19			14 41			
d		13 20			13 42								14 12					14 20			14 41			
Prestbury d		13 24																14 24						
Adlington (Cheshire) d		13 27																14 27						
Poynton d		13 30																14 30						
Bramhall d		13 33																14 33						
Cheadle Hulme d		13 37						13 59							14 24			14 37					14 59	
Stockport a		13 41			13 55	13 58		14 04		14 16			14 27		14 29	14 36		14 41			14 55	14 58	15 04	
d	13 41	13 42		13 53	13 56	13 58		14 04	14 12	14 17	14 21	14 26	14 27		14 29	14 37	14 41	14 42		14 53	14 56	14 58	15 04	15 12
Heaton Chapel d		13 45						14 08	14 16						14 33			14 45					15 08	15 16
Levenshulme d		13 48						14 11	14 19						14 36			14 48					15 11	15 19
Manchester Piccadilly 10 a	13 52	13 56	14 00	14 02	14 07	14 15		14 20	14 28	14 28	14 36	14 36	14 40	14 42	14 44	14 49	14 52	14 56	15 00	15 02	15 07	15 15	15 20	15 28
d	13 54											14 37					14 54							
Manchester Oxford Road a	13 56											14 40					14 56							
Deansgate a	14 00																15 00							

For general notes see front of timetable
For details of catering facilities see Directory of Train Operators

A From Buxton (Table 86)
B From Chester (Table 88)
C From Norwich to Liverpool Lime Street (Table 49)
D From Bournemouth (Table 51)
E From Hazel Grove (Table 86) to Preston (Table 82)
G From Bristol Temple Meads (Table 51)
H From Cleethorpes to Manchester Airport (22 June to 4 September from Doncaster) (Table 29)
J From Milford Haven (Table 128)
K From Pembroke Dock (Table 128)
L From Paignton (Table 51)
b Change at Stafford

Stoke-on-Trent and Crewe → Manchester Airport, Stockport and Manchester

Network Diagram - see first page of Table 78

	VT	NT	EM	XC	NT	NT	VT	NT	NT	XC	TP	VT	AW	NT	NT	VT	NT	EM	XC	NT	NT	VT		NT
	1 ◇		◇	1 ◇			1 ◇			1 ◇	1 ◇	1 ◇	◇			1 ◇		◇	1 ◇			1 ◇		
		A	B	C				D		E	G		H		J		A	B	C					K
	[restaurant]		[trolley]	[trolley]			[restaurant]			[trolley]	[trolley]	[restaurant]	[trolley]			[restaurant]		[trolley]	[trolley]			[restaurant]		
London Euston 15 ⊖ 65 d	13 20			13b07			13 40					14 00				14 20			14b07			14 40		
Birmingham New Street 12 68 d				13 57		13 36	14 01			14 31			14 20						14 57		14 36	15 01		
Wolverhampton 7 68 🚢 d				14 15		13 53	14 19			14 49									15 15		14 53	15 19		
Stafford 65, 68 d				14 29		14 09	14 35												15 29		15 09	15 35		
Stoke-on-Trent 50, 68 d	14 48			14 55					14 58	15 18		15 25				15 48			15 55					
Longport 50 d																								
Kidsgrove 50 d									15 05															
Crewe 10 65 d					14 33	14 50	15 11						15 28							15 33	15 50	16 12		
Sandbach d					14 40	14 57														15 40	15 57			
Holmes Chapel d					14 44	15 02														15 44	16 02			
Goostrey d						15 05															16 05			
Chelford d						15 09															16 09			
Alderley Edge d					14 53	15 13								15 49						15 53	16 13			
Wilmslow d					14 57	15 17	15 27						15 46	15 52						15 56	16 17	16 27		
Styal d																				15 59				
Manchester Airport ✈ a					15 04															16 04				
Handforth d						15 20								15 55							16 20			
Congleton d									15 12															
Macclesfield a				15 11					15 19			15 41							16 11					
d				15 12					15 20			15 41							16 12					
Prestbury d									15 24															
Adlington (Cheshire) d									15 27															
Poynton d									15 30															
Bramhall d									15 33															
Cheadle Hulme d						15 24			15 37					15 59							16 24			
Stockport a	15 16			15 27		15 29	15 36		15 41			15 55	15 58	16 04		16 16			16 27		16 29	16 36		
d	15 17	15 21	15 26	15 27		15 29	15 37	15 41	15 42		15 53	15 56	15 58	16 04	16 12	16 17	16 21	16 26	16 27		16 29	16 37		16 41
Heaton Chapel d						15 33			15 45					16 08	16 16						16 33			
Levenshulme d						15 36			15 48					16 11	16 19						16 36			
Manchester Piccadilly 10 🚢 a	15 28	15 36	15 36	15 40	15 41	15 44	15 49	15 52	15 56	16 00	16 02	16 07	16 15	16 20	16 25	16 28	16 36	16 36	16 40	16 42	16 44	16 49		16 52
d			15 37		15 42			15 54							16 27			16 37						16 54
Manchester Oxford Road a			15 40		15 46			15 56							16 29			16 40						16 56
Deansgate 🚢 a								16 00							16 32									17 00

	NT	XC	TP	VT	AW	NT	NT	VT	NT	EM	XC	NT	NT	VT	NT	NT	XC	TP	VT	AW	NT	NT	VT	NT
		1 ◇	1 ◇	1 ◇	◇			1 ◇		◇	1 ◇			1 ◇			1 ◇	1 ◇	1 ◇	◇			1 ◇	
		L	G		N		Q		A	B	C				Q		E	G		H		U		A
		[trolley]	[trolley]	[restaurant]	[trolley]			[restaurant]		[trolley]	[trolley]			[restaurant]			[trolley]	[trolley]	[restaurant]	[trolley]			⊠	
London Euston 15 ⊖ 65 d				15 00				15 20			15b07			15 40					16 00				16 20	
Birmingham New Street 12 68 d		15 31			15 20						15 57		15 36	16 01			16 31			16 20				
Wolverhampton 7 68 🚢 d		15 49									16 15		15 53	16 19			16 49							
Stafford 65, 68 d											16 29		16 09	16 35										
Stoke-on-Trent 50, 68 d	15 58	16 18		16 25				16 48			16 55					16 58	17 18		17 25				17 48	
Longport 50 d																								
Kidsgrove 50 d	16 05															17 05								
Crewe 10 65 d					16 28							16 33	16 50	17 11						17 29				
Sandbach d												16 40	16 57											
Holmes Chapel d												16 44	17 02											
Goostrey d													17 05											
Chelford d													17 09											
Alderley Edge d						16 49						16 53	17 13								17 49			
Wilmslow d					16 46	16 52						16 57	17 17	17 27						17 47	17 52			
Styal d																								
Manchester Airport ✈ a												17 04												
Handforth d						16 55							17 20								17 55			
Congleton d	16 12															17 12								
Macclesfield a	16 19			16 41							17 11					17 19			17 41					
d	16 20			16 41							17 12					17 20			17 41					
Prestbury d	16 24															17 24								
Adlington (Cheshire) d	16 27															17 27								
Poynton d	16 30															17 30								
Bramhall d	16 33															17 33								
Cheadle Hulme d	16 37					16 59							17 24			17 36					17 59			
Stockport a	16 41			16 54	16 58	17 04		17 16			17 27		17 29	17 36		17 41			17 55	17 58	18 04		18 16	
d	16 42		16 52	16 55	16 58	17 04	17 12	17 17	17 21	17 26	17 27		17 29	17 37	17 41	17 42		17 53	17 56	17 58	18 04	18 12	18 17	18 21
Heaton Chapel d	16 45					17 08	17 16						17 33			17 45					18 08	18 16		
Levenshulme d	16 48					17 11	17 19						17 36			17 48					18 11	18 19		
Manchester Piccadilly 10 🚢 a	16 56	17 00	17 02	17 07	17 15	17 20	17 25	17 28	17 36	17 37	17 40	17 42	17 44	17 49	17 52	17 56	18 00	18 02	18 07	18 15	18 20	18 28	18 28	18 36
d							17 27			17 37					17 54									
Manchester Oxford Road a							17 29			17 40					17 56									
Deansgate 🚢 a							17 32								18 00									

For general notes see front of timetable
For details of catering facilities see Directory of Train Operators

- **A** From Chester (Table 88)
- **B** From Norwich to Liverpool Lime Street (Table 49)
- **C** From Bournemouth (Table 51)
- **D** From Hazel Grove (Table 86) to Bolton (Table 82)
- **E** From Bristol Temple Meads (Table 51)
- **G** From Cleethorpes to Manchester Airport (22 June to 4 September from Doncaster) (Table 29)
- **H** From Carmarthen (Table 128)
- **J** From Hazel Grove (Table 86) to Barrow-in-Furness (Table 82)
- **K** From Hazel Grove (Table 86) to Preston (Table 82)
- **L** From Penzance (Table 135)
- **N** From Milford Haven (Table 128)
- **Q** From Buxton (Table 86) to Blackpool North (Table 82)
- **U** From Buxton (Table 86)
- **b** Change at Stafford

Stoke-on-Trent and Crewe → Manchester Airport, Stockport and Manchester

Network Diagram - see first page of Table 78

	EM	XC	NT	NT	VT	NT	NT	XC	TP	VT	AW	NT	VT	NT	NT		EM	XC	NT	VT	NT	XC	TP	VT
	◇	1 ◇			1 ◇			1 ◇	1 ◇	1 ◇	R		1 ◇				◇	1 ◇		1 ◇		1 ◇	1 ◇	1 ◇
	A	B				C		D	E		G	H			J		A	B				K	E	
	⊼	⊼			⊠			⊼	⊼	⊠	⊼		⊠				⊼	⊼		⊠		⊼	⊼	⊠
London Euston 15 ⊖ 65 d		*16b07*			16 40					17 00			17 20					*17b07*		17 40				18 00
Birmingham New Street 12 68 d		16 57		*16 36*	*17 01*			17 31			*17 20*							17 57	*17 36*	*18 01*		18 31		
Wolverhampton 7 68 ⇌ d		17 15		*16 53*	*17 19*			17 49										18 15	*17 53*	*18 19*		18 49		
Stafford 65, 68 d		17 29		*17 09*	*17 36*						*17 56*							18 29	*18 09*	*18 35*				
Stoke-on-Trent 50, 68 d		17 55					17 58	18 18		18 25			18 49					18 55			18 58	19 18		19 25
Longport 50 d																								
Kidsgrove 50 d							18 05														19 05			
Crewe 10 65 d			17 33	17 50	18 11						18 28			18 33					18 50	19 11				
Sandbach d			17 40	17 57										18 40					18 57					
Holmes Chapel d			17 44	18 02										18 44					19 02					
Goostrey d				18 05															19 05					
Chelford d				18 09															19 09					
Alderley Edge d			17 53	18 13										18 53					19 13					
Wilmslow d			17 56	18 17	18 27						18 46			18 56					19 17	19 27				
Styal d			17 59																					
Manchester Airport ✈ a			18 04											19 04										
Handforth d				18 20															19 20					
Congleton d							18 12														19 12			
Macclesfield a		18 11					18 19			18 41								19 11			19 19			19 41
d		18 12					18 20			18 41								19 12			19 20			19 41
Prestbury d							18 24														19 24			
Adlington (Cheshire) d							18 27														19 27			
Poynton d							18 30														19 30			
Bramhall d							18 33														19 33			
Cheadle Hulme d				18 24			18 37												19 24		19 37			
Stockport a		18 27		18 29	18 37		18 41			18 55	18 58		19 16					19 27	19 29	19 36	19 41			19 55
d	18 26	18 27		18 29	18 38	18 41	18 42		18 53	18 56	18 58	19 12	19 17		19 21		19 26	19 27	19 29	19 37	19 42		19 53	19 56
Heaton Chapel d				18 33			18 45					19 16									19 45			
Levenshulme d				18 36			18 48					19 19									19 48			
Manchester Piccadilly 10 ⇌ a	18 36	18 40	18 42	18 44	18 49	18 52	18 56	19 00	19 02	19 07	19 15	19 28	19 28	19 31	19 35		19 36	19 40	19 43	19 49	19 56	20 00	20 02	20 07
d	18 37					18 54								19 32			19 37							
Manchester Oxford Road a	18 40					18 56								19 36			19 40							
Deansgate ⇌ a						19 00																		

	AW	NT	VT	NT	NT	EM	XC	NT	VT	NT	XC	TP	VT	AW	NT	VT	NT	EM	NT	XC	NT	VT	NT	XC
	R		1 ◇			◇	1 ◇		1 ◇		1 ◇	1 ◇	1 ◇	R		1 ◇		◇		1 ◇		1 ◇		1 ◇
	L	H			J	A	B				N	E		G	H			Q	J	B				K
	⊼		⊠			⊼	⊼		⊠		⊼	⊼	⊠	⊼		ꝑ		⊼				ꝑ		
London Euston 15 ⊖ 65 d			18 20				*18b07*		18 40				19 00			19 20				*18b33*		19 40		
Birmingham New Street 12 68 d	*18 20*						18 57	*18 36*	*19 01*		19 31			*19 20*						19 57	*19 36*	*20 20*		20 31
Wolverhampton 7 68 ⇌ d							19 15	*18 53*	*19 19*		19 49									20 16	*19 53*	*20 37*		20 49
Stafford 65, 68 d	*18 56*						19 29	*19 09*	*19 36*					*19 56*						20 29	*20 09*	21 04		
Stoke-on-Trent 50, 68 d			19 48				19 55			19 58	20 19		20 25			20 48				20 55			20 58	21 18
Longport 50 d																								
Kidsgrove 50 d										20 05													21 05	
Crewe 10 65 d	19 28							19 50	20 11					20 28							20 50			
Sandbach d								19 57													20 57			
Holmes Chapel d								20 02													21 02			
Goostrey d								20 05													21 05			
Chelford d								20 09													21 09			
Alderley Edge d								20 13													21 13			
Wilmslow d	19 46			19 56				20 17	20 27					20 46			20 56				21 17	21 36		
Styal d																								
Manchester Airport ✈ a				20 04													21 04							
Handforth d								20 20													21 20			
Congleton d										20 12													21 12	
Macclesfield a							20 11			20 19			20 41							21 11			21 19	
d							20 12			20 20			20 41							21 12			21 20	
Prestbury d										20 24													21 24	
Adlington (Cheshire) d										20 27													21 27	
Poynton d										20 30													21 30	
Bramhall d										20 33													21 33	
Cheadle Hulme d								20 24		20 37											21 24		21 37	
Stockport a	19 58		20 16				20 27	20 29	20 36	20 41			20 55	20 58		21 16				21 27	21 29		21 41	
d	19 58	20 12	20 17		20 21	20 26	20 27	20 29	20 37	20 42		20 53	20 56	20 58	21 12	21 17		21 20	21 21	21 27	21 29		21 42	
Heaton Chapel d		20 16								20 45					21 16								21 45	
Levenshulme d		20 19								20 48					21 19								21 49	
Manchester Piccadilly 10 ⇌ a	20 15	20 28	20 28	20 32	20 35	20 36	20 40	20 43	20 49	20 56	21 00	21 02	21 07	21 15	21 28	21 28	21 32	21 32	21 35	21 40	21 44	21 55	21 56	22 00
d				20 32		20 37											21 32							
Manchester Oxford Road a				20 36		20 40											21 36							
Deansgate ⇌ a																								

For general notes see front of timetable
For details of catering facilities see Directory of Train Operators

A From Norwich to Liverpool Lime Street (Table 49)
B From Bournemouth (Table 51)
C From Buxton (Table 86) to Bolton (Table 82)
D From Paignton (Table 51)
E From Cleethorpes to Manchester Airport (22 June to 4 September from Doncaster) (Table 29)
G From Milford Haven (Table 128)
H From Buxton (Table 86)
J From Chester (Table 88)
K From Bristol Temple Meads (Table 51)
L From Carmarthen (Table 128)
N From Bristol Temple Meads (Fridays from Exeter St Davids) (Table 51)
Q From Norwich (Table 49)
b Change at Stafford

Stoke-on-Trent and Crewe → Manchester Airport, Stockport and Manchester

Network Diagram - see first page of Table 78

	VT	AW	NT	NT	NT	XC	NT	NT	VT	NT	TP	VT	NT	NT	XC	AW	NT	NT	NT	XC	VT	VT		
	1 ◇	◇				1 ◇			1 ◇		1 ◇	1 ◇			1 ◇	◇				1 ◇	1 ◇	1 ◇		
		A	B		C	D		E			G				D	H	B	J						
	🍴	🛒							🍴			🍴									🍴	🍴		
London Euston 15 ⊖ 65 d	20 00	*19 30*							20 40			21 00			*20b07*	*21 10*					21 40	22 00		
Birmingham New Street 12 68 d						20 57	*20 36*								21 57	*21c57*				22 28				
Wolverhampton 7 68 🚋 d						21 16	*20 53*								22 16	*22c16*				22 46				
Stafford 65, 68 d		*20 53*				21 29	*21 09*								22 29	22 34				22 59				
Stoke-on-Trent 50, 68 d	21 24					21 55				22 18		22 28			22 55					23 21				
Longport 50 d																								
Kidsgrove 50 d										22 25														
Crewe 10 65 d		21 28					21 50		22 13							23 05			23 13					
Sandbach d							21 57												23 19					
Holmes Chapel d							22 02												23 24					
Goostrey d							22 05												23 27					
Chelford d							22 09												23 31					
Alderley Edge d							22 13												23 35					
Wilmslow d		21 46		21 55			22 17		22 29					22 56		23 23			23 39					
Styal d																								
Manchester Airport ✈ a				22 04										23 04										
Handforth d							22 20												23 42					
Congleton d										22 32														
Macclesfield a	21 40					22 11				22 40		22 44	←		23 11						23s52			
d	21 40					22 12				22 48 →		22 44	22 48		23 12									
Prestbury d													22 53											
Adlington (Cheshire) d													22 56											
Poynton d													22 59											
Bramhall d													23 02											
Cheadle Hulme d							22 24						23 05						23 46					
Stockport a	21 55	21 58				22 25	22 29		22 38			22 58	23 10		23 25	23 32			23 51		00s08	00s59		
d	21 56	21 58	22 12		22 21	22 25	22 29	22 34	22 39		22 53	22 59	23 10		23 25	23 33	23 41	23 48	23 51					
Heaton Chapel d			22 16					22 38					23 14						23 55					
Levenshulme d			22 19					22 41					23 17						23 58					
Manchester Piccadilly 10 🚋 a	22 07	22 15	22 28	22 31	22 35	22 40	22 42	22 48	22 51		23 02	23 11	23 25	23 33	23 40	23 48	23 54	00 02	00 07	00e15	00 21	01 13		
d				22 32				22 50																
Manchester Oxford Road a				22 36				22 52																
Deansgate 🚋 a								22 55																

Saturdays

	NT	NT	TP	NT	NT	TP	AW	NT	NT	NT	EM	XC	NT	NT	NT	NT	XC	TP	AW	NT	NT		NT	NT
			1 ◇			1 ◇					◇	1 ◇					1 ◇	1 ◇	◇					
	C		K		L	N			B	C	Q				U			V	X	Y				B
											🛒	🛒					🛒	🛒						
London Euston 15 ⊖ 65 d																								
Birmingham New Street 12 68 d												05 57	*05 30*				06 31		*06 20*					
Wolverhampton 7 68 🚋 d												06 14	*05 48*				06 49		*06 18*					
Stafford 65, 68 d												06 29	*06 01*				07 01		*06 36*					
Stoke-on-Trent 50, 68 d												06 51				06 57	07 18							
Longport 50 d																								
Kidsgrove 50 d																07 04								
Crewe 10 65 d		00 44					06 27						06 33	06 49					07 27				07 30	
Sandbach d													06 40	06 56									07 37	
Holmes Chapel d													06 44	07 00									07 41	
Goostrey d														07 03									07 44	
Chelford d														07 08									07 49	
Alderley Edge d								06 49					06 53	07 12							07 49		07 53	
Wilmslow d				05 46			06 45	06 52					06 57	07 16					07 44		07 52		07 56	
Styal d																							07 59 →	
Manchester Airport ✈ a		01 16		05 53									07 04											
Handforth d								06 55						07 19							07 55			
Congleton d												07 03				07 11								
Macclesfield a												07 11				07 18	07 36							
d												07 12				07 19	07 37							
Prestbury d																07 23								
Adlington (Cheshire) d																07 26								
Poynton d																07 29								
Bramhall d																07 32								
Cheadle Hulme d								06 59						07 24		07 36					07 59			
Stockport a							06 54	07 04				07 27		07 29		07 40	07 49		07 54		08 04			
d	00 05		05 53		06 41	06 53	06 54	07 04	07 12	07 19	07 22	07 27		07 29	07 40	07 41	07 50	07 53	07 54	07 57	08 04			08 12
Heaton Chapel d								07 08	07 16					07 33		07 44					08 08			08 16
Levenshulme d								07 11	07 19					07 36		07 47					08 11			08 19
Manchester Piccadilly 10 🚋 a	00 18	01 36	06 05	06 25	06 52	07 02	07 09	07 21	07 28	07 31	07 34	07 40	07 42	07 44	07 52	07 56	08 00	08 02	08 08	08 09	08 20			08 28
d					06 54						07 34				07 54									
Manchester Oxford Road a					06 56						07 37				07 56									
Deansgate 🚋 a					06 59										08 00									

For general notes see front of timetable
For details of catering facilities see Directory of Train Operators

- **A** From Carmarthen (Table 128)
- **B** From Buxton (Table 86)
- **C** From Chester (Table 88)
- **D** From Bournemouth (Table 51)
- **E** To Wigan Wallgate (Table 82)
- **G** From Cleethorpes to Manchester Airport (22 June to 4 September from Doncaster) (Table 29)
- **H** From Maesteg (Table 128)
- **J** From Sheffield (Table 78)
- **K** From Sheffield to Manchester Airport (Table 78)
- **L** From Buxton (Table 86) to Clitheroe (Table 94)
- **N** From Doncaster to Manchester Airport (Table 29)
- **Q** From Nottingham to Liverpool Lime Street (Table 49)
- **U** From Hazel Grove (Table 86) to Preston (Table 82)
- **V** From Cleethorpes to Manchester Airport (27 June to 5 September from Doncaster) (Table 29)
- **X** From Cardiff Central (Table 131)
- **Y** From Hazel Grove (Table 86)
- **b** Change at Stafford
- **c** Change at Stafford and Crewe
- **e** Tuesday and Wednesday mornings arr. 0037

Table 84

Saturdays

Stoke-on-Trent and Crewe → Manchester Airport, Stockport and Manchester

Network Diagram - see first page of Table 78

		NT	EM	XC	NT	NT	VT	NT	NT	XC	TP	VT	AW	NT	NT	VT	NT	EM	XC	NT	NT	VT		NT	NT
			◇	1 ◇			1 ◇			1 ◇	1 ◇	1 ◇	◇			1 ◇		◇	1 ◇			1 ◇			
		A	B					C			D		E		C		A	B	G					H	
			⊼	⊼			⊡			⊼	⊼	⊡	⊼			⊡		⊼	⊼			⊡			
London Euston 15 ⊖ 65	d						06 36					06 55				07 20			07b07			07 35			
Birmingham New Street 12 68	d			06 57		06 36	07 01			07 31			07 20						07 57		07 36	08 01			
Wolverhampton 7 68 ⇌	d			07 14		06 54	07 18			07 49									08 14		07 53	08 19			
Stafford 65, 68	d			07 29		07 08	07 38												08 29		08 09	08 36			
Stoke-on-Trent 50, 68	d								07 57	08 18		08 25				08 48			08 55						08 58
Longport 50	d																								
Kidsgrove 50	d								08 04																09 05
Crewe 10 65	d			07 53		07 55	08 11						08 28							08 31	08 50	09 11			
Sandbach	d					08 02														08 38	08 57				
Holmes Chapel	d					08 08														08 42	09 02				
Goostrey	d																			08 45	09 05				
Chelford	d																			08 50	09 09				
Alderley Edge	d					08 15								08 49						08 54	09 13				
Wilmslow	d			08 10	←	08 19	08 27						08 46	08 52						08 57	09 17	09 27			
Styal	d				07 59																				
Manchester Airport ✈	a				08 05															09 04					
Handforth	d					08 22								08 55							09 20				
Congleton	d								08 11																09 12
Macclesfield	a								08 18	08 35		08 41							09 11						09 19
	d								08 19	08 37		08 41							09 12						09 20
Prestbury	d								08 23																09 24
Adlington (Cheshire)	d								08 26																09 27
Poynton	d								08 30																09 30
Bramhall	d								08 33																09 33
Cheadle Hulme	d					08 26			08 37					08 59							09 24				09 37
Stockport	a			08 20		08 31	08 37		08 41	08 49		08 55	08 58	09 04		09 16			09 27		09 29	09 36			09 41
	d	08 19	08 24	08 20		08 31	08 38	08 41	08 42	08 50	08 53	08 56	08 58	09 04	09 12	09 17	09 21	09 25	09 27		09 29	09 37		09 41	09 42
Heaton Chapel	d					08 35			08 45					09 08	09 16						09 33				09 45
Levenshulme	d								08 48					09 11	09 19						09 36				09 48
Manchester Piccadilly 10 ⇌	a	08 32	08 36	08 40	08 42	08 45	08 49	08 52	08 56	09 00	09 02	09 07	09 14	09 20	09 28	09 28	09 36	09 36	09 40	09 42	09 44	09 49		09 52	09 56
	d		08 37					08 54										09 37						09 54	
Manchester Oxford Road	a		08 40					08 56										09 40						09 56	
Deansgate ⇌	a							09 00																10 00	

		XC	TP	VT	AW	NT	NT	VT	NT	EM	XC	NT	NT	VT	NT	NT	XC	TP	VT	AW	NT	NT		VT	NT
		1 ◇	1 ◇	1 ◇	◇			1 ◇		◇	1 ◇			1 ◇			1 ◇	1 ◇	1 ◇	◇				1 ◇	
		J	D		K		C		A	L	G				H		N	D		K		C			A
		⊡ ⊼	⊼	⊡	⊼			⊡		⊼	⊼			⊡			⊡ ⊼	⊼	⊡	⊼				⊡	
London Euston 15 ⊖ 65	d			08 00				08 20			08b07			08 40					09 00					09 20	
Birmingham New Street 12 68	d	08 31			08 20						08 57		08 36	09 01			09 31			09 20					
Wolverhampton 7 68 ⇌	d	08 49									09 14		08 53	09 19			09 49								
Stafford 65, 68	d										09 29		09 09	09 35											
Stoke-on-Trent 50, 68	d	09 18		09 25				09 48			09 55					09 58	10 18		10 25					10 48	
Longport 50	d																								
Kidsgrove 50	d															10 05									
Crewe 10 65	d				09 28							09 33	09 50	10 11						10 28					
Sandbach	d											09 40	09 57												
Holmes Chapel	d											09 44	10 02												
Goostrey	d												10 05												
Chelford	d												10 09												
Alderley Edge	d					09 49						09 53	10 13								10 49				
Wilmslow	d				09 46	09 52						09 57	10 17	10 27						10 46	10 52				
Styal	d																								
Manchester Airport ✈	a											10 04													
Handforth	d					09 55							10 20								10 55				
Congleton	d															10 12									
Macclesfield	a			09 41							10 11					10 19			10 41						
	d			09 41							10 12					10 20			10 41						
Prestbury	d															10 24									
Adlington (Cheshire)	d															10 27									
Poynton	d															10 30									
Bramhall	d															10 33									
Cheadle Hulme	d					09 59							10 24			10 37					10 59				
Stockport	a			09 55	09 58	10 04		10 16			10 27		10 29	10 36		10 41			10 55	10 58	11 04			11 16	
	d		09 53	09 56	09 58	10 04	10 12	10 17	10 21	10 26	10 27		10 29	10 37	10 40	10 42		10 53	10 56	10 58	11 04	11 12		11 17	11 21
Heaton Chapel	d					10 08	10 16						10 33			10 45					11 08	11 16			
Levenshulme	d					10 11	10 19						10 36			10 48					11 11	11 19			
Manchester Piccadilly 10 ⇌	a	10 00	10 02	10 07	10 15	10 20	10 28	10 28	10 36	10 36	10 40	10 42	10 44	10 49	10 52	10 56	11 00	11 02	11 07	11 15	11 20	11 28		11 28	11 36
	d									10 37					10 54										
Manchester Oxford Road	a									10 40					10 56										
Deansgate ⇌	a														11 00										

For general notes see front of timetable
For details of catering facilities see Directory of Train Operators

- **A** From Chester (Table 88)
- **B** From Nottingham to Liverpool Lime Street (Table 49)
- **C** From Buxton (Table 86)
- **D** From Cleethorpes to Manchester Airport (27 June to 5 September from Doncaster) (Table 29)
- **E** From Cardiff Central (Table 131)
- **G** From Southampton Central (Table 51)
- **H** From Hazel Grove (Table 86) to Preston (Table 82)
- **J** From Bristol Temple Meads (Table 51)
- **K** From Carmarthen (Table 128)
- **L** From Norwich to Liverpool Lime Street (Table 49)
- **N** From Cardiff Central (Table 51)
- **b** Change at Stafford

Stoke-on-Trent and Crewe → Manchester Airport, Stockport and Manchester

Network Diagram - see first page of Table 78

	EM ◇ A	XC 1◇ B	NT	NT	VT 1◇	NT C	NT	XC 1◇ D	TP 1◇ E	VT 1◇	AW ◇ G	NT	NT H	VT 1◇	NT J	EM ◇ A	XC 1◇ B	NT	NT	VT 1◇	NT C		NT	XC 1◇ K
London Euston 15 ⊖ 65 d		09b07		08 50	09 40					10 00				10 20			10b07			10 40				
Birmingham New Street 12 68 d		09 57		09 36	10 01			10 31			10 20						10 57		10 36	11 01				11 31
Wolverhampton 7 68 ⛴ d		10 14		09 53	10 19			10 49									11 14		10 53	11 19				11 49
Stafford 65, 68 d		10 29		10 09	10 35												11 29		11 09	11 35				
Stoke-on-Trent 50, 68 d		10 55					10 58	11 18		11 25				11 48			11 55						11 58	12 18
Longport 50 d																								
Kidsgrove 50 d							11 05																12 05	
Crewe 10 65 d			10 33	10 50	11 11						11 28							11 33	11 50	12 11				
Sandbach d			10 40	10 57														11 40	11 57					
Holmes Chapel d			10 44	11 02														11 44	12 02					
Goostrey d				11 05															12 05					
Chelford d				11 09															12 09					
Alderley Edge d			10 53	11 13								11 49						11 53	12 13					
Wilmslow d			10 57	11 17	11 27						11 46	11 52						11 57	12 17	12 27				
Styal d																								
Manchester Airport ✈ a			11 04															12 04						
Handforth d				11 20								11 55							12 20					
Congleton d							11 12																12 12	
Macclesfield a		11 11					11 19			11 41							12 11						12 19	
d		11 12					11 20			11 41							12 12						12 20	
Prestbury d							11 24																12 24	
Adlington (Cheshire) d							11 27																12 27	
Poynton d							11 30																12 30	
Bramhall d							11 33																12 33	
Cheadle Hulme d				11 24			11 37					11 59							12 24				12 37	
Stockport a		11 27		11 29	11 36		11 41			11 55	11 58	12 04		12 16			12 27		12 29	12 36			12 41	
d	11 26	11 27		11 29	11 37	11 41	11 42		11 53	11 56	11 58	12 04	12 12	12 17	12 21	12 26	12 27		12 29	12 37	12 41		12 42	
Heaton Chapel d				11 33			11 45					12 08	12 16						12 33				12 45	
Levenshulme d				11 36			11 48					12 11	12 19						12 36				12 48	
Manchester Piccadilly 10 ⛴ a	11 36	11 40	11 42	11 44	11 49	11 52	11 56	12 00	12 02	12 07	12 15	12 20	12 28	12 28	12 36	12 36	12 40	12 42	12 44	12 49	12 52		12 56	13 00
d	11 37					11 54										12 37					12 54			
Manchester Oxford Road a	11 40					11 56										12 40					12 56			
Deansgate ⛴ a						12 00															13 00			

	TP 1◇ E	VT 1◇	AW ◇ G	NT	NT H	VT 1◇	NT J	EM ◇ A	XC 1◇ B	NT	NT	VT 1◇	NT C	NT	XC 1◇ L	TP 1◇ E	VT 1◇	AW ◇ N	NT	NT H	VT 1◇		NT J	EM ◇ A
London Euston 15 ⊖ 65 d		11 00				11 20			11b07			11 40					12 00				12 20			
Birmingham New Street 12 68 d			11 20						11 57		11 36	12 01			12 31			12c20						
Wolverhampton 7 68 ⛴ d									12 14		11 53	12 19			12 49									
Stafford 65, 68 d									12 29		12 09	12 35												
Stoke-on-Trent 50, 68 d		12 25				12 48			12 55					12 58	13 18		13 25				13 48			
Longport 50 d																								
Kidsgrove 50 d														13 05										
Crewe 10 65 d			12 28							12 33	12 50	13 11						13 28						
Sandbach d										12 40	12 57													
Holmes Chapel d										12 44	13 02													
Goostrey d											13 05													
Chelford d											13 09													
Alderley Edge d				12 49						12 53	13 13								13 49					
Wilmslow d			12 46	12 52						12 57	13 17	13 27						13 46	13 52					
Styal d																								
Manchester Airport ✈ a										13 04														
Handforth d				12 55							13 20								13 55					
Congleton d														13 12										
Macclesfield a		12 41							13 11					13 19			13 41							
d		12 41							13 12					13 20			13 42							
Prestbury d														13 24										
Adlington (Cheshire) d														13 27										
Poynton d														13 30										
Bramhall d														13 33										
Cheadle Hulme d				12 59							13 24			13 37					13 59					
Stockport a		12 55	12 58	13 04		13 16			13 27		13 29	13 36		13 41			13 55	13 58	14 04		14 16			
d	12 53	12 56	12 58	13 04	13 12	13 17	13 21	13 26	13 27		13 29	13 37	13 41	13 42		13 53	13 56	13 58	14 04	14 12	14 17		14 21	14 26
Heaton Chapel d				13 08	13 16						13 33			13 45					14 08	14 16				
Levenshulme d				13 11	13 19						13 36			13 48					14 11	14 19				
Manchester Piccadilly 10 ⛴ a	13 02	13 07	13 15	13 20	13 28	13 28	13 36	13 36	13 40	13 42	13 44	13 49	13 52	13 56	14 00	14 02	14 07	14 15	14 20	14 28	14 28		14 36	14 36
d								13 37					13 54											14 37
Manchester Oxford Road a								13 40					13 56											14 40
Deansgate ⛴ a													14 00											

For general notes see front of timetable
For details of catering facilities see Directory of Train Operators

A From Norwich to Liverpool Lime Street (Table 49)
B From Bournemouth (Table 51)
C From Hazel Grove (Table 86) to Preston (Table 82)
D From Paignton (Table 51)
E From Cleethorpes to Manchester Airport (27 June to 5 September from Doncaster) (Table 29)
G From Milford Haven (Table 128)
H From Buxton (Table 86)
J From Chester (Table 88)
K From Bristol Temple Meads (Table 51)
L From Plymouth (from 12 September from Bristol Temple Meads) (Table 51)
N From Carmarthen (Table 128)
b Change at Stafford
c From 7 November dep. 1201

Stoke-on-Trent and Crewe → Manchester Airport, Stockport and Manchester

Network Diagram - see first page of Table 78

	XC 1 ◇ A 🛒	NT	NT	VT 1 ◇ 🍽	NT B	NT	XC 1 ◇ C 🍽 🛒	TP 1 ◇ D 🛒	VT 1 ◇ 🍽	AW ◇ E 🛒	NT	NT G	VT 1 ◇ 🍽	NT H	EM ◇ J 🛒	XC 1 ◇ A 🛒	NT	NT	VT 1 ◇ 🍽	NT B	NT		XC 1 ◇ K 🍽 🛒	TP 1 ◇ D 🛒
London Euston 15 ⊖ 65 d	12b07			12 40					13 00				13 20			13b07			13 40					
Birmingham New Street 12 68 d	12 57		12 36	13 01			13 31			13 20						13 57		13 36	14 01				14 31	
Wolverhampton 7 68 ⛴ d	13 14		12 53	13 19			13 49									14 14		13 53	14 19				14 49	
Stafford 65, 68 d	13 29		13 09	13 35												14 29		14 09	14 35					
Stoke-on-Trent 50, 68 d	13 55					13 58	14 18		14 25				14 48			14 55					14 58		15 18	
Longport 50 d																								
Kidsgrove 50 d						14 05															15 05			
Crewe 10 65 d		13 33	13 50	14 11						14 28							14 33	14 50	15 11					
Sandbach d		13 40	13 57														14 40	14 57						
Holmes Chapel d		13 44	14 02														14 44	15 02						
Goostrey d			14 05															15 05						
Chelford d			14 09															15 09						
Alderley Edge d		13 53	14 13								14 49						14 53	15 13						
Wilmslow d		13 57	14 17	14 27						14 46	14 52						14 57	15 17	15 27					
Styal d																								
Manchester Airport ✈ a		14 04															15 04							
Handforth d			14 20								14 55							15 20						
Congleton d						14 12															15 12			
Macclesfield a	14 11					14 19			14 41							15 11					15 19			
d	14 12					14 20			14 41							15 12					15 20			
Prestbury d						14 24															15 24			
Adlington (Cheshire) d						14 27															15 27			
Poynton d						14 30															15 30			
Bramhall d						14 33															15 33			
Cheadle Hulme d			14 24			14 37					14 59							15 24			15 37			
Stockport a	14 27		14 29	14 36		14 41			14 55	14 58	15 04		15 16			15 27		15 29	15 36		15 41			
d	14 27		14 29	14 37	14 41	14 42		14 53	14 56	14 58	15 04	15 12	15 17	15 21	15 26	15 27		15 29	15 37	15 41	15 42			15 53
Heaton Chapel d			14 33			14 45					15 08	15 16						15 33			15 45			
Levenshulme d			14 36			14 48					15 11	15 19						15 36			15 48			
Manchester Piccadilly 10 ⛴ a	14 40	14 42	14 44	14 49	14 52	14 56	15 00	15 02	15 07	15 15	15 20	15 28	15 28	15 36	15 36	15 40	15 42	15 44	15 49	15 52	15 56		16 00	16 02
d					14 54										15 37					15 54				
Manchester Oxford Road a					14 56										15 40					15 56				
Deansgate ⛴ a					15 00															16 00				

	VT 1 ◇ 🍽	AW ◇ L 🛒	NT	NT G	VT 1 ◇ 🍽	NT H	EM ◇ J 🛒	XC 1 ◇ A 🛒	NT	NT	VT 1 ◇ 🍽	NT B	NT	XC 1 ◇ N 🍽 🛒	TP 1 ◇ D 🛒	VT 1 ◇ 🍽	AW ◇ E 🛒	NT	NT G	VT 1 ◇ 🍽	NT H		EM ◇ J 🛒	XC 1 ◇ A 🛒
London Euston 15 ⊖ 65 d	14 00				14 20			14b07			14 40					15 00				15 20				15b07
Birmingham New Street 12 68 d		14c20						14 57		14 36	15 01			15 31			15 20							15 57
Wolverhampton 7 68 ⛴ d								15 14		14 53	15 19			15 49										16 14
Stafford 65, 68 d								15 29		15 09	15 35													16 29
Stoke-on-Trent 50, 68 d	15 25				15 48			15 55					15 58	16 18		16 25				16 48				16 55
Longport 50 d																								
Kidsgrove 50 d													16 05											
Crewe 10 65 d		15 28							15 33	15 50	16 12						16 28							
Sandbach d									15 40	15 57														
Holmes Chapel d									15 44	16 02														
Goostrey d										16 05														
Chelford d										16 09														
Alderley Edge d			15 49						15 53	16 13								16 49						
Wilmslow d		15 46	15 52						15 56	16 17	16 27						16 46	16 52						
Styal d									15 59															
Manchester Airport ✈ a									16 04															
Handforth d			15 55							16 20								16 55						
Congleton d													16 12											
Macclesfield a	15 41							16 11					16 19			16 41								17 11
d	15 41							16 12					16 20			16 41								17 12
Prestbury d													16 24											
Adlington (Cheshire) d													16 27											
Poynton d													16 30											
Bramhall d													16 33											
Cheadle Hulme d			15 59							16 24			16 37					16 59						
Stockport a	15 55	15 58	16 04		16 16			16 27		16 29	16 36		16 41			16 54	16 58	17 04		17 16				17 27
d	15 56	15 58	16 04	16 12	16 17	16 21	16 26	16 27		16 29	16 37	16 41	16 42		16 52	16 55	16 58	17 04	17 12	17 17	17 21		17 26	17 27
Heaton Chapel d			16 08	16 16						16 33			16 45					17 08	17 16					
Levenshulme d			16 11	16 19						16 36			16 48					17 11	17 19					
Manchester Piccadilly 10 ⛴ a	16 07	16 15	16 20	16 28	16 28	16 36	16 36	16 40	16 42	16 44	16 49	16 52	16 56	17 00	17 02	17 07	17 15	17 20	17 28	17 28	17 36		17 37	17 40
d							16 37					16 54											17 37	
Manchester Oxford Road a							16 40					16 56											17 40	
Deansgate ⛴ a												17 00												

For general notes see front of timetable
For details of catering facilities see Directory of Train Operators

- **A** From Bournemouth (Table 51)
- **B** From Hazel Grove (Table 86) to Preston (Table 82)
- **C** From Paignton (Table 51)
- **D** From Cleethorpes to Manchester Airport (27 June to 5 September from Doncaster) (Table 29)
- **E** From Milford Haven (Table 128)
- **G** From Buxton (Table 86)
- **H** From Chester (Table 88)
- **J** From Norwich to Liverpool Lime Street (Table 49)
- **K** From Bristol Temple Meads (Table 51)
- **L** From Carmarthen (Table 128)
- **N** From Bristol Temple Meads (Table 51) (from 12 September from Penzance) (Table 135)
- **b** Change at Stafford
- **c** From 7 November dep. 1401

Stoke-on-Trent and Crewe → Manchester Airport, Stockport and Manchester

Network Diagram - see first page of Table 78

		NT	NT	VT	NT	NT	XC	TP	VT	AW	NT	NT	VT	NT	EM	XC	NT	NT	VT	NT	NT	XC		TP	VT
				1 ◇			1 ◇	1 ◇	1 ◇	◇			1 ◇		◇	1 ◇			1 ◇			1 ◇		1 ◇	1 ◇
					A		B	C		D		E		G	H	J				K		L		C	
London Euston 15	⊖ 65 d			15 40					16 00				16 20			*16b07*			16 40						17 00
Birmingham New Street 12	68 d		*15 36*	*16 01*			16 31			*16c20*						16 57		*16 36*	*17 01*			17 31			
Wolverhampton 7	68 d		*15 53*	*16 19*			16 49									17 14		*16 53*	*17 19*			17 49			
Stafford	65, 68 d		*16 09*	*16 35*												17 29		*17 09*	*17 36*						
Stoke-on-Trent	50, 68 d					16 58	17 18		17 25				17 48			17 55					17 58	18 18			18 25
Longport	50 d																								
Kidsgrove	50 d					17 05															18 05				
Crewe 10	65 d	16 33	16 50	17 11						17 28							17 33	17 50	18 11						
Sandbach	d	16 40	16 57														17 40	17 57							
Holmes Chapel	d	16 44	17 02														17 44	18 02							
Goostrey	d		17 05															18 05							
Chelford	d		17 09															18 09							
Alderley Edge	d	16 53	17 13								17 49						17 53	18 13							
Wilmslow	d	16 57	17 17	17 27						17 46	17 52						17 56	18 17	18 27						
Styal	d																17 59								
Manchester Airport	✈ a	17 04															18 04								
Handforth	d		17 20								17 55							18 20							
Congleton	d					17 12															18 12				
Macclesfield	a					17 19			17 41							18 11					18 19				18 41
	d					17 20			17 41							18 12					18 20				18 41
Prestbury	d					17 24															18 24				
Adlington (Cheshire)	d					17 27															18 27				
Poynton	d					17 30															18 30				
Bramhall	d					17 33															18 33				
Cheadle Hulme	d		17 24			17 37					17 59							18 24			18 37				
Stockport	a		17 29	17 36		17 41			17 55	17 58	18 04		18 16			18 27		18 29	18 36		18 41				18 55
	d		17 29	17 37	17 41	17 42		17 53	17 56	17 58	18 04	18 12	18 17	18 21	18 26	18 27		18 29	18 37	18 41	18 42			18 53	18 56
Heaton Chapel	d		17 33			17 45					18 08	18 16						18 33			18 45				
Levenshulme	d		17 36			17 48					18 11	18 19						18 36			18 48				
Manchester Piccadilly 10	a	17 42	17 44	17 49	17 52	17 56	18 00	18 02	18 07	18 15	18 20	18 28	18 28	18 36	18 36	18 40	18 42	18 44	18 49	18 52	18 56	19 00		19 02	19 07
	d				17 54										18 37					18 54					
Manchester Oxford Road	a				17 56										18 40					18 56					
Deansgate	a				18 00															19 00					

		AW	NT	VT	NT	NT	EM	XC	NT	VT	NT	XC	TP	VT	AW	NT	VT	NT	NT	EM	XC	NT		VT	NT
		R		1 ◇			◇	1 ◇		1 ◇		1 ◇	1 ◇	1 ◇	R		1 ◇			◇	1 ◇			1 ◇	
		N	E			G	H	J				B	C		D	E			G	Q	J				
London Euston 15	⊖ 65 d			17 20				*16b33*		17 40				18 00			18 20				*18b07*			18 40	
Birmingham New Street 12	68 d	*17 20*						17 57	*17 36*	*18 01*		18 31			*18e20*						18 57	*18 36*		*19 01*	
Wolverhampton 7	68 d							18 14	*17 53*	*18 19*		18 49									19 14	*18 53*		*19 19*	
Stafford	65, 68 d							18 29	*18 09*	*18 35*											19 29	*19 09*		*19 36*	
Stoke-on-Trent	50, 68 d			18 48				18 55			18 58	19 18		19 25			19 48				19 55				19 58
Longport	50 d																								
Kidsgrove	50 d										19 05														20 05
Crewe 10	65 d	18 28			18 33				18 50	19 11					19 28							19 50		20 11	
Sandbach	d				18 40				18 57													19 57			
Holmes Chapel	d				18 44				19 02													20 02			
Goostrey	d								19 05													20 05			
Chelford	d								19 09													20 09			
Alderley Edge	d				18 53				19 13													20 13			
Wilmslow	d	18 46			18 56				19 17	19 27					19 46			19 56				20 17		20 27	
Styal	d																								
Manchester Airport	✈ a				19 04													20 04							
Handforth	d								19 20													20 20			
Congleton	d										19 12														20 12
Macclesfield	a							19 11			19 19			19 41							20 11				20 19
	d							19 12			19 20			19 41							20 12				20 20
Prestbury	d										19 24														20 24
Adlington (Cheshire)	d										19 27														20 27
Poynton	d										19 30														20 30
Bramhall	d										19 33														20 33
Cheadle Hulme	d								19 24		19 37											20 24			20 37
Stockport	a	18 58		19 16				19 27	19 29	19 36	19 41			19 55	19 58		20 16				20 27	20 29		20 36	20 41
	d	18 58	19 12	19 17		19 21	19 26	19 27	19 29	19 37	19 42		19 53	19 56	19 58	20 12	20 17		20 21	20 26	20 27	20 29		20 37	20 42
Heaton Chapel	d		19 16								19 45					20 16									20 45
Levenshulme	d		19 19								19 48					20 19									20 48
Manchester Piccadilly 10	a	19 15	19 28	19 28	19 31	19 35	19 36	19 40	19 43	19 49	19 56	20 00	20 02	20 07	20 15	20 28	20 28	20 31	20 35	20 37	20 40	20 43		20 49	20 56
	d				19 32		19 37											20 32							
Manchester Oxford Road	a				19 36		19 40											20 36							
Deansgate	a																								

For general notes see front of timetable
For details of catering facilities see Directory of Train Operators

- **A** From Hazel Grove (Table 86) to Blackpool North (Table 82)
- **B** From Bristol Temple Meads (Table 51)
- **C** From Cleethorpes to Manchester Airport (27 June to 5 September from Doncaster) (Table 29)
- **D** From Carmarthen (Table 128)
- **E** From Buxton (Table 86)
- **G** From Chester (Table 88)
- **H** From Norwich to Liverpool Lime Street (Table 49)
- **J** From Bournemouth (Table 51)
- **K** From Hazel Grove (Table 86) to Bolton (Table 82)
- **L** From Paignton (Table 51)
- **N** From Milford Haven (Table 128)
- **Q** From Norwich (Table 49)
- **b** Change at Stafford
- **c** From 7 November dep. 1601
- **e** From 7 November dep. 1801

Stoke-on-Trent and Crewe → Manchester Airport, Stockport and Manchester

Network Diagram - see first page of Table 78

		XC	TP	VT	AW	NT	VT	VT	NT	EM	NT	XC	NT	VT	NT	XC	XC	XC	AW	NT	NT	XC		XC	XC
		1◇	1◇	1◇	R		1◇	1◇		◇		1◇		1◇		1◇		1◇	◇			1◇		1◇	1◇
		A	B		C	D	E	G		H	J	K				L	N	Q	U	D		V		X	Y
		☕🍴	🍴	☕	🍴		☕	☕		🍴				☕			🚌		🍴						
London Euston 15	⊖ 65 d			18b54			19 05	19 20				18c57		19e25								19f07		18f57	18f57
Birmingham New Street 12	68 d	19 31			19 20							19 57	19 36	20 20		20 31		20 31				20 57		20 57	20 57
Wolverhampton 7	68 ⛴ d	19 49										20 14	19 53	20 37		20 49		20 49				21 15		21 14	21 14
Stafford	65, 68 d											20 29	20 09	20 50								21 28		21 30	21 30
Stoke-on-Trent	50, 68 d	20 18		20 25			20 42	20 48				20 55			20 58			21 18				21 49		21 50	
Longport	50 d																								
Kidsgrove	50 d														21 05										
Crewe 10	65 d				20 28								20 50	21 19					21 28						
Sandbach	d												20 57												
Holmes Chapel	d												21 02												
Goostrey	d												21 05												
Chelford	d												21 09												
Alderley Edge	d												21 13												
Wilmslow	d				20 46				20 56				21 17	21 34		21 40	21 50		21 46		21 55				22 20
Styal	d																								
Manchester Airport	✈ a								21 05												22 04				
Handforth	d												21 20												
Congleton	d														21 12										
Macclesfield	a			20 41								21 11			21 19		22 20	21 38				22 05		22 09	
	d			20 41								21 12			21 20			21 39				22 06		22 10	
Prestbury	d														21 24										
Adlington (Cheshire)	d														21 27										
Poynton	d														21 30										
Bramhall	d														21 33										
Cheadle Hulme	d												21 24		21 37										
Stockport	a			20 55	20 58		21 16	21 16				21 27	21 29	21 44	21 41	21 50		21 53	21 58			22 19		22 24	22 35
	d		20 53	20 56	20 58	21 12	21 17	21 17		21 20	21 21	21 27	21 29	21 45	21 42	21 51		21 54	21 58	22 12		22 19		22 24	22 35
Heaton Chapel	d					21 16									21 45					22 16					
Levenshulme	d					21 19									21 49					22 19					
Manchester Piccadilly 10	⛴ a	21 00	21 02	21 07	21 15	21 28	21 28	21 28	21 31	21 32	21 35	21 40	21 43	21 56	21 57	22 05		22 05	22 15	22 28	22 31	22 40		22 40	22 48
	d								21 32												22 32				
Manchester Oxford Road	a								21 36												22 36				
Deansgate	⛴ a																								

		XC	NT	VT	VT	VT	NT	NT	NT	NT	NT	NT	XC	XC	XC	NT	VT	NT	AW	NT	NT	NT	XC		
				1◇	1◇								1◇	1◇			1◇		◇				1◇		
		N		Z	N	N	AA	J	N	N	Z	N	BB	CC	N			DD	EE		D				
		🚌		☕	☕	🚌			🚌			🚌			🚌		☕								
London Euston 15	⊖ 65 d		19e25	19 47	19 47								20g11				20h26		20j14						
Birmingham New Street 12	68 d		20 36										21 57	21 57					21 36			21k57	22 31		
Wolverhampton 7	68 ⛴ d		20 53										22 14	22 14					21 53			22k14	22 49		
Stafford	65, 68 d	21 40	21 09		22 00	22 10							22 29	22 29	22 40		22 36		22 09				23 03		
Stoke-on-Trent	50, 68 d	22 10		22 05		22 40			21 30		22 18	22 20	22 51		23 10										
Longport	50 d																								
Kidsgrove	50 d								21 55		22 25	22 45													
Crewe 10	65 d		21 50		22 27												23 01		23 06			23 11	23 28		
Sandbach	d		21 57																			23 18			
Holmes Chapel	d		22 02																			23 23			
Goostrey	d		22 05																			23 26			
Chelford	d		22 09																			23 30			
Alderley Edge	d		22 13																			23 34			
Wilmslow	d		22 17		22 43									23 12		23 15	23 17		23 24			23 38	23 44		
Styal	d																			←					
Manchester Airport	✈ a															23 23				23 23					
Handforth	d		22 20													→						23 41			
Congleton	d								22 10		22 32	23 00													
Macclesfield	a	23 10		22 21		23 30			22 30		22 39	23s20	23 07		00 10										
	d			22 21		23 30				22 40	22 40		23 08												
Prestbury	d									22 44	22 44														
Adlington (Cheshire)	d									22 47	22 47														
Poynton	d									22 50	22 50														
Bramhall	d									22 53	22 53														
Cheadle Hulme	d		22 24							22 56	22 56											23 45			
Stockport	a		22 29	22 35	22 51	23 59				23 01	23 01	23s50	23 21	23 21			23 26		23 32			23 50	23s53		
	d		22 29	22 36	22 52		22 40	22 48		23 01	23 01		23 21	23 21			23 27	23 22	23 33		23 41	23 50			
Heaton Chapel	d						22 44			23 05	23 05											23 54			
Levenshulme	d						22 47			23 08	23 08											23 57			
Manchester Piccadilly 10	⛴ a		22 43	22 51	23 04		22 53	23 00		23 16	23 16	00 10	23 35	23 35			23 39	23 43	23 48	23 51	23 54	00 07	00 09		
	d						22 54																		
Manchester Oxford Road	a						22 56																		
Deansgate	⛴ a						23 00																		

For general notes see front of timetable
For details of catering facilities see Directory of Train Operators

- **A** From Bristol Temple Meads (Table 51)
- **B** From Cleethorpes to Manchester Airport (27 June to 5 September from Doncaster) (Table 29)
- **C** From Milford Haven (Table 128)
- **D** From Buxton (Table 86)
- **E** Until 5 September
- **G** From 12 September
- **H** From Norwich (Table 49)
- **J** From Chester (Table 88)
- **K** From Bournemouth (Table 51)
- **L** Until 11 July. From Bristol Temple Meads (Table 51)
- **N** Until 11 July
- **Q** From 18 July from Bristol Temple Meads (Table 51)
- **U** From Carmarthen (Table 128)
- **V** From 12 September. From Bournemouth (Table 51)
- **X** 18 July to 5 September. From Newquay (Table 135)
- **Y** Until 11 July. From Newquay (Table 135)
- **Z** From 18 July
- **AA** To Wigan Wallgate (Table 82)
- **BB** From 18 July. From Bournemouth (Table 51)
- **CC** Until 11 July. From Bournemouth (Table 51)
- **DD** From Sheffield (Table 78)
- **EE** From Maesteg (Table 128)
- **b** From 12 September dep. 1900
- **c** Change at Stafford. From 12 September dep. 1833
- **e** From 12 September dep. 1940
- **f** Change at Stafford
- **g** Change at Stafford. 18 July to 5 September dep. 1941
- **h** From 12 September dep. 2100
- **j** From 12 September dep. 2030
- **k** Change at Stafford and Crewe

Table 84

Sundays

until 12 July

Stoke-on-Trent and Crewe → Manchester Airport, Stockport and Manchester

Network Diagram - see first page of Table 78

	NT A	NT B	TP 1◇ C	AW	NT D	NT B	NT	TP 1◇ E	AW	NT D	NT G	XC 1◇ 🛒	VT 1◇ 🍴	NT	VT 1◇ 🍴	VT 🚌	NT	TP 1◇ H	AW ◇ J	NT D	NT	XC 1◇ 🛒	XC 🚌	XC 🚌
London Euston [15] ⊖ 65 d													08 10		08 20				*08 15*					
Birmingham New Street [12] 68 d												09 01							*09 20*			10 00		
Wolverhampton [7] 68 ⛴ d												09 19										10 18		
Stafford 65, 68 d												09 32			10 05	10 10			*09 58*			10 32		10 40
Stoke-on-Trent 50, 68 d																10 40								11 10
Longport 50 d																								
Kidsgrove 50 d																								
Crewe [10] 65 d				08 28					09 28			09 59	10 19						10 32					
Sandbach d																								
Holmes Chapel d																								
Goostrey d																								
Chelford d																								
Alderley Edge d							09 26							10 19			10 44							
Wilmslow d				08 47			09 30		09 47			10 15		10 23	10 43		10 47		10 51		←	11 12	11 20	
Styal d																	10 51 →				10 51			
Manchester Airport ✈ a																					10 58			
Handforth d							09 33							10 26										
Congleton d																								
Macclesfield a																11 30							11 50	12 10
d																11 30								
Prestbury d																								
Adlington (Cheshire) d																								
Poynton d																								
Bramhall d																								
Cheadle Hulme d							09 37							10 30										
Stockport a							09 42					10 24	10 40	10 35	10 52	12 00			11 00			11 21		
d	00 02	08 22	08 31		09 08	09 22	09 43	09 52		10 03	10 12	10 25	10 41	10 39	10 53			10 53	11 00	11 07		11 23		
Heaton Chapel d					09 12		09 47			10 08				10 43						11 11				
Levenshulme d					09 15		09 50			10 11				10 46						11 14				
Manchester Piccadilly [10] ⛴ a	00 15	08 33	08 43	09 11	09 23	09 33	09 57	10 06	10 12	10 20	10 23	10 40	10 54	10 55	11 04			11 06	11 15	11 23	11 25	11 38		
d		08 35				09 35					10 26										11 26			
Manchester Oxford Road a		08 37				09 37					10 28										11 28			
Deansgate ⛴ a		08 40				09 40					10 40													

	NT		AW ◇ K 🛒	TP 1◇ L	VT 1◇ 🍴	VT 🚌	NT D	NT G	EM ◇ N 🛒	XC 1◇ Q 🛒	XC 🚌	XC 🚌	NT	VT 1◇ 🍴	VT 🚌	TP 1◇ L	AW ◇ K 🛒	NT D	NT	NT B	EM ◇ N 🛒	XC 1◇ U 🛒	XC 🚌	XC 🚌
London Euston [15] ⊖ 65 d	*08 45*				09 20									10 20			*09 45*							
Birmingham New Street [12] 68 d	*09 41*		*10 15*							10 59							*11 20*					12 01		
Wolverhampton [7] 68 ⛴ d	*09 57*									11 17												12 19		
Stafford 65, 68 d	*10 14*				11 02	11 10				11 30		11 40		12 07	12 10		*11 54*					12 34		12 40
Stoke-on-Trent 50, 68 d						11 40						12 10			12 40									13 10
Longport 50 d																								
Kidsgrove 50 d																								
Crewe [10] 65 d	11 02		11 22														12 28							
Sandbach d	11 09																							
Holmes Chapel d	11 14																							
Goostrey d	11 17																							
Chelford d	11 21																							
Alderley Edge d	11 25												12 19						12 51					
Wilmslow d	11 29		11 41		11 47					12 06	12 20		12 23	12 42			12 47		12 54			13 09	13 20	
Styal d																			12 58					
Manchester Airport ✈ a																			13 05					
Handforth d	11 32												12 26											
Congleton d																								
Macclesfield a						12 30					12 50	13 10			13 30								13 50	14 10
d						12 30									13 30									
Prestbury d																								
Adlington (Cheshire) d																								
Poynton d																								
Bramhall d																								
Cheadle Hulme d	11 36												12 30											
Stockport a	11 41				11 55	13 00				12 19			12 37	12 52	14 00		12 58					13 18		
d	11 41			11 53	11 56		12 12	12 21	12 26	12 27			12 37	12 53		12 53	12 58	13 12		13 22	13 26	13 27		
Heaton Chapel d	11 45						12 16						12 41					13 16						
Levenshulme d	11 48						12 19						12 44					13 19						
Manchester Piccadilly [10] ⛴ a	11 54		12 02	12 06	12 09		12 29	12 33	12 37	12 40			12 51	13 04		13 06	13 15	13 27	13 31	13 33	13 37	13 40		
d								12 35	12 38											13 35	13 38			
Manchester Oxford Road a								12 37	12 41											13 37	13 41			
Deansgate ⛴ a								12 40												13 40				

For general notes see front of timetable
For details of catering facilities see Directory of Train Operators

- **A** From Chester (Table 88)
- **B** To Southport (Table 82)
- **C** From Sheffield to Manchester Airport (Table 78)
- **D** From Buxton (Table 86)
- **E** From Meadowhall to Manchester Airport (Table 29)
- **G** From Chester (Table 88) to Southport (Table 82)
- **H** From Sheffield (Table 78)
- **J** From Shrewsbury (Table 131)
- **K** From Cardiff Central (Table 131)
- **L** From Cleethorpes to Manchester Airport (from 28 June from Doncaster) (Table 29)
- **N** From Nottingham to Liverpool Lime Street (Table 49)
- **Q** From Reading (Table 51)
- **U** From Southampton Central (Table 51)

Table 84

Sundays

Stoke-on-Trent and Crewe → Manchester Airport, Stockport and Manchester

until 12 July

Network Diagram - see first page of Table 78

		NT	VT	VT		TP	AW	NT	VT	NT	EM	XC	XC	NT	VT	XC	TP	VT	AW	NT	VT	NT	NT	EM	XC
			1◇			1◇	◇		1◇		◇	1◇			1◇	1◇	1◇	1◇	◇		1◇			◇	1◇
						A	B	C		D	E	G					H		B	C			J	E	G
			P	🚌			T		P		T	T	🚌		P	T		P	T		P			T	T
London Euston 15	⊖ 65 d	10b20	11 20				11 15		12 15			12c02			12 35			12 55			13 15				13c02
Birmingham New Street 12	68 d	11 42					12 20					13 01			12 35	13 31			13 20						14 01
Wolverhampton 7	68 ⛴ d	11 59										13 19			12 52	13 49									14 19
Stafford	65, 68 d	12 16	13 01	13 10			12 56					13 34			13 25										14 34
Stoke-on-Trent	50, 68 d			13a40					13 50							14 21		14 26			14 50				14 57
Longport	50 d																								
Kidsgrove	50 d																								
Crewe 10	65 d	12 56					13 29								14 13				14 28						
Sandbach	d	13 03																							
Holmes Chapel	d	13 08																							
Goostrey	d	13 11																							
Chelford	d	13 15																							
Alderley Edge	d	13 19												14 19								14 51			
Wilmslow	d	13 23	13 37				13 48					14 10	14 20	14 23	14 29				14 47			14 54			
Styal	d																					14 58			
Manchester Airport	✈ a																					15 05			
Handforth	d	13 26												14 26											
Congleton	d																								
Macclesfield	a												14 50					14 42							15 14
	d																	14 42							15 15
Prestbury	d																								
Adlington (Cheshire)	d																								
Poynton	d																								
Bramhall	d																								
Cheadle Hulme	d	13 30												14 30											
Stockport	a	13 37	13 45				13 58		14 18			14 22		14 37	14 38			14 56	14 58		15 18				15 28
	d	13 37	13 46			13 53	13 58	14 12	14 19	14 21	14 26	14 29		14 37	14 39		14 53	14 57	14 58	15 12	15 19		15 22	15 26	15 29
Heaton Chapel	d	13 41						14 16						14 41						15 16					
Levenshulme	d	13 44						14 19						14 44						15 19					
Manchester Piccadilly 10	⛴ a	13 52	13 59			14 06	14 15	14 27	14 30	14 33	14 37	14 40		14 51	14 51	15 00	15 06	15 09	15 15	15 27	15 30	15 31	15 33	15 37	15 40
	d									14 35	14 38												15 35	15 38	
Manchester Oxford Road	a									14 37	14 41												15 37	15 41	
Deansgate	⛴ a									14 40													15 40		

		NT	VT	XC	TP	VT		AW	NT	VT	NT	EM	XC	NT	VT	NT	XC	TP	VT	AW	NT	VT	NT	NT	EM
			1◇	1◇	1◇	1◇		◇		1◇		◇	1◇		1◇		1◇	1◇	1◇	R		1◇			◇
					A			K	C		D	L	G				N	A		B	C			J	L
			P	T		P		T		P		T	T		P		T		P	T		P			T
London Euston 15	⊖ 65 d	13 02	13 35			13 55				14 15			14c02		14 35				14 55			15 15			
Birmingham New Street 12	68 d	13 35		14 31				14 20					15 01		14 35		15 31			15 20					
Wolverhampton 7	68 ⛴ d	13 52		14 49									15 19		14 52		15 49								
Stafford	65, 68 d	14 22											15 34		15 25										
Stoke-on-Trent	50, 68 d			15 21		15 26				15 50			15 57			16 01	16 21		16 25			16 50			
Longport	50 d																								
Kidsgrove	50 d															16 08									
Crewe 10	65 d	14 56	15 13					15 28							16 13					16 31					
Sandbach	d	15 03																							
Holmes Chapel	d	15 08																							
Goostrey	d	15 11																							
Chelford	d	15 15																							
Alderley Edge	d	15 19												16 19									16 51		
Wilmslow	d	15 23	15 29					15 47						16 23	16 29					16 49			16 54		
Styal	d																						16 58		
Manchester Airport	✈ a																						17 05		
Handforth	d	15 26												16 26											
Congleton	d															16 15									
Macclesfield	a					15 42							16 14			16 22			16 42						
	d					15 42							16 15			16 23			16 42						
Prestbury	d															16 27									
Adlington (Cheshire)	d															16 30									
Poynton	d															16 33									
Bramhall	d															16 36									
Cheadle Hulme	d	15 30												16 30		16 39									
Stockport	a	15 37	15 38			15 56		15 58		16 18			16 28	16 37	16 38	16 44			16 56	16 58		17 18			
	d	15 37	15 39		15 54	15 57		15 58	16 12	16 19	16 21	16 26	16 29	16 37	16 39	16 44		16 54	16 57	16 58	17 12	17 19		17 22	17 27
Heaton Chapel	d	15 41							16 16					16 41							17 16				
Levenshulme	d	15 44							16 19					16 44							17 19				
Manchester Piccadilly 10	⛴ a	15 51	15 51	16 00	16 06	16 09		16 15	16 27	16 30	16 33	16 37	16 40	16 51	16 51	16 58	17 00	17 06	17 09	17 15	17 27	17 30	17 31	17 33	17 37
	d										16 35	16 38												17 35	17 38
Manchester Oxford Road	a										16 37	16 41												17 37	17 41
Deansgate	⛴ a										16 40													17 40	

For general notes see front of timetable
For details of catering facilities see Directory of Train Operators

- **A** From Cleethorpes to Manchester Airport (from 28 June from Doncaster) (Table 29)
- **B** From Cardiff Central (Table 131)
- **C** From Buxton (Table 86)
- **D** From Chester (Table 88) to Southport (Table 82)
- **E** From Norwich to Liverpool Lime Street (Table 49)
- **G** From Bournemouth (Table 51)
- **H** From Doncaster to Manchester Airport (Table 29)
- **J** To Southport (Table 82)
- **K** From Milford Haven (Table 128)
- **L** From Nottingham to Liverpool Lime Street (Table 49)
- **N** From Plymouth (Table 51)
- **b** Change at Stafford and Crewe
- **c** Change at Stafford

Table 84

Sundays

until 12 July

Stoke-on-Trent and Crewe → Manchester Airport, Stockport and Manchester

Network Diagram - see first page of Table 78

	XC	NT	VT	XC	TP	VT	AW		NT	VT	NT	EM	XC	NT	VT	XC	TP	VT	AW	NT	VT	NT	NT	EM
							R												R					
	1 ◇		1 ◇	1 ◇	1 ◇	1 ◇				1 ◇		◇	1 ◇		1 ◇	1 ◇	1 ◇	1 ◇			1 ◇			◇
	A			B	C		D		E		G	H	A			J	C		K	E			L	H
	(trolley)		(buffet)	(trolley)		(buffet)	(trolley)			(buffet)		(trolley)	(trolley)		(buffet)	(trolley)		(buffet)	(trolley)		(buffet)			(trolley)
London Euston 15 ⊖ 65 d	*15b02*		15 35			15 55				16 15			*16b02*		16 35			16 55			17 15			
Birmingham New Street 12 68 d	16 01	*15 35*		16 31			*16 20*						17 01		*16 35*	17 31			*17 20*					
Wolverhampton 7 68 ⛴ d	16 19	*15 52*		16 49									17 19		*16 52*	17 49								
Stafford 65, 68 d	16 36	*16 10*											17 36		*17 10*									
Stoke-on-Trent 50, 68 d	16 57			17 21		17 26				17 50			17 57			18 21		18 26			18 50			
Longport 50 d																								
Kidsgrove 50 d																								
Crewe 10 65 d		16 56	17 13				17 28								18 13				18 28					
Sandbach d		17 03																						
Holmes Chapel d		17 08																						
Goostrey d		17 11																						
Chelford d		17 15																						
Alderley Edge d		17 19												18 19								18 51		
Wilmslow d		17 23	17 29				17 45							18 23	18 29				18 47			18 54		
Styal d																						18 58		
Manchester Airport ✈ a																						19 05		
Handforth d		17 26												18 26										
Congleton d																								
Macclesfield a	17 14					17 42							18 14					18 42						
d	17 15					17 42							18 15					18 42						
Prestbury d																								
Adlington (Cheshire) d																								
Poynton d																								
Bramhall d																								
Cheadle Hulme d		17 30												18 30										
Stockport a	17 30	17 37	17 38			17 56	17 58			18 18			18 28	18 37	18 38			18 56	18 58		19 18			
d	17 31	17 37	17 39		17 54	17 57	17 58		18 12	18 19	18 21	18 26	18 29	18 37	18 39		18 54	18 57	18 58	19 12	19 19		19 22	19 26
Heaton Chapel d		17 41							18 16					18 41						19 16				
Levenshulme d		17 44							18 19					18 44						19 19				
Manchester Piccadilly 10 ⛴ a	17 40	17 51	17 51	18 00	18 06	18 09	18 15		18 27	18 30	18 33	18 37	18 40	18 51	18 51	19 00	19 06	19 09	19 15	19 27	19 30	19 31	19 33	19 37
d											18 35	18 38											19 35	19 38
Manchester Oxford Road a											18 37	18 41											19 37	19 41
Deansgate ⛴ a											18 40												19 40	

	XC	NT	VT	XC	TP	VT	AW	NT	VT		NT	EM	XC	NT	VT	NT	XC	TP	VT	AW	NT	VT	NT	NT
							R													R				
	1 ◇		1 ◇	1 ◇	1 ◇	1 ◇			1 ◇			◇	1 ◇		1 ◇		1 ◇	1 ◇	1 ◇			1 ◇		
	A			N	C		Q	E			G	U	A				J	C		K	E			V
	(trolley)		(buffet)	(trolley)		(buffet)	(trolley)		(buffet)			(trolley)	(trolley)		(buffet)		(trolley)		(buffet)			(buffet)		
London Euston 15 ⊖ 65 d	*17b02*		17 35			17 55			18 15				*18b02*		18 35				18 55			19 15		
Birmingham New Street 12 68 d	18 01	*17 35*		18 31									19 01		*18 35*		19 31			*19 20*				
Wolverhampton 7 68 ⛴ d	18 19	*17 52*		18 49									19 19		*18 52*		19 49							
Stafford 65, 68 d	18 39	*18 10*											19 38		*19 10*									
Stoke-on-Trent 50, 68 d	18 59			19 21		19 26			19 50				19 57			20 01	20 22		20 26			20 50		
Longport 50 d																								
Kidsgrove 50 d																20 08								
Crewe 10 65 d		18 56	19 13				19 28								20 13					20 28				
Sandbach d		19 03																						
Holmes Chapel d		19 08																						
Goostrey d		19 11																						
Chelford d		19 15																						
Alderley Edge d		19 19												20 19									20 51	
Wilmslow d		19 23	19 29				19 47							20 23	20 29					20 46			20 54	
Styal d																							20 58	
Manchester Airport ✈ a																							21 05	
Handforth d		19 26												20 26										
Congleton d																20 15								
Macclesfield a	19 16					19 42							20 14			20 22			20 42					
d	19 17					19 42							20 15			20 23			20 42					
Prestbury d																20 27								
Adlington (Cheshire) d																20 30								
Poynton d																20 33								
Bramhall d																20 36								
Cheadle Hulme d		19 30												20 30		20 39								
Stockport a	19 28	19 37	19 38			19 56	19 58		20 18				20 28	20 37	20 38	20 44			20 56	20 57		21 18		
d	19 29	19 37	19 39		19 54	19 57	19 58	20 12	20 19		20 21	20 26	20 29	20 37	20 39	20 44		20 54	20 57	20 57	21 12	21 19		21 22
Heaton Chapel d		19 41						20 16						20 41							21 16			
Levenshulme d		19 44						20 19						20 44							21 19			
Manchester Piccadilly 10 ⛴ a	19 40	19 51	19 51	20 00	20 06	20 09	20 15	20 27	20 30		20 33	20 38	20 40	20 51	20 51	20 58	21 00	21 06	21 09	21 14	21 27	21 30	21 31	21 33
d											20 35													21 35
Manchester Oxford Road a											20 37													21 37
Deansgate ⛴ a											20 40													21 40

For general notes see front of timetable
For details of catering facilities see Directory of Train Operators

- **A** From Bournemouth (Table 51)
- **B** From Paignton (Table 51)
- **C** From Cleethorpes to Manchester Airport (from 28 June from Doncaster) (Table 29)
- **D** From Pembroke Dock (Table 128)
- **E** From Buxton (Table 86)
- **G** From Chester (Table 88) to Southport (Table 82)
- **H** From Norwich to Liverpool Lime Street (Table 49)
- **J** From Bristol Temple Meads (Table 51)
- **K** From Cardiff Central (Table 131)
- **L** To Southport (Table 82)
- **N** From Penzance (Table 135)
- **Q** From Milford Haven (Table 128)
- **U** From Norwich (Table 49)
- **V** To Wigan Wallgate (Table 82)
- **b** Change at Stafford

Table 84

Stoke-on-Trent and Crewe → Manchester Airport, Stockport and Manchester

Sundays

until 12 July

Network Diagram - see first page of Table 78

		EM	XC	NT	VT	XC	TP	VT	AW	NT	VT	NT	XC	NT	VT	NT	NT	NT	NT	XC	NT	VT	VT
		◇	**1** ◇		**1** ◇	**1** ◇	**1** ◇	**1** ◇	**R**		**1** ◇		**1** ◇		**1** ◇					**1** ◇		**1** ◇	**1** ◇
		A	B			C	D		E	G		H	B			G	J			B			
		⚒	⚒		☕	⚒		☕	⚒		☕				☕							☕	☕
London Euston **15**	⊖ 65 d		19b02		19 35			19 55			20 15		20b05		20 35						20 35	21 24	21 50
Birmingham New Street **12**	68 d		20 01	19 35		20 31			20 20				21 01		21 20					22 01	21 35		
Wolverhampton **7**	68 ⛴ d		20 19	19 52		20 49			20 38				21 19		21 38					22 19	21 53		
Stafford	65, 68 d		20 38	20 10					20 52				21 38		22 04					22 38	22 14		
Stoke-on-Trent	50, 68 d		20 58			21 21		21 26			21 50		21 57						22 39	22 57		23 33	
Longport	50 d																						
Kidsgrove	50 d																		22 46				
Crewe 10	65 d			20 56	21 14				21 28						22 23						22 56		
Sandbach	d			21 03																	23 03		
Holmes Chapel	d			21 08																	23 08		
Goostrey	d			21 11																	23 11		
Chelford	d			21 15																	23 15		
Alderley Edge	d			21 19										22 19				22 51			23 19		
Wilmslow	d			21 23	21 30				21 47					22 23	22 38			22 54			23 23		
Styal	d																	22 58					
Manchester Airport	✈ a																	23 05					
Handforth	d			21 26										22 26							23 26		
Congleton	d																		22 53				
Macclesfield	a		21 15					21 42					22 14						23 00	23 13		23 49	
	d		21 16					21 42					22 15						23 01	23 14		23 51	
Prestbury	d																		23 05				
Adlington (Cheshire)	d																		23 08				
Poynton	d																		23 11				
Bramhall	d																		23 14				
Cheadle Hulme	d			21 30										22 30					23 17		23 30		
Stockport	a		21 28	21 37	21 39			21 56	21 58		22 18		22 28	22 37	22 48				23 22	23 27	23 35	00 05	00s45
	d	21 24	21 29	21 37	21 40		21 54	21 57	21 58	22 12	22 19	22 21	22 29	22 37	22 49	23 12	23 16		23 23	23 28	23 37	00 06	
Heaton Chapel	d			21 41						22 16				22 41		23 16					23 41		
Levenshulme	d			21 44						22 19				22 44		23 19					23 44		
Manchester Piccadilly 10	⛴ a	21 36	21 40	21 52	21 52	22 00	22 06	22 09	22 15	22 27	22 30	22 33	22 40	22 51	23 00	23 27	23 29	23 33	23 37	23 41	23 51	00 17	00 58
	d											22 35											
Manchester Oxford Road	a											22 37											
Deansgate	⛴ a											22 40											

Sundays

19 July to 6 September

		NT	NT	TP	AW	NT	NT	NT	TP	AW	NT		NT	XC	NT	VT	NT	VT	NT	TP	AW	NT		NT	XC
				1 ◇					**1** ◇					**1** ◇		**1** ◇		**1** ◇		**1** ◇	◇				**1** ◇
		K	L	N		G	L		Q		G		U							J	V	G			
														⚒		☕		☕							⚒
London Euston **15**	⊖ 65 d															08 10		08 20							08b15
Birmingham New Street **12**	68 d													09 01		09 20									10 00
Wolverhampton **7**	68 ⛴ d													09 19		09 19									10 18
Stafford	65, 68 d													09 34											10 33
Stoke-on-Trent	50, 68 d																	10 21							10 52
Longport	50 d																								
Kidsgrove	50 d																								
Crewe 10	65 d				08 28					09 28				09 56		10 17					10 28				
Sandbach	d																								
Holmes Chapel	d																								
Goostrey	d																								
Chelford	d																								
Alderley Edge	d							09 26							10 19				10 40						
Wilmslow	d				08 47			09 30		09 47				10 13	10 23	10 32			10 43		10 47			←	
Styal	d																		10 47					10 47	
Manchester Airport	✈ a																		→					10 55	
Handforth	d							09 33							10 26										
Congleton	d																								
Macclesfield	a																	10 37							11 09
	d																	10 39							11 10
Prestbury	d																								
Adlington (Cheshire)	d																								
Poynton	d																								
Bramhall	d																								
Cheadle Hulme	d							09 37							10 30										
Stockport	a							09 42						10 21	10 35	10 40		10 52			10 58				11 22
	d	00 02	08 22	08 31		09 08	09 22	09 43	09 52		10 03		10 12	10 22	10 39	10 41	←	10 53		10 53	10 58	11 07			11 23
Heaton Chapel	d					09 12		09 47			10 08				10 43		10 43					11 11			
Levenshulme	d					09 15		09 50			10 11				→		10 46					11 14			
Manchester Piccadilly 10	⛴ a	00 15	08 33	08 43	09 11	09 23	09 33	09 57	10 06	10 12	10 20		10 23	10 39		10 54	10 55	11 04		11 06	11 15	11 23		11 25	11 38
	d		08 35				09 35						10 26											11 26	
Manchester Oxford Road	a		08 37				09 37						10 28											11 28	
Deansgate	⛴ a		08 40				09 40						10 40												

For general notes see front of timetable
For details of catering facilities see Directory of Train Operators

A From Norwich (Table 49)
B From Bournemouth (Table 51)
C From Bristol Temple Meads (Table 51)
D From Cleethorpes to Manchester Airport (from 28 June from Doncaster) (Table 29)
E From Milford Haven (Table 128)
G From Buxton (Table 86)
H From Chester (Table 88) to Wigan Wallgate (Table 82)
J From Sheffield (Table 78)
K From Chester (Table 88)
L To Southport (Table 82)
N From Sheffield to Manchester Airport (Table 78)
Q From Meadowhall to Manchester Airport (Table 29)
U From Chester (Table 88) to Southport (Table 82)
V From Shrewsbury (Table 131)
b Change at Stafford

Table 84

Sundays

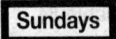

19 July to 6 September

Stoke-on-Trent and Crewe → Manchester Airport, Stockport and Manchester

Network Diagram - see first page of Table 78

	EM ◇ A	NT	AW ◇ B	TP 1◇ C	VT 1◇	NT D	NT E	EM ◇ A	XC 1◇ G	NT		VT 1◇	TP 1◇ C	AW ◇ B	NT D	NT	NT H	EM ◇ A	XC 1◇ J	NT	VT 1◇		TP 1◇ C	AW ◇ B
London Euston [15] ⊖ 65 d		08 15	08 45		09 20				09b15			10 20		09 45					10b15	10 15	11 20			11 15
Birmingham New Street [12] 68 d		09 42	10 20						11 01					11 20					12 01	11 42				12 20
Wolverhampton [7] 68 d		09 59							11 19					10 59					12 20	11 59				12c20
Stafford 65, 68 d		10 17							11 33					11 17					12 34	12 16				12 56
Stoke-on-Trent 50, 68 d					11 22				11 54			12 22							12 54		13 12			
Longport 50 d																								
Kidsgrove 50 d																								
Crewe [10] 65 d		10 56	11 22											12 28						12 56				13 29
Sandbach d		11 03																		13 03				
Holmes Chapel d		11 08																		13 08				
Goostrey d		11 11																		13 11				
Chelford d		11 15																		13 15				
Alderley Edge d		11 19								12 19						12 51				13 19				
Wilmslow d		11 23	11 41							12 23				12 47		12 54				13 23				13 48
Styal d																12 58								
Manchester Airport ✈ a																13 05								
Handforth d		11 26								12 26										13 26				
Congleton d																								
Macclesfield a					11 38				12 10			12 38							13 10		13 28			
d					11 40				12 11			12 40							13 11		13 29			
Prestbury d																								
Adlington (Cheshire) d																								
Poynton d																								
Bramhall d																								
Cheadle Hulme d		11 30								12 30										13 30				
Stockport a		11 37			11 53				12 26	12 37		12 52		12 58					13 26	13 37	13 42			13 58
d	11 27	11 37		11 53	11 54	12 12	12 21	12 26	12 27	12 37		12 53	12 53	12 58	13 12		13 22	13 26	13 27	13 37	13 43		13 53	13 58
Heaton Chapel d		11 41				12 16				12 41					13 16					13 41				
Levenshulme d		11 44				12 19				12 44					13 19					13 44				
Manchester Piccadilly [10] a	11 38	11 53	12 02	12 06	12 09	12 29	12 33	12 37	12 40	12 51		13 06	13 06	13 15	13 27	13 31	13 33	13 37	13 40	13 52	13 59		14 06	14 15
d	11 38						12 35	12 38									13 35	13 38						
Manchester Oxford Road a	11 41						12 37	12 41									13 37	13 41						
Deansgate a							12 40										13 40							

	NT D	VT 1◇	NT E	EM ◇ K	XC 1◇ L	NT	VT 1◇	XC 1◇	TP 1◇ C	VT 1◇		AW ◇ B	NT D	VT 1◇	NT	NT H	EM ◇ K	XC 1◇ L	NT	VT 1◇	XC 1◇ N		TP 1◇ C	VT 1◇
London Euston [15] ⊖ 65 d		12 15			12b02		12 35			12 55				13 15				13b02	13 02	13 35				13 55
Birmingham New Street [12] 68 d					13 01		12 35	13 31				13 20						14 01	13 35		14 31			
Wolverhampton [7] 68 d					13 19		12 52	13 49										14 19	13 52		14 49			
Stafford 65, 68 d					13 34		13 25											14 34	14 22					
Stoke-on-Trent 50, 68 d		13 50			13 57			14 21		14 26				14 50				14 57			15 21			15 26
Longport 50 d																								
Kidsgrove 50 d																								
Crewe [10] 65 d							14 13					14 28							14 56	15 13				
Sandbach d																			15 03					
Holmes Chapel d																			15 08					
Goostrey d																			15 11					
Chelford d																			15 15					
Alderley Edge d						14 19									14 51				15 19					
Wilmslow d						14 23	14 29					14 47			14 54				15 23	15 29				
Styal d															14 58									
Manchester Airport ✈ a															15 05									
Handforth d						14 26													15 26					
Congleton d																								
Macclesfield a					14 14					14 42								15 14						15 42
d					14 15					14 42								15 15						15 42
Prestbury d																								
Adlington (Cheshire) d																								
Poynton d																								
Bramhall d																								
Cheadle Hulme d						14 30													15 30					
Stockport a		14 18			14 28	14 37	14 38			14 56		14 58		15 18				15 28	15 37	15 38				15 56
d	14 12	14 19	14 21	14 26	14 29	14 37	14 39		14 53	14 57		14 58	15 12	15 19		15 22	15 26	15 29	15 37	15 39			15 54	15 57
Heaton Chapel d	14 16					14 41							15 16						15 41					
Levenshulme d	14 19					14 44							15 19						15 44					
Manchester Piccadilly [10] a	14 27	14 30	14 33	14 37	14 40	14 51	14 51	15 00	15 06	15 09		15 15	15 27	15 30	15 31	15 33	15 37	15 40	15 51	15 51	16 00		16 06	16 09
d			14 35	14 38												15 35	15 38							
Manchester Oxford Road a			14 37	14 41												15 37	15 41							
Deansgate a			14 40													15 40								

For general notes see front of timetable
For details of catering facilities see Directory of Train Operators

A From Nottingham to Liverpool Lime Street (Table 49)
B From Cardiff Central (Table 131)
C From Doncaster to Manchester Airport (Table 29)
D From Buxton (Table 86)
E From Chester (Table 88) to Southport (Table 82)
G From Reading (Table 51)
H To Southport (Table 82)
J From Southampton Central (Table 51)
K From Norwich to Liverpool Lime Street (Table 49)
L From Bournemouth (Table 51)
N From Paignton (Table 51)
b Change at Stafford
c Change at Stafford and Crewe

Table 84

Sundays

Stoke-on-Trent and Crewe → Manchester Airport, Stockport and Manchester

19 July to 6 September

Network Diagram - see first page of Table 78

	AW	NT	VT	NT	EM	XC	NT	VT	NT	XC	TP	VT	AW	NT	VT	NT	NT	EM	XC	NT	VT	XC
	◇		1 ◇		◇	1 ◇		1 ◇		1 ◇	1 ◇	1 ◇	R		1 ◇			◇	1 ◇		1 ◇	1 ◇
	A	B		C	D	E				G	H		J	B			K	D	E			L
	[trolley]		[restaurant]		[trolley]	[trolley]		[restaurant]		[trolley]		[restaurant]	[trolley]		[restaurant]			[trolley]	[trolley]		[restaurant]	[trolley]
London Euston [15] ⊖ 65 d			14 15			*14b02*		14 35				14 55			15 15				*15b02*		15 35	
Birmingham New Street [12] 68 d	*14 20*					15 01		*14 35*		15 31			*15 20*						16 01	*15 35*		16 31
Wolverhampton [7] 68 ⛴ d						15 19		*14 52*		15 49									16 19	*15 52*		16 49
Stafford 65, 68 d						15 34		*15 25*											16 36	*16 10*		
Stoke-on-Trent 50, 68 d			15 50			15 57			16 01	16 21		16 25			16 50				16 57			17 21
Longport 50 d																						
Kidsgrove 50 d									16 08													
Crewe [10] 65 d	15 28							16 13					16 31							16 56	17 13	
Sandbach d																				17 03		
Holmes Chapel d																				17 08		
Goostrey d																				17 11		
Chelford d																				17 15		
Alderley Edge d							16 19									16 51				17 19		
Wilmslow d	15 47						16 23	16 29					16 49			16 54				17 23	17 29	
Styal d																16 58						
Manchester Airport ✈ a																17 05						
Handforth d							16 26													17 26		
Congleton d									16 15													
Macclesfield a						16 14			16 22			16 42							17 14			
d						16 15			16 23			16 42							17 15			
Prestbury d									16 27													
Adlington (Cheshire) d									16 30													
Poynton d									16 33													
Bramhall d									16 36													
Cheadle Hulme d							16 30		16 39											17 30		
Stockport a	15 58		16 18			16 28	16 37	16 38	16 44			16 56	16 58		17 18				17 30	17 37	17 38	
d	15 58	16 12	16 19	16 21	16 26	16 29	16 37	16 39	16 44		16 54	16 57	16 58	17 12	17 19		17 22	17 27	17 31	17 37	17 39	
Heaton Chapel d		16 16					16 41							17 16						17 41		
Levenshulme d		16 19					16 44							17 19						17 44		
Manchester Piccadilly [10] ⛴ a	16 15	16 27	16 30	16 33	16 37	16 40	16 51	16 51	16 58	17 00	17 06	17 09	17 15	17 27	17 30	17 31	17 33	17 37	17 40	17 51	17 51	18 00
d				16 35	16 38												17 35	17 38				
Manchester Oxford Road a				16 37	16 41												17 37	17 41				
Deansgate ⛴ a				16 40													17 40					

	TP	VT	AW	NT	VT	NT	EM	XC	NT	VT	XC	TP	VT	AW	NT	VT	NT	NT	EM	XC	NT	VT
	1 ◇	1 ◇	R		1 ◇		◇	1 ◇		1 ◇	1 ◇	1 ◇	1 ◇	R		1 ◇			◇	1 ◇		1 ◇
	H		N	B		C	Q	E			U	H		J	B			K	Q	E		
		[restaurant]	[trolley]		[restaurant]		[trolley]	[trolley]		[restaurant]	[trolley]		[restaurant]	[trolley]		[restaurant]			[trolley]	[trolley]		[restaurant]
London Euston [15] ⊖ 65 d		15 55			16 15			*16b02*		16 35			16 55			17 15				*17b02*		17 35
Birmingham New Street [12] 68 d			*16 20*					17 01		*16 35*	17 31			*17 20*						18 01	*17 35*	
Wolverhampton [7] 68 ⛴ d								17 19		*16 52*	17 49									18 19	*17 52*	
Stafford 65, 68 d								17 36		*17 10*										18 39	*18 10*	
Stoke-on-Trent 50, 68 d		17 26			17 50			17 57			18 21		18 26			18 50				18 59		
Longport 50 d																						
Kidsgrove 50 d																						
Crewe [10] 65 d			17 28							18 13				18 28							18 56	19 13
Sandbach d																					19 03	
Holmes Chapel d																					19 08	
Goostrey d																					19 11	
Chelford d																					19 15	
Alderley Edge d									18 19								18 51				19 19	
Wilmslow d			17 45						18 23	18 29				18 47			18 54				19 23	19 29
Styal d																	18 58					
Manchester Airport ✈ a																	19 05					
Handforth d									18 26												19 26	
Congleton d																						
Macclesfield a		17 42						18 14					18 42							19 16		
d		17 42						18 15					18 42							19 17		
Prestbury d																						
Adlington (Cheshire) d																						
Poynton d																						
Bramhall d																						
Cheadle Hulme d									18 30												19 30	
Stockport a		17 56	17 58		18 18			18 28	18 37	18 38			18 56	18 58		19 18				19 28	19 37	19 38
d	17 54	17 57	17 58	18 12	18 19	18 21	18 26	18 29	18 37	18 39		18 54	18 57	18 58	19 12	19 19		19 22	19 26	19 29	19 37	19 39
Heaton Chapel d				18 16					18 41						19 16						19 41	
Levenshulme d				18 19					18 44						19 19						19 44	
Manchester Piccadilly [10] ⛴ a	18 06	18 09	18 15	18 27	18 30	18 33	18 37	18 40	18 51	18 51	19 00	19 06	19 09	19 15	19 27	19 30	19 31	19 33	19 37	19 40	19 51	19 51
d						18 35	18 38											19 35	19 38			
Manchester Oxford Road a						18 37	18 41											19 37	19 41			
Deansgate ⛴ a						18 40												19 40				

For general notes see front of timetable
For details of catering facilities see Directory of Train Operators

- **A** From Milford Haven (Table 128)
- **B** From Buxton (Table 86)
- **C** From Chester (Table 88) to Southport (Table 82)
- **D** From Nottingham to Liverpool Lime Street (Table 49)
- **E** From Bournemouth (Table 51)
- **G** From Plymouth (Table 51)
- **H** From Doncaster to Manchester Airport (Table 29)
- **J** From Cardiff Central (Table 131)
- **K** To Southport (Table 82)
- **L** From Paignton (Table 51)
- **N** From Pembroke Dock (Table 128)
- **Q** From Norwich to Liverpool Lime Street (Table 49)
- **U** From Bristol Temple Meads (Table 51)
- **b** Change at Stafford

Sundays

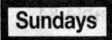

Stoke-on-Trent and Crewe → Manchester Airport, Stockport and Manchester

19 July to 6 September

Network Diagram - see first page of Table 78

	XC	TP	VT	AW	NT	VT	NT	EM	XC	NT		VT	NT	XC	TP	VT	AW	NT	VT	NT	NT		EM	XC
				R													R							
	1◊	1◊	1◊			1◊		◊	1◊			1◊		1◊	1◊	1◊			1◊				◊	1◊
	A	B		C	D		E	G	H					J	B		K	D			L		G	H
	⊼		Ⓟ	⊼		Ⓟ		⊼	⊼			Ⓟ		⊼		Ⓟ			Ⓟ				⊼	
London Euston 15 ⊖ 65 d			17 55			18 15			18b02			18 35				18 55			19 15					19b02
Birmingham New Street 12 68 d	18 31								19 01			18 35		19 31			19 20							20 01
Wolverhampton 7 68 ⛴ d	18 49								19 19			18 52		19 49										20 19
Stafford 65, 68 d									19 38			19 10												20 38
Stoke-on-Trent 50, 68 d	19 21		19 26			19 50			19 57				20 01	20 22		20 26			20 50					20 58
Longport 50 d																								
Kidsgrove 50 d													20 08											
Crewe 10 65 d				19 28								20 13					20 28							
Sandbach d																								
Holmes Chapel d																								
Goostrey d																								
Chelford d																								
Alderley Edge d										20 19										20 51				
Wilmslow d				19 47						20 23		20 29					20 46			20 54				
Styal d																				20 58				
Manchester Airport ✈ a																				21 05				
Handforth d										20 26														
Congleton d													20 15											
Macclesfield a			19 42						20 14				20 22			20 42								21 15
d			19 42						20 15				20 23			20 42								21 16
Prestbury d													20 27											
Adlington (Cheshire) d													20 30											
Poynton d													20 33											
Bramhall d													20 36											
Cheadle Hulme d										20 30			20 39											
Stockport a			19 56	19 58		20 18			20 28	20 37		20 38	20 44			20 56	20 57		21 18					21 28
d		19 54	19 57	19 58	20 12	20 19	20 21	20 26	20 29	20 37		20 39	20 44		20 54	20 57	20 57	21 12	21 19		21 22		21 24	21 29
Heaton Chapel d					20 16					20 41								21 16						
Levenshulme d					20 19					20 44								21 19						
Manchester Piccadilly 10 ⛴ a	20 00	20 06	20 09	20 15	20 27	20 30	20 33	20 38	20 40	20 51		20 51	20 58	21 00	21 06	21 09	21 14	21 27	21 30	21 31	21 33		21 36	21 40
d							20 35														21 35			
Manchester Oxford Road a							20 37														21 37			
Deansgate ⛴ a							20 40														21 40			

	NT	VT	XC	TP	VT	AW	NT	VT	NT	XC		NT	VT	NT	NT	NT	NT	XC	NT	VT	VT			
						R																		
		1◊	1◊	1◊	1◊			1◊		1◊			1◊					1◊		1◊	1◊			
			J	B		C	D		N	H				D	Q			H						
		Ⓟ			Ⓟ	⊼		Ⓟ					Ⓟ							Ⓟ	Ⓟ			
London Euston 15 ⊖ 65 d		19 35			19 55			20 15		20b05			20 35							21 24	21 50			
Birmingham New Street 12 68 d	19 35	19 35	20 31			20 20				21 01			21 20					22 01	21 35					
Wolverhampton 7 68 ⛴ d	19 52	19 52	20 49			20 38				21 19			21 38					22 19	21 53					
Stafford 65, 68 d	20 10	20 30				20 52				21 38			22 04					22 38	22 14					
Stoke-on-Trent 50, 68 d			21 21		21 26			21 50		21 57							22 39	22 57		23 33				
Longport 50 d																								
Kidsgrove 50 d																	22 46							
Crewe 10 65 d	20 56	21 14				21 28							22 23						22 56					
Sandbach d	21 03																		23 03					
Holmes Chapel d	21 08																		23 08					
Goostrey d	21 11																		23 11					
Chelford d	21 15																		23 15					
Alderley Edge d	21 19											22 19				22 51			23 19					
Wilmslow d	21 23	21 30				21 47						22 23	22 38			22 54			23 23					
Styal d																22 58								
Manchester Airport ✈ a																23 05								
Handforth d	21 26											22 26							23 26					
Congleton d																	22 53							
Macclesfield a					21 42					22 14							23 00	23 13		23 49				
d					21 42					22 15							23 01	23 14		23 51				
Prestbury d																	23 05							
Adlington (Cheshire) d																	23 08							
Poynton d																	23 11							
Bramhall d																	23 14							
Cheadle Hulme d	21 30											22 30					23 17		23 30					
Stockport a	21 37	21 39			21 56	21 58		22 18		22 28		22 37	22 48				23 22	23 27	23 35	00 05	00s46			
d	21 37	21 40		21 54	21 57	21 58	22 12	22 19	22 21	22 29		22 37	22 49	23 12	23 16		23 23	23 28	23 37	00 06				
Heaton Chapel d	21 41						22 16					22 41		23 16					23 41					
Levenshulme d	21 44						22 19					22 44		23 19					23 44					
Manchester Piccadilly 10 ⛴ a	21 52	21 52	22 00	22 06	22 09	22 15	22 27	22 30	22 33	22 40		22 51	23 00	23 27	23 29	23 33	23 37	23 41	23 51	00 17	00 58			
d									22 35															
Manchester Oxford Road a									22 37															
Deansgate ⛴ a									22 40															

For general notes see front of timetable
For details of catering facilities see Directory of Train Operators

A From Penzance (Table 135)
B From Doncaster to Manchester Airport (Table 29)
C From Milford Haven (Table 128)
D From Buxton (Table 86)
E From Chester (Table 88) to Southport (Table 82)
G From Norwich (Table 49)
H From Bournemouth (Table 51)
J From Bristol Temple Meads (Table 51)
K From Cardiff Central (Table 131)
L To Wigan Wallgate (Table 82)
N From Chester (Table 88) to Wigan Wallgate (Table 82)
Q From Sheffield (Table 78)
b Change at Stafford

Table 84

Sundays

from 13 September

Stoke-on-Trent and Crewe → Manchester Airport, Stockport and Manchester

Network Diagram - see first page of Table 78

		NT	TP	AW	NT	NT	NT	TP	AW		NT	NT	XC	VT	NT	VT	AW	NT		NT	NT	XC	NT	AW	TP
			1 ◇					1 ◇					1 ◇	1 ◇		1 ◇	◇					1 ◇		◇	1 ◇
		A	B		C	D		E			C	G					H	C		D				J	K
London Euston 15	⊖ 65 d													08 10		08 20						08b15	08 15	08c44	
Birmingham New Street 12	68 d												09 01				09 20					10 00	09 41	10e15	
Wolverhampton 7	68 d												09 19									10 18	09 57		
Stafford	65, 68 d												09 32									10 31	10 14		
Stoke-on-Trent	50, 68 d															10 21						10 52			
Longport	50 d																								
Kidsgrove	50 d																								
Crewe 10	65 d			08 28					09 28				09 58	10 20			10 28						10 56	11 22	
Sandbach	d																						11 03		
Holmes Chapel	d																						11 08		
Goostrey	d																						11 11		
Chelford	d																						11 15		
Alderley Edge	d						09 19								10 19						10 50		11 19		
Wilmslow	d			08 47			09 23		09 47				10 14		10 23		10 47				10 53		11 23	11 41	
Styal	d																				10 57				
Manchester Airport	a																				11 04				
Handforth	d						09 26								10 26								11 26		
Congleton	d																								
Macclesfield	a															10 36						11 09			
	d															10 38						11 10			
Prestbury	d																								
Adlington (Cheshire)	d																								
Poynton	d																								
Bramhall	d																								
Cheadle Hulme	d						09 30								10 30								11 30		
Stockport	a						09 38						10 23	10 41	10 35	10 51	10 58					11 21	11 37		
	d	00 02	08 31		09 08	09 22	09 40	09 52			10 07	10 19	10 24	10 42	10 39	10 52	10 58	11 11		11 12		11 22	11 37		11 53
Heaton Chapel	d				09 12		09 44				10 12				10 43					11 16			11 41		
Levenshulme	d				09 15		09 47				10 15				10 46					11 19			11 44		
Manchester Piccadilly 10	a	00 15	08 43	09 11	09 23	09 31	09 53	10 06	10 16		10 23	10 33	10 37	10 54	10 55	11 04	11 15	11 23		11 25	11 29	11 40	11 53	12 02	12 06
	d					09 35						10 35								11 27	11 30				
Manchester Oxford Road	a					09 37						10 37								11 29	11 32				
Deansgate	a					09 40						10 40								11 40					

		VT	NT	NT	EM		XC	NT	VT	TP	AW	NT	NT	NT		EM	XC	NT	VT	TP	AW	NT	VT		NT
		1 ◇			◇		1 ◇		1 ◇	1 ◇	◇					◇	1 ◇		1 ◇	1 ◇	◇		1 ◇		
			C	G	L		N			K	J	C		D		L	Q			K	J	C			G
London Euston 15	⊖ 65 d	09 20					09b15		10 20		09 45						10b15	10 15	11 20		11 15		12 15		
Birmingham New Street 12	68 d						11 01				11 20						12 01	11 42			12f20				
Wolverhampton 7	68 d						11 19				10 59						12 20	11 59			12g20				
Stafford	65, 68 d						11 32				11 17						12 34	12 16			12 56				
Stoke-on-Trent	50, 68 d	11 22					11 52		12 22								12 54		13 12				13 50		
Longport	50 d																								
Kidsgrove	50 d																								
Crewe 10	65 d										12 28							12 56			13 29				
Sandbach	d																	13 03							
Holmes Chapel	d																	13 08							
Goostrey	d																	13 11							
Chelford	d																	13 15							
Alderley Edge	d							12 19					12 51					13 19							
Wilmslow	d							12 23			12 47		12 54					13 23			13 48				
Styal	d												12 58												
Manchester Airport	a												13 05												
Handforth	d							12 26										13 26							
Congleton	d																								
Macclesfield	a	11 37					12 09		12 37								13 10		13 27						
	d	11 39					12 10		12 39								13 11		13 28						
Prestbury	d																								
Adlington (Cheshire)	d																								
Poynton	d																								
Bramhall	d																								
Cheadle Hulme	d							12 30										13 30							
Stockport	a	11 52					12 21	12 37	12 52		12 58						13 28	13 37	13 41		13 58		14 18		
	d	11 54	12 10	12 16	12 26		12 22	12 37	12 53	12 53	12 58	13 12		13 22		13 26	13 29	13 37	13 43	13 53	13 58	14 12	14 19		14 21
Heaton Chapel	d		12 15					12 41				13 16						13 41				14 16			
Levenshulme	d		12 18					12 44				13 19						13 44				14 19			
Manchester Piccadilly 10	a	12 06	12 25	12 28	12 37		12 40	12 53	13 06	13 06	13 15	13 27	13 31	13 33		13 37	13 40	13 52	13 59	14 06	14 15	14 27	14 30		14 33
	d			12 30	12 38									13 35		13 38									14 35
Manchester Oxford Road	a			12 32	12 41									13 37		13 41									14 37
Deansgate	a			12 40										13 40											14 40

For general notes see front of timetable
For details of catering facilities see Directory of Train Operators

- A From Chester (Table 88)
- B From Sheffield to Manchester Airport (Table 78)
- C From Buxton (Table 86)
- D To Southport (Table 82)
- E From Meadowhall to Manchester Airport (Table 29)
- G From Chester (Table 88) to Southport (Table 82)
- H From Shrewsbury (Table 131)
- J From Cardiff Central (Table 131)
- K From Cleethorpes to Manchester Airport (Table 29)
- L From Nottingham to Liverpool Lime Street (Table 49)
- N From Reading (Table 51)
- Q From Southampton Central (Table 51)
- b Change at Stafford
- c From 8 November only
- e From 8 November dep. 1020
- f From 8 November dep. 1201
- g Change at Stafford and Crewe

Sundays

from 13 September

Stoke-on-Trent and Crewe → Manchester Airport, Stockport and Manchester

Network Diagram - see first page of Table 78

	EM	XC	NT	VT	XC	TP	VT	AW		NT	VT	NT	NT	EM	XC	NT	VT		XC	TP	VT	AW	NT	VT
	◇	1 ◇		1 ◇	1 ◇	1 ◇	1 ◇	◇			1 ◇			◇	1 ◇		1 ◇		1 ◇	1 ◇	1 ◇	◇		1 ◇
	A	B			C	D		E		G			H	J	B				K	L		N	G	
	🛒	🛒		🍴	🛒		🍴	🛒			🍴			🛒	🛒		🍴		🛒		🍴	🛒		🍴
London Euston [15] ⊖ 65 d		12b02		12 35			12 55				13 15				13b02	13 02	13 35				13 55			14 15
Birmingham New Street [12] 68 d		13 01		12 35	13 31			13 20							14 01	13 35			14 31			14c20		
Wolverhampton [7] 68 ⛴ d		13 19		12 52	13 49										14 19	13 52			14 49					
Stafford 65, 68 d		13 34		13 25											14 34	14 22								
Stoke-on-Trent 50, 68 d		13 57			14 21		14 26				14 50				14 57				15 21		15 26			15 50
Longport 50 d																								
Kidsgrove 50 d																								
Crewe [10] 65 d				14 13				14 28								14 56	15 13					15 28		
Sandbach d																15 03								
Holmes Chapel d																15 08								
Goostrey d																15 11								
Chelford d																15 15								
Alderley Edge d			14 19									14 51				15 19								
Wilmslow d			14 23	14 29				14 47				14 54				15 23	15 29					15 47		
Styal d												14 58												
Manchester Airport ✈ a												15 05												
Handforth d			14 26													15 26								
Congleton d																								
Macclesfield a		14 14					14 42								15 14						15 42			
d		14 15					14 42								15 15						15 42			
Prestbury d																								
Adlington (Cheshire) d																								
Poynton d																								
Bramhall d																								
Cheadle Hulme d			14 30													15 30								
Stockport a		14 28	14 37	14 38			14 56	14 58			15 18				15 28	15 37	15 38				15 56	15 58		16 18
d	14 26	14 29	14 37	14 39		14 53	14 57	14 58		15 12	15 19		15 22	15 26	15 29	15 37	15 39			15 54	15 57	15 58	16 12	16 19
Heaton Chapel d			14 41							15 16						15 41							16 16	
Levenshulme d			14 44							15 19						15 44							16 19	
Manchester Piccadilly [10] ⛴ a	14 37	14 40	14 51	14 51	15 00	15 06	15 09	15 15		15 27	15 30	15 31	15 33	15 37	15 40	15 51	15 51		16 00	16 06	16 09	16 15	16 27	16 30
d	14 38												15 35	15 38										
Manchester Oxford Road a	14 41												15 37	15 41										
Deansgate ⛴ a													15 40											

	NT	EM	XC	NT		VT	NT	XC	TP	VT	AW	NT	VT		NT	NT	EM	XC	NT	VT	XC	TP		VT
		◇	1 ◇			1 ◇		1 ◇	1 ◇	1 ◇	R		1 ◇				◇	1 ◇		1 ◇	1 ◇	1 ◇		1 ◇
	Q	A	B					U	L		E	G				H	A	B			V	L		
		🛒	🛒			🍴		🛒		🍴	🛒		🍴				🛒	🛒		🍴	🛒			🍴
London Euston [15] ⊖ 65 d			14b02			14 35				14 55			15 15					15b02		15 35				15 55
Birmingham New Street [12] 68 d			15 01			14 35		15 31			15 20							16 01	15 35		16 31			
Wolverhampton [7] 68 ⛴ d			15 19			14 52		15 49										16 19	15 52		16 49			
Stafford 65, 68 d			15 34			15 25												16 36	16 10					
Stoke-on-Trent 50, 68 d			15 57				16 01	16 21		16 25			16 50					16 57			17 21			17 26
Longport 50 d																								
Kidsgrove 50 d							16 08																	
Crewe [10] 65 d						16 13					16 31								16 56	17 13				
Sandbach d																			17 03					
Holmes Chapel d																			17 08					
Goostrey d																			17 11					
Chelford d																			17 15					
Alderley Edge d				16 19											16 51				17 19					
Wilmslow d				16 23		16 29					16 49				16 54				17 23	17 29				
Styal d															16 58									
Manchester Airport ✈ a															17 05									
Handforth d				16 26															17 26					
Congleton d							16 15																	
Macclesfield a			16 14				16 22			16 42								17 14						17 42
d			16 15				16 23			16 42								17 15						17 42
Prestbury d							16 27																	
Adlington (Cheshire) d							16 30																	
Poynton d							16 33																	
Bramhall d							16 36																	
Cheadle Hulme d				16 30			16 39												17 30					
Stockport a			16 28	16 37		16 38	16 44			16 56	16 58		17 18					17 30	17 37	17 38				17 56
d	16 21	16 26	16 29	16 37		16 39	16 44		16 54	16 57	16 58	17 12	17 19			17 22	17 27	17 31	17 37	17 39		17 54		17 57
Heaton Chapel d				16 41								17 16							17 41					
Levenshulme d				16 44								17 19							17 44					
Manchester Piccadilly [10] ⛴ a	16 33	16 37	16 40	16 51		16 51	16 58	17 00	17 06	17 09	17 15	17 27	17 30		17 31	17 33	17 37	17 40	17 51	17 51	18 00	18 06		18 09
d	16 35	16 38														17 35	17 38							
Manchester Oxford Road a	16 37	16 41														17 37	17 41							
Deansgate ⛴ a	16 40															17 40								

For general notes see front of timetable
For details of catering facilities see Directory of Train Operators

- **A** From Nottingham to Liverpool Lime Street (Table 49)
- **B** From Bournemouth (Table 51)
- **C** From 8 November from Plymouth (Table 51)
- **D** From Doncaster to Manchester Airport (Table 29)
- **E** From Cardiff Central (Table 131)
- **G** From Buxton (Table 86)
- **H** To Southport (Table 82)
- **J** From Norwich to Liverpool Lime Street (Table 49)
- **K** From Paignton (from 8 November from Plymouth) (Table 51)
- **L** From Cleethorpes to Manchester Airport (Table 29)
- **N** From Carmarthen (Table 128)
- **Q** From Chester (Table 88) to Southport (Table 82)
- **U** From Plymouth (Table 51) (from 8 November from Penzance) (Table 135)
- **V** From Paignton (Table 51)
- **b** Change at Stafford
- **c** From 8 November dep. 1335

Table 84

Sundays

Stoke-on-Trent and Crewe → Manchester Airport, Stockport and Manchester

from 13 September

Network Diagram - see first page of Table 78

	AW R A ╤	NT B	VT 1◇ ⊡	NT C	EM ◇ D ╤	XC 1◇ E ╤	NT	VT 1◇ ⊡	XC 1◇ G ╤	TP 1◇ H	VT 1◇ ⊡	AW R J ╤	NT B	VT 1◇ ⊡	NT	NT K	EM ◇ D ╤	XC 1◇ E ╤	NT	VT 1◇ ⊡	XC 1◇ L ╤	TP 1◇ H
London Euston [15] ⊖ 65 d			16 15			*16b02*		16 35			16 55			17 15				*17b02*		17 35		
Birmingham New Street [12] 68 d	*16 20*					17 01		*16 35*	17 31			*17 20*						18 01	*17 35*		18 31	
Wolverhampton [7] 68 d						17 19		*16 52*	17 49									18 19	*17 52*		18 49	
Stafford 65, 68 d						17 36		*17 10*										18 39	*18 10*			
Stoke-on-Trent 50, 68 d			17 50			17 57			18 21		18 26			18 50				18 59			19 21	
Longport 50 d																						
Kidsgrove 50 d																						
Crewe [10] 65 d	17 28							18 13				18 28							18 56	19 13		
Sandbach d																			19 03			
Holmes Chapel d																			19 08			
Goostrey d																			19 11			
Chelford d																			19 15			
Alderley Edge d							18 19								18 51				19 19			
Wilmslow d	17 45						18 23	18 29				18 47			18 54				19 23	19 29		
Styal d															18 58							
Manchester Airport ✈ a															19 05							
Handforth d							18 26												19 26			
Congleton d																						
Macclesfield a						18 14					18 42							19 16				
d						18 15					18 42							19 17				
Prestbury d																						
Adlington (Cheshire) d																						
Poynton d																						
Bramhall d																						
Cheadle Hulme d							18 30												19 30			
Stockport a	17 58		18 18			18 28	18 37	18 38			18 56	18 58		19 18				19 28	19 37	19 38		
d	17 58	18 12	18 19	18 21	18 26	18 29	18 37	18 39		18 54	18 57	18 58	19 12	19 19		19 22	19 26	19 29	19 37	19 39		19 54
Heaton Chapel d		18 16					18 41						19 16						19 41			
Levenshulme d		18 19					18 44						19 19						19 44			
Manchester Piccadilly [10] a	18 15	18 27	18 30	18 33	18 37	18 40	18 51	18 51	19 00	19 06	19 09	19 15	19 27	19 30	19 31	19 33	19 37	19 40	19 51	19 51	20 00	20 06
d				18 35	18 38											19 35	19 38					
Manchester Oxford Road a				18 37	18 41											19 37	19 41					
Deansgate a				18 40												19 40						

	VT 1◇ ⊡	AW R N ╤	NT B	VT 1◇ ⊡	NT C	EM ◇ Q ╤	XC 1◇ E ╤	NT	VT 1◇ ⊡	NT	XC 1◇ U ╤	TP 1◇ H	VT 1◇ ⊡	AW R J	NT B	VT 1◇ ⊡	NT	NT V	EM ◇ Q ╤	XC 1◇ E	NT
London Euston [15] ⊖ 65 d	17 55			18 15			*18b02*		18 35				18 55			19 15				*19b02*	
Birmingham New Street [12] 68 d							19 01		*18 35*		19 31			*19 20*						20 01	*19 35*
Wolverhampton [7] 68 d							19 19		*18 52*		19 49									20 19	*19 52*
Stafford 65, 68 d							19 38		*19 10*											20 38	*20 10*
Stoke-on-Trent 50, 68 d	19 26			19 50			19 57			20 01	20 22		20 26			20 50				20 58	
Longport 50 d																					
Kidsgrove 50 d										20 08											
Crewe [10] 65 d		19 28							20 13					20 28							20 56
Sandbach d																					21 03
Holmes Chapel d																					21 08
Goostrey d																					21 11
Chelford d																					21 15
Alderley Edge d								20 19									20 51				21 19
Wilmslow d		19 47						20 23	20 29					20 46			20 54				21 23
Styal d																	20 58				
Manchester Airport ✈ a																	21 05				
Handforth d								20 26													21 26
Congleton d										20 15											
Macclesfield a	19 42						20 14			20 22			20 42							21 15	
d	19 42						20 15			20 23			20 42							21 16	
Prestbury d										20 27											
Adlington (Cheshire) d										20 30											
Poynton d										20 33											
Bramhall d										20 36											
Cheadle Hulme d								20 30		20 39											21 30
Stockport a	19 56	19 58		20 18			20 28	20 37	20 38	20 44			20 56	20 57		21 18				21 28	21 37
d	19 57	19 58	20 12	20 19	20 21	20 26	20 29	20 37	20 39	20 44		20 54	20 57	20 57	21 12	21 19		21 22	21 24	21 29	21 37
Heaton Chapel d			20 16					20 41							21 16						21 41
Levenshulme d			20 19					20 44							21 19						21 44
Manchester Piccadilly [10] a	20 09	20 15	20 27	20 30	20 33	20 38	20 40	20 51	20 51	20 58	21 00	21 06	21 09	21 14	21 27	21 30	21 31	21 33	21 36	21 40	21 52
d					20 35													21 35			
Manchester Oxford Road a					20 37													21 37			
Deansgate a					20 40													21 40			

For general notes see front of timetable
For details of catering facilities see Directory of Train Operators

- **A** From Carmarthen (Table 128)
- **B** From Buxton (Table 86)
- **C** From Chester (Table 88) to Southport (Table 82)
- **D** From Norwich to Liverpool Lime Street (Table 49)
- **E** From Bournemouth (Table 51)
- **G** From Bristol Temple Meads (Table 51) (from 8 November from Penzance) (Table 135)
- **H** From Cleethorpes to Manchester Airport (Table 29)
- **J** From Cardiff Central (Table 131)
- **K** To Southport (Table 82)
- **L** From Penzance (Table 135) (from 8 November from Plymouth) (Table 51)
- **N** From Milford Haven (Table 128)
- **Q** From Norwich (Table 49)
- **U** From Bristol Temple Meads (from 8 November from Plymouth) (Table 51)
- **V** To Wigan Wallgate (Table 82)
- **b** Change at Stafford

Sundays

from 13 September

Stoke-on-Trent and Crewe → Manchester Airport, Stockport and Manchester

Network Diagram - see first page of Table 78

		VT	XC	TP	VT	AW	NT	VT	NT	XC	NT	VT	NT	NT	NT	NT	XC	NT	XC	VT	VT
		1◇	1◇	1◇	1◇	R		1◇		1◇		1◇					1◇		1◇	1◇	1◇
			A	B		C	D		E	G			D	H			G		J		
		☕			☕	🍴		☕				☕								☕	☕
London Euston 15	⊖ 65 d	19 35			19 55			20 15		20b05		20 35						20 35	20c50	21 24	21 50
Birmingham New Street 12	68 d		20 31			20 20				21 01		21 20					22 01	21 35	22 28		
Wolverhampton 7	68 ⛴ d		20 49			20 38				21 19		21 38					22 19	21 53	22 46		
Stafford	65, 68 d					20 52				21 38		22 04					22 38	22 14	22 59		
Stoke-on-Trent	50, 68 d		21 21		21 26			21 50		21 57						22 39	22 57			23 33	
Longport	50 d																				
Kidsgrove	50 d															22 46					
Crewe 10	65 d	21 14				21 28						22 23						22 56	23 26		
Sandbach	d																	23 03			
Holmes Chapel	d																	23 08			
Goostrey	d																	23 11			
Chelford	d																	23 15			
Alderley Edge	d										22 19				22 51			23 19			
Wilmslow	d	21 30				21 47					22 23	22 38			22 54			23 23	23 43		
Styal	d														22 58						
Manchester Airport	✈ a														23 05						
Handforth	d										22 26							23 26			
Congleton	d															22 53					
Macclesfield	a				21 42					22 14						23 00	23 13			23 49	
	d				21 42					22 15						23 01	23 14			23 51	
Prestbury	d															23 05					
Adlington (Cheshire)	d															23 08					
Poynton	d															23 11					
Bramhall	d															23 14					
Cheadle Hulme	d										22 30					23 17		23 30			
Stockport	a	21 39			21 56	21 58		22 18		22 28	22 37	22 48				23 22	23 27	23 35	23s51	00 05	00s46
	d	21 40		21 54	21 57	21 58	22 12	22 19	22 21	22 29	22 37	22 49	23 12	23 16		23 23	23 28	23 37		00 06	
Heaton Chapel	d						22 16				22 41		23 16					23 41			
Levenshulme	d						22 19				22 44		23 19					23 44			
Manchester Piccadilly 10	⛴ a	21 52	22 00	22 06	22 09	22 15	22 27	22 30	22 33	22 40	22 51	23 00	23 27	23 29	23 33	23 37	23 40	23 51	00 05	00 17	00 58
	d								22 35												
Manchester Oxford Road	a								22 37												
Deansgate	⛴ a								22 40												

For general notes see front of timetable
For details of catering facilities see Directory of Train Operators

A From Bristol Temple Meads (from 8 November from Plymouth) (Table 51)
B From Cleethorpes to Manchester Airport (Table 29)
C From Milford Haven (Table 128)
D From Buxton (Table 86)
E From Chester (Table 88) to Wigan Wallgate (Table 82)
G From Bournemouth (Table 51)
H From Sheffield (Table 78)
J From 8 November from Plymouth (Table 51)
b Change at Stafford
c Change at Crewe

Manchester, Stockport and Manchester Airport → Crewe and Stoke-on-Trent

Network Diagram - see first page of Table 78

Miles	Miles	Miles		XC 1◇ A ✠	VT 1◇ ⊠	NT	XC 1◇ A ✠	TP 1◇ B	NT C	VT 1◇ ⊠	XC 1◇ D ✠	NT	NT	NT	VT 1◇ ⊠	NT E		NT G	VT 1◇ ⊠	AW ◇ H ✠	NT	VT 1◇ ⊠	NT	VT 1◇ ⊠
0	0	—	Deansgate ⇌ d																					
½	½	—	**Manchester Oxford Road** d																					
1	1	—	**Manchester Piccadilly** 10 ⇌ a																					
—	—	—	d	05 00	05 05	05 35		05 44	05 50	05 55	06 00			06 06	06 10	06 17		06 21	06 27	06 30	06 32	06 35	←	06 43
4	4	—	Levenshulme d											06 11				06 28			06 37		06 37	
5½	5½	—	Heaton Chapel d											06 14				06 31			→		06 40	
7	7	—	**Stockport** a		05 12			05 52	05 59	06 02	06 07			06 18	06 17	06 27		06 34	06 34	06 38		06 43	06 44	06 50
—	—	—	d		05 13					06 03	06 08			06 19	06 18				06 35	06 39		06 43	06 45	06 51
9¼	9¼	—	Cheadle Hulme d											06 26									06 51	
9¾	—	—	Bramhall d																				06 54	
12¼	—	—	Poynton d																				06 57	
14¼	—	—	Adlington (Cheshire) d																				07 01	
16¼	—	—	Prestbury d																				07 04	
19	—	—	**Macclesfield** a												06 30				06 47			06 55	07 07	
—	—	—	d										06 03		06 31				06 48			06 55	07 08	
27	—	—	Congleton d										06 10										07 15	
—	11½	—	Handforth d									←		06 30										
—	—	0	**Manchester Airport** ✈ d			06 05 →						06 05												
—	—	2¼	Styal d																					
—	13	4	**Wilmslow** d							06 11		06b17		06 34						06 47				06 59
—	14¾	—	Alderley Edge d									06 20		06 37										
—	17¾	—	Chelford d									06 24												
—	21½	—	Goostrey d									06 29												
—	23½	—	Holmes Chapel d									06 32		06 47										
—	27¼	—	Sandbach d				←					06 36		06 53										
—	32	—	**Crewe** 10 65 a	05 44	05 34		05 44			06 27	06 32	06 46		07 04						07 06				07 15
32½	—	—	Kidsgrove 50 a	→									06 16											
35¾	—	—	Longport 50 a																					
38¾	—	—	**Stoke-on-Trent** 50, 68 a				06 07						06 26		06 46				07 04			07 11	07 30	
—	—	—	Stafford 68 a		05 53		06 25				06 57								07 27					07 34
—	—	—	Wolverhampton 7 68 ⇌ a				06 39				07 12								07 43					*07 57*
—	—	—	Birmingham New Street 12 68 a				06 58				07 31	*07 55*							08 05					*08 17*
—	—	—	London Euston 15 ⊖ 65 a		07 28		*07c50*			08 11	*08c36*				08 22				09e34			08 49		08 55

	NT	NT J	VT 1◇ ⊠	NT	XC 1◇ D ✠	VT 1◇ ⊠	NT E	TP 1◇ B ✠		NT K	XC 1◇ A ✠	AW ◇ L ✠	VT 1◇ ⊠	NT	EM ◇ N ✠	NT	NT	NT J	VT 1◇ ⊠	NT	NT	XC 1◇ Q ✠		VT 1◇ ⊠
Deansgate ⇌ d										07 11														
Manchester Oxford Road d										07 15					07 38									
Manchester Piccadilly 10 ⇌ a										07 17					07 41									
d	06 46	06 49	07 00	07 03	07 06	07 15	07 17	07 20		07 21	07 26	07 30	07 35	07 38	07 42	07 46	07 48	07 52	07 55		08 04	08 07		08 15
Levenshulme d		06 55		07 09						07 28				07 43							08 09			
Heaton Chapel d		06 58		07 12						07 31				07 46							08 12			
Stockport a		07 01		07 16		07 22	07 26	07 28		07 34	07 34	07 38	07 43	07 50	07 53		07 57	08 01	08 03		08 16			08 22
d			07u07	07 18		07 23					07 35	07 39	07 43	07 51			07 58		08 04		08 17			08 23
Cheadle Hulme d				07 24										07 55			08 02				08 24			
Bramhall d																	08 05							
Poynton d																	08 08							
Adlington (Cheshire) d																	08 11							
Prestbury d																	08 14							
Macclesfield a											07 48		07 56				08 18							
d											07 49		07 56				08 18							
Congleton d																	08 26							
Handforth d				07 28										07 59						←	08 28			
Manchester Airport ✈ d	07 11															08 11 →				08 11				
Styal d																				08 18				
Wilmslow d	07 21			07 31								07 47		08 02					08 11	08 22	08 31			
Alderley Edge d	07 24			07 34										08a08						08 25	08 34			
Chelford d				07 38																	08 38			
Goostrey d				07 43																	08 43			
Holmes Chapel d	07 32			07 46																08 33	08 46			
Sandbach d	07 36			07 51																08 37	08 51			
Crewe 10 65 a	07 46			08 01								08 08							08 27	08 47	09 01			
Kidsgrove 50 a																	08 32							
Longport 50 a																								
Stoke-on-Trent 50, 68 a					07 43	07 48					08 06		08 12				08 42					08 43		08 48
Stafford 68 a											08 24	*08 42*							*09 09*					
Wolverhampton 7 68 ⇌ a					08 13						08 39	*08 58*							*09 27*			09 13		
Birmingham New Street 12 68 a	*08 56*				08 31						08 58	*09 18*							*09 47*	*09 56*		09 31		
London Euston 15 ⊖ 65 a	*09 38*		08 58			09 23					*09f56*		09 52						10 04					10 23

For general notes see front of timetable
For details of catering facilities see Directory of Train Operators

- **A** To Bournemouth (Table 51)
- **B** From Manchester Airport to Cleethorpes (22 June to 4 September to Doncaster) (Table 29)
- **C** To Sheffield (Table 78)
- **D** To Bristol Temple Meads (Table 51)
- **E** To Chester (Table 88)
- **G** To Hazel Grove (Table 86)
- **H** To Milford Haven (Table 128)
- **J** To Buxton (Table 86)
- **K** From Wigan Wallgate (Table 82) to Hazel Grove (Table 86)
- **L** To Carmarthen (Table 128)
- **N** From Liverpool Lime Street to Norwich (Table 49)
- **Q** To Paignton (Table 51)
- **b** Arr. 0611
- **c** Change at Crewe
- **e** By changing at Stafford, passengers may arrive at 0855
- **f** Change at Stafford

Manchester, Stockport and Manchester Airport → Crewe and Stoke-on-Trent

Network Diagram - see first page of Table 78

		NT	TP	NT	XC	AW	VT	NT	EM	NT	NT	NT	VT	NT		NT	XC	VT	NT	TP	NT	XC	AW	VT	NT
			1◇		1◇	◇	1◇		◇				1◇				1◇	1◇		1◇		1◇	◇	1◇	
		A	B	C	D	E			G			H					J		A	B	K	D	L		
			⊥		⊥	⊥	⊠		⊥				⊠				⊥	⊠		⊥		⊥	⊥	⊠	
Deansgate	d			08 12																	09 12				
Manchester Oxford Road	d			08 15					08 39												09 16				
Manchester Piccadilly 10	a			08 18					08 41												09 18				
	d	08 17	08 20	08 20	08 27	08 30	08 35	08 38	08 43	08 46	08 48	08 52	08 55			09 04	09 07	09 15	09 17	09 20	09 21	09 27	09 30	09 35	09 38
Levenshulme	d			08 28				08 43				08 58				09 09					09 28				09 43
Heaton Chapel	d			08 31				08 46				09 01				09 12					09 31				09 46
Stockport	a	08 27	08 28	08 34	08 34	08 38	08 42	08 50	08 53		08 57	09 04	09 03			09 16		09 22	09 27	09 28	09 34	09 34	09 38	09 42	09 50
	d				08 35	08 39	08 42	08 51			08 58		09 04			09 17		09 23				09 35	09 39	09 42	09 51
Cheadle Hulme	d							08 55			09 02					09 24									09 55
Bramhall	d										09 05														
Poynton	d										09 08														
Adlington (Cheshire)	d										09 11														
Prestbury	d										09 14														
Macclesfield	a				08 47		08 55				09 18											09 47		09 55	
	d				08 49		08 55				09 18											09 49		09 55	
Congleton	d										09 26														
Handforth	d							08 59						←		09 28									09 59
Manchester Airport ✈	d									09 11 →				09 11											
Styal	d																								
Wilmslow	d					08 47		09 02					09 11	09 21		09 31							09 47		10 02
Alderley Edge	d							09a08						09 24		09 34									10a08
Chelford	d															09 38									
Goostrey	d															09 43									
Holmes Chapel	d													09 32		09 46									
Sandbach	d													09 36		09 51									
Crewe 10	65 a					09 06							09 27	09 46		10 01							10 06		
Kidsgrove	50 a										09 32														
Longport	50 a																								
Stoke-on-Trent	50, 68 a				09 06		09 11				09 42						09 43	09 48				10 06		10 11	
Stafford	68 a				09 24	09 42							10 09									10 24	10 42		
Wolverhampton 7	68 a				09 39	09 56							10 27				10 13					10 39	10 56		
Birmingham New Street 12	68 a				09 58	10 17							10 47	10 55			10 31					10 58	11 18		
London Euston 15	⊖ 65 a				10b56		10 42						11 04	11 38				11 23				11b56		11 42	

		EM	NT	NT	NT	VT		NT	NT	XC	VT	NT	TP	NT	XC	AW	VT	NT	EM	NT		NT	NT	VT	NT
		◇				1◇				1◇	1◇		1◇		1◇	◇	1◇		◇					1◇	
		G			H					J		A	B	K	D	E			G				H		
		⊥				⊠				⊥	⊡		⊥		⊥	⊥	⊡		⊥					⊡	
Deansgate	d													10 12											
Manchester Oxford Road	d	09 39												10 16					10 39						
Manchester Piccadilly 10	a	09 41												10 18					10 41						
	d	09 43	09 46	09 48	09 52	09 55			10 04	10 07	10 15	10 17	10 20	10 21	10 27	10 30	10 35	10 38	10 43	10 46		10 48	10 52	10 55	
Levenshulme	d				09 58				10 09					10 28				10 43					10 58		
Heaton Chapel	d				10 01				10 12					10 31				10 46					11 01		
Stockport	a	09 53		09 57	10 04	10 03			10 16		10 22	10 27	10 28	10 34	10 34	10 38	10 42	10 50	10 53			10 57	11 04	11 03	
	d			09 58		10 04			10 17		10 23				10 35	10 39	10 42	10 51				10 58		11 04	
Cheadle Hulme	d			10 02					10 24									10 55				11 02			
Bramhall	d			10 05																		11 05			
Poynton	d			10 08																		11 08			
Adlington (Cheshire)	d			10 11																		11 11			
Prestbury	d			10 14																		11 14			
Macclesfield	a			10 18											10 47		10 55					11 18			
	d			10 18											10 49		10 55					11 18			
Congleton	d			10 26																		11 26			
Handforth	d							←	10 28									10 59							←
Manchester Airport ✈	d		10 11 →					10 11												11 11 →					11 11
Styal	d																								
Wilmslow	d					10 11		10 21	10 31							10 47		11 02						11 11	11 21
Alderley Edge	d							10 24	10 34									11a08							11 24
Chelford	d								10 38																
Goostrey	d								10 43																
Holmes Chapel	d							10 32	10 46																11 32
Sandbach	d							10 36	10 51																11 36
Crewe 10	65 a					10 27		10 46	11 01							11 06								11 27	11 46
Kidsgrove	50 a			10 32																		11 32			
Longport	50 a																								
Stoke-on-Trent	50, 68 a			10 42						10 43	10 48				11 06		11 11					11 42			
Stafford	68 a					11 09									11 24	11 42								12 09	
Wolverhampton 7	68 a					11 27				11 13					11 39	11 56								12 27	
Birmingham New Street 12	68 a					11 47		11 56		11 31					11 58	12 17								12 47	12 55
London Euston 15	⊖ 65 a					12 04		12 38			12 23				12b56		12 42							13 04	13 38

For general notes see front of timetable
For details of catering facilities see Directory of Train Operators

- **A** To Chester (Table 88)
- **B** From Manchester Airport to Cleethorpes (22 June to 4 September to Doncaster) (Table 29)
- **C** From Blackpool North (Table 82) to Hazel Grove (Table 86)
- **D** To Bournemouth (Table 51)
- **E** To Milford Haven (Table 128)
- **G** From Liverpool Lime Street to Norwich (Table 49)
- **H** To Buxton (Table 86)
- **J** To Bristol Temple Meads (Table 51)
- **K** From Preston (Table 82) to Hazel Grove (Table 86)
- **L** To Carmarthen (Table 128)
- **b** Change at Stafford

Manchester, Stockport and Manchester Airport → Crewe and Stoke-on-Trent

Network Diagram - see first page of Table 78

		NT	XC 1◇ A ✕	VT 1◇ 🍽	NT B	TP 1◇ C ✕	NT D	XC 1◇ E ✕	AW ◇ G ✕	VT 1◇ 🍽	NT	EM ◇ H ✕	NT	NT	NT B	VT 1◇ 🍽	NT	NT	XC 1◇ J ✕	VT 1◇ 🍽	NT K	TP 1◇ C ✕	NT D	XC 1◇ E ✕
Deansgate	d						11 12																12 12	
Manchester Oxford Road	d						11 16					11 39											12 16	
Manchester Piccadilly 10	a						11 18					11 41											12 18	
	d	11 04	11 07	11 15	11 17	11 20	11 21	11 27	11 30	11 35	11 38	11 43	11 46	11 48	11 52	11 55		12 04	12 07	12 15	12 17	12 20	12 21	12 27
Levenshulme	d	11 09					11 28				11 43				11 58			12 09					12 28	
Heaton Chapel	d	11 12					11 31				11 46				12 01			12 12					12 31	
Stockport	a	11 16		11 22	11 27	11 28	11 34	11 34	11 38	11 42	11 50	11 53		11 57	12 04	12 03		12 16		12 22	12 27	12 28	12 34	12 34
	d	11 17		11 23				11 35	11 39	11 42	11 51			11 58		12 04		12 17		12 23				12 35
Cheadle Hulme	d	11 24									11 55			12 02				12 24						
Bramhall	d													12 05										
Poynton	d													12 08										
Adlington (Cheshire)	d													12 11										
Prestbury	d													12 14										
Macclesfield	a							11 47		11 55				12 18										12 47
	d							11 49		11 55				12 18										12 49
Congleton	d													12 26										
Handforth	d	11 28									11 59						←	12 28						
Manchester Airport ✈	d												12 11 →				12 11							
Styal	d																							
Wilmslow	d	11 31							11 47		12 02					12 11	12 21	12 31						
Alderley Edge	d	11 34									12a08						12 24	12 34						
Chelford	d	11 38																12 38						
Goostrey	d	11 43																12 43						
Holmes Chapel	d	11 46															12 32	12 46						
Sandbach	d	11 51															12 36	12 51						
Crewe 10	65 a	12 01							12 06							12 27	12 46	13 01						
Kidsgrove	50 a													12 32										
Longport	50 a																							
Stoke-on-Trent	50, 68 a		11 43	11 48				12 06		12 11				12 42					12 43	12 48				13 06
Stafford	68 a							12 24	12 42							13 09								13 24
Wolverhampton 7	68 a		12 13					12 39	12 56							13 27			13 13					13 39
Birmingham New Street 12	68 a		12 31					12 58	13 17							13 47	13 56		13 31					13 58
London Euston 15	⊖ 65 a			13 23				13b56		13 42						14 04	14 38			14 24				14b58

		AW R L ✕	VT 1◇ 🍽	NT	EM ◇ H ✕	NT	NT	NT B	VT 1◇ 🍽	NT	NT	XC 1◇ A ✕	VT 1◇ 🍽	NT K	TP 1◇ C ✕	NT D	XC 1◇ E ✕	AW R G ✕	VT 1◇ 🍽	NT	EM ◇ H ✕	NT	NT
Deansgate	d															13 12							
Manchester Oxford Road	d				12 39											13 16					13 39		
Manchester Piccadilly 10	a				12 41											13 18					13 41		
	d	12 30	12 35	12 38	12 43	12 46	12 48	12 52	12 55		13 04	13 07	13 15	13 17	13 20	13 21	13 27	13 30	13 35	13 38	13 43	13 46	13 48
Levenshulme	d			12 43				12 58			13 09					13 28				13 43			
Heaton Chapel	d			12 46				13 01			13 12					13 31				13 46			
Stockport	a	12 38	12 42	12 50	12 53		12 57	13 04	13 03		13 16		13 22	13 27	13 28	13 34	13 34	13 38	13 42	13 50	13 53		13 57
	d	12 39	12 42	12 51			12 58		13 04		13 17		13 23				13 35	13 39	13 42	13 51			13 58
Cheadle Hulme	d			12 55			13 02				13 24									13 55			14 02
Bramhall	d						13 05																14 05
Poynton	d						13 08																14 08
Adlington (Cheshire)	d						13 11																14 11
Prestbury	d						13 14																14 14
Macclesfield	a		12 55				13 18										13 47		13 55				14 18
	d		12 55				13 18										13 49		13 55				14 18
Congleton	d						13 26																14 26
Handforth	d			12 59						←	13 28									13 59			
Manchester Airport ✈	d					13 11 →				13 11												14 11 →	
Styal	d									13 18													
Wilmslow	d	12 47		13 02					13 11	13 22	13 31							13 47		14 02			
Alderley Edge	d			13a08						13 25	13 34									14a08			
Chelford	d										13 38												
Goostrey	d										13 43												
Holmes Chapel	d									13 33	13 46												
Sandbach	d									13 37	13 51												
Crewe 10	65 a	13 06							13 27	13 47	14 01							14 06					
Kidsgrove	50 a						13 32																14 32
Longport	50 a																						
Stoke-on-Trent	50, 68 a		13 11				13 42					13 43	13 48				14 06		14 11				14 42
Stafford	68 a	13 42							14 09								14 24	14 46					
Wolverhampton 7	68 a	13 56							14 27			14 13					14 39	14 59					
Birmingham New Street 12	68 a	14 17							14 47	14 55		14 31					14 58	15 20					
London Euston 15	⊖ 65 a		14 42						15 04				15 23				15b56		15 42				

For general notes see front of timetable
For details of catering facilities see Directory of Train Operators

- **A** To Bristol Temple Meads (Table 51)
- **B** To Buxton (Table 86)
- **C** From Manchester Airport to Cleethorpes (22 June to 4 September to Doncaster) (Table 29)
- **D** From Preston (Table 82) to Hazel Grove (Table 86)
- **E** To Bournemouth (Table 51)
- **G** To Carmarthen (Table 128)
- **H** From Liverpool Lime Street to Norwich (Table 49)
- **J** To Bristol Temple Meads (Fridays to Exeter St Davids) (Table 51)
- **K** To Chester (Table 88)
- **L** To Milford Haven (Table 128)
- **b** Change at Stafford

Manchester, Stockport and Manchester Airport → Crewe and Stoke-on-Trent

Network Diagram - see first page of Table 78

		NT	VT	NT	NT	XC	VT	NT	TP	NT		XC	AW	VT	NT	EM	NT	NT	NT	VT	NT	NT	XC	VT	NT
			1◇			1◇	1◇		1◇			1◇	R	1◇		◇				1◇			1◇	1◇	
		A				B		C	D	E		G	H			J			A				K		C
			☕			🛒	☕		🛒			🛒	🛒	☕		🛒				☕			🛒	☕	
Deansgate ⇌	d									14 12															
Manchester Oxford Road	d									14 16						14 39									
Manchester Piccadilly 10 ⇌	a									14 18						14 41									
	d	13 52	13 55		14 04	14 07	14 15	14 17	14 20	14 21		14 27	14 30	14 35	14 38	14 43	14 46	14 48	14 52	14 55		15 04	15 07	15 15	15 17
Levenshulme	d	13 58			14 09					14 28					14 43				14 58			15 09			
Heaton Chapel	d	14 01			14 12					14 31					14 46				15 01			15 12			
Stockport	a	14 04	14 03		14 16		14 22	14 27	14 28	14 34		14 34	14 38	14 42	14 50	14 53		14 57	15 04	15 03		15 16		15 22	15 27
	d		14 04		14 17		14 23					14 35	14 39	14 42	14 51			14 58		15 04		15 17		15 23	
Cheadle Hulme	d				14 24										14 55			15 02				15 24			
Bramhall	d																	15 05							
Poynton	d																	15 08							
Adlington (Cheshire)	d																	15 11							
Prestbury	d																	15 14							
Macclesfield	a											14 47		14 55				15 18							
	d											14 49		14 55				15 18							
Congleton	d																	15 26							
Handforth	d			←	14 28										14 59						←	15 28			
Manchester Airport ✈	d			14 11													15 11 →				15 11				
Styal	d																								
Wilmslow	d		14 11	14 21	14 31								14 47		15 02					15 11	15 21	15 31			
Alderley Edge	d			14 24	14 34										15a08						15 24	15 34			
Chelford	d				14 38																	15 38			
Goostrey	d				14 43																	15 43			
Holmes Chapel	d			14 32	14 46																15 32	15 46			
Sandbach	d			14 36	14 51																15 36	15 51			
Crewe 10	65 a		14 27	14 46	15 01								15 06							15 27	15 46	16 01			
Kidsgrove	50 a																	15 32							
Longport	50 a																								
Stoke-on-Trent	50, 68 a					14 43	14 48					15 06		15 11				15 42					15 43	15 48	
Stafford	68 a		*15 09*									15 24	*15 42*							*16 09*					
Wolverhampton 7 ⇌	68 a		*15 27*			15 13						15 39	*15 56*							*16 26*			16 13		
Birmingham New Street 12	68 a		*15 47*	*15 56*		15 31						15 58	*16 17*							*16 47*	*16 55*		16 31		
London Euston 15 ⊖	65 a		16 04	*16 38*			16 23					*16b56*		16 42						17 04	*17 38*			17 23	

		TP		NT	XC	AW	VT	NT	EM	NT	NT	NT	VT	NT	NT	XC		VT	NT	TP	NT	XC	AW	VT	NT
		1◇			1◇	R	1◇		◇				1◇			1◇		1◇		1◇		1◇	R	1◇	
		D		E	G	L			N			A				K			C	D	Q	G	H		
		🛒			🛒	🛒	☕		🛒				☕			🛒		⊠		🛒		🛒	🛒	⊠	
Deansgate ⇌	d			15 12																	16 12				
Manchester Oxford Road	d			15 16					15 39												16 16				
Manchester Piccadilly 10 ⇌	a			15 18					15 41												16 18				
	d	15 20		15 21	15 27	15 30	15 35	15 38	15 43	15 46	15 48	15 52	15 55		16 04	16 07		16 15	16 17	16 20	16 21	16 27	16 30	16 35	16 38
Levenshulme	d			15 28				15 43				15 58			16 09						16 28				16 43
Heaton Chapel	d			15 31				15 46				16 01			16 12						16 31				16 46
Stockport	a	15 28		15 34	15 34	15 38	15 42	15 50	15 53		15 57	16 04	16 03		16 16			16 22	16 27	16 28	16 34	16 34	16 38	16 42	16 50
	d				15 35	15 39	15 42	15 51			15 58		16 04		16 17			16 23				16 35	16 39	16 42	16 51
Cheadle Hulme	d							15 55			16 02				16 24										16 55
Bramhall	d										16 05														
Poynton	d										16 08														
Adlington (Cheshire)	d										16 11														
Prestbury	d										16 14														
Macclesfield	a				15 47		15 55				16 18											16 47		16 56	
	d				15 49		15 55				16 18											16 49		16 56	
Congleton	d										16 26														
Handforth	d							15 59						←	16 28										16 59
Manchester Airport ✈	d									16 11 →				16 11											
Styal	d																								
Wilmslow	d					15 47		16 02					16 11	16 21	16 31								16 49		17 02
Alderley Edge	d							16a08						16 24	16 34										17a08
Chelford	d														16 38										
Goostrey	d														16 43										
Holmes Chapel	d													16 32	16 46										
Sandbach	d													16 36	16 51										
Crewe 10	65 a					16 06							16 27	16 46	17 01								17 08		
Kidsgrove	50 a										16 32														
Longport	50 a																								
Stoke-on-Trent	50, 68 a				16 06		16 11				16 42					16 43		16 49				17 06		17 12	
Stafford	68 a				16 24	*16 46*							*17 10*									17 24	*17 42*		
Wolverhampton 7 ⇌	68 a				16 39	*16 59*							*17 27*			17 13						17 39	*17 56*		
Birmingham New Street 12	68 a				16 58	*17 20*							*17 47*	*17 56*		17 31						17 58	*18 17*		
London Euston 15 ⊖	65 a				*17b56*		17 42						18 06	*18 38*				18 23				*18b59*		18 42	

For general notes see front of timetable
For details of catering facilities see Directory of Train Operators

A To Buxton (Table 86)
B To Paignton (Table 51)
C To Chester (Table 88)
D From Manchester Airport to Cleethorpes (22 June to 4 September to Doncaster) (Table 29)
E From Preston (Table 82) to Hazel Grove (Table 86)
G To Bournemouth (Table 51)
H To Milford Haven (Table 128)
J From Liverpool Lime Street to Nottingham (Table 49)
K To Bristol Temple Meads (Table 51)
L To Pembroke Dock (Table 128)
N From Liverpool Lime Street to Norwich (Table 49)
Q From Preston (Table 82) to Buxton (Table 86)
b Change at Stafford

Table 84 — Mondays to Fridays

Manchester, Stockport and Manchester Airport → Crewe and Stoke-on-Trent

Network Diagram - see first page of Table 78

Station		EM	NT	NT	NT	VT	NT	NT		NT	XC	NT	VT	NT	TP	NT	NT	XC	AW	VT	NT	EM		NT	NT
		◇				1 ◇					1 ◇		1 ◇		1 ◇			1 ◇	R	1 ◇		◇			
		A			B		C				D	E			G	H	C	J	K			L			
		🍴				⊠					🍴		⊠		🍴			🍴	🍴	⊠		🍴			
Deansgate 🚆	d													17 10		17 15									
Manchester Oxford Road	d	16 39												17 13		17 19						17 39			
Manchester Piccadilly 10 🚆	a	16 41												17 15		17 21						17 41			
	d	16 43	16 46	16 48	16 51	16 55	16 58			17 03	17 06	17 09	17 15	17 17	17 20	17 23	17 23	17 27	17 30	17 35	17 38	17 43		17 46	17 48
Levenshulme	d						17 03			17 08							17 28				17 43				
Heaton Chapel	d						17 06			17 11							17 31				17 46				
Stockport	a	16 53		16 57	17 01	17 03	17 10			17 15		17 17	17 22	17 27	17 28	17 32	17 35	17 35	17 39	17 43	17 50	17 53			17 57
	d			16 58		17 04				17 16			17 23	17 28				17 35	17 40	17 43	17 51				17 58
Cheadle Hulme	d			17 02						17 24				17 32							17 55				18 02
Bramhall	d			17 05										17 35											18 05
Poynton	d			17 08										17 38											18 08
Adlington (Cheshire)	d			17 11										17 41											18 11
Prestbury	d			17 14										17 44											18 14
Macclesfield	a			17 18							17 26			17 48						17 55					18 17
	d			17 18							17 27			17 48						17 55					18 18
Congleton	d			17 26										17 56											18 26
Handforth	d							←		17 28											17 59				
Manchester Airport ✈	d		17 11 →					17 11																18 11 →	
Styal	d																								
Wilmslow	d					17 11		17 21		17 31								17 44	17 48		18 02				
Alderley Edge	d							17 24		17 34											18 05				
Chelford	d									17 38															
Goostrey	d									17 43															
Holmes Chapel	d							17 32		17 46															
Sandbach	d							17 36		17 51											18 16				
Crewe 10	65 a					17 27		17 44		18 01									18 11		18 26				
Kidsgrove	50 a			17 32																					18 32
Longport	50 a																								
Stoke-on-Trent	50, 68 a			17 42							17 43		17 49	18 10						18 11					18 42
Stafford	68 a					18 09												18 25	18 42						
Wolverhampton 7	68 🚆 a					18 27					18 13							18 39	18 56						
Birmingham New Street 12	68 a					18 48		18 55			18 31							18 58	19 17						
London Euston 15	⊖ 65 a					19 08		19 38					19 23					20b02		19 42					

Station		NT	VT	NT	XC	NT	VT	NT	TP	NT	XC	AW	VT	NT		EM	NT	NT	NT	VT	NT	NT	XC	VT	NT
			1 ◇		1 ◇		1 ◇		1 ◇		1 ◇	◇	1 ◇			◇				1 ◇			1 ◇	1 ◇	
		B			N			E	G	Q	J	U				A			B				V		E
			⊠		🍴		⊠		🍴		🍴	🍴	⊠			🍴				⊠			🍴	🍽	
Deansgate 🚆	d									18 12															
Manchester Oxford Road	d									18 16						18 39									
Manchester Piccadilly 10 🚆	a									18 18						18 41									
	d	17 52	17 55		18 05	18 08	18 15	18 17	18 20	18 21	18 27	18 30	18 35	18 38		18 43	18 46	18 48	18 52	18 55		19 04	19 07	19 15	19 17
Levenshulme	d	17 58				18 13				18 28				18 43					18 58			19 09			
Heaton Chapel	d	18 01				18 16				18 31				18 46					19 01			19 12			
Stockport	a	18 04	18 03			18 20	18 22	18 27	18 28	18 34	18 34	18 38	18 42	18 50		18 53		18 57	19 04	19 03		19 16		19 22	19 27
	d		18 04			18 22	18 23				18 35	18 39	18 42	18 51				18 58		19 04		19 17		19 23	
Cheadle Hulme	d					18 30								18 55				19 02				19 24			
Bramhall	d																	19 05							
Poynton	d																	19 08							
Adlington (Cheshire)	d																	19 11							
Prestbury	d																	19 14							
Macclesfield	a				18 24								18 55					19 18						19 35	
	d				18 25								18 55					19 18						19 36	
Congleton	d										18 54							19 26							
Handforth	d			←		18 34								18 59							←	19 28			
Manchester Airport ✈	d			18 11													19 14 →				19 14				
Styal	d			18 18																					
Wilmslow	d		18 11	18 22		18 37						18 47		19 02						19 11	19 26	19 31			
Alderley Edge	d			18 25		18 40								19a08							19a32	19 34			
Chelford	d					18 44																19 38			
Goostrey	d					18 48																19 43			
Holmes Chapel	d			18 33		18 51																19 46			
Sandbach	d			18 37		18 56																19 51			
Crewe 10	65 a		18 27	18 47		19 06						19 07								19 27		20 01			
Kidsgrove	50 a																	19 32							
Longport	50 a																								
Stoke-on-Trent	50, 68 a				18 43		18 48				19 06		19 11					19 42					19 43	19 51	
Stafford	68 a		19 09								19 24	19 41								20 15		20 38			
Wolverhampton 7	68 🚆 a		19 27		19 13						19 39	19 57								20 29		20 57	20 13		
Birmingham New Street 12	68 a		19 47	19 56	19 31						19 58	20 17								20 47		21 18	20 31		
London Euston 15	⊖ 65 a		20 08				20 23					21 06	20 42							21 10				21 25	

For general notes see front of timetable
For details of catering facilities see Directory of Train Operators

- **A** From Liverpool Lime Street to Norwich (Table 49)
- **B** To Buxton (Table 86)
- **C** To Hazel Grove (Table 86)
- **D** To Cardiff Central (Table 51)
- **E** To Chester (Table 88)
- **G** From Manchester Airport to Cleethorpes (22 June to 4 September to Doncaster) (Table 29)
- **H** From Preston (Table 82) to Buxton (Table 86)
- **J** To Bournemouth (Table 51)
- **K** To Milford Haven (Table 128)
- **L** From Liverpool Lime Street to Nottingham (Table 49)
- **N** To Plymouth (Table 51)
- **Q** From Wigan Wallgate (Table 82) to Buxton (Table 86)
- **U** To Carmarthen (Table 128)
- **V** To Bristol Temple Meads (Table 51)
- **b** Change at Stafford

Manchester, Stockport and Manchester Airport → Crewe and Stoke-on-Trent

Network Diagram - see first page of Table 78

		TP 1◇ A	NT B	XC 1◇ C	AW ◇ D	EM ◇ E		NT	NT	NT G	VT 1◇	NT	NT	XC 1◇	VT 1◇	NT H	TP 1◇ A	XC 1◇	AW ◇ D	EM ◇ E		NT	NT	NT G	NT
Deansgate	d																								
Manchester Oxford Road	d					19 39		19 43												20 39		20 43			
Manchester Piccadilly 10	a					19 41		19 45												20 41		20 45			
	d	19 18	19 22	19 27	19 30	19 43		19 46	19 48	19 52	19 55		20 04	20 07	20 15	20 17	20 20	20 27	20 30	20 43		20 46	20 48	20 52	21 04
Levenshulme	d		19 28							19 58			20 09											20 58	21 09
Heaton Chapel	d		19 31							20 01			20 12											21 01	21 12
Stockport	a	19 26	19 34	19 34	19 38	19 53			19 57	20 04	20 03		20 16		20 22	20 27	20 28	20 34	20 38	20 53			20 58	21 04	21 16
	d			19 35	19 39				19 58		20 04		20 17		20 23			20 35	20 39				20 58		21 17
Cheadle Hulme	d								20 02				20 24										21 02		21 24
Bramhall	d								20 05														21 05		
Poynton	d								20 08														21 08		
Adlington (Cheshire)	d								20 11														21 11		
Prestbury	d								20 14														21 14		
Macclesfield	a			19 47					20 18						20 35			20 47					21 18		
	d			19 49					20 18						20 36			20 49					21 18		
Congleton	d								20 26														21 26		
Handforth	d											←	20 28												21 28
Manchester Airport	d							20 14 →				20 14										21 14			
Styal	d																								
Wilmslow	d				19 47						20 11	20a24	20 31						20 47			21a24			21 31
Alderley Edge	d												20 34												21 34
Chelford	d												20 38												21 38
Goostrey	d												20 43												21 43
Holmes Chapel	d												20 46												21 46
Sandbach	d												20 51												21 51
Crewe 10	65 a				20 09						20 27		21 01						21 11						22 01
Kidsgrove	50 a								20 32														21 32		
Longport	50 a																								
Stoke-on-Trent	50, 68 a			20 06					20 42					20 43	20 51			21 06					21 42		
Stafford	68 a			20 24							20 47		*21 38*					21 24	*21 43*						*22 40*
Wolverhampton 7	68 a			20 39							*21 26*		*21 57*	21 13				21 39	*22b39*						*22 57*
Birmingham New Street 12	68 a			20 58							*21 47*		*22 17*	21 36				22 00	*22 50*						*23 18*
London Euston 15	⊖ 65 a				*22 09*						22 12				22 51				*23 53*						

		VT 1◇	NT H	TP 1◇ A	XC 1◇	AW ◇ D	NT	NT	NT G	NT	XC 1◇	NT H		TP 1◇ J	EM ◇ E	AW ◇ K	NT	NT	NT	NT G	NT	NT H	NT		
Deansgate	d																								
Manchester Oxford Road	d						21 43								22 24		22 43								
Manchester Piccadilly 10	a						21 45								22 26		22 45								
	d	21 15	21 17	21 20	21 27	21 35	21 46	21 48	21 52	22 04	22 07	22 17		22 20	22 28	22 35	22 46	22 48	23 03	23 10	23 14	23 17	23 38		
Levenshulme	d								21 58	22 09									23 09				23 43		
Heaton Chapel	d								22 01	22 12									23 12				23 46		
Stockport	a	21 22	21 27	21 28	21 35	21 43		21 57	22 04	22 16	22 15	22 27		22 28	22 37	22 43		22 57	23 16	23 19	23 23	23 26	23 50		
	d	21 23			21 35	21 44		21 58		22 17	22 16					22 44		22 58	23 16		23 23		23 50		
Cheadle Hulme	d							22 02		22 24								23 02	23 23		23 27		23 54		
Bramhall	d							22 05										23 05			23 30				
Poynton	d							22 08										23 08			23 33				
Adlington (Cheshire)	d							22 11										23 11			23 37				
Prestbury	d							22 14										23 14			23 40				
Macclesfield	a	21 35			21 48			22 18			22 28							23 20			23 46				
	d	21 36			21 49			22 18			22 29														
Congleton	d							22 26																	
Handforth	d									22 28									23 27				23 58		
Manchester Airport	d						22 14										23 14								
Styal	d																								
Wilmslow	d					21 51	22a22			22 31						22 52	23a22		23 30				00 01		
Alderley Edge	d									22 34									23a36				00 04		
Chelford	d									22 38													00 08		
Goostrey	d									22 43													00 12		
Holmes Chapel	d									22 46													00 15		
Sandbach	d									22 51													00 20		
Crewe 10	65 a					22 11				23 01						23 10							00 30		
Kidsgrove	50 a							22 32																	
Longport	50 a																								
Stoke-on-Trent	50, 68 a	21 51			22 07			22 42			22 46														
Stafford	68 a				22 25						23 06														
Wolverhampton 7	68 a				22 39						23 19														
Birmingham New Street 12	68 a				23 03						23 40														
London Euston 15	⊖ 65 a	23 50																							

For general notes see front of timetable
For details of catering facilities see Directory of Train Operators

A From Manchester Airport to Cleethorpes (22 June to 4 September to Doncaster) (Table 29)
B To Hazel Grove (Table 86)
C To Southampton Central (Table 51)
D To Cardiff Central (Table 131)
E From Liverpool Lime Street to Nottingham (Table 49)
G To Buxton (Table 86)
H To Chester (Table 88)
J From Manchester Airport to Sheffield (Table 78)
K To Shrewsbury (Table 131)
b Change at Crewe and Stafford

Manchester, Stockport and Manchester Airport → Crewe and Stoke-on-Trent

Network Diagram - see first page of Table 78

		XC	VT	NT	TP	NT	VT	NT	NT	XC	NT	VT	NT	AW	VT	NT		NT	NT	VT	XC	NT	NT	XC	VT
		1◇	1◇		1◇		1◇			1◇		1◇		◇	1◇					1◇	1◇			1◇	1◇
		A			B	C				D			E	G					H		J			K	
		🛒	🍽				🍽			🛒		🍽		🛒	🍽					🍽	🛒			🛒	🍽
Deansgate ⇌	d																								
Manchester Oxford Road	d																								
Manchester Piccadilly 10 ⇌	a																								
	d	05 11	05 25	05 35	05 44	05 50	05 55			06 00	06 06	06 10	06 17	06 30	06 35	06 42		06 46	06 49	06 55	07 00		07 03	07 07	07 15
Levenshulme	d										06 11								06 55				07 09		
Heaton Chapel	d										06 14								06 58				07 12		
Stockport	a		05 33		05 52	05 59	06 02			06 07	06 18	06 17	06 27	06 38	06 43	06 50			07 01	07 03	07 08		07 16		07 22
	d		05 34				06 03			06 08	06 19	06 18		06 39	06 43	06 52				07 04	07 09		07 18		07 23
Cheadle Hulme	d										06 26					06 56							07 24		
Bramhall	d															06 59									
Poynton	d															07 02									
Adlington (Cheshire)	d															07 05									
Prestbury	d															07 08									
Macclesfield	a									06 20		06 30			06 55	07 12					07 23				
	d								06 03	06 21		06 31			06 55	07 12					07 25				
Congleton	d								06 10							07 20									
Handforth	d							←			06 30											←	07 28		
Manchester Airport ✈	d			06 05 →				06 05										07 11 →				07 11			
Styal	d																								
Wilmslow	d		05 41				06 11	06 14			06 33			06 47						07 11		07 21	07 31		
Alderley Edge	d							06 17			06 36											07 24	07 34		
Chelford	d							06 21															07 38		
Goostrey	d							06 25															07 43		
Holmes Chapel	d							06 28			06 44											07 32	07 46		
Sandbach	d							06 33			06 49											07 36	07 51		
Crewe 10	65 a	05 45	05 57				06 27	06 43			06 59			07 06						07 27		07 46	08 01		
Kidsgrove	50 a								06 16							07 28									
Longport	50 a																								
Stoke-on-Trent	50, 68 a	06 07							06 26	06 38		06 46			07 11	07 39					07 43			07 43	07 48
Stafford	68 a	06 25	06 17				*07 10*			06 57				*07 38*						*08 10*					
Wolverhampton 7 ⇌	68 a	06 39	*06 39*				*07 28*			07 12				*07 57*						*08 28*	08 16			08 13	
Birmingham New Street 12	68 a	06 58	*06 58*				*07 47*	*07 55*		07 31				*08 17*						*08 47*	08 37	*08 55*		08 31	
London Euston 15	⊖ 65 a	*07b54*	07 54				08 10					08 27		*08 59*	08 46					09 04					09 23

		NT	TP	NT	XC	AW	VT	NT	EM	NT		NT	NT	VT	XC	NT	NT	XC	VT	NT	TP	NT	XC	AW	VT
			1◇		1◇	◇	1◇		◇					1◇	1◇			1◇	1◇		1◇		1◇	◇	1◇
		E	B	L	A	N			Q				H		U			V		E	B	X	A	G	
			🛒		🛒	🛒	🍽		🛒					🍽	🛒			🛒	🍽		🛒		🛒	🛒	🍽
Deansgate ⇌	d			07 11																		08 12			
Manchester Oxford Road	d			07 15					07 38													08 15			
Manchester Piccadilly 10 ⇌	a			07 17					07 41													08 18			
	d	07 17	07 20	07 21	07 27	07 30	07 35	07 38	07 42	07 46		07 48	07 52	07 55	08 00		08 04	08 07	08 15	08 17	08 20	08 20	08 27	08 30	08 35
Levenshulme	d			07 28				07 43					07 58				08 09					08 28			
Heaton Chapel	d			07 31				07 46									08 12					08 31			
Stockport	a	07 27	07 28	07 34	07 34	07 38	07 43	07 50	07 53			07 57	08 02	08 03	08 08		08 16		08 22	08 27	08 28	08 34	08 34	08 38	08 42
	d				07 35	07 39	07 43	07 51				07 58		08 04	08 09		08 17		08 23				08 35	08 39	08 42
Cheadle Hulme	d							07 55				08 02					08 24								
Bramhall	d											08 05													
Poynton	d											08 08													
Adlington (Cheshire)	d											08 11													
Prestbury	d											08 14													
Macclesfield	a				07 48		07 56					08 18			08 23								08 48		08 55
	d				07 49		07 56					08 18			08 25								08 49		08 55
Congleton	d											08 26													
Handforth	d							07 59								←	08 28								
Manchester Airport ✈	d									08 11 →						08 11									
Styal	d															08 18									
Wilmslow	d					07 47		08 01						08 11		08 22	08 31							08 47	
Alderley Edge	d							08a07								08 25	08 34								
Chelford	d																08 38								
Goostrey	d																08 43								
Holmes Chapel	d															08 33	08 46								
Sandbach	d															08 37	08 51								
Crewe 10	65 a					08 06								08 27		08 47	09 01							09 06	
Kidsgrove	50 a											08 32													
Longport	50 a																								
Stoke-on-Trent	50, 68 a				08 06		08 12					08 42			08 44			08 43	08 48				09 06		09 12
Stafford	68 a				08 25	*08 42*								*09 09*									09 25	*09 42*	
Wolverhampton 7 ⇌	68 a				08 39	*08 58*								*09 27*	09 17			09 13					09 39	*09 56*	
Birmingham New Street 12	68 a				08 58	*09 18*								*09 47*	09 38	*09 55*		09 31					09 58	*10 17*	
London Euston 15	⊖ 65 a				*10c01*		09 42							10 04					10 23				*11c01*		10 42

For general notes see front of timetable
For details of catering facilities see Directory of Train Operators

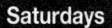

- **A** To Bournemouth (Table 51)
- **B** From Manchester Airport to Cleethorpes (27 June to 5 September to Doncaster) (Table 29)
- **C** To Sheffield (Table 78)
- **D** To Bristol Temple Meads (Table 51)
- **E** To Chester (Table 88)
- **G** To Milford Haven (Table 128)
- **H** To Buxton (Table 86)
- **J** Until 5 September. To Newquay (Table 135)
- **K** From 12 September. To Bristol Temple Meads (Table 51)
- **L** From Wigan Wallgate (Table 82) to Hazel Grove (Table 86)
- **N** To Carmarthen (Table 128)
- **Q** From Liverpool Lime Street to Norwich (Table 49)
- **U** Until 5 September. To Paignton (Table 51)
- **V** From 12 September. To Paignton (Table 51)
- **X** From Blackpool North (Table 82) to Hazel Grove (Table 86)
- **b** Change at Crewe
- **c** Change at Stafford

Table 84

Saturdays

Manchester, Stockport and Manchester Airport → Crewe and Stoke-on-Trent

Network Diagram - see first page of Table 78

		NT	EM ◇ A 🛒	NT		NT	NT B	VT 1◇ 🍽	NT	NT	XC 1◇ C 🛒	VT 1◇ 🍽	NT D	TP 1◇ E 🛒	NT G	XC 1◇ H 🛒	AW ◇ J 🛒	VT 1◇ 🍽	NT	EM ◇ A 🛒		NT	NT	NT B	VT 1◇ 🍽
Deansgate 🚋	d														09 12										
Manchester Oxford Road	d		08 39												09 16					09 39					
Manchester Piccadilly 10 🚋	a		08 41												09 18					09 41					
	d	08 38	08 43	08 46		08 48	08 52	08 55		09 04	09 07	09 15	09 17	09 20	09 21	09 27	09 30	09 35	09 38	09 43		09 46	09 48	09 52	09 55
Levenshulme	d	08 43					08 58			09 09					09 28				09 43					09 58	
Heaton Chapel	d	08 46					09 01			09 12					09 31				09 46					10 01	
Stockport	a	08 50	08 53			08 57	09 04	09 03		09 16		09 22	09 27	09 28	09 34	09 34	09 38	09 42	09 50	09 53			09 57	10 04	10 03
	d	08 51				08 58		09 04		09 17		09 23				09 35	09 39	09 42	09 51				09 58		10 04
Cheadle Hulme	d	08 55				09 02				09 24									09 55				10 02		
Bramhall	d					09 05																	10 05		
Poynton	d					09 08																	10 08		
Adlington (Cheshire)	d					09 11																	10 11		
Prestbury	d					09 14																	10 14		
Macclesfield	a					09 18										09 47		09 55					10 18		
	d					09 18										09 49		09 55					10 18		
Congleton	d					09 26																	10 26		
Handforth	d	08 59							←	09 28									09 59						
Manchester Airport ✈	d			09 11 →					09 11													10 11 →			
Styal	d																								
Wilmslow	d	09 02						09 11	09 21	09 31							09 47		10 02						10 11
Alderley Edge	d	09a08							09 24	09 34									10a08						
Chelford	d									09 38															
Goostrey	d									09 43															
Holmes Chapel	d								09 32	09 46															
Sandbach	d								09 36	09 51															
Crewe 10	65 a							09 27	09 46	10 01							10 06								10 27
Kidsgrove	50 a					09 32																	10 32		
Longport	50 a																								
Stoke-on-Trent	50, 68 a					09 42					09 43	09 48				10 06		10 12					10 42		
Stafford	68 a							10 09								10 25	10 42								11 09
Wolverhampton 7	68 🚋 a							10 27			10 13					10 39	10 56								11 27
Birmingham New Street 12	68 a							10 47	10 55		10 31					10 58	11 17								11 47
London Euston 15	⊖ 65 a							11 04	11 38			11 23				11b56		11 42							12 04

		NT	NT	XC 1◇ C 🛒	VT 1◇ 🍽	NT D	TP 1◇ E 🛒	NT G	XC 1◇ H 🛒	AW ◇ K 🛒	VT 1◇ 🍽	NT	EM ◇ A 🛒	NT		NT	NT B	VT 1◇ 🍽	NT	NT	XC 1◇ C 🛒	VT 1◇ 🍽	NT D	TP 1◇ E 🛒	NT G
Deansgate 🚋	d							10 12																	11 12
Manchester Oxford Road	d							10 16					10 39												11 16
Manchester Piccadilly 10 🚋	a							10 18					10 41												11 18
	d		10 04	10 07	10 15	10 17	10 20	10 21	10 27	10 30	10 35	10 38	10 43	10 46		10 48	10 52	10 55		11 04	11 07	11 15	11 17	11 20	11 21
Levenshulme	d		10 09					10 28				10 43					10 58			11 09					11 28
Heaton Chapel	d		10 12					10 31				10 46					11 01			11 12					11 31
Stockport	a		10 16		10 22	10 27	10 28	10 34	10 34	10 38	10 42	10 50	10 53			10 57	11 04	11 03		11 16		11 22	11 27	11 28	11 34
	d		10 17		10 23				10 35	10 39	10 42	10 51				10 58		11 04		11 17		11 23			
Cheadle Hulme	d		10 24									10 55				11 02				11 24					
Bramhall	d															11 05									
Poynton	d															11 08									
Adlington (Cheshire)	d															11 11									
Prestbury	d															11 14									
Macclesfield	a								10 47		10 55					11 18									
	d								10 49		10 55					11 18									
Congleton	d															11 26									
Handforth	d	←	10 28									10 59							←	11 28					
Manchester Airport ✈	d	10 11												11 11 →					11 11						
Styal	d																								
Wilmslow	d	10 21	10 31							10 47		11 02						11 11	11 21	11 31					
Alderley Edge	d	10 24	10 34									11a08							11 24	11 34					
Chelford	d		10 38																	11 38					
Goostrey	d		10 43																	11 43					
Holmes Chapel	d	10 32	10 46																11 32	11 46					
Sandbach	d	10 36	10 51																11 36	11 51					
Crewe 10	65 a	10 46	11 01							11 06								11 27	11 46	12 01					
Kidsgrove	50 a															11 32									
Longport	50 a																								
Stoke-on-Trent	50, 68 a			10 43	10 48				11 06		11 12					11 42					11 43	11 48			
Stafford	68 a								11 25	11 42								12 09							
Wolverhampton 7	68 🚋 a			11 13					11 39	11 56								12 27			12 13				
Birmingham New Street 12	68 a	11 55		11 31					11 58	12 17								12 47	12c55		12 31				
London Euston 15	⊖ 65 a	12 38			12 23				12b56		12 42							13 04	13 38			13 23			

For general notes see front of timetable
For details of catering facilities see Directory of Train Operators

A From Liverpool Lime Street to Norwich (Table 49)
B To Buxton (Table 86)
C To Bristol Temple Meads (Table 51)
D To Chester (Table 88)
E From Manchester Airport to Cleethorpes (27 June to 5 September to Doncaster) (Table 29)
G From Preston (Table 82) to Hazel Grove (Table 86)
H To Bournemouth (Table 51)
J To Carmarthen (Table 128)
K To Milford Haven (Table 128)
b Change at Stafford
c From 7 November arr. 1250

Table 84

Saturdays

Manchester, Stockport and Manchester Airport → Crewe and Stoke-on-Trent

Network Diagram - see first page of Table 78

	XC	AW	VT	NT	EM	NT	NT		NT	VT	NT	NT	XC	VT	NT	TP	NT	XC	AW	VT	NT	EM	NT	NT
	1 ◇	◇	1 ◇		◇					1 ◇			1 ◇	1 ◇		1 ◇		1 ◇	R	1 ◇		◇		
	A	B			C				D				E		G	H	J	A	K			C		
Deansgate d																	12 12							
Manchester Oxford Road d					11 39												12 16					12 39		
Manchester Piccadilly 10 a					11 41												12 18					12 41		
d	11 27	11 30	11 35	11 38	11 43	11 46	11 48		11 52	11 55		12 04	12 07	12 15	12 17	12 20	12 21	12 27	12 30	12 35	12 38	12 43	12 46	12 48
Levenshulme d				11 43					11 58			12 09					12 28				12 43			
Heaton Chapel d				11 46					12 01			12 12					12 31				12 46			
Stockport a	11 34	11 38	11 42	11 50	11 53		11 57		12 04	12 03		12 16		12 22	12 27	12 28	12 34	12 34	12 38	12 42	12 50	12 53		12 57
d	11 35	11 39	11 42	11 51			11 58			12 04		12 17		12 23				12 35	12 39	12 42	12 51			12 58
Cheadle Hulme d				11 55			12 02					12 24									12 55			13 02
Bramhall d							12 05																	13 05
Poynton d							12 08																	13 08
Adlington (Cheshire) d							12 11																	13 11
Prestbury d							12 14																	13 14
Macclesfield a	11 47		11 55				12 18											12 47		12 55				13 18
d	11 49		11 55				12 18											12 49		12 55				13 18
Congleton d							12 26																	13 26
Handforth d				11 59							←	12 28									12 59			
Manchester Airport d						12 11 →					12 11												13 11 →	
Styal d																								
Wilmslow d		11 47		12 02						12 11	12 21	12 31							12 47		13 02			
Alderley Edge d				12a08							12 24	12 34									13a08			
Chelford d												12 38												
Goostrey d												12 43												
Holmes Chapel d											12 32	12 46												
Sandbach d											12 36	12 51												
Crewe 10 65 a		12 06								12 27	12 46	13 01							13 06					
Kidsgrove 50 a							12 32																	13 32
Longport 50 a																								
Stoke-on-Trent 50, 68 a	12 06		12 12				12 42						12 43	12 48				13 06		13 12				13 42
Stafford 68 a	12 24	12 42								13 09								13 25	13 42					
Wolverhampton 7 68 a	12 39	12 56								13 27			13 13					13 39	13 56					
Birmingham New Street 12 68 a	12 58	13 17								13 47	13b55		13 31					13 58	14 17					
London Euston 15 ⊖ 65 a	13c56		13 42							14 04	14 38			14 23				14c56		14 42				

	NT		VT	NT	NT	NT	XC	VT	NT	TP	NT	XC	AW	VT	NT	EM	NT		NT	NT	VT	NT	NT	NT
			1 ◇				1 ◇	1 ◇		1 ◇		1 ◇	R	1 ◇		◇					1 ◇			
	D				L	N	Q		G	H	J	A	B			C				D			L	N
Deansgate d											13 12													
Manchester Oxford Road d											13 16					13 39								
Manchester Piccadilly 10 a											13 18					13 41								
d	12 52		12 55		13 04	13 04	13 07	13 15	13 17	13 20	13 21	13 27	13 30	13 35	13 38	13 43	13 46		13 48	13 52	13 55		14 04	14 04
Levenshulme d	12 58				13 09	13 09					13 28				13 43					13 58			14 09	14 09
Heaton Chapel d	13 01				13 12	13 12					13 31				13 46					14 01			14 12	14 12
Stockport a	13 04		13 03		13 16	13 16		13 22	13 27	13 28	13 34	13 34	13 38	13 42	13 50	13 53			13 57	14 04	14 03		14 16	14 16
d			13 04		13 17	13 17		13 23				13 35	13 39	13 42	13 51				13 58		14 04		14 17	14 17
Cheadle Hulme d					13 24	13 24									13 55				14 02				14 24	14 24
Bramhall d																			14 05					
Poynton d																			14 08					
Adlington (Cheshire) d																			14 11					
Prestbury d																			14 14					
Macclesfield a												13 47		13 55					14 18					
d												13 49		13 55					14 18					
Congleton d																			14 26					
Handforth d				←	13 28	13 28									13 59								14 28	14 28
Manchester Airport d				13 11													14 11 →					14 11		
Styal d				13 18																				
Wilmslow d			13 11	13 22	13 31	13 35							13 47		14 02						14 11	14 21	14 31	14 35
Alderley Edge d				13 25	13 34	13 38									14a08							14 24	14 34	14 38
Chelford d					13 38	13 42																	14 38	14 42
Goostrey d					13 43	13 46																	14 43	14 46
Holmes Chapel d				13 33	13 46	13 49																14 32	14 46	14 49
Sandbach d				13 37	13 51	13 54																14 36	14 51	14 54
Crewe 10 65 a			13 27	13 47	14 01	14 04							14 06								14 27	14 46	15 01	15 04
Kidsgrove 50 a																			14 32					
Longport 50 a																								
Stoke-on-Trent 50, 68 a							13 43	13 48				14 06		14 12					14 42					
Stafford 68 a			14 09									14 25	14 46								15 09			
Wolverhampton 7 68 a			14 27				14 13					14 39	14 59								15 27			
Birmingham New Street 12 68 a			14 47	14e55			14 31					14 58	15 18								15 47	15f55		
London Euston 15 ⊖ 65 a			15 04					15 23				15c56		15 42							16 04	16 38		

For general notes see front of timetable
For details of catering facilities see Directory of Train Operators

A To Bournemouth (Table 51)
B To Carmarthen (Table 128)
C From Liverpool Lime Street to Norwich (Table 49)
D To Buxton (Table 86)
E To Paignton (from 12 September to Bristol Temple Meads) (Table 51)
G To Chester (Table 88)
H From Manchester Airport to Cleethorpes (27 June to 5 September to Doncaster) (Table 29)
J From Preston (Table 82) to Hazel Grove (Table 86)
K To Milford Haven (Table 128)
L Until 31 October
N From 7 November
Q To Bristol Temple Meads (Table 51)
b From 7 November arr. 1417
c Change at Stafford
e From 7 November arr. 1518
f From 7 November arr. 1550

Manchester, Stockport and Manchester Airport → Crewe and Stoke-on-Trent

Network Diagram - see first page of Table 78

		XC	VT	NT	TP	NT	XC	AW	VT	NT	EM	NT		NT	NT	VT	NT	NT	NT	XC	VT	NT	TP	NT	XC
		[1] ◇	[1] ◇		[1] ◇		[1] ◇	[R]	[1] ◇		◇					[1] ◇				[1] ◇	[1] ◇		[1] ◇		[1] ◇
		A		B	C	D	E	G			H				J			K	L	N		B	C	D	E
		🛒	🍴		🛒		🛒	🛒	🍴		🛒					🍴				🛒	🍴		🛒		🛒
Deansgate 🚆	d					14 12																		15 12	
Manchester Oxford Road	d					14 16					14 39													15 16	
Manchester Piccadilly [10] 🚆	a					14 18					14 41													15 18	
	d	14 07	14 15	14 17	14 20	14 21	14 27	14 30	14 35	14 38	14 43	14 46		14 48	14 52	14 55		15 04	15 04	15 07	15 15	15 17	15 20	15 21	15 27
Levenshulme	d					14 28				14 43					14 58			15 09	15 09					15 28	
Heaton Chapel	d					14 31				14 46					15 01			15 12	15 12					15 31	
Stockport	a		14 22	14 27	14 28	14 34	14 34	14 38	14 42	14 50	14 53			14 57	15 04	15 03		15 16	15 16		15 22	15 27	15 28	15 34	15 34
	d		14 23				14 35	14 39	14 42	14 51				14 58		15 04		15 17	15 17		15 23				15 35
Cheadle Hulme	d									14 55				15 02				15 24	15 24						
Bramhall	d													15 05											
Poynton	d													15 08											
Adlington (Cheshire)	d													15 11											
Prestbury	d													15 14											
Macclesfield	a						14 47		14 55					15 18											15 47
	d						14 49		14 55					15 18											15 49
Congleton	d													15 26											
Handforth	d									14 59							←	15 28	15 28						
Manchester Airport ✈	d											15 11 →					15 11								
Styal	d																								
Wilmslow	d							14 47		15 02						15 11	15 21	15 31	15 35						
Alderley Edge	d									15a08							15 24	15 34	15 38						
Chelford	d																	15 38	15 42						
Goostrey	d																	15 43	15 46						
Holmes Chapel	d																15 32	15 46	15 49						
Sandbach	d																15 36	15 51	15 54						
Crewe [10]	65 a							15 06								15 27	15 46	16 01	16 04						
Kidsgrove	50 a													15 32											
Longport	50 a																								
Stoke-on-Trent	50, 68 a	14 43	14 48				15 06		15 12					15 42						15 43	15 48				16 06
Stafford	68 a						15 25	15 42								16 09									16 24
Wolverhampton [7]	68 🚆 a	15 13					15 39	15 56								16 27				16 13					16 39
Birmingham New Street [12]	68 a	15 31					15 58	16 17								16 47	16b55			16 31					16 58
London Euston [15]	⊖ 65 a		16 23				16c56		16 42							17 04	17b38				17 23				17c57

		AW	VT	NT	EM	NT		NT	NT	VT	NT	NT	NT	XC	VT	NT	TP	NT	XC	AW	VT	NT		EM	NT
		[R]	[1] ◇		◇					[1] ◇				[1] ◇	[1] ◇		[1] ◇		[1] ◇	[R]	[1] ◇			◇	
		Q			U				J			K	L	V		B	C	D	E	G				U	
		🛒	🍴		🛒					🍴				🛒	🍴		🛒		🛒	🛒	🍴			🛒	
Deansgate 🚆	d																	16 12							
Manchester Oxford Road	d				15 39													16 16						16 39	
Manchester Piccadilly [10] 🚆	a				15 41													16 18						16 41	
	d	15 30	15 35	15 38	15 43	15 46		15 48	15 52	15 55		16 04	16 04	16 07	16 15	16 17	16 20	16 21	16 27	16 30	16 35	16 38		16 43	16 46
Levenshulme	d			15 43					15 58			16 09	16 09					16 28				16 43			
Heaton Chapel	d			15 46					16 01			16 12	16 12					16 31				16 46			
Stockport	a	15 38	15 42	15 50	15 53			15 57	16 04	16 03		16 16	16 16		16 22	16 27	16 28	16 34	16 34	16 38	16 42	16 50		16 53	
	d	15 39	15 42	15 51				15 58		16 04		16 17	16 17		16 23				16 35	16 39	16 42	16 51			
Cheadle Hulme	d			15 55				16 02				16 24	16 24									16 55			
Bramhall	d							16 05																	
Poynton	d							16 08																	
Adlington (Cheshire)	d							16 11																	
Prestbury	d							16 14																	
Macclesfield	a		15 55					16 18											16 47		16 56				
	d		15 55					16 18											16 49		16 56				
Congleton	d							16 26																	
Handforth	d			15 59							←	16 28	16 28									16 59			
Manchester Airport ✈	d					16 11 →					16 11														17 11 →
Styal	d																								
Wilmslow	d	15 47		16 02						16 11	16 21	16 31	16 35							16 49		17 02			
Alderley Edge	d			16a08							16 24	16 34	16 38									17a08			
Chelford	d											16 38	16 42												
Goostrey	d											16 43	16 46												
Holmes Chapel	d										16 32	16 46	16 49												
Sandbach	d										16 36	16 51	16 54												
Crewe [10]	65 a	16 06								16 27	16 46	17 01	17 04							17 08					
Kidsgrove	50 a							16 32																	
Longport	50 a																								
Stoke-on-Trent	50, 68 a		16 12					16 42						16 43	16 48				17 06		17 13				
Stafford	68 a	16 46								17 09									17 25	17 42					
Wolverhampton [7]	68 🚆 a	16 59								17 27				17 13					17 39	17 56					
Birmingham New Street [12]	68 a	17 18								17 47	17e55			17 31					17 58	18 17					
London Euston [15]	⊖ 65 a		17 42							18 04	18 38				18 23				18c56		18 42				

For general notes see front of timetable
For details of catering facilities see Directory of Train Operators

- **A** To Bristol Temple Meads (from 12 September to Paignton) (Table 51)
- **B** To Chester (Table 88)
- **C** From Manchester Airport to Cleethorpes (27 June to 5 September to Doncaster) (Table 29)
- **D** From Preston (Table 82) to Hazel Grove (Table 86)
- **E** To Bournemouth (Table 51)
- **G** To Milford Haven (Table 128)
- **H** From Liverpool Lime Street to Nottingham (Table 49)
- **J** To Buxton (Table 86)
- **K** Until 31 October
- **L** From 7 November
- **N** To Bristol Temple Meads (Table 51)
- **Q** To Pembroke Dock (Table 128)
- **U** From Liverpool Lime Street to Norwich (Table 49)
- **V** To Paignton (from 12 September to Bristol Temple Meads) (Table 51)
- **b** From 7 November arr. Birmingham New Street 1718, London Euston 1737
- **c** Change at Stafford
- **e** From 7 November arr. 1750

Manchester, Stockport and Manchester Airport → Crewe and Stoke-on-Trent

Network Diagram - see first page of Table 78

	NT	NT	VT	NT	NT	NT	XC	NT	VT	NT	TP	NT	XC	AW	VT		NT	EM	NT	NT	NT	VT	NT	XC
		A	1 ◇ ⊡		B	C	1 ◇ D ✕	E	1 ◇ ⊡	G	1 ◇ H ✕	J	1 ◇ K ✕	R L ✕	1 ◇ ⊡			◇ N ✕			A	1 ◇ ⊡		1 ◇ Q ✕
Deansgate d												17 12												
Manchester Oxford Road d												17 16						17 39						
Manchester Piccadilly 10 a												17 18						17 41						
Manchester Piccadilly d	16 48	16 51	16 55		17 03	17 03	17 06	17 09	17 15	17 17	17 20	17 21	17 27	17 30	17 35		17 38	17 43	17 46	17 48	17 52	17 55		18 05
Levenshulme d		16 58			17 08	17 08		17 14				17 28					17 43				17 58			
Heaton Chapel d		17 01			17 11	17 11		17 17				17 31					17 46				18 01			
Stockport a	16 57	17 04	17 03		17 15	17 15		17 21	17 22	17 27	17 28	17 34	17 35	17 39	17 43		17 50	17 53		17 57	18 04	18 03		
Stockport d	16 58		17 04		17 16	17 16			17 23				17 35	17 40	17 43		17 51			17 58		18 04		
Cheadle Hulme d	17 02				17 24	17 24											17 55			18 02				
Bramhall d	17 05																			18 05				
Poynton d	17 08																			18 08				
Adlington (Cheshire) d	17 11																			18 11				
Prestbury d	17 14																			18 14				
Macclesfield a	17 18						17 25								17 55					18 18				18 24
Macclesfield d	17 18						17 27								17 55					18 18				18 25
Congleton d	17 26												17 54							18 26				
Handforth d				←	17 28	17 28											17 59						←	
Manchester Airport ✈ d				17 11															18 11 →				18 11	
Styal d																							18 18	
Wilmslow d			17 11	17 21	17 31	17 35								17 48			18 02					18 11	18 22	
Alderley Edge d				17 24	17 34	17 38											18a08						18 25	
Chelford d					17 38	17 42																		
Goostrey d					17 43	17 46																		
Holmes Chapel d				17 32	17 46	17 49																	18 33	
Sandbach d				17 36	17 51	17 54																	18 37	
Crewe 10 65 a			17 27	17 44	18 01	18 04								18 11								18 27	18 47	
Kidsgrove 50 a	17 32																			18 32				
Longport 50 a																								
Stoke-on-Trent 50, 68 a	17 42						17 43		17 49				18 07		18 12					18 42				18 43
Stafford 68 a			18 09										18 25	18 42								19 09		
Wolverhampton 7 68 a			18 27				18 13						18 39	18 56								19 27		19 13
Birmingham New Street 12 68 a			18 47	18b55			18 31						18 58	19 17								19 47	19c55	19 31
London Euston 15 ⊖ 65 a			19 04	20b04					19 23				19e56		19 42							20 04	21c58	

	NT	VT	NT	TP	NT	XC	AW	VT	NT		EM	NT	NT	NT	VT	NT	NT	NT	XC	NT	TP	NT	XC	AW
		1 ◇ ⊡	G	1 ◇ H ✕	U	1 ◇ K ✕	◇ V ✕	1 ◇ ⊡			◇ X ✕			A	1 ◇ ⊡		B	C	1 ◇ Y ✕	G	1 ◇ H	E	1 ◇ Z ✕	◇ AA
Deansgate d					18 12																			
Manchester Oxford Road d					18 16						18 39													
Manchester Piccadilly 10 a					18 18						18 41													
Manchester Piccadilly d	18 08	18 15	18 17	18 20	18 21	18 27	18 30	18 35	18 38		18 43	18 46	18 48	18 52	18 55		19 04	19 04	19 07	19 17	19 18	19 22	19 27	19 30
Levenshulme d	18 13				18 28				18 43					18 58			19 09	19 09				19 28		
Heaton Chapel d	18 16				18 31				18 46					19 01			19 12	19 12				19 31		
Stockport a	18 20	18 22	18 27	18 28	18 34	18 34	18 38	18 42	18 50		18 53		18 57	19 04	19 03		19 16	19 16	19 15	19 27	19 26	19 34	19 34	19 39
Stockport d	18 22	18 23				18 35	18 39	18 42	18 51				18 58		19 04		19 17	19 17	19 16				19 35	19 39
Cheadle Hulme d	18 30								18 55				19 02				19 24	19 24						
Bramhall d													19 05											
Poynton d													19 08											
Adlington (Cheshire) d													19 11											
Prestbury d													19 14											
Macclesfield a								18 55					19 18										19 47	
Macclesfield d								18 55					19 18										19 49	
Congleton d						18 54							19 26											
Handforth d	18 34								18 59							←	19 28	19 28						
Manchester Airport ✈ d												19 14 →				19 14								
Styal d																								
Wilmslow d	18 37						18 47		19 02						19 11	19 26	19 31	19 35						19 47
Alderley Edge d	18 40								19a08							19a32	19 34	19 38						
Chelford d	18 44																19 38	19 42						
Goostrey d	18 48																19 43	19 46						
Holmes Chapel d	18 51																19 46	19 49						
Sandbach d	18 56																19 51	19 54						
Crewe 10 65 a	19 06						19 08								19 27		20 01	20 04						20 06
Kidsgrove 50 a													19 32											
Longport 50 a																								
Stoke-on-Trent 50, 68 a		18 48				19 06		19 12					19 42						19 43				20 06	
Stafford 68 a						19 25	19 42								20 11								20 25	20 42
Wolverhampton 7 68 a						19 39	19 57								20 28				20 13				20 39	20 57
Birmingham New Street 12 68 a						19 58	20 17								20 47				20 31				20 58	21 17
London Euston 15 ⊖ 65 a		20 28				21f25	21g58	21h16							21g58								22j43	23k03

For general notes see front of timetable
For details of catering facilities see Directory of Train Operators

- **A** To Buxton (Table 86)
- **B** Until 31 October
- **C** From 7 November
- **D** To Cardiff Central (Table 51)
- **E** To Hazel Grove (Table 86)
- **G** To Chester (Table 88)
- **H** From Manchester Airport to Cleethorpes (27 June to 5 September to Doncaster) (Table 29)
- **J** From Preston (Table 82) to Buxton (Table 86)
- **K** To Bournemouth (Table 51)
- **L** To Haverfordwest (Table 128)
- **N** From Liverpool Lime Street to Nottingham (Table 49)
- **Q** To Bristol Temple Meads (from 12 September to Plymouth) (Table 51)
- **U** From Preston (Table 82) to Hazel Grove (Table 86)
- **V** To Carmarthen (Table 128)
- **X** From Liverpool Lime Street to Norwich (Table 49)
- **Y** To Bristol Temple Meads (Table 51)
- **Z** To Southampton Central (Table 51)
- **AA** To Cardiff Central (Table 131)
- **b** From 7 November arr. Birmingham New Street 1917, London Euston 1937
- **c** From 7 November arr. Birmingham New Street 1956, London Euston 2119
- **e** Change at Stafford
- **f** Change at Stafford. From 12 September arr. 2115
- **g** From 12 September arr. 2119
- **h** From 12 September arr. 2101
- **j** Change at Stafford. From 12 September arr. 2217
- **k** Until 31 October only. 12 September to 31 October arr. 2243

Manchester, Stockport and Manchester Airport → Crewe and Stoke-on-Trent

Network Diagram - see first page of Table 78

		VT 1 ◇	EM ◇ A	NT	NT	NT B	NT	XC 1 ◇	NT C	TP 1 ◇ D	XC 1 ◇	AW ◇ E	VT 1 ◇	EM ◇ A	NT	NT G	NT H	NT B	NT	XC 1 ◇	NT C	TP 1 ◇ D	XC 1 ◇ G
Deansgate	d																						
Manchester Oxford Road	d		19 39	19 43										20 39	20 43								
Manchester Piccadilly 10	a		19 41	19 45										20 41	20 45								
	d	19 35	19 43	19 46	19 48	19 52	20 04	20 07	20 17	20 20	20 27	20 30	20 35	20 43	20 46	20 48	20 48	20 52	21 04	21 06	21 17	21 20	21 27
Levenshulme	d					19 58	20 09											20 58	21 09				
Heaton Chapel	d					20 01	20 12											21 01	21 12				
Stockport	a	19 42	19 53		19 57	20 04	20 16	20 15	20 27	20 28	20 34	20 39	20 42	20 53		20 57	20 57	21 04	21 16		21 27	21 28	21 34
	d	19 42			19 58		20 17	20 16			20 35	20 39	20 43			20 58	20 58		21 17				21 35
Cheadle Hulme	d				20 02		20 24									21 02	21 02		21 24				
Bramhall	d				20 05											21 05	21 05						
Poynton	d				20 08											21 08	21 08						
Adlington (Cheshire)	d				20 11											21 11	21 11						
Prestbury	d				20 14											21 14	21 14						
Macclesfield	a	19 55			20 18						20 47		20 55			21 18	21 18						
	d	19 55			20 18						20 49		20 56				21 18						
Congleton	d				20 26												21 26						
Handforth	d						20 28												21 28				
Manchester Airport	d			20 14											21 14								
Styal	d																						
Wilmslow	d			20a24			20 31					20 47			21a24				21 31				21 45
Alderley Edge	d						20 34												21 34				
Chelford	d						20 38												21 38				
Goostrey	d						20 43												21 43				
Holmes Chapel	d						20 46												21 46				
Sandbach	d						20 51												21 51				
Crewe 10	65 a						21 01					21 06							22 01				
Kidsgrove	50 a				20 32												21 32						
Longport	50 a																						
Stoke-on-Trent	50, 68 a	20 12			20 42			20 43			21 06		21 11				21 42			21 43			
Stafford	68 a										21 25	*21 41*											22 32
Wolverhampton 7	68 a							21 13			21 39	*21 57*								22 13			22 50
Birmingham New Street 12	68 a							21 36			22 03	*22 19*								22 37			23 22
London Euston 15	⊖ 65 a	22b21											23c36										

		XC 1 ◇ H	AW ◇ J	EM ◇ K	XC G	NT	NT G	NT G	NT H	NT B	NT	NT C	TP 1 ◇ L	AW ◇ J	XC G	NT	NT	NT	NT B	NT	NT C	NT
Deansgate	d																					
Manchester Oxford Road	d			21 39		21 43										22 43						
Manchester Piccadilly 10	a			21 41		21 45										22 45						
	d	21 27	21 30	21 43		21 46	21 48		21 48	21 52	22 04	22 17	22 20	22 35		22 46	22 48	23 04	23 10	23 14	23 17	23 37
Levenshulme	d									21 58	22 09							23 09				23 42
Heaton Chapel	d									22 01	22 12							23 12				23 45
Stockport	a	21 34	21 38	21 52			21 58		21 58	22 04	22 16	22 27	22 28	22 43			22 57	23 16	23 19	23 23	23 26	23 49
	d	21 35	21 39				21 58		21 58		22 17			22 44			22 58	23 16		23 23		23 50
Cheadle Hulme	d						22 02		22 02		22 24						23 02	23 21		23 27		23 54
Bramhall	d						22 05		22 05								23 05			23 30		
Poynton	d						22 08		22 08								23 08			23 33		
Adlington (Cheshire)	d						22 11		22 11								23 11			23 37		
Prestbury	d						22 14		22 14								23 14			23 40		
Macclesfield	a	21 47					22 18		22 18								23 20			23 46		
	d	21 49			21 40			22 30	22 18						22 30							
Congleton	d							22 50	22 26													
Handforth	d										22 28							23 25				23 58
Manchester Airport	d					22 14										23 14						
Styal	d																					
Wilmslow	d		21 47		22a10	22a22					22 31			22 52	23a00	23a22		23 28				00 01
Alderley Edge	d										22 34							23 31				00a05
Chelford	d										22 38							23 35				
Goostrey	d										22 43							23 40				
Holmes Chapel	d										22 46							23 43				
Sandbach	d										22 51							23 48				
Crewe 10	65 a		22 10								23 01			23 10				23 58				
Kidsgrove	50 a							23 05	22 32													
Longport	50 a																					
Stoke-on-Trent	50, 68 a	22 06						23 30	22 42													
Stafford	68 a	22 33	*22 45*																			
Wolverhampton 7	68 a	22 50	*23 01*																			
Birmingham New Street 12	68 a	23 22	*23 20*																			
London Euston 15	⊖ 65 a																					

For general notes see front of timetable
For details of catering facilities see Directory of Train Operators

A From Liverpool Lime Street to Nottingham (Table 49)
B To Buxton (Table 86)
C To Chester (Table 88)
D From Manchester Airport to Cleethorpes (27 June to 5 September to Doncaster) (Table 29)
E To Hereford (from 18 July to Cardiff Central) (Table 131)
G Until 11 July
H From 18 July
J To Shrewsbury (Table 131)
K From Liverpool Lime Street to Norwich (Table 49)
L From Manchester Airport to Sheffield (Table 78)
b From 12 September arr. 2202
c From 12 September arr. 2304

Table 84

Sundays

until 12 July

Manchester, Stockport and Manchester Airport → Crewe and Stoke-on-Trent

Network Diagram - see first page of Table 78

	VT	VT	VT	XC	NT	NT	TP	NT	VT	VT	NT	XC	XC	AW	NT	NT	XC	XC	VT	XC	AW	VT	VT	NT
		1◇	1◇	1◇			1◇			1◇			1◇	◇					1◇	1◇	R		1◇	
				A		B	C				D		A	E	B					A	G			
	🚌	☕	☕	🛒					🚌	☕		🚌	🛒				🚌	🚌	☕	🛒	🛒	🚌	☕	
Deansgate d											09 15													
Manchester Oxford Road d											09 18													
Manchester Piccadilly 10 a											09 21													
d		08 05	08 20	08 27	08 42	08 55	08 58	09 04		09 20	09 23		09 27	09 30	09 51	10 01			10 20	10 26	10 30		10 35	10 41
Levenshulme d						09 00		09 09							09 58	10 07								
Heaton Chapel d						09 03		09 12							10 01	10 10								
Stockport a		08 13	08 28	08 34		09 07	09 06	09 16		09 27	09 31		09 35	09 39	10 04	10 13			10 28	10 34	10 39		10 43	
d	07 00	08 14	08 28	08 36				09 17	08 15	09 27			09 36	09 39		10 14			10 29	10 35	10 41	09 40	10 43	
Cheadle Hulme d								09 21								10 18								
Bramhall d																								
Poynton d																								
Adlington (Cheshire) d																								
Prestbury d																								
Macclesfield a	07 30								08 45													10 10		
d	07 30								08 45			09 00					09 45	10 00				10 10		
Congleton d																								
Handforth d								09 25								10 22								
Manchester Airport ✈ d					09 09																			11 08
Styal d					09 13																			11 12
Wilmslow d		08 22	08 38	08 43	09 17			09 28		09 36		09a30	09 43	09 47		10 25		10a30	10 37	10 43	10 47		10 53	11 16
Alderley Edge d					09 20			09a33								10a34								11 19
Chelford d					09 24																			11 23
Goostrey d					09 28																			11 34
Holmes Chapel d					09 31																			11 37
Sandbach d					09 36																			11 42
Crewe 10 65 a		08 39	08 54	09 01	09 44									10 06					10 53		11 07			11 50
Kidsgrove 50 a																								
Longport 50 a																								
Stoke-on-Trent 50, 68 a	08 20								09 35								10 45					11 00		
Stafford 68 a	08 50	09 07		09 28	*10 38*				10 05	10 16			10 24	*10 45*			11 15		*11 41*	11 24		11 30	11 36	
Wolverhampton 7 68 a				09 41									10 40	*11 01*					*12b40*	11 37				
Birmingham New Street 12 68 a				09 58									10 59	*11 18*					*12 05*	11 57				*12 55*
London Euston 15 ⊖ 65 a		10 58	11 08	*11c44*						12 08			*12c38*	*12 51*					12 58				13 09	

	NT	NT	VT	TP	NT	AW	XC	XC	XC	AW	VT	VT	NT	VT	NT	VT	VT	TP	NT	XC	XC	XC	AW	VT
			1◇	1◇		R			1◇	R		1◇		1◇			1◇	1◇				1◇	R	
	B			H	J	E			A	E			B					K	L			A	G	
			☕			🛒	🚌	🚌	🛒	🛒	🚌	☕		☕		🚌	☕			🚌	🚌	🛒	🛒	🚌
Deansgate d					11 11														12 11					
Manchester Oxford Road d					11 17														12 17					
Manchester Piccadilly 10 a					11 19														12 19					
d	10 52	11 02	11 09	11 18	11 22	11 24			11 27			11 35	11 52	11 55	12 04		12 15	12 18	12 22			12 26	12 30	
Levenshulme d	10 58	11 08											11 58		12 09									
Heaton Chapel d	11 01	11 11											12 01		12 12									
Stockport a	11 04	11 15	11 17	11 27	11 30	11 34			11 36	←		11 43	12 04	12 03	12 16		12 22	12 27	12 32			12 35	12 39	
d		11 17	11 17			11 40 →			11 37	11 40	10 30	11 43		12 05	12 16		12 23					12 36	12 40	
Cheadle Hulme d		11 26													12 20									
Bramhall d																								
Poynton d																								
Adlington (Cheshire) d																								
Prestbury d																								
Macclesfield a											11 00													
d							10 45	11 00			11 00									11 45	12 00			12 00
Congleton d																								
Handforth d		11 30													12 24									
Manchester Airport ✈ d																								
Styal d																								
Wilmslow d		11 33						11a30	11 44	11 48		11 53		12 12	12 27						12a30	12 43	12 48	
Alderley Edge d		11a37													12a31									
Chelford d																								
Goostrey d																								
Holmes Chapel d																								
Sandbach d																								
Crewe 10 65 a										12 07				12 28									13 08	
Kidsgrove 50 a																								
Longport 50 a																								
Stoke-on-Trent 50, 68 a							11 45				11 50					12d30				12 45				12 50
Stafford 68 a			11 58				12 15		12 26	*12 41*	12 20	12 27				13 00	13 04			13 15		13 26	*13 42*	13 20
Wolverhampton 7 68 a									12 40			*12 59*										13 40		
Birmingham New Street 12 68 a									12 58			*13 16*		*13 55*								13 58		
London Euston 15 ⊖ 65 a			13 31						*14c03*			13 53		14 12			14 40					*15c03*		

For general notes see front of timetable
For details of catering facilities see Directory of Train Operators

- **A** To Bournemouth (Table 51)
- **B** To Buxton (Table 86)
- **C** From Manchester Airport to Sheffield (Table 78)
- **D** From Wigan Wallgate (Table 82) to Chester (Table 88)
- **E** To Cardiff Central (Table 131)
- **G** To Milford Haven (Table 128)
- **H** From Manchester Airport to Cleethorpes (from 28 June to Doncaster) (Table 29)
- **J** From Southport (Table 82) to Chester (Table 88)
- **K** To Doncaster (Table 29)
- **L** From Southport (Table 82)
- **b** Change at Crewe and Stafford
- **c** Change at Stafford

Manchester, Stockport and Manchester Airport → Crewe and Stoke-on-Trent

Network Diagram - see first page of Table 78

	VT	NT	EM	NT	VT	NT	NT	XC	NT	VT	TP	NT	XC	AW	VT	EM	NT	VT	NT	XC	VT	TP	NT	XC
	1 ◇		◇ A	B	1 ◇			1 ◇ C		1 ◇	1 ◇ D	E	1 ◇ G	R H	1 ◇	◇ J	B	1 ◇		1 ◇ K	1 ◇	1 ◇ D	L	1 ◇ G
Deansgate d												13 11											14 11	
Manchester Oxford Road d												13 17				13 39							14 17	
Manchester Piccadilly 10 a												13 19				13 41							14 19	
d	12 35	12 41	12 44	12 52	12 55		13 04	13 07		13 15	13 20	13 22	13 27	13 30	13 35	13 44	13 52	13 55	14 04	14 07	14 15	14 20	14 22	14 27
Levenshulme d				12 58			13 09										13 58		14 09					
Heaton Chapel d				13 01			13 12										14 01		14 12					
Stockport a	12 44		12 53	13 04	13 03		13 16		←	13 22	13 28	13 30	13 34	13 39	13 42	13 53	14 04	14 03	14 16		14 22	14 28	14 33	14 34
d	12 44				13 05		13 17 →		13 17	13 22			13 36	13 39	13 42			14 04	14 17		14 22			14 36
Cheadle Hulme d									13 21										14 22					
Bramhall d																								
Poynton d																								
Adlington (Cheshire) d																								
Prestbury d																								
Macclesfield a													13 48		13 55									14 48
d													13 49		13 55									14 49
Congleton d																								
Handforth d						←			13 25										14 26					
Manchester Airport d		13 06 →				13 06																		
Styal d						13 10																		
Wilmslow d	12 53				13 12	13 15		13 22	13 28					13 47				14 11	14 29					
Alderley Edge d						13a19			13 31										14a33					
Chelford d									13 35															
Goostrey d									13 40															
Holmes Chapel d									13 43															
Sandbach d									13 48															
Crewe 10 65 a					13 28				13 56					14 07				14 27						
Kidsgrove 50 a																								
Longport 50 a																								
Stoke-on-Trent 50, 68 a										13 49			14 06		14 12					14 42	14 49			15 06
Stafford 68 a	13 27												14 24	*14 42*										15 24
Wolverhampton 7 68 a	*13 58*							14 13					14 40	*14 58*						15 13				15 40
Birmingham New Street 12 68 a	*14 15*				*14 55*			14 31					14 58	*15 15*				*15 55*		15 31				15 58
London Euston 15 ⊖ 65 a	14 52				15 12					15 30			*16b03*		15 48			16 11			16 30			*17b03*

	AW	VT	NT	NT	EM	NT	VT	NT	NT	XC	VT	TP	NT	XC	AW	VT	EM	NT	VT	NT	XC	VT	TP	NT
	R N	1 ◇			◇ J	B	1 ◇			1 ◇ K	1 ◇	1 ◇ D	E	1 ◇ G	R H	1 ◇	◇ J	B	1 ◇		1 ◇ K	1 ◇	1 ◇ D	L
Deansgate d													15 11											16 11
Manchester Oxford Road d					14 39								15 17				15 39							16 17
Manchester Piccadilly 10 a					14 41								15 19				15 41							16 19
d	14 30	14 35	14 41	14 41	14 44	14 52	14 55		15 04	15 07	15 15	15 20	15 22	15 27	15 30	15 35	15 44	15 52	15 55	16 04	16 07	16 15	16 20	16 22
Levenshulme d						14 58			15 09									15 58		16 09				
Heaton Chapel d						15 01			15 12									16 01		16 12				
Stockport a	14 38	14 42		14 49	14 53	15 04	15 03		15 16		15 22	15 28	15 30	15 34	15 38	15 42	15 53	16 04	16 03	16 16		16 22	16 28	16 31
d	14 39	14 42		14 51			15 04		15 17		15 22			15 36	15 39	15 42			16 04	16 17		16 23		
Cheadle Hulme d				14 55					15 22											16 22				
Bramhall d				14 58																				
Poynton d				15 01																				
Adlington (Cheshire) d				15 05																				
Prestbury d				15 08																				
Macclesfield a		14 55		15 11										15 48		15 55								
d		14 55		15 12										15 49		15 55								
Congleton d				15 19																				
Handforth d								←	15 26											16 26				
Manchester Airport d			15 06 →					15 06																
Styal d								15 10																
Wilmslow d	14 47						15 11	15 15	15 29						15 47				16 11	16 29				
Alderley Edge d								15a19	15 32											16a33				
Chelford d									15 36															
Goostrey d									15 40															
Holmes Chapel d									15 43															
Sandbach d									15 48															
Crewe 10 65 a	15 06						15 27		15 56						16 06				16 27					
Kidsgrove 50 a				15 25																				
Longport 50 a																								
Stoke-on-Trent 50, 68 a		15 12		15 35						15 42	15 49			16 06		16 12					16 42	16 48		
Stafford 68 a	*15 42*													16 24	*16 42*									
Wolverhampton 7 68 a	*15 58*									16 13				16 40	*16 58*						17 13			
Birmingham New Street 12 68 a	*16 15*						*16 55*			16 31				16 58	*17 15*				*17 55*		17 31			
London Euston 15 ⊖ 65 a		16 48					17 11				17 30			*18b04*		17 48			18 11			18 30		

For general notes see front of timetable
For details of catering facilities see Directory of Train Operators

- **A** To Norwich (Table 49)
- **B** To Buxton (Table 86)
- **C** To Paignton (Table 51)
- **D** From Manchester Airport to Cleethorpes (from 28 June to Doncaster) (Table 29)
- **E** From Southport (Table 82) to Chester (Table 88)
- **G** To Bournemouth (Table 51)
- **H** To Cardiff Central (Table 131)
- **J** From Liverpool Lime Street to Norwich (Table 49)
- **K** To Bristol Temple Meads (Table 51)
- **L** From Southport (Table 82)
- **N** To Milford Haven and Pembroke Dock (Table 128)
- **b** Change at Stafford

Table 84

Sundays

until 12 July

Manchester, Stockport and Manchester Airport → Crewe and Stoke-on-Trent

Network Diagram - see first page of Table 78

		XC	AW	VT	NT	EM	NT	VT	NT	NT	XC	VT	TP	NT	XC	AW	VT	EM	NT	VT	NT	XC	VT	TP	NT
		1 ◇	R	1 ◇		◇		1 ◇			1 ◇	1 ◇	1 ◇		1 ◇	R	1 ◇	◇		1 ◇		1 ◇	1 ◇	1 ◇	
		A	B			C	D				E		G	H	A	B		J	D			K		G	L
		🛒	🛒	🍴		🛒		🍴			🛒	🍴			🛒	🛒	🍴	🛒		🍴		🛒	🍴		
Deansgate 🚊	d													17 11											18 11
Manchester Oxford Road	d					16 39								17 17				17 39							18 17
Manchester Piccadilly 10 🚊	a					16 41								17 19				17 41							18 19
	d	16 27	16 30	16 35	16 41	16 44	16 52	16 55		17 04	17 07	17 15	17 20	17 22	17 27	17 30	17 35	17 44	17 52	17 55	18 04	18 07	18 15	18 20	18 22
Levenshulme	d						16 58			17 09									17 58		18 09				
Heaton Chapel	d						17 01			17 12									18 01		18 12				
Stockport	a	16 34	16 39	16 42		16 53	17 04	17 03		17 16		17 22	17 28	17 30	17 34	17 39	17 42	17 53	18 04	18 03	18 16		18 22	18 28	18 33
	d	16 36	16 39	16 42				17 04		17 17		17 22			17 36	17 39	17 42			18 04	18 17		18 22		
Cheadle Hulme	d									17 22											18 22				
Bramhall	d																								
Poynton	d																								
Adlington (Cheshire)	d																								
Prestbury	d																								
Macclesfield	a	16 48		16 55											17 48		17 55								
	d	16 49		16 55											17 49		17 55								
Congleton	d																								
Handforth	d								←	17 26											18 26				
Manchester Airport ✈	d				17 06				17 06																
Styal	d				→				17 10																
Wilmslow	d		16 47					17 11	17 15	17 29						17 47				18 11	18 29				
Alderley Edge	d								17a19	17 32											18a33				
Chelford	d									17 36															
Goostrey	d									17 40															
Holmes Chapel	d									17 43															
Sandbach	d									17 48															
Crewe 10	65 a		17 06					17 27		17 56						18 06				18 27					
Kidsgrove	50 a																								
Longport	50 a																								
Stoke-on-Trent	50, 68 a	17 06		17 12							17 42	17 49			18 06		18 12					18 42	18 49		
Stafford	68 a	17 24	*17 42*												18 24	*18 42*									
Wolverhampton 7	68 🚊 a	17 40	*17 58*								18 13				18 40	*18 58*						19 13			
Birmingham New Street 12	68 a	17 58	*18 15*					*18 55*			18 31				18 58	*19 15*				*19 55*		19 31			
London Euston 15	⊖ 65 a	*19b03*		18 48				19 11				19 30			*20b03*		19 48			20 11			20 30		

		XC	AW	VT	NT	NT	EM	NT	VT	NT	NT	XC	VT	TP	NT	XC	AW	VT	EM	NT	NT	XC	TP	VT	NT
		1 ◇	R	1 ◇	1		◇		1 ◇			1 ◇	1 ◇	1 ◇		1 ◇	◇	1 ◇	◇			1 ◇	1 ◇	1 ◇	
		N	B				J	D				K		G	H	Q	B		J	D		K	G		L
		🛒	🛒	🍴			🛒		🍴			🛒	🍴			🛒		🍴	🛒					🍴	
Deansgate 🚊	d														19 11										20 11
Manchester Oxford Road	d						18 39								19 17				19 39						20 17
Manchester Piccadilly 10 🚊	a						18 41								19 19				19 41						20 19
	d	18 27	18 30	18 35	18 41	18 42	18 44	18 52	18 55		19 04	19 07	19 15	19 20	19 22	19 27	19 30	19 35	19 44	19 52	20 04	20 07	20 18	20 20	20 22
Levenshulme	d							18 58			19 09									19 58	20 09				
Heaton Chapel	d							19 01			19 12									20 01	20 12				
Stockport	a	18 34	18 38	18 42		18 50	18 53	19 04	19 03		19 16		19 22	19 28	19 30	19 34	19 39	19 42	19 53	20 04	20 16	20 15	20 26	20 27	20 32
	d	18 36	18 39	18 42		18 52			19 04		19 17		19 22			19 35	19 39	19 42			20 17	20 16		20 27	
Cheadle Hulme	d					18 57					19 22										20 23				
Bramhall	d					19 00																			
Poynton	d					19 03																			
Adlington (Cheshire)	d					19 06																			
Prestbury	d					19 09																			
Macclesfield	a	18 48		18 55		19 13										19 47		19 55				20 28		20 40	
	d	18 49		18 55		19 13										19 48		19 55				20 29		20 40	
Congleton	d					19 21																			
Handforth	d									←	19 26										20 27				
Manchester Airport ✈	d				19 06					19 06															
Styal	d				→					19 10															
Wilmslow	d		18 47						19 11	19 15	19 29						19 47				20 30				
Alderley Edge	d									19a19	19 32										20a35				
Chelford	d										19 36														
Goostrey	d										19 40														
Holmes Chapel	d										19 43														
Sandbach	d										19 48														
Crewe 10	65 a		19 06						19 27		19 56						20 06								
Kidsgrove	50 a					19 28																			
Longport	50 a																								
Stoke-on-Trent	50, 68 a	19 06		19 12		19 38						19 42	19 49			20 05		20 12				20 46		20 57	
Stafford	68 a	19 24	*19 42*													20 24	*20 37*					21 08			
Wolverhampton 7	68 🚊 a	19 40	*19 58*									20 13				20 39	*20 55*					21 21			
Birmingham New Street 12	68 a	19 58	*20 15*						*20 57*			20 31				21 00	*21 15*					21 39			
London Euston 15	⊖ 65 a	*21b06*		20 48					21 14				21 34				*22 29*	22 04						22 57	

For general notes see front of timetable
For details of catering facilities see Directory of Train Operators

- **A** To Bournemouth (Table 51)
- **B** To Cardiff Central (Table 131)
- **C** From Liverpool Lime Street to Norwich (Table 49)
- **D** To Buxton (Table 86)
- **E** To Paignton (Table 51)
- **G** From Manchester Airport to Cleethorpes (from 28 June to Doncaster) (Table 29)
- **H** From Southport (Table 82) to Chester (Table 88)
- **J** From Liverpool Lime Street to Nottingham (Table 49)
- **K** To Bristol Temple Meads (Table 51)
- **L** From Southport (Table 82)
- **N** To Southampton Central (Table 51)
- **Q** To Reading (Table 51)
- **b** Change at Stafford

Table 84

Sundays until 12 July

Manchester, Stockport and Manchester Airport → Crewe and Stoke-on-Trent

Network Diagram - see first page of Table 78

	AW	NT	EM	NT	VT	NT	XC	TP	NT	AW	NT	NT	NT	XC	EM	TP	NT	AW	NT	NT	TP	NT
	◇		◇		1 ◇		1 ◇	1 ◇						1 ◇	◇	1 ◇					1 ◇	
	A		B	C				D	E			C			B	D	G		C		D	G
			✕		⊡																	
Deansgate d									21 11								22 11					23 11
Manchester Oxford Road d			20 39						21 17						22 07		22 17					23 17
Manchester Piccadilly 10 a			20 41						21 19						22 09		22 19					23 19
d	20 30	20 41	20 44	20 52	20 55	21 04	21 07	21 20	21 22	21 34	21 41	21 52	22 04	22 07	22 11	22 16	22 22	22 35	22 52	23 04	23 20	23 22
Levenshulme d				20 58		21 09						21 58	22 09						22 58	23 09		
Heaton Chapel d				21 01		21 12						22 01	22 12						23 01	23 12		
Stockport a	20 38		20 53	21 04	21 03	21 16	21 15	21 28	21 30		21 49	22 04	22 16	22 15	22 20	22 24	22 31		23 04	23 16	23 28	23 32
d	20 39				21 03	21 17	21 16				21 52		22 17	22 16						23 17		
Cheadle Hulme d						21 23					21 56		22 23							23 21		
Bramhall d											21 59											
Poynton d											22 02											
Adlington (Cheshire) d											22 05											
Prestbury d											22 08											
Macclesfield a					21 15		21 28				22 12			22 28								
d					21 15		21 29				22 13			22 29								
Congleton d											22 20											
Handforth d						21 27							22 27							23 25		
Manchester Airport ✈ d		21 06																				
Styal d		21 10																				
Wilmslow d	20 47	21 15				21 30				21 52			22 30					22 52		23 28		
Alderley Edge d		21a19				21 33							22a34							23a33		
Chelford d						21 37																
Goostrey d						21 42																
Holmes Chapel d						21 45																
Sandbach d						21 50																
Crewe 10 65 a	21 07					21 58				22 11								23 11				
Kidsgrove 50 a											22 26											
Longport 50 a																						
Stoke-on-Trent 50, 68 a					21 32		21 46				22 36			22 46								
Stafford 68 a	*21 36*						22 06			*22 41*				23 05								
Wolverhampton 7 68 a	*21 55*						22 20			*23 00*				23 18								
Birmingham New Street 12 68 a	*22 15*						22 45			*23 17*				23 41								
London Euston 15 ⊖ 65 a	*23 54*				23 32																	

Sundays 19 July to 6 September

	VT	VT	XC	NT	NT	TP	NT	VT	NT	XC	AW	NT	NT	VT	XC	AW	VT	NT	NT	NT	VT	TP
																R						
	1 ◇	1 ◇	1 ◇			1 ◇		1 ◇		1 ◇	◇			1 ◇	1 ◇		1 ◇				1 ◇	1 ◇
			H		C	D			J	H	A	C			H	K			C			L
	⊡	⊡	✕					⊡		✕				⊡	✕	✕	⊡				⊡	
Deansgate d									09 15													
Manchester Oxford Road d									09 18													
Manchester Piccadilly 10 a									09 21													
d	08 05	08 20	08 27	08 42	08 55	08 58	09 04	09 20	09 23	09 27	09 30	09 51	10 01	10 20	10 24	10 30	10 35	10 41	10 52	11 02	11 15	11 18
Levenshulme d					09 00		09 09					09 58	10 07						10 58	11 08		
Heaton Chapel d					09 03		09 12					10 01	10 10						11 01	11 11		
Stockport a	08 13	08 28	08 34		09 07	09 06	09 16	09 27	09 31	09 35	09 39	10 04	10 13	10 28	10 32	10 39	10 43		11 04	11 15	11 23	11 27
d	08 14	08 28	08 36				09 17	09 27		09 36	09 39		10 14	10 29	10 34	10 41	10 43			11 17	11 23	
Cheadle Hulme d							09 21						10 18							11 23		
Bramhall d																						
Poynton d																						
Adlington (Cheshire) d																						
Prestbury d																						
Macclesfield a		08 42						09 40		09 48					10 46		10 56					
d		08 42						09 40		09 49					10 47		10 56					
Congleton d																						
Handforth d							09 25						10 22							11 27		
Manchester Airport ✈ d				09 09														11 08				
Styal d				09 13														11 12				
Wilmslow d	08 22		08 43	09 17			09 28				09 47		10 25	10 37		10 47		11 16		11 30		
Alderley Edge d				09a21			09 31						10a29					11a20		11 33		
Chelford d							09 35													11 37		
Goostrey d							09 40													11 41		
Holmes Chapel d							09 43													11 44		
Sandbach d							09 48													11 49		
Crewe 10 65 a	08 39		09 01				09 56				10 06			10 53		11 07				11 57		
Kidsgrove 50 a																						
Longport 50 a																						
Stoke-on-Trent 50, 68 a		08 59						09 57		10 05					11 06		11 12				11 50	
Stafford 68 a	09 00		09 24				*10 31*			10 25	*10 41*			*11 31*	11 24							
Wolverhampton 7 68 a			09 40							10 40	*11 00*				11 40							
Birmingham New Street 12 68 a			09 58							10 58	*11 17*				11 58	*12 55*						
London Euston 15 ⊖ 65 a	10 58	11 03	*11b44*				*12 38*	12 08		*12b38*	*12 51*			12 58	*13b15*	*13 44*	13 01				13 31	

For general notes see front of timetable
For details of catering facilities see Directory of Train Operators

A To Cardiff Central (Table 131)
B From Liverpool Lime Street to Nottingham (Table 49)
C To Buxton (Table 86)
D From Manchester Airport to Sheffield (Table 78)
E From Southport (Table 82) to Chester (Table 88)
G From Southport (Table 82)
H To Bournemouth (Table 51)
J From Wigan Wallgate (Table 82) to Chester (Table 88)
K To Milford Haven (Table 128)
L From Manchester Airport to Doncaster (Table 29)
b Change at Stafford

Table 84 **Sundays**

Manchester, Stockport and Manchester Airport → Crewe and Stoke-on-Trent

19 July to 6 September

Network Diagram - see first page of Table 78

	NT	AW	XC	VT	NT	VT	NT		VT	TP	NT	XC	AW	VT	NT	EM	NT		VT	NT	NT	XC	VT	TP
		R	1◇	1◇		1◇			1◇	1◇		1◇	R	1◇		◇			1◇			1◇	1◇	1◇
	A	B	C		D					E	G	C	H			J	D					K		L
		✕	✕	⊡		⊡			⊡			✕	✕	⊡		✕			⊡			✕	⊡	
Deansgate d	11 11										12 11													
Manchester Oxford Road d	11 17										12 17													
Manchester Piccadilly 10 a	11 19										12 19													
d	11 22	11 24	11 27	11 35	11 52	11 55	12 04		12 15	12 18	12 22	12 26	12 30	12 35	12 41	12 44	12 52		12 55		13 04	13 07	13 15	13 20
Levenshulme d					11 58		12 09										12 58				13 09			
Heaton Chapel d					12 01		12 12										13 01				13 12			
Stockport a	11 30	11 34	11 36	11 43	12 04	12 03	12 16		12 22	12 27	12 32	12 35	12 39	12 44		12 53	13 04		13 03		13 16		13 22	13 28
d		11 40	11 37	11 43		12 05	12 17		12 23			12 36	12 40	12 44					13 05		13 17		13 22	
Cheadle Hulme d							12 23														13 21			
Bramhall d																								
Poynton d																								
Adlington (Cheshire) d																								
Prestbury d																								
Macclesfield a			11 49	11 56								12 48		12 57										
d			11 50	11 56								12 49		12 57										
Congleton d																								
Handforth d							12 27													←	13 25			
Manchester Airport ✈ d															13 06 →					13 06				
Styal d																				13 10				
Wilmslow d		11 48				12 12	12 30						12 48						13 12	13 15	13 28			
Alderley Edge d							12a34													13a19	13 31			
Chelford d																					13 35			
Goostrey d																					13 40			
Holmes Chapel d																					13 43			
Sandbach d																					13 48			
Crewe 10 65 a		12 07				12 28							13 08						13 28		13 56			
Kidsgrove 50 a																								
Longport 50 a																								
Stoke-on-Trent 50, 68 a			12 07	12 13					12 50			13 06		13 14								13 42	13 49	
Stafford 68 a		*12 41*	12 25									13 24	*13 42*											
Wolverhampton 7 68 a		*12 59*	12 40									13 40	*13 58*									14 13		
Birmingham New Street 12 68 a		*13 16*	12 58			*13 55*						13 58	*14 15*						*14 55*			14 31		
London Euston 15 ⊖ 65 a			*14b03*	13 49		14 12			14 31			*15b03*		14 50					15 12				15 30	

	NT	XC	AW	VT	EM		NT	VT	NT	XC	VT	TP	NT	XC	AW		VT	NT	NT	EM	NT	VT	NT	NT
		1◇	R	1◇	◇			1◇		1◇	1◇	1◇		1◇	R		1◇			◇		1◇		
	A	C	B		N		D			Q		L	G	C	U					N	D			
		✕	✕	⊡	✕			⊡		✕	⊡			✕	✕		⊡			✕		⊡		
Deansgate d	13 11												14 11											
Manchester Oxford Road d	13 17				13 39								14 17							14 39				
Manchester Piccadilly 10 a	13 19				13 41								14 19							14 41				
d	13 22	13 27	13 30	13 35	13 44		13 52	13 55	14 04	14 07	14 15	14 20	14 22	14 27	14 30		14 35	14 41	14 41	14 44	14 52	14 55		15 04
Levenshulme d							13 58		14 09												14 58			15 09
Heaton Chapel d							14 01		14 12												15 01			15 12
Stockport a	13 30	13 34	13 39	13 42	13 53		14 04	14 03	14 16		14 22	14 28	14 33	14 34	14 38		14 42		14 49	14 53	15 04	15 03		15 16
d		13 36	13 39	13 42				14 04	14 17		14 22			14 36	14 39		14 42		14 51			15 04		15 17
Cheadle Hulme d									14 22										14 55					15 22
Bramhall d																			14 58					
Poynton d																			15 01					
Adlington (Cheshire) d																			15 05					
Prestbury d																			15 08					
Macclesfield a		13 48		13 55										14 48			14 55		15 11					
d		13 49		13 55										14 49			14 55		15 12					
Congleton d																			15 19					
Handforth d									14 26														←	15 26
Manchester Airport ✈ d																		15 06 →					15 06	
Styal d																							15 10	
Wilmslow d			13 47					14 11	14 29						14 47							15 11	15 15	15 29
Alderley Edge d									14a33														15a19	15 32
Chelford d																								15 36
Goostrey d																								15 40
Holmes Chapel d																								15 43
Sandbach d																								15 48
Crewe 10 65 a			14 07					14 27							15 06							15 27		15 56
Kidsgrove 50 a																			15 25					
Longport 50 a																								
Stoke-on-Trent 50, 68 a		14 06		14 12						14 42	14 49			15 06			15 12		15 35					
Stafford 68 a		14 24	*14 42*											15 24	*15 42*									
Wolverhampton 7 68 a		14 40	*14 58*							15 13				15 40	*15 58*									
Birmingham New Street 12 68 a		14 58	*15 15*					*15 55*		15 31				15 58	*16 15*							*16 55*		
London Euston 15 ⊖ 65 a		*16b03*		15 48				16 11			16 30			*17b03*			16 48					17 11		

For general notes see front of timetable
For details of catering facilities see Directory of Train Operators

- **A** From Southport (Table 82) to Chester (Table 88)
- **B** To Cardiff Central (Table 131)
- **C** To Bournemouth (Table 51)
- **D** To Buxton (Table 86)
- **E** To Doncaster (Table 29)
- **G** From Southport (Table 82)
- **H** To Milford Haven (Table 128)
- **J** To Norwich (Table 49)
- **K** To Paignton (Table 51)
- **L** From Manchester Airport to Doncaster (Table 29)
- **N** From Liverpool Lime Street to Norwich (Table 49)
- **Q** To Bristol Temple Meads (Table 51)
- **U** To Milford Haven and Pembroke Dock (Table 128)
- **b** Change at Stafford

Table 84

Sundays

19 July to 6 September

Manchester, Stockport and Manchester Airport → Crewe and Stoke-on-Trent

Network Diagram - see first page of Table 78

		XC	VT	TP		NT	XC	AW	VT	EM	NT	VT	NT	XC		VT	TP	NT	XC	AW	VT	NT	EM	NT	VT
		1◇	1◇	1◇			1◇	R	1◇	◇		1◇		1◇		1◇	1◇		1◇	R	1◇		◇		1◇
		A		B		C	D	E		G	H			A			B	J	D	E			G	H	
		🛒	🍴				🛒	🛒	🍴	🛒		🍴		🛒		🍴			🛒	🛒	🍴		🛒		🍴
Deansgate 🚆	d					15 11												16 11							
Manchester Oxford Road	d					15 17				15 39								16 17					16 39		
Manchester Piccadilly 10 🚆	a					15 19				15 41								16 19					16 41		
	d	15 07	15 15	15 20		15 22	15 27	15 30	15 35	15 44	15 52	15 55	16 04	16 07		16 15	16 20	16 22	16 27	16 30	16 35	16 41	16 44	16 52	16 55
Levenshulme	d										15 58		16 09											16 58	
Heaton Chapel	d										16 01		16 12											17 01	
Stockport	a		15 22	15 28		15 30	15 34	15 38	15 42	15 53	16 04	16 03	16 16			16 22	16 28	16 31	16 34	16 39	16 42		16 53	17 04	17 03
	d		15 22				15 36	15 39	15 42			16 04	16 17			16 23			16 36	16 39	16 42				17 04
Cheadle Hulme	d												16 22												
Bramhall	d																								
Poynton	d																								
Adlington (Cheshire)	d																								
Prestbury	d																								
Macclesfield	a						15 48		15 55										16 48		16 55				
	d						15 49		15 55										16 49		16 55				
Congleton	d																								
Handforth	d												16 26												
Manchester Airport ✈	d																					17 06 →			
Styal	d																								
Wilmslow	d							15 47				16 11	16 29							16 47					17 11
Alderley Edge	d												16a33												
Chelford	d																								
Goostrey	d																								
Holmes Chapel	d																								
Sandbach	d																								
Crewe 10	65 a							16 06				16 27								17 06					17 27
Kidsgrove	50 a																								
Longport	50 a																								
Stoke-on-Trent	50, 68 a	15 42	15 49				16 06		16 12					16 42		16 48			17 06		17 12				
Stafford	68 a						16 24	*16 42*											17 24	*17 42*					
Wolverhampton 7	68 🚆 a	16 13					16 40	*16 58*						17 13					17 40	*17 58*					
Birmingham New Street 12	68 a	16 31					16 58	*17 15*				*17 55*		17 31					17 58	*18 15*					*18 55*
London Euston 15	⊖ 65 a		17 30				*18b04*		17 48			18 11				18 30			*19b03*		18 48				19 11

		NT		NT	XC	VT	TP	NT	XC	AW	VT	EM		NT	VT	NT	XC	VT	TP	NT	XC	AW		VT	NT
					1◇	1◇	1◇		1◇	R	1◇	◇			1◇		1◇	1◇	1◇		1◇	R		1◇	
					K		B	C	D	E		L		H			A		B	J	N	E			
					🛒	🍴			🛒	🛒	🍴	🛒			🍴		🛒	🍴			🛒	🛒		🍴	
Deansgate 🚆	d							17 11												18 11					
Manchester Oxford Road	d							17 17				17 39								18 17					
Manchester Piccadilly 10 🚆	a							17 19				17 41								18 19					
	d			17 04	17 07	17 15	17 20	17 22	17 27	17 30	17 35	17 44		17 52	17 55	18 04	18 07	18 15	18 20	18 22	18 27	18 30		18 35	18 41
Levenshulme	d			17 09										17 58		18 09									
Heaton Chapel	d			17 12										18 01		18 12									
Stockport	a			17 16		17 22	17 28	17 30	17 34	17 39	17 42	17 53		18 04	18 03	18 16		18 22	18 28	18 33	18 34	18 38		18 42	
	d			17 17		17 22			17 36	17 39	17 42				18 04	18 17		18 22			18 36	18 39		18 42	
Cheadle Hulme	d			17 22												18 22									
Bramhall	d																								
Poynton	d																								
Adlington (Cheshire)	d																								
Prestbury	d																								
Macclesfield	a								17 48		17 55										18 48			18 55	
	d								17 49		17 55										18 49			18 55	
Congleton	d																								
Handforth	d	←		17 26												18 26									
Manchester Airport ✈	d	17 06																							19 06 →
Styal	d	17 10																							
Wilmslow	d	17 15		17 29						17 47					18 11	18 29						18 47			
Alderley Edge	d	17a19		17 32												18a33									
Chelford	d			17 36																					
Goostrey	d			17 40																					
Holmes Chapel	d			17 43																					
Sandbach	d			17 48																					
Crewe 10	65 a			17 56						18 06					18 27							19 06			
Kidsgrove	50 a																								
Longport	50 a																								
Stoke-on-Trent	50, 68 a				17 42	17 49			18 06		18 12						18 42	18 49			19 06			19 12	
Stafford	68 a								18 24	*18 42*											19 24	*19 42*			
Wolverhampton 7	68 🚆 a				18 13				18 40	*18 58*							19 13				19 40	*19 58*			
Birmingham New Street 12	68 a				18 31				18 58	*19 15*					*19 55*		19 31				19 58	*20 15*			
London Euston 15	⊖ 65 a					19 30			*20b03*		19 48				20 11			20 30			*21b06*			20 48	

For general notes see front of timetable
For details of catering facilities see Directory of Train Operators

- **A** To Bristol Temple Meads (Table 51)
- **B** From Manchester Airport to Doncaster (Table 29)
- **C** From Southport (Table 82) to Chester (Table 88)
- **D** To Bournemouth (Table 51)
- **E** To Cardiff Central (Table 131)
- **G** From Liverpool Lime Street to Norwich (Table 49)
- **H** To Buxton (Table 86)
- **J** From Southport (Table 82)
- **K** To Paignton (Table 51)
- **L** From Liverpool Lime Street to Nottingham (Table 49)
- **N** To Southampton Central (Table 51)
- **b** Change at Stafford

Sundays

Manchester, Stockport and Manchester Airport → Crewe and Stoke-on-Trent

19 July to 6 September

Network Diagram - see first page of Table 78

	NT	EM	NT	VT	NT	NT	XC	VT	TP		NT	XC	AW	VT	EM	NT	NT	XC	TP		VT	NT	AW	NT
		◇		1 ◇			1 ◇	1 ◇	1 ◇			1 ◇	◇	1 ◇	◇			1 ◇	1 ◇		1 ◇		◇	
		A	B				C		D		E	G	H		A	B		C	D			J	H	
		🛒		☕			🛒	☕				🛒		☕	🛒						☕			
Deansgate 🚊 d											19 11											20 11		
Manchester Oxford Road d		18 39									19 17				19 39							20 17		
Manchester Piccadilly 10 🚊 a		18 41									19 19				19 41							20 19		
d	18 42	18 44	18 52	18 55		19 04	19 07	19 15	19 20		19 22	19 27	19 30	19 35	19 44	19 52	20 04	20 07	20 18		20 20	20 22	20 30	20 41
Levenshulme d			18 58			19 09										19 58	20 09							
Heaton Chapel d			19 01			19 12										20 01	20 12							
Stockport a	18 50	18 53	19 04	19 03		19 16		19 22	19 28		19 30	19 34	19 39	19 42	19 53	20 04	20 16	20 15	20 26		20 27	20 32	20 38	
d	18 52			19 04		19 17		19 22				19 35	19 39	19 42			20 17	20 16			20 27		20 39	
Cheadle Hulme d	18 57					19 22											20 23							
Bramhall d	19 00																							
Poynton d	19 03																							
Adlington (Cheshire) d	19 06																							
Prestbury d	19 09																							
Macclesfield a	19 13											19 47		19 55				20 28			20 40			
d	19 13											19 48		19 55				20 29			20 40			
Congleton d	19 21																							
Handforth d					←	19 26											20 27							
Manchester Airport ✈ d					19 06																			21 06
Styal d					19 10																			21 10
Wilmslow d				19 11	19 15	19 29							19 47				20 30						20 47	21 15
Alderley Edge d					19a19	19 32											20a35							21a19
Chelford d						19 36																		
Goostrey d						19 40																		
Holmes Chapel d						19 43																		
Sandbach d						19 48																		
Crewe 10 65 a				19 27		19 56							20 06										21 07	
Kidsgrove 50 a	19 28																							
Longport 50 a																								
Stoke-on-Trent 50, 68 a	19 38						19 42	19 49				20 05		20 12				20 46			20 57			
Stafford 68 a												20 24	*20 37*					21 07					*21 36*	
Wolverhampton 7 68 🚊 a							20 13					20 39	*20 55*					21 21					*21 55*	
Birmingham New Street 12 68 a				*20 57*			20 31					21 00	*21 15*					21 39					*22 15*	
London Euston 15 ⊖ 65 a				21 14				21 34				22b29	*22 29*	22 04							22 57		*23 59*	

	EM	NT	VT	NT	XC	TP	NT		AW	NT	NT	NT	XC	EM	TP	NT	AW		NT	NT	TP	NT
	◇		1 ◇		1 ◇	1 ◇							1 ◇	◇	1 ◇						1 ◇	
	A	B				K	E				B			A	K	J			B		K	J
	🛒		☕																			
Deansgate 🚊 d							21 11									22 11						23 11
Manchester Oxford Road d	20 39						21 17							22 07		22 17						23 17
Manchester Piccadilly 10 🚊 a	20 41						21 19							22 09		22 19						23 19
d	20 44	20 52	20 55	21 04	21 07	21 20	21 22		21 34	21 41	21 52	22 04	22 07	22 11	22 16	22 22	22 35		22 52	23 04	23 20	23 22
Levenshulme d		20 58		21 09							21 58	22 09							22 58	23 09		
Heaton Chapel d		21 01		21 12							22 01	22 12							23 01	23 12		
Stockport a	20 53	21 04	21 03	21 16	21 15	21 28	21 30			21 49	22 04	22 16	22 15	22 20	22 24	22 31			23 04	23 16	23 28	23 32
d			21 03	21 17	21 16					21 52		22 17	22 16							23 17		
Cheadle Hulme d				21 23						21 56		22 23								23 21		
Bramhall d										21 59												
Poynton d										22 02												
Adlington (Cheshire) d										22 05												
Prestbury d										22 08												
Macclesfield a			21 15		21 28					22 12			22 28									
d			21 15		21 29					22 13			22 29									
Congleton d										22 20												
Handforth d				21 27								22 27								23 25		
Manchester Airport ✈ d																						
Styal d																						
Wilmslow d				21 30					21 52			22 30					22 52			23 28		
Alderley Edge d				21 33								22a34								23a33		
Chelford d				21 37																		
Goostrey d				21 42																		
Holmes Chapel d				21 45																		
Sandbach d				21 50																		
Crewe 10 65 a				21 58					22 11								23 11					
Kidsgrove 50 a										22 26												
Longport 50 a																						
Stoke-on-Trent 50, 68 a			21 32		21 46					22 36			22 46									
Stafford 68 a					22 06				*22 41*				23 04									
Wolverhampton 7 68 🚊 a					22 20				*23 00*				23 18									
Birmingham New Street 12 68 a					22 45				*23 17*				23 41									
London Euston 15 ⊖ 65 a			23 53																			

For general notes see front of timetable
For details of catering facilities see Directory of Train Operators

A From Liverpool Lime Street to Nottingham (Table 49)
B To Buxton (Table 86)
C To Bristol Temple Meads (Table 51)
D From Manchester Airport to Doncaster (Table 29)
E From Southport (Table 82) to Chester (Table 88)
G To Reading (Table 51)
H To Cardiff Central (Table 131)
J From Southport (Table 82)
K From Manchester Airport to Sheffield (Table 78)
b Change at Stafford

Sundays

from 13 September

Manchester, Stockport and Manchester Airport → Crewe and Stoke-on-Trent

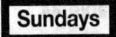

Network Diagram - see first page of Table 78

	NT	VT	VT	XC	NT	NT	TP	NT	VT	NT	XC		AW	NT	NT	VT	NT	XC	AW	VT	NT	NT	NT	VT
		1 ◇	1 ◇	1 ◇			1 ◇		1 ◇		1 ◇		◇			1 ◇		1 ◇	R	1 ◇				1 ◇
	A			B		C	D			E	B		G	C			H	B	J			C		
		⊡	⊡	⊥					⊡		⊥					⊡		⊥	⊥	⊡				⊡
Deansgate d										09 15							10 15							
Manchester Oxford Road d										09 18							10 19							
Manchester Piccadilly 10 a										09 21							10 21							
d	07 57	08 05	08 20	08 27	08 42	08 55	08 58	09 04	09 20	09 23	09 27		09 30	09 51	10 03	10 20	10 23	10 27	10 30	10 35	10 43	10 52	11 04	11 15
Levenshulme d						09 00		09 09						09 58	10 08							10 58	11 10	
Heaton Chapel d						09 03		09 12						10 01	10 11							11 01	11 13	
Stockport a	08 08	08 13	08 28	08 34		09 07	09 06	09 16	09 27	09 31	09 35		09 39	10 04	10 15	10 28	10 32	10 34	10 38	10 42		11 04	11 17	11 23
d		08 14	08 28	08 36				09 17	09 27		09 36		09 39		10 17	10 29		10 36	10 39	10 42			11 17	11 23
Cheadle Hulme d								09 21							10 23								11 24	
Bramhall d																								
Poynton d																								
Adlington (Cheshire) d																								
Prestbury d																								
Macclesfield a			08 42						09 40		09 48							10 48		10 55				
d			08 42						09 40		09 49							10 49		10 55				
Congleton d																								
Handforth d								09 25							10 27								11 28	
Manchester Airport ✈ d					09 09																11 10			
Styal d					09 13																11 15			
Wilmslow d		08 22		08 43	09 17			09 28					09 47		10 30	10 36			10 47		11 18		11 31	
Alderley Edge d					09a21			09 31							10a34						11a23		11 34	
Chelford d								09 35															11 38	
Goostrey d								09 40															11 43	
Holmes Chapel d								09 43															11 46	
Sandbach d								09 48															11 51	
Crewe 10 65 a		08 39		09 01				09 56					10 06			10 52			11 07				11 59	
Kidsgrove 50 a																								
Longport 50 a																								
Stoke-on-Trent 50, 68 a			09 04						09 57		10 05							11 06		11 12				11 50
Stafford 68 a		09 07		09 27				*10 38*			10 26		*10 45*			*11 41*		11 24						
Wolverhampton 7 68 a				09 40							10 40		*11 01*					11 40						
Birmingham New Street 12 68 a				09 58							10 58		*11 18*			*12b05*		11 58	*12 55*					
London Euston 15 ⊖ 65 a		10 58	11 08	*11c44*				*12 38*	12 08		*12c38*		*12 51*			12 58		*13c15*	*13e44*	13 09				13 31

	TP		NT	XC	AW	VT	NT	VT	NT	VT	TP	NT	XC		AW	VT	NT	EM	NT	VT	NT	NT	NT	XC
	1 ◇			1 ◇	R	1 ◇		1 ◇		1 ◇	1 ◇		1 ◇		R	1 ◇		◇		1 ◇				1 ◇
	K		L	B	G		C				N	H	B		J			Q	C			U	V	X
				⊥	⊥	⊡		⊡		⊡			⊥		⊥	⊡		⊥		⊡				⊥
Deansgate d			11 11									12 11												
Manchester Oxford Road d			11 17									12 17												
Manchester Piccadilly 10 a			11 19									12 19												
d	11 18		11 22	11 27	11 30	11 35	11 52	11 55	12 04	12 15	12 18	12 22	12 26		12 30	12 35	12 41	12 44	12 52	12 55		13 04	13 04	13 07
Levenshulme d							11 58		12 09										12 58			13 09	13 09	
Heaton Chapel d							12 01		12 12										13 01			13 12	13 12	
Stockport a	11 27		11 30	11 35	11 39	11 43	12 04	12 04	12 16	12 23	12 27	12 32	12 35		12 39	12 44		12 53	13 04	13 04		13 16	13 16	
d				11 36	11 40	11 43		12 05	12 17	12 23			12 36		12 40	12 44				13 05		13 17	13 17	
Cheadle Hulme d									12 24													13 22	13 22	
Bramhall d																								
Poynton d																								
Adlington (Cheshire) d																								
Prestbury d																								
Macclesfield a				11 48		11 56							12 48			12 57								
d				11 49		11 56							12 49			12 57								
Congleton d																								
Handforth d									12 28												←	13 26	13 26	
Manchester Airport ✈ d																	13 06 →				13 06			
Styal d																					13 10			
Wilmslow d					11 47			12 12	12 31						12 48					13 12	13 15	13 28	13f34	
Alderley Edge d									12a36												13a19	13 31	13 37	
Chelford d																						13 35	13 41	
Goostrey d																						13 40	13 45	
Holmes Chapel d																						13 43	13 48	
Sandbach d																						13 48	13 53	
Crewe 10 65 a					12 06			12 28							13 08					13 28		13 56	14 01	
Kidsgrove 50 a																								
Longport 50 a																								
Stoke-on-Trent 50, 68 a				12 06		12 13				12 50			13 06			13 14								13 42
Stafford 68 a				12 25	*12 41*								13 24		*13 42*									
Wolverhampton 7 68 a				12 40	*12 59*								13 40		*13 58*									14 13
Birmingham New Street 12 68 a				12 58	*13 16*			*13g55*					13 58		*14 15*					*14 55*				14 31
London Euston 15 ⊖ 65 a				*14c03*		13 49		14 12		14 31			*15c03*			14 50				15 12				

For general notes see front of timetable
For details of catering facilities see Directory of Train Operators

- **A** To Sheffield (Table 78)
- **B** To Bournemouth (Table 51)
- **C** To Buxton (Table 86)
- **D** From Manchester Airport to Sheffield (Table 78)
- **E** From Wigan Wallgate (Table 82) to Chester (Table 88)
- **G** To Cardiff Central (Table 131)
- **H** From Southport (Table 82)
- **J** To Milford Haven (Table 128)
- **K** From Manchester Airport to Cleethorpes (Table 29)
- **L** From Southport (Table 82) to Chester (Table 88)
- **N** To Doncaster (Table 29)
- **Q** To Norwich (Table 49)
- **U** Until 1 November
- **V** From 8 November
- **X** To Paignton (Table 51) (from 8 November to Penzance) (Table 135)
- **b** From 8 November arr. 1255
- **c** Change at Stafford
- **e** From 8 November arr. 1323
- **f** Arr. 1328
- **g** From 8 November arr. 1415

Table 84

Sundays

from 13 September

Manchester, Stockport and Manchester Airport → Crewe and Stoke-on-Trent

Network Diagram - see first page of Table 78

	VT	TP	NT		XC	AW	VT	EM	NT	VT	NT	XC	VT	TP	NT		XC	AW	VT	NT	NT	EM	NT	VT
	1 ◇	1 ◇			1 ◇	R	1 ◇	◇		1 ◇		1 ◇	1 ◇	1 ◇			1 ◇	R	1 ◇			◇		1 ◇
		A	B		C	D		E	G			H		A	J		C	K				E	G	
	☕				🛒	🛒	☕	🛒		☕		🛒	☕				🛒	🛒	☕			🛒		☕
Deansgate d			13 11												14 11									
Manchester Oxford Road d			13 17					13 39							14 17							14 39		
Manchester Piccadilly 10 a			13 19					13 41							14 19							14 41		
d	13 15	13 20	13 22		13 27	13 30	13 35	13 44	13 52	13 55	14 04	14 07	14 15	14 20	14 22		14 27	14 30	14 35	14 41	14 41	14 44	14 52	14 55
Levenshulme d									13 58		14 09												14 58	
Heaton Chapel d									14 01		14 12												15 01	
Stockport a	13 22	13 28	13 30		13 34	13 39	13 42	13 53	14 04	14 03	14 16		14 22	14 28	14 33		14 34	14 38	14 42		14 49	14 53	15 04	15 03
d	13 22				13 36	13 39	13 42			14 04	14 17		14 22				14 36	14 39	14 42		14 51			15 04
Cheadle Hulme d											14 22										14 55			
Bramhall d																					14 58			
Poynton d																					15 01			
Adlington (Cheshire) d																					15 04			
Prestbury d																					15 07			
Macclesfield a					13 48		13 55										14 48		14 55		15 11			
d					13 49		13 55										14 49		14 55		15 11			
Congleton d																					15 19			
Handforth d											14 26													
Manchester Airport d																				15 06 →				
Styal d																								
Wilmslow d						13 47				14 11	14 29							14 47						15 11
Alderley Edge d											14a33													
Chelford d																								
Goostrey d																								
Holmes Chapel d																								
Sandbach d																								
Crewe 10 65 a						14 07				14 27								15 06						15 27
Kidsgrove 50 a																					15 25			
Longport 50 a																								
Stoke-on-Trent 50, 68 a	13 49				14 06		14 12					14 42	14 49				15 06		15 12		15 35			
Stafford 68 a					14 24	*14 42*											15 24	*15 42*						
Wolverhampton 7 68 a					14 40	*14 58*						15 13					15 40	*15 58*						
Birmingham New Street 12 68 a					14 58	*15 15*				*15 55*		15 31					15 58	*16 15*						*16 55*
London Euston 15 ⊖ 65 a	15 30				*16b03*		15 48			16 11			16 30				*17b03*		16 48					17 11

	NT	NT	XC	VT	TP		NT	XC	AW	VT	EM	NT	VT	NT	XC	VT	TP		NT	XC	AW	VT	NT	EM
			1 ◇	1 ◇	1 ◇			1 ◇	R	1 ◇	◇		1 ◇		1 ◇	1 ◇	1 ◇			1 ◇	R	1 ◇		◇
			L		A		B	C	D		E	G			H		A		J	C	D			E
			🛒	☕				🛒	🛒	☕	🛒		☕		🛒	☕				🛒	🛒	☕		🛒
Deansgate d							15 11												16 11					
Manchester Oxford Road d							15 17				15 39								16 17					16 39
Manchester Piccadilly 10 a							15 19				15 41								16 19					16 41
d		15 04	15 07	15 15	15 20		15 22	15 27	15 30	15 35	15 44	15 52	15 55	16 04	16 07	16 15	16 20		16 22	16 27	16 30	16 35	16 41	16 44
Levenshulme d		15 09										15 58		16 09										
Heaton Chapel d		15 12										16 01		16 12										
Stockport a		15 16		15 22	15 28		15 30	15 34	15 38	15 42	15 53	16 04	16 03	16 16		16 22	16 28		16 31	16 34	16 39	16 42		16 53
d		15 17		15 22				15 36	15 39	15 42			16 04	16 17		16 23				16 36	16 39	16 42		
Cheadle Hulme d		15 22												16 22										
Bramhall d																								
Poynton d																								
Adlington (Cheshire) d																								
Prestbury d																								
Macclesfield a								15 48		15 55										16 48		16 55		
d								15 49		15 55										16 49		16 55		
Congleton d																								
Handforth d	←	15 26												16 26										
Manchester Airport d	15 06																						17 06 →	
Styal d	15 10																							
Wilmslow d	15 15	15 29							15 47				16 11	16 29							16 47			
Alderley Edge d	15a19	15 32												16a33										
Chelford d		15 36																						
Goostrey d		15 40																						
Holmes Chapel d		15 43																						
Sandbach d		15 48																						
Crewe 10 65 a		15 56							16 06				16 27								17 06			
Kidsgrove 50 a																								
Longport 50 a																								
Stoke-on-Trent 50, 68 a			15 42	15 49				16 06		16 12					16 42	16 48				17 06		17 12		
Stafford 68 a								16 24	*16 42*											17 24	*17 42*			
Wolverhampton 7 68 a			16 13					16 40	*16 58*						17 13					17 40	*17 58*			
Birmingham New Street 12 68 a			16 31					16 58	*17 15*				*17 55*		17 31					17 58	*18 15*			
London Euston 15 ⊖ 65 a				17 30				*18b04*		17 48			18 11			18 30				*19b03*		18 48		

For general notes see front of timetable
For details of catering facilities see Directory of Train Operators

- **A** From Manchester Airport to Cleethorpes (Table 29)
- **B** From Southport (Table 82) to Chester (Table 88)
- **C** To Bournemouth (Table 51)
- **D** To Cardiff Central (Table 131)
- **E** From Liverpool Lime Street to Norwich (Table 49)
- **G** To Buxton (Table 86)
- **H** To Bristol Temple Meads (from 8 November to Plymouth) (Table 51)
- **J** From Southport (Table 82)
- **K** To Milford Haven and Pembroke Dock (Table 128)
- **L** To Bristol Temple Meads (Table 51) (from 8 November to Penzance) (Table 135)
- **b** Change at Stafford

Table 84

Sundays

from 13 September

Manchester, Stockport and Manchester Airport → Crewe and Stoke-on-Trent

Network Diagram - see first page of Table 78

		NT	VT	NT	NT	XC	VT	TP		NT	XC	AW	VT	EM	NT	VT	NT	XC	VT	TP		NT	XC	AW	VT
			1 ◇			1 ◇	1 ◇	1 ◇			1 ◇	R	1 ◇	◇		1 ◇		1 ◇	1 ◇	1 ◇			1 ◇	R	1 ◇
		A				B		C		D	E	G		H	A			J		C		K	L	G	
			🍽			🛒	🍽				🛒	🛒	🍽	🛒		🍽		🛒	🍽				🛒	🛒	🍽
Deansgate	d									17 11												18 11			
Manchester Oxford Road	d									17 17				17 39								18 17			
Manchester Piccadilly 10	a									17 19				17 41								18 19			
	d	16 52	16 55		17 04	17 07	17 15	17 20		17 22	17 27	17 30	17 35	17 44	17 52	17 55	18 04	18 07	18 15	18 20		18 22	18 27	18 30	18 35
Levenshulme	d	16 58			17 09										17 58		18 09								
Heaton Chapel	d	17 01			17 12										18 01		18 12								
Stockport	a	17 04	17 03		17 16		17 22	17 28		17 30	17 34	17 38	17 42	17 53	18 04	18 03	18 16		18 22	18 28		18 33	18 34	18 38	18 42
	d		17 04		17 17		17 22				17 36	17 39	17 42			18 04	18 17		18 22				18 36	18 39	18 42
Cheadle Hulme	d				17 22												18 22								
Bramhall	d																								
Poynton	d																								
Adlington (Cheshire)	d																								
Prestbury	d																								
Macclesfield	a										17 48		17 55										18 48		18 55
	d										17 49		17 55										18 49		18 55
Congleton	d																								
Handforth	d			←	17 26												18 26								
Manchester Airport ✈	d			17 06																					
Styal	d			17 10																					
Wilmslow	d		17 11	17 15	17 29							17 48				18 11	18 29							18 47	
Alderley Edge	d			17a19	17 32												18a33								
Chelford	d				17 36																				
Goostrey	d				17 40																				
Holmes Chapel	d				17 43																				
Sandbach	d				17 48																				
Crewe 10	65 a		17 27		17 56							18 07				18 27								19 06	
Kidsgrove	50 a																								
Longport	50 a																								
Stoke-on-Trent	50, 68 a					17 42	17 49				18 06		18 12					18 42	18 49				19 06		19 12
Stafford	68 a										18 24	18 42											19 24	19 42	
Wolverhampton 7	68 a					18 13					18 40	18 58						19 13					19 40	19 58	
Birmingham New Street 12	68 a		18 55			18 31					18 58	19 15				19 55		19 31					19 58	20 15	
London Euston 15	⊖ 65 a		19 11				19 30				20b03		19 48			20 11			20 30				21b06		20 48

		NT	NT	EM	NT	VT	NT	NT	XC	VT		TP	NT	XC	AW	VT	EM	NT	NT	XC	TP	VT		NT	AW
				◇		1 ◇			1 ◇	1 ◇		1 ◇		1 ◇	◇	1 ◇	◇			1 ◇	1 ◇	1 ◇			◇
				H	A				N			C	D	Q	G		H	A		N	C			K	G
				🛒		🍽			🛒	🍽				🛒		🍽	🛒					🍽			
Deansgate	d												19 11											20 11	
Manchester Oxford Road	d			18 39									19 17				19 39							20 17	
Manchester Piccadilly 10	a			18 41									19 19				19 41							20 19	
	d	18 41	18 42	18 44	18 52	18 55		19 04	19 07	19 15		19 20	19 22	19 27	19 30	19 35	19 44	19 52	20 04	20 07	20 18	20 20		20 22	20 30
Levenshulme	d				18 58			19 09										19 58	20 09						
Heaton Chapel	d				19 01			19 12										20 01	20 12						
Stockport	a		18 50	18 53	19 04	19 03		19 16		19 22		19 28	19 30	19 34	19 39	19 42	19 53	20 04	20 16	20 15	20 26	20 27		20 32	20 38
	d		18 52			19 04		19 17		19 22				19 35	19 39	19 42			20 17	20 16		20 27			20 39
Cheadle Hulme	d		18 57					19 22											20 23						
Bramhall	d		19 00																						
Poynton	d		19 03																						
Adlington (Cheshire)	d		19 06																						
Prestbury	d		19 09																						
Macclesfield	a		19 13											19 47		19 55				20 28		20 40			
	d		19 13											19 48		19 55				20 29		20 40			
Congleton	d		19 21																						
Handforth	d						←	19 26											20 27						
Manchester Airport ✈	d	19 06 →					19 06																		
Styal	d						19 10																		
Wilmslow	d					19 11	19 15	19 29							19 47				20 30						20 47
Alderley Edge	d						19a19	19 32											20a35						
Chelford	d							19 36																	
Goostrey	d							19 40																	
Holmes Chapel	d							19 43																	
Sandbach	d							19 48																	
Crewe 10	65 a					19 27		19 56							20 06										21 07
Kidsgrove	50 a		19 28																						
Longport	50 a																								
Stoke-on-Trent	50, 68 a		19 38						19 42	19 49				20 05		20 12				20 46		20 57			
Stafford	68 a													20 24	20 37					21 08					21 36
Wolverhampton 7	68 a								20 13					20 39	20 55					21 21					21 55
Birmingham New Street 12	68 a					20 57			20 31					21 00	21 15					21 39					22 15
London Euston 15	⊖ 65 a					21 14				21 34				22b29	22 29	22 04						22 57			23 59

For general notes see front of timetable
For details of catering facilities see Directory of Train Operators

- **A** To Buxton (Table 86)
- **B** To Paignton (from 8 November to Plymouth) (Table 51)
- **C** From Manchester Airport to Cleethorpes (Table 29)
- **D** From Southport (Table 82) to Chester (Table 88)
- **E** To Bournemouth (Table 51)
- **G** To Cardiff Central (Table 131)
- **H** From Liverpool Lime Street to Nottingham (Table 49)
- **J** To Bristol Temple Meads (from 8 November to Plymouth) (Table 51)
- **K** From Southport (Table 82)
- **L** To Southampton Central (Table 51)
- **N** To Bristol Temple Meads (Table 51)
- **Q** To Reading (Table 51)
- **b** Change at Stafford

Table 84

Sundays

from 13 September

Manchester, Stockport and Manchester Airport → Crewe and Stoke-on-Trent

Network Diagram - see first page of Table 78

		NT	EM	NT	VT	NT	XC	TP	NT	AW	NT	NT	NT	XC	EM	TP	NT	AW	NT	NT	TP	NT
			◇		1 ◇		1 ◇	1 ◇						1 ◇	◇	1 ◇					1 ◇	
			A	B				C	D			B			A	C	E		B		C	E
			✕		☕																	
Deansgate	d								21 11								22 11					23 12
Manchester Oxford Road	d		20 39						21 17						22 07		22 17					23 17
Manchester Piccadilly 10	a		20 41						21 19						22 09		22 19					23 19
	d	20 41	20 44	20 52	20 55	21 04	21 07	21 20	21 22	21 34	21 41	21 52	22 04	22 07	22 11	22 16	22 22	22 35	22 52	23 04	23 20	23 22
Levenshulme	d			20 58		21 09						21 58	22 09						22 58	23 09		
Heaton Chapel	d			21 01		21 12						22 01	22 12						23 01	23 12		
Stockport	a		20 53	21 04	21 03	21 16	21 15	21 28	21 30		21 49	22 04	22 16	22 15	22 20	22 24	22 31		23 04	23 16	23 28	23 32
	d				21 03	21 17	21 16				21 52		22 17	22 16						23 17		
Cheadle Hulme	d					21 23					21 56		22 23							23 21		
Bramhall	d										21 59											
Poynton	d										22 02											
Adlington (Cheshire)	d										22 05											
Prestbury	d										22 08											
Macclesfield	a				21 15		21 28				22 12			22 28								
	d				21 15		21 29				22 13			22 29								
Congleton	d										22 20											
Handforth	d					21 27							22 27							23 25		
Manchester Airport ✈	d	21 06																				
Styal	d	21 10																				
Wilmslow	d	21 15				21 30				21 52			22 30					22 52		23 28		
Alderley Edge	d	21a19				21 33							22a34							23a33		
Chelford	d					21 37																
Goostrey	d					21 42																
Holmes Chapel	d					21 45																
Sandbach	d					21 50																
Crewe 10	65 a					21 58				22 11								23 11				
Kidsgrove	50 a										22 26											
Longport	50 a																					
Stoke-on-Trent	50, 68 a				21 32		21 46				22 36			22 46								
Stafford	68 a						22 06			*22 41*				23 05								
Wolverhampton 7	68 a						22 20			*23 00*				23 18								
Birmingham New Street 12	68 a						22 45			*23 17*				23 41								
London Euston 15	⊖ 65 a				23 53																	

For general notes see front of timetable
For details of catering facilities see Directory of Train Operators

A From Liverpool Lime Street to Nottingham (Table 49)
B To Buxton (Table 86)
C From Manchester Airport to Sheffield (Table 78)
D From Southport (Table 82) to Chester (Table 88)
E From Southport (Table 82)

Manchester → Manchester Airport

Network Diagram - see first page of Table 78

Miles	Station		TP	TP	TP	TP	TP	NT	TP	TP	TP	NT	NT		TP	TP	TP	NT	NT	TP	TP	NT	TP	TP	NT
			MO	MO	MX	MO																			
			1 ◇	1 ◇	1 ◇	1 ◇	1 ◇		1 ◇	1 ◇	1 ◇	1			1 ◇	1 ◇	1 ◇			1 ◇	1 ◇		1 ◇	1 ◇	
			A	B	C	D	E	G	H	A	E		J		A	E	H			E	A	J	K L	K N	
																					🛒				
—	Deansgate	d																			06 51				
—	Manchester Oxford Road	d																			06 54	06 58			
—	Manchester Piccadilly 10	a																			06 56	07 01			
0		d	00 16	00 44	00 54	01 16	04 00	04 15	04 44	04u47	05 00	05 35	05 58		06 03	06 08	06 12	06 15	06 46	06 54	06 58	07 03	07 06	07 06	07 14
3½	Mauldeth Road	d										05 42						06 22	06 53						07 21
4¼	Burnage	d										05 44						06 24	06 55						07 23
5¼	East Didsbury	d										05 46						06 26	06 57						07 25
6¾	Gatley	d										05 49						06 29	06 59						07 27
8¼	Heald Green	d										05 52						06 32	07 02		07 10				07 30
9¾	Manchester Airport	a	00 30	01 00	01 10	01 31	04 15	04 30	05 00	05 06	05 15	05 57	06 14		06 18	06 24	06 29	06 39	07 07	07 12	07 17	07 22	07 26	07 32	07 38
—	Wilmslow	84 a										06 11							07 20						
—	Crewe 10	84 a										06 46							07 46						

Station		TP	TP		NT	NT	TP	TP	NT	TP	NT	TP	TP	NT	NT		TP	TP	NT	TP	NT	TP	TP	NT	NT
		1 ◇	1 ◇				1 ◇	1 ◇		1 ◇		1 ◇	1 ◇				1 ◇	1 ◇		1 ◇		1 ◇	1 ◇		
		E	Q		U		E	A	J	V		X	Y	U			Z	AA	J	V		Z	Q	U	
			🛒				🛒	🛒		🛒		🛒	🛒				🛒	🛒		🛒		🛒	🛒		
Deansgate	d				07 28			07 51						08 29										09 29	
Manchester Oxford Road	d		07 24		07 32			07 54	07 59				08 24	08 33				08 53	08 58				09 24	09 33	
Manchester Piccadilly 10	a		07 27		07 34			07 56	08 01				08 27	08 35				08 56	09 01				09 27	09 35	
	d	07 23	07 29		07 36	07 46	07 54	07 58	08 02	08 06	08 14	08 24	08 29	08 37	08 46		08 54	08 58	09 03	09 06	09 14	09 24	09 29	09 37	09 46
Mauldeth Road	d					07 53					08 21				08 53						09 21				09 53
Burnage	d					07 55					08 23				08 55						09 23				09 55
East Didsbury	d					07 57					08 25		08 38		08 57			09 07			09 25				09 57
Gatley	d					07 59					08 27				08 59						09 27				09 59
Heald Green	d					08 02		08 10		08 21	08 30				09 02			09 12			09 30				10 02
Manchester Airport	a	07 42	07 47		07 53	08 07	08 12	08 17	08 22	08 29	08 39	08 42	08 47	08 53	09 07		09 12	09 19	09 22	09 33	09 38	09 42	09 47	09 53	10 07
Wilmslow	84 a					08 21									09 20										10 20
Crewe 10	84 a					08 47									09 46										10 46

Station		TP	TP	NT	TP		NT	TP	TP	NT	NT	TP	TP	NT	TP	NT	TP		TP	NT	NT	TP	TP	NT	TP
		1 ◇	1 ◇		1 ◇			1 ◇	1 ◇			1 ◇	1 ◇		1 ◇		1 ◇		1 ◇			1 ◇	1 ◇		1 ◇
		X	A	J	V			C	BB	U		E	A	J	V		X		Q	U		C	A	J	V
		🛒	🛒		🛒			🛒	🛒			🛒	🛒		🛒		🛒		🛒			🛒	🛒		🛒
Deansgate	d		09 51							10 29			10 51							11 29			11 51		
Manchester Oxford Road	d		09 54	09 58					10 24	10 33			10 54	10 58					11 24	11 33			11 54	11 58	
Manchester Piccadilly 10	a		09 56	10 01					10 27	10 35			10 56	11 01					11 27	11 35			11 56	12 01	
	d	09 54	09 58	10 03	10 06		10 14	10 24	10 29	10 37	10 46	10 54	10 58	11 03	11 06	11 14	11 24		11 29	11 37	11 46	11 54	11 58	12 03	12 06
Mauldeth Road	d						10 21				10 53					11 21					11 53				
Burnage	d						10 23				10 55					11 23					11 55				
East Didsbury	d						10 25				10 57					11 25					11 57				
Gatley	d						10 27				10 59					11 27					11 59				
Heald Green	d		10 10				10 30				11 02		11 10			11 30					12 02		12 10		
Manchester Airport	a	10 12	10 17	10 22	10 26		10 38	10 42	10 47	10 53	11 07	11 12	11 17	11 22	11 26	11 38	11 42		11 47	11 53	12 07	12 12	12 17	12 22	12 26
Wilmslow	84 a										11 20										12 20				
Crewe 10	84 a										11 46										12 46				

Station		NT	TP	TP	NT	NT	TP		TP	NT	TP	NT	TP	TP	NT	NT	TP	TP	NT		TP	NT	TP	TP	NT
			1 ◇	1 ◇			1 ◇		1 ◇		1 ◇		1 ◇	1 ◇			1 ◇	1 ◇			1 ◇		1 ◇	1 ◇	
			X	CC	U		C		A	J	V		X	DD	U		C	A	J		V		X	CC	U
			🛒	🛒			🛒		🛒		🛒		🛒	🛒			🛒	🛒			🛒		🛒	🛒	
Deansgate	d				12 29				12 51						13 29			13 51							14 29
Manchester Oxford Road	d			12 24	12 33				12 54	12 58				13 24	13 33			13 54	13 58					14 24	14 33
Manchester Piccadilly 10	a			12 27	12 35				12 56	13 01				13 27	13 35			13 56	14 01					14 27	14 35
	d	12 14	12 24	12 29	12 37	12 46	12 54		12 58	13 03	13 06	13 14	13 24	13 29	13 37	13 46	13 54	13 58	14 03		14 06	14 14	14 24	14 29	14 37
Mauldeth Road	d	12 21				12 53						13 21				13 53						14 21			
Burnage	d	12 23				12 55						13 23				13 55						14 23			
East Didsbury	d	12 25				12 57						13 25				13 57						14 25			
Gatley	d	12 27				12 59						13 27				13 59						14 27			
Heald Green	d	12 30				13 02			13 10			13 30				14 02		14 10				14 30			
Manchester Airport	a	12 38	12 42	12 47	12 53	13 07	13 12		13 17	13 22	13 26	13 38	13 42	13 47	13 53	14 07	14 12	14 17	14 22		14 26	14 38	14 42	14 47	14 53
Wilmslow	84 a					13 21										14 20									
Crewe 10	84 a					13 47										14 46									

Station		NT	TP	TP	NT	TP	NT	TP	TP		NT	NT	TP	TP	NT	TP	NT	TP	TP	NT	NT		TP	TP	NT
			1 ◇	1 ◇		1 ◇		1 ◇	1 ◇				1 ◇	1 ◇		1 ◇		1 ◇	1 ◇				1 ◇	1 ◇	
			C	A	J	V		X	EE		U		C	A	J	V		X	CC	U			C	A	J
			🛒	🛒		🛒		🛒	🛒				🛒	🛒		🛒		🛒	🛒				🛒	🛒	
Deansgate	d			14 51							15 29			15 51										16 51	
Manchester Oxford Road	d			14 54	14 58				15 24		15 33			15 54	15 58				16 24	16 33				16 54	16 58
Manchester Piccadilly 10	a			14 56	15 01				15 27		15 35			15 56	16 01				16 27	16 35				16 56	17 01
	d	14 46	14 54	14 58	15 03	15 06	15 14	15 24	15 29		15 37	15 46	15 54	15 58	16 03	16 06	16 14	16 24	16 29	16 37	16 46		16 54	16 58	17 03
Mauldeth Road	d	14 53					15 21					15 53					16 21				16 53				
Burnage	d	14 55					15 23					15 55					16 23				16 55				
East Didsbury	d	14 57					15 25					15 57					16 25				16 57				
Gatley	d	14 59					15 27					15 59					16 27				16 59				
Heald Green	d	15 02		15 10			15 30					16 02		16 10			16 30		16 40		17 02			17 10	
Manchester Airport	a	15 07	15 12	15 17	15 22	15 26	15 38	15 42	15 47		15 53	16 07	16 12	16 17	16 22	16 26	16 38	16 42	16 47	16 53	17 07		17 12	17 17	17 22
Wilmslow	84 a	15 20										16 20									17 20				
Crewe 10	84 a	15 46										16 46									17 44				

For general notes see front of timetable
For details of catering facilities see Directory of Train Operators

- **A** From Blackpool North (Table 82)
- **B** Until 7 September. From Middlesbrough (Table 39)
- **C** From Newcastle (Table 39)
- **D** From 14 September. From Middlesbrough (Table 39)
- **E** From York (Table 39)
- **G** From Liverpool Lime Street (Table 89)
- **H** From Sheffield (Table 78)
- **J** From Liverpool Lime Street (Table 90)
- **K** From Doncaster (Table 29)
- **L** Until 19 June and from 7 September
- **N** 22 June to 4 September
- **Q** From Barrow-in-Furness (Table 82)
- **U** From Southport (Table 82)
- **V** From Cleethorpes (22 June to 4 September from Doncaster) (Table 29)
- **X** From Middlesbrough (Table 39)
- **Y** From Blackpool North and Barrow-in-Furness (Table 82)
- **Z** From Scarborough (Table 39)
- **AA** From Edinburgh (Table 65) and Blackpool North (Table 82)
- **BB** From Glasgow Central (Table 65)
- **CC** From Windermere (Table 82)
- **DD** From Glasgow Central and Edinburgh (Table 65)
- **EE** From Edinburgh (Table 65). Until 19 June and from 7 September also conveys portion from Barrow-in-Furness (Table 82)

Manchester → Manchester Airport

Network Diagram - see first page of Table 78

	TP 1◊ A	NT	TP 1◊ B	NT C	NT	TP 1◊ D	TP 1◊ E	NT G	TP 1◊ A	NT		TP 1◊ H	TP 1◊ E	NT C	NT J	TP 1◊ D	TP 1◊ K	NT G	TP 1◊ A	NT	TP 1◊ L	NT C		TP 1◊ D
Deansgate d							17 51										18 51					19 29		
Manchester Oxford Road d			17 24	17 33			17 54	17 59					18 24	18 33			18 54	18 58			19 24	19 33		
Manchester Piccadilly 10 a			17 27	17 35			17 56	18 01					18 27	18 35			18 56	19 01			19 27	19 35		
d	17 06	17 14	17 29	17 37	17 46	17 54	17 58	18 02	18 06	18 14		18 24	18 29	18 37	18 46	18 54	18 58	19 03	19 06	19 14	19 29	19 37		19 40
Mauldeth Road d		17 21			17 53					18 21					18 53					19 21				
Burnage d		17 23			17 55					18 23					18 55					19 23				
East Didsbury d	17 19	17 25			17 57					18 25					18 57					19 25				
Gatley d	17 22	17 27			17 59					18 27					18 59					19 27				
Heald Green d	17 25	17 30	17 40		18 02		18 10			18 30			18 40		19 02		19 10			19 30				
Manchester Airport a	17 32	17 39	17 48	17 53	18 07	18 12	18 17	18 22	18 26	18 38		18 42	18 47	18 53	19 08	19 13	19 17	19 24	19 28	19 38	19 47	19 53		19 59
Wilmslow 84 a					18 21										19 23									
Crewe 10 84 a					*18 47*										*20 01*									

	NT	TP 1◊ E	TP 1◊ K	TP 1◊ A	NT C	TP 1◊ H	NT	TP 1◊ E	NT G	TP 1◊ A	TP 1◊ L		NT C	TP 1◊ D	NT	TP 1◊ E	TP 1◊ N	TP 1◊ H	NT	TP 1◊ E	TP 1◊ A	TP 1◊ E		
Deansgate d		19 51			20 29			20 51					21 29			21 51				22 51				
Manchester Oxford Road d	19 43	19 54	19 59		20 33		20 43	20 54	20 58		21 24		21 33		21 43	21 54	22 27		22 43	22 54				
Manchester Piccadilly 10 a	19 45	19 56	20 02		20 35		20 45	20 56	21 01		21 27		21 35		21 45	21 56	22 30		22 45	22 56				
d	19 46	19 58	20 03	20 06	20 37	20 40	20 46	20 58	21 03	21 06	21 29		21 37	21 40	21 46	21 58	22 32	22 40	22 46	22 58	23 06	23 54		
Mauldeth Road d	19 53			20 15			20 53			21 15					21 53				22 53			00 04		
Burnage d	19 55			20 17			20 55			21 17					21 55				22 55			00 06		
East Didsbury d	19 57			20 20			20 57			21 20					21 57				22 57			00 09		
Gatley d	19 59			20 23			20 59			21 23					21 59				22 59			00 12		
Heald Green d	20 02	20 10	20 15	20 26			21 02	21 10		21 26					22 02	22 09			23 02	23 09		00 15		
Manchester Airport a	20 07	20 17	20 24	20 35	20 53	20 57	21 07	21 17	21 24	21 35	21 47		21 53	21 57	22 10	22 17	22 47	22 57	23 08	23 17	23 26	00 22		
Wilmslow 84 a	20 24						21 24								22 22				23 22					
Crewe 10 84 a	*21 01*						*22 01*								*23 01*									

Saturdays

until 31 October

	TP 1◊ D	TP 1◊ Q	NT U	TP 1◊ V	TP 1◊ E	TP 1◊ Q	NT 1	NT G		TP 1◊ E	TP 1◊ Q	TP 1◊ V	NT	NT	TP 1◊ Q	TP 1◊ E	NT G		TP 1◊ XY	TP 1◊ XZ	NT	TP 1◊ Q	TP 1◊ N	NT C
Deansgate d																06 51								07 28
Manchester Oxford Road d																06 54	06 58						07 24	07 32
Manchester Piccadilly 10 a																06 56	07 01						07 27	07 34
d	00 54	03 44	04 15	04 44	04u47	04 54	05 35	05 58		06 03	06 08	06 12	06 15	06 46	06 54	06 58	07 03		07 06	07 06	07 14	07 23	07 29	07 36
Mauldeth Road d							05 42						06 22	06 53							07 21			
Burnage d							05 44						06 24	06 55							07 23			
East Didsbury d							05 46						06 26	06 57							07 25			
Gatley d							05 49						06 29	06 59							07 27			
Heald Green d							05 52						06 32	07 02		07 10					07 30			
Manchester Airport a	01 10	04 00	04 30	05 00	05 06	05 10	05 57	06 14		06 18	06 24	06 29	06 39	07 07	07 12	07 17	07 22		07 26	07 32	07 38	07 42	07 47	07 53
Wilmslow 84 a							06 11							07 20										
Crewe 10 84 a							06 43							07 46										

	NT	TP 1◊ Q	TP 1◊ E	NT G		TP 1◊ AA	NT 1	TP 1◊ H	TP 1◊ N	NT C	NT	TP 1◊ BB	TP 1◊ E		NT G	TP 1◊ AA	NT	TP 1◊ BB	TP 1◊ N	NT C	NT	TP 1◊ H		TP 1◊ E
Deansgate d			07 51							08 29										09 29				09 51
Manchester Oxford Road d			07 54	07 58					08 24	08 33			08 53		08 58				09 24	09 33				09 54
Manchester Piccadilly 10 a			07 56	08 01					08 27	08 35			08 56		09 01				09 27	09 35				09 56
d	07 46	07 54	07 58	08 03		08 06	08 14	08 24	08 29	08 37	08 46	08 54	08 58		09 03	09 06	09 14	09 24	09 29	09 37	09 46	09 54		09 58
Mauldeth Road d	07 53						08 21				08 53						09 21				09 53			
Burnage d	07 55						08 23				08 55						09 23				09 55			
East Didsbury d	07 57						08 25		08 38		08 57		09 07				09 25				09 57			
Gatley d	07 59						08 27				08 59						09 27				09 59			
Heald Green d	08 02		08 10			08 21	08 30				09 02		09 12				09 30				10 02			10 10
Manchester Airport a	08 07	08 12	08 17	08 22		08 29	08 37	08 42	08 47	08 53	09 08	09 12	09 19		09 22	09 26	09 38	09 42	09 47	09 53	10 07	10 12		10 17
Wilmslow 84 a	08 21										09 21										10 20			
Crewe 10 84 a	08 47										09 46										10 46			

	NT G	TP 1◊ AA	NT	TP 1◊ D	TP 1◊ CC	NT C	NT	TP 1◊ Q		TP 1◊ E	NT G	TP 1◊ AA	NT	TP 1◊ H	TP 1◊ N	NT C	NT		TP 1◊ D	TP 1◊ E	NT G	TP 1◊ AA	NT	TP 1◊ H
Deansgate d						10 29				10 51						11 29				11 51				
Manchester Oxford Road d	09 58				10 24	10 33				10 54	10 58				11 24	11 33				11 54	11 58			
Manchester Piccadilly 10 a	10 01				10 27	10 35				10 56	11 01				11 27	11 35				11 56	12 01			
d	10 03	10 06	10 14	10 24	10 29	10 37	10 46	10 54		10 58	11 03	11 06	11 14	11 24	11 29	11 37	11 46		11 54	11 58	12 03	12 06	12 14	12 24
Mauldeth Road d			10 21				10 53						11 21				11 53						12 21	
Burnage d			10 23				10 55						11 23				11 55						12 23	
East Didsbury d			10 25				10 57						11 25				11 57						12 25	
Gatley d			10 27				10 59						11 27				11 59						12 27	
Heald Green d			10 30				11 02			11 10			11 30				12 02			12 10			12 30	
Manchester Airport a	10 22	10 26	10 38	10 42	10 47	10 53	11 07	11 12		11 17	11 22	11 26	11 38	11 42	11 47	11 53	12 07		12 12	12 17	12 22	12 26	12 38	12 42
Wilmslow 84 a							11 20										12 20							
Crewe 10 84 a							11 46										12 46							

For general notes see front of timetable
For details of catering facilities see Directory of Train Operators

- A From Cleethorpes (22 June to 4 September from Doncaster) (Table 29)
- B From Glasgow Central (Table 65) and Barrow-in-Furness (Table 82)
- C From Southport (Table 82)
- D From Newcastle (Table 39)
- E From Blackpool North (Table 82)
- G From Liverpool Lime Street (Table 90)
- H From Middlesbrough (Table 39)
- J To Alderley Edge (Table 84)
- K From Windermere (Table 82)
- L From Edinburgh (Table 65)
- N From Barrow-in-Furness (Table 82)
- Q From York (Table 39)
- U From Liverpool Lime Street (Table 89)
- V From Sheffield (Table 78)
- X From Doncaster (Table 29)
- Y Until 20 June and from 12 September
- Z 27 June to 5 September
- AA From Cleethorpes (27 June to 5 September from Doncaster) (Table 29)
- BB From Scarborough (Table 39)
- CC From Glasgow Central (Table 65)

Saturdays

until 31 October

Manchester → Manchester Airport

Network Diagram - see first page of Table 78

		TP	NT	NT	TP	TP	NT	TP	NT	TP	TP	NT	NT	TP	TP	NT	TP	NT	TP	TP	NT	NT
		1◇			1◇	1◇		1◇		1◇	1◇			1◇	1◇		1◇		1◇	1◇		
		A	B		C	D	E	G		H	J	B		C	K	E	G		H	A	B	
		🚲			🚲	🚲		🚲		🚲	🚲			🚲	🚲		🚲		🚲	🚲		
Deansgate	d		12 29			12 51						13 29			13 51						14 29	
Manchester Oxford Road	d	12 24	12 33			12 54	12 58				13 24	13 33			13 54	13 58				14 24	14 33	
Manchester Piccadilly 10	a	12 27	12 35			12 56	13 01				13 27	13 35			13 56	14 01				14 27	14 35	
	d	12 29	12 37	12 46	12 54	12 58	13 03	13 06	13 14	13 24	13 29	13 37	13 46	13 54	13 58	14 03	14 06	14 14	14 24	14 29	14 37	14 46
Mauldeth Road	d			12 53					13 21				13 53					14 21				14 53
Burnage	d			12 55					13 23				13 55					14 23				14 55
East Didsbury	d			12 57					13 25				13 57					14 25				14 57
Gatley	d			12 59					13 27				13 59					14 27				14 59
Heald Green	d			13 02		13 10			13 30				14 02		14 10			14 30				15 02
Manchester Airport	a	12 47	12 53	13 07	13 12	13 17	13 22	13 33	13 38	13 42	13 47	13 53	14 07	14 12	14 17	14 22	14 26	14 38	14 42	14 47	14 53	15 07
Wilmslow	84 a			13 21									14 20									15 20
Crewe 10	84 a			13 47									14 46									15 46

		TP	TP	NT	TP	NT	TP	TP	NT	NT	TP	TP	NT	TP	NT	TP	TP	NT	NT	TP	TP	NT	TP
		1◇	1◇		1◇		1◇	1◇			1◇	1◇		1◇		1◇	1◇			1◇	1◇		1◇
		C	K	E	G		H	L	B		C	K	E	G		H	J	B		C	K	E	G
		🚲	🚲		🚲		🚲	🚲			🚲	🚲		🚲		🚲	🚲			🚲	🚲		🚲
Deansgate	d		14 51						15 29			15 51									16 51		
Manchester Oxford Road	d		14 54	14 58				15 24	15 33			15 54	15 58				16 24	16 33			16 54	16 58	
Manchester Piccadilly 10	a		14 56	15 01				15 27	15 35			15 56	16 01				16 27	16 35			16 56	17 01	
	d	14 54	14 58	15 03	15 06	15 14	15 24	15 29	15 37	15 46	15 54	15 58	16 03	16 06	16 14	16 24	16 29	16 37	16 46	16 54	16 58	17 03	17 06
Mauldeth Road	d					15 21				15 53					16 21				16 53				
Burnage	d					15 23				15 55					16 23				16 55				
East Didsbury	d					15 25				15 57					16 25				16 57				17 19
Gatley	d					15 27				15 59					16 27				16 59				17 22
Heald Green	d		15 10			15 30				16 02		16 10			16 30		16 40		17 02		17 10		17 25
Manchester Airport	a	15 12	15 17	15 22	15 26	15 38	15 42	15 47	15 53	16 07	16 12	16 17	16 22	16 26	16 38	16 42	16 47	16 53	17 07	17 12	17 17	17 22	17 32
Wilmslow	84 a									16 20									17 20				
Crewe 10	84 a									16 46									17 44				

		NT	TP	NT	NT	TP	TP	NT	TP	NT	TP	TP	NT	NT	NT	TP	TP	NT	TP	NT	TP	NT
			1◇			1◇	1◇		1◇		1◇	1◇				1◇	1◇		1◇		1◇	
			N	B		C	K	E	G		H	Q	B	U	U	C	A	E	G		N	B
			🚲			🚲	🚲		🚲		🚲	🚲				🚲	🚲		🚲		🚲	
Deansgate	d			17 29			17 51										18 51					19 29
Manchester Oxford Road	d		17 24	17 33			17 54	17 58				18 24	18 33				18 54	18 58			19 24	19 33
Manchester Piccadilly 10	a		17 27	17 35			17 56	18 01				18 27	18 35				18 56	19 01			19 27	19 35
	d	17 14	17 29	17 37	17 46	17 54	17 58	18 03	18 06	18 14	18 24	18 29	18 37	18 38	18 46	18 54	18 58	19 03	19 06	19 14	19 32	19 37
Mauldeth Road	d	17 21			17 53					18 21					18 53					19 21		
Burnage	d	17 23			17 55					18 23					18 55					19 23		
East Didsbury	d	17 25			17 57					18 25					18 57					19 25		
Gatley	d	17 27			17 59					18 27					18 59					19 27		
Heald Green	d	17 30	17 40		18 02		18 10			18 30		18 40			19 02		19 10			19 30		
Manchester Airport	a	17 36	17 48	17 53	18 07	18 12	18 17	18 22	18 26	18 38	18 42	18 47	18 53		19 08	19 13	19 17	19 24	19 28	19 38	19 50	19 53
Wilmslow	84 a				18 21									19 02	19 23							
Crewe 10	84 a				18 47										*20 01*							

		TP	NT	TP	TP	TP	NT	TP	NT	TP	NT	TP	TP	NT	TP	NT	TP	TP	NT	TP	NT	TP
		1◇		1◇	1◇	1◇		1◇		1◇		1◇	1◇		1◇		1◇	1◇		1◇		1◇
		C		K	G	J	B	H		K	E	G	N	B	C		K	H		K	U	K
					🚲	🚲						🚲	🚲									
Deansgate	d			19 51			20 29			20 51				21 29			21 51			22 51		
Manchester Oxford Road	d		19 43	19 54		20 24	20 33		20 43	20 54	20 58		21 24	21 33		21 43	21 54		22 43	22 54		
Manchester Piccadilly 10	a		19 45	19 56		20 27	20 35		20 45	20 56	21 01		21 27	21 35		21 45	21 56		22 45	22 56		
	d	19 40	19 46	19 58	20 06	20 32	20 37	20 40	20 46	20 58	21 03	21 06	21 29	21 37	21 40	21 46	21 58	22 40	22 46	22 58	23 37	23 54
Mauldeth Road	d		19 53		20 15				20 53			21 15				21 53			22 53			00 04
Burnage	d		19 55		20 17				20 55			21 17				21 55			22 55			00 06
East Didsbury	d		19 57		20 20				20 57			21 20				21 57			22 57			00 09
Gatley	d		19 59		20 23				20 59			21 23				21 59			22 59			00 12
Heald Green	d		20 02	20 10	20 26				21 02	21 10		21 26				22 02	22 09		23 02	23 09		00 15
Manchester Airport	a	19 59	20 07	20 17	20 35	20 47	20 53	20 57	21 07	21 17	21 24	21 35	21 47	21 53	21 57	22 08	22 17	22 57	23 08	23 17		00 22
Wilmslow	84 a		20 24						21 24							22 22			23 22		00 01	
Crewe 10	84 a		*21 01*						*22 01*							*23 01*			*23 58*			

Saturdays

from 7 November

		TP	TP	NT	TP	TP	TP	NT	VT	NT	TP	TP	TP	NT	NT	TP	TP	NT	TP	NT	TP	TP	NT	NT	TP
		1◇	1◇		1◇	1◇	1◇		1◇		1◇	1◇	1◇			1◇	1◇		1◇		1◇	1◇			1◇
		C	V	X	Y	K	V		Z	E	K	V	Y			V	K	E	AA		V	BB	B		V
Deansgate	d																06 51						07 28		
Manchester Oxford Road	d																06 54	06 58				07 24	07 32		
Manchester Piccadilly 10	a																06 56	07 01				07 27	07 34		
	d	00 54	03 44	04 15	04 44	04u47	04 54	05 35	05 55	05 58	06 03	06 08	06 12	06 15	06 46	06 54	06 58	07 03	07 06	07 14	07 23	07 29	07 36	07 46	07 54
Mauldeth Road	d							05 42						06 22	06 53					07 21				07 53	
Burnage	d							05 44						06 24	06 55					07 23				07 55	
East Didsbury	d							05 46						06 26	06 57					07 25				07 57	
Gatley	d							05 49						06 29	06 59					07 27				07 59	
Heald Green	d							05 52						06 32	07 02		07 10			07 30				08 02	
Manchester Airport	a	01 10	04 00	04 30	05 00	05 06	05 10	05 57		06 14	06 18	06 24	06 29	06 39	07 07	07 12	07 17	07 22	07 26	07 38	07 42	07 47	07 53	08 07	08 12
Wilmslow	84 a							06 11	06 10						07 20									08 21	
Crewe 10	84 a							06 43	06 27						07 46									08 47	

For general notes see front of timetable
For details of catering facilities see Directory of Train Operators

- **A** From Windermere (Table 82)
- **B** From Southport (Table 82)
- **C** From Newcastle (Table 39)
- **D** From Edinburgh (Table 65) and Blackpool North (Table 82)
- **E** From Liverpool Lime Street (Table 90)
- **G** From Cleethorpes (27 June to 5 September from Doncaster) (Table 29)
- **H** From Middlesbrough (Table 39)
- **J** From Glasgow Central (Table 65)
- **K** From Blackpool North (Table 82)
- **L** From Edinburgh (Table 65). Until 20 June and from 12 September also conveys portion from Barrow-in-Furness (Table 82)
- **N** From Edinburgh (Table 65)
- **Q** From Blackpool North and Barrow-in-Furness (Table 82)
- **U** To Alderley Edge (Table 84)
- **V** From York (Table 39)
- **X** From Liverpool Lime Street (Table 89)
- **Y** From Sheffield (Table 78)
- **Z** To London Euston (Table 65)
- **AA** From Doncaster (Table 29)
- **BB** From Barrow-in-Furness (Table 65)

Table 85

Saturdays

from 7 November

Manchester → Manchester Airport

Network Diagram - see first page of Table 78

Station		TP 1◇ A 🛒	NT B	TP 1◇ C 🛒	NT	TP 1◇ D	TP 1◇ E 🛒	NT G	NT	TP 1◇ H	TP 1◇ A 🛒	NT B	TP 1◇ C 🛒	NT		TP 1◇ H 🛒	TP 1◇ E 🛒	NT G	NT	TP 1◇ D 🛒	TP 1◇ A 🛒	NT B	TP 1◇ C 🛒	NT	TP 1◇ J 🛒
Deansgate 🚊	d	07 51						08 29										09 29			09 51				
Manchester Oxford Road	d	07 54	07 58				08 24	08 33			08 53	08 58					09 24	09 33			09 54	09 58			
Manchester Piccadilly 10 🚊	a	07 56	08 01				08 27	08 35			08 56	09 01					09 27	09 35			09 56	10 01			
	d	07 58	08 03	08 06	08 14	08 24	08 29	08 37	08 46	08 54	08 58	09 03	09 06	09 14		09 24	09 29	09 37	09 46	09 54	09 58	10 03	10 06	10 14	10 24
Mauldeth Road	d				08 21				08 53					09 21					09 53					10 21	
Burnage	d				08 23				08 55					09 23					09 55					10 23	
East Didsbury	d				08 25		08 38		08 57		09 07			09 25					09 57					10 25	
Gatley	d				08 27				08 59					09 27					09 59					10 27	
Heald Green	d	08 10		08 21	08 30				09 02		09 12			09 30					10 02		10 10			10 30	
Manchester Airport ✈	a	08 17	08 22	08 29	08 37	08 42	08 47	08 53	09 08	09 12	09 19	09 22	09 26	09 38		09 42	09 47	09 53	10 07	10 12	10 17	10 22	10 26	10 38	10 42
Wilmslow	84 a								09 21										10 20						
Crewe 10	84 a								09 46										10 46						

Station		TP 1◇ K 🛒	NT G	NT	TP 1◇ L 🛒	TP 1◇ A 🛒	NT B	TP 1◇ C 🛒	NT	TP 1◇ D 🛒	TP 1◇ E 🛒	NT G	NT	TP 1◇ J 🛒	TP 1◇ A 🛒	NT B	TP 1◇ C 🛒	TP 1◇ D 🛒	TP 1◇ N 🛒	NT G	NT	TP 1◇ J 🛒	TP 1◇ Q 🛒	NT B	TP 1◇ C 🛒
Deansgate 🚊	d		10 29			10 51						11 29			11 51					12 29			12 51		
Manchester Oxford Road	d	10 24	10 33			10 54	10 58				11 24	11 33			11 54	11 58			12 24	12 33			12 54	12 58	
Manchester Piccadilly 10 🚊	a	10 27	10 35			10 56	11 01				11 27	11 35			11 56	12 01			12 27	12 35			12 56	13 01	
	d	10 29	10 37	10 46	10 54	10 58	11 03	11 06	11 14	11 24	11 29	11 37	11 46	11 54	11 58	12 03	12 06	12 24	12 29	12 37	12 46	12 54	12 58	13 03	13 06
Mauldeth Road	d			10 53					11 21				11 53				12 15				12 53				13 15
Burnage	d			10 55					11 23				11 55				12 17				12 55				13 17
East Didsbury	d			10 57					11 25				11 57				12 20				12 57				13 20
Gatley	d			10 59					11 27				11 59				12 23				12 59				13 23
Heald Green	d			11 02		11 10			11 30				12 02		12 10		12 26				13 02		13 10		13 26
Manchester Airport ✈	a	10 47	10 53	11 07	11 12	11 17	11 22	11 26	11 38	11 42	11 47	11 53	12 07	12 12	12 17	12 22	12 33	12 42	12 47	12 54	13 07	13 12	13 17	13 22	13 33
Wilmslow	84 a			11 20									12 20								13 21				
Crewe 10	84 a			11 46									12 46								13 47				

Station		TP 1◇ D 🛒	TP 1◇ K 🛒	NT G	NT	TP 1◇ J 🛒		TP 1◇ A 🛒	NT B	TP 1◇ C 🛒	TP 1◇ D 🛒	TP 1◇ U 🛒	NT G	NT	TP 1◇ J 🛒	TP 1◇ A 🛒	NT B	TP 1◇ C 🛒	TP 1◇ D 🛒	TP 1◇ V 🛒	NT G	NT	TP 1◇ J 🛒	TP 1◇ A 🛒	NT B
Deansgate 🚊	d			13 29				13 51					14 29			14 51					15 29			15 51	
Manchester Oxford Road	d		13 24	13 33				13 54	13 58			14 24	14 33			14 54	14 58			15 24	15 33			15 54	15 58
Manchester Piccadilly 10 🚊	a		13 27	13 35				13 56	14 01			14 27	14 35			14 56	15 01			15 27	15 35			15 56	16 01
	d	13 24	13 29	13 37	13 46	13 54		13 58	14 03	14 06	14 24	14 29	14 37	14 46	14 54	14 58	15 03	15 06	15 24	15 29	15 37	15 46	15 54	15 58	16 03
Mauldeth Road	d				13 53					14 15				14 53				15 15				15 53			
Burnage	d				13 55					14 17				14 55				15 17				15 55			
East Didsbury	d				13 57					14 20				14 57				15 20				15 57			
Gatley	d				13 59					14 23				14 59				15 23				15 59			
Heald Green	d				14 02			14 10		14 26				15 02		15 10		15 26				16 02		16 10	
Manchester Airport ✈	a	13 42	13 47	13 53	14 07	14 12		14 17	14 22	14 33	14 42	14 47	14 54	15 07	15 12	15 17	15 22	15 33	15 42	15 47	15 53	16 07	16 12	16 17	16 22
Wilmslow	84 a				14 20									15 20								16 20			
Crewe 10	84 a				14 46									15 46								16 46			

Station		TP 1◇ C 🛒	TP 1◇ D 🛒	TP 1◇ K 🛒	NT G	NT	TP 1◇ J 🛒	TP 1◇ A 🛒	NT B	TP 1◇ C 🛒	TP 1◇ X 🛒	NT G	NT	TP 1◇ J 🛒	TP 1◇ A 🛒	NT B	TP 1◇ C 🛒	TP 1◇ D 🛒	TP 1◇ Y 🛒	NT G	NT Z	TP 1◇ J 🛒	TP 1◇ U 🛒	NT B	TP 1◇ C 🛒
Deansgate 🚊	d							16 51				17 29			17 51								18 51		
Manchester Oxford Road	d			16 24	16 33			16 54	16 58		17 24	17 33			17 54	17 58			18 24	18 33			18 54	18 58	
Manchester Piccadilly 10 🚊	a			16 27	16 35			16 56	17 01		17 27	17 35			17 56	18 01			18 27	18 35			18 56	19 01	
	d	16 06	16 24	16 29	16 37	16 46	16 54	16 58	17 03	17 06	17 29	17 37	17 46	17 54	17 58	18 03	18 06	18 24	18 29	18 37	18 46	18 54	18 58	19 03	19 06
Mauldeth Road	d	16 15				16 53				17 15			17 53				18 15				18 53				19 15
Burnage	d	16 17				16 55				17 17			17 55				18 17				18 55				19 17
East Didsbury	d	16 20				16 57				17 20			17 57				18 20				18 57				19 20
Gatley	d	16 23				16 59				17 23			17 59				18 23				18 59				19 23
Heald Green	d	16 26		16 40		17 02		17 10		17 26	17 40		18 02		18 10		18 26		18 40		19 02		19 10		19 26
Manchester Airport ✈	a	16 33	16 42	16 47	16 54	17 07	17 12	17 17	17 22	17 33	17 48	17 53	18 07	18 12	18 17	18 22	18 33	18 42	18 47	18 54	19 08	19 13	19 17	19 24	19 35
Wilmslow	84 a					17 20							18 21								19 23				
Crewe 10	84 a					17 44							18 47								*20 04*				

Station		TP 1◇ X 🛒	NT G	TP 1◇ J	NT	TP 1◇ A	TP 1◇ C 🛒	TP 1◇ K	NT G	TP 1◇ D	NT	TP 1◇ A	NT B	TP 1◇ C 🛒	TP 1◇ X 🛒	NT G	TP 1◇ J	NT	TP 1◇ A	TP 1◇ D	NT	TP 1◇ A	TP 1◇ A		
Deansgate 🚊	d		19 29			19 51			20 29			20 51				21 29			21 51			22 51			
Manchester Oxford Road	d	19 24	19 33		19 43	19 54		20 24	20 33		20 43	20 54	20 58		21 24	21 33		21 43	21 54		22 43	22 54			
Manchester Piccadilly 10 🚊	a	19 27	19 35		19 45	19 56		20 27	20 35		20 45	20 56	21 01		21 27	21 35		21 45	21 56		22 45	22 56			
	d	19 32	19 37	19 40	19 46	19 58	20 06	20 32	20 37	20 40	20 46	20 58	21 03	21 06	21 29	21 37	21 40	21 46	21 58	22 40	22 46	22 58	23 54		
Mauldeth Road	d				19 53		20 15				20 53			21 15				21 53			22 53		00 04		
Burnage	d				19 55		20 17				20 55			21 17				21 55			22 55		00 06		
East Didsbury	d				19 57		20 20				20 57			21 20				21 57			22 57		00 09		
Gatley	d				19 59		20 23				20 59			21 23				21 59			22 59		00 12		
Heald Green	d				20 02	20 10	20 26				21 02	21 10		21 26				22 02	22 09		23 02	23 09	00 15		
Manchester Airport ✈	a	19 50	19 53	19 59	20 07	20 17	20 35	20 47	20 53	20 57	21 07	21 17	21 24	21 35	21 47	21 53	21 57	22 08	22 17	22 57	23 08	23 17	00 22		
Wilmslow	84 a				20 24						21 24							22 22			23 22				
Crewe 10	84 a				*21 01*						*22 01*							*23 01*			*23 58*				

For general notes see front of timetable
For details of catering facilities see Directory of Train Operators

- **A** From Blackpool North (Table 82)
- **B** From Liverpool Lime Street (Table 90)
- **C** From Cleethorpes (Table 29)
- **D** From Middlesbrough (Table 39)
- **E** From Barrow-in-Furness (Table 82)
- **G** From Southport (Table 82)
- **H** From Scarborough (Table 39)
- **J** From Newcastle (Table 39)
- **K** From Glasgow Central (Table 65)
- **L** From York (Table 39)
- **N** From Windermere (Table 82). 🛒 from Preston
- **Q** From Edinburgh (Table 65) and Blackpool North (Table 82)
- **U** From Windermere (Table 82)
- **V** From Edinburgh (Table 65) and Barrow-in-Furness (Table 82)
- **X** From Edinburgh (Table 65)
- **Y** From Blackpool North and Barrow-in-Furness (Table 82)
- **Z** To Alderley Edge (Table 84)

Table 85

Sundays

until 6 September

Manchester → Manchester Airport

Network Diagram - see first page of Table 78

Station		TP 1◇ A	TP 1◇ B	TP C (bus)	TP 1◇ B	NT		TP 1◇ B	NT	TP C (bus)	TP 1◇ B	NT		TP 1◇	TP 1◇ B	NT D	NT E	TP 1◇ G		TP 1◇ C	NT H	TP 1◇ B	NT	TP 1◇ C	NT J
Deansgate	d																			08 53				09 51	
Manchester Oxford Road	d																			08 56	09 03			09 54	
Manchester Piccadilly 10	a																			08 59	09 05			09 57	
	d	00 45	04 06	05u00	05 21	05 41		06 38	06 41	07u00	07 38	07 41		08 09	08 38	08 42	08 42	08 47		09 00	09 07	09 38	09 41	09 58	10 01
Mauldeth Road	d					05 48			06 48			07 48				08 49	08 49						09 48		
Burnage	d					05 50			06 50			07 50				08 51	08 51						09 50		
East Didsbury	d					05 52			06 52			07 52				08 53	08 53						09 52		
Gatley	d					05 54			06 54			07 54				08 56	08 56						09 54		
Heald Green	d					05 57			06 57			07 57				08 59	08 59						09 57		
Manchester Airport	a	01 00	04 23	05 25	05 38	06 02		06 55	07 02	07 25	07 55	08 02		08 23	08 55	09 04	09 04	09 07		09 19	09 22	09 55	10 02	10 13	
Wilmslow	84 a															09 17	09 17								10 24
Crewe 10	84 a															09 44	09 56								

Station		NT H		TP 1◇ K	TP 1◇ L	NT D	NT E	TP 1◇ C		NT H	TP 1◇ N	TP 1◇ Q	NT	TP 1◇ C		NT H	TP 1◇ U	TP 1◇ A	NT J			TP 1◇ C	NT H	TP 1◇ U	TP 1◇ N
Deansgate	d							10 51						11 51								12 51			
Manchester Oxford Road	d	10 00						10 54		11 00	11 24		11 38	11 54		12 00						12 54	13 00		13 24
Manchester Piccadilly 10	a	10 03						10 57		11 03	11 27		11 41	11 57		12 02						12 57	13 02		13 27
	d	10 08		10 13	10 38	10 41	10 41	10 58		11 06	11 29	11 38	11 41	11 58		12 04	12 13	12 38	12 41			12 58	13 04	13 13	13 29
Mauldeth Road	d					10 50	10 50						11 48						12 48						
Burnage	d					10 52	10 52						11 50						12 50						
East Didsbury	d					10 54	10 54						11 52						12 52						
Gatley	d					10 57	10 57						11 54						12 54						
Heald Green	d					11 00	11 00						11 57						12 57						
Manchester Airport	a	10 24		10 30	10 55	11 05	11 05	11 17		11 21	11 47	11 55	12 02	12 17		12 19	12 29	12 55	13 02			13 17	13 19	13 29	13 47
Wilmslow	84 a					11 16	11 16												13 13						
Crewe 10	84 a					11 50	11 57												13 56						

Station		TP 1◇ L	NT	TP 1◇ C		NT H	TP 1◇ U	TP 1◇ X	TP 1◇ L	NT J		TP 1◇ C	NT H	TP 1◇ Y	TP 1◇ N	TP 1◇ L		NT	TP 1◇ C	NT H	TP 1◇ U	TP 1◇ X (catering)		TP 1◇ L	NT J
Deansgate	d			13 51								14 51							15 51						
Manchester Oxford Road	d			13 54		14 00		14 24				14 54	15 00		15 24				15 54	16 00		16 24			
Manchester Piccadilly 10	a			13 57		14 02		14 27				14 57	15 02		15 27				15 57	16 02		16 27			
	d	13 38	13 41	13 58		14 04	14 13	14 29	14 38	14 41		14 58	15 04	15 13	15 29	15 38		15 41	15 58	16 04	16 13	16 29		16 38	16 41
Mauldeth Road	d		13 48							14 48								15 48							16 48
Burnage	d		13 50							14 50								15 50							16 50
East Didsbury	d		13 52							14 52								15 52							16 52
Gatley	d		13 54							14 54								15 54							16 54
Heald Green	d		13 57							14 57								15 57							16 57
Manchester Airport	a	13 55	14 02	14 17		14 19	14 29	14 47	14 55	15 02		15 17	15 20	15 29	15 47	15 55		16 02	16 17	16 19	16 29	16 47		16 55	17 02
Wilmslow	84 a									15 14															17 13
Crewe 10	84 a									15 56															17 56

Station		TP 1◇ C	NT H	TP 1◇ U	TP 1◇ N	TP 1◇ L		NT	TP 1◇ C	NT H	NT J	TP 1◇ U		TP 1◇ Z (catering)	TP 1◇ L	NT J	TP 1◇ AA	NT H		TP 1◇ U	TP 1◇ X (catering)	TP 1◇ L	NT	TP 1◇ C	NT H
Deansgate	d	16 51							17 51								18 51							19 51	
Manchester Oxford Road	d	16 54	17 00		17 24				17 54	18 00				18 24			18 54	19 00			19 24			19 54	20 00
Manchester Piccadilly 10	a	16 57	17 02		17 27				17 57	18 02				18 27			18 57	19 02			19 27			19 57	20 02
	d	16 58	17 04	17 13	17 29	17 38		17 41	17 58	18 04	18 04	18 13		18 29	18 38	18 41	18 58	19 04		19 13	19 29	19 38	19 41	19 58	20 04
Mauldeth Road	d							17 48								18 48							19 48		
Burnage	d							17 50								18 50							19 50		
East Didsbury	d							17 52								18 52							19 52		
Gatley	d							17 54								18 54							19 54		
Heald Green	d							17 57								18 57							19 57		
Manchester Airport	a	17 17	17 19	17 29	17 47	17 55		18 02	18 17	18 19		18 29		18 47	18 55	19 02	19 17	19 19		19 29	19 47	19 55	20 02	20 17	20 19
Wilmslow	84 a										18 28					19 13									
Crewe 10	84 a															19 56									

For general notes see front of timetable
For details of catering facilities see Directory of Train Operators

- **A** From Middlesbrough (Table 39)
- **B** From York (Table 39)
- **C** From Blackpool North (Table 82)
- **D** Until 12 July
- **E** From 19 July. To Alderley Edge (Table 84)
- **G** From Sheffield (Table 78)
- **H** From Liverpool Lime Street (Table 90)
- **J** To Alderley Edge (Table 84)
- **K** From Meadowhall (Table 34)
- **L** From Newcastle (Table 39)
- **N** From Barrow-in-Furness (Table 82)
- **Q** From Scarborough (Table 39)
- **U** From Cleethorpes (from 28 June from Doncaster) (Table 29)
- **X** From Edinburgh (Table 65)
- **Y** From Doncaster (Table 29)
- **Z** From Glasgow Central (Table 65) and Barrow-in-Furness (Table 82)
- **AA** From Windermere and Blackpool North (Table 82)

Table 85

Manchester → Manchester Airport

Sundays until 6 September

Network Diagram - see first page of Table 78

	TP 1◇ A		TP 1◇ B (trolley)	TP 1◇ C	NT D	TP 1◇ E	NT G		TP 1◇ A	TP 1◇ H (trolley)	NT	TP 1◇ E	NT G		TP 1◇ A	TP 1◇ C	NT	NT G	TP 1◇ J (trolley)		NT G			
Deansgate d						20 51						21 51							23 09					
Manchester Oxford Road d			20 24			20 54	21 00			21 24		21 54	22 00					23 00	23 12		23 59			
Manchester Piccadilly 10 a			20 27			20 57	21 02			21 27		21 57	22 02					23 02	23 14		00 02			
d	20 13		20 29	20 38	20 41	20 58	21 04		21 13	21 29	21 41	21 58	22 04		22 13	22 38	22 46	23 04	23 15		00 04			
Mauldeth Road d					20 48						21 48						22 53							
Burnage d					20 50						21 50						22 55							
East Didsbury d					20 52						21 52						22 57							
Gatley d					20 54						21 54						22 59							
Heald Green d					20 57						21 57						23 02							
Manchester Airport a	20 29		20 47	20 55	21 02	21 17	21 19		21 29	21 47	22 02	22 17	22 19		22 29	22 55	23 08	23 20	23 30		00 17			
Wilmslow 84 a					21 13																			
Crewe 10 84 a					*21 58*																			

Sundays from 13 September

	TP 1◇ K	TP L (bus)	TP E (bus)	TP L (bus)	NT	NT	TP E (bus)	TP L (bus)	NT	TP 1◇	TP 1	NT D	TP 1◇ N	TP L (bus)	TP 1◇ E	NT	TP 1◇ E	NT G	TP 1◇ Q	TP 1◇ U	NT D	TP 1◇ E	NT G	TP 1◇ C
Deansgate d															09 23		09 51					10 51		
Manchester Oxford Road d															09 26		09 54	10 00				10 54	11 00	
Manchester Piccadilly 10 a															09 28		09 57	10 03				10 57	11 03	
d	00 33	04 20	05u00	05 35	05 41	06 41	07u00	07 35	07 41	07 50	08 39	08 42	08 47	09 05	09 33	09 41	09 58	10 08	10 13	10 39	10 43	10 58	11 07	11 10
Mauldeth Road d					05 48	06 48			07 48			08 49				09 48					10 51			
Burnage d					05 50	06 50			07 50			08 51				09 50					10 53			
East Didsbury d					05 52	06 52			07 52			08 53				09 52					10 55			
Gatley d					05 54	06 54			07 54			08 56				09 54					10 57			
Heald Green d					05 57	06 57			07 57			08 59				09 57					11 00			
Manchester Airport a	00 48	04 45	05 25	06 00	06 02	07 02	07 25	08 00	08 02	08 07	08 53	09 04	09 07	09 30	09 53	10 02	10 13	10 25	10 30	10 53	11 06	11 17	11 21	11 25
Wilmslow 84 a												09 16									11 17			
Crewe 10 84 a												*09 56*									*11 59*			

	NT	TP 1◇ E	NT G	TP 1◇ V	TP 1◇ X	NT D	TP 1◇ E	NT G	TP 1◇ Y		TP 1◇ X	TP 1◇ Z	NT	TP 1◇ E	NT G	TP 1◇ C	TP 1◇ X	TP 1◇ H	NT D	TP 1◇ E	NT G	TP 1◇ C	TP 1◇ AA	TP 1◇ Z
Deansgate d		11 51					12 51							13 51						14 51				
Manchester Oxford Road d	11 37	11 54	12 00				12 54	13 00				13 24		13 54	14 00			14 24		14 54	15 00			15 24
Manchester Piccadilly 10 a	11 40	11 57	12 02				12 57	13 02				13 27		13 57	14 02			14 27		14 57	15 02			15 27
d	11 41	11 58	12 04	12 10	12 12	12 41	12 58	13 04	13 10		13 13	13 29	13 41	13 58	14 04	14 10	14 13	14 29	14 41	14 58	15 04	15 10	15 13	15 29
Mauldeth Road d	11 50					12 48							13 48						14 48					
Burnage d	11 52					12 50							13 50						14 50					
East Didsbury d	11 54					12 52							13 52						14 52					
Gatley d	11 56					12 54							13 54						14 54					
Heald Green d	11 59					12 57							13 57						14 57					
Manchester Airport a	12 04	12 17	12 21	12 25	12 29	13 02	13 17	13 19	13 25		13 29	13 47	14 02	14 17	14 19	14 25	14 34	14 47	15 02	15 17	15 20	15 25	15 34	15 47
Wilmslow 84 a						13 13													15 14					
Crewe 10 84 a						*13b56*													*15 56*					

	NT		TP 1◇ E	NT G	TP 1◇ C	TP 1◇ X	TP 1◇ H (trolley)	NT D	TP 1◇ E	NT G	TP 1◇ C	TP 1◇ X	TP 1◇ Z	NT	TP 1◇ E	NT G	TP 1◇ C	TP 1◇ X	TP 1◇ CC (trolley)	NT D	TP 1◇ E	NT G	TP 1◇ C	TP 1◇ X
Deansgate d			15 51						16 51						17 51						18 51			
Manchester Oxford Road d			15 54	16 00			16 24		16 54	17 00			17 24		17 54	18 00			18 24		18 54	19 00		
Manchester Piccadilly 10 a			15 57	16 02			16 27		16 57	17 02			17 27		17 57	18 02			18 27		18 57	19 02		
d	15 41		15 58	16 04	16 10	16 13	16 29	16 41	16 58	17 04	17 10	17 13	17 29	17 41	17 58	18 04	18 10	18 13	18 29	18 41	18 58	19 04	19 10	19 13
Mauldeth Road d	15 48							16 48						17 48						18 48				
Burnage d	15 50							16 50						17 50						18 50				
East Didsbury d	15 52							16 52						17 52						18 52				
Gatley d	15 54							16 54						17 54						18 54				
Heald Green d	15 57							16 57						17 57						18 57				
Manchester Airport a	16 02		16 17	16 19	16 25	16 34	16 47	17 02	17 17	17 19	17 25	17 29	17 47	18 02	18 17	18 19	18 25	18 29	18 47	19 02	19 17	19 19	19 25	19 29
Wilmslow 84 a								17 13												19 13				
Crewe 10 84 a								*17 56*												*19 56*				

For general notes see front of timetable
For details of catering facilities see Directory of Train Operators

- **A** From Cleethorpes (from 28 June from Doncaster) (Table 29)
- **B** From Glasgow Central (Table 65) and Barrow-in-Furness (Table 82)
- **C** From Newcastle (Table 39)
- **D** To Alderley Edge (Table 84)
- **E** From Blackpool North (Table 82)
- **G** From Liverpool Lime Street (Table 90)
- **H** From Edinburgh (Table 65)
- **J** From Edinburgh (Table 65) and Blackpool North (Table 82)
- **K** From Huddersfield (Table 39)
- **L** From York (Table 39)
- **N** From Sheffield (Table 78)
- **Q** From Meadowhall (Table 29)
- **U** From Manchester Victoria (Table 39)
- **V** From Scarborough (Table 39)
- **X** From Cleethorpes (Table 29)
- **Y** From Middlesbrough (Table 39)
- **Z** From Barrow-in-Furness (Table 82)
- **AA** From Doncaster (Table 29)
- **CC** From Glasgow Central (Table 65)
- **b** From 8 November arr. 1401

Sundays

from 13 September

Manchester → Manchester Airport

Network Diagram - see first page of Table 78

		TP	NT	TP	NT	TP	TP	TP	NT	TP	NT	TP	TP	TP	NT	TP	NT	TP	NT	NT	TP	TP	NT
		1◇		1◇		1◇	1◇	1◇		1◇		1◇	1◇	1◇		1◇		1◇			1◇	1◇	
		A		B	C	D	E	G	H	B	C	D	E	A		B	C	E		C	J	D	C
		🍴						🍴						🍴							🍴		
Deansgate	d			19 51						20 51						21 51					23 09		
Manchester Oxford Road	d	19 24		19 54	20 00			20 24		20 54	21 00			21 24		21 54	22 00			23 00	23 12		23 59
Manchester Piccadilly 10	a	19 27		19 57	20 02			20 27		20 57	21 02			21 27		21 57	22 02			23 02	23 14		00 02
	d	19 29	19 41	19 58	20 04	20 10	20 13	20 29	20 41	20 58	21 04	21 10	21 13	21 29	21 41	21 58	22 04	22 13	22 46	23 04	23 15	23 26	00 04
Mauldeth Road	d		19 48						20 48						21 48				22 53				
Burnage	d		19 50						20 50						21 50				22 55				
East Didsbury	d		19 52						20 52						21 52				22 57				
Gatley	d		19 54						20 54						21 54				22 59				
Heald Green	d		19 57						20 57						21 57				23 02				
Manchester Airport	a	19 47	20 02	20 17	20 19	20 25	20 34	20 47	21 02	21 17	21 19	21 25	21 30	21 47	22 02	22 17	22 19	22 29	23 08	23 20	23 30	23 40	00 17
Wilmslow	84 a								21 13														
Crewe 10	84 a								*21 58*														

For general notes see front of timetable
For details of catering facilities see Directory of Train Operators

A From Edinburgh (Table 65)
B From Blackpool North (Table 82)
C From Liverpool Lime Street (Table 90)
D From Newcastle (Table 39)
E From Cleethorpes (Table 29)
G From Glasgow Central (Table 65) and Barrow-in-Furness (Table 82)
H To Alderley Edge (Table 84)
J From Edinburgh (Table 65) and Blackpool North (Table 82)

Table 85

Mondays to Fridays

Manchester Airport → Manchester

Network Diagram - see first page of Table 78

Miles		TP	TP	NT	TP	TP	NT	TP	TP		TP	NT	TP	TP	NT	NT	TP	TP		TP	NT	TP	TP	NT
		1◇	1◇	MX	1◇	1◇		1◇	1◇		1◇		1◇	1◇			1◇	1◇		1◇		1◇	1◇	
		A	B		A	C	D	E	A		C		G	H	J		E	A		K		L	H	J
									🛒				🛒	🛒			🛒	🛒		🛒		🛒	🛒	
—	Crewe 10 84 d			00 44																	06 33			
—	Wilmslow 84 d											05 46									06 57			
0	**Manchester Airport** ✈ d	00 01	01 00	01 20	03 40	04 00	04 34	05 15	05 29		05 37	06 01	06 18	06 23	06 41	06 46	06 55	07 00		07 05	07 17	07 28	07 35	07 41
1½	Heald Green d								05 33			06 04				06 49					07 20	07 32		
4	Gatley d											06 07				06 52					07 23			
5¼	East Didsbury d											06 10				06 55					07 26			
6¼	Burnage d											06 12				06 57					07 28			
7¼	Mauldeth Road d											06 14				06 59					07 30			
9¾	**Manchester Piccadilly** 10 🚊 a	00 15	01 14	01 36	03 53	04 14	04 47	05 33	05 44		05 51	06 25	06 31	06 39	06 56	07 11	07 13	07 14		07 22	07 42	07 43	07 49	07 56
—	d												06 33		06 58			07 15						07 58
—	**Manchester Oxford Road** a												06 35		07 00			07 17						08 00
—	Deansgate 🚊 a																							

	NT	TP	TP	NT	TP		NT	TP	TP	NT	NT	TP	TP	NT		TP	NT	TP	TP	NT	NT	TP	TP	NT
		1◇	1◇		1◇			1◇	1◇			1◇	1◇			1◇		1◇	1◇			1◇	1◇	
		E	A	N	K		Q	U	H	J		E	V	N		K		A	H	J		E	X	N
		🛒	🛒		🛒			🛒	🛒			🛒	🛒			🛒		🛒	🛒			🛒	🛒	
Crewe 10 84 d																	08 31							
Wilmslow 84 d							07 56										08 57							
Manchester Airport ✈ d	07 46	07 54	08 00	08 03	08 05		08 17	08 25	08 35	08 41	08 46	08 55	09 00	09 03		09 05	09 17	09 29	09 35	09 41	09 46	09 55	10 00	10 03
Heald Green d	07 49	07 58					08 20	08 29			08 49	08 59					09 20	09 33			09 49			
Gatley d	07 52						08 23	08 32			08 52						09 23				09 52			
East Didsbury d	07 55						08 26	08 35			08 55						09 26				09 55			
Burnage d	07 57						08 28				08 57						09 28				09 57			
Mauldeth Road d	07 59						08 30				08 59						09 30				09 59			
Manchester Piccadilly 10 🚊 a	08 11	08 13	08 14	08 21	08 22		08 42	08 44	08 49	08 58	09 11	09 13	09 14	09 18		09 22	09 42	09 44	09 52	09 59	10 11	10 13	10 14	10 18
d			08 15	08 22				08 46		09 01			09 16	09 22				09 46		10 01			10 16	10 22
Manchester Oxford Road a			08 17	08 24				08 48		09 03			09 18	09 24				09 48		10 03			10 18	10 24
Deansgate 🚊 a				08 28				08 51						09 28				09 51						10 28

	TP		NT	TP	TP	NT	NT	TP	TP	NT		TP	NT	TP	TP	NT	NT	TP	TP		NT	TP	NT	TP
	1◇			1◇	1◇			1◇	1◇			1◇		1◇	1◇			1◇	1◇			1◇		1◇
	K			A	H	J		E	Y	N		K		A	H	J		E	L		N	K		A
	🛒			🛒	🛒			🛒	🛒			🛒		🛒	🛒			🛒	🛒			🛒		🛒
Crewe 10 84 d			09 33										10 33										11 33	
Wilmslow 84 d			09 57										10 57										11 57	
Manchester Airport ✈ d	10 05		10 17	10 29	10 35	10 41	10 46	10 55	11 00	11 03		11 05	11 17	11 29	11 35	11 41	11 46	11 55	12 00		12 03	12 05	12 17	12 29
Heald Green d			10 20	10 33			10 49						11 20	11 33			11 49						12 20	12 33
Gatley d			10 23				10 52						11 23				11 52						12 23	
East Didsbury d			10 26				10 55						11 26				11 55						12 26	
Burnage d			10 28				10 57						11 28				11 57						12 28	
Mauldeth Road d			10 30				10 59						11 30				11 59						12 30	
Manchester Piccadilly 10 🚊 a	10 22		10 42	10 44	10 52	10 59	11 11	11 13	11 14	11 18		11 22	11 42	11 44	11 52	11 59	12 11	12 13	12 14		12 18	12 22	12 42	12 44
d				10 46		11 01			11 16	11 22				11 46		12 01			12 16		12 22			12 46
Manchester Oxford Road a				10 48		11 03			11 18	11 24				11 48		12 03			12 18		12 24			12 48
Deansgate 🚊 a				10 51						11 28				11 51							12 28			12 51

	TP	NT	NT	TP	TP	NT		TP	NT	TP	TP	NT	NT	TP	TP		NT	TP	NT	TP	TP	NT	NT	TP
	1◇			1◇	1◇			1◇		1◇	1◇			1◇	1◇			1◇		1◇	1◇			1◇
	H	J		E	Y	N		K		A	H	J		E	AA		N	B		A	H	J		E
	🛒			🛒	🛒			🛒		🛒	🛒			🛒	🛒			🛒		🛒	🛒			🛒
Crewe 10 84 d									12 33										13 33					
Wilmslow 84 d									12 57										13 57					
Manchester Airport ✈ d	12 35	12 41	12 46	12 55	13 00	13 03		13 05	13 17	13 29	13 35	13 41	13 46	13 55	14 00		14 03	14 05	14 17	14 29	14 35	14 41	14 46	14 55
Heald Green d			12 49						13 20	13 33			13 49						14 20	14 33			14 49	
Gatley d			12 52						13 23				13 52						14 23				14 52	
East Didsbury d			12 55						13 26				13 55						14 26				14 55	
Burnage d			12 57						13 28				13 57						14 28				14 57	
Mauldeth Road d			12 59						13 30				13 59						14 30				14 59	
Manchester Piccadilly 10 🚊 a	12 52	12 59	13 11	13 13	13 14	13 18		13 22	13 42	13 44	13 52	13 59	14 11	14 13	14 14		14 18	14 22	14 42	14 44	14 52	14 59	15 11	15 13
d		13 01			13 16	13 22				13 46		14 01			14 16		14 22			14 46		15 01		
Manchester Oxford Road a		13 03			13 18	13 24				13 48		14 03			14 18		14 24			14 48		15 03		
Deansgate 🚊 a						13 28				13 51							14 28			14 51				

	TP	NT		TP	NT	TP	TP	NT	NT	TP	TP		NT	TP	NT	TP	TP	NT	NT	TP		TP	NT	TP
	1◇			1◇		1◇	1◇			1◇	1◇			1◇		1◇	1◇			1◇		1◇		1◇
	Y	N		K		A	C	J		E	BB		N	C		A	H	J		E		G	N	K
	🛒			🛒		🛒	🛒			🛒	🛒			🛒		🛒	🛒			🛒		🛒		🛒
Crewe 10 84 d					14 33										15 33									
Wilmslow 84 d					14 57										15 56									
Manchester Airport ✈ d	15 00	15 03		15 05	15 17	15 29	15 35	15 41	15 46	15 55	16 00		16 03	16 05	16 17	16 29	16 35	16 41	16 46	16 55		17 00	17 03	17 05
Heald Green d					15 20	15 33			15 49						16 20	16 33			16 49					
Gatley d					15 23				15 52						16 23				16 52					
East Didsbury d					15 26				15 55						16 26				16 55					
Burnage d					15 28				15 57						16 28				16 57					
Mauldeth Road d					15 30				15 59						16 30				16 59					
Manchester Piccadilly 10 🚊 a	15 14	15 18		15 22	15 41	15 44	15 52	15 59	16 11	16 13	16 14		16 18	16 22	16 42	16 44	16 52	16 59	17 11	17 13		17 14	17 21	17 22
d	15 16	15 22			15 42	15 46		16 01			16 16		16 22			16 46		17 01				17 15	17 22	
Manchester Oxford Road a	15 18	15 24			15 46	15 48		16 03			16 18		16 24			16 48		17 03				17 17	17 25	
Deansgate 🚊 a		15 28				15 51							16 28											

For general notes see front of timetable
For details of catering facilities see Directory of Train Operators

- **A** To Blackpool North (Table 82)
- **B** To York (Table 39)
- **C** To Scarborough (Table 39)
- **D** To Liverpool Lime Street (Table 89)
- **E** To Cleethorpes (22 June to 4 September to Doncaster) (Table 29)
- **G** To Glasgow Central (Table 65) and Barrow-in-Furness (Table 82)
- **H** To Middlesbrough (Table 39)
- **J** To Liverpool Lime Street (Table 90)
- **K** To Newcastle (Table 39)
- **L** To Edinburgh (Table 65)
- **N** To Southport (Table 82)
- **Q** From Alderley Edge (Table 84)
- **U** To Windermere (Table 82)
- **V** To Barrow-in-Furness and Blackpool North (Table 82)
- **X** To Glasgow Central (Table 65)
- **Y** To Barrow-in-Furness (Table 82)
- **AA** To Edinburgh (Table 65). Until 19 June and from 7 September also conveys portion to Windermere (Table 82)
- **BB** To Edinburgh (Table 65) and Windermere (Table 82)

Manchester Airport → Manchester

Network Diagram - see first page of Table 78

		NT	TP 1◇ A	TP 1◇ B	NT C	NT	TP 1◇ D	TP 1◇ E		NT G	NT	TP 1◇ A	TP 1◇ B	NT C	NT	TP 1◇ D	TP 1◇ H		NT G	NT	TP 1◇ J	TP 1◇ A	NT C	NT	TP 1◇ D
Crewe 10	84 d	16 33									17 33									18 33					
Wilmslow	84 d	16 57									17 56									18 56					
Manchester Airport	d	17 17	17 27	17 35	17 41	17 46	17 55	18 00		18 03	18 17	18 29	18 35	18 41	18 46	18 55	19 00		19 03	19 09	19 20	19 29	19 41	19 46	19 55
Heald Green	d	17 20	17 31			17 49					18 20	18 33			18 49					19 12		19 33		19 49	
Gatley	d	17 23				17 52					18 23				18 52					19 15				19 52	
East Didsbury	d	17 26	17 35			17 55					18 26				18 55					19 18				19 55	
Burnage	d	17 28				17 57					18 28				18 57					19 20				19 57	
Mauldeth Road	d	17 30				17 59					18 30				18 59					19 22				19 59	
Manchester Piccadilly 10	a	17 42	17 44	17 52	17 59	18 11	18 13	18 14		18 18	18 42	18 44	18 52	18 59	19 11	19 13	19 14		19 18	19 31	19 36	19 44	19 59	20 11	20 13
	d		17 46		18 01			18 16		18 22		18 46		19 01			19 16		19 20	19 32		19 46	20 01		
Manchester Oxford Road	a		17 48		18 03			18 18		18 24		18 48		19 03			19 18		19 22	19 36		19 48	20 03		
Deansgate	a		17 51							18 28		18 51							19 26			19 51			

		TP 1◇ H	NT G	NT		TP 1◇ K	TP 1◇ A	TP 1◇ D	NT G	NT	TP 1◇ J	TP 1◇ A	NT C		TP 1◇ L	TP 1◇ H	NT	NT G	TP 1◇ N	TP 1◇ A	NT	TP 1◇ N	TP 1◇ L		
Crewe 10	84 d																								
Wilmslow	84 d			19 56						20 56							21 55				22 56				
Manchester Airport	d	20 00	20 03	20 09		20 20	20 29	20 47	21 03	21 09	21 20	21 29	21 41		21 47	22 00	22 08	22 19	22 22	22 29	23 09	23 18	23 52		
Heald Green	d			20 12			20 33	20 51		21 12		21 33			21 51		22 12			22 33	23 12				
Gatley	d			20 15				20 54		21 15					21 54		22 15				23 15				
East Didsbury	d			20 18				20 57		21 18					21 57		22 17				23 18				
Burnage	d			20 20				20 59		21 20					21 59		22 19				23 20				
Mauldeth Road	d			20 22				21 02		21 22					22 02		22 21				23 22				
Manchester Piccadilly 10	a	20 14	20 18	20 32		20 36	20 44	21 13	21 18	21 32	21 36	21 44	21 59		22 13	22 14	22 31	22 34	22 36	22 44	23 33	23 34	00 09		
	d	20 16	20 20	20 32			20 46		21 20	21 32		21 46	22 01			22 16	22 32	22 36		22 46					
Manchester Oxford Road	a	20 18	20 22	20 36			20 48		21 22	21 36		21 48	22 03			22 18	22 36	22 38		22 48					
Deansgate	a		20 26				20 51		21 26			21 51						22 41		22 51					

Saturdays

until 31 October

		TP 1◇ A	TP 1◇ N	NT	TP 1◇ A	TP 1◇ N	NT Q	TP 1◇ U	TP 1◇ A		TP 1◇ K	NT	TP 1◇ V	TP 1◇ B	NT C	NT	TP 1◇ U	TP 1◇ A		TP 1◇ J	NT	TP 1◇ X	TP 1◇ B	NT C	NT
Crewe 10	84 d			00 44																	06 33				
Wilmslow	84 d											05 46									06 57				
Manchester Airport	d	00 01	01 00	01 20	03 40	04 00	04 34	05 15	05 29		05 37	06 01	06 18	06 23	06 41	06 46	06 55	07 00		07 05	07 17	07 28	07 33	07 41	07 46
Heald Green	d								05 33			06 04				06 49					07 20	07 32			07 49
Gatley	d											06 07				06 52					07 23				07 52
East Didsbury	d											06 10				06 55					07 26				07 55
Burnage	d											06 12				06 57					07 28				07 57
Mauldeth Road	d											06 14				06 59					07 30				07 59
Manchester Piccadilly 10	a	00 15	01 14	01 36	03 53	04 14	04 47	05 33	05 44		05 51	06 25	06 31	06 39	06 56	07 11	07 13	07 14		07 22	07 42	07 43	07 48	07 56	08 11
	d												06 33		06 58			07 15						07 58	
Manchester Oxford Road	a												06 35		07 00			07 17						08 00	
Deansgate	a																								

		TP 1◇ U	TP 1◇ A	NT G	TP 1◇ J		NT	TP 1◇ Y	TP 1◇ B	NT C	NT	TP 1◇ U	TP 1◇ Z	NT G		TP 1◇ J	NT	TP 1◇ A	TP 1◇ B	NT C	NT	TP 1◇ U	TP 1◇ X		NT G
Crewe 10	84 d						07 30										08 31								
Wilmslow	84 d						07 56										08 57								
Manchester Airport	d	07 54	08 00	08 03	08 05		08 17	08 25	08 35	08 41	08 46	08 55	09 00	09 03		09 05	09 17	09 29	09 35	09 41	09 46	09 55	10 00		10 03
Heald Green	d	07 58					08 20	08 29			08 49	08 59					09 20	09 33			09 49				
Gatley	d						08 23	08 32			08 52						09 23				09 52				
East Didsbury	d						08 26	08 35			08 55						09 26				09 55				
Burnage	d						08 28				08 57						09 28				09 57				
Mauldeth Road	d						08 30				08 59						09 30				09 59				
Manchester Piccadilly 10	a	08 13	08 14	08 21	08 22		08 42	08 44	08 49	08 59	09 11	09 13	09 14	09 18		09 22	09 42	09 44	09 52	09 59	10 11	10 13	10 14		10 18
	d		08 15	08 22				08 46		09 01			09 16	09 22				09 46		10 01			10 16		10 22
Manchester Oxford Road	a		08 17	08 24				08 48		09 03			09 18	09 24				09 48		10 03			10 18		10 24
Deansgate	a			08 28				08 51						09 28				09 51							10 28

		TP 1◇ J	NT	TP 1◇ A	TP 1◇ B	NT C	NT	TP 1◇ U	TP 1◇ H		NT G	NT AA	TP 1◇ J	NT	TP 1◇ A	TP 1◇ B	NT C	NT		TP 1◇ U	TP 1◇ X	NT G	TP 1◇ J	NT	TP 1◇ A
Crewe 10	84 d		09 33											10 33										11 33	
Wilmslow	84 d		09 57									10 52		10 57										11 57	
Manchester Airport	d	10 05	10 17	10 29	10 35	10 41	10 46	10 55	11 00		11 03		11 05	11 17	11 29	11 35	11 41	11 46		11 55	12 00	12 03	12 05	12 17	12 29
Heald Green	d		10 20	10 33			10 49							11 20	11 33			11 49						12 20	12 33
Gatley	d		10 23				10 52							11 23				11 52						12 23	
East Didsbury	d		10 26				10 55							11 26				11 55						12 26	
Burnage	d		10 28				10 57							11 28				11 57						12 28	
Mauldeth Road	d		10 30				10 59							11 30				11 59						12 30	
Manchester Piccadilly 10	a	10 22	10 42	10 44	10 52	10 59	11 11	11 13	11 14		11 18	11 20	11 22	11 42	11 44	11 52	11 59	12 11		12 13	12 14	12 18	12 22	12 42	12 44
	d			10 46		11 01			11 16		11 22				11 46		12 01				12 16	12 22			12 46
Manchester Oxford Road	a			10 48		11 03			11 18		11 24				11 48		12 03				12 18	12 24			12 48
Deansgate	a			10 51							11 28				11 51							12 28			12 51

For general notes see front of timetable
For details of catering facilities see Directory of Train Operators

- **A** To Blackpool North (Table 82)
- **B** To Middlesbrough (Table 39)
- **C** To Liverpool Lime Street (Table 90)
- **D** To Cleethorpes (22 June to 4 September to Doncaster) (Table 29)
- **E** To Edinburgh (Table 65) and Barrow-in-Furness (Table 82)
- **G** To Southport (Table 82)
- **H** To Barrow-in-Furness (Table 82)
- **J** To Newcastle (Table 39)
- **K** To Scarborough (Table 39)
- **L** To Sheffield (Table 78)
- **N** To York (Table 39)
- **Q** To Liverpool Lime Street (Table 89)
- **U** To Cleethorpes (27 June to 5 September to Doncaster) (Table 29)
- **V** To Glasgow Central (Table 65) and Barrow-in-Furness (Table 82)
- **X** To Edinburgh (Table 65)
- **Y** To Windermere (Table 82)
- **Z** To Glasgow Central (Table 65) and Blackpool North (Table 82)
- **AA** From Alderley Edge (Table 84)

Table 85

Manchester Airport → Manchester

Saturdays
until 31 October

Network Diagram - see first page of Table 78

		TP 1◇ A 🛒	NT B	NT	TP 1◇ C 🛒		TP 1◇ D 🛒	NT E	TP 1◇ G 🛒	NT	TP 1◇ H 🛒	TP 1◇ A 🛒	NT B	NT		TP 1◇ C 🛒	TP 1◇ J 🛒	NT E	TP 1◇ K 🛒	NT	TP 1◇ L 🛒	TP 1◇ A	NT B		NT
Crewe 10	84 d									12 33										13 33					
Wilmslow	84 d									12 57										13 57					
Manchester Airport ✈	d	12 35	12 41	12 46	12 55		13 00	13 03	13 05	13 17	13 29	13 35	13 41	13 46		13 55	14 00	14 03	14 05	14 17	14 29	14 35	14 41		14 46
Heald Green	d			12 49						13 20	13 33			13 49						14 20	14 33				14 49
Gatley	d			12 52						13 23				13 52						14 23					14 52
East Didsbury	d			12 55						13 26				13 55						14 26					14 55
Burnage	d			12 57						13 28				13 57						14 28					14 57
Mauldeth Road	d			12 59						13 30				13 59						14 30					14 59
Manchester Piccadilly 10 🚊	a	12 52	12 59	13 11	13 13		13 14	13 18	13 22	13 42	13 44	13 52	13 59	14 11		14 13	14 14	14 18	14 22	14 42	14 44	14 52	14 59		15 11
	d		13 01				13 16	13 22			13 46		14 01				14 16	14 22			14 46		15 01		
Manchester Oxford Road	a		13 03				13 18	13 24			13 48		14 03				14 18	14 24			14 48		15 03		
Deansgate 🚊	a							13 28			13 51							14 28			14 51				

		TP 1◇ C 🛒	TP 1◇ N 🛒	NT E	TP 1◇ G 🛒	NT	TP 1◇ L 🛒	TP 1◇ A 🛒	NT B		NT	TP 1◇ C 🛒	TP 1◇ Q 🛒	NT E	TP 1◇ K	NT	TP 1◇ L 🛒	TP 1◇ A		NT B	NT	TP 1◇ C 🛒	TP 1◇ N 🛒	NT E	TP 1◇ G
Crewe 10	84 d					14 33										15 33									
Wilmslow	84 d					14 57										15 56									
Manchester Airport ✈	d	14 55	15 00	15 03	15 05	15 17	15 29	15 35	15 41		15 46	15 55	16 00	16 03	16 05	16 17	16 29	16 35		16 41	16 46	16 55	17 00	17 03	17 05
Heald Green	d					15 20	15 33				15 49					16 20	16 33				16 49				
Gatley	d					15 23					15 52					16 23					16 52				
East Didsbury	d					15 26					15 55					16 26					16 55				
Burnage	d					15 28					15 57					16 28					16 57				
Mauldeth Road	d					15 30					15 59					16 30					16 59				
Manchester Piccadilly 10 🚊	a	15 13	15 14	15 18	15 22	15 42	15 44	15 52	15 59		16 11	16 13	16 14	16 18	16 22	16 42	16 44	16 52		16 59	17 11	17 13	17 14	17 21	17 22
	d		15 16	15 22			15 46		16 01				16 16	16 22			16 46			17 01			17 15	17 22	
Manchester Oxford Road	a		15 18	15 24			15 48		16 03				16 18	16 24			16 48			17 03			17 17	17 25	
Deansgate 🚊	a			15 28			15 51							16 28											

		NT	TP 1◇ L 🛒	TP 1◇ A	NT B		NT	TP 1◇ C 🛒	TP 1◇ D 🛒	NT E	NT	TP 1◇ L 🛒	TP 1◇ A	NT B		NT	TP 1◇ C	TP 1◇ N	NT E	NT	TP 1◇ G	TP 1◇ L	NT B		NT
Crewe 10	84 d	16 33									17 33									18 33					
Wilmslow	84 d	16 57									17 56									18 56					
Manchester Airport ✈	d	17 17	17 27	17 35	17 41		17 46	17 55	18 00	18 03	18 17	18 29	18 35	18 41		18 46	18 55	19 00	19 03	19 09	19 19	19 29	19 41		19 46
Heald Green	d	17 20	17 31				17 49				18 20	18 33				18 49				19 12		19 33			19 49
Gatley	d	17 23					17 52				18 23					18 52				19 15					19 52
East Didsbury	d	17 26	17 35				17 55				18 26					18 55				19 18					19 55
Burnage	d	17 28					17 57				18 28					18 57				19 20					19 57
Mauldeth Road	d	17 30					17 59				18 30					18 59				19 22					19 59
Manchester Piccadilly 10 🚊	a	17 42	17 44	17 52	17 59		18 11	18 13	18 14	18 18	18 42	18 44	18 52	18 59		19 11	19 13	19 14	19 18	19 31	19 36	19 44	19 59		20 11
	d		17 46		18 01				18 16	18 22		18 46		19 01				19 16	19 20	19 32		19 46	20 01		
Manchester Oxford Road	a		17 48		18 03				18 18	18 24		18 48		19 03				19 18	19 22	19 36		19 48	20 03		
Deansgate 🚊	a		17 51							18 28		18 51							19 26			19 51			

		TP 1◇ C	TP 1◇ N	NT E	NT	TP 1◇ U	TP 1◇ L	TP 1◇ C	NT E		NT	TP 1◇ K	TP 1◇ L	NT B	TP 1◇ V	TP 1◇ N	NT	NT E		TP 1◇ K	TP 1◇ L	TP 1◇ X	NT		
Crewe 10	84 d																						21b50		
Wilmslow	84 d				19 56						20 56						21 55						23 15		
Manchester Airport ✈	d	19 55	20 00	20 03	20 09	20 20	20 29	20 47	21 03		21 09	21 20	21 29	21 41	21 47	22 00	22 08	22 19		22 22	22 29	23 24	23 27		
Heald Green	d				20 12		20 33	20 51			21 12		21 33		21 51		22 12				22 33		23 30		
Gatley	d				20 15			20 54			21 15				21 54		22 15						23 33		
East Didsbury	d				20 18			20 57			21 18				21 57		22 17						23 36		
Burnage	d				20 20			20 59			21 20				21 59		22 19						23 38		
Mauldeth Road	d				20 22			21 02			21 22				22 02		22 21						23 40		
Manchester Piccadilly 10 🚊	a	20 13	20 14	20 18	20 31	20 36	20 44	21 13	21 18		21 31	21 36	21 44	22 00	22 13	22 14	22 31	22 34		22 36	22 44	23 39	23 51		
	d		20 16	20 20	20 32		20 46		21 20		21 32		21 46	22 01		22 16	22 32	22 36			22 46				
Manchester Oxford Road	a		20 18	20 22	20 36		20 48		21 22		21 36		21 48	22 03		22 18	22 36	22 38			22 48				
Deansgate 🚊	a			20 26			20 51		21 26				21 51					22 41			22 51				

Saturdays
from 7 November

		TP 1◇ L	TP 1◇ K	NT	TP 1◇ L	TP 1◇ K	NT Y	TP 1◇ Z	TP 1◇ L	TP 1◇ U	NT	TP 1◇ AA 🛒	TP 1◇ A 🛒	NT B	NT	TP 1◇ Z 🛒	TP 1◇ L 🛒	TP 1◇ G 🛒	NT	TP 1◇ J 🛒	TP 1◇ A 🛒	NT B	NT	TP 1◇ Z 🛒	TP 1◇ L 🛒
Crewe 10	84 d			00 44															06 33						
Wilmslow	84 d										05 46								06 57						
Manchester Airport ✈	d	00 01	01 00	01 20	03 40	04 00	04 34	05 15	05 29	05 37	06 01	06 18	06 23	06 41	06 46	06 55	07 00	07 05	07 17	07 28	07 33	07 41	07 46	07 54	08 00
Heald Green	d								05 33		06 04				06 49				07 20	07 32			07 49	07 58	
Gatley	d										06 07				06 52				07 23				07 52		
East Didsbury	d										06 10				06 55				07 26				07 55		
Burnage	d										06 12				06 57				07 28				07 57		
Mauldeth Road	d										06 14				06 59				07 30				07 59		
Manchester Piccadilly 10 🚊	a	00 15	01 14	01 36	03 53	04 14	04 47	05 33	05 44	05 51	06 25	06 31	06 39	06 56	07 11	07 13	07 14	07 22	07 42	07 43	07 48	07 56	08 11	08 13	08 14
	d											06 33		06 58			07 15					07 58			08 15
Manchester Oxford Road	a											06 35		07 00			07 17					08 00			08 17
Deansgate 🚊	a																								

For general notes see front of timetable
For details of catering facilities see Directory of Train Operators

- **A** To Middlesbrough (Table 39)
- **B** To Liverpool Lime Street (Table 90)
- **C** To Cleethorpes (27 June to 5 September to Doncaster) (Table 29)
- **D** To Glasgow Central (Table 65)
- **E** To Southport (Table 82)
- **G** To Newcastle (Table 39)
- **H** To Blackpool North and Barrow-in-Furness (Table 82)
- **J** To Edinburgh (Table 65)
- **K** To York (Table 39)
- **L** To Blackpool North (Table 82)
- **N** To Barrow-in-Furness (Table 82)
- **Q** To Edinburgh (Table 65) and Windermere (Table 82)
- **U** To Scarborough (Table 39)
- **V** To Sheffield (Table 78)
- **X** Until 5 September to York (Table 39)
- **Y** To Liverpool Lime Street (Table 89)
- **Z** To Cleethorpes (Table 29)
- **AA** To Glasgow Central (Table 65) and Barrow-in-Furness (Table 82)
- **b** Until 11 July dep. 2227

Table 85

Saturdays
from 7 November

Manchester Airport → Manchester

Network Diagram - see first page of Table 78

		NT A	TP 1◇ B	NT	TP 1◇ C	TP 1◇ D	NT E	NT	TP 1◇ G	TP 1◇ H	NT A	TP 1◇ B	NT	TP 1◇ J		TP 1◇ D	NT E	NT	TP 1◇ G	TP 1◇ K	NT A	TP 1◇ B	NT	TP 1◇ J	TP 1◇ D
Crewe 10	84 d			07 30									08 31										09 33		
Wilmslow	84 d			07 56									08 57										09 57		
Manchester Airport	d	08 03	08 05	08 17	08 25	08 35	08 41	08 46	08 55	09 00	09 03	09 05	09 17	09 29		09 35	09 41	09 46	09 55	10 00	10 03	10 05	10 17	10 29	10 35
Heald Green	d			08 20	08 29			08 49	08 59				09 20	09 33				09 49					10 20	10 33	
Gatley	d			08 23	08 32			08 52					09 23					09 52					10 23		
East Didsbury	d			08 26	08 35			08 55					09 26					09 55					10 26		
Burnage	d			08 28				08 57					09 28					09 57					10 28		
Mauldeth Road	d			08 30				08 59					09 30					09 59					10 30		
Manchester Piccadilly 10	a	08 21	08 22	08 42	08 44	08 49	08 59	09 11	09 13	09 14	09 18	09 22	09 42	09 44		09 52	09 59	10 11	10 13	10 14	10 18	10 22	10 42	10 44	10 52
	d	08 22			08 46		09 01			09 16	09 22			09 46			10 01			10 16	10 22			10 46	
Manchester Oxford Road	a	08 24			08 48		09 03			09 18	09 24			09 48			10 03			10 18	10 24			10 48	
Deansgate	a	08 28			08 51						09 28			09 51							10 28			10 51	

		NT E	NT	TP 1◇ G	TP 1◇ L	NT A	TP 1◇ B	NT	TP 1◇ J	TP 1◇ D	NT E	NT	TP 1◇ G	TP 1◇ K	NT A	TP 1◇ B	NT	TP 1◇ J	TP 1◇ D	NT E	TP 1◇ G	TP 1◇ N	NT A	TP 1◇ B	NT
Crewe 10	84 d							10 33									11 33								12 33
Wilmslow	84 d							10 57									11 57								12 57
Manchester Airport	d	10 41	10 46	10 55	11 00	11 03	11 05	11 17	11 29	11 35	11 41	11 46	11 55	12 00	12 03	12 05	12 17	12 29	12 35	12 41	12 47	13 00	13 03	13 05	13 17
Heald Green	d		10 49					11 20	11 33			11 49					12 20	12 33			12 51				13 20
Gatley	d		10 52					11 23				11 52					12 23				12 54				13 23
East Didsbury	d		10 55					11 26				11 55					12 26				12 57				13 26
Burnage	d		10 57					11 28				11 57					12 28				12 59				13 28
Mauldeth Road	d		10 59					11 30				11 59					12 30				13 02				13 30
Manchester Piccadilly 10	a	10 59	11 11	11 13	11 14	11 18	11 22	11 42	11 44	11 52	11 59	12 11	12 13	12 14	12 18	12 22	12 42	12 44	12 52	12 59	13 13	13 14	13 18	13 22	13 42
	d	11 01			11 16	11 22			11 46		12 01			12 16	12 22			12 46		13 01		13 16	13 22		
Manchester Oxford Road	a	11 03			11 18	11 24			11 48		12 03			12 18	12 24			12 48		13 03		13 18	13 24		
Deansgate	a					11 28			11 51						12 28			12 51					13 28		

		TP 1◇ Q	TP 1◇ D	NT E	TP 1◇ G	TP 1◇ K		NT A	TP 1◇ U	NT	TP 1◇ J	TP 1◇ D	NT E	TP 1◇ G	TP 1◇ V	NT A	TP 1◇ B	NT	TP 1◇ J	TP 1◇ D	NT E	TP 1◇ G	TP 1◇ X	NT A	TP 1◇ U
Crewe 10	84 d									13 33								14 33							
Wilmslow	84 d									13 57								14 57							
Manchester Airport	d	13 29	13 35	13 41	13 47	14 00		14 03	14 05	14 17	14 29	14 35	14 41	14 47	15 00	15 03	15 05	15 17	15 29	15 35	15 41	15 47	16 00	16 03	16 05
Heald Green	d	13 33			13 51					14 20	14 33			14 51				15 20	15 33			15 51			
Gatley	d				13 54					14 23				14 54				15 23				15 54			
East Didsbury	d				13 57					14 26				14 57				15 26				15 57			
Burnage	d				13 59					14 28				14 59				15 28				15 59			
Mauldeth Road	d				14 02					14 30				15 02				15 30				16 02			
Manchester Piccadilly 10	a	13 44	13 52	13 59	14 13	14 14		14 18	14 22	14 42	14 44	14 52	14 59	15 13	15 14	15 18	15 22	15 42	15 44	15 52	15 59	16 13	16 14	16 18	16 22
	d	13 46		14 01		14 16		14 22			14 46		15 01		15 16	15 22			15 46		16 01		16 16	16 22	
Manchester Oxford Road	a	13 48		14 03		14 18		14 24			14 48		15 03		15 18	15 24			15 48		16 03		16 18	16 24	
Deansgate	a	13 51						14 28			14 51					15 28			15 51					16 28	

		NT	TP 1◇ J	TP 1◇ D	NT E	TP 1◇ G	TP 1◇ V	NT A	TP 1◇ B	NT	TP 1◇ J	TP 1◇ D	NT E	TP 1◇ G	TP 1◇ N	NT A	NT	TP 1◇ J	TP 1◇ D	NT E	TP 1◇ G	TP 1◇ L	NT A	NT	TP 1◇ B
Crewe 10	84 d	15 33								16 33							17 33							18 33	
Wilmslow	84 d	15 56								16 57							17 56							18 56	
Manchester Airport	d	16 17	16 29	16 35	16 41	16 47	17 00	17 03	17 05	17 17	17 27	17 35	17 41	17 47	18 00	18 03	18 17	18 29	18 35	18 41	18 47	19 00	19 03	19 09	19 19
Heald Green	d	16 20	16 33			16 51				17 20	17 31			17 51			18 20	18 33			18 51			19 12	
Gatley	d	16 23				16 54				17 23				17 54			18 23				18 54			19 15	
East Didsbury	d	16 26				16 57				17 26	17 35			17 57			18 26				18 57			19 18	
Burnage	d	16 28				16 59				17 28				17 59			18 28				18 59			19 20	
Mauldeth Road	d	16 30				17 02				17 30				18 02			18 30				19 02			19 22	
Manchester Piccadilly 10	a	16 42	16 44	16 52	16 59	17 13	17 14	17 21	17 22	17 42	17 44	17 52	17 59	18 13	18 14	18 18	18 42	18 44	18 52	18 59	19 13	19 14	19 18	19 31	19 36
	d		16 46		17 01		17 15	17 22			17 46		18 01		18 16	18 22		18 46		19 01		19 16	19 20	19 32	
Manchester Oxford Road	a		16 48		17 03		17 17	17 25			17 48		18 03		18 18	18 24		18 48		19 03		19 18	19 22	19 36	
Deansgate	a										17 51					18 28		18 51					19 26		

		TP 1◇ J	NT E	TP 1◇ G	TP 1◇ V	NT A	NT	TP 1◇ Y	TP 1◇ J	TP 1◇ G	NT A	NT	TP 1◇ U	TP 1◇ J	NT E	TP 1◇ Z	TP 1◇ L	NT	NT A	TP 1◇ U	TP 1◇ J	TP 1◇	NT		
Crewe 10	84 d																								
Wilmslow	84 d						19 56					20 56						21 55					23 15		
Manchester Airport	d	19 29	19 41	19 47	20 00	20 03	20 09	20 20	20 29	20 47	21 03	21 09	21 20	21 29	21 41	21 47	22 00	22 08	22 19	22 22	22 29	23 24	23 27		
Heald Green	d	19 33		19 51			20 12		20 33	20 51		21 12		21 33		21 51		22 12			22 33		23 30		
Gatley	d			19 54			20 15			20 54		21 15				21 54		22 15					23 33		
East Didsbury	d			19 57			20 18			20 57		21 18				21 57		22 17					23 36		
Burnage	d			19 59			20 20			20 59		21 20				21 59		22 19					23 38		
Mauldeth Road	d			20 02			20 22			21 02		21 22				22 02		22 21					23 40		
Manchester Piccadilly 10	a	19 44	19 59	20 13	20 14	20 18	20 31	20 36	20 44	21 13	21 18	21 31	21 36	21 44	22 00	22 13	22 14	22 31	22 34	22 36	22 44	23 39	23 51		
	d	19 46	20 01		20 16	20 20	20 32		20 46		21 20	21 32		21 46	22 01		22 16	22 32	22 36		22 46				
Manchester Oxford Road	a	19 48	20 03		20 18	20 22	20 36		20 48		21 22	21 36		21 48	22 03		22 18	22 36	22 38		22 48				
Deansgate	a	19 51				20 26			20 51		21 26			21 51					22 41		22 51				

For general notes see front of timetable
For details of catering facilities see Directory of Train Operators

- **A** To Southport (Table 82)
- **B** To Newcastle (Table 39)
- **C** To Windermere (Table 82)
- **D** To Middlesbrough (Table 39)
- **E** To Liverpool Lime Street (Table 90)
- **G** To Cleethorpes (Table 29)
- **H** To Glasgow Central (Table 65) and Blackpool North (Table 82)
- **J** To Blackpool North (Table 82)
- **K** To Edinburgh (Table 65)
- **L** To Barrow-in-Furness (Table 82)
- **N** To Glasgow Central (Table 65)
- **Q** To Blackpool North and Barrow-in-Furness (Table 82)
- **U** To York (Table 39)
- **V** To Barrow-in-Furness (Table 65)
- **X** To Edinburgh (Table 65) and Windermere (Table 82)
- **Y** To Scarborough (Table 39)
- **Z** To Sheffield (Table 78)

Table 85

Sundays

until 6 September

Manchester Airport → Manchester

Network Diagram - see first page of Table 78

	TP	TP	TP	TP	NT	TP	TP	NT	TP	TP	NT	TP	NT	TP	TP	NT	TP	TP	NT	NT	TP	TP	NT	TP
	A (bus)	1◇ B	1◇ B	A (bus)		1◇ C	1◇ D		1◇ A	1◇ D		1◇ A	E	1◇ G	1◇ H		1◇ D	1◇ J (catering)	E		1◇ D	1◇ A	E	1◇ K
Crewe 10 84 d																								
Wilmslow 84 d																								
Manchester Airport ✈ d	00 10	01 22	04 43	05 30	06 09	06 24	07 24	07 30	07 55	08 06	08 09	08 30	08 34	08 39	09 00	09 06	09 20	09 30	09 35	10 08	10 19	10 29	10 32	10 44
Heald Green d					06 12			07 33			08 12					09 09				10 11				
Gatley d					06 15			07 36			08 15					09 12				10 14				
East Didsbury d					06 18			07 39			08 18					09 15				10 17				
Burnage d					06 20			07 41			08 20					09 17				10 19				
Mauldeth Road d					06 22			07 43			08 22					09 19				10 21				
Manchester Piccadilly 10 a	00 35	01 35	04 56	05 55	06 31	06 37	07 37	07 54	08 08	08 24	08 31	08 44	08 49	08 54	09 14	09 29	09 37	09 44	09 48	10 30	10 34	10 40	10 46	10 58
d									08 11			08 46	08 50		09 16			09 46	09 50			10 43	10 50	
Manchester Oxford Road a									08 13			08 48	08 52		09 18			09 48	09 52			10 46	10 52	
Deansgate a									08 16			08 51						09 51				10 51		

	TP	NT	TP	TP	NT	TP	NT	TP	TP		NT	TP	TP	NT	TP	TP	NT	TP	TP	NT	TP	TP	NT	TP
	1◇ H	L	1◇ D	1◇ A	E	1◇ N (catering)		1◇ D	1◇ A		E	1◇ K	1◇ Q (catering)	L	1◇ D	1◇ A	E	1◇ K	1◇ N (catering)		1◇ D	1◇ A	E	1◇ K
Crewe 10 84 d																								
Wilmslow 84 d		10b43												12 54										
Manchester Airport ✈ d	11 00	11 03	11 17	11 30	11 35	12 00	12 09	12 20	12 30		12 35	12 55	13 00	13 09	13 20	13 30	13 35	13 55	14 00	14 09	14 20	14 30	14 35	14 55
Heald Green d		11 07					12 12							13 12						14 12				
Gatley d		11 10					12 15							13 15						14 15				
East Didsbury d		11 12					12 18							13 18						14 18				
Burnage d		11 14					12 20							13 20						14 20				
Mauldeth Road d		11 16					12 22							13 22						14 22				
Manchester Piccadilly 10 a	11 14	11 25	11 35	11 44	11 48	12 14	12 31	12 37	12 44		12 48	13 09	13 14	13 31	13 37	13 44	13 48	14 09	14 14	14 31	14 37	14 44	14 48	15 09
d	11 16	11 26		11 46	11 50	12 16			12 46		12 50		13 16			13 46	13 50		14 16			14 46	14 50	
Manchester Oxford Road a	11 18	11 28		11 48	11 52	12 18			12 48		12 52		13 18			13 48	13 52		14 18			14 48	14 52	
Deansgate a				11 51					12 51							13 51						14 51		

	TP	NT	TP	TP	NT	TP	TP	NT	TP	TP	NT	TP	TP	NT	TP	TP	NT	TP	TP	NT	TP	TP	NT	TP
	1◇ H	L	1◇ D	1◇ A	E	1◇ K	1◇ U (catering)		1◇ D	1◇ A	E	1◇ K	1◇ Q (catering)	L	1◇ D	1◇ A	E	1◇ K	1◇ N (catering)		1◇ C	1◇ A	E	1◇ K
Crewe 10 84 d																								
Wilmslow 84 d		14 54												16 54										
Manchester Airport ✈ d	15 00	15 09	15 20	15 30	15 35	15 55	16 00	16 09	16 20	16 30	16 35	16 55	17 00	17 09	17 20	17 30	17 35	17 55	18 00	18 09	18 20	18 30	18 35	18 55
Heald Green d		15 12						16 12						17 12						18 12				
Gatley d		15 15						16 15						17 15						18 15				
East Didsbury d		15 18						16 18						17 18						18 18				
Burnage d		15 20						16 20						17 20						18 20				
Mauldeth Road d		15 22						16 22						17 22						18 22				
Manchester Piccadilly 10 a	15 14	15 31	15 37	15 44	15 48	16 09	16 14	16 31	16 37	16 44	16 48	17 09	17 14	17 31	17 37	17 44	17 48	18 09	18 14	18 31	18 37	18 44	18 48	19 09
d	15 16			15 46	15 50		16 16			16 46	16 50		17 16			17 46	17 50		18 16			18 46	18 50	
Manchester Oxford Road a	15 18			15 48	15 52		16 18			16 48	16 52		17 18			17 48	17 52		18 18			18 48	18 52	
Deansgate a				15 51						16 51						17 51						18 51		

	TP	NT	TP	TP	NT	TP	NT	TP	TP	NT	TP	NT	TP	TP	NT	TP	NT	TP	NT	TP	NT	TP		
	1◇ H	L	1◇ D	1◇ A	E	1◇ K		1◇ V	1◇ A	E	1◇ G	L	1◇ B	1◇ A	E	1◇ G		1◇ A	E	1◇ G	L	1◇ B		
Crewe 10 84 d																								
Wilmslow 84 d		18 54										20 54									22 54			
Manchester Airport ✈ d	19 00	19 09	19 20	19 30	19 35	19 55	20 09	20 20	20 30	20 35	20 55	21 09	21 20	21 30	21 35	21 55	22 09	22 30	22 35	22 55	23 09	23 20		
Heald Green d		19 12					20 12					21 12					22 12				23 12			
Gatley d		19 15					20 15					21 15					22 15				23 15			
East Didsbury d		19 18					20 18					21 18					22 18				23 18			
Burnage d		19 20					20 20					21 20					22 20				23 20			
Mauldeth Road d		19 22					20 22					21 22					22 22				23 22			
Manchester Piccadilly 10 a	19 14	19 31	19 37	19 44	19 48	20 09	20 31	20 37	20 44	20 48	21 09	21 31	21 37	21 44	21 48	22 09	22 31	22 44	22 48	23 09	23 33	23 38		
d	19 16			19 46	19 50				20 46	20 50				21 46	21 50			22 46	22 50					
Manchester Oxford Road a	19 18			19 48	19 52				20 48	20 52				21 48	21 52			22 48	22 52					
Deansgate a				19 51					20 51					21 51				22 51						

For general notes see front of timetable
For details of catering facilities see Directory of Train Operators

- **A** To Blackpool North (Table 82)
- **B** To York (Table 39)
- **C** To Middlesbrough (Table 39)
- **D** To Newcastle (Table 39)
- **E** To Liverpool Lime Street (Table 90)
- **G** To Sheffield (Table 78)
- **H** To Barrow-in-Furness (Table 82)
- **J** To Blackpool North (Table 82) and to Glasgow Central (Table 65)
- **K** To Cleethorpes (from 28 June to Doncaster) (Table 29)
- **L** From Alderley Edge (Table 84)
- **N** To Edinburgh (Table 65)
- **Q** To Glasgow Central (Table 65) and Barrow-in-Furness (Table 82)
- **U** To Edinburgh (Table 65) and Windermere (Table 82)
- **V** To Scarborough (Table 39)
- **b** Until 12 July dep. 1047

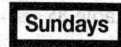

Table 85

Sundays

from 13 September

Manchester Airport → Manchester

Network Diagram - see first page of Table 78

	TP	TP	TP	TP	NT	TP	NT	TP	TP	NT	TP	TP	TP	NT	TP		TP	NT	TP	NT	TP	TP	TP	NT
								1 ◇	1 ◇		1 ◇	1 ◇	1 ◇		1 ◇		1 ◇		1 ◇		1 ◇	1 ◇	1 ◇	
	A	B	B	A		C		A	D		E	A	D		A		D		A	G	H	J	D	K
	🚌	🚌	🚌	🚌		🚌																🛒		
Crewe 10 84 d																								
Wilmslow 84 d																								10 53
Manchester Airport ✈ d	00 10	01 35	05 00	05 30	06 09	06 10	07 09	07 30	07 40	08 24	08 39	08 47	09 03	09 06	09 30		10 03	10 07	10 25	10 31	10 44	10 58	11 03	11 08
Heald Green d					06 12		07 12			08 27				09 09				10 10						11 11
Gatley d					06 15		07 15			08 30				09 12				10 13						11 14
East Didsbury d					06 18		07 18			08 33				09 15				10 16						11 17
Burnage d					06 20		07 20			08 35				09 17				10 18						11 19
Mauldeth Road d					06 22		07 22			08 37				09 19				10 20						11 21
Manchester Piccadilly 10 a	00 35	02 00	05 25	05 55	06 31	06 35	07 31	07 43	07 53	08 46	08 54	09 01	09 18	09 29	09 44		10 18	10 29	10 40	10 45	10 58	11 14	11 18	11 29
d								07 46				09 03			09 46				10 43	10 50		11 16		11 30
Manchester Oxford Road a								07 48				09 05			09 48				10 46	10 52		11 18		11 32
Deansgate a								07 51				09 08			09 51				10 51					

	TP	NT	TP	TP	NT	TP	NT	TP	TP		TP	NT	TP	NT	TP	TP	TP	NT	TP	NT	TP	TP	TP	NT
	1 ◇		1 ◇	1 ◇		1 ◇		1 ◇	1 ◇		1 ◇		1 ◇		1 ◇	1 ◇	1 ◇		1 ◇		1 ◇	1 ◇	1 ◇	
	A	G	L	D		A	G	H	N		D	K	A	G	H	L	D		A	G	H	Q	D	K
			🛒						🛒							🛒								
Crewe 10 84 d																								
Wilmslow 84 d												12 54												14 54
Manchester Airport ✈ d	11 30	11 33	11 58	12 03	12 09	12 30	12 35	12 55	12 58		13 03	13 09	13 30	13 35	13 55	13 58	14 03	14 09	14 30	14 35	14 55	14 58	15 03	15 09
Heald Green d					12 12							13 12						14 12						15 12
Gatley d					12 15							13 15						14 15						15 15
East Didsbury d					12 18							13 18						14 18						15 18
Burnage d					12 20							13 20						14 20						15 20
Mauldeth Road d					12 22							13 22						14 22						15 22
Manchester Piccadilly 10 a	11 44	11 48	12 14	12 18	12 31	12 44	12 48	13 09	13 14		13 18	13 31	13 44	13 48	14 09	14 14	14 18	14 31	14 44	14 48	15 09	15 14	15 18	15 31
d	11 46	11 50	12 16			12 46	12 50		13 16				13 46	13 50		14 16			14 46	14 50		15 16		
Manchester Oxford Road a	11 48	11 52	12 18			12 48	12 52		13 18				13 48	13 52		14 18			14 48	14 52		15 18		
Deansgate a	11 51					12 51							13 51						14 51					

	TP	NT	TP		TP	TP	NT	TP	NT	TP	TP	TP	NT	TP	NT	TP	TP	TP	NT		TP	NT	TP	TP
	1 ◇		1 ◇		1 ◇	1 ◇		1 ◇		1 ◇	1 ◇	1 ◇		1 ◇		1 ◇	1 ◇	1 ◇			1 ◇		1 ◇	1 ◇
	A	G	H		L	D		A	G	H	N	D	K	A	G	H	L	U			A	G	H	Q
					🛒						🛒						🛒							
Crewe 10 84 d																								
Wilmslow 84 d													16 54											
Manchester Airport ✈ d	15 30	15 35	15 55		15 58	16 03	16 09	16 30	16 35	16 55	16 58	17 03	17 09	17 30	17 35	17 55	17 58	18 03	18 09		18 30	18 35	18 55	18 58
Heald Green d							16 12						17 12						18 12					
Gatley d							16 15						17 15						18 15					
East Didsbury d							16 18						17 18						18 18					
Burnage d							16 20						17 20						18 20					
Mauldeth Road d							16 22						17 22						18 22					
Manchester Piccadilly 10 a	15 44	15 48	16 09		16 14	16 18	16 31	16 44	16 48	17 09	17 14	17 18	17 31	17 44	17 48	18 09	18 14	18 18	18 31		18 44	18 48	19 09	19 14
d	15 46	15 50			16 16			16 46	16 50		17 16			17 46	17 50		18 16				18 46	18 50		19 16
Manchester Oxford Road a	15 48	15 52			16 18			16 48	16 52		17 18			17 48	17 52		18 18				18 48	18 52		19 18
Deansgate a	15 51							16 51						17 51							18 51			

	TP	NT	TP	NT	TP	TP	NT	TP	NT	TP	TP	NT	TP	NT	TP	TP	NT	TP	NT	TP	NT	TP		
	1 ◇		1 ◇		1 ◇	1 ◇		1 ◇		1 ◇	1 ◇		1 ◇		1 ◇	1 ◇		1 ◇		1 ◇		1 ◇		
	D	K	A	G	H	V		A	G	E	B	K	A	G	E	X		A	G	E	K	B		
Crewe 10 84 d																								
Wilmslow 84 d		18 54										20 54									22 54			
Manchester Airport ✈ d	19 03	19 09	19 30	19 35	19 55	20 03	20 09	20 30	20 35	20 55	21 03	21 09	21 30	21 35	21 55	22 03	22 09	22 30	22 35	22 55	23 09	23 25		
Heald Green d		19 12					20 12					21 12					22 12				23 12			
Gatley d		19 15					20 15					21 15					22 15				23 15			
East Didsbury d		19 18					20 18					21 18					22 18				23 18			
Burnage d		19 20					20 20					21 20					22 20				23 20			
Mauldeth Road d		19 22					20 22					21 22					22 22				23 22			
Manchester Piccadilly 10 a	19 18	19 31	19 44	19 48	20 09	20 18	20 31	20 44	20 48	21 09	21 18	21 31	21 44	21 48	22 09	22 16	22 31	22 44	22 48	23 12	23 33	23 38		
d			19 46	19 50				20 46	20 50				21 46	21 50				22 46	22 50					
Manchester Oxford Road a			19 48	19 52				20 48	20 52				21 48	21 52				22 48	22 52					
Deansgate a			19 51					20 51					21 51					22 51						

For general notes see front of timetable
For details of catering facilities see Directory of Train Operators

- **A** To Blackpool North (Table 82)
- **B** To York (Table 39)
- **C** To Leeds (Table 39)
- **D** To Newcastle (Table 39)
- **E** To Sheffield (Table 78)
- **G** To Liverpool Lime Street (Table 90)
- **H** To Cleethorpes (Table 29)
- **J** To Glasgow Central (Table 65)
- **K** From Alderley Edge (Table 84)
- **L** To Edinburgh (Table 65)
- **N** To Glasgow Central (Table 65) and Barrow-in-Furness (Table 82)
- **Q** To Barrow-in-Furness (Table 82)
- **U** To Middlesbrough (Table 39)
- **V** To Scarborough (Table 39)
- **X** To Manchester Victoria

Manchester → Hazel Grove and Buxton

Network Diagram - see first page of Table 78

Mondays to Fridays

Miles	Station		NT A	NT	NT	NT B	NT	NT C	NT	NT D	NT	NT D	NT	NT D	NT	NT D	NT	NT D	NT	NT D
—	Deansgate	d				07 11	07 28	08 12	08 29	09 12	09 29	10 12	10 29	11 12	11 29	12 12	12 29	13 12	13 29	14 12
—	Manchester Oxford Road	d				07 15	07 38	08 15	08 39	09 16	09 39	10 16	10 39	11 16	11 39	12 16	12 39	13 16	13 39	14 16
0	**Manchester Piccadilly** 10	84 d	05 50	06 21	06 49	07 21	07 52	08 20	08 52	09 21	09 52	10 21	10 52	11 21	11 52	12 21	12 52	13 21	13 52	14 21
3	Levenshulme	84 d		06 28	06 55	07 28		08 28	08 58	09 28	09 58	10 28	10 58	11 28	11 58	12 28	12 58	13 28	13 58	14 28
4½	Heaton Chapel	84 d		06 31	06 58	07 31		08 31	09 01	09 31	10 01	10 31	11 01	11 31	12 01	12 31	13 01	13 31	14 01	14 31
6	**Stockport**	84 d	06 00	06 35	07 02	07 35	08 01	08 35	09 05	09 35	10 05	10 35	11 05	11 35	12 05	12 35	13 05	13 35	14 05	14 35
7	Davenport	d		06 39	07 06	07 39	08 05	08 39	09 09	09 39	10 09	10 39	11 09	11 39	12 09	12 39	13 09	13 39	14 09	14 39
7¾	Woodsmoor	d		06 41	07 08	07 41	08 07	08 41	09 11	09 41	10 11	10 41	11 11	11 41	12 11	12 41	13 11	13 41	14 11	14 41
8¾	**Hazel Grove**	a	06 06	06 45	07 10	07 45	08 09	08 45	09 13	09 45	10 13	10 45	11 13	11 45	12 13	12 45	13 13	13 45	14 13	14 45
—		d			07 10		08 10		09 13		10 13		11 13		12 13		13 13		14 13	
11	Middlewood	d			07 15				09 18		10 18				12 18				14 18	
12½	Disley	d			07 19		08 17		09 22		10 22		11 20		12 22		13 20		14 22	
14¼	New Mills Newtown	d			07 22		08 20		09 25		10 25		11 24		12 25		13 24		14 25	
15¼	Furness Vale	d			07 24		08 23		09 28		10 28		11 26		12 28		13 26		14 28	
16¼	Whaley Bridge	d			07 28		08 26		09 31		10 31		11 29		12 31		13 29		14 31	
20½	Chapel-en-le-Frith	d			07 35		08 33		09 38		10 38		11 36		12 38		13 36		14 38	
22¾	Dove Holes	d			07 40				09 43		10 43				12 43				14 43	
25¾	**Buxton**	a			07 50		08 44		09 53		10 53		11 50		12 53		13 50		14 53	

Station		NT E	NT G	NT D	NT	NT D	NT	NT	NT D	NT	NT	NT B	NT	NT	NT	NT	NT	NT
Deansgate	d	14 29	14 29	15 12	15 29	16 12	16 12		17 15	16 51	17 15	18 12	18 12	18 51	19 29	20 29	21 29	22 51
Manchester Oxford Road	d	14 39	14 39	15 16	15 39	16 16	16 39		17 19	17 07	17 39	18 16	18 39	19 07	19 39	20 39	21 33	22 54
Manchester Piccadilly 10	84 d	14 52	14 52	15 21	15 52	16 21	16 51	16 58	17 23	17 23	17 52	18 21	18 52	19 22	19 52	20 52	21 52	23 10
Levenshulme	84 d	14 58	14 58	15 28	15 58	16 28		17 03		17 28	17 58	18 28	18 58	19 28	19 58	20 58	21 58	
Heaton Chapel	84 d	15 01	15 01	15 31	16 01	16 31		17 06		17 31	18 01	18 31	19 01	19 31	20 01	21 01	22 01	
Stockport	84 d	15 05	15 08	15 35	16 05	16 35	17 02	17 10	17 32	17 35	18 05	18 35	19 05	19 35	20 05	21 05	22 05	23 20
Davenport	d	15 09	15 12	15 39	16 09	16 39	17 05	17 14		17 39	18 09	18 39	19 09	19 39	20 09	21 09	22 09	23 23
Woodsmoor	d	15 11	15 14	15 41	16 11	16 41	17 07	17 16		17 41	18 11	18 41	19 11	19 41	20 11	21 11	22 11	23 25
Hazel Grove	a	15 13	15 16	15 45	16 13	16 43	17 09	17 20	17 39	17 45	18 13	18 43	19 13	19 45	20 13	21 13	22 13	23 27
	d	15 13	15 17		16 13	16 46	17 10		17 39		18 13	18 46	19 13		20 13	21 13	22 13	23 28
Middlewood	d				16 18		17 14				18 18		19 18		20 18	21 18	22 18	23 32
Disley	d	15 20	15 24		16 22	16 53	17 18		17 46		18 22	18 53	19 22		20 22	21 22	22 22	23 36
New Mills Newtown	d	15 24	15 28		16 25	16 56	17 22		17 47		18 25	18 56	19 25		20 25	21 25	22 25	23 40
Furness Vale	d	15 26	15 30		16 28	16 59	17 25		17 50		18 28	18 59	19 28		20 28	21 28	22 28	23 42
Whaley Bridge	d	15 29	15 33		16 31	17 02	17 28		17 53		18 31	19 02	19 31		20 31	21 31	22 31	23 45
Chapel-en-le-Frith	d	15 36	15 40		16 38	17 09	17 35		18 01		18 38	19 09	19 38		20 38	21 38	22 38	23 52
Dove Holes	d				16 43		17 40				18 43		19 43		20 43	21 43	22 43	23 57
Buxton	a	15 50	15 54		16 53	17 22	17 50		18 14		18 53	19 22	19 53		20 53	21 53	22 53	00 07

Saturdays

Station		NT A	NT	NT B	NT	NT C	NT	NT D	NT	NT D	NT	NT D	NT	NT D	NT	NT D	NT	NT D
Deansgate	d			07 11	07 28	08 12	08 29	09 12	09 29	10 12	10 29	11 12	11 29	12 12	12 29	13 12	13 29	14 12
Manchester Oxford Road	d			07 15	07 38	08 15	08 39	09 16	09 39	10 16	10 39	11 16	11 39	12 16	12 39	13 16	13 39	14 16
Manchester Piccadilly 10	84 d	05 50	06 49	07 21	07 52	08 20	08 52	09 21	09 52	10 21	10 52	11 21	11 52	12 21	12 52	13 21	13 52	14 21
Levenshulme	84 d		06 55	07 28	07 58	08 28	08 58	09 28	09 58	10 28	10 58	11 28	11 58	12 28	12 58	13 28	13 58	14 28
Heaton Chapel	84 d		06 58	07 31		08 31	09 01	09 31	10 01	10 31	11 01	11 31	12 01	12 31	13 01	13 31	14 01	14 31
Stockport	84 d	06 00	07 02	07 35	08 03	08 35	09 05	09 35	10 05	10 35	11 05	11 35	12 05	12 35	13 05	13 35	14 05	14 35
Davenport	d		07 06	07 39	08 07	08 39	09 09	09 39	10 09	10 39	11 09	11 39	12 09	12 39	13 09	13 39	14 09	14 39
Woodsmoor	d		07 08	07 41	08 09	08 41	09 11	09 41	10 11	10 41	11 11	11 41	12 11	12 41	13 11	13 41	14 11	14 41
Hazel Grove	a	06 06	07 10	07 45	08 11	08 45	09 13	09 45	10 13	10 45	11 13	11 45	12 13	12 45	13 13	13 45	14 13	14 45
	d		07 10		08 11		09 13		10 13		11 13		12 13		13 13		14 13	
Middlewood	d		07 15				09 18		10 18				12 18				14 18	
Disley	d		07 19		08 18		09 22		10 22		11 20		12 22		13 20		14 22	
New Mills Newtown	d		07 22		08 21		09 25		10 25		11 23		12 25		13 23		14 25	
Furness Vale	d		07 24		08 24		09 28		10 27		11 26		12 27		13 26		14 27	
Whaley Bridge	d		07 28		08 27		09 31		10 31		11 29		12 31		13 29		14 31	
Chapel-en-le-Frith	d		07 35		08 34		09 38		10 38		11 36		12 38		13 36		14 38	
Dove Holes	d		07 40				09 43		10 43				12 43				14 43	
Buxton	a		07 50		08 46		09 53		10 53		11 50		12 53		13 50		14 53	

Station		NT	NT D	NT	NT D	NT	NT	NT D	NT	NT D	NT	NT	NT	NT	NT	NT
Deansgate	d	14 29	15 12	15 29	16 12	16 12	16 51	17 12	17 29	18 12	18 12	18 51	19 29	20 29	21 29	22 51
Manchester Oxford Road	d	14 39	15 16	15 39	16 16	16 39	16 54	17 16	17 39	18 16	18 39	19 07	19 39	20 39	21 39	22 54
Manchester Piccadilly 10	84 d	14 52	15 21	15 52	16 21	16 52	17 09	17 21	17 52	18 21	18 52	19 22	19 52	20 52	21 52	23 10
Levenshulme	84 d	14 58	15 28	15 58	16 28	16 58	17 14	17 28	17 58	18 28	18 58	19 28	19 58	20 58	21 58	
Heaton Chapel	84 d	15 01	15 31	16 01	16 31	17 01	17 17	17 31	18 01	18 31	19 01	19 31	20 01	21 01	22 01	
Stockport	84 d	15 05	15 35	16 05	16 35	17 05	17 32	17 35	18 05	18 35	19 05	19 35	20 05	21 05	22 05	23 20
Davenport	d	15 09	15 39	16 09	16 39	17 09		17 39	18 09	18 39	19 09	19 39	20 09	21 09	22 09	23 23
Woodsmoor	d	15 11	15 41	16 11	16 41	17 11		17 41	18 11	18 41	19 11	19 41	20 11	21 11	22 11	23 25
Hazel Grove	a	15 13	15 45	16 13	16 45	17 13	17 39	17 43	18 13	18 45	19 13	19 45	20 13	21 13	22 13	23 27
	d	15 13		16 13		17 13		17 46	18 13		19 13		20 13	21 13	22 13	23 28
Middlewood	d			16 18				17 50			19 18		20 18	21 18	22 18	23 32
Disley	d	15 20		16 22		17 20		17 54	18 20		19 22		20 22	21 22	22 22	23 36
New Mills Newtown	d	15 24		16 25		17 24		17 58	18 24		19 25		20 25	21 25	22 25	23 40
Furness Vale	d	15 26		16 27		17 26		18 00	18 26		19 28		20 27	21 28	22 28	23 42
Whaley Bridge	d	15 29		16 31		17 29		18 03	18 29		19 31		20 31	21 31	22 31	23 45
Chapel-en-le-Frith	d	15 36		16 38		17 36		18 10	18 36		19 38		20 38	21 38	22 38	23 52
Dove Holes	d			16 43				18 15			19 43		20 43	21 43	22 43	23 57
Buxton	a	15 50		16 53		17 50		18 25	18 50		19 53		20 53	21 53	22 53	00 07

For general notes see front of timetable
For details of catering facilities see Directory of Train Operators

A To Sheffield (Table 78)
B From Wigan Wallgate (Table 82)
C From Blackpool North (Table 82)
D From Preston (Table 82)
E Until 19 June and from 7 September
G 22 June to 4 September

From 5 October Northern will be operating a revised service due to seasonal difficulties, when services will arrive at their destination 2 minutes later than shown

From 10 October Northern will be operating a revised service due to seasonal difficulties, when services will arrive at their destination 2 minutes later than shown

Sundays

Manchester → Hazel Grove and Buxton

Network Diagram - see first page of Table 78

			NT	NT	NT	NT	NT	NT	NT	NT	NT	NT	NT	NT	NT	NT	NT
Deansgate	🚋	d	.....	09b15	10 15	11c27	12 11	13c27	14c27	15c27	16c27	17c27	18c27	19c27	20c27	21 11	22e27
Manchester Oxford Road		d	08f05	09g18	10 19	11h38	12 34	13 39	14 39	15 39	16 39	17 39	18 39	19 39	20 39	21 34	22j37
Manchester Piccadilly 10	84 🚋	d	08 55	09 51	10 52	11 52	12 52	13 52	14 52	15 52	16 52	17 52	18 52	19 52	20 52	21 52	22 52
Levenshulme	84	d	09 00	09 58	10 58	11 58	12 58	13 58	14 58	15 58	16 58	17 58	18 58	19 58	20 58	21 58	22 58
Heaton Chapel	84	d	09 03	10 01	11 01	12 01	13 01	14 01	15 01	16 01	17 01	18 01	19 01	20 01	21 01	22 01	23 01
Stockport	84	d	09 10	10 05	11 05	12 05	13 05	14 05	15 05	16 05	17 05	18 05	19 05	20 05	21 05	22 05	23 05
Davenport		d	09 13	10 09	11 09	12 09	13 09	14 09	15 09	16 09	17 09	18 09	19 09	20 09	21 09	22 09	23 09
Woodsmoor		d	09 15	10 11	11 11	12 11	13 11	14 11	15 11	16 11	17 11	18 11	19 11	20 11	21 11	22 11	23 11
Hazel Grove		a	09 17	10 13	11 13	12 13	13 13	14 13	15 13	16 13	17 13	18 13	19 13	20 13	21 13	22 13	23 13
		d	09 18	10 13	11 13	12 13	13 13	14 13	15 13	16 13	17 13	18 13	19 13	20 13	21 13	22 13	23 13
Middlewood		d	09 22	10 18	11 18	12 18	13 18	14 18	15 18	16 18	17 18	18 18	19 18	20 18	21 18	22 18	23 18
Disley		d	09 26	10 22	11 22	12 22	13 22	14 22	15 22	16 22	17 22	18 22	19 22	20 22	21 22	22 22	23 22
New Mills Newtown		d	09 30	10 25	11 25	12 25	13 25	14 25	15 25	16 25	17 25	18 25	19 25	20 25	21 25	22 25	23 25
Furness Vale		d	09 32	10 28	11 28	12 28	13 28	14 28	15 28	16 28	17 28	18 28	19 28	20 28	21 28	22 28	23 28
Whaley Bridge		d	09 35	10 31	11 31	12 31	13 31	14 31	15 31	16 31	17 31	18 31	19 31	20 31	21 31	22 31	23 31
Chapel-en-le-Frith		d	09 42	10 38	11 38	12 38	13 38	14 38	15 38	16 38	17 38	18 38	19 38	20 38	21 38	22 38	23 38
Dove Holes		d	09 47	10 43	11 43	12 43	13 43	14 43	15 43	16 43	17 43	18 43	19 43	20 43	21 43	22 43	23 43
Buxton		a	09 55	10 51	11 51	12 51	13 51	14 51	15 51	16 51	17 51	18 51	19 51	20 51	21 51	22 51	23 51

For general notes see front of timetable
For details of catering facilities see Directory of Train Operators

b From 13 September dep. 0923
c Change at Manchester Oxford Road and Manchester Piccadilly
e From 13 September dep. 2211
f From 13 September dep. 0746
g From 13 September dep. 0926
h From 13 September dep. 1137
j From 13 September dep. 2234

Buxton and Hazel Grove → Manchester

Network Diagram - see first page of Table 78

Miles	Station		NT A	NT	NT B	NT	NT C	NT	NT	EM ◇ D	NT	NT E	NT	NT E	NT	NT E	NT	NT E	NT	NT E
0	**Buxton**	d	05 59		06 23		06 50		07 24		07 48		08 27		09 27		10 30		11 27	
3	Dove Holes	d			06 29		06 56		07 30				08 33		09 33				11 33	
5¼	Chapel-en-le-Frith	d	06 08		06 34		07 01		07 35		07 57		08 38		09 38		10 39		11 38	
9½	Whaley Bridge	d	06 14		06 40		07 07		07 41		08 03		08 44		09 44		10 45		11 44	
10½	Furness Vale	d	06 17		06 43		07 10		07 44		08 06		08 47		09 47		10 48		11 47	
11½	New Mills Newtown	d	06 20		06 46		07 13		07 47		08 10		08 50		09 50		10 51		11 50	
13¼	Disley	d	06 24		06 49		07 17		07 51		08 14		08 53		09 53		10 55		11 53	
14¾	Middlewood	d			06 53		07 21		07 55				08 57		09 57				11 57	
17	**Hazel Grove**	a	06 32		06 59		07 27		08 00		08 22		09 03		10 03		11 03		12 03	
—		d	06 33	06 50	07 00	07 22	07 27	07 48	08 01	08 17	08 22	08 32	09 04	09 33	10 04	10 33	11 04	11 33	12 04	12 33
18	Woodsmoor	d	06 35	06 52	07 02	07 24	07 30	07 50	08 03			08 34	09 06	09 35	10 06	10 35	11 06	11 35	12 06	12 35
18¾	Davenport	d	06 37	06 54	07 04	07 27	07 32	07 53	08 06			08 37	09 08	09 37	10 08	10 37	11 08	11 37	12 08	12 37
19¾	**Stockport**	84 a	06 41	06 58	07 08	07 31	07 37	07 57	08 10	08 24		08 41	09 12	09 41	10 12	10 41	11 12	11 41	12 12	12 41
21¼	Heaton Chapel	84 a			07 15		07 41						09 16		10 16		11 16		12 16	
22¾	Levenshulme	84 a			07 18		07 44						09 19		10 19		11 19		12 19	
25¾	**Manchester Piccadilly** 10	84 a	06 52	07 10	07 26	07 45	07 52	08 09	08 25	08 36	08 39	08 52	09 28	09 52	10 28	10 52	11 28	11 52	12 28	12 52
—	Manchester Oxford Road	a	06 56		07 29	*08 00*	07 56	*08 24*		08 40	*08 52*	08 56	*09 48*	09 56	*10 48*	10 56	*11 48*	11 56	*12 48*	12 56
—	Deansgate	a	06 59	*07 32*	07 32	*08b17*	07 59	*08 28*	*08 51*	*08 51*	*09 00*	09 00	*09 51*	10 00	*10 51*	11 00	*11 51*	12 00	*12 51*	13 00

Station		NT	NT E	NT	NT E	NT	NT G	NT H	NT	NT E	NT C	NT C	NT	NT G	NT	NT	NT	NT	NT
Buxton	d	12 30		13 25		14 30			15 47		16 30	16 59	17 27	17 59	18 27	19 27	20 27	21 27	22 56
Dove Holes	d			13 31					15 53				17 33		18 33	19 33	20 33	21 33	23 02
Chapel-en-le-Frith	d	12 39		13 36		14 39			15 58		16 39	17 08	17 38	18 08	18 38	19 38	20 38	21 38	23 07
Whaley Bridge	d	12 45		13 42		14 45			16 04		16 45	17 14	17 44	18 14	18 44	19 44	20 44	21 44	23 13
Furness Vale	d	12 48		13 45		14 48			16 07		16 48	17 17	17 47	18 17	18 47	19 47	20 47	21 47	23 16
New Mills Newtown	d	12 51		13 48		14 51			16 10		16 51	17 20	17 50	18 20	18 50	19 50	20 50	21 50	23 19
Disley	d	12 55		13 51		14 55			16 14		16 55	17 24	17 53	18 24	18 53	19 53	20 53	21 53	23 22
Middlewood	d			13 55					16 18				17 57		18 57	19 57	20 57	21 57	23 26
Hazel Grove	a	13 03		14 01		15 03			16 23		17 03	17 32	18 03	18 32	19 03	20 03	21 03	22 03	23 31
	d	13 04	13 33	14 01	14 33	15 04	15 33	16 04		16 33	17 04	17 33	18 04	18 33	19 04	20 04	21 04	22 04	23 32
Woodsmoor	d	13 06	13 35	14 03	14 35	15 06	15 35	16 06		16 35	17 06	17 35	18 06	18 35	19 06	20 06	21 06	22 06	23 34
Davenport	d	13 08	13 37	14 05	14 37	15 08	15 37	16 08		16 37	17 08	17 37	18 08	18 37	19 08	20 08	21 08	22 08	23 36
Stockport	84 a	13 12	13 41	14 09	14 41	15 12	15 41	16 12		16 41	17 12	17 41	18 12	18 41	19 12	20 12	21 12	22 12	23 40
Heaton Chapel	84 a	13 16		14 16		15 16		16 16			17 16		18 16		19 16	20 16	21 16	22 16	
Levenshulme	84 a	13 19		14 19		15 19		16 19			17 19		18 19		19 19	20 19	21 19	22 19	
Manchester Piccadilly 10	84 a	13 28	13 52	14 28	14 52	15 28	15 52	16 25		16 52	17 25	17 52	18 28	18 52	19 28	20 28	21 28	22 28	23 54
Manchester Oxford Road	a	*13 48*	13 56	*14 48*	14 56	*15 46*	15 56	16 29		16 56	17 29	17 56	*18 48*	18 56	*19 48*	*20 48*	*21 40*	*22 48*	
Deansgate	a	*13 51*	14 00	*14 51*	15 00	*15 51*	16 00	16 32		17 00	17 32	18 00	*18 51*	19 00	*19 51*	*20 51*	*21 46*	*22 51*	

Saturdays

Station		NT A	NT	NT E	NT	NT	EM ◇ D	NT E	NT	NT E	NT	NT E	NT	NT E	NT	NT E	NT	NT E
Buxton	d	05 59	06 27			07 27		07 56	08 27		09 27		10 30		11 27		12 30	
Dove Holes	d		06 33			07 33		08 02	08 33		09 33				11 33			
Chapel-en-le-Frith	d	06 08	06 38			07 38		08 07	08 38		09 38		10 39		11 38		12 39	
Whaley Bridge	d	06 14	06 44			07 44		08 13	08 44		09 44		10 45		11 44		12 45	
Furness Vale	d	06 17	06 47			07 47		08 16	08 47		09 47		10 48		11 47		12 48	
New Mills Newtown	d	06 20	06 50			07 50		08 19	08 50		09 50		10 51		11 50		12 51	
Disley	d	06 24	06 53			07 53		08 22	08 53		09 53		10 55		11 53		12 55	
Middlewood	d		06 57			07 57		08 26	08 57		09 57				11 57			
Hazel Grove	a	06 32	07 03			08 03		08 32	09 03		10 03		11 03		12 03		13 03	
	d	06 33	07 03	07 32	07 48	08 03	08 17	08 33	09 04	09 33	10 04	10 33	11 04	11 33	12 04	12 33	13 04	13 33
Woodsmoor	d	06 35	07 05	07 34	07 50	08 05		08 35	09 06	09 35	10 06	10 35	11 06	11 35	12 06	12 35	13 06	13 35
Davenport	d	06 37	07 07	07 36	07 53	08 07		08 37	09 08	09 37	10 08	10 37	11 08	11 37	12 08	12 37	13 08	13 37
Stockport	84 a	06 41	07 12	07 40	07 57	08 12	08 24	08 41	09 12	09 41	10 12	10 40	11 12	11 41	12 12	12 41	13 12	13 41
Heaton Chapel	84 a		07 16			08 16			09 16		10 16		11 16		12 16		13 16	
Levenshulme	84 a		07 19			08 19			09 19		10 19		11 19		12 19		13 19	
Manchester Piccadilly 10	84 a	06 52	07 28	07 52	08 09	08 28	08 36	08 52	09 28	09 52	10 28	10 52	11 28	11 52	12 28	12 52	13 28	13 52
Manchester Oxford Road	a	06 56	*07 52*	07 56	*08 24*	*08 48*	08 40	08 56	*09 48*	09 56	*10 48*	10 56	*11 48*	11 56	*12 48*	12 56	*13 48*	13 56
Deansgate	a	06 59	*08 00*	08 00	*08 28*	*08 51*	*08 51*	09 00	*09 51*	10 00	*10 51*	11 00	*11 51*	12 00	*12 51*	13 00	*13 51*	14 00

For general notes see front of timetable
For details of catering facilities see Directory of Train Operators

A To Clitheroe (Table 94)
B To Wigan North Western (Table 82)
C To Blackpool North (Table 82)
D From Nottingham to Liverpool Lime Street (Table 49)
E To Preston (Table 82)
G To Bolton (Table 82)
H To Barrow-in-Furness (Table 82)
b Change at Manchester Piccadilly and Manchester Oxford Road

From 5 October Northern will be operating a revised service due to seasonal difficulties. Trains will run up to 5 minutes earlier between Buxton and Hazel Grove. Customers should check times with NRES

From 10 October Northern will be operating a revised service due to seasonal difficulties. Trains will run up to 5 mins earlier between Buxton and Hazel Grove. Customers should check times with NRES

Table 86

Saturdays

Buxton and Hazel Grove → Manchester

Network Diagram - see first page of Table 78

Station		NT	NT A	NT	NT A	NT	NT A	NT	NT B	NT	NT C	NT	NT	NT	NT	NT
Buxton	d	13 27		14 30		15 27		16 30		17 27		18 27	19 27	20 27	21 27	22 56
Dove Holes	d	13 33				15 33				17 33		18 33	19 33	20 33	21 33	23 02
Chapel-en-le-Frith	d	13 38		14 39		15 38		16 39		17 38		18 38	19 38	20 38	21 38	23 07
Whaley Bridge	d	13 44		14 45		15 44		16 45		17 44		18 44	19 44	20 44	21 44	23 13
Furness Vale	d	13 47		14 48		15 47		16 48		17 47		18 47	19 47	20 47	21 47	23 16
New Mills Newtown	d	13 50		14 51		15 50		16 51		17 50		18 50	19 50	20 50	21 50	23 19
Disley	d	13 53		14 55		15 53		16 55		17 53		18 53	19 53	20 53	21 53	23 22
Middlewood	d	13 57				15 57				17 57		18 57	19 57	20 57	21 57	23 26
Hazel Grove	a	14 03		15 03		16 03		17 03		18 03		19 03	20 03	21 03	22 03	23 32
	d	14 04	14 33	15 04	15 33	16 04	16 33	17 04	17 33	18 04	18 33	19 04	20 04	21 04	22 04	23 33
Woodsmoor	d	14 06	14 35	15 06	15 35	16 06	16 35	17 06	17 35	18 06	18 35	19 06	20 06	21 06	22 06	23 35
Davenport	d	14 08	14 37	15 08	15 37	16 08	16 37	17 08	17 37	18 08	18 37	19 08	20 08	21 08	22 08	23 37
Stockport 84	a	14 12	14 41	15 12	15 41	16 12	16 41	17 12	17 41	18 12	18 41	19 12	20 12	21 12	22 12	23 40
Heaton Chapel 84	a	14 16		15 16		16 16		17 16		18 16		19 16	20 16	21 16	22 16	
Levenshulme 84	a	14 19		15 19		16 19		17 19		18 19		19 19	20 19	21 19	22 19	
Manchester Piccadilly 10 84 (ship symbol)	a	14 28	14 52	15 28	15 52	16 28	16 52	17 28	17 52	18 28	18 52	19 28	20 28	21 28	22 28	23 54
Manchester Oxford Road	a	*14 48*	14 56	*15 48*	15 56	*16 48*	16 56	*17 48*	17 56	*18 48*	18 56	*19 48*	*20 48*	*21 40*	22 48	
Deansgate (ship symbol)	a	*14 51*	15 00	*15 51*	16 00	*17 00*	17 00	*17 51*	18 00	*18 51*	19 00	*19 51*	*20 51*	*21 46*	22 51	

Sundays

Station		NT	NT D	NT E	NT D	NT E	NT E	NT D	NT	NT
Buxton	d	08 23	09 19	09 23	10 23	10 27	11 26	11 27	12 27	13 27
Dove Holes	d	08 29	09 25	09 29	10 29	10 33	11 32	11 33	12 33	13 33
Chapel-en-le-Frith	d	08 34	09 30	09 34	10 34	10 38	11 37	11 38	12 38	13 38
Whaley Bridge	d	08 40	09 36	09 40	10 40	10 44	11 43	11 44	12 44	13 44
Furness Vale	d	08 43	09 39	09 43	10 43	10 47	11 46	11 47	12 47	13 47
New Mills Newtown	d	08 46	09 42	09 46	10 46	10 50	11 49	11 50	12 50	13 50
Disley	d	08 49	09 45	09 49	10 49	10 53	11 52	11 53	12 53	13 53
Middlewood	d	08 53	09 49	09 53	10 53	10 57	11 56	11 57	12 57	13 57
Hazel Grove	a	08 59	09 55	09 59	10 58	11 02	12 02	12 03	13 03	14 03
	d	09 00	09 55	09 59	10 59	11 03	12 02	12 04	13 04	14 04
Woodsmoor	d	09 02	09 57	10 01	11 01	11 05	12 04	12 06	13 06	14 06
Davenport	d	09 04	09 59	10 03	11 03	11 07	12 06	12 08	13 08	14 08
Stockport 84	a	09 08	10 03	10 07	11 07	11 11	12 10	12 12	13 12	14 12
Heaton Chapel 84	a	09 12	10 08	10 12	11 11		12 15	12 16	13 16	14 16
Levenshulme 84	a	09 15	10 11	10 15	11 14		12 18	12 19	13 19	14 19
Manchester Piccadilly 10 84 (ship symbol)	a	09 23	10 20	10 23	11 23	11 23	12 25	12 29	13 27	14 27
Manchester Oxford Road	a	*09 37*	*10 46*	*10 37*	*11 37*	*11 48*	*12 41*	*12 48*	*13 41*	*14 41*
Deansgate (ship symbol)	a	*09 40*	*10 51*	*10 40*	*11 40*	*11 51*	*12 51*	*12 51*	*13 51*	*14 51*

Station		NT	NT	NT	NT	NT	NT	NT	NT	NT
Buxton	d	14 27	15 27	16 27	17 27	18 27	19 27	20 27	21 27	22 27
Dove Holes	d	14 33	15 33	16 33	17 33	18 33	19 33	20 33	21 33	22 33
Chapel-en-le-Frith	d	14 38	15 38	16 38	17 38	18 38	19 38	20 38	21 38	22 38
Whaley Bridge	d	14 44	15 44	16 44	17 44	18 44	19 44	20 44	21 44	22 44
Furness Vale	d	14 47	15 47	16 47	17 47	18 47	19 47	20 47	21 47	22 47
New Mills Newtown	d	14 50	15 50	16 50	17 50	18 50	19 50	20 50	21 50	22 50
Disley	d	14 53	15 53	16 53	17 53	18 53	19 53	20 53	21 53	22 53
Middlewood	d	14 57	15 57	16 57	17 57	18 57	19 57	20 57	21 57	22 57
Hazel Grove	a	15 03	16 03	17 03	18 03	19 03	20 03	21 03	22 03	23 03
	d	15 04	16 04	17 04	18 04	19 04	20 04	21 04	22 04	23 04
Woodsmoor	d	15 06	16 06	17 06	18 06	19 06	20 06	21 06	22 06	23 06
Davenport	d	15 08	16 08	17 08	18 08	19 08	20 08	21 08	22 08	23 08
Stockport 84	a	15 12	16 12	17 12	18 12	19 12	20 12	21 12	22 12	23 12
Heaton Chapel 84	a	15 16	16 16	17 16	18 16	19 16	20 16	21 16	22 16	23 16
Levenshulme 84	a	15 19	16 19	17 19	18 19	19 19	20 19	21 19	22 19	23 19
Manchester Piccadilly 10 84 (ship symbol)	a	15 27	16 27	17 27	18 27	19 27	20 27	21 27	22 27	23 27
Manchester Oxford Road	a	*15 41*	*16 41*	*17 41*	*18 41*	*19 41*	*20 48*	*21 48*	*22 48*	
Deansgate (ship symbol)	a	*15 51*	*16 51*	*17 51*	*18 51*	*19 51*	*20 51*	*21 51*	*22 51*	

For general notes see front of timetable
For details of catering facilities see Directory of Train Operators

A To Preston (Table 82)
B To Blackpool North (Table 82)
C To Bolton (Table 82)
D Until 6 September
E From 13 September

From 10 October Northern will be operating a revised service due to seasonal difficulties. Trains will run up to 5 mins earlier between Buxton and Hazel Grove. Customers should check times with NRES

Network Diagram for Tables 88, 89, 90, 91

DM-12/06(2)
Design BAJS

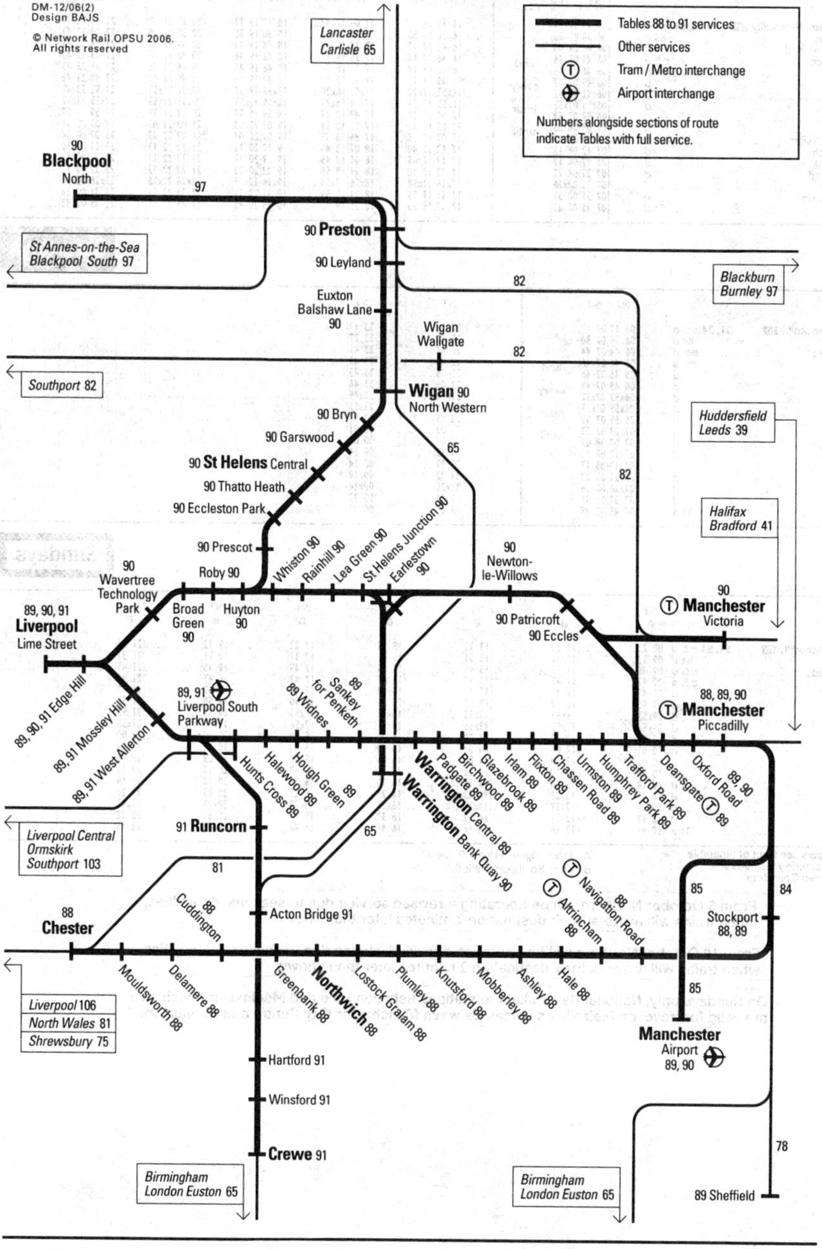
Tables 88 to 91 services
Other services
Tram / Metro interchange
Airport interchange
Numbers alongside sections of route indicate Tables with full service.
Lancaster Carlisle 65
90 Blackpool North
97
St Annes-on-the-Sea Blackpool South 97
90 Preston
90 Leyland
Euxton Balshaw Lane 90
Blackburn Burnley 97
82
Wigan Wallgate
82
Southport 82
Wigan 90 North Western
90 Bryn
90 Garswood
65
90 St Helens Central
90 Thatto Heath
90 Eccleston Park
82
Huddersfield Leeds 39
Halifax Bradford 41
90 Prescot
90 Wavertree Technology Park
Roby 90
Whiston 90
Rainhill 90
Lea Green 90
St Helens Junction 90
Earlestown 90
90 Newton-le-Willows
90 Manchester Victoria
89, 90, 91 Liverpool Lime Street
Broad Green 90
Huyton 90
90 Patricroft
90 Eccles
89, 91 Liverpool South Parkway
89 Sankey for Penketh
89 Widnes
88, 89, 90 Manchester Piccadilly
89, 90, 91 Edge Hill
89, 91 Mossley Hill
89, 91 West Allerton
Hunts Cross 89
Halewood 89
Hough Green 89
Warrington Central 89
Warrington Bank Quay 90
Padgate 89
Birchwood 89
Glazebrook 89
Irlam 89
Flixton 89
Chassen Road 89
Urmston 89
Humphrey Park 89
Trafford Park 89
Deansgate 89
Oxford Road 89, 90
91 Runcorn
65
Liverpool Central Ormskirk Southport 103
81
88 Cuddington
88 Navigation Road
88 Altrincham
85
84
88 Chester
Acton Bridge 91
Stockport 88, 89
85
Mouldsworth 88
Delamere 88
Greenbank 88
Northwich 88
Lostock Gralam 88
Plumley 88
Knutsford 88
Mobberley 88
Ashley 88
Hale 88
Manchester Airport 89, 90
Liverpool 106
North Wales 81
Shrewsbury 75
Hartford 91
Winsford 91
Crewe 91
78
Birmingham London Euston 65
Birmingham London Euston 65
89 Sheffield

Manchester → Northwich and Chester

Network Diagram - see first page of Table 88

Mondays to Fridays

Miles	Station		NT	NT		NT	NT	NT	NT	NT	NT	NT	NT	NT	NT
½	**Manchester Piccadilly** 10	81, 84 ⛴ d	06 17	07 17		16 17	*16 43*	17 09	*17 43*	18 17	19 17	20 17	21 17	22 17	23 17
6¼	**Stockport**	84 d	06 30	07 30		16 30	16 58	17 19	17 58	18 30	19 30	20 30	21 30	22 30	23 27
14¾	Navigation Road	⛴ d	06 44	07 44		16 44	17 12	17 33	18 12	18 44	19 44	20 44	21 44	22 44	23 41
15¼	**Altrincham**	⛴ a	06 46	07 46	and	16 46	17 14	17 35	18 14	18 46	19 46	20 46	21 46	22 46	23 43
—		d	06 46	07 46		16 46	17 14	17 35	18 14	18 46	19 46	20 46	21 46	22 46	23 43
16	Hale	d	06 49	07 49	every	16 49	17 17	17 38	18 17	18 49	19 49	20 49	21 49	22 49	23 46
17¾	Ashley	d	06x52	07x52		16x52	17x20	17x41	18x20	18x52	19x52	20x52	21x52	22x52	23x49
18½	Mobberley	d	06x55	07x55	hour	16x55	17x23	17x44	18x23	18x55	19x55	20x55	21x55	22x55	23x52
22¼	Knutsford	d	06 59	07 59		16 59	17 27	17 49	18 27	18 59	19 59	20 59	21 59	22 59	23 57
24¾	Plumley	d	07 03	08 03	until	17 03	17 31	17 53	18 31	19 03	20 03	21 03	22 03	23 03	00 01
26¾	Lostock Gralam	d	07 07	08 07		17 07	17 35	17 56	18 35	19 07	20 07	21 07	22 07	23 07	00 04
28¼	**Northwich**	d	07 12	08 12		17 12	17 40	18 02	18 40	19 12	20 12	21 12	22 12	23 12	00 10
30	Greenbank	d	07 17	08 17		17 17	17 45	18 06	18 45	19 17	20 17	21 17	22 17	23 17	00 14
32¾	Cuddington	d	07 22	08 22		17 22	17 50	18 11	18 50	19 22	20 22	21 22	22 22	23 22	00 19
35¾	Delamere	d	07x26	08x26		17x26	17x54	18x16	18x54	19x26	20x26	21x26	22x26	23x26	00x24
38¾	Mouldsworth	d	07 31	08 31		17 31	17 59	18 21	18 59	19 31	20 31	21 31	22 31	23 31	00 28
45¼	**Chester**	81 a	07 45	08 45		17 45	18 13	18 35	19 13	19 45	20 45	21 45	22 45	23 45	00 43

Saturdays

Station		NT	NT		NT	NT
Manchester Piccadilly 10	81, 84 ⛴ d	06 17	07 17		22 17	23 17
Stockport	84 d	06 30	07 30		22 30	23 27
Navigation Road	⛴ d	06 44	07 44		22 44	23 41
Altrincham	⛴ a	06 46	07 46	and	22 46	23 43
	d	06 46	07 46		22 46	23 43
Hale	d	06 49	07 49	every	22 49	23 46
Ashley	d	06x52	07x52		22x52	23x49
Mobberley	d	06x55	07x55	hour	22x55	23x52
Knutsford	d	06 59	07 59		22 59	23 57
Plumley	d	07 03	08 03	until	23 03	00 01
Lostock Gralam	d	07 07	08 07		23 07	00 04
Northwich	d	07 12	08 12		23 12	00 10
Greenbank	d	07 17	08 17		23 17	00 14
Cuddington	d	07 22	08 22		23 22	00 19
Delamere	d	07x26	08x26		23x26	00x24
Mouldsworth	d	07 31	08 31		23 31	00 28
Chester	81 a	07 45	08 45		23 45	00 43

Sundays

Station		NT A	NT B	NT B	NT B	NT B	NT B	NT B
Manchester Piccadilly 10	81, 84 ⛴ d	09 23	11 22	13 22	15 22	17 22	19 22	21 22
Stockport	84 d	09 32	11 31	13 31	15 31	17 31	19 31	21 31
Navigation Road	⛴ d	09 45	11 45	13 45	15 45	17 45	19 45	21 45
Altrincham	⛴ a	09 47	11 47	13 47	15 47	17 47	19 47	21 47
	d	09 48	11 47	13 47	15 47	17 47	19 47	21 47
Hale	d	09 50	11 50	13 50	15 50	17 50	19 50	21 50
Ashley	d	09x53	11x53	13x53	15x53	17x53	19x53	21x53
Mobberley	d	09x56	11x56	13x56	15x56	17x56	19x56	21x56
Knutsford	d	10 01	12 00	14 00	16 00	18 00	20 00	22 00
Plumley	d	10 05	12 04	14 04	16 04	18 04	20 04	22 04
Lostock Gralam	d	10 08	12 08	14 08	16 08	18 08	20 08	22 08
Northwich	d	10 14	12 13	14 13	16 13	18 13	20 13	22 13
Greenbank	d	10 18	12 18	14 18	16 18	18 18	20 18	22 18
Cuddington	d	10 23	12 23	14 23	16 23	18 23	20 23	22 23
Delamere	d	10x28	12x27	14x27	16x27	18x27	20x27	22x27
Mouldsworth	d	10 32	12 32	14 32	16 32	18 32	20 32	22 32
Chester	81 a	10 47	12 46	14 46	16 46	18 46	20 46	22 46

For general notes see front of timetable
For details of catering facilities see Directory of Train Operators

A From Wigan Wallgate (Table 82)
B From Southport (Table 82)

From 5 October Northern will be operating a revised service due to seasonal difficulties, when trains will arrive at their destination 2 minutes later than shown

From 10 October Northern will be operating a revised service due to seasonal difficulties, when trains will arrive at their destination 2 minutes later than shown

On Sundays only, National Rail Tickets to stations between Hale and Mouldsworth inclusive are valid for travel on Metrolink services between Manchester City Centre and Altrincham.

Chester and Northwich → Manchester

Network Diagram - see first page of Table 88

Miles			NT	NT	NT	NT	NT	NT		NT	NT	NT	NT	NT	NT
0	**Chester**	81 d	06 05	06 35	07 03	07 35	08 07	09 07		17 07	18 07	19 07	20 07	21 07	22 48
6½	Mouldsworth	d	06 16	06 46	07 14	07 46	08 18	09 18		17 18	18 18	19 18	20 18	21 18	22 59
9½	Delamere	d	06x21	06x51	07x19	07x51	08x23	09x23		17x23	18x23	19x23	20x23	21x23	23x04
12½	Cuddington	d	06 25	06 55	07 23	07 55	08 27	09 27	and	17 27	18 27	19 27	20 27	21 27	23 08
15¼	Greenbank	d	06 30	07 00	07 28	08 00	08 32	09 32		17 32	18 32	19 32	20 32	21 32	23 13
17	**Northwich**	d	06 35	07 05	07 33	08 05	08 37	09 37	every	17 37	18 37	19 37	20 37	21 37	23 17
18½	Lostock Gralam	d	06 38	07 08	07 36	08 08	08 40	09 40		17 40	18 40	19 40	20 40	21 40	23 20
20½	Plumley	d	06 41	07 11	07 40	08 11	08 43	09 43	hour	17 43	18 43	19 43	20 43	21 43	23 24
23	Knutsford	d	06 46	07 17	07 45	08 17	08 49	09 49		17 49	18 49	19 49	20 49	21 49	23 29
26¾	Mobberley	d	06x50	07x21	07x49	08x21	08x53	09x53	until	17x53	18x53	19x53	20x53	21x53	23x33
27½	Ashley	d	06x54	07x24	07x53	08x24	08x56	09x56		17x56	18x56	19x56	20x56	21x56	23x36
29¼	Hale	d	06 57	07 28	07 57	08 28	08 59	09 59		17 59	18 59	19 59	20 59	21 59	23 39
30	**Altrincham**	🚊 a	07 01	07 32	08 01	08 32	09 04	10 04		18 04	19 04	20 04	21 04	22 04	23 44
—		d	07 02	07 33	08 02	08 33	09 04	10 04		18 04	19 04	20 04	21 04	22 04	23 44
30½	Navigation Road	🚊 d	07 04	07 35	08 04	08 35	09 06	10 06		18 06	19 06	20 06	21 06	22 06	23 46
38¾	**Stockport**	84 a	07 18	07 56	08 19	08 56	09 21	10 21		18 21	19 21	20 21	21 21	22 21	00b02
44¾	**Manchester Piccadilly** 10	81, 84 🚊 a	07 31	*08 21*	08 32	*09 20*	09 36	10 36		18 36	19 35	20 35	21 35	22 35	00 18

Saturdays

		NT	NT	NT	NT		NT	NT	NT	NT	NT	NT
Chester	81 d	06 05	07 03	08 07	09 07		17 07	18 07	19 07	20 07	21 33	22 49
Mouldsworth	d	06 16	07 14	08 18	09 18		17 18	18 18	19 18	20 18	21 45	23 00
Delamere	d	06x21	07x19	08x23	09x23		17x23	18x23	19x23	20x23	21x49	23x05
Cuddington	d	06 25	07 23	08 27	09 27		17 27	18 27	19 27	20 27	21 54	23 09
Greenbank	d	06 30	07 28	08 32	09 32	and	17 32	18 32	19 32	20 32	21 58	23 14
Northwich	d	06 35	07 33	08 37	09 37		17 37	18 37	19 37	20 37	22 03	23 18
Lostock Gralam	d	06 38	07 36	08 40	09 40	every	17 40	18 40	19 40	20 40	22 06	23 21
Plumley	d	06 41	07 40	08 43	09 43		17 43	18 43	19 43	20 43	22 10	23 25
Knutsford	d	06 46	07 45	08 49	09 49	hour	17 49	18 49	19 49	20 49	22 15	23 30
Mobberley	d	06x50	07x49	08x53	09x53		17x53	18x53	19x53	20x53	22x19	23x34
Ashley	d	06x54	07x53	08x56	09x56	until	17x56	18x56	19x56	20x56	22x23	23x37
Hale	d	06 57	07 57	08 59	09 59		17 59	18 59	19 59	20 59	22 26	23 40
Altrincham	🚊 a	07 01	08 01	09 04	10 04		18 04	19 04	20 04	21 04	22 30	23 45
	d	07 02	08 02	09 04	10 04		18 04	19 04	20 04	21 04	22 31	23 45
Navigation Road	🚊 d	07 04	08 04	09 06	10 06		18 06	19 06	20 06	21 06	22 33	23 47
Stockport	84 a	07 18	08 19	09 21	10 21		18 21	19 21	20 21	21 21	22 47	00 02
Manchester Piccadilly 10	81, 84 🚊 a	07 31	08 32	09 36	10 36		18 36	19 35	20 35	21 35	23 00	00 15

Sundays

		NT A	NT B	NT B	NT A	NT C	NT C	NT C	NT C	NT D
Chester	81 d	08§59	09§06	11§03	11§08	13 08	15 08	17 08	19 08	21 08
Mouldsworth	d	09§09	09§16	11§13	11§18	13 18	15 18	17 18	19 18	21 18
Delamere	d	09x14	09x21	11x18	11x23	13x23	15x23	17x23	19x23	21x23
Cuddington	d	09§18	09§25	11§22	11§27	13 27	15 27	17 27	19 27	21 27
Greenbank	d	09§23	09§30	11§27	11§32	13 32	15 32	17 32	19 32	21 32
Northwich	d	09§28	09§35	11§32	11§37	13 37	15 37	17 37	19 37	21 37
Lostock Gralam	d	09§31	09§38	11§35	11§40	13 40	15 40	17 40	19 40	21 40
Plumley	d	09§34	09§41	11§38	11§43	13 43	15 43	17 43	19 43	21 43
Knutsford	d	09§40	09§47	11§44	11§49	13 49	15 49	17 49	19 49	21 49
Mobberley	d	09x44	09x51	11x48	11x53	13x53	15x53	17x53	19x53	21x53
Ashley	d	09x47	09x54	11x51	11x56	13x56	15x56	17x56	19x56	21x56
Hale	d	09§50	09§57	11§54	11§59	13 59	15 59	17 59	19 59	21 59
Altrincham	🚊 a	09§55	10§02	11§59	12§04	14 04	16 04	18 04	20 04	22 04
	d	09§55	10§02	11§59	12§04	14 04	16 04	18 04	20 04	22 04
Navigation Road	🚊 d	09§57	10§04	12§01	12§06	14 06	16 06	18 06	20 06	22 06
Stockport	84 a	10§12	10§19	12§16	12§21	14 21	16 21	18 21	20 21	22 21
Manchester Piccadilly 10	81, 84 🚊 a	10§23	10§33	12§28	12§33	14 33	16 33	18 33	20 33	22 33

For general notes see front of timetable
For details of catering facilities see Directory of Train Operators

A Until 6 September. To Southport (Table 82)
B From 13 September. To Southport (Table 82)
C To Southport (Table 82)
D To Wigan Wallgate (Table 82)
b Saturday mornings arr. 0005

From 5 October Northern will be operating a revised service due to seasonal difficulties. Customers should check with NRES for precise times

From 10 October Northern will be operating a revised service due to seasonal difficulties. Customers should check with NRES for precise times

On Sundays only, National Rail Tickets from stations between Mouldsworth and Hale inclusive are valid for travel on Metrolink services between Altrincham and Manchester City Centre.

Liverpool → Warrington Central → Manchester and Manchester Airport

Network Diagram - see first page of Table 88

Miles	Station		NT	NT	NT	NT	NT	TP 1◇ A		NT	EM ◇ B	NT	NT	NT	NT		TP 1◇ A	NT	EM ◇ B	NT	NT	NT	TP 1◇ A
0	**Liverpool Lime Street 10**	90, 91 d	03 38	05 13		05 49	06 13	06 16		06 21	06 47		06 50	07 13			07 16	07 26	07 42	07 51	08 13		08 22
1¾	Edge Hill	90, 91 d				05 53							06 54					07 30					
3¾	Mossley Hill	91 d				05 58				06 29			06 59					07 35		07 59			
4½	West Allerton	91 d				06 00				06 31			07 01					07 37		08 01			
—	Liverpool Central 10	103 d											06b43						07b29	07b44			
5½	**Liverpool South Parkway 7**	91, 103 d				06 03				06 34	06 57		07 04					07 40	07 52	08 04			
7¼	Hunts Cross	103 d				06 07							07 08						07 59	08 08			
8¼	Halewood	d				06 09							07 10							08 10			
10½	Hough Green	d				06 13				06 41			07 14					07 47		08 14			
12¼	Widnes	d				06 17				06 44	07 07		07 18				07 33		08 05	08 18			
16	Sankey for Penketh	d				06 22							07 23							08 23			
18½	**Warrington Central**	a				06 28		06 37		06 52	07 15		07 29				07 39	07 56	08 13	08 28		←	08 43
—		d			06 02			06 38		06 53	07 15	07 22					07 40	07 57	08 13	08 28 →		08 28	08 44
20¼	Padgate	d			06 05					06 56		07 25						08 00					
21¾	Birchwood	d			06 08			06 43		06 59	07 20	07 28					07 45	08 03	08 18			08 33	08 49
24½	Glazebrook	d			06 13					07 04		07 33						08 08					
25¾	Irlam	d			06 16					07 07		07 36					07 50	08 11				08 39	
28	Flixton	d			06 20					07 11		07 40						08 15				08 43	
28½	Chassen Road	d			06 22					07 13		07 42						08 17				08 45	
29	Urmston	d			06 24					07 15		07 44						08 19				08 47	
30¼	Humphrey Park	d			06 26					07 17		07 46						08 21				08 49	
31	Trafford Park	d			06 29					07 20		07 49			←			08 24				08 52	
34	Deansgate	84, 85 a			06 36					07 29		07 58 →			07 58			08 31				08 59	
34½	**Manchester Oxford Road**	84, 85 a			06 41		06 57	07 00		07 36	07 38			07 57	08 03		08 04	08 36	08 38		08 57	09 04	09 05
35	**Manchester Piccadilly 10**	78, 84, 85 a	04 14	05 57	06 56		07 01	07 09		07 56	07 41			08 01	08 18		08 08	08 50	08 41		09 01	09 18	09 09
—	Stockport	84 a	05 12	06 17	07 34		07 22	07 28			07 53			08 22	08 34		08 28		08 53		09 22	09 34	09 28
—	Sheffield 7	78 a	06 49					08 10			08 34						09 08		09 35				10 08
44¾	**Manchester Airport**	85 a	04 30	06 14	07 17		07 22	07 42		08 17	08c12			08 22	08 47		08 42	09 19	09c12		09 22	09 47	09 42

Station		NT		EM ◇ B	NT	NT	NT	TP 1◇ A	NT		EM ◇ B	NT	NT	NT	TP 1◇ A	NT		EM ◇ B	NT	NT	NT	TP 1◇ A	NT
Liverpool Lime Street 10	90, 91 d	08 26		08 52	08 55	09 13		09 22	09 27		09 52	09 55	10 13		10 22	10 27		10 52	10 55	11 13		11 22	11 27
Edge Hill	90, 91 d	08 30			08 59							09 59							10 59				
Mossley Hill	91 d	08 35			09 04				09 35			10 04				10 35			11 04				11 35
West Allerton	91 d	08 37			09 06				09 37			10 06				10 37			11 06				11 37
Liverpool Central 10	103 d				08b44							09b44							10b44				
Liverpool South Parkway 7	91, 103 d	08 40		09 03	09 09				09 40		10 03	10 09				10 40		11 03	11 09				11 40
Hunts Cross	103 d				09 13							10 13							11 13				
Halewood	d				09 16							10 16							11 16				
Hough Green	d	08 47			09 20		←		09 47			10 20		←		10 47			11 20		←		11 47
Widnes	d	08 50		09 11	09 23 →		09 23		09 50		10 11	10 23 →		10 23		10 50		11 11	11 23 →		11 23		11 50
Sankey for Penketh	d						09 28							10 28							11 28		
Warrington Central	a	08 58		09 18			09 33	09 43	09 58		10 18			10 33	10 43	10 58		11 18			11 33	11 43	11 58
	d	08 59		09 19			09 34	09 44	09 59		10 19			10 34	10 44	10 59		11 19			11 34	11 44	11 59
Padgate	d	09 02							10 02							11 02							12 02
Birchwood	d	09 05					09 38	09 49	10 05					10 38	10 49	11 05					11 38	11 49	12 05
Glazebrook	d								10 10														12 10
Irlam	d	09 11					09 44		10 13					10 44		11 11					11 44		12 13
Flixton	d	09 15							10 17							11 15							12 17
Chassen Road	d								10 19														12 19
Urmston	d	09 18					09 49		10 21					10 49		11 18					11 49		12 21
Humphrey Park	d	09 20														11 20							
Trafford Park	d	09 23														11 23							
Deansgate	84, 85 a	09 31					09 59		10 31					10 59		11 31					11 59		12 31
Manchester Oxford Road	84, 85 a	09 36		09 39		09 57	10 04	10 05	10 36		10 39		10 57	11 04	11 05	11 36		11 39		11 57	12 04	12 05	12 36
Manchester Piccadilly 10	78, 84, 85 a	09 56		09 41		10 01	10 18	10 09	10 56		10 41		11 01	11 18	11 09	11 56		11 41		12 01	12 18	12 09	12 56
Stockport	84 a			09 53		10 22	10 34	10 28			10 53		11 22	11 34	11 28			11 53		12 22	12 34	12 28	
Sheffield 7	78 a			10 35				11 08			11 35				12 08			12 35				13 08	
Manchester Airport	85 a	10 17		10c12		10 22	10 47	10 42	11 17		11c12		11 22	11 47	11 42	12 17		12c12		12 22	12 47	12 42	13 17

Station		EM ◇ B	NT		NT	NT	TP 1◇ A	NT	EM ◇ B	NT		NT	NT	TP 1◇ A	NT	EM ◇ C	NT		NT	NT	TP 1◇ A	NT	EM ◇ B
Liverpool Lime Street 10	90, 91 d	11 52	11 55		12 13		12 22	12 27	12 52	12 55		13 13		13 22	13 27	13 52	13 55		14 13		14 22	14 27	14 52
Edge Hill	90, 91 d		11 59							12 59							13 59						
Mossley Hill	91 d		12 04					12 35		13 04					13 35		14 04					14 35	
West Allerton	91 d		12 06					12 37		13 06					13 37		14 06					14 37	
Liverpool Central 10	103 d		11b44							12b44							13b44						
Liverpool South Parkway 7	91, 103 d	12 03	12 09					12 40	13 03	13 09					13 40	14 03	14 09					14 40	15 03
Hunts Cross	103 d		12 13							13 13							14 13						
Halewood	d		12 16							13 16							14 16						
Hough Green	d		12 20			←		12 47		13 20			←		13 47		14 20			←		14 47	
Widnes	d	12 11	12 23 →			12 23		12 50	13 11	13 23 →			13 23		13 50	14 11	14 23 →			14 23		14 50	15 11
Sankey for Penketh	d					12 28							13 28							14 28			
Warrington Central	a	12 18				12 33	12 43	12 58	13 18				13 33	13 43	13 58	14 18				14 33	14 43	14 58	15 18
	d	12 19				12 34	12 44	12 59	13 19				13 34	13 44	13 59	14 19				14 34	14 44	14 59	15 19
Padgate	d							13 02							14 02							15 02	
Birchwood	d					12 38	12 49	13 05					13 38	13 49	14 05					14 38	14 49	15 05	
Glazebrook	d														14 10								
Irlam	d					12 44		13 11					13 44		14 13					14 44		15 11	
Flixton	d							13 15							14 17							15 15	
Chassen Road	d														14 19								
Urmston	d					12 49		13 18					13 49		14 21					14 49		15 18	
Humphrey Park	d							13 20														15 20	
Trafford Park	d							13 23														15 23	
Deansgate	84, 85 a					12 59		13 31					13 59		14 31					14 59		15 31	
Manchester Oxford Road	84, 85 a	12 39			12 57	13 04	13 05	13 36	13 39			13 57	14 04	14 05	14 36	14 39			14 57	15 04	15 05	15 36	15 39
Manchester Piccadilly 10	78, 84, 85 a	12 41			13 01	13 18	13 09	13 56	13 41			14 01	14 18	14 09	14 56	14 41			15 01	15 18	15 09	15 56	15 41
Stockport	84 a	12 53			13 22	13 34	13 28		13 53			14 22	14 34	14 28		14 53			15 22	15 34	15 28		15 53
Sheffield 7	78 a	13 35					14 08		14 35					15 08		15 34					16 08		16 35
Manchester Airport	85 a	13c12			13 22	13 47	13 42	14 17	14c12			14 22	14 47	14 42	15 17	15c12			15 22	15 47	15 42	16 17	16c12

For general notes see front of timetable
For details of catering facilities see Directory of Train Operators

A To Scarborough (Table 39)
B To Norwich (Table 49)
C To Nottingham (Table 49)

b Change at Hunts Cross
c Change at Manchester Piccadilly

Liverpool → Warrington Central → Manchester and Manchester Airport

Network Diagram - see first page of Table 88

		NT	NT	NT		TP 1 ◇ A	NT	EM ◇ B	NT	NT	NT		TP 1 ◇ C	NT	EM ◇ D	NT	NT	NT		TP 1 ◇ C	NT	EM ◇ B	NT
Liverpool Lime Street 10	90, 91 d	14 55	15 13			15 22	15 27	15 52	15 55	16 13			16 22	16 27	16 52	16 55	17 06			17 22	17 25	17 52	17 55
Edge Hill	90, 91 d	14 59							15 59							16 59					17 29		17 59
Mossley Hill	91 d	15 04					15 35		16 04					16 35		17 04					17 34		18 04
West Allerton	91 d	15 06					15 37		16 06					16 37		17 06					17 36		18 06
Liverpool Central 10	103 d	14b44							15b44							16b44					17b14		17b44
Liverpool South Parkway 7	91, 103 ✈ d	15 09					15 40	16 03	16 09					16 40	17 03	17 09					17 39	18 03	18 09
Hunts Cross	103 d	15 13							16 13							17 13					17 43		18 13
Halewood	d	15 16							16 16							17 16					17 46		18 16
Hough Green	d	15 20		←			15 47		16 20		←			16 47		17 20		←			17 50		18 20
Widnes	d	15 23		15 23			15 50	16 11	16 23		16 23			16 50	17 11	17 23		17 23			17 53	18 11	18 23
Sankey for Penketh	d	→		15 28					→		16 28					→		17 28			17 58		→
Warrington Central	a			15 33		15 43	15 58	16 18			16 33		16 43	16 58	17 18			17 33		17 43	18 03	18 18	
	d			15 34		15 44	15 59	16 19			16 34		16 44	16 59	17 19			17 34		17 44	18 04	18 19	
Padgate	d						16 02							17 02							18 07		
Birchwood	d			15 38		15 49	16 05				16 38		16 49	17 05				17 38		17 49	18 10		
Glazebrook	d						16 10																
Irlam	d			15 44			16 13				16 44			17 11				17 44			18 16		
Flixton	d						16 17							17 15									
Chassen Road	d						16 19														18 20		
Urmston	d			15 49			16 21				16 49			17 18				17 49			18 22		
Humphrey Park	d													17 20									
Trafford Park	d													17 23									
Deansgate	84, 85 ⛴ a			15 59			16 30				16 59			17 31				17 59			18 32		
Manchester Oxford Road	84, 85 a		15 57	16 04		16 05	16 36	16 38		16 57	17 04		17 05	17 36	17 38		17 57	18 03		18 05	18 36	18 39	
Manchester Piccadilly 10	78, 84, 85 ⛴ a		16 01	16 18		16 09	16 56	16 41		17 01	17 15		17 09	17 56	17 41		18 01	18 18		18 09	18 56	18 41	
Stockport	84 a		16 22	16 34		16 28		16 53		17 22			17c27		17 53		18 22	18 34		18 28		18 53	
Sheffield 7	78 ⛴ a					17 08		17 37					18 15		18 41					19 10		19 33	
Manchester Airport	85 ✈ a		16 22	16 47		16 42	17 17	17e12		17 22			17 48	18 17	18e12		18 22	18 47		18 42	19 17	19e13	

		NT	NT	TP 1 ◇ C	NT		EM ◇ D	NT	TP 1 ◇ E	NT	EM ◇ G	NT		NT	TP 1 ◇ H	NT	EM ◇ D	NT	TP 1 ◇ E		NT		
Liverpool Lime Street 10	90, 91 d	18 13		18 22	18 25		18 52	18 55	19 22		19 52	19 55		20 09	20 22	20 55	21 37	21 55	22 30		23 38		
Edge Hill	90, 91 d				18 29			18 59				19 59				20 59		21 59			23 42		
Mossley Hill	91 d				18 34			19 04				20 04				21 04		22 04			23 47		
West Allerton	91 d				18 36			19 06				20 06				21 06		22 06			23 50		
Liverpool Central 10	103 d				18b14			18b44				19b44				20b44		21b44			23b29		
Liverpool South Parkway 7	91, 103 ✈ d				18 39		19 03	19 09			20 03	20 09				21 09	21 47	22 09			23 53		
Hunts Cross	103 d				18 43			19 13				20 13				21 13		22 13			23 56		
Halewood	d				18 46			19 16				20 16				21 16		22 16			23 59		
Hough Green	d		←		18 50			19 20				20 20				21 20		22 20			00 03		
Widnes	d		18 23		18 53		19 11	19 23			20 11	20 23				21 23	21 55	22 23			00 06		
Sankey for Penketh	d		18 28		18 58			19 28				20 28				21 28		22 28			00 11		
Warrington Central	a		18 33	18 43	19 03		19 18	19 34	19 43		20 18	20 34			20 43	21 33	22 03	22 33	22 52		00 16		
	d		18 34	18 44	19 03		19 19		19 44	19 56	20 19				20 44	21 34	22 03	22 34	22 52		00 17		
Padgate	d				19 06					19 59						21 37		22 37					
Birchwood	d		18 38	18 49	19 09				19 49	20 02					20 49	21 40		22 40	22 57				
Glazebrook	d				19 14					20 07						21 45		22 45					
Irlam	d		18 44		19 17					20 10						21 48		22 48					
Flixton	d									20 14						21 52		22 52					
Chassen Road	d									20 16						21 54		22 54					
Urmston	d		18 49		19 22					20 18						21 56		22 56					
Humphrey Park	d									20 20						21 58		22 58					
Trafford Park	d									20 23						22 01		23 01					
Deansgate	84, 85 ⛴ a		18 59		19 32					20 31						22 08		23 08					
Manchester Oxford Road	84, 85 a	18 57	19 04	19 05	19 36		19 39		20 05	20 36	20 39			20 57	21 05	22 13	22 23	23 13	23 14				
Manchester Piccadilly 10	78, 84, 85 ⛴ a	19 01	19 27	19 09	19 45		19 41		20 09	20 45	20 41			21 01	21 09		22 26	23 37	23 19		00 40		
Stockport	84 a	19 22		19 34			19 53		20 28		20 53			21 22	21 28		22 37		23 50				
Sheffield 7	78 ⛴ a	20 08					20 36		21 08		21 35				22 08		23 35		01 08				
Manchester Airport	85 ✈ a	19 24		19 47	20 07		20e17		20 53	21 07	21e17			21 24	21 47	22 47	22e57	00f22	00 22		01 10		

For general notes see front of timetable
For details of catering facilities see Directory of Train Operators

A To Middlesbrough (Table 39)
B To Norwich (Table 49)
C To Scarborough (Table 39)
D To Nottingham (Table 49)
E To York (Table 39)
G To Nottingham (Table 34)
H To Hull (Table 39)

b Change at Hunts Cross
c Change at Manchester Oxford Road
e Change at Manchester Piccadilly
f Change at Manchester Oxford Road and Manchester Piccadilly

Table 89

Saturdays

Liverpool → Warrington Central → Manchester and Manchester Airport

Network Diagram - see first page of Table 88

Station		NT	NT	NT	NT	TP 1 ◇ A		NT	EM ◇ B	NT	NT	TP 1 ◇ A		NT	EM ◇ B	NT	NT	NT		TP 1 ◇ A	NT	EM ◇ B	NT
Liverpool Lime Street 10	90, 91 d	03 38	05 13	05 49	06 13	06 16		06 26	06 49	06 55	07 13	07 16		07 26	07 42	07 51	08 13			08 22	08 26	08 52	08 55
Edge Hill	90, 91 d			05 53						06 59				07 30							08 30		08 59
Mossley Hill	91 d			05 58				06 34		07 04				07 35		07 59					08 35		09 04
West Allerton	91 d			06 00				06 36		07 06				07 37		08 01					08 37		09 06
Liverpool Central 10	103 d									06b43					07b29	07b44							08b44
Liverpool South Parkway 7	91, 103 ✈ d			06 03				06 39	06 59	07 09				07 40	07 52	08 04					08 40	09 03	09 09
Hunts Cross	103 d			06 07						07 13					07 59	08 08							09 13
Halewood	d			06 09						07 16						08 10							09 16
Hough Green	d			06 13				06 46		07 20				07 47		08 14					08 47		09 20
Widnes	d			06 17				06 49	07 07	07 23		07 33			08 05	08 18					08 50	09 11	09 23 →
Sankey for Penketh	d			06 22						07 28						08 23							
Warrington Central	a			06 28		06 37		06 57	07 15	07 34		07 39		07 56	08 13	08 28		←		08 43	08 58	09 18	
	d					06 38		06 58	07 15			07 40		07 57	08 13	08 28 →		08 28		08 44	08 59	09 19	
Padgate	d							07 01						08 00							09 02		
Birchwood	d					06 43		07 04	07 20			07 45		08 03	08 18			08 33		08 49	09 05		
Glazebrook	d							07 09						08 08									
Irlam	d							07 12				07 50		08 11				08 39			09 11		
Flixton	d							07 16						08 15				08 43			09 15		
Chassen Road	d							07 18						08 17				08 45					
Urmston	d							07 20						08 19				08 47			09 18		
Humphrey Park	d							07 22						08 21				08 49			09 20		
Trafford Park	d							07 25						08 24				08 52			09 23		
Deansgate	84, 85 ⛴ a							07 32						08 31				08 59			09 31		
Manchester Oxford Road	84, 85 a				06 57	07 00		07 37	07 38		07 57	08 04		08 36	08 38		08 57	09 04		09 05	09 36	09 39	
Manchester Piccadilly 10	78, 84, 85 ⛴ a	04 14	05 57		07 01	07 09		07 56	07 41		08 01	08 08		08 50	08 41		09 01	09 18		09 09	09 56	09 41	
Stockport	84 a	05 33	06 17		07 22	07 28			07 53		08 22	08 28			08 53		09 22	09 34		09 28		09 53	
Sheffield 7	78 ⛴ a	06 49	07 57			08 10			08 34			09 08			09 35					10 08		10 35	
Manchester Airport	85 ✈ a	04 30	06 14		07 22	07 42		08 17	08c12		08 22	08 42		09 19	09c12		09 22	09 47		09 42	10 17	10c12	

Station		NT	NT	TP 1 ◇ A		NT	EM ◇ B	NT	NT	NT		TP 1 ◇ A	NT	EM ◇ B	NT	NT		NT	TP 1 ◇ A	NT	EM ◇ B	NT	NT
Liverpool Lime Street 10	90, 91 d	09 13		09 22		09 26	09 52	09 55	10 13			10 22	10 27	10 52	10 55	11 13			11 22	11 27	11 52	11 55	12 13
Edge Hill	90, 91 d							09 59							10 59							11 59	
Mossley Hill	91 d					09 35		10 04					10 35		11 04					11 35		12 04	
West Allerton	91 d					09 37		10 06					10 37		11 06					11 37		12 06	
Liverpool Central 10	103 d							09b44							10b44							11b44	
Liverpool South Parkway 7	91, 103 ✈ d					09 40	10 03	10 09					10 40	11 03	11 09					11 40	12 03	12 09	
Hunts Cross	103 d							10 13							11 13							12 13	
Halewood	d							10 16							11 16							12 16	
Hough Green	d		←			09 47		10 20		←			10 47		11 20			←		11 47		12 20	
Widnes	d		09 23			09 50	10 11	10 23 →		10 23			10 50	11 11	11 23 →			11 23		11 50	12 11	12 23 →	
Sankey for Penketh	d		09 28							10 28								11 28					
Warrington Central	a		09 33	09 43		09 58	10 18			10 33		10 43	10 58	11 18				11 33	11 43	11 58	12 18		
	d		09 34	09 44		09 59	10 19			10 34		10 44	10 59	11 19				11 34	11 44	11 59	12 19		
Padgate	d					10 02							11 02							12 02			
Birchwood	d		09 38	09 49		10 05				10 38		10 49	11 05					11 38	11 49	12 05			
Glazebrook	d					10 10														12 10			
Irlam	d		09 44			10 13				10 44			11 11					11 44		12 13			
Flixton	d					10 17							11 15							12 17			
Chassen Road	d					10 19														12 19			
Urmston	d		09 49			10 21				10 49			11 18					11 49		12 21			
Humphrey Park	d												11 20										
Trafford Park	d												11 23										
Deansgate	84, 85 ⛴ a		09 59			10 31				10 59			11 31					11 59		12 31			
Manchester Oxford Road	84, 85 a	09 57	10 04	10 05		10 36	10 39		10 57	11 04		11 05	11 36	11 39		11 57		12 04	12 05	12 36	12 39		12 57
Manchester Piccadilly 10	78, 84, 85 ⛴ a	10 01	10 18	10 09		10 56	10 41		11 01	11 18		11 09	11 56	11 41		12 01		12 18	12 09	12 56	12 41		13 01
Stockport	84 a	10 22	10 34	10 28			10 53		11 22	11 34		11 28		11 53		12 22		12 34	12 28		12 53		13 22
Sheffield 7	78 ⛴ a			11 08			11 35					12 08		12 35					13 08		13 35		
Manchester Airport	85 ✈ a	10 22	10 47	10 42		11 17	11c12		11 22	11 47		11 42	12 17	12c12		12 22		12 47	12 42	13 17	13c12		13 22

For general notes see front of timetable
For details of catering facilities see Directory of Train Operators

A To Scarborough (Table 39)
B To Norwich (Table 49)
b Change at Hunts Cross
c Change at Manchester Piccadilly

Table 89

Liverpool → Warrington Central → Manchester and Manchester Airport

Network Diagram - see first page of Table 88

		NT		TP 1 ◇ A	NT	EM ◇ B	NT	NT		NT	TP 1 ◇ A	NT	EM ◇ C	NT		NT	NT	TP 1 ◇ A	NT	EM ◇ B		NT	NT
Liverpool Lime Street 10	90, 91 d			12 22	12 27	12 52	12 55	13 13			13 22	13 27	13 52	13 55		14 13		14 22	14 27	14 52		14 55	15 13
Edge Hill	90, 91 d						12 59							13 59								14 59	
Mossley Hill	91 d				12 35		13 04					13 35		14 04					14 35			15 04	
West Allerton	91 d				12 37		13 06					13 37		14 06					14 37			15 06	
Liverpool Central 10	103 d						12b44							13b44								14b44	
Liverpool South Parkway 7	91, 103 d				12 40	13 03	13 09					13 40	14 03	14 09					14 40	15 03		15 09	
Hunts Cross	103 d						13 13							14 13								15 13	
Halewood	d						13 16							14 16								15 16	
Hough Green	d	←			12 47		13 20			←		13 47		14 20			←		14 47			15 20	
Widnes	d	12 23			12 50	13 11	13 23 →			13 23		13 50	14 11	14 23 →			14 23		14 50	15 11		15 23 →	
Sankey for Penketh	d	12 28								13 28							14 28						
Warrington Central	a	12 33		12 43	12 58	13 18				13 33	13 43	13 58	14 18				14 33	14 43	14 58	15 18			
	d	12 34		12 44	12 59	13 19				13 34	13 44	13 59	14 19				14 34	14 44	14 59	15 19			
Padgate	d				13 02							14 02							15 02				
Birchwood	d	12 38		12 49	13 05					13 38	13 49	14 05					14 38	14 49	15 05				
Glazebrook	d											14 10											
Irlam	d	12 44			13 11					13 44		14 13					14 44		15 11				
Flixton	d				13 15							14 17							15 15				
Chassen Road	d											14 19											
Urmston	d	12 49			13 18					13 49		14 21					14 49		15 18				
Humphrey Park	d				13 20														15 20				
Trafford Park	d				13 23														15 23				
Deansgate	84, 85 a	12 59			13 31					13 59		14 31					14 59		15 31				
Manchester Oxford Road	84, 85 a	13 04		13 05	13 36	13 39		13 57		14 04	14 05	14 36	14 39			14 57	15 04	15 05	15 36	15 39			15 57
Manchester Piccadilly 10	78, 84, 85 a	13 18		13 09	13 56	13 41		14 01		14 18	14 09	14 56	14 41			15 01	15 18	15 09	15 56	15 41			16 01
Stockport	84 a	13 34		13 28		13 53		14 22		14 34	14 28		14 53			15 22	15 34	15 28		15 53			16 22
Sheffield 7	78 a			14 08		14 35					15 08		15 35					16 08		16 35			
Manchester Airport	85 a	13 47		13 42	14 17	14c12		14 22		14 47	14 42	15 17	15c12			15 22	15 47	15 42	16 17	16c12			16 22

		NT	TP 1 ◇ A	NT	EM ◇ B	NT		NT	NT	TP 1 ◇ A	NT	EM ◇ C		NT	NT	NT	TP 1 ◇ A	NT		EM ◇ B	NT	NT	NT
Liverpool Lime Street 10	90, 91 d		15 22	15 27	15 52	15 55		16 13		16 22	16 27	16 52		16 55	17 06		17 22	17 25		17 52	17 55	18 13	
Edge Hill	90, 91 d					15 59								16 59				17 29			17 59		
Mossley Hill	91 d			15 35		16 04					16 35			17 04				17 34			18 04		
West Allerton	91 d			15 37		16 06					16 37			17 06				17 36			18 06		
Liverpool Central 10	103 d					15b44								16b44				17b14			17b44		
Liverpool South Parkway 7	91, 103 d			15 40	16 03	16 09					16 40	17 03		17 09				17 39		18 03	18 09		
Hunts Cross	103 d					16 13								17 13				17 43			18 13		
Halewood	d					16 16								17 16				17 46			18 16		
Hough Green	d	←		15 47		16 20			←		16 47			17 20		←		17 50			18 20		←
Widnes	d	15 23		15 50	16 11	16 23 →			16 23		16 50	17 11		17 23 →		17 23		17 54		18 11	18 23 →		18 23
Sankey for Penketh	d	15 28							16 28							17 28		17 58					18 28
Warrington Central	a	15 33	15 43	15 58	16 18				16 33	16 43	16 58	17 18				17 33	17 43	18 03		18 18			18 33
	d	15 34	15 44	15 59	16 19				16 34	16 44	16 59	17 19				17 34	17 44	18 04		18 19			18 34
Padgate	d			16 02							17 02							18 07					
Birchwood	d	15 38	15 49	16 05					16 38	16 49	17 05					17 38	17 49	18 10					18 38
Glazebrook	d			16 10																			
Irlam	d	15 44		16 13					16 44		17 11					17 44		18 16					18 44
Flixton	d			16 17							17 15												
Chassen Road	d			16 19														18 20					
Urmston	d	15 49		16 21					16 49		17 18					17 49		18 22					18 49
Humphrey Park	d										17 20												
Trafford Park	d										17 23												
Deansgate	84, 85 a	15 59		16 30					16 59		17 31					17 59		18 32					18 59
Manchester Oxford Road	84, 85 a	16 04	16 05	16 36	16 38			16 57	17 04	17 05	17 36	17 38			17 57	18 04	18 05	18 36		18 39		18 57	19 04
Manchester Piccadilly 10	78, 84, 85 a	16 18	16 09	16 56	16 41			17 01	17 18	17 09	17 56	17 41			18 01	18 18	18 09	18 56		18 41		19 01	19 27
Stockport	84 a	16 34	16 28		16 53			17 22	17 34	17 28		17 53			18 22	18 34	18 28			18 53		19 26	19 53
Sheffield 7	78 a		17 08		17 37					18 15		18 34					19 10			19 35		20 08	
Manchester Airport	85 a	16 47	16 42	17 17	17c12			17 22	17 48	17 48	18 17	18c12			18 22	18 47	18 42	19 17		19c13		19 24	19 50

		TP 1 ◇ A	NT	EM ◇ C		NT	TP 1 ◇ D	NT	EM ◇ C	NT		NT	TP 1 ◇ E	EM ◇ E	NT	NT		TP 1 ◇ G	NT
Liverpool Lime Street 10	90, 91 d	18 22	18 25	18 52		18 55	19 22		19 52	19 55		20 09	20 22	20 52	20 55	21 55		22 30	23 38
Edge Hill	90, 91 d		18 29			18 59				19 59					20 59	21 59			23 42
Mossley Hill	91 d		18 34			19 04				20 04					21 04	22 04			23 47
West Allerton	91 d		18 36			19 06				20 06					21 06	22 06			23 49
Liverpool Central 10	103 d		18b14			18b44				19b44					20b44	21b44			23b29
Liverpool South Parkway 7	91, 103 d		18 39	19 03		19 09			20 03	20 09				21 03	21 09	22 09			23 52
Hunts Cross	103 d		18 43			19 13				20 13					21 13	22 13			23 56
Halewood	d		18 46			19 16				20 16					21 16	22 16			23 59
Hough Green	d		18 50			19 20				20 20					21 20	22 20			00 03
Widnes	d		18 53	19 11		19 23			20 11	20 23				21 11	21 23	22 23			00 06
Sankey for Penketh	d		18 58			19 28				20 28					21 28	22 28			00 11
Warrington Central	a	18 43	19 03	19 18		19 34	19 43		20 18	20 34			20 43	21 18	21 33	22 33		22 52	00 16
	d	18 44	19 03	19 19			19 44	19 56	20 19				20 44	21 19	21 34	22 34		22 52	00 17
Padgate	d		19 06					19 59							21 37	22 37			
Birchwood	d	18 49	19 09				19 49	20 02					20 49		21 40	22 40		22 57	
Glazebrook	d		19 14					20 07							21 45	22 45			
Irlam	d		19 17					20 10							21 48	22 48			
Flixton	d							20 14							21 52	22 52			
Chassen Road	d							20 16							21 54	22 54			
Urmston	d		19 22					20 18							21 56	22 56			
Humphrey Park	d							20 20							21 58	22 58			
Trafford Park	d							20 23							22 01	23 01			
Deansgate	84, 85 a		19 32					20 31							22 08	23 08			
Manchester Oxford Road	84, 85 a	19 05	19 36	19 39			20 05	20 36	20 39			20 57	21 05	21 39	22 13	23 13		23 14	
Manchester Piccadilly 10	78, 84, 85 a	19 09	19 45	19 41			20 09	20 45	20 41			21 01	21 09	21 41	22 45	23 37		23 19	00 39
Stockport	84 a	19 34		19 53			20 28		20 53			21 27	21 28	21 52				23 49	
Sheffield 7	78 a	20 35		20 35			21 08		21 34				22 08	22 31					
Manchester Airport	85 a	19 50	20 07	20c17			20 47	21 07	21c17			21 24	21 47	22c17	23 08	00e22		00 22	

For general notes see front of timetable
For details of catering facilities see Directory of Train Operators

A To Scarborough (Table 39)
B To Norwich (Table 49)
C To Nottingham (Table 49)
D To York (Table 39)
E To Hull (from 12 September to York) (Table 39)
G To York (from 12 September to Huddersfield) (Table 39)

b Change at Hunts Cross
c Change at Manchester Piccadilly
e Change at Manchester Oxford Road and Manchester Piccadilly

Sundays

until 6 September

Liverpool → Warrington Central → Manchester and Manchester Airport

Network Diagram - see first page of Table 88

		NT	TP 1 ◇ A	NT	NT	TP 1 ◇ B		NT	NT	TP 1 ◇ C	NT	NT		TP 1 ◇ B	NT	NT	TP 1 ◇ C	NT		EM ◇ D ⚮	NT	TP 1 ◇ B	NT
Liverpool Lime Street 10	90, 91 d	08 05	08 22	08 26	09 01	09 22		09 26	10 01	10 22	10 26	11 01		11 22	11 26	12 01	12 22	12 26		12 52	13 01	13 22	13 26
Edge Hill	90, 91 d																						
Mossley Hill	91 d			08 34				09 34			10 34				11 34			12 34					13 34
West Allerton	91 d			08 36				09 36			10 36				11 36			12 36					13 36
Liverpool Central 10	103 d			08b14				09b14			10b14				11b14			12b14					13b14
Liverpool South Parkway 7	91, 103 ✈ d			08 39				09 39			10 39				11 39			12 39		13 03			13 39
Hunts Cross	103 d			08 43				09 43			10 43				11 43			12 43					13 43
Halewood	d			08 46				09 46			10 46				11 46			12 46					13 46
Hough Green	d			08 50				09 50			10 50				11 50			12 50					13 50
Widnes	d			08 53				09 53			10 53				11 53			12 53		13 11			13 53
Sankey for Penketh	d																						
Warrington Central	a		08 43	09 01		09 43		10 01		10 43	11 01			11 43	12 01		12 43	13 01		13 18		13 43	14 01
	d		08 44	09 02		09 44		10 02		10 44	11 02			11 44	12 02		12 44	13 02		13 19		13 44	14 02
Padgate	d																						
Birchwood	d		08 49	09 06		09 49		10 06		10 49	11 06			11 49	12 06		12 49	13 06				13 49	14 06
Glazebrook	d																						
Irlam	d			09 12				10 12			11 12				12 12			13 12					14 12
Flixton	d																						
Chassen Road	d																						
Urmston	d			09 17				10 17			11 17				12 17			13 17					14 17
Humphrey Park	d																						
Trafford Park	d																						
Deansgate	84, 85 ⛴ a			09 27				10 27			11 27				12 27			13 27					14 27
Manchester Oxford Road	84, 85 a	09 01	09 05	09 31	09 59	10 05		10 31	10 59	11 05	11 31	11 59		12 05	12 31	12 59	13 05	13 31		13 39	13 59	14 05	14 31
Manchester Piccadilly 10	78, 84, 85 ⛴ a	09 05	09 09	09 48	10 03	10 10		10 50	11 03	11 09	11 41	12 02		12 09	12 57	13 02	13 09			13 41	14 02	14 09	
Stockport	84 a		09 27			10 28		11 30	11c27	11 30	12 32	12 22		12 32	13 30	13 22	13 28			13 53	14 22	14 28	
Sheffield 7	78 ⛴ a		11 06			12 06			12 08	13 06		13 08		13e37			14 08			14f43		15 08	
Manchester Airport	85 ✈ a	09 22	09 55	10 13	10 24	10 55		11 17	11 21	11 47	12 02	12 19		12 55	13 17	13 19	13 47			14g17	14 19	14 47	

		EM ◇ D ⚮	NT	TP 1 ◇ C		NT	EM ◇ D ⚮	NT	TP 1 ◇ B	NT		EM ◇ D ⚮	NT	TP 1 ◇ C	NT	EM ◇ E ⚮		NT	TP 1 ◇ B	NT	EM ◇ E ⚮	NT	TP 1 ◇ B
Liverpool Lime Street 10	90, 91 d	13 52	14 01	14 22		14 26	14 52	15 01	15 22	15 26		15 52	16 01	16 22	16 26	16 52		17 01	17 22	17 26	17 52	18 01	18 22
Edge Hill	90, 91 d																						
Mossley Hill	91 d					14 34				15 34					16 34					17 34			
West Allerton	91 d					14 36				15 36					16 36					17 36			
Liverpool Central 10	103 d					14b14				15b14					16b14					17b14			
Liverpool South Parkway 7	91, 103 ✈ d	14 03				14 39	15 03			15 39		16 03			16 39	17 03				17 39	18 03		
Hunts Cross	103 d					14 43				15 43					16 43					17 43			
Halewood	d					14 46				15 46					16 46					17 46			
Hough Green	d					14 50				15 50					16 50					17 50			
Widnes	d	14 11				14 53	15 11			15 53		16 11			16 53	17 11				17 53	18 11		
Sankey for Penketh	d																						
Warrington Central	a	14 18		14 43		15 01	15 18		15 43	16 01		16 18		16 43	17 01	17 18			17 43	18 01	18 18		18 43
	d	14 19		14 44		15 02	15 19		15 44	16 02		16 19		16 44	17 02	17 19			17 44	18 02	18 19		18 44
Padgate	d																						
Birchwood	d			14 49		15 06			15 49	16 06				16 49	17 06				17 49	18 06			18 49
Glazebrook	d																						
Irlam	d					15 12				16 12					17 12					18 12			
Flixton	d																						
Chassen Road	d																						
Urmston	d					15 17				16 17					17 17					18 17			
Humphrey Park	d																						
Trafford Park	d																						
Deansgate	84, 85 ⛴ a					15 27				16 27					17 27					18 27			
Manchester Oxford Road	84, 85 a	14 39	14 59	15 05		15 31	15 39	15 59	16 05	16 31		16 38	16 59	17 05	17 31	17 38		17 59	18 05	18 31	18 39	18 59	19 05
Manchester Piccadilly 10	78, 84, 85 ⛴ a	14 41	15 02	15 09			15 41	16 02	16 09			16 41	17 02	17 09		17 41		18 02	18 09		18 41	19 02	19 09
Stockport	84 a	14 53	15 22	15 28			15 53	16 22	16 28			16 53	17 22	17 28		17 53		18 22	18 28		18 53	19 22	19 28
Sheffield 7	78 ⛴ a	15 33		16 08			16 36		17 08			17 36		18 08		18 37			19 08		19 34		20 08
Manchester Airport	85 ✈ a	15g17	15 20	15 47			16g17	16 19	16 47			17g17	17 19	17 47		18g17		18 19	18 47		19g17	19 19	19 47

For general notes see front of timetable
For details of catering facilities see Directory of Train Operators

A To Hull (Table 39)
B To Scarborough (Table 39)
C To Middlesbrough (Table 39)
D To Norwich (Table 49)
E To Nottingham (Table 49)
b Change at Hunts Cross
c From 19 July arr. 1123
e From 19 July arr. 1342
f Until 12 July arr. 1439
g Change at Manchester Piccadilly

Table 89

Sundays

until 6 September

Liverpool → Warrington Central → Manchester and Manchester Airport

Network Diagram - see first page of Table 88

		NT		EM	NT	TP	NT	EM		NT	TP	NT	NT	EM		NT	TP	NT	NT	NT			
				◇ A		[1] ◇ B		◇ A			[1] ◇ C			◇ A			[1] ◇ B						
Liverpool Lime Street [10]	90, 91 d	18 26		18 52	19 01	19 22	19 26	19 52		20 01	20 22	20 26	21 01	21 22		21 26	21 52	22 01	22 26	23 01			
Edge Hill	90, 91 d																						
Mossley Hill	91 d	18 34					19 34					20 34				21 34			22 34				
West Allerton	91 d	18 36					19 36					20 36				21 36			22 36				
Liverpool Central [10]	103 d	18b14					19b14					20b14				21b14			22b14				
Liverpool South Parkway [7]	91, 103 d	18 39		19 03			19 39	20 03				20 39				21 39			22 39				
Hunts Cross	103 d	18 43					19 43					20 43				21 43			22 43				
Halewood	d	18 46					19 46					20 46				21 46			22 46				
Hough Green	d	18 50					19 50					20 50				21 50			22 50				
Widnes	d	18 53		19 11			19 53	20 11				20 53		21 39		21 53			22 53				
Sankey for Penketh	d																						
Warrington Central	a	19 01		19 18		19 43	20 01	20 18			20 43	21 01		21 47		22 01	22 13		23 01				
	d	19 02		19 19		19 44	20 02	20 19			20 44	21 02		21 47		22 02	22 14		23 02				
Padgate	d																						
Birchwood	d	19 06				19 49	20 06				20 49	21 06				22 06	22 19		23 06				
Glazebrook	d																						
Irlam	d	19 12					20 12					21 12				22 12			23 12				
Flixton	d																						
Chassen Road	d																						
Urmston	d	19 17					20 17					21 17				22 17			23 17				
Humphrey Park	d																						
Trafford Park	d																						
Deansgate	84, 85 a	19 27					20 27					21 27				22 27			23 27				
Manchester Oxford Road	84, 85 a	19 31		19 39	19 59	20 05	20 31	20 39		20 59	21 05	21 31	21 59	22 07		22 31	22 35	22 59	23 31	23 59			
Manchester Piccadilly [10]	78, 84, 85 a			19 41	20 02	20 09		20 41		21 02	21 09	21 57	22 02	22 09			22 40	23 02		00 02			
Stockport	84 a			19 53	20 26	20 27		20 53			21 28			22 20		23 32	23 04	23 28					
Sheffield [7]	78 a			20 34	21 08	21 36		21 36			22 11		23 06	23c25				00 15					
Manchester Airport	85 a			20e17	20 19	20 47		21e17		21 19	21 47	22 17	22 19	22e55				23 20	00 17	00 17			

Sundays

13 September to 1 November

		NT	TP	TP	NT	NT		NT	TP	TP	NT	NT		NT	TP	TP	NT	NT		NT	TP	TP	NT
				[1] ◇ D						[1] ◇ E						[1] ◇ D						[1] ◇ E	
		Bus	Bus			Bus			Bus			Bus			Bus			Bus			Bus		
Liverpool Lime Street [10]	90, 91 d	07 45		08 19		08 45		09 01		09 22		09 45		10 01		10 22		10 45		11 01		11 22	
Edge Hill	90, 91 d																						
Mossley Hill	91 d	07 58				08 58						09 58						10 58					
West Allerton	91 d	08 02				09 02						10 02						11 02					
Liverpool Central [10]	103 d																						
Liverpool South Parkway [7]	91, 103 d	08 07				09 07						10 07						11 07					
Hunts Cross	103 d	08 13				09 13						10 13						11 13					
Halewood	d	08 19				09 19						10 19						11 19					
Hough Green	d	08 29				09 29						10 29						11 29					
Widnes	d	08 38				09 38						10 38						11 38					
Sankey for Penketh	d																						
Warrington Central	a	08 53				09 53						10 53						11 53					
	d		08 05		09 02				09 10		10 02				10 10		11 02				11 10		12 02
Padgate	d																						
Birchwood	d				09 06						10 06						11 06						12 06
Glazebrook	d																						
Irlam	d				09 12						10 12						11 12						12 12
Flixton	d																						
Chassen Road	d																						
Urmston	d				09 17						10 17						11 17						12 17
Humphrey Park	d																						
Trafford Park	d																						
Deansgate	84, 85 a				09 27						10 27						11 27						12 27
Newton-le-Willows	90 d		08a25	08 35					09a30	09 40					10a30	10 40					11a30	11 40	
Manchester Victoria	90 a			08 56						10 03						11 03						12 03	
Manchester Oxford Road	84, 85 a				09 31			09 59			10 31			10 59			11 31			11 59			12 31
Manchester Piccadilly [10]	78, 84, 85 a				09 49			10 03			10 50			11 03			11 40			12 02			12 57
Stockport	84 a				10 32			10 28			11 30			11 23			12 32			12 23			13 30
Sheffield [7]	78 a							12f08						12 08						13 08			
Manchester Airport	85 a				10 13			10 25			11 17			11 21			12 04			12 21			13 17

For general notes see front of timetable
For details of catering facilities see Directory of Train Operators

- **A** To Nottingham (Table 49)
- **B** To York (Table 39)
- **C** To Newcastle (Table 39)
- **D** To Middlesbrough (Table 39)
- **E** To Scarborough (Table 39)
- **b** Change at Hunts Cross
- **c** Until 12 July arr. 2323
- **e** Change at Manchester Piccadilly
- **f** 13 September arr. 1206

Table 89

Sundays

13 September to 1 November

Liverpool → Warrington Central → Manchester and Manchester Airport

Network Diagram - see first page of Table 88

	NT	NT	TP		TP	NT	NT	NT	TP		TP	NT	NT	NT	TP		TP	NT	NT	NT	TP	TP
					[1] ◇ A						[1] ◇ B						[1] ◇ A					[1] ◇ B
	🚌		🚌				🚌		🚌				🚌		🚌				🚌		🚌	
Liverpool Lime Street [10] 90, 91 d	11 45	12 01			12 22		12 45	13 01			13 22		13 45	14 01			14 22		14 45	15 01		15 22
Edge Hill 90, 91 d																						
Mossley Hill 91 d	11 58						12 58						13 58						14 58			
West Allerton 91 d	12 02						13 02						14 02						15 02			
Liverpool Central [10] 103 d																						
Liverpool South Parkway [7] 91, 103 ✈ d	12 07						13 07						14 07						15 07			
Hunts Cross 103 d	12 13						13 13						14 13						15 13			
Halewood d	12 19						13 19						14 19						15 19			
Hough Green d	12 29						13 29						14 29						15 29			
Widnes d	12 38						13 38						14 38						15 38			
Sankey for Penketh d																						
Warrington Central a	12 53						13 53						14 53						15 53			
d			12 10			13 02			13 10			14 02			14 10			15 02			15 10	
Padgate d																						
Birchwood d						13 06						14 06						15 06				
Glazebrook d																						
Irlam d						13 12						14 12						15 12				
Flixton d																						
Chassen Road d																						
Urmston d						13 17						14 17						15 17				
Humphrey Park d																						
Trafford Park d																						
Deansgate 84, 85 🚌 a						13 27						14 27						15 27				
Newton-le-Willows 90 d			12a30		12 40				13a30		13 40				14a30		14 40				15a30	15 40
Manchester Victoria 90 🚌 a					13 03						14 03						15 03					16 03
Manchester Oxford Road 84, 85 a		12 59				13 31		13 59				14 31		14 59				15 31		15 59		
Manchester Piccadilly [10] 78, 84, 85 🚌 a		13 02				13 41		14 02				14 41		15 02				15 41		16 02		
Stockport 84 a		13 22				13 53		14 22				14 53		15 22				15 53		16 22		
Sheffield [7] 78 🚌 a		14 08						15 08						16 08						17 08		
Manchester Airport 85 ✈ a		13 19				14 17		14 19				15 17		15 20				16 17		16 19		

	NT		NT	NT	TP	TP	NT		NT	NT	TP	TP	NT		NT	NT	TP	TP	NT		NT	NT
						[1] ◇ A						[1] ◇ B						[1] ◇ B				
			🚌		🚌				🚌		🚌				🚌		🚌				🚌	
Liverpool Lime Street [10] 90, 91 d			15 45	16 01		16 22			16 45	17 01		17 22			17 45	18 01		18 22			18 45	19 01
Edge Hill 90, 91 d																						
Mossley Hill 91 d			15 58						16 58						17 58						18 58	
West Allerton 91 d			16 02						17 02						18 02						19 02	
Liverpool Central [10] 103 d																						
Liverpool South Parkway [7] 91, 103 ✈ d			16 07						17 07						18 07						19 07	
Hunts Cross 103 d			16 13						17 13						18 13						19 13	
Halewood d			16 19						17 19						18 19						19 19	
Hough Green d			16 29						17 29						18 29						19 29	
Widnes d			16 38						17 38						18 38						19 38	
Sankey for Penketh d																						
Warrington Central a			16 53						17 53						18 53						19 53	
d	16 02				16 10		17 02				17 10		18 02				18 10		19 02			
Padgate d																						
Birchwood d	16 06						17 06						18 06						19 06			
Glazebrook d																						
Irlam d	16 12						17 12						18 12						19 12			
Flixton d																						
Chassen Road d																						
Urmston d	16 17						17 17						18 17						19 17			
Humphrey Park d																						
Trafford Park d																						
Deansgate 84, 85 🚌 a	16 27						17 27						18 27						19 27			
Newton-le-Willows 90 d					16a30	16 40					17a30	17 40					18a30	18 40				
Manchester Victoria 90 🚌 a						17 03						18 03						19 03				
Manchester Oxford Road 84, 85 a	16 31			16 59			17 31			17 59			18 31			18 59			19 31			19 59
Manchester Piccadilly [10] 78, 84, 85 🚌 a	16 41			17 02			17 41			18 02			18 41			19 02			19 41			20 02
Stockport 84 a	16 53			17 22			17 53			18 22			18 53			19 22			19 53			20 26
Sheffield [7] 78 🚌 a				18 08						19 08						20 08						21 08
Manchester Airport 85 ✈ a	17 17			17 19			18 17			18 19			19 17			19 19			20 17			20 19

For general notes see front of timetable
For details of catering facilities see Directory of Train Operators

A To Middlesbrough (Table 39)
B To Scarborough (Table 39)

Table 89

Sundays

Liverpool → Warrington Central → Manchester and Manchester Airport

13 September to 1 November

Network Diagram - see first page of Table 88

Station		TP	TP 1◇ A	NT	NT	NT	TP	TP 1◇ B	NT	NT	NT	TP	TP 1◇ A	NT	NT	NT	NT	NT
Liverpool Lime Street 10	90, 91 d		19 22		19 45	20 01		20 22		20 45	21 01		21 52		21 45	22 01		23 01
Edge Hill	90, 91 d																	
Mossley Hill	91 d				19 58					20 58					21 58			
West Allerton	91 d				20 02					21 02					22 02			
Liverpool Central 10	103 d																	
Liverpool South Parkway 7	91, 103 ✈ d				20 07					21 07					22 07			
Hunts Cross	103 d				20 13					21 13					22 13			
Halewood	d				20 19					21 19					22 19			
Hough Green	d				20 29					21 29					22 29			
Widnes	d				20 38					21 38					22 38			
Sankey for Penketh	d																	
Warrington Central	a				20 53					21 53					22 53			
	d	19 10		20 02			20 10		21 02			21 40		22 02			23 02	
Padgate	d																	
Birchwood	d			20 06					21 06					22 06			23 06	
Glazebrook	d																	
Irlam	d			20 12					21 12					22 12			23 12	
Flixton	d																	
Chassen Road	d																	
Urmston	d			20 17					21 17					22 17			23 17	
Humphrey Park	d																	
Trafford Park	d																	
Deansgate	84, 85 ⛴ a			20 27					21 27					22 27			23 27	
Newton-le-Willows	90 d	19a30	19 40				20a30	20 40				22a00	22 08					
Manchester Victoria	90 ⛴ a		20 03					21 03					22 30					
Manchester Oxford Road	84, 85 a			20 31		20 59			21 31		21 59			22 31		22 59	23 31	23 59
Manchester Piccadilly 10	78, 84, 85 ⛴ a			20 41		21 02			21 57		22 02					23 02		00 02
Stockport	84 a			20 53		21 28					22b20			23 32		23 28		
Sheffield 7	78 ⛴ a					22 11					23 06					00 15		
Manchester Airport	85 ✈ a			21 17		21 19			22 17		22 19					23 20		00 17

Sundays

from 8 November

Station		TP	TP 1◇ C	NT	NT	TP	TP 1◇ D	NT	NT	TP	TP 1◇ C	NT	NT	TP	TP 1◇ D	NT	NT	TP
Liverpool Lime Street 10	90, 91 d		08 19	08 26	09 01		09 22	09 26	10 01		10 22	10 26	11 01		11 22	11 26	12 01	
Edge Hill	90, 91 d																	
Mossley Hill	91 d			08 34				09 34				10 34				11 34		
West Allerton	91 d			08 36				09 36				10 36				11 36		
Liverpool Central 10	103 d			08c14				09c14				10c14				11c14		
Liverpool South Parkway 7	91, 103 ✈ d			08 39				09 39				10 39				11 39		
Hunts Cross	103 d			08 43				09 43				10 43				11 43		
Halewood	d			08 46				09 46				10 46				11 46		
Hough Green	d			08 50				09 50				10 50				11 50		
Widnes	d			08 53				09 53				10 53				11 53		
Sankey for Penketh	d																	
Warrington Central	a			09 01				10 01				11 01				12 01		
	d	08 05		09 02		09 10		10 02		10 10		11 02		11 10		12 02		12 10
Padgate	d																	
Birchwood	d			09 06				10 06				11 06				12 06		
Glazebrook	d																	
Irlam	d			09 12				10 12				11 12				12 12		
Flixton	d																	
Chassen Road	d																	
Urmston	d			09 17				10 17				11 17				12 17		
Humphrey Park	d																	
Trafford Park	d																	
Deansgate	84, 85 ⛴ a			09 27				10 27				11 27				12 27		
Newton-le-Willows	90 d	08a25	08 35			09a30	09 40			10a30	10 40			11a30	11 40			12a30
Manchester Victoria	90 ⛴ a		08 56				10 03				11 03				12 03			
Manchester Oxford Road	84, 85 a			09 31	09 59			10 31	10 59			11 31	11 59			12 31	12 59	
Manchester Piccadilly 10	78, 84, 85 ⛴ a			09 49	10 03			10 50	11 03			11 40	12 02			12 57	13 02	
Stockport	84 a			10 32	10 28			11 30	11 23			12 32	12 23			13 30	13 22	
Sheffield 7	78 ⛴ a								12 08				13 08				14 08	
Manchester Airport	85 ✈ a			10 13	10 25			11 17	11 21			12 04	12 21			13 17	13 19	

For general notes see front of timetable
For details of catering facilities see Directory of Train Operators

A To York (Table 39)
B To Newcastle (Table 39)
C To Middlesbrough (Table 39)
D To Scarborough (Table 39)

b Change at Manchester Oxford Road
c Change at Hunts Cross

Sundays

from 8 November

Liverpool → Warrington Central → Manchester and Manchester Airport

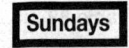

Network Diagram - see first page of Table 88

		TP 1◇ A	NT	EM ◇ B 🍴	NT	TP 🚌	TP 1◇ C	NT	EM ◇ B 🍴	NT	TP 🚌	TP 1◇ A	NT	EM ◇ B 🍴	NT	TP 🚌	TP 1◇ C	NT
Liverpool Lime Street 10	90, 91 d	12 22	12 26	12 52	13 01		13 22	13 26	13 52	14 01		14 22	14 26	14 52	15 01		15 22	15 26
Edge Hill	90, 91 d																	
Mossley Hill	91 d		12 34					13 34					14 34					15 34
West Allerton	91 d		12 36					13 36					14 36					15 36
Liverpool Central 10	103 d		12b14					13b14					14b14					15b14
Liverpool South Parkway 7	91, 103 ✈ d		12 39	13 03				13 39	14 03				14 39	15 03				15 39
Hunts Cross	103 d		12 43					13 43					14 43					15 43
Halewood	d		12 46					13 46					14 46					15 46
Hough Green	d		12 50					13 50					14 50					15 50
Widnes	d		12 53	13 11				13 53	14 11				14 53	15 11				15 53
Sankey for Penketh	d																	
Warrington Central	a		13 01	13 18				14 01	14 18				15 01	15 18				16 01
	d		13 02	13 19		13 10		14 02	14 19		14 10		15 02	15 19		15 10		16 02
Padgate	d																	
Birchwood	d		13 06					14 06					15 06					16 06
Glazebrook	d																	
Irlam	d		13 12					14 12					15 12					16 12
Flixton	d																	
Chassen Road	d																	
Urmston	d		13 17					14 17					15 17					16 17
Humphrey Park	d																	
Trafford Park	d																	
Deansgate	84, 85 🚊 a		13 27					14 27					15 27					16 27
Newton-le-Willows	90 d	12 40				13a30	13 40				14a30	14 40				15a30	15 40	
Manchester Victoria	90 🚊 a	13 03					14 03					15 03					16 03	
Manchester Oxford Road	84, 85 a		13 31	13 39	13 59			14 31	14 39	14 59			15 31	15 39	15 59			16 31
Manchester Piccadilly 10	78, 84, 85 🚊 a			13 41	14 02				14 41	15 02				15 41	16 02			
Stockport	84 a			13 53	*14 22*				14 53	*15 22*				15 53	*16 22*			
Sheffield 7	78 🚊 a			14 39	*15 08*				15 37	*16 08*				16 36	*17 08*			
Manchester Airport	85 ✈ a			*14c17*	14 19			*15 17*	*15c17*	15 20				*16c17*	16 19			

		EM ◇ B 🍴	NT	TP 🚌	TP 1◇ A	NT	EM ◇ D 🍴	NT	TP 🚌	TP 1◇ C	NT	EM ◇ D 🍴	NT	TP 🚌	TP 1◇ C	NT	EM ◇ D 🍴	NT
Liverpool Lime Street 10	90, 91 d	15 52	16 01		16 22	16 26	16 52	17 01		17 22	17 26	17 52	18 01		18 22	18 26	18 52	19 01
Edge Hill	90, 91 d																	
Mossley Hill	91 d					16 34					17 34					18 34		
West Allerton	91 d					16 36					17 36					18 36		
Liverpool Central 10	103 d					16b14					17b14					18b14		
Liverpool South Parkway 7	91, 103 ✈ d	16 03				16 39	17 03				17 39	18 03				18 39	19 03	
Hunts Cross	103 d					16 43					17 43					18 43		
Halewood	d					16 46					17 46					18 46		
Hough Green	d					16 50					17 50					18 50		
Widnes	d	16 11				16 53	17 11				17 53	18 11				18 53	19 11	
Sankey for Penketh	d																	
Warrington Central	a	16 18				17 01	17 18				18 01	18 18				19 01	19 18	
	d	16 19		16 10		17 02	17 19		17 10		18 02	18 19		18 10		19 02	19 19	
Padgate	d																	
Birchwood	d					17 06					18 06					19 06		
Glazebrook	d																	
Irlam	d					17 12					18 12					19 12		
Flixton	d																	
Chassen Road	d																	
Urmston	d					17 17					18 17					19 17		
Humphrey Park	d																	
Trafford Park	d																	
Deansgate	84, 85 🚊 a					17 27					18 27					19 27		
Newton-le-Willows	90 d			16a30	16 40				17a30	17 40				18a30	18 40			
Manchester Victoria	90 🚊 a				17 03					18 03					19 03			
Manchester Oxford Road	84, 85 a	16 38	16 59			17 31	17 38	17 59			18 31	18 39	18 59			19 31	19 39	19 59
Manchester Piccadilly 10	78, 84, 85 🚊 a	16 41	17 02				17 41	18 02				18 41	19 02				19 41	20 02
Stockport	84 a	16 53	*17 22*				17 53	*18 22*				18 53	*19 22*				19 53	*20 26*
Sheffield 7	78 🚊 a	17 36	*18 08*				18 37	*19 08*				19 34	*20 08*				20 34	*21 08*
Manchester Airport	85 ✈ a	*17c17*	17 19			*18 17*	*18c17*	18 19				*19c17*	19 19				*20c17*	20 19

For general notes see front of timetable
For details of catering facilities see Directory of Train Operators

A To Middlesbrough (Table 39)
B To Norwich (Table 49)
C To Scarborough (Table 39)
D To Nottingham (Table 49)

b Change at Hunts Cross
c Change at Manchester Piccadilly

Sundays

Liverpool → Warrington Central → Manchester and Manchester Airport

from 8 November

Network Diagram - see first page of Table 88

		TP	TP	NT	EM	NT	TP	TP	NT	NT	EM	NT	TP	TP	NT	NT	NT
		🚌	1 ◇ A		◇ B 🍴		🚌	1 ◇ C			◇ B		🚌	1 ◇ A			
Liverpool Lime Street 10	90, 91 d		19 22	19 26	19 52	20 01		20 22	20 26	21 01	21 22	21 26		21 52	22 01	22 26	23 01
Edge Hill	90, 91 d																
Mossley Hill	91 d			19 34					20 34			21 34				22 34	
West Allerton	91 d			19 36					20 36			21 36				22 36	
Liverpool Central 10	103 d			19b14					20b14			21b14				22b14	
Liverpool South Parkway 7	91, 103 ✈ d			19 39	20 03				20 39			21 39				22 39	
Hunts Cross	103 d			19 43					20 43			21 43				22 43	
Halewood	d			19 46					20 46			21 46				22 46	
Hough Green	d			19 50					20 50			21 50				22 50	
Widnes	d			19 53	20 11				20 53		21 39	21 53				22 53	
Sankey for Penketh	d																
Warrington Central	a			20 01	20 18				21 01		21 47	22 01				23 01	
	d	19 10		20 02	20 19		20 10		21 02		21 47	22 02	21 40			23 02	
Padgate	d																
Birchwood	d			20 06					21 06			22 06				23 06	
Glazebrook	d																
Irlam	d			20 12					21 12			22 12				23 12	
Flixton	d																
Chassen Road	d																
Urmston	d			20 17					21 17			22 17				23 17	
Humphrey Park	d																
Trafford Park	d																
Deansgate	84, 85 🚇 a			20 27					21 27			22 27				23 27	
Newton-le-Willows	90 d	19a30	19 40				20a30	20 40					22a00	22 08			
Manchester Victoria	90 🚇 a		20 03					21 03						22 30			
Manchester Oxford Road	84, 85 a			20 31	20 39	20 59			21 31	21 59	22 07	22 31			22 59	23 31	23 59
Manchester Piccadilly 10	78, 84, 85 🚇 a				20 41	21 02			21 57	22 02	22 09				23 02		00 02
Stockport	84 a				20 53	21 28					22 20	23 32			23 28		
Sheffield 7	78 🚇 a				21 36	22 11				23 06	23 23				00 15		
Manchester Airport	85 ✈ a				21c17	21 19			22 17	22 19	23c08				23 20		00 17

For general notes see front of timetable
For details of catering facilities see Directory of Train Operators

A To York (Table 39)
B To Nottingham (Table 49)
C To Newcastle (Table 39)
b Change at Hunts Cross
c Change at Manchester Piccadilly

Manchester Airport and Manchester → Warrington Central → Liverpool

Network Diagram - see first page of Table 88

Miles	Station		NT	NT	NT	NT	NT	NT	TP 1 ◇		NT	EM ◇ A	NT	NT	TP 1 ◇ B	NT	NT		EM ◇ C	NT	NT	NT	TP 1 ◇ D
0	**Manchester Airport**	85 ✈ d	04 34			05b37	06 18	06 41				07c05	07 00	07 41					08c05	08 03	08 41		
—	Sheffield 7	78 d						05 11				06 20							07 35				
—	Stockport	84 d						06e41				07 22	07 10	07 31	07 42				08 24	08 14	08e41		08 42
9¾	**Manchester Piccadilly 10**	78, 84, 85 d	04 49			06 03	06 33	06 58	07 07			07 34	07 27	07 58	08 07	←			08 37	08 29	09 01		09 07
10¼	**Manchester Oxford Road**	84, 85 d				06 27	06 46	07 01	07 11			07 37	07 39	08 03 →	08 11	08 03	08 15		08 41	08 44	09 04		09 11
10¾	Deansgate	84, 85 d				06 29							07 41				08 17			08 46			
13¾	Trafford Park	d				06 34							07 46										
14½	Humphrey Park	d				06 36																	
15¾	Urmston	d				06 38	06 53						07 49				08 24			08 52			
16¼	Chassen Road	d				06 40											08 26						
16¾	Flixton	d				06 43							07 52				08 29						
19	Irlam	d				06 47	06 58						07 56				08 33			08 57			
20¼	Glazebrook	d				06 50							07 59				08 36						
23	Birchwood	d				06 54	07 04		07 24				08 04		08 24		08 40			09 03			09 24
24½	Padgate	d				06 57							08 07							09 06			
26¼	**Warrington Central**	a				07 01	07 12		07 29			07 53	08 10		08 29		08 45		08 57	09 09			09 29
—		d		06 03	06 37	07 01			07 29		07 35	07 53	08 11		08 29		08 46		08 57	09 10		←	09 29
28¾	Sankey for Penketh	d		06 07	06 41	07 05					07 39		08 15							09 14 →		09 14	
32½	Widnes	d		06 12	06 46	07 11					07 44	08 01	08 20				08 54		09 05			09 19	
34¼	Hough Green	d		06 15	06 49	07 14					07 47	08 05	08 24				08 57					09 23	
36½	Halewood	d		06 20	06 54	07 18					07 52		08 28									09 27	
37½	Hunts Cross	89 d		06 23	06 57	07 22					07 55	08s10	08 32									09 30	
39¼	**Liverpool South Parkway 7**	91, 103 ✈ a		06 27	07 01	07 27					07 59	08 18	08 37				09 06		09 15			09 35	
—	Liverpool Central 10	103 a		06 53	07 23	07 53					08 23	08f38	08f53						09 38			09f53	
40¼	West Allerton	91 a		06 31	07 05	07 30					08 03		08 40				09 10					09 38	
41	Mossley Hill	91 a		06 33	07 07	07 33					08 06		08 43				09 12					09 41	
43	Edge Hill	90, 91 a		06 39	07 13	07 39					08 11		08 48									09 46	
44¾	**Liverpool Lime Street 10**	90, 91 a	05 30	06 45	07 19	07 47		07 49	07 57		08 18	08 31	08 55		08 57	08 59	09 23		09 31		09 48	09 53	09 57

Station		NT	EM ◇ C	NT	NT		NT	TP 1 ◇ E	NT	EM ◇ G	NT	NT	NT		TP 1 ◇ E	NT	EM ◇ G	NT	NT	NT	TP 1 ◇ E		NT
Manchester Airport	85 ✈ d		09c05	09 03	09 41					10c05	10 03	10 41					11c05	11 03	11 41				
Sheffield 7	78 d		08 42							09 42							10 42						
Stockport	84 d		09 25		09e41			09 42		10 26		10e41			10 42		11 26		11e41		11 42		
Manchester Piccadilly 10	78, 84, 85 d		09 37	09 22	10 01			10 07		10 37	10 22	11 01			11 07		11 37	11 22	12 01		12 07		
Manchester Oxford Road	84, 85 d	09 16	09 41	09 44	10 04			10 11	10 16	10 41	10 44	11 04			11 11	11 16	11 41	11 44	12 04		12 11		12 16
Deansgate	84, 85 d	09 18		09 46					10 18		10 46					11 18		11 46					12 18
Trafford Park	d	09 23														11 23							
Humphrey Park	d	09 25														11 25							
Urmston	d	09 27		09 52					10 24		10 52					11 27		11 52					12 24
Chassen Road	d								10 26														12 26
Flixton	d	09 30							10 29							11 30							12 29
Irlam	d	09 34		09 57					10 33		10 57					11 34		11 57					12 33
Glazebrook	d								10 36														12 36
Birchwood	d	09 40		10 03				10 24	10 40		11 03				11 24	11 40		12 03			12 24		12 40
Padgate	d			10 06							11 06							12 06					
Warrington Central	a	09 45	09 57	10 09				10 29	10 45	10 57	11 09				11 29	11 45	11 57	12 09			12 29		12 45
	d	09 46	09 57	10 10			←	10 29	10 46	10 57	11 10		←		11 29	11 46	11 57	12 10		←	12 29		12 46
Sankey for Penketh	d			10 14 →			10 14				11 14 →		11 14					12 14 →		12 14			
Widnes	d	09 54	10 05				10 19		10 54	11 05			11 19			11 54	12 05			12 19			12 54
Hough Green	d	09 57					10 23		10 57				11 23			11 57				12 23			12 57
Halewood	d						10 27						11 27							12 27			
Hunts Cross	89 d						10 30						11 30							12 30			
Liverpool South Parkway 7	91, 103 ✈ a	10 06	10 15				10 35		11 06	11 15			11 35			12 06	12 15			12 35			13 06
Liverpool Central 10	103 a		10 38				10f53			11 38			11f53				12 38			12f53			
West Allerton	91 a	10 10					10 38		11 10				11 38			12 10				12 38			13 10
Mossley Hill	91 a	10 12					10 41		11 12				11 41			12 12				12 41			13 12
Edge Hill	90, 91 a						10 46						11 46							12 46			
Liverpool Lime Street 10	90, 91 a	10 23	10 31		10 48		10 53	10 57	11 23	11 31		11 48	11 53		11 57	12 23	12 31		12 48	12 53	12 57		13 23

Station		EM ◇ G	NT	NT	NT	TP 1 ◇ E	NT	EM ◇ G		NT	NT	NT	TP 1 ◇ E	NT	EM ◇ G	NT		NT	NT	TP 1 ◇ E	NT	EM ◇ G	NT
Manchester Airport	85 ✈ d	12c05	12 03	12 41				13c05		13 03	13 41				14c05	14 03		14 41				15c05	15 03
Sheffield 7	78 d	11 42						12 42							13 42							14 42	
Stockport	84 d	12 26		12e41		12 42		13 26			13e41		13 42		14 26			14e41		14 42		15 26	
Manchester Piccadilly 10	78, 84, 85 d	12 37	12 22	13 01		13 07		13 37		13 22	14 01		14 07		14 37	14 22		15 01		15 07		15 37	15 22
Manchester Oxford Road	84, 85 d	12 41	12 44	13 04		13 11	13 16	13 41		13 44	14 04		14 11	14 16	14 41	14 44		15 04		15 11	15 16	15 41	15 44
Deansgate	84, 85 d		12 46				13 18			13 46				14 18		14 46					15 18		15 46
Trafford Park	d						13 23														15 23		
Humphrey Park	d						13 25														15 25		
Urmston	d		12 52				13 27			13 52				14 24		14 52					15 27		15 52
Chassen Road	d													14 26									
Flixton	d						13 30							14 29							15 30		
Irlam	d		12 57				13 34			13 57				14 33		14 57					15 34		15 57
Glazebrook	d													14 36									
Birchwood	d		13 03			13 24	13 40			14 03			14 24	14 40		15 03				15 24	15 40		16 03
Padgate	d		13 06							14 06						15 06							16 06
Warrington Central	a	12 57	13 09			13 29	13 45	13 57		14 09			14 29	14 45	14 57	15 09				15 29	15 45	15 57	16 09
	d	12 57	13 10		←	13 29	13 46	13 57		14 10		←	14 29	14 46	14 57	15 10			←	15 29	15 45	15 57	16 10
Sankey for Penketh	d		13 14 →		13 14					14 14 →		14 14				15 14 →			15 14				16 14 →
Widnes	d	13 05			13 19		13 54	14 05				14 19		14 54	15 05				15 19		15 53	16 05	
Hough Green	d				13 23		13 57					14 23		14 57					15 23		15 56		
Halewood	d				13 27							14 27							15 27		16 01		
Hunts Cross	89 d				13 30							14 30							15 30				
Liverpool South Parkway 7	91, 103 ✈ a	13 15			13 35		14 06	14 15				14 35		15 06	15 15				15 35		16 07	16 15	
Liverpool Central 10	103 a	13 38			13f53			14 38				14f53			15 38				15f53			16 38	
West Allerton	91 a				13 38		14 10					14 38		15 10					15 38		16 11		
Mossley Hill	91 a				13 41		14 12					14 41		15 12					15 41		16 13		
Edge Hill	90, 91 a				13 46							14 46							15 46				
Liverpool Lime Street 10	90, 91 a	13 31		13 48	13 53	13 57	14 23	14 31			14 48	14 53	14 57	15 23	15 31			15 48	15 53	15 57	16 25	16 31	

For general notes see front of timetable
For details of catering facilities see Directory of Train Operators

A From Nottingham (Table 49)
B From Hull (Table 39)
C From Nottingham (Table 34)
D From Newcastle (Table 39)
E From Scarborough (Table 39)
G From Norwich (Table 49)
b Change at Manchester Piccadilly and Manchester Oxford Road
c Change at Manchester Piccadilly
e Change at Manchester Oxford Road
f Change at Hunts Cross

Manchester Airport and Manchester → Warrington Central → Liverpool

Network Diagram - see first page of Table 88

		NT	NT	TP [1]◇ A ⊼		NT	EM ◇ B ⊼	NT	NT	NT	TP [1]◇ A ⊼	NT		EM ◇ B ⊼	NT	NT	NT	TP [1]◇ A ⊼	NT	NT		EM ◇ B ⊼	NT
Manchester Airport	85 d	15 41					16b05	16 03	16 41					17b05		17 03	17 41					18b03	
Sheffield [7]	78 d						15 42							16 42								17 40	
Stockport	84 d	15c41		15 42			16 26	16 12	16c41		16 42			17 26		17 12	17 37	17 42				18 26	
Manchester Piccadilly [10]	78, 84, 85 d	16 01		16 07			16 37	16 27	17 01		17 07			17 37		17 27	18 01	18 07	←			18 37	18 22
Manchester Oxford Road	84, 85 d	16 04		16 11		16 16	16 41	16 43	17 04		17 11	17 13		17 42		17 44	18 04	18 11	18 04	18 16		18 41	18 44
Deansgate	84, 85 d					16 18		16 45				17 15				17 46	→			18 18			18 46
Trafford Park	d							16 51				17 20				17 51				18 23			18 51
Humphrey Park	d											17 22				17 53				18 25			18 53
Urmston	d					16 24		16 54				17 25				17 55				18 27			18 55
Chassen Road	d					16 26						17 27				17 57				18 29			18 57
Flixton	d					16 29		16 57				17 29				18 00				18 32			19 00
Irlam	d					16 33		17 01				17 33		17 52		18 04				18 36			19 04
Glazebrook	d					16 36						17 36				18 07							19 07
Birchwood	d			16 24		16 40		17 07			17 24	17 41		17 58		18 12		18 24		18 41			19 11
Padgate	d					16 43		17 10				17 44				18 15							19 14
Warrington Central	a			16 29		16 47	16 57	17 13		←	17 29	17 48		18 03		18 18		18 29		18 46		18 57	19 20
	d		←	16 29		16 47	16 57	17 14 →		17 14	17 29	17 48		18 03		18 19		18 29		18 47		18 57	
Sankey for Penketh	d		16 14							17 18		17 52								18 51			
Widnes	d		16 19			16 55	17 05			17 23		17 58		18 11						18 56		19 05	
Hough Green	d		16 23			16 58				17 27		18 01				18 28				18 59			
Halewood	d		16 27							17 31		18 06								19 04			
Hunts Cross	89 d		16 30							17 34	17 40	18 09				18 33				19 07		19 12	
Liverpool South Parkway [7]	91, 103 a		16 35			17 07	17 15			17 39		18 14		18 21		18 38				19 13		19 18	
Liverpool Central [10]	103 a		16e53				17 38				18 08	18 38		18 53		19 08						19e38	
West Allerton	91 a		16 38			17 11				17 42		18 18			←	18 42				19 16			
Mossley Hill	91 a		16 41			17 13				17 45		18 20			18 20	18 44				19 18			
Edge Hill	90, 91 a		16 46							17 50		→			18 30	18 50				19 26			
Liverpool Lime Street [10]	90, 91 a	16 48	16 53	16 57		17 25	17 31		17 48	17 58	18 00			18 35	18 38	18 57		18 59	19 00	19 35		19 35	

		NT	TP [1]◇ A ⊼	NT	EM ◇ B ⊼	NT	NT	NT		TP [1]◇ A	NT	EM ◇ B ⊼	NT	TP [1]◇ A	NT	NT		NT	TP [1]◇ A	NT	NT		
Manchester Airport	85 d	18 41			19c09		19 41					20c09		20 29		21c09		21 41			22 29		
Sheffield [7]	78 d				18 42							19 42				20 11		20 32	20 32				
Stockport	84 d	18c41	18 42		19 26		19 37			19 42		20 26	19 26	20 42		21 17		21 29	21 42		22 35		
Manchester Piccadilly [10]	78, 84, 85 d	19 01	19 07		19 37	19 32	20 01			20 07		20 37	20 32	21 07		21 38		22 01	22 07		23 14		
Manchester Oxford Road	84, 85 d	19 04	19 11		19 41	19 44	20 04			20 11		20 41	20 44	21 11		21 44		22 04	22 11		23 27		
Deansgate	84, 85 d					19 46							20 46			21 46					23 29		
Trafford Park	d					19 51							20 51			21 51					23 34		
Humphrey Park	d					19 53							20 53			21 53					23 36		
Urmston	d					19 55							20 55			21 55					23 38		
Chassen Road	d					19 57							20 57			21 57					23 40		
Flixton	d					20 00							21 00			22 00					23 43		
Irlam	d					20 04		←					21 04			22 04					23 47		
Glazebrook	d					20 07		20 07					21 07			22 07					23 50		
Birchwood	d		19 24			→		20 11		20 24			21 11	21 24		22 11			22 24		23 54		
Padgate	d							20 14					21 14			22 14					23 57		
Warrington Central	a		19 29		19 57			20 18		20 29		20 57	21 20	21 29		22 20			22 29		00 01		
	d		19 29	19 34	19 57			20 18		20 29	20 49	20 57		21 29	21 49				22 29	22 49	00 01		
Sankey for Penketh	d			19 38							20 53				21 53					22 53	00 05		
Widnes	d			19 43	20 05						20 58	21 05			21 58					22 58	00 11		
Hough Green	d			19 46				20 28			21 01				22 01					23 01	00 13		
Halewood	d			19 51							21 06				22 06					23 06	00 18		
Hunts Cross	89 d			19 54				20 33			21 09				22 09					23 09	00 21		
Liverpool South Parkway [7]	91, 103 a			19 58	20 15			20 38			21 11	21 19			22 11					23 11	00 27		
Liverpool Central [10]	103 a			20 23				21 08			21 38				22 38					23 38			
West Allerton	91 a			20 02				20 41			21 15				22 15					23 15			
Mossley Hill	91 a			20 05				20 44			21 18				22 18					23 18			
Edge Hill	90, 91 a			20 10							21 23				22 23					23 23			
Liverpool Lime Street [10]	90, 91 a	19 48	19 57	20 18	20 35		20 48	20 56		20 59	21 30	21 35		21 57	22 30			22 48	22 58	23 30	00 41		

For general notes see front of timetable
For details of catering facilities see Directory of Train Operators

A From Scarborough (Table 39)
B From Norwich (Table 49)
b Change at Manchester Piccadilly
c Change at Manchester Oxford Road
e Change at Hunts Cross

Manchester Airport and Manchester → Warrington Central → Liverpool

Network Diagram - see first page of Table 88

		NT	NT	NT	NT	NT	TP	NT	EM	NT	NT	TP	NT	NT	EM	NT	NT	NT	TP	NT
							1 ◇		◇ A ✠			1 ◇ B ✠			◇ A ✠				1 ◇ C ✠	
Manchester Airport	85 ✈ d	04 34			05b15	06 41			07c05	07 00	07 41				08c05	08 03	08 41			
Sheffield 7	78 ⛴ d					05 11			06 20				←		07 35					
Stockport	84 d					06e41			07 22		07 29	07 41	07 40		08 24		08e41		08 42	
Manchester Piccadilly 10	78, 84, 85 ⛴ d	04 49			05 50	06 58	07 07		07 34	07 15	07 58	08 07			08 37	08 22	09 01		09 07	
Manchester Oxford Road	84, 85 d				06 22	07 01	07 11		07 37	07 39	08 03	08 11	08 03	08 15	08 41	08 44	09 04		09 11	09 16
Deansgate	84, 85 ⛴ d				06 24					07 41	→			08 17		08 46				09 18
Trafford Park	d				06 29					07 46										09 23
Humphrey Park	d				06 31															09 25
Urmston	d				06 33					07 49				08 24		08 52				09 27
Chassen Road	d				06 35									08 26						
Flixton	d				06 38					07 52				08 29						09 30
Irlam	d				06 42					07 56				08 33		08 57				09 34
Glazebrook	d				06 45					07 59				08 36						
Birchwood	d				06 49		07 24			08 04		08 24		08 40		09 03			09 24	09 40
Padgate	d				06 52					08 07						09 06				
Warrington Central	a				06 56		07 29		07 53	08 10		08 29		08 45	08 57	09 09			09 29	09 45
	d		06 03	06 37	06 56		07 29	07 40	07 53	08 11		08 29		08 46	08 57	09 10		←	09 29	09 46
Sankey for Penketh	d		06 07	06 41	07 00			07 44		08 15						09 14		09 14		
Widnes	d		06 12	06 46	07 06			07 49	08 01	08 20				08 54	09 05	→		09 19		09 54
Hough Green	d		06 15	06 49	07 09			07 52	08 05	08 24				08 57				09 23		09 57
Halewood	d		06 20	06 54	07 13			07 57		08 28								09 27		
Hunts Cross	89 d		06 23	06 57	07 17			08 00	08s10	08 32								09 30		
Liverpool South Parkway 7	91, 103 ✈ a		06 27	07 01	07 22			08 02	08 18	08 37				09 06	09 15			09 35		10 06
Liverpool Central 10	103 a		06 53	07 23	07f38			08 23	08f38	08f53					09 38			09f53		
West Allerton	91 a		06 31	07 05	07 25			08 06		08 40				09 10				09 38		10 10
Mossley Hill	91 a		06 33	07 07	07 28			08 09		08 43				09 12				09 41		10 12
Edge Hill	90, 91 a		06 39	07 13	07 34			08 14		08 48								09 46		
Liverpool Lime Street 10	90, 91 a	05 30	06 45	07 20	07 40	07 49	07 57	08 21	08 31	08 55		08 57	08 59	09 23	09 31		09 48	09 53	09 57	10 23

		EM	NT	NT	NT	TP	NT	EM	NT	NT	NT	TP	NT	EM	NT	NT	NT	TP	NT	EM
		◇ A ✠				1 ◇ D ✠		◇ E ✠				1 ◇ D		◇ E ✠				1 ◇ D ✠		◇ E ✠
Manchester Airport	85 ✈ d	09c05	09 03	09 41				10c05	10 03	10 41				11c05	11 03	11 41				12c05
Sheffield 7	78 ⛴ d	08 42						09 42						10 42						11 42
Stockport	84 d	09 25		09e41		09 42		10 26		10e40		10 42		11 26		11e41		11 42		12 26
Manchester Piccadilly 10	78, 84, 85 ⛴ d	09 37	09 22	10 01		10 07		10 37	10 22	11 01		11 07		11 37	11 22	12 01		12 07		12 37
Manchester Oxford Road	84, 85 d	09 41	09 44	10 04		10 11	10 16	10 41	10 44	11 04		11 11	11 16	11 41	11 44	12 04		12 11	12 16	12 41
Deansgate	84, 85 ⛴ d		09 46				10 18		10 46				11 18		11 46				12 18	
Trafford Park	d												11 23							
Humphrey Park	d												11 25							
Urmston	d		09 52				10 24		10 52				11 27		11 52				12 24	
Chassen Road	d						10 26												12 26	
Flixton	d						10 29						11 30						12 29	
Irlam	d		09 57				10 33		10 57				11 34		11 57				12 33	
Glazebrook	d						10 36												12 36	
Birchwood	d		10 03			10 24	10 40		11 03			11 24	11 40		12 03			12 24	12 40	
Padgate	d		10 06						11 06						12 06					
Warrington Central	a	09 57	10 09			10 29	10 45	10 57	11 09			11 29	11 45	11 57	12 09			12 29	12 45	12 57
	d	09 57	10 10		←	10 29	10 46	10 57	11 10		←	11 29	11 46	11 57	12 10		←	12 29	12 46	12 57
Sankey for Penketh	d		10 14		10 14				11 14		11 14				12 14		12 14			
Widnes	d	10 05	→		10 19		10 54	11 05	→		11 19		11 54	12 05	→		12 19		12 54	13 05
Hough Green	d				10 23		10 57				11 23		11 57				12 23		12 57	
Halewood	d				10 27						11 27						12 27			
Hunts Cross	89 d				10 30						11 30						12 30			
Liverpool South Parkway 7	91, 103 ✈ a	10 15			10 35		11 06	11 15			11 35		12 06	12 15			12 35		13 06	13 15
Liverpool Central 10	103 a	10 38			10f53			11 38			11f53			12 38			12f53			13 38
West Allerton	91 a				10 38		11 10				11 38		12 10				12 38		13 10	
Mossley Hill	91 a				10 41		11 12				11 41		12 12				12 41		13 12	
Edge Hill	90, 91 a				10 46						11 46						12 46			
Liverpool Lime Street 10	90, 91 a	10 31		10 48	10 53	10 57	11 23	11 31		11 48	11 53	11 57	12 23	12 31		12 48	12 53	12 57	13 23	13 31

For general notes see front of timetable
For details of catering facilities see Directory of Train Operators

- **A** From Nottingham (Table 49)
- **B** From Hull (Table 39)
- **C** From Newcastle (Table 39)
- **D** From Scarborough (Table 39)
- **E** From Norwich (Table 49)
- **b** Change at Manchester Piccadilly and Manchester Oxford Road
- **c** Change at Manchester Piccadilly
- **e** Change at Manchester Oxford Road
- **f** Change at Hunts Cross

Manchester Airport and Manchester → Warrington Central → Liverpool

Network Diagram - see first page of Table 88

	NT	NT	NT	TP 1◇ A	NT	EM ◇ B		NT	NT	NT	TP 1◇ A	NT	EM ◇ B		NT	NT	NT	TP 1◇ A	NT	EM ◇ B		NT
Manchester Airport 85 d	12 03	12 41				13b05		13 03	13 41				14b05		14 03	14 41				15b05		15 03
Sheffield 78 d						12 42							13 42							14 42		
Stockport 84 d		12c41		12 42		13 26			13c41		13 42		14 26			14c41		14 42		15 26		
Manchester Piccadilly 78, 84, 85 d	12 22	13 01		13 07		13 37		13 22	14 01		14 07		14 37		14 22	15 01		15 07		15 37		15 22
Manchester Oxford Road 84, 85 d	12 44	13 04		13 11	13 16	13 41		13 44	14 04		14 11	14 16	14 41		14 44	15 04		15 11	15 16	15 41		15 44
Deansgate 84, 85 d	12 46				13 18			13 46				14 18			14 46				15 18			15 46
Trafford Park d					13 23														15 23			
Humphrey Park d					13 25														15 25			
Urmston d	12 52				13 27			13 52				14 24			14 52				15 27			15 52
Chassen Road d												14 26										
Flixton d					13 30							14 29							15 30			
Irlam d	12 57				13 34			13 57				14 33			14 57				15 34			15 57
Glazebrook d												14 36										
Birchwood d	13 03			13 24	13 40			14 03			14 24	14 40			15 03			15 24	15 40			16 03
Padgate d	13 06							14 06							15 06							16 06
Warrington Central a	13 09			13 29	13 45	13 57		14 09			14 29	14 45	14 57		15 09			15 29	15 45	15 57		16 09
d	13 10		←	13 29	13 46	13 57		14 10		←	14 29	14 46	14 57		15 10		←	15 29	15 45	15 57		16 10
Sankey for Penketh d	13 14 →		13 14					14 14 →		14 14					15 14 →		15 14					16 14 →
Widnes d			13 19		13 54	14 05				14 19		14 54	15 05				15 19		15 53	16 05		
Hough Green d			13 23		13 57					14 23		14 57					15 23		15 56			
Halewood d			13 27							14 27							15 27		16 01			
Hunts Cross 89 d			13 30							14 30							15 30					
Liverpool South Parkway 91, 103 a			13 35		14 06	14 15				14 35		15 06	15 15				15 35		16 07	16 15		
Liverpool Central 103 a			13e53			14 38				14e53			15 38				15e53			16 38		
West Allerton 91 a			13 38		14 10					14 38		15 10					15 38		16 11			
Mossley Hill 91 a			13 41		14 12					14 41		15 12					15 41		16 13			
Edge Hill 90, 91 a			13 46							14 46							15 46					
Liverpool Lime Street 90, 91 a		13 48	13 53	13 57	14 23	14 31			14 48	14 53	14 57	15 23	15 31			15 48	15 53	15 57	16 25	16 31		

	NT	NT	TP 1◇ A	NT	EM ◇ B	NT		NT	NT	TP 1◇ A	NT C	NT D	EM ◇ B		NT C	NT D	NT	NT	TP 1◇ A	NT		NT
Manchester Airport 85 d	15 41				16b05	16 03		16 41					17b05				17 03	17 41				
Sheffield 78 d					15 42								16 42									
Stockport 84 d	15c41		15 42		16 26			16c41		16 42			17 26					17 37	17 42			
Manchester Piccadilly 78, 84, 85 d	16 01		16 07		16 37	16 22		17 01		17 07			17 37				17 22	18 01	18 07	←		
Manchester Oxford Road 84, 85 d	16 04		16 11	16 16	16 41	16 43		17 04		17 11	17 13	17 16	17 42				17 44	18 04 →	18 11	18 04		18 16
Deansgate 84, 85 d				16 18		16 45					17 15	17 18					17 46					18 18
Trafford Park d						16 51					17 20	17 23					17 51					18 23
Humphrey Park d											17 22	17 25					17 53					18 25
Urmston d				16 24		16 54					17 25	17 27					17 55					18 27
Chassen Road d				16 26							17 27	17 29					17 57					18 29
Flixton d				16 29		16 57					17 29	17 32					18 00					18 32
Irlam d				16 33		17 01					17 33	17 36	17 52				18 04					18 36
Glazebrook d				16 36							17 36	17 39					18 07					
Birchwood d			16 24	16 40		17 07				17 24	17 41	17 44	17 58				18 12		18 24			18 41
Padgate d				16 43		17 10					17 44	17 47					18 15					
Warrington Central a			16 29	16 47	16 57	17 13			←	17 29	17 48	17 50	18 03				18 18		18 29			18 46
d		←	16 29	16 47	16 57	17 14 →			17 14	17 29	17 48	17 51	18 03				18 19		18 29			18 47
Sankey for Penketh d		16 14							17 18		17 52	17 55										18 51
Widnes d		16 19		16 55	17 05				17 23		17 58	18 01	18 11									18 56
Hough Green d		16 23		16 58					17 27		18 01	18 03					18 28					18 59
Halewood d		16 27							17 31		18 06	18 08										19 04
Hunts Cross 89 d		16 30							17 34	17 40	18 09	18 12					18 33					19 07
Liverpool South Parkway 91, 103 a		16 35		17 07	17 15				17 39		18 14	18 17	18 21				18 38					19 11
Liverpool Central 103 a		16e53			17 38					18 08	18 38	18 38					19e08					
West Allerton 91 a		16 38		17 11					17 42		18 18	18 21			←	←	18 42					19 15
Mossley Hill 91 a		16 41		17 13					17 45		18 20 →	18 23 →			18 20	18 23	18 44					19 18
Edge Hill 90, 91 a		16 46							17 50						18 30	18 30	18 50					19 26
Liverpool Lime Street 90, 91 a	16 48	16 53	16 57	17 25	17 31			17 48	17 58	18 00			18 35		18 38	18 38	18 57		18 59	19 00		19 35

	EM ◇ B	NT	NT	TP 1◇ A	NT	EM ◇ B		NT	NT	NT	TP 1◇ E	NT	NT	TP 1◇ A	NT	NT	NT	TP 1◇ A	NT	NT		
Manchester Airport 85 d	18b03	18 03	18 41			19c09			19 41				20 09	20 29		21c09	21 41			22 29		
Sheffield 78 d	17 40					18 42								19 42		20 11	20 31					
Stockport 84 d	18 26		18c41	18 42		19 26			19 37		19 42		19 26	20 42		21 17	21 29	21 45		22 40		
Manchester Piccadilly 78, 84, 85 d	18 37	18 22	19 01	19 07		19 37		19 32	20 01		20 07		20 32	21 07		21 38	22 01	22 07		22 54		
Manchester Oxford Road 84, 85 d	18 41	18 44	19 04	19 11		19 41		19 44	20 04		20 11		20 44	21 11		21 44	22 03	22 11		23 20		
Deansgate 84, 85 d		18 46						19 46					20 46			21 46				23 22		
Trafford Park d		18 51						19 51					20 51			21 51				23 27		
Humphrey Park d		18 53						19 53					20 53			21 53				23 29		
Urmston d		18 55						19 55					20 55			21 55				23 31		
Chassen Road d		18 57						19 57					20 57			21 57				23 33		
Flixton d		19 00						20 00					21 00			22 00				23 36		
Irlam d		19 04						20 04		←			21 04			22 04				23 40		
Glazebrook d		19 07						20 07 →		20 07			21 07			22 07				23 43		
Birchwood d		19 11		19 24						20 11	20 24		21 11	21 24		22 11		22 24		23 47		
Padgate d		19 14								20 14			21 14			22 14				23 50		
Warrington Central a	18 57	19 20		19 29		19 57				20 18	20 29		21 20	21 29		22 20		22 29		23 54		
d	18 57			19 29	19 34	19 57				20 18	20 29	20 49		21 29	21 49			22 29	22 49	23 54		
Sankey for Penketh d					19 38							20 53			21 53				22 53	23 58		
Widnes d	19 05				19 43	20 05						20 58			21 58				22 58	00 04		
Hough Green d					19 46					20 28		21 01			22 01				23 01	00 06		
Halewood d					19 51							21 06			22 06				23 06	00 11		
Hunts Cross 89 d	19 12				19 54					20 33		21 09			22 09				23 09	00 14		
Liverpool South Parkway 91, 103 a	19 18				19 58	20 18				20 38		21 15			22 11				23 11	00 20		
Liverpool Central 103 a	19e38				20 23	20 53				21 08		21 38			22 38				23 38			
West Allerton 91 a					20 02					20 41		21 19			22 15				23 15			
Mossley Hill 91 a					20 05					20 44		21 21			22 18				23 18			
Edge Hill 90, 91 a					20 10							21 27			22 23				23 23			
Liverpool Lime Street 90, 91 a	19 35		19 48	19 57	20 18	20 34			20 48	20 55	20 59	21 34		21 57	22 30		22 48	22 58	23 30	00 34		

For general notes see front of timetable
For details of catering facilities see Directory of Train Operators

- A From Scarborough (Table 39)
- B From Norwich (Table 49)
- C Until 31 October
- D From 7 November
- E From Hull (from 12 September from Scarborough) (Table 39)
- b Change at Manchester Piccadilly
- c Change at Manchester Oxford Road
- e Change at Hunts Cross

Table 89

Sundays

until 6 September

Manchester Airport and Manchester → Warrington Central → Liverpool

Network Diagram - see first page of Table 88

		NT	NT	NT	TP 1 ◇	NT		NT	TP 1 ◇ A	NT	NT	TP 1 ◇		EM ◇ B	NT	NT	TP 1 ◇ C	EM ◇ D		NT	NT	TP 1 ◇ E	EM ◇ D
Manchester Airport	85 ✈ d	06b40	08c06	08 34	08 39	09 00		09 35			10 32			11e03	11 03	11 35		12e00			12 35		13e00
Sheffield 7	78 d				07 50						09 20			10 41		10f19		11 38					12 41
Stockport	84 d		08 22	08 22	08 31	09 22			09 43	10 12	10g25	10 41		11 27		11f23	11f41	12 26		12 21	12 27	12 37	13 26
Manchester Piccadilly 10	78, 84, 85 d	07h44	08 35	08 50	09 07	09 35		09 50	10 07	10 26	10 50	11 07		11 38	11 35	11 50	12 07	12 38		12 35	12 50	13 07	13 38
Manchester Oxford Road	84, 85 d	08 06	08 45	08 54	09 10	09 45		09 53	10 10	10 45	10 53	11 10		11 42	11 45	11 53	12 10	12 42		12 45	12 53	13 10	13 42
Deansgate	84, 85 d	08 08	08 47			09 47				10 47					11 47					12 47			
Trafford Park	d																						
Humphrey Park	d																						
Urmston	d	08 14	08 53			09 53				10 53					11 53					12 53			
Chassen Road	d																						
Flixton	d																						
Irlam	d	08 19	08 58			09 58				10 58					11 58					12 58			
Glazebrook	d																						
Birchwood	d	08 25	09 04		09 24	10 04			10 24	11 04		11 24			12 04		12 24			13 04		13 24	
Padgate	d																						
Warrington Central	a	08 30	09 09		09 29	10 09			10 29	11 09		11 29		11 58	12 09		12 29	12 58		13 09		13 29	13 58
	d	08 30	09 09		09 29	10 09			10 29	11 09		11 29		11 59	12 09		12 29	12 58		13 09		13 29	13 58
Sankey for Penketh	d																						
Widnes	d	08 38	09 17			10 17				11 17				12 06	12 17			13 06		13 17			14 06
Hough Green	d	08 42	09 21			10 21				11 21					12 21					13 21			
Halewood	d	08 46	09 25			10 25				11 25					12 25					13 25			
Hunts Cross	89 d	08 49	09 28			10 28				11 28					12 28					13 28			
Liverpool South Parkway 7	91, 103 ✈ a	08 54	09 33			10 33				11 33				12 16	12 33			13 16		13 33			14 16
Liverpool Central 10	103 a	09 23	09j53			10j53				11j53					12j53					13j53			
West Allerton	91 a	08 57	09 36			10 36				11 36					12 36					13 36			
Mossley Hill	91 a	09 00	09 39			10 39				11 39					12 39					13 39			
Edge Hill	90, 91 a																						
Liverpool Lime Street 10	90, 91 a	09 09	09 48	09 53	09 57	10 50		10 55	10 57	11 48	11 53	11 59		12 30	12 48	12 53	12 57	13 30		13 48	13 53	13 57	14 30

		NT	NT	TP 1 ◇ E		EM ◇ G	NT	NT	TP 1 ◇ H	EM ◇ G		NT	NT	TP 1 ◇ E	EM ◇ D	NT		NT	TP 1 ◇ H	EM ◇ D	NT	NT	TP 1 ◇ E
Manchester Airport	85 ✈ d		13 35			14e00		14 35		15e00			15 35		16e00			16 35		17e00		17 35	
Sheffield 7	78 d					13 38				14 39					15 37					16 44			
Stockport	84 d	13 22	13 27	13 37		14 26	14 21	14 29	14 39	15 26		15 22	15 29	15 39	16 26	16 21		16 29	16 39	17 27	17 22	17 31	17 39
Manchester Piccadilly 10	78, 84, 85 d	13 35	13 50	14 07		14 38	14 35	14 50	15 07	15 38		15 35	15 50	16 07	16 38	16 35		16 50	17 07	17 38	17 35	17 50	18 07
Manchester Oxford Road	84, 85 d	13 45	13 53	14 10		14 42	14 45	14 53	15 10	15 42		15 45	15 53	16 10	16 42	16 45		16 53	17 10	17 42	17 45	17 53	18 10
Deansgate	84, 85 d	13 47					14 47					15 47				16 47					17 47		
Trafford Park	d																						
Humphrey Park	d																						
Urmston	d	13 53					14 53					15 53				16 53					17 53		
Chassen Road	d																						
Flixton	d																						
Irlam	d	13 58					14 58					15 58				16 58					17 58		
Glazebrook	d																						
Birchwood	d	14 04		14 24			15 04		15 24			16 04		16 24		17 04			17 24		18 04		18 24
Padgate	d																						
Warrington Central	a	14 09		14 29		14 58	15 09		15 29	15 58		16 09		16 29	16 58	17 09			17 29	17 58	18 09		18 29
	d	14 09		14 29		14 58	15 09		15 29	15 58		16 09		16 29	16 58	17 09			17 29	17 58	18 09		18 29
Sankey for Penketh	d																						
Widnes	d	14 17				15 06	15 17			16 06		16 17			17 06	17 17				18 06	18 17		
Hough Green	d	14 21					15 21					16 21				17 21					18 21		
Halewood	d	14 25					15 25					16 25				17 25					18 25		
Hunts Cross	89 d	14 28					15 28					16 28				17 28					18 28		
Liverpool South Parkway 7	91, 103 ✈ a	14 33				15 16	15 33			16 16		16 33			17 16	17 33				18 16	18 33		
Liverpool Central 10	103 a	14j53					15j53					16j53				17j53					18j53		
West Allerton	91 a	14 36					15 36					16 36				17 36					18 36		
Mossley Hill	91 a	14 39					15 39					16 39				17 39					18 39		
Edge Hill	90, 91 a																						
Liverpool Lime Street 10	90, 91 a	14 48	14 53	14 57		15 30	15 48	15 53	15 57	16 30		16 48	16 53	16 57	17 30	17 48		17 53	17 57	18 30	18 48	18 53	18 57

For general notes see front of timetable
For details of catering facilities see Directory of Train Operators

- **A** From York (Table 39)
- **B** From 19 July. From Nottingham (Table 49)
- **C** From Newcastle (Table 39)
- **D** From Nottingham (Table 49)
- **E** From Scarborough (Table 39)
- **G** From Norwich (Table 49)
- **H** From Middlesbrough (Table 39)
- **b** Change at Manchester Piccadilly and Manchester Oxford Road. By bus from Manchester Piccadilly
- **c** Change at Manchester Piccadilly and Manchester Oxford Road
- **e** Change at Manchester Piccadilly
- **f** Until 12 July only
- **g** From 19 July dep. 1022
- **h** By bus
- **j** Change at Hunts Cross

Table 89

Manchester Airport and Manchester → Warrington Central → Liverpool

until 6 September

Network Diagram - see first page of Table 88

	EM		NT	NT	TP	EM	NT		NT	TP	NT	NT	TP		NT	NT	TP	NT	NT			
	◇ A trolley				[1] ◇ B	◇ A trolley				[1] ◇ C			[1] ◇ B				[1] ◇ C					
Manchester Airport 85 ✈ d	18b00			18 35		19b00			19 35		19c55	20 35			20c55	21 35		21c55	22 35			
Sheffield [7] 78 d	17 44					18 37						19 35				20 35			21 11			
Stockport 84 d	18 26		18 21	18 29	18 39	19 26	19 22		19 29	19 39	20 21	20 29	20 39		21 22	21 29	21 40	22 21	22 29			
Manchester Piccadilly [10] 78, 84, 85 d	18 38		18 35	18 50	19 07	19 38	19 35		19 50	20 07	20 35	20 50	21 07		21 35	21 50	22 07	22 35	22 50			
Manchester Oxford Road 84, 85 d	18 42		18 45	18 53	19 10	19 42	19 45		19 53	20 10	20 45	20 53	21 10		21 45	21 53	22 10	22 45	22 53			
Deansgate 84, 85 d			18 47				19 47				20 47				21 47			22 47				
Trafford Park d																						
Humphrey Park d																						
Urmston d			18 53				19 53				20 53				21 53			22 53				
Chassen Road d																						
Flixton d																						
Irlam d			18 58				19 58				20 58				21 58			22 58				
Glazebrook d																						
Birchwood d			19 04		19 24		20 04			20 24	21 04		21 24		22 04		22 24	23 04				
Padgate d																						
Warrington Central a	18 58		19 09		19 29	19 58	20 09			20 29	21 09		21 29		22 09		22 29	23 09				
d	18 58		19 09		19 29	19 58	20 09			20 29	21 09		21 29		22 09		22 29	23 09				
Sankey for Penketh d																						
Widnes d	19 06		19 17			20 06	20 17				21 17				22 17			23 17				
Hough Green d			19 21				20 21				21 21				22 21			23 21				
Halewood d			19 25				20 25				21 25				22 25			23 25				
Hunts Cross 89 d			19 28				20 28				21 28				22 28			23 28				
Liverpool South Parkway [7] 91, 103 ✈ a	19 16		19 33			20 16	20 33				21 33				22 33			23 33				
Liverpool Central [10] 103 a			19e53				20e53				21e53				22e53							
West Allerton 91 a			19 36				20 36				21 36				22 36			23 36				
Mossley Hill 91 a			19 39				20 39				21 39				22 39			23 39				
Edge Hill 90, 91 a																						
Liverpool Lime Street [10] 90, 91 a	19 30		19 48	19 53	19 57	20 30	20 48		20 53	20 57	21 48	21 53	21 57		22 48	22 53	22 57	23 48	23 53			

Sundays

13 September to 1 November

	NT	NT	NT	TP	NT		TP	NT	TP	NT	TP		NT	NT	TP	NT	TP		NT	NT	TP	NT
		bus		[1] ◇	bus		bus		[1] ◇ D	bus	bus				[1] ◇ D	bus	bus				[1] ◇ E	bus
Manchester Airport 85 ✈ d			08 47					09c03					10c03	10 31					11 08	11 33		
Sheffield [7] 78 d														09 20						09f20		
Stockport 84 d								09 22					10 19	10 24					11 12	11 22		
Manchester Piccadilly [10] 78, 84, 85 d			09 03					09 35					10 35	10 50					11 30	11 50		
Manchester Oxford Road 84, 85 d	07 45		09 11					09 45					10 45	10 53					11 45	11 53		
Manchester Victoria 90 d				09 15					10 15						11 09						12 09	
Newton-le-Willows 90 d				09 33			09 45		10 33		10 45				11 27		11 40				12 27	
Deansgate 84, 85 d	07 47		09 13					09 47					10 47						11 47			
Trafford Park d																						
Humphrey Park d																						
Urmston d	07 53		09 19					09 53					10 53						11 53			
Chassen Road d																						
Flixton d																						
Irlam d	07 58		09 24					09 58					10 58						11 58			
Glazebrook d																						
Birchwood d	08 04		09 30					10 04					11 04						12 04			
Padgate d																						
Warrington Central a	08 11		09 37				10 05	10 11			11 05		11 11				12 00		12 11			
d		08 30			09 45					10 20						11 20						12 20
Sankey for Penketh d																						
Widnes d		08 45			10 00					10 35						11 35						12 35
Hough Green d		08 54			10 09					10 44						11 44						12 44
Halewood d		09 04			10 19					10 54						11 54						12 54
Hunts Cross 89 d		09 10			10 25					11 00						12 00						13 00
Liverpool South Parkway [7] 91, 103 ✈ a		09 16			10 31					11 06						12 06						13 06
Liverpool Central [10] 103 a																						
West Allerton 91 a		09 21			10 36					11 11						12 11						13 11
Mossley Hill 91 a		09 27			10 42					11 17						12 17						13 17
Edge Hill 90, 91 a																						
Liverpool Lime Street [10] 90, 91 a		09 42		09 57	10 57				10 57	11 32				11 53	11 57	12 32				12 53	12 57	13 32

For general notes see front of timetable
For details of catering facilities see Directory of Train Operators

A From Norwich (Table 49)
B From Middlesbrough (Table 39)
C From Scarborough (Table 39)
D From York (Table 39)
E From Newcastle (Table 39)
b Change at Manchester Piccadilly
c Change at Manchester Piccadilly and Manchester Oxford Road
e Change at Hunts Cross
f 13 September dep. 1019

Table 89

Sundays

Manchester Airport and Manchester → Warrington Central → Liverpool

13 September to 1 November

Network Diagram - see first page of Table 88

Station		TP	NT	NT		TP	NT	TP	NT	NT		TP	NT	TP	NT	NT		TP	NT	TP	NT	NT	TP
						1 ◇ A						1 ◇ A						1 ◇ B					1 ◇ A
		bus					bus	bus					bus	bus					bus	bus			
Manchester Airport	85 ✈ d		12b03	12 35					13b03	13 35					14b03	14 35					15b03	15 35	
Sheffield 7	78 d			11 38						12 41						13 38						14 39	
Stockport	84 d		12 16	12 26					13 22	13 29					14 21	14 29					15 22	15 29	
Manchester Piccadilly 10	78, 84, 85 d		12 30	12 50					13 35	13 50					14 35	14 50					15 35	15 50	
Manchester Oxford Road	84, 85 d		12 45	12 53					13 45	13 53					14 45	14 53					15 45	15 53	
Manchester Victoria	90 d					13 09						14 09						15 09					16 09
Newton-le-Willows	90 d	12 40				13 27		13 40				14 27		14 40				15 27		15 40			16 27
Deansgate	84, 85 d		12 47						13 47						14 47						15 47		
Trafford Park	d																						
Humphrey Park	d																						
Urmston	d		12 53						13 53						14 53						15 53		
Chassen Road	d																						
Flixton	d																						
Irlam	d		12 58						13 58						14 58						15 58		
Glazebrook	d																						
Birchwood	d		13 04						14 04						15 04						16 04		
Padgate	d																						
Warrington Central	a	13 00	13 11					14 00	14 11					15 00	15 11					16 00	16 11		
	d						13 20						14 20						15 20				
Sankey for Penketh	d																						
Widnes	d						13 35						14 35						15 35				
Hough Green	d						13 44						14 44						15 44				
Halewood	d						13 54						14 54						15 54				
Hunts Cross	89 d						14 00						15 00						16 00				
Liverpool South Parkway 7	91, 103 ✈ a						14 06						15 06						16 06				
Liverpool Central 10	103 a																						
West Allerton	91 a						14 11						15 11						16 11				
Mossley Hill	91 a						14 17						15 17						16 17				
Edge Hill	90, 91 a																						
Liverpool Lime Street 10	90, 91 a			13 53		13 57	14 32			14 53		14 57	15 32			15 53		15 57	16 32			16 53	16 57

Station		NT		TP	NT	NT	TP	NT		TP	NT	NT	TP	NT		TP	NT	NT	TP	NT		TP	NT
							1 ◇ B						1 ◇ A						1 ◇ B				
		bus		bus				bus		bus				bus		bus				bus		bus	
Manchester Airport	85 ✈ d				16b03	16 35					17b03	17 35					18b03	18 35					19b03
Sheffield 7	78 d					15 37						16 44						17 44					
Stockport	84 d				16 21	16 29					17 22	17 31					18 21	18 29					19 22
Manchester Piccadilly 10	78, 84, 85 d				16 35	16 50					17 35	17 50					18 35	18 50					19 35
Manchester Oxford Road	84, 85 d				16 45	16 53					17 45	17 53					18 45	18 53					19 45
Manchester Victoria	90 d						17 09						18 09						19 09				
Newton-le-Willows	90 d			16 40			17 27			17 40			18 27			18 40			19 27			19 40	
Deansgate	84, 85 d				16 47						17 47						18 47						19 47
Trafford Park	d																						
Humphrey Park	d																						
Urmston	d				16 53						17 53						18 53						19 53
Chassen Road	d																						
Flixton	d																						
Irlam	d				16 58						17 58						18 58						19 58
Glazebrook	d																						
Birchwood	d				17 04						18 04						19 04						20 04
Padgate	d																						
Warrington Central	a			17 00	17 11					18 00	18 11					19 00	19 11					20 00	20 11
	d	16 20						17 20						18 20						19 20			
Sankey for Penketh	d																						
Widnes	d	16 35						17 35						18 35						19 35			
Hough Green	d	16 44						17 44						18 44						19 44			
Halewood	d	16 54						17 54						18 54						19 54			
Hunts Cross	89 d	17 00						18 00						19 00						20 00			
Liverpool South Parkway 7	91, 103 ✈ a	17 06						18 06						19 06						20 06			
Liverpool Central 10	103 a																						
West Allerton	91 a	17 11						18 11						19 11						20 11			
Mossley Hill	91 a	17 17						18 17						19 17						20 17			
Edge Hill	90, 91 a																						
Liverpool Lime Street 10	90, 91 a	17 32				17 53	17 57	18 32				18 53	18 57	19 32				19 53	19 57	20 32			

For general notes see front of timetable
For details of catering facilities see Directory of Train Operators

A From Scarborough (Table 39)
B From Middlesbrough (Table 39)
b Change at Manchester Piccadilly and Manchester Oxford Road

Table 89

Sundays

Manchester Airport and Manchester → Warrington Central → Liverpool

13 September to 1 November

Network Diagram - see first page of Table 88

Station		NT	TP [1]◇ A	NT (bus)	TP (bus)	NT		NT	TP [1]◇ B	NT (bus)	TP (bus)	NT		NT	TP [1]◇ A	NT (bus)	TP (bus)	NT		NT	NT (bus)		
Manchester Airport	85 (air) d	19 35				20b03		20 35				21b03		21 35				22b03		22 35			
Sheffield [7]	78 (ship) d	18 37						19 35						20 35						21 11			
Stockport	84 d	19 29				20 21		20 29				21 22		21 29				22 21		22 29			
Manchester Piccadilly [10]	78, 84, 85 (ship) d	19 50				20 35		20 50				21 35		21 50				22 35		22 50			
Manchester Oxford Road	84, 85 d	19 53				20 45		20 53				21 45		21 53				22 45		22 53			
Manchester Victoria	90 (ship) d		20 09						21 09						22 09								
Newton-le-Willows	90 d		20 27		20 40				21 27		21 40				22 27		22 40						
Deansgate	84, 85 (ship) d					20 47						21 47						22 47					
Trafford Park	d																						
Humphrey Park	d																						
Urmston	d					20 53						21 53						22 53					
Chassen Road	d																						
Flixton	d																						
Irlam	d					20 58						21 58						22 58					
Glazebrook	d																						
Birchwood	d					21 04						22 04						23 04					
Padgate	d																						
Warrington Central	a				21 00	21 11					22 00	22 11					23 00	23 11					
	d			20 20						21 20						22 20					23 20		
Sankey for Penketh	d																						
Widnes	d			20 35						21 35						22 35					23 35		
Hough Green	d			20 44						21 44						22 44					23 44		
Halewood	d			20 54						21 54						22 54					23 54		
Hunts Cross	89 d			21 00						22 00						23 00					23 59		
Liverpool South Parkway [7]	91, 103 (air) a			21 06						22 06						23 06					00 06		
Liverpool Central [10]	103 a																						
West Allerton	91 a			21 11						22 11						23 11					00 11		
Mossley Hill	91 a			21 17						22 17						23 17					00 17		
Edge Hill	90, 91 a																						
Liverpool Lime Street [10]	90, 91 a	20 53	20 57	21 32				21 53	21 57	22 32				22 53	22 57	23 32				23 53	00 32		

Sundays

from 8 November

Station		NT	TP [1]◇	NT	TP (bus)	NT	TP [1]◇ C	TP (bus)	NT	NT	TP [1]◇ C	TP (bus)	NT	NT	TP [1]◇ D	EM ◇ E (trolley)	TP (bus)	NT	NT	TP [1]◇ A	EM ◇ E (trolley)	TP (bus)	NT
Manchester Airport	85 (air) d			08 47		09b03			10b03	10 31			11 08	11 33		12c03			12 35		13c03		
Sheffield [7]	78 (ship) d									09 20						11 38					12 41		
Stockport	84 d					09 22			10 19	10 24			11 12	11 22		12 26		12 16			13 26		13 22
Manchester Piccadilly [10]	78, 84, 85 (ship) d			09 03		09 35			10 35	10 50			11 30	11 50		12 38		12 30	12 50		13 38		13 35
Manchester Oxford Road	84, 85 d	07 45		09 11		09 45			10 45	10 53			11 45	11 53		12 42		12 45	12 53		13 42		13 45
Manchester Victoria	90 (ship) d		09 15				10 15				11 09				12 09					13 09			
Newton-le-Willows	90 d		09 33		09 45		10 33	10 45			11 27	11 40			12 27		12 40			13 27		13 40	
Deansgate	84, 85 (ship) d	07 47		09 13		09 47			10 47				11 47					12 47					13 47
Trafford Park	d																						
Humphrey Park	d																						
Urmston	d	07 53		09 19		09 53			10 53				11 53					12 53					13 53
Chassen Road	d																						
Flixton	d																						
Irlam	d	07 58		09 24		09 58			10 58				11 58					12 58					13 58
Glazebrook	d																						
Birchwood	d	08 04		09 30		10 04			11 04				12 04					13 04					14 04
Padgate	d																						
Warrington Central	a	08 09		09 35	10 05	10 09		11 05	11 09			12 00	12 09			12 58	13 00	13 09			13 58	14 00	14 09
	d	08 31		09 35		10 09			11 09				12 09			12 58		13 09			13 58		14 09
Sankey for Penketh	d																						
Widnes	d	08 39		09 43		10 17			11 17				12 17			13 06		13 17			14 06		14 17
Hough Green	d	08 42		09 47		10 21			11 21				12 21					13 21					14 21
Halewood	d	08 46		09 51		10 25			11 25				12 25					13 25					14 25
Hunts Cross	89 d	08 49		09 54		10 28			11 28				12 28					13 28					14 28
Liverpool South Parkway [7]	91, 103 (air) a	08 55		09 59		10 33			11 33				12 33			13 16		13 33			14 16		14 33
Liverpool Central [10]	103 a	09 23		10 23		10e53			11e53				12e53					13e53					14e53
West Allerton	91 a	08 58		10 02		10 36			11 36				12 36					13 36					14 36
Mossley Hill	91 a	09 00		10 05		10 39			11 39				12 39					13 39					14 39
Edge Hill	90, 91 a																						
Liverpool Lime Street [10]	90, 91 a	09 10	09 57	10 14		10 50	10 57		11 48	11 53	11 57		12 48	12 53	12 57	13 30		13 48	13 53	13 57	14 30		14 48

For general notes see front of timetable
For details of catering facilities see Directory of Train Operators

A From Scarborough (Table 39)
B From Middlesbrough (Table 39)
C From York (Table 39)
D From Newcastle (Table 39)
E From Nottingham (Table 49)

b Change at Manchester Piccadilly and Manchester Oxford Road
c Change at Manchester Piccadilly
e Change at Hunts Cross

Table 89

Sundays

from 8 November

Manchester Airport and Manchester → Warrington Central → Liverpool

Network Diagram - see first page of Table 88

Station	Table		NT	TP 1 ◇ A	EM ◇ B 🛒	TP 🚌	NT	NT	TP 1 ◇ C	EM ◇ D 🛒	TP 🚌	NT	NT	TP 1 ◇ A	EM ◇ B 🛒	TP 🚌	NT	NT	TP 1 ◇ C	EM ◇ B 🛒	TP 🚌	NT	NT	TP 1 ◇ A
Manchester Airport	85 ✈	d	13 35		14b03			14 35		15b03			15 35		16b03			16 35		17b03			17 35	
Sheffield 7	78 🚢	d			13 38					14 39					15 37					16 44				
Stockport	84	d	13 29		14 26		14 21	14 29		15 26		15 22	15 29		16 26		16 21	16 29		17 27		17 22	17 31	
Manchester Piccadilly 10	78, 84, 85 🚢	d	13 50		14 38		14 35	14 50		15 38		15 35	15 50		16 38		16 35	16 50		17 38		17 35	17 50	
Manchester Oxford Road	84, 85	d	13 53		14 42		14 45	14 53		15 42		15 45	15 53		16 42		16 45	16 53		17 42		17 45	17 53	
Manchester Victoria	90 🚢	d		14 09					15 09					16 09					17 09					18 09
Newton-le-Willows	90	d		14 27		14 40			15 27		15 40			16 27		16 40			17 27		17 40			18 27
Deansgate	84, 85 🚢	d					14 47					15 47					16 47					17 47		
Trafford Park		d																						
Humphrey Park		d																						
Urmston		d					14 53					15 53					16 53					17 53		
Chassen Road		d																						
Flixton		d																						
Irlam		d					14 58					15 58					16 58					17 58		
Glazebrook		d																						
Birchwood		d					15 04					16 04					17 04					18 04		
Padgate		d																						
Warrington Central		a			14 58	15 00	15 09			15 58	16 00	16 09			16 58	17 00	17 09			17 58	18 00	18 09		
		d			14 58		15 09			15 58		16 09			16 58		17 09			17 58		18 09		
Sankey for Penketh		d																						
Widnes		d			15 06		15 17			16 06		16 17			17 06		17 17			18 06		18 17		
Hough Green		d					15 21					16 21					17 21					18 21		
Halewood		d					15 25					16 25					17 25					18 25		
Hunts Cross	89	d					15 28					16 28					17 28					18 28		
Liverpool South Parkway 7	91, 103 ✈	a			15 16		15 33			16 16		16 33			17 16		17 33			18 16		18 33		
Liverpool Central 10	103	a					15c53					16c53					17c53					18c53		
West Allerton	91	a					15 36					16 36					17 36					18 36		
Mossley Hill	91	a					15 39					16 39					17 39					18 39		
Edge Hill	90, 91	a																						
Liverpool Lime Street 10	90, 91	a	14 53	14 57	15 30		15 48	15 53	15 57	16 30		16 48	16 53	16 57	17 30		17 48	17 53	17 57	18 30		18 48	18 53	18 57

Station	Table		EM ◇ D 🛒	TP 🚌	NT	NT	TP 1 ◇ C	EM ◇ D 🛒	TP 🚌	NT	NT	TP 1 ◇ A	TP 🚌	NT	NT	TP 1 ◇ C	TP 🚌	NT	NT	TP 1 ◇ A	TP 🚌	NT	NT
Manchester Airport	85 ✈	d	18b03			18 35		19b03			19 35			20e03	20 35			21e03	21 35			22e03	22 35
Sheffield 7	78 🚢	d	17 44					18 37							19 35				20 35				21 11
Stockport	84	d	18 26		18 21	18 29		19 26		19 22	19 29			20 21	20 29			21 22	21 29			22 21	22 29
Manchester Piccadilly 10	78, 84, 85 🚢	d	18 38		18 35	18 50		19 38		19 35	19 50			20 35	20 50			21 35	21 50			22 35	22 50
Manchester Oxford Road	84, 85	d	18 42		18 45	18 53		19 42		19 45	19 53			20 45	20 53			21 45	21 53			22 45	22 53
Manchester Victoria	90 🚢	d					19 09					20 09				21 09				22 09			
Newton-le-Willows	90	d		18 40			19 27		19 40			20 27	20 40			21 27	21 40			22 27	22 40		
Deansgate	84, 85 🚢	d			18 47					19 47				20 47				21 47				22 47	
Trafford Park		d																					
Humphrey Park		d																					
Urmston		d			18 53					19 53				20 53				21 53				22 53	
Chassen Road		d																					
Flixton		d																					
Irlam		d			18 58					19 58				20 58				21 58				22 58	
Glazebrook		d																					
Birchwood		d			19 04					20 04				21 04				22 04				23 04	
Padgate		d																					
Warrington Central		a	18 58	19 00	19 09			19 58	20 00	20 09			21 00	21 09			22 00	22 09			23 00	23 09	
		d	18 58		19 09			19 58		20 09				21 09				22 09				23 09	
Sankey for Penketh		d																					
Widnes		d	19 06		19 17			20 06		20 17				21 17				22 17				23 17	
Hough Green		d			19 21					20 21				21 21				22 21				23 21	
Halewood		d			19 25					20 25				21 25				22 25				23 25	
Hunts Cross	89	d			19 28					20 28				21 28				22 28				23 28	
Liverpool South Parkway 7	91, 103 ✈	a	19 16		19 33			20 16		20 33				21 33				22 33				23 33	
Liverpool Central 10	103	a			19c53					20c53				21c53				22c53					
West Allerton	91	a			19 36					20 36				21 36				22 36				23 36	
Mossley Hill	91	a			19 39					20 39				21 39				22 39				23 39	
Edge Hill	90, 91	a																					
Liverpool Lime Street 10	90, 91	a	19 30		19 48	19 53	19 57	20 30		20 48	20 53	20 57		21 48	21 53	21 57		22 48	22 53	22 57		23 48	23 53

For general notes see front of timetable
For details of catering facilities see Directory of Train Operators

- **A** From Scarborough (Table 39)
- **B** From Nottingham (Table 49)
- **C** From Middlesbrough (Table 39)
- **D** From Norwich (Table 49)
- **b** Change at Manchester Piccadilly
- **c** Change at Hunts Cross
- **e** Change at Manchester Piccadilly and Manchester Oxford Road

Liverpool and St Helens → Newton-le-Willows, Wigan, Preston and Manchester

Network Diagram - see first page of Table 88

Miles	Miles	Miles	Miles			NT	AW	NT	NT	NT	NT	AW	NT	NT	NT	NT	NT	NT	AW	NT	AW	NT	NT	NT	NT
							A					A							A ✕	B	◇ C ✕				
0	0	0	—	**Liverpool Lime Street [10]**	89, 91 d	05 13		05 31	05 46	06 01	06 13		06 16	06 31	06 46	06 57	07 01	07 13		07 16		07 31	07 46	07 57	08 01
1¾	1¾	1¾	—	Edge Hill	89, 91 d			05 35	05 50	06 05			06 20	06 35	06 50		07 05			07 20		07 35	07 50		08 05
2½	2½	2½	—	Wavertree Technology Park	d	05 19		05 37	05 52	06 07	06 19		06 22	06 37	06 52		07 07	07 19		07 22		07 37	07 52		08 07
3½	3½	3½	—	Broad Green	d			05 40	05 55	06 10			06 25	06 40	06 55		07 10			07 26		07 40	07 55		08 10
5	5	5	—	Roby	d			05 44	05 59	06 14			06 29	06 44	06 59		07 14			07 29		07 44	07 59		08 14
5½	5½	5½	—	Huyton	d			05 46	06 01	06 16			06 31	06 46	07 01	07 06	07 16			07 31		07 46	08 01	08 06	08 16
—	7¾	—	—	Prescot	d			05 51		06 21				06 51			07 21					07 51			08 21
—	8¾	—	—	Eccleston Park	d			05 53		06 23				06 53			07 23					07 53			08 23
—	9¾	—	—	Thatto Heath	d			05 56		06 26				06 56			07 26					07 56			08 26
—	11¼	—	—	**St Helens Central**	a			05 59		06 29				06 59		07 15	07 29					07 59		08 15	08 29
—	—	—	—		d			06 00		06 30				07 00		07 15	07 30					08 00		08 15	08 30
—	15	—	—	Garswood	d			06 07		06 37				07 07			07 37					08 07			08 37
—	16¼	—	—	Bryn	d			06 10		06 40				07 10			07 40					08 10			08 40
7½	—	7½	—	Whiston	d				06 05				06 35		07 05					07 35			08 05		
9	—	9	—	Rainhill	d				06 08				06 38		07 08					07 38			08 08		
10¾	—	10¾	—	Lea Green	d				06 11				06 41		07 11			07 28		07 41			08 11		
12	—	12	—	**St Helens Junction**	d	05 29			06 14		06 29		06 44		07 14			07 31		07 44			08 14		
—	—	—	—	Warrington Bank Quay	d		06 06					06 40							07 39		08 08				
14¾	—	14¾	—	Earlestown [8]	d		06 12		06 19			06 47	06 50		07 19				07 46	07 49	08 16		08 19		
—	—	—	—	Warrington Bank Quay	a								07 01							*08 23*					
16¼	—	16¼	0	**Newton-le-Willows**	d	05 35	06 15		06 22		06 35	06 50			07 22			07 37	07 49	07 52	08 19		08 22		
—	20	23¼	—	**Wigan North Western**	a			06 21		06 51				07 21		07 30	07 51					08 21		08 30	08 51
—	—	—	—		65 d											07 31								08 31	
—	28¼	31½	—	Euxton Balshaw Lane	d											07 41								08 41	
—	31	34¼	—	Leyland	82 a											07 46								08 46	
—	35	38¼	—	**Preston [8]**	65, 82 a									*07 51*		07 56	*08 13*					*08 51*		08 55	*09 38*
—	52½	—	—	Blackpool North	97 a											*08b29*	*09b05*							*09b25*	
26¾	—	—	10½	Patricroft	d				06 34						07 34					08 04			08 34		
27¾	—	—	11½	Eccles	d				06 36						07 36					08 06			08 36		
31¾	—	—	—	**Manchester Victoria**	⛴ a				06 49						07 49					08 19			08 49		
—	—	—	15¾	**Manchester Oxford Road**	a		06 35				06 57	07 09						07 57	08 09		08 41				
—	—	—	16¼	**Manchester Piccadilly [10]**	⛴ a	05 57	06 46				07 01	07 18						08 01	08 18		08 50				
—	—	—	26	**Manchester Airport**	85 ✈ a	06 14					07 22							08 22							

		NT	NT	NT	NT	AW	NT	NT	NT	NT	NT	NT	AW	NT	NT	NT	NT	NT	NT	AW	NT	NT	NT	NT	NT
					D	◇ C ✕						D	◇ C ✕						D	◇ C ✕					
Liverpool Lime Street [10]	89, 91 d	08 13	08 16	08 31	08 44		08 57	09 01	09 13	09 16	09 31	09 46		09 57	10 01	10 13	10 16	10 31	10 46		10 57	11 01	11 13	11 16	11 31
Edge Hill	89, 91 d		08 20	08 35	08 50			09 05		09 20	09 35	09 50			10 05		10 20	10 35	10 50			11 05		11 20	11 35
Wavertree Technology Park	d	08 19	08 22	08 37	08 52			09 07	09 19	09 22	09 37	09 52			10 07	10 19	10 22	10 37	10 52			11 07	11 19	11 22	11 37
Broad Green	d		08 25	08 40	08 55			09 10		09 25	09 40	09 55			10 10		10 25	10 40	10 55			11 10		11 25	11 40
Roby	d		08 29	08 44	08 59			09 14		09 29	09 44	09 59			10 14		10 29	10 44	10 59			11 14		11 29	11 44
Huyton	d		08 31	08 46	09 01		09 06	09 16		09 31	09 46	10 01		10 06	10 16		10 31	10 46	11 01		11 06	11 16		11 31	11 46
Prescot	d			08 51				09 21			09 51				10 21			10 51				11 21			11 51
Eccleston Park	d			08 53				09 23			09 53				10 23			10 53				11 23			11 53
Thatto Heath	d			08 56				09 26			09 56				10 26			10 56				11 26			11 56
St Helens Central	a			08 59			09 15	09 29			09 59			10 15	10 29			10 59			11 15	11 29			11 59
	d			09 00			09 15	09 30			10 00			10 15	10 30			11 00			11 15	11 30			12 00
Garswood	d			09 07				09 37			10 07				10 37			11 07				11 37			12 07
Bryn	d			09 10				09 40			10 10				10 40			11 10				11 40			12 10
Whiston	d		08 35		09 05					09 35		10 05					10 35		11 05					11 35	
Rainhill	d		08 38		09 08					09 38		10 08					10 38		11 08					11 38	
Lea Green	d		08 41		09 11					09 41		10 11					10 41		11 11					11 41	
St Helens Junction	d	08 29	08 44		09 14				09 29	09 44		10 14				10 29	10 44		11 14				11 29	11 44	
Warrington Bank Quay	d					09 19							10 19							11 19					
Earlestown [8]	d		08 50		09 19	09 26				09 50		10 19	10 26				10 50		11 19	11 26				11 50	
Warrington Bank Quay	a		09 01							10 01							11 01							12 01	
Newton-le-Willows	d	08 35			09 22	09 29			09 35			10 22	10 29			10 35			11 22	11 29			11 35		
Wigan North Western	a			09 21			09 30	09 51			10 21			10 30	10 51			11 21			11 30	11 51			12 21
	65 d						09 31							10 31							11 31				
Euxton Balshaw Lane	d						09 41							10 41							11 41				
Leyland	82 a						09 46							10 46							11 46				
Preston [8]	65, 82 a			*09 51*			09 54	*10 38*			*10 51*			10 54	*11 38*			*11 51*			11 54	*12 38*			*12 51*
Blackpool North	97 a						10 20							11 20							12 20				
Patricroft	d				09 34							10 34							11 34						
Eccles	d				09 36							10 36							11 36						
Manchester Victoria	⛴ a				09 47							10 49							11 49						
Manchester Oxford Road	a	08 57				09 48			09 57				10 48			10 57				11 48			11 57		
Manchester Piccadilly [10]	⛴ a	09 01				09 57			10 01				10 57			11 01				11 57			12 01		
Manchester Airport	85 ✈ a	09 22							10 22							11 22							12 22		

For general notes see front of timetable
For details of catering facilities see Directory of Train Operators

A From Chester (Table 81)
B To Huddersfield (Table 39)
C From Llandudno (Table 81)
D To Stalybridge (Table 39)
b Change at Wigan North Western and Preston

Liverpool and St Helens → Newton-le-Willows, Wigan, Preston and Manchester

Network Diagram - see first page of Table 88

			NT	AW	NT	NT	NT	NT	NT	NT	AW	NT	NT	NT	NT	NT	NT	AW	NT	NT	NT	NT	NT	NT	AW	NT
			A	◇ B						A	◇ B						A	◇ B						A	◇ B	
Liverpool Lime Street [10]	89, 91	d	11 46		11 57	12 01	12 13	12 16	12 31	12 46		12 57	13 01	13 13	13 16	13 31	13 46		13 57	14 01	14 13	14 16	14 31	14 46		14 57
Edge Hill	89, 91	d	11 50			12 05		12 20	12 35	12 50			13 05		13 20	13 35	13 50			14 05		14 20	14 35	14 50		
Wavertree Technology Park		d	11 52			12 07	12 19	12 22	12 37	12 52			13 07	13 19	13 22	13 37	13 52			14 07	14 19	14 22	14 37	14 52		
Broad Green		d	11 55			12 10		12 25	12 40	12 55			13 10		13 25	13 40	13 55			14 10		14 25	14 40	14 55		
Roby		d	11 59			12 14		12 29	12 44	12 59			13 14		13 29	13 44	13 59			14 14		14 29	14 44	14 59		
Huyton		d	12 01		12 06	12 16		12 31	12 46	13 01		13 06	13 16		13 31	13 46	14 01		14 06	14 16		14 31	14 46	15 01		15 06
Prescot		d				12 21			12 51				13 21			13 51				14 21			14 51			
Eccleston Park		d				12 23			12 53				13 23			13 53				14 23			14 53			
Thatto Heath		d				12 26			12 56				13 26			13 56				14 26			14 56			
St Helens Central		a			12 15	12 29			12 59			13 15	13 29			13 59			14 15	14 29			14 59			15 15
		d			12 15	12 30			13 00			13 15	13 30			14 00			14 15	14 30			15 00			15 15
Garswood		d				12 37			13 07				13 37			14 07				14 37			15 07			
Bryn		d				12 40			13 10				13 40			14 10				14 40			15 10			
Whiston		d	12 05					12 35		13 05					13 35		14 05					14 35		15 05		
Rainhill		d	12 08					12 38		13 08					13 38		14 08					14 38		15 08		
Lea Green		d	12 11					12 41		13 11					13 41		14 11					14 41		15 11		
St Helens Junction		d	12 14				12 29	12 44		13 14				13 29	13 44		14 14				14 29	14 44		15 14		
Warrington Bank Quay		d		12 19							13 19							14 19							15 19	
Earlestown [8]		d	12 19	12 26				12 50		13 19	13 26				13 50		14 19	14 26				14 50		15 19	15 26	
Warrington Bank Quay		a						13 01							14 01							15 01				
Newton-le-Willows		d	12 22	12 29			12 35			13 22	13 29			13 35			14 22	14 29			14 35			15 22	15 29	
Wigan North Western		a			12 30	12 51			13 21			13 30	13 51			14 21			14 30	14 51			15 21			15 30
	65	d			12 31							13 31							14 31							15 31
Euxton Balshaw Lane		d			12 41							13 41							14 41							15 41
Leyland	82	a			12 46							13 46							14 46							15 46
Preston [8]	65, 82	a			12 54	*13 38*			*13 51*			13 54	*14 38*			*14 51*			14 54	*15 38*			*15 51*			15 54
Blackpool North	97	a			13 21							14 20							15 20							16 20
Patricroft		d	12 34							13 34							14 34							15 34		
Eccles		d	12 36							13 36							14 36							15 36		
Manchester Victoria		a	12 50							13 47							14 50							15 49		
Manchester Oxford Road		a		12 48			12 57				13 48			13 57				14 48			14 57				15 48	
Manchester Piccadilly [10]		a		12 57			13 01				13 57			14 01				14 57			15 01				15 57	
Manchester Airport	85	a					13 22							14 22							15 22					

			NT	NT	NT	NT	NT	AW	NT	NT	NT	NT	AW	NT	NT	NT	NT	NT	NT	AW	NT	NT	NT	NT	NT	NT
							C	◇ B					◇ B		C					◇ B						
Liverpool Lime Street [10]	89, 91	d	15 01	15 13	15 16	15 31	15 46		15 57	16 01	16 13	16 16		16 31	16 46	16 57	17 01	17 06	17 10		17 19	17 27	17 35	17 44	17 48	18 01
Edge Hill	89, 91	d	15 05		15 20	15 35	15 50			16 05		16 20		16 35	16 50		17 05		17 14			17 31	17 39		17 52	18 05
Wavertree Technology Park		d	15 07	15 19	15 22	15 37	15 52			16 07	16 19	16 22		16 37	16 52		17 07	17 12	17 16			17 33	17 41	17 49	17 54	18 07
Broad Green		d	15 10		15 25	15 40	15 55			16 10		16 25		16 40	16 55		17 10		17 19			17 36	17 44	17 52	17 57	18 10
Roby		d	15 14		15 29	15 44	15 59			16 14		16 29		16 44	16 59		17 14		17 23			17 40	17 48		18 01	18 14
Huyton		d	15 16		15 31	15 46	16 01		16 06	16 16		16 31		16 46	17 01	17 06	17 16	17 19	17 25		17 29	17 42	17 50	17 57	18 03	18 16
Prescot		d	15 21			15 51				16 21				16 51			17 21				17 33			18 02		18 21
Eccleston Park		d	15 23			15 53				16 23				16 53			17 23				17 36			18 05		18 23
Thatto Heath		d	15 26			15 56				16 26				16 56			17 26				17 38			18 07		18 26
St Helens Central		a	15 29			15 59			16 15	16 29				16 59		17 15	17 29				17 42	17 51		18 11		18 29
		d	15 30			16 00			16 15	16 30				17 00		17 15	17 30				17 42	17 51		18 11		18 30
Garswood		d	15 37			16 07				16 37				17 07			17 37				17 49			18 19		18 37
Bryn		d	15 40			16 10				16 40				17 10			17 40				17 52			18 22		18 40
Whiston		d			15 35		16 05					16 35			17 05				17 28				17 54		18 07	
Rainhill		d			15 38		16 08					16 38			17 08				17 32				17 57		18 10	
Lea Green		d			15 41		16 11					16 41			17 11			17 26	17 35				18 00		18 13	
St Helens Junction		d		15 29	15 44		16 14				16 29	16 44			17 14			17 29	17 39				18 03		18 16	
Warrington Bank Quay		d						16 19					16 51							17 49						
Earlestown [8]		d			15 50		16 19	16 26				16 49	16 59		17 19				17 44	17 57			18 08		18 21	
Warrington Bank Quay		a			16 01							*17 25*			*17 52*				*18 23*							
Newton-le-Willows		d		15 35			16 22	16 29			16 35	16 52	17 02		17 22			17 35	17 47	18 00			18 11		18 24	
Wigan North Western		a	15 51			16 21			16 29	16 51				17 21		17 30	17 52				18 04	18 05		18 30		18 49
	65	d							16 31							17 31						18 06		18 31		18 49
Euxton Balshaw Lane		d							16 43							17 41						18 17		18 41		19 01
Leyland	82	a							16 48							17 46						18 22		18 46		19 06
Preston [8]	65, 82	a				*16 42*			16 56	*17 38*				*17 51*		17 54					*18 51*	18 31		18 54		19 15
Blackpool North	97	a							17 23							18 20						*19 09*		19 20		*20 00*
Patricroft		d					16 34					17 04			17 34				17 59				18 23			
Eccles		d					16 36					17 06			17 36				18 01				18 25		18 36	
Manchester Victoria		a					16 49					17 19			17 47				18 12				18 40		18 49	
Manchester Oxford Road		a		15 57				16 48			16 57		17 21					17 57		18 19						
Manchester Piccadilly [10]		a		16 01				16 57			17 01		17 30					18 01		18 28						
Manchester Airport	85	a		16 22							17 22							18 22								

For general notes see front of timetable
For details of catering facilities see Directory of Train Operators

A To Stalybridge (Table 39)
B From Llandudno (Table 81)
C To Huddersfield (Table 39)

Liverpool and St Helens → Newton-le-Willows, Wigan, Preston and Manchester

Network Diagram - see first page of Table 88

Mondays to Fridays

	NT	NT	AW ◇ A	NT	NT	AW B	NT	NT	NT	AW ◇ A	NT	NT	NT	NT	AW ◇ A	NT	NT	AW B	NT	NT	NT	NT	AW B
Liverpool Lime Street 10 89, 91 d	18 13	18 16		18 31	18 46		19 01	19 12	19 23		19 42	20 09	20 12	20 25		20 42	21 12		21 42	22 12	23 02	23 16	
Edge Hill 89, 91 d		18 20		18 35	18 50		19 05	19 16			19 46		20 16			20 46	21 16		21 46	22 16	23 06	23 20	
Wavertree Technology Park d	18 19	18 22		18 37	18 52		19 07	19 18			19 48	20 15	20 18			20 48	21 18		21 48	22 18	23 08	23 22	
Broad Green d		18 25		18 40	18 55		19 10	19 21			19 51		20 21			20 51	21 21		21 51	22 21	23 11	23 26	
Roby d		18 29		18 44	18 59		19 14	19 25			19 55		20 25			20 55	21 25		21 55	22 25	23 15	23 30	
Huyton d		18 31		18 46	19 01		19 16	19 27	19 32		19 57		20 27	20 34		20 57	21 27		21 57	22 27	23 17	23 32	
Prescot d				18 51			19 21				20 02					21 02			22 02		23 22		
Eccleston Park d				18 53			19 23				20 04					21 04			22 04		23 24		
Thatto Heath d				18 56			19 26				20 07					21 07			22 07		23 27		
St Helens Central a				18 59			19 29		19 40		20 10			20 42		21 10			22 10		23 30		
d				19 00			19 30		19 41		20 11			20 43		21 11			22 11		23 31		
Garswood d				19 07			19 37				20 18					21 18			22 18		23 38		
Bryn d				19 10			19 40				20 21					21 21			22 21		23 41		
Whiston d		18 35			19 05			19 31					20 31				21 31			22 31		23 36	
Rainhill d		18 38			19 08			19 34					20 34				21 34			22 34		23 39	
Lea Green d		18 41			19 11			19 37					20 37				21 37			22 37		23 42	
St Helens Junction d	18 29	18 44			19 14			19 40				20 25	20 40				21 40			22 40		23 45	
Warrington Bank Quay d			18 46			19 19				20 19					21 19			22 19					23 49
Earlestown 8 d		18 50	18 57		19 19	19 26		19 45		20 26			20 45		21 26		21 45	22 26		22 45		23 50	23 56
Warrington Bank Quay a		19 01						*20 25*					*21 25*				*22 23*			*23 47*			
Newton-le-Willows d	18 35		19 00		19 22	19 29		19 48		20 29		20 35	20 48		21 29		21 48	22 29		22 48		23 53	23 59
Wigan North Western a				19 21			19 51		19 54		20 32			20 57		21 32			22 28		23 48		
65 d									19 55					20 57					22 28		23 48		
Euxton Balshaw Lane d									20 05					21 08					22 39		23 59		
Leyland 82 a									20 10					21 16					22 44		00 04		
Preston 8 65, 82 a				*19 51*			*20 14*		20 18		*20 51*			21 22		*22 53*			22 54		00 13		
Blackpool North 97 a							*20b54*		20 44		*21b48*			21 53					23 21		*00c48*		
Patricroft d					19 34			20 00					21 00				22 00			23 00		00 05	
Eccles d					19 36			20 02					21 02				22 02			23 02		00 08	
Manchester Victoria a					19 49			20 16					21 15				22 15			23 15		00 21	
Manchester Oxford Road a	18 57		19 21			19 48				20 48		20 57			21 48			22 50					
Manchester Piccadilly 10 a	19 01		19 29			19 57				20 57		21 01			21 57			22 58					00 28
Manchester Airport 85 a	19 24											21 24											

Saturdays

	NT	AW B	NT	NT	NT	NT	AW B	NT	NT	NT C	NT	NT	NT	AW B	NT D	AW ◇ A	NT	NT	NT		NT	NT	NT	NT
Liverpool Lime Street 10 89, 91 d	05 13		05 31	05 46	06 01	06 13		06 16	06 31	06 46	06 57	07 01	07 13		07 16		07 31	07 46	07 57		08 01	08 13	08 16	08 31
Edge Hill 89, 91 d			05 35	05 50	06 05			06 20	06 35	06 50		07 05			07 20		07 35	07 50			08 05		08 20	08 35
Wavertree Technology Park d	05 19		05 37	05 52	06 07	06 19		06 22	06 37	06 52		07 07	07 19		07 22		07 37	07 52			08 07	08 19	08 22	08 37
Broad Green d			05 40	05 55	06 10			06 25	06 40	06 55		07 10			07 25		07 40	07 55			08 10		08 25	08 40
Roby d			05 44	05 59	06 14			06 29	06 44	06 59		07 14			07 29		07 44	07 59			08 14		08 29	08 44
Huyton d			05 46	06 01	06 16			06 31	06 46	07 01	07 06	07 16			07 31		07 46	08 02	08 06		08 16		08 31	08 46
Prescot d			05 51		06 21				06 51			07 21					07 51				08 21			08 51
Eccleston Park d			05 53		06 23				06 53			07 23					07 53				08 23			08 53
Thatto Heath d			05 56		06 26				06 56			07 26					07 56				08 26			08 56
St Helens Central a			05 59		06 29				06 59		07 15	07 29					07 59		08 15		08 29			08 59
d			06 00		06 30				07 00		07 15	07 30					08 00		08 15		08 30			09 00
Garswood d			06 07		06 37				07 07			07 37					08 07				08 37			09 07
Bryn d			06 10		06 40				07 10			07 40					08 10				08 40			09 10
Whiston d				06 05				06 35		07 05					07 35			08 05					08 35	
Rainhill d				06 08				06 38		07 08					07 38			08 08					08 38	
Lea Green d				06 11				06 41		07 11			07 28		07 41			08 11					08 41	
St Helens Junction d	05 29			06 14		06 29		06 44		07 14			07 31		07 44			08 14				08 29	08 44	
Warrington Bank Quay d		06 06					06 40							07 39		08 08								
Earlestown 8 d		06 12		06 19			06 47	06 50		07 19				07 46	07 49	08 16		08 19					08 50	
Warrington Bank Quay a								07 01							*08 23*								09 01	
Newton-le-Willows d	05 35	06 15		06 22		06 35	06 50			07 22			07 37	07 49	07 52	08 19		08 22				08 35		
Wigan North Western a			06 21		06 51				07 21		07 30	07 51					08 21		08 30		08 51			09 21
65 d											07 31								08 31					
Euxton Balshaw Lane d											07 41								08 41					
Leyland 82 a											07 46								08 46					
Preston 8 65, 82 a									*07 51*		07 54	*08 36*					*08 52*		08 54		*09 38*			*09 51*
Blackpool North 97 a											08 18								09 20					
Patricroft d				06 34						07 34					08 04			08 34						
Eccles d				06 36						07 36					08 06			08 36						
Manchester Victoria a				06 49						07 49					08 19			08 49						
Manchester Oxford Road a		06 35				06 57	07 09						07 57	08 09		08 41						08 57		
Manchester Piccadilly 10 a	05 57	06 46				07 01	07 18						08 01	08 18		08 50						09 01		
Manchester Airport 85 a	06 14					07 22							08 22									09 22		

For general notes see front of timetable
For details of catering facilities see Directory of Train Operators

A From Llandudno (Table 81)
B From Chester (Table 81)
C To Stalybridge (Table 39)
D To Huddersfield (Table 39)
b Change at Wigan North Western and Preston. From 5 October arr. 2 mins. later
c Change at Leyland

Liverpool and St Helens → Newton-le-Willows, Wigan, Preston and Manchester

Network Diagram - see first page of Table 88

Station																									
		NT	AW	NT	NT	NT	NT	NT	NT	AW	NT	NT	NT	NT	NT	NT	AW	NT		NT	NT	NT	NT	NT	AW
		A	◇ B						A	◇ B						A	◇ B							A	◇ B
Liverpool Lime Street 10	89, 91 d	08 44		08 57	09 01	09 13	09 16	09 31	09 46		09 57	10 01	10 13	10 16	10 31	10 46		10 57		11 01	11 13	11 16	11 31	11 46	
Edge Hill	89, 91 d	08 50			09 05		09 20	09 35	09 50			10 05		10 20	10 35	10 50				11 05		11 20	11 35	11 50	
Wavertree Technology Park	d	08 52			09 07	09 19	09 22	09 37	09 52			10 07	10 19	10 22	10 37	10 52				11 07	11 19	11 22	11 37	11 52	
Broad Green	d	08 55			09 10		09 25	09 40	09 55			10 10		10 24	10 40	10 55				11 10		11 25	11 40	11 55	
Roby	d	08 59			09 14		09 29	09 44	09 59			10 14		10 29	10 44	10 59				11 14		11 29	11 44	11 59	
Huyton	d	09 01		09 06	09 16		09 31	09 46	10 01		10 06	10 16		10 31	10 46	11 01		11 06		11 16		11 31	11 46	12 01	
Prescot	d				09 21			09 51				10 21			10 51					11 21			11 51		
Eccleston Park	d				09 23			09 53				10 23			10 53					11 23			11 53		
Thatto Heath	d				09 26			09 56				10 26			10 56					11 26			11 56		
St Helens Central	a			09 15	09 29			09 59			10 15	10 29			10 59			11 15		11 29			11 59		
	d			09 15	09 30			10 00			10 15	10 30			11 00			11 15		11 30			12 00		
Garswood	d				09 37			10 07				10 37			11 07					11 37			12 07		
Bryn	d				09 40			10 10				10 40			11 10					11 40			12 10		
Whiston	d	09 05					09 35		10 05					10 35		11 05						11 35		12 05	
Rainhill	d	09 08					09 38		10 08					10 38		11 08						11 38		12 08	
Lea Green	d	09 11					09 41		10 11					10 41		11 11						11 41		12 11	
St Helens Junction	d	09 14				09 29	09 44		10 14				10 29	10 44		11 14					11 29	11 44		12 14	
Warrington Bank Quay	d		09 19							10 19							11 19								12 19
Earlestown 8	d	09 19	09 26				09 50		10 19	10 26				10 50		11 19	11 26					11 50		12 19	12 26
Warrington Bank Quay	a						10 01							11 01								12 01			
Newton-le-Willows	d	09 22	09 29			09 35			10 22	10 29			10 35			11 22	11 29				11 35			12 22	12 29
Wigan North Western	a			09 30	09 51			10 21			10 30	10 53			11 21			11 30		11 51			12 21		
	65 d			09 31							10 31							11 31							
Euxton Balshaw Lane	d			09 41							10 41							11 41							
Leyland	82 a			09 46							10 46							11 46							
Preston 8	65, 82 a			09 54	*10 38*			*10 51*			10 54	*11 38*			*11 51*			11 54		*12b38*					
Blackpool North	97 a			10 20							11 20							12 20		*13c21*					
Patricroft	d	09 34							10 34							11 34								12 34	
Eccles	d	09 36							10 36							11 36								12 36	
Manchester Victoria	a	09 47							10 49							11 49								12 49	
Manchester Oxford Road	a		09 48			09 57				10 48			10 57				11 48				11 57				12 48
Manchester Piccadilly 10	a		09 57			10 01				10 57			11 01				11 57				12 01				12 57
Manchester Airport	85 a					10 22							11 22								12 22				

Station																									
		NT	NT	NT	NT	NT	NT	AW	NT	NT	NT	NT	NT	NT	AW	NT		NT	NT	NT	NT	NT	AW	NT	NT
							A	◇ B						A	◇ B							A	◇ B		
Liverpool Lime Street 10	89, 91 d	11 57	12 01	12 13	12 16	12 31	12 46		12 57	13 01	13 13	13 16	13 31	13 46		13 57		14 01	14 13	14 16	14 31	14 46		14 57	15 01
Edge Hill	89, 91 d		12 05		12 20	12 35	12 50			13 05		13 20	13 35	13 50				14 05		14 20	14 35	14 50			15 05
Wavertree Technology Park	d		12 07	12 19	12 22	12 37	12 52			13 07	13 19	13 22	13 37	13 52				14 07	14 19	14 22	14 37	14 52			15 07
Broad Green	d		12 10		12 25	12 40	12 55			13 10		13 25	13 40	13 55				14 10		14 25	14 40	14 55			15 10
Roby	d		12 14		12 29	12 44	12 59			13 14		13 29	13 44	13 59				14 14		14 29	14 44	14 59			15 14
Huyton	d	12 06	12 16		12 31	12 46	13 01		13 06	13 16		13 31	13 46	14 01		14 06		14 16		14 31	14 46	15 01		15 06	15 16
Prescot	d		12 21			12 51				13 21			13 51					14 21			14 51				15 21
Eccleston Park	d		12 23			12 53				13 23			13 53					14 23			14 53				15 23
Thatto Heath	d		12 26			12 56				13 26			13 56					14 26			14 56				15 26
St Helens Central	a	12 15	12 29			12 59			13 15	13 29			13 59			14 15		14 29			14 59			15 15	15 29
	d	12 15	12 30			13 00			13 15	13 30			14 00			14 15		14 30			15 00			15 15	15 30
Garswood	d		12 37			13 07				13 37			14 07					14 37			15 07				15 37
Bryn	d		12 40			13 10				13 40			14 10					14 40			15 10				15 40
Whiston	d				12 35		13 05					13 35		14 05						14 35		15 05			
Rainhill	d				12 38		13 08					13 38		14 08						14 38		15 08			
Lea Green	d				12 41		13 11					13 41		14 11						14 41		15 11			
St Helens Junction	d			12 29	12 44		13 14				13 29	13 44		14 14					14 29	14 44		15 14			
Warrington Bank Quay	d							13 19							14 19								15 19		
Earlestown 8	d				12 50		13 19	13 26				13 50		14 19	14 26					14 50		15 19	15 26		
Warrington Bank Quay	a				13 01							14 01								15 01					
Newton-le-Willows	d			12 35			13 22	13 29			13 35			14 22	14 29				14 35			15 22	15 29		
Wigan North Western	a	12 30	12 51			13 21			13 30	13 51			14 21			14 30		14 51			15 21			15 30	15 51
	65 d	12 31							13 31							14 31								15 31	
Euxton Balshaw Lane	d	12 41							13 41							14 41								15 41	
Leyland	82 a	12 46							13 46							14 46								15 46	
Preston 8	65, 82 a	12 54	*13e38*						13 54	*14f38*						14 54		*15g38*						15 54	*16h38*
Blackpool North	97 a	13 21							14 20							15 20								16 20	
Patricroft	d						13 34							14 34								15 34			
Eccles	d						13 36							14 36								15 36			
Manchester Victoria	a						13 49							14 50								15 49			
Manchester Oxford Road	a			12 57				13 48			13 57				14 48				14 57				15 48		
Manchester Piccadilly 10	a			13 01				13 57			14 01				14 57				15 01				15 57		
Manchester Airport	85 a			13 22							14 22								15 22						

For general notes see front of timetable
For details of catering facilities see Directory of Train Operators

- **A** To Stalybridge (Table 39)
- **B** From Llandudno (Table 81)
- **b** From 7 November arr. 1223
- **c** From 7 November arr. 1300, change at Wigan North Western and Preston
- **e** From 7 November arr. 1354
- **f** From 7 November arr. 1454
- **g** From 7 November arr. 1554
- **h** From 7 November arr. 1654

Saturdays

Liverpool and St Helens → Newton-le-Willows, Wigan, Preston and Manchester

Network Diagram - see first page of Table 88

	NT	NT	NT	NT	AW	NT	NT	NT	NT	NT	NT	AW	NT		NT	NT	NT	NT	NT	NT	NT	NT	AW	NT
				A	◇ B 🛒						A	◇ B 🛒											◇ B 🛒	
Liverpool Lime Street 10 89, 91 d	15 13	15 16	15 31	15 46		15 57	16 01	16 13	16 16	16 31	16 46		16 57		17 01	17 06	17 10	17 19	17 27	17 35	17 44	17 48		18 01
Edge Hill 89, 91 d		15 20	15 35	15 50			16 05		16 20	16 35	16 50				17 05		17 14		17 31	17 39		17 52		18 05
Wavertree Technology Park d	15 19	15 22	15 37	15 52			16 07	16 19	16 22	16 37	16 52				17 07	17 12	17 16		17 33	17 41	17 49	17 54		18 07
Broad Green d		15 25	15 40	15 55			16 10		16 25	16 40	16 55				17 10		17 19		17 36	17 44	17 52	17 57		18 10
Roby d		15 29	15 44	15 59			16 14		16 29	16 44	16 59				17 14		17 23		17 40	17 48		18 01		18 14
Huyton d		15 31	15 46	16 01		16 06	16 16		16 31	16 46	17 01		17 06		17 16	17 20	17 25	17 29	17 41	17 50	17 57	18 03		18 16
Prescot d			15 51				16 21			16 51					17 21			17 33			18 02			18 21
Eccleston Park d			15 53				16 23			16 53					17 23			17 36			18 05			18 23
Thatto Heath d			15 56				16 26			16 56					17 26			17 38			18 07			18 26
St Helens Central a			15 59			16 15	16 29			16 59			17 15		17 29			17 42	17 50		18 11			18 29
d			16 00			16 15	16 30			17 00			17 15		17 30			17 42	17 50		18 11			18 30
Garswood d			16 07				16 37			17 07					17 37			17 49			18 19			18 37
Bryn d			16 10				16 40			17 10					17 40			17 52			18 22			18 40
Whiston d		15 35		16 05					16 35		17 05						17 28			17 54		18 07		
Rainhill d		15 38		16 08					16 38		17 08						17 32			17 57		18 10		
Lea Green d		15 41		16 11					16 41		17 11					17 26	17 35			18 00		18 13		
St Helens Junction d	15 29	15 44		16 14				16 29	16 44		17 14					17 29	17 39			18 03		18 16		
Warrington Bank Quay d					16 19							17 19											18 19	
Earlestown 8 d		15 50		16 19	16 26				16 49		17 19	17 26					17 44			18 08		18 21	18 26	
Warrington Bank Quay a		16 01							*17 25*								*18 24*							
Newton-le-Willows d	15 35			16 22	16 29			16 35	16 52		17 22	17 29				17 35	17 47			18 11		18 24	18 29	
Wigan North Western a			16 21			16 30	16 51			17 21			17 30		17 52			18 04	18 05		18 30			18 49
65 d						16 31							17 31						18 05		18 31			18 49
Euxton Balshaw Lane d						16 41							17 41						18 16		18 41			19 01
Leyland 82 a						16 46							17 46						18 21		18 46			19 06
Preston 8 65, 82 a						16 54	17b38						17 54					18c38	18 31		18 54			19 15
Blackpool North 97 a						17 20							18 20						*19 09*		19 20			20f00
Patricroft d				16 34					17 04		17 34						17 59			18 23				
Eccles d				16 36					17 06		17 36						18 01			18 25		18 36		
Manchester Victoria a				16 49					17 19		17 47						18 15			18 40		18 49		
Manchester Oxford Road a	15 57				16 48			16 57				17 48				17 57							18 48	
Manchester Piccadilly 10 a	16 01				16 57			17 01				17 57				18 01							18 57	
Manchester Airport 85 ✈ a	16 22							17 22								18 22								

	NT	NT	NT	NT	AW	NT	NT	NT	AW	NT	NT	NT	NT	AW	NT	NT	AW	NT	NT	NT	NT	AW		
					◇ B 🛒				◇ B 🛒					◇ B			C					C		
Liverpool Lime Street 10 89, 91 d	18 13	18 16	18 31	18 46		19 01	19 12	19 23		19 42	20 09	20 12	20 25		20 42	21 12		21 42	22 12	23 02	23 16			
Edge Hill 89, 91 d		18 20	18 35	18 50		19 06	19 16			19 46		20 16			20 46	21 16		21 46	22 16	23 06	23 20			
Wavertree Technology Park d	18 19	18 22	18 37	18 52		19 07	19 18			19 48	20 15	20 18			20 48	21 18		21 48	22 18	23 08	23 22			
Broad Green d		18 25	18 40	18 55		19 10	19 21			19 51		20 21			20 51	21 21		21 51	22 21	23 11	23 26			
Roby d		18 29	18 44	18 59		19 14	19 25			19 55		20 25			20 55	21 25		21 55	22 25	23 15	23 30			
Huyton d		18 31	18 46	19 01		19 16	19 27	19 32		19 57		20 27	20 34		20 57	21 27		21 57	22 27	23 17	23 32			
Prescot d			18 51			19 21				20 02					21 02			22 02		23 22				
Eccleston Park d			18 53			19 23				20 04					21 04			22 04		23 24				
Thatto Heath d			18 56			19 26				20 07					21 07			22 07		23 27				
St Helens Central a			18 59			19 29		19 40		20 10			20 42		21 10			22 10		23 30				
d			19 00			19 30		19 41		20 11			20 43		21 11			22 11		23 31				
Garswood d			19 07			19 37				20 18					21 18			22 18		23 38				
Bryn d			19 10			19 40				20 21					21 21			22 21		23 41				
Whiston d		18 35		19 05			19 31					20 31				21 31			22 31		23 36			
Rainhill d		18 38		19 08			19 34					20 34				21 34			22 34		23 39			
Lea Green d		18 41		19 11			19 37					20 37				21 37			22 37		23 42			
St Helens Junction d	18 29	18 44		19 14			19 40				20 25	20 40				21 40			22 40		23 45			
Warrington Bank Quay d					19 19				20 19					21 19			22 19					23 49		
Earlestown 8 d		18 50		19 19	19 26		19 45		20 26			20 45		21 26		21 45	22 27		22 45		23 50	23 56		
Warrington Bank Quay a		19 01					*20 29*					*21 26*				*22 23*			*23 47*					
Newton-le-Willows d	18 35			19 22	19 29		19 48		20 29		20 35	20 48		21 29		21 48	22 30		22 48		23 53	23 59		
Wigan North Western a			19 21			19 51		19 54		20 30			20 57		21 32			22 28		23 48				
65 d								19 55					20 57					22 28		23 48				
Euxton Balshaw Lane d								20 05					21 08					22 39		23 59				
Leyland 82 a								20 10					21 16					22 44		00 07				
Preston 8 65, 82 a			19g59			20h38		20 18		20h59			21 22					22 54		00 16				
Blackpool North 97 a								20 44					21 53					23 21						
Patricroft d				19 34			20 00					21 00				22 00			23 00		00 05			
Eccles d				19 36			20 02					21 02				22 02			23 02		00 08			
Manchester Victoria a				19 49			20 15					21 15				22 15			23 15		00 21			
Manchester Oxford Road a	18 57				19 48				20 48		20 57			21 48			22 50							
Manchester Piccadilly 10 a	19 01				19 57				20 57		21 01			21 57			22 58					00 26		
Manchester Airport 85 ✈ a	19 24										21 24													

For general notes see front of timetable
For details of catering facilities see Directory of Train Operators

- **A** To Stalybridge (Table 39)
- **B** From Llandudno (Table 81)
- **C** From Chester (Table 81)
- **b** From 7 November arr. 1754
- **c** From 7 November arr. 1854
- **f** Until 3 October arr. 1948, change at Leyland
- **g** From 7 November arr. 2018
- **h** From 7 November arr. 2122

Table 90

Sundays

until 6 September

Liverpool and St Helens → Newton-le-Willows, Wigan, Preston and Manchester

Network Diagram - see first page of Table 88

		NT	NT	AW	NT	NT	NT	AW	NT	AW	NT	NT	AW	NT	NT	AW	NT	NT	AW	NT	NT	AW	NT	NT	AW
				A		B	C	◇ D		A 🛒			A 🛒			A 🛒			A 🛒			A 🛒			A 🛒
Liverpool Lime Street [10]	89, 91 d	08 05	08 31		09 01	09 31	09 31		10 01		10 31	11 01		11 31	12 01		12 31	13 01		13 31	14 01		14 31	15 01	
Edge Hill	89, 91 d																								
Wavertree Technology Park	d	08 11	08 37		09 07	09 37	09 37		10 07		10 37	11 07		11 37	12 07		12 37	13 07		13 37	14 07		14 37	15 07	
Broad Green	d	08 14	08 40		09 10	09 40	09 40		10 10		10 40	11 10		11 40	12 10		12 40	13 10		13 40	14 10		14 40	15 10	
Roby	d	08 17	08 43		09 13	09 43	09 43		10 13		10 43	11 13		11 43	12 13		12 43	13 13		13 43	14 13		14 43	15 13	
Huyton	d	08 19	08 46		09 16	09 46	09 46		10 16		10 46	11 16		11 46	12 16		12 46	13 16		13 46	14 16		14 46	15 16	
Prescot	d		08 50			09 50	09 50				10 50			11 50			12 50			13 50			14 50		
Eccleston Park	d																								
Thatto Heath	d		08 54			09 54	09 54				10 54			11 54			12 54			13 54			14 54		
St Helens Central	a		08 57			09 57	09 57				10 57			11 57			12 57			13 57			14 57		
	d		08 58			09 58	09 58				10 58			11 58			12 58			13 58			14 58		
Garswood	d		09 05			10 05	10 05				11 05			12 05			13 05			14 05			15 05		
Bryn	d																								
Whiston	d	08 23			09 19				10 19			11 19			12 19			13 19			14 19			15 19	
Rainhill	d	08 26			09 22				10 22			11 22			12 22			13 22			14 22			15 22	
Lea Green	d	08 29			09 26				10 26			11 26			12 26			13 26			14 26			15 26	
St Helens Junction	d	08 32			09 29				10 29			11 29			12 29			13 29			14 29			15 29	
Warrington Bank Quay	d			09 10				10 12		11 03			12 03			13 03			14 03			15 03			16 03
Earlestown [8]	d	08 37		09 17	09 33			10 19	10 33	11 10		11 33	12 10		12 33	13 10		13 33	14 10		14 33	15 10		15 33	16 10
Warrington Bank Quay	a				*10 27*				*11 29*			*12 27*			*13 28*			*14 27*			*15 28*			*16 27*	
Newton-le-Willows	d	08 40		09 20	09 36			10 22	10 36	11 13		11 36	12 13		12 36	13 13		13 36	14 13		14 36	15 13		15 36	16 13
Wigan North Western	a		09 13			10 13	10 13				11 13			12 13			13 13			14 13			15 13		
	65 d		09 14			10 14	10 16				11 14			12 14			13 14			14 14			15 14		
Euxton Balshaw Lane	d		09 24			10 26	10 28				11 24			12 24			13 24			14 24			15 24		
Leyland	82 a		09 29			10 31	10 33				11 29			12 29			13 29			14 29			15 29		
Preston [8]	65, 82 a		09 37			10 39	10 41				11 37			12 37			13 37			14 37			15 37		
Blackpool North	97 a		10 06			11 09	11 09				12 07			13 07			14 07			15 07			16 07		
Patricroft	d																								
Eccles	d	08 52			09 49				10 49			11 49			12 49			13 49			14 49			15 49	
Manchester Victoria	[connection] a																								
Manchester Oxford Road	a	09 01		09 39	09 59			10 41	10 59	11 32		11 59	12 32		12 59	13 32		13 59	14 32		14 59	15 32		15 59	16 32
Manchester Piccadilly [10]	[connection] a	09 05		09 48	10 03			10 50	11 03	11 41		12 02	12 41		13 02	13 41		14 02	14 41		15 02	15 41		16 02	16 41
Manchester Airport	85 [air link] a	09 22			10 24				11 21			12 19			13 19			14 19			15 20			16 19	

		NT	NT	AW	NT	NT	AW	NT	NT	AW	NT	NT	AW	NT	NT	AW	NT	NT	AW	NT	NT	AW	NT	NT	
				◇ D 🛒			◇ D 🛒			A			A			A			A			A			
Liverpool Lime Street [10]	89, 91 d	15 31	16 01		16 31	17 01		17 31	18 01		18 31	19 01		19 31	20 01		20 31	21 01		21 31	22 01		22 31	23 01	
Edge Hill	89, 91 d																								
Wavertree Technology Park	d	15 37	16 07		16 37	17 07		17 37	18 07		18 37	19 07		19 37	20 07		20 37	21 07		21 37	22 07		22 37	23 07	
Broad Green	d	15 40	16 10		16 40	17 10		17 40	18 10		18 40	19 10		19 40	20 10		20 40	21 10		21 40	22 10		22 40	23 10	
Roby	d	15 43	16 13		16 43	17 13		17 43	18 13		18 43	19 13		19 43	20 13		20 43	21 13		21 43	22 13		22 43	23 13	
Huyton	d	15 46	16 16		16 46	17 16		17 46	18 16		18 46	19 16		19 46	20 16		20 46	21 16		21 46	22 16		22 46	23 16	
Prescot	d	15 50			16 50			17 50			18 50			19 50			20 50			21 50			22 50		
Eccleston Park	d																								
Thatto Heath	d	15 54			16 54			17 54			18 54			19 54			20 54			21 54			22 54		
St Helens Central	a	15 57			16 57			17 57			18 57			19 57			20 57			21 57			22 57		
	d	15 58			16 58			17 58			18 58			19 58			20 58			21 58			22 58		
Garswood	d	16 05			17 05			18 05			19 05			20 05			21 05			22 05			23 05		
Bryn	d																								
Whiston	d		16 19			17 19			18 19			19 19			20 19			21 19			22 19			23 19	
Rainhill	d		16 22			17 22			18 22			19 22			20 22			21 22			22 22			23 22	
Lea Green	d		16 26			17 26			18 26			19 26			20 26			21 26			22 26			23 26	
St Helens Junction	d		16 29			17 29			18 29			19 29			20 29			21 29			22 29			23 29	
Warrington Bank Quay	d			17 03			18 03			19 03			20 03			21 03			22 03			22 36			
Earlestown [8]	d		16 33	17 10		17 33	18 10		18 33	19 10		19 33	20 10		20 33	21 10		21 33	22 10		22 33	22 44		23 33	
Warrington Bank Quay	a		*17 27*			*18 27*			*19 28*			*20 29*			*21 27*			*22 27*			*23 27*			*23 55*	
Newton-le-Willows	d		16 36	17 13		17 36	18 13		18 36	19 13		19 36	20 13		20 36	21 13		21 36	22 13		22 36	22 47		23 36	
Wigan North Western	a	16 13			17 13			18 13			19 13			20 13			21 13			22 13			23 13		
	65 d	16 14			17 14			18 14			19 14			20 14			21 14			22 14			23 14		
Euxton Balshaw Lane	d	16 24			17 24			18 24			19 24			20 24			21 24			22 24					
Leyland	82 a	16 29			17 29			18 29			19 29			20 29			21 29			22 29			23 27		
Preston [8]	65, 82 a	16 37			17 37			18 37			19 37			20 37			21 37			22 37			23 35		
Blackpool North	97 a	17 07			18 07			19 07			20 07			21 07			22 07			23 07			00 04		
Patricroft	d																								
Eccles	d		16 49			17 49			18 49			19 49			20 49			21 49			22 49			23 49	
Manchester Victoria	[connection] a																								
Manchester Oxford Road	a		16 59	17 32		17 59	18 32		18 59	19 32		19 59	20 32		20 59	21 32		21 59	22 32		22 59	23 06		23 59	
Manchester Piccadilly [10]	[connection] a		17 02	17 41		18 02	18 41		19 02	19 41		20 02	20 41		21 02	21 41		22 02	22 41		23 02	23 15		00 02	
Manchester Airport	85 [air link] a		17 19			18 19			19 19			20 19			21 19			22 19			23 20			00 17	

For general notes see front of timetable
For details of catering facilities see Directory of Train Operators

A From Chester (Table 81)
B From 19 July
C Until 12 July
D From Holyhead (Table 81)

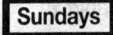

Table 90

Sundays

from 13 September

Liverpool and St Helens → Newton-le-Willows, Wigan, Preston and Manchester

Network Diagram - see first page of Table 88

Station		TP 1 ◇ A	NT	NT	AW B	NT	TP 1 ◇ C	NT D	NT E	AW B	NT	TP 1 ◇ A	AW B	NT	NT	TP 1 ◇ C	AW B	NT	NT	TP 1 ◇ A	AW B	NT	EM ◇ G	NT	TP 1 ◇ C
Liverpool Lime Street 10	89, 91 d	08 19	08 22	08 31		09 01	09 22	09 31	09 31		10 01	10 22		10 31	11 01	11 22		11 31	12 01	12 22		12 31	12 57	13 01	13 22
Edge Hill	89, 91 d																								
Wavertree Technology Park	d		08 28	08 37		09 07		09 37	09 37		10 07			10 37	11 07			11 37	12 07			12 37		13 07	
Broad Green	d		08 31	08 40		09 10		09 40	09 40		10 10			10 40	11 10			11 40	12 10			12 40		13 10	
Roby	d		08 34	08 43		09 13		09 43	09 43		10 13			10 43	11 13			11 43	12 13			12 43		13 13	
Huyton	d		08 36	08 46		09 16		09 46	09 46		10 16			10 46	11 16			11 46	12 16			12 46		13 16	
Prescot	d			08 50				09 50	09 50					10 50				11 50				12 50			
Eccleston Park	d																								
Thatto Heath	d			08 54				09 54	09 54					10 54				11 54				12 54			
St Helens Central	a			08 57				09 57	09 57					10 57				11 57				12 57			
	d			08 58				09 58	09 58					10 58				11 58				12 58			
Garswood	d			09 05				10 05	10 05					11 05				12 05				13 05			
Bryn	d																								
Whiston	d		08 40			09 19					10 19				11 19				12 19					13 19	
Rainhill	d		08 43			09 22					10 22				11 22				12 22					13 22	
Lea Green	d		08 46			09 26					10 26				11 26				12 26					13 26	
St Helens Junction	d		08 49			09 29					10 29				11 29				12 29					13 29	
Warrington Bank Quay	d				09 10					10 12			11 03				12 03				13 03				
Earlestown 8	d		08 54		09 17	09 33				10 19	10 33		11 10		11 33		12 10		12 33		13 10			13 33	
Warrington Bank Quay	a					*10 27*					*11 29*				*12 27*				*13 28*					*14 27*	
Newton-le-Willows	d	08 35	08 57		09 20	09 36	09 40			10 22	10 36	10 40	11 13		11 36	11 40	12 13		12 36	12 40	13 13		13 17	13 36	13 40
Wigan North Western	a			09 13				10 13	10 13					11 13				12 13				13 13			
	65 d			09 14				10 14	10 16					11 14				12 14				13 14			
Euxton Balshaw Lane	d			09 24				10 26	10 28					11 24				12 24				13 24			
Leyland	82 a			09 29				10 31	10 33					11 29				12 29				13 29			
Preston 8	65, 82 a			09 37				10 39	10 41					11 37				12 37				13 37			
Blackpool North	97 a			10 06				11 09	11 09					12 07				13 07				14 07			
Patricroft	d																								
Eccles	d		09 09			09 49					10 49				11 49				12 49					13 49	
Manchester Victoria	a	08 56					10 03					11 03				12 03				13 03					14 03
Manchester Oxford Road	a		09 20		09 39	09 59				10 41	10 59		11 32		11 59		12 32		12 59		13 32		13 39	13 59	
Manchester Piccadilly 10	a				09 49	10 03				10 50	11 03		11 41		12 02		12 41		13 02		13 41		13 41	14 02	
Manchester Airport	85 a					10 25					11 21				12 21				13 19					14 19	

Station		AW B	NT	EM ◇ G	NT	TP 1 ◇ A	AW B	NT	EM ◇ G	NT	TP 1 ◇ C	AW B	NT	EM ◇ G	NT	TP 1 ◇ A	AW ◇ H	NT	EM ◇ J	NT	TP 1 ◇ C	AW B	NT	EM ◇ J	NT
Liverpool Lime Street 10	89, 91 d		13 31	13 57	14 01	14 22		14 31	14 57	15 01	15 22		15 31	15 57	16 01	16 22		16 31	16 57	17 01	17 22		17 31	17 57	18 01
Edge Hill	89, 91 d																								
Wavertree Technology Park	d		13 37		14 07			14 37		15 07			15 37		16 07			16 37		17 07			17 37		18 07
Broad Green	d		13 40		14 10			14 40		15 10			15 40		16 10			16 40		17 10			17 40		18 10
Roby	d		13 43		14 13			14 43		15 13			15 43		16 13			16 43		17 13			17 43		18 13
Huyton	d		13 46		14 16			14 46		15 16			15 46		16 16			16 46		17 16			17 46		18 16
Prescot	d		13 50					14 50					15 50					16 50					17 50		
Eccleston Park	d																								
Thatto Heath	d		13 54					14 54					15 54					16 54					17 54		
St Helens Central	a		13 57					14 57					15 57					16 57					17 57		
	d		13 58					14 58					15 58					16 58					17 58		
Garswood	d		14 05					15 05					16 05					17 05					18 05		
Bryn	d																								
Whiston	d				14 19					15 19					16 19					17 19					18 19
Rainhill	d				14 22					15 22					16 22					17 22					18 22
Lea Green	d				14 26					15 26					16 26					17 26					18 26
St Helens Junction	d				14 29					15 29					16 29					17 29					18 29
Warrington Bank Quay	d	14 03					15 03					16 03					17 03					18 03			
Earlestown 8	d	14 10			14 33		15 10			15 33		16 10			16 33		17 10			17 33		18 10			18 33
Warrington Bank Quay	a				*15 28*					*16 27*					*17 27*					*18 27*					*19 28*
Newton-le-Willows	d	14 13		14 17	14 36	14 40	15 13		15 17	15 36	15 40	16 13		16 17	16 36	16 40	17 13		17 17	17 36	17 40	18 13		18 17	18 36
Wigan North Western	a		14 13					15 13					16 13					17 13					18 13		
	65 d		14 14					15 14					16 14					17 14					18 14		
Euxton Balshaw Lane	d		14 24					15 24					16 24					17 24					18 24		
Leyland	82 a		14 29					15 29					16 29					17 29					18 29		
Preston 8	65, 82 a		14 37					15 37					16 37					17 37					18 37		
Blackpool North	97 a		15 07					16 07					17 07					18 07					19 07		
Patricroft	d																								
Eccles	d				14 49					15 49					16 49					17 49					18 49
Manchester Victoria	a					15 03					16 03					17 03					18 03				
Manchester Oxford Road	a	14 32		14 39	14 59		15 32		15 39	15 59		16 32		16 38	16 59		17 32		17 38	17 59		18 32		18 39	18 59
Manchester Piccadilly 10	a	14 41		14 41	15 02		15 41		15 41	16 02		16 41		16 41	17 02		17 41		17 41	18 02		18 41		18 41	19 02
Manchester Airport	85 a				15 20					16 19					17 19					18 19					19 19

For general notes see front of timetable
For details of catering facilities see Directory of Train Operators

- **A** To Middlesbrough (Table 39)
- **B** From Chester (Table 81)
- **C** To Scarborough (Table 39)
- **D** From 8 November
- **E** Until 1 November
- **G** Until 1 November. To Norwich (Table 49)
- **H** From Holyhead (Table 81)
- **J** Until 1 November. To Nottingham (Table 49)

Liverpool and St Helens → Newton-le-Willows, Wigan, Preston and Manchester

Network Diagram - see first page of Table 88

Station			TP	AW	NT	EM	NT	TP	AW	NT	EM	NT	TP	AW	NT	NT	EM	NT	TP	AW	NT	AW	NT	NT
			1st class ◇			◇		1st class ◇			◇		1st class ◇				◇		1st class ◇					
			A	B		C		D	B		C		E	B			C		D	B		B		
						catering					catering													
Liverpool Lime Street (10)	89, 91	d	18 22		18 31	18 57	19 01	19 22		19 31	19 57	20 01	20 22		20 31	21 01	21 23	21 31	21 52		22 01		22 31	23 01
Edge Hill	89, 91	d																						
Wavertree Technology Park		d			18 37		19 07			19 37		20 07			20 37	21 07		21 37			22 07		22 37	23 07
Broad Green		d			18 40		19 10			19 40		20 10			20 40	21 10		21 40			22 10		22 40	23 10
Roby		d			18 43		19 13			19 43		20 13			20 43	21 13		21 43			22 13		22 43	23 13
Huyton		d			18 46		19 16			19 46		20 16			20 46	21 16		21 46			22 16		22 46	23 16
Prescot		d			18 50					19 50					20 50			21 50					22 50	
Eccleston Park		d																						
Thatto Heath		d			18 54					19 54					20 54			21 54					22 54	
St Helens Central		a			18 57					19 57					20 57			21 57					22 57	
		d			18 58					19 58					20 58			21 58					22 58	
Garswood		d			19 05					20 05					21 05			22 05					23 05	
Bryn		d																						
Whiston		d					19 19					20 19				21 19					22 19			23 19
Rainhill		d					19 22					20 22				21 22					22 22			23 22
Lea Green		d					19 26					20 26				21 26					22 26			23 26
St Helens Junction		d					19 29					20 29				21 29					22 29			23 29
Warrington Bank Quay		d		19 03					20 03					21 03						22 03		22 36		
Earlestown (8)		d		19 10			19 33		20 10			20 33		21 10		21 33				22 10	22 33	22 44		23 33
Warrington Bank Quay		a					20 29					21 27				22 27					23 27			23 55
Newton-le-Willows		d	18 40	19 13		19 17	19 36	19 40	20 13		20 17	20 36	20 40	21 13		21 36	21 42		22 08	22 13	22 36	22 47		23 36
Wigan North Western		a			19 13					20 13					21 13			22 13					23 13	
	65	d			19 14					20 14					21 14			22 14					23 14	
Euxton Balshaw Lane		d			19 24					20 24					21 24			22 24						
Leyland	82	a			19 29					20 29					21 29			22 29					23 27	
Preston (8)	65, 82	a			19 37					20 37					21 37			22 37					23 35	
Blackpool North	97	a			20 07					21 07					22 07			23 07					00 04	
Patricroft		d																						
Eccles		d					19 49					20 49				21 49					22 49			23 49
Manchester Victoria	(ferry)	a	19 03					20 03					21 03						22 30					
Manchester Oxford Road		a		19 32		19 39	19 59		20 32		20 39	20 59		21 32		21 59	22 07			22 32	22 59	23 06		23 59
Manchester Piccadilly (10)	(ferry)	a		19 41		19 41	20 02		20 41		20 41	21 02		21 41		22 02	22 09			22 41	23 02	23 15		00 02
Manchester Airport	85 (air)	a					20 19					21 19				22 19					23 20			00 17

For general notes see front of timetable
For details of catering facilities see Directory of Train Operators

A To Scarborough (Table 39)
B From Chester (Table 81)
C Until 1 November. To Nottingham (Table 49)
D To York (Table 39)
E To Newcastle (Table 39)

Manchester, Preston, Wigan and Newton-le-Willows → St Helens and Liverpool

Network Diagram - see first page of Table 88

Miles	Miles	Miles	Miles			NT	NT	NT	AW ◇ A	NT	NT	NT	AW ◇ A	NT	NT	NT	NT	NT	NT	NT	AW ◇ A	NT	NT	NT	NT
—	—	—	0	**Manchester Airport** 85 ✈	d									06 41								07 41			
—	—	—	9¾	**Manchester Piccadilly** 10	d				05 50				06 50	06 58							07 50	07 58			
—	—	—	10¼	**Manchester Oxford Road**	d				05 53				06 53	07 01							07 53	08 03			
0	—	—	—	**Manchester Victoria**	d		05 39			06 09						07 09			07 39				08 09		
4	—	—	14½	Eccles	d		05 46			06 16						07 16			07 46				08 17		
5	—	—	15½	Patricroft	d		05 49			06 19						07 19			07 49				08 19		
—	—	—	—	Blackpool North 97	d			*04b57*			*05b45*						*06b34*	07 02						*07b18*	
—	0	0	—	**Preston** 8 65, 82	d			*05 30*			*06 16*						*07 17*	07 30						*07 58*	
—	4	4	—	Leyland 82	d													07 35							
—	6¾	6¾	—	Euxton Balshaw Lane	d													07 40							
—	15	15	—	**Wigan North Western** 65	a													07 50							
—	—	—	—		d			06 08			06 38	06 47			07 08		07 38	07 50		07 58				08 28	
15½	—	22	26	**Newton-le-Willows**	d		06 01		06 12	06 31		07 00	07 12	07 19		07 31			08 01		08 12	08 21	08 31		
—	—	—	—	Warrington Bank Quay	d					*06 06*		*06 40*							*07 39*				*08 08*		
17	—	23½	27½	Earlestown 8	d		06 04		06 15	06 34		07 03	07 15			07 34			08 04		08 15		08 34		
—	—	—	—	Warrington Bank Quay	a				06 25				07 22								08 23				
19¾	—	26¼	30¼	**St Helens Junction**	d		06 09			06 39		07 09		07 24		07 39			08 09			08 26	08 39		
21	—	27½	31½	Lea Green	d		06 12			06 42		07 12				07 42			08 12			08 29	08 42		
22¾	—	29¼	33¼	Rainhill	d		06 16			06 46		07 16		07 29		07 46			08 16			08 34	08 46		
24¼	—	30¾	34¾	Whiston	d		06 19			06 49		07 19				07 49			08 19			08 37	08 49		
—	18¾	—	—	Bryn	d			06 15			06 45				07 15		07 45			08 05				08 35	
—	20	—	—	Garswood	d			06 19			06 49				07 19		07 49	07 59		08 09				08 39	
—	23¾	—	—	**St Helens Central**	a			06 25			06 55				07 25		07 55	08 06		08 15				08 45	
—	—	—	—		d	05 56		06 26			06 56				07 26		07 56	08 06		08 16				08 46	08 56
—	25¼	—	—	Thatto Heath	d	05 59		06 29			06 59				07 29		07 59			08 19				08 49	08 59
—	26¼	—	—	Eccleston Park	d	06 02		06 32			07 02				07 32		08 02			08 22				08 52	09 02
—	27¼	—	—	Prescot	d	06 04		06 34			07 04				07 34		08 04	08 12		08 24				08 54	09 04
26¼	29½	32¾	36¾	Huyton	d	06 08	06 23	06 38		06 53	07 08	07 23		07 34	07 38	07 53	08 08	08 16	08 23	08 28		08 41	08 53	08 58	09 08
26¾	30	33¼	37¼	Roby	d	06 10	06 25	06 40		06 55	07 10	07 25			07 40	07 55	08 10		08 25	08 30			08 55	09 00	09 10
28¼	31½	34¾	38¾	Broad Green	d	06 13	06 28	06 43		06 58	07 13	07 28			07 43	07 58	08 13	08 20	08 28	08 33		08 45	08 58	09 03	09 13
29¼	32½	35¾	39¾	Wavertree Technology Park	d	06 16	06 31	06 46		07 01	07 16	07 31		07 39	07 46	08 01	08 16	08 24	08 31	08 37		08 48	09 01	09 06	09 16
30	33¼	36½	40½	Edge Hill 89, 91	d	06 19	06 34	06 49		07 04	07 19	07 34			07 49	08 04	08 19		08 34	08 41			09 04	09 09	09 19
31¾	35	38¼	42¼	**Liverpool Lime Street** 10 89, 91	a	06 28	06 43	06 58		07 13	07 28	07 43		07 49	07 58	08 13	08 28	08 35	08 43	08 50		08 59	09 13	09 18	09 28

		NT B	AW ◇ A	NT	NT	NT	NT	NT	NT B	AW ◇ A	NT	NT	NT	NT	NT	NT B	AW ◇ A	NT	NT	NT	NT	NT	NT B	AW ◇ A	NT
Manchester Airport 85 ✈	d			08 41							09 41							10 41							11 41
Manchester Piccadilly 10	d		08 50	09 01						09 50	10 01						10 50	11 01						11 50	12 01
Manchester Oxford Road	d		08 53	09 04						09 53	10 04						10 53	11 04						11 53	12 04
Manchester Victoria	d	08 39							09 39							10 39							11 39		
Eccles	d	08 46							09 46							10 46							11 46		
Patricroft	d	08 49							09 49							10 49							11 49		
Blackpool North 97	d				*07b36*	08 29		*08b45*					09 37		*09b45*					10 37		*10b45*			
Preston 8 65, 82	d				*08 17*	09 04		*09 17*					10 04		*10 17*					11 04		*11 17*			
Leyland 82	d					09 09							10 09							11 09					
Euxton Balshaw Lane	d					09 14							10 14							11 14					
Wigan North Western 65	a					09 24							10 24							11 24					
	d				09 08	09 24		09 38				10 08	10 24		10 38				11 08	11 24		11 38			
Newton-le-Willows	d	09 01	09 12	09 22					10 01	10 12	10 22					11 01	11 12	11 22					12 01	12 12	12 22
Warrington Bank Quay	d						09 22							10 22							11 22				
Earlestown 8	d	09 04	09 15				09 34		10 04	10 15				10 34		11 04	11 15				11 34		12 04	12 15	
Warrington Bank Quay	a		09 25							10 25							11 25							12 25	
St Helens Junction	d	09 09		09 27			09 39		10 09		10 27			10 39		11 09		11 27			11 39		12 09		12 27
Lea Green	d	09 12					09 42		10 12					10 42		11 12					11 42		12 12		
Rainhill	d	09 16					09 46		10 16					10 46		11 16					11 46		12 16		
Whiston	d	09 19					09 49		10 19					10 49		11 19					11 49		12 19		
Bryn	d				09 15			09 45				10 15			10 45				11 15			11 45			
Garswood	d				09 19			09 49				10 19			10 49				11 19			11 49			
St Helens Central	a				09 25	09 39		09 55				10 25	10 39		10 55				11 25	11 39		11 55			
	d				09 26	09 39		09 56				10 26	10 39		10 56				11 26	11 39		11 56			
Thatto Heath	d				09 29			09 59				10 29			10 59				11 29			11 59			
Eccleston Park	d				09 32			10 02				10 32			11 02				11 32			12 02			
Prescot	d				09 34			10 04				10 34			11 04				11 34			12 04			
Huyton	d	09 23			09 38	09 48	09 53	10 08	10 23			10 38	10 48	10 53	11 08	11 23			11 38	11 48	11 53	12 08	12 23		
Roby	d	09 25			09 40		09 55	10 10	10 25			10 40		10 55	11 10	11 25			11 40		11 55	12 10	12 25		
Broad Green	d	09 28			09 43		09 58	10 13	10 28			10 43		10 58	11 13	11 28			11 43		11 58	12 13	12 28		
Wavertree Technology Park	d	09 31		09 38	09 46		10 01	10 16	10 31		10 38	10 46		11 01	11 16	11 31		11 38	11 46		12 01	12 16	12 31		12 38
Edge Hill 89, 91	d	09 34			09 50		10 04	10 19	10 34			10 49		11 04	11 19	11 34			11 49		12 04	12 19	12 34		
Liverpool Lime Street 10 89, 91	a	09 43		09 48	09 58	10 02	10 13	10 28	10 43		10 48	10 58	11 02	11 13	11 28	11 43		11 48	11 58	12 02	12 13	12 28	12 43		12 48

For general notes see front of timetable
For details of catering facilities see Directory of Train Operators

A To Llandudno (Table 81)
B From Stalybridge (Table 39)
b Change at Preston and Wigan North Western

Manchester, Preston, Wigan and Newton-le-Willows → St Helens and Liverpool

Network Diagram - see first page of Table 88

		NT	NT	NT	NT	NT	AW	NT	NT	NT	NT	NT	NT	AW	NT	NT	NT	NT	NT	NT	AW	NT	NT	NT	NT
						A	◇ B						A	◇ B						A	◇ B				
Manchester Airport	85 ✈ d							12 41							13 41							14 41			
Manchester Piccadilly 10	d						12 50	13 01						13 50	14 01						14 50	15 01			
Manchester Oxford Road	d						12 53	13 04						13 53	14 04						14 53	15 04			
Manchester Victoria	d					12 39							13 39							14 39					
Eccles	d					12 46							13 46							14 46					
Patricroft	d					12 49							13 49							14 50					
Blackpool North	97 d		11 37		*11b45*					12 37		*12b45*					13 37		*13b45*					14 37	
Preston 8	65, 82 d		12 04		*12 17*					13 04		*13 17*					14 04		*14 17*					15 04	
Leyland	82 d		12 09							13 09							14 09							15 09	
Euxton Balshaw Lane	d		12 14							13 14							14 14							15 14	
Wigan North Western	65 a		12 24							13 24							14 24							15 24	
	d	12 08	12 24		12 38				13 08	13 24		13 38				14 08	14 24		14 38				15 08	15 24	
Newton-le-Willows	d					13 01	13 12	13 22					14 01	14 12	14 22					15 01	15 12	15 22			
Warrington Bank Quay	d			12 22							13 22							14 22							15 22
Earlestown 8	d			12 34		13 04	13 15				13 34		14 04	14 15				14 34		15 04	15 15				15 34
Warrington Bank Quay	a						13 25							14 25							15 25				
St Helens Junction	d			12 39		13 09		13 27			13 39		14 09		14 27			14 39		15 09		15 27			15 39
Lea Green	d			12 42		13 12					13 42		14 12					14 42		15 12					15 42
Rainhill	d			12 46		13 16					13 46		14 16					14 46		15 16					15 46
Whiston	d			12 49		13 19					13 49		14 19					14 49		15 19					15 49
Bryn	d	12 15			12 45				13 15			13 45				14 15			14 45				15 15		
Garswood	d	12 19			12 49				13 19			13 49				14 19			14 49				15 19		
St Helens Central	a	12 25	12 39		12 55				13 25	13 39		13 55				14 25	14 39		14 55				15 25	15 39	
	d	12 26	12 39		12 56				13 26	13 39		13 56				14 26	14 39		14 56				15 26	15 39	
Thatto Heath	d	12 29			12 59				13 29			13 59				14 29			14 59				15 29		
Eccleston Park	d	12 32			13 02				13 32			14 02				14 32			15 02				15 32		
Prescot	d	12 34			13 04				13 34			14 04				14 34			15 04				15 34		
Huyton	d	12 38	12 48	12 53	13 08	13 23			13 38	13 48	13 53	14 08	14 23			14 38	14 48	14 53	15 08	15 23			15 38	15 48	15 53
Roby	d	12 40		12 55	13 10	13 25			13 40		13 55	14 10	14 25			14 40		14 55	15 10	15 25			15 40		15 55
Broad Green	d	12 43		12 58	13 13	13 28			13 43		13 58	14 13	14 28			14 43		14 58	15 13	15 28			15 43		15 58
Wavertree Technology Park	d	12 46		13 01	13 16	13 31		13 38	13 46		14 01	14 16	14 31		14 38	14 46		15 01	15 16	15 31		15 38	15 46		16 01
Edge Hill	89, 91 d	12 49		13 04	13 19	13 34			13 50		14 04	14 19	14 34			14 50		15 04	15 19	15 34			15 50		16 04
Liverpool Lime Street 10	89, 91 a	12 58	13 02	13 13	13 28	13 43		13 48	13 58	14 02	14 13	14 28	14 43		14 48	14 58	15 02	15 13	15 28	15 43		15 48	15 58	16 02	16 13

		NT	NT	AW	NT	NT	NT	NT	NT	NT	AW	NT	NT	NT	NT	NT	AW	NT	NT	AW	NT	NT	NT	NT	NT
			A	◇ B						A	◇ B						C			◇ B					
Manchester Airport	85 ✈ d				15 41							16 41									17 41				
Manchester Piccadilly 10	d			15 50	16 01						16 50	17 01					17 19			17 50	18 01				
Manchester Oxford Road	d			15 53	16 04						16 53	17 04					17 22			17 53	18 04				
Manchester Victoria	d		15 39							16 39					17 09			17 37							18 39
Eccles	d		15 46							16 46					17 17			17 46			18 11				18 46
Patricroft	d		15 49							16 49					17 19			17 49							18 49
Blackpool North	97 d	*14b45*					15 37		*15b45*					16 35		*16b41*						17 37	*17b20*	*17 37*	
Preston 8	65, 82 d	*15 17*					16 04		*16 17*					17 04		*17 17*						18 04	*17 56*	*18 17*	
Leyland	82 d						16 09							17 09								18 09			
Euxton Balshaw Lane	d						16 14							17 14								18 14			
Wigan North Western	65 a						16 24							17 24								18 24			
	d	15 38				16 08	16 24		16 38				17 08	17 24		17 38			18 08			18 24	18 21	18 35	
Newton-le-Willows	d		16 01	16 12	16 22					17 01	17 12	17 22			17 31		17 40	18 01		18 12	18 24		18 34		19 01
Warrington Bank Quay	d							16 22							*16 51*								*17 49*		
Earlestown 8	d		16 04	16 15				16 34		17 04	17 15				17 34		17 44	18 04		18 15			18 37		19 04
Warrington Bank Quay	a			16 26							17 25						17 52			18 23					
St Helens Junction	d		16 09		16 27			16 39		17 09		17 27			17 39			18 09			18 29		18 41		19 09
Lea Green	d		16 12					16 42		17 12					17 42			18 12			18 32		18 44		19 12
Rainhill	d		16 16					16 46		17 16					17 46			18 16			18 36		18 48		19 16
Whiston	d		16 19					16 49		17 19					17 49			18 19					18 51		19 19
Bryn	d	15 45				16 15			16 45				17 15			17 45			18 15					18 45	
Garswood	d	15 49				16 19			16 49				17 19			17 49			18 19					18 49	
St Helens Central	a	15 55				16 25	16 39		16 55				17 25	17 39		17 55			18 25			18 39		18 55	
	d	15 56				16 26	16 39		16 56				17 26	17 39		17 56			18 26			18 39		18 56	
Thatto Heath	d	15 59				16 29			16 59				17 29			17 59			18 29					18 59	
Eccleston Park	d	16 02				16 32			17 02				17 32			18 02			18 32					19 02	
Prescot	d	16 04				16 34			17 04				17 34			18 04			18 34					19 04	
Huyton	d	16 08	16 23			16 38	16 48	16 53	17 08	17 23			17 38	17 48	17 53	18 08		18 23	18 38		18 41	18 48	18 55	19 08	19 23
Roby	d	16 10	16 25			16 40		16 55	17 10	17 25			17 40		17 55	18 10		18 25			18 43		18 57	19 10	19 25
Broad Green	d	16 13	16 28			16 43		16 58	17 13	17 28			17 43		17 58	18 13		18 28			18 47		19 00	19 13	19 28
Wavertree Technology Park	d	16 16	16 31		16 38	16 46		17 01	17 16	17 31		17 38	17 46		18 01	18 16		18 31	18 43		18 50		19 03	19 16	19 31
Edge Hill	89, 91 d	16 19	16 34			16 50		17 04	17 19	17 34			17 49		18 04	18 19		18 34	18 46				19 06	19 19	19 34
Liverpool Lime Street 10	89, 91 a	16 28	16 43		16 48	16 58	17 05	17 13	17 28	17 43		17 48	17 58	18 02	18 13	18 28		18 43	18 54		19 00	19 03	19 16	19 28	19 43

For general notes see front of timetable
For details of catering facilities see Directory of Train Operators

A From Stalybridge (Table 39)
B To Llandudno (Table 81)
C To Chester (Table 81)
b Change at Preston and Wigan North Western

Manchester, Preston, Wigan and Newton-le-Willows → St Helens and Liverpool

Network Diagram - see first page of Table 88

	AW A	NT	NT	NT	NT	NT	AW A	NT	NT	NT	NT	NT	NT	AW A	NT	AW A	NT	NT	AW A	NT	NT	NT	AW A	
Manchester Airport 85 ✈ d		18 41						19 41									21 41							
Manchester Piccadilly 10 d	18 50	19 01					19 50	20 01						20 50		21 50	22 01		22 12				23 14	
Manchester Oxford Road d	18 53	19 04					19 53	20 04						20 53		21 53	22 04		22 29				23 17	
Manchester Victoria d						19 39						20 39			21 39					22 39		23 09		
Eccles d						19 46						20 46			21 46					22 46		23 16		
Patricroft d						19 49						20 49			21 49					22 49		23 19		
Blackpool North 97 d				18 37					*18b45*	19 37	*19 37*		20 38					*20b45*			22 14			
Preston 8 65, 82 d				19 04					*19 17*	20 04	*20 08*		21 04					*21 17*			22 43			
Leyland 82 d				19 09						20 09			21 09								22 48			
Euxton Balshaw Lane d				19 14						20 14			21 14								22 53			
Wigan North Western 65 a				19 24						20 24			21 23								23 02			
d			19 08	19 24					20 08	20 24	20 38		21 23					22 25			23 03			
Newton-le-Willows d	19 12	19 22				20 01	20 12	20 22				21 01		21 12	22 01	22 12	22 22		22 47	23 01		23 31	23 36	
Warrington Bank Quay d					19 22							*20 19*			*21 19*					*22 19*				
Earlestown 8 d	19 16				19 34	20 04	20 15					21 04		21 15	22 04	22 15			22 50	23 04		23 34	23 39	
Warrington Bank Quay a	19 24						20 25							21 25		22 23			22 58				23 47	
St Helens Junction d		19 27			19 39	20 09		20 27				21 09			22 09		22 27			23 09		23 39		
Lea Green d					19 42	20 12						21 12			22 12					23 12		23 42		
Rainhill d					19 46	20 16						21 16			22 16					23 16		23 46		
Whiston d					19 49	20 19						21 19			22 19					23 19		23 49		
Bryn d			19 15						20 15		20 45		21 30					22 32			23 10			
Garswood d			19 19						20 19		20 49		21 34					22 36			23 14			
St Helens Central a			19 25	19 39					20 25	20 39	20 55		21 40					22 42			23 20			
d			19 26	19 39					20 26	20 39	20 56		21 41					22 43			23 21			
Thatto Heath d			19 29						20 29		20 59		21 44					22 46			23 24			
Eccleston Park d			19 32						20 32		21 02		21 47					22 49			23 27			
Prescot d			19 34						20 34		21 04		21 49					22 51			23 29			
Huyton d			19 38	19 48	19 53	20 23			20 38	20 48	21 08	21 23	21 53		22 23			22 55		23 23	23 33	23 53		
Roby d			19 40		19 55	20 25			20 40		21 10	21 25	21 55		22 25			22 57		23 25	23 35	23 55		
Broad Green d			19 43		19 58	20 28			20 43		21 13	21 28	22 00		22 28			23 00		23 28	23 38	23 58		
Wavertree Technology Park d		19 38	19 46		20 01	20 31		20 38	20 46		21 16	21 31	22 03		22 31		22 38	23 03		23 31	23 41	00 01		
Edge Hill 89, 91 d			19 49		20 04	20 34			20 49		21 19	21 34	22 06		22 34			23 06		23 34	23 46	00 04		
Liverpool Lime Street 10 89, 91 a		19 48	19 58	20 02	20 13	20 43		20 48	20 58	21 02	21 28	21 43	22 14		22 43		22 48	23 15		23 43	23 54	00 13		

Saturdays

	NT	NT	NT	AW ◇ B	NT	NT	NT	AW ◇ B	NT	NT	NT	NT	NT	NT	NT	AW ◇ B	NT	NT	NT		NT	NT C	AW ◇ B	NT
Manchester Airport 85 ✈ d									06 41								07 41							08 41
Manchester Piccadilly 10 d				05 50				06 50	06 58							07 50	07 58						08 50	09 01
Manchester Oxford Road d				05 53				06 53	07 01							07 53	08 03						08 53	09 04
Manchester Victoria d		05 39			06 09						07 09			07 39				08 09				08 39		
Eccles d		05 46			06 16						07 16			07 46				08 17				08 46		
Patricroft d		05 49			06 19						07 19			07 49				08 19				08 49		
Blackpool North 97 d						*05b45*						*06b34*	07 02						*07b18*					
Preston 8 65, 82 d						*06 17*						*07 17*	07 30						*07 58*					
Leyland 82 d													07 35											
Euxton Balshaw Lane d													07 40											
Wigan North Western 65 a													07 50											
d			06 08			06 38	06 47			07 08		07 38	07 50		07 58				08 28					
Newton-le-Willows d		06 01		06 12	06 31		07 00	07 12	07 19		07 31			08 01		08 12	08 21	08 31				09 01	09 12	09 22
Warrington Bank Quay d					*06 06*		*06 40*							*07 39*				*08 08*						
Earlestown 8 d		06 04		06 15	06 34		07 03	07 15			07 34			08 04		08 15		08 34				09 04	09 15	
Warrington Bank Quay a				06 25				07 23								08 23							09 25	
St Helens Junction d		06 09			06 39		07 09		07 24		07 39			08 09			08 26	08 39				09 09		09 27
Lea Green d		06 12			06 42		07 12				07 42			08 12			08 29	08 42				09 12		
Rainhill d		06 16			06 46		07 16		07 29		07 46			08 16			08 33	08 46				09 16		
Whiston d		06 19			06 49		07 19				07 49			08 19			08 37	08 49				09 19		
Bryn d			06 15			06 45				07 15		07 45			08 05				08 35					
Garswood d			06 19			06 49				07 19		07 49	07 59		08 09				08 39					
St Helens Central a			06 25			06 55				07 25		07 55	08 06		08 15				08 45					
d	05 56		06 26			06 56				07 26		07 56	08 06		08 16				08 46		08 56			
Thatto Heath d	05 59		06 29			06 59				07 29		07 59			08 19				08 49		08 59			
Eccleston Park d	06 02		06 32			07 02				07 32		08 02			08 22				08 52		09 02			
Prescot d	06 04		06 34			07 04				07 34		08 04	08 12		08 24				08 54		09 04			
Huyton d	06 08	06 23	06 38		06 53	07 08	07 23		07 34	07 38	07 53	08 08	08 16	08 23	08 28		08 41	08 53	08 58		09 08	09 23		
Roby d	06 10	06 25	06 40		06 55	07 10	07 25			07 40	07 55	08 10		08 25	08 30			08 55	09 00		09 10	09 25		
Broad Green d	06 13	06 28	06 43		06 58	07 13	07 28			07 43	07 58	08 13	08 20	08 28	08 33		08 45	08 58	09 03		09 13	09 28		
Wavertree Technology Park d	06 16	06 31	06 46		07 01	07 16	07 31		07 39	07 46	08 01	08 16	08 24	08 31	08 36		08 48	09 01	09 06		09 16	09 31		09 38
Edge Hill 89, 91 d	06 19	06 36	06 49		07 04	07 19	07 34			07 49	08 04	08 19		08 34	08 40			09 05	09 09		09 19	09 34		
Liverpool Lime Street 10 89, 91 a	06 28	06 43	06 58		07 13	07 28	07 43		07 49	07 58	08 13	08 28	08 34	08 43	08 48		08 59	09 13	09 18		09 28	09 43		09 48

For general notes see front of timetable
For details of catering facilities see Directory of Train Operators

A To Chester (Table 81)
B To Llandudno (Table 81)
C From Stalybridge (Table 39)
b Change at Preston and Wigan North Western

Manchester, Preston, Wigan and Newton-le-Willows → St Helens and Liverpool

Network Diagram - see first page of Table 88

		NT	NT	NT	NT	NT	AW	NT	NT	NT	NT	NT	NT	AW	NT	NT	NT	NT		NT	NT	AW	NT	NT	NT
						A	◇ B						A	◇ B							A	◇ B			
Manchester Airport	85 ✈ d							09 41							10 41								11 41		
Manchester Piccadilly 10	d						09 50	10 01						10 50	11 01							11 50	12 01		
Manchester Oxford Road	d						09 53	10 04						10 53	11 04							11 53	12 04		
Manchester Victoria	d					09 39							10 39								11 39				
Eccles	d					09 46							10 46								11 46				
Patricroft	d					09 49							10 49								11 49				
Blackpool North	97 d	07b29	08 38		08b45					09 37		09b45					10 37			10b45					11 37
Preston 8	65, 82 d	08 17	09 04		09 17					10 04		10 17					11 04			11 17					12 04
Leyland	82 d		09 09							10 09							11 09								12 09
Euxton Balshaw Lane	d		09 14							10 14							11 14								12 14
Wigan North Western	65 a		09 24							10 24							11 24								12 24
	d	09 08	09 24		09 38				10 08	10 24		10 38				11 08	11 24			11 38				12 08	12 24
Newton-le-Willows	d					10 01	10 12	10 22					11 01	11 12	11 22						12 01	12 12	12 22		
Warrington Bank Quay	d			09 22							10 22							11 22							
Earlestown 8	d			09 34		10 04	10 15				10 34		11 04	11 15				11 34			12 04	12 15			
Warrington Bank Quay	a						10 25							11 25								12 25			
St Helens Junction	d			09 39		10 09		10 27			10 39		11 09		11 27			11 39			12 09		12 27		
Lea Green	d			09 42		10 12					10 42		11 12					11 42			12 12				
Rainhill	d			09 46		10 16					10 46		11 16					11 46			12 16				
Whiston	d			09 49		10 19					10 49		11 19					11 49			12 19				
Bryn	d	09 15			09 45				10 15			10 45				11 15				11 45				12 15	
Garswood	d	09 19			09 49				10 19			10 49				11 19				11 49				12 19	
St Helens Central	a	09 25	09 39		09 55				10 25	10 39		10 55				11 25	11 39			11 55				12 25	12 39
	d	09 26	09 39		09 56				10 26	10 39		10 56				11 26	11 39			11 56				12 26	12 39
Thatto Heath	d	09 29			09 59				10 29			10 59				11 29				11 59				12 29	
Eccleston Park	d	09 32			10 02				10 32			11 02				11 32				12 02				12 32	
Prescot	d	09 34			10 04				10 34			11 04				11 34				12 04				12 34	
Huyton	d	09 38	09 48	09 53	10 08	10 23			10 38	10 48	10 53	11 08	11 23			11 38	11 48	11 53		12 08	12 23			12 38	12 48
Roby	d	09 40		09 55	10 10	10 25			10 40		10 55	11 10	11 25			11 40		11 55		12 10	12 25			12 40	
Broad Green	d	09 43		09 58	10 13	10 28			10 43		10 58	11 13	11 28			11 43		11 58		12 13	12 28			12 43	
Wavertree Technology Park	d	09 46		10 01	10 16	10 31		10 38	10 46		11 01	11 16	11 31		11 38	11 46		12 01		12 16	12 31		12 38	12 46	
Edge Hill	89, 91 d	09 48		10 04	10 21	10 34			10 49		11 04	11 19	11 34			11 49		12 04		12 19	12 34			12 49	
Liverpool Lime Street 10	89, 91 a	09 58	10 02	10 13	10 29	10 43		10 48	10 58	11 02	11 13	11 28	11 43		11 48	11 58	12 02	12 13		12 28	12 43		12 48	12 58	13 02

		NT	NT	NT	AW	NT	NT	NT	NT	NT	NT	AW	NT	NT	NT	NT		NT	NT	AW	NT	NT	NT	NT	NT
				A	◇ B						A	◇ B							A	◇ B					
Manchester Airport	85 ✈ d					12 41							13 41								14 41				
Manchester Piccadilly 10	d				12 50	13 01						13 50	14 01							14 50	15 01				
Manchester Oxford Road	d				12 53	13 04						13 53	14 04							14 53	15 04				
Manchester Victoria	d			12 39							13 39								14c38						
Eccles	d			12 46							13 46								14 46						
Patricroft	d			12 49							13 49								14 49						
Blackpool North	97 d							12 37		12e45					13 37			13e45					14 37		14e45
Preston 8	65, 82 d		12f17					13 04		13e17					14 04			14e17					15 04		15e17
Leyland	82 d							13 09							14 09								15 09		
Euxton Balshaw Lane	d							13 14							14 14								15 14		
Wigan North Western	65 a							13 24							14 24								15 24		
	d		12 38				13 08	13 24		13 38				14 08	14 24			14 38				15 08	15 24		15 38
Newton-le-Willows	d			13 01	13 12	13 22					14 01	14 12	14 22						15 01	15 12	15 22				
Warrington Bank Quay	d	12 22							13 22							14 22								15 22	
Earlestown 8	d	12 34		13 04	13 15				13 34		14 04	14 15				14 34			15 04	15 15				15 34	
Warrington Bank Quay	a				13 25							14 25								15 25					
St Helens Junction	d	12 39		13 09		13 27			13 39		14 09		14 27			14 39			15 09		15 27			15 39	
Lea Green	d	12 42		13 12					13 42		14 12					14 42			15 12					15 42	
Rainhill	d	12 46		13 16					13 46		14 16					14 46			15 16					15 46	
Whiston	d	12 49		13 19					13 49		14 19					14 49			15 19					15 49	
Bryn	d		12 45				13 15			13 45				14 15				14 45				15 15			15 45
Garswood	d		12 49				13 19			13 49				14 19				14 49				15 19			15 49
St Helens Central	a		12 55				13 25	13 39		13 55				14 25	14 39			14 55				15 25	15 39		15 55
	d		12 56				13 26	13 39		13 56				14 26	14 39			14 56				15 26	15 39		15 56
Thatto Heath	d		12 59				13 29			13 59				14 29				14 59				15 29			15 59
Eccleston Park	d		13 02				13 32			14 02				14 32				15 02				15 32			16 02
Prescot	d		13 04				13 34			14 04				14 34				15 04				15 34			16 04
Huyton	d	12 53	13 08	13 23			13 38	13 48	13 53	14 08	14 23			14 38	14 48	14 53		15 08	15 23			15 38	15 48	15 53	16 08
Roby	d	12 55	13 10	13 25			13 40		13 55	14 10	14 25			14 40		14 55		15 10	15 25			15 40		15 55	16 10
Broad Green	d	12 58	13 13	13 28			13 43		13 58	14 13	14 28			14 43		14 58		15 13	15 28			15 43		15 58	16 13
Wavertree Technology Park	d	13 01	13 16	13 31		13 38	13 46		14 01	14 16	14 31		14 38	14 46		15 01		15 16	15 31		15 38	15 46		16 01	16 16
Edge Hill	89, 91 d	13 04	13 19	13 34			13 50		14 04	14 19	14 34			14 50		15 04		15 19	15 34			15 50		16 04	16 19
Liverpool Lime Street 10	89, 91 a	13 13	13 28	13 43		13 48	13 58	14 02	14 13	14 28	14 43		14 48	14 58	15 02	15 13		15 28	15 43		15 48	15 58	16 02	16 13	16 28

For general notes see front of timetable
For details of catering facilities see Directory of Train Operators

A From Stalybridge (Table 39)
B To Llandudno (Table 81)
b Change at Preston and Wigan North Western
c Until 31 October dep. 1 min. later
e Until 31 October only
f From 7 November dep. 1204

Table 90

Saturdays

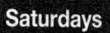

Manchester, Preston, Wigan and Newton-le-Willows → St Helens and Liverpool

Network Diagram - see first page of Table 88

	NT	AW	NT	NT	NT	NT	NT	NT	AW	NT	NT	NT	NT		NT	NT	NT	AW	NT	NT	NT	NT	NT	AW
	A	◇ B 🛒						A	◇ B 🛒							A		◇ B 🛒					A	C 🛒
Manchester Airport 85 ✈ d			15 41							16 41									17 41					
Manchester Piccadilly 10 d		15 50	16 01						16 50	17 01								17 50	18 01					18 50
Manchester Oxford Road d		15 53	16 04						16 53	17 04								17 53	18 04					18 53
Manchester Victoria d	15 39							16 39					17 09			17 39							18 39	
Eccles d	15 46							16 46					17 17			17 46			18 11				18 46	
Patricroft d	15 49							16 49					17 19			17 49							18 49	
Blackpool North 97 d					15 37		15b45					16 35			16b41					17 37	17b18			
Preston 8 65, 82 d					16 04		16b17					17 04			17b17					18 04	17b58	18b17		
Leyland 82 d					16 09							17 09								18 09				
Euxton Balshaw Lane d					16 14							17 14								18 14				
Wigan North Western 65 a					16 24							17 24								18 24				
d				16 08	16 24		16 38				17 08	17 24			17 38		18 08			18 24	18 21	18 35		
Newton-le-Willows d	16 01	16 12	16 22					17 01	17 12	17 22			17 31			18 01		18 12	18 24		18 34		19 01	19 12
Warrington Bank Quay d						16 22							*17 19*								*18 19*			
Earlestown 8 d	16 04	16 15				16 34		17 04	17 15				17 34			18 04		18 15			18 37		19 04	19 16
Warrington Bank Quay a		16 25							17 25									18 24						19 25
St Helens Junction d	16 09		16 27			16 39		17 09		17 27			17 39			18 09			18 29		18 41		19 09	
Lea Green d	16 12					16 42		17 12					17 42			18 12			18 32		18 44		19 12	
Rainhill d	16 16					16 46		17 16					17 46			18 16			18 36		18 48		19 16	
Whiston d	16 19					16 49		17 19					17 49			18 19					18 51		19 19	
Bryn d				16 15			16 45				17 15				17 45		18 15					18 45		
Garswood d				16 19			16 49				17 19				17 49		18 19					18 49		
St Helens Central a				16 25	16 39		16 55				17 25	17 39			17 55		18 25			18 39		18 55		
d				16 26	16 39		16 56				17 26	17 39			17 56		18 26			18 39		18 56		
Thatto Heath d				16 29			16 59				17 29				17 59		18 29					18 59		
Eccleston Park d				16 32			17 02				17 32				18 02		18 32					19 02		
Prescot d				16 34			17 04				17 34				18 04		18 34					19 04		
Huyton d	16 23			16 38	16 48	16 53	17 08	17 23			17 38	17 48	17 53		18 08	18 23	18 38		18 41	18 48	18 55	19 08	19 23	
Roby d	16 25			16 40		16 55	17 10	17 25			17 40		17 55		18 10	18 25			18 43		18 57	19 10	19 25	
Broad Green d	16 28			16 43		16 58	17 13	17 28			17 43		17 58		18 13	18 28			18 47		19 00	19 13	19 28	
Wavertree Technology Park d	16 31		16 38	16 46		17 01	17 16	17 31		17 38	17 46		18 01		18 16	18 31	18 43		18 50		19 03	19 16	19 31	
Edge Hill 89, 91 d	16 34			16 49		17 04	17 19	17 34			17 50		18 04		18 19	18 34	18 46				19 06	19 19	19 34	
Liverpool Lime Street 10 89, 91 a	16 43		16 48	16 58	17 05	17 13	17 28	17 43		17 48	17 58	18 02	18 13		18 28	18 43	18 54		19 00	19 02	19 15	19 28	19 43	

	NT	NT	NT	NT	NT	AW	NT	NT	NT	NT	NT	NT	AW	NT	AW	NT	NT	AW	NT	NT	NT	AW		
						C							C		C			C				C		
Manchester Airport 85 ✈ d	18 41						19 41									21 41								
Manchester Piccadilly 10 d	19 01					19 50	20 01						20 50		21 50	22 01		22 26				23 14		
Manchester Oxford Road d	19 04					19 53	20 04						20 53		21 53	22 03		22 29				23 17		
Manchester Victoria d					19 39						20 39			21 39					22 39		23 09			
Eccles d					19 46						20 46			21 46					22 46		23 16			
Patricroft d					19 49						20 49			21 49					22 49		23 19			
Blackpool North 97 d			18 37					18b45	19 37	19b45		20 38					20b45			22 14				
Preston 8 65, 82 d			19 04					19b17	20 04	20b17		21 04					21b20			22 43				
Leyland 82 d			19 09						20 09			21 09								22 48				
Euxton Balshaw Lane d			19 14						20 14			21 14								22 53				
Wigan North Western 65 a			19 24						20 24			21 24								23 02				
d		19 08	19 24					20 08	20 24	20 38		21 24					22 25			23 03				
Newton-le-Willows d	19 22				20 01	20 12	20 22				21 01		21 12	22 01	22 12	22 22		22 47	23 01		23 31	23 36		
Warrington Bank Quay d				19 22							*20 19*			*21 19*					*22 19*					
Earlestown 8 d				19 34	20 04	20 15					21 04		21 15	22 04	22 15			22 50	23 04		23 34	23 39		
Warrington Bank Quay a						20 29							21 26		22 23			22 58				23 47		
St Helens Junction d	19 27			19 39	20 09		20 27				21 09			22 09		22 27			23 09		23 39			
Lea Green d				19 42	20 12						21 12			22 12					23 12		23 42			
Rainhill d				19 46	20 16						21 16			22 16					23 16		23 46			
Whiston d				19 49	20 19						21 19			22 19					23 19		23 49			
Bryn d		19 15						20 15		20 45		21 31					22 32			23 10				
Garswood d		19 19						20 19		20 49		21 35					22 36			23 14				
St Helens Central a		19 25	19 39					20 25	20 39	20 55		21 41					22 42			23 20				
d		19 26	19 39					20 26	20 39	20 56		21 42					22 43			23 21				
Thatto Heath d		19 29						20 29		20 59		21 45					22 46			23 24				
Eccleston Park d		19 32						20 32		21 02		21 48					22 49			23 27				
Prescot d		19 34						20 34		21 04		21 50					22 51			23 29				
Huyton d		19 38	19 48	19 53	20 23			20 38	20 48	21 08	21 23	21 54		22 23			22 55		23 23	23 33	23 53			
Roby d		19 40		19 55	20 25			20 40		21 10	21 25	21 56		22 25			22 57		23 25	23 35	23 55			
Broad Green d		19 43		19 58	20 28			20 43		21 13	21 28	22 00		22 28			23 00		23 28	23 38	23 58			
Wavertree Technology Park d	19 38	19 46		20 01	20 31		20 38	20 46		21 16	21 31	22 05		22 31		22 38	23 03		23 31	23 41	00 01			
Edge Hill 89, 91 d		19 49		20 04	20 34			20 49		21 19	21 34	22 10		22 34			23 06		23 34	23 46	00 04			
Liverpool Lime Street 10 89, 91 a	19 48	19 58	20 02	20 13	20 43		20 48	20 58	21 02	21 28	21 43	22 14		22 43		22 48	23 15		23 43	23 54	00 13			

For general notes see front of timetable
For details of catering facilities see Directory of Train Operators

A From Stalybridge (Table 39)
B To Llandudno (Table 81)
C To Chester (Table 81)

b Until 31 October only

Table 90

Sundays

until 6 September

Manchester, Preston, Wigan and Newton-le-Willows → St Helens and Liverpool

Network Diagram - see first page of Table 88

			AW A 🚌	NT	NT	NT	NT	NT B	NT C	AW A	NT	NT	AW A	NT	NT	AW A 🛒	NT	NT	AW A 🛒
Manchester Airport	85 ✈	d			08 34		09 35				10 32			11 35			12 35		
Manchester Piccadilly [10]	🚢	d	07 44		08 50		09 50			09 56	10 50		10 55	11 50		11 56	12 50		12 56
Manchester Oxford Road		d	07 54		08 54		09 53			09 59	10 53		10 59	11 53		11 59	12 53		12 59
Manchester Victoria	🚢	d																	
Eccles		d			09 01		10 00				11 00			12 00			13 00		
Patricroft		d																	
Blackpool North	97	d				08 50		09 50	09 50			10 50			11 50			12 50	
Preston [8]	65, 82	d				09 15		10 15	10 15			11 15			12 15			13 15	
Leyland	82	d				09 21		10 21	10 21			11 21			12 21			13 21	
Euxton Balshaw Lane		d				09 25		10 25	10 25			11 25			12 25			13 25	
Wigan North Western	65	a				09 35		10 35	10 38			11 35			12 35			13 35	
		d		08 36		09 36		10 36	10 38			11 36			12 36			13 36	
Newton-le-Willows		d	08 19		09 14		10 13			10 18	11 13		11 20	12 13		12 18	13 13		13 18
Warrington Bank Quay		d					*09 10*				*10 12*			*11 03*			*12 03*		
Earlestown [8]		d	08 27		09 16		10 16			10 21	11 16		11 23	12 16		12 21	13 16		13 21
Warrington Bank Quay		a	08 42							10 27			11 29			12 27			13 28
St Helens Junction		d			09 21		10 21				11 21			12 21			13 21		
Lea Green		d			09 24		10 24				11 24			12 24			13 24		
Rainhill		d			09 28		10 28				11 28			12 28			13 28		
Whiston		d			09 31		10 31				11 31			12 31			13 31		
Bryn		d																	
Garswood		d		08 46		09 46		10 46	10 48			11 46			12 46			13 46	
St Helens Central		a		08 52		09 52		10 52	10 54			11 52			12 52			13 52	
		d		08 53		09 53		10 53	10 55			11 53			12 53			13 53	
Thatto Heath		d		08 56		09 56		10 56	10 58			11 56			12 56			13 56	
Eccleston Park		d																	
Prescot		d		09 00		10 00		11 00	11 02			12 00			13 00			14 00	
Huyton		d		09 05	09 35	10 05	10 35	11 05	11 07		11 35	12 05		12 35	13 05		13 35	14 05	
Roby		d		09 07	09 37	10 07	10 37	11 07	11 09		11 37	12 07		12 37	13 07		13 37	14 07	
Broad Green		d		09 10	09 40	10 10	10 40	11 10	11 12		11 40	12 10		12 40	13 10		13 40	14 10	
Wavertree Technology Park		d		09 13	09 43	10 13	10 43	11 13	11 15		11 43	12 13		12 43	13 13		13 43	14 13	
Edge Hill	89, 91	d																	
Liverpool Lime Street [10]	89, 91	a		09 22	09 53	10 22	10 55	11 22	11 24		11 53	12 22		12 53	13 22		13 53	14 22	

			NT	NT	AW A 🛒	NT	NT	AW A 🛒	NT	NT	AW A 🛒	NT	NT	AW A 🛒	NT	NT	AW A 🛒	NT
Manchester Airport	85 ✈	d	13 35			14 35			15 35			16 35			17 35			18 35
Manchester Piccadilly [10]	🚢	d	13 50		13 56	14 50		14 56	15 50		15 56	16 50		16 56	17 50		17 56	18 50
Manchester Oxford Road		d	13 53		13 59	14 53		14 59	15 53		15 59	16 53		16 59	17 53		17 59	18 53
Manchester Victoria	🚢	d																
Eccles		d	14 00			15 00			16 00			17 00			18 00			19 00
Patricroft		d																
Blackpool North	97	d		13 50			14 50			15 50			16 50			17 50		
Preston [8]	65, 82	d		14 15			15 15			16 15			17 15			18 15		
Leyland	82	d		14 21			15 21			16 21			17 21			18 21		
Euxton Balshaw Lane		d		14 25			15 25			16 25			17 25			18 25		
Wigan North Western	65	a		14 35			15 35			16 35			17 35			18 35		
		d		14 36			15 36			16 36			17 36			18 36		
Newton-le-Willows		d	14 13		14 18	15 13		15 18	16 13		16 18	17 13		17 18	18 13		18 18	19 13
Warrington Bank Quay		d	*13 03*			*14 03*			*15 03*			*16 03*			*17 03*			*18 03*
Earlestown [8]		d	14 16		14 21	15 16		15 21	16 16		16 21	17 16		17 21	18 16		18 21	19 16
Warrington Bank Quay		a			14 27			15 28			16 27			17 27			18 27	
St Helens Junction		d	14 21			15 21			16 21			17 21			18 21			19 21
Lea Green		d	14 24			15 24			16 24			17 24			18 24			19 24
Rainhill		d	14 28			15 28			16 28			17 28			18 28			19 28
Whiston		d	14 31			15 31			16 31			17 31			18 31			19 31
Bryn		d																
Garswood		d		14 46			15 46			16 46			17 46			18 46		
St Helens Central		a		14 52			15 52			16 52			17 52			18 52		
		d		14 53			15 53			16 53			17 53			18 53		
Thatto Heath		d		14 56			15 56			16 56			17 56			18 56		
Eccleston Park		d																
Prescot		d		15 00			16 00			17 00			18 00			19 00		
Huyton		d	14 35	15 05		15 35	16 05		16 35	17 05		17 35	18 05		18 35	19 05		19 35
Roby		d	14 37	15 07		15 37	16 07		16 37	17 07		17 37	18 07		18 37	19 07		19 37
Broad Green		d	14 40	15 10		15 40	16 10		16 40	17 10		17 40	18 10		18 40	19 10		19 40
Wavertree Technology Park		d	14 43	15 13		15 43	16 13		16 43	17 13		17 43	18 13		18 43	19 13		19 43
Edge Hill	89, 91	d																
Liverpool Lime Street [10]	89, 91	a	14 53	15 22		15 53	16 22		16 53	17 22		17 53	18 22		18 53	19 22		19 53

For general notes see front of timetable
For details of catering facilities see Directory of Train Operators

A To Chester (Table 81)
B From 19 July
C Until 12 July

Table 90

Sundays

until 6 September

Manchester, Preston, Wigan and Newton-le-Willows → St Helens and Liverpool

Network Diagram - see first page of Table 88

	NT	AW A	NT	NT	AW A	NT	NT	AW A	NT	NT	AW A	NT	NT	AW A	AW A
Manchester Airport 85 ✈ d			19 35			20 35			21 35			22 35			
Manchester Piccadilly 10 ⛴ d		18 56	19 50		19 56	20 50		20 56	21 50		21 56	22 50		22 56	23 25
Manchester Oxford Road d		18 59	19 53		19 59	20 53		20 59	21 53		21 59	22 53		22 59	23 28
Manchester Victoria ⛴ d															
Eccles d			20 00			21 00			22 00			23 00			
Patricroft d															
Blackpool North 97 d	18 50			19 50			20 50			21 50			22 44		
Preston 8 65, 82 d	19 15			20 15			21 15			22 15			23 09		
Leyland 82 d	19 21			20 21			21 21			22 21			23 15		
Euxton Balshaw Lane d	19 25			20 25			21 25			22 25			23 19		
Wigan North Western 65 a	19 35			20 35			21 35			22 35			23 29		
d	19 36			20 36			21 36			22 36			23 30		
Newton-le-Willows d		19 18	20 13		20 18	21 13		21 18	22 13		22 18	23 13		23 18	23 46
Warrington Bank Quay d			*19 03*			*20 03*			*21 03*			*22 36*			
Earlestown 8 d		19 21	20 16		20 21	21 16		21 21	22 16		22 21	23 16		23 21	23 49
Warrington Bank Quay a		19 28			20 29			21 27			22 27			23 27	23 55
St Helens Junction d			20 21			21 21			22 21			23 21			
Lea Green d			20 24			21 24			22 24			23 24			
Rainhill d			20 28			21 28			22 28			23 28			
Whiston d			20 31			21 31			22 31			23 31			
Bryn d															
Garswood d	19 46			20 46			21 46			22 47			23 40		
St Helens Central a	19 52			20 52			21 52			22 54			23 46		
d	19 53			20 53			21 53			22 54			23 47		
Thatto Heath d	19 56			20 56			21 56			22 58			23 50		
Eccleston Park d															
Prescot d	20 00			21 00			22 00			23 02			23 54		
Huyton d	20 05		20 35	21 05		21 35	22 05		22 35	23 06		23 35	23 59		
Roby d	20 07		20 37	21 07		21 37	22 07		22 37	23 08		23 37	00 01		
Broad Green d	20 10		20 40	21 10		21 40	22 10		22 40	23 12		23 40	00 04		
Wavertree Technology Park d	20 13		20 43	21 13		21 43	22 13		22 43	23 15		23 43	00 07		
Edge Hill 89, 91 d															
Liverpool Lime Street 10 89, 91 a	20 22		20 53	21 22		21 53	22 22		22 53	23 23		23 53	00 16		

Sundays

from 13 September

	AW A 🚌	NT	NT	TP 1 ◇	NT	NT	AW A	TP 1 ◇ B	NT C	NT D	NT	AW A	TP 1 ◇ B	NT	NT	AW A 🍴	TP 1 ◇ E	NT	EM ◇ G 🍴	NT	AW A 🍴	TP 1 ◇ H	NT	EM ◇ G 🍴
Manchester Airport 85 ✈ d											10 31				11 33					12 35				
Manchester Piccadilly 10 ⛴ d	07 44					09 50	09 53				10 50	10 55			11 50	11 56			12 38	12 50	12 56			13 38
Manchester Oxford Road d	07 54					09 53	09 59				10 53	10 59			11 53	11 59			12 42	12 53	12 59			13 42
Manchester Victoria ⛴ d			08 53	09 15				10 15					11 09				12 09					13 09		
Eccles d			09 00			10 00					11 00				12 00					13 00				
Patricroft d																								
Blackpool North 97 d					08 50				09 50	09 50				10 50				11 50					12 50	
Preston 8 65, 82 d					09 15				10 15	10 15				11 15				12 15					13 15	
Leyland 82 d					09 21				10 21	10 21				11 21				12 21					13 21	
Euxton Balshaw Lane d					09 25				10 25	10 25				11 25				12 25					13 25	
Wigan North Western 65 a					09 35				10 35	10 38				11 35				12 35					13 35	
d		08 36			09 36				10 36	10 38				11 36				12 36					13 36	
Newton-le-Willows d	08 19		09 13	09 33		10 13	10 18	10 33			11 13	11 20	11 27		12 13	12 18	12 27		13 00	13 13	13 18	13 27		14 00
Warrington Bank Quay d						*09 10*					*10 12*				*11 03*					*12 03*				
Earlestown 8 d	08 27		09 16			10 16	10 21				11 16	11 23			12 16	12 21				13 16	13 21			
Warrington Bank Quay a	08 42						10 27					11 29				12 27					13 28			
St Helens Junction d			09 21			10 21					11 21				12 21					13 21				
Lea Green d			09 24			10 24					11 24				12 24					13 24				
Rainhill d			09 28			10 28					11 28				12 28					13 28				
Whiston d			09 31			10 31					11 31				12 31					13 31				
Bryn d																								
Garswood d		08 46			09 46				10 46	10 48				11 46				12 46					13 46	
St Helens Central a		08 52			09 52				10 52	10 54				11 52				12 52					13 52	
d		08 53			09 53				10 53	10 55				11 53				12 53					13 53	
Thatto Heath d		08 56			09 56				10 56	10 58				11 56				12 56					13 56	
Eccleston Park d																								
Prescot d		09 00			10 00				11 00	11 02				12 00				13 00					14 00	
Huyton d		09 05	09 35		10 05	10 35			11 05	11 07	11 35			12 05	12 35			13 05		13 35			14 05	
Roby d		09 07	09 37		10 07	10 37			11 07	11 09	11 37			12 07	12 37			13 07		13 37			14 07	
Broad Green d		09 10	09 40		10 10	10 40			11 10	11 12	11 40			12 10	12 40			13 10		13 40			14 10	
Wavertree Technology Park d		09 13	09 43		10 13	10 43			11 13	11 15	11 43			12 13	12 43			13 13		13 43			14 13	
Edge Hill 89, 91 d																								
Liverpool Lime Street 10 89, 91 a		09 22	09 53	09 57	10 22	10 53		10 57	11 22	11 24	11 53		11 57	12 22	12 53		12 57	13 22	13 30	13 53		13 57	14 22	14 30

For general notes see front of timetable
For details of catering facilities see Directory of Train Operators

- **A** To Chester (Table 81)
- **B** From York (Table 39)
- **C** From 8 November
- **D** Until 1 November
- **E** From Newcastle (Table 39)
- **G** Until 1 November. From Nottingham (Table 49)
- **H** From Scarborough (Table 39)

Table 90

Sundays

from 13 September

Manchester, Preston, Wigan and Newton-le-Willows → St Helens and Liverpool

Network Diagram - see first page of Table 88

Station		NT	AW	TP	NT	EM	NT	AW	TP	NT	EM	NT	AW	TP	NT	EM	NT	AW	TP	NT	EM	NT	AW	TP	NT
			A	1 ◇ B		◇ C		A	1 ◇ D		◇ E		A	1 ◇ B		◇ C		A	1 ◇ D		◇ C		A	1 ◇ B	
Manchester Airport 85 ✈	d	13 35					14 35					15 35					16 35					17 35			
Manchester Piccadilly 10	d	13 50	13 56			14 38	14 50	14 56			15 38	15 50	15 56			16 38	16 50	16 56			17 38	17 50	17 56		
Manchester Oxford Road	d	13 53	13 59			14 42	14 53	14 59			15 42	15 53	15 59			16 42	16 53	16 59			17 42	17 53	17 59		
Manchester Victoria	d			14 09					15 09					16 09					17 09					18 09	
Eccles	d	14 00					15 00					16 00					17 00					18 00			
Patricroft	d																								
Blackpool North 97	d				13 50					14 50					15 50					16 50					17 50
Preston 8 65, 82	d				14 15					15 15					16 15					17 15					18 15
Leyland 82	d				14 21					15 21					16 21					17 21					18 21
Euxton Balshaw Lane	d				14 25					15 25					16 25					17 25					18 25
Wigan North Western 65	a				14 35					15 35					16 35					17 35					18 35
	d				14 36					15 36					16 36					17 36					18 36
Newton-le-Willows	d	14 13	14 18	14 27		15 00	15 13	15 18	15 27		16 00	16 13	16 18	16 27		17 00	17 13	17 18	17 27		18 00	18 13	18 18	18 27	
Warrington Bank Quay	d	*13 03*					*14 03*					*15 03*					*16 03*					*17 03*			
Earlestown 8	d	14 16	14 21				15 16	15 21				16 16	16 21				17 16	17 21				18 16	18 21		
Warrington Bank Quay	a		14 27					15 28					16 27					17 27					18 27		
St Helens Junction	d	14 21					15 21					16 21					17 21					18 21			
Lea Green	d	14 24					15 24					16 24					17 24					18 24			
Rainhill	d	14 28					15 28					16 28					17 28					18 28			
Whiston	d	14 31					15 31					16 31					17 31					18 31			
Bryn	d																								
Garswood	d				14 46					15 46					16 46					17 46					18 46
St Helens Central	a				14 52					15 52					16 52					17 52					18 52
	d				14 53					15 53					16 53					17 53					18 53
Thatto Heath	d				14 56					15 56					16 56					17 56					18 56
Eccleston Park	d																								
Prescot	d				15 00					16 00					17 00					18 00					19 00
Huyton	d	14 35			15 05		15 35			16 05		16 35			17 05		17 35			18 05		18 35			19 05
Roby	d	14 37			15 07		15 37			16 07		16 37			17 07		17 37			18 07		18 37			19 07
Broad Green	d	14 40			15 10		15 40			16 10		16 40			17 10		17 40			18 10		18 40			19 10
Wavertree Technology Park	d	14 43			15 13		15 43			16 13		16 43			17 13		17 43			18 13		18 43			19 13
Edge Hill 89, 91	d																								
Liverpool Lime Street 10 89, 91	a	14 53		14 57	15 22	15 30	15 53		15 57	16 22	16 30	16 53		16 57	17 22	17 30	17 53		17 57	18 22	18 30	18 53		18 57	19 22

Station		EM	NT	AW	TP	NT	EM	NT	AW	TP	NT	NT	AW	TP	NT	NT	AW	TP	NT	NT	NT	AW	AW		
		◇ E		A	1 ◇ D		◇ E		A	1 ◇ B			A	1 ◇ D			A	1 ◇ B				A	A		
Manchester Airport 85 ✈	d		18 35					19 35				20 35				21 35				22 35					
Manchester Piccadilly 10	d	18 38	18 50	18 56			19 38	19 50	19 56			20 50	20 56			21 50	21 56			22 50		22 56	23 25		
Manchester Oxford Road	d	18 42	18 53	18 59			19 42	19 53	19 59			20 53	20 59			21 53	21 59			22 53		22 59	23 28		
Manchester Victoria	d				19 09					20 09				21 09				22 09							
Eccles	d		19 00					20 00				21 00				22 00				23 00					
Patricroft	d																								
Blackpool North 97	d					18 50					19 50				20 50				21 50		22 44				
Preston 8 65, 82	d					19 15					20 15				21 15				22 15		23 09				
Leyland 82	d					19 21					20 21				21 21				22 21		23 15				
Euxton Balshaw Lane	d					19 25					20 25				21 25				22 25		23 19				
Wigan North Western 65	a					19 35					20 35				21 35				22 35		23 29				
	d					19 36					20 36				21 36				22 36		23 30				
Newton-le-Willows	d	19 00	19 13	19 18	19 27		20 00	20 13	20 18	20 27		21 13	21 18	21 27		22 13	22 18	22 27		23 13		23 18	23 46		
Warrington Bank Quay	d		*18 03*					*19 03*				*20 03*				*21 03*				*22 36*					
Earlestown 8	d		19 16	19 21				20 16	20 21			21 16	21 21			22 16	22 21			23 16		23 21	23 49		
Warrington Bank Quay	a			19 28					20 29				21 27				22 27					23 27	23 55		
St Helens Junction	d		19 21					20 21				21 21				22 21				23 21					
Lea Green	d		19 24					20 24				21 24				22 24				23 24					
Rainhill	d		19 28					20 28				21 28				22 28				23 28					
Whiston	d		19 31					20 31				21 31				22 31				23 31					
Bryn	d																								
Garswood	d					19 46					20 46				21 46				22 47		23 40				
St Helens Central	a					19 52					20 52				21 52				22 54		23 46				
	d					19 53					20 53				21 53				22 54		23 47				
Thatto Heath	d					19 56					20 56				21 56				22 58		23 50				
Eccleston Park	d																								
Prescot	d					20 00					21 00				22 00				23 02		23 54				
Huyton	d		19 35			20 05		20 35			21 05	21 35			22 05	22 35			23 06	23 35	23 59				
Roby	d		19 37			20 07		20 37			21 07	21 37			22 07	22 37			23 08	23 37	00 01				
Broad Green	d		19 40			20 10		20 40			21 10	21 40			22 10	22 40			23 12	23 40	00 04				
Wavertree Technology Park	d		19 43			20 13		20 43			21 13	21 43			22 13	22 43			23 15	23 43	00 07				
Edge Hill 89, 91	d																								
Liverpool Lime Street 10 89, 91	a	19 30	19 53		19 57	20 22	20 30	20 53		20 57	21 22	21 53		21 57	22 22	22 53		22 57	23 23	23 53	00 16				

For general notes see front of timetable
For details of catering facilities see Directory of Train Operators

A To Chester (Table 81)
B From Scarborough (Table 39)
C Until 1 November. From Nottingham (Table 49)
D From Middlesbrough (Table 39)
E Until 1 November. From Norwich (Table 49)

Liverpool → Runcorn and Crewe

Network Diagram - see first page of Table 88

Miles			VT	NT	VT	NT	LM	EM	NT	VT	LM	NT	LM	EM	VT	NT	LM	NT	LM	VT	EM
			1 ◇		1 ◇		1 ◇	◇		1 ◇	1 ◇		1 ◇	◇	1 ◇		1 ◇		1 ◇	1 ◇	◇
				A		B		C	A			B		C		B		B			C
			⊠		⊠			🛒		⊠				🛒	⊠					⊠	🛒
0	**Liverpool Lime Street** 10	90 d	05 27	05 49	06 05	06 21	06 31	06 47	06 50	07 00	07 05	07 26	07 34	07 42	07 48	07 51	08 04	08 26	08 34	08 48	08 52
1¾	Edge Hill	90 d		05 53					06 54			07 30						08 30			
3¾	Mossley Hill	d		05 58		06 29			06 59			07 35				07 59		08 35			
4½	West Allerton	d		06 00		06 31			07 01			07 37				08 01		08 37			
5½	**Liverpool South Parkway** 7 ✈	a		06 03		06 34	06 40	06 57	07 04		07 14	07 40	07 43	07 52		08 04	08 15	08 40	08 43		09 02
—		d					06 41				07 15		07 44				08 15		08 44		
13	**Runcorn**	a	05 42		06 20		06 48				07 22		07 51		08 03		08 24		08 51	09 03	
—		d	05 43		06 21		06 49			07u15	07 23		07 52		08 04		08 25		08 52	09 04	
21	Acton Bridge	d					06 57				07 32						08 34		09 01		
23¾	Hartford	d					07 02				07 36		08 04						09 06		
28	Winsford	d					07 06						08 08								
35½	**Crewe** 10	65 a	06 00				07 14				07 48		08 19				08 47		09 20		
—	Birmingham New Street 12	65 a	*06b58*				08 17				08 47		09 18				09 47		10 17		
—	London Euston ⊖	65 a	07 50		08 26		*09c38*			09 01	*09b56*		*10c04*		09 56		*10b56*			10 56	

		NT	LM	NT	LM	VT	EM	NT	LM	NT	LM	VT	EM	NT	LM	NT	LM	VT	EM	NT	LM
			1 ◇		1 ◇	1 ◇	◇		1 ◇		1 ◇	1 ◇	◇		1 ◇		1 ◇	1 ◇	◇		1 ◇
		B		B			C	B		B			C	B		B			C	B	
						⊠	🛒					☕	🛒					☕	🛒		
Liverpool Lime Street 10	90 d	08 55	09 04	09 27	09 34	09 48	09 52	09 55	10 04	10 27	10 34	10 48	10 52	10 55	11 04	11 27	11 34	11 48	11 52	11 55	12 04
Edge Hill	90 d	08 59						09 59						10 59						11 59	
Mossley Hill	d	09 04		09 35				10 04		10 35				11 04		11 35				12 04	
West Allerton	d	09 06		09 37				10 06		10 37				11 06		11 37				12 06	
Liverpool South Parkway 7 ✈	a	09 09	09 15	09 40	09 43		10 02	10 09	10 15	10 40	10 43		11 02	11 09	11 15	11 40	11 43		12 02	12 09	12 15
	d		09 15		09 44				10 15		10 44				11 15		11 44				12 15
Runcorn	a		09 24		09 51	10 03			10 24		10 51	11 03			11 24		11 51	12 03			12 24
	d		09 25		09 52	10 04			10 25		10 52	11 04			11 25		11 52	12 04			12 25
Acton Bridge	d																				
Hartford	d				10 04						11 04						12 04				
Winsford	d				10 08						11 08						12 08				
Crewe 10	65 a		09 44		10 19				10 45		11 19				11 45		12 19				12 45
Birmingham New Street 12	65 a		10 47		11 18				11 47		12 17				12 47		13 17				13 47
London Euston ⊖	65 a		*11c38*		*12c04*	11 56			*12c38*		*13c04*	12 56			*13c38*		*14c04*	13 56			*14c38*

		NT	LM	VT	EM	NT	LM	NT	LM	VT	EM	NT	LM	NT	LM	VT	EM	NT	LM	NT
			1 ◇	1 ◇	◇		1 ◇		1 ◇	1 ◇	◇		1 ◇		1 ◇	1 ◇	◇		1 ◇	
		B			C	B		B			D	B		B			C	B		B
				☕	🛒					☕	🛒					☕	🛒			
Liverpool Lime Street 10	90 d	12 27	12 34	12 48	12 52	12 55	13 04	13 27	13 34	13 48	13 52	13 55	14 04	14 27	14 34	14 48	14 52	14 55	15 04	15 27
Edge Hill	90 d					12 59						13 59						14 59		
Mossley Hill	d	12 35				13 04		13 35				14 04		14 35				15 04		15 35
West Allerton	d	12 37				13 06		13 37				14 06		14 37				15 06		15 37
Liverpool South Parkway 7 ✈	a	12 40	12 43		13 02	13 09	13 15	13 40	13 43		14 02	14 09	14 15	14 40	14 43		15 02	15 09	15 15	15 40
	d		12 44				13 15		13 44				14 15		14 44				15 15	
Runcorn	a		12 51	13 03			13 24		13 51	14 03			14 24		14 51	15 03			15 24	
	d		12 52	13 04			13 25		13 52	14 04			14 25		14 52	15 04			15 25	
Acton Bridge	d		13 01																	
Hartford	d		13 06						14 04						15 04					
Winsford	d								14 08						15 08					
Crewe 10	65 a		13 20				13 44		14 19				14 44		15 19				15 44	
Birmingham New Street 12	65 a		14 17				14 47		15 20				15 47		16 17				16 47	
London Euston ⊖	65 a			14 58			*15c38*		*16c04*	15 56			*16c38*		*17c04*	16 56			*17c38*	

		LM	VT	EM	NT	LM	NT	LM	VT	EM	NT	LM	NT	LM	VT	EM	NT	LM	NT	LM	VT
		1 ◇	1 ◇	◇		1 ◇		1 ◇	1 ◇	◇		1 ◇		1 ◇	1 ◇	◇		1 ◇		1 ◇	1 ◇
				C	B		B			D	B		B			C	B		B		
			☕	🛒					⊠	🛒					⊠	🛒					⊠
Liverpool Lime Street 10	90 d	15 34	15 48	15 52	15 55	16 04	16 27	16 34	16 48	16 52	16 55	17 04	17 25	17 34	17 48	17 52	17 55	18 04	18 25	18 34	18 48
Edge Hill	90 d				15 59						16 59		17 29				17 59		18 29		
Mossley Hill	d				16 04		16 35				17 04		17 34				18 04		18 34		
West Allerton	d				16 06		16 37				17 06		17 36				18 06		18 36		
Liverpool South Parkway 7 ✈	a	15 43		16 02	16 09	16 15	16 40	16 43		17 02	17 09	17 15	17 39	17 43		18 02	18 09	18 14	18 39	18 44	
	d	15 44				16 15		16 44				17 15		17 44				18 15		18 44	
Runcorn	a	15 51	16 03			16 24		16 52	17 03			17 24		17 51	18 03			18 24		18 52	19 03
	d	15 52	16 04			16 25		16 53	17 04			17 25		17 52	18 04			18 25		18 52	19 04
Acton Bridge	d							17 01						18 01							
Hartford	d	16 04						17 06						18 06						19 04	
Winsford	d	16 08										17 38						18 38		19 08	
Crewe 10	65 a	16 19				16 44		17 19				17 46		18 20				18 47		19 16	19 21
Birmingham New Street 12	65 a	17 20				17 47		18 17				18 48		19 17				19 47		20 17	
London Euston ⊖	65 a	*18c06*	17 56			*18c38*			18 59			*19c38*			20 02			*21b06*		*21c10*	21 06

		EM	NT	LM	LM	VT	EM	NT	LM	LM	VT	NT	LM	EM	NT	LM	LM	NT
		◇		1 ◇	1 ◇	1 ◇	◇		1 ◇	1 ◇	1 ◇		1 ◇	◇		1 ◇	1	
		D	A				D	A				B		D	B			E
		🛒				☕	🛒				☕							
Liverpool Lime Street 10	90 d	18 52	18 55	19 11	19 34	19 48	19 52	19 55	20 04	20 34	20 48	20 55	21 34	21 37	21 55	22 34	23 34	23 38
Edge Hill	90 d		18 59					19 59				20 59			21 59			23 42
Mossley Hill	d		19 04					20 04				21 04			22 04			23 47
West Allerton	d		19 06					20 06				21 06			22 06			23 50
Liverpool South Parkway 7 ✈	a	19 02	19 09	19 20	19 43		20 02	20 09	20 15	20 43		21 09	21 43	21 47	22 09	22 44	23 44	23 53
	d			19 21	19 44				20 15	20 44			21 44			22 44	23 45	
Runcorn	a			19 28	19 51	20 03			20 24	20 51	21 03		21 51			22 52	23 53	
	d			19 29	19 52	20 04			20 25	20 52	21 04		21 52			22 52	23 53	
Acton Bridge	d			19 40												23 02	00 03	
Hartford	d				20 04					21 04			22 04			23 07	00 07	
Winsford	d				20 08					21 08			22 08			23 11	00 12	
Crewe 10	65 a			19 53	20 16	20 21			20 45	21 16	21 22		22 16			23 22	00 22	
Birmingham New Street 12	65 a			20 47	21 18				21 47	22 17	*22 50*		23 18					
London Euston ⊖	65 a				*22b12*	22 09					23 53							

For general notes see front of timetable
For details of catering facilities see Directory of Train Operators

- **A** To Warrington Central (Table 89)
- **B** To Manchester Oxford Road (Table 89)
- **C** To Norwich (Table 49)
- **D** To Nottingham (Table 49)
- **E** To Manchester Piccadilly (Table 89)
- **b** Change at Stafford
- **c** Change at Crewe

Table 91

Saturdays

Liverpool → Runcorn and Crewe

Network Diagram - see first page of Table 88

		VT	NT	NT	LM	VT	EM	NT	LM	VT	NT	LM	EM	VT	NT	LM	NT	LM	VT		EM	NT	LM	NT	LM
		1◇			1◇	1◇	◇		1◇	1◇		1◇	◇	1◇		1◇		1◇	1◇		◇		1◇		1◇
			A	B			C	A			B		C		B		B				C	B		B	
		☕				☕	🛒			☕			🛒	☕					☕		🛒				
Liverpool Lime Street 10	90 d	05 47	05 49	06 26	06 33	06 45	06 49	06 55	07 05	07 19	07 26	07 34	07 42	07 48	07 51	08 04	08 26	08 34	08 48		08 52	08 55	09 04	09 26	09 34
Edge Hill	90 d		05 53					06 59			07 30						08 30					08 59			
Mossley Hill	d		05 58	06 34				07 04			07 35				07 59		08 35					09 04		09 35	
West Allerton	d		06 00	06 36				07 06			07 37				08 01		08 37					09 06		09 37	
Liverpool South Parkway 7	a		06 03	06 39	06 42		06 59	07 09	07 14		07 40	07 43	07 52		08 04	08 14	08 40	08 43			09 02	09 09	09 15	09 40	09 43
	d				06 43				07 15			07 44				08 15		08 44					09 15		09 44
Runcorn	a	06 02			06 50	07 00			07 22	07 35		07 51		08 03		08 24		08 51	09 03				09 24		09 51
	d	06 03			06 51	07 01			07 23	07 36		07 52		08 04		08 25		08 52	09 04				09 25		09 52
Acton Bridge	d								07 32							08 34		09 01							
Hartford	d				07 02				07 36			08 04						09 06							10 04
Winsford	d				07 06							08 08													10 08
Crewe 10	65 a				07 14	07 18			07 47	07 52		08 19				08 47		09 20					09 44		10 19
Birmingham New Street 12	65 a				08 17				08 47	08b58		09 18				09 47		10 17					10 47		11 17
London Euston ⊖	65 a	08 05			09c04	08 59			09b46	09 46		10c04		10 01		11b01			11 01				11c38		12c04

		VT	EM	NT	LM	NT	LM	VT	EM	NT	LM	NT	LM	VT	EM	NT		LM	NT	LM	VT	EM	NT	LM	NT
		1◇	◇		1◇		1◇	1◇	◇		1◇		1◇	1◇	◇			1◇		1◇	1◇	◇		1◇	
			C	B		B			C	B		B			C	B			B			C	B		B
		☕	🛒					☕	🛒					☕	🛒						☕	🛒			
Liverpool Lime Street 10	90 d	09 48	09 52	09 55	10 04	10 27	10 34	10 48	10 52	10 55	11 04	11 27	11 34	11 48	11 52	11 55		12 04	12 27	12 34	12 48	12 52	12 55	13 04	13 27
Edge Hill	90 d			09 59						10 59						11 59							12 59		
Mossley Hill	d			10 04		10 35				11 04		11 35				12 04			12 35				13 04		13 35
West Allerton	d			10 06		10 37				11 06		11 37				12 06			12 37				13 06		13 37
Liverpool South Parkway 7	a		10 02	10 09	10 15	10 40	10 43		11 02	11 09	11 15	11 40	11 43		12 02	12 09		12 15	12 40	12 43		13 02	13 09	13 15	13 40
	d				10 15		10 44				11 15		11 44					12 15		12 44				13 15	
Runcorn	a	10 03			10 24		10 51	11 03			11 24		11 51	12 03				12 24		12 51	13 03			13 24	
	d	10 04			10 25		10 52	11 04			11 25		11 52	12 04				12 25		12 52	13 04			13 25	
Acton Bridge	d																			13 01					
Hartford	d						11 04						12 04							13 06					
Winsford	d						11 08						12 08												
Crewe 10	65 a				10 45		11 19				11 44		12 19					12 44		13 20				13 44	
Birmingham New Street 12	65 a				11 47		12 17				12 47		13 17					13 47		14 17				14 47	
London Euston ⊖	65 a	11 56			12c38		13c04	12 56			13c38		14c04	13 56				14c38		15e38	14 56			15c38	

		LM	VT	EM	NT	LM	NT	LM	VT	EM	NT	LM	NT		LM	VT	EM	NT	LM	NT	LM	VT	EM	NT	LM
		1◇	1◇	◇		1◇		1◇	1◇	◇		1◇			1◇	1◇	◇		1◇		1◇	1◇	◇		1◇
				D	B		B			C	B		B				C	B		B			D	B	
			☕	🛒					☕	🛒						☕	🛒					☕	🛒		
Liverpool Lime Street 10	90 d	13 34	13 48	13 52	13 55	14 04	14 27	14 34	14 48	14 52	14 55	15 04	15 27		15 34	15 48	15 52	15 55	16 04	16 27	16 34	16 48	16 52	16 55	17 04
Edge Hill	90 d				13 59						14 59							15 59						16 59	
Mossley Hill	d				14 04		14 35				15 04		15 35					16 04		16 35				17 04	
West Allerton	d				14 06		14 37				15 06		15 37					16 06		16 37				17 06	
Liverpool South Parkway 7	a	13 43		14 02	14 09	14 15	14 40	14 43		15 02	15 09	15 15	15 40		15 43		16 02	16 09	16 15	16 40	16 43		17 02	17 09	17 15
	d	13 44				14 15		14 44				15 15			15 44				16 15		16 44				17 15
Runcorn	a	13 51	14 03			14 24		14 51	15 03			15 24			15 51	16 03			16 24		16 51	17 03			17 24
	d	13 52	14 04			14 25		14 52	15 04			15 25			15 52	16 04			16 25		16 52	17 04			17 25
Acton Bridge	d																				17 01				
Hartford	d	14 04						15 04							16 04						17 06				
Winsford	d	14 08						15 08							16 08										17 38
Crewe 10	65 a	14 19				14 44		15 19				15 44			16 19				16 44		17 20				17 46
Birmingham New Street 12	65 a	15 18				15 47		16 17				16 47			17 18				17 47		18 17				18 47
London Euston ⊖	65 a	16c04	15 56			16c38		17c04	16 56			17f38			18c04	17 57			18c38			18 56			19g56

		NT	LM	VT	EM	NT	LM	NT	LM	VT	EM	NT	LM	LM	VT	EM	NT	LM	EM	NT	LM	NT	NT		
			1◇	1◇	◇		1◇		1◇	1◇	◇		1◇	1◇	1◇	◇		1◇	◇		1◇				
		B			C	B		B			D	A				D	A		D	B		B	E		
				☕	🛒					☕	🛒				☕	🛒									
Liverpool Lime Street 10	90 d	17 25	17 34	17 48	17 52	17 55	18 04	18 25	18 34	18 48	18 52	18 55	19 04	19 34	19 48	19 52	19 55	20 34	20 52	20 55	21 34	21 55	23 38		
Edge Hill	90 d	17 29				17 59		18 29				18 59					19 59			20 59		21 59	23 42		
Mossley Hill	d	17 34				18 04		18 34				19 04					20 04			21 04		22 04	23 47		
West Allerton	d	17 36				18 06		18 36				19 06					20 06			21 06		22 06	23 49		
Liverpool South Parkway 7	a	17 39	17 43		18 02	18 09	18 14	18 39	18 44		19 02	19 09	19 14	19 43		20 02	20 09	20 43	21 02	21 09	21 43	22 09	23 52		
	d		17 44				18 15		18 44				19 14	19 44				20 44			21 44				
Runcorn	a		17 51	18 03			18 24		18 52	19 03			19 23	19 51	20 03			20 51			21 51				
	d		17 52	18 04			18 25		18 52	19 04			19 23	19 52	20 04			20 52			21 52				
Acton Bridge	d		18 01										19 36												
Hartford	d		18 05						19 04					20 04				21 03			22 04				
Winsford	d						18 38		19 08					20 08				21 07			22 08				
Crewe 10	65 a		18 19				18 46		19 19				19 49	20 16				21 15			22 18				
Birmingham New Street 12	65 a		19 17				19 47		20 17				20 47	21 17				22 19			23 20				
London Euston ⊖	65 a		20c04	19 56			21h25		21j58	21k25			22m43	23n03	22q43										

For general notes see front of timetable
For details of catering facilities see Directory of Train Operators

- **A** To Warrington Central (Table 89)
- **B** To Manchester Oxford Road (Table 89)
- **C** To Norwich (Table 49)
- **D** To Nottingham (Table 49)
- **E** To Manchester Piccadilly (Table 89)

- **b** Change at Stafford
- **c** Change at Crewe
- **e** Change at Crewe. From 7 November arr. 1508
- **f** Change at Crewe. From 7 November arr. 1737
- **g** Until 31 October change at Stafford. From 7 November arr. 1937, change at Crewe
- **h** Change at Stafford. From 12 September arr. 2115
- **j** Change at Crewe. From 12 September arr. 2119
- **k** From 12 September arr. 2115
- **m** Change at Stafford. From 12 September arr. 2217
- **n** Until 31 October only. Change at Crewe. 12 September to 31 October arr. 2243
- **q** From 12 September arr. 2117

Table 91

Liverpool → Runcorn and Crewe

Sundays until 6 September

Network Diagram - see first page of Table 88

		VT	VT	NT	VT	NT	VT	VT	NT	VT	NT	LM	VT	NT	LM	VT	EM	NT
		1 ◇	1 ◇		1 ◇		1 ◇	1 ◇		1 ◇		1 ◇	1 ◇		1 ◇	1 ◇	◇	
		A	B	C		C	A	B	C		C			C			D	C
Liverpool Lime Street 10	d	08 15	08 15	08 26	08 38	09 26	09 36	09 36	10 26	10 38	11 26	11 34	11 48	12 26	12 34	12 48	12 52	13 26
Mossley Hill	d			08 34		09 34			10 34		11 34			12 34				13 34
West Allerton	d			08 36		09 36			10 36		11 36			12 36				13 36
Liverpool South Parkway 7	a			08 39		09 39			10 39		11 39	11 43		12 39	12 43		13 02	13 39
	d											11 44			12 44			
Runcorn	a	08 33	08 33		08 53		09 51	09 51		10 53		11 51	12 03		12 51	13 03		
	d	08 34	08 34		08 54		09 52	09 52		10 54		11 52	12 04		12 52	13 04		
Hartford	d											12 04			13 03			
Winsford	d											12 08			13 07			
Crewe 10	65 a		08 54		09 11		10 10	10 12		11 12		12 19			13 18			
Birmingham New Street 12	65 a		09 58		10b59		11c18	11c17		12 55		13 16			14 15			
London Euston ⊖	65 a	11 03	11 07		11 44		12 38	12 38		13 15		14e12	14 03		15e12	15 03		

		LM	VT	EM	NT	LM	VT	EM	NT	LM	VT	EM	VT	NT	LM	VT	EM
		1 ◇	1 ◇	◇		1 ◇	1 ◇	◇		1 ◇	1 ◇	◇	1 ◇		1 ◇	1 ◇	◇
				D	C			D	C			D		C			E
Liverpool Lime Street 10	d	13 34	13 48	13 52	14 26	14 34	14 48	14 52	15 26	15 34	15 48	15 52	16 18	16 26	16 34	16 48	16 52
Mossley Hill	d				14 34				15 34					16 34			
West Allerton	d				14 36				15 36					16 36			
Liverpool South Parkway 7	a	13 43		14 02	14 39	14 43		15 02	15 39	15 43		16 02		16 39	16 43		17 02
	d	13 44				14 44				15 44					16 44		
Runcorn	a	13 51	14 03			14 51	15 03			15 51	16 03		16 33		16 51	17 03	
	d	13 52	14 04			14 52	15 04			15 52	16 04		16 34		16 52	17 04	
Hartford	d	14 03				15 03				16 03					17 03		
Winsford	d	14 07				15 07				16 07					17 07		
Crewe 10	65 a	14 18				15 19				16 18			16 50		17 18		
Birmingham New Street 12	65 a	15 15				16 15				17 15			17 55		18 15		
London Euston ⊖	65 a	16e11	16 03			17e11	17 03			18e11	18 04		18 44		19e11	19 03	

		NT	LM	VT	EM	NT	LM	VT	EM	NT	LM	VT	EM	NT	LM	VT	NT	LM	NT
			1 ◇	1 ◇	◇		1 ◇	1 ◇	◇		1 ◇	1 ◇	◇		1 ◇	1 ◇		1	
		C			E	C			E	C			E	C			C		C
Liverpool Lime Street 10	d	17 26	17 34	17 48	17 52	18 26	18 34	18 48	18 52	19 26	19 34	19 48	19 52	20 26	20 34	20 48	21 26	21 34	22 26
Mossley Hill	d	17 34				18 34				19 34				20 34			21 34		22 34
West Allerton	d	17 36				18 36				19 36				20 36			21 36		22 36
Liverpool South Parkway 7	a	17 39	17 43		18 02	18 39	18 43		19 02	19 39	19 43		20 02	20 39	20 43		21 39	21 43	22 39
	d		17 44				18 44				19 44				20 44			21 44	
Runcorn	a		17 51	18 03			18 51	19 03			19 51	20 03			20 51	21 03		21 51	
	d		17 52	18 04			18 52	19 04			19 52	20 04			20 52	21 04		21 52	
Hartford	d		18 03				19 03				20 03				21 03			22 03	
Winsford	d		18 07				19 07				20 07				21 07			22 07	
Crewe 10	65 a		18 19				19 19				20 15	20 22			21 15	21 22		22 17	
Birmingham New Street 12	65 a		19 15				20 15				21 15	21c39			22 15	22c40		23 17	
London Euston ⊖	65 a		20e11	20 03			21e14	21 06				22 29				23f59			

Sundays from 13 September

		NT	VT	NT	VT	NT	NT	VT	NT	NT	VT	NT	NT	LM	NT	VT	NT	LM	NT	VT	EM	NT	LM
			1 ◇		1 ◇			1 ◇			1 ◇			1 ◇		1 ◇		1 ◇		1 ◇	◇		1 ◇
		G		H		G	H		G	H		G	H		G		H		G		J	H	K
Liverpool Lime Street 10	d	07 45	08 15	08 26	08 38	08 45	09 26	09 36	09 45	10 26	10 38	10 45	11 26	11 34	11 45	11 48	12 26	12 34	12 45	12 48	12 52	13 26	13 34
Mossley Hill	d	07 58		08 34		08 58	09 34		09 58	10 34		10 58	11 34		11 58		12 34		12 58			13 34	
West Allerton	d	08 02		08 36		09 02	09 36		10 02	10 36		11 02	11 36		12 02		12 36		13 02			13 36	
Liverpool South Parkway 7	a	08 07		08 39		09 07	09 39		10 07	10 39		11 07	11 39	11 43	12 07		12 39	12 43	13 07		13 02	13 39	13 43
	d													11 44				12 44					13 44
Runcorn	a		08 33		08 53			09 51			10 53			11 51		12 03		12 51		13 03			13 51
	d		08 34		08 54			09 52			10 54			11 52		12 04		12 52		13 04			13 52
Hartford	d													12 04				13 03					14 03
Winsford	d													12 08				13 07					14 07
Crewe 10	65 a		08 54		09 11			10 10			11 12			12 19				13 18					14 18
Birmingham New Street 12	65 a		09 58		10c58			11c18			12 55			13 16				14 15					15 15
London Euston ⊖	65 a		11 03		11 44			12 38			13 15			14e12		14 03		15e12		15 03			16e11

For general notes see front of timetable
For details of catering facilities see Directory of Train Operators

- **A** Until 12 July
- **B** From 19 July
- **C** To Manchester Oxford Road (Table 89)
- **D** To Norwich (Table 49)
- **E** To Nottingham (Table 49)
- **G** Until 1 November. To Warrington Central (Table 89)
- **H** From 8 November. To Manchester Oxford Road (Table 89)
- **J** From 8 November. To Norwich (Table 49)
- **K** Until 1 November
- **b** Change at Stafford. From 19 July arr. 1058
- **c** Change at Stafford
- **e** Change at Crewe
- **f** Until 12 July arr. 2354

Table 91 **Sundays**

from 13 September

Liverpool → Runcorn and Crewe

Network Diagram - see first page of Table 88

		LM	NT	VT	EM	NT	LM	NT		VT	EM	NT	LM	NT	VT	EM	VT	NT		LM	NT	VT	EM	NT	LM
		1◇		1◇	◇		1◇			1◇	◇		1◇		1◇	◇	1◇			1◇		1◇	◇		1◇
		A	B		C	D		B			C	D		B		C		D			B		E	D	
			🚌	☕	🛒			🚌		☕	🛒			🚌	☕	🛒	☕				🚌	☕	🛒		
Liverpool Lime Street 10	d	13 34	13 45	13 48	13 52	14 26	14 34	14 45		14 48	14 52	15 26	15 34	15 45	15 48	15 52	16 18	16 26		16 34	16 45	16 48	16 52	17 26	17 34
Mossley Hill	d		13 58			14 34		14 58				15 34		15 58				16 34			16 58			17 34	
West Allerton	d		14 02			14 36		15 02				15 36		16 02				16 36			17 02			17 36	
Liverpool South Parkway 7 ✈	a	13 43	14 07		14 02	14 39	14 43	15 07			15 02	15 39	15 43	16 07		16 02		16 39		16 43	17 07		17 02	17 39	17 43
	d	13 44					14 44						15 44							16 44					17 44
Runcorn	a	13 51		14 03			14 51			15 03			15 51		16 03		16 33			16 51		17 03			17 51
	d	13 52		14 04			14 52			15 04			15 52		16 04		16 34			16 52		17 04			17 52
Hartford	d	14 03					15 03						16 03							17 03					18 03
Winsford	d	14 07					15 07						16 07							17 07					18 07
Crewe 10	65 a	14 20					15 19						16 18				16 50			17 18					18 19
Birmingham New Street 12	65 a	15 15					16 15						17 15				*17 55*			18 15					19 15
London Euston ⊖	65 a	*16b44*		16 03			*17b11*			17 03			*18b11*		18 04		18 44			*19b11*		19 03			*20b11*

		NT	VT	EM	NT	LM		NT	VT	EM	NT	LM	NT	VT	EM	NT	LM	NT	VT	NT	LM	NT	NT		
			1◇	◇		1◇			1◇	◇		1◇		1◇	◇		1◇		1◇		1				
		B		E	D			B		E	D		B		E	D		B		D		B	D		
		🚌	☕	🛒				🚌	☕	🛒			🚌	☕	🛒			🚌	☕			🚌			
Liverpool Lime Street 10	d	17 45	17 48	17 52	18 26	18 34		18 45	18 48	18 52	19 26	19 34	19 45	19 48	19 52	20 26	20 34	20 45	20 48	21 26	21 34	21 45	22 26		
Mossley Hill	d	17 58			18 34			18 58			19 34		19 58			20 34		20 58		21 34		21 58	22 34		
West Allerton	d	18 02			18 36			19 02			19 36		20 02			20 36		21 02		21 36		22 02	22 36		
Liverpool South Parkway 7 ✈	a	18 07		18 02	18 39	18 43		19 07		19 02	19 39	19 43	20 07		20 02	20 39	20 43	21 07		21 39	21 43	22 07	22 39		
	d					18 44						19 44					20 44				21 44				
Runcorn	a		18 03			18 51			19 03			19 51		20 03			20 51		21 03		21 51				
	d		18 04			18 52			19 04			19 52		20 04			20 52		21 04		21 52				
Hartford	d					19 03						20 03					21 03				22 03				
Winsford	d					19 07						20 07					21 07				22 07				
Crewe 10	65 a					19 19						20 15		20 22			21 15		21 22		22 17				
Birmingham New Street 12	65 a					20 15						21 15		*21c39*			22 15		*22c40*		23 17				
London Euston ⊖	65 a		20 03			*21b14*			21 06					22 29					23 59						

For general notes see front of timetable
For details of catering facilities see
Directory of Train Operators

A From 8 November

B Until 1 November.
To Warrington Central (Table 89)

C From 8 November.
To Norwich (Table 49)

D From 8 November.
To Manchester Oxford Road (Table 89)

E From 8 November.
To Nottingham (Table 49)

b Change at Crewe

c Change at Stafford

Crewe and Runcorn → Liverpool

Network Diagram - see first page of Table 88

Miles			NT	NT	LM	NT		LM	LM	NT	VT		NT	LM	EM	LM		NT	LM	VT	NT		EM	LM	NT
			MX		1◇			1◇	1◇		1◇			1◇	◇	1◇			1◇	1◇			◇	1◇	
			A	B		B				A			B		C			A	D		A		C	E	A
											⊠				🛒					⊠			🛒		
—	London Euston	⊖ 65 d									05 35					05b47			06b36	07 07				07b10	
—	Birmingham New Street [12]	65 d						05 30	06 01		06c20			06 36		07 01			07 36					08 01	
0	**Crewe [10]**	65 d			06 02			06 31	06 57		07 24			07 31		07 58			08 31					08 58	
7½	Winsford	d			06 09			06 41	07 04					07 42		08 05								09 07	
11¾	Hartford	d			06 14			06 46	07 09					07 47		08 10								09 12	
14½	Acton Bridge	d			06 18			06 51	07 14					07 51		08 14									
22½	**Runcorn**	a			06 26			06 57	07 22		07 40			07 59		08 22			08 48	08 54				09 21	
—		d			06 27			06 57	07 22		07 40			07 59		08 23			08 48	08 54				09 21	
30	**Liverpool South Parkway [7]**	✈ a			06 35			07 08	07 31					08 09		08 31			08 59					09 31	
—		d	00 27	06 27	06 36	07 01		07 08	07 31	07 27			07 59	08 10	08 18	08 32		08 37	08 59		09 06		09 15	09 31	09 35
31	West Allerton	d		06 31		07 05				07 30			08 03					08 40			09 10				09 38
31¾	Mossley Hill	d		06 33		07 07				07 33			08 06					08 43			09 12				09 41
33¾	Edge Hill	90 d		06 39		07 13				07 39			08 11					08 48							09 46
35½	**Liverpool Lime Street [10]**	90 a	00 41	06 45	06 48	07 19		07 20	07 41	07 47	08 02		08 18	08 20	08 31	08 43		08 55	09 09	09 15	09 23		09 31	09 42	09 53

		LM	VT	NT		EM	LM	NT	LM		VT	NT	EM	LM		NT	LM	VT	NT		EM	LM	NT	LM	VT
		1◇	1◇			◇	1◇		1◇		1◇		◇	1◇			1◇	1◇			◇	1◇		1◇	1◇
				A		C		A				A	G			A			A		G		A		
			⊠			🛒					⊠		🛒					☕			🛒				☕
London Euston	⊖ 65 d	07b35	08 07				08b10		08b40		09 07			09b10			09b40	10 07				10b10		10b40	11 07
Birmingham New Street [12]	65 d	08 36					09 01		09 36					10 01			10 36					11 01		11 36	
Crewe [10]	65 d	09 31					09 57		10 31					10 57			11 31					11 57		12 31	
Winsford	d													11 06											
Hartford	d						10 10							11 11								12 10			
Acton Bridge	d						10 14															12 14			
Runcorn	a	09 48	09 54				10 21		10 48		10 54			11 21			11 48	11 54				12 21		12 48	12 54
	d	09 48	09 54				10 22		10 48		10 54			11 21			11 48	11 54				12 22		12 48	12 54
Liverpool South Parkway [7]	✈ a	09 59					10 31		10 59					11 31			11 59					12 31		12 59	
	d	09 59		10 06		10 15	10 32	10 35	10 59			11 06	11 15	11 31		11 35	11 59		12 06		12 15	12 32	12 35	12 59	
West Allerton	d			10 10				10 38				11 10				11 38			12 10				12 38		
Mossley Hill	d			10 12				10 41				11 12				11 41			12 12				12 41		
Edge Hill	90 d							10 46								11 46							12 46		
Liverpool Lime Street [10]	90 a	10 09	10 15	10 23		10 31	10 43	10 53	11 09		11 15	11 23	11 31	11 42		11 53	12 09	12 15	12 23		12 31	12 43	12 53	13 09	13 15

		NT		EM	LM	NT	LM		VT	NT	EM	LM		NT	LM	VT	NT		EM	LM	NT	LM		VT	NT
				◇	1◇		1◇		1◇		◇	1◇			1◇	1◇			◇	1◇		1◇		1◇	
		A		G		A				A	G			A			A		G		A				A
				🛒					☕		🛒					☕			🛒					☕	
London Euston	⊖ 65 d				11b10		11b40		12 07			12b10			12b40	13 07				13c07		13b40		14 07	
Birmingham New Street [12]	65 d				12 01		12 36					13 01			13 36					14 01		14 36			
Crewe [10]	65 d				12 57		13 31					13 57			14 31					14 57		15 31			
Winsford	d				13 06							14 06								15 06					
Hartford	d				13 11							14 11								15 11					
Acton Bridge	d																								
Runcorn	a				13 21		13 48		13 54			14 21			14 48	14 54				15 21		15 48		15 54	
	d				13 21		13 48		13 54			14 21			14 48	14 54				15 21		15 48		15 54	
Liverpool South Parkway [7]	✈ a				13 31		13 59					14 31			14 59					15 31		15 59			
	d	13 06		13 15	13 31	13 35	13 59			14 06	14 15	14 31		14 35	14 59		15 06		15 15	15 31	15 35	15 59			16 07
West Allerton	d	13 10				13 38				14 10				14 38			15 10				15 38				16 11
Mossley Hill	d	13 12				13 41				14 12				14 41			15 12				15 41				16 13
Edge Hill	90 d					13 46								14 46							15 46				
Liverpool Lime Street [10]	90 a	13 23		13 31	13 42	13 53	14 09		14 15	14 23	14 31	14 42		14 53	15 09	15 15	15 23		15 31	15 42	15 53	16 09		16 15	16 25

		EM	LM	NT	LM		VT	NT	EM	LM		NT	LM	VT	EM		NT	LM	NT	LM		VT	NT	EM	LM
		◇	1◇		1◇		1◇		◇	1◇			1◇	1◇	◇			1◇		1◇		1◇		◇	1◇
		G		A				A	G			A			G		A		A				A	G	
		🛒					☕		🛒					⊠	🛒							⊠		🛒	
London Euston	⊖ 65 d		14b10		14b40		15 07			15b10			15b40	16 07				16b10		16b40		17 07			17c07
Birmingham New Street [12]	65 d		15 01		15 36					16 01			16 36					17 01		17 36					18 01
Crewe [10]	65 d		15 57		16 31					16 57			17 31					18 01		18 31		18 45			19 02
Winsford	d									17 06								18 08							19 09
Hartford	d		16 11							17 11								18 13		18 44					
Acton Bridge	d																			18 50					
Runcorn	a		16 24		16 48		16 54			17 21			17 48	17 54				18 23		18 57		19 02			19 22
	d		16 24		16 48		16 54			17 21			17 48	17 54				18 23		18 57		19 02			19 22
Liverpool South Parkway [7]	✈ a		16 33		16 59					17 31			17 59					18 33		19 07					19 32
	d	16 15	16 33	16 35	16 59			17 07	17 15	17 31		17 39	17 59		18 22		18 14	18 33	18 38	19 07			19 13	19 18	19 32
West Allerton	d			16 38				17 11				17 42					18 18		18 42				19 16		
Mossley Hill	d			16 41				17 13				17 45					18 20		18 44				19 18		
Edge Hill	90 d			16 46								17 50					18 30		18 50				19 26		
Liverpool Lime Street [10]	90 a	16 31	16 43	16 53	17 09		17 15	17 25	17 31	17 42		17 58	18 09	18 15	18 35		18 38	18 43	18 57	19 17		19 23	19 35	19 35	19 42

For general notes see front of timetable
For details of catering facilities see Directory of Train Operators

A From Manchester Oxford Road (Table 89)
B From Warrington Central (Table 89)
C From Nottingham (Table 49)
D From Birmingham International (Table 68)
E From Walsall (Table 70)
G From Norwich (Table 49)
b Change at Crewe
c Change at Stafford

Crewe and Runcorn → Liverpool

Network Diagram - see first page of Table 88

		VT	NT	LM	VT	LM	EM	VT	NT	LM	VT	NT	EM	LM	VT	NT	LM	NT	VT
		1◇		1◇	1◇	1◇	◇	1◇		1◇	1◇		◇	1◇	1◇		1◇		1◇
			A				B		C			A	B			A		A	
		⊠			⊠		[T]	⊠			[P]		[T]		[P]				[P]
London Euston ⊖	65 d	17 33		17b40	18 07			18 33		18b40	19 07			19c40	20 07		20b40		21 07
Birmingham New Street 12	65 d	18 20		18 36				19 20		19 36				20 36			21 36		21 36
Crewe 10	65 d	19 18		19 31	19 45			20 18		20 31				21 31			22 31		22 48
Winsford	d			19 42						20 40				21 39			22 39		
Hartford	d			19 47						20 45				21 44			22 44		
Acton Bridge	d																22 48		
Runcorn	a	19 34		19 55	20 01			20 34		20 55	21 00			21 53	21 58		22 56		23 07
	d	19 34		19 55	20 01			20 34		20 55	21 00			21 53	21 58		22 56		23 07
Liverpool South Parkway 7 ✈	a			20 08		←				21 05				22 04			23 08		
	d		19 58	20 08 →		20 08	20 15		20 38	21 05		21 11	21 20	22 04		22 11	23 09	23 11	
West Allerton	d		20 02						20 41			21 15				22 15		23 15	
Mossley Hill	d		20 05						20 44			21 18				22 18		23 18	
Edge Hill	90 d		20 10									21 23				22 23		23 23	
Liverpool Lime Street 10	90 a	19 55	20 18		20 22	20 23	20 35	20 55	20 56	21 15	21 21	21 30	21 35	22 14	22 20	22 30	23 21	23 30	23 35

Saturdays

		NT	NT	NT	LM	NT	LM	NT	LM	EM	LM	NT	LM	VT	NT	EM	LM	NT	LM	VT	NT	EM	LM	NT	LM
					1◇		1◇		1◇	◇	1◇		1◇	1◇		◇	1◇		1◇	1◇		◇	1◇		1◇
		C	A	A		C		A		D		C			C	D		C			C	D		C	
										[T]				[P]		[T]				[P]		[T]			
London Euston ⊖	65 d										06c05		06b36	07 07					07b35	08 07			08c07		08b40
Birmingham New Street 12	65 d				05 30		06 01		06 36		07 01		07 36				08 01		08 36				09 01		09 36
Crewe 10	65 d				06 31		06 58		07 34		08 00		08 31	08 43			08 58		09 31				09 57		10 31
Winsford	d				06 41		07 05		07 44		08 07						09 07								
Hartford	d				06 46		07 10		07 49		08 12						09 12						10 10		
Acton Bridge	d				06 51				07 53		08 16												10 14		
Runcorn	a				06 57		07 20		08 01		08 24		08 48	08 59			09 22		09 48	09 54			10 21		10 48
	d				06 57		07 21		08 01		08 25		08 48	08 59			09 22		09 48	09 54			10 22		10 48
Liverpool South Parkway 7 ✈	a				07 08		07 30		08 11		08 33		08 59				09 31		09 59				10 31		10 59
	d	00 27	06 27	07 01	07 08	07 22	07 31	08 02	08 12	08 18	08 34	08 37	08 59		09 06	09 15	09 31	09 35	09 59		10 06	10 15	10 32	10 35	10 59
West Allerton	d		06 31	07 05		07 25		08 06				08 40			09 10			09 38			10 10			10 38	
Mossley Hill	d		06 33	07 07		07 28		08 09				08 43			09 12			09 41			10 12			10 41	
Edge Hill	90 d		06 39	07 13		07 34		08 14				08 48						09 46						10 46	
Liverpool Lime Street 10	90 a	00 41	06 45	07 20	07 20	07 40	07 41	08 21	08 22	08 31	08 45	08 55	09 09	09 21	09 23	09 31	09 42	09 53	10 09	10 15	10 23	10 31	10 43	10 53	11 09

		VT	NT	EM	LM	NT	LM	VT	NT	EM	LM	NT	LM	VT	NT	EM	LM	NT	LM	VT	NT	EM	LM	NT
		1◇		◇	1◇		1◇	1◇		◇	1◇		1◇	1◇		◇	1◇		1◇	1◇		◇	1◇	
			C	B		C			C	B		C			C	B		C			C	B		C
		[P]		[T]				[P]		[T]				[P]		[T]				[P]		[T]		
London Euston ⊖	65 d	09 07			09c07		09b40	10 07			10c07		10b40	11 07			11b10		11b40	12 07			12b10	
Birmingham New Street 12	65 d				10 01		10 36				11 01		11 36				12 01		12 36				13 01	
Crewe 10	65 d				10 57		11 31				11 57		12 31				12 57		13 31				13 57	
Winsford	d				11 06												13 06						14 06	
Hartford	d				11 11						12 10						13 11						14 11	
Acton Bridge	d										12 14													
Runcorn	a	10 54			11 21		11 48	11 54			12 21		12 48	12 54			13 21		13 48	13 54			14 21	
	d	10 54			11 21		11 48	11 54			12 22		12 48	12 54			13 21		13 48	13 54			14 21	
Liverpool South Parkway 7 ✈	a				11 31		11 59				12 31		12 59				13 31		13 59				14 31	
	d		11 06	11 15	11 31	11 35	11 59		12 06	12 15	12 32	12 35	12 59		13 06	13 15	13 31	13 35	13 59		14 06	14 15	14 31	14 35
West Allerton	d		11 10			11 38			12 10			12 38			13 10			13 38			14 10			14 38
Mossley Hill	d		11 12			11 41			12 12			12 41			13 12			13 41			14 12			14 41
Edge Hill	90 d					11 46						12 46						13 46						14 46
Liverpool Lime Street 10	90 a	11 15	11 23	11 31	11 42	11 53	12 09	12 15	12 23	12 31	12 43	12 53	13 09	13 15	13 23	13 31	13 42	13 53	14 09	14 15	14 23	14 31	14 42	14 53

		LM	VT	NT	EM	LM	NT	LM	VT	NT	EM	LM	NT	LM	VT	NT	EM	LM	NT	LM	VT	EM	NT	NT
		1◇	1◇		◇	1◇		1◇	1◇		◇	1◇		1◇	1◇		◇	1◇		1◇	1◇	◇		
				C	B		C			C	B		C			C	B		C			B	E	G
			[P]		[T]				[P]		[T]				[P]		[T]				[P]	[T]		
London Euston ⊖	65 d	12b40	13 07			13e07		13b40	14 07			14b10		14b40	15 07			15b10		15b40	16 07			
Birmingham New Street 12	65 d	13 36				14 01		14 36				15 01		15 36				16 01		16 36				
Crewe 10	65 d	14 31				14 57		15 31				15 57		16 31				16 57		17 31				
Winsford	d					15 06												17 06						
Hartford	d					15 11						16 11						17 11						
Acton Bridge	d											16 15												
Runcorn	a	14 48	14 54			15 21		15 48	15 54			16 24		16 48	16 54			17 21		17 48	17 54			
	d	14 48	14 54			15 21		15 48	15 54			16 24		16 48	16 54			17 21		17 48	17 54			
Liverpool South Parkway 7 ✈	a	14 59				15 31		15 59				16 33		16 59				17 31		17 59				
	d	14 59		15 06	15 15	15 31	15 35	15 59		16 07	16 15	16 33	16 35	16 59		17 07	17 15	17 31	17 39	17 59		18 22	18⌇14	18⌇17
West Allerton	d			15 10			15 38			16 11			16 38			17 11			17 42				18⌇18	18⌇21
Mossley Hill	d			15 12			15 41			16 13			16 41			17 13			17 45				18⌇20	18⌇23
Edge Hill	90 d						15 46						16 46						17 50				18⌇30	18⌇30
Liverpool Lime Street 10	90 a	15 09	15 15	15 23	15 31	15 42	15 53	16 09	16 15	16 25	16 31	16 43	16 53	17 09	17 15	17 25	17 31	17 42	17 58	18 09	18 15	18 35	18⌇38	18⌇38

For general notes see front of timetable
For details of catering facilities see Directory of Train Operators

- **A** From Warrington Central (Table 89)
- **B** From Norwich (Table 49)
- **C** From Manchester Oxford Road (Table 89)
- **D** From Nottingham (Table 49)
- **E** Until 31 October. From Manchester Oxford Road (Table 89)
- **G** From 7 November. From Manchester Oxford Road (Table 89)
- **b** Change at Crewe
- **c** Change at Stafford
- **e** Until 31 October change at Stafford. From 7 November dep. 1310, change at Crewe

Table 91

Saturdays

Crewe and Runcorn → Liverpool

Network Diagram - see first page of Table 88

		LM	VT	NT	LM	VT	NT	EM	VT	NT	LM	EM	VT	NT	LM	VT	VT	NT	NT	NT	VT	VT	NT
		1 ◇	1 ◇		1 ◇	1 ◇		◇	1 ◇		1 ◇	◇	1 ◇		1 ◇	1 ◇	1 ◇				1 ◇	1 ◇	
				A			A	B		C		B		A		D	E	G	H	C	D	E	C
			☕			☕		🛒	☕			🛒	☕			☕	☕				☕	☕	
London Euston	⊖ 65 d	*16b10*	16 33		*16b40*	17 07			18 07		*17b40*		18 33		*18b40*	18ʃ57	19ʃ07				19ʃ41	20ʃ11	
Birmingham New Street 12	65 d	17 01			17 36						18 36				19 36						*20c57*	*20c57*	
Crewe 10	65 d	18 00			18 31						19 37				20 31	20ʃ48	20ʃ47				22ʃ03	22ʃ13	
Winsford	d	18 08									19 48				20 40								
Hartford	d	18 13			18 44						19 53				20 45								
Acton Bridge	d										19 57												
Runcorn	a	18 23	18 31		18 52	18 58			19 54		20 05		20 32		20 55	21ʃ05	21ʃ04				22ʃ20	22ʃ30	
	d	18 23	18 31		18 52	18 58			19 54		20 05		20 32		20 55	21ʃ05	21ʃ04				22ʃ20	22ʃ30	
Liverpool South Parkway 7	✈ a	18 33			19 03						20 15				21 05								
	d	18 33		18 38	19 03		19 11	19 18		19 58	20 16	20 19		20 38	21 05			21ʃ15	21ʃ15	22 11			23 11
West Allerton	d			18 42			19 15			20 02				20 41				21ʃ19	21ʃ20	22 15			23 15
Mossley Hill	d			18 44			19 18			20 05				20 44				21ʃ21	21ʃ22	22 18			23 18
Edge Hill	90 d			18 50			19 26			20 10								21ʃ27	21ʃ27	22 23			23 23
Liverpool Lime Street 10	90 a	18 43	18 54	18 57	19 13	19 19	19 35	19 35	20 15	20 18	20 26	20 34	20 53	20 55	21 15	21ʃ26	21ʃ25	21ʃ34	21ʃ34	22 30	22ʃ41	22ʃ52	23 30

Sundays

until 6 September

		NT	NT	NT	NT	VT	LM	LM	NT	VT	LM	EM	NT	VT	VT	LM	EM	NT	VT	LM
						1 ◇	1 ◇	1 ◇		1 ◇	1 ◇	◇		1 ◇	1 ◇	1 ◇	◇		1 ◇	1 ◇
		A	A	A	A		J	K	A			L	A	K	J		N	A		
						☕				☕		🛒		☕	☕		🛒		☕	
London Euston	⊖ 65 d					08 15	*08c15*	*08c20*		09e15	*09f20*			10ʃ15	10ʃ15	*10g20*			11 15	*11h20*
Birmingham New Street 12	65 d					*09 20*	09ʃ42	09ʃ41		*10j15*	10 42			*11ʃ20*	*11ʃ20*	11 42			*12 20*	12 35
Crewe 10	65 d					10 31	10ʃ38	10ʃ39		11 32	11 38			12ʃ21	12ʃ32	12 38			13 18	13 31
Winsford	d						10ʃ45	10ʃ46			11 45					12 45				13 38
Hartford	d						10ʃ50	10ʃ51			11 50					12 50				13 43
Runcorn	a					10 47	11ʃ00	11ʃ01		11 48	12 00			12ʃ37	12ʃ48	13 00			13 34	13 53
	d					10 47	11ʃ00	11ʃ01		11 48	12 00			12ʃ37	12ʃ48	13 00			13 34	13 53
Liverpool South Parkway 7	✈ a						11ʃ10	11ʃ11			12 10					13 10				14 03
	d	00 20	08 54	09 33	10 33		11ʃ10	11ʃ11	11 33		12 10	12ʃ17	12 33			13 10	13 16	13 33		14 03
West Allerton	d		08 57	09 36	10 36				11 36				12 36					13 36		
Mossley Hill	d		09 00	09 39	10 39				11 39				12 39					13 39		
Liverpool Lime Street 10	a	00 34	09 09	09 48	10 50	11 08	11ʃ20	11ʃ21	11 48	12 09	12 20	12ʃ30	12 48	13ʃ03	13ʃ09	13 20	13 30	13 48	13 56	14 13

		VT	EM	NT	LM	VT	EM	NT	LM	VT	EM	NT	LM	VT	EM	NT	LM	VT	EM
		1 ◇	◇		1 ◇	1 ◇	◇		1 ◇	1 ◇	◇		1 ◇	1 ◇	◇		1 ◇	1 ◇	◇
			N	A			B	A			B	A			N	A			N
		☕	🛒			☕	🛒			☕	🛒			☕	🛒			☕	🛒
London Euston	⊖ 65 d	12 02			*12b35*	13 02			*13b35*	14 02			*14b35*	15 02			*15b35*	16 02	
Birmingham New Street 12	65 d				13 35				14 35				15 35				16 35		
Crewe 10	65 d	13 45			14 31	14 45			15 31	15 45			16 34				17 31		
Winsford	d				14 38				15 38				16 41				17 38		
Hartford	d				14 43				15 43				16 46				17 43		
Runcorn	a	14 01			14 53	15 01			15 53	16 01			16 55	16 58			17 53	17 56	
	d	14 01			14 53	15 01			15 53	16 01			16 56	16 58			17 53	17 56	
Liverpool South Parkway 7	✈ a				15 03				16 03				17 05				18 03		
	d		14 16	14 33	15 03		15 16	15 33	16 03		16 16	16 33	17 06		17 16	17 33	18 03		18 16
West Allerton	d			14 36				15 36				16 36				17 36			
Mossley Hill	d			14 39				15 39				16 39				17 39			
Liverpool Lime Street 10	a	14 23	14 30	14 48	15 13	15 23	15 30	15 48	16 13	16 22	16 30	16 48	17 16	17 22	17 30	17 48	18 13	18 19	18 30

		NT	LM	VT	EM	NT	LM	VT	EM	NT	LM	VT	NT	VT	VT	NT	NT	VT
			1 ◇	1 ◇	◇		1 ◇	1 ◇	◇		1 ◇	1 ◇		1 ◇	1 ◇			1 ◇
		A			B	A			B	A			A			A	A	
				☕	🛒			☕	🛒			☕		☕	☕			☕
London Euston	⊖ 65 d		*16b35*	17 02			*17b35*	18 02			*18b35*	19 02		20 02	20 05			21 20
Birmingham New Street 12	65 d		17 35				18 35				19 35			*20 20*				*22c01*
Crewe 10	65 d		18 31				19 31				20 31	20 50		21 46	21 55			23 47
Winsford	d		18 38				19 38				20 38							
Hartford	d		18 43				19 43				20 43							
Runcorn	a		18 53	18 56			19 53	19 57			20 53	21 06		22 02	22 11			00 07
	d		18 53	18 56			19 53	19 57			20 53	21 06		22 02	22 11			00 07
Liverpool South Parkway 7	✈ a		19 03				20 03				21 03							
	d	18 33	19 03		19 17	19 33	20 03		20 16	20 33	21 03		21 33			22 33	23 33	
West Allerton	d	18 36				19 36				20 36			21 36			22 36	23 36	
Mossley Hill	d	18 39				19 39				20 39			21 39			22 39	23 39	
Liverpool Lime Street 10	a	18 48	19 13	19 19	19 30	19 48	20 13	20 19	20 30	20 48	21 13	21 27	21 48	22 23	22 32	22 48	23 48	00 34

For general notes see front of timetable
For details of catering facilities see Directory of Train Operators

- **A** From Manchester Oxford Road (Table 89)
- **B** From Norwich (Table 49)
- **C** From Warrington Central (Table 89)
- **D** Until 5 September
- **E** From 12 September
- **G** From 12 September. From Warrington Central (Table 89)
- **H** Until 5 September. From Warrington Central (Table 89)
- **J** From 19 July
- **K** Until 12 July
- **L** From 19 July. From Nottingham (Table 49)
- **N** From Nottingham (Table 49)
- **b** Change at Crewe
- **c** Change at Stafford
- **e** By changing at Stafford until 12 July only, passengers may depart at 0920
- **f** Change at Stafford. From 19 July dep. 0915
- **g** Change at Stafford. From 19 July dep. 1015
- **h** Change at Stafford. From 19 July dep. 1115
- **j** From 19 July dep. 1020

Sundays

from 13 September

Crewe and Runcorn → Liverpool

Network Diagram - see first page of Table 88

	NT A	NT B	NT C	NT B	NT C	NT B	VT 1◇	LM 1◇	NT C	NT B	VT 1◇	LM 1◇	NT C		NT B	VT 1◇	LM 1◇	EM ◇ D	NT C	NT B	VT 1◇	LM 1◇	VT 1◇	EM ◇ E
London Euston ⊖ 65 d							08 15				09 15					10 15					11 15		12 02	
Birmingham New Street 65 d							*09 20*	09 41			*10b15*	10 42				*11 20*	11 42				*12c20*	12 35		
Crewe 65 d							10 31	10 39			11 32	11 38				12 32	12 38				13 18	13 31	13 45	
Winsford d								10 46				11 45					12 45					13 38		
Hartford d								10 51				11 50					12 50					13 43		
Runcorn a							10 47	11 01			11 48	12 00				12 48	13 00				13 34	13 53	14 01	
d							10 47	11 01			11 48	12 00				12 48	13 00				13 34	13 53	14 01	
Liverpool South Parkway a								11 11				12 10					13 10					14 03		
d	00 20	08 55	09 16	09 59	10 31	10 33		11 11	11 06	11 33		12 10	12 06		12 33		13 10	13 16	13 06	13 33		14 03		14 16
West Allerton d		08 58	09 21	10 02	10 36	10 36			11 11	11 36			12 11		12 36				13 11	13 36				
Mossley Hill d		09 00	09 27	10 05	10 42	10 39			11 17	11 39			12 17		12 39				13 17	13 39				
Liverpool Lime Street a	00 34	09 10	09 42	10 14	10 57	10 50	11 08	11 21	11 32	11 48	12 09	12 20	12 32		12 48	13 09	13 20	13 30	13 32	13 48	13 56	14 13	14 23	14 30

	NT C	NT B	LM 1◇	VT 1◇	EM ◇ E		NT C	NT B	LM 1◇	VT 1◇	EM ◇ G	NT C	NT B	LM 1◇	VT 1◇	EM ◇ E	NT C	NT B	LM 1◇		VT 1◇	EM ◇ E	NT C	NT B
London Euston ⊖ 65 d			*12e35*	13 02					*13e35*	14 02				*14e35*	15 02				*15e35*		16 02			
Birmingham New Street 65 d			13 35						14 35					15 35					16 35					
Crewe 65 d			14 31	14 45					15 31	15 45				16 34					17 31					
Winsford d			14 38						15 38					16 41					17 38					
Hartford d			14 43						15 43					16 46					17 43					
Runcorn a			14 53	15 01					15 53	16 01				16 55	16 58				17 53		17 56			
d			14 53	15 01					15 53	16 01				16 56	16 58				17 53		17 56			
Liverpool South Parkway a			15 03						16 03					17 05					18 03					
d	14 06	14 33	15 03		15 16		15 06	15 33	16 03		16 16	16 06	16 33	17 06		17 16	17 06	17 33	18 03			18 16	18 06	18 33
West Allerton d	14 11	14 36					15 11	15 36				16 11	16 36				17 11	17 36					18 11	18 36
Mossley Hill d	14 17	14 39					15 17	15 39				16 17	16 39				17 17	17 39					18 17	18 39
Liverpool Lime Street a	14 32	14 48	15 13	15 23	15 30		15 32	15 48	16 13	16 22	16 30	16 32	16 48	17 16	17 22	17 30	17 32	17 48	18 13		18 19	18 30	18 32	18 48

	LM 1◇	VT 1◇	EM ◇ G	NT C	NT B	LM 1◇	VT 1◇	EM ◇ G	NT C	NT B	LM 1◇	VT 1◇	NT C	NT B	VT 1◇	VT 1◇	NT C	NT B	NT C	NT B	NT C	VT 1◇		
London Euston ⊖ 65 d	*16e35*	17 02				*17e35*	18 02				*18e35*	19 02			20 02	20 05						21 20		
Birmingham New Street 65 d	17 35					18 35					19 35				*20 20*	*20f20*						*22f28*		
Crewe 65 d	18 31					19 31					20 31	20 50			21 46	21 55						23 47		
Winsford d	18 38					19 38					20 38													
Hartford d	18 43					19 43					20 43													
Runcorn a	18 53	18 56				19 53	19 57				20 53	21 06			22 02	22 11						00 07		
d	18 53	18 56				19 53	19 57				20 53	21 06			22 02	22 11						00 07		
Liverpool South Parkway a	19 03					20 03					21 03													
d	19 03		19 17	19 06	19 33	20 03		20 16	20 06	20 33	21 03		21 06	21 33			22 06	22 33	23 06	23 33	00 06			
West Allerton d				19 11	19 36				20 11	20 36			21 11	21 36			22 11	22 36	23 11	23 36	00 11			
Mossley Hill d				19 17	19 39				20 17	20 39			21 17	21 39			22 17	22 39	23 17	23 39	00 17			
Liverpool Lime Street a	19 13	19 19	19 30	19 32	19 48	20 13	20 19	20 30	20 32	20 48	21 13	21 27	21 32	21 48	22 23	22 32	22 32	22 48	23 32	23 48	00 32	00 34		

For general notes see front of timetable
For details of catering facilities see
Directory of Train Operators

- **A** From Manchester Oxford Road (Table 89)
- **B** From 8 November. From Manchester Oxford Road (Table 89)
- **C** Until 1 November. From Warrington Central (Table 89)
- **D** From 8 November. From Nottingham (Table 53)
- **E** From 8 November. From Nottingham (Table 49)
- **G** From 8 November. From Norwich (Table 49)
- **b** From 8 November dep. 1020
- **c** From 8 November dep. 1201, change at Stafford
- **e** Change at Crewe
- **f** Change at Stafford

Network Diagram for Tables 94, 95

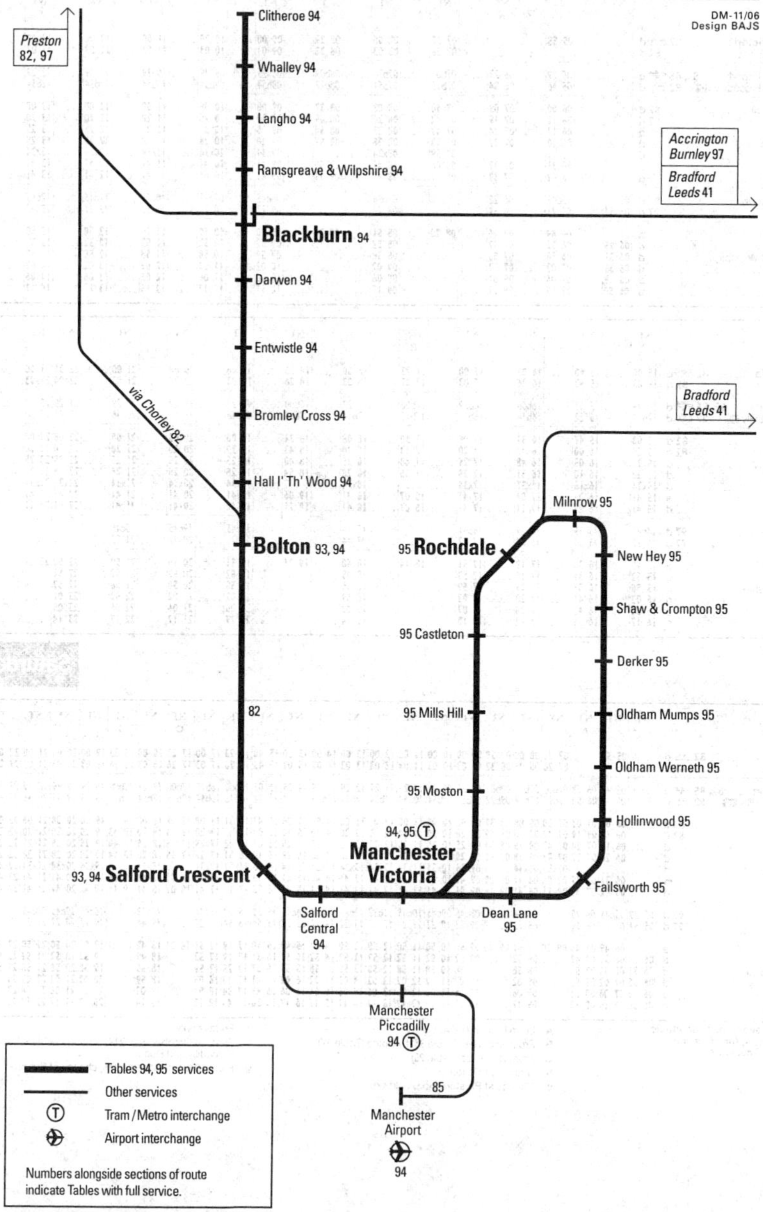
DM-11/06
Design BAJS
Preston
82, 97
Clitheroe 94
Whalley 94
Langho 94
Ramsgreave & Wilpshire 94
Accrington
Burnley 97
Bradford
Leeds 41
Blackburn 94
Darwen 94
Entwistle 94
via Chorley 82
Bromley Cross 94
Hall I' Th' Wood 94
Bolton 93, 94
Bradford
Leeds 41
Milnrow 95
95 Rochdale
New Hey 95
Shaw & Crompton 95
95 Castleton
Derker 95
82
95 Mills Hill
Oldham Mumps 95
Oldham Werneth 95
95 Moston
Hollinwood 95
94, 95
Manchester
Victoria
93, 94 Salford Crescent
Failsworth 95
Salford
Central
94
Dean Lane
95
Manchester
Piccadilly
94
85
Manchester
Airport
94
Tables 94, 95 services
Other services
Tram / Metro interchange
Airport interchange
Numbers alongside sections of route
indicate Tables with full service.

Manchester and Bolton → Blackburn → Clitheroe

Network Diagram - see first page of Table 94

Miles			NT	NT	NT A	NT	NT	NT	NT	NT	NT	NT	NT	NT
0	**Manchester Victoria**	82 d		05 55		07 23	08 00	08 29	09 00	10 00	11 00	12 00	13 00	14 00
3/4	Salford Central	82 d				07 26	08 03	08 32	09 03	10 03	11 03	12 03	13 03	14 03
—	Manchester Airport	82, 85 d		05 29	06 23	07b00	07b28	08b03	08 25	09 29	10 29	11 29	12 29	13 29
—	Manchester Piccadilly 10	82 d		05 46	06 54	07b15	07b54	08b22	08b54	09b54	10b54	11b54	12b54	13b54
1 3/4	Salford Crescent	82 d		06 00	07 03	07 30	08 08	08 37	09 08	10 08	11 08	12 08	13 08	14 08
10 3/4	**Bolton**	82 d		06 12	07 19	07 42	08 20	08 49	09 20	10 20	11 20	12 20	13 20	14 20
12 1/2	Hall I' Th' Wood	d		06 17	07 24	07 47	08 25	08 54	09 25	10 25	11 25	12 25	13 25	14 25
13 1/2	Bromley Cross	d		06 20	07 27	07 53	08 28	08 57	09 28	10 28	11 28	12 28	13 28	14 28
16 1/2	Entwistle	d				07x59	08x34		09x34	10x34	11x34	12x34	13x34	14x34
20 1/4	Darwen	a		06 31	07 39	08 06	08 41	09 09	09 41	10 41	11 41	12 41	13 41	14 41
—		d		06 42	07 39	08 11	08 41	09 11	09 41	10 41	11 41	12 41	13 41	14 41
—	Blackpool North	97 d	05 29	05c45	06 28		07c36		08c45	09c45	10c45	11c45	12c45	13c45
—	Preston 8	97 d	05 54	06 21	06 54		08 22		09 22	10 22	11 22	12 22	13 22	14 22
24 1/2	**Blackburn**	a		06 49	07 46	08 20	08 51	09 20	09 50	10 50	11 50	12 50	13 50	14 50
—		d	06 25	06 52	07 47		08 52		09 52	10 52	11 52	12 52	13 52	14 52
27 1/4	Ramsgreave & Wilpshire	d	06 31	06 58	07 53		08 58		09 58	10 58	11 58	12 58	13 58	14 58
29 3/4	Langho	d	06 35	07 02	07 57		09 02		10 02	11 02	12 02	13 02	14 02	15 02
31 3/4	Whalley	d	06 39	07 06	08 01		09 06		10 06	11 06	12 06	13 06	14 06	15 06
34 3/4	**Clitheroe**	a	06 50	07 15	08 12		09 17		10 17	11 17	12 15	13 17	14 17	15 17

		NT	NT	NT	NT	NT B	NT	NT C	NT	NT	NT	NT	NT
Manchester Victoria	82 d	15 00	15 40	16 23	17 00	17 23	18 00	18 23	19 00	20 00	21 00	22 01	23 00
Salford Central	82 d	15 03	15 43	16 26	17 03	17 27	18 03	18 26	19 03	20 03	21 03	22e04	23e03
Manchester Airport	82, 85 d	14 29	15 03	16b00	16b29	17b00	17 27	18b00	18 29	19 29	20 29	21 29	22 29
Manchester Piccadilly 10	82 d	14b54	15 22	16b16	16b54	17b15	17b54	18b16	18 46	19 46	20 46	21 46	22 50
Salford Crescent	82 d	15 08	15 47	16 31	17 08	17 30	18 08	18 31	19 08	20 08	21 08	22 08	23 08
Bolton	82 d	15 20	16 00	16 43	17 20	17 43	18 20	18 43	19 20	20 20	21 20	22 20	23 20
Hall I' Th' Wood	d	15 25	16 05	16 48	17 25	17 48	18 25	18 48	19 25	20 25	21 25	22 25	23 25
Bromley Cross	d	15 28	16 10	16 51	17 28	17 55	18 28	18 54	19 28	20 28	21 28	22 28	23 28
Entwistle	d	15x34	16x16	16x57	17x34		18x34		19x34	20x34	21x34	22x34	23x34
Darwen	a	15 41	16 23	17 04	17 41	18 07	18 41	19 06	19 41	20 41	21 41	22 41	23 41
	d	15 41	16 23	17 11	17 41	18 07	18 41	19 11	19 42	20 41	21 41	22 41	23 41
Blackpool North	97 d	14c45	15 29	16 29	16c41		17 14		18c45	19c45	20c45		
Preston 8	97 d	15 22	15 54	16 54	17 22		17 44		19 22	20 22	21 22		
Blackburn	a	15 49	16 30	17 19	17 51	18 14	18 48	19 21	19 51	20 50	21 50	22 50	23 51
	d	15 52	16 31	17 19	17 53		18 49		19 52	20 52	21 52	22 51	
Ramsgreave & Wilpshire	d	15 58	16 37	17 25	17 59		18 55		19 58	20 58	21 58	22 57	
Langho	d	16 02	16 41	17 30	18 03		18 59		20 02	21 02	22 02	23 01	
Whalley	d	16 06	16 45	17 34	18 07		19 03		20 06	21 06	22 06	23 05	
Clitheroe	a	16 17	16 56	17 44	18 18		19 14		20 17	21 17	22 17	23 14	

Saturdays

		NT	NT	NT A	NT	NT	NT	NT	NT	NT	NT	NT	NT
Manchester Victoria	82 d		05 55		07 23	08 00	08 29	09 00	10 00	11 00	12 00	13 00	14 00
Salford Central	82 d				07 26	08 03	08 32	09 03	10 03	11 03	12 03	13 03	14 03
Manchester Airport	82, 85 d		05 29	06 23	07b00	07b28	08b03	08 25	09 29	10 29	11 29	12 29	13 29
Manchester Piccadilly 10	82 d		05 46	06 54	07b15	07b54	08b22	08b54	09b54	10b54	11b54	12b54	13b54
Salford Crescent	82 d		06 00	07 03	07 30	08 08	08 37	09 08	10 08	11 08	12 08	13 08	14 08
Bolton	82 d		06 12	07 19	07 42	08 20	08 49	09 20	10 20	11 20	12 20	13 20	14 20
Hall I' Th' Wood	d		06 17	07 24	07 47	08 25	08 54	09 25	10 25	11 25	12 25	13 25	14 25
Bromley Cross	d		06 20	07 27	07 53	08 28	08 57	09 28	10 28	11 28	12 28	13 28	14 28
Entwistle	d				07x59	08x34		09x34	10x34	11x34	12x34	13x34	14x34
Darwen	a		06 31	07 39	08 06	08 41	09 09	09 41	10 41	11 41	12 41	13 41	14 41
	d		06 42	07 39	08 11	08 41	09 11	09 41	10 41	11 41	12 41	13 41	14 41
Blackpool North	97 d	05 29	05c45	06 28		07c44		08c45	09c45	10c45	11c37	12c45	13c45
Preston 8	97 d	05 54	06 21	06 54		08 22		09 22	10 22	11 22	12 22	13 22	14 22
Blackburn	a		06 49	07 46	08 20	08 51	09 20	09 50	10 50	11 50	12 50	13 50	14 50
	d	06 25	06 52	07 47		08 52		09 52	10 52	11 52	12 52	13 52	14 52
Ramsgreave & Wilpshire	d	06 31	06 58	07 53		08 58		09 58	10 58	11 58	12 58	13 58	14 58
Langho	d	06 35	07 02	07 57		09 02		10 02	11 02	12 02	13 02	14 02	15 02
Whalley	d	06 39	07 06	08 01		09 06		10 06	11 06	12 06	13 06	14 06	15 06
Clitheroe	a	06 50	07 15	08 12		09 17		10 17	11 17	12 17	13 17	14 17	15 17

		NT	NT	NT	NT	NT C	NT	NT C	NT	NT	NT	NT	NT
Manchester Victoria	82 d	15 00	15 40	16 23	17 00	17 23	18 00	18 23	19 00	20 00	21 00	22 00	23 05
Salford Central	82 d	15 03	15 43	16 26	17 03	17 26	18 03	18 26	19 03	20 03	21 03	22 03	23 08
Manchester Airport	82, 85 d	14 29	15 03	16b00	16b29	17b00	17 27	18b00	18 29	19 29	20 29	21 29	22f29
Manchester Piccadilly 10	82 d	14b54	15 22	16b16	16b54	17b15	17b54	18b16	18 46	19 46	20 46	21 46	22g54
Salford Crescent	82 d	15 08	15 47	16 31	17 08	17 31	18 08	18 31	19 08	20 08	21 08	22 08	23 12
Bolton	82 d	15 20	16 00	16 43	17 20	17 43	18 20	18 43	19 20	20 20	21 20	22 20	23 24
Hall I' Th' Wood	d	15 25	16 05	16 48	17 25	17 48	18 25	18 48	19 25	20 25	21 25	22 25	23 29
Bromley Cross	d	15 28	16 10	16 51	17 28	17 55	18 28	18 54	19 28	20 28	21 28	22 28	23 32
Entwistle	d	15x34	16x16	16x57	17x34		18x34		19x34	20x34	21x34	22x34	23x38
Darwen	a	15 41	16 23	17 04	17 41	18 07	18 41	19 06	19 41	20 41	21 41	22 41	23 45
	d	15 41	16 23	17 11	17 41	18 07	18 41	19 11	19 42	20 41	21 41	22 41	23 45
Blackpool North	97 d	14c45	15 29	16 29	16c41		17 18		18c45	19c45	20c45		
Preston 8	97 d	15 22	15 54	16 54	17 22		17 44		19 22	20 22	21 22		
Blackburn	a	15 49	16 30	17 19	17 51	18 21	18 48	19 21	19 51	20 50	21 50	22 50	23 54
	d	15 52	16 31	17 19	17 53		18 49		19 52	20 52	21 52	22 51	
Ramsgreave & Wilpshire	d	15 58	16 37	17 25	17 59		18 55		19 58	20 58	21 58	22 57	
Langho	d	16 02	16 41	17 30	18 03		18 59		20 02	21 02	22 02	23 01	
Whalley	d	16 06	16 45	17 34	18 07		19 03		20 06	21 06	22 06	23 05	
Clitheroe	a	16 17	16 56	17 44	18 18		19 14		20 17	21 17	22 17	23 16	

For general notes see front of timetable
For details of catering facilities see Directory of Train Operators

- A From Buxton (Table 86)
- B From Rochdale (Table 95) to Colne (Table 97)
- C From Rochdale (Table 95)
- b Change at Bolton
- c Change at Preston and Blackburn
- e Fridays only
- f From 10 October dep. 2141, change at Manchester Piccadilly and Bolton
- g From 10 October dep. 2216, change at Bolton

Manchester and Bolton → Blackburn → Clitheroe

Sundays
until 6 September

Network Diagram - see first page of Table 94

	NT	NT A	NT	NT A	NT	NT	NT	NT	NT	NT	NT	NT	NT	NT	NT	NT	NT
Manchester Victoria 82 d	08 01		09 00		10 00	11 00	12 00	13 00	14 00	15 00	16 00	17 00	18 00	19 00	20 00	21 00	22 00
Salford Central 82 d																	
Manchester Airport 82, 85 d	06b40		08 30		09 30	10 29	11 30	12 30	13 30	14 30	15 30	16 30	17 30	18 30	19 30	20 30	21 30
Manchester Piccadilly 10 82 d	06b55		08 46		09 46	10 43	11 46	12 46	13 46	14 46	15 46	16 46	17 46	18 46	19 46	20 46	21 46
Salford Crescent 82 d	08 08		09 08		10 08	11 08	12 08	13 08	14 08	15 08	16 08	17 08	18 08	19 08	20 08	21 08	22 08
Bolton 82 d	08 20		09 20		10 20	11 20	12 20	13 20	14 20	15 20	16 20	17 20	18 20	19 20	20 20	21 20	22 20
Hall I' Th' Wood d	08 25		09 25		10 25	11 25	12 25	13 25	14 25	15 25	16 25	17 25	18 25	19 25	20 25	21 25	22 25
Bromley Cross d	08 28		09 28		10 28	11 28	12 28	13 28	14 28	15 28	16 28	17 28	18 28	19 28	20 28	21 28	22 28
Entwistle d	08x34		09x34		10x34	11x34	12x34	13x34	14x34	15x34	16x34	17x34	18x34	19x34	20x34	21x34	22x34
Darwen a	08 41		09 41		10 41	11 41	12 41	13 41	14 41	15 41	16 41	17 41	18 41	19 41	20 41	21 41	22 41
d	08 41		09 41		10 41	11 41	12 41	13 41	14 41	15 41	16 41	17 41	18 41	19 41	20 41	21 41	22 41
Blackpool North 97 d		08 36	08 36	09 20	09c20	10 11	11c20	12 11	13c20	14 11	15c20	16 11	17c20	18 11	19c20	20c20	
Preston 8 97 d	08 16	09 05		10 00	10 05	10 37	12 05	12 37	14 05	14 37	16 05	16 37	18 05	18 37	20 05	21 05	
Blackburn a	08 48	09 25	09 48	10 19	10 48	11 48	12 48	13 48	14 48	15 48	16 48	17 48	18 48	19 48	20 48	21 48	22 48
d	08 57	09 27	09 48	10 22	10 48	11 48	12 50	13 48	14 50	15 48	16 50	17 48	18 50	19 48	20 50	21 48	
Ramsgreave & Wilpshire d	09 03	09 34	09 54	10 28	10 54	11 54	12 56	13 54	14 56	15 54	16 56	17 54	18 56	19 54	20 56	21 54	
Langho d	09 07	09 39	09 58	10 33	10 58	11 58	13 00	13 58	15 00	15 58	17 00	17 58	19 00	19 58	21 00	21 58	
Whalley d	09 11	09 43	10 02	10 38	11 02	12 02	13 04	14 02	15 04	16 02	17 04	18 02	19 04	20 02	21 04	22 02	
Clitheroe a	09 20	09 50	10 13	10 44	11 13	12 13	13 13	14 13	15 13	16 13	17 13	18 13	19 13	20 13	21 13	22 13	

Sundays
from 13 September

	NT	NT bus	NT	NT bus	NT	NT bus	NT	NT bus	NT	NT bus	NT	NT bus	NT
Manchester Victoria 82 d	08 01		09 00		10 00		11 00		12 00		13 00		14 00
Salford Central 82 d													
Manchester Airport 82, 85 d	07 30				09 30		10 25		11 30		12 30		13 30
Manchester Piccadilly 10 82 d	07 46				09 46		10 43		11 46		12 46		13 46
Salford Crescent 82 d	08 09		09 08		10 08		11 08		12 08		13 08		14 08
Bolton 82 d	08 21		09 20		10 20		11 20		12 20		13 20		14 20
Hall I' Th' Wood d	08 26		09 25		10 25		11 25		12 25		13 25		14 25
Bromley Cross d	08 29		09 28		10 28		11 28		12 28		13 28		14 28
Entwistle d	08x35		09x34		10x34		11x34		12x34		13x34		14x34
Darwen a	08 42		09 41		10 41		11 41		12 41		13 41		14 41
d	08 42		09 41		10 41		11 41		12 41		13 41		14 41
Blackpool North 97 d													
Preston 8 97 d													
Blackburn a	08 49		09 48		10 48		11 48		12 48		13 48		14 48
d		09 00		10 00		11 00		12 00		13 00		14 00	
Ramsgreave & Wilpshire d		09 08		10 08		11 08		12 08		13 08		14 08	
Langho d		09 13		10 13		11 13		12 13		13 13		14 13	
Whalley d		09 24		10 24		11 24		12 24		13 24		14 24	
Clitheroe a		09 36		10 36		11 36		12 36		13 36		14 36	

	NT bus	NT	NT bus	NT	NT bus	NT	NT bus	NT	NT bus	NT	NT bus	NT	NT bus	NT	NT bus
Manchester Victoria 82 d		15 00		16 00		17 00		18 00		19 00		20 00		21 00	
Salford Central 82 d															
Manchester Airport 82, 85 d		14 30		15 30		16 30		17 30		18 30		19 30		20 30	
Manchester Piccadilly 10 82 d		14 46		15 46		16 46		17 46		18 46		19 46		20 46	
Salford Crescent 82 d		15 08		16 08		17 08		18 08		19 08		20 08		21 08	
Bolton 82 d		15 20		16 20		17 20		18 20		19 20		20 20		21 20	
Hall I' Th' Wood d		15 25		16 25		17 25		18 25		19 25		20 25		21 25	
Bromley Cross d		15 28		16 28		17 28		18 28		19 28		20 28		21 28	
Entwistle d		15x34		16x34		17x34		18x34		19x34		20x34		21x34	
Darwen a		15 41		16 41		17 41		18 41		19 41		20 41		21 41	
d		15 41		16 41		17 41		18 41		19 41		20 41		21 41	
Blackpool North 97 d															
Preston 8 97 d															
Blackburn a		15 48		16 48		17 48		18 48		19 48		20 48		21 48	
d	15 00		16 00		17 00		18 00		19 00		20 00		21 00		22 00
Ramsgreave & Wilpshire d	15 08		16 08		17 08		18 08		19 08		20 08		21 08		22 08
Langho d	15 13		16 13		17 13		18 13		19 13		20 13		21 13		22 13
Whalley d	15 24		16 24		17 24		18 24		19 24		20 24		21 24		22 24
Clitheroe a	15 36		16 36		17 36		18 36		19 36		20 36		21 36		22 36

For general notes see front of timetable
For details of catering facilities see Directory of Train Operators

A To Carlisle (Table 36)
b Change at Bolton
c Change at Preston and Blackburn

Clitheroe → Blackburn → Bolton and Manchester

Network Diagram - see first page of Table 94

Mondays to Fridays

Miles	Station		NT	NT A	NT	NT	NT	NT	NT	NT	NT	NT	NT	NT	NT	NT	NT	NT B	NT	NT	NT	NT	NT	NT	NT
0	**Clitheroe**	d	.	.	07 07	07 40	.	08 26	.	09 40	10 40	11 40	12 40	13 40	14 40	15 26	16 40	17 09	18 09	18 40	.	19 40	20 40	21 40	22 40
2½	Whalley	d	.	.	07 13	07 46	.	08 32	.	09 46	10 46	11 46	12 46	13 46	14 46	15 32	16 46	17 15	18 15	18 46	.	19 46	20 46	21 46	22 46
4½	Langho	d	.	.	07 17	07 50	.	08 36	.	09 50	10 50	11 50	12 50	13 50	14 50	15 36	16 50	17 19	18 19	18 50	.	19 50	20 50	21 50	22 50
7	Ramsgreave & Wilpshire	d	.	.	07 22	07 55	.	08 41	.	09 55	10 55	11 55	12 55	13 55	14 55	15 41	16 55	17 24	18 24	18 55	.	19 55	20 55	21 55	22 55
9¾	**Blackburn**	a	.	.	07 28	08 02	.	08 47	.	10 01	11 01	12 01	13 01	14 01	15 01	15 47	17 01	17 30	18 30	19 01	.	20 01	21 01	22 01	23 01
—		d	06 28	07 00	07 29	08 03	08 32	09 03	09 31	10 03	11 03	12 03	13 03	14 03	15 03	15 51	17 03	17 31	18 31	19 03	19 31	20 03	21 03	22 03	23 03
—	Preston 8	97 a	.	.	08 00	08 38	.	09 32	.	10 32	11 32	12 32	13 32	14 32	15 32	16 32	17 32	18 00	19 00	19 32	.	20 32	21 32	22 49	23 54
—	Blackpool North	97 a	.	.	08b44	09 05	.	10 00	.	11 00	12 00	13 00	14 00	15 00	16 00	17 00	18 06	18b46	19 33	20 00	.	21 00	22 00	23b48	00b48
14	Darwen	a	06 35	07 08	07 37	08 10	08 39	09 11	09 38	10 10	11 10	12 10	13 10	14 10	15 10	15 58	17 10	17 38	18 38	19 10	19 38	20 10	21 10	22 10	23 10
—		d	06 35	07 08	07 40	08 10	08 42	09 11	09 41	10 10	11 10	12 10	13 10	14 10	15 10	15 58	17 10	17 41	18 41	19 10	19 42	20 10	21 10	22 10	23 10
17¾	Entwistle	d	06x42	07x15	.	08x17	.	.	.	10x17	11x17	12x17	13x17	14x17	15x17	.	17x17	17x48	18x48	19x17	19x49	20x17	21x17	22x17	23x17
20¾	Bromley Cross	d	06 48	07 20	07 51	08 23	08 52	09 22	09 52	10 23	11 23	12 23	13 23	14 23	15 23	16 08	17 23	17 54	18 54	19 23	19 54	20 23	21 23	22 23	23 23
21¾	Hall I' Th' Wood	d	06 50	07 23	07 53	08 25	08 55	09 23	09 55	10 25	11 25	12 25	13 25	14 25	15 25	16 10	17 25	17 56	18 56	19 25	19 57	20 25	21 25	22 25	23 25
23½	**Bolton**	82 a	06 55	07 30	07 58	08 30	09 02	09 30	10 00	10 30	11 30	12 30	13 30	14 30	15 30	16 17	17 30	18 01	19 01	19 31	20 02	20 30	21 30	22 30	23 30
32½	Salford Crescent	82 a	07 15	07 43	08 17	08 43	09 15	09 43	10 13	10 43	11 43	12 43	13 43	14 43	15 43	16 30	17 43	18 15	19 14	19 44	20 15	20 43	21 43	22 43	23 43
—	Manchester Piccadilly 10	82 a	07c27	07c56	08c27	08c56	09c27	09c56	10c27	10c56	11c56	12c56	13c56	14c56	15c56	16 56	17c56	18c27	19c27	20c02	20 35	20c56	21c56	22c56	23c53
—	Manchester Airport	82, 85 ✈ a	07c47	08c17	08c47	09c19	09c47	10c17	10c47	11c17	12c17	13c17	14c17	15c17	16c17	17 17	18c17	18c47	19c47	20c24	20 53	21c17	23 17	00e22	00c22
33½	Salford Central	82 a	07 18	07 46	08 20	08 46	09 18	09 46	10 16	10 46	11 46	12 46	13 46	14 46	15 46	16 33	17 46	18 17	19 17	19 46	20 18	20 46	21 46	22f46	.
34¼	**Manchester Victoria**	82 a	07 26	07 51	08 25	08 51	09 26	09 51	10 21	10 51	11 51	12 51	13 51	14 51	15 53	16 40	17 52	18 24	19 22	19 52	20 23	20 51	21 51	22 51	23 50

Saturdays

Station		NT	NT	NT	NT	NT B	NT	NT	NT	NT	NT	NT	NT	NT	NT	NT	NT B	NT	NT	NT	NT	NT	NT	NT	
Clitheroe	d	.	.	07 07	07 40	.	08 26	.	09 40	10 40	11 40	12 40	13 40	14 40	15 26	16 40	17 09	18 09	18 40	.	19 40	20 40	21 40	22 46	.
Whalley	d	.	.	07 13	07 46	.	08 32	.	09 46	10 46	11 46	12 46	13 46	14 46	15 32	16 46	17 15	18 15	18 46	.	19 46	20 46	21 46	22 52	.
Langho	d	.	.	07 17	07 50	.	08 36	.	09 50	10 50	11 50	12 50	13 50	14 50	15 36	16 50	17 19	18 19	18 50	.	19 50	20 50	21 50	22 56	.
Ramsgreave & Wilpshire	d	.	.	07 22	07 55	.	08 41	.	09 55	10 55	11 55	12 55	13 55	14 55	15 41	16 55	17 24	18 24	18 55	.	19 55	20 55	21 55	23 01	.
Blackburn	a	.	.	07 28	08 02	.	08 47	.	10 01	11 01	12 01	13 01	14 01	15 01	15 47	17 01	17 30	18 30	19 01	.	20 01	21 01	22 01	23 07	.
	d	06 28	07 00	07 29	08 03	08 32	09 03	09 31	10 03	11 03	12 03	13 03	14 03	15 03	15 51	17 03	17 31	18 31	19 03	19 31	20 03	21 03	22 03	23 09	.
Preston 8	97 a	.	.	08 00	08 38	.	09 32	.	10 32	11 32	12 32	13 32	14 32	15 32	16 32	17 32	18 00	19 00	19 32	.	20 32	21 32	22 49	23 54	.
Blackpool North	97 a	.	.	08b44	09 05	.	10 00	.	11 00	12 00	13 00	14 00	15 00	16 00	17 00	18 06	18b48	19b48	20 00	.	21 00	22 00	23b48	00b40	.
Darwen	a	06 35	07 07	07 37	08 10	08 39	09 11	09 38	10 10	11 10	12 10	13 10	14 10	15 10	15 58	17 10	17 38	18 38	19 10	19 38	20 10	21 10	22 10	23 16	.
	d	06 35	07 08	07 40	08 10	08 42	09 11	09 41	10 10	11 10	12 10	13 10	14 10	15 10	15 58	17 10	17 41	18 41	19 10	19 42	20 10	21 10	22 10	23 16	.
Entwistle	d	06x42	07x15	.	08x17	.	.	.	10x17	11x17	12x17	13x17	14x17	15x17	.	17x17	17x48	18x48	19x17	19x49	20x17	21x17	22x17	23x23	.
Bromley Cross	d	06 48	07 20	07 51	08 23	08 53	09 22	09 52	10 23	11 23	12 23	13 23	14 23	15 23	16 08	17 23	17 54	18 54	19 23	19 54	20 23	21 23	22 23	23 29	.
Hall I' Th' Wood	d	06 50	07 23	07 53	08 25	08 55	09 23	09 55	10 25	11 25	12 25	13 25	14 25	15 25	16 10	17 25	17 56	18 56	19 25	19 57	20 25	21 25	22 25	23 31	.
Bolton	82 a	06 55	07 30	07 58	08 30	09 02	09 30	10 00	10 30	11 30	12 30	13 30	14 30	15 30	16 17	17 30	18 01	19 01	19 31	20 02	20 30	21 30	22 30	23 36	.
Salford Crescent	82 a	07 15	07 43	08 17	08 43	09 15	09 43	10 13	10 43	11 43	12 43	13 43	14 43	15 43	16 30	17 43	18 14	19 14	19 44	20 15	20 43	21 43	22 43	23 50	.
Manchester Piccadilly 10	82 a	07c27	07c56	08c27	08c56	09c27	09c56	10c27	10c56	11c56	12c56	13c56	14c56	15c56	16 56	17c56	18c27	19c27	.	20c27	20c56	21c56	22c56	.	.
Manchester Airport	82, 85 ✈ a	07c47	08c17	08c47	09c19	09c47	10c17	10c47	11c17	12c17	13c17	14c17	15c17	16c17	17 17	18c17	18c47	19c50	.	20c47	21c17	22c17	23c17	.	.
Salford Central	82 a	07 19	07 46	08 20	08 46	09 18	09 46	10 16	10 46	11 46	12 46	13 46	14 46	15 46	16 33	17 46	18 17	19 17	19 46	20 17	20 46	21 46	22 46	.	.
Manchester Victoria	82 a	07 22	07 51	08 25	08 51	09 26	09 51	10 23	10 51	11 51	12 51	13 51	14 51	15 53	16 40	17 54	18 26	19 22	19 52	20 23	20 51	21 51	22 51	23 59	.

Sundays

until 6 September

Station		NT	NT		NT	NT		NT	NT		NT	NT		NT	NT		NT C	NT	NT	NT C	NT	NT	NT		
Clitheroe	d	.	09 40	.	10 40	11 40	.	12 40	13 40	.	14 40	15 40	.	16 40	17 40	.	17 58	18 40	19 40	19 55	20 40	21 40	22 40	.	.
Whalley	d	.	09 46	.	10 46	11 46	.	12 46	13 46	.	14 46	15 46	.	16 46	17 46	.	18 04	18 46	19 46	20 04	20 46	21 46	22 46	.	.
Langho	d	.	09 50	.	10 50	11 50	.	12 50	13 50	.	14 50	15 50	.	16 50	17 50	.	18 09	18 50	19 50	20 09	20 50	21 50	22 50	.	.
Ramsgreave & Wilpshire	d	.	09 55	.	10 55	11 55	.	12 55	13 55	.	14 55	15 55	.	16 55	17 55	.	18 14	18 55	19 55	20 14	20 55	21 55	22 55	.	.
Blackburn	a	.	10 01	.	11 02	12 01	.	13 01	14 01	.	15 01	16 01	.	17 01	18 01	.	18 23	19 01	20 01	20 22	21 01	22 01	23 01	.	.
	d	09 03	10 03	.	11 03	12 03	.	13 03	14 03	.	15 03	16 03	.	17 03	18 03	.	18 28	19 03	20 03	20 25	21 03	22 03	23 03	.	.
Preston 8	97 a	.	10 27	.	12 13	12 42	.	14 13	14 42	.	16 13	16 42	.	18 13	18 42	.	18 50	20 14	20 42	20 47	22 13	22 42	.	.	.
Blackpool North	97 a	.	10 53	.	12 38	13 38	.	14 38	15g40	.	16 38	17 38	.	18 38	19 38	.	19 38	20 39	21 16	21 16	22 38	00b04	.	.	.
Darwen	a	09 10	10 10	.	11 10	12 10	.	13 10	14 10	.	15 10	16 10	.	17 10	18 10	.	.	19 10	20 10	.	21 10	22 10	23 10	.	.
	d	09 10	10 10	.	11 10	12 10	.	13 10	14 10	.	15 10	16 10	.	17 10	18 10	.	.	19 10	20 10	.	21 10	22 10	23 10	.	.
Entwistle	d	09x17	10x17	.	11x17	12x17	.	13x17	14x17	.	15x17	16x17	.	17x17	18x17	.	.	19x17	20x17	.	21x17	22x17	23x17	.	.
Bromley Cross	d	09 22	10 22	.	11 22	12 22	.	13 22	14 22	.	15 22	16 22	.	17 22	18 22	.	.	19 22	20 22	.	21 22	22 22	23 22	.	.
Hall I' Th' Wood	d	09 23	10 23	.	11 23	12 23	.	13 23	14 23	.	15 23	16 23	.	17 23	18 23	.	.	19 23	20 23	.	21 23	22 23	23 23	.	.
Bolton	82 a	09 30	10 30	.	11 30	12 30	.	13 30	14 30	.	15 30	16 30	.	17 30	18 30	.	.	19 30	20 30	.	21 30	22 30	23 30	.	.
Salford Crescent	82 a	09 43	10 43	.	11 43	12 43	.	13 43	14 43	.	15 43	16 43	.	17 43	18 43	.	.	19 43	20 43	.	21 43	22 43	23 43	.	.
Manchester Piccadilly 10	82 a	09c57	10c57	.	11c57	12c57	.	13c57	14c57	.	15c57	16c57	.	17c57	18c57	.	.	19c57	20c57	.	21c57	23 14	00c15	.	.
Manchester Airport	82, 85 ✈ a	10c13	11c17	.	12c17	13c17	.	14c17	15c17	.	16c17	17c17	.	18c17	19c17	.	.	20c17	21c17	.	22c17	23 30	01h00	.	.
Salford Central	82 a	.	.	.	.	.	.	.	.	.	.	.	.	.	.	.	.	.	.	.	.	.	.	.	.
Manchester Victoria	82 a	09 51	10 51	.	11 51	12 51	.	13 51	14 51	.	15 51	16 51	.	17 51	18 51	.	.	19 51	20 51	.	21 51	22 51	23 51	.	.

For general notes see front of timetable
For details of catering facilities see Directory of Train Operators

- **A** From Colne (Table 97)
- **B** To Rochdale (Table 95)
- **C** From Carlisle (Table 36)
- **b** Change at Blackburn and Preston
- **c** Change at Bolton
- **e** Change at Salford Crescent and Manchester Piccadilly
- **f** Fridays only
- **g** 19 July to 6 September arr. 1539
- **h** Change at Bolton and Manchester Piccadilly

Table 94

Sundays

from 13 September

Clitheroe → Blackburn → Bolton and Manchester

Network Diagram - see first page of Table 94

		NT	NT 🚌	NT	NT 🚌	NT	NT 🚌	NT	NT 🚌	NT	NT 🚌	NT	NT 🚌	NT	NT 🚌	NT	NT 🚌	NT
Clitheroe	d		09 19		10 19		11 19		12 19		13 19		14 19		15 19		16 19	
Whalley	d		09 31		10 31		11 31		12 31		13 31		14 31		15 31		16 31	
Langho	d		09 42		10 42		11 42		12 42		13 42		14 42		15 42		16 42	
Ramsgreave & Wilpshire	d		09 47		10 47		11 47		12 47		13 47		14 47		15 47		16 47	
Blackburn	a		09 55		10 55		11 55		12 55		13 55		14 55		15 55		16 55	
	d	09 03		10 03		11 03		12 03		13 03		14 03		15 03		16 03		17 03
Preston 8 97	a																	
Blackpool North 97	a																	
Darwen	a	09 10		10 10		11 10		12 10		13 10		14 10		15 10		16 10		17 10
	d	09 10		10 10		11 10		12 10		13 10		14 10		15 10		16 10		17 10
Entwistle	d	09x17		10x17		11x17		12x17		13x17		14x17		15x17		16x17		17x17
Bromley Cross	d	09 22		10 22		11 22		12 22		13 22		14 22		15 22		16 22		17 22
Hall I' Th' Wood	d	09 23		10 23		11 23		12 23		13 23		14 23		15 23		16 23		17 23
Bolton 82	a	09 30		10 30		11 30		12 30		13 30		14 30		15 30		16 30		17 30
Salford Crescent 82	a	09 43		10 43		11 43		12 43		13 43		14 43		15 43		16 43		17 43
Manchester Piccadilly 10 82	a	09c57		10c57		11c57		12c57		13c57		14c57		15c57		16c57		17c57
Manchester Airport 82, 85 ✈	a	10c13		11c17		12c17		13c17		14c17		15c17		16c17		17c17		18c17
Salford Central 82	a																	
Manchester Victoria 82	a	09 51		10 51		11 51		12 51		13 51		14 51		15 51		16 51		17 51

		NT 🚌	NT	NT 🚌	NT	NT 🚌	NT	NT 🚌	NT	NT 🚌	NT	NT 🚌	NT
Clitheroe	d	17 19		18 19		19 19		20 19		21 19		22 19	
Whalley	d	17 31		18 31		19 31		20 31		21 31		22 31	
Langho	d	17 42		18 42		19 42		20 42		21 42		22 42	
Ramsgreave & Wilpshire	d	17 47		18 47		19 47		20 47		21 47		22 47	
Blackburn	a	17 55		18 55		19 55		20 55		21 55		22 55	
	d		18 03		19 03		20 03		21 03		22 03		23 03
Preston 8 97	a												
Blackpool North 97	a												
Darwen	a		18 10		19 10		20 10		21 10		22 10		23 10
	d		18 10		19 10		20 10		21 10		22 10		23 10
Entwistle	d		18x17		19x17		20x17		21x17		22x17		23x17
Bromley Cross	d		18 22		19 22		20 22		21 22		22 22		23 22
Hall I' Th' Wood	d		18 23		19 23		20 23		21 23		22 23		23 23
Bolton 82	a		18 30		19 30		20 30		21 30		22 30		23 30
Salford Crescent 82	a		18 43		19 43		20 43		21 43		22 43		23 43
Manchester Piccadilly 10 82	a		18c57		19c57		20c57		21c57		23c14		00c15
Manchester Airport 82, 85 ✈	a		19c17		20c17		21c17		22c17		23c30		01c31
Salford Central 82	a												
Manchester Victoria 82	a		18 51		19 51		20 51		21 51		22 51		23 51

For general notes see front of timetable
For details of catering facilities see
Directory of Train Operators

c Change at Bolton

Table 95

Mondays to Saturdays
until 3 October

Manchester → Oldham and Rochdale

Network Diagram - see first page of Table 94

Miles	Miles			NT SO A	NT B	NT SX C	NT SO D	NT	NT	NT E	NT	NT G	NT	NT	NT H	NT	NT	NT J	NT	NT G	NT	NT	NT H	NT	NT K
—	—	Liverpool Lime Street 10	90 d									05 46								06 46				07 16	
—	—	Bolton	82 d									05b43					06 56		07 25	07c30			07 43		07e59
—	—	Salford Crescent	82 d									06f38					07 15		07 38	07c43		07 51	08 02		08 13
—	—	Salford Central	82 d									06f41					07 19		07 41	07c46		07 55	08 05		08 16
0	0	**Manchester Victoria**	d	05 40	05 54	06 17	06 21	06 28	06 35	06 43		06 58	07 03	07 09	07 17		07 38	07 47	07 53	08 00		08 09	08 22	08 24	08 30
—	4	Moston	d			06 23		06 34				07 04			07 23					08 06					08 36
—	5¾	Mills Hill	d			06 28		06 39				07 09			07 28					08 11					08 40
—	8¾	Castleton	d			06 33		06 44				07 14			07 33					08 16					08 45
2½	—	Dean Lane	d						06 41					07 15			07 44					08 15			
3½	—	Failsworth	d						06 44					07 18			07 47					08 18			
4¼	—	Hollinwood	d						06 46					07 20			07 49					08 20			
6¼	—	Oldham Werneth	d						06 51		←			07 25		←	07 54					08 25			
7½	—	**Oldham Mumps**	d						06 54 →		06 54		07 16	07 28 →		07 28	07 57		08 07			08 28		08 37	
8	—	Derker	d								06 57		07 19				08 00					08 31			
10	—	Shaw & Crompton	a								07 00		07 25			07 33	08 06		08 12		←	08 37		08 44	
—	—		d								07 01					07 37			08 12 →		08 12			08 44 →	
11¾	—	New Hey	d								07 04					07 40					08 16				
12¾	—	Milnrow	d								07 07					07 43					08 18				
14¾	10¼	**Rochdale**	a	05 54	06 08	06 36	06 34	06 49		06 56	07 14	07 17			07 36	07 50		08 01		08 19	08 27		08 34		08 51

		NT	NT	NT J	NT	NT G	NT	NT	NT H	NT	NT SO L	NT SX	NT	NT	NT J	NT		NT G	NT	NT	NT H	NT	NT N	NT	NT
Liverpool Lime Street 10	90 d				07 46											08 44									
Bolton	82 d			08c12	08 25	08 31			08 39		09 03	09 02				09 25		09 31			09 39		10 03		
Salford Crescent	82 d		08 17	08c30	08 38	08 44		08 50	09g02		09 16	09 16			09 27	09 38		09 44			10 03		10 15		
Salford Central	82 d		08 20	08c32	08 41	08 46		08 53	09g04		09 18	09 18			09 31	09 41		09 46			10 05		10 17		
Manchester Victoria	d		08 38	08 48	08 54	09 00		09 09	09 22	09 24	09 33	09 33		09 38	09 48	09 54		10 00		10 09	10 21	10 24	10 30		10 38
Moston	d					09 06					09 39	09 39						10 06					10 36		
Mills Hill	d					09 11					09 44	09 44						10 11					10 40		
Castleton	d					09 16					09 49	09 49						10 16					10 45		
Dean Lane	d		08 44					09 15						09 44						10 15					10 44
Failsworth	d		08 47					09 18						09 47						10 18					10 47
Hollinwood	d		08 49					09 20						09 49						10 20					10 49
Oldham Werneth	d		08 54					09 25						09 54						10 25					10 54
Oldham Mumps	d		08 57		09 07			09 28		09 37				09 57		10 07				10 28		10 37			10 57
Derker	d		09 00					09 31						10 00						10 31					11 00
Shaw & Crompton	a	←	09 06		09 12		←	09 37		09 44			←	10 06		10 12			←	10 37		10 44		←	11 06
	d	08 44			09 12 →		09 12			09 44 →			09 44			10 12 →			10 12			10 44 →		10 44	
New Hey	d	08 47					09 16						09 47						10 16					10 47	
Milnrow	d	08 50					09 18						09 50						10 18					10 50	
Rochdale	a	08 57		09 02		09 19	09 27		09 35		09 52	09 54	09 57		10 02			10 19	10 27		10 34		10 51	10 57	

		NT J	NT	NT G	NT	NT	NT H	NT	NT N	NT	NT	NT J	NT	NT G	NT	NT	NT H	NT	NT N	NT	NT	NT J	NT	NT G	NT
Liverpool Lime Street 10	90 d		09 46										10 46											11 46	
Bolton	82 d	10h13	10 25	10 31			10 39		11 03			11h13	11 25	11 31			11 39		12 03		12 03	12h13	12 25	12 31	
Salford Crescent	82 d	10 34	10 38	10 44			11 03		11 15			11 34	11 38	11 44			12 03		12 15			12 34	12 38	12 44	
Salford Central	82 d	10 36	10 41	10 46			11 05		11 17			11 36	11 41	11 46			12 05		12 17			12 36	12 41	12 46	
Manchester Victoria	d	10 48	10 54	11 00		11 09	11 21	11 24	11 30		11 38	11 48	11 54	12 00		12 09	12 21	12 24	12 30		12 38	12 48	12 54	13 00	
Moston	d			11 06					11 36					12 06					12 36					13 06	
Mills Hill	d			11 11					11 40					12 11					12 40					13 11	
Castleton	d			11 16					11 45					12 16					12 45					13 16	
Dean Lane	d					11 15					11 44					12 15					12 44				
Failsworth	d					11 18					11 47					12 18					12 47				
Hollinwood	d					11 20					11 49					12 20					12 49				
Oldham Werneth	d					11 25					11 54					12 25					12 54				
Oldham Mumps	d		11 07			11 28		11 37			11 57		12 07			12 28		12 37			12 57		13 07		
Derker	d					11 31					12 00					12 31					13 00				
Shaw & Crompton	a		11 12		←	11 37		11 44		←	12 06		12 12		←	12 37		12 44		←	13 06		13 12		←
	d		11 12 →		11 12			11 44 →		11 44			12 12 →		12 12			12 44 →		12 44			13 12 →		13 12
New Hey	d				11 16					11 47					12 16					12 47					13 16
Milnrow	d				11 18					11 50					12 18					12 50					13 18
Rochdale	a	11 02		11 19	11 27		11 34		11 51	11 57		12 02		12 19	12 27		12 34		12 51	12 57		13 02		13 19	13 27

		NT	NT H	NT	NT N	NT	NT	NT J		NT	NT G	NT	NT	NT H	NT	NT N	NT	NT	NT J	NT	NT G	NT	NT	NT H	NT
Liverpool Lime Street 10	90 d									12 46											13 46				
Bolton	82 d		12 39		13 03			13h13		13 25	13 31			13 39		14 03			14h13	14 25	14 31			14 39	
Salford Crescent	82 d		13 03		13 15			13 34		13 38	13 44			14 03		14 15			14 34	14 38	14 44			15 03	
Salford Central	82 d		13 05		13 17			13 36		13 41	13 46			14 05		14 17			14 36	14 41	14 46			15 05	
Manchester Victoria	d	13 09	13 21	13 24	13 30		13 38	13 48		13 54	14 00		14 09	14 21	14 24	14 30		14 37	14 48	14 54	15 00		15 09	15 21	15 24
Moston	d				13 36						14 06					14 36					15 06				
Mills Hill	d				13 40						14 11					14 40					15 11				
Castleton	d				13 45						14 16					14 45					15 16				
Dean Lane	d	13 15					13 44						14 15					14 44					15 15		
Failsworth	d	13 18					13 47						14 18					14 47					15 18		
Hollinwood	d	13 20					13 49						14 20					14 49					15 20		
Oldham Werneth	d	13 25					13 54						14 25					14 54					15 25		
Oldham Mumps	d	13 28		13 37			13 57			14 07			14 28		14 37			14 57		15 07			15 28		15 37
Derker	d	13 31					14 00						14 31					15 00					15 31		
Shaw & Crompton	a	13 37		13 44		←	14 06			14 12		←	14 37		14 44		←	15 06		15 12		←	15 37		15 44
	d			13 44 →		13 44				14 12 →		14 12			14 44 →		14 44			15 12 →		15 12			15 44 →
New Hey	d					13 47						14 16					14 47					15 16			
Milnrow	d					13 50						14 18					14 50					15 18			
Rochdale	a		13 34		13 51	13 57		14 02			14 19	14 27		14 34		14 51	14 57		15 02		15 19	15 27		15 34	

For general notes see front of timetable
For details of catering facilities see Directory of Train Operators

- **A** Until 11 July. To Hebden Bridge (Table 41)
- **B** All Mondays to Fridays, also Saturdays from 18 July. Mondays to Fridays to Selby (Saturdays to Leeds) (Table 41)
- **C** To Selby (Table 41)
- **D** To Selby (Until 11 July to Hebden Bridge) (Table 41)
- **E** Mondays to Fridays to Selby (Saturdays until 11 July to Hebden Bridge from 18 July to Leeds) (Table 41)
- **G** To Leeds (Table 41)
- **H** To Leeds (Saturdays until 11 July to Todmorden) (Table 41)
- **J** To Selby (Saturdays until 11 July to Hebden Bridge) (Table 41)
- **K** From Kirkby (Table 82)
- **L** From Blackburn (Table 94)
- **N** From Wigan Wallgate (Table 82)
- **b** Mondays to Fridays only. Change at Salford Crescent and Manchester Victoria
- **c** Saturdays only
- **e** Change at Manchester Victoria
- **f** Mondays to Fridays only
- **g** Saturdays dep. Salford Crescent 0903, Salford Central 0906
- **h** Change at Salford Crescent and Manchester Victoria

Table 95

Mondays to Saturdays

until 3 October

Manchester → Oldham and Rochdale

Network Diagram - see first page of Table 94

		NT A	NT	NT	NT B	NT	NT C	NT	NT	NT D	NT	NT A	NT	NT	NT B	NT	NT C	NT	NT	NT D	NT	NT A	NT	NT	NT E
Liverpool Lime Street 10	90 d					14 46										15 46						16b16			
Bolton	82 d	15 03			15c13	15 25	15 31			15 39		16 03			16 17	16 25				16 39		17 03		17 03	
Salford Crescent	82 d	15 15			15 34	15 38	15 44			16 03		16 15			16 34	16 38				17 03		17 15			
Salford Central	82 d	15 17			15 36	15 41	15 46			16 05		16 17			16e36	16e42				17 05		17 17			
Manchester Victoria	d	15 30		15 38	15 48	15 54	16 00		16 09	16 21	16 24	16 30		16 38	16 48	16 54	17 00		17 09	17 18	17 23	17 30		17 38	17 41
Moston	d	15 36					16 06					16 36					17 06			17 24		17 36			17 47
Mills Hill	d	15 40					16 11					16 40					17 11			17 29		17 40			17 52
Castleton	d	15 45					16 16					16 45					17 16			17 34		17 45			17 57
Dean Lane	d			15 44					16 15					16 44					17 15					17 44	
Failsworth	d			15 47					16 18					16 47					17 18					17 47	
Hollinwood	d			15 49					16 20					16 49					17 20					17 49	
Oldham Werneth	d			15 54					16 25					16 54					17 25					17 54	
Oldham Mumps	d			15 57		16 07			16 28		16 37			16 57		17 07			17 28		17 37			17 57	
Derker	d			16 00					16 31					17 00					17 31					18 00	
Shaw & Crompton	a		←	16 06		16 12		←	16 37		16 44		←	17 06		17 12		←	17 37		17 44		←	18 06	
	d		15 44			16 12 →		16 12			16 44 →		16 44			17 12 →		17 12			17 44 →		17 44		
New Hey	d		15 47					16 16					16 47					17 16					17 47		
Milnrow	d		15 50					16 18					16 50					17 18					17 50		
Rochdale	a	15 51	15 57		16 02		16 19	16 27		16 35		16 51	16 57		17 02		17 19	17 27		17 37		17 51	17 57		18 02

		NT	NT C	NT	NT D	NT G	NT	NT H	NT	NT C	NT	NT D	NT	NT	NT C	NT	NT	NT C	NT	NT J	NT SO C	NT J	NT
Liverpool Lime Street 10	90 d	16 46			17 10			17 35		17 48				18 46	19 12			20 12		21 12		22 12	
Bolton	82 d	17 25	17 31		17 39	18 02		18c13		18 30		18 39		19 31	19c35		20 31	20c35	21 31	21c35	22 25	22c35	
Salford Crescent	82 d	17 38	17 44		18 03	18 15		18 33		18 43		19 03		19 44	20 03		20 44	21 03	21 44	22 03	22 38	23 03	
Salford Central	82 d	17 41	17 46		18 05	18 17		18 36		18 46		19 05		19 46	20 05		20 46	21 05	21 46	22f05	22 41	23g05	
Manchester Victoria	d	17 54	18 00		18 21	18 26	18 35	18 48		19 00	19 08	19 20		20 08	20 21		21 00	21 21	22 00	22 21	22 54	23 20	23 24
Moston	d					18 32				19 06		19 27			20 27			21 27		22 27		23 26	
Mills Hill	d		18 09			18 36				19 10		19 32			20 32			21 32		22 32		23 31	
Castleton	d		18 14			18 41				19 15		19 37			20 37			21 37		22 37		23 36	
Dean Lane	d						18 41				19 14			20 14			21 06		22 06				23 30
Failsworth	d						18 44				19 17			20 17			21 09		22 09				23 33
Hollinwood	d						18 46				19 19			20 19			21 12		22 12				23 36
Oldham Werneth	d						18 51		←		19 24		←	20 24		←	21 16		22 16				23 40
Oldham Mumps	d	18 07					18 54 →		18 54		19 27 →		19 27	20 27 →		20 27	21 20		22 20				23 44
Derker	d								18 57				19 30			20 30	21 22		22 22				23 46
Shaw & Crompton	a	18 12		←					19 00				19 35			20 35	21 26		22 26				23 50
	d	18 12 →		18 12					19 00				19 35			20 35	21 26		22 26				23 50
New Hey	d			18 16					19 04				19 38			20 38	21 29		22 29				23 53
Milnrow	d			18 18					19 06				19 41			20 41	21 32		22 32				23 56
Rochdale	a		18 18	18 27	18 35	18 49		19 01	19 14	19 19		19 40	19 49		20 40	20 49	21 39	21 40	22 39	22 42	23 07	23 41	00 05

Mondays to Saturdays

from 5 October

		NT K	NT SX L	NT SO L	NT	NT K	NT C	NT C	NT L	NT C	NT C	NT N	NT L	NT C	NT C	NT SO Q	NT SX	NT L	NT C	NT C	NT A	NT L
Liverpool Lime Street 10	90 d																					
Bolton	82 d															09 03					10 03	
Salford Crescent	82 d											08 13				09 16					10 15	
Salford Central	82 d											08 16				09 18					10 17	
Manchester Victoria	d	05 54	06 17	06 21	06 28	06 43	06 58	07 17	07 48	08 00	08 22	08 28	08 48	09 00	09 22	09 33	09 33	09 48	10 00	10 21	10 28	10 48
Moston	d		06 23		06 34		07 04	07 23		08 06		08 34		09 06		09 39	09 39		10 06		10 34	
Mills Hill	d		06 28		06 39		07 09	07 28		08 11		08 38		09 11		09 44	09 44		10 11		10 38	
Castleton	d		06 33		06 44		07 14	07 33		08 16		08 43		09 16		09 49	09 49		10 16		10 43	
Rochdale	a	06 08	06 36	06 34	06 49	06 56	07 17	07 36	08 01	08 19	08 34	08 49	09 02	09 19	09 35	09 52	09 54	10 02	10 19	10 34	10 49	11 02

		NT C	NT C	NT A	NT L	NT C	NT C	NT A	NT L	NT C	NT C	NT L	NT L	NT C	NT C	NT A	NT L	NT C	NT C	NT A	NT L
Liverpool Lime Street 10	90 d																				
Bolton	82 d			11 03				12 03				13 03				14 03				15 03	
Salford Crescent	82 d			11 15				12 15				13 15				14 15				15 15	
Salford Central	82 d			11 17				12 17				13 17				14 17				15 17	
Manchester Victoria	d	11 00	11 21	11 28	11 48	12 00	12 21	12 28	12 48	13 00	13 21	13 28	13 48	14 00	14 21	14 28	14 48	15 00	15 21	15 28	15 48
Moston	d	11 06		11 34		12 06		12 34		13 06		13 34		14 06		14 34		15 06		15 34	
Mills Hill	d	11 11		11 38		12 11		12 38		13 11		13 38		14 11		14 38		15 11		15 38	
Castleton	d	11 16		11 43		12 16		12 43		13 16		13 43		14 16		14 43		15 16		15 43	
Rochdale	a	11 19	11 34	11 49	12 02	12 19	12 34	12 49	13 02	13 19	13 34	13 49	14 02	14 19	14 34	14 49	15 02	15 19	15 34	15 49	16 02

		NT C	NT C	NT A	NT L	NT C	NT C	NT A	NT U	NT C	NT C	NT G	NT C	NT C	NT C	NT C	NT C	NT	NT SO C	NT
Liverpool Lime Street 10	90 d																			
Bolton	82 d			16 03				17 03				18 02								
Salford Crescent	82 d			16 15				17 15				18 15								
Salford Central	82 d			16 17				17 17				18 17								
Manchester Victoria	d	16 00	16 21	16 28	16 48	17 00	17 18	17 28	17 43	18 00	18 21	18 26	18 48	19 00	19 21	20 21	21 21	22 21	22 54	23 20
Moston	d	16 06		16 34		17 06	17 24	17 34	17 49			18 32		19 06	19 27	20 27	21 27	22 27		23 26
Mills Hill	d	16 11		16 38		17 11	17 29	17 38	17 54	18 09		18 36		19 10	19 32	20 32	21 32	22 32		23 31
Castleton	d	16 16		16 43		17 16	17 34	17 43	17 59	18 14		18 41		19 15	19 37	20 37	21 37	22 37		23 36
Rochdale	a	16 19	16 35	16 49	17 02	17 19	17 37	17 49	18 02	18 18	18 35	18 49	19 01	19 19	19 40	20 40	21 40	22 42	23 07	23 41

For general notes see front of timetable
For details of catering facilities see Directory of Train Operators

- **A** From Wigan Wallgate (Table 82)
- **B** To Selby (Saturdays until 11 July to Hebden Bridge) (Table 41)
- **C** To Leeds (Table 41)
- **D** To Leeds (Saturdays until 11 July to Todmorden) (Table 41)
- **E** To York (Saturdays until 11 July to Hebden Bridge) (Table 41)
- **G** From Clitheroe (Table 94)
- **H** To Leeds (Saturdays until 11 July to Hebden Bridge) (Table 41)
- **J** Mondays to Fridays to Leeds (Table 41)
- **K** To Selby (Saturdays to Leeds) (Table 41)
- **L** To Selby (Table 41)
- **N** From Kirkby (Table 82)
- **Q** From Blackburn (Table 94)
- **U** To York (Table 41)
- **b** Change at Manchester Victoria
- **c** Change at Salford Crescent and Manchester Victoria
- **e** Saturdays dep. 1 min. later
- **f** Fridays and Saturdays dep. 2205
- **g** Fridays and Saturdays dep. 2305

Sundays
until 27 September

Manchester → Oldham and Rochdale

Network Diagram - see first page of Table 94

		NT A	NT	NT A	NT	NT A	NT	NT A	NT	NT A	NT	NT A	NT	NT A	NT	NT A	NT	NT A
Liverpool Lime Street 10	90 d	*08b19*		*09b22*		*10b22*		*11b22*		*12b22*		*13b22*		*14b22*		*15b22*		*16b22*
Bolton	82 d			*09 31*		*10 31*		*11 31*		*12 31*		*13 31*		*14 31*		*15 31*		*16 31*
Salford Crescent	82 d			*09 44*		*10 44*		*11 44*		*12 44*		*13 44*		*14 44*		*15 44*		*16 44*
Salford Central	82 d																	
Manchester Victoria	d	09 08	09 35	10 08	10 35	11 08	11 35	12 08	12 35	13 08	13 35	14 08	14 35	15 08	15 35	16 08	16 35	17 08
Moston	d	09 15		10 15		11 15		12 15		13 15		14 15		15 15		16 15		17 15
Mills Hill	d	09 19		10 19		11 19		12 19		13 19		14 19		15 19		16 19		17 19
Castleton	d	09 24		10 24		11 24		12 24		13 24		14 24		15 24		16 24		17 24
Dean Lane	d		09 41		10 41		11 41		12 41		13 41		14 41		15 41		16 41	
Failsworth	d		09 44		10 44		11 44		12 44		13 44		14 44		15 44		16 44	
Hollinwood	d		09 46		10 46		11 46		12 46		13 46		14 46		15 46		16 46	
Oldham Werneth	d		09 51		10 51		11 51		12 51		13 51		14 51		15 51		16 51	
Oldham Mumps	d		09 54		10 54		11 54		12 54		13 54		14 54		15 54		16 54	
Derker	d		09 57		10 57		11 57		12 57		13 57		14 57		15 57		16 57	
Shaw & Crompton	a		10 00		11 00		12 00		13 00		14 00		15 00		16 00		17 00	
	d		10 00		11 00		12 00		13 00		14 00		15 00		16 00		17 00	
New Hey	d		10 04		11 04		12 04		13 04		14 04		15 04		16 04		17 04	
Milnrow	d		10 06		11 06		12 06		13 06		14 06		15 06		16 06		17 06	
Rochdale	a	09 28	10 13	10 28	11 14	11 28	12 14	12 28	13 14	13 28	14 14	14 28	15 14	15 28	16 14	16 28	17 14	17 28

		NT	NT A	NT	NT A	NT B	NT A	NT	NT A	NT	NT A	NT	NT
Liverpool Lime Street 10	90 d		*17b22*		*18b22*		*19b22*		*20b22*			*21 52*	
Bolton	82 d		*17 31*		*18 31*		*19 31*		*20 31*		*21 31*		*22 31*
Salford Crescent	82 d		*17 44*		*18 44*		*19 44*		*20 44*		*21 44*		*22 44*
Salford Central	82 d												
Manchester Victoria	d	17 35	18 08	18 35	19 08	19 35	20 08	20 35	21 08	21 35	22 08	22 35	23 20
Moston	d		18 15		19 15		20 15		21 15		22 15		
Mills Hill	d		18 19		19 19		20 19		21 19		22 19		
Castleton	d		18 24		19 24		20 24		21 24		22 24		
Dean Lane	d	17 41		18 41		19 41		20 41		21 41		22 41	23 26
Failsworth	d	17 44		18 44		19 44		20 44		21 44		22 44	23 29
Hollinwood	d	17 46		18 46		19 46		20 46		21 46		22 46	23 31
Oldham Werneth	d	17 51		18 51		19 51		20 51		21 51		22 51	23 36
Oldham Mumps	d	17 54		18 54		19 54		20 54		21 54		22 54	23 39
Derker	d	17 57		18 57		19 57		20 57		21 57		22 57	23 42
Shaw & Crompton	a	18 00		19 00		20 00		21 00		22 00		23 00	23 45
	d	18 00		19 00		20 00		21 00		22 00		23 00	23 45
New Hey	d	18 04		19 04		20 04		21 04		22 04		23 04	23 49
Milnrow	d	18 06		19 06		20 06		21 06		22 06		23 06	23 51
Rochdale	a	18 14	18 28	19 14	19 28	20 13	20 28	21 13	21 28	22 13	22 28	23 13	23 58

Sundays
from 4 October

		NT A	NT A	NT A	NT A	NT A	NT A	NT A	NT A	NT A	NT A	NT A	NT A	NT A	NT A
Liverpool Lime Street 10	90 d														
Bolton	82 d														
Salford Crescent	82 d														
Salford Central	82 d														
Manchester Victoria	d	09 08	10 08	11 08	12 08	13 08	14 08	15 08	16 08	17 08	18 08	19 08	20 08	21 08	22 08
Moston	d	09 15	10 15	11 15	12 15	13 15	14 15	15 15	16 15	17 15	18 15	19 15	20 15	21 15	22 15
Mills Hill	d	09 19	10 19	11 19	12 19	13 19	14 19	15 19	16 19	17 19	18 19	19 19	20 19	21 19	22 19
Castleton	d	09 24	10 24	11 24	12 24	13 24	14 24	15 24	16 24	17 24	18 24	19 24	20 24	21 24	22 24
Rochdale	a	09 28	10 28	11 28	12 28	13 28	14 28	15 28	16 28	17 28	18 28	19 28	20 28	21 28	22 28

For general notes see front of timetable
For details of catering facilities see
Directory of Train Operators

A To Leeds (Table 41)
B 13, 20 and 27 September
b From 13 September only

Rochdale and Oldham → Manchester

Network Diagram - see first page of Table 94

Miles	Miles			NT	NT SX A	NT	NT	NT SO B	NT	NT SX A	NT SO C		NT	NT B		NT	NT E	NT	NT	NT J		NT	NT E	NT	NT A
0	0	**Rochdale**	d	06 18	06 24		06 49	06 55		07 16	07 16		07 24	07 30			07 52		07 54	08 00			08 14		08 30
2	—	Milnrow	d	06 22			06 53						07 28			←			08 00			←			
3	—	New Hey	d	06 24			06 55						07 30			07 30			08 02			08 02			
4¾	—	Shaw & Crompton	a	06 28			06 59						→			07 34			→			08 06			
—	—		d	06 28			07 02									07 37		07 51				08 06		08 21	
6¾	—	Derker	d	06 32		←	07 06		←									07 55						08 25	
7¼	—	**Oldham Mumps**	d	06 35		06 35	07 08		07 08							07 42		07 57				08 11		08 27	
8½	—	Oldham Werneth	d	→		06 38	→		07 11									08 00						08 30	
10¼	—	Hollinwood	d			06 41			07 14									08 03						08 33	
11¼	—	Failsworth	d			06 43			07 17									08 06						08 36	
12¼	—	Dean Lane	d			06 46			07 19									08 08						08 38	
—	1½	Castleton	d		06 27			06 58		07 19	07 19			07 33			07 55			08 03			08 17		08 33
—	4½	Mills Hill	d		06 32			07 03		07 24	07 24			07 37			08 00			08 08			08 22		08 37
—	6¼	Moston	d		06 35			07 06		07 27	07 27			07 40			08 03			08 11			08 25		08 40
14¾	10¼	**Manchester Victoria**	a		06 48	06 55		07 17	07 28	07 37	07 38			07 53		08 00	08 14	08 17		08 22		08 30	08 38	08 47	08 53
—	—	Salford Central	82 a		07 04	07b04		07 26	07c50	07 50				08 03		08e13		08 25		08 36			08 49		09 03
—	—	Salford Crescent	82 a		07 07	07g07		07 29	07h53	07 53				08 07		08j17		08 29		08 39			08 52		09 07
—	—	Bolton	82 a		07 23	07m23		07 41	08n19	08q14				08 19		08r27		08 40		08 55			09q14		09 19
—	—	Liverpool Lime Street 10	90 a			08 13			08 43							09 13						09 43			

		NT	NT B	NT	NT	NT J	NT		NT K	NT	NT A	NT	NT L	NT	NT	NT J		NT	NT E		NT	NT A	NT	NT L	
Rochdale	d	08 31	08 51		08 56	09 00			09 14		09 30	09 31	09 51		09 56	10 00			10 14			10 30	10 31	10 51	
Milnrow	d	08 35			09 00		←					09 35			10 00			←					10 35		
New Hey	d	08 37			09 02		09 02					09 37			10 02			10 02					10 37		
Shaw & Crompton	a	08 41			→		09 06					09 41			→			10 06					10 41		
	d	08 41		08 51			09 06			09 21		09 41		09 51				10 06			10 21		10 41		
Derker	d			08 55						09 25				09 55							10 25				
Oldham Mumps	d	08 46		08 57			09 11			09 27		09 46		09 57				10 11			10 27		10 46		
Oldham Werneth	d			09 00						09 30				10 00							10 30				
Hollinwood	d			09 03						09 33				10 03							10 33				
Failsworth	d			09 06						09 36				10 06							10 36				
Dean Lane	d			09 08						09 38				10 08							10 38				
Castleton	d					09 03					09 33					10 03						10 33			
Mills Hill	d					09 08					09 37					10 08						10 38			
Moston	d					09 11					09 40					10 11						10 41			
Manchester Victoria	a	09 06	09 08	09 17		09 22	09 30		09 32	09 47	09 53	10 06	10 07	10 17		10 21		10 30	10 32		10 47	10 53	11 06	11 08	
Salford Central	82 a			09 25		09 35			09 49		10 03			10 25		10 36			10 49			11 03			
Salford Crescent	82 a			09 29		09 39			09 52		10 07			10 29		10 39			10 52			11 07			
Bolton	82 a			09 40		09 55			10q14		10 19			10 40		10 55			11q14			11 19			
Liverpool Lime Street 10	90 a								10 43										11 43						

		NT	NT		NT J	NT		NT E	NT	NT A	NT	NT L			NT	NT	NT J	NT	NT E	NT	NT A		NT	NT L	
Rochdale	d		10 56		11 00			11 14		11 30	11 31	11 51				11 56	12 00		12 14		12 30		12 31	12 51	
Milnrow	d		11 00			←					11 35					12 00		←					12 35		
New Hey	d		11 02			11 02					11 37					12 02		12 02					12 37		
Shaw & Crompton	a		→			11 06					11 41					→		12 06					12 41		
	d	10 51				11 06			11 21		11 41				11 51			12 06		12 21			12 41		
Derker	d	10 55							11 25						11 55					12 25					
Oldham Mumps	d	10 57				11 11			11 27		11 46				11 57			12 11		12 27			12 46		
Oldham Werneth	d	11 00							11 30						12 00					12 30					
Hollinwood	d	11 03							11 33						12 03					12 33					
Failsworth	d	11 06							11 36						12 06					12 36					
Dean Lane	d	11 08							11 38						12 08					12 38					
Castleton	d				11 03					11 33							12 03				12 33				
Mills Hill	d				11 08					11 38							12 08				12 38				
Moston	d				11 11					11 41							12 11				12 41				
Manchester Victoria	a	11 17			11 21	11 30		11 32	11 47	11 53	12 06	12 08			12 17		12 21	12 30	12 32	12 47	12 53		13 06	13 08	
Salford Central	82 a	11 25			11 36			11 49		12 03					12 25		12 35		12 49		13 03				
Salford Crescent	82 a	11 29			11 39			11 52		12 07					12 29		12 39		12 52		13 07				
Bolton	82 a	11 40			11 55			12q14		12 19					12 40		12 55		13q14		13 19				
Liverpool Lime Street 10	90 a							12 43											13 43						

For general notes see front of timetable
For details of catering facilities see Directory of Train Operators

- **A** From Leeds (Table 41)
- **B** From Leeds (until 11 July from Hebden Bridge) (Table 41)
- **C** From 18 July. From Leeds (Table 41)
- **E** All Mondays to Fridays, also Saturdays from 18 July from Leeds. Until 11 July from Todmorden (Table 41)
- **J** To Wigan Wallgate (Table 82)
- **K** Mondays to Fridays from Selby. Saturdays until 11 July from Todmorden. Saturdays from 18 July from Leeds (Table 41)
- **L** Saturdays until 11 July from Hebden Bridge (Table 41). All Mondays to Fridays, also Saturdays from 18 July from Leeds (Table 41)
- **N** All Mondays to Fridays, also Saturdays from 18 July. From Leeds (Table 41)
- **Q** Until 11 July. From Todmorden (Table 41)
- **b** Saturdays arr. 0709
- **c** Saturdays arr. 0803
- **e** Saturdays arr. 0810
- **g** Saturdays arr. 0712
- **h** Saturdays arr. 0807
- **j** Saturdays arr. 0813
- **m** Saturdays arr. 0726
- **n** Mondays to Fridays arr. 0814, change at Manchester Victoria and Salford Crescent
- **q** Change at Manchester Victoria and Salford Crescent
- **r** Saturdays arr. 0823

Rochdale and Oldham → Manchester

Network Diagram - see first page of Table 94

Station		NT	NT	NT A	NT	NT B	NT	NT C		NT	NT D	NT	NT	NT A	NT	NT B	NT		NT C	NT	NT D	NT	NT	NT A	NT
Rochdale	d		12 56	13 00		13 14		13 30		13 31	13 51		13 56	14 00		14 14			14 30	14 31	14 51		14 56	15 00	
Milnrow	d		13 00		←					13 35			14 00		←					14 35			15 00		←
New Hey	d		13 02 →		13 02					13 37			14 02 →		14 02					14 37			15 02 →		15 02
Shaw & Crompton	a				13 06					13 41					14 06					14 41					15 06
	d	12 51			13 06		13 21			13 41		13 51			14 06		14 21			14 41		14 51			15 06
Derker	d	12 55					13 25					13 55					14 25					14 55			
Oldham Mumps	d	12 57			13 11		13 27			13 46		13 57			14 11		14 27			14 46		14 57			15 11
Oldham Werneth	d	13 00					13 30					14 00					14 30					15 00			
Hollinwood	d	13 03					13 33					14 03					14 33					15 03			
Failsworth	d	13 06					13 36					14 06					14 36					15 06			
Dean Lane	d	13 08					13 38					14 08					14 38					15 08			
Castleton	d			13 03				13 33						14 03					14 33					15 03	
Mills Hill	d			13 08				13 38						14 08					14 38					15 08	
Moston	d			13 11				13 41						14 11					14 41					15 11	
Manchester Victoria	a	13 17		13 21	13 30	13 32	13 47	13 53		14 06	14 07	14 17		14 21	14 30	14 32	14 47		14 53	15 06	15 08	15 17		15 21	15 30
Salford Central	82 a	13 25		13 36		13 49		14 03				14 25		14 36		14 49			15 03			15 25		15 35	
Salford Crescent	82 a	13 29		13 39		13 52		14 07				14 29		14 39		14 52			15 07			15 29		15 39	
Bolton	82 a	13 40		13 55		14b14		14 19				14 40		14 55		15b14			15 19			15 40		15 55	
Liverpool Lime Street 10	90 a					14 43										15 43									

Station		NT B	NT	NT C		NT	NT SX C	NT SO E	NT	NT	NT A	NT	NT G		NT	NT C	NT	NT D	NT	NT	NT SO H	NT SX J		NT	NT B
Rochdale	d	15 14		15 30		15 31	15 51	15 51		15 56	16 00		16 14			16 30	16 31	16 51		16 56	17 00	17 00			17 14
Milnrow	d					15 35				16 00		←					16 35			17 00				←	
New Hey	d					15 37				16 02 →		16 02					16 37			17 02 →				17 02	
Shaw & Crompton	a					15 41						16 06					16 41							17 06	
	d		15 21			15 41			15 51			16 06			16 21		16 41		16 50					17 06	
Derker	d		15 25						15 55						16 25				16 54						
Oldham Mumps	d		15 27			15 46			15 57			16 11			16 27		16 46		16 56					17 11	
Oldham Werneth	d		15 30						16 00						16 30				16 59						
Hollinwood	d		15 33						16 03						16 33				17 02						
Failsworth	d		15 36						16 06						16 36				17 05						
Dean Lane	d		15 38						16 08						16 38				17 07						
Castleton	d			15 33							16 03					16 33					17 03	17 03			
Mills Hill	d			15 38							16 08					16 38					17 08	17 08			
Moston	d			15 41							16 11					16 41					17 11	17 11			
Manchester Victoria	a	15 32	15 47	15 53		16 06	16 07	16 08	16 18		16 21	16 31	16 32		16 47	16 53	17 06	17 07	17 17		17 23	17 23		17 30	17 32
Salford Central	82 a	15 43		16 10			16 23	16 23	16 26		16 39	16 39	16 49			17 03		17 22	17c39		17 26	17 27		17 39	17 43
Salford Crescent	82 a	15 46		16 13			16 26	16 26	16 30		16 42	16 42	16 52			17 07		17 25	17e42		17 30	17 29		17 42	17 46
Bolton	82 a	15 59		16 23			16 37	16 37	16 42		16 58	16 58	17b14			17 19		17 37	18f01		17 42	17 42		18 01	18b05
Liverpool Lime Street 10	90 a	16 43											17 43			18 13									18 43

Station		NT	NT SO C	NT SX C	NT	NT D	NT	NT	NT H		NT	NT K	NT SO L	NT	NT	NT SO C	NT SX C	NT		NT D	NT	NT SX C	NT SO N	NT	NT C
Rochdale	d		17 30	17 30	17 31	17 51		17 56	18 00			18 14	18 16		18 31	18 32	18 32			18 51	19 00	19 15	19 16	19 23	19 32
Milnrow	d				17 35			18 00			←				18 35			←						19 27	
New Hey	d				17 37			18 02 →			18 02				18 37 →			18 37						19 29	
Shaw & Crompton	a				17 41						18 06							18 41						19 33	
	d	17 21			17 41		17 51				18 06			18 21				18 41						19 33	
Derker	d	17 25					17 55							18 25										19 37	
Oldham Mumps	d	17 27			17 46		17 57				18 11			18 27				18 46						19 40 →	
Oldham Werneth	d	17 30					18 00							18 30											
Hollinwood	d	17 33					18 03							18 33											
Failsworth	d	17 36					18 06							18 36											
Dean Lane	d	17 37					18 08							18 38											
Castleton	d		17 33	17 33					18 03							18 35	18 35				19 03				19 35
Mills Hill	d		17 38	17 38					18 08							18 40	18 40				19 08				19 40
Moston	d		17 41	17 41					18 11							18 43	18 43				19 11				19 43
Manchester Victoria	a	17 47	17 51	17 53	18 06	18 07	18 17		18 21		18 30	18 32	18 33	18 47		18 53	18 54	19 06		19 07	19 21	19 32	19 32		19 54
Salford Central	82 a		18 03	18 03		18 23			18 26			18 48	18 48			19 03	19 03				19 31				20 03
Salford Crescent	82 a		18 07	18 07		18 26			18 30			18 51	18 51			19 07	19 07				19 34				20 07
Bolton	82 a		18 19	18 19		18 37	18 42		18 42			19b06	19b06			19 20	19 20				19 45				20 19
Liverpool Lime Street 10	90 a											19 43	19 43									20 43	20 43		

For general notes see front of timetable
For details of catering facilities see Directory of Train Operators

- **A** To Wigan Wallgate (Table 82)
- **B** Saturdays until 11 July from Todmorden. All Mondays to Fridays, also Saturdays from 18 July from Leeds (Table 41)
- **C** From Leeds (Table 41)
- **D** Saturdays until 11 July from Hebden Bridge. All Mondays to Fridays, also Saturdays from 18 July from Leeds (Table 41)
- **E** Until 11 July from Hebden Bridge. From 18 July from Leeds (Table 41)
- **G** All Mondays to Fridays, also Saturdays from 18 July from Leeds. Saturdays until 11 July from Todmorden (Table 41)
- **H** To Blackburn (Table 94)
- **J** To Colne (Table 97)
- **K** All Mondays to Fridays, also Saturdays from 18 July. From Leeds (Table 41)
- **L** Until 11 July. From Todmorden (Table 41)
- **N** Until 11 July from Todmorden. From 18 July from Leeds (Table 41)
- **b** Change at Manchester Victoria and Salford Crescent
- **c** Saturdays arr. 1726
- **e** Saturdays arr. 1730
- **f** Saturdays arr. 1742

Table 95

Mondays to Saturdays

until 3 October

Rochdale and Oldham → Manchester

Network Diagram - see first page of Table 94

	NT	NT	NT	NT		NT	NT	NT	NT	NT	NT	NT	NT		NT	NT	NT	NT	NT	NT	NT			
			SO	SX		SO		SO	SX	SO						SO	SX		SO					
		A	B				C			D	E		J			J	J				J			
Rochdale d		19 52	19 53	19 56		19 56	20 14			20 20	20 52	20 56	21 52		21 56	22 52	22 52	22 56	23 04		23 52			
Milnrow d				20 00		20 00						21 00			22 00			23 00						
New Hey d				20 02		20 02						21 02			22 02			23 02						
Shaw & Crompton a				20 06		20 06						21 06			22 06			23 06						
d				20 06		20 06						21 06			22 06			23 06						
Derker d	←			20 10		20 10		←	←			21 10			22 10			23 10		←				
Oldham Mumps d	19 40			20 13		20 13		20 13	20 13			21 13			22 13			23 13		23 13				
Oldham Werneth d	19 43			→		→		20 16	20 16			21 16			22 16			→		23 16				
Hollinwood d	19 46							20 19	20 19			21 19			22 19					23 19				
Failsworth d	19 48							20 21	20 21			21 21			22 21					23 21				
Dean Lane d	19 51							20 24	20 24			21 24			22 24					23 24				
Castleton d		19 55	19 56								20 55		21 55				22 55		23 07					
Mills Hill d		20 00	20 01								21 00		22 00				23 00		23 12					
Moston d		20 03	20 04								21 03		22 03				23 03		23 15					
Manchester Victoria a	20 00	20 15	20 15				20 32	20 35	20 36	20 37	21 14	21 33	22 14		22 33	23 08	23 14		23 26	23 33	00 08			
Salford Central 82 a	20 13	20 25	20 25					21 03	21 03	21 03	21 25	22b04	22c25		23e03	23 19	23f23							
Salford Crescent 82 a	20 16	20 29	20 29					21 07	21 07	21 07	21 29	22 07	22 29		23g07	23 22	23h25							
Bolton 82 a		20 40	20 40					21 19	21 19	21 19	21 40	22 19	22 40		23j19	23 32	23 40							
Liverpool Lime Street 10 90 a		21 43					21 43					22 43			23 43									

Mondays to Saturdays

from 5 October

	NT	NT	NT	NT	NT		NT	NT	NT	NT	NT		NT	NT	NT	NT	NT		NT	NT	NT	NT	NT	NT
	SX	SO																						
	J	J	J	J	J		K	J	J	J	L		N	J	J	L	J		J	J	L	J	J	J
Rochdale d	06 24	06 55	07 16	07 30	07 52		08 00	08 14	08 30	08 51	09 04		09 14	09 30	09 51	10 05	10 14		10 30	10 51	11 04	11 14	11 30	11 51
Castleton d	06 27	06 58	07 19	07 33	07 55		08 03	08 17	08 33		09 07			09 33		10 08			10 33		11 07		11 33	
Mills Hill d	06 32	07 03	07 24	07 37	08 00		08 08	08 22	08 37		09 12			09 37		10 13			10 38		11 12		11 38	
Moston d	06 35	07 06	07 27	07 40	08 03		08 11	08 25	08 40		09 15			09 40		10 16			10 41		11 15		11 41	
Manchester Victoria a	06 48	07 17	07 38	07 53	08 14		08 22	08 38	08 53	09 08	09 26		09 32	09 53	10 07	10 26	10 32		10 53	11 08	11 26	11 32	11 53	12 08
Salford Central 82 a							08 36				09 35					10 36					11 36			
Salford Crescent 82 a							08 39				09 39					10 39					11 39			
Bolton 82 a							08 55				09 55					10 55					11 55			
Liverpool Lime Street 10 90 a																								

	NT		NT	NT	NT	NT	NT		NT	NT	NT	NT	NT		NT	NT	NT	NT	NT		NT	NT	NT	NT
	L		J	J	J	L	J		J	J	L	J	J		J	L	J	J	J		L	J	J	J
Rochdale d	12 04		12 14	12 30	12 51	13 04	13 14		13 30	13 51	14 04	14 14	14 30		14 51	15 04	15 14	15 30	15 51		16 04	16 14	16 30	16 51
Castleton d	12 07			12 33		13 07			13 33		14 07		14 33			15 07		15 33			16 07		16 33	
Mills Hill d	12 12			12 38		13 12			13 38		14 12		14 38			15 12		15 38			16 12		16 38	
Moston d	12 15			12 41		13 15			13 41		14 15		14 41			15 15		15 41			16 15		16 41	
Manchester Victoria a	12 25		12 32	12 53	13 08	13 25	13 32		13 53	14 07	14 25	14 32	14 53		15 08	15 25	15 32	15 53	16 08		16 25	16 32	16 53	17 07
Salford Central 82 a	12 35					13 36					14 36					15 35					16 39			
Salford Crescent 82 a	12 39					13 39					14 39					15 39					16 42			
Bolton 82 a	12 55					13 55					14 57					15 55					16 58			
Liverpool Lime Street 10 90 a																								

	NT	NT	NT		NT	NT	NT	NT	NT		NT	NT	NT	NT	NT		NT	NT	NT	NT	NT	NT		
																			SO	SX	SO			
	Q	J	J		J	U	J	J	J			J	J	V	J		J	J	J	J		J		
Rochdale d	17 00	17 14	17 30		17 51	18 00	18 14	18 32	18 51		19 00	19 15	19 32	19 52	20 14		20 52	21 52	22 52	22 52	23 04	23 52		
Castleton d	17 03		17 33			18 03		18 35			19 03		19 35	19 55			20 55	21 55		22 55	23 07			
Mills Hill d	17 08		17 38			18 08		18 40			19 08		19 40	20 00			21 00	22 00		23 00	23 12			
Moston d	17 11		17 41			18 11		18 43			19 11		19 43	20 03			21 03	22 03		23 03	23 15			
Manchester Victoria a	17 23	17 32	17 53		18 07	18 21	18 32	18 54	19 07		19 21	19 32	19 54	20 15	20 32		21 14	22 14	23 08	23 14	23 26	00 08		
Salford Central 82 a	17 26					18 26																		
Salford Crescent 82 a	17 29					18 30																		
Bolton 82 a	17 42					18 42																		
Liverpool Lime Street 10 90 a																								

For general notes see front of timetable
For details of catering facilities see Directory of Train Operators

- **A** All Mondays to Fridays, also Saturdays until 11 July. Saturdays from Hebden Bridge. Mondays to Fridays from Selby (Table 41)
- **B** From 18 July. From Leeds (Table 41)
- **C** All Mondays to Fridays, also Saturdays from 18 July. From Leeds (Table 41)
- **D** Until 11 July. From Todmorden (Table 41)
- **E** Saturdays until 11 July from Leeds. All Mondays to Fridays, also Saturdays from 18 July from Leeds (Table 41)
- **J** From Leeds (Table 41)
- **K** From Todmorden (Table 41) to Wigan Wallgate (Table 82)
- **L** To Wigan Wallgate (Table 82)
- **N** From Selby (Saturdays from Leeds) (Table 41)
- **Q** To Colne (Table 97)
- **U** To Blackburn (Table 94)
- **V** From Selby (Table 41)
- **b** Fridays and Saturdays only. Saturdays arr. 2203
- **c** Fridays and Saturdays only
- **e** Fridays and Saturdays only. Saturdays arr. 2248
- **f** Fridays only
- **g** Saturdays arr. 2251
- **h** Fridays arr. 2326
- **j** Saturdays arr. 2306, change at Manchester Victoria and Salford Crescent

Sundays
until 27 September

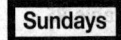

Rochdale and Oldham → Manchester

Network Diagram - see first page of Table 94

		NT	NT A	NT A	NT	NT A	NT	NT A	NT	NT A	NT	NT A	NT	NT A	NT	NT A	NT	NT A
Rochdale	d	09 23	09 41	10 17	10 23	11 09	11 23	12 09	12 23	13 09	13 23	14 09	14 23	15 09	15 23	16 09	16 23	17 09
Milnrow	d	09 27			10 27		11 27		12 27		13 27		14 27		15 27		16 27	
New Hey	d	09 29			10 29		11 29		12 29		13 29		14 29		15 29		16 29	
Shaw & Crompton	a	09 33			10 33		11 33		12 33		13 33		14 33		15 33		16 33	
	d	09 33			10 33		11 33		12 33		13 33		14 33		15 33		16 33	
Derker	d	09 37			10 37		11 37		12 37		13 37		14 37		15 37		16 37	
Oldham Mumps	d	09 40			10 40		11 40		12 40		13 40		14 40		15 40		16 40	
Oldham Werneth	d	09 43			10 43		11 43		12 43		13 43		14 43		15 43		16 43	
Hollinwood	d	09 46			10 46		11 46		12 46		13 46		14 46		15 46		16 46	
Failsworth	d	09 48			10 48		11 48		12 48		13 48		14 48		15 48		16 48	
Dean Lane	d	09 51			10 51		11 51		12 51		13 51		14 51		15 51		16 51	
Castleton	d		09 44	10 20		11 12		12 12		13 12		14 12		15 12		16 12		17 12
Mills Hill	d		09 49	10 25		11 17		12 17		13 17		14 17		15 17		16 17		17 17
Moston	d		09 52	10 28		11 20		12 20		13 20		14 20		15 20		16 20		17 20
Manchester Victoria	a	09 59	10 02	10 38	10 59	11b30	11 59	12b30	12 59	13b30	13 59	14c30	14 59	15b30	15 59	16b30	16 59	17b30
Salford Central	82 a																	
Salford Crescent	82 a		*10 29*	*11 06*	*11 29*	*12 06*	*12 29*	*13 06*	*13 29*	*14 06*	*14 29*	*15 06*	*15 29*	*16 06*	*16 29*	*17 06*	*17 29*	*18 06*
Bolton	82 a		*10 40*	*11 19*	*11 40*	*12 19*	*12 40*	*13 19*	*13 40*	*14 19*	*14 40*	*15 19*	*15 40*	*16 19*	*16 40*	*17 19*	*17 40*	*18 19*
Liverpool Lime Street 10	90 a		*10e57*		*11f57*		*12f57*		*13f57*		*14e59*		*15f57*		*16f57*		*17f57*	

		NT	NT A	NT	NT A	NT	NT A	NT	NT B	NT C	NT	NT D	NT E
Rochdale	d	17 23	18 09	18 23	19 09	19 23	20 19	20 23	21 11	21 20	21 23	22 51	22 58
Milnrow	d	17 27		18 27		19 27		20 27			21 27		
New Hey	d	17 29		18 29		19 29		20 29			21 29		
Shaw & Crompton	a	17 33		18 33		19 33		20 33			21 33		
	d	17 33		18 33		19 33		20 33			21 33		
Derker	d	17 37		18 37		19 37		20 37			21 37		
Oldham Mumps	d	17 40		18 40		19 40		20 40			21 40		
Oldham Werneth	d	17 43		18 43		19 43		20 43			21 43		
Hollinwood	d	17 46		18 46		19 46		20 46			21 46		
Failsworth	d	17 48		18 48		19 48		20 48			21 48		
Dean Lane	d	17 51		18 51		19 51		20 51			21 51		
Castleton	d		18 12		19 12		20 22		21 14	21 23		22 54	23 01
Mills Hill	d		18 17		19 17		20 27		21 19	21 28		22 59	23 06
Moston	d		18 20		19 20		20 30		21 22	21 31		23 02	23 09
Manchester Victoria	a	17 59	18b30	18 59	19b30	19 59	20 41	20 59	21 33	21 41	21 59	23 12	23 18
Salford Central	82 a												
Salford Crescent	82 a	*18 29*	*19 06*	*19 29*	*20 06*	*20 29*	*21 06*	*21 29*	*22 06*	*22 06*			
Bolton	82 a	*18 40*	*19 19*	*19 40*	*20 19*	*20 40*	*21 19*	*21 40*	*22 19*	*22 19*			
Liverpool Lime Street 10	90 a	*18f57*		*19f57*		*20f57*		*21f57*			*22f57*		

Sundays
from 4 October

		NT A	NT A	NT A	NT A	NT A	NT A	NT A	NT A	NT A	NT A	NT A	NT A	NT A	NT G
Rochdale	d	09 41	10 17	11 12	12 11	13 11	14 11	15 11	16 11	17 11	18 11	19 11	20 19	21 11	22 58
Castleton	d	09 44	10 20	11 15	12 14	13 14	14 14	15 14	16 14	17 14	18 14	19 14	20 22	21 14	23 01
Mills Hill	d	09 49	10 25	11 20	12 19	13 19	14 19	15 19	16 19	17 19	18 19	19 19	20 27	21 19	23 06
Moston	d	09 52	10 28	11 23	12 22	13 22	14 22	15 22	16 22	17 22	18 22	19 22	20 30	21 22	23 09
Manchester Victoria	a	10 02	10 38	11 32	12 32	13 32	14 33	15 33	16 33	17 33	18 33	19 33	20 41	21 33	23 18
Salford Central	82 a														
Salford Crescent	82 a														
Bolton	82 a														
Liverpool Lime Street 10	90 a														

For general notes see front of timetable
For details of catering facilities see Directory of Train Operators

A From Leeds (Table 41)
B From 19 July. From Leeds (Table 41)
C Until 12 July. From Leeds (Table 41)
D Until 6 September. From York (Table 41)
E From 13 September. From York (Table 41)
G From York (Table 41)
b From 13 September arr. 2 mins. later
c From 13 September arr. 3 mins. later
e From 13 September only
f 13, 20 and 27 September only

Network Diagram for Tables 97, 98, 99, 100

DM-15/08
Design BAJS

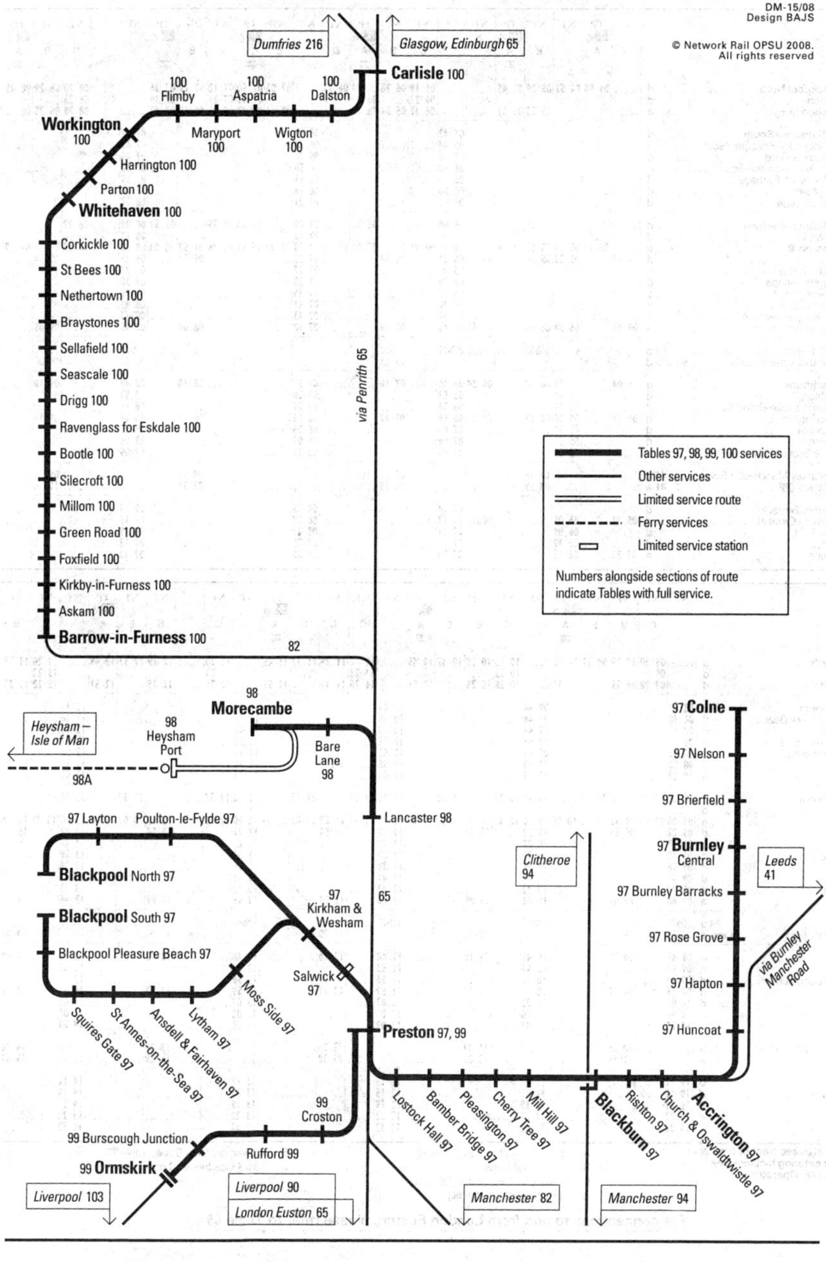
Dumfries 216
Glasgow, Edinburgh 65
Carlisle 100
100 Flimby
100 Aspatria
100 Dalston
Workington 100
Maryport 100
Wigton 100
Harrington 100
Parton 100
Whitehaven 100
Corkickle 100
St Bees 100
Nethertown 100
Braystones 100
Sellafield 100
Seascale 100
Drigg 100
Ravenglass for Eskdale 100
Bootle 100
Silecroft 100
Millom 100
Green Road 100
Foxfield 100
Kirkby-in-Furness 100
Askam 100
Barrow-in-Furness 100
via Penrith 65
82
Tables 97, 98, 99, 100 services
Other services
Limited service route
Ferry services
Limited service station
Numbers alongside sections of route indicate Tables with full service.
98
Morecambe
Heysham – Isle of Man
98 Heysham Port
98A
Bare Lane 98
Lancaster 98
97 Layton
Poulton-le-Fylde 97
Blackpool North 97
Blackpool South 97
Blackpool Pleasure Beach 97
97 Kirkham & Wesham
65
Salwick 97
Moss Side 97
Squires Gate 97
St Annes-on-the-Sea 97
Ansdell & Fairhaven 97
Lytham 97
Preston 97, 99
99 Croston
99 Burscough Junction
Rufford 99
99 Ormskirk
Liverpool 103
Liverpool 90
London Euston 65
Manchester 82
Manchester 94
Clitheroe 94
97 Colne
97 Nelson
97 Brierfield
97 Burnley Central
Leeds 41
97 Burnley Barracks
97 Rose Grove
97 Hapton
97 Huncoat
via Burnley Manchester Road
Lostock Hall 97
Bamber Bridge 97
Pleasington 97
Cherry Tree 97
Mill Hill 97
Blackburn 97
Rishton 97
Church & Oswaldtwistle 97
Accrington 97

Blackpool → Preston → Blackburn, Accrington, Burnley and Colne

Network Diagram - see first page of Table 97

Miles	Miles			NT	TP 1◇ A	NT	NT B	TP 1◇ A	NT	NT	NT C	NT B	TP 1◇ A	NT D	NT	NT E	TP 1◇	NT C	NT B	TP 1◇	NT		NT C	NT B	TP 1◇ A
—	0	**Blackpool North**	d		04 50	04 57	05 29	05 45			06 19	06 28	06 34	06 53		07 02	07 10	07 18	07 29	07 36			08 20	08 29	08 45
—	1¼	Layton	d								06 22		06 37				07 13	07 21		07 39			08 23		
—	3¼	Poulton-le-Fylde	d				05 35	05 51			06 27	06 34	06 41			07 08	07 17	07 26	07 35	07 43			08 28	08 35	08 51
0	—	**Blackpool South**	d							05 42					06 42						07 42				
½	—	Blackpool Pleasure Beach	d							05 44					06 44						07 44				
1¾	—	Squires Gate	d							05 46					06 46						07 46				
3¼	—	St Annes-on-the-Sea	d							05 50					06 50						07 50				
5¼	—	Ansdell & Fairhaven	d							05 53					06 53						07 53				
6½	—	Lytham	d							05 56					06 56						07 56				
9	—	Moss Side	d							06 01					07 01						08 01				
12¼	9¾	Kirkham & Wesham	d							06 08	06 36		06 50		07 09		07 26	07 35		07 52	08 09		08 37		
14¾	12¼	Salwick	d												07 13						08 13				
20	17½	**Preston** 8	a		05 14	05 20	05 52	06 08		06 19	06 46	06 52	07 01	07 15	07 20	07 28	07 37	07 46	07 52	08 03	08 20		08 47	08 52	09 09
—	—		d	04 47		05 22	05 54		06 17	06 21		06 54			07 22				07 54		08 22			08 54	
22¾	—	Lostock Hall	d							06 26					07 27						08 27				
24	—	Bamber Bridge	d							06 29					07 30						08 30				
29	—	Pleasington	d							06 37					07 38						08 38				
30	—	Cherry Tree	d							06 40					07 41						08 41				
30¾	—	Mill Hill (Lancashire)	d							06 42					07 43						08 43				
32	—	**Blackburn**	a	05 03		05 38	06 09		06 33	06 45		07 09			07 50				08 09		08 46			09 09	
—	—	Clitheroe 94	a				*06b50*			*07b15*		*08b12*									*09b17*				
—	—	Manchester Victoria 94 🚌	d									*05 55*									*07 23*			*08 00*	
—	—	**Blackburn**	d	05 04		05 39	06 10		06 34	06 48		07 10			07 51				08 10		08 48			09 10	
35¾	—	Rishton	d			05 44				06 53					07 56						08 53				
37½	—	Church & Oswaldtwistle	d			05 47				06 56					07 59						08 56				
38¼	—	**Accrington**	d	05 11		05 50	06 17		06 41	06 59		07 17			08 02				08 17		08 59			09 17	
40	—	Huncoat	d			05 54				07 03					08 06						09 03				
41½	—	Hapton	d			05 57				07 06					08 09						09 06				
43	—	Rose Grove	d			06 00				07 09					08 12						09 09				
—	—	Burnley Manchester Road 41	a				06 26					07 26							08 26					09 26	
—	—	Leeds 10 41	a				07 39					08 39							09 39					10 40	
44	—	Burnley Barracks	d							07 14					08 15						09 12				
44½	—	**Burnley Central**	d	05 21		06 05			06a53	07 17					08 18						09 15				
46¾	—	Brierfield	d			06 09				07 21					08 22						09 19				
48	—	Nelson	d			06 12				07 24					08 25						09 22				
50	—	**Colne**	a	05 35		06 22				07 34					08 35						09 32				

		NT	NT C	NT B	NT E	TP 1◇ A	NT	NT C	NT B	NT E	TP 1◇ A	NT	NT C	NT B	NT E	TP 1◇ A	NT	NT C		NT B	NT E	TP 1◇ A	NT	NT C	NT B
Blackpool North	d		09 20	09 29	09 37	09 45		10 20	10 29	10 37	10 45		11 20	11 29	11 37	11 45		12 20		12 29	12 37	12 45		13 20	13 29
Layton	d		09 23					10 23					11 23					12 23						13 23	
Poulton-le-Fylde	d		09 28	09 35		09 51		10 28	10 35		10 51		11 28	11 35		11 51		12 28		12 35		12 51		13 28	13 35
Blackpool South	d	08 44					09 44					10 44					11 44						12 44		
Blackpool Pleasure Beach	d	08 46					09 46					10 46					11 46						12 46		
Squires Gate	d	08 48					09 48					10 48					11 48						12 48		
St Annes-on-the-Sea	d	08 52					09 52					10 52					11 52						12 52		
Ansdell & Fairhaven	d	08 55					09 55					10 55					11 55						12 55		
Lytham	d	08 58					09 58					10 58					11 58						12 58		
Moss Side	d	09 03					10 03					11 03					12 03						13 03		
Kirkham & Wesham	d	09 10	09 37		09 52		10 10	10 37		10 52		11 10	11 37		11 52		12 10	12 37			12 52		13 10	13 37	
Salwick	d																								
Preston 8	a	09 20	09 47	09 52	10 02	10 09	10 20	10 47	10 52	11 02	11 09	11 20	11 47	11 52	12 02	12 09	12 20	12 47		12 52	13 02	13 09	13 20	13 47	13 52
	d	09 22		09 54			10 22		10 54			11 22		11 54			12 22			12 54			13 22		13 54
Lostock Hall	d	09 27					10 27					11 27					12 27						13 27		
Bamber Bridge	d	09 30					10 30					11 30					12 30						13 30		
Pleasington	d	09 38					10 38					11 38					12 38						13 38		
Cherry Tree	d	09 41					10 41					11 41					12 41						13 41		
Mill Hill (Lancashire)	d	09 43					10 43					11 43					12 43						13 43		
Blackburn	a	09 46		10 09			10 46		11 09			11 46		12 09			12 46			13 09			13 46		14 10
Clitheroe 94	a	*10b17*					*11b17*					*12b15*					*13b17*						*14b17*		
Manchester Victoria 94 🚌	d	*08 29*		*09 00*					*10 00*					*11 00*						*12 00*					*13 00*
Blackburn	d	09 48		10 10			10 48		11 10			11 48		12 10			12 48			13 10			13 48		14 10
Rishton	d	09 53					10 53					11 53					12 53						13 53		
Church & Oswaldtwistle	d	09 56					10 56					11 56					12 56						13 56		
Accrington	d	09 59		10 17			10 59		11 17			11 59		12 17			12 59			13 17			13 59		14 17
Huncoat	d	10 03					11 03					12 03					13 03						14 03		
Hapton	d	10 06					11 06					12 06					13 06						14 06		
Rose Grove	d	10 09					11 09					12 09					13 09						14 09		
Burnley Manchester Road 41	a			10 26					11 27					12 26						13 26					14 26
Leeds 10 41	a			11 39					12 39					13 38						14 39					15 39
Burnley Barracks	d	10 12					11 12					12 12					13 12						14 12		
Burnley Central	d	10 15					11 15					12 15					13 15						14 15		
Brierfield	d	10 19					11 19					12 19					13 19						14 19		
Nelson	d	10 22					11 22					12 22					13 22						14 22		
Colne	a	10 32					11 32					12 32					13 32						14 32		

For general notes see front of timetable
For details of catering facilities see Directory of Train Operators

A To Manchester Airport (Table 82)
B To York (Table 40)
C To Manchester Victoria (Table 82)
D To Hazel Grove (Table 86)
E To Liverpool Lime Street (Table 90)
b From 5 October arr. 2 mins. later

For connections to and from London Euston, please refer to Table 65

Blackpool → Preston → Blackburn, Accrington, Burnley and Colne

Network Diagram - see first page of Table 97

		NT A	TP 1◇ B 🛒	NT	NT C	NT D	NT A	TP 1◇ B 🛒	NT	NT C	NT D	NT A	TP 1◇ B 🛒	NT	NT C		NT D	NT A	TP 1◇ B 🛒	NT	NT D	TP 1◇ B 🛒	NT A	NT E	NT
Blackpool North	d	13 37	13 45		14 20	14 29	14 37	14 45		15 20	15 29	15 37	15 45		16 20		16 29	16 35	16 41		17 14	17 20	17 37		
Layton	d				14 23					15 23					16 23				16 44			17 23			
Poulton-le-Fylde	d		13 51		14 28	14 35		14 51		15 28	15 35		15 51		16 28		16 35		16 48		17 20	17 27			
Blackpool South	d			13 44					14 44					15 44						16 44					17 44
Blackpool Pleasure Beach	d			13 46					14 46					15 46						16 46					17 46
Squires Gate	d			13 48					14 48					15 48						16 48					17 48
St Annes-on-the-Sea	d			13 52					14 52					15 52						16 52					17 52
Ansdell & Fairhaven	d			13 55					14 55					15 55						16 55					17 55
Lytham	d			13 58					14 58					15 58						16 58					17 58
Moss Side	d			14 03					15 03					16 02						17 03					18 03
Kirkham & Wesham	d	13 52		14 10	14 37		14 52		15 10	15 37		15 52		16 10	16 37			16 52	16 58	17 10	17 29		17 52		18 10
Salwick	d													16 15											
Preston 8	a	14 02	14 09	14 20	14 47	14 52	15 02	15 09	15 20	15 47	15 52	16 02	16 09	16 22	16 47		16 52	17 02	17 09	17 20	17 44	17 45	18 02		18 20
	d			14 22		14 54			15 22		15 54			16 22			16 54			17 22	17 44				18 24
Lostock Hall	d			14 27					15 27					16 27						17 27	17 51				18 30
Bamber Bridge	d			14 30					15 30					16 30						17 30	17 54				18 33
Pleasington	d			14 38					15 38					16 38						17 38	18 01				18 41
Cherry Tree	d			14 41					15 41					16 41						17 41	18 05				18 44
Mill Hill (Lancashire)	d			14 43					15 43					16 43						17 43	18 08				18 46
Blackburn	a			14 46		15 09			15 46		16 09			16 48			17 09			17 47	18 11				18 52
Clitheroe 94	a			15b17					16b17		16b56						17b44			18b18	19b14				
Manchester Victoria 94	d					*14 00*					*15 00*			*15 40*						*16 23*	*17 00*			17 23	*18 00*
Blackburn	d			14 48		15 10			15 48		16 10			16 50			17 10			17 48	18 11			18 16	18 53
Rishton	d			14 53					15 53					16 55						17 53					18 58
Church & Oswaldtwistle	d			14 56					15 56					16 58						17 56					19 01
Accrington	d			14 59		15 17			15 59		16 17			17 01			17 17			17 59	18 19			18 23	19 04
Huncoat	d			15 03					16 03					17 05						18 03					19 08
Hapton	d			15 06					16 06					17 08						18 06					19 11
Rose Grove	d			15 09					16 09					17 11						18 09					19 14
Burnley Manchester Road 41	a					15 26					16 26						17 26				18 27				
Leeds 10 41	a					16 39					17 39						18 39				19 40				
Burnley Barracks	d			15 12					16 12					17 14						18 12					19 17
Burnley Central	d			15 15					16 15					17 17						18a20				18 34	19 20
Brierfield	d			15 19					16 19					17 21										18 39	19 24
Nelson	d			15 22					16 22					17 24										18 42	19 27
Colne	a			15 32					16 32					17 34										18 51	19 37

		NT C	NT D	NT A	TP 1◇ B 🛒	NT	NT C	NT A	TP 1◇ B	NT	NT C	NT D	NT A	TP 1◇ B	NT	NT C	TP 1◇ B	NT	NT A	NT C	TP 1◇ B	NT C	NT		
Blackpool North	d	18 20	18 29	18 37	18 45		19 20	19 37	19 45		20 20	20 29	20 38	20 45		21 20	21 45		22 14	22 20	22 45	23 13			
Layton	d	18 23					19 23				20 23					21 23				22 23		23 16			
Poulton-le-Fylde	d	18 28	18 35		18 51		19 28		19 51		20 28	20 35		20 51		21 28	21 51			22 28	22 51	23 21			
Blackpool South	d					18 44				19 44					20 44			22 00					23 30		
Blackpool Pleasure Beach	d					18 46				19 46					20 46			22 02					23 32		
Squires Gate	d					18 48				19 48					20 48			22 04					23 34		
St Annes-on-the-Sea	d					18 52				19 52					20 52			22 08					23 38		
Ansdell & Fairhaven	d					18 55				19 55					20 55			22 11					23 41		
Lytham	d					18 58				19 58					20 58			22 14					23 44		
Moss Side	d					19 03				20 03					21 03			22 19					23 49		
Kirkham & Wesham	d	18 37		18 52		19 10	19 37			20 10	20 37				21 10	21 37		22 26		22 37		23 30	23 56		
Salwick	d																								
Preston 8	a	18 47	18 52	19 02	19 09	19 20	19 47	20 02	20 09	20 20	20 46	20 53	21 02	21 09	21 20	21 47	22 09	22 36	22 41	22 47	23 09	23 40	00 08		
	d		18 54			19 22				20 22		20 54			21 22			22 38							
Lostock Hall	d					19 27				20 27					21 27			22 43							
Bamber Bridge	d					19 30				20 30					21 30			22 46							
Pleasington	d					19 38				20 38					21 38			22 54							
Cherry Tree	d					19 41				20 41					21 41			22 57							
Mill Hill (Lancashire)	d					19 43				20 43					21 43			22 59							
Blackburn	a		19 09			19 46				20 46		21 09			21 46			23 04							
Clitheroe 94	a					20b17				21b17					22b17										
Manchester Victoria 94	d					*18 23*				*19 00*		*20 00*						*22 01*							
Blackburn	d		19 10			19 48				20 48		21 10			21 48			23 05							
Rishton	d					19 53				20 53					21 53			23 10							
Church & Oswaldtwistle	d					19 56				20 56					21 56			23 13							
Accrington	d		19 17			19 59				20 59		21 17			21 59			23 16							
Huncoat	d					20 03				21 03					22 03			23 20							
Hapton	d					20 06				21 06					22 06			23 23							
Rose Grove	d					20 09				21 09					22 09			23 26							
Burnley Manchester Road 41	a		19 26									21 28													
Leeds 10 41	a		20 38									22 41													
Burnley Barracks	d					20 12				21 12					22 12			23 29							
Burnley Central	d					20 15				21 15					22 15			23 32							
Brierfield	d					20 19				21 19					22 19			23 36							
Nelson	d					20 22				21 22					22 22			23 39							
Colne	a					20 32				21 32					22 32			23 49							

For general notes see front of timetable
For details of catering facilities see Directory of Train Operators

- **A** To Liverpool Lime Street (Table 90)
- **B** To Manchester Airport (Table 82)
- **C** To Manchester Victoria (Table 82)
- **D** To York (Table 40)
- **E** From Rochdale (Table 95)
- **b** From 5 October arr. 2 mins. later

For connections to and from London Euston, please refer to Table 65

Table 97

Saturdays

Blackpool → Preston → Blackburn, Accrington, Burnley and Colne

Network Diagram - see first page of Table 97

Station		NT	TP 1◇ A	NT	NT B	TP 1◇ A	NT	NT C	NT B	TP 1◇ A 🚲	NT D	NT
Blackpool North	d		04 50	04 57	05 29	05 45		06 19	06 28	06 34	06 53	
Layton	d							06 22		06 37		
Poulton-le-Fylde	d				05 35	05 51		06 27	06 34	06 41		
Blackpool South	d						05 42					06 42
Blackpool Pleasure Beach	d						05 44					06 44
Squires Gate	d						05 46					06 46
St Annes-on-the-Sea	d						05 50					06 50
Ansdell & Fairhaven	d						05 53					06 53
Lytham	d						05 56					06 56
Moss Side	d						06 01					07 01
Kirkham & Wesham	d						06 08	06 36		06 50		07 09
Salwick	d											07 13
Preston 8	a		05 14	05 20	05 52	06 08	06 19	06 46	06 52	07 01	07 15	07 20
	d	04 47		05 22	05 54		06 21		06 54			07 22
Lostock Hall	d						06 26					07 27
Bamber Bridge	d						06 29					07 30
Pleasington	d						06 37					07 38
Cherry Tree	d						06 40					07 41
Mill Hill (Lancashire)	d						06 42					07 43
Blackburn	a	05 03		05 38	06 09		06 45		07 09			07 50
Clitheroe 94	a				06b50		07b15		08b12			
Manchester Victoria 94 🚌	d								05 55			
Blackburn	d	05 04		05 39	06 10		06 48		07 10			07 51
Rishton	d			05 44			06 53					07 56
Church & Oswaldtwistle	d			05 47			06 56					07 59
Accrington	d	05 11		05 50	06 17		06 59		07 17			08 02
Huncoat	d			05 54			07 03					08 06
Hapton	d			05 57			07 06					08 09
Rose Grove	d			06 00			07 09					08 12
Burnley Manchester Road 41	a				06 26				07 26			
Leeds 10 41	a				07c39				08e41			
Burnley Barracks	d						07 14					08 15
Burnley Central	d	05 21		06 05			07 17					08 18
Brierfield	d			06 09			07 21					08 22
Nelson	d			06 12			07 24					08 25
Colne	a	05 35		06 22			07 34					08 35

Station		NT E	NT C	NT B	TP 1◇ A 🚲	NT	NT C	NT B	NT E	TP 1◇ A 🚲	NT	TP 1◇ G	NT C
Blackpool North	d	07 02	07 18	07 29	07 44		08 20	08 29	08 38	08 45		09 14	09 20
Layton	d		07 21		07 47		08 23						09 23
Poulton-le-Fylde	d	07 08	07 26	07 35	07 51		08 28	08 35		08 51		09 20	09 28
Blackpool South	d					07 42					08 44		
Blackpool Pleasure Beach	d					07 44					08 46		
Squires Gate	d					07 46					08 48		
St Annes-on-the-Sea	d					07 50					08 52		
Ansdell & Fairhaven	d					07 53					08 55		
Lytham	d					07 56					08 58		
Moss Side	d					08 01					09 03		
Kirkham & Wesham	d		07 35		08 00	08 09	08 37				09 10		09 37
Salwick	d					08 13							
Preston 8	a	07 28	07 46	07 52	08 11	08 20	08 47	08 52	09 02	09 09	09 20	09 39	09 47
	d			07 54		08 22		08 54			09 22		
Lostock Hall	d					08 27					09 27		
Bamber Bridge	d					08 30					09 30		
Pleasington	d					08 38					09 38		
Cherry Tree	d					08 41					09 41		
Mill Hill (Lancashire)	d					08 43					09 43		
Blackburn	a			08 09		08 46		09 09			09 46		
Clitheroe 94	a					09b17					10b17		
Manchester Victoria 94 🚌	d					07 23		08 00			08 29		
Blackburn	d			08 10		08 48		09 10			09 48		
Rishton	d					08 53					09 53		
Church & Oswaldtwistle	d					08 56					09 56		
Accrington	d			08 17		08 59		09 17			09 59		
Huncoat	d					09 03					10 03		
Hapton	d					09 06					10 06		
Rose Grove	d					09 09					10 09		
Burnley Manchester Road 41	a			08 26				09 26					
Leeds 10 41	a			09e41				10e41					
Burnley Barracks	d					09 12					10 12		
Burnley Central	d					09 15					10 15		
Brierfield	d					09 19					10 19		
Nelson	d					09 22					10 22		
Colne	a					09 32					10 32		

Station		NT B	NT E	TP 1◇ A 🚲	NT	NT C	NT B	NT E	TP 1◇ A 🚲	NT	NT C	NT B
Blackpool North	d	09 29	09 37	09 45		10 20	10 29	10 37	10 45		11 15	11 24
Layton	d					10 23					11 18	
Poulton-le-Fylde	d	09 35		09 51		10 28	10 35		10 51		11 23	11 31
Blackpool South	d				09 44					10 44		
Blackpool Pleasure Beach	d				09 46					10 46		
Squires Gate	d				09 48					10 48		
St Annes-on-the-Sea	d				09 52					10 52		
Ansdell & Fairhaven	d				09 55					10 55		
Lytham	d				09 58					10 58		
Moss Side	d				10 03					11 03		
Kirkham & Wesham	d				10 10	10 37				11 10	11 32	
Salwick	d											
Preston 8	a	09 52	10 02	10 09	10 20	10 47	10 52	11 02	11 09	11 20	11 42	11 52
	d	09 54			10 22		10 54			11 22		11 54
Lostock Hall	d				10 27					11 27		
Bamber Bridge	d				10 30					11 30		
Pleasington	d				10 38					11 38		
Cherry Tree	d				10 41					11 41		
Mill Hill (Lancashire)	d				10 43					11 43		
Blackburn	a	10 09			10 46		11 09			11 46		12 09
Clitheroe 94	a				11b17					12b17		
Manchester Victoria 94 🚌	d	09 00					10 00					11 00
Blackburn	d	10 10			10 48		11 10			11 48		12 10
Rishton	d				10 53					11 53		
Church & Oswaldtwistle	d				10 56					11 56		
Accrington	d	10 17			10 59		11 17			11 59		12 17
Huncoat	d				11 03					12 03		
Hapton	d				11 06					12 06		
Rose Grove	d				11 09					12 09		
Burnley Manchester Road 41	a	10 26					11 27					12 26
Leeds 10 41	a	11e41					12e43					13f43
Burnley Barracks	d				11 12					12 12		
Burnley Central	d				11 15					12 15		
Brierfield	d				11 19					12 19		
Nelson	d				11 22					12 22		
Colne	a				11 32					12 32		

Station		TP 1◇ 🚲	NT E	NT	NT C	NT B	NT E	TP 1◇ A 🚲	NT	NT C	NT B	NT E
Blackpool North	d	11 32	11 37		12 20	12 29	12 37	12 45		13 20	13 29	13 37
Layton	d				12 23					13 23		
Poulton-le-Fylde	d	11 38			12 28	12 35		12 51		13 28	13 35	
Blackpool South	d			11 44					12 44			
Blackpool Pleasure Beach	d			11 46					12 46			
Squires Gate	d			11 48					12 48			
St Annes-on-the-Sea	d			11 52					12 52			
Ansdell & Fairhaven	d			11 55					12 55			
Lytham	d			11 58					12 58			
Moss Side	d			12 03					13 03			
Kirkham & Wesham	d			12 10	12 37				13 10	13 37		
Salwick	d											
Preston 8	a	11 58	12 02	12 20	12 47	12 52	13 02	13 09	13 20	13 47	13 53	14 02
	d			12 22		12 54			13 22		13 54	
Lostock Hall	d			12 27					13 27			
Bamber Bridge	d			12 30					13 30			
Pleasington	d			12 38					13 38			
Cherry Tree	d			12 41					13 41			
Mill Hill (Lancashire)	d			12 43					13 43			
Blackburn	a			12 46		13 09			13 46		14 10	
Clitheroe 94	a			13b17					14b17			
Manchester Victoria 94 🚌	d					12 00					13 00	
Blackburn	d			12 48		13 10			13 48		14 10	
Rishton	d			12 53					13 53			
Church & Oswaldtwistle	d			12 56					13 56			
Accrington	d			12 59		13 17			13 59		14 17	
Huncoat	d			13 03					14 03			
Hapton	d			13 06					14 06			
Rose Grove	d			13 09					14 09			
Burnley Manchester Road 41	a					13 26					14 26	
Leeds 10 41	a					14e41					15e41	
Burnley Barracks	d			13 12					14 12			
Burnley Central	d			13 15					14 15			
Brierfield	d			13 19					14 19			
Nelson	d			13 22					14 22			
Colne	a			13 32					14 32			

For general notes see front of timetable
For details of catering facilities see Directory of Train Operators

A To Manchester Airport (Table 82)
B To York (Table 40)
C To Manchester Victoria (Table 82)
D To Hazel Grove (Table 86)
E To Liverpool Lime Street (Table 90)
G To Barrow-in-Furness (Table 82)

b From 10 October arr. 2 mins. later
c Until 11 July arr. 0732
e From 18 July arr. 2 mins. earlier
f From 18 July arr. 4 mins. earlier

For connections to and from London Euston, please refer to Table 65

Table 97

Saturdays

Blackpool → Preston → Blackburn, Accrington, Burnley and Colne

Network Diagram - see first page of Table 97

		TP 1◇	NT	NT	NT	NT	TP 1◇	NT	NT	NT	NT	TP 1◇	NT	NT	NT	NT	TP 1◇	NT	TP 1◇	NT	NT	NT	NT
		A		B	C	D	A		B	C	D	A		B	C	D	A		A	C	D		B
Blackpool North	d	13 45		14 20	14 29	14 37	14 45		15 20	15 29	15 37	15 45		16 20	16 29	16 35	16 41		17 11	17 18	17 37		18 20
Layton	d			14 23					15 23					16 23			16 44		17 14				18 23
Poulton-le-Fylde	d	13 51		14 28	14 35		14 51		15 28	15 35		15 51		16 28	16 35		16 48		17 18	17 24			18 28
Blackpool South	d		13 44					14 44					15 44					16 44				17 44	
Blackpool Pleasure Beach	d		13 46					14 46					15 46					16 46				17 46	
Squires Gate	d		13 48					14 48					15 48					16 48				17 48	
St Annes-on-the-Sea	d		13 52					14 52					15 52					16 52				17 52	
Ansdell & Fairhaven	d		13 55					14 55					15 55					16 55				17 55	
Lytham	d		13 58					14 58					15 58					16 58				17 58	
Moss Side	d		14 03					15 03					16 03					17 03				18 03	
Kirkham & Wesham	d		14 10	14 37				15 10	15 37				16 10	16 37			16 58	17 10		17 33		18 10	18 37
Salwick	d												16 15										
Preston 8	a	14 09	14 20	14 47	14 52	15 02	15 09	15 20	15 47	15 52	16 02	16 09	16 22	16 47	16 52	17 02	17 09	17 20	17 39	17 44	18 02	18 22	18 47
	d		14 22		14 54			15 22		15 54			16 22		16 54			17 22		17 44		18 24	
Lostock Hall	d		14 27					15 27					16 27					17 27		17 51		18 30	
Bamber Bridge	d		14 30					15 30					16 30					17 30		17 54		18 33	
Pleasington	d		14 38					15 38					16 38					17 38		18 01		18 41	
Cherry Tree	d		14 41					15 41					16 41					17 41		18 05		18 44	
Mill Hill (Lancashire)	d		14 43					15 43					16 43					17 43		18 08		18 46	
Blackburn	a		14 46		15 09			15 46		16 09			16 48		17 09			17 47		18 11		18 52	
Clitheroe 94	a		15b17					16b17		16c56					17b44			18b18		19b14			
Manchester Victoria 94	d				14 00					15 00			15 40					16 23		17 00		18 00	
Blackburn	d		14 48		15 10			15 48		16 10			16 48		17 10			17 48		18 11		18 53	
Rishton	d		14 53					15 53					16 53					17 53				18 58	
Church & Oswaldtwistle	d		14 56					15 56					16 56					17 56				19 01	
Accrington	d		14 59		15 17			15 59		16 17			16 59		17 17			17 59		18 19		19 04	
Huncoat	d		15 03					16 03					17 03					18 03				19 08	
Hapton	d		15 06					16 06					17 06					18 06				19 11	
Rose Grove	d		15 09					16 09					17 09					18 09				19 14	
Burnley Manchester Road 41	a				15 26					16 26					17 26					18 27			
Leeds 10 41	a				16e41					17e42					18f41					19f43			
Burnley Barracks	d		15 12					16 12					17 12					18 12				19 17	
Burnley Central	d		15 15					16 15					17 15					18 15				19 20	
Brierfield	d		15 19					16 19					17 19					18 19				19 24	
Nelson	d		15 22					16 22					17 22					18 22				19 27	
Colne	a		15 32					16 32					17 32					18 32				19 37	

		NT	NT	TP 1◇	NT	NT	NT	TP 1◇	NT	NT	NT	NT	TP 1◇	NT	NT	TP 1◇	NT	NT	NT	TP 1◇	NT	NT
		C	D	A		B	D	A		B	C	D	A		B	A		D	B	A	B	
Blackpool North	d	18 29	18 37	18 45		19 20	19 37	19 45		20 20	20 29	20 38	20 45		21 20	21 45		22 14	22 20	22 45	23 02	
Layton	d					19 23				20 23					21 23				22 23		23 05	
Poulton-le-Fylde	d	18 35		18 51		19 28		19 51		20 28	20 35		20 51		21 28	21 51			22 28	22 51	23 10	
Blackpool South	d				18 44				19 44					20 44			22 00					23 30
Blackpool Pleasure Beach	d				18 46				19 46					20 46			22 02					23 32
Squires Gate	d				18 48				19 48					20 48			22 04					23 34
St Annes-on-the-Sea	d				18 52				19 52					20 52			22 08					23 38
Ansdell & Fairhaven	d				18 55				19 55					20 55			22 11					23 41
Lytham	d				18 58				19 58					20 58			22 14					23 44
Moss Side	d				19 03				20 03					21 03			22 19					23 49
Kirkham & Wesham	d				19 10	19 37			20 10	20 37				21 10	21 37		22 26		22 37		23 19	23 56
Salwick	d																					
Preston 8	a	18 52	19 02	19 09	19 20	19 47	20 02	20 09	20 20	20 47	20 53	21 02	21 09	21 20	21 47	22 09	22 36	22 41	22 47	23 09	23 29	00 08
	d	18 54			19 22				20 22		20 54			21 22			22 38					
Lostock Hall	d				19 27				20 27					21 27			22 43					
Bamber Bridge	d				19 30				20 30					21 30			22 46					
Pleasington	d				19 38				20 38					21 38			22 54					
Cherry Tree	d				19 41				20 41					21 41			22 57					
Mill Hill (Lancashire)	d				19 43				20 43					21 43			22 59					
Blackburn	a	19 09			19 46				20 46		21 09			21 46			23 06					
Clitheroe 94	a				20b17				21b17					22b17								
Manchester Victoria 94	d				18 23				19 00		20 00											
Blackburn	d	19 10			19 48				20 48		21 10			21 48								
Rishton	d				19 53				20 53					21 53								
Church & Oswaldtwistle	d				19 56				20 56					21 56								
Accrington	d	19 17			19 59				20 59		21 17			21 59								
Huncoat	d				20 03				21 03					22 03								
Hapton	d				20 06				21 06					22 06								
Rose Grove	d				20 09				21 09					22 09								
Burnley Manchester Road 41	a	19 26									21 28											
Leeds 10 41	a	20g42									22h39											
Burnley Barracks	d				20 12				21 12					22 12								
Burnley Central	d				20 15				21 15					22 15								
Brierfield	d				20 19				21 19					22 19								
Nelson	d				20 22				21 22					22 22								
Colne	a				20 32				21 32					22 32								

For general notes see front of timetable
For details of catering facilities see Directory of Train Operators

A To Manchester Airport (Table 82)
B To Manchester Victoria (Table 82)
C To York (Table 40)
D To Liverpool Lime Street (Table 90)
b From 10 October arr. 2 mins. later
c From 18 July arr. 3 mins. earlier
e From 18 July arr. 2 mins. earlier
f From 18 July arr. 1 min. earlier
g Until 11 July arr. 2036
h Until 11 July arr. 2227

For connections to and from London Euston, please refer to Table 65

Blackpool → Preston → Blackburn, Accrington, Burnley and Colne

Network Diagram - see first page of Table 97

		TP	NT	TP	NT	NT	TP	NT	NT	NT	NT	NT	NT	NT	TP	NT	NT	NT	TP	NT	NT	NT
		1 ◇		1 ◇			1 ◇								1 ◇				1 ◇			
		A		B	C	D	E	G	H	J	C	D	K	L	E	G	N	C	E	G	N	C
Blackpool North	d	07 48		08 14	08 20	08 36	08 44	08 50	09 01	09 11	09 20				09 44	09 50	10 11	10 20	10 44	10 50	11 13	11 20
Layton	d				08 23						09 23							10 23				11 23
Poulton-le-Fylde	d	07 54		08 20	08 28	08 42	08 50	08 56	09 07	09 17	09 28				09 50	09 56	10 17	10 28	10 50	10 56	11 19	11 28
Blackpool South	d												09 28									
Blackpool Pleasure Beach	d												09 30									
Squires Gate	d												09 32									
St Annes-on-the-Sea	d												09 36									
Ansdell & Fairhaven	d												09 39									
Lytham	d												09 42									
Moss Side	d												09 47									
Kirkham & Wesham	d				08 37	08 51					09 37		09 54					10 37				11 37
Salwick	d																					
Preston 8	a	08 12		08 38	08 47	09 02	09 08	09 14	09 24	09 34	09 47		10 04		10 08	10 14	10 34	10 47	11 08	11 14	11 36	11 47
	d		08 16			09 05			09 27	09 37		10 00	10 05	10 05			10 37				11 38	
Lostock Hall	d		08 21			09 11						10 05	10 11	10 11								
Bamber Bridge	d		08 24			09 14						10 08	10 14	10 14								
Pleasington	d												10 21	10 21								
Cherry Tree	d												10 24	10 24								
Mill Hill (Lancashire)	d												10 27	10 27								
Blackburn	a		08 35			09 25			09 42	09 52		10 19	10 30	10 30			10 54				11 53	
Clitheroe 94	a		*09b20*			09 50						10 44	*11b13*				*12b13*					
Manchester Victoria 94 🚌	d								*08 01*	*09 00*			*09 00*	*09 00*			*10 00*				*11 00*	
Blackburn	d		08 37						09 44	09 54			10 31	10 31			10 54				11 54	
Rishton	d												10 36	10 36								
Church & Oswaldtwistle	d												10 39	10 39								
Accrington	d		08 44						09 51	10 01			10 42	10 42			11 01				12 01	
Huncoat	d												10 47	10 47								
Hapton	d												10 50	10 50								
Rose Grove	d		08 51										10 53	10 53								
Burnley Manchester Road 41	a								10 00	10 10							11 10				12 10	
Leeds 10 41	a								11 21	11c21							12e11				13f22	
Burnley Barracks	d												10 56	10 56								
Burnley Central	d		08 56										10 58	10 58								
Brierfield	d		09 00										11 03	11 03								
Nelson	d		09 03										11 06	11 06								
Colne	a		09 13										11 15	11 15								

		NT	NT	TP	NT	NT	NT	NT	TP	NT	NT	NT	NT	NT	TP	NT	NT	NT	NT	TP	NT	NT
				1 ◇					1 ◇						1 ◇					1 ◇		
		K	L	E	G	N	C	K	E	G	N	C	K	L	E	G	N	C	K	E	G	N
Blackpool North	d			11 44	11 50	12 11	12 20		12 44	12 50	13 13	13 20			13 44	13 50	14 11	14 20		14 44	14 50	15 13
Layton	d						12 23					13 23						14 23				
Poulton-le-Fylde	d			11 50	11 56	12 17	12 28		12 50	12 56	13 19	13 28			13 50	13 56	14 17	14 28		14 50	14 56	15 19
Blackpool South	d	11 27						12 27					13 27						14 27			
Blackpool Pleasure Beach	d	11 29						12 29					13 29						14 29			
Squires Gate	d	11 31						12 31					13 31						14 31			
St Annes-on-the-Sea	d	11 35						12 35					13 35						14 35			
Ansdell & Fairhaven	d	11 38						12 38					13 38						14 38			
Lytham	d	11 41						12 41					13 41						14 41			
Moss Side	d	11 46						12 46					13 46						14 46			
Kirkham & Wesham	d	11 53					12 37	12 53				13 37	13 53					14 37	14 53			
Salwick	d																					
Preston 8	a	12 03		12 08	12 14	12 34	12 47	13 03	13 08	13 14	13 36	13 47	14 03		14 08	14 14	14 34	14 47	15 03	15 08	15 14	15 36
	d	12 05	12 05			12 37					13 38		14 05	14 05			14 37					15 37
Lostock Hall	d	12 11	12 11										14 11	14 11								
Bamber Bridge	d	12 14	12 14										14 14	14 14								
Pleasington	d	12 21	12 21										14 21	14 21								
Cherry Tree	d	12 24	12 24										14 24	14 24								
Mill Hill (Lancashire)	d	12 27	12 27										14 27	14 27								
Blackburn	a	12 30	12 30			12 52					13 53		14 30	14 30			14 52					15 53
Clitheroe 94	a	*13b13*				*14b13*							*15b13*				*16b13*					
Manchester Victoria 94 🚌	d					*12 00*					*13 00*						*14 00*					*15 00*
Blackburn	d	12 31	12 31			12 54					13 54		14 31	14 31			14 54					15 54
Rishton	d	12 36	12 36										14 36	14 36								
Church & Oswaldtwistle	d	12 39	12 39										14 39	14 39								
Accrington	d	12 42	12 42			13 01					14 01		14 42	14 42			15 01					16 01
Huncoat	d	12 47	12 47										14 47	14 47								
Hapton	d	12 50	12 50										14 50	14 50								
Rose Grove	d	12 53	12 53										14 53	14 53								
Burnley Manchester Road 41	a					13 10					14 10						15 10					16 10
Leeds 10 41	a					14g22					15h22						16j22					17k21
Burnley Barracks	d	12 56	12 56										14 56	14 56								
Burnley Central	d	12 58	12 58										14 58	14 58								
Brierfield	d	13 03	13 03										15 03	15 03								
Nelson	d	13 06	13 06										15 06	15 06								
Colne	a	13 15	13 15										15 15	15 15								

For general notes see front of timetable
For details of catering facilities see Directory of Train Operators

A Until 6 September. To Manchester Airport (Table 82)
B From 13 September. To Manchester Airport (Table 82)
C To Manchester Victoria (Table 82)
D Until 6 September. To Carlisle (Table 36)
E To Manchester Airport (Table 82)
G To Liverpool Lime Street (Table 90)
H From 13 September. To York (Table 40)
J Until 6 September. To York (Table 40)
K Until 1 November
L From 8 November
N To York (Table 40)
b Until 6 September only
c Until 12 July arr. 1109
e From 19 July arr. 1222
f Until 12 July arr. 1310
g Until 12 July arr. 1408
h Until 12 July arr. 1511
j Until 12 July arr. 1611
k Until 12 July arr. 1712

For connections to and from London Euston, please refer to Table 65

Sundays

Blackpool → Preston → Blackburn, Accrington, Burnley and Colne

Network Diagram - see first page of Table 97

		NT	NT	NT	TP 1 ◊	NT	NT	NT	NT	TP 1 ◊	NT	NT	NT	TP 1 ◊	NT	NT	TP 1 ◊	NT	NT	NT	NT	TP 1 ◊
		A	B	C	D	E	G	A	B	D	E	G	A	H	B	C	J	E	G	A	B	D
Blackpool North	d	15 20			15 44	15 50	16 11	16 20		16 44	16 50	17 11	17 20	17 40			17 44	17 50	18 11	18 20		18 44
Layton	d	15 23						16 23					17 23							18 23		
Poulton-le-Fylde	d	15 28			15 50	15 56	16 17	16 28		16 50	16 56	17 17	17 28	17 46			17 50	17 56	18 17	18 28		18 50
Blackpool South	d		15 27						16 27						17 24						18 27	
Blackpool Pleasure Beach	d		15 29						16 29						17 26						18 29	
Squires Gate	d		15 31						16 31						17 28						18 31	
St Annes-on-the-Sea	d		15 35						16 35						17 32						18 35	
Ansdell & Fairhaven	d		15 38						16 38						17 35						18 38	
Lytham	d		15 41						16 41						17 38						18 41	
Moss Side	d		15 46						16 46						17 43						18 46	
Kirkham & Wesham	d	15 37	15 53					16 37	16 53				17 37		17 50					18 37	18 53	
Salwick	d																					
Preston 8	a	15 47	16 03		16 08	16 14	16 34	16 47	17 03	17 08	17 14	17 34	17 47	18 04	18 00		18 08	18 14	18 34	18 47	19 03	19 08
	d		16 05	16 05			16 37					17 37			18 05	18 05			18 37			
Lostock Hall	d		16 11	16 11											18 11	18 11						
Bamber Bridge	d		16 14	16 14											18 14	18 14						
Pleasington	d		16 21	16 21											18 21	18 21						
Cherry Tree	d		16 24	16 24											18 24	18 24						
Mill Hill (Lancashire)	d		16 27	16 27											18 27	18 27						
Blackburn	a		16 30	16 30			16 52					17 52			18 30	18 30			18 52			
Clitheroe 94	a		*17b13*				*18b13*								*19b13*				*20b13*			
Manchester Victoria 94 🚌	d						*16 00*					*17 00*							*18 00*			
Blackburn	d		16 31	16 31			16 54					17 54			18 31	18 31			18 54			
Rishton	d		16 36	16 36											18 36	18 36						
Church & Oswaldtwistle	d		16 39	16 39											18 39	18 39						
Accrington	d		16 42	16 42			17 01					18 01			18 42	18 42			19 01			
Huncoat	d		16 47	16 47											18 47	18 47						
Hapton	d		16 50	16 50											18 50	18 50						
Rose Grove	d		16 53	16 53											18 53	18 53						
Burnley Manchester Road 41	a						17 10					18 10							19 10			
Leeds 10 41	a						18c21					19c21							20e23			
Burnley Barracks	d		16 56	16 56											18 56	18 56						
Burnley Central	d		16 58	16 58											18 58	18 58						
Brierfield	d		17 03	17 03											19 03	19 03						
Nelson	d		17 06	17 06											19 06	19 06						
Colne	a		17 15	17 15											19 15	19 15						

		NT	NT	NT	NT	NT	TP 1 ◊	NT	NT	NT	NT	TP 1 ◊	NT	NT	NT	NT	NT	TP 1 ◊	NT	NT	TP 1 ◊
		E	G	A	B	C	D	E	K	A	B	D	E	K	A	B	E		E	🚌	D
Blackpool North	d	18 50	19 13	19 20			19 44	19 50	20 11	20 20		20 44	20 50	21 13	21 20		21 50	21 56	22 44		23 00
Layton	d			19 23						20 23					21 23						23 03
Poulton-le-Fylde	d	18 56	19 19	19 28			19 50	19 56	20 17	20 28		20 50	20 56	21 19	21 28		21 56	22 02	22 50		23 07
Blackpool South	d				19 27						20 27					21 27					
Blackpool Pleasure Beach	d				19 29						20 29					21 29					
Squires Gate	d				19 31						20 31					21 31					
St Annes-on-the-Sea	d				19 35						20 35					21 35					
Ansdell & Fairhaven	d				19 38						20 38					21 38					
Lytham	d				19 41						20 41					21 41					
Moss Side	d				19 46						20 46					21 46					
Kirkham & Wesham	d			19 37	19 53					20 37	20 53				21 37	21 53					23 16
Salwick	d																				
Preston 8	a	19 14	19 36	19 47	20 03		20 08	20 14	20 34	20 47	21 03	21 08	21 14	21 36	21 47	22 03	22 14	22 20	23 08		23 26
	d		19 37		20 05	20 05			20 37		21 05			21 38		22 05					
Lostock Hall	d				20 11	20 11					21 11					22 11					
Bamber Bridge	d				20 14	20 14					21 14					22 14					
Pleasington	d				20 21	20 21					21 21					22 21					
Cherry Tree	d				20 24	20 24					21 24					22 24					
Mill Hill (Lancashire)	d				20 27	20 27					21 27					22 27					
Blackburn	a		19 53		20 30	20 30			20 52		21 30			21 53		22 30					
Clitheroe 94	a				*21b13*						*22b13*										
Manchester Victoria 94 🚌	d		*19 00*						*20 00*					*21 00*							
Blackburn	d		19 54		20 31	20 31			20 54		21 31			21 54		22 31				23 15	
Rishton	d				20 36	20 36					21 36					22 36				23 25	
Church & Oswaldtwistle	d				20 39	20 39					21 39					22 39				23 37	
Accrington	d		20 01		20 42	20 42			21 01		21 42			22 01		22 42				23 41	
Huncoat	d				20 47	20 47					21 47					22 47				23 47	
Hapton	d				20 50	20 50					21 50					22 50				23 53	
Rose Grove	d				20 53	20 53					21 53					22 53				23 59	
Burnley Manchester Road 41	a		20 10						21 10					22 10							
Leeds 10 41	a		21f22						22g22					23h26							
Burnley Barracks	d				20 56	20 56					21 56					22 56				00 03	
Burnley Central	d				20 58	20 58					22a00					22 58				00 08	
Brierfield	d				21 03	21 03										23 03				00 16	
Nelson	d				21 06	21 06										23 06				00 21	
Colne	a				21 15	21 15										23 15				00 29	

For general notes see front of timetable
For details of catering facilities see Directory of Train Operators

- **A** To Manchester Victoria (Table 82)
- **B** Until 1 November
- **C** From 8 November
- **D** To Manchester Airport (Table 82)
- **E** To Liverpool Lime Street (Table 90)
- **G** To York (Table 40)
- **H** Until 6 September. To Manchester Airport (Table 82)
- **J** From 13 September. To Manchester Airport (Table 82)
- **K** From 19 July
- **b** Until 6 September only
- **c** Until 12 July arr. 10 mins. earlier
- **e** Until 12 July arr. 2008
- **f** Until 12 July arr. 2108
- **g** Until 12 July arr. 2209
- **h** Until 12 July arr. 2309

For connections to and from London Euston, please refer to Table 65

Colne, Burnley, Accrington and Blackburn → Preston → Blackpool

Network Diagram - see first page of Table 97

Miles	Miles		NT MX A	TP 1◇ B	NT C	NT D	NT A	NT	NT	TP 1◇ B	NT	NT A	NT E	NT G	TP 1◇ B	NT	NT A	NT E	NT H	NT	TP 1◇	NT A	NT J
0	—	**Colne** d			05 38	05 40		06 28								07 50				08 50			
2	—	Nelson d			05 43	05 45		06 33								07 55				08 55			
3¼	—	Brierfield d			05 46	05 48		06 36								07 58				08 58			
5½	—	**Burnley Central** d			05 51	05 53		06 41			07 03					08 03				09 03			
6	—	Burnley Barracks d			05 53	05 55					07 05					08 05				09 05			
—	—	Leeds [10] 41 d							05 51				06 51					07 51					08 51
—	—	Burnley Manchester Road 41 d							06 57				07 57					08 57					09 57
7	—	Rose Grove d			05 56	05 58					07 08					08 08				09 08			
8½	—	Hapton d			05 59	06 01					07 11					08 11				09 11			
10	—	Huncoat d			06 02	06 04					07 14					08 14				09 14			
11¾	—	Accrington d			06 07	06 09		06 51	07 06		07 19		08 06			08 19		09 06		09 19			10 06
12½	—	Church & Oswaldtwistle d			06 09	06 11					07 21					08 21				09 21			
14¼	—	Rishton d			06 12	06 14					07 24					08 24				09 24			
18	—	**Blackburn** a			06 21	06 23		06 59	07 16		07 33		08 14			08 33		09 14		09 33			10 14
—	—	Manchester Victoria 94 a			*07 26*	*07 26*		07 51	*08 25*		*08 51*		*09 26*			*09 51*		*10 21*		*10 51*			
—	—	Clitheroe 94 d									*07b07*		*07b40*					*08 26*					*09b40*
—	—	**Blackburn** d			06 23	06 25			07 16		07 35		08 15			08 35		09 15		09 35			10 15
19¼	—	Mill Hill (Lancashire) d			06 26	06 28					07 38		08 18			08 38				09 38			
20	—	Cherry Tree d			06 28	06 30					07 40					08 40				09 40			
21	—	Pleasington d			06 30	06 32					07 42					08 42				09 42			
26	—	Bamber Bridge d			06 37	06 39			07 26		07 49		08 27			08 49				09 49			
27¼	—	Lostock Hall d			06 40	06 42			07 28		07 52		08 30			08 52				09 52			
30	—	**Preston [8]** a			06 50	06 50			07 36		08 00		08 38			09 00		09 32		10 00			10 32
—	—	d	00 19	06 34	07 00	07 00	07 13		07 38	07 59	08 02	08 15	08 40	08 51	08 59	09 02	09 19	09 34	09 55	10 02	10 08	10 19	10 34
35¼	5¼	Salwick d			07 07	07 07					08 09												
37¼	7¼	Kirkham & Wesham d	00 28	06 43	07 11	07 11	07 22			08 09	08 13	08 25				09 11	09 28		10 05	10 11		10 28	
41	—	Moss Side d			07 17	07 17					08 19					09 17				10 17			
43½	—	Lytham d			07 21	07 21					08 23					09 21				10 21			
44¾	—	Ansdell & Fairhaven d			07 24	07 24					08 26					09 24				10 24			
46¾	—	St Annes-on-the-Sea d			07 28	07 28					08 30					09 28				10 28			
48¼	—	Squires Gate d			07 32	07 32					08 34					09 32				10 32			
49½	—	Blackpool Pleasure Beach d			07 34	07 34					08 36					09 34				10 34			
50	—	**Blackpool South** a			07 37	07 37					08 41					09 39				10 39			
—	14½	Poulton-le-Fylde d	00 36	06 53			07 30		07 54	08 18		08 33	08 56		09 16		09 36	09 50			10 25	10 36	10 50
—	16¼	Layton d	00 43	06 56			07 34			08 22		08 37					09 43					10 43	
—	17½	**Blackpool North** a	00c50	07 03			07c43		08 05	08 29		08c46	09 05	09c18	09 25		09c53	10 00	10 20		10 35	10c50	11 00

	TP 1◇ B	NT H	NT	NT A	NT E	TP 1◇ B	NT H	NT	NT A	NT E	TP 1◇ B	NT H	NT	NT A	NT E	TP 1◇ B	NT H	NT	NT A	NT E	TP 1◇ B	NT H	NT
Colne d			09 50					10 50					11 50					12 50					13 50
Nelson d			09 55					10 55					11 55					12 55					13 55
Brierfield d			09 58					10 58					11 58					12 58					13 58
Burnley Central d			10 03					11 03					12 03					13 03					14 03
Burnley Barracks d			10 05					11 05					12 05					13 05					14 05
Leeds [10] 41 d					09 51					10 51					11 51					12 51			
Burnley Manchester Road 41 d					10 57					11 57					12 57					13 57			
Rose Grove d			10 08					11 08					12 08					13 08					14 08
Hapton d			10 11					11 11					12 11					13 11					14 11
Huncoat d			10 14					11 14					12 14					13 14					14 14
Accrington d			10 19		11 06			11 19		12 06			12 19		13 06			13 19		14 06			14 19
Church & Oswaldtwistle d			10 21					11 21					12 21					13 21					14 21
Rishton d			10 24					11 24					12 24					13 24					14 24
Blackburn a			10 33		11 14			11 33		12 14			12 33		13 14			13 33		14 14			14 33
Manchester Victoria 94 a			*11 51*					*12 51*					*13 51*					*14 51*					*15 53*
Clitheroe 94 d					*10b40*					*11b40*					*12b40*					*13b40*			
Blackburn d			10 35		11 15			11 35		12 15			12 35		13 15			13 35		14 15			14 35
Mill Hill (Lancashire) d			10 38					11 38					12 38					13 38					14 38
Cherry Tree d			10 40					11 40					12 40					13 40					14 40
Pleasington d			10 42					11 42					12 42					13 42					14 42
Bamber Bridge d			10 49					11 49					12 49					13 49					14 49
Lostock Hall d			10 52					11 52					12 52					13 52					14 52
Preston [8] a			11 00		11 32			12 00		12 32			13 00		13 32			14 00		14 32			15 00
d	10 38	10 55	11 02	11 19	11 34	11 38	11 55	12 02	12 19	12 34	12 38	12 55	13 02	13 19	13 34	13 38	13 55	14 02	14 19	14 34	14 38	14 55	15 02
Salwick d								12 09															
Kirkham & Wesham d		11 05	11 11	11 28			12 05	12 13	12 28			13 05	13 11	13 28			14 05	14 11	14 28			15 05	15 11
Moss Side d			11 17					12 19					13 17					14 17					15 17
Lytham d			11 21					12 23					13 21					14 21					15 21
Ansdell & Fairhaven d			11 24					12 26					13 24					14 24					15 24
St Annes-on-the-Sea d			11 28					12 30					13 28					14 28					15 28
Squires Gate d			11 32					12 34					13 32					14 32					15 32
Blackpool Pleasure Beach d			11 34					12 36					13 34					14 34					15 34
Blackpool South a			11 39					12 39					13 39					14 39					15 39
Poulton-le-Fylde d	10 56			11 36	11 50	11 56			12 36	12 50	12 56			13 36	13 50	13 56			14 36	14 50	14 56		
Layton d				11 43					12 43					13 43					14 43				
Blackpool North a	11 05	11 20		11c50	12 00	12 05	12 20		12c50	13 00	13 05	13 21		13c50	14 00	14 05	14 20		14c50	15 00	15 05	15 20	

For general notes see front of timetable
For details of catering facilities see Directory of Train Operators

- **A** From Manchester Victoria (Table 82)
- **B** From Manchester Airport (Table 82)
- **C** From 5 October
- **D** Until 2 October
- **E** From York (Table 40)
- **G** From Buxton (Table 86)
- **H** From Liverpool Lime Street (Table 90)
- **J** From Selby (Table 40)
- **b** From 5 October dep. 5 mins. earlier
- **c** Until 2 October arr. 2 mins. earlier

For connections to and from London Euston, please refer to Table 65

Colne, Burnley, Accrington and Blackburn → Preston → Blackpool

Network Diagram - see first page of Table 97

		NT	NT	TP	NT	NT		NT	TP	NT	NT	NT	TP	NT	NT	NT	NT	NT	NT	TP	NT	NT		NT	NT
				1 ◇					1 ◇				1 ◇							1 ◇					
		A	B	C	D			B	C	D		A	C	B	D		E	G	B	C	G	D			
				⚯					⚯				⚯							⚯					
Colne	d					14 50					15 50					16 50								17 50	
Nelson	d					14 55					15 55					16 55								17 55	
Brierfield	d					14 58					15 58					16 58								17 58	
Burnley Central	d					15 03					16 03					17 03								18 03	18 26
Burnley Barracks	d					15 05					16 05					17 05								18 05	
Leeds 10	41 d		13 51					14 51						15 51					16 51						
Burnley Manchester Road	41 d		14 57					15 57						16 58					17 57						
Rose Grove	d					15 08					16 08					17 08								18 08	
Hapton	d					15 11					16 11					17 11								18 11	
Huncoat	d					15 14					16 14					17 14								18 14	
Accrington	d		15 06			15 19		16 06			16 19			17 06		17 19			18 06					18 19	18 36
Church & Oswaldtwistle	d					15 21					16 21					17 21								18 21	
Rishton	d					15 24					16 24					17 24								18 24	
Blackburn	a		15 14			15 33		16 14			16 33			17 14		17 34			18 14					18 34	18 44
Manchester Victoria	94 ⛴ a					*16 40*					*17 52*			*18 24*					*19 22*						*19 52*
Clitheroe	94 d		*14b40*					*15 26*						*16b40*		*17c09*								*18b09*	
Blackburn	d		15 15			15 35		16 15			16 35			17 15		17 35			18 15					18 35	18 44
Mill Hill (Lancashire)	d					15 38					16 38					17 38								18 38	
Cherry Tree	d					15 40					16 40					17 40								18 40	
Pleasington	d					15 42					16 42					17 42								18 42	
Bamber Bridge	d					15 49					16 49					17 49								18 49	
Lostock Hall	d					15 52					16 52					17 52								18 52	
Preston 8	a		15 32			16 00		16 32			17 00			17 32		18 00			18 33					19 00	19 05
	d	15 19	15 34	15 38	15 55	16 02		16 34	16 38	16 58	17 02	17 21	17 32	17 36	17 55	18 02	18 18	18 26	18 34	18 40	18 49	18 55		19 02	19 08
Salwick	d					16 09																			
Kirkham & Wesham	d	15 28			16 05	16 13			16 47	17 07	17 11	17 30	17 41		18 05	18 11	18 27			18 49		19 05		19 11	
Moss Side	d					16 19					17 17					18 17								19 17	
Lytham	d					16 23					17 21					18 21								19 21	
Ansdell & Fairhaven	d					16 26					17 24					18 24								19 24	
St Annes-on-the-Sea	d					16 30					17 28					18 28								19 28	
Squires Gate	d					16 34					17 32					18 32								19 32	
Blackpool Pleasure Beach	d					16 36					17 34					18 34								19 34	
Blackpool South	a					16 41					17 39					18 39								19 39	
Poulton-le-Fylde	d	15 36	15 50	15 56				16 50	16 57			17 38	17 51	17 56	18 13		18 35	18 43	18 50	18 59					
Layton	d	15 43							17 00			17 43	17 54				18 39			19 02					
Blackpool North	a	15e50	16 00	16 05	16 20			17 00	17 07	17 23		17e50	18 02	18 06	18 21		18e48	18e55	19 00	19 09	19e16	19 20			19 33

		NT	NT	TP	NT	NT	NT	NT	TP	NT	NT	NT	NT	TP	NT	NT	TP	NT	NT	NT	TP	TP	NT		
				1 ◇					1 ◇					1 ◇			1 ◇				1 ◇	1 ◇			
		A	B	C		D	A		C		A	D	B	C		A	C		D	A	C	H			
				⚯																					
Colne	d				18 55					19 50					20 50			21 44					22 55		
Nelson	d				19 00					19 55					20 55			21 49					23 00		
Brierfield	d				19 03					19 58					20 58			21 52					23 03		
Burnley Central	d				19 08					20 03					21 03			21 57					23 08		
Burnley Barracks	d				19 10					20 05					21 05			21 59					23 10		
Leeds 10	41 d		17 51					18 51					19 51												
Burnley Manchester Road	41 d		18 57					19 57					20 57												
Rose Grove	d				19 13					20 08					21 08			22 02					23 13		
Hapton	d				19 16					20 11					21 11			22 05							
Huncoat	d				19 19					20 14					21 14			22 08							
Accrington	d		19 06		19 24			20 06		20 19			21 06		21 19			22 13					23 20		
Church & Oswaldtwistle	d				19 26					20 21					21 21			22 15							
Rishton	d				19 29					20 24					21 24			22 18							
Blackburn	a		19 14		19 34			20 14		20 33			21 14		21 33			22 23					23 28		
Manchester Victoria	94 ⛴ a		*20 23*		*20 51*					*21 51*					*22f49*			*23 50*							
Clitheroe	94 d		*18b40*					*19b40*					*20b40*					*21b40*					*22b40*		
Blackburn	d		19 15		19 35			20 15		20 35			21 15		21 35			22 24					23 30		
Mill Hill (Lancashire)	d				19 38					20 38					21 38			22 27					23 33		
Cherry Tree	d				19 40					20 40					21 40			22 29							
Pleasington	d				19 42					20 42					21 42			22 31							
Bamber Bridge	d				19 49					20 49					21 49			22 38					23 41		
Lostock Hall	d				19 52					20 52					21 52			22 41					23 43		
Preston 8	a		19 32		20 00			20 32		21 00			21 32		22 02			22 49					23 54		
	d	19 20	19 34	19 38	20 02	20 19	20 25	20 34	20 38	21 02	21 19	21 24	21 34	21 38		22 19	22 35	22 51	22 56	23 19	23 35	23 51			
Salwick	d																								
Kirkham & Wesham	d	19 29			20 11		20 35			21 11	21 28					22 28		23 00		23 28					
Moss Side	d				20 17					21 17								23 06							
Lytham	d				20 21					21 21								23 10							
Ansdell & Fairhaven	d				20 24					21 24								23 13							
St Annes-on-the-Sea	d				20 28					21 28								23 17							
Squires Gate	d				20 32					21 32								23 21							
Blackpool Pleasure Beach	d				20 34					21 34								23 23							
Blackpool South	a				20 39					21 39								23 28							
Poulton-le-Fylde	d	19 37	19 50	19 56			20 43	20 50	20 56		21 36		21 50	21 56		22 36	22 52			23 36	23 52	00 10			
Layton	d	19 43					20 47				21 40					22 43				23 40					
Blackpool North	a	19e50	20 00	20 05		20 44	20e56	21 00	21 06		21e50	21 53	22 00	22 06		22e50	23 01		23 21	23e50	00 01	00 20			

For general notes see front of timetable
For details of catering facilities see Directory of Train Operators

A From Manchester Victoria (Table 82)
B From York (Table 40)
C From Manchester Airport (Table 82)
D From Liverpool Lime Street (Table 90)
E From Manchester Victoria (Table 40)
G From Buxton (Table 86)
H From Windermere (Table 83)
b From 5 October dep. 5 mins. earlier
c From 5 October dep. 2 mins. earlier
e Until 2 October arr. 2 mins. earlier
f Fridays arr. 2251

For connections to and from London Euston, please refer to Table 65

Colne, Burnley, Accrington and Blackburn → Preston → Blackpool

Network Diagram - see first page of Table 97

Station		NT A	TP 1◇ B	NT C	NT D	NT A	NT E	NT G	TP 1◇ B	NT	NT A	NT H	NT G	TP 1◇ B	NT	NT A	NT H	NT G	NT	TP 1◇	NT A	NT H	TP 1◇ B
Colne	d			05 38	05 40					06 50					07 50				08 50				
Nelson	d			05 43	05 45					06 55					07 55				08 55				
Brierfield	d			05 46	05 48					06 58					07 58				08 58				
Burnley Central	d			05 51	05 53					07 03					08 03				09 03				
Burnley Barracks	d			05 53	05 55					07 05					08 05				09 05				
Leeds 10	41 d						05b51					06c51					07c51					08c51	
Burnley Manchester Road	41 d						06 57					07 57					08 57					09 57	
Rose Grove	d			05 56	05 58					07 08					08 08				09 08				
Hapton	d			05 59	06 01					07 11					08 11				09 11				
Huncoat	d			06 02	06 04					07 14					08 14				09 14				
Accrington	d			06 07	06 09		07 06			07 19		08 06			08 19		09 06		09 19			10 06	
Church & Oswaldtwistle	d			06 09	06 11					07 21					08 21				09 21				
Rishton	d			06 12	06 14					07 24					08 24				09 24				
Blackburn	a			06 21	06 23		07 16			07 33		08 14			08 33		09 14		09 33			10 14	
Manchester Victoria	94 ⛴ a			*07 22*	*07 22*		*08 25*			*08 51*		*09 26*			*09 51*		*10 23*		*10 51*				
Clitheroe	94 d									*07e07*		*07 40*			*07e40*		*08 26*						
Blackburn	d			06 23	06 25		07 16			07 35		08 15			08 35		09 15		09 35			10 15	
Mill Hill (Lancashire)	d			06 26	06 28					07 38		08 18			08 38				09 38				
Cherry Tree	d			06 28	06 30					07 40					08 40				09 40				
Pleasington	d			06 30	06 32					07 42					08 42				09 42				
Bamber Bridge	d			06 37	06 39		07 26			07 49		08 27			08 49				09 49				
Lostock Hall	d			06 40	06 42		07 28			07 52		08 30			08 52				09 52				
Preston 8	a			06 50	06 50		07 36			08 00		08 38			09 00		09 32		10 00			10 32	
	d	00 19	06 34	07 00	07 00	07 13	07 38	07 55	07 59	08 02	08 15	08 40	08 55	08 59	09 02	09 19	09 34	09 55	10 02	10 08	10 19	10 34	10 38
Salwick	d			07 07	07 07					08 09													
Kirkham & Wesham	d	00 28	06 43	07 11	07 11	07 22			08 09	08 13	08 25				09 11	09 28			10 11		10 28		
Moss Side	d			07 17	07 17					08 19					09 17				10 17				
Lytham	d			07 21	07 21					08 23					09 21				10 21				
Ansdell & Fairhaven	d			07 24	07 24					08 26					09 24				10 24				
St Annes-on-the-Sea	d			07 28	07 28					08 30					09 28				10 28				
Squires Gate	d			07 32	07 32					08 34					09 32				10 32				
Blackpool Pleasure Beach	d			07 34	07 34					08 36					09 34				10 34				
Blackpool South	a			07 37	07 37					08 41					09 39				10 39				
Poulton-le-Fylde	d	00 36	06 53			07 30	07 54		08 18		08 33	08 56		09 16		09 36	09 50			10 25	10 36	10 50	10 56
Layton	d	00 41	06 56			07 34			08 22		08 37					09 43					10 43		
Blackpool North	a	00f50	07 03			07f43	08 05	08 18	08 29		08f46	09 05	09 20	09 25		09f50	10 00	10 20		10 35	10f50	11 00	11 05

Station		NT G	NT	NT A	NT H	TP 1◇ B	NT G	NT	NT A	NT H	TP 1◇ B	NT G	NT	NT A	NT H	TP 1◇ B	NT G	NT	NT A	NT H	TP 1◇ B	NT G
Colne	d		09 50					10 50					11 50					12 50				
Nelson	d		09 55					10 55					11 55					12 55				
Brierfield	d		09 58					10 58					11 58					12 58				
Burnley Central	d		10 03					11 03					12 03					13 03				
Burnley Barracks	d		10 05					11 05					12 05					13 05				
Leeds 10	41 d				09c51					10c51					11c51					12c51		
Burnley Manchester Road	41 d				10 57					11 57					12 57					13 57		
Rose Grove	d		10 08					11 08					12 08					13 08				
Hapton	d		10 11					11 11					12 11					13 11				
Huncoat	d		10 14					11 14					12 14					13 14				
Accrington	d		10 19		11 06			11 19		12 06			12 19		13 06			13 19		14 06		
Church & Oswaldtwistle	d		10 21					11 21					12 21					13 21				
Rishton	d		10 24					11 24					12 24					13 24				
Blackburn	a		10 33		11 14			11 33		12 14			12 33		13 14			13 33		14 14		
Manchester Victoria	94 ⛴ a		*11 51*					*12 51*					*13 51*					*14 51*				
Clitheroe	94 d		*09e40*					*10e40*					*11e40*					*12e40*				
Blackburn	d		10 35		11 15			11 35		12 15			12 35		13 15			13 35		14 15		
Mill Hill (Lancashire)	d		10 38					11 38					12 38					13 38				
Cherry Tree	d		10 40					11 40					12 40					13 40				
Pleasington	d		10 42					11 42					12 42					13 42				
Bamber Bridge	d		10 49					11 49					12 49					13 49				
Lostock Hall	d		10 52					11 52					12 52					13 52				
Preston 8	a		11 00		11 32			12 00		12 32			13 00		13 32			14 00		14 32		
	d	10 55	11 02	11 19	11 34	11 38	11 55	12 02	12 19	12 34	12 38	12 55	13 02	13 19	13 34	13 38	13 55	14 02	14 19	14 34	14 38	14 55
Salwick	d							12 09														
Kirkham & Wesham	d		11 11	11 28				12 13	12 28				13 11	13 28				14 11	14 28			
Moss Side	d		11 17					12 19					13 17					14 17				
Lytham	d		11 21					12 23					13 21					14 21				
Ansdell & Fairhaven	d		11 24					12 26					13 24					14 24				
St Annes-on-the-Sea	d		11 28					12 30					13 28					14 28				
Squires Gate	d		11 32					12 34					13 32					14 32				
Blackpool Pleasure Beach	d		11 34					12 36					13 34					14 34				
Blackpool South	a		11 39					12 39					13 39					14 39				
Poulton-le-Fylde	d			11 36	11 50	11 56			12 36	12 50	12 56			13 36	13 50	13 56			14 36	14 50	14 56	
Layton	d			11 44					12 43					13 43					14 43			
Blackpool North	a	11 20		11f51	12 00	12 05	12 20		12f50	13 00	13 05	13 21		13f50	14 00	14 05	14 20		14f50	15 00	15 05	15 20

For general notes see front of timetable
For details of catering facilities see Directory of Train Operators

- **A** From Manchester Victoria (Table 82)
- **B** From Manchester Airport (Table 82)
- **C** From 10 October
- **D** Until 3 October
- **E** From 18 July
- **G** From Liverpool Lime Street (Table 90)
- **H** From York (Table 40)
- **b** Until 11 July dep. 0603
- **c** Until 11 July dep. 7 mins. later
- **e** From 10 October dep. 5 mins. earlier
- **f** Until 3 October arr. 2 mins. earlier

For connections to and from London Euston, please refer to Table 65

Table 97

Saturdays

Colne, Burnley, Accrington and Blackburn → Preston → Blackpool

Network Diagram - see first page of Table 97

Station	d/a	NT	NT	NT	TP	NT	NT	NT	TP	NT	NT	NT	TP	NT	NT	NT	NT		NT	TP	NT	NT	NT	NT
			A	B	1 ◇ C	D		B	1 ◇ C	D		A	1 ◇ C	B	D		A		B	1 ◇ C	E	D		A
Colne	d	13 50					14 50				15 50					16 50							17 50	
Nelson	d	13 55					14 55				15 55					16 55							17 55	
Brierfield	d	13 58					14 58				15 58					16 58							17 58	
Burnley Central	d	14 03					15 03				16 03					17 03							18 03	
Burnley Barracks	d	14 05					15 05				16 05					17 05							18 05	
Leeds 10	41 d			13b51				14b51						15b51					16b51					
Burnley Manchester Road	41 d			14 57				15 57						16 58					17 57					
Rose Grove	d	14 08					15 08				16 08					17 08							18 08	
Hapton	d	14 11					15 11				16 11					17 11							18 11	
Huncoat	d	14 14					15 14				16 14					17 14							18 14	
Accrington	d	14 19		15 06			15 19	16 06			16 19			17 06		17 19			18 06				18 19	
Church & Oswaldtwistle	d	14 21					15 21				16 21					17 21							18 21	
Rishton	d	14 24					15 24				16 24					17 24							18 24	
Blackburn	a	14 33		15 14			15 33	16 14			16 33			17 14		17 34			18 14				18 34	
Manchester Victoria	94 a	15 53					16 40				17 54			18 26					19 22				19 52	
Clitheroe	94 d	13c40					14e40							16e40		17e09							18e09	
Blackburn	d	14 35		15 15			15 35	16 15			16 35			17 15		17 35			18 15				18 35	
Mill Hill (Lancashire)	d	14 38					15 38				16 38					17 38							18 38	
Cherry Tree	d	14 40					15 40				16 40					17 40							18 40	
Pleasington	d	14 42					15 42				16 42					17 42							18 42	
Bamber Bridge	d	14 49					15 49				16 49					17 49							18 49	
Lostock Hall	d	14 52					15 52				16 52					17 52							18 52	
Preston 8	a	15 00		15 32			16 00	16 32			17 00			17 32		18 00			18 33				19 00	
	d	15 02	15 19	15 34	15 38	15 55	16 02	16 34	16 38	16 55	17 02	17 21	17 32	17 36	17 55	18 02	18 18		18 34	18 40	18 50	18 55	19 02	19 20
Salwick	d						16 09																	
Kirkham & Wesham	d	15 11	15 28				16 13		16 47		17 11	17 30	17 41			18 11	18 27			18 49			19 11	19 29
Moss Side	d	15 17					16 19				17 17					18 17							19 17	
Lytham	d	15 21					16 23				17 21					18 21							19 21	
Ansdell & Fairhaven	d	15 24					16 26				17 24					18 24							19 24	
St Annes-on-the-Sea	d	15 28					16 30				17 28					18 28							19 28	
Squires Gate	d	15 32					16 34				17 32					18 32							19 32	
Blackpool Pleasure Beach	d	15 34					16 36				17 34					18 34							19 34	
Blackpool South	a	15 39					16 41				17 39					18 39							19 39	
Poulton-le-Fylde	d		15 36	15 50	15 56			16 50	16 57			17 38	17 51	17 56			18 35		18 50	18 59				19 37
Layton	d		15 43						17 00			17 43	17 54				18 43			19 02				19 43
Blackpool North	a		15f50	16 00	16 05	16 20		17 00	17 07	17 20		17f50	18 02	18 06	18 20		18f50		19 00	19 09	19f18	19 20		19f50

Station	d/a	NT	TP	NT	NT		NT	NT	TP	NT	NT	NT	NT	TP		NT	NT	TP	NT	NT	NT	TP	NT
		B	1 ◇ C		D		A	B	1 ◇ C		A	D	B	1 ◇ C			A	1 ◇ C		D	A	1 ◇ C	
Colne	d			18 50						19 50						20 50			21 44				22 55
Nelson	d			18 55						19 55						20 55			21 49				23 00
Brierfield	d			18 58						19 58						20 58			21 52				23 03
Burnley Central	d			19 03						20 03						21 03			21 57				23 08
Burnley Barracks	d			19 05						20 05						21 05			21 59				23 10
Leeds 10	41 d	17b51						18b51					19g51										
Burnley Manchester Road	41 d	18 57						19 57					20 57										
Rose Grove	d			19 08						20 08						21 08			22 02				23 13
Hapton	d			19 11						20 11						21 11			22 05				
Huncoat	d			19 14						20 14						21 14			22 08				
Accrington	d	19 06		19 19				20 06		20 19			21 06			21 19			22 13				23 20
Church & Oswaldtwistle	d			19 21						20 21						21 21			22 15				
Rishton	d			19 24						20 24						21 24			22 18				
Blackburn	a	19 14		19 33				20 14		20 33			21 14			21 33			22 23				23 28
Manchester Victoria	94 a	20 23		20 51						21 51						22 51			23 59				
Clitheroe	94 d			18e40						19e40						20e40			21e40				22e46
Blackburn	d	19 15		19 35				20 15		20 35			21 15			21 35			22 24				23 30
Mill Hill (Lancashire)	d			19 38						20 38						21 38			22 27				23 33
Cherry Tree	d			19 40						20 40						21 40			22 29				
Pleasington	d			19 42						20 42						21 42			22 31				
Bamber Bridge	d			19 49						20 49						21 49			22 38				23 41
Lostock Hall	d			19 52						20 52						21 52			22 41				23 43
Preston 8	a	19 32		20 00				20 32		21 00			21 32			22 02			22 49				23 54
	d	19 34	19 38	20 02	20 19		20 25	20 34	20 38	21 02	21 19	21 24	21 34	21 38			22 19	22 35	22 51	22 56	23 19	23 35	
Salwick	d																						
Kirkham & Wesham	d			20 11			20 35			21 11	21 28						22 28		23 00		23 28		
Moss Side	d			20 17						21 17									23 06				
Lytham	d			20 21						21 21									23 10				
Ansdell & Fairhaven	d			20 24						21 24									23 13				
St Annes-on-the-Sea	d			20 28						21 28									23 17				
Squires Gate	d			20 32						21 32									23 21				
Blackpool Pleasure Beach	d			20 34						21 34									23 23				
Blackpool South	a			20 39						21 39									23 28				
Poulton-le-Fylde	d	19 50	19 56				20 43	20 50	20 56		21 36		21 50	21 56			22 36	22 52			23 36	23 52	
Layton	d						20 47				21 40						22 40				23 40		
Blackpool North	a	20 00	20 05		20 44		20f56	21 00	21 06		21f50	21 53	22 00	22 06			22f50	23 01		23 21	23f50	00 01	

For general notes see front of timetable
For details of catering facilities see Directory of Train Operators

A From Manchester Victoria (Table 82)
B From York (Table 40)
C From Manchester Airport (Table 82)
D From Liverpool Lime Street (Table 90)
E From Hazel Grove (Table 86)
b Until 11 July dep. 7 mins. later
c From 10 October dep. 1335
e From 10 October dep. 5 mins. earlier
f Until 3 October arr. 2 mins. earlier
g Until 11 July dep. 4 mins. later

For connections to and from London Euston, please refer to Table 65

Table 97

Sundays

Colne, Burnley, Accrington and Blackburn → Preston → Blackpool

Network Diagram - see first page of Table 97

		NT A	TP 1◇ B	NT C	TP 1◇ D	NT A	TP 1◇ D		NT E	TP 1◇ B	NT A	NT G	NT C	NT		TP 1◇ H	NT E	NT J	NT A	TP 1◇ H	NT E		NT C	NT J	NT A
Colne	d											09 16	09 16												
Nelson	d											09 21	09 21												
Brierfield	d											09 24	09 24												
Burnley Central	d											09 29	09 29												
Burnley Barracks	d											09 31	09 31												
Leeds 10	41 d													08b45				09c35						10 34	
Burnley Manchester Road	41 d													09 50				10 39						11 39	
Rose Grove	d											09 34	09 34												
Hapton	d											09 37	09 37												
Huncoat	d											09 40	09 40												
Accrington	d											09 45	09 45	09 59				10 48						11 47	
Church & Oswaldtwistle	d											09 47	09 47												
Rishton	d											09 50	09 50												
Blackburn	a											09 55	09 55	10 07				10 56						11 55	
Manchester Victoria	94 a											*10 51*	*10 51*					*11 51*						*12 51*	
Clitheroe	94 d													*09e40*										*10 40*	
Blackburn	d											09 57	09 57	10 07				10 56						11 56	
Mill Hill (Lancashire)	d											10 00	10 00												
Cherry Tree	d											10 02	10 02												
Pleasington	d											10 04	10 04												
Bamber Bridge	d											10 11	10 11												
Lostock Hall	d											10 14	10 14												
Preston 8	a											10 22	10 22	10 27				11 13						12 13	
	d	00 11	08 32	08 49	08 57	09 19	09 34		09 39	09 51	10 19		10 24	10 29		10 34	10 40	11 15	11 21	11 34	11 39		11 44	12 14	12 20
Salwick	d																								
Kirkham & Wesham	d	00 21		08 58		09 28					10 28		10 33						11 31				11 53		12 29
Moss Side	d			09 04									10 39										11 59		
Lytham	d			09 08									10 43										12 03		
Ansdell & Fairhaven	d			09 11									10 46										12 06		
St Annes-on-the-Sea	d			09 15									10 50										12 10		
Squires Gate	d			09 19									10 54										12 14		
Blackpool Pleasure Beach	d			09 21									10 56										12 16		
Blackpool South	a			09 24									10 59										12 19		
Poulton-le-Fylde	d	00 29	08 49		09 14	09 36	09 51		09 57	10 08	10 36			10 46		10 51	10 59	11 32	11 39	11 51	11 57			12 31	12 37
Layton	d	00 33				09 41					10 41								11 44						12 42
Blackpool North	a	00 42	08 58		09 25	09 46	10 00		10 06	10 17	10 46			10 53		11 00	11 09	11 39	11 49	12 00	12 07			12 38	12 47

		TP 1◇ H	NT E	NT G	NT C	NT J		NT A	TP 1◇ H	NT E	NT C	NT J	NT A		TP 1◇ H	NT E	NT G	NT C	NT J	NT A		TP 1◇ H	NT E	NT C	NT J
Colne	d			11 35	11 35												13 35	13 35							
Nelson	d			11 40	11 40												13 40	13 40							
Brierfield	d			11 43	11 43												13 43	13 43							
Burnley Central	d			11 48	11 48												13 48	13 48							
Burnley Barracks	d			11 50	11 50												13 50	13 50							
Leeds 10	41 d					11f35						12 35							13g35						14 35
Burnley Manchester Road	41 d					12 39						13 39							14 39						15 39
Rose Grove	d			11 53	11 53												13 53	13 53							
Hapton	d			11 56	11 56												13 56	13 56							
Huncoat	d			11 59	11 59												13 59	13 59							
Accrington	d			12 04	12 04	12 47						13 47					14 04	14 04	14 47						15 47
Church & Oswaldtwistle	d			12 06	12 06												14 06	14 06							
Rishton	d			12 09	12 09												14 09	14 09							
Blackburn	a			12 14	12 14	12 55						13 55					14 14	14 14	14 55						15 55
Manchester Victoria	94 a					*13 51*						*14 51*							*15 51*						*16 51*
Clitheroe	94 d				*11e40*							*12e40*						*13e40*							*14e40*
Blackburn	d			12 16	12 16	12 56						13 56					14 16	14 16	14 56						15 56
Mill Hill (Lancashire)	d			12 19	12 19												14 19	14 19							
Cherry Tree	d			12 21	12 21												14 21	14 21							
Pleasington	d			12 23	12 23												14 23	14 23							
Bamber Bridge	d			12 30	12 30												14 30	14 30							
Lostock Hall	d			12 33	12 33												14 33	14 33							
Preston 8	a			12 42	12 42	13 13						14 13					14 41	14 42	15 13						16 13
	d	12 34	12 39		12 44	13 14		13 20	13 34	13 39	13 44	14 14	14 20		14 34	14 39		14 44	15 14	15 20		15 34	15 39	15 44	16 14
Salwick	d																								
Kirkham & Wesham	d				12 53			13 29			13 53		14 29					14 53		15 29				15 53	
Moss Side	d				12 59						13 59							14 59						15 59	
Lytham	d				13 03						14 03							15 03						16 03	
Ansdell & Fairhaven	d				13 06						14 06							15 06						16 06	
St Annes-on-the-Sea	d				13 10						14 10							15 10						16 10	
Squires Gate	d				13 14						14 14							15 14						16 14	
Blackpool Pleasure Beach	d				13 16						14 16							15 16						16 16	
Blackpool South	a				13 19						14 19							15 19						16 19	
Poulton-le-Fylde	d	12 51	12 57			13 31		13 37	13 51	13 57		14 30	14 37		14 51	14 57			15 32	15 37		15 51	15 57		16 31
Layton	d							13 42					14 42							15 43					
Blackpool North	a	13 00	13 07			13 38		13 47	14 00	14 07		14 38	14 47		15 00	15 07			15 40	15 48		16 00	16 07		16 38

For general notes see front of timetable
For details of catering facilities see Directory of Train Operators

- **A** From Manchester Victoria (Table 82)
- **B** From 13 September. From Manchester Airport (Table 82)
- **C** Until 1 November
- **D** Until 6 September. From Manchester Airport (Table 82)
- **E** From Liverpool Lime Street (Table 90)
- **G** From 8 November
- **H** From Manchester Airport (Table 82)
- **J** From York (Table 40)
- **b** Until 12 July dep. 0902
- **c** Until 12 July dep. 0945
- **e** Until 6 September only
- **f** Until 12 July dep. 1149
- **g** Until 12 July dep. 1346

For connections to and from London Euston, please refer to Table 65

Table 97

Sundays

Colne, Burnley, Accrington and Blackburn → Preston → Blackpool

Network Diagram - see first page of Table 97

		NT	TP	NT	NT	NT	NT	NT	TP	NT	NT	NT	NT	TP	NT	NT	NT	NT	NT	NT	TP	NT
			1 ◇						1 ◇					1 ◇							1 ◇	
		A	B	C	D	E	G	A	B	C	E	G	A	B	C	D	E	H	G	A	B	C
Colne	d				15 35	15 35										17 35	17 35					
Nelson	d				15 40	15 40										17 40	17 40					
Brierfield	d				15 43	15 43										17 43	17 43					
Burnley Central	d				15 48	15 48										17 48	17 48					
Burnley Barracks	d				15 50	15 50										17 50	17 50					
Leeds 10	41 d						15b35					16 35							17c35			
Burnley Manchester Road	41 d						16 39					17 39							18 39			
Rose Grove	d				15 53	15 53										17 53	17 53					
Hapton	d				15 56	15 56										17 56	17 56					
Huncoat	d				15 59	15 59										17 59	17 59					
Accrington	d				16 04	16 04	16 47					17 47				18 04	18 04		18 47			
Church & Oswaldtwistle	d				16 06	16 06										18 06	18 06					
Rishton	d				16 09	16 09										18 09	18 09					
Blackburn	a				16 14	16 14	16 55					17 55				18 14	18 14		18 55			
Manchester Victoria	94 a						*17 51*					*18 51*							*19 51*			
Clitheroe	94 d					*15e40*						*16e40*					*17e40*	17 58				
Blackburn	d				16 16	16 16	16 56					17 56				18 16	18 16	18 28	18 56			
Mill Hill (Lancashire)	d				16 19	16 19										18 19	18 19					
Cherry Tree	d				16 21	16 21										18 21	18 21					
Pleasington	d				16 23	16 23										18 23	18 23					
Bamber Bridge	d				16 30	16 30										18 30	18 30	18 37				
Lostock Hall	d				16 33	16 33										18 33	18 33	18 40				
Preston 8	a				16 43	16 42	17 13					18 13				18 43	18 42	18 50	19 13			
	d	16 20	16 34	16 39		16 44	17 14	17 20	17 34	17 39	17 44	18 14	18 20	18 34	18 39		18 44		19 14	19 20	19 34	19 39
Salwick	d																					
Kirkham & Wesham	d	16 29				16 53		17 29			17 53		18 29				18 53			19 29		
Moss Side	d					16 59					17 59						18 59					
Lytham	d					17 03					18 03						19 03					
Ansdell & Fairhaven	d					17 06					18 06						19 06					
St Annes-on-the-Sea	d					17 10					18 10						19 10					
Squires Gate	d					17 14					18 14						19 14					
Blackpool Pleasure Beach	d					17 16					18 16						19 16					
Blackpool South	a					17 19					18 19						19 19					
Poulton-le-Fylde	d	16 37	16 51	16 57			17 31	17 37	17 51	17 57		18 31	18 37	18 51	18 57				19 31	19 37	19 51	19 57
Layton	d	16 42						17 42					18 42							19 42		
Blackpool North	a	16 47	17 00	17 07			17 38	17 47	18 00	18 07		18 38	18 47	19 00	19 07				19 38	19 47	20 00	20 07

		NT	NT	NT	TP	NT	NT	NT	NT	NT	NT	TP	NT	NT	NT	TP	NT	NT	NT	TP
					1 ◇							1 ◇				1 ◇				1 ◇
		E	G	A	B	C	D	E	H	G	A	B	C	G	A	B	C		C	B
Colne	d						19 35	19 35										21 35		
Nelson	d						19 40	19 40										21 40		
Brierfield	d						19 43	19 43										21 43		
Burnley Central	d						19 48	19 48										21 48		
Burnley Barracks	d						19 50	19 50										21 50		
Leeds 10	41 d		18 34							19f35				20 35						
Burnley Manchester Road	41 d		19 39							20 39				21 39						
Rose Grove	d						19 53	19 53										21 53		
Hapton	d						19 56	19 56										21 56		
Huncoat	d						19 59	19 59										21 59		
Accrington	d		19 47				20 04	20 04		20 47				21 47				22 04		
Church & Oswaldtwistle	d						20 06	20 06										22 06		
Rishton	d						20 09	20 09										22 09		
Blackburn	a		19 56				20 14	20 14		20 55				21 55				22 14		
Manchester Victoria	94 a		*20 51*							*21 51*				*22 51*				*23 51*		
Clitheroe	94 d		*18e40*					*19e40*	19 55					*20e40*				*21e40*		
Blackburn	d		19 57				20 16	20 16	20 25	20 56				21 56				22 16		
Mill Hill (Lancashire)	d						20 19	20 19										22 19		
Cherry Tree	d						20 21	20 21										22 21		
Pleasington	d						20 23	20 23										22 23		
Bamber Bridge	d						20 30	20 30	20 34									22 30		
Lostock Hall	d						20 33	20 33	20 38									22 33		
Preston 8	a		20 14				20 43	20 42	20 47	21 13				22 13				22 42		
	d	19 44	20 15	20 20	20 34	20 39		20 44	20 49	21 14	21 20	21 34	21 39	22 14	22 20	22 34	22 38		23 38	23 47
Salwick	d																			
Kirkham & Wesham	d	19 53		20 29				20 53	20 59		21 29				22 29					23 56
Moss Side	d	19 59						20 59												
Lytham	d	20 03						21 03												
Ansdell & Fairhaven	d	20 06						21 06												
St Annes-on-the-Sea	d	20 10						21 10												
Squires Gate	d	20 14						21 14												
Blackpool Pleasure Beach	d	20 16						21 16												
Blackpool South	a	20 19						21 19												
Poulton-le-Fylde	d		20 32	20 37	20 51	20 57			21 07	21 31	21 37	21 51	21 57	22 31	22 37	22 51	22 57		23 55	00 05
Layton	d			20 43							21 42				22 42					
Blackpool North	a		20 39	20 48	21 00	21 07			21 16	21 38	21 47	22 00	22 07	22 38	22 47	23 00	23 07		00 04	00 14

For general notes see front of timetable
For details of catering facilities see Directory of Train Operators

A From Manchester Victoria (Table 82)
B From Manchester Airport (Table 82)
C From Liverpool Lime Street (Table 90)
D From 8 November
E Until 1 November
G From York (Table 40)
H Until 6 September. From Carlisle (Table 36)
b Until 12 July dep. 1547
c Until 12 July dep. 1746
e Until 6 September only
f Until 12 July dep. 1949

For connections to and from London Euston, please refer to Table 65

Lancaster — Morecambe and Heysham

Network Diagram - see first page of Table 97

Mondays to Fridays

Miles			TP 1 A	NT	NT	NT	NT	NT	NT	NT B	NT	NT	NT B	NT	NT	NT	NT B	NT	NT	NT	NT	NT B	NT	NT	NT	NT	NT
0	Lancaster 3 .. 82	d	05 45	06 38	07 25	07 58	08 35	09 15	10 05	10 27	11 23	12 02	12 28	13 44	14 27	15 25	16 03	16 19	16 51	17 38	18 33	18 49	19 40	20 22	21 03	22 06	22 35
2½	Bare Lane	d	05 51	06 44	07 31	08 04	08 41	09 21	10 11	10 34	11 29	12 08	12 34	13 50	14 33	15 31	16 09	16 26	16 57	17 44	18 39	18 55	19 46	20 28	21 09	22 12	22 41
4¼	Morecambe	a	05 55	06 49	07 36	08 09	08 46	09 26	10 16	10 40	11 34	12 13	12 39	13 55	14 38	15 36	16 13	16 30	17 02	17 49	18 44	19 01	19 50	20 32	21 13	22 16	22 45
—		d	.	.	.	.	.	.	.	.	.	.	12 42	.	.	.	.	.	.	.	.	.	.	.	.	.	.
8½	Heysham Port	a	...	...	...	...	...	...	...	...	...	...	12 57	...	...	...	...	...	...	...	...	...	...	...	...	...	...

Saturdays

		TP 1 A	NT	NT	NT	NT	NT	NT	NT B	NT	NT	NT B	NT	NT	NT	NT C	NT D	NT	NT	NT	NT	NT B	NT E	NT G	NT	NT	NT	NT
Lancaster 6 .. 82	d	05 45	06 38	07 25	07 57	08 35	09 15	10 05	10 27	11 23	12 02	12 25	13 24	14 27	15 25	15 49	15 54	16 03	17 04	17 37	18 21	18 47	19 37	19 40	20 22	21 03	22 06	22 35
Bare Lane	d	05 51	06 44	07 31	08 03	08 41	09 21	10 11	10 34	11 29	12 08	12 31	13 30	14 33	15 31	15 56	16 00	16 09	17 10	17 43	18 27	18 53	19 43	19 46	20 28	21 09	22 12	22 41
Morecambe	a	05 55	06 49	07 36	08 08	08 46	09 26	10 16	10 40	11 34	12 13	12 36	13 35	14 38	15 36	16 02	16 06	16 14	17 15	17 48	18 32	18 59	19 47	19 50	20 32	21 13	22 16	22 45
	d	.	.	.	.	.	.	.	.	.	.	12 39	.	.	.	.	.	.	.	.	.	.	.	.	.	.	.	.
Heysham Port	a	...	...	...	...	...	...	...	...	...	...	12 54	...	...	...	...	...	...	...	...	...	...	...	...	...	...	...	...

Sundays

		NT H	NT J	NT K	NT L	NT J	NT H	NT J	NT N	NT	NT J	NT J	NT B	NT B	NT
Lancaster 6 .. 82	d	10 45	11 05	11 54	11 58	12 04	12 59	13 20	14 27	15 04	15 45	16 26	16 50	19 20	21 18
Bare Lane	d	10 51	11 11	12 00	12 04	12 10	13 05	13 26	14 34	15 10	15 51	16 32	16 56	19 26	21 24
Morecambe	a	10 55	11 15	12 05	12 09	12 14	13 09	13 31	14 39	15 14	15 55	16 36	17 01	19 30	21 28
	d	.	.	12 08	12 12	.	.	13 34	.	.	.	.	.	.	.
Heysham Port	a	...	...	12 23	12 27	...	...	13 49	...	...	...	...	...	...	...

Mondays to Fridays

Miles			NT	NT	NT	NT	NT	NT	NT	NT Q	NT	NT	NT Q	NT	NT	NT	NT Q	NT	NT U	NT	NT	NT Q	NT	NT	NT	NT	NT V
0	Heysham Port	d	...	...	...	...	...	...	...	...	...	...	13 15	...	...	...	...	...	...	...	...	...	...	...	...	...	...
4¼	Morecambe	a	.	.	.	.	.	.	.	.	.	.	13 25	.	.	.	.	.	.	.	.	.	.	.	.	.	.
—		d	06 19	07 03	07 40	08 11	08 51	09 41	10 33	10 41	11 39	12 32	13 29	13 58	14 42	15 45	16 19	16 34	17 03	17 56	19 00	19 08	19 55	20 40	21 36	22 20	22 55
6	Bare Lane	d	06 23	07 07	07 44	08 15	08 55	09 45	10 37	10 45	11 43	12 36	13 36	14 02	14 46	15 49	16a23	16 38	17 07	18 00	19 04	19 12	19 59	20 44	21 40	22 24	22 59
8½	Lancaster 3 .. 82	a	06 30	07 14	07 51	08 22	09 03	09 52	10 44	10 52	11 50	12 43	13 42	14 09	14 53	15 56	.....	16 45	17 14	18 07	19 11	19 19	20 06	20 51	21 47	22 31	23 05

Saturdays

		NT	NT	NT	NT	NT	NT	NT	NT Q	NT	NT G	NT E	NT Q	NT	NT	NT	NT Q	NT	NT	NT	NT	NT Q	NT E	NT G	NT	NT	NT
Heysham Port	d	...	...	...	...	...	...	...	...	...	...	...	13 15	...	...	...	...	...	...	...	...	...	...	...	...	...	...
Morecambe	a	.	.	.	.	.	.	.	.	.	.	.	13 25	.	.	.	.	.	.	.	.	.	.	.	.	.	.
	d	06 19	07 03	07 38	08 12	08 51	09 41	10 33	10 41	11 40	12 32	12 35	13 29	13 58	14 42	15 44	16 19	16 40	17 20	17 56	18 58	19 09	19 51	19 55	20 40	21 36	22 20
Bare Lane	d	06 23	07 07	07 42	08 16	08 55	09 45	10 37	10 45	11 44	12 36	12 39	13 36	14 02	14 46	15 48	16 24	16 44	17 24	18 00	19 02	19 13	19 55	19 59	20 44	21 40	22 24
Lancaster 6 .. 82	a	06 30	07 14	07 49	08 23	09 03	09 52	10 44	10 52	11 51	12 43	12 46	13 42	14 09	14 53	15 54	16 30	16 50	17 31	18 07	19 09	19 20	20 02	20 06	20 51	21 47	22 31

Sundays

		NT J	NT J	NT N	NT J	NT J	NT J	NT N	NT	NT J	NT J	NT Q	NT Q	NT
Heysham Port	d	...	...	...	12 42	...	14 00	...	...	...	...	...	...	...
Morecambe	a	.	.	.	12 52	.	14 10	.	.	.	.	.	.	.
	d	11 20	11 35	12 20	12 56	13 23	14 15	14 35	15 21	16 03	16 42	17 45	20 00	21 41
Bare Lane	d	11 24	11 39	12 24	13 03	13 27	14 22	14 39	15 25	16 07	16 46	17 49	20 04	21 45
Lancaster 6 .. 82	a	11 31	11 45	12 30	13 12	13 33	14 31	14 46	15 31	16 15	16 52	17 55	20 11	21 51

For general notes see front of timetable
For details of catering facilities see Directory of Train Operators

- **A** To Windermere (Table 83)
- **B** From Leeds (Table 36)
- **C** Until 31 October. From Leeds (Table 36)
- **D** From 7 November. From Leeds (Table 36)
- **E** From 7 November
- **G** Until 31 October
- **H** Until 13 September. From Leeds (Table 36)
- **J** Until 13 September
- **K** 19 July to 6 September
- **L** Until 12 July and 13 September
- **N** Until 13 September. To Leeds (Table 36)
- **Q** To Leeds (Table 36)
- **U** To Barrow-in-Furness (Table 82)
- **V** To Preston (Table 65)

To and from The Isle of Man via Heysham and Liverpool

One Class only on ship

		R	NT	R	R	R	R	R	R	R
		A			B	C	D	E	G	H
London Euston 15	65 d	.	.	.	.	.	.	.	.	.
Birmingham New Street 12	65 d	.	.	.	.	.	.	.	.	.
Crewe 10	65 d	.	.	.	.	.	.	.	.	.
Manchester Piccadilly 10	82, 89 d	.	.	.	.	.	.	.	.	.
Preston 10	82 d	.	.	.	.	.	.	.	.	.
Lancaster 8	98 d	.	12 28	.	.	.	.	.	.	.
Morecambe	98 d	.	12 42	.	.	.	.	.	.	.
Heysham Port	a	.	12 57	.	.	.	.	.	.	.
Liverpool Lime Street	a	.	.	.	.	.	.	.	.	.
Liverpool Landing Stage	d	11 30	.	.	18 00	18 30	19 30	20 00	20 30	21 30
Heysham Port	d	.	.	14 15	.	.	.	.	.	.
Douglas (Isle of Man)	a	14 00	.	17 45	20 30	21 00	22 00	22 30	23 00	23 59

Saturdays

One Class only on ship

		R	NT	R	R	R	R
		J		K	L	N	Q
London Euston 15	65 d	.	.	.	.	.	.
Birmingham New Street 12	65 d	.	.	.	.	.	.
Crewe 10	65 d	.	.	.	.	.	.
Manchester Piccadilly 10	82, 89 d	.	.	.	.	.	.
Preston 10	82 d	.	.	.	.	.	.
Lancaster 8	98 d	.	12 25	.	.	.	.
Morecambe	98 d	.	12 39	.	.	.	.
Heysham Port	a	.	12 54	.	.	.	.
Liverpool Lime Street	a	.	.	.	.	.	.
Liverpool Landing Stage	d	11 30	.	.	14b00	19 30	21 30
Heysham Port	d	.	.	14 15	.	.	.
Douglas (Isle of Man)	a	14 00	.	17 45	18 15	22 00	23 59

Sundays

One Class only on ship

		R	NT	R	R	R	R
		U	V	X	Y	Z	AA
London Euston 15	65 d	.	.	.	.	.	.
Birmingham New Street 12	65 d	.	.	.	.	.	.
Crewe 10	65 d	.	.	.	.	.	.
Manchester Piccadilly 10	82, 89 d	.	.	.	.	.	.
Preston 10	82 d	.	.	.	.	.	.
Lancaster 8	98 d	.	13 20	.	.	.	.
Morecambe	98 d	.	13 34	.	.	.	.
Heysham Port	a	.	13 49	.	.	.	.
Liverpool Lime Street	a	.	.	.	.	.	.
Liverpool Landing Stage	d	11 30	.	.	14b00	19 30	20 00
Heysham Port	d	.	.	14 15	.	.	.
Douglas (Isle of Man)	a	14 00	.	17 45	18 15	22 00	22 30

For general notes see front of timetable
For details of catering facilities see Directory of Train Operators

A 18 May, 25 May to 2 June, 17 June to 7 September, 11, 14, 18, 21, 25 and 28 September and 2 October
B 3 June
C 12 June
D Until 26 May, 17 June to 26 August, 8 September to 19 October and 22, 26 and 29 October
E 1 June
G 4 June, 27, 28 and 31 August and 1 to 7 September
H 27, 28 and 29 May and 5 June
J 23 May, 20 June and 3 October
K Until 31 October
L From 7 November
N 23 May, 20 June to 22 August, 12 September to 31 October
Q 30 May
U 21, 28 June and 5 July, 19 July to 16 August
V Until 13 September
X Until 1 November
Y From 8 November
Z 17 and 24 May, 21 June to 16 August, 13 September to 1 November
AA 31 May
b Sailing departs from Birkenhead

Reservations: Customers, including all children, must obtain an advance reservation for the ship. This can be obtained free of charge from stations, appointed Agents or direct from The Isle of Man Steam Packet Company Offices in Douglas, Isle of Man.Customers without a reservation may not be able to travel if the ship is fully reserved.

Customers travelling via Liverpool should allow a minimum of 45 minutes for the transfer to and from the ship. Bus transfers between Liverpool Lime Street and the Landing Stage are available free of charge for customers with through rail tickets.

To and from The Isle of Man via Heysham and Liverpool

One Class only on ship

Mondays to Fridays

		A	B	C	D	E	G	NT	H	J
		R	R	R	R	R	R		R	R
Douglas (Isle of Man)	⛴ d	07 00	07 30	08 00	08 15	08 45	09 15		15 30	17 15
Heysham Port	⛴ a			11 30	11 45	12 15	12 45			
Liverpool Landing Stage	⛴ a	09 30	10 00						18 00	19 45
Liverpool Lime Street	d									
Heysham Port	d							13 15		
Morecambe	98 a							13 25		
Lancaster [8]	98 a							13 42		
Preston [10]	82 a									
Manchester Piccadilly [10]	82, 89 ⛴ a									
Crewe [10]	65 a									
Birmingham New Street [12]	65 a									
London Euston [15]	65 a									

Saturdays

One Class only on ship

		K	L	N	Q	U	NT	V	X
		R	R	R	R	R		R	R
Douglas (Isle of Man)	⛴ d	07 30	08 00	08 00	08 15	08 45		15 30	17 15
Heysham Port	⛴ a			11 30	11 45	12 15			
Liverpool Landing Stage	⛴ a	10 00	12b15					18 00	20 45
Liverpool Lime Street	d								
Heysham Port	d						13 15		
Morecambe	98 a						13 25		
Lancaster [8]	98 a						13 42		
Preston [10]	82 a								
Manchester Piccadilly [10]	82, 89 ⛴ a								
Crewe [10]	65 a								
Birmingham New Street [12]	65 a								
London Euston [15]	65 a								

Sundays

One Class only on ship

		Y	Z	AA	NT BB	CC
		R	R	R		R
Douglas (Isle of Man)	⛴ d	07 30	08 00	08 45		15 30
Heysham Port	⛴ a			12 15		
Liverpool Landing Stage	⛴ a	10 00	12b15			18 00
Liverpool Lime Street	d					
Heysham Port	d				12 42	
Morecambe	98 a				12 52	
Lancaster [8]	98 a				13 12	
Preston [10]	82 a					
Manchester Piccadilly [10]	82, 89 ⛴ a					
Crewe [10]	65 a					
Birmingham New Street [12]	65 a					
London Euston [15]	65 a					

For general notes see front of timetable
For details of catering facilities see Directory of Train Operators

- **A** 1, 2 and 4 June
- **B** 18 May, 25 to 29 May, 17 June to 27 August, 31 August to 7 September, 11, 14, 18, 21, 25 and 28 September and 2 and 9 October
- **C** 2 to 5 June and 30 June
- **D** 20, 21 and 28 August
- **E** Until 27 May, 1 and 8 June, 10 to 29 June, 1 July to 19 August, 24 to 27 August and from 31 August
- **G** 9 June
- **H** Until 26 May, 1 and 4 June, 17 June to 28 August, 7 September to 19 October and 22, 26, 29 and 30 October
- **J** 27, 28 and 29 May
- **K** 23 and 30 May, 20 June to 22 August, 5 September to 3 October
- **L** From 7 November
- **N** 30 May and 6 June
- **Q** 22 and 29 August
- **U** 23 May, 13 June to 15 August, 5 September to 31 October
- **V** 23 May, 20 June to 29 August, 12 September to 3 October
- **X** 30 May
- **Y** 21, 28 June and 5 July, 19 July to 16 August
- **Z** From 8 November
- **AA** Until 1 November
- **BB** Until 13 September
- **CC** 17, 24 and 31 May, 21 June to 30 August, 13 September to 1 November
- **b** Sailing arrives at Birkenhead

Reservations: Customers, including all children, must obtain an advance reservation for the ship. This can be obtained free of charge from stations, appointed Agents or direct from The Isle of Man Steam Packet Company Offices in Douglas, Isle of Man. Customers without a reservation may not be able to travel if the ship is fully reserved.

Customers travelling via Liverpool should allow a minimum of 45 minutes for the transfer to and from the ship. Bus transfers between Liverpool Lime Street and the Landing Stage are available free of charge for customers with through rail tickets.

Ormskirk — Preston

Network Diagram - see first page of Table 97

Miles			NT	NT	NT	NT	NT	NT	NT	NT	NT	NT	NT	NT
—	Liverpool Central 10	103 d	06 10	07 25	08 40	10 10	11 40	12 55	14 10	15 55	17 10	18 25	19 40	21 40
0	**Ormskirk**	d	06 58	08 06	09 17	10 54	12 17	13 40	14 53	16 38	17 52	19 08	20 19	22 17
2½	Burscough Junction	d	07 02	08 10	09 21	10 58	12 21	13 44	14 57	16 42	17 56	19 12	20 23	22 21
5½	Rufford	d	07 07	08 15	09 25	11 03	12 25	13 49	15 01	16 46	18 01	19 17	20 27	22 25
8	Croston	d	07 11	08 19	09 30	11 07	12 30	13 54	15 06	16 51	18 06	19 21	20 32	22 30
15	**Preston 3**	a	07 29	08 36	09 47	11 24	12 47	14 12	15b23	17 07	18 23	19 39	20 49	22 46

Mondays to Saturdays

Miles			NT	NT	NT	NT	NT	NT	NT	NT	NT	NT	NT	NT
0	**Preston 3**	d	06 25	07 33	08 41	10 07	11 32	12 59	14 17	15 39	17 10	18 34	19 42	21 37
7	Croston	d	06 36	07 45	08 52	10 19	11 43	13 11	14 28	15 51	17 22	18 47	19 53	21 49
9½	Rufford	d	06 41	07 50	08 57	10 24	11 48	13 16	14 33	15 56	17 27	18 51	19 58	21 53
12½	Burscough Junction	d	06 46	07 55	09 02	10 29	11 53	13 21	14 38	16 01	17 32	18 56	20 03	21 58
15	**Ormskirk**	a	06 55	08 04	09 11	10 38	12 00	13 30	14 45	16 10	17 41	19 05	20 12	22 07
—	Liverpool Central 10	103 a	07 35	08 50	09 50	11 20	12 35	14 05	15 20	16 50	18 20	19 50	20 50	22 50

For general notes see front of timetable
For details of catering facilities see Directory of Train Operators

b Saturdays arr. 1 minute later

No Sunday Service

Barrow-in-Furness → Whitehaven and Carlisle

Network Diagram - see first page of Table 97

Miles			NT	NT	NT	NT	NT		NT	NT	NT	NT	NT		NT	NT	NT	NT	NT	NT	NT	NT	NT	NT		
					A					A																
—	Lancaster 6	82 d			05 42				07 36	08 58	10 16				12 14	13 32	15 33	16 14	16 54		18 25			20 14		
0	**Barrow-in-Furness**	d		06 00	06 50	08 01			09 10	10 11	11 19		12 31		13 31	14 54	16 41	17 28	18 05		19 35			21 25		
6	Askam	d		06 10	07 00	08 11			09 20	10 21	11 29		12 41		13 41	15 04	16 51	17 40	18 15		19 45			21 35		
9¼	Kirkby-in-Furness	d		06 14	07x04	08x15			09x24	10x25	11x33		12x45		13x45	15x08	16x55	17x44	18x19		19x49			21x39		
11¼	Foxfield	d		06x18	07x08	08x18			09x27	10x28	11x36		12x48		13x48	15x11	16x58	17x48	18x22		19x52			21x42		
13½	Green Road	d		06x24	07x12	08x22			09x31	10x32	11x40		12x52		13x52	15x15	17x02	17x51	18x26		19x56			21x46		
16	Millom	a		06 29	07 19	08 28			09 37	10 38	11 46		12 58		13 58	15 21	17 08	17 58	18 35		20 05			21 55		
—		d		06 29	07 19	08 29			09 38	10 39	11 47		12 59		13 58	15 22	17 09	17 58								
19	Silecroft	d		06x34	07x24				09x42	10x43	11x51		13x03		14x03	15x26	17x13	18x03								
24½	Bootle	d		06x41	07x31				09x49	10x50	11x58		13x10		14x09	15x33	17x20	18x09								
29¼	Ravenglass for Eskdale	d		06 47	07 37	08 44			09 55	10 56	12 04		13 15		14 15	15 39	17 26	18 15								
31	Drigg	d		06x51	07x41				09x58	10x59	12x07		13x18		14x18	15x42	17x29	18x18								
33¼	Seascale	d		06x54	07x44	08x49			10x01	11x02	12x10		13x21		14x21	15x45	17x32	18x21								
35	Sellafield	d		07 02	07 51	08a58			10 10	11 10	12 15		13 28		14 27	15 51	17 39	18 27								
37	Braystones	d		07x05	07x54										14x31			18x31								
38¼	Nethertown	d		07x08	07x57										14x33			18x33								
41¼	St Bees	d		07 12	08 01				10 20	11 19	12 25		13 38		14 38	16 00	17 49	18b45								
44¾	Corkickle	d		07x17	08x06				10x25	11x24	12x30		13x43		14x43	16x05	17x54	18x50								
45¾	**Whitehaven**	a		07 20	08 10				10 27	11 27	12 33		13 45		14 46	16 09	17 57	18 53								
—		d	06 30	07 25	08 11		09 02		10 28	11 29	12 35	13 05	13 47		14 48	16 11	17 58	18 55		19 31		20 30	21 50			
47	Parton	d	06x33	07x29	08x15		09x05		10x31	11x32	12x39		13x50		14x51	16x15	18x02	18x58		19x34		20x33	21x53			
50½	Harrington	d	06x41	07x37	08x23		09x13		10x40	11x40	12x47		13x58		14x59	16x23	18x10	19x06		19x42		20x41	22x01			
52¼	**Workington**	d	06 48	07 43	08 29		09 20		10 46	11 47	12 53	13 22	14 05		15 06	16 29	18 16	19 12		19 49		20 48	22a10			
56	Flimby	d	06x52	07x48	08x34		09x24		10x50	11x51	12x58		14x09		15x10	16x34	18x21	19x17		19x53		20x52				
58	Maryport	d	06 56	07 51	08 37		09 28		10 54	11 55	13 01	13 30	14 13		15 14	16 37	18 26	19 20		19 57		20 56				
65½	Aspatria	d	07x05	08x01	08x47		09x37		11x03	12x04	13x11		14x22		15x23	16x47	18x36	19x30		20x06		21x05				
71¾	Wigton	d	07 15	08 11	08 57		09 47		11 13	12 14	13 21	13 50	14 32		15 33	16 57	18 46	19 40		20 16		21 15				
81¼	Dalston	d	07x24	08x19	09x05		09x56		11x22	12x23	13x29		14x41		15x42	17x05	18x54	19x48		20x25		21x24				
85¼	**Carlisle 8**	a	07 38	08 34	09 21		10 13		11 37	12 39	13 45	14 11	14 57		15 58	17 21	19 08	20 04		20 41		21 39				

Saturdays

		NT	NT	NT		NT	NT	NT		NT	NT	NT		NT	NT	NT		NT	NT	NT	NT	NT	NT	NT		
										A																
Lancaster 6	82 d							07 36		09 02	10 20			11 28	12 14	13 32		14 22	16 14	16 59		18 14		20 18		
Barrow-in-Furness	d		06 00	07 05		08 01		09 07		10 11	11 22			12 34	13 50	14 50		15 33	17 25	18 10		19 30		21 25		
Askam	d		06 10	07 15		08 11		09 17		10 21	11 32			12 44	14 00	15 00		15 43	17 35	18 20		19 40		21 35		
Kirkby-in-Furness	d		06x14	07x19		08x15		09x21		10x25	11x36			12x48	14x04	15x04		15x47	17x39	18x24		19x44		21x39		
Foxfield	d		06x17	07x23		08x18		09x24		10x28	11x39			12x51	14x07	15x07		15x50	17x42	18x27		19x47		21x42		
Green Road	d		06x21	07x27		08x22		09x28		10x32	11x43			12x55	14x11	15x11		15x54	17x46	18x31		19x51		21x46		
Millom	a		06 25	07 34		08 28		09 34		10 38	11 49			13 01	14 17	15 17		16 00	17 52	18 40		20 00		21 55		
	d		06 26	07 34		08 29		09 35		10 39	11 50			13 02	14 18	15 18		16 01	17 53							
Silecroft	d		06x30	07x39				09x39		10x43	11x54			13x06	14x22	15x22		16x05	17x57							
Bootle	d		06x37	07x46				09x46		10x50	12x01			13x13	14x29	15x29		16x12	18x04							
Ravenglass for Eskdale	d		06 42	07 52		08 44		09 52		10 56	12 07			13 19	14 35	15 35		16 18	18 10							
Drigg	d		06x45	07x56				09x55		10x59	12x10			13x22	14x38	15x38		16x21	18x13							
Seascale	d		06x50	07x59		08x49		09x58		11x04	12x13			13x25	14x41	15x41		16x24	18x16							
Sellafield	d		06 55	08 06		08a58		10 04		11 10	12 19			13 31	14 47	15c51		16 30	18 22							
Braystones	d		06x59	08x09														16x34	18x26							
Nethertown	d		07x01	08x12														16x36	18x28							
St Bees	d		07 06	08 16				10 14		11 19	12 29			13 40	14 56	16 01		16c46	18 33							
Corkickle	d		07x11	08x21				10x19		11x24	12x34			13x45	15x01	16x06		16x51	18x38							
Whitehaven	a		07 14	08 25				10 22		11 27	12 39			13 49	15 05	16 09		16 54	18 41							
	d	06 30	07 17	08 26			09 15	10 24		11 29		12 54		13 51	15 06	16 11		16 56	18 43		19 31		20 30			
Parton	d	06x33	07x21	08x30			09x18	10x27		11x32		12x57		13x54	15x10	16x15		17x00	18x46		19x34		20x33			
Harrington	d	06x41	07x29	08x38			09x26	10x35		11x40		13x05		14x02	15x18	16x23		17x08	18x54		19x42		20x41			
Workington	d	06 48	07 36	08 44			09 33	10 42		11 47		13 12		14 09	15 24	16 29		17 14	19 01		19 49		20 48			
Flimby	d	06x52	07x40	08x49			09x37	10x46		11x51		13x16		14x13	15x29	16x34		17x19	19x05		19x53		20x52			
Maryport	d	06 56	07 44	08 52			09 41	10 50		11 55		13 20		14 17	15 32	16 37		17 22	19 09		19 57		20 56			
Aspatria	d	07x05	07x53	09x02			09x50	10x59		12x04		13x29		14x26	15x42	16x47		17x32	19x18		20x06		21x05			
Wigton	d	07 15	08 03	09 12			10 00	11 09		12 14		13 39		14 36	15 52	16 57		17 42	19 28		20 16		21 15			
Dalston	d	07x24	08x12	09x20			10x08	11x18		12x23		13x48		14x45	16x00	17x05		17x50	19x37		20x25		21x24			
Carlisle 8	a	07 38	08 26	09 36			10 24	11 34		12 39		14 04		15 01	16 16	17 21		18 06	19 53		20 41		21 39			

Sundays

		NT					NT					NT
Whitehaven	d	12 57					16 28					20 28
Parton	d	13x00					16x31					20x31
Harrington	d	13x08					16x39					20x39
Workington	d	13 15					16 46					20 46
Flimby	d	13x19					16x50					20x50
Maryport	d	13 23					16 54					20 54
Aspatria	d	13x32					17x03					21x03
Wigton	d	13 42					17 13					21 13
Dalston	d	13x50					17x21					21x21
Carlisle 8	a	14 07					17 37					21 38

For general notes see front of timetable
For details of catering facilities see Directory of Train Operators

A From Preston (Table 82)
b Arr. 1838
c Arr. 5 mins. earlier

No Sunday Service Whitehaven to Barrow-in-Furness

Carlisle and Whitehaven → Barrow-in-Furness

Network Diagram - see first page of Table 97

Mondays to Fridays

Miles	Station		NT B	NT	NT	NT	NT	NT	NT	NT	NT	NT	NT	NT B	NT	NT	NT C	NT	NT	NT	NT	NT
0	**Carlisle** 8	d				07 44		08 44	09 40	10 43	11 49	12 47	14 20	15 12	16 31	17 27	18 11		19 15	20 33		21 50
4	Dalston	d				07x52		08x52	09x48	10x51	11x57	12x55	14x28	15x20	16x39	17x35	18x19		19x23	20x41		21x58
11½	Wigton	d				08 01		09 01	09 57	11 00	12 06	13 04	14 37	15 29	16 48	17 44	18 28		19 32	20 50		22 07
19¾	Aspatria	d				08x11		09x11	10x07	11x10	12x16	13x14	14x47	15x39	16x58	17x54	18x38		19x42	21x00		22x17
27¼	Maryport	d		06 00		08 21		09 21	10 17	11 20	12 26	13 24	14 57	15 49	17 08	18 04	18 48		19 52	21 10		22 27
29¼	Flimby	d		06x03		08x24		09x24	10x20	11x23	12x29	13x27	15x00	15x52	17x11	18x07	18x51		19x55	21x13		22x30
33	**Workington**	d		06 09		08 33		09 33	10 29	11 32	12 38	13 36	15 09	16 01	17 20	18 16	19 00		20 04	21 22		22 39
34¾	Harrington	d		06x13		08x36		09x36	10x32	11x35	12x41	13x39	15x12	16x04	17x23	18x19	19x03		20x07	21x25		22x42
38¼	Parton	d		06x21		08x45		09x45	10x42	11x44	12x50	13x48	15x21	16x13	17x32	18x28	19x12		20x16	21x34		22x51
39½	**Whitehaven**	a		06 26		08 54		09 51	10 47	11 50	12 59	13 54	15 27	16 19	17 38	18 34	19 21		20 25	21 43		23 00
—		d		06 28	07 28			09 52	10 48	11 51		13 56	15 28	16 20	17 39	18 35						
40½	Corkickle	d		06x30	07x30			09x54	10x50	11x53		13x58	15x30	16x22	17x41	18x37						
44	St Bees	d		06 35	07 35			10 00	10 56	11 59		14 03	15 36	16 31	17 50	18 43						
47	Nethertown	d		06x39					11x00				15x40		17x54							
48¼	Braystones	d		06x42					11x02				15x42		17x57							
50¼	Sellafield	d		06 48	07 48		09 07	10 11	11 08	12 10		14 14	15b54	16 42	18 03	18 54						
52	Seascale	d		06x51	07x51		09x10	10x14	11x11	12x13		14x17	15x57	16x45	18x07	18x57						
54¼	Drigg	d		06x54	07x54		09x13	10x17	11x14	12x16		14x20	16x01	16x49	18x11	19x00						
56	Ravenglass for Eskdale	d		06 57	07 57		09 16	10 20	11 18	12 20		14 23	16 04	16 52	18 14	19 03						
60¾	Bootle	d		07x03	08x03		09x22	10x26	11x23	12x25		14x29	16x10	16x58	18x20	19x09						
66¼	Silecroft	d		07x09	08x09		09x28	10x32	11x30	12x32		14x35	16x17	17x05	18x27	19x15						
69¼	Millom	a		07 16	08 14		09 35	10 39	11 37	12 39		14 42	16 24	17 12	18 34	19 22						
—		d	06 10	07 17	08 15		09 36	10 40	11 37	12 39		14 43	16 25	17 13	18 34	19 23		20 10			22 02	
71¾	Green Road	d	06x14	07x21	08x19		09x40	10x44	11x41	12x43		14x47	16x29	17x17	18x39	19x27		20x14			22x06	
73¾	Foxfield	d	06x17	07x24	08x22		09x43	10x47	11x44	12x47		14x50	16x33	17x21	18x43	19x30		20x17			22x09	
76	Kirkby-in-Furness	d	06x21	07x28	08x26		09x47	10x51	11x48	12x51		14x54	16x38	17x26	18x47	19x34		20x21			22x13	
79¼	Askam	d	06 26	07 33	08 31		09 52	10 56	11 53	12 56		14 59	16 43	17 31	18 52	19 39		20 26			22 18	
85¼	**Barrow-in-Furness**	a	06 42	07 49	08 49		10 07	11 14	12 09	13 14		15 17	16 59	17 47	19 10	19 57		20 43			22 35	
—	Lancaster 8 82	a	08 03	09 07	*10 26*		11 20	*12 18*	13 15	*14 18*		*16 18*	*18 20*	19 04		*21 11*		*22 44*				

Saturdays

Station		NT	NT	NT	NT	NT	NT	NT	NT	NT	NT	NT	NT B	NT	NT	NT C	NT	NT	NT	NT	NT
Carlisle 8	d			07 44		08 37	09 40	10 43	11 39		12 48	14 21	15 25	16 30	17 40	18 11		19 00	20 05		21 45
Dalston	d			07x52		08x45	09x48	10x51	11x47		12x56	14x29	15x33	16x38	17x48	18x19		19x08	20x13		21x53
Wigton	d			08 01		08 54	09 57	11 00	11 56		13 05	14 38	15 42	16 47	17 57	18 28		19 17	20 22		22 02
Aspatria	d			08x11		09x04	10x07	11x10	12x06		13x15	14x48	15x52	16x57	18x07	18x39		19x27	20x32		22x12
Maryport	d		06 26	08 21		09 14	10 17	11 20	12 16		13 25	14 58	16 02	17 07	18 17	18 49		19 37	20 42		22 22
Flimby	d		06x29	08x24		09x17	10x20	11x23	12x19		13x28	15x01	16x05	17x10	18x20	18x53		19x40	20x45		22x25
Workington	d		06 37	08 33		09 26	10 29	11 32	12 28		13 37	15 10	16 14	17 19	18 29	19 01		19 49	20 54		22 34
Harrington	d		06x41	08x36		09x29	10x32	11x35	12x31		13x40	15x14	16x18	17x23	18x32	19x05		19x52	20x57		22x37
Parton	d		06x49	08x45		09x38	10x41	11x44	12x40		13x49	15x22	16x26	17x31	18x41	19x14		20x01	21x06		22x46
Whitehaven	a		06 55	08 54		09 44	10 47	11 50	12 49		13 55	15 28	16 32	17 37	18 47	19 23		20 10	21 15		22 55
	d		06 57			09 45	10 48	11 51		12 54	13 57	15 30	16 34	17 39	18 48						
Corkickle	d		06x59			09x47	10x50	11x53		12x56	13x59	15x32	16x36	17x41	18x50						
St Bees	d		07c10			09 53	10 56	11 59		13 01	14 04	15 37	16 43	17 46	18 56						
Nethertown	d		07x14				11x00					15x41		17x50							
Braystones	d		07x16				11x02					15x44		17x53							
Sellafield	d		07 22		09 07	10 03	11 08	12 10		13 12	14 15	15 50	16 53	17 59	19 06						
Seascale	d		07x25		09x10	10x06	11x11	12x13		13x15	14x18	15x53	16x56	18x02	19x09						
Drigg	d		07x28		09x13	10x09	11x14	12x16		13x18	14x21	15x56	16x59	18x05	19x12						
Ravenglass for Eskdale	d		07 32		09 16	10 13	11 18	12 20		13 21	14 24	15 59	17 03	18 08	19 16						
Bootle	d		07x37		09x22	10x18	11x23	12x25		13x27	14x30	16x05	17x08	18x14	19x21						
Silecroft	d		07x44		09x28	10x25	11x30	12x32		13x33	14x36	16x11	17x15	18x20	19x28						
Millom	a		07 51		09 35	10 32	11 37	12 39		13 40	14 43	16 18	17 22	18 27	19 35						
	d	06 10	07 51		09 36	10 32	11 37	12 39		13 41	14 44	16 19	17 22	18 28	19 36		20 10			22 02	
Green Road	d	06x14	07x55		09x40	10x36	11x41	12x43		13x45	14x48	16x23	17x26	18x32	19x40		20x14			22x06	
Foxfield	d	06x17	07x59		09x43	10x40	11x44	12x47		13x48	14x51	16x26	17x30	18x35	19x43		20x17			22x09	
Kirkby-in-Furness	d	06x21	08x03		09x47	10x44	11x48	12x51		13x52	14x55	16x30	17x34	18x39	19x47		20x21			22x13	
Askam	d	06 26	08 08		09 52	10 49	11 53	12 56		13 57	15 00	16 35	17 39	18 44	19 52		20 26			22 18	
Barrow-in-Furness	a	06 42	08 24		10 07	11 07	12 09	13 14		14 13	15 16	16 53	17 55	19 02	20 10		20 44			22 35	
Lancaster 6 82	a	*08 26*	09 33		11 20	*12 18*	13 15	*14 18*		15 21	16 23	*18 17*	19 04	*20 45*			*22 44*				

Sundays

Station		NT	NT	NT
Carlisle 8	d	15 00	19 00	21 50
Dalston	d	15x08	19x08	21x58
Wigton	d	15 17	19 17	22 07
Aspatria	d	15x27	19x27	22x17
Maryport	d	15 37	19 37	22 27
Flimby	d	15x40	19x40	22x30
Workington	d	15 49	19 49	22 39
Harrington	d	15x52	19x52	22x42
Parton	d	16x01	20x01	22x51
Whitehaven	a	16 10	20 10	23 00

For general notes see front of timetable
For details of catering facilities see Directory of Train Operators

B To Preston (Table 82)
C From Newcastle (Table 48)
b Arr. 1548
c Arr. 0704

No Sunday Service Whitehaven to Barrow-in-Furness

Network Diagram for Tables 101, 103, 106, 109

DM-14/06(2)
Design BAJS

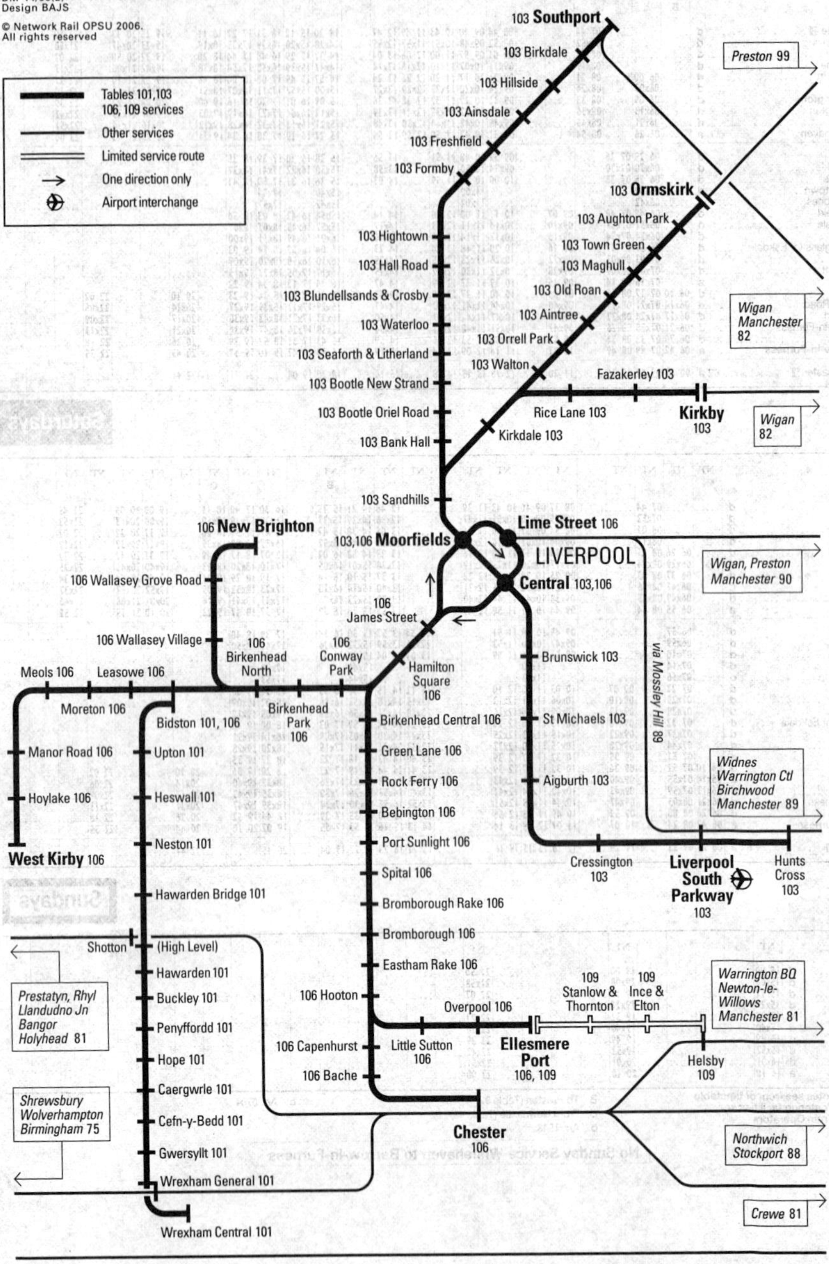
Tables 101,103 106, 109 services
Other services
Limited service route
One direction only
Airport interchange
103 Southport
103 Birkdale
103 Hillside
103 Ainsdale
103 Freshfield
103 Formby
103 Hightown
103 Hall Road
103 Blundellsands & Crosby
103 Waterloo
103 Seaforth & Litherland
103 Bootle New Strand
103 Bootle Oriel Road
103 Bank Hall
103 Sandhills
Preston 99
103 Ormskirk
103 Aughton Park
103 Town Green
103 Maghull
103 Old Roan
103 Aintree
103 Orrell Park
103 Walton
Wigan Manchester 82
Fazakerley 103
Rice Lane 103
Kirkby 103
Wigan 82
Kirkdale 103
Lime Street 106
106 New Brighton
103,106 Moorfields
LIVERPOOL
Central 103,106
Wigan, Preston Manchester 90
106 Wallasey Grove Road
106 James Street
106 Wallasey Village
106 Birkenhead North
106 Conway Park
Hamilton Square 106
Brunswick 103
via Mossley Hill 89
Meols 106
Leasowe 106
Moreton 106
Bidston 101, 106
Birkenhead Park 106
Birkenhead Central 106
St Michaels 103
Manor Road 106
Upton 101
Green Lane 106
Widnes Warrington Ctl Birchwood Manchester 89
Rock Ferry 106
Aigburth 103
Hoylake 106
Heswall 101
Bebington 106
West Kirby 106
Neston 101
Port Sunlight 106
Cressington 103
Liverpool South Parkway 103
Hunts Cross 103
Spital 106
Hawarden Bridge 101
Bromborough Rake 106
Bromborough 106
Shotton (High Level)
Hawarden 101
Eastham Rake 106
Warrington BQ Newton-le-Willows Manchester 81
Prestatyn, Rhyl Llandudno Jn Bangor Holyhead 81
Buckley 101
106 Hooton
109 Stanlow & Thornton
109 Ince & Elton
Overpool 106
Penyffordd 101
106 Capenhurst
Little Sutton 106
Ellesmere Port 106, 109
Helsby 109
Hope 101
106 Bache
Caergwrle 101
Shrewsbury Wolverhampton Birmingham 75
Cefn-y-Bedd 101
Chester 106
Northwich Stockport 88
Gwersyllt 101
Wrexham General 101
Wrexham Central 101
Crewe 81

Table 101

Mondays to Saturdays

Wrexham → Bidston

Network Diagram - see first page of Table 101

Miles			AW	AW	AW	AW	AW	AW	AW	AW	AW	AW	AW	AW	AW	AW	AW
				BHX		BHX		BHX		BHX		BHX		BHX		SO	
0	**Wrexham Central**	d		07 28	08 30	09 30	10 30	11 30	12 30	13 30	14 30	15 30	16 30	17 43	19 44	19 46	21 55
½	**Wrexham General**	a		07 30	08 32	09 32	10 32	11 32	12 32	13 32	14 32	15 32	16 32	17 45	19 46	19 48	21 57
—		d	06 31	07 30	08 32	09 32	10 32	11 32	12 32	13 32	14 32	15 32	16 32	17 45	19 46		21 57
2¼	Gwersyllt	d	06x35	07 34	08x36	09x36	10x36	11x36	12x36	13x36	14x36	15x36	16x36	17x49	19x50		22x01
4	Cefn-y-Bedd	d	06x40	07 39	08x41	09x41	10x41	11x41	12x41	13x41	14x41	15x41	16x41	17x54	19x55		22x06
4¾	Caergwrle	d	06x42	07 41	08x43	09x43	10x43	11x43	12x43	13x43	14x43	15x43	16x43	17x56	19x57		22x08
5¼	Hope (Flintshire)	d	06x44	07 43	08x45	09x45	10x45	11x45	12x45	13x45	14x45	15x45	16x45	17x58	19x59		22x10
7¼	Penyffordd	d	06x48	07 47	08x49	09x49	10x49	11x49	12x49	13x49	14x49	15x49	16x49	18x02	20x03		22x14
8½	Buckley	d	06x51	07 50	08x52	09x52	10x52	11x52	12x52	13x52	14x52	15x52	16x52	18x05	20x06		22x17
10½	Hawarden	d	06x55	07 54	08x56	09x56	10x56	11x56	12x56	13x56	14x56	15x56	16x56	18x09	20x10		22x21
12¾	Shotton High Level	d	06 59	07 59	09 00	10 00	11 00	12 00	13 00	14 00	15 00	16 00	17 00	18 13	20 14		22 25
13¼	Hawarden Bridge	d	07x01	08x01									17x02				
18¾	Neston	d	07x10	08 10	09x10	10x10	11x10	12x10	13x10	14x10	15x10	16x10	17x11	18x23	20x24		22x35
21¼	Heswall	d	07x15	08 15	09x15	10x15	11x15	12x15	13x15	14x15	15x15	16x15	17x16	18x28	20x29		22x40
25½	Upton	d	07x21	08 21	09x21	10x21	11x21	12x21	13x21	14x21	15x21	16x21	17x22	18x34	20x35		22x46
27½	**Bidston**	a	07 29	08 29	09 29	10 29	11 29	12 29	13 29	14 29	15 29	16 29	17 29	18 44	20 43		22 54
—	Liverpool Lime Street 10	106 a	*07 53*	*08 53*	*09 53*	*10 53*	*11 53*	*12 53*	*13 53*	*14 53*	*15 53*	*16 53*	*17 53*	*19 08*	*21 33*		*23 33*

Sundays

		AW	AW	AW	AW	AW	AW
Wrexham Central	d		11 11	13 41	16 11	18 41	21 11
Wrexham General	a		11 13	13 43	16 13	18 43	21 13
	d	08 44	11 14	13 44	16 14	18 44	21 14
Gwersyllt	d	08x48	11x18	13x48	16x18	18x48	21x18
Cefn-y-Bedd	d	08x53	11x23	13x53	16x23	18x53	21x23
Caergwrle	d	08x55	11x25	13x55	16x25	18x55	21x25
Hope (Flintshire)	d	08x57	11x27	13x57	16x27	18x57	21x27
Penyffordd	d	09x01	11x31	14x01	16x31	19x01	21x31
Buckley	d	09x04	11x34	14x04	16x34	19x04	21x34
Hawarden	d	09x08	11x38	14x08	16x38	19x08	21x38
Shotton High Level	d	09 12	11 42	14 12	16 42	19 12	21 42
Hawarden Bridge	d						
Neston	d	09x22	11x52	14x22	16x52	19x22	21x52
Heswall	d	09x27	11x57	14x27	16x57	19x27	21x57
Upton	d	09x33	12x03	14x33	17x03	19x33	22x03
Bidston	a	09 41	12 11	14 41	17 11	19 41	22 11
Liverpool Lime Street 10	106 a	*10 03*	*12 33*	*15 03*	*17 33*	*20 03*	*22 33*

For general notes see front of timetable
For details of catering facilities see Directory of Train Operators

Table 101

Mondays to Saturdays

Bidston → Wrexham

Network Diagram - see first page of Table 101

Miles			AW BHX	AW	AW BHX		AW	AW BHX	AW		AW BHX	AW	AW BHX		AW	AW BHX	AW		AW BHX	AW SO	AW SX	AW SO	AW SX
—	Liverpool Lime Street 10	106 d		06 53	08 08		09 08	10 08	11 08		12 08	13 08	14 08		15 08	16 08	17 23		18 23	20 03	20 03	22 03	22 03
0	**Bidston**	d		07 31	08 31		09 32	10 32	11 32		12 32	13 32	14 32		15 32	16 31	17 45		18 46	20 45	20 56	22 45	22 56
2	Upton	d		07 33	08x33		09x34	10x34	11x34		12x34	13x34	14x34		15x34	16x33	17 47		18x48	20x49	20x58	22x49	22x58
6¼	Heswall	d		07 40	08x40		09x41	10x41	11x41		12x41	13x41	14x41		15x41	16x40	17 54		18x55	20x56	21x05	22x56	23x05
8¾	Neston	d		07 45	08x45		09x46	10x46	11x46		12x46	13x46	14x46		15x46	16x45	17 59		19x00	21x01	21x10	23x01	23x10
14¼	Hawarden Bridge	d		07x53	08x53											16x53	18x07						
14¾	Shotton High Level	d		07 55	08 55		09 55	10 55	11 55		12 55	13 55	14 55		15 55	16 55	18 09		19 09	21 10	21 19	23 11	23 20
17½	Hawarden	d		08 00	09x00		10x00	11x00	12x00		13x00	14x00	15x00		16x00	17x00	18 14		19x14	21x15	21x24	23x16	23x25
19	Buckley	d		08 05	09x05		10x05	11x05	12x05		13x05	14x05	15x05		16x05	17x05	18 19		19x19	21x20	21x29	23x21	23x30
20¼	Penyffordd	d		08 08	09x08		10x08	11x08	12x08		13x08	14x08	15x08		16x08	17x08	18 22		19x22	21x23	21x32	23x24	23x33
22¼	Hope (Flintshire)	d		08 12	09x12		10x12	11x12	12x12		13x12	14x12	15x12		16x12	17x12	18 26		19x26	21x27	21x36	23x28	23x37
22¾	Caergwrle	d		08 14	09x14		10x14	11x14	12x14		13x14	14x14	15x14		16x14	17x14	18 28		19x28	21x29	21x38	23x30	23x39
23½	Cefn-y-Bedd	d		08 16	09x16		10x16	11x16	12x16		13x16	14x16	15x16		16x16	17x16	18 30		19x30	21x31	21x40	23x32	23x41
25¼	Gwersyllt	d		08 20	09x20		10x20	11x20	12x20		13x20	14x20	15x20		16x20	17x20	18 34		19x34	21x35	21x44	23x36	23x47
27	**Wrexham General**	a		08 27	09 27		10 27	11 27	12 27		13 27	14 27	15 27		16 27	17 27	18 41		19 41	21 40	21 51	23 41	23 54
—		d	07 10	08 27	09 27		10 27	11 27	12 27		13 27	14 27	15 27		16 27	17 27	18 41		19 41	21 40	21 51		
27½	**Wrexham Central**	a	07 13	08 32	09 32		10 32	11 32	12 32		13 32	14 32	15 32		16 32	17 32	18 46		19 46	21 45	21 56		

Sundays

		AW			AW			AW			AW			AW			AW
Liverpool Lime Street 10	106 d	09 33			12 03			14 33			17 03			19 33			22 03
Bidston	d	09 57			12 27			14 57			17 27			19 57			22 27
Upton	d	09x59			12x29			14x59			17x29			19x59			22x29
Heswall	d	10x06			12x36			15x06			17x36			20x06			22x36
Neston	d	10x11			12x41			15x11			17x41			20x11			22x41
Hawarden Bridge	d																
Shotton High Level	d	10 20			12 50			15 20			17 50			20 20			22 50
Hawarden	d	10x25			12x55			15x25			17x55			20x25			22x55
Buckley	d	10x30			13x00			15x30			18x00			20x30			23x00
Penyffordd	d	10x33			13x03			15x33			18x03			20x33			23x03
Hope (Flintshire)	d	10x37			13x07			15x37			18x07			20x37			23x07
Caergwrle	d	10x39			13x09			15x39			18x09			20x39			23x09
Cefn-y-Bedd	d	10x41			13x11			15x41			18x11			20x41			23x11
Gwersyllt	d	10x45			13x15			15x45			18x15			20x45			23x15
Wrexham General	a	10 52			13 22			15 52			18 22			20 52			23 25
	d	10 53			13 23			15 53			18 23			20 53			
Wrexham Central	a	10 58			13 28			15 58			18 28			20 58			

For general notes see front of timetable
For details of catering facilities see
Directory of Train Operators

Llandudno → Blaenau Ffestiniog

Network Diagram - see first page of Table 81

Mondays to Saturdays

Miles	Station		AW ◇	AW ◇	AW ◇	AW ◇	AW ◇	AW ◇
0	**Llandudno**	81 d		07 10	10 20	13 20	16 20	19 03
1¾	Deganwy	81 d		07 14	10x24	13x24	16x24	19x07
—	Crewe 10	81 d		06b24	08c49	11e49	14f21	17g49
—	Chester	81 d		06 44	09 26	12 26	15 26	18h27
—	Rhyl	81 d		07 16	09 58	12 58	15 58	18h59
—	Bangor (Gwynedd)	81 d	04 57	07b08	10 02	13 07	16 02	18 00
3	**Llandudno Junction**	81 d	05 35	07 39	10 33	13 33	16 33	19 20
5	Glan Conwy	d		07x42	10x36	13x36	16x36	19x23
8½	Tal-y-Cafn	d		07 48	10 42	13 42	16 42	19 29
11½	Dolgarrog	d		07x53	10x47	13x47	16x47	19x34
14½	North Llanrwst	d		08x00	10x53	13x53	16x53	19x40
15	Llanrwst	d	05 53	08 02	10 55	13 55	16 55	19 42
18½	Betws-y-Coed	d	05 59	08 08	11 01	14 01	17 01	19 48
22¾	Pont-y-Pant	d		08x16	11x09	14x09	17x09	19x56
24¼	Dolwyddelan	d		08x19	11x12	14x12	17x12	19x59
26	Roman Bridge	d		08x23	11x16	14x16	17x16	20x03
31	**Blaenau Ffestiniog**	a	06 26	08 40	11 33	14 33	17 33	20 19

Sundays

Station		AW ◇ A	AW B (bus)	AW B (bus)	AW ◇ A	AW ◇ A	AW B (bus)
Llandudno	81 d	10 22	10 15	13 15	13 30	15 45	16 00
Deganwy	81 d	10x26	10 30	13 20	13x34	15 49	16 15
Crewe 10	81 d	08 27		11 27	11 27	14 27	14 27
Chester	81 d	09 02		12 03	12 03	15 02	15 02
Rhyl	81 d	09 34		12 37	12 37	15 36	15 36
Bangor (Gwynedd)	81 d	09 08	09 18	12j15	13 14	15 08	15 08
Llandudno Junction	81 d	10 32	10 35	13 35	13 40	16 15	16 20
Glan Conwy	d	10x35	10 40	13 40	13x43	16x18	16 25
Tal-y-Cafn	d	10 41	10 48	13 48	13 49	16 24	16 33
Dolgarrog	d	10x46	10 53	13 53	13x54	16x29	16 38
North Llanrwst	d	10x52	10 58	13 58	14x00	16x35	16 43
Llanrwst	d	10 54	11 00	14 00	14 02	16 37	16 45
Betws-y-Coed	d	11 00	11 10	14 10	14 08	16 43	16 55
Pont-y-Pant	d	11x08	11 20	14 20	14x16	16x51	17 05
Dolwyddelan	d	11x11	11 25	14 25	14x19	16x54	17 10
Roman Bridge	d	11x15	11 32	14 32	14x23	16x58	17 17
Blaenau Ffestiniog	a	11 30	11 45	14 45	14 38	17 13	17 30

For general notes see front of timetable
For details of catering facilities see Directory of Train Operators

A Until 6 September
B From 13 September

b Saturdays dep. Crewe 0623, Bangor 0717
c Change at Chester and Llandudno Junction. Saturdays dep. 0821
e Change at Chester and Llandudno Junction. Saturdays until 31 October dep. 1150, from 7 November dep. 1121
f Saturdays until 31 October dep. 1450, from 7 November dep. 1449
g Saturdays from 7 November dep. 1721
h Saturdays dep. Chester 1826, Rhyl 1858
j 13 September to 1 November only

Blaenau Ffestiniog → Llandudno

Network Diagram - see first page of Table 81

Miles			AW ◇	AW ◇	AW ◇	AW SO ◇	AW SX ◇	AW ◇	AW ◇
—	**Blaenau Ffestiniog**	d	06 30	08 52	11 52	14 52	14 52	17 37	20 23
—	Roman Bridge	d	06x40	09x02	12x02	15x02	15x02	17x47	20x33
6¾	Dolwyddelan	d	06x43	09x06	12x06	15x06	15x06	17x51	20x37
8¼	Pont-y-Pant	d	06x46	09x09	12x09	15x09	15x09	17x54	20x40
12½	Betws-y-Coed	d	06 56	09 19	12 19	15 19	15 19	18 04	20 50
16	Llanrwst	d	07 02	09 25	12 25	15 25	15 25	18 10	20 56
16½	North Llanrwst	d	07x03	09x26	12x26	15x26	15x26	18x11	20x57
19½	Dolgarrog	d	07x09	09x33	12x33	15x33	15x33	18x18	21x04
22½	Tal-y-Cafn	d	07x14	09x39	12x39	15x39	15x39	18x24	21x10
26	Glan Conwy	d	07x20	09x45	12x45	15x45	15x45	18x30	21x16
28	**Llandudno Junction**	81 a	07 26	09 51	12 51	15 51	15 51	18 35	21 23
—	Bangor (Gwynedd)	81 a	07 49	10 36	13 31	16b36	16 36	19c22	22e22
—	Rhyl	81 a	07f56	10 41	13 41	16 41	16 33	19 12	21 47
—	Chester	81 a	08f31	11 15	14 15	17 14	17 10	19 49	22 23
—	Crewe 10	81 a	08 54	11g54	14g54	17g54	17g54	20g17	22 46
29¼	Deganwy	81 a	07 54	10x03	13x03	16x03	16x07	18x44	21x28
31	**Llandudno**	81 a	08 06	10 08	13 09	16 09	16 13	18 49	21 35

Sundays

		AW ◇ A	AW B Bus	AW ◇ A	AW B Bus	AW ◇ A	AW B Bus
Blaenau Ffestiniog	d	11 45	11 50	15 03	15 00	17 30	17 50
Roman Bridge	d	11x55	12 00	15x13	15 10	17x40	18 00
Dolwyddelan	d	11x58	12 05	15x16	15 15	17x44	18 05
Pont-y-Pant	d	12x01	12 09	15x19	15 19	17x48	18 09
Betws-y-Coed	d	12 11	12 20	15 29	15 30	17 57	18 20
Llanrwst	d	12 17	12 30	15 35	15 40	18 03	18 30
North Llanrwst	d	12x18	12 33	15x36	15 43	18x05	18 33
Dolgarrog	d	12x24	12 38	15x42	15 48	18x11	18 38
Tal-y-Cafn	d	12x29	12 43	15x47	15 53	18x17	18 43
Glan Conwy	d	12x35	12 51	15x53	16 01	18x23	18 51
Llandudno Junction	81 a	12 40	13 00	15 59	16 10	18 29	19 00
Bangor (Gwynedd)	81 a	13 10	14 18	17 12	17 12	19 46	19 46
Rhyl	81 a	13 48	13 48	16 53	16 43	19 42	19 42
Chester	81 a	14 23	14 23	17 32	17 20	20 19	20 19
Crewe 10	81 a	14 52	14 52	18g18	17 43	20 48	20 48
Deganwy	81 a	12x45	13 05	16 07	16 15	18x34	19 05
Llandudno	81 a	12 51	13 20	16 14	16 30	18 40	19 20

For general notes see front of timetable
For details of catering facilities see Directory of Train Operators

A Until 6 September
B From 13 September
b From 7 November arr. 1617
c Saturdays until 31 October arr. 1921, from 7 November arr. 1931
e Saturdays arr. 2242
f Saturdays arr. 5 mins. earlier
g Change at Llandudno Junction and Chester

Merseyrail

These notes apply to Tables 103 and 106

Spring Holiday

Monday 25 May — A normal Saturday service will operate

Late Summer Holiday

Monday 31 August — A normal Saturday service will operate

Hunts Cross and Liverpool → Kirkby, Ormskirk and Southport

Network Diagram - see first page of Table 101

Miles	Miles	Miles			ME	ME	ME	ME	ME	ME	ME	ME		ME	ME	ME	ME		ME	ME	ME	ME	ME	ME
0	—	—	**Hunts Cross**	89 d					06 06		06 21				06 36		06 51				07 06			07 21
1½	—	—	**Liverpool South Parkway** 7	89 ⇄ d					06 09		06 24				06 39		06 54				07 09			07 24
2½	—	—	Cressington	d					06 12		06 27				06 42		06 57				07 12			07 27
3¼	—	—	Aigburth	d					06 14		06 29				06 44		06 59				07 14			07 29
4½	—	—	St Michaels	d					06 16		06 31				06 46		07 01				07 16			07 31
5¾	—	—	Brunswick	d					06 19		06 34				06 49		07 04				07 19			07 34
7¼	—	—	**Liverpool Central** 10	a					06 23		06 38				06 53		07 08				07 23			07 38
—	0	0		d		05 55	06 08	06 10	06 23	06 25	06 38	06 40		06 50	06 53	06 55	07 08		07 10	07 20	07 23	07 25	07 35	07 38
7¾	½	½	**Moorfields** 10	d		05 57	06 10	06 12	06 25	06 27	06 40	06 42		06 52	06 55	06 57	07 10		07 12	07 22	07 25	07 27	07 37	07 40
9¼	2	2	Sandhills	d	05 59	06 01	06 14	06 16	06 29	06 31	06 44	06 46		06 56	06 59	07 01	07 14		07 16	07 26	07 29	07 31	07 41	07 44
—	3	3	Kirkdale	d		06 04		06 19		06 34		06 49		06 59		07 04			07 19	07 29		07 34	07 44	
—	—	4¼	Rice Lane	d		06 07				06 37				07 02						07 32			07 47	
—	—	5¾	Fazakerley	d		06 10				06 40				07 03						07 34			07 49	
—	—	7½	**Kirkby**	a		06 13				06 43				07 08						07 38			07 53	
—	4¼	—	Walton (Merseyside)	d				06 22				06 52				07 07			07 22			07 37		
—	4½	—	Orrell Park	d				06 23				06 53				07 08			07 23			07 38		
—	5½	—	Aintree	d				06 26				06 56				07 11			07 26			07 41		
—	6¼	—	Old Roan	d				06 28				06 58				07 13			07 28			07 43		
—	8	—	Maghull	d				06 31				07 01				07 16			07 31			07 46		
—	10½	—	Town Green	d				06 35				07 05				07 20			07 35			07 50		
—	11½	—	Aughton Park	d				06 37				07 07				07 22			07 37			07 52		
—	12¾	—	**Ormskirk**	a				06 42				07 12				07 27			07 42			07 57		
10	—	—	Bank Hall	d	06 01		06 16		06 31		06 46				07 01		07 16				07 31			07 46
10¾	—	—	Bootle Oriel Road	d	06 03		06 18		06 33		06 48				07 03		07 18				07 33			07 48
11	—	—	Bootle New Strand	d	06 05		06 20		06 35		06 50				07 05		07 20				07 35			07 50
12	—	—	Seaforth & Litherland	d	06 07		06 22		06 37		06 52				07 07		07 22				07 37			07 52
13¼	—	—	Waterloo (Merseyside)	d	06 09		06 24		06 39		06 54				07 09		07 24				07 39			07 54
14¼	—	—	Blundellsands & Crosby	d	06 12		06 27		06 42		06 57				07 12		07 27				07 42			07 57
15	—	—	Hall Road	d	06 14		06 29		06 44		06 59				07 14		07 29				07 44			07 59
17	—	—	Hightown	d	06 17		06 32		06 47		07 02				07 17		07 32				07 47			08 02
19	—	—	Formby	d	06 21		06 36		06 51		07 06				07 21		07 36				07 51			08 06
20	—	—	Freshfield	d	06 23		06 38		06 53		07 08				07 23		07 38				07 53			08 08
22¾	—	—	Ainsdale	d	06 27		06 42		06 57		07 12				07 27		07 42				07 57			08 12
24½	—	—	Hillside	d	06 30		06 45		07 00		07 15				07 30		07 45				08 00			08 15
25¼	—	—	Birkdale	d	06 32		06 47		07 02		07 17				07 32		07 47				08 02			08 17
26¼	—	—	**Southport**	a	06 37		06 52		07 07		07 22				07 37		07 52				08 07			08 22

		ME	ME	ME	ME	ME	ME		ME	ME	ME SX	ME	ME	ME	ME	ME		ME	ME	ME	ME	ME
Hunts Cross	89 d			07 36			07 51		16 51				17 06			17 21				17 36		
Liverpool South Parkway 7	89 ⇄ d			07 39			07 54		16 54				17 09			17 24				17 39		
Cressington	d			07 42			07 57		16 57				17 12			17 27				17 42		
Aigburth	d			07 44			07 59		16 59				17 14			17 29				17 44		
St Michaels	d			07 46			08 01		17 01				17 16			17 31				17 46		
Brunswick	d			07 49			08 04		17 04				17 19			17 34				17 49		
Liverpool Central 10	a			07 53			08 08		17 08				17 23			17 38				17 53		
	d	07 40	07 50	07 53	07 55	08 05	08 08		17 08	17 10	17 13	17 20	17 23	17 25	17 35	17 38		17 40	17 50	17 53	17 55	18 05
Moorfields 10	d	07 42	07 52	07 55	07 57	08 07	08 10		17 10	17 12	17 15	17 22	17 25	17 27	17 37	17 40		17 42	17 52	17 55	17 57	18 07
Sandhills	d	07 46	07 56	07 59	08 01	08 11	08 14		17 14	17 16	17 19	17 26	17 29	17 31	17 41	17 44		17 46	17 56	17 59	18 01	18 11
Kirkdale	d	07 49	07 59		08 04	08 14				17 19		17 29		17 34	17 44			17 49	17 59		18 04	18 14
Rice Lane	d		08 02			08 17		and at				17 32			17 47				18 02			18 17
Fazakerley	d		08 04			08 19		the same				17 34			17 49				18 04			18 19
Kirkby	a		08 08			08 23						17 38			17 53				18 08			18 23
Walton (Merseyside)	d	07 52			08 07			minutes		17 22				17 37				17 52			18 07	
Orrell Park	d	07 53			08 08			past		17 23				17 38				17 53			18 08	
Aintree	d	07 56			08 11					17 26				17 41				17 56			18 11	
Old Roan	d	07 58			08 13			each		17 28				17 43				17 58			18 13	
Maghull	d	08 01			08 16					17 31				17 46				18 01			18 16	
Town Green	d	08 05			08 20			hour until		17 35				17 50				18 05			18 20	
Aughton Park	d	08 07			08 22					17 37				17 52				18 07			18 22	
Ormskirk	a	08 12			08 27					17 42				17 57				18 12			18 27	
Bank Hall	d			08 01			08 16		17 16		17 21		17 31			17 46				18 01		
Bootle Oriel Road	d			08 03			08 18		17 18		17 23		17 33			17 48				18 03		
Bootle New Strand	d			08 05			08 20		17 20		17 25		17 35			17 50				18 05		
Seaforth & Litherland	d			08 07			08 22		17 22		17 27		17 37			17 52				18 07		
Waterloo (Merseyside)	d			08 09			08 24		17 24		17 29		17 39			17 54				18 09		
Blundellsands & Crosby	d			08 12			08 27		17 27		17 32		17 42			17 57				18 12		
Hall Road	d			08 14			08 29		17 29		17 34		17 44			17 59				18 14		
Hightown	d			08 17			08 32		17 32		17 37		17 47			18 02				18 17		
Formby	d			08 21			08 36		17 36		17 41		17 51			18 06				18 21		
Freshfield	d			08 23			08 38		17 38		17 43		17 53			18 08				18 23		
Ainsdale	d			08 27			08 42		17 42		17 47		17 57			18 12				18 27		
Hillside	d			08 30			08 45		17 45		17 50		18 00			18 15				18 30		
Birkdale	d			08 32			08 47		17 47		17 52		18 02			18 17				18 32		
Southport	a			08 37			08 52		17 52		17 57		18 07			18 22				18 37		

For general notes see front of timetable
For details of catering facilities see
Directory of Train Operators

Hunts Cross and Liverpool → Kirkby, Ormskirk and Southport

Network Diagram - see first page of Table 101

	ME	ME	ME	ME	ME		ME	ME	ME	ME	ME	ME	ME	ME		ME	ME	ME	ME		ME	ME	ME
Hunts Cross 89 d	17 51			18 06				18 21			18 36			18 51			19 06		19 21			19 36	
Liverpool South Parkway 7 89 ✈ d	17 54			18 09				18 24			18 39			18 54			19 09		19 24			19 39	
Cressington d	17 57			18 12				18 27			18 42			18 57			19 12		19 27			19 42	
Aigburth d	17 59			18 14				18 29			18 44			18 59			19 14		19 29			19 44	
St Michaels d	18 01			18 16				18 31			18 46			19 01			19 16		19 31			19 46	
Brunswick d	18 04			18 19				18 34			18 49			19 04			19 19		19 34			19 49	
Liverpool Central 10 a	18 08			18 23				18 38			18 53			19 08			19 23		19 38			19 53	
d	18 08	18 10	18 20	18 23	18 25		18 35	18 38	18 40	18 50	18 53	18 55	19 05	19 08		19 10	19 23	19 25	19 38		19 40	19 53	19 55
Moorfields 10 d	18 10	18 12	18 22	18 25	18 27		18 37	18 40	18 42	18 52	18 55	18 57	19 07	19 10		19 12	19 25	19 27	19 40		19 42	19 55	19 57
Sandhills d	18 14	18 16	18 26	18 29	18 31		18 41	18 44	18 46	18 56	18 59	19 01	19 11	19 14		19 16	19 29	19 31	19 44		19 46	19 59	20 01
Kirkdale d		18 19	18 29		18 34		18 44		18 49	18 59		19 04	19 14			19 19		19 34			19 49		20 04
Rice Lane d			18 32				18 47			19 02			19 17					19 37					20 07
Fazakerley d			18 34				18 49			19 04			19 19					19 40					20 10
Kirkby a			18 38				18 53			19 08			19 23					19 43					20 13
Walton (Merseyside) d		18 22			18 37				18 52			19 07				19 22					19 52		
Orrell Park d		18 23			18 38				18 53			19 08				19 23					19 53		
Aintree d		18 26			18 41				18 56			19 11				19 26					19 56		
Old Roan d		18 28			18 43				18 58			19 13				19 28					19 58		
Maghull d		18 31			18 46				19 01			19 16				19 31					20 01		
Town Green d		18 35			18 50				19 05			19 20				19 35					20 05		
Aughton Park d		18 37			18 52				19 07			19 22				19 37					20 07		
Ormskirk a		18 42			18 57				19 12			19 27				19 42					20 12		
Bank Hall d	18 16			18 31				18 46			19 01			19 16			19 31		19 46			20 01	
Bootle Oriel Road d	18 18			18 33				18 48			19 03			19 18			19 33		19 48			20 03	
Bootle New Strand d	18 20			18 35				18 50			19 05			19 20			19 35		19 50			20 05	
Seaforth & Litherland d	18 22			18 37				18 52			19 07			19 22			19 37		19 52			20 07	
Waterloo (Merseyside) d	18 24			18 39				18 54			19 09			19 24			19 39		19 54			20 09	
Blundellsands & Crosby d	18 27			18 42				18 57			19 12			19 27			19 42		19 57			20 12	
Hall Road d	18 29			18 44				18 59			19 14			19 29			19 44		19 59			20 14	
Hightown d	18 32			18 47				19 02			19 17			19 32			19 47		20 02			20 17	
Formby d	18 36			18 51				19 06			19 21			19 36			19 51		20 06			20 21	
Freshfield d	18 38			18 53				19 08			19 23			19 38			19 53		20 08			20 23	
Ainsdale d	18 42			18 57				19 12			19 27			19 42			19 57		20 12			20 27	
Hillside d	18 45			19 00				19 15			19 30			19 45			20 00		20 15			20 30	
Birkdale d	18 47			19 02				19 17			19 32			19 47			20 02		20 17			20 32	
Southport a	18 52			19 07				19 22			19 37			19 52			20 07		20 22			20 37	

	ME	ME	ME	ME	ME		ME	ME	ME	ME	ME	ME	ME	ME		ME	ME	ME			
Hunts Cross 89 d	19 51		20 06		20 21		22 21		22 36		22 51		23 06			23 21					
Liverpool South Parkway 7 89 ✈ d	19 54		20 09		20 24		22 24		22 39		22 54		23 09			23 24					
Cressington d	19 57		20 12		20 27		22 27		22 42		22 57		23 12			23 27					
Aigburth d	19 59		20 14		20 29		22 29		22 44		22 59		23 14			23 29					
St Michaels d	20 01		20 16		20 31		22 31		22 46		23 01		23 16			23 31					
Brunswick d	20 04		20 19		20 34		22 34		22 49		23 04		23 19			23 34					
Liverpool Central 10 a	20 08		20 23		20 38		22 38		22 53		23 08		23 23			23 38					
d	20 08	20 10	20 23	20 25	20 38		22 38	22 40	22 53	22 55	23 08	23 10	23 23	23 25		23 38	23 40	23 55			
Moorfields 10 d	20 10	20 12	20 25	20 27	20 40		22 40	22 42	22 55	22 57	23 10	23 12	23 25	23 27		23 40	23 42	23 57			
Sandhills d	20 14	20 16	20 29	20 31	20 44		22 44	22 46	22 59	23 01	23 14	23 16	23 29	23 31		23 44	23 46	00 01			
Kirkdale d		20 19		20 34				22 49		23 04		23 19		23 34			23 49	00 04			
Rice Lane d				20 37						23 07				23 37				00 07	and at		
Fazakerley d				20 40						23 10				23 40				00 10	the same		
Kirkby a				20 43						23 13				23 43				00 13			
Walton (Merseyside) d		20 22						22 52				23 22					23 52		minutes		
Orrell Park d		20 23						22 53				23 23					23 53				
Aintree d		20 26						22 56				23 26					23 56		past		
Old Roan d		20 28						22 58				23 28					23 58				
Maghull d		20 31						23 01				23 31					00 01		each		
Town Green d		20 35						23 05				23 35					00 05				
Aughton Park d		20 37						23 07				23 37					00 07		hour until		
Ormskirk a		20 42						23 12				23 42					00 12				
Bank Hall d	20 16		20 31		20 46		22 46		23 01		23 16		23 31			23 46					
Bootle Oriel Road d	20 18		20 33		20 48		22 48		23 03		23 18		23 33			23 48					
Bootle New Strand d	20 20		20 35		20 50		22 50		23 05		23 20		23 35			23 50					
Seaforth & Litherland d	20 22		20 37		20 52		22 52		23 07		23 22		23 37			23 52					
Waterloo (Merseyside) d	20 24		20 39		20 54		22 54		23 09		23 24		23 39			23 54					
Blundellsands & Crosby d	20 27		20 42		20 57		22 57		23 12		23 27		23 42			23 57					
Hall Road d	20 29		20 44		20 59		22 59		23 14		23 29		23 44			23 59					
Hightown d	20 32		20 47		21 02		23 02		23 17		23 32		23 47			00 02					
Formby d	20 36		20 51		21 06		23 06		23 21		23 36		23 51			00 06					
Freshfield d	20 38		20 53		21 08		23 08		23 23		23 38		23 53			00 08					
Ainsdale d	20 42		20 57		21 12		23 12		23 27		23 42		23 57			00 12					
Hillside d	20 45		21 00		21 15		23 15		23 30		23 45		23 59			00 15					
Birkdale d	20 47		21 02		21 17		23 17		23 32		23 47		00 02			00 17					
Southport a	20 52		21 07		21 22		23 22		23 37		23 52		00 07			00 22					

For general notes see front of timetable
For details of catering facilities see
Directory of Train Operators

Sundays

Hunts Cross and Liverpool → Kirkby, Ormskirk and Southport

Network Diagram - see first page of Table 101

		ME	ME	ME	ME	ME	ME	ME	ME	ME	ME	ME	ME	ME	ME A	ME	ME	ME	ME A
Hunts Cross 89	d			08 06			08 36			09 06			09 36				10 06		
Liverpool South Parkway 7 89 ✈	d			08 09			08 39			09 09			09 39				10 09		
Cressington	d			08 12			08 42			09 12			09 42				10 12		
Aigburth	d			08 14			08 44			09 14			09 44				10 14		
St Michaels	d			08 16			08 46			09 16			09 46				10 16		
Brunswick	d			08 19			08 49			09 19			09 49				10 19		
Liverpool Central 10	a			08 23			08 53			09 23			09 53				10 23		
	d	08 08	08 10	08 23	08 25	08 40	08 53	08 55	09 10	09 23	09 25	09 40	09 53	09 55	10 08	10 10	10 23	10 25	10 38
Moorfields 10	d	08 10	08 12	08 25	08 27	08 42	08 55	08 57	09 12	09 25	09 27	09 42	09 55	09 57	10 10	10 12	10 25	10 27	10 40
Sandhills	d	08 14	08 16	08 29	08 31	08 46	08 59	09 01	09 16	09 29	09 31	09 46	09 59	10 01	10 14	10 16	10 29	10 31	10 44
Kirkdale	d		08 19		08 34	08 49		09 04	09 19		09 34	09 49		10 04		10 19		10 34	
Rice Lane	d				08 37			09 07			09 37			10 07				10 37	
Fazakerley	d				08 40			09 10			09 40			10 10				10 40	
Kirkby	a				08 43			09 13			09 43			10 13				10 43	
Walton (Merseyside)	d		08 22			08 52			09 22			09 52				10 22			
Orrell Park	d		08 23			08 53			09 23			09 53				10 23			
Aintree	d		08 26			08 56			09 26			09 56				10 26			
Old Roan	d		08 28			08 58			09 28			09 58				10 28			
Maghull	d		08 31			09 01			09 31			10 01				10 31			
Town Green	d		08 35			09 05			09 35			10 05				10 35			
Aughton Park	d		08 37			09 07			09 37			10 07				10 37			
Ormskirk	a		08 42			09 12			09 42			10 12				10 42			
Bank Hall	d	08 16		08 31			09 01			09 31			10 01		10 16		10 31		10 46
Bootle Oriel Road	d	08 18		08 33			09 03			09 33			10 03		10 18		10 33		10 48
Bootle New Strand	d	08 20		08 35			09 05			09 35			10 05		10 20		10 35		10 50
Seaforth & Litherland	d	08 22		08 37			09 07			09 37			10 07		10 22		10 37		10 52
Waterloo (Merseyside)	d	08 24		08 39			09 09			09 39			10 09		10 24		10 39		10 54
Blundellsands & Crosby	d	08 27		08 42			09 12			09 42			10 12		10 27		10 42		10 57
Hall Road	d	08 29		08 44			09 14			09 44			10 14		10 29		10 44		10 59
Hightown	d	08 32		08 47			09 17			09 47			10 17		10 32		10 47		11 02
Formby	d	08 36		08 51			09 21			09 51			10 21		10 36		10 51		11 06
Freshfield	d	08 38		08 53			09 23			09 53			10 23		10 38		10 53		11 08
Ainsdale	d	08 42		08 57			09 27			09 57			10 27		10 42		10 57		11 12
Hillside	d	08 45		09 00			09 30			10 00			10 30		10 45		11 00		11 15
Birkdale	d	08 47		09 02			09 32			10 02			10 32		10 47		11 02		11 17
Southport	a	08 52		09 07			09 37			10 07			10 37		10 52		11 07		11 22

		ME	ME	ME	ME	ME A	ME	ME A	ME B	ME	ME		ME	ME
Hunts Cross 89	d			22 36				23 06	23 06					
Liverpool South Parkway 7 89 ✈	d			22 39				23 09	23 09					
Cressington	d			22 42				23 12	23 12					
Aigburth	d			22 44				23 14	23 14					
St Michaels	d			22 46				23 16	23 16					
Brunswick	d			22 49				23 19	23 19					
Liverpool Central 10	a			22 53				23 23	23 23					
	d	10 40	22 40	22 53	22 55	23 08	23 10	23 23	23 23	23 25	23 38		23 40	23 55
Moorfields 10	d	10 42	22 42	22 55	22 57	23 10	23 12	23 25	23 25	23 27	23 40		23 42	23 57
Sandhills	d	10 46	22 46	22 59	23 01	23 14	23 16	23a29	23 29	23 31	23 44		23 46	00 01
Kirkdale	d	10 49	22 49		23 04		23 19			23 34			23 49	00 04
Rice Lane	d				23 07					23 37		and at the same minutes past each hour until		00 07
Fazakerley	d				23 10					23 40				00 10
Kirkby	a				23 13					23 43				00 13
Walton (Merseyside)	d	10 52	22 52				23 22						23 52	
Orrell Park	d	10 53	22 53				23 23						23 53	
Aintree	d	10 56	22 56				23 26						23 56	
Old Roan	d	10 58	22 58				23 28						23 58	
Maghull	d	11 01	23 01				23 31						00 01	
Town Green	d	11 05	23 05				23 35						00 05	
Aughton Park	d	11 07	23 07				23 37						00 07	
Ormskirk	a	11 12	23 12				23 42						00 12	
Bank Hall	d			23 01		23 16			23 31		23 46			
Bootle Oriel Road	d			23 03		23 18			23 33		23 48			
Bootle New Strand	d			23 05		23 20			23 35		23 50			
Seaforth & Litherland	d			23 07		23 22			23 37		23 52			
Waterloo (Merseyside)	d			23 09		23 24			23 39		23 54			
Blundellsands & Crosby	d			23 12		23 27			23 42		23 57			
Hall Road	d			23 14		23 29			23 44		23 59			
Hightown	d			23 17		23 32			23 47		00 02			
Formby	d			23 21		23 36			23 51		00 06			
Freshfield	d			23 23		23 38			23 53		00 08			
Ainsdale	d			23 27		23 42			23 57		00 12			
Hillside	d			23 30		23 45			00 01		00 15			
Birkdale	d			23 32		23 47			00 02		00 17			
Southport	a			23 37		23 52			00 07		00 22			

For general notes see front of timetable
For details of catering facilities see
Directory of Train Operators

A Until 27 September
B From 4 October

Southport, Ormskirk and Kirkby → Liverpool and Hunts Cross

Network Diagram - see first page of Table 101

Miles	Miles	Miles			ME	ME	ME	ME	ME	ME	ME	ME	ME		ME	ME	ME	ME	ME	ME	ME	ME	ME	ME
0	—	—	**Southport**	d				05 43		05 58		06 13			06 28		06 43			06 58			07 13	
1	—	—	Birkdale	d				05 47		06 02		06 17			06 32		06 47			07 02			07 17	
2	—	—	Hillside	d				05 49		06 04		06 19			06 34		06 49			07 04			07 19	
3½	—	—	Ainsdale	d				05 52		06 07		06 22			06 37		06 52			07 07			07 22	
6¼	—	—	Freshfield	d				05 56		06 11		06 26			06 41		06 56			07 11			07 26	
7¼	—	—	Formby	d				05 58		06 13		06 28			06 43		06 58			07 13			07 28	
9¼	—	—	Hightown	d				06 02		06 17		06 32			06 47		07 02			07 17			07 32	
11¼	—	—	Hall Road	d				06 05		06 20		06 35			06 50		07 05			07 20			07 35	
12	—	—	Blundellsands & Crosby	d				06 07		06 22		06 37			06 52		07 07			07 22			07 37	
13	—	—	Waterloo (Merseyside)	d				06 10		06 25		06 40			06 55		07 10			07 25			07 40	
14¼	—	—	Seaforth & Litherland	d				06 12		06 27		06 42			06 57		07 12			07 27			07 42	
15¼	—	—	Bootle New Strand	d				06 15		06 30		06 45			07 00		07 15			07 30			07 45	
15½	—	—	Bootle Oriel Road	d				06 16		06 31		06 46			07 01		07 16			07 31			07 46	
16¼	—	—	Bank Hall	d				06 18		06 33		06 48			07 03		07 18			07 33			07 48	
—	0	—	**Ormskirk**	d			05 50				06 20					06 50			07 05			07 20		
—	1¼	—	Aughton Park	d			05 53				06 23					06 53			07 08			07 23		
—	2¼	—	Town Green	d			05 55				06 25					06 55			07 10			07 25		
—	4¾	—	Maghull	d			06 00				06 30					07 00			07 15			07 30		
—	6½	—	Old Roan	d			06 03				06 33					07 03			07 18			07 33		
—	7¼	—	Aintree	d			06 05				06 35					07 05			07 20			07 35		
—	8¼	—	Orrell Park	d			06 07				06 37					07 07			07 22			07 37		
—	8½	—	Walton (Merseyside)	d			06 09				06 39					07 09			07 24			07 39		
—	—	0	**Kirkby**	d	05 48				06 18				06 48					07 13			07 28			07 43
—	—	1¾	Fazakerley	d	05 51				06 21				06 51					07 16			07 31			07 46
—	—	3¼	Rice Lane	d	05 54				06 24				06 54					07 19			07 34			07 49
—	9¾	4½	Kirkdale	d	05 57		06 12		06 27		06 42		06 57			07 12		07 22	07 27		07 37	07 42		07 52
17	10¾	5½	Sandhills	d	06 00	06 06	06 14	06 21	06 30	06 36	06 44	06 51	07 00		07 06	07 14	07 21	07 25	07 29	07 36	07 40	07 44	07 51	07 55
18½	12¼	7	**Moorfields** 10	d	06 03	06 10	06 18	06 25	06 33	06 40	06 48	06 55	07 03		07 10	07 18	07 25	07 28	07 33	07 40	07 43	07 48	07 55	07 58
19	12¾	7½	**Liverpool Central** 10	a	06 06	06 13	06 20	06 28	06 36	06 43	06 50	06 58	07 06		07 13	07 20	07 28	07 31	07 35	07 43	07 46	07 50	07 58	08 01
—	—	—		d		06 14		06 29		06 43		06 59			07 14		07 29			07 44			07 59	
20½	—	—	Brunswick	d		06 17		06 32		06 47		07 02			07 17		07 32			07 47			08 02	
21¾	—	—	St Michaels	d		06 20		06 35		06 49		07 05			07 20		07 35			07 50			08 05	
23	—	—	Aigburth	d		06 22		06 37		06 52		07 07			07 22		07 37			07 52			08 07	
23¾	—	—	Cressington	d		06 24		06 39		06 54		07 09			07 24		07 39			07 54			08 09	
24¾	—	—	**Liverpool South Parkway** 7 89 ✈	d		06 27		06 42		06 56		07 12			07 27		07 42			07 57			08 12	
26¼	—	—	**Hunts Cross** 89	a		06 31		06 46		07 01		07 16			07 31		07 46			08 01			08 16	

		ME		ME	ME	ME	ME	ME	ME SX	ME	ME	ME		ME SX	ME	ME		ME	ME	ME	ME	ME	ME	ME
Southport	d			07 28			07 43		07 48		07 58			08 03		08 13				08 28			08 43	
Birkdale	d			07 32			07 47		07 52		08 02			08 07		08 17				08 32			08 47	
Hillside	d			07 34			07 49		07 54		08 04			08 09		08 19				08 34			08 49	
Ainsdale	d			07 37			07 52		07 57		08 07			08 12		08 22				08 37			08 52	
Freshfield	d			07 41			07 56		08 01		08 11			08 16		08 26				08 41			08 56	
Formby	d			07 43			07 58		08 03		08 13			08 18		08 28				08 43			08 58	
Hightown	d			07 47			08 02		08 07		08 17			08 22		08 32				08 47			09 02	
Hall Road	d			07 50			08 05		08 10		08 20			08 25		08 35				08 50			09 05	
Blundellsands & Crosby	d			07 52			08 07		08 12		08 22			08 27		08 37				08 52			09 07	
Waterloo (Merseyside)	d			07 55			08 10		08 15		08 25			08 30		08 40				08 55			09 10	
Seaforth & Litherland	d			07 57			08 12		08 17		08 27			08 32		08 42				08 57			09 12	
Bootle New Strand	d			08 00			08 15		08 20		08 30			08 35		08 45				09 00			09 15	
Bootle Oriel Road	d			08 01			08 16		08 21		08 31			08 36		08 46				09 01			09 16	
Bank Hall	d			08 03			08 18		08 23		08 33			08 38		08 48				09 03			09 18	
Ormskirk	d	07 35				07 50				08 05					08 20				08 35			08 50		
Aughton Park	d	07 38				07 53				08 08					08 23				08 38			08 53		
Town Green	d	07 40				07 55				08 10					08 25				08 40			08 55		
Maghull	d	07 45				08 00				08 15					08 30				08 45			09 00		
Old Roan	d	07 48				08 03				08 18					08 33				08 48			09 03		
Aintree	d	07 50				08 05				08 20					08 35				08 50			09 05		
Orrell Park	d	07 52				08 07				08 22					08 37				08 52			09 07		
Walton (Merseyside)	d	07 54				08 09				08 24					08 39				08 54			09 09		
Kirkby	d				07 58			08 13				08 28						08 43			08 58			09 13
Fazakerley	d				08 01			08 16				08 31						08 46			09 01			09 16
Rice Lane	d				08 04			08 19				08 34						08 49			09 04			09 19
Kirkdale	d	07 57			08 07	08 12		08 22		08 27		08 37			08 42			08 52	08 57		09 07	09 12		09 22
Sandhills	d	07 59		08 06	08 10	08 14	08 21	08 25	08 27	08 29	08 36	08 40		08 42	08 44	08 51		08 55	08 59	09 06	09 10	09 14	09 21	09 25
Moorfields 10	d	08 03		08 10	08 13	08 18	08 25	08 28	08 31	08 33	08 40	08 43		08 46	08 48	08 55		08 58	09 03	09 10	09 13	09 18	09 25	09 28
Liverpool Central 10	a	08 05		08 13	08 16	08 20	08 28	08 31	08 33	08 35	08 43	08 46		08 48	08 50	08 58		09 01	09 05	09 13	09 16	09 20	09 28	09 31
	d			08 14			08 29				08 44					08 59				09 14			09 29	
Brunswick	d			08 17			08 32				08 47					09 02				09 17			09 32	
St Michaels	d			08 20			08 35				08 50					09 05				09 20			09 35	
Aigburth	d			08 22			08 37				08 52					09 07				09 22			09 37	
Cressington	d			08 24			08 39				08 54					09 09				09 24			09 39	
Liverpool South Parkway 7 89 ✈	d			08 27			08 42				08 57					09 12				09 27			09 42	
Hunts Cross 89	a			08 31			08 46				09 01					09 16				09 31			09 46	

For general notes see front of timetable
For details of catering facilities see Directory of Train Operators

Southport, Ormskirk and Kirkby → Liverpool and Hunts Cross

Network Diagram - see first page of Table 101

		ME	ME	ME	ME	ME	ME	ME	ME	ME	ME	ME	ME	ME	ME	ME	ME	ME	
Southport	d		08 58			09 13	18 13			18 28			18 43			18 58			
Birkdale	d		09 02			09 17	18 17			18 32			18 47			19 02			
Hillside	d		09 04			09 19	18 19			18 34			18 49			19 04			
Ainsdale	d		09 07			09 22	18 22			18 37			18 52			19 07			
Freshfield	d		09 11			09 26	18 26			18 41			18 56			19 11			
Formby	d		09 13			09 28	18 28			18 43			18 58			19 13			
Hightown	d		09 17			09 32	18 32			18 47			19 02			19 17			
Hall Road	d		09 20			09 35	18 35			18 50			19 05			19 20			
Blundellsands & Crosby	d		09 22			09 37	18 37			18 52			19 07			19 22			
Waterloo (Merseyside)	d		09 25			09 40	18 40			18 55			19 10			19 25			
Seaforth & Litherland	d		09 27			09 42	18 42			18 57			19 12			19 27			
Bootle New Strand	d		09 30			09 45	18 45			19 00			19 15			19 30			
Bootle Oriel Road	d		09 31			09 46	18 46			19 01			19 16			19 31			
Bank Hall	d		09 33			09 48	18 48			19 03			19 18			19 33			and at the same minutes past each hour until
Ormskirk	d	09 05			09 20				18 35			18 50			19 05			19 20	
Aughton Park	d	09 08			09 23				18 38			18 53			19 08			19 23	
Town Green	d	09 10			09 25				18 40			18 55			19 10			19 25	
Maghull	d	09 15			09 30				18 45			19 00			19 15			19 30	
Old Roan	d	09 18			09 33				18 48			19 03			19 18			19 33	
Aintree	d	09 20			09 35				18 50			19 05			19 20			19 35	
Orrell Park	d	09 22			09 37				18 52			19 07			19 22			19 37	
Walton (Merseyside)	d	09 24			09 39				18 54			19 09			19 24			19 39	
Kirkby	d			09 28				18 43			18 58			19 13			19 28		
Fazakerley	d			09 31				18 46			19 01			19 16			19 31		
Rice Lane	d			09 34				18 49			19 04			19 19			19 34		
Kirkdale	d	09 27		09 37	09 42			18 52	18 57		19 07	19 12		19 22	19 27		19 37	19 42	
Sandhills	d	09 29	09 36	09 40	09 44	09 51	18 51	18 55	18 59	19 06	19 10	19 14	19 21	19 25	19 29	19 36	19 40	19 44	
Moorfields 10	d	09 33	09 40	09 43	09 48	09 55	18 55	18 58	19 03	19 10	19 13	19 18	19 25	19 28	19 33	19 40	19 43	19 48	
Liverpool Central 10	a	09 35	09 43	09 46	09 50	09 58	18 58	19 01	19 05	19 13	19 16	19 20	19 28	19 31	19 35	19 43	19 46	19 50	
	d		09 44			09 59	18 59			19 14			19 29			19 44			
Brunswick	d		09 47			10 02	19 02			19 17			19 32			19 47			
St Michaels	d		09 50			10 05	19 05			19 20			19 35			19 50			
Aigburth	d		09 52			10 07	19 07			19 22			19 37			19 52			
Cressington	d		09 54			10 09	19 09			19 24			19 39			19 54			
Liverpool South Parkway 7	89 ✈ d		09 57			10 12	19 12			19 27			19 42			19 57			
Hunts Cross	89 a		10 01			10 16	19 16			19 31			19 46			20 01			

		ME	ME	ME	ME	ME	ME	ME	ME	ME	ME	ME	ME	ME	ME	ME	ME	ME	ME
Southport	d	19 13		19 28		19 43		19 58			22 13		22 28		22 43		22 58		23 16
Birkdale	d	19 17		19 32		19 47		20 02			22 17		22 32		22 47		23 02		23 20
Hillside	d	19 19		19 34		19 49		20 04			22 19		22 34		22 49		23 04		23 22
Ainsdale	d	19 22		19 37		19 52		20 07			22 22		22 37		22 52		23 07		23 25
Freshfield	d	19 26		19 41		19 56		20 11			22 26		22 41		22 56		23 11		23 29
Formby	d	19 28		19 43		19 58		20 13			22 28		22 43		22 58		23 13		23 31
Hightown	d	19 32		19 47		20 02		20 17			22 32		22 47		23 02		23 17		23 35
Hall Road	d	19 35		19 50		20 05		20 20			22 35		22 50		23 05		23 20		23 38
Blundellsands & Crosby	d	19 37		19 52		20 07		20 22			22 37		22 52		23 07		23 22		23 40
Waterloo (Merseyside)	d	19 40		19 55		20 10		20 25			22 40		22 55		23 10		23 25		23 43
Seaforth & Litherland	d	19 42		19 57		20 12		20 27			22 42		22 57		23 12		23 27		23 45
Bootle New Strand	d	19 45		20 00		20 15		20 30			22 45		23 00		23 15		23 30		23 48
Bootle Oriel Road	d	19 46		20 01		20 16		20 31			22 46		23 01		23 16		23 31		23 49
Bank Hall	d	19 48		20 03		20 18		20 33			22 48		23 03		23 18		23 33		23 51
Ormskirk	d				19 50				20 20	22 20				22 50				23 20	
Aughton Park	d				19 53				20 23	22 23				22 53				23 23	
Town Green	d				19 55				20 25	22 25				22 55				23 25	
Maghull	d				20 00				20 30	22 30				23 00				23 30	
Old Roan	d				20 03				20 33	22 33				23 03				23 33	
Aintree	d				20 05				20 35	22 35				23 05				23 35	
Orrell Park	d				20 07				20 37	22 37				23 07				23 37	
Walton (Merseyside)	d				20 09				20 39	22 39				23 09				23 39	
Kirkby	d		19 48				20 18					22 48				23 18			
Fazakerley	d		19 51				20 21					22 51				23 21			
Rice Lane	d		19 54				20 24					22 54				23 24			
Kirkdale	d		19 57		20 12		20 27		20 42	22 42		22 57		23 12		23 27		23 42	
Sandhills	d	19 51	20 00	20 06	20 14	20 21	20 30	20 36	20 44	22 44	22 51	23 00	23 06	23 14	23 21	23 30	23 36	23 44	23 55
Moorfields 10	d	19 55	20 03	20 10	20 18	20 25	20 33	20 40	20 48	22 48	22 55	23 03	23 10	23 18	23 25	23 33	23 40	23 48	23 58
Liverpool Central 10	a	19 58	20 06	20 13	20 20	20 28	20 36	20 43	20 50	22 50	22 58	23 06	23 13	23 20	23 28	23 36	23 43	23 50	00 01
	d	19 59		20 14		20 29		20 44			22 59		23 14		23 29		23 44		
Brunswick	d	20 02		20 17		20 32		20 47			23 02		23 17		23 32		23 47		
St Michaels	d	20 05		20 20		20 35		20 50			23 05		23 20		23 35		23 50		
Aigburth	d	20 07		20 22		20 37		20 52			23 07		23 22		23 37		23 52		
Cressington	d	20 09		20 24		20 39		20 54			23 09		23 24		23 39		23 54		
Liverpool South Parkway 7	89 ✈ d	20 12		20 27		20 42		20 57			23 12		23 27		23 42		23 57		
Hunts Cross	89 a	20 16		20 31		20 46		21 01			23 18		23 32		23 46		00 01		

and
the s
minu
pa
ea
hour

For general notes see front of timetable
For details of catering facilities see
Directory of Train Operators

Table 103

Sundays

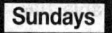

Southport, Ormskirk and Kirkby → Liverpool and Hunts Cross

Network Diagram - see first page of Table 101

		ME	ME	ME	ME	ME	ME	ME	ME	ME	ME	ME	ME	ME	ME	ME	ME
Southport	d			07 58			08 28			08 58			09 28			09 58	
Birkdale	d			08 02			08 32			09 02			09 32			10 02	
Hillside	d			08 04			08 34			09 04			09 34			10 04	
Ainsdale	d			08 07			08 37			09 07			09 37			10 07	
Freshfield	d			08 11			08 41			09 11			09 41			10 11	
Formby	d			08 13			08 43			09 13			09 43			10 13	
Hightown	d			08 17			08 47			09 17			09 47			10 17	
Hall Road	d			08 20			08 50			09 20			09 50			10 20	
Blundellsands & Crosby	d			08 22			08 52			09 22			09 52			10 22	
Waterloo (Merseyside)	d			08 25			08 55			09 25			09 55			10 25	
Seaforth & Litherland	d			08 27			08 57			09 27			09 57			10 27	
Bootle New Strand	d			08 30			09 00			09 30			10 00			10 30	
Bootle Oriel Road	d			08 31			09 01			09 31			10 01			10 31	
Bank Hall	d			08 33			09 03			09 33			10 03			10 33	
Ormskirk	d				08 20			08 50			09 20			09 50			10 20
Aughton Park	d				08 23			08 53			09 23			09 53			10 23
Town Green	d				08 25			08 55			09 25			09 55			10 25
Maghull	d				08 30			09 00			09 30			10 00			10 30
Old Roan	d				08 33			09 03			09 33			10 03			10 33
Aintree	d				08 35			09 05			09 35			10 05			10 35
Orrell Park	d				08 37			09 07			09 37			10 07			10 37
Walton (Merseyside)	d				08 39			09 09			09 39			10 09			10 39
Kirkby	d		08 18			08 48			09 18			09 48			10 18		
Fazakerley	d		08 21			08 51			09 21			09 51			10 21		
Rice Lane	d		08 24			08 54			09 24			09 54			10 24		
Kirkdale	d		08 27		08 42	08 57		09 12	09 27		09 42	09 57		10 12	10 27		10 42
Sandhills	d		08 30	08 36	08 44	09 00	09 06	09 14	09 30	09 36	09 44	10 00	10 06	10 14	10 30	10 36	10 44
Moorfields 10	d		08 33	08 40	08 48	09 03	09 10	09 18	09 33	09 40	09 48	10 03	10 10	10 18	10 33	10 40	10 48
Liverpool Central 10	a		08 36	08 43	08 50	09 06	09 13	09 20	09 36	09 43	09 50	10 06	10 13	10 20	10 36	10 43	10 50
	d	08 14		08 44			09 14			09 44			10 14			10 44	
Brunswick	d	08 17		08 47			09 17			09 47			10 17			10 47	
St Michaels	d	08 20		08 50			09 20			09 50			10 20			10 50	
Aigburth	d	08 22		08 52			09 22			09 52			10 22			10 52	
Cressington	d	08 24		08 54			09 24			09 54			10 24			10 54	
Liverpool South Parkway 7	89 ⇄ d	08 27		08 57			09 27			09 57			10 27			10 57	
Hunts Cross	89 a	08 31		09 01			09 31			10 01			10 31			11 01	

		ME A	ME	ME	ME	ME A	ME A	ME	ME	ME	ME	
Southport	d	10 13		10 28		10 43	22 43		22 58		23 16	
Birkdale	d	10 17		10 32		10 47	22 47		23 02		23 20	
Hillside	d	10 19		10 34		10 49	22 49		23 04		23 22	
Ainsdale	d	10 22		10 37		10 52	22 52		23 07		23 25	
Freshfield	d	10 26		10 41		10 56	22 56		23 11		23 29	
Formby	d	10 28		10 43		10 58	22 58		23 13		23 31	
Hightown	d	10 32		10 47		11 02	23 02		23 17		23 35	
Hall Road	d	10 35		10 50		11 05	23 05		23 20		23 38	
Blundellsands & Crosby	d	10 37		10 52		11 07	23 07		23 22		23 40	
Waterloo (Merseyside)	d	10 40		10 55		11 10	23 10		23 25		23 43	
Seaforth & Litherland	d	10 42		10 57		11 12	23 12		23 27		23 45	
Bootle New Strand	d	10 45		11 00		11 15	23 15		23 30		23 48	
Bootle Oriel Road	d	10 46		11 01		11 16	23 16		23 31		23 49	
Bank Hall	d	10 48		11 03		11 18	23 18		23 33		23 51	and at
Ormskirk	d				10 50					23 20		the same
Aughton Park	d				10 53					23 23		minutes
Town Green	d				10 55					23 25		past
Maghull	d				11 00					23 30		each
Old Roan	d				11 03					23 33		hour until
Aintree	d				11 05					23 35		
Orrell Park	d				11 07					23 37		
Walton (Merseyside)	d				11 09					23 39		
Kirkby	d		10 48					23 18				
Fazakerley	d		10 51					23 21				
Rice Lane	d		10 54					23 24				
Kirkdale	d		10 57		11 12			23 27		23 42		
Sandhills	d	10 51	11 00	11 06	11 14	11 21	23 21	23 30	23 36	23 44	23 55	
Moorfields 10	d	10 55	11 03	11 10	11 18	11 25	23 25	23 33	23 40	23 48	23 58	
Liverpool Central 10	a	10 58	11 06	11 13	11 20	11 28	23 28	23 36	23 43	23 50	00 01	
	d			11 14					23 44			
Brunswick	d			11 17					23 47			
St Michaels	d			11 20					23 50			
Aigburth	d			11 22					23 52			
Cressington	d			11 24					23 54			
Liverpool South Parkway 7	89 ⇄ d			11 27					23 57			
Hunts Cross	89 a			11 31					00 01			

For general notes see front of timetable
For details of catering facilities see Directory of Train Operators

A Until 27 September

Liverpool and Birkenhead → New Brighton, West Kirby, Ellesmere Port and Chester

Network Diagram - see first page of Table 101

Miles	Miles	Miles	Miles			ME	ME	ME	ME	ME	ME	ME	ME	ME	ME	ME	ME	ME	ME	ME	ME	ME	ME	ME
0	—	0	0	**Moorfields 10**	d	05 36	05 56	06 06	06 16	06 21	06 26	06 41	06 46	06 51	06 56	07 11	07 16	07 21	07 26	07 31	07 36	07 41	07 46	07 51
½	—	½	½	**Liverpool Lime Street 10**	d	05 38	05 58	06 08	06 18	06 23	06 28	06 43	06 48	06 53	06 58	07 13	07 18	07 23	07 28	07 33	07 38	07 43	07 48	07 53
1	—	1	1	**Liverpool Central 10**	d	05 40	06 00	06 10	06 20	06 25	06 30	06 45	06 50	06 55	07 00	07 15	07 20	07 25	07 30	07 35	07 40	07 45	07 50	07 55
1½	—	1½	1½	James Street	d	05 42	06 02	06 12	06 22	06 27	06 32	06 47	06 52	06 57	07 02	07 17	07 22	07 27	07 32	07 37	07 42	07 47	07 52	07 57
2¾	—	2¾	2¾	Hamilton Square	d	05 45	06 05	06 15	06 25	06 30	06 35	06 50	06 55	07 00	07 05	07 20	07 25	07 30	07 35	07 40	07 45	07 50	07 55	08 00
—	—	3¼	3¼	Conway Park	d				06 27	06 32			06 57	07 02			07 27	07 32		07 42	07 47		07 57	08 02
—	—	4	4	Birkenhead Park	d				06 29	06 34			06 59	07 04			07 29	07 34		07 44	07 49		07 59	08 04
—	—	4¾	4¾	Birkenhead North	d				06 32	06 37			07 02	07 07			07 32	07 37		07 47	07 52		08 02	08 07
—	—	—	6¼	Wallasey Village	d				06 37				07 07				07 37			07 52			08 07	
—	—	—	6½	Wallasey Grove Road	d				06 38				07 08				07 38			07 53			08 08	
—	—	—	7¾	**New Brighton**	a				06 43				07 13				07 43			07 58			08 13	
—	—	5¼	—	Bidston	d					06 40				07 10				07 40			07 55			08 10
—	—	6½	—	Leasowe	d					06 42				07 12				07 42			07 57			08 12
—	—	7	—	Moreton (Merseyside)	d					06 44				07 14				07 44			07 59			08 14
—	—	8¼	—	Meols	d					06 48				07 18				07 48			08 03			08 18
—	—	9½	—	Manor Road	d					06 50				07 20				07 50			08 05			08 20
—	—	10	—	Hoylake	d					06 52				07 22				07 52			08 07			08 22
—	—	11¼	—	**West Kirby**	a					06 57				07 27				07 57			08 12			08 27
3	—	—	—	Birkenhead Central	d	05 47	06 07	06 17			06 37	06 52			07 07	07 22			07 37			07 52		
3¾	—	—	—	Green Lane	d	05 49	06 09	06 19			06 39	06 54			07 09	07 24			07 39			07 54		
4½	—	—	—	Rock Ferry	d	05 52	06 12	06 22			06 42	06 57			07 12	07 27			07 42			07 57		
5½	—	—	—	Bebington	d	05 54	06 14	06 24			06 44	06 59			07 14	07 29			07 44			07 59		
6½	—	—	—	Port Sunlight	d	05 56	06 16	06 26			06 46	07 01			07 16	07 31			07 46			08 01		
7	—	—	—	Spital	d	05 58	06 18	06 28			06 48	07 03			07 18	07 33			07 48			08 03		
7¾	—	—	—	Bromborough Rake	d	06 00	06 20	06 30			06 50	07 05			07 20	07 35			07 50			08 05		
8½	—	—	—	Bromborough	d	06 02	06 22	06 32			06 52	07 07			07 22	07 37			07 52			08 07		
9	—	—	—	Eastham Rake	d	06 05	06 25	06 35			06 55	07 10			07 25	07 40			07 55			08 10		
10	0	—	—	Hooton	d	06 07	06 27	06 37			06 57	07 12			07 27	07 42			07 57			08 12		
—	1½	—	—	Little Sutton	d		06 31				07 01				07 31				08 01					
—	2½	—	—	Overpool	d		06 33				07 03				07 33				08 03					
—	4	—	—	**Ellesmere Port**	a		06 37				07 07				07 37				08 07					
13	—	—	—	Capenhurst	d	06 12		06 42				07 17				07 47						08 17		
16¾	—	—	—	Bache	d	06 17		06 47				07 22				07 52						08 22		
18¼	—	—	—	**Chester**	a	06 26		06 56				07 26				07 56						08 26		

		ME	ME	ME		ME	ME	ME	ME	ME	ME	ME	ME	ME	ME	ME	ME SX	ME	ME	ME	ME SX
Moorfields 10	d	07 56	08 01	08 06		15 11	15 16	15 21	15 26	15 31	15 36	15 41	15 46	15 51	15 56	16 01	16 03	16 06	16 11	16 16	16 18
Liverpool Lime Street 10	d	07 58	08 03	08 08		15 13	15 18	15 23	15 28	15 33	15 38	15 43	15 48	15 53	15 58	16 03	16 05	16 08	16 13	16 18	16 20
Liverpool Central 10	d	08 00	08 05	08 10		15 15	15 20	15 25	15 30	15 35	15 40	15 45	15 50	15 55	16 00	16 05	16 07	16 10	16 15	16 20	16 22
James Street	d	08 02	08 07	08 12		15 17	15 22	15 27	15 32	15 37	15 42	15 47	15 52	15 57	16 02	16 07	16 09	16 12	16 17	16 22	16 24
Hamilton Square	d	08 05	08 10	08 15		15 20	15 25	15 30	15 35	15 40	15 45	15 50	15 55	16 00	16 05	16 10	16a12	16 15	16 20	16 25	16a27
Conway Park	d		08 12	08 17			15 27	15 32		15 42	15 47		15 57	16 02		16 12		16 17		16 27	
Birkenhead Park	d		08 14	08 19			15 29	15 34		15 44	15 49		15 59	16 04		16 14		16 19		16 29	
Birkenhead North	d		08 17	08 22			15 32	15 37		15 47	15 52		16 02	16 07		16 17		16 22		16 32	
Wallasey Village	d		08 22				15 37			15 52			16 07			16 22				16 37	
Wallasey Grove Road	d		08 23				15 38			15 53			16 08			16 23				16 38	
New Brighton	a		08 28		and at		15 43			15 58			16 13			16 28				16 43	
Bidston	d			08 25	the same			15 40			15 55			16 10				16 25			
Leasowe	d			08 27				15 42			15 57			16 12				16 27			
Moreton (Merseyside)	d			08 29	minutes			15 44			15 59			16 14				16 29			
Meols	d			08 33				15 48			16 03			16 18				16 33			
Manor Road	d			08 35	past			15 50			16 05			16 20				16 35			
Hoylake	d			08 37				15 52			16 07			16 22				16 37			
West Kirby	a			08 42	each			15 57			16 12			16 27				16 42			
Birkenhead Central	d	08 07			hour until	15 22			15 37			15 52			16 07				16 22		
Green Lane	d	08 09				15 24			15 39			15 54			16 09				16 24		
Rock Ferry	d	08 12				15 27			15 42			15 57			16 12				16 27		
Bebington	d	08 14				15 29			15 44			15 59			16 14				16 29		
Port Sunlight	d	08 16				15 31			15 46			16 01			16 16				16 31		
Spital	d	08 18				15 33			15 48			16 03			16 18				16 33		
Bromborough Rake	d	08 20				15 35			15 50			16 05			16 20				16 35		
Bromborough	d	08 22				15 37			15 52			16 07			16 22				16 37		
Eastham Rake	d	08 25				15 40			15 55			16 10			16 25				16 40		
Hooton	d	08 27				15 42			15 57			16 12			16 27				16 42		
Little Sutton	d	08 31							16 01						16 31						
Overpool	d	08 33							16 03						16 33						
Ellesmere Port	a	08 37							16 07						16 37						
Capenhurst	d					15 47						16 17							16 47		
Bache	d					15 52						16 22							16 52		
Chester	a					15 56						16 26							16 56		

For general notes see front of timetable
For details of catering facilities see Directory of Train Operators

Liverpool and Birkenhead → New Brighton, West Kirby, Ellesmere Port and Chester

Network Diagram - see first page of Table 101

		ME	ME	ME	ME SX	ME	ME SX	ME SO	ME	ME SX	ME	ME	ME	ME SX	ME	ME SX	ME SO	ME	ME SX	ME	ME	ME	ME SX
Moorfields 10	d	16 21	16 26	16 31	16 33	16 36	16 41	16 41	16 46	16 48	16 51	16 56	17 01	17 03	17 06	17 11	17 11	17 16	17 18	17 21	17 26	17 31	17 33
Liverpool Lime Street 10	d	16 23	16 28	16 33	16 35	16 38	16 43	16 43	16 48	16 50	16 53	16 58	17 03	17 05	17 08	17 13	17 13	17 18	17 20	17 23	17 28	17 33	17 35
Liverpool Central 10	d	16 25	16 30	16 35	16 37	16 40	16 45	16 45	16 50	16 52	16 55	17 00	17 05	17 07	17 10	17 15	17 15	17 20	17 22	17 25	17 30	17 35	17 37
James Street	d	16 27	16 32	16 37	16 39	16 42	16 47	16 47	16 52	16 54	16 57	17 02	17 07	17 09	17 12	17 17	17 17	17 22	17 24	17 27	17 32	17 37	17 39
Hamilton Square	d	16 30	16 35	16 40	16 42	16 45	16 50	16 50	16 55	16 57	17 00	17 05	17 10	17 12	17 15	17 20	17 20	17 25	17 27	17 30	17 35	17 40	17 42
Conway Park	d	16 32		16 42		16 47			16 57		17 02		17 12		17 17			17 27		17 32		17 42	
Birkenhead Park	d	16 34		16 44		16 49			16 59		17 04		17 14		17 19			17 29		17 34		17 44	
Birkenhead North	d	16 37		16 47		16 52			17 02		17 07		17 17		17 22			17 32		17 37		17 47	
Wallasey Village	d			16 52					17 07				17 22					17 37				17 52	
Wallasey Grove Road	d			16 53					17 08				17 23					17 38				17 53	
New Brighton	a			16 58					17 13				17 28					17 43				17 58	
Bidston	d	16 40				16 55					17 10				17 25					17 40			
Leasowe	d	16 42				16 57					17 12				17 27					17 42			
Moreton (Merseyside)	d	16 44				16 59					17 14				17 29					17 44			
Meols	d	16 48				17 03					17 18				17 33					17 48			
Manor Road	d	16 50				17 05					17 20				17 35					17 50			
Hoylake	d	16 52				17 07					17 22				17 37					17 52			
West Kirby	a	16 57				17 12					17 27				17 42					17 57			
Birkenhead Central	d		16 37		16 45		16 52	16 52		17 00		17 07		17 15		17 22	17 22		17 30		17 37		17 45
Green Lane	d		16 39		16 47		16 54	16 54		17 02		17 09		17 17		17 24	17 24		17 32		17 39		17 47
Rock Ferry	d		16 42		16 49		16 57	16 57		17 04		17 12		17 19		17 27	17 27		17 34		17 42		17 49
Bebington	d		16 44		16 52		16 59	16 59		17 07		17 14		17 22		17 29	17 29		17 37		17 44		17 52
Port Sunlight	d		16 46		16 54		17 01	17 01		17 09		17 16		17 24		17 31	17 31		17 39		17 46		17 54
Spital	d		16 48		16 56		17 03	17 03		17 11		17 18		17 26		17 33	17 33		17 41		17 48		17 56
Bromborough Rake	d		16 50		16 58		17 05	17 05		17 13		17 20		17 28		17 35	17 35		17 43		17 50		17 58
Bromborough	d		16 52		17 00		17 07	17 07		17 15		17 22		17 30		17 37	17 37		17 45		17 52		18 00
Eastham Rake	d		16 55		17 02		17 10	17 10		17 17		17 25		17 32		17 40	17 40		17 47		17 55		18 02
Hooton	d		16 57		17 04		17 12	17 12		17 19		17 27		17 34		17 42	17 42		17 49		17 57		18 04
Little Sutton	d		17 01				17 16					17 31				17 46					18 01		
Overpool	d		17 03				17 18					17 33				17 48					18 03		
Ellesmere Port	a		17 07				17 23					17 37				17 53					18 07		
Capenhurst	d				17 09			17 17		17 24				17 39			17 47		17 54				18 09
Bache	d				17 15			17 22		17 30				17 45			17 52		18 00				18 15
Chester	a				17 18			17 26		17 33				17 48			17 56		18 03				18 18

		ME	ME SX	ME SO	ME	ME SX	ME	ME	ME	ME	ME	ME	ME	ME	ME	ME	ME	ME	ME	ME	ME	ME
Moorfields 10	d	17 36	17 41	17 41	17 46	17 48	17 51	17 56	18 01	18 06	18 11	18 16	18 21	18 26	18 31	18 36	18 41	18 46	18 51	18 56	19 01	19 06
Liverpool Lime Street 10	d	17 38	17 43	17 43	17 48	17 50	17 53	17 58	18 03	18 08	18 13	18 18	18 23	18 28	18 33	18 38	18 43	18 48	18 53	18 58	19 03	19 08
Liverpool Central 10	d	17 40	17 45	17 45	17 50	17 52	17 55	18 00	18 05	18 10	18 15	18 20	18 25	18 30	18 35	18 40	18 45	18 50	18 55	19 00	19 05	19 10
James Street	d	17 42	17 47	17 47	17 52	17 54	17 57	18 02	18 07	18 12	18 17	18 22	18 27	18 32	18 37	18 42	18 47	18 52	18 57	19 02	19 07	19 12
Hamilton Square	d	17 45	17 50	17 50	17 55	17 57	18 00	18 05	18 10	18 15	18 20	18 25	18 30	18 35	18 40	18 45	18 50	18 55	19 00	19 05	19 10	19 15
Conway Park	d	17 47			17 57		18 02		18 12	18 17		18 27	18 32		18 42	18 47		18 57	19 02		19 12	19 17
Birkenhead Park	d	17 49			17 59		18 04		18 14	18 19		18 29	18 34		18 44	18 49		18 59	19 04		19 14	19 19
Birkenhead North	d	17 52			18 02		18 07		18 17	18 22		18 32	18 37		18 47	18 52		19 02	19 07		19 17	19 22
Wallasey Village	d				18 07				18 22			18 37			18 52			19 07			19 22	
Wallasey Grove Road	d				18 08				18 23			18 38			18 53			19 08			19 23	
New Brighton	a				18 13				18 28			18 43			18 58			19 13			19 28	
Bidston	d	17 55					18 10			18 25			18 40			18 55			19 10			19 25
Leasowe	d	17 57					18 12			18 27			18 42			18 57			19 12			19 27
Moreton (Merseyside)	d	17 59					18 14			18 29			18 44			18 59			19 14			19 29
Meols	d	18 03					18 18			18 33			18 48			19 03			19 18			19 33
Manor Road	d	18 05					18 20			18 35			18 50			19 05			19 20			19 35
Hoylake	d	18 07					18 22			18 37			18 52			19 07			19 22			19 37
West Kirby	a	18 12					18 27			18 42			18 57			19 12			19 27			19 42
Birkenhead Central	d		17 52	17 52		18 00		18 07			18 22			18 37			18 52			19 07		
Green Lane	d		17 54	17 54		18 02		18 09			18 24			18 39			18 54			19 09		
Rock Ferry	d		17 57	17 57		18 04		18 12			18 27			18 42			18 57			19 12		
Bebington	d		17 59	17 59		18 07		18 14			18 29			18 44			18 59			19 14		
Port Sunlight	d		18 01	18 01		18 09		18 16			18 31			18 46			19 01			19 16		
Spital	d		18 03	18 03		18 11		18 18			18 33			18 48			19 03			19 18		
Bromborough Rake	d		18 05	18 05		18 13		18 20			18 35			18 50			19 05			19 20		
Bromborough	d		18 07	18 07		18 15		18 22			18 37			18 52			19 07			19 22		
Eastham Rake	d		18 10	18 10		18 17		18 25			18 40			18 55			19 10			19 25		
Hooton	d		18 12	18 12		18 19		18 27			18 42			18 57			19 12			19 27		
Little Sutton	d		18 16					18 31						19 01						19 31		
Overpool	d		18 18					18 33						19 03						19 33		
Ellesmere Port	a		18 23					18 37						19 07						19 37		
Capenhurst	d			18 17		18 24					18 47						19 17					
Bache	d			18 22		18 30					18 52						19 22					
Chester	a			18 26		18 33					18 56						19 26					

For general notes see front of timetable
For details of catering facilities see
Directory of Train Operators

Liverpool and Birkenhead → New Brighton, West Kirby, Ellesmere Port and Chester

Network Diagram - see first page of Table 101

Mondays to Saturdays

		ME	ME	ME	ME	ME	ME	ME	ME	
Moorfields 10	d	19 11	19 16	19 26	19 31	19 41	19 46	19 56	20 01	
Liverpool Lime Street 10	d	19 13	19 18	19 28	19 33	19 43	19 48	19 58	20 03	
Liverpool Central 10	d	19 15	19 20	19 30	19 35	19 45	19 50	20 00	20 05	
James Street	d	19 17	19 22	19 32	19 37	19 47	19 52	20 02	20 07	
Hamilton Square	d	19 20	19 25	19 35	19 40	19 50	19 55	20 05	20 10	
Conway Park	d		19 27		19 42		19 57		20 12	
Birkenhead Park	d		19 29		19 44		19 59		20 14	
Birkenhead North	d		19 32		19 47		20 02		20 17	
Wallasey Village	d		19 37				20 07			
Wallasey Grove Road	d		19 38				20 08			
New Brighton	a		19 43				20 13			and at
Bidston	d				19 50				20 20	
Leasowe	d				19 52				20 22	the same
Moreton (Merseyside)	d				19 54				20 24	
Meols	d				19 58				20 28	minutes
Manor Road	d				20 00				20 30	
Hoylake	d				20 02				20 32	past
West Kirby	a				20 07				20 37	each
Birkenhead Central	d	19 22		19 37		19 52		20 07		
Green Lane	d	19 24		19 39		19 54		20 09		hour until
Rock Ferry	d	19 27		19 42		19 57		20 12		
Bebington	d	19 29		19 44		19 59		20 14		
Port Sunlight	d	19 31		19 46		20 01		20 16		
Spital	d	19 33		19 48		20 03		20 18		
Bromborough Rake	d	19 35		19 50		20 05		20 20		
Bromborough	d	19 37		19 52		20 07		20 22		
Eastham Rake	d	19 40		19 55		20 10		20 25		
Hooton	d	19 42		19 57		20 12		20 27		
Little Sutton	d			20 01				20 31		
Overpool	d			20 03				20 33		
Ellesmere Port	a			20 07				20 37		
Capenhurst	d	19 47				20 17				
Bache	d	19 52				20 22				
Chester	a	19 56				20 26				

		ME	ME	ME	ME	ME	ME	ME
Moorfields 10	d	23 11	23 16	23 26	23 31	23 41	23 46	23 56
Liverpool Lime Street 10	d	23 13	23 18	23 28	23 33	23 43	23 48	23 58
Liverpool Central 10	d	23 15	23 20	23 30	23 35	23 45	23 50	23 59
James Street	d	23 17	23 22	23 32	23 37	23 47	23 52	00 02
Hamilton Square	d	23 20	23 25	23 35	23 40	23 50	23 55	00a05
Conway Park	d		23 27		23 42		23 57	
Birkenhead Park	d		23 29		23 44		23 59	
Birkenhead North	d		23 32		23 47		00 02	
Wallasey Village	d		23 37				00 07	
Wallasey Grove Road	d		23 38				00 08	
New Brighton	a		23 43				00 13	
Bidston	d				23 50			
Leasowe	d				23 52			
Moreton (Merseyside)	d				23 54			
Meols	d				23 58			
Manor Road	d				23 59			
Hoylake	d				00 02			
West Kirby	a				00 07			
Birkenhead Central	d	23 22		23 37		23 52		
Green Lane	d	23 24		23 39		23 54		
Rock Ferry	d	23 27		23 42		23 57		
Bebington	d	23 29		23 44		23 59		
Port Sunlight	d	23 31		23 46		00 01		
Spital	d	23 33		23 48		00 03		
Bromborough Rake	d	23 35		23 50		00 05		
Bromborough	d	23 37		23 52		00 07		
Eastham Rake	d	23 40		23 55		00 10		
Hooton	d	23 42		23 57		00 12		
Little Sutton	d			00 01				
Overpool	d			00 03				
Ellesmere Port	a			00 07				
Capenhurst	d	23 47				00 17		
Bache	d	23 52				00 22		
Chester	a	23 56				00 26		

Sundays

		ME	ME	ME	ME	ME	ME	ME	ME	ME	ME	
Moorfields 10	d	07 56	08 01	08 11	08 16	08 26	08 31	08 41	08 46	08 56	09 01	
Liverpool Lime Street 10	d	07 58	08 03	08 13	08 18	08 28	08 33	08 43	08 48	08 58	09 03	
Liverpool Central 10	d	08 00	08 05	08 15	08 20	08 30	08 35	08 45	08 50	09 00	09 05	
James Street	d	08 02	08 07	08 17	08 22	08 32	08 37	08 47	08 52	09 02	09 07	
Hamilton Square	d	08 05	08 10	08 20	08 25	08 35	08 40	08 50	08 55	09 05	09 10	
Conway Park	d		18 12		08 27		08 42		08 57		09 12	
Birkenhead Park	d		18 14		08 29		08 44		08 59		09 14	
Birkenhead North	d		18 17		08 32		08 47		09 02		09 17	
Wallasey Village	d				08 37				09 07			
Wallasey Grove Road	d				08 38				09 08			
New Brighton	a				08 43				09 13			and at
Bidston	d		08 20				08 50				09 20	
Leasowe	d		08 22				08 52				09 22	the same
Moreton (Merseyside)	d		08 24				08 54				09 24	
Meols	d		08 28				08 58				09 28	minutes
Manor Road	d		08 30				09 00				09 30	
Hoylake	d		08 32				09 02				09 32	past
West Kirby	a		08 37				09 07				09 37	each
Birkenhead Central	d	08 07		08 22		08 37		08 52		09 07		
Green Lane	d	08 09		08 24		08 39		08 54		09 09		hour until
Rock Ferry	d	08 12		08 27		08 42		08 57		09 12		
Bebington	d	08 14		08 29		08 44		08 59		09 14		
Port Sunlight	d	08 16		08 31		08 46		09 01		09 16		
Spital	d	08 18		08 33		08 48		09 03		09 18		
Bromborough Rake	d	08 20		08 35		08 50		09 05		09 20		
Bromborough	d	08 22		08 37		08 52		09 07		09 22		
Eastham Rake	d	08 25		08 40		08 55		09 10		09 25		
Hooton	d	08 27		08 42		08 57		09 12		09 27		
Little Sutton	d	08 31				09 01				09 31		
Overpool	d	08 33				09 03				09 33		
Ellesmere Port	a	08 37				09 07				09 37		
Capenhurst	d			08 47				09 17				
Bache	d			08 52				09 22				
Chester	a			08 56				09 26				

		ME	ME	ME	ME	ME	ME	ME
Moorfields 10	d	23 11	23 16	23 26	23 31	23 41	23 46	23 56
Liverpool Lime Street 10	d	23 13	23 18	23 28	23 33	23 43	23 48	23 58
Liverpool Central 10	d	23 15	23 20	23 30	23 35	23 45	23 50	23 59
James Street	d	23 17	23 22	23 32	23 37	23 47	23 52	00 02
Hamilton Square	d	23 20	23 25	23 35	23 40	23 50	23 55	00a05
Conway Park	d		23 27		23 42		23 57	
Birkenhead Park	d		23 29		23 44		23 59	
Birkenhead North	d		23 32		23 47		00 02	
Wallasey Village	d		23 37				00 07	
Wallasey Grove Road	d		23 38				00 08	
New Brighton	a		23 43				00 13	
Bidston	d				23 50			
Leasowe	d				23 52			
Moreton (Merseyside)	d				23 54			
Meols	d				23 58			
Manor Road	d				23 59			
Hoylake	d				00 02			
West Kirby	a				00 07			
Birkenhead Central	d	23 22		23 37		23 52		
Green Lane	d	23 24		23 39		23 54		
Rock Ferry	d	23 27		23 42		23 57		
Bebington	d	23 29		23 44		23 59		
Port Sunlight	d	23 31		23 46		00 01		
Spital	d	23 33		23 48		00 03		
Bromborough Rake	d	23 35		23 50		00 05		
Bromborough	d	23 37		23 52		00 07		
Eastham Rake	d	23 40		23 55		00 10		
Hooton	d	23 42		23 57		00 12		
Little Sutton	d			00 01				
Overpool	d			00 03				
Ellesmere Port	a			00 07				
Capenhurst	d	23 47				00 17		
Bache	d	23 52				00 22		
Chester	a	23 56				00 26		

For general notes see front of timetable
For details of catering facilities see Directory of Train Operators

Chester, Ellesmere Port, West Kirby and New Brighton → Birkenhead and Liverpool

Network Diagram - see first page of Table 101

Miles	Miles	Miles	Miles			ME	ME	ME	ME	ME	ME	ME	ME	ME	ME	ME	ME		ME	ME	ME	ME	ME	ME	ME	ME
0	—	—	—	**Chester**	d						06 00				06 30							07 00				
1½	—	—	—	Bache	d						06 03				06 33							07 03				
5¼	—	—	—	Capenhurst	d						06 09				06 39							07 09				
—	0	—	—	**Ellesmere Port**	d									06 19					06 49						07 19	
—	1½	—	—	Overpool	d									06 22					06 52						07 22	
—	2½	—	—	Little Sutton	d									06 24					06 54						07 24	
8¼	4	—	—	Hooton	d		05 39			05 59	06 14			06 29	06 44				06 59			07 14			07 29	
9¼	—	—	—	Eastham Rake	d		05 41			06 01	06 16			06 31	06 46				07 01			07 16			07 31	
9¾	—	—	—	Bromborough	d		05 43			06 03	06 18			06 33	06 48				07 03			07 18			07 33	
10½	—	—	—	Bromborough Rake	d		05 45			06 05	06 20			06 35	06 50				07 05			07 20			07 35	
11¼	—	—	—	Spital	d		05 47			06 07	06 22			06 37	06 52				07 07			07 22			07 37	
11¾	—	—	—	Port Sunlight	d		05 49			06 09	06 24			06 39	06 54				07 09			07 24			07 39	
12¾	—	—	—	Bebington	d		05 51			06 11	06 26			06 41	06 56				07 11			07 26			07 41	
13¾	—	—	—	Rock Ferry	d	05 44	05 54			06 14	06 29			06 44	06 59				07 14			07 29			07 44	
14½	—	—	—	Green Lane	d	05 47	05 57			06 17	06 32			06 47	07 02				07 17			07 32			07 47	
15	—	—	—	Birkenhead Central	d	05 49	05 59			06 19	06 34			06 49	07 04				07 19			07 34			07 49	
—	—	0	—	**West Kirby**	d				05 51				06 21				06 51				07 06			07 21		
—	—	1	—	Hoylake	d				05 54				06 24				06 54				07 09			07 24		
—	—	1¾	—	Manor Road	d				05 56				06 26				06 56				07 11			07 26		
—	—	3	—	Meols	d				05 58				06 28				06 58				07 13			07 28		
—	—	4¼	—	Moreton (Merseyside)	d				06 01				06 31				07 01				07 16			07 31		
—	—	4¾	—	Leasowe	d				06 03				06 33				07 03				07 18			07 33		
—	—	5¾	—	Bidston	d				06 06				06 36				07 06				07 21			07 36		
—	—	—	0	**New Brighton**	d			05 53				06 23				06 53				07 08			07 23			07 38
—	—	—	1¼	Wallasey Grove Road	d			05 57				06 27				06 57				07 12			07 27			07 42
—	—	—	1½	Wallasey Village	d			05 59				06 29				06 59				07 14			07 29			07 44
—	—	6½	3	Birkenhead North	d			06 04	06 09			06 34	06 39			07 04	07 09			07 19	07 24		07 34	07 39		07 49
—	—	7½	3¾	Birkenhead Park	d			06 06	06 11			06 36	06 41			07 06	07 11			07 21	07 26		07 36	07 41		07 51
—	—	8¼	4½	Conway Park	d			06 09	06 14			06 39	06 44			07 09	07 14			07 24	07 29		07 39	07 44		07 54
15½	—	8¾	5	Hamilton Square	d	05 51	06 01	06 11	06 16	06 21	06 36	06 41	06 46	06 51	07 06	07 11	07 16		07 21	07 26	07 31	07 36	07 41	07 46	07 51	07 56
16¾	—	9¾	6¼	James Street	d	05 54	06 04	06 14	06 19	06 24	06 39	06 44	06 49	06 54	07 09	07 14	07 19		07 24	07 29	07 34	07 39	07 44	07 49	07 54	07 59
17¼	—	10¼	7¾	**Moorfields** 10	a	05 56	06 06	06 16	06 21	06 26	06 41	06 46	06 51	06 56	07 11	07 16	07 21		07 26	07 31	07 36	07 41	07 46	07 51	07 56	08 01
17¾	—	10¾	8¼	**Liverpool Lime Street** 10	a	05 58	06 08	06 18	06 23	06 28	06 43	06 48	06 53	06 58	07 13	07 18	07 23		07 28	07 33	07 38	07 43	07 48	07 53	07 58	08 03
18½	—	11¼	8¾	**Liverpool Central** 10	a	06 00	06 10	06 20	06 25	06 30	06 45	06 50	06 55	07 00	07 15	07 20	07 25		07 30	07 35	07 40	07 45	07 50	07 55	08 00	08 05

		ME SX	ME	ME SX	ME SO	ME	ME SX		ME	ME	ME	ME SX	ME	ME SX	ME SO	ME	ME SX	ME	ME	ME		ME SX	ME	ME	ME	ME SX
Chester	d	07 22			07 30		07 37					07 52			08 00		08 07							08 30		
Bache	d	07 26			07 33		07 41					07 56			08 03		08 11							08 33		
Capenhurst	d	07 32			07 39		07 47					08 02			08 09		08 17							08 39		
Ellesmere Port	d			07 31						07 49				08 01					08 19							
Overpool	d			07 34						07 52				08 04					08 22							
Little Sutton	d			07 36						07 54				08 06					08 24							
Hooton	d	07 36		07 44	07 44		07 51			07 59		08 06		08 14	08 14		08 21		08 29			08 36		08 44		08 51
Eastham Rake	d	07 38		07 46	07 46		07 53			08 01		08 08		08 16	08 16		08 23		08 31			08 38		08 46		08 53
Bromborough	d	07 41		07 48	07 48		07 56			08 03		08 11		08 18	08 18		08 26		08 33			08 41		08 48		08 56
Bromborough Rake	d	07 43		07 50	07 50		07 58			08 05		08 13		08 20	08 20		08 28		08 35			08 43		08 50		08 58
Spital	d	07 45		07 52	07 52		08 00			08 07		08 15		08 22	08 22		08 30		08 37			08 45		08 52		09 00
Port Sunlight	d	07 47		07 54	07 54		08 02			08 09		08 17		08 24	08 24		08 32		08 39			08 47		08 54		09 02
Bebington	d	07 49		07 56	07 56		08 04			08 11		08 19		08 26	08 26		08 34		08 41			08 49		08 56		09 04
Rock Ferry	d	07 52		07 59	07 59		08 07			08 14		08 22		08 29	08 29		08 37		08 44			08 52		08 59		09 07
Green Lane	d	07 54		08 02	08 02		08 09			08 17		08 24		08 32	08 32		08 39		08 47			08 54		09 02		09 09
Birkenhead Central	d	07 57		08 04	08 04		08 12			08 19		08 27		08 34	08 34		08 42		08 49			08 57		09 04		09 12
West Kirby	d		07 36						07 51				08 06					08 21					08 36			
Hoylake	d		07 39						07 54				08 09					08 24					08 39			
Manor Road	d		07 41						07 56				08 11					08 26					08 41			
Meols	d		07 43						07 58				08 13					08 28					08 43			
Moreton (Merseyside)	d		07 46						08 01				08 16					08 31					08 46			
Leasowe	d		07 48						08 03				08 18					08 33					08 48			
Bidston	d		07 51						08 06				08 21					08 36					08 51			
New Brighton	d					07 53					08 08					08 23				08 38					08 53	
Wallasey Grove Road	d					07 57					08 12					08 27				08 42					08 57	
Wallasey Village	d					07 59					08 14					08 29				08 44					08 59	
Birkenhead North	d		07 54			08 04			08 09		08 19		08 24			08 34		08 39		08 49			08 54		09 04	
Birkenhead Park	d		07 56			08 06			08 11		08 21		08 26			08 36		08 41		08 51			08 56		09 06	
Conway Park	d		07 59			08 09			08 14		08 24		08 29			08 39		08 44		08 54			08 59		09 09	
Hamilton Square	d	07 59	08 01	08 06	08 06	08 11	08 14		08 16	08 21	08 26	08 29	08 31	08 36	08 36	08 41	08 44	08 46	08 51	08 56		08 59	09 01	09 06	09 11	09 14
James Street	d	08 02	08 04	08 09	08 09	08 14	08 17		08 19	08 24	08 29	08 32	08 34	08 39	08 39	08 44	08 47	08 49	08 54	08 59		09 02	09 04	09 09	09 14	09 17
Moorfields 10	a	08 03	08 06	08 11	08 11	08 16	08 18		08 21	08 26	08 31	08 33	08 36	08 41	08 41	08 46	08 48	08 51	08 56	09 01		09 03	09 06	09 11	09 16	09 18
Liverpool Lime Street 10	a	08 05	08 08	08 13	08 13	08 18	08 20		08 23	08 28	08 33	08 35	08 38	08 43	08 43	08 48	08 50	08 53	08 58	09 03		09 05	09 08	09 13	09 18	09 20
Liverpool Central 10	a	08 07	08 10	08 15	08 15	08 20	08 22		08 25	08 30	08 35	08 37	08 40	08 45	08 45	08 50	08 52	08 55	09 00	09 05		09 07	09 10	09 15	09 20	09 22

For general notes see front of timetable
For details of catering facilities see
Directory of Train Operators

Chester, Ellesmere Port, West Kirby and New Brighton → Birkenhead and Liverpool

Network Diagram - see first page of Table 101

		ME	ME	ME	ME	ME	ME	ME	ME	ME	ME	ME	ME		ME	ME	ME	ME	ME	ME	ME	ME	ME
Chester	d					09 00						09 30								18 00			
Bache	d					09 03						09 33								18 03			
Capenhurst	d					09 09						09 39								18 09			
Ellesmere Port	d		08 49						09 19								17 49						18 19
Overpool	d		08 52						09 22								17 52						18 22
Little Sutton	d		08 54						09 24								17 54						18 24
Hooton	d		08 59			09 14			09 29			09 44					17 59			18 14			18 29
Eastham Rake	d		09 01			09 16			09 31			09 46					18 01			18 16			18 31
Bromborough	d		09 03			09 18			09 33			09 48					18 03			18 18			18 33
Bromborough Rake	d		09 05			09 20			09 35			09 50					18 05			18 20			18 35
Spital	d		09 07			09 22			09 37			09 52					18 07			18 22			18 37
Port Sunlight	d		09 09			09 24			09 39			09 54		**and at**			18 09			18 24			18 39
Bebington	d		09 11			09 26			09 41			09 56					18 11			18 26			18 41
Rock Ferry	d		09 14			09 29			09 44			09 59		**the same**			18 14			18 29			18 44
Green Lane	d		09 17			09 32			09 47			10 02					18 17			18 32			18 47
Birkenhead Central	d		09 19			09 34			09 49			10 04		**minutes**			18 19			18 34			18 49
West Kirby	d	08 51			09 06			09 21			09 36			**past**		17 51			18 06			18 21	
Hoylake	d	08 54			09 09			09 24			09 39					17 54			18 09			18 24	
Manor Road	d	08 56			09 11			09 26			09 41			**each**		17 56			18 11			18 26	
Meols	d	08 58			09 13			09 28			09 43					17 58			18 13			18 28	
Moreton (Merseyside)	d	09 01			09 16			09 31			09 46			**hour until**		18 01			18 16			18 31	
Leasowe	d	09 03			09 18			09 33			09 48					18 03			18 18			18 33	
Bidston	d	09 06			09 21			09 36			09 51					18 06			18 21			18 36	
New Brighton	d			09 08			09 23			09 38			09 53		17 53			18 08			18 23		
Wallasey Grove Road	d			09 12			09 27			09 42			09 57		17 57			18 12			18 27		
Wallasey Village	d			09 14			09 29			09 44			09 59		17 59			18 14			18 29		
Birkenhead North	d	09 09		09 19	09 24		09 34	09 39		09 49	09 54		10 04		18 04	18 09		18 19	18 24		18 34	18 39	
Birkenhead Park	d	09 11		09 21	09 26		09 36	09 41		09 51	09 56		10 06		18 06	18 11		18 21	18 26		18 36	18 41	
Conway Park	d	09 14		09 24	09 29		09 39	09 44		09 54	09 59		10 09		18 09	18 14		18 24	18 29		18 39	18 44	
Hamilton Square	d	09 16	09 21	09 26	09 31	09 36	09 41	09 46	09 51	09 56	10 01	10 06	10 11		18 11	18 16	18 21	18 26	18 31	18 36	18 41	18 46	18 51
James Street	d	09 19	09 24	09 29	09 34	09 39	09 44	09 49	09 54	09 59	10 04	10 09	10 14		18 14	18 19	18 24	18 29	18 34	18 39	18 44	18 49	18 54
Moorfields 10	a	09 21	09 26	09 31	09 36	09 41	09 46	09 51	09 56	10 01	10 06	10 11	10 16		18 16	18 21	18 26	18 31	18 36	18 41	18 46	18 51	18 56
Liverpool Lime Street 10	a	09 23	09 28	09 33	09 38	09 43	09 48	09 53	09 58	10 03	10 08	10 13	10 18		18 18	18 23	18 28	18 33	18 38	18 43	18 48	18 53	18 58
Liverpool Central 10	a	09 25	09 30	09 35	09 40	09 45	09 50	09 55	10 00	10 05	10 10	10 15	10 20		18 20	18 25	18 30	18 35	18 40	18 45	18 50	18 55	19 00

		ME	ME	ME		ME	ME	ME	ME	ME	ME	ME	ME		ME	ME	ME	ME	ME	ME	ME
Chester	d			18 30					19 00				19 30					23 00			23 30
Bache	d			18 33					19 03				19 33					23 03			23 33
Capenhurst	d			18 39					19 09				19 39					23 09			23 39
Ellesmere Port	d						18 49				19 19					22 49				23 19	
Overpool	d						18 52				19 22					22 52				23 22	
Little Sutton	d						18 54				19 24					22 54				23 24	
Hooton	d			18 44			18 59		19 14		19 29		19 44			22 59		23 14		23 29	23a45
Eastham Rake	d			18 46			19 01		19 16		19 31		19 46			23 01		23 16		23 31	
Bromborough	d			18 48			19 03		19 18		19 33		19 48			23 03		23 18		23 33	
Bromborough Rake	d			18 50			19 05		19 20		19 35		19 50			23 05		23 20		23 35	
Spital	d			18 52			19 07		19 22		19 37		19 52			23 07		23 22		23 37	
Port Sunlight	d			18 54			19 09		19 24		19 39		19 54	**and at**		23 09		23 24		23 39	
Bebington	d			18 56			19 11		19 26		19 41		19 56			23 11		23 26		23 41	
Rock Ferry	d			18 59			19 14		19 29		19 44		19 59	**the same**		23 14		23 29		23 44	
Green Lane	d			19 02			19 17		19 32		19 47		20 02			23 17		23 32		23 47	
Birkenhead Central	d			19 04			19 19		19 34		19 49		20 04	**minutes**		23 19		23 34		23 49	
West Kirby	d		18 36					19 01				19 31		**past**			23 01				
Hoylake	d		18 39					19 04				19 34					23 04				
Manor Road	d		18 41					19 06				19 36		**each**			23 06				
Meols	d		18 43					19 08				19 38					23 08				
Moreton (Merseyside)	d		18 46					19 11				19 41		**hour until**			23 11				
Leasowe	d		18 48					19 13				19 43					23 13				
Bidston	d		18 51					19 16				19 46					23 16				
New Brighton	d	18 38				18 53				19 23					22 53				23 23		
Wallasey Grove Road	d	18 42				18 57				19 27					22 57				23 27		
Wallasey Village	d	18 44				18 59				19 29					22 59				23 29		
Birkenhead North	d	18 49	18 54			19 04		19 19		19 34		19 49			23 04		23 19		23 34		
Birkenhead Park	d	18 51	18 56			19 06		19 21		19 36		19 51			23 06		23 21		23 36		
Conway Park	d	18 54	18 59			19 09		19 24		19 39		19 54			23 09		23 24		23 39		
Hamilton Square	d	18 56	19 01	19 06		19 11	19 21	19 26	19 36	19 41	19 51	19 56	20 06		23 11	23 21	23 26	23 36	23 41	23 51	
James Street	d	18 59	19 04	19 09		19 14	19 24	19 29	19 39	19 44	19 54	19 59	20 09		23 14	23 24	23 29	23 39	23 44	23 54	
Moorfields 10	a	19 01	19 06	19 11		19 16	19 26	19 31	19 41	19 46	19 56	20 01	20 11		23 16	23 26	23 31	23 41	23 46	23 56	
Liverpool Lime Street 10	a	19 03	19 08	19 13		19 18	19 28	19 33	19 43	19 48	19 58	20 03	20 13		23 18	23 28	23 33	23 43	23 48	23 58	
Liverpool Central 10	a	19 05	19 10	19 15		19 20	19 30	19 35	19 45	19 50	20 00	20 05	20 15		23 20	23 30	23 35	23 45	23 50	23 59	

For general notes see front of timetable
For details of catering facilities see
Directory of Train Operators

Sundays

Chester, Ellesmere Port, West Kirby and New Brighton → Birkenhead and Liverpool

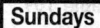

Network Diagram - see first page of Table 101

		ME	ME	ME		ME	ME	ME	ME	ME	ME	ME	ME			ME	ME	ME	ME	ME		ME	ME		
Chester	d								08 00				08 30						23 00				23 30		
Bache	d								08 03				08 33						23 03				23 33		
Capenhurst	d								08 09				08 39						23 09				23 39		
Ellesmere Port	d						07 49				08 19						22 49					23 19			
Overpool	d						07 52				08 22						22 52					23 22			
Little Sutton	d						07 54				08 24						22 54					23 24			
Hooton	d			07 44			07 59		08 14		08 29		08 44				22 59		23 14			23 29	23a45		
Eastham Rake	d			07 46			08 01		08 16		08 31		08 46				23 01		23 16			23 31			
Bromborough	d			07 48			08 03		08 18		08 33		08 48				23 03		23 18			23 33			
Bromborough Rake	d			07 50			08 05		08 20		08 35		08 50				23 05		23 20			23 35			
Spital	d			07 52			08 07		08 22		08 37		08 52				23 07		23 22			23 37			
Port Sunlight	d			07 54			08 09		08 24		08 39		08 54	and at			23 09		23 24			23 39			
Bebington	d			07 56			08 11		08 26		08 41		08 56				23 11		23 26			23 41			
Rock Ferry	d	07 44	07 49	07 59			08 14		08 29		08 44		08 59	the same			23 14		23 29			23 44			
Green Lane	d	07 47	07 52	08 02			08 17		08 32		08 47		09 02				23 17		23 32			23 47			
Birkenhead Central	d	07 49	07 54	08 04			08 19		08 34		08 49		09 04	minutes			23 19		23 34			23 49			
West Kirby	d							08 01				08 31		past				23 01							
Hoylake	d		08a32					08 04				08 34						23 04							
Manor Road	d		08 30					08 06				08 36		each				23 06							
Meols	d		08 28					08 08				08 38						23 08							
Moreton (Merseyside)	d		08 24					08 11				08 41		hour until				23 11							
Leasowe	d		08 22					08 13				08 43						23 13							
Bidston	d		08 20					08 16				08 46						23 16							
New Brighton	d					07 53				08 23						22 53				23 23					
Wallasey Grove Road	d					07 57				08 27						22 57				23 27					
Wallasey Village	d					07 59				08 29						22 59				23 29					
Birkenhead North	d		08 17			08 04		08 19		08 34		08 49				23 04		23 19		23 34					
Birkenhead Park	d		08 14			08 06		08 21		08 36		08 51				23 06		23 21		23 36					
Conway Park	d		08 12			08 09		08 24		08 39		08 54				23 09		23 24		23 39					
Hamilton Square	d	07 51	07 56	08 06		08 11	08 21	08 26	08 36	08 41	08 51	08 56	09 06			23 11	23 21	23 26	23 36	23 41		23 51			
James Street	d	07 54	07 59	08 09		08 14	08 24	08 29	08 39	08 44	08 54	08 59	09 09			23 14	23 24	23 29	23 39	23 44		23 54			
Moorfields 10	a	07 56	08 01	08 11		08 16	08 26	08 31	08 41	08 46	08 56	09 01	09 11			23 16	23 26	23 31	23 41	23 46		23 56			
Liverpool Lime Street 10	a	07 58	08 03	08 13		08 18	08 28	08 33	08 43	08 48	08 58	09 03	09 13			23 18	23 28	23 33	23 43	23 48		23 58			
Liverpool Central 10	a	08 00	08 05	08 15		08 20	08 30	08 35	08 45	08 50	09 00	09 05	09 15			23 20	23 30	23 35	23 45	23 50		23 59			

For general notes see front of timetable
For details of catering facilities see
Directory of Train Operators

Table 109

Mondays to Saturdays

Helsby — Ellesmere Port

Network Diagram - see first page of Table 101

Miles			NT	NT	NT	NT
—	Warrington Bank Quay	81 d	05 52		14 26	15 26
0	**Helsby**	d	06 06	06 35	15 17	15 47
2	Ince & Elton	d	06 09	06 38	15 20	15 50
$2\frac{3}{4}$	Stanlow & Thornton	d	06 11	06 40	15 22	15 52
$5\frac{1}{4}$	**Ellesmere Port**	a	06 18	06 47	15 28	15 58
—	Hooton	106 a	06 59	07 29	15 59	16 29
—	Liverpool Lime Street	106 a	07 28	07 58	16 28	16 58

Mondays to Saturdays

Miles			NT	NT SX	NT SO	NT	NT
—	Liverpool Lime Street	106 d		05 58	05 58	14 28	14 58
—	Hooton	106 d				14 57	15 27
0	**Ellesmere Port**	d	06 21	06 56	06 56	15 31	16 01
$2\frac{1}{2}$	Stanlow & Thornton	d	06 25	07 00	07 00	15 35	16 05
$3\frac{1}{4}$	Ince & Elton	d	06 28	07 03	07 03	15 38	16 08
$5\frac{1}{4}$	**Helsby**	a	06 32	07 06	07 06	15 42	16 11
—	Warrington Bank Quay	81 a		07 23	07 38	16b12	16 34

For general notes see front of timetable
For details of catering facilities see
Directory of Train Operators

b Saturdays arr. 1616

No Sunday Service

Network Diagram for Tables 114, 115

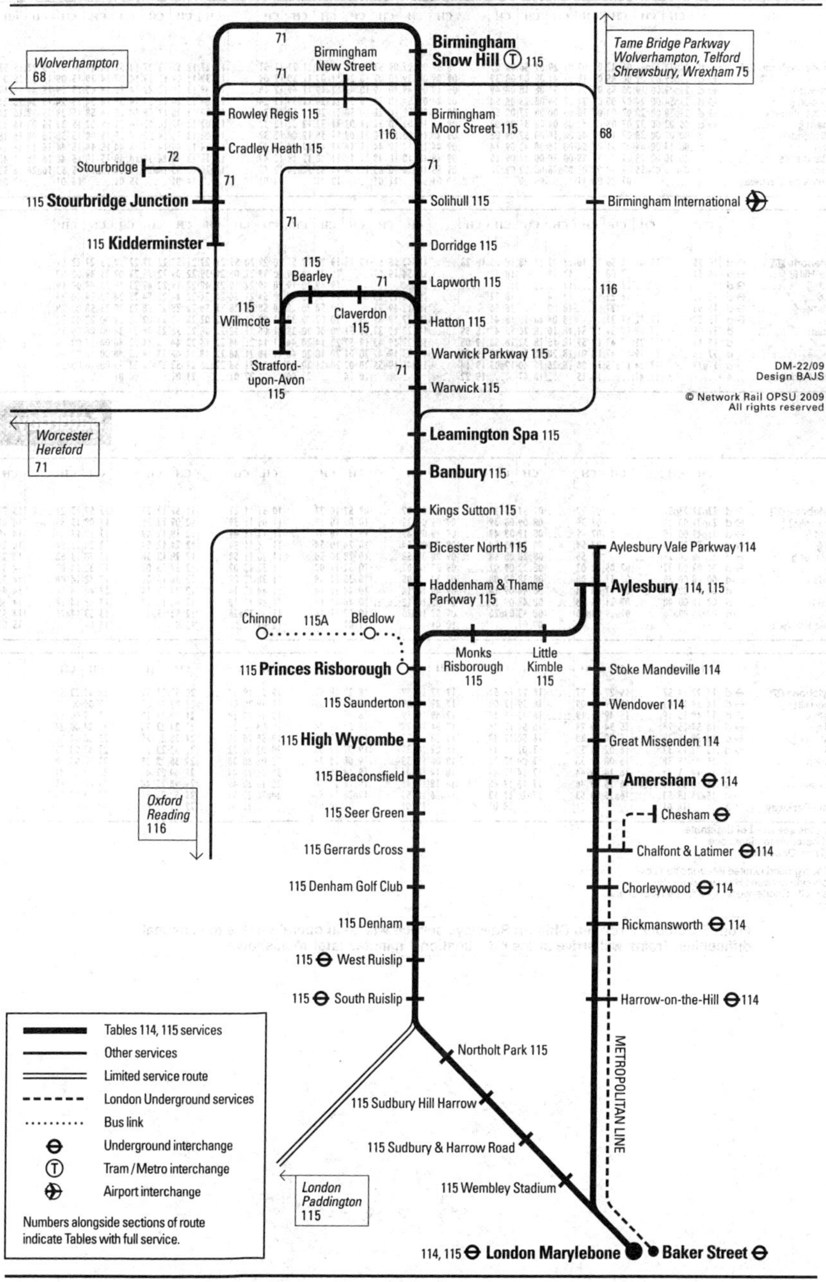

Birmingham Snow Hill 115
Birmingham New Street
Birmingham Moor Street 115
Wolverhampton 68
Tame Bridge Parkway Wolverhampton, Telford Shrewsbury, Wrexham 75
Rowley Regis 115
Cradley Heath 115
Stourbridge
115 Stourbridge Junction
115 Kidderminster
Birmingham International
Solihull 115
Dorridge 115
Lapworth 115
Hatton 115
Warwick Parkway 115
Warwick 115
115 Bearley
115 Wilmcote
Claverdon 115
Stratford-upon-Avon 115
Worcester Hereford 71
Leamington Spa 115
Banbury 115
Kings Sutton 115
Bicester North 115
Haddenham & Thame Parkway 115
Aylesbury Vale Parkway 114
Aylesbury 114, 115
Chinnor
115A
Bledlow
115 Princes Risborough
Monks Risborough 115
Little Kimble 115
Stoke Mandeville 114
Wendover 114
Great Missenden 114
115 Saunderton
115 High Wycombe
115 Beaconsfield
115 Seer Green
115 Gerrards Cross
115 Denham Golf Club
115 Denham
115 West Ruislip
115 South Ruislip
Oxford Reading 116
Amersham 114
Chesham
Chalfont & Latimer 114
Chorleywood 114
Rickmansworth 114
Harrow-on-the-Hill 114
METROPOLITAN LINE
Northolt Park 115
115 Sudbury Hill Harrow
115 Sudbury & Harrow Road
115 Wembley Stadium
London Paddington 115
114, 115 London Marylebone
Baker Street
71
72
68
116
DM-22/09
Design BAJS
© Network Rail OPSU 2009
All rights reserved
Tables 114, 115 services
Other services
Limited service route
London Underground services
Bus link
Underground interchange
Tram / Metro interchange
Airport interchange
Numbers alongside sections of route indicate Tables with full service.

London → Amersham and Aylesbury

Network Diagram - See first page of Table 114

Miles			CH ◇	CH MX	CH	CH	CH	CH	CH		CH ◇	CH	CH ◇	CH	CH	CH	CH		CH	CH	CH	CH	CH	CH	CH	CH
0	**London Marylebone** 10	⊖ d	23p27	23p57	06 32	07 07	07 29	07 56	08 27		08 57	09 27	09 57	10 27	10 57	11 27	11 57		12 27	12 57	13 27	13 57	14 27	14 57	15 27	15 57
9	Harrow-on-the-Hill 3 §	⊖ d	23p39	00 09	06 45	07 19	07 41	08 08	08 39		09 09	09 39	10 09	10 39	11 09	11 39	12 09		12 39	13 09	13 39	14 09	14 39	15 09	15 39	16 09
17	Rickmansworth §	⊖ d	23p49	00 19	06 56	07 29	07 51	08 18	08 49		09 19	09 49	10 19	10 49	11 19	11 49	12 18		12 49	13 19	13 49	14 19	14 49	15 19	15 49	16 19
19¼	Chorleywood §	⊖ d	23p54	00 24	07 00	07 34	07 56	08 23	08 54		09 24	09 54	10 24	10 54	11 24	11 54	12 24		12 54	13 24	13 54	14 24	14 54	15 24	15 54	16 24
21½	Chalfont & Latimer §	⊖ d	23p58	00 28	07 04	07 38	08 00	08 27	08 58		09 28	09 58	10 28	10 58	11 28	11 58	12 28		12 58	13 28	13 58	14 28	14 58	15 28	15 58	16 28
23½	**Amersham §**	⊖ d	00 02	00 32	07 08	07 42	08 04	08 31	09 02		09 32	10 02	10 32	11 02	11 32	12 02	12 32		13 02	13 32	14 02	14 32	15 02	15 32	16 02	16 32
28¾	Great Missenden	d	00 08	00 38	07 15	07 48	08 10	08 37	09 08		09 38	10 08	10 38	11 08	11 38	12 08	12 37		13 08	13 38	14 08	14 38	15 08	15 38	16 08	16 38
33¼	Wendover	d	00 14	00 44	07 21	07 54	08 16	08 43	09 14		09 44	10 14	10 44	11 14	11 44	12 14	12 43		13 14	13 44	14 14	14 44	15 14	15 44	16 14	16 44
35¼	Stoke Mandeville	d	00 18	00 48	07 25	07 58	08 20	08 47	09 18		09 48	10 18	10 48	11 18	11 48	12 18	12 47		13 18	13 48	14 18	14 48	15 18	15 48	16 18	16 48
37¾	**Aylesbury**	d	00a26	00a56	07 30	08 03	08a28	08 52	09a26		09 53	10a26	10 53	11a26	11 53	12a26	12 53		13a26	13 53	14a26	14 53	15a26	15 53	16a26	16 53
40½	**Aylesbury Vale Parkway**	a			07 39	08 11		09 00			10 01		11 01		12 01		13 01			14 01		15 01		16 01		17 01

		CH		CH	CH	CH	CH	CH	CH	CH		CH	CH	CH	CH	CH	CH	CH ◇	CH	CH	CH	CH	CH ◇	CH		
London Marylebone 10	⊖ d	16 25		16 42	16 56	17 16	17 27	17 48	18 06	18 23		18 42	18 57	19 15	19 27	19 57	20 27	20 57	21 27	21 57	22 27	22 57	23 27	23 57		
Harrow-on-the-Hill 3 §	⊖ d	16 37			17 08		17 39		18 18			18 54	19 09		19 39	20 09	20 39	21 09	21 39	22 09	22 39	23 09	23 39	00 09		
Rickmansworth §	⊖ d				17 18		17 50								19 49	20 19	20 49	21 19	21 49	22 19	22 49	23 19	23 49	00 19		
Chorleywood §	⊖ d	16 51			17 23		17 54		18 32			19 08	19 23		19 54	20 24	20 54	21 24	21 54	22 24	22 54	23 24	23 54	00 24		
Chalfont & Latimer §	⊖ d	16 55			17 27		18 00		18 36			19 12	19 27		19 58	20 28	20 58	21 28	21 58	22 28	22 58	23 28	23 58	00 28		
Amersham §	⊖ d	16 59		17 12	17 31		18 04	18 19	18 41			19 17	19 31		20 02	20 32	21 02	21 32	22 02	22 32	23 02	23 32	00 02	00 32		
Great Missenden	d	17 05		17 19	17 37	17 51	18 10	18 26	18 47	18 59		19 23	19 37	19 51	20 08	20 38	21 08	21 38	22 08	22 38	23 08	23 38	00 08	00 38		
Wendover	d	17 11		17 25	17 43	17 57	18 16	18 32	18 53	19 05		19 29	19 43	19 57	20 14	20 44	21 14	21 44	22 14	22 44	23 14	23 44	00 14	00 44		
Stoke Mandeville	d	17 15		17 29	17 47	18 01	18 20	18 36	18 57	19 09		19 33	19 47	20 01	20 18	20 48	21 18	21 48	22 18	22 48	23 18	23 48	00 18	00 48		
Aylesbury	d	17a23		17 34	17a55	18 06	18a26	18 40	19a05	19 14		19a41	19a55	20 07	20a26	20 53	21a26	21 53	22a26	22 53	23a26	23 53	00a26	00a56		
Aylesbury Vale Parkway	a			17 41		18 15		18 47		19 22				20 14		21 09		22 01		23 01		00 01				

Saturdays

		CH ◇	CH		CH	CH		CH	CH		CH	CH		CH	CH		CH	CH		CH	CH		CH	CH		CH
London Marylebone 10	⊖ d	23p27	23p57			07 27		07 57	08 27		08 57	09 27		09 57	10 27		10 57	11 27		11 57	12 27		12 57	13 27		13 57
Harrow-on-the-Hill 3 §	⊖ d	23p39	00 09			07 39		08 09	08 39		09 09	09 39		10 09	10 39		11 09	11 39		12 09	12 39		13 09	13 39		14 09
Rickmansworth §	⊖ d	23p49	00 19			07 49		08 19	08 49		09 19	09 49		10 19	10 49		11 19	11 49		12 19	12 49		13 19	13 49		14 19
Chorleywood §	⊖ d	23p54	00 24			07 54		08 24	08 54		09 24	09 54		10 24	10 54		11 24	11 54		12 24	12 54		13 24	13 54		14 24
Chalfont & Latimer §	⊖ d	23p58	00 28			07 58		08 28	08 58		09 28	09 58		10 28	10 58		11 28	11 58		12 28	12 58		13 28	13 58		14 28
Amersham §	⊖ d	00 02	00 32		07 05	08 02		08 32	09 02		09 32	10 02		10 32	11 02		11 32	12 02		12 32	13 02		13 32	14 02		14 32
Great Missenden	d	00 08	00 38		07 11	08 08		08 38	09 08		09 38	10 08		10 38	11 08		11 38	12 08		12 38	13 08		13 38	14 08		14 38
Wendover	d	00 14	00 44		07 17	08 14		08 44	09 14		09 44	10 14		10 44	11 14		11 44	12 14		12 44	13 14		13 44	14 14		14 44
Stoke Mandeville	d	00 18	00 48		07 21	08 18		08 48	09 18		09 48	10 18		10 48	11 18		11 48	12 18		12 48	13 18		13 48	14 18		14 48
Aylesbury	d	00a26	00a56		07a29	08a26		08 53	09a26		09 53	10a26		10 53	11a26		11 53	12a26		12 53	13a26		13 53	14a26		14 53
Aylesbury Vale Parkway	a							09 01			10 01			11 01			12 01			13 01			14 01			15 01

		CH	CH		CH	CH		CH	CH		CH	CH		CH	CH		CH	CH		CH	CH		CH	CH		
London Marylebone 10	⊖ d	14 27	14 57		15 27	15 57		16 27	16 57		17 27	17 57		18 27	18 57		19 27	19 57		20 57	21 57		22 57	23 57		
Harrow-on-the-Hill 3 §	⊖ d	14 39	15 09		15 39	16 09		16 39	17 09		17 39	18 09		18 39	19 09		19 39	20 09		21 09	22 09		23 09	00 09		
Rickmansworth §	⊖ d	14 49	15 19		15 49	16 19		16 49	17 19		17 49	18 19		18 49	19 19		19 49	20 19		21 19	22 19		23 19	00 19		
Chorleywood §	⊖ d	14 54	15 24		15 54	16 24		16 54	17 24		17 54	18 24		18 54	19 24		19 54	20 24		21 24	22 24		23 24	00 24		
Chalfont & Latimer §	⊖ d	14 58	15 28		15 58	16 28		16 58	17 28		17 58	18 28		18 58	19 28		19 58	20 28		21 28	22 28		23 28	00 28		
Amersham §	⊖ d	15 02	15 32		16 02	16 32		17 02	17 32		18 02	18 32		19 02	19 32		20 02	20 32		21 32	22 32		23 32	00 32		
Great Missenden	d	15 08	15 38		16 08	16 38		17 08	17 38		18 08	18 38		19 08	19 38		20 08	20 38		21 38	22 38		23 38	00 38		
Wendover	d	15 14	15 44		16 14	16 44		17 14	17 44		18 14	18 44		19 14	19 44		20 14	20 44		21 44	22 44		23 44	00 44		
Stoke Mandeville	d	15 18	15 48		16 18	16 48		17 18	17 48		18 18	18 48		19 18	19 48		20 18	20 48		21 48	22 48		23 48	00 48		
Aylesbury	d	15a26	15 53		16a26	16 53		17a26	17 53		18a26	18 53		19a26	19 53		20a26	20 53		21 53	22 53		23 53	00a56		
Aylesbury Vale Parkway	a		16 01			17 01			18 01			19 01			20 01			21 01		22 01	23 01		00 01			

For general notes see front of timetable
For details of catering facilities see Directory of Train Operators

§ London Underground Limited (Metropolitan Line) services operate between Harrow-on-the-Hill, Rickmansworth, Chorleywood, Chalfont & Latimer and Amersham

From 5 October a revised Chiltern Railways service will be in operation due to seasonal difficulties. Trains will arrive at their destination 3 minutes later than shown

Table 114

Sundays

London → Amersham and Aylesbury

Network Diagram - See first page of Table 114

		CH	CH	CH	CH	CH	CH	CH	CH	CH	CH	CH	CH	CH
London Marylebone 10	⊖ d		23p57		08 27	09 27	10 27	11 27	12 27	13 27	14 27		15 27	
Harrow-on-the-Hill 3 §	⊖ d		00 09		08 39	09 39	10 39	11 39	12 39	13 39	14 39		15 39	
Rickmansworth §	⊖ d		00 19		08 49	09 49	10 49	11 49	12 49	13 49	14 49		15 49	
Chorleywood §	⊖ d		00 24		08 54	09 54	10 54	11 54	12 54	13 54	14 54		15 54	
Chalfont & Latimer §	⊖ d		00 28		08 58	09 58	10 58	11 58	12 58	13 58	14 58		15 58	
Amersham §	⊖ d	00 02	00 32	08 32	09 02	10 02	11 02	12 02	13 02	14 02	15 02	15 32	16 02	16 32
Great Missenden	d	00 08	00 38	08 38	09 08	10 08	11 08	12 08	13 08	14 08	15 08	15 38	16 08	16 38
Wendover	d	00 14	00 44	08 44	09 14	10 14	11 14	12 14	13 14	14 14	15 14	15 44	16 14	16 44
Stoke Mandeville	d	00 18	00 48	08 48	09 18	10 18	11 18	12 18	13 18	14 18	15 18	15 48	16 18	16 48
Aylesbury	d	00a26	00a56	08a56	09 23	10 23	11 23	12 23	13 23	14 23	15 23	15a56	16 23	16a56
Aylesbury Vale Parkway	a				09 31	10 31	11 31	12 31	13 31	14 31	15 31		16 31	

		CH	CH	CH	CH	CH	CH	CH	CH	CH	CH	CH	CH	CH
London Marylebone 10	⊖ d	16 27		17 27		18 27		19 27		20 27		21 27	22 27	23 27
Harrow-on-the-Hill 3 §	⊖ d	16 39		17 39		18 39		19 39		20 39		21 39	22 39	23 39
Rickmansworth §	⊖ d	16 49		17 49		18 49		19 49		20 49		21 49	22 49	23 49
Chorleywood §	⊖ d	16 54		17 54		18 54		19 54		20 54		21 54	22 54	23 54
Chalfont & Latimer §	⊖ d	16 58		17 58		18 58		19 58		20 58		21 58	22 58	23 58
Amersham §	⊖ d	17 02	17 32	18 02	18 32	19 02	19 32	20 02	20 32	21 02	21 32	22 02	23 02	00 02
Great Missenden	d	17 08	17 38	18 08	18 38	19 08	19 38	20 08	20 38	21 08	21 38	22 08	23 08	00 08
Wendover	d	17 14	17 44	18 14	18 44	19 14	19 44	20 14	20 44	21 14	21 44	22 14	23 14	00 14
Stoke Mandeville	d	17 18	17 48	18 18	18 48	19 18	19 48	20 18	20 48	21 18	21 48	22 18	23 18	00 18
Aylesbury	d	17 23	17a56	18 23	18a56	19 23	19a56	20 23	20a56	21 23	21a56	22 23	23 23	00a26
Aylesbury Vale Parkway	a	17 31		18 31		19 31		20 31		21 31		22 31	23 31	

For general notes see front of timetable
For details of catering facilities see Directory of Train Operators

§ London Underground Limited (Metropolitan Line) services operate between Harrow-on-the-Hill, Rickmansworth, Chorleywood, Chalfont & Latimer and Amersham

From 4 October a revised Chiltern Railways service will be in operation due to seasonal difficulties. Trains will arrive at their destination 3 minutes later than shown

Mondays to Fridays

until 2 October

Aylesbury and Amersham → London

Network Diagram - See first page of Table 114

Miles			CH	CH	CH	CH	CH	CH	CH	CH	CH	CH	CH	CH ◇	CH	CH	CH	CH	CH	CH	CH ◇	CH
0	Aylesbury Vale Parkway	d	05 26	06 01		06 38		07 11		07 45		08 20		09 05	09 30		10 30		11 30		12 30	
2¾	Aylesbury	d	05 31	06 06	06 26	06 43	06 57	07 16	07 29	07 50	08 06	08 25	08 39	09 10	09 37	10 05	10 35	11 05	11 35	12 05	12 35	13 05
5¼	Stoke Mandeville	d	05 35	06 10	06 30	06 47	07 01	07 20	07 33	07 54	08 10	08 29	08 43	09 14	09 41	10 09	10 39	11 09	11 39	12 09	12 39	13 09
7¼	Wendover	d	05 39	06 14	06 34	06 51	07 05	07 24	07 37	07 58	08 14	08 33	08 47	09 18	09 45	10 13	10 43	11 13	11 43	12 13	12 43	13 13
11¾	Great Missenden	d	05 45	06 20	06 40	06 57	07 11	07 30	07 43	08 04	08 20	08 39	08 53	09 24	09 51	10 19	10 49	11 19	11 49	12 19	12 49	13 19
17	Amersham §	⊖ d	05 52	06 27	06 47		07 18	07 38	07 51	08 12	08 27		09 00	09 31	09 58	10 26	10 56	11 26	11 56	12 26	12 56	13 26
19	Chalfont & Latimer §	⊖ d		06 33	06 51		07 22		07 55		08 31		09 04	09 35	10 02	10 30	11 00	11 30	12 00	12 30	13 00	13 30
21¼	Chorleywood §	⊖ d		06 36	06 54		07 25		07 58		08 34		09 07	09 38	10 05	10 33	11 03	11 33	12 03	12 33	13 03	13 33
23½	Rickmansworth §	⊖ d			06 59				08 03				09 12	09 43	10 10	10 38	11 08	11 38	12 08	12 38	13 08	13 38
31½	Harrow-on-the-Hill [3] §	⊖ d	06 10	06 50	07 10		07 39		08 14		08 48		09 23	09 54	10 21	10 49	11 19	11 49	12 19	12 49	13 19	13 49
40½	London Marylebone [10]	⊖ a	06 25	07 04	07 25	07 37	07 56	08 14	08 29	08 44	09 05	09 19	09 39	10 09	10 37	11 05	11 35	12 05	12 35	13 05	13 35	14 05

		CH	CH	CH	CH	CH	CH	CH	CH	CH	CH	CH	CH	CH ◇	CH ◇	CH	CH	CH	CH	CH
Aylesbury Vale Parkway	d	13 30		14 30		15 30		16 30		17 28		18 18			19 30		20 30		21 30	22 30
Aylesbury	d	13 35	14 05	14 35	15 05	15 35	16 05	16 35	17 05	17 35	17 55	18 26	18 45	19 15	19 35	20 05	20 35	21 05	21 35	22 35
Stoke Mandeville	d	13 39	14 09	14 39	15 09	15 39	16 09	16 39	17 09	17 39	17 59	18 30	18 49	19 19	19 39	20 09	20 39	21 09	21 39	22 39
Wendover	d	13 43	14 13	14 43	15 13	15 43	16 13	16 43	17 13	17 43	18 03	18 34	18 53	19 23	19 43	20 13	20 43	21 13	21 43	22 43
Great Missenden	d	13 49	14 19	14 49	15 19	15 49	16 19	16 49	17 19	17 49	18 09	18 40	18 59	19 29	19 49	20 19	20 49	21 19	21 49	22 49
Amersham §	⊖ d	13 56	14 26	14 56	15 26	15 56	16 26	16 56	17 26	17 56	18 16	18 47	19 06	19 36	19 56	20 26	20 56	21 26	21 56	22 56
Chalfont & Latimer §	⊖ d	14 00	14 30	15 00	15 30	16 00	16 30	17 00	17 30	18 00	18 20	18 51	19 10	19 40	20 00	20 30	21 00	21 30	22 00	23 00
Chorleywood §	⊖ d	14 03	14 33	15 03	15 33	16 03	16 33	17 03	17 33	18 03	18 23	18 54	19 13	19 43	20 03	20 33	21 03	21 33	22 03	23 03
Rickmansworth §	⊖ d	14 08	14 38	15 08	15 38	16 08	16 38	17 08	17 38	18 08	18 28	18 59	19 18	19 48	20 08	20 38	21 08	21 38	22 08	23 08
Harrow-on-the-Hill [3] §	⊖ d	14 19	14 49	15 19	15 49	16 19	16 49	17 19	17 49	18 19	18 39	19 10	19 29	19 59	20 19	20 49	21 19	21 49	22 19	23 19
London Marylebone [10]	⊖ a	14 35	15 05	15 35	16 05	16 35	17 05	17 35	18 05	18 35	18 55	19 26	19 45	20 15	20 35	21 05	21 35	22 05	22 35	23 35

Mondays to Fridays

from 5 October

		CH	CH	CH	CH	CH	CH	CH	CH	CH	CH	CH	CH ◇	CH	CH	CH	CH	CH	CH	CH ◇	CH	CH
Aylesbury Vale Parkway	d	05 23	05 58		06 35		07 08		07 42		08 17		09 02	09 27		10 27		11 27		12 27		13 27
Aylesbury	d	05 31	06 03	06 23	06 40	06 54	07 13	07 26	07 47	08 03	08 22	08 36	09 07	09 34	10 02	10 32	11 02	11 32	12 02	12 32	13 02	13 32
Stoke Mandeville	d	05 35	06 07	06 27	06 44	06 58	07 17	07 30	07 51	08 07	08 26	08 40	09 11	09 38	10 06	10 36	11 06	11 36	12 06	12 36	13 06	13 36
Wendover	d	05 39	06 11	06 31	06 48	07 02	07 21	07 34	07 55	08 11	08 30	08 44	09 15	09 42	10 10	10 40	11 10	11 40	12 10	12 40	13 10	13 40
Great Missenden	d	05 45	06 17	06 37	06 54	07 08	07 27	07 40	08 01	08 17	08 36	08 50	09 21	09 48	10 16	10 46	11 16	11 46	12 16	12 46	13 16	13 46
Amersham §	⊖ d	05 52	06 24	06 44		07 15	07 35	07 48	08 09	08 24		08 57	09 28	09 55	10 23	10 53	11 23	11 53	12 23	12 53	13 23	13 53
Chalfont & Latimer §	⊖ d		06 30	06 48		07 19		07 52		08 28		09 01	09 32	09 59	10 27	10 57	11 27	11 57	12 27	12 57	13 27	13 57
Chorleywood §	⊖ d		06 35	06 53		07 24		07 57		08 33		09 06	09 37	10 04	10 32	11 02	11 32	12 02	12 32	13 02	13 32	14 02
Rickmansworth §	⊖ d			06 59				08 03				09 12	09 43	10 10	10 38	11 08	11 38	12 08	12 38	13 08	13 38	14 08
Harrow-on-the-Hill [3] §	⊖ d	06 10	06 50	07 10		07 39		08 14		08 48		09 23	09 54	10 21	10 49	11 19	11 49	12 19	12 49	13 19	13 49	14 19
London Marylebone [10]	⊖ a	06 25	07 04	07 25	07 37	07 55	08 14	08 29	08 44	09 05	09 19	09 39	10 09	10 37	11 05	11 35	12 05	12 35	13 05	13 35	14 05	14 35

		CH	CH	CH	CH	CH	CH	CH	CH	CH	CH	CH	CH ◇	CH ◇	CH	CH	CH	CH	CH
Aylesbury Vale Parkway	d		14 27		15 27		16 27		17 25		18 15			19 27		20 27		21 27	22 27
Aylesbury	d	14 02	14 32	15 02	15 32	16 02	16 32	17 02	17 32	17 52	18 23	18 42	19 12	19 32	20 02	20 32	21 02	21 32	22 32
Stoke Mandeville	d	14 06	14 36	15 06	15 36	16 06	16 36	17 06	17 36	17 56	18 27	18 46	19 16	19 36	20 06	20 36	21 06	21 36	22 36
Wendover	d	14 10	14 40	15 10	15 40	16 10	16 40	17 10	17 40	18 00	18 31	18 50	19 20	19 40	20 10	20 40	21 10	21 40	22 40
Great Missenden	d	14 16	14 46	15 16	15 46	16 16	16 46	17 16	17 46	18 06	18 37	18 56	19 26	19 46	20 16	20 46	21 16	21 46	22 46
Amersham §	⊖ d	14 23	14 53	15 23	15 53	16 23	16 53	17 23	17 53	18 13	18 44	19 03	19 33	19 53	20 23	20 53	21 23	21 53	22 53
Chalfont & Latimer §	⊖ d	14 27	14 57	15 27	15 57	16 27	16 57	17 27	17 57	18 17	18 48	19 07	19 37	19 57	20 27	20 57	21 27	21 57	22 57
Chorleywood §	⊖ d	14 32	15 02	15 32	16 02	16 32	17 02	17 32	18 02	18 22	18 53	19 12	19 42	20 02	20 32	21 02	21 32	22 02	23 02
Rickmansworth §	⊖ d	14 38	15 08	15 38	16 08	16 38	17 08	17 38	18 08	18 28	18 59	19 18	19 48	20 08	20 38	21 08	21 38	22 08	23 08
Harrow-on-the-Hill [3] §	⊖ d	14 49	15 19	15 49	16 19	16 49	17 19	17 49	18 19	18 39	19 10	19 29	19 59	20 19	20 49	21 19	21 49	22 19	23 19
London Marylebone [10]	⊖ a	15 05	15 35	16 05	16 35	17 05	17 35	18 05	18 35	18 55	19 26	19 45	20 15	20 35	21 05	21 35	22 05	22 35	23 35

Saturdays

until 3 October

		CH	CH	CH	CH	CH	CH	CH	CH	CH	CH	CH	CH	CH	CH	CH	CH	CH
Aylesbury Vale Parkway	d			07 00	07 30		08 30		09 30		10 30		11 30		12 30		13 30	
Aylesbury	d	06 05	06 35	07 05	07 35	08 05	08 35	09 05	09 35	10 05	10 35	11 05	11 35	12 05	12 35	13 05	13 35	14 05
Stoke Mandeville	d	06 09	06 39	07 09	07 39	08 09	08 39	09 09	09 39	10 09	10 39	11 09	11 39	12 09	12 39	13 09	13 39	14 09
Wendover	d	06 13	06 43	07 13	07 43	08 13	08 43	09 13	09 43	10 13	10 43	11 13	11 43	12 13	12 43	13 13	13 43	14 13
Great Missenden	d	06 19	06 49	07 19	07 49	08 19	08 49	09 19	09 49	10 19	10 49	11 19	11 49	12 19	12 49	13 19	13 49	14 19
Amersham §	⊖ d	06 26	06a58	07 26	07 56	08 26	08 56	09 26	09 56	10 26	10 56	11 26	11 56	12 26	12 56	13 26	13 56	14 26
Chalfont & Latimer §	⊖ d	06 30		07 30	08 00	08 30	09 00	09 30	10 00	10 30	11 00	11 30	12 00	12 30	13 00	13 30	14 00	14 30
Chorleywood §	⊖ d	06 33		07 33	08 03	08 33	09 03	09 33	10 03	10 33	11 03	11 33	12 03	12 33	13 03	13 33	14 03	14 33
Rickmansworth §	⊖ d	06 38		07 38	08 08	08 38	09 08	09 38	10 08	10 38	11 08	11 38	12 08	12 38	13 08	13 38	14 08	14 38
Harrow-on-the-Hill [3] §	⊖ d	06 49		07 49	08 19	08 49	09 19	09 49	10 19	10 49	11 19	11 49	12 19	12 49	13 19	13 49	14 19	14 49
London Marylebone [10]	⊖ a	07 04		08 04	08 34	09 04	09 34	10 05	10 35	11 05	11 35	12 04	12 35	13 05	13 35	14 05	14 35	15 05

For general notes see front of timetable
For details of catering facilities see Directory of Train Operators

§ London Underground Limited (Metropolitan Line) services operate between Harrow-on-the-Hill, Rickmansworth, Chorleywood, Chalfont & Latimer and Amersham

Table 114

Aylesbury and Amersham → London

Saturdays until 3 October

Network Diagram - See first page of Table 114

		CH	CH	CH	CH	CH	CH	CH	CH	CH	CH	CH	CH	CH	CH
Aylesbury Vale Parkway	d	14 30		15 30		16 30		17 30		18 30		19 46	20 46	21 46	
Aylesbury	d	14 35	15 05	15 35	16 05	16 35	17 05	17 35	18 05	18 35	19 05	20 05	21 05	22 05	23 20
Stoke Mandeville	d	14 39	15 09	15 39	16 09	16 39	17 09	17 39	18 09	18 39	19 09	20 09	21 09	22 09	23 24
Wendover	d	14 43	15 13	15 43	16 13	16 43	17 13	17 43	18 13	18 43	19 13	20 13	21 13	22 13	23 28
Great Missenden	d	14 49	15 19	15 49	16 19	16 49	17 19	17 49	18 19	18 49	19 19	20 19	21 19	22 19	23 34
Amersham §	⊖ d	14 56	15 26	15 56	16 26	16 56	17 26	17 56	18 26	18 56	19 26	20 26	21 26	22 26	23a43
Chalfont & Latimer §	⊖ d	15 00	15 30	16 00	16 30	17 00	17 30	18 00	18 30	19 00	19 30	20 30	21 30	22 30	
Chorleywood §	⊖ d	15 03	15 33	16 03	16 33	17 03	17 33	18 03	18 33	19 03	19 33	20 33	21 33	22 33	
Rickmansworth §	⊖ d	15 08	15 38	16 08	16 38	17 08	17 38	18 08	18 38	19 08	19 38	20 38	21 38	22 38	
Harrow-on-the-Hill 3 §	⊖ d	15 19	15 49	16 19	16 49	17 19	17 49	18 19	18 49	19 19	19 49	20 49	21 49	22 49	
London Marylebone 10	⊖ a	15 34	16 05	16 34	17 05	17 35	18 05	18 35	19 05	19 35	20 05	21 04	22 05	23 04	

Saturdays from 10 October

		CH	CH	CH	CH	CH	CH	CH	CH	CH	CH	CH	CH	CH	CH	CH	CH	CH
Aylesbury Vale Parkway	d			06 57	07 27		08 27		09 27		10 27		11 27		12 27		13 27	
Aylesbury	d	06 02	06 32	07 02	07 32	08 02	08 32	09 02	09 32	10 02	10 32	11 02	11 32	12 02	12 32	13 02	13 32	14 02
Stoke Mandeville	d	06 06	06 36	07 06	07 36	08 06	08 36	09 06	09 36	10 06	10 36	11 06	11 36	12 06	12 36	13 06	13 36	14 06
Wendover	d	06 10	06 40	07 10	07 40	08 10	08 40	09 10	09 40	10 10	10 40	11 10	11 40	12 10	12 40	13 10	13 40	14 10
Great Missenden	d	06 16	06 46	07 16	07 46	08 16	08 46	09 16	09 46	10 16	10 46	11 16	11 46	12 16	12 46	13 16	13 46	14 16
Amersham §	⊖ d	06 23	06a55	07 23	07 53	08 23	08 53	09 23	09 53	10 23	10 53	11 23	11 53	12 23	12 53	13 23	13 53	14 23
Chalfont & Latimer §	⊖ d	06 27		07 27	07 57	08 27	08 57	09 27	09 57	10 27	10 57	11 27	11 57	12 27	12 57	13 27	13 57	14 27
Chorleywood §	⊖ d	06 32		07 32	08 02	08 32	09 02	09 32	10 02	10 32	11 02	11 32	12 02	12 32	13 02	13 32	14 02	14 32
Rickmansworth §	⊖ d	06 38		07 38	08 08	08 38	09 08	09 38	10 08	10 38	11 08	11 38	12 08	12 38	13 08	13 38	14 08	14 38
Harrow-on-the-Hill 3 §	⊖ d	06 49		07 49	08 19	08 49	09 19	09 49	10 19	10 49	11 19	11 49	12 19	12 49	13 19	13 49	14 19	14 49
London Marylebone 10	⊖ a	07 04		08 04	08 34	09 04	09 34	10 05	10 35	11 05	11 35	12 04	12 35	13 05	13 35	14 05	14 35	15 05

		CH	CH	CH	CH	CH	CH	CH	CH	CH	CH	CH	CH	CH	CH
Aylesbury Vale Parkway	d	14 27		15 27		16 27		17 27		18 27		19 46	20 46	21 46	
Aylesbury	d	14 32	15 02	15 32	16 02	16 32	17 02	17 32	18 02	18 32	19 02	20 02	21 02	22 02	23 17
Stoke Mandeville	d	14 36	15 06	15 36	16 06	16 36	17 06	17 36	18 06	18 36	19 06	20 06	21 06	22 06	23 21
Wendover	d	14 40	15 10	15 40	16 10	16 40	17 10	17 40	18 10	18 40	19 10	20 10	21 10	22 10	23 25
Great Missenden	d	14 46	15 16	15 46	16 16	16 46	17 16	17 46	18 16	18 46	19 16	20 16	21 16	22 16	23 31
Amersham §	⊖ d	14 53	15 23	15 53	16 23	16 53	17 23	17 53	18 23	18 53	19 23	20 23	21 23	22 23	23a40
Chalfont & Latimer §	⊖ d	14 57	15 27	15 57	16 27	16 57	17 27	17 57	18 27	18 57	19 27	20 27	21 27	22 27	
Chorleywood §	⊖ d	15 02	15 32	16 02	16 32	17 02	17 32	18 02	18 32	19 02	19 32	20 32	21 32	22 32	
Rickmansworth §	⊖ d	15 08	15 38	16 08	16 38	17 08	17 38	18 08	18 38	19 08	19 38	20 38	21 38	22 38	
Harrow-on-the-Hill 3 §	⊖ d	15 19	15 49	16 19	16 49	17 19	17 49	18 19	18 49	19 19	19 49	20 49	21 49	22 49	
London Marylebone 10	⊖ a	15 34	16 05	16 34	17 05	17 35	18 05	18 35	19 05	19 35	20 05	21 04	22 05	23 04	

Sundays until 27 September

		CH	CH	CH	CH	CH	CH	CH	CH	CH	CH	CH	CH
Aylesbury Vale Parkway	d	07 30	08 30	09 00	10 00	11 00	12 00	13 00	14 00	15 00		16 00	
Aylesbury	d	07 35	08 35	09 05	10 05	11 05	12 05	13 05	14 05	15 05	15 35	16 05	16 35
Stoke Mandeville	d	07 39	08 39	09 09	10 09	11 09	12 09	13 09	14 09	15 09	15 39	16 09	16 39
Wendover	d	07 43	08 43	09 13	10 13	11 13	12 13	13 13	14 13	15 13	15 43	16 13	16 43
Great Missenden	d	07 49	08 49	09 19	10 19	11 19	12 19	13 19	14 19	15 19	15 49	16 19	16 49
Amersham §	⊖ d	07 56	08 56	09 26	10 26	11 26	12 26	13 26	14 26	15 26	15a58	16 26	16a58
Chalfont & Latimer §	⊖ d	08 00	09 00	09 30	10 30	11 30	12 30	13 30	14 30	15 30		16 30	
Chorleywood §	⊖ d	08 03	09 03	09 33	10 33	11 33	12 33	13 33	14 33	15 33		16 33	
Rickmansworth §	⊖ d	08 08	09 08	09 38	10 38	11 38	12 38	13 38	14 38	15 38		16 38	
Harrow-on-the-Hill 3 §	⊖ d	08 19	09 19	09 49	10 49	11 49	12 49	13 49	14 49	15 49		16 49	
London Marylebone 10	⊖ a	08 34	09 34	10 04	11 05	12 05	13 04	14 05	15 05	16 05		17 05	

		CH	CH	CH	CH	CH	CH	CH	CH	CH	CH	CH	CH
Aylesbury Vale Parkway	d	17 00		18 00		19 00		20 00		21 00		22 00	
Aylesbury	d	17 05	17 35	18 05	18 35	19 05	19 35	20 05	20 35	21 05	21 35	22 05	22 35
Stoke Mandeville	d	17 09	17 39	18 09	18 39	19 09	19 39	20 09	20 39	21 09	21 39	22 09	22 39
Wendover	d	17 13	17 43	18 13	18 43	19 13	19 43	20 13	20 43	21 13	21 43	22 13	22 43
Great Missenden	d	17 19	17 49	18 19	18 49	19 19	19 49	20 19	20 49	21 19	21 49	22 19	22 49
Amersham §	⊖ d	17 26	17a58	18 26	18a58	19 26	19a58	20 26	20a58	21 26	21a58	22a28	22 56
Chalfont & Latimer §	⊖ d	17 30		18 30		19 30		20 30		21 30			23 00
Chorleywood §	⊖ d	17 33		18 33		19 33		20 33		21 33			23 03
Rickmansworth §	⊖ d	17 38		18 38		19 38		20 38		21 38			23 08
Harrow-on-the-Hill 3 §	⊖ d	17 49		18 49		19 49		20 49		21 49			23 19
London Marylebone 10	⊖ a	18 05		19 05		20 05		21 04		22 05			23 35

Sundays from 4 October

		CH	CH	CH	CH	CH	CH	CH	CH	CH	CH	CH	CH
Aylesbury Vale Parkway	d	07 27	08 27	08 57	09 57	10 57	11 57	12 57	13 57	14 57		15 57	
Aylesbury	d	07 32	08 32	09 02	10 02	11 02	12 02	13 02	14 02	15 02	15 32	16 02	16 32
Stoke Mandeville	d	07 36	08 36	09 06	10 06	11 06	12 06	13 06	14 06	15 06	15 36	16 06	16 36
Wendover	d	07 40	08 40	09 10	10 10	11 10	12 10	13 10	14 10	15 10	15 40	16 10	16 40
Great Missenden	d	07 46	08 46	09 16	10 16	11 16	12 16	13 16	14 16	15 16	15 46	16 16	16 46
Amersham §	⊖ d	07 53	08 53	09 23	10 23	11 23	12 23	13 23	14 23	15 23	15a55	16 23	16a55
Chalfont & Latimer §	⊖ d	07 57	08 57	09 27	10 27	11 27	12 27	13 27	14 27	15 27		16 27	
Chorleywood §	⊖ d	08 02	09 02	09 32	10 32	11 32	12 32	13 32	14 32	15 32		16 32	
Rickmansworth §	⊖ d	08 08	09 08	09 38	10 38	11 38	12 38	13 38	14 38	15 38		16 38	
Harrow-on-the-Hill 3 §	⊖ d	08 19	09 19	09 49	10 49	11 49	12 49	13 49	14 49	15 49		16 49	
London Marylebone 10	⊖ a	08 34	09 34	10 04	11 05	12 05	13 04	14 05	15 05	16 05		17 05	

		CH	CH	CH	CH	CH	CH	CH	CH	CH	CH	CH	CH
Aylesbury Vale Parkway	d	16 57		17 57		18 57		19 57		20 57		21 57	
Aylesbury	d	17 02	17 32	18 02	18 32	19 02	19 32	20 02	20 32	21 02	21 32	22 02	22 32
Stoke Mandeville	d	17 06	17 36	18 06	18 36	19 06	19 36	20 06	20 36	21 06	21 36	22 06	22 36
Wendover	d	17 10	17 40	18 10	18 40	19 10	19 40	20 10	20 40	21 10	21 40	22 10	22 40
Great Missenden	d	17 16	17 46	18 16	18 46	19 16	19 46	20 16	20 46	21 16	21 46	22 16	22 46
Amersham §	⊖ d	17 23	17a55	18 23	18a55	19 23	19a55	20 23	20a55	21 23	21a55	22a25	22 53
Chalfont & Latimer §	⊖ d	17 27		18 27		19 27		20 27		21 27			22 57
Chorleywood §	⊖ d	17 32		18 32		19 32		20 32		21 32			23 02
Rickmansworth §	⊖ d	17 38		18 38		19 38		20 38		21 38			23 08
Harrow-on-the-Hill 3 §	⊖ d	17 49		18 49		19 49		20 49		21 49			23 19
London Marylebone 10	⊖ a	18 05		19 05		20 05		21 04		22 05			23 35

For general notes see front of timetable
For details of catering facilities see Directory of Train Operators

§ London Underground Limited (Metropolitan Line) services operate between Harrow-on-the-Hill, Rickmansworth, Chorleywood, Chalfont & Latimer and Amersham

London → High Wycombe, Aylesbury, Banbury, Stratford-upon-Avon, Birmingham Snow Hill and Kidderminster

Network Diagram - See first page of Table 114

Miles	Miles	Miles	Station		CH MX ◇	CH MO	CH MX	CH MX	CH MX ◇	CH MO	CH MO	CH MX	LM A	CH	CH B	CH C	CH	CH	CH	CH ◇	CH	CH	CH	CH	CH
0	—	—	**London Marylebone [10]** ⊖	d	22p20	22p45	23p10	23p30	23p54	23p45		00 10					06 00		06 27	06 50	06 53	07 20	07 23		07 26
—	—	0	**London Paddington [15]** ⊖	d																					
6½	—	—	Wembley Stadium	d		22p54	23p19	23p39		23p54		00 19					06 09		06 36		07 02				07 35
8	—	—	Sudbury & Harrow Road	d																					
8¾	—	—	Sudbury Hill Harrow	d																					07 39
9¾	—	—	Northolt Park	d		22p59		23p44		23p59		00 24					06 14		06 41						07 42
11½	—	—	South Ruislip § ⊖	d		23p03		23p48		00 03		00 28					06 18		06 45				07 38		
13¼	—	12	West Ruislip [3] § ⊖	d		23p06		23p51		00 06		00 31							06 48		07 11				07 47
16	—	—	Denham	d		23p11		23p56		00 11		00 36					06 24		06 53		07 16		07 43		07 51
17	—	—	Denham Golf Club	d		23p13		23p58		00 13		00 38							06 55						07 54
18¾	—	—	Gerrards Cross [1]	d		23p16	23p33	00 01	00 15	00 16		00 41					06 28		06 58		07 21		07 48		07 57
21¼	—	—	Seer Green	d		23p21		00 06		00 21		00 46					06 33				07 26				08 02
23	—	—	Beaconsfield	d		23p24	23p39	00 09	00 21	00 24		00 49					06 36		07 04		07 30		07 54		08 05
27¾	—	—	**High Wycombe [1]**	d		23p30	23p45	00 15	00 27	00 30		00 55			06 07	06 10	06 42		07a14	07 20	07a38	07 50	08 00		08 11
32¾	—	—	Saunderton	d		23p37		00 22	00 34	00 37		01 02			06 13	06 16	06 49						08 07		
36	0	—	**Princes Risborough [2]**	d		23p43	23p56	00 27	00 40	00 43	00 48	01 07			06 19	06 21	06 55	07 08		07 31		08 00	08 12	08 18	08a24
—	1½	—	Monks Risborough	d				00 31			00 51	01 11						07 11						08 21	
—	3	—	Little Kimble	d				00 34			00 55	01 14						07 15						08 25	
—	7½	—	**Aylesbury**	a				00 49			01 06	01 29						07 26						08 36	
41¾	—	—	Haddenham & Thame Parkway	d	23p02	23p50	00 03		00 47	00 50					06 26	06 28	07 02			07 37		08 06			
54¾	—	—	**Bicester North [3]**	a	23p13	00 03	00 16		01 00	01 03					06 41	06 43	07 15			07 48		08 18	08 27		
—	—	—		d	23p13	00 04	00 16		01 00	01 04					06 41	06 43	07 15			07 49		08 19	08 27		
65¼	—	—	Kings Sutton	d		00 16			01 12						06 54	06 56	07 26						08 39		
68¾	—	—	**Banbury**	d	23p30	00a25	00a40		01a21	01a24					07 02	07 02	07a38			08 05		08 35	08 45		
88¾	—	0	**Leamington Spa [8]**	d	23p48									06 55	07 22	07 22				08 24		08 53	09 03		
90¾	—	2	Warwick	d	23p53									06 59	07 26	07 26				08 28		08 57	09 08		
92	—	3¼	Warwick Parkway	d	23p56									07 02	07 30	07 30				08 32		09 01	09 11		
94¾	—	6	Hatton	d										07 07	07 34	07 34						09 07	09 17		
—	—	7¾	Claverdon	d									06x34	07 12									09 22		
—	—	10	Bearley	d									06x38	07 17											
—	—	11½	Wilmcote	d									06 42	07 21											
—	—	15¼	**Stratford-upon-Avon**	a									06 46	07 30									09 40		
99	—	—	Lapworth	a																		09 12			
101½	—	—	Dorridge	a	00 07										07 42	07 42				08 42		09 16			
104¾	—	—	Solihull	a	00 12										07 50	07 50				08 48		09 20			
111¼	—	—	**Birmingham Moor Street**	a	00 22										08 03	08 03				08 59		09 32			
112	—	—	**Birmingham Snow Hill** ⛴	a	00 32										08 14	08 11				09 07		09 41			
—	—	—	Rowley Regis	a																					
—	—	—	Cradley Heath	a																					
—	—	—	**Stourbridge Junction [2]**	a																					
—	—	—	**Kidderminster**	a																					

Station		CH	CH	CH	CH	CH ◇	CH	CH	CH 🍴	CH 🍴	CH	CH ◇ 🍴	CH	CH	CH	CH ◇ 🍴	CH ◇	CH	CH ◇ 🍴	CH ◇	CH	CH ◇ 🍴	CH	CH ◇ 🍴	CH
London Marylebone [10] ⊖	d	07 50	07 53	08 00	08 20	08 24	08 31		08 50	08 54	09 03	09 20		09 24	09 30	09 50	09 54	10 00	10 20	10 24	10 30	10 50		10 54	11 00
London Paddington [15] ⊖	d																								
Wembley Stadium	d			08 09			08 40				09 13				09 39			10 09			10 39				11 09
Sudbury & Harrow Road	d																								
Sudbury Hill Harrow	d			08 13			08 44								09 43						10 43				
Northolt Park	d					08 36									09 46			10 14			10 46				11 14
South Ruislip § ⊖	d			08 18							09 20							10 18							11 18
West Ruislip [3] § ⊖	d			08 21			08 51								09 51						10 51				
Denham	d			08 26			08 55				09 26				09 55			10 24			10 55				11 24
Denham Golf Club	d						08 58								09 58						10 58				
Gerrards Cross [1]	d		08 14	08 30		08 46	09 01				09 31			09 45	10 01		10 15	10 28		10 45	11 01			11 15	11 28
Seer Green	d		08 18	08 35		08 50					09 35				10 06			10 33			11 06				11 33
Beaconsfield	d		08 22	08 38		08 54	09 07				09 39			09 51	10 09		10 21	10 36		10 51	11 09			11 21	11 36
High Wycombe [1]	d	08 20	08 28	08a47	08 50	09 00	09a16		09 20	09 25	09a48	09 50		09 58	10a19	10 20	10 28	10a45	10 50	10 58	11a18			11 28	11a48
Saunderton	d		08 35			09 07								10 04						11 04					
Princes Risborough [2]	d		08 41		09 01	09 12		09 17		09 35		10 01	10 11	10a13			10 38		11 01	11 10			11 11	11 38	
Monks Risborough	d							09 20					10 14										11 14		
Little Kimble	d							09 24					10 18										11 18		
Aylesbury	a							09 35					10 29										11 29		
Haddenham & Thame Parkway	d		08 48		09 07	09 19				09 42		10 07					10 45		11 07	11 16				11 45	
Bicester North [3]	a		09 06		09 18	09 36				09 55		10 18					11 01		11 18	11 33		11 38		11 59	
	d				09 19					09 55		10 19							11 19			11 39		11 59	
Kings Sutton	d									10 08														12 12	
Banbury	d	08 57			09 35				09 57	10 14		10 35				10 57			11 35			11 57		12 17	
Leamington Spa [8]	d	09 15			09 54				10 15	10 34		10 54				11 15			11 54			12 15		12 38	
Warwick	d	09 19			09 58				10 19	10 38		10 59				11 19			11 59			12 19		12 42	
Warwick Parkway	d	09 22			10 02				10 22			11 02				11 22			12 02			12 22			
Hatton	d				10 07					10 45									12 07					12 49	
Claverdon	d																							12 54	
Bearley	d									10 53														12 59	
Wilmcote	d									10 57															
Stratford-upon-Avon	a									11 09														13 11	
Lapworth	a				10 12														12 13						
Dorridge	a	09 33			10 16				10 33			11 13				11 33			12 17			12 33			
Solihull	a	09 38			10 22				10 38			11 18				11 38			12 22			12 38			
Birmingham Moor Street	a	09 49			10 33				10 49			11 30				11 49			12 34			12 49			
Birmingham Snow Hill ⛴	a	10 01			10 41				11 01			11 41				12 01			12 42			13 02			
Rowley Regis	a																								
Cradley Heath	a																								
Stourbridge Junction [2]	a																								
Kidderminster	a																								

For general notes see front of timetable
For details of catering facilities see Directory of Train Operators

§ London Underground Limited (Central Line) also operate services between South Ruislip and West Ruislip at frequent intervals

A From Birmingham Snow Hill (Table 71)
B From 5 October
C Until 2 October

From 5 October a revised Chiltern Railways service will be in operation due to seasonal difficulties. Trains will arrive at their destination 3 minutes later than shown

London → High Wycombe, Aylesbury, Banbury, Stratford-upon-Avon, Birmingham Snow Hill and Kidderminster

Network Diagram - See first page of Table 114

		CH ⟂	CH	CH	CH	CH ◇ ⟂	CH ◇		CH	CH	CH	CH	CH ◇	CH	CH	CH	CH	CH	CH	CH	CH ◇	CH	CH	CH	CH
London Marylebone 10 ⊖	d	11 20			11 30	11 50	11 54		12 00	12 20	12 24	12 30	12 50		12 54	13 00	13 20		13 24	13 30	13 50	13 54	14 00	14 20	14 24
London Paddington 15 ⊖	d			11 20																					
Wembley Stadium	d				11 39				12 09			12 39				13 09				13 39			14 09		
Sudbury & Harrow Road	d																								
Sudbury Hill Harrow	d				11 43							12 43								13 43					
Northolt Park	d				11 46				12 14			12 46				13 14				13 46			14 14		
South Ruislip § ⊖	d								12 18							13 18							14 18		
West Ruislip 3 § ⊖	d				11 51							12 51								13 51					
Denham	d				11 55				12 24			12 55				13 24				13 55			14 24		
Denham Golf Club	d				11 58							12 58								13 58					
Gerrards Cross 1	d			11 45	12 01		12 15		12 28		12 45	13 01			13 15	13 28			13 45	14 01		14 15	14 28		14 45
Seer Green	d				12 06				12 33			13 06				13 33				14 06			14 33		
Beaconsfield	d			11 51	12 09		12 21		12 36		12 51	13 09			13 21	13 36			13 51	14 09		14 21	14 36		14 51
High Wycombe 1	d	11 50		11 58	12a18		12 28		12a45	12 50	12 58	13a18			13 28	13a45	13 50		13 58	14a18		14 28	14a45	14 50	14 58
Saunderton	d			12 04							13 04								14 04						15 04
Princes Risborough 2	d	12 01	12 11	12a13			12 38			13 01	13 10			13 11	13 38		14 01	14 11	14a13			14 38		15 01	15 10
Monks Risborough	d		12 14											13 14				14 14							
Little Kimble	d		12 18											13 18				14 18							
Aylesbury	a		12 29											13 29				14 29							
Haddenham & Thame Parkway	d	12 07					12 45			13 07	13 16				13 45		14 07					14 45		15 07	15 16
Bicester North 3	a	12 18				12 39	13 01			13 18	13 34		13 39		13 59		14 18				14 39	15 01		15 18	15 34
	d	12 19				12 39				13 19			13 39		13 59		14 19				14 39			15 19	
Kings Sutton	d														14 12										
Banbury	d	12 35				12 57				13 35			13 57		14 17		14 35				14 57			15 35	
Leamington Spa 8	d	12 54				13 15				13 54			14 15		14 38		14 54				15 15			15 54	
Warwick	d	12 59				13 19				13 59			14 19		14 42		14 59				15 19			15 59	
Warwick Parkway	d	13 02				13 22				14 02			14 22				15 02				15 22			16 02	
Hatton	d									14 07					14 49									16 07	
Claverdon	d																								
Bearley	d														14 57										
Wilmcote	d																								
Stratford-upon-Avon	a														15 09										
Lapworth	a									14 13														16 13	
Dorridge	a	13 13				13 33				14 17			14 32				15 13				15 33			16 17	
Solihull	a	13 18				13 38				14 22			14 39				15 18				15 38			16 22	
Birmingham Moor Street	a	13 31				13 49				14 34			14 49				15 33				15 49			16 34	
Birmingham Snow Hill ⛴	a	13 41				14 01				14 42			15 02				15 41				16 01			16 42	
Rowley Regis	a																								
Cradley Heath	a																								
Stourbridge Junction 2	a																								
Kidderminster	a																								

		CH	CH	CH	CH ◇	CH	CH	CH	CH	CH	CH	CH ◇ ⟂	CH	CH	CH	CH	CH ⟂	CH	CH	CH	CH	CH ◇ A ⟂	CH	CH	CH
London Marylebone 10 ⊖	d	14 30	14 50		14 54	15 00	15 20		15 24	15 30	15 42	16 00	16 03	16 06	16 10	16 14	16 30		16 36	16 39	16 47	17 00	17 03		17 06
London Paddington 15 ⊖	d																								
Wembley Stadium	d	14 39				15 09				15 39					16 19	16 23				16 48					17 15
Sudbury & Harrow Road	d															16 26									
Sudbury Hill Harrow	d	14 43								15 43						16 29									
Northolt Park	d	14 46				15 14				15 46						16 32				16 53					
South Ruislip § ⊖	d					15 18								16 21						16 57					
West Ruislip 3 § ⊖	d	14 51								15 51					16 28						17 04				17 24
Denham	d	14 55				15 24				15 55					16 33					17 03					17 29
Denham Golf Club	d	14 58													16 35										17 31
Gerrards Cross 1	d	15 01			15 15	15 28			15 48	16 00	16 03			16 29	16 39	16a45				17 07	17 10				17 34
Seer Green	d	15 06				15 33			15 53						16 43						17 15				
Beaconsfield	d	15 09			15 21	15 36			15 56	16 06	16 09			16 35	16 47					17 13	17 18				
High Wycombe 1	d	15a18			15 28	15a45	15 50		16 02	16a15	16 17		16 32	16 41	16a57				17 05	17 19	17a27		17 33		17 45
Saunderton	d								16 09					16 48											17 52
Princes Risborough 2	d			15 11	15 38		16 01	16 07	16a21		16 26		16 43	16a57				17 00	17 16	17a33			17 44	17 49	17 57
Monks Risborough	d			15 14				16 10										17 03						17 52	
Little Kimble	d			15 18				16 14										17 07						17 56	
Aylesbury	a			15 29				16 25										17 18						18 07	
Haddenham & Thame Parkway	d				15 45		16 07				16 33		16 49						17 22				17 50		18 04
Bicester North 3	a		15 38		15 59		16 18				16 50		17 00						17 33				18 01		18 22
	d		15 39		15 59		16 19						17 01						17 33				18 01		
Kings Sutton	d				16 12								17 12										18 14		
Banbury	d		15 57		16 17		16 35					17 03	17a25				17 33		17 49			18 03	18a25		
Leamington Spa 8	d		16 15		16 38		16 54					17 22					17 50		18 07			18 23			
Warwick	d		16 19		16 42		16 59					17 27					17 56								
Warwick Parkway	d		16 22				17 02					17 30					17 59		18 14			18 29			
Hatton	d				16 49														18 20						
Claverdon	d				16 54																				
Bearley	d				16 59																				
Wilmcote	d				17 02														18 30						
Stratford-upon-Avon	a				17 12														18 41						
Lapworth	a						17 10										18 08								
Dorridge	a		16 33				17 14					17 42					18 12					18 39			
Solihull	a		16 38				17 20					17 48					18 17					18 45			
Birmingham Moor Street	a		16 49				17 32					17 58					18 28					18 56			
Birmingham Snow Hill ⛴	a		17 01				17 41					18 12					18 41					19 01			
Rowley Regis	a																					19 24			
Cradley Heath	a																					19 29			
Stourbridge Junction 2	a																					19 35			
Kidderminster	a																					19 48			

For general notes see front of timetable
For details of catering facilities see Directory of Train Operators

A ⟂ to Birmingham Snow Hill

§ London Underground Limited (Central Line) also operate services between South Ruislip and West Ruislip at frequent intervals

From 5 October a revised Chiltern Railways service will be in operation due to seasonal difficulties. Trains will arrive at their destination 3 minutes later than shown

London → High Wycombe, Aylesbury, Banbury, Stratford-upon-Avon, Birmingham Snow Hill and Kidderminster

Network Diagram - See first page of Table 114

		CH	CH	CH	CH	CH	CH	CH	CH	CH	CH	CH	CH	CH	CH	CH	CH	CH	CH	CH	CH	CH	CH	CH	CH
										◇ A											A				
London Marylebone 10	⊖ d	17 10	17 19	17 30	17 33	17 36	17 41	17 45	17 51	18 00	18 03	18 09		18 12	18 15	18 19	18 30	18 33	18 37	18 46	19 00	19 03	19 07	19 11	19 30
London Paddington 15	⊖ d																								
Wembley Stadium	d	17 19					17 50	17 54							18 24	18 28			18 46					19 20	
Sudbury & Harrow Road	d	17 22														18 31								19 23	
Sudbury Hill Harrow	d					17 48										18 34								19 26	
Northolt Park	d	17 26			17 46				18 04							18 36				18 59				19 28	
South Ruislip §	⊖ d	17 29					17 58								18 31					19 02			19 22		
West Ruislip 3 §	⊖ d					17 54								18 29					18 55					19 33	
Denham	d				17 53										18 37					19 08				19 38	
Denham Golf Club	d													18 34										19 40	
Gerrards Cross 1	d		17 40			18a04		18 09				18 30			18 41	18a49			19 02	19 13			19 30	19 44	
Seer Green	d		17 45		18 00				18 16					18 40					19 06				19 34		
Beaconsfield	d	17 43	17 48		18 04			18 15	18 20					18 43	18 48			18 58	19 10	19 18			19 38		
High Wycombe 1	d	17a53	17 55		18a13		18 15	18 21	18a29			18 41		18 50	18a58			19 05	19 16	19 25		19 33	19 44	19a58	
Saunderton	d							18 28						18 56					19 23				19 51		
Princes Risborough 2	d		18a08				18 25	18 33			18 42	18 50	18 55	19a05				19 14	19 28	19 34		19 43	19a59		
Monks Risborough	d							18 37												19 39					
Little Kimble	d							18 40												19 44					
Aylesbury	a							18 55					19 11						19 49	19 59					
Haddenham & Thame Parkway	d			18 13			18 31				18 49	18 59						19 21				19 50			20 11
Bicester North 3	a			18 24			18 42				19 01	19 16					19 20	19 41				20 03			20 22
	d			18 25			18 42				19 02						19 21					20 03			20 22
Kings Sutton	d										19 12											20 15			
Banbury	d			18 39			18 58			19 03	19a28						19 36				20 03	20a26			20 38
Leamington Spa 8	d			18 58			19 16			19 22							19 54				20 23				20 56
Warwick	d			19 03			19 20										19 59								21 00
Warwick Parkway	d			19 06						19 28							20 02				20 29				21 04
Hatton	d			19 11			19 27										20 07								21 09
Claverdon	d						19 33																		
Bearley	d																								
Wilmcote	d																								
Stratford-upon-Avon	a						19 51																		
Lapworth	a			19 17													20 13								21 14
Dorridge	a			19 21						19 38							20 17				20 39				21 18
Solihull	a			19 27						19 44							20 22				20 45				21 24
Birmingham Moor Street	a			19 38						19 56							20 33				20 57				21 36
Birmingham Snow Hill	a			19 47						20 01							20 44				21 03				21 47
Rowley Regis	a									20 24											21 19				
Cradley Heath	a									20 29											21 25				
Stourbridge Junction 2	a									20 35											21 32				
Kidderminster	a									20 50											21 49				

		CH	CH	CH	CH	CH	CH	CH	CH	CH	CH	CH	CH	CH	CH	CH	CH	CH	CH	CH	CH	CH	CH
																			FX	FO		FO	FX
		◇				◇		◇		◇			◇			◇						◇	◇
London Marylebone 10	⊖ d	19 33	19 36	19 40	20 00	20 06	20 10	20 30	20 33	21 00	21 03	21 18	21 33	21 40	22 03	22 20	22 23	22 40	23 10	23 10	23 30	23 54	23 54
London Paddington 15	⊖ d																						
Wembley Stadium	d			19 49			20 19		20 42		21 12			21 49			22 32	22 49	23 19	23 19	23 39		
Sudbury & Harrow Road	d								20 45														
Sudbury Hill Harrow	d								20 48														
Northolt Park	d			19 54			20 24				21 17			21 54			22 37				23 44		
South Ruislip §	⊖ d			19 58					20 53					21 58				22 56			23 48		
West Ruislip 3 §	⊖ d			20 01			20 29				21 22						22 42				23 51		
Denham	d			20 06			20 34		20 58		21 27			22 04			22 47	23 02			23 56		
Denham Golf Club	d						20 36				21 29						22 49				23 58		
Gerrards Cross 1	d		19 57	20 10		20 27	20 40		21 03		21 33	21 39		22 08	22 24		22 53	23 07	23 33	23 33	00 01	00 15	00 15
Seer Green	d			20 14			20 44		21 07		21 37			22 13			22 57	23 11			00 06		
Beaconsfield	d	19 57	20 03	20 18		20 33	20 47		21 11		21 41	21 47		22 16	22 30		23 01	23 15	23 39	23 39	00 09	00 21	00 21
High Wycombe 1	d	20 04	20 10	20a27		20 40	20 54	21 00	21 17		21 47	21 53		22 23	22 36		23 07	23 21	23 45	23 45	00 15	00 27	00 27
Saunderton	d						21 00				21 54			22 29			23 14				00 22	00 34	00 34
Princes Risborough 2	d	20 15	20 20			20 49	21 06	21 11	21a30		21 59	22 03		22 36	22 46		23 19	23 31	23 56	23 56	00 27	00 40	00 40
Monks Risborough	d						21 09				22 03						23 23				00 31		
Little Kimble	d						21 13				22 06						23 26				00 34		
Aylesbury	a						21 27				22 20			22 54			23 40				00 49		
Haddenham & Thame Parkway	d	20 21	20 27			20 56		21 17		21 41		22 09	22 16		22 53	23 02		23 38	00 03	00 03		00 47	00 47
Bicester North 3	a	20 32	20 43		20 50	21 13		21 28		21 54		22 24	22 27		23 09	23 13		23 51	00 16	00 16		01 00	01 00
	d	20 32			20 50			21 28		21 54			22 28			23 13		23 52	00 16	00 16		01 00	01 00
Kings Sutton	d							21 41										00 04				01 12	01 12
Banbury	d	20 49			21 06			21 47		22 10			22 42			23 30		00a14	00a40	00 33		01 18	01a21
Leamington Spa 8	d	21 07			21 25			22 05		22 30			23 00			23 48				00 52		01a39	
Warwick	d	21 12						22 10					23 05			23 53				00 56			
Warwick Parkway	d				21 31			22 14		22 35			23 07			23 56				01a06			
Hatton	d	21 19						22 19															
Claverdon	d	21 24																					
Bearley	d	21 29																					
Wilmcote	d	21 33																					
Stratford-upon-Avon	a	21 43																					
Lapworth	a							22 24															
Dorridge	a				21 41			22 28		22 46			23 18			00 07							
Solihull	a				21 47			22 35		22 51			23 23			00 12							
Birmingham Moor Street	a				21 58			22 49		23 00			23 33			00 22							
Birmingham Snow Hill	a				22 04			22 58		23 05			23 45			00 32							
Rowley Regis	a				22 24					23 31													
Cradley Heath	a				22 29					23 37													
Stourbridge Junction 2	a				22 35					23 50													
Kidderminster	a				22 50																		

For general notes see front of timetable
For details of catering facilities see
Directory of Train Operators

§ London Underground Limited (Central Line) also operate services between South Ruislip and West Ruislip at frequent intervals

A to Birmingham Snow Hill

From 5 October a revised Chiltern Railways service will be in operation due to seasonal difficulties. Trains will arrive at their destination 3 minutes later than shown

London → High Wycombe, Aylesbury, Banbury, Stratford-upon-Avon, Birmingham Snow Hill and Kidderminster

Network Diagram - See first page of Table 114

		CH ◇	CH	CH	CH ◇	CH	CH	CH	CH	CH	CH ◇	CH		CH	CH	CH	CH	CH	CH	CH	CH	CH ◇	CH	CH ◇	CH
London Marylebone 10 ⊖	d	22p20	23p10	23p30	23p54	00 10		06 27			07 24			08 18	08 24	08 45		08 54	09 18		09 24	09 45	10 00	10 18	10 24
London Paddington 15 ⊖	d																								
Wembley Stadium	d		23p19	23p39		00 19		06 36			07 33				08 33						09 33		10 09		10 33
Sudbury & Harrow Road	d																								
Sudbury Hill Harrow	d																								
Northolt Park	d			23p44		00 24		06 41			07 38				08 38						09 38		10 14		10 38
South Ruislip § ⊖	d			23p48		00 28		06 45			07 42				08 42						09 42		10 18		
West Ruislip 3 § ⊖	d			23p51		00 31		06 48			07 45				08 45						09 45				10 43
Denham	d			23p56		00 36		06 53			07 50				08 50						09 50		10 24		10 48
Denham Golf Club	d			23p58		00 38		06 55			07 52				08 52						09 52				10 50
Gerrards Cross 1	d		23p33	00 01	00 15	00 41		06 59			07 55			08 39	08 55			09 15	09 39		09 55		10 28		10 54
Seer Green	d			00 06		00 46		07 03			08 00				09 00						10 00		10 33		10 58
Beaconsfield	d		23p39	00 09	00 21	00 49		07 07			08 03			08 45	09 03			09 21	09 45		10 03		10 36		11 01
High Wycombe 1	d		23p45	00 15	00 27	00 55	06 10	07 13			08 10			08 51	09a13	09 14		09 28	09 51		10a13	10 15	10a45	10 48	11a11
Saunderton	d			00 22	00 34	01 02	06 16	07 21			08 16			08 58					09 58					10 54	
Princes Risborough 2	d		23p56	00 27	00 40	01 07	06 22	07 26	07 30		08 22	08 30		09 04		09 24	09 28	09 39	10 04	10 11				11 01	
Monks Risborough	d			00 31		01 11			07 33			08 33					09 31			10 14					
Little Kimble	d			00 34		01 14			07 37			08 37					09 35			10 18					
Aylesbury	a			00 49		01 29			07 47			08 47					09 45			10 28					
Haddenham & Thame Parkway	d	23p02	00 03		00 47		06 29	07 33			08 29			09 11		09 31		09 45	10 11			10 30		11 07	
Bicester North 3	a	23p13	00 16		01 00		06 41	07 43			08 41			09 22		09 42		09 59	10 22			10 42		11 18	
	d	23p13	00 16		01 00		06 42	07 44			08 42			09 22		09 42		10 00	10 22			10 42		11 19	
Kings Sutton	d				01 12		06 53				08 53							10 11							
Banbury	d	23p30	00 33		01 18		07 02	08 01		08 40	08 58			09 39		09 58		10 19	10 39			10 58		11 35	
Leamington Spa 8	d	23p48	00 52		01a39		07 21	08 20		09 00	09 17			09 58		10 17		10 38	10 58			11 17		11 54	
Warwick	d	23p53	00 56				07 25	08 24		09 04	09 21			10 02		10 21		10 42	11 02			11 21		11 59	
Warwick Parkway	d	23p56	01a06				07 29	08 28		09 08	09 25			10 06		10 25			11 06			11 25		12 02	
Hatton	d							08 33		09 12						10 30		10 49						12 07	
Claverdon	d																	10 54							
Bearley	d																	10 59							
Wilmcote	d																	11 03							
Stratford-upon-Avon	a									09 36								11 13							
Lapworth	a							08 38								10 35								12 13	
Dorridge	a	00 07					07 40	08 42			09 35			10 16		10 39			11 16			11 35		12 17	
Solihull	a	00 12					07 45	08 50			09 41			10 22		10 45			11 22			11 42		12 22	
Birmingham Moor Street	a	00 22					07 57	09 00			09 51			10 33		10 54			11 33			11 51		12 34	
Birmingham Snow Hill ⛴	a	00 32					08 08	09 11			10 02			10 41		11 04			11 41			12 01		12 42	
Rowley Regis	a																								
Cradley Heath	a																								
Stourbridge Junction 2	a																								
Kidderminster	a																								

For general notes see front of timetable
For details of catering facilities see Directory of Train Operators

§ London Underground Limited (Central Line) also operate services between South Ruislip and West Ruislip at frequent intervals

From 10 October a revised Chiltern Railways service will be in operation due to seasonal difficulties. Trains will arrive at their destination 3 minutes later than shown

Table 115

Saturdays

London → High Wycombe, Aylesbury, Banbury, Stratford-upon-Avon, Birmingham Snow Hill and Kidderminster

Network Diagram - See first page of Table 114

		CH ◇		CH	CH ◇	CH	CH	CH	CH ◇	CH	CH	CH	CH	CH ◇		CH	CH	CH	CH	CH ◇	CH	CH	CH	CH	CH
London Marylebone 10 ⊖	d	10 50			10 53	11 00	11 20	11 30	11 50		11 53	12 20	12 24	12 50			12 53	13 20	13 24	13 50		13 53	14 20	14 24	14 50
London Paddington 15 ⊖	d																								
Wembley Stadium	d					11 09		11 39			12 02		12 33						13 33			14 02		14 33	
Sudbury & Harrow Road	d																								
Sudbury Hill Harrow	d																								
Northolt Park	d					11 14		11 44					12 38						13 38					14 38	
South Ruislip § ⊖	d					11 18		11 48					12 42						13 42					14 42	
West Ruislip 3 § ⊖	d							11 51					12 45						13 45					14 45	
Denham	d					11 24		11 56					12 50						13 50					14 50	
Denham Golf Club	d							11 58					12 52						13 52					14 52	
Gerrards Cross 1	d				11 14	11 28		12 01			12 16		12 55				13 14		13 55			14 16		14 55	
Seer Green	d					11 33		12 06					13 00						14 00					15 00	
Beaconsfield	d				11 20	11 36		12 09			12 22		13 03				13 20		14 03			14 22		15 03	
High Wycombe 1	d				11 27	11a45	11 49	12a19			12 28	12 50	13a13				13 27	13 50	14a13			14 28	14 50	15a13	
Saunderton	d				11 33						12 35						13 33					14 35			
Princes Risborough 2	d			11 08	11 39		12 00			12 10	12 41	13 01				13 11	13 39	14 01			14 11	14 41	15 01		
Monks Risborough	d			11 11						12 13						13 14					14 14				
Little Kimble	d			11 15						12 17						13 18					14 18				
Aylesbury	a			11 25						12 27						13 28					14 28				
Haddenham & Thame Parkway	d				11 45		12 06				12 48	13 07					13 45	14 07				14 48	15 07		
Bicester North 3	a	11 41			11 59		12 17		12 42		13 03	13 18		13 41			13 59	14 18		14 41		15 04	15 18		15 41
	d	11 42			12 00		12 18		12 42			13 19		13 42			14 00	14 19		14 42			15 19		15 42
Kings Sutton	d				12 11												14 11								
Banbury	d	11 58			12 19		12 34		12 58			13 35		13 58			14 19	14 35		14 58			15 35		15 58
Leamington Spa 8	d	12 17			12 38		12 53		13 17			13 54		14 17			14 38	14 54		15 17			15 54		16 17
Warwick	d	12 21			12 42		12 59		13 21			13 59		14 21			14 42	14 59		15 21			15 59		16 21
Warwick Parkway	d	12 25					13 02		13 25			14 02		14 25				15 02		15 25			16 02		16 25
Hatton	d				12 49							14 07					14 49						16 07		
Claverdon	d																								
Bearley	d				12 58																				
Wilmcote	d				13 00												15 00								
Stratford-upon-Avon	a				13 11												15 10								
Lapworth	a											14 13											16 13		
Dorridge	a	12 35					13 13		13 36			14 17		14 36				15 13		15 36			16 17		16 35
Solihull	a	12 41					13 19		13 42			14 22		14 41				15 19		15 41			16 22		16 42
Birmingham Moor Street	a	12 52					13 32		13 52			14 34		14 52				15 32		15 52			16 33		16 53
Birmingham Snow Hill ⛴	a	13 01					13 41		14 01			14 42		15 01				15 41		16 01			16 41		17 02
Rowley Regis	a																								
Cradley Heath	a																								
Stourbridge Junction 2	a																								
Kidderminster	a																								

		CH	CH ◇	CH		CH	CH	CH	CH	CH	CH	CH	CH	CH	CH	CH		CH	CH	CH	CH	CH	CH	CH	CH
London Marylebone 10 ⊖	d		14 53	15 00		15 20	15 30	15 50		15 53	16 00	16 20	16 24	16 50		16 53		17 00	17 20	17 24	17 50		17 53	18 00	18 15
London Paddington 15 ⊖	d																								
Wembley Stadium	d			15 09			15 39				16 09		16 33					17 09		17 33				18 09	
Sudbury & Harrow Road	d																								
Sudbury Hill Harrow	d																								
Northolt Park	d			15 14			15 44				16 14		16 38					17 14		17 38				18 14	
South Ruislip § ⊖	d			15 18							16 18		16 42					17 18						18 18	
West Ruislip 3 § ⊖	d						15 49						16 45							17 43					
Denham	d			15 24			15 54				16 24		16 50					17 24		17 48				18 24	
Denham Golf Club	d						15 56						16 52							17 50					
Gerrards Cross 1	d		15 14	15 28			16 00			16 14	16 28		16 55			17 14		17 28		17 54			18 14	18 28	
Seer Green	d			15 33			16 04				16 33		17 00					17 33		17 58				18 33	
Beaconsfield	d		15 20	15 36			16 07			16 20	16 36		17 03			17 20		17 36		18 01			18 20	18 36	
High Wycombe 1	d		15 27	15a45		15 49	16a17			16 27	16a45	16 50	17a13			17 27		17a45	17 50	18a11			18 27	18a45	18 47
Saunderton	d		15 33							16 33						17 33							18 33		
Princes Risborough 2	d	15 05	15 39			16 00			16 05	16 39		17 01			17 11	17 39			18 01			18 08	18 39		18 56
Monks Risborough	d	15 08							16 08						17 14							18 11			
Little Kimble	d	15 12							16 12						17 18							18 15			
Aylesbury	a	15 22							16 22						17 28							18 25			19 14
Haddenham & Thame Parkway	d		15 45			16 06				16 45		17 07				17 45			18 07				18 45		
Bicester North 3	a		15 59			16 17		16 41		17 02		17 18		17 42		17 59			18 18		18 45		19 02		
	d		16 00			16 18		16 42				17 19		17 42		18 00			18 19		18 45				
Kings Sutton	d		16 11													18 11									
Banbury	d		16 19			16 34		16 58				17 35		17 58		18 19			18 35		19 03				
Leamington Spa 8	d		16 38			16 53		17 17				17 54		18 17		18 38			18 54		19 23				
Warwick	d		16 42			16 59		17 21				17 59		18 21		18 42			18 59		19 27				
Warwick Parkway	d					17 02		17 25				18 02		18 25					19 02		19 30				
Hatton	d		16 49			17 07						18 07				18 49			19 07						
Claverdon	d		16 54													18 54									
Bearley	d		16 59													18 59									
Wilmcote	d															19 03									
Stratford-upon-Avon	a		17 11													19 13									
Lapworth	a					17 13						18 13							19 13						
Dorridge	a					17 17		17 35				18 17		18 36					19 17		19 41				
Solihull	a					17 22		17 42				18 22		18 41					19 22		19 48				
Birmingham Moor Street	a					17 33		17 53				18 33		18 54					19 33		19 58				
Birmingham Snow Hill ⛴	a					17 41		18 02				18 41		19 04					19 41		20 06				
Rowley Regis	a																								
Cradley Heath	a																								
Stourbridge Junction 2	a																								
Kidderminster	a																								

For general notes see front of timetable
For details of catering facilities see Directory of Train Operators

§ London Underground Limited (Central Line) also operate services between South Ruislip and West Ruislip at frequent intervals

From 10 October a revised Chiltern Railways service will be in operation due to seasonal difficulties. Trains will arrive at their destination 3 minutes later than shown

London → High Wycombe, Aylesbury, Banbury, Stratford-upon-Avon, Birmingham Snow Hill and Kidderminster

Network Diagram - See first page of Table 114

Station		CH	CH	CH	CH	CH		CH	CH	CH	CH	CH ◇	CH	CH	CH ◇	CH	CH	CH ◇	CH	CH	CH	CH	CH		
London Marylebone 10	⊖ d	18 20	18 30	18 50		18 53		19 00	19 20		19 30	20 00	20 05	20 40	20 50	21 15	21 40	22 00	22 10	22 45	23 10	23 14	23 45		
London Paddington 15	⊖ d																								
Wembley Stadium	d		18 39					19 09			19 39		20 14			21 24			22 19	22 54	23 19	23 23	23 54		
Sudbury & Harrow Road	d																								
Sudbury Hill Harrow	d																								
Northolt Park	d		18 44					19 14			19 44		20 19			21 29			22 24			23 28			
South Ruislip §	⊖ d							19 18					20 23			21 33			22 28			23 32			
West Ruislip 3 §	⊖ d		18 49								19 49		20 26			21 36			22 31			23 35			
Denham	d		18 54					19 24			19 54		20 31			21 41			22 36			23 40			
Denham Golf Club	d		18 56								19 56		20 33			21 43			22 38			23 42			
Gerrards Cross 1	d		19 00			19 14		19 28			20 00		20 37	21 01		21 46	22 01		22 41	23 08	23 33	23 45	00 08		
Seer Green	d		19 04					19 33			20 04		20 41			21 51			22 46			23 50			
Beaconsfield	d		19 07			19 20		19 36			20 07		20 45	21 07		21 54	22 07		22 49	23 14	23 39	23 53	00 14		
High Wycombe 1	d	18 50	19a17			19 27		19 43	19 50		20 13	20 30	20 51	21 13	21 21	22 00	22 13		22 55	23 20	23 45	23 59	00 20		
Saunderton	d					19 33					20 20			21 20		22 07			23 02			00 06			
Princes Risborough 2	d	19 01			19 08	19 39		19 54	20 01	20 05	20 27	20 41	21 01	21 27	21 31	22 14	22 24		23 07	23 32	23 56	00 12	00 32		
Monks Risborough	d				19 11					20 08	20 30			21 30		22 17			23 11			00 16			
Little Kimble	d				19 15					20 12	20 34			21 34		22 21			23 14			00 19			
Aylesbury	a				19 25			20 12		20 22	20 47		21 19	21 47		22 34			23 29			00 34			
Haddenham & Thame Parkway	d	19 07				19 45			20 07			20 48			21 38		22 31			23 38	00 03		00 38		
Bicester North 3	a	19 18		19 45		19 59			20 18			21 00			21 50		22 47	22 51		23 52	00 15		00 51		
	d	19 19		19 45		20 00			20 19			21 00			21 51			22 51		23 52	00 16		00 52		
Kings Sutton	d					20 11														00 03			01 03		
Banbury	d	19 35		20 03		20 19			20 35			21 19			22 07			23 06		00a14	00a36		01a14		
Leamington Spa 8	d	19 53		20 23		20 38			20 54			21 38			22 27			23 24							
Warwick	d	19 59		20 27		20 42			20 59			21 42			22 31			23 28							
Warwick Parkway	d	20 02		20 30					21 02			21 46			22 35			23 34							
Hatton	d	20 07				20 49			21 07																
Claverdon	d					20 54																			
Bearley	d																								
Wilmcote	d																								
Stratford-upon-Avon	a					21 10																			
Lapworth	a	20 13							21 13																
Dorridge	a	20 17		20 41					21 17			21 57			22 46			23 32							
Solihull	a	20 22		20 47					21 22			22 03			22 51			23 49							
Birmingham Moor Street	a	20 34		20 58					21 33			22 15			23 02			23 59							
Birmingham Snow Hill	⛴ a	20 42		21 06					21 41			22 26			23 10			00 10							
Rowley Regis	a																								
Cradley Heath	a																								
Stourbridge Junction 2	a																								
Kidderminster	a																								

For general notes see front of timetable
For details of catering facilities see Directory of Train Operators

§ London Underground Limited (Central Line) also operate services between South Ruislip and West Ruislip at frequent intervals

From 10 October a revised Chiltern Railways service will be in operation due to seasonal difficulties. Trains will arrive at their destination 3 minutes later than shown

London → High Wycombe, Aylesbury, Banbury, Stratford-upon-Avon, Birmingham Snow Hill and Kidderminster

Network Diagram - See first page of Table 114

Station		CH	CH	CH	CH	CH		CH	CH	CH	CH	CH		CH	CH	CH	CH	CH		CH	CH	CH	CH	CH	CH
London Marylebone 10 ⊖	d	22p45	23p10	23p14	23p45	00 10		07 35	07 50	08 10	08 54	09 15		09 33	09 54	10 17	10 50	10 54		11 20	11 33	11 50	11 54	12 20	12 33
London Paddington 15 ⊖	d																								
Wembley Stadium	d	22p54	23p19	23p23	23p54	00 19		07 44	07 59		09 03			09 42	10 03			11 03			11 42		12 03		12 42
Sudbury & Harrow Road	d																								
Sudbury Hill Harrow	d																								
Northolt Park	d			23p28		00 24			08 04		09 08				10 08			11 08					12 08		
South Ruislip § ⊖	d			23p32		00 28		07 51	08 08		09 12				10 12			11 12					12 12		
West Ruislip 3 § ⊖	d			23p35		00 31			08 11		09 15				10 15			11 15					12 15		
Denham	d			23p40		00 36		07 57	08 16		09 20				10 20			11 20					12 20		
Denham Golf Club	d			23p42		00 38			08 18		09 22							11 22							
Gerrards Cross 1	d	23p08	23p33	23p45	00 08	00 41		08 02	08 21		09 25	09 36		09 56	10 24	10 38		11 25		11 41	11 56		12 24	12 41	12 56
Seer Green	d			23p50		00 46			08 26		09 30				10 28			11 30					12 28		
Beaconsfield	d	23p14	23p39	23p53	00 14	00 49		08 08	08 29		09 33	09 42		10 02	10 32	10 44		11 33		11 47	12 02		12 32	12 47	13 02
High Wycombe 1	d	23p20	23p45	23p59	00 20	00 55		08 14	08 35	08 40	09 39	09 49		10 08	10 38	10 51		11 39		11 54	12 08		12 38	12 54	13 08
Saunderton	d			00 06		01 02			08 42		09 46				10 45			11 46					12 45		
Princes Risborough 2	d	23p32	23p56	00 12	00 32	01 07		08 25	08 47	08 51	09 51	09 59		10 18	10 50	11 01		11 51		12 04	12 18		12 50	13 04	13 18
Monks Risborough	d			00 16		01 11			08 51		09 55				10 54			11 55					12 54		
Little Kimble	d			00 19		01 14			08 54		09 58				10 57			11 58					12 57		
Aylesbury	a			00 34		01 29			09 09		10 13				11 11			12 13					13 11		
Haddenham & Thame Parkway	d	23p38	00 03		00 38			08 32		08 58		10 06		10 25		11 08				12 11	12 25			13 11	13 25
Bicester North 3	a	23p52	00 15		00 51			08 48		09 09		10 19		10 39		11 21	11 45			12 24	12 39	12 44		13 24	13 41
	d	23p52	00 16		00 52					09 09		10 20		10 39		11 22	11 45			12 25	12 39	12 45		13 25	
Kings Sutton	d	00 03			01 03					09 21				10 53							12 53				
Banbury	d	00a14	00a36		01a14					09 27		10 36		11 01		11 38	12 02			12 41	13 01	13 05		13 41	
Leamington Spa 8	d									09 46		10 58		11 21		11 58	12 22			13 01	13 21	13 25		14 01	
Warwick	d									09 51		11 02		11 25		12 02				13 05	13 25			14 05	
Warwick Parkway	d									09 54		11 06				12 06	12 27			13 09		13 31		14 09	
Hatton	d									09 59				11 31		12 11					13 31				
Claverdon	d																								
Bearley	d																								
Wilmcote	d													11 49							13 43				
Stratford-upon-Avon	a													11 59							13 54				
Lapworth	a									10 05						12 16								14 16	
Dorridge	a									10 09		11 17				12 19	12 38			13 19		13 42		14 20	
Solihull	a									10 14		11 23				12 25	12 44			13 25		13 47		14 26	
Birmingham Moor Street	a									10 26		11 32				12 35	12 55			13 37		13 58		14 37	
Birmingham Snow Hill	a									10 39		11 45				12 44	13 03			13 46		14 08		14 45	
Rowley Regis	a																								
Cradley Heath	a																								
Stourbridge Junction 2	a																								
Kidderminster	a																								

For general notes see front of timetable
For details of catering facilities see Directory of Train Operators

§ London Underground Limited (Central Line) also operate services between South Ruislip and West Ruislip at frequent intervals

From 4 October a revised Chiltern Railways service will be in operation due to seasonal difficulties. Trains will arrive at their destination 3 minutes later than shown

Table 115

Sundays

London → High Wycombe, Aylesbury, Banbury, Stratford-upon-Avon, Birmingham Snow Hill and Kidderminster

Network Diagram - See first page of Table 114

	CH		CH	CH	CH	CH	CH		CH	CH	CH	CH	CH		CH	CH	CH	CH	CH		CH	CH	CH	CH
London Marylebone 10 ⊖ d	12 50		12 54	13 20	13 33	13 50	13 54		14 20	14 33	14 50	14 54	15 20		15 33	15 50	15 54	16 20	16 35		16 57	17 00	17 20	17 35
London Paddington 15 ⊖ d																								
Wembley Stadium d			13 03		13 42		14 03			14 42		15 03			15 42		16 03		16 44			17 09		17 44
Sudbury & Harrow Road d																								
Sudbury Hill Harrow d																								
Northolt Park d			13 08				14 08					15 08					16 08					17 14		
South Ruislip § ⊖ d			13 12				14 12					15 12					16 12					17 18		
West Ruislip 3 § ⊖ d			13 15				14 15					15 15					16 15					17 21		
Denham d			13 20				14 20					15 20					16 20					17 26		
Denham Golf Club d			13 22									15 22										17 28		
Gerrards Cross 1 d			13 25	13 41	13 56		14 24		14 41	14 56		15 25	15 41		15 56		16 24	16 41	16 58			17 31	17 41	17 58
Seer Green d			13 30				14 28					15 30					16 28					17 36		
Beaconsfield d			13 33	13 47	14 02		14 32		14 47	15 02		15 33	15 47		16 02		16 32	16 47	17 04			17 39	17 47	18 04
High Wycombe 1 d			13 39	13 54	14 08		14 38		14 54	15 08		15 39	15 54		16 08		16 38	16 54	17 10			17 45	17 54	18 10
Saunderton d			13 46				14 45					15 46					16 45					17 52		
Princes Risborough 2 d			13 51	14 04	14 18		14 50		15 04	15 18		15 51	16 04		16 18		16 50	17 04	17 20			17 57	18 04	18 20
Monks Risborough d			13 55				14 54					15 55					16 54					18 01		
Little Kimble d			13 58				14 57					15 58					16 57					18 04		
Aylesbury a			14 13				15 11					16 13					17 12					18 19		
Haddenham & Thame Parkway d				14 11	14 25				15 11	15 25			16 11		16 25			17 11	17 27				18 11	18 27
Bicester North 3 a	13 44			14 24	14 39	14 44			15 24	15 41	15 44		16 24		16 39	16 44		17 24	17 43		17 51		18 24	18 41
d	13 45			14 25	14 39	14 45			15 25		15 45		16 25		16 39	16 45		17 25			17 52		18 25	18 41
Kings Sutton d					14 53										16 53									18 53
Banbury d	14 02			14 41	15 01	15 05			15 40		16 02		16 41		17 01	17 05		17 41			18 09		18 41	19 01
Leamington Spa 8 d	14 22			15 01	15 21	15 25			15 59		16 22		17 01		17 21	17 25		18 01			18 29		19 01	19 21
Warwick d				15 05	15 25				16 03				17 05		17 25			18 05					19 05	19 25
Warwick Parkway d	14 27			15 09		15 31			16 06		16 27		17 09			17 31		18 09			18 34		19 09	
Hatton d					15 31				16 11						17 31			18 13						19 31
Claverdon d																								
Bearley d																								
Wilmcote d					15 43										17 43									19 43
Stratford-upon-Avon a					15 54										17 54									19 54
Lapworth a									16 16									18 18						
Dorridge a	14 38			15 19		15 41			16 20		16 38		17 19			17 42		18 22			18 45		19 19	
Solihull a	14 44			15 25		15 48			16 26		16 44		17 25			17 47		18 29			18 51		19 27	
Birmingham Moor Street a	14 55			15 35		15 58			16 36		16 55		17 37			17 59		18 41			19 01		19 38	
Birmingham Snow Hill a	15 03			15 49		16 06			16 49		17 03		17 46			18 07		18 49			19 10		19 46	
Rowley Regis a																								
Cradley Heath a																								
Stourbridge Junction 2 a																								
Kidderminster a																								

	CH	CH	CH		CH	CH	CH	CH	CH		CH	CH	CH	CH	CH		CH	CH	CH	CH	CH	CH		
London Marylebone 10 ⊖ d	17 57	18 00	18 20		18 35	18 57	19 00	19 22	19 35		19 57	20 00	20 20	20 50	21 10		21 40	22 00	22 10	22 45		23 45		
London Paddington 15 ⊖ d																								
Wembley Stadium d		18 09			18 44		19 09		19 44			20 09			21 19				22 19	22 54		23 54		
Sudbury & Harrow Road d																								
Sudbury Hill Harrow d																								
Northolt Park d		18 14					19 14					20 14			21 24				22 24	22 59		23 59		
South Ruislip § ⊖ d		18 18					19 18					20 18			21 28				22 28	23 03		00 03		
West Ruislip 3 § ⊖ d		18 21					19 21					20 21			21 31				22 31	23 06		00 06		
Denham d		18 26					19 26					20 26			21 36				22 36	23 11		00 11		
Denham Golf Club d							19 28								21 38					23 13		00 13		
Gerrards Cross 1 d		18 30	18 41		18 58		19 31	19 43	19 58			20 30	20 41	21 11	21 41		22 01		22 40	23 16		00 16		
Seer Green d		18 34					19 36					20 34			21 46				22 44	23 21		00 21		
Beaconsfield d		18 38	18 47		19 04		19 39	19 49	20 04			20 38	20 47	21 17	21 49		22 07		22 48	23 24		00 24		
High Wycombe 1 d		18 44	18 54		19 10		19 45	19 56	20 10			20 44	20 54	21 24	21 55		22 13		22 54	23 30		00 30		
Saunderton d		18 51					19 52					20 51			22 02				23 01	23 37		00 37		
Princes Risborough 2 d		18 56	19 04		19 20		19 57	20 07	20 20			20 56	21 04	21 34	22 07		22 24		23 06	23 43	23 48	00 43		
Monks Risborough d		19 00					20 01					21 00			22 11				23 10		23 51			
Little Kimble d		19 03					20 04					21 03			22 14				23 13		23 55			
Aylesbury a		19 17					20 19					21 18			22 29				23 27		00 06			
Haddenham & Thame Parkway d			19 11		19 27			20 14	20 27				21 11	21 41			22 31			23 50		00 50		
Bicester North 3 a	18 51		19 24		19 40	19 52		20 27	20 41		20 52		21 24	21 54			22 47	22 51		00 03		01 03		
d	18 52		19 25		19 41	19 52		20 27	20 41		20 52		21 25	21 55				22 51		00 04		01 04		
Kings Sutton d									20 53											00 16				
Banbury d	19 09		19 41		20a02	20 09		20 44	21a04		21 09		21 41	22 11				23 06		00a25		01a24		
Leamington Spa 8 d	19 29		20 03			20 29		21 03			21 29		22 01	22 31				23 24						
Warwick d			20 08					21 08					22 05	22 35				23 28						
Warwick Parkway d	19 34		20 11			20 34		21 11			21 34		22 09	22 39				23 32						
Hatton d														22 43										
Claverdon d																								
Bearley d																								
Wilmcote d																								
Stratford-upon-Avon a																								
Lapworth a			20 20											22 48										
Dorridge a	19 45		20 23			20 45		21 22			21 45		22 20	22 52				23 43						
Solihull a	19 51		20 30			20 51		21 29			21 51		22 25	22 59				23 47						
Birmingham Moor Street a	20 01		20 42			21 01		21 40			22 01		22 37	23 10				23 58						
Birmingham Snow Hill a	20 10		20 53			21 10		21 48			22 10		22 45	23 18				00 08						
Rowley Regis a																								
Cradley Heath a																								
Stourbridge Junction 2 a																								
Kidderminster a																								

For general notes see front of timetable
For details of catering facilities see Directory of Train Operators

§ London Underground Limited (Central Line) also operate services between South Ruislip and West Ruislip at frequent intervals

From 4 October a revised Chiltern Railways service will be in operation due to seasonal difficulties. Trains will arrive at their destination 3 minutes later than shown

Kidderminster, Birmingham Snow Hill, Stratford-upon-Avon, Banbury, Aylesbury and High Wycombe → London

Network Diagram - See first page of Table 114

Miles	Miles	Miles			CH	CH	CH	CH	CH	CH	CH	CH	CH	CH	CH	CH	CH	CH	CH	LM	CH	CH	CH	CH
					A	B						⊼						◇ ⊼						
—	—	—	**Kidderminster**	d																				
—	—	—	**Stourbridge Junction** 2	d																				
—	—	—	Cradley Heath	d																				
—	—	—	Rowley Regis	d																				
0	—	—	**Birmingham Snow Hill**	d														05 43		05 55				
3/4	—	—	**Birmingham Moor Street**	d														05 46		05 58				
7 1/4	—	—	Solihull	d														05 56		06 13				
10 1/2	—	—	Dorridge	d														06 01		06 21				
13	—	—	Lapworth	d																06 25				
—	—	0	**Stratford-upon-Avon**	d															06 10					
—	—	2 3/4	Wilmcote	d															06 14	06a42				
—	—	4 1/4	Bearley	d															06 20					
—	—	7 1/2	Claverdon	d															06 25					
17 1/4	—	9 1/4	Hatton	d															06 31					
20	—	12	Warwick Parkway	d								05 40						06 12						
21 1/4	—	13 1/4	Warwick	d														06 15	06 38					
23 1/4	—	15 1/4	**Leamington Spa** 8	d								05 45						06 20	06a45					
43 1/4	—	—	**Banbury**	d				05 24				06 03					06 25	06 38						06 53
46 1/4	—	—	Kings Sutton	d				05 28									06 29							
57 1/4	—	—	**Bicester North** 3	a				05 40				06 17					06 42	06 53						07 07
—	—	—		d				05 40		05 55		06 17					06 42	06 54					06 59	07 10
70 1/4	—	—	Haddenham & Thame Parkway	d				05 53		06 08		06 30					06 55						07 12	07 23
—	0	—	**Aylesbury**	d	05 02	05 05	05 35		05 49				06 19		06 29									
—	4 1/2	—	Little Kimble	d	05 10	05 13			05 57						06 37									
—	6	—	Monks Risborough	d	05 14	05 17			06 01						06 41									
76	7 1/2	—	**Princes Risborough** 2	d	05 18	05 20	05 48	06 01	06 05	06 15		06 36	06 32		06 45		07 03						07 19	07 30
79 1/4	—	—	Saunderton	d	05 23	05 25			06 10						06 50								07 24	
84 1/4	—	—	**High Wycombe** 1	d	05 30	05 32	05 58	06 12	06 17	06 25	06 29		06 50	06 55	07 02	07 08	07 13					07 21	07 31	
89	—	—	Beaconsfield	d	05 37	05 38	06 04	06 18	06 23		06 35		06 56	07 01	07 08		07 20					07 27	07 37	
90 3/4	—	—	Seer Green	d	05 40	05 41	06 07				06 38					07 16						07 30		
93 1/4	—	—	Gerrards Cross 1	d	05 45	05 45	06 11	06 24	06 28		06 42		07 01	07 06	07 14	07 20						07 34	07 43	
95	—	—	Denham Golf Club	d	05 48	05 48			06 31					07 09										
96	—	—	Denham	d	05 50	05 50	06 15				06 46			07 12								07 38		
98 3/4	—	0	West Ruislip 3 §	⊖ d	05 55	05 55			06 39		06 50		07 08								07 36			
100 1/2	—	—	South Ruislip §	⊖ d	05 58	05 58		06 52	06 43					07 18								07 44		
102 1/4	—	—	Northolt Park	d	06 02	06 02			06 46		06 55		07 13								07 41			
103 3/4	—	—	Sudbury Hill Harrow	d					06 49												07 43			
104	—	—	Sudbury & Harrow Road	d					06 51												07 46			
105 1/2	—	—	Wembley Stadium	d	06 07	06 07		06 39	06 54		07 00											07 51		
—	—	12	**London Paddington** 15	⊖ a																				
112	—	—	**London Marylebone** 10	⊖ a	06 24	06 21	06 39	06 51	07 11	06 59	07 15	07 18	07 29	07 36	07 42	07 46	07 50	07 53			08 01	08 05	08 08	08 11

		CH	CH	CH	CH	CH	CH	CH	CH	CH	CH	CH	CH	CH	CH	CH	CH	CH	CH	CH	CH	CH	CH
		⊼							◇ ⊼					⊼				⊼	◇ ⊼				⊼
Kidderminster	d								06 10					06 30					06 56				07 30
Stourbridge Junction 2	d								06 18					06 39					07 07				07 40
Cradley Heath	d								06 24					06 44					07 14				07 45
Rowley Regis	d								06 30					06 50					07 22				07 53
Birmingham Snow Hill	d	06 14							06 50					07 14					07 45				08 12
Birmingham Moor Street	d	06 17							06 53					07 17					07 48				08 15
Solihull	d	06 27							07 03					07 28					07 58				08 25
Dorridge	d	06 32							07 08					07 33					08 03				08 30
Lapworth	d																		08 07				
Stratford-upon-Avon	d							06 46										07 36					
Wilmcote	d																	07 40					
Bearley	d																	07 46					
Claverdon	d																	07 51					
Hatton	d							07 03										07 56	08 13				
Warwick Parkway	d	06 44						07 09	07 19					07 45					08 19				08 41
Warwick	d							07 13						07 48				08 05	08 23				08 44
Leamington Spa 8	d	06 49						07 18	07 24					07 52				08 09	08 27				08 49
Banbury	d	07 07				07 18		07 36	07 42				07 51	08 10				08 28	08 45				09 09
Kings Sutton	d																	08 33					
Bicester North 3	a					07 31		07 50					08 05	08 26				08 46	08 59				
	d					07 33	07 40	07 51					08 05	08 26				08 47	08 59			09 11	
Haddenham & Thame Parkway	d					07 46	07 53	08 03					08 16	08 37				08 58	09 11			09 24	
Aylesbury	d				07 28					07 55							08 40						
Little Kimble	d				07 36					08 03							08 48						
Monks Risborough	d				07 40					08 07							08 52						
Princes Risborough 2	d				07 44	07 53	07 59			08a13			08 23			08 55	08a59	09 06				09 32	
Saunderton	d						08 04						08 29			09 00						09 36	
High Wycombe 1	d		07 45	07 50	07 55		08 11					08 31	08 36		08 55	09 07		09 16			09 35	09 43	09 48
Beaconsfield	d			07 56	08 01		08 17					08 37	08 42		09 01	09 13		09 22			09 41	09 49	
Seer Green	d				08 05								08 46			09 16					09 44		
Gerrards Cross 1	d		07 54	08 02			08 22				08 17	08 43	08 49		09 06	09 20		09 27		09 42	09 48	09 54	
Denham Golf Club	d			08 05											09 09								
Denham	d			08 07		08 16					08 21	08 47			09 12					09 46			
West Ruislip 3 §	⊖ d				08 14						08c40				09 16						09 55		
South Ruislip §	⊖ d			08 13									08 57		09 21					09 52			
Northolt Park	d		08 04								08 45					09 28				09 55			
Sudbury Hill Harrow	d										08 47				09 24								
Sudbury & Harrow Road	d										08 50				09 26								
Wembley Stadium	d		08 09	08 20		08 26						08 58	09 04		09 29						10 03		
London Paddington 15	⊖ a																						
London Marylebone 10	⊖ a	08 16	08 25	08 33	08 36	08 40	08 48	08 51	08 54		09 08	09 13	09 17	09 25	09 43	09 47		09 55	10 01	10 13	10 17	10 21	10 25

For general notes see front of timetable
For details of catering facilities see Directory of Train Operators

§ London Underground Limited (Central Line) also operate services between South Ruislip and West Ruislip at frequent intervals

A From 5 October
B Until 2 October
c Arr. 0824

From 5 October a revised Chiltern Railways service will be in operation due to seasonal difficulties. Trains will arrive at their destination 3 minutes later than shown

Kidderminster, Birmingham Snow Hill, Stratford-upon-Avon, Banbury, Aylesbury and High Wycombe → London

Network Diagram - See first page of Table 114

		CH ◇	CH	CH	CH	CH	CH ◇ 🍴	CH	CH	CH ◇	CH		CH	CH	CH ◇	CH	CH ◇	CH ◇	CH	CH	CH	CH ◇	CH	CH	CH ◇
Kidderminster	d						08 10																		
Stourbridge Junction 2	d						08 23																		
Cradley Heath	d						08 28																		
Rowley Regis	d						08 34																		
Birmingham Snow Hill ⛴	d						08 52			09 12					09 52			10 12				10 52			11 12
Birmingham Moor Street	d						08 55			09 15					09 55			10 15				10 55			11 15
Solihull	d						09 05			09 25					10 05			10 25				11 05			11 25
Dorridge	d						09 10			09 30					10 10			10 30				11 10			11 30
Lapworth	d									09 34								10 34							
Stratford-upon-Avon	d													09 42											
Wilmcote	d													09 46											
Bearley	d													09 52											
Claverdon	d																								
Hatton	d									09 40				10 01				10 40							
Warwick Parkway	d						09 21			09 45				10 06	10 21			10 45				11 21			11 41
Warwick	d						09 24			09 49				10 10	10 24			10 49				11 24			11 45
Leamington Spa 8	d						09 29			09 54				10 14	10 29			10 54				11 29			11 52
Banbury	d	09 15					09 47			10 12				10 32	10 47			11 12				11 47			12 09
Kings Sutton	d													10 37											
Bicester North 3	a	09 28					10 03			10 28				10 48	11 03			11 28				12 03			12 24
	d	09 29				09 47	10 04			10 28				10 48	11 04		11 13	11 28			11 44	12 04			12 24
Haddenham & Thame Parkway	d	09 42				10 00				10 40				11 00			11 26	11 40			11 57				12 36
Aylesbury	d		09 40								10 38								11 38						
Little Kimble	d		09 48								10 46								11 46						
Monks Risborough	d		09 52								10 50								11 50						
Princes Risborough 2	d	09 49	09a59			10 06			10 32	10 47	10a56			11 06			11 33	11 47	11a56		12 04			12 33	12 43
Saunderton	d								10 36								11 38							12 38	
High Wycombe 1	d	09 59			10 04	10 17		10 32	10 43	10 57			11 02	11 17		11 32	11 44	11 57		12 02	12 15		12 32	12 44	12 53
Beaconsfield	d				10 10	10 23		10 38	10 49				11 08	11 23		11 38	11 51			12 08	12 21		12 38	12 51	
Seer Green	d				10 13			10 41					11 11			11 41				12 11			12 41		
Gerrards Cross 1	d			10 03	10 17	10 29		10 45	10 54				11 15	11 29		11 45	11 56			12 15	12 26		12 45	12 56	
Denham Golf Club	d			10 06				10 48								11 48							12 48		
Denham	d			10 08	10 21			10 50					11 19			11 50				12 19			12 50		
West Ruislip 3 §	⊖ d			10 12				10 55								11 55							12 55		
South Ruislip §	⊖ d				10 27								11 25							12 25					
Northolt Park	d				10 30			11 00					11 28			12 00				12 28			13 00		
Sudbury Hill Harrow	d				10 33								11 31							12 31					
Sudbury & Harrow Road	d																								
Wembley Stadium	d				10 37			11 05					11 35			12 05				12 35			13 05		
London Paddington 15	⊖ a			10 41																					
London Marylebone 10	⊖ a	10 36			10 50	10 55	10 58	11 19	11 22	11 30			11 48	11 57	12 02	12 18	12 21	12 30		12 48	12 51	12 59	13 18	13 21	13 29

		CH		CH	CH	CH	CH	CH	CH ◇	CH	CH	CH	CH	CH	CH		CH ◇	CH	CH	CH	CH	CH	CH ◇	CH ◇	CH
Kidderminster	d																								
Stourbridge Junction 2	d																								
Cradley Heath	d																								
Rowley Regis	d																								
Birmingham Snow Hill ⛴	d					11 52			12 12				12 52				13 12				13 52			14 12	
Birmingham Moor Street	d					11 55			12 15				12 55				13 15				13 55			14 15	
Solihull	d					12 05			12 25				13 05				13 25				14 05			14 25	
Dorridge	d					12 10			12 30				13 10				13 30				14 10			14 30	
Lapworth	d								12 34															14 34	
Stratford-upon-Avon	d				11 40															13 40					
Wilmcote	d																								
Bearley	d				11 48																				
Claverdon	d																			13 51					
Hatton	d				11 57				12 40											13 57				14 40	
Warwick Parkway	d					12 21			12 45				13 21				13 41				14 21			14 45	
Warwick	d				12 03	12 24			12 49				13 24				13 45			14 03	14 24			14 49	
Leamington Spa 8	d				12 08	12 29			12 54				13 29				13 52			14 08	14 29			14 54	
Banbury	d				12 27	12 47			13 12				13 47				14 09			14 27	14 47			15 12	
Kings Sutton	d				12 32															14 32					
Bicester North 3	a				12 44	13 03			13 28				14 03				14 24			14 43	15 03			15 28	
	d				12 44	13 04		13 13	13 28			13 44	14 04				14 24			14 44	15 04		15 13	15 28	
Haddenham & Thame Parkway	d				12 57			13 26	13 40			13 57					14 36			14 57			15 26	15 40	
Aylesbury	d	12 38									13 44							14 38							15 38
Little Kimble	d	12 46									13 52							14 46							15 46
Monks Risborough	d	12 50									13 56							14 50							15 50
Princes Risborough 2	d	12a56			13 06			13 33	13 47		14a02	14 04			14 33		14 43	14a56		15 06			15 33	15 47	15a56
Saunderton	d							13 38							14 38								15 38		
High Wycombe 1	d			13 02	13 17		13 32	13 44	13 57	14 02		14 15		14 32	14 44		14 53		15 02	15 16		15 32	15 44	15 57	
Beaconsfield	d			13 08	13 23		13 38	13 51		14 08		14 21		14 38	14 51				15 08	15 22		15 38	15 51		
Seer Green	d			13 11			13 41			14 11				14 41					15 11			15 41			
Gerrards Cross 1	d			13 15	13 29		13 45	13 56		14 15		14 26		14 45	14 56				15 15	15 27		15 45	15 56		
Denham Golf Club	d						13 48							14 48								15 48			
Denham	d			13 19			13 50			14 19				14 50					15 19			15 50			
West Ruislip 3 §	⊖ d						13 55							14 55								15 55			
South Ruislip §	⊖ d			13 25						14 25									15 25						
Northolt Park	d			13 28			14 00			14 28				15 00					15 28			16 00			
Sudbury Hill Harrow	d			13 31						14 31									15 31						
Sudbury & Harrow Road	d																								
Wembley Stadium	d			13 35			14 05			14 35				15 05					15 35			16 05			
London Paddington 15	⊖ a																								
London Marylebone 10	⊖ a			13 49	13 56	13 59	14 18	14 21	14 30	14 48		14 51	14 59	15 18	15 21		15 28		15 48	15 53	16 00	16 19	16 22	16 31	

For general notes see front of timetable
For details of catering facilities see Directory of Train Operators

§ London Underground Limited (Central Line) also operate services between South Ruislip and West Ruislip at frequent intervals

From 5 October a revised Chiltern Railways service will be in operation due to seasonal difficulties. Trains will arrive at their destination 3 minutes later than shown

Kidderminster, Birmingham Snow Hill, Stratford-upon-Avon, Banbury, Aylesbury and High Wycombe → London

Network Diagram - See first page of Table 114

		CH	CH ◇	CH	CH	CH		CH ◇	CH	CH	CH	CH ◇	CH	CH	CH ◇	CH	CH	CH	CH		CH	CH	CH	CH	CH
Kidderminster	d																								
Stourbridge Junction 2	d																								
Cradley Heath	d																								
Rowley Regis	d																								
Birmingham Snow Hill	d			14 52				15 12					15 52				16 12						16 52		
Birmingham Moor Street	d			14 55				15 15					15 55				16 15						16 55		
Solihull	d			15 05				15 25					16 05				16 25						17 05		
Dorridge	d			15 10				15 30					16 10				16 30						17 10		
Lapworth	d																16 34								
Stratford-upon-Avon	d											15 40													
Wilmcote	d																								
Bearley	d											15 48													
Claverdon	d																								
Hatton	d											15 57					16 40								
Warwick Parkway	d			15 21				15 41					16 21				16 45						17 20		
Warwick	d			15 24				15 44				16 03	16 24				16 49						17 23		
Leamington Spa 8	d			15 29				15 49				16 08	16 29				16 54						17 28		
Banbury	d			15 47				16 07				16 27	16 47				17 12						17 46		17 51
Kings Sutton	d											16 32													17 56
Bicester North 3	a			16 03				16 23				16 43	17 03				17 28						18 02		18 09
	d		15 44	16 04				16 24				16 44	17 04		17 17		17 28						18 03		18 10
Haddenham & Thame Parkway	d		15 57					16 36				16 57			17 30		17 40						18 14		18 22
Aylesbury	d								16 39							17 23						18 10			
Little Kimble	d								16 47							17 31						18 18			
Monks Risborough	d								16 51							17 35						18 22			
Princes Risborough 2	d		16 04			16 36		16 43	16a57			17 06			17 37	17a42	17 46		17 55		18 15	18a28			18 30
Saunderton	d					16 40						17 12			17 42										18 35
High Wycombe 1	d	16 02	16 15		16 32	16 47		16 53			17 05	17 19	17 26	17 36	17 48		17 56	18 01	18 06		18 25		18 30	18 35	18 41
Beaconsfield	d	16 08	16 21		16 38	16 53					17 11	17 25		17 42	17 55			18 07	18 12		18 31			18 41	18 47
Seer Green	d	16 11			16 41						17 14			17 45					18 15						18 51
Gerrards Cross 1	d	16 15	16 26		16 45	16 59				17 09	17 18	17 30		17 49	18 00			18 13	18 19		18 36			18 46	18 55
Denham Golf Club	d				16 48					17 12									18 22						
Denham	d	16 19			16 50					17 14	17 22			17 53					18 24					18 50	
West Ruislip 3 §	⊖ d				16 55						17 26			17 57				18 19						18 55	
South Ruislip §	⊖ d	16 25								17 20									18 30						
Northolt Park	d	16 28			17 00						17 32			18 02				18 24						19 00	
Sudbury Hill Harrow	d	16 31								17 24								18 27							
Sudbury & Harrow Road	d																								
Wembley Stadium	d	16 35			17 05					17 28	17 37			18 07				18 31						19 05	
London Paddington 15	⊖ a																								
London Marylebone 10	⊖ a	16 49	16 53	17 01	17 21	17 25		17 31		17 42	17 53	17 56	18 05	18 24	18 28		18 33	18 46	18 49		19 02		19 08	19 18	19 21

		CH ◇	CH	CH	CH	CH	CH	CH	CH ◇	CH		CH ◇	CH	CH	CH	CH ◇	CH	CH ◇	CH	CH ◇	CH	CH	CH		
Kidderminster	d																								
Stourbridge Junction 2	d																								
Cradley Heath	d																								
Rowley Regis	d																								
Birmingham Snow Hill	d	17 10			17 52				18 12					19 12				20 12		21 15					
Birmingham Moor Street	d	17 13			17 55				18 15					19 15				20 15		21 18					
Solihull	d	17 23			18 05				18 25					19 25				20 25		21 27					
Dorridge	d	17 30			18 12				18 30					19 32				20 32		21 33					
Lapworth	d	17 34							18 34					19 36				20 36		21 37					
Stratford-upon-Avon	d			17 40												19 43	20 00						23 00		
Wilmcote	d			17 44													20 04								
Bearley	d			17 50																					
Claverdon	d			17 55												19 54									
Hatton	d	17 40		18 01					18 40					19 42		19 59	20 17	20 42		21 42					
Warwick Parkway	d	17 45			18 23				18 45					19 47		20 06		20 47		21 47					
Warwick	d	17 49		18 08	18 26				18 49					19 50		20 09	20 23	20 50		21 51			23 21		
Leamington Spa 8	d	17 54		18 12	18 30				18 54					19 54		20 14	20a33	20 54		21 55			23 25		
Banbury	d	18 12		18 32	18 48				19 12			19 35		20 12		20 32		21 12		22 14			23a43		
Kings Sutton	d								19 17							20 37				22 19					
Bicester North 3	a	18 27		18 48	19 04				19 30			19 49		20 27		20 50		21 27		22 30					
	d	18 28		18 48	19 04			19 20	19 30			19 50		20 27		20 50		21 27		22 30	22 37				
Haddenham & Thame Parkway	d	18 40		19 02				19 33	19 42			20 03		20 39		21 03		21 39		22 41					
Aylesbury	d						19 14						20 16						21 37			23 00			
Little Kimble	d												20 24						21 45			23 08			
Monks Risborough	d						19 25						20 28						21 49			23 12			
Princes Risborough 2	d	18 47		19 10		19 25	19a33	19 40	19 49			20 10	20 31	20 46		21 10		21 46	21 52	22 47	22 52	23 15			
Saunderton	d							19 45					20 36						21 57		22 57				
High Wycombe 1	d	18 57	19 07	19 20	19 28	19 36		19 51	19 59	20 06		20 20	20 43	20 56	21 06	21 20		21 56	22 06	22 59	23 04	23 25			
Beaconsfield	d		19 13	19 26		19 42		19 58		20 12		20 26	20 49		21 12	21 26			22 12		23 10	23 31			
Seer Green	d		19 16			19 45				20 15					21 15				22 15		23 13				
Gerrards Cross 1	d		19 20	19 31		19 49		20 03		20 19		20 31	20 54		21 19	21 31			22 19		23 17	23 37			
Denham Golf Club	d		19 23							20 22					21 22				22 22		23 20				
Denham	d		19 25			19 53				20 24					21 24				22 24		23 23				
West Ruislip 3 §	⊖ d					19 57				20 29					21 29				22 29		23 27				
South Ruislip §	⊖ d		19 31							20 32					21 32				22 32		23 31				
Northolt Park	d		19 35			20 02				20 36					21 36				22 36		23 34				
Sudbury Hill Harrow	d		19 37																						
Sudbury & Harrow Road	d																								
Wembley Stadium	d		19 41			20 07				20 41				21 18	21 41			22 18	22 41	23 19	23 39	23 50			
London Paddington 15	⊖ a																								
London Marylebone 10	⊖ a	19 33	19 55	19 58	20 06	20 21		20 29	20 35	20 55		20 58	21 19	21 32	21 54	21 57		22 32	22 55	23 33	23 53	00 04			

For general notes see front of timetable
For details of catering facilities see Directory of Train Operators

§ London Underground Limited (Central Line) also operate services between South Ruislip and West Ruislip at frequent intervals

From 5 October a revised Chiltern Railways service will be in operation due to seasonal difficulties. Trains will arrive at their destination 3 minutes later than shown

Table 115

Saturdays

Kidderminster, Birmingham Snow Hill, Stratford-upon-Avon, Banbury, Aylesbury and High Wycombe → London

Network Diagram - See first page of Table 114

		CH	CH	CH	CH	CH	CH	CH	CH	CH	CH	CH	CH	CH	CH	CH	CH	CH	CH ◇	CH	CH ◇	CH
Kidderminster	d									06 37			07 14						08 13			
Stourbridge Junction 2	d									06 45			07 22						08 26			
Cradley Heath	d									06 50			07 27						08 32			
Rowley Regis	d									06 56			07 33						08 37			
Birmingham Snow Hill	d						06 12	06 37		07 12			07 52		08 12				08 52		09 12	
Birmingham Moor Street	d						06 15	06 40		07 15			07 55		08 15				08 55		09 15	
Solihull	d						06 25	06 50		07 25			08 05		08 25				09 05		09 25	
Dorridge	d						06 31	06 55		07 31			08 11		08 32				09 11		09 31	
Lapworth	d									07 35					08 36						09 35	
Stratford-upon-Avon	d											07 35										
Wilmcote	d																					
Bearley	d																					
Claverdon	d											07 47										
Hatton	d									07 41		07 57			08 42							
Warwick Parkway	d						06 41	07 06		07 45			08 22		08 46				09 22		09 44	
Warwick	d						06 45	07 09		07 48		08 04	08 25		08 49				09 25		09 47	
Leamington Spa 8	d						06 49	07 14		07 53		08 09	08 30		08 53				09 30		09 52	
Banbury	d			06 05	06 34		07 07	07 34		08 13		08 29	08 49		09 13			09 28	09 49		10 13	
Kings Sutton	d			06 09								08 33						09 32				
Bicester North 3	a			06 22	06 49		07 23	07 49		08 28		08 45			09 28			09 44			10 27	
	d			06 22	06 49		07 24	07 49		08 28		08 46			09 28			09 46			10 28	
Haddenham & Thame Parkway	d			06 35	07 01		07 35	08 01		08 40		08 59			09 40			09 59			10 40	
Aylesbury	d	05 15	05 56			06 56			07 56					09 08			09 48					10 38
Little Kimble	d	05 23	06 04			07 04			08 04					09 16			09 56					10 46
Monks Risborough	d	05 27	06 08			07 08			08 08					09 20			10 00					10 50
Princes Risborough 2	d	05 30	06 11	06 43		07 11	07 43		08 11	08 47		09 06		09 23	09 47		10a06	10 09			10 47	10a59
Saunderton	d	05 35	06 16			07 16			08 16					09 28				10 13				
High Wycombe 1	d	05 42	06 23	06 53		07 23	07 53		08 23	08 57	09 04	09 18		09 34	09 57	10 04		10 20		10 34	10 57	
Beaconsfield	d	05 48	06 29	06 59		07 29	07 59		08 29		09 10	09 24		09 40		10 10		10 26		10 40		
Seer Green	d	05 51	06 32			07 32			08 32		09 13			09 43		10 13				10 43		
Gerrards Cross 1	d	05 55	06 36	07 04		07 36	08 04		08 36		09 17	09 30		09 47		10 17		10 32		10 47		
Denham Golf Club	d	05 58	06 39			07 39			08 39					09 50						10 50		
Denham	d	06 00	06 41			07 41			08 41		09 21			09 52		10 21				10 52		
West Ruislip 3 §	⊖ d	06 05	06 46			07 46			08 46					09 57						10 57		
South Ruislip §	⊖ d	06 08	06 49			07 49			08 49		09 27					10 27						
Northolt Park	d	06 12	06 53			07 53			08 53		09 30			10 02		10 30				11 02		
Sudbury Hill Harrow	d																					
Sudbury & Harrow Road	d																					
Wembley Stadium	d	06 17	06 58	07 17		07 58			08 58		09 35			10 07		10 35				11 07		
London Paddington 15	⊖ a																					
London Marylebone 10	⊖ a	06 31	07 11	07 31	07 47	08 11	08 29	08 47	09 12	09 30	09 50	09 55	10 01	10 23	10 34	10 50		10 58	11 02	11 20	11 32	

For general notes see front of timetable
For details of catering facilities see Directory of Train Operators

§ London Underground Limited (Central Line) also operate services between South Ruislip and West Ruislip at frequent intervals

From 10 October a revised Chiltern Railways service will be in operation due to seasonal difficulties. Trains will arrive at their destination 3 minutes later than shown

Kidderminster, Birmingham Snow Hill, Stratford-upon-Avon, Banbury, Aylesbury and High Wycombe → London

Network Diagram - See first page of Table 114

		CH		CH	CH ◇	CH	CH ◇	CH		CH	CH	CH ◇	CH	CH ◇		CH	CH	CH	CH	CH		CH	CH	CH	CH
Kidderminster	d				09 03																				
Stourbridge Junction 2	d				09 15																				
Cradley Heath	d				09 21																				
Rowley Regis	d				09 26																				
Birmingham Snow Hill	d				09 52		10 12					10 52		11 12				11 52		12 12				12 52	
Birmingham Moor Street	d				09 55		10 15					10 55		11 15				11 55		12 15				12 55	
Solihull	d				10 05		10 25					11 05		11 25				12 05		12 25				13 05	
Dorridge	d				10 11		10 31					11 11		11 31				12 11		12 31				13 11	
Lapworth	d						10 35													12 35					
Stratford-upon-Avon	d			09 38													11 38								
Wilmcote	d			09 42													11 42								
Bearley	d			09 48													11 48								
Claverdon	d			09 53																					
Hatton	d			09 57			10 41										11 57			12 41					
Warwick Parkway	d				10 22		10 45					11 22		11 41				12 22		12 45				13 22	
Warwick	d			10 04	10 25		10 48					11 25		11 45			12 04	12 25		12 48				13 25	
Leamington Spa 8	d			10 09	10 30		10 53					11 30		11 49			12 09	12 30		12 53				13 30	
Banbury	d			10 29	10 49		11 13				11 29	11 49		12 07			12 29	12 49		13 13				13 49	
Kings Sutton	d										11 33						12 33								
Bicester North 3	a			10 45	11 04		11 28				11 45	12 04		12 23			12 45	13 04		13 27				14 03	
	d			10 46	11 04		11 28				11 46	12 04		12 24			12 46	13 04		13 28			13 46	14 04	
Haddenham & Thame Parkway	d			10 59			11 40				11 59			12 35			12 59			13 40			13 59		
Aylesbury	d							11 38								12 38						13 38			
Little Kimble	d							11 46								12 46						13 46			
Monks Risborough	d							11 50								12 50						13 50			
Princes Risborough 2	d			11 06			11 47	11a56			12 06			12 43		12a56	13 06			13 47		13a56	14 06		
Saunderton	d			11 11							12 11						13 11						14 11		
High Wycombe 1	d	11 04		11 18		11 34	11 57			12 04	12 18		12 34	12 53			13 18		13 38	13 57			14 18		14 38
Beaconsfield	d	11 10		11 24		11 40				12 10	12 24		12 40				13 24		13 44				14 24		14 44
Seer Green	d	11 13				11 43				12 13			12 43						13 47						14 47
Gerrards Cross 1	d	11 17		11 30		11 47				12 17	12 30		12 47				13 30		13 51				14 30		14 51
Denham Golf Club	d					11 50							12 50						13 54						14 54
Denham	d	11 21				11 52				12 21			12 52						13 57						14 57
West Ruislip 3 §	⊖ d					11 57							12 57						14 01						15 01
South Ruislip §	⊖ d	11 27								12 27			13 00						14 05						15 05
Northolt Park	d	11 30				12 02				12 30			13 04						14 08						15 08
Sudbury Hill Harrow	d																								
Sudbury & Harrow Road	d																								
Wembley Stadium	d	11 35				12 07				12 35			13 09				13 43		14 13				14 43		15 13
London Paddington 15	⊖ a																								
London Marylebone 10	⊖ a	11 50		11 56	11 59	12 21	12 30			12 48	12 58	13 01	13 23	13 26			13 58	14 01	14 28	14 32			14 58	15 01	15 27

		CH	CH	CH		CH	CH	CH	CH	CH		CH	CH	CH	CH	CH		CH	CH	CH	CH	CH		CH	CH
Kidderminster	d																								
Stourbridge Junction 2	d																								
Cradley Heath	d																								
Rowley Regis	d																								
Birmingham Snow Hill	d	13 12				13 52		14 12					14 57		15 12					15 52		16 12			
Birmingham Moor Street	d	13 15				13 55		14 15					14 55		15 15					15 55		16 15			
Solihull	d	13 25				14 05		14 25					15 05		15 25					16 05		16 25			
Dorridge	d	13 31				14 11		14 31					15 11		15 31					16 11		16 31			
Lapworth	d							14 35														16 35			
Stratford-upon-Avon	d			13 40															15 39						
Wilmcote	d																		15 43						
Bearley	d																								
Claverdon	d																		15 52						
Hatton	d			13 57				14 41											15 57			16 41			
Warwick Parkway	d	13 41				14 22		14 45					15 22		15 41					16 22		16 45			
Warwick	d	13 45		14 04		14 25		14 48					15 25		15 45				16 04	16 25		16 48			
Leamington Spa 8	d	13 49		14 09		14 30		14 53					15 30		15 49				16 09	16 30		16 53			
Banbury	d	14 07		14 29		14 49		15 13					15 49		16 07				16 29	16 49		17 13			
Kings Sutton	d			14 33															16 33						
Bicester North 3	a	14 23		14 45		15 03		15 28					16 03		16 23				16 45	17 03		17 28			
	d	14 24		14 46		15 04		15 28				15 46	16 04		16 24				16 46	17 04		17 28			
Haddenham & Thame Parkway	d	14 35		14 59				15 40				15 59			16 35				16 59			17 40			
Aylesbury	d		14 38						15 38							16 38								17 38	
Little Kimble	d		14 46						15 46							16 46								17 46	
Monks Risborough	d		14 50						15 50							16 50								17 50	
Princes Risborough 2	d	14 43	14a56	15 06				15 47	15a56			16 06			16 43	16a56			17 06			17 47		17a56	
Saunderton	d			15 11								16 11							17 11						
High Wycombe 1	d	14 53		15 18			15 34	15 57		16 04		16 18		16 34	16 53			17 04	17 18		17 34	17 57			18 04
Beaconsfield	d			15 24			15 40			16 10		16 24		16 40				17 10	17 24		17 40				18 10
Seer Green	d						15 43			16 13				16 43				17 13			17 43				18 13
Gerrards Cross 1	d			15 30			15 47			16 17		16 30		16 47				17 17	17 30		17 47				18 17
Denham Golf Club	d						15 50							16 50							17 50				
Denham	d						15 52			16 21				16 52				17 21			17 52				18 21
West Ruislip 3 §	⊖ d						15 57							16 57							17 57				
South Ruislip §	⊖ d						16 00			16 27								17 27							18 27
Northolt Park	d						16 04			16 30				17 02				17 30			18 02				18 30
Sudbury Hill Harrow	d																								
Sudbury & Harrow Road	d																								
Wembley Stadium	d			15 43			16 09			16 35				17 07				17 35			18 07				18 35
London Paddington 15	⊖ a																								
London Marylebone 10	⊖ a	15 30		15 58		16 01	16 22	16 37		16 48		16 55	16 59	17 20	17 29			17 49	17 58	18 01	18 20	18 32			18 48

For general notes see front of timetable
For details of catering facilities see Directory of Train Operators

§ London Underground Limited (Central Line) also operate services between South Ruislip and West Ruislip at frequent intervals

From 10 October a revised Chiltern Railways service will be in operation due to seasonal difficulties. Trains will arrive at their destination 3 minutes later than shown

Table 115

Saturdays

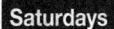

Kidderminster, Birmingham Snow Hill, Stratford-upon-Avon, Banbury, Aylesbury and High Wycombe → London

Network Diagram - See first page of Table 114

		CH	CH	CH	CH	CH	CH	CH	CH	CH	CH	CH	CH	CH	CH	CH	CH	CH	CH	CH
														◇	◇	◇			◇	
Kidderminster	d																			
Stourbridge Junction 2	d																			
Cradley Heath	d																			
Rowley Regis	d																			
Birmingham Snow Hill	d		16 52		17 12				17 52			18 12		19 10		20 10			21 11	
Birmingham Moor Street	d		16 55		17 15				17 55			18 15		19 13		20 13			21 14	
Solihull	d		17 05		17 25				18 05			18 25		19 23		20 23			21 23	
Dorridge	d		17 11		17 31				18 11			18 32		19 30		20 30			21 30	
Lapworth	d				17 35							18 36		19 34		20 34			21 34	
Stratford-upon-Avon	d							17 36							19 53		21 15			
Wilmcote	d							17 40												
Bearley	d							17 46							20 01					
Claverdon	d							17 51												
Hatton	d				17 41			17 57				18 42		19 40	20 10	20 40	21a33		21 40	
Warwick Parkway	d		17 22		17 45				18 22			18 46		19 44	20 16	20 44			21 44	
Warwick	d		17 25		17 48			18 04	18 25			18 49		19 47	20 19	20 47			21 47	
Leamington Spa 8	d		17 30		17 53			18 09	18 30			18 53		19 52	20 23	20 52			21 52	
Banbury	d		17 49		18 13			18 29	18 49			19 13		20 13	20 42	21 15			22 15	
Kings Sutton	d							18 33							20 47				22 20	
Bicester North 3	a		18 04		18 28			18 45	19 03			19 28		20 28	20 59	21 29			22 32	
	d	17 46	18 04		18 28			18 46	19 04			19 29	20 00	20 29	21 00	21 30			22 32	
Haddenham & Thame Parkway	d	17 59			18 40			18 59				19 42	20 13	20 42	21 13	21 43			22 45	
Aylesbury	d					18 38					19 30							21 53		22 45
Little Kimble	d					18 46					19 38							22 01		22 53
Monks Risborough	d					18 50					19 42							22 05		22 57
Princes Risborough 2	d	18 06			18 47	18a56		19 06			19a48	19 50	20 21	20 50	21 21	21 52		22 08	22 54	23 00
Saunderton	d	18 11						19 11					20 26		21 26			22 13		23 05
High Wycombe 1	d	18 18	18 28	18 34	18 57		19 04	19 18	19 28	19 34		20 00	20 33	21 00	21 33	22 02		22 20	23 04	23 12
Beaconsfield	d	18 24		18 40			19 10	19 24		19 40		20 06	20 39	21 06	21 39	22 08		22 26		23 18
Seer Green	d			18 43			19 13			19 43			20 42		21 42			22 29		23 21
Gerrards Cross 1	d	18 30		18 47			19 17	19 30		19 47		20 11	20 46	21 11	21 46	22 13		22 34		23 26
Denham Golf Club	d			18 50						19 50			20 49		21 49			22 37		23 29
Denham	d			18 52			19 21			19 52			20 52		21 52			22 39		23 31
West Ruislip 3 §	⊖ d			18 57						19 57			20 56		21 56			22 44		23 36
South Ruislip §	⊖ d						19 27			20 00			21 00		22 00			22 47		23 39
Northolt Park	d			19 02			19 30			20 04			21 03		22 03			22 51		23 43
Sudbury Hill Harrow	d																			
Sudbury & Harrow Road	d																			
Wembley Stadium	d			19 07			19 35			20 09			21 08		22 08	22 27		22 57	23 27	23 49
London Paddington 15	⊖ a																			
London Marylebone 10	⊖ a	18 56	19 02	19 21	19 30		19 48	19 56	20 02	20 23		20 37	21 21	21 37	22 21	22 40		23 10	23 40	00 03

For general notes see front of timetable
For details of catering facilities see
Directory of Train Operators

§ London Underground Limited (Central Line) also operate services between South Ruislip and West Ruislip at frequent intervals

From 10 October a revised Chiltern Railways service will be in operation due to seasonal difficulties. Trains will arrive at their destination 3 minutes later than shown

Table 115

Sundays

Kidderminster, Birmingham Snow Hill, Stratford-upon-Avon, Banbury, Aylesbury and High Wycombe → London

Network Diagram - See first page of Table 114

		CH	CH	CH	CH	CH	CH	CH	CH	CH	CH	CH	CH	CH	CH	CH	CH	CH	CH	CH
Kidderminster	d																			
Stourbridge Junction 2	d																			
Cradley Heath	d																			
Rowley Regis	d																			
Birmingham Snow Hill	d							08 40		09 10		09 40		10 10		10 40		11 10		11 40
Birmingham Moor Street	d							08 43		09 13		09 43		10 13		10 43		11 13		11 43
Solihull	d							08 52		09 22		09 52		10 22		10 52		11 22		11 52
Dorridge	d							08 58		09 28		09 58		10 28		10 58		11 28		11 58
Lapworth	d															11 02				
Stratford-upon-Avon	d												10 00							
Wilmcote	d												10 04							
Bearley	d																			
Claverdon	d																			
Hatton	d												10 17			11 07				
Warwick Parkway	d							09 09		09 38		10 09		10 38		11 12		11 38		12 09
Warwick	d							09 12		09 41			10 25	10 41				11 41		
Leamington Spa 8	d							09 17		09 47		10 16	10 29	10 47		11 18		11 47		12 16
Banbury	d					09 03		09 36	09 47	10 06		10 35	10 48	11 06		11 37		12 06		12 35
Kings Sutton	d					09 08							10 53							
Bicester North 3	a					09 19		09 52	10 01	10 21		10 50	11 05	11 21		11 53		12 21		12 50
	d			08 24	09 02	09 20		09 52	10 02	10 22		10 51	11 06	11 22		11 53	12 06	12 22		12 51
Haddenham & Thame Parkway	d			08 35	09 15	09 33			10 15			11 04	11 19			12 06	12 19			13 04
Aylesbury	d	07 27	08 18				09 30				10 28				11 30				12 28	
Little Kimble	d	07 35	08 26				09 38				10 36				11 38				12 36	
Monks Risborough	d	07 39	08 30				09 42				10 40				11 42				12 40	
Princes Risborough 2	d	07 42	08 33	08 43	09 22	09 41	09 45		10 22		10 43	11 12	11 26		11 45	12 15	12 26		12 43	13 12
Saunderton	d	07 47		08 48			09 50				10 48				11 50				12 48	
High Wycombe 1	d	07 54	08 43	08 55	09 32	09 52	09 57		10 32		10 55	11 22	11 36		11 57	12 25	12 36		12 55	13 22
Beaconsfield	d	08 00	08 49	09 01	09 38		10 03		10 38		11 01	11 28	11 42		12 03	12 31	12 42		13 01	13 28
Seer Green	d	08 03		09 04			10 06				11 04				12 06				13 04	
Gerrards Cross 1	d	08 07	08 55	09 08	09 43		10 10		10 43		11 08	11 34	11 48		12 10	12 36	12 48		13 08	13 34
Denham Golf Club	d	08 10					10 13								12 13					
Denham	d	08 13		09 12			10 16				11 12				12 16				13 12	
West Ruislip 3 §	⊖ d	08 17		09 16			10 20				11 16				12 20				13 16	
South Ruislip §	⊖ d	08 21		09 20			10 24				11 20				12 24				13 20	
Northolt Park	d	08 24		09 23			10 27				11 23				12 27				13 23	
Sudbury Hill Harrow	d																			
Sudbury & Harrow Road	d																			
Wembley Stadium	d	08 29		09 28			10 32				11 28		12 01		12 32		13 01		13 28	
London Paddington 15	⊖ a																			
London Marylebone 10	⊖ a	08 42	09 20	09 43	10 09	10 25	10 47	10 51	11 10	11 23	11 42	11 58	12 17	12 22	12 47	13 01	13 14	13 22	13 42	13 58

For general notes see front of timetable
For details of catering facilities see
Directory of Train Operators

§ London Underground Limited (Central Line) also operate services between South Ruislip and West Ruislip at frequent intervals

From 4 October a revised Chiltern Railways service will be in operation due to seasonal difficulties. Trains will arrive at their destination 3 minutes later than shown

Table 115

Sundays

Kidderminster, Birmingham Snow Hill, Stratford-upon-Avon, Banbury, Aylesbury and High Wycombe → London

Network Diagram - See first page of Table 114

		CH		CH	CH	CH		CH	CH	CH		CH	CH	CH		CH	CH	CH		CH	CH	CH		CH	CH
Kidderminster	d																								
Stourbridge Junction 2	d																								
Cradley Heath	d																								
Rowley Regis	d																								
Birmingham Snow Hill	d			12 10		12 40			13 10			13 40		14 10			14 40			15 10		15 40			16 10
Birmingham Moor Street	d			12 13		12 43			13 13			13 43		14 13			14 43			15 13		15 43			16 13
Solihull	d			12 22		12 52			13 22			13 52		14 22			14 52			15 22		15 52			16 22
Dorridge	d			12 28		12 58			13 28			13 58		14 28			14 58			15 28		15 58			16 28
Lapworth	d											14 02										16 02			
Stratford-upon-Avon	d	12 00											14 00											16 00	
Wilmcote	d	12 04											14 04											16 04	
Bearley	d																								
Claverdon	d																								
Hatton	d	12 17										14 07	14 17									16 07		16 17	
Warwick Parkway	d			12 38		13 09			13 38			14 12		14 38			15 09			15 38		16 12			16 38
Warwick	d	12 25		12 41					13 41				14 25	14 41						15 41				16 25	16 41
Leamington Spa 8	d	12 29		12 47		13 16			13 47			14 18	14 29	14 47			15 16			15 47		16 18		16 29	16 47
Banbury	d	12 48		13 06		13 35			14 06			14 37	14 48	15 06			15 35			16 06		16 37		16 48	17 06
Kings Sutton	d	12 53											14 53											16 53	
Bicester North 3	a	13 05		13 21		13 51			14 21			14 52	15 05	15 21			15 50			16 22		16 52		17 05	17 22
	d	13 06		13 22		13 51		14 06	14 22			14 53	15 06	15 22			15 51	16 06		16 22		16 53		17 06	17 22
Haddenham & Thame Parkway	d	13 19				14 04		14 19				15 06	15 19				16 04	16 19				17 06		17 19	
Aylesbury	d				13 30					14 28						15 30					16 30				
Little Kimble	d				13 38					14 36						15 38					16 38				
Monks Risborough	d				13 42					14 40						15 42					16 42				
Princes Risborough 2	d	13 26			13 45	14 12		14 26		14 43		15 15	15 26			15 45	16 12	16 26			16 45	17 15		17 26	
Saunderton	d				13 50					14 48						15 50					16 50				
High Wycombe 1	d	13 36			13 57	14 22		14 36		14 55		15 25	15 36			15 57	16 22	16 36			16 57	17 25		17 36	
Beaconsfield	d	13 42			14 03	14 28		14 42		15 01		15 31	15 42			16 03	16 28	16 42			17 03	17 31		17 42	
Seer Green	d				14 06					15 04						16 06					17 06				
Gerrards Cross 1	d	13 48			14 10	14 34		14 48		15 08		15 36	15 48			16 10	16 34	16 48			17 10	17 36		17 48	
Denham Golf Club	d				14 13											16 13									
Denham	d				14 16					15 12						16 16					17 16				
West Ruislip 3 §	⊖ d				14 20					15 16						16 20					17 20				
South Ruislip §	⊖ d				14 24					15 20						16 24					17 24				
Northolt Park	d				14 27					15 23						16 27					17 27				
Sudbury Hill Harrow	d																								
Sudbury & Harrow Road	d																								
Wembley Stadium	d	14 01			14 32			15 01		15 28			16 01			16 32		17 01			17 32			18 01	
London Paddington 15	⊖ a																								
London Marylebone 10	⊖ a	14 16		14 22	14 47	15 00		15 14	15 23	15 42		16 01	16 16	16 22		16 47	16 58	17 14		17 23	17 47	18 02		18 16	18 21

		CH	CH	CH		CH	CH	CH		CH	CH	CH		CH	CH	CH		CH	CH	CH					
Kidderminster	d																								
Stourbridge Junction 2	d																								
Cradley Heath	d																								
Rowley Regis	d																								
Birmingham Snow Hill	d		16 40			17 10		17 40			18 10			18 40	19 10			20 15		21 15					
Birmingham Moor Street	d		16 43			17 13		17 43			18 13			18 43	19 13			20 18		21 18					
Solihull	d		16 52			17 22		17 52			18 22			18 52	19 21			20 28		21 28					
Dorridge	d		16 58			17 28		17 58			18 28			18 58	19 29			20 35		21 35					
Lapworth	d							18 02							19 33										
Stratford-upon-Avon	d									18 00						19 57									
Wilmcote	d									18 04						20 01									
Bearley	d																								
Claverdon	d																								
Hatton	d							18 07		18 17					19 38	20 14									
Warwick Parkway	d		17 09			17 38		18 12			18 38			19 09	19 43			20 46		21 46					
Warwick	d					17 41				18 25	18 41				19 46	20 22		20 49		21 49					
Leamington Spa 8	d		17 16			17 47		18 18		18 29	18 47			19 16	19 54	20 26		20 54		21 54					
Banbury	d		17 35			18 06		18 37		18 48	19 06			19 35	20 13	20 48		21 13		22 15					
Kings Sutton	d									18 53						20 53				22 20					
Bicester North 3	a		17 50			18 22		18 52		19 05	19 22			19 50	20 30	21 06		21 29		22 33					
	d		17 51	18 06		18 22		18 53		19 06	19 22			19 51	20 30	21 06		21 30		22 34					
Haddenham & Thame Parkway	d		18 04	18 19				19 06		19 19				20 04	20 43	21 19		21 43		22 47					
Aylesbury	d	17 30					18 28					19 30							22 32						
Little Kimble	d	17 38					18 36					19 38							22 40						
Monks Risborough	d	17 42					18 40					19 42							22 44						
Princes Risborough 2	d	17 45	18 12	18 26			18 43	19 15		19 26		19 45		20 12	20 51	21 26		21 51	22a50	22 55					
Saunderton	d	17 50					18 48					19 50			20 56			21 56		23 00					
High Wycombe 1	d	17 57	18 22	18 36			18 55	19 25		19 36		19 57		20 22	21 03	21 36		22 03		23 07					
Beaconsfield	d	18 03	18 28	18 42			19 01	19 31		19 42		20 03		20 28	21 09	21 42		22 09		23 13					
Seer Green	d	18 06					19 04					20 06			21 12			22 12		23 16					
Gerrards Cross 1	d	18 10	18 34	18 48			19 08	19 36		19 48		20 10		20 34	21 16	21 48		22 16		23 20					
Denham Golf Club	d	18 13										20 13						22 19							
Denham	d	18 16					19 12					20 16			21 21			22 21		23 24					
West Ruislip 3 §	⊖ d	18 20					19 16					20 20			21 26			22 26		23 28					
South Ruislip §	⊖ d	18 24					19 20					20 24			21 29			22 29		23 32					
Northolt Park	d	18 27					19 23					20 27			21 33			22 33		23 35					
Sudbury Hill Harrow	d																								
Sudbury & Harrow Road	d																								
Wembley Stadium	d	18 32		19 01			19 28			20 01		20 32			21 38	22 01		22 38		23 40					
London Paddington 15	⊖ a																								
London Marylebone 10	⊖ a	18 48	18 58	19 14		19 22	19 42	20 02		20 16	20 21	20 48		20 58	21 52	22 16		22 52		23 53					

For general notes see front of timetable
For details of catering facilities see Directory of Train Operators

§ London Underground Limited (Central Line) also operate services between South Ruislip and West Ruislip at frequent intervals

From 4 October a revised Chiltern Railways service will be in operation due to seasonal difficulties. Trains will arrive at their destination 3 minutes later than shown

Table 115A

Mondays to Fridays

Chinnor — Princes Risborough

Bus Service

		CH	CH	CH	CH	CH	CH
Chinnor, Lower Road	d	06 12	06 40	07 34	08 00	09 07	09 36
Chinnor, Estover Way	d	06 14	06 42	07 36	08 02	09 09	09 38
Chinnor, The Wheatsheaf	d	06 15	06 43	07 37	08 03	09 10	09 39
Chinnor, The Red Lion	d	06 18	06 46	07 40	08 06	09 13	09 42
Bledlow, Village Hall	d	06 21	06 49	07 43	08 09	09 16	09 45
Princes Risborough	a	06 28	06 56	07 50	08 16	09 23	09 52

Mondays to Fridays

		CH	CH	CH	CH	CH	CH	CH
Princes Risborough	d	16 50	17 19	18 12	18 47	19 17	20 19	20 54
Bledlow, Village Hall	d	16 57	17 26	18 19	18 54	19 24	20 26	21 01
Chinnor, Lower Road	d	17 00	17 29	18 22	18 57	19 27	20 29	21 04
Chinnor, Estover Way	d	17 02	17 31	18 24	18 59	19 29	20 31	21 06
Chinnor, The Wheatsheaf	d	17 03	17 32	18 25	19 00	19 30	20 32	21 07
Chinnor, The Red Lion	a	17 06	17 35	18 28	19 03	19 33	20 35	21 10

For general notes see front of timetable
For details of catering facilities see
Directory of Train Operators

NO SATURDAY OR SUNDAY SERVICE

Network Diagram for Tables 116, 117, 118, 119, 120, 121, 122, 126

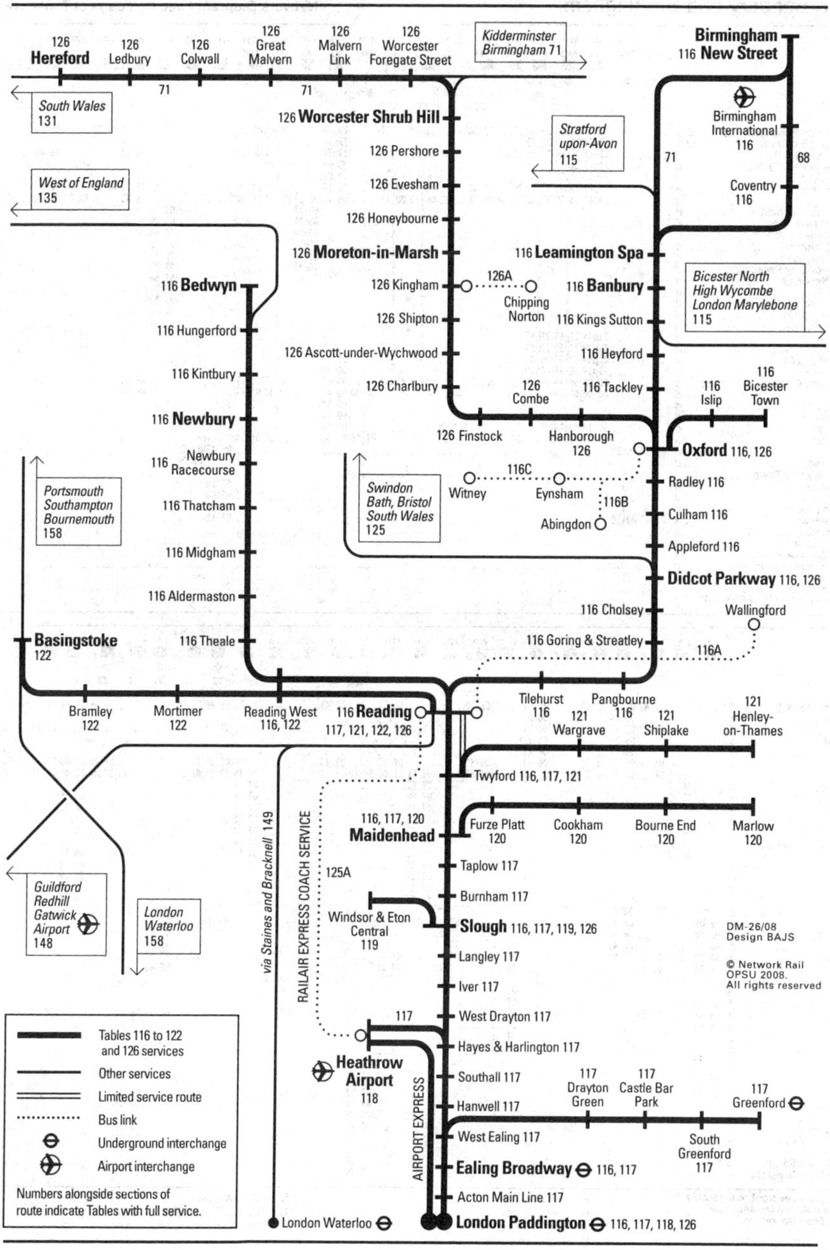

London and Reading → Bedwyn, Oxford, Bicester, Banbury and Birmingham

Network Diagram - see first page of Table 116

Miles	Miles			CH	CH	GW	GW	GW	GW	GW	GW	GW	GW	GW	GW	GW	GW	GW	GW	GW	GW	GW	GW	GW	GW	XC
				MX	MX	MX	MO	MO	MX	MX	MO	MO	MO	MO	MX	MX	MO	MX								
						1	1	1	1 ◇	1 ◇		1 ◇	1 ◇		1	1	1 ◇	1 ◇	1	1	1	1 ◇	1 ◇	1	1 ◇	1 ◇
				A	B		C	D			E 🚌	D	C	E 🚌			C									
										☕		☕	☕										☕		☕	🛒
0	—	**London Paddington 15** ⊖	d			22p45	22p44	22p43	23p20	23p30		23p37	23p37		23p29		23p47	00 21				05 16	05 27		05 30	
5¾	—	Ealing Broadway ⊖	d			22p54	22p52	22p52							23p37		23p55									
18½	—	Slough 3	d			23p12	23p15	23p15	23p39			23p55			23p54		00 08	00 40				05 34			05 49	
24¼	—	Maidenhead 3	d			23p23	23p24	23p24							00 01		00 15									
31	—	Twyford 3	d			23p31	23p32	23p32							00 09											
36	—	**Reading 7**	a			23p40	23p43	23p43	00 04	00 07		00 15	00 15		00 19		00 28	01 00				05 51	05 55		06 05	
—	0		d			23p40	23p50	23p50	00 04	00 08		00 15	00 15		00 19	00 20	00 29	01 00			05 21	05 52		05 57	06 07	06 10
—	1	Reading West	d													00s23					05 23					
—	5¼	Theale	d													00s29					05 29					
—	8¾	Aldermaston	d													00s34					05 34					
—	10¾	Midgham	d													00s37					05 38					
—	13½	Thatcham	d													00s42					05 43					
—	16½	Newbury Racecourse	d													00s47					05 47					
—	17	**Newbury**	a													00 52					05 50					
—	—		d																		05 50					
—	22½	Kintbury	d																		05 57					
—	25½	Hungerford	d																		06 01					
—	30½	**Bedwyn**	a																		06 11					
38¾	—	Tilehurst	d			23p44	23p55	23p55							00 23									06 01		
41½	—	Pangbourne	d			23p49	23p59	23p59							00 28									06 05 →		
44¾	—	Goring & Streatley	d			23p54	00 05	00 05							00 33											
48½	—	Cholsey	d			23p59	00 10	00 10							00 38											
53¼	—	**Didcot Parkway**	a			00 06	00 16	00 17		00 25		00s33	00s33		00 45		00 43	01 19				06 07			06 21	
—	—		d			00 06	00 17				00 25			00 40	00 45		00 44	01 19				06 07				
55¼	—	Appleford	d												00 50											
56¼	—	Culham	d												00 52											
58½	—	Radley	d			00 14	00 24				00 40				00 56											
63½	—	**Oxford**	a			00 23	00 34		00 34		00 55			01 05	01 06		00 59	01 34				06 22				06 34
—	0		d	00 20	00 20														05 45	05 51						06 35
—	5¾	Islip	d																	06 04						
—	11¾	**Bicester Town**	a																	06 17						
72½	—	Tackley	d																05 54							
75¼	—	Heyford	d																05 58							
82¾	—	Kings Sutton	d																06 07							
86¼	—	**Banbury**	a	00 47	00 50														06 14							06 52
106¼	—	Leamington Spa 3	a																							07 10
—	—	Warwick	a																							*07 26*
—	—	Warwick Parkway	a																							*07 29*
—	—	Stratford-upon-Avon	a																							
115¾	—	Coventry	a																							07 22
126½	—	Birmingham International	a																							07 37
135	—	**Birmingham New Street 12**	a																							07 49

		GW	GW	GW	GW	GW	XC	GW	GW	GW	GW	GW	GW	XC	GW	GW	GW	GW	GW	GW	GW	XC	GW	GW	GW	GW
		1	1	1 ◇	1	1 ◇	1 ◇	1	1	1 ◇	1	1	1 ◇	1 ◇	1 ◇	1 ◇	1	1	1	1 ◇	1	1 ◇	1 ◇	1	1 ◇	1
																			G		G					
							🛒			☕				🛒	☕				🛒	☕	🛒	🛒	☕			
London Paddington 15 ⊖	d			05 42	05 22	05 58		05 57		06 30			06 33		06 45				06 48	07 00			07 15	07 18	07 22	06 57
Ealing Broadway ⊖	d				05 30			06 05																		07 05
Slough 3	d			06 04	05 57	06 13		06 29					06 48						07 04						07 37	07 29
Maidenhead 3	d				06 04			06 37																		07 37
Twyford 3	d				06 12			06 45																		07 45
Reading 7	a			06 20	06 21	06 28		06 53		06 55			07 03		07 10				07 20	07 25			07 40	07 48	07 52	07 53
	d		06 15	06 21	06 23	06 30	06 40	06 53		06 57		07 01	07 05	07 10				07 19	07 21	07 27		07 40	07 41	07 48	07 53	07 53
Reading West	d		06 17									07 03						07 21								
Theale	d		06 23									07 09						07 28						07 56		
Aldermaston	d		06 28									07 14						07 33						08 01		
Midgham	d		06 32									07 18						07 36								
Thatcham	d		06 37									07 23						07 41						08 07		
Newbury Racecourse	d		06 41									07 27						07 46								
Newbury	a		06 47									07 30						07 51						08 13		
	d											07 30												08 13		
Kintbury	d											07 37												08 19		
Hungerford	d											07 41												08 24		
Bedwyn	a											07 51												08 34		
Tilehurst	d	←			06 28			06 58			←								07 25		←					07 58
Pangbourne	d	06 05			06 32			07 02 →			07 02								07 30 →		07 30					08 02
Goring & Streatley	d	06 10			06 37				←		07 07										07 35					08 07 →
Cholsey	d	06 15			06 42 →				06 42		07 12										07 40					
Didcot Parkway	a	06 22		06 39					06 50	07 11	07 19		07 22			←	←			07 41	07 47		07 55			
	d	06 25		06 39					07 03		07 33 →		07 26 →			07 26	07 33				07 48					
Appleford	d																07 37									
Culham	d								07 08								07 39									
Radley	d	06 33							07 12								07 43									
Oxford	a	06 41		06 53		06 59	07 04		07 20					07 34		07 39	07 53				08 00	08 04			08 19	
	d	06 42					07 05		07 25					07 35								08 05				
Islip	d								07 38																	
Bicester Town	a								07 53																	
Tackley	d	06 50																								
Heyford	d	06 55																								
Kings Sutton	d	07 03																								
Banbury	a	07 11					07 24							07 52								08 24				
Leamington Spa 8	a						07 41							08 10								08 41				
Warwick	a						*08 04*							*08 28*								*08 56*				
Warwick Parkway	a						*08 08*							*08 31*								*09 01*				
Stratford-upon-Avon	a																					*09b40*				
Coventry	a													08 22												
Birmingham International	a													08 37												
Birmingham New Street 12	a						08 17							08 49								09 17				

For general notes see front of timetable
For details of catering facilities see Directory of Train Operators

A Until 2 October
B From 6 October
C From 14 September
D Until 7 September
E Until 31 August
G To Great Malvern (Table 126)
b From 5 October arr. 3 minutes later

Table 116

Mondays to Fridays

London and Reading → Bedwyn, Oxford, Bicester, Banbury and Birmingham

Network Diagram - see first page of Table 116

Station		GW 1◇ ☕	GW 1	XC 1◇ 🛒	GW 1◇ ☕	GW 1	GW 1	GW 1	GW 1◇ ☕	GW 1◇	GW 1	GW 1◇ ☕	GW 1	GW 1	XC 1◇ 🛒	GW 1	GW 1◇ ☕	GW 1◇ ☕	GW 1◇ ☕	GW 1	GW 1◇ ☕		XC 1◇ 🛒	GW 1	GW 1◇ ☕	GW 1
London Paddington 15 ⊖	d	07 30			07 45				07 48	07 52	07 27	08 00					08 15	08 18	08 22	07 57	08 30				08 45	
Ealing Broadway ⊖	d										07 35									08 05						
Slough 3	d									08 06	07 59								08 37	08 29						
Maidenhead 3	d										08 07									08 37						
Twyford 3	d										08 15									08 45						
Reading 7	a	07 56			08 10				08 15	08 21	08 23	08 26					08 40	08 45	08 52	08 53	08 56				09 10	
	d			08 10				08 12	08 16	08 22	08 23	08 27		08 34	08 40		08 41	08 48	08 53	08 53	08 57		09 10			09 12
Reading West	d							08 14																		09 14
Theale	d							08 20						08 41				08 56								09 20
Aldermaston	d							08 25						08 46												09 25
Midgham	d							08 29																		09 29
Thatcham	d							08 34						08 53				09 04								09 34
Newbury Racecourse	d							08 38																		09 38
Newbury	a							08 42						09 03				09 12								09 44
	d							08 42										09 12								
Kintbury	d							08 49										09 21								
Hungerford	d							08 53										09 30								
Bedwyn	a							09 03																		
Tilehurst	d										08 28					←				08 58				←		
Pangbourne	d						←				08 32					08 32				09 02				09 02		
Goring & Streatley	d						08 07				→					08 37				→				09 07		
Cholsey	d						08 12									08 42								09 12		
Didcot Parkway	a						08 20		08 32			08 41				08 50	08 55				09 12			09 23		
	d		08 09				08 25									08 55								09 25		
Appleford	d		08 13													09 00										
Culham	d		08 15													09 02										
Radley	d		08 19				08 33									09 06										
Oxford	a		08 31	08 34			08 42			08 48					09 04	09 16			09 20				09 34	09 40		
	d			08 35		08 41							08 53		09 05								09 35			
Islip	d					08 54																				
Bicester Town	a					09 07																				
Tackley	d												09 02													
Heyford	d												09 06													
Kings Sutton	d												09 15													
Banbury	a			08 52									09 22		09 24								09 52			
Leamington Spa 8	a			09 10											09 41								10 10			
Warwick	a														*09 58*								*10 36*			
Warwick Parkway	a														*10 01*											
Stratford-upon-Avon	a																						*11b08*			
Coventry	a			09 22																			10 22			
Birmingham International	a			09 37																			10 37			
Birmingham New Street 12	a			09 49											10 17								10 49			

Station		GW 1◇	GW 1	GW 1◇ ☕	GW 1◇ A ☕	GW 1	XC 1◇ 🛒	GW 1	GW 1◇ ☕	GW 1	GW 1	GW 1◇ 🛒	GW 1◇ ☕	XC 1◇ 🛒	GW 1	GW 1◇ ☕	GW 1	GW 1◇ ☕	GW 1◇	GW 1	GW 1◇ ☕	GW 1◇ A ☕	GW 1	XC 1◇ 🛒	GW 1	GW 1◇ ☕
London Paddington 15 ⊖	d	08 51	08 27	09 00	09 06				09 15	09 18	08 57	09 21	09 30			09 45		09 48	09 50	09 27	10 00	10 06				10 15
Ealing Broadway ⊖	d		08 35								09 05									09 35						
Slough 3	d	09 06	08 59								09 27	09 37							10 06	09 57						
Maidenhead 3	d		09 06								09 34									10 04						
Twyford 3	d		09 16								09 42									10 12						
Reading 7	a	09 21	09 23	09 26	09 31				09 40	09 48	09 52	09 52	09 56			10 10		10 15	10 21	10 22	10 26	10 31				10 40
	d	09 22	09 23				09 40		09 41	09 48	09 53	09 53	09 57	10 10			10 12	10 16	10 22	10 23				10 40		10 41
Reading West	d																10 14									
Theale	d									09 56							10 20									
Aldermaston	d																10 25									
Midgham	d																10 29									
Thatcham	d									10 04							10 34									
Newbury Racecourse	d																10 38									
Newbury	a									10 10							10 44									
	d									10 10																
Kintbury	d									10 17																
Hungerford	d									10 21																
Bedwyn	a									10 31																
Tilehurst	d		09 28								09 58				←					10 28						
Pangbourne	d		09 32								10 02				10 02					10 32						
Goring & Streatley	d		09 37					←			→				10 07					10 37					←	
Cholsey	d		09 42					09 42							10 12					10 42					10 42	
Didcot Parkway	a	09 37	→					09 50	09 55				10 12		10 21			10 32		→					10 49	10 55
	d	09 38						09 55							10 25										10 55	
Appleford	d																								11 00	
Culham	d							10 01																		
Radley	d							10 05																	11 05	
Oxford	a	09 52					10 04	10 14				10 18		10 34	10 40				10 48					11 04	11 14	
	d					10 00	10 05							10 35									11 00	11 05		
Islip	d					10 13																	11 13			
Bicester Town	a					10 26																	11 26			
Tackley	d																									
Heyford	d																									
Kings Sutton	d																									
Banbury	a						10 24							10 52										11 24		
Leamington Spa 8	a						10 41							11 10										11 41		
Warwick	a						*10 58*																	*11 58*		
Warwick Parkway	a						*11 02*																	*12 02*		
Stratford-upon-Avon	a																									
Coventry	a													11 22												
Birmingham International	a													11 37												
Birmingham New Street 12	a						11 17							11 49										12 17		

For general notes see front of timetable
For details of catering facilities see
Directory of Train Operators

A From 7 September
b From 5 October arr. 3 minutes later

London and Reading → Bedwyn, Oxford, Bicester, Banbury and Birmingham

Network Diagram - see first page of Table 116

		GW	GW	GW	GW	GW	XC	GW	GW	GW	GW	GW	GW	GW	XC	GW	GW	GW	GW	GW	GW	XC	GW	GW	GW	GW
		1	1	1 ◊	1 ◊	1	1 ◊	1	1 ◊	1	1 ◊	1	1 ◊	1 ◊	1 ◊	1	1 ◊	1	1	1 ◊	1 ◊	1 ◊	1	1 ◊	1	1 ◊
														A												
				☕	☕		🛒		☕				☕	☕	🛒		☕			☕	☕	🛒		☕		☕
London Paddington 15 ⊖	d	10 18	09 57	10 22	10 30				10 45		10 51	10 27	11 00	11 06			11 15	11 18	10 57	11 22	11 30			11 45		11 48
Ealing Broadway ⊖	d		10 05									10 35							11 05							
Slough 3	d		10 27	10 37							11 06	10 57							11 27	11 37						
Maidenhead 3	d		10 34									11 04							11 34							
Twyford 3	d		10 42									11 12							11 42							
Reading 7	a	10 48	10 52	10 52	10 56				11 10		11 21	11 22	11 26	11 31			11 40	11 48	11 52	11 52	11 56			12 10		12 15
	d	10 48	10 53	10 53	10 57		11 10			11 12	11 22	11 23			11 40		11 41	11 48	11 53	11 53	11 57	12 10			12 12	12 16
Reading West	d									11 14															12 14	
Theale	d	10 56								11 20								11 56							12 20	
Aldermaston	d									11 25															12 25	
Midgham	d									11 29															12 29	
Thatcham	d	11 04								11 34								12 04							12 34	
Newbury Racecourse	d									11 38															12 38	
Newbury	a	11 10								11 44								12 10							12 44	
	d	11 10																12 10								
Kintbury	d	11 17																12 17								
Hungerford	d	11 21																12 21								
Bedwyn	a	11 31																12 31								
Tilehurst	d		10 58					←				11 28							11 58				←			
Pangbourne	d		11 02					11 02				11 32				←			12 02				12 02			
Goring & Streatley	d		→					11 07				11 37				11 37			→				12 07			
Cholsey	d							11 12				→				11 42							12 12			
Didcot Parkway	a				11 12			11 20			11 37					11 50	11 55				12 12		12 20			12 32
	d							11 25			11 37					11 55							12 25			
Appleford	d																									
Culham	d																									
Radley	d															12 03										
Oxford	a			11 18			11 34	11 40			11 52				12 04	12 12				12 18		12 34	12 40			
	d					11 23	11 35								12 05							12 35				
Islip	d																									
Bicester Town	a																									
Tackley	d					11 32																				
Heyford	d					11 36																				
Kings Sutton	d					11 45																				
Banbury	a					11 52	11 52								12 24							12 52				
Leamington Spa 8	a						12 10								12 41							13 10				
Warwick	a						*12 40*								*12 58*											
Warwick Parkway	a														*13 02*											
Stratford-upon-Avon	a						*13b11*																			
Coventry	a						12 22															13 22				
Birmingham International	a						12 37															13 37				
Birmingham New Street 12	a						12 49								13 17							13 49				

		GW	GW	GW	GW	XC	GW	GW	GW	GW	GW	GW	GW	XC	GW	GW	GW		GW	GW	GW	GW	XC	GW	GW	GW
		1 ◊	1	1 ◊	1 ◊	1 ◊	1	1 ◊	1 ◊	1	1 ◊	1 ◊	1	1 ◊	1 ◊	1	1		1 ◊	1	1 ◊	1 ◊	1 ◊	1	1 ◊	1
					A																	A				
				☕	☕	🛒		☕	☕			☕		🛒	☕						☕	☕	🛒		☕	
London Paddington 15 ⊖	d	11 50	11 27	12 00	12 06			12 15	12 18	11 57	12 22	12 30			12 45				12 50	12 27	13 00	13 06			13 15	13 18
Ealing Broadway ⊖	d		11 35							12 05										12 35						
Slough 3	d	12 06	11 57							12 27	12 37								13 06	12 57						
Maidenhead 3	d		12 04							12 34										13 04						
Twyford 3	d		12 12							12 42										13 12						
Reading 7	a	12 21	12 22	12 26	12 31			12 40	12 45	12 50	12 52	12 57			13 10				13 21	13 22	13 26	13 31			13 40	13 48
	d	12 22	12 23			12 40		12 41	12 48	12 53	12 53	12 57		13 10			13 12		13 22	13 23			13 40		13 41	13 48
Reading West	d																13 14									
Theale	d								12 56								13 20									13 56
Aldermaston	d																13 25									
Midgham	d																13 29									
Thatcham	d								13 04								13 34									14 04
Newbury Racecourse	d																13 38									
Newbury	a								13 12								13 44									14 10
	d								13 12																	14 10
Kintbury	d																									14 17
Hungerford	d								13 21																	14 21
Bedwyn	a								13 30																	14 31
Tilehurst	d		12 28							12 58										13 28						
Pangbourne	d		12 32				←			13 02						←				13 32				←		
Goring & Streatley	d		12 37				12 37			13 07						13 07				13 37				13 37		
Cholsey	d		→				12 42			→						13 12				→				13 42		
Didcot Parkway	a						12 50	12 55				13 12				13 20			13 37					13 50	13 55	
	d						12 55									13 25			13 37					13 55		
Appleford	d																									
Culham	d																									
Radley	d						13 03																	14 03		
Oxford	a	12 48				13 04	13 12				13 19			13 34		13 40			13 51				14 04	14 12		
	d					13 05							13 26	13 35									14 05			
Islip	d												13 39													
Bicester Town	a												13 52													
Tackley	d																									
Heyford	d																									
Kings Sutton	d																									
Banbury	a					13 24								13 52									14 24			
Leamington Spa 8	a					13 41								14 10									14 41			
Warwick	a					*13 58*								*14 41*									*14 58*			
Warwick Parkway	a					*14 02*																	*15 02*			
Stratford-upon-Avon	a													*15b09*												
Coventry	a													14 22												
Birmingham International	a													14 37												
Birmingham New Street 12	a					14 17								14 49									15 17			

For general notes see front of timetable
For details of catering facilities see Directory of Train Operators

A From 7 September
b From 5 October arr. 3 minutes later

London and Reading → Bedwyn, Oxford, Bicester, Banbury and Birmingham

Network Diagram - see first page of Table 116

	GW	GW	GW	GW	XC	GW	GW	GW	GW	GW	GW	GW	GW
	1	1◇	1◇	1	1◇	1	1◇	1	1◇	1◇	1	1◇	1◇
													A
			☕		🛒		☕		☕			☕	☕
London Paddington 15 ⊖ d	12 57	13 21	13 30				13 45		13 48	13 51	13 27	14 00	14 06
Ealing Broadway ⊖ d	13 05										13 35		
Slough 3 d	13 27	13 37								14 06	13 57		
Maidenhead 3 d	13 34										14 04		
Twyford 3 d	13 42										14 12		
Reading 7 a	13 52	13 52	13 57				14 10		14 15	14 21	14 21	14 26	14 31
d	13 53	13 53	13 57		14 10			14 12	14 16	14 22	14 23		
Reading West d								14 14					
Theale d								14 20					
Aldermaston d								14 25					
Midgham d								14 29					
Thatcham d								14 34					
Newbury Racecourse d								14 38					
Newbury a								14 44					
d													
Kintbury d													
Hungerford d													
Bedwyn a													
Tilehurst d	13 58					←					14 28		
Pangbourne d	14 02					14 02					14 32		
Goring & Streatley d	→					14 07					14 37		
Cholsey d						14 12					→		
Didcot Parkway a			14 12			14 20			14 32				
d						14 25							
Appleford d													
Culham d													
Radley d													
Oxford a		14 18			14 34	14 40				14 48			
d				14 23	14 35								
Islip d													
Bicester Town a													
Tackley d				14 32									
Heyford d				14 36									
Kings Sutton d				14 45									
Banbury a				14 52	14 52								
Leamington Spa 8 a					15 10								
Warwick a													
Warwick Parkway a													
Stratford-upon-Avon a													
Coventry a					15 22								
Birmingham International a					15 37								
Birmingham New Street 12 a					15 49								

	GW	XC	GW	GW	GW	GW	GW	GW	XC	GW	GW	GW
	1	1◇	1	1◇	1	1	1◇	1◇	1◇	1	1◇	1
								B				
		🛒		☕				☕	🛒		☕	
London Paddington 15 ⊖ d				14 15	14 18	13 57	14 21	14 30			14 45	
Ealing Broadway ⊖ d						14 05						
Slough 3 d						14 27	14 37					
Maidenhead 3 d						14 34						
Twyford 3 d						14 42						
Reading 7 a				14 40	14 48	14 52	14 52	14 56			15 10	
d		14 40		14 41	14 48	14 53	14 53	14 57	15 10			15 12
Reading West d												15 14
Theale d					14 56							15 20
Aldermaston d												15 25
Midgham d												15 29
Thatcham d					15 04							15 34
Newbury Racecourse d												15 38
Newbury a					15 10							15 44
d					15 10							
Kintbury d					15 17							
Hungerford d					15 21							
Bedwyn a					15 31							
Tilehurst d						14 58				←		
Pangbourne d			←			15 02				15 02		
Goring & Streatley d			14 37			→				15 07		
Cholsey d			14 42							15 12		
Didcot Parkway a			14 50	14 55				15 12		15 22		
d			14 55							15 25		
Appleford d												
Culham d												
Radley d			15 03									
Oxford a		15 04	15 12				15 18		15 34	15 40		
d	15 00	15 05							15 35			
Islip d	15 13											
Bicester Town a	15 26											
Tackley d												
Heyford d												
Kings Sutton d												
Banbury a		15 24							15 52			
Leamington Spa 8 a		15 41							16 10			
Warwick a		*15 58*							*16 41*			
Warwick Parkway a		*16 02*										
Stratford-upon-Avon a									*17b12*			
Coventry a									16 22			
Birmingham International a									16 37			
Birmingham New Street 12 a		16 17							16 49			

	GW	GW	GW	GW	XC	GW	GW	GW	GW	GW	GW	GW	GW
	1◇	1	1◇	1◇	1◇	1	1◇	1	1	1◇	1◇	1	1
				A							B		
			☕	☕	🛒		☕				☕		
London Paddington 15 ⊖ d	14 50	14 27	15 00	15 06			15 15	15 18	14 57	15 22	15 30		
Ealing Broadway ⊖ d		14 35							15 05				
Slough 3 d	15 06	14 57							15 27	15 37			
Maidenhead 3 d		15 04							15 34				
Twyford 3 d		15 12							15 42				
Reading 7 a	15 21	15 22	15 25	15 31			15 40	15 48	15 52	15 52	15 57		
d	15 22	15 23			15 40		15 41	15 48	15 53	15 53	15 57		
Reading West d													
Theale d								15 56					
Aldermaston d													
Midgham d													
Thatcham d								16 04					
Newbury Racecourse d													
Newbury a								16 10					
d								16 10					
Kintbury d								16 17					
Hungerford d								16 21					
Bedwyn a								16 31					
Tilehurst d		15 28							15 58				
Pangbourne d		15 32							16 02				
Goring & Streatley d		15 37				←			→				
Cholsey d		15 42				15 42							
Didcot Parkway a	15 37	→				15 50	15 55				16 12		
d	15 37					15 55							
Appleford d													
Culham d						16 01							
Radley d						16 05							
Oxford a	15 50				16 04	16 14				16 19			
d					16 05							16 23	16 30
Islip d													16 43
Bicester Town a													16 56
Tackley d												16 32	
Heyford d												16 36	
Kings Sutton d												16 45	
Banbury a					16 24							16 52	
Leamington Spa 8 a					16 41								
Warwick a					*16 58*								
Warwick Parkway a					*17 02*								
Stratford-upon-Avon a													
Coventry a													
Birmingham International a													
Birmingham New Street 12 a					17 17								

	XC	GW	GW	GW	GW	GW	GW	GW	GW	XC	GW	GW
	1◇	1	1◇	1	1◇	1◇	1	1◇	1◇	1◇	1	1◇
									A			
	🛒		☕		☕	☕		☕	☕	🛒		☕
London Paddington 15 ⊖ d			15 45		15 48	15 51	15 27	16 00	16 06			16 15
Ealing Broadway ⊖ d							15 35					
Slough 3 d						16 06	15 55					
Maidenhead 3 d							16 03					
Twyford 3 d							16 11					
Reading 7 a			16 10		16 15	16 21	16 22	16 26	16 31			16 40
d	16 10			16 12	16 16	16 22	16 23			16 40		16 41
Reading West d				16 14								
Theale d				16 20								
Aldermaston d				16 25								
Midgham d				16 29								
Thatcham d				16 34								
Newbury Racecourse d				16 38								
Newbury a				16 44								
d												
Kintbury d												
Hungerford d												
Bedwyn a												
Tilehurst d		←					16 28					
Pangbourne d		16 02					16 32					
Goring & Streatley d		16 07					16 37				←	
Cholsey d		16 12					16 42				16 42	
Didcot Parkway a		16 20			16 32		→				16 50	16 55
d		16 25									16 55	
Appleford d											17 00	
Culham d											17 02	
Radley d											17 06	
Oxford a	16 34	16 40				16 47				17 04	17 16	
d	16 35									17 05		
Islip d												
Bicester Town a												
Tackley d												
Heyford d												
Kings Sutton d												
Banbury a	16 52									17 24		
Leamington Spa 8 a	17 10									17 41		
Warwick a	*17 26*									*17 55*		
Warwick Parkway a	*17 30*									*17 59*		
Stratford-upon-Avon a										*18b41*		
Coventry a	17 22											
Birmingham International a	17 37											
Birmingham New Street 12 a	17 49									18 17		

For general notes see front of timetable
For details of catering facilities see Directory of Train Operators

A From 7 September
B To Weston-super-Mare (Table 134)
b From 5 October arr. 3 minutes later

London and Reading → Bedwyn, Oxford, Bicester, Banbury and Birmingham

Network Diagram - see first page of Table 116

Station		GW	GW	GW	GW	GW	GW	XC	GW	GW	GW	GW	GW		GW	GW	GW	GW	GW	GW	XC	GW	GW	GW	GW	GW
		1	1	1	1 ◇	1 ◇	1 ◇	1 ◇	1	1 ◇	1	1	1 ◇		1	1 ◇	1 ◇	1 ◇	1	1 ◇	1 ◇	1	1 ◇	1 ◇	1	1 ◇
						A											B	C		D						A
						☕	☕	🛒		☕						☕	☕	☕		☕	🛒		☕	☕		☕
London Paddington 15 ⊖	d		16 18	15 57	16 22	16 30	16 33			16 45			16 51		16 27	17 00	17 03	17 03		17 06			17 15	17 22	17 18	17 30
Ealing Broadway ⊖	d			16 05											16 35											
Slough 3	d			16 26	16 37		16 48								16 53											
Maidenhead 3	d			16 33											17 04										17 39	
Twyford 3	d			16 41											17 12					17 28					17 47	
Reading 7	a		16 48	16 52	16 52	16 56	17 03			17 10			17 16		17 22	17 25		17 30		17 36			17 40	17 50	17 55	17 55
	d		16 48	16 53	16 53	16 57	17 04	17 10		17 11		17 12	17 17		17 23	17 27	17u31	17 31		17 36	17 40		17 41	17 50	17 56	17 57
Reading West	d											17 14														
Theale	d		16 56									17 20								17 45						
Aldermaston	d		17 01									17 25														
Midgham	d											17 29														
Thatcham	d		17 08									17 34								17 55						
Newbury Racecourse	d											17 38														
Newbury	a		17 14				17 19				←	17 44					17 47	17 47		18 01						
	d	17 08	17 25				17 20				17 25									18 01						
Kintbury	d	17 14	→								17 32									18 09						
Hungerford	d	17 19					17a29				17 36									18 15						
Bedwyn	a	17 28									17 46									18 24						
Tilehurst	d			16 58					←						17 28							←			18 00	
Pangbourne	d			17 02					17 02						17 32							17 32			18 04	
Goring & Streatley	d			→					17 07						→							17 37			→	
Cholsey	d								17 12													17 42				
Didcot Parkway	a				17 08	17 12			17 20	17 25			17 32			17 40						17 54	17 55			18 10
	d				17 09				17 25				17 33									17 55				
Appleford	d								17 30																	
Culham	d								17 32																	
Radley	d								17 36																	
Oxford	a				17 23			17 34	17 44				17 48								18 04	18 11		18 15		
	d							17 35	17 44										17 54		18 05					
Islip	d																		18 07							
Bicester Town	a																		18 20							
Tackley	d								17 54																	
Heyford	d								17 58																	
Kings Sutton	d								18 07																	
Banbury	a							17 52	18 15												18 24					
Leamington Spa 8	a							18 10													18 41					
Warwick	a																				*19 03*					
Warwick Parkway	a							*18 28*													*19 06*					
Stratford-upon-Avon	a																									
Coventry	a							18 22																		
Birmingham International	a							18 37																		
Birmingham New Street 12	a							18 49													19 17					

Station		GW	XC	GW	GW	GW	GW	GW	GW	GW	GW	GW	GW	GW	GW	XC	GW	GW	GW	GW	GW	GW	GW	XC	GW	GW
		1 ◇	1 ◇	1	1 ◇	1	1	1 ◇	1	1 ◇	1 ◇	1	1	1 ◇	1 ◇	1 ◇	1	1 ◇	1 ◇	1	1 ◇	1 ◇	1	1 ◇	1	1 ◇
														C	E						G					
		☕	🛒		☕			☕		☕	☕			☕	☕	🛒		☕	☕		☕	☕		🛒		☕
London Paddington 15 ⊖	d	17 33			17 45			17 48	17 36	17 51	18 00		17 25	18 03	18 06			18 15	18 21	18 18	18 30	18 36				18 45
Ealing Broadway ⊖	d												17 33													
Slough 3	d												17 58													
Maidenhead 3	d								17 59				18 10							18 39						
Twyford 3	d								18 08				18 17		18 28					18 47						
Reading 7	a	18 00			18 10			18 15	18 16	18 20	18 25		18 26	18 30	18 36			18 40	18 50	18 55	18 55	19 02				19 10
	d	18 01	18 10				18 12	18 16	18 18	18 21	18 27		18 27		18 36	18 40		18 41	18 51	18 56	18 57	19 03		19 10		
Reading West	d						18 14																			
Theale	d						18 20								18 45											
Aldermaston	d						18 25																			
Midgham	d						18 29																			
Thatcham	d						18 34								18 55											
Newbury Racecourse	d						18 38																			
Newbury	a	18 16					18 44								19 01							19 18				
	d					18 23									19 01							19 19				
Kintbury	d					18 29									19 09											
Hungerford	d					18 34									19 15							19a28				
Bedwyn	a					18 43									19 24											
Tilehurst	d			←					18 23				18 31							19 00					←	
Pangbourne	d			18 04					18 27			←	18 36							19 04					19 04	
Goring & Streatley	d			18 09					18 32			18 32	18 41				←			→					19 09	
Cholsey	d			18 14					→			18 38	18 46				18 46								19 14	
Didcot Parkway	a			18 22				18 32			18 41	18 45	→				18 53	18 55			19 11				19 22	
	d			18 25								18 45					18 55								19 25	
Appleford	d																19 01								19 30	
Culham	d			18 31																					19 32	
Radley	d			18 35								18 53					19 06								19 36	
Oxford	a		18 34	18 45						18 48		19 02				19 04	19 14		19 18					19 34	19 45	
	d		18 35													19 05	19 14						19 23	19 35		
Islip	d																						19 36			
Bicester Town	a																						19 49			
Tackley	d																19 23									
Heyford	d																19 28									
Kings Sutton	d																19 38									
Banbury	a		18 52													19 24	19 45							19 52		
Leamington Spa 8	a		19 10													19 41								20 10		
Warwick	a		*19b20*													*19 58*										
Warwick Parkway	a		*19 27*													*20 02*								*20 28*		
Stratford-upon-Avon	a		*19c51*																							
Coventry	a		19 22																					20 22		
Birmingham International	a		19 37																					20 37		
Birmingham New Street 12	a		19 50													20 17								20 49		

For general notes see front of timetable
For details of catering facilities see Directory of Train Operators

- **A** To Taunton (Table 134)
- **B** Until 4 September
- **C** From 7 September
- **D** To Westbury (Table 135)
- **E** To Frome (Table 123)
- **G** To Weston-super-Mare (Table 134)
- **b** Change at Banbury
- **c** Change at Banbury. From 5 October arr. 3 minutes later

London and Reading → Bedwyn, Oxford, Bicester, Banbury and Birmingham

Network Diagram - see first page of Table 116

		GW	GW	GW	GW	GW	GW	GW	GW	GW	XC	GW	GW	GW	GW	GW	GW	GW	GW	XC	GW	GW	GW	GW	GW	GW
		1	1	1	1 ◇	1	1 ◇	1	1 ◇	1	1 ◇	1	1	1 ◇	1	1 ◇	1	1	1 ◇	1 ◇	1	1 ◇	1 ◇	1 ◇	1	1 ◇
																			A							
					☕				☕	✕	🛒			☕		☕			☕			☕	☕			☕
London Paddington 15 ⊖	d			18 33	18 48		18 51	18 25	19 00	19 03				19 15		19 22		19 18	19 30			19 45	19 48	19 50	19 27	20 00
Ealing Broadway ⊖	d							18 33																	19 35	
Slough 3	d						19 06	18 58								19 37								20 06	19 59	
Maidenhead 3	d			18 53				19 10										19 39							20 09	
Twyford 3	d			19 03				19 18										19 47							20 17	
Reading 7	a			19 12	19 15	←	19 21	19 26	19 26	19 31				19 40		19 52		19 55	19 57			20 10	20 15	20 21	20 25	20 26
	d		19 12	19 17	19 16	19 17	19 22	19 27	19 27	19 32	19 40			19 41	19 42	19 53		19 56	19 57	20 10		20 11	20 16	20 22	20 25	20 27
Reading West	d		19 14	→											19 44											
Theale	d		19 20												19 50											
Aldermaston	d		19 25												19 55											
Midgham	d		19 29												19 59											
Thatcham	d		19 34												20 04											
Newbury Racecourse	d		19 38												20 08											
Newbury	a		19 45							19 47					20 16							20 27				
	d	19 28													20 32											
Kintbury	d	19 34													20 38											
Hungerford	d	19 39													20 42											
Bedwyn	a	19 48													20 52											
Tilehurst	d					19 24		19 31										20 00			←				20 29	
Pangbourne	d					19 29		19 35				←	←					20 04			20 04				20 34	
Goring & Streatley	d					19 35		19 40				19 35	19 40					→			20 09				→	
Cholsey	d					→		→				19 41	19 46								20 14					
Didcot Parkway	a				19 32				19 41			19 49	19 54	19 55			←		20 12		20 22		20 32			20 41
	d											19 55	20 08				20 08				20 25					
Appleford	d												→								20 30					
Culham	d																				20 32					
Radley	d											20 04					20 16				20 36					
Oxford	a						19 50				20 04	20 14				20 21	20 26			20 34	20 45			20 49		
	d										20 05									20 35						
Islip	d																									
Bicester Town	a																									
Tackley	d																									
Heyford	d																									
Kings Sutton	d																									
Banbury	a										20 24									20 52						
Leamington Spa 8	a										20 41									21 10						
Warwick	a										*21 00*															
Warwick Parkway	a										*21 03*									*21 30*						
Stratford-upon-Avon	a										*21b43*															
Coventry	a																			21 22						
Birmingham International	a																			21 37						
Birmingham New Street 12	a										21 22									21 49						

		GW	GW	GW	XC	GW	GW	GW	GW	GW	XC	XC	GW	GW	GW	GW	GW	GW	GW	XC	GW	GW	XC	GW	GW	GW
		1	1	1	1 ◇	1 ◇	1	1 ◇	1	1 ◇	1 ◇	1 ◇	1	1 ◇	1	1	1 ◇	1	1 ◇	1 ◇	1	1 ◇	1 ◇	1	1	1 ◇
						☕		☕		☕				☕					☕							☕
London Paddington 15 ⊖	d					20 15		20 20	19 57	20 35				20 45	20 27		20 51		21 15		20 57	21 21				21 45
Ealing Broadway ⊖	d								20 05						20 35						21 05					
Slough 3	d							20 35	20 27						20 57		21 07				21 27	21 37				
Maidenhead 3	d								20 34						21 04						21 34					
Twyford 3	d								20 42						21 12						21 42					
Reading 7	a					20 40		20 50	20 52	21 00				21 10	21 20		21 23	←	21 40		21 51	21 53		←		22 10
	d				20 40	20 41	20 41	20 51	20 54	21 01		21 10		21 11	21 27		21 23	21 27	21 41	21 45	21 57	21 54		21 57	22 01	22 11
Reading West	d						20 44								→						→				22 03	
Theale	d						20 50																		22 10	
Aldermaston	d						20 55																		22 15	
Midgham	d						20 58																		22 18	
Thatcham	d						21 03																		22 23	
Newbury Racecourse	d						21 08																		22 28	
Newbury	a						21 11			21 17															22 31	
	d						21 22																		22 31	
Kintbury	d						21 29																		22 37	
Hungerford	d						21 33																		22 42	
Bedwyn	a						21 43																		22 52	
Tilehurst	d			←					20 59									21 32						22 02		
Pangbourne	d			20 34					21 03				←					21 36						22 07		
Goring & Streatley	d			20 39					21 08				21 08					21 41						22 12		
Cholsey	d			20 44					→				21 13					21 46						22 17		
Didcot Parkway	a			20 51		20 55							21 22	21 25				21 54	22 00					22 25		22 30
	d			20 55									21 25					21 55						22 25		
Appleford	d																	21 59								
Culham	d																	22 02								
Radley	d			21 03														22 06								
Oxford	a			21 12	21 21			21 16			←	21 34	21 40				21 53	22 15		22 28		22 24	←	22 39		
	d	20 54	20 59		21 22						21 22	21 35				21 42				22 30			22 30			
Islip	d		21 12		→															→						
Bicester Town	a		21 25																							
Tackley	d	21 02														21 51										
Heyford	d	21 06														21 55										
Kings Sutton	d	21 15														22 04										
Banbury	a	21 23									21 40	21 52				22 11							22 52			
Leamington Spa 8	a										21 59	22 10				*23 05*							23 10			
Warwick	a										*22c10*					*23 10*							*23 52*			
Warwick Parkway	a										*22c13*	*22 33*				*23 13*							*23 56*			
Stratford-upon-Avon	a																									
Coventry	a											22 22														
Birmingham International	a											22 33														
Birmingham New Street 12	a										22 35	22 50											23 55			

For general notes see front of timetable
For details of catering facilities see Directory of Train Operators

A To Weston-super-Mare (Table 134)
b From 5 October arr. 3 minutes later
c Change at Banbury

London and Reading → Bedwyn, Oxford, Bicester, Banbury and Birmingham

Network Diagram - see first page of Table 116

		GW	GW	GW	GW	GW	GW	GW	GW	GW	GW	GW	GW	GW	GW	GW	GW	GW	GW	GW	GW	GW	GW	GW
		FO		FX		FO		FO	FX	FO			FX		FO	FX	FO	FX		FO	FO	FX	FX	
		1◇	1	1◇	1	1	1	1◇	1◇	1◇	1	1	1◇	1	1◇	1◇	1◇	1◇	1	1◇	1◇	1◇	1◇	1
		A		B																				
		☕		☕				☕	☕						☕	☕					☕		☕	
London Paddington 15 ⊖	d	21 48	21 27	21 48				22 15	22 15	22 21	21 57		22 21		22 45	22 45	22 48	22 48	22 45	23 20	23 30	23 20	23 30	23 29
Ealing Broadway ⊖	d		21 35								22 05								22 54					23 37
Slough 3	d	22 03	21 54	22 03						22 37	22 33		22 42				23 06	23 06	23 12	23 39		23 39		23 54
Maidenhead 3	d		22 01								22 41								23 23					00 01
Twyford 3	d		22 09								22 49								23 31					00 09
Reading 7	a	22 19	22 20	22 23			←	22 40	22 49	22 53	22 58		23 06		23 10	23 20	23 21	23 34	23 40	23 54	00 01	00 04	00 07	00 19
	d	22 23	22 27	22 23			22 27	22 41	22 50	22 53	22 58	23 00	23 06		23 11	23 21	23 21	23 34	23 40	23 54	00 02	00 04	00 08	00 19
Reading West	d		↪									23 02												
Theale	d											23 08												
Aldermaston	d											23 13												
Midgham	d											23 17												
Thatcham	d											23 22												
Newbury Racecourse	d											23 26												
Newbury	a											23 29												
	d											23 29												
Kintbury	d											23 36												
Hungerford	d											23 40												
Bedwyn	a											23 50												
Tilehurst	d						22 32				23 02								23 44					00 23
Pangbourne	d						22 37				23 07			←					23 49					00 28
Goring & Streatley	d						22 42				23 12			23 12					23 54					00 33
Cholsey	d						22 47				↪			23 17					23 59					00 38
Didcot Parkway	a						22 57	23 01	23 08					23 25	23 30	23 39			00 06		00 20		00 25	00 45
	d						22 57							23 28					00 06					00 45
Appleford	d						23 02																	00 50
Culham	d						23 04																	00 52
Radley	d						23 08												00 14					00 56
Oxford	a	22 51		22 51			23 20			23 26			23 39	23 44			23 49	00 13	00 23	00 29		00 34		01 06
	d				22 56	23 01																		
Islip	d					23 14																		
Bicester Town	a					23 27																		
Tackley	d				23 06																			
Heyford	d				23 10																			
Kings Sutton	d				23 19																			
Banbury	a				23 26																			
Leamington Spa 8	a				*00 54*																			
Warwick	a				*00 58*																			
Warwick Parkway	a				*01 08*																			
Stratford-upon-Avon	a																							
Coventry	a																							
Birmingham International	a																							
Birmingham New Street 12	a																							

For general notes see front of timetable
For details of catering facilities see Directory of Train Operators

A ☕ until 4 September
B ☕ until 3 September

Table 116

Saturdays

until 5 September

London and Reading → Bedwyn, Oxford, Bicester, Banbury and Birmingham

Network Diagram - see first page of Table 116

		CH	GW 1	GW 1◇ ꟼ	GW 1	GW 1	GW 1◇	GW 1	GW 1	GW 1	GW 1	GW 1◇	GW 1	XC 1◇ ⊼	GW 1	GW 1	GW 1◇	GW 1	GW 1	XC 1◇ ⊼	GW 1	GW 1◇	GW 1◇ ꟼ		GW 1	XC 1◇ ⊼
London Paddington 15	⊖ d		22p45	23p30	23p29		00 21					05 21				05 25	05 50					06 21	06 30		05 57	
Ealing Broadway	⊖ d		22p54		23p37											05 33									06 05	
Slough 3	d		23p12		23p54		00 39					05 37				05 51	06 07					06 37			06 31	
Maidenhead 3	d		23p23		00 01											06 02									06 42	
Twyford 3	d		23p31		00 09											06 10									06 50	
Reading 7	a		23p40	00 01	00 19		00 55					05 52				06 17	06 22					06 51	06 56		06 56	
	d		23p40	00 02	00 19	00 20	00 56	05 10		05 41	05 45	05 54		06 10	06 12	06 18	06 23			06 46	06 48	06 53	06 57		07 01	07 10
Reading West	d					00s23		05 13		05 44					06 14											
Theale	d					00s29		05 19		05 50					06 20						06 55					
Aldermaston	d					00s34		05 24		05 55					06 25											
Midgham	d					00s37		05 27		05 58					06 29											
Thatcham	d					00s42		05 32		06 03					06 34						07 04					
Newbury Racecourse	d					00s47		05 37		06 08					06 38											
Newbury	a					00 52		05 39		06 10					06 44						07 09					
	d							05 39		06 10											07 09					
Kintbury	d							05 46		06 17											07 16					
Hungerford	d							05 50		06 21											07 20					
Bedwyn	a							05 59		06 30											07 29					
Tilehurst	d		23p44		00 23						05 49		←			06 22			←						07 05	
Pangbourne	d		23p49		00 28						05 53 →		05 53			06 27 →			06 27						07 10	
Goring & Streatley	d		23p54		00 33								05 58						06 32						07 15 →	
Cholsey	d		23p59		00 38								06 03						06 37							
Didcot Parkway	a		00 06	00 20	00 45		01 13					06 07	06 12				06 37		06 44				07 12			
	d		00 06		00 45		01 14					06 08	06 13				06 38		06 44							
Appleford	d				00 50								06 17													
Culham	d				00 52								06 20													
Radley	d		00 14		00 56								06 24						06 52							
Oxford	a		00 23		01 06		01 30					06 23	06 32	06 34			06 52		07 03	07 10		07 18				07 34
	d	00 20							06 16					06 36				07 00		07 12						07 36
Islip	d																	07 13								
Bicester Town	a																	07 25								
Tackley	d								06 25																	
Heyford	d								06 29																	
Kings Sutton	d								06 38																	
Banbury	a	00 47							06 46					06 52						07 30						07 52
Leamington Spa 8	a													07 10						07 48						08 10
Warwick	a													*07 25*						*08 00*						*08 24*
Warwick Parkway	a													*07 28*						*08 04*						*08 27*
Stratford-upon-Avon	a																									
Coventry	a													07 24												08 22
Birmingham International	a													07 37												08 37
Birmingham New Street 12	a													07 49						08 17						08 49

For general notes see front of timetable
For details of catering facilities see Directory of Train Operators

London and Reading → Bedwyn, Oxford, Bicester, Banbury and Birmingham

Network Diagram - see first page of Table 116

		GW	GW	GW	GW	GW	GW	GW	GW	GW	XC	GW	GW	GW	XC	GW	GW	GW	GW	GW	GW	XC	GW		GW	GW
		1	1	1	1 ◇	1	1	1	1 ◇	1	1 ◇	1	1 ◇	1	1 ◇	1	1 ◇	1	1	1 ◇	1 ◇	1 ◇	1		1 ◇	1
									☕		🛒		☕	☕	🛒		☕				☕	🛒			☕	
London Paddington 15 ⊖	d			06 27	06 50				07 00			06 57	07 21	07 30			07 45		07 27	07 50	08 00				08 15	
Ealing Broadway ⊖	d			06 35								07 05							07 35							
Slough 3	d			06 57	07 07							07 27	07 37						07 57	08 07						
Maidenhead 3	d			07 04								07 34							08 04							
Twyford 3	d			07 12								07 42							08 12							
Reading 7	a			07 20	07 21			←	07 26			07 51	07 51	07 56			08 10		08 20	08 22	08 26				08 40	
	d		07 11	07 23	07 22			07 23		07 35	07 45	07 53	07 53	07 57	08 10			08 18	08 23	08 23		08 40			08 41	
Reading West	d		07 14	→														08 21								
Theale	d		07 21							07 44								08 28								
Aldermaston	d		07 26															08 33								
Midgham	d		07 29															08 36								
Thatcham	d		07 34							07 52								08 41								
Newbury Racecourse	d		07 39															08 46								
Newbury	a		07 43							07 58								08 50								
	d									07 58																08 58
Kintbury	d									08 04																09 04
Hungerford	d									08 09																09 09
Bedwyn	a									08 18																09 17
Tilehurst	d							07 28				07 58				←			08 28							
Pangbourne	d	←						07 32				08 02 →				08 02			08 32							
Goring & Streatley	d	07 15						07 37								08 07			08 37				←			
Cholsey	d	07 20						07 42								08 12			08 42 →				08 42			
Didcot Parkway	a	07 30						07 49						08 12		08 20							08 50		08 56	
	d	07 30						07 51								08 25							08 55			
Appleford	d																						09 00			
Culham	d							07 56																		
Radley	d							08 00															09 05			
Oxford	a	07 43			07 48			08 09			08 13		08 19		08 34	08 40				08 48		09 04	09 14			
	d					07 53	08 07				08 15				08 36							09 07				
Islip	d						08 20																			
Bicester Town	a						08 32																			
Tackley	d					08 02																				
Heyford	d					08 06																				
Kings Sutton	d					08 15																				
Banbury	a					08 23					08 34				08 52							09 24				
Leamington Spa 8	a										08 52				09 10							09 42				
Warwick	a										*09 04*				*09 21*							*10 02*				
Warwick Parkway	a										*09 07*				*09 26*							*10 05*				
Stratford-upon-Avon	a										*09 36*															
Coventry	a														09 22											
Birmingham International	a														09 37											
Birmingham New Street 12	a										09 17				09 49							10 17				

		GW	GW	GW	GW	GW	GW	XC	GW	GW	GW	GW	GW	GW	XC	GW	GW	GW	GW	GW	GW	XC	GW		GW	GW
		1	1	1 ◇	1 ◇	1	1	1 ◇	1 ◇	1	1	1	1 ◇	1 ◇	1 ◇	1	1	1	1	1 ◇	1 ◇	1 ◇	1 ◇		1	1
				☕	☕	☕		🛒	☕					☕	🛒						☕	🛒	☕			
London Paddington 15 ⊖	d	08 18	07 57	08 21	08 30	08 35			08 45			08 27	08 50	09 00			09 18	08 57		09 21	09 30		09 45			
Ealing Broadway ⊖	d		08 05									08 35						09 05								
Slough 3	d		08 27	08 39								08 57	09 07					09 27		09 39						
Maidenhead 3	d		08 34									09 04						09 34								
Twyford 3	d		08 42									09 12						09 42								
Reading 7	a	08 48	08 51	08 53	08 57				09 10			09 20	09 22	09 26			09 47	09 51		09 53	09 57		10 10			
	d	08 48	08 53	08 54	08 57	09u04		09 10			09 12	09 23	09 23		09 40		09 47	09 53		09 54	09 57	10 10				10 12
Reading West	d										09 14															10 14
Theale	d	08 56									09 20						09 55									10 20
Aldermaston	d										09 25															10 25
Midgham	d										09 29															10 29
Thatcham	d	09 04									09 34						10 04									10 34
Newbury Racecourse	d										09 38															10 38
Newbury	a	09 10				09 20					09 44						10 09									10 44
	d	09 27															10 09									
Kintbury	d	09 33															10 17									
Hungerford	d	09 38															10 20									
Bedwyn	a	09 46															10 30									
Tilehurst	d		08 58									09 28						09 58								
Pangbourne	d		09 02							←		09 32						10 02							←	
Goring & Streatley	d		09 07 →							09 07		09 37				←		10 07 →							10 07	
Cholsey	d									09 12		09 42 →				09 42									10 12	
Didcot Parkway	a				09 12					09 19						09 50					10 12				10 20	
	d									09 25						09 55									10 25	
Appleford	d																									
Culham	d															10 01										
Radley	d															10 05										
Oxford	a			09 18				09 34		09 40			09 48		10 04	10 14				10 20		10 34			10 40	
	d						09 27	09 36							10 07				10 16			10 36				
Islip	d						09 41																			
Bicester Town	a						09 53																			
Tackley	d																		10 25							
Heyford	d																		10 29							
Kings Sutton	d																		10 40							
Banbury	a							09 52							10 24				10 48			10 52				
Leamington Spa 8	a							10 10							10 42							11 10				
Warwick	a							*10b21*							*11 02*							*11b21*				
Warwick Parkway	a							*10b25*							*11 05*							*11b24*				
Stratford-upon-Avon	a							*11 13*																		
Coventry	a							10 22														11 22				
Birmingham International	a							10 37														11 37				
Birmingham New Street 12	a							10 49							11 17							11 49				

For general notes see front of timetable
For details of catering facilities see
Directory of Train Operators

b Change at Banbury

Table 116

Saturdays

London and Reading → Bedwyn, Oxford, Bicester, Banbury and Birmingham

until 5 September

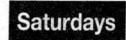

Network Diagram - see first page of Table 116

		GW 1	GW 1◇	GW 1◇ ⊏	GW 1	XC 1◇ ✕	GW 1	GW 1◇ ⊏	GW 1	GW 1	GW 1◇ ⊏	GW 1◇ ⊏	GW 1 ⊏	XC 1◇ ✕	GW 1◇ ⊏	GW 1	GW 1	GW 1	GW 1◇	GW 1◇ ⊏	XC 1◇ ✕	GW 1	GW 1		GW 1	GW 1
London Paddington 15	⊖ d	09 27	09 50	10 00				10 15	10 18	09 57	10 21	10 30	10 35		10 45			10 27	10 50	11 00					11 18	10 57
Ealing Broadway	⊖ d	09 35								10 05								10 35								11 05
Slough 3	d	09 57	10 07							10 27	10 39							10 57	11 07							11 27
Maidenhead 3	d	10 04								10 34								11 04								11 34
Twyford 3	d	10 12								10 42								11 12								11 42
Reading 7	a	10 20	10 22	10 26				10 40	10 48	10 51	10 53	10 57	11 03		11 10			11 20	11 22	11 26					11 48	11 51
	d	10 23	10 23			10 40		10 41	10 48	10 53	10 54	10 57		11 10			11 12	11 23	11 23		11 40				11 48	11 53
Reading West	d																11 14									
Theale	d								10 55								11 20								11 55	
Aldermaston	d																11 25									
Midgham	d																11 29									
Thatcham	d								11 04								11 34								12 04	
Newbury Racecourse	d																11 38									
Newbury	a								11 09								11 44								12 09	
	d								11 20																12 23	
Kintbury	d								11 28																12 30	
Hungerford	d								11 31																12 33	
Bedwyn	a								11 42																12 43	
Tilehurst	d	10 28								10 58								11 28								11 58
Pangbourne	d	10 32								11 02						←		11 32				←				12 02
Goring & Streatley	d	10 37					←			11 07						11 07		11 37				11 37				12 07
Cholsey	d	10 42					10 42			→						11 12		→				11 42				→
Didcot Parkway	a	→					10 50	10 56				11 12				11 20						11 50				
	d						10 55									11 25						11 55				
Appleford	d						11 00																			
Culham	d																									
Radley	d						11 05															12 05				
Oxford	a		10 48			11 04	11 14				11 19			11 34		11 40			11 48		12 04	12 14				
	d				11 00	11 07								11 36							12 07		12 16			
Islip	d				11 13																					
Bicester Town	a				11 25																					
Tackley	d																						12 25			
Heyford	d																						12 29			
Kings Sutton	d																						12 39			
Banbury	a					11 24								11 52							12 24		12 46			
Leamington Spa 8	a					11 42								12 10							12 42					
Warwick	a					*11 58*								*12b21*							*12 58*					
Warwick Parkway	a					*12 02*								*12b25*							*13 02*					
Stratford-upon-Avon	a													*13 11*												
Coventry	a													12 22												
Birmingham International	a													12 37												
Birmingham New Street 12	a					12 17								12 49							13 17					

		GW 1◇ ⊏	GW 1◇ ⊏	GW 1	XC 1◇ ✕	GW 1◇ ⊏	GW 1	GW 1	GW 1◇	GW 1	GW 1◇ ⊏	XC 1◇ ✕	GW 1	GW 1◇ ⊏	GW 1	GW 1	GW 1◇	GW 1◇ ⊏	GW 1 ⊏	XC 1◇ ✕	GW 1◇ ⊏	GW 1	GW 1		GW 1	GW 1
London Paddington 15	⊖ d	11 21	11 30			11 45			11 50	11 27	12 00			12 15	12 18	11 57	12 21	12 30	12 35		12 45					
Ealing Broadway	⊖ d									11 35						12 05										
Slough 3	d	11 39								11 57						12 27	12 39									
Maidenhead 3	d									12 04						12 34										
Twyford 3	d									12 12						12 42										
Reading 7	a	11 53	11 57			12 11			12 19	12 20	12 26			12 40	12 48	12 51	12 54	12 57	13 03		13 10					
	d	11 54	11 57		12 10			12 14	12 20	12 23		12 40		12 41	12 48	12 53	12 54	12 57	13 04	13 10						13 12
Reading West	d							12 17																		13 14
Theale	d							12 23							12 56											13 20
Aldermaston	d							12 28																		13 25
Midgham	d							12 31																		13 29
Thatcham	d							12 36							13 04											13 34
Newbury Racecourse	d							12 41																		13 38
Newbury	a							12 45							13 10				13 20							13 44
	d																								13 25	
Kintbury	d																								13 31	
Hungerford	d																								13 36	
Bedwyn	a																								13 44	
Tilehurst	d									12 27						12 58										
Pangbourne	d						←			12 32			←			13 02						←				
Goring & Streatley	d						12 07			12 37			12 37			13 07						13 07				
Cholsey	d						12 12			→			12 42			→						13 12				
Didcot Parkway	a		12 12				12 20						12 49	12 56				13 12				13 20				
	d						12 25						12 55									13 25				
Appleford	d																									
Culham	d																									
Radley	d												13 05													
Oxford	a	12 18			12 34		12 40		12 48			13 04	13 14				13 20			13 34		13 40				
	d			12 30	12 36							13 07								13 36			13 41			
Islip	d			12 43																			13 54			
Bicester Town	a			12 55																			14 06			
Tackley	d																									
Heyford	d																									
Kings Sutton	d																									
Banbury	a				12 52							13 24								13 52						
Leamington Spa 8	a				13 10							13 42								14 10						
Warwick	a				*13b21*							*13 58*								*14b21*						
Warwick Parkway	a				*13b25*							*14 02*								*14b26*						
Stratford-upon-Avon	a																			*15 10*						
Coventry	a				13 22															14 22						
Birmingham International	a				13 37															14 37						
Birmingham New Street 12	a				13 49							14 17								14 49						

For general notes see front of timetable
For details of catering facilities see Directory of Train Operators

b Change at Banbury

Table 116

Saturdays

until 5 September

London and Reading → Bedwyn, Oxford, Bicester, Banbury and Birmingham

Network Diagram - see first page of Table 116

		GW	GW	GW	XC	GW	GW	GW	GW	GW	GW	XC	GW	GW	GW	GW	GW	GW	GW	XC	GW	GW	GW		GW	GW
		1	1◊	1◊ 🍴	1◊ 🛒	1	1	1	1	1◊ 🍴	1◊ 🍴	1◊ 🛒	1◊ 🍴	1	1	1	1◊	1◊ 🍴	1	1◊ 🛒	1	1◊ 🍴	1		1	1◊ 🍴
London Paddington 15	⊖ d	12 27	12 50	13 00			13 18	12 57		13 21	13 30		13 45			13 27	13 50	14 00				14 15	14 18		13 57	14 21
Ealing Broadway	⊖ d	12 35						13 05								13 35									14 05	
Slough 3	d	12 57	13 07					13 27		13 39						13 57	14 07								14 27	14 39
Maidenhead 3	d	13 04						13 34								14 04									14 34	
Twyford 3	d	13 12						13 42								14 12									14 42	
Reading 7	a	13 20	13 22	13 26			13 48	13 51		13 53	13 57		14 10			14 20	14 22	14 26				14 40	14 48		14 51	14 53
	d	13 23	13 23		13 40		13 48	13 53		13 54	13 57	14 10			14 12	14 23	14 23			14 40		14 41	14 48		14 53	14 54
Reading West	d														14 14											
Theale	d						13 55								14 20								14 55			
Aldermaston	d														14 25											
Midgham	d														14 29											
Thatcham	d						14 04								14 34								15 04			
Newbury Racecourse	d														14 38											
Newbury	a						14 09								14 44								15 09			
	d						14 09																15 09			
Kintbury	d						14 17																15 17			
Hungerford	d						14 20																15 22			
Bedwyn	a						14 31																15 33			
Tilehurst	d	13 28						13 57								14 28									14 58	
Pangbourne	d	13 32				←		14 02						←		14 32					←				15 02	
Goring & Streatley	d	13 37				13 37		14 07						14 07		14 37					14 37				15 07	
Cholsey	d	→				13 42		→						14 12		→					14 42				→	
Didcot Parkway	a					13 50					14 12			14 19							14 50	14 56				
	d					13 55								14 25							14 55					
Appleford	d																									
Culham	d																									
Radley	d					14 05															15 05					
Oxford	a		13 48		14 04	14 14				14 18		14 34		14 40			14 48			15 04	15 14					15 18
	d				14 07				14 16			14 36							14 57	15 07						
Islip	d																		15 10							
Bicester Town	a																		15 22							
Tackley	d								14 25																	
Heyford	d								14 29																	
Kings Sutton	d								14 38																	
Banbury	a				14 24				14 46			14 52								15 24						
Leamington Spa 8	a				14 42							15 10								15 42						
Warwick	a				*14 58*							*15b21*								*15 58*						
Warwick Parkway	a				*15 02*							*15b25*								*16 02*						
Stratford-upon-Avon	a																									
Coventry	a											15 22														
Birmingham International	a											15 37														
Birmingham New Street 12	a				15 17							15 49								16 17						

		GW	XC	GW	GW	GW	GW	GW	GW	GW	XC	GW	GW	GW	GW	GW	GW	XC	GW	GW	GW	GW	GW		GW	XC
		1◊ 🍴	1◊ 🛒	1◊ 🍴	1	1	1	1◊	1◊ 🍴	1	1◊ 🛒	1	1	1	1	1◊ 🍴	1◊ 🍴	1◊ 🛒	1◊ 🍴	1	1	1	1◊		1◊ 🍴	1◊ 🛒
London Paddington 15	⊖ d	14 30		14 45			14 27	14 50	15 00				15 18	14 57		15 21	15 30		15 45			15 27	15 50		16 00	
Ealing Broadway	⊖ d						14 35							15 05								15 35				
Slough 3	d						14 57	15 07						15 27		15 39						15 57	16 07			
Maidenhead 3	d						15 04							15 34								16 04				
Twyford 3	d						15 12							15 42								16 12				
Reading 7	a	14 57		15 10			15 20	15 22	15 26				15 48	15 51		15 53	15 57		16 10			16 20	16 22		16 27	
	d	14 57	15 10			15 12	15 23	15 23			15 40		15 48	15 53		15 54	15 57	16 10			16 12	16 23	16 23			16 40
Reading West	d					15 14															16 14					
Theale	d					15 20							15 55								16 20					
Aldermaston	d					15 25															16 25					
Midgham	d					15 29															16 29					
Thatcham	d					15 34							16 04								16 34					
Newbury Racecourse	d					15 38															16 38					
Newbury	a					15 44							16 09								16 44					
	d												16 09													
Kintbury	d												16 17													
Hungerford	d												16 20													
Bedwyn	a												16 31													
Tilehurst	d						15 28							15 58								16 28				
Pangbourne	d				←		15 32							16 02						←		16 32				
Goring & Streatley	d				15 07		15 37					←		16 07						16 07		16 37				
Cholsey	d				15 12		15 42					15 42		→						16 12		16 42				
Didcot Parkway	a	15 12			15 20		→					15 49					16 12			16 20		→				
	d				15 25							15 55								16 25						
Appleford	d																									
Culham	d											16 01														
Radley	d											16 05														
Oxford	a		15 34		15 40			15 48			16 04	16 14				16 18		16 34		16 40			16 48			17 04
	d		15 36							16 01	16 07				16 16			16 36								17 07
Islip	d									16 14																
Bicester Town	a									16 26																
Tackley	d														16 25											
Heyford	d														16 29											
Kings Sutton	d														16 39											
Banbury	a		15 52								16 24				16 46			16 52								17 24
Leamington Spa 8	a		16 10								16 42							17 10								17 42
Warwick	a		*16b21*								*16 57*							*17b22*								*17 58*
Warwick Parkway	a		*16b24*								*17 01*							*17b25*								*18 02*
Stratford-upon-Avon	a		*17 11*																							
Coventry	a		16 22															17 22								
Birmingham International	a		16 37															17 37								
Birmingham New Street 12	a		16 49								17 17							17 49								18 17

For general notes see front of timetable
For details of catering facilities see Directory of Train Operators

b Change at Banbury

Saturdays

until 5 September

London and Reading → Bedwyn, Oxford, Bicester, Banbury and Birmingham

Network Diagram - see first page of Table 116

		GW 1	GW 1	GW 1◇	GW 1	GW 1	GW 1◇	GW 1◇	XC 1◇	GW 1◇	GW 1	GW 1	GW 1	GW 1◇	GW 1◇	XC 1◇	GW 1	GW 1	GW 1	GW 1	GW 1◇	GW 1◇	XC 1◇		GW 1◇	GW 1
																						B				
				☕			☕	☕	🛒	☕					☕	🛒					☕	☕	🛒		☕	
London Paddington 15	⊖ d			16 15	16 18	15 57	16 21	16 30		16 45			16 27	16 50	17 00			17 18	16 57		17 21	17 30			17 45	
Ealing Broadway	⊖ d					16 05							16 35						17 05							
Slough 3	d					16 27	16 39						16 57	17 07					17 27		17 39					
Maidenhead 3	d					16 34							17 04						17 34							
Twyford 3	d					16 42							17 12						17 42							
Reading 7	a			16 40	16 48	16 51	16 53	16 57		17 10			17 20	17 22	17 26			17 48	17 51		17 53	17 57			18 11	
	d			16 41	16 48	16 53	16 54	16 57	17 10			17 12	17 23	17 23		17 40		17 48	17 53		17 54	17 57	18 10			
Reading West	d											17 14														
Theale	d				16 55							17 20						17 55								
Aldermaston	d											17 25														
Midgham	d											17 29														
Thatcham	d				17 04							17 34						18 04								
Newbury Racecourse	d											17 38														
Newbury	a				17 09							17 44						18 09								
	d				17 09													18 09								
Kintbury	d				17 17													18 17								
Hungerford	d				17 20													18 20								
Bedwyn	a				17 31													18 30								
Tilehurst	d					16 58							17 28						17 58							
Pangbourne	d					17 02					←		17 32						18 02							←
Goring & Streatley	d		←			17 07					17 07		17 37				←		18 07							18 07
Cholsey	d		16 42			→					17 12		17 42				17 42		→							18 12
Didcot Parkway	a		16 49	16 56				17 12			17 20		→				17 49					18 12				18 20
	d		16 55								17 25						17 55									18 25
Appleford	d		17 00																							
Culham	d																18 01									
Radley	d		17 05														18 05									
Oxford	a		17 14				17 18		17 34		17 40			17 48		18 04	18 14				18 18		18 34			18 40
	d	17 10							17 36							18 07				18 16			18 36			
Islip	d	17 26																								
Bicester Town	a	17 38																								
Tackley	d																			18 25						
Heyford	d																			18 29						
Kings Sutton	d																			18 38						
Banbury	a								17 52							18 24				18 46			18 52			
Leamington Spa 8	a								18 10							18 42							19 10			
Warwick	a								18b21							18 58							19 26			
Warwick Parkway	a								18b26							19 02							19 30			
Stratford-upon-Avon	a								19 13																	
Coventry	a								18 22														19 22			
Birmingham International	a								18 37														19 37			
Birmingham New Street 12	a								18 49							19 17							19 49			

		GW 1	GW 1	GW 1	GW 1◇	GW 1◇	XC 1◇	GW 1	GW 1◇	GW 1	GW 1	GW 1	GW 1◇	GW 1◇	XC 1◇	GW 1◇	GW 1	GW 1	GW 1	GW 1◇	GW 1◇	GW 1◇	GW 1		XC 1◇	GW 1
						☕	🛒		☕				☕	☕	🛒	☕					☕	☕			🛒	
London Paddington 15	⊖ d		17 27		17 50	18 00			18 15	18 18	17 57		18 21	18 30		18 45		18 27		18 50	19 00	19 06				
Ealing Broadway	⊖ d		17 35								18 05							18 35								
Slough 3	d		17 57		18 07						18 27		18 39					18 57		19 07						
Maidenhead 3	d		18 04								18 34							19 04								
Twyford 3	d		18 12								18 42							19 12								
Reading 7	a		18 20		18 22	18 27			18 40	18 48	18 51		18 53	18 57		19 11		19 20		19 22	19 26	19 32				
	d	18 12	18 23		18 23		18 40		18 41	18 48	18 53		18 54	18 57	19 10			19 23		19 23		19 32			19 40	
Reading West	d	18 14																								
Theale	d	18 20								18 55																
Aldermaston	d	18 25																								
Midgham	d	18 29																								
Thatcham	d	18 34								19 04																
Newbury Racecourse	d	18 38																								
Newbury	a	18 44								19 09												19 48				
	d									19 09																
Kintbury	d									19 17																
Hungerford	d									19 20																
Bedwyn	a									19 30																
Tilehurst	d		18 28								18 58							19 28								
Pangbourne	d		18 32								19 02						←	19 32								
Goring & Streatley	d		18 37					←			19 07						19 07	19 37								←
Cholsey	d		18 42					18 42			→						19 12	19 42								19 42
Didcot Parkway	a		→					18 49	18 56					19 12			19 20	→								19 49
	d							18 55									19 25									19 55
Appleford	d							19 00																		20 01
Culham	d																									
Radley	d							19 05																		20 05
Oxford	a				18 48		19 04	19 14					19 18		19 34		19 40			19 48					20 04	20 14
	d			18 41			19 07					19 16			19 36				19 48				19 56		20 07	
Islip	d			18 54															20 01							
Bicester Town	a			19 06															20 13							
Tackley	d											19 25											20 05			
Heyford	d											19 29											20 09			
Kings Sutton	d											19 38											→			
Banbury	a						19 24					19 46			19 52										20 24	
Leamington Spa 8	a						19 42								20 10										20 42	
Warwick	a						19 58								20 26											
Warwick Parkway	a						20 02								20 30											
Stratford-upon-Avon	a														21 10											
Coventry	a														20 22											
Birmingham International	a														20 37											
Birmingham New Street 12	a						20 17								20 49										21 17	

For general notes see front of timetable
For details of catering facilities see
Directory of Train Operators

B To Weston-super-Mare (Table 134)
b Change at Banbury

Table 116

Saturdays

until 5 September

London and Reading → Bedwyn, Oxford, Bicester, Banbury and Birmingham

Network Diagram - see first page of Table 116

		GW	GW	GW	GW	GW	XC	GW	GW	GW	GW	GW	GW	GW	XC	GW	GW	GW	GW	GW	GW	GW	XC		GW	GW
		1	1	1 ◇	1 ◇	1	1 ◇	1 ◇	1	1	1 ◇	1 ◇	1 ◇	1	1 ◇	1	1 ◇	1	1	1	1 ◇	1 ◇	1 ◇		1 ◇	1
					☕		🛒	☕			🛒	☕	☕		🛒		☕					☕	🛒		☕	
London Paddington 15 ⊖	d		18 57	19 21	19 30			19 45		19 27	19 50	20 00	20 06				20 15		19 57		20 21	20 30			20 45	
Ealing Broadway ⊖	d		19 05							19 35									20 05							
Slough 3	d		19 27	19 38						19 57	20 07								20 27							
Maidenhead 3	d		19 34							20 04									20 34							
Twyford 3	d		19 42							20 12									20 42							
Reading 7	a		19 51	19 53	19 57			20 10		20 20	20 21	20 27	20 31				20 40		20 51		20 52	20 57			21 10	
	d	19 49	19 53	19 54	19 57		20 10			20 23	20 23	20 27	20 31		20 40		20 41	20 49	20 53		20 53	20 57	21 10			
Reading West	d	19 52																20 52								
Theale	d	19 58																20 58								
Aldermaston	d	20 03																21 03								
Midgham	d	20 06																21 06								
Thatcham	d	20 11																21 11								
Newbury Racecourse	d	20 16																21 16								
Newbury	a	20 18											20 46					21 18								
	d	20 18																21 32								
Kintbury	d	20 25																21 39								
Hungerford	d	20 29																21 43								
Bedwyn	a	20 38																21 52								
Tilehurst	d		19 58							20 28									20 58							
Pangbourne	d		20 02						←	20 32									21 02							←
Goring & Streatley	d		20 07						20 07	20 37						←			21 07							21 07
Cholsey	d		→						20 12	20 42						20 42			→							21 12
Didcot Parkway	a				20 12				20 20	→		20 41				20 49	20 56					21 12				21 20
	d								20 25							20 55										21 25
Appleford	d															21 00										
Culham	d																									
Radley	d															21 05										
Oxford	a			20 20			20 34		20 40		20 47				21 04	21 14					21 20		21 34			21 40
	d						20 36							21 00	21 07					21 20			21 36			
Islip	d													21 13												
Bicester Town	a													21 25												
Tackley	d					←														21 29						
Heyford	d					20 09														21 33						
Kings Sutton	d					20 18														21 42						
Banbury	a					20 25	20 52								21 24					21 49			21 52			
Leamington Spa 8	a					*20 54*	21 10								21 42								22 10			
Warwick	a					*20 58*	*21 42*																*22 31*			
Warwick Parkway	a					*21 02*	*21 46*																*22 34*			
Stratford-upon-Avon	a																									
Coventry	a						21 22								21 55								22 22			
Birmingham International	a						21 37								22 12								22 37			
Birmingham New Street 12	a						21 49								22 25								22 54			

		GW	GW	XC	GW	GW	GW	GW	GW	GW	GW	GW	GW	GW	GW	GW	GW	GW	GW	GW	GW	GW	GW	GW		
		1	1 ◇	1 ◇	1	1	1	1	1 ◇	1	1 ◇	1	1 ◇	1 ◇	1	🚌	1 ◇	1 ◇	1	1 ◇	1	1 ◇	1 ◇	1		
				🛒							☕			☕			☕					☕				
London Paddington 15 ⊖	d	20 27	20 50				20 57		21 21		21 30		21 50	22 00	21 57		22 30	22 32		23 00	22 45	23 30	23 33	23 20		
Ealing Broadway ⊖	d	20 35					21 05								22 05						22 55			23 28		
Slough 3	d	20 57	21 09				21 27						22 07		22 27			22 50		23 17	23 21		23 50	23 54		
Maidenhead 3	d	21 04					21 34								22 34						23 30			00 05		
Twyford 3	d	21 12					21 42								22 42						23 38			00 13		
Reading 7	a	21 20	21 24				21 51		21 52	←	21 57		22 22	22 27	22 51		22 55	23 06		23 33	23 44	23 59	00 07	00 20		
	d	21 23	21 24	21 40		21 51	21 53		21 52	21 53	21 57		22 22	22 27	22 53		23 00	23 07	23 12	23 34	23 49	23 59	00 08	00 21		
Reading West	d					21 54	→												23 14							
Theale	d					22 02													23 20							
Aldermaston	d					22 07													23 25							
Midgham	d					22 10													23 29							
Thatcham	d					22 15													23 34							
Newbury Racecourse	d					22 20													23 38							
Newbury	a					22 22													23 41							
	d					22 22													23 41							
Kintbury	d					22 29													23 48							
Hungerford	d					22 33													23 52							
Bedwyn	a					22 41													00 01							
Tilehurst	d	21 28			←					21 58		←			22 57						23 53			00 25		
Pangbourne	d	21 32			21 32					22 02		22 02			23 02						23 58					
Goring & Streatley	d	→			21 37					→		22 07			23 07						00 03			00 32		
Cholsey	d				21 42							22 12			23 12						00 08			00 37		
Didcot Parkway	a		21 39		21 49				22 08		22 12	22 20	22 37	22 42	23 19		23 22	23 28		23 50	00 15	00 18	00 24	00 44		
	d		21 39		21 55				22 09			22 25	22 37		23 20			23 28		23 50	00 17		00 24	00 45		
Appleford	d																									
Culham	d				22 01																					
Radley	d				22 05																00s24					
Oxford	a		21 53	22 04	22 14				22 21			22 40	22 49		23 33			23 42		00 04	00 33		00 38	00 59		
	d			22 07				22 17								23 40										
Islip	d							22 30																		
Bicester Town	a							22 42																		
Tackley	d															00s01										
Heyford	d															00s15										
Kings Sutton	d															00b30										
Banbury	a			22 24												00 40										
Leamington Spa 8	a			22 42																						
Warwick	a			*23 26*																						
Warwick Parkway	a			*23 29*																						
Stratford-upon-Avon	a																									
Coventry	a																									
Birmingham International	a																									
Birmingham New Street 12	a			23 17																						

For general notes see front of timetable
For details of catering facilities see
Directory of Train Operators

b Kings Sutton V. Square. Stops to set down only

Table 116

Saturdays

from 12 September

London and Reading → Bedwyn, Oxford, Bicester, Banbury and Birmingham

Network Diagram - see first page of Table 116

		CH	CH	GW	GW	GW	GW	GW	GW	GW	GW	GW	GW	GW	XC	GW	GW	GW	GW	GW	XC	GW	GW	GW	GW	XC
				1	1 ◇	1	1	1 ◇	1	1	1	1	1 ◇	1	1 ◇	1	1	1 ◇	1	1	1 ◇	1	1 ◇	1 ◇	1	1 ◇
		A	B		☕										🛒						🛒			☕		🛒
London Paddington 15 ⊖	d			22p45	23p30	23p29		00 21					05 21				05 25	05 50					06 21	06 30	05 57	
Ealing Broadway ⊖	d			22p54		23p37											05 33								06 05	
Slough 3	d			23p12		23p54		00 39					05 37				05 51	06 07					06 37		06 31	
Maidenhead 3	d			23p23		00 01											06 02								06 42	
Twyford 3	d			23p31		00 09											06 10								06 50	
Reading 7	a			23p40	00 01	00 19		00 55					05 52				06 17	06 22					06 51	06 56	06 56	
	d			23p40	00 02	00 19	00 20	00 56	05 10		05 41	05 45	05 54		06 10	06 12	06 18	06 23			06 46	06 48	06 53	06 57	07 01	07 10
Reading West	d						00s23		05 13		05 44					06 14										
Theale	d						00s29		05 19		05 50					06 20						06 55				
Aldermaston	d						00s34		05 24		05 55					06 25										
Midgham	d						00s37		05 27		05 58					06 29										
Thatcham	d						00s42		05 32		06 03					06 34						07 04				
Newbury Racecourse	d						00s47		05 37		06 08					06 38										
Newbury	a						00 52		05 39		06 10					06 44						07 09				
	d								05 39		06 10											07 09				
Kintbury	d								05 46		06 17											07 16				
Hungerford	d								05 50		06 21											07 20				
Bedwyn	a								05 59		06 30											07 29				
Tilehurst	d			23p44		00 23						05 49		←			06 22			←					07 05	
Pangbourne	d			23p49		00 28						05 53		05 53			06 27			06 27					07 10	
Goring & Streatley	d			23p54		00 33						→		05 58			→			06 32					07 15	
Cholsey	d			23p59		00 38								06 03						06 37					→	
Didcot Parkway	a			00 06	00 20	00 45		01 13					06 07	06 12				06 37		06 44				07 12		
	d			00 06		00 45		01 14					06 08	06 13				06 38		06 44						
Appleford	d					00 50								06 17												
Culham	d					00 52								06 20												
Radley	d			00 14		00 56								06 24						06 52						
Oxford	a			00 23		01 06		01 30					06 23	06 32	06 34			06 52		07 03	07 10		07 18			07 34
	d	00§20	00§20							06 16					06 36				07 00		07 12					07 36
Islip	d	§	§																07 13							
Bicester Town	a	§	§																07 25							
Tackley	d	§	§							06 25																
Heyford	d	§	§							06 29																
Kings Sutton	d	§	§							06 38																
Banbury	a	00§47	00§50							06 46					06 52						07 30					07 52
Leamington Spa 8	a														07 10						07 48					08 10
Warwick	a														*07 25*						*08 00*					*08 24*
Warwick Parkway	a														*07 28*						*08 04*					*08 27*
Stratford-upon-Avon	a																									
Coventry	a														07 24											08 22
Birmingham International	a														07 37											08 37
Birmingham New Street 12	a														07 49						08 17					08 49

For general notes see front of timetable
For details of catering facilities see Directory of Train Operators

A Until 3 October
B From 10 October

Table 116

Saturdays

from 12 September

London and Reading → Bedwyn, Oxford, Bicester, Banbury and Birmingham

Network Diagram - see first page of Table 116

		GW 1	GW 1	GW 1	GW 1 ◇	GW 1	GW 1	GW 1	GW 1 ◇ ☕	XC 1 ◇ 🛒	GW 1	GW 1	GW 1 ◇ ☕	GW 1 ◇ ☕	XC 1 ◇ 🛒	GW 1	GW 1 ◇ ☕	GW 1	GW 1	GW 1 ◇	GW 1 ◇ ☕	XC 1 ◇ 🛒	GW 1	GW 1 ◇ ☕	GW 1	GW 1 ◇ ☕
London Paddington 15 ⊖	d			06 27	06 50				07 00			06 57	07 21	07 30			07 45		07 27	07 50	08 00			08 15		08 18
Ealing Broadway ⊖	d			06 35								07 05							07 35							
Slough 3	d			06 57	07 07							07 27	07 37						07 57	08 07						
Maidenhead 3	d			07 04								07 34							08 04							
Twyford 3	d			07 12								07 42							08 12							
Reading 7	a			07 20	07 21			←	07 26			07 51	07 51	07 56			08 10		08 20	08 22	08 26			08 40		08 45
	d		07 11	07 23	07 22			07 23		07 45	07 48	07 53	07 53	07 57	08 10			08 12	08 23	08 23		08 40		08 41		08 49
Reading West	d		07 14	→														08 14								
Theale	d		07 21								07 57							08 20								08 58
Aldermaston	d		07 26															08 25								
Midgham	d		07 29															08 29								
Thatcham	d		07 34								08 05							08 34								09 07
Newbury Racecourse	d		07 39															08 38								
Newbury	a		07 43								08 11							08 44								09 13
	d										08 11														08 58	09 14
Kintbury	d										08 17														09 04	
Hungerford	d										08 22														09 09	09 23
Bedwyn	a										08 31														09 17	09 30
Tilehurst	d							07 28				07 58				←			08 28							
Pangbourne	d	←						07 32				08 02				08 02			08 32							
Goring & Streatley	d	07 15						07 37				→				08 07			08 37				←			
Cholsey	d	07 20						07 42								08 12			08 42				08 42			
Didcot Parkway	a	07 30						07 49						08 11		08 20			→				08 50	08 56		
	d	07 30						07 51								08 25							08 55			
Appleford	d																						09 00			
Culham	d							07 56																		
Radley	d							08 00															09 05			
Oxford	a	07 43			07 48			08 09		08 13			08 19		08 34	08 40				08 48		09 04	09 14			
	d					07 53	08 07			08 15					08 36							09 07				
Islip	d						08 20																			
Bicester Town	a						08 32																			
Tackley	d					08 02																				
Heyford	d					08 06																				
Kings Sutton	d					08 15																				
Banbury	a					08 23				08 34					08 52							09 24				
Leamington Spa 8	a									08 52					09 10							09 42				
Warwick	a									*09 04*					*09 21*							*10 02*				
Warwick Parkway	a									*09 07*					*09 26*							*10 05*				
Stratford-upon-Avon	a									*09b36*																
Coventry	a														09 22											
Birmingham International	a														09 37											
Birmingham New Street 12	a									09 17					09 49							10 17				

		GW 1	GW 1 ◇ ☕	GW 1 ◇ ☕	GW 1	XC 1 ◇ 🛒	GW 1 ◇ ☕	GW 1	GW 1	GW 1	GW 1 ◇	GW 1 ◇ ☕	GW 1 ◇ ☕	XC 1 ◇ 🛒	GW 1	GW 1	GW 1	GW 1	GW 1 ◇	GW 1 ◇ ☕	XC 1 ◇ 🛒	GW 1 ◇ ☕	GW 1	GW 1	GW 1	GW 1 ◇
London Paddington 15 ⊖	d	07 57	08 21	08 30			08 45			08 27	08 50	09 00	09 06			09 18	08 57		09 21	09 30		09 45			09 27	09 50
Ealing Broadway ⊖	d	08 05								08 35							09 05								09 35	
Slough 3	d	08 27	08 39							08 57	09 07						09 27		09 39						09 57	10 07
Maidenhead 3	d	08 34								09 04							09 34								10 04	
Twyford 3	d	08 42								09 12							09 42								10 12	
Reading 7	a	08 51	08 53	08 57			09 10			09 20	09 22	09 26	09 31			09 47	09 51		09 53	09 57		10 10			10 20	10 22
	d	08 53	08 54	08 57		09 10			09 12	09 23	09 23			09 40		09 47	09 53		09 54	09 57	10 10			10 12	10 23	10 23
Reading West	d								09 14															10 14		
Theale	d								09 20							09 55								10 20		
Aldermaston	d								09 25															10 25		
Midgham	d								09 29															10 29		
Thatcham	d								09 34							10 04								10 34		
Newbury Racecourse	d								09 38															10 38		
Newbury	a								09 44							10 09								10 44		
	d															10 09										
Kintbury	d															10 17										
Hungerford	d															10 20										
Bedwyn	a															10 30										
Tilehurst	d	08 58								09 28							09 58								10 28	
Pangbourne	d	09 02						←		09 32							10 02						←		10 32	
Goring & Streatley	d	09 07						09 07		09 37					←		10 07						10 07		10 37	
Cholsey	d	→						09 12		09 42					09 42		→						10 12		10 42	
Didcot Parkway	a			09 12				09 19		→					09 50					10 12			10 20		→	
	d							09 25							09 55								10 25			
Appleford	d																									
Culham	d														10 01											
Radley	d														10 05											
Oxford	a		09 18			09 34		09 40			09 48			10 04	10 14				10 20		10 34		10 40			10 48
	d				09 27	09 36								10 07				10 16			10 36					
Islip	d				09 41																					
Bicester Town	a				09 53																					
Tackley	d																	10 25								
Heyford	d																	10 29								
Kings Sutton	d																	10 40								
Banbury	a					09 52								10 24				10 48			10 52					
Leamington Spa 8	a					10 10								10 42							11 10					
Warwick	a					*10c21*								*11 02*							*11c21*					
Warwick Parkway	a					*10c25*								*11 05*							*11c24*					
Stratford-upon-Avon	a					*11b13*																				
Coventry	a					10 22															11 22					
Birmingham International	a					10 37															11 37					
Birmingham New Street 12	a					10 49								11 17							11 49					

For general notes see front of timetable
For details of catering facilities see Directory of Train Operators

b From 10 October arr. 3 minutes later
c Change at Banbury

Table 116

Saturdays

from 12 September

London and Reading → Bedwyn, Oxford, Bicester, Banbury and Birmingham

Network Diagram - see first page of Table 116

		GW	GW	GW	XC	GW	GW	GW	GW	GW	GW	XC	GW
		1 ◇	1 ◇	1	1 ◇	1	1 ◇	1	1	1 ◇	1 ◇	1 ◇	1 ◇
		🍴	🍴		🛒		🍴			🍴	🍴	🛒	🍴
London Paddington 15 ⊖	d	10 00	10 06				10 15	10 18	09 57	10 21	10 30		10 45
Ealing Broadway ⊖	d								10 05				
Slough 3	d								10 27	10 39			
Maidenhead 3	d								10 34				
Twyford 3	d								10 42				
Reading 7	a	10 26	10 32				10 40	10 48	10 51	10 53	10 57		11 10
	d				10 40		10 41	10 48	10 53	10 54	10 57	11 10	
Reading West	d												
Theale	d							10 55					
Aldermaston	d												
Midgham	d												
Thatcham	d							11 04					
Newbury Racecourse	d												
Newbury	a							11 09					
	d							11 09					
Kintbury	d							11 17					
Hungerford	d							11 20					
Bedwyn	a							11 31					
Tilehurst	d								10 58				
Pangbourne	d								11 02				
Goring & Streatley	d					←			11 07				
Cholsey	d					10 42			→				
Didcot Parkway	a					10 50	10 56				11 12		
	d					10 55							
Appleford	d					11 00							
Culham	d												
Radley	d					11 05							
Oxford	a				11 04	11 14				11 19		11 34	
	d			11 00	11 07							11 36	
Islip	d			11 13									
Bicester Town	a			11 25									
Tackley	d												
Heyford	d												
Kings Sutton	d												
Banbury	a				11 24							11 52	
Leamington Spa 8	a				11 42							12 10	
Warwick	a				*11 58*							*12b21*	
Warwick Parkway	a				*12 02*							*12b25*	
Stratford-upon-Avon	a											*13c11*	
Coventry	a											12 22	
Birmingham International	a											12 37	
Birmingham New Street 12	a				12 17							12 49	

		GW	GW	GW	GW	GW	GW	XC	GW	GW	GW	GW	GW	GW
		1	1	1	1 ◇	1 ◇	1 ◇	1 ◇	1	1	1	1	1 ◇	1 ◇
						🍴	🍴	🛒					🍴	🍴
London Paddington 15 ⊖	d			10 27	10 50	11 00	11 06			11 18	10 57		11 21	11 30
Ealing Broadway ⊖	d			10 35							11 05			
Slough 3	d			10 57	11 07						11 27		11 39	
Maidenhead 3	d			11 04							11 34			
Twyford 3	d			11 12							11 42			
Reading 7	a			11 20	11 22	11 26	11 31			11 48	11 51		11 53	11 57
	d		11 12	11 23	11 23			11 40		11 48	11 53		11 54	11 57
Reading West	d		11 14											
Theale	d		11 20							11 55				
Aldermaston	d		11 25											
Midgham	d		11 29											
Thatcham	d		11 34							12 04				
Newbury Racecourse	d		11 38											
Newbury	a		11 44							12 09				
	d									12 09				
Kintbury	d									12 17				
Hungerford	d									12 20				
Bedwyn	a									12 31				
Tilehurst	d			11 28							11 58			
Pangbourne	d	←		11 32					←		12 02			
Goring & Streatley	d	11 07		11 37					11 37		12 07			
Cholsey	d	11 12		→					11 42		→			
Didcot Parkway	a	11 20							11 50					12 12
	d	11 25							11 55					
Appleford	d													
Culham	d													
Radley	d								12 05					
Oxford	a	11 40			11 48			12 04	12 14				12 18	
	d							12 07				12 16		
Islip	d													
Bicester Town	a													
Tackley	d											12 25		
Heyford	d											12 29		
Kings Sutton	d											12 39		
Banbury	a							12 24				12 46		
Leamington Spa 8	a							12 42						
Warwick	a							*12 58*						
Warwick Parkway	a							*13 02*						
Stratford-upon-Avon	a													
Coventry	a													
Birmingham International	a													
Birmingham New Street 12	a							13 17						

		GW	XC	GW	GW	GW	GW	GW	GW	GW	XC	GW	GW
		1	1 ◇	1 ◇	1	1	1	1 ◇	1 ◇	1 ◇	1 ◇	1	1 ◇
			🛒	🍴					🍴	🍴	🛒		🍴
London Paddington 15 ⊖	d			11 45			11 27	11 50	12 00	12 06			12 15
Ealing Broadway ⊖	d						11 35						
Slough 3	d						11 57	12 07					
Maidenhead 3	d						12 04						
Twyford 3	d						12 12						
Reading 7	a			12 10			12 20	12 22	12 26	12 31			12 40
	d		12 10			12 12	12 23	12 23			12 40		12 41
Reading West	d					12 14							
Theale	d					12 20							
Aldermaston	d					12 25							
Midgham	d					12 29							
Thatcham	d					12 34							
Newbury Racecourse	d					12 38							
Newbury	a					12 44							
	d												
Kintbury	d												
Hungerford	d												
Bedwyn	a												
Tilehurst	d						12 27						
Pangbourne	d				←		12 32					←	
Goring & Streatley	d				12 07		12 37					12 37	
Cholsey	d				12 12		→					12 42	
Didcot Parkway	a				12 20							12 49	12 56
	d				12 25							12 55	
Appleford	d												
Culham	d												
Radley	d											13 05	
Oxford	a		12 34		12 40			12 48			13 04	13 14	
	d	12 30	12 36								13 07		
Islip	d	12 43											
Bicester Town	a	12 55											
Tackley	d												
Heyford	d												
Kings Sutton	d												
Banbury	a		12 52								13 24		
Leamington Spa 8	a		13 10								13 42		
Warwick	a		*13b21*								*13 58*		
Warwick Parkway	a		*13b25*								*14 02*		
Stratford-upon-Avon	a												
Coventry	a		13 22										
Birmingham International	a		13 37										
Birmingham New Street 12	a		13 49								14 17		

		GW	GW	GW	GW	XC	GW	GW	GW	GW	GW	GW	GW	GW
		1 ◇	1	1 ◇	1 ◇	1 ◇	1 ◇	1	1	1	1	1 ◇	1 ◇	1 ◇
		🍴			🍴	🛒	🍴						🍴	🍴
London Paddington 15 ⊖	d	12 18	11 57	12 21	12 30		12 45			12 27		12 50	13 00	13 06
Ealing Broadway ⊖	d		12 05							12 35				
Slough 3	d		12 27	12 39						12 57		13 07		
Maidenhead 3	d		12 34							13 04				
Twyford 3	d		12 42							13 12				
Reading 7	a	12 45	12 51	12 54	12 57		13 10			13 20		13 22	13 26	13 31
	d	12 49	12 53	12 54	12 57	13 10			13 12	13 23		13 23		
Reading West	d								13 14					
Theale	d	12 58							13 20					
Aldermaston	d								13 25					
Midgham	d								13 29					
Thatcham	d	13 07							13 34					
Newbury Racecourse	d								13 38					
Newbury	a	13 13							13 44					
	d	13 14												
Kintbury	d													
Hungerford	d	13 23												
Bedwyn	a	13 30												
Tilehurst	d		12 58							13 28				
Pangbourne	d		13 02					←		13 32				
Goring & Streatley	d		13 07					13 07		13 37				
Cholsey	d		→					13 12		→				
Didcot Parkway	a				13 12			13 20						
	d							13 25						
Appleford	d													
Culham	d													
Radley	d													
Oxford	a			13 20		13 34		13 40				13 48		
	d					13 36					13 41			
Islip	d										13 54			
Bicester Town	a										14 06			
Tackley	d													
Heyford	d													
Kings Sutton	d													
Banbury	a					13 52								
Leamington Spa 8	a					14 10								
Warwick	a					*14b21*								
Warwick Parkway	a					*14b26*								
Stratford-upon-Avon	a					*15c10*								
Coventry	a					14 22								
Birmingham International	a					14 37								
Birmingham New Street 12	a					14 49								

For general notes see front of timetable
For details of catering facilities see Directory of Train Operators

b Change at Banbury
c From 10 October arr. 3 minutes later

Saturdays

from 12 September

London and Reading → Bedwyn, Oxford, Bicester, Banbury and Birmingham

Network Diagram - see first page of Table 116

		XC	GW	GW	GW	GW	GW	GW	XC	GW	GW	GW	GW	GW	GW	GW	GW	XC	GW	GW	GW	GW	GW	GW	XC	GW
		1◇	1	1	1	1	1◇	1◇	1◇	1◇	1	1	1	1◇	1◇	1◇	1	1◇	1	1◇	1	1	1◇	1◇	1◇	1◇
		🛒					☕	☕	🛒	☕					☕	☕		🛒		☕			☕	☕	🛒	☕
London Paddington 15 ⊖	d			13 18	12 57		13 21	13 30		13 45			13 27	13 50	14 00	14 06				14 15	14 18	13 57	14 21	14 30		14 45
Ealing Broadway ⊖	d				13 05								13 35									14 05				
Slough 3	d				13 27		13 39						13 57	14 07								14 27	14 39			
Maidenhead 3	d				13 34								14 04									14 34				
Twyford 3	d				13 42								14 12									14 42				
Reading 7	a			13 48	13 51		13 53	13 57		14 10			14 20	14 22	14 26	14 31				14 40	14 48	14 51	14 53	14 57		15 10
	d	13 40		13 48	13 53		13 54	13 57	14 10			14 12	14 23	14 23				14 40		14 41	14 48	14 53	14 54	14 57	15 10	
Reading West	d											14 14														
Theale	d			13 55								14 20									14 55					
Aldermaston	d											14 25														
Midgham	d											14 29														
Thatcham	d			14 04								14 34									15 04					
Newbury Racecourse	d											14 38														
Newbury	a			14 09								14 44									15 09					
	d			14 09																	15 09					
Kintbury	d			14 17																	15 17					
Hungerford	d			14 20																	15 20					
Bedwyn	a			14 31																	15 31					
Tilehurst	d				13 57								14 28									14 58				
Pangbourne	d		←		14 02						←		14 32						←			15 02				
Goring & Streatley	d		13 37		14 07						14 07		14 37						14 37			15 07				
Cholsey	d		13 42		→						14 12		→						14 42			→				
Didcot Parkway	a		13 50					14 12			14 19								14 50	14 56				15 12		
	d		13 55								14 25								14 55							
Appleford	d																									
Culham	d																									
Radley	d		14 05																15 05							
Oxford	a	14 04	14 14				14 18		14 34		14 40			14 48				15 04	15 14				15 18		15 34	
	d	14 07				14 16			14 36								14 57	15 07							15 36	
Islip	d																15 10									
Bicester Town	a																15 22									
Tackley	d					14 25																				
Heyford	d					14 29																				
Kings Sutton	d					14 38																				
Banbury	a	14 24				14 46			14 52									15 24							15 52	
Leamington Spa 8	a	14 42							15 10									15 42							16 10	
Warwick	a	*14 58*							*15b21*									*15 58*							*16b21*	
Warwick Parkway	a	*15 02*							*15b25*									*16 02*							*16b24*	
Stratford-upon-Avon	a																								*17c11*	
Coventry	a								15 22																16 22	
Birmingham International	a								15 37																16 37	
Birmingham New Street 12	a	15 17							15 49									16 17							16 49	

		GW	GW	GW	GW	GW	GW	GW	XC	GW	GW	GW	GW	GW	GW	XC	GW	GW	GW	GW	GW	GW	GW	XC	GW	GW
		1	1	1	1◇	1◇	1◇	1	1◇	1	1	1	1	1◇	1◇	1◇	1◇	1	1	1	1◇	1◇	1◇	1◇	1	1
						☕	☕		🛒					☕	☕	🛒	☕					☕	☕	🛒		
London Paddington 15 ⊖	d			14 27	14 50	15 00	15 06				15 18	14 57		15 21	15 30		15 45			15 27	15 50	16 00	16 06			
Ealing Broadway ⊖	d			14 35								15 05								15 35						
Slough 3	d			14 57	15 07							15 27		15 39						15 57	16 07					
Maidenhead 3	d			15 04								15 34								16 04						
Twyford 3	d			15 12								15 42								16 12						
Reading 7	a			15 20	15 22	15 26	15 33				15 48	15 51		15 53	15 57		16 10			16 20	16 22	16 26	16 32			
	d		15 12	15 23	15 23				15 40		15 48	15 53		15 54	15 57	16 10			16 12	16 23	16 23			16 40		
Reading West	d		15 14																16 14							
Theale	d		15 20								15 55								16 20							
Aldermaston	d		15 25																16 25							
Midgham	d		15 29																16 29							
Thatcham	d		15 34								16 04								16 34							
Newbury Racecourse	d		15 38																16 38							
Newbury	a		15 44								16 09								16 44							
	d										16 09															
Kintbury	d										16 17															
Hungerford	d										16 20															
Bedwyn	a										16 31															
Tilehurst	d			15 28								15 58								16 28						
Pangbourne	d	←		15 32								16 02								16 32						
Goring & Streatley	d	15 07		15 37						←		16 07						←		16 37						←
Cholsey	d	15 12		15 42						15 42		→						16 07		16 42						16 42
Didcot Parkway	a	15 20		→						15 49					16 12			16 12		→						16 49
	d	15 25								15 55								16 20								16 55
Appleford	d																	16 25								17 00
Culham	d									16 01																
Radley	d									16 05																17 05
Oxford	a	15 40			15 48				16 04	16 14				16 18		16 34		16 40			16 48			17 04		17 14
	d							16 01	16 07				16 16			16 36								17 07	17 10	
Islip	d							16 14																	17 26	
Bicester Town	a							16 26																	17 38	
Tackley	d												16 25													
Heyford	d												16 29													
Kings Sutton	d												16 39													
Banbury	a								16 24				16 46			16 52								17 24		
Leamington Spa 8	a								16 42							17 10								17 42		
Warwick	a								*16 57*							*17b22*								*17 58*		
Warwick Parkway	a								*17 01*							*17b25*								*18 02*		
Stratford-upon-Avon	a																									
Coventry	a															17 22										
Birmingham International	a															17 37										
Birmingham New Street 12	a								17 17							17 49								18 17		

For general notes see front of timetable
For details of catering facilities see
Directory of Train Operators

b Change at Banbury
c From 10 October arr. 3 minutes later

Table 116

Saturdays

from 12 September

London and Reading → Bedwyn, Oxford, Bicester, Banbury and Birmingham

Network Diagram - see first page of Table 116

		GW	GW	GW	GW	GW	XC	GW	GW	GW	GW	GW	GW	GW	XC	GW	GW	GW	GW	GW	GW	XC	GW	GW	GW	GW
		1◇	1	1	1◇	1◇	1◇	1◇	1	1	1	1◇	1◇	1◇	1◇	1	1	1	1	1◇	1◇	1◇	1◇	1	1	1
																					A					
		☕			☕	☕	🛒	☕					☕	☕	🛒					☕	☕	🛒	☕			
London Paddington 15	⊖ d	16 15	16 18	15 57	16 21	16 30		16 45			16 27	16 50	17 00	17 06			17 18	16 57		17 21	17 30		17 45			17 27
Ealing Broadway	⊖ d			16 05							16 35							17 05								17 35
Slough 3	d			16 27	16 39						16 57	17 07						17 27		17 39						17 57
Maidenhead 3	d			16 34							17 04							17 34								18 04
Twyford 3	d			16 42							17 12							17 42								18 12
Reading 7	a	16 40	16 48	16 51	16 53	16 57		17 10			17 20	17 22	17 26	17 31			17 48	17 51		17 53	17 57		18 11			18 20
	d	16 41	16 48	16 53	16 54	16 57	17 10			17 12	17 23	17 23			17 40		17 48	17 53		17 54	17 57	18 10			18 12	18 23
Reading West	d									17 14															18 14	
Theale	d		16 55							17 20							17 55								18 20	
Aldermaston	d									17 25															18 25	
Midgham	d									17 29															18 29	
Thatcham	d		17 04							17 34							18 04								18 34	
Newbury Racecourse	d									17 38															18 38	
Newbury	a		17 09							17 44							18 09								18 44	
	d		17 09														18 09									
Kintbury	d		17 17														18 17									
Hungerford	d		17 20														18 20									
Bedwyn	a		17 31														18 30									
Tilehurst	d			16 58							17 28							17 58								18 28
Pangbourne	d			17 02					←		17 32							18 02						←		18 32
Goring & Streatley	d			17 07					17 07		17 37					←		18 07						18 07		18 37
Cholsey	d			→					17 12		17 42					17 42		→						18 12		18 42
Didcot Parkway	a	16 56				17 12			17 20		→					17 49					18 12			18 20		→
	d								17 25							17 55								18 25		
Appleford	d																									
Culham	d															18 01										
Radley	d															18 05										
Oxford	a				17 18		17 34		17 40			17 48			18 04	18 14				18 18		18 34		18 40		
	d						17 36								18 07				18 16			18 36				
Islip	d																									
Bicester Town	a																									
Tackley	d																		18 25							
Heyford	d																		18 29							
Kings Sutton	d																		18 38							
Banbury	a						17 52								18 24				18 46			18 52				
Leamington Spa 8	a						18 10								18 42							19 10				
Warwick	a						18b21								18 58							19 26				
Warwick Parkway	a						18b26								19 02							19 30				
Stratford-upon-Avon	a						19c13																			
Coventry	a						18 22															19 22				
Birmingham International	a						18 37															19 37				
Birmingham New Street 12	a						18 49								19 17							19 49				

		GW	GW	GW	GW	XC	GW	GW	GW	GW	GW	GW	GW	XC	GW	GW	GW	GW	GW	GW	GW	GW	XC	GW	GW	GW
		1	1◇	1◇	1◇	1◇	1	1◇	1	1	1	1◇	1◇	1◇	1◇	1	1	1	1◇	1◇	1◇	1	1◇	1	1◇	1
				☕	☕	🛒		☕				☕	☕	🛒	☕					☕	☕		🛒		☕	
London Paddington 15	⊖ d		17 50	18 00	18 06			18 15	18 18	17 57		18 21	18 30		18 45		18 27		18 50	19 00	19 06				19 15	
Ealing Broadway	⊖ d									18 05							18 35									
Slough 3	d		18 07							18 27		18 39					18 57		19 07							
Maidenhead 3	d									18 34							19 04									
Twyford 3	d									18 42							19 12									
Reading 7	a		18 22	18 27	18 31			18 40	18 48	18 51		18 53	18 57		19 11		19 20		19 22	19 26	19 32				19 40	
	d		18 23			18 40		18 41	18 48	18 53		18 54	18 57	19 10			19 23		19 23		19 32		19 40		19 41	19 49
Reading West	d																									19 52
Theale	d								18 55																	19 58
Aldermaston	d																									20 03
Midgham	d																									20 06
Thatcham	d								19 04																	20 11
Newbury Racecourse	d																									20 16
Newbury	a								19 09												19 48					20 18
	d								19 09																	20 18
Kintbury	d								19 17																	20 25
Hungerford	d								19 20																	20 29
Bedwyn	a								19 30																	20 38
Tilehurst	d									18 58							19 28									
Pangbourne	d									19 02						←	19 32									
Goring & Streatley	d						←			19 07						19 07	19 37							←		
Cholsey	d						18 42			→						19 12	19 42							19 42		
Didcot Parkway	a						18 49	18 56					19 12			19 20	→							19 49	19 55	
	d						18 55									19 25								19 55		
Appleford	d						19 00																			
Culham	d																							20 01		
Radley	d						19 05																	20 05		
Oxford	a		18 48			19 04	19 14					19 18		19 34		19 40			19 48				20 04	20 14		
	d	18 41				19 07					19 16			19 36				19 48				19 56	20 07			
Islip	d	18 54																20 01								
Bicester Town	a	19 06																20 13								
Tackley	d										19 25											20 05				
Heyford	d										19 29											20 09				
Kings Sutton	d										19 38											→				
Banbury	a					19 24					19 46			19 52									20 24			
Leamington Spa 8	a					19 42								20 10									20 42			
Warwick	a					19 58								20 26												
Warwick Parkway	a					20 02								20 30												
Stratford-upon-Avon	a													21c10												
Coventry	a													20 22												
Birmingham International	a													20 37												
Birmingham New Street 12	a					20 17								20 49									21 17			

For general notes see front of timetable
For details of catering facilities see Directory of Train Operators

A To Weston-super-Mare (Table 134)
b Change at Banbury
c From 10 October arr. 3 minutes later

Table 116

Saturdays

from 12 September

London and Reading → Bedwyn, Oxford, Bicester, Banbury and Birmingham

Network Diagram - see first page of Table 116

		GW	GW	GW	GW	XC	GW	GW	GW	GW	GW	GW	GW	XC	GW	GW	GW	GW	GW	GW	GW	XC	GW	GW	GW	GW
		1	1 ◇	1 ◇	1	1 ◇	1 ◇	1	1	1 ◇	1 ◇	1 ◇	1	1 ◇	1	1 ◇	1	1	1	1 ◇	1 ◇	1 ◇	1 ◇	1	1	1 ◇
				☕		trolley	☕			trolley	☕	☕		trolley		☕					☕	trolley	☕			
London Paddington [15] ⊖	d	18 57	19 21	19 30			19 45		19 27	19 50	20 00	20 06				20 15		19 57		20 21	20 30		20 45		20 27	20 50
Ealing Broadway ⊖	d	19 05							19 35									20 05							20 35	
Slough [3]	d	19 27	19 38						19 57	20 07								20 27							20 57	21 09
Maidenhead [3]	d	19 34							20 04									20 34							21 04	
Twyford [3]	d	19 42							20 12									20 42							21 12	
Reading [7]	a	19 51	19 53	19 57			20 10		20 20	20 21	20 27	20 32				20 40		20 51		20 52	20 57		21 10		21 20	21 24
	d	19 53	19 54	19 57		20 10			20 23	20 23	20 27	20 32		20 40		20 41	20 49	20 53		20 53	20 57	21 10			21 23	21 24
Reading West	d																20 52									
Theale	d																20 58									
Aldermaston	d																21 03									
Midgham	d																21 06									
Thatcham	d																21 11									
Newbury Racecourse	d																21 16									
Newbury	a											20 46					21 18									
	d																21 32									
Kintbury	d																21 39									
Hungerford	d																21 43									
Bedwyn	a																21 52									
Tilehurst	d	19 58							20 28									20 58							21 28	
Pangbourne	d	20 02						←	20 32									21 02						←	21 32	
Goring & Streatley	d	20 07						20 07	20 37						←			21 07						21 07	→	
Cholsey	d	→						20 12	20 42						20 42			→						21 12		
Didcot Parkway	a			20 12				20 20	→		20 41				20 49	20 56					21 12			21 20		21 39
	d							20 25							20 55									21 25		21 39
Appleford	d														21 00											
Culham	d																									
Radley	d														21 05											
Oxford	a		20 20			20 34		20 40		20 47				21 04	21 14					21 20		21 34		21 40		21 53
	d					20 36							21 00	21 07					21 20			21 36				
Islip	d												21 13													
Bicester Town	a												21 25													
Tackley	d				←														21 29							
Heyford	d				20 09														21 33							
Kings Sutton	d				20 18														21 42							
Banbury	a				20 25	20 52								21 24					21 49			21 52				
Leamington Spa [8]	a				*20 54*	21 10								21 42								22 10				
Warwick	a				*20 58*	*21 42*																*22 31*				
Warwick Parkway	a				*21 02*	*21 46*																*22 34*				
Stratford-upon-Avon	a																									
Coventry	a					21 22								21 55								22 22				
Birmingham International	a					21 37								22 12								22 37				
Birmingham New Street [12]	a					21 49								22 25								22 54				

		XC	GW	GW	GW	GW	GW	GW	GW	GW	GW	GW	GW	GW	GW	GW	GW	GW	GW	GW	GW	GW	GW	GW
		1 ◇	1	1	1	1	1 ◇	1	1 ◇	1	1 ◇	1 ◇	1	bus	1 ◇	1 ◇	bus	1	1 ◇	bus	1	1 ◇	1 ◇	1
		trolley							☕			☕			☕							☕		
London Paddington [15] ⊖	d				20 57		21 21		21 30		21 50	22 00	21 57		22 30	22 32			23 00		22 45	23 30	23 33	23 20
Ealing Broadway ⊖	d				21 05								22 05								22 55			23 28
Slough [3]	d				21 27						22 07		22 27			22 50			23 17		23 21		23 50	23 54
Maidenhead [3]	d				21 34								22 34								23 30			00 05
Twyford [3]	d				21 42								22 42								23 38			00 13
Reading [7]	a				21 51		21 52	←	21 57		22 22	22 27	22 51		22 55	23 06			23 33		23 44	23 59	00 07	00 20
	d	21 40		21 51	21 53		21 52	21 53	21 57		22 22	22 27	22 53		23 00	23 07		23 12	23 34		23 49	23 59	00 08	00 20
Reading West	d			21 54	→													23 14						
Theale	d			22 02														23 20						
Aldermaston	d			22 07														23 25						
Midgham	d			22 10														23 29						
Thatcham	d			22 15														23 34						
Newbury Racecourse	d			22 20														23 38						
Newbury	a			22 22														23 41						
	d			22 22														23 41						
Kintbury	d			22 29														23 48						
Hungerford	d			22 33														23 52						
Bedwyn	a			22 41														00 01						
Tilehurst	d		←					21 58		←			22 57								23 53			00 24
Pangbourne	d		21 32					22 02		22 02			23 02								23 58			
Goring & Streatley	d		21 37					→		22 07			23 07								00 03			00 31
Cholsey	d		21 42							22 12			23 12								00 08			00 36
Didcot Parkway	a		21 49				22 08		22 12	22 20	22 37	22 42	23 19		23 22	23 29			23 51		00 15	00 18	00 25	00 45
	d		21 55				22 09			22 25	22 37		23 20				23 36			23 58				
Appleford	d																							
Culham	d		22 01																					
Radley	d		22 05																					
Oxford	a	22 04	22 14				22 21			22 40	22 49		23 33				00 01			00 23				
	d	22 07				22 17								23 40										
Islip	d					22 30																		
Bicester Town	a					22 42																		
Tackley	d													00s01										
Heyford	d													00s15										
Kings Sutton	d													00b30										
Banbury	a	22 24												00 40										
Leamington Spa [8]	a	22 42																						
Warwick	a	*23 26*																						
Warwick Parkway	a	*23 29*																						
Stratford-upon-Avon	a																							
Coventry	a																							
Birmingham International	a																							
Birmingham New Street [12]	a	23 17																						

For general notes see front of timetable
For details of catering facilities see
Directory of Train Operators

b Kings Sutton V. Square. Stops to set down only

Table 116

Sundays

until 12 July

London and Reading → Bedwyn, Oxford, Bicester, Banbury and Birmingham

Network Diagram - see first page of Table 116

		GW	GW	GW	GW	GW	GW	GW	GW	GW	GW	XC	GW	GW	GW	GW	GW	GW	GW	GW	GW	XC	GW	GW	GW	GW
		1	1 ◇	1	1		1 ◇	1 ◇		1	1	1 ◇	1 ◇	1 ◇	1 ◇	1 ◇	1 ◇	1	1	1	1 ◇	1 ◇	1 ◇	1 ◇	1 ◇	1
								A																	B	
London Paddington 15 ⊖	d	22p45	23p33		23p20		08 00	08 03			07 43		08 30	08 35	08 42	08 57	09 00		08 43	09 04	09 30		09 35	09 57	10 00	
Ealing Broadway ⊖	d	22p55			23p28						07 50								08 52							
Slough 3	d	23p21	23p50		23p54			08 21			08 22				09 01				09 16	09 23			09 51			
Maidenhead 3	d	23p30			00 05			08 29			08 32								09 27	09 32						
Twyford 3	d	23p38			00 13						08 40								09 35							
Reading 7	a	23p44	00 07		00 20		08 36	08 43			08 49		09 14	09 19	09 24	09 31	09 36		09 43	09 46	10 04		10 12	10 32	10 36	
	d	23p49	00 08	00 15	00 21	08 14	08 38	08 44	08 44		08 49	09 11	09 16		09 26	09 32	09 37		09 44	09 47	10 05	10 11	10 12		10 37	
Reading West	d			00s18		08 17														09 50						
Theale	d			00s24		08 23			08 51											09 56						
Aldermaston	d			00s29		08 28														10 01						
Midgham	d			00s32		08 31														10 04						
Thatcham	d			00s37		08 36			09 00											10 09						
Newbury Racecourse	d			00s42																						
Newbury	a			00 45		08 43			09 05							09 47				10 15						
	d								09 06											10 15						
Kintbury	d								09 12											10 22						
Hungerford	d								09 17											10 26						
Bedwyn	a								09 24											10 35						
Tilehurst	d	23p53			00 25						08 53								09 48							
Pangbourne	d	23p58									08 58								09 52							
Goring & Streatley	d	00 03			00 32						09 03								09 57							
Cholsey	d	00 08			00 37						09 08								10 02							
Didcot Parkway	a	00 15	00 24		00 44		08 53	08 58			09 12		09 30		09 40		09 52		10 08		10 20		10 28		10 52	
	d	00 17	00 24		00 45			09 03			09 12				09 41				10 09				10 28			
Appleford	d																		10 14							
Culham	d																									
Radley	d	00s24									09 21								10 19							
Oxford	a	00 33	00 38		00 59			09 15			09 30	09 35			09 54				10 27			10 35	10 42			
	d									09 26		09 37						10 00				10 37				10 56
Islip	d									09 39																11 09
Bicester Town	a									09 51																11 21
Tackley	d																	10 09								
Heyford	d																	10 13								
Kings Sutton	d																	10 22								
Banbury	a											09 52						10 30				10 52				
Leamington Spa 8	a											10 10						*10 55*				11 10				
Warwick	a																	*11 01*				*11 22*				
Warwick Parkway	a																	*11 05*				*12 05*				
Stratford-upon-Avon	a																					*11 59*				
Coventry	a											10 22										11 22				
Birmingham International	a											10 38										11 38				
Birmingham New Street 12	a											10 51										11 51				

For general notes see front of timetable
For details of catering facilities see Directory of Train Operators

A To Great Malvern (Table 126)
B To Weston-super-Mare (Table 134)

Table 116

Sundays

until 12 July

London and Reading → Bedwyn, Oxford, Bicester, Banbury and Birmingham

Network Diagram - see first page of Table 116

		GW 1	GW 1	GW 1◇	XC 1◇	GW 1◇	GW 1◇	GW 1◇	GW 1◇	GW 1	GW 1	GW 1◇	GW 1	XC 1◇
									A					
				☕	🛒	☕	☕	☕	☕			☕		🛒
London Paddington 15 ⊖	d	09 43	10 04	10 27		10 37	10 42	10 57	11 00	10 43	11 04	11 27		
Ealing Broadway ⊖	d	09 50								10 50				
Slough 3	d	10 16	10 23				10 59			11 16	11 23			
Maidenhead 3	d	10 27	10 32							11 27	11 31			
Twyford 3	d	10 35								11 35				
Reading 7	a	10 43	10 46	11 02		11 13	11 20	11 31	11 36	11 42	11 46	12 02		
	d	10 43	10 47		11 11	11 14	11 20		11 37	11 43	11 47			12 11
Reading West	d		10 50											
Theale	d		10 56								11 54			
Aldermaston	d		11 01											
Midgham	d		11 04											
Thatcham	d		11 09								12 03			
Newbury Racecourse	d													
Newbury	a		11 17								12 08			
	d										12 09			
Kintbury	d										12 15			
Hungerford	d										12 20			
Bedwyn	a										12 29			
Tilehurst	d	10 48								11 48				
Pangbourne	d	10 52								11 52				
Goring & Streatley	d	10 57								11 57				
Cholsey	d	11 02								12 02				
Didcot Parkway	a	11 08				11 29	11 36		11 52	12 08				
	d	11 09					11 36			12 09				
Appleford	d													
Culham	d													
Radley	d	11 17								12 17				
Oxford	a	11 25			11 35		11 50			12 25				12 35
	d				11 37								12 26	12 37
Islip	d												12 39	
Bicester Town	a												12 51	
Tackley	d													
Heyford	d													
Kings Sutton	d													
Banbury	a				11 52									12 52
Leamington Spa 8	a				12 10									13 10
Warwick	a				*13 04*									*13 22*
Warwick Parkway	a				*12 27*									*13 30*
Stratford-upon-Avon	a													*13 52*
Coventry	a				12 22									13 22
Birmingham International	a				12 38									13 37
Birmingham New Street 12	a				12 51									13 49

		GW 1◇	GW 1◇	GW 1◇	GW 1◇	GW 1	GW 1	XC 1◇	GW 1◇	GW 1	XC 1◇	GW 1◇	GW 1◇
		☕		☕	☕			🛒	☕		🛒	☕	☕
London Paddington 15 ⊖	d	11 37	11 42	11 57	12 00	11 43	12 04		12 27			12 37	12 42
Ealing Broadway ⊖	d					11 50							
Slough 3	d		12 00			12 16	12 23						12 59
Maidenhead 3	d					12 27	12 31						
Twyford 3	d					12 35							
Reading 7	a	12 13	12 19	12 31	12 36	12 43	12 46		13 02			13 13	13 20
	d	12 14	12 22	12 32	12 37	12 43	12 47	12 54			13 11	13 14	13 20
Reading West	d						12 50						
Theale	d						12 56						
Aldermaston	d						13 01						
Midgham	d						13 04						
Thatcham	d						13 09						
Newbury Racecourse	d												
Newbury	a			12 47			13 17						
	d												
Kintbury	d												
Hungerford	d												
Bedwyn	a												
Tilehurst	d					12 48							
Pangbourne	d					12 52							
Goring & Streatley	d					12 57				←			
Cholsey	d					13 02				13 02			
Didcot Parkway	a	12 29	12 37		12 52	→				13 08		13 29	13 36
	d		12 38							13 09			13 36
Appleford	d									13 14			
Culham	d												
Radley	d									13 19			
Oxford	a		12 50					13 15		13 27	13 35		13 50
	d							13 17			13 37		
Islip	d												
Bicester Town	a												
Tackley	d												
Heyford	d												
Kings Sutton	d												
Banbury	a							13 34			13 52		
Leamington Spa 8	a							13 51			14 10		
Warwick	a							*14 04*					
Warwick Parkway	a							*14 07*			*14 27*		
Stratford-upon-Avon	a												
Coventry	a										14 22		
Birmingham International	a										14 35		
Birmingham New Street 12	a							14 18			14 49		

		GW 1◇	GW 1◇	GW 1		XC 1◇	GW 1	GW 1	GW 1	XC 1◇	GW 1◇	GW 1◇	GW 1◇	GW 1◇
		☕	☕			🛒				🛒	☕	☕	☕	☕
London Paddington 15 ⊖	d	12 57	13 00					12 43	13 04		13 37	13 42	13 57	14 00
Ealing Broadway ⊖	d							12 50						
Slough 3	d							13 16	13 23			13 58		
Maidenhead 3	d							13 27	13 31					
Twyford 3	d							13 35						
Reading 7	a	13 31	13 36					13 43	13 46		14 13	14 20	14 31	14 36
	d		13 37			13 40		13 43	13 47	14 11	14 14	14 21	14 32	14 37
Reading West	d													
Theale	d								13 54					
Aldermaston	d													
Midgham	d													
Thatcham	d								14 03					
Newbury Racecourse	d													
Newbury	a								14 08				14 47	
	d								14 09					
Kintbury	d								14 15					
Hungerford	d								14 20					
Bedwyn	a								14 29					
Tilehurst	d							13 48						
Pangbourne	d							13 52						
Goring & Streatley	d							13 57						
Cholsey	d							14 02						
Didcot Parkway	a		13 52					14 08			14 29	14 36		14 52
	d							14 09				14 37		
Appleford	d													
Culham	d													
Radley	d							14 17						
Oxford	a					14 03		14 25		14 35		14 50		
	d			13 56		14 06	14 20			14 37				
Islip	d			14 09										
Bicester Town	a			14 21										
Tackley	d						14 29							
Heyford	d						14 33							
Kings Sutton	d						14 42							
Banbury	a					14 24	14 50			14 52				
Leamington Spa 8	a					14 41				15 10				
Warwick	a					*15 04*				*15 24*				
Warwick Parkway	a					*15 08*				*15 31*				
Stratford-upon-Avon	a									*15 54*				
Coventry	a									15 22				
Birmingham International	a									15 35				
Birmingham New Street 12	a					15 09				15 49				

		XC 1◇	GW 1	GW 1	GW 1	GW 1◇	XC 1◇	GW 1◇	GW 1◇	GW 1◇	GW 1◇	XC 1◇	GW 1
											A		
		🛒				☕	🛒	☕	🛒	☕	☕	🛒	
London Paddington 15 ⊖	d			13 43	14 06	14 27		14 37	14 42	14 57	15 00		14 43
Ealing Broadway ⊖	d			13 50									14 50
Slough 3	d			14 16	14 23				15 00				15 16
Maidenhead 3	d			14 27	14 31								15 27
Twyford 3	d			14 35									15 35
Reading 7	a			14 43	14 46	15 02		15 13	15 20	15 31	15 36		15 43
	d	14 40		14 43	14 47		15 11	15 14	15 20		15 37	15 40	15 43
Reading West	d				14 50								
Theale	d				14 56								
Aldermaston	d				15 01								
Midgham	d				15 04								
Thatcham	d				15 09								
Newbury Racecourse	d												
Newbury	a				15 17								
	d												
Kintbury	d												
Hungerford	d												
Bedwyn	a												
Tilehurst	d			14 48									15 48
Pangbourne	d			14 52									15 52
Goring & Streatley	d			14 57									15 57
Cholsey	d			15 02									16 02
Didcot Parkway	a			15 08				15 29	15 36		15 52		16 08
	d			15 09					15 36				16 09
Appleford	d			15 14									
Culham	d												
Radley	d			15 19									16 17
Oxford	a	15 03		15 27			15 35		15 50			16 03	16 25
	d	15 06	15 26				15 37					16 06	
Islip	d		15 39										
Bicester Town	a		15 51										
Tackley	d												
Heyford	d												
Kings Sutton	d												
Banbury	a	15 24					15 52					16 24	
Leamington Spa 8	a	15 41					16 10					16 41	
Warwick	a	*16 03*										*17 04*	
Warwick Parkway	a	*16 05*					*16 27*					*17 08*	
Stratford-upon-Avon	a												
Coventry	a						16 22						
Birmingham International	a						16 35						
Birmingham New Street 12	a	16 09					16 49					17 09	

For general notes see front of timetable
For details of catering facilities see
Directory of Train Operators

A To Weston-super-Mare (Table 134)

Table 116

Sundays

until 12 July

London and Reading → Bedwyn, Oxford, Bicester, Banbury and Birmingham

Network Diagram - see first page of Table 116

		GW	XC	GW	GW	GW	GW	GW	XC	GW	GW	GW	GW	XC	GW	GW	GW	GW	XC	GW	GW	GW	GW	XC	GW	GW
		1	1◇	1◇	1◇	1◇	1◇	1	1◇	1	1	1	1◇	1◇	1◇	1◇	1◇	1◇	1◇	1	1	1	1◇	1◇	1◇	1◇
			🛒	☕	☕	☕	☕		🛒				☕	🛒	☕	☕	☕	☕	🛒				☕	🛒	☕	🛒
London Paddington 15 ⊖	d	15 06		15 37	15 42	15 57	16 00				15 43	16 06	16 27		16 37	16 42	16 57	17 00			16 43	17 06	17 30		17 37	17 42
Ealing Broadway ⊖	d										15 50										16 50					
Slough 3	d	15 23			15 58						16 16	16 23				16 59					17 16	17 23				17 59
Maidenhead 3	d	15 31									16 27	16 31									17 27	17 31				
Twyford 3	d										16 35										17 35					
Reading 7	a	15 46		16 15	16 20	16 31	16 36				16 43	16 46	17 02		17 15	17 20	17 31	17 36			17 43	17 46	18 04		18 15	18 20
	d	15 47	16 11	16 16	16 21	16 32	16 37		16 40		16 43	16 47		17 11	17 16	17 21		17 37	17 40		17 43	17 47		18 11	18 16	18 21
Reading West	d											16 50														
Theale	d	15 54										16 56										17 54				
Aldermaston	d											17 01														
Midgham	d											17 04														
Thatcham	d	16 03										17 09										18 03				
Newbury Racecourse	d																									
Newbury	a	16 08				16 47						17 17										18 08				
	d	16 09																				18 09				
Kintbury	d	16 15																				18 15				
Hungerford	d	16 20																				18 20				
Bedwyn	a	16 29																				18 29				
Tilehurst	d										16 48										17 48					
Pangbourne	d										16 52										17 52					
Goring & Streatley	d										16 57										17 57					
Cholsey	d										17 02										18 02					
Didcot Parkway	a			16 31	16 36		16 52				17 08				17 31	17 37		17 52			18 08				18 31	18 37
	d				16 37						17 09					17 38					18 09					18 38
Appleford	d																				18 14					
Culham	d																									
Radley	d										17 17										18 19					
Oxford	a		16 35		16 49				17 03		17 25			17 35		17 50			18 03		18 27			18 35		18 50
	d		16 37					16 56	17 06	17 19				17 37					18 06	18 26				18 37		
Islip	d							17 09												18 39						
Bicester Town	a							17 21												18 51						
Tackley	d									17 28																
Heyford	d									17 32																
Kings Sutton	d									17 41																
Banbury	a		16 52						17 24	17 50				17 52					18 24					18 52		
Leamington Spa 8	a		17 10						17 41					18 10					18 41					19 10		
Warwick	a		*17 22*						*18 04*										*19 04*					*19 25*		
Warwick Parkway	a		*17 30*						*18 08*					*18 34*					*19 08*					*19 34*		
Stratford-upon-Avon	a		*17 54*																					*19 54*		
Coventry	a		17 22											18 22										19 22		
Birmingham International	a		17 35											18 35										19 35		
Birmingham New Street 12	a		17 49						18 09					18 49					19 09					19 49		

		GW	GW	XC	GW	GW	GW	XC	GW	GW	GW	GW	GW	XC	GW	GW	GW	XC	GW	GW	GW	GW	XC	GW	GW	GW
		1◇	1◇	1◇	1	1	1◇	1◇	1◇	1◇	1◇	1◇	1	1◇	1	1	1◇	1◇	1◇	1◇	1◇	1◇	1◇	1	1	1
		☕	☕	🛒			☕	🛒	☕	☕	☕	☕		🛒			☕	🛒	☕	☕	☕	☕	🛒			
London Paddington 15 ⊖	d	17 57	18 00		17 43	18 06	18 27		18 37	18 42	18 57	19 00			18 43	19 06	19 30		19 37	19 42	19 57	20 00				19 43
Ealing Broadway ⊖	d				17 50										18 50											19 50
Slough 3	d				18 16	18 23				18 59					19 16	19 23				19 57						20 16
Maidenhead 3	d				18 27	18 31									19 27	19 31										20 27
Twyford 3	d				18 35										19 35											20 35
Reading 7	a	18 31	18 36		18 43	18 46	19 01		19 15	19 20	19 31	19 36			19 43	19 51	20 04		20 16	20 17	20 31	20 36				20 43
	d	18 32	18 37	18 40	18 43	18 47		19 11	19 16	19 20		19 37		19 40	19 43	19 54		20 11	20 16	20 20	20 32	20 37	20 40	20 44		20 47
Reading West	d					18 50																		20 47		
Theale	d					18 56										20 03								20 56		
Aldermaston	d					19 01																		21 01		
Midgham	d					19 04																		21 04		
Thatcham	d					19 09										20 12								21 09		
Newbury Racecourse	d																							21 14		
Newbury	a	18 47				19 17										20 17					20 48			21 18		
	d															20 18										
Kintbury	d															20 24										
Hungerford	d															20 29										
Bedwyn	a															20 37										
Tilehurst	d				18 48										19 48											20 51
Pangbourne	d				18 52										19 52											20 56
Goring & Streatley	d				18 57										19 57											21 01
Cholsey	d				19 02										20 02											21 06
Didcot Parkway	a		18 52		19 08				19 31	19 36		19 52			20 08				20 31	20 35		20 52				21 12
	d				19 09					19 36					20 09					20 36						21 12
Appleford	d																									
Culham	d																									
Radley	d				19 17										20 17											21 19
Oxford	a			19 04	19 25			19 35		19 50				20 04	20 25			20 35		20 48			21 03			21 27
	d			19 06				19 37					19 56	20 06				20 37					21 06		21 26	
Islip	d												20 09												21 39	
Bicester Town	a												20 21												21 51	
Tackley	d																									
Heyford	d																									
Kings Sutton	d																									
Banbury	a			19 24				19 52						20 24				20 52					21 24			
Leamington Spa 8	a			19 41				20 10						20 41				21 10					21 41			
Warwick	a			*20 06*										*21 07*									*22 05*			
Warwick Parkway	a			*20 10*				*20 34*						*21 11*				*21 34*					*22 08*			
Stratford-upon-Avon	a																									
Coventry	a			19 53				20 22						20 53				21 22					21 53			
Birmingham International	a			20 03				20 37						21 03				21 35					22 03			
Birmingham New Street 12	a			20 15				20 49						21 20				21 49					22 20			

For general notes see front of timetable
For details of catering facilities see
Directory of Train Operators

Sundays

until 12 July

London and Reading → Bedwyn, Oxford, Bicester, Banbury and Birmingham

Network Diagram - see first page of Table 116

		GW	XC	GW	GW	GW	GW	XC	GW	GW	GW	GW	GW	GW	GW	GW	GW	GW	GW	GW	GW	GW	GW	GW
		1 ◇	1 ◇	1 ◇	1 ◇	1 ◇	1 ◇	1 ◇	1	1	1 ◇	1 ◇	1	1	1 ◇	1		1	1 ◇	1		1 ◇	1	1 ◇
							A																	
																	🚌				🚌			
		🍴	🛒	🍴		🍴	🍴	🛒			🍴	🍴			🍴							🍴		🍴
London Paddington 15 ⊖	d	20 29		20 37	20 42	20 57	21 00			20 43	21 27	21 37		21 43	22 03			22 15	22 42	22 43		23 03		23 37
Ealing Broadway ⊖	d									20 50				21 50				22 24		22 52				
Slough 3	d				20 59					21 16	21 49			22 15				22 46	23 01	23 15				23 55
Maidenhead 3	d									21 27				22 31				22 56		23 24				
Twyford 3	d									21 35				22 39				23 04		23 32				
Reading 7	a	21 03		21 15	21 18	21 31	21 36			21 44	22 08	22 14		22 46	22 50	⟵		23 11	23 18	23 43		23 46	⟵	00 15
	d		21 11	21 16	21 22		21 37	21 40	21 44	21 47	22 10	22 15	22 44	22 54	22 50	22 54		23 12	23 20	23 50		23 46	23 50	00 15
Reading West	d												22 47	⟶				23 16		⟶				
Theale	d								21 51				22 53					23 23						
Aldermaston	d												22 58											
Midgham	d												23 01											
Thatcham	d								22 00				23 06					23 31						
Newbury Racecourse	d												23 11											
Newbury	a								22 05				23 15					23 38						
	d								22 06															
Kintbury	d								22 12															
Hungerford	d								22 17															
Bedwyn	a								22 24															
Tilehurst	d									21 51						22 58							23 55	
Pangbourne	d									21 56						23 03							23 59	
Goring & Streatley	d									22 01						23 07							00 05	
Cholsey	d									22 06						23 12							00 10	
Didcot Parkway	a			21 31	21 37		21 53			22 12	22 25	22 31			23 06	23 20			23 36			00s02	00 17	00s33
	d				21 38					22 13	22 26						23 25				23 45			
Appleford	d																							
Culham	d																							
Radley	d									22 20							23 40							
Oxford	a		21 35		21 51			22 04		22 28	22 39						23 55				00 10			
	d		21 37					22 06																
Islip	d																							
Bicester Town	a																							
Tackley	d																							
Heyford	d																							
Kings Sutton	d																							
Banbury	a		21 52					22 24																
Leamington Spa 8	a		22 10					22 41																
Warwick	a		22 34					23 25																
Warwick Parkway	a		22 37					23 28																
Stratford-upon-Avon	a																							
Coventry	a		22 22					22 53																
Birmingham International	a		22 32					23 03																
Birmingham New Street 12	a		23 06					23 35																

For general notes see front of timetable
For details of catering facilities see Directory of Train Operators

A To Weston-super-Mare (Table 134)

Sundays

London and Reading → Bedwyn, Oxford, Bicester, Banbury and Birmingham

19 July to 6 September

Network Diagram - see first page of Table 116

		GW	GW	GW	GW	GW	GW	GW	GW	GW	GW	XC	GW	GW	GW	GW	GW	GW	GW	GW	GW	XC	GW	GW	GW	GW
		1	1 ◇	1	1		1 ◇	1 ◇		1	1	1 ◇	1 ◇	1 ◇	1 ◇	1 ◇	1 ◇	1	1	1	1 ◇	1 ◇	1 ◇	1 ◇	1 ◇	1
								A																	B	
							☕					🛒	☕	☕		☕	☕				☕	🛒	☕	☕	☕	
London Paddington 15 ⊖	d	22p45	23p33		23p20		08 00	08 03			07 43		08 30	08 35	08 42	08 57	09 00		08 43	09 04	09 30		09 35	09 57	10 00	
Ealing Broadway ⊖	d	22p55			23p28						07 50								08 52							
Slough 3	d	23p21	23p50		23p54			08 21			08 22				09 01				09 16	09 23			09 51			
Maidenhead 3	d	23p30			00 05			08 29			08 32								09 27	09 32						
Twyford 3	d	23p38			00 13						08 40								09 35							
Reading 7	a	23p44	00 07		00 20		08 36	08 43			08 49		09 14	09 19	09 24	09 31	09 36		09 43	09 46	10 04		10 12	10 32	10 36	
	d	23p49	00 08	00 15	00 21	08 14	08 38	08 44	08 44		08 49	09 11	09 16		09 26	09 32	09 37		09 44	09 47	10 05	10 11	10 12		10 37	
Reading West	d			00s18		08 17														09 50						
Theale	d			00s24		08 23			08 51											09 56						
Aldermaston	d			00s29		08 28														10 01						
Midgham	d			00s32		08 31														10 04						
Thatcham	d			00s37		08 36			09 00											10 09						
Newbury Racecourse	d			00s42																						
Newbury	a			00 45		08 43			09 05							09 47				10 15						
	d								09 06											10 15						
Kintbury	d								09 12											10 22						
Hungerford	d								09 17											10 26						
Bedwyn	a								09 24											10 35						
Tilehurst	d	23p53			00 25						08 53								09 48							
Pangbourne	d	23p58									08 58								09 52							
Goring & Streatley	d	00 03			00 32						09 03								09 57							
Cholsey	d	00 08			00 37						09 08								10 02							
Didcot Parkway	a	00 15	00 24		00 44		08 55	08 58			09 12		09 30		09 40		09 52		10 08		10 20		10 28		10 52	
	d	00 17	00 24		00 45			09 03			09 12				09 41				10 09				10 28			
Appleford	d																		10 14							
Culham	d																									
Radley	d	00s24									09 21								10 19							
Oxford	a	00 33	00 38		00 59			09 15			09 30	09 35			09 54				10 27			10 35	10 42			
	d									09 26		09 37						10 00				10 37				10 56
Islip	d									09 39																11 09
Bicester Town	a									09 51																11 21
Tackley	d																	10 09								
Heyford	d																	10 13								
Kings Sutton	d																	10 22								
Banbury	a											09 52						10 30				10 52				
Leamington Spa 8	a											10 10						*10 55*				11 10				
Warwick	a																	*11 01*				*11 22*				
Warwick Parkway	a																	*11 05*				*12 05*				
Stratford-upon-Avon	a																					*11 59*				
Coventry	a											10 22										11 22				
Birmingham International	a											10 38										11 38				
Birmingham New Street 12	a											10 51										11 51				

For general notes see front of timetable
For details of catering facilities see Directory of Train Operators

A To Great Malvern (Table 126)
B To Weston-super-Mare (Table 134)

Table 116

Sundays

London and Reading → Bedwyn, Oxford, Bicester, Banbury and Birmingham

19 July to 6 September

Network Diagram - see first page of Table 116

		GW	GW	GW	XC	GW	GW	GW	GW	GW	GW	GW	GW	XC	GW	GW	GW	GW	GW	GW	XC	GW	GW	XC	GW	GW
		1	1	1 ◇	1 ◇	1 ◇	1 ◇	1 ◇	1 ◇	1	1	1 ◇	1	1 ◇	1 ◇	1 ◇	1 ◇	1 ◇	1	1	1 ◇	1 ◇	1	1 ◇	1 ◇	1 ◇
									A																	
				☕	🛒	☕	☕	☕	☕			☕		🛒	☕		☕	☕			🛒	☕		🛒	☕	☕
London Paddington 15	⊖ d	09 43	10 04	10 27		10 37	10 42	10 57	11 00	10 43	11 04	11 27			11 37	11 42	11 57	12 00	11 43	12 04		12 27			12 37	12 42
Ealing Broadway	⊖ d	09 50								10 50									11 50							
Slough 3	d	10 16	10 23				10 59			11 16	11 23					12 00			12 16	12 23						12 59
Maidenhead 3	d	10 27	10 32							11 27	11 31								12 27	12 31						
Twyford 3	d	10 35								11 35									12 35							
Reading 7	a	10 43	10 46	11 02		11 13	11 20	11 31	11 36	11 42	11 46	12 02			12 13	12 19	12 31	12 36	12 43	12 46		13 02			13 13	13 20
	d	10 43	10 47		11 11	11 14	11 20		11 37	11 43	11 47			12 11	12 14	12 22	12 32	12 37	12 43	12 47	12 54			13 11	13 14	13 20
Reading West	d		10 50																	12 50						
Theale	d		10 56								11 54									12 56						
Aldermaston	d		11 01																	13 01						
Midgham	d		11 04																	13 04						
Thatcham	d		11 09								12 03									13 09						
Newbury Racecourse	d																									
Newbury	a		11 17								12 08						12 47			13 17						
	d										12 09															
Kintbury	d										12 15															
Hungerford	d										12 20															
Bedwyn	a										12 29															
Tilehurst	d	10 48								11 48									12 48							
Pangbourne	d	10 52								11 52									12 52							
Goring & Streatley	d	10 57								11 57									12 57				←			
Cholsey	d	11 02								12 02									13 02				13 02			
Didcot Parkway	a	11 08				11 29	11 36		11 52	12 08					12 29	12 37		12 52	→				13 08		13 29	13 36
	d	11 09					11 36			12 09						12 38							13 09			13 36
Appleford	d																						13 14			
Culham	d																									
Radley	d	11 17								12 17													13 19			
Oxford	a	11 25			11 35		11 50			12 25				12 35		12 50					13 15		13 27	13 35		13 50
	d				11 36								12 26	12 37							13 17			13 37		
Islip	d												12 39													
Bicester Town	a												12 51													
Tackley	d																									
Heyford	d																									
Kings Sutton	d																									
Banbury	a				11 52									12 52							13 34			13 52		
Leamington Spa 8	a				12 10									13 10							13 51			14 10		
Warwick	a				*13 04*									*13 22*							*14 04*					
Warwick Parkway	a				*12 27*									*13 30*							*14 07*			*14 27*		
Stratford-upon-Avon	a													*13 52*												
Coventry	a				12 22									13 22										14 22		
Birmingham International	a				12 38									13 37										14 35		
Birmingham New Street 12	a				12 51									13 49							14 18			14 49		

		GW	GW	GW		XC	GW	GW	GW	XC	GW	GW	GW	GW	XC	GW	GW	GW	GW	XC	GW	GW	GW	GW	XC	GW
		1 ◇	1 ◇	1		1 ◇	1	1	1	1 ◇	1 ◇	1 ◇	1 ◇	1 ◇	1 ◇	1	1	1	1 ◇	1 ◇	1 ◇	1 ◇	1 ◇	1 ◇	1 ◇	1
																								A		
		☕	☕			🛒				🛒	☕	☕	☕	☕	🛒				☕	🛒	☕	🛒	☕	☕	🛒	
London Paddington 15	⊖ d	12 57	13 00					12 43	13 04		13 37	13 42	13 57	14 00			13 43	14 06	14 27		14 37	14 42	14 57	15 00		14 43
Ealing Broadway	⊖ d							12 50									13 50									14 50
Slough 3	d							13 16	13 23			13 58					14 16	14 23				15 00				15 16
Maidenhead 3	d							13 27	13 31								14 27	14 31								15 27
Twyford 3	d							13 35									14 35									15 35
Reading 7	a	13 31	13 36					13 43	13 46		14 13	14 20	14 31	14 36			14 43	14 46	15 02		15 13	15 20	15 31	15 36		15 43
	d		13 37			13 40		13 43	13 47	14 11	14 14	14 21	14 32	14 37	14 40		14 43	14 47		15 11	15 14	15 20		15 37	15 40	15 43
Reading West	d																	14 50								
Theale	d								13 54									14 56								
Aldermaston	d																	15 01								
Midgham	d																	15 04								
Thatcham	d								14 03									15 09								
Newbury Racecourse	d																									
Newbury	a								14 08				14 47					15 17								
	d								14 09																	
Kintbury	d								14 15																	
Hungerford	d								14 20																	
Bedwyn	a								14 29																	
Tilehurst	d							13 48									14 48									15 48
Pangbourne	d							13 52									14 52									15 52
Goring & Streatley	d							13 57									14 57									15 57
Cholsey	d							14 02									15 02									16 02
Didcot Parkway	a		13 52					14 08			14 29	14 36		14 52			15 08				15 29	15 36		15 52		16 08
	d							14 09				14 37					15 09					15 36				16 09
Appleford	d																15 14									
Culham	d																									
Radley	d							14 17									15 19									16 17
Oxford	a					14 03		14 25		14 35		14 50			15 03		15 27			15 35		15 50			16 03	16 25
	d			13 56		14 06	14 20			14 37					15 06	15 26				15 37					16 06	
Islip	d			14 09												15 39										
Bicester Town	a			14 21												15 51										
Tackley	d						14 29																			
Heyford	d						14 33																			
Kings Sutton	d						14 42																			
Banbury	a					14 24	14 50			14 52					15 24					15 52					16 24	
Leamington Spa 8	a					14 41				15 10					15 41					16 10					16 41	
Warwick	a					*15 04*				*15 24*					*16 03*										*17 04*	
Warwick Parkway	a					*15 08*				*15 31*					*16 05*					*16 27*					*17 08*	
Stratford-upon-Avon	a									*15 54*																
Coventry	a									15 22										16 22						
Birmingham International	a									15 35										16 35						
Birmingham New Street 12	a					15 09				15 49					16 09					16 49					17 09	

For general notes see front of timetable
For details of catering facilities see Directory of Train Operators

A To Weston-super-Mare (Table 134)

Table 116

Sundays

London and Reading → Bedwyn, Oxford, Bicester, Banbury and Birmingham

19 July to 6 September

Network Diagram - see first page of Table 116

Station		GW	XC	GW	GW	GW	GW	GW	XC	GW	GW	GW	GW	XC	GW	GW	GW	GW	XC	GW	GW	GW	GW	XC	GW	GW
		1	1◇	1◇	1◇	1◇	1◇	1	1◇	1	1	1	1◇	1◇	1◇	1◇	1◇	1◇	1◇	1	1	1	1◇	1◇	1◇	1◇
			🛒	☕	☕	☕	☕		🛒				☕	🛒	☕	☕	☕	☕	🛒				☕	🛒	☕	🛒
London Paddington 15 ⊖	d	15 06		15 37	15 42	15 57	16 00				15 43	16 06	16 27		16 37	16 42	16 57	17 00			16 43	17 06	17 30		17 37	17 42
Ealing Broadway ⊖	d										15 50										16 50					
Slough 3	d	15 23			15 58						16 16	16 23				16 59					17 16	17 23				17 58
Maidenhead 3	d	15 31									16 27	16 31									17 27	17 31				
Twyford 3	d										16 35										17 35					
Reading 7	a	15 46		16 15	16 20	16 31	16 36				16 43	16 46	17 02		17 15	17 20	17 31	17 36			17 43	17 46	18 04		18 15	18 20
	d	15 47	16 11	16 16	16 21	16 32	16 37		16 40		16 43	16 47		17 11	17 16	17 21		17 37	17 40		17 43	17 47		18 11	18 16	18 21
Reading West	d											16 50														
Theale	d	15 54										16 56										17 54				
Aldermaston	d											17 01														
Midgham	d											17 04														
Thatcham	d	16 03										17 09										18 03				
Newbury Racecourse	d																									
Newbury	a	16 08				16 47						17 17										18 08				
	d	16 09																				18 09				
Kintbury	d	16 15																				18 15				
Hungerford	d	16 20																				18 20				
Bedwyn	a	16 29																				18 29				
Tilehurst	d										16 48										17 48					
Pangbourne	d										16 52										17 52					
Goring & Streatley	d										16 57										17 57					
Cholsey	d										17 02										18 02					
Didcot Parkway	a			16 31	16 36		16 52				17 08				17 31	17 37		17 52			18 08				18 31	18 36
	d				16 37						17 09					17 38					18 09					18 37
Appleford	d																				18 14					
Culham	d																									
Radley	d										17 17										18 19					
Oxford	a		16 35		16 49				17 03		17 25			17 35		17 50			18 03		18 27			18 35		18 50
	d		16 37					16 56	17 06	17 19				17 37					18 06	18 26				18 36		
Islip	d							17 09												18 39						
Bicester Town	a							17 21												18 51						
Tackley	d									17 28																
Heyford	d									17 32																
Kings Sutton	d									17 41																
Banbury	a		16 52						17 24	17 50				17 52					18 24					18 52		
Leamington Spa 8	a		17 10						17 41					18 10					18 41					19 10		
Warwick	a		*17 22*						*18 04*										*19 04*					*19 25*		
Warwick Parkway	a		*17 30*						*18 08*					*18 34*					*19 08*					*19 34*		
Stratford-upon-Avon	a		*17 54*																					*19 54*		
Coventry	a		17 22											18 22										19 22		
Birmingham International	a		17 35											18 35										19 35		
Birmingham New Street 12	a		17 49						18 09					18 49					19 09					19 49		

Station		GW	GW	XC	GW	GW	GW	XC	GW	GW	GW	GW	GW	XC	GW	GW	GW	XC	GW	GW	GW	GW	XC	GW	GW	GW
		1◇	1◇	1◇	1	1	1◇	1◇	1◇	1◇	1◇	1◇	1	1◇	1	1	1◇	1◇	1◇	1◇	1◇	1◇	1◇	1	1	1
		☕	☕	🛒			☕	🛒	☕	☕	☕	☕		🛒			☕	🛒	☕	☕	☕	☕	🛒			
London Paddington 15 ⊖	d	17 57	18 00		17 43	18 06	18 27		18 37	18 42	18 57	19 00			18 43	19 06	19 30		19 37	19 42	19 57	20 00				19 43
Ealing Broadway ⊖	d				17 50										18 50											19 50
Slough 3	d				18 16	18 23				18 59					19 16	19 23				19 57						20 16
Maidenhead 3	d				18 27	18 31									19 27	19 31										20 27
Twyford 3	d				18 35										19 35											20 35
Reading 7	a	18 31	18 36		18 43	18 46	19 01		19 15	19 20	19 31	19 36			19 43	19 51	20 04		20 16	20 17	20 31	20 36				20 43
	d	18 32	18 37	18 40	18 43	18 47		19 11	19 16	19 20		19 37		19 40	19 43	19 54		20 11	20 16	20 20	20 32	20 37	20 40	20 44		20 47
Reading West	d					18 50																		20 47		
Theale	d					18 56										20 03								20 56		
Aldermaston	d					19 01																		21 01		
Midgham	d					19 04																		21 04		
Thatcham	d					19 09										20 12								21 09		
Newbury Racecourse	d																							21 14		
Newbury	a	18 47				19 17										20 17					20 48			21 18		
	d															20 18										
Kintbury	d															20 24										
Hungerford	d															20 29										
Bedwyn	a															20 37										
Tilehurst	d				18 48										19 48											20 51
Pangbourne	d				18 52										19 52											20 56
Goring & Streatley	d				18 57										19 57											21 01
Cholsey	d				19 02										20 02											21 06
Didcot Parkway	a		18 52		19 08				19 31	19 36		19 52			20 08				20 31	20 35		20 52				21 12
	d				19 09					19 36					20 09					20 36						21 12
Appleford	d																									
Culham	d																									
Radley	d				19 17										20 17											21 19
Oxford	a			19 03	19 25			19 35		19 50				20 03	20 25			20 35		20 48			21 03			21 27
	d			19 06				19 37					19 56	20 06				20 37					21 06		21 26	
Islip	d												20 09												21 39	
Bicester Town	a												20 21												21 51	
Tackley	d																									
Heyford	d																									
Kings Sutton	d																									
Banbury	a			19 24				19 52						20 24				20 52					21 24			
Leamington Spa 8	a			19 41				20 10						20 41				21 10					21 41			
Warwick	a			*20 06*										*21 07*									*22 05*			
Warwick Parkway	a			*20 10*				*20 34*						*21 11*				*21 34*					*22 08*			
Stratford-upon-Avon	a																									
Coventry	a			19 53				20 22						20 53				21 22					21 53			
Birmingham International	a			20 03				20 35						21 03				21 35					22 03			
Birmingham New Street 12	a			20 15				20 49						21 20				21 49					22 20			

For general notes see front of timetable
For details of catering facilities see Directory of Train Operators

London and Reading → Bedwyn, Oxford, Bicester, Banbury and Birmingham

Network Diagram - see first page of Table 116

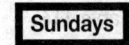

		GW	XC	GW	GW	GW	GW	XC	GW	GW	GW	GW	GW	GW	GW	GW	GW	GW	GW	GW	GW	GW	GW	GW
		1 ◇	1 ◇	1 ◇	1 ◇	1 ◇	1 ◇	1 ◇	1	1	1 ◇	1 ◇	1	1	1 ◇	1		1	1 ◇	1		1 ◇	1	1 ◇
							A										🚌				🚌			
		☕	🛒	☕		☕	☕	🛒			☕	☕			☕							☕		☕
London Paddington 15 ⊖	d	20 29		20 37	20 42	20 57	21 00			20 43	21 27	21 37		21 43	22 03			22 15	22 42	22 43		23 03		23 37
Ealing Broadway ⊖	d									20 50				21 50				22 24		22 52				
Slough 3	d				20 59					21 16	21 49			22 15				22 46	23 01	23 15				23 55
Maidenhead 3	d									21 27				22 31				22 56		23 24				
Twyford 3	d									21 35				22 39				23 04		23 32				
Reading 7	a	21 03		21 15	21 18	21 31	21 36			21 44	22 08	22 14		22 46	22 50	←		23 11	23 18	23 43		23 46	←	00 15
	d		21 11	21 16	21 22		21 37	21 40	21 44	21 47	22 10	22 15	22 44	22 54	22 50	22 54		23 12	23 20	23 50		23 46	23 50	00 15
Reading West	d												22 47	→				23 16		→				
Theale	d								21 51				22 53					23 23						
Aldermaston	d												22 58											
Midgham	d												23 01											
Thatcham	d								22 00				23 06					23 31						
Newbury Racecourse	d												23 11											
Newbury	a								22 05				23 15					23 38						
	d								22 06															
Kintbury	d								22 12															
Hungerford	d								22 17															
Bedwyn	a								22 24															
Tilehurst	d									21 51						22 58							23 55	
Pangbourne	d									21 56						23 03							23 59	
Goring & Streatley	d									22 01						23 07							00 05	
Cholsey	d									22 06						23 12							00 10	
Didcot Parkway	a			21 31	21 37		21 53			22 12	22 25	22 31			23 06	23 20			23 36			00s02	00 17	00s33
	d				21 38					22 13	22 26						23 25				23 45			
Appleford	d																							
Culham	d																							
Radley	d									22 20							23 40							
Oxford	a		21 35		21 51			22 03		22 28	22 39						23 55				00 10			
	d		21 36					22 06																
Islip	d																							
Bicester Town	a																							
Tackley	d																							
Heyford	d																							
Kings Sutton	d																							
Banbury	a		21 52					22 24																
Leamington Spa 8	a		22 10					22 41																
Warwick	a		22 34					23 25																
Warwick Parkway	a		22 37					23 28																
Stratford-upon-Avon	a																							
Coventry	a		22 22					22 53																
Birmingham International	a		22 32					23 03																
Birmingham New Street 12	a		22 47					23 20																

For general notes see front of timetable
For details of catering facilities see Directory of Train Operators

A To Weston-super-Mare (Table 134)

Table 116

Sundays
from 13 September

London and Reading → Bedwyn, Oxford, Bicester, Banbury and Birmingham

Network Diagram - see first page of Table 116

		GW	GW	GW	GW	GW	GW	GW	GW	GW	GW	GW	GW	GW	GW	XC	GW	GW	GW	GW	GW		GW	XC	GW	GW
		1	1 ◇		1	1			1 ◇	1	1 ◇		1	1	1 ◇	1 ◇	1 ◇	1 ◇	1 ◇	1	1		1 ◇	1 ◇	1 ◇	1 ◇
											A															
				🚌			🚌		☕		🛒				☕	🛒		☕	☕				☕	🛒	☕	☕
London Paddington 15	⊖ d	22p45	23p33			23p20			08 00	07 44	08 03				08 30		08 42	08 57	09 03	08 44			09 30		09 35	09 57
Ealing Broadway	⊖ d	22p55				23p28				07 52										08 52						
Slough 3	d	23p21	23p50			23p54				08 14	08 25						09 01			09 15					09 57	
Maidenhead 3	d	23p30				00 05				08 24	08 32									09 24						
Twyford 3	d	23p38				00 13				08 32										09 32						
Reading 7	a	23p44	00 07			00 20			08 32	08 41	08 44			←	09 03		09 20	09 31	09 36	09 41			10 02		10 11	10 31
	d	23p49	00 08		00 15	00 20		08 14	08 34	08 48	08 44	08 44		08 48	09 05	09 11	09 22	09 32	09 37	09 43	09 44		10 05	10 11	10 11	
Reading West	d				00s18			08 17		↪											09 47					
Theale	d				00s24			08 23				08 51									09 53					
Aldermaston	d				00s29			08 28													09 58					
Midgham	d				00s32			08 31													10 01					
Thatcham	d				00s37			08 36				09 00									10 06					
Newbury Racecourse	d				00s42																					
Newbury	a				00 45			08 43				09 05						09 47			10 12					
	d											09 06									10 12					
Kintbury	d											09 12									10 18					
Hungerford	d											09 17									10 23					
Bedwyn	a											09 24									10 31					
Tilehurst	d	23p53				00 24								08 52						09 47						
Pangbourne	d	23p58												08 57						09 52						
Goring & Streatley	d	00 03				00 31								09 02						09 57						
Cholsey	d	00 08				00 36								09 07						10 02						
Didcot Parkway	a	00 15	00 25			00 45			08 49		08 58			09 11	09 21		09 37		09 53	10 08			10 20		10 27	
	d			00 32			00 51				09 03			09 12			09 38			10 09					10 27	
Appleford	d						01s01													10 14						
Culham	d						01s11																			
Radley	d			00s47			01s21							09 21						10 19						
Oxford	a			01 02			01 36				09 15			09 30		09 35	09 52			10 27				10 35	10 41	
	d												09 26			09 37								10 37		
Islip	d												09 39													
Bicester Town	a												09 51													
Tackley	d																									
Heyford	d																									
Kings Sutton	d																									
Banbury	a															09 52								10 52		
Leamington Spa 8	a															10 10								11 10		
Warwick	a															*11 01*								*11 22*		
Warwick Parkway	a															*11 05*								*12 05*		
Stratford-upon-Avon	a																							*11b59*		
Coventry	a															10 22								11 22		
Birmingham International	a															10 38								11 38		
Birmingham New Street 12	a															10 51								11 51		

For general notes see front of timetable
For details of catering facilities see Directory of Train Operators

A To Great Malvern (Table 126)
b From 4 October arr. 3 minutes later

Table 116

Sundays

from 13 September

London and Reading → Bedwyn, Oxford, Bicester, Banbury and Birmingham

Network Diagram - see first page of Table 116

		GW 1◇ A ⊐P	GW 1	GW 1	GW 1	GW 1◇ ⊐P	XC 1◇ ⊐o	GW 1◇ ⊐P	GW 1◇ ⊐P	GW 1◇ A ⊐P	GW 1	GW 1	GW 1◇ ⊐P	GW 1	GW 1◇ ⊐P	XC 1◇ ⊐o	GW 1◇	GW 1◇ ⊐P	GW 1◇ ⊐P		GW 1	GW 1	XC 1◇ ⊐o	GW 1	GW 1◇ ⊐P	XC 1◇ ⊐o
London Paddington 15	⊖ d	10 03		09 44		10 37		10 42	10 57	11 03	10 44		11 27		11 37		11 42	11 57	12 03		11 43				12 37	
Ealing Broadway	⊖ d			09 52							10 52										11 52					
Slough 3	d			10 15				11 05			11 15						12 02				12 15					
Maidenhead 3	d			10 27							11 27										12 27					
Twyford 3	d			10 35							11 35										12 35					
Reading 7	a	10 36		10 42		11 10		11 19	11 31	11 36	11 42		12 02		12 10		12 18	12 31	12 36		12 43				13 10	
	d	10 37		10 43	10 44	11 11	11 11	11 20		11 37	11 43	11 44			12 11	12 11	12 22	12 32	12 37		12 43	12 44	12 54		13 11	13 11
Reading West	d				10 47																	12 47				
Theale	d				10 53							11 51										12 53				
Aldermaston	d				10 58																	12 58				
Midgham	d				11 01																	13 01				
Thatcham	d				11 06							12 00										13 06				
Newbury Racecourse	d				11 11																	13 11				
Newbury	a				11 15							12 05						12 47				13 15				
	d											12 06														
Kintbury	d											12 12														
Hungerford	d											12 17														
Bedwyn	a											12 25														
Tilehurst	d			10 48							11 48										12 48					
Pangbourne	d			10 52							11 52										12 52					
Goring & Streatley	d			10 57							11 57										12 57			←		
Cholsey	d			11 02							12 02										13 02			13 02		
Didcot Parkway	a	10 52		11 08		11 26		11 35		11 52	12 08				12 26		12 37		12 52		→			13 08	13 26	
	d			11 09				11 36			12 09						12 38							13 09		
Appleford	d																							13 14		
Culham	d																									
Radley	d			11 17							12 17													13 19		
Oxford	a			11 25			11 35	11 49			12 25					12 35	12 50						13 16	13 27		13 35
	d		10 56				11 37							12 26		12 37							13 17			13 37
Islip	d		11 09											12 39												
Bicester Town	a		11 21											12 51												
Tackley	d																									
Heyford	d																									
Kings Sutton	d																									
Banbury	a						11 52									12 52							13 35			13 52
Leamington Spa 8	a						12 10									13 10							13 52			14 10
Warwick	a						*13 04*									*13 22*							*14 04*			
Warwick Parkway	a						*12 27*									*13 30*							*14 07*			*14 27*
Stratford-upon-Avon	a															*13b52*										
Coventry	a						12 22									13 22										14 22
Birmingham International	a						12 38									13 37										14 35
Birmingham New Street 12	a						12 51									13 49							14 20			14 49

		GW 1◇ ⊐P	GW 1◇ ⊐P	GW 1◇ ⊐P	GW 1	XC 1◇ ⊐o	GW 1	GW 1	GW 1◇ ⊐P	XC 1◇ ⊐o	GW 1◇ ⊐P	GW 1◇ ⊐P	GW 1◇ ⊐P	XC 1◇ ⊐o	GW 1	GW 1	GW 1		GW 1◇ ⊐P	XC 1◇ ⊐o	GW 1◇ ⊐o	GW 1◇ ⊐P	GW 1◇ B ⊐P	XC 1◇ ⊐o	GW 1	GW 1
London Paddington 15	⊖ d	12 42	12 57	13 03			12 44		13 37		13 42	13 57	14 03			13 44			14 37		14 42	14 57	15 03		14 44	
Ealing Broadway	⊖ d						12 52									13 52									14 52	
Slough 3	d	13 05					13 15				14 05					14 15					15 05				15 15	
Maidenhead 3	d						13 27									14 27									15 27	
Twyford 3	d						13 35									14 35									15 35	
Reading 7	a	13 19	13 31	13 36			13 43		14 10		14 19	14 31	14 36			14 43			15 10		15 20	15 31	15 36		15 43	
	d	13 20		13 37		13 40	13 43	13 44	14 11	14 11	14 20	14 32	14 37	14 40		14 43	14 44		15 11	15 11	15 20		15 37	15 40	15 43	15 44
Reading West	d																14 47									
Theale	d							13 51									14 53									15 51
Aldermaston	d																14 58									
Midgham	d																15 01									
Thatcham	d							14 00									15 06									16 00
Newbury Racecourse	d																15 11									
Newbury	a							14 05				14 47					15 15									16 05
	d							14 06																		16 06
Kintbury	d							14 12																		16 12
Hungerford	d							14 17																		16 17
Bedwyn	a							14 25																		16 25
Tilehurst	d						13 48									14 48									15 48	
Pangbourne	d						13 52									14 52									15 52	
Goring & Streatley	d						13 57									14 57									15 57	
Cholsey	d						14 02									15 02									16 02	
Didcot Parkway	a	13 35		13 52			14 08		14 26		14 35		14 52			15 08			15 26		15 36		15 52		16 08	
	d	13 36					14 09				14 36					15 09					15 36				16 09	
Appleford	d															15 14										
Culham	d																									
Radley	d						14 17									15 19									16 17	
Oxford	a	13 49				14 03	14 25			14 35	14 49			15 03		15 27				15 35	15 50			16 03	16 25	
	d				13 56	14 06				14 37				15 06	15 26					15 37				16 06		
Islip	d				14 09										15 39											
Bicester Town	a				14 21										15 51											
Tackley	d																									
Heyford	d																									
Kings Sutton	d																									
Banbury	a					14 24				14 52				15 24						15 52				16 24		
Leamington Spa 8	a					14 41				15 10				15 41						16 10				16 41		
Warwick	a					*15 04*				*15 24*				*16 03*										*17 04*		
Warwick Parkway	a					*15 08*				*15 31*				*16 05*						*16 27*				*17 08*		
Stratford-upon-Avon	a									*15b54*																
Coventry	a									15 22										16 22						
Birmingham International	a									15 35										16 35						
Birmingham New Street 12	a					15 09				15 49				16 09						16 49				17 09		

For general notes see front of timetable
For details of catering facilities see Directory of Train Operators

A To Weston-super-Mare (Table 134)
B To Taunton (Table 134)
b From 4 October arr. 3 minutes later

Table 116

Sundays

from 13 September

London and Reading → Bedwyn, Oxford, Bicester, Banbury and Birmingham

Network Diagram - see first page of Table 116

		GW	XC	GW	GW	GW	GW	XC	GW	GW	GW	GW	XC	GW	GW		GW	XC	GW	GW	GW	GW	GW	XC	GW	GW
		1 ◇	1 ◇	1 ◇	1 ◇	1 ◇	1	1 ◇	1	1	1 ◇	1 ◇	1 ◇	1 ◇	1 ◇		1 ◇	1 ◇	1	1	1	1 ◇	1 ◇	1 ◇	1 ◇	1 ◇
		🍴	🛒	🍴	🍴	🍴		🛒			🍴	🍴	🛒	🍴	🍴		🍴	🛒				🍴	🍴	🛒	🛒	🍴
London Paddington 15 ⊖	d	15 37		15 42	15 57	16 03			15 44		16 27	16 37		16 42	16 57		17 03			16 44		17 30	17 37		17 42	17 57
Ealing Broadway ⊖	d								15 52											16 52						
Slough 3	d			16 05					16 15					17 03						17 15					18 03	
Maidenhead 3	d								16 27											17 27						
Twyford 3	d								16 35											17 35						
Reading 7	a	16 10		16 19	16 31	16 36			16 43		17 04	17 10		17 19	17 31		17 36			17 43		18 04	18 10		18 19	18 31
	d	16 11	16 11	16 20	16 32	16 37		16 40	16 43	16 44		17 11	17 11	17 20			17 37	17 40		17 43	17 44		18 11	18 11	18 20	18 32
Reading West	d									16 47																
Theale	d									16 53											17 51					
Aldermaston	d									16 58																
Midgham	d									17 01																
Thatcham	d									17 06											18 00					
Newbury Racecourse	d									17 11																
Newbury	a				16 47					17 15											18 05					18 47
	d																				18 06					
Kintbury	d																				18 12					
Hungerford	d																				18 17					
Bedwyn	a																				18 25					
Tilehurst	d								16 48											17 48						
Pangbourne	d								16 52											17 52						
Goring & Streatley	d								16 57											17 57						
Cholsey	d								17 02											18 02						
Didcot Parkway	a	16 26		16 35		16 52			17 08			17 26		17 36			17 52			18 08			18 26		18 36	
	d			16 36					17 09					17 37						18 09					18 37	
Appleford	d																			18 14						
Culham	d																									
Radley	d								17 17											18 19						
Oxford	a		16 35	16 49				17 03	17 25				17 35	17 49				18 03		18 27				18 35	18 49	
	d		16 37				16 56	17 06					17 37					18 06	18 26					18 37		
Islip	d						17 09												18 39							
Bicester Town	a						17 21												18 51							
Tackley	d																									
Heyford	d																									
Kings Sutton	d																									
Banbury	a		16 52					17 24					17 52					18 24						18 52		
Leamington Spa 8	a		17 10					17 41					18 10					18 41						19 10		
Warwick	a		*17 22*					*18 04*										*19 04*						*19 25*		
Warwick Parkway	a		*17 30*					*18 08*					*18 34*					*19 08*						*19 34*		
Stratford-upon-Avon	a		*17b54*																					*19b54*		
Coventry	a		17 22										18 22											19 22		
Birmingham International	a		17 35										18 35											19 35		
Birmingham New Street 12	a		17 49					18 09					18 49					19 09						19 49		

		GW	XC	GW	GW	GW	GW	XC	GW	GW	GW	GW	XC		GW	GW	GW	GW	XC	GW	GW	GW	XC	GW	GW	GW
		1 ◇	1 ◇	1	1	1 ◇	1 ◇	1 ◇	1 ◇	1 ◇	1 ◇	1	1 ◇		1	1	1 ◇	1 ◇	1 ◇	1 ◇	1 ◇	1 ◇	1 ◇	1	1	1
		🍴	🛒			🍴	🍴	🛒	🍴	🍴	🍴		🛒				🍴	🍴	🛒	🍴	🍴	🍴	🛒			
London Paddington 15 ⊖	d	18 03		17 44		18 27	18 37		18 42	18 57	19 03				18 44		19 30	19 37		19 42	19 57	20 03			19 44	
Ealing Broadway ⊖	d			17 52											18 52										19 52	
Slough 3	d			18 15					19 06						19 15					20 05					20 15	
Maidenhead 3	d			18 27											19 27										20 27	
Twyford 3	d			18 35											19 35										20 35	
Reading 7	a	18 36		18 43		19 04	19 10		19 20	19 31	19 36				19 43		20 04	20 10		20 17	20 31	20 36			20 43	
	d	18 37	18 40	18 43	18 44		19 11	19 11	19 20		19 37		19 40		19 43	19 44		20 11	20 11	20 20	20 32	20 37	20 40		20 43	20 44
Reading West	d				18 47																					20 47
Theale	d				18 53											19 51										20 56
Aldermaston	d				18 58																					21 01
Midgham	d				19 01																					21 04
Thatcham	d				19 06											20 00										21 09
Newbury Racecourse	d				19 11																					21 14
Newbury	a				19 15											20 05					20 48					21 18
	d															20 06										
Kintbury	d															20 12										
Hungerford	d															20 17										
Bedwyn	a															20 25										
Tilehurst	d			18 48											19 48										20 48	
Pangbourne	d			18 52											19 52										20 52	
Goring & Streatley	d			18 57											19 57										20 57	
Cholsey	d			19 02											20 02										21 02	
Didcot Parkway	a	18 52		19 08			19 26		19 36		19 52				20 08			20 26		20 35		20 52			21 10	
	d			19 09					19 36						20 09					20 36					21 11	
Appleford	d																									
Culham	d																									
Radley	d			19 17											20 17										21 18	
Oxford	a		19 03	19 25				19 35	19 50				20 03		20 25				20 35	20 48			21 03		21 26	
	d		19 06					19 37				19 56	20 06						20 37				21 06	21 26		
Islip	d											20 09												21 39		
Bicester Town	a											20 21												21 51		
Tackley	d																									
Heyford	d																									
Kings Sutton	d																									
Banbury	a		19 24					19 52					20 24						20 52				21 24			
Leamington Spa 8	a		19 41					20 10					20 41						21 10				21 41			
Warwick	a		*20 06*										*21 07*										*22 05*			
Warwick Parkway	a		*20 10*					*20 34*					*21 11*						*21 34*				*22 08*			
Stratford-upon-Avon	a																									
Coventry	a		19 53					20 22					20 53						21 22				21 53			
Birmingham International	a		20 03					20 37					21 03						21 35				22 03			
Birmingham New Street 12	a		20 15					20 49					21 20						21 49				22 20			

For general notes see front of timetable
For details of catering facilities see Directory of Train Operators

b From 4 October arr. 3 minutes later

Table 116

Sundays

from 13 September

London and Reading → Bedwyn, Oxford, Bicester, Banbury and Birmingham

Network Diagram - see first page of Table 116

		GW	GW	XC	GW	GW	GW	XC	GW	GW	GW	GW	GW	GW	GW	GW	GW	GW	GW	GW	GW	GW	GW	GW
		1 ◇	1 ◇	1 ◇	1 ◇	1 ◇	1 ◇	1 ◇	1	1	1 ◇	1 ◇	1	1	1 ◇	1	1	1 ◇	1 ◇	1	1 ◇	1	1 ◇	1 ◇
							A																	
		🍽	🍽	🛒		🍽	🍽	🛒				🍽			🍽			🍽			🍽		🍽	
London Paddington 15 ⊖	d	20 29	20 37		20 42	20 57	21 03			20 44	21 27	21 37		21 44	22 03		22 15	22 37	22 42	22 44	23 03		23 37	23 47
Ealing Broadway ⊖	d									20 52				21 52			22 24			22 52				23 55
Slough 3	d				21 05					21 15	21 53			22 15			22 46		23 01	23 15				00 08
Maidenhead 3	d									21 27				22 31			22 56			23 24				00 15
Twyford 3	d									21 35				22 39			23 04			23 32				
Reading 7	a	21 04	21 10		21 19	21 31	21 36			21 44	22 07	22 13		22 46	22 50	←	23 11	23 14	23 18	23 43	23 46	←	00 15	00 28
	d		21 11	21 11	21 22		21 37	21 40	21 44	21 47	22 08	22 14	22 44	22 54	22 50	22 54	23 12	23 14	23 20	23 50	23 46	23 50	00 15	00 29
Reading West	d												22 47	→			23 16			→				
Theale	d								21 51				22 53				23 23							
Aldermaston	d												22 58											
Midgham	d												23 01											
Thatcham	d								22 00				23 06				23 31							
Newbury Racecourse	d												23 11											
Newbury	a								22 05				23 15				23 38							
	d								22 06															
Kintbury	d								22 12															
Hungerford	d								22 17															
Bedwyn	a								22 24															
Tilehurst	d									21 51						22 58						23 55		
Pangbourne	d									21 56						23 03						23 59		
Goring & Streatley	d									22 01						23 07						00 05		
Cholsey	d									22 06						23 12						00 10		
Didcot Parkway	a		21 26		21 38		21 53			22 12	22 23	22 29			23 06	23 18		23s30	23 35		00s02	00 16	00s33	00 43
	d				21 38					22 13	22 24					23 20			23 35			00 17		00 44
Appleford	d																							
Culham	d																							
Radley	d									22 20						23 26						00 24		
Oxford	a			21 35	21 51			22 03		22 28	22 37					23 35			23 49			00 34		00 59
	d			21 37				22 06																
Islip	d																							
Bicester Town	a																							
Tackley	d																							
Heyford	d																							
Kings Sutton	d																							
Banbury	a			21 52				22 24																
Leamington Spa 8	a			22 10				22 41																
Warwick	a			22 34				23 25																
Warwick Parkway	a			22 37				23 28																
Stratford-upon-Avon	a																							
Coventry	a			22 22				22 53																
Birmingham International	a			22 32				23 03																
Birmingham New Street 12	a			23 06				23 35																

For general notes see front of timetable
For details of catering facilities see Directory of Train Operators

A To Weston-super-Mare (Table 134)

Birmingham, Banbury, Bicester, Oxford and Bedwyn → Reading and London

Network Diagram - see first page of Table 116

Miles	Miles			GW	GW	GW	GW	GW	GW	GW	GW	GW	GW	GW	GW	GW	GW	GW	GW	GW	GW	GW	GW	GW	GW
				MO	MO	MO	MX	MO	MO	MX	MO		MO												
				1	1	1 ◇	1 ◇		1 ◇	1		1	1	1	1 ◇	1	1	1	1	1	1	1 ◇	1	1	1
				A		B		C	C		C	D	C												
								🚌			🚌				☕							☕			
0	—	**Birmingham New Street 12**	d																						
8½	—	Birmingham International	d																						
19¼	—	Coventry	d																						
—	—	Stratford-upon-Avon	d																						
—	—	Warwick Parkway	d																						
—	—	Warwick	d																						
28¾	—	Leamington Spa 8	d																						
48¾	—	**Banbury**	d							23p50															
52½	—	Kings Sutton	d							23p54															
59¾	—	Heyford	d							00 03															
62½	—	Tackley	d							00 07															
—	0	**Bicester Town**	d																						
—	6	Islip	d																						
71½	11¾	**Oxford**	a							00 18															
—	—		d			00 01	00 06	00 05		00 19	03 40	04 00		05 03		05 34		05 45			06 02				06 07
76½	—	Radley	d							00 26				05 09				05 51							06 13
78¾	—	Culham	d							00 30															06 17
79¾	—	Appleford	d							00 32															06 19
81¾	—	**Didcot Parkway**	a			00 13	00 19	00 30		00 39	04 05	04 12		05 18		05 46		06 00			06 14				06 26
—	—		d	23p50		00 14	00 21		00 35	00 43		04 12	04 12	05 18	05 41	05 46		06 00		06 12	06 16	06 29			06 31
86½	—	Cholsey	d	23p56						00 49		04 18	04 18	05 24		05 52				06 18			←		06 37
90¼	—	Goring & Streatley	d	00 01						00 54		04 23	04 23	05 29		05 57				06 25			06 25		06 42
93½	—	Pangbourne	d	00 05						00 59		04 28	04 28	05 33		06 02				→			06 31		06 47
96¼	—	Tilehurst	d	00 10						01 03		04 32	04 32	05 38		06 06							06 36		→
—	0	**Bedwyn**	d																					06 07	
—	5	Hungerford	d																					06 13	
—	8	Kintbury	d																					06 17	
—	13½	**Newbury**	a																					06 24	
—	—		d		23p45												05 40		05 58					06 25	
—	14	Newbury Racecourse	d		23p47												05 42								
—	17	Thatcham	d		23p52												05 47		06 02					06 30	
—	19¾	Midgham	d		23p57												05 51								
—	21¾	Aldermaston	d		00 01												05 55								
—	25¾	Theale	d		00 06												06 00		06 10					06 38	
—	29½	Reading West	d		00s13												06 07		06 17					06 46	
99	30½	**Reading 7**	a	00 14	00 17	00 30	00 38		00 52	01 09		04 38	04 38	05 44	05 57	06 12	06 12	06 16	06 21		06 30	06 43	06 43	06 49	
—	—		d	00 15		00 32	00 39		00 54	01 10		04 41	04 41	05 44	05 57	06 15		06 16	06 22		06 32	06 45	06 46	06 50	
104	—	Twyford 3	a	00 21		00 38			01 00	01 17		04 48	04 48	05 50		06 21		06 23					06 53		
110¾	—	Maidenhead 3	a	00 29		00 47			01 07	01 25		04 56	04 56	05 58		06 29		06 31			06 42		07 02		
116½	—	Slough 3	a	00 36		00 55	00 56		01 15	01 32		05 03	05 03	06 10		06 40			06 40		06 50	06 58			
129¼	—	Ealing Broadway	⊖ a	00 59		01 12			01 31	01 48		05 28	05 28	06 35		07 05									
135	—	**London Paddington 15**	⊖ a	01 11		01 22	01 17		01 41	02 00		05 41	05 41	06 49	06 24	07 17		06 54	07 00		07 09	07 16	07 26	07 23	

		GW	GW	GW	GW	GW	GW	GW	GW	GW	GW	GW	GW	GW	GW	GW	GW	GW	GW	GW	XC	GW	GW	GW	GW
		1	1 ◇	1	1 ◇	1	1	1	1 ◇	1 ◇	1	1	1 ◇	1	1	1 ◇	1 ◇	1 ◇	1	1	1 ◇	1 ◇	1	1	1 ◇
																		E							
			☕		☕				☕	☕			☕			☕	☕	☕			trolley	☕			trolley
Birmingham New Street 12	d																				06 04				
Birmingham International	d																				06 14				
Coventry	d																				06 25				
Stratford-upon-Avon	d																								
Warwick Parkway	d										05 40										06 12				
Warwick	d																				06 15				
Leamington Spa 8	d										05 45										06 38				
Banbury	d										06 08								06 32		06 55				
Kings Sutton	d										06 12								06 36						
Heyford	d										06 21								06 45						
Tackley	d										06 25								06 49						
Bicester Town	d											06 24													
Islip	d											06 35													
Oxford	a										06 36	06 50							07 00		07 14				
	d		06 28								06 37		06 56						07 01	07 10	07 15			07 21	07 31
Radley	d										06 43								07 08					07 27	
Culham	d										06 47								07 12					07 31	
Appleford	d										06 49								07 14					07 33	
Didcot Parkway	a		06 42								06 56		07 09						07 22				←	07 40	
	d	06 39	06 42		06 46				07 00		07 01		07 10				07 20		07 28			07 29	07 28	07 49	
Cholsey	d	06 45				←					07 07			←					→	07 26			07 34	→	
Goring & Streatley	d	06 50		←		06 50					07 12			07 12						07 32			07 39		
Pangbourne	d	→		06 47		06 54					→			07 17						07 38			07 44		
Tilehurst	d			06 51		06 59								07 21						07 44			07 48		
Bedwyn	d							06 23										06 46							
Hungerford	d							06 28		06 39								06 53							
Kintbury	d							06 33										06 59							
Newbury	a							06 40		06 49								07 08							
	d							06 40		06 50					06 56			07 09							
Newbury Racecourse	d							06 42							06 58										
Thatcham	d							06 47		06 57					07 03			07 16							
Midgham	d							06 52							07 07										
Aldermaston	d							06 55							07 11										
Theale	d							07 00		07 07					07 16			07 25							
Reading West	d							07 07							07 23			07 34							
Reading 7	a		06 57	06 59	07 02	07 05	←	07 12	07 14	07 20			07 26	07 27	07 28		07 36	07 38			07 40	07 44	07 54		07 56
	d		06 58	07 10	07 02	07 07	07 10		07 15	07 21			07 27	07 30		07 31	07 37	07 39				07 45	07 55		07 57
Twyford 3	a			→			07 16							07 37									08 02		
Maidenhead 3	a					07 18	07 24							07 45						08 00			08 10		
Slough 3	a						07 36							07 55									08 20		
Ealing Broadway	⊖ a						08 03							08 19											
London Paddington 15	⊖ a		07 29		07 32	07 43	08 14		07 44	07 52			07 59	08 32		08 02	08 07	08 09		08 24		08 14	08 47		08 29

For general notes see front of timetable
For details of catering facilities see Directory of Train Operators

- **A** Until 7 September
- **B** From 7 September
- **C** Until 31 August
- **D** All Tuesdays to Fridays, also Mondays from 7 September
- **E** From Frome (Table 123)

Birmingham, Banbury, Bicester, Oxford and Bedwyn → Reading and London

Network Diagram - see first page of Table 116

		GW	GW	GW	XC	GW	GW	GW	GW	GW	GW	GW	GW	GW		GW	GW	XC	GW	GW	GW	GW	GW	GW	GW
		1	1 ◊	1 ◊	1 ◊	1 ◊	1	1 ◊	1	1 ◊	1	1	1	1 ◊		1 ◊	1 ◊	1 ◊	1	1 ◊	1	1 ◊	1	1	1 ◊
								A												A					
			☕	☕	🛒	☕		☕		☕				☕		☕		🛒		☕		☕			☕
Birmingham New Street 12	d				06 33													07 04							
Birmingham International	d																	07 14							
Coventry	d																	07 25							
Stratford-upon-Avon	d				*06 10*								*06b10*					*06 46*							
Warwick Parkway	d				*06 44*								*06c44*					*07 19*							
Warwick	d				*06 38*								*06b38*					*07 13*							
Leamington Spa 8	d				07 00													07 38							
Banbury	d				07 19								07 27					07 55							
Kings Sutton	d												07 31												
Heyford	d												07 40												
Tackley	d												07 44												
Bicester Town	d																							07 57	
Islip	d																							08 08	
Oxford	a				07 41								07 55					08 14						08 23	
	d				07 42					07 51			07 55				08 06	08 15					08 21		
Radley	d												08 02										08 27		
Culham	d												08 06												
Appleford	d												08 09												
Didcot Parkway	a						⟵						08 15				08 19		⟵				08 36		
	d		07 45			07 54	07 49	08 00					08 15 →			08 17	08 20		08 15	08 30			08 37		08 47
Cholsey	d						07 55												08 22				08 43		
Goring & Streatley	d						08 00												08 27				08 48 →		
Pangbourne	d						08 04												08 32						
Tilehurst	d						08 09												08 37						
Bedwyn	d	07 07										07 56													
Hungerford	d	07 12		07 36								08 01													
Kintbury	d	07 17										08 06													
Newbury	a	07 24		07 46								08 14													
	d	07 24		07 47							07 55											08 31			
Newbury Racecourse	d	07 26									07 57														
Thatcham	d	07 32									08 02														
Midgham	d	07 36									08 07														
Aldermaston	d	07 40									08 10														
Theale	d	07 45									08 16														
Reading West	d	07 52									08 23														
Reading 7	a	07 57	08 01	08 07	08 13	08 13	08 15	08 16	⟵	08 22	08 27					08 33	08 36	08 40	08 43	08 44	⟵	08 51			09 02
	d		08 02	08 08		08 14	08 19 →	08 18	08 19	08 23				08 34		08 36	08 38		08 47 →	08 45	08 47	08 52			09 02
Twyford 3	a								08 25												08 54				
Maidenhead 3	a								08 33												09 02				
Slough 3	a																								
Ealing Broadway	⊖ a																								
London Paddington 15	⊖ a		08 32	08 38		08 40		08 45	08 59	08 53				09 00		09 06	09 10			09 14	09 26	09 21			09 29

		GW	GW	GW	GW	XC	GW	GW	GW	GW	GW	GW	GW	GW	XC	GW	GW	GW	GW	GW	GW	GW	GW	GW	XC
															R										
		1	1	1 ◊	1	1 ◊	1 ◊	1 ◊	1	1 ◊	1	1 ◊	1 ◊	1	1	1 ◊	1	1 ◊	1 ◊	1	1 ◊	1	1	1 ◊	1 ◊
															B										
				☕		🛒	☕	☕		☕		✕			🛒	☕			☕		☕			☕	🛒
Birmingham New Street 12	d					07 33									08 04										08 33
Birmingham International	d														08 14										
Coventry	d														08 25										
Stratford-upon-Avon	d														*07 36*										
Warwick Parkway	d					*07 43*									*08 19*										*08 41*
Warwick	d					*07 46*									*08 23*										*08 44*
Leamington Spa 8	d					08 00									08 38										09 00
Banbury	d					08 19									08 55										09 19
Kings Sutton	d																								
Heyford	d																								
Tackley	d																								
Bicester Town	d																						09 12		
Islip	d																						09 23		
Oxford	a					08 41									09 14								09 38		09 41
	d				08 37	08 42		08 50					09 01	09 07	09 15			09 31				09 37			09 42
Radley	d													09 13											
Culham	d													09 17											
Appleford	d				08 45																				
Didcot Parkway	a				08 51						⟵		09 13	09 24						⟵		09 50			
	d			08 53	09 01 →		09 00				09 01		09 14	09 31 →		09 29				09 31	09 53	10 01			
Cholsey	d	⟵									09 07									09 37		10 07			
Goring & Streatley	d	08 48									09 12									09 42		10 12 →			
Pangbourne	d	08 53									09 17									09 47					
Tilehurst	d	08 57									09 21									09 51					
Bedwyn	d								08 40																
Hungerford	d								08 45																
Kintbury	d								08 50																
Newbury	a								08 57																
	d		08 36						08 57								09 22								
Newbury Racecourse	d		08 38														09 24								
Thatcham	d		08 43						09 02								09 29								
Midgham	d		08 47														09 33								
Aldermaston	d		08 51														09 37								
Theale	d		08 56						09 10								09 42								
Reading West	d		09 03														09 49								
Reading 7	a	09 03	09 07	09 08		09 13	09 14	09 15	09 20		09 28		09 32		09 40	09 44	09 54	09 55		09 57	10 07				10 13
	d	09 03		09 09			09 16	09 18	09 21	09 29	09 33	09 35	09 37			09 45		09 56	10 02	10 03	10 09			10 11	
Twyford 3	a	09 09									09 39									10 09					
Maidenhead 3	a	09 17									09 47									10 17					
Slough 3	a	09 24									09 54		09 51					10 09		10 24					
Ealing Broadway	⊖ a	09 49									10 19									10 49					
London Paddington 15	⊖ a	10 01		09 39			09 44	09 47	09 55	09 59	10 31	10 02	10 10			10 14		10 28	10 30	11 01	10 37			10 39	

For general notes see front of timetable
For details of catering facilities see Directory of Train Operators

A From Weston-super-Mare (Table 134)
B From Nottingham (Table 57)

b Until 2 October only. Change at Leamington Spa and Banbury
c Until 2 October only

Birmingham, Banbury, Bicester, Oxford and Bedwyn → Reading and London

Network Diagram - see first page of Table 116

		GW	GW	GW	GW	GW	GW	GW	XC	GW	GW	GW	GW	GW	GW	GW	GW	GW	XC	GW	GW	GW	GW	GW	GW
		1	1 ◇	1	1 ◇	1	1	1	1 ◇	1 ◇	1	1 ◇	1 ◇	1	1 ◇	1	1	1 ◇	1 ◇	1	1	1 ◇	1	1 ◇	1
					☕				🛒	☕		☕			☕			☕	🛒					☕	
Birmingham New Street 12	d								09 04										09 33						
Birmingham International	d								09 14																
Coventry	d								09 25																
Stratford-upon-Avon	d																								
Warwick Parkway	d								*09 21*										*09 45*						
Warwick	d								*09 24*										*09 49*						
Leamington Spa 8	d								09 38										10 00						
Banbury	d							09 39	09 55										10 19						
Kings Sutton	d							09 43																	
Heyford	d							09 52																	
Tackley	d							09 56																	
Bicester Town	d																			10 29					
Islip	d																			10 40					
Oxford	a							10 10	10 14										10 41	10 55					
	d		10 01				10 07		10 15				10 31				10 37		10 42			11 01			
Radley	d						10 13																		
Culham	d																								
Appleford	d																								
Didcot Parkway	a						10 22							←			10 51								
	d				10 17		10 31 →			10 29				10 31	10 47		11 01							11 17	
Cholsey	d			←										10 37			11 07						←		
Goring & Streatley	d			10 12										10 42			11 12 →						11 12		
Pangbourne	d			10 17										10 47									11 17		
Tilehurst	d			10 21										10 51									11 21		
Bedwyn	d	09 36																		10 36					
Hungerford	d	09 41																		10 41					
Kintbury	d	09 46																		10 46					
Newbury	a	09 53																		10 53					
	d	09 53									10 13									10 53					
Newbury Racecourse	d										10 15														
Thatcham	d	09 58									10 20									10 58					
Midgham	d										10 24														
Aldermaston	d										10 28														
Theale	d	10 06									10 33									11 06					
Reading West	d										10 40														
Reading 7	a	10 16	10 25	10 29	10 32	←			10 40	10 44	10 45		10 55	10 59	11 01	←			11 13	11 16		11 25	11 27	11 32	←
	d	10 18	10 26	10 33 →	10 32	10 33				10 45		10 52	10 56	11 03 →	11 02	11 03		11 13		11 18		11 26	11 33 →	11 32	11 33
Twyford 3	a					10 39										11 09									11 39
Maidenhead 3	a					10 47										11 17									11 47
Slough 3	a		10 39			10 54							11 09			11 24						11 39			11 54
Ealing Broadway ⊖	a					11 19										11 49									12 19
London Paddington 15 ⊖	a	10 54	10 59		11 02	11 31				11 14		11 23	11 30		11 32	12 01		11 40		11 54		11 58		12 00	12 31

		GW	XC	GW		GW	GW	GW	GW	GW	GW	GW	GW	XC	GW	GW	GW	GW	GW	GW	GW	XC	GW	GW	GW
		1	1 ◇	1 ◇		1	1 ◇	1 ◇	1 ◇	1	1 ◇	1 ◇	1	1 ◇	1	1	1 ◇	1	1 ◇	1	1	1 ◇	1 ◇	1	1 ◇
			🛒	☕			☕	🛒	☕		☕	☕		🛒					☕			🛒	☕		
Birmingham New Street 12	d		10 04											10 33								11 04			
Birmingham International	d		10 14																			11 14			
Coventry	d		10 25																			11 25			
Stratford-upon-Avon	d		*09 42*																						
Warwick Parkway	d		*10 21*											*10 45*								*11 21*			
Warwick	d		*10 24*											*10 49*								*11 24*			
Leamington Spa 8	d		10 38											11 00								11 38			
Banbury	d		10 55											11 19								11 55			
Kings Sutton	d																								
Heyford	d																								
Tackley	d																								
Bicester Town	d															11 29									
Islip	d															11 40									
Oxford	a		11 14											11 41		11 56						12 14			
	d	11 07	11 15					11 31					11 37	11 42			12 01				12 07	12 15			12 31
Radley	d	11 13																			12 13				
Culham	d																								
Appleford	d																								
Didcot Parkway	a	11 22								←			11 50								12 22				
	d	11 31 →		11 29						11 31	11 53		12 01						12 17		12 31 →		12 29		
Cholsey	d									11 37			12 07					←							
Goring & Streatley	d									11 42			12 12 →					12 12							
Pangbourne	d									11 47								12 17							
Tilehurst	d									11 51								12 21							
Bedwyn	d														11 36										
Hungerford	d														11 41										
Kintbury	d														11 46										
Newbury	a														11 53										
	d					11 13									11 53									12 13	
Newbury Racecourse	d					11 15																		12 15	
Thatcham	d					11 20									11 58									12 20	
Midgham	d					11 24																		12 24	
Aldermaston	d					11 28																		12 28	
Theale	d					11 33									12 06									12 33	
Reading West	d					11 40																		12 40	
Reading 7	a		11 40	11 44		11 45		11 55		11 59	12 07			12 13	12 16		12 25	12 27	12 32	←		12 40	12 44	12 45	12 55
	d			11 45			11 52	11 56	12 02	12 03	12 09	12 11			12 18		12 26	12 33 →	12 32	12 33			12 45		12 56
Twyford 3	a									12 09										12 39					
Maidenhead 3	a									12 17										12 47					
Slough 3	a							12 09		12 24							12 39			12 54					13 09
Ealing Broadway ⊖	a									12 49										13 19					
London Paddington 15 ⊖	a			12 14			12 25	12 29	12 32	13 01	12 37	12 40			12 54		13 00		13 08	13 31			13 14		13 28

For general notes see front of timetable
For details of catering facilities see Directory of Train Operators

Birmingham, Banbury, Bicester, Oxford and Bedwyn → Reading and London

Network Diagram - see first page of Table 116

		GW	GW	GW	GW	GW	XC	GW	GW	GW	GW	GW	GW	GW	XC	GW	GW	GW	GW	GW	GW	GW	GW	GW	XC
		1	1 ◇ ☕	1	1 ◇ ☕	1	1 ◇ 🛒	1 ☕	1 ◇	1	1 ◇ ☕	1	1	1	1 ◇ 🛒	1 ◇ ☕	1	1	1 ◇ 🛒	1 ◇ ☕	1	1 ◇ ☕	1 ◇ ☕	1	1 ◇ 🛒
Birmingham New Street 12	d						11 33								12 04										12 33
Birmingham International	d														12 14										
Coventry	d														12 25										
Stratford-upon-Avon	d													*11 40*											
Warwick Parkway	d						*11 41*								*12 21*										*12 45*
Warwick	d						*11 45*							*12 04*	*12 24*										*12 49*
Leamington Spa 8	d						12 00							*12 08*	12 38										13 00
Banbury	d						12 19							12 39	12 55										13 19
Kings Sutton	d													12 43											
Heyford	d													12 52											
Tackley	d													12 56											
Bicester Town	d																								
Islip	d																								
Oxford	a						12 41							13 10	13 14										13 41
	d					12 37	12 42		13 01				13 07		13 15				13 31					13 37	13 42
Radley	d												13 13												
Culham	d																								
Appleford	d																								
Didcot Parkway	a	←				12 49							13 24								←			13 49	
	d	12 31	12 47			13 01					13 17		13 31 →			13 29					13 31	13 53		14 01	
Cholsey	d	12 37				13 07				←											13 37			14 07	
Goring & Streatley	d	12 42				13 12 →				13 12											13 42			14 12 →	
Pangbourne	d	12 47								13 17											13 47				
Tilehurst	d	12 51								13 21											13 51				
Bedwyn	d																	13 12							
Hungerford	d																	13 17							
Kintbury	d																	13 22							
Newbury	a																	13 29							
	d																13 13	13 29							
Newbury Racecourse	d																13 15								
Thatcham	d																13 20	13 34							
Midgham	d																13 24								
Aldermaston	d																13 28								
Theale	d																13 33	13 42							
Reading West	d																13 40								
Reading 7	a	12 57	13 01	←			13 13		13 25	13 27	13 32	←			13 40	13 44	13 45	13 51	13 55		13 59	14 07			14 13
	d	13 03 →	13 02	13 03	13 11			13 18	13 26	13 33 →	13 32	13 33				13 45		13 52	13 56	14 02	14 03	14 09	14 11		
Twyford 3	a			13 09								13 39									14 09				
Maidenhead 3	a			13 17								13 47									14 17				
Slough 3	a			13 24					13 39			13 54							14 09		14 24				
Ealing Broadway	⊖ a			13 49								14 19									14 49				
London Paddington 15	⊖ a		13 30	14 01	13 40			13 44	13 59		14 06	14 31				14 14		14 25	14 29	14 32	15 01	14 37	14 40		

		GW	GW	GW	GW	GW	GW	XC	GW	GW	GW	GW	GW	GW	GW	GW		GW	GW	XC	GW	GW	GW	GW	GW
		1 ◇ ☕	1 ◇	1	1 ◇ ☕	1	1	1 ◇ 🛒	1 ◇ ☕	1	1 ✕	1 ◇	1	1	1 ◇ ☕	1		1 ◇ ☕	1	1 ◇ 🛒	1	1 ◇	1	1 ◇ ☕	1
Birmingham New Street 12	d							13 04												13 33					
Birmingham International	d							13 14																	
Coventry	d							13 25																	
Stratford-upon-Avon	d																								
Warwick Parkway	d							*13 21*												*13 41*					
Warwick	d							*13 24*												*13 45*					
Leamington Spa 8	d							13 38												14 00					
Banbury	d							13 55												14 19					
Kings Sutton	d																								
Heyford	d																								
Tackley	d																								
Bicester Town	d												14 00												
Islip	d												14 11												
Oxford	a							14 14					14 32							14 41					
	d		14 01				14 07	14 15				14 31							14 37	14 42		15 01			
Radley	d						14 13																		
Culham	d																								
Appleford	d						14 17																		
Didcot Parkway	a						14 24							←					14 51						
	d				14 17		14 31 →		14 29					14 31	14 47				15 01					15 17	
Cholsey	d			←										14 37					15 07				←		
Goring & Streatley	d			14 12										14 42					15 12 →				15 12		
Pangbourne	d			14 17										14 47									15 17		
Tilehurst	d			14 21										14 51									15 21		
Bedwyn	d	13 31																			14 36				
Hungerford	d	13 39																			14 41				
Kintbury	d																				14 46				
Newbury	a	13 49																			14 53				
	d	13 49								14 13											14 53				
Newbury Racecourse	d									14 15															
Thatcham	d	13 56								14 20											14 58				
Midgham	d									14 24															
Aldermaston	d									14 28															
Theale	d	14 05								14 33											15 06				
Reading West	d									14 40															
Reading 7	a	14 17	14 25	14 27	14 32	←		14 40	14 44	14 45		14 55		14 59	15 01	←				15 13	15 16	15 26	15 27	15 32	←
	d	14 18	14 26	14 33 →	14 32	14 33			14 45		14 52	14 56		15 03 →	15 02	15 03		15 11			15 18	15 26	15 33 →	15 32	15 33
Twyford 3	a					14 39										15 09									15 39
Maidenhead 3	a					14 47										15 17									15 47
Slough 3	a		14 39			14 54						15 09				15 24						15 39			15 54
Ealing Broadway	⊖ a					15 19										15 49									16 19
London Paddington 15	⊖ a	14 44	15 01		15 07	15 31			15 14		15 23	15 28			15 30	16 01		15 39			15 54	16 00		16 09	16 31

For general notes see front of timetable
For details of catering facilities see Directory of Train Operators

Birmingham, Banbury, Bicester, Oxford and Bedwyn → Reading and London

Network Diagram - see first page of Table 116

		GW	XC	GW	GW	GW	GW	GW	GW	GW	GW	GW	GW	XC	GW	GW	GW	GW	GW	GW	GW	XC	GW	GW	GW
		1	1◇ ⊤	1◇ ☕	1	1◇ ✕	1◇ ☕	1◇ ☕	1	1◇ ☕	1	1	1◇ ☕	1◇ ⊤	1	1	1◇	1	1◇ ☕	1	1	1◇ ⊤	1◇ ☕	1	1◇ ☕
Birmingham New Street 12	d		14 04											14 33								15 04			
Birmingham International	d		14 14																			15 14			
Coventry	d		14 25																			15 25			
Stratford-upon-Avon	d		13 40																						
Warwick Parkway	d		14 21											14 45								15 21			
Warwick	d		14 24											14 49								15 24			
Leamington Spa 8	d		14 38											15 00								15 38			
Banbury	d		14 55									15 07		15 19								15 55			
Kings Sutton	d											15 11													
Heyford	d											15 20													
Tackley	d											15 24													
Bicester Town	d															15 29									
Islip	d															15 40									
Oxford	a		15 14									15 38		15 41		15 56						16 14			
	d	15 07	15 15				15 31				15 37			15 42			16 01				16 07	16 15			
Radley	d	15 13																			16 13				
Culham	d	15 17																							
Appleford	d																				16 17				
Didcot Parkway	a	15 24							←		15 50										16 24				
	d	15 31		15 29					15 31	15 53	16 01								16 17		16 31		16 29		
Cholsey	d	→							15 37		16 07							←			→				
Goring & Streatley	d								15 42		16 12							16 12							
Pangbourne	d								15 47		→							16 17							
Tilehurst	d								15 51									16 21							
Bedwyn	d														15 36										
Hungerford	d														15 41										
Kintbury	d														15 46										
Newbury	a														15 53										
	d				15 13										15 53									16 13	
Newbury Racecourse	d				15 15																			16 15	
Thatcham	d				15 20										15 58									16 20	
Midgham	d				15 24																			16 24	
Aldermaston	d				15 28																			16 28	
Theale	d				15 33										16 06									16 33	
Reading West	d				15 40																			16 40	
Reading 7	a		15 40	15 44	15 45		15 55		15 59	16 07				16 13	16 16		16 25	16 27	16 32	←		16 40	16 44	16 45	
	d			15 45		15 52	15 56	16 02	16 03	16 09			16 13		16 18		16 26	16 33	16 32	16 33			16 45		16 52
Twyford 3	a								16 09									→		16 39					
Maidenhead 3	a								16 17											16 47					
Slough 3	a						16 09		16 24								16 39			16 54					
Ealing Broadway	⊖ a								16 49											17 19					
London Paddington 15	⊖ a			16 14		16 21	16 28	16 30	17 01	16 39			16 44		16 54		16 58		17 01	17 31			17 14		17 24

		GW	GW	GW	GW	GW	GW	XC	GW	GW	GW	GW	GW	GW	GW	GW	XC	GW	GW	GW	GW	GW	GW	GW	GW
		1◇ ☕	1	1◇ ☕	1	1	1◇ ☕	1◇ ⊤	1◇ ☕	1	1	1◇	1	1◇ ☕	1	1	1◇ ⊤	1	1◇ ☕	1	1◇ ☕	1◇ ☕	1	1	1◇ ☕
Birmingham New Street 12	d							15 33									16 04								
Birmingham International	d																16 14								
Coventry	d																16 25								
Stratford-upon-Avon	d																15 40								
Warwick Parkway	d							15 41									16 21								
Warwick	d							15 44									16 24								
Leamington Spa 8	d							16 00									16 38								
Banbury	d							16 19									16 55								
Kings Sutton	d																								
Heyford	d																								
Tackley	d																								
Bicester Town	d																	17 00							
Islip	d																	17 11							
Oxford	a							16 41									17 14	17 26							
	d	16 31				16 37		16 42			16 47	17 01				17 07	17 15							17 31	17 37
Radley	d					16 43										17 13								17 37	
Culham	d															17 17									
Appleford	d																							17 41	
Didcot Parkway	a		←			16 52					17 04					17 24							←	17 48	
	d		16 31	16 47		17 01							←	17 17		17 31			17 29				17 31	18 01	
Cholsey	d		16 37			17 07							17 07			→							17 37	→	
Goring & Streatley	d		16 42			→							17 12										17 42		
Pangbourne	d		16 47										17 17										17 47		
Tilehurst	d		16 51										17 21										17 51		
Bedwyn	d									16 44															
Hungerford	d								16 39	16 49															
Kintbury	d									16 54															
Newbury	a								16 49	17 03															
	d								16 49											17 13					
Newbury Racecourse	d																			17 15					
Thatcham	d								16 56											17 20					
Midgham	d																			17 24					
Aldermaston	d																			17 28					
Theale	d								17 05											17 33					
Reading West	d																			17 40					
Reading 7	a	16 55	16 59	17 01	←			17 13	17 17			17 25	17 29	17 32	←		17 40		17 44	17 45			17 57		18 02
	d	16 56	17 03	17 02	17 03		17 11		17 18			17 26	17 33	17 32	17 33				17 45		17 52	17 58	17 58		18 03
Twyford 3	a		→		17 09								→		17 39								18 05		
Maidenhead 3	a				17 17										17 47								18 13		
Slough 3	a	17 09			17 24				17 31			17 39			17 54								18 20		
Ealing Broadway	⊖ a				17 49										18 19								18 49		
London Paddington 15	⊖ a	17 27		17 30	18 01		17 39		17 54			17 59		18 02	18 31				18 14		18 21	18 24	19 00		18 30

For general notes see front of timetable
For details of catering facilities see
Directory of Train Operators

Birmingham, Banbury, Bicester, Oxford and Bedwyn → Reading and London

Network Diagram - see first page of Table 116

		GW 1◇ 🍽	XC 1◇ 🛒	GW 1	GW 1◇ 🍽	GW 1		GW 1◇	GW 1	GW 1◇ 🍽	GW 1	GW 1	XC 1◇ 🛒	GW 1	GW 1◇ 🍽	GW 1◇ 🍽	GW 1◇	GW 1	GW 1◇ 🍽	GW 1	GW 1	GW 1◇ 🍽	XC 1◇ 🛒	GW 1	GW 1
Birmingham New Street 12	d		16 33										17 04										17 33		
Birmingham International	d												17 14												
Coventry	d												17 25												
Stratford-upon-Avon	d																								
Warwick Parkway	d		16 45										17 20										17 45		
Warwick	d		16 49										17 23										17 49		
Leamington Spa 8	d		17 00										17 38										18 00		
Banbury	d		17 19	17 22									17 55										18 19		
Kings Sutton	d			17 26																					
Heyford	d			17 35																					
Tackley	d			17 39																					
Bicester Town	d																							18 26	
Islip	d																							18 37	
Oxford	a		17 41	17 53									18 14										18 41	18 52	
	d		17 42					18 01				18 07	18 15				18 31				18 37		18 42		
Radley	d											18 13													
Culham	d											18 17													
Appleford	d																				18 45				
Didcot Parkway	a								←			18 24						←			18 51				
	d	17 53							18 01	18 17		18 31 →			18 29			18 31	18 47		19 01				
Cholsey	d								18 07									18 37			19 07 →				
Goring & Streatley	d								18 12									18 42							
Pangbourne	d								18 17									18 47							
Tilehurst	d								18 21									18 51							
Bedwyn	d					17 36								17 55											
Hungerford	d					17 41								18 00											
Kintbury	d					17 46								18 05											
Newbury	a					17 53								18 12											
	d					17 53								18 13											18 53
Newbury Racecourse	d													18 15											
Thatcham	d					17 58								18 20											18 58
Midgham	d													18 24											
Aldermaston	d					18 04								18 28											
Theale	d					18 09								18 33											19 06
Reading West	d													18 40											
Reading 7	a	18 07	18 13			18 21		18 25	18 27	18 32	←		18 40	18 45	18 47		18 55	19 00	19 01	←			19 13		19 16
	d	18 09			18 15	18 22		18 26	18 33 →	18 32	18 33				18 47	18 52	18 56	19 03 →	19 02	19 03		19 11			19 18
Twyford 3	a										18 39									19 09					
Maidenhead 3	a										18 47									19 21					
Slough 3	a							18 39			18 54						19 09			19 29					
Ealing Broadway	⊖ a										19 19									19 53					
London Paddington 15	⊖ a	18 39			18 44	18 54		18 59		19 02	19 30				19 14	19 24	19 29		19 32	20 04		19 38			19 54

		GW 1◇	GW 1	GW 1	GW 1◇ 🍽	GW 1	GW 1	XC 1◇ 🛒	GW 1◇ 🍽	GW 1◇	GW 1	GW 1◇ 🍽	GW 1 🍽	GW 1	XC 1◇ 🛒	GW 1◇ 🍽	GW 1	GW 1◇	GW 1	GW 1◇ A 🍽	GW 1	XC 1◇ 🛒	GW 1	GW 1◇ 🍽	GW 1
Birmingham New Street 12	d							18 04							18 33							19 04			
Birmingham International	d							18 14														19 14			
Coventry	d							18 25														19 25			
Stratford-upon-Avon	d							17 42																	
Warwick Parkway	d							18 23							18 45										
Warwick	d							18 26							18 49										
Leamington Spa 8	d							18 38							19 00							19 38			
Banbury	d							18 55		19 01					19 19							19 55			
Kings Sutton	d									19 05															
Heyford	d									19 14															
Tackley	d									19 18															
Bicester Town	d																						20 00		
Islip	d																						20 11		
Oxford	a							19 14		19 30					19 41							20 14	20 26		
	d	19 01					19 10	19 15		19 31				19 37	19 42			20 01			20 07	20 15			
Radley	d						19 16														20 13				
Culham	d																				20 17				
Appleford	d																								
Didcot Parkway	a						19 25				←			19 49					←		20 24				
	d			←	19 17		19 31 →		19 29		19 31			20 01 →		19 59			20 01		20 32 →			20 29	
Cholsey	d			19 07							19 37								20 07						
Goring & Streatley	d			19 12							19 42								20 12						
Pangbourne	d			19 17							19 47								20 17						
Tilehurst	d			19 21							19 51								20 21						
Bedwyn	d		19 03																	19 44					19 55
Hungerford	d		19 08																	19 51					20 00
Kintbury	d		19 13																	19 57					20 05
Newbury	a		19 22																	20 06					20 12
	d												19 45				19 50			20 06					20 13
Newbury Racecourse	d																19 52								20 15
Thatcham	d																19 57			20 12					20 20
Midgham	d																20 01								20 24
Aldermaston	d																20 05								20 28
Theale	d																20 10			20 21					20 33
Reading West	d																20 16								20 40
Reading 7	a	19 26		19 27	19 32	←		19 40	19 45	19 55	19 57		20 07		20 13	20 14	20 22	20 25	20 27	20 33		20 40		20 44	20 45
	d	19 26		19 33 →	19 32	19 33			19 46	19 56	19 58	20 02	20 08			20 15		20 26	20 33	20 34				20 45	
Twyford 3	a					19 42					20 04								20 39						
Maidenhead 3	a					19 50					20 12								20 47						
Slough 3	a	19 39				19 57				20 09	20 19								20 54						
Ealing Broadway	⊖ a					20 22					20 49								21 19						
London Paddington 15	⊖ a	20 00			20 07	20 33			20 14	20 29	20 59	20 32	20 39			20 46		20 57	21 29	21 01				21 14	

For general notes see front of timetable
For details of catering facilities see Directory of Train Operators

A From Westbury (Table 135)

Table 116

Birmingham, Banbury, Bicester, Oxford and Bedwyn → Reading and London

Network Diagram - see first page of Table 116

		GW	GW	GW	GW	GW	GW	XC	GW	GW	GW	XC	GW	GW	GW	GW	GW FO	GW FX	GW FO	GW FX	GW	XC	GW	GW	GW
		1◇	1◇	1	1	1◇	1	1◇	1◇	1	1	1◇	1◇	1	1◇	1	1◇	1◇	1◇	1◇	1	1◇	1	1	1◇
		⊏P	⊏P			⊏P		⊥					⊏P		⊏P				⊏P	⊏P					
Birmingham New Street 12	d							19 33				20 04										20 33			
Birmingham International	d											20 14													
Coventry	d											20 25													
Stratford-upon-Avon	d											19 43										20 00			
Warwick Parkway	d							19 47				20 06										20 47			
Warwick	d							19 50				20 09										20 50			
Leamington Spa 8	d							20 00				20 38										21 00			
Banbury	d			20 01				20 19				20 55										21 19			
Kings Sutton	d			20 05																					
Heyford	d			20 14																					
Tackley	d			20 18																					
Bicester Town	d																						21 30		
Islip	d																						21 41		
Oxford	a			20 32				20 41				21 14										21 41	21 56		
	d		20 31				20 37	20 42	21 01		21 07	21 15					21 31	21 31			21 38	21 42			22 11
Radley	d										21 13										21 44				
Culham	d										21 17														
Appleford	d						20 45																		
Didcot Parkway	a				←		20 51				21 24					←					21 53				22 24
	d				20 32	20 47	21 01			←	21 31 →		21 28			21 31			21 50	21 50	22 01			←	22 27 →
Cholsey	d				20 37		21 07 →			21 07						21 37					22 07 →			22 07	
Goring & Streatley	d				20 42					21 12						21 42								22 12	
Pangbourne	d				20 47					21 17						21 47								22 17	
Tilehurst	d				20 51					21 21						21 51								22 21	
Bedwyn	d													21 06											
Hungerford	d													21 11											
Kintbury	d													21 16											
Newbury	a													21 23											
	d													21 23	21 42										
Newbury Racecourse	d													21 25											
Thatcham	d													21 30											
Midgham	d													21 35											
Aldermaston	d													21 38											
Theale	d													21 43											
Reading West	d													21 50											
Reading 7	a		20 55		21 00	21 01		21 13	21 25	21 29		21 40	21 43	21 55	22 00	22 03	22 06	22 06	22 11	22 11		22 19		22 27	
	d	20 52	20 56			21 02			21 26	21 33			21 45		22 01		22 06	22 06	22 14	22 14				22 46 →	
Twyford 3	a									21 39															
Maidenhead 3	a									21 47															
Slough 3	a		21 09						21 39	21 58							22 21	22 28							
Ealing Broadway	⊖ a									22 21															
London Paddington 15	⊖ a	21 21	21 29			21 32			21 58	22 32			22 14		22 30		22 40	22 52	22 44	22 55					

		GW	XC	GW	GW	GW	GW FO	GW FX	GW	GW FO	GW FX	GW	GW	GW	GW	GW	GW	XC FO	XC FX	GW FO	CH	CH	GW
		1	1◇	1	1◇	1	1◇	1◇	1◇	1◇	1◇	1	1	1◇	1	1	1◇	1◇	1◇	1			1
																	A				B	C	
									⊏P	⊏P	⊏P						⊏P	⊥	⊥				
Birmingham New Street 12	d		21 04															22 04	22 04				
Birmingham International	d		21 14															22 14	22 14				
Coventry	d		21 25															22 25	22 25				
Stratford-upon-Avon	d																				23 00	23 00	
Warwick Parkway	d											21 47									22b53	22b53	
Warwick	d											21 50									23 21	23 21	
Leamington Spa 8	d		21 38									21 55						22 38	22 38		23 25	23 25	
Banbury	d	21 40	21 55									22 19						22 55	22 55		23 44	23 44	23 50
Kings Sutton	d	21 44										22 23											23 54
Heyford	d	21 53										22 32											00 03
Tackley	d	21 57										22 36											00 07
Bicester Town	d																			23 30			
Islip	d																			23 41			
Oxford	a	22 11	22 14									22 50						23 14	23 14	23 56	00 14	00 17	00 18
	d		22 15				22 33	22 33					22 55	23 05				23 15	23 16				00 19
Radley	d												23 01										00 26
Culham	d												23 05										00 30
Appleford	d												23 07										00 32
Didcot Parkway	a				←								23 14	23 18	←								00 39
	d				22 27				22 46				23 21 →	23 18	23 21		23 34						00 43
Cholsey	d														23 27								00 49
Goring & Streatley	d														23 32								00 54
Pangbourne	d														23 37								00 59
Tilehurst	d														23 41								01 03
Bedwyn	d			21 55												23 00							
Hungerford	d			22 00												23 05							
Kintbury	d			22 05												23 10							
Newbury	a			22 12												23 17							
	d			22 13												23 17							
Newbury Racecourse	d			22 15												23 19							
Thatcham	d			22 20												23 24							
Midgham	d			22 24												23 29							
Aldermaston	d			22 28												23 32							
Theale	d			22 33												23 37							
Reading West	d			22 40												23 44							
Reading 7	a		22 40	22 45	22 45	←	22 58	22 58	23 03					23 34	23 48	23 49	23 55	23 57	23 57				01 09
	d				22 46	22 46	22 59	22 59	23 05	23 08	23 08			23 35			23 56						01 10
Twyford 3	a					22 55																	01 17
Maidenhead 3	a					23 03								23 46									01 25
Slough 3	a				23 03	23 15	23 12	23 18						23 54									01 32
Ealing Broadway	⊖ a					23 52																	01 48
London Paddington 15	⊖ a				23 24	00 03	23 30	23 37	23 40	23 41	23 51			00 21			00 33						02 00

For general notes see front of timetable
For details of catering facilities see Directory of Train Operators

A From Taunton (Table 134)
B Until 2 October
C From 5 October

b Change at Leamington Spa

Table 116

Saturdays

until 5 September

Birmingham, Banbury, Bicester, Oxford and Bedwyn → Reading and London

Network Diagram - see first page of Table 116

		GW	GW	GW	GW	GW	GW	GW	GW	GW	GW	GW	GW	GW	GW	GW	GW	GW	XC	GW	GW	GW	GW	GW	GW
		1 ◇	1	1	1	1	1 ◇	1	1	1 ◇	1	1 ◇	1	1	1 ◇	1	1 ◇	1	1 ◇	1 ◇	1	1 ◇	1	1	1 ◇
							☕					☕					☕		🛒	☕		☕			☕
Birmingham New Street 12	d																		06 04						
Birmingham International	d																		06 14						
Coventry	d																		06 25						
Stratford-upon-Avon	d																								
Warwick Parkway	d																								
Warwick	d																								
Leamington Spa 8	d																		06 38						
Banbury	d		23p50																06 55				07 02		
Kings Sutton	d		23p54																				07 07		
Heyford	d		00 03																				07 15		
Tackley	d		00 07																				07 20		
Bicester Town	d																								
Islip	d																								
Oxford	a		00 18																07 14				07 31		
	d	00 06	00 19	03 59	05 07	05 37			06 07	06 31				06 37	07 01			07 07	07 16			07 31			
Radley	d		00 26		05 13				06 13									07 13							
Culham	d		00 30		05 17													07 17							
Appleford	d		00 32						06 18																
Didcot Parkway	a	00 19	00 39	04 10	05 24	05 48			06 24					06 49				07 24						←	
	d	00 20	00 43	04 10	05 31	06 01	06 29		06 31			06 59		07 01			07 17	07 31 →		07 30				07 31	07 47
Cholsey	d		00 49		05 37	06 07			06 37					07 07		←								07 37	
Goring & Streatley	d		00 54		05 42	06 12			06 42					07 12 →		07 12								07 42	
Pangbourne	d		00 59		05 47	06 17			06 47							07 17								07 47	
Tilehurst	d		01 03		05 51	06 21			06 51							07 21								07 51	
Bedwyn	d							06 05					06 37												
Hungerford	d							06 11					06 43												
Kintbury	d							06 15					06 47												
Newbury	a							06 22					06 54												
	d							06 22					06 54								07 13				
Newbury Racecourse	d							06 24													07 15				
Thatcham	d							06 29					06 59								07 20				
Midgham	d							06 34													07 24				
Aldermaston	d							06 37													07 28				
Theale	d							06 42					07 07								07 33				
Reading West	d							06 49													07 42				
Reading 7	a	00 38	01 09	04 27	05 57	06 27	06 43	06 52	06 57	07 00	←	07 14	07 20		07 27	07 27	07 32		07 40	07 44	07 45	07 54		07 57	08 01
	d	00 39	01 10	04 40	06 03	06 33	06 45	06 52	07 03 →	07 00	07 03	07 15	07 21		07 27	07 33	07 33			07 46		07 56		07 58	08 03
Twyford 3	a		01 17	04 46	06 09	06 39					07 09					07 39								08 09	
Maidenhead 3	a		01 25	04 54	06 17	06 47					07 17					07 47								08 17	
Slough 3	a	00 53	01 32	05 01	06 24	06 54				07 16	07 24					07 54						08 09		08 24	
Ealing Broadway	⊖ a		01 48	05 19	06 49	07 19					07 49					08 19								08 49	
London Paddington 15	⊖ a	01 11	02 00	05 31	07 01	07 31	07 14	07 24		07 37	08 01	07 44	07 54		07 59	08 31	08 02			08 14		08 29		09 01	08 32

For general notes see front of timetable
For details of catering facilities see
Directory of Train Operators

Table 116

Saturdays

until 5 September

Birmingham, Banbury, Bicester, Oxford and Bedwyn → Reading and London

Network Diagram - see first page of Table 116

		GW	XC	GW	GW	GW	GW	GW	GW		GW	XC	GW	GW	GW	GW	GW	GW	GW	GW	XC	GW	GW	GW	GW
		[1]	[1] ◇	[1] ◇	[1]	[1] ◇	[1]	[1]	[1] ◇		[1]	[1] ◇	[1] ◇	[1]	[1] ◇	[1] ◇	[1]	[1] ◇	[1] ◇	[1]	[1] ◇	[1] ◇	[1]	[1] ◇	[1]
																						A			
			🛒	☕					☕			🛒	☕		☕	☕		☕	☕		🛒	☕			
Birmingham New Street [12]	d		06 33									07 04									07 33				
Birmingham International	d											07 14													
Coventry	d											07 25													
Stratford-upon-Avon	d																								
Warwick Parkway	d		*06 41*									*07 06*									*07 45*				
Warwick	d		*06 45*									*07 09*									*07 48*				
Leamington Spa [8]	d		07 00									07 38									08 00				
Banbury	d		07 19									07 55									08 19				
Kings Sutton	d																								
Heyford	d																								
Tackley	d																								
Bicester Town	d						07 36																		
Islip	d						07 47																		
Oxford	a		07 40				08 03					08 14									08 40				
	d	07 37	07 43			08 01					08 07	08 16				08 31				08 37	08 43			09 01	
Radley	d										08 13														
Culham	d																								
Appleford	d										08 18														
Didcot Parkway	a	07 49						←			08 24						←			08 49					←
	d	08 01 →		08 00				08 01	08 17		08 31 →		08 30				08 31	08 47	08 52	09 01 →		09 00			09 01
Cholsey	d							08 07									08 37								09 07
Goring & Streatley	d							08 12									08 42								09 12
Pangbourne	d							08 17									08 47								09 17
Tilehurst	d							08 21									08 51								09 21
Bedwyn	d				07 37																		08 37		
Hungerford	d				07 43																		08 43		
Kintbury	d				07 47																		08 47		
Newbury	a				07 54																		08 55		
	d				07 54									08 13	08 34								08 55		
Newbury Racecourse	d													08 15											
Thatcham	d				07 59									08 20									09 00		
Midgham	d													08 24											
Aldermaston	d													08 28											
Theale	d				08 07									08 33									09 08		
Reading West	d													08 40											
Reading [7]	a		08 13	08 14	08 19	08 24		08 27	08 32			08 40	08 44	08 45	08 52	08 56	08 57	09 02	09 07		09 13	09 14	09 19	09 25	09 27
	d			08 16	08 21	08 25		08 33	08 33				08 46		08 52	08 57	09 03	09 04	09 09			09 16	09 20	09 26	09 33
Twyford [3]	a							08 39									09 09								09 39
Maidenhead [3]	a							08 47									09 17								09 47
Slough [3]	a					08 39		08 54								09 10	09 24							09 39	09 54
Ealing Broadway	⊖ a							09 19									09 49								10 19
London Paddington [15]	⊖ a			08 44	08 55	08 59		09 31	09 02				09 14		09 21	09 29	10 01	09 32	09 37			09 44	09 54	09 59	10 31

		GW	GW	GW	GW	XC	GW	GW	GW	GW	GW	GW	GW	GW	XC	GW	GW	GW	GW	GW	XC	GW	GW	GW	GW
						R																			
		[1] ◇	[1] ◇	[1]	[1]	[1]	[1] ◇	[1] ◇	[1]	[1]	[1]	[1] ◇	[1] ◇	[1]	[1] ◇	[1]	[1] ◇	[1]	[1] ◇	[1]	[1] ◇	[1]	[1] ◇	[1]	[1] ◇
						B																			
		☕	☕			🛒	☕	☕				☕	☕		🛒				☕		🛒		☕		☕
Birmingham New Street [12]	d					08 04									08 33						09 04				
Birmingham International	d					08 14															09 14				
Coventry	d					08 25															09 25				
Stratford-upon-Avon	d					*07 35*																			
Warwick Parkway	d					*08 23*									*08 46*						*09 22*				
Warwick	d					*08 26*									*08 49*						*09 25*				
Leamington Spa [8]	d					08 38									09 00						09 38				
Banbury	d					08 55				09 02					09 19						09 55				
Kings Sutton	d									09 07															
Heyford	d									09 15															
Tackley	d									09 20															
Bicester Town	d				08 45																	09 57			
Islip	d				08 56																	10 08			
Oxford	a				09 12	09 14				09 32					09 40						10 14	10 24			
	d			09 07		09 16		09 31						09 37	09 43		10 01			10 07	10 16				
Radley	d			09 13																10 13					
Culham	d			09 17																					
Appleford	d																								
Didcot Parkway	a			09 24							←			09 49						10 21					
	d	09 18		09 31 →			09 29				09 31	09 47		10 01					10 22	10 31 →			10 29		
Cholsey	d										09 37			10 07				←							
Goring & Streatley	d										09 42			10 12 →				10 12							
Pangbourne	d										09 47							10 17							
Tilehurst	d										09 51							10 21							
Bedwyn	d															09 37									
Hungerford	d															09 43									
Kintbury	d															09 47									
Newbury	a															09 54									
	d								09 23							09 54								10 13	
Newbury Racecourse	d								09 26															10 15	
Thatcham	d								09 31							09 59								10 20	
Midgham	d								09 36															10 24	
Aldermaston	d								09 39															10 28	
Theale	d								09 44							10 07								10 33	
Reading West	d								09 51															10 40	
Reading [7]	a	09 33				09 40	09 44	09 55	09 56		09 57	10 01			10 10	10 17	10 25	10 27	10 35		10 40		10 45	10 45	
	d	09 34	09 37				09 45	09 56			10 03	10 03	10 10			10 18	10 25	10 33	10 37				10 45		10 53
Twyford [3]	a										10 09							10 39							
Maidenhead [3]	a										10 17							10 47							
Slough [3]	a							10 09			10 24						10 40	10 54							
Ealing Broadway	⊖ a										10 49							11 19							
London Paddington [15]	⊖ a	10 02	10 08				10 14	10 29			11 01	10 32	10 38			10 52	10 59	11 31	11 08				11 14		11 24

For general notes see front of timetable
For details of catering facilities see Directory of Train Operators

A From Taunton (Table 134)
B From Nottingham (Table 57)

Table 116

Birmingham, Banbury, Bicester, Oxford and Bedwyn → Reading and London

Saturdays

until 5 September

Network Diagram - see first page of Table 116

		GW	GW	GW	GW	GW	XC	GW	GW	GW	GW	XC	GW	GW	GW	GW	GW	GW	GW	GW	GW	XC	GW	GW	GW
		1◇	1	1◇	1	1◇	1◇	1	1◇	1	1	1◇	1◇	1	1	1◇	1	1	1◇	1◇	1	1◇	1	1◇	1
		☕		☕		☕	🛒					🛒	☕		☕	☕			☕	☕		🛒			
Birmingham New Street 12	d						09 33					10 04										10 33			
Birmingham International	d											10 14													
Coventry	d											10 25													
Stratford-upon-Avon	d											*09 38*													
Warwick Parkway	d						*09 44*					*10 22*										*10 45*			
Warwick	d						*09 47*					*10 25*										*10 48*			
Leamington Spa 8	d						10 00					10 38										11 00			
Banbury	d						10 19					10 55					11 02					11 19			
Kings Sutton	d																11 07								
Heyford	d																11 15								
Tackley	d																11 20								
Bicester Town	d																						11 30		
Islip	d																						11 41		
Oxford	a						10 40					11 14					11 31					11 40	11 56		
	d	10 31			10 37		10 43		11 01		11 07	11 16				11 31					11 37	11 43		12 01	
Radley	d										11 13														
Culham	d																								
Appleford	d																								
Didcot Parkway	a		←		10 49						11 25							←			11 49				
	d		10 31	10 47	11 01						11 31		11 29					11 31	11 47		12 01				
Cholsey	d		10 37		11 07					←	→							11 37			12 07				
Goring & Streatley	d		10 42		11 12					11 12								11 42			12 12				
Pangbourne	d		10 47		→					11 17								11 47			→				
Tilehurst	d		10 51							11 21								11 51							
Bedwyn	d							10 40																	11 48
Hungerford	d							10 46																	11 54
Kintbury	d							10 50																	11 58
Newbury	a							10 57																	12 05
	d							10 57						11 13											12 05
Newbury Racecourse	d													11 15											
Thatcham	d							11 02						11 20											12 10
Midgham	d													11 24											
Aldermaston	d													11 28											
Theale	d							11 10						11 33											12 18
Reading West	d													11 40											
Reading 7	a	10 55	10 58	11 01			11 13	11 21	11 24	11 27		11 40	11 44	11 45		11 55		11 58	12 02			12 13		12 24	12 26
	d	10 56	11 03	11 03		11 13		11 21	11 25	11 33			11 45		11 53	11 56		12 03	12 03	12 11				12 24	12 28
Twyford 3	a		11 09							11 39								12 09							
Maidenhead 3	a		11 17							11 47								12 17							
Slough 3	a	11 09	11 24						11 39	11 54						12 09		12 24						12 39	
Ealing Broadway	⊖ a		11 49							12 19								12 49							
London Paddington 15	⊖ a	11 29	12 01	11 32		11 40		11 55	11 59	12 31			12 14		12 23	12 29		13 01	12 32	12 39				12 59	13 03

		GW	GW	GW	XC	GW	GW	GW	GW	GW	GW	GW	GW	GW	GW	XC	GW	GW	GW	GW	XC	GW	GW	GW	GW
		1	1◇	1	1◇	1	1	1◇	1	1	1	1◇	1	1	1	1◇	1	1◇	1	1	1◇	1	1◇	1	1
			☕		🛒	☕	☕	☕				☕		☕		🛒	☕				🛒		☕		
Birmingham New Street 12	d				11 04											11 33					12 04				
Birmingham International	d				11 14																12 14				
Coventry	d				11 25																12 25				
Stratford-upon-Avon	d																				*11 38*				
Warwick Parkway	d				*11 22*											*11 41*					*12 22*				
Warwick	d				*11 25*											*11 45*					*12 25*				
Leamington Spa 8	d				11 38											12 00					12 38				
Banbury	d				11 55											12 19					12 55				
Kings Sutton	d																								
Heyford	d																								
Tackley	d																								
Bicester Town	d																					12 59			
Islip	d																					13 10			
Oxford	a				12 14											12 40					13 14	13 26			
	d			12 07	12 16			12 31							12 37	12 43		13 01		13 07	13 16				
Radley	d			12 13																13 13					
Culham	d																								
Appleford	d																								
Didcot Parkway	a			12 21							←				12 49					13 22					
	d		12 22	12 31			12 29				12 31	12 47			13 01					13 31			13 29		
Cholsey	d	←		→							12 37				13 07				←	→					
Goring & Streatley	d	12 12									12 42				13 12				13 12						
Pangbourne	d	12 17									12 47				→				13 17						
Tilehurst	d	12 21									12 51								13 21						
Bedwyn	d									12 32															
Hungerford	d									12 38															
Kintbury	d									12 42															
Newbury	a									12 49															
	d								12 24															13 13	13 29
Newbury Racecourse	d								12 26															13 15	
Thatcham	d								12 31															13 20	13 34
Midgham	d								12 36															13 24	
Aldermaston	d								12 39															13 28	
Theale	d								12 44															13 33	13 42
Reading West	d								12 51															13 40	
Reading 7	a	12 32	12 36		12 40		12 48	12 54	12 57		12 57	13 01	←			13 13		13 25	13 27		13 40		13 44	13 45	13 51
	d	12 33	12 38			12 42	12 50	12 55			13 03	13 01	13 03	13 11			13 20	13 25	13 33				13 45		13 52
Twyford 3	a	12 39									→		13 09						13 39						
Maidenhead 3	a	12 47											13 17						13 47						
Slough 3	a	12 54						13 09					13 24					13 40	13 54						
Ealing Broadway	⊖ a	13 19											13 49						14 19						
London Paddington 15	⊖ a	13 31	13 10			13 14	13 22	13 29				13 32	14 01	13 39			13 54	13 59	14 31				14 14		14 22

For general notes see front of timetable
For details of catering facilities see
Directory of Train Operators

Birmingham, Banbury, Bicester, Oxford and Bedwyn → Reading and London

Network Diagram - see first page of Table 116

		GW	GW	GW	GW	GW	GW	XC	GW	GW	GW	GW	GW	XC	GW	GW	GW	GW	GW	GW	GW	GW	XC	GW	GW
		1◇	1	1	1◇	1◇	1	1◇	1	1◇	1	1◇	1	1◇	1◇	1	1	1◇	1	1	1◇	1	1◇	1	1
					☕	☕		🛒				☕		🛒	☕		☕	☕		☕	☕		🛒		
Birmingham New Street [12]	d							12 33						13 04									13 33		
Birmingham International	d													13 14											
Coventry	d													13 25											
Stratford-upon-Avon	d																								
Warwick Parkway	d							*12 45*						*13 22*									*13 41*		
Warwick	d							*12 48*						*13 25*									*13 45*		
Leamington Spa [8]	d							13 00						13 38									14 00		
Banbury	d		13 02					13 19						13 55									14 19		
Kings Sutton	d		13 07																						
Heyford	d		13 15																						
Tackley	d		13 20																						
Bicester Town	d																								14 17
Islip	d																								14 28
Oxford	a		13 32					13 40						14 14									14 40		14 45
	d	13 31					13 37	13 43		14 01			14 07	14 16				14 31				14 37	14 43		
Radley	d												14 13												
Culham	d																								
Appleford	d												14 18												
Didcot Parkway	a			←			13 49						14 24						←			14 49			
	d			13 31	13 47		14 01					14 22	14 31 →		14 30				14 31			15 01			
Cholsey	d			13 37			14 07				←								14 37			15 07			
Goring & Streatley	d			13 42			14 12 →				14 12								14 42			15 12 →			
Pangbourne	d			13 47							14 17								14 47						
Tilehurst	d			13 51							14 21								14 51						
Bedwyn	d								13 40															14 37	
Hungerford	d								13 46															14 43	
Kintbury	d								13 50															14 47	
Newbury	a								13 57															14 54	
	d								13 57							14 13								14 54	
Newbury Racecourse	d															14 15									
Thatcham	d								14 02							14 20								14 59	
Midgham	d															14 24									
Aldermaston	d															14 28									
Theale	d								14 10							14 33								15 07	
Reading West	d															14 40									
Reading [7]	a	13 55		13 59	14 02			14 13	14 17	14 25	14 27	14 36		14 40	14 44	14 45		14 55	14 58				15 13	15 17	
	d	13 55		14 03	14 03	14 11			14 19	14 26	14 33	14 38			14 46		14 53	14 56	15 03	15 04	15 11			15 19	
Twyford [3]	a			14 09							14 39								15 09						
Maidenhead [3]	a			14 17							14 47								15 17						
Slough [3]	a	14 10		14 24						14 39	14 54							15 09	15 24						
Ealing Broadway	⊖ a			14 49							15 19								15 49						
London Paddington [15]	⊖ a	14 29		15 01	14 32	14 39			14 54	14 59	15 31	15 09			15 14		15 23	15 29	16 01	15 32	15 39			15 55	

		GW	GW	GW	GW	XC	GW	GW	GW	GW	GW	GW	GW	GW	GW	XC	GW	GW	GW	GW	GW	GW	GW	XC	GW
		1◇	1	1	1	1◇	1◇	1	1◇	1	1	1	1◇	1◇	1	1◇	1	1	1◇	1	1	1◇	1	1◇	1◇
						🛒	☕	☕			☕		☕	☕		🛒				☕		☕		🛒	☕
Birmingham New Street [12]	d					14 04										14 33								15 04	
Birmingham International	d					14 14																		15 14	
Coventry	d					14 25																		15 25	
Stratford-upon-Avon	d					*13 40*																			
Warwick Parkway	d					*14 22*										*14 45*								*15 22*	
Warwick	d					*14 25*										*14 48*								*15 25*	
Leamington Spa [8]	d					14 38										15 00								15 38	
Banbury	d					14 55				15 02						15 19								15 55	
Kings Sutton	d									15 07															
Heyford	d									15 15															
Tackley	d									15 20															
Bicester Town	d																	15 28							
Islip	d																	15 39							
Oxford	a					15 14				15 32						15 40		15 55						16 14	
	d	15 01			15 07	15 16			15 31						15 37	15 43			16 01				16 07	16 16	
Radley	d				15 13																		16 13		
Culham	d				15 17																				
Appleford	d																						16 18		
Didcot Parkway	a				15 24							←			15 49								16 24		
	d				15 31 →		15 29					15 31	15 47		16 01							16 22	16 31 →		16 29
Cholsey	d		←									15 37			16 07						←				
Goring & Streatley	d		15 12									15 42			16 12 →						16 12				
Pangbourne	d		15 17									15 47									16 17				
Tilehurst	d		15 21									15 51									16 21				
Bedwyn	d																15 42								
Hungerford	d																15 48								
Kintbury	d																15 52								
Newbury	a																15 59								
	d			15 05													15 59			16 06					
Newbury Racecourse	d			15 07																					
Thatcham	d			15 12													16 04								
Midgham	d			15 16																					
Aldermaston	d			15 20																					
Theale	d			15 25													16 12								
Reading West	d			15 32																					
Reading [7]	a	15 25	15 27	15 37		15 40	15 44		15 55			16 02	16 02			16 13	16 19		16 24	16 28	16 29	16 36		16 40	16 44
	d	15 25	15 33				15 45	15 51	15 56		16 00	16 03	16 04	16 11			16 21		16 25	16 28	16 33	16 38			16 45
Twyford [3]	a		15 39									16 09									16 39				
Maidenhead [3]	a		15 47									16 17									16 47				
Slough [3]	a	15 40	15 54									16 24									16 54				
Ealing Broadway	⊖ a		16 19									16 49									17 19				
London Paddington [15]	⊖ a	15 59	16 31				16 14	16 21	16 26		16 29	17 01	16 32	16 37			16 54		16 56	16 59	17 31	17 06			17 14

For general notes see front of timetable
For details of catering facilities see Directory of Train Operators

Saturdays

until 5 September

Birmingham, Banbury, Bicester, Oxford and Bedwyn → Reading and London

Network Diagram - see first page of Table 116

	GW	GW	GW	GW	GW	GW	GW	XC	GW	GW	GW	GW	GW	GW	XC	GW	GW	GW	GW	GW	GW	GW	GW	GW
	1	1	1 ◇	1	1 ◇	1 ◇	1	1 ◇	1	1 ◇	1	1	1	1	1 ◇	1 ◇	1	1	1 ◇	1	1 ◇	1 ◇	1	1
		☕	☕		☕	☕		🛒					☕		🛒	☕		☕	☕		☕	☕		
Birmingham New Street 12 d								15 33							16 04									
Birmingham International d															16 14									
Coventry d															16 25									
Stratford-upon-Avon d															15 39									
Warwick Parkway d								15 41							16 22									
Warwick d								15 45							16 25									
Leamington Spa 8 d								16 00							16 38									
Banbury d								16 19							16 55									
Kings Sutton d																								
Heyford d																								
Tackley d																								
Bicester Town d											16 35													
Islip d											16 46													
Oxford a								16 40			17 02				17 14									
d			16 31				16 37	16 43		17 01				17 07	17 16				17 31					17 37
Radley d														17 13										
Culham d														17 17										
Appleford d																								
Didcot Parkway a				←			16 49							17 24						←				17 49
d				16 31	16 47		17 01							17 31 →		17 29				17 31	17 47			18 01
Cholsey d				16 37			17 07					←								17 37				18 07
Goring & Streatley d				16 42			17 12 →					17 12								17 42				18 12 →
Pangbourne d				16 47								17 17								17 47				
Tilehurst d				16 51								17 21								17 51				
Bedwyn d									16 40														17 14	
Hungerford d									16 46														17 20	
Kintbury d									16 50														17 24	
Newbury a									16 57														17 31	
d	16 13								16 57								17 15						17 39	
Newbury Racecourse d	16 15																17 17						17 42	
Thatcham d	16 20								17 02								17 22						17 47	
Midgham d	16 24																17 27						17 51	
Aldermaston d	16 28																17 30						17 55	
Theale d	16 33								17 10								17 35						18 00	
Reading West d	16 40																17 42						18 08	
Reading 7 a	16 45		16 55	16 58	17 01			17 13	17 17	17 25		17 27			17 40	17 44	17 47		17 55	17 58	18 01		18 11	
d		16 50	16 56	17 03	17 03	17 11			17 19	17 25		17 33	17 36			17 45		17 52	17 57	18 03	18 03	18 11		
Twyford 3 a				17 09								17 39								18 09				
Maidenhead 3 a				17 17								17 47								18 17				
Slough 3 a			17 09	17 24						17 40		17 54							18 10	18 24				
Ealing Broadway ⊖ a				17 49								18 19								18 49				
London Paddington 15 ⊖ a		17 21	17 29	18 01	17 32	17 38			17 54	17 59		18 31	18 08			18 14		18 21	18 29	19 01	18 32	18 38		

	XC	GW	GW	GW	GW	GW	GW	XC	GW	GW	GW	GW	GW	GW	GW	GW	GW	XC	GW	GW	GW	GW	XC	GW
	1 ◇	1	1	1 ◇	1	1 ◇	1	1 ◇	1 ◇	1	1 ◇	1 ◇	1	1	1 ◇	1 ◇	1	1 ◇	1	1 ◇	1	1	1 ◇	1 ◇
	🛒					☕		🛒	☕		☕	☕			☕	☕		🛒					🛒	☕
Birmingham New Street 12 d	16 33							17 04										17 33					18 04	
Birmingham International d								17 14															18 14	
Coventry d								17 25															18 25	
Stratford-upon-Avon d																							17 36	
Warwick Parkway d	16 45							17 22										17 45					18 22	
Warwick d	16 48							17 25										17 48					18 25	
Leamington Spa 8 d	17 00							17 38										18 00					18 38	
Banbury d	17 19		17 23					17 55										18 19					18 55	
Kings Sutton d			17 28																					
Heyford d			17 36																					
Tackley d			17 41																					
Bicester Town d													18 04											
Islip d													18 15											
Oxford a	17 40		17 53					18 14					18 31					18 40					19 14	
d	17 43			18 01			18 07	18 16				18 31					18 37	18 43		19 01		19 07	19 16	
Radley d							18 13															19 13		
Culham d																						19 17		
Appleford d							18 18																	
Didcot Parkway a							18 24		←					←			18 49					19 24		
d						18 22	18 31 →		18 29					18 31	18 47		19 01					19 31 →		19 29
Cholsey d					←									18 37			19 07				←			
Goring & Streatley d					18 12									18 42			19 12 →				19 12			
Pangbourne d					18 17									18 47							19 17			
Tilehurst d					18 21									18 51							19 21			
Bedwyn d		17 37																	18 37					
Hungerford d		17 43																	18 43					
Kintbury d		17 47																	18 47					
Newbury a		17 54																	18 54					
d		17 54								18 13									18 54					
Newbury Racecourse d										18 15														
Thatcham d		17 59								18 20									18 59					
Midgham d										18 24														
Aldermaston d										18 28														
Theale d		18 07								18 33									19 07					
Reading West d										18 40														
Reading 7 a	18 13	18 17		18 25	18 27	18 36		18 40	18 43	18 45		18 55		18 58	19 01			19 13	19 17	19 25	19 27		19 40	19 43
d		18 19		18 25	18 33	18 38			18 45		18 51	18 56		19 03	19 03	19 11			19 19	19 25	19 33			19 45
Twyford 3 a					18 39									19 09							19 39			
Maidenhead 3 a					18 47									19 17							19 47			
Slough 3 a				18 40	18 54							19 09		19 24						19 40	19 54			
Ealing Broadway ⊖ a					19 19									19 49							20 19			
London Paddington 15 ⊖ a		18 55		18 59	19 31	19 08			19 14		19 22	19 29		20 01	19 32	19 39			19 52	19 59	20 31			20 14

For general notes see front of timetable
For details of catering facilities see Directory of Train Operators

Table 116

Saturdays

until 5 September

Birmingham, Banbury, Bicester, Oxford and Bedwyn → Reading and London

Network Diagram - see first page of Table 116

		GW 1	GW 1◇ ☕	GW 1	GW 1◇ ☕	GW 1	GW 1◇ ☕	GW 1	XC 1◇ 🛒	GW 1	GW 1◇	GW 1	GW 1	GW 1◇ ☕	GW 1	XC 1◇ 🛒	GW 1◇ ☕	GW 1◇ ☕	GW 1	GW 1◇ ☕	GW 1	GW 1◇ ☕	GW 1	XC 1◇ 🛒	GW 1
Birmingham New Street 12	d								18 33							19 04								19 33	
Birmingham International	d															19 14									
Coventry	d															19 25									
Stratford-upon-Avon	d																								
Warwick Parkway	d								*18 46*							*18 46*								*19 44*	
Warwick	d								*18 49*							*18 49*								*19 47*	
Leamington Spa 8	d								19 00							19 38								20 00	
Banbury	d			19 02					19 19							19 55			20 02					20 19	
Kings Sutton	d			19 07															20 07						
Heyford	d			19 15															20 15						
Tackley	d			19 20															20 20						
Bicester Town	d									19 18															20 30
Islip	d									19 29															20 41
Oxford	a			19 32					19 40	19 45						20 14			20 32					20 40	20 56
	d		19 31					19 37	19 43		20 01				20 07	20 16		20 31					20 37	20 43	
Radley	d														20 13										
Culham	d																								
Appleford	d														20 18										
Didcot Parkway	a					←		19 49							20 24						←		20 49		
	d					19 31		20 01						20 22	20 31 →		20 29				20 31	20 47	21 01		
Cholsey	d					19 37		20 07				←									20 37		21 07		
Goring & Streatley	d					19 42		20 12				20 12									20 42		21 12		
Pangbourne	d					19 47		→				20 17									20 47		→		
Tilehurst	d					19 51						20 21									20 51				
Bedwyn	d												19 37												
Hungerford	d												19 43												
Kintbury	d												19 47												
Newbury	a												19 54												
	d	19 13					19 49						19 54												
Newbury Racecourse	d	19 15											19 56												
Thatcham	d	19 20											20 01												
Midgham	d	19 24											20 06												
Aldermaston	d	19 28											20 09												
Theale	d	19 33											20 14												
Reading West	d	19 40											20 21												
Reading 7	a	19 45	19 55			19 57	20 06		20 13		20 25	20 27	20 28	20 36		20 40	20 44	20 52			20 57	21 07		21 13	
	d		19 56		20 02	20 03	20 15				20 25	20 33		20 38			20 45	20 53		21 01	21 03	21 09			
Twyford 3	a					20 09						20 39									21 09				
Maidenhead 3	a					20 17						20 47									21 17				
Slough 3	a		20 09			20 24					20 40	20 54						21 10			21 24				
Ealing Broadway	⊖ a					20 49						21 19									21 49				
London Paddington 15	⊖ a		20 29		20 32	21 01	20 45				20 59	21 31		21 07			21 14	21 29		21 32	22 01	21 36			

		GW 1◇	GW 1	GW 1	GW 1	XC 1◇ 🛒	GW 1◇ ☕	GW 1 ☕	GW 1◇ ☕	GW 1◇	XC 1◇ 🛒	GW 1	GW 1	GW 1◇	XC 1◇ 🛒	GW 1	GW 1◇	GW 1	GW 1◇ ☕	GW 1◇	GW 1	GW 1◇ A ☕	GW 1	GW 1
Birmingham New Street 12	d					20 04					20 33				21 04									
Birmingham International	d					20 14									21 14									
Coventry	d					20 25									21 25									
Stratford-upon-Avon	d					*19 53*																		
Warwick Parkway	d					*20 16*					*20 44*													
Warwick	d					*20 19*					*20 47*													
Leamington Spa 8	d					20 38					21 00				21 38									
Banbury	d		20 38			20 55					21 19				21 55			22 02						
Kings Sutton	d		20 43															22 07						
Heyford	d		20 51															22 15						
Tackley	d		20 56															22 20						
Bicester Town	d												21 37											22 50
Islip	d												21 48											23 01
Oxford	a		21 08			21 14					21 40		22 03		22 14			22 32						23 16
	d	21 01				21 16				21 37	21 43	21 50		22 08	22 16		22 31			23 01			23 07	
Radley	d											21 56											23 13	
Culham	d																						23 17	
Appleford	d																						23 20	
Didcot Parkway	a									21 49		22 04								23 13			23 25	
	d						21 34		21 47	21 50		22 04							22 47	23 14		23 32	23 36	
Cholsey	d			←								22 10											23 42	
Goring & Streatley	d			21 12								22 15											23 47	
Pangbourne	d			21 17								22 21											23 51	
Tilehurst	d			21 21								22 24											23 56	
Bedwyn	d				20 48											22 00					23 00			
Hungerford	d				20 54											22 06					23 06			
Kintbury	d				20 58											22 10					23 10			
Newbury	a				21 05											22 17					23 17			
	d				21 05											22 17					23 17			
Newbury Racecourse	d				21 07											22 19					23 19			
Thatcham	d				21 12											22 24					23 24			
Midgham	d				21 17											22 29					23 29			
Aldermaston	d				21 20											22 32					23 32			
Theale	d				21 25											22 37					23 37			
Reading West	d				21 32											22 44					23 44			
Reading 7	a	21 25		21 27	21 37	21 40	21 48		21 58	22 04	22 13	22 31		22 34	22 40	22 50	22 55		23 01	23 30	23 50	23 52	00 01	
	d	21 25		21 33			21 50	21 59	22 00	22 05		22 32		22 35			22 56		23 03	23 31		23 53	00 03	
Twyford 3	a			21 39								22 39											00 09	
Maidenhead 3	a			21 47								22 47											00 17	
Slough 3	a	21 40		21 54						22 22		22 54		22 49			23 17			23 48			00 28	
Ealing Broadway	⊖ a			22 19								23 19											00 52	
London Paddington 15	⊖ a	21 59		22 31			22 16	22 26	22 32	22 39		23 28		23 08			23 36		23 38	00 10		00 33	01 02	

For general notes see front of timetable
For details of catering facilities see Directory of Train Operators

A From Taunton (Table 134)

Table 116

Saturdays

from 12 September

Birmingham, Banbury, Bicester, Oxford and Bedwyn → Reading and London

Network Diagram - see first page of Table 116

		GW	GW	GW	GW	GW	GW	GW	GW	GW	GW	GW	GW	GW	GW	GW	GW	GW	XC	GW	GW	GW	GW	GW	GW
		1 ◇	1	1	1	1	1 ◇ ☕	1	1	1 ◇	1	1 ◇ ☕	1	1	1 ◇	1	1 ◇ ☕	1	1 ◇ 🛒	1 ◇ ☕	1	1 ◇ ☕	1	1	1 ◇ ☕
Birmingham New Street 12	d																		06 04						
Birmingham International	d																		06 14						
Coventry	d																		06 25						
Stratford-upon-Avon	d																								
Warwick Parkway	d																								
Warwick	d																								
Leamington Spa 8	d																		06 38						
Banbury	d		23p50																06 55				07 02		
Kings Sutton	d		23p54																				07 07		
Heyford	d		00 03																				07 15		
Tackley	d		00 07																				07 20		
Bicester Town	d																								
Islip	d																								
Oxford	a		00 18																07 14				07 31		
	d	00 06	00 19	03 59	05 07	05 37			06 07	06 31				06 37	07 01			07 07	07 16			07 31			
Radley	d		00 26		05 13				06 13									07 13							
Culham	d		00 30		05 17													07 17							
Appleford	d		00 32						06 18																
Didcot Parkway	a	00 19	00 39	04 10	05 24	05 48			06 24					06 49				07 24						←	
	d	00 20	00 43	04 10	05 31	06 01	06 29		06 31			06 59		07 01			07 17	07 31		07 30				07 31	07 47
Cholsey	d		00 49		05 37	06 07			06 37					07 07		←		→						07 37	
Goring & Streatley	d		00 54		05 42	06 12			06 42					07 12		07 12								07 42	
Pangbourne	d		00 59		05 47	06 17			06 47					→		07 17								07 47	
Tilehurst	d		01 03		05 51	06 21			06 51							07 21								07 51	
Bedwyn	d							06 05					06 37												
Hungerford	d							06 11					06 43												
Kintbury	d							06 15					06 47												
Newbury	a							06 22					06 54												
	d							06 22					06 54								07 13				
Newbury Racecourse	d							06 24													07 15				
Thatcham	d							06 29					06 59								07 20				
Midgham	d							06 34													07 24				
Aldermaston	d							06 37													07 28				
Theale	d							06 42					07 07								07 33				
Reading West	d							06 49													07 42				
Reading 7	a	00 38	01 09	04 27	05 57	06 27	06 43	06 52	06 57	07 00	←	07 14	07 20		07 27	07 27	07 32		07 40	07 44	07 45	07 54		07 59	08 01
	d	00 39	01 10	04 40	06 03	06 33	06 45	06 52	07 03	07 00	07 03	07 15	07 21		07 27	07 33	07 33			07 46		07 56		08 03	08 03
Twyford 3	a		01 17	04 46	06 09	06 39			→		07 09					07 39								08 09	
Maidenhead 3	a		01 25	04 54	06 17	06 47					07 17					07 47								08 17	
Slough 3	a	00 53	01 32	05 01	06 24	06 54				07 16	07 24					07 54						08 09		08 24	
Ealing Broadway ⊖	a		01 48	05 19	06 49	07 19					07 49					08 19								08 49	
London Paddington 15 ⊖	a	01 11	02 00	05 31	07 01	07 31	07 14	07 24		07 37	08 01	07 44	07 54		07 59	08 31	08 02			08 14		08 29		09 01	08 32

For general notes see front of timetable
For details of catering facilities see
Directory of Train Operators

Table 116

Saturdays

Birmingham, Banbury, Bicester, Oxford and Bedwyn → Reading and London

from 12 September

Network Diagram - see first page of Table 116

		GW	XC	GW	GW	GW	GW	GW	GW	GW	XC	GW	GW	GW	GW	GW		GW	GW	GW	XC	GW	GW	GW	GW
		1	1◇	1◇	1	1◇	1	1	1◇	1	1◇	1◇	1	1◇	1◇	1		1◇	1◇	1	1◇	1◇	1	1◇	1
																						A			
			🛒	☕					☕		🛒	☕		☕	☕			☕	☕		🛒	☕			
Birmingham New Street 12	d		06 33								07 04										07 33				
Birmingham International	d										07 14														
Coventry	d										07 25														
Stratford-upon-Avon	d																								
Warwick Parkway	d		*06 41*								*07 06*										*07 45*				
Warwick	d		*06 45*								*07 09*										*07 48*				
Leamington Spa 8	d		07 00								07 38										08 00				
Banbury	d		07 19								07 55										08 19				
Kings Sutton	d																								
Heyford	d																								
Tackley	d																								
Bicester Town	d						07 36																		
Islip	d						07 47																		
Oxford	a		07 40				08 03				08 14										08 40				
	d	07 37	07 43			08 01				08 07	08 16				08 31					08 37	08 43			09 01	
Radley	d									08 13															
Culham	d																								
Appleford	d									08 18															
Didcot Parkway	a	07 49								08 24										08 49					
	d	08 01 →		08 00				← 08 01	08 17	08 31 →		08 30				← 08 31		08 47	08 52	09 01 →		09 00			← 09 01
Cholsey	d							08 07								08 37									09 07
Goring & Streatley	d							08 12								08 42									09 12
Pangbourne	d							08 17								08 47									09 17
Tilehurst	d							08 21								08 51									09 21
Bedwyn	d				07 37																		08 37		
Hungerford	d				07 43																		08 43		
Kintbury	d				07 47																		08 47		
Newbury	a				07 54																		08 55		
	d				07 54								08 13	08 34									08 55		
Newbury Racecourse	d												08 15												
Thatcham	d				07 59								08 20										09 00		
Midgham	d												08 24												
Aldermaston	d												08 28												
Theale	d				08 07								08 33												
Reading West	d												08 40										09 08		
Reading 7	a		08 13	08 14	08 16	08 25		08 27	08 32		08 40	08 44	08 45	08 52	08 56	08 57		09 02	09 07		09 13	09 14	09 19	09 25	09 27
	d			08 16	08 18	08 26		08 33	08 33			08 46		08 52	08 57	09 03		09 04	09 09			09 16	09 20	09 26	09 33
Twyford 3	a							08 39								09 09									09 39
Maidenhead 3	a							08 47								09 17									09 47
Slough 3	a					08 39		08 54							09 10	09 24								09 39	09 54
Ealing Broadway	⊖ a							09 19								09 49									10 19
London Paddington 15	⊖ a			08 44	08 55	08 59		09 31	09 02			09 14		09 21	09 29	10 01		09 32	09 37			09 44	09 54	09 59	10 31

		GW	GW	GW	GW	XC	GW	GW	GW	GW	GW	GW	GW	GW	XC	GW	GW	GW	GW	GW	GW	XC	GW	GW	GW
						R																			
		1◇	1◇	1	1	1	1◇	1◇	1	1	1	1◇	1◇	1	1◇	1	1◇	1	1◇	1◇	1	1◇	1	1◇	1
						B																			
		☕	☕			🛒	☕	☕				☕	☕		🛒				☕	☕		🛒		☕	
Birmingham New Street 12	d					08 04									08 33							09 04			
Birmingham International	d					08 14																09 14			
Coventry	d					08 25																09 25			
Stratford-upon-Avon	d					*07 35*																			
Warwick Parkway	d					*08 23*									*08 46*							*09 22*			
Warwick	d					*08 26*									*08 49*							*09 25*			
Leamington Spa 8	d					08 38									09 00							09 38			
Banbury	d					08 55				09 02					09 19							09 55			
Kings Sutton	d									09 07															
Heyford	d									09 15															
Tackley	d									09 20															
Bicester Town	d				08 45																		09 57		
Islip	d				08 56																		10 08		
Oxford	a				09 12	09 14				09 32					09 40							10 14	10 24		
	d			09 07		09 16		09 31						09 37	09 43		10 01				10 07	10 16			
Radley	d			09 13																	10 13				
Culham	d			09 17																					
Appleford	d																								
Didcot Parkway	a			09 24										09 49							10 21				
	d	09 18		09 31 →			09 29				← 09 31	09 47		10 01					10 17	10 22	10 31 →			10 29	
Cholsey	d										09 37			10 07				←							
Goring & Streatley	d										09 42			10 12 →				10 12							
Pangbourne	d										09 47							10 17							
Tilehurst	d										09 51							10 21							
Bedwyn	d															09 37									
Hungerford	d															09 43									
Kintbury	d															09 47									
Newbury	a															09 54									
	d								09 23							09 54									10 13
Newbury Racecourse	d								09 26																10 15
Thatcham	d								09 31							09 59									10 20
Midgham	d								09 36																10 24
Aldermaston	d								09 39																10 28
Theale	d								09 44																10 33
Reading West	d								09 51							10 07									10 40
Reading 7	a	09 33				09 40	09 44	09 55	09 56		09 57	10 01			10 13	10 17	10 25	10 27	10 32	10 35		10 40		10 45	10 45
	d	09 34	09 37				09 45	09 56			10 03	10 03	10 10			10 18	10 25	10 33	10 33	10 37				10 45	
Twyford 3	a										10 09							10 39							
Maidenhead 3	a										10 17							10 47							
Slough 3	a							10 09			10 24						10 40	10 54							
Ealing Broadway	⊖ a										10 49							11 19							
London Paddington 15	⊖ a	10 02	10 08				10 14	10 29			11 01	10 32	10 38			10 52	10 59	11 31	11 02	11 08				11 14	

For general notes see front of timetable
For details of catering facilities see Directory of Train Operators

A From Taunton (Table 134)
B From Nottingham (Table 57)

Table 116

Saturdays

from 12 September

Birmingham, Banbury, Bicester, Oxford and Bedwyn → Reading and London

Network Diagram - see first page of Table 116

		GW	GW	GW	GW	GW	GW	XC	GW	GW		GW	GW	XC	GW	GW	GW	GW	GW	GW	GW	GW	GW	XC	GW
		1◇	1◇	1	1◇	1	1◇	1◇	1	1◇		1	1	1◇	1◇	1	1	1◇	1	1	1◇	1◇	1	1◇	1
		☕	☕		☕		☕	🛒						🛒	☕		☕	☕			☕	☕		🛒	
Birmingham New Street 12	d							09 33						10 04										10 33	
Birmingham International	d													10 14											
Coventry	d													10 25											
Stratford-upon-Avon	d													*09 38*											
Warwick Parkway	d							*09 44*						*10 22*										*10 45*	
Warwick	d							*09 47*						*10 25*										*10 48*	
Leamington Spa 8	d							10 00						10 38										11 00	
Banbury	d							10 19						10 55					11 02					11 19	
Kings Sutton	d																		11 07						
Heyford	d																		11 15						
Tackley	d																		11 20						
Bicester Town	d																								
Islip	d																								
Oxford	a							10 40						11 14					11 31					11 40	
	d		10 31			10 37		10 43		11 01			11 07	11 16				11 31					11 37	11 43	
Radley	d												11 13												
Culham	d																								
Appleford	d			←																←					
Didcot Parkway	a					10 49							11 25										11 49		
	d			10 31	10 47	11 01							11 31 →		11 29					11 31	11 47		12 01		
Cholsey	d			10 37		11 07						←								11 37			12 07		
Goring & Streatley	d			10 42		11 12 →						11 12								11 42			12 12 →		
Pangbourne	d			10 47								11 17								11 47					
Tilehurst	d			10 51								11 21								11 51					
Bedwyn	d								10 40																11 37
Hungerford	d								10 46																11 43
Kintbury	d								10 50																11 47
Newbury	a								10 57																11 54
	d								10 57							11 13									11 54
Newbury Racecourse	d															11 15									
Thatcham	d								11 02							11 20									11 59
Midgham	d															11 24									
Aldermaston	d															11 28									
Theale	d								11 10							11 33									12 07
Reading West	d															11 40									
Reading 7	a		10 55	10 58	11 01			11 13	11 21	11 25		11 27		11 40	11 44	11 45		11 55		11 58	12 02			12 13	12 15
	d	10 53	10 56	11 03	11 03		11 13		11 21	11 27		11 33			11 45		11 53	11 56		12 03	12 03	12 11			12 17
Twyford 3	a			11 09								11 39								12 09					
Maidenhead 3	a			11 17								11 47								12 17					
Slough 3	a		11 09	11 24						11 40		11 54						12 09		12 24					
Ealing Broadway	⊖ a			11 49								12 19								12 49					
London Paddington 15	⊖ a	11 24	11 29	12 01	11 32		11 40		11 55	11 59		12 31			12 14		12 23	12 29		13 01	12 32	12 39			12 52

		GW	GW	GW	GW	GW	XC	GW	GW	GW	GW	GW	GW	GW	GW	GW	XC	GW	GW	GW	GW	XC	GW	GW	GW
		1	1◇	1	1◇	1	1◇	1◇	1	1◇	1◇	1	1◇	1	1◇	1	1◇	1◇	1◇	1	1	1◇	1	1◇	1
					☕		🛒	☕		☕	☕		☕		☕		🛒	☕				🛒		☕	
Birmingham New Street 12	d						11 04										11 33					12 04			
Birmingham International	d						11 14															12 14			
Coventry	d						11 25															12 25			
Stratford-upon-Avon	d																					*11 38*			
Warwick Parkway	d						*11 22*										*11 41*					*12 22*			
Warwick	d						*11 25*										*11 45*					*12 25*			
Leamington Spa 8	d						11 38										12 00					12 38			
Banbury	d						11 55										12 19					12 55			
Kings Sutton	d																								
Heyford	d																								
Tackley	d																								
Bicester Town	d	11 30																					12 59		
Islip	d	11 41																					13 10		
Oxford	a	11 56					12 14										12 40					13 14	13 26		
	d		12 01			12 07	12 16				12 31					12 37	12 43		13 01		13 07	13 16			
Radley	d					12 13															13 13				
Culham	d																								
Appleford	d											←													
Didcot Parkway	a					12 21										12 49					13 22				
	d				12 22	12 31 →		12 29				12 31	12 47			13 01					13 31 →			13 29	
Cholsey	d			←								12 37				13 07				←					
Goring & Streatley	d			12 12								12 42				13 12 →				13 12					
Pangbourne	d			12 17								12 47								13 17					
Tilehurst	d			12 21								12 51								13 21					
Bedwyn	d																								
Hungerford	d																								
Kintbury	d																								
Newbury	a																								
	d								12 13																13 13
Newbury Racecourse	d								12 15																13 15
Thatcham	d								12 20																13 20
Midgham	d								12 24																13 24
Aldermaston	d								12 28																13 28
Theale	d								12 33																13 33
Reading West	d								12 40																13 40
Reading 7	a		12 25	12 28	12 36		12 40	12 44	12 45		12 54	12 57	13 01	←			13 13		13 25	13 27		13 40		13 44	13 45
	d		12 25	12 33	12 38			12 45		12 54	12 55	13 03 →	13 01	13 03	13 12			13 20	13 25	13 33				13 45	
Twyford 3	a			12 39										13 09						13 39					
Maidenhead 3	a			12 47										13 17						13 47					
Slough 3	a		12 40	12 54							13 09			13 24					13 40	13 54					
Ealing Broadway	⊖ a			13 19										13 49						14 19					
London Paddington 15	⊖ a		12 59	13 31	13 06			13 14		13 21	13 29		13 32	14 01	13 41			13 46	13 59	14 31				14 14	

For general notes see front of timetable
For details of catering facilities see
Directory of Train Operators

Table 116

Saturdays

from 12 September

Birmingham, Banbury, Bicester, Oxford and Bedwyn → Reading and London

Network Diagram - see first page of Table 116

		GW	GW	GW		GW	GW	GW	GW	XC	GW	GW	GW	GW	GW	XC	GW	GW	GW	GW	GW	GW	GW	GW	XC
		1	1 ◊	1		1	1 ◊	1 ◊	1	1 ◊	1 ◊	1 ◊	1	1 ◊	1	1 ◊	1 ◊	1	1 ◊	1 ◊	1	1 ◊	1 ◊	1	1 ◊
							☕	☕		🛒	☕			☕		🛒	☕		☕	☕		☕	☕		🛒
Birmingham New Street 12	d									12 33						13 04									13 33
Birmingham International	d															13 14									
Coventry	d															13 25									
Stratford-upon-Avon	d																								
Warwick Parkway	d									*12 45*						*13 22*									*13 41*
Warwick	d									*12 48*						*13 25*									*13 45*
Leamington Spa 8	d									13 00						13 38									14 00
Banbury	d			13 02						13 19						13 55									14 19
Kings Sutton	d			13 07																					
Heyford	d			13 15																					
Tackley	d			13 20																					
Bicester Town	d																								
Islip	d																								
Oxford	a			13 32						13 40						14 14									14 40
	d		13 31						13 37	13 43		14 01			14 07	14 16				14 31				14 37	14 43
Radley	d														14 13										
Culham	d																								
Appleford	d														14 18										
Didcot Parkway	a					←			13 49						14 24						←			14 49	
	d					13 31	13 47		14 01					14 22	14 31		14 29				14 31	14 47		15 01	
Cholsey	d					13 37			14 07				←		→						14 37			15 07	
Goring & Streatley	d					13 42			14 12				14 12								14 42			15 12	
Pangbourne	d					13 47			→				14 17								14 47			→	
Tilehurst	d					13 51							14 21								14 51				
Bedwyn	d	13 07									13 33														
Hungerford	d	13 13									13 40														
Kintbury	d	13 17																							
Newbury	a	13 24									13 49														
	d	13 28									13 50							14 13							
Newbury Racecourse	d																	14 15							
Thatcham	d	13 33									13 57							14 20							
Midgham	d																	14 24							
Aldermaston	d																	14 28							
Theale	d	13 41									14 06							14 33							
Reading West	d																	14 40							
Reading 7	a	13 51	13 55			13 59	14 02			14 13	14 19	14 25	14 27	14 36		14 40	14 43	14 45		14 55	14 58	15 01			15 13
	d	13 51	13 55			14 03	14 03	14 11			14 19	14 26	14 33	14 38			14 45		14 53	14 56	15 03	15 03	15 11		
Twyford 3	a					14 09							14 39								15 09				
Maidenhead 3	a					14 17							14 47								15 17				
Slough 3	a		14 10			14 24							14 54								15 24				
Ealing Broadway	⊖ a					14 49						14 39	15 19							15 09	15 49				
London Paddington 15	⊖ a	14 24	14 29			15 01	14 32	14 39			14 45	14 59	15 31	15 09			15 14		15 22	15 29	16 01	15 32	15 39		

		GW	GW	GW	GW	GW	XC	GW	GW	GW	GW	GW	GW	GW	GW	XC	GW	GW	GW	GW		GW	GW	GW	XC
		1	1	1 ◊	1	1	1 ◊	1 ◊	1	1 ◊	1 ◊	1	1	1 ◊	1	1 ◊	1	1 ◊	1	1 ◊		1	1 ◊	1	1 ◊
							🛒	☕		☕				☕		🛒		☕					☕		🛒
Birmingham New Street 12	d						14 04									14 33									15 04
Birmingham International	d						14 14																		15 14
Coventry	d						14 25																		15 25
Stratford-upon-Avon	d						*13 40*																		
Warwick Parkway	d						*14 22*									*14 45*									*15 22*
Warwick	d						*14 25*									*14 48*									*15 25*
Leamington Spa 8	d						14 38									15 00									15 38
Banbury	d						14 55					15 02				15 19									15 55
Kings Sutton	d											15 07													
Heyford	d											15 15													
Tackley	d											15 20													
Bicester Town	d		14 17														15 28								
Islip	d		14 28														15 39								
Oxford	a		14 45				15 14					15 32				15 40	15 55								16 14
	d			15 01		15 07	15 16				15 31				15 37	15 43				16 01				16 07	16 16
Radley	d					15 13																		16 13	
Culham	d					15 17																			
Appleford	d																							16 18	
Didcot Parkway	a					15 24							←		15 49									16 24	
	d					15 31		15 29					15 31	15 47	16 01								16 22	16 31	
Cholsey	d				←	→							15 37		16 07							←		→	
Goring & Streatley	d				15 12								15 42		16 12							16 12			
Pangbourne	d				15 17								15 47		→							16 17			
Tilehurst	d				15 21								15 51									16 21			
Bedwyn	d	14 37																	15 37						
Hungerford	d	14 43																	15 43						
Kintbury	d	14 47																	15 47						
Newbury	a	14 54																	15 54						
	d	14 54							15 13										15 54						
Newbury Racecourse	d								15 15																
Thatcham	d	14 59							15 20										15 59						
Midgham	d								15 24																
Aldermaston	d								15 28																
Theale	d	15 07							15 33										16 07						
Reading West	d								15 40																
Reading 7	a	15 17		15 25	15 27		15 40	15 44	15 45		15 55		15 59	16 01		16 10			16 16	16 24		16 27	16 36		16 40
	d	15 19		15 25	15 33			15 45		15 53	15 56		16 03	16 03				16 11	16 18	16 25		16 33	16 38		
Twyford 3	a				15 39								16 09									16 39			
Maidenhead 3	a				15 47								16 17									16 47			
Slough 3	a			15 40	15 54								16 24									16 54			
Ealing Broadway	⊖ a				16 19								16 49							16 39		17 19			
London Paddington 15	⊖ a	15 55		15 59	16 31			16 14		16 23	16 29		17 01	16 32				16 41	16 55	16 59		17 31	17 06		

For general notes see front of timetable
For details of catering facilities see
Directory of Train Operators

Table 116

Birmingham, Banbury, Bicester, Oxford and Bedwyn → Reading and London

Network Diagram - see first page of Table 116

		GW 1◇ ☕	GW 1	GW 1◇ ☕	GW 1◇ ☕	GW 1	GW 1◇ ☕	GW 1	XC 1◇ 🛒	GW 1◇ ☕	GW 1	GW 1◇	GW 1	GW 1	GW 1◇ ☕	GW 1	XC 1◇ 🛒	GW 1◇ ☕	GW 1◇ ☕	GW 1◇ ☕	GW 1	GW 1◇ ☕	GW 1◇ ☕	GW 1	XC 1◇ 🛒
Birmingham New Street [12]	d								15 33								16 04								16 33
Birmingham International	d																16 14								
Coventry	d																16 25								
Stratford-upon-Avon	d																15 39								
Warwick Parkway	d								15 41								16 22								16 45
Warwick	d								15 45								16 25								16 48
Leamington Spa [8]	d								16 00								16 38								17 00
Banbury	d								16 19								16 55								17 19
Kings Sutton	d																								
Heyford	d																								
Tackley	d																								
Bicester Town	d												16 35												
Islip	d												16 46												
Oxford	a								16 40				17 02				17 14								17 40
	d				16 31			16 37	16 43			17 01				17 07	17 16			17 31				17 37	17 43
Radley	d															17 13									
Culham	d															17 17									
Appleford	d																								
Didcot Parkway	a					←		16 49								17 24					←			17 49	
	d	16 29				16 31	16 47	17 01								17 31 →		17 29			17 31	17 47		18 01	
Cholsey	d					16 37		17 07						←							17 37			18 07	
Goring & Streatley	d					16 42		17 12 →						17 12							17 42			18 12 →	
Pangbourne	d					16 47								17 17							17 47				
Tilehurst	d					16 51								17 21							17 51				
Bedwyn	d										16 37				16 53										
Hungerford	d										16 43				17 00										
Kintbury	d										16 47														
Newbury	a										16 54				17 09										
	d		16 13								16 54				17 10										
Newbury Racecourse	d		16 15								16 56														
Thatcham	d		16 20								17 01				17 17										
Midgham	d		16 24								17 06														
Aldermaston	d		16 28								17 09														
Theale	d		16 33								17 14				17 26										
Reading West	d		16 40								17 21														
Reading [7]	a	16 44	16 45		16 55	16 58	17 01		17 10		17 25	17 25		17 27	17 39		17 40	17 44		17 55	17 58	18 01			18 13
	d	16 45		16 51	16 56	17 03	17 03			17 11		17 25		17 33	17 41			17 45	17 54	17 57	18 03	18 03	18 11		
Twyford [3]	a					17 09								17 39							18 09				
Maidenhead [3]	a					17 17								17 47							18 17				
Slough [3]	a				17 09	17 24						17 40		17 54						18 10	18 24				
Ealing Broadway	⊖ a					17 49								18 19							18 49				
London Paddington [15]	⊖ a	17 14		17 21	17 29	18 01	17 32			17 38		17 59		18 31	18 08			18 14	18 21	18 29	19 01	18 32	18 38		

		GW 1	GW 1	GW 1◇	GW 1	GW 1◇ ☕	GW 1	XC 1◇ 🛒	GW 1◇ ☕	GW 1	GW 1◇ ☕	GW 1◇ ☕	GW 1	GW 1		GW 1◇ ☕	GW 1◇ ☕	GW 1	XC 1◇ 🛒	GW 1	GW 1◇	GW 1	GW 1	XC 1◇ 🛒	GW 1◇ ☕
Birmingham New Street [12]	d							17 04											17 33					18 04	
Birmingham International	d							17 14																18 14	
Coventry	d							17 25																18 25	
Stratford-upon-Avon	d																							17 36	
Warwick Parkway	d							17 22											17 45					18 22	
Warwick	d							17 25											17 48					18 25	
Leamington Spa [8]	d							17 38											18 00					18 38	
Banbury	d		17 23					17 55											18 19					18 55	
Kings Sutton	d		17 28																						
Heyford	d		17 36																						
Tackley	d		17 41																						
Bicester Town	d												18 04												
Islip	d												18 15												
Oxford	a		17 53					18 14					18 31						18 40					19 14	
	d			18 01			18 07	18 16				18 31						18 37	18 43		19 01		19 07	19 16	
Radley	d						18 13																19 13		
Culham	d																						19 17		
Appleford	d						18 18																		
Didcot Parkway	a						18 24							←				18 49					19 24		
	d					18 22	18 31 →		18 29					18 31		18 47		19 01					19 31 →		19 29
Cholsey	d				←									18 37				19 07				←			
Goring & Streatley	d				18 12									18 42				19 12 →				19 12			
Pangbourne	d				18 17									18 47								19 17			
Tilehurst	d				18 21									18 51								19 21			
Bedwyn	d	17 37																		18 37					
Hungerford	d	17 43																		18 43					
Kintbury	d	17 47																		18 47					
Newbury	a	17 54																		18 54					
	d	17 54								18 13										18 54					
Newbury Racecourse	d									18 15															
Thatcham	d	17 59								18 20										18 59					
Midgham	d									18 24															
Aldermaston	d									18 28															
Theale	d	18 07								18 33										19 07					
Reading West	d									18 40															
Reading [7]	a	18 17		18 25	18 27	18 36		18 40	18 44	18 45		18 55		18 58		19 01			19 13	19 17	19 25	19 27		19 40	19 44
	d	18 19		18 25	18 33	18 38			18 45		18 51	18 56		19 03		19 03	19 11			19 19	19 25	19 33			19 45
Twyford [3]	a				18 39									19 09								19 39			
Maidenhead [3]	a				18 47									19 17								19 47			
Slough [3]	a			18 40	18 54							19 09		19 24							19 40	19 54			
Ealing Broadway	⊖ a				19 19									19 49								20 19			
London Paddington [15]	⊖ a	18 55		18 59	19 31	19 08			19 14		19 22	19 29		20 01		19 32	19 39			19 52	19 59	20 31			20 14

For general notes see front of timetable
For details of catering facilities see Directory of Train Operators

Table 116

Birmingham, Banbury, Bicester, Oxford and Bedwyn → Reading and London

Saturdays

from 12 September

Network Diagram - see first page of Table 116

		GW	GW	GW	GW	GW	GW	GW	XC	GW	GW	GW	GW	GW	GW	XC	GW	GW	GW	GW	GW	GW	GW	XC	GW
		1	1 ◇	1	1 ◇	1	1 ◇	1	1 ◇	1	1 ◇	1	1	1 ◇	1	1 ◇	1 ◇	1 ◇	1	1 ◇	1	1 ◇	1	1 ◇	1
			☕		☕		☕		🍴					☕		🍴	☕	☕		☕		☕		🍴	
Birmingham New Street 12	d								18 33							19 04								19 33	
Birmingham International	d															19 14									
Coventry	d															19 25									
Stratford-upon-Avon	d																								
Warwick Parkway	d								*18 46*															*19 44*	
Warwick	d								*18 49*															*19 47*	
Leamington Spa 8	d								19 00							19 38								20 00	
Banbury	d			19 02					19 19							19 55			20 02					20 19	
Kings Sutton	d			19 07															20 07						
Heyford	d			19 15															20 15						
Tackley	d			19 20															20 20						
Bicester Town	d									19 18															20 30
Islip	d									19 29															20 41
Oxford	a			19 32					19 40	19 45						20 14			20 32					20 40	20 56
	d		19 31					19 37	19 43		20 01				20 07	20 16		20 31					20 37	20 43	
Radley	d														20 13										
Culham	d																								
Appleford	d														20 18										
Didcot Parkway	a					←		19 49							20 24						←		20 49		
	d					19 31		20 01						20 22	20 31 →		20 29				20 31	20 47	21 01		
Cholsey	d					19 37		20 07				←									20 37		21 07		
Goring & Streatley	d					19 42		20 12 →				20 12									20 42		21 12 →		
Pangbourne	d					19 47						20 17									20 47				
Tilehurst	d					19 51						20 21									20 51				
Bedwyn	d												19 39												
Hungerford	d												19 45												
Kintbury	d												19 49												
Newbury	a												19 56												
	d	19 13					19 50						19 56												
Newbury Racecourse	d	19 15											19 58												
Thatcham	d	19 20											20 03												
Midgham	d	19 24											20 08												
Aldermaston	d	19 28											20 11												
Theale	d	19 33											20 16												
Reading West	d	19 40											20 23												
Reading 7	a	19 45	19 55			19 57	20 07		20 13		20 25	20 27	20 29	20 36		20 40	20 44	20 52			20 57	21 07		21 13	
	d		19 56		20 02	20 03	20 09				20 25	20 33		20 38			20 45	20 53		21 01	21 03	21 09			
Twyford 3	a					20 09						20 39									21 09				
Maidenhead 3	a					20 17						20 47									21 17				
Slough 3	a		20 09			20 24					20 40	20 54						21 10			21 24				
Ealing Broadway	⊖ a					20 49						21 19									21 49				
London Paddington 15	⊖ a		20 29		20 32	21 01	20 37				20 59	21 31		21 07			21 14	21 29		21 32	22 01	21 36			

		GW	GW	GW	GW	XC	GW	GW	GW	XC	GW	GW	GW	XC	GW	GW	GW	GW	GW	GW	GW	GW	GW
		1 ◇	1	1	1	1 ◇	1 ◇	1 ◇	1 ◇	1 ◇	1	1	1 ◇	1 ◇	1	1 ◇	1	1 ◇	1 ◇	1	1 ◇	1	1
																					A		
						🍴	☕	☕		🍴				🍴				☕			☕		
Birmingham New Street 12	d					20 04				20 33				21 04									
Birmingham International	d					20 14								21 14									
Coventry	d					20 25								21 25									
Stratford-upon-Avon	d					*19 53*																	
Warwick Parkway	d					*20 16*				*20 44*													
Warwick	d					*20 19*				*20 47*													
Leamington Spa 8	d					20 38				21 00				21 38									
Banbury	d		20 38			20 55				21 19				21 55			22 02						
Kings Sutton	d		20 43														22 07						
Heyford	d		20 51														22 15						
Tackley	d		20 56														22 20						
Bicester Town	d											21 37											22 50
Islip	d											21 48											23 01
Oxford	a		21 08			21 14				21 40		22 03		22 14			22 32						23 16
	d	21 01				21 16			21 37	21 43	21 50		22 08	22 16		22 31			23 01			23 07	
Radley	d										21 56											23 13	
Culham	d																					23 17	
Appleford	d																					23 20	
Didcot Parkway	a								21 49		22 04								23 13			23 25	
	d						21 34	21 47	21 50		22 04							22 47	23 14		23 32	23 36	
Cholsey	d			←							22 10											23 42	
Goring & Streatley	d			21 12							22 15											23 47	
Pangbourne	d			21 17							22 21											23 51	
Tilehurst	d			21 21							22 24											23 56	
Bedwyn	d				20 48										22 00					23 00			
Hungerford	d				20 54										22 06					23 06			
Kintbury	d				20 58										22 10					23 10			
Newbury	a				21 05										22 17					23 17			
	d				21 05										22 17					23 17			
Newbury Racecourse	d				21 07										22 19					23 19			
Thatcham	d				21 12										22 24					23 24			
Midgham	d				21 17										22 29					23 29			
Aldermaston	d				21 20										22 32					23 32			
Theale	d				21 25										22 37					23 37			
Reading West	d				21 32										22 44					23 44			
Reading 7	a	21 25		21 27	21 37	21 40	21 48	21 58	22 04	22 13	22 31		22 34	22 40	22 50	22 55		23 01	23 30	23 50	23 52	00 01	
	d	21 25		21 33			21 50	22 00	22 05		22 32		22 35			22 56		23 03	23 31		23 53	00 03	
Twyford 3	a			21 39							22 39											00 09	
Maidenhead 3	a			21 47							22 47											00 17	
Slough 3	a	21 40		21 54					22 22		22 54		22 49			23 12			23 48			00 28	
Ealing Broadway	⊖ a			22 19							23 19											00 52	
London Paddington 15	⊖ a	21 59		22 31			22 16	22 32	22 39		23 28		23 08			23 30		23 36	00 10		00 33	01 02	

For general notes see front of timetable
For details of catering facilities see
Directory of Train Operators

A From Taunton (Table 134)

Birmingham, Banbury, Bicester, Oxford and Bedwyn → Reading and London

Network Diagram - see first page of Table 116

		GW	GW	GW	GW	GW	GW	GW	GW	GW		GW	GW	GW	GW	GW	XC	GW	GW	GW		GW	GW	GW	GW
		1	1	1	1◇ ☕	1◇	1◇ ☕	1◇ ☕	1	1		1◇	1◇ ☕	1	1◇ ☕	1	1◇ 🍴	1◇ ☕	1	1		1◇ 🍴	1◇ ☕	1◇ ☕	1
Birmingham New Street 12	d																09 04								
Birmingham International	d																09 14								
Coventry	d																09 25								
Stratford-upon-Avon	d																								
Warwick Parkway	d																*09 10*								
Warwick	d																*09 13*								
Leamington Spa 8	d																09 38								
Banbury	d																09 55								
Kings Sutton	d																								
Heyford	d																								
Tackley	d																								
Bicester Town	d																		10 03						
Islip	d																		10 14						
Oxford	a																10 14		10 30						
	d	23p07		08 05		08 38				09 05		09 38				10 05	10 16					10 38			
Radley	d	23p13		08 12						09 11						10 11									
Culham	d	23p17																							
Appleford	d	23p20														10 16									
Didcot Parkway	a	23p25		08 20		08 50				09 21		09 50				10 21						10 50			
	d	23p36	07 45	08 21	08 39	08 50	09 10			09 26		09 51	09 59		10 17	10 21				←		10 51	10 59	11 17	
Cholsey	d	23p42		08 27						09 32						10 27 →				10 27					
Goring & Streatley	d	23p47	07 53	08 32						09 37										10 33					
Pangbourne	d	23p51		08 37						09 41										10 37					
Tilehurst	d	23p56		08 42						09 46										10 42					
Bedwyn	d													09 35											10 54
Hungerford	d													09 41											11 00
Kintbury	d													09 46											11 04
Newbury	a													09 52											11 11
	d								09 05					09 53				10 27							11 11
Newbury Racecourse	d								09 07					09 55											
Thatcham	d								09 12					10 00											11 16
Midgham	d								09 17					10 05											
Aldermaston	d								09 20					10 08											
Theale	d								09 25					10 13											11 24
Reading West	d								09 33					10 21											
Reading 7	a	00 01	08 04	08 47	08 55	09 06	09 26		09 36	09 51		10 06	10 12	10 25	10 31		10 42	10 44		10 46		11 07	11 13	11 31	11 37
	d	00 03	08 04	08 50	08 56	09 06	09 27	09 30	09 36	09 52		10 10	10 15	10 26	10 32			10 46		10 52		11 10	11 15	11 32	11 37
Twyford 3	a	00 09		08 56						09 58										10 58					
Maidenhead 3	a	00 17		09 04					09 48	10 06				10 39						11 06					11 50
Slough 3	a	00 28	08 22	09 11		09 25			09 57	10 13		10 30		10 48						11 13		11 30			11 59
Ealing Broadway	⊖ a	00 52		09 34						10 36										11 36					
London Paddington 15	⊖ a	01 02	08 44	09 43	09 34	09 46	10 06	10 10	10 17	10 47		10 53	10 55	11 08	11 10			11 22		11 47		11 54	11 55	12 09	12 23

		GW	XC	GW	GW	GW	GW	GW		GW	GW	GW	GW	GW	GW	XC	GW	GW		GW	XC	GW	GW	GW	GW
		1	1◇ 🍴	1◇ ☕	1	1◇ ☕	1	1		1◇	1◇ ☕	1	1◇ ☕	1	1	1◇ 🍴	1	1◇ 🍴		1◇ ☕	1◇ 🍴	1◇ ☕	1◇ ☕	1	1
Birmingham New Street 12	d		10 04													11 04					11 33				
Birmingham International	d		10 14													11 14									
Coventry	d		10 25													11 25									
Stratford-upon-Avon	d		*10 00*																						
Warwick Parkway	d		*10 10*													*11 12*					*11 39*				
Warwick	d		*10 25*													*10 42*					*11 42*				
Leamington Spa 8	d		10 38													11 38					12 00				
Banbury	d		10 55					11 00								11 55					12 19				
Kings Sutton	d							11 05																	
Heyford	d							11 14																	
Tackley	d							11 19																	
Bicester Town	d											11 33													
Islip	d											11 44													
Oxford	a		11 14					11 29				12 00				12 14					12 47				
	d	11 05	11 16							11 38					12 05	12 16		12 42			12 47				13 05
Radley	d	11 11													12 11										13 11
Culham	d																								
Appleford	d														12 16										
Didcot Parkway	a	11 21								11 50					12 21										13 21
	d	11 21			←					11 50	11 59		12 17		12 21		←			12 59			13 17		13 21
Cholsey	d	11 27 →			11 27										12 27 →		12 27								13 27 →
Goring & Streatley	d				11 33												12 33								
Pangbourne	d				11 37												12 37								
Tilehurst	d				11 42												12 42								
Bedwyn	d																							12 54	
Hungerford	d																							13 00	
Kintbury	d																							13 04	
Newbury	a																							13 11	
	d					11 26								12 03										13 11	
Newbury Racecourse	d													12 05											
Thatcham	d													12 10										13 16	
Midgham	d													12 15											
Aldermaston	d													12 18											
Theale	d													12 23										13 24	
Reading West	d													12 31											
Reading 7	a		11 42		11 46	11 47	←			12 07	12 13		12 31	12 35		12 42	12 47	13 09		13 13	13 15		13 31	13 37	
	d			11 44	11 52 →	11 50	11 52			12 10	12 15		12 32	12 36			12 52	13 10		13 15		13 22	13 32	13 37	
Twyford 3	a						11 58										12 58								
Maidenhead 3	a						12 06							12 48			13 06							13 48	
Slough 3	a						12 13			12 32				12 59			13 13	13 29						13 59	
Ealing Broadway	⊖ a						12 36										13 36								
London Paddington 15	⊖ a			12 28		12 32	12 47			12 51	12 55		13 10	13 23			13 47	13 53		13 55		14 08	14 09	14 23	

For general notes see front of timetable
For details of catering facilities see
Directory of Train Operators

Table 116

Sundays

until 12 July

Birmingham, Banbury, Bicester, Oxford and Bedwyn → Reading and London

Network Diagram - see first page of Table 116

		XC	GW	GW	GW	GW		GW	XC	GW	GW	GW	GW	XC	GW	GW		GW	GW	XC	GW	GW	GW	GW	GW
		1 ◇ 🛒	1	1	1 ◇ 🍴	1		1 ◇ 🛒	1 ◇ 🛒	1 ◇ 🍴	1 ◇ 🍴	1	1	1 ◇ 🛒	1 ◇ 🍴	1		1 ◇	1 ◇ 🍴	1 ◇ 🛒	1	1 ◇ 🍴	1 ◇ 🍴	1	1
Birmingham New Street 12	d	12 04							12 33					13 04						13 33					
Birmingham International	d	12 14												13 14											
Coventry	d	12 25												13 25											
Stratford-upon-Avon	d	*12 00*																							
Warwick Parkway	d	*12 10*							*12 39*					*13 09*						*13 39*					
Warwick	d	*12 25*							*12 42*											*13 42*					
Leamington Spa 8	d	12 38							13 00					13 38						14 00					
Banbury	d	12 55							13 19					13 55						14 19					
Kings Sutton	d																								
Heyford	d																								
Tackley	d																								
Bicester Town	d		13 03																		14 33				
Islip	d		13 14																		14 44				
Oxford	a	13 14	13 30						13 41					14 14						14 45	15 00				
	d	13 16						13 38	13 43				14 05	14 16				14 42		14 45					15 05
Radley	d												14 11												15 11
Culham	d																								
Appleford	d												14 16												
Didcot Parkway	a							13 50					14 21												15 21
	d			←				13 50		13 59	14 17		14 21			←			14 59				15 17		15 21
Cholsey	d			13 27									14 27 →			14 27									15 27 →
Goring & Streatley	d			13 33												14 33									
Pangbourne	d			13 37												14 37									
Tilehurst	d			13 42												14 42									
Bedwyn	d																							14 54	
Hungerford	d																							15 00	
Kintbury	d																							15 04	
Newbury	a																							15 11	
	d				13 31							14 03												15 11	
Newbury Racecourse	d											14 05													
Thatcham	d											14 10												15 16	
Midgham	d											14 15													
Aldermaston	d											14 18													
Theale	d											14 23												15 24	
Reading West	d											14 31													
Reading 7	a	13 42		13 46	13 48	←		14 07	14 13	14 13	14 31	14 35		14 42		14 46		15 09	15 14	15 15			15 31	15 37	
	d			13 52 →	13 49	13 52		14 10		14 15	14 32	14 36			14 45	14 52		15 10	15 15			15 22	15 32	15 37	
Twyford 3	a					13 58										14 58									
Maidenhead 3	a					14 06						14 48				15 06								15 48	
Slough 3	a					14 13		14 30				14 59				15 13		15 30						16 00	
Ealing Broadway	⊖ a					14 36										15 36									
London Paddington 15	⊖ a				14 24	14 47		14 52		14 55	15 09	15 23			15 25	15 47		15 53	15 55			16 08	16 10	16 23	

		XC	GW	GW		XC	GW	GW	GW	GW	GW	XC	GW	GW		GW	GW	GW	XC	GW	GW	GW	GW	GW	GW
		1 ◇ 🛒	1 ◇ 🍴	1		1 ◇ 🛒	1 ◇ 🍴	1 ◇ 🍴	1 ◇ 🍴	1	1	1 ◇ 🛒	1	1		1 ◇ 🍴	1	1	1 ◇ 🛒	1 ◇ 🍴	1 ◇ 🍴	1 ◇ 🍴	1 ◇ 🍴	1	1
Birmingham New Street 12	d	14 04				14 33						15 04							15 33						
Birmingham International	d	14 14										15 14													
Coventry	d	14 25										15 25													
Stratford-upon-Avon	d	*14 00*																							
Warwick Parkway	d	*14 12*				*14 39*						*15 10*							*15 38*						
Warwick	d	*14 25*				*14 42*													*15 40*						
Leamington Spa 8	d	14 38				15 00						15 38							16 00						
Banbury	d	14 55				15 19						15 55					16 00		16 19						
Kings Sutton	d																16 05								
Heyford	d																16 14								
Tackley	d																16 18								
Bicester Town	d												16 03												
Islip	d												16 14												
Oxford	a	15 14				15 41						16 14	16 30				16 33		16 41						
	d	15 16				15 43		15 50			16 05	16 16							16 43			16 50			17 05
Radley	d										16 11														17 11
Culham	d																								
Appleford	d										16 16														
Didcot Parkway	a							16 02			16 21											17 01			17 21
	d			←			15 59	16 02	16 17		16 21			←						16 59		17 03	17 17		17 21
Cholsey	d			15 27							16 27 →			16 27											17 27 →
Goring & Streatley	d			15 33										16 33											
Pangbourne	d			15 37										16 37											
Tilehurst	d			15 42										16 42											
Bedwyn	d																							16 54	
Hungerford	d																							17 00	
Kintbury	d																							17 04	
Newbury	a																							17 11	
	d									16 03						16 30								17 11	
Newbury Racecourse	d									16 05															
Thatcham	d									16 10														17 16	
Midgham	d									16 15															
Aldermaston	d									16 18															
Theale	d									16 23														17 24	
Reading West	d									16 31															
Reading 7	a	15 42		15 46		16 13	16 14	16 19	16 31	16 35		16 42		16 46		16 47		←	17 15	17 14		17 21	17 31	17 35	
	d		15 48	15 52			16 15	16 23	16 32	16 36				16 52 →		16 49		16 52		17 15	17 20	17 22	17 32	17 36	
Twyford 3	a			15 58														16 58							
Maidenhead 3	a			16 06						16 48								17 06						17 48	
Slough 3	a			16 15				16 48		16 59								17 15				17 51		17 58	
Ealing Broadway	⊖ a			16 39														17 38							
London Paddington 15	⊖ a		16 24	16 49			16 53	17 06	17 10	17 23						17 28		17 48		17 53	18 08	18 10	18 15	18 18	

For general notes see front of timetable
For details of catering facilities see Directory of Train Operators

until 12 July

Birmingham, Banbury, Bicester, Oxford and Bedwyn → Reading and London

Network Diagram - see first page of Table 116

		XC 1◇ 🛒		GW 1◇ ☕	GW 1◇ ☕	GW 1	XC 1◇ 🛒	GW 1◇ ☕	GW 1◇ ☕	GW 1	GW 1◇ ☕	GW 1		GW 1	XC 1◇ 🛒	GW 1	GW 1◇ ☕	GW 1	GW 1◇ ☕	GW 1◇ ☕	GW 1◇ ☕	XC 1◇ 🛒		GW 1◇ ☕	GW 1◇ ☕
Birmingham New Street 12	d	16 04					16 33								17 04							17 33			
Birmingham International	d	16 14													17 14										
Coventry	d	16 25													17 25										
Stratford-upon-Avon	d	*16 00*																							
Warwick Parkway	d	*16 12*					*16 39*								*17 10*										
Warwick	d	*16 25*					*16 42*																		
Leamington Spa 8	d	16 38					17 00								17 38							18 00			
Banbury	d	16 55					17 19								17 55	18 00						18 19			
Kings Sutton	d															18 07									
Heyford	d															18 16									
Tackley	d															18 20									
Bicester Town	d									17 33															
Islip	d									17 44															
Oxford	a	17 14					17 41			18 00					18 14	18 31						18 45			
	d	17 16					17 43		17 50					18 05	18 16					18 40		18 45			
Radley	d													18 11											
Culham	d																								
Appleford	d													18 16											
Didcot Parkway	a								18 03					18 21						18 53					
	d					←		17 59	18 03		18 17			18 21				←		18 54	18 59				19 17
Cholsey	d					17 27								18 27 →				18 27							
Goring & Streatley	d					17 33												18 33							
Pangbourne	d					17 37												18 37							
Tilehurst	d					17 42												18 42							
Bedwyn	d																								
Hungerford	d																								
Kintbury	d																								
Newbury	a																								
	d											18 03							18 35						
Newbury Racecourse	d											18 05													
Thatcham	d											18 10													
Midgham	d											18 15													
Aldermaston	d											18 18													
Theale	d											18 23													
Reading West	d											18 31													
Reading 7	a	17 42				17 46	18 13	18 14	18 21		18 31	18 35			18 42			18 46	18 53	19 09	19 15	19 15			19 31
	d			17 44	17 50	17 52		18 15	18 22		18 32	18 36					18 47	18 52	18 57	19 13	19 16			19 27	19 32
Twyford 3	a					17 58												18 58							
Maidenhead 3	a					18 06						18 49						19 06							
Slough 3	a					18 15			18 48			18 59						19 15		19 34					
Ealing Broadway	⊖ a					18 39												19 38							
London Paddington 15	⊖ a			18 23	18 26	18 49		18 53	19 08		19 10	19 23					19 28	19 48	19 42	19 53	19 55			20 07	20 12

		GW 1	GW 1	XC 1◇ 🛒	GW 1	GW 1◇ ☕	GW 1◇ ☕	GW 1	XC 1◇ 🛒	GW 1◇ ☕		GW 1◇ ☕	GW 1	GW 1◇ ☕	GW 1◇ ☕	GW 1	GW 1◇ ☕	XC 1◇ 🛒	GW 1	XC 1◇ 🛒		GW 1◇ ☕	GW 1◇ ☕	GW 1	GW 1◇ ☕
Birmingham New Street 12	d			18 04					18 33									19 04		19 33					
Birmingham International	d			18 14														19 14							
Coventry	d			18 25														19 25							
Stratford-upon-Avon	d			*18 00*																					
Warwick Parkway	d			*18 12*					*18 39*									*19 10*		*19 43*					
Warwick	d			*18 25*					*18 42*											*19 46*					
Leamington Spa 8	d			18 38					19 00									19 38		20 00					
Banbury	d			18 55					19 19									19 55		20 19					
Kings Sutton	d																								
Heyford	d																								
Tackley	d																								
Bicester Town	d				19 03																			20 33	
Islip	d				19 14																			20 44	
Oxford	a			19 14	19 30				19 41									20 14		20 41				21 00	
	d		19 05	19 16					19 43			19 50				20 05		20 16		20 43					
Radley	d		19 11													20 11									
Culham	d																								
Appleford	d																								
Didcot Parkway	a		19 21									20 04				20 21									
	d		19 21					←		19 59		20 05		20 17		20 21			←				20 59		
Cholsey	d		19 27 →					19 27								20 27 →			20 27						
Goring & Streatley	d							19 33											20 33						
Pangbourne	d							19 37											20 37						
Tilehurst	d							19 42											20 42						
Bedwyn	d	18 54																							
Hungerford	d	19 00																							
Kintbury	d	19 04																							
Newbury	a	19 11																							
	d	19 11											19 53		20 16										
Newbury Racecourse	d												19 55												
Thatcham	d	19 16											20 00												
Midgham	d												20 05												
Aldermaston	d												20 08												
Theale	d	19 24											20 13												
Reading West	d												20 21												
Reading 7	a	19 35		19 42				19 46	20 13	20 14		20 22	20 24	20 31	20 34			20 42	20 46	21 13			21 16		
	d	19 36				19 43	19 47	19 52		20 15		20 24		20 32	20 35		20 42		20 52			21 14	21 17		21 25
Twyford 3	a							19 58											20 58						
Maidenhead 3	a	19 48						20 06											21 06						
Slough 3	a	19 57						20 15				20 48							21 15						
Ealing Broadway	⊖ a							20 38											21 38						
London Paddington 15	⊖ a	20 18				20 23	20 25	20 47		20 53		21 06		21 11	21 13		21 21		21 47			21 56	21 56		22 07

For general notes see front of timetable
For details of catering facilities see Directory of Train Operators

Table 116

Sundays

until 12 July

Birmingham, Banbury, Bicester, Oxford and Bedwyn → Reading and London

Network Diagram - see first page of Table 116

		GW 1 ◇ ☕	GW 1	XC 1 ◇ 🛒	GW 1	XC 1 ◇ 🛒	GW 1 ◇ ☕	GW 1 ◇		GW 1	GW 1 ◇ ☕	GW 1 ◇ ☕	XC 1 ◇ 🛒	GW 1	GW 1	GW 1	GW 1 ◇ ☕	GW 🚌		GW 1 ◇	GW	GW 1	GW 1
Birmingham New Street 12	d			20 04		20 33							21 04										
Birmingham International	d			20 14									21 14										
Coventry	d			20 25									21 24										
Stratford-upon-Avon	d			*19 57*																			
Warwick Parkway	d					*20 46*																	
Warwick	d			*20 22*		*20 49*																	
Leamington Spa 8	d			20 38		21 00							21 35										
Banbury	d			20 55		21 19																	
Kings Sutton	d																						
Heyford	d																						
Tackley	d																						
Bicester Town	d														22 03								
Islip	d														22 14								
Oxford	a			21 14		21 38							22 08		22 30								
	d			21 16	21 21	21 40		21 50					22 10	22 21				23 00					
Radley	d				21 27									22 27				23 15					
Culham	d																						
Appleford	d																						
Didcot Parkway	a				21 36			22 03						22 35				23 35					
	d	21 17			21 36		22 01	22 05						22 35			23 11			23 40		23 50	
Cholsey	d				21 42									22 41								23 56	
Goring & Streatley	d				21 47									22 46								00 01	
Pangbourne	d				21 52									22 51								00 05	
Tilehurst	d				21 56									22 55								00 10	
Bedwyn	d		20 54													22 35							
Hungerford	d		21 00													22 41							
Kintbury	d		21 04													22 45							
Newbury	a		21 11													22 52							
	d		21 12							21 53	22 09					22 53					23 23		23 45
Newbury Racecourse	d									21 55						22 55					23 25		23 47
Thatcham	d		21 17							22 00						23 00					23 30		23 52
Midgham	d									22 05						23 05					23 35		23 57
Aldermaston	d									22 08						23 08					23 38		00 01
Theale	d		21 25							22 13						23 13					23 43		00 06
Reading West	d									22 21						23 21					23s50		00s13
Reading 7	a	21 31	21 33	21 42	22 02	22 12	22 17	22 22		22 24	22 28		22 42	23 00		23 24	23 26			23 52	23 53	00 14	00 17
	d	21 32			22 10		22 23	22 24			22 30	22 35		23 00			23 28			23 52		00 15	
Twyford 3	a				22 16									23 06								00 21	
Maidenhead 3	a				22 24									23 14								00 29	
Slough 3	a				22 33			22 47						23 22						00 12		00 36	
Ealing Broadway	⊖ a				22 56									23 44								00 59	
London Paddington 15	⊖ a	22 16			23 05		23 08	23 15			23 17	23 22		23 54			00 06			00 35		01 11	

For general notes see front of timetable
For details of catering facilities see Directory of Train Operators

Table 116

Sundays

19 July to 6 September

Birmingham, Banbury, Bicester, Oxford and Bedwyn → Reading and London

Network Diagram - see first page of Table 116

		GW	GW	GW	GW	GW	GW	GW	GW	GW	GW		GW	GW	GW	GW	GW	XC	GW	GW	GW	GW		GW	GW
		1	1	1	1 ◇	1 ◇	1	1	1 ◇	1 ◇	1		1 ◇	1 ◇	1	1 ◇	1	1 ◇	1 ◇	1	1	1 ◇		1 ◇	1 ◇
														A											
			(bus)		(catering)				(catering)	(catering)				(catering)		(catering)		(trolley)	(catering)			(catering)		(trolley)	(catering)
Birmingham New Street 12	d																	09 04							
Birmingham International	d																	09 14							
Coventry	d																	09 25							
Stratford-upon-Avon	d																								
Warwick Parkway	d																	*09 10*							
Warwick	d																	*09 13*							
Leamington Spa 8	d																	09 38							
Banbury	d																	09 55							
Kings Sutton	d																								
Heyford	d																								
Tackley	d																								
Bicester Town	d																			10 03					
Islip	d																			10 14					
Oxford	a																	10 14		10 30					
	d	23p07		08 21		08 31					09 05		09 38				10 05	10 16						10 38	
Radley	d	23p13		08 28							09 11						10 11								
Culham	d	23p17																							
Appleford	d	23p20		08 33													10 16								
Didcot Parkway	a	23p25		08 38		08 43	←				09 21		09 50				10 21							10 50	
	d	23p36	07 05	08 47 →	08 39	08 44	08 47		09 19		09 26		09 51	09 59		10 17	10 21				←			10 51	10 59
Cholsey	d	23p42					08 53				09 32						10 27 →				10 27				
Goring & Streatley	d	23p47	07 30				08 58				09 37										10 33				
Pangbourne	d	23p51					09 02				09 41										10 37				
Tilehurst	d	23p56					09 07				09 46										10 42				
Bedwyn	d														09 35										
Hungerford	d														09 41										
Kintbury	d														09 46										
Newbury	a														09 52										
	d							08 55							09 53				10 27						
Newbury Racecourse	d							08 57							09 55										
Thatcham	d							09 02							10 00										
Midgham	d							09 07							10 05										
Aldermaston	d							09 10							10 08										
Theale	d							09 15							10 13										
Reading West	d							09 22							10 21										
Reading 7	a	00 01	07 55		08 55	09 06	09 12	09 25	09 34		09 51		10 06	10 12	10 25	10 31		10 42	10 44		10 46			11 07	11 13
	d	00 03			08 56	09 06	09 18	09 26	09 34	09 46	09 52		10 10	10 15	10 26	10 32			10 46		10 52	11 01		11 10	11 15
Twyford 3	a	00 09					09 24				09 58										10 58				
Maidenhead 3	a	00 17					09 30	09 38			10 06				10 39						11 06				
Slough 3	a	00 28				09 25	09 45	09 48			10 13		10 30		10 48						11 13			11 30	
Ealing Broadway	⊖ a	00 52					10 06				10 36										11 36				
London Paddington 15	⊖ a	01 02			09 34	09 46	10 17	10 07	10 10	10 22	10 47		10 53	10 55	11 08	11 10			11 22		11 47	11 36		11 54	11 55

For general notes see front of timetable
For details of catering facilities see Directory of Train Operators

A From Weston-super-Mare (Table 134)

Table 116

Sundays

Birmingham, Banbury, Bicester, Oxford and Bedwyn → Reading and London

19 July to 6 September

Network Diagram - see first page of Table 116

Station		GW 1◇ ⊡	GW 1	GW 1	XC 1◇ ⊤	GW 1	GW 1◇ ⊡	GW 1	GW 1	GW 1◇	GW 1◇ ⊡	GW 1	GW 1◇ ⊡	GW 1	GW 1	XC 1◇ ⊤	GW 1	GW 1◇ ⊤	GW 1◇ ⊡	XC 1◇ ⊤	GW 1◇ ⊡	GW 1◇ ⊡	GW 1
Birmingham New Street 12	d				10 04											11 04				11 33			
Birmingham International	d				10 14											11 14							
Coventry	d				10 25											11 25							
Stratford-upon-Avon	d				*10 00*																		
Warwick Parkway	d				*10 10*											*11 12*				*11 39*			
Warwick	d				*10 25*											*10 42*				*11 42*			
Leamington Spa 8	d				10 38											11 38				12 00			
Banbury	d				10 55				11 00							11 55				12 19			
Kings Sutton	d								11 05														
Heyford	d								11 14														
Tackley	d								11 19														
Bicester Town	d											11 33											
Islip	d											11 44											
Oxford	a				11 14				11 29			12 00				12 14				12 47			
	d			11 05	11 16					11 38					12 05	12 16		12 42		12 47			
Radley	d			11 11											12 11								
Culham	d																						
Appleford	d														12 16								
Didcot Parkway	a			11 21						11 50					12 21								
	d	11 17		11 21		←				11 50	11 59		12 17		12 21		←		12 59			13 17	
Cholsey	d			11 27		11 27									12 27		12 27						
Goring & Streatley	d			→		11 33									→		12 33						
Pangbourne	d					11 37											12 37						
Tilehurst	d					11 42											12 42						
Bedwyn	d		10 54																				12 54
Hungerford	d		11 00																				13 00
Kintbury	d		11 04																				13 04
Newbury	a		11 11																				13 11
	d		11 11				11 26							12 03									13 11
Newbury Racecourse	d													12 05									
Thatcham	d		11 16											12 10									13 16
Midgham	d													12 15									
Aldermaston	d													12 18									
Theale	d		11 24											12 23									13 24
Reading West	d													12 31									
Reading 7	a	11 31	11 37		11 42	11 46	11 47	←		12 07	12 13		12 31	12 35		12 42	12 47	13 09	13 13	13 15		13 31	13 37
	d	11 32	11 37			11 52	11 50	11 52		12 10	12 15		12 32	12 36			12 52	13 10	13 15		13 22	13 32	13 37
Twyford 3	a					→		11 58									12 58						
Maidenhead 3	a		11 50					12 06						12 48			13 06						13 48
Slough 3	a		11 59					12 13		12 32				12 59			13 13	13 29					13 59
Ealing Broadway	⊖ a							12 36									13 36						
London Paddington 15	⊖ a	12 09	12 23				12 27	12 47		12 51	12 55		13 10	13 23			13 47	13 53	13 55		14 08	14 09	14 23

Station		GW 1	XC 1◇ ⊤	GW 1	GW 1	GW 1◇ ⊡	GW 1	GW 1◇ ⊤	XC 1◇ ⊤	GW 1◇ ⊡	GW 1◇ ⊡	GW 1	GW 1	XC 1◇ ⊤	GW 1◇ ⊡	GW 1	GW 1◇	GW 1◇ ⊡	XC 1◇ ⊤	GW 1	GW 1◇ ⊡	GW 1◇ ⊡	GW 1
Birmingham New Street 12	d		12 04						12 33					13 04					13 33				
Birmingham International	d		12 14											13 14									
Coventry	d		12 25											13 25									
Stratford-upon-Avon	d		*12 00*																				
Warwick Parkway	d		*12 10*						*12 39*					*13 09*					*13 39*				
Warwick	d		*12 25*						*12 42*										*13 42*				
Leamington Spa 8	d		12 38						13 00					13 38					14 00				
Banbury	d		12 55						13 19					13 55					14 19				
Kings Sutton	d																						
Heyford	d																						
Tackley	d																						
Bicester Town	d			13 03																14 33			
Islip	d			13 14																14 44			
Oxford	a		13 14	13 30					13 41					14 14					14 45	15 00			
	d	13 05	13 16					13 38	13 43				14 05	14 16			14 42		14 45				
Radley	d	13 11											14 11										
Culham	d																						
Appleford	d												14 16										
Didcot Parkway	a	13 21						13 50					14 21										
	d	13 21			←			13 50		13 59	14 17		14 21			←		14 59				15 17	
Cholsey	d	13 27			13 27								14 27			14 27							
Goring & Streatley	d	→			13 33								→			14 33							
Pangbourne	d				13 37											14 37							
Tilehurst	d				13 42											14 42							
Bedwyn	d																						14 54
Hungerford	d																						15 00
Kintbury	d																						15 04
Newbury	a																						15 11
	d					13 31						14 03											15 11
Newbury Racecourse	d											14 05											
Thatcham	d											14 10											15 16
Midgham	d											14 15											
Aldermaston	d											14 18											
Theale	d											14 23											15 24
Reading West	d											14 31											
Reading 7	a		13 42		13 46	13 48	←	14 07	14 13	14 13	14 31	14 35		14 42		14 46	15 09	15 14	15 15			15 31	15 37
	d				13 52	13 49	13 52	14 10		14 15	14 32	14 36			14 45	14 52	15 10	15 15			15 22	15 32	15 37
Twyford 3	a				→		13 58									14 58							
Maidenhead 3	a						14 06					14 48				15 06							15 48
Slough 3	a						14 13	14 30				14 59				15 13	15 30						16 00
Ealing Broadway	⊖ a						14 36									15 36							
London Paddington 15	⊖ a					14 24	14 47	14 52		14 55	15 09	15 23			15 25	15 47	15 53	15 55			16 08	16 10	16 23

For general notes see front of timetable
For details of catering facilities see Directory of Train Operators

Birmingham, Banbury, Bicester, Oxford and Bedwyn → Reading and London

Network Diagram - see first page of Table 116

		GW	XC	GW	GW	XC	GW	GW	GW	GW	GW		XC	GW	GW	GW	GW	GW	XC	GW	GW	GW		GW	GW
		1	1 ◇	1 ◇	1	1 ◇	1 ◇	1 ◇	1 ◇	1	1		1 ◇	1	1	1 ◇	1	1	1 ◇	1 ◇	1 ◇	1 ◇		1 ◇	1
Birmingham New Street 12	d		14 04			14 33							15 04						15 33						
Birmingham International	d		14 14										15 14												
Coventry	d		14 25										15 25												
Stratford-upon-Avon	d		14 00																						
Warwick Parkway	d		14 12			14 39							15 10						15 38						
Warwick	d		14 25			14 42													15 40						
Leamington Spa 8	d		14 38			15 00							15 38						16 00						
Banbury	d		14 55			15 19							15 55				16 00		16 19						
Kings Sutton	d																16 05								
Heyford	d																16 14								
Tackley	d																16 18								
Bicester Town	d													16 03											
Islip	d													16 14											
Oxford	a		15 14			15 41							16 14	16 30			16 33		16 41						
	d	15 05	15 16			15 43		15 50			16 05		16 16						16 43			16 50			
Radley	d	15 11									16 11														
Culham	d																								
Appleford	d										16 16														
Didcot Parkway	a	15 21						16 02			16 21											17 01			
	d	15 21			←		15 59	16 02	16 17		16 21				←					16 59		17 03		17 17	
Cholsey	d	15 27			15 27						16 27				16 27										
Goring & Streatley	d	→			15 33						→				16 33										
Pangbourne	d				15 37										16 37										
Tilehurst	d				15 42										16 42										
Bedwyn	d																								16 54
Hungerford	d																								17 00
Kintbury	d																								17 04
Newbury	a																								17 11
	d									16 03						16 30									17 11
Newbury Racecourse	d									16 05															
Thatcham	d									16 10															17 16
Midgham	d									16 15															
Aldermaston	d									16 18															
Theale	d									16 23															17 24
Reading West	d									16 31															
Reading 7	a		15 42		15 46	16 13	16 14	16 19	16 31	16 35			16 42		16 46	16 47		←	17 13	17 14		17 21		17 31	17 35
	d			15 48	15 52		16 15	16 23	16 32	16 36					16 52 →	16 49		16 52		17 15	17 20	17 22		17 32	17 36
Twyford 3	a				15 58													16 58							
Maidenhead 3	a				16 06					16 48								17 06							17 48
Slough 3	a				16 15			16 48		16 59								17 15				17 51			17 58
Ealing Broadway	⊖ a				16 39													17 38							
London Paddington 15	⊖ a			16 24	16 49		16 53	17 06	17 10	17 23						17 28		17 48		17 53	18 08	18 10		18 15	18 18

		GW	XC	GW	GW	GW	XC	GW	GW	GW	GW		GW	GW	XC	GW	GW	GW	GW	GW	GW	XC		GW	GW
		1	1 ◇	1 ◇	1 ◇	1	1 ◇	1 ◇	1 ◇	1	1 ◇		1	1	1 ◇	1	1 ◇	1	1 ◇	1 ◇	1 ◇	1 ◇		1 ◇	1 ◇
Birmingham New Street 12	d		16 04				16 33								17 04							17 39			
Birmingham International	d		16 14												17 14										
Coventry	d		16 25												17 25										
Stratford-upon-Avon	d		16 00																						
Warwick Parkway	d		16 12				16 39								17 10										
Warwick	d		16 25				16 42																		
Leamington Spa 8	d		16 38				17 00								17 38							18 00			
Banbury	d		16 55				17 19								17 55	18 00						18 19			
Kings Sutton	d															18 07									
Heyford	d															18 16									
Tackley	d															18 20									
Bicester Town	d									17 33															
Islip	d									17 44															
Oxford	a		17 14				17 41			18 00					18 14	18 31						18 45			
	d	17 05	17 16				17 43		17 50					18 05	18 16					18 40		18 45			
Radley	d	17 11												18 11											
Culham	d																								
Appleford	d													18 16											
Didcot Parkway	a	17 21							18 03					18 21						18 53					
	d	17 21				←		17 59	18 03		18 17			18 21				←		18 54	18 59				19 17
Cholsey	d	17 27				17 27								18 27				18 27							
Goring & Streatley	d	→				17 33								→				18 33							
Pangbourne	d					17 37												18 37							
Tilehurst	d					17 42												18 42							
Bedwyn	d																								
Hungerford	d																								
Kintbury	d																								
Newbury	a																								
	d												18 03						18 35						
Newbury Racecourse	d												18 05												
Thatcham	d												18 10												
Midgham	d												18 15												
Aldermaston	d												18 18												
Theale	d												18 23												
Reading West	d												18 31												
Reading 7	a		17 42			17 46	18 10	18 14	18 21		18 31		18 35		18 42			18 46	18 53	19 09	19 15	19 15			19 31
	d			17 44	17 50	17 52		18 15	18 22		18 32		18 36				18 47	18 52	18 57	19 13	19 16			19 27	19 32
Twyford 3	a					17 58												18 58							
Maidenhead 3	a					18 06							18 49					19 06							
Slough 3	a					18 15			18 48				18 59					19 15		19 34					
Ealing Broadway	⊖ a					18 39												19 38							
London Paddington 15	⊖ a			18 23	18 26	18 49		18 53	19 08		19 10		19 23				19 28	19 48	19 42	19 53	19 55			20 07	20 12

For general notes see front of timetable
For details of catering facilities see Directory of Train Operators

Table 116

Sundays

Birmingham, Banbury, Bicester, Oxford and Bedwyn → Reading and London

19 July to 6 September

Network Diagram - see first page of Table 116

		GW	GW	XC	GW	GW	GW	GW	XC	GW	GW		GW	GW	GW	GW	GW	XC	GW	XC	GW	GW		GW	GW
		1	1	1◇	1	1◇	1◇	1	1◇	1◇	1◇		1	1◇	1◇	1	1◇	1◇	1	1◇	1◇	1◇		1	1◇
				🛒		☕	☕		🛒	☕	☕			☕	☕		☕	🛒		🛒	☕	☕			☕
Birmingham New Street 12	d			18 04					18 33									19 04		19 33					
Birmingham International	d			18 14														19 14							
Coventry	d			18 25														19 25							
Stratford-upon-Avon	d			18 00																					
Warwick Parkway	d			18 12					18 39									19 10		19 43					
Warwick	d			18 25					18 42											19 46					
Leamington Spa 8	d			18 38					19 00									19 38		20 00					
Banbury	d			18 55					19 19									19 55		20 19					
Kings Sutton	d																								
Heyford	d																								
Tackley	d																								
Bicester Town	d				19 03																			20 33	
Islip	d				19 14																			20 44	
Oxford	a			19 14	19 30				19 41									20 14		20 41				21 00	
	d		19 05	19 16					19 43		19 50					20 05		20 16		20 43					
Radley	d		19 11													20 11									
Culham	d																								
Appleford	d																								
Didcot Parkway	a		19 21								20 04					20 21									
	d		19 21					←		19 59	20 05			20 17		20 21			←			20 59			
Cholsey	d		19 27 →					19 27								20 27 →			20 27						
Goring & Streatley	d							19 33											20 33						
Pangbourne	d							19 37											20 37						
Tilehurst	d							19 42											20 42						
Bedwyn	d	18 54																							
Hungerford	d	19 00																							
Kintbury	d	19 04																							
Newbury	a	19 11																							
	d	19 11											19 53		20 16										
Newbury Racecourse	d												19 55												
Thatcham	d	19 16											20 00												
Midgham	d												20 05												
Aldermaston	d												20 08												
Theale	d	19 24											20 13												
Reading West	d												20 21												
Reading 7	a	19 35		19 42				19 46	20 13	20 14	20 22		20 24	20 31	20 34			20 42	20 46	21 13		21 16			
	d	19 36				19 43	19 47	19 52		20 15	20 24			20 32	20 35		20 42		20 52		21 14	21 17			21 25
Twyford 3	a							19 58											20 58						
Maidenhead 3	a	19 48						20 06											21 06						
Slough 3	a	19 57						20 15			20 48								21 15						
Ealing Broadway	⊖ a							20 38											21 38						
London Paddington 15	⊖ a	20 18				20 23	20 25	20 47		20 53	21 06			21 11	21 13		21 21		21 47		21 56	21 56			22 07

		GW	GW	XC	GW	XC	GW	GW	GW	GW	GW		XC	GW	GW	GW	GW	GW	GW	GW	GW	GW			
		1◇	1	1◇	1	1◇	1◇	1◇	1	1◇	1◇		1◇	1	1	1	1◇	🚌	1◇		1	1			
		☕		🛒		🛒	☕			☕	☕		🛒				☕								
Birmingham New Street 12	d			20 04		20 33							21 04												
Birmingham International	d			20 14									21 14												
Coventry	d			20 25									21 24												
Stratford-upon-Avon	d			19 57																					
Warwick Parkway	d					20 46																			
Warwick	d			20 22		20 49																			
Leamington Spa 8	d			20 38		21 00							21 35												
Banbury	d			20 55		21 19																			
Kings Sutton	d																								
Heyford	d																								
Tackley	d																								
Bicester Town	d														22 03										
Islip	d														22 14										
Oxford	a			21 14		21 38							22 08		22 30										
	d			21 16	21 21	21 40		21 50					22 10	22 21				23 00							
Radley	d				21 27									22 27				23 15							
Culham	d																								
Appleford	d																								
Didcot Parkway	a				21 36			22 03						22 35				23 35							
	d	21 17			21 36		22 01	22 05						22 35			23 11		23 40		23 50				
Cholsey	d				21 42									22 41							23 56				
Goring & Streatley	d				21 47									22 46							00 01				
Pangbourne	d				21 52									22 51							00 05				
Tilehurst	d				21 56									22 55							00 10				
Bedwyn	d		20 54													22 35									
Hungerford	d		21 00													22 41									
Kintbury	d		21 04													22 45									
Newbury	a		21 11													22 52									
	d		21 12						21 53	22 09						22 53				23 23		23 45			
Newbury Racecourse	d								21 55							22 55				23 25		23 47			
Thatcham	d		21 17						22 00							23 00				23 30		23 52			
Midgham	d								22 05							23 05				23 35		23 57			
Aldermaston	d								22 08							23 08				23 38		00 01			
Theale	d		21 25						22 13							23 13				23 43		00 06			
Reading West	d								22 21							23 21				23s50		00s13			
Reading 7	a	21 31	21 33	21 42	22 02	22 10	22 17	22 22	22 24	22 28			22 42	23 00		23 24	23 26		23 52	23 53	00 14	00 17			
	d	21 32			22 10		22 23	22 24		22 30	22 35			23 00			23 28		23 52		00 15				
Twyford 3	a				22 16									23 06							00 21				
Maidenhead 3	a				22 24									23 14							00 29				
Slough 3	a				22 33			22 47						23 22					00 12		00 36				
Ealing Broadway	⊖ a				22 56									23 44							00 59				
London Paddington 15	⊖ a	22 16			23 05		23 08	23 15		23 17	23 22			23 54			00 06		00 35		01 11				

For general notes see front of timetable
For details of catering facilities see Directory of Train Operators

Table 116

Sundays

from 13 September

Birmingham, Banbury, Bicester, Oxford and Bedwyn → Reading and London

Network Diagram - see first page of Table 116

		GW	GW	GW	GW	GW	GW	GW	GW	GW	GW	GW	GW	GW	GW	GW	XC	GW	GW	GW	GW	GW	GW
		1	1	1	1	1 ◇	1 ◇	1	1 ◇	1 ◇	1	1 ◇	1 ◇	1	1 ◇	1	1 ◇	1 ◇	1	1	1 ◇	1 ◇	1
				🚌		⊡P			⊡P	⊡P		⊡P					✠	⊡P			⊡P	✠	
Birmingham New Street 12	d																09 04						
Birmingham International	d																09 14						
Coventry	d																09 25						
Stratford-upon-Avon	d																						
Warwick Parkway	d																*09 10*						
Warwick	d																*09 13*						
Leamington Spa 8	d																09 38						
Banbury	d																09 55						
Kings Sutton	d																						
Heyford	d																						
Tackley	d																						
Bicester Town	d																		10 03				
Islip	d																		10 14				
Oxford	a																10 14		10 30				
	d	23p07		07 45							09 05		09 50			10 05	10 16					10 50	
Radley	d	23p13									09 11					10 11							
Culham	d	23p17																					
Appleford	d	23p20														10 16							
Didcot Parkway	a	23p25		08 10							09 21		10 02			10 21						11 02	
	d	23p36	07 45		08 21	08 39	08 50		09 10		09 25	09 59	10 03		10 17	10 21				←	10 59	11 04	
Cholsey	d	23p42			08 27						09 31					10 27				10 27			
Goring & Streatley	d	23p47	07 53		08 32						09 36					→				10 33			
Pangbourne	d	23p51			08 37						09 40									10 37			
Tilehurst	d	23p56			08 42						09 45									10 42			
Bedwyn	d													09 35									10 42
Hungerford	d													09 41									10 48
Kintbury	d													09 46									10 52
Newbury	a													09 52									10 59
	d							08 53						09 53				10 27					11 00
Newbury Racecourse	d							08 55						09 55									
Thatcham	d							09 00						10 00									11 05
Midgham	d							09 05						10 05									
Aldermaston	d							09 08						10 08									
Theale	d							09 13						10 13									11 13
Reading West	d							09 21						10 21									
Reading 7	a	00 01	08 04		08 47	08 55	09 06	09 24	09 26		09 50	10 12	10 18	10 24	10 31		10 42	10 44		10 46	11 13	11 20	11 21
	d	00 03	08 04		08 52	08 56	09 06		09 27	09 33	09 52	10 15	10 20		10 32			10 52		10 52	11 15	11 22	
Twyford 3	a	00 09			08 58						09 58									10 58			
Maidenhead 3	a	00 17			09 06						10 06									11 06			
Slough 3	a	00 28	08 20		09 13		09 22				10 13		10 35							11 13		11 38	
Ealing Broadway	⊖ a	00 52			09 38						10 38									11 38			
London Paddington 15	⊖ a	01 02	08 44		09 49	09 43	09 51		10 06	10 09	10 49	10 52	10 58		11 08			11 30		11 49	11 53	12 01	

For general notes see front of timetable
For details of catering facilities see
Directory of Train Operators

Table 116

Birmingham, Banbury, Bicester, Oxford and Bedwyn → Reading and London

Sundays

from 13 September

Network Diagram - see first page of Table 116

		GW 1◇ 🍽		GW 1	XC 1◇ 🛒	GW 1	GW 1◇ 🍽	GW 1	GW 1◇ 🍽	GW 1◇		GW 1	GW 1	GW 1◇ 🍽	GW 1	XC 1◇ 🛒	GW 1	XC 1◇ 🛒		GW 1◇ 🍽	GW 1◇ 🛒	GW 1	GW 1◇ 🍽	GW 1	XC 1◇ 🛒
Birmingham New Street 12	d				10 04											11 04		11 33							12 04
Birmingham International	d				10 14											11 14									12 14
Coventry	d				10 25											11 25									12 25
Stratford-upon-Avon	d				*10 00*																				*12 00*
Warwick Parkway	d				*10 10*											*11 12*		*11 39*							*12 10*
Warwick	d				*10 25*											*10 42*		*11 42*							*12 25*
Leamington Spa 8	d				10 38											11 38		12 00							12 38
Banbury	d				10 55											11 55		12 19							12 55
Kings Sutton	d																								
Heyford	d																								
Tackley	d																								
Bicester Town	d												11 33												
Islip	d												11 44												
Oxford	a				11 14								12 00			12 14		12 41							13 14
	d			11 05	11 16					11 50					12 05	12 16		12 43			12 50			13 05	13 16
Radley	d			11 11											12 11									13 11	
Culham	d																								
Appleford	d														12 16										
Didcot Parkway	a			11 21						12 02					12 22						13 02			13 21	
	d	11 17		11 21		←			11 59	12 03				12 17	12 22		←			12 59	13 04		13 17	13 21	
Cholsey	d			11 27 →		11 27									12 28 →		12 28							13 27 →	
Goring & Streatley	d					11 33											12 34								
Pangbourne	d					11 37											12 38								
Tilehurst	d					11 42											12 43								
Bedwyn	d																					12 42			
Hungerford	d																					12 48			
Kintbury	d																					12 52			
Newbury	a																					12 59			
	d						11 26					11 53										13 00			
Newbury Racecourse	d											11 55													
Thatcham	d											12 00										13 05			
Midgham	d											12 05													
Aldermaston	d											12 08													
Theale	d											12 13										13 13			
Reading West	d											12 21													
Reading 7	a	11 31			11 42	11 46	11 47	←	12 13	12 19		12 24		12 31		12 42	12 47	13 13		13 13	13 20	13 21	13 31		13 42
	d	11 32				11 52 →	11 50	11 52	12 15	12 21				12 32			12 52			13 15	13 20		13 32		
Twyford 3	a							11 58									12 58								
Maidenhead 3	a							12 06									13 06								
Slough 3	a							12 13		12 35							13 13								
Ealing Broadway	⊖ a							12 38									13 38				13 36				
London Paddington 15	⊖ a	12 08					12 32	12 49	12 53	13 00				13 08			13 49			13 53	14 00		14 08		

		GW 1	GW 1	GW 1◇ 🍽		GW 1	XC 1◇ 🛒	GW 1◇ 🍽	GW 1◇ 🛒	GW 1	GW 1◇ 🍽	GW 1		XC 1◇ 🛒	GW 1◇ 🍽	GW 1	XC 1◇ 🛒	GW 1◇ 🍽	GW 1◇	GW 1		GW 1	GW 1◇ 🍽	GW 1	XC 1◇ 🛒
Birmingham New Street 12	d						12 33							13 04			13 33								14 04
Birmingham International	d													13 14											14 14
Coventry	d													13 25											14 25
Stratford-upon-Avon	d																								*14 00*
Warwick Parkway	d						*12 39*							*13 09*			*13 39*								*14 12*
Warwick	d						*12 42*										*13 42*								*14 25*
Leamington Spa 8	d						13 00							13 38			14 00								14 38
Banbury	d						13 19							13 55			14 19								14 55
Kings Sutton	d																								
Heyford	d																								
Tackley	d																								
Bicester Town	d	13 03																				14 33			
Islip	d	13 14																				14 44			
Oxford	a	13 30					13 41							14 14			14 41					15 00			15 14
	d						13 43		13 50			14 05		14 16			14 43		14 50					15 05	15 16
Radley	d											14 11												15 11	
Culham	d																								
Appleford	d											14 16													
Didcot Parkway	a								14 02			14 21							15 03					15 21	
	d		←					13 59	14 03		14 17	14 21				←		14 59	15 04				15 17	15 21	
Cholsey	d		13 27									14 27 →				14 27								15 27 →	
Goring & Streatley	d		13 33													14 33									
Pangbourne	d		13 37													14 37									
Tilehurst	d		13 42													14 42									
Bedwyn	d																			14 42					
Hungerford	d																			14 48					
Kintbury	d																			14 52					
Newbury	a																			14 59					
	d			13 31						13 53										15 00					
Newbury Racecourse	d									13 55															
Thatcham	d									14 00										15 05					
Midgham	d									14 05															
Aldermaston	d									14 08															
Theale	d									14 13										15 13					
Reading West	d									14 21															
Reading 7	a		13 46	13 48		←	14 13	14 13	14 19	14 24	14 31			14 42		14 46	15 13	15 14	15 20	15 21			15 31		15 42
	d		13 52 →	13 49		13 52		14 15	14 21		14 32				14 45	14 52		15 15	15 20				15 32		
Twyford 3	a					13 58										14 58									
Maidenhead 3	a					14 06										15 06									
Slough 3	a					14 13			14 35							15 13									
Ealing Broadway	⊖ a					14 38										15 38			15 35						
London Paddington 15	⊖ a			14 29		14 49		14 53	14 58		15 08				15 30	15 49		15 53	16 01				16 08		

For general notes see front of timetable
For details of catering facilities see Directory of Train Operators

Sundays

from 13 September

Birmingham, Banbury, Bicester, Oxford and Bedwyn → Reading and London

Network Diagram - see first page of Table 116

		GW	GW	XC	GW	GW	GW	GW	GW	XC	GW	GW	GW	GW	XC	GW	GW	GW	GW	GW	GW	XC
		1◇	1	1◇	1◇	1◇	1	1◇	1	1◇	1	1	1◇	1	1◇	1◇	1◇	1	1◇	1◇	1	1◇
Birmingham New Street 12	d			14 33						15 04					15 33							16 04
Birmingham International	d									15 14												16 14
Coventry	d									15 25												16 25
Stratford-upon-Avon	d																					*16 00*
Warwick Parkway	d			*14 39*						*15 10*					*15 38*							*16 12*
Warwick	d			*14 42*											*15 40*							*16 25*
Leamington Spa 8	d			15 00						15 38					16 00							16 38
Banbury	d			15 19						15 55					16 19							16 55
Kings Sutton	d																					
Heyford	d																					
Tackley	d																					
Bicester Town	d										16 03											
Islip	d										16 14											
Oxford	a			15 41						16 14	16 30				16 41							17 14
	d			15 43		15 50			16 05	16 16					16 43				16 50		17 05	17 16
Radley	d								16 11												17 11	
Culham	d																					
Appleford	d								16 16													
Didcot Parkway	a					16 01			16 21										17 01		17 21	
	d		⟵		15 59	16 01		16 17	16 21			⟵				16 59			17 03	17 17	17 21	
Cholsey	d		15 27						16 27 →			16 27									17 27 →	
Goring & Streatley	d		15 33									16 33										
Pangbourne	d		15 37									16 37										
Tilehurst	d		15 42									16 42										
Bedwyn	d																	16 42				
Hungerford	d																	16 48				
Kintbury	d																	16 52				
Newbury	a																	16 59				
	d						15 53						16 30					17 00				
Newbury Racecourse	d						15 55															
Thatcham	d						16 00											17 05				
Midgham	d						16 05															
Aldermaston	d						16 08															
Theale	d						16 13											17 13				
Reading West	d						16 21															
Reading 7	a		15 46	16 13	16 14	16 19	16 24	16 31		16 42		16 46	16 48	⟵	17 13	17 14		17 21	17 21	17 31		17 42
	d	15 48	15 52		16 15	16 20		16 32				16 52 →	16 48	16 52		17 15	17 19		17 22	17 32		
Twyford 3	a		15 58											16 58								
Maidenhead 3	a		16 06											17 06								
Slough 3	a		16 15			16 34								17 15					17 39			
Ealing Broadway	⊖ a		16 39											17 39								
London Paddington 15	⊖ a	16 29	16 49		16 53	16 59		17 08					17 33	17 49		17 53	17 59		18 06	18 09		

		GW	GW	GW	XC	GW	GW	GW	GW	GW	GW	XC	GW	GW	GW	XC	GW	GW	GW	GW	GW	GW	XC
		1◇	1◇	1	1◇	1◇	1◇	1	1	1◇	1	1◇	1◇	1	1◇	1◇	1◇	1◇	1	1◇	1◇	1	1◇
Birmingham New Street 12	d				16 33							17 04				17 33							18 04
Birmingham International	d											17 14											18 14
Coventry	d											17 25											18 25
Stratford-upon-Avon	d																						*18 00*
Warwick Parkway	d				*16 39*							*17 10*				*17 39*							*18 12*
Warwick	d				*16 42*											*17 42*							*18 25*
Leamington Spa 8	d				17 00							17 38				18 00							18 38
Banbury	d				17 19							17 55				18 19							18 55
Kings Sutton	d																						
Heyford	d																						
Tackley	d																						
Bicester Town	d								17 33														
Islip	d								17 44														
Oxford	a				17 41				18 00			18 14				18 41							19 14
	d				17 43		17 50				18 05	18 16				18 43		18 50				19 05	19 16
Radley	d										18 11											19 11	
Culham	d																						
Appleford	d										18 16												
Didcot Parkway	a						18 03				18 21							19 02				19 21	
	d			⟵		17 59	18 03			18 17	18 21			⟵			18 59	19 03			19 17	19 21	
Cholsey	d			17 27							18 27 →			18 27								19 27 →	
Goring & Streatley	d			17 33										18 33									
Pangbourne	d			17 37										18 37									
Tilehurst	d			17 42										18 42									
Bedwyn	d																		18 42				
Hungerford	d																		18 48				
Kintbury	d																		18 52				
Newbury	a																		18 59				
	d							17 53							18 35				19 00				
Newbury Racecourse	d							17 55															
Thatcham	d							18 00											19 05				
Midgham	d							18 05															
Aldermaston	d							18 08															
Theale	d							18 13											19 13				
Reading West	d							18 21															
Reading 7	a			17 46	18 13	18 14	18 20	18 24		18 31		18 42		18 46	18 52	19 13	19 15	19 19	19 21		19 31		19 42
	d	17 45	17 50	17 52		18 15	18 22			18 32			18 47	18 52	18 53		19 16	19 21		19 22	19 32		
Twyford 3	a			17 58										18 58									
Maidenhead 3	a			18 06										19 06									
Slough 3	a			18 15			18 35							19 15				19 35					
Ealing Broadway	⊖ a			18 39										19 39									
London Paddington 15	⊖ a	18 29	18 40	18 49		18 53	19 04			19 08			19 31	19 49	19 43		19 53	20 01		20 03	20 10		

For general notes see front of timetable
For details of catering facilities see Directory of Train Operators

Table 116

Sundays

from 13 September

Birmingham, Banbury, Bicester, Oxford and Bedwyn → Reading and London

Network Diagram - see first page of Table 116

		GW		GW	GW	GW	XC	GW	GW	GW		GW	GW	XC	GW	GW	GW	XC		GW	GW	GW	GW	GW	GW
		1		1◇	1◇	1	1◇	1◇	1◇	1		1◇	1	1◇	1◇	1◇	1	1◇		1◇	1◇	1◇	1	1◇	1
																						A			
				🍴	🍴		🛒	🍴	🍴			🍴		🛒	🍴	🍴		🛒		🍴	🍴	🛒		🍴	
Birmingham New Street 12	d						18 33							19 04				19 33							
Birmingham International	d													19 14											
Coventry	d													19 25											
Stratford-upon-Avon	d																								
Warwick Parkway	d													*19 10*				*19 43*							
Warwick	d						*18 42*											*19 46*							
Leamington Spa 8	d						19 00							19 38				20 00							
Banbury	d						19 19							19 55				20 19							
Kings Sutton	d																								
Heyford	d																								
Tackley	d																								
Bicester Town	d	19 03																					20 33		
Islip	d	19 14																					20 44		
Oxford	a	19 30					19 41							20 14				20 41					21 00		
	d						19 43		19 50				20 05	20 16				20 43				20 50			
Radley	d												20 11												
Culham	d																								
Appleford	d																								
Didcot Parkway	a								20 04				20 21									21 04			
	d					←		19 59	20 05			20 17	20 21				←				20 59	21 05		21 17	
Cholsey	d					19 27							20 27				20 27								
Goring & Streatley	d					19 33							→				20 33								
Pangbourne	d					19 37											20 37								
Tilehurst	d					19 42											20 42								
Bedwyn	d																								20 54
Hungerford	d																								21 00
Kintbury	d																								21 04
Newbury	a																								21 11
	d									19 53					20 21										21 12
Newbury Racecourse	d									19 55															
Thatcham	d									20 00															21 17
Midgham	d									20 05															
Aldermaston	d									20 08															
Theale	d									20 13															21 25
Reading West	d									20 21															
Reading 7	a					19 46	20 10	20 14	20 20	20 24		20 31		20 42	20 43		20 46	21 13			21 16	21 19		21 31	21 33
	d			19 43	19 47	19 52		20 15	20 21			20 32			20 43	20 45	20 52			21 14	21 17	21 19		21 32	
Twyford 3	a					19 58											20 58								
Maidenhead 3	a					20 06											21 06					21 33			
Slough 3	a					20 15			20 34								21 15					21 39			
Ealing Broadway	⊖ a					20 39											21 39								
London Paddington 15	⊖ a			20 29	20 39	20 49		20 53	21 01			21 11			21 29	21 39	21 49			21 53	21 59	22 07		22 11	

		XC	GW	GW		XC	GW	GW	GW	GW	GW	XC		GW	GW	GW	GW	GW	GW	GW		GW			
		1◇	1◇	1		1◇	1◇	1◇	1	1◇	1◇	1◇		1	1	1◇	1	1◇		1		1			
		🛒	🍴			🛒	🍴			🍴	🍴	🛒						🍴							
Birmingham New Street 12	d	20 04				20 33						21 04													
Birmingham International	d	20 14										21 14													
Coventry	d	20 25										21 24													
Stratford-upon-Avon	d	*19 57*																							
Warwick Parkway	d					*20 46*																			
Warwick	d	*20 22*				*20 49*																			
Leamington Spa 8	d	20 38				21 00						21 35													
Banbury	d	20 55				21 19																			
Kings Sutton	d																								
Heyford	d																								
Tackley	d																								
Bicester Town	d														22 03										
Islip	d														22 14										
Oxford	a	21 14				21 40						22 08			22 30										
	d	21 16		21 21		21 40		21 50				22 10		22 21		22 50				23 15					
Radley	d			21 27										22 27						23 22					
Culham	d																								
Appleford	d																								
Didcot Parkway	a			21 36				22 03						22 35		22 59				23 30					
	d		21 31	21 36			22 01	22 05						22 35		23 00		23 11		23 30					
Cholsey	d			21 42										22 41						23 36					
Goring & Streatley	d			21 47										22 46						23 41					
Pangbourne	d			21 52										22 51						23 46					
Tilehurst	d			21 56										22 55						23 50					
Bedwyn	d																22 35								
Hungerford	d																22 41								
Kintbury	d																22 45								
Newbury	a																22 52								
	d								21 53	22 09							22 53		23 23			23 45			
Newbury Racecourse	d								21 55								22 55		23 25			23 47			
Thatcham	d								22 00								23 00		23 30			23 52			
Midgham	d								22 05								23 05		23 35			23 57			
Aldermaston	d								22 08								23 08		23 38			00 01			
Theale	d								22 13								23 13		23 43			00 06			
Reading West	d								22 21								23 21		23s50			00s13			
Reading 7	a	21 42	21 46	22 02		22 12	22 17	22 21	22 24	22 28		22 42		23 00		23 16	23 24	23 26	23 53	23 56		00 17			
	d		21 47	22 06			22 19	22 24		22 29	22 35			23 00		23 16		23 28		23 56					
Twyford 3	a			22 12										23 06						00 02					
Maidenhead 3	a			22 20										23 14						00 10					
Slough 3	a			22 29				22 47						23 22		23 36				00 20					
Ealing Broadway	⊖ a			22 56										23 44						00 42					
London Paddington 15	⊖ a		22 29	23 05			23 08	23 15		23 17	23 22			23 54		00 01		00 06		00 52					

For general notes see front of timetable
For details of catering facilities see Directory of Train Operators

A From Hereford (Table 126)

Table 116A

Mondays to Fridays

Reading — Wallingford

Bus Service

		GW	GW	GW	GW	GW	GW	GW	GW	GW
Reading	d	00 35	07 27	08 27	09 25	10 25	11 25	12 25	13 25	14 25
Wallingford Market Place	a	01 10	07 59	08 59	09 58	10 58	11 58	12 58	13 58	14 58

		GW	GW	GW	GW	GW	GW	GW	GW	GW
Reading	d	15 25	16 35	17 35	18 35	19 35	20 35	21 35	22 35	23 35
Wallingford Market Place	a	15 58	17 10	18 10	19 10	20 10	21 10	22 10	23 10	00 10

Saturdays

		GW	GW	GW	GW	GW	GW	GW	GW
Reading	d	08 27	09 25	10 25	11 25	12 25	13 25	14 25	15 25
Wallingford Market Place	a	08 59	09 58	10 58	11 58	12 58	13 58	14 58	15 58

		GW	GW	GW	GW	GW	GW	GW	GW
Reading	d	16 35	17 35	18 35	19 35	20 35	21 35	22 35	23 35
Wallingford Market Place	a	17 10	18 10	19 10	20 10	21 10	22 10	23 10	00 10

Sundays

		GW	GW	GW	GW	GW	GW	GW	GW	GW
Reading	d	00 35	11 25	13 25	15 25	17 25	19 25	21 25	23 25	23 35
Wallingford Market Place	a	01 10	11 58	13 58	15 58	17 58	19 58	21 58	23 58	00 10

Mondays to Fridays

		GW	GW	GW	GW	GW	GW	GW	GW	GW	GW	GW	GW
Wallingford Market Place	d	06 07	06 47	07 40	08 40	09 40	10 40	11 40	12 40	13 40	14 40	15 50	16 50
Reading	a	06 40	07 25	08 20	09 18	10 18	11 18	12 18	13 18	14 18	15 18	16 28	17 28

		GW	GW	GW	GW	GW	GW	GW FX	GW FO
Wallingford Market Place	d	17 50	18 50	19 50	20 50	21 50	22 50	23 50	23 55
Reading	a	18 28	19 28	20 28	21 28	22 28	23 28	00 28	00 33

Saturdays

		GW	GW	GW	GW	GW	GW	GW	GW
Wallingford Market Place	d	07 40	08 40	09 40	10 40	11 40	12 40	13 40	14 40
Reading	a	08 20	09 18	10 18	11 18	12 18	13 18	14 18	15 18

		GW	GW	GW	GW	GW	GW	GW	GW	GW
Wallingford Market Place	d	15 50	16 50	17 50	18 50	19 50	20 50	21 50	22 50	23 50
Reading	a	16 28	17 28	18 28	19 28	20 28	21 28	22 28	23 28	00 28

Sundays

		GW	GW	GW	GW	GW	GW	GW	GW
Wallingford Market Place	d	10 40	12 40	14 40	16 40	18 40	20 40	22 40	23 50
Reading	a	11 18	13 18	15 18	17 18	19 18	21 18	23 18	00 28

For general notes see front of timetable
For details of catering facilities see Directory of Train Operators

Table 116B

Mondays to Fridays

Oxford → Abingdon
Bus Service

	GW	GW	GW	GW	GW	GW	GW	GW	GW	GW	GW	GW	GW	GW	GW	GW	GW	GW	GW	GW	GW	GW	GW	GW	GW
Oxford d	06 11	06 30	06 50	07 14	07 32	07 52	08 12	08 34	08 56	09 20	09 40	10 00	10 20	10 40	11 00	11 20	11 40	12 00	12 20	12 40	13 00	13 20	13 40	14 00	14 20
Abingdon High Street a	06 41	07 00	07 20	07 44	08 02	08 22	08 42	09 04	09 26	09 50	10 10	10 30	10 50	11 10	11 30	11 50	12 10	12 30	12 50	13 10	13 30	13 50	14 10	14 30	14 50

	GW	GW	GW	GW	GW	GW	GW	GW	GW	GW	GW	GW	GW	GW	GW	GW	GW	GW	GW	GW	GW	GW	GW	GW	
Oxford d	14 40	15 00	15 15	15 25	15 45	16 05	16 25	16 45	17 05	17 25	17 45	18 05	18 23	18 40	19 10	19 40	20 10	20 40	21 10	21 40	22 10	22 40	23 10	23 40	
Abingdon High Street a	15 10	15 30	15 45	15 55	16 15	16 35	16 55	17 15	17 35	17 55	18 15	18 35	18 53	19 10	19 40	20 10	20 40	21 10	21 40	22 10	22 40	23 10	23 40	00 09	

Saturdays

	GW	GW	GW	GW	GW	GW	GW	GW	GW	GW	GW	GW		GW	GW	GW	GW	GW	GW	GW	GW	GW	GW	GW	GW	GW
Oxford d	06 50	07 10	07 30	08 10	08 30	09 03	09 23	09 43	10 03	10 23	10 43	11 03		11 23	11 43	12 03	12 23	12 43	13 03	13 23	13 43	14 03	14 23	14 43	15 03
Abingdon High Street a	07 20	07 40	08 00	08 40	09 00	09 33	09 53	10 13	10 33	10 53	11 13	11 33		11 53	12 13	12 33	12 53	13 13	13 33	13 53	14 13	14 33	14 53	15 13	15 33

	GW	GW		GW	GW	GW	GW	GW	GW	GW	GW	GW	GW	GW	GW	GW	GW	GW	GW	GW	GW	GW		
Oxford d	15 23	15 43		16 03	16 23	16 43	17 03	17 23	17 43	18 03	18 26	18 40	18 55	19 10	19 40	20 10	20 40	21 10	21 30	22 10	22 30	23 10	23 30		
Abingdon High Street a	15 53	16 13		16 33	16 53	17 13	17 33	17 53	18 13	18 33	18 56	19 10	19 25	19 40	20 10	20 40	21 10	21 40	22 00	22 40	23 00	23 40	23 59		

Sundays

	GW	GW		GW	GW		GW	GW		GW	GW		GW	GW		GW	GW		GW	GW		GW	GW		GW
Oxford d	08 00	08 40		09 00	09 40		10 10	10 40		11 10	11 40		12 10	12 40		13 10	13 40		14 10	14 40		15 10	15 40		16 10
Abingdon High Street a	08 30	09 10		09 30	10 10		10 40	11 10		11 40	12 10		12 40	13 10		13 40	14 10		14 40	15 10		15 40	16 10		16 40

	GW	GW		GW	GW		GW	GW		GW	GW		GW	GW		GW	GW		GW	GW					
Oxford d	16 40	17 10		17 40	18 10		18 40	19 10		19 40	20 10		20 40	21 10		21 40	22 10		22 40	23 10					
Abingdon High Street a	17 10	17 40		18 10	18 40		19 10	19 40		20 10	20 40		21 10	21 40		22 10	22 40		23 10	23 40					

For general notes see front of timetable
For details of catering facilities see
Directory of Train Operators

Table 116B

Mondays to Fridays

Abingdon → Oxford

Bus Service

	GW	GW	GW	GW	GW	GW	GW	GW	GW	GW	GW	GW	GW	GW	GW	GW	GW	GW	GW	GW	GW	GW	GW	GW	GW
Abingdon High Street d	05 40	05 57	06 15	06 35	06 52	07 12	07 32	07 52	08 12	08 32	08 52	09 14	09 37	10 00	10 20	10 40	11 00	11 20	11 40	12 00	12 20	12 40	13 00	13 20	13 40
Oxford a	06 10	06 27	06 45	07 05	07 22	07 42	08 02	08 22	08 42	09 02	09 22	09 44	10 07	10 30	10 50	11 10	11 30	11 50	12 10	12 30	12 50	13 10	13 30	13 50	14 10

	GW	GW	GW	GW	GW	GW	GW	GW	GW	GW	GW	GW	GW	GW	GW	GW	GW	GW	GW	GW	GW	GW	GW	GW	
Abingdon High Street d	14 00	14 20	14 40	15 00	15 20	15 40	15 57	16 17	16 37	16 57	17 17	17 37	17 57	18 17	18 37	19 00	19 30	20 00	20 30	21 00	21 30	22 00	22 30	23 00	....
Oxford a	14 30	14 50	15 10	15 30	15 50	16 10	16 27	16 47	17 07	17 27	17 47	18 07	18 27	18 47	19 07	19 30	20 00	20 30	21 00	21 30	22 00	22 30	23 00	23 30	.

Saturdays

	GW	GW	GW	GW	GW	GW	GW	GW	GW	GW	GW	GW		GW	GW	GW	GW	GW	GW	GW	GW	GW	GW	GW	GW
Abingdon High Street d	06 20	06 40	07 00	07 20	08 00	08 20	08 30	08 50	09 10	09 30	09 50	10 10	....	10 30	10 50	11 10	11 30	11 50	12 10	12 30	12 50	13 10	13 30	13 50	14 10
Oxford a	06 50	07 10	07 30	07 50	08 30	08 50	09 00	09 20	09 40	10 00	10 20	10 40	.	11 00	11 20	11 40	12 00	12 20	12 40	13 00	13 20	13 40	14 00	14 20	14 40

	GW	GW		GW	GW	GW	GW	GW	GW	GW	GW	GW	GW	GW	GW	GW	GW	GW	GW	GW	GW	GW	GW		
Abingdon High Street d	14 30	14 50	....	15 10	15 30	15 50	16 10	16 30	16 50	17 10	17 30	17 50	18 10	18 40	18 55	19 25	19 55	20 25	20 55	21 25	22 00	22 20	23 00	....	....
Oxford a	15 00	15 20	.	15 40	16 00	16 20	16 40	17 00	17 20	17 40	18 00	18 20	18 40	19 08	19 23	19 53	20 23	20 53	21 23	21 53	22 30	22 50	23 30	.	.

Sundays

	GW	GW		GW	GW		GW	GW		GW	GW		GW	GW		GW	GW		GW	GW		GW	GW		GW
Abingdon High Street d	07 30	08 10	....	08 30	08 50	....	09 10	09 40	....	10 10	10 40	....	11 10	11 40	....	12 10	12 40	....	13 10	13 40	....	14 10	14 40	....	15 10
Oxford a	08 00	08 40	.	09 00	09 20	.	09 40	10 10	.	10 40	11 10	.	11 40	12 10	.	12 40	13 10	.	13 40	14 10	.	14 40	15 10	.	15 40

	GW	GW		GW	GW		GW	GW		GW	GW		GW	GW		GW	GW		GW	GW		GW			
Abingdon High Street d	15 40	16 10	....	16 40	17 10	....	17 40	18 10	....	18 40	19 10	....	19 40	20 10	....	20 40	21 10	....	21 40	22 10	....	22 40	....	....	....
Oxford a	16 10	16 40	.	17 10	17 40	.	18 10	18 40	.	19 10	19 40	.	20 10	20 40	.	21 10	21 40	.	22 10	22 40	.	23 10	.	.	.

For general notes see front of timetable
For details of catering facilities see
Directory of Train Operators

Table 116C

Mondays to Fridays

Oxford → Eynsham → Witney
Bus Service

	GW	GW	GW	GW	GW	GW	GW	GW	GW	GW	GW	GW	GW	GW	GW	GW	GW	GW	GW	GW	GW	GW
Oxford d	00 47	00 47	05 59	06 54	07 14	07 19	07 39	07 59	08 19	08 39	08 59	09 14	09 29	09 44	09 59	10 14	10 29	10 44	10 59	11 14	11 29	11 44
Eynsham Church a	01 00	01 00	06 14	07 09	07 29	07 36	07 57	08 17	08 37	08 57	09 17	09 32	09 47	10 02	10 17	10 32	10 47	11 02	11 17	11 32	11 47	12 02
Witney Market Place a	01 12	01 12	06 27	07 21	07 41	07 51	08 14	08 34	08 54	09 14	09 34	09 49	10 04	10 19	10 34	10 49	11 04	11 19	11 34	11 49	12 04	12 19

	GW	GW	GW	GW	GW	GW	GW	GW	GW	GW	GW	GW	GW	GW	GW	GW	GW	GW	GW	GW	GW	GW
Oxford d	11 59	12 14	12 29	12 44	12 59	13 14	13 29	13 44	13 59	14 14	14 29	14 44	14 59	15 14	15 29	15 44	15 59	16 14	16 29	16 39	16 49	16 59
Eynsham Church a	12 17	12 32	12 47	13 02	13 17	13 32	13 47	14 02	14 17	14 32	14 47	15 02	15 17	15 32	15 47	16 02	16 17	16 32	16 47	17 03	17 14	17 24
Witney Market Place a	12 34	12 49	13 04	13 19	13 34	13 49	14 04	14 19	14 34	14 49	15 04	15 19	15 34	15 49	16 04	16 19	16 34	16 49	17 04	17 22	17 35	17 43

	GW	GW	GW	GW	GW	GW	GW	GW	GW	GW	GW	GW	GW	GW	GW	GW	GW	GW	GW	GW
Oxford d	17 09	17 19	17 29	17 39	17 49	17 59	18 12	18 27	18 47	19 22	19 57	20 37	20 52	21 17	21 57	22 27	23 07	23 47	23 47	23 52
Eynsham Church a	17 34	17 44	17 54	18 04	18 14	18 24	18 35	18 45	19 05	19 37	20 10	20 50	21 05	21 30	22 10	22 40	23 20	23 59	00 01	00 08
Witney Market Place a	17 53	18 03	18 13	18 23	18 33	18 43	18 52	19 02	19 22	19 52	20 22	21 02	21 17	21 42	22 22	22 52	23 32	00 12	00 12	00 24

Saturdays

	GW	GW	GW	GW	GW	GW	GW	GW	GW	GW	GW	GW	GW	GW	GW	GW	GW	GW	GW	GW
Oxford d	00 17	00 47	01 47	06 35	07 22	07 52	08 17	08 38	08 59	09 14	09 29	09 44	09 59	10 14	10 29	10 44	10 59	11 14	11 29	11 44
Eynsham Church a	00 30	01 00	02 00	06 50	07 37	08 07	08 33	08 55	09 16	09 32	09 47	10 02	10 17	10 32	10 47	11 02	11 17	11 32	11 47	12 02
Witney Market Place a	00 42	01 12	02 12	07 02	07 49	08 19	08 48	09 10	09 31	09 49	10 04	10 19	10 32	10 49	11 04	11 19	11 32	11 49	12 04	12 19

	GW	GW	GW	GW	GW	GW	GW	GW	GW	GW	GW	GW	GW	GW	GW	GW	GW	GW	GW	GW
Oxford d	11 59	12 14	12 29	12 44	12 59	13 14	13 29	13 44	13 59	14 14	14 29	14 44	14 59	15 14	15 29	15 44	15 59	16 14	16 29	16 44
Eynsham Church a	12 17	12 32	12 47	13 02	13 17	13 32	13 47	14 02	14 17	14 32	14 47	15 02	15 17	15 32	15 47	16 02	16 17	16 32	16 47	17 02
Witney Market Place a	12 32	12 49	13 04	13 19	13 32	13 49	14 04	14 19	14 32	14 49	15 04	15 19	15 32	15 49	16 04	16 19	16 32	16 49	17 04	17 19

	GW	GW	GW	GW	GW	GW	GW	GW	GW	GW	GW	GW	GW	GW	GW	GW	GW
Oxford d	16 59	17 14	17 29	17 44	17 54	18 09	18 29	18 47	19 22	19 57	20 37	20 52	21 17	21 57	22 27	23 07	23 47
Eynsham Church a	17 17	17 32	17 47	17 52	18 02	18 17	18 39	18 55	19 37	20 10	20 50	21 05	21 30	22 10	22 40	23 20	23 59
Witney Market Place a	17 32	17 49	18 04	18 19	18 29	18 44	19 04	19 22	19 52	20 22	21 02	21 17	21 42	22 22	22 52	23 32	00 12

Sundays

	GW	GW	GW	GW	GW	GW	GW	GW	GW	GW	GW	GW	GW	GW
Oxford d	00 17	00 47	01 17	01 47	08 22	09 22	10 22	11 22	11 52	12 22	12 52	13 22	13 52	14 22
Eynsham Church a	00 30	01 00	01 30	02 00	08 38	09 38	10 38	11 38	12 08	12 38	13 08	13 38	14 08	14 38
Witney Market Place a	00 42	01 12	01 42	02 12	08 54	09 54	10 54	11 54	12 24	12 54	13 24	13 54	14 24	14 54

	GW	GW	GW	GW	GW	GW	GW	GW	GW	GW	GW	GW	GW	GW	GW	GW
Oxford d	14 52	15 22	15 52	16 22	16 52	17 22	17 52	18 22	18 52	19 22	20 22	21 22	22 22	23 12	23 47	23 52
Eynsham Church a	15 08	15 38	16 08	16 38	17 08	17 38	18 08	18 38	19 08	19 38	20 38	21 38	22 38	23 28	23 59	00 08
Witney Market Place a	15 24	15 54	16 24	16 54	17 24	17 54	18 24	18 54	19 24	19 54	20 54	21 54	22 54	23 44	00 12	00 24

For general notes see front of timetable
For details of catering facilities see Directory of Train Operators

Table 116C

Mondays to Fridays

Witney → Eynsham → Oxford

Bus Service

		GW	GW	GW	GW	GW	GW	GW	GW	GW	GW	GW	GW	GW	GW	GW	GW	GW	GW	GW	GW	GW
Witney Market Place	d	05 20	06 12	06 28	06 44	06 59	07 14	07 24	07 34	07 44	07 54	08 05	08 25	08 40	08 55	09 10	09 25	09 40	09 55	10 10	10 25	10 40
Eynsham Witney Road	d	05 29	06 26	06 42	06 58	07 13	07 28	07 38	07 48	07 58	08 08	08 19	08 39	08 54	09 09	09 24	09 39	09 54	10 09	10 24	10 39	10 54
Oxford	a	05 50	06 50	07 10	07 30	07 45	08 10	08 20	08 30	08 40	08 50	09 11	09 21	09 32	09 37	09 52	10 07	10 22	10 37	10 52	11 07	11 22

		GW	GW	GW	GW	GW	GW	GW	GW	GW	GW	GW	GW	GW	GW	GW	GW	GW	GW	GW	GW	GW
Witney Market Place	d	10 55	11 10	11 25	11 40	11 55	12 10	12 25	12 40	12 55	13 10	13 25	13 40	13 55	14 10	14 25	14 40	14 55	15 10	15 25	15 40	16 00
Eynsham Witney Road	d	11 09	11 24	11 39	11 54	12 09	12 24	12 39	12 54	13 09	13 24	13 39	13 54	14 09	14 24	14 39	14 54	15 09	15 24	15 39	15 54	16 14
Oxford	a	11 37	11 52	12 07	12 22	12 37	12 52	13 07	13 22	13 37	13 52	14 07	14 22	14 37	14 52	15 07	15 22	15 37	15 52	16 07	16 22	16 42

		GW	GW	GW	GW	GW	GW	GW	GW	GW	GW	GW	GW	GW	GW	GW	GW	GW	GW	GW	GW	GW
Witney Market Place	d	16 10	16 30	16 50	17 10	17 21	17 34	17 56	18 22	18 52	19 00	19 35	20 04	20 12	20 34	20 40	21 04	21 44	22 24	23 04	23 34	23 34
Eynsham Witney Road	d	16 24	16 44	17 04	17 24	17 35	17 48	18 10	18 38	19 08	19 16	19 50	20 19	20 28	20 49	20 55	21 18	21 58	22 38	23 18	23 48	23 48
Oxford	a	16 52	17 12	17 32	17 52	18 03	18 16	18 38	19 03	19 33	19 41	20 11	20 40	20 53	21 10	21 19	21 40	22 20	23 00	23 40	00 10	00 10

Saturdays

		GW	GW	GW	GW	GW	GW	GW	GW	GW	GW	GW	GW	GW	GW	GW	GW	GW	GW
Witney Market Place	d	05 52	06 42	07 12	07 32	07 53	08 10	08 25	08 40	08 55	09 10	09 25	09 40	09 55	10 10	10 25	10 40	10 55	11 10
Eynsham Witney Road	d	06 01	06 51	07 21	07 45	08 07	08 24	08 39	08 54	09 09	09 24	09 39	09 54	10 09	10 24	10 39	10 54	11 09	11 24
Oxford	a	06 25	07 15	07 45	08 09	08 31	08 52	09 07	09 22	09 37	09 52	10 07	10 22	10 37	10 52	11 07	11 22	11 37	11 52

		GW	GW	GW	GW	GW	GW	GW	GW	GW	GW	GW	GW	GW	GW	GW	GW	GW	GW
Witney Market Place	d	11 25	11 40	11 55	12 10	12 25	12 40	12 55	13 10	13 25	13 40	13 55	14 10	14 25	14 40	14 55	15 10	15 25	15 40
Eynsham Witney Road	d	11 39	11 54	12 09	12 24	12 39	12 54	13 09	13 24	13 39	13 54	14 09	14 24	14 39	14 54	15 09	15 24	15 39	15 54
Oxford	a	12 07	12 22	12 37	12 52	13 07	13 22	13 37	13 52	14 07	14 22	14 37	14 52	15 07	15 22	15 37	15 52	16 07	16 22

		GW	GW	GW	GW	GW	GW	GW	GW	GW	GW	GW	GW	GW	GW	GW	GW	GW	GW	GW
Witney Market Place	d	15 55	16 10	16 25	16 40	16 55	17 15	17 35	17 58	18 25	18 52	19 00	19 38	20 12	20 40	21 04	21 44	22 24	23 04	23 34
Eynsham Witney Road	d	16 09	16 24	16 39	16 54	17 09	17 29	17 49	18 12	18 41	19 08	19 16	19 54	20 29	20 55	21 18	21 58	22 38	23 18	23 48
Oxford	a	16 37	16 52	17 07	17 22	17 37	17 57	18 17	18 40	19 06	19 33	19 41	20 19	20 53	21 19	21 40	22 20	23 00	23 40	00 10

Sundays

		GW	GW	GW	GW	GW	GW	GW	GW	GW	GW	GW	GW	GW	GW	GW	GW	GW	GW	GW	GW	GW	GW	GW	GW	GW
Witney Market Place	d	07 35	08 35	09 35	10 35	11 05	11 35	12 05	12 35	13 05	13 35	14 05	14 35	15 05	15 35	16 05	16 35	17 05	17 35	18 05	18 35	19 35	20 35	21 35	22 35	23 34
Eynsham Witney Road	d	07 51	08 51	09 51	10 51	11 21	11 51	12 21	12 51	13 21	13 51	14 21	14 51	15 21	15 51	16 21	16 51	17 21	17 51	18 21	18 51	19 51	20 51	21 51	22 51	23 48
Oxford	a	08 08	09 08	10 08	11 08	11 38	12 08	12 38	13 08	13 38	14 08	14 38	15 08	15 38	16 08	16 38	17 08	17 38	18 08	18 38	19 08	20 08	21 08	22 08	23 08	00 10

For general notes see front of timetable
For details of catering facilities see
Directory of Train Operators

London → Greenford and Reading
(Local services only)

Network Diagram - see first page of Table 116

Miles	Miles	Miles				GW MX 1	GW MX 1	GW MO 1 ◇ A	GW MO 1	GW MX 1	GW MX 1 ◇	GW MO 1	GW MX 1	GW 1	GW 1	HC	HC	GW 1 ◇	GW 1 B	GW 1 ◇	GW 1 B	HC	GW 1	GW 1 ◇	GW 1
0	0	0	**London Paddington 15**	⊖ d	23 15		23p29	23p47	23p53	23 48	00 21	00 34	00 34	01 34	03 34	04 42	05 13	05 16	05 22	05 30		05 33	05 37	05 42	05 45
4¼	4¼	4¼	Acton Main Line	d						23 54															05 51
5¾	5¾	5¾	**Ealing Broadway**	⊖ d	23 24		23p37	23p55	00 02	23 58		00 42	00 42	01 42	03 42	04 50	05 21		05 30			05 41	05 50		05 54
6½	6½	6½	West Ealing	d						00 01												05 43			05 57
—	7¼	—	Drayton Green	d																					05 59
—	7½	—	Castle Bar Park	d																					06 01
—	8¼	—	South Greenford	d																					06 04
—	9¼	—	**Greenford**	⊖ a																					06 09
7¼	—	7¼	Hanwell	d						00 03												05 45			
9	—	9	Southall	d	23 29				00 07	00 07		00 47	00 47	01 47	03 48	04 54	05 25		05 36		←	05 49	05 55		
10¾	—	10¾	Hayes & Harlington	d	23 33		23p44		00 11	00 12		00 51	00 51	01 51	03 52	04 58	05 29		05 42 →		05 42	05 53	08 02		
—	—	14¾	**Heathrow Terminals 1-2-3 2**	✈ a												05 04	05 35					05 59			
—	—	16½	**Heathrow Terminal 4**	✈ a												05 10	05 41					06 10			
—	—	—	**Heathrow Terminal 5**	✈ a												*05b33*	*05b46*					*06b16*			
13¼	—	—	West Drayton	d					00 15	00 16		00 55	00 55	01 55	03 56						05 46		06 06 →		
14¾	—	—	Iver	d						00 19											05 49				
16¼	—	—	Langley	d					00 20	00 22		01 00	01 00								05 52				
18½	—	—	**Slough 3**	a			23p53	00 07	00 24	00 28	00 40	01 05	01 05	02 04	04 04			05 33		05 48	05 57			06 04	
—	—	—		d			23p54	00 08	00 24	00 28	00 40	01 05	01 05	02 04	04 05			05 34		05 49	05 57			06 04	
21	—	—	Burnham	d					00 28	00 32		01 09	01 09												
22½	—	—	Taplow	d						00 35			01 13												
24¼	—	—	**Maidenhead 3**	d			00 01	00 15	00 34	00 40		01 15	01 16	02 11	04 12						06 04 →				
31	—	—	**Twyford 3**	d		00 07	00 09		00 42	00 49		01 23	01 24	02 19	04 20										
36	—	—	**Reading 7**	a		00 17	00 19	00 28	00 49	00 58	01 00	01 32	01 33	02 29	04 30			05 51		06 05				06 20	
—	—	—	Oxford	a			01 06	00 59			01 34							06 22						06 53	

		GW 1 B	GW 1	GW 1 ◇	GW 1	GW 1	HC	GW 1	GW 1	GW 1	GW 1 ◇	GW 1	GW 1	HC	GW 1	GW 1	GW 1		GW 1	HC	GW 1	GW 1	GW 1 ◇	GW 1	GW 1
London Paddington 15	⊖ d		05 57	05 58			06 03	06 12	06 15	06 27	06 33			06 33	06 42	06 45	06 48		06 57	07 03	07 12	07 15	07 22		
Acton Main Line	d								06 21							06 51						07 21			
Ealing Broadway	⊖ d		06 05				06 11	06 20	06 24	06 35				06 41	06 50	06 54			07 05	07 11	07 20	07 24			
West Ealing	d						06 13		06 27					06 43		06 57				07 13		07 27			
Drayton Green	d								06 29							06 59						07 29			
Castle Bar Park	d								06 31							07 01						07 31			
South Greenford	d								06 34							07 04						07 34			
Greenford	⊖ a								06 41							07 09						07 39			
Hanwell	d						06 15							06 45						07 15					←
Southall	d		06 10			←	06 19	06 25						06 49	06 55				07 10	07 19	07 25 →				07 25
Hayes & Harlington	d		06 14 →			06 14	06 23	06 32		06 42				06 53	07 02				07 14	07 23					07 32
Heathrow Terminals 1-2-3 2	✈ a						06 29							06 59						07 29					
Heathrow Terminal 4	✈ a						06 40							07 10						07 40					
Heathrow Terminal 5	✈ a				←		*06b46*						←	*07b16*				←		*07b46*					
West Drayton	d				06 06	06 18		06 40		06 46 →			06 46		07 06 →			07 06	07 18						07 36
Iver	d					06 21							06 49						07 21						
Langley	d					06 25							06 52						07 25						
Slough 3	a			06 13	06 13	06 29		06 47			06 48		06 57				07 04	07 13	07 29				07 37		07 43
	d			06 13	06 13	06 29		06 47			06 48		06 57				07 04	07 13	07 29				07 37		07 43
Burnham	d				06 17			06 51				←						07 17							07 47
Taplow	d	←			06 21			06 54 →				06 54						07 21						←	07 51
Maidenhead 3	d	06 04			06 25	06 37						06 58	07 04					07 25	07 37 →					07 37	07 55
Twyford 3	d	06 12			06 33	06 45						07 06	07 12					07 33						07 45	08 03
Reading 7	a	06 21		06 28	06 44	06 53					07 03	07 15	07 25				07 20	07 41					07 52	07 53	08 11
Oxford	a	07 20		06 59	*07 34*	07 53					07 39	*08c00*	*08 04*				08 00						08 19	08 42	

		GW 1	HC	GW 1	GW 1	GW 1 ◇	GW 1		GW 1	GW 1	HC	GW 1	GW 1	GW 1	GW 1	GW 1 ◇	GW 1	GW 1	GW 1	HC	GW 1	GW 1	GW 1	GW 1 ◇	GW 1
London Paddington 15	⊖ d	07 27	07 33	07 42	07 45	07 52				07 57	08 03	08 05		08 12	08 15	08 22			08 27	08 33	08 38	08 42	08 45	08 51	
Acton Main Line	d				07 51										08 21								08 51		
Ealing Broadway	⊖ d	07 35	07 41	07 50	07 54					08 05	08 11			08 20	08 24				08 35	08 41	08 46	08 50	08 54		
West Ealing	d		07 43		07 57						08 13				08 27					08 43		08 52	08 57		
Drayton Green	d				07 59										08 29								08 59		
Castle Bar Park	d				08 01										08 31								09 01		
South Greenford	d				08 04										08 34								09 04		
Greenford	⊖ a				08 09										08 39								09 09		
Hanwell	d		07 45						←		08 15							←		08 45		08 55			
Southall	d	07 40	07 49	07 55 →					07 55	08 10	08 19		←	08 25 →				08 25	08 40	08 49	08 52	08 59 →			
Hayes & Harlington	d	07 44	07 53						08 02	08 14 →	08 23		08 14					08 32	08 44	08 53	08 56				
Heathrow Terminals 1-2-3 2	✈ a		07 59								08 29									08 59					
Heathrow Terminal 4	✈ a		08 10								08 40									09 10					
Heathrow Terminal 5	✈ a		*08b16*								*08b46*									*09b16*					
West Drayton	d	07 48							08 06				08 18					08 36	08 48						
Iver	d	07 51											08 21						08 51						
Langley	d	07 55											08 25						08 55						
Slough 3	a	07 59				08 06			08 13			08 25	08 29			08 37		08 43	08 59		09 05			09 06	
	d	07 59				08 06			08 13			08 26	08 29			08 37		08 43	08 59		09 05			09 06	
Burnham	d								08 17									08 47			09 09				
Taplow	d						←		08 21								←	08 51			09 12 →				←
Maidenhead 3	d	08 07 →					08 07		08 25			08 34	08 37 →				08 37	08 55	09 06 →						09 06
Twyford 3	d						08 15		08 33			08 42					08 45	09 03							09 16
Reading 7	a					08 21	08 23		08 42			08 52				08 52	08 53	09 11						09 21	09 23
Oxford	a					08 48	09 16					*09 34*				09 20	09 40							09 52	10 14

For general notes see front of timetable
For details of catering facilities see Directory of Train Operators
For fast services between London Paddington and Reading see Table 116

A From 14 September
B To Bicester Town (Table 116)
b Change at Heathrow Terminals 1-2-3
c Change at Reading and Didcot Parkway

London → Greenford and Reading

(Local services only)

Network Diagram - see first page of Table 116

		GW 1	GW 1	GW 1	HC	GW 1	GW 1	GW 1 ◇	GW 1	GW 1	HC	GW 1	GW 1	GW 1 ◇	GW 1	GW 1	GW 1	HC	GW 1	GW 1	GW 1 ◇	GW 1	GW 1	HC	GW 1
London Paddington 15 ⊖	d			08 57	09 03	09 12	09 15	09 21		09 27	09 33	09 42	09 45	09 50			09 57	10 03	10 12	10 15	10 22		10 27	10 33	10 42
Acton Main Line	d						09 21						09 51							10 21					
Ealing Broadway ⊖	d			09 05	09 11	09 20	09 24			09 35	09 41	09 50	09 54				10 05	10 11	10 20	10 24			10 35	10 41	10 50
West Ealing	d				09 13		09 27				09 43		09 57					10 13		10 27				10 43	
Drayton Green	d						09 29						09 59							10 29					
Castle Bar Park	d						09 31						10 01							10 31					
South Greenford	d						09 34						10 04							10 34					
Greenford ⊖	a						09 39						10 09							10 39					
Hanwell	d		←		09 15						09 45					←		10 15				←		10 45	
Southall	d		08 59		09 19	09 25					09 49	09 55 →				09 55		10 19	10 25 →			10 25		10 49	10 55 →
Hayes & Harlington	d		09 02	09 12	09 23	09 32				09 42	09 53					10 02	10 12	10 23				10 32	10 42	10 53	
Heathrow Terminals 1-2-3 2 ✈	a				09 29						09 59							10 29						10 59	
Heathrow Terminal 4 ✈	a				09 40						10 10							10 40						11 10	
Heathrow Terminal 5 ✈	a				*09b46*				←		*10b16*							*10b46*						*11b16*	
West Drayton	d		09 06	09 16		09 36 →			09 36	09 46						10 06	10 16					10 36	10 46		
Iver	d		09 10	09 19						09 49							10 19						10 49		
Langley	d		09 13	09 22						09 52							10 22						10 52		
Slough 3	a		09 18	09 27				09 37	09 43	09 57				10 06		10 13	10 27				10 37	10 43	10 57		
	d		09 18	09 27				09 37	09 43	09 57				10 06		10 13	10 27				10 37	10 43	10 57		
Burnham	d	←							09 47							10 17						10 47			
Taplow	d	09 12							09 51						←	10 21						10 51			
Maidenhead 3	d	09 16	09 24	09 34					09 55	10 04 →					10 04	10 25	10 34					10 55	11 04 →		
Twyford 3	d	09 24	09a35	09 42					10 03						10 12	10 33	10 42					11 03			
Reading 7	a	09 35		09 52				09 52	10 17					10 21	10 22	10 43	10 52				10 52	11 11			
Oxford	a			10 40				10 18						10 48	11 14		11 40				11 18				

		GW 1	GW 1 ◇	GW 1	GW 1	GW 1	HC	GW 1	GW 1	GW 1 ◇	GW 1		GW 1	HC	GW 1	GW 1	GW 1 ◇	GW 1	GW 1	GW 1	HC	GW 1	GW 1	GW 1 ◇	GW 1
London Paddington 15 ⊖	d	10 45	10 51			10 57	11 03	11 12	11 15	11 22			11 27	11 33	11 42	11 45	11 50			11 57	12 03	12 12	12 15	12 22	
Acton Main Line	d	10 51							11 21							11 51							12 21		
Ealing Broadway ⊖	d	10 54				11 05	11 11	11 20	11 24				11 35	11 41	11 50	11 54				12 05	12 11	12 20	12 24		
West Ealing	d	10 57					11 13		11 27					11 43		11 57					12 13		12 27		
Drayton Green	d	10 59							11 29							11 59							12 29		
Castle Bar Park	d	11 01							11 31							12 01							12 31		
South Greenford	d	11 04							11 34							12 04							12 34		
Greenford ⊖	a	11 09							11 39							12 09							12 39		
Hanwell	d				←		11 15				←			11 45					←		12 15				←
Southall	d				10 55		11 19	11 25 →			11 25			11 49	11 55 →				11 55		12 19	12 25 →			12 25
Hayes & Harlington	d				11 02	11 12	11 23				11 32		11 42	11 53					12 02	12 12	12 23				12 32
Heathrow Terminals 1-2-3 2 ✈	a						11 29							11 59							12 29				
Heathrow Terminal 4 ✈	a						11 40							12 10							12 40				
Heathrow Terminal 5 ✈	a						*11b46*							*12b16*							*12b46*				
West Drayton	d				11 06	11 16					11 36		11 46						12 06	12 16					12 36
Iver	d					11 19							11 49							12 19					
Langley	d					11 22							11 52							12 22					
Slough 3	a		11 06		11 13	11 27				11 37	11 43		11 57				12 06		12 13	12 27				12 37	12 43
	d		11 06		11 13	11 27				11 37	11 43		11 57				12 06		12 13	12 27				12 37	12 43
Burnham	d				11 17						11 47								12 17						12 47
Taplow	d			←	11 21						11 51							←	12 21						12 51
Maidenhead 3	d			11 04	11 25	11 34					11 55		12 04 →					12 04	12 25	12 34					12 55
Twyford 3	d			11 12	11 33	11 42					12 03							12 12	12 33	12 42					13 03
Reading 7	a		11 21	11 22	11 43	11 52				11 52	12 17						12 21	12 22	12 43	12 50				12 52	13 11
Oxford	a		11 52	12 12		12 40				12 18	*13 04*						12 48	13 12		13 40				13 19	

		GW 1	HC	GW 1	GW 1	GW 1 ◇	GW 1	GW 1	GW 1	HC	GW 1	GW 1	GW 1 ◇	GW 1	GW 1	HC	GW 1	GW 1	GW 1 ◇	GW 1	GW 1	HC	GW 1	GW 1	GW 1 ◇
London Paddington 15 ⊖	d	12 27	12 33	12 42	12 45	12 50			12 57	13 03	13 12	13 15	13 21		13 27	13 33	13 42	13 45	13 51		13 57	14 03	14 12	14 15	14 21
Acton Main Line	d				12 51							13 21						13 51						14 21	
Ealing Broadway ⊖	d	12 35	12 41	12 50	12 54				13 05	13 11	13 20	13 24			13 35	13 41	13 50	13 54			14 05	14 11	14 20	14 24	
West Ealing	d		12 43		12 57					13 13		13 27				13 43		13 57				14 13		14 27	
Drayton Green	d				12 59							13 29						13 59						14 29	
Castle Bar Park	d				13 01							13 31						14 01						14 31	
South Greenford	d				13 04							13 34						14 04						14 34	
Greenford ⊖	a				13 10							13 39						14 09						14 39	
Hanwell	d		12 45					←		13 15				←		13 45				←		14 15			
Southall	d		12 49	12 55 →				12 55		13 19	13 25 →			13 25		13 49	13 55 →			13 55		14 19	14 25 →		
Hayes & Harlington	d	12 42	12 53					13 02	13 12	13 23				13 32	13 42	13 53				14 02	14 12	14 23			
Heathrow Terminals 1-2-3 2 ✈	a		12 59							13 29						13 59						14 29			
Heathrow Terminal 4 ✈	a		13 10							13 40						14 10						14 40			
Heathrow Terminal 5 ✈	a		*13b16*							*13b46*						*14b16*						*14b46*			
West Drayton	d	12 46						13 06	13 16					13 36	13 46					14 06	14 16				
Iver	d	12 49							13 19						13 49						14 19				
Langley	d	12 52							13 22						13 52						14 22				
Slough 3	a	12 57				13 06		13 13	13 27				13 37	13 43	13 57				14 06	14 13	14 27				14 37
	d	12 57				13 06		13 13	13 27				13 37	13 43	13 57				14 06	14 13	14 27				14 37
Burnham	d							13 17						13 47						14 17					
Taplow	d						←	13 21						13 51						14 21					
Maidenhead 3	d	13 04 →					13 04	13 25	13 34					13 55	14 04					14 25	14 34				
Twyford 3	d						13 12	13 33	13 42					14 03	14 12					14 33	14 42				
Reading 7	a					13 21	13 22	13 43	13 52				13 52	14 17	14 21				14 21	14 43	14 52				14 52
Oxford	a					13 51	14 12		14 40				14 18	*15 04*	15 12				14 48		15 40				15 18

For general notes see front of timetable
For details of catering facilities see Directory of Train Operators

For fast services between London Paddington and Reading see Table 116

b Change at Heathrow Terminals 1-2-3

London → Greenford and Reading
(Local services only)

Network Diagram - see first page of Table 116

		GW	GW	HC	GW	GW	GW	GW	GW	GW	HC	GW	GW	GW	GW		GW	HC	GW	GW	GW	GW	GW	GW	HC
		1	1		1	1	1 ◇	1	1	1		1	1	1 ◇	1		1		1	1	1 ◇ ☕	1	1	1 A	
London Paddington 15 ⊖	d		14 27	14 33	14 42	14 45	14 50			14 57	15 03	15 12	15 15	15 22			15 27	15 33	15 42	15 45	15 51			15 57	16 03
Acton Main Line	d					14 51							15 21							15 51					
Ealing Broadway ⊖	d		14 35	14 41	14 50	14 54				15 05	15 11	15 20	15 24				15 35	15 41	15 50	15 54				16 05	16 11
West Ealing	d			14 43		14 57					15 13		15 27					15 43		15 57					16 13
Drayton Green	d					14 59							15 29							15 59					
Castle Bar Park	d					15 01							15 31							16 01					
South Greenford	d					15 04							15 34							16 04					
Greenford ⊖	a					15 09							15 39							16 09					
Hanwell	d	←		14 45					←		15 15							15 45							16 15
Southall	d	14 25		14 49	14 55				14 55		15 19	15 25			←		15 40	15 49	15 55				←	16 10	16 19
Hayes & Harlington	d	14 32	14 42	14 53	→				15 02	15 12	15 23	15 32			15 32		15 44	15 53	16 02				16 02	16 14	16 23
Heathrow Terminals 1-2-3 2 ✈	a			14 59							15 29	→						15 59	→						16 29
Heathrow Terminal 4 ✈	a			15 10							15 40							16 10							16 40
Heathrow Terminal 5 ✈	a			15b16							15b46							16b16							16b46
West Drayton	d	14 36	14 46						15 06	15 16					15 36		15 48						16 06	16 19	
Iver	d		14 49							15 19					15 39								16 09		
Langley	d		14 52							15 22					15 43								16 13		
Slough 3	a	14 43	14 57				15 06		15 13	15 27				15 37	15 47		15 55				16 06		16 17	16 26	
	d	14 43	14 57				15 06		15 13	15 27				15 37	15 47		15 55				16 06		16 17	16 26	
Burnham	d	14 47							15 17						15 51								16 21		
Taplow	d	14 51						←	15 21						15 55							←	16 25		
Maidenhead 3	d	14 55	15 04					15 04	15 25	15 34					15 59		16 03					16 03	16 29	16 33	
Twyford 3	d	15 03	→					15 12	15 33	15 42					16 07		→					16 11	16 37	16 41	
Reading 7	a	15 11					15 21	15 22	15 42	15 52				15 52	16 17						16 21	16 22	16 45	16 52	
Oxford	a						15 50	16 14		16 40				16 19	*17 04*						16 47	17 16		17 44	

		GW	GW	GW	GW	GW	GW	GW	HC	GW	GW	GW	HC	GW	GW	GW	GW	GW	GW	GW	GW	GW	GW	HC	GW
		1	1	1 ◇	1	1 ◇ ☕	1	1		1	1	1		1 ◇ B ☕	1	1	1 C	1	1	1	1	1 C	1 A		1
London Paddington 15 ⊖	d	16 12	16 15	16 22	16 27	16 33			16 33	16 42	16 45	16 57	17 03	17 06			17 12	17 15	17 18	17 18			17 25	17 33	17 36
Acton Main Line	d		16 21								16 51									17 24					
Ealing Broadway ⊖	d	16 20	16 24		16 35				16 41	16 50	16 54	17 05	17 11					17 23		17 27			17 33	17 41	
West Ealing	d		16 27						16 43		16 57		17 13							17 30				17 43	
Drayton Green	d		16 29								16 59									17 32					
Castle Bar Park	d		16 31								17 01									17 34					
South Greenford	d		16 34								17 04									17 37					
Greenford ⊖	a		16 39								17 09									17 42					
Hanwell	d							←	16 45				17 15											17 45	
Southall	d	16 25			16 40		←	16 40	16 49	16 55		17 10	17 19					17 28					17 38	17 49	
Hayes & Harlington	d	16 32			→		16 32	16 44	16 53	17 02		17 14	17 23					17 32					17 42	17 53	
Heathrow Terminals 1-2-3 2 ✈	a	→							16 59				17 29											17 59	
Heathrow Terminal 4 ✈	a								17 10				17 40											18 10	
Heathrow Terminal 5 ✈	a								17b16				17b46											18b16	
West Drayton	d						16 37			17 07		17 19				←		17 37					17 47		
Iver	d						16 40			17 10		17 22				17 22		17 40					17 50		
Langley	d						16 44			19 14		→				17 26		17 44					→		
Slough 3	a			16 37		16 48	16 48	16 53		17 18					←	17 30	17 35	→				←			
	d			16 37		16 48	16 48	16 53		17 18					17 18	17 30	17 36					17 36			
Burnham	d						16 52			→					17 22	17 34	→				←				
Taplow	d						16 56								17 26	17 38					17 38				
Maidenhead 3	d						17 00	17 04							17 30	→			17 39		17 43	17 48			17 59
Twyford 3	d						17 08	17 12						17 28	17 38				17 47		17 51	17a58			18 08
Reading 7	a			16 52		17 03	17 16	17 22						17 36	17 46				17 55		18 00				18 16
Oxford	a			17 23		*17 34*	*18 04*	18 11						*18 15*					18 45		*18 34*				19 02

		GW	GW	GW	GW	GW	GW	HC	GW	GW	GW	GW	GW	GW	GW	GW	GW	GW	GW		GW	GW	HC	GW	GW
		1	1 A	1 D	1	1	1		1 ◇ E ☕	1	1	1 C	1	1	1	1	1 C	1	1		1	1		1	1 D
London Paddington 15 ⊖	d			17 42	17 45	17 48	17 57	18 03	18 06			18 12	18 15	18 18	18 18			18 25	18 33				18 33		18 42
Acton Main Line	d					17 54									18 24										
Ealing Broadway ⊖	d				17 53	17 57	18 05	18 11					18 23		18 27			18 33					18 41		
West Ealing	d					18 00		18 13							18 30								18 43		
Drayton Green	d					18 02									18 32										
Castle Bar Park	d					18 04									18 34										
South Greenford	d					18 07									18 37										
Greenford ⊖	a					18 12									18 42										
Hanwell	d							18 15															18 45		
Southall	d				17 58		18 10	18 19					18 28					18 38					18 49		
Hayes & Harlington	d				18 02		18 14	18 23					18 32					18 42					18 53		
Heathrow Terminals 1-2-3 2 ✈	a							18 29															18 59		
Heathrow Terminal 4 ✈	a							18 40															19 10		
Heathrow Terminal 5 ✈	a							18b46		←													19b16		
West Drayton	d		←		18 07		18 19			18 07	←		18 37					18 47				←			
Iver	d	←	17 50		→		18 22				18 22							18 50			←	18 50			
Langley	d	17 44	17 54				→			18 12	18 26		18 42					→			18 42	18 54			
Slough 3	a	17 49	17 58	18 05						18 16	18 30	18 35	→				←				18 46	18 58			19 05
	d	17 49	17 58	18 05						18 16	18 30	18 36					18 36				18 46	18 58			19 05
Burnham	d	17 53	18 02							18 20	18 34	→				←					18 50	19 02		←	
Taplow	d	17 56	18 06								18 38					18 38						19 06		19 06	
Maidenhead 3	d	18a05	18 10	18a18						18 26	→			18 39		18 43	18 48		18 53		18 57	→		19 10	19a18
Twyford 3	d		18 17						18 28	18 34				18 47		18 51	18a58		19 03		19 07			19 18	
Reading 7	a		18 26						18 36	18 43				18 55		19 00			19 12		19 15			→	
Oxford	a		19 14							*19 18*				19 45		*19 34*			20 14						

For general notes see front of timetable
For details of catering facilities see Directory of Train Operators

For fast services between London Paddington and Reading see Table 116

- **A** To Banbury (Table 116)
- **B** To Westbury (Table 135)
- **C** To Henley-on-Thames (Table 121)
- **D** To Bourne End (Table 120)
- **E** To Frome (Table 123)
- **b** Change at Heathrow Terminals 1-2-3

London → Greenford and Reading

(Local services only)

Network Diagram - see first page of Table 116

Station		GW	GW	GW	GW	GW	GW	HC	GW	GW	GW	GW	GW	GW	GW	GW	GW	GW	HC	GW	GW	GW	GW	GW	GW
		1	1	1 ◇	1	1	1		1	1	1	1	1	1 ◇	1	1	1	1		1	1	1 ◇	1	1	1
									A					☕											
London Paddington 15 ⊖	d	18 45	18 48	18 51			18 57	19 03	19 06	19 12	19 15	19 18		19 22				19 27	19 33	19 42	19 45	19 50			19 57
Acton Main Line	d		18 54								19 21										19 51				
Ealing Broadway ⊖	d	18 53	18 57				19 05	19 11		19 20	19 24							19 35	19 41	19 50	19 54				20 05
West Ealing	d		19 00					19 13			19 27								19 43		19 57				
Drayton Green	d		19 02								19 29										19 59				
Castle Bar Park	d		19 04								19 31										20 01				
South Greenford	d		19 07								19 34										20 04				
Greenford ⊖	a		19 12								19 39										20 09				
Hanwell	d					←		19 15											19 45						
Southall	d	18 58				18 58	19 10	19 19		19 25							←	19 40	19 49	19 55				←	
Hayes & Harlington	d	→				19 02	19 14	19 23		19 32							19 32	19 44	19 53	20 02				20 02	20 12
Heathrow Terminals 1-2-3 2 ✈	a							19 29		→									19 59	→					
Heathrow Terminal 4 ✈	a							19 40											20 10						
Heathrow Terminal 5 ✈	a							19b46											20b16						
West Drayton	d						19 19						←					19 48						20 06	20 16
Iver	d						19 22						19 22					19 51						20 09	20 19
Langley	d						→						19 26					19 55						20 13	20 22
Slough 3	a			19 06		19 11							19 30	19 37			19 41	19 59				20 06		20 17	20 27
	d			19 06		19 11							19 30	19 37			19 41	19 59				20 06		20 17	20 27
Burnham	d					19 15							19 34			←	19 45	20 03						20 21	
Taplow	d												19 38		←	19 38	19 48						←	20 25	
Maidenhead 3	d				←	19 21			19 28			19 39	→		19 39	19 43	19 52	20 09					20 09	20 29	20 34
Twyford 3	d				19 18	19c36			19a38			→			19 47	19 51	20 00	→					20 17	20 37	→
Reading 7	a			19 21	19 26	19 45								19 52	19 55	20 00	20 09					20 21	20 25	20 45	
Oxford	a			19 50	20 26									20 21	20 45	20 34						20 49	21 12	21 34	

Station		HC	GW	GW	GW	GW	GW	GW	HC	GW	GW	GW	GW	GW	HC	GW	GW	GW	GW	GW	HC	GW	GW	GW	GW
																							FO		FX
			1	1	1 ◇	1	1	1		1	1	1 ◇	1	1		1	1	1 ◇	1	1		1	1 ◇	1	1 ◇
																							B		C
					☕																		☕		☕
London Paddington 15 ⊖	d	20 03	20 12	20 15	20 20			20 27	20 33	20 42	20 45	20 51		20 57	21 03	21 12	21 15	21 21		21 27	21 33	21 42	21 48		21 48
Acton Main Line	d			20 21							20 51						21 21								
Ealing Broadway ⊖	d	20 11	20 20	20 24				20 35	20 41	20 50	20 54			21 05	21 11	21 20	21 24			21 35	21 41	21 50			
West Ealing	d	20 13		20 27					20 43		20 57				21 13		21 27				21 43				
Drayton Green	d			20 29							20 59						21 29								
Castle Bar Park	d			20 31							21 01						21 31								
South Greenford	d			20 34							21 04						21 34								
Greenford ⊖	a			20 39							21 09						21 39								
Hanwell	d	20 15					←		20 45				←		21 15				←		21 45				
Southall	d	20 19	20 25				20 25		20 49	20 55			20 55		21 19	21 25			21 25		21 49	21 55			
Hayes & Harlington	d	20 23	→				20 32	20 42	20 53	→			21 02	21 12	21 23	→			21 32	21 42	21 53	22 02			
Heathrow Terminals 1-2-3 2 ✈	a	20 29							20 59						21 29						21 59	→			
Heathrow Terminal 4 ✈	a	20 40							21 10						21 40						22 10				
Heathrow Terminal 5 ✈	a	20b46							21b16						21b46						22b16				
West Drayton	d						20 36	20 46					21 06	21 16					21 36	21 46					
Iver	d							20 49						21 19											
Langley	d							20 52						21 22											
Slough 3	a				20 35		20 43	20 57				21 07	21 13	21 27				21 37	21 43	21 54			22 03		22 03
	d				20 35		20 43	20 57				21 07	21 13	21 27				21 37	21 43	21 54			22 03		22 03
Burnham	d						20 47						21 17						21 47						
Taplow	d					←	20 51						21 21						21 51					←	
Maidenhead 3	d					20 34	20 55	21 04					21 25	21 34					21 55	22 01				22 01	
Twyford 3	d					20 42	21 03	21 12					21 33	21 42					22 03	→				22 09	
Reading 7	a				20 50	20 52	21 11	21 20				21 23	21 43	21 51				21 53	22 11				22 19	22 20	22 23
Oxford	a				21 16	21 40		22 15				21 53		22 39				22 24					22 51	23 15	22 51

Station		GW	GW	HC	GW	GW	GW	GW	GW	GW	GW	HC	GW	GW	GW	GW	GW	HC	GW	GW	GW	GW	GW		
					FX	FO	FO		FX	FX	FO			FO	FX				FO		FX				
		1	1		1	1	1 ◇	1	1 ◇	1	1		1	1 ◇	1 ◇	1	1		1 ◇	1	1 ◇	1	1		
London Paddington 15 ⊖	d		21 57	22 03	22 10	22 10	22 21		22 21			22 33	22 45	22 48	22 48		22 59	23 03	23 20		23 20	23 29	23 48		
Acton Main Line	d												22 51			←							23 54		
Ealing Broadway ⊖	d		22 05	22 11	22 18	22 18						22 41	22 54			22 54	23 07	23 11				23 37	23 58		
West Ealing	d			22 13								22 43	→					23 13					00 01		
Drayton Green	d																								
Castle Bar Park	d																								
South Greenford	d																								
Greenford ⊖	a																								
Hanwell	d			22 15								22 45						23 15					00 03		
Southall	d	←		22 19	22 23	22 23					←	22 49					23 12	23 19					00 07		
Hayes & Harlington	d	22 02	22 12	22 23	22 27	22 27					22 27	22 53				23 02	23 18	23 23				23 44	00 12		
Heathrow Terminals 1-2-3 2 ✈	a			22 29		→						22 59						23 29							
Heathrow Terminal 4 ✈	a			22 40								23 10						23 40							
Heathrow Terminal 5 ✈	a			22b46								23b16						23b46							
West Drayton	d	22 06	22 16		22 31						22 31						23 22						00 16		
Iver	d	22 09	22 19								22 34						23 25						00 19		
Langley	d	22 13	22 22								22 38						23 28						00 22		
Slough 3	a	22 18	22 28		22 39		22 37		22 42	←	22 43			23 06	23 06	23 12	23 34		23 36		23 38	23 53	00 28		
	d	22 18	22 33		22 45		22 37		22 42	22 45	22 45			23 06	23 06	23 12	23 34		23 39		23 39	23 54	00 28		
Burnham	d	22 22			→					22 49	22 49					23 16							00 32		
Taplow	d	22 26						←		22 52	22 52					23 19				←			00 35		
Maidenhead 3	d	22 30	22 41					22 41		22 56	22 56					23 23	23 41			23 41		00 01	00 40		
Twyford 3	d	22 38	→					22 49		23 04	23 04					23 31	→			23 49		00 09	00 49		
Reading 7	a	22 46					22 53	22 58	23 06	23 14	23 14			23 21	23 34	23 40			23 54	23 58	00 04	00 19	00 58		
Oxford	a	23 39					23 26	23 44	23 39					23 49	00 13	00 23			00 29		00 34	01 06			

For general notes see front of timetable
For details of catering facilities see Directory of Train Operators

For fast services between London Paddington and Reading see Table 116

A To Henley-on-Thames (Table 121)
B ☕ until 4 September
C ☕ until 3 September
b Change at Heathrow Terminals 1-2-3
c Arr. 1929

London → Greenford and Reading
(Local services only)

Network Diagram - see first page of Table 116

		GW 1	GW 1	GW 1	GW 1 ◇	GW 1	GW 1	GW 1	GW 1	HC	HC	GW ◇	GW 1	HC	GW 1	GW 1 ◇		GW 1	HC	GW 1	GW 1	GW ◇ (catering)	GW 1	GW 1	GW 1
London Paddington 15 ⊖	d		23p29	23p48	00 21		00 34	01 44	03 34	04 42	05 13	05 21	05 25	05 33	05 45	05 50		05 57	06 03	06 12	06 15	06 21			06 27
Acton Main Line	d			23p54											05 51						06 21				
Ealing Broadway ⊖	d		23p37	23p58			00 42	01 52	03 42	04 50	05 21		05 33	05 41	05 54			06 05	06 11	06 20	06 24				06 35
West Ealing	d			00 01										05 43	05 57				06 13		06 27				
Drayton Green	d														05 59						06 29				
Castle Bar Park	d														06 01						06 31				
South Greenford	d														06 04						06 34				
Greenford ⊖	a														06 09						06 39				
Hanwell	d			00 03										05 45					06 15					←	
Southall	d			00 07			00 47	01 57	03 47	04 54	05 25		05 38	05 49				06 10	06 19	06 25				06 25	
Hayes & Harlington	d		23p44	00 12			00 51	02 01	03 51	04 58	05 29		05 42	05 53				06 15	06 23	→				06 32	06 42
Heathrow Terminals 1-2-3 2 ✈	a									05 04	05 35			05 59					06 29						
Heathrow Terminal 4 ✈	a									05 10	05 41			06 10					06 40						
Heathrow Terminal 5 ✈	a									*05b33*	*05b46*			*06b16*					*06b46*						
West Drayton	d			00 16			00 55	02 05	03 55									06 19						06 36	06 46
Iver	d			00 19														06 22							06 49
Langley	d			00 22			01 00											06 25							06 52
Slough 3	a		23p53	00 28	00 38		01 05	02 13	04 03			05 37	05 50			06 06		06 30				06 36		06 42	06 57
	d		23p54	00 28	00 39		01 05	02 13	04 03			05 37	05 51			06 07		06 31				06 37		06 43	06 57
Burnham	d			00 32		←	01 09						05 55					06 35					←	06 47	
Taplow	d			00 35		00 35	01 13						05 58					06 38					06 38	06 51	
Maidenhead 3	d		00 01	→		00 40	01 16	02 21	04 11				06 02					→					06 42	06 55	07 04
Twyford 3	d	00 07	00 09			00 49	01 24	02 29	04 19				06 10										06 50	07 03	07 12
Reading 7	a	00 17	00 19		00 55	00 58	01 33	02 38	04 30			05 52	06 17			06 22						06 51	06 56	07 11	07 20
Oxford	a		01 06		01 30							06 23	07 03			06 51						07 18	07 43		08 09

		HC	GW 1	GW 1	GW 1 ◇	GW 1	GW 1	HC	GW 1	GW 1		GW 1 ◇ (catering)	GW 1	GW 1	HC	GW 1	GW 1	GW 1 ◇	GW 1	GW 1	HC	GW 1	GW 1	GW 1 ◇ (catering)	GW 1
London Paddington 15 ⊖	d	06 33	06 42	06 45	06 50		06 57	07 03	07 12	07 15		07 21		07 27	07 33	07 42	07 45	07 50		07 57	08 03	08 12	08 15	08 21	
Acton Main Line	d			06 51						07 21							07 51						08 21		
Ealing Broadway ⊖	d	06 41	06 50	06 54			07 05	07 11	07 20	07 24				07 35	07 41	07 50	07 54			08 05	08 11	08 20	08 24		
West Ealing	d	06 43		06 57				07 13		07 27					07 43		07 57				08 13		08 27		
Drayton Green	d			06 59						07 29							07 59						08 29		
Castle Bar Park	d			07 01						07 31							08 01						08 31		
South Greenford	d			07 04						07 34							08 04						08 34		
Greenford ⊖	a			07 09						07 39							08 09						08 39		
Hanwell	d	06 45				←		07 15					←		07 45				←		08 15				←
Southall	d	06 49	06 55			06 55		07 19	07 25				07 25		07 49	07 55			07 55		08 19	08 25			08 25
Hayes & Harlington	d	06 53	→			07 02	07 12	07 23	→				07 32	07 42	07 53	→			08 02	08 12	08 23	→			08 32
Heathrow Terminals 1-2-3 2 ✈	a	06 59						07 29							07 59						08 29				
Heathrow Terminal 4 ✈	a	07 10						07 40							08 10						08 40				
Heathrow Terminal 5 ✈	a	*07b16*						*07b46*							*08b16*						*08b46*				
West Drayton	d					07 06	07 16						07 36	07 46					08 06	08 16					08 36
Iver	d						07 19							07 49						08 19					
Langley	d						07 22							07 52						08 22					
Slough 3	a				07 06	07 13	07 27					07 36	07 42	07 57				08 06	08 13	08 27				08 38	08 42
	d				07 07	07 13	07 27					07 37	07 43	07 57				08 07	08 13	08 27				08 39	08 43
Burnham	d					07 17							07 47						08 17						08 47
Taplow	d					07 21							07 51						08 21						08 51
Maidenhead 3	d					07 25	07 34						07 55	08 04					08 25	08 34					08 55
Twyford 3	d					07 33	07 42						08 03	08 12					08 33	08 42					09 03
Reading 7	a				07 22	07 43	07 51					07 51	08 11	08 20				08 22	08 43	08 51				08 53	09 11
Oxford	a				07 48		08 40					08 19		09 14				08 48		09 40				09 18	

		GW 1	HC	GW 1		GW 1	GW 1 ◇	GW 1	GW 1	HC	GW 1	GW 1	GW 1 ◇	GW 1	GW 1	HC	GW 1	GW 1	GW 1 ◇	GW 1		GW 1	HC	GW 1	GW 1
London Paddington 15 ⊖	d	08 27	08 33	08 42		08 45	08 50		08 57	09 03	09 12	09 15	09 21		09 27	09 33	09 42	09 45	09 50			09 57	10 03	10 12	10 15
Acton Main Line	d					08 51						09 21						09 51							10 21
Ealing Broadway ⊖	d	08 35	08 41	08 50		08 54			09 05	09 11	09 20	09 24			09 35	09 41	09 50	09 54				10 05	10 11	10 20	10 24
West Ealing	d		08 43			08 57				09 13		09 27				09 43		09 57					10 13		10 27
Drayton Green	d					08 59						09 29						09 59							10 29
Castle Bar Park	d					09 01						09 31						10 01							10 31
South Greenford	d					09 04						09 34						10 04							10 34
Greenford ⊖	a					09 09						09 39						10 09							10 39
Hanwell	d		08 45					←		09 15				←		09 45				←			10 15		
Southall	d		08 49	08 55				08 55		09 19	09 25			09 25		09 49	09 55			09 55			10 19	10 25	
Hayes & Harlington	d	08 42	08 53	→				09 02	09 12	09 23	→			09 32	09 42	09 53	→			10 02		10 12	10 23	→	
Heathrow Terminals 1-2-3 2 ✈	a		08 59							09 29						09 59							10 29		
Heathrow Terminal 4 ✈	a		09 10							09 40						10 10							10 40		
Heathrow Terminal 5 ✈	a		*09b16*							*09b46*						*10b16*							*10b46*		
West Drayton	d	08 46						09 06	09 16					09 36	09 46					10 06		10 16			
Iver	d	08 49							09 19						09 49							10 19			
Langley	d	08 52							09 22						09 52							10 22			
Slough 3	a	08 57					09 06	09 13	09 27				09 38	09 42	09 57				10 06	10 13		10 27			
	d	08 57					09 07	09 13	09 27				09 39	09 43	09 57				10 07	10 13		10 27			
Burnham	d							09 17						09 47						10 17					
Taplow	d							09 21						09 51						10 21					
Maidenhead 3	d	09 04						09 25	09 34					09 55	10 04					10 25		10 34			
Twyford 3	d	09 12						09 33	09 42					10 03	10 12					10 33		10 42			
Reading 7	a	09 20					09 22	09 43	09 51				09 54	10 11	10 20				10 22	10 43		10 51			
Oxford	a	10 14					09 48		10 40				10 20		11 14				10 48			11 40			

For general notes see front of timetable
For details of catering facilities see Directory of Train Operators

For fast services between London Paddington and Reading see Table 116

b Change at Heathrow Terminals 1-2-3

London → Greenford and Reading
(Local services only)

Network Diagram - see first page of Table 116

		GW 1◇	GW 1	GW 1	HC	GW 1	GW 1	GW 1◇	GW 1	GW 1	HC	GW 1	GW 1	GW 1◇		GW 1	GW 1	HC	GW 1	GW 1	GW 1◇	GW 1	GW 1	HC	GW 1
																					A				
London Paddington 15 ⊖	d	10 21		10 27	10 33	10 42	10 45	10 50		10 57	11 03	11 12	11 15	11 21			11 27	11 33	11 42	11 45	11 50		11 57	12 03	12 12
Acton Main Line	d						10 51						11 21							11 51					
Ealing Broadway ⊖	d			10 35	10 41	10 50	10 54			11 05	11 11	11 20	11 24				11 35	11 41	11 50	11 54			12 05	12 11	12 20
West Ealing	d				10 43		10 57				11 13		11 27					11 43		11 57				12 13	
Drayton Green	d						10 59						11 29							11 59					
Castle Bar Park	d						11 01						11 31							12 01					
South Greenford	d						11 04						11 34							12 04					
Greenford ⊖	a						11 09						11 39							12 09					
Hanwell	d		←		10 45				←		11 15					←		11 45				←		12 15	
Southall	d		10 25		10 49	10 55 →			10 55		11 19	11 25 →				11 25		11 49	11 55 →			11 55		12 19	12 25 →
Hayes & Harlington	d		10 32	10 42	10 53				11 02	11 12	11 23					11 32	11 42	11 53				12 02	12 12	12 23	
Heathrow Terminals 1-2-3 2 ✈	a				10 59						11 29							11 59						12 29	
Heathrow Terminal 4 ✈	a				11 10						11 40							12 10						12 40	
Heathrow Terminal 5 ✈	a				11b16						11b46							12b16						12b46	
West Drayton	d		10 36	10 46					11 06	11 16						11 36	11 46					12 06	12 16		
Iver	d			10 49						11 19							11 49						12 19		
Langley	d			10 52						11 22							11 52						12 22		
Slough 3	a	10 38	10 42	10 57				11 06	11 13	11 27				11 38		11 42	11 57				12 06	12 13	12 27		
	d	10 39	10 43	10 57				11 07	11 13	11 27				11 39		11 43	11 57				12 07	12 13	12 27		
Burnham	d		10 47						11 17							11 47						12 17			
Taplow	d		10 51						11 21							11 51						12 21			
Maidenhead 3	d		10 55	11 04					11 25	11 34						11 55	12 04					12 25	12 34		
Twyford 3	d		11 03	11 12					11 33	11 42						12 03	12 12					12 33	12 42		
Reading 7	a	10 53	11 11	11 20				11 22	11 43	11 51				11 53		12 11	12 20				12 22	12 43	12 51		
Oxford	a	11 19		12 14				11 48		12 40				12 18		12 48	13 14				12 48		13 40		

		GW 1	GW 1◇	GW 1	GW 1	HC	GW 1	GW 1		GW 1◇	GW 1	GW 1	HC	GW 1	GW 1	GW 1◇	GW 1	GW 1	HC	GW 1	GW 1	GW 1◇	GW 1	GW 1	HC
			B																						
London Paddington 15 ⊖	d	12 15	12 21		12 27	12 33	12 42	12 45		12 50		12 57	13 03	13 12	13 15	13 21		13 27	13 33	13 42	13 45	13 50		13 57	14 03
Acton Main Line	d	12 21						12 51							13 21						13 51				
Ealing Broadway ⊖	d	12 24			12 35	12 41	12 50	12 54				13 05	13 11	13 20	13 24			13 35	13 41	13 50	13 54			14 05	14 11
West Ealing	d	12 27				12 43		12 57					13 13		13 27				13 43		13 57				14 13
Drayton Green	d	12 29						12 59							13 29						13 59				
Castle Bar Park	d	12 31						13 01							13 31						14 01				
South Greenford	d	12 34						13 04							13 34						14 04				
Greenford ⊖	a	12 39						13 09							13 39						14 09				
Hanwell	d			←		12 45					←		13 15				←		13 45				←		14 15
Southall	d			12 25		12 49	12 55 →				12 55		13 19	13 25 →			13 25		13 49	13 55 →			13 55		14 19
Hayes & Harlington	d			12 32	12 42	12 53					13 02	13 12	13 23				13 32	13 42	13 53				14 02	14 12	14 23
Heathrow Terminals 1-2-3 2 ✈	a					12 59							13 29						13 59						14 29
Heathrow Terminal 4 ✈	a					13 10							13 40						14 10						14 40
Heathrow Terminal 5 ✈	a					13b16							13b46						14b16						14b46
West Drayton	d			12 36	12 46						13 06	13 16					13 36	13 46					14 06	14 16	
Iver	d				12 49							13 19						13 49						14 19	
Langley	d				12 52							13 22						13 52						14 22	
Slough 3	a		12 38	12 42	12 57					13 06	13 13	13 27				13 38	13 42	13 57				14 06	14 13	14 27	
	d		12 39	12 43	12 57					13 07	13 13	13 27				13 39	13 43	13 57				14 07	14 13	14 27	
Burnham	d			12 47							13 17						13 47						14 17		
Taplow	d			12 51							13 21						13 51						14 21		
Maidenhead 3	d			12 55	13 04						13 25	13 34					13 55	14 04					14 25	14 34	
Twyford 3	d			13 03	13 12						13 33	13 42					14 03	14 12					14 33	14 42	
Reading 7	a		12 54	13 11	13 20					13 22	13 43	13 51				13 53	14 11	14 20				14 22	14 43	14 51	
Oxford	a		13 20		14 14					13 48		14 40				14 18		15 14				14 48		15 40	

		GW 1		GW 1	GW 1◇	GW 1	GW 1	HC	GW 1	GW 1	GW 1◇	GW 1	GW 1	HC	GW 1	GW 1	GW 1◇	GW 1		GW 1	HC	GW 1	GW 1	GW 1◇	GW 1
London Paddington 15 ⊖	d	14 12		14 15	14 21		14 27	14 33	14 42	14 45	14 50		14 57	15 03	15 12	15 15	15 21			15 27	15 33	15 42	15 45	15 50	
Acton Main Line	d			14 21						14 51						15 21							15 51		
Ealing Broadway ⊖	d	14 20		14 24			14 35	14 41	14 50	14 54			15 05	15 11	15 20	15 24				15 35	15 41	15 50	15 54		
West Ealing	d			14 27				14 43		14 57				15 13		15 27					15 43		15 57		
Drayton Green	d			14 29						14 59						15 29							15 59		
Castle Bar Park	d			14 31						15 01						15 31							16 01		
South Greenford	d			14 34						15 04						15 34							16 04		
Greenford ⊖	a			14 39						15 09						15 39							16 09		
Hanwell	d					←		14 45				←		15 15				←			15 45				←
Southall	d	14 25 →				14 25		14 49	14 55 →			14 55		15 19	15 25 →			15 25			15 49	15 55 →			15 55
Hayes & Harlington	d					14 32	14 42	14 53				15 02	15 12	15 23				15 32		15 42	15 53				16 02
Heathrow Terminals 1-2-3 2 ✈	a							14 59						15 29							15 59				
Heathrow Terminal 4 ✈	a							15 10						15 40							16 10				
Heathrow Terminal 5 ✈	a							15b16						15b46							16b16				
West Drayton	d					14 36	14 46					15 06	15 16					15 36		15 46					16 06
Iver	d						14 49						15 19							15 49					
Langley	d						14 52						15 22							15 52					
Slough 3	a				14 38	14 42	14 57				15 06	15 13	15 27				15 38	15 42		15 57				16 06	16 13
	d				14 39	14 43	14 57				15 07	15 13	15 27				15 39	15 43		15 57				16 07	16 13
Burnham	d					14 47						15 17						15 47							16 17
Taplow	d					14 51						15 21						15 51							16 21
Maidenhead 3	d					14 55	15 04					15 25	15 34					15 55		16 04					16 25
Twyford 3	d					15 03	15 12					15 33	15 42					16 03		16 12					16 33
Reading 7	a				14 53	15 11	15 20				15 22	15 43	15 51				15 53	16 11		16 20				16 22	16 43
Oxford	a				15 18		16 14				15 48		16 40				16 18			17 14				16 48	

For general notes see front of timetable
For details of catering facilities see Directory of Train Operators

For fast services between London Paddington and Reading see Table 116

A From 12 September
B Until 5 September
b Change at Heathrow Terminals 1-2-3

Table 117

London → Greenford and Reading

(Local services only)

Saturdays

Network Diagram - see first page of Table 116

	GW 1	HC	GW 1	GW 1	GW 1 ◇	GW 1	GW 1	HC	GW 1	GW 1	GW 1 ◇		GW 1	GW 1	HC	GW 1	GW 1	GW 1 ◇	GW 1	GW 1	HC	GW 1	GW 1	GW 1 ◇
London Paddington 15 ⊖ d	15 57	16 03	16 12	16 15	16 21		16 27	16 33	16 42	16 45	16 50			16 57	17 03	17 12	17 15	17 21		17 27	17 33	17 42	17 45	17 50
Acton Main Line d				16 21						16 51							17 21						17 51	
Ealing Broadway ⊖ d	16 05	16 11	16 20	16 24			16 35	16 41	16 50	16 54				17 05	17 11	17 20	17 24			17 35	17 41	17 50	17 54	
West Ealing d		16 13		16 27				16 43		16 57					17 13		17 27				17 43		17 57	
Drayton Green d				16 29						16 59							17 29						17 59	
Castle Bar Park d				16 31						17 01							17 31						18 01	
South Greenford d				16 34						17 04							17 34						18 04	
Greenford ⊖ a				16 39						17 09							17 39						18 09	
Hanwell d		16 15				←		16 45					←		17 15				←		17 45			
Southall d		16 19	16 25			16 25		16 49	16 55				16 55		17 19	17 25			17 25		17 49	17 55		
Hayes & Harlington d	16 12	16 23	→			16 32	16 42	16 53	→				17 02	17 12	17 23	→			17 32	17 42	17 53	→		
Heathrow Terminals 1-2-3 2 ✈ a		16 29						16 59							17 29						17 59			
Heathrow Terminal 4 ✈ a		16 40						17 10							17 40						18 10			
Heathrow Terminal 5 ✈ a		16b46						17b16							17b46						18b16			
West Drayton d	16 16					16 36	16 46						17 06	17 16					17 36	17 46				
Iver d	16 19						16 49							17 19						17 49				
Langley d	16 22						16 52							17 22						17 52				
Slough 3 a	16 27				16 38	16 42	16 57				17 06		17 13	17 27				17 38	17 42	17 57				18 06
d	16 27				16 39	16 43	16 57				17 07		17 13	17 27				17 39	17 43	17 57				18 07
Burnham d						16 47							17 17						17 47					
Taplow d						16 51							17 21						17 51					
Maidenhead 3 d	16 34					16 55	17 04						17 25	17 34					17 55	18 04				
Twyford 3 d	16 42					17 03	17 12						17 33	17 42					18 03	18 12				
Reading 7 a	16 51				16 53	17 11	17 20				17 22		17 43	17 51				17 53	18 11	18 20				18 22
Oxford a	17 40				17 18		18 14				17 48			18 40				18 18		19 14				18 48

	GW 1	GW 1	HC	GW 1	GW 1		GW 1 ◇	GW 1	GW 1	HC	GW 1	GW 1	GW 1 ◇	GW 1	GW 1	HC	GW 1	GW 1	GW 1 ◇	GW 1	GW 1		HC	GW 1
London Paddington 15 ⊖ d		17 57	18 03	18 12	18 15		18 21		18 27	18 33	18 42	18 45	18 50		18 57	19 03	19 12	19 15	19 21		19 27		19 33	19 42
Acton Main Line d					18 21							18 51						19 21						
Ealing Broadway ⊖ d		18 05	18 11	18 20	18 24				18 35	18 41	18 50	18 54			19 05	19 11	19 20	19 24			19 35		19 41	19 50
West Ealing d			18 13		18 27					18 43		18 57				19 13		19 27					19 43	
Drayton Green d					18 29							18 59						19 29						
Castle Bar Park d					18 31							19 01						19 31						
South Greenford d					18 34							19 04						19 34						
Greenford ⊖ a					18 39							19 09						19 39						
Hanwell d	←		18 15					←		18 45				←		19 15				←			19 45	
Southall d	17 55		18 19	18 25				18 25		18 49	18 55			18 55		19 19	19 25			19 25			19 49	19 55
Hayes & Harlington d	18 02	18 12	18 23	→				18 32	18 42	18 53	→			19 02	19 12	19 23	→			19 32	19 42		19 53	→
Heathrow Terminals 1-2-3 2 ✈ a			18 29							18 59						19 29							19 59	
Heathrow Terminal 4 ✈ a			18 40							19 10						19 40							20 10	
Heathrow Terminal 5 ✈ a			18b46							19b16						19b46							20b16	
West Drayton d	18 06	18 16						18 36	18 46					19 06	19 16					19 36	19 46			
Iver d		18 19							18 49						19 19						19 49			
Langley d		18 22							18 52						19 22						19 52			
Slough 3 a	18 13	18 27					18 38	18 42	18 57				19 06	19 13	19 27				19 37	19 42	19 57			
d	18 13	18 27					18 39	18 43	18 57				19 07	19 13	19 27				19 38	19 43	19 57			
Burnham d	18 17							18 47						19 17						19 47				
Taplow d	18 21							18 51						19 21						19 51				
Maidenhead 3 d	18 25	18 34						18 55	19 04					19 25	19 34					19 55	20 04			
Twyford 3 d	18 33	18 42						19 03	19 12					19 33	19 42					20 03	20 12			
Reading 7 a	18 43	18 51					18 53	19 11	19 20				19 22	19 43	19 51				19 53	20 11	20 20			
Oxford a		19 40					19 18		20 14				19 48		20 40				20 20		21 14			

	GW 1	GW 1 ◇	GW 1	GW 1	HC	GW 1	GW 1	GW 1	HC	GW 1	GW 1	GW 1 ◇	GW 1	GW 1	HC		GW 1	GW 1	HC	GW 1	GW ◇	GW 1	GW 1	HC
London Paddington 15 ⊖ d	19 45	19 50		19 57	20 03	20 12	20 15	20 27	20 33	20 42	20 45	20 50		20 57	21 03		21 12	21 15	21 33	21 42	21 50		21 57	22 03
Acton Main Line d	19 51						20 21				20 51							21 21						
Ealing Broadway ⊖ d	19 54			20 05	20 11	20 20	20 24	20 35	20 41	20 50	20 54			21 05	21 11		21 20	21 24	21 41	21 50			22 05	22 11
West Ealing d	19 57				20 13		20 27		20 43		20 57				21 13			21 27	21 43					22 13
Drayton Green d	19 59						20 29				20 59							21 29						
Castle Bar Park d	20 01						20 31				21 01							21 31						
South Greenford d	20 04						20 34				21 04							21 34						
Greenford ⊖ a	20 09						20 39				21 09							21 39						
Hanwell d			←		20 15				20 45				←		21 15				21 45			←		22 15
Southall d			19 55		20 19	20 25			20 49	20 55			20 55		21 19		21 25		21 49	21 55		21 55		22 19
Hayes & Harlington d			20 02	20 12	20 23	20 32		20 42	20 53	→			21 02	21 12	21 23		21 32		21 53	→		22 02	22 12	22 23
Heathrow Terminals 1-2-3 2 ✈ a					20 29				20 59						21 29				21 59					22 29
Heathrow Terminal 4 ✈ a					20 40				21 10						21 40				22 10					22 40
Heathrow Terminal 5 ✈ a					20b46				21b16						21b46				22b16					22b46
West Drayton d			20 06	20 16		20 36		20 46					21 06	21 16			21 36					22 06	22 16	
Iver d				20 19				20 49						21 19									22 19	
Langley d				20 22				20 52						21 22			21 41						22 22	
Slough 3 a		20 07	20 13	20 27		20 42		20 57				21 07	21 13	21 27			21 44				22 06	22 13	22 27	
d		20 07	20 13	20 27		20 43		20 57				21 07	21 13	21 27			21 45				22 07	22 13	22 27	
Burnham d			20 17			20 47							21 17				21 49					22 17		
Taplow d			20 21			20 51							21 21				21 53					22 21		
Maidenhead 3 d			20 25	20 34		20 55		21 04					21 25	21 34			21 57					22 25	22 34	
Twyford 3 d			20 33	20 42		21 03		21 12					21 33	21 42			22 05					22 33	22 42	
Reading 7 a		20 21	20 43	20 51		21 11		21 20				21 23	21 43	21 51			22 13				22 22	22 43	22 51	
Oxford a		20 47	*21 20*	21 40				22 14				21 53	*22 21*	22 40							22 49		23 33	

For general notes see front of timetable
For details of catering facilities see Directory of Train Operators

For fast services between London Paddington and Reading see Table 116

b Change at Heathrow Terminals 1-2-3

Table 117

Saturdays

London → Greenford and Reading

(Local services only)

Network Diagram - see first page of Table 116

	GW 1 A	GW 1 B	GW 1 ◇ A	GW 1 ◇ B	GW 1 B	GW 1 A	HC	GW 1 A	GW 1 C	GW 1 ◇ A	GW 1 ◇ B	GW 1 A	GW 1 C	HC	GW 1 A	GW 1 C	GW 1 ◇ A	GW 1 ◇ B	GW 1 A	GW 1 C	GW 1
London Paddington 15 ⊖ d	22 12	22 12	22 32	22 32			22 33	22 45	22 45	23 00	23 00			23 03	23 20	23 20	23 33	23 33			23 42
Acton Main Line d								22 51	22 51												
Ealing Broadway ⊖ d	22 20	22 20					22 41	22 55	22 55					23 11	23 28	23 28					23 50
West Ealing d							22 43							23 13							
Drayton Green d																					
Castle Bar Park d																					
South Greenford d																					
Greenford ⊖ a																					
Hanwell d							22 45							23 15							
Southall d	22 25	22 25					22 49	23 00	23 00			←	←	23 19	23 33	23 33			←	←	23 56
Hayes & Harlington d	22 32	22 32					22 53	23 04	23 04			23 04	23 04	23 23	23 37	23 37			23 37	23 37	00 01
Heathrow Terminals 1-2-3 2 ✈ a							22 59	→	→					23 29	→	→					
Heathrow Terminal 4 ✈ a							23 10							23 40							
Heathrow Terminal 5 ✈ a							23b16							23b46							
West Drayton d	22 36	22 36										23 08	23 08						23 41	23 41	00 06
Iver d												23 11	23 11						23 44	23 44	
Langley d	22 41	22 41										23 14	23 14						23 48	23 48	
Slough 3 a	22 44	22 44	22 49	22 49						23 16	23 16	23 19	23 19				23 49	23 49	23 53	23 53	00 13
d	22 45	22 45	22 50	22 50						23 17	23 17	23 21	23 21				23 50	23 50	23 54	23 54	00 13
Burnham d	22 49	22 49			←	←						23 25	23 25						23 58	23 58	00 17
Taplow d	22 53	22 53			22 53	22 53													00 01	00 01	00 21
Maidenhead 3 d	→	→			22 57	22 59						23 30	23 30						00 05	00 05	00 25
Twyford 3 d					23 05	23 06						23 38	23 38						00 13	00 13	00 33
Reading 7 a			23 06	23 06	23 13	23 14				23 33	23 33	23 44	23 44				00 07	00 07	00 20	00 20	00 42
Oxford a			23 42	00c01						00 04	00c23	00 33					00 38		00 59	01c36	

Sundays

until 6 September

	GW 1	GW 1	GW 1	GW 1	GW 1	HC	HC	GW 1	HC	GW 1	GW ◇ D	GW 1	HC	GW 1	GW ◇	GW 1	GW 1	HC	GW 1	GW 1 ◇	HC
London Paddington 15 ⊖ d	23 20	23p42	00 05	00 30	01 00		06 12	06 44	07 12	07 43	08 03		08 12	08 15	08 42	08 43	09 04	09 07	09 15	09 35	09 37
Acton Main Line d																					
Ealing Broadway ⊖ d	23 28	23p50	00 13	00 38	01 08	05 20	06 20	06 52	07 20	07 50			08 20	08 24		08 52		09 15	09 24		09 45
West Ealing d																					
Drayton Green d																					
Castle Bar Park d																					
South Greenford d																					
Greenford ⊖ a																					
Hanwell d																					
Southall d	23 33	23p56	00 19	00 44	01 13	05 24	06 24	06 58	07 24	07 56			08 24	08 29		08 58		09 19	09 29		09 49
Hayes & Harlington d	23p37	00 01	00 23	00 48	01 17	05 28	06 28	07 02	07 28	08 00			08 28	08 33		09 02		09 23	09 33		09 53
Heathrow Terminals 1-2-3 2 ✈ a						05 34	06 34		07 34				08 34					09 30			09 59
Heathrow Terminal 4 ✈ a						05 40	06 40		07 40				08 40					09 40			10 10
Heathrow Terminal 5 ✈ a						05b47	06b50		07b50				08b50					09b46			10b16
West Drayton d	23p41	00 06	00 27	00 52				07 06		08 04				08 37		09 06			09 37		
Iver d	23p44		00 30																		
Langley d	23p48		00 33	00 56				07 11		08 09				08 42		09 10			09 42		
Slough 3 a	23p53	00 13	00 37	01 00	01 25			07 14		08 12	08 20	←		08 46	09 00	09 14	09 22		09 46	09 50	
d	23p54	00 13	00 38	01 01	01 26			07 14		08 22	08 21	08 22		08 46	09 01	09 16	09 23		09 46	09 51	
Burnham d	23p58	00 17	00 42					07 19		→		08 27				09 20					
Taplow d	00 01	00 21	00 45																		
Maidenhead 3 d	00 05	00 25	00 49	01 08	01 33			07 24			08 29	08 32		08 54		09 27	09 32		09 54		
Twyford 3 d	00 13	00 33	00 57	01 16	01 41			07 32				08 40		09 02		09 35			10 02		
Reading 7 a	00 20	00 42	01 05	01 24	01 49			07 41			08 43	08 49		09 11	09 24	09 43	09 46		10 10	10 12	
Oxford a	00 59										09 15	09 30			09 54	10 27	10 35			10 42	

	GW 1	GW 1	HC	GW 1	HC	GW 1 ◇	GW 1	GW 1	HC	GW 1	HC	GW 1 ◇	GW 1	GW 1	HC	GW 1	HC	GW 1 ◇	GW 1	GW 1
London Paddington 15 ⊖ d	09 43	10 04	10 07	10 15	10 37	10 42	10 43	11 04	11 07	11 15	11 37	11 42	11 43	12 04	12 07	12 15	12 37	12 42	12 43	13 04
Acton Main Line d																				
Ealing Broadway ⊖ d	09 50		10 15	10 24	10 45		10 50		11 15	11 24	11 45		11 50		12 15	12 24	12 45		12 50	
West Ealing d																				
Drayton Green d																				
Castle Bar Park d																				
South Greenford d																				
Greenford ⊖ a																				
Hanwell d																				
Southall d	09 56		10 19	10 29	10 49		10 56		11 19	11 29	11 49		11 56		12 19	12 29	12 49		12 56	
Hayes & Harlington d	10 02		10 23	10 33	10 53		11 02		11 23	11 33	11 53		12 02		12 23	12 33	12 53		13 02	
Heathrow Terminals 1-2-3 2 ✈ a			10 29		10 59				11 29		11 59				12 29		12 59			
Heathrow Terminal 4 ✈ a			10 40		11 10				11 40		12 10				12 40		13 10			
Heathrow Terminal 5 ✈ a			10b46		11b16				11b46		12b16				12b46		13b16			
West Drayton d	10 06			10 37			11 06			11 37			12 07			12 37			13 06	
Iver d																				
Langley d	10 10			10 42			11 10			11 42			12 10			12 42			13 10	
Slough 3 a	10 14	10 23		10 46		10 58	11 14	11 22		11 46		11 59	12 14	12 22		12 46		12 58	13 14	13 22
d	10 16	10 23		10 46		10 59	11 16	11 23		11 46		12 00	12 16	12 23		12 46		12 59	13 16	13 23
Burnham d	10 20						11 20						12 20						13 20	
Taplow d																				
Maidenhead 3 d	10 27	10 32		10 54			11 27	11 31		11 54			12 27	12 31		12 54			13 27	13 31
Twyford 3 d	10 35			11 02			11 35			12 02			12 35			13 02			13 35	
Reading 7 a	10 43	10 46		11 10		11 20	11 42	11 46		12 10		12 19	12 43	12 46		13 10		13 20	13 43	13 46
Oxford a	11 25	11 35				11 50	12 25	12 35				12 50	13 27	13 15				13 50	14 25	14 35

For general notes see front of timetable
For details of catering facilities see Directory of Train Operators

For fast services between London Paddington and Reading see Table 116

- **A** Until 5 September
- **B** From 12 September
- **C** From 12 September. To Didcot Parkway (Table 116)
- **D** To Great Malvern (Table 126)
- **b** Change at Heathrow Terminals 1-2-3
- **c** Change at Didcot Parkway. By bus

Table 117

Sundays

London → Greenford and Reading

(Local services only)

until 6 September

Network Diagram - see first page of Table 116

		HC	GW 1	HC		GW 1 ◇	GW 1	GW 1	HC	GW 1		HC	GW 1 ◇	GW 1	GW 1	HC		GW 1	HC	GW 1 ◇	GW 1	GW 1		HC	GW 1
London Paddington 15 ⊖	d	13 07	13 15	13 37		13 42	13 43	14 06	14 07	14 15		14 37	14 42	14 43	15 06	15 07		15 15	15 37	15 42	15 43	16 06		16 07	16 15
Acton Main Line	d																								
Ealing Broadway ⊖	d	13 15	13 24	13 45			13 50		14 15	14 24		14 45		14 50		15 15		15 24	15 45		15 50			16 15	16 24
West Ealing	d																								
Drayton Green	d																								
Castle Bar Park	d																								
South Greenford	d																								
Greenford ⊖	a																								
Hanwell	d																								
Southall	d	13 19	13 29	13 49			13 56		14 19	14 29		14 49		14 56		15 19		15 29	15 49		15 56			16 19	16 29
Hayes & Harlington	d	13 23	13 33	13 53			14 02		14 23	14 33		14 53		15 02		15 23		15 33	15 53		16 02			16 23	16 33
Heathrow Terminals 1-2-3 2 ✈	a	13 29		13 59					14 29			14 59				15 29			15 59					16 29	
Heathrow Terminal 4 ✈	a	13 40		14 10					14 40			15 10				15 40			16 10					16 40	
Heathrow Terminal 5 ✈	a	13b46		14b16					14b46			15b16				15b46			16b16					16b46	
West Drayton	d		13 37				14 06			14 37				15 06				15 37			16 06				16 37
Iver	d																								
Langley	d		13 42				14 10			14 42				15 10				15 42			16 10				16 42
Slough 3	a		13 46			13 57	14 14	14 22		14 46			14 59	15 14	15 22			15 46		15 57	16 14	16 22			16 46
	d		13 46			13 58	14 16	14 23		14 46			15 00	15 16	15 23			15 46		15 58	16 16	16 23			16 46
Burnham	d						14 20							15 20				15 50			16 20				16 50
Taplow	d																								
Maidenhead 3	d		13 54				14 27	14 31		14 54				15 27	15 31			15 56			16 27	16 31			16 56
Twyford 3	d		14 02				14 35			15 02				15 35				16 04			16 35				17 04
Reading 7	a		14 10			14 20	14 43	14 46		15 10			15 20	15 43	15 46			16 12		16 20	16 43	16 46			17 12
Oxford	a					14 50	15 27	15 35					15 50	16 25	16 35					16 49	17 25	17 35			

		HC	GW 1 ◇	GW 1	GW 1	HC		GW 1	HC	GW 1 ◇ A	GW 1 ◇ B	GW 1		GW 1	HC	GW 1	HC	GW 1 ◇		GW 1	GW 1	HC	GW 1	HC	GW 1 ◇
London Paddington 15 ⊖	d	16 37	16 42	16 43	17 06	17 07		17 15	17 37	17 42	17 42	17 43		18 06	18 07	18 15	18 37	18 42		18 43	19 06	19 07	19 15	19 37	19 42
Acton Main Line	d																								
Ealing Broadway ⊖	d	16 45		16 50		17 15		17 24	17 45			17 50			18 15	18 24	18 45			18 50		19 15	19 24	19 45	
West Ealing	d																								
Drayton Green	d																								
Castle Bar Park	d																								
South Greenford	d																								
Greenford ⊖	a																								
Hanwell	d																								
Southall	d	16 49		16 56		17 19		17 29	17 49			17 56			18 19	18 29	18 49			18 56		19 19	19 29	19 49	
Hayes & Harlington	d	16 53		17 02		17 23		17 33	17 53			18 02			18 23	18 33	18 53			19 02		19 23	19 33	19 53	
Heathrow Terminals 1-2-3 2 ✈	a	16 59				17 29			17 59						18 29		18 59					19 29		19 59	
Heathrow Terminal 4 ✈	a	17 10				17 40			18 10						18 40		19 10					19 40		20 10	
Heathrow Terminal 5 ✈	a	17b16				17b46			18b16						18b46		19b16					19b46		20b16	
West Drayton	d			17 06				17 37				18 06				18 37				19 06			19 37		
Iver	d																								
Langley	d			17 10				17 42				18 10				18 42				19 10			19 42		
Slough 3	a		16 59	17 14	17 22			17 46		17 57	17 59	18 14		18 22		18 46		18 58		19 14	19 22		19 46		19 57
	d		16 59	17 16	17 23			17 47		17 58	17 59	18 16		18 23		18 46		18 59		19 16	19 23		19 47		19 57
Burnham	d			17 20				17 51				18 20				18 50				19 20			19 51		
Taplow	d																								
Maidenhead 3	d			17 27	17 31			17 56				18 27		18 31		18 56				19 27	19 31		19 56		
Twyford 3	d			17 35				18 04				18 35				19 04				19 35			20 04		
Reading 7	a		17 20	17 43	17 46			18 12		18 20	18 20	18 43		18 46		19 12		19 20		19 43	19 51		20 12		20 17
Oxford	a		17 50	18 27	18 35					18 50	18 50	19 25		19 35				19 50		20 25	20 35				20 48

		GW 1		HC	GW 1	HC	GW ◇	GW 1		HC	GW 1	GW 1 ◇	GW 1	GW 1 C		HC	GW 1 D	GW 1 ◇	GW 1 C	HC	GW 1	GW 1 ◇	GW 1		
London Paddington 15 ⊖	d	19 43		20 07	20 15	20 37	20 42	20 43		21 07	21 15	21 27		21 43		22 12	22 15	22 42	22 43	23 12	23 15	23 37	23 53		
Acton Main Line	d																								
Ealing Broadway ⊖	d	19 50		20 15	20 24	20 45		20 50		21 15	21 24			21 50		22 20	22 24		22 52	23 20	23 24		00 02		
West Ealing	d																								
Drayton Green	d																								
Castle Bar Park	d																								
South Greenford	d																								
Greenford ⊖	a																								
Hanwell	d																								
Southall	d	19 56		20 19	20 29	20 49		20 56		21 19	21 29			21 56		22 24	22 29		22 58	23 24	23 29		00 07		
Hayes & Harlington	d	20 02		20 23	20 33	20 53		21 02		21 23	21 33			22 02		22 28	22 33		23 02	23 28	23 33		00 11		
Heathrow Terminals 1-2-3 2 ✈	a			20 29		20 59				21 29						22 34				23 34					
Heathrow Terminal 4 ✈	a			20 40		21 10				21 40						22 40				23 40					
Heathrow Terminal 5 ✈	a			20b46		21b16				21b46						22b50				23b50					
West Drayton	d	20 06			20 37			21 06			21 37			22 06			22 37		23 06		23 37		00 15		
Iver	d																								
Langley	d	20 10			20 42			21 10			21 41			22 10			22 42		23 10		23 42		00 20		
Slough 3	a	20 14			20 46		20 59	21 14			21 46	21 48	←	22 14			22 46	22 59	23 14		23 46	23 54	00 24		
	d	20 16			20 46		20 59	21 16			21 59	21 49	21 59	22 15			22 46	23 01	23 15		23 46	23 55	00 24		
Burnham	d	20 20			20 50			21 19			→		22 03	22 19			22 50		23 19		23 50		00 28		
Taplow	d																								
Maidenhead 3	d	20 27			20 56			21 27					22 08	22c31			22 56		23 24		23 56		00 34		
Twyford 3	d	20 35			21 04			21 35					22 16	22 39			23 04		23 32		00 04		00 42		
Reading 7	a	20 43			21 12		21 18	21 44				22 08	22 23	22 46			23 11	23 18	23 43		00 12	00 15	00 49		
Oxford	a	21 27					21 51	22 28				22 39		23e55				00e10	00e55			01f05			

For general notes see front of timetable
For details of catering facilities see Directory of Train Operators

For fast services between London Paddington and Reading see Table 116

A From 19 July
B Until 12 July
C To Didcot Parkway (Table 116)
D To Newbury (Table 116)

b Change at Heathrow Terminals 1-2-3
c Arr. 2225
e Change at Didcot Parkway. By bus
f Change at Didcot Parkway.By bus

Table 117

London → Greenford and Reading

(Local services only)

Sundays

from 13 September

Network Diagram - see first page of Table 116

		GW	GW	GW	GW		GW	HC	HC	GW		HC	GW	GW	HC		GW	GW	GW	HC		GW	GW	GW	HC
		1	1	1	1		1			1			1	1 ◇			1	◇	1			1	1 ◇	1	
		A												B 🛒				🛒					☕		
London Paddington 15	⊖ d	23p20	23p42	00 05	00 30		01 00		06 12	06 44		07 12	07 44	08 03	08 12		08 15	08 42	08 44	09 12		09 15	09 35	09 44	10 12
Acton Main Line	d																								
Ealing Broadway	⊖ d	23p28	23p50	00 13	00 38		01 08	05 20	06 20	06 52		07 20	07 52		08 20		08 24		08 52	09 20		09 24		09 52	10 20
West Ealing	d																								
Drayton Green	d																								
Castle Bar Park	d																								
South Greenford	d																								
Greenford	⊖ a																								
Hanwell	d																								
Southall	d	23p33	23p56	00 19	00 44		01 13	05 24	06 24	06 58		07 24	07 58		08 24		08 29		08 58	09 24		09 29		09 58	10 24
Hayes & Harlington	d	23p37	00 01	00 23	00 48		01 17	05 28	06 28	07 02		07 28	08 02		08 28		08 33		09 02	09 28		09 33		10 02	10 28
Heathrow Terminals 1-2-3 2	✈ a							05 34	06 34			07 34			08 34					09 34					10 34
Heathrow Terminal 4	✈ a							05 40	06 40			07 40			08 40					09 40					10 40
Heathrow Terminal 5	✈ a							*05b47*	*06b50*			*07b50*			*08b50*					*09b50*					*10b50*
West Drayton	d	23p41	00 06	00 27	00 52					07 06			08 06				08 37		09 06			09 37		10 06	
Iver	d	23p44		00 30																					
Langley	d	23p48		00 33	00 56					07 11			08 11				08 42		09 10			09 42		10 10	
Slough 3	a	23p53	00 13	00 37	01 00		01 25			07 14			08 14	08 24			08 46	09 01	09 14			09 46	09 56	10 14	
	d	23p54	00 13	00 38	01 01		01 26			07 14			08 14	08 25			08 46	09 01	09 15			09 46	09 57	10 15	
Burnham	d	23p58	00 17	00 42						07 19			08 19						09 19					10 19	
Taplow	d	00 01	00 21	00 45																					
Maidenhead 3	d	00 05	00 25	00 49	01 08		01 33			07 24			08 24	08 32			08 54		09 24			09 54		10 27	
Twyford 3	d	00 13	00 33	00 57	01 16		01 41			07 32			08 32				09 02		09 32			10 02		10 35	
Reading 7	a	00 20	00 42	01 05	01 24		01 49			07 41			08 41	08 44			09 10	09 20	09 41			10 10	10 11	10 42	
Oxford	a	*01c36*											09 30	09 15				09 52	10 27				10 41	11 25	

		GW	GW		GW	HC	GW	GW		GW	HC	GW	GW		GW	HC	GW	GW		GW	HC	GW	GW		GW
		1	1 ◇		1		1	1 ◇		1		1	1 ◇		1		1	1 ◇		1		1	1 ◇		1
			☕										☕					☕					🛒		
London Paddington 15	⊖ d	10 15	10 42		10 44	11 12	11 15	11 42		11 43	12 12	12 15	12 42		12 44	13 12	13 15	13 42		13 44	14 12	14 15	14 42		14 44
Acton Main Line	d																								
Ealing Broadway	⊖ d	10 24			10 52	11 20	11 24			11 52	12 20	12 24			12 52	13 20	13 24			13 52	14 20	14 24			14 52
West Ealing	d																								
Drayton Green	d																								
Castle Bar Park	d																								
South Greenford	d																								
Greenford	⊖ a																								
Hanwell	d																								
Southall	d	10 29			10 58	11 24	11 29			11 58	12 24	12 29			12 58	13 24	13 29			13 58	14 24	14 29			14 58
Hayes & Harlington	d	10 33			11 02	11 28	11 33			12 02	12 28	12 33			13 02	13 28	13 33			14 02	14 28	14 33			15 02
Heathrow Terminals 1-2-3 2	✈ a					11 34					12 34					13 34					14 34				
Heathrow Terminal 4	✈ a					11 40					12 40					13 40					14 40				
Heathrow Terminal 5	✈ a					*11b50*					*12b50*					*13b50*					*14b50*				
West Drayton	d	10 37			11 06		11 37			12 06		12 37			13 06		13 37			14 06		14 37			15 06
Iver	d																								
Langley	d	10 42			11 10		11 42			12 10		12 42			13 10		13 42			14 10		14 42			15 10
Slough 3	a	10 46	11 04		11 14		11 46	12 01		12 14		12 46	13 04		13 14		13 46	14 04		14 14		14 46	15 04		15 14
	d	10 46	11 05		11 15		11 46	12 02		12 15		12 46	13 05		13 15		13 46	14 05		14 15		14 46	15 05		15 15
Burnham	d				11 19					12 19					13 19					14 19					15 19
Taplow	d																								
Maidenhead 3	d	10 54			11 27		11 54			12 27		12 54			13 27		13 54			14 27		14 54			15 27
Twyford 3	d	11 02			11 35		12 02			12 35		13 02			13 35		14 02			14 35		15 02			15 35
Reading 7	a	11 10	11 19		11 42		12 10	12 18		12 43		13 10	13 19		13 43		14 10	14 19		14 43		15 10	15 20		15 43
Oxford	a		11 49		12 25			12 50		13 27			13 49		14 25			14 49		15 27			15 50		16 25

		HC	GW	GW	GW		HC	GW	GW	GW		HC	GW	GW	GW		HC	GW	GW	GW		HC	GW	GW	GW
			1	1 ◇	1			1	1 ◇	1			1	1 ◇	1			1	1 ◇	1			1	1 ◇	1
				☕					☕					🛒					☕					☕	
London Paddington 15	⊖ d	15 12	15 15	15 42	15 44		16 12	16 15	16 42	16 44		17 12	17 15	17 42	17 44		18 12	18 15	18 42	18 44		19 12	19 15	19 42	19 44
Acton Main Line	d																								
Ealing Broadway	⊖ d	15 20	15 24		15 52		16 20	16 24		16 52		17 20	17 24		17 52		18 20	18 24		18 52		19 20	19 24		19 52
West Ealing	d																								
Drayton Green	d																								
Castle Bar Park	d																								
South Greenford	d																								
Greenford	⊖ a																								
Hanwell	d																								
Southall	d	15 24	15 29		15 58		16 24	16 29		16 58		17 24	17 29		17 58		18 24	18 29		18 58		19 24	19 29		19 58
Hayes & Harlington	d	15 28	15 33		16 02		16 28	16 33		17 02		17 28	17 33		18 02		18 28	18 33		19 02		19 28	19 33		20 02
Heathrow Terminals 1-2-3 2	✈ a	15 34					16 34					17 34					18 34					19 34			
Heathrow Terminal 4	✈ a	15 40					16 40					17 40					18 40					19 40			
Heathrow Terminal 5	✈ a	*15b50*					*16b50*					*17b50*					*18b50*					*19b50*			
West Drayton	d		15 37		16 06			16 37		17 06			17 37		18 06			18 37		19 06			19 37		20 06
Iver	d																								
Langley	d		15 42		16 10			16 42		17 10			17 42		18 10			18 42		19 10			19 42		20 10
Slough 3	a		15 46	16 04	16 14			16 46	17 03	17 14			17 46	18 03	18 14			18 46	19 05	19 14			19 46	20 05	20 14
	d		15 46	16 05	16 15			16 46	17 03	17 15			17 47	18 03	18 15			18 46	19 06	19 15			19 47	20 05	20 15
Burnham	d		15 50		16 19			16 50		17 19			17 51		18 19			18 50		19 19			19 51		20 19
Taplow	d																								
Maidenhead 3	d		15 56		16 27			16 56		17 27			17 56		18 27			18 56		19 27			19 56		20 27
Twyford 3	d		16 04		16 35			17 04		17 35			18 04		18 35			19 04		19 35			20 04		20 35
Reading 7	a		16 12	16 19	16 43			17 12	17 19	17 43			18 12	18 19	18 43			19 12	19 20	19 43			20 12	20 17	20 43
Oxford	a			16 49	17 25				17 49	18 27				18 49	19 25				19 50	20 25				20 48	21 26

For general notes see front of timetable
For details of catering facilities see Directory of Train Operators

For fast services between London Paddington and Reading see Table 116

A To Didcot Parkway (Table 116)
B To Great Malvern (Table 126)
b Change at Heathrow Terminals 1-2-3
c Change at Didcot Parkway. By bus

Sundays

from 13 September

London → Greenford and Reading
(Local services only)

Network Diagram - see first page of Table 116

		HC	GW 1	GW 1	GW 1	HC	GW 1	GW 1	GW 1	GW 1	HC	GW 1 A	GW 1 ◇	GW 1	HC	GW 1	GW 1 ◇	GW 1
London Paddington 15 ⊖	d	20 12	20 15	20 42	20 44	21 12	21 15	21 27		21 44	22 12	22 15	22 42	22 44	23 12	23 15	23 47	23 53
Acton Main Line	d																	
Ealing Broadway ⊖	d	20 20	20 24		20 52	21 20	21 24			21 52	22 20	22 24		22 52	23 20	23 24	23 55	00 02
West Ealing	d																	
Drayton Green	d																	
Castle Bar Park	d																	
South Greenford	d																	
Greenford ⊖	a																	
Hanwell	d																	
Southall	d	20 24	20 29		20 58	21 24	21 29			21 58	22 24	22 29		22 58	23 24	23 29		00 07
Hayes & Harlington	d	20 28	20 33		21 02	21 28	21 33			22 02	22 28	22 33		23 02	23 28	23 33		00 11
Heathrow Terminals 1-2-3 2 ✈	a	20 34				21 34					22 34				23 34			
Heathrow Terminal 4 ✈	a	20 40				21 40					22 40				23 40			
Heathrow Terminal 5 ✈	a	20b50				21b50					22b50				23b50			
West Drayton	d		20 37		21 06		21 37			22 06		22 37		23 06		23 37		00 15
Iver	d																	
Langley	d		20 42		21 10		21 41			22 10		22 42		23 10		23 42		00 20
Slough 3	a		20 46	21 04	21 14		21 45	21 52		22 13		22 46	22 59	23 14		23 46	00 07	00 24
	d		20 46	21 05	21 15		21 46	21 53		22 15		22 46	23 01	23 15		23 46	00 08	00 24
Burnham	d		20 50		21 19		21 50			22 19		22 50		23 19		23 50		00 28
Taplow	d								←									
Maidenhead 3	d		20 56		21 27		21 55		21 55	22c31		22 56		23 24		23 56	00 15	00 34
Twyford 3	d		21 04		21 35		→		22 03	22 39		23 04		23 32		00 04		00 42
Reading 7	a		21 12	21 19	21 44			22 07	22 10	22 46		23 11	23 18	23 43		00 12	00 28	00 49
Oxford	a			21 51	22 28			22 37		23 35			23 49	00 34			00 59	

For general notes see front of timetable
For details of catering facilities see Directory of Train Operators

For fast services between London Paddington and Reading see Table 116

A To Newbury (Table 116)
b Change at Heathrow Terminals 1-2-3
c Arr. 2225

Reading and Greenford → London

(Local services only)

Network Diagram - see first page of Table 116

Miles	Miles	Miles			GW	HC	GW	GW	GW	GW	GW	GW	GW	GW	GW		GW	GW	GW	GW	GW	HC	GW	HC	GW
					MX		MO	MO	MO	MO	MO	MX	MO	MX	MO		MX				MO				
					1		1	◇	1	1	1	1	1 ◇	1 ◇	1 ◇		1	1	1	1	1		1		1
								A		B	C		D		E		G			H	J				
—	—	—	Oxford	d						23p15			00 01	00 06			00 19			04 00	03b40				
0	—	—	**Reading 7**	d	23p15		23p35	23p52		23p56	00 15	00 15	00 32	00 39	00 54		01 10	02 24	03 54	04 41	04 41		05 14		05 39
5	—	—	**Twyford 3**	d	23p22		23p41			00 03	00 21	00 21	00 38		01 00		01 17	02 30	04 00	04 48	04 48		05 20		05 45
11¾	—	—	**Maidenhead 3**	d	23p29		23p49			00 11	00 29	00 29	00 47		01 08		01 25	02 38	04 08	04 56	04 56		05 28		05 53
13½	—	—	Taplow	d	23p33							00 32											05 32		
15	—	—	Burnham	d	23p36		23p54			00 15		00 35											05 35		
17½	—	—	**Slough 3**	a	23p41		23p58	00 12		00 20	00 36	00 40	00 55	00 56	01 15		01 32	02 45	04 15	05 03	05 03		05 40		06 01
—	—	—		d	23p41		23p59	00 12		00 20	00 36	00 40	00 55	00 57	01 15		01 32	02 45	04 15	05 03	05 03		05 40		06 01
19¾	—	—	Langley	d	23p45		00 03			00 24	00 40	00 44								05 07	05 07		05 44		
21¼	—	—	Iver	d	23p48															05 10	05 10		05 47		
22¾	—	—	West Drayton	d	23p52		00 08			00 29	00 45	00 49						02 52	04 22	05 14	05 14		05 51		
—	—	—	**Heathrow Terminal 5** ✈	d		23c53																05e07		05e42	
—	—	0	**Heathrow Terminal 4** ✈	d		00 01																05 23		05 51	
—	—	1¾	**Heathrow Terminals 1-2-3 2** ✈	d		00 07			←													05 29		05 57	
25¼	—	5¾	Hayes & Harlington	d	23p56	00 13	00 16		00 16	00 33	00 50	00 54	01 05		01 24		01 41	02 57	04 27	05 19	05 19	05 35	05 55	06 03	06 10
27	—	7½	Southall	d	23p59	00 16	→		00 20	00 37	00 53	00 57						03 00	04 30	05 22	05 22	05 38	05 59	06 06	06 13
28¾	—	9¼	Hanwell	d																		05 41		06 09	
—	0	—	**Greenford** ⊖	d																					
—	1	—	South Greenford	d																					
—	1¾	—	Castle Bar Park	d																					
—	2	—	Drayton Green	d																					
29½	2¾	10	West Ealing	d																		05 43		06 11	
30¼	3½	11	**Ealing Broadway** ⊖	d	00 06	00 21			00 25	00 42	00 59	01 03	01 12		01 31		01 48	03 06	04 36	05 28	05 28	05 46	06 05	06 14	06 19
31¾	5	12¼	Acton Main Line	d																05 31	05 31		06 08		
36	9¼	16½	**London Paddington 15** ⊖	a	00 17	00 30		00 35	00 38	00 52	01 11	01 14	01 22	01 17	01 41		02 00	03 18	04 47	05 41	05 41	05 56	06 16	06 24	06 30

		GW	GW	GW	GW		GW	HC	GW	GW	GW	GW	GW	GW	GW	GW	GW		GW	HC	GW	GW	GW	GW	GW
		1	1	1	1		1		1	1	1	1	1	1	1	1	1 ◇		1		1	1	1	1	1
Oxford	d	05 03							05 34	05 45			06 02												
Reading 7	d	05 44	06 02				06 07		06 15	06 16	06 22		06 32		06 32	06 37	06 45				06 46				06 57
Twyford 3	d	05 50					06 13		06 21	06 23					06 38	06 43					06 54				07 03
Maidenhead 3	d	05 58					06 21		06 29	06 31			06 43		06 46	06 53					07 03			←	07 11
Taplow	d	06 02					06 24		06 32							06 57								06 57	
Burnham	d	06 05					06 27		06 35						06 50	→								07 01	
Slough 3	a	06 10	06 17				06 32		06 40		06 40		06 50		06 55		06 58							07 06	07 18
	d	06 10	06 17				06 32		06 40		06 40		06 50		06 55		06 59					←		07 06	07 20
Langley	d	06 14					06 36		06 44						06 59				←			06 59		07 11	
Iver	d	06 17							06 47			←			→				06 47			07 02		07 14	
West Drayton	d	06 20					06 41		→			06 41							06 51			07 06		07 18	
Heathrow Terminal 5 ✈	d						→	06e12												06e42					
Heathrow Terminal 4 ✈	d							06 21												06 51					
Heathrow Terminals 1-2-3 2 ✈	d				←			06 27												06 57					
Hayes & Harlington	d	06 25			06 25			06 33				06 46							06 56	07 03		07 11		07 23	
Southall	d	→			06 29			06 36				06 50							07 00	07 06		07 15		07 27	
Hanwell	d							06 39												07 09					
Greenford ⊖	d			06 16										06 46									07 16		
South Greenford	d			06 19										06 49									07 19		
Castle Bar Park	d			06 22										06 52									07 22		
Drayton Green	d			06 24										06 54									07 24		
West Ealing	d			06 26				06 41						06 56						07 11			07 26		
Ealing Broadway ⊖	d			06 29	06 35			06 44				06 55		06 59					07 05	07 14		07 20	07 29	07 33	
Acton Main Line	d			06 33	06 38									07 03									07 33		
London Paddington 15 ⊖	a		06 38	06 42	06 49			06 54		06 54	07 00	07 07	07 09	07 12			07 16		07 17	07 24	07 26	07 33	07 42	07 44	07 47

		GW	GW	HC	GW	GW	GW		GW	GW	GW	GW	HC	GW	GW	GW	GW	GW	GW		GW	GW	HC	GW	GW
		1	1		1	1	1		1	1	1	1		1	1	1	1	1	1		1	1		1	1
						K					L	G				K	G				G				
Oxford	d		06 28		06 07							06 37		06 56	07 10						07 01	07 31			07 21
Reading 7	d	07 02	07 07		07 10							07 30		07 42							07 55	08 06		08 12	08 19
Twyford 3	d	07 08			07 16	07 22						07 37		07 48		07 56					08 02	08a12		08 18	08 26
Maidenhead 3	d	07 16	07 18		07 24	07 31					07 41	07 45		07 56	08 00	08 04					08 11			08 26	08 34
Taplow	d				07 28									08 00										08 29	
Burnham	d	07 21			07 31							07 50		08 03							08 15			08 32	
Slough 3	a	07 26			07 36						07 49	07 55		08 07							08 20			→	
	d	07 26			07 36						07 50	07 55		08 08							08 20				
Langley	d	07 30			07 41					←		08 00		08 12					←						
Iver	d				07 44		←			07 44				08 15			←		08 15						
West Drayton	d	07 35			→		07 35			07 48		08 05		→			08 05		08 19						
Heathrow Terminal 5 ✈	d	→		07e12								→	07e42										08e12		
Heathrow Terminal 4 ✈	d			07 21									07 51										08 21		
Heathrow Terminals 1-2-3 2 ✈	d			07 27									07 57										08 27		
Hayes & Harlington	d			07 33			07 40			07 53			08 03				08 09		08 24				08 33		
Southall	d			07 36			07 44			07 57			08 06				08 13		08 28				08 36		
Hanwell	d			07 39									08 09										08 39		
Greenford ⊖	d								07 46									08 16							
South Greenford	d								07 49									08 19							
Castle Bar Park	d								07 52									08 22							
Drayton Green	d								07 54									08 24							
West Ealing	d			07 41					07 56				08 11					08 26					08 41		
Ealing Broadway ⊖	d			07 44			07 49		07 59	08 03			08 14				08 19	08 29	08 32				08 44		
Acton Main Line	d								08 03									08 33							
London Paddington 15 ⊖	a		07 43	07 54		07 57	08 02		08 12	08 14	08 17		08 24		08 24	08 29	08 32	08 42	08 44		08 47		08 54		08 59

For general notes see front of timetable
For details of catering facilities see Directory of Train Operators

For fast services between Reading and London Paddington see Table 116

- **A** Until 7 September
- **B** From 14 September
- **C** Until 7 September from Didcot Parkway (Table 116)
- **D** From 7 September
- **E** Until 31 August. From Didcot Parkway
- **G** From Banbury (Table 116)
- **H** All Tuesdays to Fridays, also Mondays from 7 September
- **J** Until 31 August. From Didcot Parkway (Table 116)
- **K** From Henley-on-Thames (Table 121)
- **L** From Bourne End (Table 120)
- **b** Change at Didcot Parkway. By bus
- **c** Previous night.Change at Heathrow Terminals 1-2-3. Sunday evenings dept. 2357
- **e** Change at Heathrow Terminals 1-2-3

Reading and Greenford → London
(Local services only)

Network Diagram - see first page of Table 116

Station		GW 1	GW 1	GW 1	GW 1 A	HC	GW 1	GW 1	GW 1		GW 1	GW 1	HC	GW 1	GW 1	GW 1	GW 1 ◇	GW 1	GW 1	HC	GW 1		GW 1	GW 1 ◇	GW 1
Oxford	d						*07 51*	07 55						08 21		08 37	09 01						*09 15*	09 31	
Reading 7	d						08 31	08 47						09 03	09 17	09 33	09 37				←		09 48	09 56	
Twyford 3	d						08 37	08 54						09 09	09 24	09 39					09 39		09 54		
Maidenhead 3	d				08 41		08 45	09 03						09 17	09 33	→					09 47		10 02		
Taplow	d			←			08 49								09 36								→		
Burnham	d			08 32			08 52								09 39										
Slough 3	a			08 37	08 49		08 57							09 24	09 44		09 51				09 54			10 09	
	d	08 25		08 37	08 50		08 57					09 14		09 24	09 44		09 51				09 54			10 10	
Langley	d	08 30		08 42			09 01		←					09 28							09 58				
Iver	d			08 45			09 04		09 04					09 31							10 01				←
West Drayton	d	08 35		08 49			→		09 08			09 21		09 35	09 51						10 05				10 05
Heathrow Terminal 5 ✈	d					*08b42*							*09b12*							*09b42*	→				
Heathrow Terminal 4 ✈	d					08 51							09 21							09 51					
Heathrow Terminals 1-2-3 2 ✈	d					08 57							09 27						←	09 57					
Hayes & Harlington	d	08 39		08 53		09 03			09 13			09 26	09 33	09 40	09 56				09 56	10 03					10 10
Southall	d	08 43		08 57		09 06			09 17			09 30	09 36	09 43	→					10 06					10 13
Hanwell	d					09 09							09 39							10 09					
Greenford ⊖	d		08 46								09 16							09 46							
South Greenford	d		08 49								09 19							09 49							
Castle Bar Park	d		08 52								09 22							09 52							
Drayton Green	d		08 54								09 24							09 54							
West Ealing	d		08 56			09 11					09 26		09 41					09 56		10 11					
Ealing Broadway ⊖	d	08 49	08 59	09 03		09 14			09 23		09 29	09 36	09 44	09 49				09 59	10 03	10 14					10 19
Acton Main Line	d		09 03								09 33							10 03							
London Paddington 15 ⊖	a	09 02	09 12	09 18	09 21	09 24		09 26	09 35		09 42	09 47	09 54	10 01			10 10	10 12	10 16	10 24				10 28	10 31

Station		GW 1	GW 1	HC	GW 1	GW 1	GW 1 ◇	GW 1	GW 1	GW 1	HC		GW 1	GW 1	GW 1 ◇	GW 1	GW 1	GW 1	HC	GW 1	GW 1	GW 1 ◇	GW 1		GW 1
Oxford	d				09 07		10 01						09 37	*10 15*	10 31					10 07		11 01			
Reading 7	d				10 03	10 18	10 26						10 33	10 48	10 56					11 03	11 18	11 26			
Twyford 3	d		←		10 09	10 24				←			10 39	10 54				←		11 09	11 24				
Maidenhead 3	d		10 02		10 17	10 32				10 32			10 47	11 02				11 02		11 17	11 32				
Taplow	d		10 06			→				10 36				→				11 06			→				
Burnham	d		10 09							10 39								11 09							
Slough 3	a		10 14		10 24		10 39			10 44			10 54		11 09			11 14		11 24		11 39			
	d		10 14		10 24		10 40			10 44			10 54		11 10			11 14		11 24		11 40			
Langley	d				10 28								10 58							11 28					
Iver	d				10 31			←					11 01			←				11 31			←		
West Drayton	d		10 21		10 35			10 35		10 51			11 05			11 05		11 21		11 35			11 35		
Heathrow Terminal 5 ✈	d			*10b12*	→						*10b42*		→						*11b12*	→					
Heathrow Terminal 4 ✈	d			10 21							10 51								11 21						
Heathrow Terminals 1-2-3 2 ✈	d			10 27							10 57								11 27						
Hayes & Harlington	d		10 26	10 33				10 40		10 56	11 03					11 10		11 26	11 33				11 40		
Southall	d			10 36				10 43			11 06					11 13			11 36				11 43		
Hanwell	d			10 39							11 09								11 39						
Greenford ⊖	d	10 16							10 46								11 16								11 46
South Greenford	d	10 19							10 49								11 19								11 49
Castle Bar Park	d	10 22							10 52								11 22								11 52
Drayton Green	d	10 24							10 54								11 24								11 54
West Ealing	d	10 26		10 41					10 56		11 11						11 26		11 41						11 56
Ealing Broadway ⊖	d	10 29	10 33	10 44				10 49	10 59	11 03	11 14					11 19	11 29	11 33	11 44				11 49		11 59
Acton Main Line	d	10 33							11 03								11 33								12 03
London Paddington 15 ⊖	a	10 42	10 46	10 54			10 59	11 01	11 12	11 16	11 24				11 30	11 31	11 42	11 46	11 54			11 58	12 01		12 12

Station		GW 1	HC	GW 1	GW 1	GW 1 ◇	GW 1	GW 1	GW 1	HC	GW 1	GW 1		GW 1 ◇	GW 1	GW 1	GW 1	HC	GW 1	GW 1	GW 1 ◇	GW 1	GW 1	GW 1	HC
Oxford	d			10 37	*11 15*	11 31					11 07			12 01					11 37	*12 15*	12 31				
Reading 7	d			11 33	11 48	11 56					12 03	12 18		12 26					12 33	12 48	12 56				
Twyford 3	d	←		11 39	11 54				←		12 09	12 24					←		12 39	12 54				←	
Maidenhead 3	d	11 32		11 47	12 02				12 02		12 17	12 32					12 32		12 47	13 02				13 02	
Taplow	d	11 36			→				12 06			→					12 36			→				13 06	
Burnham	d	11 39							12 09								12 39							13 09	
Slough 3	a	11 44		11 54		12 09			12 14		12 24			12 39			12 44		12 54		13 09			13 14	
	d	11 44		11 54		12 10			12 14		12 24			12 40			12 44		12 54		13 10			13 14	
Langley	d			11 58							12 28								12 58						
Iver	d			12 01			←				12 31				←				13 01			←			
West Drayton	d	11 51		12 05			12 05		12 21		12 35				12 35		12 51		13 05			13 05		13 21	
Heathrow Terminal 5 ✈	d		*11b42*	→						*12b12*	→							*12b42*	→						*13b12*
Heathrow Terminal 4 ✈	d		11 51							12 21								12 51							13 21
Heathrow Terminals 1-2-3 2 ✈	d		11 57							12 27								12 57							13 27
Hayes & Harlington	d	11 56	12 03				12 10		12 26	12 33					12 40		12 56	13 03				13 10		13 26	13 33
Southall	d		12 06				12 13			12 36					12 43			13 06				13 13			13 36
Hanwell	d		12 09							12 39								13 09							13 39
Greenford ⊖	d							12 16								12 46							13 16		
South Greenford	d							12 19								12 49							13 19		
Castle Bar Park	d							12 22								12 52							13 22		
Drayton Green	d							12 24								12 54							13 24		
West Ealing	d		12 11					12 26		12 41						12 56		13 11					13 26		13 41
Ealing Broadway ⊖	d	12 03	12 14				12 19	12 29	12 33	12 44					12 49	12 59	13 03	13 14				13 19	13 29	13 33	13 44
Acton Main Line	d							12 33								13 03							13 33		
London Paddington 15 ⊖	a	12 16	12 24			12 29	12 31	12 42	12 46	12 54				13 00	13 01	13 12	13 16	13 24			13 28	13 31	13 42	13 46	13 54

For general notes see front of timetable
For details of catering facilities see Directory of Train Operators

For fast services between Reading and London Paddington see Table 116

A From Bourne End (Table 120)
b Change at Heathrow Terminals 1-2-3

Reading and Greenford → London

(Local services only)

Network Diagram - see first page of Table 116

		GW 1		GW 1	GW 1◇	GW 1	GW 1	GW 1	HC	GW 1	GW 1	GW 1◇ 🛒	GW 1	GW 1		GW 1	HC	GW 1	GW 1	GW 1◇	GW 1	GW 1	GW 1	HC	GW 1
Oxford	d	12 07			13 01					12 37	*13 15*	13 31						13 07		14 01					13 37
Reading 7	d	13 03		13 18	13 26					13 33	13 48	13 56						14 03	14 18	14 26					14 33
Twyford 3	d	13 09		13 24				←		13 39	13 54					←		14 09	14 24				←		14 39
Maidenhead 3	d	13 17		13 32				13 32		13 47	14 02					14 02		14 17	14 32				14 32		14 47
Taplow	d			→				13 36			→					14 06			→				14 36		
Burnham	d							13 39								14 09							14 39		
Slough 3	a	13 24			13 39			13 44		13 54		14 09				14 14		14 24		14 39			14 44		14 54
	d	13 24			13 39			13 44		13 54		14 10				14 14		14 24		14 40			14 44		14 54
Langley	d	13 28								13 58								14 28							14 58
Iver	d	13 31				←				14 01			←					14 31			←				15 01
West Drayton	d	13 35				13 35		13 51		14 05			14 05			14 21		14 35			14 35		14 51		15 05
Heathrow Terminal 5 ✈	d	→							*13b42*	→							*14b12*	→						*14b42*	→
Heathrow Terminal 4 ✈	d								13 51								14 21							14 51	
Heathrow Terminals 1-2-3 2 ✈	d								13 57								14 27							14 57	
Hayes & Harlington	d					13 40		13 56	14 03				14 10			14 26	14 33				14 40		14 56	15 03	
Southall	d					13 43			14 06				14 13				14 36				14 43			15 06	
Hanwell	d								14 09								14 39							15 09	
Greenford Θ	d						13 46							14 16								14 46			
South Greenford	d						13 49							14 19								14 49			
Castle Bar Park	d						13 52							14 22								14 52			
Drayton Green	d						13 54							14 24								14 54			
West Ealing	d						13 56		14 11					14 26			14 41					14 56		15 11	
Ealing Broadway Θ	d					13 49	13 59	14 03	14 14				14 19	14 29		14 33	14 44				14 49	14 59	15 03	15 14	
Acton Main Line	d						14 03							14 33								15 03			
London Paddington 15 Θ	a				13 59	14 01	14 12	14 16	14 24			14 29	14 31	14 42		14 46	14 54			15 01	15 01	15 12	15 16	15 24	

		GW 1	GW 1◇	GW 1		GW 1	GW 1	HC	GW 1	GW 1	GW 1◇	GW 1	GW 1	GW 1	HC	GW 1		GW 1	GW 1◇ ☕	GW 1	GW 1	GW 1	HC	GW 1	GW 1
Oxford	d	*14 15*	14 31						14 07		15 01					14 37		*15 15*	15 31					15 07	
Reading 7	d	14 48	14 56						15 03	15 18	15 26					15 33		15 48	15 56					16 03	16 18
Twyford 3	d	14 54					←		15 09	15 24				←		15 39		15 54				←		16 09	16 24
Maidenhead 3	d	15 02					15 02		15 17	15 32				15 32		15 47		16 02				16 02		16 17	16 32
Taplow	d	→					15 06			→				15 36				→				16 06			→
Burnham	d						15 09							15 39								16 09			
Slough 3	a		15 09				15 14		15 24		15 39			15 44		15 54			16 09			16 14		16 24	
	d		15 10				15 14		15 24		15 39			15 44		15 54			16 10			16 14		16 24	
Langley	d								15 28							15 58								16 28	
Iver	d			←					15 31			←				16 01				←				16 31	
West Drayton	d			15 05			15 21		15 35			15 35		15 51		16 05				16 05		16 21		16 35	
Heathrow Terminal 5 ✈	d							*15b12*	→						*15b42*	→							*16b12*	→	
Heathrow Terminal 4 ✈	d							15 21							15 51								16 21		
Heathrow Terminals 1-2-3 2 ✈	d							15 27							15 57								16 27		
Hayes & Harlington	d			15 10			15 26	15 33				15 40		15 56	16 03					16 10		16 26	16 33		
Southall	d			15 13				15 36				15 43			16 06					16 13			16 36		
Hanwell	d							15 39							16 09								16 39		
Greenford Θ	d					15 16							15 46								16 16				
South Greenford	d					15 19							15 49								16 19				
Castle Bar Park	d					15 22							15 52								16 22				
Drayton Green	d					15 24							15 54								16 24				
West Ealing	d					15 26		15 41					15 56		16 11						16 26		16 41		
Ealing Broadway Θ	d			15 19		15 29	15 33	15 44				15 49	15 59	16 03	16 14					16 19	16 29	16 33	16 44		
Acton Main Line	d					15 33							16 03								16 33				
London Paddington 15 Θ	a		15 28	15 31		15 42	15 46	15 54			16 00	16 01	16 12	16 16	16 24				16 27	16 31	16 42	16 46	16 54		

		GW 1◇	GW 1	GW 1	GW 1	HC		GW 1	GW 1	GW 1◇ ☕	GW 1	GW 1	GW 1	HC	GW 1	GW 1◇ ☕	GW 1	GW 1◇		GW 1	GW 1	GW 1	HC	GW 1	GW 1
Oxford	d	16 01						15 37	*16 15*	16 31					16 07			17 01						16 37	
Reading 7	d	16 26						16 33	16 48	16 56					17 03	17 18	17 18	17 26						17 33	17 42
Twyford 3	d				←			16 39	16 54				←		17 09		17 24					←		17 39	17 48
Maidenhead 3	d				16 32			16 47	17 02				17 02		17 17		17 32					17 32		17 47	17 56
Taplow	d				16 36				→				17 06				→					17 36			17 59
Burnham	d				16 39								17 09									17 39			18 02
Slough 3	a	16 39			16 44			16 54		17 09			17 14		17 24	17 31		17 39				17 44		17 54	18 07
	d	16 40			16 44			16 54		17 10			17 14		17 24	17 32		17 40				17 44		17 54	18 07
Langley	d							16 58							17 28									17 58	
Iver	d		←					17 01			←				17 31					←				18 01	
West Drayton	d		16 35		16 51			17 05			17 05		17 21		17 35					17 35		17 51		18 05	18 14
Heathrow Terminal 5 ✈	d					*16b42*		→						*17b12*	→								*17b42*		
Heathrow Terminal 4 ✈	d					16 51								17 21									17 51		
Heathrow Terminals 1-2-3 2 ✈	d					16 57								17 27									17 57		
Hayes & Harlington	d		16 40		16 56	17 03					17 10		17 26	17 33						17 40		17 56	18 03	18 10	18 19
Southall	d		16 43			17 06					17 13			17 36						17 43			18 06	18 13	
Hanwell	d					17 09								17 39									18 09		
Greenford Θ	d			16 46								17 16									17 46				
South Greenford	d			16 49								17 19									17 49				
Castle Bar Park	d			16 52								17 22									17 52				
Drayton Green	d			16 54								17 24									17 54				
West Ealing	d			16 56		17 11						17 26		17 41							17 56		18 11		
Ealing Broadway Θ	d		16 49	16 59	17 03	17 14					17 19	17 29	17 33	17 44						17 49	17 59	18 03	18 14	18 19	18 26
Acton Main Line	d			17 03								17 33									18 03				
London Paddington 15 Θ	a	16 58	17 01	17 12	17 16	17 24				17 27	17 31	17 42	17 46	17 54		17 54		17 59		18 01	18 12	18 16	18 24	18 31	18 37

For general notes see front of timetable
For details of catering facilities see Directory of Train Operators

For fast services between Reading and London Paddington see Table 116

b Change at Heathrow Terminals 1-2-3

Reading and Greenford → London

(Local services only)

Network Diagram - see first page of Table 116

		GW 1	GW 1	HC	GW 1	GW 1	GW 1	GW 1 ◇		GW 1	GW 1	GW 1	HC	GW 1	GW 1	GW 1 ◇	GW 1	GW 1	GW 1	HC		GW 1	GW 1	GW 1 ◇	GW 1
Oxford	d		*17 15*		17 07		*17 37*	18 01						17 31	*18 15*	18 31						18 07		19 01	
Reading 7	d		17 54		17 58		18 18	18 26						18 33	18 48	18 56						19 03	19 18	19 26	
Twyford 3	d				18 05		18 24					←		18 39	18 54				←			19 09	19 24		
Maidenhead 3	d		18 08		18 13	18 25	18 32					18 32		18 48	19 02				19 02			19 21	19 32		
Taplow	d						→					18 36			→				19 06				→		
Burnham	d											18 39							19 09						
Slough 3	a		18 16		18 20	18 33		18 39				18 44		18 54		19 09			19 14			19 29		19 39	
	d		18 17		18 24	18 33		18 40				18 44		18 54		19 10			19 14			19 29		19 39	
Langley	d				18 28									18 58								19 33			
Iver	d				18 31									19 01			←					19 36			←
West Drayton	d				18 35							18 51		19 05			19 05		19 21			19 39			19 39
Heathrow Terminal 5 ✈	d			18b12									18b42	→						19b12		→			
Heathrow Terminal 4 ✈	d			18 21									18 51							19 21					
Heathrow Terminals 1-2-3 2 ✈	d			18 27						←			18 57							19 27					
Hayes & Harlington	d		18 27	18 33	18 40	18 44				18 44		18 56	19 03				19 10		19 26	19 33					19 44
Southall	d			18 36	18 43	→							19 06				19 13			19 36					19 47
Hanwell	d			18 39									19 09							19 39					
Greenford ⊖	d	18 16									18 46							19 16							
South Greenford	d	18 19									18 49							19 19							
Castle Bar Park	d	18 22									18 52							19 22							
Drayton Green	d	18 24									18 54							19 24							
West Ealing	d	18 26		18 41							18 56		19 11					19 26		19 41					
Ealing Broadway ⊖	d	18 29	18 34	18 44	18 49					18 53	18 59	19 05	19 14				19 19	19 29	19 33	19 44					19 53
Acton Main Line	d	18 33									19 03							19 33							
London Paddington 15 ⊖	a	18 42	18 46	18 54	19 00			18 59		19 04	19 12	19 18	19 24			19 29	19 30	19 42	19 46	19 54				20 00	20 04

		GW 1	GW 1	HC	GW 1	GW 1	GW 1 ◇	GW 1	GW 1	GW 1		HC	GW 1	GW 1	GW 1	HC	GW 1	GW 1	GW 1 ◇ ☕	GW 1	GW 1	HC		GW 1	GW 1 ◇
Oxford	d				18 37	*19 15*	19 31						19 10				19c37	*20 15*	20 31						21 01
Reading 7	d				19 33	19 48	19 56						19 58		20 18		20 33	20 48	20 56					21 18	21 26
Twyford 3	d		←		19 42	19 54				←			20 04		20 24		20 39	20 54			←			21 24	
Maidenhead 3	d		19 32		19 50	20 02				20 02			20 12		20 32		20 47	21 02			21 02			→	
Taplow	d		19 36			→				20 06					20 36			→			21 06				
Burnham	d		19 39							20 09					20 39						21 09				
Slough 3	a		19 44		19 57		20 09			20 14			20 19		20 44		20 54		21 09		21 14				21 39
	d		19 44		19 57		20 10			20 14			20 24		20 44		20 54		21 10		21 14				21 40
Langley	d				20 01								20 28				20 58				21 17				
Iver	d				20 04			←					20 31				21 01				21 20				
West Drayton	d		19 51		20 08			20 08		20 21			20 35		20 51		21 05				21 24				
Heathrow Terminal 5 ✈	d			19b42	→							20b12				20b42						21b12			
Heathrow Terminal 4 ✈	d			19 51								20 21				20 51						21 21			
Heathrow Terminals 1-2-3 2 ✈	d			19 57								20 27				20 57						21 27			
Hayes & Harlington	d		19 56	20 03				20 13		20 26		20 33	20 40		20 56	21 03	21 10				21 28	21 33			
Southall	d			20 06				20 16				20 36	20 43			21 06	21 13					21 36			
Hanwell	d			20 09								20 39				21 09						21 39			
Greenford ⊖	d	19 46							20 16					20 46						21 16					
South Greenford	d	19 49							20 19					20 49						21 19					
Castle Bar Park	d	19 52							20 22					20 52						21 22					
Drayton Green	d	19 54							20 24					20 54						21 24					
West Ealing	d	19 56		20 11					20 26			20 41		20 56		21 11				21 26		21 41			
Ealing Broadway ⊖	d	19 59	20 03	20 14				20 22	20 29	20 33		20 44	20 49	20 59	21 03	21 14	21 19			21 29	21 35	21 44			
Acton Main Line	d	20 03							20 33					21 03						21 33					
London Paddington 15 ⊖	a	20 12	20 16	20 24			20 29	20 33	20 42	20 46		20 54	20 59	21 12	21 16	21 24	21 29		21 29	21 42	21 48	21 54			21 58

		GW 1	GW 1	HC	GW 1	GW FO 1 ◇	GW FX 1	GW FX 1 ◇	HC	GW FX 1	GW FO 1	GW 1 ◇		HC	GW 1	GW FO 1	GW FX 1	GW FO 1	HC	GW 1	GW 1	GW 1 ◇			
Oxford	d				20 37	21 31	*21 15*	21 31				22 11			21 38	22 33	22 33					23 05			
Reading 7	d		←		21 33	22 06	22 00	22 06			22 15	22 46			22 46	23 59	22 59				23 15	23 35			
Twyford 3	d		21 24		21 39		22 06				22 22				22 55						23 22				
Maidenhead 3	d		21 32		21 47		22 14				22 30				23 03						23 29	23 47			
Taplow	d				21 50		22 17				22 33				23 07						23 33				
Burnham	d				21 53		22 20				22 36				23 10						23 36				
Slough 3	a		21 40		21 58	22 21	22 25	22 28		←	22 41	23 03			23 15	23 12	23 18			←	23 41	23 54			
	d		21 40		21 58	22 22	22 35	22 28		22 35	22 41	22 04			23 27	23 13	23 18			23 27	23 41	23 55			
Langley	d		21 44		22 02		→			22 39	22 45				→					23 31	23 45				
Iver	d		21 47		22 05					22 42	22 48							←		23 34	23 48				
West Drayton	d		21 51		22 09					22 46	22 52							23 23		23 38	23 52				
Heathrow Terminal 5 ✈	d			21b42					22b12					22b42					23b12						
Heathrow Terminal 4 ✈	d			21 51					22 21					22 51					23 21						
Heathrow Terminals 1-2-3 2 ✈	d			21 57					22 27					22 57					23 27						
Hayes & Harlington	d		21 55	22 03	22 14				22 33	22 51	22 56			23 03				23 28	23 33	23 43	23 56				
Southall	d		21 59	22 06					22 36	22 54	23 00			23 06				23 31	23 36	23 47	23 59				
Hanwell	d			22 09					22 39					23 09					23 39						
Greenford ⊖	d	21 46																							
South Greenford	d	21 49																							
Castle Bar Park	d	21 52																							
Drayton Green	d	21 54																							
West Ealing	d	21 56		22 11					22 41					23 11					23 41						
Ealing Broadway ⊖	d	21 59	22 04	22 14	22 21				22 44	23 00	23 05			23 14				23 37	23 44	23 52	00 06				
Acton Main Line	d	22 03																							
London Paddington 15 ⊖	a	22 14	22 16	22 24	22 32	22 40		22 52	22 54	23 10	23 17	23 24		23 24		23 30	23 37	23 48	23 54	00 03	00 17	00 21			

For general notes see front of timetable
For details of catering facilities see Directory of Train Operators

For fast services between Reading and London Paddington see Table 116

b Change at Heathrow Terminals 1-2-3

c By changing at Reading, passengers may depart at 2001

Saturdays

Reading and Greenford → London

(Local services only)

Network Diagram - see first page of Table 116

Station		GW 1	HC	GW 1	GW 1 ◇	GW 1	GW 1 A	GW 1	GW 1	HC	GW 1	HC	GW 1	GW 1	GW 1		HC	GW 1	GW 1	GW 1	HC	GW 1	GW 1	GW 1 ◇	GW 1
Oxford	d				00 06		00 19		03 59									05 07				05 37		06 31	
Reading 7	d	23p15		00 15	00 39		01 10	04 10	04 40		05 10		05 33		05 48			06 03		06 18		06 33	06 48	07 00	
Twyford 3	d	23p22		00 21			01 17	04 16	04 46		05 16		05 39		05 54			06 09		06 24		06 39	06 54		
Maidenhead 3	d	23p29		00 29			01 25	04 24	04 54		05 24		05 47		06 02			06 17		06 32		06 47	07 02		
Taplow	d	23p33		00 32							05 28				06 06					06 36			07 06		
Burnham	d	23p36		00 35							05 31				06 09					06 39			07 09		
Slough 3	a	23p41		00 40	00 53		01 32	04 31	05 01		05 35		05 54		06 13			06 24		06 43		06 54	07 13	07 16	
	d	23p41		00 40	00 53		01 32	04 32	05 02		05 36		05 54		06 14			06 24		06 44		06 54	07 14	07 17	
Langley	d	23p45		00 44							05 40		05 58					06 28				06 58			
Iver	d	23p48									05 43		06 01					06 31				07 01			
West Drayton	d	23p52		00 49				04 38			05 45		06 05		06 21			06 35		06 51		07 05	07 21		
Heathrow Terminal 5 ✈	d		23b53							05c07		05c42					06c12				06c42				
Heathrow Terminal 4 ✈	d		00 01							05 23		05 51					06 21				06 51				
Heathrow Terminals 1-2-3 2 ✈	d		00 07			←				05 29		05 57					06 27				06 57				
Hayes & Harlington	d	23p56	00 13	00 54		00 54	01 41	04 43	05 11	05 35	05 51	06 03	06 10		06 26		06 33	06 40		06 56	07 03	07 10	07 26		
Southall	d	23p59	00 16	→		00 57		04 46	05 14	05 38	05 54	06 06	06 13				06 36	06 43			07 06	07 13	→		
Hanwell	d									05 41		06 09					06 39				07 09				
Greenford ⊖	d													06 16					06 46						07 16
South Greenford	d													06 19					06 49						07 19
Castle Bar Park	d													06 22					06 52						07 22
Drayton Green	d													06 24					06 54						07 24
West Ealing	d									05 43		06 11		06 26			06 41		06 56		07 11				07 26
Ealing Broadway ⊖	d	00 06	00 21			01 03	01 48	04 52	05 20	05 46	06 00	06 14	06 19	06 29	06 33		06 44	06 49	06 59	07 03	07 14	07 19			07 29
Acton Main Line	d								05 23		06 03			06 33					07 03						07 33
London Paddington 15 ⊖	a	00 17	00 30		01 11	01 14	02 00	05 01	05 31	05 56	06 11	06 24	06 31	06 42	06 46		06 54	07 01	07 12	07 16	07 24	07 31		07 37	07 42

Station		GW 1	HC	GW 1	GW 1	GW 1	HC	GW 1		GW 1	GW 1 ◇	GW 1	GW 1	GW 1	HC	GW 1 B	GW 1 C	GW 1	GW 1 ◇	GW 1 B	GW 1 C	GW 1	GW 1		HC
Oxford	d			06 07				06 37		*07 16*	07 31					07 07	07 07		08 01						
Reading 7	d			07 03		07 18		07 33		07 48	07 56					07 58	08 03	08 18	08 26						
Twyford 3	d			07 09		07 24		07 39		07 54				←		08 09	08 09	08 24					←		
Maidenhead 3	d			07 17		07 32		07 47		08 02				08 02		08 17	08 17	08 32					08 32		
Taplow	d					07 36				→				08 06				→					08 36		
Burnham	d					07 39								08 09									08 39		
Slough 3	a			07 24		07 43		07 54			08 09			08 13		08 24	08 24		08 39				08 43		
	d			07 24		07 44		07 54			08 10			08 14		08 24	08 24		08 40				08 44		
Langley	d			07 28				07 58								08 28	08 28								
Iver	d			07 31				08 01				←				08 31	08 31			←	←				
West Drayton	d			07 35		07 51		08 05				08 05		08 21		08 35	08 35			08 35	08 35		08 51		
Heathrow Terminal 5 ✈	d		07c12				07c42	→							08c12	→	→								08c42
Heathrow Terminal 4 ✈	d		07 21				07 51								08 21										08 51
Heathrow Terminals 1-2-3 2 ✈	d	←	07 27				07 57								08 27										08 57
Hayes & Harlington	d	07 26	07 33	07 40		07 56	08 03					08 10		08 26	08 33					08 40	08 40		08 56		09 03
Southall	d		07 36	07 43			08 06					08 13			08 36					08 43	08 43				09 06
Hanwell	d		07 39				08 09								08 39										09 09
Greenford ⊖	d				07 46								08 16									08 46			
South Greenford	d				07 49								08 19									08 49			
Castle Bar Park	d				07 52								08 22									08 52			
Drayton Green	d				07 54								08 24									08 54			
West Ealing	d		07 41		07 56		08 11						08 26		08 41							08 56			09 11
Ealing Broadway ⊖	d	07 33	07 44	07 49	07 59	08 03	08 14					08 19	08 29	08 33	08 44					08 49	08 49	08 59	09 03		09 14
Acton Main Line	d				08 03								08 33									09 03			
London Paddington 15 ⊖	a	07 46	07 54	08 01	08 12	08 16	08 24				08 30	08 31	08 42	08 46	08 54				08 59	09 01	09 01	09 12	09 16		09 24

Station		GW 1	GW 1	GW 1 ◇	GW 1	GW 1	GW 1	HC	GW 1	GW 1	GW 1 ◇	GW 1	GW 1	GW 1	HC		GW 1	GW 1	GW 1 ◇	GW 1	GW 1	GW 1	HC	GW 1	GW 1
Oxford	d	07 37	*08 16*	08 31					08 07		09 01						08 37	*09 16*	09 31					09 07	
Reading 7	d	08 33	08 48	08 57					09 03	09 18	09 26						09 33	09 48	09 56					10 03	10 18
Twyford 3	d	08 39	08 54				←		09 09	09 24				←			09 39	09 54				←		10 09	10 24
Maidenhead 3	d	08 47	09 02				09 02		09 17	09 32				09 32			09 47	10 02				10 02		10 17	10 32
Taplow	d		→				09 06			→				09 36				→				10 06			→
Burnham	d						09 09							09 39								10 09			
Slough 3	a	08 54		09 10			09 13		09 24		09 39			09 43			09 54		10 09			10 13		10 24	
	d	08 54		09 11			09 14		09 24		09 40			09 44			09 54		10 10			10 14		10 24	
Langley	d	08 58							09 28								09 58							10 28	
Iver	d	09 01			←				09 31			←					10 01			←				10 31	
West Drayton	d	09 05			09 05		09 21		09 35			09 35		09 51			10 05			10 05		10 21		10 35	
Heathrow Terminal 5 ✈	d	→						09c12	→						09c42		→						10c12	→	
Heathrow Terminal 4 ✈	d							09 21							09 51								10 21		
Heathrow Terminals 1-2-3 2 ✈	d							09 27							09 57								10 27		
Hayes & Harlington	d				09 10		09 26	09 33				09 40		09 56	10 03					10 10		10 26	10 33		
Southall	d				09 13			09 36				09 43			10 06					10 13			10 36		
Hanwell	d							09 39							10 09								10 39		
Greenford ⊖	d					09 16							09 46								10 16				
South Greenford	d					09 19							09 49								10 19				
Castle Bar Park	d					09 22							09 52								10 22				
Drayton Green	d					09 24							09 54								10 24				
West Ealing	d					09 26		09 41					09 56		10 11						10 26		10 41		
Ealing Broadway ⊖	d				09 19	09 29	09 33	09 44				09 49	09 59	10 03	10 14					10 19	10 29	10 33	10 44		
Acton Main Line	d					09 33							10 03								10 33				
London Paddington 15 ⊖	a			09 30	09 31	09 42	09 46	09 54			09 59	10 01	10 12	10 16	10 24				10 29	10 31	10 42	10 46	10 54		

For general notes see front of timetable
For details of catering facilities see Directory of Train Operators

For fast services between Reading and London Paddington see Table 116

A From Banbury (Table 116)
B Until 5 September
C From 12 September

b Previous night. Change at Heathrow Terminals 1-2-3
c Change at Heathrow Terminals 1-2-3

Table 117

Saturdays

Reading and Greenford → London

(Local services only)

Network Diagram - see first page of Table 116

	GW 1	GW 1	GW 1	GW 1	HC	GW 1	GW 1	GW 1 ◇	GW 1	GW 1	GW 1	HC	GW 1	GW 1	GW 1	GW 1	GW 1	GW 1	HC	GW 1	GW 1	GW 1 ◇
Oxford d	10 01					09 37	*10 16*	10 31					10 07		11 01					10 37	*11 16*	11 31
Reading 7 d	10 25					10 33	10 48	10 56					11 03	11 18	11 25					11 33	11 48	11 56
Twyford 3 d				←		10 39	10 54				←		11 09	11 24				←		11 39	11 54	
Maidenhead 3 d				10 32		10 47	11 02				11 02		11 17	11 32				11 32		11 47	12 02	
Taplow d				10 36			→				11 06			→				11 36			→	
Burnham d				10 39							11 09							11 39				
Slough 3 a	10 40			10 43		10 54		11 09			11 13		11 24		11 39			11 43		11 54		12 09
d	10 40			10 44		10 54		11 10			11 14		11 24		11 40			11 44		11 54		12 10
Langley d						10 58							11 28							11 58		
Iver d		←				11 01			←				11 31			←				12 01		
West Drayton d		10 35		10 51		11 05			11 05		11 21		11 35			11 35		11 51		12 05		
Heathrow Terminal 5 ✈ d					10b42	→						11b12	→						11b42	→		
Heathrow Terminal 4 ✈ d					10 51							11 21							11 51			
Heathrow Terminals 1-2-3 2 ✈ d					10 57							11 27							11 57			
Hayes & Harlington d		10 40		10 56	11 03				11 10		11 26	11 33				11 40		11 56	12 03			
Southall d		10 43			11 06				11 13			11 36				11 43			12 06			
Hanwell d					11 09							11 39							12 09			
Greenford ⊖ d			10 46							11 16							11 46					
South Greenford d			10 49							11 19							11 49					
Castle Bar Park d			10 52							11 22							11 52					
Drayton Green d			10 54							11 24							11 54					
West Ealing d			10 56		11 11					11 26		11 41					11 56		12 11			
Ealing Broadway ⊖ d		10 49	10 59	11 03	11 14				11 19	11 29	11 33	11 44				11 49	11 59	12 03	12 14			
Acton Main Line d			11 03							11 33							12 03					
London Paddington 15 ⊖ a	10 59	11 01	11 12	11 16	11 24			11 29	11 31	11 42	11 46	11 54			11 59	12 01	12 12	12 16	12 24			12 30

	GW 1	GW 1	GW 1	HC	GW 1	GW 1	GW 1 ◇ A	GW 1 ◇ B	GW 1	GW 1	GW 1	HC	GW 1	GW 1	GW 1 ◇	GW 1	GW 1	GW 1	HC	GW 1	GW 1	GW 1 ◇	GW 1
Oxford d					11 07		12 01	12 01					11 37	*12 16*	12 31					12 07		13 01	
Reading 7 d					12 03	12 18	12 24	12 25					12 33	12 48	12 55					13 03	13 18	13 25	
Twyford 3 d			←		12 09	12 24					←		12 39	12 54				←		13 09	13 24		
Maidenhead 3 d			12 02		12 17	12 32					12 32		12 47	13 02				13 02		13 17	13 32		
Taplow d			12 06			→					12 36			→				13 06			→		
Burnham d			12 09								12 39							13 09					
Slough 3 a			12 13		12 24		12 39	12 40			12 43		12 54		13 09			13 13		13 24		13 40	
d			12 14		12 24		12 39	12 40			12 44		12 54		13 10			13 14		13 24		13 40	
Langley d					12 28								12 58							13 28			
Iver d	←				12 31				←				13 01			←				13 31			←
West Drayton d	12 05		12 21		12 35				12 35		12 51		13 05			13 05		13 21		13 35			13 35
Heathrow Terminal 5 ✈ d				12b12	→							12b42	→						13b12	→			
Heathrow Terminal 4 ✈ d				12 21								12 51							13 21				
Heathrow Terminals 1-2-3 2 ✈ d				12 27								12 57							13 27				
Hayes & Harlington d	12 10		12 26	12 33					12 40		12 56	13 03				13 10		13 26	13 33				13 40
Southall d	12 13			12 36					12 43			13 06				13 13			13 36				13 43
Hanwell d				12 39								13 09							13 39				
Greenford ⊖ d		12 16								12 46							13 16						
South Greenford d		12 19								12 49							13 19						
Castle Bar Park d		12 22								12 52							13 22						
Drayton Green d		12 24								12 54							13 24						
West Ealing d		12 26		12 41						12 56		13 11					13 26		13 41				
Ealing Broadway ⊖ d	12 19	12 29	12 33	12 44					12 49	12 59	13 03	13 14				13 19	13 29	13 33	13 44				13 49
Acton Main Line d		12 33								13 03							13 33						
London Paddington 15 ⊖ a	12 31	12 42	12 46	12 54			12 59	12 59	13 01	13 12	13 16	13 24			13 30	13 31	13 42	13 46	13 54			13 59	14 01

	GW 1	GW 1	HC	GW 1	GW 1	GW 1 ◇	GW 1	GW 1	GW 1	HC	GW 1	GW 1	GW 1 ◇	GW 1	GW 1	GW 1	HC	GW 1	GW 1	GW 1 ◇	GW 1	GW 1
Oxford d				12 37	*13 16*	13 31					13 07		14 01					13 37	*14 16*	14 31		
Reading 7 d				13 33	13 48	13 55					14 03	14 18	14 25					14 33	14 48	14 56		
Twyford 3 d		←		13 39	13 54				←		14 09	14 24				←		14 39	14 54			
Maidenhead 3 d		13 32		13 47	14 02				14 02		14 17	14 32				14 32		14 47	15 02			
Taplow d		13 36			→				14 06			→				14 36			→			
Burnham d		13 39							14 09							14 39						
Slough 3 a		13 43		13 54		14 10			14 13		14 24		14 40			14 43		14 54		15 09		
d		13 44		13 54		14 10			14 14		14 24		14 40			14 44		14 54		15 10		
Langley d				13 58							14 28							14 58				
Iver d				14 01			←				14 31			←				15 01			←	
West Drayton d		13 51		14 05			14 05		14 21		14 35			14 35		14 51		15 05			15 05	
Heathrow Terminal 5 ✈ d			13b42	→						14b12	→						14b42	→				
Heathrow Terminal 4 ✈ d			13 51							14 21							14 51					
Heathrow Terminals 1-2-3 2 ✈ d			13 57							14 27							14 57					
Hayes & Harlington d		13 56	14 03				14 10		14 26	14 33				14 40		14 56	15 03				15 10	
Southall d			14 06				14 13			14 36				14 43			15 06				15 13	
Hanwell d			14 09							14 39							15 09					
Greenford ⊖ d	13 46							14 16							14 46							15 16
South Greenford d	13 49							14 19							14 49							15 19
Castle Bar Park d	13 52							14 22							14 52							15 22
Drayton Green d	13 54							14 24							14 54							15 24
West Ealing d	13 56		14 11					14 26		14 41					14 56		15 11					15 26
Ealing Broadway ⊖ d	13 59	14 03	14 14				14 19	14 29	14 33	14 44				14 49	14 59	15 03	15 14				15 19	15 29
Acton Main Line d	14 03							14 33							15 03							15 33
London Paddington 15 ⊖ a	14 12	14 16	14 24			14 29	14 31	14 42	14 46	14 54			14 59	15 01	15 12	15 16	15 24			15 29	15 31	15 42

For general notes see front of timetable
For details of catering facilities see Directory of Train Operators

For fast services between Reading and London Paddington see Table 116

A Until 5 September
B From 12 September
b Change at Heathrow Terminals 1-2-3

Table 117

Reading and Greenford → London

(Local services only)

Network Diagram - see first page of Table 116

		GW 1	HC	GW 1	GW 1	GW 1 ◇	GW 1	GW 1	GW 1	HC	GW 1	GW 1	GW 1	HC	GW 1		GW 1	GW 1 ◇ A	GW 1	GW 1	GW 1	HC	GW 1	GW 1	GW 1 ◇ ꟾP
Oxford	d			14 07		15 01					14 37		*15 16*		15b07			16 01					15c37	*16 16*	16 31
Reading 7	d			15 03	15 18	15 25					15 33		15 48		16 03		16 18	16 25					16 33	16 48	16 56
Twyford 3	d	←		15 09	15 24				←		15 39		15 54		16 09		16 24				←		16 39	16 54	
Maidenhead 3	d	15 02		15 17	15 32				15 32		15 47		16 02		16 17		16 32				16 32		16 47	17 02	
Taplow	d	15 06			→				15 36				16 06				→				16 36			→	
Burnham	d	15 09							15 39				16 09								16 39				
Slough 3	a	15 13		15 24		15 40			15 43		15 54		16 13		16 24			16 39			16 43		16 54		17 09
	d	15 14		15 24		15 40			15 44		15 54		16 14		16 24			16 40			16 44		16 54		17 10
Langley	d			15 28							15 58				16 28								16 58		
Iver	d			15 31			←				16 01				16 31				←				17 01		
West Drayton	d	15 21		15 35			15 35		15 51		16 05		16 21		16 35				16 35		16 51		17 05		
Heathrow Terminal 5 ✈	d		*15e12*	→						*15e42*				*16e12*	→							*16e42*	→		
Heathrow Terminal 4 ✈	d		15 21							15 51				16 21								16 51			
Heathrow Terminals 1-2-3 2 ✈	d		15 27							15 57				16 27								16 57			
Hayes & Harlington	d	15 26	15 33				15 40		15 56	16 03	16 10		16 26	16 33					16 40		16 56	17 03			
Southall	d		15 36				15 43			16 06	16 13			16 36					16 43			17 06			
Hanwell	d		15 39							16 09				16 39								17 09			
Greenford ⊖	d							15 46				16 16								16 46					
South Greenford	d							15 49				16 19								16 49					
Castle Bar Park	d							15 52				16 22								16 52					
Drayton Green	d							15 54				16 24								16 54					
West Ealing	d		15 41					15 56		16 11		16 26		16 41						16 56		17 11			
Ealing Broadway ⊖	d	15 33	15 44				15 49	15 59	16 03	16 14	16 19	16 29	16 33	16 44					16 49	16 59	17 03	17 14			
Acton Main Line	d							16 03				16 33								17 03					
London Paddington 15 ⊖	a	15 46	15 54			15 59	16 01	16 12	16 16	16 24	16 31	16 42	16 46	16 54				16 59	17 01	17 12	17 16	17 24			17 30

		GW 1	GW 1	GW 1	HC	GW 1	GW 1	GW 1 ◇		GW 1	GW 1	GW 1	HC	GW 1	GW 1	GW 1 ◇ ꟾP	GW 1	GW 1	GW 1	HC	GW 1	GW 1	GW 1 ◇		GW 1
Oxford	d					16 07		17 01						16 37	*17 16*	17 31					17 07		18 01		
Reading 7	d					17 03	17 18	17 25						17 33	17 48	17 57					18 03	18 18	18 25		
Twyford 3	d			←		17 09	17 24					←		17 39	17 54				←		18 09	18 24			
Maidenhead 3	d			17 02		17 17	17 32					17 32		17 47	18 02				18 02		18 17	18 32			
Taplow	d			17 06			→					17 36			→				18 06			→			
Burnham	d			17 09								17 39							18 09						
Slough 3	a			17 13		17 24		17 40				17 43		17 54		18 10			18 13		18 24		18 40		
	d			17 14		17 24		17 40				17 44		17 54		18 11			18 14		18 24		18 40		
Langley	d					17 28								17 58							18 28				
Iver	d	←				17 31				←				18 01			←				18 31				←
West Drayton	d	17 05		17 21		17 35				17 35		17 51		18 05			18 05		18 21		18 35				18 35
Heathrow Terminal 5 ✈	d				*17e12*	→							*17e42*	→						*18e12*	→				
Heathrow Terminal 4 ✈	d				17 21								17 51							18 21					
Heathrow Terminals 1-2-3 2 ✈	d				17 27								17 57							18 27					
Hayes & Harlington	d	17 10		17 26	17 33					17 40		17 56	18 03				18 10		18 26	18 33					18 40
Southall	d	17 13			17 36					17 43			18 06				18 13			18 36					18 43
Hanwell	d				17 39								18 09							18 39					
Greenford ⊖	d		17 16								17 46							18 16							
South Greenford	d		17 19								17 49							18 19							
Castle Bar Park	d		17 22								17 52							18 22							
Drayton Green	d		17 24								17 54							18 24							
West Ealing	d		17 26		17 41						17 56		18 11					18 26		18 41					
Ealing Broadway ⊖	d	17 19	17 29	17 33	17 44					17 49	17 59	18 03	18 14				18 19	18 29	18 33	18 44					18 49
Acton Main Line	d		17 33								18 03							18 33							
London Paddington 15 ⊖	a	17 31	17 42	17 46	17 54			17 59		18 01	18 12	18 16	18 24			18 29	18 31	18 42	18 46	18 54			18 59		19 01

		GW 1	GW 1	HC	GW 1	GW 1	GW 1 ◇ ꟾP	GW 1	GW 1	GW 1	HC	GW 1	GW 1	GW 1 ◇	GW 1		GW 1	GW 1	HC	GW 1	GW 1	GW 1 ◇ ꟾP	GW 1	GW 1	GW 1
Oxford	d				17 37	*18 16*	18 31					18 07		19 01						18 37	*19 16*	19 31			
Reading 7	d				18 33	18 48	18 56					19 03	19 18	19 25						19 33	19 48	19 56			
Twyford 3	d		←		18 39	18 54				←		19 09	19 24					←		19 39	19 54				←
Maidenhead 3	d		18 32		18 47	19 02				19 02		19 17	19 32					19 32		19 47	20 02				20 02
Taplow	d		18 36			→				19 06			→					19 36			→				20 06
Burnham	d		18 39							19 09								19 39							20 09
Slough 3	a		18 43		18 54		19 09			19 13		19 24		19 40				19 43		19 54		20 09			20 13
	d		18 44		18 54		19 10			19 14		19 24		19 40				19 44		19 54		20 10			20 14
Langley	d				18 58							19 28								19 58					
Iver	d				19 01			←				19 31			←					20 01			←		
West Drayton	d		18 51		19 05			19 05		19 21		19 35			19 35			19 51		20 05			20 05		20 21
Heathrow Terminal 5 ✈	d			*18e42*	→						*19e12*	→							*19e42*	→					
Heathrow Terminal 4 ✈	d			18 51							19 21								19 51						
Heathrow Terminals 1-2-3 2 ✈	d			18 57							19 27								19 57						
Hayes & Harlington	d		18 56	19 03				19 10		19 26	19 33				19 40			19 56	20 03				20 10		20 26
Southall	d			19 06				19 13			19 36				19 43				20 06				20 13		
Hanwell	d			19 09							19 39								20 09						
Greenford ⊖	d	18 46							19 16								19 46							20 16	
South Greenford	d	18 49							19 19								19 49							20 19	
Castle Bar Park	d	18 52							19 22								19 52							20 22	
Drayton Green	d	18 54							19 24								19 54							20 24	
West Ealing	d	18 56		19 11					19 26		19 41						19 56		20 11					20 26	
Ealing Broadway ⊖	d	18 59	19 03	19 14				19 19	19 29	19 33	19 44				19 49		19 59	20 03	20 14				20 19	20 29	20 33
Acton Main Line	d	19 03							19 33								20 03							20 33	
London Paddington 15 ⊖	a	19 12	19 16	19 24			19 29	19 31	19 42	19 46	19 54			19 59	20 01		20 12	20 16	20 24			20 29	20 31	20 42	20 46

For general notes see front of timetable
For details of catering facilities see Directory of Train Operators

For fast services between Reading and London Paddington see Table 116

A From 12 September

b By changing at Reading, passengers may depart at 1531

c By changing at Reading, passengers may depart at 1601

e Change at Heathrow Terminals 1-2-3

Reading and Greenford → London

(Local services only)

Saturdays

Network Diagram - see first page of Table 116

Station		HC	GW 1	GW 1	GW 1 ◇	GW 1	GW 1	GW 1		HC	GW 1	GW 1	GW 1 ◇	GW 1	GW 1	GW 1	HC	GW 1	GW 1	GW 1	GW 1	GW 1	GW 1		HC
Oxford	d		19 07		20 01						19 37	*20 16*	20 31					20 07		21 01					
Reading 7	d		20 03	20 18	20 25						20 33	20 48	20 53					21 03	21 18	21 25					
Twyford 3	d		20 09	20 24				←			20 39	20 54				←		21 09	21 24				←		
Maidenhead 3	d		20 17	20 32				20 32			20 47	21 02				21 02		21 17	21 32				21 32		
Taplow	d			→				20 36				→				21 06			→				21 36		
Burnham	d							20 39								21 09							21 39		
Slough 3	a		20 24		20 40			20 43			20 54		21 10			21 13		21 24		21 40			21 43		
	d		20 24		20 40			20 44			20 54		21 10			21 14		21 24		21 40			21 44		
Langley	d		20 28								20 58							21 28							
Iver	d		20 31			←					21 01			←				21 31			←				
West Drayton	d		20 35			20 35		20 51			21 05			21 05		21 21		21 35			21 35		21 51		
Heathrow Terminal 5	d	*20b12*	→							*20b42*	→						*21b12*	→							*21b42*
Heathrow Terminal 4	d	20 21								20 51							21 21								21 51
Heathrow Terminals 1-2-3 2	d	20 27								20 57							21 27								21 57
Hayes & Harlington	d	20 33				20 40		20 56		21 03				21 10		21 26	21 33				21 40		21 56		22 03
Southall	d	20 36				20 43				21 06				21 13			21 36				21 43				22 06
Hanwell	d	20 39								21 09							21 39								22 09
Greenford	⊖ d						20 46								21 16							21 46			
South Greenford	d						20 49								21 19							21 49			
Castle Bar Park	d						20 52								21 22							21 52			
Drayton Green	d						20 54								21 24							21 54			
West Ealing	d	20 41					20 56			21 11					21 26		21 41					21 56			22 11
Ealing Broadway	⊖ d	20 44				20 49	20 59	21 03		21 14				21 19	21 29	21 33	21 44				21 49	21 59	22 03		22 14
Acton Main Line	d						21 03								21 33							22 03			
London Paddington 15	⊖ a	20 54			20 59	21 01	21 12	21 16		21 24			21 30	21 31	21 42	21 46	21 54			21 59	22 01	22 12	22 16		22 24

Station		GW 1	GW 1	GW 1	GW 1	HC	GW 1	GW 1	GW 1 ◇	GW 1	HC	GW 1	GW 1	GW 1 ◇ A	GW 1		GW 1 ◇ B	GW 1	HC	GW 1	GW ◇	GW 1	GW 1		
Oxford	d	20 37	*21 16*	21 37				21 50	22 08				*22 16*	22 31			22 31				23 01		23 07		
Reading 7	d	21 33	21 48	22 05			22 18	22 32	22 35			←	22 48	22 56			22 56			23 18	23 31		00 03		
Twyford 3	d	21 39	21 54				22 24	22 39				22 39	22 54		←					23 24			00 09		
Maidenhead 3	d	21 47	22 02				22 32	→				22 47	23 02		23 02					23 32			00 17		
Taplow	d		22 06				22 36						→		23 06					23 36			00 21		
Burnham	d		22 09				22 39								23 09					23 39			00 24		
Slough 3	a	21 54	22 13	22 22			22 43		22 49			22 54		23 12	23 13		23 17			23 43	23 48		00 28		
	d	21 54	22 14	22 22			22 44		22 50			22 54		23 13	23 14		23 18			23 44	23 49		00 29		
Langley	d	21 58										22 58											00 33		
Iver	d	22 01										23 01											00 36		
West Drayton	d	22 05	22 21				22 51					23 05			23 21					23 51			00 39		
Heathrow Terminal 5	d					*22b12*					*22b42*								*23b12*						
Heathrow Terminal 4	d					22 21					22 51								23 21						
Heathrow Terminals 1-2-3 2	d				←	22 27				←	22 57							←	23 27			←			
Hayes & Harlington	d	22 10	22 26		22 26	22 33	22 56			22 56	23 03	23 10			23 26			23 26	23 33	23 56		23 56	00 44		
Southall	d	22 13	→			22 36	→				23 06	23 13			→				23 36	→		23 59	00 47		
Hanwell	d					22 39					23 09								23 39						
Greenford	⊖ d																								
South Greenford	d																								
Castle Bar Park	d																								
Drayton Green	d																								
West Ealing	d					22 41					23 11								23 41						
Ealing Broadway	⊖ d	22 19			22 33	22 44				23 03	23 14	23 19						23 33	23 44			00 03	00 53		
Acton Main Line	d																								
London Paddington 15	⊖ a	22 31		22 39	22 46	22 54			23 08	23 16	23 24	23 28		23 30			23 36	23 46	23 54		00 10	00 16	01 02		

Sundays

until 6 September

Station		GW 1	HC	GW 1	HC	GW 1	HC	GW 1		HC	GW 1	GW 1	GW 1 C	GW 1 D	GW 1 ◇ D	GW 1 ◇ C		HC	GW 1 C	GW 1 D	GW 1 D	GW 1 C	GW 1 C	GW 1 D	HC
Oxford	d			23p07									08 05		08 31	08 38				08 21					
Reading 7	d	23p18		00 03		06 22		07 22			08 04	08 22	08 50	08 50	09 06	09 06			09 18	09 18	09 26	09 36			
Twyford 3	d	23p24		00 09		06 28		07 28				08 28	08 56	08 56					09 24	09 24					
Maidenhead 3	d	23p32		00 17		06 36		07 36				08 36	09 04	09 04					09 36	09 36	09 38	09 49			
Taplow	d	23p36		00 21																					
Burnham	d	23p39		00 24		06 41		07 41				08 41							09 40	09 40					
Slough 3	a	23p43		00 28		06 45		07 45			08 22	08 45	09 11	09 11	09 25	09 25			09 45	09 45	09 48	09 57			
	d	23p44		00 29		06 46		07 46			08 23	08 46	09 12	09 12	09 27	09 27			09 45	09 45	09 48	09 58			
Langley	d			00 33		06 50		07 50				08 50	09 16	09 16					09 47	09 47					
Iver	d			00 36																					
West Drayton	d	23p51		00 39		06 55		07 55				08 55	09 21	09 21					09 53	09 53					
Heathrow Terminal 5	d		*23c53*		*06b03*		*07b03*			*08b03*								*09b13*							*09b42*
Heathrow Terminal 4	d		00 01		06 07		07 07			08 07								09 21							09 51
Heathrow Terminals 1-2-3 2	d		00 07		06 13		07 13			08 13								09 27					←	←	09 57
Hayes & Harlington	d	23p56	00 13	00 44	06 19	07 02	07 19	08 02		08 19		09 02	09 25	09 25				09 33	09 59	09 59			09 59	09 59	10 03
Southall	d	23p59	00 16	00 47	06 22	07 05	07 22	08 05		08 22		09 05	09 29	09 29				09 36	→	→			10 02	10 02	10 06
Hanwell	d																								
Greenford	⊖ d																								
South Greenford	d																								
Castle Bar Park	d																								
Drayton Green	d																								
West Ealing	d																								
Ealing Broadway	⊖ d	00 03	00 21	00 53	06 27	07 11	07 27	08 11		08 27		09 11	09 34	09 34				09 41					10 08	10 08	10 11
Acton Main Line	d																								
London Paddington 15	⊖ a	00 16	00 30	01 02	06 36	07 20	07 36	08 20		08 36	08 44	09 20	09 43	09 43	09 46	09 46		09 50			10 07	10 17	10 17	10 17	10 20

For general notes see front of timetable
For details of catering facilities see Directory of Train Operators

For fast services between Reading and London Paddington see Table 116

A From 12 September
B Until 5 September
C Until 12 July
D From 19 July

b Change at Heathrow Terminals 1-2-3
c Previous night. Change at Heathrow Terminals 1-2-3

Sundays

until 6 September

Reading and Greenford → London

(Local services only)

Network Diagram - see first page of Table 116

		GW		HC	GW	GW	GW	GW	HC	GW		HC	GW	GW	HC	GW	GW	HC		GW	GW	HC	GW	GW	HC
		1			1 ◇	1	1	1		1			1 ◇	1		1	1			◇	1		1	1	
Oxford	d	09 05			09 38					10 05			10 38				11 05			11 38				12 05	
Reading 7	d	09 52			10 10	10 18	10 26			10 52			11 10	11 18		11 37	11 52			12 10	12 18		12 36	12 52	
Twyford 3	d	09 58				10 24				10 58				11 24			11 58				12 24			12 58	
Maidenhead 3	d	10 06				10 36	10 40			11 06				11 36		11 50	12 06				12 36		12 49	13 06	
Taplow	d																								
Burnham	d					10 40								11 40							12 40				
Slough 3	a	10 13			10 30	10 45	10 48			11 13			11 30	11 45		11 59	12 13			12 32	12 45		12 59	13 13	
	d	10 14			10 30	10 45	10 48			11 14			11 30	11 45		11 59	12 14			12 33	12 45		13 00	13 14	
Langley	d	10 18				10 47				11 18				11 49			12 18				12 49			13 18	
Iver	d																								
West Drayton	d	10 23				10 53				11 23				11 53			12 23				12 54			13 23	
Heathrow Terminal 5 ✈	d			10b12					10b42			11b12			11b42			12b12				12b42			13b12
Heathrow Terminal 4 ✈	d			10 21					10 51			11 21			11 51			12 21				12 51			13 21
Heathrow Terminals 1-2-3 2 ✈	d			10 27				←	10 57			11 27			11 57			12 27				12 57			13 27
Hayes & Harlington	d	10 27		10 33		10 59		10 59	11 03	11 27		11 33		11 59	12 03		12 27	12 33			12 59	13 03		13 27	13 33
Southall	d	10 31		10 36		→		11 02	11 06	11 31		11 36		12 02	12 06		12 31	12 36			13 02	13 06		13 31	13 36
Hanwell	d																								
Greenford ⊖	d																								
South Greenford	d																								
Castle Bar Park	d																								
Drayton Green	d																								
West Ealing	d																								
Ealing Broadway ⊖	d	10 36		10 41				11 08	11 11	11 36		11 41		12 08	12 11		12 36	12 41			13 08	13 11		13 36	13 41
Acton Main Line	d																								
London Paddington 15 ⊖	a	10 47		10 50	10 53		11 08	11 17	11 20	11 47		11 50	11 54	12 17	12 20	12 23	12 47	12 50		12 51	13 17	13 20	13 23	13 47	13 50

		GW	GW	HC		GW	GW	HC	GW	GW	HC	GW		GW	HC	GW	GW	HC	GW	GW		HC	GW	GW	GW
		1 ◇	1			1	1		1 ◇	1		1		1		1 ◇	1		1	1			1	1 ◇	1
Oxford	d	12 42				*12 47*	13 05		13 38	*13 43*				14 05		14 42			*14 47*	15 05			*15 43*	15 50	
Reading 7	d	13 10	13 18			13 37	13 52		14 10	14 18		14 36		14 52		15 10	15 18		15 37	15 52			16 18	16 23	
Twyford 3	d		13 24				13 58			14 24				14 58			15 24			15 58			16 24		
Maidenhead 3	d		13 36			13 49	14 06			14 36		14 49		15 06			15 36		15 49	16 06			16 36		
Taplow	d																								
Burnham	d		13 40							14 40							15 40			16 11			16 40		
Slough 3	a	13 29	13 45			13 59	14 13		14 30	14 45		14 59		15 13		15 30	15 45		16 00	16 15			16 45	16 48	
	d	13 30	13 45			14 00	14 14		14 30	14 45		15 00		15 14		15 30	15 45		16 00	16 16			16 45	16 48	
Langley	d		13 49				14 18			14 49				15 18			15 49			16 21			16 49		
Iver	d																								
West Drayton	d		13 53				14 23			14 53				15 23			15 53			16 26			16 54		
Heathrow Terminal 5 ✈	d			13b42				14b12			14b42				15b12			15b42				16b12			
Heathrow Terminal 4 ✈	d			13 51				14 21			14 51				15 21			15 51				16 21			
Heathrow Terminals 1-2-3 2 ✈	d			13 57				14 27			14 57				15 27			15 57				16 27			←
Hayes & Harlington	d		13 59	14 03			14 27	14 33		14 59	15 03			15 27	15 33		15 59	16 03		16 30		16 33	16 59		16 59
Southall	d		14 02	14 06			14 31	14 36		15 02	15 06			15 31	15 36		16 02	16 06		16 34		16 36	→		17 02
Hanwell	d																								
Greenford ⊖	d																								
South Greenford	d																								
Castle Bar Park	d																								
Drayton Green	d																								
West Ealing	d																								
Ealing Broadway ⊖	d		14 08	14 11			14 36	14 41		15 08	15 11			15 36	15 41		16 08	16 11		16 39		16 41			17 08
Acton Main Line	d																								
London Paddington 15 ⊖	a	13 53	14 17	14 20		14 23	14 47	14 50	14 52	15 17	15 20	15 23		15 47	15 50	15 53	16 17	16 20	16 23	16 49		16 51		17 06	17 17

		HC	GW	GW	HC	GW		GW	GW	GW	HC	GW	HC	GW		GW	GW	HC	GW	GW	HC	GW		GW	GW
			1	1		1		1 ◇	1	1		1		1		1 ◇	1		1	1		1 ◇		1	1
Oxford	d			16 05		*16 43*		16 50				17 05		*17 43*		17 50				18 05		18 40			
Reading 7	d		16 36	16 52		17 18		17 22		17 36		17 52		18 18		18 22			18 36	18 52		19 13		19 18	19 36
Twyford 3	d			16 58		17 24						17 58		18 24						18 58				19 24	
Maidenhead 3	d		16 49	17 06		17 36				17 49		18 06		18 36					18 49	19 06				19 36	19 49
Taplow	d																								
Burnham	d			17 11		17 40						18 11		18 40						19 11				19 40	
Slough 3	a		16 59	17 15		17 45		17 51		17 58		18 15		18 45		18 48			18 59	19 15		19 34		19 45	19 57
	d		17 00	17 16		17 45		17 51		17 59		18 16		18 45		18 48			18 59	19 16		19 34		19 45	19 58
Langley	d			17 20		17 49						18 21		18 49						19 20				19 49	
Iver	d																								
West Drayton	d			17 25		17 54						18 26		18 54						19 25				19 54	
Heathrow Terminal 5 ✈	d	16b42			17b12						17b42		18b12					18b42			19b12				
Heathrow Terminal 4 ✈	d	16 51			17 21						17 51		18 21					18 51			19 21				
Heathrow Terminals 1-2-3 2 ✈	d	16 57			17 27				←		17 57		18 27				←	18 57			19 27				
Hayes & Harlington	d	17 03		17 29	17 33	17 59			17 59		18 03	18 30	18 33	18 59			18 59	19 03		19 29	19 33			19 59	
Southall	d	17 06		17 33	17 36	→			18 02		18 06	18 34	18 36	→			19 02	19 06		19 33	19 36			20 02	
Hanwell	d																								
Greenford ⊖	d																								
South Greenford	d																								
Castle Bar Park	d																								
Drayton Green	d																								
West Ealing	d																								
Ealing Broadway ⊖	d	17 11		17 38	17 41				18 08		18 11	18 39	18 41				19 08	19 11		19 38	19 41			20 08	
Acton Main Line	d																								
London Paddington 15 ⊖	a	17 20	17 23	17 48	17 50			18 10	18 17	18 18	18 20	18 49	18 51			19 08	19 17	19 20	19 23	19 48	19 51	19 53		20 17	20 18

For general notes see front of timetable
For details of catering facilities see Directory of Train Operators

For fast services between Reading and London Paddington see Table 116

b Change at Heathrow Terminals 1-2-3

Table 117

Reading and Greenford → London
(Local services only)

Sundays

until 6 September

Network Diagram - see first page of Table 116

		HC	GW 1	HC	GW 1	GW 1 ◇ ☕	GW 1	HC		GW 1	HC	HC	GW 1	GW 1	GW 1	HC		GW 1	GW 1	GW 1	GW 1 ◇	GW 1			
Oxford	d		19 05		19 43	19 50				20 05			20 43	21 21	21 50				22 21		23b50				
Reading 7	d		19 52		20 18	20 24				20 52			21 40	22 10	22 24			22 40	23 00	23 35	23 52				
Twyford 3	d		19 58		20 24					20 58			21 46	22 16				22 46	23 07	23 41					
Maidenhead 3	d		20 06		20c36					21 06			21 54	22 24				22 54	23 15	23 49					
Taplow	d																								
Burnham	d		20 11		20 40					21 11			21 59	22 29				22 58		23 54					
Slough 3	a		20 15		20 45	20 48				21 15			22 03	22 33	22 47			23 03	23 22	23 58	00 12				
	d		20 16		20 45	20 49				21 16			22 08	22 34	22 48			23 03	23 22	23 59	00 12				
Langley	d		20 20		20 49					21 20			22 12	22 38				23 07	23 26	00 03					
Iver	d																								
West Drayton	d		20 25		20 54					21 25			22 17	22 43				23 12	23 31	00 08					
Heathrow Terminal 5 ✈	d	19e42		20e12				20e42			21e12	22e03				23e03									
Heathrow Terminal 4 ✈	d	19 51		20 21				20 51			21 21	22 07				23 07									
Heathrow Terminals 1-2-3 2 ✈	d	19 57		20 27			←	20 57			21 27	22 13				23 13						←			
Hayes & Harlington	d	20 03	20 29	20 33	20 59		20 59	21 03		21 29	21 33	22 19	22 22	22 47		23 19		23 23	23 36	00 16		00 16			
Southall	d	20 06	20 33	20 36	→		21 02	21 06		21 33	21 36	22 22	22 26	22 51		23 22			23 39	→		00 20			
Hanwell	d																								
Greenford ⊖	d																								
South Greenford	d																								
Castle Bar Park	d																								
Drayton Green	d																								
West Ealing	d																								
Ealing Broadway ⊖	d	20 11	20 38	20 41			21 08	21 11		21 38	21 41	22 27	22 31	22 56		23 27		23 31	23 45			00 25			
Acton Main Line	d																								
London Paddington 15 ⊖	a	20 20	20 47	20 50		21 06	21 17	21 20		21 47	21 50	22 36	22 40	23 05	23 15	23 36		23 40	23 54		00 35	00 38			

Sundays

from 13 September

		GW 1	HC	GW 1	HC	GW 1	HC		GW 1	HC	GW 1	GW 1	HC	GW 1 A		GW 1 ◇	GW 1	HC	GW 1	GW 1	GW 1 ◇		GW 1	HC	GW 1
Oxford	d			23p07										07f45					09 05		09 50				10 05
Reading 7	d	23p18		00 03		06 22			07 22		08 04	08 22		08 52		09 06	09 18		09 52	10 18	10 20				10 52
Twyford 3	d	23p24		00 09		06 28			07 28			08 28		08 58			09 24		09 58	10 24			←		10 58
Maidenhead 3	d	23p32		00 17		06 36			07 36			08 36		09 06			09 36		10 06	10 36 →			10 36		11 06
Taplow	d	23p36		00 21																					
Burnham	d	23p39		00 24		06 41			07 41			08 41					09 40						10 40		
Slough 3	a	23p43		00 28		06 45			07 45		08 20	08 45		09 13		09 22	09 45		10 13		10 35		10 45		11 13
	d	23p44		00 29		06 46			07 46		08 21	08 46		09 18		09 23	09 48		10 18		10 35		10 48		11 18
Langley	d			00 33		06 50			07 50			08 50		09 22			09 50		10 22				10 50		11 22
Iver	d			00 36																					
West Drayton	d	23p51		00 39		06 55			07 55			08 55		09 27			09 56		10 27				10 56		11 27
Heathrow Terminal 5 ✈	d		23g53		06e03		07e03			08e03			09e03					10e03						11e03	
Heathrow Terminal 4 ✈	d		00 01		06 07		07 07			08 07			09 07					10 07						11 07	
Heathrow Terminals 1-2-3 2 ✈	d		00 07		06 13		07 13			08 13			09 13					10 13						11 13	
Hayes & Harlington	d	23p56	00 13	00 44	06 19	07 02	07 19		08 02	08 19		09 02	09 19	09 32			10 02	10 19	10 32				11 02	11 19	11 32
Southall	d	23p59	00 16	00 47	06 22	07 05	07 22		08 05	08 22		09 05	09 22				10 05	10 22					11 05	11 22	
Hanwell	d																								
Greenford ⊖	d																								
South Greenford	d																								
Castle Bar Park	d																								
Drayton Green	d																								
West Ealing	d																								
Ealing Broadway ⊖	d	00 03	00 21	00 53	06 27	07 11	07 27		08 11	08 27		09 11	09 27	09 39			10 11	10 27	10 39				11 11	11 27	11 39
Acton Main Line	d																								
London Paddington 15 ⊖	a	00 16	00 30	01 02	06 36	07 20	07 36		08 20	08 36	08 44	09 20	09 36	09 49		09 51	10 20	10 36	10 49		10 58		11 20	11 36	11 49

For general notes see front of timetable
For details of catering facilities see Directory of Train Operators

For fast services between Reading and London Paddington see Table 116

A From Didcot Parkway (Table 116)
b Change at Didcot Parkway. Until 30 August dep. 2300, by bus
c Arr. 2031
e Change at Heathrow Terminals 1-2-3
f Change at Didcot Parkway. By bus
g Previous night. Change at Heathrow Terminals 1-2-3

Table 117

Sundays

from 13 September

Reading and Greenford → London

(Local services only)

Network Diagram - see first page of Table 116

		GW	GW	GW	HC	GW		GW	GW	GW	HC	GW	GW		GW	GW	HC	GW	GW	GW		GW	HC	GW	GW
		1	1 ◊	1		1		1	1	1		1	1		1 ◊	1		1	1	1 ◊		1		1	1
Oxford	d	*10 16*	10 50			11 05		*11 16*	11 50			12 05	*12 43*		12 50			13 05	*13 43*	13 50				14 05	*14 43*
Reading 7	d	11 18	11 22			11 52		12 18	12 21			12 52	13 18		13 20			13 52	14 18	14 21				14 52	15 18
Twyford 3	d	11 24		←		11 58		12 24		←		12 58	13 24			←		13 58	14 24			←		14 58	15 24
Maidenhead 3	d	11b36 →		11 36		12 06		12 36 →		12 36		13 06	13 36 →			13 36		14 06	14 36 →			14 36		15 06	15 36 →
Taplow	d																								
Burnham	d			11 40						12 40						13 40						14 40			
Slough 3	a		11 38	11 45		12 13			12 35	12 45		13 13			13 36	13 45		14 13		14 35		14 45		15 13	
	d		11 38	11 48		12 18			12 36	12 48		13 18			13 37	13 48		14 18		14 36		14 48		15 18	
Langley	d			11 52		12 22				12 52		13 22				13 52		14 22				14 52		15 22	
Iver	d																								
West Drayton	d			11 57		12 27				12 53		13 27				13 57		14 27				14 57		15 27	
Heathrow Terminal 5 ✈	d				*12c03*						*13c03*						*14c03*						*15c03*		
Heathrow Terminal 4 ✈	d				12 07						13 07						14 07						15 07		
Heathrow Terminals 1-2-3 2 ✈	d				12 13						13 13						14 13						15 13		
Hayes & Harlington	d			12 02	12 19	12 32				13 02	13 19	13 32				14 02	14 19	14 32				15 02	15 19	15 32	
Southall	d			12 05	12 22					13 05	13 22					14 05	14 22					15 05	15 22		
Hanwell	d																								
Greenford ⊖	d																								
South Greenford	d																								
Castle Bar Park	d																								
Drayton Green	d																								
West Ealing	d																								
Ealing Broadway ⊖	d			12 11	12 27	12 39				13 11	13 27	13 39				14 11	14 27	14 39				15 11	15 27	15 39	
Acton Main Line	d																								
London Paddington 15 ⊖	a		12 01	12 20	12 36	12 49			13 00	13 20	13 36	13 49			14 00	14 21	14 36	14 49		14 58		15 20	15 36	15 49	

		GW	GW	HC	GW		GW	GW	GW	HC	GW	GW		GW	GW	HC	GW	GW	GW		GW	HC	GW	GW	GW
		1 ◊	1		1		1	1 ◊	1		1	1		1 ◊	1		1	1	1 ◊		1		1	1	1 ◊
Oxford	d	14 50			15 05		*15 43*	15 50			16 05	*16 43*		16 50			17 05	*17 43*	17 50				18 05	*18 43*	18 50
Reading 7	d	15 20			15 52		16 18	16 20			16 52	17 18		17 22			17 52	18 18	18 22				18 52	19 18	19 21
Twyford 3	d		←		15 58		16 24		←		16 58	17 24			←		17 58	18 24			←		18 58	19 24	
Maidenhead 3	d		15 36		16 06		16e36 →		16 36		17 06	17 36 →			17 36		18 06	18 36 →			18 36		19 06	19 36 →	
Taplow	d																								
Burnham	d		15 40		16 11				16 40		17 11				17 40		18 11				18 40		19 11		
Slough 3	a	15 35	15 45		16 15			16 34	16 45		17 15			17 39	17 45		18 15		18 35		18 45		19 15		19 35
	d	15 35	15 48		16 18			16 34	16 48		17 19			17 39	17 48		18 19		18 35		18 48		19 19		19 35
Langley	d		15 52		16 22				16 52		17 23				17 52		18 23				18 52		19 23		
Iver	d																								
West Drayton	d		15 57		16 27				16 57		17 28				17 57		18 28				18 57		19 28		
Heathrow Terminal 5 ✈	d			*16c03*						*17c03*						*18c03*						*19c03*			
Heathrow Terminal 4 ✈	d			16 07						17 07						18 07						19 07			
Heathrow Terminals 1-2-3 2 ✈	d			16 13						17 13						18 13						19 13			
Hayes & Harlington	d		16 02	16 19	16 32				17 02	17 19	17 32				18 02	18 19	18 32				19 02	19 19	19 32		
Southall	d		16 05	16 22					17 05	17 22					18 05	18 22					19 05	19 22			
Hanwell	d																								
Greenford ⊖	d																								
South Greenford	d																								
Castle Bar Park	d																								
Drayton Green	d																								
West Ealing	d																								
Ealing Broadway ⊖	d		16 11	16 27	16 39				17 11	17 27	17 39				18 11	18 27	18 39				19 11	19 27	19 39		
Acton Main Line	d																								
London Paddington 15 ⊖	a	16 01	16 20	16 36	16 49			16 59	17 20	17 36	17 49			18 06	18 20	18 36	18 49		19 04		19 20	19 36	19 49		20 01

		GW	HC	GW		GW	GW	GW	HC	GW	GW		GW	HC	GW	GW	HC	GW		GW	GW	GW	GW		
		1		1		1	1 ◊	1		1	1 ◊ A		1		1	1		1		1	1 ◊	1	1		
Oxford	d			19 05		*19 16*	19 50			20 05	20 50				21 21	21 50				22 21	22 50		23 15		
Reading 7	d			19 52		20 18	20 21			20 52	21 19		21 24		22 06	22 24		22 40		23 00	23 16	23 35	23 56		
Twyford 3	d	←		19 58		20 24		←		20 58			21 30		22 12			22 46		23 07		23 41	00 03		
Maidenhead 3	d	19 36		20 06		20f36 →		20 36		21 06	21 33		21 38		22 20			22 54		23 15		23 49	00 11		
Taplow	d																								
Burnham	d	19 40		20 11				20 40		21 11			21 43		22 25			22 58				23 54	00 15		
Slough 3	a	19 45		20 15			20 34	20 45		21 15	21 39		21 48		22 29	22 47		23 03		23 22	23 36	23 58	00 20		
	d	19 48		20 19			20 35	20 48		21 19	21 39		21 48		22 34	22 48		23 03		23 22	23 37	23 59	00 20		
Langley	d	19 52		20 23				20 52		21 23			21 52		22 38			23 07		23 26		00 03	00 24		
Iver	d																								
West Drayton	d	19 57		20 28				20 57		21 28			21 57		22 43			23 12		23 31		00 08	00 29		
Heathrow Terminal 5 ✈	d		*20c03*						*21c03*					*22c03*			*23c03*								
Heathrow Terminal 4 ✈	d		20 07						21 07					22 07			23 07								
Heathrow Terminals 1-2-3 2 ✈	d		20 13						21 13					22 13			23 13								
Hayes & Harlington	d	20 02	20 19	20 32				21 02	21 19	21 32			22 02	22 19	22 47		23 19	23 23		23 36		00 16	00 33		
Southall	d	20 05	20 22					21 05	21 22				22 05	22 22	22 51		23 22			23 39		00 20	00 37		
Hanwell	d																								
Greenford ⊖	d																								
South Greenford	d																								
Castle Bar Park	d																								
Drayton Green	d																								
West Ealing	d																								
Ealing Broadway ⊖	d	20 11	20 27	20 39				21 11	21 27	21 39			22 11	22 27	22 56		23 27	23 31		23 45		00 25	00 42		
Acton Main Line	d																								
London Paddington 15 ⊖	a	20 20	20 36	20 49			21 01	21 20	21 36	21 49	22 07		22 20	22 36	23 05	23 15	23 36	23 40		23 54	00 01	00 38	00 52		

For general notes see front of timetable
For details of catering facilities see Directory of Train Operators

For fast services between Reading and London Paddington see Table 116

A From Hereford (Table 126)
b Arr. 1131
c Change at Heathrow Terminals 1-2-3
e Arr. 1631
f Arr. 2031

Table 118

Mondays to Fridays

London → Heathrow Airport

Network Diagram - see first page of Table 116

Miles			HX 1	HX 1	HX 1	HX 1		HX 1	HX 1	HX 1	HX 1		HX 1	HX 1	HX 1	HX 1		HX 1	HX 1	HX 1	HX 1		HX 1	HX 1	HX 1
0	London Paddington 15	⊖ d	05 10	05 25	05 40	05 55	.....	06 10	06 25	06 40	06 55	.....	07 10	07 25	07 40	07 55	.....	08 10	08 25	08 40	08 55	.....	09 10	09 25	09 40
14¾	Heathrow Terminals 1-2-3 2	✈ a	05 26	05 40	05 55	06 10	.	06 25	06 40	06 55	07 10	.	07 25	07 40	07 55	08 10	.	08 25	08 40	08 55	09 10	.	09 25	09 40	09 55
—	Heathrow Terminal 4	✈ a	*05 41*	*05 48*	*06 10*	*06 18*	.....	*06 40*	*06 48*	*07 10*	*07 18*	.....	*07 40*	*07 48*	*08 10*	*08 18*	.....	*08 40*	*08 48*	*09 10*	*09 18*	.....	*09 40*	*09 48*	*10 10*
16¼	Heathrow Terminal 5	✈ a	05 33	05 46	06 01	06 16	.	06 31	06 46	07 01	07 16	.	07 31	07 46	08 01	08 16	.	08 31	08 46	09 01	09 16	.	09 31	09 46	10 01

		HX 1	HX 1	HX 1		HX 1	HX 1	HX 1	HX 1		HX 1	HX 1	HX 1	HX 1		HX 1	HX 1	HX 1	HX 1		HX 1	HX 1	HX 1	HX 1	HX 1
London Paddington 15	⊖ d	09 55	10 10	10 25	.....	10 40	10 55	11 10	11 25	.....	11 40	11 55	12 10	12 25	.....	12 40	12 55	13 10	13 25	.....	13 40	13 55	14 10	14 25	14 40
Heathrow Terminals 1-2-3 2	✈ a	10 10	10 25	10 40	.	10 55	11 10	11 25	11 40	.	11 55	12 10	12 25	12 40	.	12 55	13 10	13 25	13 40	.	13 55	14 10	14 25	14 40	14 55
Heathrow Terminal 4	✈ a	*10 18*	*10 40*	*10 48*	.....	*11 10*	*11 18*	*11 40*	*11 48*	.....	*12 10*	*12 18*	*12 40*	*12 48*	.....	*13 10*	*13 18*	*13 40*	*13 48*	.....	*14 10*	*14 18*	*14 40*	*14 48*	*15 10*
Heathrow Terminal 5	✈ a	10 16	10 31	10 46	.	11 01	11 16	11 31	11 46	.	12 01	12 16	12 31	12 46	.	13 01	13 16	13 31	13 46	.	14 01	14 16	14 31	14 46	15 01

		HX 1		HX 1	HX 1	HX 1	HX 1		HX 1	HX 1	HX 1	HX 1		HX 1	HX 1	HX 1	HX 1		HX 1	HX 1	HX 1	HX 1		HX 1	HX 1
London Paddington 15	⊖ d	14 55	.....	15 10	15 25	15 40	15 55	.....	16 10	16 25	16 40	16 55	.....	17 10	17 25	17 40	17 55	.....	18 10	18 25	18 40	18 55	.....	19 10	19 25
Heathrow Terminals 1-2-3 2	✈ a	15 10	.	15 25	15 40	15 55	16 10	.	16 25	16 40	16 55	17 10	.	17 25	17 40	17 55	18 10	.	18 25	18 40	18 55	19 10	.	19 25	19 40
Heathrow Terminal 4	✈ a	*15 18*	.....	*15 40*	*15 48*	*16 10*	*16 18*	.....	*16 40*	*16 48*	*17 10*	*17 18*	.....	*17 40*	*17 48*	*18 10*	*18 18*	.....	*18 40*	*18 48*	*19 10*	*19 18*	.....	*19 40*	*19 48*
Heathrow Terminal 5	✈ a	15 16	.	15 31	15 46	16 01	16 16	.	16 31	16 46	17 01	17 16	.	17 31	17 46	18 01	18 16	.	18 31	18 46	19 01	19 16	.	19 31	19 46

		HX 1	HX 1	HX 1	HX 1		HX 1	HX 1	HX 1	HX 1		HX 1	HX 1	HX 1	HX 1		HX 1	HX 1	HX 1	HX 1					
London Paddington 15	⊖ d	19 40	19 55	20 10	20 25	.....	20 40	20 55	21 10	21 25	.....	21 40	21 55	22 10	22 25	.....	22 40	22 55	23 10	23 25	.....	.....	.....	.....	.....
Heathrow Terminals 1-2-3 2	✈ a	19 55	20 10	20 25	20 40	.	20 55	21 10	21 25	21 40	.	21 55	22 10	22 25	22 40	.	22 55	23 10	23 25	23 40	.	.	.	.	.
Heathrow Terminal 4	✈ a	*20 10*	*20 18*	*20 40*	*20 48*	.....	*21 10*	*21 18*	*21 40*	*21 48*	.....	*22 10*	*22 18*	*22 40*	*22 48*	.....	*23 10*	*23 18*	*23 40*	*23 48*	.....	.....	.....	.....	.....
Heathrow Terminal 5	✈ a	20 01	20 16	20 31	20 46	.	21 01	21 16	21 31	21 46	.	22 01	22 16	22 31	22 46	.	23 01	23 16	23 31	23 46	.	.	.	.	.

Saturdays

		HX 1	HX 1	HX 1		HX 1	HX 1	HX 1		HX 1	HX 1	HX 1		HX 1	HX 1	HX 1		HX 1	HX 1	HX 1		HX 1	HX 1	HX 1	HX 1
London Paddington 15	⊖ d	05 10	05 25	05 40	.....	05 55	06 10	06 25	.....	06 40	06 55	07 10	.....	07 25	07 40	07 55	.....	08 10	08 25	08 40	.....	08 55	09 10	09 25	09 40
Heathrow Terminals 1-2-3 2	✈ a	05 26	05 41	05 55	.	06 10	06 25	06 40	.	06 55	07 10	07 25	.	07 40	07 55	08 10	.	08 25	08 40	08 55	.	09 10	09 25	09 40	09 55
Heathrow Terminal 4	✈ a	*05 41*	*05 48*	*06 10*	.....	*06 18*	*06 40*	*06 48*	.....	*07 10*	*07 18*	*07 40*	.....	*07 48*	*08 10*	*08 18*	.....	*08 40*	*08 48*	*09 10*	.....	*09 18*	*09 40*	*09 48*	*10 10*
Heathrow Terminal 5	✈ a	05 33	05 46	06 01	.	06 16	06 31	06 46	.	07 01	07 16	07 31	.	07 46	08 01	08 16	.	08 31	08 46	09 01	.	09 16	09 31	09 46	10 01

		HX 1		HX 1	HX 1	HX 1		HX 1	HX 1	HX 1		HX 1	HX 1	HX 1		HX 1	HX 1	HX 1		HX 1	HX 1	HX 1		HX 1	HX 1
London Paddington 15	⊖ d	09 55	.....	10 10	10 25	10 40	.....	10 55	11 10	11 25	.....	11 40	11 55	12 10	.....	12 25	12 40	12 55	.....	13 10	13 25	13 40	.....	13 55	14 10
Heathrow Terminals 1-2-3 2	✈ a	10 10	.	10 25	10 40	10 55	.	11 10	11 25	11 40	.	11 55	12 10	12 25	.	12 40	12 55	13 10	.	13 25	13 40	13 55	.	14 10	14 25
Heathrow Terminal 4	✈ a	*10 18*	.....	*10 40*	*10 48*	*11 10*	.....	*11 18*	*11 40*	*11 48*	.....	*12 10*	*12 18*	*12 40*	.....	*12 48*	*13 10*	*13 18*	.....	*13 40*	*13 48*	*14 10*	.....	*14 18*	*14 40*
Heathrow Terminal 5	✈ a	10 16	.	10 31	10 46	11 01	.	11 16	11 31	11 46	.	12 01	12 16	12 31	.	12 46	13 01	13 16	.	13 31	13 46	14 01	.	14 16	14 31

		HX 1	HX 1	HX 1		HX 1	HX 1	HX 1		HX 1	HX 1	HX 1		HX 1	HX 1	HX 1		HX 1	HX 1	HX 1		HX 1	HX 1	HX 1	HX 1
London Paddington 15	⊖ d	14 25	14 40	14 55	.....	15 10	15 25	15 40	.....	15 55	16 10	16 25	.....	16 40	16 55	17 10	.....	17 25	17 40	17 55	.....	18 10	18 25	18 40	18 55
Heathrow Terminals 1-2-3 2	✈ a	14 40	14 55	15 10	.	15 25	15 40	15 55	.	16 10	16 25	16 40	.	16 55	17 10	17 25	.	17 40	17 55	18 10	.	18 25	18 40	18 55	19 10
Heathrow Terminal 4	✈ a	*14 48*	*15 10*	*15 18*	.....	*15 40*	*15 48*	*16 10*	.....	*16 18*	*16 40*	*16 48*	.....	*17 10*	*17 18*	*17 40*	.....	*17 48*	*18 10*	*18 18*	.....	*18 40*	*18 48*	*19 10*	*19 18*
Heathrow Terminal 5	✈ a	14 46	15 01	15 16	.	15 31	15 46	16 01	.	16 16	16 31	16 46	.	17 01	17 16	17 31	.	17 46	18 01	18 16	.	18 31	18 46	19 01	19 16

		HX 1		HX 1	HX 1	HX 1		HX 1	HX 1	HX 1		HX 1	HX 1	HX 1		HX 1	HX 1	HX 1	HX 1	HX 1	HX 1	HX 1	HX 1		
London Paddington 15	⊖ d	19 10	.....	19 25	19 40	19 55	.....	20 10	20 25	20 40	.....	20 55	21 10	21 25	.....	21 40	21 55	22 10	22 25	22 40	22 55	23 10	23 25	.....	.....
Heathrow Terminals 1-2-3 2	✈ a	19 25	.	19 40	19 55	20 10	.	20 25	20 40	20 55	.	21 10	21 25	21 40	.	21 55	22 10	22 25	22 40	22 55	23 10	23 25	23 40	.	.
Heathrow Terminal 4	✈ a	*19 40*	.....	*19 48*	*20 10*	*20 18*	.....	*20 40*	*20 48*	*21 10*	.....	*21 18*	*21 40*	*21 48*	.	*22 10*	*22 18*	*22 40*	*22 48*	*23 10*	*23 18*	*23 40*	*23 48*	.	.....
Heathrow Terminal 5	✈ a	19 31	.	19 46	20 01	20 16	.	20 31	20 46	21 01	.	21 16	21 31	21 46	.	22 01	22 16	22 31	22 46	23 01	23 16	23 31	23 46	.	.

Sundays

until 6 September

		HX 1	HX 1	HX 1		HX 1	HX 1	HX 1		HX 1	HX 1	HX 1		HX 1	HX 1	HX 1		HX 1	HX 1	HX 1		HX 1	HX 1	HX 1	HX 1
London Paddington 15	⊖ d	05 10	05 25	05 40	.....	05 55	06 10	06 25	.....	06 40	06 55	07 10	.....	07 25	07 40	07 55	.....	08 10	08 25	08 40	.....	08 55	09 10	09 25	09 40
Heathrow Terminals 1-2-3 2	✈ a	05 26	05 41	05 56	.	06 11	06 26	06 41	.	06 56	07 11	07 26	.	07 41	07 56	08 11	.	08 26	08 41	08 56	.	09 11	09 25	09 40	09 55
Heathrow Terminal 4	✈ a	*05 40*	*05 51*	*06 06*	.....	.....	*06 35*	*06 53*	.....	*07 06*	.....	*07 35*	.....	*07 53*	*08 06*	.....	.....	*08 35*	*08 53*	*09 06*	.....	*09 19*	*09 40*	*09 48*	*10 10*
Heathrow Terminal 5	✈ a	05 32	05 47	06 03	.	06 17	06 32	06 50	.	07 03	07 17	07 32	.	07 50	08 03	08 17	.	08 32	08 50	09 03	.	09 17	09 31	09 46	10 01

		HX 1		HX 1	HX 1	HX 1		HX 1	HX 1	HX 1		HX 1	HX 1	HX 1		HX 1	HX 1	HX 1		HX 1	HX 1	HX 1		HX 1	HX 1
London Paddington 15	⊖ d	09 55	.....	10 10	10 25	10 40	.....	10 55	11 10	11 25	.....	11 40	11 55	12 10	.....	12 25	12 40	12 55	.....	13 10	13 25	13 40	.....	13 55	14 10
Heathrow Terminals 1-2-3 2	✈ a	10 10	.	10 25	10 40	10 55	.	11 10	11 25	11 40	.	11 55	12 10	12 25	.	12 40	12 55	13 10	.	13 25	13 40	13 55	.	14 10	14 25
Heathrow Terminal 4	✈ a	*10 18*	.....	*10 40*	*10 48*	*11 10*	.....	*11 18*	*11 40*	*11 48*	.....	*12 10*	*12 18*	*12 40*	.....	*12 48*	*13 10*	*13 18*	.....	*13 40*	*13 48*	*14 10*	.....	*14 18*	*14 40*
Heathrow Terminal 5	✈ a	10 16	.	10 31	10 46	11 01	.	11 16	11 31	11 46	.	12 01	12 16	12 31	.	12 46	13 01	13 16	.	13 31	13 46	14 01	.	14 16	14 31

For general notes see front of timetable
For details of catering facilities see Directory of Train Operators

Table 118

London → Heathrow Airport

Sundays
until 6 September

Network Diagram - see first page of Table 116

	HX 1	HX 1	HX 1		HX 1	HX 1	HX 1		HX 1	HX 1	HX 1		HX 1	HX 1	HX 1		HX 1	HX 1	HX 1		HX 1	HX 1	HX 1	HX 1
London Paddington 15 ⊖ d	14 25	14 40	14 55	.....	15 10	15 25	15 40	.....	15 55	16 10	16 25	.....	16 40	16 55	17 10	.....	17 25	17 40	17 55	.....	18 10	18 25	18 40	18 55
Heathrow Terminals 1-2-3 2 ✈ a	14 40	14 55	15 10	.	15 25	15 40	15 55	.	16 10	16 25	16 40	.	16 55	17 10	17 25	.	17 40	17 55	18 10	.	18 25	18 40	18 55	19 10
Heathrow Terminal 4 ✈ a	*14 48*	*15 10*	*15 18*	.....	*15 40*	*15 48*	*16 10*	.....	*16 18*	*16 40*	*16 48*	.....	*17 10*	*17 18*	*17 40*	.....	*17 48*	*18 10*	*18 18*	.....	*18 40*	*18 48*	*19 10*	*19 18*
Heathrow Terminal 5 ✈ a	14 46	15 01	15 16	.	15 31	15 46	16 01	.	16 16	16 31	16 46	.	17 01	17 16	17 31	.	17 46	18 01	18 16	.	18 31	18 46	19 01	19 16

	HX 1		HX 1	HX 1	HX 1		HX 1	HX 1	HX 1		HX 1	HX 1	HX 1		HX 1	HX 1	HX 1	HX 1	HX 1	HX 1	HX 1	HX 1		
London Paddington 15 ⊖ d	19 10	.....	19 25	19 40	19 55	.....	20 10	20 25	20 40	.....	20 55	21 10	21 25	.....	21 40	21 55	22 10	22 25	22 40	22 55	23 10	23 25	.....	.....
Heathrow Terminals 1-2-3 2 ✈ a	19 25	.	19 40	19 55	20 10	.	20 25	20 40	20 55	.	21 10	21 25	21 40	.	21 56	22 11	22 26	22 41	22 56	23 11	23 26	23 41	.	.
Heathrow Terminal 4 ✈ a	*19 40*	.....	*19 48*	*20 10*	*20 18*	.....	*20 40*	*20 48*	*21 10*	.....	*21 18*	*21 40*	*21 53*	.....	*22 06*	.....	*22 35*	*22 53*	*23 06*	.....	*23 35*	*23 53*	.....	.....
Heathrow Terminal 5 ✈ a	19 31	.	19 46	20 01	20 16	.	20 31	20 46	21 01	.	21 16	21 31	21 46	.	22 03	22 17	22 32	22 50	23 03	23 17	23 32	23 50	.	.

Sundays
from 13 September

	HX 1	HX 1	HX 1		HX 1	HX 1	HX 1		HX 1	HX 1	HX 1		HX 1	HX 1	HX 1		HX 1	HX 1	HX 1		HX 1	HX 1	HX 1	HX 1
London Paddington 15 ⊖ d	05 10	05 25	05 40	.....	05 55	06 10	06 25	.....	06 40	06 55	07 10	.....	07 25	07 40	07 55	.....	08 10	08 25	08 40	.....	08 55	09 10	09 25	09 40
Heathrow Terminals 1-2-3 2 ✈ a	05 26	05 41	05 56	.	06 11	06 26	06 41	.	06 56	07 11	07 26	.	07 41	07 56	08 11	.	08 26	08 41	08 56	.	09 11	09 26	09 41	09 56
Heathrow Terminal 4 ✈ a	*05 40*	*05 51*	*06 06*	.....	.....	*06 35*	*06 53*	.....	*07 06*	.....	*07 35*	.....	*07 53*	*08 06*	.....	.....	*08 35*	*08 53*	*09 06*	.....	.....	*09 35*	*09 53*	*10 06*
Heathrow Terminal 5 ✈ a	05 32	05 47	06 03	.	06 17	06 32	06 50	.	07 03	07 17	07 32	.	07 50	08 03	08 17	.	08 32	08 50	09 03	.	09 17	09 32	09 50	10 03

	HX 1		HX 1	HX 1	HX 1		HX 1	HX 1	HX 1		HX 1	HX 1	HX 1		HX 1	HX 1	HX 1		HX 1	HX 1	HX 1		HX 1	HX 1
London Paddington 15 ⊖ d	09 55	.....	10 10	10 25	10 40	.....	10 55	11 10	11 25	.....	11 40	11 55	12 10	.....	12 25	12 40	12 55	.....	13 10	13 25	13 40	.....	13 55	14 10
Heathrow Terminals 1-2-3 2 ✈ a	10 11	.	10 26	10 41	10 56	.	11 11	11 26	11 41	.	11 56	12 11	12 26	.	12 41	12 56	13 11	.	13 26	13 41	13 56	.	14 11	14 26
Heathrow Terminal 4 ✈ a	.....	.....	*10 35*	*10 53*	*11 06*	.....	.....	*11 35*	*11 53*	.....	*12 06*	.....	*12 35*	.....	*12 53*	*13 06*	.....	.....	*13 35*	*13 53*	*14 06*	.....	.....	*14 35*
Heathrow Terminal 5 ✈ a	10 17	.	10 32	10 50	11 03	.	11 17	11 32	11 50	.	12 03	12 17	12 32	.	12 50	13 03	13 17	.	13 32	13 50	14 03	.	14 17	14 32

	HX 1	HX 1	HX 1		HX 1	HX 1	HX 1		HX 1	HX 1	HX 1		HX 1	HX 1	HX 1		HX 1	HX 1	HX 1		HX 1	HX 1	HX 1	HX 1
London Paddington 15 ⊖ d	14 25	14 40	14 55	.....	15 10	15 25	15 40	.....	15 55	16 10	16 25	.....	16 40	16 55	17 10	.....	17 25	17 40	17 55	.....	18 10	18 25	18 40	18 55
Heathrow Terminals 1-2-3 2 ✈ a	14 41	14 56	15 11	.	15 26	15 41	15 56	.	16 11	16 26	16 41	.	16 56	17 11	17 26	.	17 41	17 56	18 11	.	18 26	18 41	18 56	19 11
Heathrow Terminal 4 ✈ a	*14 53*	*15 06*	.....	.....	*15 35*	*15 53*	*16 06*	.....	.....	*16 35*	*16 53*	.....	*17 06*	.....	*17 35*	.....	*17 53*	*18 06*	.....	.....	*18 35*	*18 53*	*19 06*	.....
Heathrow Terminal 5 ✈ a	14 50	15 03	15 17	.	15 32	15 50	16 03	.	16 17	16 32	16 50	.	17 03	17 17	17 32	.	17 50	18 03	18 17	.	18 32	18 50	19 03	19 17

	HX 1		HX 1	HX 1	HX 1		HX 1	HX 1	HX 1		HX 1	HX 1	HX 1		HX 1	HX 1	HX 1	HX 1	HX 1	HX 1	HX 1	HX 1		
London Paddington 15 ⊖ d	19 10	.....	19 25	19 40	19 55	.....	20 10	20 25	20 40	.....	20 55	21 10	21 25	.....	21 40	21 55	22 10	22 25	22 40	22 55	23 10	23 25	.....	.....
Heathrow Terminals 1-2-3 2 ✈ a	19 26	.	19 41	19 56	20 11	.	20 26	20 41	20 56	.	21 11	21 26	21 41	.	21 56	22 11	22 26	22 41	22 56	23 11	23 26	23 41	.	.
Heathrow Terminal 4 ✈ a	*19 35*	.....	*19 53*	*20 06*	.....	.....	*20 35*	*20 53*	*21 06*	.....	.....	*21 35*	*21 53*	.....	*22 06*	.....	*22 35*	*22 53*	*23 06*	.....	*23 35*	*23 53*	.....	.....
Heathrow Terminal 5 ✈ a	19 32	.	19 50	20 03	20 17	.	20 32	20 50	21 03	.	21 17	21 32	21 50	.	22 03	22 17	22 32	22 50	23 03	23 17	23 32	23 50	.	.

For general notes see front of timetable
For details of catering facilities see
Directory of Train Operators

Heathrow Airport → London

Mondays to Fridays

Network Diagram - see first page of Table 116

Miles		HX 1	HX 1	HX 1	HX 1		HX 1	HX 1	HX 1	HX 1		HX 1	HX 1	HX 1	HX 1		HX 1	HX 1	HX 1	HX 1		HX 1	HX 1	HX 1
0	Heathrow Terminal 5 ✈ d	05 07	05 27	05 42	05 57	.....	06 12	06 27	06 42	06 57	.....	07 12	07 27	07 42	07 57	.....	08 12	08 27	08 42	08 57	.....	09 12	09 27	09 42
—	Heathrow Terminal 4 ✈ d	.	05 23	05 31	05 51	.	06 01	06 21	06 31	06 51	.	07 01	07 21	07 31	07 51	.	08 01	08 21	08 31	08 51	.	09 01	09 21	09 31
1½	Heathrow Terminals 1-2-3 [2] ✈ d	05 12	05 33	05 48	06 03	.....	06 18	06 33	06 48	07 03	.....	07 18	07 33	07 48	08 03	.....	08 18	08 33	08 48	09 03	.....	09 18	09 33	09 48
16¼	London Paddington [15] ⊖ a	05 28	05 49	06 04	06 19	.	06 34	06 49	07 05	07 19	.	07 35	07 49	08 04	08 19	.	08 35	08 49	09 04	09 19	.	09 35	09 50	10 05

	HX 1	HX 1	HX 1		HX 1	HX 1	HX 1	HX 1		HX 1	HX 1	HX 1	HX 1		HX 1	HX 1	HX 1	HX 1		HX 1	HX 1	HX 1	HX 1	HX 1
Heathrow Terminal 5 ✈ d	09 57	10 12	10 27	.....	10 42	10 57	11 12	11 27	.....	11 42	11 57	12 12	12 27	.....	12 42	12 57	13 12	13 27	.....	13 42	13 57	14 12	14 27	14 42
Heathrow Terminal 4 ✈ d	09 51	10 01	10 21	.	10 31	10 51	11 01	11 21	.	11 31	11 51	12 01	12 21	.	12 31	12 51	13 01	13 21	.	13 31	13 51	14 01	14 21	14 31
Heathrow Terminals 1-2-3 [2] ✈ d	10 03	10 18	10 33	.....	10 48	11 03	11 18	11 33	.....	11 48	12 03	12 18	12 33	.....	12 48	13 03	13 18	13 33	.....	13 48	14 03	14 18	14 33	14 48
London Paddington [15] ⊖ a	10 19	10 34	10 49	.	11 05	11 19	11 34	11 49	.	12 05	12 19	12 34	12 49	.	13 05	13 19	13 35	13 49	.	14 04	14 19	14 34	14 49	15 04

	HX 1		HX 1	HX 1	HX 1	HX 1		HX 1	HX 1	HX 1	HX 1		HX 1	HX 1	HX 1	HX 1		HX 1	HX 1	HX 1	HX 1		HX 1	HX 1
Heathrow Terminal 5 ✈ d	14 57	.....	15 12	15 27	15 42	15 57	.....	16 12	16 27	16 42	16 57	.....	17 12	17 27	17 42	17 57	.....	18 12	18 27	18 42	18 57	.....	19 12	19 27
Heathrow Terminal 4 ✈ d	14 51	.	15 01	15 21	15 31	15 51	.	16 01	16 21	16 31	16 51	.	17 01	17 21	17 31	17 51	.	18 01	18 21	18 31	18 51	.	19 01	19 21
Heathrow Terminals 1-2-3 [2] ✈ d	15 03	.....	15 18	15 33	15 48	16 03	.....	16 18	16 33	16 48	17 03	.....	17 18	17 33	17 48	18 03	.....	18 18	18 33	18 48	19 03	.....	19 18	19 33
London Paddington [15] ⊖ a	15 19	.	15 35	15 49	16 05	16 19	.	16 35	16 49	17 04	17 19	.	17 35	17 49	18 05	18 19	.	18 34	18 49	19 05	19 19	.	19 35	19 49

	HX 1	HX 1	HX 1	HX 1		HX 1	HX 1	HX 1	HX 1		HX 1	HX 1	HX 1	HX 1		HX 1	HX 1	HX 1	HX 1		HX 1	HX 1		
Heathrow Terminal 5 ✈ d	19 42	19 57	20 12	20 27	.....	20 42	20 57	21 12	21 27	.....	21 42	21 57	22 12	22 27	.....	22 42	22 57	23 12	23 27	.....	23 42	23 53	.....	.....
Heathrow Terminal 4 ✈ d	19 31	19 51	20 01	20 21	.	20 31	20 51	21 01	21 21	.	21 31	21 51	22 01	22 21	.	22 31	22 51	23 01	23 21	.	23 31		.	.
Heathrow Terminals 1-2-3 [2] ✈ d	19 48	20 03	20 18	20 33	.....	20 48	21 03	21 18	21 33	.....	21 48	22 03	22 18	22 33	.....	22 48	23 03	23 18	23 33	.....	23 48	23a57	.	.
London Paddington [15] ⊖ a	20 04	20 19	20 35	20 49	.	21 04	21 19	21 34	21 49	.	22 04	22 19	22 34	22 49	.	23 04	23 19	23 34	23 49	.	00 04	00 30	.....	.....

Saturdays

	HX 1	HX 1	HX 1	HX 1		HX 1	HX 1	HX 1	HX 1		HX 1	HX 1	HX 1	HX 1		HX 1	HX 1	HX 1	HX 1		HX 1	HX 1	HX 1	HX 1
Heathrow Terminal 5 ✈ d	05 07	05 27	05 42	05 57	.....	06 12	06 27	06 42	06 57	.....	07 12	07 27	07 42	07 57	.....	08 12	08 27	08 42	08 57	.....	09 12	09 27	09 42	09 57
Heathrow Terminal 4 ✈ d	.	05 23	05 31	05 51	.	06 01	06 21	06 31	06 51	.	07 01	07 21	07 31	07 51	.	08 01	08 21	08 31	08 51	.	09 01	09 21	09 31	09 51
Heathrow Terminals 1-2-3 [2] ✈ d	05 12	05 33	05 48	06 03	.....	06 18	06 33	06 48	07 03	.....	07 18	07 33	07 48	08 03	.....	08 18	08 33	08 48	09 03	.....	09 18	09 33	09 48	10 03
London Paddington [15] ⊖ a	05 28	05 49	06 04	06 19	.	06 34	06 49	07 04	07 19	.	07 34	07 49	08 04	08 19	.	08 34	08 49	09 04	09 19	.	09 34	09 49	10 04	10 19

	HX 1	HX 1		HX 1	HX 1	HX 1	HX 1		HX 1	HX 1	HX 1	HX 1		HX 1	HX 1	HX 1	HX 1		HX 1	HX 1	HX 1	HX 1		HX 1
Heathrow Terminal 5 ✈ d	10 12	10 27	.....	10 42	10 57	11 12	11 27	.....	11 42	11 57	12 12	12 27	.....	12 42	12 57	13 12	13 27	.....	13 42	13 57	14 12	14 27	.....	14 42
Heathrow Terminal 4 ✈ d	10 01	10 21	.	10 31	10 51	11 01	11 21	.	11 31	11 51	12 01	12 21	.	12 31	12 51	13 01	13 21	.	13 31	13 51	14 01	14 21	.	14 31
Heathrow Terminals 1-2-3 [2] ✈ d	10 18	10 33	.....	10 48	11 03	11 18	11 33	.....	11 48	12 03	12 18	12 33	.....	12 48	13 03	13 18	13 33	.....	13 48	14 03	14 18	14 33	.....	14 48
London Paddington [15] ⊖ a	10 34	10 49	.	11 04	11 19	11 34	11 49	.	12 04	12 19	12 34	12 49	.	13 04	13 19	13 34	13 49	.	14 04	14 19	14 34	14 49	.	15 04

	HX 1	HX 1	HX 1	HX 1		HX 1	HX 1	HX 1	HX 1		HX 1	HX 1	HX 1	HX 1		HX 1	HX 1	HX 1	HX 1		HX 1	HX 1	HX 1	HX 1
Heathrow Terminal 5 ✈ d	14 57	15 12	15 27	15 42	.....	15 57	16 12	16 27	16 42	.....	16 57	17 12	17 27	17 42	.....	17 57	18 12	18 27	18 42	.....	18 57	19 12	19 27	19 42
Heathrow Terminal 4 ✈ d	14 51	15 01	15 21	15 31	.	15 51	16 01	16 21	16 31	.	16 51	17 01	17 21	17 31	.	17 51	18 01	18 21	18 31	.	18 51	19 01	19 21	19 31
Heathrow Terminals 1-2-3 [2] ✈ d	15 03	15 18	15 33	15 48	.....	16 03	16 18	16 33	16 48	.....	17 03	17 18	17 33	17 48	.....	18 03	18 18	18 33	18 48	.....	19 03	19 18	19 33	19 48
London Paddington [15] ⊖ a	15 19	15 34	15 49	16 04	.	16 19	16 34	16 49	17 04	.	17 19	17 34	17 49	18 04	.	18 19	18 34	18 49	19 04	.	19 19	19 34	19 49	20 04

	HX 1	HX 1		HX 1	HX 1	HX 1	HX 1		HX 1	HX 1	HX 1	HX 1		HX 1	HX 1	HX 1	HX 1		HX 1	HX 1	HX 1			
Heathrow Terminal 5 ✈ d	19 57	20 12	.....	20 27	20 42	20 57	21 12	.....	21 27	21 42	21 57	22 12	.....	22 27	22 42	22 57	23 12	.....	23 27	23 42	23 53	.....	.....	.....
Heathrow Terminal 4 ✈ d	19 51	20 01	.	20 21	20 31	20 51	21 01	.	21 21	21 31	21 51	22 01	.	22 21	22 31	22 51	23 01	.	23 21	23 31		.	.	.
Heathrow Terminals 1-2-3 [2] ✈ d	20 03	20 18	.....	20 33	20 48	21 03	21 18	.....	21 33	21 48	22 03	22 18	.....	22 33	22 48	23 03	23 18	.....	23 33	23 48	23a57	.....	.	.....
London Paddington [15] ⊖ a	20 19	20 34	.	20 49	21 04	21 19	21 34	.	21 49	22 04	22 19	22 34	.	22 49	23 04	23 19	23 34	.	23 49	00 04	00 30	.	.	.

Sundays

until 6 September

	HX 1	HX 1	HX 1	HX 1		HX 1	HX 1	HX 1	HX 1		HX 1	HX 1	HX 1	HX 1		HX 1	HX 1	HX 1	HX 1		HX 1	HX 1	HX 1	HX 1
Heathrow Terminal 5 ✈ d	05 03	05 18	05 33	05 48	.....	06 03	06 18	06 33	06 48	.....	07 03	07 18	07 33	07 48	.....	08 03	08 18	08 33	08 48	.....	09 00	09 13	09 27	09 42
Heathrow Terminal 4 ✈ d	.	.	.	.	.	05 53	06 07	06 22	06 40	.	06 53	07 07	07 22	07 40	.	07 53	08 07	08 22	08 40	.	08 53	09 06	09 21	09 31
Heathrow Terminals 1-2-3 [2] ✈ d	05 08	05 23	05 38	05 53	.....	06 08	06 23	06 38	06 53	.....	07 08	07 23	07 38	07 53	.....	08 08	08 23	08 38	08 53	.....	09 06	09 19	09 33	09 48
London Paddington [15] ⊖ a	05 24	05 39	05 54	06 09	.	06 24	06 39	06 54	07 09	.	07 24	07 39	07 54	08 09	.	08 24	08 39	08 54	09 09	.	09 22	09 35	09 49	10 04

	HX 1	HX 1		HX 1	HX 1	HX 1	HX 1		HX 1	HX 1	HX 1	HX 1		HX 1	HX 1	HX 1	HX 1		HX 1	HX 1	HX 1	HX 1		HX 1
Heathrow Terminal 5 ✈ d	09 57	10 12	.....	10 27	10 42	10 57	11 12	.....	11 27	11 42	11 57	12 12	.....	12 27	12 42	12 57	13 12	.....	13 27	13 42	13 57	14 12	.....	14 27
Heathrow Terminal 4 ✈ d	09 51	10 01	.	10 21	10 31	10 51	11 01	.	11 21	11 31	11 51	12 01	.	12 21	12 31	12 51	13 01	.	13 21	13 31	13 51	14 01	.	14 21
Heathrow Terminals 1-2-3 [2] ✈ d	10 03	10 18	.....	10 33	10 48	11 03	11 18	.....	11 33	11 48	12 03	12 18	.....	12 33	12 48	13 03	13 18	.....	13 33	13 48	14 03	14 18	.....	14 33
London Paddington [15] ⊖ a	10 19	10 34	.	10 49	11 04	11 19	11 34	.	11 49	12 04	12 19	12 34	.	12 49	13 04	13 19	13 34	.	13 49	14 04	14 19	14 34	.	14 49

For general notes see front of timetable
For details of catering facilities see
Directory of Train Operators

Table 118

Heathrow Airport → London

Sundays

until 6 September

Network Diagram - see first page of Table 116

	HX 1	HX 1	HX 1	HX 1		HX 1	HX 1	HX 1	HX 1		HX 1	HX 1	HX 1	HX 1		HX 1	HX 1	HX 1	HX 1		HX 1	HX 1	HX 1	HX 1
Heathrow Terminal 5 ✈ d	14 42	14 57	15 12	15 27	.....	15 42	15 57	16 12	16 27	.....	16 42	16 57	17 12	17 27	.....	17 42	17 57	18 12	18 27	.....	18 42	18 57	19 12	19 27
Heathrow Terminal 4 ✈ d	*14 31*	*14 51*	*15 01*	*15 21*	.	*15 31*	*15 51*	*16 01*	*16 21*	.	*16 31*	*16 51*	*17 01*	*17 21*	.	*17 31*	*17 51*	*18 01*	*18 21*	.	*18 31*	*18 51*	*19 01*	*19 21*
Heathrow Terminals 1-2-3 2 ✈ d	14 48	15 03	15 18	15 33	.....	15 48	16 03	16 18	16 33	.....	16 48	17 03	17 18	17 33	.....	17 48	18 03	18 18	18 33	.....	18 48	19 03	19 18	19 33
London Paddington 15 ⊖ a	15 04	15 19	15 34	15 49	.	16 03	16 19	16 34	16 49	.	17 04	17 19	17 34	17 49	.	18 04	18 20	18 34	18 49	.	19 04	19 19	19 34	19 49

	HX 1	HX 1		HX 1	HX 1	HX 1	HX 1		HX 1	HX 1	HX 1	HX 1		HX 1	HX 1	HX 1	HX 1		HX 1	HX 1	HX 1	HX 1		
Heathrow Terminal 5 ✈ d	19 42	19 57	.....	20 12	20 27	20 42	20 57	.....	21 12	21 27	21 48	22 03	.....	22 18	22 33	22 48	23 03	.....	23 18	23 33	23 48	23 57	.....	.....
Heathrow Terminal 4 ✈ d	*19 31*	*19 51*	.	*20 01*	*20 21*	*20 31*	*20 51*	.	*21 01*	*21 21*	*21 40*	*21 53*	.	*22 07*	*22 22*	*22 40*	*22 53*	.	*23 07*	*23 22*	*23 40*	.	.	.
Heathrow Terminals 1-2-3 2 ✈ d	19 48	20 03	.....	20 18	20 33	20 48	21 03	.....	21 18	21 33	21 53	22 08	.....	22 23	22 38	22 53	23 08	.....	23 23	23 38	23 53	00a01	.....	.....
London Paddington 15 ⊖ a	20 04	20 19	.	20 34	20 49	21 04	21 19	.	21 34	21 49	22 09	22 24	.	22 43	22 54	23 10	23 24	.	23 43	23 56	00 09	*00 30*	.	.

Sundays

from 13 September

	HX 1	HX 1	HX 1	HX 1		HX 1	HX 1	HX 1	HX 1		HX 1	HX 1	HX 1	HX 1		HX 1	HX 1	HX 1	HX 1		HX 1	HX 1	HX 1	HX 1
Heathrow Terminal 5 ✈ d	05 03	05 18	05 33	05 48	.....	06 03	06 18	06 33	06 48	.....	07 03	07 18	07 33	07 48	.....	08 03	08 18	08 33	08 48	.....	09 03	09 18	09 33	09 48
Heathrow Terminal 4 ✈ d	.	.	.	.	.	*05 53*	*06 07*	*06 22*	*06 40*	.	*06 53*	*07 07*	*07 22*	*07 40*	.	*07 53*	*08 07*	*08 22*	*08 40*	.	*08 53*	*09 07*	*09 22*	*09 40*
Heathrow Terminals 1-2-3 2 ✈ d	05 08	05 23	05 38	05 53	.....	06 08	06 23	06 38	06 53	.....	07 08	07 23	07 38	07 53	.....	08 08	08 23	08 38	08 53	.....	09 08	09 23	09 38	09 53
London Paddington 15 ⊖ a	05 24	05 39	05 54	06 09	.	06 24	06 39	06 54	07 09	.	07 24	07 39	07 54	08 09	.	08 24	08 39	08 54	09 09	.	09 24	09 41	09 54	10 11

	HX 1	HX 1		HX 1	HX 1	HX 1	HX 1		HX 1	HX 1	HX 1	HX 1		HX 1	HX 1	HX 1	HX 1		HX 1	HX 1	HX 1	HX 1		HX 1
Heathrow Terminal 5 ✈ d	10 03	10 18	.....	10 33	10 48	11 03	11 18	.....	11 33	11 48	12 03	12 18	.....	12 33	12 48	13 03	13 18	.....	13 33	13 48	14 03	14 18	.....	14 33
Heathrow Terminal 4 ✈ d	*09 53*	*10 07*	.	*10 22*	*10 40*	*10 53*	*11 07*	.	*11 22*	*11 40*	*11 53*	*12 07*	.	*12 22*	*12 40*	*12 53*	*13 07*	.	*13 22*	*13 40*	*13 53*	*14 07*	.	*14 22*
Heathrow Terminals 1-2-3 2 ✈ d	10 08	10 23	.....	10 38	10 53	11 08	11 23	.....	11 38	11 53	12 08	12 23	.....	12 38	12 53	13 08	13 23	.....	13 38	13 53	14 08	14 23	.....	14 38
London Paddington 15 ⊖ a	10 24	10 39	.	10 54	11 09	11 24	11 39	.	11 54	12 09	12 24	12 39	.	12 54	13 09	13 24	13 39	.	13 54	14 09	14 24	14 39	.	14 54

	HX 1	HX 1	HX 1	HX 1		HX 1	HX 1	HX 1	HX 1		HX 1	HX 1	HX 1	HX 1		HX 1	HX 1	HX 1	HX 1		HX 1	HX 1	HX 1	HX 1
Heathrow Terminal 5 ✈ d	14 48	15 03	15 18	15 33	.....	15 48	16 03	16 18	16 33	.....	16 48	17 03	17 18	17 33	.....	17 48	18 03	18 18	18 33	.....	18 48	19 03	19 18	19 33
Heathrow Terminal 4 ✈ d	*14 40*	*14 53*	*15 07*	*15 22*	.	*15 40*	*15 53*	*16 07*	*16 22*	.	*16 40*	*16 53*	*17 07*	*17 22*	.	*17 40*	*17 53*	*18 07*	*18 22*	.	*18 40*	*18 53*	*19 07*	*19 22*
Heathrow Terminals 1-2-3 2 ✈ d	14 53	15 08	15 23	15 38	.....	15 53	16 08	16 23	16 38	.....	16 53	17 08	17 23	17 38	.....	17 53	18 08	18 23	18 38	.....	18 53	19 08	19 23	19 38
London Paddington 15 ⊖ a	15 09	15 24	15 39	15 54	.	16 09	16 24	16 39	16 54	.	17 09	17 24	17 39	17 54	.	18 10	18 24	18 41	18 54	.	19 09	19 24	19 41	19 54

	HX 1	HX 1		HX 1	HX 1	HX 1	HX 1		HX 1	HX 1	HX 1	HX 1		HX 1	HX 1	HX 1	HX 1		HX 1	HX 1	HX 1	HX 1		
Heathrow Terminal 5 ✈ d	19 48	20 03	.....	20 18	20 33	20 48	21 03	.....	21 18	21 33	21 48	22 03	.....	22 18	22 33	22 48	23 03	.....	23 18	23 33	23 48	23 57	.....	.....
Heathrow Terminal 4 ✈ d	*19 40*	*19 53*	.	*20 07*	*20 22*	*20 40*	*20 53*	.	*21 07*	*21 22*	*21 40*	*21 53*	.	*22 07*	*22 22*	*22 40*	*22 53*	.	*23 07*	*23 22*	*23 40*	.	.	.
Heathrow Terminals 1-2-3 2 ✈ d	19 53	20 08	.....	20 23	20 38	20 53	21 08	.....	21 23	21 38	21 53	22 08	.....	22 23	22 38	22 53	23 08	.....	23 23	23 38	23 53	00a01	.....	.....
London Paddington 15 ⊖ a	20 09	20 24	.	20 41	20 54	21 12	21 24	.	21 41	21 54	22 09	22 24	.	22 39	22 54	23 10	23 24	.	23 43	23 56	00 09	*00 30*	.	.

For general notes see front of timetable
For details of catering facilities see
Directory of Train Operators

Slough → Windsor & Eton

Network Diagram - see first page of Table 116

Mondays to Fridays

Miles			GW 1	GW 1	GW 1		GW 1	GW 1	GW 1		GW 1	GW 1	GW 1		GW 1	GW 1	GW 1		GW 1	GW 1	GW 1		GW 1	GW 1	GW 1	GW 1
—	London Paddington 15 ⊖	d	05 16	05 30	05 58	.....	.....	06 33	.....	.....	06 42	07 22	07 52	.....	08 05	08 22	08 51	.....	08 57	09 12	09 51	.....	09 57	10 22	10 51	10 57
—	Reading 7	d	04 41	05 14	05 44	.	06 07	06 32	06 45	.	07 02	07 10	07 42	.	07 55	08 12	08 31	.	09 03	09 17	09 37	.	10 03	10 26	10 33	11 03
0	Slough 3	d	05 38	05 58	06 18	.....	06 37	06 55	07 13	.....	07 31	07 54	08 13	.....	08 31	08 54	09 14	.....	09 33	09 53	10 11	.....	10 30	10 50	11 10	11 30
2¾	Windsor & Eton Central	a	05 44	06 04	06 24	.	06 43	07 01	07 19	.	07 37	08 00	08 19	.	08 37	09 00	09 20	.	09 39	09 59	10 17	.	10 36	10 56	11 16	11 36

		GW 1		GW 1	GW 1	GW 1		GW 1	GW 1	GW 1		GW 1	GW 1	GW 1		GW 1	GW 1	GW 1		GW 1	GW 1	GW 1		GW 1	GW 1	GW 1
London Paddington 15 ⊖	d	11 22	.....	11 51	11 57	12 22	.....	12 50	12 57	13 22	.....	13 51	13 57	14 21	.....	14 50	14 57	.....	.....	15 51	16 22	16 33	.....	16 42	17 12	17 15
Reading 7	d	11 26	.	11 33	12 03	12 26	.	12 33	13 03	13 26	.	13 33	14 03	14 26	.	14 33	15 03	15 26	.	15 56	16 26	16 33	.	16 56	17 18	17 33
Slough 3	d	11 50	.....	12 10	12 30	12 50	.....	13 10	13 30	13 50	.....	14 10	14 30	14 50	.....	15 10	15 30	15 50	.....	16 21	16 43	17 01	.....	17 21	17 40	17 58
Windsor & Eton Central	a	11 56	.	12 16	12 36	12 56	.	13 16	13 36	13 56	.	14 16	14 36	14 56	.	15 16	15 36	15 56	.	16 27	16 49	17 07	.	17 27	17 46	18 04

		GW 1	GW 1		GW 1	GW 1	GW 1		GW 1	GW 1	GW 1		GW 1	GW 1	GW 1		GW 1	GW 1	GW 1		GW 1	GW 1				
London Paddington 15 ⊖	d	17 42	18 12	.....	18 15	18 51	19 22	.....	.....	19 51	20 20	.....	20 27	20 51	21 21	.....	21 27	21 48	.....	.....	22 21	22 48	.....	.....	.....	.....
Reading 7	d	17 42	17 58	.	18 33	18 56	19 03	.	19 33	19 56	19 58	.	20 33	20 56	.	.	21 26	21 33	22 06	.	.	.	.	.	.	.
Slough 3	d	18 16	18 40	.....	18 58	19 16	19 40	.....	20 00	20 20	20 40	.....	21 00	21 20	21 40	.....	22 00	22 20	22 40	.....	23 00	23 20	.....	.....	.....	.....
Windsor & Eton Central	a	18 22	18 46	.	19 04	19 22	19 46	.	20 06	20 26	20 46	.	21 06	21 26	21 46	.	22 06	22 26	22 46	.	23 06	23 26	.	.	.	.

Saturdays

		GW 1	GW 1	GW 1		GW 1	GW 1	GW 1		GW 1	GW 1	GW 1		GW 1	GW 1	GW 1		GW 1	GW 1	GW 1		GW 1	GW 1	GW 1		GW 1
London Paddington 15 ⊖	d	05 50	06 21	06 50	.....	07 21	07 50	08 21	.....	08 50	09 21	09 50	.....	10 21	10 50	11 21	.....	.....	12 21	12 50	.....	13 21	13 50	14 21	.....	14 50
Reading 7	d	05 48	06 18	07 00	.	07 18	07 56	08 26	.	08 57	09 26	09 56	.	10 25	10 56	11 27	.	11 56	.	12 55	.	13 25	13 55	14 26	.	14 56
Slough 3	d	06 20	06 50	07 20	.....	07 50	08 20	08 50	.....	09 20	09 50	10 20	.....	10 50	11 20	11 50	.....	12 20	12 50	13 20	.....	13 50	14 20	14 50	.....	15 20
Windsor & Eton Central	a	06 26	06 56	07 26	.	07 56	08 26	08 56	.	09 26	09 56	10 26	.	10 56	11 26	11 56	.	12 26	12 56	13 26	.	13 56	14 26	14 56	.	15 26

		GW 1	GW 1	GW 1		GW 1	GW 1	GW 1		GW 1	GW 1	GW 1		GW 1	GW 1	GW 1		GW 1	GW 1	GW 1		GW 1	GW 1			
London Paddington 15 ⊖	d	15 21	15 50	16 21	.....	16 50	17 21	17 50	.....	18 21	18 50	19 21	.....	19 50	20 12	20 50	.....	21 12	21 50	22 32	.....	23 00	23 33	.....	.....	.....
Reading 7	d	15 25	15 48	.	.	16 56	17 25	17 57	.	18 25	18 56	19 25	.	19 56	20 25	20 53	.	21 25	21 48	22 35	.	22 56	23 31	.	.	.
Slough 3	d	15 50	16 20	16 50	.....	17 20	17 50	18 20	.....	18 50	19 20	19 50	.....	20 20	20 50	21 20	.....	21 50	22 20	22 55	.....	23 21	23 55	.....	.....	.....
Windsor & Eton Central	a	15 56	16 26	16 56	.	17 26	17 56	18 26	.	18 56	19 26	19 56	.	20 26	20 56	21 26	.	21 56	22 26	23 01	.	23 27	00 01	.	.	.

Sundays

		GW 1	GW 1		GW 1	GW 1		GW 1	GW 1		GW 1	GW 1		GW 1	GW 1		GW 1	GW 1		GW 1	GW 1		GW 1	GW 1		GW 1
London Paddington 15 ⊖	d	.....	08 15	.....	.....	09 15	.....	.....	10 15	.....	.....	11 15	.....	11 43	12 15	.....	.....	13 15	.....	.....	14 15	.....	.....	15 15	.....	.....
Reading 7	d	07 22	08 22	.	.	.	.	09 52	.	.	10 52	.	.	11 52	.	.	12 52	.	.	13 52	.	.	17 02	.	.	15 52
Slough 3	d	08 22	08 52	.....	09 22	09 52	.....	10 22	10 52	.....	11 22	11 52	.....	12 22	12 52	.....	13 22	13 52	.....	14 22	14 52	.....	15 22	15 52	.....	16 22
Windsor & Eton Central	a	08 28	08 58	.	09 28	09 58	.	10 28	10 58	.	11 28	11 58	.	12 28	12 58	.	13 28	13 58	.	14 28	14 58	.	15 28	15 58	.	16 28

		GW 1	GW 1		GW 1	GW 1		GW 1	GW 1		GW 1	GW 1		GW 1	GW 1		GW 1	GW 1		GW 1	GW 1					
London Paddington 15 ⊖	d	16 15	.....	.....	17 15	.....	.....	18 15	.....	.....	19 15	.....	.....	20 15	.....	.....	.....	.....	.....	22 15	.....	.....	.....	.....	.....	.....
Reading 7	d	.	16 52	.	.	17 52	.	18 22	18 52	.	.	19 52	.	.	20 52	.	.	.	.	22 24	22 40	.	.	.	.	.
Slough 3	d	16 52	17 22	.....	17 52	18 22	.....	18 52	19 22	.....	19 52	20 22	.....	20 52	21 22	.....	21 52	22 22	.....	22 52	23 22	.....	.....	.....	.....	.....
Windsor & Eton Central	a	16 58	17 28	.	17 58	18 28	.	18 58	19 28	.	19 58	20 28	.	20 58	21 28	.	21 58	22 28	.	22 58	23 28	.	.	.	.	.

For general notes see front of timetable
For details of catering facilities see
Directory of Train Operators

Windsor & Eton → Slough

Network Diagram - see first page of Table 116

Mondays to Fridays

Miles			GW 1	GW 1	GW 1		GW 1	GW 1	GW 1		GW 1	GW 1	GW 1		GW 1	GW 1	GW 1		GW 1	GW 1	GW 1		GW 1	GW 1	GW 1	GW 1
0	Windsor & Eton Central	d	05 48	06 08	06 28	.....	06 46	07 04	07 22	.....	07 40	08 04	08 22	.....	08 40	09 04	09 24	.....	09 42	10 02	10 20	.....	10 40	11 00	11 20	11 40
2¾	Slough 3	a	05 54	06 14	06 34	.	06 52	07 10	07 28	.	07 46	08 10	08 28	.	08 46	09 10	09 30	.	09 48	10 08	10 26	.	10 46	11 06	11 26	11 46
—	Reading 7	a	06 20	06 53	07 03	.....	07 25	07 41	07 52	.....	08 21	08 42	08 52	.....	09 21	09 52	10 17	.....	10 21	10 43	10 52	.....	11 21	11 43	11 52	12 21
—	London Paddington 15	a	06 30	06 38	07 00	.	07 16	07 47	08 14	.	08 17	08 47	09 18	.	09 21	09 49	.	.	10 10	10 46	10 59	.	.	11 28	11 58	.

		GW 1		GW 1	GW 1	GW 1		GW 1	GW 1	GW 1		GW 1	GW 1	GW 1		GW 1	GW 1	GW 1		GW 1	GW 1	GW 1		GW 1	GW 1	GW 1
Windsor & Eton Central	d	12 00	.....	12 20	12 40	13 00	.....	13 20	13 40	14 00	.....	14 20	14 40	15 00	.....	15 20	15 40	16 00	.....	16 30	16 52	17 10	.....	17 30	17 49	18 07
Slough 3	a	12 06	.	12 26	12 46	13 06	.	13 26	13 46	14 06	.	14 26	14 46	15 06	.	15 26	15 46	16 06	.	16 36	16 58	17 16	.	17 36	17 55	18 13
Reading 7	a	12 43	.....	12 52	13 21	13 43	.....	13 52	14 21	14 43	.....	14 52	15 21	15 42	.....	15 52	16 21	16 45	.....	17 03	17 46	18 00	.....	.....	18 26	18 43
London Paddington 15	a	12 29	.	12 59	.	13 28	.	13 59	.	14 29	.	14 59	.	15 28	.	16 00	.	16 28	.	16 58	17 28	17 55	.	.	18 37	18 46

		GW 1	GW 1		GW 1	GW 1	GW 1		GW 1	GW 1	GW 1		GW 1	GW 1	GW 1		GW 1	GW 1	GW 1		GW 1	GW 1				
Windsor & Eton Central	d	18 28	18 49	.....	19 07	19 27	19 50	.....	20 10	20 30	20 50	.....	21 10	21 30	21 50	.....	22 10	22 30	22 50	.....	23 10	23 30	.....	.....	.....	.....
Slough 3	a	18 34	18 55	.	19 13	19 33	19 56	.	20 16	20 36	20 56	.	21 16	21 36	21 56	.	22 16	22 36	22 56	.	23 16	23 36	.	.	.	.
Reading 7	a	19 15	19 21	.....	.....	19 52	20 21	.....	20 50	21 11	21 23	.....	21 51	22 11	.....	.....	.....	.....	.....	.....	.....	.....	.....	.....	.....	.....
London Paddington 15	a	18 59	19 29	.	.	19 59	20 29	.	21 01	21 16	21 29	.	.	.	.	.	.	.	.	.	.	00 17	.	.	.	.

Saturdays

		GW 1	GW 1		GW 1	GW 1		GW 1	GW 1		GW 1	GW 1		GW 1	GW 1		GW 1	GW 1		GW 1	GW 1		GW 1	GW 1		GW 1
Windsor & Eton Central	d	06 30	07 00	.....	07 30	08 00	.....	08 30	09 00	.....	09 30	10 00	.....	10 30	11 00	.....	11 30	12 00	.....	12 30	13 00	.....	13 30	14 00	.....	14 30
Slough 3	a	06 36	07 06	.	07 36	08 06	.	08 36	09 06	.	09 36	10 06	.	10 36	11 06	.	11 36	12 06	.	12 36	13 06	.	13 36	14 06	.	14 36
Reading 7	a	07 11	07 43	.....	08 11	08 43	.....	08 53	09 43	.....	09 53	10 43	.....	10 53	11 43	.....	11 53	12 43	.....	.....	13 43	.....	13 53	14 43	.....	14 53
London Paddington 15	a	07 16	07 37	.	08 16	08 30	.	08 59	09 30	.	09 59	10 29	.	10 59	11 30	.	11 59	12 30	.	12 59	13 30	.	13 59	14 29	.	14 59

		GW 1	GW 1		GW 1	GW 1		GW 1	GW 1		GW 1	GW 1		GW 1	GW 1		GW 1	GW 1	GW 1	GW 1	GW 1	GW 1	GW 1	GW 1		
Windsor & Eton Central	d	15 00	15 30	.....	16 00	16 30	.....	17 00	17 30	.....	18 00	18 30	.....	19 00	19 30	.....	20 00	20 30	21 00	21 30	22 00	22 30	23 04	23 32	.....	.....
Slough 3	a	15 06	15 36	.	16 06	16 36	.	17 06	17 36	.	18 06	18 36	.	19 06	19 36	.	20 06	20 36	21 06	21 36	22 06	22 36	23 10	23 38	.	.
Reading 7	a	15 43	15 53	.....	16 43	16 53	.....	17 43	17 53	.....	18 43	18 52	.....	19 43	20 11	.....	20 43	21 11	21 43	22 13	22 43	23 06	23 33	00 07	.....	.....
London Paddington 15	a	15 29	15 59	.	16 46	.	.	17 30	17 59	.	18 29	18 59	.	19 30	19 59	.	20 30	20 59	21 30	21 59	22 40	23 08	.	00 10	.	.

Sundays

		GW 1	GW 1		GW 1	GW 1		GW 1	GW 1		GW 1	GW 1		GW 1	GW 1		GW 1	GW 1		GW 1	GW 1		GW 1	GW 1		GW 1
Windsor & Eton Central	d	00 05	08 32	.....	09 02	09 32	.....	10 02	10 32	.....	11 02	11 32	.....	12 02	12 32	.....	13 02	13 32	.....	14 02	14 32	.....	15 02	15 32	.....	16 02
Slough 3	a	00 11	08 38	.	09 08	09 38	.	10 08	10 38	.	11 08	11 38	.	12 08	12 38	.	13 08	13 38	.	14 08	14 38	.	15 08	15 38	.	16 08
Reading 7	a	01 05	.....	.....	.....	10 10	.....	.....	11 10	.....	11 42	12 10	.....	12 43	13 10	.....	13 43	14 10	.....	14 43	15 10	.....	15 43	16 12	.....	16 43
London Paddington 15	a	01 02	09 20	.	.	.	.	.	.	.	.	.	.	.	.	.	.	.	.	.	.	.	.	.	.	16 49

		GW 1	GW 1		GW 1	GW 1		GW 1	GW 1		GW 1	GW 1		GW 1	GW 1		GW 1	GW 1		GW 1	GW 1		GW 1			
Windsor & Eton Central	d	16 32	17 02	.....	17 32	18 02	.....	18 32	19 02	.....	19 32	20 02	.....	20 32	21 02	.....	21 32	22 02	.....	22 32	23 02	.....	23 32	.....	.....	.....
Slough 3	a	16 38	17 08	.	17 38	18 08	.	18 38	19 08	.	19 38	20 08	.	20 38	21 08	.	21 38	22 08	.	22 38	23 08	.	23 38	.	.	.
Reading 7	a	17 12	17 43	.....	18 12	18 43	.....	19 12	19 43	.....	20 12	20 43	.....	21 12	21 44	.....	.....	22 46	.....	23 11	23 43	.....	00 12	.....	.....	.....
London Paddington 15	a	.	.	.	.	18 49	.	.	.	.	.	.	.	.	.	.	.	23 05	.	23 15	23 54	.	.	.	.	.

For general notes see front of timetable
For details of catering facilities see
Directory of Train Operators

Maidenhead → Marlow

Network Diagram - see first page of Table 116

Mondays to Fridays

Miles			GW MX 1	GW 1	GW 1	GW 1	GW 1	GW 1	GW 1	GW 1	GW 1	GW 1	GW 1	GW 1	GW 1	GW 1	GW 1	GW 1	GW 1
—	London Paddington 15 ⊖	d		03 34			05b43		06b33		06 57		07 27		08b22	08 57	09 57	10 57	11 57
—	Reading 7	d		04 41	05 14		06 15		06 46		07 10		07 55		08 31	09 17	10 18	11 18	12 18
0	**Maidenhead 3**	d	23p45	05 25	05 49		06 32		07 09		07 42		08 13		09 04	09 38	10 38	11 38	12 38
1¼	Furze Platt	d	23p49	05 29	05 53		06 36		07 13		07 46		08 17		09 08	09 42	10 42	11 42	12 42
3	Cookham	d	23p52	05 32							07 49		08 20		09 11	09 45	10 45	11 45	12 45
4½	Bourne End 3	a	23p56	05 36	06 01		06 44		07 21		07 53		08 24		09 15	09 49	10 49	11 49	12 49
—		d	00 01	05 40		06 18		06 49		07 28		07 58		08 27		09 53	10 53	11 53	12 53
7¼	**Marlow**	a	00 08	05 48		06 25		06 56		07 35		08 05		08 34		10 01	11 01	12 01	13 01

		GW 1	GW 1	GW 1	GW 1	GW 1	GW 1	GW 1	GW 1	GW 1	GW 1	GW 1	GW 1	GW 1	GW 1	GW 1	GW 1	GW 1
London Paddington 15 ⊖	d	12 57	13 57	14 57	15 57	17 18	17 42		18 18		18 42		19 18		19 57	20 57	21 57	22 59
Reading 7	d	13 18	14 18	15 18	16 18	17 18	17 58		18 18		18 48		19 18		20 18	21 18	22c00	23 15
Maidenhead 3	d	13 38	14 38	15 38	16 38	17 46	18 18		18 49		19 18		19 51		20 42	21 38	22 46	23 45
Furze Platt	d	13 42	14 42	15 42	16 42	17 50	18 23		18 53		19 23		19 55		20 46	21 42	22 50	23 49
Cookham	d	13 45	14 45	15 45	16 45	17 53	18 26		18 56		19 26		19 58		20 49	21 45	22 53	23 52
Bourne End 3	a	13 49	14 49	15 49	16 49	17 57	18 32		19 00		19 32		20 02		20 53	21 49	22 57	23 56
	d	13 53	14 53	15 53	16 53	18 01		18 35		19 05		19 35		20 05	20 57	21 53	23 01	00 01
Marlow	a	14 01	15 01	16 01	17 01	18 09		18 42		19 12		19 42		20 12	21 05	22 01	23 09	00 08

Saturdays

		GW 1	GW 1	GW 1	GW 1	GW 1	GW 1	GW 1	GW 1	GW 1	GW 1	GW 1	GW 1	GW 1	GW 1	GW 1	GW 1	GW 1	GW 1	GW 1
London Paddington 15 ⊖	d		05 25	06 57	07 57	08 57	09 57	10 57	11 57	12 57	13 57	14 57	15 57	16 57	17 57	18 57	19 57	20 57	21 57	23b00
Reading 7	d		06 18	07 18	08 18	09 18	10 18	11 18	12 18	13 18	14 18	15 18	16 18	17 18	18 18	19 18	20 18	21 18	22 18	23 18
Maidenhead 3	d	23p45	06 38	07 38	08 38	09 38	10 38	11 38	12 38	13 38	14 38	15 38	16 38	17 38	18 38	19 38	20 38	21 38	22 38	23 38
Furze Platt	d	23p49	06 42	07 42	08 42	09 42	10 42	11 42	12 42	13 42	14 42	15 42	16 42	17 42	18 42	19 42	20 42	21 42	22 42	23 42
Cookham	d	23p52	06 45	07 45	08 45	09 45	10 45	11 45	12 45	13 45	14 45	15 45	16 45	17 45	18 45	19 45	20 45	21 45	22 45	23 45
Bourne End 3	a	23p56	06 49	07 49	08 49	09 49	10 49	11 49	12 49	13 49	14 49	15 49	16 49	17 49	18 49	19 49	20 49	21 49	22 49	23 49
	d	00 01	06 53	07 53	08 53	09 53	10 53	11 53	12 53	13 53	14 53	15 53	16 53	17 53	18 53	19 53	20 53	21 53	22 53	23 53
Marlow	a	00 08	07 01	08 01	09 01	10 01	11 01	12 01	13 01	14 01	15 01	16 01	17 01	18 01	19 01	20 01	21 01	22 01	23 01	00 01

Sundays

		GW 1	GW 1	GW 1	GW 1	GW 1	GW 1	GW 1	GW 1	GW 1	GW 1	GW 1	GW 1	GW 1
London Paddington 15 ⊖	d	08e43	10f04	11g04	12h04	13j04	14k06	15m06	16n06	17q06	18r06	19t06	19v43	20w43
Reading 7	d	09 18	10 18	11 18	12 18	13 18	14 18	15 18	16 18	17 18	18 18	19 18	20 18	20y52
Maidenhead 3	d	09 35	10 35	11 35	12 35	13 35	14 35	15 35	16 35	17 35	18 35	19 35	20 35	21 40
Furze Platt	d	09 39	10 39	11 39	12 38	13 39	14 39	15 39	16 39	17 39	18 39	19 39	20 39	21 44
Cookham	d	09 42	10 42	11 42	12 41	13 42	14 41	15 42	16 42	17 42	18 42	19 42	20 42	21 47
Bourne End 3	a	09 47	10 47	11 47	12 47	13 47	14 47	15 47	16 47	17 47	18 47	19 47	20 47	21 52
	d	09 51	10 51	11 51	12 50	13 51	14 51	15 50	16 51	17 51	18 51	19 51	20 51	21 56
Marlow	a	09 58	10 58	11 58	12 58	13 58	14 58	15 58	16 58	17 58	18 58	19 58	20 58	22 03

For general notes see front of timetable
For details of catering facilities see Directory of Train Operators

- b Change at Slough and Maidenhead
- c Fridays dep. 2215
- e From 13 September dep. 0844
- f From 13 September dep. 0944
- g From 13 September dep. 1044
- h From 13 September dep. 1143
- j From 13 September dep. 1244
- k From 13 September dep. 1344
- m From 13 September dep. 1444
- n From 13 September dep. 1544
- q From 13 September dep. 1644
- r From 13 September dep. 1744
- t From 13 September dep. 1844
- v From 13 September dep. 1944
- w From 13 September dep. 2044
- y From 13 September dep. 2124

Table 120

Marlow → Maidenhead

Mondays to Fridays

Network Diagram - see first page of Table 116

Miles			GW MX 1	GW 1	GW 1	GW 1	GW 1	GW 1	GW 1	GW 1	GW 1	GW 1	GW 1	GW 1	GW 1	GW 1	GW 1	GW 1	GW 1
0	**Marlow**	d	00 11	06 04		06 39		07 18		07 47		08 17		08 37		10 06	11 06	12 06	13 06
2¾	Bourne End 3	a	00 18	06 11		06 46		07 25		07 54		08 24		08 44		10 13	11 13	12 13	13 13
—		d	00 22		06 14		06 49		07 28		07 57		08 28	08 48	09 19	10 17	11 17	12 17	13 17
4¼	Cookham	d	00 26		06 17		06 52		07 31		08 00		08 31	08 52	09 22	10 21	11 21	12 21	13 21
6	Furze Platt	d	00 29		06 21		06 56		07 35		08 04		08 35	08 55	09 26	10 24	11 24	12 24	13 24
7¼	**Maidenhead 3**	a	00 34		06 25		07 00		07 39		08 08		08 39	09 00	09 30	10 29	11 29	12 29	13 29
—	Reading 7	a	00 58		06 53		07 25		08 11		08 42		09 11	09 23	09 52	10 52	11 52	12 50	13 52
—	London Paddington 15 ⊖	a	02 00		06 54		07 26		08 17		08 47		09 21	09 27	10b10	11 16	12 16	13 16	14 16

		GW 1	GW 1	GW 1	GW 1	GW 1	GW 1	GW 1	GW 1	GW 1	GW 1	GW 1	GW 1	GW 1	GW 1	GW 1	GW 1
Marlow	d	14 06	15 06	16 06	17 06	18 24		18 54		19 25		19 55		20 15	21 08	22 04	23 13
Bourne End 3	a	14 13	15 13	16 13	17 13	18 31		19 01		19 32		20 02		20 22	21 15	22 11	23 20
	d	14 17	15 17	16 17	17 17		18 34		19 04		19 36		20 11	20 26	21 19	22 15	23 24
Cookham	d	14 21	15 21	16 21	17 21		18 37		19 07		19 39		20 14	20 30	21 23	22 19	23 28
Furze Platt	d	14 24	15 24	16 24	17 24		18 41		19 11		19 43		20 18	20 33	21 26	22 22	23 31
Maidenhead 3	a	14 29	15 29	16 29	17 29		18 45		19 15		19 47		20 22	20 38	21 31	22 27	23 36
Reading 7	a	14 52	15 52	16 52	17 55		19c12		19 45		20 09		20 45	21 11	21 51	22 46	23 58
London Paddington 15 ⊖	a	15 16	16 16	17 16	18 16		19b29		19b59		20b29		21 16	21b29	22 32	23e43	00 21

Saturdays

		GW 1	GW 1	GW 1	GW 1	GW 1	GW 1	GW 1	GW 1	GW 1	GW 1	GW 1	GW 1	GW 1	GW 1	GW 1	GW 1	GW 1	GW 1
Marlow	d	00 11	07 06	08 06	09 06	10 06	11 06	12 06	13 06	14 06	15 06	16 06	17 06	18 06	19 06	20 06	21 06	22 06	23 06
Bourne End 3	a	00 18	07 13	08 13	09 13	10 13	11 13	12 13	13 13	14 13	15 13	16 13	17 13	18 13	19 13	20 13	21 13	22 13	23 13
	d	00 22	07 17	08 17	09 17	10 17	11 17	12 17	13 17	14 17	15 17	16 17	17 17	18 17	19 17	20 17	21 17	22 17	23 17
Cookham	d	00 26	07 21	08 21	09 21	10 21	11 21	12 21	13 21	14 21	15 21	16 21	17 21	18 21	19 21	20 21	21 21	22 21	23 21
Furze Platt	d	00 29	07 24	08 24	09 24	10 24	11 24	12 24	13 24	14 24	15 24	16 24	17 24	18 24	19 24	20 24	21 24	22 24	23 24
Maidenhead 3	a	00 34	07 29	08 29	09 29	10 29	11 29	12 29	13 29	14 29	15 29	16 29	17 29	18 29	19 29	20 29	21 29	22 29	23 29
Reading 7	a	00 58	07 51	08 51	09 51	10 51	11 51	12 51	13 51	14 51	15 51	16 51	17 51	18 51	19 51	20 51	21 51	22 51	00 20
London Paddington 15 ⊖	a	02 00	08 16	09 16	10 16	11 16	12 16	13 16	14 16	15 16	16 16	17 16	18 16	19 16	20 16	21 16	22 16	23 16	00 16

Sundays

		GW 1	GW 1	GW 1	GW 1	GW 1	GW 1	GW 1	GW 1	GW 1	GW 1	GW 1	GW 1	GW 1	GW 1
Marlow	d	00 06	10 01	11 01	12 01	13 01	14 01	15 01	16 01	17 01	18 01	19 01	20 01	21 01	22 06
Bourne End 3	a	00 13	10 08	11 08	12 08	13 08	14 08	15 08	16 08	17 08	18 08	19 08	20 08	21 08	22 13
	d	00 17	10 12	11 12	12 12	13 12	14 12	15 12	16 12	17 12	18 12	19 12	20 12	21 12	22 17
Cookham	d	00 21	10 16	11 16	12 16	13 16	14 16	15 16	16 16	17 16	18 16	19 16	20 16	21 16	22 20
Furze Platt	d	00 24	10 20	11 20	12 20	13 20	14 20	15 20	16 20	17 20	18 20	19 20	20 20	21 20	22 24
Maidenhead 3	a	00 29	10 24	11 24	12 24	13 24	14 24	15 24	16 24	17 24	18 24	19 24	20 24	21 24	22 28
Reading 7	a	01 05	10f43	11 42	12 43	13 43	14 43	15 43	16 43	17 43	18 43	19 43	20 43	21 44	22 46
London Paddington 15 ⊖	a		11g08	12h17	13j17	14k17	15m17	16n17	17q20	18r20	19t20	20v17	21w20	22y40	23 40

For general notes see front of timetable
For details of catering facilities see Directory of Train Operators

- b Change at Maidenhead and Slough
- c 29 June to 4 September arr. 1915
- e Change at Maidenhead and Slough. Fridays arr. 2312
- f From 13 September arr. 1042
- g From 13 September arr. 1120
- h From 13 September arr. 1220
- j From 13 September arr. 1320
- k From 13 September arr. 1421
- m From 13 September arr. 1520
- n From 13 September arr. 1620
- q Until 6 September arr. 1706, change at Maidenhead and Slough
- r Until 6 September arr. 1810, change at Maidenhead and Slough
- t Until 6 September arr. 1908, change at Maidenhead and Slough
- v From 13 September arr. 2020
- w Until 6 September arr. 2106, change at Maidenhead and Slough
- y From 13 September arr. 2207

Twyford → Henley-on-Thames

Network Diagram - see first page of Table 116

Mondays to Fridays

Miles			GW 1	GW 1	GW 1	GW 1	GW 1	GW 1	GW 1	GW 1	GW 1	GW 1	GW 1	GW 1	GW 1
—	London Paddington 15 ⊖	d	03 34	05b30	05 57	06b33	07b22	07b52	08 27	08 57	09b51	10 27	11b22	11 57	12b50
—	Reading 7	d	05 14	06 07	06 37	07 10	08 06	08 31	09 03	09 33	10 18	11 03	11 48	12 33	13 18
0	**Twyford 3**	d	05 42	06 21	06 50	07 27	08 14	08 44	09 22	09 53	10 36	11 21	12 06	12 51	13 36
1¾	Wargrave	d	05 46	06 25	06 54	07 31	08 19	08 48	09 26	09 57	10 40	11 25	12 10	12 55	13 40
2¾	Shiplake	d	05 49	06 28	06 57	07 34	08 22	08 51	09 29	10 00	10 43	11 28	12 13	12 58	13 43
4½	**Henley-on-Thames**	a	05 54	06 33	07 02	07 39	08 26	08 56	09 34	10 05	10 48	11 33	12 18	13 03	13 48

		GW 1	GW 1	GW 1	GW 1	GW 1	GW 1	GW 1	GW 1	GW 1	GW 1	GW 1	GW 1	GW 1	GW 1
London Paddington 15 ⊖	d	13 27	14b21	14 57	15 57	17 06	17 12	18 06	18 12	19 06	19b22	19 57	20 57	21 57	22b48
Reading 7	d	14 03	14 48	15 33	16 33	17 18	17 42	18 18	18 48	19 18	19 58	20 33	21 33	22c00	23 15
Twyford 3	d	14 21	15 06	15 48	16 47	17 30	17 58	18 31	18 58	19 38	20 09	20 48	21 48	22 52	23 37
Wargrave	d	14 25	15 10	15 52	16 51	17 34	18 03	18 35	19 03	19 42	20 13	20 52	21 52	22 56	23 41
Shiplake	d	14 28	15 13	15 55	16 54	17 37	18 06	18 38	19 06	19 45	20 16	20 55	21 55	22 59	23 44
Henley-on-Thames	a	14 33	15 18	16 00	16 59	17 42	18 13	18 43	19 13	19 51	20 21	21 00	22 00	23 04	23 49

Saturdays

		GW 1	GW 1	GW 1	GW 1	GW 1	GW 1	GW 1	GW 1	GW 1	GW 1	GW 1	GW 1	GW 1	GW 1	GW 1	GW 1	GW 1	GW 1
London Paddington 15 ⊖	d	05 25	06 57	07 57	08 57	09 57	10 57	11 57	12 57	13 57	14 57	15 57	16 57	17 57	18 57	19 57	20 57	21 57	23b00
Reading 7	d	06 33	07 33	08 33	09 33	10 33	11 33	12 33	13 33	14 33	15 33	16 33	17 33	18 33	19 33	20 33	21 33	22 32	23 18
Twyford 3	d	06 50	07 50	08 50	09 50	10 50	11 50	12 50	13 50	14 50	15 50	16 50	17 50	18 50	19 50	20 50	21 50	22 50	23 50
Wargrave	d	06 54	07 54	08 54	09 54	10 54	11 54	12 54	13 54	14 54	15 54	16 54	17 54	18 54	19 54	20 54	21 54	22 54	23 54
Shiplake	d	06 57	07 57	08 57	09 57	10 57	11 57	12 57	13 57	14 57	15 57	16 57	17 57	18 57	19 57	20 57	21 57	22 57	23 57
Henley-on-Thames	a	07 02	08 02	09 02	10 02	11 02	12 02	13 02	14 02	15 02	16 02	17 02	18 02	19 02	20 02	21 02	22 02	23 02	00 02

Sundays

		GW 1 A	GW 1 B	GW 1	GW 1	GW 1	GW 1	GW 1	GW 1	GW 1	GW 1	GW 1	GW 1	GW 1	GW 1
London Paddington 15 ⊖	d	08 44	08 43	09e43	10e43	11 43	12e43	13e43	14e43	15e43	16e43	17e43	18e43	19e43	20e43
Reading 7	d	09 18	09 18	10 18	11 18	12 18	13 18	14 18	15 18	16 18	17 18	18 18	19 18	20 18	20f52
Twyford 3	d	09 38	09 41	10 38	11 38	12 38	13 38	14 38	15 38	16 38	17 38	18 38	19 38	20 38	21 38
Wargrave	d	09 42	09 45	10 42	11 42	12 42	13 42	14 42	15 42	16 42	17 42	18 42	19 42	20 42	21 42
Shiplake	d	09 45	09 48	10 45	11 45	12 45	13 45	14 45	15 45	16 45	17 45	18 45	19 45	20 45	21 45
Henley-on-Thames	a	09 51	09 53	10 50	11 50	12 50	13 50	14 50	15 50	16 50	17 50	18 50	19 50	20 50	21 50

For general notes see front of timetable
For details of catering facilities see Directory of Train Operators

- A From 13 September
- B Until 6 September
- b Change at Slough and Twyford
- c Fridays dep. 2215
- e From 13 September dep. 1 minute later
- f From 13 September dep. 2124

Table 121

Mondays to Fridays

Henley-on-Thames → Twyford

Network Diagram - see first page of Table 116

Miles			GW 1	GW 1	GW 1	GW 1	GW 1	GW 1	GW 1	GW 1	GW 1	GW 1	GW 1	GW 1	GW 1
0	**Henley-on-Thames**	d	06 06	06 36	07 09	07 43	08 29	09 01	09 37	10 09	10 54	11 39	12 24	13 09	13 54
1¾	Shiplake	d	06 10	06 40	07 13	07 47	08 33	09 05	09 41	10 13	10 58	11 43	12 28	13 13	13 58
2¾	Wargrave	d	06 13	06 43	07 16	07 50	08 36	09 08	09 44	10 16	11 01	11 46	12 31	13 16	14 01
4½	**Twyford 3**	a	06 18	06 48	07 21	07 56	08 41	09 13	09 49	10 21	11 06	11 51	12 36	13 21	14 06
—	Reading 7	a	06 44	07 15	07 41	08 11	08 53	09 23	10 17	10 43	11 22	12 17	12 50	13 43	14 21
—	London Paddington 15	⊖ a	06 54	07 26	07 57	08 29	09 27	10b10	10 46	11 16	11b58	12 46	13b28	14 16	14b59

		GW 1	GW 1	GW 1	GW 1	GW 1	GW 1	GW 1	GW 1	GW 1	GW 1	GW 1	GW 1	GW 1	GW 1
Henley-on-Thames	d	14 39	15 24	16 20	17 09	17 46	18 17	18 46	19 16	19 55	20 24	21 07	22 07	23 07	23 52
Shiplake	d	14 43	15 28	16 24	17 13	17 50	18 21	18 50	19 20	19 59	20 28	21 11	22 11	23 11	23 56
Wargrave	d	14 46	15 31	16 27	17 16	17 53	18 24	18 53	19 23	20 02	20 31	21 14	22 14	23 14	23 59
Twyford 3	a	14 51	15 36	16 32	17 21	17 58	18 29	18 58	19 28	20 07	20 36	21 19	22 19	23 19	00 04
Reading 7	a	15 11	15 52	16 45	17 36	18 16	18 43	19c12	19 45	20 25	20 52	21 43	22 46	23 40	00 17
London Paddington 15	⊖ a	15 46	16b28	17b28	18 16	19 00	19b29	19b59	20b29	21 16	21b29	22 16	23e43	00 17	01f14

Saturdays

		GW 1	GW 1	GW 1	GW 1	GW 1	GW 1	GW 1	GW 1	GW 1	GW 1	GW 1	GW 1	GW 1	GW 1	GW 1	GW 1	GW 1
Henley-on-Thames	d	07 24	08 24	09 24	10 24	11 24	12 24	13 24	14 24	15 24	16 24	17 24	18 24	19 24	20 24	21 24	22 24	23 24
Shiplake	d	07 28	08 28	09 28	10 28	11 28	12 28	13 28	14 28	15 28	16 28	17 28	18 28	19 28	20 28	21 28	22 28	23 28
Wargrave	d	07 31	08 31	09 31	10 31	11 31	12 31	13 31	14 31	15 31	16 31	17 31	18 31	19 31	20 31	21 31	22 31	23 31
Twyford 3	a	07 36	08 36	09 36	10 36	11 36	12 36	13 36	14 36	15 36	16 36	17 36	18 36	19 36	20 36	21 36	22 36	23 36
Reading 7	a	07 51	08 51	09 51	10 51	11 51	12 51	13 51	14 51	15 51	16 51	17 51	18 51	19 51	20 51	21 51	22 51	00 20
London Paddington 15	⊖ a	08b30	09b30	10b29	11b30	12b30	13b30	14b29	15b29	16 31	17b30	18b29	19b30	20b30	21b30	22 31	23 28	01 02

Sundays

		GW 1	GW 1	GW 1	GW 1	GW 1	GW 1	GW 1	GW 1	GW 1	GW 1	GW 1	GW 1	GW 1	GW 1
Henley-on-Thames	d	00 08	10 03	11 03	12 03	13 03	14 03	15 03	16 03	17 03	18 03	19 03	20 03	21 03	22 01
Shiplake	d	00 12	10 07	11 07	12 07	13 07	14 07	15 07	16 07	17 07	18 07	19 07	20 07	21 07	22 05
Wargrave	d	00 15	10 10	11 10	12 10	13 10	14 10	15 10	16 10	17 10	18 10	19 10	20 10	21 10	22 08
Twyford 3	a	00 20	10 15	11 15	12 15	13 15	14 15	15 15	16 15	17 15	18 15	19 15	20 15	21 15	22 13
Reading 7	a	00 42	10g43	11 42	12 43	13 43	14 43	15 43	16 43	17 43	18 43	19 43	20 43	21 44	22h23
London Paddington 15	⊖ a		11j20	12k17	13m17	14n17	15q17	16r17	17t20	18v20	19w20	20y17	21z20	22A40	23B05

For general notes see front of timetable
For details of catering facilities see Directory of Train Operators

- **A** From 13 September arr. 2220
- **B** From 13 September arr. 2340
- **b** Change at Twyford and Slough
- **c** 29 June to 4 September arr. 1915
- **e** Change at Twyford and Slough. Fridays arr. 2312
- **f** Mondays to Fridays change at Twyford. Fridays arr. 0111, change at Twyford and Slough
- **g** From 13 September arr. 1042
- **h** From 13 September arr. 2246
- **j** Until 6 September arr. 1108, change at Twyford and Slough
- **k** From 13 September arr. 1220
- **m** From 13 September arr. 1320
- **n** From 13 September arr. 1421
- **q** From 13 September arr. 1520
- **r** From 13 September arr. 1620
- **t** Until 6 September arr. 1706, change at Twyford and Slough
- **v** Until 6 September arr. 1810, change at Twyford and Slough
- **w** Until 6 September arr. 1908, change at Twyford and Slough
- **y** From 13 September arr. 2020
- **z** Until 6 September arr. 2106, change at Twyford and Slough

Table 122

Mondays to Fridays

Reading → Basingstoke

Network Diagram - see first page of Table 116

Miles		GW 1	GW 1	GW 1	GW 1	GW 1	XC 1◇ (catering)	GW 1	GW 1	XC 1◇ (catering)	GW 1	GW 1	XC R 1 (catering)	GW 1	GW 1	XC 1◇ (catering)	GW 1	GW 1
—	London Paddington 15 ⊖ d	03 34	05 27	05 58	06 30	07 00		07 30	08 00		08 30	09 00		09 30	10 00		10 30	11 00
0	**Reading 7** d	05 39	06 07	06 39	07 07	07 39	07 45	08 07	08 39	08 45	09 07	09 39	09 45	10 07	10 39	10 45	11 07	11 39
1	Reading West d	05 42	06 10	06 42	07 10	07 42		08 10	08 42		09 10	09 42		10 10	10 42		11 10	11 42
7¼	Mortimer d	05 50	06 18	06 50	07 18	07 50		08 18	08 50		09 18	09 50		10 18	10 50		11 18	11 50
10¾	Bramley (Hants) d	05 55	06 23	06 55	07 23	07 55		08 23	08 55		09 23	09 55		10 23	10 55		11 23	11 55
15½	**Basingstoke** a	06 03	06 31	07 03	07 31	08 03	08 08	08 31	09 03	09 08	09 34	10 03	10 08	10 32	11 03	11 08	11 31	12 03

	XC 1◇ (catering)	GW 1	GW 1	XC 1◇ (catering)	GW 1	GW 1	XC 1◇ (catering)	GW 1	GW 1	XC 1◇ (catering)	GW 1	GW 1	XC 1◇ (catering)	GW 1	GW 1	XC 1◇ (catering)	GW 1
London Paddington 15 ⊖ d		11 30	12 00		12 30	13 00		13 30	14 00		14 30	15 00		15 30	16 00		16 30
Reading 7 d	11 45	12 07	12 39	12 45	13 07	13 39	13 45	14 07	14 39	14 45	15 07	15 39	15 45	16 07	16 39	16 45	17 07
Reading West d		12 10	12 42		13 10	13 42		14 10	14 42		15 10	15 42		16 10	16 42		17 10
Mortimer d		12 18	12 50		13 18	13 50		14 18	14 50		15 18	15 50		16 18	16 50		17 18
Bramley (Hants) d		12 23	12 55		13 23	13 55		14 23	14 55		15 23	15 55		16 23	16 55		17 23
Basingstoke a	12 08	12 32	13 03	13 08	13 31	14 03	14 08	14 31	15 03	15 07	15 31	16 03	16 08	16 31	17 03	17 08	17 32

	GW 1	XC 1◇ (catering)	GW 1	GW 1	XC 1◇ (catering)	GW 1	GW 1	XC 1◇ (catering)	GW 1	GW 1	XC 1◇	GW 1	GW 1	XC 1◇	GW 1	XC 1◇	GW 1	GW 1
London Paddington 15 ⊖ d	17 00	17 06	17 33	18 00	18 06	18b30	19 00	19 03	19 30	20 00		20 35	20 51		21 21	21 48	21c48	22e45
Reading 7 d	17 39	17 45	18 07	18 39	18 45	19 07	19 37	19 45	20 07	20 37	20 45	21 07	21 39	21 45	22 10	22 45	22 52	23 34
Reading West d	17 42		18 10	18 42		19 10	19 40		20 10	20 40		21 10	21 42		22 13		22 55	23 37
Mortimer d	17 50		18 18	18 50		19 18	19 48		20 18	20 48		21 18	21 50		22 21		23 03	23 45
Bramley (Hants) d	17 55		18 23	18 55		19 23	19 53		20 23	20 53		21 23	21 55		22 26		23 08	23 50
Basingstoke a	18 05	18 08	18 32	19 05	19 08	19 31	20 03	20 09	20 31	21 01	21 08	21 31	22 03	22 08	22 34	23 12	23 18	23 58

Saturdays

	GW 1	GW 1	GW 1	GW 1	XC 1◇ (catering)	GW 1	GW 1	XC 1◇ (catering)	GW 1	GW 1	XC R 1 (catering)	GW 1	GW 1	XC 1◇ (catering)	GW 1	GW 1	XC 1◇ (catering)
London Paddington 15 ⊖ d	05 21	05 50	06 30	07 00		07 30	08 00		08 30	09f00		09 30	10g00		10 30	11h00	
Reading 7 d	06 07	06 39	07 07	07 39	07 45	08 07	08 39	08 45	09 07	09 39	09 45	10 07	10 39	10 45	11 07	11 39	11 45
Reading West d	06 10	06 42	07 10	07 42		08 10	08 42		09 10	09 42		10 10	10 42		11 10	11 42	
Mortimer d	06 18	06 50	07 18	07 50		08 18	08 50		09 18	09 50		10 18	10 50		11 18	11 50	
Bramley (Hants) d	06 23	06 55	07 23	07 55		08 23	08 55		09 23	09 55		10 23	10 55		11 23	11 55	
Basingstoke a	06 32	07 03	07 32	08 03	08 08	08 31	09 03	09 08	09 31	10 03	10 08	10 31	11 03	11 08	11 31	12 03	12 08

	GW 1 A	GW 1 B	GW 1	XC 1◇ (catering)	GW 1 A	GW 1 B	GW 1	XC 1◇ (catering)	GW 1	GW 1	XC 1◇ (catering)	GW 1	GW 1	XC 1◇ (catering)	GW 1	GW 1	XC 1◇ (catering)
London Paddington 15 ⊖ d	11 30	11 30	12 06		12 30	12 30	13 06		13 30	14 06		14 30	15 00	15 06	15 30	16 06	
Reading 7 d	12 07	12 10	12 39	12 45	13 07	13 07	13 39	13 45	14 07	14 39	14 45	15 07	15 39	15 45	16 07	16 39	16 45
Reading West d	12 10	12 13	12 42		13 10	13 10	13 42		14 10	14 42		15 10	15 42		16 10	16 42	
Mortimer d	12 18	12 21	12 50		13 18	13 20	13 50		14 18	14 50		15 18	15 50		16 18	16 50	
Bramley (Hants) d	12 23	12 26	12 55		13 23	13 25	13 55		14 23	14 55		15 23	15 55		16 23	16 55	
Basingstoke a	12 31	12 34	13 03	13 08	13 31	13 33	14 03	14 08	14 31	15 03	15 08	15 31	16 03	16 08	16 31	17 03	17 08

	GW 1	GW 1	XC 1◇ (catering)	GW 1	GW 1	XC 1◇ (catering)	GW 1	GW 1	XC 1◇ (catering)	GW 1	GW 1	XC 1◇ (catering)	GW 1	GW 1	XC 1◇ (catering)	GW 1	GW 1	XC 1◇ (catering)	GW 1
London Paddington 15 ⊖ d	16 30	17 06		17 30	18 06		18 30	19 06		19 30	20 06		20 30	20 50		21 30	22 00		22 30
Reading 7 d	17 07	17 39	17 45	18 07	18 39	18 45	19 07	19 39	19 45	20 07	20 39	20 45	21 07	21 39	21 45	22 07	22 39	22 45	23 07
Reading West d	17 10	17 42		18 10	18 42		19 10	19 42		20 10	20 42		21 10	21 42		22 10	22 42		23 10
Mortimer d	17 18	17 50		18 18	18 50		19 18	19 50		20 18	20 50		21 18	21 50		22 18	22 50		23 18
Bramley (Hants) d	17 23	17 55		18 23	18 55		19 23	19 55		20 23	20 55		21 23	21 55		22 23	22 55		23 23
Basingstoke a	17 31	18 03	18 08	18 31	19 03	19 08	19 31	20 03	20 08	20 31	21 03	21 08	21 31	22 03	22 08	22 31	23 03	23 11	23 31

For general notes see front of timetable
For details of catering facilities see Directory of Train Operators

- **A** From 12 September
- **B** Until 5 September
- **b** 29 June to 4 September dep. 1833
- **c** Fridays dep. 2215
- **e** Fridays dep. 2248
- **f** From 12 September dep. 0906
- **g** From 12 September dep. 1006
- **h** From 12 September dep. 1106

Sundays

Reading → Basingstoke

Network Diagram - see first page of Table 116

		GW	GW	GW	XC	GW	XC	GW	XC	GW	XC	GW	XC	GW	XC	GW	XC	GW
		1	1	1	R 1	1	1 ◇	1	1 ◇	1	1 ◇	1	1 ◇	1	1 ◇	1	1 ◇	1
London Paddington 15 ⊖	d		06 44	08 42	09b00	09 35	10c00	10 42	11e00	11 42	12f00	12 42	13g00	13 42	14h00	14 42	14j57	15 42
Reading 7	d	07 37	08 37	09 37	09 51	10 37	10 50	11 37	11 51	12 37	12 51	13 37	13 51	14 37	14 51	15 37	15 51	16 37
Reading West	d	07 40	08 40	09 40		10 40		11 40		12 40		13 40		14 40		15 40		16 40
Mortimer	d	07 48	08 48	09 48		10 48		11 48		12 48		13 48		14 48		15 48		16 48
Bramley (Hants)	d	07 53	08 53	09 53		10 53		11 53		12 53		13 53		14 53		15 53		16 53
Basingstoke	a	08 01	09 01	10 01	10 09	11 01	11 09	12 01	12 09	13 01	13 09	14 01	14 09	15 01	15 09	16 01	16 09	17 01

		XC	GW	XC	GW	XC	GW	XC	GW	XC	GW	XC	XC	GW	GW
		1 ◇	1	1 ◇	1	1 ◇	1	1 ◇	1	1 ◇	1	1 ◇	1 ◇	1	1
London Paddington 15 ⊖	d	16k00	16 42	17m00	17 42	18n00	18 42	19q00	19 42	20r00	20 42	21t00		21 37	22 42
Reading 7	d	16 51	17 37	17 51	18 37	18 51	19 37	19 51	20 37	20 51	21 37	21 51	22 12	22 37	23 37
Reading West	d		17 40		18 40		19 40		20 40		21 40			22 41	23 40
Mortimer	d		17 48		18 48		19 48		20 48		21 48			22 49	23 48
Bramley (Hants)	d		17 53		18 53		19 53		20 53		21 53			22 54	23 53
Basingstoke	a	17 09	18 01	18 09	19 01	19 09	20 01	20 09	21 01	21 09	22 01	22 11	22 30	23 02	00 01

For general notes see front of timetable
For details of catering facilities see Directory of Train Operators

- b From 13 September dep. 0903
- c From 13 September dep. 1003
- e From 13 September dep. 1103
- f From 13 September dep. 1203
- g From 13 September dep. 1303
- h From 13 September dep. 1403
- j From 13 September dep. 1503
- k From 13 September dep. 1603
- m From 13 September dep. 1703
- n From 13 September dep. 1803
- q From 13 September dep. 1903
- r From 13 September dep. 2003
- t From 13 September dep. 2103

Basingstoke → Reading

Network Diagram - see first page of Table 116

Mondays to Fridays

Miles			GW MX	GW MO	XC		GW	GW	XC		GW	GW	XC		GW	GW	XC		GW	GW	XC		GW	GW	XC	GW
0	Basingstoke	d	00 02	00 07	05 47		06 07	06 37	06 47		07 07	07 37	07 47		08 07	08 37	08 47		09 07	09 37	09 47		10 07	10 37	10 47	11 07
5	Bramley (Hants)	d	00 09	00 14	.		06 14	06 44	.		07 14	07 44	.		08 14	08 44	.		09 14	09 44	.		10 14	10 44	.	11 14
8¼	Mortimer	d	00 14	00 19	.		06 19	06 49	.		07 19	07 49	.		08 19	08 49	.		09 19	09 49	.		10 19	10 49	.	11 19
14½	Reading West	d	00 22	00 26	.		06 27	06 57	.		07 27	07 57	.		08 27	08 57	.		09 27	09 57	.		10 27	10 57	.	11 27
15½	Reading 7	a	00 26	00 30	06 05		06 32	07 00	07 05		07 31	08 00	08 05		08 30	09 00	09 05		09 30	10 00	10 05		10 30	11 00	11 05	11 30
—	London Paddington 15 ⊖	a	01 17	01b41	06 54	.	07 16	07 43	07 45	.	08 11	08 39	08 41	.	09 10	09 39	09 45	.	10 10	10 39	10 54	.	11 15	.	11 42	12 15

		GW		XC	GW	GW		XC	GW	GW		XC	GW	GW		XC	GW	GW		XC	GW	GW		XC	GW	GW
Basingstoke	d	11 37		11 47	12 07	12 37		12 47	13 07	13 37		13 47	14 07	14 37		14 47	15 07	15 37		15 47	16 07	16 37		16 47	17 07	17 37
Bramley (Hants)	d	11 44		.	12 14	12 44		.	13 14	13 44		.	14 14	14 44		.	15 14	15 44		.	16 14	16 44		.	17 14	17 44
Mortimer	d	11 49		.	12 19	12 49		.	13 19	13 49		.	14 19	14 49		.	15 19	15 49		.	16 19	16 49		.	17 19	17 49
Reading West	d	11 57		.	12 27	12 57		.	13 27	13 57		.	14 27	14 57		.	15 27	15 57		.	16 27	16 57		.	17 27	17 57
Reading 7	a	12 00		12 05	12 30	13 00		13 05	13 30	14 00		14 05	14 30	15 00		15 05	15 30	16 00		16 05	16 30	17 00		17 05	17 30	18 00
London Paddington 15 ⊖	a	12 39	.	12 54	13 15	13 42	.	13 44	14 15	14 39	.	14 45	15 15	15 42	.	15 54	16 15	16 40	.	16 45	17 15	17 42	.	17 55	18 15	18 40

		XC	GW		GW	XC	GW		GW	XC	GW		GW	XC	GW		GW	GW	GW		GW
Basingstoke	d	17 47	18 07		18 37	18 47	19 07		19 37	19 47	20 07		20 37	20 47	21 07		21 42	22 24	22 55		23 30
Bramley (Hants)	d	.	18 14		18 44	.	19 14		19 44	.	20 14		20 44	.	21 14		21 49	22 31	23 02		23 37
Mortimer	d	.	18 19		18 49	.	19 19		19 49	.	20 19		20 49	.	21 19		21 54	22 36	23 07		23 42
Reading West	d	.	18 27		18 57	.	19 27		19 57	.	20 27		20 57	.	21 27		22 02	22 44	23 15		23 50
Reading 7	a	18 05	18 31		19 00	19 05	19 31		20 00	20 05	20 30		21 01	21 05	21 30		22 05	22 47	23 18		23 53
London Paddington 15 ⊖	a	18 45	19 15	.	19 42	19 54	20 15	.	20 39	20 46	21 15	.	.	21c58	22 15	.	22e55	23f37	00 21	.	01g14

Saturdays

		GW	XC	GW		XC	GW	XC		GW	XC	GW		GW	XC	GW		GW	XC	GW		GW	XC	GW		GW
Basingstoke	d	00 02	05 41	06 37		06 47	07 07	07 25		07 37	07 47	08 07		08 37	08 47	09 07		09 37	09 47	10 07		10 37	10 47	11 07		11 37
Bramley (Hants)	d	00 09	.	06 44		.	07 14	.		07 44	.	08 14		08 44	.	09 14		09 44	.	10 14		10 44	.	11 14		11 44
Mortimer	d	00 14	.	06 49		.	07 19	.		07 49	.	08 19		08 49	.	09 19		09 49	.	10 19		10 49	.	11 19		11 49
Reading West	d	00 22	.	06 57		.	07 27	.		07 57	.	08 27		08 57	.	09 27		09 57	.	10 27		10 57	.	11 27		11 57
Reading 7	a	00 26	05 59	07 00		07 04	07 31	07 41		08 00	08 04	08 31		09 00	09 04	09 31		10 00	10 04	10 31		11 00	11 04	11 31		12 00
London Paddington 15 ⊖	a	02h00	07 15	.	.	07 45	08 15	08 30	.	.	08 45	09 15	.	09 37	09 45	10 15	.	10 42	10 52	11 15	.	.	11 42	12 15	.	.

		XC	GW	GW		XC	GW	GW		XC	GW	GW		XC	GW	GW A		GW B	XC	GW		GW	XC	GW		GW
Basingstoke	d	11 47	12 07	12 37		12 47	13 07	13 37		13 47	14 07	14 37		14 47	15 07	15 37		15 37	15 47	16 07		16 37	16 47	17 07		17 37
Bramley (Hants)	d	.	12 14	12 44		.	13 14	13 44		.	14 14	14 44		.	15 14	15 44		15 44	.	16 14		16 44	.	17 14		17 44
Mortimer	d	.	12 19	12 49		.	13 19	13 49		.	14 19	14 49		.	15 19	15 49		15 49	.	16 19		16 49	.	17 19		17 49
Reading West	d	.	12 27	12 57		.	13 27	13 57		.	14 27	14 57		.	15 27	15 57		15 59	.	16 27		16 57	.	17 27		17 57
Reading 7	a	12 04	12 31	13 00		13 04	13 31	14 00		14 04	14 31	15 00		15 04	15 31	16 00		16 02	16 04	16 31		17 00	17 04	17 31		18 00
London Paddington 15 ⊖	a	12 42	13j10	.	.	13 42	14 15	.	.	14 42	15 09	.	.	15 42	16 15	.	.	.	16 42	17 06	.	.	17 42	18k15	.	.

		XC	GW	GW		XC	GW	GW		XC	GW B	GW A		GW	XC	GW		GW	GW	GW		GW	GW
Basingstoke	d	17 47	18 07	18 37		18 47	19 07	19 37		19 47	20 07	20 07		20 37	20 47	21 07		21 37	22 07	22 37		23 07	23 37
Bramley (Hants)	d	.	18 14	18 44		.	19 14	19 44		.	20 14	20 14		20 44	.	21 14		21 44	22 14	22 44		23 14	23 44
Mortimer	d	.	18 19	18 49		.	19 19	19 49		.	20 19	20 19		20 49	.	21 19		21 49	22 19	22 49		23 19	23 49
Reading West	d	.	18 27	18 57		.	19 27	19 58		.	20 27	20 29		20 57	.	21 27		21 57	22 27	22 57		23 27	23 57
Reading 7	a	18 04	18 31	19 00		19 04	19 31	20 01		20 04	20 31	20 33		21 00	21 04	21 31		22 00	22 31	23 00		23 31	00 01
London Paddington 15 ⊖	a	18 42	19 08	.	.	19 42	20 15	20m45	.	20n45	21 07	21 15	.	21 36	21 59	22 16	.	23 08	23q36	00 10	.	00 33	.

For general notes see front of timetable
For details of catering facilities see Directory of Train Operators

A From 12 September
B Until 5 September

b Until 31 August only
c 29 June to 4 September arr. 2200
e Fridays arr. 2245
f Fridays arr. 2332
g Fridays arr. 0111
h From 12 September arr. 0111

j From 12 September arr. 1306
k From 12 September arr. 1808
m From 12 September arr. 2037
n From 12 September arr. 2059
q From 12 September arr. 2330

Table 122

Sundays

Basingstoke → Reading

Network Diagram - see first page of Table 116

		GW	GW	XC	GW	GW	XC	GW	XC	GW	XC	GW	XC	GW
		1	1	1 ◇	1	1	1 ◇	1	1 ◇	1	1 ◇	1	1 ◇	1
					A	B								
				⚲			⚲		⚲		⚲		⚲	
Basingstoke	d	08 07	09 07	09 47	10 07	10 07	10 47	11 07	11 47	12 07	12 47	13 07	13 47	14 07
Bramley (Hants)	d	08 14	09 14	.	10 14	10 14	.	11 14	.	12 14	.	13 14	.	14 14
Mortimer	d	08 19	09 19	.	10 19	10 19	.	11 19	.	12 19	.	13 19	.	14 19
Reading West	d	08 27	09 27	.	10 27	10 28	.	11 27	.	12 27	.	13 27	.	14 27
Reading 7	a	08 30	09 30	10 04	10 30	10 31	11 04	11 30	12 04	12 30	13 04	13 30	14 04	14 30
London Paddington 15	⊖ a	09b34	10c49	10e55	11 30	11 22	11f55	12g23	12h55	13j47	13k55	14m23	14n55	15q25

		XC	GW	XC	GW	XC	GW	XC	GW	XC	GW	XC	GW	XC	GW	GW	GW
		1 ◇	1	1 ◇	1	1 ◇	1	1 ◇	1	1 ◇	1	1 ◇	1	1 ◇	1	1	1
		⚲		⚲		⚲		⚲		⚲		⚲		⚲			
Basingstoke	d	14 47	15 07	15 47	16 07	16 47	17 07	17 47	18 07	18 47	19 07	19 47	20 07	20 47	21 07	22 07	23 07
Bramley (Hants)	d	.	15 14	.	16 14	.	17 14	.	18 14	.	19 14	.	20 14	.	21 14	22 15	23 14
Mortimer	d	.	15 19	.	16 19	.	17 19	.	18 19	.	19 19	.	20 19	.	21 19	22 20	23 19
Reading West	d	.	15 27	.	16 27	.	17 27	.	18 27	.	19 27	.	20 27	.	21 27	22 30	23 27
Reading 7	a	15 04	15 30	16 04	16 30	17 04	17 30	18 04	18 30	19 04	19 30	20 04	20 30	21 04	21 30	22 33	23 30
London Paddington 15	⊖ a	15r55	16t23	16 53	17v28	17 53	18w23	18 53	19y28	19 53	20z23	20 53	21C21	21D56	22E40	23 40	00G35

For general notes see front of timetable
For details of catering facilities see Directory of Train Operators

- **A** From 13 September
- **B** Until 6 September
- **C** From 13 September arr. 2129
- **D** From 13 September arr. 2153
- **E** From 13 September arr. 2229
- **G** Sundays arr. 0052
- **b** From 13 September arr. 0943
- **c** Until 12 July arr. 1047. 19 July to 6 September arr. 1022
- **e** From 13 September arr. 1052
- **f** From 13 September arr. 1153
- **g** From 13 September arr. 1232
- **h** From 13 September arr. 1253
- **j** From 13 September arr. 1349
- **k** From 13 September arr. 1353
- **m** From 13 September arr. 1429
- **n** From 13 September arr. 1453
- **q** From 13 September arr. 1530
- **r** From 13 September arr. 1553
- **t** From 13 September arr. 1629
- **v** From 13 September arr. 1733
- **w** From 13 September arr. 1829
- **y** From 13 September arr. 1931
- **z** From 13 September arr. 2029

Network Diagram for Table 123

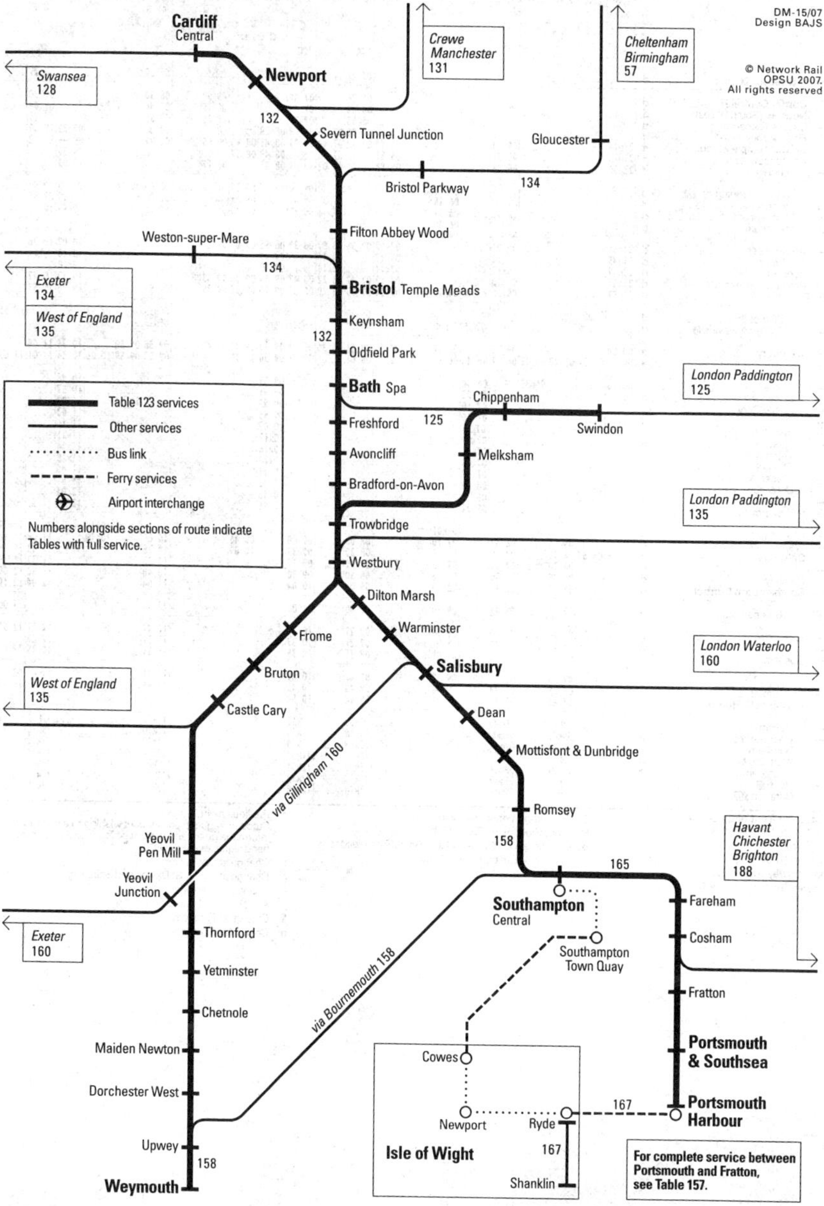

DM-15/07
Design BAJS
© Network Rail
OPSU 2007.
All rights reserved
Cardiff
Central
Newport
Swansea
128
Crewe
Manchester
131
Cheltenham
Birmingham
57
132
Severn Tunnel Junction
Gloucester
Bristol Parkway
134
Filton Abbey Wood
Weston-super-Mare
134
Exeter
134
West of England
135
Bristol Temple Meads
Keynsham
132
Oldfield Park
Bath Spa
Chippenham
London Paddington
125
Freshford
125
Swindon
Avoncliff
Melksham
Bradford-on-Avon
London Paddington
135
Trowbridge
Westbury
Table 123 services
Other services
Bus link
Ferry services
Airport interchange
Numbers alongside sections of route indicate Tables with full service.
Dilton Marsh
Frome
Warminster
Salisbury
London Waterloo
160
Bruton
West of England
135
Castle Cary
Dean
Mottisfont & Dunbridge
via Gillingham 160
Romsey
Havant
Chichester
Brighton
188
Yeovil
Pen Mill
158
165
Yeovil
Junction
Southampton
Central
Fareham
Exeter
160
Thornford
Southampton
Town Quay
Cosham
Yetminster
via Bournemouth 158
Fratton
Chetnole
Portsmouth
& Southsea
Maiden Newton
Cowes
Dorchester West
Newport
Ryde
167
Portsmouth
Harbour
Upwey
Isle of Wight
167
158
Shanklin
Weymouth
For complete service between Portsmouth and Fratton, see Table 157.

South Wales and Bristol → Weymouth and Portsmouth

Network Diagram - see first page of Table 123

Miles	Miles	Miles			GW MX	GW	GW	GW	GW ◇	GW ◇	GW A	GW	GW ◇ ⊼	GW B	GW ◇ ⊼	GW ◇ C	SW 1 ◇ D	GW	GW ◇ ⊼	GW 1 ◇ ⊡	GW	GW ◇ E	GW ◇ ⊼	GW
—	—	—	Swansea 7	d									05 27		06 29			06b59	07 29				08 29	
0	0	—	**Cardiff Central 7**	d									06 28		07 30			08 00	08 30				09 30	
11¾	11¾	—	Newport (South Wales)	d									06 42		07 44			08 15	08 44				09 44	
21¾	21¾	—	Severn Tunnel Jn	d									06 53		07 55			08 25	08 55				09c25	
33¾	33¾	—	Filton Abbey Wood	d									07 09	07 28	08 09	08 28		08 42	09 09			09 22	10 09	
38½	38½	—	**Bristol Temple Meads 10**	d	23p16				05 44			06 44	07 22	07 49	08 22	08 41	08 50	09 05	09 22			09 49	10 22	
42¾	42¾	—	Keynsham	d	23p23				05 51			06 51		07 56		08 48	08 57					09 56		
48¾	48¾	—	Oldfield Park	d	23p30				05 58			06 58		08 03		08 55		09 17				10 03		
—	—	—	London Paddington 15 ⊖	d								05 27		06 30	07 00		07 30		08 00	08 18		08 30	09 00	
—	—	0	Swindon	d							06 15	06 25		07 30	08 00		08 25		09 00			09 30	09 55	
—	—	16¾	Chippenham	d							06 31	06 40		07 45	08 15		08 40		09 15			09 45	10 10	
—	—	23	Melksham	d							06 40													
49¾	49¾	—	**Bath Spa 7**	d	23p35				06 01			07 02	07 36	08 07	08 37	08 58	09 07	09 21	09 36			10 07	10 36	
56¼	56¼	—	Freshford	d	23p45				06 12			07 12		08 16		09 09						10 16		
57¾	57¾	—	Avoncliff	d	23e47				06x15			07x14		08x18		09x10						10x18		
59	59	—	Bradford-on-Avon	d	23p51				06 18			07 18	07 47	08 22	08 47	09 14	09 20	09 33				10 22	10 47	
62¼	62¼	28½	Trowbridge	d	23p57				06 25		06 50	07 24	07 53	08 28	08 53	09 20	09 27	09 39	09 51			10 28	10 53	
—	—	—	Plymouth	d									05 30			07f47			06g55		07 47			08 55
—	—	—	Exeter St Davids 6	d						05f46	05h10		06 38		06h42	08f49			08h25		08 49			09 57
66¼	66¼	32½	**Westbury**	a	00 04				06 32		06 57	07 33	08 01	08 36	09 01	09 27	09 33	09 48	09 58	09 58		10 36	11 00	
—	—	—		d	00 04	05 24	05 49	06 25	06 37	06 44	06 58		08 01		09 01	09 30	09 39		09 58	09 59	10 08	10 36	11 01	11 07
—	72	—	Frome	d	00a16			06a35		06 54						09 39						10 46		
—	82½	—	Bruton	d						07 05						09 51						10 57		
—	86	—	Castle Cary	a						07 10						09 55				10 16		11 02		
—	—	—		d						07 10						09 56						11 03		
—	97¾	—	Yeovil Pen Mill	d						07j34						10 09						11 16		
—	101	—	Thornford	d						07x38						10x13						11x21		
—	102	—	Yetminster	d						07x41						10x16						11x24		
—	104	—	Chetnole	d						07x45						10x20						11x28		
—	110½	—	Maiden Newton	d						07 57						10 31						11 40		
—	118¼	—	Dorchester West	d						08 08						10 42						11 51		
—	122¾	—	Upwey	a						08 14						10 48						12 01		
—	125¼	—	**Weymouth**	a						08 21						10 56						12 08		
67¾	—	—	Dilton Marsh	d							07x01										10x10			11x09
71	—	—	Warminster	d		05 32	05 56		06 43		07 10		08 08		09 08		09 46		10 06		10a19		11 08	11 16
90¾	—	—	**Salisbury**	a		05 53	06 19		07 10		07 36		08 32		09 32		10 09		10 28				11 32	11 38
—	—	—		d			06 20		07 11		07 36		08 32		09 32				10 30				11 32	11 39
107¼	—	—	Romsey	d			06 38		07 30		07 56		08 50		09 50				10 48				11 50	12 00
115½	—	—	**Southampton Central**	a			06 49		07 41		08 09		09 04		10 04				11 04				12 04	12 19
—	—	—	Bournemouth	a			07 44		08 43		09 10		10 00		11 00				12 00					13 00
130	—	—	Fareham	a			07 14		08 05		08 56		09 27		10 27				11 27				12 27	12 56
—	—	—		d			07 15		08 06				09 27		10 27				11 27				12 27	
135¾	—	—	Cosham	a			07 23		08 14		09 05		09 35		10 35				11 35				12 35	13 04
139½	—	—	Fratton	a			07 34		08 21		09 37		09 41		10 41				11 41				12 41	13 37
140½	—	—	Portsmouth & Southsea	a			07 38		08 24		09 42		09 45		10 45				11 45				12 45	13 42
141¼	—	—	**Portsmouth Harbour**	a			07 45		08 30				09 54		10 54				11 54				12 54	
—	—	—	Havant	a			07k46		08m40				09k53		10k53				11k55				12k55	
—	—	—	Chichester 4	a			08k08		09m00				10k10		11k10				12k10				13k10	
—	—	—	Barnham	a			08k16		09m08				10k18		11k18				12k18				13k18	
—	—	—	Worthing 4	a			08k56		09m24				10k54		11k54				12k54				13k54	
—	—	—	Shoreham-by-Sea	a			09k04		09m34				11k04		12k04				13k04				14k04	
—	—	—	Hove 2	a			09k14		09m43				11k13		12k13				13k13				14k13	
—	—	—	Brighton 10	a			09k18		09m48				11k18		12k18				13k18				14k18	

For general notes see front of timetable
For details of catering facilities see Directory of Train Operators

- **A** From Gloucester (Table 125)
- **B** From Bristol Parkway (Table 132)
- **C** From Worcester Shrub Hill (Table 57)
- **D** To London Waterloo (Table 160)
- **E** From Gloucester (Table 134)
- **b** Change at Cardiff Central and Bristol Temple Meads
- **c** Change at Bristol Temple Meads
- **e** Previous night.
- Stops on request, passengers wishing to alight must inform the guard and those wishing to join must give a hand signal to the driver
- **f** Change at Castle Cary
- **g** Change at Exeter St Davids and Salisbury
- **h** Change at Salisbury
- **j** Arr. 0723
- **k** Change at Fareham
- **m** Change at Fratton

Table 123

South Wales and Bristol → Weymouth and Portsmouth

Network Diagram - see first page of Table 123

		GW A	GW ◇	GW 1 ◇	GW ◇ B	GW ◇	GW ◇ A	SW 1 ◇	GW 1 ◇ C	GW ◇	GW B	GW ◇	GW	GW ◇ A	GW ◇	GW 1 ◇	GW B	SW 1 ◇	GW ◇	GW	GW ◇ A	GW D	GW ◇
Swansea 7	d		09 29			10 29		10b55		11 29		12 29			13 29				14 29			14b55	15 29
Cardiff Central 7	d		10 30			11 30		12 00		12 30		13 30			14 30				15 30			16c00	16 30
Newport (South Wales)	d		10 44			11 44		12 15		12 44		13 44			14 44				15 44			16c15	16 44
Severn Tunnel Jn	d		10c25			11c25		12 25				13c25			14c25				15c25			16c25	16 55
Filton Abbey Wood	d	10 22	11 09		11 22	12 09	12 22	12 42		13 09	13 22	14 09		14 22	15 09		15 22		16 09		16 22	16 49	17 09
Bristol Temple Meads 10	d	10 49	11 22		11 49	12 22	12 39	13 10		13 22	13 49	14 22		14 49	15 22		15 43	15 52	16 22		16 49	17 07	17 22
Keynsham	d	10 56			11 56		12 46				13 56			14 56			15 50				16 56	17 14	
Oldfield Park	d	11 03			12 03		12 53				14 03			15 03			15 57				17 03	17 21	17 32
London Paddington 15 ⊖	d	09 30	10 00	11 06	10 30	11 00		11 30	12 18	12 00	12 30	13 00		13 30	14 00	15 06		14 30	15 00		15 30		16 00
Swindon	d	10 30	10 55		11 30	11 55		12 30		12 55	13 30	13 55		14 30	14 55			15 30	15 55		16 30		16 55
Chippenham	d	10 45	11 10		11 45	12 10		12 45		13 10	13 45	14 10		14 45	15 10			15 45	16 10		16 45		17 10
Melksham	d																						
Bath Spa 7	d	11 07	11 36		12 07	12 36	12 57	13 22		13 36	14 07	14 36		15 07	15 36		16 01	16 07	16 36		17 07	17 25	17 36
Freshford	d	11 16			12 16		13 06				14 16			15 16			16 09				17 16	17 34	
Avoncliff	d	11x18			12x18		13x07				14x18			15x18			16x11				17x18	17x36	
Bradford-on-Avon	d	11 22	11 47		12 22	12 47	13 12	13 35		13 47	14 22	14 47		15 22	15 47		16 15	16 22	16 47		17 22	17 40	17 47
Trowbridge	d	11 28	11 53		12 28	12 53	13 18	13 42		13 53	14 28	14 53		15 28	15 53		16 21	16 28	16 53		17 28	17 46	17 53
Plymouth	d				10e44		10f44					12g21	12 55										15g00
Exeter St Davids 6	d		10h10		10j54		11 54			12h10		13h35	13 57		14h10								16h10
Westbury	a	11 36	12 01	12 21	12 36	13 01	13 25	13 48	13 57	14 01	14 36	15 01		15 36	16 01	16 21	16 28	16 36	17 01		17 36	17 56	18 01
	d		12 01	12 22	12 37	13 01	13 27	13 53	13 59	14 02		15 01	15 08	15 36	16 01	16 22		16 39	17 01	17 08	17 38		18 01
Frome	d				12 47				14 09					15 46							17 47		
Bruton	d				12 57									15 57							17 59		
Castle Cary	a			12 39	13 03				14 22					16 02		16 41					18 04		
	d				13 04									16 10							18 05		
Yeovil Pen Mill	d				13 17									16 23							18k24		
Thornford	d				13x22									16x28							18x28		
Yetminster	d				13x25									16x31							18x31		
Chetnole	d				13x29									16x35							18x35		
Maiden Newton	d				13 41									16 47							18 47		
Dorchester West	d				13 54									16 57							18 58		
Upwey	a				14 01									17 02							19 05		
Weymouth	a				14 09									17 10							19 12		
Dilton Marsh	d						13x29						15x10							17x10			
Warminster	d		12 08			13 08	13 36	14 00		14 08		15 08	15a19		16 08			16 47	17 08	17a18			18 08
Salisbury	a		12 32			13 32	13 58	14 25		14 32		15 32			16 32			17 09	17 32				18 32
	d		12 32			13 32	13 59			14 32		15 32			16 32				17 32				18 32
Romsey	d		12 50			13 50	14 20			14 50		15 50			16 50				17 50				18 50
Southampton Central	a		13 04			14 04	14 32			15 04		16 04			17 04				18 04				19 04
Bournemouth	a		14 00			15 00	15 15			16 00		17 04			18 04				18 49				20 02
Fareham	a		13 27			14 27	14 55			15 27		16 27			17 27				18 27				19 27
	d		13 27			14 27	14 56			15 27		16 27			17 27				18 27				19 27
Cosham	a		13 35			14 35	15 04			15 35		16 35			17 35				18 35				19 35
Fratton	a		13 41			14 41	15 37			15 41		16 41			17 41				18 48				19 41
Portsmouth & Southsea	a		13 45			14 45	15 42			15 45		16 45			17 45				18 52				19 45
Portsmouth Harbour	a		13 54			14 54				15 54		16 54			17 54				18 58				19 54
Havant	a		13m55			14m55	15 10			15m57		16m51			17m55				18m50				19m52
Chichester 4	a		14m10			15m10	15 21			16m12		17m06			18m10				19m05				20m06
Barnham	a		14m18			15m18	15 29			16m20		17m20			18m20				19m13				20m14
Worthing 4	a		14m54				15 45			16m54		17n43			18m52				19m51				20m52
Shoreham-by-Sea	a		15m04				15 56			17m04		17n53			19m02				20m02				21m02
Hove 2	a		15m13				16 07			17m13		18n04			19m13				20m13				21m13
Brighton 10	a		15m18				16 14			17m18		18n09			19m18				20m18				21m18

For general notes see front of timetable
For details of catering facilities see Directory of Train Operators

- **A** From Great Malvern (Table 71)
- **B** From Gloucester (Table 134)
- **C** To Taunton (Table 135)
- **D** From Bristol Parkway (Table 132)
- **b** Change at Cardiff Central and Bristol Temple Meads
- **c** Change at Bristol Temple Meads
- **e** Change at Exeter St Davids and Castle Cary
- **f** Change at Exeter St Davids and Westbury
- **g** Change at Exeter St Davids and Salisbury
- **h** Change at Salisbury
- **j** Change at Castle Cary
- **k** Arr. 1819
- **m** Change at Fareham
- **n** Change at Fratton

South Wales and Bristol → Weymouth and Portsmouth

Network Diagram - see first page of Table 123

		GW	GW	GW	GW		GW	GW	GW	GW	GW	GW	GW		GW	GW	GW	GW	GW	GW	GW		SW	GW		
		[1] ◇	◇	[1] ◇			[1] ◇	◇			[1] ◇	◇	[1] ◇			◇	[1] ◇	◇	[1] ◇	◇			[1]			
			A		B				C	D					A			E								
		🍴		🍴			🍴	🛒			🍴	🛒	🍴				🍴		🍴							
Swansea [7]	d				15b55			16 29				17 29				18 29				19 29				20b29		
Cardiff Central [7]	d				17c00			17 30				18 30				19 30				20 30				21 30		
Newport (South Wales)	d				17c15			17 44				18 44				19 44				20 44				21 44		
Severn Tunnel Jn	d				17c25			17 55				18 55				19c25				20c21				21 56		
Filton Abbey Wood	d		17 22		17 49			18 09		18 22		19 09			19 22	20 09		20 22		21 09			21 57	22 13		
Bristol Temple Meads [10]	d		17 49		18 07			18 22		18 49		19 22			19 49	20 22		20 49		21 22	22 00		22 25	23 16		
Keynsham	d		17 56		18 14					18 56					19 56			20 56			22 07			23 23		
Oldfield Park	d		18 03		18 21					19 03					20 03			21 03			22 14			23 30		
London Paddington [15] ⊖	d	16 33	16 30	17 06			17 33	17 00	17 45	17 30	18 06	18 00	18 36		18 30	19 00	19 45	19 30	20 35	20 00	20 45			21 45		
Swindon	d		17 30					18 00	18 44	18 30		19 00			19 30	20 00		20 30		21 00	21 45			22 50		
Chippenham	d		17 45					18 15	19 01	18 45		19 15			19 45	20 15		20 45		21 15	22 00			23 05		
Melksham	d								19 11																	
Bath Spa [7]	d		18 07		18 25			18 36		19 07		19 37			20 07	20 37		21 07		21 37	22 18		22 38	23 35		
Freshford	d		18 16		18 34					19 16					20 16			21 16			22 28			23 45		
Avoncliff	d		18x18		18x36					19x18					20x18			21x18			22x29			23x47		
Bradford-on-Avon	d		18 22		18 40			18 47		19 22		19 47			20 22	20 47		21 22		21 47	22 34		22 51	23 51		
Trowbridge	d		18 28		18 46			18 53	19 20	19 28		19 53			20 28	20 53		21 28		21 53	22 40		22 57	23 57		
Plymouth	d		16e57						16 57							18f00		18g43								
Exeter St Davids [6]	d		18e00						18 00			18h10				19h10		19e54		20h15						
Westbury	a	18 04	18 36	18 54	18 56		18 59	19 00	19 27	19 36	19 52	20 01	20 04		20 36	21 01	21 05	21 35	21 56	22 01	22 47		23 04	00 04		
	d	18 05	18 39				19 01	19 01	19 40		19 53	20 01	20 05		20 36	21 01	21 05	21 35	21 57	22 01			23 04	00 04		
Frome	d		18 49								20a08				20a47			21 49						00a16		
Bruton	d		19 00															22 01								
Castle Cary	a	18 22	19 05				19 17						20 22				21 27	22 06	22 14							
	d		19 06															22 06								
Yeovil Pen Mill	d		19 19															22 20								
Thornford	d		19x24															22x24								
Yetminster	d		19x27															22x27								
Chetnole	d		19x31															22x31								
Maiden Newton	d		19 43															22 43								
Dorchester West	d		19 55															22 53								
Upwey	a		20 01															23 00								
Weymouth	a		20 08															23 07								
Dilton Marsh	d								19x42											22x04						
Warminster	d							19 08	19 49			20 08				21 08				22 08			23 11			
Salisbury	a							19 32	20 12			20 32				21 32				22 32			23 34			
	d							19 32	20 13			20 32				21 32				22 32						
Romsey	d							19 50	20 35			20 50				21 50				22 50						
Southampton Central	a							20 04	20 48			21 04				22 02				23 03						
Bournemouth	a							21 00				22 09				23 17				00 16						
Fareham	a							20 27				21 27				22 42				23 25						
	d							20 27				21 27				22 42				23 25						
Cosham	a							20 44				21 49				22j46				23 59						
Fratton	a							20 41				21 41				22 56				23 40						
Portsmouth & Southsea	a							20 45				21 45				22 59				23 44						
Portsmouth Harbour	a							20 54				21 52				23 04				23 53						
Havant	a							20k50				21k55				23k14										
Chichester [4]	a							21k05				22k06				23k25										
Barnham	a							21k14				22k14				23k33										
Worthing [4]	a							21k54				22k52														
Shoreham-by-Sea	a							22k04				23k02														
Hove [2]	a							22k16				23m43														
Brighton [10]	a							22k21				23m48														

For general notes see front of timetable
For details of catering facilities see Directory of Train Operators

A From Gloucester (Table 134)
B From Bristol Parkway (Table 132)
C From Worcester Foregate Street (Table 71)
D From Cheltenham Spa (Table 57)
E From Great Malvern (Table 71)
b Change at Cardiff Central and Bristol Temple Meads
c Change at Bristol Temple Meads
e Change at Castle Cary
f Change at Exeter St Davids and Salisbury
g Change at Exeter St Davids and Castle Cary
h Change at Salisbury
j Change at Southampton Central
k Change at Fareham
m Change at Fratton

Table 123

Saturdays
until 5 September

South Wales and Bristol → Weymouth and Portsmouth

Network Diagram - see first page of Table 123

		GW	GW	GW	GW	GW	GW	GW	GW	GW	GW	SW	GW	GW	GW	GW	GW	GW	GW	GW
				◇				◇		◇	◇	1 ◇	1	◇		◇	◇			1
											A	B				C			A	
										(trolley)			(buffet)	(trolley)			(trolley)			(buffet)
Swansea 7	d						03 59	05 29		06 29				07 29			08 29			
Cardiff Central 7	d						04 55	06 30		07 30				08 30			09 30			
Newport (South Wales)	d						05 09	06 44		07 44				08 44			09 44			
Severn Tunnel Jn	d							06 55		07 55							09b26			
Filton Abbey Wood	d							07 10		08 10	08 23			09 09		09 23	10 09		10 28	
Bristol Temple Meads 10	d	23p16		05 49			06 49	07 22	07 49	08 22	08 41	08 50		09 22		09 49	10 22		10 49	
Keynsham	d	23p23		05 56			06 56		07 56		08 48	08 57				09 56			10 56	
Oldfield Park	d	23p30		06 03			07 03		08 03		08 55					10 03			11 03	
London Paddington 15	⊖ d								06 30	07 00		07 30	08 35	08 00		08 30	09 00		09 30	10 35
Swindon	d								07 30	07 55		08 30		08 55		09 30	09 55		10 30	
Chippenham	d								07 45	08 10		08 45		09 10		09 45	10 10		10 45	
Melksham	d																			
Bath Spa 7	d	23p35		06 07			07 07	07 36	08 07	08 36	08 58	09 07		09 36		10 07	10 36		11 07	
Freshford	d	23p45		06 16			07 16		08 16		09 09					10 16			11 16	
Avoncliff	d	23c47		06x18			07x18		08x18		09x10					10x18			11x18	
Bradford-on-Avon	d	23p51		06 22			07 22	07 47	08 22	08 47	09 14	09 20		09 47		10 22	10 47		11 22	
Trowbridge	d	23p57		06 28			07 28	07 53	08 28	08 53	09 20	09 27		09 53		10 28	10 53		11 28	
Plymouth	d							05 40			07e47			07 47				08 52		
Exeter St Davids 6	d			05f10				06 41			08e49			08 49				09 54		
Westbury	a	00 04		06 35			07 35	08 01	08 35	09 01	09 27	09 34	09 56	10 03		10 34	11 00		11 35	11 54
	d	00 04	05 26	06 39	06 47	07 06		08 01		09 01	09 30	09 39	09 58	10 03	10 10	10 35	11 01	11 07		11 55
Frome	d	00a16			06 56						09 39					10 45				
Bruton	d				07 08						09 51					10 57				
Castle Cary	a				07 14						09 56		10 14			11 02				12 12
	d				07 15						09 56					11 02				
Yeovil Pen Mill	d				07g39						10 10					11 16				
Thornford	d				07x44						10x14					11x20				
Yetminster	d				07x47						10x17					11x23				
Chetnole	d				07x51						10x21					11x27				
Maiden Newton	d				08 03						10 33					11 41				
Dorchester West	d				08 14						10 40					11h56				
Upwey	a				08 20						10 50					12 02				
Weymouth	a				08 26						10 55					12 08				
Dilton Marsh	d					07x09									10x13			11x10		
Warminster	d		05 34	06 46		07 15		08 08		09 08		09 46		10 08	10a19		11 08	11 16		
Salisbury	a		05 58	07 15		07 35		08 32		09 32		10 09		10 31			11 32	11 38		
	d			07 24		07 37		08 33		09 33				10 32			11 33	11 39		
Romsey	d			07 44		07 56		08 51		09 51				10 50			11 51	12 00		
Southampton Central	a			08 02		08 07		09 02		10 02				11 02			12 02	12 20		
Bournemouth	a					09 10		10 00		11 00				12 00			13 00	13 15		
Fareham	a			08 27		08 39		09 27		10 27				11 27			12 27	12 56		
	d			08 27				09 27		10 27				11 27			12 27			
Cosham	a			08 35		08 49		09 35		10 35				11 35			12 35	13 04		
Fratton	a			08 42		09j07		09 42		10 43				11 42			12 42	13 37		
Portsmouth & Southsea	a			08 46		09 42		09 46		10 46				11 46			12 46	13 42		
Portsmouth Harbour	a			08 52				09 52		10 53				11 52			12 52			
Havant	a			08k55				09k55		10k55				11k55			12k55			
Chichester 4	a			09k10				10k10		11k10				12k10			13k10			
Barnham	a			09k18				10k18		11k18				12k18			13k18			
Worthing 4	a			09k54				10k54		11k54				12k54			13k54			
Shoreham-by-Sea	a			10k04				11k04		12k04				13k04			14k04			
Hove 2	a			10k13				11k13		12k13				13k13			14k13			
Brighton 10	a			10k18				11k18		12k18				13k18			14k18			

For general notes see front of timetable
For details of catering facilities see Directory of Train Operators

A From Worcester Shrub Hill (Table 57)
B To London Waterloo (Table 160)
C From Gloucester (Table 134)
b Change at Bristol Temple Meads
c Previous night.
Stops on request, passengers wishing to alight must inform the guard and those wishing to join must give a hand signal to the driver
e Change at Castle Cary
f Change at Salisbury
g Arr. 0727
h Arr. 1151
j Change at Southampton Central and Cosham
k Change at Fareham

Table 123

Saturdays
until 5 September

South Wales and Bristol → Weymouth and Portsmouth

Network Diagram - see first page of Table 123

		GW ◇ 🛒	GW ◇ A	GW ◇ 🛒	GW ◇ B	SW [1] ◇	GW [1] 🍴	GW ◇ 🛒	GW A	GW ◇ 🛒	GW	GW ◇ C 🛒	GW ◇ 🛒	GW	GW [1] ◇ 🍴	GW A	SW [1] ◇	GW ◇ 🛒	GW ◇ B	GW ◇ 🛒
Swansea [7]	d	09 29		10 29		10b55		11 29		12 29			13 29					14 29		15 29
Cardiff Central [7]	d	10 30		11 30		12 00		12 30		13 30			14 30					15 30		16 30
Newport (South Wales)	d	10 44		11 44		12 15		12 44		13 44			14 44					15 44		16 44
Severn Tunnel Jn	d	10c25		11c25		12 25				13c26			14c25					15c25		16 55
Filton Abbey Wood	d	11 09	11 23	12 09	12 28	12 42		13 09	13 23	14 09		14 25	15 09			15 22		16 09	16 28	17 10
Bristol Temple Meads [10]	d	11 22	11 49	12 22	12 43	13 15		13 22	13 49	14 22		14 49	15 22			15 38	15 52	16 22	16 49	17 22
Keynsham	d		11 56		12 50				13 56			14 56				15 45			16 56	
Oldfield Park	d		12 03		12 57				14 03			15 03				15 52			17 03	
London Paddington [15] ⊖	d	10 00	10 30	11 00		11 30	12 35	12 00	12 30	13 00		13 30	14 00	14 15	15 06		14 30	15 00	15 30	16 00
Swindon	d	10 55	11 30	11 55		12 30		12 55	13 30	13 55		14 30	14 55	15 20			15 30	15 55	16 30	16 55
Chippenham	d	11 10	11 45	12 10		12 45		13 10	13 45	14 10		14 45	15 10	15 36			15 45	16 10	16 45	17 10
Melksham	d													15 46						
Bath Spa [7]	d	11 36	12 07	12 36	13 00	13 27		13 36	14 07	14 36		15 07	15 36			15 56	16 07	16 36	17 07	17 36
Freshford	d		12 16						14 16			15 16				16 06			17 16	
Avoncliff	d		12x18						14x18			15x18				16x09			17x18	
Bradford-on-Avon	d	11 47	12 22	12 47	13 13	13 40		13 47	14 22	14 47		15 22	15 47			16 12	16 24	16 47	17 22	17 47
Trowbridge	d	11 53	12 28	12 53	13 19	13 47		13 53	14 28	14 53		15 28	15 53	15 59		16 18	16 30	16 53	17 28	17 53
Plymouth	d	09 34						10e43		12e21		13f01						14g25		14h48
Exeter St Davids [6]	d	10 37		11h08				12h10		13h35		14j11	14 11					15 32		16h10
Westbury	a	12 01	12 35	13 01	13 26	13 53	13 59	14 01	14 35	15 01		15 35	16 01	16 06	16 23	16 28	16 37	17 01	17 35	18 01
	d	12 01	12 36	13 01	13 27	13 54	14 00	14 01		15 01	15 08	15 36	16 01	16 08	16 23		16 39	17 01	17 38	18 01
Frome	d		12 48									15 46							17 47	
Bruton	d		12 59									15 57							17 59	
Castle Cary	a		13 04				14 17					16 02			16 41				18 04	
	d		13 05									16 03							18 05	
Yeovil Pen Mill	d		13 18									16 16							18 19	
Thornford	d		13x23									16x21							18x24	
Yetminster	d		13x26									16x24							18x28	
Chetnole	d		13x30									16x28							18x32	
Maiden Newton	d		13 42									16k46							18 45	
Dorchester West	d		13 55									16 56							18 54	
Upwey	a		14 02									17 02							19 02	
Weymouth	a		14 08									17 07							19 08	
Dilton Marsh	d				13x30						15x11			16x10						
Warminster	d	12 08		13 08	13 36	14 02		14 08		15 08	15a17		16 08	16a16			16 47	17 08		18 08
Salisbury	a	12 32		13 32	13 58	14 25		14 32		15 32			16 32				17 09	17 32		18 32
	d	12 33		13 33	13 59			14 33		15 33			16 33					17 33		18 33
Romsey	d	12 51		13 51	14 19			14 51		15 51			16 51					17 51		18 51
Southampton Central	a	13 02		14 02	14 32			15 02		16 02			17 02					18 02		19 02
Bournemouth	a	14 00		15 00	15 15			16 00		17 00			18 00					19 00		20 00
Fareham	a	13 27		14 27	14 54			15 27		16 27			17 27					18 27		19 27
	d	13 27		14 27	14 55			15 27		16 27			17 27					18 27		19 27
Cosham	a	13 35		14 35	15 03			15 35		16 35			17 35					18 35		19 35
Fratton	a	13 42		14 42	15 37			15 42		16 42			17 42					18 43		19 43
Portsmouth & Southsea	a	13 46		14 46	15 42			15 46		16 46			17 46					18 47		19 46
Portsmouth Harbour	a	13 52		14 52				15 52		16 52			17 52					18 52		19 52
Havant	a	13m55		14m55	15 10			15m55		16m55			17m55					18m50		19m51
Chichester [4]	a	14m10		15m10	15 21			16m10		17m10			18m10					19m05		20m06
Barnham	a	14m18		15m18	15 29			16m18		17m18			18m18					19m14		20m14
Worthing [4]	a	14m54			15 44			16m54		17m54			18m54					19m53		20m52
Shoreham-by-Sea	a	15m04			15 55			17m04		18m04			19m04					20m03		21m02
Hove [2]	a	15m13			16 07			17m13		18m13			19m13					20m14		21m13
Brighton [10]	a	15m18			16 14			17m18		18m18			19m18					20m19		21m18

For general notes see front of timetable
For details of catering facilities see Directory of Train Operators

A From Gloucester (Table 134)
B From Great Malvern (Table 71)
C From Worcester Foregate Street (Table 71)
b Change at Cardiff Central and Bristol Temple Meads
c Change at Bristol Temple Meads
e Change at Exeter St Davids and Salisbury
f Change at Exeter St Davids and Castle Cary
g Change at Exeter St Davids and Westbury
h Change at Salisbury
j Change at Castle Cary
k Arr. 1638
m Change at Fareham

Table 123

South Wales and Bristol → Weymouth and Portsmouth

Network Diagram - see first page of Table 123

	GW 1 ◇ ⊡	GW ◇ A	GW ◇ ⚒		GW	GW B	GW ◇ ⚒		GW 1 ◇ ⊡	GW A	GW ◇ ⚒		GW 1 ◇ ⊡	GW ◇ B	GW C		GW ◇ ⚒	GW	SW 1		GW				
Swansea 7 d			16 29				17 29				18 29						19 29		20b00		20b55				
Cardiff Central 7 d			17 30				18 30				19 30						20 30		21 00		22 00				
Newport (South Wales) d			17 44				18 44				19 44						20 44		21 15		22 16				
Severn Tunnel Jn d			17 55				18c25				19c25						20c15		21 25		22 33				
Filton Abbey Wood d		17 23	18 10			18 28	19 09			19 25	20 09			20 27			21 09		21 42		22 52				
Bristol Temple Meads 10 d		17 49	18 22			18 49	19 22			19 49	20 22			20 49			21 22	21 51	22 23		23 10				
Keynsham d		17 56				18 56				19 56				20 56				21 56			23 17				
Oldfield Park d		18 03				19 03				20 03				21 03				22 03			23 23				
London Paddington 15 ⊖ d	17 06	16 30	17 00			17 30	18 00		19 06	18 30	19 00		20 06	19 30	20 00		20 00	20 30			21 30				
Swindon d		17 30	17 55			18 30	18 55			19 30	19 55			20 30	21 08		21 00	21 30			22 30				
Chippenham d		17 45	18 10			18 45	19 11			19 46	20 10			20 45	21 24		21 15	21 45			22 45				
Melksham d															21 34										
Bath Spa 7 d		18 07	18 36			19 07	19 36			20 07	20 36			21 07			21 37	22 07	22 36		23 27				
Freshford d		18 16				19 16				20 16				21 16				22 16			23 36				
Avoncliff d		18x18				19x18				20x18				21x18				22x18			23x38				
Bradford-on-Avon d		18 22	18 47			19 22	19 47			20 22	20 47			21 22			21 47	22 22	22 47		23 42				
Trowbridge d		18 28	18 53			19 28	19 53			20 28	20 53			21 28	21 43		21 53	22 28	22 53		23 48				
Plymouth d		16e25															19f12								
Exeter St Davids 6 d		18g02					18h10				19h10						20h15								
Westbury a	18 22	18 35	19 01			19 35	20 01		20 27	20 35	21 01		21 24	21 36	21 51		22 01	22 37	23 02		23 55				
d	18 22	18 36	19 01		19 09		20 01		20 28	20 37	21 01		21 24	21 39			22 01		23 04		23 55				
Frome d		18 46								20a46				21 49							00a05				
Bruton d		18 57												22 00											
Castle Cary a	18 40	19 02							20 45				21 43	22 05											
d		19 05												22 06											
Yeovil Pen Mill d		19 19												22 19											
Thornford d		19x23												22x24											
Yetminster d		19x26												22x27											
Chetnole d		19x30												22x31											
Maiden Newton d		19 43												22 43											
Dorchester West d		19 54												22 53											
Upwey a		20 02												22 59											
Weymouth a		20 08												23 05											
Dilton Marsh d					19x12												22x04								
Warminster d			19 08		19 18		20 08				21 08						22 08		23 11						
Salisbury a			19 32		19 41		20 32				21 32						22 31		23 34						
d			19 33		19 41		20 33				21 33						22 32								
Romsey d			19 51		20 02		20 51				21 51						22 52								
Southampton Central a			20 02		20 18		21 02				22 02						23 02								
Bournemouth a					21 00		22 09				23 16						00 16								
Fareham a			20 27		20 56		21 27				22 26						23 27								
d			20 27				21 27				22 26						23 28								
Cosham a			20 44		21 04		21 49				22 48						23 58								
Fratton a			20 41		21 37		21 43				22 40						23 41								
Portsmouth & Southsea a			20 45		21 42		21 46				22 44						23 45								
Portsmouth Harbour a			20 51				21 52				22 52						23 49								
Havant a			20j50				21j55				22j54														
Chichester 4 a			21j05				22j06				23j09														
Barnham a			21j14				22k18				23k26														
Worthing 4 a			21j54				22j52				23k59														
Shoreham-by-Sea a			22j04				23k32				00k09														
Hove 2 a			22j16				23k43				00k20														
Brighton 10 a			22j21				23k48				00k25														

For general notes see front of timetable
For details of catering facilities see Directory of Train Operators

A From Gloucester (Table 134)
B From Great Malvern (Table 71)
C From Cheltenham Spa (Table 125)
b Change at Cardiff Central and Bristol Temple Meads
c Change at Bristol Temple Meads
e Change at Exeter St Davids and Castle Cary
f Change at Exeter St Davids and Salisbury
g Change at Castle Cary
h Change at Salisbury
j Change at Fareham
k Change at Fratton

Saturdays

from 12 September

South Wales and Bristol → Weymouth and Portsmouth

Network Diagram - see first page of Table 123

		GW	GW	GW ◇	GW	GW	GW	GW ◇	GW	GW ◇	GW ◇ A	SW 1 ◇ B	GW 1 ◇	GW ◇	GW	GW ◇ C	GW ◇	GW	GW A	GW ◇
Swansea 7	d						03 59	05 29		06 29				07 29			08 29			09 29
Cardiff Central 7	d						04 55	06 30		07 30				08 30			09 30			10 30
Newport (South Wales)	d						05 09	06 44		07 44				08 44			09 44			10 44
Severn Tunnel Jn	d							06 55		07 55				08b25			09b26			10b25
Filton Abbey Wood	d							07 10		08 10	08 23			09 09		09 23	10 09		10 28	11 09
Bristol Temple Meads 10	d	23p16		05 49			06 49	07 22	07 49	08 22	08 41	08 50		09 22		09 49	10 22		10 49	11 22
Keynsham	d	23p23		05 56			06 56		07 56		08 48	08 57				09 56			10 56	
Oldfield Park	d	23p30		06 03			07 03		08 03		08 55					10 03			11 03	
London Paddington 15 ⊖	d								06 30	07 00		07 30	08 18	08 00		08 30	09 00		09 30	10 00
Swindon	d								07 30	07 55		08 30		08 55		09 30	09 55		10 30	10 55
Chippenham	d								07 45	08 10		08 45		09 10		09 45	10 10		10 45	11 10
Melksham	d																			
Bath Spa 7	d	23p35		06 07			07 07	07 36	08 07	08 36	08 58	09 07		09 36		10 07	10 36		11 07	11 36
Freshford	d	23p45		06 16			07 16		08 16		09 09					10 16			11 16	
Avoncliff	d	23c47		06x18			07x18		08x18		09x10					10x18			11x18	
Bradford-on-Avon	d	23p51		06 22			07 22	07 47	08 22	08 47	09 14	09 20		09 47		10 22	10 47		11 22	11 47
Trowbridge	d	23p57		06 28			07 28	07 53	08 28	08 53	09 20	09 27		09 53		10 28	10 53		11 28	11 53
Plymouth	d							05 40			07e47			07 47				08 52		
Exeter St Davids 6	d			05f10				06 41			08e49			08 49				09 54		10f10
Westbury	a	00 04		06 35			07 35	08 01	08 35	09 01	09 27	09 34	09 59	10 03		10 34	11 00		11 35	12 01
	d	00 04	05 26	06 39	06 47	07 06		08 01		09 01	09 30	09 39	10 00	10 03	10 10	10 35	11 01	11 07		12 01
Frome	d	00a16			06 56						09 39					10 45				
Bruton	d				07 08						09 51					10 57				
Castle Cary	a				07 14						09 56		10 17			11 02				
	d				07 15						09 56					11 02				
Yeovil Pen Mill	d				07g39						10 10					11 16				
Thornford	d				07x44						10x14					11x20				
Yetminster	d				07x47						10x17					11x23				
Chetnole	d				07x51						10x21					11x27				
Maiden Newton	d				08 03						10 33					11 41				
Dorchester West	d				08 14						10 40					11h56				
Upwey	a				08 20						10 50					12 02				
Weymouth	a				08 26						10 55					12 08				
Dilton Marsh	d					07x09									10x13			11x10		
Warminster	d		05 34	06 46		07 15		08 08		09 08		09 46		10 08	10a19		11 08	11 16		12 08
Salisbury	a		05 58	07 15		07 35		08 32		09 32		10 09		10 31			11 32	11 38		12 32
	d			07 24		07 37		08 33		09 33				10 32			11 33	11 39		12 33
Romsey	d			07 44		07 56		08 51		09 51				10 50			11 51	12 00		12 51
Southampton Central	a			08 02		08 07		09 02		10 02				11 02			12 02	12 20		13 02
Bournemouth	a					09 10		10 00		11 00				12 00			13 00	13 15		14 00
Fareham	a			08 27		08 39		09 27		10 27				11 27			12 27	12 56		13 27
	d			08 27				09 27		10 27				11 27			12 27			13 27
Cosham	a			08 35		08 49		09 35		10 35				11 35			12 35	13 04		13 35
Fratton	a			08 42		09j07		09 42		10 43				11 42			12 42	13 37		13 42
Portsmouth & Southsea	a			08 46		09 42		09 46		10 46				11 46			12 46	13 42		13 46
Portsmouth Harbour	a			08 52				09 52		10 53				11 52			12 52			13 52
Havant	a			08k55				09k55		10k55				11k55			12k55			13k55
Chichester 4	a			09k10				10k10		11k10				12k10			13k10			14k10
Barnham	a			09k18				10k18		11k18				12k18			13k18			14k18
Worthing 4	a			09k54				10k54		11k54				12k54			13k54			14k54
Shoreham-by-Sea	a			10k04				11k04		12k04				13k04			14k04			15k04
Hove 2	a			10k13				11k13		12k13				13k13			14k13			15k13
Brighton 10	a			10k18				11k18		12k18				13k18			14k18			15k18

For general notes see front of timetable
For details of catering facilities see Directory of Train Operators

A From Worcester Shrub Hill (Table 57)
B To London Waterloo (Table 160)
C From Gloucester (Table 134)
b Change at Bristol Temple Meads
c Previous night.
Stops on request, passengers wishing to alight must inform the guard and those wishing to join must give a hand signal to the driver
e Change at Castle Cary
f Change at Salisbury
g Arr. 0727
h Arr. 1151
j Change at Southampton Central and Cosham
k Change at Fareham

Table 123

Saturdays

from 12 September

South Wales and Bristol → Weymouth and Portsmouth

Network Diagram - see first page of Table 123

		GW	GW	GW	GW	SW	GW	GW	GW	GW	GW	GW	GW	GW	GW	GW	SW	GW	GW	GW
		1 ◇	◇	◇	◇	1 ◇	1 ◇	◇	◇	◇		◇	◇		1 ◇		1 ◇	◇		◇
			A		B		C		A			D				A				B
		⊐		⊼			⊐	⊼		⊼		⊼	⊼		⊐			⊼		
Swansea 7	d			10 29		10b55		11 29		12 29			13 29					14 29		
Cardiff Central 7	d			11 30		12 00		12 30		13 30			14 30					15 30		
Newport (South Wales)	d			11 44		12 15		12 44		13 44			14 44					15 44		
Severn Tunnel Jn	d			11c25		12 25				13c26			14c25					15c25		
Filton Abbey Wood	d		11 23	12 09	12 28	12 42		13 09	13 23	14 09		14 25	15 09			15 22		16 09		16 28
Bristol Temple Meads 10	d		11 49	12 22	12 43	13 15		13 22	13 49	14 22		14 49	15 22			15 38	15 52	16 22		16 49
Keynsham	d		11 56		12 50				13 56			14 56				15 45				16 56
Oldfield Park	d		12 03		12 57				14 03			15 03				15 52				17 03
London Paddington 15 ⊖	d	11 06	10 30	11 00		11 30	12 18	12 00	12 30	13 00		13 30	14 00	14 15	15 06		14 30	15 00		15 30
Swindon	d		11 30	11 55		12 30		12 55	13 30	13 55		14 30	14 55	15 20			15 30	15 55		16 30
Chippenham	d		11 45	12 10		12 45		13 10	13 45	14 10		14 45	15 10	15 36			15 45	16 10		16 45
Melksham	d													15 46						
Bath Spa 7	d		12 07	12 36	13 00	13 27		13 36	14 07	14 36		15 07	15 36			15 56	16 07	16 36		17 07
Freshford	d		12 16						14 16			15 16				16 06				17 16
Avoncliff	d		12x18						14x18			15x18				16x09				17x18
Bradford-on-Avon	d		12 22	12 47	13 13	13 40		13 47	14 22	14 47		15 22	15 47			16 12	16 24	16 47		17 22
Trowbridge	d		12 28	12 53	13 19	13 47		13 53	14 28	14 53		15 28	15 53	15 59		16 18	16 30	16 53		17 28
Plymouth	d		10e43	09f25						12f21	12 54									
Exeter St Davids 6	d		11g54	11h08	11 54			12h10		13h35	13 56		14h10							
Westbury	a	12 22	12 35	13 01	13 26	13 53	13 59	14 01	14 35	15 01		15 35	16 01	16 06	16 23	16 28	16 37	17 01		17 35
	d	12 22	12 36	13 01	13 27	13 54	13 59	14 01		15 01	15 08	15 36	16 01		16 23		16 39	17 01	17 08	17 38
Frome	d		12 48				14 09					15 46								17 47
Bruton	d		12 59									15 57								17 59
Castle Cary	a	12 40	13 04				14 21					16 02			16 41					18 04
	d		13 05									16 09								18 05
Yeovil Pen Mill	d		13 18									16 23								18 19
Thornford	d		13x23									16x27								18x24
Yetminster	d		13x26									16x30								18x28
Chetnole	d		13x30									16x34								18x32
Maiden Newton	d		13 42									16 46								18 45
Dorchester West	d		13 55									16 56								18 54
Upwey	a		14 02									17 03								19 02
Weymouth	a		14 08									17 07								19 08
Dilton Marsh	d				13x30						15x11								17x11	
Warminster	d			13 08	13 36	14 02		14 08		15 08	15a17		16 08				16 47	17 08	17a19	
Salisbury	a			13 32	13 58	14 25		14 32		15 32			16 32				17 09	17 32		
	d			13 33	13 59			14 33		15 33			16 33					17 33		
Romsey	d			13 51	14 19			14 51		15 51			16 51					17 51		
Southampton Central	a			14 02	14 32			15 02		16 02			17 02					18 02		
Bournemouth	a			15 00	15 15			16 00		17 00			18 00					19 00		
Fareham	a			14 27	14 54			15 27		16 27			17 27					18 27		
	d			14 27	14 55			15 27		16 27			17 27					18 27		
Cosham	a			14 35	15 03			15 35		16 35			17 35					18 35		
Fratton	a			14 42	15 37			15 42		16 42			17 42					18 43		
Portsmouth & Southsea	a			14 46	15 42			15 46		16 46			17 46					18 47		
Portsmouth Harbour	a			14 52				15 52		16 52			17 52					18 52		
Havant	a			14j55	15 10			15j55		16j55			17j55					18j50		
Chichester 4	a			15j10	15 21			16j10		17j10			18j10					19j05		
Barnham	a			15j18	15 29			16j18		17j18			18j18					19j14		
Worthing 4	a				15 44			16j54		17j54			18j54					19j53		
Shoreham-by-Sea	a				15 55			17j04		18j04			19j04					20j03		
Hove 2	a				16 07			17j13		18j13			19j13					20j14		
Brighton 10	a				16 14			17j18		18j18			19j18					20j19		

For general notes see front of timetable
For details of catering facilities see Directory of Train Operators

A From Gloucester (Table 134)
B From Great Malvern (Table 71)
C To Taunton (Table 135)
D From Worcester Foregate Street (Table 71)
b Change at Cardiff Central and Bristol Temple Meads
c Change at Bristol Temple Meads
e Change at Exeter St Davids and Castle Cary
f Change at Exeter St Davids and Salisbury
g Change at Castle Cary
h Change at Salisbury
j Change at Fareham

Saturdays
from 12 September

South Wales and Bristol → Weymouth and Portsmouth

Network Diagram - see first page of Table 123

		GW ◇	GW [1] ◇	GW ◇ A	GW ◇	GW	GW B	GW ◇	GW [1] ◇	GW A	GW ◇	GW [1] ◇	GW ◇ B	GW C	GW ◇	GW	SW [1]	GW
Swansea [7]	d	15 29			16 29			17 29			18 29				19 29		20b00	20b55
Cardiff Central [7]	d	16 30			17 30			18 30			19 30				20 30	20 30	21 00	22 00
Newport (South Wales)	d	16 44			17 44			18 44			19 44				20 44		21 15	22 16
Severn Tunnel Jn	d	16 55			17 55			18c25			19c25				20c15		21 25	22 33
Filton Abbey Wood	d	17 10		17 23	18 10		18 28	19 09		19 25	20 09		20 27		21 09		21 42	22 52
Bristol Temple Meads [10]	d	17 22		17 49	18 22		18 49	19 22		19 49	20 22		20 49		21 22	21 51	22 23	23 10
Keynsham	d			17 56			18 56			19 56			20 56			21 56		23 17
Oldfield Park	d			18 03			19 03			20 03			21 03			22 03		23 23
London Paddington [15] ⊖	d	16 00	17 06	16 30	17 00		17 30	18 00	19 06	18 30	19 00	20 06	19 30	20 00	20 00	20 30		21 30
Swindon	d	16 55		17 30	17 55		18 30	18 55		19 30	19 55		20 30	21 08	21 00	21 30		22 30
Chippenham	d	17 10		17 45	18 10		18 45	19 11		19 46	20 10		20 45	21 24	21 15	21 45		22 45
Melksham	d													21 34				
Bath Spa [7]	d	17 36		18 07	18 36		19 07	19 36		20 07	20 36		21 07		21 37	22 07	22 36	23 27
Freshford	d			18 16			19 16			20 16			21 16			22 16		23 36
Avoncliff	d			18x18			19x18			20x18			21x18			22x18		23x38
Bradford-on-Avon	d	17 47		18 22	18 47		19 22	19 47		20 22	20 47		21 22		21 47	22 22	22 47	23 42
Trowbridge	d	17 53		18 28	18 53		19 28	19 53		20 28	20 53		21 28	21 43	21 53	22 28	22 53	23 48
Plymouth	d	15e04		16f57											18e43			
Exeter St Davids [6]	d	16g10		18f02				18g10			19g10				20g15			
Westbury	a	18 01	18 22	18 35	19 01		19 35	20 01	20 27	20 35	21 01	21 24	21 36	21 51	22 01	22 37	23 02	23 55
	d	18 01	18 22	18 36	19 01	19 09		20 01	20 28	20 37	21 01	21 25	21 39		22 01		23 04	23 55
Frome	d			18 46						20a46			21 49					00a05
Bruton	d			18 57									22 00					
Castle Cary	a		18 40	19 02					20 45			21 43	22 05					
	d			19 02									22 06					
Yeovil Pen Mill	d			19 19									22 19					
Thornford	d			19x23									22x24					
Yetminster	d			19x26									22x27					
Chetnole	d			19x30									22x31					
Maiden Newton	d			19 43									22 43					
Dorchester West	d			19 54									22 53					
Upwey	a			20 02									22 59					
Weymouth	a			20 08									23 05					
Dilton Marsh	d					19x12									22x04			
Warminster	d	18 08			19 08	19 18		20 08			21 08				22 08		23 11	
Salisbury	a	18 32			19 32	19 41		20 32			21 32				22 31		23 34	
	d	18 33			19 33	19 41		20 33			21 33				22 32			
Romsey	d	18 51			19 51	20 02		20 51			21 51				22 52			
Southampton Central	a	19 02			20 02	20 18		21 02			22 02				23 02			
Bournemouth	a	20 00				21 00		22 09			23 16				00 16			
Fareham	a	19 27			20 27	20 56		21 27			22 26				23 27			
	d	19 27			20 27			21 27			22 26				23 28			
Cosham	a	19 35			20 44	21 04		21 49			22 48				23 58			
Fratton	a	19 43			20 41	21 37		21 43			22 40				23 41			
Portsmouth & Southsea	a	19 46			20 45	21 42		21 46			22 44				23 45			
Portsmouth Harbour	a	19 52			20 51			21 52			22 52				23 49			
Havant	a	19h51			20h50			21h55			22h54							
Chichester [4]	a	20h06			21h05			22h06			23h09							
Barnham	a	20h14			21h14			22j18			23j26							
Worthing [4]	a	20h52			21h54			22h52			23j59							
Shoreham-by-Sea	a	21h02			22h04			23j32			00j09							
Hove [2]	a	21h13			22h16			23j43			00j20							
Brighton [10]	a	21h18			22h21			23j48			00j25							

For general notes see front of timetable
For details of catering facilities see Directory of Train Operators

A From Gloucester (Table 134)
B From Great Malvern (Table 71)
C From Cheltenham Spa (Table 125)
b Change at Cardiff Central and Bristol Temple Meads
c Change at Bristol Temple Meads
e Change at Exeter St Davids and Salisbury
f Change at Castle Cary
g Change at Salisbury
h Change at Fareham
j Change at Fratton

Table 123

Sundays

until 6 September

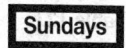

South Wales and Bristol → Weymouth and Portsmouth

Network Diagram - see first page of Table 123

		GW	GW ◇	GW	GW 1 ◇	GW 1 ◇	GW ◇	GW ◇	GW ◇	GW 1 ◇	GW ◇	GW ◇	GW 1 ◇	GW ◇	GW 1 ◇	GW ◇	SW 1 ◇ A	GW ◇
Swansea 7	d						07 59	08 59	09 59		10 59			11 59		12 59		13 59
Cardiff Central 7	d		08 05				09 15	10 15	11 15		12 15			13 15		14 15		15 15
Newport (South Wales)	d		08 23				09 29	10 29	11 29		12 29			13 29		14 29		15 29
Severn Tunnel Jn	d		08 39				09 39	10 39	11 39		12 39			13 39		14 39		15 39
Filton Abbey Wood	d		08 54				09 56	10 54	11 54		12 57			13 54		14 55		15 56
Bristol Temple Meads 10	d		09 10	09 15			10 10	11 10	12 10		13 10			14 10		15 10	16 04	16 10
Keynsham	d		09 17	09 22				11 17			13 17					15 17	16 11	
Oldfield Park	d		09 24	09 30				11 24			13 24					15 24		
London Paddington 15 ⊖	d				08 57	09 57			10 00	11 27	11 00		12 57	12 00	13 57	13 00	14 00	
Swindon	d								11b10		12c10			13e11		14f11	15 11	
Chippenham	d								11g26		12h26			13j26		14k26	15 26	
Melksham	d																	
Bath Spa 7	d		09 27	09 33			10 22	11 27	12 22		13 27			14 24		15 27	16 20	16 24
Freshford	d			09 43			10 32		12 32					14 33				16 35
Avoncliff	d			09x45			10x34		12x34					14x36				16x37
Bradford-on-Avon	d		09 39	09 49			10 38	11 39	12 38		13 39			14 39		15 39	16 31	16 41
Trowbridge	d		09 45	09 55			10 44	11 46	12 44		13 46			14 45		15 45	16 37	16 47
Plymouth	d						08 40		10m40		11 45			12n00		13 44		14q06
Exeter St Davids 6	d		08 38				09 49		11 47		12 51			13q18		14 46		15q20
Westbury	a		09 53	10 02	10 22		10 51	11 53	12 51	13 01	13 53		14 17	14 52		15 52	16 44	16 54
	d	09 00	09 55	10 03			11 00	12 03	12 57	13 03	14 03	14 15		15 00		15 58	16 46	16 58
Frome	d	09 09		10 12								14 28						
Bruton	d	09 21		10 24								14 40						
Castle Cary	a	09 26		10 29		11 34				13 19		14 45			15 34			
	d	09 26		10 29								14 46						
Yeovil Pen Mill	d	09 40		10 43								15 00						
Thornford	d	09x44		10x47								15x04						
Yetminster	d	09x47		10x50								15x07						
Chetnole	d	09x51		10x54								15x11						
Maiden Newton	d	10 03		11 06								15 23						
Dorchester West	d	10 13		11 16								15 33						
Upwey	a	10 20		11 23								15 40						
Weymouth	a	10 25		11 27								15 45						
Dilton Marsh	d		09x58					12x06			14x06					16x01		17x01
Warminster	d		10 04				11 07	12 12	13 04		14 12			15 07		16 07	16 53	17 07
Salisbury	a		10 28				11 29	12 34	13 27		14 39			15 30		16 30	17 16	17 30
	d		10 31				11 31	12 36	13 29		14 48			15 31		16 31		17 31
Romsey	d		10 50				11 49	12 56	13 47		15 10			15 51		16 49		17 49
Southampton Central	a		11 00				12 04	13 06	13 58		15 20			16 05		17 04		18 04
Bournemouth	a		12 23				13 23	14 23	14 35		16 23			17 23		18 23		19 23
Fareham	a		11 25				12 28	13 33	14 22		15 50			16 28		17 28		18 28
	d		11 26				12 29	13 34	14 23		15 51			16 29		17 29		18 29
Cosham	a		11 33				12 37	13 41	14 31		16 00			16 37		17 37		18 37
Fratton	a		11 40				12 44	14 04	14 38		16 30			16 44		17 44		18 44
Portsmouth & Southsea	a		11 44				12 47	14 08	14 41		16 33			16 47		17 47		18 47
Portsmouth Harbour	a		11 53				12 53	14 13	14 48		16 53			16 53		17 53		18 51
Havant	a		11r59				12r59	14 03	14r59		16 11			16r59		17r59		18r59
Chichester 4	a		12r14				13r14	14 19	15r14		16 22			17r14		18r14		19r14
Barnham	a		12r22				13r22	14 27	15r22		16 30			17r22		18r22		19r22
Worthing 4	a		12r37				13r37	14 44	15r37		16 45			17r37		18r37		19r37
Shoreham-by-Sea	a		12r47				13r47	14 51	15r47		16 51			17r47		18r47		19r47
Hove 2	a		12r53				13r53	14 57	15r53		16 58			17r53		18r53		19r53
Brighton 10	a		13t05				14t05	15 04	16t05		17 05			18t05		19t05		20t05

For general notes see front of timetable
For details of catering facilities see Directory of Train Operators

- **A** To London Waterloo (Table 160)
- **b** From 19 July dep. 1121
- **c** From 19 July dep. 1221
- **e** From 19 July dep. 1321
- **f** From 19 July dep. 1421
- **g** From 19 July dep. 1137
- **h** From 19 July dep. 1238
- **j** From 19 July dep. 1338
- **k** From 19 July dep. 1438
- **m** From 19 July dep. 1042
- **n** Change at Exeter St Davids and Salisbury
- **q** Change at Salisbury
- **r** Change at Fratton
- **t** Change at Fratton and Hove

Sundays

until 6 September

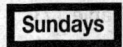

South Wales and Bristol → Weymouth and Portsmouth

Network Diagram - see first page of Table 123

Station		GW 1 ◇	GW ◇	GW ◇	GW ◇ A	GW ◇	GW	GW 1 ◇	GW ◇	GW ◇	GW 1 ◇	GW ◇	GW 1 ◇	GW ◇	GW ◇	SW 1	GW	GW ◇
Swansea 7	d		14 59	15 30		15 59				16 59		17 59			18 59			20 35
Cardiff Central 7	d		16 15	16 40		17 15			17 45	18 15		19 15			20 15			22 05
Newport (South Wales)	d		16 29	16 54		17 29			17 59	18 29		19 29			20 29			22 24
Severn Tunnel Jn	d		16 39			17 39				18 39					20 39			22 41
Filton Abbey Wood	d		16 55	17 17		17 54			18 22	18 56		19 52		19 59	20 54			22 58
Bristol Temple Meads 10	d		17 10	17 40	17 44	18 10			18 50	19 10		20 10		20 50	21 10	21 35	22 15	23 10
Keynsham	d		17 17		17 51	18 17				19 17				20 57			22 22	
Oldfield Park	d		17 24		17 58	18 24				19 24				21 04			22 29	
London Paddington 15 ⊖	d	15 57		16 00			17 00	17 57	17 00	17 30	18 57	18 00	19 57	19 00	19 30	20 00		21 00
Swindon	d			17 11			18 31		18 11	18 33		19 11		20 11	20 34	21 11		22 14
Chippenham	d			17 26			18 47		18 26	18 52		19 26		20 26	20 49	21 26		22 28
Melksham	d						18 57											
Bath Spa 7	d		17 27	17 52	18 01	18 27			19 02	19 27		20 22		21 07	21 23	21 49	22 32	23 22
Freshford	d				18 11							20 32		21 18			22 43	
Avoncliff	d				18x14							20x34		21x21			22x46	
Bradford-on-Avon	d		17 39	18 04	18 17	18 39			19 14	19 39		20 38		21 24	21 34	22 00	22 49	23 34
Trowbridge	d		17 45	18 11	18 23	18 45	19 06		19 20	19 45		20 44		21 30	21 40	22 06	22 55	23 40
Plymouth	d		15 43			16b02			16 45			18 10		19c15	19 15			
Exeter St Davids 6	d		16 45			17b18			17 47			19b20		20c20	20 20			
Westbury	a	17 22	17 52	18 18	18 30	18 54	19 13	19 26	19 27	19 52		20 51	21 27	21 37	21 47	22 13	23 02	23 47
	d	17 24	18 00	18 19	18 30	18 58			19 29	19 53		20 55	21 28	21 38	21 55	22 15		23 50
Frome	d				18 39									21 48				
Bruton	d				18 51									21 59				
Castle Cary	a	17 40			18 56						20 29		21 45	22 04				
	d				19 00									22 05				
Yeovil Pen Mill	d				19 14									22 18				
Thornford	d				19x18									22x23				
Yetminster	d				19x21									22x26				
Chetnole	d				19x25									22x30				
Maiden Newton	d				19 37									22 42				
Dorchester West	d				19 48									22 52				
Upwey	a				19 55									22 58				
Weymouth	a				20 01									23 03				
Dilton Marsh	d			18x22						19x56								23x53
Warminster	d		18 07	18 28		19 05			19 37	20 02		21 02			22 02	22 22		23a59
Salisbury	a		18 30	18 53		19 29			19 59	20 25		21 25			22 25	22 46		
	d		18 31	18 57		19 30			20 00	20 30		21 29			22 29			
Romsey	d		18 49	19 15		19 48			20 19	20 48		21 47			22 48			
Southampton Central	a		19 04	19 26		19 58			20 29	20 59		21 58			22 59			
Bournemouth	a			20 23		20 35			21 23	22 23		22 35			00 21			
Fareham	a		19 28	19 48		20 23			20 54	21 22		22 22			23 21			
	d		19 29	19 49		20 24			20 55	21 23		22 23			23 22			
Cosham	a		19 37	19 58		20 54			21 19	21 54		22 54			23 54			
Fratton	a		19 44	20 30		20 39			21 09	21 36		22 36			23 37			
Portsmouth & Southsea	a		19 47	20 33		20 43			21 15	21 39		22 39			23 40			
Portsmouth Harbour	a		19 53			20 49			21 26	21 48		22 46			23 48			
Havant	a		19e59	20 10		20e59				21e49		22e49						
Chichester 4	a		20e14	20 21		21e14				22e14		23e14						
Barnham	a		20e22	20 29		21e22				22e22		23e22						
Worthing 4	a		20e37	20 51		22e01				23e01								
Shoreham-by-Sea	a		20e47	20 57		22e11				23e11								
Hove 2	a		20e53	21 04		22e23				23e24								
Brighton 10	a		21f05	21 10		22e27				23e29								

For general notes see front of timetable
For details of catering facilities see Directory of Train Operators

A From Weston-super-Mare (Table 134)
b Change at Salisbury
c Change at Castle Cary
e Change at Fratton
f Change at Fratton and Hove

Sundays

from 13 September

South Wales and Bristol → Weymouth and Portsmouth

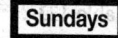

Network Diagram - see first page of Table 123

		GW	GW	GW	GW	GW	GW	GW	GW	GW	GW	GW	GW	GW	SW	GW	GW	GW
		◇	1 ◇	1 ◇	◇	◇	◇	1 ◇	◇	1 ◇	◇	◇	1 ◇	◇	1 ◇	◇	1 ◇	◇
															A			
		🛒	🍽	🍽	🛒	🛒	🛒	🍽	🛒	🍽		🛒	🍽	🛒		🛒	🍽	🛒
Swansea 7	d				07 59	08 59	09 59		10 59			11 59		12 59		13 59		14 59
Cardiff Central 7	d	08 05			09 15	10 15	11 15		12 15			13 15		14 15		15 15		16 15
Newport (South Wales)	d	08 23			09 29	10 29	11 29		12 29			13 29		14 29		15 29		16 29
Severn Tunnel Jn	d	08 39			09 39	10 39	11 39		12 39			13 39		14 39		15 39		16 39
Filton Abbey Wood	d	08 54			09 56	10 54	11 54		12 57		13 01	13 54		14 55		15 56		16 55
Bristol Temple Meads 10	d	09 10			10 10	11 10	12 10		13 10		13 40	14 10		15 10	16 04	16 10		17 10
Keynsham	d	09 17				11 17			13 17		13 47			15 17	16 11			17 17
Oldfield Park	d	09 24				11 24			13 24		13 54			15 24				17 24
London Paddington 15 ⊖	d		08 57	09 57	08 00	09 03	10 03	11 27	11 03	12 57	12 03		13 57	13 03	14 03		15 57	15 03
Swindon	d				09 08	10 10	11 10		12 10		13 11			14 11	15 11			16 11
Chippenham	d				09 25	10 27	11 26		12 26		13 26			14 26	15 26			16 26
Melksham	d																	
Bath Spa 7	d	09 27			10 22	11 27	12 22		13 27		13 57	14 23		15 27	16 20	16 24		17 27
Freshford	d				10 32		12 32				14 08	14 33				16 35		
Avoncliff	d				10x34		12x34				14x11	14x36				16x37		
Bradford-on-Avon	d	09 39			10 38	11 39	12 38		13 39		14 14	14 39		15 39	16 31	16 41		17 39
Trowbridge	d	09 45			10 44	11 46	12 44		13 46		14 20	14 45		15 45	16 37	16 47		17 45
Plymouth	d				08 40		10 40		11 45					13 44		14b06		15 43
Exeter St Davids 6	d	08 38			09 49		11 47		12 51			13b18		14 46		15b20		16 45
Westbury	a	09 53	10 22		10 51	11 53	12 51	13 01	13 53	14 17	14 29	14 52		15 52	16 44	16 54	17 22	17 52
	d	09 55			11 00	12 03	12 57	13 03	14 03		14 30	15 00		15 58	16 46	16 58	17 24	18 00
Frome	d										14c49							
Bruton	d										15 00							
Castle Cary	a			11 33				13 19			15 05		15 34				17 40	
	d										15 06							
Yeovil Pen Mill	d										15 19							
Thornford	d										15x24							
Yetminster	d										15x27							
Chetnole	d										15x31							
Maiden Newton	d										15 43							
Dorchester West	d										15 53							
Upwey	a										15 59							
Weymouth	a										16 05							
Dilton Marsh	d	09x58				12x06			14x06					16x01		17x01		
Warminster	d	10 04			11 07	12 12	13 04		14 12			15 07		16 07	16 53	17 07		18 07
Salisbury	a	10 28			11 29	12 34	13 27		14 39			15 30		16 30	17 16	17 30		18 30
	d	10 31			11 31	12 36	13 29		14 48			15 31		16 31		17 31		18 31
Romsey	d	10 50			11 49	12 56	13 47		15 10			15 51		16 49		17 49		18 49
Southampton Central	a	11 00			12 04	13 06	13 58		15 20			16 05		17 04		18 04		19 04
Bournemouth	a	12 23			13 23	14 23	14 35		16 23			17 23		18 23		19 23		
Fareham	a	11 25			12 28	13 33	14 22		15 50			16 28		17 28		18 28		19 28
	d	11 26			12 29	13 34	14 23		15 51			16 29		17 29		18 29		19 29
Cosham	a	11 33			12 37	13 41	14 31		16 00			16 37		17 37		18 37		19 37
Fratton	a	11 40			12 44	14 04	14 38		16 30			16 44		17 44		18 44		19 44
Portsmouth & Southsea	a	11 44			12 47	14 08	14 41		16 33			16 47		17 47		18 47		19 47
Portsmouth Harbour	a	11 53			12 53	14 13	14 48		16 53			16 53		17 53		18 51		19 53
Havant	a	11e59			12e59	14 03	14e59		16 11			16e59		17e59		18e59		19e59
Chichester 4	a	12e14			13e14	14 19	15e14		16 22			17e14		18e14		19e14		20e14
Barnham	a	12e22			13e22	14 27	15e22		16 30			17e22		18e22		19e22		20e22
Worthing 4	a	12e37			13e37	14 44	15e37		16 45			17e37		18e37		19e37		20e37
Shoreham-by-Sea	a	12e47			13e47	14 51	15e47		16 51			17e47		18e47		19e47		20e47
Hove 2	a	12e53			13e53	14 59	15e53		16 58			17e53		18e53		19e53		20e53
Brighton 10	a	13f00			14f00	15 06	16f00		17 05			18f00		19f00		20f00		21f00

For general notes see front of timetable
For details of catering facilities see Directory of Train Operators

A To London Waterloo (Table 160)
b Change at Salisbury
c Arr. 1439
e Change at Fratton
f Change at Fratton and Hove

Table 123

Sundays

from 13 September

South Wales and Bristol → Weymouth and Portsmouth

Network Diagram - see first page of Table 123

		GW ◇ 🍴	GW ◇ A	GW ◇ 🍴	GW	GW 1 ◇ 🍽	GW ◇ 🍴	GW ◇ 🍴	GW 1 ◇ 🍽	GW ◇ 🍴	GW 1 ◇ 🍽	GW ◇	GW ◇ 🍴	SW 1	GW	GW ◇ 🍴
Swansea 7	d	15 30		15 59				16 59		17 59			18 59			20 35
Cardiff Central 7	d	16 40		17 15			17 45	18 15		19 15			20 15			22 05
Newport (South Wales)	d	16 54		17 29			17 59	18 29		19 29			20 29			22 24
Severn Tunnel Jn	d			17 39				18 39					20 39			22 41
Filton Abbey Wood	d	17 17		17 54			18 22	18 56		19 52		19 59	20 54			22 58
Bristol Temple Meads 10	d	17 40	17 44	18 10			18 50	19 10		20 10		20 50	21 10	21 35	22 15	23 10
Keynsham	d		17 51	18 17				19 17				20 57			22 22	
Oldfield Park	d		17 58	18 24				19 24				21 04			22 29	
London Paddington 15 ⊖	d	*16 03*			*17 03*	17 57	*17 03*	*17 30*	18 57	*18 03*	19 57	*19 03*	*19 30*	*20 03*		*21 03*
Swindon	d	*17 11*			18 31		*18 11*	*18 33*		*19 11*		*20 11*	*20 34*	*21 11*		*22 14*
Chippenham	d	*17 26*			18 47		*18 26*	*18 52*		*19 26*		*20 26*	*20 49*	*21 26*		*22 28*
Melksham	d				18 57											
Bath Spa 7	d	17 52	18 01	18 27			19 02	19 27		20 22		21 07	21 23	21 49	22 32	23 22
Freshford	d		18 11							20 32		21 18			22 43	
Avoncliff	d		18x14							20x34		21x21			22x46	
Bradford-on-Avon	d	18 04	18 17	18 39			19 14	19 39		20 38		21 24	21 34	22 00	22 49	23 34
Trowbridge	d	18 11	18 23	18 45	19 06		19 20	19 45		20 44		21 30	21 40	22 06	22 55	23 40
Plymouth	d			*16b02*			*16 45*			*18 10*		*19c15*	*19 15*			
Exeter St Davids 6	d			*17b18*			*17 47*			*19b20*		*20c20*	*20 20*			
Westbury	a	18 18	18 30	18 54	19 13	19 26	19 27	19 52		20 51	21 27	21 37	21 47	22 13	23 02	23 47
	d	18 19	18 30	18 58			19 29	19 53		20 55	21 28	21 38	21 55	22 15		23 50
Frome	d		18 39									21 48				
Bruton	d		18 51									21 59				
Castle Cary	a		18 56						20 29		21 45	22 04				
	d		19 00									22 05				
Yeovil Pen Mill	d		19 14									22 18				
Thornford	d		19x18									22x23				
Yetminster	d		19x21									22x26				
Chetnole	d		19x25									22x30				
Maiden Newton	d		19 37									22 42				
Dorchester West	d		19 48									22 52				
Upwey	a		19 55									22 58				
Weymouth	a		20 01									23 03				
Dilton Marsh	d	18x22						19x56								23x53
Warminster	d	18 28		19 05			19 37	20 02		21 02			22 02	22 22		23a59
Salisbury	a	18 53		19 29			19 59	20 25		21 25			22 25	22 46		
	d	18 57		19 30			20 00	20 30		21 29			22 29			
Romsey	d	19 15		19 48			20 19	20 48		21 47			22 48			
Southampton Central	a	19 26		19 58			20 29	20 59		21 58			22 59			
Bournemouth	a	*20 23*		*20 35*			*21 23*	*22 23*		*22 35*			*00 21*			
Fareham	a	19 48		20 23			20 54	21 22		22 22			23 21			
	d	19 49		20 24			20 55	21 23		22 23			23 22			
Cosham	a	19 58		*20 54*			*21 19*	*21 54*		*22 54*			*23 54*			
Fratton	a	*20 30*		20 39			21 09	21 36		22 36			23 37			
Portsmouth & Southsea	a	*20 33*		20 43			21 15	21 39		22 39			23 40			
Portsmouth Harbour	a			20 49			21 26	21 48		22 48			23 48			
Havant	a	20 10		20e59			21e32	21e49		22e49						
Chichester 4	a	20 21		21e14			21e53	22e14		23e14						
Barnham	a	20 29		21e22			22e01	22e22		23e22						
Worthing 4	a	20 51		22e01			22e29	23e01								
Shoreham-by-Sea	a	20 57		22e11			22e39	23e11								
Hove 2	a	21 04		22e23			22e51	23e24								
Brighton 10	a	21 10		22e27			22e56	23e29								

For general notes see front of timetable
For details of catering facilities see Directory of Train Operators

A From Weston-super-Mare (Table 134)
b Change at Salisbury
c Change at Castle Cary
e Change at Fratton

Portsmouth and Weymouth → Bristol and South Wales

Network Diagram - see first page of Table 123

Miles	Miles	Miles	Station		GW	GW	GW	GW	GW	GW	GW	SW	GW	GW	GW	GW	GW	GW	GW	GW	GW	GW	GW	GW
						1 ◇	1 ◇	A		B	1 ◇	1	◇ C	D	◇	1 ◇	◇	◇ C	A	◇	◇ D	1 ◇	◇	◇ A
						⊡	⊡				⊡				⊼	⊡	⊼			⊼		⊡	⊼	
—	—	—	Brighton 10	d																05b30			07b06	
—	—	—	Hove 2	d																05b34			07b10	
—	—	—	Shoreham-by-Sea	d																05b45			07b16	
—	—	—	Worthing 4	d																05b55			07b23	
—	—	—	Barnham	d											05c20					06b18			07b44	
—	—	—	Chichester 4	d											05c28					06b26			07b52	
—	—	—	Havant	d											05c39					06b40			08b03	
0	—	—	**Portsmouth Harbour**	d											06 00					06 51			08 22	
¾	—	—	Portsmouth & Southsea	d											06 04					06 55			08 27	
1¾	—	—	Fratton	d											06 08					06 59			08 31	
5½	—	—	Cosham	d											06 15					07 07	07 38		08 39	
11¼	—	—	Fareham	a											06 23					07 17			08 46	
—	—	—		d											06 24					07 18	07 47		08 47	
—	—	—	Bournemouth	d											05e57					06 56	07 30		08 10	
25¾	—	—	**Southampton Central**	d											06 46					07 47	08 23		09 10	
34	—	—	Romsey	d											07 00					08 00	08 35		09 21	
50½	—	—	**Salisbury**	a											07 18					08 20	09 00		09 40	
—	—	—		d				06 04				06 40			07 19					08 21	09 03		09 41	
70¼	—	—	Warminster	d				06 25				07 00		07 23	07 39					08 41	09 23		10 01	
73½	—	—	Dilton Marsh	d				06x29						07x27	07x44						09x28			
—	0	—	**Weymouth**	d									05 35					06 40						08 50
—	2½	—	Upwey	d									05 40					06 45						08 55
—	7	—	Dorchester West	d									05 49					06 53						09 04
—	14¾	—	Maiden Newton	d									06 00					07f05						09 15
—	21¼	—	Chetnole	d									06x08					07x12						09x23
—	23½	—	Yetminster	d									06x11					07x15						09x26
—	24¼	—	Thornford	d									06x13					07x18						09x28
—	27½	—	Yeovil Pen Mill	d									06 21					07g31						09 36
—	39¼	—	Castle Cary	a									06 33					07 43						09 48
—	—	—		d							06 38		06 46			07 30		07 43				09 40		09 51
—	42¾	—	Bruton	d									06 52					07 49						09 57
—	53¼	—	Frome	d			06 07		06 46				07 05					08 02						10h15
75	59	0	**Westbury**	a			06 17	06 33	06 55		07 01	07 06	07 14	07 32	07 46	07 48	←	08 15		08 47	09 33	09 58	10 07	10 25
—	—	—		d	05 58	06 08	06 18	06 34	06 55	07 02	07 05	07 07	07 18	07 38	07 54	07 51	07 54	08 17	08 45	08 54	09 38	09 59	10 08	10 38
—	—	—	Exeter St Davids 6	a											→					10j32	11 12		11j42	11k12
—	—	—	Plymouth	a																11m56	12n25		12m56	12q25
79	63	4	Trowbridge	d	06 04			06 40	07 01	07 08		07 13	07 24	07 44			08 00	08 23	08 51	09 00	09 44		10 14	10 44
82¼	66¼	—	Bradford-on-Avon	d	06 10			06 46	07 07			07 20	07 30	07 50			08 06	08 29	08 57	09 08	09 50		10 20	10 50
83½	67½	—	Avoncliff	d	06x12			06x48	07x09				07x32	07x52				08x31	08x59		09x52			10x52
84½	68½	—	Freshford	d	06 15			06 51	07 13				07 36	07 55			08 10	08 34	09 02		09 55			10 55
91½	75½	—	Bath Spa 7	a	06 26			07 02	07 24			07 32	07 47	08 06			08 21	08 45	09 13	09 20	10 06		10 33	11 06
—	—	9½	Melksham	d						07 17														
—	—	15¾	Chippenham	a	06 54					07 30		07 54		08 24			08 44	09 24		09 54	10 25		10 54	11 24
—	—	32½	Swindon	a	07 09					07 48		08 09		08 40			09 04	09 39		10 09	10 41		11 09	11 39
—	—	—	London Paddington 15 ⊖	a	08 15	07 52	08 11			09 06	08 38	09 15		09 45		09 21	10 15	10 42		11 15	11 42	11 23	12 15	12 42
92½	76½	—	Oldfield Park	a	06 30			07 06	07 28			07 36	07 51	08 10			08 24	08 49	09 17		10 10			11 10
98½	82½	—	Keynsham	a	06 37			07 13	07 35			07 43	07 57	08 17			08 32	08 56	09 24	09 30	10 17			11 17
103	87	—	**Bristol Temple Meads 10**	a	06 45			07 21	07 45			07 52	08 06	08 29			08 39	09 04	09 35	09 39	10 29		10 47	11 29
107½	91½	—	Filton Abbey Wood	a	07 02			07 44	08 00				08 21	08 48			09 01	09 20	09 48	10 01	10 48		11 01	11 48
119½	119½	—	Severn Tunnel Jn	a	07 14								08r48					09r46		10r46			11r46	
129½	113½	—	Newport (South Wales)	a	07 27				08 26				09r01				09 25	09r58		10 23			11 26	
141¼	125¼	—	**Cardiff Central 7**	a	07 45				08 46				09t23				09 43	10r18		10 42			11 44	
—	—	—	Swansea 7	a	08 49				09v47								10v45			11v45			12v47	

For general notes see front of timetable
For details of catering facilities see Directory of Train Operators

A To Gloucester (Table 134)
B To Cheltenham Spa (Table 125)
C To Bristol Parkway (Table 132)
D To Great Malvern (Table 71)
b Change at Fareham
c Change at Fratton
e From 28 September dep. 0554
f Arr. 0702
g Arr. 0727
h Arr. 1009
j Change at Salisbury
k Change at Castle Cary
m Change at Salisbury and Exeter St Davids
n Change at Westbury and Exeter St Davids
q Change at Castle Cary and Exeter St Davids
r Change at Bristol Temple Meads
t Change at Bristol Parkway
v Change at Newport (South Wales)

Portsmouth and Weymouth → Bristol and South Wales

Network Diagram - see first page of Table 123

		GW	GW	GW	SW	GW	GW	GW	GW	GW	GW	GW	GW	SW	GW	GW	GW	GW	GW	GW	GW	GW	GW	GW
			1 ◇	◇	1 ◇	◇	◇	◇	1 ◇	◇		◇	◇	1 ◇	◇	1 ◇	◇		◇	1 ◇	◇	◇		◇
					A	B		C			D	E		A	C			B		G	C		B	
			⊡	⊥			⊥		⊡	⊥			⊥			✕	⊥		⊥	⊡		⊥		⊥
Brighton 10	d			08b07		09 00	09c03			10c03			11c03				12c03		13c03			14c03		15c03
Hove 2	d			08b11		09 04	09c07			10c07			11c07				12c07		13c07			14c07		15c07
Shoreham-by-Sea	d			08b20		09 13	09c17			10c16			11c16				12c16		13c16			14c16		15c16
Worthing 4	d			08b28		09 22	09c25			10c25			11c25				12c25		13c25			14c25		15c25
Barnham	d			09e00		09 38	09e58			10e57			11e57				12e57		13e57			14e57		15e57
Chichester 4	d			09e08		09 47	10e06			11e05			12e05				13e05		14e05			15e05		16e05
Havant	d			09e23		09 59	10e20			11e19			12e19				13e19		14e19			15e19		16e19
Portsmouth Harbour	d			09 22		09 33	10 22			11 22			12 22				13 22		14 22			15 22		16 22
Portsmouth & Southsea	d			09 27		09 38	10 27			11 27			12 27				13 27		14 27			15 27		16 27
Fratton	d			09 31		09 43	10 31			11 31			12 31				13 31		14 31			15 31		16 31
Cosham	d			09 39		10 05	10 39			11 39		11 46	12 39				13 39		14 39			15 39		16 39
Fareham	a			09 46		10 14	10 46			11 46			12 46				13 46		14 46			15 46		16 46
	d			09 47		10 14	10 47			11 47		11 54	12 47				13 47		14 47			15 47		16 47
Bournemouth	d			09 18		09 55	10 22			11 22		11 45	12 22				13 22		14 22			15 22		16 22
Southampton Central	d			10 10		10 42	11 10			12 10		12 26	13 10				14 10		15 10			16 10		17 10
Romsey	d			10 21		10 54	11 21			12 21		12 39	13 21				14 21		15 21			16 21		17 21
Salisbury	a			10 40		11 13	11 40			12 40		13 02	13 40				14 40		15 40			16 40		17 40
	d			10 41	10 52	11 14	11 41			12 41		13 06	13 41	13 52			14 41		15 41			16 41		17 41
Warminster	d	10 25		11 01	11 12	11 33	12 01			13 01		13 31	14 01	14 12			15 01	15 28	16 01			17 01	17 28	18 01
Dilton Marsh	d	10x29										13x35						15x32					17x32	
Weymouth	d							11 10							13 10						15 10			
Upwey	d							11 16							13 16						15 16			
Dorchester West	d							11 24							13 25						15 25			
Maiden Newton	d							11 42							13f43						15 36			
Chetnole	d							11x49							13x50						15x45			
Yetminster	d							11x52							13x53						15x48			
Thornford	d							11x55							13x56						15x50			
Yeovil Pen Mill	d							12 03							14 04						15 57			
Castle Cary	a							12 14							14 16						16 09			
	d							12 22	12 45						14 16	14 44				15 41	16 10			
Bruton	d							12 27							14 22						16 16			
Frome	d							12 39							14 35					15 56	16 29			
Westbury	a	10 33		11 07	11 18	11 38	12 07	12g48	13 04	13 07		13 39	14 07	14 18	14 44	15 02	15 07	15 36	16 07	16 06	16 38	17 07	17 36	18 08
	d		11 03	11 08	11 19	11 38	12 08	12 49	13 05	13 08	13 38	13 42	14 08	14 19	14 45	15 03	15 08	15 38	16 07	16 09	16 38	17 08	17 38	18 08
Exeter St Davids 6	a			12h29			13 32	13j32					15h42						17 34		17j34		19 17	19h57
Plymouth	a			13k48			14 39	14j39					16k56						18 38		18j38		20m25	21m17
Trowbridge	d			11 14	11 25	11 44	12 14	12 55		13 14	13 44	13 51	14 14	14 25	14 51		15 14	15 44	16 14		16 44	17 14	17 44	18 14
Bradford-on-Avon	d			11 20	11 31	11 50	12 20	13 01		13 20	13 50	13 57	14 20	14 31	14 57		15 20	15 50	16 20		16 50	17 20	17 50	18 20
Avoncliff	d					11x52		13x03			13x52	13x59			14x59			15x52			16x52		17x52	
Freshford	d					11 55		13 05			13 55	14 02			15 02			15 55			16 55		17 55	
Bath Spa 7	a			11 33	11 45	12 06	12 33	13 17		13 33	14 06	14 13	14 33	14 45	15 13		15 33	16 05	16 33		17 06	17 33	18 06	18 35
Melksham	d																							
Chippenham	a			11 54		12 24	12 54			13 54	14 24		14 54	15 24			15 54	16 24	16 54		17 24	17 54	18 24	18 54
Swindon	a			12 09		12 40	13 09			14 09	14 39		15 09	15 39			16 09	16 39	17 09		17 39	18 09	18 39	19 09
London Paddington 15 ⊖	a		12 25	13 15		13 42	14 15		14 44	15 15	15 42		16 15	16 45		16 21	17 15	17 42	18 15	17 54	18 45	19 15	19 42	20 15
Oldfield Park	a					12 10		13 20				14 17			15 17			16 09			17 10		18 10	
Keynsham	a					12 17		13 27				14 25			15 24			16 17			17 17		18 16	
Bristol Temple Meads 10	a			11 47	12 05	12 29	12 47	13 36		13 47		14 35	14 47	15 05	15 34		15 47	16 29	16 47		17 29	17 47	18 28	18 50
Filton Abbey Wood	a			12 01	12 29	12 48	13 01	13 48		14 01	14 29	14 47	15 01	15 30	15 48		16 01	16 48	17 01		17 48	18 01	18 48	19 01
Severn Tunnel Jn	a				12 45		13n46			14n50				15 46			16n46		17 13			18 14		19 13
Newport (South Wales)	a			12 24	13 01		13 25			14 24			15 25	15 58			16 24		17 27			18 27		19 27
Cardiff Central 7	a			12 42	13 24		13 44			14 45			15 43	16 18			16 43		17 45			18 45		19 45
Swansea 7	a			13q45			14q45			15q45			16q47				17q44		19 01			19 55		20 49

For general notes see front of timetable
For details of catering facilities see Directory of Train Operators

- A From London Waterloo (Table 160)
- B To Great Malvern (Table 71)
- C To Gloucester (Table 134)
- D To Bristol Parkway (Table 134)
- E To Worcester Foregate Street (Table 71)
- G From Taunton (Table 135)
- b Change at Barnham and Fareham
- c Change at Fratton
- e Change at Fareham
- f Arr. 1334
- g Arr. 1133
- h Change at Salisbury
- j Change at Castle Cary
- k Change at Salisbury and Exeter St Davids
- m Change at Westbury and Exeter St Davids
- n Change at Bristol Temple Meads
- q Change at Newport (South Wales)

Table 123

Mondays to Fridays

Portsmouth and Weymouth → Bristol and South Wales

Network Diagram - see first page of Table 123

		GW A	GW FX ◇ ⊼	GW FO ◇ ⊼	GW ◇	GW [1] ⊏	GW [1] ◇ ⊏	GW ◇	GW B	GW ◇ C	GW ◇ ⊼	GW [1]	GW	GW [1] ◇ ⊏	GW ◇	GW	SW [1] ◇	GW ◇	GW ◇	GW	GW	GW
Brighton [10]	d		16b03	16b03						17 00	17b03				18b00				19b00			20b03
Hove [2]	d		16b07	16b07						17 04	17b07				18b04				19b04			20b07
Shoreham-by-Sea	d		16b16	16b16						17 13	17b16				18b16				19b16			20b19
Worthing [4]	d		16b25	16b25						17 22	17b25				18b27				19b26			20b29
Barnham	d		16c57	16c57						17 39	17c57				18c54				19c53			20b51
Chichester [4]	d		17c05	17c05						17 47	18c05				19c02				20c01			20b59
Havant	d		17c19	17c19						17 58	18c22				19c20				20c22			21b10
Portsmouth Harbour	d		17 22	17 22						17 33	18 22				19 22				20 22			21 22
Portsmouth & Southsea	d		17 27	17 27						17 38	18 27				19 27				20 27			21 27
Fratton	d		17 31	17 31						17 43	18 31				19 31				20 31			21 31
Cosham	d		17 39	17 39						18 05	18 39				19 39				20 29			21e44
Fareham	a		17 46	17 46						18 12	18 46				19 46				20 46			21 46
	d		17 47	17 47						18 13	18 47				19 47				20 47			21 47
Bournemouth	d		17 22	17 22						17 59	18 22				19 22				20 22			21 12
Southampton Central	d		18 10	18 10						18 42	19 10				20 10				21 10	21 20		22 22
Romsey	d		18 21	18 21						18 54	19 21				20 21				21 21	21 31		22 33
Salisbury	a		18 40	18 40						19 12	19 40				20 40				21 40	21 51		22 58
	d		18 41	18 41						19 13	19 41				20 41		20 57		21 41	21 53		23 00
Warminster	d		19 01	19 01						19 32	20 01				21 01		21 17		22 01	22 15		23 20
Dilton Marsh	d									19x37										22x20		23x24
Weymouth	d				17 30													20 24				
Upwey	d				17 35													20 29				
Dorchester West	d				17 45													20 37				
Maiden Newton	d				17 56													20 49				
Chetnole	d				18x04													20x56				
Yetminster	d				18x07													20x59				
Thornford	d				18x09													21x02				
Yeovil Pen Mill	d				18 19													21 10				
Castle Cary	a				18 35													21 22				
	d				18 36	18 53		←						20 45				21 22				
Bruton	d				18 42			18 42										21 28				
Frome	d							19f05				20 18				21 01		21 41				
Westbury	a		19 08	19 08		19 11		19 17		19 40	20 08	20 29		21 03	21 08	21 11	21 23	21 51	22 07	22 25		23 30
	d	18 38	19 08	19 08		19 11	19 17	19 17	19 32	19 41	20 08		20 38	21 04	21 08		21 24	21 55	22 08		22 32	
Exeter St Davids [6]	a		20g36	20g36	20h10					21 16	21g54						23j20	22k39				
Plymouth	a		21m48	21m48	21n17						23q38						00r25	23t55				
Trowbridge	d	18 44	19 14	19 14	→			19 23	19 38	19 47	20 14		20 44		21 14		21 30	22 01	22 14		22 38	
Bradford-on-Avon	d	18 50	19 20	19 20				19 29		19 53	20 20		20 50		21 20		21 36	22 07	22 20		22 44	
Avoncliff	d	18x52						19x31		19x55			20x52					22x09			22x46	
Freshford	d	18 55						19 35		19 57			20 55					22 13			22 49	
Bath Spa [7]	a	19 06	19 35	19 35				19 46		20 10	20 35		21 06		21 35		21 50	22 24	22 33		23 00	
Melksham	d								19 47													
Chippenham	a		19 54	19 54					20 01		20 54						22 09		22 57			
Swindon	a		20 09	20 09					20 21		21 09						22 25		23 14			
London Paddington [15] ⊖	a		21 15	21 15		20 39	21 01		21 32		22 15			22 30			23v37		00 33			
Oldfield Park	a	19 10						19 50		20 12			21 10					22 28			23 04	
Keynsham	a	19 17						19 57		20 19			21 17				21 58	22 35			23 12	
Bristol Temple Meads [10]	a	19 29	19 49	19 49				20 05		20 29	20 50		21 29		21 50		22 06	22 45	22 47		23 21	
Filton Abbey Wood	a	19 48	20 11	20 01				20 21		20 48	21 01				22 01				23 01			
Severn Tunnel Jn	a			20 16				20 36			21w45				22 17				23 16			
Newport (South Wales)	a		20 37	20 28				20 47			21 27				22 37				23 35			
Cardiff Central [7]	a		20 56	20 46				21 07			21 45				22 59				23 58			
Swansea [7]	a		22y03	21z46				22y20			23 07				00 28				02D15			

For general notes see front of timetable
For details of catering facilities see Directory of Train Operators

- **A** To Cheltenham Spa (Table 57)
- **B** To Cheltenham Spa (Table 125)
- **C** To Worcester Shrub Hill (Table 57)
- **D** Saturday mornings arr. 0155
- **b** Change at Fratton
- **c** Change at Fareham
- **e** Change at Southampton Central
- **f** Arr. 1856
- **g** Change at Salisbury
- **h** Change at Castle Cary
- **j** From 7 September arr. 2328
- **k** Change at Castle Cary. From 7 September arr. 2219
- **m** Change at Salisbury and Exeter St Davids
- **n** Change at Castle Cary and Exeter St Davids
- **q** Change at Salisbury and Exeter St Davids. From 7 September arr. 2319
- **r** Tuesday to Saturday mornings from 8 September arr. 0035
- **t** Change at Castle Cary. From 7 September arr. 2330
- **v** Fridays arr. 2332
- **w** Change at Bristol Temple Meads
- **y** Change at Bristol Temple Meads and Cardiff Central
- **z** Change at Newport (South Wales)

Portsmouth and Weymouth → Bristol and South Wales

Network Diagram - see first page of Table 123

		GW A	GW	SW 1	GW B	GW 1 ◇ ⊏P	GW ◇	GW ◇ A	GW	GW ◇	GW C	GW 1 ◇ ⊏P	GW ◇	GW ◇ A	GW	GW 1 ⊏P	GW ◇	SW 1 ◇ D
Brighton 10	d									05b27			07c03				08c03	
Hove 2	d									05b31			07c07				08c07	
Shoreham-by-Sea	d									05b43			07c16				08c16	
Worthing 4	d									05b53			07c25				08c25	
Barnham	d						05c30			06c27			07b57				08b57	
Chichester 4	d						05c38			06c35			08b05				09b05	
Havant	d						05c49			06c46			08b20				09b19	
Portsmouth Harbour	d						06 00			07 05			08 22				09 22	
Portsmouth & Southsea	d						06 04			07 09			08 27				09 27	
Fratton	d						06 08			07 14			08 31				09 31	
Cosham	d						06 19			07 21	07 46		08 39				09 39	
Fareham	a						06 27			07 29			08 46				09 46	
	d						06 28			07 30	07 54		08 47				09 47	
Bournemouth	d						05 42			06 42	07 45		08 22				09 22	
Southampton Central	d						06 52			07 54	08 27		09 10				10 10	
Romsey	d						07 11			08 12	08 38		09 21				10 21	
Salisbury	a						07 29			08 30	09 03		09 40				10 40	
	d	06 03		06 40			07 30			08 34	09 04		09 41				10 41	10 52
Warminster	d	06 23		07 00	07 23		07 50			08 54	09 25		10 01		10 25		11 01	11 12
Dilton Marsh	d	06x27			07x28		07x54				09x29				10x30			
Weymouth	d							06 40						08 52				
Upwey	d							06 45						08 57				
Dorchester West	d							06 53						09 05				
Maiden Newton	d							07 05						09 17				
Chetnole	d							07x12						09x24				
Yetminster	d							07x15						09x27				
Thornford	d							07x18						09x30				
Yeovil Pen Mill	d							07e30						09 38				
Castle Cary	a							07 42						09 50				
	d					07 33		07 43				09 40		09 57				
Bruton	d							07 49						10 03				
Frome	d		06 37					08 02						10 17				
Westbury	a	06 33	06 46	07 06	07 31	07 51	07 58	08 12		08 58	09 33	09 58	10 07	10 27	10 33		11 07	11 18
	d	06 38	06 51	07 07	07 38	07 56	08 02	08 17	09 03	09 08	09 38	09 59	10 08	10 38		11 02	11 08	11 19
Exeter St Davids 6	a									10f29	11 04		12f01	11g04			12f30	
Plymouth	a									11h56	12j26		13h14	12k26			13h48	
Trowbridge	d	06 44	06 57	07 13	07 44		08 08	08 23	09 09	09 14	09 44		10 14	10 44			11 14	11 25
Bradford-on-Avon	d	06 49	07 03	07 19	07 50		08 14	08 29		09 20	09 50		10 20	10 50			11 20	11 31
Avoncliff	d	06x51	07x05		07x52			08x32			09x52			10x52				
Freshford	d	06 55	07 09		07 55			08 34			09 55			10 55				
Bath Spa 7	a	07 06	07 20	07 32	08 07		08 31	08 45		09 33	10 07		10 34	11 08			11 33	11 45
Melksham	d								09 18									
Chippenham	a	07 24		07 54			08 54	09 24	09 30	09 54			10 54				11 54	12 24
Swindon	a	07 40		08 09			09 09	09 39	09 49	10 09			11 09				12 09	12 40
London Paddington 15	⊖ a	08 45		09 15		09 21	10 15	10 42	11 08	11 15		11 24	12 15			12 23	13 22	13 42
Oldfield Park	a	07 10	07 24	07 36	08 10			08 49			10 10			11 10				
Keynsham	a	07 17	07 31	07 43	08 17			08 56			10 17			11 17				
Bristol Temple Meads 10	a	07 29	07 39	07 52	08 30		08 45	09 05		09 47	10 29		10 48	11 29			11 47	12 00
Filton Abbey Wood	a	07 48	08 01	08 31	08 48		09 01	09 45		10 01	10 48		11 01	11 48			12 01	12 31
Severn Tunnel Jn	a			08 47				09m46		10m47			11m46					12 46
Newport (South Wales)	a		08 26	09 00			09 24	09m59		10 23			11 24				12 23	13 00
Cardiff Central 7	a		08 45	09 21			09 42	10m16		10 42			11 43	12m41			12 41	13 21
Swansea 7	a		09 56				10n45			11n45			12n45	13q45			13 45	

For general notes see front of timetable
For details of catering facilities see Directory of Train Operators

- **A** To Gloucester (Table 134)
- **B** To Great Malvern (Table 71)
- **C** To Worcester Foregate Street (Table 71)
- **D** From London Waterloo (Table 160)
- **b** Change at Fareham
- **c** Change at Fratton
- **e** Arr. 0724
- **f** Change at Salisbury
- **g** Change at Castle Cary
- **h** Change at Salisbury and Exeter St Davids
- **j** Change at Westbury and Exeter St Davids
- **k** Change at Castle Cary and Exeter St Davids
- **m** Change at Bristol Temple Meads
- **n** Change at Newport (South Wales)
- **q** Change at Bristol Temple Meads and Cardiff Central

Table 123

Saturdays
until 5 September

Portsmouth and Weymouth → Bristol and South Wales

Network Diagram - see first page of Table 123

		GW ◇ A	GW 1 ☕	GW ◇	GW ◇ B	GW ◇	GW A	GW ◇	SW 1 ◇ C	GW ◇ B	GW	GW ◇	GW 1 ☕	GW A	GW ◇	GW ◇ B	GW 1 ☕	GW ◇
Brighton 10	d	09 00		09b03		10b03		11b03				12b03			13b03			14b03
Hove 2	d	09 04		09b07		10b07		11b07				12b07			13b07			14b07
Shoreham-by-Sea	d	09 13		09b17		10b16		11b16				12b16			13b16			14b16
Worthing 4	d	09 22		09b25		10b25		11b25				12b25			13b25			14b25
Barnham	d	09 41		09c57		10c57		11c57				12c57			13c57			14c57
Chichester 4	d	09 49		10c05		11c05		12c05				13c05			14c05			15c05
Havant	d	10 00		10c19		11c19		12c19				13c19			14c19			15c19
Portsmouth Harbour	d	09e29		10 22		11 22		12 22				13 22			14 22			15 22
Portsmouth & Southsea	d	09 38		10 27		11 27		12 27				13 27			14 27			15 27
Fratton	d	09 43		10 31		11 31		12 31				13 31			14 31			15 31
Cosham	d	10 06		10 39		11 39	11 46	12 39				13 39			14 39			15 39
Fareham	a	10 15		10 46		11 46		12 46				13 46			14 46			15 46
	d	10 16		10 47		11 47	11 54	12 47				13 47			14 47			15 47
Bournemouth	d	09 59		10 22		11 22	11 45	12 22				13 22			14 22			15 22
Southampton Central	d	10 42		11 10		12 10	12 27	13 10				14 10			15 10			16 10
Romsey	d	10 53		11 21		12 21	12 38	13 21				14 21			15 21			16 21
Salisbury	a	11 13		11 40		12 40	13 03	13 40				14 40			15 40			16 40
	d	11 13		11 41		12 41	13 04	13 41	13 52			14 41			15 41			16 41
Warminster	d	11 34		12 01		13 01	13 25	14 01	14 12			15 01		15 28	16 01	16 28		17 01
Dilton Marsh	d						13x29							15x33		16x33		
Weymouth	d				11 10					13 10								
Upwey	d				11 15					13 15								
Dorchester West	d				11 26					13 24								
Maiden Newton	d				11f41					13g44								
Chetnole	d				11x49					13x51								
Yetminster	d				11x52					13x54								
Thornford	d				11x54					13x57								
Yeovil Pen Mill	d				12 02					14 05								
Castle Cary	a				12 14					14 17								
	d		11 23		12 22					14 18			15 08				16 18	
Bruton	d				12 27					14 24								
Frome	d				12 40					14 37								
Westbury	a	11 38	11 41	12 07	12 49	13 07	13 33	14 07	14 18	14 47		15 07	15 26	15 36	16 07	16 36	16 36	17 07
	d	11 38	11 43	12 08	12 52	13 08	13 38	14 08	14 19	14 48	15 05	15 08	15 28	15 38	16 08	16 38	16 38	17 08
Exeter St Davids 6	a	13 06		13h42		14h26	15 06	15h42							17 33			
Plymouth	a	14j23		15k11		15m48	16j25	16h58							18 38			
Trowbridge	d	11 44		12 14	12 58	13 14	13 44	14 14	14 25	14 54	15 11	15 14		15 44	16 14	16 44		17 14
Bradford-on-Avon	d	11 50		12 20	13 04	13 20	13 50	14 20	14 31	15 00		15 20		15 50	16 20	16 50		17 20
Avoncliff	d	11x52					13x52			15x02				15x52		16x52		
Freshford	d	11 55					13 55			15 06				15 55		16 55		
Bath Spa 7	a	12 08		12 33	13 16	13 33	14 08	14 33	14 45	15 17		15 34		16 07	16 33	17 07		17 33
Melksham	d										15 20							
Chippenham	a			12 54		13 54		14 54	15 24		15 28	15 54			16 54			17 54
Swindon	a			13 09		14 09		15 09	15 39		15 48	16 10			17 09			18 09
London Paddington 15 ⊖	a		13 14	14 15		15 15		16 15	16 42		17 06	17 15	16 59		18 15		18 08	19 15
Oldfield Park	a	12 10			13 20		14 10			15 21				16 10		17 10		
Keynsham	a	12 17			13 27		14 17			15 28				16 17		17 17		
Bristol Temple Meads 10	a	12 29		12 47	13 36	13 47	14 29	14 47	15 05	15 35		15 48		16 30	16 47	17 29		17 47
Filton Abbey Wood	a	12 48		13 01	13 48	14 01	14 48	15 01	15 30	15 48		16 01		16 48	17 01	17 48		18 01
Severn Tunnel Jn	a			13n46		14n47			15 49			16n47			17 14			18 13
Newport (South Wales)	a			13 25		14 23		15 24	16 01			16 23			17 26			18 25
Cardiff Central 7	a			13 42		14 43		15 42	16 18			16 41			17 45			18 43
Swansea 7	a			14q45		15q45		16q45				17 45			18q47			19q45

For general notes see front of timetable
For details of catering facilities see Directory of Train Operators

A To Great Malvern (Table 71)
B To Gloucester (Table 134)
C From London Waterloo (Table 160)
b Change at Fratton
c Change at Fareham
e Change at Fratton and Cosham
f Arr. 1135
g Arr. 1333
h Change at Salisbury
j Change at Westbury and Exeter St Davids
k Change at Salisbury and Exeter St Davids. Until 20 June arr. 1453
m Change at Salisbury and Exeter St Davids
n Change at Bristol Temple Meads
q Change at Newport (South Wales)

Portsmouth and Weymouth → Bristol and South Wales

Network Diagram - see first page of Table 123

		GW ◇ A	GW ◇	GW ◇	GW ◇	GW 1 ◇ (catering)	GW ◇	GW B	GW 1 ◇ (catering)	GW ◇	GW	GW 1	GW ◇	SW 1 ◇ C	GW ◇	GW ◇	GW
Brighton 10	d		15b03		16b03			17 00		17b03			18b03			19b03	
Hove 2	d		15b07		16b07			17 04		17b07			18b07			19b07	
Shoreham-by-Sea	d		15b16		16b16			17 13		17b17			18b16			19b19	
Worthing 4	d		15b25		16b25			17 22		17b25			18b25			19b29	
Barnham	d		15c57		16c57			17 38		17c57			18c57			19c57	
Chichester 4	d		16c05		17c05			17 46		18c05			19c05			20c05	
Havant	d		16c19		17c19			18 00		18c19			19c19			20c26	
Portsmouth Harbour	d		16 22		17 22			17 33		18 22			19 22			20 22	
Portsmouth & Southsea	d		16 27		17 27			17 38		18 27			19 27			20 27	
Fratton	d		16 31		17 31			17 43		18 31			19 31			20 31	
Cosham	d		16 39		17 39			18 06		18 39			19 39			20 32	20 46
Fareham	a		16 46		17 46			18 14		18 46			19 46			20 44	
	d		16 47		17 47			18 15		18 47			19 47			20 48	20 54
Bournemouth	d		16 22		17 22			17 59		18 22			19 22			20 22	
Southampton Central	d		17 10		18 10			18 45		19 10			20 10			21 12	21 27
Romsey	d		17 21		18 21			18 56		19 21			20 21			21 23	21 38
Salisbury	a		17 40		18 40			19 15		19 40			20 40			21 42	22 03
	d		17 41		18 41			19 16		19 41			20 41	20 57		21 43	22 04
Warminster	d		18 01		19 01			19 37		20 01			21 01	21 17		22 03	22 25
Dilton Marsh	d							19x42									22x29
Weymouth	d	16 10		17 30											20 24		
Upwey	d	16 15		17 35											20 29		
Dorchester West	d	16 26		17 44											20 37		
Maiden Newton	d	16e42		17 55											20 49		
Chetnole	d	16x49		18x03											20x56		
Yetminster	d	16x52		18x06											20x59		
Thornford	d	16x55		18x08											21x02		
Yeovil Pen Mill	d	17 03		18f24											21 10		
Castle Cary	a	17 15		18 36											21 22		
	d	17 15		18 42		18 53	←		19 47						21 22		
Bruton	d	17 21		18 48			18 48								21 28		
Frome	d	17 34					19g06					20 53			21 41		
Westbury	a	17 43	18 07		19 07	19 11	19 16	19 45	20 05	20 07		21 02	21 07	21 23	21 51	22 08	22 33
	d	17 44	18 08		19 08	19 12	19 17	19 48	20 06	20 08	20 38		21 08	21 24	21 55	22 08	22 38
Exeter St Davids 6	a		19 33	19h33						21 39		22 36	22 36		22h36		
Plymouth	a		20 36	20h36						22 42		23 47	23 47		23h47		
Trowbridge	d	17 50	18 14	→	19 14		19 23	19 54		20 14	20 44		21 14	21 30	22 01	22 14	22 44
Bradford-on-Avon	d	17 56	18 20		19 20		19 29	20 00		20 20	20 50		21 20	21 36	22 07	22 20	22 50
Avoncliff	d	17x58					19x31	20x02			20x52				22x09		22x52
Freshford	d	18 01					19 34	20 05			20 55				22 13		22 55
Bath Spa 7	a	18 11	18 33		19 33		19 45	20 16		20 33	21 07		21 37	21 50	22 24	22 35	23 08
Melksham	d																
Chippenham	a		18 54		19 54					20 57				22 11		22 57	
Swindon	a		19 09		20 09					21 13				22 27		23 13	
London Paddington 15 ⊖	a		20 15		21 15	20 45			21 32	22 16				23 38		00 33	
Oldfield Park	a	18 15					19 49	20 20			21 10				22 28		23 10
Keynsham	a	18 22					19 56	20 27			21 17			21 58	22 35		23 17
Bristol Temple Meads 10	a	18 35	18 47		19 47		20 04	20 35		20 47	21 26		21 51	22 06	22 45	22 50	23 28
Filton Abbey Wood	a	18 48	19 01		20 01		20 27	20 48		21 01			22 01			23 01	
Severn Tunnel Jn	a		19j44				20 44			21j51			22 18			23 16	
Newport (South Wales)	a		19 23		20 23		20 54			21 23			22 36			23 34	
Cardiff Central 7	a		19 42		20 41		21 16			21 41			22 56			23 54	
Swansea 7	a		20 49		21 45					22 45			00 02				

For general notes see front of timetable
For details of catering facilities see Directory of Train Operators

- **A** To Great Malvern (Table 71)
- **B** To Cheltenham Spa (Table 57)
- **C** From London Waterloo (Table 160)
- **b** Change at Fratton
- **c** Change at Fareham
- **e** Arr. 1635
- **f** Arr. 1815
- **g** Arr. 1901
- **h** Change at Castle Cary
- **j** Change at Bristol Temple Meads

Table 123

Saturdays

from 12 September

Portsmouth and Weymouth → Bristol and South Wales

Network Diagram - see first page of Table 123

Station		GW	GW	SW	GW	GW	GW	GW	GW	GW	GW	GW	GW	GW	GW	GW	GW	SW
				1		**1** ◇	◇	◇		◇		**1** ◇	◇	◇		**1**	◇	**1** ◇
		A			B			A			C			A				D
						☕						☕				☕		
Brighton 10	d									05b27			07c03				08c03	
Hove 2	d									05b31			07c07				08c07	
Shoreham-by-Sea	d									05b43			07c16				08c16	
Worthing 4	d									05b53			07c25				08c25	
Barnham	d						05c30			06c27			07b57				08b57	
Chichester 4	d						05c38			06c35			08b05				09b05	
Havant	d						05c49			06c46			08b20				09b19	
Portsmouth Harbour	d						06 00			07 05			08 22				09 22	
Portsmouth & Southsea	d						06 04			07 09			08 27				09 27	
Fratton	d						06 08			07 14			08 31				09 31	
Cosham	d						06 19			07 21	07 46		08 39				09 39	
Fareham	a						06 27			07 29			08 46				09 46	
	d						06 28			07 30	07 54		08 47				09 47	
Bournemouth	d						05 42			06 42	07 45		08 22				09 22	
Southampton Central	d						06 52			07 54	08 27		09 10				10 10	
Romsey	d						07 11			08 12	08 38		09 21				10 21	
Salisbury	a						07 29			08 30	09 03		09 40				10 40	
	d	06 03		06 40			07 30			08 34	09 04		09 41				10 41	10 52
Warminster	d	06 23		07 00	07 23		07 50			08 54	09 25		10 01		10 25		11 01	11 12
Dilton Marsh	d	06x27			07x28		07x54				09x29				10x30			
Weymouth	d							06 40						08 52				
Upwey	d							06 45						08 57				
Dorchester West	d							06 53						09 05				
Maiden Newton	d							07 05						09 17				
Chetnole	d							07x12						09x24				
Yetminster	d							07x15						09x27				
Thornford	d							07x18						09x30				
Yeovil Pen Mill	d							07e30						09 38				
Castle Cary	a							07 42						09 50				
	d					07 33		07 43				09 40		09 57				
Bruton	d							07 49						10 03				
Frome	d		06 37					08 02						10 17				
Westbury	a	06 33	06 46	07 06	07 31	07 51	07 58	08 12		08 58	09 33	09 58	10 07	10 27	10 33		11 07	11 18
	d	06 38	06 51	07 07	07 38	07 56	08 02	08 17	09 03	09 08	09 38	09 59	10 08	10 38		11 02	11 08	11 19
Exeter St Davids 6	a									10f29	11 13		12f01	11g13			12f30	
Plymouth	a									11h55	12j48		13h10	12k48			13h48	
Trowbridge	d	06 44	06 57	07 13	07 44		08 08	08 23	09 09	09 14	09 44		10 14	10 44			11 14	11 25
Bradford-on-Avon	d	06 49	07 03	07 19	07 50		08 14	08 29		09 20	09 50		10 20	10 50			11 20	11 31
Avoncliff	d	06x51	07x05		07x52			08x32			09x52			10x52				
Freshford	d	06 55	07 09		07 55			08 34			09 55			10 55				
Bath Spa 7	a	07 06	07 20	07 32	08 07		08 31	08 45		09 33	10 07		10 34	11 08			11 33	11 45
Melksham	d								09 18									
Chippenham	a	07 24		07 54			08 54	09 24	09 30	09 54			10 54				11 54	12 24
Swindon	a	07 40		08 09			09 09	09 39	09 49	10 09			11 09				12 09	12 40
London Paddington 15 ⊖	a	08 45		09 15		09 21	10 15	10 42	11 02	11 15		11 24	12 15			12 23	13 15	13 42
Oldfield Park	a	07 10	07 24	07 36	08 10			08 49			10 10			11 10				
Keynsham	a	07 17	07 31	07 43	08 17			08 56			10 17			11 17				
Bristol Temple Meads 10	a	07 29	07 39	07 52	08 30		08 45	09 05		09 47	10 29		10 48	11 29			11 47	12 00
Filton Abbey Wood	a	07 48	08 01	08 31	08 48		09 01	09 45		10 01	10 48		11 01	11 48			12 01	12 31
Severn Tunnel Jn	a			08 47				09m46		10m47			11m46					12 46
Newport (South Wales)	a		08 26	09 00			09 24	09m59		10 23			11 24				12 23	13 00
Cardiff Central 7	a		08 45	09 21			09 42	10m16		10 42			11 43				12 41	13 21
Swansea 7	a		09 56				10n45			11n45			12n45				13 45	

For general notes see front of timetable
For details of catering facilities see Directory of Train Operators

- **A** To Gloucester (Table 134)
- **B** To Great Malvern (Table 71)
- **C** To Worcester Foregate Street (Table 71)
- **D** From London Waterloo (Table 160)
- **b** Change at Fareham
- **c** Change at Fratton
- **e** Arr. 0724
- **f** Change at Salisbury
- **g** Change at Castle Cary
- **h** Change at Salisbury and Exeter St Davids
- **j** Change at Westbury and Exeter St Davids
- **k** Change at Castle Cary and Exeter St Davids
- **m** Change at Bristol Temple Meads
- **n** Change at Newport (South Wales)

Saturdays

from 12 September

Portsmouth and Weymouth → Bristol and South Wales

Network Diagram - see first page of Table 123

		GW	GW	GW	GW	GW	GW	GW	SW	GW	GW	GW	GW	GW	GW	GW	GW	GW
		◇	◇	◇	1 ◇	◇		◇	1 ◇	◇	1 ◇		◇		◇	1 ◇	◇	◇
		A		B	☕		A		C	B	☕			A		D ☕	B	
Brighton 10	d	09 00	09b03			10b03		11b03					12b03		13b03			14b03
Hove 2	d	09 04	09b07			10b07		11b07					12b07		13b07			14b07
Shoreham-by-Sea	d	09 13	09b17			10b16		11b16					12b16		13b16			14b16
Worthing 4	d	09 22	09b25			10b25		11b25					12b25		13b25			14b25
Barnham	d	09 41	09c57			10c57		11c57					12c57		13c57			14c57
Chichester 4	d	09 49	10c05			11c05		12c05					13c05		14c05			15c05
Havant	d	10 00	10c19			11c19		12c19					13c19		14c19			15c19
Portsmouth Harbour	d	09e29	10 22			11 22		12 22					13 22		14 22			15 22
Portsmouth & Southsea	d	09 38	10 27			11 27		12 27					13 27		14 27			15 27
Fratton	d	09 43	10 31			11 31		12 31					13 31		14 31			15 31
Cosham	d	10 06	10 39			11 39	11 46	12 39					13 39		14 39			15 39
Fareham	a	10 15	10 46			11 46		12 46					13 46		14 46			15 46
	d	10 16	10 47			11 47	11 54	12 47					13 47		14 47			15 47
Bournemouth	d	09 59	10 22			11 22	11 45	12 22					13 22		14 22			15 22
Southampton Central	d	10 42	11 10			12 10	12 27	13 10					14 10		15 10			16 10
Romsey	d	10 53	11 21			12 21	12 38	13 21					14 21		15 21			16 21
Salisbury	a	11 13	11 40			12 40	13 03	13 40					14 40		15 40			16 40
	d	11 13	11 41			12 41	13 04	13 41	13 52				14 41		15 41			16 41
Warminster	d	11 34	12 01			13 01	13 25	14 01	14 12				15 01	15 28	16 01			17 01
Dilton Marsh	d						13x29							15x33				
Weymouth	d			11 10						13 10							15 09	
Upwey	d			11 15						13 15							15 14	
Dorchester West	d			11 26						13 24							15 22	
Maiden Newton	d			11f41						13g44							15 34	
Chetnole	d			11x49						13x51							15x41	
Yetminster	d			11x52						13x54							15x44	
Thornford	d			11x54						13x57							15x47	
Yeovil Pen Mill	d			12 02						14 05							15 55	
Castle Cary	a			12 14						14 17							16 07	
	d			12 22	12 45					14 18	14 44					16 00	16 08	
Bruton	d			12 27						14 24							16 14	
Frome	d			12 40						14 37						16 14	16 27	
Westbury	a	11 38	12 07	12 49	13 03	13 07	13 33	14 07	14 18	14 47	15 02		15 07	15 36	16 07	16 23	16 37	17 07
	d	11 38	12 08	12 52	13 05	13 08	13 38	14 08	14 19	14 48	15 03	15 05	15 08	15 38	16 08	16 25	16 38	17 08
Exeter St Davids 6	a		13 32	13h32		14j26		15j42							17 33		17h33	
Plymouth	a		14 36	14h36		15k48		16j58							18 38		18h38	
Trowbridge	d	11 44	12 14	12 58		13 14	13 44	14 14	14 25	14 54		15 11	15 14	15 44	16 14		16 44	17 14
Bradford-on-Avon	d	11 50	12 20	13 04		13 20	13 50	14 20	14 31	15 00			15 20	15 50	16 20		16 50	17 20
Avoncliff	d	11x52					13x52			15x02				15x52			16x52	
Freshford	d	11 55					13 55			15 06				15 55			16 55	
Bath Spa 7	a	12 08	12 33	13 16		13 33	14 08	14 33	14 45	15 17			15 34	16 07	16 33		17 06	17 33
Melksham	d											15 20						
Chippenham	a		12 54			13 54		14 54	15 24			15 28	15 54		16 54		17 24	17 54
Swindon	a		13 09			14 09		15 09	15 39			15 48	16 09		17 09		17 39	18 09
London Paddington 15 ⊖	a		14 15		14 45	15 15		16 15	16 42		16 23	17 06	17 15		18 15	18 08	18 42	19 15
Oldfield Park	a	12 10		13 20			14 10			15 21				16 10			17 10	
Keynsham	a	12 17		13 27			14 17			15 28				16 17			17 16	
Bristol Temple Meads 10	a	12 29	12 47	13 36		13 47	14 29	14 47	15 05	15 35			15 48	16 30	16 47		17 28	17 47
Filton Abbey Wood	a	12 48	13 01	13 48		14 01	14 48	15 01	15 30	15 48			16 01	16 48	17 01		17 48	18 01
Severn Tunnel Jn	a		13m46			14m47			15 49				16m47		17 14			18 13
Newport (South Wales)	a		13 25			14 23		15 24	16 01				16 23		17 26			18 25
Cardiff Central 7	a		13 42			14 43		15 42	16 18				16 41		17 45			18 43
Swansea 7	a		14n45			15n45		16n45					17 45		18n47			19n45

For general notes see front of timetable
For details of catering facilities see Directory of Train Operators

A To Great Malvern (Table 71)
B To Gloucester (Table 134)
C From London Waterloo (Table 160)
D From Taunton (Table 135)
b Change at Fratton
c Change at Fareham
e Change at Fratton and Cosham
f Arr. 1135
g Arr. 1333
h Change at Castle Cary
j Change at Salisbury
k Change at Salisbury and Exeter St Davids
m Change at Bristol Temple Meads
n Change at Newport (South Wales)

Saturdays

from 12 September

Portsmouth and Weymouth → Bristol and South Wales

Network Diagram - see first page of Table 123

		GW	GW	GW	GW	GW	GW	GW	GW	GW	GW	GW	GW	GW	SW	GW	GW	GW
			◇		◇	◇	[1] ◇	◇		[1] ◇	◇		[1]	◇	[1] ◇	◇	◇	
		A		B			🍴		B	🍴					C			
Brighton [10]	d		15b03			16b03			17 00		17b03			18b03			19b03	
Hove [2]	d		15b07			16b07			17 04		17b07			18b07			19b07	
Shoreham-by-Sea	d		15b16			16b16			17 13		17b17			18b16			19b19	
Worthing [4]	d		15b25			16b25			17 22		17b25			18b25			19b29	
Barnham	d		15c57			16c57			17 38		17c57			18c57			19c57	
Chichester [4]	d		16c05			17c05			17 46		18c05			19c05			20c05	
Havant	d		16c19			17c19			18 00		18c19			19c19			20c26	
Portsmouth Harbour	d		16 22			17 22			17 33		18 22			19 22			20 22	
Portsmouth & Southsea	d		16 27			17 27			17 38		18 27			19 27			20 27	
Fratton	d		16 31			17 31			17 43		18 31			19 31			20 31	
Cosham	d		16 39			17 39			18 06		18 39			19 39			20 32	20 46
Fareham	a		16 46			17 46			18 14		18 46			19 46			20 44	
	d		16 47			17 47			18 15		18 47			19 47			20 48	20 54
Bournemouth	d		16 22			17 22			17 59		18 22			19 22			20 22	
Southampton Central	d		17 10			18 10			18 45		19 10			20 10			21 12	21 27
Romsey	d		17 21			18 21			18 56		19 21			20 21			21 23	21 38
Salisbury	a		17 40			18 40			19 15		19 40			20 40			21 42	22 03
	d		17 41			18 41			19 16		19 41			20 41	20 57		21 43	22 04
Warminster	d	17 28	18 01			19 01			19 37		20 01			21 01	21 17		22 03	22 25
Dilton Marsh	d	17 33							19x42									22x29
Weymouth	d				17 30											20 24		
Upwey	d				17 35											20 29		
Dorchester West	d				17 44											20 37		
Maiden Newton	d				17 55											20 49		
Chetnole	d				18x03											20x56		
Yetminster	d				18x06											20x59		
Thornford	d				18x08											21x02		
Yeovil Pen Mill	d				18e24											21 10		
Castle Cary	a				18 36											21 22		
	d				18 42		18 53	←		19 47						21 22		
Bruton	d				18 48			18 48								21 28		
Frome	d							19f06					20 53			21 41		
Westbury	a	17 36	18 07			19 07	19 11	19 16	19 45	20 05	20 07		21 02	21 07	21 23	21 51	22 08	22 33
	d	17 44	18 08	18 38		19 08	19 12	19 17	19 48	20 06	20 08	20 38		21 08	21 24	21 55	22 08	22 38
Exeter St Davids [6]	a		19 32		19g32						21 39			22 37		22g37		
Plymouth	a		20 35		20g35						22 42			23 48		22g48		
Trowbridge	d	17 50	18 14	18 44	→	19 14		19 23	19 54		20 14	20 44		21 14	21 30	22 01	22 14	22 44
Bradford-on-Avon	d	17 56	18 20	18 50		19 20		19 29	20 00		20 20	20 50		21 20	21 36	22 07	22 20	22 50
Avoncliff	d	17x58		18x52				19x31	20x02			20x52				22x09		22x52
Freshford	d	18 01		18 55				19 34	20 05			20 55				22 13		22 55
Bath Spa [7]	a	18 11	18 33	19 07		19 33		19 45	20 16		20 33	21 07		21 37	21 50	22 24	22 35	23 08
Melksham	d																	
Chippenham	a		18 54			19 54					20 57				22 11		22 57	
Swindon	a		19 09			20 09					21 13				22 27		23 13	
London Paddington [15]	⊖ a		20 15			21 15	20 37			21 32	22 16				23 36		00 33	
Oldfield Park	a	18 15		19 10				19 49	20 20			21 10				22 28		23 10
Keynsham	a	18 22		19 17				19 56	20 27			21 17			21 58	22 35		23 17
Bristol Temple Meads [10]	a	18 35	18 47	19 29		19 47		20 04	20 35		20 47	21 26		21 51	22 06	22 45	22 50	23 28
Filton Abbey Wood	a	18 48	19 01	19 48		20 01		20 27	20 48		21 01			22 01			23 01	
Severn Tunnel Jn	a		19h44					20 44			21h51			22 18			23 16	
Newport (South Wales)	a		19 23			20 23		20 54			21 23			22 36			23 34	
Cardiff Central [7]	a		19 42			20 41		21 16			21 41			22 56			23 54	
Swansea [7]	a		20 49			21 45		22j20			22 45			00 02				

For general notes see front of timetable
For details of catering facilities see Directory of Train Operators

A To Great Malvern (Table 71)
B To Cheltenham Spa (Table 57)
C From London Waterloo (Table 160)
b Change at Fratton
c Change at Fareham
e Arr. 1815
f Arr. 1901
g Change at Castle Cary
h Change at Bristol Temple Meads
j Change at Bristol Temple Meads and Cardiff Central

Sundays

until 6 September

Portsmouth and Weymouth → Bristol and South Wales

Network Diagram - see first page of Table 123

		GW	GW	GW	GW	GW	GW	GW	GW	GW	GW	GW	SW	GW	GW	GW	GW	GW
			1 ◇		1 ◇	1 ◇	◇		1 ◇	◇	◇	1 ◇	1 ◇	◇		1 ◇	◇	◇
					A	B							C					
			🍽		🍽	🍽	🛒	🛒	🍽	🛒		🍽		🛒		🍽	🛒	🛒
Brighton 10	d						07b18			09b12	11 08			11b12			12b12	13b12
Hove 2	d						07b22			09b22	11 12			11b22			12b22	13b22
Shoreham-by-Sea	d						07b33			09b33	11 18			11b33			12b33	13b33
Worthing 4	d						07b43			09b43	11 27			11b43			12b43	13b43
Barnham	d						08b06			10b06	11 43			12b06			13b06	14b06
Chichester 4	d						08b14			10b14	11 55			12b14			13b14	14b14
Havant	d						08b39			10b53	12 10			12b51			13b51	14b51
Portsmouth Harbour	d						09 08			11 08	11c32			13 08			14 08	15 08
Portsmouth & Southsea	d						09 12			11 12	11 42			13 12			14 12	15 12
Fratton	d						09 16			11 16	11 46			13 16			14 16	15 16
Cosham	d						09 23			11 23	12 23			13 23			14 23	15 23
Fareham	a						09 31			11 31	12 31			13 31			14 31	15 31
	d						09 32			11 32	12 32			13 32			14 32	15 32
Bournemouth	d						08 50			10 50	11 50			12 50			13 50	14 50
Southampton Central	d						09 54			11 54	12 54			13 54			14 54	15 54
Romsey	d						10 05			12 06	13 06			14 06			15 06	16 06
Salisbury	a						10 24			12 24	13 24			14 24			15 24	16 24
	d						10 30			12 28	13 28		13 58	14 28			15 28	16 28
Warminster	d						10 50			12 48	13 47		14 18	14 48			15 48	16 48
Dilton Marsh	d						10x55							14x53			15x53	16x53
Weymouth	d							11 11							14 10			
Upwey	d							11 16							14 15			
Dorchester West	d							11 24							14 23			
Maiden Newton	d							11 36							14 35			
Chetnole	d							11x44							14x43			
Yetminster	d							11x47							14x46			
Thornford	d							11x50							14x49			
Yeovil Pen Mill	d							11 57							14e59			
Castle Cary	a							12 09							15 11			
	d		09 29					12 11	12 34						15 12	15 33		
Bruton	d							12 16							15 18			
Frome	d	09 35						12 29							15 31			
Westbury	a	09 44	09 46	←			10 57	12 39	12 52	12 53	13 54		14 24	14 55	15 40	15 50	15 55	16 55
	d	09 56	09 49	09 56	10 53	10 53	10 58		12 53	12 55	13 55	13 57	14 25	15 01	15 41	15 51	15 58	16 59
Exeter St Davids 6	a	→					12f49			14 12	15 24			16f49	16g22			18 37
Plymouth	a						14h14			15j29	16 29			18h24	17g29			19 38
Trowbridge	d			10 02			11 04			13 01	14 01		14 32	15 07	15 47		16 04	17 05
Bradford-on-Avon	d			10 07			11 10			13 07	14 07		14 38	15 13	15 52		16 10	17 11
Avoncliff	d			10x10						13x10	14x10				15x55		16x13	
Freshford	d			10 13						13 13	14 12				15 57		16 16	
Bath Spa 7	a			10 24			11 25			13 25	14 23		14 54	15 27	16 08		16 28	17 25
Melksham	d																	
Chippenham	a			10k54			12m24			14n24			15 24	16 24			16 54	17 54
Swindon	a			11q10			12r40			14t40			15 40	16 40			17 10	18 10
London Paddington 15 ⊖	a		11 22	12v28	12 27	12 32	13 55		14 24	15 55		15 25	16 53	17 53		17 28	18 23	19 28
Oldfield Park	a			10 28			11 28			13 28	14 27				16 12			17 28
Keynsham	a			10 35			11 35			13 35	14 34				16 19			17 35
Bristol Temple Meads 10	a			10 43			11 43			13 43	14 42		15 08	15 40	16 28		16 41	17 43
Filton Abbey Wood	a						11 55			13 55	14 55			15 55	16 50		16 55	17 55
Severn Tunnel Jn	a						12 10			14 07	15 07			16 07			17 10	18 07
Newport (South Wales)	a						12 24			14 21	15 21			16 21			17 24	18 21
Cardiff Central 7	a						12 39			14 37	15 38			16 39			17 40	18 39
Swansea 7	a						13 50			15 52	16 50			17 52			18 55	19 54

For general notes see front of timetable
For details of catering facilities see Directory of Train Operators

A From 19 July
B Until 12 July
C From London Waterloo (Table 160)

b Change at Fratton
c Change at Fratton and Cosham
e Arr. 1454
f Change at Salisbury
g Change at Castle Cary
h Change at Salisbury and Exeter St Davids
j Change at Westbury and Exeter St Davids

k From 19 July arr. 1110
m From 19 July arr. 1210
n From 19 July arr. 1409
q From 19 July arr. 1134
r From 19 July arr. 1233
t From 19 July arr. 1434
v From 19 July arr. 1255

Table 123

Sundays

until 6 September

Portsmouth and Weymouth → Bristol and South Wales

Network Diagram - see first page of Table 123

		GW	GW	GW 1 ◇	GW ◇	GW ◇	GW 1 ◇	GW ◇	GW ◇	GW A	GW ◇	GW 1 ◇	SW 1 ◇ B	GW ◇	GW ◇	GW 1 ◇	GW ◇	GW ◇	GW ◇
Brighton 10	d				14b12	15 45					16b12			17 45				18b12	20b12
Hove 2	d				14b22	15 49					16b22			17 49				18b22	20b22
Shoreham-by-Sea	d				14b33	15 55					16b33			17 55				18b33	20b33
Worthing 4	d				14b43	16 06					16b43			18 06				18b43	20b43
Barnham	d				15b06	16 23					17b06			18 23				19b06	21b06
Chichester 4	d				15b14	16 34					17b14			18 34				19b14	21b14
Havant	d				15b51	16 48		16b51			17b51			18 48	18b51			19b51	21b51
Portsmouth Harbour	d				16 08	16 17		17 08			18 08			18 17	19 08			20 08	22 03
Portsmouth & Southsea	d				16 12	16 22		17 12			18 12			18 22	19 12			20 12	22 12
Fratton	d				16 16	16 26		17 16			18 16			18 26	19 16			20 16	22 16
Cosham	d				16 23	16 55		17 23			18 23			18 55	19 23			20 23	22 23
Fareham	a				16 31	17 02		17 31			18 31			19 02	19 31			20 31	22 31
	d				16 32	17 03		17 32			18 32			19 03	19 32			20 32	22 32
Bournemouth	d				15 50	16 40		16 50			17 50			18 50				19 50	
Southampton Central	d				16 54	17 26		17 54			18 54			19 30	19 54			20 54	
Romsey	d				17 06	17 39		18 06			19 06			19 42	20 06			21 06	23 09
Salisbury	a				17 24	18 01		18 24			19 24			20 00	20 24			21 24	23 27
	d				17 28	18 02		18 28			19 28		19 58	20 03	20 28			21 28	23 28
Warminster	d				17 48	18 22		18 48			19 48		20 18	20 28	20 48			21 48	23 53
Dilton Marsh	d					18x27								20x33				21x53	23x58
Weymouth	d		16 13						18 00								20 09		
Upwey	d		16 18						18 05								20 14		
Dorchester West	d		16 26						18 13								20 22		
Maiden Newton	d		16 38						18 25								20 34		
Chetnole	d		16x46						18x32								20x41		
Yetminster	d		16x49						18x35								20x44		
Thornford	d		16x52						18x38								20x47		
Yeovil Pen Mill	d		16 59						18 46								20 55		
Castle Cary	a		17 11						18 57								21 06		
	d		17 11	17 37					18 59			20 05				21 12	21 16		
Bruton	d		17 17						19 05								21 22		
Frome	d		17 30						19 18								21 35		
Westbury	a		17 39	17 54	17 57	18 30		18 53	19 27		19 53	20 24	20 24	20 36	20 53	21 30	21 44	21 55	00 02
	d	17 05	17 40	17 57	18 01	18 34	18 58	19 01	19 30	19 35	20 01	20 25	20 31	20 39	21 01	21 30	21 46	22 01	
Exeter St Davids 6	a		18c37					20 33	21c21						22 37		22c37	00e30	
Plymouth	a		19c40					21 37	22c31						23 44		23c44		
Trowbridge	d	17 11	17 46		18 07	18 40		19 07	19 36	19 42	20 07		20 37	20 45	21 07		21 52	22 07	
Bradford-on-Avon	d		17 52			18 46		19 13	19 42		20 13		20 43	20 52	21 13		21 58	22 13	
Avoncliff	d		17x55			18x49			19x45					20x55			22x01		
Freshford	d		17 57			18 52			19 48					20 57			22 04		
Bath Spa 7	a		18 08		18 25	19 03		19 27	20 01		20 27		20 59	21 15	21 27		22 15	22 28	
Melksham	d	17 21								19 52									
Chippenham	a	17 31			18 54	19 24		19 54	20 24	20 02			21 25		22 30				
Swindon	a	17 48			19 11	19 40		20 10	20 40	20 20			21 41		22 46				
London Paddington 15 ⊖	a	19 10		19 42	20 25	20 53	20 23	21 21	21 56	21 56		21 56	23 08		00 06	23 17			
Oldfield Park	a		18 12			19 06			20 04					21 19			22 18		
Keynsham	a		18 20			19 14			20 12				21 07	21 26			22 26		
Bristol Temple Meads 10	a		18 28		18 38	19 22		19 40	20 20		20 40		21 16	21 34	21 40		22 34	22 41	
Filton Abbey Wood	a		18 47		18 55			19 55	20 50		20 55				21 57			22 55	
Severn Tunnel Jn	a				19 07			20 10			21 07				22 12			23 09	
Newport (South Wales)	a				19 21			20 24			21 21				22 33			23 28	
Cardiff Central 7	a				19 38			20 40			21 38				22 58			23 49	
Swansea 7	a				20 55			21 52			23 00				00 03			01 02	

For general notes see front of timetable
For details of catering facilities see Directory of Train Operators

A To Cheltenham Spa (Table 125)
B From London Waterloo (Table 160)
b Change at Fratton
c Change at Castle Cary
e Change at Salisbury

Table 123

Sundays

from 13 September

Portsmouth and Weymouth → Bristol and South Wales

Network Diagram - see first page of Table 123

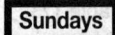

		GW	GW	GW	GW	GW	GW	GW	GW	GW	SW	GW	GW	GW	GW	GW	GW	GW
			1 ◇		1 ◇	◇	1 ◇	◇	◇	1 ◇	1 ◇	◇	◇	1 ◇	◇	◇		1 ◇
											A							
			☕		☕	🛒	☕	🛒		☕		🛒		☕	🛒	🛒		☕
Brighton 10	d					07b22		09b17	11 10			11b17			12b17	13b17		
Hove 2	d					07b26		09b26	11 14			11b26			12b26	13b26		
Shoreham-by-Sea	d					07b37		09b38	11 20			11b38			12b38	13b38		
Worthing 4	d					07b47		09b48	11 29			11b48			12b48	13b48		
Barnham	d					08b20		10b12	11 46			12b12			13b12	14b12		
Chichester 4	d					08b28		10b20	11 58			12b20			13b20	14b20		
Havant	d					08b49		10b53	12 10			12b51			13b51	14b51		
Portsmouth Harbour	d					09 08		11 08	11c32			13 08			14 08	15 08		
Portsmouth & Southsea	d					09 12		11 12	11 42			13 12			14 12	15 12		
Fratton	d					09 16		11 16	11 46			13 16			14 16	15 16		
Cosham	d					09 23		11 23	12 23			13 23			14 23	15 23		
Fareham	a					09 31		11 31	12 31			13 31			14 31	15 31		
	d					09 32		11 32	12 32			13 32			14 32	15 32		
Bournemouth	d					08 50		10 50	11 50			12 50			13 50	14 50		
Southampton Central	d					09 54		11 54	12 54			13 54			14 54	15 54		
Romsey	d					10 05		12 06	13 06			14 06			15 06	16 06		
Salisbury	a					10 24		12 24	13 24			14 24			15 24	16 24		
	d					10 30		12 28	13 28		13 58	14 28			15 28	16 28		
Warminster	d					10 50		12 48	13 47		14 18	14 48			15 48	16 48		
Dilton Marsh	d					10x55						14x53			15x53	16x53		
Weymouth	d												14 00					
Upwey	d												14 05					
Dorchester West	d												14 13					
Maiden Newton	d												14 25					
Chetnole	d												14x32					
Yetminster	d												14x35					
Thornford	d												14x38					
Yeovil Pen Mill	d												14 46					
Castle Cary	a												14 57					
	d		09 29				12 34						14 59	15 33				17 37
Bruton	d												15 05					
Frome	d	09 35											15 18					
Westbury	a	09 44	09 46	⟵		10 57	12 52	12 53	13 54		14 24	14 55	15 27	15 50	15 55	16 55		17 54
	d	09 56	09 49	09 56	10 53	10 58	12 53	12 55	13 55	13 57	14 25	15 01	15 27	15 51	15 58	16 59	17 05	17 57
Exeter St Davids 6	a	⟶				12e49		14 12	15 24			16e49	16f22			18 37		
Plymouth	a					14g14		15h27	16 29			18g22	17f29			19 38		
Trowbridge	d			10 02		11 04		13 01	14 01		14 32	15 07	15 33		16 04	17 05	17 11	
Bradford-on-Avon	d			10 07		11 10		13 07	14 07		14 38	15 13	15 39		16 10	17 11		
Avoncliff	d			10x10				13x10	14x10				15x42		16x13			
Freshford	d			10 13				13 13	14 12				15 45		16 16			
Bath Spa 7	a			10 24		11 25		13 25	14 23		14 54	15 27	15 56		16 28	17 25		
Melksham	d																17 21	
Chippenham	a			11 24		12 24		14 24			15 24		16 24		16 54	17 54	17 31	
Swindon	a			11 40		12 40		14 40			15 40		16 40		17 10	18 10	17 48	
London Paddington 15 ⊖	a		11 30	12 53	12 32	13 53	14 29	15 53		15 30	16 53		17 53	17 33	18 40	19 31	19 08	19 43
Oldfield Park	a			10 28		11 28		13 28	14 27				16 00			17 28		
Keynsham	a			10 35		11 35		13 35	14 34				16 08			17 35		
Bristol Temple Meads 10	a			10 43		11 43		13 43	14 42		15 08	15 40	16 16		16 41	17 43		
Filton Abbey Wood	a					11 55		13 55	14 55			15 55	16 50		16 55	17 55		
Severn Tunnel Jn	a					12 10		14 07	15 07			16 07			17 10	18 07		
Newport (South Wales)	a					12 24		14 21	15 21			16 21			17 24	18 21		
Cardiff Central 7	a					12 39		14 40	15 38			16 39			17 40	18 39		
Swansea 7	a					13 47		15 47	16 47			17 52			18 53	19 54		

For general notes see front of timetable
For details of catering facilities see Directory of Train Operators

- **A** From London Waterloo (Table 160)
- **b** Change at Fratton
- **c** Change at Fratton and Cosham
- **e** Change at Salisbury
- **f** Change at Castle Cary
- **g** Change at Salisbury and Exeter St Davids
- **h** Change at Westbury and Exeter St Davids

Table 123

Sundays

from 13 September

Portsmouth and Weymouth → Bristol and South Wales

Network Diagram - see first page of Table 123

		GW	GW	GW	GW	GW	GW	GW	GW	SW	GW	GW	GW	GW	GW	GW
		◇	◇	[1] ◇	◇	◇		◇	[1] ◇	[1] ◇	◇	◇	[1] ◇	◇	◇	◇
							A			B						
		⊼		⊡	⊼			⊼	⊡			⊼	⊡		⊼	⊼
Brighton [10]	d	14b17	15 47					16b17			17 47				18b17	20b17
Hove [2]	d	14b26	15 51					16b26			17 51				18b26	20b26
Shoreham-by-Sea	d	14b38	15 57					16b38			17 57				18b38	20b38
Worthing [4]	d	14b48	16 08					16b48			18 08				18b48	20b48
Barnham	d	15b12	16 25					17b12			18 25				19b12	21b12
Chichester [4]	d	15b20	16 34					17b20			18 34				19b20	21b20
Havant	d	15b51	16 48		16b51			17b51			18 48	18b51			19b51	21b51
Portsmouth Harbour	d	16 08	16 17		17 08			18 08			18 17	19 08			20 08	22 03
Portsmouth & Southsea	d	16 12	16 22		17 12			18 12			18 22	19 12			20 12	22 12
Fratton	d	16 16	16 26		17 16			18 16			18 26	19 16			20 16	22 16
Cosham	d	16 23	16 55		17 23			18 23			18 55	19 23			20 23	22 23
Fareham	a	16 31	17 02		17 31			18 31			19 02	19 31			20 31	22 31
	d	16 32	17 03		17 32			18 32			19 03	19 32			20 32	22 32
Bournemouth	d	15 50	16 40		16 50			17 50			18 50				19 50	
Southampton Central	d	16 54	17 26		17 54			18 54			19 30	19 54			20 54	
Romsey	d	17 06	17 39		18 06			19 06			19 42	20 06			21 06	23 09
Salisbury	a	17 24	18 01		18 24			19 24			20 00	20 24			21 24	23 27
	d	17 28	18 02		18 28			19 28		19 58	20 03	20 28			21 28	23 28
Warminster	d	17 48	18 22		18 48			19 48		20 18	20 28	20 48			21 48	23 53
Dilton Marsh	d		18x27								20x33				21x53	23x58
Weymouth	d					18 00								20 09		
Upwey	d					18 05								20 14		
Dorchester West	d					18 13								20 22		
Maiden Newton	d					18 25								20 34		
Chetnole	d					18x32								20x41		
Yetminster	d					18x35								20x44		
Thornford	d					18x38								20x47		
Yeovil Pen Mill	d					18 46								20 55		
Castle Cary	a					18 57								21 06		
	d					18 59			20 05				21 12	21 16		
Bruton	d					19 05								21 22		
Frome	d					19 18								21 35		
Westbury	a	17 57	18 30		18 53	19 27		19 53	20 24	20 24	20 36	20 53	21 30	21 44	21 55	00 02
	d	18 01	18 34	18 58	19 01	19 30	19 35	20 01	20 25	20 31	20 39	21 01	21 30	21 46	22 01	
Exeter St Davids [6]	a				20 33	21c21				22 37		22 37		22c37	00e30	
Plymouth	a				21 37	22c31				23 44		23 44		23c44		
Trowbridge	d	18 07	18 40		19 07	19 36	19 42	20 07		20 37	20 45	21 07		21 52	22 07	
Bradford-on-Avon	d		18 46		19 13	19 42		20 13		20 43	20 52	21 13		21 58	22 13	
Avoncliff	d		18x49			19x45					20x55			22x01		
Freshford	d		18 52			19 48					20 57			22 04		
Bath Spa [7]	a	18 25	19 03		19 27	20 01		20 27		20 59	21 15	21 27		22 15	22 28	
Melksham	d						19 52									
Chippenham	a	18 54	19 24		19 54	20 24	20 02			21 25		22 30				
Swindon	a	19 11	19 40		20 10	20 40	20 20			21 41		22 46				
London Paddington [15] ⊖	a	20 39	20 53	20 29	21 39	21 59	21 59		21 53	23 08		00 06	23 17			
Oldfield Park	a		19 06			20 04					21 19			22 18		
Keynsham	a		19 14			20 12				21 07	21 26			22 26		
Bristol Temple Meads [10]	a	18 38	19 22		19 40	20 20		20 40		21 16	21 34	21 40		22 34	22 41	
Filton Abbey Wood	a	18 55			19 55	20 50		20 55				21 57			22 55	
Severn Tunnel Jn	a	19 07			20 10			21 07				22 12			23 09	
Newport (South Wales)	a	19 21			20 24			21 21				22 33			23 28	
Cardiff Central [7]	a	19 38			20 40			21 38				22 58			23 49	
Swansea [7]	a	20 54			21 47			22 47				23f57			01 02	

For general notes see front of timetable
For details of catering facilities see Directory of Train Operators

A To Cheltenham Spa (Table 125)
B From London Waterloo (Table 160)
b Change at Fratton
c Change at Castle Cary
e Change at Salisbury
f Change at Newport (South Wales)

Route Diagram for Table 125

DM-12/06
Design BAJS

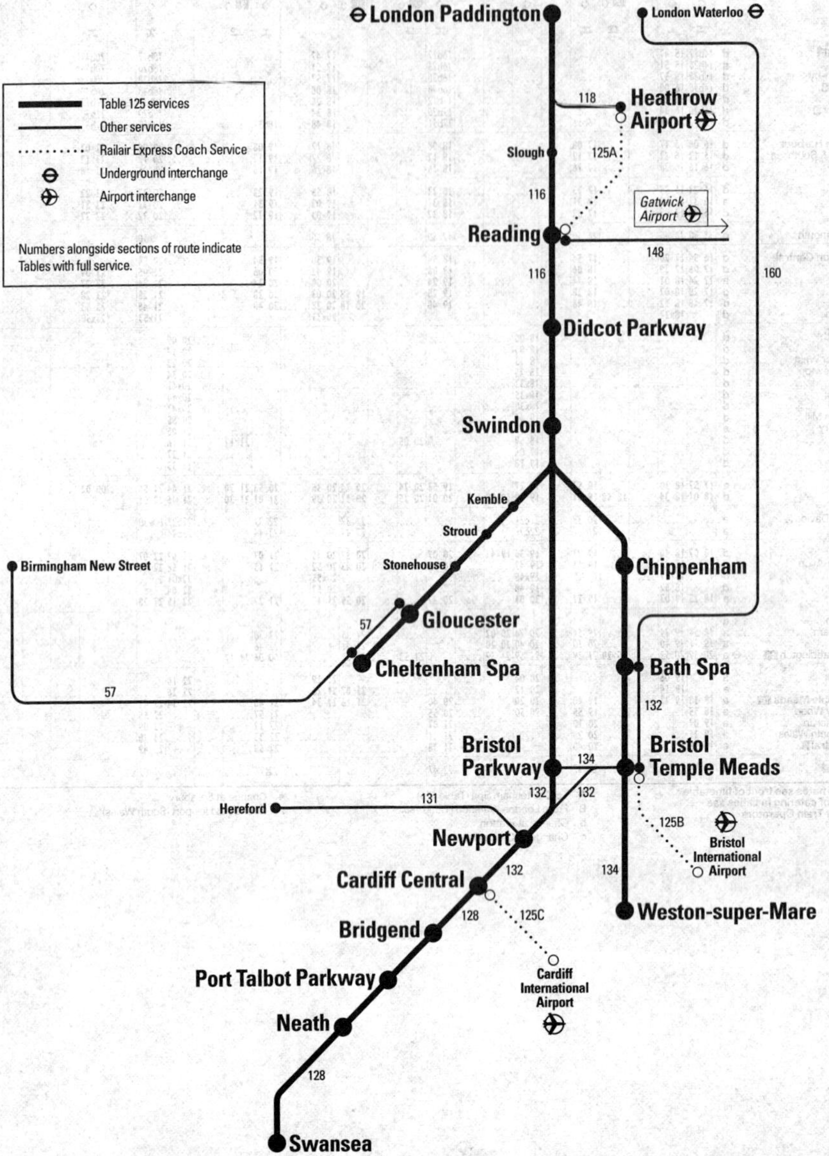

Table 125 services
Other services
Railair Express Coach Service
Underground interchange
Airport interchange
Numbers alongside sections of route indicate Tables with full service.
London Paddington
London Waterloo
118
Heathrow Airport
Slough
125A
116
Gatwick Airport
Reading
148
116
160
Didcot Parkway
Swindon
Kemble
Stroud
Stonehouse
Chippenham
Birmingham New Street
Gloucester
57
Cheltenham Spa
Bath Spa
57
132
Bristol Parkway
134
Bristol Temple Meads
132
132
131
Hereford
125B
Newport
Bristol International Airport
132
134
Cardiff Central
128
125C
Weston-super-Mare
Bridgend
Cardiff International Airport
Port Talbot Parkway
Neath
128
Swansea

Table 125

Mondays to Fridays

London and Oxford → Swindon, Cheltenham Spa, Bristol, Weston-super-Mare and South Wales

Route Diagram - see first page of Table 125

Miles	Miles	Miles			GW	GW	GW	GW	GW	GW	GW	GW	GW	GW	GW	GW	GW	GW	GW	GW	GW
					MX	MX	MX	MO	MO												
						1◇	1◇	1◇	1◇		1◇	1◇	1◇	1◇		1◇	1◇	1◇	1◇	1◇	1◇
								A	B	C					D			E			
						☕	☕	☕	☕		☕	☕	☕	☕		☕	☕	☕	☕	☕	☕
0	0	0	**London Paddington** [15] ⊖	d		22p45	23p30	23p37	23p37		05 27	05 30	06 30	06 45		07 00	07 15	07 30	07 45	07 48	08 00
—	—	—	**London Waterloo** [15] ⊖	d																	
18½	18½	18½	Slough [3]	d				23p55			04 05	05 49	06 13	06 48			06 57	07 13	07 37		07 43
—	—	—	Heathrow Central Bus Stn 🚌	d							05 00		06 00				06 30	06 57			
—	—	—	Gatwick Airport [10]	d										05 31			05 56	06b00			
36	36	36	**Reading** [7]	d		23p21	00 08	00 15	00 15		05 57	06 07	06 57	07 11		07 27	07 41	07 57	08 11	08 16	08 27
—	—	—	Oxford	d			00 06					06 02	06 37			07 01	07 21			08 06	08 21
53¼	53¼	53¼	Didcot Parkway	d		23p39	00 26					06 22	07 12			07 42	07 56			08 33	08 42
77¼	77¼	77¼	**Swindon**	a		23p58	00 46	00s52	00s52		06 24	06 41	07 29	07 39		07 59	08 14	08 25	08 39	08 53	09 00
—	—	—		d	23p33	23p58	00 46			06 15	06 25	06 50	07 30	07 40	07 54	08 00	08 15	08 25	08 40	08 54	09 00
—	—	91	Kemble	d	23p47							07 10			08 07					09 07	
—	—	102¼	Stroud	d	00 02							07 25			08 22					09 22	
—	—	105	Stonehouse	d	00 07							07 30			08 27					09 28	
—	—	113¾	Gloucester [7]	a	00 24							07 49			08 50					09 44	
—	—	120¼	**Cheltenham Spa**	a	00 53							08 04			09 03					10 03	
—	—	—	**Birmingham New Street** [12]	a								08 56			09 56					10 56	
—	94	—	Chippenham	d			01 00	01s08	01s08	06a31	06 40		07 45			08 15		08 40			09 15
—	107	—	Bath Spa [7]	a			01 15	01s22	01s22		06 53		08 00			08 30		08 55			09 28
111¾	—	—	Bristol Parkway [7]	a		00 25								08 06			08 41		09 06		
—	—	—		d		00 25								08 07			08 42		09 07		
117¾	118½	—	**Bristol Temple Meads** [10]	a			01 29	01 38	01 38		07 08		08 17			08 44		09 10			09 44
—	137½	—	Weston-super-Mare	a							07 47					09 24		10 03			10 22
133½	—	—	Newport (South Wales)	a		00 54	02s10				07 44			08 30			09 05		09 29		
—	—	—	Hereford [7]	a							08 53			09 53					10 26		
145¼	—	—	**Cardiff Central** [7]	a		01 14	02 33				08 01			08 48			09 22		09 48		
165½	—	—	Bridgend	a		01 39					08 22			09 09					10 09		
177¾	—	—	Port Talbot Parkway	a		01 52					08 35			09 23					10 23		
183¼	—	—	Neath	a		01 59					08 44			09 30					10 30		
192¾	—	—	**Swansea** [7]	a		02 14					08 57			09 46					10 44		

		GW	GW	GW	GW	GW	GW	GW	GW	GW	GW	SW	GW	GW	GW	GW	GW	GW	GW	GW	GW
		1◇	1◇	1◇		1◇	1◇	1◇	1◇	1◇	1◇	1◇	1◇	1◇	1◇		1◇	1◇	1◇	1◇	1◇
											G										
		☕	☕	☕		☕	☕	☕	☕	☕	☕		☕	☕	☕		☕	☕	☕	☕	☕
London Paddington [15] ⊖	d	08 15	08 30	08 45		09 00	09 15	09 30	09 45	09 48	10 00		10 15	10 30	10 45		11 00	11 15	11 30	11 45	11 48
London Waterloo [15] ⊖	d											09 20									
Slough [3]	d	08 06	08 13	08 37		08 43	09 06		09 27		09 43		10 06	10 13	10 37		10 43	11 06	11 13	11 37	
Heathrow Central Bus Stn 🚌	d	07 20	07 40			08 00	08 20	08 40	09 00		09 20		09 40		10 00		10 15	10 35	10 55		11 15
Gatwick Airport [10]	d	07 00		07b07		07 58			08b15				09 07				10 03			10b10	
Reading [7]	d	08 41	08 57	09 11		09 27	09 41	09 57	10 11	10 16	10 27		10 41	10 57	11 11		11 27	11 41	11 57	12 11	12 16
Oxford	d	08 37					09 37			10 07			10 37					11 37			12 07
Didcot Parkway	d	08 56	09 12				09 56	10 12		10 33			10 56	11 12				11 56	12 12		12 33
Swindon	a	09 14	09 30	09 39		09 55	10 14	10 30	10 39	10 53	10 55		11 14	11 30	11 39		11 55	12 14	12 30	12 39	12 53
	d	09 15	09 30	09 40	09 54	09 55	10 15	10 30	10 40	10 54	10 55		11 15	11 30	11 40	11 54	11 55	12 15	12 30	12 40	12 54
Kemble	d				10 07					11 07						12 07					13 07
Stroud	d				10 22					11 22						12 22					13 22
Stonehouse	d				10 27					11 28						12 27					13 28
Gloucester [7]	a				10 50					11 44						12 50					13 44
Cheltenham Spa	a				11 03					12 03						13 03					14 03
Birmingham New Street [12]	a				11 56					12 56						13 56					14 56
Chippenham	d		09 45			10 10		10 45			11 10			11 45			12 10		12 45		
Bath Spa [7]	a		10 00			10 25		11 00			11 25	11 45		12 00			12 25		13 00		
Bristol Parkway [7]	a	09 41		10 06			10 41		11 06				11 41		12 06			12 41		13 06	
	d	09 42		10 07			10 42		11 07				11 42		12 07			12 42		13 07	
Bristol Temple Meads [10]	a		10 15			10 39		11 15			11 42	12 05		12 15			12 39		13 15		
Weston-super-Mare	a		11 00			11 21		12 00			12 06			13 00			13 21		14 00		
Newport (South Wales)	a	10 04		10 29			11 05		11 31				12 04		12 29			13 04		13 29	
Hereford [7]	a			11 53			12 26		12 53						13 53					14 26	
Cardiff Central [7]	a	10 21		10 47			11 23		11 48				12 21		12 48			13 22		13 48	
Bridgend	a			11 09					12 09						13 09					14 09	
Port Talbot Parkway	a			11 23					12 23						13 23					14 23	
Neath	a			11 30					12 30						13 30					14 30	
Swansea [7]	a			11 43					12 45						13 44					14 44	

For general notes see front of timetable
For details of catering facilities see Directory of Train Operators

- **A** Until 7 September
- **B** From 14 September
- **C** From Gloucester
- **D** From Westbury (Table 123)
- **E** To Penzance (Table 135)
- **G** To Paignton (Table 135)
- **b** Change at Redhill and Reading

London and Oxford → Swindon, Cheltenham Spa, Bristol, Weston-super-Mare and South Wales

Route Diagram - see first page of Table 125

		GW 1◇ ☕	GW 1◇ ☕		GW 1◇ ☕	GW 1◇ ☕	GW	GW 1◇ ☕		SW 1◇	GW 1◇ ☕	GW 1◇ ☕	GW 1◇ ☕		GW 1◇ ☕	GW 1◇ ☕	GW 1◇ ☕	GW 1◇ ☕		GW 1◇ ☕	GW	GW 1◇ ☕	GW 1◇ ☕		GW 1◇ ☕
London Paddington 15 ⊖	d	12 00	12 15		12 30	12 45		13 00			13 15	13 30	13 45		13 48	14 00	14 15	14 30		14 45		15 00	15 15		15 30
London Waterloo 15 ⊖	d									12 20															
Slough 3	d	*11 43*	*12 06*		*12 27*	*12 37*		*12 43*			*13 06*	*13 13*	*13 37*			*13 43*	*14 06*	*14 13*		*14 37*		*14 43*	*15 06*		*15 13*
Heathrow Central Bus Stn 🚌	d		*11 35*		*11 55*			*12 15*			*12 35*	*12 55*			*13 15*		*13 35*	*13 55*				*14 15*	*14 35*		*14 55*
Gatwick Airport 10	d	*11 03*				*11b08*		*12 03*					*12b08*			*13 03*				*13b08*		*14 03*			
Reading 7	d	12 27	12 41		12 57	13 11		13 27			13 41	13 57	14 11		14 16	14 27	14 41	14 57		15 11		15 27	15 41		15 57
Oxford	d		*12 37*								*13 37*				*14 07*		*14 37*						*15 37*		
Didcot Parkway	d		12 56		13 12						13 56	14 12			14 33		14 56	15 12					15 56		16 12
Swindon	a	12 55	13 14		13 30	13 39		13 55			14 14	14 30	14 39		14 53	14 55	15 14	15 30		15 39		15 55	16 14		16 30
	d	12 55	13 15		13 30	13 40	13 54	13 55			14 15	14 30	14 40		14 54	14 55	15 15	15 30		15 40	15 54	15 55	16 15		16 30
Kemble	d						14 07								15 07						16 07				
Stroud	d						14 22								15 22						16 22				
Stonehouse	d						14 27								15 28						16 27				
Gloucester 7	a						14 50								15 44						16 50				
Cheltenham Spa	a						15 03								16 03						17 03				
Birmingham New Street 12	a						*15 56*								*16 56*						*17 56*				
Chippenham	d	13 10			13 45			14 10				14 45				15 10		15 45				16 10			16 45
Bath Spa 7	a	13 25			14 00			14 25		14 45		15 00				15 25		16 00				16 25			17 00
Bristol Parkway 7	a		13 41			14 06					14 41		15 06				15 41			16 06			16 41		
	d		13 42			14 07					14 42		15 07				15 42			16 07			16 42		
Bristol Temple Meads 10	a	13 41			14 15			14 39		15 05		15 15				15 40		16 15				16 39			17 15
Weston-super-Mare	a	*14 21*			*15 00*			*15 25*				*16 00*				*16 24*		16 52				*17 27*			17 52
Newport (South Wales)	a		14 04			14 29					15 05		15 29				16 04			16 29			17 05		
Hereford 7	a					*15 53*							*16 25*							*17 53*					
Cardiff Central 7	a		14 21			14 48					15 23		15 48				16 21			16 48			17 22		
Bridgend	a					15 09							16 09							17 09					
Port Talbot Parkway	a					15 23							16 23							17 23					
Neath	a					15 30							16 30							17 30					
Swansea 7	a					15 44							16 45							17 44					

		GW 1◇ ☕	GW 1◇ ☕	GW 1◇ ☕	GW 1◇ ☕		GW 1◇ A ☕	GW 1◇ ☕	GW	GW 1◇ ☕		GW 1◇ ☕	GW 1◇ A ☕	GW 1◇ B ☕	GW C		GW 1◇ ☕	GW 1◇ ☕	GW 1◇ ☕	GW 1◇ ☕		GW 1◇ ☕	GW 1◇ ☕	GW 1◇ ☕	GW 1◇ ☕
London Paddington 15 ⊖	d	15 45	15 48	16 00	16 15		16 30	16 45		17 00		17 15	17 30	17 45			17 48	18 00	18 15	18 30		18 45	18 48	19 00	19 15
London Waterloo 15 ⊖	d																								
Slough 3	d	*15 37*		*15 47*	*16 06*		*16 17*	*16 48*				*16 53*	*17 18*	*17 30*					*17 58*	*18 16*		*18 30*		*18 46*	*19 06*
Heathrow Central Bus Stn 🚌	d		*15 15*		*15 35*		*15 55*			*16 15*		*16 35*		*16 55*				*17 15*	*17 35*			*17 55*		*18 15*	*18 35*
Gatwick Airport 10	d	*14b08*			*15 03*			*15b08*		*16 03*				*16b08*					*17 03*					*17b23*	*18 03*
Reading 7	d	16 11	16 16	16 27	16 41		16 57	17 11		17 27		17 41	17 57	18 11			18 16	18 27	18 41	18 57		19 11	19 16	19 27	19 41
Oxford	d		*16 07*				*16 47*			*17 07*		*17 31*					*18 07*		*18 37*				*19 10*		*19 37*
Didcot Parkway	d		16 33		16 56		17 12	17 26		17 42		17 56	18 12				18 33	18 42	18 56	19 12			19 33	19 42	19 56
Swindon	a	16 39	16 54	16 55	17 15		17 30	17 45		18 00		18 15	18 30	18 39			18 53	19 00	19 15	19 30		19 39	19 53	20 00	20 14
	d	16 40	16 54	16 55	17 15		17 30	17 45	17 54	18 00		18 15	18 30	18 40	18 44		18 54	19 00	19 15	19 30		19 40	19 54	20 00	20 15
Kemble	d		17 07						18 07								19 07						20 07		
Stroud	d		17 22						18 22								19 22						20 22		
Stonehouse	d		17 28						18 27								19 27						20 28		
Gloucester 7	a		17 46						18 50								19 45						20 44		
Cheltenham Spa	a		18 03						19 03								20 03						21 03		
Birmingham New Street 12	a		*18 56*						*19 56*								*20 56*						*21 57*		
Chippenham	d			17 10			17 45			18 15			18 45		19a01			19 15		19 45				20 15	
Bath Spa 7	a			17 25			18 00			18 28			19 00					19 28		20 00				20 28	
Bristol Parkway 7	a	17 06			17 41			18 12				18 41		19 10					19 42			20 06			20 41
	d	17 07			17 42			18 12				18 42		19 10					19 42			20 07			20 42
Bristol Temple Meads 10	a			17 41			18 15			18 44			19 15					19 43		20 15				20 44	
Weston-super-Mare	a			*18 25*			18 52			*19 28*			19 49					*20 29*		20 55				*21 27*	
Newport (South Wales)	a	17 29			18 05			18 36				19 10		19 37					20 06			20 29			21 04
Hereford 7	a	*18 26*						*19 56*						*20 39*					*21 16*						*22 00*
Cardiff Central 7	a	17 48			18 22			18 53				19 27		19 53					20 27			20 48			21 21
Bridgend	a	18 09			18 44			19 15				19 49		20 15					20 48			21 09			21 44
Port Talbot Parkway	a	18 23			18 57			19 28				20 02		20 28					21 01			21 23			21 57
Neath	a	18 30			19 04			19 36				20 10		20 36					21 09			21 30			22 05
Swansea 7	a	18 48			19 19			19 49				20 24		20 49					21 25			21 46			22 18

For general notes see front of timetable
For details of catering facilities see Directory of Train Operators

A To Taunton (Table 134)
B To Carmarthen (Table 128)
C From Worcester Foregate Street (Table 71)
b Change at Redhill and Reading

London and Oxford → Swindon, Cheltenham Spa, Bristol, Weston-super-Mare and South Wales

Route Diagram - see first page of Table 125

Mondays to Fridays

		GW A	GW 1◇	GW 1◇	GW 1◇	GW 1◇	GW 1◇	GW B	GW FX 1◇	GW FO 1◇	GW 1◇ C	GW FO 1◇	GW FX 1◇	GW	GW FO 1◇	GW FX 1◇	GW FO 1◇	GW FX 1◇
London Paddington 15 ⊖	d		19 30	19 48	20 00	20 15	20 45		21 15	21 15	21 45	22 15	22 15		22 45	22 45	23 30	23 30
London Waterloo 15 ⊖	d																	
Slough 3	d		19 11	19 41		20 06	20 35		21 07	21 07	21 37	22 03	22 03		22 37	22 45	23 39	
Heathrow Central Bus Stn (bus)	d			18 55	19 15	19 40	20 10		20 40	20 40	21 10	21 40	21 40		22 15	22 15	23 05	
Gatwick Airport 10	d				18b23	19 16			20 03	20 03	20b11	21 03	21 03		21b11			
Reading 7	d		19 57	20 16	20 27	20 41	21 11		21 41	21 41	22 11	22 41	22 50		23 11	23 21	00 02	00 08
Oxford	d			20 07		20 37			21 38	21 38		22 33	22 33		23 05	23 05		
Didcot Parkway	d		20 12	20 33	20 42	20 56	21 26		22 00	22 00	22 30	23 01	23 09		23 30	23 39	00 25	00 26
Swindon	a		20 30	20 53	21 00	21 15	21 45		22 19	22 19	22 49	23 20	23 26		23 49	23 58	00 42	00 46
	d	20 23	20 30	20 54	21 00	21 15	21 45	21 54	22 20	22 20	22 50	23 21	23 26	23 33	23 50	23 58	00 43	00 46
Kemble	d	20 37		21 11				22 07						23 47				
Stroud	d	20 52		21 26				22 22						00 02				
Stonehouse	d	20 57		21 31				22 27						00 07				
Gloucester 7	a	21 13		21 47				22 45						00 24				
Cheltenham Spa	a	21 29		22 03				23 03						00c53				
Birmingham New Street 12	a			23 35														
Chippenham	d		20 45		21 15		22 00				23 05	23 35	23 41				00 58	01 00
Bath Spa 7	a		21 00		21 28		22 11				23 19	23 49	23 56				01 13	01 15
Bristol Parkway 7	a					21 41			22 46	22 46					00 16	00 25		
	d					21 42			22 46	22 46					00 17	00 25		
Bristol Temple Meads 10	a		21 15		21 44		22 30				23 33	00 03	00 10				01 27	01 29
Weston-super-Mare	a		21 50		22 27		23 43				00s06							
Newport (South Wales)	a					22 04			23 16	23 15					00 39	00 54	02s03	02s10
Hereford 7	a					23 04				01 46					01 46	01 55		
Cardiff Central 7	a					22 25			23 39	23 39					00 55	01 14	02 22	02 33
Bridgend	a					22 57			23 59	23 59					01 20	01 39		
Port Talbot Parkway	a					23 10			00 11	00 11					01 33	01 52		
Neath	a					23 17			00 19	00 19					01 41	01 59		
Swansea 7	a					23 32			00 34	00 34					01 54	02 15		

Saturdays

		GW	GW 1◇	GW 1◇	GW	GW 1◇	GW 1◇	GW 1 D	GW 1◇	GW 1◇	GW 1◇	GW 1◇	GW 1◇ E	GW 1◇ G	GW 1◇ H	GW	GW 1◇	GW 1◇	GW 1◇	SW 1◇	GW 1◇	GW 1◇ G
London Paddington 15 ⊖	d		22p45	23p30		06 30	07 00	07 30	07 45	08 00	08 15	08 30	08 45	09 00	09 00		09 30	09 45	10 00		10 15	10 30
London Waterloo 15 ⊖	d																			09 20		
Slough 3	d					06 07	06 57	07 13	07 37	07 57	08 07	08 13	08 39	08 57	08 57		09 13	09 39	09 57		10 07	10 13
Heathrow Central Bus Stn (bus)	d					06 00			07 00		07 30		08 00				08 30	09 00			09 30	
Gatwick Airport 10	d			21e11			06 04			07 03			07b10	08 03	08 03			08b08	09 03			
Reading 7	d		23p11	00 02		06 57	07 27	07 57	08 11	08 27	08 41	08 57	09 11	09 27	09 27		09 57	10 11	10 27		10 41	10 57
Oxford	d					06 37		07 37			08 37						09 37				10 37	
Didcot Parkway	d		23p30	00 25		07 12		08 12			08 56	09 12					10 12				10 56	11 12
Swindon	a		23p49	00 42		07 30	07 55	08 30	08 39	08 55	09 15	09 30	09 39	09 55	09 55		10 30	10 39	10 55		11 15	11 30
	d	23p33	23p50	00 43	07 16	07 30	07 55	08 30	08 40	08 55	09 15	09 30	09 40	09 55	09 55	10 14	10 30	10 40	10 55		11 15	11 30
Kemble	d	23p47			07 30						09 30					10 28					11 30	
Stroud	d	00 02			07 45						09 45					10 43					11 45	
Stonehouse	d	00 07			07 50						09 50					10 48					11 50	
Gloucester 7	a	00 24			08 06						10 06					11 07					12 07	
Cheltenham Spa	a	00 52			08 24						10 23					11 22					12 23	
Birmingham New Street 12	a				09 26						11 26					12 26					13 26	
Chippenham	d			00 58		07 45	08 10	08 45		09 10		09 45		10 10	10 10		10 45		11 10			11 45
Bath Spa 7	a			01 13		08 00	08 24	09 00		09 24		10 00		10 25	10 25		11 00		11 25	11 45		12 00
Bristol Parkway 7	a		00 16						09 06				10 06					11 06				
	d		00 17						09 07				10 07					11 07				
Bristol Temple Meads 10	a			01 27		08 15	08 39	09 15		09 39		10 15		10 39	10 39		11 15		11 39	12 00		12 15
Weston-super-Mare	a					09 00	09 22	10 00		10 22		11 00		11 07	11 21		12 00		12 22			12 36
Newport (South Wales)	a		00 39	02s03					09 31				10 31					11 31				
Hereford 7	a		01 55						10 53				11 53					12 56				
Cardiff Central 7	a		00 56	02 22					09 48				10 48					11 48				
Bridgend	a		01 20						10 09				11 09					12 09				
Port Talbot Parkway	a		01 33						10 23				11 22					12 23				
Neath	a		01 41						10 30				11 30					12 30				
Swansea 7	a		01 54						10 44				11 43					12 44				

For general notes see front of timetable
For details of catering facilities see Directory of Train Operators

- A From Westbury (Table 123)
- B From 7 September to Worcester Shrub Mill (Table 57)
- C Until 4 September To Exeter St Davids (Table 135)
- D From 12 September To Penzance (Table 135)
- E Until 5 September to Pembroke Dock (Table 128)
- G Until 5 September
- H From 12 September
- b Change at Redhill and Reading
- c Saturday mornings arr.0052
- e Saturdays. Change at Redhill and Reading

Table 125

Saturdays

London and Oxford → Swindon, Cheltenham Spa, Bristol, Weston-super-Mare and South Wales

Route Diagram - see first page of Table 125

		GW A	GW	GW	GW	GW	GW	GW	GW	GW B	GW A	GW	GW	SW	GW	GW	GW	GW	GW	GW	GW B
London Paddington 15 ⊖	d	10 30	10 45	11 00		11 30	11 45	12 00	12 15	12 30	12 30	12 45	13 00			13 30	13 45	14 00	14 15		14 30
London Waterloo 15 ⊖	d													12 20							
Slough 3	d	10 13	10 39	10 57		11 13	11 39	11 57		12 13	12 13	12b39	12 57			13 13	13 39	13 57	14 07		14 13
Heathrow Central Bus Stn	d		10 00			10 30	11 00		11 30			12 00				12 30	13 00		13 30		
Gatwick Airport 10	d		09c08	10 03			10c08	11 03				11c08	12 03				12c08	13 03			
Reading 7	d	10 57	11 11	11 27		11 57	12 11	12 27	12 41	12 57	12 57	13 11	13 27			13 57	14 11	14 27	14 41		14 57
Oxford	d					11 37			12 37							13 37			14 37		
Didcot Parkway	d	11 12				12 12			12 56	13 12	13 12					14 12			14 56		15 12
Swindon	a	11 30	11 39	11 55		12 30	12 39	12 55	13 15	13 30	13 30	13 39	13 55			14 30	14 39	14 55	15 15		15 30
	d	11 30	11 40	11 55	12 14	12 30	12 40	12 55	13 15	13 30	13 30	13 40	13 55		14 14	14 30	14 40	14 55	15 15	15 20	15 30
Kemble	d				12 28				13 30						14 28				15 30		
Stroud	d				12 43				13 45						14 43				15 45		
Stonehouse	d				12 48				13 50						14 48				15 50		
Gloucester 7	a				13 07				14 06						15 08				16 06		
Cheltenham Spa	a				13 22				14 23						15 25				16 23		
Birmingham New Street 12	a				14 26				15 26						16 26				17 26		
Chippenham	d	11 45		12 10		12 45		13 10		13 45	13 45		14 10			14 45		15 10		15a36	15 45
Bath Spa 7	a	12 00		12 25		13 00		13 25		14 00	14 00		14 25	14 45		15 00		15 25			16 00
Bristol Parkway 7	a		12 06				13 06					14 06					15 06				
	d		12 07				13 07					14 07					15 07				
Bristol Temple Meads 10	a	12 15		12 40		13 15		13 40		14 15	14 15		14 39	15 05		15 15		15 39			16 15
Weston-super-Mare	a	13 00		13 22		14 00		14 22		14 36	15 00		15 23			16 00		16 22			16 36
Newport (South Wales)	a		12 31				13 31					14 31					15 31				
Hereford 7	a		13 53				14 53					15 53					16 55				
Cardiff Central 7	a		12 48				13 48					14 48					15 48				
Bridgend	a		13 09				14 09					15 09					16 09				
Port Talbot Parkway	a		13 23				14 23					15 23					16 23				
Neath	a		13 30				14 30					15 30					16 30				
Swansea 7	a		13 44				14 44					15 44					16 44				

		GW A	GW	GW	GW	GW B	GW A	GW	GW	GW	GW C	GW	GW	GW	GW	GW D	GW	GW	GW E	GW	GW E
London Paddington 15 ⊖	d	14 30	14 45	15 00		15 30	15 30	15 45	16 00	16 15	16 30	16 45	17 00		17 30	17 45	18 00	18 15	18 30	18 45	19 00
London Waterloo 15 ⊖	d																				
Slough 3	d	14 13	14 39	14 57		15 13	15 13	15 39	15 57	16 07	16 13	16 39	16 57		17 13	17 39	17 57	18 07	18 13	18 39	18 57
Heathrow Central Bus Stn	d		14 00			14 30	14 30	15 00		15 30		16 00			16 30	17 00		17 30		18 00	
Gatwick Airport 10	d		13c08	14 03				14c08	15 03			15c08	16 03			16c08	17 03			17c08	18 03
Reading 7	d	14 57	15 11	15 27		15 57	15 57	16 11	16 27	16 41	16 57	17 11	17 27		17 57	18 11	18 27	18 41	18 57	19 11	19 27
Oxford	d					15 37	15 37			16 37					17 37			18 37			
Didcot Parkway	d	15 12				16 12	16 12			16 56	17 12				18 12			18 56	19 12		
Swindon	a	15 30	15 39	15 55		16 30	16 30	16 39	16 55	17 15	17 30	17 39	17 55		18 30	18 40	18 55	19 15	19 30	19 40	19 55
	d	15 30	15 40	15 55	16 14	16 30	16 30	16 40	16 55	17 15	17 30	17 40	17 55	18 14	18 30	18 40	18 55	19 15	19 30	19 40	19 55
Kemble	d				16 28					17 30				18 28				19 30			
Stroud	d				16 43					17 45				18 43				19 45			
Stonehouse	d				16 48					17 50				18 48				19 50			
Gloucester 7	a				17 08					18 06				19 08				20 06			
Cheltenham Spa	a				17 25					18 23				19 25				20 23			
Birmingham New Street 12	a				18 26					19 26				20 26				21e41			
Chippenham	d	15 45		16 10		16 45	16 45		17 10		17 45		18 10		18 45		19 11		19 46		20 10
Bath Spa 7	a	16 00		16 25		17 00	17 00		17 25		18 00		18 25		19 00		19 25		20 00		20 25
Bristol Parkway 7	a		16 06					17 06				18 06				19 13				20 07	
	d		16 07					17 07				18 07				19 13				20 07	
Bristol Temple Meads 10	a	16 15		16 39		17 15	17 15		17 39		18 15		18 39		19 15		19 40		20 15		20 42
Weston-super-Mare	a	17 00		17 22		17 36	18 00		18 21		18 36		19 23		19 52		20 23		20 36		21 26
Newport (South Wales)	a		16 31					17 31				18 31				19 36				20 31	
Hereford 7	a		17 53					18 55				19 53				20 39					
Cardiff Central 7	a		16 48					17 48				18 48				19 53				20 48	
Bridgend	a		17 09					18 09				19 09				20 14				21 09	
Port Talbot Parkway	a		17 23					18 23				19 23				20 27				21 23	
Neath	a		17 30					18 30				19 30				20 36				21 30	
Swansea 7	a		17 44					18 47				19 44				20 49				21 45	

For general notes see front of timetable
For details of catering facilities see Directory of Train Operators

- **A** From 12 September
- **B** Until 5 September
- **C** To Paignton (Table 135)
- **D** To Carmarthen (Table 128)
- **E** To Taunton (Table 134)
- **b** From 12 September dep. 1238
- **c** Change at Redhill and Reading
- **e** From 12 September arr. 2138

Table 125

Saturdays

London and Oxford → Swindon, Cheltenham Spa, Bristol, Weston-super-Mare and South Wales

Route Diagram - see first page of Table 125

		GW	GW 1◇ A	GW 1◇	GW 1◇	GW 1◇	SW 1◇	GW B	GW 1◇	GW 1◇ C	GW 1◇	GW 1◇ A	GW 1◇ D	GW	GW 1◇	GW 1◇ E	GW 1◇ G	GW E (bus)	GW 1◇ E	GW 1◇ G
London Paddington 15 ⊖	d		19 15	19 30	19 45	20 00			20 15	20 30	20 45	21 30	21 30		22 00	22 30	22 30		23 30	23 30
London Waterloo 15 ⊖	d						19 20													
Slough 3	d		19 07	19 13	19 38	19 57			20 07	20 13	20 27	21 13	21 13		21 45	22 27	22 27		23 21	23 21
Heathrow Central Bus Stn (bus)	d		18 30	18 30	19 00	19 20				19 50		20 50	20 50		21 30	22 00	22 00		23 05	23 05
Gatwick Airport 10	d				18b08	19 03					19b08	20 03	20 03		21 03				21b11	21b11
Reading 7	d		19 41	19 57	20 11	20 27			20 41	20 57	21 11	21 57	21 57		22 27	23 00	23 00		23 59	23 59
Oxford	d		19 37	19 37		20 07			20 37			21 50	21 50			23 01	23 01		23 07	23 07
Didcot Parkway	d		19 56	20 12		20 42			20 56	21 12		22 12	22 12		22 42	23 22	23 22		00 18	00 18
Swindon	a		20 14	20 30	20 39	21 00			21 15	21 30	21 44	22 29	22 30		23 00	23 41	23 41		00 37	00 37
	d	20 00	20 15	20 30	20 40	21 00		21 08	21 15	21 30	21 46	22 30	22 30	22 35	23 00	23 41	23 41	23 49	00 37	00 37
Kemble	d	20 15							21 30					22 49						
Stroud	d	20 30							21 45					23 04						
Stonehouse	d	20 35							21 50					23 09						
Gloucester 7	a	20 51							22 05					23 25						
Cheltenham Spa	a	21 05							22 23											
Birmingham New Street 12	a	22c07																		
Chippenham	d			20 45		21 15		21a24		21 45		22 45	22 45				23 56	00 24		00 52
Bath Spa 7	a			21 00		21 30	21 50			22 00		23 00	23 00				00 10	00 59		01 07
Bristol Parkway 7	a		20 41		21 06						22 11				23 28					
	d		20 42		21 07						22 11				23 29					
Bristol Temple Meads 10	a			21 15		21 45	22 06			22 15		23 15	23 15			00 16	00 25	01 29	01 15	01 23
Weston-super-Mare	a					22 27				22s48										
Newport (South Wales)	a		21 04		21 31						22 46				23 58					
Hereford 7	a		21 58		22e58															
Cardiff Central 7	a		21 21		21 48						23 06				00 19					
Bridgend	a		21 43		22 09						23 28									
Port Talbot Parkway	a		21 56		22 22						23 41									
Neath	a		22 04		22 30						23 49									
Swansea 7	a		22 18		22 44						00 02									

Sundays

until 12 July

		GW 1◇	GW 1◇ H	GW 1◇	GW 1◇	GW 1◇	GW 1◇	GW	GW 1◇	GW 1◇	GW 1◇ J	GW 1◇	GW 1◇	GW 1◇ K	GW 1◇	GW 1◇ J	GW 1◇	SW 1◇
London Paddington 15 ⊖	d	23p30	08 00	08 30	08 35	09 00	09 30		10 00	10 27	10 37	11 00	11 37	12 00	12 27	12 37	13 00	
London Waterloo 15 ⊖	d																	12 15
Slough 3	d		07 14	08 22	08 46	09 01	09 23		09 51	10 23		10 59	11 23	12 00	12 23		12 59	
Heathrow Central Bus Stn (bus)	d		07 30	08 00		08 30	09 00		09 30	10 00		10 30	11 00	11 30	12 00		12 30	
Gatwick Airport 10	d		06 06	07 08			08 08			09 08			10 08		11 08			
Reading 7	d	23p59	08 38	09 16	09 20	09 37	10 05		10 37	11 05	11 14	11 37	12 14	12 37	13 05	13 14	13 37	
Oxford	d		08 05	09 05			09 38		10 05		11 05		12 05			13 05		
Didcot Parkway	d	00 18	08 53	09 31		09 53	10 21		10 53		11 30	11 53	12 30	12 53		13 30	13 53	
Swindon	a	00 37	09 12	09 48	09 53	10 08	10 38		11 10	11 34	11 47	12 10	12 47	13 11	13 34	13 47	14 10	
	d	00 37	09 12	09 50	09 55	10 10	10 40	10 45	11 10	11 35	11 47	12 10	12 47	13 11	13 40	13 47	14 11	
Kemble	d				10 08			10 59		11 49					13 54			
Stroud	d				10 23			11 14		12 05					14 09			
Stonehouse	d				10 28			11 19		12 10					14 14			
Gloucester 7	a				10 44			11 35		12 26					14 32			
Cheltenham Spa	a				11 02			11 48		12 46					14 48			
Birmingham New Street 12	a				12 28			13 34		14 28					15 40			
Chippenham	d	00 52	09 29			10 26			11 26			12 26		13 26			14 26	
Bath Spa 7	a	01 07	09 45			10 41			11 41			12 40		13 40			14 40	14 54
Bristol Parkway 7	a			10 15			11 05				12 14		13 14			14 14		
	d			10 17			11 07				12 16		13 16			14 16		
Bristol Temple Meads 10	a	01 23	09 59			10 56			11 57			12 54		13 56			14 55	15 08
Weston-super-Mare	a		10 41			11 38			12 31			13 32		14 37			15 48	16 26
Newport (South Wales)	a			10 38			11 30				12 37		13 39			14 39		
Hereford 7	a			11 44			12 49				13 47		14 49			16 02		
Cardiff Central 7	a			10 55			11 47				12 54		13 56			14 56		
Bridgend	a			11 17			12 09				13 16		14 19			15 18		
Port Talbot Parkway	a			11 30			12 22				13 29		14 31			15 31		
Neath	a			11 37			12 29				13 36		14 38			15 38		
Swansea 7	a			11 52			12 44				13 50		14 58			15 52		

For general notes see front of timetable
For details of catering facilities see Directory of Train Operators

A From 12 September
B From Cheltenham Spa
C To Exeter St Davids (Table 135)
D Until 5 September
E 18 July to 5 September
G Until 11 July and from 12 September
H To Penzance (Table 135)
J To Carmarthen (Table 128)
K To Plymouth (Table 135)
b Change at Redhill and Reading
c From 12 September arr. 2158
e Until 11 July arr. 2350, by bus

Table 125

Sundays

until 12 July

London and Oxford → Swindon, Cheltenham Spa, Bristol, Weston-super-Mare and South Wales

Route Diagram - see first page of Table 125

		GW	GW 1◇	GW 1◇	GW 1◇	GW 1◇	GW 1◇	GW 1◇	GW 1◇	GW 1◇	GW 1◇	GW 1◇	GW	GW	GW 1◇	GW 1◇	GW 1◇
						A	B										
London Paddington 15 ⊖	d		13 37	14 00	14 27	14 37	15 00	15 37	16 00	16 27	16 37	17 00			17 30	17 37	18 00
London Waterloo 15 ⊖	d																
Slough 3	d		13 23	13 58	14 23		15 00	15 23	15 58	16 23		16 59			17 23		17 59
Heathrow Central Bus Stn 🚌	d		13 00	13 30	14 00		14 30	15 00	15 30	16 00		16 30			17 00		17 30
Gatwick Airport 10	d		12 08		13 08			14 08		15 08					16 08		
Reading 7	d		14 14	14 37	15 05	15 14	15 37	16 16	16 37	17 05	17 16	17 37			18 04	18 16	18 37
Oxford	d		14 05			15 05		16 05			17 05					18 05	
Didcot Parkway	d		14 30	14 53		15 30	15 53	16 32	16 53		17 32	17 53				18 32	18 53
Swindon	a		14 47	15 11	15 34	15 47	16 11	16 48	17 11	17 38	17 49	18 10			18 33	18 49	19 11
	d	14 21	14 47	15 11	15 35	15 47	16 11	16 51	17 11	17 39	17 51	18 11	18 22	18 31	18 33	18 51	19 11
Kemble	d	14 36			15 49					17 52			18 36				
Stroud	d	14 51			16 04					18 07			18 50				
Stonehouse	d	14 56			16 09					18 12			18 55				
Gloucester 7	a	15 19			16 25					18 28			19 18				
Cheltenham Spa	a	15 33			16 46					18 48			19 47				
Birmingham New Street 12	a	16 26			17 40					19 40			20b50				
Chippenham	d			15 26			16 26		17 26			18 26		18a47	18 52		19 26
Bath Spa 7	a			15 40			16 40		17 42			18 40			19 12		19 40
Bristol Parkway 7	a		15 14			16 16		17 17			18 16					19 16	
	d		15 16			16 16		17 18			18 18					19 18	
Bristol Temple Meads 10	a			15 55			16 55		17 57			18 55			19 28		19 55
Weston-super-Mare	a			16 57			17 36		18 34			19 37			20 02		20 36
Newport (South Wales)	a		15 37			16 39		17 39			18 41					19 39	
Hereford 7	a		17 02			17 49		18 44			19 47					20 52	
Cardiff Central 7	a		15 54			16 56		17 56			18 58					19 56	
Bridgend	a		16 16			17 18		18 18			19 19					20 18	
Port Talbot Parkway	a		16 29			17 31		18 31			19 32					20 31	
Neath	a		16 36			17 38		18 39			19 40					20 39	
Swansea 7	a		16 50			17 52		18 55			19 54					20 55	

		GW 1◇	GW 1◇	GW 1◇	SW 1◇	GW	GW 1◇	GW 1◇	GW 1◇	GW 1◇	GW 1◇	GW 1◇	GW 1◇	GW	GW 1◇	GW 1◇	GW 1◇
				C		D											
London Paddington 15 ⊖	d	18 27	18 37	19 00			19 30	19 37	20 00	20 29	20 37	21 00	21 37		22 03	23 03	23 37
London Waterloo 15 ⊖	d				18 15												
Slough 3	d	18 23		18 59			19 23		19 57	20 16		20 59	21 49		21 59	23 01	23 55
Heathrow Central Bus Stn 🚌	d	18 00		18 30			19 00		19 20	19 50		20 20	20 50		21 30	22 00	23 05
Gatwick Airport 10	d	17 08					18 08			19 08			20 08		21 08	22 07	
Reading 7	d	19 05	19 16	19 37			20 05	20 16	20 37	21 05	21 16	21 37	22 15		22 50	23 46	00 15
Oxford	d		19 05					20 05				21 21	21 50		22 21		
Didcot Parkway	d		19 32	19 53				20 32	20 53		21 32	21 53	22 32		23 06		
Swindon	a	19 34	19 49	20 11			20 34	20 49	21 10	21 34	21 51	22 14	22 50		23 25	00s22	00s52
	d	19 36	19 51	20 11		20 24	20 34	20 51	21 11	21 36	21 52	22 14	22 51	22 57	23 26		
Kemble	d	19 49				20 38				21 49				23 11			
Stroud	d	20 04				20 53				22 04				23 26			
Stonehouse	d	20 09				20 58				22 09				23 31			
Gloucester 7	a	20 25				21 16				22 25				23 47			
Cheltenham Spa	a	20 46				21 28				22 46				00 04			
Birmingham New Street 12	a	21 45				22 40				23 43							
Chippenham	d			20 26			20 49		21 26			22 28			23 41	00s37	01s08
Bath Spa 7	a			20 40	20 59		21 05		21 40			22 42			23 55	00s52	01s22
Bristol Parkway 7	a		20 16					21 16			22 17		23 17				
	d		20 18					21 18			22 19		23 18				
Bristol Temple Meads 10	a			20 55	21 16		21 22		21 55			22 58			00 10	01 06	01 38
Weston-super-Mare	a			21 27					23 03			23 32					
Newport (South Wales)	a		20 39					21 44			22 46		23 46				
Hereford 7	a		21 47								00 04						
Cardiff Central 7	a		20 56					22 04			23 07		00 06				
Bridgend	a		21 18					22 26			23 29		00 28				
Port Talbot Parkway	a		21 31					22 39			23 42		00 41				
Neath	a		21 38					22 47			23 49		00 49				
Swansea 7	a		21 52					23 00			00 03		01 02				

For general notes see front of timetable
For details of catering facilities see Directory of Train Operators

A To Carmarthen (Table 128)
B To Taunton (Table 134)
C To Exeter St Davids (Table 135)
D From Westbury (Table 123)
b Change at Gloucester and Cheltenham Spa

Table 125

Sundays

London and Oxford → Swindon, Cheltenham Spa, Bristol, Weston-super-Mare and South Wales

19 July to 6 September

Route Diagram - see first page of Table 125

		GW	GW 1 ◇	GW	GW		GW 1 ◇ A	GW	GW	GW 1 ◇		GW 1 ◇	GW 1 ◇	GW	GW		GW	GW 1 ◇	GW	GW 1 ◇		GW 1 ◇	GW 1 ◇ B	GW 1 ◇	GW 1 ◇
		(bus)	(trolley)	(bus)	(bus)		(trolley)	(bus)	(bus)	(trolley)		(trolley)	(trolley)	(bus)	(bus)		(bus)	(trolley)		(trolley)		(trolley)	(trolley)	(trolley)	(trolley)
London Paddington 15 ⊖	d		23p30				08 00			08 30		08 35	09 00					09 30		10 00		10 27	10 37	11 00	11 37
London Waterloo 15 ⊖	d																								
Slough 3	d						07 14			08 22		08 46	09 01					09 23		09 51		10 23		10 59	11 23
Heathrow Central Bus Stn (bus)	d						07 30			08 00			08 30					09 00		09 30		10 00		10 30	11 00
Gatwick Airport 10	d						07 08											08 08				09 08			10 08
Reading 7	d		23p59				08 38			09 16		09 20	09 37					10 05		10 37		11 05	11 14	11 37	12 14
Oxford	d						08 31			09 05								09 38		10 05			11 05		12 05
Didcot Parkway	d		00 18				08 55			09 31			09 53					10 21		10 53			11 30	11 53	12 30
Swindon	a		00 37				09 14			09 48		09 53	10 08					10 38		11 11		11 34	11 47	12 10	12 47
	d	23p49	00 37	00 43			09 14		09 20	09 50		09 55	10 10	10 20			10 20	10 40	10 45	11 21		11 35	11 47	12 21	12 47
Kemble	d											10 08							10 59			11 49			
Stroud	d											10 23							11 14			12 05			
Stonehouse	d											10 28							11 19			12 10			
Gloucester 7	a											10 44							11 35			12 26			
Cheltenham Spa	a							09 40				11 02							11 48			12 46			
Birmingham New Street 12	a											11 50							12 50			13 40			
Chippenham	d	00 24		01 18	08 25				09a55						10 40		10a55			11 37				12 38	
Bath Spa 7	a	00 59		01 53	09 00			10 15						11 10	11 15					12 00				12 59	
Bristol Parkway 7	a									10 15								11 05					12 14		13 14
	d									10 17								11 07					12 16		13 16
Bristol Temple Meads 10	a	01 29	01 15	02 23	09 43		09 49						10 47	11 40						12 16				13 13	
Weston-super-Mare	a						10 41						11 38							12 50				13 50	
Newport (South Wales)	a									10 38								11 30					12 37		13 39
Hereford 7	a									11 44								12 49					13 47		14 49
Cardiff Central 7	a									10 55								11 47					12 54		13 56
Bridgend	a									11 17								12 09					13 16		14 19
Port Talbot Parkway	a									11 30								12 22					13 29		14 31
Neath	a									11 37								12 29					13 36		14 38
Swansea 7	a									11 52								12 44					13 50		14 58

		GW 1 ◇ C	SW 1 ◇		GW 1 ◇	GW 1 ◇ B	GW 1 ◇	GW		GW 1 ◇	GW 1 ◇	GW 1 ◇	GW 1 ◇ B		GW 1 ◇ D	GW 1 ◇	GW 1 ◇	GW 1 ◇		GW 1 ◇	GW 1 ◇	GW	GW		GW 1 ◇
		(trolley)			(trolley)	(trolley)	(trolley)			(trolley)	(trolley)	(trolley)	(trolley)		(trolley)	(trolley)	(trolley)	(trolley)		(trolley)	(trolley)				(trolley)
London Paddington 15 ⊖	d	12 00			12 27	12 37	13 00			13 37	14 00	14 27	14 37		15 00	15 37	16 00	16 27		16 37	17 00				17 30
London Waterloo 15 ⊖	d		12 15																						
Slough 3	d	12 00			12 23		12 59			13 23	13 58	14 23			15 00	15 23	15 58	16 23			16 59				17 23
Heathrow Central Bus Stn (bus)	d	11 30			12 00		12 30			13 00	13 30	14 00			14 30	15 00	15 30	16 00			16 30				17 00
Gatwick Airport 10	d				11 08					12 08		13 08				14 08		15 08							16 08
Reading 7	d	12 37			13 05	13 14	13 37			14 14	14 37	15 05	15 14		15 37	16 16	16 37	17 05		17 16	17 37				18 04
Oxford	d					13 05				14 05			15 05			16 05				17 05					
Didcot Parkway	d	12 53				13 30	13 53			14 30	14 53		15 30		15 53	16 32	16 53			17 32	17 53				
Swindon	a	13 11			13 34	13 47	14 10			14 47	15 11	15 34	15 47		16 11	16 48	17 11	17 38		17 49	18 10				18 33
	d	13 21			13 40	13 47	14 21	14 21		14 47	15 11	15 35	15 47		16 11	16 51	17 11	17 39		17 51	18 11	18 22	18 31		18 33
Kemble	d				13 54			14 36				15 49						17 52				18 36			
Stroud	d				14 09			14 51				16 04						18 07				18 50			
Stonehouse	d				14 14			14 56				16 09						18 12				18 55			
Gloucester 7	a				14 32			15 19				16 25						18 28				19 18			
Cheltenham Spa	a				14 48			15 33				16 46						18 48				19 47			
Birmingham New Street 12	a				15 40			16 26				17 40						19 40				20b50			
Chippenham	d	13 38					14 38				15 26				16 26		17 26				18 26		18a47		18 52
Bath Spa 7	a	14 00	14 54				15 00				15 40				16 40		17 42				18 40				19 12
Bristol Parkway 7	a					14 14				15 14			16 16			17 17				18 16					
	d					14 16				15 16			16 16			17 18				18 18					
Bristol Temple Meads 10	a	14 16	15 08				15 15				15 55				16 55		17 57				18 55				19 28
Weston-super-Mare	a	15 48					16 26				16 57				17 36		18 34				19 37				20 02
Newport (South Wales)	a					14 39				15 37			16 39			17 39				18 41					
Hereford 7	a					16 02				17 02			17 49			18 44				19 47					
Cardiff Central 7	a					14 56				15 54			16 56			17 56				18 58					
Bridgend	a					15 18				16 16			17 18			18 18				19 19					
Port Talbot Parkway	a					15 31				16 29			17 31			18 31				19 32					
Neath	a					15 38				16 36			17 38			18 39				19 40					
Swansea 7	a					15 52				16 50			17 52			18 55				19 54					

For general notes see front of timetable
For details of catering facilities see Directory of Train Operators

- **A** To Penzance (Table 135)
- **B** To Carmarthen (Table 128)
- **C** To Plymouth (Table 135)
- **D** To Taunton (Table 134)
- **b** Change at Gloucester and Cheltenham Spa

Table 125

Sundays

19 July to 6 September

London and Oxford → Swindon, Cheltenham Spa, Bristol, Weston-super-Mare and South Wales

Route Diagram - see first page of Table 125

		GW	GW	GW	GW		GW	SW	GW	GW		GW	GW	GW	GW		GW	GW	GW	GW		GW	GW		
		1◇	1◇	1◇	1◇		1◇	1◇		1◇		1◇	1◇	1◇	1◇		1◇	1◇		1◇		1◇	1◇		
							A		B																
		☕	☕	☕	☕		☕			☕		☕	☕	☕	☕		☕	☕		☕		☕	☕		
London Paddington 15 ⊖	d	17 37	18 00	18 27	18 37		19 00			19 30		19 37	20 00	20 29	20 37		21 00	21 37		22 03		23 03	23 37		
London Waterloo 15 ⊖	d							18 15																	
Slough 3	d		*17 58*	*18 23*			*18 59*			*19 23*			*19 57*	*20 16*			*20 59*	*21 49*		*21 59*		*23 01*	23 55		
Heathrow Central Bus Stn 🚌	d		*17 30*	*18 00*			*18 30*			*19 00*			*19 20*	*19 50*			*20 20*	*20 50*		*21 30*		*22 00*	*23 05*		
Gatwick Airport 10	d			*17 08*						*18 08*				*19 08*				*20 08*		*21 08*		*22 07*	*22 07*		
Reading 7	d	18 16	18 37	19 05	19 16		19 37			20 05		20 16	20 37	21 05	21 16		21 37	22 15		22 50		23 46	00 15		
Oxford	d	*18 05*			*19 05*							*20 05*					*21 21*	*21 50*		*22 21*					
Didcot Parkway	d	18 32	18 53		19 32		19 53					20 32	20 53		21 32		21 53	22 32		23 06					
Swindon	a	18 49	19 11	19 34	19 49		20 11			20 34		20 49	21 10	21 34	21 51		22 14	22 50		23 25		00s22	00s52		
	d	18 51	19 11	19 36	19 51		20 11		20 24	20 34		20 51	21 11	21 36	21 52		22 14	22 51	22 57	23 26					
Kemble	d			19 49					20 38					21 49					23 11						
Stroud	d			20 04					20 53					22 04					23 26						
Stonehouse	d			20 09					20 58					22 09					23 31						
Gloucester 7	a			20 25					21 16					22 25					23 47						
Cheltenham Spa	a			20 46					21 28					22 46					00 04						
Birmingham New Street 12	a			*21 45*					*22 40*					*23 43*											
Chippenham	d		19 26				20 26			20 49			21 26				22 28			23 41		00s37	01s08		
Bath Spa 7	a		19 40				20 40	20 59		21 05			21 40				22 42			23 55		00s52	01s22		
Bristol Parkway 7	a	19 16			20 16							21 16			22 17			23 17							
	d	19 18			20 18							21 18			22 19			23 18							
Bristol Temple Meads 10	a		19 55				20 55	21 16		21 22			21 55				22 58			00 10		01 06	01 38		
Weston-super-Mare	a		*20 36*				21 27						*23 03*				23 32								
Newport (South Wales)	a	19 39			20 39							21 44			22 46			23 46							
Hereford 7	a	*20 52*			*21 47*										*00 04*										
Cardiff Central 7	a	19 56			20 56							22 04			23 07			00 06							
Bridgend	a	20 18			21 18							22 26			23 29			00 28							
Port Talbot Parkway	a	20 31			21 31							22 39			23 42			00 41							
Neath	a	20 39			21 38							22 47			23 49			00 49							
Swansea 7	a	20 55			21 52							23 00			00 03			01 02							

Sundays

from 13 September

		GW	GW		GW	GW		GW	GW		GW	GW		GW	GW		GW	GW		GW	GW		GW	GW	SW
		1◇	1◇		1◇	1◇		1◇	1◇			1◇		1◇	1◇		1◇	1◇		1◇	1◇		1◇	1◇	1◇
			C												D					E			D		
		☕	☕		☕	☕		☕	☕			☕		☕	☕		☕	☕		☕	☕		☕	☕	
London Paddington 15 ⊖	d	23p30	08 00		08 30			09 03	09 30			10 03			10 37		11 03	11 37		12 03			12 37	13 03	
London Waterloo 15 ⊖	d																								12 15
Slough 3	d		*07 14*		*08 25*			*09 01*	*09 15*			*09 57*			*10 15*		*11 05*	*11 15*		*12 02*			*12 15*	*13 05*	
Heathrow Central Bus Stn 🚌	d		*07 30*		*08 00*			*08 30*	*09 00*			*09 30*			*10 00*		*10 30*	*11 00*		*11 30*			*12 00*	*12 30*	
Gatwick Airport 10	d		*06 06*		*07 08*				*08 08*						*09 08*			*10 08*					*11 08*		
Reading 7	d	23p59	08 34		09 05			09 37	10 05			10 37			11 11		11 37	12 11		12 37			13 11	13 37	
Oxford	d		*07b45*					*09 05*	*09 50*			*10 05*			*11 05*			*12 05*					*13 05*		
Didcot Parkway	d	00 18	08 49		09 22			09 53	10 21			10 53			11 27		11 53	12 27		12 53			13 27	13 53	
Swindon	a	00 37	09 08		09 40			10 10	10 38			11 10			11 44		12 10	12 44		13 11			13 44	14 10	
	d	00 37	09 08		09 42	09 55		10 10	10 40		10 45	11 10		11 35	11 46		12 10	12 46		13 11	13 40		13 46	14 11	
Kemble	d					10 08					10 59			11 49							13 54				
Stroud	d					10 23					11 14			12 05							14 09				
Stonehouse	d					10 28					11 19			12 10							14 14				
Gloucester 7	a					10 44					11 35			12 26							14 32				
Cheltenham Spa	a					11 02					11 48			12 46							14 49				
Birmingham New Street 12	a					*11c50*					*12e45*			*13f40*							*15g40*				
Chippenham	d	00 52	09 25					10 27				11 26					12 26			13 26				14 26	
Bath Spa 7	a	01 07	09 38					10 42				11 41					12 40			13 40				14 40	14 54
Bristol Parkway 7	a				10 07				11 05						12 11			13 11					14 11		
	d				10 09				11 07						12 13			13 13					14 13		
Bristol Temple Meads 10	a	01 23	09 52					10 58				11 57					12 54			13 56				14 55	15 08
Weston-super-Mare	a		*10 41*					*11 38*				12 34					13 32			*14 37*				*15 48*	*16 26*
Newport (South Wales)	a				10 30				11 30						12 34			13 34					14 34		
Hereford 7	a				*11 44*				*12 49*						*13 47*			*14 49*					*16 02*		
Cardiff Central 7	a				10 47				11 47						12 51			13 51					14 51		
Bridgend	a				11 09				12 09						13 13			14 13					15 13		
Port Talbot Parkway	a				11 23				12 22						13 26			14 26					15 26		
Neath	a				11 31				12 29						13 33			14 33					15 33		
Swansea 7	a				11 45				12 44						13 47			14 49					15 47		

For general notes see front of timetable
For details of catering facilities see Directory of Train Operators

A To Exeter St Davids (Table 135)
B From Westbury (Table 123)
C To Penzance (Table 135)
D To Carmarthen (Table 128)
E To Plymouth (Table 135)
b By bus
c From 8 November arr. 1232
e From 8 November arr. 1323
f From 8 November arr. 1422
g From 8 November arr. 1611

Sundays
from 13 September

London and Oxford → Swindon, Cheltenham Spa, Bristol, Weston-super-Mare and South Wales

Route Diagram - see first page of Table 125

		GW	GW	GW	GW	GW	GW	GW	GW	GW	GW	GW	GW	GW	GW	GW	GW
				1 ◇	1 ◇	1 ◇	1 ◇	1 ◇	1 ◇	1 ◇	1 ◇	1 ◇	1 ◇			1 ◇	1 ◇
		A	B				C	D									
				☕	☕	☕	☕	☕	☕	☕	☕	☕	☕			☕	☕
London Paddington [15] ⊖	d			13 37	14 03		14 37	15 03	15 37	16 03	16 27	16 37	17 03			17 30	17 37
London Waterloo [15] ⊖	d																
Slough [3]	d			13 15	14 05		14 15	15 05	15 15	16 05	16 15		17 03			17 15	
Heathrow Central Bus Stn 🚌	d			13 00	13 30		14 00	14 30	15 00	15 30	16 00		16 30			17 00	
Gatwick Airport [10]	d			12 08			13 08		14 08		15 08					16 08	
Reading [7]	d			14 11	14 37		15 11	15 37	16 11	16 37	17 05	17 11	17 37			18 04	18 11
Oxford	d			14 05			15 05		16 05			17 05					18 05
Didcot Parkway	d			14 27	14 53		15 27	15 53	16 27	16 53		17 27	17 53				18 27
Swindon	a			14 43	15 11		15 44	16 11	16 43	17 11	17 38	17 44	18 10			18 33	18 44
	d	14 21	14 21	14 46	15 11	15 35	15 46	16 11	16 46	17 11	17 39	17 46	18 11	18 22	18 31	18 33	18 46
Kemble	d	14 36	14 36			15 49					17 52			18 36			
Stroud	d	14 51	14 51			16 04					18 07			18 50			
Stonehouse	d	14 56	14 56			16 09					18 12			18 55			
Gloucester [7]	a	15 19	15 19			16 25					18 28			19 18			
Cheltenham Spa	a	15 33	15 37			16 46					18 48			19 47			
Birmingham New Street [12]	a	16 26	17 11			17b41					19c40			20e55			
Chippenham	d				15 26			16 26		17 26			18 26		18a47	18 52	
Bath Spa [7]	a				15 40			16 40		17 42			18 40			19 12	
Bristol Parkway [7]	a			15 11			16 13		17 12			18 11					19 13
	d			15 13			16 13		17 13			18 13					19 13
Bristol Temple Meads [10]	a				15 55			16 55		17 57			18 55			19 28	
Weston-super-Mare	a				16 57			17 36		18 34			19 37			20 02	
Newport (South Wales)	a			15 34			16 39		17 38			18 39					19 37
Hereford [7]	a			17 02			17 49		18 44			19 47					20 52
Cardiff Central [7]	a			15 51			16 56		17 54			18 57					19 54
Bridgend	a			16 13			17 18		18 16			19 20					20 17
Port Talbot Parkway	a			16 26			17 31		18 29			19 33					20 30
Neath	a			16 33			17 38		18 37			19 41					20 38
Swansea [7]	a			16 47			17 52		18 53			19 54					20 54

		GW	GW	GW	GW	SW	GW	GW	GW	GW	GW	GW	GW	GW	GW	GW	GW	GW	GW
		1 ◇	1 ◇	1 ◇	1 ◇	1 ◇		1 ◇	1 ◇	1 ◇	1 ◇	1 ◇	1 ◇	1 ◇		1 ◇	1 ◇	1 ◇	1 ◇
					E		G												
		☕	☕	☕	☕			☕	☕	☕	☕	☕	☕	☕		☕	☕	☕	☕
London Paddington [15] ⊖	d	18 03	18 27	18 37	19 03			19 30	19 37	20 03	20 29	20 37	21 03	21 37		22 03	22 37	23 03	23 37
London Waterloo [15] ⊖	d					18 15													
Slough [3]	d	18 03	18 15		19 06			19 15		20 05	20 15		21 05	21 53			22 15	23 01	23 15
Heathrow Central Bus Stn 🚌	d	17 30	18 00		18 30			19 00		19 20	19 50		20 20	20 50		21 30	22 00		23 05
Gatwick Airport [10]	d		17 08					18 08			19 08			20 08		21 08		22 07	22 07
Reading [7]	d	18 37	19 05	19 11	19 37			20 05	20 11	20 37	21 05	21 11	21 37	22 14		22 50	23 14	23 46	00 15
Oxford	d			19 05					20 05			20 50	21 21	21 50		22 50			
Didcot Parkway	d	18 53		19 27	19 53				20 27	20 53		21 27	21 53	22 30		23 06			
Swindon	a	19 11	19 34	19 44	20 11			20 34	20 45	21 10	21 34	21 45	22 14	22 48		23 25	23s49	00s22	00s52
	d	19 11	19 36	19 46	20 11		20 28	20 34	20 46	21 11	21 36	21 46	22 14	22 51	22 57	23 26			
Kemble	d		19 49				20 42				21 49				23 11				
Stroud	d		20 04				20 57				22 04				23 26				
Stonehouse	d		20 09				21 02				22 09				23 31				
Gloucester [7]	a		20 28				21 17				22 25				23 47				
Cheltenham Spa	a		20 46				21 34				22 46				00 04				
Birmingham New Street [12]	a		21f45				22g40				23g43								
Chippenham	d	19 26			20 26			20 49		21 26			22 28			23 41		00s37	01s08
Bath Spa [7]	a	19 40			20 40	20 59		21 05		21 40			22 42			23 55		00s52	01s22
Bristol Parkway [7]	a			20 11					21 11			22 11		23 17			00s16		
	d			20 13					21 13			22 13		23 18					
Bristol Temple Meads [10]	a	19 55			20 55	21 16		21 22		21 55			22 58			00 10	00 30	01 06	01 38
Weston-super-Mare	a	20h36			21 27					23 03			23 32						
Newport (South Wales)	a			20 34					21 34			22 40		23 46					
Hereford [7]	a			21 47								00 04							
Cardiff Central [7]	a			20 51					21 51			23 01		00 06					
Bridgend	a			21 13					22 13			23 23		00 28					
Port Talbot Parkway	a			21 26					22 26			23 36		00 41					
Neath	a			21 33					22 33			23 43		00 49					
Swansea [7]	a			21 47					22 47			23 57		01 02					

For general notes see front of timetable
For details of catering facilities see Directory of Train Operators

A Until 1 November
B From 8 November
C To Carmarthen (Table 128)
D To Taunton (Table 134)
E To Exeter St Davids (Table 135)
G From Westbury (Table 123)
b From 8 November arr. 1811
c From 8 November arr. 2011
e Change at Gloucester and Cheltenham Spa. From 8 November arr. 2127
f From 8 November arr. 2220
g From 8 November arr. 2355
h From 8 November arr. 2053

South Wales, Weston-super-Mare, Bristol, Cheltenham Spa and Swindon → Oxford and London

Route Diagram - see first page of Table 125

Miles	Miles	Miles			GW 1◇	GW	GW 1◇	GW 1◇	GW 1◇	GW 1◇	GW 1◇	GW 1◇	GW 1◇	GW 1◇	GW 1◇	GW 1◇	GW	GW 1◇	GW 1◇	GW 1◇	GW 1◇	GW 1◇	GW 1◇	GW	GW 1◇
						A							B				C					D			E
					☕		☕	☕	☕	☕	☕	☕	☕	☕	☕	☕		☕	☕	☕	☕	☕	☕		☕
0	—	—	**Swansea 7**	d				03 59		04 58				05 27				05 59		06 29			06 59		
9½	—	—	Neath	d				04 10		05 10				05 39				06 10		06 40			07 10		
15	—	—	Port Talbot Parkway	d				04 18		05 18				05 46				06 18		06 48			07 18		
27¼	—	—	Bridgend	d				04 30		05 29				05 58				06 30		07 00			07 30		
47½	—	—	**Cardiff Central 7**	d				05 15		05 54				06 23				06 55		07 25			07 55		
—	—	—	Hereford 7	d										05 23						06 42			07 13		
59¼	—	—	Newport (South Wales)	d				05 33		06 08				06 37				07 09		07 39			08 09		
—	0	—	Weston-super-Mare	d									06 01			06 20			06 49			07 24			07 49
—	19	—	**Bristol Temple Meads 10**	d	04 47		05 30		06 00			06 30	06 40			07 00			07 30			08 00		08 13	08 30
81	—	—	Bristol Parkway 7	a				06 00		06 29				06 58				07 30		08 00			08 31		
—	—	—		d	04u57			06 01		06 31				07 00				07 32		08 02			08 32		
—	30½	—	Bath Spa 7	d			05 43		06 13			06 43	06 52			07 13			07 43			08 13		08 31	08 43
—	43½	—	Chippenham	d			05 55		06 25			06 55	07 05			07 25	07 30		07 55			08 25		08 45	08 55
—	—	—	Birmingham New Street 12	d											05 00						06 42				
—	—	0	**Cheltenham Spa**	d							05 55				06 30						07 30				
—	—	6½	Gloucester 7	d		05 19					06 12				06 47						07 45				
—	—	15½	Stonehouse	d		05 32					06 25				07 00						07 59				
—	—	18	Stroud	d		05 37					06 31				07 06						08 04				
—	—	29¼	Kemble	d		05 51					06 46				07 21						08 19				
115½	60¼	43	**Swindon**	a	05 23	06 06	06 09	06 27	06 39	06 56	07 00	07 09	07 19	07 25	07 35	07 39	07 48	07 57	08 09	08 27	08 33	08 40	08 58	09 04	09 10
—	—	—		d	05 23		06 11	06 28	06 41	06 58	07 02	07 11	07 21	07 27	07 36	07 41		07 59	08 11	08 29	08 35	08 41	08 59		09 11
139½	84¼	67	Didcot Parkway	a	05 41		06 28	06 45	06 58		07 19	07 28		07 43	07 54	08 00		08 16	08 28	08 46	08 52	08 58			09 28
—	—	—	Oxford	a	06 22		06 53		07 20		07 39			08 00		08 31		08 42		09 16		09 40			09 52
156¾	101½	84½	**Reading 7**	a	05 57		06 43	07 02	07 14	07 29	07 36	07 44		08 01	08 13	08 16		08 33	08 44	09 02	09 08	09 14	09 27		09 44
—	—	—	Gatwick Airport 10	a	07 50				09 01							09 58							10 50		
—	—	—	Heathrow Terminal 1 Bus	a	07 29		08 09	08 29	08 49			09 09		09 29		09 49			09 59		10 19		10 39		10 59
174¼	119	101¾	Slough 3	a	06 32		06 58	07 36	07 55	08 07		08 20		08 37		08 57			09 24		09 44		09 51		10 09
—	—	—	**London Waterloo 15** ⊖	a																					
192¾	137½	120¼	**London Paddington 15** ⊖	a	06 24		07 16	07 32	07 44	08 02	08 07	08 14	08 17	08 32	08 40	08 44		09 06	09 14	09 29	09 39	09 44	09 59		10 14

		GW 1◇	GW 1◇	SW 1◇	GW 1◇		GW 1◇	GW 1◇	GW 1◇	GW 1◇	GW	GW 1◇	GW 1◇	GW 1◇	GW 1◇	GW 1◇	GW 1◇	GW 1◇	GW 1◇	GW 1◇	GW	GW 1◇	GW 1◇	GW 1◇	GW 1◇
									G	H										J					
		☕	☕		☕		☕	☕	☕	☕		☕	☕	☕	☕	☕	☕	☕	☕	☕		☕	☕	☕	☕
Swansea 7	d	07 29					07 59		08 29					09 29					10 29					11 29	
Neath	d	07 40					08 10		08 40					09 40					10 40					11 40	
Port Talbot Parkway	d	07 48					08 18		08 48					09 48					10 48					11 48	
Bridgend	d	08 00					08 30		09 00					10 00					11 00					12 00	
Cardiff Central 7	d	08 25					08 55		09 25			09 55		10 25			10 55		11 25			11 55		12 25	
Hereford 7	d	07 44					08 14		08 42								10 12		10 42					11 42	
Newport (South Wales)	d	08 39					09 09		09 39			10 09		10 39			11 09		11 39			12 09		12 39	
Weston-super-Mare	d				08 06			08 40		09 28			09 45			10 10		10 40		11 10			11 45		
Bristol Temple Meads 10	d			08 50	09 00			09 30		10 00			10 30			11 00		11 30		12 00			12 30		
Bristol Parkway 7	a	09 00					09 30		10 00			10 30		11 00			11 30		12 00			12 30		13 00	
	d	09 02					09 32		10 02			10 32		11 02			11 32		12 02			12 32		13 02	
Bath Spa 7	d			09 07	09 13			09 43		10 13			10 43			11 13		11 43		12 13			12 43		
Chippenham	d				09 25			09 55		10 25			10 55			11 25		11 55		12 25			12 55		
Birmingham New Street 12	d		07 42								08 42				09 42						10 42				11 42
Cheltenham Spa	d		08 31								09 40				10 31						11 40				12 31
Gloucester 7	d		08 46								09 54				10 46						11 54				12 46
Stonehouse	d		08 59								10 06				10 59						12 06				12 59
Stroud	d		09 04								10 11				11 04						12 11				13 04
Kemble	d		09 19								10 25				11 19						12 25				13 19
Swindon	a	09 27	09 34		09 39		09 57	10 09	10 27	10 41	10 42	10 57	11 09	11 27	11 34	11 39	11 57	12 09	12 27	12 40	12 42	12 57	13 09	13 27	13 34
	d	09 29	09 35		09 41		09 59	10 11	10 29	10 41		10 59	11 11	11 29	11 35	11 41	11 59	12 11	12 29	12 41		12 59	13 11	13 29	13 35
Didcot Parkway	a		09 52				10 16	10 28	10 46			11 16	11 28		11 52		12 16	12 28	12 46			13 16	13 28		13 52
Oxford	a						10 40		11 14			11 40	11 52				12 40		13 12			13 40	13 51		
Reading 7	a	10 01	10 07		10 09		10 32	10 44	11 01	11 11		11 32	11 44	12 00	12 07	12 09	12 32	12 44	13 01	13 11		13 32	13 44	14 00	14 07
Gatwick Airport 10	a				11 50					12 50						13 50				14 50					
Heathrow Terminal 1 Bus	a				11 19			11 59	12 19	12 39			12 59			13 19		13 59	14 19	14 39			14 59		
Slough 3	a				10 39			11 09		11 39			12 09			12 39		13 09		13 39			14 09		
London Waterloo 15 ⊖	a			11 49																					
London Paddington 15 ⊖	a	10 30	10 37		10 49		11 02	11 14	11 32	11 40		12 00	12 14	12 32	12 39	12 42	13 08	13 14	13 30	13 40		14 06	14 14	14 32	14 37

For general notes see front of timetable
For details of catering facilities see Directory of Train Operators

- **A** To Southampton Central (Table 123)
- **B** Until 26 June and from 7 September
- **C** To Cheltenham Spa
- **D** From Exeter St Davids (Table 135)
- **E** From Plymouth (Table 135)
- **G** From Carmarthen (Table 128)
- **H** From Paignton (Table 135)
- **J** From Penzance (Table 135)

South Wales, Weston-super-Mare, Bristol, Cheltenham Spa and Swindon → Oxford and London

Route Diagram - see first page of Table 125

		GW 1 ◇ ☕	SW 1 ◇	GW 1 ◇ ☕	GW 1 ◇ ☕	GW 1 ◇ ☕	GW 1 ◇ ☕		GW	GW 1 ◇ ☕	GW 1 ◇ ☕	GW 1 ◇ ☕	GW 1 ◇ ☕	GW 1 ◇ ☕	GW 1 ◇ ☕	GW 1 ◇ ☕	GW 1 ◇ ☕	SW 1 ◇	GW 1 ◇ ☕	GW	GW 1 ◇ ☕	GW 1 ◇ ☕	GW 1 ◇ ☕	GW 1 ◇ ☕	GW 1 ◇ ☕
Swansea 7	d					12 29						13 29					14 29						15 29		
Neath	d					12 40						13 40					14 40						15 40		
Port Talbot Parkway	d					12 48						13 48					14 48						15 48		
Bridgend	d					13 00						14 00					15 00						16 00		
Cardiff Central 7	d			12 55		13 25				13 55		14 25			14 55		15 25				15 55		16 25		
Hereford 7	d			12 12		12 42						13 42			14 12		14 42						15 42		
Newport (South Wales)	d			13 09		13 39				14 09		14 39			15 09		15 39				16 09		16 39		
Weston-super-Mare	d	12 10			12 40		13 10				13 40			14 10		14 40			15 10			15 46			16 10
Bristol Temple Meads 10	d	13 00	13 10		13 30		14 00				14 30			15 00		15 30		15 52	16 00			16 30			17 00
Bristol Parkway 7	a			13 30		14 00				14 30		15 00			15 30		16 00				16 30		17 00		
	d			13 32		14 02				14 32		15 02			15 32		16 02				16 32		17 02		
Bath Spa 7	d	13 13	13 22		13 43		14 13				14 43			15 13		15 43		16 07	16 13			16 43			17 13
Chippenham	d	13 25			13 55		14 25				14 55			15 25		15 55			16 25			16 55			17 25
Birmingham New Street 12	d								12 42				13 42							14 42				15 42	
Cheltenham Spa	d								13 40				14 31							15 40				16 31	
Gloucester 7	d								13 54				14 46							15 54				16 46	
Stonehouse	d								14 06				14 59							16 06				16 59	
Stroud	d								14 11				15 04							16 11				17 04	
Kemble	d								14 25				15 19							16 25				17 19	
Swindon	a	13 39		13 57	14 09	14 27	14 39		14 42	14 57	15 09	15 27	15 34	15 39	15 57	16 09	16 27		16 39	16 42	16 57	17 09	17 27	17 34	17 39
	d	13 41		13 59	14 11	14 29	14 41			14 59	15 11	15 29	15 35	15 41	15 59	16 11	16 29		16 41		16 59	17 11	17 29	17 35	17 41
Didcot Parkway	a			14 16	14 28	14 46				15 16	15 28		15 52		16 16	16 28	16 46				17 16	17 28		17 52	
Oxford	a			14 40		15 12				15 40	15 50				16 40		17 16				17 44	17 48			
Reading 7	a	14 09		14 32	14 44	15 01	15 09			15 32	15 44	16 01	16 07	16 11	16 32	16 44	17 01		17 09		17 32	17 44	17 57	18 07	18 13
Gatwick Airport 10	a	15 50					16 58							17 54					19 00						19 53
Heathrow Terminal 1 Bus	a	15 19			15 59		16 19				16 59		17 19	17 39		17 59			18 19			18 59			19 29
Slough 3	a	14 39			15 09		15 39				16 09			16 39		17 09			17 31		18 07	18 16			18 39
London Waterloo 15 ⊖	a		16 19															18 45							
London Paddington 15 ⊖	a	14 40		15 07	15 14	15 30	15 39			16 09	16 14	16 30	16 39	16 44	17 01	17 14	17 30		17 39		18 02	18 14	18 24	18 39	18 44

		GW 1 ◇ ☕	GW 1 ◇ ☕	GW 1 ◇ ☕	GW 1 ◇ ☕	GW A	GW 1 ◇ ☕	GW 1 ◇ ☕	GW 1 ◇ ☕	GW 1 ◇ ☕	GW 1 ◇ ☕	GW B	GW 1 ◇ ☕	GW	GW 1 ◇ ☕	GW FO 1 ◇ ☕	GW FX 1 ◇ ☕	GW 1	C ☕	GW FO 1 ◇ ☕	GW FX 1 ◇ ☕	GW	GW 1 ◇ D ☕		
Swansea 7	d			16 29					17 29				18 29			19 29	19 29			20 29	20 29				
Neath	d			16 40					17 40				18 40			19 40	19 40			20 40	20 40				
Port Talbot Parkway	d			16 48					17 48				18 48			19 48	19 48			20 48	20 48				
Bridgend	d			17 00					18 00				19 00			20 00	20 00			21 00	21 00				
Cardiff Central 7	d	16 55		17 25			17 55		18 25				19 25			20 25	20 25			21 25	21 25				
Hereford 7	d	16 12		16 42									18 42							20 10	20 10				
Newport (South Wales)	d	17 09		17 39			18 09		18 39				19 39			20 39	20 39			21 39	21 39				
Weston-super-Mare	d		17 10		17 16			18 10			18 40				19 51								21 58		
Bristol Temple Meads 10	d		17 30		18 00			18 30			19 30				20 30				21 47				22 33		
Bristol Parkway 7	a	17 30		18 00			18 30		19 00				20 00			21 02	21 02			22 02	22 02				
	d	17 32		18 02			18 32		19 02				20 02			21 02	21 02			22 02	22 02				
Bath Spa 7	d		17 43		18 13			18 43			19 43				20 43				22 00				22 46		
Chippenham	d		17 55		18 25			18 55			19 55	20 02			20 55				22 12				22 58		
Birmingham New Street 12	d					16 42				17 42				19 12				19 42				21 12			
Cheltenham Spa	d					17 40				18 31				20 00				20 48				22 00			
Gloucester 7	d					17 54				18 52				20 13				21 05				22 13			
Stonehouse	d					18 06				19 05				20 25				21 18				22 25			
Stroud	d					18 11				19 10				20 30				21 23				22 30			
Kemble	d					18 25				19 24				20 44				21 37				22 45			
Swindon	a	17 57	18 09	18 27	18 39	18 41	18 57	19 09	19 27	19 40	20 09	20 21	20 27	21 02	21 09	21 29	21 29	21 53	22 27	22 32	22 32	23 02	23 14		
	d	17 59	18 11	18 29	18 41		18 59	19 11	19 29	19 41	20 11		20 29		21 11	21 29	21 29		22 33	22 33	22 33		23 15		
Didcot Parkway	a	18 16	18 28	18 46			19 16	19 28		19 58	20 28		20 46		21 27	21 50	21 50		22 46				23 33		
Oxford	a	18 45	19 02	19 14			19 45	20 14		20 26			21 12			22 15	22 15		23 15				00 23		
Reading 7	a	18 32	18 47	19 01	19 09		19 32	19 45	20 00	20 14	20 44		21 01		21 43	22 11	22 11		23 03	23 07	23 07		23 55		
Gatwick Airport 10	a				20 50					22 04			23 04			00 10	00 10			01 02	01 02				
Heathrow Terminal 1 Bus	a		19 59		20 29			20 55		21 25	21 55				22 55	23 55	23 55								
Slough 3	a		19 09		19 39			20 09	20 44	20 54	21 09		21 39		22b25	22 54	22 58			23 41	23 41		00 40		
London Waterloo 15 ⊖	a																								
London Paddington 15 ⊖	a	19 02	19 14	19 32	19 38		20 07	20 14	20 32	20 46	21 14		21 32		22 14	22 44	22 55		23 40	23 41	23 51		00 33		

For general notes see front of timetable
For details of catering facilities see Directory of Train Operators

A From Worcester Foregate Street (Table 71) to Southampton Central (Table 123)
B To Cheltenham Spa
C From Penzance (Table 135)
D From Taunton (Table 134)
b Fridays arr. 2221

South Wales, Weston-super-Mare, Bristol, Cheltenham Spa and Swindon → Oxford and London

Route Diagram - see first page of Table 125

		GW	GW	GW	GW	GW	GW	GW	GW	GW	GW	GW	GW	GW	GW	GW	SW	GW	GW	GW	GW	GW
		1◇		1◇	1◇	1◇	1◇	1◇	1◇	1◇	1◇	1◇	1◇	1◇	1◇	1◇	1◇	1◇		1◇	1◇	1◇
													A					B		C		D
		☕		☕	☕	☕	☕	☕	☕	☕	☕	☕	☕	☕	☕	☕		☕		☕	☕	☕
Swansea [7]	d			03 59	04 59		05 29		05 59		06 29			06 59		07 29				07 59		
Neath	d			04 10	05 10		05 40		06 10		06 40			07 10		07 40				08 10		
Port Talbot Parkway	d			04 18	05 18		05 48		06 18		06 48			07 18		07 48				08 18		
Bridgend	d			04 30	05 30		06 00		06 30		07 00			07 30		08 00				08 30		
Cardiff Central [7]	d			04 55	05 55		06 25		06 55		07 25			07 55		08 25				08 55		
Hereford [7]	d						*05 42*							*07 13*		*07 48*				*08 14*		
Newport (South Wales)	d			05 09	06 09		06 39		07 09		07 39			08 09		08 39				09 09		
Weston-super-Mare	d							06 24					07 25		*07 39*			08 29				*08 40*
Bristol Temple Meads [10]	d	05 30		06 00		06 30		07 00		07 30			08 00		08 30		08 50	09 00				09 30
Bristol Parkway [7]	a			05 37	06 30		07 00		07 30		08 00			08 31		09 00				09 30		
	d			05 42	06 32		07 02		07 32		08 02			08 32		09 02				09 32		
Bath Spa [7]	d	05 43		06 13		06 43		07 13		07 43			08 13		08 43		09 07	09 13				09 43
Chippenham	d	05 55		06 25		06 55		07 25		07 55			08 25		08 55			09 25	09 30			09 55
Birmingham New Street [12]	d											*06 42*									*08 12*	
Cheltenham Spa	d		05 30									07 29									09 00	
Gloucester [7]	d		05 44									07 45									09 16	
Stonehouse	d		05 56									07 57									09 29	
Stroud	d		06 01									08 03									09 34	
Kemble	d		06 16									08 17									09 48	
Swindon	a	06 09	06 32	06 39	06 57	07 09	07 27	07 40	07 57	08 09	08 27	08 33	08 39	08 58	09 09	09 27		09 39	09 49	09 57	10 02	10 09
	d	06 11		06 41	06 59	07 11	07 29	07 41	07 59	08 11	08 29	08 35	08 41	08 59	09 11	09 29		09 41		09 59	10 04	10 11
Didcot Parkway	a	06 28		06 58	07 16	07 28	07 46	07 59	08 16	08 28	08 46	08 51	08 58	09 16	09 28	09 46				10 16	10 21	10 28
Oxford	a	*06 56*			*07 43*		*08 09*		*08 40*		*09 14*			*09 40*		*10 14*				*10 40*		
Reading [7]	a	06 43		07 14	07 32	07 44	08 01	08 14	08 32	08 44	09 02	09 07	09 14	09 33	09 44	10 01		10 09		10 32	10 35	10 45
Gatwick Airport [10]	a			*08 50*				*09 50*					*10 50*					*11 50*				
Heathrow Terminal 1 Bus	a	*08 09*		*08 39*		*09 09*		*09 39*		*10 09*			*10 39*		*11 09*			*11 39*				*12 09*
Slough [3]	a	*07 16*		*07 54*		*08 09*		*08 39*		*09 10*			*09 39*		*10 09*			*10 40*				*11 09*
London Waterloo [15] ⊖	a																11 49					
London Paddington [15] ⊖	a	07 14		07 44	08 02	08 14	08 32	08 44	09 02	09 14	09 32	09 37	09 44	10 02	10 14	10 32		10 38		11 02	11 08	11 14

		GW	GW	GW	GW	GW	GW	GW	GW	GW	GW	GW	GW	GW	GW	GW	GW	GW	GW	GW	SW	GW
		1◇	1◇	1◇		1◇	1◇	1◇	1◇	1◇	1◇	1	1◇	1◇	1◇		1◇	1◇	1◇	1◇	1◇	1◇
		E							C	D	C	G	H	D	C							C
		☕	☕	☕		☕	☕	☕	☕	☕	☕	☕	☕	☕	☕		☕	☕	☕	☕		☕
Swansea [7]	d		08 29				09 29						10 29					11 29				
Neath	d		08 40				09 40						10 40					11 40				
Port Talbot Parkway	d		08 48				09 48						10 48					11 48				
Bridgend	d		09 00				10 00						11 00					12 00				
Cardiff Central [7]	d		09 25				10 25						11 25					12 25				
Hereford [7]	d		*08 42*				*09 47*						*10 42*					*11 44*				
Newport (South Wales)	d		09 39				10 39						11 39					12 39				
Weston-super-Mare	d	09 02		*09 10*		*09 40*		*10 10*			*10 43*	*10 43*		11 33	*11 09*		*11 40*		*12 10*			*12 40*
Bristol Temple Meads [10]	d	09 30		10 00		10 30		11 00			11 30	11 30		12 00	12 00		12 30		13 00		13 15	13 30
Bristol Parkway [7]	a		10 00				11 00						12 00					13 00				
	d		10 02				11 02						12 02					13 02				
Bath Spa [7]	d	09 43		10 13		10 43		11 13			11 43	11 43		12 13	12 13		12 43		13 13		13 27	13 43
Chippenham	d	09 55		10 25		10 55		11 25			11 55	11 55		12 25	12 25		12 55		13 25			13 55
Birmingham New Street [12]	d				*09 12*				*10 12*	*10 12*						*11 12*				*12 12*		
Cheltenham Spa	d				10 01				11 00	11 00						12 01				13 00		
Gloucester [7]	d				10 15				11 16	11 16						12 15				13 16		
Stonehouse	d				10 27				11 29	11 29						12 27				13 29		
Stroud	d				10 32				11 34	11 34						12 32				13 34		
Kemble	d				10 47				11 48	11 48						12 47				13 48		
Swindon	a	10 09	10 27	10 39	11 02	11 09	11 27	11 39	12 02	12 02	12 09	12 09	12 27	12 40	12 40	13 02	13 09	13 27	13 39	14 02		14 09
	d	10 11	10 29	10 41		11 11	11 29	11 41	12 04	12 04	12 11	12 11	12 29	12 41	12 41		13 11	13 29	13 41	14 04		14 11
Didcot Parkway	a	10 28	10 46			11 28	11 46		12 21	12 21	12 28	12 28	12 46				13 28	13 46		14 21		14 28
Oxford	a		*11 14*				*12 14*						*13 14*					*14 14*				
Reading [7]	a	10 45	11 01	11 12		11 44	12 02	12 09	12 36	12 36	12 44	12 48	13 01	13 09	13 10		13 44	14 02	14 09	14 36		14 43
Gatwick Airport [10]	a			*12 50*				*13 50*						*14 50*	*14 50*				*15 50*			
Heathrow Terminal 1 Bus	a	*12 09*		*12 39*		*13 09*		*13 39*			*14 09*	*14 09*		*14 39*	*14 39*		*15 09*		*15 39*			*16 09*
Slough [3]	a	*11 09*		*11 40*		*12 09*		*12b39*			*13 09*	*13 09*		*13 40*	*13 40*		*14 10*		*14 39*			*15 09*
London Waterloo [15] ⊖	a																				16 19	
London Paddington [15] ⊖	a	11 14	11 32	11 40		12 14	12 32	12 39	13 06	13 10	13 14	13 22	13 32	13 39	13 41		14 14	14 32	14 39	15 09		15 14

For general notes see front of timetable
For details of catering facilities see Directory of Train Operators

A From Taunton (Table 134)
B From Exeter St Davids (Table 135)
C From 12 September
D Until 5 September
E From 12 September. From Paignton (Table 135)
G Until 5 September. From Paignton (Table 135)
H From Carmarthen (Table 128)
b From 12 September arr. 1240

South Wales, Weston-super-Mare, Bristol, Cheltenham Spa and Swindon → Oxford and London

Route Diagram - see first page of Table 125

		GW 1◇ A	GW 1◇ B	GW 1◇ C	GW 1◇		GW	GW 1◇	GW 1◇ C	GW 1◇ A	GW 1◇	GW		GW 1◇	GW 1◇ C	GW 1◇ A	GW 1◇	SW 1◇	GW 1◇		GW	GW 1◇	GW 1◇	GW 1◇	GW 1◇
Swansea 7	d		12 29	12 29					13 29	13 29							14 29						15 29		
Neath	d		12 40	12 40					13 40	13 40							14 40						15 40		
Port Talbot Parkway	d		12 48	12 48					13 48	13 48							14 48						15 48		
Bridgend	d		13 00	13 00					14 00	14 00							15 00						16 00		
Cardiff Central 7	d		13 25	13 25					14 25	14 25							15 25						16 25		
Hereford 7	d		12 42	12 42					13 44	13 44							14 42						15 42		
Newport (South Wales)	d		13 39	13 39					14 39	14 39							15 39						16 39		
Weston-super-Mare	d	13 01			13 10			13 40			14 10				14 40	15 01			15b27			15 40		16 10	
Bristol Temple Meads 10	d	13 30			14 00			14 30			15 00				15 30	15 30		15 52	16 00			16 30		17 00	
Bristol Parkway 7	a		14 00	14 00					15 00	15 00							16 00						17 00		
	d		14 02	14 02					15 02	15 02							16 02						17 02		
Bath Spa 7	d	13 43			14 13			14 43			15 13				15 43	15 43		16 07	16 13			16 43		17 13	
Chippenham	d	13 55			14 25			14 55			15 25	15 28			15 55	15 55			16 25			16 55		17 25	
Birmingham New Street 12	d						13 12							14 12							15 12				16 12
Cheltenham Spa	d						14 01							15 00							16 01				17 00
Gloucester 7	d						14 15							15 16							16 15				17 16
Stonehouse	d						14 27							15 29							16 27				17 29
Stroud	d						14 32							15 34							16 32				17 34
Kemble	d						14 47							15 48							16 47				17 48
Swindon	a	14 09	14 27	14 27	14 39		15 02	15 09	15 27	15 27	15 39	15 48		16 02	16 09	16 10	16 27		16 39		17 02	17 09	17 27	17 39	18 02
	d	14 11	14 29	14 29	14 41			15 11	15 29	15 29	15 41			16 04	16 11	16 11	16 29		16 41			17 11	17 29	17 41	18 04
Didcot Parkway	a	14 29		14 46				15 28	15 46	15 46				16 21	16 28	16 28	16 46					17 28	17 46		18 21
Oxford	a	15 14		15 14					16 14	16 14							17 14						18 14		
Reading 7	a	14 44	15 01	15 01	15 09			15 44	16 01	16 02	16 09			16 36	16 44	16 44	17 01		17 09			17 44	18 01	18 09	18 36
Gatwick Airport 10	a				16 50						17 50								18 50					19 50	
Heathrow Terminal 1 Bus	a	16 09			16 39			17 09			17 39				18 09	18 09			18 39			19 09		19 39	
Slough 3	a	15 09			15 40			16 24			16c43				17 09	17 09			17 40			18 10		18 40	
London Waterloo 15 ⊖	a																	18 49							
London Paddington 15 ⊖	a	15 14	15 32	15 32	15 39			16 14	16 32	16 32	16 42			17 06	17 14	17 14	17 32		17 38			18 14	18 32	18 38	19 08

		GW 1◇ A	GW 1◇ C	GW 1◇		GW 1◇	GW	GW 1◇ A	GW 1◇ C	GW 1◇ B	GW 1◇ C		GW 1◇	GW 1◇	GW 1◇	GW D	GW 1◇	GW 1◇		GW	GW 1◇ E	GW 1◇ G	GW 1◇ H		
Swansea 7	d			16 29						17 29	17 29				18 29			19 29							
Neath	d			16 40						17 40	17 40				18 40			19 40							
Port Talbot Parkway	d			16 48						17 48	17 48				18 48			19 48							
Bridgend	d			17 00						18 00	18 00				19 00			20 00							
Cardiff Central 7	d			17 25						18 25	18 25				19 25			20 25							
Hereford 7	d			16 42											18 43										
Newport (South Wales)	d			17 39						18 39	18 39				19 39			20 39							
Weston-super-Mare	d	17 01	16 40			17 10		18 01	17 40					18 40			20 10				20 51	20 51	21 59		
Bristol Temple Meads 10	d	17 30	17 30			18 00		18 30	18 30					19 30			20 33				21 44	21 44	22 33		
Bristol Parkway 7	a			18 00						19 00	19 00				20 00			21 00							
	d			18 02						19 02	19 02				20 02			21 02							
Bath Spa 7	d	17 43	17 43			18 13		18 43	18 43					19 43			20 46				22 00	22 00	22 46		
Chippenham	d	17 55	17 55			18 25		18 55	18 55					19 55			20 58				22 12	22 12	22 58		
Birmingham New Street 12	d						17 12						18 12			19 12				20 30					
Cheltenham Spa	d						18 01						19 00			20 01				21 19					
Gloucester 7	d						18 15						19 16			20 15				21 35					
Stonehouse	d						18 27						19 29			20 27				21 47					
Stroud	d						18 32						19 34			20 32				21 52					
Kemble	d						18 47						19 48			20 47				22 07					
Swindon	a	18 09	18 09	18 27		18 39	19 02	19 09	19 09	19 27	19 27		20 02	20 09	20 27	21 03	21 13	21 27		22 22	22 27	22 27	23 13		
	d	18 11	18 11	18 29		18 41		19 11	19 11	19 29	19 29		20 04	20 11	20 29		21 14	21 29			22 28	22 28	23 14		
Didcot Parkway	a	18 28	18 28	18 46				19 28	19 28				20 21	20 28	20 46		21 31	21 46			22 45	22 45	23 31		
Oxford	a			19 14				20 14	20 14						21 14		21 52	22 14			23 40	23 40	00 04		
Reading 7	a	18 43	18 44	19 01		19 09		19 43	19 44	20 00	20 01		20 36	20 44	21 07		21 48	21 58			23 01	23 01	23 52		
Gatwick Airport 10	a					20 50				21 59	21 59				23 03		00 10				01 02	01 02			
Heathrow Terminal 1 Bus	a	20 09	20 09			20 39				21 19	21 19		21 49					23 55							
Slough 3	a	19 09	19 09			19 40		20 09	20 09	20 40	20 40			21 10	21 40			22 22			23 43	23 43	00 28		
London Waterloo 15 ⊖	a																								
London Paddington 15 ⊖	a	19 14	19 14	19 32		19 39		20 14	20 14	20 32	20 32		21 07	21 14	21 36		22 16	22 32			23 36	23 38	00 33		

For general notes see front of timetable
For details of catering facilities see Directory of Train Operators

A Until 5 September

B Until 5 September. From Pembroke Dock (Table 128)

C From 12 September

D To Westbury (Table 123)

E From 12 September. From Penzance (Table 135)

G Until 5 September. From Penzance (Table 135)

H From Taunton (Table 134)

b From 12 September dep. 1529

c From 12 September arr. 1639

Table 125

Sundays

until 12 July

South Wales, Weston-super-Mare, Bristol, Cheltenham Spa and Swindon → Oxford and London

Route Diagram - see first page of Table 125

		GW	GW	GW	GW	GW	GW	GW	GW	GW	GW	GW	GW	GW	GW	GW	GW	GW
		1 ◇	1 ◇	1 ◇	1 ◇	1 ◇		1 ◇	1 ◇	1 ◇	1 ◇	1 ◇	1 ◇ A	1 ◇	1 ◇		1 ◇ A	1 ◇
		☕	☕	☕	☕	☕		☕	☕	☕	☕	☕	☕	☕	☕		☕	☕
Swansea [7]	d					07 59			08 59			09 59			10 59			11 59
Neath	d					08 11			09 11			10 11			11 11			12 11
Port Talbot Parkway	d					08 18			09 18			10 18			11 18			12 18
Bridgend	d					08 30			09 30			10 30			11 30			12 30
Cardiff Central [7]	d			07 45		08 55			09 55			10 55			11 55			12 55
Hereford [7]	d											10 11						12 03
Newport (South Wales)	d			08 03		09 09			10 09			11 09			12 09			13 09
Weston-super-Mare	d				08 26			09 14			10 21		10 51				12 07	
Bristol Temple Meads [10]	d	07 40	08 10		09 00			10 00		10 30	11 00		12 00				13 00	
Bristol Parkway [7]	a			08 34		09 30			10 30			11 30			12 30			13 30
	d			08 34		09 32			10 32			11 32			12 32			13 32
Bath Spa [7]	d	07 53	08 23		09 13			10 13		10 43	11 13		12 13				13 13	
Chippenham	d	08 05	08 35		09 25			10 25		10 55	11 25		12 25				13 25	
Birmingham New Street [12]	d													10 14		11 30		
Cheltenham Spa	d						09 35							11 46		12 35		
Gloucester [7]	d						09 49							12 04		12 49		
Stonehouse	d						10 01							12 18		13 01		
Stroud	d						10 06							12 23		13 06		
Kemble	d						10 20							12 37		13 20		
Swindon	a	08 20	08 50	09 00	09 39	09 57	10 35	10 40	10 56	11 10	11 40	11 57	12 40	12 51	12 57	13 36	13 40	13 57
	d	08 20	08 50	09 00	09 41	09 59		10 41	10 59	11 11	11 41	11 59	12 41	12 53	12 59		13 41	13 59
Didcot Parkway	a	08 39	09 09		09 58	10 16		10 58	11 16		11 58	12 16	12 58		13 16		13 58	14 16
Oxford	a	09 15	09 54		10 27	10 42		11 25	11 50		12 25	12 50	13 27		13 50		14 25	14 50
Reading [7]	a	08 55	09 26	09 29	10 12	10 31		11 13	11 31	11 42	12 13	12 31	13 13	13 22	13 31		14 13	14 31
Gatwick Airport [10]	a	10 30		11 32		12 27				13 32		14 25			15 32			16 25
Heathrow Terminal 1 Bus	a	10 09		10 39	11 39	12 09		12 39		13 09	13 39	14 09		14 39	15 09		15 39	16 09
Slough [3]	a	09 25		09 57	10 48	11 13		11 59		12 13	12 59	13 13		13 59	14 13		14 59	15 13
London Waterloo [15]	⊖ a																	
London Paddington [15]	⊖ a	09 34	10 06	10 10	10 55	11 10		11 55	12 09	12 28	12 55	13 10	13 55	14 08	14 09		14 55	15 09

		GW	GW	GW	GW	GW	GW	GW	SW	GW	GW	GW	GW	GW	GW	GW	GW
		1 ◇	1 ◇	1 ◇	1 ◇	1 ◇	1 ◇	1 ◇	1 ◇	1 ◇	1 ◇		1 ◇		1 ◇	1 ◇ A	1 ◇ B
		☕	☕	☕	☕	☕	☕	☕		☕	☕		☕		☕	☕	☕
Swansea [7]	d			12 59		13 59				14 59					15 59		
Neath	d			13 11		14 11				15 11					16 11		
Port Talbot Parkway	d			13 18		14 18				15 18					16 18		
Bridgend	d			13 30		14 30				15 30					16 30		
Cardiff Central [7]	d			13 55		14 55				15 55					16 55		
Hereford [7]	d			12 42		13 39				14 55					15 43		
Newport (South Wales)	d			14 09		15 09				16 09					17 09		
Weston-super-Mare	d	13 21			14 21						15 50		16 14			17 01	17 24
Bristol Temple Meads [10]	d	14 00			15 00		16 00		16 04		16 30		17 00			17 30	18 00
Bristol Parkway [7]	a			14 30		15 30				16 30					17 30		
	d			14 32		15 32				16 32					17 32		
Bath Spa [7]	d	14 13			15 13		16 13		16 20		16 43		17 13			17 43	18 13
Chippenham	d	14 25			15 25		16 25				16 55		17 25	17 31		17 55	18 25
Birmingham New Street [12]	d		12 30					14 43				15 43					
Cheltenham Spa	d		13 46					15 46				16 33					
Gloucester [7]	d		14 04					16 04				16 47					
Stonehouse	d		14 16					16 16				16 59					
Stroud	d		14 22					16 22				17 04					
Kemble	d		14 36					16 36				17 19					
Swindon	a	14 40	14 50	14 57	15 40	15 57	16 40	16 50		16 57	17 10	17 34	17 40	17 48	17 57	18 10	18 40
	d	14 41	14 51	14 59	15 41	15 59	16 41	16 51		16 59	17 11		17 41		17 59	18 11	18 41
Didcot Parkway	a	14 58		15 16	15 58	16 16	16 58			17 16			17 58		18 16		18 59
Oxford	a	15 27		15 50	16 25	16 49	17 25			17 50			18 27		18 50		19 25
Reading [7]	a	15 14	15 19	15 31	16 14	16 31	17 14	17 19		17 31	17 42		18 14		18 31	18 44	19 15
Gatwick Airport [10]	a			17 32		18 27					19 32					20 27	
Heathrow Terminal 1 Bus	a		16 39	17 09	17 39	18 09		18 39			19 09		19 39			20 09	
Slough [3]	a		16 00	16 15	16 48	17 15	17 51	17 58			18 15		18 48			19 15	
London Waterloo [15]	⊖ a								18 58								
London Paddington [15]	⊖ a	15 55	16 08	16 10	16 53	17 10	17 53	18 08		18 15	18 23		18 53		19 10	19 28	19 55

For general notes see front of timetable
For details of catering facilities see Directory of Train Operators

A From Plymouth (Table 135)
B From Paignton (Table 135)

Table 125

Sundays

until 12 July

South Wales, Weston-super-Mare, Bristol, Cheltenham Spa and Swindon → Oxford and London

Route Diagram - see first page of Table 125

		GW	GW	GW	GW	GW	GW	GW	GW	GW	GW	GW	GW	GW	GW	GW
		1 ◇	1 ◇	1 ◇	1 ◇	1 ◇	1 ◇			1 ◇	1 ◇	1 ◇	1 ◇	1 ◇	1 ◇	
			A	B			C	D				A		A	B	
		☕	☕	☕	☕	☕	☕			☕	☕	☕	☕	☕	☕	
Swansea [7]	d		16 59			17 59						18 59		19 59		
Neath	d		17 11			18 11						19 11		20 11		
Port Talbot Parkway	d		17 18			18 18						19 18		20 18		
Bridgend	d		17 30			18 30						19 30		20 30		
Cardiff Central [7]	d		17 55			18 55						19 55		20 55		
Hereford [7]	d		16 42			17 43						18 57		19 35		
Newport (South Wales)	d		18 09			19 09						20 09		21 09		
Weston-super-Mare	d			17 50	18 16		18 53						20 38		20 55	
Bristol Temple Meads [10]	d			18 30	19 00		19 30			20 00			21 00		22 05	
Bristol Parkway [7]	a		18 30			19 30						20 30		21 30		
	d		18 32			19 32						20 32		21 32		
Bath Spa [7]	d			18 43	19 13		19 43			20 13			21 13		22 19	
Chippenham	d			18 55	19 25		19 55	20 04		20 25			21 25		22 31	
Birmingham New Street [12]	d	16 43							18 30		18 43					20 43
Cheltenham Spa	d	17 46							19 14		19 46					21 46
Gloucester [7]	d	18 05							19 34		20 05					21 59
Stonehouse	d	18 18							19 48		20 17					22 12
Stroud	d	18 23							19 53		20 23					22 17
Kemble	d	18 37							20 07		20 38					22 32
Swindon	a	18 51	18 57	19 11	19 40	19 56	20 10	20 20	20 23	20 40	20 53	20 57	21 41	21 57	22 46	22 47
	d	18 53	18 59	19 11	19 41	19 59	20 11			20 41	20 54	20 59	21 41	21 59	22 52	
Didcot Parkway	a		19 16		19 58	20 16				20 59		21 16	22 00		23 10	
Oxford	a		19 50		20 25	20 48				21 27		21 51	22 28		23b55	
Reading [7]	a	19 23	19 31	19 43	20 14	20 31	20 42			21 16	21 25	21 31	22 17	22 35	23 26	
Gatwick Airport [10]	a			21 32			22 25					23 33		00 41		
Heathrow Terminal 1 Bus 🚌	a	20 39		21 19		21 49	21 55					22 55		23 55		
Slough [3]	a	19 57		20 15	20 48		21 15					22 03	22 47	23 22	23 58	
London Waterloo [15] (Underground)	a															
London Paddington [15] (Underground)	a	20 07	20 12	20 25	20 53	21 11	21 21			21 56	22 07	22 16	23 08	23 22	00 06	

Sundays

19 July to 6 September

		GW	GW	GW	GW	GW	GW	GW	GW	GW	GW	GW	GW	GW	GW	GW	GW	GW	GW	GW
			1 ◇	1 ◇	1 ◇	1 ◇		1 ◇		1 ◇	1 ◇			1 ◇	1 ◇	1 ◇	1 ◇	1 ◇	1 ◇	
																	B			
		🚌					🚌		🚌				🚌							
			☕	☕	☕	☕		☕		☕	☕			☕	☕	☕	☕	☕	☕	
Swansea [7]	d							07 59						08 59		09 59			10 59	
Neath	d							08 11						09 11		10 11			11 11	
Port Talbot Parkway	d							08 18						09 18		10 18			11 18	
Bridgend	d							08 30						09 30		10 30			11 30	
Cardiff Central [7]	d			07 45				08 55						09 55		10 55			11 55	
Hereford [7]	d															10 11				
Newport (South Wales)	d			08 03				09 09						10 09		11 09			12 09	
Weston-super-Mare	d					08 26					09 14				10 12		10 51			
Bristol Temple Meads [10]	d		07 45		08 25	09 00				09 40	10 00				10 45		11 45			
Bristol Parkway [7]	a			08 34				09 30						10 30		11 30			12 30	
	d			08 34				09 32						10 32		11 32			12 32	
Bath Spa [7]	d	07 00			08 38		08 43		09 43	09 53			←		10 58		11 58			
Chippenham	d	07 35					09 18		10 18 →				10 18		11 10		12 10			
Birmingham New Street [12]	d																	10 16		11 12
Cheltenham Spa	d											09 35						11 46		12 35
Gloucester [7]	d											09 49						12 04		12 49
Stonehouse	d											10 01						12 18		13 01
Stroud	d											10 06						12 23		13 06
Kemble	d											10 20						12 37		13 20
Swindon	a	08 10	08 17	09 00		09 31	09 53	09 57			10 32	10 35	10 53	10 56	11 34	11 57	12 33	12 51	12 57	13 36
	d		08 20	09 00		09 41		09 59			10 41			10 59	11 41	11 59	12 41	12 53	12 59	
Didcot Parkway	a		08 39	09 18		09 58		10 16			10 58			11 16	11 58	12 16	12 58		13 16	
Oxford	a		09 15	09 54		10 27		10 42			11 25			11 50	12 25	12 50	13 27		13 50	
Reading [7]	a		08 55	09 34	09 46	10 12		10 31		11 01	11 13			11 31	12 13	12 31	13 13	13 22	13 31	
Gatwick Airport [10]	a		10 30		11 32			12 27						13 32		14 25			15 32	
Heathrow Terminal 1 Bus 🚌	a		10 09		11 09	11 39		12 09			12 39			13 09	13 39	14 09		14 39	15 09	
Slough [3]	a		09 25	10 13	10 30	10 48		11 13		11 30	11 59			12 13	12 59	13 13		13 59	14 13	
London Waterloo [15] (Underground)	a																			
London Paddington [15] (Underground)	a		09 34	10 10	10 22	10 55		11 10		11 36	11 55			12 09	12 55	13 10	13 55	14 08	14 09	

For general notes see front of timetable
For details of catering facilities see
Directory of Train Operators

A From Carmarthen (Table 128)
B From Plymouth (Table 135)
C From Taunton (Table 134)
D To Cheltenham Spa
b By bus

Table 125

Sundays

19 July to 6 September

South Wales, Weston-super-Mare, Bristol, Cheltenham Spa and Swindon → Oxford and London

Route Diagram - see first page of Table 125

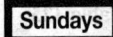

		GW 1◇ A		GW 1◇	GW 1◇	GW 1◇		GW 1◇	GW 1◇	GW 1◇		GW 1◇	GW 1◇	SW 1◇		GW 1◇	GW 1◇	GW		GW 1◇	GW	GW 1◇		GW 1◇ A	GW 1◇ B
Swansea 7	d			11 59				12 59		13 59						14 59						15 59			
Neath	d			12 11				13 11		14 11						15 11						16 11			
Port Talbot Parkway	d			12 18				13 18		14 18						15 18						16 18			
Bridgend	d			12 30				13 30		14 30						15 30						16 30			
Cardiff Central 7	d			12 55				13 55		14 55						15 55						16 55			
Hereford 7	d			*12 03*				*12 42*		*13 39*						*14 55*						*15 43*			
Newport (South Wales)	d			13 09				14 09		15 09						16 09						17 09			
Weston-super-Mare	d				13 15				14 21								*15 50*			*16 14*				17 01	17 24
Bristol Temple Meads 10	d	12 45			13 45				15 00			16 00		16 04			16 30			17 00				17 30	18 00
Bristol Parkway 7	a			13 30				14 30		15 30						16 30						17 30			
	d			13 32				14 32		15 32						16 32						17 32			
Bath Spa 7	d	12 58			13 58				15 13			16 13		16 20			16 43			17 13				17 43	18 13
Chippenham	d	13 10			14 10				15 25			16 25					16 55			17 25	17 31			17 55	18 25
Birmingham New Street 12	d					*11 45*							*14 43*					*15 43*							
Cheltenham Spa	d					13 46							15 46					16 33							
Gloucester 7	d					14 04							16 04					16 47							
Stonehouse	d					14 16							16 16					16 59							
Stroud	d					14 22							16 22					17 04							
Kemble	d					14 36							16 36					17 19							
Swindon	a	13 39		13 57	14 34	14 50		14 57	15 40	15 57		16 40	16 50			16 57	17 10	17 34		17 40	17 48	17 57		18 10	18 40
	d	13 41		13 59	14 41	14 51		14 59	15 41	15 59		16 41	16 51			16 59	17 11			17 41		17 59		18 11	18 41
Didcot Parkway	a	13 58		14 16	14 58			15 16	15 58	16 16		16 58				17 16				17 58		18 16			18 59
Oxford	a	*14 25*		*14 50*	*15 27*			*15 50*	*16 25*	*16 49*		*17 25*				*17 50*				*18 27*		*18 50*			*19 25*
Reading 7	a	14 13		14 31	15 14	15 19		15 31	16 14	16 31		17 14	17 19			17 31	17 42			18 14		18 31		18 44	19 15
Gatwick Airport 10	a			*16 25*				*17 32*		*18 27*							*19 32*							*20 27*	
Heathrow Terminal 1 Bus	a	*15 39*		*16 09*		*16 39*		*17 09*	*17 39*	*18 09*			*18 39*				*19 09*			*19 39*				*20 09*	
Slough 3	a	*14 59*		*15 13*		*16 00*		*16 15*	*16 48*	*17 15*		*17 51*	*17 58*				*18 15*			*18 48*				*19 15*	
London Waterloo 15 ⊖	a													18 58											
London Paddington 15 ⊖	a	14 55		15 09	15 55	16 08		16 10	16 53	17 10		17 53	18 08			18 15	18 23			18 53		19 10		19 28	19 55

		GW 1◇	GW 1◇ C	GW 1◇ A		GW 1◇	GW 1◇	GW 1◇ D		GW E	GW	GW 1◇		GW 1◇	GW 1◇ C	GW 1◇		GW 1◇ C	GW 1◇ A	GW
Swansea 7	d		16 59				17 59								18 59			19 59		
Neath	d		17 11				18 11								19 11			20 11		
Port Talbot Parkway	d		17 18				18 18								19 18			20 18		
Bridgend	d		17 30				18 30								19 30			20 30		
Cardiff Central 7	d		17 55				18 55								19 55			20 55		
Hereford 7	d		*16 42*				*17 43*								*18 57*			*19 35*		
Newport (South Wales)	d		18 09				19 09								20 09			21 09		
Weston-super-Mare	d			*17 50*		*18 16*		18 53								20 38			*20 55*	
Bristol Temple Meads 10	d			18 30		19 00		19 30				20 00				21 00			22 05	
Bristol Parkway 7	a		18 30				19 30								20 30			21 30		
	d		18 32				19 32								20 32			21 32		
Bath Spa 7	d			18 43		19 13		19 43				20 13				21 13			22 19	
Chippenham	d			18 55		19 25		19 55		20 04		20 25				21 25			22 31	
Birmingham New Street 12	d	*16 43*									*18 30*			*18 43*						*20 43*
Cheltenham Spa	d	17 46									*19 14*			19 46						21 46
Gloucester 7	d	18 05									19 34			20 05						21 59
Stonehouse	d	18 18									19 48			20 17						22 12
Stroud	d	18 23									19 53			20 23						22 17
Kemble	d	18 37									20 07			20 38						22 32
Swindon	a	18 51	18 57	19 11		19 40	19 56	20 10		20 20	20 23	20 40		20 53	20 57	21 41		21 57	22 46	22 47
	d	18 53	18 59	19 11		19 41	19 59	20 11				20 41		20 54	20 59	21 41		21 59	22 52	
Didcot Parkway	a		19 16			19 58	20 16					20 59			21 16	22 00			23 10	
Oxford	a		*19 50*			*20 25*	*20 48*					*21 27*			*21 51*	*22 28*			23b55	
Reading 7	a	19 23	19 31	19 43		20 14	20 31	20 42				21 16		21 25	21 31	22 17		22 35	23 26	
Gatwick Airport 10	a			*21 32*				*22 25*							*23 33*			*00 41*		
Heathrow Terminal 1 Bus	a	*20 39*		*21 19*			*21 49*	*21 55*							*22 55*			*23 55*		
Slough 3	a	*19 57*		*20 15*		*20 48*		*21 15*							*22 03*	*22 47*		*23 22*	*23 58*	
London Waterloo 15 ⊖	a																			
London Paddington 15 ⊖	a	20 07	20 12	20 25		20 53	21 11	21 21				21 56		22 07	22 16	23 08		23 22	00 06	

For general notes see front of timetable
For details of catering facilities see Directory of Train Operators

A From Plymouth (Table 135)
B From Paignton (Table 135)
C From Carmarthen (Table 128)
D From Taunton (Table 134)
E To Cheltenham Spa
b By bus

Table 125

Sundays

from 13 September

South Wales, Weston-super-Mare, Bristol, Cheltenham Spa and Swindon → Oxford and London

Route Diagram - see first page of Table 125

		GW	GW	GW	GW	GW	GW	GW	GW	GW	GW	GW	GW	GW	GW	GW	GW	GW	GW	GW	GW	GW	GW	GW	SW
		1◇	1◇	1◇	1◇	1◇		1◇	1◇	1◇	1◇	1◇	1◇	1◇		1◇	1◇	1◇	1◇	1◇	1◇	1◇	1◇	1◇	1◇
												A				A									
		☕	☕	☕	☕	☕		☕	☕	☕	☕	☕	☕	☕		☕	☕	☕	☕	☕	☕	☕	☕	☕	
Swansea 7	d					07 59			08 59		09 59			10 59			11 59			12 59		13 59			
Neath	d					08 11			09 11		10 11			11 11			12 11			13 11		14 11			
Port Talbot Parkway	d					08 18			09 18		10 18			11 18			12 18			13 18		14 18			
Bridgend	d					08 30			09 30		10 30			11 30			12 30			13 30		14 30			
Cardiff Central 7	d			07 45		08 55			09 55		10 55			11 55			12 55			13 55		14 55			
Hereford 7	d										*10 11*						*12 03*			*12 42*		*13 39*			
Newport (South Wales)	d			08 03		09 09			10 09		11 09			12 09			13 09			14 09		15 09			
Weston-super-Mare	d				08 26			*09 14*		10 26		*10 51*				*12b22*		13 21			14 21				
Bristol Temple Meads 10	d	07 40	08 10		09 00			10 00		11 00		12 00				13 00		14 00			15 00		16 00		16 04
Bristol Parkway 7	a			08 34		09 30			10 30		11 30			12 30			13 30			14 30		15 30			
	d			08 34		09 32			10 32		11 32			12 32			13 32			14 32		15 32			
Bath Spa 7	d	07 53	08 23		09 13			10 13		11 13		12 13				13 13		14 13			15 13		16 13		16 20
Chippenham	d	08 05	08 35		09 25			10 25		11 25		12 25				13 25		14 25			15 25		16 25		
Birmingham New Street 12	d												*10 30*		*11 30*				*12c30*					*14e43*	
Cheltenham Spa	d						09 35						11 46		12 35				13 46					15 46	
Gloucester 7	d						09 49						12 04		12 49				14 04					16 04	
Stonehouse	d						10 01						12 18		13 01				14 17					16 16	
Stroud	d						10 06						12 23		13 06				14 23					16 22	
Kemble	d						10 20						12 37		13 20				14 37					16 36	
Swindon	a	08 20	08 50	09 00	09 39	09 57	10 35	10 40	10 56	11 40	11 57	12 40	12 51	12 57	13 36	13 40	13 57	14 40	14 51	14 57	15 40	15 57	16 40	16 50	
	d	08 20	08 50	09 00	09 41	09 59		10 41	10 59	11 41	11 59	12 41		12 59		13 41	13 59	14 41		14 59	15 41	15 59	16 41	16 51	
Didcot Parkway	a	08 39	09 09		09 58	10 16		10 58	11 16	11 58	12 16	12 58		13 16		13 58	14 16	14 58		15 16	15 58	16 16	16 58		
Oxford	a	*09 15*	*09 52*		*10 27*	*10 41*		*11 25*	*11 49*	*12 25*	*12 50*	*13 27*		*13 49*		*14 25*	*14 49*	*15 27*		*15 50*	*16 25*	*16 49*	*17 25*		
Reading 7	a	08 55	09 26	09 33	10 12	10 31		11 13	11 31	12 13	12 31	13 13		13 31		14 13	14 31	15 14		15 31	16 14	16 31	17 14	17 19	
Gatwick Airport 10	a	*10 31*		*11 31*		*12 31*			*13 31*		*14 31*			*15 31*			*16 31*			*17 31*		*18 31*			
Heathrow Terminal 1 Bus 🚌	a	*10 09*	*10 39*	*11 09*	*11 39*	*12 09*		*12 39*	*13 09*	*13 39*	*14 09*	*14 39*		*15 09*		*15 39*	*16 09*	*16 39*		*17 09*	*17 39*	*18 09*		*18 39*	
Slough 3	a	*09 22*		*10 13*	*10 35*	*11 13*		*11 38*	*12 13*	*12 35*	*13 13*	*13 36*		*14 13*		*14 35*	*15 13*			*16 15*		*17 15*	*17 39*		
London Waterloo 15 ⊖	a																								18 58
London Paddington 15 ⊖	a	09 43	10 06	10 09	10 52	11 08		11 53	12 08	12 53	13 08	13 53		14 08		14 53	15 08	15 53		16 08	16 53	17 08	17 53	17 59	

		GW	GW	GW	GW	GW	GW	GW	GW	GW	GW	GW	GW	GW	GW	GW	GW	GW	GW	GW	GW	GW	GW	GW	
		1◇	1◇		1◇		1◇	1◇	1◇	1◇	1◇	1◇	1◇	1◇	1◇			1◇	1◇	1◇	1◇	1◇	1◇		
								A	B		C	A			D	E			C			C	A		
		☕	☕		☕		☕	☕	☕	☕	☕	☕	☕	☕	☕			☕	☕	☕	☕	☕	☕		
Swansea 7	d	14 59					15 59				16 59			17 59					18 59			19 59			
Neath	d	15 11					16 11				17 11			18 11					19 11			20 11			
Port Talbot Parkway	d	15 18					16 18				17 18			18 18					19 18			20 18			
Bridgend	d	15 30					16 30				17 30			18 30					19 30			20 30			
Cardiff Central 7	d	15 55					16 55				17 55			18 55					19 55			20 55			
Hereford 7	d	*14 55*					*15 43*				*16 42*			*17 43*					*18 57*			*19 35*			
Newport (South Wales)	d	16 09					17 09				18 09			19 09					20 09			21 09			
Weston-super-Mare	d		*15 50*		*16 14*			17 01	17 25			*17 50*	*18 16*		18 53						20 38		*20 55*		
Bristol Temple Meads 10	d		16 30		17 00			17 30	18 00			18 30	19 00		19 30			20 00			21 00		22 05		
Bristol Parkway 7	a	16 30					17 30				18 30			19 30					20 30			21 30			
	d	16 32					17 32				18 32			19 32					20 32			21 32			
Bath Spa 7	d		16 43		17 13			17 43	18 13			18 43	19 13		19 43			20 13			21 13		22 19		
Chippenham	d		16 55		17 25	17 31		17 55	18 25			18 55	19 25		19 55	20 04		20 25			21 25		22 31		
Birmingham New Street 12	d			*15f43*						*16g43*							*18h30*			*19j12*				*20k43*	
Cheltenham Spa	d			16 33						17 46							*19m14*			20 05				21 46	
Gloucester 7	d			16 47						18 05							19 34			20 23				21 59	
Stonehouse	d			16 59						18 18							19 48			20 36				22 12	
Stroud	d			17 04						18 23							19 53			20 42				22 17	
Kemble	d			17 19						18 37							20 07			20 57				22 32	
Swindon	a	16 57	17 10	17 34	17 40	17 48	17 57	18 10	18 40	18 51	18 57	19 11	19 40	19 56	20 10	20 20	20 23	20 40	20 57	21 11	21 41	21 57	22 46	22 47	
	d	16 59	17 11		17 41		17 59	18 11	18 41	18 53	18 59	19 11	19 41	19 59	20 11			20 41	20 59	21 11	21 41	21 59	22 52		
Didcot Parkway	a	17 16			17 58		18 16		18 59		19 16		19 58	20 16				20 59	21 16	21 30	22 00		23 10		
Oxford	a	*17 49*			*18 27*		*18 49*		*19 25*		*19 50*		*20 25*	*20 48*				*21 26*		*21 51*	*22 28*		*23 35*		
Reading 7	a	17 31	17 41		18 14		18 31	18 44	19 15	19 22	19 31	19 46	20 14	20 31	20 45			21 16	21 31	21 46	22 17	22 35	23 26		
Gatwick Airport 10	a		*19 31*					*20 31*				*21 31*			*22 31*					*23 31*		*00 41*			
Heathrow Terminal 1 Bus 🚌	a		*19 09*		*19 39*			*20 09*		*20 39*		*21 19*		*21 49*	*21 55*					*22 55*		*23 55*			
Slough 3	a		*18 15*		*18 35*			*19 15*			*20 15*		*20 34*		*21 15*			*21 48*		*22 29*	*22 47*	*23 22*	*23 58*		
London Waterloo 15 ⊖	a																								
London Paddington 15 ⊖	a	18 09	18 40		18 53		19 08	19 31	19 53	20 03	20 10	20 39	20 53	21 11	21 39			21 59	22 11	22 29	23 08	23 22	00 06		

For general notes see front of timetable
For details of catering facilities see Directory of Train Operators

- **A** From Plymouth (Table 135)
- **B** From Paignton (Table 135)
- **C** From Carmarthen (Table 128)
- **D** From Taunton (Table 134)
- **E** To Cheltenham Spa
- **b** From 8 November dep. 1207
- **c** From 8 November dep. 1142
- **e** From 8 November dep. 1430
- **f** From 8 November dep. 1530
- **g** From 8 November dep. 1630
- **h** From 8 November dep. 1730
- **j** From 8 November dep. 1842
- **k** From 8 November dep. 1942
- **m** From 8 November dep. 1906

Mondays to Fridays

Reading → Heathrow Railair Link
Express Coach Service

Sunday service operates on Bank Holiday Mondays.

		GW	GW	GW	GW	GW	GW	GW	GW	GW	GW	GW	GW	GW	GW	GW	GW	GW
Reading	d	04 00	05 00	05 30	05 55	06 08	06 20	06 40	07 00	07 20	07 40	08 00	08 20	08 40	09 05	09 25	09 45	10 05
Heathrow Terminal 1 Bus	a	04 50	05 50	06 20	06 45	07 02	07 29	07 49	08 09	08 29	08 49	09 09	09 29	09 49	09 59	10 19	10 39	10 59
Heathrow Terminal 2 Bus	a	04 53	05 53	06 23	06 48	07 05	07 32	07 52	08 12	08 32	08 52	09 12	09 32	09 52	10 02	10 22	10 42	11 02
Heathrow Terminal 3 Bus	a	04 55	05 55	06 25	06 50	07 08	07 35	07 55	08 15	08 35	08 55	09 15	09 35	09 55	10 05	10 25	10 45	11 05

		GW	GW	GW	GW	GW	GW	GW	GW	GW	GW	GW	GW	GW	GW	GW	GW	GW
Reading	d	10 25	10 45	11 05	11 25	11 45	12 05	12 25	12 45	13 05	13 25	13 45	14 05	14 25	14 45	15 05	15 25	15 45
Heathrow Terminal 1 Bus	a	11 19	11 39	11 59	12 19	12 39	12 59	13 19	13 39	13 59	14 19	14 39	14 59	15 19	15 39	15 59	16 19	16 39
Heathrow Terminal 2 Bus	a	11 22	11 42	12 02	12 22	12 42	13 02	13 22	13 42	14 02	14 22	14 42	15 02	15 22	15 42	16 02	16 22	16 42
Heathrow Terminal 3 Bus	a	11 25	11 45	12 05	12 25	12 45	13 05	13 25	13 45	14 05	14 25	14 45	15 05	15 25	15 45	16 05	16 25	16 45

		GW	GW	GW	GW	GW	GW	GW	GW	GW	GW	GW	GW	GW	GW	GW	GW
Reading	d	16 05	16 25	16 45	17 05	17 25	17 45	18 05	18 35	19 05	19 35	20 05	20 35	21 05	22 05	23 05	23 05
Heathrow Terminal 1 Bus	a	16 59	17 19	17 39	17 59	18 19	18 39	18 59	19 29	19 59	20 29	20 55	21 25	21 55	22 55	23 55	23 55
Heathrow Terminal 2 Bus	a	17 02	17 22	17 42	18 02	18 22	18 42	19 02	19 32	20 02	20 32	20 58	21 28	21 58	22 58	23 58	23 58
Heathrow Terminal 3 Bus	a	17 05	17 25	17 45	18 05	18 25	18 45	19 05	19 35	20 05	20 35	21 00	21 30	22 00	23 00	00 01	00 01

Saturdays

		GW	GW	GW	GW	GW	GW	GW	GW	GW	GW	GW	GW	GW	GW	GW	GW	GW
Reading	d	04 00	05 00	05 45	06 15	06 45	07 15	07 45	08 15	08 45	09 15	09 45	10 15	10 45	11 15	11 45	12 15	12 45
Heathrow Terminal 1 Bus	a	04 50	05 50	06 39	07 09	07 39	08 09	08 39	09 09	09 39	10 09	10 39	11 09	11 39	12 09	12 39	13 09	13 39
Heathrow Terminal 2 Bus	a	04 53	05 53	06 42	07 12	07 42	08 12	08 42	09 12	09 42	10 12	10 42	11 12	11 42	12 12	12 42	13 12	13 42
Heathrow Terminal 3 Bus	a	04 55	05 55	06 45	07 15	07 45	08 15	08 45	09 15	09 45	10 15	10 45	11 15	11 45	12 15	12 45	13 15	13 45

		GW	GW	GW	GW	GW	GW	GW	GW	GW	GW	GW	GW	GW	GW	GW	GW	GW
Reading	d	13 15	13 45	14 15	14 45	15 15	15 45	16 15	16 45	17 15	17 45	18 15	18 45	19 15	19 45	20 25	20 55	23 05
Heathrow Terminal 1 Bus	a	14 09	14 39	15 09	15 39	16 09	16 39	17 09	17 39	18 09	18 39	19 09	19 39	20 09	20 39	21 19	21 49	23 55
Heathrow Terminal 2 Bus	a	14 12	14 42	15 12	15 42	16 12	16 42	17 12	17 42	18 12	18 42	19 12	19 42	20 12	20 42	21 22	21 52	23 58
Heathrow Terminal 3 Bus	a	14 15	14 45	15 15	15 45	16 15	16 45	17 15	17 45	18 15	18 45	19 15	19 45	20 15	20 45	21 25	21 55	00 01

Sundays

Also Bank Holiday Mondays.

		GW	GW	GW	GW	GW	GW	GW	GW	GW	GW	GW	GW	GW	GW	GW	GW	GW	GW	GW
Reading	d	04 00	05 00	05 45	06 15	06 45	07 15	07 45	08 15	08 45	09 15	09 45	10 15	10 45	11 15	11 45	12 15	12 45	13 15	13 45
Heathrow Terminal 1 Bus	a	04 50	05 50	06 39	07 09	07 39	08 09	08 39	09 09	09 39	10 09	10 39	11 09	11 39	12 09	12 39	13 09	13 39	14 09	14 39
Heathrow Terminal 2 Bus	a	04 53	05 53	06 42	07 12	07 42	08 12	08 42	09 12	09 42	10 12	10 42	11 12	11 42	12 12	12 42	13 12	13 42	14 12	14 42
Heathrow Terminal 3 Bus	a	04 55	05 55	06 45	07 15	07 45	08 15	08 45	09 15	09 45	10 15	10 45	11 15	11 45	12 15	12 45	13 15	13 45	14 15	14 45

		GW	GW	GW	GW	GW	GW	GW	GW	GW	GW	GW	GW	GW	GW	GW	GW	GW
Reading	d	14 15	14 45	15 15	15 45	16 15	16 45	17 15	17 45	18 15	18 45	19 15	19 45	20 25	20 55	21 15	22 05	23 05
Heathrow Terminal 1 Bus	a	15 09	15 39	16 09	16 39	17 09	17 39	18 09	18 39	19 09	19 39	20 09	20 39	21 19	21 49	21 55	22 55	23 55
Heathrow Terminal 2 Bus	a	15 12	15 42	16 12	16 42	17 12	17 42	18 12	18 42	19 12	19 42	20 12	20 42	21 22	21 52	21 57	22 58	23 58
Heathrow Terminal 3 Bus	a	15 15	15 45	16 15	16 45	17 15	17 45	18 15	18 45	19 15	19 45	20 15	20 45	21 25	21 55	22 00	23 00	00 01

For general notes see front of timetable
For details of catering facilities see
Directory of Train Operators

Heathrow → Reading Railair Link
Express Coach Service

Sunday service operates on Bank Holiday Mondays.

		GW	GW	GW	GW	GW	GW	GW	GW	GW	GW	GW	GW	GW	GW	GW	GW	GW
Heathrow Central Bus Stn	d	00 05	05 00	06 00	06 30	06 57	07 20	07 40	08 00	08 20	08 40	09 00	09 20	09 40	10 00	10 15	10 35	10 55
Reading	a	00 51	05 46	06 46	07 21	07 48	08 21	08 46	09 06	09 26	09 39	09 59	10 13	10 33	10 53	11 08	11 28	11 48

		GW	GW	GW	GW	GW	GW	GW	GW	GW	GW	GW	GW	GW	GW	GW	GW	GW
Heathrow Central Bus Stn	d	11 15	11 35	11 55	12 15	12 35	12 55	13 15	13 35	13 55	14 15	14 35	14 55	15 15	15 35	15 55	16 15	16 35
Reading	a	12 08	12 28	12 48	13 08	13 28	13 48	14 08	14 28	14 48	15 08	15 28	15 48	16 08	16 28	16 48	17 14	17 34

		GW	GW	GW	GW	GW	GW	GW	GW	GW	GW	GW	GW	GW	GW	GW	GW
Heathrow Central Bus Stn	d	16 55	17 15	17 35	17 55	18 15	18 35	18 55	19 15	19 40	20 10	20 40	21 10	21 40	22 15	23 05	23 59
Reading	a	17 54	18 14	18 34	18 54	19 14	19 34	19 54	20 14	20 31	21 01	21 31	22 01	22 31	23 01	23 51	00 43

Saturdays

		GW	GW	GW	GW	GW	GW	GW	GW	GW	GW	GW	GW	GW	GW	GW	GW	GW
Heathrow Central Bus Stn	d	05 00	06 00	07 00	07 30	08 00	08 30	09 00	09 30	10 00	10 30	11 00	11 30	12 00	12 30	13 00	13 30	14 00
Reading	a	05 46	06 46	07 53	08 23	08 53	09 23	09 53	10 23	10 53	11 23	11 53	12 23	12 53	13 23	13 53	14 23	14 53

		GW	GW	GW	GW	GW	GW	GW	GW	GW	GW	GW	GW	GW	GW	GW	GW	GW	GW
Heathrow Central Bus Stn	d	14 30	15 00	15 30	16 00	16 30	17 00	17 30	18 00	18 30	19 00	19 20	19 50	20 20	20 50	21 30	22 00	23 05	23 59
Reading	a	15 23	15 53	16 23	16 53	17 23	17 53	18 23	18 53	19 23	19 53	20 13	20 43	21 13	21 43	22 19	22 49	23 51	00 43

Sundays

Also Bank Holiday Mondays.

		GW	GW	GW	GW	GW	GW	GW	GW	GW	GW	GW	GW	GW	GW	GW	GW	GW	GW	GW
Heathrow Central Bus Stn	d	00 05	05 00	06 00	07 00	07 30	08 00	08 30	09 00	09 30	10 00	10 30	11 00	11 30	12 00	12 30	13 00	13 30	14 00	14 30
Reading	a	00 51	05 46	06 46	07 53	08 23	08 53	09 23	09 53	10 23	10 53	11 23	11 53	12 23	12 53	13 23	13 53	14 23	14 53	15 23

		GW	GW	GW	GW	GW	GW	GW	GW	GW	GW	GW	GW	GW	GW	GW	GW	GW
Heathrow Central Bus Stn	d	15 00	15 30	16 00	16 30	17 00	17 30	18 00	18 30	19 00	19 20	19 50	20 20	20 50	21 30	22 00	23 05	23 59
Reading	a	15 53	16 23	16 53	17 23	17 53	18 23	18 53	19 23	19 53	20 13	20 43	21 13	21 43	22 19	22 49	23 51	00 43

For general notes see front of timetable
For details of catering facilities see Directory of Train Operators

Bristol — Bristol International Airport

Bus service

		GW	GW	GW	GW	GW	GW	GW	GW	GW	GW	GW	GW	GW	GW	GW	GW	GW	GW	GW	GW	GW	GW
											SX												
Bristol Temple Meads	d	02 40	03 55	05 25	06 10	06 25	06 40	06 55	07 10	07 25	07 40	07 55	08 10	08 25	08 40	08 55	09 10	09 25	09 40	09 55	10 10	10 25	10 40
Bristol Internatl Airport	a	03 05	04 20	05 50	06 35	06 50	07 05	07 20	07 35	07 50	08 05	08 20	08 35	08 50	09 05	09 20	09 35	09 50	10 05	10 20	10 35	10 50	11 05

		GW	GW	GW	GW	GW	GW	GW	GW	GW	GW	GW	GW	GW	GW	GW	GW	GW	GW	GW	GW	GW	GW
																							SX
Bristol Temple Meads	d	10 55	11 10	11 25	11 40	11 55	12 10	12 25	12 40	12 55	13 10	13 25	13 40	13 55	14 10	14 25	14 40	14 55	15 10	15 25	15 40	15 55	16 10
Bristol Internatl Airport	a	11 20	11 35	11 50	12 05	12 20	12 35	12 50	13 05	13 20	13 35	13 50	14 05	14 20	14 35	14 50	15 05	15 20	15 35	15 50	16 05	16 20	16 35

		GW	GW	GW	GW	GW	GW	GW	GW	GW	GW	GW	GW	GW	GW	GW	GW	GW	GW	GW	GW		
			SX	SX	SX		SX		SX		SX		SX										
Bristol Temple Meads	d	16 25	16 40	16 55	17 10	17 25	17 40	17 55	18 10	18 25	18 40	18 55	19 10	19 25	19 55	20 25	20 55	21 25	21 55	22 25	22 55		
Bristol Internatl Airport	a	16 50	17 05	17 20	17 35	17 50	18 05	18 20	18 35	18 50	19 05	19 20	19 35	19 50	20 20	20 50	21 20	21 50	22 20	22 50	23 20		

Sundays

		GW	GW	GW	GW	GW	GW	GW	GW	GW	GW	GW	GW	GW	GW	GW	GW	GW	GW
Bristol Temple Meads	d	02 40	03 55	05 25	05 55	06 25	06 55	07 25	07 55	08 25	08 55	09 25	09 55	10 25	10 55	11 25	11 55	12 25	12 55
Bristol Internatl Airport	a	03 05	04 20	05 45	06 20	06 50	07 20	07 50	08 20	08 50	09 20	09 50	10 20	10 50	11 20	11 50	12 20	12 50	13 20

		GW	GW	GW	GW	GW	GW	GW	GW	GW	GW	GW	GW	GW	GW	GW	GW	GW	GW
Bristol Temple Meads	d	13 25	13 55	14 25	14 40	14 55	15 10	15 25	15 40	15 55	16 10	16 25	16 40	16 55	17 10	17 25	17 40	17 55	18 10
Bristol Internatl Airport	a	13 50	14 20	14 50	15 05	15 20	15 35	15 50	16 05	16 20	16 35	16 50	17 05	17 20	17 35	17 50	18 05	18 20	18 35

		GW	GW	GW	GW	GW	GW	GW	GW	GW	GW	GW	GW	GW	GW	GW	GW		
Bristol Temple Meads	d	18 25	18 40	18 55	19 10	19 25	19 55	20 10	20 25	20 40	20 55	21 10	21 40	21 55	22 10	22 25	22 55		
Bristol Internatl Airport	a	18 50	19 05	19 20	19 35	19 50	20 20	20 35	20 50	21 05	21 20	21 35	22 05	22 20	22 35	22 50	23 20		

Mondays to Saturdays

		GW	GW	GW	GW	GW	GW	GW	GW	GW	GW	GW	GW	GW	GW	GW	GW	GW	GW	GW	GW	GW	GW
Bristol Internatl Airport	d	03 05	04 20	06 15	06 45	07 00	07 15	07 30	07 45	08 00	08 15	08 30	08 45	09 00	09 15	09 30	09 45	10 00	10 15	10 30	10 45	11 00	11 15
Bristol Temple Meads	a	03 30	04 45	06 40	07 10	07 25	07 40	07 55	08 10	08 25	08 40	08 55	09 10	09 25	09 40	09 55	10 10	10 25	10 40	10 55	11 10	11 25	11 40

		GW	GW	GW	GW	GW	GW	GW	GW	GW	GW	GW	GW	GW	GW	GW	GW	GW	GW	GW	GW	GW	GW
																					SX		SX
Bristol Internatl Airport	d	11 30	11 45	12 00	12 15	12 30	12 45	13 00	13 15	13 30	13 45	14 00	14 15	14 30	14 45	15 00	15 15	15 30	15 45	16 00	16 15	16 30	16 45
Bristol Temple Meads	a	11 55	12 10	12 25	12 40	12 55	13 10	13 25	13 40	13 55	14 10	14 25	14 40	14 55	15 10	15 25	15 40	15 55	16 10	16 25	16 40	16 55	17 10

		GW	GW	GW	GW	GW	GW	GW	GW	GW	GW	GW	GW	GW	GW	GW	GW	GW	GW	GW	GW		
			SX		SX		SX		SX		SX												
Bristol Internatl Airport	d	17 00	17 15	17 30	17 45	18 00	18 15	18 30	18 45	19 00	19 15	19 30	20 00	20 30	21 00	21 30	22 00	22 15	22 45	23 15	23 45		
Bristol Temple Meads	a	17 25	17 40	17 55	18 10	18 25	18 40	18 55	19 10	19 25	19 40	19 55	20 25	20 55	21 25	21 55	22 25	22 40	23 10	23 40	00 10		

Sundays

		GW	GW	GW	GW	GW	GW	GW	GW	GW	GW	GW	GW	GW	GW	GW	GW	GW	GW
Bristol Internatl Airport	d	03 05	04 20	06 00	07 00	07 30	08 00	08 30	09 00	09 30	10 00	10 30	11 00	12 00	12 30	13 00	13 30	14 00	14 30
Bristol Temple Meads	a	03 30	04 45	06 25	07 25	07 55	08 25	08 55	09 25	09 55	10 25	10 55	11 25	12 25	12 55	13 25	13 55	14 25	14 55

		GW	GW	GW	GW	GW	GW	GW	GW	GW	GW	GW	GW	GW	GW	GW	GW	GW	GW
Bristol Internatl Airport	d	14 45	15 00	15 15	15 30	15 45	16 00	16 15	16 30	16 45	17 00	17 15	17 30	17 45	18 00	18 15	18 30	18 45	19 00
Bristol Temple Meads	a	15 10	15 25	15 40	15 55	16 10	16 25	16 40	16 55	17 10	17 25	17 40	17 55	18 10	18 25	18 40	18 55	19 10	19 25

		GW	GW	GW	GW	GW	GW	GW	GW	GW	GW	GW	GW	GW	GW	GW	GW	GW	
Bristol Internatl Airport	d	19 15	19 30	19 45	20 00	20 15	20 30	20 45	21 15	21 30	21 45	22 00	22 15	22 30	22 45	23 00	23 15	23 30	
Bristol Temple Meads	a	19 40	19 55	20 10	20 25	20 40	20 55	21 10	21 40	21 55	22 10	22 25	22 40	22 55	23 10	23 25	23 40	23 55	

Table 125C

Mondays to Fridays

Cardiff — Cardiff International Airport

Bus Service

		GW	GW	GW	GW	GW	GW	GW	GW	GW	GW	GW	GW	GW
Cardiff Central Bus Stn	d	05 10	08 00	08 57	10 02	11 02	12 02	13 02	14 02	15 02	16 02	17 12	17 40	18 20
Cardiff International Apt	a	05 39	08 35	09 26	10 31	11 31	12 31	13 31	14 31	15 31	16 33	17 50	18 12	18 50

Saturdays

		GW	GW	GW	GW	GW	GW	GW	GW	GW	GW	GW	GW	GW
Cardiff Central Bus Stn	d	05 10	08 02	09 02	10 02	11 02	12 02	13 02	14 02	15 02	16 02	17 12	17 40	18 20
Cardiff International Apt	a	05 39	08 31	09 31	10 31	11 31	12 31	13 31	14 31	15 31	16 31	17 41	18 12	18 49

Sundays

		GW	GW	GW	GW	GW	GW	GW
Cardiff Central Bus Stn	d	08 30	10 02	12 02	14 02	16 02	18 02	19 15
Cardiff International Apt	a	08 59	10 31	12 31	14 31	16 31	18 31	19 44

Mondays to Fridays

		GW	GW	GW	GW	GW	GW	GW	GW	GW	GW	GW	GW	GW	GW	GW
Cardiff International Apt	d	07 16	07 51	09 35	10 35	11 05	11 35	12 35	13 35	14 35	15 05	15 35	16 40	17 41	18 51	20 25
Cardiff Central Bus Stn	a	07 50	08 32	10 06	11 06	11 36	12 06	13 06	14 06	15 06	15 36	16 06	17 16	18 12	19 21	20 55

Saturdays

		GW	GW	GW	GW	GW	GW	GW	GW	GW	GW	GW	GW	GW
Cardiff International Apt	d	07 25	08 00	09 35	10 35	11 35	12 35	13 35	14 35	15 35	16 40	17 40	18 51	20 25
Cardiff Central Bus Stn	a	07 56	08 31	10 06	11 06	12 06	13 06	14 06	15 06	16 06	17 11	18 11	19 23	20 55

Sundays

		GW	GW	GW	GW	GW	GW	GW
Cardiff International Apt	d	09 05	10 40	12 40	14 40	16 40	18 40	20 25
Cardiff Central Bus Stn	a	09 35	11 10	13 10	15 10	17 10	19 10	21 01

For general notes see front of timetable
For details of catering facilities see Directory of Train Operators

London and Oxford → Worcester and Hereford

Network Diagram - see first page of Table 116

Miles			GW	GW	GW	GW	GW	GW	GW	GW	GW	GW	GW	GW	GW	GW	GW	GW	GW	GW	GW	GW	GW
			MX	MX																			
			1 ◇		1	1 ◇	1	1 ◇	1 ◇	1 ◇	1 ◇	1 ◇	1 ◇	1 ◇	1	1 ◇	1 ◇	1 ◇	1 ◇	1 ◇		1 ◇	
			A	B																A	C	A	C
			☕	🚌			🍴	☕	🍴	☕	☕			☕		☕	☕	☕	☕	☕	🚌	☕	🚌
0	**London Paddington** [15] ⊖	d	21p48			05 42	06 48	08 22	09 21	10 22	11 22	13 21	14 21	15 51		17 22	17 51	18 21	19 22	20 20		21 48	
18½	Slough [3]	d	22p03			06 04	07 04	08 37	09 37	10 37	11 37	13 37	14 37	16 06					19 37	20 35		22 03	
36	Reading [7]	d	22p23			06 21	07 21	08 53	09 53	10 53	11 53	13 53	14 53	16 22		17 50	18 21	18 51	19 53	20 51		22 23	
53¼	Didcot Parkway	d				06 39	07 48																
63½	**Oxford**	d	22p52	22p58		06 54	08 04	09 21		11 19	12 19	14 19	15 19	16 47	17 31	18 16	18 54	19 19	20 22	21 17	21 23	22 52	22 58
70½	Hanborough	d	23p02	23b23		07 04		09 31	10 35	11 29	12 29	14 29	15 29	16 58	17 40	18 26		19 29	20 32	21 27	21 48	23 02	23s23
71½	Combe	d													17 43								
75	Finstock	d													17 48								
76¾	Charlbury	d	23p10	23b43		07 12		09 39	10 42	11 37	12 37	14 37	15 36	17 06	17 52	18 35	19 09	19 38	20 40	21 35	22 08	23 10	23s43
80½	Ascott-under-Wychwood	d													17 57								
81¾	Shipton	d	23p18	23 25											18 00		19 16					23 18	00s02
84¾	Kingham	d	23p23	00 15		07 22	08 25	09 49	10 51	11 47	12 47	14 47	15 45	17 15	18 05	18 45	19 22	19 48	20 50	21 45	22 31	23 23	00 15
91¾	Moreton-in-Marsh	a	23p32	00 37		07 31	08 33	09 58	11 00	11 56	12 56	14 56	15 58	17 24	18 13	18 54	19 31	19 57	20 59	21 54	22 53	23 32	00 37
—		d	23p34	00 37	05 37	07 31	08 34	09 59	11 01	11 57	12 57	14 57		17 26	18 14	18 55	19 35	19 59	21 00	21 55	22 53	23 34	00 37
101¾	Honeybourne	d	23p45	01s02		07 43	08 46	10 11		12 09	13 09	15 09		17 37	18 26	19 07		20 10	21 12	22 06	23 18	23 45	01s02
106¾	Evesham	a	23p54	01 27	05 51	07 51	08 53	10 19	11 16	12 17	13 17	15 17		17 46	18 33	19 15	19 52	20 19	21 20	22 15	23 43	23 54	01 27
—		d	23p55	01 27	06 06	07 56	08 54	10 29	11 18	12 29	13 19	15 19		17 47	18 41	19 21	19 57	20 20	21 25	22 16	23 43	23 55	01 27
112¾	Pershore	d	00 03	01s42	06 14	08 05	09 02	10 37		12 37	13 27	15 27		17 55	18 49	19 29	20 05	20 28	21 33	22 24	23 58	00 03	01s42
120½	**Worcester Shrub Hill** [7]	a	00 16	01 02	06 30	08 17	09 16	10 51	11 35	12 50	13 39	15 39		18 08	19 11	19 44	20 23	20 41	21 45	22 36	00s28	00 16	02 12
121¼	**Worcester Foregate Street** [7]	a			06 36	08 21	09 19	10 55	11 42	12 54	13 43	15 47			19 17	19 48		20 45	21 52	22 47	00s38		
128	Malvern Link	a					09 28	11 05		13 03	13 53	15 57				19 58		20 54	22 05	22 56	00s58		
128¾	Great Malvern	a				08 37	09 34	11 09		13 07	14 00	16 04				20 02		20 58	22 09	23 03	01 08		
131¾	Colwall	a						11 15		13 15						20 08		21 04	22 27				
136	Ledbury	a						11 23		13 23						20 16		21 12	22 35				
149¾	**Hereford** [7]	a						11 47		13 48						20 37		21 36	22 57				

Saturdays

		GW	GW	GW	GW	GW	GW	GW	GW	GW	GW	GW	GW	GW	GW	GW	GW
		1 ◇		1 ◇	1 ◇	1 ◇	1 ◇	1 ◇	1 ◇	1 ◇	1 ◇	1 ◇	1 ◇	1 ◇	1 ◇	1 ◇	1 ◇
		D	E														
			🚌				☕	☕	☕	☕	☕	☕	☕	☕	☕	🍴	
London Paddington [15] ⊖	d	21p48		05 21	06 21	07 21	08 21	10 21	11 21	13 21	14 21	15 21	16 21	17 21	18 21	19 50	21 50
Slough [3]	d	22p03		05 37	06 37	07 37	08 39	10 39	11 39	13 39	14 39	15 39	16 39	17 39	18 39	20 07	22 07
Reading [7]	d	22p23		05 54	06 53	07 53	08 54	10 54	11 54	13 54	14 54	15 54	16 54	17 54	18 54	20 23	22 22
Didcot Parkway	d			06 08													22 37
Oxford	d	22p52	22p58	06 24	07 18	08 20	09 20	11 20	12 24	14 20	15 20	16 20	17 20	18 20	19 20	20 49	22 50
Hanborough	d	23p02	23b23	06 34	07 31	08 31	09 31	11 31	12 34	14 31	15 31	16 31	17 31	18 31	19 31	20 58	23 00
Combe	d																
Finstock	d																
Charlbury	d	23p10	23b43	06 42	07 39	08 39	09 39	11 39	12 42	14 39	15 39	16 39	17 39	18 39	19 39	21 06	23 07
Ascott-under-Wychwood	d																
Shipton	d	23p18	00s02							14 46			17 47			21 12	23 14
Kingham	d	23p23	00 15	06 52	07 49	08 49	09 49	11 49	12 52	14 52	15 49	16 49	17 53	18 49	19 49	21 17	23 19
Moreton-in-Marsh	a	23p32	00 37	07 00	07 57	08 57	09 57	11 57	13 00	15 00	15 57	16 57	18 01	18 57	19 57	21 25	23 27
	d	23p34	00 37	07 02	08 00	09 00	10 00	12 00	13 03	15 03	16 00	17 00	18 03	19 00	20 00	21 28	23 29
Honeybourne	d	23p45	01s02	07 13	08 11	09 11	10 11	12 11	13 14	15 14	16 11	17 11	18 15	19 11	20 11	21 39	23 40
Evesham	a	23p54	01 27	07 21	08 22	09 22	10 19	12 19	13 22	15 22	16 19	17 22	18 22	19 19	20 19	21 46	23 47
	d	23p55	01 27	07 23	08 24	09 24	10 24	12 21	13 28	15 28	16 25	17 24	18 25	19 22	20 27	21 49	23 49
Pershore	d	00 03	01s42	07 31	08 32	09 32	10 32	12 29	13 36	15 36	16 33	17 32	18 33	19 30	20 35	21 56	23 57
Worcester Shrub Hill [7]	a	00 16	01 24	07 42	08 44	09 43	10 44	12 41	13 48	15 48	16 44	17 44	18 44	19 41	20 46	22 08	00 11
Worcester Foregate Street [7]	a			07 46	08 48	09 48	10 48	12 48	13 52	15 52	16 48	17 48	18 54	19 45	20 50	22 11	
Malvern Link	a			07 56	08 59	09 57	10 57	12 57	14 01	16 02	16 58	17 57	19 03		21 00	22 20	
Great Malvern	a			08 04	09 07	10 05	11 01	13 01	14 09	16 09	17 06	18 05	19 07		21 04	22 27	
Colwall	a						11 13	13 13					19 13		21 10		
Ledbury	a						11 21	13 21					19 21		21 18		
Hereford [7]	a						11 40	13 40					19 45		21 37		

For general notes see front of timetable
For details of catering facilities see Directory of Train Operators

A Until 4 September
B From 8 September
C From 7 September
D Until 5 September
E From 12 September
b Previous night.
Stops to set down only

Table 126

Sundays
until 6 September

London and Oxford → Worcester and Hereford

Network Diagram - see first page of Table 116

		GW 1 ◇	GW 1 ◇	GW 1 ◇	GW 1 ◇	GW 1 ◇	GW 1 ◇	GW 1 ◇	GW 1 ◇	GW 1 ◇	GW 1 ◇	GW 1 ◇	GW 1 ◇
									A	B			
			☕	☕	☕	🍴	☕	☕	🍴	🍴	☕		☕
London Paddington 15 ⊖	d	08 03	09 35	10 42	12 42	14 42	15 42	16 42	17 42	17 42	18 42	19 42	21 27
Slough 3	d	08 21	09 51	10 59	12 59	15 00	15 58	16 59	17 58	17 59	18 59	19 57	21 49
Reading 7	d	08 44	10 12	11 20	13 20	15 20	16 21	17 21	18 21	18 21	19 20	20 20	22 10
Didcot Parkway	d	09 03	10 28	11 36	13 36	15 36	16 37	17 38	18 37	18 38	19 36	20 36	22 26
Oxford	d	09 15	10 43	11 50	13 50	15 50	16 50	17 50	18 53	18 53	19 50	20 50	22 40
Hanborough	d	09 26	10 54	12 01	14 01	16 01		18 01	19 02	19 02	20 02	20 59	22 55
Combe	d												
Finstock	d												
Charlbury	d	09 34	11 02	12 09	14 09	16 09	17 04	18 09	19 10	19 10	20 10	21 08	23 03
Ascott-under-Wychwood	d												
Shipton	d												
Kingham	d	09 43	11 12	12 20	14 19	16 19	17 14	18 19	19 19	19 19	20 20	21 17	23 13
Moreton-in-Marsh	a	09 51	11 20	12 28	14 28	16 27	17 23	18 27	19 27	19 27	20 28	21 25	23 21
	d	09 57	11 23	12 30	14 31	16 29	17 24	18 29	19 29	19 29	20 30	21 27	23 22
Honeybourne	d	10 08	11 34	12 42		16 40		18 40	19 41	19 41	20 41	21 38	23 34
Evesham	a	10 15	11 42	12 49	14 47	16 48	17 40	18 48	19 48	19 48	20 49	21 44	23 40
	d	10 17	11 44	12 52	14 49	16 50	17 48	18 51	19 51	19 51	20 55	21 48	23 43
Pershore	d	10 25	11 52	13 00	14 57	16 58	17 56	18 59	19 58	19 58	21 03	21 58	23 51
Worcester Shrub Hill 7	a	10 36	12 03	13 11	15 09	17 10	18 08	19 11	20 08	20 08	21 14	22 07	00 04
Worcester Foregate Street 7	a	10 38	12 07	13 15	15 13	17 14		19 15	20 15	20 15	21 18	22 24	
Malvern Link	a	10 49	12 18	13 25	15 22	17 24		19 25	20 24	20 24	21 28	22 32	
Great Malvern	a	10 54	12 21	13 29	15 26	17 27		19 29	20 29	20 29	21 32	22 40	
Colwall	a		12 27	13 35	15 33	17 34					21 38		
Ledbury	a		12 35	13 43	15 41	17 42					21 46		
Hereford 7	a		12 58	14 05	16 06	18 01					22 05		

Sundays
from 13 September

		GW 1 ◇	GW 1 ◇	GW 1 ◇	GW 1 ◇	GW 1 ◇	GW 1 ◇	GW 1 ◇	GW 1 ◇	GW 1 ◇	GW 1 ◇	GW 1 ◇	GW 1 ◇
		🍴	☕	☕	☕	☕	🍴	☕	☕	🍴	☕	☕	☕
London Paddington 15 ⊖	d	08 03	09 35	10 42	12 42	13 42	14 42	15 42	16 42	17 42	18 42	19 42	21 27
Slough 3	d	08 25	09 57	11 05	13 05	14 05	15 05	16 05	17 03	18 03	19 06	20 05	21 53
Reading 7	d	08 44	10 11	11 20	13 20	14 20	15 20	16 20	17 20	18 20	19 20	20 20	22 08
Didcot Parkway	d	09 03	10 27	11 36	13 36	14 36	15 36	16 36	17 37	18 37	19 36	20 36	22 24
Oxford	d	09 15	10 43	11 50	13 50	14 50	15 50	16 50	17 50	18 53	19 50	20 50	22 40
Hanborough	d	09 26	10 54	12 01	14 01		16 01		18 01	19 02	20 02	20 59	22 55
Combe	d												
Finstock	d												
Charlbury	d	09 34	11 02	12 09	14 09	15 04	16 09	17 04	18 09	19 10	20 10	21 08	23 03
Ascott-under-Wychwood	d												
Shipton	d												
Kingham	d	09 43	11 12	12 20	14 19	15 15	16 19	17 14	18 19	19 19	20 20	21 17	23 13
Moreton-in-Marsh	a	09 51	11 20	12 28	14 27	15 23	16 27	17 23	18 27	19 27	20 28	21 25	23 21
	d	09 57	11 23	12 30	14 29	15 26	16 29	17 24	18 29	19 29	20 30	21 27	23 22
Honeybourne	d	10 08	11 34	12 42		15 37	16 41		18 40	19 41	20 41	21 38	23 34
Evesham	a	10 15	11 42	12 49	14 45	15 47	16 48	17 40	18 48	19 48	20 49	21 44	23 40
	d	10 17	11 44	12 52	14 48	15 49	16 50	17 48	18 51	19 51	20 55	21 48	23 43
Pershore	d	10 25	11 52	13 00	14 57	15 57	16 58	17 56	18 59	19 58	21 03	21 58	23 51
Worcester Shrub Hill 7	a	10 36	12 03	13 11	15 09	16 09	17 10	18 08	19 11	20 09	21 14	22 07	00 04
Worcester Foregate Street 7	a	10 39	12 07	13 15	15 13		17 14		19 15	20 15	21 18	22 24	
Malvern Link	a	10 49	12 18	13 25	15 22		17 24		19 25	20 24	21 28	22 32	
Great Malvern	a	10 54	12 21	13 29	15 26		17 27		19 29	20 29	21 32	22 40	
Colwall	a		12 27	13 35	15 33		17 34				21 38		
Ledbury	a		12 35	13 43	15 41		17 42				21 46		
Hereford 7	a		12 55	14 05	16 06		18 01				22 05		

For general notes see front of timetable
For details of catering facilities see Directory of Train Operators

A From 19 July
B Until 12 July

Table 126

Hereford and Worcester → Oxford and London

Network Diagram - see first page of Table 116

Miles			GW	GW	GW	GW	GW	GW	GW	GW	GW	GW	GW	GW	GW	GW	GW	GW	GW	GW	GW	GW	GW	GW
			MX																FO	FX		FO	FX	
				1 ◇	1 ◇	1 ◇	1	1 ◇	1 ◇	1 ◇	1 ◇	1 ◇	1 ◇	1	1 ◇	1 ◇	1 ◇	1	1 ◇	1 ◇		1 ◇	1 ◇	
			A																B	C	D		C	D
			(bus)																		(bus)			(bus)
				(buffet)	(buffet)					(trolley)	(trolley)	(buffet)	(buffet)		(buffet)		(buffet)							
0	Hereford 7	d				05 35		06 43				13 11			15 11							21 53	21 53	
13¾	Ledbury	d				05 52		06 59				13 28			15 27							22 11	22 11	
18	Colwall	d				05 59		07 07				13 35			15 35							22 18	22 18	
20¾	Great Malvern	d			05 17	06 05		07 14	08 58	09 54		13 47	14 34		15 40	17 00						22 24	22 24	
21¾	Malvern Link	d			05 20	06 09		07 18	09 00	09 56		13 51	14 37		15 44	17 03						22 28	22 28	
28½	Worcester Foregate Street 7	d			05 31	06 20	06 50	07 30	09 09	10 05	12 06	14 02	14 52		16 01	17 20	18 47	19 27	20 59	20 59		22 39	22 39	
29¼	Worcester Shrub Hill 7	d	23p00	05 02	05 35	06 26	06 52	07 35	09 12	10 08	12 08	14 06	14 56		16 06	17 24	18 50	19 29	21 03	21 03	21 09	22 43	22 43	23 00
37	Pershore	d	23p25		05 44	06 35	07 01	07 44	09 21	10 17	12 17	14 15	15 05		16 15	17 34	19 08	19 45	21 12	21 12	21 34	22 52	22 52	23 25
43	Evesham	a	23p45	05 16	05 53	06 44	07 09	07 53	09 29	10 26	12 26	14 24	15 14		16 24	17 43	19 17	19 54	21 22	21 22	21 54	23 01	23 01	23 45
—		d	23p45	05 18	05 55	06 45	07 10	07 54	09 30	10 27	12 27	14 26	15 22		16 30	17 49	19 19	20 22	21 27	21 27	21 54	23 06	23 06	23 45
48	Honeybourne	d	00s05		06 02	06 52		08 01	09 37	10 34	12 34	14 33	15 29		16 37	17 56		20 29	21 34	21 34	22 14	23 12	23 12	00s05
58	Moreton-in-Marsh	a	00 35	05 34	06 14	07 05	07 26	08 14	09 49	10 47	12 47	14 45	15 41		16 49	18 09	19 35	20 42	21 46	21 46	22 44	23 25	23 25	00 35
—		d	00 35	05 48	06 16	07 06	07 26	08 15	09 49	10 48	12 48	14 47	15 43	16 14	16 51	18 10	19 36	20 43	21 48	21 48	22 44	23 26	23 26	00 35
65	Kingham	d	00 55	05 56	06 24	07 15	07 35	08 24	09 57	10 57	12 57	14 55	15 51	16 21	16 59	18b25	19 45	20 52	21 56	21 56	23 04	23 35	23 35	00 55
68	Shipton	d					07 39								17 05									
69¼	Ascott-under-Wychwood	d					07 44																	
73	Charlbury	d	01 20	06 06	06 34	07 26	07 49	08 35	10 07	11 06	13 06	15 05	16 01	16 31	17 18	18 47	19 55	21 01	22 06	22 06	23 29	23 45	23 45	01 20
74¾	Finstock	d					07 53																	
78¼	Combe	d					07 58																	
79¼	Hanborough	d		06 14	06 42	07 34	08 01		10 14	11 14	13 14	15 13	16 09		17 26		20 03	21 09	22 14	22 14	23 49			
86¼	Oxford	a	01 58	06 25	06 53	07 46	08 12	08 49	10 25	11 27	13 24	15 24	16 27	16 46	17 37	19 01	20 23	21 20	22 27	22 27	00 15	23 59	23 59	01 58
96½	Didcot Parkway	a		06 42	07 09									17 04								00 19	00 19	
113¾	Reading 7	a		06 57	07 26	08 22		09 15	10 55	11 55	13 55	15 55	16 55		18 02	19 26	20 55		23 22	22 58		00 38	00 38	
131¼	Slough 3	a							11 09	12 09	14 09	16 09	17 09			19 39	21 09		23 12	23 18		00 53	00 56	
149¾	London Paddington 15	⊖ a		07 29	07 59	08 53		09 47	11 30	12 29	14 29	16 27	17 27		18 30	20 00	21 29		23 38	23 37		01 11	01 17	

Saturdays

		GW	GW	GW	GW	GW	GW	GW	GW	GW	GW	GW	GW	GW	GW	GW	HX
			1 ◇	1 ◇	1 ◇	1 ◇	1 ◇	1 ◇	1 ◇	1 ◇	1 ◇	1 ◇	1 ◇	1 ◇	1 ◇	1	1
		E															
		(bus)															
			(buffet)	(buffet)	(buffet)	(buffet)	(buffet)	(buffet)	(buffet)	(buffet)	(buffet)	(buffet)	(buffet)	(buffet)			
Hereford 7	d				07 10				12 13		15 10					20 20	23 53
Ledbury	d				07 30				12 32		15 29					20 40	
Colwall	d				07 38				12 40		15 37					20 48	23a57
Great Malvern	d		05 39	06 35	07 43	08 43	09 43	10 32	12 45	14 32	15 43	16 32	17 43	18 29		20 53	22 40
Malvern Link	d		05 43	06 39	07 47	08 47	09 47	10 36	12 49	14 36	15 47	16 36	17 47	18 32		20 57	22 43	*00 30*
Worcester Foregate Street 7	d		05 54	06 50	07 58	08 56	09 58	10 58	13 00	14 57	15 59	16 58	17 58	18 44	20 02	21 10	22 51
Worcester Shrub Hill 7	d	23p00	05 58	06 54	08 03	09 03	10 03	11 02	13 05	15 01	16 06	17 02	18 03	19 00	20 06	21 25	22 55
Pershore	d	23p25	06 07	07 03	08 12	09 12	10 12	11 11	13 14	15 10	16 15	17 11	18 12	19 09	20 15	21 34	23 04
Evesham	a	23p45	06 15	07 11	08 20	09 20	10 21	11 19	13 24	15 18	16 23	17 19	18 20	19 17	20 23	21 42	23 13
	d	23p45	06 25	07 25	08 27	09 27	10 27	11 27	13 26	15 25	16 28	17 27	18 27	19 27	20 37	21 54	
Honeybourne	d	23 53	06 32	07 32	08 34	09 34	10 34	11 34	13 34	15 32	16 35	17 34	18 34	19 34	20 44	22 01	
Moreton-in-Marsh	a	00 35	06 43	07 43	08 46	09 46	10 46	11 46	13 46	15 44	16 47	17 46	18 46	19 47	20 57	22 13	
	d	00 35	06 46	07 45	08 48	09 48	10 48	11 48	13 48	15 45	16 48	17 48	18 48	19 48	20 58	22 15	
Kingham	d	00 55	06 55	07 54	08 57	09 57	10 57	11 57	13 57	15 54	16 57	17 57	18 57	19 57	21 07	22 24	
Shipton	d		07 00	08 00						16 00						22 30	
Ascott-under-Wychwood	d																
Charlbury	d	01 20	07 08	08 08	09 08	10 08	11 08	12 08	14 08	16 08	17 08	18 08	19 08	20 08	21 18	22 38	
Finstock	d																
Combe	d																
Hanborough	d		07 16	08 16	09 16	10 16	11 16	12 16	14 16	16 16	17 16	18 16	19 16	20 16	21 26	22 46	
Oxford	a	01 58	07 26	08 26	09 26	10 28	11 26	12 26	14 26	16 26	17 26	18 26	19 26	20 27	21 36	22 56	
Didcot Parkway	a														21 49	23 13	
Reading 7	a		07 54	08 56	09 55	10 55	11 55	12 54	14 55	16 55	17 55	18 55	19 55	20 52	22 04	23 30	
Slough 3	a		08 09	09 10	10 09	11 09	12 09	13 09	15 09	17 09	18 10	19 09	20 09	21 10	22 22	23 48	
London Paddington 15	⊖ a		08 29	09 29	10 29	11 29	12 29	13 29	15 29	17 29	18 29	19 29	20 29	21 29	22 39	00 10	

For general notes see front of timetable
For details of catering facilities see Directory of Train Operators

A From 8 September
B Until 4 September
C Until 3 September
D From 7 September
E From 12 September
b Arr. 1819

Table 126

Hereford and Worcester → Oxford and London

Sundays
until 6 September

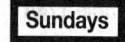

Network Diagram - see first page of Table 116

		GW 1 ◇	GW 1 ◇	GW 1 ◇	GW 1 ◇	GW 1 ◇	GW 1 ◇	GW 1 ◇	GW 1 ◇	GW 1 ◇	GW 1 ◇	GW 1 ◇
Hereford 7	d				13 28	14 30		16 30		18 30		
Ledbury	d				13 46	14 55		16 47		18 48		
Colwall	d				13 53	15 02		16 55		18 55		
Great Malvern	d	09 00	11 07	13 10	13 59	15 08		17 00		19 08	20 08	20 55
Malvern Link	d	09 03	11 10	13 13	14 03	15 12		17 04		19 12	20 12	20 59
Worcester Foregate Street 7	d	09 12	11 19	13 23	14 14	15 24		17 22		19 25	20 25	21 10
Worcester Shrub Hill 7	d	09 16	11 23	13 27	14 19	15 26	16 27	17 27	18 25	19 29	20 28	21 18
Pershore	d	09 25	11 32	13 36	14 28	15 36	16 37	17 36	18 35	19 38	20 38	21 28
Evesham	a	09 33	11 40	13 44	14 36	15 44	16 45	17 45	18 45	19 45	20 46	21 36
	d	09 34	11 46	13 47	14 51	15 51	16 52	17 50	18 53	19 53	20 53	21 53
Honeybourne	d	09 40	11 52	13 52		15 57	16 59		19 00	20 00	21 00	22 00
Moreton-in-Marsh	a	09 53	12 04	14 05	15 06	16 09	17 11	18 05	19 12	20 12	21 12	22 12
	d	09 55	12 07	14 07	15 09	16 12	17 12	18 07	19 13	20 13	21 13	22 13
Kingham	d	10 03	12 15	14 15	15 16	16 20	17 22	18 15	19 22	20 22	21 22	22 21
Shipton	d											
Ascott-under-Wychwood	d											
Charlbury	d	10 13	12 24	14 25	15 27	16 29	17 32	18 25	19 31	20 31	21 32	22 31
Finstock	d											
Combe	d											
Hanborough	d	10 21	12 32	14 33	15 35	16 38	17 40		19 40	20 40	21 40	22 39
Oxford	a	10 34	12 42	14 42	15 48	16 50	17 50	18 40	19 49	20 49	21 49	22 48
Didcot Parkway	a	10 50			16 02	17 01	18 03	18 53	20 04	21 04	22 03	
Reading 7	a	11 07	13 09	15 09	16 19	17 21	18 21	19 09	20 22	21 19	22 22	
Slough 3	a	11 30	13 29	15 30	16 48	17 51	18 48	19 34	20 48	21 41	22 47	
London Paddington 15 ⊖	a	11 54	13 53	15 53	17 06	18 10	19 08	19 53	21 06	22 07	23 15	

Sundays
from 13 September

		GW 1 ◇	GW 1 ◇	GW 1 ◇	GW 1 ◇	GW 1 ◇	GW 1 ◇	GW 1 ◇	GW 1 ◇	GW 1 ◇	GW 1 ◇	GW 1 ◇	HX 1
Hereford 7	d				13 28	14 30		16 30		18 30			23 57
Ledbury	d				13 46	14 55		16 47		18 48			
Colwall	d				13 53	15 02		16 55		18 55			00 01
Great Malvern	d	09 00	11 07	13 10	13 59	15 08		17 00		19 08	20 08	20 55	
Malvern Link	d	09 03	11 10	13 13	14 03	15 12		17 04		19 12	20 12	20 59	*00 30*
Worcester Foregate Street 7	d	09 12	11 19	13 23	14 14	15 23		17 23		19 24	20 24	21 10	
Worcester Shrub Hill 7	d	09 17	11 23	13 27	14 19	15 26	16 27	17 27	18 25	19 29	20 28	21 18	
Pershore	d	09 26	11 32	13 36	14 28	15 36	16 37	17 36	18 35	19 38	20 38	21 28	
Evesham	a	09 34	11 40	13 44	14 36	15 44	16 45	17 45	18 45	19 45	20 46	21 36	
	d	09 36	11 46	13 47	14 50	15 51	16 52	17 50	18 53	19 53	20 53	21 53	
Honeybourne	d	09 42	11 52	13 52		15 57	16 59	17 58	19 00	19 59	21 00	22 00	
Moreton-in-Marsh	a	09 55	12 04	14 05	15 05	16 09	17 11	18 09	19 12	20 12	21 12	22 12	
	d	09 56	12 07	14 07	15 07	16 12	17 12	18 12	19 13	20 13	21 13	22 13	
Kingham	d	10 04	12 15	14 15	15 15	16 20	17 22	18 21	19 22	20 22	21 22	22 21	
Shipton	d												
Ascott-under-Wychwood	d												
Charlbury	d	10 15	12 24	14 25	15 26	16 29	17 32	18 31	19 31	20 31	21 32	22 31	
Finstock	d												
Combe	d												
Hanborough	d	10 22	12 32	14 33	15 34	16 38	17 40		19 40	20 40	21 40	22 39	
Oxford	a	10 34	12 48	14 50	15 48	16 50	17 50	18 49	19 49	20 49	21 49	22 48	
Didcot Parkway	a	11 02	13 02	15 03	16 01	17 01	18 03	19 02	20 04	21 04	22 03	22 59	
Reading 7	a	11 20	13 20	15 20	16 19	17 21	18 20	19 19	20 20	21 19	22 21	23 16	
Slough 3	a	11 38	13 36	15 35	16 34	17 39	18 35	19 35	20 34	21 39	22 47	23 36	
London Paddington 15 ⊖	a	12 01	14 00	16 01	16 59	18 06	19 04	20 01	21 01	22 07	23 15	00 01	

For general notes see front of timetable
For details of catering facilities see
Directory of Train Operators

Table 126A

Mondays to Fridays

Kingham — Chipping Norton
Bus Service

		GW 🚌	GW 🚌	GW 🚌	GW 🚌	GW 🚌	GW 🚌	GW 🚌	GW 🚌	GW 🚌	GW 🚌	GW 🚌	GW 🚌	GW 🚌
Kingham	d	07 07	07 43	08 35	09 32	11 30	13 15	14 05	16 20	17 15	18 08	18 50	19 20	19 50
Chipping Norton West St	a	07 18	07 56	08 48	09 50	11 48	13 28	14 18	16 33	17 28	18 21	19 03	19 33	20 03

Saturdays

		GW 🚌	GW 🚌	GW 🚌	GW 🚌	GW 🚌	GW 🚌	GW 🚌	GW 🚌	GW 🚌	GW 🚌	GW 🚌
Kingham	d	08 10	09 15	10 10	11 15	12 10	13 10	15 15	16 15	17 15	18 18	19 45
Chipping Norton West St	a	08 23	09 28	10 29	11 34	12 29	13 23	15 28	16 28	17 28	18 31	19 58

Mondays to Fridays

		GW 🚌	GW 🚌	GW 🚌	GW 🚌	GW 🚌	GW 🚌	GW 🚌	GW 🚌	GW 🚌	GW 🚌	GW 🚌	GW 🚌	GW 🚌
Chipping Norton West St	d	06 52	07 20	08 00	09 00	10 48	12 35	13 35	15 55	16 40	17 35	18 25	19 05	19 35
Kingham	a	07 05	07 33	08 13	09 13	11 03	12 50	13 48	16 08	16 55	17 48	18 38	19 16	19 47

Saturdays

		GW 🚌	GW 🚌	GW 🚌	GW 🚌	GW 🚌	GW 🚌	GW 🚌	GW 🚌	GW 🚌	GW 🚌
Chipping Norton West St	d	07 40	08 35	09 30	10 40	11 40	13 35	15 40	16 45	17 40	19 25
Kingham	a	07 53	08 48	09 43	10 58	11 58	13 48	15 53	16 58	17 53	19 38

For general notes see front of timetable
For details of catering facilities see
Directory of Train Operators

No Sunday Service

Route Diagram for Tables 127, 128

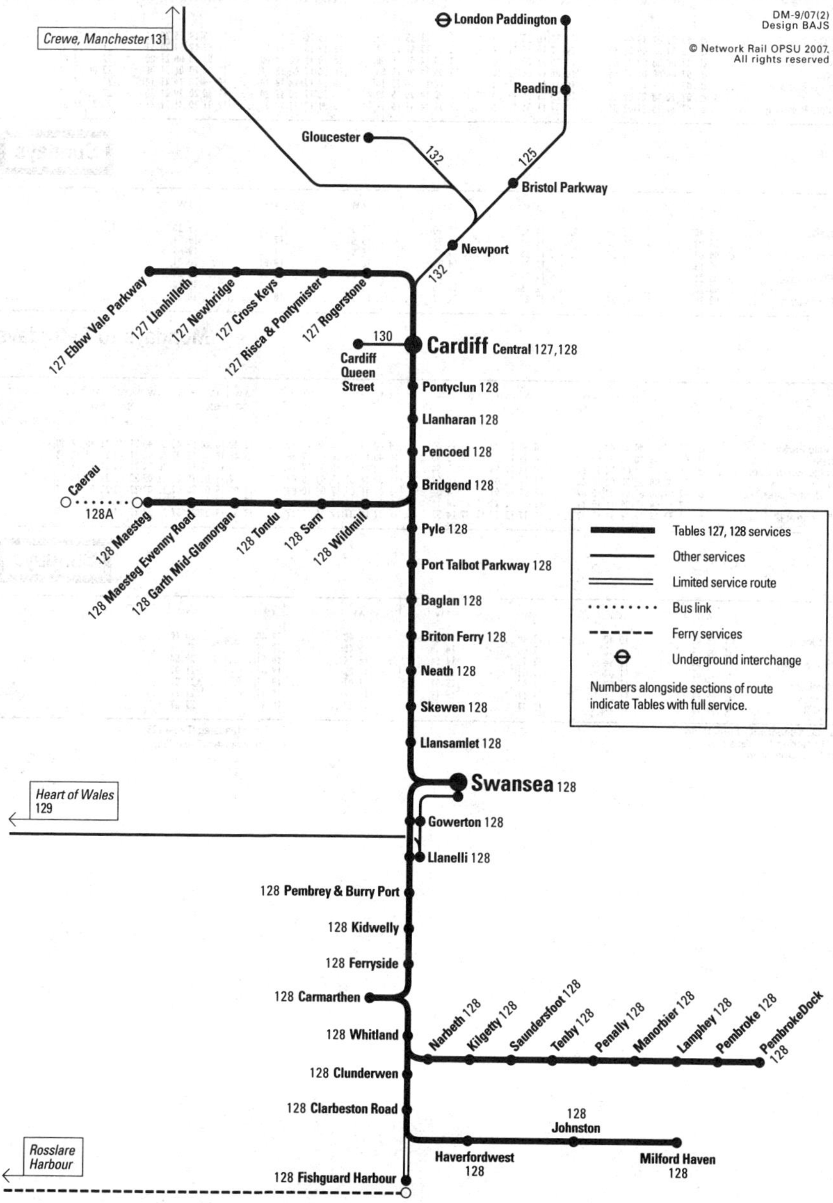
DM-9/07(2)
Design BAJS
© Network Rail OPSU 2007.
All rights reserved
Crewe, Manchester 131
London Paddington
Reading
Gloucester
132
125
Bristol Parkway
Newport
132
127 Ebbw Vale Parkway
127 Llanhilleth
127 Newbridge
127 Cross Keys
127 Risca & Pontymister
127 Rogerstone
130
Cardiff Queen Street
Cardiff Central 127,128
Pontyclun 128
Llanharan 128
Pencoed 128
Bridgend 128
Caerau
128A
128 Maesteg
128 Maesteg Ewenny Road
128 Garth Mid-Glamorgan
128 Tondu
128 Sarn
128 Wildmill
Pyle 128
Port Talbot Parkway 128
Baglan 128
Briton Ferry 128
Neath 128
Skewen 128
Llansamlet 128
Swansea 128
Heart of Wales 129
Gowerton 128
Llanelli 128
128 Pembrey & Burry Port
128 Kidwelly
128 Ferryside
128 Carmarthen
128 Whitland
128 Clunderwen
128 Clarbeston Road
Narbeth 128
Kilgetty 128
Saundersfoot 128
Tenby 128
Penally 128
Manorbier 128
Lamphey 128
Pembroke 128
PembrokeDock 128
128 Johnston
Haverfordwest 128
Milford Haven 128
Rosslare Harbour
128 Fishguard Harbour
Tables 127, 128 services
Other services
Limited service route
Bus link
Ferry services
Underground interchange
Numbers alongside sections of route indicate Tables with full service.

Cardiff Central — Ebbw Vale Parkway

Route Diagram - see first page of Table 127

Miles			AW	AW A	AW	AW	AW	AW	AW	AW	AW	AW	AW	AW	AW	AW	AW	AW	AW
0	Cardiff Central 7	d	06 35	07 39	08 35	09 35	10 35	11 35	12 35	13 35	14 35	15 35	16 35	17 35	18 35	19 35	20 35	21 35	22 35
14	Rogerstone	d	06 57	08 00	08 57	09 57	10 57	11 57	12 57	13 57	14 57	15 57	16 57	17 57	18 57	19 57	20 57	21 57	22 57
15¼	Risca & Pontymister	d	07 00	08 04	09 00	10 00	11 00	12 00	13 00	14 00	15 00	16 00	17 00	18 00	19 00	20 00	21 00	22 00	23 00
17¾	Cross Keys	d	07 06	08 09	09 06	10 06	11 06	12 06	13 06	14 06	15 06	16 06	17 06	18 06	19 06	20 06	21 06	22 06	23 06
20¾	Newbridge (Ebbw Vale)	d	07 14	08 17	09 14	10 14	11 14	12 14	13 14	14 14	15 14	16 14	17 14	18 14	19 14	20 14	21 14	22 14	23 14
23¼	Llanhilleth	d	07 20	08 23	09 20	10 20	11 20	12 20	13 20	14 20	15 20	16 20	17 20	18 20	19 20	20 20	21 20	22 20	23 20
28¾	Ebbw Vale Parkway	a	07 31	08 31	09 31	10 31	11 31	12 31	13 31	14 31	15 31	16 31	17 31	18 31	19 31	20 31	21 31	22 31	23 31

Sundays

		AW	AW	AW	AW	AW	AW	AW
Cardiff Central 7	d	07 40	09 30	11 30	13 30	15 30	17 30	19 30
Rogerstone	d	08 03	09 51	11 51	13 51	15 51	17 51	19 51
Risca & Pontymister	d	08 07	09 55	11 55	13 55	15 55	17 55	19 55
Cross Keys	d	08 13	10 01	12 01	14 01	16 01	18 01	20 01
Newbridge (Ebbw Vale)	d	08 21	10 09	12 09	14 09	16 09	18 09	20 09
Llanhilleth	d	08 28	10 16	12 16	14 16	16 16	18 16	20 16
Ebbw Vale Parkway	a	08 39	10 27	12 27	14 27	16 27	18 27	20 27

Mondays to Saturdays

Miles			AW	AW	AW	AW	AW	AW	AW	AW	AW	AW	AW B	AW	AW SO	AW SX	AW	AW	AW SX	AW SO	AW
0	Ebbw Vale Parkway	d	06 40	07 40	08 40	09 40	10 40	11 40	12 40	13 40	14 40	15 40	16 40	17 40	18 40	18 40	19 40	20 40	21 40	21 40	22 40
5¼	Llanhilleth	d	06 48	07 48	08 48	09 48	10 48	11 48	12 48	13 48	14 48	15 48	16 48	17 48	18 48	18 48	19 48	20 48	21 48	21 48	22 48
8	Newbridge (Ebbw Vale)	d	06 54	07 54	08 54	09 54	10 54	11 54	12 54	13 54	14 54	15 54	16 54	17 54	18 54	18 54	19 54	20 54	21 54	21 54	22 54
11½	Cross Keys	d	07 02	08 02	09 02	10 02	11 02	12 02	13 02	14 02	15 02	16 02	17 02	18 02	19 02	19 02	20 02	21 02	22 02	22 02	23 02
13¾	Risca & Pontymister	d	07 07	08 07	09 07	10 07	11 07	12 07	13 07	14 07	15 07	16 07	17 07	18 07	19 07	19 07	20 07	21 07	22 07	22 07	23 07
14¾	Rogerstone	d	07 11	08 11	09 11	10 11	11 11	12 11	13 11	14 11	15 11	16 11	17 11	18 11	19 11	19 11	20 11	21 11	22 11	22 11	23 11
28¾	Cardiff Central 7	a	07 37	08 37	09 37	10 37	11 37	12 37	13 37	14 37	15 37	16 37	17 36	18 37	19 37	19 39	20 37	21 37	22 37	22 39	23 37

Sundays

		AW	AW	AW	AW	AW	AW	AW
Ebbw Vale Parkway	d	08 40	10 40	12 40	14 40	16 40	18 40	20 40
Llanhilleth	d	08 48	10 48	12 48	14 48	16 48	18 48	20 48
Newbridge (Ebbw Vale)	d	08 54	10 54	12 54	14 54	16 54	18 54	20 54
Cross Keys	d	09 02	11 02	13 02	15 02	17 02	19 02	21 02
Risca & Pontymister	d	09 07	11 07	13 07	15 07	17 07	19 07	21 07
Rogerstone	d	09 11	11 11	13 11	15 11	17 11	19 11	21 11
Cardiff Central 7	a	09 37	11 37	13 37	15 37	17 37	19 37	21 37

For general notes see front of timetable
For details of catering facilities see Directory of Train Operators

A From Maesteg (Table 128)
B To Swansea (Table 128)

Cardiff → Maesteg, Swansea and West Wales

Route Diagram - see first page of Table 127

Miles	Miles			AW MX R	AW MO ◇	AW MX ◇	AW MX	GW MX 1◇	GW MO 1◇ A	GW MO 1◇ B	GW MX 1◇	AW R C	AW ◇	AW	AW	AW	AW	AW ◇	AW	AW ◇	AW D	AW ◇ E	GW 1◇	AW ◇ G	AW ◇ H
—	—	London Paddington 15 ⊖	d					21p15	21p37	21p37	22p45												05 27		
—	—	Reading 7	d					21p41	22p14	22p15	23p21												05 57		
—	—	Manchester Piccadilly 10	d	17p30																					
—	—	Gloucester 7	d																		05 50				
—	—	Bristol Parkway 7	d					22p46	23p18	23p18	00 25														
—	—	Newport (South Wales)	d	20p44				23p18	23p47	23p47	00 55										06 44	07 35	07 45		08 01
—	—	Cardiff Queen Street 3	d																	*06 26*	*06 44*	*07 46*	*07 51*	*07 56*	*08 06*
0	—	**Cardiff Central 7**	d	21p06	22p35		23p15	23p40	00 09	00 09	01 16							05 40	05 51	06 52	07 04	07 58	08 01	08 09	08 20
11	—	Pontyclun	d				23p29											05 52	06 03		07 16				08 32
14	—	Llanharan	d				23p34											05 57	06 08		07 21				08 37
16¼	—	Pencoed	d				23p39											06 02	06 12		07 25				08 41
20¼	0	Bridgend	d	21p28	22p54		23p45	23p59	00 29	00 29	01 39							06 08	06 20	07 12	07 32	08 17	08 22	08 29	08 49
—	1	Wildmill	d																06 22		07 35				08 51
—	2¼	Sarn	d																06 25		07 38				08 54
—	3	Tondu	d																06 29		07 41				08 58
—	7	Garth (Mid Glamorgan)	d																06 38		07 51				09 07
—	7¾	Maesteg (Ewenny Road)	d																06 41		07 53				09 10
—	8¼	Maesteg	a																06 46		07 59				09 14
26¼	—	Pyle	d	21p35			23p53											06 16		07 20				08 37	
32½	—	Port Talbot Parkway	d	21p43	23p07		00 01	00 11	00 42	00 42	01 52							06 24		07 28		08 30	08 35	08 45	
34½	—	Baglan	d				00 05											06 28		07 32				08 49	
36¼	—	Briton Ferry	d				00 08											06 31		07 35				08 52	
38	—	Neath	d	21p50	23p14		00 12	00 19	00 50	00 50	01 59							06 35		07 39		08 37	08 44	08 56	
41¾	—	Skewen	d				00 16											06 39		07 43				09 00	
43½	—	Llansamlet	d				00 20											06 43		07 47				09 04	
47½	—	**Swansea 7**	a	22p03	23p26		00 28	00 34	01 02	01 02	02 14							06 52		07 55		08 49	08 57	09 13	
—	—		d	22p27	23p32	23p45	00 45						04 36				05 50	06 54		08 05		09 00		09 15	
53	—	Gowerton	d	22b37	23b42		00c56										06x01			08x16		09x15			
58¾	—	Llanelli	a	22p44	23p49	00 01	01s02						04 52				06 08	07 10		08 22		09 19		09 32	
—	—		d	22p44	23p49	00 01											06 08	07 11		08 23		09 19			
62¾	—	Pembrey & Burry Port	d	22p50	23p55	00 07	01s08										06 14	07 17		08 28		09 24			
68	—	Kidwelly	d	22b56	00x01		01c14										06x21	07x23		08x35		09x34			
72¼	—	Ferryside	d	23b01	00x07		01c20										06x27	07x29		08x41		09x39			
79¼	—	**Carmarthen**	a	23p13	00 19	00 27	01 37										06 40	07 42		08 53		09 51			
—	—		d	23p17	00 21	00 30								04 55	05 45	06 05	06 43	07 44		08 56		09 55			
93¼	0	Whitland	a	23p31	00 36	00 45								05 11	05 59	06 19	06 58	07 59		09 10		10 13			
—	—		d	23p32	00 36	00 45								05 11	05 59	06 20	06 58	08 00		09 10		10 14			
—	5¼	Narberth	d												06x08		07x07			09x19					
—	10¾	Kilgetty	d												06x17		07x17			09x28					
—	11½	Saundersfoot	d												06x18		07x19			09x29					
—	15¾	**Tenby**	a												06 25		07 26			09 36					
—	—		d												06 30		07 42			09 43					
—	17	Penally	d												06x33		07x45			09x46					
—	20¼	Manorbier	d												06 40		07 52			09 53					
—	23¾	Lamphey	d												06x47		07x59			10x00					
—	25¼	Pembroke	d												06 50		08 02			10 03					
—	27¼	**Pembroke Dock**	a												07 04		08 17			10 17					
98¾	—	Clunderwen	d	23b38										05x18		06x26		08x06				10x20			
105¼	0	Clarbeston Road	d	23b45	00x48	00x59								05x26		06x33		08x13				10x27			
—	5¼	Haverfordwest	d	23p54										05e40		06 41		08 22				10 35			
—	10	Johnston	d	00x01										05x47		06x49		08x29				10x43			
—	14	**Milford Haven**	a	00 11										05 57		07 04		08 44				10 58			
121	—	**Fishguard Harbour**	a		01 17	01 26																			
—	—		⛴ d									02 45													
—	—	Rosslare Harbour	⛴ a									06 15													

For general notes see front of timetable
For details of catering facilities see Directory of Train Operators

A From 14 September
B Until 7 September
C Ship service
D From Cheltenham Spa (Table 57)
E From Crewe (Table 131)
G To Shrewsbury (Table 129)
H From Chester (Table 131)
b Previous night.
Stops on request, passengers wishing to alight must inform the guard and those wishing to join must give a hand signal to the driver
c Stops, on request, to set down only
e Arr. 0534

Table 128

Mondays to Fridays

Cardiff → Maesteg, Swansea and West Wales

Route Diagram - see first page of Table 127

		GW	AW	AW	AW	AW	GW	AW	AW	GW	AW	AW		AW	AW	AW	GW	AW	AW	AW	GW	AW	AW	AW	AW
		1 ◇	◇				1 ◇	◇		1 ◇	◇	◇					1 ◇	◇		◇	1 ◇	◇			
			A			B			B										B						B
		🍽	🛒	🛒			🍽	🛒		🍽	🛒	🛒		🛒			🍽	🛒			🍽	🛒	🛒		
London Paddington 15 ⊖	d	06 45					07 45			08 45							09 45				10 45				
Reading 7	d	07 11					08 11			09 11							10 11				11 11				
Manchester Piccadilly 10 ⛴	d							06 30				07 30						08 30				09 30			
Gloucester 7	d					07 58			08 58										10 58						11 59
Bristol Parkway 7	d	08 07					09 07			10 07							11 07				12 07				
Newport (South Wales)	d	08 31	08 33			08 52	09 31	09 33	09 52	10 31		10 40				10 57	11 31	11 33	11 52		12 31	12 33			12 52
Cardiff Queen Street 3	d	08 36	08 51		09 01	09 06	09 36	09 51	10 06	10 36	10 41	10 51			11 01	11 06	11 36	11 51	12 06		12 36	12 46		13 01	13 06
Cardiff Central 7	d	08 48	09 04		09 14	09 18	09 48	10 04	10 18	10 48	10 54	11 04			11 14	11 18	11 48	12 04	12 18		12 48	13 04		13 14	13 18
Pontyclun	d					09 30			10 30							11 30			12 30						13 30
Llanharan	d					09 35			10 35							11 35			12 35						13 35
Pencoed	d					09 39			10 39							11 39			12 39						13 39
Bridgend	d	09 09	09 23		09 34	09 46	10 09	10 23	10 46	11 10		11 23			11 34	11 46	12 09	12 23	12 46		13 09	13 23		13 34	13 46
Wildmill	d					09 49			10 49							11 49			12 49						13 49
Sarn	d					09 52			10 52							11 52			12 52						13 52
Tondu	d					09 55			10 55							11 55			12 55						13 55
Garth (Mid Glamorgan)	d					10 05			11 05							12 05			13 05						14 05
Maesteg (Ewenny Road)	d					10 07			11 07							12 07			13 07						14 07
Maesteg	a					10 10			11 12							12 12			13 12						14 12
Pyle	d				09 42										11 42									13 42	
Port Talbot Parkway	d	09 23	09 36		09 50		10 23	10 36		11 23		11 36			11 50		12 23	12 36			13 23	13 36		13 50	
Baglan	d				09 54										11 54									13 54	
Briton Ferry	d				09 57										11 57									13 57	
Neath	d	09 30	09 43		10 01		10 30	10 43		11 30		11 43			12 01		12 30	12 43			13 30	13 43		14 01	
Skewen	d				10 05										12 05									14 05	
Llansamlet	d				10 09										12 09									14 09	
Swansea 7	a	09 46	09 55		10 20		10 44	10 55		11 43		11 55			12 20		12 45	12 55			13 44	13 55		14 20	
	d		10 00	10 05				11 00				12 00		12 05				13 00		13 16		14 00	14 05		
Gowerton	d			10x17										12x17									14x17		
Llanelli	a		10 15	10 24				11 16			11 58	12 15		12 24				13 15		13 32		14 15	14 24		
	d		10 16	10 24				11 17			11 58	12 16		12 24				13 16				14 16	14 24		
Pembrey & Burry Port	d		10 21	10 30				11 22				12 21		12 30				13 21				14 21	14 30		
Kidwelly	d			10x37										12x37									14x37		
Ferryside	d			10x43										12x43									14x43		
Carmarthen	a		10 41	10 56				11 42				12 41		12 56				13 41				14 41	14 56		
	d			10 59				11 45						12 59				13 44					14 59		
Whitland	a			11 13				11 59			12 33			13 13				13 58					15 13		
	d			11 13				12 00			12 34			13 13				13 59					15 13		
Narberth	d			11x22										13x22									15x22		
Kilgetty	d			11x31										13x31									15x31		
Saundersfoot	d			11x32										13x32									15x32		
Tenby	a			11 39										13 39									15 39		
	d			11 43										13 43									15 43		
Penally	d			11x46										13x46									15x46		
Manorbier	d			11 53										13 53									15 53		
Lamphey	d			12x00										14x00									16x00		
Pembroke	d			12 03										14 03									16 03		
Pembroke Dock	a			12 17										14 17									16 17		
Clunderwen	d							12x06										14x05							
Clarbeston Road	d							12x13										14x12							
Haverfordwest	d							12 21										14 20							
Johnston	d							12x29										14x28							
Milford Haven	a							12 44										14 44							
Fishguard Harbour	a										13 15														
⛴	d																								
Rosslare Harbour ⛴	a																								

For general notes see front of timetable
For details of catering facilities see Directory of Train Operators

A From Crewe (Table 131)
B From Cheltenham Spa (Table 57)

Cardiff → Maesteg, Swansea and West Wales

Route Diagram - see first page of Table 127

		AW	GW	AW	AW	GW	AW	AW	AW	AW	GW	AW	AW	GW	AW	AW	AW	AW	AW	AW	GW	AW	AW	GW	AW
		R	1 ◇	◇		1 ◇	◇				1 ◇	R		1 ◇		R		◇	◇		1 ◇	R		1 ◇	
		A								B			B					C		D			B		B
			🍴	☕		🍴	☕	☕			🍴	☕		🍴	☕	☕	☕	☕			🍴	☕		🍴	
London Paddington 15 ⊖	d		11 45			12 45					13 45			14 45							15 45			16 15	
Reading 7	d		12 11			13 11					14 11			15 11							16 11			16 41	
Manchester Piccadilly 10 ⛴	d			10 30			11 30					12 30				13 30						14 30			
Gloucester 7	d									13 59			14 58										16 58		
Bristol Parkway 7	d		13 07			14 07					15 07			16 07							17 07			17 42	
Newport (South Wales)	d		13 31	13 37		14 31	14 33			14 53	15 31	15 33	15 52	16 31		16 34		16 59		17b11	17 31	17 33	17 52	18 05	
Cardiff Queen Street 3	d		*13 36*	*13 51*	*14 11*	*14 36*	*14 51*		*15 01*	*15 06*	*15 36*	*15 51*	*16 06*	*16 36*		*16 51*		*17 11*		*17 26*	*17 36*	*17 51*	*18 01*	*18 11*	
Cardiff Central 7	d		13 48	14 04	14 21	14 48	15 04		15 14	15 18	15 48	16 04	16 18	16 48		17 04		17 21		17 38	17 48	18 04	18 12	18 22	←
Pontyclun	d				14 33					15 30			16 30					17 32					18 24		
Llanharan	d				14 38					15 35			16 35					17 38					18 29		18 29
Pencoed	d				14 42					15 39			16 39					17 41					→		18 33
Bridgend	d		14 09	14 23	14 49	15 09	15 23		15 34	15 46	16 09	16 23	16 46	17 09		17 25		17 48		17 59	18 09	18 24		18 44	18 49
Wildmill	d				14 52					15 49			16 49					17 51							18 52
Sarn	d				14 55					15 52			16 52					17 54							18 55
Tondu	d				14 58					15 55			16 55					17 57							18 58
Garth (Mid Glamorgan)	d				15 08					16 05			17 05					18 07							19 08
Maesteg (Ewenny Road)	d				15 10					16 07			17 07					18 09							19 10
Maesteg	a				15 15					16 12			17 12					18 14							19 15
Pyle	d								15 42							17 31				18 07					
Port Talbot Parkway	d		14 23	14 36		15 23	15 36		15 50		16 23	16 36		17 23		17 39				18 16	18 23	18 42		18 57	
Baglan	d								15 54							17 40				18 20					
Briton Ferry	d								15 57							17 45				18 23					
Neath	d		14 30	14 43		15 30	15 43		16 01		16 30	16 43		17 30		17 49				18 27	18 30	18 49		19 04	
Skewen	d								16 05							17 52				18 31					
Llansamlet	d								16 09							17 56				18 35					
Swansea 7	a		14 44	14 55		15 44	15 55		16 20		16 45	16 55		17 44		18 05				18 46	18 48	19 01		19 19	
	d			15 00			16 00	16 05				17 05			17 51	18 09			18 21			19 05			
Gowerton	d							16x17				17x16			18x02	18x19						19x18			
Llanelli	a			15 18			16 15	16 24				17 23			18 09	18 26			18 37			19 25			
	d			15 19			16 16	16 24				17 23			18 09	18 26						19 25			
Pembrey & Burry Port	d			15 24			16 21	16 30				17 29			18 15	18 32						19 31			
Kidwelly	d							16x37				17x35			18x22	18x38									
Ferryside	d							16x43				17x40			18x28	18x43									
Carmarthen	a			15 44			16 41	16 56				17 52			18 41	19 00	←					19 50			
	d			15 47				16 59				17 55			19 05 →		19 05					19 55			
Whitland	a			16 01				17 13				18 13					19 19					20 09			
	d			16 02				17 13				18 14					19 19					20 10			
Narberth	d							17x22									19x28								
Kilgetty	d							17x31									19x37								
Saundersfoot	d							17x32									19x38								
Tenby	a							17 39									19 45								
	d							17 43									19 52								
Penally	d							17x46									19x55								
Manorbier	d							17 53									20 02								
Lamphey	d							18x00									20x09								
Pembroke	d							18 03									20 12								
Pembroke Dock	a							18 17									20 22								
Clunderwen	d			16x08								18x20										20x16			
Clarbeston Road	d			16x15								18x27										20x23			
Haverfordwest	d			16 23								18 35										20 31			
Johnston	d			16x31								18x43										20x39			
Milford Haven	a			16 46								18 58										20 54			
Fishguard Harbour	a																								
⛴	d	14 30																							
Rosslare Harbour ⛴	a	18 00																							

For general notes see front of timetable
For details of catering facilities see Directory of Train Operators

A Ship service
B From Cheltenham Spa (Table 57)
C From Holyhead (Table 131)
D From Ebbw Vale Parkway (Table 127)
b From 7 September dep. 1712

Cardiff → Maesteg, Swansea and West Wales

Route Diagram - see first page of Table 127

		GW	AW	AW	GW	GW	AW	GW	AW	GW	GW	AW	AW	GW	AW	AW	GW	AW	AW	AW	GW	GW FO	GW FX
		1 ◇	R	A	1 ◇	1 ◇	R	1 ◇	A	1 ◇	1 ◇	R	A	1 ◇	◇		1 ◇		◇		1 ◇	1 ◇	1 ◇
London Paddington 15 ⊖	d	16 45			17 15	17 45				18 15	18 45			19 15			20 15				21 15	22 45	22 45
Reading 7	d	17 11			17 41	18 11				18 41	19 11			19 41			20 41				21 41	23 11	23 21
Manchester Piccadilly 10	d		15 30				16 30					17 30			18 30								
Gloucester 7	d			17 59					18 58				19 58										
Bristol Parkway 7	d	18 12			18 42	19 10				19 42	20 07			20 42			21 42				22 46	00 17	00 25
Newport (South Wales)	d	18 38	18 43	18 53	19 10	19 37	19 33		19 52	20 08	20 31	20 44	20 52	21 05	21 50	21 59	22 05			22 46	23 18	00 40	00 55
Cardiff Queen Street 3	d		18 51	18 56	19 06	19 36	19 46		19 56	20 16	20 36	20 56		20 56	21 56		22 16			22 55	23 20	00 56	
Cardiff Central 7	d	18 53	19 04	19 12	19 27	19 53	20 01		20 13	20 28	20 48	21 06	21 10	21 23	22 13	22 25	22 35	←		23 15	23 40	00 57	01 16
Pontyclun	d			19 28					20 25				21 22			22 37				23 29			
Llanharan	d			19 33					20 30				21 27			22 42 →		22 42		23 34			
Pencoed	d			19 37					20 34				21 32					22 46		23 39			
Bridgend	d	19 15	19 23	19 45	19 49	20 15	20 22		20 41	20 48	21 09	21 28	21 41	21 44	22 33		22 57	23 02		23 45	23 59	01 20	01 39
Wildmill	d			19 48					20 44				21 43					23 05					
Sarn	d			19 51					20 47				21 46					23 08					
Tondu	d			19 54					20 50				21 50					23 11					
Garth (Mid Glamorgan)	d			20 04					21 00				21 59					23 21					
Maesteg (Ewenny Road)	d			20 06					21 02				22 02					23 23					
Maesteg	a			20 11					21 05				22 06					23 29					
Pyle	d		19 30									21 35								23 53			
Port Talbot Parkway	d	19 28	19 38		20 02	20 28	20 35			21 01	21 23	21 43		21 57	22 47		23 10			00 01	00 11	01 33	01 52
Baglan	d		19 41																	00 05			
Briton Ferry	d		19 44					←												00 08			
Neath	d	19 36	19 48		20 10	20 36 →		20 36		21 09	21 30	21 50		22 05	22 55		23 17			00 12	00 19	01 41	01 59
Skewen	d		19 53																	00 16			
Llansamlet	d		19 57																	00 20			
Swansea 7	a	19 49	20 05		20 24			20 49		21 23	21 46	22 03		22 18	23 07		23 32			00 28	00 34	01 54	02 14
	d		20 10					21 00				22 27			23 10				23 45	00 45			
Gowerton	d											22x37			23x21					00b56			
Llanelli	a		20 25				21 05	21 16				22 44			23 27				00 01	01s02			
	d		20 26				21 05	21 16				22 44			23 28				00 01				
Pembrey & Burry Port	d		20 31				21 11	21 23				22 50			23 33				00 07	01s08			
Kidwelly	d		20x37									22x56			23x40					01b14			
Ferryside	d		20x43									23x01			23x46					01b20			
Carmarthen	a		20 55				21 30	21 48				23 13			00 04				00 27	01 37			
	d		21 00				22 04					23 17							00 30				
Whitland	a		21 14				22 20					23 31							00 45				
	d		21 14				22 21					23 32							00 45				
Narberth	d		21x23																				
Kilgetty	d		21x33																				
Saundersfoot	d		21x35																				
Tenby	a		21 42																				
	d		21 45																				
Penally	d		21x48																				
Manorbier	d		21x55																				
Lamphey	d		22x02																				
Pembroke	d		22 05																				
Pembroke Dock	a		22 18																				
Clunderwen	d						22x27					23x38											
Clarbeston Road	d						22x34					23x45							00x59				
Haverfordwest	d						22 42					23 54											
Johnston	d						22x50					00x01											
Milford Haven	a						23 05					00 11											
Fishguard Harbour	a																		01 26				
⛴	d																						
Rosslare Harbour ⛴	a																						

For general notes see front of timetable
For details of catering facilities see Directory of Train Operators

A From Cheltenham Spa (Table 57)
b Stops, on request, to set down only

Table 128

Saturdays

Cardiff → Maesteg, Swansea and West Wales

Route Diagram - see first page of Table 127

Station		AW	AW	AW	AW	GW	GW	AW	AW	AW	AW	AW	AW	AW	AW	GW		AW	AW	AW	GW	GW	AW	AW	AW
		R [trolley]	◇			1 ◇ [buffet]	1 ◇ [buffet]	R A	◇			[trolley]	[trolley]	◇ [trolley]		1 ◇ B		◇ C	◇ B		1	1 ◇ D [buffet]	B	◇ E [trolley]	◇ G
London Paddington 15 ⊖	d					21p15	22p45																		
Reading 7	d					21p41	23p11																		
Manchester Piccadilly 10	d	17p30																							
Gloucester 7	d																			05 50					
Bristol Parkway 7	d					22p46	00 17															07 11			
Newport (South Wales)	d	20p44				23p18	00 40													06 44		07 34		07 38	
Cardiff Queen Street 3	d																	*06 26*	*06 26*	*06 44*		*07 41*		*07 51*	*07 56*
Cardiff Central 7	d	21p06			23p15	23p40	00 56							05 40	05 51			06 52	06 52	07 04		07 52		08 04	08 09
Pontyclun	d				23p29									05 52	06 03					07 16					
Llanharan	d				23p34									05 57	06 08					07 21					
Pencoed	d				23p39									06 02	06 12					07 25					
Bridgend	d	21p28			23p45	23p59	01 20							06 08	06 20			07 12	07 12	07 32		08 09		08 23	08 29
Wildmill	d														06 22					07 35					
Sarn	d														06 25					07 38					
Tondu	d														06 29					07 41					
Garth (Mid Glamorgan)	d														06 38					07 51					
Maesteg (Ewenny Road)	d														06 41					07 53					
Maesteg	a														06 46					07 59					
Pyle	d	21p35			23p53									06 16				07 20	07 20						08 37
Port Talbot Parkway	d	21p43			00 01	00 11	01 33							06 24				07 28	07 28			08 23		08 36	08 45
Baglan	d				00 05									06 28				07 32	07 32						08 49
Briton Ferry	d				00 08									06 31				07 35	07 35						08 52
Neath	d	21p50			00 12	00 19	01 41							06 35				07 39	07 39			08 30		08 43	08 56
Skewen	d				00 16									06 39				07 43	07 43						09 00
Llansamlet	d				00 20									06 43				07 47	07 47						09 04
Swansea 7	a	22p03			00 28	00 34	01 54							06 51				07 55	07 55			08 45		08 55	09 13
	d	22p27	23p45	00 05	00 45				04 36				05 50	06 54		07 24		08 05	08 05		08 13			09 00	09 15
Gowerton	d	22c37		00x16	00e56								06x01					08x16	08x16					09x15	
Llanelli	a	22p44	00 01	00 23	01s02				04 52				06 08	07 10		07 44		08 22	08 22		08 29			09 19	09 31
	d	22p44	00 01	00 23									06 08	07 11		07 45		08 23	08 23		08 34			09 19	
Pembrey & Burry Port	d	22p50	00 07	00 29	01s08								06 14	07 17		07 52		08 28	08 28		08 41			09 24	
Kidwelly	d	22c56		00x36	01e14								06x21	07x23				08x35	08x35					09x34	
Ferryside	d	23c01		00x41	01e20								06x27	07x29				08x41	08x41					09x39	
Carmarthen	a	23p13	00 27	00 59	01 37								06 40	07 42		08 13		08 53	08 53		09 08			09 51	
	d	23p17	00 30							04 55	05 45	06 05	06 43	07 44		08 20		08 56					09 40	09 55	
Whitland	a	23p31	00 45							05 11	05 59	06 19	06 58	07 59		08 37		09 10					09 56	10 13	
	d	23p32	00 45							05 11	05 59	06 20	06 58	08 00		08 39		09 10					09 56	10 14	
Narberth	d										06x08		07x07			08x48		09x19					10x05		
Kilgetty	d										06x17		07x17			08x57		09x28					10x14		
Saundersfoot	d										06x18		07x19			09x00		09x29					10x15		
Tenby	a										06 25		07 26			09 08		09 36					10 27		
	d										06 30		07 42			09 12		09 43							
Penally	d										06x33		07x45			09x16		09x46							
Manorbier	d										06 40		07 52			09 24		09 53							
Lamphey	d										06x47		07x59			09x33		10x00							
Pembroke	d										06 50		08 02			09 38		10 03							
Pembroke Dock	a										07 04		08 17			09 49		10 17							
Clunderwen	d	23c38								05x18		06x26		08x06										10x20	
Clarbeston Road	d	23c45	00x59							05x26		06x33		08x13										10x27	
Haverfordwest	d	23p54								05f40		06 41		08 22										10 35	
Johnston	d	00x01								05x47		06x49		08x29										10x43	
Milford Haven	a	00 11								05 57		07 04		08 44										10 58	
Fishguard Harbour	a		01 26																						
	d							02 45																	
Rosslare Harbour	a							06 15																	

For general notes see front of timetable
For details of catering facilities see Directory of Train Operators

A Ship service

B Until 5 September
C From 12 September
D From Bristol Temple Meads (Table 132)
E From Crewe (Table 131)
G To Shrewsbury (Table 129)

c Previous night.
Stops on request, passengers wishing to alight must inform the guard and those wishing to join must give a hand signal to the driver
e Stops, on request, to set down only
f Arr. 0534

Cardiff → Maesteg, Swansea and West Wales

Route Diagram - see first page of Table 127

		AW	AW	AW	AW	AW	AW	GW	AW	AW		GW	GW	AW	GW	AW	AW	AW	AW	AW	AW	GW	AW	AW	AW
					◇			1 ◇	◇			1 ◇	1 ◇	◇	1 ◇	◇	◇					1 ◇	◇		◇
		A	B	C	D		E			E		C	B		C	B	C	B			C			E	
			⌶	⌶	⌶			⎍	⌶			⎍	⎍	⌶	⎍	⌶	⌶	⌶			⌶	⎍	⌶		
London Paddington 15 ⊖	d							07 45				08 45	08 45									09 45			
Reading 7	d							08 11				09 11	09 11									10 11			
Manchester Piccadilly 10	d								06 30							07 30	07 30						08 30		
Gloucester 7	d						07 58			08 58														10 58	
Bristol Parkway 7	d							09 07				10 07	10 07									11 07			
Newport (South Wales)	d	08 01			08 37		08 52	09 31	09 33	09 52		10 31	10 31			10 37	10 37					11 31	11 33	11 52	
Cardiff Queen Street 3	d	08 11			08 51	09 01	09 06	09 36	09 51	10 06		10 36	10 36	10 41		10 51	10 51		11 01	11 11		11 36	11 51	12 06	
Cardiff Central 7	d	08 22			09 04	09 14	09 18	09 48	10 04	10 18		10 48	10 48	10 55		11 04	11 04		11 14	11 21		11 48	12 04	12 18	
Pontyclun	d	08 34					09 30			10 30										11 33				12 30	
Llanharan	d	08 38					09 35			10 35										11 38				12 35	
Pencoed	d	08 42					09 39			10 39										11 42				12 39	
Bridgend	d	08 49			09 23	09 34	09 46	10 09	10 23	10 46		11 09	11 09			11 23	11 23		11 34	11 49		12 09	12 23	12 46	
Wildmill	d	08 52					09 49			10 49										11 52				12 49	
Sarn	d	08 55					09 52			10 52										11 55				12 52	
Tondu	d	08 58					09 55			10 55										11 58				12 55	
Garth (Mid Glamorgan)	d	09 08					10 05			11 05										12 08				13 05	
Maesteg (Ewenny Road)	d	09 10					10 07			11 07										12 10				13 07	
Maesteg	a	09 15					10 12			11 12										12 15				13 12	
Pyle	d					09 42													11 42						
Port Talbot Parkway	d				09 36	09 50		10 23	10 36			11 23	11 23			11 36	11 36		11 50			12 23	12 36		
Baglan	d					09 54													11 54						
Briton Ferry	d					09 57													11 57						
Neath	d				09 43	10 01		10 30	10 43			11 30	11 30			11 43	11 43		12 01			12 30	12 43		
Skewen	d					10 05													12 05						
Llansamlet	d					10 09													12 09						
Swansea 7	a				09 56	10 20		10 44	10 55			11 43	11 43		←	11 55	11 55		12 20			12 44	12 55		
	d		09 50	09 50	10 05				11 00			11 51 →			11 51	12 00	12 05	12 05			12 35		13 00		13 16
Gowerton	d		10x01	10x01														12x17			12x52				
Llanelli	a		10 08	10 08	10 23				11 16					11 58	12 07	12 15	12 20	12 24			12 59		13 15		13 32
	d		10 08	10 08	10 24				11 17					11 58	12 08	12 16	12 21	12 24			12 59		13 16		
Pembrey & Burry Port	d		10 14	10 14	10 29				11 22						12 15	12 21	12 26	12 30			13 05		13 21		
Kidwelly	d		10x21	10x21														12x37			13x12				
Ferryside	d		10x27	10x27														12x43			13x18				
Carmarthen	a		10 40	10 40	10 51				11 45						12 40	12 46	12 51	12 56			13 31		13 41		
	d		10 56	10 56					11 48						12 46			12 59					13 44		
Whitland	a		11 10	11 14					12 02					12 33	13 04			13 13					13 58		
	d		11 10	11 14					12 03					12 34	13 05			13 13					13 59		
Narberth	d		11x19	11x23														13x22							
Kilgetty	d		11x28	11x32														13x31							
Saundersfoot	d		11x29	11x33											13 25			13x32							
Tenby	a		11 36	11 40											13 35			13 39							
	d		11 41	11 43											13 41			13 43							
Penally	d		11x44	11x46														13x46							
Manorbier	d		11 50	11 52											13 51			13 53							
Lamphey	d		11x57	11x59														14x00							
Pembroke	d		12 00	12 02											14 03			14 03							
Pembroke Dock	a		12 15	12 17											14 14			14 17							
Clunderwen	d								12x09														14x05		
Clarbeston Road	d								12x16														14x12		
Haverfordwest	d								12 24														14 20		
Johnston	d								12x32														14x28		
Milford Haven	a								12 47														14 44		
Fishguard Harbour	a													13 15											
⛴	d																								
Rosslare Harbour ⛴	a																								

For general notes see front of timetable
For details of catering facilities see Directory of Train Operators

- **A** From Shrewsbury (Table 131)
- **B** From 12 September
- **C** Until 5 September
- **D** From Crewe (Table 131)
- **E** From Cheltenham Spa (Table 57)

Table 128

Saturdays

Cardiff → Maesteg, Swansea and West Wales

Route Diagram - see first page of Table 127

	AW	GW	AW		AW	AW	AW	AW	GW	AW	AW	GW	AW	AW	AW	AW	AW	GW	AW		AW	GW	AW	AW
	A	1 ◇	◇		B		C	R D	1 ◇	◇		1 ◇	◇	B	A		C	1 ◇	R		C	1 ◇		R
London Paddington 15 ⊖ d		10 45							11 45			12 45						13 45				14 45		
Reading 7 d		11 11							12 11			13 11						14 11				15 11		
Manchester Piccadilly 10 d			09 30							10 30			11 30						12 30					13 30
Gloucester 7 d							11 58										13 58				14 58			
Bristol Parkway 7 d		12 07							13 07			14 07						15 07				16 07		
Newport (South Wales) d		12 31	12 34				12 52		13 31	13 33		14 31	14 37				14 52	15 31	15 33		15 52	16 31		16 33
Cardiff Queen Street 3 d		12 36	12 46			13 01	13 06		13 36	13 51	14 11	14 36	14 51			15 01	15 06	15 36	15 51		16 06	16 36		16 51
Cardiff Central 7 d		12 48	13 04			13 14	13 18		13 48	14 04	14 21	14 48	15 04			15 14	15 18	15 48	16 04		16 18	16 48		17 04
Pontyclun d							13 30				14 33						15 30				16 30			
Llanharan d							13 35				14 38						15 35				16 35			
Pencoed d							13 39				14 42						15 39				16 39			
Bridgend d		13 09	13 23			13 34	13 46		14 09	14 23	14 49	15 09	15 23			15 34	15 46	16 09	16 23		16 46	17 09		17 25
Wildmill d							13 49				14 52						15 49				16 49			
Sarn d							13 52				14 55						15 52				16 52			
Tondu d							13 55				14 58						15 55				16 55			
Garth (Mid Glamorgan) d							14 05				15 08						16 05				17 05			
Maesteg (Ewenny Road) d							14 07				15 10						16 07				17 07			
Maesteg a							14 12				15 15						16 12				17 12			
Pyle d						13 42										15 42								17 31
Port Talbot Parkway d		13 23	13 36			13 50			14 23	14 36		15 23	15 36			15 50		16 23	16 36			17 23		17 39
Baglan d						13 54										15 54								17 40
Briton Ferry d						13 57										15 57								17 45
Neath d		13 30	13 43			14 01			14 30	14 43		15 30	15 43			16 01		16 30	16 43			17 30		17 49
Skewen d						14 05										16 05								17 52
Llansamlet d						14 09										16 09								17 56
Swansea 7 a		13 44	13 55			14 20			14 44	14 55		15 44	15 55			16 20		16 44	16 56			17 44		18 05
d	13 35		14 00		14 05					15 00			16 00	16 05	16 05				17 05				17 51	18 09
Gowerton d	13x46				14x17									16x17	16x17				17x16				18x02	18x19
Llanelli a	13 53		14 15		14 24					15 18			16 15	16 24	16 24				17 23				18 09	18 26
d	13 53		14 16		14 24					15 19			16 16	16 24	16 24				17 23				18 09	18 26
Pembrey & Burry Port d	13 59		14 21		14 30					15 24			16 21	16 30	16 30				17 29				18 15	18 32
Kidwelly d	14x06				14x37									16x37	16x37				17x35				18x22	18x38
Ferryside d	14x12				14x43									16x43	16x43				17x40				18x28	18x43
Carmarthen a	14 27		14 46		14 56					15 44			16 46	16 56	16 56				17 52				18 41	19 00
d	14 47				14 59					15 47				16 59	17 05				17 55				19 05	
Whitland a	15 01				15 13					16 01				17 13	17 19				18 13				19 19	
d	15 01				15 13					16 02				17 13	17 32				18 14				19 19	
Narberth d	15x10				15x22									17x22	17x40								19x28	
Kilgetty d	15x19				15x31									17x31	17x49								19x37	
Saundersfoot d	15x20				15x32									17x32	17x51								19x38	
Tenby a	15 29				15 39									17 39	17 58								19 45	
d	15 33				15 43									17 43	18 01								19 52	
Penally d	15x36				15x46									17x46	18x04								19x55	
Manorbier d	15 43				15 53									17 53	18 11								20 02	
Lamphey d	15x50				16x00									18x00	18x18								20x09	
Pembroke d	15 53				16 03									18 03	18 21								20 12	
Pembroke Dock a	16 07				16 17									18 17	18 35								20 22	
Clunderwen d										16x08									18x20					
Clarbeston Road d										16x15									18x27					
Haverfordwest d										16 23									18 35					
Johnston d										16x31									18x43					
Milford Haven a										16 46									18 58					
Fishguard Harbour a																								
d								14 30																
Rosslare Harbour a								18 00																

For general notes see front of timetable
For details of catering facilities see Directory of Train Operators

A Until 5 September
B From 12 September
C From Cheltenham Spa (Table 57)
D Ship service

Cardiff → Maesteg, Swansea and West Wales

Route Diagram - see first page of Table 127

		AW	AW	AW	GW	AW	AW	GW	AW	AW	GW	AW	GW	AW	GW	AW	AW	GW	GW	AW	AW	AW	GW
		R	◇		1 ◇	R		1 ◇	R		1 ◇	R	1 ◇		1 ◇	R		1 ◇	1 ◇	◇	◇		1 ◇
		A		B			C			C				C			C	D					
		⇌			⊏P	⇌		⊏P	⇌		⊏P	⇌	⊏P		⊏P	⇌		⊏P	⊏P	⇌			⊏P
London Paddington 15 ⊖	d				15 45			16 45			17 45				18 45			19 15	19 45				20 45
Reading 7	d				16 11			17 11			18 11				19 11			19 41	20 11				21 11
Manchester Piccadilly 10 ⛴	d					14 30			15 30			16 30				17 30				18 30			
Gloucester 7	d						16 58			17 58				18 58			19 58						
Bristol Parkway 7	d				17 07			18 07			19 13				20 07			20 42	21 07				22 11
Newport (South Wales)	d	16 59		17 06	17 31	17 33	17 52	18 31	18 39	18 52	19 36	19 30		19 52	20 31	20 39	20 52	21 05	21 31	21 50		22 10	22 46
Cardiff Queen Street 3	d	17 11		17 26	17 36	17 51	18 06	18 36	18 51	19 01	19 36	19 46		19 56	20 36	20 56			21 36	21 56		22 26	22 55
Cardiff Central 7	d	17 21		17 38	17 48	18 04	18 18	18 48	19 04	19 16	19 54	20 00		20 13	20 48	21 06	21 10	21 23	21 48	22 16		22 43	23 07
Pontyclun	d	17 32					18 30			19 28				20 25			21 22					22 55	
Llanharan	d	17 38					18 35			19 33				20 30			21 27					23 00	
Pencoed	d	17 41					18 39			19 37				20 34			21 30					23 04	
Bridgend	d	17 48		17 58	18 09	18 23	18 46	19 09	19 23	19 45	20 14	20 22		20 41	21 09	21 28	21 41	21 44	22 09	22 36		23 10	23 28
Wildmill	d	17 51					18 49			19 48				20 44			21 43						
Sarn	d	17 54					18 52			19 51				20 47			21 46						
Tondu	d	17 57					18 55			19 54				20 50			21 50						
Garth (Mid Glamorgan)	d	18 07					19 05			20 04				21 00			21 59						
Maesteg (Ewenny Road)	d	18 09					19 07			20 06				21 02			22 02						
Maesteg	a	18 14					19 12			20 11				21 07			22 06						
Pyle	d			18 06					19 30							21 35						23 18	
Port Talbot Parkway	d			18 14	18 23	18 36		19 23	19 38		20 27	20 35			21 23	21 43		21 57	22 23	22 50		23 27	23 41
Baglan	d			18 18					19 41													23 30	
Briton Ferry	d			18 21					19 44													23 34	
Neath	d			18 25	18 30	18 43		19 30	19 48		20 36 →		← 20 36		21 30	21 50		22 05	22 30	22 58		23 38	23 49
Skewen	d			18 29					19 53													23 41	
Llansamlet	d			18 33					19 57													23 45	
Swansea 7	a			18 44	18 47	18 56		19 44	20 05				20 49		21 44	22 03		22 18	22 44	23 10		23 53	00 02
	d		18 21			19 05			20 10				21 00			22 27				23 13	23 45	00 08	
Gowerton	d					19x18										22x37				23x24		00b19	
Llanelli	a		18 37			19 25			20 25			21 05	21 25			22 44				23 30	00 01	00s25	
	d					19 25			20 26			21 05	21 25			22 44				23 31	00 01		
Pembrey & Burry Port	d					19 31			20 31			21 11	21 32			22 50				23 36	00 07	00s31	
Kidwelly	d								20x37							22x56				23x43		00b38	
Ferryside	d								20x43							23x01				23x49		00b44	
Carmarthen	a					19 50			20 55			21 30	21 55			23 13				00 07	00 27	01 01	
	d					19 55			21 00			22 04				23 17					00 30		
Whitland	a					20 09			21 14			22 20				23 31					00 45		
	d					20 10			21 14			22 21				23 32					00 45		
Narberth	d								21x23														
Kilgetty	d								21x33														
Saundersfoot	d								21x35														
Tenby	a								21 42														
	d								21 45														
Penally	d								21x48														
Manorbier	d								21 55														
Lamphey	d								22x02														
Pembroke	d								22 05														
Pembroke Dock	a								22 20														
Clunderwen	d					20x16						22x27				23x38							
Clarbeston Road	d					20x23						22x34				23x45					00x59		
Haverfordwest	d					20 31						22 42				23a53							
Johnston	d					20x39						22x50											
Milford Haven	a					20 54						23 05											
Fishguard Harbour	a																				01 26		
⛴	d																						
Rosslare Harbour ⛴	a																						

For general notes see front of timetable
For details of catering facilities see Directory of Train Operators

- **A** From Holyhead (Table 131)
- **B** From Ebbw Vale Parkway (Table 127)
- **C** From Cheltenham Spa (Table 57)
- **D** From 12 September
- **b** Stops, on request, to set down only

Table 128

Sundays

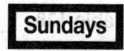

until 6 September

Cardiff → Maesteg, Swansea and West Wales

Route Diagram - see first page of Table 127

		AW	AW	AW	AW	AW	AW	AW	AW	AW	GW	AW	GW	AW	AW	AW	GW	GW	AW	AW
		◇		R A			◇			◇	1 ◇	◇ B	1 ◇	R A			1 ◇	1 ◇	R	◇
London Paddington 15	⊖ d										08 30		09 30				10 37	11 37		
Reading 7	d										09 16		10 05				11 14	12 14		
Manchester Piccadilly 10	d																		10 30	
Gloucester 7	d																			
Bristol Parkway 7	d										10 17		11 07				12 16	13 16		
Newport (South Wales)	d										10 40	11 02	11 32				12 39	13 39	13 36	
Cardiff Queen Street 3	d								*09 16*		*10 36*	*10 51*	*11 16*				*12 36*	*13 16*	*13 51*	
Cardiff Central 7	d		22p43				08 30		09 55		10 57	11 20	11 49				12 56	13 56	14 06	
Pontyclun	d		22p55				08 42													
Llanharan	d		23p00				08 47													
Pencoed	d		23p04				08 51													
Bridgend	d		23p10				08 58		10 15		11 18	11 40	12 10				13 17	14 19	14 25	
Wildmill	d																			
Sarn	d																			
Tondu	d																			
Garth (Mid Glamorgan)	d																			
Maesteg (Ewenny Road)	d																			
Maesteg	a																			
Pyle	d		23p18				09 06													
Port Talbot Parkway	d		23p27				09 14		10 29		11 31	11 54	12 23				13 30	14 32	14 38	
Baglan	d		23p30				09 17													
Briton Ferry	d		23p34				09 21													
Neath	d		23p38				09 25		10 37		11 38	12 02	12 30				13 36	14 39	14 46	
Skewen	d		23p41				09 29													
Llansamlet	d		23p45				09 33													
Swansea 7	a		23p53				09 40		10 49		11 52	12 14	12 44				13 50	14 58	15 01	
	d	23p45	00 08				09 45		10 54	11 04		12 17					14 03		15 06	15 16
Gowerton	d		00b19				09x56		11x05	11x15		12x28								15x27
Llanelli	a	00 01	00s25				10 02		11 11	11 22		12 34					14 22		15 24	15 34
	d	00 01					10 06		11 12			12 35					14 22		15 25	
Pembrey & Burry Port	d	00 07	00s31				10 12		11 18			12 40					14 28		15 31	
Kidwelly	d		00b38				10x18		11x24			12x47								
Ferryside	d		00b44				10x24		11x30			12x53								
Carmarthen	a	00 27	01 01				10 37		11 43			13 05					14 53		15 50	
	d	00 30			08 20	09 35	10 39	10 46	11 50			13 08			14 05	14 20			16 05	
Whitland	a	00 45			08 34	09 47	10 54	11 01	12 05			13 23			14 21	14 34			16 19	
	d	00 45			08 35	09 48	10 55	11 01	12 05			13 24			14 21	14 34			16 20	
Narberth	d					09x55		11x10	12x13							14x43				
Kilgetty	d					10x04		11x19	12x22							14x53				
Saundersfoot	d					10x05		11x20	12x23							14x55				
Tenby	a					10 12		11 28	12 39							15 02				
	d					10 16		11 32								15 21				
Penally	d					10x19		11x35								15x24				
Manorbier	d					10 24		11 41								15 31				
Lamphey	d					10x32		11x49								15x38				
Pembroke	d					10 35		11 52								15 42				
Pembroke Dock	a					10 49		12 03								15 55				
Clunderwen	d				08x41		11x01								14x28				16x26	
Clarbeston Road	d	00x59			08x48		11x09								14x36				16x33	
Haverfordwest	d				08 56		11 18								14 44				16 41	
Johnston	d				09x04		11x26								14x52				16x49	
Milford Haven	a				09 15		11 37								15 05				17 04	
Fishguard Harbour	a	01 26										14 00								
	⛴ d			02 45										14 30						
Rosslare Harbour	⛴ a			06 15										18 00						

For general notes see front of timetable
For details of catering facilities see Directory of Train Operators

A Ship service
B From Hereford (Table 131)
b Stops, on request, to set down only

Cardiff → Maesteg, Swansea and West Wales

Route Diagram - see first page of Table 127

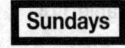

		GW	GW	AW	AW	GW	GW	AW		GW	GW	AW	GW	AW	GW	AW	GW	GW
		1 ◇	1 ◇		R	1 ◇	1 ◇	R		1 ◇	1 ◇	◇	1 ◇	◇	1 ◇	◇	1 ◇	1 ◇
								A										
		☕	☕		🛒	☕	☕	🛒		☕	☕		☕		☕		☕	☕
London Paddington 15 ⊖	d	12 37	13 37			14 37	15 37			16 37	17 37		18 37		19 37		20 37	21 37
Reading 7	d	13 14	14 14			15 14	16 16			17 16	18 16		19 16		20 16		21 16	22 15
Manchester Piccadilly 10	d				12 30			14 30										
Gloucester 7	d																	
Bristol Parkway 7	d	14 16	15 16			16 16	17 18			18 18	19 18		20 18		21 18		22 19	23 18
Newport (South Wales)	d	14 39	15 39		15 44	16 39	17 39	17 29		18 41	19 39	*19 46*	20 41	*21 06*	21 45		22 47	23 47
Cardiff Queen Street 3	d	*14 36*	*15 16*		*15 51*	*16 36*	*17 16*	*17 51*		*18 36*	*19 16*	*19 51*	*20 36*	*21 16*	*21 51*		*22 36*	*22 36*
Cardiff Central 7	d	14 58	15 56		16 20	16 56	17 58	18 07		18 58	19 58	20 22	20 58	21 32	22 06	22 35	23 08	00 09
Pontyclun	d				16 32									21 44				
Llanharan	d				16 36									21 48				
Pencoed	d				16 40									21 52				
Bridgend	d	15 19	16 17		16 47	17 19	18 19	18 27		19 19	20 19	20 42	21 19	21 59	22 27	22 54	23 29	00 29
Wildmill	d																	
Sarn	d																	
Tondu	d																	
Garth (Mid Glamorgan)	d																	
Maesteg (Ewenny Road)	d																	
Maesteg	a																	
Pyle	d													22 06				
Port Talbot Parkway	d	15 32	16 30		17 00	17 32	18 32	18 39		19 32	20 32	20 54	21 32	22 14	22 39	23 07	23 43	00 42
Baglan	d													22 18				
Briton Ferry	d													22 21				
Neath	d	15 39	16 36		17 07	17 39	18 40	18 46		19 40	20 40	21 01	21 39	22 25	22 48	23 14	23 50	00 50
Skewen	d													22 30				
Llansamlet	d													22 34				
Swansea 7	a	15 52	16 50		17 19	17 52	18 55	18 59		19 54	20 55	21 15	21 52	22 41	23 00	23 26	00 03	01 02
	d	16 03			17 24	18 03		19 20				21 19		23 10		23 32		
Gowerton	d				17x34			19x31				21x29				23x42		
Llanelli	a	16 21			17 41	18 20		19 37				21 36		23 28		23 49		
	d	16 21			17 41	18 21		19 39				21 36		23 29		23 49		
Pembrey & Burry Port	d	16 28			17 47	18 27		19 45				21 42		23 35		23 55		
Kidwelly	d				17x53							21x48				00x01		
Ferryside	d				17x59							21x54				00x07		
Carmarthen	a	16 51			18 13	18 52		20 04				22 06		23 57		00 19		
	d			17 00	18 16			20 09				22 11				00 21		
Whitland	a			17 14	18 30			20 23				22 25				00 36		
	d			17 19	18 32			20 28	20 35			22 27				00 36		
Narberth	d			17x28				20x37										
Kilgetty	d			17x38				20x46										
Saundersfoot	d			17x40				20x48										
Tenby	a			17 47				20 57										
	d			17 50				21 00										
Penally	d			17x53				21x03										
Manorbier	d			18 00				21 09										
Lamphey	d			18x07				21x17										
Pembroke	d			18 11				21 20										
Pembroke Dock	a			18 25				21 35										
Clunderwen	d				18x38				20x41			22x33						
Clarbeston Road	d				18x46				20x48			22x40				00x48		
Haverfordwest	d				18 54				20 57			22 48						
Johnston	d				19x02				21x05			22x56						
Milford Haven	a				19 17				21 20			23 11						
Fishguard Harbour	a															01 17		
⛴	d																	
Rosslare Harbour ⛴	a																	

For general notes see front of timetable
For details of catering facilities see Directory of Train Operators

A 🛒 to Milford Haven

Sundays

from 13 September

Cardiff → Maesteg, Swansea and West Wales

Route Diagram - see first page of Table 127

		AW	AW	AW	AW	AW	GW	AW	AW	GW	AW	AW	AW	GW	GW	AW	AW	GW
		◇		R A	◇ (trolley)	◇	1 ◇ (catering)	(trolley)	◇ B (trolley)	1 ◇ (catering)	R A	(trolley)	(trolley)	1 ◇ (catering)	1 ◇ (catering)	R (trolley)	◇	1 ◇ (catering)
London Paddington 15 ⊖	d						08 30			09 30				10 37	11 37			12 37
Reading 7	d						09 05			10 05				11 11	12 11			13 11
Manchester Piccadilly 10	d															10 30		
Gloucester 7	d																	
Bristol Parkway 7	d						10 09			11 07				12 13	13 13			14 13
Newport (South Wales)	d				09 10		10 32		11 02	11 32				12 35	13 35	13 41		14 35
Cardiff Queen Street 3	d				09 16		10 36		10 51	11 16				12 36	13 16	13 51		14 36
Cardiff Central 7	d		22p43		09 30		10 49		11 20	11 49				12 53	13 53	14 04		14 53
Pontyclun	d		22p55		09 42													
Llanharan	d		23p00		09 48													
Pencoed	d		23p04		09 52													
Bridgend	d		23p10		09 58		11 10		11 40	12 10				13 13	14 13	14 23		15 13
Wildmill	d																	
Sarn	d																	
Tondu	d																	
Garth (Mid Glamorgan)	d																	
Maesteg (Ewenny Road)	d																	
Maesteg	a																	
Pyle	d		23p18		10 06													
Port Talbot Parkway	d		23p27		10 14		11 24		11 54	12 23				13 27	14 27	14 36		15 27
Baglan	d		23p30		10 17													
Briton Ferry	d		23p34		10 21													
Neath	d		23p38		10 25		11 32		12 02	12 30				13 33	14 33	14 43		15 33
Skewen	d		23p41		10 29													
Llansamlet	d		23p45		10 33													
Swansea 7	a		23p53		10 40		11 45		12 14	12 44				13 47	14 49	14 56		15 47
	d	23p45	00 08		10 43	11 09			12 17					13 53		15 06	15 16	15 53
Gowerton	d		00b19		10x54	11x20			12x28								15x27	
Llanelli	a	00 01	00s25		11 00	11 27			12 34					14 10		15 24	15 34	16 10
	d	00 01			11 06				12 35					14 10		15 25		16 10
Pembrey & Burry Port	d	00 07	00s31		11 12				12 40					14 16		15 31		16 17
Kidwelly	d		00b38		11x18				12x47									
Ferryside	d		00b44		11x24				12x53									
Carmarthen	a	00 27	01 01		11 37				13 05					14 41		15 50		16 40
	d	00 30			12 05				13 08			14 05	14 20			16 05		
Whitland	a	00 45			12 20				13 23			14 21	14 34			16 19		
	d	00 45			12 24			12 28	13 24			14 21	14 34			16 20		
Narberth	d							12x37					14x43					
Kilgetty	d							12x46					14x53					
Saundersfoot	d							12x48					14x55					
Tenby	a							13 00					15 02					
	d												15 21					
Penally	d												15x24					
Manorbier	d												15 31					
Lamphey	d												15x38					
Pembroke	d												15 42					
Pembroke Dock	a												15 55					
Clunderwen	d				12x31							14x28				16x26		
Clarbeston Road	d	00x59			12x38							14x36				16x33		
Haverfordwest	d				12 47							14 44				16 41		
Johnston	d				12x55							14x52				16x49		
Milford Haven	a				13 06							15 05				17 04		
Fishguard Harbour	a	01 26							14 00									
(ship)	d			02 45							14 30							
Rosslare Harbour (ship)	a			06 15							18 00							

For general notes see front of timetable
For details of catering facilities see Directory of Train Operators

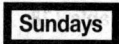

A Ship service
B From Hereford (Table 131)
b Stops, on request, to set down only

Cardiff → Maesteg, Swansea and West Wales

Route Diagram - see first page of Table 127

		GW		AW	AW		GW	GW		AW			GW	GW		AW	GW		AW	GW	AW	GW	GW
					R					R													
		1 ◇					1 ◇	1 ◇					1 ◇	1 ◇		◇	1 ◇		◇	1 ◇	◇	1 ◇	1 ◇
										A													
		☕			🍴		☕	☕		🍴			☕	☕			☕			☕		☕	☕
London Paddington 15 ⊖	d	13 37					14 37	15 37					16 37	17 37			18 37			19 37		20 37	21 37
Reading 7	d	14 11					15 11	16 11					17 11	18 11			19 11			20 11		21 11	22 14
Manchester Piccadilly 10	d				12 30					14 30													
Gloucester 7	d																						
Bristol Parkway 7	d	15 13					16 13	17 13					18 13	19 13			20 13			21 13		22 13	23 18
Newport (South Wales)	d	15 35			15 44		16 39	17 39		17b29			18 39	19 39		19 46	20 36			21 36	21 41	22 41	23 47
Cardiff Queen Street 3	d	15 16			15 51		16 36	17 16		17 51			18 36	19 16		19 51	20 36		21 16		21 51	22 36	
Cardiff Central 7	d	15 53			16 20		16 56	17 56		18 07			18 59	19 56		20 22	20 51		21 32	21 51	22 35	23 02	00 09
Pontyclun	d				16 32														21 44				
Llanharan	d				16 36														21 48				
Pencoed	d				16 40														21 52				
Bridgend	d	16 13			16 47		17 19	18 17		18 27			19 20	20 17		20 42	21 14		21 59	22 14	22 54	23 23	00 29
Wildmill	d																						
Sarn	d																						
Tondu	d																						
Garth (Mid Glamorgan)	d																						
Maesteg (Ewenny Road)	d																						
Maesteg	a																						
Pyle	d																		22 06				
Port Talbot Parkway	d	16 27			17 00		17 32	18 30		18 39			19 33	20 30		20 54	21 26		22 14	22 26	23 07	23 37	00 42
Baglan	d																		22 18				
Briton Ferry	d																		22 21				
Neath	d	16 33			17 07		17 39	18 38		18 46			19 42	20 38		21 01	21 34		22 25	22 34	23 14	23 44	00 50
Skewen	d																		22 30				
Llansamlet	d																		22 34				
Swansea 7	a	16 47			17 19		17 52	18 53		18 59			19 54	20 54		21 15	21 47		22 41	22 47	23 26	23 57	01 02
	d				17 24		18 03			19 20						21 19			22 54		23 32		
Gowerton	d				17x34					19x31						21x29					23x42		
Llanelli	a				17 41		18 20			19 37						21 36			23 09		23 49		
	d				17 41		18 21			19 39						21 36			23 10		23 49		
Pembrey & Burry Port	d				17 47		18 27			19 45						21 42			23 16		23 55		
Kidwelly	d				17x53											21x48					00x01		
Ferryside	d				17x59											21x54					00x07		
Carmarthen	a				18 13		18 52			20 04						22 06			23 38		00 19		
	d			17 00	18 16					20 09						22 11					00 21		
Whitland	a			17 14	18 30					20 23						22 25					00 36		
	d			17 19	18 32					20 28	20 35					22 27					00 36		
Narberth	d			17x28						20x37													
Kilgetty	d			17x38						20x46													
Saundersfoot	d			17x40						20x48													
Tenby	a			17 47						20 57													
	d			17 50						21 00													
Penally	d			17x53						21x03													
Manorbier	d			18 00						21 09													
Lamphey	d			18x07						21x17													
Pembroke	d			18 11						21 20													
Pembroke Dock	a			18 25						21 35													
Clunderwen	d				18x38						20x41					22x33							
Clarbeston Road	d				18x46						20x48					22x40					00x48		
Haverfordwest	d				18 54						20 57					22 48							
Johnston	d				19x02						21x05					22x56							
Milford Haven	a				19 17						21 20					23 11							
Fishguard Harbour	a																				01 17		
⛴	d																						
Rosslare Harbour ⛴	a																						

For general notes see front of timetable
For details of catering facilities see Directory of Train Operators

A 🍴 to Milford Haven
b From 8 November dep. 1735

West Wales, Swansea and Maesteg → Cardiff

Route Diagram - see first page of Table 127

Miles	Miles			AW MO ◇	AW MX	AW ◇	GW 1 ◇ 🍴	GW 1 ◇ 🍴	GW 1 ◇ 🍴	AW ◇ 🛒	GW 1 ◇ 🍴	GW 1 ◇ 🍴	AW A	AW ◇ 🛒	GW 1 ◇ 🍴	AW	GW 1 ◇ 🍴	AW	AW ◇ 🛒	AW B	GW 1 ◇ 🍴	GW 1 ◇ 🍴	AW ◇ 🛒	AW B
—	—	Rosslare Harbour ⛴	d																					
—	—	**Fishguard Harbour** ⛴	a																					
0	—		d			01 50																		
—	0	**Milford Haven**	d	21p35	00 15														06 05				07 05	
—	4	Johnston	d	21b42	00x22														06x12				07x12	
—	8¾	Haverfordwest	d	21p50	00 30														06 20				07 20	
15¾	14	Clarbeston Road	d	21b58	00x37	02x10													06x27				07x27	
22¼	—	Clunderwen	d	22b06	00x44														06x33				07x33	
—	0	**Pembroke Dock**	d																					
—	2	Pembroke	d																					
—	3½	Lamphey	d																					
—	7	Manorbier	d																					
—	10¼	Penally	d																					
—	11½	**Tenby**	a																					
—	—		d																					
—	15¾	Saundersfoot	d																					
—	16½	Kilgetty	d																					
—	22	Narberth	d																					
27¾	27¼	Whitland	a	22p12	00 50	02 22													06 39				07 39	
—	—		d	22p13	00 50	02 22													06 40				07 40	
41¾	—	**Carmarthen**	a	22p30	01 12	02 39													06 56				07 56	
—	—		d	22p35		02 44				05 04				05 50		06 18			07 00			07 30	07 59	
48¾	—	Ferryside	d	22b45										06x00		06x28						07 42	08x09	
53	—	Kidwelly	d	22b51										06x05		06x33						07 49	08x14	
58¼	—	Pembrey & Burry Port	d	22p59						05 22				06 12		06 40			07 18			07 56	08 21	
62¼	—	Llanelli	a	23p05		03 06				05 27				06 17		06 45			07 23			08 02	08 26	
—	—		d	23p05		03 07				05 28				06 18		06 46			07 24			08 04	08 27	
68	—	Gowerton	d	23b13										06x24		06x52			07x30				08x33	
73½	—	**Swansea** 7	a	23p27		03 25								06 37		07 06			07 43			08 22	08 46	
—	—		d	23p37			03 59	04 58	05 27		05 59	06 29		06 40	06 59	07 09	07 29		07 45		07 59	08 29	08 55	
77½	—	Llansamlet	d													07 16								
79¼	—	Skewen	d													07 20								
83	—	Neath	d	23p48			04 10	05 10	05 39		06 10	06 40		06 51	07 10	07 24	07 40		07 56		08 10	08 40	09 06	
84¾	—	Briton Ferry	d													07 27								
86½	—	Baglan	d													07 31								
88½	—	Port Talbot Parkway	d	23p56			04 18	05 18	05 46	06 01	06 18	06 48		06 58	07 18	07 35	07 48		08 03		08 18	08 48	09 13	
94¾	—	Pyle	d											07 04		07 42			08 10					
—	0	Maesteg	d										06 46							08 00				09 15
—	½	Maesteg (Ewenny Road)	d										06 48							08 02				09 17
—	1¼	Garth (Mid Glamorgan)	d										06 51							08 05				09 20
—	5¼	Tondu	d										07 00							08 14				09 29
—	6	Sarn	d										07 03							08 17				09 32
—	7¼	Wildmill	d										07 05							08 19				09 34
100¾	8¼	Bridgend	d	00 09			04 30	05 29	05 58	06 15	06 30	07 00	07 09	07 17	07 30	07 50	08 00	←	08 17	08 23	08 30	09 00	09 25	09 38
104¾	—	Pencoed	d							06 21			07 15			08 07			08 23					09 44
107	—	Llanharan	d							06 24				07 24		08 11		08 11		08 31				09 48
110	—	Pontyclun	d							06 29			07 22			→		08 15	08 30					09 52
121	—	**Cardiff Central** 7	a	00 50			04 56	05 51	06 20	06 43	06 52	07 22	07 36	07 40	07 52		08 22	08 34	08 44	08 48	08 52	09 22	09 47	10 07
—	—	Cardiff Queen Street 3	a				*05 29*	*06 14*	*06 39*	*06 54*	*07 09*	*07 34*	*07 49*	*07 54*	*08 04*		*08 34*	*08 44*	*08 54*	*08 59*	*09 04*	*09 34*	*09 59*	*10 19*
—	—	Newport (South Wales)	a				05 32	06 07	06 36	07 02	07 08	07 38	*07 58*	08 03	08 08		08 38	*08 58*	09 03	09 25	09 08	09 38	10 03	10 25
—	—	Bristol Parkway 7	a				06 00	06 29	06 58		07 30	08 00			08 31		09 00				09 30	10 00		
—	—	Gloucester 7	a																	10 20				11 20
—	—	Manchester Piccadilly 10 ⛴	a							10 15				11 15					12 15				13 15	
—	—	Reading 7	a				07 02	07 29	08 01		08 33	09 02			09 27		10 01				10 32	11 01		
—	—	London Paddington 15 ⊖	a				07 32	08 02	08 32		09 06	09 29			09 59		10 30				11 02	11 32		

For general notes see front of timetable
For details of catering facilities see Directory of Train Operators

A To Ebbw Vale Parkway (Table 127)
B To Cheltenham Spa (Table 57)

b Previous night.
Stops on request, passengers wishing to alight must inform the guard and those wishing to join must give a hand signal to the driver

West Wales, Swansea and Maesteg → Cardiff

Route Diagram - see first page of Table 127

		AW	AW	GW	AW	AW	AW	GW	AW	AW	AW	AW		GW	AW	AW	GW	AW	AW	AW	AW	AW	AW	GW
		◇	◇	1 ◇		◇		1 ◇	◇					1 ◇	◇		1 ◇	◇	R	◇				1 ◇
		A								B						B			C					
			T	P	T	T		P	T			T		P	T		P	T					T	P
Rosslare Harbour ⛴	d																		09 00					
Fishguard Harbour ⛴	a																		12 30					
	d																							
Milford Haven	d								09 10									11 10						
Johnston	d								09x17									11x17						
Haverfordwest	d								09 25									11 25						
Clarbeston Road	d								09x32									11x32						
Clunderwen	d								09x38									11x38						
Pembroke Dock	d		07 05									09 05											11 05	
Pembroke	d		07 13									09 13											11 13	
Lamphey	d		07x16									09x16											11x16	
Manorbier	d		07 25									09 24											11 25	
Penally	d		07x30									09x29											11x30	
Tenby	a		07 33									09 32											11 33	
	d		07 36									09 40											11 41	
Saundersfoot	d		07x44									09x47											11x48	
Kilgetty	d		07x46									09x49											11x50	
Narberth	d		07x56									09x58											11x59	
Whitland	a		08 04						09 44			10 06						11 44					12 07	
	d		08 06						09 45			10 09						11 45					12 10	
Carmarthen	a		08 24						10 01			10 26						12 01					12 27	
	d		08 30		09 00				10 05			10 30			11 00			12 05					12 30	
Ferryside	d		08x40		09x10										11x10									
Kidwelly	d		08x45		09x16										11x15									
Pembrey & Burry Port	d		08 51		09 23				10 22			10 49			11 22			12 23					12 49	
Llanelli	a		08 57		09 29				10 28			10 55			11 27			12 28					12 55	
	d	08 45	09 00		09 30				10 28			10 55			11 28			12 29		12 33			12 55	
Gowerton	d	08x53	09x06									11x02			11x34								13x02	
Swansea 7	a	09 08	09 22		09 50	←			10 45			11 22			11 46			12 46		13 01			13 22	
	d	09 11	09 55	09 29		09 55		10 29	10 55		11 10			11 29	11 55		12 29	12 50				13 10		13 29
Llansamlet	d	09 18	→								11 17											13 17		
Skewen	d	09 22									11 21											13 21		
Neath	d	09 26		09 40		10 06		10 40	11 06		11 25			11 40	12 06		12 40	13 06				13 25		13 40
Briton Ferry	d	09 29									11 28											13 28		
Baglan	d	09 33									11 32											13 32		
Port Talbot Parkway	d	09 37		09 48		10 13		10 48	11 13		11 36			11 48	12 13		12 48	13 13				13 36		13 48
Pyle	d	09 44									11 43											13 43		
Maesteg	d						10 15			11 15						12 15					13 15			
Maesteg (Ewenny Road)	d						10 17			11 17						12 17					13 17			
Garth (Mid Glamorgan)	d						10 20			11 20						12 20					13 20			
Tondu	d						10 29			11 29						12 29					13 29			
Sarn	d						10 32			11 32						12 32					13 32			
Wildmill	d						10 34			11 34						12 34					13 34			
Bridgend	d	09 52		10 00		10 25	10 38	11 00	11 25	11 38	11 55			12 00	12 25	12 38	13 00	13 25			13 38	13 52		14 00
Pencoed	d						10 44			11 44						12 44					13 44			
Llanharan	d						10 48			11 48						12 48					13 48			
Pontyclun	d						10 52			11 52						12 52					13 52			
Cardiff Central 7	a	10 17		10 22		10 48	11 09	11 22	11 47	12 08	12 17			12 22	12 47	13 07	13 22	13 47			14 07	14 15		14 22
Cardiff Queen Street 3	a	10 29		10 34		10 59	11 19	11 34	11b59	12 19	12 29			12 34	12 59	13 19	13 34	13 59			14 19	14 29		14 34
Newport (South Wales)	a			10 38		11 03	11 32	11 38	12 03	12 25				12 38	13 03	13 25	13 38	14 03						14 38
Bristol Parkway 7	a			11 00				12 00						13 00			14 00							15 00
Gloucester 7	a									13 20						14 20								
Manchester Piccadilly 10 ⛴	a					14 15			15 15						16 15			17 15						
Reading 7	a			12 00				13 01						14 00			15 01							16 01
London Paddington 15 ⊖	a			12 32				13 30						14 32			15 30							16 30

For general notes see front of timetable
For details of catering facilities see Directory of Train Operators

A From Shrewsbury (Table 129)
B To Cheltenham Spa (Table 57)
C Ship service
b Until 4 September only

West Wales, Swansea and Maesteg → Cardiff

Route Diagram - see first page of Table 127

		AW	AW	GW	AW	AW	AW	AW	AW	GW	AW	AW	GW	AW	AW	AW	AW	GW	AW	AW	AW	GW	AW	AW
					R	R					R			R										
		◇		1 ◇						1 ◇			1 ◇					1 ◇	◇	◇		1 ◇	◇	
			A			A						A			A									A
		🛒		☕	🛒	🛒			🛒	☕	🛒		☕	🛒			🛒	☕	🛒			☕		
Rosslare Harbour ⛴	d																							
Fishguard Harbour ⛴	a																							
	d					13 27																		
Milford Haven	d				13 10									15 10									17 10	
Johnston	d				13x17									15x17									17x17	
Haverfordwest	d				13 25									15 25									17 25	
Clarbeston Road	d				13x32									15x32									17x32	
Clunderwen	d				13x38									15x38									17x39	
Pembroke Dock	d								13 05								15 05							
Pembroke	d								13 13								15 13							
Lamphey	d								13x16								15x16							
Manorbier	d								13 25								15 25							
Penally	d								13x30								15x30							
Tenby	a								13 33								15 33							
	d								13 41								15 42							
Saundersfoot	d								13x48								15x49							
Kilgetty	d								13x50								15x51							
Narberth	d								13x59								16x00							
Whitland	a				13 44	13 59			14 07					15 44			16 08						17 45	
	d				13 45	13 59			14 10					15 45			16 11						17 45	
Carmarthen	a				14 01	14 16			14 27					16 01			16 28						18 02	
	d	13 00			14 05	14 19			14 30		15 05			16 05			16 31		17 01				18 06	
Ferryside	d	13x10							14x40								16x41		17x11				18x16	
Kidwelly	d	13x15							14x46								16x47		17x17				18x21	
Pembrey & Burry Port	d	13 22			14 23				14 53		15 23			16 23			16 54		17 23				18 28	
Llanelli	a	13 27			14 28	14 43			14 59		15 28			16 28			17 00		17 28				18 34	
	d	13 28			14 29	14 43			15 00		15 29			16 29			17 01		17 29	17 36			18 34	
Gowerton	d				14x35									16x35			17x08			17x44				
Swansea 7	a	13 48			14 48				15 22		15 46			16 48			17 22		17 46	18 06			18 53	
	d	13 55		14 29	14 55			15 10		15 29	15 55		16 29	16 55		17 10		17 29	17 55			18 29	19 10 →	19 00
Llansamlet	d							15 17								17 17								
Skewen	d							15 21								17 21								
Neath	d	14 06		14 40	15 06			15 25		15 40	16 06		16 40	17 06		17 25		17 40	18 06			18 40		19 11
Briton Ferry	d							15 28								17 28								
Baglan	d							15 32								17 32								
Port Talbot Parkway	d	14 13		14 48	15 13			15 36		15 48	16 13		16 48	17 13		17 36		17 48	18 13			18 48		19 18
Pyle	d							15 43								17 43								
Maesteg	d		14 15				15 17					16 15			17 15						18 20			
Maesteg (Ewenny Road)	d		14 17				15 19					16 17			17 17						18 22			
Garth (Mid Glamorgan)	d		14 20				15 22					16 20			17 20						18 25			
Tondu	d		14 29				15 31					16 29			17 29						18 34			
Sarn	d		14 32				15 34					16 32			17 32						18 37			
Wildmill	d		14 34				15 36					16 34			17 34						18 39			
Bridgend	d	14 25	14 38	15 00	15 25		15 40	15 52		16 00	16 25	16 38	17 00	17 25	17 38	17 54		18 00	18 26		18 43	19 00		19 32
Pencoed	d		14 44				15 46					16 44			17 44						18 49			
Llanharan	d		14 48				15 50					16 48			17 48						18 53			
Pontyclun	d		14 52				15 54					16 52			17 52	18 04					18 57			
Cardiff Central 7	a	14 47	15 07	15 22	15 48	16 04	16 09	16 15		16 22	16 47	17 07	17 22	17 47	18 07	18 18		18 22	18 47		19 13	19 22		19 56
Cardiff Queen Street 3	a	*14 59*	*15 19*	*15 34*	*15 59*	*16 14*	*16 19*	*16 29*		*16 34*	*16 59*	*17 19*	*17 34*	*17 59*	*18 19*	*18 29*		*18 34*	*19 04*		*19 29*	*19 34*		*20 09*
Newport (South Wales)	a	15 03	15 25	15 38	16 03	16 18				16 38	17 03	17 25	17 38	18 03	18 25			18 38	19 03			19 38		20 28
Bristol Parkway 7	a			16 00						17 00			18 00					19 00				20 00		
Gloucester 7	a		16 21			17 15						18 21			19 20									21 21
Manchester Piccadilly 10 ⛴	a	18 15			19 15						20 15			21 15					22 15					
Reading 7	a			17 01						17 57			19 01					20 00				21 01		
London Paddington 15 ⊖	a			17 30						18 24			19 32					20 32				21 32		

For general notes see front of timetable
For details of catering facilities see
Directory of Train Operators

A To Cheltenham Spa (Table 57)

West Wales, Swansea and Maesteg → Cardiff

Route Diagram - see first page of Table 127

		AW	AW	AW	GW	GW	AW	AW	GW	GW	AW	AW	AW	AW	AW	AW	AW	AW	AW	AW	AW	AW
					FO	FX			FO	FX					FO	FX						
		◇	◇		■1 ◇	■1 ◇	◇		■1 ◇	■1 ◇	◇			◇								R
							A	B							B	B						C
				H	IP	IP			IP	IP												
Rosslare Harbour ⛴	d																					21 15
Fishguard Harbour ⛴	a																					00 45
	d																					
Milford Haven	d										19 10						21 20				23 15	
Johnston	d										19x17						21x27				23x22	
Haverfordwest	d										19 25						21 35				23 30	
Clarbeston Road	d										19x32						21x42				23x39	
Clunderwen	d										19x38						21x48				23x47	
Pembroke Dock	d			17 05									19 16						21 11	22 24		
Pembroke	d			17 13									19 24						21 19	22 32		
Lamphey	d			17x16									19x27						21x22	22x35		
Manorbier	d			17 25									19 36						21 31	22 44		
Penally	d			17x30									19x41						21x36	22x49		
Tenby	a			17 33									19 44						21 39	22 51		
	d			17 41									19 47						21 44	22 51		
Saundersfoot	d			17x48									19x54						21x52	22x58		
Kilgetty	d			17x50									19x56						21x54	23x00		
Narberth	d			17x59									20x05						22x04	23x09		
Whitland	a			18 07							19 44		20 13				21 54		22 12	23 17	23 56	
	d			18 10							19 45		20 16				21 55		22 15	23 20	23 57	
Carmarthen	a			18 27							20 02		20 33				22 16		22 32	23 40	00 18	
	d			18 30			19 08				20 05		20 36						22 35			
Ferryside	d			18x40									20x46						22x45			
Kidwelly	d			18x46									20x52						22x51			
Pembrey & Burry Port	d			18 53			19 26				20 23		20 59						22 58			
Llanelli	a			18 59			19 31				20 28		21 05						23 04			
	d			19 00			19 32				20 29		21 10	21 44					23 05			
Gowerton	d			19x07										21x52					23x12			
Swansea 7	a		←	19 20			19 49				20 50		21 33	22 13					23 27			
	d		19 10		19 29	19 29	20 00		20 29	20 29	20 55		21 35					22 32				
Llansamlet	d		19 17										21 42					22 39				
Skewen	d		19 21										21 46					22 43				
Neath	d		19 25		19 40	19 40	20 11		20 40	20 40	21 06		21 50					22 47				
Briton Ferry	d		19 28										21 53					22 50				
Baglan	d		19 32										21 57					22 54				
Port Talbot Parkway	d		19 36		19 48	19 48	20 18		20 48	20 48	21 13		22 01					22 58				
Pyle	d		19 43										22 08					23 05				
Maesteg	d	19 17						20 15				21 15			22 15	22 15						
Maesteg (Ewenny Road)	d	19 19						20 17				21 17			22 17	22 17						
Garth (Mid Glamorgan)	d	19 22						20 20				21 20			22 20	22 20						
Tondu	d	19 31						20 29				21 29			22 29	22 29						
Sarn	d	19 34						20 32				21 32			22 32	22 32						
Wildmill	d	19 36						20 34				21 34			22 34	22 34						
Bridgend	d	19 40	19 51		20 00	20 00	20 30	20 38	21 00	21 00	21 25	21 38	22 16		22 38	22 38		23 13				
Pencoed	d	19 46						20 44				21 44			22 44	22 44						
Llanharan	d	19 49						20 48				21 48			22 48	22 48						
Pontyclun	d	19 54						20 52				21 52			22 52	22 52						
Cardiff Central 7	a	20 07	20 15		20 22	20 22	20 51	21 06	21 22	21 22	21 47	22 10	22 39		23 07	23 07		23 38				
Cardiff Queen Street 3	a		*20 29*		*20 34*	*20 34*	*21 04*	*21 29*	*21 34*	*21 34*	*22 04*	*22 29*	*22 49*		*23 18*	*23 18*						
Newport (South Wales)	a	20 24			20 38	20 38	21 08	21 27	21 38	21 38			*23 15*		23 35	23 39		*00 48*				
Bristol Parkway 7	a				21 02	21 02			22 02	22 02												
Gloucester 7	a							22 22							00 36	00 39						
Manchester Piccadilly 10 ⛴	a	23 48																				
Reading 7	a				22 11	22 11			23 07	23 07												
London Paddington 15 ⊖	a				22 44	22 55			23 41	23 51												

For general notes see front of timetable
For details of catering facilities see Directory of Train Operators

A To Chester (Table 131)
B To Cheltenham Spa (Table 57)
C Ship service

Table 128

Saturdays

West Wales, Swansea and Maesteg → Cardiff

Route Diagram - see first page of Table 127

		AW	AW	GW	GW	GW	AW	GW	GW	AW	AW	GW	AW	GW	AW	AW	AW	GW	GW	AW	AW	AW	AW	GW
			◇	1 ◇	1 ◇	1 ◇	◇	1 ◇	1 ◇		◇	1 ◇		1 ◇		◇		1 ◇	1 ◇	◇		◇		1 ◇
										A							B	C			B	D		
				🛒	🛒	🛒	✕	🛒	🛒		✕	🛒		🛒		✕		🛒	🛒	✕			✕	🛒
Rosslare Harbour ⛴	d																							
Fishguard Harbour ⛴	a																							
	d		01 50																					
Milford Haven	d	00 15														06 05				07 05				
Johnston	d	00x22														06x12				07x12				
Haverfordwest	d	00 30														06 20				07 20				
Clarbeston Road	d	00x37	02x10													06x27				07x27				
Clunderwen	d	00x44														06x33				07x33				
Pembroke Dock	d																							
Pembroke	d																							
Lamphey	d																							
Manorbier	d																							
Penally	d																							
Tenby	a																							
	d																							
Saundersfoot	d																							
Kilgetty	d																							
Narberth	d																							
Whitland	a	00 50	02 22													06 39				07 39				
	d	00 50	02 22													06 40				07 40				
Carmarthen	a	01 12	02 39													06 56				07 56				
	d		02 44				05 04				05 50		06 18			07 00				07 59			08 30	
Ferryside	d										06x00		06x28							08x09			08x40	
Kidwelly	d										06x05		06x33							08x14			08x46	
Pembrey & Burry Port	d						05 22				06 12		06 40			07 18				08 21			08 53	
Llanelli	a		03 06				05 27				06 17		06 45			07 23				08 26			08 59	
	d		03 06				05 28				06 18		06 46			07 24				08 27		08 45	09 00	
Gowerton	d										06x24		06x52			07x30				08x33		08x53	09x07	
Swansea 7	a		03 25								06 37		07 06			07 43				08 46		09 07	09 22	
	d			03 59	04 59	05 29		05 59	06 29		06 40	06 59	07 09	07 29		07 45		07 59	08 29	08 55		09 10		09 29
Llansamlet	d												07 16									09 17		
Skewen	d												07 20									09 21		
Neath	d			04 10	05 10	05 40		06 10	06 40		06 51	07 10	07 24	07 40		07 56		08 10	08 40	09 06		09 25		09 40
Briton Ferry	d												07 27									09 29		
Baglan	d												07 31									09 32		
Port Talbot Parkway	d			04 18	05 18	05 48	06 01	06 18	06 48		06 58	07 18	07 35	07 48		08 03		08 18	08 48	09 13		09 36		09 48
Pyle	d										07 04		07 42			08 10						09 43		
Maesteg	d									06 46							08 00				09 17			
Maesteg (Ewenny Road)	d									06 48							08 02				09 19			
Garth (Mid Glamorgan)	d									06 51							08 05				09 22			
Tondu	d									07 00							08 14				09 31			
Sarn	d									07 03							08 17				09 34			
Wildmill	d									07 05							08 19				09 36			
Bridgend	d			04 30	05 30	06 00	06 13	06 30	07 00	07 09	07 17	07 30	07 50	08 00		08 17	08 23	08 30	09 00	09 25	09 40	09 55		10 00
Pencoed	d						06 19			07 15			08 07		←	08 23					09 46			
Llanharan	d						06 23				07 24		08 11 →		08 11		08 31				09 50			
Pontyclun	d						06 27			07 22					08 15	08 30					09 54			
Cardiff Central 7	a			04 53	05 52	06 22	06 41	06 52	07 22	07 36	07 40	07 52		08 22	08 34	08 44	08 48	08 52	09 22	09 47	10 09	10 17		10 22
Cardiff Queen Street 3	a			*05 29*	*06 14*	*06 39*	*06 54*	*07 09*	*07 34*	*07 49*	*07 54*	*08 04*		*08 34*	*08 44*	*08 54*	*08 59*	*09 04*	*09 34*	*09 59*	*10 19*	*10 29*		*10 34*
Newport (South Wales)	a			05 09	06 08	06 38	07 02	07 08	07 38	*07 58*	08 03	08 08		08 38	*08 58*	09 03	09 25	09 08	09 38	10 03	10 25			10 38
Bristol Parkway 7	a			05 37	06 30	07 00		07 30	08 00			08 31		09 00				09 30	10 00					11 00
Gloucester 7	a																10 21				11 21			
Manchester Piccadilly 10 ⛴	a						10 15				11 15					12 15				13 15				
Reading 7	a			07 14	07 32	08 01		08 32	09 02			09 33		10 01				10 32	11 01					12 02
London Paddington 15 ⊖	a			07 44	08 02	08 32		09 02	09 32			10 02		10 32				11 02	11 32					12 32

For general notes see front of timetable
For details of catering facilities see Directory of Train Operators

A To Ebbw Vale Parkway (Table 127)
B To Cheltenham Spa (Table 57)
C From 12 September
D From Shrewsbury (Table 129)

Table 128

Saturdays

West Wales, Swansea and Maesteg → Cardiff

Route Diagram - see first page of Table 127

Station		AW	AW	AW	GW	AW	AW	AW	AW	AW		GW	AW	AW	GW	GW	AW	AW	AW	AW	AW	AW	AW	GW
		◇			[1] ◇	◇						[1] ◇	◇		[1]	[1] ◇	◇	◇					Ⓡ	[1] ◇
			A				B		A	C				B	A	C					C	A	D	C
		⊼	⊼		🍽	⊼				⊼		🍽	⊼		🍽	🍽	⊼				⊼	⊼		🍽
Rosslare Harbour ⛴	d																						09 00	
Fishguard Harbour ⛴	a																						12 30	
	d																							
Milford Haven	d					09 10											11 10							
Johnston	d					09x17											11x17							
Haverfordwest	d					09 25											11 25							
Clarbeston Road	d					09x32											11x32							
Clunderwen	d					09x38											11x38							
Pembroke Dock	d	07 05	08⌇35							09⌇05					10⌇02						11⌇05			
Pembroke	d	07 13	08⌇43							09⌇13					10⌇12						11⌇13			
Lamphey	d	07x16	08x46							09x16											11x16			
Manorbier	d	07 25	08⌇55							09⌇25					10⌇25						11⌇25			
Penally	d	07x30	09x00							09x30											11x30			
Tenby	a	07 33	09⌇03							09⌇33					10⌇34						11⌇33			
	d	07 36	09⌇08							09⌇40					10⌇38						11⌇40	11⌇42		
Saundersfoot	d	07x44	09x15							09x47					10⌇48						11x47	11x49		
Kilgetty	d	07x46	09x17							09x49											11x49	11x51		
Narberth	d	07x56	09x26							09x59											11x58	12x00		
Whitland	a	08 04	09⌇39			09 44				10⌇06					11⌇08		11 44				12⌇06	12⌇08		
	d	08 06				09 45			10⌇08	10⌇09					11⌇09		11 45				12⌇09	12⌇09		
Carmarthen	a	08 25				10 01			10⌇26	10⌇26					11⌇27		12 01				12⌇26	12⌇26		
	d	09 00			09 35	10 05			10⌇30	10⌇30			11 00		11⌇36		12 05				12⌇30	12⌇30		
Ferryside	d	09x10											11x10											
Kidwelly	d	09x15											11x15											
Pembrey & Burry Port	d	09 21			09 56	10 22			10⌇49	10⌇49			11 22		11⌇57		12 23				12⌇49	12⌇50		
Llanelli	a	09 27			10 01	10 28			10⌇55	10⌇55			11 27		12⌇02		12 28				12⌇55	12⌇56		
	d	09 27			10 03	10 28			10⌇55	10⌇55			11 28		12⌇03		12 29	12 33			12⌇55	12⌇56		
Gowerton	d								11x02	11x02			11x34								13x02	13x03		
Swansea [7]	a	09 46			10 21	10 45			11⌇16	11⌇22			11 46		12⌇22		12 46	13 01			13⌇22	13⌇22		
	d	09 55			10 29	10 55		11 10				11 29	11 55		12⌇29	12⌇29	12 50			13 10				13⌇29
Llansamlet	d							11 17												13 17				
Skewen	d							11 21												13 21				
Neath	d	10 06			10 40	11 06		11 25				11 40	12 06		12⌇40	12⌇40	13 06			13 25				13⌇40
Briton Ferry	d							11 28												13 28				
Baglan	d							11 32												13 32				
Port Talbot Parkway	d	10 13			10 48	11 13		11 36				11 48	12 13		12⌇48	12⌇48	13 13			13 36				13⌇48
Pyle	d							11 43												13 43				
Maesteg	d			10 15			11 15							12 17					13 15					
Maesteg (Ewenny Road)	d			10 17			11 17							12 19					13 17					
Garth (Mid Glamorgan)	d			10 20			11 20							12 22					13 20					
Tondu	d			10 29			11 29							12 31					13 29					
Sarn	d			10 32			11 32							12 34					13 32					
Wildmill	d			10 34			11 34							12 36					13 34					
Bridgend	d	10 25		10 38	11 00	11 25	11 38	11 55				12 00	12 25	12 40	13⌇00	13⌇00	13 25		13 38	13 52				14⌇00
Pencoed	d			10 44			11 44							12 46					13 44					
Llanharan	d			10 48			11 48							12 50					13 48					
Pontyclun	d			10 52			11 52							12 54					13 52					
Cardiff Central [7]	a	10 47		11 13	11 22	11 47	12 07	12 17				12 22	12 47	13 09	13⌇22	13⌇22	13 47		14 10	14 16				14⌇22
Cardiff Queen Street [3]	a	*10 59*		*11 24*	*11 34*	*11 59*	*12 19*	*12 29*				*12 34*	*12 59*	*13 19*	*13⌇34*	*13⌇34*	*13 59*		*14 24*	*14 29*				*14⌇34*
Newport (South Wales)	a	11 03		*11 32*	11 38	12 03	12 25					12 38	13 03	13 25	13⌇38	13⌇38	14 03							14⌇38
Bristol Parkway [7]	a				12 00							13 00			14⌇00	14⌇00								15⌇00
Gloucester [7]	a						13 21							14 21										
Manchester Piccadilly [10] ⛴	a	14 15				15 15							16 15				17 15							
Reading [7]	a				13 01							14 02			15⌇01	15⌇01								16⌇01
London Paddington [15] ⊖	a				13 32							14 32			15⌇32	15⌇32								16⌇32

For general notes see front of timetable
For details of catering facilities see Directory of Train Operators

A Until 5 September
B To Cheltenham Spa (Table 57)
C From 12 September
D Ship service

West Wales, Swansea and Maesteg → Cardiff

Route Diagram - see first page of Table 127

		GW	AW	AW	GW	AW	AW	AW	AW	AW	GW	AW	AW	GW	AW	AW	AW	GW	AW	GW	AW	AW	AW	AW
		■1 ◇	◇		■1 ◇	R	◇				■1 ◇	R		■1 ◇	R			■1 ◇		■1 ◇	◇	◇		
		A		B				B	C				B			B		A	D	D			A	
		[restaurant]	[buffet]		[restaurant]	[buffet]	[buffet]			[buffet]	[restaurant]	[buffet]		[restaurant]	[buffet]			[restaurant]	[buffet]	[restaurant]	[buffet]		[buffet]	
Rosslare Harbour	⛴ d																							
Fishguard Harbour	⛴ a																							
	d						13 27																	
Milford Haven	d					13 10									15 10									
Johnston	d					13x17									15x17									
Haverfordwest	d					13 25									15 25									
Clarbeston Road	d					13x32									15x32									
Clunderwen	d					13x38									15x38									
Pembroke Dock	d									13 05								14 55	15 05				16 35	
Pembroke	d									13 13								15 05	15 13				16 43	
Lamphey	d									13x16								15x08	15x16				16x46	
Manorbier	d									13 25								15 20	15 25				16 55	
Penally	d									13x30								15x26	15x30				17x00	
Tenby	a									13 33								15 29	15 33				17 03	
	d									13 41								15 35	15 42				17 03	
Saundersfoot	d									13x48								15 45	15x49				17x10	
Kilgetty	d									13x50								15x48	15x51				17x12	
Narberth	d									13x59								15x58	16x00				17x21	
Whitland	a					13 44	13 59			14 07					15 44			16 07	16 08				17 29	
	d					13 45	13 59			14 10					15 45			16 09	16 11				17 31	
Carmarthen	a					14 01	14 16			14 27					16 01			16 26	16 28				17 48	
	d		13 00			14 05	14 19			14 30		15 05			16 05			16 33	16 31		17 01		18 30 →	
Ferryside	d		13x10							14x40								16x44	16x41		17x11			
Kidwelly	d		13x15							14x46								16x50	16x47		17x17			
Pembrey & Burry Port	d		13 22			14 23				14 53		15 23			16 23			16 57	16 54		17 23			
Llanelli	a		13 27			14 28	14 43			14 59		15 28			16 28			17 03	17 00		17 28			
	d		13 28			14 29	14 43			15 00		15 29			16 29			17 04	17 01		17 29	17 36		
Gowerton	d					14x35									16x35				17x08			17x44		
Swansea ■7	a		13 48			14 48				15 22		15 46			16 48			17 21	17 22		17 46	18 06		
	d	13 29	13 55		14 29	14 55			15 10		15 29	15 55		16 29	16 55		17 10	17 29		17 29	17 56			
Llansamlet	d								15 17								17 17							
Skewen	d								15 21								17 21							
Neath	d	13 40	14 06		14 40	15 06			15 25		15 40	16 06		16 40	17 06		17 25	17 40		17 40	18 07			
Briton Ferry	d								15 28								17 28							
Baglan	d								15 32								17 32							
Port Talbot Parkway	d	13 48	14 13		14 48	15 13			15 36		15 48	16 13		16 48	17 13		17 36	17 48		17 48	18 14			
Pyle	d								15 43								17 43							
Maesteg	d			14 15				15 17					16 15			17 15								18 20
Maesteg (Ewenny Road)	d			14 17				15 19					16 17			17 17								18 22
Garth (Mid Glamorgan)	d			14 20				15 22					16 20			17 20								18 25
Tondu	d			14 29				15 31					16 29			17 29								18 34
Sarn	d			14 32				15 34					16 32			17 32								18 37
Wildmill	d			14 34				15 36					16 34			17 34								18 39
Bridgend	d	14 00	14 25	14 38	15 00	15 25		15 40	15 52		16 00	16 25	16 38	17 00	17 25	17 38	17 55	18 00		18 00	18 26			18 43
Pencoed	d			14 44				15 46					16 44			17 44								18 49
Llanharan	d			14 48				15 50					16 48			17 48								18 53
Pontyclun	d			14 52				15 54					16 52			17 52	18 05							18 57
Cardiff Central ■7	a	14 22	14 47	15 07	15 22	15 47	16 02	16 09	16 16		16 22	16 47	17 07	17 22	17 47	18 07	18 18	18 22		18 22	18 47			19 15
Cardiff Queen Street ■3	a	14 34	14 59	15 19	15 34	15 59	16 14	16 19	16 29		16 34	16 59	17 19	17 34	17 59	18 19	18 29	18 34		18 34	19 04			19 29
Newport (South Wales)	a	14 38	15 03	15 25	15 38	16 03		16 23	16 32		16 38	17 03	17 27	17 38	18 03	18 25		18 38		18 38	19 03			
Bristol Parkway ■7	a	15 00			16 00						17 00			18 00				19 00		19 00				
Gloucester ■7	a			16 21				17 21					18 20			19 20								
Manchester Piccadilly ■10	⛴ a		18 15			19 15						20 15			21 15						22 15			
Reading ■7	a	16 02			17 01						18 01			19 01				20 00		20 01				
London Paddington ■15	⊖ a	16 32			17 32						18 32			19 32				20 32		20 32				

For general notes see front of timetable
For details of catering facilities see Directory of Train Operators

A Until 5 September
B To Cheltenham Spa (Table 57)
C To Abergavenny (Table 131)
D From 12 September

Table 128

Saturdays

West Wales, Swansea and Maesteg → Cardiff

Route Diagram - see first page of Table 127

		GW	AW	AW	AW	AW	AW	GW	AW	AW	AW	AW	AW	AW	AW	AW	AW	AW	AW	AW	AW	AW
		1 ◇		◇	◇			1 ◇	◇		◇	◇			◇							R
			A			B	C		D		E	G										H
		🍽				🍴	🍴	🍽														
Rosslare Harbour ⛴	d																					21 15
Fishguard Harbour ⛴	a																					00 45
	d																					
Milford Haven	d				17 10						19 10	19 10					21 20				23 15	
Johnston	d				17x17						19x17	19x17					21x27				23x22	
Haverfordwest	d				17 25						19 25	19 25					21 35				23 30	
Clarbeston Road	d				17x32						19x32	19x32					21x42				23x39	
Clunderwen	d				17x39						19x38	19x38					21x48				23x47	
Pembroke Dock	d						17 05							19 16					21 11	22 24		
Pembroke	d						17 13							19 24					21 19	22 32		
Lamphey	d						17x16							19x27					21x22	22x35		
Manorbier	d						17 25							19 36					21 31	22 44		
Penally	d						17x30							19x41					21x36	22x49		
Tenby	a						17 33							19 44					21 39	22 51		
	d						17 41							19 47					21 44	22 51		
Saundersfoot	d						17x48							19x54					21x52	22x58		
Kilgetty	d						17x50							19x56					21x54	23x00		
Narberth	d						17x59							20x05					22x04	23x09		
Whitland	a				17 45		18 07				19 44	19 44		20 13			21 54		22 12	23 17	23 56	
	d				17 45		18 10				19 45	19 45		20 14			21 55		22 15	23 20	23 57	
Carmarthen	a				18 02	←	18 27				20 02	20 02		20 33			22 16		22 32	23 40	00 18	
	d				18 06	18 30	18 30		19 08		20 05	20 05		20 35					22 35			
Ferryside	d				18x16	18x40	18x40							20x46					22x45			
Kidwelly	d				18x21	18x46	18x46							20x52					22x51			
Pembrey & Burry Port	d				18 28	18 53	18 53		19 26		20 23	20 23		20 59					22 58			
Llanelli	a				18 34	18 59	18 59		19 31		20 28	20 28		21 05					23 04			
	d				18 34	19 00	19 00		19 32		20 29	20 29		21 06	21 44				23 05			
Gowerton	d					19x07	19x07								21x52				23x12			
Swansea 7	a				18 51	19 22	19 22		19 49		20 50	20 50		21 24	22 13				23 29			
	d	18 29	19 00		19 10			19 29	20 00		20 55	20 55		21 35				22 20				
Llansamlet	d				19 17									21 42				22 27				
Skewen	d				19 21									21 46				22 31				
Neath	d	18 40	19 11		19 25			19 40	20 11		21 06	21 06		21 50				22 35				
Briton Ferry	d				19 28									21 53				22 38				
Baglan	d				19 32									21 57				22 42				
Port Talbot Parkway	d	18 48	19 18		19 36			19 48	20 18		21 13	21 13		22 01				22 46				
Pyle	d				19 43									22 08				22 53				
Maesteg	d			19 15						20 15			21 15			22 15						
Maesteg (Ewenny Road)	d			19 17						20 17			21 17			22 17						
Garth (Mid Glamorgan)	d			19 20						20 20			21 20			22 20						
Tondu	d			19 29						20 29			21 29			22 29						
Sarn	d			19 32						20 32			21 32			22 32						
Wildmill	d			19 34						20 34			21 34			22 34						
Bridgend	d	19 00	19 32	19 38	19 53			20 00	20 30	20 38	21 25	21 25	21 38	22 16		22 39		23 01				
Pencoed	d			19 44						20 44			21 44			22 45						
Llanharan	d			19 47						20 48			21 48			22 49						
Pontyclun	d			19 52						20 52			21 52			22 53						
Cardiff Central 7	a	19 22	19 55	20 05	20 18			20 22	20 51	21 07	21 46	21 49	22 09	22 39		23 08		23 26				
Cardiff Queen Street 3	a	*19 34*	*20 09*		*20 29*			*20 34*	*21 04*	*21 29*	*22 04*	*22 04*	*22 29*	*22 49*		23b*18*						
Newport (South Wales)	a	19 38	20 28	20 24				20 38	21 08	21 28	22 05	*22 13*				23 37						
Bristol Parkway 7	a	20 00						21 00														
Gloucester 7	a		21 22							22 22						00 42						
Manchester Piccadilly 10 🚌	a			23 48																		
Reading 7	a	21 07						21 58														
London Paddington 15 ⊖	a	21 36						22 32														

For general notes see front of timetable
For details of catering facilities see Directory of Train Operators

A To Cheltenham Spa (Table 57)
B Until 5 September
C From 12 September
D To Chester (Table 131)
E From 18 July. To Hereford (Table 131)
G Until 11 July
H Ship service
b Until 5 September only

Table 128

West Wales, Swansea and Maesteg → Cardiff

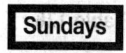

Route Diagram - see first page of Table 127

		AW	GW	GW		GW	GW	AW		GW	AW	GW		AW	GW	AW		GW	AW	AW		AW	GW	AW
		◇	1 ◇	1 ◇		1 ◇	1 ◇	◇		1 ◇	R	1 ◇		R	1 ◇			1 ◇	R				1 ◇	◇
											A													
Rosslare Harbour ⛴	d										09 00													
Fishguard Harbour ⛴	a										12 30													
	d	01 50																				14 30		
Milford Haven	d							09 25											13 35					
Johnston	d							09x32											13x42					
Haverfordwest	d							09 40											13 50					
Clarbeston Road	d							09x47											13x57					
Clunderwen	d							09x53											14x04					
Pembroke Dock	d													11 00		12 40								
Pembroke	d													11 08		12 48								
Lamphey	d													11x11		12x51								
Manorbier	d													11 19		13 00								
Penally	d													11x25		13x05								
Tenby	a													11 28		13 06								
	d													11 34		13 08				13 58				
Saundersfoot	d													11x40		13x16				14x06				
Kilgetty	d													11x42		13x18				14x08				
Narberth	d													11x50		13x28				14x18				
Whitland	a	02 21						09 59						11 58		13 36			14 10	14 26		15 01		
	d	02 22						10 00						12 01		13 39			14 12	14 29		15 02		
Carmarthen	a	02 38						10 16						12 17		13 57			14 28	14 46		15 20		
	d	02 41						10 20						12 35		14 00			14 42					
Ferryside	d							10x30						12x45		14x10								
Kidwelly	d							10x35						12x51		14x16								
Pembrey & Burry Port	d							10 42						12 58		14 23			15 00					
Llanelli	a	03 03						10 47						13 03		14 29			15 05					
	d	03 04						10 48						13 04		14 30			15 06					15 45
Gowerton	d							10x54								14x37								15x52
Swansea 7	a	03 21						11 10						13 21		14 51			15 23					16 13
	d	03 35	07 59	08 59		09 59	10 59	11 22		11 59		12 59		13 46	13 59			14 59	15 30				15 59	
Llansamlet	d							11 29																
Skewen	d							11 33																
Neath	d	03 46	08 11	09 11		10 11	11 11	11 37		12 11		13 11		13 57	14 11			15 11	15 41				16 11	
Briton Ferry	d							11 40																
Baglan	d							11 44																
Port Talbot Parkway	d	03 53	08 18	09 18		10 18	11 18	11 48		12 18		13 18		14 04	14 18			15 18	15 48				16 18	
Pyle	d							11 54																
Maesteg	d																							
Maesteg (Ewenny Road)	d																							
Garth (Mid Glamorgan)	d																							
Tondu	d																							
Sarn	d																							
Wildmill	d																							
Bridgend	d	04 05	08 30	09 30		10 30	11 30	12 02		12 30		13 30		14 16	14 30			15 30	16 00				16 30	
Pencoed	d							12 08											16 06					
Llanharan	d							12 12											16 10					
Pontyclun	d							12 16											16 14					
Cardiff Central 7	a	04 30	08 52	09 52		10 52	11 52	12 30		12 52		13 52		14 37	14 52			15 52	16 29				16 52	
Cardiff Queen Street 3	a		*09 09*	*10 09*		*11 09*	*12 09*			*13 09*		*14 09*			*15 09*			*16 09*					*17 09*	
Newport (South Wales)	a		09 08	10 08		11 08	12 08	12 57		13 08		14 08		15 13	15 08			16 08	16 57				17 08	
Bristol Parkway 7	a		09 30	10 30		11 30	12 30			13 30		14 30			15 30			16 30					17 30	
Gloucester 7	a																							
Manchester Piccadilly 10 🚌	a							16 15						18 15					20 15					
Reading 7	a		10 31	11 31		12 31	13 31			14 31		15 31			16 31			17 31					18 31	
London Paddington 15 ⊖	a		11 10	12 09		13 10	14 09			15 09		16 10			17 10			18 15					19 10	

For general notes see front of timetable
For details of catering facilities see Directory of Train Operators

A Ship service

Table 128

Sundays

until 6 September

West Wales, Swansea and Maesteg → Cardiff

Route Diagram - see first page of Table 127

		GW	AW	AW	GW	GW	AW	AW	GW	AW	AW	AW	AW	AW	AW	AW	AW
			R														R
		1 ◇			1 ◇	1 ◇		◇	1 ◇	◇	◇		◇	◇			
								A		B	C		C				D
		☕	🍴	🍴	☕	☕			☕								
Rosslare Harbour ⛴	d																21 15
Fishguard Harbour ⛴	a																00 45
	d																
Milford Haven	d		15 35				17 35					19 35		21 35		23 15	
Johnston	d		15x42				17x42					19x42		21x42		23x22	
Haverfordwest	d		15 50				17 50					19 50		21 50		23 30	
Clarbeston Road	d		15x57				17x57					19x58		21x58		23x37	
Clunderwen	d		16x03				18x03					20x05		22x06		23x44	
Pembroke Dock	d			16 05							19 05				22 05		
Pembroke	d			16 13							19 13				22 13		
Lamphey	d			16x16							19x16				22x16		
Manorbier	d			16 25							19 25				22 25		
Penally	d			16x30							19x30				22x30		
Tenby	a			16 33							19 33				22 33		
	d			16 33							19 33				22 33		
Saundersfoot	d			16x41							19x40				22x41		
Kilgetty	d			16x43							19x42				22x43		
Narberth	d			16x53							19x51				22x53		
Whitland	a		16 09	17 01			18 09				19 59	20 11		22 12	23 01	23 50	
	d		16 10	17 04			18 10				20 04	20 12		22 13	23 04	23 51	
Carmarthen	a		16 26	17 25			18 27				20 21	20 30	←	22 30	23 25	00 07	
	d	16 09	16 31			18 05		18 35	19 09		20 35 →		20 35	22 35			
Ferryside	d		16x41					18x45					20x45	22x45			
Kidwelly	d		16x46					18x50					20x51	22x51			
Pembrey & Burry Port	d	16 29	16 53			18 25		18 57	19 29				20 59	22 59			
Llanelli	a	16 34	16 58			18 30		19 03	19 34				21 05	23 05			
	d	16 36	16 59			18 32		19 03	19 36	19 52			21 05	23 05			
Gowerton	d		17x05					19x10		19x59			21x12	23x13			
Swansea 7	a	16 52	17 18			18 48		19 26	19 52	20 13			21 26	23 27			
	d	16 59	17 35		17 59	18 59		19 36	19 59	20 35			21 35	23 37			
Llansamlet	d												21 42				
Skewen	d												21 46				
Neath	d	17 11	17 47		18 11	19 11		19 47	20 11	20 46			21 50	23 48			
Briton Ferry	d												21 53				
Baglan	d												21 57				
Port Talbot Parkway	d	17 18	17 54		18 18	19 18		19 54	20 18	20 54			22 01	23 56			
Pyle	d												22 08				
Maesteg	d																
Maesteg (Ewenny Road)	d																
Garth (Mid Glamorgan)	d																
Tondu	d																
Sarn	d																
Wildmill	d																
Bridgend	d	17 30	18 06		18 30	19 30		20 06	20 30	21 07			22 16	00 09			
Pencoed	d												22 22				
Llanharan	d												22 26				
Pontyclun	d												22 30				
Cardiff Central 7	a	17 52	18 27		18 52	19 52		20 27	20 52	21 30			22 44	00 50			
Cardiff Queen Street 3	a	*18 09*			*19 09*	*20 09*			*21 09*	*22 09*							
Newport (South Wales)	a	18 08	18 57		19 08	20 08		20 53	21 08	*22 23*			23 08				
Bristol Parkway 7	a	18 30			19 30	20 30			21 30								
Gloucester 7	a																
Manchester Piccadilly 10 ⛴	a		22 15														
Reading 7	a	19 31			20 31	21 31			22 35								
London Paddington 15 ⊖	a	20 12			21 11	22 16			23 22								

For general notes see front of timetable
For details of catering facilities see Directory of Train Operators

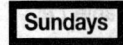

A To Crewe (Table 131)
B From Shrewsbury (Table 129)
C To Hereford (Table 131)
D Ship service

Table 128

Sundays

from 13 September

West Wales, Swansea and Maesteg → Cardiff

Route Diagram - see first page of Table 127

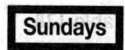

		AW	GW	GW	GW	GW	AW	GW	AW	GW	AW	GW	AW	GW	AW	AW	GW
		◇	1 ◇	1 ◇	1 ◇	1 ◇	◇	1 ◇	R	1 ◇	R	1 ◇		1 ◇	R		1 ◇
									A								
Rosslare Harbour ⛴	d								09 00								
Fishguard Harbour ⛴	a								12 30								
	d	01 50														14 10	
Milford Haven	d														13 35		
Johnston	d														13x42		
Haverfordwest	d														13 50		
Clarbeston Road	d														13x57		
Clunderwen	d														14x04		
Pembroke Dock	d																
Pembroke	d																
Lamphey	d																
Manorbier	d																
Penally	d																
Tenby	a																
	d												13 08				
Saundersfoot	d												13x16				
Kilgetty	d												13x18				
Narberth	d												13x28				
Whitland	a	02 21											13 36		14 10	14 41	
	d	02 22											13 39		14 12	14 42	
Carmarthen	a	02 38											13 57		14 28	15 00	
	d	02 41					10 30				12 35		14 00		14 42		
Ferryside	d						10x40				12x45		14x10				
Kidwelly	d						10x45				12x51		14x16				
Pembrey & Burry Port	d						10 52				12 58		14 23		15 00		
Llanelli	a	03 03					10 57				13 03		14 29		15 05		
	d	03 04					10 58				13 04		14 30		15 06		
Gowerton	d						11x04						14x37				
Swansea 7	a	03 21					11 17				13 21		14 51		15 23		
	d	03 35	07 59	08 59	09 59	10 59	11 22	11 59		12 59	13 46	13 59		14 59	15 30		15 59
Llansamlet	d						11 29										
Skewen	d						11 33										
Neath	d	03 46	08 11	09 11	10 11	11 11	11 37	12 11		13 11	13 57	14 11		15 11	15 41		16 11
Briton Ferry	d						11 40										
Baglan	d						11 44										
Port Talbot Parkway	d	03 53	08 18	09 18	10 18	11 18	11 48	12 18		13 18	14 04	14 18		15 18	15 48		16 18
Pyle	d						11 54										
Maesteg	d																
Maesteg (Ewenny Road)	d																
Garth (Mid Glamorgan)	d																
Tondu	d																
Sarn	d																
Wildmill	d																
Bridgend	d	04 05	08 30	09 30	10 30	11 30	12 02	12 30		13 30	14 16	14 30		15 30	16 00		16 30
Pencoed	d						12 08								16 06		
Llanharan	d						12 12								16 10		
Pontyclun	d						12 16								16 14		
Cardiff Central 7	a	04 30	08 52	09 52	10 52	11 52	12 30	12 52		13 52	14 37	14 52		15 52	16 29		16 52
Cardiff Queen Street 3	a		*09 09*	*10 09*	*11 09*	*12 09*		*13 09*		*14 09*	*15 09*			*16 09*			*17 09*
Newport (South Wales)	a		09 08	10 08	11 08	12 08	12 57	13 08		14 08	15 13	15 08		16 08	16b57		17 08
Bristol Parkway 7	a		09 30	10 30	11 30	12 30		13 30		14 30		15 30		16 30			17 30
Gloucester 7	a																
Manchester Piccadilly 10 ⛴	a						16 15				18 15				20 15		
Reading 7	a		10 31	11 31	12 31	13 31		14 31		15 31		16 31		17 31			18 31
London Paddington 15 ⊖	a		11 08	12 08	13 08	14 08		15 08		16 08		17 08		18 09			19 08

For general notes see front of timetable
For details of catering facilities see Directory of Train Operators

A Ship service
b By changing at Cardiff Central, passengers may arrive at 1652

Table 128

Sundays

from 13 September

West Wales, Swansea and Maesteg → Cardiff

Route Diagram - see first page of Table 127

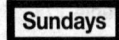

		AW	GW	AW	AW	GW	GW	AW	AW	GW	AW	AW	AW	AW	AW	AW	AW
		◇	1 ◇	R		1 ◇	1 ◇		◇	1 ◇	◇	◇		◇			R
									A		B	C					D
Rosslare Harbour	d																21 15
Fishguard Harbour	a																00 45
	d																
Milford Haven	d			15 35				17 35					19 35	21 35		23 15	
Johnston	d			15x42				17x42					19x42	21x42		23x22	
Haverfordwest	d			15 50				17 50					19 50	21 50		23 30	
Clarbeston Road	d			15x57				17x57					19x58	21x58		23x37	
Clunderwen	d			16x03				18x03					20x05	22x06		23x44	
Pembroke Dock	d				16 05							19 05			22 05		
Pembroke	d				16 13							19 13			22 13		
Lamphey	d				16x16							19x16			22x16		
Manorbier	d				16 25							19 25			22 25		
Penally	d				16x30							19x30			22x30		
Tenby	a				16 33							19 33			22 33		
	d				16 33							19 33			22 33		
Saundersfoot	d				16x41							19x40			22x41		
Kilgetty	d				16x43							19x42			22x43		
Narberth	d				16x53							19x51			22x53		
Whitland	a			16 09	17 01			18 09				19 59	20 11	22 12	23 01	23 50	
	d			16 10	17 04			18 10				20 04	20 12	22 13	23 04	23 51	
Carmarthen	a			16 26	17 25			18 27				20 21	20 30	22 30	23 25	00 07	
	d		16 09	16 31			18 05		18 35	19 09		20 35		22 35			
Ferryside	d			16x41					18x45			20x45		22x45			
Kidwelly	d			16x46					18x50			20x51		22x51			
Pembrey & Burry Port	d		16 29	16 53			18 25		18 57	19 29		20 59		22 59			
Llanelli	a		16 34	16 58			18 30		19 03	19 34		21 05		23 05			
	d	15 45	16 36	16 59			18 32		19 03	19 36	19 52	21 05		23 05			
Gowerton	d	15x52		17x05					19x10		19x59	21x12		23x13			
Swansea 7	a	16 13	16 52	17 18			18 48		19 26	19 52	20 13	21 26		23 27			
	d		16 59	17 35		17 59	18 59		19 36	19 59	20 35	21 35		23 37			
Llansamlet	d											21 42					
Skewen	d											21 46					
Neath	d		17 11	17 47		18 11	19 11		19 47	20 11	20 46	21 50		23 48			
Briton Ferry	d											21 53					
Baglan	d											21 57					
Port Talbot Parkway	d		17 18	17 54		18 18	19 18		19 54	20 18	20 54	22 01		23 56			
Pyle	d											22 08					
Maesteg	d																
Maesteg (Ewenny Road)	d																
Garth (Mid Glamorgan)	d																
Tondu	d																
Sarn	d																
Wildmill	d																
Bridgend	d		17 30	18 06		18 30	19 30		20 06	20 30	21 07	22 16		00 09			
Pencoed	d											22 22					
Llanharan	d											22 26					
Pontyclun	d											22 30					
Cardiff Central 7	a		17 52	18 27		18 52	19 52		20 27	20 52	21 30	22 44		00 50			
Cardiff Queen Street 3	a		*18 09*			*19 09*	*20 09*			*21 09*	*22 09*						
Newport (South Wales)	a		18 08	18 57		19 08	20 08		20 53	21 08	22 23	23 08					
Bristol Parkway 7	a		18 30			19 30	20 30			21 30							
Gloucester 7	a																
Manchester Piccadilly 10	a			22 15													
Reading 7	a		19 31			20 31	21 31			22 35							
London Paddington 15	⊖ a		20 10			21 11	22 11			23 22							

For general notes see front of timetable
For details of catering facilities see Directory of Train Operators

A To Crewe (Table 131)
B From Shrewsbury (Table 129)
C To Hereford (Table 131)
D Ship service

Table 128A

Mondays to Fridays

Maesteg — Caerau
Bus Service

	AW	AW	AW	AW	AW	AW	AW	AW	AW	AW	AW	AW	AW	AW	AW	AW	AW
Cardiff Central .. 128 d	05 51	07 04	08 20	09 18	10 18	11 18	12 18	13 18	14 21	15 18	16 18	17 21	18b22	19 12	20 13	21 10	22b35
Bridgend . . 128 d	06 20	07 32	08 49	09 46	10 46	11 46	12 46	13 46	14 49	15 46	16 46	17 48	18 49	19 45	20 41	21 41	23 02
Maesteg d	**06 51**	**08 05**	**09 20**	**10 20**	**11 20**	**12 20**	**13 20**	**14 20**	**15 20**	**16 20**	**17 20**	**18 20**	**19 20**	**20 20**	**21 20**	**22 20**	**23 34**
Caerau (Square) . . a	**07 00**	**08 14**	**09 29**	**10 29**	**11 29**	**12 29**	**13 29**	**14 29**	**15 29**	**16 29**	**17 29**	**18 29**	**19 29**	**20 29**	**21 29**	**22 29**	**23 43**
Caerau Park a	**07 10**	**08 24**	**09 39**	**10 39**	**11 39**	**12 39**	**13 39**	**14 39**	**15 39**	**16 39**	**17 39**	**18 39**	**19 39**	**20 39**	**21 39**	**22 39**	**23 53**

Saturdays

	AW	AW	AW	AW	AW	AW	AW	AW	AW	AW	AW	AW	AW	AW	AW	AW
Cardiff Central .. 128 d	05 51	07 04	08 22	09 18	10 18	11 21	12 18	13 18	14 21	15 18	16 18	17 21	18 18	19 16	20 13	21 10
Bridgend . . 128 d	06 20	07 32	08 49	09 46	10 46	11 49	12 46	13 46	14 49	15 46	16 46	17 48	18 46	19 45	20 41	21 41
Maesteg d	**06 51**	**08 05**	**09 20**	**10 20**	**11 20**	**12 20**	**13 20**	**14 20**	**15 20**	**16 20**	**17 20**	**18 20**	**19 20**	**20 20**	**21 20**	**22 20**
Caerau (Square) . . a	**07 00**	**08 14**	**09 29**	**10 29**	**11 29**	**12 29**	**13 29**	**14 29**	**15 29**	**16 29**	**17 29**	**18 29**	**19 29**	**20 29**	**21 29**	**22 29**
Caerau Park a	**07 10**	**08 24**	**09 39**	**10 39**	**11 39**	**12 39**	**13 39**	**14 39**	**15 39**	**16 39**	**17 39**	**18 39**	**19 39**	**20 39**	**21 39**	**22 39**

Mondays to Fridays

	AW	AW	AW	AW	AW	AW	AW	AW	AW	AW	AW	AW	AW	AW	AW	AW
Caerau Park d	**06 21**	**07 35**	**08 50**	**09 50**	**10 50**	**11 50**	**12 50**	**13 50**	**14 50**	**15 50**	**16 50**	**17 50**	**18 50**	**19 50**	**20 50**	**21 50**
Caerau (Square) . . d	**06 31**	**07 45**	**09 00**	**10 00**	**11 00**	**12 00**	**13 00**	**14 00**	**15 00**	**16 00**	**17 00**	**18 00**	**19 00**	**20 00**	**21 00**	**22 00**
Maesteg a	**06 41**	**07 55**	**09 10**	**10 10**	**11 10**	**12 10**	**13 10**	**14 10**	**15 10**	**16 10**	**17 10**	**18 10**	**19 10**	**20 10**	**21 10**	**22 10**
Bridgend . . 128 a	07 08	08 22	09 37	10 37	11 37	12 37	13 37	14 37	15 39	16 37	17 37	18 42	19 39	20 37	21 37	22 37
Cardiff Central .. 128 a	07 36	08 48	10 07	11 09	12 08	13 07	14 07	15 07	16 09	17 07	18 07	19 13	20 07	21 06	22 10	23 07

Saturdays

	AW	AW	AW	AW	AW	AW	AW	AW	AW	AW	AW	AW	AW	AW	AW	AW
Caerau Park d	**06 21**	**07 35**	**08 50**	**09 50**	**10 50**	**11 50**	**12 50**	**13 50**	**14 50**	**15 50**	**16 50**	**17 50**	**18 50**	**19 50**	**20 50**	**21 50**
Caerau (Square) . . d	**06 31**	**07 45**	**09 00**	**10 00**	**11 00**	**12 00**	**13 00**	**14 00**	**15 00**	**16 00**	**17 00**	**18 00**	**19 00**	**20 00**	**21 00**	**22 00**
Maesteg a	**06 41**	**07 55**	**09 10**	**10 10**	**11 10**	**12 10**	**13 10**	**14 10**	**15 10**	**16 10**	**17 10**	**18 10**	**19 10**	**20 10**	**21 10**	**22 10**
Bridgend . . 128 a	07 08	08 22	09 39	10 37	11 37	12 39	13 37	14 37	15 39	16 37	17 37	18 42	19 37	20 37	21 37	22 37
Cardiff Central .. 128 a	07 36	08 48	10 09	11 13	12 07	13 09	14 07	15 07	16 09	17 07	18 07	19 15	20 05	21 07	22 09	23 08

For general notes see front of timetable
For details of catering facilities see
Directory of Train Operators

b Change at Bridgend and Maesteg

No Sunday Service

Network Diagram for Tables 129, 131

DM-16/08
Design BAJS

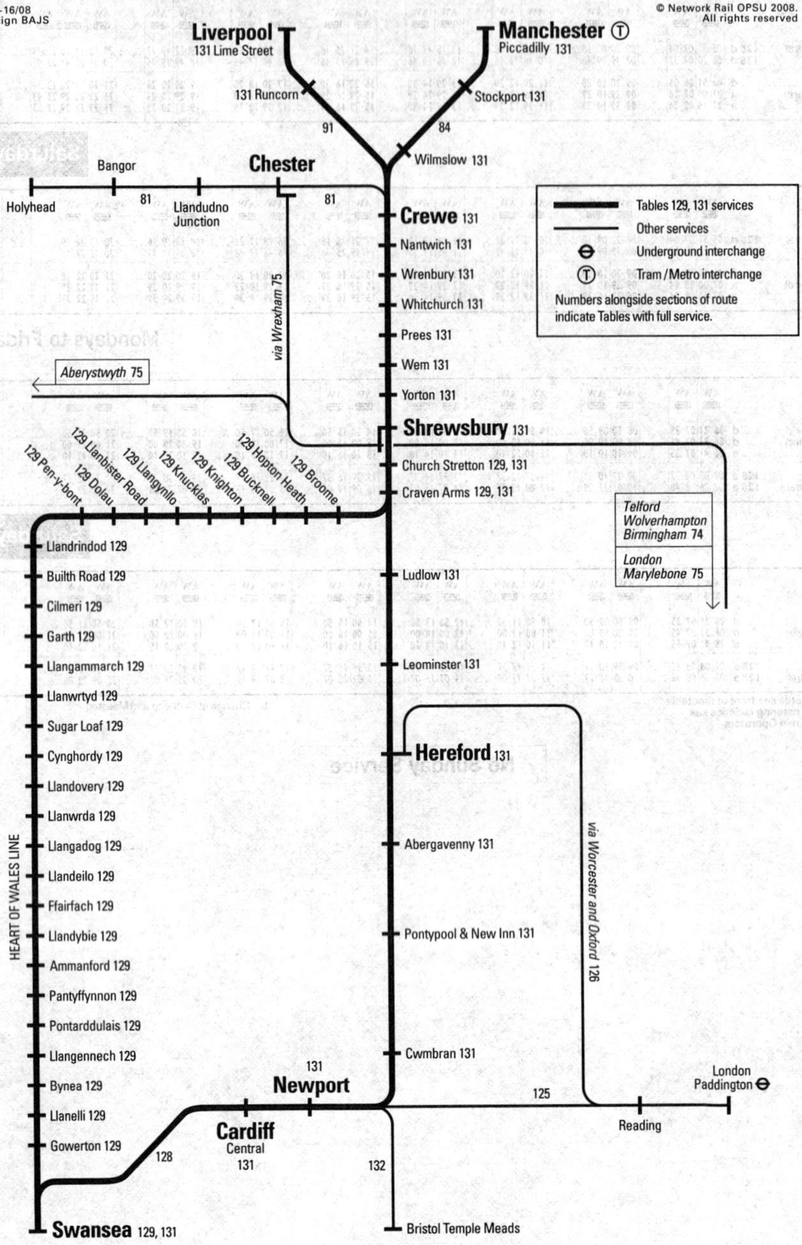
Liverpool
131 Lime Street
Manchester
Piccadilly 131
131 Runcorn
Stockport 131
91
84
Wilmslow 131
Bangor
Chester
Holyhead
81
Llandudno
Junction
81
Crewe 131
Nantwich 131
Wrenbury 131
Whitchurch 131
Prees 131
Wem 131
Yorton 131
via Wrexham 75
Aberystwyth 75
Shrewsbury 131
Church Stretton 129, 131
Craven Arms 129, 131
129 Pen-y-bont
129 Dolau
129 Llanbister Road
129 Llangynllo
129 Knucklas
129 Knighton
129 Bucknell
129 Hopton Heath
129 Broome
Telford
Wolverhampton
Birmingham 74
London
Marylebone 75
Tables 129, 131 services
Other services
Underground interchange
Tram / Metro interchange
Numbers alongside sections of route indicate Tables with full service.
Llandrindod 129
Builth Road 129
Cilmeri 129
Garth 129
Llangammarch 129
Llanwrtyd 129
Sugar Loaf 129
Cynghordy 129
Llandovery 129
Llanwrda 129
Llangadog 129
Llandeilo 129
Ffairfach 129
Llandybie 129
Ammanford 129
Pantyffynnon 129
Pontarddulais 129
Llangennech 129
Bynea 129
Llanelli 129
Gowerton 129
HEART OF WALES LINE
Ludlow 131
Leominster 131
Hereford 131
Abergavenny 131
Pontypool & New Inn 131
Cwmbran 131
via Worcester and Oxford 126
131
Newport
London
Paddington
125
Reading
Cardiff
Central
131
128
132
Bristol Temple Meads
Swansea 129, 131

Table 129

Mondays to Fridays

Swansea → Shrewsbury

HEART OF WALES LINE

Route Diagram - see first page of Table 129

Miles				AW ◇	AW ◇ A	AW ◇	AW ◇
0	**Swansea** 7	128	d	04 36	09 15	13 16	18 21
5½	Gowerton	128	d				
11¼	Llanelli	128	d	04 53	09 35	13 35	18 39
14	Bynea		d	04x58	09x40	13x39	18x43
16	Llangennech		d	05x01	09x43	13x43	18x47
18½	Pontarddulais		d	05x05	09x47	13x47	18x51
23	Pantyffynnon		d	05 13	09 55	13 54	18 58
24¼	Ammanford		d	05 16	09 58	13 57	19 01
26	Llandybie		d	05 20	10 02	14 02	19 06
30	Ffairfach		d	05x27	10x09	14x09	19x13
30¾	Llandeilo		a	05 30	10 12	14 11	19 15
—			d	05 32	10 14	14 14	19 18
36½	Llangadog		d	05 42	10 24	14 23	19 27
38¼	Llanwrda		d	05 45	10 27	14 27	19 31
42	Llandovery		a	05 52	10 34	14 33	19 37
—			d	05 54	10 36	14 36	19 40
46¾	Cynghordy		d	06x02	10x44	14x44	19x48
49½	Sugar Loaf		d	06x10	10x52	14x52	19x56
53½	Llanwrtyd		a	06 16	11 58	14 58	20 02
—			d	06 19	11 05	15 00	20 06
56¾	Llangammarch		d	06x24	11x11	15x06	20x12
58½	Garth (Powys)		d	06x28	11x14	15x09	20x15
62	Cilmeri		d	06x33	11x19	15x14	20x20
64	Builth Road		d	06x36	11x22	15x17	20x23
69¾	Llandrindod		a	06 47	11 34	15 29	20 35
—			d	06 55	11 38	15 39	20 39
73¼	Pen-y-bont		d	07x02	11x45	15x46	20x46
76¼	Dolau		d	07 07	11 50	15 51	20 51
79¾	Llanbister Road		d	07x13	11x57	15x56	20x57
82¾	Llangynllo		d	07x18	12x02	16x01	21x02
86¼	Knucklas		d	07x24	12x08	16x07	21x08
89¼	Knighton		a	07 30	12 13	16 13	21 13
—			d	07 31	12 15	16 15	21 16
93½	Bucknell		d	07 37	12 21	16 21	21 22
96½	Hopton Heath		d	07x41	12x25	16x25	21x26
99	Broome		d	07x45	12x29	16x29	21x30
101½	Craven Arms	131	a	07 52	12 36	16 36	21 37
108¾	Church Stretton	131	a	08 05	12 49	16 49	21 50
121½	**Shrewsbury**	131	a	08 21	13 07	17 10	22 07

Saturdays

			AW ◇	AW ◇ A	AW ◇	AW ◇
Swansea 7	128	d	04 36	09 15	13 16	18 21
Gowerton	128	d				
Llanelli	128	d	04 53	09 35	13 35	18 39
Bynea		d	04x58	09x40	13x39	18x43
Llangennech		d	05x01	09x43	13x43	18x47
Pontarddulais		d	05x05	09x47	13x47	18x51
Pantyffynnon		d	05 13	09 55	13 54	18 58
Ammanford		d	05 16	09 58	13 57	19 01
Llandybie		d	05 20	10 02	14 02	19 06
Ffairfach		d	05x27	10x09	14x09	19x13
Llandeilo		a	05 30	10 12	14 11	19 15
		d	05 32	10 14	14 14	19 18
Llangadog		d	05 42	10 24	14 23	19 27
Llanwrda		d	05 45	10 27	14 27	19 31
Llandovery		a	05 52	10 34	14 33	19 37
		d	05 54	10 36	14 36	19 40
Cynghordy		d	06x02	10x44	14x44	19x48
Sugar Loaf		d	06x10	10x52	14x52	19x56
Llanwrtyd		a	06 16	10 58	14 58	20 02
		d	06 19	11 05	15 00	20 06
Llangammarch		d	06x24	11x11	15x06	20x12
Garth (Powys)		d	06x28	11x14	15x09	20x15
Cilmeri		d	06x33	11x19	15x14	20x20
Builth Road		d	06x36	11x22	15x17	20x23
Llandrindod		a	06 47	11 34	15 29	20 35
		d	06 55	11 38	15 39	20 39
Pen-y-bont		d	07x02	11x45	15x46	20x46
Dolau		d	07 07	11 50	15 51	20 51
Llanbister Road		d	07x13	11x57	15x56	20x57
Llangynllo		d	07x18	12x02	16x01	21x02
Knucklas		d	07x24	12x08	16x07	21x08
Knighton		a	07 30	12 13	16 13	21 13
		d	07 31	12 15	16 15	21 16
Bucknell		d	07 37	12 21	16 21	21 22
Hopton Heath		d	07x41	12x25	16x25	21x26
Broome		d	07x45	12x29	16x29	21x30
Craven Arms	131	a	07 52	12 36	16 36	21 37
Church Stretton	131	a	08 05	12 49	16 49	21 50
Shrewsbury	131	a	08 21	13 07	17 10	22 07

For general notes see front of timetable
For details of catering facilities see Directory of Train Operators

A From Cardiff Central (Table 128)

Table 129

Sundays

Swansea → Shrewsbury
HEART OF WALES LINE

Route Diagram - see first page of Table 129

		AW ◇ A	AW ◇ B	AW ◇
Swansea 7	128 d	11\04	11\09	15 16
Gowerton	128 d	11x15	11x20	15x27
Llanelli	128 d	11\27	11\27	15 35
Bynea	d	11x32	11x32	15x40
Llangennech	d	11x36	11x36	15x43
Pontarddulais	d	11x40	11x40	15x47
Pantyffynnon	d	11\47	11\47	15 55
Ammanford	d	11\50	11\50	15 58
Llandybie	d	11\55	11\55	16 02
Ffairfach	d	12x02	12x02	16x09
Llandeilo	a	12\04	12\04	16 12
	d	12\07	12\07	16 14
Llangadog	d	12\16	12\16	16 24
Llanwrda	d	12\20	12\20	16 27
Llandovery	a	12\26	12\26	16 34
	d	12\29	12\29	16 36
Cynghordy	d	12x37	12x37	16x44
Sugar Loaf	d	12x45	12x45	16x52
Llanwrtyd	a	12\51	12\51	16 58
	d	12\53	12\53	17 01
Llangammarch	d	12x59	12x59	17x06
Garth (Powys)	d	13x02	13x02	17x10
Cilmeri	d	13x07	13x07	17x15
Builth Road	d	13x10	13x10	17x18
Llandrindod	a	13\22	13\22	17 29
	d	13\45	13\45	17 58
Pen-y-bont	d	13x52	13x52	18x05
Dolau	d	13\57	13\57	18 10
Llanbister Road	d	14x02	14x02	18x15
Llangynllo	d	14x07	14x07	18x20
Knucklas	d	14x13	14x13	18x26
Knighton	a	14\19	14\19	18 32
	d	14\21	14\21	18 34
Bucknell	d	14\27	14\27	18 40
Hopton Heath	d	14x31	14x31	18x44
Broome	d	14x35	14x35	18x48
Craven Arms	131 a	14\42	14\42	18 58
Church Stretton	131 a	14\55	14\55	19 11
Shrewsbury	131 a	15\13	15\13	19 29

For general notes see front of timetable
For details of catering facilities see Directory of Train Operators

A Until 6 September
B From 13 September

Shrewsbury → Swansea

HEART OF WALES LINE

Route Diagram - see first page of Table 129

Miles			AW ◇ A	AW ◇	AW ◇	AW ◇
0	**Shrewsbury**	131 d	05 19	09 05	14 05	18 05
12¾	Church Stretton	131 d	05 36	09 22	14 23	18 23
20	Craven Arms	131 d	05 53	09 35	14 36	18 35
22½	Broome	d	05x55	09x40	14x41	18x40
25	Hopton Heath	d	05x59	09x44	14x45	18x44
28	Bucknell	d	06x03	09x48	14x49	18x48
32¼	Knighton	d	06 12	09 57	14 58	18 57
34¾	Knucklas	d	06x17	10x02	15x03	19x02
38¾	Llangynllo	d	06x25	10x10	15x11	19x10
41¾	Llanbister Road	d	06x29	10x14	15x15	19x14
45¼	Dolau	d	06x35	10x20	15x21	19x20
48½	Pen-y-bont	d	06x39	10x24	15x25	19x24
51¾	Llandrindod	a	06 48	10 33	15 34	19 33
—		d	06 53	10 33	15 36	19 33
57½	Builth Road	d	07x02	10x42	15x45	19x42
59½	Cilmeri	d	07x05	10x45	15x48	19x45
63	Garth (Powys)	d	07x10	10x50	15x53	19x50
64¾	Llangammarch	d	07x13	10x54	15x57	19x54
68	Llanwrtyd	a	07 19	11 00	16 03	20 00
—		d	07 22	11 07	16 05	20 11
70¾	Sugar Loaf	d	07x28	11x13	16x11	20x17
74¾	Cynghordy	d	07x34	11x19	16x18	20x23
79½	Llandovery	a	07 44	11 29	16 27	20 33
—		d	07 46	11 31	16 30	20 35
83¼	Llanwrda	d	07x52	11x37	16x35	20x41
85	Llangadog	d	07x55	11x40	16x39	20x44
90¾	Llandeilo	a	08 04	11 49	16 48	20 53
—		d	08 07	11 52	16 50	20 56
91½	Ffairfach	d	08 09	11 54	16 53	20 58
95½	Llandybie	d	08x16	12x01	17x00	21x05
97¼	Ammanford	d	08x20	12x05	17x04	21x09
98½	Pantyffynnon	d	08 23	12 08	17 07	21 12
103¼	Pontarddulais	d	08x30	12x15	17x13	21x19
105½	Llangennech	d	08x34	12x19	17x17	21x23
107½	Bynea	d	08x37	12x22	17x20	21x26
110¼	Llanelli	128 a	08 41	12 28	17 26	21 40
116	Gowerton	128 a	08x53	....	17x44	21x52
121½	**Swansea 7**	128 a	09 08	13 01	18 06	22 13

Saturdays

		AW ◇ A	AW ◇	AW ◇	AW ◇
Shrewsbury	131 d	05 19	09 05	14 05	18 05
Church Stretton	131 d	05 36	09 22	14 23	18 23
Craven Arms	131 d	05 50	09 35	14 36	18 35
Broome	d	05x55	09x40	14x41	18x40
Hopton Heath	d	05x59	09x44	14x45	18x44
Bucknell	d	06x03	09x48	14x49	18x48
Knighton	d	06 12	09 57	14 58	18 57
Knucklas	d	06x17	10x02	15x03	19x02
Llangynllo	d	06x25	10x10	15x11	19x10
Llanbister Road	d	06x29	10x14	15x15	19x14
Dolau	d	06x35	10x20	15x21	19x20
Pen-y-bont	d	06x39	10x24	15x25	19x24
Llandrindod	a	06 48	10 33	15 34	19 33
	d	06 53	10 33	15 36	19 33
Builth Road	d	07x02	10x42	15x45	19x42
Cilmeri	d	07x05	10x45	15x48	19x45
Garth (Powys)	d	07x10	10x50	15x53	19x50
Llangammarch	d	07x13	10x54	15x57	19x54
Llanwrtyd	a	07 19	11 00	16 03	20 00
	d	07 22	11 07	16 05	20 11
Sugar Loaf	d	07x28	11x13	16x11	20x17
Cynghordy	d	07x34	11x19	16x18	20x23
Llandovery	a	07 44	11 29	16 27	20 33
	d	07 46	11 31	16 30	20 35
Llanwrda	d	07x52	11x37	16x35	20x41
Llangadog	d	07x55	11x40	16x39	20x44
Llandeilo	a	08 04	11 49	16 48	20 53
	d	08 07	11 52	16 50	20 56
Ffairfach	d	08 09	11 54	16 53	20 58
Llandybie	d	08x16	12x01	17x00	21x05
Ammanford	d	08x20	12x05	17x04	21x09
Pantyffynnon	d	08 23	12 08	17 07	21 12
Pontarddulais	d	08x30	12x15	17x13	21x19
Llangennech	d	08x34	12x19	17x17	21x23
Bynea	d	08x37	12x22	17x20	21x26
Llanelli	128 a	08 41	12 28	17 32	21 40
Gowerton	128 a	08x53		17x44	21x52
Swansea 7	128 a	09 07	13 01	18 06	22 13

For general notes see front of timetable
For details of catering facilities see Directory of Train Operators

A To Cardiff Central (Table 128)

Sundays

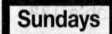

Shrewsbury → Swansea
HEART OF WALES LINE

Route Diagram - see first page of Table 129

			AW ◇	AW ◇ A
Shrewsbury	131	d	12 07	16 25
Church Stretton	131	d	12 24	16 42
Craven Arms	131	d	12 36	16 54
Broome		d	12x42	17x00
Hopton Heath		d	12x46	17x04
Bucknell		d	12x50	17x08
Knighton		d	12 58	17 17
Knucklas		d	13x03	17x22
Llangynllo		d	13x11	17x30
Llanbister Road		d	13x15	17x34
Dolau		d	13x21	17x40
Pen-y-bont		d	13x25	17x44
Llandrindod		a	13 33	17 53
		d	13 36	17 55
Builth Road		d	13x45	18x04
Cilmeri		d	13x48	18x07
Garth (Powys)		d	13x53	18x12
Llangammarch		d	13x56	18x16
Llanwrtyd		a	14 02	18 22
		d	14 08	18 24
Sugar Loaf		d	14x14	18x30
Cynghordy		d	14x20	18x37
Llandovery		a	14 30	18 46
		d	14 32	18 49
Llanwrda		d	14x38	18x54
Llangadog		d	14x41	18x58
Llandeilo		a	14 50	19 07
		d	15 05	19 09
Ffairfach		d	15 07	19 12
Llandybie		d	15x14	19x19
Ammanford		d	15x18	19x23
Pantyffynnon		d	15 21	19 26
Pontarddulais		d	15x28	19x32
Llangennech		d	15x32	19x36
Bynea		d	15x35	19x39
Llanelli	128	a	15 40	19 47
Gowerton	128	a	15x52	19x59
Swansea 7	128	a	16 13	20 13

For general notes see front of timetable
For details of catering facilities see Directory of Train Operators

A To Cardiff Central (Table 128)

Network Diagram for Table 130

DM-27/08
Design BAJS

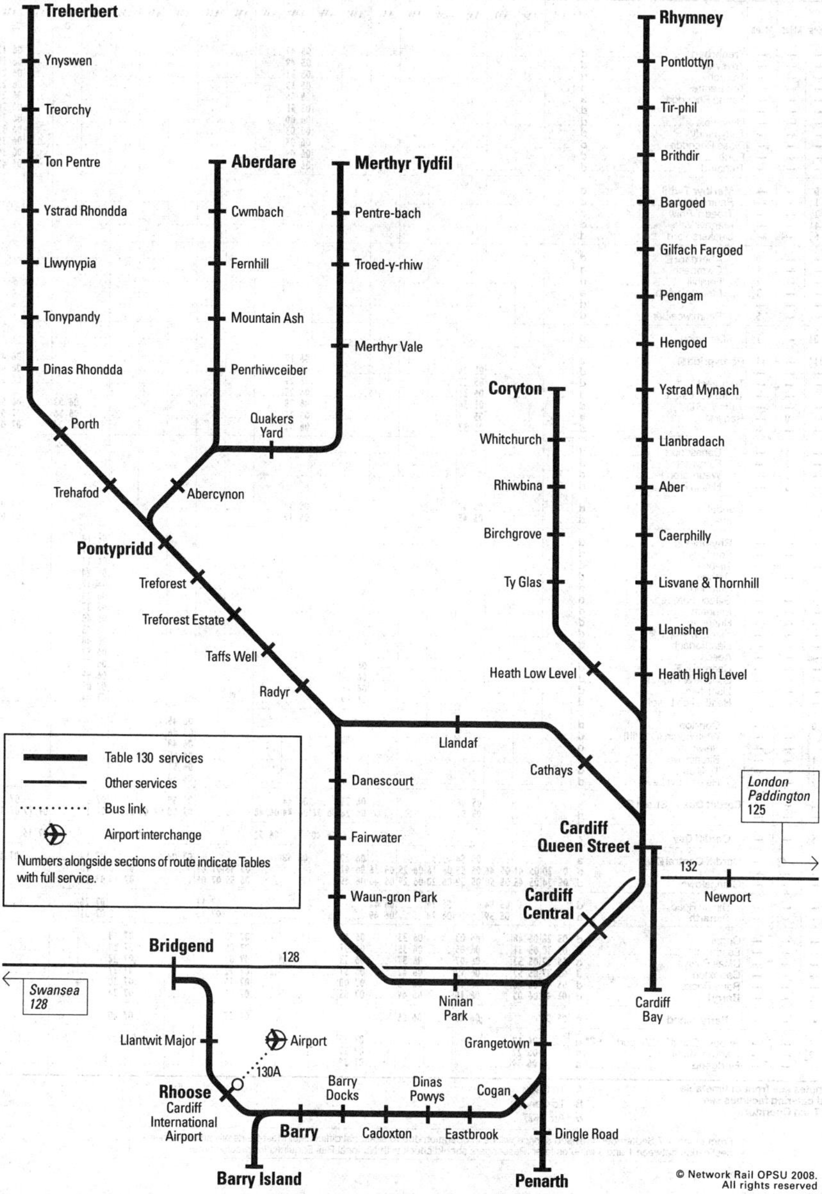

Treherbert
Ynyswen
Treorchy
Ton Pentre
Ystrad Rhondda
Llwynypia
Tonypandy
Dinas Rhondda
Porth
Trehafod
Aberdare
Cwmbach
Fernhill
Mountain Ash
Penrhiwceiber
Quakers Yard
Abercynon
Merthyr Tydfil
Pentre-bach
Troed-y-rhiw
Merthyr Vale
Pontypridd
Treforest
Treforest Estate
Taffs Well
Radyr
Rhymney
Pontlottyn
Tir-phil
Brithdir
Bargoed
Gilfach Fargoed
Pengam
Hengoed
Ystrad Mynach
Llanbradach
Aber
Caerphilly
Lisvane & Thornhill
Llanishen
Heath High Level
Coryton
Whitchurch
Rhiwbina
Birchgrove
Ty Glas
Heath Low Level
Llandaf
Cathays
Danescourt
Fairwater
Waun-gron Park
Cardiff Queen Street
Cardiff Central
London Paddington 125
132
Newport
Cardiff Bay
Table 130 services
Other services
Bus link
Airport interchange
Numbers alongside sections of route indicate Tables with full service.
Bridgend
128
Swansea 128
Ninian Park
Llantwit Major
Airport
130A
Rhoose Cardiff International Airport
Barry Docks
Dinas Powys
Grangetown
Cogan
Barry
Cadoxton
Eastbrook
Dingle Road
Barry Island
Penarth

Treherbert, Aberdare, Merthyr, Pontypridd, Rhymney and Coryton → Cardiff, Penarth, Barry, Barry Island and Bridgend

Network Diagram - see first page of Table 130

Miles	Miles	Miles	Miles	Miles	Station		AW	AW	AW	AW	AW	AW	AW	AW	AW	AW	AW	AW	AW	AW	AW	AW	AW	AW	AW	AW
																				A				B		
0	—	—	—	—	**Treherbert**	d										05 47										06 17
½	—	—	—	—	Ynyswen	d										05 49										06 19
1½	—	—	—	—	Treorchy	d										05 51										06 21
2¾	—	—	—	—	Ton Pentre	d										05 53										06 23
3¼	—	—	—	—	Ystrad Rhondda	a										05 56										06 26
—	—	—	—	—		d										05 58										06 28
4½	—	—	—	—	Llwynypia	d										06 00										06 30
5½	—	—	—	—	Tonypandy	d										06 03										06 33
6	—	—	—	—	Dinas Rhondda	d										06 05										06 35
7½	—	—	—	—	Porth	d										06 09										06 39
8¾	—	—	—	—	Trehafod	d										06 12										06 42
—	—	0	—	—	**Merthyr Tydfil**	d																				
—	—	1½	—	—	Pentre-bach	d																				
—	—	2¾	—	—	Troed Y Rhiw	d																				
—	—	4½	—	—	Merthyr Vale	d																				
—	—	6¾	—	—	Quakers Yard	d																				
—	—	—	—	0	**Aberdare [3]**	d																				
—	—	—	—	1½	Cwmbach	d																				
—	—	—	—	2¾	Fernhill	d																				
—	—	—	—	3¾	Mountain Ash	a																				
—	—	—	—	—		d																				
—	—	—	—	5	Penrhiwceiber	d																				
—	—	8¼	—	7¾	Abercynon	d																				
10¾	—	11½	—	11	**Pontypridd [3]**	a										06 17										06 47
—	—	—	—	—		d				05 24						06 18										06 48
11½	—	—	—	—	Trefforest	d				05 27						06 21										06 51
14	—	—	—	—	Trefforest Estate	d				05 31						06 25										
16¼	—	—	—	—	Taffs Well [3]	d				05 34						06 28								06 53		06 58
18¼	—	—	0	—	Radyr [3]	a				05 37						06 31								06 56		07 01
—	—	—	—	—		d				05 37						06 31								07 04		07 01
																								→		
—	—	—	1½	—	Danescourt	d																				
—	—	—	2	—	Fairwater	d																				
—	—	—	2¼	—	Waun-gron Park	d																				
—	—	—	3¾	—	Ninian Park	d																				
19¼	—	—	—	—	Llandaf	d				05 40						06 34										07 04
21¾	—	—	—	—	Cathays	d				05 45						06 39										07 09
—	0	—	—	—	**Rhymney [3]**	d																06 14			
—	1	—	—	—	Pontlottyn	d																06 17			
—	3½	—	—	—	Tir-phil	d																06 21			
—	4½	—	—	—	Brithdir	d																06 24			
—	6	—	—	—	Bargoed	d																06b32			
—	6½	—	—	—	Gilfach Fargoed	d																06 34			
—	7½	—	—	—	Pengam	d																06 37			
—	9¼	—	—	—	Hengoed	d																06 40			
—	10½	—	—	—	Ystrad Mynach [3]	d																06 43			
—	13	—	—	—	Llanbradach	d																06 48			
—	15	—	—	—	Aber	d																06 52			
—	15¾	—	—	—	Caerphilly [3]	d							06 10									06 55			
—	18¼	—	—	—	Lisvane & Thornhill	d							06 14									06 59			
—	19¼	—	—	—	Llanishen	d							06 16									07 01			
—	20¼	—	—	—	Heath High Level	d							06 19									07 04			
—	—	0	—	—	**Coryton**	d														06 45						
—	—	½	—	—	Whitchurch (Cardiff)	d														06 46						
—	—	¾	—	—	Rhiwbina	d														06 48						
—	—	1¼	—	—	Birchgrove	d														06 50						
—	—	1½	—	—	Ty Glas	d														06 51						
—	—	2¼	—	—	Heath Low Level	d														06 54						
22½	22¾	4¾	—	—	**Cardiff Queen Street [3]**	a				05 48				06 25		06 44				06 59			07 09			07 14
—	—	—	—	—		d				05 51				06 26	06 36	06 44	06 48			07 00	07 00		07 11		07 12	07 16
—	—	5¾	—	—	**Cardiff Bay**	a									06 40		06 52				07 04				07 16	
23	23¼	—	4¾	—	**Cardiff Central [7]**	a				05 54				06 29		06 48				07 04			07 14			07 18
—	—	—	—	—		d	05 20	05 41	05 46	05 55	06 16	06 25	06 36	06 41				06 55	07 01			07 10	07 16			
24	24¼	—	—	—	Grangetown	d	05 24	05 45	05 50	05 59	06 20	06 29	06 40	06 45				06 59	07 05			07 14	07 20			
—	26¾	—	—	—	Dingle Road	d			05 54		06 24		06 44						07 11				07 26			
—	27	—	—	—	**Penarth**	a			05 59		06 28		06 49						07 16				07 31			
25¾	—	—	—	—	Cogan	d	05 28	05 48		06 03		06 33		06 48				07 03				07 18				
26½	—	—	—	—	Eastbrook	d	05 30	05 51		06 05		06 35		06 51				07 05				07 20				
27½	—	—	—	—	Dinas Powys	d	05 32	05 53		06 07		06 37		06 53				07 07				07 22				
29½	—	—	—	—	Cadoxton	d	05 37	05 57		06 12		06 42		06 57				07 12				07 27				
30¼	—	—	—	—	Barry Docks	d	05 40	06 00		06 15		06 45		07 00				07 15				07 30				
31½	—	0	—	—	**Barry [3]**	d	05 44	06 05		06 19		06 49		07 05				07 19				07 34				
32¼	—	—	—	—	**Barry Island**	a	05 50			06 25		06 55						07 25				07 40				
—	—	3¼	—	—	Rhoose Cardiff Int Airport ✈	d		06 12						07 12												
—	—	9¾	—	—	Llantwit Major	d		06 22						07 22												
—	—	19	—	—	**Bridgend**	a		06 39						07 39												

For general notes see front of timetable
For details of catering facilities see Directory of Train Operators

A To Radyr
B To Coryton
b Arr. 0627

From Monday 7 September a revised service will be in operation due to seasonal difficulties. Most trains will arrive at their destination between 1 and 3 minutes later. Passengers should check with National Rail Enquiries for precise times.

Treherbert, Aberdare, Merthyr, Pontypridd, Rhymney and Coryton → Cardiff, Penarth, Barry, Barry Island and Bridgend

Network Diagram - see first page of Table 130

		AW A	AW		AW	AW	AW B	AW	AW	AW	AW	AW A	AW	AW	AW	AW	AW	AW B	AW	AW	AW	AW	AW A	AW		AW
Treherbert	d										06 47											07 17				
Ynyswen	d										06 49											07 19				
Treorchy	d										06 51											07 21				
Ton Pentre	d										06 53											07 23				
Ystrad Rhondda	a										06 56											07 26				
	d										06 58											07 28				
Llwynypia	d										07 00											07 30				
Tonypandy	d										07 03											07 33				
Dinas Rhondda	d										07 05											07 35				
Porth	d										07 09											07 39				
Trehafod	d										07 12											07 42				
Merthyr Tydfil	d							06 38											07 08							
Pentre-bach	d							06 42											07 12							
Troed Y Rhiw	d							06 45											07 15							
Merthyr Vale	d							06 50											07 20							
Quakers Yard	d							06 55											07 25							
Aberdare 3	d		06 22											06 52												07 22
Cwmbach	d		06 25											06 55												07 25
Fernhill	d		06 28											06 58												07 28
Mountain Ash	a		06 31											07 01												07 31
	d		06 34											07 04												07 34
Penrhiwceiber	d		06 37											07 07												07 37
Abercynon	d		06 43					06 59						07 13					07 29							07 43
Pontypridd 3	a		06 53					07 07			07 17			07 23					07 37			07 47				07 53
	d		06 54					07 09			07 18			07 24					07 39			07 48				07 54
Trefforest	d		06 57					07 12			07 21			07 27					07 42			07 51				07 57
Trefforest Estate	d		07 01					07 16											07 46							
Taffs Well 3	d		07 04					07 20			07 28			07 34					07 50			07 58				08 04
Radyr 3	a	←	07 07					07 23			07 31			07 37					07 53			08 01				08 07
	d	07 04	07 07					07 23			07 31	07 34		07 37					07 53			08 01	08 04			08 07
Danescourt	d	07 08										07 38											08 08			
Fairwater	d	07 10										07 40											08 10			
Waun-gron Park	d	07 12										07 42											08 12			
Ninian Park	d	07 15										07 45											08 15			
Llandaf	d		07 10					07 26			07 34		←	07 40					07 56			08 04		←		08 10
Cathays	d		07 15					07 31			07 39		07 39	07 45					08 01			08 09		08 09		08 15
Rhymney 3	d					06 37					→				07 02							→				
Pontlottyn	d					06 40									07 05											
Tir-phil	d					06 44									07 09											
Brithdir	d					06 47									07 12											
Bargoed	d					06 51				07 02					07 17					07 32						
Gilfach Fargoed	d									07 04					07 19											
Pengam	d					06 55				07 07					07 22					07 37						
Hengoed	d					06 59				07 10					07 25					07 40						
Ystrad Mynach 3	d					07 01				07 13					07 28					07 43						
Llanbradach	d					07 06				07 18					07 33					07 48						
Aber	d					07 10				07 22					07 37					07 52						
Caerphilly 3	d					07 13				07 25					07 40					07 55						
Lisvane & Thornhill	d					07 17				07 29					07 44					07 59						
Llanishen	d					07 19				07 31					07 46					08 01						
Heath High Level	d					07 22				07 34					07 49					08 04						
Coryton	d						07 15											07 45								
Whitchurch (Cardiff)	d						07 16											07 46								
Rhiwbina	d						07 18											07 48								
Birchgrove	d						07 20											07 50								
Ty Glas	d						07 21											07 51								
Heath Low Level	d						07 24											07 54								
Cardiff Queen Street 3	a		07 19			07 27	07 29	07 35		07 39			07 44		07 49	07 54		07 59	08 04	08 09				08 14		08 19
	d		07 21		07 24	07 28	07 31	07 36	07 36	07 41			07 46	07 48	07 51	07 56	08 00	08 01	08 06	08 11	08 12			08 16		08 21
Cardiff Bay	a				07 28				07 40					07 52			08 04				08 16					
Cardiff Central 7	a	07 20	07 24			07 31	07 34	07 40		07 44		07 50	07 51		07 54	07 59		08 04	08 09	08 14			08 20	08 22		08 24
	d		07 25			07 32		07 41		07 46					07 55	08 01			08 10	08 16						08 25
Grangetown	d		07 29			07 36		07 45		07 50					07 59	08 05			08 14	08 20						08 29
Dingle Road	d					07 41				07 56						08 11				08 26						
Penarth	a					07 46				08 01						08 16				08 31						
Cogan	d		07 33					07 48							08 03				08 18							08 33
Eastbrook	d		07 35					07 51							08 05				08 20							08 35
Dinas Powys	d		07 37					07 53							08 07				08 22							08 37
Cadoxton	d		07 42					07 57							08 12				08 27							08 42
Barry Docks	d		07 45					08 00							08 15				08 30							08 45
Barry 3	d		07 49					08 05							08 19				08 34							08 49
Barry Island	a		07 55												08 25				08 40							08 55
Rhoose Cardiff Int Airport ✈	d							08 12																		
Llantwit Major	d							08 22																		
Bridgend	a							08 39																		

For general notes see front of timetable
For details of catering facilities see Directory of Train Operators

A To Coryton
B To Radyr

From Monday 7 September a revised service will be in operation due to seasonal difficulties. Most trains will arrive at their destination between 1 and 3 minutes later. Passengers should check with National Rail Enquiries for precise times.

Treherbert, Aberdare, Merthyr, Pontypridd, Rhymney and Coryton → Cardiff, Penarth, Barry, Barry Island and Bridgend

Network Diagram - see first page of Table 130

		AW	AW	AW	AW	AW	AW	AW	AW	AW	AW	AW	AW	AW	AW	AW	AW	AW	AW	AW	AW	AW	AW	AW	AW
				A					B						A					B					A
Treherbert	d							07 45											08 17						
Ynyswen	d							07 47											08 19						
Treorchy	d							07 49											08 21						
Ton Pentre	d							07 51											08 23						
Ystrad Rhondda	a							07 54											08 26						
	d							07 58											08 28						
Llwynypia	d							08 00											08 30						
Tonypandy	d							08 03											08 33						
Dinas Rhondda	d							08 05											08 35						
Porth	d							08 09											08 39						
Trehafod	d							08 12											08 42						
Merthyr Tydfil	d				07 38											08 08									
Pentre-bach	d				07 42											08 12									
Troed Y Rhiw	d				07 45											08 15									
Merthyr Vale	d				07 50											08 20									
Quakers Yard	d				07 55											08 25									
Aberdare 3	d											07 52										08 22			
Cwmbach	d											07 55										08 25			
Fernhill	d											07 58										08 28			
Mountain Ash	a											08 01										08 31			
	d											08 04										08 34			
Penrhiwceiber	d											08 07										08 37			
Abercynon	d				07 59							08 13				08 29						08 43			
Pontypridd 3	a				08 07			08 17				08 23				08 37			08 47			08 53			
	d				08 09			08 18				08 24				08 39			08 48			08 54			
Trefforest	d				08 12			08 21				08 27				08 42			08 51			08 57			
Trefforest Estate	d				08 16											08 46									
Taffs Well 3	d				08 20			08 28				08 34				08 50			08 58			09 04			
Radyr 3	a				08 23			08 31				08 37				08 53			09 01			09 07			
	d				08 23			08 31	08 34			08 37				08 53			09 01	09 04		09 07			
Danescourt	d								08 38											09 08					
Fairwater	d								08 40											09 10					
Waun-gron Park	d								08 42											09 12					
Ninian Park	d								08 45											09 15					
Llandaf	d				08 26			08 34		←		08 40				08 56			09 04		←	09 10			
Cathays	d				08 31			08 39		08 39		08 45				09 01			09 09		09 09	09 15			
Rhymney 3	d		07 24				07 44	→											→					08 30	
Pontlottyn	d		07 27				07 47																	08 33	
Tir-phil	d		07 31				07 51																	08 37	
Brithdir	d		07 34				07 54																	08 40	
Bargoed	d		07b45				08 02						08 17				08 32							08 47	
Gilfach Fargoed	d		07 47										08 19												
Pengam	d		07 50				08 07						08 22				08 37							08 52	
Hengoed	d		07 54				08 10						08 25				08 40							08 55	
Ystrad Mynach 3	d		07 57				08 13						08 28				08 43							08 58	
Llanbradach	d		08 02				08 18						08 33				08 48							09 03	
Aber	d		08 07				08 22						08 37				08 52							09 07	
Caerphilly 3	d		08 10				08 25						08 40				08 55							09 10	
Lisvane & Thornhill	d		08 14				08 29						08 44				08 59							09 14	
Llanishen	d		08 16				08 31						08 46				09 01							09 16	
Heath High Level	d		08 19				08 34						08 49				09 04							09 19	
Coryton	d			08 15											08 45										09 15
Whitchurch (Cardiff)	d			08 16											08 46										09 16
Rhiwbina	d			08 18											08 48										09 18
Birchgrove	d			08 20											08 50										09 20
Ty Glas	d			08 21											08 51										09 21
Heath Low Level	d			08 24											08 54										09 24
Cardiff Queen Street 3	a		08 24	08 29	08 34		08 39			08 44		08 49	08 54		08 59	09 04	09 09				09 14	09 19		09 24	09 29
	d	08 24	08 26	08 31	08 36	08 36	08 41			08 46	08 48	08 51	08 56	09 00	09 01	09 06	09 11	09 12			09 16	09 21	09 24	09 26	09 31
Cardiff Bay	a	08 28				08 40					08 52			09 04				09 16					09 28		
Cardiff Central 7	a		08 29	08 34	08 39		08 47		08 50	08 52		08 54	08 59		09 04	09 09	09 14			09 20	09 22	09 24		09 29	09 34
	d		08 31		08 41							08 55	09 01			09 10	09 16					09 25		09 31	
Grangetown	d		08 35		08 45							08 59	09 05			09 14	09 20					09 29		09 35	
Dingle Road	d		08 41										09 11				09 26							09 41	
Penarth	a		08 46										09 16				09 31							09 46	
Cogan	d				08 48							09 03				09 18						09 33			
Eastbrook	d				08 51							09 05				09 20						09 35			
Dinas Powys	d				08 53							09 07				09 22						09 37			
Cadoxton	d				08 57							09 12				09 27						09 42			
Barry Docks	d				09 00							09 15				09 30						09 45			
Barry 3	d				09 05							09 19				09 34						09 49			
Barry Island	a											09 25				09 40						09 55			
Rhoose Cardiff Int Airport ✈	d				09 12																				
Llantwit Major	d				09 22																				
Bridgend	a				09 39																				

For general notes see front of timetable
For details of catering facilities see
Directory of Train Operators

A To Radyr
B To Coryton
b Arr. 0737

From Monday 7 September a revised service will be in operation due to seasonal difficulties. Most trains will arrive at their destination between 1 and 3 minutes later. Passengers should check with National Rail Enquiries for precise times.

Treherbert, Aberdare, Merthyr, Pontypridd, Rhymney and Coryton → Cardiff, Penarth, Barry, Barry Island and Bridgend

Network Diagram - see first page of Table 130

		AW	AW	AW	AW	AW	AW	AW	AW	AW	AW	AW	AW	AW	AW	AW	AW	AW	AW		AW	AW	AW	AW	AW	AW
						A						B					A						B			
Treherbert	d				08 47											09 17										
Ynyswen	d				08 49											09 19										
Treorchy	d				08 51											09 21										
Ton Pentre	d				08 53											09 23										
Ystrad Rhondda	a				08 56											09 26										
	d				08 58											09 28										
Llwynypia	d				09 00											09 30										
Tonypandy	d				09 03											09 33										
Dinas Rhondda	d				09 05											09 35										
Porth	d				09 09											09 39										
Trehafod	d				09 12											09 42										
Merthyr Tydfil	d	08 38											09 08											09 38		
Pentre-bach	d	08 42											09 12											09 42		
Troed Y Rhiw	d	08 45											09 15											09 45		
Merthyr Vale	d	08 50											09 20											09 50		
Quakers Yard	d	08 55											09 25											09 55		
Aberdare 3	d								08 52										09 22							
Cwmbach	d								08 55										09 25							
Fernhill	d								08 58										09 28							
Mountain Ash	a								09 01										09 31							
	d								09 04										09 34							
Penrhiwceiber	d								09 07										09 37							
Abercynon	d	08 59							09 13				09 29						09 43					09 59		
Pontypridd 3	a	09 07			09 17				09 23				09 37			09 47			09 53					10 07		
	d	09 09			09 18				09 24				09 39			09 48			09 54					10 09		
Trefforest	d	09 12			09 21				09 27				09 42			09 51			09 57					10 12		
Trefforest Estate	d	09 16											09 46											10 16		
Taffs Well 3	d	09 20			09 28				09 34				09 50			09 58			10 04					10 20		
Radyr 3	a	09 23			09 31				09 37				09 53			10 01			10 07					10 23		
	d	09 23			09 31	09 34			09 37				09 53			10 01	10 04		10 07					10 23		
Danescourt	d					09 38											10 08									
Fairwater	d					09 40											10 10									
Waun-gron Park	d					09 42											10 12									
Ninian Park	d					09 45											10 15									
Llandaf	d	09 26			09 34		←		09 40				09 56			10 04		←	10 10					10 26		
Cathays	d	09 31			09 39		09 39		09 45				10 01			10 09		10 09	10 15					10 31		
Rhymney 3	d				↪											↪						09 29				
Pontlottyn	d																					09 32				
Tir-phil	d																					09 36				
Brithdir	d																					09 39				
Bargoed	d			09 02						09 17				09 32								09b47				10 02
Gilfach Fargoed	d									09 19																
Pengam	d			09 07						09 22				09 37								09 52				10 07
Hengoed	d			09 10						09 25				09 40								09 55				10 10
Ystrad Mynach 3	d			09 13						09 28				09 43								09 58				10 13
Llanbradach	d			09 18						09 33				09 48								10 03				10 18
Aber	d			09 22						09 37				09 52								10 07				10 22
Caerphilly 3	d			09 25						09 40				09 55								10 10				10 25
Lisvane & Thornhill	d			09 29						09 44				09 59								10 14				10 29
Llanishen	d			09 31						09 46				10 01								10 16				10 31
Heath High Level	d			09 34						09 49				10 04								10 19				10 34
Coryton	d											09 45											10 15			
Whitchurch (Cardiff)	d											09 46											10 16			
Rhiwbina	d											09 48											10 18			
Birchgrove	d											09 50											10 20			
Ty Glas	d											09 51											10 21			
Heath Low Level	d											09 54											10 24			
Cardiff Queen Street 3	a	09 34		09 39			09 44		09 49	09 54		09 59	10 04	10 09				10 14	10 19			10 24	10 29	10 34		10 39
	d	09 36	09 36	09 41			09 46	09 48	09 51	09 56	10 00	10 01	10 06	10 11	10 12			10 16	10 21		10 24	10 26	10 31	10 36	10 36	10 41
Cardiff Bay	a		09 40					09 52			10 04				10 16						10 28				10 40	
Cardiff Central 7	a	09 39		09 44		09 50	09 52		09 54	09 59		10 04	10 09	10 14			10 20	10 22	10 24			10 29	10 34	10 39		10 44
	d	09 41		09 46					09 55	10 01			10 10	10 16					10 25			10 31		10 41		10 46
Grangetown	d	09 45		09 50					09 59	10 05			10 14	10 20					10 29			10 35		10 45		10 50
Dingle Road	d			09 56						10 11				10 26								10 41				10 56
Penarth	a			10 01						10 16				10 31								10 46				11 01
Cogan	d	09 48							10 03				10 18						10 33					10 48		
Eastbrook	d	09 51							10 05				10 20						10 35					10 51		
Dinas Powys	d	09 53							10 07				10 22						10 37					10 53		
Cadoxton	d	09 57							10 12				10 27						10 42					10 57		
Barry Docks	d	10 00							10 15				10 30						10 45					11 00		
Barry 3	d	10 05							10 19				10 34						10 49					11 05		
Barry Island	a								10 25				10 40						10 55							
Rhoose Cardiff Int Airport ✈	d	10 12																						11 12		
Llantwit Major	d	10 22																						11 22		
Bridgend	a	10 39																						11 39		

For general notes see front of timetable
For details of catering facilities see Directory of Train Operators

A To Coryton
B To Radyr
b Arr. 0942

From Monday 7 September a revised service will be in operation due to seasonal difficulties. Most trains will arrive at their destination between 1 and 3 minutes later. Passengers should check with National Rail Enquiries for precise times.

Treherbert, Aberdare, Merthyr, Pontypridd, Rhymney and Coryton → Cardiff, Penarth, Barry, Barry Island and Bridgend

Network Diagram - see first page of Table 130

		AW	AW	AW	AW	AW	AW	AW	AW	AW	AW	AW	AW	AW	AW	AW	AW		AW	AW	AW	AW	AW	AW	AW	AW
			A						B					A						B					A	
Treherbert	d	09 47																	10 17					10 47		
Ynyswen	d	09 49																	10 19					10 49		
Treorchy	d	09 51																	10 21					10 51		
Ton Pentre	d	09 53																	10 23					10 53		
Ystrad Rhondda	a	09 56																	10 26					10 56		
	d	09 58																	10 28					10 58		
Llwynypia	d	10 00																	10 30					11 00		
Tonypandy	d	10 03																	10 33					11 03		
Dinas Rhondda	d	10 05																	10 35					11 05		
Porth	d	10 09																	10b52					11 09		
Trehafod	d	10 12																	10 55					11 12		
Merthyr Tydfil	d									10 04											10 38					
Pentre-bach	d									10 08											10 42					
Troed Y Rhiw	d									10 11											10 45					
Merthyr Vale	d									10 16											10 50					
Quakers Yard	d									10 22											10 55					
Aberdare 3	d					09 52									10 22											
Cwmbach	d					09 55									10 25											
Fernhill	d					09 58									10 28											
Mountain Ash	a					10 01									10 31											
	d					10 04									10 34											
Penrhiwceiber	d					10 07									10 37											
Abercynon	d					10 13				10 26					10 43						10 59					
Pontypridd 3	a	10 17				10 23				10 32					10 53				11 00		11 08			11 17		
	d	10 18				10 24					10 39				10 54				11 04		11 09			11 18		
Trefforest	d	10 21				10 27					10 42				10 57				11 07		11 12			11 21		
Trefforest Estate	d										10 46										11 16					
Taffs Well 3	d	10 28				10 34					10 50				11 04				11 13		11 20			11 28		
Radyr 3	a	10 31				10 37					10 53				11 07				11 17		11 23			11 31		
	d	10 31	10 34			10 37					10 53			11 04	11 07				11 17		11 23			11 31	11 34	
Danescourt	d		10 38											11 08											11 38	
Fairwater	d		10 40											11 10											11 40	
Waun-gron Park	d		10 42											11 12											11 42	
Ninian Park	d		10 45											11 15											11 45	
Llandaf	d	10 34		←		10 40					10 56				11 10						11 26			11 34		←
Cathays	d	10 39		10 39		10 45					11 01				11 15						11 31			11 39		11 39
Rhymney 3	d	→															10 29							→		
Pontlottyn	d																10 32									
Tir-phil	d																10 36									
Brithdir	d																10 39									
Bargoed	d						10 17					10 32					10c47						11 02			
Gilfach Fargoed	d						10 19																			
Pengam	d						10 22					10 37					10 52						11 07			
Hengoed	d						10 25					10 40					10 55						11 10			
Ystrad Mynach 3	d						10 28					10 43					10 58						11 13			
Llanbradach	d						10 33					10 48					11 03						11 18			
Aber	d						10 37					10 52					11 07						11 22			
Caerphilly 3	d						10 40					10 55					11 10						11 25			
Lisvane & Thornhill	d						10 44					10 59					11 14						11 29			
Llanishen	d						10 46					11 01					11 16						11 31			
Heath High Level	d						10 49					11 04					11 19						11 34			
Coryton	d								10 45											11 15						
Whitchurch (Cardiff)	d								10 46											11 16						
Rhiwbina	d								10 48											11 18						
Birchgrove	d								10 50											11 20						
Ty Glas	d								10 51											11 21						
Heath Low Level	d								10 54											11 24						
Cardiff Queen Street 3	a			10 44		10 49	10 54		10 59		11 04	11 09			11 19		11 24			11 29	11 34		11 39			11 44
	d			10 46	10 48	10 51	10 56	11 00	11 01		11 06	11 11	11 12		11 21	11 24	11 26			11 31	11 36	11 36	11 41			11 46
Cardiff Bay	a				10 52			11 04					11 16			11 28						11 40				
Cardiff Central 7	a		10 50	10 52		10 54	10 59		11 04		11 09	11 14		11 20	11 24		11 29		11 34	11 34	11 39		11 44		11 50	11 52
	d					10 55	11 01				11 10	11 16			11 25		11 31				11 41		11 46			
Grangetown	d					10 59	11 05				11 14	11 20			11 29		11 35				11 45		11 50			
Dingle Road	d						11 11					11 26					11 41						11 56			
Penarth	a						11 16					11 31					11 46						12 01			
Cogan	d					11 03					11 18				11 33						11 48					
Eastbrook	d					11 05					11 20				11 35						11 51					
Dinas Powys	d					11 07					11 22				11 37						11 53					
Cadoxton	d					11 12					11 27				11 42						11 57					
Barry Docks	d					11 15					11 30				11 45						12 00					
Barry 3	d					11 19					11 34				11 49						12 05					
Barry Island	a					11 25					11 40				11 55											
Rhoose Cardiff Int Airport ✈	d																				12 12					
Llantwit Major	d																				12 22					
Bridgend	a																				12 39					

For general notes see front of timetable
For details of catering facilities see Directory of Train Operators

A To Coryton
B To Radyr
b Arr. 1038
c Arr. 1042

From Monday 7 September a revised service will be in operation due to seasonal difficulties. Most trains will arrive at their destination between 1 and 3 minutes later. Passengers should check with National Rail Enquiries for precise times.

Treherbert, Aberdare, Merthyr, Pontypridd, Rhymney and Coryton → Cardiff, Penarth, Barry, Barry Island and Bridgend

Network Diagram - see first page of Table 130

		AW	AW	AW	AW	AW A	AW	AW	AW	AW	AW B	AW	AW	AW	AW		AW A	AW	AW	AW	AW	AW B	AW	AW	AW	AW
Treherbert	d									11 17											11 47					
Ynyswen	d									11 19											11 49					
Treorchy	d									11 21											11 51					
Ton Pentre	d									11 23											11 53					
Ystrad Rhondda	a									11 26											11 56					
	d									11 28											11 58					
Llwynypia	d									11 30											12 00					
Tonypandy	d									11 33											12 03					
Dinas Rhondda	d									11 35											12 05					
Porth	d									11 39											12 09					
Trehafod	d									11 42											12 12					
Merthyr Tydfil	d						11 08											11 38								
Pentre-bach	d						11 12											11 42								
Troed Y Rhiw	d						11 15											11 45								
Merthyr Vale	d						11 20											11 50								
Quakers Yard	d						11 25											11 55								
Aberdare 3	d		10 52										11 22													
Cwmbach	d		10 55										11 25													
Fernhill	d		10 58										11 28													
Mountain Ash	a		11 01										11 31													
	d		11 04										11 34													
Penrhiwceiber	d		11 07										11 37													
Abercynon	d		11 13				11 29						11 43					11 59								
Pontypridd 3	a		11 23				11 37			11 47			11 53					12 07			12 17					
	d		11 24				11 39			11 48			11 54					12 09			12 18					
Trefforest	d		11 27				11 42			11 51			11 57					12 12			12 21					
Trefforest Estate	d						11 46											12 16								
Taffs Well 3	d		11 34				11 50			11 58			12 04					12 20			12 28					
Radyr 3	a		11 37				11 53			12 01			12 07					12 23			12 31					
	d		11 37				11 53			12 01	12 04		12 07					12 23			12 31	12 34				
Danescourt	d										12 08											12 38				
Fairwater	d										12 10											12 40				
Waun-gron Park	d										12 12											12 42				
Ninian Park	d										12 15											12 45				
Llandaf	d		11 40				11 56			12 04		←	12 10					12 26			12 34		←			
Cathays	d		11 45				12 01			12 09		12 09	12 15					12 31			12 39		12 39			
Rhymney 3	d									→					11 29						→					
Pontlottyn	d														11 32											
Tir-phil	d														11 36											
Brithdir	d														11 39											
Bargoed	d			11 17				11 32							11b47					12 02					12 17	
Gilfach Fargoed	d			11 19																					12 19	
Pengam	d			11 22				11 37							11 52					12 07					12 22	
Hengoed	d			11 25				11 40							11 55					12 10					12 25	
Ystrad Mynach 3	d			11 28				11 43							11 58					12 13					12 28	
Llanbradach	d			11 33				11 48							12 03					12 18					12 33	
Aber	d			11 37				11 52							12 07					12 22					12 37	
Caerphilly 3	d			11 40				11 55							12 10					12 25					12 40	
Lisvane & Thornhill	d			11 44				11 59							12 14					12 29					12 44	
Llanishen	d			11 46				12 01							12 16					12 31					12 46	
Heath High Level	d			11 49				12 04							12 19					12 34					12 49	
Coryton	d					11 45											12 15									
Whitchurch (Cardiff)	d					11 46											12 16									
Rhiwbina	d					11 48											12 18									
Birchgrove	d					11 50											12 20									
Ty Glas	d					11 51											12 21									
Heath Low Level	d					11 54											12 24									
Cardiff Queen Street 3	a		11 49	11 54		11 59	12 04	12 09				12 14	12 19		12 24		12 29	12 34		12 39			12 44		12 54	
	d	11 48	11 51	11 56	12 00	12 01	12 06	12 11	12 12			12 16	12 21	12 24	12 26		12 31	12 36	12 36	12 41			12 46	12 48	12 56	13 00
Cardiff Bay	a	11 52			12 04				12 16					12 28					12 40					12 52		13 04
Cardiff Central 7	a		11 54	11 59		12 04	12 09	12 14			12 20	12 22	12 24		12 29		12 34	12 39		12 44		12 50	12 52		12 59	
	d		11 55	12 01			12 10	12 16					12 25		12 31			12 41		12 46			12 55		13 01	
Grangetown	d		11 59	12 05			12 14	12 20					12 29		12 35			12 45		12 50			12 59		13 05	
Dingle Road	d			12 11				12 26							12 41					12 56					13 11	
Penarth	a			12 16				12 31							12 46					13 01					13 16	
Cogan	d		12 03				12 18						12 33					12 48					13 03			
Eastbrook	d		12 05				12 20						12 35					12 51					13 05			
Dinas Powys	d		12 07				12 22						12 37					12 53					13 07			
Cadoxton	d		12 12				12 27						12 42					12 57					13 12			
Barry Docks	d		12 15				12 30						12 45					13 00					13 15			
Barry 3	d		12 19				12 34						12 49					13 05					13 19			
Barry Island	a		12 25				12 40						12 55										13 25			
Rhoose Cardiff Int Airport ✈	d																	13 12								
Llantwit Major	d																	13 22								
Bridgend	a																	13 39								

For general notes see front of timetable
For details of catering facilities see Directory of Train Operators

A To Radyr
B To Coryton
b Arr. 1142

From Monday 7 September a revised service will be in operation due to seasonal difficulties. Most trains will arrive at their destination between 1 and 3 minutes later. Passengers should check with National Rail Enquiries for precise times.

Treherbert, Aberdare, Merthyr, Pontypridd, Rhymney and Coryton → Cardiff, Penarth, Barry, Barry Island and Bridgend

Network Diagram - see first page of Table 130

		AW	AW	AW	AW	AW	AW	AW	AW	AW	AW	AW	AW		AW	AW	AW	AW	AW	AW	AW	AW	AW	AW	AW	AW
		A					B					A						B						A		
Treherbert	d					12 17											12 47									
Ynyswen	d					12 19											12 49									
Treorchy	d					12 21											12 51									
Ton Pentre	d					12 23											12 53									
Ystrad Rhondda	a					12 26											12 56									
	d					12 28											12 58									
Llwynypia	d					12 30											13 00									
Tonypandy	d					12 33											13 03									
Dinas Rhondda	d					12 35											13 05									
Porth	d					12 39											13 09									
Trehafod	d					12 42											13 12									
Merthyr Tydfil	d		12 08										12 38												13 08	
Pentre-bach	d		12 12										12 42												13 12	
Troed Y Rhiw	d		12 15										12 45												13 15	
Merthyr Vale	d		12 20										12 50												13 20	
Quakers Yard	d		12 25										12 55												13 25	
Aberdare 3	d								12 22												12 52					
Cwmbach	d								12 25												12 55					
Fernhill	d								12 28												12 58					
Mountain Ash	a								12 31												13 01					
	d								12 34												13 04					
Penrhiwceiber	d								12 37												13 07					
Abercynon	d		12 29						12 43				12 59								13 13				13 29	
Pontypridd 3	a		12 37			12 48			12 53				13 07				13 17				13 23				13 37	
	d		12 39			12 48			12 54				13 09				13 18				13 24				13 39	
Trefforest	d		12 42			12 51			12 57				13 12				13 21				13 27				13 42	
Trefforest Estate	d		12 46										13 16												13 46	
Taffs Well 3	d		12 50			12 58			13 04				13 20				13 28				13 34				13 50	
Radyr 3	a		12 53			13 01			13 07				13 23				13 31				13 37				13 53	
	d		12 53			13 01	13 04		13 07				13 23				13 31	13 34			13 37				13 53	
Danescourt	d						13 08											13 38								
Fairwater	d						13 10											13 40								
Waun-gron Park	d						13 12											13 42								
Ninian Park	d						13 15											13 45								
Llandaf	d		12 56			13 04		←	13 10				13 26				13 34		←		13 40				13 56	
Cathays	d		13 01			13 09		13 09	13 15				13 31				13 39		13 39		13 45				14 01	
Rhymney 3	d					→					12 29						→									
Pontlottyn	d										12 32															
Tir-phil	d										12 36															
Brithdir	d										12 39															
Bargoed	d			12 32							12b47					13 02						13 17				13 32
Gilfach Fargoed	d																					13 19				
Pengam	d			12 37							12 52					13 07						13 22				13 37
Hengoed	d			12 40							12 55					13 10						13 25				13 40
Ystrad Mynach 3	d			12 43							12 58					13 13						13 28				13 43
Llanbradach	d			12 48							13 03					13 18						13 33				13 48
Aber	d			12 52							13 07					13 22						13 37				13 52
Caerphilly 3	d			12 55							13 10					13 25						13 40				13 55
Lisvane & Thornhill	d			12 59							13 14					13 29						13 44				13 59
Llanishen	d			13 01							13 16					13 31						13 46				14 01
Heath High Level	d			13 04							13 19					13 34						13 49				14 04
Coryton	d	12 45										13 15												13 45		
Whitchurch (Cardiff)	d	12 46										13 16												13 46		
Rhiwbina	d	12 48										13 18												13 48		
Birchgrove	d	12 50										13 20												13 50		
Ty Glas	d	12 51										13 21												13 51		
Heath Low Level	d	12 54										13 24												13 54		
Cardiff Queen Street 3	a	12 59	13 04	13 09				13 14	13 19		13 24	13 29	13 34			13 39			13 44		13 49	13 54		13 59	14 04	14 09
	d	13 01	13 06	13 11	13 12			13 16	13 21	13 24	13 26	13 31	13 36		13 36	13 41			13 46	13 48	13 51	13 56	14 00	14 01	14 06	14 11
Cardiff Bay	a				13 16					13 28					13 40					13 52			14 04			
Cardiff Central 7	a	13 04	13 09	13 14			13 20	13 22	13 24		13 29	13 34	13 39			13 44		13 50	13 52		13 54	13 59		14 04	14 09	14 14
	d		13 10	13 16					13 25		13 31		13 41			13 46					13 55	14 01			14 10	14 16
Grangetown	d		13 14	13 20					13 29		13 35		13 45			13 50					13 59	14 05			14 14	14 20
Dingle Road	d			13 26							13 41					13 56						14 11				14 26
Penarth	a			13 31							13 46					14 01						14 16				14 31
Cogan	d		13 18						13 33				13 48								14 03				14 18	
Eastbrook	d		13 20						13 35				13 51								14 05				14 20	
Dinas Powys	d		13 22						13 37				13 53								14 07				14 22	
Cadoxton	d		13 27						13 42				13 57								14 12				14 27	
Barry Docks	d		13 30						13 45				14 00								14 15				14 30	
Barry 3	d		13 34						13 49				14 05								14 19				14 34	
Barry Island	a		13 40						13 55												14 25				14 40	
Rhoose Cardiff Int Airport ✈	d												14 12													
Llantwit Major	d												14 22													
Bridgend	a												14 39													

For general notes see front of timetable
For details of catering facilities see Directory of Train Operators

A To Radyr
B To Coryton
b Arr. 1242

From Monday 7 September a revised service will be in operation due to seasonal difficulties. Most trains will arrive at their destination between 1 and 3 minutes later. Passengers should check with National Rail Enquiries for precise times.

Treherbert, Aberdare, Merthyr, Pontypridd, Rhymney and Coryton → Cardiff, Penarth, Barry, Barry Island and Bridgend

Network Diagram - see first page of Table 130

		AW	AW	AW A	AW	AW	AW	AW	AW B	AW	AW		AW	AW	AW A	AW	AW	AW	AW	AW	AW B	AW	AW	AW	AW A	AW
Treherbert	d		13 17											13 47												
Ynyswen	d		13 19											13 49												
Treorchy	d		13 21											13 51												
Ton Pentre	d		13 23											13 53												
Ystrad Rhondda	a		13 26											13 56												
	d		13 28											13 58												
Llwynypia	d		13 30											14 00												
Tonypandy	d		13 33											14 03												
Dinas Rhondda	d		13 35											14 05												
Porth	d		13 39											14 09												
Trehafod	d		13 42											14 12												
Merthyr Tydfil	d									13 38												14 08				
Pentre-bach	d									13 42												14 12				
Troed Y Rhiw	d									13 45												14 15				
Merthyr Vale	d									13 50												14 20				
Quakers Yard	d									13 55												14 25				
Aberdare 3	d																	13 52								14 22
Cwmbach	d																	13 55								14 25
Fernhill	d																	13 58								14 28
Mountain Ash	a																	14 01								14 31
	d																	14 04								14 34
Penrhiwceiber	d																	14 07								14 37
Abercynon	d					13 45				13 59								14 13				14 29				14 43
Pontypridd 3	a		13 47			13 53				14 07				14 17				14 23				14 37				14 53
	d		13 48			13 54				14 09				14 18				14 24				14 39				14 54
Trefforest	d		13 51			13 57				14 12				14 21				14 27				14 42				14 57
Trefforest Estate	d									14 16												14 46				
Taffs Well 3	d		13 58			14 04				14 20				14 28				14 34				14 50				15 04
Radyr 3	a		14 01			14 07				14 23				14 31				14 37				14 53				15 07
	d		14 01	14 04		14 07				14 23				14 31	14 34			14 37				14 53			15 04	15 07
Danescourt	d			14 08											14 38										15 08	
Fairwater	d			14 10											14 40										15 10	
Waun-gron Park	d			14 12											14 42										15 12	
Ninian Park	d			14 15											14 45										15 15	
Llandaf	d		14 04		←	14 10				14 26				14 34		←		14 40				14 56				15 10
Cathays	d		14 09		14 09	14 15				14 31				14 39		14 39		14 45				15 01				15 15
Rhymney 3	d		↪					13 29						↪												
Pontlottyn	d							13 32																		
Tir-phil	d							13 36																		
Brithdir	d							13 39																		
Bargoed	d							13b47					14 02						14 17				14 32			
Gilfach Fargoed	d																		14 19							
Pengam	d							13 52					14 07						14 22				14 37			
Hengoed	d							13 55					14 10						14 25				14 40			
Ystrad Mynach 3	d							13 58					14 13						14 28				14 43			
Llanbradach	d							14 03					14 18						14 33				14 48			
Aber	d							14 07					14 22						14 37				14 52			
Caerphilly 3	d							14 10					14 25						14 40				14 55			
Lisvane & Thornhill	d							14 14					14 29						14 44				14 59			
Llanishen	d							14 16					14 31						14 46				15 01			
Heath High Level	d							14 19					14 34						14 49				15 04			
Coryton	d								14 15												14 45					
Whitchurch (Cardiff)	d								14 16												14 46					
Rhiwbina	d								14 18												14 48					
Birchgrove	d								14 20												14 50					
Ty Glas	d								14 21												14 51					
Heath Low Level	d								14 24												14 54					
Cardiff Queen Street 3	a				14 14	14 19		14 24	14 29	14 34			14 39			14 44		14 49	14 54		14 59	15 04	15 09			15 19
	d	14 12			14 16	14 21	14 24	14 26	14 31	14 36	14 36		14 41			14 46	14 48	14 51	14 56	15 00	15 01	15 06	15 11	15 12		15 21
Cardiff Bay	a	14 16					14 28				14 40						14 52			15 04				15 16		
Cardiff Central 7	a			14 20	14 22	14 24		14 29	14 34	14 39			14 44		14 50	14 52		14 54	14 59		15 04	15 09	15 14		15 20	15 24
	d					14 25		14 31		14 41			14 46					14 55	15 01			15 10	15 16			15 25
Grangetown	d					14 29		14 35		14 45			14 50					14 59	15 05			15 14	15 20			15 29
Dingle Road	d							14 41					14 56						15 11				15 26			
Penarth	a							14 46					15 01						15 16				15 31			
Cogan	d					14 33				14 48								15 03				15 18				15 33
Eastbrook	d					14 35				14 51								15 05				15 20				15 35
Dinas Powys	d					14 37				14 53								15 07				15 22				15 37
Cadoxton	d					14 42				14 57								15 12				15 27				15 42
Barry Docks	d					14 45				15 00								15 15				15 30				15 45
Barry 3	d					14 49				15 05								15 19				15 34				15 49
Barry Island	a					14 55												15 25				15 40				15 55
Rhoose Cardiff Int Airport ✈	d									15 12																
Llantwit Major	d									15 22																
Bridgend	a									15 39																

For general notes see front of timetable
For details of catering facilities see
Directory of Train Operators

A To Coryton
B To Radyr
b Arr. 1342

From Monday 7 September a revised service will be in operation due to seasonal difficulties. Most trains will arrive at their destination between 1 and 3 minutes later. Passengers should check with National Rail Enquiries for precise times.

Treherbert, Aberdare, Merthyr, Pontypridd, Rhymney and Coryton → Cardiff, Penarth, Barry, Barry Island and Bridgend

Network Diagram - see first page of Table 130

		AW	AW	AW	AW	AW	AW	AW	AW	AW	AW	AW	AW	AW	AW	AW	AW	AW	AW	AW	AW	AW	AW	AW	AW
					A					B						A						B			
Treherbert	d			14 17					14 47												15 17				
Ynyswen	d			14 19					14 49												15 19				
Treorchy	d			14 21					14 51												15 21				
Ton Pentre	d			14 23					14 53												15 23				
Ystrad Rhondda	a			14 26					14 56												15 26				
	d			14 28					14 58												15 28				
Llwynypia	d			14 30					15 00												15 30				
Tonypandy	d			14 33					15 03												15 33				
Dinas Rhondda	d			14 35					15 05												15 35				
Porth	d			14b52					15 09												15 39				
Trehafod	d			14 55					15 12												15 42				
Merthyr Tydfil	d					14 38											15 04								
Pentre-bach	d					14 42											15 08								
Troed Y Rhiw	d					14 45											15 11								
Merthyr Vale	d					14 50											15 16								
Quakers Yard	d					14 55											15 22								
Aberdare 3	d												14 52											15 22	
Cwmbach	d												14 55											15 25	
Fernhill	d												14 58											15 28	
Mountain Ash	a												15 01											15 31	
	d												15 04											15 34	
Penrhiwceiber	d												15 07											15 37	
Abercynon	d					14 59							15 13				15 26							15 43	
Pontypridd 3	a			15 00		15 07			15 17				15 23				15 32				15 47			15 53	
	d			15 04		15 09			15 18				15 24					15 39			15 48			15 54	
Trefforest	d			15 07		15 12			15 21				15 27					15 42			15 51			15 57	
Trefforest Estate	d					15 16												15 46							
Taffs Well 3	d			15 13		15 20			15 28				15 34					15 50			15 58			16 04	
Radyr 3	a			15 17		15 23			15 31				15 37					15 53			16 01			16 07	
	d			15 17		15 23			15 31	15 34			15 37					15 53			16 01	16 04		16 07	
Danescourt	d									15 38												16 08			
Fairwater	d									15 40												16 10			
Waun-gron Park	d									15 42												16 12			
Ninian Park	d									15 45												16 15			
Llandaf	d					15 26			15 34		←		15 40					15 56			16 04		←	16 10	
Cathays	d					15 31			15 39		15 39		15 45					16 01			16 09		16 09	16 15	
Rhymney 3	d		14 29						→												→				
Pontlottyn	d		14 32																						
Tir-phil	d		14 36																						
Brithdir	d		14 39																						
Bargoed	d		14c47					15 02						15 17					15 32						
Gilfach Fargoed	d													15 19											
Pengam	d		14 52					15 07						15 22					15 37						
Hengoed	d		14 55					15 10						15 25					15 40						
Ystrad Mynach 3	d		14 58					15 13						15 28					15 43						
Llanbradach	d		15 03					15 18						15 33					15 48						
Aber	d		15 07					15 22						15 37					15 52						
Caerphilly 3	d		15 10					15 25						15 40					15 55						
Lisvane & Thornhill	d		15 14					15 29						15 44					15 59						
Llanishen	d		15 16					15 31						15 46					16 01						
Heath High Level	d		15 19					15 34						15 49					16 04						
Coryton	d				15 15											15 45									
Whitchurch (Cardiff)	d				15 16											15 46									
Rhiwbina	d				15 18											15 48									
Birchgrove	d				15 20											15 50									
Ty Glas	d				15 21											15 51									
Heath Low Level	d				15 24											15 54									
Cardiff Queen Street 3	a		15 24		15 29	15 34		15 39			15 44		15 49	15 54		15 59		16 04	16 09				16 14	16 19	
	d	15 24	15 26		15 31	15 36	15 36	15 41			15 46	15 48	15 51	15 56	16 00	16 01		16 06	16 11	16 12			16 16	16 21	16 24
Cardiff Bay	a	15 28					15 40					15 52			16 04					16 16					16 28
Cardiff Central 7	a		15 29	15 34	15 34	15 39		15 44		15 50	15 52		15 54	15 59		16 05		16 09	16 14			16 20	16 22	16 24	
	d		15 31			15 41		15 46					15 55	16 01				16 10	16 16					16 25	
Grangetown	d		15 35			15 45		15 50					15 59	16 05				16 14	16 20					16 29	
Dingle Road	d		15 41					15 56						16 11					16 26						
Penarth	a		15 46					16 01						16 16					16 31						
Cogan	d					15 48							16 03					16 18						16 33	
Eastbrook	d					15 51							16 05					16 20						16 35	
Dinas Powys	d					15 53							16 07					16 22						16 37	
Cadoxton	d					15 57							16 12					16 27						16 42	
Barry Docks	d					16 00							16 15					16 30						16 45	
Barry 3	d					16 05							16 19					16 34						16 49	
Barry Island	a												16 25					16 40						16 55	
Rhoose Cardiff Int Airport ✈	d					16 12																			
Llantwit Major	d					16 22																			
Bridgend	a					16 39																			

For general notes see front of timetable
For details of catering facilities see Directory of Train Operators

A To Radyr
B To Coryton
b Arr. 1438
c Arr. 1442

From Monday 7 September a revised service will be in operation due to seasonal difficulties. Most trains will arrive at their destination between 1 and 3 minutes later. Passengers should check with National Rail Enquiries for precise times.

Table 130

Mondays to Fridays

Treherbert, Aberdare, Merthyr, Pontypridd, Rhymney and Coryton → Cardiff, Penarth, Barry, Barry Island and Bridgend

Network Diagram - see first page of Table 130

		AW	AW	AW	AW	AW	AW		AW	AW	AW	AW	AW	AW	AW	AW	AW	AW	AW	AW	AW	AW	AW	AW	AW	AW
			A						B						A					B					A	
Treherbert	d						15 47												16 17							
Ynyswen	d						15 49												16 19							
Treorchy	d						15 51												16 21							
Ton Pentre	d						15 53												16 23							
Ystrad Rhondda	a						15 56												16 26							
	d						15 58												16 28							
Llwynypia	d						16 00												16 30							
Tonypandy	d						16 03												16 33							
Dinas Rhondda	d						16 05												16 35							
Porth	d						16 09												16 39							
Trehafod	d						16 12												16 42							
Merthyr Tydfil	d			15 38												16 08										16 38
Pentre-bach	d			15 42												16 12										16 42
Troed Y Rhiw	d			15 45												16 15										16 45
Merthyr Vale	d			15 50												16 20										16 50
Quakers Yard	d			15 55												16 25										16 55
Aberdare 3	d											15 52										16 22				
Cwmbach	d											15 55										16 25				
Fernhill	d											15 58										16 28				
Mountain Ash	a											16 01										16 31				
	d											16 04										16 34				
Penrhiwceiber	d											16 07										16 37				
Abercynon	d			15 59								16 13				16 29						16 43				16 59
Pontypridd 3	a			16 08			16 17					16 23				16 37			16 47			16 53				17 07
	d			16 09			16 18					16 24				16 39			16 48			16 54				17 09
Trefforest	d			16 12			16 21					16 27				16 42			16 51			16 57				17 12
Trefforest Estate	d			16 16												16 46										17 16
Taffs Well 3	d			16 20			16 28					16 34				16 50			16 58			17 04				17 20
Radyr 3	a			16 23			16 31					16 37				16 53			17 01			17 07				17 23
	d			16 23			16 31		16 34			16 37				16 53			17 01	17 04		17 07				17 23
Danescourt	d								16 38											17 08						
Fairwater	d								16 40											17 10						
Waun-gron Park	d								16 42											17 12						
Ninian Park	d								16 45											17 15						
Llandaf	d			16 26			16 34			←		16 40				16 56			17 04		←	17 10				17 26
Cathays	d			16 31			16 39			16 39		16 45				17 01			17 09		17 09	17 15				17 31
Rhymney 3	d	15 29					→												→					16 29		
Pontlottyn	d	15 32																						16 32		
Tir-phil	d	15 36																						16 36		
Brithdir	d	15 39																						16 39		
Bargoed	d	15b47				16 02							16 17				16 32							16c47		
Gilfach Fargoed	d												16 19													
Pengam	d	15 52				16 07							16 22				16 37							16 52		
Hengoed	d	15 55				16 10							16 25				16 40							16 55		
Ystrad Mynach 3	d	15 58				16 13							16 28				16 43							16 58		
Llanbradach	d	16 03				16 18							16 33				16 48							17 03		
Aber	d	16 07				16 22							16 37				16 52							17 07		
Caerphilly 3	d	16 10				16 25							16 40				16 55							17 10		
Lisvane & Thornhill	d	16 14				16 29							16 44				16 59							17 14		
Llanishen	d	16 16				16 31							16 46				17 01							17 16		
Heath High Level	d	16 19				16 34							16 49				17 04							17 19		
Coryton	d		16 15												16 45										17 15	
Whitchurch (Cardiff)	d		16 16												16 46										17 16	
Rhiwbina	d		16 18												16 48										17 18	
Birchgrove	d		16 20												16 50										17 20	
Ty Glas	d		16 21												16 51										17 21	
Heath Low Level	d		16 24												16 54										17 24	
Cardiff Queen Street 3	a	16 24	16 29	16 34		16 39				16 44		16 49	16 54		16 59	17 04	17 09				17 14	17 19		17 24	17 29	17 34
	d	16 26	16 31	16 36	16 36	16 41				16 46	16 48	16 51	16 56	17 00	17 01	17 06	17 11	17 12			17 16	17 21	17 24	17 26	17 31	17 36
Cardiff Bay	a				16 40						16 52			17 04				17 16					17 28			
Cardiff Central 7	a	16 32	16 34	16 39		16 44			16 50	16 52		16 54	16 59		17 04	17 09	17 14			17 20	17 22	17 24		17 29	17 34	17 39
	d			16 41		16 46						16 55	17 01			17 10	17 16					17 25		17 31		17 41
Grangetown	d			16 45		16 50						16 59	17 05			17 14	17 20					17 29		17 35		17 45
Dingle Road	d					16 56							17 11				17 26							17 41		
Penarth	a					17 01							17 16				17 31							17 46		
Cogan	d			16 48								17 03				17 18						17 33				17 48
Eastbrook	d			16 51								17 05				17 20						17 35				17 51
Dinas Powys	d			16 53								17 07				17 22						17 37				17 53
Cadoxton	d			16 57								17 12				17 27						17 42				17 57
Barry Docks	d			17 00								17 15				17 30						17 45				18 00
Barry 3	d			17 05								17 19				17 34						17 49				18 05
Barry Island	a											17 25				17 40						17 55				
Rhoose Cardiff Int Airport ✈	d			17 12																						18 12
Llantwit Major	d			17 22																						18 22
Bridgend	a			17 39																						18 39

For general notes see front of timetable
For details of catering facilities see Directory of Train Operators

A To Radyr
B To Coryton
b Arr. 1542
c Arr. 1642

From Monday 7 September a revised service will be in operation due to seasonal difficulties. Most trains will arrive at their destination between 1 and 3 minutes later. Passengers should check with National Rail Enquiries for precise times.

Treherbert, Aberdare, Merthyr, Pontypridd, Rhymney and Coryton → Cardiff, Penarth, Barry, Barry Island and Bridgend

Network Diagram - see first page of Table 130

		AW	AW	AW	AW A		AW	AW	AW	AW	AW	AW B	AW	AW	AW	AW	AW A	AW	AW	AW	AW	AW B	AW	AW	AW	AW A
Treherbert	d			16 47											17 17										17 47	
Ynyswen	d			16 49											17 19										17 49	
Treorchy	d			16 51											17 21										17 51	
Ton Pentre	d			16 53											17 23										17 53	
Ystrad Rhondda	a			16 56											17 26										17 56	
	d			16 58											17 28										17 58	
Llwynypia	d			17 00											17 30										18 00	
Tonypandy	d			17 03											17 33										18 03	
Dinas Rhondda	d			17 05											17 35										18 05	
Porth	d			17 09											17 39										18 09	
Trehafod	d			17 12											17 42										18 12	
Merthyr Tydfil	d												17 08										17 38			
Pentre-bach	d												17 12										17 42			
Troed Y Rhiw	d												17 15										17 45			
Merthyr Vale	d												17 20										17 50			
Quakers Yard	d												17 25										17 55			
Aberdare 3	d								16 52										17 22							
Cwmbach	d								16 55										17 25							
Fernhill	d								16 58										17 28							
Mountain Ash	a								17 01										17 31							
	d								17 04										17 34							
Penrhiwceiber	d								17 07										17 37							
Abercynon	d								17 13				17 29						17 43				17 59			
Pontypridd 3	a			17 17					17 23				17 37		17 47				17 53				18 07		18 17	
	d			17 18					17 24				17 39		17 48				17 54				18 09		18 18	
Trefforest	d			17 21					17 27				17 42		17 51				17 57				18 12		18 21	
Trefforest Estate	d												17 46										18 16			
Taffs Well 3	d			17 28					17 34				17 50		17 58				18 04				18 20		18 28	
Radyr 3	a			17 31					17 37				17 53		18 01				18 07				18 23		18 31	
	d			17 31	17 34				17 37				17 53		18 01		18 04		18 07				18 23		18 31	18 34
Danescourt	d				17 38												18 08									18 38
Fairwater	d				17 40												18 10									18 40
Waun-gron Park	d				17 42												18 12									18 42
Ninian Park	d				17 45												18 15									18 45
Llandaf	d			17 34			←		17 40				17 56		18 04			←	18 10				18 26		18 34	
Cathays	d			17 39			17 39		17 45				18 01		18 09			18 09	18 15				18 31		18 39	
Rhymney 3	d			→											→						17 29				→	
Pontlottyn	d																				17 32					
Tir-phil	d																				17 36					
Brithdir	d																				17 39					
Bargoed	d		17 02							17 17				17 32							17b47					
Gilfach Fargoed	d									17 19																
Pengam	d		17 07							17 22				17 37							17 52					
Hengoed	d		17 10							17 25				17 40							17 55					
Ystrad Mynach 3	d		17 13							17 28				17 43							17 58					
Llanbradach	d		17 18							17 33				17 48							18 03					
Aber	d		17 22							17 37				17 52							18 07					
Caerphilly 3	d		17 25							17 40				17 55							18 10					
Lisvane & Thornhill	d		17 29							17 44				17 59							18 14					
Llanishen	d		17 31							17 46				18 01							18 16					
Heath High Level	d		17 34							17 49				18 04							18 19					
Coryton	d											17 45										18 15				
Whitchurch (Cardiff)	d											17 46										18 16				
Rhiwbina	d											17 48										18 18				
Birchgrove	d											17 50										18 20				
Ty Glas	d											17 51										18 21				
Heath Low Level	d											17 54										18 24				
Cardiff Queen Street 3	a		17 39				17 44		17 49	17 54		17 59	18 04	18 09				18 14	18 19		18 24	18 29	18 34			
	d	17 36	17 41				17 46	17 48	17 51	17 56	18 00	18 01	18 06	18 11		18 12		18 16	18 21	18 24	18 26	18 31	18 36	18 36		
Cardiff Bay	a	17 40						17 52			18 04					18 16				18 28				18 40		
Cardiff Central 7	a		17 44		17 50		17 52		17 54	17 59		18 04	18 09	18 14			18 20	18 22	18 24		18 29	18 34	18 39			18 50
	d		17 46						17 55	18 01			18 10	18 16					18 25		18 31		18 41			
Grangetown	d		17 50						17 59	18 05			18 14	18 20					18 29		18 35		18 45			
Dingle Road	d		17 56							18 11				18 26							18 41					
Penarth	a		18 01							18 16				18 31							18 46					
Cogan	d								18 03				18 18						18 33				18 48			
Eastbrook	d								18 05				18 20						18 35				18 51			
Dinas Powys	d								18 07				18 22						18 37				18 53			
Cadoxton	d								18 12				18 27						18 42				18 57			
Barry Docks	d								18 15				18 30						18 45				19 00			
Barry 3	d								18 19				18 34						18 49				19 05			
Barry Island	a								18 25				18 40						18 55							
Rhoose Cardiff Int Airport ✈	d																						19 12			
Llantwit Major	d																						19 22			
Bridgend	a																						19 39			

For general notes see front of timetable
For details of catering facilities see Directory of Train Operators

A To Coryton
B To Radyr
b Arr. 1742

From Monday 7 September a revised service will be in operation due to seasonal difficulties. Most trains will arrive at their destination between 1 and 3 minutes later. Passengers should check with National Rail Enquiries for precise times.

Treherbert, Aberdare, Merthyr, Pontypridd, Rhymney and Coryton → Cardiff, Penarth, Barry, Barry Island and Bridgend

Network Diagram - see first page of Table 130

		AW	AW	AW	AW	AW	AW	AW	AW	AW	AW	AW	AW	AW	AW A	AW	AW	AW	AW	AW	AW	AW	AW	AW
Treherbert	d									18 17								18 47						
Ynyswen	d									18 19								18 49						
Treorchy	d									18 21								18 51						
Ton Pentre	d									18 23								18 53						
Ystrad Rhondda	a									18 26								18 56						
	d									18 28								18 58						
Llwynypia	d									18 30								19 00						
Tonypandy	d									18 33								19 03						
Dinas Rhondda	d									18 35								19 05						
Porth	d									18 39								19 09						
Trehafod	d									18 42								19 12						
Merthyr Tydfil	d							18 08								18 38							19 08	
Pentre-bach	d							18 12								18 42							19 12	
Troed Y Rhiw	d							18 15								18 45							19 15	
Merthyr Vale	d							18 20								18 50							19 20	
Quakers Yard	d							18 25								18 55							19 25	
Aberdare 3	d			17 52								18 22								18 52				
Cwmbach	d			17 55								18 25								18 55				
Fernhill	d			17 58								18 28								18 58				
Mountain Ash	a			18 01								18 31								19 01				
	d			18 04								18 34								19 04				
Penrhiwceiber	d			18 07								18 37								19 07				
Abercynon	d			18 13				18 29				18 43				18 59				19 13			19 29	
Pontypridd 3	a			18 23				18 37		18 47		18 53				19 07		19 17		19 23			19 37	
	d			18 24				18 39		18 48		18 54				19 09		19 18		19 24			19 39	
Trefforest	d			18 27				18 42		18 51		18 57				19 12		19 21		19 27			19 42	
Trefforest Estate	d							18 46								19 16							19 46	
Taffs Well 3	d			18 34				18 50		18 58		19 04				19 20		19 28		19 34			19 50	
Radyr 3	a			18 37				18 53		19 01		19 07				19 23		19 31		19 37			19 53	
	d			18 37				18 53		19 01	19 04	19 07				19 23		19 31		19 37			19 53	
Danescourt	d										19 08													
Fairwater	d										19 10													
Waun-gron Park	d										19 12													
Ninian Park	d										19 15													
Llandaf	d	←		18 40				18 56		19 04		19 10				19 26		19 34		19 40			19 56	
Cathays	d	18 39		18 45				19 01		19 09		19 15				19 31		19 39		19 45			20 01	
Rhymney 3	d																							
Pontlottyn	d																							
Tir-phil	d																							
Brithdir	d																							
Bargoed	d				18 17									18 48										
Gilfach Fargoed	d				18 19									18 50										
Pengam	d				18 22									18 53										
Hengoed	d				18 25									18 56										
Ystrad Mynach 3	d				18 28									18 59										
Llanbradach	d				18 33									19 04										
Aber	d				18 37									19 08										
Caerphilly 3	d				18 40									19 11							19 40			
Lisvane & Thornhill	d				18 44									19 15							19 44			
Llanishen	d				18 46									19 17							19 46			
Heath High Level	d				18 49									19 20							19 49			
Coryton	d						18 45								19 15									
Whitchurch (Cardiff)	d						18 46								19 16									
Rhiwbina	d						18 48								19 18									
Birchgrove	d						18 50								19 20									
Ty Glas	d						18 51								19 21									
Heath Low Level	d						18 54								19 24									
Cardiff Queen Street 3	a	18 44		18 49	18 54		18 59	19 04		19 14		19 19		19 24	19 29	19 35		19 44		19 49	19 54		20 04	
	d	18 46	18 48	18 51	18 56	19 00	19 01	19 06	19 12	19 16		19 21	19 24	19 26	19 31	19 36	19 36	19 46	19 48	19 51	19 56	20 00	20 06	20 12
Cardiff Bay	a		18 52			19 04			19 16				19 28				19 40		19 52			20 04		20 16
Cardiff Central 7	a	18 53		18 54	18 59		19 06	19 10		19 22	19 22	19 24		19 29	19 34	19 40		19 52		19 57	19 59		20 10	
	d			18 55	19 01							19 25		19 31		19 41					20 01			
Grangetown	d			18 59	19 05							19 29		19 35		19 45					20 05			
Dingle Road	d				19 11									19 41							20 11			
Penarth	a				19 16									19 46							20 16			
Cogan	d			19 03								19 33				19 48								
Eastbrook	d			19 05								19 35				19 51								
Dinas Powys	d			19 07								19 37				19 53								
Cadoxton	d			19 12								19 42				19 57								
Barry Docks	d			19 15								19 45				20 00								
Barry 3	d			19 19								19 49				20 05								
Barry Island	a			19 25								19 55												
Rhoose Cardiff Int Airport ✈	d															20 12								
Llantwit Major	d															20 22								
Bridgend	a															20 39								

For general notes see front of timetable
For details of catering facilities see Directory of Train Operators

A To Radyr

From Monday 7 September a revised service will be in operation due to seasonal difficulties. Most trains will arrive at their destination between 1 and 3 minutes later. Passengers should check with National Rail Enquiries for precise times.

Treherbert, Aberdare, Merthyr, Pontypridd, Rhymney and Coryton → Cardiff, Penarth, Barry, Barry Island and Bridgend

Network Diagram - see first page of Table 130

		AW	AW	AW	AW	AW	AW	AW	AW	AW	AW	AW	AW	AW	AW	AW	AW	AW	AW	AW	AW	AW	AW	AW	AW
						A																A			
Treherbert	d	19 17								19 47						20 17									
Ynyswen	d	19 19								19 49						20 19									
Treorchy	d	19 21								19 51						20 21									
Ton Pentre	d	19 23								19 53						20 23									
Ystrad Rhondda	a	19 26								19 56						20 26									
	d	19 28								19 58						20 28									
Llwynypia	d	19 30								20 00						20 30									
Tonypandy	d	19 33								20 03						20 33									
Dinas Rhondda	d	19 35								20 05						20 35									
Porth	d	19 39								20 09						20 39									
Trehafod	d	19 42								20 12						20 42									
Merthyr Tydfil	d						19 38																20 38		
Pentre-bach	d						19 42																20 42		
Troed Y Rhiw	d						19 45																20 45		
Merthyr Vale	d						19 50																20 50		
Quakers Yard	d						19 55																20 55		
Aberdare 3	d											19 52						20 22							
Cwmbach	d											19 55						20 25							
Fernhill	d											19 58						20 28							
Mountain Ash	a											20 01						20 31							
	d											20 04						20 34							
Penrhiwceiber	d											20 07						20 37							
Abercynon	d			19 43			19 59					20 13						20 43					20 59		
Pontypridd 3	a	19 47		19 53			20 07			20 17		20 23				20 47		20 53					21 07		
	d	19 48		19 54			20 09			20 18		20 24				20 48		20 54					21 09		
Trefforest	d	19 51		19 57			20 12			20 21		20 27				20 51		20 57					21 12		
Trefforest Estate	d						20 16																21 16		
Taffs Well 3	d	19 58		20 04			20 20			20 28		20 34				20 58		21 04					21 20		
Radyr 3	a	20 01		20 07			20 23			20 31		20 37				21 01		21 07					21 23		
	d	20 01	20 04	20 07			20 23			20 31		20 37				21 01	21 04	21 07					21 23		
Danescourt	d		20 08														21 08		←						
Fairwater	d		20 10														21 10		21 10						
Waun-gron Park	d		20 12														→		21 12						
Ninian Park	d		20 15																21 15						
Llandaf	d	20 04		20 10			20 26			20 34		20 40				21 04		21 10					21 26		
Cathays	d	20 09		20 15			20 31			20 39		20 45				21 09		21 15					21 31		
Rhymney 3	d								19 45																20 48
Pontlottyn	d								19 48																20 51
Tir-phil	d								19 52																20 55
Brithdir	d								19 55																20 58
Bargoed	d								19 59																21 02
Gilfach Fargoed	d								20 01																21 04
Pengam	d								20 04																21 07
Hengoed	d								20 07																21 10
Ystrad Mynach 3	d								20 10																21 13
Llanbradach	d								20 15																21 18
Aber	d								20 19																21 22
Caerphilly 3	d								20 22				20 40												21 25
Lisvane & Thornhill	d								20 26				20 44												21 29
Llanishen	d								20 28				20 46												21 31
Heath High Level	d								20 31				20 49												21 34
Coryton	d					20 15																21 15			
Whitchurch (Cardiff)	d					20 16																21 16			
Rhiwbina	d					20 18																21 18			
Birchgrove	d					20 20																21 20			
Ty Glas	d					20 21																21 21			
Heath Low Level	d					20 24																21 24			
Cardiff Queen Street 3	a	20 14		20 19		20 29	20 34		20 39	20 44		20 49	20 54			21 14		21 19				21 29	21 34		21 42
	d	20 16		20 21	20 24	20 31	20 36	20 36	20 41	20 46	20 48	20 51	20 56	21 00	21 12	21 16		21 21		21 24		21 31	21 36	21 36	21 44
Cardiff Bay	a				20 28			20 40			20 52			21 04	21 16					21 28				21 40	
Cardiff Central 7	a	20 19	20 22	20 24		20 34	20 39		20 47	20 52		20 57	20 59			21 21		21 24	21 25			21 34	21 39		21 47
	d	20 20		20 31			20 41						21 01					21 25			21 31		21 41		
Grangetown	d	20 24		20 35			20 45						21 05					21 29			21 35		21 45		
Dingle Road	d			20 41									21 11								21 41				
Penarth	a			20 46									21 16								21 46				
Cogan	d	20 28					20 48											21 33					21 48		
Eastbrook	d	20 30					20 51											21 35					21 51		
Dinas Powys	d	20 32					20 53											21 37					21 53		
Cadoxton	d	20 37					20 57											21 42					21 57		
Barry Docks	d	20 40					21 00											21 45					22 00		
Barry 3	d	20 44					21 05											21 49					22 05		
Barry Island	a	20 50																21 55							
Rhoose Cardiff Int Airport ✈	d						21 12																22 12		
Llantwit Major	d						21 22																22 22		
Bridgend	a						21 39																22 39		

For general notes see front of timetable
For details of catering facilities see
Directory of Train Operators

A To Radyr

From Monday 7 September a revised service will be in operation due to seasonal difficulties. Most trains will arrive at their destination between 1 and 3 minutes later. Passengers should check with National Rail Enquiries for precise times.

Table 130

Mondays to Fridays

Treherbert, Aberdare, Merthyr, Pontypridd, Rhymney and Coryton → Cardiff, Penarth, Barry, Barry Island and Bridgend

Network Diagram - see first page of Table 130

		AW	AW	AW	AW	AW	AW	AW	AW	AW	AW	AW	AW	AW	AW	AW	AW	AW	AW		AW	AW	AW	AW		
								A																		
Treherbert	d						21 17																			
Ynyswen	d						21 19																			
Treorchy	d						21 21																			
Ton Pentre	d						21 23																			
Ystrad Rhondda	a						21 26																			
	d						21 28																			
Llwynypia	d						21 30																			
Tonypandy	d						21 33																			
Dinas Rhondda	d						21 35																			
Porth	d						21 39																			
Trehafod	d						21 42																			
Merthyr Tydfil	d										21 38										22 38					
Pentre-bach	d										21 42										22 42					
Troed Y Rhiw	d										21 45										22 45					
Merthyr Vale	d										21 50										22 50					
Quakers Yard	d										21 55										22 55					
Aberdare 3	d		20 52											21 52										22 52		
Cwmbach	d		20 55											21 55										22 55		
Fernhill	d		20 58											21 58										22 58		
Mountain Ash	a		21 01											22 01										23 01		
	d		21 04											22 04										23 04		
Penrhiwceiber	d		21 07											22 07										23 07		
Abercynon	d		21 13								21 59			22 14							22 59			23 13		
Pontypridd 3	a		21 23				21 47				22 07			22 24							23 07			23 23		
	d		21 24				21 48				22 09			22 29							23 09			23 29		
Trefforest	d		21 27				21 51				22 12			22 32							23 12			23 32		
Trefforest Estate	d										22 16															
Taffs Well 3	d		21 34				21 58				22 20			22 39							23 20			23 38		
Radyr 3	a		21 37				22 01				22 23			22 42							23 23			23 42		
	d		21 37				22 01	22 04			22 23			22 42				23 10			23 23			23 42		
Danescourt	d							22 08																		
Fairwater	d							22 10																		
Waun-gron Park	d							22 12																		
Ninian Park	d							22 15																		
Llandaf	d		21 40				22 04				22 26			22 45				23 12			23 26			23 45		
Cathays	d		21 45				22 09				22 31			22 50				23 16			23 31			23 49		
Rhymney 3	d									21 33																
Pontlottyn	d									21 36																
Tir-phil	d									21 40																
Brithdir	d									21 43																
Bargoed	d									21 47																
Gilfach Fargoed	d									21 49																
Pengam	d									21 52																
Hengoed	d									21 55																
Ystrad Mynach 3	d									21 58																
Llanbradach	d									22 03																
Aber	d									22 07																
Caerphilly 3	d			21 40						22 10																
Lisvane & Thornhill	d			21 45						22 14																
Llanishen	d			21 47						22 16																
Heath High Level	d			21 49						22 19																
Coryton	d															22 45										
Whitchurch (Cardiff)	d															22 46										
Rhiwbina	d															22 48										
Birchgrove	d															22 50										
Ty Glas	d															22 51										
Heath Low Level	d															22 54										
Cardiff Queen Street 3	a		21 49	21 54			22 14			22 24	22 34			22 54		22 59		23 19			23 34			23 53		
	d	21 48	21 51	21 56	22 00	22 12	22 16		22 24	22 26	22 36	22 36	22 48	22 55	23 00	23 01	23 12	23 20	23 24		23 36	23 36	23 48	23 56		
Cardiff Bay	a	21 52			22 04	22 16			22 28			22 40	22 52		23 04		23 16		23 28			23 40	23 52			
Cardiff Central 7	a		21 57	21 59			22 22	22 20		22 29	22 39			23 01		23 06		23 25			23 42			00 02		
	d			22 01			22 25			22 31	22 41			23 12				23 30								
Grangetown	d			22 05			22 29			22 35	22 45			23 16				23 34								
Dingle Road	d			22 11						22 41				23 20												
Penarth	a			22 16						22 46				23 25												
Cogan	d						22 33				22 48							23 37								
Eastbrook	d						22 35				22 51							23 40								
Dinas Powys	d						22 37				22 53							23 42								
Cadoxton	d						22 42				22 57							23 46								
Barry Docks	d						22 45				23 00							23 49								
Barry 3	d						22 49				23 05							23 54								
Barry Island	a						22 55											23 59								
Rhoose Cardiff Int Airport ✈	d										23 12															
Llantwit Major	d										23 22															
Bridgend	a										23 39															

For general notes see front of timetable
For details of catering facilities see Directory of Train Operators

A To Coryton

From Monday 7 September a revised service will be in operation due to seasonal difficulties. Most trains will arrive at their destination between 1 and 3 minutes later. Passengers should check with National Rail Enquiries for precise times.

Treherbert, Aberdare, Merthyr, Pontypridd, Rhymney and Coryton → Cardiff, Penarth, Barry, Barry Island and Bridgend

Network Diagram - see first page of Table 130

		AW	AW	AW	AW	AW	AW	AW	AW	AW	AW	AW	AW	AW	AW	AW	AW		AW	AW	AW	AW	AW	AW	AW	AW
													A	B	C					B			B			
Treherbert	d										05 47											06 17				
Ynyswen	d										05 49											06 19				
Treorchy	d										05 51											06 21				
Ton Pentre	d										05 53											06 23				
Ystrad Rhondda	a										05 56											06 26				
	d										05 58											06 28				
Llwynypia	d										06 00											06 30				
Tonypandy	d										06 03											06 33				
Dinas Rhondda	d										06 05											06 35				
Porth	d										06 09											06 39				
Trehafod	d										06 12											06 42				
Merthyr Tydfil	d																									
Pentre-bach	d																									
Troed Y Rhiw	d																									
Merthyr Vale	d																									
Quakers Yard	d																									
Aberdare 3	d																							06 22		
Cwmbach	d																							06 25		
Fernhill	d																							06 28		
Mountain Ash	a																							06 31		
	d																							06 34		
Penrhiwceiber	d																							06 37		
Abercynon	d																							06 43		
Pontypridd 3	a										06 17											06 47		06 53		
	d				05 24						06 18											06 48		06 54		
Trefforest	d				05 27						06 21											06 51		06 57		
Trefforest Estate	d				05 31						06 25													07 01		
Taffs Well 3	d				05 34						06 28									06 53		06 58		07 04		
Radyr 3	a				05 37						06 31									06 56		07 01	←	07 07		
	d				05 37						06 31									07 04		07 01	07 04	07 07		
Danescourt	d																			→			07 08			
Fairwater	d																						07 10			
Waun-gron Park	d																						07 12			
Ninian Park	d																						07 15			
Llandaf	d				05 40						06 34											07 04		07 10		
Cathays	d				05 45						06 39											07 09		07 15		
Rhymney 3	d																		06 14							06 37
Pontlottyn	d																		06 17							06 40
Tir-phil	d																		06 21							06 44
Brithdir	d																		06 24							06 47
Bargoed	d																		06b32							06 51
Gilfach Fargoed	d																		06 34							
Pengam	d																		06 37							06 55
Hengoed	d																		06 40							06 59
Ystrad Mynach 3	d																		06 43							07 01
Llanbradach	d																		06 48							07 06
Aber	d																		06 52							07 10
Caerphilly 3	d								06 10										06 55							07 13
Lisvane & Thornhill	d								06 14										06 59							07 17
Llanishen	d								06 16										07 01							07 19
Heath High Level	d								06 19										07 04							07 22
Coryton	d														06 45											
Whitchurch (Cardiff)	d														06 46											
Rhiwbina	d														06 48											
Birchgrove	d														06 50											
Ty Glas	d														06 51											
Heath Low Level	d														06 54											
Cardiff Queen Street 3	a				05 48				06 25		06 44				06 59				07 09			07 14		07 19		07 27
	d				05 51				06 26	06 36	06 44	06 48			07 00	07 00			07 11		07 12	07 16		07 21	07 24	07 28
Cardiff Bay	a									06 40		06 52				07 04					07 16				07 28	
Cardiff Central 7	a				05 54				06 29		06 48				07 04				07 14			07 18	07 20	07 24		07 31
	d	05 20	05 41	05 46	05 55	06 16	06 25	06 36	06 41				06 55	07 01			07 10		07 16					07 25		07 31
Grangetown	d	05 24	05 45	05 50	05 59	06 20	06 29	06 40	06 45				06 59	07 05			07 14		07 20					07 29		07 35
Dingle Road	d			05 54		06 24		06 44						07 11					07 26							07 41
Penarth	a			05 59		06 28		06 49						07 16					07 31							07 46
Cogan	d	05 28	05 48		06 03		06 33		06 48				07 03				07 18							07 33		
Eastbrook	d	05 30	05 51		06 05		06 35		06 51				07 05				07 20							07 35		
Dinas Powys	d	05 32	05 53		06 07		06 37		06 53				07 07				07 22							07 37		
Cadoxton	d	05 37	05 57		06 12		06 42		06 57				07 12				07 27							07 42		
Barry Docks	d	05 40	06 00		06 15		06 45		07 00				07 15				07 30							07 45		
Barry 3	d	05 44	06 05		06 19		06 49		07 05				07 19				07 34							07 49		
Barry Island	a	05 50			06 25		06 55						07 25				07 40							07 55		
Rhoose Cardiff Int Airport ✈	d		06 12						07 12																	
Llantwit Major	d		06 22						07 22																	
Bridgend	a		06 39						07 39																	

For general notes see front of timetable
For details of catering facilities see Directory of Train Operators

A From Hereford (Table 131)
B To Coryton
C To Radyr

b Arr. 0627

From Saturday 12 September a revised service will be in operation due to seasonal difficulties. Most trains will arrive at their destination between 1 and 3 minutes later. Passengers should check with National Rail Enquiries for precise times.

Table 130

Saturdays

Treherbert, Aberdare, Merthyr, Pontypridd, Rhymney and Coryton → Cardiff, Penarth, Barry, Barry Island and Bridgend

Network Diagram - see first page of Table 130

		AW A	AW	AW	AW	AW	AW B	AW	AW	AW	AW	AW	AW A	AW	AW	AW	AW	AW B	AW	AW	AW	AW	AW A	AW	AW
Treherbert	d					06 47											07 17								
Ynyswen	d					06 49											07 19								
Treorchy	d					06 51											07 21								
Ton Pentre	d					06 53											07 23								
Ystrad Rhondda	a					06 56											07 26								
	d					06 58											07 28								
Llwynypia	d					07 00											07 30								
Tonypandy	d					07 03											07 33								
Dinas Rhondda	d					07 05											07 35								
Porth	d					07 09											07 39								
Trehafod	d					07 12											07 42								
Merthyr Tydfil	d		06 38											07 08										07 38	
Pentre-bach	d		06 42											07 12										07 42	
Troed Y Rhiw	d		06 45											07 15										07 45	
Merthyr Vale	d		06 50											07 20										07 50	
Quakers Yard	d		06 55											07 25										07 55	
Aberdare [3]	d									06 52										07 22					
Cwmbach	d									06 55										07 25					
Fernhill	d									06 58										07 28					
Mountain Ash	a									07 01										07 31					
	d									07 04										07 34					
Penrhiwceiber	d									07 07										07 37					
Abercynon	d		06 59							07 13				07 29						07 43				07 59	
Pontypridd [3]	a		07 07			07 17				07 23				07 37			07 47			07 53				08 07	
	d		07 09			07 18				07 24				07 39			07 48			07 54				08 09	
Trefforest	d		07 12			07 21				07 27				07 42			07 51			07 57				08 12	
Trefforest Estate	d		07 16											07 46										08 16	
Taffs Well [3]	d		07 20			07 28				07 34				07 50			07 58			08 04				08 20	
Radyr [3]	a		07 23			07 31				07 37				07 53			08 01			08 07				08 23	
	d		07 23			07 31	07 34			07 37				07 53			08 01	08 04		08 07				08 23	
Danescourt	d						07 38											08 08							
Fairwater	d						07 40											08 10							
Waun-gron Park	d						07 42											08 12							
Ninian Park	d						07 45											08 15							
Llandaf	d		07 26			07 34		←		07 40				07 56			08 04		←	08 10				08 26	
Cathays	d		07 31			07 39		07 39		07 45				08 01			08 09		08 09	08 15				08 31	
Rhymney [3]	d					→					07 02						→					07 24			
Pontlottyn	d										07 05											07 27			
Tir-phil	d										07 09											07 31			
Brithdir	d										07 12											07 34			
Bargoed	d				07 02						07 17				07 32							07b45			
Gilfach Fargoed	d				07 04						07 19											07 47			
Pengam	d				07 07						07 22				07 37							07 50			
Hengoed	d				07 10						07 25				07 40							07 54			
Ystrad Mynach [3]	d				07 13						07 28				07 43							07 57			
Llanbradach	d				07 18						07 33				07 48							08 02			
Aber	d				07 22						07 37				07 52							08 07			
Caerphilly [3]	d				07 25						07 40				07 55							08 10			
Lisvane & Thornhill	d				07 29						07 44				07 59							08 14			
Llanishen	d				07 31						07 46				08 01							08 16			
Heath High Level	d				07 34						07 49				08 04							08 19			
Coryton	d	07 15											07 45										08 15		
Whitchurch (Cardiff)	d	07 16											07 46										08 16		
Rhiwbina	d	07 18											07 48										08 18		
Birchgrove	d	07 20											07 50										08 20		
Ty Glas	d	07 21											07 51										08 21		
Heath Low Level	d	07 24											07 54										08 24		
Cardiff Queen Street [3]	a	07 29	07 35		07 39			07 44		07 49	07 54		07 59	08 04	08 09				08 14	08 19		08 24	08 29	08 34	
	d	07 31	07 36	07 36	07 41			07 46	07 48	07 51	07 56	08 00	08 01	08 06	08 11	08 12			08 16	08 21	08 24	08 26	08 31	08 36	08 36
Cardiff Bay	a			07 40					07 52			08 04				08 16					08 28				08 40
Cardiff Central [7]	a	07 34	07 39		07 44		07 50	07 52		07 54	07 59		08 04	08 09	08 14			08 20	08 22	08 24		08 29	08 34	08 39	
	d		07 41		07 46					07 55	08 01			08 10	08 16					08 25		08 31		08 41	
Grangetown	d		07 45		07 50					07 59	08 05			08 14	08 20					08 29		08 35		08 45	
Dingle Road	d				07 56						08 11				08 26							08 41			
Penarth	a				08 01						08 16				08 31							08 46			
Cogan	d		07 48							08 03				08 18						08 33				08 48	
Eastbrook	d		07 51							08 05				08 20						08 35				08 51	
Dinas Powys	d		07 53							08 07				08 22						08 37				08 53	
Cadoxton	d		07 57							08 12				08 27						08 42				08 57	
Barry Docks	d		08 00							08 15				08 30						08 45				09 00	
Barry [3]	d		08 05							08 19				08 34						08 49				09 05	
Barry Island	a									08 25				08 40						08 55					
Rhoose Cardiff Int Airport ✈	d		08 12																					09 12	
Llantwit Major	d		08 22																					09 22	
Bridgend	a		08 39																					09 39	

For general notes see front of timetable
For details of catering facilities see Directory of Train Operators

A To Radyr
B To Coryton
b Arr. 0737

From Saturday 12 September a revised service will be in operation due to seasonal difficulties. Most trains will arrive at their destination between 1 and 3 minutes later. Passengers should check with National Rail Enquiries for precise times.

Treherbert, Aberdare, Merthyr, Pontypridd, Rhymney and Coryton → Cardiff, Penarth, Barry, Barry Island and Bridgend

Network Diagram - see first page of Table 130

Station		AW	AW	AW	AW		AW	AW	AW	AW	AW	AW	AW	AW	AW	AW	AW	AW	AW	AW	AW	AW		AW	AW	AW
				A							B					A					B					
Treherbert	d		07 45												08 17											08 47
Ynyswen	d		07 47												08 19											08 49
Treorchy	d		07 49												08 21											08 51
Ton Pentre	d		07 51												08 23											08 53
Ystrad Rhondda	a		07 54												08 26											08 56
	d		07 58												08 28											08 58
Llwynypia	d		08 00												08 30											09 00
Tonypandy	d		08 03												08 33											09 03
Dinas Rhondda	d		08 05												08 35											09 05
Porth	d		08 09												08 39											09 09
Trehafod	d		08 12												08 42											09 12
Merthyr Tydfil	d											08 08										08 38				
Pentre-bach	d											08 12										08 42				
Troed Y Rhiw	d											08 15										08 45				
Merthyr Vale	d											08 20										08 50				
Quakers Yard	d											08 25										08 55				
Aberdare 3	d							07 52										08 22								
Cwmbach	d							07 55										08 25								
Fernhill	d							07 58										08 28								
Mountain Ash	a							08 01										08 31								
	d							08 04										08 34								
Penrhiwceiber	d							08 07										08 37								
Abercynon	d							08 13				08 29						08 43				08 59				
Pontypridd 3	a		08 17					08 23				08 37			08 47			08 53				09 07				09 17
	d		08 18					08 24				08 39			08 48			08 54				09 09				09 18
Trefforest	d		08 21					08 27				08 42			08 51			08 57				09 12				09 21
Trefforest Estate	d											08 46										09 16				
Taffs Well 3	d		08 28					08 34				08 50			08 58			09 04				09 20				09 28
Radyr 3	a		08 31					08 37				08 53			09 01			09 07				09 23				09 31
	d		08 31	08 34				08 37				08 53			09 01	09 04		09 07				09 23				09 31
Danescourt	d			08 38												09 08										
Fairwater	d			08 40												09 10										
Waun-gron Park	d			08 42												09 12										
Ninian Park	d			08 45												09 15										
Llandaf	d		08 34		←			08 40				08 56			09 04		←	09 10				09 26				09 34
Cathays	d		08 39		08 39			08 45				09 01			09 09		09 09	09 15				09 31				09 39
Rhymney 3	d	07 44	→												→					08 30						→
Pontlottyn	d	07 47																		08 33						
Tir-phil	d	07 51																		08 37						
Brithdir	d	07 54																		08 40						
Bargoed	d	08 02							08 17				08 32							08 47					09 02	
Gilfach Fargoed	d								08 19																	
Pengam	d	08 07							08 22				08 37							08 52					09 07	
Hengoed	d	08 10							08 25				08 40							08 55					09 10	
Ystrad Mynach 3	d	08 13							08 28				08 43							08 58					09 13	
Llanbradach	d	08 18							08 33				08 48							09 03					09 18	
Aber	d	08 22							08 37				08 52							09 07					09 22	
Caerphilly 3	d	08 25							08 40				08 55							09 10					09 25	
Lisvane & Thornhill	d	08 29							08 44				08 59							09 14					09 29	
Llanishen	d	08 31							08 46				09 01							09 16					09 31	
Heath High Level	d	08 34							08 49				09 04							09 19					09 34	
Coryton	d										08 45										09 15					
Whitchurch (Cardiff)	d										08 46										09 16					
Rhiwbina	d										08 48										09 18					
Birchgrove	d										08 50										09 20					
Ty Glas	d										08 51										09 21					
Heath Low Level	d										08 54										09 24					
Cardiff Queen Street 3	a	08 39			08 44			08 49	08 54		08 59	09 04	09 09				09 14	09 19		09 24	09 29	09 34			09 39	
	d	08 41			08 46		08 48	08 51	08 56	09 00	09 01	09 06	09 11	09 12			09 16	09 21	09 24	09 26	09 31	09 36		09 36	09 41	
Cardiff Bay	a						08 52			09 04				09 16					09 28					09 40		
Cardiff Central 7	a	08 47		08 50	08 52			08 54	08 59		09 04	09 09	09 14			09 20	09 22	09 24		09 29	09 34	09 39			09 44	
	d							08 55	09 01			09 10	09 16					09 25		09 31		09 41			09 46	
Grangetown	d							08 59	09 05			09 14	09 20					09 29		09 35		09 45			09 50	
Dingle Road	d								09 11				09 26							09 41					09 56	
Penarth	a								09 16				09 31							09 46					10 01	
Cogan	d							09 03				09 18						09 33				09 48				
Eastbrook	d							09 05				09 20						09 35				09 51				
Dinas Powys	d							09 07				09 22						09 37				09 53				
Cadoxton	d							09 12				09 27						09 42				09 57				
Barry Docks	d							09 15				09 30						09 45				10 00				
Barry 3	d							09 19				09 34						09 49				10 05				
Barry Island	a							09 25				09 40						09 55								
Rhoose Cardiff Int Airport ✈	d																					10 12				
Llantwit Major	d																					10 22				
Bridgend	a																					10 39				

For general notes see front of timetable
For details of catering facilities see Directory of Train Operators

A To Coryton
B To Radyr

From Saturday 12 September a revised service will be in operation due to seasonal difficulties. Most trains will arrive at their destination between 1 and 3 minutes later. Passengers should check with National Rail Enquiries for precise times.

Table 130

Saturdays

Treherbert, Aberdare, Merthyr, Pontypridd, Rhymney and Coryton → Cardiff, Penarth, Barry, Barry Island and Bridgend

Network Diagram - see first page of Table 130

		AW A	AW	AW	AW	AW	AW	AW B	AW	AW	AW	AW	AW A	AW	AW	AW		AW	AW B	AW	AW	AW	AW	AW A	AW	AW
Treherbert	d											09 17											09 47			
Ynyswen	d											09 19											09 49			
Treorchy	d											09 21											09 51			
Ton Pentre	d											09 23											09 53			
Ystrad Rhondda	a											09 26											09 56			
	d											09 28											09 58			
Llwynypia	d											09 30											10 00			
Tonypandy	d											09 33											10 03			
Dinas Rhondda	d											09 35											10 05			
Porth	d											09 39											10 09			
Trehafod	d											09 42											10 12			
Merthyr Tydfil	d								09 08											09 38						
Pentre-bach	d								09 12											09 42						
Troed Y Rhiw	d								09 15											09 45						
Merthyr Vale	d								09 20											09 50						
Quakers Yard	d								09 25											09 55						
Aberdare 3	d				08 52										09 22											
Cwmbach	d				08 55										09 25											
Fernhill	d				08 58										09 28											
Mountain Ash	a				09 01										09 31											
	d				09 04										09 34											
Penrhiwceiber	d				09 07										09 37											
Abercynon	d				09 13				09 29						09 43					09 59						
Pontypridd 3	a				09 23				09 37			09 47			09 53					10 07			10 17			
	d				09 24				09 39			09 48			09 54					10 09			10 18			
Trefforest	d				09 27				09 42			09 51			09 57					10 12			10 21			
Trefforest Estate	d								09 46											10 16						
Taffs Well 3	d				09 34				09 50			09 58			10 04					10 20			10 28			
Radyr 3	a				09 37				09 53			10 01			10 07					10 23			10 31			
	d	09 34			09 37				09 53			10 01	10 04		10 07					10 23			10 31	10 34		
Danescourt	d	09 38											10 08											10 38		
Fairwater	d	09 40											10 10											10 40		
Waun-gron Park	d	09 42											10 12											10 42		
Ninian Park	d	09 45											10 15											10 45		
Llandaf	d		←		09 40				09 56			10 04		←	10 10					10 26			10 34		←	
Cathays	d		09 39		09 45				10 01			10 09		10 09	10 15					10 31			10 39		10 39	
Rhymney 3	d											→						09 29					→			
Pontlottyn	d																	09 32								
Tir-phil	d																	09 36								
Brithdir	d																	09 39								
Bargoed	d					09 17				09 32								09b47				10 02				
Gilfach Fargoed	d					09 19																				
Pengam	d					09 22				09 37								09 52				10 07				
Hengoed	d					09 25				09 40								09 55				10 10				
Ystrad Mynach 3	d					09 28				09 43								09 58				10 13				
Llanbradach	d					09 33				09 48								10 03				10 18				
Aber	d					09 37				09 52								10 07				10 22				
Caerphilly 3	d					09 40				09 55								10 10				10 25				
Lisvane & Thornhill	d					09 44				09 59								10 14				10 29				
Llanishen	d					09 46				10 01								10 16				10 31				
Heath High Level	d					09 49				10 04								10 19				10 34				
Coryton	d							09 45											10 15							
Whitchurch (Cardiff)	d							09 46											10 16							
Rhiwbina	d							09 48											10 18							
Birchgrove	d							09 50											10 20							
Ty Glas	d							09 51											10 21							
Heath Low Level	d							09 54											10 24							
Cardiff Queen Street 3	a		09 44		09 49	09 54		09 59	10 04	10 09				10 14	10 19			10 24	10 29	10 34		10 39			10 44	
	d		09 46	09 48	09 51	09 56	10 00	10 01	10 06	10 11	10 12			10 16	10 21	10 24		10 26	10 31	10 36	10 36	10 41			10 46	10 48
Cardiff Bay	a			09 52			10 04				10 16					10 28					10 40					10 52
Cardiff Central 7	a	09 50	09 52		09 54	09 59		10 04	10 09	10 14			10 20	10 22	10 24			10 29	10 34	10 39		10 44		10 50	10 52	
	d				09 55	10 01			10 10	10 16					10 25			10 31		10 41		10 46				
Grangetown	d				09 59	10 05			10 14	10 20					10 29			10 35		10 45		10 50				
Dingle Road	d					10 11				10 26								10 41				10 56				
Penarth	a					10 16				10 31								10 46				11 01				
Cogan	d				10 03				10 18						10 33					10 48						
Eastbrook	d				10 05				10 20						10 35					10 51						
Dinas Powys	d				10 07				10 22						10 37					10 53						
Cadoxton	d				10 12				10 27						10 42					10 57						
Barry Docks	d				10 15				10 30						10 45					11 00						
Barry 3	d				10 19				10 34						10 49					11 05						
Barry Island	a				10 25				10 40						10 55											
Rhoose Cardiff Int Airport	d																			11 12						
Llantwit Major	d																			11 22						
Bridgend	a																			11 39						

For general notes see front of timetable
For details of catering facilities see Directory of Train Operators

A To Coryton
B To Radyr
b Arr. 0942

From Saturday 12 September a revised service will be in operation due to seasonal difficulties. Most trains will arrive at their destination between 1 and 3 minutes later. Passengers should check with National Rail Enquiries for precise times.

Table 130

Saturdays

Treherbert, Aberdare, Merthyr, Pontypridd, Rhymney and Coryton → Cardiff, Penarth, Barry, Barry Island and Bridgend

Network Diagram - see first page of Table 130

Station		AW	AW	AW	AW A	AW	AW	AW	AW	AW B	AW	AW	AW	AW	AW A	AW	AW	AW	AW	AW B	AW	AW	AW	AW	AW
Treherbert	d													10 17					10 47						
Ynyswen	d													10 19					10 49						
Treorchy	d													10 21					10 51						
Ton Pentre	d													10 23					10 53						
Ystrad Rhondda	a													10 26					10 56						
	d													10 28					10 58						
Llwynypia	d													10 30					11 00						
Tonypandy	d													10 33					11 03						
Dinas Rhondda	d													10 35					11 05						
Porth	d													10b52					11 09						
Trehafod	d													10 55					11 12						
Merthyr Tydfil	d					10 04										10 38									
Pentre-bach	d					10 08										10 42									
Troed Y Rhiw	d					10 11										10 45									
Merthyr Vale	d					10 16										10 50									
Quakers Yard	d					10 22										10 55									
Aberdare 3	d	09 52									10 22												10 52		
Cwmbach	d	09 55									10 25												10 55		
Fernhill	d	09 58									10 28												10 58		
Mountain Ash	a	10 01									10 31												11 01		
	d	10 04									10 34												11 04		
Penrhiwceiber	d	10 07									10 37												11 07		
Abercynon	d	10 13				10 26					10 43					10 59							11 13		
Pontypridd 3	a	10 23				10 32					10 53			11 00		11 08			11 17				11 23		
	d	10 24					10 39				10 54			11 04		11 09			11 18				11 24		
Trefforest	d	10 27					10 42				10 57			11 07		11 12			11 21				11 27		
Trefforest Estate	d						10 46									11 16									
Taffs Well 3	d	10 34					10 50				11 04			11 13		11 20			11 28				11 34		
Radyr 3	a	10 37					10 53				11 07			11 17		11 23			11 31				11 37		
	d	10 37					10 53			11 04	11 07			11 17		11 23			11 31	11 34			11 37		
Danescourt	d									11 08										11 38					
Fairwater	d									11 10										11 40					
Waun-gron Park	d									11 12										11 42					
Ninian Park	d									11 15										11 45					
Llandaf	d	10 40					10 56				11 10					11 26			11 34		←		11 40		
Cathays	d	10 45					11 01				11 15					11 31			11 39		11 39		11 45		
Rhymney 3	d												10 29						→						
Pontlottyn	d												10 32												
Tir-phil	d												10 36												
Brithdir	d												10 39												
Bargoed	d		10 17					10 32					10c47					11 02						11 17	
Gilfach Fargoed	d		10 19																					11 19	
Pengam	d		10 22					10 37					10 52					11 07						11 22	
Hengoed	d		10 25					10 40					10 55					11 10						11 25	
Ystrad Mynach 3	d		10 28					10 43					10 58					11 13						11 28	
Llanbradach	d		10 33					10 48					11 03					11 18						11 33	
Aber	d		10 37					10 52					11 07					11 22						11 37	
Caerphilly 3	d		10 40					10 55					11 10					11 25						11 40	
Lisvane & Thornhill	d		10 44					10 59					11 14					11 29						11 44	
Llanishen	d		10 46					11 01					11 16					11 31						11 46	
Heath High Level	d		10 49					11 04					11 19					11 34						11 49	
Coryton	d				10 45										11 15										
Whitchurch (Cardiff)	d				10 46										11 16										
Rhiwbina	d				10 48										11 18										
Birchgrove	d				10 50										11 20										
Ty Glas	d				10 51										11 21										
Heath Low Level	d				10 54										11 24										
Cardiff Queen Street 3	a	10 49	10 54		10 59		11 04	11 09			11 19		11 24		11 29	11 34		11 39			11 44		11 49	11 54	
	d	10 51	10 56	11 00	11 01		11 06	11 11	11 12		11 21	11 24	11 26		11 31	11 36	11 36	11 41			11 46	11 48	11 51	11 56	12 00
Cardiff Bay	a			11 04					11 16			11 28					11 40					11 52			12 04
Cardiff Central 7	a	10 54	10 59		11 04		11 09	11 14		11 20	11 24		11 29	11 34	11 34	11 39		11 44		11 50	11 52		11 54	11 59	
	d	10 55	11 01				11 10	11 16			11 25		11 31			11 41		11 46					11 55	12 01	
Grangetown	d	10 59	11 05				11 14	11 20			11 29		11 35			11 45		11 50					11 59	12 05	
Dingle Road	d		11 11					11 26					11 41					11 56						12 11	
Penarth	a		11 16					11 31					11 46					12 01						12 16	
Cogan	d	11 03					11 18				11 33					11 48							12 03		
Eastbrook	d	11 05					11 20				11 35					11 51							12 05		
Dinas Powys	d	11 07					11 22				11 37					11 53							12 07		
Cadoxton	d	11 12					11 27				11 42					11 57							12 12		
Barry Docks	d	11 15					11 30				11 45					12 00							12 15		
Barry 3	d	11 19					11 34				11 49					12 05							12 19		
Barry Island	a	11 25					11 40				11 55												12 25		
Rhoose Cardiff Int Airport ✈	d															12 12									
Llantwit Major	d															12 22									
Bridgend	a															12 39									

For general notes see front of timetable
For details of catering facilities see Directory of Train Operators

A To Radyr
B To Coryton
b Arr. 1038
c Arr. 1042

From Saturday 12 September a revised service will be in operation due to seasonal difficulties. Most trains will arrive at their destination between 1 and 3 minutes later. Passengers should check with National Rail Enquiries for precise times.

Table 130

Saturdays

Treherbert, Aberdare, Merthyr, Pontypridd, Rhymney and Coryton → Cardiff, Penarth, Barry, Barry Island and Bridgend

Network Diagram - see first page of Table 130

		AW A	AW	AW		AW	AW	AW B	AW	AW	AW	AW	AW A	AW	AW	AW	AW	AW B	AW	AW	AW		AW	AW A	AW	AW
Treherbert	d						11 17										11 47									
Ynyswen	d						11 19										11 49									
Treorchy	d						11 21										11 51									
Ton Pentre	d						11 23										11 53									
Ystrad Rhondda	a						11 26										11 56									
	d						11 28										11 58									
Llwynypia	d						11 30										12 00									
Tonypandy	d						11 33										12 03									
Dinas Rhondda	d						11 35										12 05									
Porth	d						11 39										12 09									
Trehafod	d						11 42										12 12									
Merthyr Tydfil	d		11 08											11 38											12 08	
Pentre-bach	d		11 12											11 42											12 12	
Troed Y Rhiw	d		11 15											11 45											12 15	
Merthyr Vale	d		11 20											11 50											12 20	
Quakers Yard	d		11 25											11 55											12 25	
Aberdare 3	d									11 22																
Cwmbach	d									11 25																
Fernhill	d									11 28																
Mountain Ash	a									11 31																
	d									11 34																
Penrhiwceiber	d									11 37																
Abercynon	d		11 29							11 43				11 59											12 29	
Pontypridd 3	a		11 37				11 47			11 53				12 07			12 17								12 37	
	d		11 39				11 48			11 54				12 09			12 18								12 39	
Trefforest	d		11 42				11 51			11 57				12 12			12 21								12 42	
Trefforest Estate	d		11 46											12 16											12 46	
Taffs Well 3	d		11 50				11 58			12 04				12 20			12 28								12 50	
Radyr 3	a		11 53				12 01			12 07				12 23			12 31								12 53	
	d		11 53				12 01	12 04		12 07				12 23			12 31	12 34							12 53	
Danescourt	d							12 08										12 38								
Fairwater	d							12 10										12 40								
Waun-gron Park	d							12 12										12 42								
Ninian Park	d							12 15										12 45								
Llandaf	d		11 56				12 04		←	12 10				12 26			12 34		←						12 56	
Cathays	d		12 01				12 09		12 09	12 15				12 31			12 39		12 39						13 01	
Rhymney 3	d						→					11 29					→									
Pontlottyn	d											11 32														
Tir-phil	d											11 36														
Brithdir	d											11 39														
Bargoed	d			11 32								11b47				12 02					12 17					12 32
Gilfach Fargoed	d																				12 19					
Pengam	d			11 37								11 52				12 07					12 22					12 37
Hengoed	d			11 40								11 55				12 10					12 25					12 40
Ystrad Mynach 3	d			11 43								11 58				12 13					12 28					12 43
Llanbradach	d			11 48								12 03				12 18					12 33					12 48
Aber	d			11 52								12 07				12 22					12 37					12 52
Caerphilly 3	d			11 55								12 10				12 25					12 40					12 55
Lisvane & Thornhill	d			11 59								12 14				12 29					12 44					12 59
Llanishen	d			12 01								12 16				12 31					12 46					13 01
Heath High Level	d			12 04								12 19				12 34					12 49					13 04
Coryton	d	11 45											12 15											12 45		
Whitchurch (Cardiff)	d	11 46											12 16											12 46		
Rhiwbina	d	11 48											12 18											12 48		
Birchgrove	d	11 50											12 20											12 50		
Ty Glas	d	11 51											12 21											12 51		
Heath Low Level	d	11 54											12 24											12 54		
Cardiff Queen Street 3	a	11 59	12 04	12 09					12 14	12 19		12 24	12 29	12 34		12 39			12 44		12 54			12 59	13 04	13 09
	d	12 01	12 06	12 11		12 12			12 16	12 21	12 24	12 26	12 31	12 36	12 36	12 41			12 46	12 48	12 56		13 00	13 01	13 06	13 11
Cardiff Bay	a					12 16					12 28				12 40					12 52			13 04			
Cardiff Central 7	a	12 04	12 09	12 14				12 20	12 22	12 24		12 29	12 34	12 39		12 44		12 50	12 52		12 59			13 04	13 09	13 14
	d		12 10	12 16						12 25		12 31		12 41		12 46			12 55		13 01				13 10	13 16
Grangetown	d		12 14	12 20						12 29		12 35		12 45		12 50			12 59		13 05				13 14	13 20
Dingle Road	d			12 26								12 41				12 56					13 11					13 26
Penarth	a			12 31								12 46				13 01					13 16					13 31
Cogan	d		12 18							12 33				12 48					13 03						13 18	
Eastbrook	d		12 20							12 35				12 51					13 05						13 20	
Dinas Powys	d		12 22							12 37				12 53					13 07						13 22	
Cadoxton	d		12 27							12 42				12 57					13 12						13 27	
Barry Docks	d		12 30							12 45				13 00					13 15						13 30	
Barry 3	d		12 34							12 49				13 05					13 19						13 34	
Barry Island	a		12 40							12 55									13 25						13 40	
Rhoose Cardiff Int Airport ✈	d													13 12												
Llantwit Major	d													13 22												
Bridgend	a													13 39												

For general notes see front of timetable
For details of catering facilities see Directory of Train Operators

A To Radyr
B To Coryton
b Arr. 1142

From Saturday 12 September a revised service will be in operation due to seasonal difficulties. Most trains will arrive at their destination between 1 and 3 minutes later. Passengers should check with National Rail Enquiries for precise times.

Table 130

Saturdays

Treherbert, Aberdare, Merthyr, Pontypridd, Rhymney and Coryton → Cardiff, Penarth, Barry, Barry Island and Bridgend

Network Diagram - see first page of Table 130

Station		AW	AW	AW A	AW	AW	AW	AW	AW B	AW	AW	AW	AW	AW A	AW		AW	AW	AW	AW	AW B	AW	AW	AW	AW	AW A
Treherbert	d		12 17										12 47												13 17	
Ynyswen	d		12 19										12 49												13 19	
Treorchy	d		12 21										12 51												13 21	
Ton Pentre	d		12 23										12 53												13 23	
Ystrad Rhondda	a		12 26										12 56												13 26	
	d		12 28										12 58												13 28	
Llwynypia	d		12 30										13 00												13 30	
Tonypandy	d		12 33										13 03												13 33	
Dinas Rhondda	d		12 35										13 05												13 35	
Porth	d		12 39										13 09												13 39	
Trehafod	d		12 42										13 12												13 42	
Merthyr Tydfil	d									12 38												13 08				
Pentre-bach	d									12 42												13 12				
Troed Y Rhiw	d									12 45												13 15				
Merthyr Vale	d									12 50												13 20				
Quakers Yard	d									12 55												13 25				
Aberdare 3	d					12 22												12 52								
Cwmbach	d					12 25												12 55								
Fernhill	d					12 28												12 58								
Mountain Ash	a					12 31												13 01								
	d					12 34												13 04								
Penrhiwceiber	d					12 37												13 07								
Abercynon	d					12 43				12 59								13 13				13 29				
Pontypridd 3	a		12 48			12 53				13 07			13 17					13 23				13 37			13 47	
	d		12 48			12 54				13 09			13 18					13 24				13 39			13 48	
Trefforest	d		12 51			12 57				13 12			13 21					13 27				13 42			13 51	
Trefforest Estate	d									13 16												13 46				
Taffs Well 3	d		12 58			13 04				13 20			13 28					13 34				13 50			13 58	
Radyr 3	a		13 01			13 07				13 23			13 31					13 37				13 53			14 01	
	d		13 01	13 04		13 07				13 23			13 31	13 34				13 37				13 53			14 01	14 04
Danescourt	d			13 08										13 38												14 08
Fairwater	d			13 10										13 40												14 10
Waun-gron Park	d			13 12										13 42												14 12
Ninian Park	d			13 15										13 45												14 15
Llandaf	d		13 04		←	13 10				13 26			13 34		←			13 40				13 56			14 04	
Cathays	d		13 09		13 09	13 15				13 31			13 39		13 39			13 45				14 01			14 09	
Rhymney 3	d		→					12 29					→												→	
Pontlottyn	d							12 32																		
Tir-phil	d							12 36																		
Brithdir	d							12 39																		
Bargoed	d							12b47				13 02							13 17				13 32			
Gilfach Fargoed	d																		13 19							
Pengam	d							12 52				13 07							13 22				13 37			
Hengoed	d							12 55				13 10							13 25				13 40			
Ystrad Mynach 3	d							12 58				13 13							13 28				13 43			
Llanbradach	d							13 03				13 18							13 33				13 48			
Aber	d							13 07				13 22							13 37				13 52			
Caerphilly 3	d							13 10				13 25							13 40				13 55			
Lisvane & Thornhill	d							13 14				13 29							13 44				13 59			
Llanishen	d							13 16				13 31							13 46				14 01			
Heath High Level	d							13 19				13 34							13 49				14 04			
Coryton	d								13 15												13 45					
Whitchurch (Cardiff)	d								13 16												13 46					
Rhiwbina	d								13 18												13 48					
Birchgrove	d								13 20												13 50					
Ty Glas	d								13 21												13 51					
Heath Low Level	d								13 24												13 54					
Cardiff Queen Street 3	a				13 14	13 19		13 24	13 29	13 34		13 39			13 44			13 49	13 54		13 59	14 04	14 09			
	d	13 12			13 16	13 21	13 24	13 26	13 31	13 36	13 36	13 41			13 46		13 48	13 51	13 56	14 00	14 01	14 06	14 11	14 12		
Cardiff Bay	a	13 16					13 28				13 40						13 52			14 04				14 16		
Cardiff Central 7	a			13 20	13 22	13 24		13 29	13 34	13 39		13 44		13 50	13 52			13 54	13 59		14 04	14 09	14 14			14 20
	d					13 25		13 31		13 41		13 46						13 55	14 01			14 10	14 16			
Grangetown	d					13 29		13 35		13 45		13 50						13 59	14 05			14 14	14 20			
Dingle Road	d							13 41				13 56							14 11				14 26			
Penarth	a							13 46				14 01							14 16				14 31			
Cogan	d					13 33				13 48								14 03				14 18				
Eastbrook	d					13 35				13 51								14 05				14 20				
Dinas Powys	d					13 37				13 53								14 07				14 22				
Cadoxton	d					13 42				13 57								14 12				14 27				
Barry Docks	d					13 45				14 00								14 15				14 30				
Barry 3	d					13 49				14 05								14 19				14 34				
Barry Island	a					13 55												14 25				14 40				
Rhoose Cardiff Int Airport ✈	d									14 12																
Llantwit Major	d									14 22																
Bridgend	a									14 39																

For general notes see front of timetable
For details of catering facilities see Directory of Train Operators

A To Coryton
B To Radyr
b Arr. 1242

From Saturday 12 September a revised service will be in operation due to seasonal difficulties. Most trains will arrive at their destination between 1 and 3 minutes later. Passengers should check with National Rail Enquiries for precise times.

Table 130

Saturdays

Treherbert, Aberdare, Merthyr, Pontypridd, Rhymney and Coryton → Cardiff, Penarth, Barry, Barry Island and Bridgend

Network Diagram - see first page of Table 130

Station		AW	AW	AW	AW	AW	AW	AW	AW		AW	AW	AW	AW	AW	AW	AW	AW	AW	AW	AW	AW	AW	AW	AW	AW
						A						B						A				B				
Treherbert	d										13 47															14 17
Ynyswen	d										13 49															14 19
Treorchy	d										13 51															14 21
Ton Pentre	d										13 53															14 23
Ystrad Rhondda	a										13 56															14 26
	d										13 58															14 28
Llwynypia	d										14 00															14 30
Tonypandy	d										14 03															14 33
Dinas Rhondda	d										14 05															14 35
Porth	d										14 09															14b52
Trehafod	d										14 12															14 55
Merthyr Tydfil	d						13 38												14 08							
Pentre-bach	d						13 42												14 12							
Troed Y Rhiw	d						13 45												14 15							
Merthyr Vale	d						13 50												14 20							
Quakers Yard	d						13 55												14 25							
Aberdare 3	d														13 52								14 22			
Cwmbach	d														13 55								14 25			
Fernhill	d														13 58								14 28			
Mountain Ash	a														14 01								14 31			
	d														14 04								14 34			
Penrhiwceiber	d														14 07								14 37			
Abercynon	d		13 45				13 59								14 13				14 29				14 43			
Pontypridd 3	a		13 53				14 07				14 17				14 23				14 37				14 53			15 00
	d		13 54				14 09				14 18				14 24				14 39				14 54			15 04
Trefforest	d		13 57				14 12				14 21				14 27				14 42				14 57			15 07
Trefforest Estate	d						14 16												14 46							
Taffs Well 3	d		14 04				14 20				14 28				14 34				14 50				15 04			15 13
Radyr 3	a		14 07				14 23				14 31				14 37				14 53				15 07			15 17
	d		14 07				14 23				14 31	14 34			14 37				14 53			15 04	15 07			15 17
Danescourt	d											14 38										15 08				
Fairwater	d											14 40										15 10				
Waun-gron Park	d											14 42										15 12				
Ninian Park	d											14 45										15 15				
Llandaf	d	←	14 10				14 26				14 34		←		14 40				14 56				15 10			
Cathays	d	14 09	14 15				14 31				14 39		14 39		14 45				15 01				15 15			
Rhymney 3	d				13 29						↳														14 29	
Pontlottyn	d				13 32																				14 32	
Tir-phil	d				13 36																				14 36	
Brithdir	d				13 39																				14 39	
Bargoed	d				13c47				14 02							14 17				14 32					14e47	
Gilfach Fargoed	d															14 19										
Pengam	d				13 52				14 07							14 22				14 37					14 52	
Hengoed	d				13 55				14 10							14 25				14 40					14 55	
Ystrad Mynach 3	d				13 58				14 13							14 28				14 43					14 58	
Llanbradach	d				14 03				14 18							14 33				14 48					15 03	
Aber	d				14 07				14 22							14 37				14 52					15 07	
Caerphilly 3	d				14 10				14 25							14 40				14 55					15 10	
Lisvane & Thornhill	d				14 14				14 29							14 44				14 59					15 14	
Llanishen	d				14 16				14 31							14 46				15 01					15 16	
Heath High Level	d				14 19				14 34							14 49				15 04					15 19	
Coryton	d					14 15												14 45								
Whitchurch (Cardiff)	d					14 16												14 46								
Rhiwbina	d					14 18												14 48								
Birchgrove	d					14 20												14 50								
Ty Glas	d					14 21												14 51								
Heath Low Level	d					14 24												14 54								
Cardiff Queen Street 3	a	14 14	14 19		14 24	14 29	14 34		14 39				14 44		14 49	14 54		14 59	15 04	15 09			15 19		15 24	
	d	14 16	14 21	14 24	14 26	14 31	14 36	14 36	14 41				14 46	14 48	14 51	14 56	15 00	15 01	15 06	15 11	15 12		15 21	15 24	15 26	
Cardiff Bay	a			14 28				14 40						14 52			15 04				15 16			15 28		
Cardiff Central 7	a	14 22	14 24		14 29	14 34	14 39		14 44			14 50	14 52		14 54	14 59		15 04	15 09	15 14		15 20	15 24		15 29	15 34
	d		14 25		14 31		14 41		14 46						14 55	15 01			15 10	15 16			15 25		15 31	
Grangetown	d		14 29		14 35		14 45		14 50						14 59	15 05			15 14	15 20			15 29		15 35	
Dingle Road	d				14 41				14 56							15 11				15 26					15 41	
Penarth	a				14 46				15 01							15 16				15 31					15 46	
Cogan	d		14 33				14 48								15 03				15 18				15 33			
Eastbrook	d		14 35				14 51								15 05				15 20				15 35			
Dinas Powys	d		14 37				14 53								15 07				15 22				15 37			
Cadoxton	d		14 42				14 57								15 12				15 27				15 42			
Barry Docks	d		14 45				15 00								15 15				15 30				15 45			
Barry 3	d		14 49				15 05								15 19				15 34				15 49			
Barry Island	a		14 55												15 25				15 40				15 55			
Rhoose Cardiff Int Airport ✈	d						15 12																			
Llantwit Major	d						15 22																			
Bridgend	a						15 39																			

For general notes see front of timetable
For details of catering facilities see Directory of Train Operators

A To Radyr
B To Coryton
b Arr. 1438
c Arr. 1342
e Arr. 1442

From Saturday 12 September a revised service will be in operation due to seasonal difficulties. Most trains will arrive at their destination between 1 and 3 minutes later. Passengers should check with National Rail Enquiries for precise times.

Treherbert, Aberdare, Merthyr, Pontypridd, Rhymney and Coryton → Cardiff, Penarth, Barry, Barry Island and Bridgend

Network Diagram - see first page of Table 130

		AW A	AW		AW	AW	AW	AW B	AW	AW	AW	AW	AW	AW A	AW	AW	AW	AW	AW	AW B		AW	AW	AW	AW	AW A
Treherbert	d						14 47												15 17							
Ynyswen	d						14 49												15 19							
Treorchy	d						14 51												15 21							
Ton Pentre	d						14 53												15 23							
Ystrad Rhondda	a						14 56												15 26							
	d						14 58												15 28							
Llwynypia	d						15 00												15 30							
Tonypandy	d						15 03												15 33							
Dinas Rhondda	d						15 05												15 35							
Porth	d						15 09												15 39							
Trehafod	d						15 12												15 42							
Merthyr Tydfil	d		14 38												15 04											
Pentre-bach	d		14 42												15 08											
Troed Y Rhiw	d		14 45												15 11											
Merthyr Vale	d		14 50												15 16											
Quakers Yard	d		14 55												15 22											
Aberdare 3	d										14 52												15 22			
Cwmbach	d										14 55												15 25			
Fernhill	d										14 58												15 28			
Mountain Ash	a										15 01												15 31			
	d										15 04												15 34			
Penrhiwceiber	d										15 07												15 37			
Abercynon	d		14 59								15 13				15 26								15 43			
Pontypridd 3	a		15 07				15 17				15 23				15 32				15 47				15 53			
	d		15 09				15 18				15 24					15 39			15 48				15 54			
Trefforest	d		15 12				15 21				15 27					15 42			15 51				15 57			
Trefforest Estate	d		15 16													15 46										
Taffs Well 3	d		15 20				15 28				15 34					15 50			15 58				16 04			
Radyr 3	a		15 23				15 31				15 37					15 53			16 01				16 07			
	d		15 23				15 31	15 34			15 37					15 53			16 01	16 04			16 07			
Danescourt	d							15 38												16 08						
Fairwater	d							15 40												16 10						
Waun-gron Park	d							15 42												16 12						
Ninian Park	d							15 45												16 15						
Llandaf	d		15 26				15 34		↩		15 40					15 56			16 04			↩	16 10			
Cathays	d		15 31				15 39		15 39		15 45					16 01			16 09			16 09	16 15			
Rhymney 3	d						↪												↪						15 29	
Pontlottyn	d																								15 32	
Tir-phil	d																								15 36	
Brithdir	d																								15 39	
Bargoed	d					15 02						15 17					15 32								15b47	
Gilfach Fargoed	d											15 19														
Pengam	d					15 07						15 22					15 37								15 52	
Hengoed	d					15 10						15 25					15 40								15 55	
Ystrad Mynach 3	d					15 13						15 28					15 43								15 58	
Llanbradach	d					15 18						15 33					15 48								16 03	
Aber	d					15 22						15 37					15 52								16 07	
Caerphilly 3	d					15 25						15 40					15 55								16 10	
Lisvane & Thornhill	d					15 29						15 44					15 59								16 14	
Llanishen	d					15 31						15 46					16 01								16 16	
Heath High Level	d					15 34						15 49					16 04								16 19	
Coryton	d	15 15												15 45												16 15
Whitchurch (Cardiff)	d	15 16												15 46												16 16
Rhiwbina	d	15 18												15 48												16 18
Birchgrove	d	15 20												15 50												16 20
Ty Glas	d	15 21												15 51												16 21
Heath Low Level	d	15 24												15 54												16 24
Cardiff Queen Street 3	a	15 29	15 34			15 39			15 44		15 49	15 54		15 59		16 04	16 09					16 14	16 19		16 24	16 29
	d	15 31	15 36		15 36	15 41			15 46	15 48	15 51	15 56	16 00	16 01		16 06	16 11	16 12				16 16	16 21	16 24	16 26	16 31
Cardiff Bay	a				15 40					15 52			16 04					16 16						16 28		
Cardiff Central 7	a	15 34	15 39			15 44		15 50	15 52		15 54	15 59		16 05		16 09	16 14			16 20		16 22	16 24		16 32	16 34
	d		15 41			15 46					15 55	16 01				16 10	16 16						16 25			
Grangetown	d		15 45			15 50					15 59	16 05				16 14	16 20						16 29			
Dingle Road	d					15 56						16 11					16 26									
Penarth	a					16 01						16 16					16 31									
Cogan	d		15 48								16 03					16 18							16 33			
Eastbrook	d		15 51								16 05					16 20							16 35			
Dinas Powys	d		15 53								16 07					16 22							16 37			
Cadoxton	d		15 57								16 12					16 27							16 42			
Barry Docks	d		16 00								16 15					16 30							16 45			
Barry 3	d		16 05								16 19					16 34							16 49			
Barry Island	a										16 25					16 40							16 55			
Rhoose Cardiff Int Airport ✈	d		16 12																							
Llantwit Major	d		16 22																							
Bridgend	a		16 39																							

For general notes see front of timetable
For details of catering facilities see Directory of Train Operators

A To Radyr
B To Coryton
b Arr. 1542

From Saturday 12 September a revised service will be in operation due to seasonal difficulties. Most trains will arrive at their destination between 1 and 3 minutes later. Passengers should check with National Rail Enquiries for precise times.

Table 130

Saturdays

Treherbert, Aberdare, Merthyr, Pontypridd, Rhymney and Coryton → Cardiff, Penarth, Barry, Barry Island and Bridgend

Network Diagram - see first page of Table 130

Station		AW	AW	AW	AW	AW A	AW	AW	AW	AW	AW	AW B	AW	AW		AW	AW	AW A	AW	AW	AW	AW	AW B	AW	AW	AW
Treherbert	d				15 47												16 17									
Ynyswen	d				15 49												16 19									
Treorchy	d				15 51												16 21									
Ton Pentre	d				15 53												16 23									
Ystrad Rhondda	a				15 56												16 26									
	d				15 58												16 28									
Llwynypia	d				16 00												16 30									
Tonypandy	d				16 03												16 33									
Dinas Rhondda	d				16 05												16 35									
Porth	d				16 09												16 39									
Trehafod	d				16 12												16 42									
Merthyr Tydfil	d	15 38											16 08											16 38		
Pentre-bach	d	15 42											16 12											16 42		
Troed Y Rhiw	d	15 45											16 15											16 45		
Merthyr Vale	d	15 50											16 20											16 50		
Quakers Yard	d	15 55											16 25											16 55		
Aberdare 3	d								15 52											16 22						
Cwmbach	d								15 55											16 25						
Fernhill	d								15 58											16 28						
Mountain Ash	a								16 01											16 31						
	d								16 04											16 34						
Penrhiwceiber	d								16 07											16 37						
Abercynon	d	15 59							16 13				16 29							16 43				16 59		
Pontypridd 3	a	16 08			16 17				16 23				16 37				16 47			16 53				17 07		
	d	16 09			16 18				16 24				16 39				16 48			16 54				17 09		
Trefforest	d	16 12			16 21				16 27				16 42				16 51			16 57				17 12		
Trefforest Estate	d	16 16											16 46											17 16		
Taffs Well 3	d	16 20			16 28				16 34				16 50				16 58			17 04				17 20		
Radyr 3	a	16 23			16 31				16 37				16 53				17 01			17 07				17 23		
	d	16 23			16 31	16 34			16 37				16 53				17 01	17 04		17 07				17 23		
Danescourt	d					16 38												17 08								
Fairwater	d					16 40												17 10								
Waun-gron Park	d					16 42												17 12								
Ninian Park	d					16 45												17 15								
Llandaf	d	16 26			16 34		←		16 40				16 56				17 04		←	17 10				17 26		
Cathays	d	16 31			16 39		16 39		16 45				17 01				17 09		17 09	17 15				17 31		
Rhymney 3	d				→												→					16 29				
Pontlottyn	d																					16 32				
Tir-phil	d																					16 36				
Brithdir	d																					16 39				
Bargoed	d			16 02						16 17				16 32								16b47				17 02
Gilfach Fargoed	d									16 19																
Pengam	d			16 07						16 22				16 37								16 52				17 07
Hengoed	d			16 10						16 25				16 40								16 55				17 10
Ystrad Mynach 3	d			16 13						16 28				16 43								16 58				17 13
Llanbradach	d			16 18						16 33				16 48								17 03				17 18
Aber	d			16 22						16 37				16 52								17 07				17 22
Caerphilly 3	d			16 25						16 40				16 55								17 10				17 25
Lisvane & Thornhill	d			16 29						16 44				16 59								17 14				17 29
Llanishen	d			16 31						16 46				17 01								17 16				17 31
Heath High Level	d			16 34						16 49				17 04								17 19				17 34
Coryton	d											16 45											17 15			
Whitchurch (Cardiff)	d											16 46											17 16			
Rhiwbina	d											16 48											17 18			
Birchgrove	d											16 50											17 20			
Ty Glas	d											16 51											17 21			
Heath Low Level	d											16 54											17 24			
Cardiff Queen Street 3	a	16 34		16 39			16 44		16 49	16 54		16 59	17 04	17 09					17 14	17 19		17 24	17 29	17 34		17 39
	d	16 36	16 36	16 41			16 46	16 48	16 51	16 56	17 00	17 01	17 06	17 11		17 12			17 16	17 21	17 24	17 26	17 31	17 36	17 36	17 41
Cardiff Bay	a		16 40					16 52			17 04					17 16					17 28				17 40	
Cardiff Central 7	a	16 39		16 44		16 50	16 52		16 54	16 59		17 05	17 09	17 14				17 20	17 22	17 24		17 29	17 34	17 39		17 44
	d	16 41		16 46					16 55	17 01			17 10	17 16						17 25		17 31		17 41		17 46
Grangetown	d	16 45		16 50					16 59	17 05			17 14	17 20						17 29		17 35		17 45		17 50
Dingle Road	d			16 56						17 11				17 26								17 41				17 56
Penarth	a			17 01						17 16				17 31								17 46				18 01
Cogan	d	16 48							17 03				17 18							17 33				17 48		
Eastbrook	d	16 51							17 05				17 20							17 35				17 51		
Dinas Powys	d	16 53							17 07				17 22							17 37				17 53		
Cadoxton	d	16 57							17 12				17 27							17 42				17 57		
Barry Docks	d	17 00							17 15				17 30							17 45				18 00		
Barry 3	d	17 05							17 19				17 34							17 49				18 05		
Barry Island	a								17 25				17 40							17 55						
Rhoose Cardiff Int Airport ✈	d	17 12																						18 12		
Llantwit Major	d	17 22																						18 22		
Bridgend	a	17 39																						18 39		

For general notes see front of timetable
For details of catering facilities see Directory of Train Operators

A To Coryton
B To Radyr
b Arr. 1642

From Saturday 12 September a revised service will be in operation due to seasonal difficulties. Most trains will arrive at their destination between 1 and 3 minutes later. Passengers should check with National Rail Enquiries for precise times.

Treherbert, Aberdare, Merthyr, Pontypridd, Rhymney and Coryton → Cardiff, Penarth, Barry, Barry Island and Bridgend

Network Diagram - see first page of Table 130

		AW	AW	AW	AW	AW	AW	AW		AW	AW	AW	AW	AW	AW	AW	AW	AW	AW	AW	AW	AW	AW	AW	AW	AW
			A							B					A					B				A		
Treherbert	d	16 47											17 17										17 47			
Ynyswen	d	16 49											17 19										17 49			
Treorchy	d	16 51											17 21										17 51			
Ton Pentre	d	16 53											17 23										17 53			
Ystrad Rhondda	a	16 56											17 26										17 56			
	d	16 58											17 28										17 58			
Llwynypia	d	17 00											17 30										18 00			
Tonypandy	d	17 03											17 33										18 03			
Dinas Rhondda	d	17 05											17 35										18 05			
Porth	d	17 09											17 39										18 09			
Trehafod	d	17 12											17 42										18 12			
Merthyr Tydfil	d										17 08										17 38					
Pentre-bach	d										17 12										17 42					
Troed Y Rhiw	d										17 15										17 45					
Merthyr Vale	d										17 20										17 50					
Quakers Yard	d										17 25										17 55					
Aberdare 3	d					16 52											17 22									
Cwmbach	d					16 55											17 25									
Fernhill	d					16 58											17 28									
Mountain Ash	a					17 01											17 31									
	d					17 04											17 34									
Penrhiwceiber	d					17 07											17 37									
Abercynon	d					17 13					17 29						17 43				17 59					
Pontypridd 3	a	17 17				17 23					17 37		17 47				17 53				18 07		18 17			
	d	17 18				17 24					17 39		17 48				17 54				18 09		18 18			
Trefforest	d	17 21				17 27					17 42		17 51				17 57				18 12		18 21			
Trefforest Estate	d										17 46										18 16					
Taffs Well 3	d	17 28				17 34					17 50		17 58				18 04				18 20		18 28			
Radyr 3	a	17 31				17 37					17 53		18 01				18 07				18 23		18 31			
	d	17 31	17 34			17 37					17 53		18 01		18 04		18 07				18 23		18 31	18 34		
Danescourt	d		17 38												18 08									18 38		
Fairwater	d		17 40												18 10									18 40		
Waun-gron Park	d		17 42												18 12									18 42		
Ninian Park	d		17 45												18 15									18 45		
Llandaf	d	17 34		←		17 40					17 56		18 04			←	18 10				18 26		18 34		←	
Cathays	d	17 39		17 39		17 45					18 01		18 09			18 09	18 15				18 31		18 39		18 39	
Rhymney 3	d	↪											↪						17 29				↪			
Pontlottyn	d																		17 32							
Tir-phil	d																		17 36							
Brithdir	d																		17 39							
Bargoed	d						17 17					17 32							17b47							
Gilfach Fargoed	d						17 19																			
Pengam	d						17 22					17 37							17 52							
Hengoed	d						17 25					17 40							17 55							
Ystrad Mynach 3	d						17 28					17 43							17 58							
Llanbradach	d						17 33					17 48							18 03							
Aber	d						17 37					17 52							18 07							
Caerphilly 3	d						17 40					17 55							18 10							
Lisvane & Thornhill	d						17 44					17 59							18 14							
Llanishen	d						17 46					18 01							18 16							
Heath High Level	d						17 49					18 04							18 19							
Coryton	d									17 45										18 15						
Whitchurch (Cardiff)	d									17 46										18 16						
Rhiwbina	d									17 48										18 18						
Birchgrove	d									17 50										18 20						
Ty Glas	d									17 51										18 21						
Heath Low Level	d									17 54										18 24						
Cardiff Queen Street 3	a			17 44		17 49	17 54			17 59	18 04	18 09				18 14	18 19		18 24	18 29	18 34				18 44	
	d			17 46	17 48	17 51	17 56	18 00		18 01	18 06	18 11		18 12		18 16	18 21	18 24	18 26	18 31	18 36	18 36			18 46	18 48
Cardiff Bay	a				17 52			18 04						18 16				18 28				18 40				18 52
Cardiff Central 7	a		17 50	17 52		17 54	17 59			18 04	18 09	18 14			18 20	18 22	18 24		18 29	18 34	18 39			18 50	18 52	
	d					17 55	18 01				18 10	18 16					18 25		18 31		18 41					
Grangetown	d					17 59	18 05				18 14	18 20					18 29		18 35		18 45					
Dingle Road	d						18 11					18 26							18 41							
Penarth	a						18 16					18 31							18 46							
Cogan	d					18 03					18 18						18 33				18 48					
Eastbrook	d					18 05					18 20						18 35				18 51					
Dinas Powys	d					18 07					18 22						18 37				18 53					
Cadoxton	d					18 12					18 27						18 42				18 57					
Barry Docks	d					18 15					18 30						18 45				19 00					
Barry 3	d					18 19					18 34						18 49				19 05					
Barry Island	a					18 25					18 40						18 55									
Rhoose Cardiff Int Airport ✈	d																				19 12					
Llantwit Major	d																				19 22					
Bridgend	a																				19 39					

For general notes see front of timetable
For details of catering facilities see Directory of Train Operators

A To Coryton
B To Radyr
b Arr. 1742

From Saturday 12 September a revised service will be in operation due to seasonal difficulties. Most trains will arrive at their destination between 1 and 3 minutes later. Passengers should check with National Rail Enquiries for precise times.

Table 130

Saturdays

Treherbert, Aberdare, Merthyr, Pontypridd, Rhymney and Coryton → Cardiff, Penarth, Barry, Barry Island and Bridgend

Network Diagram - see first page of Table 130

		AW		AW	AW	AW	AW	AW	AW	AW	AW	AW	AW	AW A	AW	AW	AW	AW	AW		AW	AW	AW	AW	AW	AW
Treherbert	d								18 17								18 47								19 17	
Ynyswen	d								18 19								18 49								19 19	
Treorchy	d								18 21								18 51								19 21	
Ton Pentre	d								18 23								18 53								19 23	
Ystrad Rhondda	a								18 26								18 56								19 26	
	d								18 28								18 58								19 28	
Llwynypia	d								18 30								19 00								19 30	
Tonypandy	d								18 33								19 03								19 33	
Dinas Rhondda	d								18 35								19 05								19 35	
Porth	d								18 39								19 09								19 39	
Trehafod	d								18 42								19 12								19 42	
Merthyr Tydfil	d						18 08								18 38								19 08			
Pentre-bach	d						18 12								18 42								19 12			
Troed Y Rhiw	d						18 15								18 45								19 15			
Merthyr Vale	d						18 20								18 50								19 20			
Quakers Yard	d						18 25								18 55								19 25			
Aberdare 3	d	17 52									18 22								18 52							
Cwmbach	d	17 55									18 25								18 55							
Fernhill	d	17 58									18 28								18 58							
Mountain Ash	a	18 01									18 31								19 01							
	d	18 04									18 34								19 04							
Penrhiwceiber	d	18 07									18 37								19 07							
Abercynon	d	18 13					18 29				18 43				18 59				19 13				19 29			
Pontypridd 3	a	18 23					18 37		18 47		18 53				19 07		19 17		19 23				19 37		19 47	
	d	18 24					18 39		18 48		18 54				19 09		19 18		19 24				19 39		19 48	
Trefforest	d	18 27					18 42		18 51		18 57				19 12		19 21		19 27				19 42		19 51	
Trefforest Estate	d						18 46								19 16								19 46			
Taffs Well 3	d	18 34					18 50		18 58		19 04				19 20		19 28		19 34				19 50		19 58	
Radyr 3	a	18 37					18 53		19 01		19 07				19 23		19 31		19 37				19 53		20 01	
	d	18 37					18 53		19 01	19 04	19 07				19 23		19 31		19 37				19 53		20 01	20 04
Danescourt	d									19 08																20 08
Fairwater	d									19 10																20 10
Waun-gron Park	d									19 12																→
Ninian Park	d									19 15																
Llandaf	d	18 40					18 56		19 04		19 10				19 26		19 34		19 40				19 56		20 04	
Cathays	d	18 45					19 01		19 09		19 15				19 31		19 39		19 45				20 01		20 09	
Rhymney 3	d																									
Pontlottyn	d																									
Tir-phil	d																									
Brithdir	d																									
Bargoed	d			18 17									18 48													
Gilfach Fargoed	d			18 19									18 50													
Pengam	d			18 22									18 53													
Hengoed	d			18 25									18 56													
Ystrad Mynach 3	d			18 28									18 59													
Llanbradach	d			18 33									19 04													
Aber	d			18 37									19 08													
Caerphilly 3	d			18 40									19 11								19 40					
Lisvane & Thornhill	d			18 44									19 15								19 44					
Llanishen	d			18 46									19 17								19 46					
Heath High Level	d			18 49									19 20								19 49					
Coryton	d					18 45								19 15												
Whitchurch (Cardiff)	d					18 46								19 16												
Rhiwbina	d					18 48								19 18												
Birchgrove	d					18 50								19 20												
Ty Glas	d					18 51								19 21												
Heath Low Level	d					18 54								19 24												
Cardiff Queen Street 3	a	18 49		18 54		18 59	19 04		19 14		19 19		19 24	19 29	19 35		19 44		19 49		19 54		20 04		20 14	
	d	18 51		18 56	19 00	19 01	19 06	19 12	19 16		19 21	19 24	19 26	19 31	19 36	19 36	19 46	19 48	19 51		19 56	20 00	20 06	20 12	20 16	
Cardiff Bay	a				19 04			19 16				19 28				19 40		19 52				20 04		20 16		
Cardiff Central 7	a	18 54		18 59		19 06	19 10		19 22	19 22	19 24		19 29	19 34	19 40		19 52		19 57		19 59		20 10		20 19	
	d	18 55		19 01							19 25		19 31		19 41						20 01				20 20	
Grangetown	d	18 59		19 05							19 29		19 35		19 45						20 05				20 24	
Dingle Road	d			19 11									19 41								20 11					
Penarth	a			19 16									19 46								20 16					
Cogan	d	19 03									19 33				19 48										20 28	
Eastbrook	d	19 05									19 35				19 51										20 30	
Dinas Powys	d	19 07									19 37				19 53										20 32	
Cadoxton	d	19 12									19 42				19 57										20 37	
Barry Docks	d	19 15									19 45				20 00										20 40	
Barry 3	d	19 19									19 49				20 05										20 44	
Barry Island	a	19 25									19 55														20 50	
Rhoose Cardiff Int Airport ✈	d														20 12											
Llantwit Major	d														20 22											
Bridgend	a														20 39											

For general notes see front of timetable
For details of catering facilities see Directory of Train Operators

A To Radyr

From Saturday 12 September a revised service will be in operation due to seasonal difficulties. Most trains will arrive at their destination between 1 and 3 minutes later. Passengers should check with National Rail Enquiries for precise times.

Treherbert, Aberdare, Merthyr, Pontypridd, Rhymney and Coryton → Cardiff, Penarth, Barry, Barry Island and Bridgend

Network Diagram - see first page of Table 130

		AW	AW	AW	AW	AW	AW	AW	AW	AW	AW	AW	AW		AW	AW	AW	AW	AW	AW	AW	AW	AW	AW	AW	AW
					A																	A				
Treherbert	d								19 47							20 17										
Ynyswen	d								19 49							20 19										
Treorchy	d								19 51							20 21										
Ton Pentre	d								19 53							20 23										
Ystrad Rhondda	a								19 56							20 26										
	d								19 58							20 28										
Llwynypia	d								20 00							20 30										
Tonypandy	d								20 03							20 33										
Dinas Rhondda	d								20 05							20 35										
Porth	d								20 09							20 39										
Trehafod	d								20 12							20 42										
Merthyr Tydfil	d					19 38																	20 38			
Pentre-bach	d					19 42																	20 42			
Troed Y Rhiw	d					19 45																	20 45			
Merthyr Vale	d					19 50																	20 50			
Quakers Yard	d					19 55																	20 55			
Aberdare 3	d										19 52							20 22								
Cwmbach	d										19 55							20 25								
Fernhill	d										19 58							20 28								
Mountain Ash	a										20 01							20 31								
	d										20 04							20 34								
Penrhiwceiber	d										20 07							20 37								
Abercynon	d	19 43				19 59					20 13							20 43					20 59			
Pontypridd 3	a	19 53				20 07			20 17		20 23					20 47		20 53					21 07			
	d	19 54				20 09			20 18		20 24					20 48		20 54					21 09			
Trefforest	d	19 57				20 12			20 21		20 27					20 51		20 57					21 12			
Trefforest Estate	d					20 16																	21 16			
Taffs Well 3	d	20 04				20 20			20 28		20 34					20 58		21 04					21 20			
Radyr 3	a	20 07				20 23			20 31		20 37					21 01		21 07					21 23			
	d	20 07				20 23			20 31		20 37					21 01	21 04	21 07					21 23			
Danescourt	d		←														21 08		←							
Fairwater	d		20 10														21 10 →		21 10							
Waun-gron Park	d		20 12																21 12							
Ninian Park	d		20 15																21 15							
Llandaf	d	20 10				20 26			20 34		20 40					21 04		21 10					21 26			
Cathays	d	20 15				20 31			20 39		20 45					21 09		21 15					21 31			
Rhymney 3	d							19 45																	20 48	
Pontlottyn	d							19 48																	20 51	
Tir-phil	d							19 52																	20 55	
Brithdir	d							19 55																	20 58	
Bargoed	d							19 59																	21 02	
Gilfach Fargoed	d							20 01																	21 04	
Pengam	d							20 04																	21 07	
Hengoed	d							20 07																	21 10	
Ystrad Mynach 3	d							20 10																	21 13	
Llanbradach	d							20 15																	21 18	
Aber	d							20 19																	21 22	
Caerphilly 3	d							20 22				20 40													21 25	
Lisvane & Thornhill	d							20 26				20 44													21 29	
Llanishen	d							20 28				20 46													21 31	
Heath High Level	d							20 31				20 49													21 34	
Coryton	d				20 15																	21 15				
Whitchurch (Cardiff)	d				20 16																	21 16				
Rhiwbina	d				20 18																	21 18				
Birchgrove	d				20 20																	21 20				
Ty Glas	d				20 21																	21 21				
Heath Low Level	d				20 24																	21 24				
Cardiff Queen Street 3	a	20 19			20 29	20 34		20 39	20 44		20 49	20 54				21 14		21 19				21 29	21 34		21 42	
	d	20 21		20 24	20 31	20 36	20 36	20 41	20 46	20 48	20 51	20 56	21 00		21 12	21 16		21 21		21 24		21 31	21 36	21 36	21 44	21 48
Cardiff Bay	a			20 28			20 40			20 52			21 04		21 16					21 28				21 40		21 52
Cardiff Central 7	a	20 24	20 25		20 34	20 39		20 47	20 52		20 57	20 59				21 21		21 24	21 25			21 34	21 39		21 51	
	d	20 31				20 41						21 01						21 25			21 31		21 41			
Grangetown	d	20 35				20 45						21 05						21 29			21 35		21 45			
Dingle Road	d	20 41										21 11									21 41					
Penarth	a	20 46										21 16									21 46					
Cogan	d					20 48												21 33					21 48			
Eastbrook	d					20 51												21 35					21 51			
Dinas Powys	d					20 53												21 37					21 53			
Cadoxton	d					20 57												21 42					21 57			
Barry Docks	d					21 00												21 45					22 00			
Barry 3	d					21 05												21 49					22 05			
Barry Island	a																	21 55								
Rhoose Cardiff Int Airport ✈	d					21 12																	22 12			
Llantwit Major	d					21 22																	22 22			
Bridgend	a					21 39																	22 39			

For general notes see front of timetable
For details of catering facilities see Directory of Train Operators

A To Radyr

From Saturday 12 September a revised service will be in operation due to seasonal difficulties. Most trains will arrive at their destination between 1 and 3 minutes later. Passengers should check with National Rail Enquiries for precise times.

Table 130

Saturdays

Treherbert, Aberdare, Merthyr, Pontypridd, Rhymney and Coryton → Cardiff, Penarth, Barry, Barry Island and Bridgend

Network Diagram - see first page of Table 130

		AW	AW	AW	AW	AW	AW		AW	AW	AW	AW	AW	AW	AW	AW	AW	AW	AW	AW	AW	AW	AW
Treherbert	d					21 17																	
Ynyswen	d					21 19																	
Treorchy	d					21 21																	
Ton Pentre	d					21 23																	
Ystrad Rhondda	a					21 26																	
	d					21 28																	
Llwynypia	d					21 30																	
Tonypandy	d					21 33																	
Dinas Rhondda	d					21 35																	
Porth	d					21 39																	
Trehafod	d					21 42																	
Merthyr Tydfil	d										21 38									22 38			
Pentre-bach	d										21 42									22 42			
Troed Y Rhiw	d										21 45									22 45			
Merthyr Vale	d										21 50									22 50			
Quakers Yard	d										21 55									22 55			
Aberdare 3	d	20 52												21 52									22 52
Cwmbach	d	20 55												21 55									22 55
Fernhill	d	20 58												21 58									22 58
Mountain Ash	a	21 01												22 01									23 01
	d	21 04												22 04									23 04
Penrhiwceiber	d	21 07												22 07									23 07
Abercynon	d	21 13									21 59			22 14						22 59			23 13
Pontypridd 3	a	21 23				21 47					22 07			22 23						23 07			23 22
	d	21 24				21 48					22 09			22 29						23 09			23 29
Trefforest	d	21 27				21 51					22 12			22 32						23 12			23 32
Trefforest Estate	d										22 16												
Taffs Well 3	d	21 34				21 58					22 20			22 39						23 20			23 38
Radyr 3	a	21 37				22 01					22 23			22 42						23 23			23 42
	d	21 37				22 01	22 04				22 23			22 42				23 10		23 23			23 42
Danescourt	d						22 08																
Fairwater	d						22 10																
Waun-gron Park	d						22 12																
Ninian Park	d						22 15																
Llandaf	d	21 40				22 04					22 26			22 45				23 12		23 26			23 45
Cathays	d	21 45				22 09					22 31			22 50				23 16		23 31			23 49
Rhymney 3	d									21 33													
Pontlottyn	d									21 36													
Tir-phil	d									21 40													
Brithdir	d									21 43													
Bargoed	d									21 47													
Gilfach Fargoed	d									21 49													
Pengam	d									21 52													
Hengoed	d									21 55													
Ystrad Mynach 3	d									21 58													
Llanbradach	d									22 03													
Aber	d									22 07													
Caerphilly 3	d		21 40							22 10													
Lisvane & Thornhill	d		21 45							22 14													
Llanishen	d		21 47							22 16													
Heath High Level	d		21 49							22 19													
Coryton	d															22 45							
Whitchurch (Cardiff)	d															22 46							
Rhiwbina	d															22 48							
Birchgrove	d															22 50							
Ty Glas	d															22 51							
Heath Low Level	d															22 54							
Cardiff Queen Street 3	a	21 49	21 54			22 14				22 24	22 34			22 54		22 59		23 19		23 34			23 53
	d	21 51	21 56	22 00	22 12	22 16			22 24	22 26	22 36	22 36	22 48	22 55	23 00	23 01	23 12	23 20	23 24	23 36	23 36	23 48	23 56
Cardiff Bay	a			22 04	22 16				22 28			22 40	22 52		23 04		23 16		23 28		23 40	23 52	
Cardiff Central 7	a	21 57	21 59			22 22	22 20			22 29	22 41			23 00		23 06		23 25		23 42			00 02
	d		22 01			22 25				22 31				23 12				23 30					
Grangetown	d		22 05			22 29				22 35				23 16				23 34					
Dingle Road	d		22 11							22 41				23 20									
Penarth	a		22 16							22 46				23 25									
Cogan	d					22 33												23 37					
Eastbrook	d					22 35												23 40					
Dinas Powys	d					22 37												23 42					
Cadoxton	d					22 42												23 46					
Barry Docks	d					22 45												23 49					
Barry 3	d					22 49												23 54					
Barry Island	a					22 55												23 59					
Rhoose Cardiff Int Airport ✈	d																						
Llantwit Major	d																						
Bridgend	a																						

For general notes see front of timetable
For details of catering facilities see Directory of Train Operators

From Saturday 12 September a revised service will be in operation due to seasonal difficulties. Most trains will arrive at their destination between 1 and 3 minutes later. Passengers should check with National Rail Enquiries for precise times.

Sundays

Treherbert, Aberdare, Merthyr, Pontypridd, Rhymney and Coryton → Cardiff, Penarth, Barry, Barry Island and Bridgend

Network Diagram - see first page of Table 130

		AW	AW	AW A	AW	AW	AW	AW	AW	AW	AW	AW	AW	AW	AW	AW	AW		AW	AW	AW	AW	AW B	AW	AW	AW
Treherbert	d					08 17																		10 17		
Ynyswen	d					08 19																		10 19		
Treorchy	d					08 21																		10 21		
Ton Pentre	d					08 23																		10 23		
Ystrad Rhondda	a					08 26																		10 26		
	d					08 28																		10 28		
Llwynypia	d					08 30																		10 30		
Tonypandy	d					08 33																		10 33		
Dinas Rhondda	d					08 35																		10 35		
Porth	d					08 39																		10 39		
Trehafod	d					08 42																		10 42		
Merthyr Tydfil	d															09 38										
Pentre-bach	d															09 42										
Troed Y Rhiw	d															09 45										
Merthyr Vale	d															09 50										
Quakers Yard	d															09 55										
Aberdare 3	d																			09 52						
Cwmbach	d																			09 55						
Fernhill	d																			09 58						
Mountain Ash	a																			10 01						
	d																			10 04						
Penrhiwceiber	d																			10 07						
Abercynon	d															09 59				10 13						
Pontypridd 3	a					08 47										10 07				10 23				10 47		
	d					08 48										10 09				10 24				10 48		
Trefforest	d					08 51										10 12				10 27				10 51		
Trefforest Estate	d																									
Taffs Well 3	d					08 58										10 20				10 34				10 58		
Radyr 3	a					09 01										10 23				10 37				11 01		
	d					09 01										10 23				10 37				11 01		
Danescourt	d																									
Fairwater	d																									
Waun-gron Park	d																									
Ninian Park	d																									
Llandaf	d					09 04										10 26				10 40				11 04		
Cathays	d					09 09										10 31				10 45				11 09		
Rhymney 3	d												09 22													
Pontlottyn	d												09 25													
Tir-phil	d												09 29													
Brithdir	d												09 32													
Bargoed	d												09 37													
Gilfach Fargoed	d												09 39													
Pengam	d												09 42													
Hengoed	d												09 45													
Ystrad Mynach 3	d												09 48													
Llanbradach	d												09 53													
Aber	d												09 57													
Caerphilly 3	d												10 00													
Lisvane & Thornhill	d												10 04													
Llanishen	d												10 06													
Heath High Level	d												10 09													
Coryton	d																									
Whitchurch (Cardiff)	d																									
Rhiwbina	d																									
Birchgrove	d																									
Ty Glas	d																									
Heath Low Level	d																									
Cardiff Queen Street 3	a					09 14							10 14			10 34				10 49				11 14		
	d			09 00	09 12	09 16	09 24	09 36	09 48		10 00	10 12	10 16	10 24		10 36	10 36		10 48	10 51	11 00	11 12		11 16	11 24	11 36
Cardiff Bay	a			09 04	09 16		09 28	09 40	09 52		10 04	10 16		10 28			10 40		10 52		11 04	11 16			11 28	11 40
Cardiff Central 7	a					09 18							10 18			10 39				10 54				11 18		
	d	08 25	08 41			09 25				09 55			10 25		10 31	10 41				10 55			11 14	11 25		
Grangetown	d	08 29	08 45			09 29				09 59			10 29		10 35	10 45				10 59				11 29		
Dingle Road	d														10 41											
Penarth	a														10 44											
Cogan	d	08 33	08 49			09 33				10 03			10 33			10 48				11 03				11 33		
Eastbrook	d	08 35	08 51			09 35				10 05			10 35			10 51				11 05				11 35		
Dinas Powys	d	08 37	08 53			09 37				10 07			10 37			10 53				11 07				11 37		
Cadoxton	d	08 42	08 58			09 42				10 12			10 42			10 57				11 12				11 42		
Barry Docks	d	08 45	09 01			09 45				10 15			10 45			11 00				11 15				11 45		
Barry 3	d	08 49	09 05			09 49				10 19			10 49			11 05				11 19			11 33	11 49		
Barry Island	a	08 55				09 55				10 25			10 55							11 25			11 40	11 55		
Rhoose Cardiff Int Airport ✈	d		09 12													11 12										
Llantwit Major	d		09 22													11 22										
Bridgend	a		09 39													11 39										

For general notes see front of timetable
For details of catering facilities see Directory of Train Operators

A From Cardiff Central
B Until 6 September. From Newport (South Wales) (Table 132)

From Sunday 13 September a revised service will be in operation due to seasonal difficulties. Most trains will arrive at their destination between 1 and 3 minutes later. Passengers should check with National Rail Enquiries for precise times.

Table 130

Sundays

Treherbert, Aberdare, Merthyr, Pontypridd, Rhymney and Coryton → Cardiff, Penarth, Barry, Barry Island and Bridgend

Network Diagram - see first page of Table 130

		AW	AW	AW	AW	AW	AW	AW	AW	AW	AW		AW	AW	AW	AW	AW	AW	AW	AW	AW	AW	AW	AW	AW	AW
Treherbert	d															12 17										
Ynyswen	d															12 19										
Treorchy	d															12 21										
Ton Pentre	d															12 23										
Ystrad Rhondda	a															12 26										
	d															12 28										
Llwynypia	d															12 30										
Tonypandy	d															12 33										
Dinas Rhondda	d															12 35										
Porth	d															12 39										
Trehafod	d															12 42										
Merthyr Tydfil	d								11 38																	13 38
Pentre-bach	d								11 42																	13 42
Troed Y Rhiw	d								11 45																	13 45
Merthyr Vale	d								11 50																	13 50
Quakers Yard	d								11 55																	13 55
Aberdare 3	d		10 52																	12 52						
Cwmbach	d		10 55																	12 55						
Fernhill	d		10 58																	12 58						
Mountain Ash	a		11 01																	13 01						
	d		11 04																	13 04						
Penrhiwceiber	d		11 07																	13 07						
Abercynon	d		11 13						11 59											13 13						13 59
Pontypridd 3	a		11 23						12 07							12 47				13 23						14 07
	d		11 24						12 09							12 48				13 24						14 09
Trefforest	d		11 27						12 12							12 51				13 27						14 12
Trefforest Estate	d																									
Taffs Well 3	d		11 34						12 20							12 58				13 34						14 20
Radyr 3	a		11 37						12 23							13 01				13 37						14 23
	d		11 37						12 23							13 01				13 37						14 23
Danescourt	d																									
Fairwater	d																									
Waun-gron Park	d																									
Ninian Park	d																									
Llandaf	d		11 40						12 26							13 04				13 40						14 26
Cathays	d		11 45						12 31							13 09				13 45						14 31
Rhymney 3	d					11 22																	13 22			
Pontlottyn	d					11 25																	13 25			
Tir-phil	d					11 29																	13 29			
Brithdir	d					11 32																	13 32			
Bargoed	d					11 37																	13 37			
Gilfach Fargoed	d					11 39																	13 39			
Pengam	d					11 42																	13 42			
Hengoed	d					11 45																	13 45			
Ystrad Mynach 3	d					11 48																	13 48			
Llanbradach	d					11 53																	13 53			
Aber	d					11 57																	13 57			
Caerphilly 3	d					12 00																	14 00			
Lisvane & Thornhill	d					12 04																	14 04			
Llanishen	d					12 06																	14 06			
Heath High Level	d					12 09																	14 09			
Coryton	d																									
Whitchurch (Cardiff)	d																									
Rhiwbina	d																									
Birchgrove	d																									
Ty Glas	d																									
Heath Low Level	d																									
Cardiff Queen Street 3	a		11 49			12 14			12 34							13 14				13 49			14 14			14 34
	d	11 48	11 51	12 00	12 12	12 16	12 24		12 36	12 36	12 48			13 00	13 12	13 16	13 24	13 36	13 48	13 51	14 00	14 12	14 16	14 24		14 36
Cardiff Bay	a	11 52		12 04	12 16		12 28			12 40	12 52			13 04	13 16		13 28	13 40	13 52		14 04	14 16		14 28		
Cardiff Central 7	a		11 54			12 18			12 39							13 18				13 54			14 18			14 39
	d		11 55			12 25		12 31	12 41				12 55			13 25				13 55			14 25		14 31	14 41
Grangetown	d		11 59			12 29		12 35	12 45				12 59			13 29				13 59			14 29		14 35	14 45
Dingle Road	d							12 41																	14 41	
Penarth	a							12 46																	14 46	
Cogan	d		12 03			12 33			12 48				13 03			13 33				14 03			14 33			14 48
Eastbrook	d		12 05			12 35			12 51				13 05			13 35				14 05			14 35			14 51
Dinas Powys	d		12 07			12 37			12 53				13 07			13 37				14 07			14 37			14 53
Cadoxton	d		12 12			12 42			12 57				13 12			13 42				14 12			14 42			14 57
Barry Docks	d		12 15			12 45			13 00				13 15			13 45				14 15			14 45			15 00
Barry 3	d		12 19			12 49			13 05				13 19			13 49				14 19			14 49			15 05
Barry Island	a		12 25			12 55							13 25			13 55				14 25			14 55			
Rhoose Cardiff Int Airport ✈	d								13 12																	15 12
Llantwit Major	d								13 22																	15 22
Bridgend	a								13 39																	15 39

For general notes see front of timetable
For details of catering facilities see Directory of Train Operators

From Sunday 13 September a revised service will be in operation due to seasonal difficulties. Most trains will arrive at their destination between 1 and 3 minutes later. Passengers should check with National Rail Enquiries for precise times.

Table 130

Sundays

Treherbert, Aberdare, Merthyr, Pontypridd, Rhymney and Coryton → Cardiff, Penarth, Barry, Barry Island and Bridgend

Network Diagram - see first page of Table 130

		AW	AW	AW	AW		AW	AW	AW	AW	AW	AW	AW	AW	AW	AW	AW	AW	AW	AW	AW	AW		AW	AW	AW
Treherbert	d							14 17																	16 17	
Ynyswen	d							14 19																	16 19	
Treorchy	d							14 21																	16 21	
Ton Pentre	d							14 23																	16 23	
Ystrad Rhondda	a							14 26																	16 26	
	d							14 28																	16 28	
Llwynypia	d							14 30																	16 30	
Tonypandy	d							14 33																	16 33	
Dinas Rhondda	d							14 35																	16 35	
Porth	d							14 39																	16 39	
Trehafod	d							14 42																	16 42	
Merthyr Tydfil	d																	15 38								
Pentre-bach	d																	15 42								
Troed Y Rhiw	d																	15 45								
Merthyr Vale	d																	15 50								
Quakers Yard	d																	15 55								
Aberdare 3	d											14 52														
Cwmbach	d											14 55														
Fernhill	d											14 58														
Mountain Ash	a											15 01														
	d											15 04														
Penrhiwceiber	d											15 07														
Abercynon	d											15 13						15 59								
Pontypridd 3	a							14 47				15 23						16 07							16 47	
	d							14 48				15 24						16 09							16 48	
Trefforest	d							14 51				15 27						16 12							16 51	
Trefforest Estate	d																									
Taffs Well 3	d							14 58				15 34						16 20							16 58	
Radyr 3	a							15 01				15 37						16 23							17 01	
	d							15 01				15 37						16 23							17 01	
Danescourt	d																									
Fairwater	d																									
Waun-gron Park	d																									
Ninian Park	d																									
Llandaf	d							15 04				15 40						16 26							17 04	
Cathays	d							15 09				15 45						16 31							17 09	
Rhymney 3	d														15 22											
Pontlottyn	d														15 25											
Tir-phil	d														15 29											
Brithdir	d														15 32											
Bargoed	d														15 37											
Gilfach Fargoed	d														15 39											
Pengam	d														15 42											
Hengoed	d														15 45											
Ystrad Mynach 3	d														15 48											
Llanbradach	d														15 53											
Aber	d														15 57											
Caerphilly 3	d														16 00											
Lisvane & Thornhill	d														16 04											
Llanishen	d														16 06											
Heath High Level	d														16 09											
Coryton	d																									
Whitchurch (Cardiff)	d																									
Rhiwbina	d																									
Birchgrove	d																									
Ty Glas	d																									
Heath Low Level	d																									
Cardiff Queen Street 3	a							15 14				15 49			16 14			16 34							17 14	
	d	14 36	14 48		15 00		15 12	15 16	15 24	15 36	15 48	15 51	16 00	16 12	16 16	16 24		16 36	16 36	16 48		17 00		17 12	17 16	17 24
Cardiff Bay	a	14 40	14 52		15 04		15 16		15 28	15 40	15 52		16 04	16 16		16 28			16 40	16 52		17 04		17 16		17 28
Cardiff Central 7	a							15 18				15 54			16 18			16 39							17 18	
	d			14 55				15 25				15 55			16 25		16 31	16 41			16 55				17 25	
Grangetown	d			14 59				15 29				15 59			16 29		16 35	16 45			16 59				17 29	
Dingle Road	d																16 41									
Penarth	a																16 46									
Cogan	d			15 03				15 33				16 03			16 33			16 48			17 03				17 33	
Eastbrook	d			15 05				15 35				16 05			16 35			16 51			17 05				17 35	
Dinas Powys	d			15 07				15 37				16 07			16 37			16 53			17 07				17 37	
Cadoxton	d			15 12				15 42				16 12			16 42			16 57			17 12				17 42	
Barry Docks	d			15 15				15 45				16 15			16 45			17 00			17 15				17 45	
Barry 3	d			15 19				15 49				16 19			16 49			17 05			17 19				17 49	
Barry Island	a			15 25				15 55				16 25			16 55						17 25				17 55	
Rhoose Cardiff Int Airport ✈	d																	17 12								
Llantwit Major	d																	17 22								
Bridgend	a																	17 39								

For general notes see front of timetable
For details of catering facilities see
Directory of Train Operators

From Sunday 13 September a revised service will be in operation due to seasonal difficulties. Most trains will arrive at their destination between 1 and 3 minutes later. Passengers should check with National Rail Enquiries for precise times.

Table 130

Sundays

Treherbert, Aberdare, Merthyr, Pontypridd, Rhymney and Coryton → Cardiff, Penarth, Barry, Barry Island and Bridgend

Network Diagram - see first page of Table 130

		AW	AW	AW	AW	AW	AW	AW	AW	AW	AW	AW	AW	AW	AW	AW	AW	AW	AW	AW	AW	AW	AW	AW
														A										
Treherbert	d														18 17						20 17			
Ynyswen	d														18 19						20 19			
Treorchy	d														18 21						20 21			
Ton Pentre	d														18 23						20 23			
Ystrad Rhondda	a														18 26						20 26			
	d														18 28						20 28			
Llwynypia	d														18 30						20 30			
Tonypandy	d														18 33						20 33			
Dinas Rhondda	d														18 35						20 35			
Porth	d														18 39						20 39			
Trehafod	d														18 42						20 42			
Merthyr Tydfil	d									17 38									19 38					21 38
Pentre-bach	d									17 42									19 42					21 42
Troed Y Rhiw	d									17 45									19 45					21 45
Merthyr Vale	d									17 50									19 50					21 50
Quakers Yard	d									17 55									19 55					21 55
Aberdare 3	d			16 52												18 52						20 52		
Cwmbach	d			16 55												18 55						20 55		
Fernhill	d			16 58												18 58						20 58		
Mountain Ash	a			17 01												19 01						21 01		
	d			17 04												19 04						21 04		
Penrhiwceiber	d			17 07												19 07						21 07		
Abercynon	d			17 13						17 59						19 13			19 59			21 13		21 59
Pontypridd 3	a			17 23						18 07					18 47	19 23			20 07		20 47	21 23		22 07
	d			17 24						18 09					18 48	19 24			20 09		20 48	21 24		22 09
Trefforest	d			17 27						18 12					18 51	19 27			20 12		20 51	21 27		22 12
Trefforest Estate	d																							
Taffs Well 3	d			17 34						18 20					18 58	19 34			20 20		20 58	21 34		22 20
Radyr 3	a			17 37						18 23					19 01	19 37			20 23		21 01	21 37		22 23
	d			17 37						18 23					19 01	19 37			20 23		21 01	21 37		22 23
Danescourt	d																							
Fairwater	d																							
Waun-gron Park	d																							
Ninian Park	d																							
Llandaf	d			17 40						18 26					19 04	19 40			20 26		21 04	21 40		22 26
Cathays	d			17 45						18 31					19 09	19 45			20 31		21 09	21 45		22 31
Rhymney 3	d						17 22										19 22							
Pontlottyn	d						17 25										19 25							
Tir-phil	d						17 29										19 29							
Brithdir	d						17 32										19 32							
Bargoed	d						17 37										19 37							
Gilfach Fargoed	d						17 39										19 39							
Pengam	d						17 42										19 42							
Hengoed	d						17 45										19 45							
Ystrad Mynach 3	d						17 48										19 48							
Llanbradach	d						17 53										19 53							
Aber	d						17 57										19 57							
Caerphilly 3	d						18 00										20 00							
Lisvane & Thornhill	d						18 04										20 04							
Llanishen	d						18 06										20 06							
Heath High Level	d						18 09										20 09							
Coryton	d																							
Whitchurch (Cardiff)	d																							
Rhiwbina	d																							
Birchgrove	d																							
Ty Glas	d																							
Heath Low Level	d																							
Cardiff Queen Street 3	a			17 49			18 14			18 34					19 14	19 49	20 14		20 34		21 14	21 49		22 34
	d	17 36	17 48	17 51	18 00	18 12	18 16	18 24		18 36	18 36	18 48		19 00	19 16	19 51	20 16		20 36		21 16	21 51		22 36
Cardiff Bay	a	17 40	17 52		18 04	18 16		18 28			18 40	18 52												
Cardiff Central 7	a			17 54			18 18			18 39				19 03	19 18	19 54	20 18		20 39		21 18	21 57		22 41
	d			17 55			18 25		18 31	18 41			18 55		19 25	19 55	20 25	20 31	20 41	20 55	21 25		22 25	
Grangetown	d			17 59			18 29		18 35	18 45			18 59		19 29	19 59	20 29	20 35	20 45	20 59	21 29		22 29	
Dingle Road	d								18 41									20 41						
Penarth	a								18 46									20 46						
Cogan	d			18 03			18 33			18 48			19 03		19 33	20 03	20 33		20 48	21 03	21 33		22 33	
Eastbrook	d			18 05			18 35			18 51			19 05		19 35	20 05	20 35		20 51	21 05	21 35		22 35	
Dinas Powys	d			18 07			18 37			18 53			19 07		19 37	20 07	20 37		20 53	21 07	21 37		22 37	
Cadoxton	d			18 12			18 42			18 57			19 12		19 42	20 12	20 42		20 57	21 12	21 42		22 42	
Barry Docks	d			18 15			18 45			19 00			19 15		19 45	20 15	20 45		21 00	21 15	21 45		22 45	
Barry 3	d			18 19			18 49			19 05			19 19		19 49	20 19	20 49		21 05	21 19	21 49		22 49	
Barry Island	a			18 25			18 55						19 25		19 55	20 25	20 55			21 25	21 55		22 55	
Rhoose Cardiff Int Airport ✈	d									19 12									21 12					
Llantwit Major	d									19 22									21 22					
Bridgend	a									19 39									21 39					

For general notes see front of timetable
For details of catering facilities see Directory of Train Operators

A From Cardiff Bay

From Sunday 13 September a revised service will be in operation due to seasonal difficulties. Most trains will arrive at their destination between 1 and 3 minutes later. Passengers should check with National Rail Enquiries for precise times.

Bridgend, Barry Island, Barry, Penarth and Cardiff → Coryton. Rhymney, Pontypridd, Merthyr, Aberdare and Treherbert

Network Diagram - see first page of Table 130

Miles	Miles	Miles	Miles	Miles			AW		AW	AW	AW	AW	AW	AW	AW	AW	AW	AW	AW	AW	AW	AW	AW	AW A	AW	AW
—	—	0	—	—	**Bridgend**	d										05 42										
—	—	9¼	—	—	Llantwit Major	d										05 56										
—	—	15¾	—	—	Rhoose Cardiff Int Airport ✈	d										06 06										
0	—	—	—	—	**Barry Island**	d								05 53							06 26					
¾	—	19	—	—	**Barry** 3	d								05 57		06 15					06 30					
2	—	—	—	—	Barry Docks	d								06 01		06 19					06 34					
2¾	—	—	—	—	Cadoxton	d								06 04		06 22					06 37					
4¾	—	—	—	—	Dinas Powys	d								06 08		06 26					06 41					
5¾	—	—	—	—	Eastbrook	d								06 10		06 28					06 43					
6½	—	—	—	—	Cogan	d								06 12		06 30					06 45					
—	0	—	—	—	**Penarth**	d						06 02						06 32								07 02
—	¼	—	—	—	Dingle Road	d						06 04						06 34								07 04
8¼	2¾	—	—	—	Grangetown	d						06 08		06 16		06 34		06 38			06 49					07 08
9¼	3¾	—	—	—	**Cardiff Central** 7	a						06 13		06 21		06 39		06 44			06 54					07 14
—	—	—	0	—		d	05 26		05 46	05 56	06 11	06 15	06 19	06 26	06 36	06 41		06 46	06 51		06 56	07 06		07 06	07 11	07 16
—	—	0	—	—	**Cardiff Bay**	d											06 42			06 54			07 06			
9¾	4¼	1	—	—	**Cardiff Queen Street** 3	a	05 29		05 49	05 59	06 14	06 19	06 24	06 29	06 39	06 44	06 46	06 49	06 54	06 58	07 00	07 09	07 10		07 14	07 19
—	—	—	—	—		d	05 30		05 50	06 00	06 15	06 20	06 25	06 30	06 40	06 45		06 50	06 55		07 00	07 10			07 15	07 20
—	—	3½	—	—	Heath Low Level	d							06 30						07 00							
—	—	4¼	—	—	Ty Glas	d							06 33						07 03							
—	—	4¾	—	—	Birchgrove	d							06 34						07 04							
—	—	5¼	—	—	Rhiwbina	d							06 36						07 06							
—	—	5½	—	—	Whitchurch (Cardiff)	d							06 38						07 08							
—	—	6	—	—	**Coryton**	a							06 43						07 13							
—	6¾	—	—	—	Heath High Level	d			05 54			06 25						06 55								07 25
—	7¾	—	—	—	Llanishen	d			05 57			06 28						06 58								07 28
—	8¾	—	—	—	Lisvane & Thornhill	d			06 00			06 30						07 00								07 30
—	11¼	—	—	—	Caerphilly 3	d			06a09			06 36						07 06								07 36
—	12	—	—	—	Aber	d						06 38						07 08								07 38
—	14	—	—	—	Llanbradach	d						06 42						07 12								07 42
—	16¾	—	—	—	Ystrad Mynach 3	d						06 47						07 17								07 47
—	17¾	—	—	—	Hengoed	d						06 50						07 20								07 50
—	19½	—	—	—	Pengam	d						06 53						07 23								07 53
—	20½	—	—	—	Gilfach Fargoed	d																				
—	21	—	—	—	Bargoed	d						07a01						07a31								08a01
—	22½	—	—	—	Brithdir	d																				
—	23½	—	—	—	Tir-phil	d																				
—	26	—	—	—	Pontlottyn	d																				
—	27	—	—	—	**Rhymney** 3	a																				
10½	—	—	—	—	Cathays	d	05 33			06 03	06 18			06 33	06 43	06 48					07 03	07 13			07 18	
13	—	—	—	—	Llandaf	d	05 37			06 07	06 22			06 37	06 47	06 52					07 07	07 17			07 22	
—	—	—	1	—	Ninian Park	d																		07 10		
—	—	—	2½	—	Waun-gron Park	d																		07 13		
—	—	—	3	—	Fairwater	d																		07 15		
—	—	—	3½	—	Danescourt	d																		07 17		
14	—	—	4¾	—	Radyr 3	a	05 39			06 10	06 24			06 40	06 50	06 54					07 10	07 20		07 24	07 25	
—	—	—	—	—		d	05 40			06 10	06 24			06 40	06 50	06 55					07 10	07 20			07 25	
16	—	—	—	—	Taffs Well 3	d	05 43			06 14	06 28			06 44	06 54	06 59					07 14	07 24			07 29	
18¼	—	—	—	—	Trefforest Estate	d	05 47			06 18				06 48							07 18					
20¾	—	—	—	—	Trefforest	d	05 52			06 22	06 35			06 52	07 01	07 06					07 22	07 31			07 36	
21¾	—	0	—	0	**Pontypridd** 3	a	05 55			06 25	06 38			06 55	07 04	07 09					07 27	07 34			07 39	
—	—	—	—	—		d	05 57	06 11		06 27	06 41			06 57	07 06	07 11					07 27	07 36			07 41	
—	—	3¼	—	3¼	Abercynon	d	06 04	06 19		06 34	06 49			07 04		07 19					07 34				07 49	
—	—	—	—	6	Penrhiwceiber	d		06 24			06 54					07 24									07 54	
—	—	—	—	7¼	Mountain Ash	a		06 28			06 58					07 28									07 58	
—	—	—	—	—		d		06 33			07 03					07 33									08 03	
—	—	—	—	8½	Fernhill	d		06 35			07 05					07 35									08 05	
—	—	—	—	9½	Cwmbach	d		06 39			07 09					07 39									08 09	
—	—	—	—	11	**Aberdare** 3	a		06 46			07 16					07 46									08 16	
—	—	4¾	—	—	Quakers Yard	d	06 09			06 39				07 09							07 39					
—	—	7	—	—	Merthyr Vale	d	06 17			06 47				07 17							07 47					
—	—	8¾	—	—	Troed Y Rhiw	d	06 20			06 50				07 20							07 50					
—	—	10	—	—	Pentre-bach	d	06 23			06 53				07 23							07 53					
—	—	11½	—	—	**Merthyr Tydfil**	a	06 31			07 01				07 31							08 01					
23½	—	—	—	—	Trehafod	d									07 11							07 41				
24¾	—	—	—	—	Porth	d									07 15							07 45				
26¼	—	—	—	—	Dinas Rhondda	d									07 19							07 49				
26¾	—	—	—	—	Tonypandy	d									07 21							07 51				
27¾	—	—	—	—	Llwynypia	d									07 23							07 53				
29	—	—	—	—	Ystrad Rhondda	a									07 26							07 56				
—	—	—	—	—		d									07 29							07 59				
29½	—	—	—	—	Ton Pentre	d									07 31							08 01				
30¾	—	—	—	—	Treorchy	d									07 34							08 04				
31¾	—	—	—	—	Ynyswen	d									07 37							08 07				
32¼	—	—	—	—	**Treherbert**	a									07 43							08 13				

For general notes see front of timetable
For details of catering facilities see
Directory of Train Operators

A From Coryton

From Monday 7 September a revised service will be in operation due to seasonal difficulties. Most trains will arrive at their destination between 1 and 3 minutes later. Passengers should check with National Rail Enquiries for precise times.

Bridgend, Barry Island, Barry, Penarth and Cardiff → Coryton. Rhymney, Pontypridd, Merthyr, Aberdare and Treherbert

Network Diagram - see first page of Table 130

		AW	AW A	AW		AW	AW	AW	AW B	AW	AW	AW	AW C	AW	AW	AW	AW	AW	AW B	AW	AW	AW	AW C	AW	AW	AW
Bridgend	d									06 42																
Llantwit Major	d									06 56																
Rhoose Cardiff Int Airport ✈	d									07 06																
Barry Island	d			06 56											07 26					07 41				07 56		
Barry 3	d			07 00						07 15					07 30					07 45				08 00		
Barry Docks	d			07 04						07 19					07 34					07 49				08 04		
Cadoxton	d			07 07						07 22					07 37					07 52				08 07		
Dinas Powys	d			07 11						07 26					07 41					07 56				08 11		
Eastbrook	d			07 13						07 28					07 43					07 58				08 13		
Cogan	d			07 15						07 30					07 45					08 00				08 15		
Penarth	d					07 17						07 32				07 47					08 02				08 17	
Dingle Road	d					07 19						07 34				07 49					08 04				08 19	
Grangetown	d			07 19		07 23				07 34		07 38			07 49	07 54				08 04	08 08			08 19	08 23	
Cardiff Central 7	a			07 24		07 29				07 39		07 44			07 54	08 00				08 09	08 14			08 24	08 29	
	d		07 21	07 26		07 31		07 36	07 36	07 41		07 46	07 51		07 56	08 01	08 06		08 06	08 11	08 16		08 21	08 26	08 31	
Cardiff Bay	d	07 18					07 30				07 42			07 54				08 06				08 18				08 30
Cardiff Queen Street 3	a	07 22	07 24	07 29		07 34	07 34	07 39		07 44	07 46	07 49	07 54	07 58	07 59	08 04	08 09	08 10		08 14	08 19	08 22	08 24	08 29	08 34	08 34
	d		07 25	07 30		07 35		07 40		07 45		07 50	07 55		08 00	08 05	08 10			08 15	08 20		08 25	08 30	08 35	
Heath Low Level	d		07 30										08 00										08 30			
Ty Glas	d		07 33										08 03										08 33			
Birchgrove	d		07 34										08 04										08 34			
Rhiwbina	d		07 36										08 06										08 36			
Whitchurch (Cardiff)	d		07 38										08 08										08 38			
Coryton	a		07 43										08 13										08 43			
Heath High Level	d					07 40						07 55				08 10					08 25				08 40	
Llanishen	d					07 43						07 58				08 13					08 28				08 43	
Lisvane & Thornhill	d					07 45						08 00				08 15					08 30				08 45	
Caerphilly 3	d					07 51						08 06				08 21					08 36				08 51	
Aber	d					07 53						08 08				08 23					08 38				08 53	
Llanbradach	d					07 57						08 12				08 27					08 42				08 57	
Ystrad Mynach 3	d					08 02						08 17				08 32					08 47				09 02	
Hengoed	d					08 05						08 20				08 35					08 50				09 05	
Pengam	d					08 08						08 23				08 38					08 53				09 08	
Gilfach Fargoed	d															08 41										
Bargoed	d					08 14						08a31				08a48					08 59				09a16	
Brithdir	d					08 18															09 03					
Tir-phil	d					08 21															09 06					
Pontlottyn	d					08 25															09 10					
Rhymney 3	a					08 28															09 16					
Cathays	d			07 33				07 43		07 48					08 03		08 13			08 18				08 33		
Llandaf	d			07 37				07 47		07 52					08 07		08 17			08 22				08 37		
Ninian Park	d								07 40										08 10							
Waun-gron Park	d								07 43										08 13							
Fairwater	d								07 45										08 15							
Danescourt	d								07 47										08 17							
Radyr 3	a			07 40				07 50	07 54	07 55					08 10		08 20		08 24	08 25				08 40		
	d			07 40				07 50		07 55					08 10		08 20			08 25				08 40		
Taffs Well 3	d			07 44				07 54		07 59					08 14		08 24			08 29				08 44		
Trefforest Estate	d			07 48											08 18									08 48		
Trefforest	d			07 52				08 01		08 06					08 23		08 31			08 36				08 52		
Pontypridd 3	a			07 55				08 04		08 09					08 26		08 34			08 39				08 55		
	d			07 57				08 06		08 11					08 27		08 36			08 41				08 57		
Abercynon	d			08 04						08 19					08 34					08 49				09 04		
Penrhiwceiber	d									08 24										08 54						
Mountain Ash	a									08 28										08 58						
	d									08 33										09 03						
Fernhill	d									08 35										09 05						
Cwmbach	d									08 39										09 09						
Aberdare 3	a									08 46										09 16						
Quakers Yard	d			08 09											08 39									09 09		
Merthyr Vale	d			08 17											08 47									09 17		
Troed Y Rhiw	d			08 20											08 50									09 20		
Pentre-bach	d			08 23											08 53									09 23		
Merthyr Tydfil	a			08 31											09 01									09 31		
Trehafod	d							08 11									08 41									
Porth	d							08 15									08 45									
Dinas Rhondda	d							08 19									08 49									
Tonypandy	d							08 21									08 51									
Llwynypia	d							08 23									08 53									
Ystrad Rhondda	a							08 26									08 56									
	d							08 29									08 59									
Ton Pentre	d							08 31									09 01									
Treorchy	d							08 34									09 04									
Ynyswen	d							08 37									09 07									
Treherbert	a							08 43									09 13									

For general notes see front of timetable
For details of catering facilities see Directory of Train Operators

A From Taffs Well
B From Coryton
C From Radyr

From Monday 7 September a revised service will be in operation due to seasonal difficulties. Most trains will arrive at their destination between 1 and 3 minutes later. Passengers should check with National Rail Enquiries for precise times.

Bridgend, Barry Island, Barry, Penarth and Cardiff → Coryton. Rhymney, Pontypridd, Merthyr, Aberdare and Treherbert

Network Diagram - see first page of Table 130

		AW	AW A	AW	AW	AW	AW B	AW	AW	AW	AW	AW	AW A	AW	AW	AW	AW B	AW	AW	AW	AW	AW A	AW	AW	AW
Bridgend	d			07 42																			08 42		
Llantwit Major	d			07 56																			08 56		
Rhoose Cardiff Int Airport ✈	d			08 06																			09 06		
Barry Island	d								08 26					08 41				08 56							
Barry 3	d			08 15					08 30					08 45				09 00					09 15		
Barry Docks	d			08 19					08 34					08 49				09 04					09 19		
Cadoxton	d			08 22					08 37					08 52				09 07					09 22		
Dinas Powys	d			08 26					08 41					08 56				09 11					09 26		
Eastbrook	d			08 28					08 43					08 58				09 13					09 28		
Cogan	d			08 30					08 45					09 00				09 15					09 30		
Penarth	d					08 32				08 47									09 17						09 32
Dingle Road	d					08 34				08 49									09 19						09 34
Grangetown	d			08 34		08 38			08 49	08 53				09 04				09 19	09 23				09 34		09 38
Cardiff Central 7	a			08 39		08 44			08 54	08 59				09 09				09 24	09 29				09 39		09 44
	d	08 36	08 36	08 41		08 46	08 51		08 56	09 01	09 06		09 06	09 11	09 16		09 21	09 26	09 31		09 36	09 36	09 41		09 46
Cardiff Bay	d				08 42			08 54				09 06				09 18				09 30				09 42	
Cardiff Queen Street 3	a	08 39		08 44	08 46	08 49	08 54	08 58	08 59	09 04	09 09	09 10		09 14	09 19	09 22	09 24	09 29	09 34	09 34	09 39		09 44	09 46	09 49
	d	08 40		08 45		08 50	08 55		09 00	09 05	09 10			09 15	09 20		09 25	09 30	09 35		09 40		09 45		09 50
Heath Low Level	d						09 00										09 30								
Ty Glas	d						09 03										09 33								
Birchgrove	d						09 04										09 34								
Rhiwbina	d						09 06										09 36								
Whitchurch (Cardiff)	d						09 08										09 38								
Coryton	a						09 13										09 43								
Heath High Level	d					08 55				09 10					09 25				09 40						09 55
Llanishen	d					08 58				09 13					09 28				09 43						09 58
Lisvane & Thornhill	d					09 00				09 15					09 30				09 45						10 00
Caerphilly 3	d					09 06				09 21					09 36				09 51						10 06
Aber	d					09 08				09 23					09 38				09 53						10 08
Llanbradach	d					09 12				09 27					09 42				09 57						10 12
Ystrad Mynach 3	d					09 17				09 32					09 47				10 02						10 17
Hengoed	d					09 20				09 35					09 50				10 05						10 20
Pengam	d					09 23				09 38					09 53				10 08						10 23
Gilfach Fargoed	d									09 41															
Bargoed	d					09a31				09a48					09 59				10a16						10a31
Brithdir	d														10 03										
Tir-phil	d														10 06										
Pontlottyn	d														10 10										
Rhymney 3	a														10 16										
Cathays	d	08 43		08 48					09 03		09 13			09 18				09 33			09 43		09 48		
Llandaf	d	08 47		08 52					09 07		09 17			09 22				09 37			09 47		09 52		
Ninian Park	d		08 40										09 10									09 40			
Waun-gron Park	d		08 43										09 13									09 43			
Fairwater	d		08 45										09 15									09 45			
Danescourt	d		08 47										09 17									09 47			
Radyr 3	a	08 50	08 54	08 55					09 10		09 20		09 24	09 25				09 40			09 50	09 54	09 55		
	d	08 50		08 55					09 10		09 20			09 25				09 40			09 50		09 55		
Taffs Well 3	d	08 54		08 59					09 14		09 24			09 29				09 44			09 54		09 59		
Trefforest Estate	d								09 18									09 48							
Trefforest	d	09 01		09 06					09 22		09 31			09 36				09 52			10 01		10 06		
Pontypridd 3	a	09 04		09 09					09 25		09 34			09 39				09 55			10 04		10 09		
	d	09 06		09 11					09 27		09 36			09 41				09 57			10 06		10 11		
Abercynon	d			09 19					09 34					09 49				10 04					10 19		
Penrhiwceiber	d			09 24										09 54									10 24		
Mountain Ash	a			09 28										09 58									10 28		
	d			09 33										10 03									10 33		
Fernhill	d			09 35										10 05									10 35		
Cwmbach	d			09 39										10 09									10 39		
Aberdare 3	a			09 46										10 16									10 46		
Quakers Yard	d								09 39									10 09							
Merthyr Vale	d								09 47									10 17							
Troed Y Rhiw	d								09 50									10 20							
Pentre-bach	d								09 53									10 23							
Merthyr Tydfil	a								10 01									10 31							
Trehafod	d	09 11									09 41										10 11				
Porth	d	09 15									09 45										10 15				
Dinas Rhondda	d	09 19									09 49										10 19				
Tonypandy	d	09 21									09 51										10 21				
Llwynypia	d	09 23									09 53										10 23				
Ystrad Rhondda	a	09 26									09 56										10 26				
	d	09 29									09 59										10 29				
Ton Pentre	d	09 31									10 01										10 31				
Treorchy	d	09 34									10 04										10 34				
Ynyswen	d	09 37									10 07										10 37				
Treherbert	a	09 43									10 13										10 43				

For general notes see front of timetable
For details of catering facilities see Directory of Train Operators

A From Coryton
B From Radyr

From Monday 7 September a revised service will be in operation due to seasonal difficulties. Most trains will arrive at their destination between 1 and 3 minutes later. Passengers should check with National Rail Enquiries for precise times.

Bridgend, Barry Island, Barry, Penarth and Cardiff → Coryton. Rhymney, Pontypridd, Merthyr, Aberdare and Treherbert

Network Diagram - see first page of Table 130

Station		AW A		AW	AW	AW	AW	AW	AW	AW B	AW	AW	AW	AW A	AW	AW	AW	AW	AW B	AW	AW	AW	AW A	AW		AW
Bridgend	d																				09 42					
Llantwit Major	d																				09 56					
Rhoose Cardiff Int Airport ✈	d																				10 06					
Barry Island	d				09 26						09 41				09 56											
Barry 3	d				09 30						09 45				10 00						10 15					
Barry Docks	d				09 34						09 49				10 04						10 19					
Cadoxton	d				09 37						09 52				10 07						10 22					
Dinas Powys	d				09 41						09 56				10 11						10 26					
Eastbrook	d				09 43						09 58				10 13						10 28					
Cogan	d				09 45						10 00				10 15						10 30					
Penarth	d					09 47						10 02				10 17						10 32				
Dingle Road	d					09 49						10 04				10 19						10 34				
Grangetown	d				09 49	09 53					10 04	10 08			10 19	10 23					10 34	10 38				
Cardiff Central 7	a				09 54	09 59					10 09	10 14			10 24	10 29					10 42	10 44				
	d	09 51			09 56	10 01		10 06		10 06	10 11	10 16		10 21	10 26	10 31		10 36	10 36			10 46	10 51			10 54
Cardiff Bay	d			09 54					10 06				10 18				10 30			10 42				10 54		
Cardiff Queen Street 3	a	09 54		09 58	09 59	10 04		10 09	10 10		10 14	10 19	10 22	10 24	10 29	10 34	10 34	10 39		10 46		10 49	10 54	10 58		
	d	09 55			10 00	10 05		10 10			10 15	10 20		10 25	10 30	10 35		10 40				10 50	10 55			
Heath Low Level	d	10 00												10 30									11 00			
Ty Glas	d	10 03												10 33									11 03			
Birchgrove	d	10 04												10 34									11 04			
Rhiwbina	d	10 06												10 36									11 06			
Whitchurch (Cardiff)	d	10 08												10 38									11 08			
Coryton	a	10 13												10 43									11 13			
Heath High Level	d					10 10						10 25				10 40						10 55				
Llanishen	d					10 13						10 28				10 43						10 58				
Lisvane & Thornhill	d					10 15						10 30				10 45						11 00				
Caerphilly 3	d					10 21						10 36				10 51						11 06				
Aber	d					10 23						10 38				10 53						11 08				
Llanbradach	d					10 27						10 42				10 57						11 12				
Ystrad Mynach 3	d					10 32						10 47				11 02						11 17				
Hengoed	d					10 35						10 50				11 05						11 20				
Pengam	d					10 38						10 53				11 08						11 23				
Gilfach Fargoed	d					10 41																				
Bargoed	d					10a48						10 59				11a16						11a31				
Brithdir	d											11 03														
Tir-phil	d											11 06														
Pontlottyn	d											11 10														
Rhymney 3	a											11 16														
Cathays	d				10 03			10 13			10 18				10 33			10 43								
Llandaf	d				10 07			10 17			10 22				10 37			10 47								
Ninian Park	d									10 10									10 40							
Waun-gron Park	d									10 13									10 43							
Fairwater	d									10 15									10 45							
Danescourt	d									10 17									10 47							
Radyr 3	a				10 10			10 20		10 24	10 25				10 40			10 50	10 54							11 05
	d				10 10			10 20			10 25				10 40			10 50								11 20 ↪
Taffs Well 3	d				10 14			10 24			10 29				10 44			10 54								
Trefforest Estate	d				10 18										10 48											
Trefforest	d				10 22			10 31			10 36				10 52			11 01								
Pontypridd 3	a				10 30			10 34			10 39				10 55			11 04								
	d						10 35	10 36			10 41				10 57			11 06								
Abercynon	d						10 41				10 49				11 04											
Penrhiwceiber	d										10 54															
Mountain Ash	a										10 58															
	d										11 03															
Fernhill	d										11 05															
Cwmbach	d										11 09															
Aberdare 3	a										11 16															
Quakers Yard	d						10 45								11 09											
Merthyr Vale	d						10 52								11 17											
Troed Y Rhiw	d						10 55								11 20											
Pentre-bach	d						10 58								11 23											
Merthyr Tydfil	a						11 06								11 31											
Trehafod	d							10 41										11 11								
Porth	d							10 45										11 15								
Dinas Rhondda	d							10 49										11 19								
Tonypandy	d							10 51										11 21								
Llwynypia	d							10 53										11 23								
Ystrad Rhondda	a							10 56										11 26								
	d							10 59										11 29								
Ton Pentre	d							11 01										11 31								
Treorchy	d							11 04										11 34								
Ynyswen	d							11 07										11 37								
Treherbert	a							11 13										11 43								

For general notes see front of timetable
For details of catering facilities see Directory of Train Operators

A From Radyr
B From Coryton

From Monday 7 September a revised service will be in operation due to seasonal difficulties. Most trains will arrive at their destination between 1 and 3 minutes later. Passengers should check with National Rail Enquiries for precise times.

Bridgend, Barry Island, Barry, Penarth and Cardiff → Coryton. Rhymney, Pontypridd, Merthyr, Aberdare and Treherbert

Network Diagram - see first page of Table 130

		AW	AW	AW	AW	AW	AW	AW	AW	AW	AW	AW	AW	AW	AW	AW	AW	AW	AW	AW	AW	AW		AW	AW	AW
						A				B					A					B						
Bridgend	d																	10 42								
Llantwit Major	d																	10 56								
Rhoose Cardiff Int Airport ✈	d																	11 06								
Barry Island	d	10 26					10 41				10 56											11 26				
Barry 3	d	10 30					10 45				11 00							11 15				11 30				
Barry Docks	d	10 34					10 49				11 04							11 19				11 34				
Cadoxton	d	10 37					10 52				11 07							11 22				11 37				
Dinas Powys	d	10 41					10 56				11 11							11 26				11 41				
Eastbrook	d	10 43					10 58				11 13							11 28				11 43				
Cogan	d	10 45					11 00				11 15							11 30				11 45				
Penarth	d		10 47					11 02				11 17							11 32					11 47		
Dingle Road	d		10 49					11 04				11 19							11 34					11 49		
Grangetown	d	10 49	10 53				11 04	11 08			11 19	11 23						11 34	11 38			11 49		11 53		
Cardiff Central 7	a	10 54	10 59				11 09	11 14			11 24	11 29						11 43	11 44			11 54		12 00		
	d	10 56	11 01			11 06	11 11	11 16		11 21	11 26	11 31		11 36	11 36	11 41			11 46	11 51		11 56		12 01	12 06	
Cardiff Bay	d			11 06					11 18				11 30				11 42				11 54					12 06
Cardiff Queen Street 3	a	10 59	11 04	11 10			11 14	11 19	11 22	11 24	11 29	11 34	11 34	11 39		11 44	11 46		11 49	11 54	11 58	11 59		12 04	12 09	12 10
	d	11 00	11 05				11 15	11 20		11 25	11 30	11 35		11 40		11 45			11 50	11 55		12 00		12 05	12 10	
Heath Low Level	d									11 30										12 00						
Ty Glas	d									11 33										12 03						
Birchgrove	d									11 34										12 04						
Rhiwbina	d									11 36										12 06						
Whitchurch (Cardiff)	d									11 38										12 08						
Coryton	a									11 43										12 13						
Heath High Level	d		11 10					11 25				11 40							11 55					12 10		
Llanishen	d		11 13					11 28				11 43							11 58					12 13		
Lisvane & Thornhill	d		11 15					11 30				11 45							12 00					12 15		
Caerphilly 3	d		11 21					11 36				11 51							12 06					12 21		
Aber	d		11 23					11 38				11 53							12 08					12 23		
Llanbradach	d		11 27					11 42				11 57							12 12					12 27		
Ystrad Mynach 3	d		11 32					11 47				12 02							12 17					12 32		
Hengoed	d		11 35					11 50				12 05							12 20					12 35		
Pengam	d		11 38					11 53				12 08							12 23					12 38		
Gilfach Fargoed	d		11 41																					12 41		
Bargoed	d		11a48					11 59				12a16							12a31					12a48		
Brithdir	d							12 03																		
Tir-phil	d							12 06																		
Pontlottyn	d							12 10																		
Rhymney 3	a							12 16																		
Cathays	d	11 03					11 18				11 33			11 43		11 48						12 03			12 13	
Llandaf	d	11 07					11 22				11 37			11 47		11 52						12 07			12 17	
Ninian Park	d					11 10									11 40											
Waun-gron Park	d					11 13									11 43											
Fairwater	d					11 15									11 45											
Danescourt	d					11 17									11 47											
Radyr 3	a	11 10			←	11 24	11 25				11 40			11 50	11 54	11 55						12 10			12 20	
	d	11 10			11 20		11 25				11 40			11 50		11 55						12 10			12 20	
Taffs Well 3	d	11 14			11 24		11 29				11 44			11 54		11 59						12 14			12 24	
Trefforest Estate	d	11 18									11 48											12 18				
Trefforest	d	11 22			11 31		11 36				11 52			12 01		12 06						12 22			12 31	
Pontypridd 3	a	11 25			11 34		11 39				11 55			12 04		12 09						12 25			12 34	
	d	11 27			11 36		11 41				11 57			12 06		12 11						12 27			12 36	
Abercynon	d	11 34					11 49				12 04					12 19						12 34				
Penrhiwceiber	d						11 54									12 24										
Mountain Ash	a						11 58									12 28										
	d						12 03									12 33										
Fernhill	d						12 05									12 35										
Cwmbach	d						12 09									12 39										
Aberdare 3	a						12 16									12 46										
Quakers Yard	d	11 39									12 09											12 39				
Merthyr Vale	d	11 47									12 17											12 47				
Troed Y Rhiw	d	11 50									12 20											12 50				
Pentre-bach	d	11 53									12 23											12 53				
Merthyr Tydfil	a	12 01									12 31											13 01				
Trehafod	d				11 41									12 11											12 41	
Porth	d				11 45									12 15											12 45	
Dinas Rhondda	d				11 49									12 19											12 49	
Tonypandy	d				11 51									12 21											12 51	
Llwynypia	d				11 53									12 23											12 53	
Ystrad Rhondda	a				11 56									12 26											12 56	
	d				11 59									12 29											12 59	
Ton Pentre	d				12 01									12 31											13 01	
Treorchy	d				12 04									12 34											13 04	
Ynyswen	d				12 07									12 37											13 07	
Treherbert	a				12 13									12 43											13 13	

For general notes see front of timetable
For details of catering facilities see Directory of Train Operators

A From Coryton
B From Radyr

From Monday 7 September a revised service will be in operation due to seasonal difficulties. Most trains will arrive at their destination between 1 and 3 minutes later. Passengers should check with National Rail Enquiries for precise times.

Bridgend, Barry Island, Barry, Penarth and Cardiff → Coryton. Rhymney, Pontypridd, Merthyr, Aberdare and Treherbert

Network Diagram - see first page of Table 130

		AW A	AW	AW	AW	AW B	AW	AW	AW	AW	AW A	AW	AW	AW	AW B	AW	AW	AW	AW	AW	AW A		AW	AW	AW	AW B
Bridgend	d											11 42														
Llantwit Major	d											11 56														
Rhoose Cardiff Int Airport ✈	d											12 06														
Barry Island	d		11 41				11 56										12 26						12 41			
Barry [3]	d		11 45				12 00					12 15					12 30						12 45			
Barry Docks	d		11 49				12 04					12 19					12 34						12 49			
Cadoxton	d		11 52				12 07					12 22					12 37						12 52			
Dinas Powys	d		11 56				12 11					12 26					12 41						12 56			
Eastbrook	d		11 58				12 13					12 28					12 43						12 58			
Cogan	d		12 00				12 15					12 30					12 45						13 00			
Penarth	d			12 02				12 17						12 32				12 47						13 02		
Dingle Road	d			12 04				12 19						12 34				12 49						13 04		
Grangetown	d		12 04	12 08			12 19	12 23				12 34		12 38			12 49	12 53					13 04	13 08		
Cardiff Central [7]	a		12 09	12 14			12 24	12 29				12 39		12 44			12 54	12 59					13 09	13 14		
	d	12 06	12 11	12 16		12 21	12 26	12 31		12 36	12 36	12 41		12 46	12 51		12 56	13 01	13 06		13 06		13 11	13 16		13 21
Cardiff Bay	d				12 18				12 30				12 42			12 54				13 06					13 18	
Cardiff Queen Street [3]	a		12 14	12 19	12 22	12 24	12 29	12 34	12 34	12 39		12 44	12 46	12 49	12 54	12 58	12 59	13 04	13 09	13 10			13 14	13 19	13 22	13 24
	d		12 15	12 20		12 25	12 30	12 35		12 40		12 45		12 50	12 55		13 00	13 05	13 10				13 15	13 20		13 25
Heath Low Level	d					12 30									13 00											13 30
Ty Glas	d					12 33									13 03											13 33
Birchgrove	d					12 34									13 04											13 34
Rhiwbina	d					12 36									13 06											13 36
Whitchurch (Cardiff)	d					12 38									13 08											13 38
Coryton	a					12 43									13 13											13 43
Heath High Level	d			12 25				12 40						12 55				13 10						13 25		
Llanishen	d			12 28				12 43						12 58				13 13						13 28		
Lisvane & Thornhill	d			12 30				12 45						13 00				13 15						13 30		
Caerphilly [3]	d			12 36				12 51						13 06				13 21						13 36		
Aber	d			12 38				12 53						13 08				13 23						13 38		
Llanbradach	d			12 42				12 57						13 12				13 27						13 42		
Ystrad Mynach [3]	d			12 47				13 02						13 17				13 32						13 47		
Hengoed	d			12 50				13 05						13 20				13 35						13 50		
Pengam	d			12 53				13 08						13 23				13 38						13 53		
Gilfach Fargoed	d																	13 41								
Bargoed	d			12 59				13a16						13a31				13a48						13 59		
Brithdir	d			13 03																				14 03		
Tir-phil	d			13 06																				14 06		
Pontlottyn	d			13 10																				14 10		
Rhymney [3]	a			13 16																				14 16		
Cathays	d		12 18				12 33			12 43		12 48					13 03		13 13				13 18			
Llandaf	d		12 22				12 37			12 47		12 52					13 07		13 17				13 22			
Ninian Park	d	12 10									12 40										13 10					
Waun-gron Park	d	12 13									12 43										13 13					
Fairwater	d	12 15									12 45										13 15					
Danescourt	d	12 17									12 47										13 17					
Radyr [3]	a	12 24	12 25				12 40			12 50	12 54	12 55					13 10		13 20		13 24		13 25			
	d		12 25				12 40			12 50		12 55					13 10		13 20				13 25			
Taffs Well [3]	d		12 29				12 44			12 54		12 59					13 14		13 24				13 29			
Trefforest Estate	d						12 48										13 18									
Trefforest	d		12 36				12 52			13 01		13 06					13 22		13 31				13 36			
Pontypridd [3]	a		12 42				12 55			13 04		13 09					13 25		13 34				13 39			
	d						12 57			13 06		13 11					13 27		13 36				13 41			
Abercynon	d						13 04					13 19					13 34						13 49			
Penrhiwceiber	d											13 24											13 54			
Mountain Ash	a											13 28											13 58			
	d											13 33											14 03			
Fernhill	d											13 35											14 05			
Cwmbach	d											13 39											14 09			
Aberdare [3]	a											13 46											14 16			
Quakers Yard	d						13 09										13 39									
Merthyr Vale	d						13 17										13 47									
Troed Y Rhiw	d						13 20										13 50									
Pentre-bach	d						13 23										13 53									
Merthyr Tydfil	a						13 31										14 01									
Trehafod	d									13 11									13 41							
Porth	d									13 15									13 45							
Dinas Rhondda	d									13 19									13 49							
Tonypandy	d									13 21									13 51							
Llwynypia	d									13 23									13 53							
Ystrad Rhondda	a									13 26									13 56							
	d									13 29									13 59							
Ton Pentre	d									13 31									14 01							
Treorchy	d									13 34									14 04							
Ynyswen	d									13 37									14 07							
Treherbert	a									13 44									14 13							

For general notes see front of timetable
For details of catering facilities see Directory of Train Operators

A From Coryton
B From Radyr

From Monday 7 September a revised service will be in operation due to seasonal difficulties. Most trains will arrive at their destination between 1 and 3 minutes later. Passengers should check with National Rail Enquiries for precise times.

Bridgend, Barry Island, Barry, Penarth and Cardiff → Coryton. Rhymney, Pontypridd, Merthyr, Aberdare and Treherbert

Network Diagram - see first page of Table 130

		AW	AW	AW	AW	AW A	AW	AW	AW	AW B	AW	AW	AW	AW	AW	AW A	AW	AW	AW	AW B		AW	AW	AW	AW	AW A
Bridgend	d						12 42																			
Llantwit Major	d						12 56																			
Rhoose Cardiff Int Airport ✈	d						13 06																			
Barry Island	d	12 56										13 26					13 41					13 56				
Barry 3	d	13 00					13 15					13 30					13 45					14 00				
Barry Docks	d	13 04					13 19					13 34					13 49					14 04				
Cadoxton	d	13 07					13 22					13 37					13 52					14 07				
Dinas Powys	d	13 11					13 26					13 41					13 56					14 11				
Eastbrook	d	13 13					13 28					13 43					13 58					14 13				
Cogan	d	13 15					13 30					13 45					14 00					14 15				
Penarth	d		13 17						13 32				13 47					14 02					14 17			
Dingle Road	d		13 19						13 34				13 49					14 04					14 19			
Grangetown	d	13 19	13 23				13 34		13 38			13 49	13 53				14 04	14 08				14 19	14 23			
Cardiff Central 7	a	13 24	13 29				13 39		13 44			13 54	13 59				14 09	14 14				14 24	14 29			
	d	13 26	13 31		13 36	13 36	13 41		13 46	13 51		13 56	14 01	14 06		14 06	14 11	14 16		14 21		14 26	14 31		14 36	14 36
Cardiff Bay	d			13 30				13 42			13 54				14 06				14 18					14 30		
Cardiff Queen Street 3	a	13 29	13 34	13 34	13 39		13 44	13 46	13 49	13 54	13 58	13 59	14 04	14 09	14 10		14 14	14 19	14 22	14 24		14 29	14 34	14 34	14 39	
	d	13 30	13 35		13 40		13 45		13 50	13 55		14 00	14 05	14 10			14 15	14 20		14 25		14 30	14 35		14 40	
Heath Low Level	d									14 00										14 30						
Ty Glas	d									14 03										14 33						
Birchgrove	d									14 04										14 34						
Rhiwbina	d									14 06										14 36						
Whitchurch (Cardiff)	d									14 08										14 38						
Coryton	a									14 13										14 43						
Heath High Level	d		13 40						13 55				14 10					14 25					14 40			
Llanishen	d		13 43						13 58				14 13					14 28					14 43			
Lisvane & Thornhill	d		13 45						14 00				14 15					14 30					14 45			
Caerphilly 3	d		13 51						14 06				14 21					14 36					14 51			
Aber	d		13 53						14 08				14 23					14 38					14 53			
Llanbradach	d		13 57						14 12				14 27					14 42					14 57			
Ystrad Mynach 3	d		14 02						14 17				14 32					14 47					15 02			
Hengoed	d		14 05						14 20				14 35					14 50					15 05			
Pengam	d		14 08						14 23				14 38					14 53					15 08			
Gilfach Fargoed	d												14 41													
Bargoed	d		14a16						14a31				14a48					14 59					15a16			
Brithdir	d																	15 03								
Tir-phil	d																	15 06								
Pontlottyn	d																	15 10								
Rhymney 3	a																	15 16								
Cathays	d	13 33			13 43		13 48					14 03		14 13			14 18					14 33			14 43	
Llandaf	d	13 37			13 47		13 52					14 07		14 17			14 22					14 37			14 47	
Ninian Park	d					13 40										14 10										14 40
Waun-gron Park	d					13 43										14 13										14 43
Fairwater	d					13 45										14 15										14 45
Danescourt	d					13 47										14 17										14 47
Radyr 3	a	13 40			13 50	13 54	13 55					14 10		14 20		14 24	14 25					14 40			14 50	14 54
	d	13 40			13 50		13 55					14 10		14 20			14 25					14 40			14 50	
Taffs Well 3	d	13 44			13 54		13 59					14 14		14 24			14 29					14 44			14 54	
Trefforest Estate	d	13 48										14 18										14 48				
Trefforest	d	13 52			14 01		14 06					14 22		14 31			14 36					14 52			15 01	
Pontypridd 3	a	13 55			14 04		14 09					14 25		14 34			14 39					14 55			15 04	
	d	13 57			14 06		14 11					14 27		14 36			14 41					14 57			15 06	
Abercynon	d	14 04					14 19					14 34					14 49					15 04				
Penrhiwceiber	d						14 24										14 54									
Mountain Ash	a						14 28										14 58									
	d						14 33										15 03									
Fernhill	d						14 35										15 05									
Cwmbach	d						14 39										15 09									
Aberdare 3	a						14 46										15 16									
Quakers Yard	d	14 09										14 39										15 09				
Merthyr Vale	d	14 17										14 47										15 17				
Troed Y Rhiw	d	14 20										14 50										15 20				
Pentre-bach	d	14 23										14 53										15 23				
Merthyr Tydfil	a	14 31										15 01										15 31				
Trehafod	d				14 11									14 41											15 11	
Porth	d				14 15									14 45											15 15	
Dinas Rhondda	d				14 19									14 49											15 19	
Tonypandy	d				14 21									14 51											15 21	
Llwynypia	d				14 23									14 53											15 23	
Ystrad Rhondda	a				14 26									14 56											15 26	
	d				14 29									14 59											15 29	
Ton Pentre	d				14 31									15 01											15 31	
Treorchy	d				14 34									15 04											15 34	
Ynyswen	d				14 37									15 07											15 37	
Treherbert	a				14 43									15 13											15 43	

For general notes see front of timetable
For details of catering facilities see Directory of Train Operators

A From Coryton
B From Radyr

From Monday 7 September a revised service will be in operation due to seasonal difficulties. Most trains will arrive at their destination between 1 and 3 minutes later. Passengers should check with National Rail Enquiries for precise times.

Bridgend, Barry Island, Barry, Penarth and Cardiff → Coryton. Rhymney, Pontypridd, Merthyr, Aberdare and Treherbert

Network Diagram - see first page of Table 130

		AW	AW	AW	AW	AW	AW	AW	AW	AW	AW	AW	AW	AW	AW	AW	AW	AW	AW		AW	AW	AW	AW	AW	AW
						A							B				A						B			
Bridgend	d	13 42																						14 42		
Llantwit Major	d	13 56																						14 56		
Rhoose Cardiff Int Airport ✈	d	14 06																						15 06		
Barry Island	d							14 26						14 41				14 56								
Barry 3	d	14 15						14 30						14 45				15 00						15 15		
Barry Docks	d	14 19						14 34						14 49				15 04						15 19		
Cadoxton	d	14 22						14 37						14 52				15 07						15 22		
Dinas Powys	d	14 26						14 41						14 56				15 11						15 26		
Eastbrook	d	14 28						14 43						14 58				15 13						15 28		
Cogan	d	14 30						14 45						15 00				15 15						15 30		
Penarth	d			14 32					14 47						15 02				15 17							15 32
Dingle Road	d			14 34					14 49						15 04				15 19							15 34
Grangetown	d	14 34		14 38				14 49	14 53					15 04	15 08			15 19	15 23					15 34		15 38
Cardiff Central 7	a	14 39		14 44				14 54	14 59					15 09	15 14			15 24	15 29					15 39		15 44
	d	14 41		14 46	14 51	14 51		14 56	15 01				15 06	15 11	15 16		15 21	15 26	15 31			15 36	15 36	15 41		15 46
Cardiff Bay	d		14 42				14 54			15 06						15 18					15 30				15 42	
Cardiff Queen Street 3	a	14 44	14 46	14 49		14 54	14 58	14 59	15 04	15 10				15 14	15 19	15 22	15 24	15 29	15 34		15 34	15 39		15 44	15 46	15 49
	d	14 45		14 50		14 55		15 00	15 05					15 15	15 20		15 25	15 30	15 35			15 40		15 45		15 50
Heath Low Level	d					15 00											15 30									
Ty Glas	d					15 03											15 33									
Birchgrove	d					15 04											15 34									
Rhiwbina	d					15 06											15 36									
Whitchurch (Cardiff)	d					15 08											15 38									
Coryton	a					15 13											15 43									
Heath High Level	d			14 55					15 10						15 25				15 40							15 55
Llanishen	d			14 58					15 13						15 28				15 43							15 58
Lisvane & Thornhill	d			15 00					15 15						15 30				15 45							16 00
Caerphilly 3	d			15 06					15 21						15 36				15 51							16 06
Aber	d			15 08					15 23						15 38				15 53							16 08
Llanbradach	d			15 12					15 27						15 42				15 57							16 12
Ystrad Mynach 3	d			15 17					15 32						15 47				16 02							16 17
Hengoed	d			15 20					15 35						15 50				16 05							16 20
Pengam	d			15 23					15 38						15 53				16 08							16 23
Gilfach Fargoed	d								15 41																	
Bargoed	d			15a31					15a48						15 59				16a16							16a31
Brithdir	d														16 03											
Tir-phil	d														16 06											
Pontlottyn	d														16 10											
Rhymney 3	a														16 16											
Cathays	d	14 48						15 03						15 18				15 33				15 43		15 48		
Llandaf	d	14 52						15 07						15 22				15 37				15 47		15 52		
Ninian Park	d												15 10										15 40			
Waun-gron Park	d												15 13										15 43			
Fairwater	d												15 15										15 45			
Danescourt	d												15 17										15 47			
Radyr 3	a				15 08			15 10				←	15 24	15 25				15 40				15 50	15 54	15 55		
	d	14 55			15 20 →			15 10				15 20		15 25				15 40				15 50		15 55		
Taffs Well 3	d	14 59						15 14				15 24		15 29				15 44				15 54		15 59		
Trefforest Estate	d							15 18										15 48								
Trefforest	d	15 06						15 22				15 31		15 36				15 52				16 01		16 06		
Pontypridd 3	a	15 09						15 30				15 34		15 39				15 55				16 04		16 09		
	d	15 11									15 35	15 36		15 41				15 57				16 06		16 11		
Abercynon	d	15 19									15 41			15 49				16 04						16 19		
Penrhiwceiber	d	15 24												15 54										16 24		
Mountain Ash	a	15 28												15 58										16 28		
	d	15 33												16 03										16 33		
Fernhill	d	15 35												16 05										16 35		
Cwmbach	d	15 39												16 09										16 39		
Aberdare 3	a	15 46												16 16										16 46		
Quakers Yard	d										15 45							16 09								
Merthyr Vale	d										15 52							16 17								
Troed Y Rhiw	d										15 55							16 20								
Pentre-bach	d										15 58							16 23								
Merthyr Tydfil	a										16 06							16 31								
Trehafod	d											15 41										16 11				
Porth	d											15 45										16 15				
Dinas Rhondda	d											15 49										16 19				
Tonypandy	d											15 51										16 21				
Llwynypia	d											15 53										16 23				
Ystrad Rhondda	a											15 56										16 26				
	d											15 59										16 29				
Ton Pentre	d											16 01										16 31				
Treorchy	d											16 04										16 34				
Ynyswen	d											16 07										16 37				
Treherbert	a											16 13										16 43				

For general notes see front of timetable
For details of catering facilities see Directory of Train Operators

A From Radyr
B From Coryton

From Monday 7 September a revised service will be in operation due to seasonal difficulties. Most trains will arrive at their destination between 1 and 3 minutes later. Passengers should check with National Rail Enquiries for precise times.

Bridgend, Barry Island, Barry, Penarth and Cardiff → Coryton. Rhymney, Pontypridd, Merthyr, Aberdare and Treherbert

Network Diagram - see first page of Table 130

		AW	AW	AW	AW	AW	AW	AW	AW	AW	AW	AW	AW	AW	AW	AW	AW	AW		AW	AW	AW	AW	AW	AW	AW
		A						B				A					B					A				
Bridgend	d																	15 42								
Llantwit Major	d																	15 56								
Rhoose Cardiff Int Airport ✈	d																	16 06								
Barry Island	d			15 26					15 41				15 56											16 26		
Barry 3	d			15 30					15 45				16 00					16 15						16 30		
Barry Docks	d			15 34					15 49				16 04					16 19						16 34		
Cadoxton	d			15 37					15 52				16 07					16 22						16 37		
Dinas Powys	d			15 41					15 56				16 11					16 26						16 41		
Eastbrook	d			15 43					15 58				16 13					16 28						16 43		
Cogan	d			15 45					16 00				16 15					16 30						16 45		
Penarth	d				15 47					16 02				16 17							16 32					
Dingle Road	d				15 49					16 04				16 19							16 34					
Grangetown	d			15 49	15 53				16 04	16 08			16 19	16 23				16 34			16 38			16 49		
Cardiff Central 7	a			15 54	15 59				16 09	16 14			16 24	16 29				16 39			16 44			16 54		
	d	15 51		15 56	16 01	16 06		16 06	16 11	16 16		16 21	16 26	16 31		16 36	16 36	16 41			16 46	16 51		16 56	17 01	17 06
Cardiff Bay	d		15 54				16 06				16 18				16 30					16 42			16 54			
Cardiff Queen Street 3	a	15 54	15 58	15 59	16 04	16 09	16 10		16 14	16 19	16 22	16 24	16 29	16 34	16 34	16 39		16 44		16 46	16 49	16 54	16 58	16 59	17 04	17 09
	d	15 55		16 00	16 05	16 10			16 15	16 20		16 25	16 30	16 35		16 40		16 45			16 50	16 55		17 00	17 05	17 10
Heath Low Level	d	16 00										16 30										17 00				
Ty Glas	d	16 03										16 33										17 03				
Birchgrove	d	16 04										16 34										17 04				
Rhiwbina	d	16 06										16 36										17 06				
Whitchurch (Cardiff)	d	16 08										16 38										17 08				
Coryton	a	16 13										16 43										17 13				
Heath High Level	d				16 10					16 25				16 40							16 55				17 10	
Llanishen	d				16 13					16 28				16 43							16 58				17 13	
Lisvane & Thornhill	d				16 15					16 30				16 45							17 00				17 15	
Caerphilly 3	d				16 21					16 36				16 51							17 06				17 21	
Aber	d				16 23					16 38				16 53							17 08				17 23	
Llanbradach	d				16 27					16 42				16 57							17 12				17 27	
Ystrad Mynach 3	d				16 32					16 47				17 02							17 17				17 33	
Hengoed	d				16 35					16 50				17 05							17 20				17 35	
Pengam	d				16 38					16 53				17 08							17 23				17 39	
Gilfach Fargoed	d				16 41																				17 42	
Bargoed	d				16a48					16 59				17a16							17a31				17 47	
Brithdir	d									17 03															17 50	
Tir-phil	d									17 06															17 53	
Pontlottyn	d									17 10															17 58	
Rhymney 3	a									17 16															18 04	
Cathays	d			16 03		16 13			16 18				16 33			16 43		16 48						17 03		17 13
Llandaf	d			16 07		16 17			16 22				16 37			16 47		16 52						17 07		17 17
Ninian Park	d							16 10									16 40									
Waun-gron Park	d							16 13									16 43									
Fairwater	d							16 15									16 45									
Danescourt	d							16 17									16 47									
Radyr 3	a			16 10		16 20		16 24	16 25				16 40			16 50	16 54	16 55						17 10		17 20
	d			16 10		16 20			16 25				16 40			16 50		16 55						17 10		17 20
Taffs Well 3	d			16 14		16 24			16 29				16 44			16 54		16 59						17 14		17 24
Trefforest Estate	d			16 18									16 48											17 18		
Trefforest	d			16 22		16 31			16 36				16 52			17 01		17 06						17 22		17 31
Pontypridd 3	a			16 25		16 34			16 39				16 55			17 04		17 09						17 25		17 34
	d			16 27		16 36			16 41				16 57			17 06		17 11						17 27		17 36
Abercynon	d			16 34					16 49				17 04					17 19						17 34		
Penrhiwceiber	d								16 54									17 24								
Mountain Ash	a								16 58									17 28								
	d								17 03									17 33								
Fernhill	d								17 05									17 35								
Cwmbach	d								17 09									17 39								
Aberdare 3	a								17 16									17 46								
Quakers Yard	d			16 39									17 09											17 39		
Merthyr Vale	d			16 47									17 17											17 47		
Troed Y Rhiw	d			16 50									17 20											17 50		
Pentre-bach	d			16 53									17 23											17 53		
Merthyr Tydfil	a			17 01									17 31											18 01		
Trehafod	d					16 41										17 11										17 41
Porth	d					16 45										17 15										17 45
Dinas Rhondda	d					16 49										17 19										17 49
Tonypandy	d					16 51										17 21										17 51
Llwynypia	d					16 53										17 23										17 53
Ystrad Rhondda	a					16 56										17 26										17 56
	d					16 59										17 29										17 59
Ton Pentre	d					17 01										17 31										18 01
Treorchy	d					17 04										17 34										18 04
Ynyswen	d					17 07										17 37										18 07
Treherbert	a					17 13										17 43										18 13

For general notes see front of timetable
For details of catering facilities see
Directory of Train Operators

A From Radyr
B From Coryton

From Monday 7 September a revised service will be in operation due to seasonal difficulties. Most trains will arrive at their destination between 1 and 3 minutes later. Passengers should check with National Rail Enquiries for precise times.

Bridgend, Barry Island, Barry, Penarth and Cardiff → Coryton. Rhymney, Pontypridd, Merthyr, Aberdare and Treherbert

Network Diagram - see first page of Table 130

		AW	AW	AW	AW	AW	AW	AW	AW	AW	AW	AW	AW	AW	AW	AW	AW	AW	AW	AW	AW	AW	AW	AW	AW
			A				B					A				B						A			
Bridgend	d												16 42												
Llantwit Major	d												16 56												
Rhoose Cardiff Int Airport ✈	d												17 06												
Barry Island	d			16 41				16 56										17 26					17 41		
Barry 3	d			16 45				17 00					17 15					17 30					17 45		
Barry Docks	d			16 49				17 04					17 19					17 34					17 49		
Cadoxton	d			16 52				17 07					17 22					17 37					17 52		
Dinas Powys	d			16 56				17 11					17 26					17 41					17 56		
Eastbrook	d			16 58				17 13					17 28					17 43					17 58		
Cogan	d			17 00				17 15					17 30					17 45					18 00		
Penarth	d				17 02				17 17						17 32				17 47					18 02	
Dingle Road	d				17 04				17 19						17 34				17 49					18 04	
Grangetown	d			17 04	17 08			17 19	17 23				17 34		17 38			17 49	17 53				18 04	18 08	
Cardiff Central 7	a			17 09	17 14			17 24	17 29				17 39		17 44			17 54	17 59				18 09	18 14	
	d		17 06	17 11	17 16		17 21	17 26	17 31		17 36	17 36	17 41		17 46	17 51		17 56	18 01	18 06		18 06	18 11	18 16	
Cardiff Bay	d	17 06				17 18				17 30				17 42			17 54				18 06				18 18
Cardiff Queen Street 3	a	17 10		17 14	17 19	17 22	17 24	17 29	17 34	17 34	17 39		17 44	17 46	17 49	17 54	17 58	17 59	18 04	18 09	18 10		18 14	18 19	18 22
	d			17 15	17 20		17 25	17 30	17 35		17 40		17 45		17 50	17 55		18 00	18 05	18 10			18 15	18 20	
Heath Low Level	d						17 30									18 00									
Ty Glas	d						17 33									18 03									
Birchgrove	d						17 34									18 04									
Rhiwbina	d						17 36									18 06									
Whitchurch (Cardiff)	d						17 38									18 08									
Coryton	a						17 43									18 13									
Heath High Level	d				17 25				17 40						17 55				18 10					18 25	
Llanishen	d				17 28				17 43						17 59				18 13					18 28	
Lisvane & Thornhill	d				17 30				17 45						18 02				18 15					18 30	
Caerphilly 3	d				17 36				17 51						18 07				18 21					18 36	
Aber	d				17 38				17 53						18 10				18 23					18 38	
Llanbradach	d				17 42				17 57						18 14				18 27					18 42	
Ystrad Mynach 3	d				17 47				18 02						18 20				18 32					18a51	
Hengoed	d				17 50				18 05						18 23				18 35						
Pengam	d				17 53				18 08						18 27				18 38						
Gilfach Fargoed	d								18 11						18 30				18 41						
Bargoed	d				18a01				18 16						18b44				18a48						
Brithdir	d								18 20						18 48										
Tir-phil	d								18 23						18 51										
Pontlottyn	d								18 27						18 55										
Rhymney 3	a								18 33						19 01										
Cathays	d			17 18				17 33			17 43		17 48					18 03		18 13			18 18		
Llandaf	d			17 22				17 37			17 47		17 52					18 07		18 17			18 22		
Ninian Park	d		17 10									17 40										18 10			
Waun-gron Park	d		17 13									17 43										18 13			
Fairwater	d		17 15									17 45										18 15			
Danescourt	d		17 17									17 47										18 17			
Radyr 3	a		17 24	17 25				17 40			17 50	17 54	17 55					18 10		18 20		18 24	18 25		
	d			17 25				17 40			17 50		17 55					18 10		18 20			18 25		
Taffs Well 3	d			17 29				17 44			17 54		17 59					18 14		18 24			18 29		
Trefforest Estate	d							17 48										18 18							
Trefforest	d			17 36				17 52			18 01		18 06					18 22		18 31			18 36		
Pontypridd 3	a			17 39				17 55			18 04		18 09					18 25		18 34			18 42		
	d			17 41				17 57			18 06		18 11					18 27		18 36					
Abercynon	d			17 49				18 04					18 19					18 34							
Penrhiwceiber	d			17 54									18 24												
Mountain Ash	a			17 58									18 28												
	d			18 03									18 33												
Fernhill	d			18 05									18 35												
Cwmbach	d			18 09									18 39												
Aberdare 3	a			18 16									18 46												
Quakers Yard	d							18 09										18 39							
Merthyr Vale	d							18 17										18 47							
Troed Y Rhiw	d							18 20										18 50							
Pentre-bach	d							18 23										18 53							
Merthyr Tydfil	a							18 31										19 01							
Trehafod	d										18 11									18 41					
Porth	d										18 15									18 45					
Dinas Rhondda	d										18 19									18 49					
Tonypandy	d										18 21									18 51					
Llwynypia	d										18 23									18 53					
Ystrad Rhondda	a										18 26									18 56					
	d										18 29									18 59					
Ton Pentre	d										18 31									19 01					
Treorchy	d										18 34									19 04					
Ynyswen	d										18 37									19 07					
Treherbert	a										18 43									19 13					

For general notes see front of timetable
For details of catering facilities see Directory of Train Operators

A From Coryton
B From Radyr
b Arr. 1834

From Monday 7 September a revised service will be in operation due to seasonal difficulties. Most trains will arrive at their destination between 1 and 3 minutes later. Passengers should check with National Rail Enquiries for precise times.

Bridgend, Barry Island, Barry, Penarth and Cardiff → Coryton. Rhymney, Pontypridd, Merthyr, Aberdare and Treherbert

Network Diagram - see first page of Table 130

		AW	AW	AW	AW		AW	AW	AW	AW	AW	AW	AW	AW	AW	AW		AW	AW	AW	AW	AW	AW	AW	AW	AW
		A					B				A												B			
Bridgend	d							17 42																18 42		
Llantwit Major	d							17 56																18 56		
Rhoose Cardiff Int Airport ✈	d							18 06																19 06		
Barry Island	d		17 56										18 26					18 41		18 56						
Barry 3	d		18 00					18 15					18 30					18 45		19 00				19 15		
Barry Docks	d		18 04					18 19					18 34					18 49		19 04				19 19		
Cadoxton	d		18 07					18 22					18 37					18 52		19 07				19 22		
Dinas Powys	d		18 11					18 26					18 41					18 56		19 11				19 26		
Eastbrook	d		18 13					18 28					18 43					18 58		19 13				19 28		
Cogan	d		18 15					18 30					18 45					19 00		19 15				19 30		
Penarth	d				18 17					18 32				18 47							19 17					
Dingle Road	d				18 19					18 34				18 49							19 19					
Grangetown	d		18 19		18 23			18 34		18 38			18 49	18 53				19 04		19 19	19 23			19 34		
Cardiff Central 7	a		18 24		18 29			18 39		18 45			18 55	18 59				19 09		19 24	19 29			19 39		
	d	18 21	18 26		18 31	18 36	18 36	18 41			18 51			19 01	19 06			19 11		19 26	19 31		19 36	19 41		19 51
Cardiff Bay	d			18 30					18 42			18 54				19 06			19 18			19 30			19 42	
Cardiff Queen Street 3	a	18 24	18 29	18 34	18 34	18 38		18 44	18 46		18 54	18 58		19 04	19 09	19 10		19 14	19 22	19 29	19 34	19 34		19 44	19 46	19 54
	d	18 25	18 30		18 35	18 40		18 50			18 55			19 05	19 10			19 15		19 30	19 35			19 45		19 55
Heath Low Level	d	18 30									19 00															20 00
Ty Glas	d	18 33									19 03															20 03
Birchgrove	d	18 34									19 04															20 04
Rhiwbina	d	18 36									19 06															20 06
Whitchurch (Cardiff)	d	18 38									19 08															20 08
Coryton	a	18 43									19 13															20 13
Heath High Level	d				18 40									19 10							19 40					
Llanishen	d				18 43									19 13							19 43					
Lisvane & Thornhill	d				18 45									19 15							19 45					
Caerphilly 3	d				18 51									19a24							19 51					
Aber	d				18 53																19 53					
Llanbradach	d				18 57																19 57					
Ystrad Mynach 3	d				19 02																20 02					
Hengoed	d				19 05																20 05					
Pengam	d				19 08																20 08					
Gilfach Fargoed	d				19 11																20 11					
Bargoed	d				19 16																20 16					
Brithdir	d				19 20																20 20					
Tir-phil	d				19 23																20 23					
Pontlottyn	d				19 27																20 27					
Rhymney 3	a				19 33																20 33					
Cathays	d		18 33			18 43		18 52							19 13			19 18		19 33				19 48		
Llandaf	d		18 37			18 47		18 56							19 17			19 22		19 37				19 52		
Ninian Park	d						18 40																19 40			
Waun-gron Park	d						18 43																19 43			
Fairwater	d						18 45																19 45			
Danescourt	d						18 47																19 47			
Radyr 3	a		18 40			18 50	18 54	18 58							19 20			19 25		19 40			19 54	19 55		
	d		18 40			18 50		18 58							19 20			19 25		19 40				19 55		
Taffs Well 3	d		18 44			18 54		19 03							19 24			19 29		19 44				19 59		
Trefforest Estate	d		18 48																	19 48						
Trefforest	d		18 52			19 01		19 10							19 31			19 36		19 52				20 06		
Pontypridd 3	a		18 55			19 04		19 13							19 34			19 39		19 55				20 09		
	d		18 57			19 06		19 14							19 36			19 41		19 57				20 11		
Abercynon	d		19 04					19 21										19 49		20 04				20 21		
Penrhiwceiber	d							19 26										19 54						20 27		
Mountain Ash	a							19 30										19 56						20 30		
	d							19 33										20 03						20 33		
Fernhill	d							19 35										20 05						20 35		
Cwmbach	d							19 39										20 09						20 39		
Aberdare 3	a							19 46										20 16						20 46		
Quakers Yard	d		19 09																	20 09						
Merthyr Vale	d		19 17																	20 17						
Troed Y Rhiw	d		19 20																	20 20						
Pentre-bach	d		19 23																	20 23						
Merthyr Tydfil	a		19 31																	20 31						
Trehafod	d					19 11									19 41											
Porth	d					19 15									19 45											
Dinas Rhondda	d					19 19									19 49											
Tonypandy	d					19 21									19 51											
Llwynypia	d					19 23									19 53											
Ystrad Rhondda	a					19 26									19 56											
	d					19 29									19 59											
Ton Pentre	d					19 31									20 01											
Treorchy	d					19 34									20 04											
Ynyswen	d					19 37									20 07											
Treherbert	a					19 43									20 13											

For general notes see front of timetable
For details of catering facilities see Directory of Train Operators

A From Radyr
B From Coryton

From Monday 7 September a revised service will be in operation due to seasonal difficulties. Most trains will arrive at their destination between 1 and 3 minutes later. Passengers should check with National Rail Enquiries for precise times.

Bridgend, Barry Island, Barry, Penarth and Cardiff → Coryton. Rhymney, Pontypridd, Merthyr, Aberdare and Treherbert

Network Diagram - see first page of Table 130

		AW	AW	AW	AW	AW	AW	AW	AW	AW	AW	AW	AW	AW	AW		AW	AW	AW	AW	AW	AW	AW	AW	AW	AW
										A													A			
Bridgend	d										19 42														20 42	
Llantwit Major	d										19 56														20 56	
Rhoose Cardiff Int Airport ✈	d										20 06														21 06	
Barry Island	d		19 26				19 56													20 56						
Barry 3	d		19 30				20 00				20 15									21 00					21 15	
Barry Docks	d		19 34				20 04				20 19									21 04					21 19	
Cadoxton	d		19 37				20 07				20 22									21 07					21 22	
Dinas Powys	d		19 41				20 11				20 26									21 11					21 26	
Eastbrook	d		19 43				20 13				20 28									21 13					21 28	
Cogan	d		19 45				20 15				20 30									21 15					21 30	
Penarth	d			19 47				20 17							20 47									21 17		
Dingle Road	d			19 49				20 19							20 49									21 19		
Grangetown	d		19 49	19 54			20 19	20 23			20 34				20 53					21 19				21 23	21 34	
Cardiff Central 7	a		19 56	19 59			20 24	20 30			20 39				20 59					21 24				21 37	21 39	
	d		20 01	20 06			20 26	20 31		20 36	20 41		20 51		21 01		21 06			21 26		21 31	21 36		21 41	
Cardiff Bay	d	19 54			20 06	20 18			20 30			20 42		20 54				21 06	21 18		21 30					21 42
Cardiff Queen Street 3	a	19 58	20 04	20 09	20 10	20 22	20 29	20 34	20 34		20 44	20 46	20 54	20 58	21 04		21 09	21 10	21 22	21 29	21 34	21 34			21 44	21 46
	d		20 05	20 10			20 30	20 35			20 45		20 55		21 05		21 10			21 30		21 35			21 45	
Heath Low Level	d												21 00													
Ty Glas	d												21 03													
Birchgrove	d												21 04													
Rhiwbina	d												21 06													
Whitchurch (Cardiff)	d												21 08													
Coryton	a												21 13													
Heath High Level	d		20 10					20 40							21 10							21 40				
Llanishen	d		20 13					20 43							21 13							21 43				
Lisvane & Thornhill	d		20 15					20 45							21 15							21 45				
Caerphilly 3	d		20a28					20 51							21a28							21 51				
Aber	d							20 53														21 53				
Llanbradach	d							20 57														21 57				
Ystrad Mynach 3	d							21 02														22 02				
Hengoed	d							21 05														22 05				
Pengam	d							21 08														22 08				
Gilfach Fargoed	d							21 11														22 11				
Bargoed	d							21 16														22 16				
Brithdir	d							21 20														22 20				
Tir-phil	d							21 23														22 23				
Pontlottyn	d							21 27														22 27				
Rhymney 3	a							21 33														22 33				
Cathays	d			20 13			20 33				20 48						21 13			21 33					21 48	
Llandaf	d			20 17			20 37				20 52						21 17			21 37					21 52	
Ninian Park	d									20 40													21 40			
Waun-gron Park	d									20 43													21 43			
Fairwater	d									20 45													21 45			
Danescourt	d									20 47													21 47			
Radyr 3	a			20 20			20 40			20 54	20 55						21 20			21 40			21 54		21 55	
	d			20 20			20 40				20 55						21 20			21 40					21 55	
Taffs Well 3	d			20 24			20 44				20 59						21 24			21 44					21 59	
Trefforest Estate	d						20 48													21 48						
Trefforest	d			20 31			20 52				21 06						21 31			21 52					22 06	
Pontypridd 3	a			20 35			20 55				21 09						21 34			21 55					22 09	
	d			20 36			20 57				21 11						21 36			21 57					22 11	
Abercynon	d						21 04				21 19									22 04					22 19	
Penrhiwceiber	d										21 24														22 24	
Mountain Ash	a										21 28														22 28	
	d										21 33														22 33	
Fernhill	d										21 35														22 35	
Cwmbach	d										21 39														22 39	
Aberdare 3	a										21 46														22 46	
Quakers Yard	d						21 09													22 09						
Merthyr Vale	d						21b17													22 17						
Troed Y Rhiw	d						21 20													22 20						
Pentre-bach	d						21 23													22 23						
Merthyr Tydfil	a						21 31													22 31						
Trehafod	d			20 41													21 41									
Porth	d			20 45													21 45									
Dinas Rhondda	d			20 49													21 49									
Tonypandy	d			20 51													21 51									
Llwynypia	d			20 53													21 53									
Ystrad Rhondda	a			20 56													21 56									
	d			20 59													21 59									
Ton Pentre	d			21 01													22 01									
Treorchy	d			21 04													22 04									
Ynyswen	d			21 07													22 07									
Treherbert	a			21 13													22 13									

For general notes see front of timetable
For details of catering facilities see Directory of Train Operators

A From Coryton
b Arr. 2114

From Monday 7 September a revised service will be in operation due to seasonal difficulties. Most trains will arrive at their destination between 1 and 3 minutes later. Passengers should check with National Rail Enquiries for precise times.

Bridgend, Barry Island, Barry, Penarth and Cardiff → Coryton. Rhymney, Pontypridd, Merthyr, Aberdare and Treherbert

Network Diagram - see first page of Table 130

		AW	AW	AW	AW	AW	AW A	AW	AW	AW	AW	AW	AW	AW		AW	AW	AW	AW	AW	AW	AW	AW	AW
Bridgend	d										21 42												22 42	
Llantwit Major	d										21 56												22 56	
Rhoose Cardiff Int Airport ✈	d										22 06												23 06	
Barry Island	d							21 56											22 56					
Barry 3	d							22 00			22 15								23 00				23 15	
Barry Docks	d							22 04			22 19								23 04				23 19	
Cadoxton	d							22 07			22 22								23 07				23 22	
Dinas Powys	d							22 11			22 26								23 11				23 26	
Eastbrook	d							22 13			22 28								23 13				23 28	
Cogan	d							22 15			22 30								23 15				23 30	
Penarth	d		21 47							22 17							22 47				23 26			
Dingle Road	d		21 49							22 19							22 49				23 28			
Grangetown	d		21 53					22 19		22 23	22 34						22 53		23 19		23 32		23 34	
Cardiff Central 7	a		21 59					22 24		22 31	22 39						23 00		23 24		23 38		23 42	
	d		22 01	22 06			22 21	22 26		22 35	22 41		22 46				23 15		23 26					
Cardiff Bay	d	21 54			22 06	22 18			22 30			22 42		22 54		23 06		23 18		23 30		23 42		23 54
Cardiff Queen Street 3	a	21 58	22 04	22 09	22 10	22 22	22 24	22 29	22 34	22 38	22 44	22 46	22 49	22 58		23 10	23 18	23 22	23 29	23 34		23 46		23 58
	d		22 05	22 10			22 25	22 30		22 39	22 45		22 50				23 19		23 30					
Heath Low Level	d						22 30																	
Ty Glas	d						22 33																	
Birchgrove	d						22 34																	
Rhiwbina	d						22 36																	
Whitchurch (Cardiff)	d						22 38																	
Coryton	a						22 43																	
Heath High Level	d		22 10							22 44							23 24							
Llanishen	d		22 13							22 47							23 27							
Lisvane & Thornhill	d		22 15							22 49							23 29							
Caerphilly 3	d		22a24							22 55							23 35							
Aber	d									22 57							23 37							
Llanbradach	d									23 01							23 41							
Ystrad Mynach 3	d									23 06							23a50							
Hengoed	d									23 09														
Pengam	d									23 12														
Gilfach Fargoed	d									23 15														
Bargoed	d									23 20														
Brithdir	d									23 24														
Tir-phil	d									23 27														
Pontlottyn	d									23 31														
Rhymney 3	a									23 37														
Cathays	d			22 13				22 33			22 48		22 53						23 33					
Llandaf	d			22 17				22 37			22 52		22 57						23 37					
Ninian Park	d																							
Waun-gron Park	d																							
Fairwater	d																							
Danescourt	d																							
Radyr 3	a			22 20				22 40			22 55		22 59						23 40					
	d			22 20				22 40			22 55		22 59						23 40					
Taffs Well 3	d			22 24				22 44			22 59		23 03						23 44					
Trefforest Estate	d							22 48											23 48					
Trefforest	d			22 31				22 52			23 06		23 10						23 52					
Pontypridd 3	a			22 34				22 55			23 09		23 14						23 58					
	d			22 36				22 57			23 11		23 15											
Abercynon	d							23 04			23 19													
Penrhiwceiber	d										23 24													
Mountain Ash	a										23 28													
	d										23 33													
Fernhill	d										23 35													
Cwmbach	d										23 39													
Aberdare 3	a										23 46													
Quakers Yard	d							23 09																
Merthyr Vale	d							23 17																
Troed Y Rhiw	d							23 20																
Pentre-bach	d							23 23																
Merthyr Tydfil	a							23 31																
Trehafod	d			22 41									23 20											
Porth	d			22 45									23 24											
Dinas Rhondda	d			22 49									23 28											
Tonypandy	d			22 51									23 30											
Llwynypia	d			22 53									23 32											
Ystrad Rhondda	a			22 56									23 35											
	d			22 59									23 38											
Ton Pentre	d			23 01									23 40											
Treorchy	d			23 04									23 43											
Ynyswen	d			23 07									23 46											
Treherbert	a			23 14									23 52											

For general notes see front of timetable
For details of catering facilities see Directory of Train Operators

A From Radyr

From Monday 7 September a revised service will be in operation due to seasonal difficulties. Most trains will arrive at their destination between 1 and 3 minutes later. Passengers should check with National Rail Enquiries for precise times.

Table 130

Saturdays

Bridgend, Barry Island, Barry, Penarth and Cardiff → Coryton, Rhymney, Pontypridd, Merthyr, Aberdare and Treherbert

Network Diagram - see first page of Table 130

		AW		AW	AW	AW	AW	AW	AW	AW	AW	AW	AW	AW	AW	AW		AW	AW	AW A	AW	AW	AW	AW B	AW	AW
Bridgend	d										05 42															
Llantwit Major	d										05 56															
Rhoose Cardiff Int Airport ✈	d										06 06															
Barry Island	d								05 53							06 26									06 56	
Barry [3]	d								05 57		06 15					06 30									07 00	
Barry Docks	d								06 01		06 19					06 34									07 04	
Cadoxton	d								06 04		06 22					06 37									07 07	
Dinas Powys	d								06 08		06 26					06 41									07 11	
Eastbrook	d								06 10		06 28					06 43									07 13	
Cogan	d								06 12		06 30					06 45									07 15	
Penarth	d						06 02						06 32									07 02				07 17
Dingle Road	d						06 04						06 34									07 04				07 19
Grangetown	d						06 08		06 16		06 34		06 38			06 49						07 08			07 19	07 23
Cardiff Central [7]	a						06 13		06 21		06 39		06 44			06 54						07 14			07 24	07 29
	d	05 26		05 46	05 56	06 11	06 15	06 19	06 26	06 36	06 41		06 46	06 51		06 56		07 06		07 06	07 11	07 16		07 21	07 26	07 31
Cardiff Bay	d											06 42			06 54				07 06				07 18			
Cardiff Queen Street [3]	a	05 29		05 49	05 59	06 14	06 19	06 24	06 29	06 39	06 44	06 46	06 49	06 54	06 58	06 59		07 09	07 10		07 14	07 19	07 22	07 24	07 29	07 34
	d	05 30		05 50	06 00	06 15	06 20	06 25	06 30	06 40	06 45		06 50	06 55		07 00		07 10			07 15	07 20		07 25	07 30	07 35
Heath Low Level	d							06 30						07 00										07 30		
Ty Glas	d							06 33						07 03										07 33		
Birchgrove	d							06 34						07 04										07 34		
Rhiwbina	d							06 36						07 06										07 36		
Whitchurch (Cardiff)	d							06 38						07 08										07 38		
Coryton	a							06 43						07 13										07 43		
Heath High Level	d			05 54			06 25						06 55									07 25				07 40
Llanishen	d			05 57			06 28						06 58									07 28				07 43
Lisvane & Thornhill	d			06 00			06 30						07 00									07 30				07 45
Caerphilly [3]	d			06a09			06 36						07 06									07 36				07 51
Aber	d						06 38						07 08									07 38				07 53
Llanbradach	d						06 42						07 12									07 42				07 57
Ystrad Mynach [3]	d						06 47						07 17									07 47				08 02
Hengoed	d						06 50						07 20									07 50				08 05
Pengam	d						06 53						07 23									07 53				08 08
Gilfach Fargoed	d																									
Bargoed	d						07a01						07a31									08a01				08 14
Brithdir	d																									08 18
Tir-phil	d																									08 21
Pontlottyn	d																									08 25
Rhymney [3]	a																									08 28
Cathays	d	05 33			06 03	06 18			06 33	06 43	06 48					07 03		07 13			07 18				07 33	
Llandaf	d	05 37			06 07	06 22			06 37	06 47	06 52					07 07		07 17			07 22				07 37	
Ninian Park	d																			07 10						
Waun-gron Park	d																			07 13						
Fairwater	d																			07 15						
Danescourt	d																			07 17						
Radyr [3]	a	05 39			06 10	06 24			06 40	06 50	06 54					07 10		07 20		07 24	07 25				07 40	
	d	05 40			06 10	06 24			06 40	06 50	06 55					07 10		07 20			07 25				07 40	
Taffs Well [3]	d	05 43			06 14	06 28			06 44	06 54	06 59					07 14		07 24			07 29				07 44	
Trefforest Estate	d	05 47			06 18				06 48							07 18									07 48	
Trefforest	d	05 52			06 22	06 35			06 52	07 01	07 06					07 22		07 31			07 36				07 52	
Pontypridd [3]	a	05 55			06 25	06 38			06 55	07 04	07 09					07 25		07 34			07 39				07 55	
	d	05 57	06 11		06 27	06 41			06 57	07 06	07 11					07 27		07 36			07 41				07 57	
Abercynon	d	06 04	06 19		06 34	06 49			07 04		07 19					07 34					07 49				08 04	
Penrhiwceiber	d		06 24			06 54					07 24										07 54					
Mountain Ash	a		06 28			06 58					07 28										07 58					
	d		06 33			07 03					07 33										08 03					
Fernhill	d		06 35			07 05					07 35										08 05					
Cwmbach	d		06 39			07 09					07 39										08 09					
Aberdare [3]	a		06 46			07 16					07 46										08 16					
Quakers Yard	d	06 09			06 39				07 09							07 39									08 09	
Merthyr Vale	d	06 17			06 47				07 17							07 47									08 17	
Troed Y Rhiw	d	06 20			06 50				07 20							07 50									08 20	
Pentre-bach	d	06 23			06 53				07 23							07 53									08 23	
Merthyr Tydfil	a	06 31			07 01				07 31							08 01									08 31	
Trehafod	d									07 11								07 41								
Porth	d									07 15								07 45								
Dinas Rhondda	d									07 19								07 49								
Tonypandy	d									07 21								07 51								
Llwynypia	d									07 23								07 53								
Ystrad Rhondda	a									07 26								07 56								
	d									07 29								07 59								
Ton Pentre	d									07 31								08 01								
Treorchy	d									07 34								08 04								
Ynyswen	d									07 37								08 07								
Treherbert	a									07 43								08 13								

For general notes see front of timetable
For details of catering facilities see Directory of Train Operators

A From Coryton
B From Taffs Well

From Saturday 12 September a revised service will be in operation due to seasonal difficulties. Most trains will arrive at their destination between 1 and 3 minutes later. Passengers should check with National Rail Enquiries for precise times.

Bridgend, Barry Island, Barry, Penarth and Cardiff → Coryton, Rhymney, Pontypridd, Merthyr, Aberdare and Treherbert

Network Diagram - see first page of Table 130

		AW	AW	AW	AW	AW	AW	AW	AW	AW	AW	AW	AW	AW	AW	AW	AW	AW	AW	AW	AW	AW	AW	AW	AW
				A				B						A				B					A		
Bridgend	d				06 42																			07 42	
Llantwit Major	d				06 56																			07 56	
Rhoose Cardiff Int Airport ✈	d				07 06																			08 06	
Barry Island	d									07 26					07 41				07 56						
Barry 3	d				07 15					07 30					07 45				08 00					08 15	
Barry Docks	d				07 19					07 34					07 49				08 04					08 19	
Cadoxton	d				07 22					07 37					07 52				08 07					08 22	
Dinas Powys	d				07 26					07 41					07 56				08 11					08 26	
Eastbrook	d				07 28					07 43					07 58				08 13					08 28	
Cogan	d				07 30					07 45					08 00				08 15					08 30	
Penarth	d						07 32				07 47					08 02				08 17					
Dingle Road	d						07 34				07 49					08 04				08 19					
Grangetown	d				07 34		07 38			07 49	07 53				08 04	08 08			08 19	08 23				08 34	
Cardiff Central 7	a				07 39		07 44			07 55	07 59				08 09	08 14			08 24	08 29				08 39	
	d		07 36	07 36	07 41		07 46	07 51		07 56	08 01	08 06		08 06	08 11	08 16		08 21	08 26	08 31		08 36	08 36	08 41	
Cardiff Bay	d	07 30				07 42			07 54				08 06				08 18				08 30				08 42
Cardiff Queen Street 3	a	07 34	07 39		07 44	07 46	07 49	07 54	07 58	07 59	08 04	08 09	08 10		08 14	08 19	08 22	08 24	08 29	08 34	08 34	08 39		08 44	08 46
	d		07 40		07 45		07 50	07 55		08 00	08 05	08 10			08 15	08 20		08 25	08 30	08 35		08 40		08 45	
Heath Low Level	d							08 00										08 30							
Ty Glas	d							08 03										08 33							
Birchgrove	d							08 04										08 34							
Rhiwbina	d							08 06										08 36							
Whitchurch (Cardiff)	d							08 08										08 38							
Coryton	a							08 13										08 43							
Heath High Level	d						07 55				08 10					08 25				08 40					
Llanishen	d						07 58				08 13					08 28				08 43					
Lisvane & Thornhill	d						08 00				08 15					08 30				08 45					
Caerphilly 3	d						08 06				08 21					08 36				08 51					
Aber	d						08 08				08 23					08 38				08 53					
Llanbradach	d						08 12				08 27					08 42				08 57					
Ystrad Mynach 3	d						08 17				08 32					08 47				09 02					
Hengoed	d						08 20				08 35					08 50				09 05					
Pengam	d						08 23				08 38					08 53				09 08					
Gilfach Fargoed	d										08 41														
Bargoed	d						08a31				08a48					08 59				09a16					
Brithdir	d															09 03									
Tir-phil	d															09 06									
Pontlottyn	d															09 10									
Rhymney 3	a															09 16									
Cathays	d		07 43		07 48					08 03		08 13			08 18				08 33			08 43		08 48	
Llandaf	d		07 47		07 52					08 07		08 17			08 22				08 37			08 47		08 52	
Ninian Park	d			07 40										08 10									08 40		
Waun-gron Park	d			07 43										08 13									08 43		
Fairwater	d			07 45										08 15									08 45		
Danescourt	d			07 47										08 17									08 47		
Radyr 3	a		07 50	07 54	07 55					08 10		08 20		08 24	08 25				08 40			08 50	08 54	08 55	
	d		07 50		07 55					08 10		08 20			08 25				08 40			08 50		08 55	
Taffs Well 3	d		07 54		07 59					08 14		08 24			08 29				08 44			08 54		08 59	
Trefforest Estate	d									08 18									08 48						
Trefforest	d		08 01		08 06					08 22		08 31			08 36				08 52			09 01		09 06	
Pontypridd 3	a		08 04		08 09					08 25		08 34			08 39				08 55			09 04		09 09	
	d		08 06		08 11					08 27		08 36			08 41				08 57			09 06		09 11	
Abercynon	d				08 19					08 34					08 49				09 04					09 19	
Penrhiwceiber	d				08 24										08 54									09 24	
Mountain Ash	a				08 28										08 58									09 28	
	d				08 33										09 03									09 33	
Fernhill	d				08 35										09 05									09 35	
Cwmbach	d				08 39										09 09									09 39	
Aberdare 3	a				08 46										09 16									09 46	
Quakers Yard	d									08 39									09 09						
Merthyr Vale	d									08 47									09 17						
Troed Y Rhiw	d									08 50									09 20						
Pentre-bach	d									08 53									09 23						
Merthyr Tydfil	a									09 01									09 31						
Trehafod	d		08 11									08 41										09 11			
Porth	d		08 15									08 45										09 15			
Dinas Rhondda	d		08 19									08 49										09 19			
Tonypandy	d		08 21									08 51										09 21			
Llwynypia	d		08 23									08 53										09 23			
Ystrad Rhondda	a		08 26									08 56										09 26			
	d		08 29									08 59										09 29			
Ton Pentre	d		08 31									09 01										09 31			
Treorchy	d		08 34									09 04										09 34			
Ynyswen	d		08 37									09 07										09 37			
Treherbert	a		08 43									09 13										09 43			

For general notes see front of timetable
For details of catering facilities see Directory of Train Operators

A From Coryton
B From Radyr

From Saturday 12 September a revised service will be in operation due to seasonal difficulties. Most trains will arrive at their destination between 1 and 3 minutes later. Passengers should check with National Rail Enquiries for precise times.

Bridgend, Barry Island, Barry, Penarth and Cardiff → Coryton, Rhymney, Pontypridd, Merthyr, Aberdare and Treherbert

Network Diagram - see first page of Table 130

	AW		AW A	AW	AW	AW	AW	AW	AW B	AW	AW	AW	AW A	AW	AW	AW	AW		AW B	AW	AW	AW	AW A	AW	AW
Bridgend d																				08 42					
Llantwit Major d																				08 56					
Rhoose Cardiff Int Airport ✈ d																				09 06					
Barry Island d					08 26					08 41				08 56											09 26
Barry 3 d					08 30					08 45				09 00						09 15					09 30
Barry Docks d					08 34					08 49				09 04						09 19					09 34
Cadoxton d					08 37					08 52				09 07						09 22					09 37
Dinas Powys d					08 41					08 56				09 11						09 26					09 41
Eastbrook d					08 43					08 58				09 13						09 28					09 43
Cogan d					08 45					09 00				09 15						09 30					09 45
Penarth d	08 32					08 47									09 17							09 32			
Dingle Road d	08 34					08 49									09 19							09 34			
Grangetown d	08 38				08 49	08 53				09 04				09 19	09 23					09 34		09 38			09 49
Cardiff Central 7 a	08 44				08 54	08 59				09 09				09 24	09 29					09 39		09 44			09 54
d	08 46		08 51		08 56	09 01	09 06		09 06	09 11	09 16		09 21	09 26	09 31		09 36		09 36	09 41		09 46	09 51		09 56
Cardiff Bay d				08 54				09 06				09 18				09 30					09 42			09 54	
Cardiff Queen Street 3 a	08 49		08 54	08 58	08 59	09 04	09 09	09 10		09 14	09 19	09 22	09 24	09 29	09 34	09 34	09 39			09 44	09 46	09 49	09 54	09 58	09 59
d	08 50		08 55		09 00	09 05	09 10			09 15	09 20		09 25	09 30	09 35		09 40			09 45		09 50	09 55		10 00
Heath Low Level d			09 00										09 30										10 00		
Ty Glas d			09 03										09 33										10 03		
Birchgrove d			09 04										09 34										10 04		
Rhiwbina d			09 06										09 36										10 06		
Whitchurch (Cardiff) d			09 08										09 38										10 08		
Coryton a			09 13										09 43										10 13		
Heath High Level d	08 55					09 10					09 25				09 40							09 55			
Llanishen d	08 58					09 13					09 28				09 43							09 58			
Lisvane & Thornhill d	09 00					09 15					09 30				09 45							10 00			
Caerphilly 3 d	09 06					09 21					09 36				09 51							10 06			
Aber d	09 08					09 23					09 38				09 53							10 08			
Llanbradach d	09 12					09 27					09 42				09 57							10 12			
Ystrad Mynach 3 d	09 17					09 32					09 47				10 02							10 17			
Hengoed d	09 20					09 35					09 50				10 05							10 20			
Pengam d	09 23					09 38					09 53				10 08							10 23			
Gilfach Fargoed d						09 41																			
Bargoed d	09a31					09a48					09 59				10a16							10a31			
Brithdir d											10 03														
Tir-phil d											10 06														
Pontlottyn d											10 10														
Rhymney 3 a											10 16														
Cathays d					09 03		09 13			09 18				09 33			09 43			09 48					10 03
Llandaf d					09 07		09 17			09 22				09 37			09 47			09 52					10 07
Ninian Park d									09 10										09 40						
Waun-gron Park d									09 13										09 43						
Fairwater d									09 15										09 45						
Danescourt d									09 17										09 47						
Radyr 3 a					09 10		09 20		09 24	09 25				09 40			09 50		09 54	09 55					10 10
d					09 10		09 20			09 25				09 40			09 50			09 55					10 10
Taffs Well 3 d					09 14		09 24			09 29				09 44			09 54			09 59					10 14
Trefforest Estate d					09 18									09 48											10 18
Trefforest d					09 22		09 31			09 36				09 52			10 01			10 06					10 22
Pontypridd 3 a					09 25		09 34			09 39				09 55			10 04			10 09					10 30
d					09 27		09 36			09 41				09 57			10 06			10 11					
Abercynon d					09 34					09 49				10 04						10 19					
Penrhiwceiber d										09 54										10 24					
Mountain Ash a										09 58										10 28					
d										10 03										10 33					
Fernhill d										10 05										10 35					
Cwmbach d										10 09										10 39					
Aberdare 3 a										10 16										10 46					
Quakers Yard d					09 39									10 09											
Merthyr Vale d					09 47									10b17											
Troed Y Rhiw d					09 50									10 20											
Pentre-bach d					09 53									10 23											
Merthyr Tydfil a					10 01									10 31											
Trehafod d							09 41										10 11								
Porth d							09 45										10 15								
Dinas Rhondda d							09 49										10 19								
Tonypandy d							09 51										10 21								
Llwynypia d							09 53										10 23								
Ystrad Rhondda a							09 56										10 26								
d							09 59										10 29								
Ton Pentre d							10 01										10 31								
Treorchy d							10 04										10 34								
Ynyswen d							10 07										10 37								
Treherbert a							10 13										10 43								

For general notes see front of timetable
For details of catering facilities see Directory of Train Operators

A From Radyr
B From Coryton
b Arr. 1014

From Saturday 12 September a revised service will be in operation due to seasonal difficulties. Most trains will arrive at their destination between 1 and 3 minutes later. Passengers should check with National Rail Enquiries for precise times.

Bridgend, Barry Island, Barry, Penarth and Cardiff → Coryton, Rhymney, Pontypridd, Merthyr, Aberdare and Treherbert

Network Diagram - see first page of Table 130

Station		AW	AW	AW	AW	AW A	AW	AW	AW	AW B	AW
Bridgend	d										
Llantwit Major	d										
Rhoose Cardiff Int Airport ✈	d										
Barry Island	d						09 41				09 56
Barry 3	d						09 45				10 00
Barry Docks	d						09 49				10 04
Cadoxton	d						09 52				10 07
Dinas Powys	d						09 56				10 11
Eastbrook	d						09 58				10 13
Cogan	d						10 00				10 15
Penarth	d	09 47						10 02			
Dingle Road	d	09 49						10 04			
Grangetown	d	09 53					10 04	10 08			10 19
Cardiff Central 7	a	09 59					10 09	10 14			10 24
	d	10 01		10 06		10 06	10 11	10 16		10 21	10 26
Cardiff Bay	d				10 06				10 18		
Cardiff Queen Street 3	a	10 04		10 09	10 10		10 14	10 19	10 22	10 24	10 29
	d	10 05		10 10			10 15	10 20		10 25	10 30
Heath Low Level	d									10 30	
Ty Glas	d									10 33	
Birchgrove	d									10 34	
Rhiwbina	d									10 36	
Whitchurch (Cardiff)	d									10 38	
Coryton	a									10 43	
Heath High Level	d	10 10						10 25			
Llanishen	d	10 13						10 28			
Lisvane & Thornhill	d	10 15						10 30			
Caerphilly 3	d	10 21						10 36			
Aber	d	10 23						10 38			
Llanbradach	d	10 27						10 42			
Ystrad Mynach 3	d	10 32						10 47			
Hengoed	d	10 35						10 50			
Pengam	d	10 38						10 53			
Gilfach Fargoed	d	10 41									
Bargoed	d	10a48						10 59			
Brithdir	d							11 03			
Tir-phil	d							11 06			
Pontlottyn	d							11 10			
Rhymney 3	a							11 16			
Cathays	d			10 13			10 18				10 33
Llandaf	d			10 17			10 22				10 37
Ninian Park	d					10 10					
Waun-gron Park	d					10 13					
Fairwater	d					10 15					
Danescourt	d					10 17					
Radyr 3	a			10 20		10 24	10 25				10 40
	d			10 20			10 25				10 40
Taffs Well 3	d			10 24			10 29				10 44
Trefforest Estate	d										10 48
Trefforest	d			10 31			10 36				10 52
Pontypridd 3	a			10 34			10 39				10 55
	d		10 35	10 36			10 41				10 57
Abercynon	d		10 41				10 49				11 04
Penrhiwceiber	d						10 54				
Mountain Ash	a						10 58				
	d						11 03				
Fernhill	d						11 05				
Cwmbach	d						11 09				
Aberdare 3	a						11 16				
Quakers Yard	d		10 45								11 09
Merthyr Vale	d		10 52								11 17
Troed Y Rhiw	d		10 55								11 20
Pentre-bach	d		10 58								11 23
Merthyr Tydfil	a		11 06								11 31
Trehafod	d			10 41							
Porth	d			10 45							
Dinas Rhondda	d			10 49							
Tonypandy	d			10 51							
Llwynypia	d			10 53							
Ystrad Rhondda	a			10 56							
	d			10 59							
Ton Pentre	d			11 01							
Treorchy	d			11 04							
Ynyswen	d			11 07							
Treherbert	a			11 13							

Station		AW	AW	AW	AW A	AW	AW	AW	AW	AW B	AW	AW	AW	AW	AW
Bridgend	d						09 42								
Llantwit Major	d						09 56								
Rhoose Cardiff Int Airport ✈	d						10 06								
Barry Island	d											10 26			
Barry 3	d						10 15					10 30			
Barry Docks	d						10 19					10 34			
Cadoxton	d						10 22					10 37			
Dinas Powys	d						10 26					10 41			
Eastbrook	d						10 28					10 43			
Cogan	d						10 30					10 45			
Penarth	d	10 17						10 32					10 47		
Dingle Road	d	10 19						10 34					10 49		
Grangetown	d	10 23					10 34	10 38				10 49	10 53		
Cardiff Central 7	a	10 29					10 42	10 44				10 54	10 59		
	d	10 31		10 36	10 36			10 46	10 51	10 51		10 56	11 01		
Cardiff Bay	d		10 30			10 42					10 54			11 06	
Cardiff Queen Street 3	a	10 34	10 34	10 39		10 46		10 49		10 54	10 58	10 59	11 04	11 10	
	d	10 35		10 40				10 50		10 55		11 00	11 05		
Heath Low Level	d									11 00					
Ty Glas	d									11 03					
Birchgrove	d									11 04					
Rhiwbina	d									11 06					
Whitchurch (Cardiff)	d									11 08					
Coryton	a									11 13					
Heath High Level	d	10 40						10 55					11 10		
Llanishen	d	10 43						10 58					11 13		
Lisvane & Thornhill	d	10 45						11 00					11 15		
Caerphilly 3	d	10 51						11 06					11 21		
Aber	d	10 53						11 08					11 23		
Llanbradach	d	10 57						11 12					11 27		
Ystrad Mynach 3	d	11 02						11 17					11 32		
Hengoed	d	11 05						11 20					11 35		
Pengam	d	11 08						11 23					11 38		
Gilfach Fargoed	d												11 41		
Bargoed	d	11a16						11a31					11a48		
Brithdir	d														
Tir-phil	d														
Pontlottyn	d														
Rhymney 3	a														
Cathays	d			10 43								11 03			
Llandaf	d			10 47								11 07			
Ninian Park	d				10 40										
Waun-gron Park	d				10 43										
Fairwater	d				10 45										
Danescourt	d				10 47										
Radyr 3	a			10 50	10 54				11 02			11 10			←
	d			10 50					11 20 →			11 10			11 20
Taffs Well 3	d			10 54								11 14			11 24
Trefforest Estate	d											11 18			
Trefforest	d			11 01								11 22			11 31
Pontypridd 3	a			11 04								11 25			11 34
	d			11 06								11 27			11 36
Abercynon	d											11 34			
Penrhiwceiber	d														
Mountain Ash	a														
	d														
Fernhill	d														
Cwmbach	d														
Aberdare 3	a														
Quakers Yard	d											11 39			
Merthyr Vale	d											11 47			
Troed Y Rhiw	d											11 50			
Pentre-bach	d											11 53			
Merthyr Tydfil	a											12 01			
Trehafod	d			11 11											11 41
Porth	d			11 15											11 45
Dinas Rhondda	d			11 19											11 49
Tonypandy	d			11 21											11 51
Llwynypia	d			11 23											11 53
Ystrad Rhondda	a			11 26											11 56
	d			11 29											11 59
Ton Pentre	d			11 31											12 01
Treorchy	d			11 34											12 04
Ynyswen	d			11 37											12 07
Treherbert	a			11 43											12 13

For general notes see front of timetable
For details of catering facilities see Directory of Train Operators

A From Coryton
B From Radyr

From Saturday 12 September a revised service will be in operation due to seasonal difficulties. Most trains will arrive at their destination between 1 and 3 minutes later. Passengers should check with National Rail Enquiries for precise times.

Table 130

Saturdays

Bridgend, Barry Island, Barry, Penarth and Cardiff → Coryton, Rhymney, Pontypridd, Merthyr, Aberdare and Treherbert

Network Diagram - see first page of Table 130

		AW A	AW	AW		AW	AW B	AW	AW	AW	AW	AW A	AW	AW	AW	AW	AW B	AW	AW	AW		AW	AW	AW A	AW	AW
Bridgend	d													10 42												
Llantwit Major	d													10 56												
Rhoose Cardiff Int Airport ✈	d													11 06												
Barry Island	d		10 41					10 56											11 26						11 41	
Barry 3	d		10 45					11 00						11 15					11 30						11 45	
Barry Docks	d		10 49					11 04						11 19					11 34						11 49	
Cadoxton	d		10 52					11 07						11 22					11 37						11 52	
Dinas Powys	d		10 56					11 11						11 26					11 41						11 56	
Eastbrook	d		10 58					11 13						11 28					11 43						11 58	
Cogan	d		11 00					11 15						11 30					11 45						12 00	
Penarth	d			11 02					11 17							11 32				11 47						12 02
Dingle Road	d			11 04					11 19							11 34				11 49						12 04
Grangetown	d		11 04	11 08				11 19	11 23					11 34		11 38			11 49	11 53					12 04	12 08
Cardiff Central 7	a		11 09	11 14				11 24	11 29					11 41		11 44			11 54	11 59					12 09	12 14
	d	11 06	11 11	11 16			11 21	11 26	11 31		11 36	11 36	11 41			11 46	11 51		11 56	12 01		12 06		12 06	12 11	12 16
Cardiff Bay	d					11 18				11 30					11 42			11 54					12 06			
Cardiff Queen Street 3	a		11 14	11 19		11 22	11 24	11 29	11 34	11 34	11 39		11 44		11 46	11 49	11 54	11 58	11 59	12 04		12 09	12 10		12 14	12 19
	d		11 15	11 20			11 25	11 30	11 35		11 40		11 45			11 50	11 55		12 00	12 05		12 10			12 15	12 20
Heath Low Level	d						11 30										12 00									
Ty Glas	d						11 33										12 03									
Birchgrove	d						11 34										12 04									
Rhiwbina	d						11 36										12 06									
Whitchurch (Cardiff)	d						11 38										12 08									
Coryton	a						11 43										12 13									
Heath High Level	d			11 25					11 40							11 55				12 10						12 25
Llanishen	d			11 28					11 43							11 58				12 13						12 28
Lisvane & Thornhill	d			11 30					11 45							12 00				12 15						12 30
Caerphilly 3	d			11 36					11 51							12 06				12 21						12 36
Aber	d			11 38					11 53							12 08				12 23						12 38
Llanbradach	d			11 42					11 57							12 12				12 27						12 42
Ystrad Mynach 3	d			11 47					12 02							12 17				12 32						12 47
Hengoed	d			11 50					12 05							12 20				12 35						12 50
Pengam	d			11 53					12 08							12 23				12 38						12 53
Gilfach Fargoed	d																			12 41						
Bargoed	d			11 59					12a16							12a31				12a48						12 59
Brithdir	d			12 03																						13 03
Tir-phil	d			12 06																						13 06
Pontlottyn	d			12 10																						13 10
Rhymney 3	a			12 16																						13 16
Cathays	d		11 18					11 33			11 43		11 48						12 03			12 13			12 18	
Llandaf	d		11 22					11 37			11 47		11 52						12 07			12 17			12 22	
Ninian Park	d	11 10										11 40												12 10		
Waun-gron Park	d	11 13										11 43												12 13		
Fairwater	d	11 15										11 45												12 15		
Danescourt	d	11 17										11 47												12 17		
Radyr 3	a	11 24	11 25					11 40			11 50	11 54	11 54						12 10			12 20		12 24	12 25	
	d		11 25					11 40			11 50		11 55						12 10			12 20			12 25	
Taffs Well 3	d		11 29					11 44			11 54		11 59						12 14			12 24			12 29	
Trefforest Estate	d							11 48											12 18							
Trefforest	d		11 36					11 52			12 01		12 06						12 22			12 31			12 36	
Pontypridd 3	a		11 39					11 55			12 04		12 09						12 25			12 34			12 42	
	d		11 41					11 57			12 06		12 11						12 27			12 36				
Abercynon	d		11 49					12 04					12 19						12 34							
Penrhiwceiber	d		11 54										12 24													
Mountain Ash	a		11 58										12 28													
	d		12 03										12 33													
Fernhill	d		12 05										12 35													
Cwmbach	d		12 09										12 39													
Aberdare 3	a		12 16										12 46													
Quakers Yard	d							12 09											12 39							
Merthyr Vale	d							12b17											12 47							
Troed Y Rhiw	d							12 20											12 50							
Pentre-bach	d							12 23											12 53							
Merthyr Tydfil	a							12 31											13 01							
Trehafod	d										12 11											12 41				
Porth	d										12 15											12 45				
Dinas Rhondda	d										12 19											12 49				
Tonypandy	d										12 21											12 51				
Llwynypia	d										12 23											12 53				
Ystrad Rhondda	a										12 26											12 56				
	d										12 29											12 59				
Ton Pentre	d										12 31											13 01				
Treorchy	d										12 34											13 04				
Ynyswen	d										12 37											13 07				
Treherbert	a										12 44											13 13				

For general notes see front of timetable
For details of catering facilities see Directory of Train Operators

A From Coryton
B From Radyr
b Arr. 1214

From Saturday 12 September a revised service will be in operation due to seasonal difficulties. Most trains will arrive at their destination between 1 and 3 minutes later. Passengers should check with National Rail Enquiries for precise times.

Bridgend, Barry Island, Barry, Penarth and Cardiff → Coryton, Rhymney, Pontypridd, Merthyr, Aberdare and Treherbert

Network Diagram - see first page of Table 130

		AW	AW A	AW	AW	AW	AW	AW B	AW	AW	AW	AW A	AW	AW	AW	AW	AW	AW B	AW	AW	AW	AW A	AW	AW	AW
Bridgend	d								11 42																
Llantwit Major	d								11 56																
Rhoose Cardiff Int Airport ✈	d								12 06																
Barry Island	d			11 56										12 26					12 41				12 56		
Barry 3	d			12 00					12 15					12 30					12 45				13 00		
Barry Docks	d			12 04					12 19					12 34					12 49				13 04		
Cadoxton	d			12 07					12 22					12 37					12 52				13 07		
Dinas Powys	d			12 11					12 26					12 41					12 56				13 11		
Eastbrook	d			12 13					12 28					12 43					12 58				13 13		
Cogan	d			12 15					12 30					12 45					13 00				13 15		
Penarth	d				12 17						12 32				12 47					13 02				13 17	
Dingle Road	d				12 19						12 34				12 49					13 04				13 19	
Grangetown	d			12 19	12 23				12 34		12 38			12 49	12 53				13 04	13 08			13 19	13 23	
Cardiff Central 7	a			12 24	12 29				12 39		12 44			12 54	12 59				13 09	13 14			13 24	13 29	
	d		12 21	12 26	12 31		12 36	12 36	12 41		12 46	12 51		12 56	13 01	13 06		13 06	13 11	13 16		13 21	13 26	13 31	
Cardiff Bay	d	12 18				12 30				12 42			12 54				13 06				13 18				13 30
Cardiff Queen Street 3	a	12 22	12 24	12 29	12 34	12 34	12 39		12 44	12 46	12 49	12 54	12 58	12 59	13 04	13 09	13 10		13 14	13 19	13 22	13 24	13 29	13 34	13 34
	d		12 25	12 30	12 35		12 40		12 45		12 50	12 55		13 00	13 05	13 10			13 15	13 20		13 25	13 30	13 35	
Heath Low Level	d		12 30									13 00										13 30			
Ty Glas	d		12 33									13 03										13 33			
Birchgrove	d		12 34									13 04										13 34			
Rhiwbina	d		12 36									13 06										13 36			
Whitchurch (Cardiff)	d		12 38									13 08										13 38			
Coryton	a		12 43									13 13										13 43			
Heath High Level	d				12 40						12 55				13 10					13 25				13 40	
Llanishen	d				12 43						12 58				13 13					13 28				13 43	
Lisvane & Thornhill	d				12 45						13 00				13 15					13 30				13 45	
Caerphilly 3	d				12 51						13 06				13 21					13 36				13 51	
Aber	d				12 53						13 08				13 23					13 38				13 53	
Llanbradach	d				12 57						13 12				13 27					13 42				13 57	
Ystrad Mynach 3	d				13 02						13 17				13 32					13 47				14 02	
Hengoed	d				13 05						13 20				13 35					13 50				14 05	
Pengam	d				13 08						13 23				13 38					13 53				14 08	
Gilfach Fargoed	d														13 41										
Bargoed	d				13a16						13a31				13a48					13 59				14a16	
Brithdir	d																			14 03					
Tir-phil	d																			14 06					
Pontlottyn	d																			14 10					
Rhymney 3	a																			14 16					
Cathays	d			12 33			12 43		12 48					13 03		13 13			13 18				13 33		
Llandaf	d			12 37			12 47		12 52					13 07		13 17			13 22				13 37		
Ninian Park	d							12 40										13 10							
Waun-gron Park	d							12 43										13 13							
Fairwater	d							12 45										13 15							
Danescourt	d							12 47										13 17							
Radyr 3	a			12 40			12 50	12 54	12 55					13 10		13 20		13 24	13 25				13 40		
	d			12 40			12 50		12 55					13 10		13 20			13 25				13 40		
Taffs Well 3	d			12 44			12 54		12 59					13 14		13 24			13 29				13 44		
Trefforest Estate	d			12 48										13 18									13 48		
Trefforest	d			12 52			13 01		13 06					13 22		13 31			13 36				13 52		
Pontypridd 3	a			12 55			13 04		13 09					13 25		13 34			13 39				13 55		
	d			12 57			13 06		13 11					13 27		13 36			13 41				13 57		
Abercynon	d			13 04					13 19					13 34					13 49				14 04		
Penrhiwceiber	d								13 24										13 54						
Mountain Ash	a								13 28										13 58						
	d								13 33										14 03						
Fernhill	d								13 35										14 05						
Cwmbach	d								13 39										14 09						
Aberdare 3	a								13 46										14 16						
Quakers Yard	d			13 09										13 39									14 09		
Merthyr Vale	d			13 17										13b47									14 17		
Troed Y Rhiw	d			13 20										13 50									14 20		
Pentre-bach	d			13 23										13 53									14 23		
Merthyr Tydfil	a			13 31										14 01									14 31		
Trehafod	d						13 11									13 41									
Porth	d						13 15									13 45									
Dinas Rhondda	d						13 19									13 49									
Tonypandy	d						13 21									13 51									
Llwynypia	d						13 23									13 53									
Ystrad Rhondda	a						13 26									13 56									
	d						13 29									13 59									
Ton Pentre	d						13 31									14 01									
Treorchy	d						13 34									14 04									
Ynyswen	d						13 37									14 07									
Treherbert	a						13 43									14 13									

For general notes see front of timetable
For details of catering facilities see Directory of Train Operators

A From Radyr
B From Coryton
b Arr. 1344

From Saturday 12 September a revised service will be in operation due to seasonal difficulties. Most trains will arrive at their destination between 1 and 3 minutes later. Passengers should check with National Rail Enquiries for precise times.

Table 130

Saturdays

Bridgend, Barry Island, Barry, Penarth and Cardiff → Coryton, Rhymney, Pontypridd, Merthyr, Aberdare and Treherbert

Network Diagram - see first page of Table 130

		AW	AW A	AW	AW	AW		AW B	AW	AW	AW	AW	AW	AW A	AW	AW	AW	AW B	AW	AW	AW	AW		AW A	AW	AW
Bridgend	d			12 42																					13 42	
Llantwit Major	d			12 56																					13 56	
Rhoose Cardiff Int Airport ✈	d			13 06																					14 06	
Barry Island	d									13 26					13 41				13 56							
Barry 3	d			13 15						13 30					13 45				14 00						14 15	
Barry Docks	d			13 19						13 34					13 49				14 04						14 19	
Cadoxton	d			13 22						13 37					13 52				14 07						14 22	
Dinas Powys	d			13 26						13 41					13 56				14 11						14 26	
Eastbrook	d			13 28						13 43					13 58				14 13						14 28	
Cogan	d			13 30						13 45					14 00				14 15						14 30	
Penarth	d					13 32					13 47					14 02				14 17						
Dingle Road	d					13 34					13 49					14 04				14 19						
Grangetown	d			13 34		13 38				13 49	13 53				14 04	14 08			14 19	14 23					14 34	
Cardiff Central 7	a			13 39		13 44				13 54	13 59				14 09	14 14			14 24	14 29					14 39	
	d	13 36	13 36	13 41		13 46		13 51		13 56	14 01	14 06		14 06	14 11	14 16		14 21	14 26	14 31		14 36		14 36	14 41	
Cardiff Bay	d				13 42				13 54				14 06				14 18				14 30					14 42
Cardiff Queen Street 3	a	13 39		13 44	13 46	13 49		13 54	13 58	13 59	14 04	14 09	14 10		14 14	14 19	14 22	14 24	14 29	14 34	14 34	14 39			14 44	14 46
	d	13 40		13 45		13 50		13 55		14 00	14 05	14 10			14 15	14 20		14 25	14 30	14 35		14 40			14 45	
Heath Low Level	d							14 00										14 30								
Ty Glas	d							14 03										14 33								
Birchgrove	d							14 04										14 34								
Rhiwbina	d							14 06										14 36								
Whitchurch (Cardiff)	d							14 08										14 38								
Coryton	a							14 13										14 43								
Heath High Level	d					13 55					14 10					14 25				14 40						
Llanishen	d					13 58					14 13					14 28				14 43						
Lisvane & Thornhill	d					14 00					14 15					14 30				14 45						
Caerphilly 3	d					14 06					14 21					14 36				14 51						
Aber	d					14 08					14 23					14 38				14 53						
Llanbradach	d					14 12					14 27					14 42				14 57						
Ystrad Mynach 3	d					14 17					14 32					14 47				15 02						
Hengoed	d					14 20					14 35					14 50				15 05						
Pengam	d					14 23					14 38					14 53				15 08						
Gilfach Fargoed	d										14 41															
Bargoed	d					14a31					14a48					14 59				15a16						
Brithdir	d															15 03										
Tir-phil	d															15 06										
Pontlottyn	d															15 10										
Rhymney 3	a															15 16										
Cathays	d	13 43		13 48						14 03		14 13			14 18				14 33			14 43			14 48	
Llandaf	d	13 47		13 52						14 07		14 17			14 22				14 37			14 47			14 52	
Ninian Park	d		13 40											14 10										14 40		
Waun-gron Park	d		13 43											14 13										14 43		
Fairwater	d		13 45											14 15										14 45		
Danescourt	d		13 47											14 17										14 47		
Radyr 3	a	13 50	13 54	13 55						14 10		14 20		14 24	14 25				14 40			14 50		14 54	14 55	
	d	13 50		13 55						14 10		14 20			14 25				14 40			14 50			14 55	
Taffs Well 3	d	13 54		13 59						14 14		14 24			14 29				14 44			14 54			14 59	
Trefforest Estate	d									14 18									14 48							
Trefforest	d	14 01		14 06						14 22		14 31			14 36				14 52			15 01			15 06	
Pontypridd 3	a	14 04		14 09						14 25		14 34			14 39				14 55			15 04			15 09	
	d	14 06		14 11						14 27		14 36			14 41				14 57			15 06			15 11	
Abercynon	d			14 19						14 34					14 49				15 04						15 19	
Penrhiwceiber	d			14 24											14 54										15 24	
Mountain Ash	a			14 28											14 58										15 28	
	d			14 33											15 03										15 33	
Fernhill	d			14 35											15 05										15 35	
Cwmbach	d			14 39											15 09										15 39	
Aberdare 3	a			14 46											15 16										15 46	
Quakers Yard	d									14 39									15 09							
Merthyr Vale	d									14 47									15b17							
Troed Y Rhiw	d									14 50									15 20							
Pentre-bach	d									14 53									15 23							
Merthyr Tydfil	a									15 01									15 31							
Trehafod	d	14 11										14 41										15 11				
Porth	d	14 15										14 45										15 15				
Dinas Rhondda	d	14 19										14 49										15 19				
Tonypandy	d	14 21										14 51										15 21				
Llwynypia	d	14 23										14 53										15 23				
Ystrad Rhondda	a	14 26										14 56										15 26				
	d	14 29										14 59										15 29				
Ton Pentre	d	14 31										15 01										15 31				
Treorchy	d	14 34										15 04										15 34				
Ynyswen	d	14 37										15 07										15 37				
Treherbert	a	14 43										15 13										15 43				

For general notes see front of timetable
For details of catering facilities see Directory of Train Operators

A From Coryton
B From Radyr
b Arr. 1514

From Saturday 12 September a revised service will be in operation due to seasonal difficulties. Most trains will arrive at their destination between 1 and 3 minutes later. Passengers should check with National Rail Enquiries for precise times.

Table 130

Saturdays

Bridgend, Barry Island, Barry, Penarth and Cardiff → Coryton, Rhymney, Pontypridd, Merthyr, Aberdare and Treherbert

Network Diagram - see first page of Table 130

		AW	AW	AW A	AW	AW	AW	AW	AW	AW	AW B	AW	AW	AW	AW A		AW	AW	AW	AW	AW B	AW	AW	AW	AW A	AW
Bridgend	d																					14 42				
Llantwit Major	d																					14 56				
Rhoose Cardiff Int Airport ✈	d																					15 06				
Barry Island	d					14 26						14 41					14 56									
Barry 3	d					14 30						14 45					15 00					15 15				
Barry Docks	d					14 34						14 49					15 04					15 19				
Cadoxton	d					14 37						14 52					15 07					15 22				
Dinas Powys	d					14 41						14 56					15 11					15 26				
Eastbrook	d					14 43						14 58					15 13					15 28				
Cogan	d					14 45						15 00					15 15					15 30				
Penarth	d	14 32					14 47						15 02					15 17						15 32		
Dingle Road	d	14 34					14 49						15 04					15 19						15 34		
Grangetown	d	14 38				14 49	14 53					15 04	15 08				15 19	15 23				15 34		15 38		
Cardiff Central 7	a	14 44				14 54	14 59					15 09	15 14				15 24	15 29				15 39		15 44		
	d	14 46	14 51	14 51		14 56	15 01				15 06	15 11	15 16		15 21		15 26	15 31		15 36	15 36	15 41		15 46	15 51	
Cardiff Bay	d				14 54			15 06						15 18					15 30				15 42			15 54
Cardiff Queen Street 3	a	14 49		14 54	14 58	14 59	15 04	15 10				15 14	15 19	15 22	15 24		15 29	15 34	15 34	15 39		15 44	15 46	15 49	15 54	15 58
	d	14 50		14 55		15 00	15 05					15 15	15 20		15 25		15 30	15 35		15 40		15 45		15 50	15 55	
Heath Low Level	d			15 00											15 30										16 00	
Ty Glas	d			15 03											15 33										16 03	
Birchgrove	d			15 04											15 34										16 04	
Rhiwbina	d			15 06											15 36										16 06	
Whitchurch (Cardiff)	d			15 08											15 38										16 08	
Coryton	a			15 13											15 43										16 13	
Heath High Level	d	14 55					15 10						15 25					15 40						15 55		
Llanishen	d	14 58					15 13						15 28					15 43						15 58		
Lisvane & Thornhill	d	15 00					15 15						15 30					15 45						16 00		
Caerphilly 3	d	15 06					15 21						15 36					15 51						16 06		
Aber	d	15 08					15 23						15 38					15 53						16 08		
Llanbradach	d	15 12					15 27						15 42					15 57						16 12		
Ystrad Mynach 3	d	15 17					15 32						15 47					16 02						16 17		
Hengoed	d	15 20					15 35						15 50					16 05						16 20		
Pengam	d	15 23					15 38						15 53					16 08						16 23		
Gilfach Fargoed	d						15 41																			
Bargoed	d	15a31					15a48						15 59					16a16						16a31		
Brithdir	d												16 03													
Tir-phil	d												16 06													
Pontlottyn	d												16 10													
Rhymney 3	a												16 16													
Cathays	d					15 03						15 18					15 33			15 43		15 48				
Llandaf	d					15 07						15 22					15 37			15 47		15 52				
Ninian Park	d										15 10										15 40					
Waun-gron Park	d										15 13										15 43					
Fairwater	d										15 15										15 45					
Danescourt	d										15 17										15 47					
Radyr 3	a		15 08			15 10				←	15 24	15 25					15 40			15 50	15 54	15 55				
	d		15 20 →			15 10				15 20		15 25					15 40			15 50		15 55				
Taffs Well 3	d					15 14				15 24		15 29					15 44			15 54		15 59				
Trefforest Estate	d					15 18											15 48									
Trefforest	d					15 22				15 31		15 36					15 52			16 01		16 06				
Pontypridd 3	a					15 30				15 34		15 39					15 55			16 04		16 09				
	d								15 35	15 36		15 41					15 57			16 06		16 11				
Abercynon	d								15 41			15 49					16 04					16 19				
Penrhiwceiber	d											15 54										16 24				
Mountain Ash	a											15 58										16 28				
	d											16 03										16 33				
Fernhill	d											16 05										16 35				
Cwmbach	d											16 09										16 39				
Aberdare 3	a											16 16										16 46				
Quakers Yard	d								15 45								16 09									
Merthyr Vale	d								15 52								16 17									
Troed Y Rhiw	d								15 55								16 20									
Pentre-bach	d								15 58								16 23									
Merthyr Tydfil	a								16 06								16 31									
Trehafod	d									15 41										16 11						
Porth	d									15 45										16 15						
Dinas Rhondda	d									15 49										16 19						
Tonypandy	d									15 51										16 21						
Llwynypia	d									15 53										16 23						
Ystrad Rhondda	a									15 56										16 26						
	d									15 59										16 29						
Ton Pentre	d									16 01										16 31						
Treorchy	d									16 04										16 34						
Ynyswen	d									16 07										16 37						
Treherbert	a									16 13										16 43						

For general notes see front of timetable
For details of catering facilities see Directory of Train Operators

A From Radyr
B From Coryton

From Saturday 12 September a revised service will be in operation due to seasonal difficulties. Most trains will arrive at their destination between 1 and 3 minutes later. Passengers should check with National Rail Enquiries for precise times.

Bridgend, Barry Island, Barry, Penarth and Cardiff → Coryton, Rhymney, Pontypridd, Merthyr, Aberdare and Treherbert

Network Diagram - see first page of Table 130

		AW	AW	AW	AW	AW	AW	AW	AW	AW	AW	AW	AW	AW	AW	AW	AW	AW	AW	AW	AW	AW	AW	AW
						A				B					A				B					
Bridgend	d															15 42								
Llantwit Major	d															15 56								
Rhoose Cardiff Int Airport ✈	d															16 06								
Barry Island	d	15 26					15 41				15 56										16 26			
Barry 3	d	15 30					15 45				16 00					16 15					16 30			
Barry Docks	d	15 34					15 49				16 04					16 19					16 34			
Cadoxton	d	15 37					15 52				16 07					16 22					16 37			
Dinas Powys	d	15 41					15 56				16 11					16 26					16 41			
Eastbrook	d	15 43					15 58				16 13					16 28					16 43			
Cogan	d	15 45					16 00				16 15					16 30					16 45			
Penarth	d		15 47					16 02				16 17						16 32						
Dingle Road	d		15 49					16 04				16 19						16 34						
Grangetown	d	15 49	15 53				16 04	16 08			16 19	16 23				16 34		16 38			16 49			
Cardiff Central 7	a	15 54	15 59				16 09	16 14			16 24	16 29				16 39		16 44			16 54			
	d	15 56	16 01	16 06		16 06	16 11	16 16		16 21	16 26	16 31		16 36	16 36	16 41		16 46	16 51		16 56	17 01	17 06	
Cardiff Bay	d				16 06				16 18				16 30				16 42			16 54				17 06
Cardiff Queen Street 3	a	15 59	16 04	16 09	16 10		16 14	16 19	16 22	16 24	16 29	16 34	16 34	16 39		16 44	16 46	16 49	16 54	16 58	16 59	17 04	17 09	17 10
	d	16 00	16 05	16 10			16 15	16 20		16 25	16 30	16 35		16 40		16 45		16 50	16 55		17 00	17 05	17 10	
Heath Low Level	d									16 30									17 00					
Ty Glas	d									16 33									17 03					
Birchgrove	d									16 34									17 04					
Rhiwbina	d									16 36									17 06					
Whitchurch (Cardiff)	d									16 38									17 08					
Coryton	a									16 43									17 13					
Heath High Level	d		16 10					16 25				16 40						16 55				17 10		
Llanishen	d		16 13					16 28				16 43						16 58				17 13		
Lisvane & Thornhill	d		16 15					16 30				16 45						17 00				17 15		
Caerphilly 3	d		16 21					16 36				16 51						17 06				17 21		
Aber	d		16 23					16 38				16 53						17 08				17 23		
Llanbradach	d		16 27					16 42				16 57						17 12				17 27		
Ystrad Mynach 3	d		16 32					16 47				17 02						17 17				17 33		
Hengoed	d		16 35					16 50				17 05						17 20				17 35		
Pengam	d		16 38					16 53				17 08						17 23				17 39		
Gilfach Fargoed	d		16 41																			17 42		
Bargoed	d		16a48					16 59				17a16						17a31				17 47		
Brithdir	d							17 03														17 50		
Tir-phil	d							17 06														17 53		
Pontlottyn	d							17 10														17 58		
Rhymney 3	a							17 16														18 04		
Cathays	d	16 03		16 13			16 18				16 33			16 43		16 48					17 03		17 13	
Llandaf	d	16 07		16 17			16 22				16 37			16 47		16 52					17 07		17 17	
Ninian Park	d					16 10									16 40									
Waun-gron Park	d					16 13									16 43									
Fairwater	d					16 15									16 45									
Danescourt	d					16 17									16 47									
Radyr 3	a	16 10		16 20		16 24	16 25				16 40			16 50	16 54	16 55					17 10		17 20	
	d	16 10		16 20			16 25				16 40			16 50		16 55					17 10		17 20	
Taffs Well 3	d	16 14		16 24			16 29				16 44			16 54		16 59					17 14		17 24	
Trefforest Estate	d	16 18									16 48										17 18			
Trefforest	d	16 22		16 31			16 36				16 52			17 01		17 06					17 22		17 31	
Pontypridd 3	a	16 25		16 34			16 39				16 55			17 04		17 09					17 25		17 34	
	d	16 27		16 36			16 41				16 57			17 06		17 11					17 27		17 36	
Abercynon	d	16 34					16 49				17 04					17 19					17 34			
Penrhiwceiber	d						16 54									17 24								
Mountain Ash	a						16 58									17 28								
	d						17 03									17 33								
Fernhill	d						17 05									17 35								
Cwmbach	d						17 09									17 39								
Aberdare 3	a						17 16									17 46								
Quakers Yard	d	16 39									17 09										17 39			
Merthyr Vale	d	16 47									17 17										17 47			
Troed Y Rhiw	d	16 50									17 20										17 50			
Pentre-bach	d	16 53									17 23										17 53			
Merthyr Tydfil	a	17 01									17 31										18 01			
Trehafod	d			16 41										17 11									17 41	
Porth	d			16 45										17 15									17 45	
Dinas Rhondda	d			16 49										17 19									17 49	
Tonypandy	d			16 51										17 21									17 51	
Llwynypia	d			16 53										17 23									17 53	
Ystrad Rhondda	a			16 56										17 26									17 56	
	d			16 59										17 29									17 59	
Ton Pentre	d			17 01										17 31									18 01	
Treorchy	d			17 04										17 34									18 04	
Ynyswen	d			17 07										17 37									18 07	
Treherbert	a			17 13										17 43									18 13	

For general notes see front of timetable
For details of catering facilities see Directory of Train Operators

A From Coryton
B From Radyr

From Saturday 12 September a revised service will be in operation due to seasonal difficulties. Most trains will arrive at their destination between 1 and 3 minutes later. Passengers should check with National Rail Enquiries for precise times.

Bridgend, Barry Island, Barry, Penarth and Cardiff → Coryton, Rhymney, Pontypridd, Merthyr, Aberdare and Treherbert

Network Diagram - see first page of Table 130

		AW A	AW	AW	AW	AW B	AW	AW	AW	AW	AW A	AW	AW	AW	AW B	AW	AW	AW	AW	AW	AW A	AW	AW	AW	AW B
Bridgend	d											16 42													
Llantwit Major	d											16 56													
Rhoose Cardiff Int Airport ✈	d											17 06													
Barry Island	d		16 41				16 56										17 26					17 41			
Barry 3	d		16 45				17 00					17 15					17 30					17 45			
Barry Docks	d		16 49				17 04					17 19					17 34					17 49			
Cadoxton	d		16 52				17 07					17 22					17 37					17 52			
Dinas Powys	d		16 56				17 11					17 26					17 41					17 56			
Eastbrook	d		16 58				17 13					17 28					17 43					17 58			
Cogan	d		17 00				17 15					17 30					17 45					18 00			
Penarth	d			17 02				17 17						17 32				17 47					18 02		
Dingle Road	d			17 04				17 19						17 34				17 49					18 04		
Grangetown	d		17 04	17 08			17 19	17 23				17 34		17 38			17 49	17 53				18 04	18 08		
Cardiff Central 7	a		17 09	17 14			17 24	17 29				17 39		17 44			17 54	17 59				18 09	18 14		
	d	17 06	17 11	17 16		17 21	17 26	17 31		17 36	17 36	17 41		17 46	17 51		17 56	18 01	18 06		18 06	18 11	18 16		18 21
Cardiff Bay	d				17 18				17 30				17 42			17 54				18 06				18 18	
Cardiff Queen Street 3	a		17 14	17 19	17 22	17 24	17 29	17 34	17 34	17 39		17 44	17 46	17 49	17 54	17 58	17 59	18 04	18 09	18 10		18 14	18 19	18 22	18 24
	d		17 15	17 20		17 25	17 30	17 35		17 40		17 45		17 50	17 55		18 00	18 05	18 10			18 15	18 20		18 25
Heath Low Level	d					17 30									18 00										18 30
Ty Glas	d					17 33									18 03										18 33
Birchgrove	d					17 34									18 04										18 34
Rhiwbina	d					17 36									18 06										18 36
Whitchurch (Cardiff)	d					17 38									18 08										18 38
Coryton	a					17 43									18 13										18 43
Heath High Level	d			17 25				17 40						17 55				18 10					18 25		
Llanishen	d			17 28				17 43						17 59				18 13					18 28		
Lisvane & Thornhill	d			17 30				17 45						18 02				18 15					18 30		
Caerphilly 3	d			17 36				17 51						18 07				18 21					18 36		
Aber	d			17 38				17 53						18 10				18 23					18 38		
Llanbradach	d			17 42				17 57						18 14				18 27					18 42		
Ystrad Mynach 3	d			17 47				18 02						18 20				18 32					18a51		
Hengoed	d			17 50				18 05						18 23				18 35							
Pengam	d			17 53				18 08						18 27				18 38							
Gilfach Fargoed	d							18 11						18 30				18 41							
Bargoed	d			18a01				18 16						18b44				18a48							
Brithdir	d							18 20						18 48											
Tir-phil	d							18 23						18 51											
Pontlottyn	d							18 27						18 55											
Rhymney 3	a							18 33						19 01											
Cathays	d		17 18				17 33			17 43		17 48					18 03		18 13			18 18			
Llandaf	d		17 22				17 37			17 47		17 52					18 07		18 17			18 22			
Ninian Park	d	17 10									17 40										18 10				
Waun-gron Park	d	17 13									17 43										18 13				
Fairwater	d	17 15									17 45										18 15				
Danescourt	d	17 17									17 47										18 17				
Radyr 3	a	17 24	17 25				17 40			17 50	17 54	17 55					18 10		18 20		18 24	18 25			
	d		17 25				17 40			17 50		17 55					18 10		18 20			18 25			
Taffs Well 3	d		17 29				17 44			17 54		17 59					18 14		18 24			18 29			
Trefforest Estate	d						17 48										18 18								
Trefforest	d		17 36				17 52			18 01		18 06					18 22		18 31			18 36			
Pontypridd 3	a		17 39				17 55			18 04		18 09					18 25		18 34			18 42			
	d		17 41				17 57			18 06		18 11					18 27		18 36						
Abercynon	d		17 49				18 04					18 19					18 34								
Penrhiwceiber	d		17 54									18 24													
Mountain Ash	a		17 58									18 28													
	d		18 03									18 33													
Fernhill	d		18 05									18 35													
Cwmbach	d		18 09									18 39													
Aberdare 3	a		18 16									18 46													
Quakers Yard	d						18 09										18 39								
Merthyr Vale	d						18 17										18 47								
Troed Y Rhiw	d						18 20										18 50								
Pentre-bach	d						18 23										18 53								
Merthyr Tydfil	a						18 31										19 01								
Trehafod	d									18 11									18 41						
Porth	d									18 15									18 45						
Dinas Rhondda	d									18 19									18 49						
Tonypandy	d									18 21									18 51						
Llwynypia	d									18 23									18 53						
Ystrad Rhondda	a									18 26									18 56						
	d									18 29									18 59						
Ton Pentre	d									18 31									19 01						
Treorchy	d									18 34									19 04						
Ynyswen	d									18 37									19 07						
Treherbert	a									18 43									19 13						

For general notes see front of timetable
For details of catering facilities see Directory of Train Operators

A From Coryton
B From Radyr
b Arr. 1834

From Saturday 12 September a revised service will be in operation due to seasonal difficulties. Most trains will arrive at their destination between 1 and 3 minutes later. Passengers should check with National Rail Enquiries for precise times.

Bridgend, Barry Island, Barry, Penarth and Cardiff → Coryton, Rhymney, Pontypridd, Merthyr, Aberdare and Treherbert

Network Diagram - see first page of Table 130

		AW	AW	AW		AW A	AW	AW	AW		AW B	AW	AW	AW	AW	AW	AW	AW	AW	AW	AW	AW A	AW	AW	AW	AW
Bridgend	d						17 42																18 42			
Llantwit Major	d						17 56																18 56			
Rhoose Cardiff Int Airport ✈	d						18 06																19 06			
Barry Island	d	17 56											18 26				18 41		18 56							
Barry 3	d	18 00					18 15						18 30				18 45		19 00				19 15			
Barry Docks	d	18 04					18 19						18 34				18 49		19 04				19 19			
Cadoxton	d	18 07					18 22						18 37				18 52		19 07				19 22			
Dinas Powys	d	18 11					18 26						18 41				18 56		19 11				19 26			
Eastbrook	d	18 13					18 28						18 43				18 58		19 13				19 28			
Cogan	d	18 15					18 30						18 45				19 00		19 15				19 30			
Penarth	d			18 17					18 32					18 47						19 17						
Dingle Road	d			18 19					18 34					18 49						19 19						
Grangetown	d	18 19		18 23			18 34		18 38				18 49	18 53			19 04		19 19	19 23			19 34			
Cardiff Central 7	a	18 24		18 29			18 39		18 45				18 55	18 59			19 09		19 24	19 29			19 39			
	d	18 26		18 31	18 36	18 36	18 41				18 51			19 01	19 06		19 11		19 26	19 31		19 36	19 41		19 51	
Cardiff Bay	d		18 30					18 42				18 54				19 06		19 18			19 30			19 42		19 54
Cardiff Queen Street 3	a	18 29	18 34	18 34	18 38		18 44	18 46			18 54	18 58		19 04	19 09	19 10	19 14	19 22	19 29	19 34	19 34		19 44	19 46	19 54	19 58
	d	18 30		18 35	18 40		18 50				18 55			19 05	19 10		19 15		19 30	19 35			19 45		19 55	
Heath Low Level	d										19 00														20 00	
Ty Glas	d										19 03														20 03	
Birchgrove	d										19 04														20 04	
Rhiwbina	d										19 06														20 06	
Whitchurch (Cardiff)	d										19 08														20 08	
Coryton	a										19 13														20 13	
Heath High Level	d			18 40										19 10						19 40						
Llanishen	d			18 43										19 13						19 43						
Lisvane & Thornhill	d			18 45										19 15						19 45						
Caerphilly 3	d			18 51										19a24						19 51						
Aber	d			18 53																19 53						
Llanbradach	d			18 57																19 57						
Ystrad Mynach 3	d			19 02																20 02						
Hengoed	d			19 05																20 05						
Pengam	d			19 08																20 08						
Gilfach Fargoed	d			19x11																20 11						
Bargoed	d			19 16																20 16						
Brithdir	d			19 20																20 20						
Tir-phil	d			19 23																20 23						
Pontlottyn	d			19 27																20 27						
Rhymney 3	a			19 33																20 33						
Cathays	d	18 33			18 43		18 52								19 13		19 18		19 33				19 48			
Llandaf	d	18 37			18 47		18 56								19 17		19 22		19 37				19 52			
Ninian Park	d					18 40																19 40				
Waun-gron Park	d					18 43																19 43				
Fairwater	d					18 45																19 45				
Danescourt	d					18 47																19 47				
Radyr 3	a	18 40			18 50	18 54	18 58								19 20		19 25		19 40			19 54	19 55			
	d	18 40			18 50		18 58								19 20		19 25		19 40				19 55			
Taffs Well 3	d	18 44			18 54		19 03								19 24		19 29		19 44				19 59			
Trefforest Estate	d	18 48																	19 48							
Trefforest	d	18 52			19 01		19 10								19 31		19 36		19 52				20 06			
Pontypridd 3	a	18 55			19 04		19 13								19 34		19 39		19 55				20 09			
	d	18 57			19 06		19 14								19 36		19 41		19 57				20 11			
Abercynon	d	19 04					19 21										19 49		20 04				20 21			
Penrhiwceiber	d						19 26										19 54						20 27			
Mountain Ash	a						19 30										19 56						20 30			
	d						19 33										20 03						20 33			
Fernhill	d						19 35										20 05						20 35			
Cwmbach	d						19 39										20 09						20 39			
Aberdare 3	a						19 46										20 16						20 46			
Quakers Yard	d	19 09																	20 09							
Merthyr Vale	d	19 17																	20 17							
Troed Y Rhiw	d	19 20																	20 20							
Pentre-bach	d	19 23																	20 23							
Merthyr Tydfil	a	19 31																	20 31							
Trehafod	d				19 11										19 41											
Porth	d				19 15										19 45											
Dinas Rhondda	d				19 19										19 49											
Tonypandy	d				19 21										19 51											
Llwynypia	d				19 23										19 53											
Ystrad Rhondda	a				19 26										19 56											
	d				19 29										19 59											
Ton Pentre	d				19 31										20 01											
Treorchy	d				19 34										20 04											
Ynyswen	d				19 37										20 07											
Treherbert	a				19 43										20 13											

For general notes see front of timetable
For details of catering facilities see Directory of Train Operators

A From Coryton
B From Radyr

From Saturday 12 September a revised service will be in operation due to seasonal difficulties. Most trains will arrive at their destination between 1 and 3 minutes later. Passengers should check with National Rail Enquiries for precise times.

Bridgend, Barry Island, Barry, Penarth and Cardiff → Coryton, Rhymney, Pontypridd, Merthyr, Aberdare and Treherbert

Network Diagram - see first page of Table 130

		AW		AW	AW	AW	AW	AW	AW	AW A	AW	AW	AW	AW	AW	AW	AW	AW		AW	AW	AW	AW A	AW	AW	AW
Bridgend	d										19 42														20 42	
Llantwit Major	d										19 56														20 56	
Rhoose Cardiff Int Airport ✈	d										20 06														21 06	
Barry Island	d	19 26					19 56													20 56						
Barry 3	d	19 30					20 00				20 15									21 00					21 15	
Barry Docks	d	19 34					20 04				20 19									21 04					21 19	
Cadoxton	d	19 37					20 07				20 22									21 07					21 22	
Dinas Powys	d	19 41					20 11				20 26									21 11					21 26	
Eastbrook	d	19 43					20 13				20 28									21 13					21 28	
Cogan	d	19 45					20 15				20 30									21 15					21 30	
Penarth	d			19 47				20 17							20 47									21 17		
Dingle Road	d			19 49				20 19							20 49									21 19		
Grangetown	d	19 49		19 54			20 19	20 23			20 34				20 53					21 19				21 23	21 34	
Cardiff Central 7	a	19 56		19 59			20 24	20 29			20 39				20 59					21 24				21 37	21 39	
	d	20 01		20 06			20 26	20 31		20 36	20 41		20 51		21 01	21 06				21 26		21 31	21 36		21 41	
Cardiff Bay	d				20 06	20 18			20 30			20 42		20 54			21 06	21 18			21 30					21 42
Cardiff Queen Street 3	a	20 04		20 09	20 10	20 22	20 29	20 34	20 34		20 44	20 46	20 54	20 58	21 04	21 09	21 10	21 22		21 29	21 34	21 34			21 44	21 46
	d	20 06		20 10			20 30	20 35			20 45		20 55		21 05	21 10				21 30		21 35			21 45	
Heath Low Level	d												21 00													
Ty Glas	d												21 03													
Birchgrove	d												21 04													
Rhiwbina	d												21 06													
Whitchurch (Cardiff)	d												21 08													
Coryton	a												21 13													
Heath High Level	d	20 10						20 40							21 10							21 40				
Llanishen	d	20 13						20 43							21 13							21 43				
Lisvane & Thornhill	d	20 16						20 45							21 15							21 45				
Caerphilly 3	d	20a28						20 51							21a28							21 51				
Aber	d							20 53														21 53				
Llanbradach	d							20 57														21 57				
Ystrad Mynach 3	d							21 02														22 02				
Hengoed	d							21 05														22 05				
Pengam	d							21 08														22 08				
Gilfach Fargoed	d							21 11														22 11				
Bargoed	d							21 16														22 16				
Brithdir	d							21 20														22 20				
Tir-phil	d							21 23														22 23				
Pontlottyn	d							21 27														22 27				
Rhymney 3	a							21 33														22 33				
Cathays	d			20 13			20 33				20 48					21 13				21 33					21 48	
Llandaf	d			20 17			20 37				20 52					21 17				21 37					21 52	
Ninian Park	d									20 40													21 40			
Waun-gron Park	d									20 43													21 43			
Fairwater	d									20 45													21 45			
Danescourt	d									20 47													21 47			
Radyr 3	a			20 20			20 40			20 54	20 55					21 20				21 40			21 54		21 55	
	d			20 20			20 40				20 55					21 20				21 40					21 55	
Taffs Well 3	d			20 24			20 44				20 59					21 24				21 44					21 59	
Trefforest Estate	d						20 48													21 48						
Trefforest	d			20 31			20 52				21 06					21 31				21 52					22 06	
Pontypridd 3	a			20 35			20 55				21 09					21 34				21 55					22 09	
	d			20 36			20 57				21 11					21 36				21 57					22 11	
Abercynon	d						21 04				21 19									22 04					22 19	
Penrhiwceiber	d										21 24														22 24	
Mountain Ash	a										21 28														22 28	
	d										21 33														22 33	
Fernhill	d										21 35														22 35	
Cwmbach	d										21 39														22 39	
Aberdare 3	a										21 46														22 46	
Quakers Yard	d						21 09													22 09						
Merthyr Vale	d						21 17													22 17						
Troed Y Rhiw	d						21 20													22 20						
Pentre-bach	d						21 23													22 23						
Merthyr Tydfil	a						21 31													22 31						
Trehafod	d			20 41												21 41										
Porth	d			20 45												21 45										
Dinas Rhondda	d			20 49												21 49										
Tonypandy	d			20 51												21 51										
Llwynypia	d			20 53												21 53										
Ystrad Rhondda	a			20 56												21 56										
	d			20 59												21 59										
Ton Pentre	d			21 01												22 01										
Treorchy	d			21 04												22 04										
Ynyswen	d			21 07												22 07										
Treherbert	a			21 13												22 13										

For general notes see front of timetable
For details of catering facilities see Directory of Train Operators

A From Coryton

From Saturday 12 September a revised service will be in operation due to seasonal difficulties. Most trains will arrive at their destination between 1 and 3 minutes later. Passengers should check with National Rail Enquiries for precise times.

Table 130

Saturdays

Bridgend, Barry Island, Barry, Penarth and Cardiff → Coryton, Rhymney, Pontypridd, Merthyr, Aberdare and Treherbert

Network Diagram - see first page of Table 130

		AW	AW	AW	AW	AW	AW	AW	AW	AW	AW	AW	AW	AW	AW	AW	AW	AW	AW	AW	AW	AW	AW
							A																
Bridgend	d										21 42											22 42	
Llantwit Major	d										21 56											22 56	
Rhoose Cardiff Int Airport ✈	d										22 06											23 06	
Barry Island	d							21 56										22 56					
Barry 3	d							22 00			22 15							23 00				23 15	
Barry Docks	d							22 04			22 19							23 04				23 19	
Cadoxton	d							22 07			22 22							23 07				23 22	
Dinas Powys	d							22 11			22 26							23 11				23 26	
Eastbrook	d							22 13			22 28							23 13				23 28	
Cogan	d							22 15			22 30							23 15				23 30	
Penarth	d		21 47							22 17						22 47				23 26			
Dingle Road	d		21 49							22 19						22 49				23 28			
Grangetown	d		21 53					22 19		22 23	22 34					22 53		23 19		23 32		23 34	
Cardiff Central 7	a		21 59					22 24		22 31	22 39					23 00		23 24		23 38		23 42	
	d		22 01	22 06			22 21	22 26		22 35	22 41		22 46			23 15		23 26					
Cardiff Bay	d	21 54			22 06	22 18			22 30			22 42		22 54	23 06		23 18		23 30		23 42		23 54
Cardiff Queen Street 3	a	21 58	22 04	22 09	22 10	22 22	22 24	22 29	22 34	22 38	22 44	22 46	22 49	22 58	23 10	23 18	23 22	23 29	23 34		23 46		23 58
	d		22 05	22 10			22 25	22 30		22 39	22 45		22 50			23 19		23 30					
Heath Low Level	d						22 30																
Ty Glas	d						22 33																
Birchgrove	d						22 34																
Rhiwbina	d						22 36																
Whitchurch (Cardiff)	d						22 38																
Coryton	a						22 43																
Heath High Level	d		22 10							22 44						23 24							
Llanishen	d		22 13							22 47						23 27							
Lisvane & Thornhill	d		22 15							22 49						23 29							
Caerphilly 3	d		22a24							22 55						23 35							
Aber	d									22 57						23 37							
Llanbradach	d									23 01						23 41							
Ystrad Mynach 3	d									23 06						23a50							
Hengoed	d									23 09													
Pengam	d									23 12													
Gilfach Fargoed	d									23 15													
Bargoed	d									23 20													
Brithdir	d									23 24													
Tir-phil	d									23 27													
Pontlottyn	d									23 31													
Rhymney 3	a									23 37													
Cathays	d			22 13				22 33			22 48		22 53					23 33					
Llandaf	d			22 17				22 37			22 52		22 57					23 37					
Ninian Park	d																						
Waun-gron Park	d																						
Fairwater	d																						
Danescourt	d																						
Radyr 3	a			22 20				22 40			22 55		22 59					23 40					
	d			22 20				22 40			22 55		22 59					23 40					
Taffs Well 3	d			22 24				22 44			22 59		23 03					23 44					
Trefforest Estate	d							22 48										23 48					
Trefforest	d			22 31				22 52			23 06		23 10					23 52					
Pontypridd 3	a			22 34				22 55			23 09		23 14					23 58					
	d			22 36				22 57			23 11		23 15										
Abercynon	d							23 04			23 19												
Penrhiwceiber	d										23 24												
Mountain Ash	a										23 28												
	d										23 33												
Fernhill	d										23 35												
Cwmbach	d										23 39												
Aberdare 3	a										23 46												
Quakers Yard	d							23 09															
Merthyr Vale	d							23 17															
Troed Y Rhiw	d							23 20															
Pentre-bach	d							23 23															
Merthyr Tydfil	a							23 31															
Trehafod	d			22 41									23 20										
Porth	d			22 45									23 24										
Dinas Rhondda	d			22 49									23 28										
Tonypandy	d			22 51									23 30										
Llwynypia	d			22 53									23 32										
Ystrad Rhondda	a			22 56									23 35										
	d			22 59									23 38										
Ton Pentre	d			23 01									23 40										
Treorchy	d			23 04									23 43										
Ynyswen	d			23 07									23 46										
Treherbert	a			23 13									23 52										

For general notes see front of timetable
For details of catering facilities see Directory of Train Operators

A From Radyr

From Saturday 12 September a revised service will be in operation due to seasonal difficulties. Most trains will arrive at their destination between 1 and 3 minutes later. Passengers should check with National Rail Enquiries for precise times.

Table 130

Sundays

Bridgend, Barry Island, Barry, Penarth and Cardiff → Coryton, Rhymney, Pontypridd, Merthyr, Aberdare and Treherbert

Network Diagram - see first page of Table 130

		AW	AW	AW A	AW	AW	AW	AW	AW	AW	AW	AW	AW	AW	AW	AW	AW	AW	AW	AW	AW	AW
Bridgend	d																	09 42				
Llantwit Major	d																	09 56				
Rhoose Cardiff Int Airport ✈	d																	10 06				
Barry Island	d								08 56						09 56					10 26		
Barry 3	d								09 00						10 00			10 15		10 30		
Barry Docks	d								09 04						10 04			10 19		10 34		
Cadoxton	d								09 07						10 07			10 22		10 37		
Dinas Powys	d								09 11						10 11			10 26		10 41		
Eastbrook	d								09 13						10 13			10 28		10 43		
Cogan	d								09 15						10 15			10 30		10 45		
Penarth	d																				10 47	
Dingle Road	d																				10 49	
Grangetown	d								09 19						10 19			10 34		10 49	10 53	
Cardiff Central 7	a								09 24						10 24			10 42		10 56	10 59	
	d	08 26	08 41	08 54	09 06				09 41			10 06			10 26							11 06
Cardiff Bay	d					09 06	09 18	09 30		09 42	09 54		10 06	10 18		10 30	10 42		10 54			
Cardiff Queen Street 3	a	08 29	08 44	08 57	09 09	09 10	09 22	09 34	09 44	09 46	09 58	10 09	10 10	10 22	10 29	10 34	10 46		10 58			11 09
	d	08 30	08 45		09 10				09 45			10 10			10 30							11 10
Heath Low Level	d																					
Ty Glas	d																					
Birchgrove	d																					
Rhiwbina	d																					
Whitchurch (Cardiff)	d																					
Coryton	a																					
Heath High Level	d											10 15										
Llanishen	d											10 18										
Lisvane & Thornhill	d											10 20										
Caerphilly 3	d											10 26										
Aber	d											10 28										
Llanbradach	d											10 32										
Ystrad Mynach 3	d											10 37										
Hengoed	d											10 40										
Pengam	d											10 43										
Gilfach Fargoed	d											10 46										
Bargoed	d											10 49										
Brithdir	d											10 53										
Tir-phil	d											10 56										
Pontlottyn	d											11 00										
Rhymney 3	a											11 06										
Cathays	d	08 33	08 48		09 13				09 48						10 33							11 13
Llandaf	d	08 37	08 52		09 17				09 52						10 37							11 17
Ninian Park	d																					
Waun-gron Park	d																					
Fairwater	d																					
Danescourt	d																					
Radyr 3	a	08 40	08 55		09 20				09 55						10 40							11 20
	d	08 40	08 55		09 20				09 55						10 40							11 20
Taffs Well 3	d	08 44	08 59		09 24				09 59						10 44							11 24
Trefforest Estate	d																					
Trefforest	d	08 52	09 06		09 31				10 06						10 52							11 31
Pontypridd 3	a	08 55	09 09		09 34				10 09						10 55							11 34
	d	08 57	09 11		09 36				10 11						10 57							11 36
Abercynon	d	09 04	09 19						10 19						11 04							
Penrhiwceiber	d		09 24						10 24													
Mountain Ash	a		09 28						10 28													
	d		09 31						10 31													
Fernhill	d		09 33						10 33													
Cwmbach	d		09 37						10 37													
Aberdare 3	a		09 44						10 44													
Quakers Yard	d	09 09													11 09							
Merthyr Vale	d	09 17													11 17							
Troed Y Rhiw	d	09 20													11 20							
Pentre-bach	d	09 23													11 23							
Merthyr Tydfil	a	09 31													11 31							
Trehafod	d				09 41																	11 41
Porth	d				09 45																	11 45
Dinas Rhondda	d				09 49																	11 49
Tonypandy	d				09 51																	11 51
Llwynypia	d				09 53																	11 53
Ystrad Rhondda	a				09 56																	11 56
	d				09 59																	11 59
Ton Pentre	d				10 01																	12 01
Treorchy	d				10 04																	12 04
Ynyswen	d				10 07																	12 07
Treherbert	a				10 13																	12 13

For general notes see front of timetable
For details of catering facilities see Directory of Train Operators

A To Cardiff Bay

From Sunday 13 September a revised service will be in operation due to seasonal difficulties. Most trains will arrive at their destination between 1 and 3 minutes later. Passengers should check with National Rail Enquiries for precise times.

Table 130

Sundays

Bridgend, Barry Island, Barry, Penarth and Cardiff → Coryton, Rhymney, Pontypridd, Merthyr, Aberdare and Treherbert

Network Diagram - see first page of Table 130

		AW	AW	AW	AW	AW	AW	AW	AW	AW	AW	AW	AW	AW	AW	AW	AW	AW	AW	AW	AW
Bridgend	d													11 42							
Llantwit Major	d													11 56							
Rhoose Cardiff Int Airport ✈	d													12 06							
Barry Island	d				10 56			11 26			11 56					12 26					
Barry [3]	d				11 00			11 30			12 00			12 15		12 30					
Barry Docks	d				11 04			11 34			12 04			12 19		12 34					
Cadoxton	d				11 07			11 37			12 07			12 22		12 37					
Dinas Powys	d				11 11			11 41			12 11			12 26		12 41					
Eastbrook	d				11 13			11 43			12 13			12 28		12 43					
Cogan	d				11 15			11 45			12 15			12 30		12 45					
Penarth	d																12 47				
Dingle Road	d																12 49				
Grangetown	d				11 19			11 49			12 19			12 34		12 49	12 53				
Cardiff Central [7]	a				11 24			11 57			12 24			12 42		12 56	12 59				
	d				11 41			12 06			12 26							13 06			
Cardiff Bay	d	11 06	11 18	11 30		11 42	11 54		12 06	12 18		12 30	12 42		12 54				13 06	13 18	13 30
Cardiff Queen Street [3]	a	11 10	11 22	11 34	11 44	11 46	11 58	12 09	12 10	12 22	12 29	12 34	12 46		12 58			13 09	13 10	13 22	13 34
	d				11 45			12 10			12 30							13 10			
Heath Low Level	d																				
Ty Glas	d																				
Birchgrove	d																				
Rhiwbina	d																				
Whitchurch (Cardiff)	d																				
Coryton	a																				
Heath High Level	d							12 15													
Llanishen	d							12 18													
Lisvane & Thornhill	d							12 20													
Caerphilly [3]	d							12 26													
Aber	d							12 28													
Llanbradach	d							12 32													
Ystrad Mynach [3]	d							12 37													
Hengoed	d							12 40													
Pengam	d							12 43													
Gilfach Fargoed	d							12 46													
Bargoed	d							12 49													
Brithdir	d							12 53													
Tir-phil	d							12 56													
Pontlottyn	d							13 00													
Rhymney [3]	a							13 06													
Cathays	d				11 48						12 33							13 13			
Llandaf	d				11 52						12 37							13 17			
Ninian Park	d																				
Waun-gron Park	d																				
Fairwater	d																				
Danescourt	d																				
Radyr [3]	a				11 55						12 40							13 20			
	d				11 55						12 40							13 20			
Taffs Well [3]	d				11 59						12 44							13 24			
Trefforest Estate	d																				
Trefforest	d				12 06						12 52							13 31			
Pontypridd [3]	a				12 09						12 55							13 34			
	d				12 11						12 57							13 36			
Abercynon	d				12 19						13 04										
Penrhiwceiber	d				12 24																
Mountain Ash	a				12 28																
	d				12 31																
Fernhill	d				12 33																
Cwmbach	d				12 37																
Aberdare [3]	a				12 44																
Quakers Yard	d										13 09										
Merthyr Vale	d										13 17										
Troed Y Rhiw	d										13 20										
Pentre-bach	d										13 23										
Merthyr Tydfil	a										13 31										
Trehafod	d																	13 41			
Porth	d																	13 45			
Dinas Rhondda	d																	13 49			
Tonypandy	d																	13 51			
Llwynypia	d																	13 53			
Ystrad Rhondda	a																	13 56			
	d																	13 59			
Ton Pentre	d																	14 01			
Treorchy	d																	14 04			
Ynyswen	d																	14 07			
Treherbert	a																	14 13			

For general notes see front of timetable
For details of catering facilities see Directory of Train Operators

From Sunday 13 September a revised service will be in operation due to seasonal difficulties. Most trains will arrive at their destination between 1 and 3 minutes later. Passengers should check with National Rail Enquiries for precise times.

Table 130 **Sundays**

Bridgend, Barry Island, Barry, Penarth and Cardiff → Coryton, Rhymney, Pontypridd, Merthyr, Aberdare and Treherbert

Network Diagram - see first page of Table 130

		AW	AW	AW	AW	AW	AW	AW	AW	AW	AW	AW	AW	AW	AW	AW	AW	AW	AW	AW	AW
Bridgend	d										13 42										
Llantwit Major	d										13 56										
Rhoose Cardiff Int Airport ✈	d										14 06										
Barry Island	d	12 56			13 26			13 56					14 26						14 56		
Barry 3	d	13 00			13 30			14 00			14 15		14 30						15 00		
Barry Docks	d	13 04			13 34			14 04			14 19		14 34						15 04		
Cadoxton	d	13 07			13 37			14 07			14 22		14 37						15 07		
Dinas Powys	d	13 11			13 41			14 11			14 26		14 41						15 11		
Eastbrook	d	13 13			13 43			14 13			14 28		14 43						15 13		
Cogan	d	13 15			13 45			14 15			14 30		14 45						15 15		
Penarth	d													14 47							
Dingle Road	d													14 49							
Grangetown	d	13 19			13 49			14 19			14 34		14 49	14 53					15 19		
Cardiff Central 7	a	13 24			13 57			14 24			14 42		14 56	14 59					15 24		
	d	13 41			14 06			14 26							15 06				15 41		
Cardiff Bay	d		13 42	13 54		14 06	14 18		14 30	14 42		14 54				15 06	15 18	15 30		15 42	15 54
Cardiff Queen Street 3	a	13 44	13 46	13 58	14 09	14 10	14 22	14 29	14 34	14 46		14 58			15 09	15 10	15 22	15 34	15 44	15 46	15 58
	d	13 45			14 10			14 30							15 10				15 45		
Heath Low Level	d																				
Ty Glas	d																				
Birchgrove	d																				
Rhiwbina	d																				
Whitchurch (Cardiff)	d																				
Coryton	a																				
Heath High Level	d				14 15																
Llanishen	d				14 18																
Lisvane & Thornhill	d				14 20																
Caerphilly 3	d				14 26																
Aber	d				14 28																
Llanbradach	d				14 32																
Ystrad Mynach 3	d				14 37																
Hengoed	d				14 40																
Pengam	d				14 43																
Gilfach Fargoed	d				14 46																
Bargoed	d				14 49																
Brithdir	d				14 53																
Tir-phil	d				14 56																
Pontlottyn	d				15 00																
Rhymney 3	a				15 06																
Cathays	d	13 48						14 33							15 13				15 48		
Llandaf	d	13 52						14 37							15 17				15 52		
Ninian Park	d																				
Waun-gron Park	d																				
Fairwater	d																				
Danescourt	d																				
Radyr 3	a	13 55						14 40							15 20				15 55		
	d	13 55						14 40							15 20				15 55		
Taffs Well 3	d	13 59						14 44							15 24				15 59		
Trefforest Estate	d																				
Trefforest	d	14 06						14 52							15 31				16 06		
Pontypridd 3	a	14 09						14 55							15 34				16 09		
	d	14 11						14 57							15 36				16 11		
Abercynon	d	14 19						15 04											16 19		
Penrhiwceiber	d	14 24																	16 24		
Mountain Ash	a	14 28																	16 28		
	d	14 31																	16 31		
Fernhill	d	14 33																	16 33		
Cwmbach	d	14 37																	16 37		
Aberdare 3	a	14 44																	16 44		
Quakers Yard	d							15 09													
Merthyr Vale	d							15 17													
Troed Y Rhiw	d							15 20													
Pentre-bach	d							15 23													
Merthyr Tydfil	a							15 31													
Trehafod	d														15 41						
Porth	d														15 45						
Dinas Rhondda	d														15 49						
Tonypandy	d														15 51						
Llwynypia	d														15 53						
Ystrad Rhondda	a														15 56						
	d														15 59						
Ton Pentre	d														16 01						
Treorchy	d														16 04						
Ynyswen	d														16 07						
Treherbert	a														16 13						

For general notes see front of timetable
For details of catering facilities see Directory of Train Operators

From Sunday 13 September a revised service will be in operation due to seasonal difficulties. Most trains will arrive at their destination between 1 and 3 minutes later. Passengers should check with National Rail Enquiries for precise times.

Table 130

Sundays

Bridgend, Barry Island, Barry, Penarth and Cardiff → Coryton, Rhymney, Pontypridd, Merthyr, Aberdare and Treherbert

Network Diagram - see first page of Table 130

		AW	AW	AW	AW	AW	AW	AW	AW	AW	AW	AW A	AW	AW	AW	AW	AW	AW	AW	AW	AW	AW
Bridgend	d							15 42														
Llantwit Major	d							15 56														
Rhoose Cardiff Int Airport ✈	d							16 06														
Barry Island	d	15 26			15 56					16 26		16 41					16 56			17 26		
Barry 3	d	15 30			16 00			16 15		16 30		16 45					17 00			17 30		
Barry Docks	d	15 34			16 04			16 19		16 34							17 04			17 34		
Cadoxton	d	15 37			16 07			16 22		16 37							17 07			17 37		
Dinas Powys	d	15 41			16 11			16 26		16 41							17 11			17 41		
Eastbrook	d	15 43			16 13			16 28		16 43							17 13			17 43		
Cogan	d	15 45			16 15			16 30		16 45							17 15			17 45		
Penarth	d										16 47											
Dingle Road	d										16 49											
Grangetown	d	15 49			16 19			16 34		16 49	16 53						17 19			17 49		
Cardiff Central 7	a	15 57			16 24			16 42		16 56	16 59	17 02					17 24			17 57		
	d	16 06			16 26								17 06				17 41			18 06		
Cardiff Bay	d		16 06	16 18		16 30	16 42		16 54					17 06	17 18	17 30		17 42	17 54		18 06	18 18
Cardiff Queen Street 3	a	16 09	16 10	16 22	16 29	16 34	16 46		16 58				17 09	17 10	17 22	17 34	17 44	17 46	17 58	18 09	18 10	18 22
	d	16 10			16 30								17 10				17 45			18 10		
Heath Low Level	d																					
Ty Glas	d																					
Birchgrove	d																					
Rhiwbina	d																					
Whitchurch (Cardiff)	d																					
Coryton	a																					
Heath High Level	d	16 15																		18 15		
Llanishen	d	16 18																		18 18		
Lisvane & Thornhill	d	16 20																		18 20		
Caerphilly 3	d	16 26																		18 26		
Aber	d	16 28																		18 28		
Llanbradach	d	16 32																		18 32		
Ystrad Mynach 3	d	16 37																		18 37		
Hengoed	d	16 40																		18 40		
Pengam	d	16 43																		18 43		
Gilfach Fargoed	d	16 46																		18 46		
Bargoed	d	16 49																		18 49		
Brithdir	d	16 53																		18 53		
Tir-phil	d	16 56																		18 56		
Pontlottyn	d	17 00																		19 00		
Rhymney 3	a	17 06																		19 06		
Cathays	d				16 33								17 13				17 48					
Llandaf	d				16 37								17 17				17 52					
Ninian Park	d																					
Waun-gron Park	d																					
Fairwater	d																					
Danescourt	d																					
Radyr 3	a				16 40								17 20				17 55					
	d				16 40								17 20				17 55					
Taffs Well 3	d				16 44								17 24				17 59					
Trefforest Estate	d																					
Trefforest	d				16 52								17 31				18 06					
Pontypridd 3	a				16 55								17 34				18 09					
	d				16 57								17 36				18 11					
Abercynon	d				17 04												18 19					
Penrhiwceiber	d																18 24					
Mountain Ash	a																18 28					
	d																18 31					
Fernhill	d																18 33					
Cwmbach	d																18 37					
Aberdare 3	a																18 44					
Quakers Yard	d				17 09																	
Merthyr Vale	d				17 17																	
Troed Y Rhiw	d				17 20																	
Pentre-bach	d				17 23																	
Merthyr Tydfil	a				17 31																	
Trehafod	d												17 41									
Porth	d												17 45									
Dinas Rhondda	d												17 49									
Tonypandy	d												17 51									
Llwynypia	d												17 53									
Ystrad Rhondda	a												17 56									
	d												17 59									
Ton Pentre	d												18 01									
Treorchy	d												18 04									
Ynyswen	d												18 07									
Treherbert	a												18 13									

For general notes see front of timetable
For details of catering facilities see Directory of Train Operators

A Until 6 Sept.
To Newport (South Wales) (Table 132)

From Sunday 13 September a revised service will be in operation due to seasonal difficulties. Most trains will arrive at their destination between 1 and 3 minutes later. Passengers should check with National Rail Enquiries for precise times.

Table 130

Sundays

Bridgend, Barry Island, Barry, Penarth and Cardiff → Coryton, Rhymney, Pontypridd, Merthyr, Aberdare and Treherbert

Network Diagram - see first page of Table 130

		AW		AW	AW	AW	AW		AW	AW	AW	AW		AW	AW	AW	AW	AW	AW	AW	AW	AW	AW	AW		
							A																			
Bridgend	d					17 42										19 42							21 42			
Llantwit Major	d					17 56										19 56							21 56			
Rhoose Cardiff Int Airport ✈	d					18 06										20 06							22 06			
Barry Island	d	17 56							18 26			18 56		19 26	19 56		20 26			20 56	21 26	21 56		22 56		
Barry 3	d	18 00				18 15			18 30			19 00		19 30	20 00	20 15	20 30			21 00	21 30	22 00	22 15	23 00		
Barry Docks	d	18 04				18 19			18 34			19 04		19 34	20 04	20 19	20 34			21 04	21 34	22 04	22 19	23 04		
Cadoxton	d	18 07				18 22			18 37			19 07		19 37	20 07	20 22	20 37			21 07	21 37	22 07	22 22	23 07		
Dinas Powys	d	18 11				18 26			18 41			19 11		19 41	20 11	20 26	20 41			21 11	21 41	22 11	22 26	23 11		
Eastbrook	d	18 13				18 28			18 43			19 13		19 43	20 13	20 28	20 43			21 13	21 43	22 13	22 28	23 13		
Cogan	d	18 15				18 30			18 45			19 15		19 45	20 15	20 30	20 45			21 15	21 45	22 15	22 30	23 15		
Penarth	d									18 47								20 47								
Dingle Road	d									18 49								20 49								
Grangetown	d	18 19				18 34			18 49	18 53		19 19		19 49	20 19	20 34	20 49	20 53		21 19	21 49	22 19	22 34	23 19		
Cardiff Central 7	a	18 24				18 42			18 56	18 59		19 24		19 57	20 24	20 42	20 54	20 59		21 27	21 54	22 27	22 42	23 27		
	d	18 26									19 06	19 41		20 06	20 26		21 06		21 16		22 06					
Cardiff Bay	d			18 30	18 42		18 54																			
Cardiff Queen Street 3	a	18 29		18 34	18 46		18 57				19 09	19 44		20 09	20 29		21 09		21 19		22 09					
	d	18 30									19 10	19 45		20 10	20 30		21 10		21 20		22 10					
Heath Low Level	d																									
Ty Glas	d																									
Birchgrove	d																									
Rhiwbina	d																									
Whitchurch (Cardiff)	d																									
Coryton	a																									
Heath High Level	d													20 15					21 25							
Llanishen	d													20 18					21 28							
Lisvane & Thornhill	d													20 20					21 30							
Caerphilly 3	d													20 26					21 36							
Aber	d													20 28					21 38							
Llanbradach	d													20 32					21 42							
Ystrad Mynach 3	d													20 37					21 47							
Hengoed	d													20 40					21 50							
Pengam	d													20 43					21 53							
Gilfach Fargoed	d													20 46					21 56							
Bargoed	d													20 49					21 59							
Brithdir	d													20 53					22 03							
Tir-phil	d													20 56					22 06							
Pontlottyn	d													21 00					22 10							
Rhymney 3	a													21 06					22 16							
Cathays	d	18 33									19 13	19 48			20 33		21 13				22 13					
Llandaf	d	18 37									19 17	19 52			20 37		21 17				22 17					
Ninian Park	d																									
Waun-gron Park	d																									
Fairwater	d																									
Danescourt	d																									
Radyr 3	a	18 40									19 20	19 55			20 40		21 20				22 20					
	d	18 40									19 20	19 55			20 40		21 20				22 20					
Taffs Well 3	d	18 44									19 24	19 59			20 44		21 24				22 24					
Trefforest Estate	d																									
Trefforest	d	18 52									19 31	20 06			20 52		21 31				22 31					
Pontypridd 3	a	18 55									19 34	20 09			20 55		21 34				22 34					
	d	18 57									19 36	20 11			20 57		21 36				22 36					
Abercynon	d	19 04										20 19			21 04											
Penrhiwceiber	d											20 24														
Mountain Ash	a											20 28														
	d											20 31														
Fernhill	d											20 33														
Cwmbach	d											20 37														
Aberdare 3	a											20 44														
Quakers Yard	d	19 09													21 09											
Merthyr Vale	d	19 17													21 17											
Troed Y Rhiw	d	19 20													21 20											
Pentre-bach	d	19 23													21 23											
Merthyr Tydfil	a	19 31													21 31											
Trehafod	d										19 41						21 41				22 41					
Porth	d										19 45						21 45				22 45					
Dinas Rhondda	d										19 49						21 49				22 49					
Tonypandy	d										19 51						21 51				22 51					
Llwynypia	d										19 53						21 53				22 53					
Ystrad Rhondda	a										19 56						21 56				22 56					
	d										19 59						21 59				22 59					
Ton Pentre	d										20 01						22 01				23 01					
Treorchy	d										20 04						22 04				23 04					
Ynyswen	d										20 07						22 07				23 07					
Treherbert	a										20 13						22 13				23 13					

For general notes see front of timetable
For details of catering facilities see Directory of Train Operators

A To Cardiff Central

From Sunday 13 September a revised service will be in operation due to seasonal difficulties. Most trains will arrive at their destination between 1 and 3 minutes later. Passengers should check with National Rail Enquiries for precise times.

Table 130A

Mondays to Saturdays

Rhoose (Cardiff Intl Airport) — Cardiff International Airport

Bus Service

		AW	AW	AW	AW	AW	AW	AW	AW	AW	AW	AW	AW	AW	AW	AW	AW	AW	AW
Rhoose Cardiff Int Airport	d	06 16	07 16	08 16	09 16	10 16	11 16	12 16	13 16	14 16	15 16	16 16	17 16	18 16	19 16	20 16	21 16	22 16	23 16
Cardiff International Apt	a	06 23	07 23	08 23	09 23	10 23	11 23	12 23	13 23	14 23	15 23	16 23	17 23	18 23	19 23	20 23	21 23	22 23	23 23

Sundays

		AW	AW	AW	AW	AW	AW	AW	AW	AW	AW	AW	AW	AW	AW
Rhoose Cardiff Int Airport	d	09 16	10 16	11 16	12 16	13 16	14 16	15 16	16 16	17 16	18 16	19 16	20 16	21 16	22 16
Cardiff International Apt	a	09 23	10 23	11 23	12 23	13 23	14 23	15 23	16 23	17 23	18 23	19 23	20 23	21 23	22 23

Mondays to Saturdays

		AW	AW	AW	AW	AW	AW	AW	AW	AW	AW	AW	AW	AW	AW	AW	AW	AW	AW
Cardiff International Apt	d	05 51	06 51	07 51	08 51	09 51	10 51	11 51	12 51	13 51	14 51	15 51	16 51	17 51	18 51	19 51	20 51	21 51	22 51
Rhoose Cardiff Int Airport	a	05 58	06 58	07 58	08 58	09 58	10 58	11 58	12 58	13 58	14 58	15 58	16 58	17 58	18 58	19 58	20 58	21 58	22 58

Sundays

		AW	AW	AW	AW	AW	AW	AW	AW	AW	AW	AW	AW	AW	AW	AW
Cardiff International Apt	d	08 51	09 51	10 51	11 51	12 51	13 51	14 51	15 51	16 51	17 51	18 51	19 51	20 51	21 51	22 51
Rhoose Cardiff Int Airport	a	08 58	09 58	10 58	11 58	12 58	13 58	14 58	15 58	16 58	17 58	18 58	19 58	20 58	21 58	22 58

For general notes see front of timetable
For details of catering facilities see
Directory of Train Operators

Cardiff → Crewe, Liverpool and Manchester

Route Diagram - see first page of Table 129

Miles	Miles			AW MX ◇	AW MX	AW	AW ◇	AW ◇ ⊼	AW ◇ ⊼	AW ◇	AW	AW ◇ A ⊼	AW ◇ ⊼	AW ◇ A ⊼	AW	AW ◇ B ⊼	AW ◇ ⊼	AW ◇ B ⊼
—	—	Swansea [7]	d					03 59		04 36		05 27	05 59	06 40		07 45	07 59	08 55
0	0	**Cardiff Central [7]**	d	21p55	00 30		04 35	05 10	05 40			06 50	07 20	07 50		08 50	09 20	09 50
—	—	London Paddington [15] ⊖	d											05 27		06 45	07 45	
—	—	Reading [7]	d											05 57		07 11	08 11	
—	—	Bristol Temple Meads [10]	d									05 54	06 50	07 15		07 53	08 54	09 21
11¾	11¾	**Newport (South Wales)**	d	22p13	00 59		04 53	05 28	05 57			07 04	07 34	08 05		09 05	09 34	10 05
18¾	18¾	Cwmbran	d	22p23	01 10		05 04	05 38	06 08			07 15	07 45	08 15		09 15	09 45	10 15
21¾	21¾	Pontypool and New Inn	d	22p29	01 16		05 09	05 44	06 13				07 49				09 49	
31¼	31¼	Abergavenny	d	22p39	01 27		05 19	05 53	06 19			07 28	08 00	08 28		09 28	10 00	10 28
55¼	55¼	**Hereford [7]**	a	23p05	01 55		05 43	06 18	06 47			07 52	08 26	08 53		09 53	10 26	10 53
—	—		d	23p07			05 48	06 25	06 49			07 55	08 28	08 55		09 55	10 28	10 55
67¾	67¾	Leominster	d	23p20			06 02	06 38	07 02			08 08		09 08		10 08		11 08
78¾	78¾	Ludlow	d	23p32			06 13	06 49	07 13			08 19	08 49	09 19		10 19	10 49	11 19
86	86	Craven Arms	d	23p41			06 21	06 58	07 22	07 53		08 28		09 28		10 28		11 28
93¼	93¼	Church Stretton	d	23p51			06 30	07 07	07 31	08 06		08 37		09 37		10 37		11 37
106	106	**Shrewsbury**	a	00 06			06 44	07 21	07 45	08 21		08 51	09 15	09 51		10 51	11 15	11 51
—	—		d	00 07		05 44	06 46	07 24	07 46		08 26	08 53	09 24	09 53	10 26	10 53	11 24	11 53
113¼	113¼	Yorton	d	00x15		05x53					08x35				10x35			
116¾	116¾	Wem	d	00 21		05 59	06 57		07 58		08 41				10 41			
120	120	Prees	d	00x25		06x03					08x45				10x45			
125	125	Whitchurch (Shrops)	d	00 32		06 10	07 06		08 07		08 52				10 52			
129¾	129¾	Wrenbury	d	00x39		06x17					08x59				10x59			
134¼	134¼	Nantwich	d	00 43		06 23	07 16		08 17		09 05				11 05			
138¾	138¾	**Crewe [10]**	a	01 00		06 35	07 25		08 26		09 17	09 25		10 26	11 17	11 25		12 25
—	—	Chester	a			07 18	08 45	08 20	09 12			10 09	10 20	11 09		12 12	12 19	13 12
—	—	Llandudno Junction	a			08 35	09b48	09 14	10b14			11 04	11 14	12 00			13 14	14b14
—	—	Bangor (Gwynedd)	a					09 31	10b36			11 27	11 38	12 16			13 31	14b36
—	—	Holyhead	a					10 05	11b19				12 13	12 50			14 14	15b11
—	161¼	Runcorn	a			07 22	08 22		09 21		09 48	10 21		11 21	11 48	12 21		13 21
—	174½	**Liverpool Lime Street [10]**	a			07 41	08 43		09 42		10 09	10 43		11 42	12 09	12 43		13 42
157¾	—	Wilmslow	a			07 16	07 44		08 45			09 45		10 45		11 45		12 45
163¾	—	Stockport	a			07 29	07 54		08 58			09 58		10 58		11 58		12 58
169¾	—	**Manchester Piccadilly [10]** 🚢	a			07 44	08 08		09 15			10 15		11 15		12 15		13 15

		GW [1] ◇ ⊡	AW	AW ◇ C ⊼	AW ◇	AW ◇ ⊼	AW ◇ B ⊼	GW [1] ◇ ⊡	AW	AW ◇ A ⊼	AW ◇ ⊼	AW ◇ D ⊼	AW	AW ◇ A ⊼	AW ◇	AW [R] ⊼	AW [R] B ⊼	AW [R] [1] ⊠
Swansea [7]	d			09 55	09 15		10 55			11 55		12 50		13 55	13 16		14 55	
Cardiff Central [7]	d			10 50	08 09	11 20	11 50			12 50	13 20	13 50		14 50		15 20	15 50	16 15
London Paddington [15] ⊖	d	08 22		08 45		09 15	09 45	10 22		10 45	11 45			12 45		13 45		14 15
Reading [7]	d	08 53		09 11		09 41	10 11	10 53		11 11	12 11			13 11		14 11		14 41
Bristol Temple Meads [10]	d			09 54		10 54	11 21			11 54	12 54	13 21		13 54		14 54	15 21	15 54
Newport (South Wales)	d			11 05		11 34	12 05			13 05	13 34	14 05		15 05		15 34	16 05	16 29
Cwmbran	d			11 15		11 45	12 15			13 15	13 45	14 15		15 15		15 44	16 15	16 39
Pontypool and New Inn	d					11 50					13 50					15 49	16 21	
Abergavenny	d			11 28		12 01	12 28			13 28	14 01	14 28		15 28		15 59	16 31	16 55
Hereford [7]	a	11 47		11 53		12 26	12 53	13 48		13 53	14 26	14 53		15 53		16 25	16 55	
	d			11 55		12 28	12 55			13 55	14 28	14 55		15 55		16 28	16 57	
Leominster	d			12 08			13 08			14 08		15 08		16 08			17 08	
Ludlow	d			12 19		12 49	13 19			14 19	14 49	15 19		16 19		16 49	17 19	
Craven Arms	d			12 28	12 36		13 28			14 28		15 28		16 28	16 37		17 28	
Church Stretton	d			12 37	12 49		13 37			14 37		15 37			16 50		17 37	
Shrewsbury	a			12 51	13 07	13 15	13 51			14 51	15 15	15 51		16 50	17 10	17 15	17 53	18 08
	d		12 26	12 53		13 24	13 53		14 26	14 53	15 24	15 53	16 26	16 52		17 24	17 54	18 09
Yorton	d		12x35						14x35				16x35					
Wem	d		12 41						14 41				16 41	17 03				
Prees	d		12x45						14x45				16x45					
Whitchurch (Shrops)	d		12 52						14 52				16 52					
Wrenbury	d		12x59						14x59				16x59					
Nantwich	d		13 05						15 05				17 05					
Crewe [10]	a		13 17	13 25			14 26		15 17	15 25		16 26	17 17	17 26			18 25	18 45
Chester	a			14 12		14 20	15 45			16 12	16 20	17 12		18 09		18 21		19 09
Llandudno Junction	a					15 14	16b48				17 14	18b16		18 59		19 15		19 55
Bangor (Gwynedd)	a					15 31					17 36	18b38		19 22		19 33		20 12
Holyhead	a					16 14					18 19	19b13				20 14		20 49
Runcorn	a		13 48	14 21			15 21		15 48	16 24		17 21	17 48	18 23			19 02	19c22
Liverpool Lime Street [10]	a		14 09	14 42			15 42		16 09	16 43		17 42	18 09	18 43			19 23	19c42
Wilmslow	a			13 45			14 45			15 45		16 45		17 45			18 45	19c27
Stockport	a			13 58			14 58		15 58	15 58		16 58		17 58			18 58	19c36
Manchester Piccadilly [10] 🚢	a			14 15			15 15			16 15		17 15		18 15			19 15	19c49

For general notes see front of timetable
For details of catering facilities see Directory of Train Operators

A From Carmarthen (Table 128)
B From Milford Haven (Table 128)
C From Pembroke Dock (Table 128)
D From Milford Haven (Table 128). ⊼ to Cardiff Central
b Change at Crewe and Chester
c Change at Crewe

Cardiff → Crewe, Liverpool and Manchester

Route Diagram - see first page of Table 129

		AW	AW R A ⌶	AW R ⌶	AW R B ⌶	AW	AW ◇ A ⌶	GW 1 ◇ ☕	AW ◇	AW ◇	AW ◇ C	GW 1 ◇ ☕	AW ◇ A	GW 1 ◇ ☕	AW ◇
Swansea 7	d		15 55		16 55		17 55		18 29	18 21	19 00		20 00		20 55
Cardiff Central 7	d		16 50	17 20	17 50		18 50		19 34		20 10		20 53		21 55
London Paddington 15 ⊖	d		14 45	15 45			16 45	17 22	17 45		18 15	18 21	19 15	19 22	20 15
Reading 7	d		15 11	16 11			17 11	17 50	18 11		18 41	18 51	19 41	19 53	20 41
Bristol Temple Meads 10	d		15 54	16 54	17 21		17 54		18 54		19 21		20 15		21 19
Newport (South Wales)	d		17 05	17 34	18 05		19 06		19 48		20 26		21 10		22 13
Cwmbran	d		17 15	17 45	18 16		19 16		19 58		20 36		21 21		22 23
Pontypool and New Inn	d			17 49	18 22				20 03		20 42				22 29
Abergavenny	d		17 28	18 00	18 31		19 32		20 12		20 51		21 34		22 39
Hereford 7	a		17 53	18 26	18 56		19 56	20 37	20 39		21 16	21 36	22 00	22 57	23 05
	d		17 55	18 28	18 57		19 58		20 39		21 17		22 01		23 07
Leominster	d		18 08	18 41	19 08		20 11		20 53		21 31		22 15		23 20
Ludlow	d		18 19	18 52	19 19		20 22		21 04		21 42		22 26		23 32
Craven Arms	d		18 28		19 28		20 28		21 12	21 37	21 50		22 34		23 41
Church Stretton	d		18 37		19 37		20 37		21 21	21 50	22 04		22 43		23 51
Shrewsbury	a		18 51	19 18	19 53		20 54		21 37	22 07	22 18		22 57		00 06
	d	18 26	18 53	19 24	19 55	20 29	20 55		21 39		22 19		23 01		00 07
Yorton	d	18x35				20x38					22x27		23x09		00x15
Wem	d	18 41				20 44					22 32		23 14		00 21
Prees	d	18x45				20x48					22x36		23x18		00x25
Whitchurch (Shrops)	d	18 52				20 55					22 43		23 25		00 32
Wrenbury	d	18x59				21x02					22x49		23x31		00x39
Nantwich	d	19 05				21 08					22 54		23 37		00 43
Crewe 10	a	19 17	19 25		20 26	21 19	21 26				23 03		23 48		01 00
Chester	a		20 16	20 20	21 10		22 15		22 34		23 42		00 27		
Llandudno Junction	a		21 05	21 20	22 06				23 49				01 28		
Bangor (Gwynedd)	a		21 22	21 37	22 22				00 12				01 45		
Holyhead	a		21 56	22 19	22 56				00 55				02 15		
Runcorn	a	19 55	20 01			21 53	22 56								
Liverpool Lime Street 10	a		20 22			22 14	23 21								
Wilmslow	a		19 45		20 45		21 45				23 23				
Stockport	a		19 58		20 58		21 58				23 32				
Manchester Piccadilly 10	a		20 15		21 15		22 15				23 48		01b36		

Saturdays

		AW ◇	AW	AW	AW ◇	AW ◇ ⌶	AW ◇ ⌶	AW ◇	AW	AW ◇ A ⌶	AW ◇ ⌶	AW ◇ A ⌶	AW
Swansea 7	d					03 59		04 36		05 29	05 59	06 40	
Cardiff Central 7	d	21p55	00 30		04 40	05 21	05 40			06 50	07 20	07 50	
London Paddington 15 ⊖	d												
Reading 7	d												
Bristol Temple Meads 10	d										06 50	07 21	
Newport (South Wales)	d	22p13	00 53		04 57	05 35	05 54			07 04	07 34	08 05	
Cwmbran	d	22p23	01 04		05 07	05 45	06 04			07 15	07 45	08 15	
Pontypool and New Inn	d	22p29	01 10		05 13	05 51	06 10				07 49		
Abergavenny	d	22p39	01 20		05 22	06 00	06 19			07 28	08 00	08 28	
Hereford 7	a	23p05	01 46		05 47	06 25	06 47			07 52	08 26	08 53	
	d	23p07	01 48		05 48	06 26	06 49			07 55	08 28	08 55	
Leominster	d	23p20	02 01		06 02	06 40	07 02			08 08		09 08	
Ludlow	d	23p32	02 13		06 13	06 51	07 13			08 19	08 49	09 19	
Craven Arms	d	23p41	02 22		06 21	06 59	07 22	07 53		08 28		09 28	
Church Stretton	d	23p51	02a33		06 30	07 08	07 31	08 06		08 37		09 37	
Shrewsbury	a	00 06			06 44	07 22	07 45	08 21		08 51	09 15	09 51	
	d	00 07		05 44	06 46	07 24	07 46		08 26	08 53	09 24	09 53	10 26
Yorton	d	00x15		05x53					08x35				10x35
Wem	d	00 21		05 59	06 57		07 58		08 41				10 41
Prees	d	00x25		06x03					08x45				10x45
Whitchurch (Shrops)	d	00 32		06 10	07 06		08 06		08 52				10 52
Wrenbury	d	00x39		06x17					08x59				10x59
Nantwich	d	00 43		06 23	07 16		08 16		09 05				11 05
Crewe 10	a	01 00		06 35	07 25		08 25		09 17	09 25		10 25	11 17
Chester	a			07 23	08 45	08 19	09 45			10 12	10 19	11 12	
Llandudno Junction	a			08 14	09e48	09 14	10e48				11 14	12 04	
Bangor (Gwynedd)	a			08 36	10e36	09 31					11 36	12 23	
Holyhead	a			09 19	11e19	10 05					12 11	12 56	
Runcorn	a			07 20	08 24		08 59		09 48	10 21		11 21	11 48
Liverpool Lime Street 10	a			07 41	08 45		09 21		10 09	10 43		11 42	12 09
Wilmslow	a			07 16	07 44		08 45			09 45		10 45	
Stockport	a			07 29	07 54		08 58			09 58		10 58	
Manchester Piccadilly 10	a			07 44	08 08		09 14			10 15		11 15	

		AW ◇ B ⌶	AW ◇ ⌶	AW ◇ B ⌶	GW 1 ◇ ☕	AW	AW ◇ D ⌶	AW ◇	AW ◇ ⌶	AW ◇ B ⌶	GW 1 ◇ ☕	AW	AW ◇ A ⌶
Swansea 7	d	07 45		08 55			09 55	09 15		10 55			11 55
Cardiff Central 7	d	08 50	09 20	09 50			10 50	08 09	11 20	11 50			12 50
London Paddington 15 ⊖	d			07 45	08 21		08 45			09 45	10 21		10 45
Reading 7	d			08 11	08 54		09 11			10 11	10 54		11 11
Bristol Temple Meads 10	d	08 20	08 54	09 21			10 21		10 54	11 21			12 21
Newport (South Wales)	d	09 05	09 34	10 05			11 05		11 34	12 05			13 05
Cwmbran	d	09 15	09 45	10 15			11 15		11 45	12 15			13 15
Pontypool and New Inn	d		09 49						11 50				
Abergavenny	d	09 28	10 00	10 28			11 28		12 01	12 32			13 28
Hereford 7	a	09 53	10 26	10 53	11 40		11 53		12 26	12 56	13 40		13 53
	d	09 55	10 28	10 55			11 55		12 28	12 58			13 55
Leominster	d	10 08		11 08			12 08			13 11			14 08
Ludlow	d	10 19	10 49	11 19			12 19		12 49	13 22			14 19
Craven Arms	d	10 28		11 28			12 28	12 36		13 28			14 28
Church Stretton	d	10 37		11 37			12 37	12 49		13 37			14 37
Shrewsbury	a	10 51	11 15	11 51			12 54	13 07	13 15	13 54			14 51
	d	10 53	11 24	11 53		12 26	12 55		13 24	13 55		14 26	14 53
Yorton	d					12x35						14x35	
Wem	d					12 41						14 41	
Prees	d					12x45						14x45	
Whitchurch (Shrops)	d					12 52						14 52	
Wrenbury	d					12x59						14x59	
Nantwich	d					13 05						15 05	
Crewe 10	a	11 25		12 25		13 17	13 26			14 26		15 17	15 25
Chester	a		12 19	13 12					14 20	15c12			
Llandudno Junction	a		13 14	14e14					15 14	16f01			
Bangor (Gwynedd)	a		13 31	14e36					15 31	16g17			
Holyhead	a		14 14	15e11					16 14	16h51			
Runcorn	a	12 21		13 21		13 48	14 21			15 21		15 48	16 24
Liverpool Lime Street 10	a	12 43		13 42		14 09	14 42			15 42		16 09	16 43
Wilmslow	a	11 45		12 45			13 45			14 45			15 45
Stockport	a	11 58		12 58			13 58			14 58			15 58
Manchester Piccadilly 10	a	12 15		13 15			14 15			15 15			16 15

For general notes see front of timetable
For details of catering facilities see Directory of Train Operators

- A From Carmarthen (Table 128)
- B From Milford Haven (Table 128)
- C From Maesteg (Table 128)
- D From Pembroke Dock (Table 128)
- b Change at Crewe
- c From 7 November arr. 1510
- e Change at Crewe and Chester
- f Until 31 October arr. 1614, change at Crewe and Chester
- g Until 31 October arr. 1636, change at Crewe and Chester
- h Until 31 October arr. 1711, change at Crewe and Chester

Cardiff → Crewe, Liverpool and Manchester

Route Diagram - see first page of Table 129

Saturdays

Station		AW	AW	AW	AW	AW	AW	AW	AW	AW	AW	AW	AW	GW	AW	AW	AW	AW	AW	GW	AW	AW	AW	AW
								[R]			[R]		[R]											
		◇	◇		◇	◇	◇					◇		[1] ◇		◇	◇	◇	◇	[1] ◇	◇	◇		
			A		B			A			B		A			B			C		B	D	E	G (bus)
		🍴	🍴		🍴		🍴	🍴			🍴	🍴	🍴	☕		🍴				☕				
Swansea 7	d		12 50		13 55	13 16		14 55	15 10		15 55		16 55			17 56	18 29	18 21	19 00		20 00	20§55		20§55
Cardiff Central 7	d	13 20	13 50		14 50		15 20	15 50	16 19		16 50	17 20	17 50			18 50	19 34		20 10		20 53	21§49		22§00
London Paddington 15 ⊖	d		11 45		12 45			13 45			14 45		15 45	16 21		16 45	17 45			18 21	18b45	19§45		19§45
Reading 7	d		12 11		13 11			14 11			15 11		16 11	16 54		17 11	18 11			18 53	19c11	20§11		20§11
Bristol Temple Meads 10	d	12 54	13 21		14 21		14 54		15 54		16 21	16 54	17 21			18 21	18 54		19 21		20 21	20§54		21§28
Newport (South Wales)	d	13 34	14 05		15 05		15 34	16 05	16 34		17 05	17 34	18 05			19 05	19 48		20 26		21 10	22§07		22§30
Cwmbran	d	13 45	14 15		15 15		15 45	16 15	16 44		17 15	17 45	18 15			19 15	19 58		20 36		21 21	22§19		22§45
Pontypool and New Inn	d	13 50					15 49	16 21	16 50			17 50	18 21				20 03		20 42			22§24		22§55
Abergavenny	d	14 01	14 28		15 28		16 00	16 30	17a03		17 28	18 01	18 30			19 28	20 13		20 51		21 34	22§34		23§10
Hereford 7	a	14 26	14 53		15 53		16 25	16 55			17 53	18 26	18 55	19 45		19 53	20 39		21 16	21 37	21 58	22§58		23§50
	d	14 28	14 55		15 55		16 28	16 56			17 55	18 28	18 57			19 55	20 39		21 17		22 00			
Leominster	d		15 08		16 08			17 08			18 08	18 41	19 10			20 08	20 52		21 31		22 14			
Ludlow	d	14 49	15 19		16 19		16 49	17 19			18 19	18 52	19 21			20 19	21 03		21 42		22 25			
Craven Arms	d		15 28			16 37		17 28			18 28		19 30			20 28	21 12	21 37	21 50		22 33			
Church Stretton	d		15 37			16 50		17 37			18 37		19 39			20 37	21 21	21 50	22 02		22 42			
Shrewsbury	a	15 15	15 51		16 45	17 10	17 15	17 52			18 51	19 18	19 53			20 51	21 35	22 07	22 16		22 56			
	d	15 24	15 53	16 26	16 48		17 24	17 54		18 26	18 53	19 24	19 55		20 29	20 53	21 37		22 19		23 06		23 50	
Yorton	d			16x35						18x35					20x38				22x27		23x14		23x58	
Wem	d			16 41	17 00					18 41					20 44				22 32		23 19		00 03	
Prees	d			16x45						18x45					20x48				22x36		23x23		00x07	
Whitchurch (Shrops)	d			16 52	17 09					18 52					20 55				22 43		23 30		00 14	
Wrenbury	d			16x59						18x59					21x02				22x49		23x36		00x19	
Nantwich	d			17 05						19 05					21 08				22 54		23 42		00 25	
Crewe 10	a		16 25	17 17	17 25			18 25		19 17	19 25		20 26		21 19	21 27			23 04		23 53		00 34	
Chester	a	16 21	17 12				18 20	19 10				20 20	21 21				22 31		23 42		00 24			
Llandudno Junction	a	17 14	18e16				19 14	20 06				21 20	22 19				23 33							
Bangor (Gwynedd)	a	17 36	18e38				19 31	20 22				21 37	22 42				00f38							
Holyhead	a	18 19	19e13				20 16	20 56				22 19	23 15				02f02							
Runcorn	a		17 21	17 48	18 23						20 05		21g05			22h20								
Liverpool Lime Street 10	a		17 42	18 09	18 43						20 26		21j26			22k41								
Wilmslow	a		16 45		17 45			18 45			19 45		20 45			21 45			23 24					
Stockport	a		16 58		17 58			18 58			19 58		20 58			21 58			23 32					
Manchester Piccadilly 10	a		17 15		18 15			19 15			20 15		21 15			22 15			23 48					

Sundays

Station		AW	AW	AW	AW	AW	AW	AW	AW	GW	GW	AW	GW	AW	AW	AW	AW	GW
																[R]	[R]	
			◇	◇	◇	◇	◇	◇	◇	[1] ◇	[1] ◇	◇	[1] ◇	◇	◇			[1] ◇
		E	H	J	K					J	L	N		L	J		Q	
						🍴	🍴	🍴	🍴	☕	☕	🍴	☕			🍴	🍴	☕
Swansea 7	d						07 59	08 59	09 59			11 22		11§04	11§09	11 59	13m46	
Cardiff Central 7	d					08 30	09 35	10 40	11 45			12 45				13 45	15 00	
London Paddington 15 ⊖	d							08 30	09 30	09§35	09§35	10 37	10 42			11 37	12 37	12 42
Reading 7	d							09n16	10 05	10§11	10§12	11q14	11 20			12r14	13t14	13 20
Bristol Temple Meads 10	d							09 50				11 48					13 48	
Newport (South Wales)	d					08 49	09 50	10 54	11 59			12 59				13 59	15 14	
Cwmbran	d					08 59	10 00	11 04	12 09			13 09				14 09	15 25	
Pontypool and New Inn	d					09 05	10 06	11 10	12 15							14 15		
Abergavenny	d					09 14	10 16	11 19	12 24			13 22				14 24	15 38	
Hereford 7	a					09 39	10 40	11 44	12 49	12§55	12§58	13 47	14 05			14 49	16 02	16 06
	d					09 43	10 43	11 52	12 58			13 55				14 50	16 04	
Leominster	d					09 57	10 56	12 05	13 11			14 08				15 04		
Ludlow	d					10 08	11 07	12 16	13 22			14 19				15 15	16 25	
Craven Arms	d					10 16		12 25				14 28		14§42	14§42			
Church Stretton	d					10 25		12 34				14 37		14§55	14§55			
Shrewsbury	a					10 39	11 33	12 50	13 48			14 51		15§13	15§13	15 41	16 51	
	d	23p50	09§55	09§55	09§55	10 41	11 36	12 52	13 51			14 53				15 42	16 53	
Yorton	d	23v58					11x45									15x51		
Wem	d	00 03				10 52	11 50									15 56		
Prees	d	00x07					11x55									16x01		
Whitchurch (Shrops)	d	00 14				11 01	12 02									16 08		
Wrenbury	d	00x19					12x08									16x14		
Nantwich	d	00 25				11 11	12 14									16 20		
Crewe 10	a	00 34	10§25	10§26	10§31	11 21	12 25	13 26	14 25			15 25				16 29	17 25	
Chester	a		11§00	11§00	11§22	12w20	13y18	14 18	15 18			16z18				17 19	18 19	
Llandudno Junction	a		11§54	11§54	12§53	13 55	14 55	15 55	16 55			17 55				18U55		
Bangor (Gwynedd)	a		12§10	12§10	13§10	14 18	15 12	16 18	17 12			18 18				19V12		
Holyhead	a		12§43	12§43	13§45	14 55	15 55	16X55	17 55			18 55				19Y55		
Runcorn	a		11§00	11§01		11 48	13 00	14 01	15 01			16 01				17 53	18 53	
Liverpool Lime Street 10	a		11§20	11§21		12 09	13 20	14 23	15 23			16 22				18 13	19 13	
Wilmslow	a		10§46	10§46	10§50	11 40	12 46	13 47	14 46			15 46				16 49	17 45	
Stockport	a		10§58	10§58	11§00	12Z37	12 58	13 58	14 58			15 58				16 58	17 58	
Manchester Piccadilly 10	a		11§15	11§15	11§15	12 02	13 15	14 15	15 15			16 15				17 15	18 15	

For general notes see front of timetable
For details of catering facilities see Directory of Train Operators

- **A** From Milford Haven (Table 128)
- **B** From Carmarthen (Table 128)
- **C** From Maesteg (Table 128)
- **D** From 18 July. From Milford Haven (Table 128)
- **E** From Birmingham New Street (Table 74)
- **G** Until 11 July
- **H** 19 July to 6 September
- **J** From 13 September
- **K** Until 12 July
- **L** Until 6 September
- **N** Until 6 September from Milford Haven, from 13 September from Carmarthen (Table 128)
- **Q** Until 6 September from Pembroke Dock, from 13 September from Carmarthen (Table 128)
- **U** Until 6 September arr. 1825, change at Crewe and Chester
- **V** Until 6 September arr. 1842, change at Crewe and Chester
- **X** From 13 September arr. 1654
- **Y** Until 6 September arr. 1925, change at Crewe and Chester
- **Z** Until 12 July arr. 1155
- **b** From 12 September dep. 1915
- **c** From 12 September dep. 1941
- **e** Change at Crewe and Chester
- **f** By bus
- **g** From 12 September arr. 2104
- **h** From 12 September arr. 2230
- **j** From 12 September arr. 2125
- **k** From 12 September arr. 2252
- **m** Also, connection applies. Swansea. Change at Cardiff Central. Dep. 1359
- **n** From 13 September dep. 0905
- **q** From 13 September dep. 1111
- **r** From 13 September dep. 1211
- **t** From 13 September dep. 1311
- **v** Previous night. Stops on request, passengers wishing to alight must inform the guard and those wishing to join must give a hand signal to the driver
- **w** From 13 September arr. 1218
- **y** From 13 September arr. 1315
- **z** From 13 September arr. 1647

Table 131

Sundays

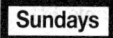

Cardiff → Crewe, Liverpool and Manchester

Route Diagram - see first page of Table 129

	AW R	AW R	AW R A	GW 1 ◇	AW R	AW ◇	AW R	AW R A	AW	AW ◇ B	AW ◇ C	GW 1 ◇	AW ◇ D
Swansea 7 d	13 59	14 59	15 30		15 59	15 16		17 35	17 59		19 36		21 35
Cardiff Central 7 d	15 20	16 00	16 45		17 20		17 40	18 45	19 45		20 40		22 50
London Paddington 15 ⊖ d		13 37	14 37	14 42			15 37	16 37	17 37		18 37	18 42	20 37
Reading 7 d		14b14	15c14	15 20			16e16	17f16	18g16		19h16	19 20	21j16
Bristol Temple Meads 10 d	14 48		15 48		16 48			17 48	18 48		19 48		21 48
Newport (South Wales) d	15 34	16 14	16 59		17 34		17 54	18 59	20 00		20 55		23 10
Cwmbran d	15 44	16 25	17 09		17 44		18 04	19 09	20 10		21 05		23 19
Pontypool and New Inn d	15 49		17 15				18 10		20 16		21 11		23 25
Abergavenny d	16 00	16 38	17 24		17 58		18 20	19 22	20 26		21 21		23 35
Hereford 7 a	16 25	17 02	17 49	18 01	18 23		18 44	19 47	20 52		21 47	22 05	00 04
d	16 26	17 04	17 53		18 24		18 49	19 49	20 54		21 49		
Leominster d	16 39		18 07				19 03	20 03	21 08		22 02		
Ludlow d	16 50	17 26	18 18		18 45		19 14	20 14	21 19		22 14		
Craven Arms d	17 00		18 26			18 58		20 22	21 29		22 23		
Church Stretton d	17 09		18 35			19 11		20 31	21 38		22 33		
Shrewsbury a	17 23	17 52	18 49		19 11	19 29	19 40	20 45	21 55		22 48		
d	17 30	17 54	18 51		19 32		19 41	20 48		22 32	22 54		
Yorton d							19x50				23x03		
Wem d							19 54				23 08		
Prees d							19x59				23x13		
Whitchurch (Shrops) d							20 06				23 20		
Wrenbury d							20x12				23x26		
Nantwich d							20 18				23 32		
Crewe 10 a		18 25	19 22				20 27	21 21		23 02	23 47		
Chester a	18 25	19 14	20 16		20 31		21 17	22k18		23 26	00 31		
Llandudno Junction a	19 23	20 07	21 11		21 29		22 08	23 50			01 24		
Bangor (Gwynedd) a	19 46	20 29	21 28		21 52		22 25	00 12			01 40		
Holyhead a	20 20	21 02	22 02		22 38		22 59	00 49			02 15		
Runcorn a		19 53	20 53				21 06	22 02		00m07			
Liverpool Lime Street 10 a		20 13	21 13				21 27	22 23		00m34			
Wilmslow a		18 46	19 46				20 45	21 46		23m42			
Stockport a		18 58	19 58				20 57	21 58		23m51			
Manchester Piccadilly 10 a		19 15	20 15				21 14	22 15		00m05			

For general notes see front of timetable
For details of catering facilities see Directory of Train Operators

A From Milford Haven (Table 128)
B From Birmingham International (Table 75)
C From Carmarthen (Table 128)
D From Pembroke Dock (Table 128)
b From 13 September dep. 1411
c From 13 September dep. 1511
e From 13 September dep. 1611
f From 13 September dep. 1711
g From 13 September dep. 1811
h From 13 September dep. 1911
j From 13 September dep. 2111
k From 13 September arr. 2221
m Change at Crewe

Manchester, Liverpool and Crewe → Cardiff

Route Diagram - see first page of Table 129

Miles	Miles			AW MX ◇	AW	GW 1 ◇ ☕	AW ◇	AW ◇ A ⊤	GW 1 ◇ ☕	AW ◇ B	AW ◇ C ⊤	AW ◇ ⊤	AW ◇ A ⊤	AW	AW 1 ◇ ⊠	AW ◇ C ⊤	AW ◇	AW ◇ B ⊤
0	—	**Manchester Piccadilly 10**	d	21p35							05 05		06 30		06b43	07 30		
6	—	Stockport	d	21p44							05 13		06 39		06b51	07 39		
12	—	Wilmslow	d	21p51									06 47		06b59	07 47		
—	0	**Liverpool Lime Street 10**	d										05 27		06b31	07 05		
—	13	Runcorn	d										05 43		06b49	07 23		
—	—	Holyhead	d									04 25	04 50		05 32	05 53		06 27
—	—	Bangor (Gwynedd)	d									04 57	05 16		06 02	06 20		07 08
—	—	Llandudno Junction	d									05 15	05 34	05 46	06 21	06 38		07 25
—	—	Chester	d					04 23		05 15	04 55	06 22	06 26	06 43	07 08	07 35		08 22
31	35½	**Crewe 10**	d	22p12				04 54			05 55		07 09	07 15	07 35	08 08		
35½	40	Nantwich	d	22p21				05 01			06 03			07 22		08 16		
40	44½	Wrenbury	d	22c26							06x08			07x28				
44¾	49¼	Whitchurch (Shrops)	d	22p33				05 12			06 15			07 35		08 27		
49¾	54¼	Prees	d	22c39							06x21			07x41				
53	57½	Wem	d	22p44				05 20			06 26			07 47		08 36		
56½	61	Yorton	d	22c49							06x31							
63¾	68¼	**Shrewsbury**	a	22p59				05 33		06 10	06 41	07 18	07 42	08 00	08 09	08 48		09 17
—	—		d	23p01			05 19	05 40		06 13	06 44	07 19	07 44		08 10	08 50	09 05	09 21
76½	81	Church Stretton	d	23p16			05 36	05 55		06 29	06 59		07 59				09 22	
83¾	88¼	Craven Arms	d	23p24			05 50	06 03		06 37	07 07		08 07				09 35	
91	95½	Ludlow	d	23p32				06 11		06 45	07 15	07 47	08 15			09 27		09 48
102	106½	Leominster	d	23p43				06 22		06 56	07 26	07 58	08 26			09 28		
114½	119	**Hereford 7**	a	23p57				06 36		07 10	07 42	08 12	08 40			09 42		10 11
—	—		d	23p59	05 23	05 35		06 42	06 43	07 13	07 44	08 14	08 42			09 44		10 12
138½	143	Abergavenny	d	00 25	05 48			07 05		07 36	08 07	08 37	09 05			10 07		10 35
148	152½	Pontypool and New Inn	d	00 34	05 59			07 15		07 46		08 47				10 17		
151	155½	Cwmbran	d	00 39	06 04			07 20		07 51	08 19	08 52	09 17			10 22		10 48
158	162½	**Newport (South Wales)**	a	00 49	06 15			07 33		08 01	08 30	09 01	09 30		09 40	10 34		10 57
—	—	Bristol Temple Meads 10	a		07 18			08 18		08 51	09 18	09 53	10 18		10 51	11 18		11 51
—	—	Reading 7	a		08 01	08 22		09 02	09 15	09 27	10 01	10 32	11 01		11 32			12 32
—	—	London Paddington 15	⊖ a		08 32	08 51		09 29	09 47	09 59	10 30	11 03	11 32		12 02			13 03
169¾	174¼	**Cardiff Central 7**	a	01 10	06 56		10 17	07 51		08 17	08 55	09 22	09 52		09 58	10 55		11 15
—	—	Swansea 7	a				09 08	08 49		09 47	09 55	10 45	10 55		11 45	11 55	13 01	12 47

		AW ◇ A ⊤	AW	AW ◇ C ⊤	AW ◇ ⊤	AW ◇ A ⊤	AW	GW 1 ◇ ☕	AW ◇ C ⊤	AW R ⊤	AW R A ⊤	AW ◇	AW	GW 1 ◇ ☕	AW R C ⊤	AW ◇ B ⊤	AW R A ⊤	AW
Manchester Piccadilly 10	d	08 30		09 30		10 30			11 30		12 30				13 30		14 30	
Stockport	d	08 39		09 39		10 39			11 39		12 39				13 39		14 39	
Wilmslow	d	08 47		09 47		10 47			11 47		12 47				13 47		14 47	
Liverpool Lime Street 10	d	08 04		09 04		10 04			11 04		12 04				13 04		14 04	
Runcorn	d	08 25		09 25		10 25			11 25		12 25				13 25		14 25	
Holyhead	d	06 55		07e15	08 05	08 55			09e23	10 33					11f23	12 38		
Bangor (Gwynedd)	d	07 22		08e02	09 02	09 22			10e02	11 06					12 24	13 07		
Llandudno Junction	d	07 40		08e25	09 25	09 40			10e25	11 25					12 42	13 25		
Chester	d	08 35		09 35	10 22	10 35			11 35	12 22	12 35				13 35	14 22	14 35	
Crewe 10	d	09 12	09 26	10 12		11 12	11 26		12 12		13 12		13 26		14 12		15 12	15 26
Nantwich	d		09 34				11 34						13 34					15 34
Wrenbury	d		09x40				11x40						13x40					15x40
Whitchurch (Shrops)	d		09 47				11 47						13 47					15 47
Prees	d		09x53				11x53						13x53					15x53
Wem	d		09 58				11 58						13 58					15 58
Yorton	d		10x03				12x03						14x03					16x03
Shrewsbury	a	09 41	10 18	10 41	11 17	11 41	12 18		12 41	13 17	13 41		14 18		14 41	15 17	15 41	16 18
	d	09 44		10 44	11 21	11 44			12 44	13 21	13 44	14 05			14 44	15 21	15 44	
Church Stretton	d	09 59		10 59		11 59			12 59		13 59	14 23			14 59		15 59	
Craven Arms	d	10 07		11 07		12 07			13 07		14 07	14 36			15 07		16 07	
Ludlow	d	10 15		11 15	11 48	12 15			13 15	13 48	14 15				15 15	15 48	16 15	
Leominster	d	10 26		11 26		12 26			13 26		14 26				15 26		16 26	
Hereford 7	a	10 40		11 40	12 11	12 40			13 40	14 11	14 40				15 40	16 11	16 40	
	d	10 42		11 42	12 12	12 42		13 11	13 42	14 12	14 42			15 11	15 42	16 12	16 42	
Abergavenny	d	11 05		12 05	12 35	13 13			14 05	14 35	15 05				16 05	16 35	17 05	
Pontypool and New Inn	d				12 45					14 45						16 45		
Cwmbran	d	11 18		12 18	12 50	13 25			14 18	14 50	15 18				16 18	16 50	17 18	
Newport (South Wales)	a	11 30		12 29	12 59	13 34			14 30	14 59	15 30				16 34	16 59	17 33	
Bristol Temple Meads 10	a	12 18		13 17	13 51	14 19			15 18	15 51	16 18				17 18	17 51	18 18	
Reading 7	a	13 01		14 00	14 32	15 01		15 55	16 01	16 32	17 01			18 02	17 57	18 32	19 01	
London Paddington 15	⊖ a	13 32		14 32	15 03	15 32		16 27	16 30	17 03	17 32			18 30	18 26	19 03	19 32	
Cardiff Central 7	a	11 55		12 54	13 20	13 54			14 54	15 20	15 53				16 54	17 17	17 52	
Swansea 7	a	12 55		13 55	14 45	14 55			15 55	16 47	16 55	18 06			18 05	18 46	19 01	

For general notes see front of timetable
For details of catering facilities see Directory of Train Operators

A To Milford Haven (Table 128)
B To Maesteg (Table 128)
C To Carmarthen (Table 128)
b Change at Crewe
c Previous night.
Stops on request, passengers wishing to alight must inform the guard and those wishing to join must give a hand signal to the driver
e Change at Chester and Crewe
f Change at Bangor (Gwynedd) and Crewe

Manchester, Liverpool and Crewe → Cardiff

Route Diagram - see first page of Table 129

Mondays to Fridays

Station		AW R A ✠	AW ◇ ✠	AW R B ✠	AW ◇	AW	AW R B ✠	AW ◇ ✠	AW ◇ C ✠	GW FO 1 ◇ D	GW FX 1 ◇ E	AW ◇	AW ◇	AW ◇	AW ◇
Manchester Piccadilly 10	d	15 30		16 30			17 30		18 30			19 30	20 30	21 35	22 35
Stockport	d	15 39		16 39			17 40		18 39			19 39	20 39	21 44	22 44
Wilmslow	d	15 47		16 49			17 48		18 47			19 47	20 47	21 51	22 52
Liverpool Lime Street 10	d	15 04		16 04			17 04		18 04			19 11	20 04	20 48	21 34
Runcorn	d	15 25		16 25			17 25		18 25			19 29	20 25	21 04	21 52
Holyhead	d	13 58	14 32				15b23	16 36				17b21	18 23	19c21	20 37
Bangor (Gwynedd)	d	14 25	15 02				16b02	17 04				18b00	19 02	20 20	21 06
Llandudno Junction	d	14 43	15 25				16b25	17 22				18b23	19 25	20 38	21 29
Chester	d	14 55	16 22	16 35			17 35	18 20	17 55			19 35	20 17	21 35	22 25
Crewe 10	d	16 12		17 12		17 26	18 12		19 12			20 12	21 12	22 12	23 14
Nantwich	d	16 20				17 34	18 20		19 20			20 21	21 20	22 21	23 22
Wrenbury	d					17x40			19x25				21x25	22x26	23x27
Whitchurch (Shrops)	d	16 31				17 47	18 31		19 33				21 33	22 33	23 34
Prees	d					17x53			19x38				21x39	22x39	23x40
Wem	d	16 39				17 58	18 39		19 44				21 44	22 44	23 45
Yorton	d					18x03			19x49				21x49	22x49	23x50
Shrewsbury	a	16 52	17 17	17 41		18 18	18 52	19 15	19 59			20 45	21 59	22 59	00 04
	d	16 53	17 21	17 44	18 05		18 56	19 16	20 01			20 51	22 01	23 01	
Church Stretton	d	17 09		17 59	18 23		19 11		20 16			21 06	22 16	23 16	
Craven Arms	d	17 17		18 07	18 35		19 19		20 24			21 14	22 24	23 24	
Ludlow	d	17 25	17 48	18 15			19 27	19 45	20 32			21 22	22 32	23 32	
Leominster	d	17 35		18 26			19 38		20 43			21 33	22 43	23 43	
Hereford 7	a	17 50	18 11	18 40			19 52	20 08	20 58			21 50	22 57	23 57	
	d	17 51	18 12	18 42			19 54	20 10	21 01	21 53	21 53	21 54	22 59	23 59	
Abergavenny	d	18 14	18 35	19 05			20 17	20 33	21 24			22 19	23 22	00 25	
Pontypool and New Inn	d		18 45					20 43				22 29		00 34	
Cwmbran	d	18 27	18 50	19 18			20 29	20 48	21 36			22 34	23 35	00 39	
Newport (South Wales)	a	18 41	18 59	19 32			20 42	20 57	21 48			22 44	23 46	00 49	
Bristol Temple Meads 10	a		19 53	20 18				22 30	23 07			00 03			
Reading 7	a			21 01				23 07		00 38	00 38				
London Paddington 15	⊖ a			21 32				23e53		01 11	01 17				
Cardiff Central 7	a	18 59	19 20	19 49			20 58	21 19	22 09			23 04	00 11	01 10	
Swansea 7	a	20 05	20 25	21 25	22 13		22 03		23 07			00 28	02f15		

Saturdays

Station		AW ◇	AW G	AW ◇	AW ◇ B ✠	GW 1 ◇ ⊐	AW H	AW ◇ C ✠	AW ◇ ✠	AW ◇ B ✠	AW	AW ◇ C ✠	AW ◇
Manchester Piccadilly 10	d	21p35						05 11		06 30		07 30	
Stockport	d	21p44								06 39		07 39	
Wilmslow	d	21p51								06 47		07 47	
Liverpool Lime Street 10	d										06 33	07 19	
Runcorn	d										06 51	07 36	
Holyhead	d								04 25				
Bangor (Gwynedd)	d								04 57				
Llandudno Junction	d								05 15	05 46			
Chester	d				04 23			04 55	06 12	06 43		07 17	
Crewe 10	d	22p12			04 54			05 55		07 13	07 26	08 08	
Nantwich	d	22p21			05 01			06 03			07 34	08 16	
Wrenbury	d	22k26						06x08			07x40		
Whitchurch (Shrops)	d	22p33			05 12			06 15			07 47	08 27	
Prees	d	22k39						06x21			07x53		
Wem	d	22p44			05 20			06 26			07 58	08 36	
Yorton	d	22k49						06x31			08x03		
Shrewsbury	a	22p59			05 33			06 41	07 17	07 41	08 18	08 48	
	d	23p01		05 19	05 40		06 13	06 44	07 19	07 44		08 50	09 05
Church Stretton	d	23p16		05 36	05 55		06 29	06 59		07 59			09 22
Craven Arms	d	23p24		05 50	06 03		06 37	07 07		08 07			09 35
Ludlow	d	23p32			06 11		06 45	07 15	07 47	08 15		09 17	
Leominster	d	23p43			06 22		06 56	07 26	07 58	08 26		09 28	
Hereford 7	a	23p57			06 36		07 10	07 40	08 12	08 40		09 42	
	d	23p59	05 42		06 50	07 10	07 13	07 48	08 14	08 42		09 44	
Abergavenny	d	00 25	06 07		07 13		07 36	08 11	08 37	09 05		10 07	
Pontypool and New Inn	d	00 34	06 18		07 23		07 46		08 47			10 17	
Cwmbran	d	00 39	06 23		07 28		07 51	08 23	08 52	09 18		10 22	
Newport (South Wales)	a	00 49	06 34		07 38		08 01	08 34	09 01	09 30		10 34	
Bristol Temple Meads 10	a		07 18		08 18		08 52	09 18	09 51	10 18		11 18	
Reading 7	a		08 01			09 55	09 33	10 01	11 01	11 01		12 02	
London Paddington 15	⊖ a		08 32			10 29	10 02	10 32	11 32	11 32		12 32	
Cardiff Central 7	a	01 10	06 54	10 17	07 55		08 19	08 52	09 23	09 54		10 53	
Swansea 7	a		08 45	09n07	08 55			09 56	10 45	10 55		11 55	13 01

Station		AW ◇ ✠	AW ◇ B ✠	AW	AW ◇ C ✠	AW ◇ ✠	GW 1 ◇ ⊐	AW ◇ B ✠	AW	AW ◇ C ✠	AW ◇ ✠	AW R B ✠	AW ◇
Manchester Piccadilly 10	d		08 30		09 30			10 30		11 30		12 30	
Stockport	d		08 39		09 39			10 39		11 39		12 39	
Wilmslow	d		08 47		09 47			10 47		11 47		12 47	
Liverpool Lime Street 10	d		08 04		09 04			10 04		11 04		12 04	
Runcorn	d		08 25		09 25			10 25		11 25		12 25	
Holyhead	d	06 33	06 50		07g55	08 20		08 55		09b23	10 33		
Bangor (Gwynedd)	d	07 08	07 17		08h22	09 02		09 22		10b02	11 06		
Llandudno Junction	d	07 25	07 35		08j40	09 25		09 40		10b25	11 25		
Chester	d	08 22	08 35		09 35	10 22		10 35		11 35	12 22		
Crewe 10	d		09 13	09 26	10 13			11 13	11 26	12 12		13 12	
Nantwich	d			09 34					11 34				
Wrenbury	d			09x40					11x40				
Whitchurch (Shrops)	d			09 47					11 47				
Prees	d			09x53					11x53				
Wem	d			09 58					11 58				
Yorton	d			10x03					12x03				
Shrewsbury	a	09 17	09 41	10 18	10 41	11 17		11 41	12 18	12 41	13 17	13 41	
	d	09 21	09 44		10 44	11 21		11 44		12 44	13 21	13 44	14 05
Church Stretton	d		09 59		10 59			11 59		12 59		13 59	14 23
Craven Arms	d		10 07		11 07			12 07		13 07		14 07	14 36
Ludlow	d	09 48	10 15		11 15	11 48		12 15		13 15	13 48	14 15	
Leominster	d		10 26		11 26			12 26		13 26		14 26	
Hereford 7	a	10 11	10 40		11 42	12 11		12 40		13 42	14 11	14 40	
	d	10 12	10 42		11 44	12 12	12 13	12 42		13 44	14 12	14 42	
Abergavenny	d	10 35	11 05		12 07	12 35		13 05		14 07	14 35	15 05	
Pontypool and New Inn	d					12 45					14 45		
Cwmbran	d	10 48	11 18		12 19	12 50		13 18		14 20	14 50	15 18	
Newport (South Wales)	a	10 57	11 30		12 34	12 59		13 30		14 34	14 59	15 30	
Bristol Temple Meads 10	a	11 52	12 18		13 18	13 52		14 18		15 18	15 52	16 18	
Reading 7	a		13 01		14 02		14 55	15 01		16m02		17 01	
London Paddington 15	⊖ a		13 32		14 32		15 29	15 32		16 32		17 32	
Cardiff Central 7	a	11 20	11 54		12 54	13 20		13 54		14 54	15 21	15 54	
Swansea 7	a	12 45	12 55		13 55	14 45		14 55		15 55	16 45	16 56	18 06

For general notes see front of timetable
For details of catering facilities see Directory of Train Operators

- **A** To Pembroke Dock (Table 128)
- **B** To Milford Haven (Table 128)
- **C** To Carmarthen (Table 128)
- **D** Until 4 September
- **E** Until 3 September
- **G** To Barry Island (Table 130)
- **H** To Maesteg (Table 128)
- **b** Change at Chester and Crewe
- **c** Change at Bangor (Gwynedd) and Crewe
- **e** Fridays arr. 2343
- **f** Saturday mornings arr. 0155
- **g** From 7 November dep. 0752
- **h** From 7 November dep. 0819
- **j** From 7 November dep. 0837
- **k** Previous night.
- Stops on request, passengers wishing to alight must inform the guard and those wishing to join must give a hand signal to the driver
- **m** From 12 September arr. 1601
- **n** Also, connection applies. Swansea. Change at Cardiff Central. Arr. 1145

Manchester, Liverpool and Crewe → Cardiff

Route Diagram - see first page of Table 129

Saturdays

		AW	GW	AW	AW	AW	AW	AW	AW	AW	AW	AW	AW	AW	GW	AW	AW	AW	AW	AW	AW	AW	AW
			1 ◇	R	R	R		R	◇	R	◇		R	◇	1 ◇	◇	◇	◇	◇	◇			◇
				A	B	C		D		C			E			A		G	H		H	G 🚌	
			🍽	🛒	🛒	🛒		🛒	🛒	🛒			🛒	🛒		🛒							
Manchester Piccadilly 10	d			13 30		14 30		15 30		16 30			17 30			18 30	19 30	20 30	20 30	21 30			22 35
Stockport	d			13 39		14 39		15 39		16 39			17 40			18 39	19 39	20 39	20 39	21 39			22 44
Wilmslow	d			13 47		14 47		15 47		16 49			17 48			18 47	19 47	20 47	20 47	21 47			22 52
Liverpool Lime Street 10	d			*13 04*		*14 04*		*15 04*		*16 04*			*17 04*			*18 04*	*19 04*	*19 34*	*19 34*	*20 34*			*21 34*
Runcorn	d			*13 25*		*14 25*		*15 25*		*16 25*			*17 25*			*18 25*	*19 23*	*19 52*	*19 52*	*20 52*			*21 52*
Holyhead	d				12 38				14 23				*15c23*	16 38			*16c38*	*18 23*	*18 23*				*20 37*
Bangor (Gwynedd)	d				13 07				14 54				*16c02*	17 07			*17c07*	*19 02*	*19 02*				*21 06*
Llandudno Junction	d				13 25				15 17				*16c25*	17 25		*16c53*	*17c53*	*19 25*	*19 25*	*19c51*			*21 29*
Chester	d				14 22	*14 35*		*15e35*	16 22				*17 35*	18 22		*17 55*	*18 55*	*20 35*	*20 35*	*20 55*			*22 25*
Crewe 10	d	13 26		14 12		15 12	15 26	16 12		17 13		17 26	18 12			19 12	20 12	21 11	21 11	22 12			23 14
Nantwich	d	13 34					15 34	16 20				17 34	18 20			19 20	20 20	21 19	21 19	22 20			23 22
Wrenbury	d	13x40					15x40					17x40				19x25		21x24	21x24	22x25			23x27
Whitchurch (Shrops)	d	13 47					15 47	16 31				17 47	18 31			19 33		21 30	21 30	22 33			23 34
Prees	d	13x53					15x53					17x53				19x38		21x36	21x36	22x39			23x40
Wem	d	13 58					15 58	16 39				17 58	18 39			19 44		21 41	21 41	22 44			23 45
Yorton	d	14x03					16x03					18x03				19x49		21x46	21x46	22x49			23x50
Shrewsbury	a	14 18		14 41	15 17	15 41	16 18	16 52	17 17	17 41		18 18	18 52	19 18		19 59	20 44	21 56	21 56	23 03			00 04
	d			14 44	15 21	15 44		16 53	17 21	17 44	18 05		18 53	19 19		20 01	20 46	21 56	21 56				
Church Stretton	d			14 59		15 59		17 09		17 59	18 23		19 09			20 16	20 59	22 12	22 12				
Craven Arms	d			15 07		16 07		17 17		18 07	18 35		19 17			20 24	21 07	22 20	22 20				
Ludlow	d			15 15	15 49	16 15		17 25	17 49	18 15			19 25	19 48		20 32	21 17	22 28	22 28				
Leominster	d			15 26		16 26		17 35		18 26			19 35			20 43	21 28	22 38	22 38				
Hereford 7	a			15 40	16 12	16 40		17 50	18 14	18 40			19 50	20 10		20 58	21 42	22 55	22 55				
	d		15 10	15 42	16 13	16 42		17 51	18 16	18 43			19 51	20 12	20 20	21 01	21 45		22 54		23 13	23 02	
Abergavenny	d			16 05	16 36	17 05		18 14	18 39	19 07			20 14	20 35		21 24	22 08		23 17		23 36	23 42	
Pontypool and New Inn	d				16 46				18 49					20 45			22 18		23 27			23 57	
Cwmbran	d			16 18	16 51	17 18		18 27	18 54	19 20			20 27	20 50		21 36	22 23		23 32		23 48	00 07	
Newport (South Wales)	a			16 30	16 59	17 33		18 37	19 04	19 30			20 37	20 59		21 48	22 41		23 43		00 04	00 22	
Bristol Temple Meads 10	a			*17 18*	*17 52*	*18 18*		*19 18*	*19 52*	*20 18*			*21 18*	*21 50*		*23 00*							
Reading 7	a		17 55	*18 01*		*19 01*				*21 07*					23 30								
London Paddington 15 ⊖	a		18 29	*18 32*		*19 32*				*21 36*					00 10								
Cardiff Central 7	a			16 54	17 18	17 54		18 54	19 26	19 48			20 54	21 20		22 09	23 05		00 08		00 24	00 52	
Swansea 7	a			18 05	*18 44*	18 56		20 05	*20 49*	*21 45*	22 13		22 03	*22 45*		23 10							

Sundays

		AW	AW	AW	AW	AW	AW	AW	GW	GW	AW	AW	AW	GW	GW	AW	AW	GW
				◇	◇	R	R	◇	1 ◇	1 ◇	R	R	◇	1 ◇	1 ◇	R	R	1 ◇
		J 🚌	🚌	K		L	N		Q	U	V	Q		Q	V	C		V
				🛒		🛒	🛒		🍽	🍽	🛒	🛒		🍽	🍽	🛒	🛒	🍽
Manchester Piccadilly 10	d				09 30	10 30	10 30				11 24	11 30				12 30	13 30	
Stockport	d				09 39	10 39	10 41				11 40	11 40				12 40	13 39	
Wilmslow	d				09 47	10 47	10 47				11 48	11 47				12 48	13 47	
Liverpool Lime Street 10	d				*08 38*	*09 36*	*09 36*				*10 38*	*10 38*				*11 34*	*12 34*	
Runcorn	d				*08 54*	*09 52*	*09 52*				*10 54*	*10 54*				*11 52*	*12 52*	
Holyhead	d					*08 50*	*08 40*						10 20			*10 55*		
Bangor (Gwynedd)	d				*07f43*	*09 18*	*09 08*						10 59			*11 22*		
Llandudno Junction	d				*08f01*	*09 36*	*09 26*						11 22			*11 40*		
Chester	d				*09g40*	*10 35*	*10 27*				*11 28*	*11 28*	12 22			*12 33*	*13h28*	
Crewe 10	d				10 11	11 13	11 13				12 13	12 13				13 13	14 13	
Nantwich	d				10 21											13 20		
Wrenbury	d				10x27											13x26		
Whitchurch (Shrops)	d				10 34											13 33		
Prees	d				10x40											13x39		
Wem	d				10 46											13 44		
Yorton	d				10x51											13x49		
Shrewsbury	a				11 00	11 41	11 41				12 41	12 41	13 17			13 57	14 41	
	d		07 50		11 02	11 44	11 44	12 07			12 44	12 44	13 19			14 00	14 44	
Church Stretton	d		08 15		11 18			12 24					13 35				14 59	
Craven Arms	d		08 35		11 26			12 36					13 43				15 07	
Ludlow	d		08 55		11 35	12 11	12 11				13 11	13 11	13 51			14 27	15 15	
Leominster	d		09 20		11 46	12 22	12 22				13 22	13 22	14 02			14 38	15 26	
Hereford 7	a		09 50		12 01	12 36	12 36				13 36	13 36	14 16			14 52	15 40	
	d	23p02		10 11	12 03	12 42	12 42		13 28	13 28	13 39	13 39	14 19	14 30	14 30	14 55	15 43	16 30
Abergavenny	d	23p42		10 34	12 27	13 05	13 05				14 02	14 02	14 42			15 18	16 06	
Pontypool and New Inn	d	23p57		10 45		13 15	13 15						14 52				16 16	
Cwmbran	d	00 07		10 50	12 40	13 20	13 20				14 14	14 14	14 57			15 30	16 21	
Newport (South Wales)	a	00 22		11 00	12 50	13 39	13 34				14 25	14 25	15 10			15 42	16 34	
Bristol Temple Meads 10	a			*12 04*	*14 04*	*15 05*	*15 05*						*16 06*			*17 05*	*17 25*	
Reading 7	a			*12 31*	*14 31*	*15 31*	*15 31*		16 19	16 19	*16 31*	*16 31*		17 21	17 21	*17 31*	*18 31*	19 09
London Paddington 15 ⊖	a			*13j08*	*15k08*	*16 08*	*16 10*		16 59	17 06	*17 10*	*17 08*		18 06	18 10	*18m15*	*19n10*	19 53
Cardiff Central 7	a	00 52		11 17	13 12	13 57	13 50				14 46	14 46	15 30			16 00	16 56	
Swansea 7	a			12 14	*14q49*	14 56	15 01	16 13			*15 52*	*15 47*	*16r50*			17 19		

For general notes see front of timetable
For details of catering facilities see Directory of Train Operators

- **A** To Carmarthen (Table 128)
- **B** To Maesteg (Table 128)
- **C** To Milford Haven (Table 128)
- **D** To Pembroke Dock (Table 128)
- **E** To Haverfordwest (Table 128)
- **G** Until 11 July
- **H** From 18 July
- **J** Until 12 July
- **K** To Fishguard Harbour (Table 128)
- **L** From 13 September. To Milford Haven (Table 128)
- **N** Until 6 September. To Milford Haven (Table 128)
- **Q** From 13 September
- **U** Unil 6 September
- **V** Until 6 September
- **c** Change at Chester and Crewe
- **e** From 7 November dep. 1455
- **f** Until 6 September only
- **g** Until 6 September arr. 0927
- **h** From 8 November dep. 1318
- **j** Until 6 September arr. 1310
- **k** Until 6 September arr. 1509
- **m** From 13 September arr. 1809
- **n** From 13 September arr. 1908
- **q** Until 6 September arr. 1458
- **r** From 13 September arr. 1647

Table 131

Sundays

Manchester, Liverpool and Crewe → Cardiff

Route Diagram - see first page of Table 129

		GW	AW	AW	AW	AW	GW	AW	AW	AW	AW	AW	AW	AW	AW	AW
		1 ◇	R	R	◇	R	1 ◇	R	R	R	R	R	R	◇	◇	
		A	B	C					D	A		A				
		☕	✠	✠		✠	✠	✠	✠	✠	✠	✠	✠			
Manchester Piccadilly 10	d		14 30	14 30		15 30		16 30	17 30	17 30		18 30	18b30	19 30	20 30	21 34
Stockport	d		14 39	14 39		15 39		16 39	17 39	17 39		18 39	18 39	19 39	20 39	21 17
Wilmslow	d		14 47	14 47		15 47		16 47	17 47	17 47		18 47	18 47	19 47	20 47	21 52
Liverpool Lime Street 10	d		13 34	13 34		14 34		16 18	16 34	16 34		17 34	17 34	18 34	19 48	21 34
Runcorn	d		13 52	13 52		14 52		16 34	16 52	16 52		17 52	17 52	18 52	20 04	21 52
Holyhead	d		12 47	12 47		13 55		14c30		15 30	16 25	16c25	16c25	17 30	18 25	20 35
Bangor (Gwynedd)	d		13 14	13 14		14 22		15c08		15 59	17 04	17c04	17c04	17 59	19 04	21 14
Llandudno Junction	d		13 32	13 32		14 40		15c26		16 25	17 25	17c25	17c25	18 24	19 24	21 37
Chester	d		14 33	14 33		15 33		16 27	17 35	17 35	18 24	18 35	18 35	19 22	20 27	22 35
Crewe 10	d		15 13	15 13		16 13		17 13	18 13	18 13		19 13	19 13	20 13	21 13	23 20
Nantwich	d							17 20				19 20	19 20		21 20	23 28
Wrenbury	d							17x26				19x25	19x25		21x25	23x35
Whitchurch (Shrops)	d							17 33				19 32	19 32		21 34	23 43
Prees	d							17x39				19x38	19x38		21x39	23x49
Wem	d							17 44				19 43	19 43		21 45	23 55
Yorton	d							17x49				19x47	19x47		21x49	23x59
Shrewsbury	a		15 41	15 41		16 41		18 00	18 41	18 41	19 19	19 57	19 57	20 41	22 00	00 11
	d		15 44	15 44	16 25	16 44		18 02	18 44	18 44	19 22	19 59	19 59	20 44	22 02	
Church Stretton	d				16 42	16 59					19 38			20 59	22 18	
Craven Arms	d				16 54	17 07					19 46			21 07	22 27	
Ludlow	d		16 11	16 11		17 15		18 30	19 11	19 11	19 54	20 27	20 27	21 15	22 35	
Leominster	d		16 22	16 22		17 26		18 40			20 05	20 37	20 37	21 26	22 47	
Hereford 7	a		16 39	16 39		17 40		18 55	19 34	19 34	20 19	20 52	20 52	21 40	23 01	
	d	16 30	16 42	16 42		17 43	18 30	18 57	19 35	19 35	20 21	20 53	20 53	21 43	23 04	
Abergavenny	d		17 05	17 05		18 06		19 20	19 58	19 58	20 44	21 16	21 16	22 06	23 27	
Pontypool and New Inn	d					18 16					20 54			22 16	23 38	
Cwmbran	d		17 17	17 17		18 21		19 33	20 11	20 11	20 59	21 29	21 29	22 21	23 43	
Newport (South Wales)	a		17 28	17 34		18 34		19 44	20 25	20 28	21 08	21 39	21 40	22 31	23 53	
Bristol Temple Meads 10	a		18 31	18 31		20 02		21 04				23 07	23 07			
Reading 7	a	19 19	19 31	19 31		20 31	21 19	21 31	22 35	22 35						
London Paddington 15 ⊖	a	20 01	20e12	20 10		21 11	22 07	22f16	23 22	23 22						
Cardiff Central 7	a		17 43	17 49	21 30	18 55		20 05	20 49	20 44	21 30	22 05	22 05	22 57	00 19	
Swansea 7	a		18 59	18 59	20 13	19 54		21 15	21 52	21 47	23g00	23 26	23 26	00 03		

For general notes see front of timetable
For details of catering facilities see Directory of Train Operators

A From 13 September

B Until 1 November. To Milford Haven and Pembroke Dock (Table 128)

C From 8 November. To Milford Haven and Pembroke Dock (Table 128)

D Until 6 September

c Change at Chester and Crewe

e From 13 September arr. 2010

f From 13 September arr. 2211

g From 13 September arr. 2247

Network Diagram for Tables 132, 133 ,134

DM-26/05
Design BAJS

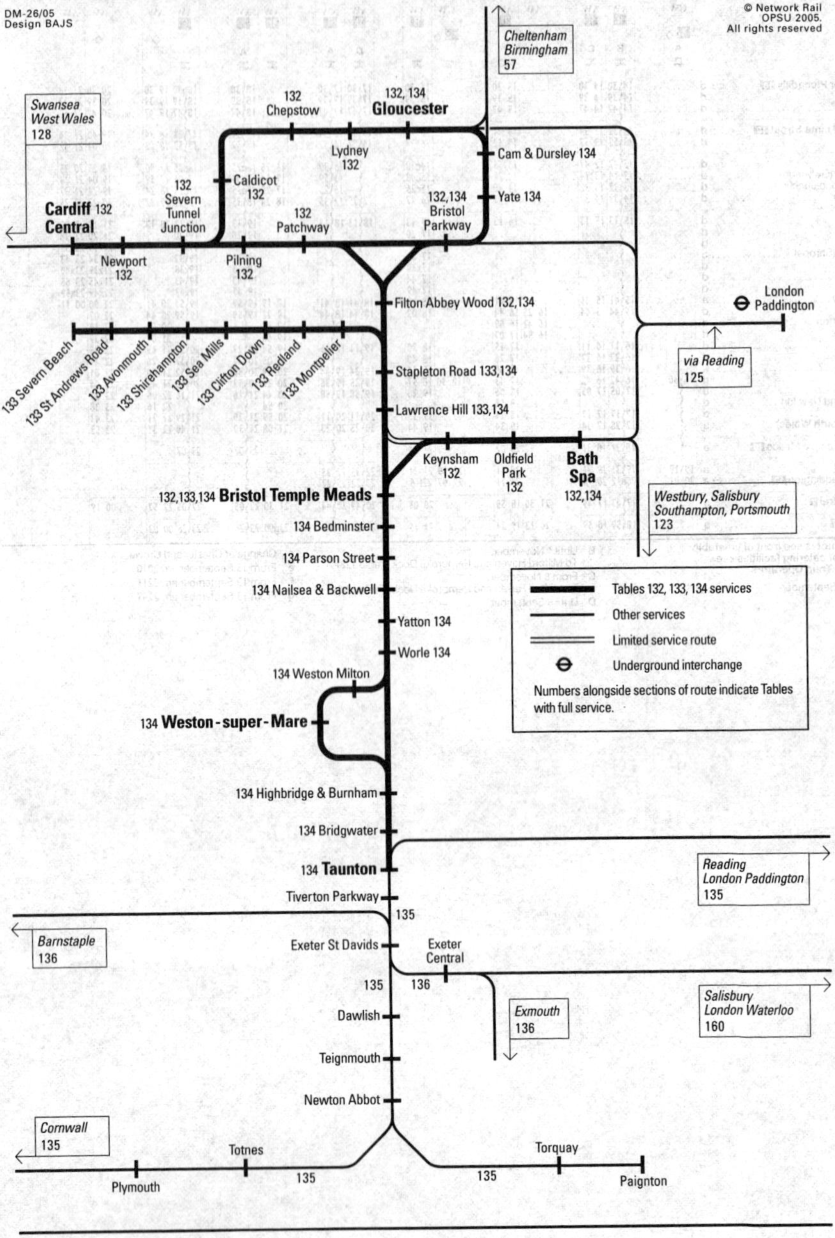
Cheltenham
Birmingham
57
Swansea
West Wales
128
132
Chepstow
132, 134
Gloucester
Lydney
132
Cam & Dursley 134
Caldicot
132
132
Severn
Tunnel
Junction
Cardiff 132
Central
132
Patchway
132,134
Bristol
Parkway
Yate 134
Newport
132
Pilning
132
Filton Abbey Wood 132,134
London
Paddington
via Reading
125
133 Severn Beach
133 St Andrews Road
133 Avonmouth
133 Shirehampton
133 Sea Mills
133 Clifton Down
133 Redland
133 Montpelier
Stapleton Road 133,134
Lawrence Hill 133,134
Keynsham
132
Oldfield
Park
132
Bath
Spa
132,134
132,133,134 Bristol Temple Meads
Westbury, Salisbury
Southampton, Portsmouth
123
134 Bedminster
134 Parson Street
134 Nailsea & Backwell
Tables 132, 133, 134 services
Other services
Limited service route
Underground interchange
Numbers alongside sections of route indicate Tables with full service.
Yatton 134
Worle 134
134 Weston Milton
134 Weston-super-Mare
134 Highbridge & Burnham
134 Bridgwater
134 Taunton
Reading
London Paddington
135
Tiverton Parkway
135
Barnstaple
136
Exeter St Davids
Exeter
Central
135
136
Salisbury
London Waterloo
160
Exmouth
136
Dawlish
Teignmouth
Newton Abbot
Cornwall
135
Totnes
Torquay
135
135
Plymouth
Paignton

Cardiff → Gloucester, Bristol and Bath Spa

Network Diagram - see first page of Table 132

Miles	Miles	Miles			AW	AW	AW	AW	GW	GW	GW	AW	GW	GW		GW	GW	GW	AW	GW	GW	GW	GW	GW	XC	AW
					MX	MX																				
							◇	◇	[1] ◇	◇	[1] ◇	◇	[1] ◇	[1] ◇		[1] ◇	[1] ◇			[1] ◇	[1] ◇	◇	[1] ◇		[1] ◇	◇
					A												B		C			D		E	G	
								⊥	⊡		⊡	⊥	⊡	⊡		⊡	⊡			⊡	⊡	⊥	⊡			⊥
0	0	0	**Cardiff Central [7]**	d	23p19	00 30	04 35	05 10			05 15	05 40		05 54					06 12	06 23		06 28			06 40	06 50
11¾	11¾	11¾	Newport (South Wales)	a	23p39	00 48	04 51	05 26			05 32	05 56		06 07					06 26	06 36		06 41			06 53	07 02
—	—	—		d	23p40						05 33			06 08					06 28	06 37		06 42			06 55	
21¾	21¾	21¾	Severn Tunnel Jn	d	23p58														06 38			06 53			07 05	
—	—	22½	Caldicot	d	00 01														06 40						07 08	
—	—	29¼	Chepstow	d	00 09														06 49						07 16	
—	—	37	Lydney	d	00 18														06 58						07 25	
—	—	56½	**Gloucester [7]**	a	00 39														07 20						07 44	
28¾	28¾	—	Pilning	d																						
32¼	32¼	—	Patchway	d																		07 06				
—	33½	—	**Bristol Parkway [7]**	a							06 00			06 29						06 58						
—	—	—		d																				07 25		
33¾	—	—	Filton Abbey Wood	d																		07 09		07 28		
38¼	—	—	**Bristol Temple Meads [10]**	a																		07 18		07 40		
—	—	—		d					05 30	05 44			06 00			06 30	06 40	06 44			07 00	07 22	07 30	07 49		
42¾	—	—	Keynsham	d						05 51								06 51						07 56		
48¾	—	—	Oldfield Park	d						05 58								06 58						08 03		
49¾	—	—	**Bath Spa [7]**	a					05 41	06 00			06 11			06 41	06 51	07 01			07 11	07 35	07 41	08 05		

		GW		XC	AW	AW	GW	GW	GW	GW	GW	XC	AW		GW	GW	SW	GW	GW	GW	GW	GW	GW	XC		AW
		[1] ◇		[1] ◇		◇	[1] ◇	[1] ◇		◇	[1] ◇	[1] ◇	◇		◇	[1] ◇	[1] ◇		[1] ◇	[1] ◇		◇	[1] ◇	[1] ◇		◇
				H	C				J						K		L	N								
		⊡		⊥		⊥	⊡	⊡		⊥	⊡					⊡			⊡	⊡		⊥	⊡			
Cardiff Central [7]	d	06 55		07 00	07 12	07 20	07 25			07 30		07 45	07 50			07 55		08 00		08 25		08 30		08 45		08 50
Newport (South Wales)	a	07 08		07 13	07 26	07 32	07 38			07 43		07 58	08 03			08 08		08 13		08 38		08 43		08 58		09 03
	d	07 09		07 15	07 27		07 39			07 44		08 00				08 09		08 15		08 39		08 44		09 00		
Severn Tunnel Jn	d			07 26	07 38					07 55								08 25				08 55				
Caldicot	d				07 40																					
Chepstow	d				07 49																					
Lydney	d				07 58																					
Gloucester [7]	a				08 20							08 44												09 44		
Pilning	d																									
Patchway	d			07 40														08 39								
Bristol Parkway [7]	a	07 30					08 00									08 31				09 00						
	d														08 25											
Filton Abbey Wood	d			07 44						08 09					08 28			08 42				09 09				
Bristol Temple Meads [10]	a			07 52						08 18					08 37			08 51				09 18				
	d							08 00	08 13	08 22	08 30				08 41		08 50		09 00		09 05	09 22	09 30			
Keynsham	d								08 20						08 48		08 57									
Oldfield Park	d								08 27						08 55						09 17					
Bath Spa [7]	a							08 11	08 29	08 35	08 41				08 58		09 04		09 11		09 19	09 34	09 41			

		GW	GW	GW	GW	AW	AW	GW	GW	GW	XC		AW	GW	GW	GW	GW	AW	GW	GW	GW	XC		AW	GW	GW
		◇	[1] ◇		[1] ◇		◇	[1] ◇	◇	[1] ◇	[1] ◇		◇		[1] ◇		[1] ◇		[1] ◇	◇	[1] ◇	[1] ◇		◇	◇	[1] ◇
		Q		N		A								U		N		A							Q	
			⊡		⊡		⊥	⊡	⊥	⊡					⊡		⊡		⊡	⊥	⊡					⊡
Cardiff Central [7]	d		08 55	09 00		09 12	09 20	09 25	09 30		09 45		09 50		09 55	10 00		10 12	10 25	10 30		10 45		10 50		10 55
Newport (South Wales)	a		09 08	09 13		09 25	09 32	09 38	09 43		09 58		10 03		10 08	10 13		10 25	10 38	10 43		10 58		11 03		11 08
	d		09 09	09 15		09 27		09 39	09 44		10 00				10 09	10 15		10 27	10 39	10 44		11 00				11 09
Severn Tunnel Jn	d			09 25		09 38										10 25		10 38								
Caldicot	d					09 40												10 40								
Chepstow	d					09 49												10 49								
Lydney	d					09 58												10 58								
Gloucester [7]	a					10 20					10 44							11 20				11 44				
Pilning	d																									
Patchway	d			09 39												10 39										
Bristol Parkway [7]	a		09 30					10 00							10 30				11 00							11 30
	d	09 19												10 19											11 19	
Filton Abbey Wood	d	09 22		09 42					10 09					10 22		10 42				11 09					11 22	
Bristol Temple Meads [10]	a	09 35		09 53					10 18					10 38		10 51				11 18					11 35	
	d	09 49			10 00				10 22	10 30				10 49			11 00			11 22	11 30				11 49	
Keynsham	d	09 56												10 56											11 56	
Oldfield Park	d	10 03												11 03											12 03	
Bath Spa [7]	a	10 05			10 13				10 35	10 41				11 06			11 11			11 35	11 41				12 05	

For general notes see front of timetable
For details of catering facilities see Directory of Train Operators

- **A** From Maesteg (Table 128) to Cheltenham Spa (Table 57)
- **B** Until 26 June and from 7 September
- **C** To Cheltenham Spa (Table 57)
- **D** To Portsmouth Harbour (Table 123)
- **E** To Westbury (Table 123)
- **G** To Nottingham (Table 57)
- **H** To Manchester Piccadilly (Table 51)
- **J** To Swindon (Table 125)
- **K** From Worcester Shrub Hill (Table 57) to Weymouth (Table 123)
- **L** To London Waterloo (Table 160)
- **N** To Taunton (Table 134)
- **Q** From Gloucester (Table 134) to Weymouth (Table 123)
- **U** From Great Malvern (Table 71) to Westbury (Table 123)

Cardiff → Gloucester, Bristol and Bath Spa

Network Diagram - see first page of Table 132

		GW	AW	GW	GW	GW	GW	XC	AW	GW		GW	GW	GW	AW	GW	SW	GW	GW	XC	AW		GW	GW	GW	GW
			◇	[1] ◇	[1] ◇	◇	[1] ◇	[1] ◇	◇	◇		[1] ◇		[1] ◇		[1] ◇	[1] ◇	◇	[1] ◇	[1] ◇	◇			[1] ◇		[1] ◇
		A								B			A		C								D		A	
			🛒	☕	☕	🛒	☕					☕		☕		☕		🛒	☕					☕		☕
Cardiff Central [7]	d	11 00	11 20		11 25	11 30		11 45	11 50			11 55	12 00		12 12	12 25		12 30		12 45	12 50			12 55	13 00	
Newport (South Wales)	a	11 13	11 32		11 38	11 43		11 58	12 03			12 08	12 13		12 25	12 38		12 43		12 58	13 03			13 08	13 13	
	d	11 15			11 39	11 44		12 00				12 09	12 15		12 28	12 39		12 44		13 00				13 09	13 15	
Severn Tunnel Jn	d	11 25											12 25		12 39										13 25	
Caldicot	d														12 42											
Chepstow	d														12 51											
Lydney	d														13 00											
Gloucester [7]	a							12 44							13 20					13 44						
Pilning	d																									
Patchway	d	11 39											12 39												13 39	
Bristol Parkway [7]	a				12 00							12 30				13 00								13 30		
	d									12 19													13 19			
Filton Abbey Wood	d	11 42				12 09				12 22			12 42					13 09					13 22		13 42	
Bristol Temple Meads [10]	a	11 51				12 18				12 35			12 51					13 17					13 36		13 51	
	d			12 00		12 22	12 30			12 39				13 00			13 10	13 22	13 30				13 49			14 00
Keynsham	d									12 46													13 56			
Oldfield Park	d									12 53													14 03			
Bath Spa [7]	a			12 11		12 35	12 41			12 56				13 11			13 21	13 35	13 41				14 06			14 11

		AW	AW	GW	GW	GW	XC	AW	GW		GW	GW	GW	GW	GW	GW	XC	AW	GW	GW		GW	SW	GW	AW	AW
																										[R]
			◇	[1] ◇	◇	[1] ◇	[1] ◇	◇	◇		[1] ◇		[1] ◇	[1] ◇	◇	[1] ◇	[1] ◇	◇		[1] ◇			[1] ◇	[1] ◇		
		C							E			A							D			A			C	
			🛒	☕	🛒	☕					☕		☕	☕	🛒	☕				☕				☕		🛒
Cardiff Central [7]	d	13 12	13 20	13 25	13 30		13 45	13 50			13 55	14 00		14 25	14 30		14 45	14 50		14 55		15 00			15 12	15 20
Newport (South Wales)	a	13 25	13 32	13 38	13 43		13 58	14 03			14 08	14 13		14 38	14 43		14 58	15 03		15 08		15 13			15 25	15 32
	d	13 28		13 39	13 44		14 00				14 09	14 15		14 39	14 44		15 00			15 09		15 15			15 28	
Severn Tunnel Jn	d	13 39										14 25										15 25			15 38	
Caldicot	d	13 41																							15 41	
Chepstow	d	13 50																							15 50	
Lydney	d	13 59																							15 59	
Gloucester [7]	a	14 20					14 44										15 44								16 21	
Pilning	d																									
Patchway	d											14 39										15 39				
Bristol Parkway [7]	a			14 00							14 30			15 00						15 30						
	d								14 19										15 19							
Filton Abbey Wood	d				14 09				14 22			14 42			15 09				15 22			15 42				
Bristol Temple Meads [10]	a				14 19				14 40			14 53			15 18				15 37			15 51				
	d				14 22	14 30			14 49				15 00		15 22	15 30			15 43				15 52	16 00		
Keynsham	d								14 56										15 50							
Oldfield Park	d								15 03										15 57							
Bath Spa [7]	a				14 35	14 41			15 05				15 11		15 35	15 41			15 59				16 05	16 11		

		GW	GW	XC	AW	GW	GW	GW		GW	GW	GW	AW	AW	GW	GW	GW	XC	AW		GW	GW	GW	GW	GW	AW
					[R]									[R]					[R]							
		[1] ◇	◇	[1] ◇		[1] ◇	◇	[1] ◇			[1] ◇			[1]	[1] ◇	◇	[1] ◇	[1] ◇			◇	[1] ◇		[1] ◇		
							E			A		G	H								J		A		G	C
		☕	🛒		🛒	☕		☕			☕			⊠	☕	🛒	☕					☕		☕		
Cardiff Central [7]	d	15 25	15 30	15 45	15 50			15 55		16 00			16 05	16 15	16 25	16 30		16 45	16 50			16 55	17 00			17 12
Newport (South Wales)	a	15 38	15 42	15 58	16 03			16 08		16 13			16 18	16 27	16 38	16 43		16 58	17 03			17 08	17 13			17 25
	d	15 39	15 44	16 00				16 09		16 15			16 21		16 39	16 44		17 00				17 09	17 15			17 28
Severn Tunnel Jn	d									16 25			16 33			16 55							17 25			17 39
Caldicot	d												16 35													17 41
Chepstow	d												16 44													17 50
Lydney	d												16 53													17 59
Gloucester [7]	a			16 44									17 15					17 44								18 21
Pilning	d																									
Patchway	d									16 39													17 39			
Bristol Parkway [7]	a	16 00						16 30							17 00							17 30				
	d						16 19					16 46									17 19				17 46	
Filton Abbey Wood	d		16 09				16 22			16 42		16 49				17 09					17 22		17 42		17 49	
Bristol Temple Meads [10]	a		16 18				16 38			16 51		17 02				17 18					17 37		17 51		18 02	
	d		16 22			16 30	16 49				17 00	17 07				17 22	17 30				17 49			18 00	18 07	
Keynsham	d						16 56					17 14									17 56				18 14	
Oldfield Park	d						17 03					17 21				17 32					18 03				18 21	
Bath Spa [7]	a		16 35			16 41	17 06				17 11	17 24				17 35	17 41				18 06			18 11	18 24	

For general notes see front of timetable
For details of catering facilities see Directory of Train Operators

- **A** To Taunton (Table 134)
- **B** From Great Malvern (Table 71) to Brighton (Table 123)
- **C** From Maesteg (Table 128) to Cheltenham Spa (Table 57)
- **D** From Gloucester (Table 134) to Westbury (Table 123)
- **E** From Great Malvern (Table 71) to Weymouth (Table 123)
- **G** To Westbury (Table 123)
- **H** From Fishguard Harbour (Table 128) to Cheltenham Spa (Table 57)
- **J** From Gloucester (Table 134) to Weymouth (Table 123)

Cardiff → Gloucester, Bristol and Bath Spa

Network Diagram - see first page of Table 132

		AW	GW	GW	GW	XC	AW		GW	GW	GW	AW	GW	GW	GW	XC	AW	GW		GW	GW	GW	AW	GW	GW	GW
		R 🛒	1◇ 🍴	◇ 🛒	1◇ 🍴	1◇	R		A	1◇ 🍴	B	C	1◇ 🍴	◇ 🛒	1◇ 🍴	1◇	◇ 🛒	D		B	1◇ 🍴	◇	◇	1◇ 🍴	◇ E	B
Cardiff Central 7	d	17 20	17 25	17 30		17 45	17 50			17 55	18 00	18 12	18 25	18 30		18 45	18 50			19 00	19 25	19 30	19 34			19 55
Newport (South Wales)	a	17 32	17 38	17 43		17 58	18 03			18 08	18 13	18 25	18 38	18 43		18 58	19 03			19 13	19 38	19 42	19 46			20 08
	d		17 39	17 44		18 00				18 09	18 15	18 27	18 39	18 44		19 00				19 15	19 39	19 44				20 10
Severn Tunnel Jn	d			17 55							18 25	18 38		18 55						19 25						20 21
Caldicot	d											18 40														
Chepstow	d											18 49														
Lydney	d											18 58														
Gloucester 7	a					18 44						19 20				19 44										
Pilning	d																									
Patchway	d										18 39									19 39						20 34
Bristol Parkway 7	a		18 00							18 30			19 00								20 00					
	d								18 19									19 19							20 19	
Filton Abbey Wood	d			18 09					18 22		18 42			19 09				19 22		19 42		20 09			20 22	20 38
Bristol Temple Meads 10	a			18 18					18 37		18 53			19 18				19 36		19 53		20 18			20 38	20 48
	d			18 22	18 30				18 49					19 22	19 30			19 49				20 22		20 30	20 49	
Keynsham	d								18 56									19 56							20 56	
Oldfield Park	d								19 03									20 03							21 03	
Bath Spa 7	a			18 34	18 41				19 06					19 35	19 41			20 05				20 35		20 41	21 06	

		XC	AW	AW	GW	GW		AW	GW	GW	XC	AW	GW	SW	GW	XC	AW		GW	GW	GW	GW	AW FO	AW FX		
		1◇	◇	G	1◇ 🍴	◇		◇	1◇ 🍴		1◇ H	C	1◇ 🍴	1		1◇	◇		1◇ 🍴	J			C	C		
Cardiff Central 7	d	20 00	20 10	20 15	20 25	20 30		20 53			21 00	21 14	21 25		21 30	21 50	21 55			22 00		23 00	23 19	23 19		
Newport (South Wales)	a	20 13	20 24	20 28	20 38	20 43		21 08			21 13	21 27	21 38		21 43	22 03	22 12			22 15		23 15	23 35	23 39		
	d	20 15		20 30	20 39	20 44					21 15	21 29	21 39		21 44	22 05				22 17		23 16	23 37	23 40		
Severn Tunnel Jn	d			20 41							21 25	21 40			21 56					22 33		23 32	23 55	23 58		
Caldicot	d			20 43							21 28	21 42											23 57	00 01		
Chepstow	d			20 52							21 36	21 51											00 06	00 09		
Lydney	d			21 01							21 45	22 01											00 15	00 18		
Gloucester 7	a	20 56		21 21							22 04	22 22				22 46							00 36	00 39		
Pilning	d																									
Patchway	d														22 09					22 48		23 46				
Bristol Parkway 7	a				21 02								22 02							22 51						
	d																			22 54						
Filton Abbey Wood	d					21 09									22 13					22 58		23 50				
Bristol Temple Meads 10	a					21 19									22 30					23 07		00 03				
	d					21 22			21 47	22 00				22 25					22 33		23 16					
Keynsham	d									22 07											23 23					
Oldfield Park	d									22 14											23 30					
Bath Spa 7	a					21 35			21 59	22 17				22 36					22 44		23 32					

Saturdays

		AW	AW	AW	GW	GW	GW	AW	AW	GW	GW	GW	GW		AW	GW	GW	XC	AW	GW	GW	GW	XC	AW	AW	GW
		C		◇	1◇ 🍴	◇	1◇ K 🍴	◇ 🛒	◇ 🛒	1◇ 🍴	1◇ 🍴		1◇ 🍴		L	1◇ 🍴	◇	1◇ N	◇	1◇ 🍴	1◇ 🍴		1◇ Q 🍴 🛒	L	◇ 🛒	1◇ 🍴
Cardiff Central 7	d	23p19	00 30	04 40			04 55	05 21	05 40		05 55				06 12	06 25	06 30	06 40	06 50	06 55			07 00	07 12	07 20	07 25
Newport (South Wales)	a	23p35	00 48	04 55			05 09	05 33	05 52		06 08				06 25	06 38	06 43	06 53	07 02	07 08			07 13	07 25	07 32	07 38
	d	23p37					05 09				06 09				06 28	06 39	06 44	06 55		07 09			07 14	07 27		07 39
Severn Tunnel Jn	d	23p55													06 39		06 55	07 05					07 25	07 38		
Caldicot	d	23p57													06 41			07 08						07 40		
Chepstow	d	00 06													06 50			07 16						07 49		
Lydney	d	00 15													06 59			07 25						07 58		
Gloucester 7	a	00 36													07 20			07 46						08 21		
Pilning	d																									
Patchway	d																						07 37			
Bristol Parkway 7	a						05 37				06 30					07 00				07 30						08 00
	d						05 42																			
Filton Abbey Wood	d																07 10						07 41			
Bristol Temple Meads 10	a						05 53										07 18						07 51			
	d				05 30	05 49	06 00			06 30		06 49	07 00				07 22				07 30	07 49				
Keynsham	d					05 56						06 56										07 56				
Oldfield Park	d					06 03						07 03										08 03				
Bath Spa 7	a				05 41	06 05	06 11			06 41		07 05	07 11				07 35				07 41	08 05				

For general notes see front of timetable
For details of catering facilities see Directory of Train Operators

- **A** From Cheltenham Spa (Table 57) to Westbury (Table 123)
- **B** To Taunton (Table 134)
- **C** From Maesteg (Table 128) to Cheltenham Spa (Table 57)
- **D** From Gloucester (Table 134) to Frome (Table 123)
- **E** From Great Malvern (Table 71) to Weymouth (Table 123)
- **G** From Swansea (Table 128) to Cheltenham Spa (Table 57)
- **H** To Birmingham New Street (Table 57)
- **J** To Exeter St Davids (Table 135)
- **K** From Swansea (Table 125)
- **L** To Cheltenham Spa (Table 57)
- **N** To Nottingham (Table 57)
- **Q** To Manchester Piccadilly (Table 51)

Cardiff → Gloucester, Bristol and Bath Spa

Network Diagram - see first page of Table 132

		GW	GW		GW	XC	AW	GW	GW	SW	GW	GW	GW	GW	GW	XC		AW	GW	GW	GW	AW	AW	GW	GW	GW
		1 ◇	◇		1 ◇	1 ◇	◇	◇	1 ◇	1 ◇		1 ◇	1 ◇	◇	1 ◇	1 ◇		◇	◇	1 ◇			◇	1 ◇	1 ◇	◇
								A		B	C								D	E	C	G				
		☕	🛒		☕		🛒		☕			☕	☕	🛒	☕			🛒		☕			🛒	☕	☕	🛒
Cardiff Central 7	d		07 30			07 45	07 50		07 55		08 00		08 25	08 30		08 45		08 50		08 55	09 00	09 12	09 20		09 25	09 30
Newport (South Wales)	a		07 43			07 58	08 03		08 08		08 13		08 38	08 43		08 58		09 03		09 08	09 13	09 25	09 32		09 38	09 43
	d		07 44			08 00			08 09		08 15		08 39	08 44		09 00				09 09	09 15	09 27			09 39	09 44
Severn Tunnel Jn	d		07 55								08 25										09 26	09 38				
Caldicot	d																					09 40				
Chepstow	d																					09 50				
Lydney	d																					09 58				
Gloucester 7	a					08 46										09 46						10 21				
Pilning	d										08 32															
Patchway	d										08 40										09 38					
Bristol Parkway 7	a								08 31				09 00							09 30					10 00	
	d							08 20											09 19							
Filton Abbey Wood	d		08 10					08 23			08 43			09 09					09 23		09 42					10 09
Bristol Temple Meads 10	a		08 18					08 34			08 52			09 18					09 35		09 51					10 18
	d	08 00	08 22		08 30			08 41		08 50		09 00		09 22	09 30				09 49					10 00		10 22
Keynsham	d							08 48		08 57									09 56							
Oldfield Park	d							08 55											10 03							
Bath Spa 7	a	08 11	08 35		08 41			08 58		09 04		09 11		09 35	09 41				10 05					10 11		10 35

		GW	XC	AW	GW	GW		GW	AW	GW	GW	GW	XC	AW	GW	GW	AW	GW	GW		GW	GW	XC	AW	GW	GW
		1 ◇	1 ◇	◇				1 ◇		1 ◇	◇	1	1 ◇	◇	◇		◇	1	1 ◇		◇	1 ◇	1 ◇	◇	◇	
					H	C			G						D	C									J	C
		☕		🛒				☕		☕	🛒	☕		🛒			🛒	☕	☕		🛒	☕		🛒		
Cardiff Central 7	d		09 45	09 50		10 00			10 12	10 25	10 30		10 45	10 50		11 00	11 20		11 25		11 30		11 45	11 50		12 00
Newport (South Wales)	a		09 58	10 03		10 13			10 25	10 38	10 43		10 58	11 03		11 13	11 32		11 38		11 43		11 58	12 03		12 13
	d		10 00			10 15			10 27	10 39	10 44		11 00			11 15			11 39		11 44		12 00			12 15
Severn Tunnel Jn	d					10 25			10 38							11 25										12 25
Caldicot	d								10 40																	
Chepstow	d								10 49																	
Lydney	d								10 58																	
Gloucester 7	a		10 46						11 21				11 46										12 46			
Pilning	d																									
Patchway	d					10 39										11 39										12 39
Bristol Parkway 7	a									11 00									12 00							
	d				10 25										11 19										12 25	
Filton Abbey Wood	d				10 28	10 42					11 09				11 23	11 42					12 09				12 28	12 42
Bristol Temple Meads 10	a				10 39	10 52					11 18				11 35	11 52					12 18				12 39	12 52
	d	10 30			10 49			11 00			11 22	11 30			11 49			12 00			12 22	12 30			12 43	
Keynsham	d				10 56										11 56										12 50	
Oldfield Park	d				11 03										12 03										12 57	
Bath Spa 7	a	10 41			11 05			11 11			11 35	11 41			12 05			12 11			12 35	12 41			13 00	

		GW	AW	GW	SW	GW	GW	XC	AW		GW	GW	GW	AW	AW	GW	GW	GW	XC	AW	GW	GW		GW	GW	GW
		1 ◇		1 ◇	1 ◇	◇	1 ◇	1 ◇	◇				1 ◇		◇	1	◇	1 ◇	1 ◇	◇	◇			1 ◇	1 ◇	◇
			G								K	C		G							L	C				
		☕		☕		🛒	☕		🛒				☕		🛒	☕	🛒	☕		🛒	🛒			☕	☕	🛒
Cardiff Central 7	d		12 12	12 25		12 30		12 45	12 50			13 00		13 12	13 20	13 25	13 30		13 45	13 50		14 00			14 25	14 30
Newport (South Wales)	a		12 25	12 38		12 43		12 58	13 03			13 13		13 25	13 32	13 38	13 43		13 58	14 03		14 13			14 38	14 43
	d		12 27	12 39		12 44		13 00				13 15		13 27		13 39	13 44		14 00			14 15			14 39	14 44
Severn Tunnel Jn	d		12 38									13 26		13 39								14 25				
Caldicot	d		12 40											13 40												
Chepstow	d		12 49											13 49												
Lydney	d		12 58											13 58												
Gloucester 7	a		13 21					13 46						14 21					14 46							
Pilning	d																									
Patchway	d											13 39										14 39				
Bristol Parkway 7	a			13 00												14 00									15 00	
	d										13 19										14 21					
Filton Abbey Wood	d					13 09					13 23	13 43					14 09				14 25	14 42				15 09
Bristol Temple Meads 10	a					13 18					13 35	13 52					14 18				14 37	14 53				15 18
	d	13 00			13 15	13 22	13 30				13 49		14 00				14 22	14 30			14 49			15 00		15 22
Keynsham	d										13 56										14 56					
Oldfield Park	d										14 03										15 03					
Bath Spa 7	a	13 11			13 26	13 35	13 41				14 05		14 11				14 35	14 41			15 05			15 11		15 35

For general notes see front of timetable
For details of catering facilities see Directory of Train Operators

- **A** From Worcester Shrub Hill (Table 57) to Weymouth (Table 123)
- **B** To London Waterloo (Table 160)
- **C** To Taunton (Table 134)
- **D** From Gloucester (Table 134) to Weymouth (Table 123)
- **E** From 12 September
- **G** From Maesteg (Table 128) to Cheltenham Spa (Table 57)
- **H** From Worcester Shrub Hill (Table 57) to Westbury (Table 123)
- **J** From Great Malvern (Table 71) to Brighton (Table 123)
- **K** From Gloucester (Table 134) to Westbury (Table 123)
- **L** From Worcester Foregate Street (Table 71) to Weymouth (Table 123)

Table 132

Cardiff → Gloucester, Bristol and Bath Spa

Network Diagram - see first page of Table 132

		GW	XC	AW	GW	SW	GW	AW	AW	GW	GW	GW		GW	XC	AW	GW	GW	GW	AW	AW	GW	GW	GW	XC	AW
		1 ◇ 🍽	1 ◇	◇ 🛒	A	1 ◇	B	C	◇ 🛒	1 ◇ 🍽	1 ◇ 🍽	◇ 🛒		1 ◇ 🍽	1 ◇	R 🛒	◇ D	B	1 ◇ 🍽	C		1 ◇ 🍽	◇ 🛒	1 ◇ 🍽	1 ◇	R 🛒
Cardiff Central 7	d		14 45	14 50			15 00	15 12	15 20		15 25	15 30			15 45	15 50		16 00		16 12	16 19	16 25	16 30		16 45	16 50
Newport (South Wales)	a		14 58	15 03			15 13	15 25	15 32		15 38	15 43			15 58	16 03		16 13		16 23	16 32	16 38	16 43		16 58	17 03
	d		15 00				15 15	15 27			15 39	15 44			16 00			16 15		16 27		16 39	16 44		17 00	
Severn Tunnel Jn	d						15 25	15 39										16 25		16 38			16 55			
Caldicot	d							15 40												16 40						
Chepstow	d							15 49												16 49						
Lydney	d							15 58												16 58						
Gloucester 7	a		15 46					16 21							16 46					17 21					17 46	
Pilning	d																									
Patchway	d						15 39											16 39								
Bristol Parkway 7	a										16 00											17 00				
	d				15 18												16 24									
Filton Abbey Wood	d				15 22		15 42					16 09					16 28	16 42					17 10			
Bristol Temple Meads 10	a				15 34		15 52					16 18					16 39	16 52					17 18			
	d	15 30			15 38	15 52				16 00		16 22		16 30			16 49		17 00				17 22	17 30		
Keynsham	d				15 45												16 56									
Oldfield Park	d				15 52												17 03									
Bath Spa 7	a	15 41			15 54	16 05				16 11		16 35		16 41			17 05		17 11				17 35	17 41		

		GW		GW	AW	AW	GW	GW	GW	GW	XC	AW	GW	GW	AW		GW	GW	GW	XC	AW	GW	GW	GW	GW	AW
		◇ E		B	C	◇ 🛒	1 ◇ 🍽	1 ◇ 🍽	◇ 🛒	1 ◇ 🍽	1 ◇	R 🛒	G	B	C		1 ◇ 🍽	◇ 🛒	1 ◇ 🍽	1 ◇	◇ 🛒	H	B	1 ◇ 🍽	◇ 🛒	◇
Cardiff Central 7	d			17 00	17 12	17 20		17 25	17 30		17 45	17 50		18 00	18 12		18 25	18 30		18 45	18 50		19 00	19 25	19 30	19 34
Newport (South Wales)	a			17 13	17 27	17 32		17 38	17 43		17 58	18 03		18 13	18 25		18 38	18 43		18 58	19 03		19 13	19 38	19 42	19 46
	d			17 15	17 27			17 39	17 44		18 00			18 15	18 27		18 39	18 44		19 00			19 15	19 39	19 44	
Severn Tunnel Jn	d			17 25	17 38				17 55					18 25	18 38								19 25			
Caldicot	d				17 40										18 40											
Chepstow	d				17 49										18 49											
Lydney	d				17 58										18 58											
Gloucester 7	a				18 20						18 46				19 20					19 46						
Pilning	d																									
Patchway	d			17 39										18 39									19 39			
Bristol Parkway 7	a							18 00									19 00							20 00		
	d	17 19											18 25									19 21				
Filton Abbey Wood	d	17 23		17 42					18 10				18 28	18 42				19 09				19 25	19 42		20 09	
Bristol Temple Meads 10	a	17 35		17 52					18 18				18 39	18 52				19 18				19 38	19 52		20 18	
	d	17 49					18 00		18 22	18 30			18 49					19 22	19 30			19 49			20 22	
Keynsham	d	17 56											18 56									19 56				
Oldfield Park	d	18 03											19 03									20 03				
Bath Spa 7	a	18 05					18 11		18 35	18 41			19 05					19 35	19 41			20 05			20 35	

		GW	GW	GW	XC		AW	AW	GW	GW	XC	AW	GW	GW	GW	AW	AW	SW		GW	GW	AW	GW	AW		
		1 ◇ 🍽	◇ D		1 ◇ J		◇	K	1 ◇ 🍽	◇ 🛒	1 ◇	◇	1 ◇ 🍽	L		N	◇ Q	1		1 ◇ 🍽		U 🚌		N		
Cardiff Central 7	d			19 50	20 00		20 10	20 15	20 25	20 30	20 50	20 53		21 00		21 15	21 49				22 00	22 00		23 20		
Newport (South Wales)	a			20 03	20 13		20 24	20 28	20 38	20 43	21 03	21 08		21 13		21 28	22 05				22 13	22 30		23 37		
	d			20 05	20 15			20 30	20 39	20 44	21 05			21 15		21 30					22 16			23 40		
Severn Tunnel Jn	d			20 15	20 25			20 41						21 25		21 41					22 33			23 57		
Caldicot	d				20 28			20 43								21 43								23 59		
Chepstow	d				20 36			20 52								21 52								00 08		
Lydney	d				20 45			21 01								22 01								00 17		
Gloucester 7	a				21 04			21 22			21 48					22 22								00 42		
Pilning	d																									
Patchway	d			20 29										21 39							22 48					
Bristol Parkway 7	a								21 00																	
	d		20 23																							
Filton Abbey Wood	d		20 27	20 38						21 09				21 42							22 52					
Bristol Temple Meads 10	a		20 39	20 48						21 18				21 50							23 00					
	d	20 33	20 49							21 22			21 44		21 51			22 23		22 33			23 10			
Keynsham	d		20 56												21 56								23 17			
Oldfield Park	d		21 03												22 03								23 23			
Bath Spa 7	a	20 44	21 05							21 35			21 58		22 07			22 34		22 44			23 26			

For general notes see front of timetable
For details of catering facilities see Directory of Train Operators

- **A** From Gloucester (Table 134) to Westbury (Table 123)
- **B** To Taunton (Table 134)
- **C** From Maesteg (Table 128) to Cheltenham Spa (Table 57)
- **D** From Great Malvern (Table 71) to Weymouth (Table 123)
- **E** From Gloucester (Table 134) to Weymouth (Table 123)
- **G** From Great Malvern (Table 71) to Westbury (Table 123)
- **H** From Gloucester (Table 134) to Frome (Table 123)
- **J** Until 5 September. To Nottingham (Table 57)
- **K** From Swansea (Table 128) to Cheltenham Spa (Table 57)
- **L** To Exeter St Davids (Table 135)
- **N** From Maesteg (Table 128)
- **Q** From 18 July
- **U** Until 11 July

Cardiff → Gloucester, Bristol and Bath Spa

Network Diagram - see first page of Table 132

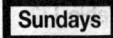

Station		AW	GW	GW	GW	GW	GW	AW	GW	GW	GW	GW	AW	GW		GW	GW	GW	XC	AW	AW	GW	GW	GW	XC	AW
			1◇	1◇	1◇	1◇	◇	◇		1◇	1◇	◇	◇	1◇		1◇	1◇	◇	1◇		◇	1◇	1◇	◇	1◇	◇
		A										B								C						
			☕	☕	☕	☕	🛒	🛒		☕	☕	🛒	🛒	☕		☕	☕	🛒			🛒	☕	☕	🛒		🛒
Cardiff Central 7	d	23p20			07 45		08 05	08 30		08 55		09 15	09 35			09 55		10 15	10 20	10 30	10 40	10 55		11 15	11 20	11 45
Newport (South Wales)	a	23p37			08 01		08 21	08 47		09 08		09 27	09 48			10 08		10 27	10 32	10 43	10 52	11 08		11 27	11 32	11 57
	d	23p40			08 03		08 23			09 09		09 29				10 09		10 29	10 34	10 45		11 09		11 29	11 34	
Severn Tunnel Jn	d	23p57					08 39					09 39						10 39		10 56				11 39		
Caldicot	d	23p59																		10 58						
Chepstow	d	00 08																		11 07						
Lydney	d	00 17																		11 16						
Gloucester 7	a	00 42																	11 16	11 42					12 16	
Pilning	d																									
Patchway	d											09 52														
Bristol Parkway 7	a				08 34					09 30						10 30						11 30				
	d																									
Filton Abbey Wood	d						08 54					09 56						10 54						11 54		
Bristol Temple Meads 10	a						09 04					10 06						11 03						12 04		
	d		07 40	08 10		09 00	09 10		09 15		10 00	10 10		10 30			11 00	11 10					12 00	12 10		
Keynsham	d						09 17		09 22									11 17								
Oldfield Park	d						09 24		09 30									11 24								
Bath Spa 7	a		07 52	08 21		09 12	09 26		09 32		10 11	10 21		10 41			11 12	11 26					12 12	12 21		

Station		GW	GW	GW	XC		AW	AW	GW	GW	GW	AW	XC	GW	GW	GW	AW	XC	GW		AW	GW	SW	GW	AW	XC
												R									R				R	
		1◇	1◇	◇	1◇			◇	1◇	1◇	◇		1◇	1◇	1◇	◇		1◇	1◇			1◇	1◇	◇		1◇
				D			C										C						E	B		
		☕	☕	🛒				🛒	☕	☕	🛒	🛒		☕	☕	🛒			☕		🛒	☕		🛒		
Cardiff Central 7	d	11 55		12 15	12 20		12 30	12 45	12 55		13 15	13 45	13 50	13 55		14 15	14 30	14 50	14 55		15 00			15 15	15 20	15 50
Newport (South Wales)	a	12 08		12 27	12 32		12 43	12 57	13 08		13 27	13 57	14 02	14 08		14 27	14 43	15 02	15 08		15 13			15 27	15 32	16 02
	d	12 09		12 29	12 34		12 45		13 09		13 29		14 04	14 09		14 29	14 45	15 04	15 09					15 29		16 04
Severn Tunnel Jn	d			12 39			12 56				13 39					14 39	14 56							15 39		
Caldicot	d						12 58										14 58									
Chepstow	d						13 07										15 07									
Lydney	d						13 16										15 16									
Gloucester 7	a				13 16		13 37						14 46				15 37	15 46								16 46
Pilning	d																									
Patchway	d			12 51																				15 52		
Bristol Parkway 7	a	12 30							13 30					14 30					15 30							
	d																									
Filton Abbey Wood	d			12 57							13 54					14 55								15 56		
Bristol Temple Meads 10	a			13 05							14 04					15 05								16 06		
	d		13 00	13 10						14 00	14 10				15 00	15 10						16 00	16 04	16 10		
Keynsham	d			13 17												15 17							16 11			
Oldfield Park	d			13 24												15 24										
Bath Spa 7	a		13 12	13 26						14 11	14 22				15 12	15 26						16 12	16 18	16 24		

Station		GW	AW	GW	GW	GW	AW	GW	GW	AW		XC	GW	AW	GW	GW	GW	AW	AW	GW	GW	XC	GW	GW		GW
			R							R								R	R							
		1◇		1◇	1◇	◇		1◇	◇			1◇	1◇		◇	1◇	◇			1◇	◇	1◇	1◇	1◇		◇
							C							G	H											B
		☕	🛒	☕	☕	🛒		☕	🛒	🛒			☕			☕	🛒			☕	🛒		☕	☕		🛒
Cardiff Central 7	d	15 55	16 00			16 15	16 30		16 40	16 45		16 50	16 55	17 05			17 15	17 20	17 40		17 45	17 50	17 55			18 15
Newport (South Wales)	a	16 08	16 13			16 27	16 43		16 52	16 57		17 02	17 08	17 18			17 27	17 32	17 52		17 57	18 02	18 08			18 27
	d	16 09				16 29	16 45		16 54			17 04	17 09				17 29				17 59	18 04	18 09			18 29
Severn Tunnel Jn	d					16 39	16 56										17 39									18 39
Caldicot	d						16 58																			
Chepstow	d						17 07																			
Lydney	d						17 16																			
Gloucester 7	a						17 37					17 46										18 46				
Pilning	d																									
Patchway	d																									18 52
Bristol Parkway 7	a	16 30											17 30										18 30			
	d																									
Filton Abbey Wood	d					16 55			17 17								17 54				18 22					18 56
Bristol Temple Meads 10	a					17 05			17 25								18 04				18 31					19 06
	d			16 30	17 00	17 10		17 30	17 40						17 44	18 00	18 10			18 30	18 50			19 00		19 10
Keynsham	d					17 17									17 51		18 17									19 17
Oldfield Park	d					17 24									17 58		18 24									19 24
Bath Spa 7	a			16 41	17 12	17 25		17 42	17 51						18 00	18 12	18 26			18 41	19 01			19 12		19 26

For general notes see front of timetable
For details of catering facilities see Directory of Train Operators

A From Maesteg (Table 128)
B To Portsmouth Harbour (Table 123)
C To Cheltenham Spa (Table 57)
D To Brighton (Table 123)
E To London Waterloo (Table 160)
G From Barry Island (Table 130)
H From Weston-super-Mare (Table 134)

Table 132

Sundays

until 12 July

Cardiff → Gloucester, Bristol and Bath Spa

Network Diagram - see first page of Table 132

		AW	AW	GW	XC	GW	GW	GW	AW	XC	GW	GW	GW	GW	AW	AW	XC	GW	SW	GW	GW	GW	AW	AW	
			R																						
				1◇	1◇	1◇	1◇	◇		1◇	1◇	◇	1◇	◇		◇	1◇	1◇	1	1◇		◇		◇	
		A																				B			
			🛒	☕		☕	☕	🛒			☕		☕	🛒				☕		☕		🛒			
Cardiff Central [7]	d	18 30	18 45		18 50	18 55		19 15	19 45	19 50	19 55			20 15	20 30	20 40	20 50	20 55				22 05	22 30	22 50	
Newport (South Wales)	a	18 43	18 57		19 03	19 08		19 28	19 58	20 02	20 08			20 27	20 43	20 53	21 02	21 08				22 23	22 47	23 08	
	d	18 45			19 04	19 09		19 29		20 04	20 09			20 29	20 45		21 04	21 09				22 24	22 49		
Severn Tunnel Jn	d	18 56												20 39	20 56							22 41	23 06		
Caldicot	d	18 58													20 58								23 08		
Chepstow	d	19 07													21 07								23 17		
Lydney	d	19 16													21 16								23 26		
Gloucester [7]	a	19 38			19 46					20 46					21 40		21 46						23 50		
Pilning	d																								
Patchway	d																					22 54			
Bristol Parkway [7]	a					19 30					20 30							21 30							
	d																								
Filton Abbey Wood	d							19 52						20 54								22 58			
Bristol Temple Meads [10]	a							20 02						21 04								23 07			
	d			19 30			20 00	20 10				20 50	21 00	21 10					21 35	22 05	22 15	23 10			
Keynsham	d											20 57									22 22				
Oldfield Park	d											21 04									22 29				
Bath Spa [7]	a			19 42			20 11	20 21				21 07	21 13	21 21					21 47	22 18	22 32	23 21			

Sundays

19 July to 6 September

		AW	GW	GW	GW	AW	GW	GW	GW		GW	AW	GW	GW	GW	AW	AW	GW		GW	GW	AW	XC	GW	GW	GW
			1◇	1◇	◇	◇	◇	1◇	1◇		◇	◇	1◇	1◇	◇		◇	1◇		1◇	◇	◇	1◇	1◇	1◇	◇
		C									D					A										E
			☕	☕	🛒	🛒		☕	☕		🛒	🛒	☕	☕	🛒		🛒	☕		☕	🛒	🛒		☕	☕	🛒
Cardiff Central [7]	d	23p20		07 45	08 05	08 30		08 55			09 15	09 35	09 55		10 15	10 30	10 40	10 55			11 15	11 45	11 50	11 55		12 15
Newport (South Wales)	a	23p37		08 01	08 21	08 47		09 08			09 27	09 48	10 08		10 27	10 43	10 52	11 08			11 27	11 57	12 02	12 08		12 27
	d	23p40		08 03	08 23			09 09			09 29		10 09		10 29	10 45		11 09			11 29		12 04	12 09		12 29
Severn Tunnel Jn	d	23p57			08 39						09 39				10 39	10 56					11 39					12 39
Caldicot	d	23p59														10 58										
Chepstow	d	00 08														11 07										
Lydney	d	00 17														11 16										
Gloucester [7]	a	00 42														11 42							12 46			
Pilning	d																									
Patchway	d										09 52															12 51
Bristol Parkway [7]	a			08 34				09 30					10 30					11 30						12 30		
	d																									
Filton Abbey Wood	d				08 54						09 56				10 54						11 54					12 57
Bristol Temple Meads [10]	a				09 04						10 06				11 03						12 04					13 05
	d		08 25		09 10		09 15		09 40		10 10			10 45	11 10					11 45	12 10				12 45	13 10
Keynsham	d				09 17		09 22								11 17											13 17
Oldfield Park	d				09 24		09 30								11 24											13 24
Bath Spa [7]	a		08 36		09 26		09 32		09 51		10 21			10 58	11 26					11 57	12 21				12 58	13 26

		AW	AW	XC		GW	GW	GW	AW	XC	GW	GW	GW		AW	XC	GW	AW	GW	SW	GW	AW		XC	GW	AW
									R									R				R				R
			◇	1◇		1◇	1◇	◇		1◇	1◇	1◇	◇			1◇	1◇		1◇	1◇	◇			1◇	1◇	
		A													A					G	D					
			🛒			☕	☕	🛒	🛒		☕	☕	🛒				☕	🛒	☕		🛒				☕	🛒
Cardiff Central [7]	d	12 30	12 45	12 50		12 55		13 15	13 45	13 50	13 55		14 15		14 30	14 50	14 55	15 00			15 15	15 20		15 50	15 55	16 00
Newport (South Wales)	a	12 43	12 57	13 02		13 08		13 27	13 57	14 02	14 08		14 27		14 43	15 02	15 08	15 13			15 27	15 32		16 02	16 08	16 13
	d	12 45		13 04		13 09		13 29		14 04	14 09		14 29		14 45	15 04	15 09				15 29			16 04	16 09	
Severn Tunnel Jn	d	12 56						13 39					14 39		14 56						15 39					
Caldicot	d	12 58													14 58											
Chepstow	d	13 07													15 07											
Lydney	d	13 16													15 16											
Gloucester [7]	a	13 37		13 46						14 46					15 37	15 46								16 46		
Pilning	d																									
Patchway	d																				15 52					
Bristol Parkway [7]	a					13 30					14 30						15 30								16 30	
	d																									
Filton Abbey Wood	d							13 54					14 55								15 56					
Bristol Temple Meads [10]	a							14 04					15 05								16 06					
	d						13 45	14 10				15 00	15 10						16 00	16 04	16 10					
Keynsham	d												15 17							16 11						
Oldfield Park	d												15 24													
Bath Spa [7]	a						13 58	14 22				15 12	15 26						16 12	16 18	16 24					

For general notes see front of timetable
For details of catering facilities see Directory of Train Operators

- **A** To Cheltenham Spa (Table 57)
- **B** To Warminster (Table 123)
- **C** From Maesteg (Table 128)
- **D** To Portsmouth Harbour (Table 123)
- **E** To Brighton (Table 123)
- **G** To London Waterloo (Table 160)

Sundays

19 July to 6 September

Cardiff → Gloucester, Bristol and Bath Spa

Network Diagram - see first page of Table 132

		GW	GW	GW	AW	GW	GW	AW R		XC	GW	GW	AW	GW	GW	AW R	AW R		GW	GW	XC	GW	GW	GW	AW	AW R
		1◇	1◇	◇		1◇	◇			1◇	1◇	◇		1◇	◇				1◇	◇	1◇	1◇	1◇	◇		
					A							B	C											D	A	
		☕	☕	🛒		☕	🛒	🛒			☕			☕	🛒				☕	🛒		☕	☕	🛒		🛒
Cardiff Central 7	d			16 15	16 30		16 40	16 45		16 50	16 55		17 05		17 15	17 20	17 40			17 45	17 50	17 55		18 15	18 30	18 45
Newport (South Wales)	a			16 27	16 43		16 52	16 57		17 02	17 08		17 18		17 27	17 32	17 52			17 57	18 02	18 08		18 27	18 43	18 57
	d			16 29	16 45		16 54			17 04	17 09				17 29					17 59	18 04	18 09		18 29	18 45	
Severn Tunnel Jn	d			16 39	16 56										17 39									18 39	18 56	
Caldicot	d				16 58																				18 58	
Chepstow	d				17 07																				19 07	
Lydney	d				17 16																				19 16	
Gloucester 7	a				17 37					17 46											18 46				19 38	
Pilning	d																									
Patchway	d																							18 52		
Bristol Parkway 7	a										17 30											18 30				
	d																									
Filton Abbey Wood	d			16 55			17 17								17 54					18 22				18 56		
Bristol Temple Meads 10	a			17 05			17 25								18 04					18 31				19 06		
	d	16 30	17 00	17 10		17 30	17 40					17 44		18 00	18 10				18 30	18 50			19 00	19 10		
Keynsham	d			17 17								17 51			18 17									19 17		
Oldfield Park	d			17 24								17 58			18 24									19 24		
Bath Spa 7	a	16 41	17 12	17 25		17 42	17 51					18 00		18 12	18 26				18 41	19 01			19 12	19 26		

		GW	XC		GW	GW	GW	AW	XC	GW	GW	GW		GW	AW	AW	XC	GW	SW	GW	GW	GW	AW	AW		
		1◇	1◇		1◇	1◇	◇		1◇	1◇	◇	1◇		◇		◇	1◇	1◇	1	1◇		◇		◇		
																						E				
		☕			☕	☕	🛒			☕		☕		🛒				☕		☕		🛒				
Cardiff Central 7	d		18 50		18 55		19 15	19 45	19 50	19 55				20 15	20 30	20 40	20 50	20 55				22 05	22 30	22 50		
Newport (South Wales)	a		19 03		19 08		19 28	19 58	20 02	20 08				20 27	20 43	20 53	21 02	21 08				22 23	22 47	23 08		
	d		19 04		19 09		19 29		20 04	20 09				20 29	20 45		21 04	21 09				22 24	22 49			
Severn Tunnel Jn	d													20 39	20 56							22 41	23 06			
Caldicot	d														20 58								23 08			
Chepstow	d														21 07								23 17			
Lydney	d														21 16								23 26			
Gloucester 7	a		19 46						20 46						21 40		21 46						23 50			
Pilning	d																									
Patchway	d																					22 54				
Bristol Parkway 7	a				19 30					20 30								21 30								
	d																									
Filton Abbey Wood	d						19 52							20 54								22 58				
Bristol Temple Meads 10	a						20 02							21 04								23 07				
	d	19 30				20 00	20 10				20 50	21 00		21 10					21 35	22 05	22 15	23 10				
Keynsham	d										20 57										22 22					
Oldfield Park	d										21 04										22 29					
Bath Spa 7	a	19 42				20 11	20 21				21 07	21 13		21 21					21 47	22 18	22 32	23 21				

Sundays

from 13 September

		AW	GW	GW	GW		GW	GW	AW	GW		GW	GW	AW	GW		GW	GW	XC	AW		AW	XC	GW	GW	GW
			1◇	1◇	1◇		1◇	◇	◇	1◇		1◇	◇	◇	1◇		1◇	◇	1◇			◇	1◇	1◇	1◇	◇
		G											D						H	A			J			
			☕	☕	☕		☕	🛒	🛒	☕		☕	🛒	🛒	☕		☕	🛒				🛒		☕	☕	🛒
Cardiff Central 7	d	23p20			07 45			08 05	08 30	08 55			09 15	09 35	09 55			10 15	10 25	10 30		10 40	10 50	10 55		11 15
Newport (South Wales)	a	23p37			08 01			08 21	08 47	09 08			09 27	09 48	10 08			10 27	10 37	10 43		10 52	11 02	11 08		11 27
	d	23p40			08 03			08 23		09 09			09 29		10 09			10 29	10 39	10 45			11 04	11 09		11 29
Severn Tunnel Jn	d	23p57						08 39					09 39					10 39		10 56						11 39
Caldicot	d	23p59																		10 58						
Chepstow	d	00 08																		11 07						
Lydney	d	00 17																		11 16						
Gloucester 7	a	00 42																	11 21	11 42			11 46			
Pilning	d																									
Patchway	d												09 52													
Bristol Parkway 7	a				08 34					09 30					10 30									11 30		
	d																									
Filton Abbey Wood	d							08 54					09 56					10 54								11 54
Bristol Temple Meads 10	a							09 04					10 06					11 03								12 04
	d		07 40	08 10			09 00	09 10				10 00	10 10				11 00	11 10							12 00	12 10
Keynsham	d							09 17										11 17								
Oldfield Park	d							09 24										11 24								
Bath Spa 7	a		07 52	08 21			09 12	09 26				10 11	10 21				11 12	11 26							12 12	12 21

For general notes see front of timetable
For details of catering facilities see Directory of Train Operators

A To Cheltenham Spa (Table 57)
B From Weston-super-Mare (Table 134)
C From Barry Island (Table 130)
D To Portsmouth Harbour (Table 123)
E To Warminster (Table 123)
G From Maesteg (Table 128)
H From 8 November
J Until 1 November

Sundays

from 13 September

Cardiff → Gloucester, Bristol and Bath Spa

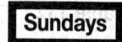

Network Diagram - see first page of Table 132

Station		XC	AW	XC	GW	GW	GW	XC	AW	AW	XC	GW	GW	GW	GW	XC	AW	XC	GW	GW	GW
		[1] ◇ A	◇	[1] ◇ B	[1] ◇	[1] ◇	◇ C	[1] ◇ A	D	◇	[1] ◇ B	[1] ◇	◇	[1] ◇	◇	[1] ◇ A	[R]	[1] ◇ B	[1] ◇	[1] ◇	◇
Cardiff Central [7]	d	11 25	11 45	11 50	11 55		12 15	12 25	12 30	12 45	12 50	12 55			13 15	13 25	13 45	13 50	13 55		14 15
Newport (South Wales)	a	11 37	11 57	12 02	12 08		12 27	12 37	12 43	12 57	13 02	13 08			13 27	13 37	13 57	14 02	14 08		14 27
	d	11 39		12 04	12 09		12 29	12 39	12 45		13 04	13 09			13 29	13 39		14 04	14 09		14 29
Severn Tunnel Jn	d						12 39		12 56						13 39						14 39
Caldicot	d								12 58												
Chepstow	d								13 07												
Lydney	d								13 16												
Gloucester [7]	a	12 21		12 46				13 21	13 37		13 46					14 21		14 46			
Pilning	d																				
Patchway	d						12 51														
Bristol Parkway [7]	a				12 30							13 30							14 30		
	d																				
Filton Abbey Wood	d						12 57								13 54						14 55
Bristol Temple Meads [10]	a						13 05								14 04						15 05
	d					13 00	13 10						13 40	14 00	14 10					15 00	15 10
Keynsham	d						13 17						13 47								15 17
Oldfield Park	d						13 24						13 54								15 24
Bath Spa [7]	a					13 12	13 26						13 57	14 11	14 23					15 12	15 26

Station		XC	AW	XC	GW	AW	GW	SW	GW	AW	XC	XC	GW	AW	GW	GW	GW	XC	AW	GW	GW
		[1] ◇ A	D	[1] ◇ B	[1] ◇	[R]	[1] ◇	[1] ◇ E	◇ G	[R]	[1] ◇ A	[1] ◇ B	[1] ◇	[R]	[1] ◇	[1] ◇	◇	[1] ◇ A	D	[1] ◇	◇
Cardiff Central [7]	d	14 25	14 30	14 50	14 55	15 00			15 15	15 20	15 25	15 50	15 55	16 00			16 15	16 25	16 30		16 40
Newport (South Wales)	a	14 37	14 43	15 02	15 08	15 13			15 27	15 32	15 37	16 02	16 08	16 13			16 27	16 37	16 43		16 52
	d	14 39	14 45	15 04	15 09				15 29		15 39	16 04	16 09				16 29	16 39	16 45		16 54
Severn Tunnel Jn	d		14 56						15 39								16 39		16 56		
Caldicot	d		14 58																16 58		
Chepstow	d		15 07																17 07		
Lydney	d		15 16																17 16		
Gloucester [7]	a	15 21	15 37	15 46							16 21	16 46						17 21	17 37		
Pilning	d																				
Patchway	d								15 52												
Bristol Parkway [7]	a				15 30								16 30								
	d																				
Filton Abbey Wood	d								15 56								16 55				17 17
Bristol Temple Meads [10]	a								16 06								17 05				17 25
	d						16 00	16 04	16 10						16 30	17 00	17 10			17 30	17 40
Keynsham	d							16 11									17 17				
Oldfield Park	d																17 24				
Bath Spa [7]	a						16 12	16 18	16 24						16 41	17 12	17 25			17 42	17 51

Station		AW	XC	GW	GW	GW	GW	AW	XC	AW	GW	GW	XC	GW	GW	GW	XC	AW	AW	GW	GW	GW
		[R]	[1] ◇ B	[1] ◇	◇ H	[1] ◇	◇	[R]	[1] ◇ A	[R]	[1] ◇	◇	[1] ◇ B	[1] ◇	[1] ◇	◇ G	[1] ◇ A	D	[R]	[1] ◇	[1] ◇	[1] ◇
Cardiff Central [7]	d	16 45	16 50	16 55			17 15	17 20	17 25	17 40		17 45	17 50	17 55		18 15	18 25	18 30	18 45		18 55	
Newport (South Wales)	a	16 57	17 02	17 08			17 27	17 32	17 37	17 52		17 57	18 02	18 08		18 27	18 37	18 43	18 57		19 08	
	d		17 04	17 09			17 29		17 39			17 59	18 04	18 09		18 29	18 39	18 45			19 09	
Severn Tunnel Jn	d						17 39									18 39		18 56				
Caldicot	d																	18 58				
Chepstow	d																	19 07				
Lydney	d																	19 16				
Gloucester [7]	a		17 46						18 21				18 46				19 21	19 38				
Pilning	d																					
Patchway	d															18 52						
Bristol Parkway [7]	a			17 30										18 30							19 30	
	d																					
Filton Abbey Wood	d						17 54					18 22				18 56						
Bristol Temple Meads [10]	a						18 04					18 31				19 06						
	d				17 44	18 00	18 10				18 30	18 50			19 00	19 10				19 30		20 00
Keynsham	d				17 51		18 17									19 17						
Oldfield Park	d				17 58		18 24									19 24						
Bath Spa [7]	a				18 00	18 12	18 26				18 41	19 01			19 12	19 26				19 42		20 11

For general notes see front of timetable
For details of catering facilities see Directory of Train Operators

A From 8 November
B Until 1 November
C To Brighton (Table 123)
D To Cheltenham Spa (Table 57)
E To London Waterloo (Table 160)
G To Portsmouth Harbour (Table 123)
H From Weston-super-Mare (Table 134)

Table 132

Sundays

from 13 September

Cardiff → Gloucester, Bristol and Bath Spa

Network Diagram - see first page of Table 132

		GW ◇	XC 1 ◇ A	AW	XC 1 ◇ B	GW 1 ◇	GW ◇	GW 1 ◇	GW ◇	XC 1 ◇ A	AW	AW ◇	XC 1 ◇ B	GW 1 ◇	SW 1	GW 1 ◇	GW	GW ◇ C	AW	AW ◇
Cardiff Central 7	d	19 15	19 25	19 45	19 50	19 55			20 15	20 25	20 30	20 40	20 50	20 55				22 05	22 30	22 50
Newport (South Wales)	a	19 28	19 37	19 58	20 02	20 08			20 27	20 37	20 43	20 53	21 02	21 08				22 23	22 47	23 08
	d	19 29	19 39		20 04	20 09			20 29	20 39	20 45		21 04	21 09				22 24	22 49	
Severn Tunnel Jn	d								20 39		20 56							22 41	23 06	
Caldicot	d										20 58								23 08	
Chepstow	d										21 07								23 17	
Lydney	d										21 16								23 26	
Gloucester 7	a		20 21		20 46					21 21	21 40		21 46						23 50	
Pilning	d																			
Patchway	d																	22 54		
Bristol Parkway 7	a					20 30								21 30						
	d																			
Filton Abbey Wood	d	19 52							20 54									22 58		
Bristol Temple Meads 10	a	20 02							21 04									23 07		
	d	20 10					20 50	21 00	21 10						21 35	22 05	22 15	23 10		
Keynsham	d						20 57										22 22			
Oldfield Park	d						21 04										22 29			
Bath Spa 7	a	20 21					21 07	21 13	21 21						21 47	22 18	22 32	23 21		

For general notes see front of timetable
For details of catering facilities see Directory of Train Operators

A From 8 November
B Until 1 November
C To Warminster (Table 123)

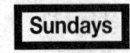

Bath Spa, Bristol and Gloucester → Cardiff

Network Diagram - see first page of Table 132

Miles	Miles	Miles			AW MX A	AW MX ◇	GW MX [1]◇ 🍴	GW MX [1]◇ 🍴	GW	AW	AW B	GW	XC [1]◇ C 🛒	GW	AW ◇ 🛒	GW [1]◇ D 🍴	XC [1]◇ C 🛒		AW ◇	GW E	GW G	GW H	SW [1]	GW [1]◇ 🍴	GW ◇ J	GW [1]◇ K 🍴
0	—	—	**Bath Spa [7]**	d				01 15						06 28		06 56					07 04	07 25	07 34		07 48	08 00
1	—	—	Oldfield Park	d										06 31							07 06	07 28	07 37		07 51	
7	—	—	Keynsham	d										06 38							07 14	07 35	07 44		07 58	08 09
11½	—	—	**Bristol Temple Meads [10]**	a				01 29						06 45		07 08					07 21	07 45	07 52		08 06	08 17
—	—	—		d				01 34	05 54			06 22		06 50		07 15				07 19	07 34	07 53			08 10	
16	—	—	Filton Abbey Wood	d					06 01			06 33		07 02		07 22				07 30	07 44	08 00			08 21	
—	0	—	**Bristol Parkway [7]**	a																07 33	07 48				08 29	
—	—	—		d			00 25													07 40				08 07		
17½	—	—	Patchway	d					06 06			06 38								07 44		08 05				
21	4¾	—	Pilning	d																						
—	—	0	**Gloucester [7]**	d	23p13						05 50		06 17				07 01									
—	—	19½	Lydney	d	23p33						06 09		06 36				07 20									
—	—	27¼	Chepstow	d	23p42						06 19		06 45				07 29									
—	—	34	Caldicot	d	23p51						06 26		06 54				07 38									
28	11¾	34½	Severn Tunnel Jn	d	23p54				06 17		06 29	06 49	06 57	07 15			07 41			07 56						
38	21¾	44¾	Newport (South Wales)	a	00 13		00 54	02s10	06 29		06 41	07 01	07 11	07 27		07 44	07 52			08 08		08 26		08 30		
—	—	—		d	00 14	00 50	00 55		06 30	06 36	06 44	07 03	07 11	07 28	07 35	07 45	07 54		08 01	08 09		08 27		08 31		
49¾	33½	56½	**Cardiff Central [7]**	a	00 35	01 10	01 14	02 33	06 47	06 56	07 00	07 20	07 31	07 45	07 51	08 01	08 13		08 17	08 25		08 46		08 48		

		AW ◇ 🛒	AW B	AW ◇ 🛒	GW [1]◇ 🍴	GW L	XC [1]◇ 🛒	GW N		GW ◇ 🛒	GW [1]◇ 🍴	GW [1]◇ 🍴	AW ◇ 🛒	AW [1]◇ 🍴	AW B	GW ◇ J	GW [1]◇ 🍴	GW L	GW [1]◇ 🍴	XC [1]◇ 🛒	GW Q	GW ◇ 🛒		GW [1]◇ 🍴	GW [1]◇ 🍴	GW [1]◇ 🍴
Bath Spa [7]	d							08 08		08 22	08 30					08 47	08 55				09 15	09 22		09 30		10 00
Oldfield Park	d							08 10		08 24						08 49					09 17					
Keynsham	d							08 17		08 33						08 57					09 25	09 31				
Bristol Temple Meads [10]	a							08 29		08 39	08 45					09 04	09 10				09 35	09 39		09 44		10 15
	d					08 21		08 41		08 54						09 10		09 21			09 41	09 54				
Filton Abbey Wood	d					08 33		08 48		09 01						09 20		09 30			09 48	10 01				
Bristol Parkway [7]	a							08 52								09 28					09 52					
	d				08 42							09 07							09 42						10 07	
Patchway	d					08 36												09 35								
Pilning	d																									
Gloucester [7]	d		07 58				08 27								08 58					09 23						
Lydney	d		08 17												09 17											
Chepstow	d		08 27												09 27											
Caldicot	d		08 35												09 35											
Severn Tunnel Jn	d		08 38			08 49									09 38			09 46								
Newport (South Wales)	a		08 50		09 05	09 01	09 11			09 25		09 29			09 50			09 58	10 04	10 11		10 23			10 29	
	d	08 33	08 52	09 02	09 05	09 02	09 11			09 26		09 31	09 33	09 41	09 52			10 00	10 05	10 11		10 23			10 31	
Cardiff Central [7]	a	08 55	09 09	09 22	09 23	09 24	09 31			09 43		09 48	09 52	09 58	10 09			10 18	10 23	10 31		10 42			10 47	

		AW ◇ 🛒	AW ◇ 🛒	GW L	GW [1]◇ 🍴	XC [1]◇ 🛒	GW ◇ U	GW [1]◇ 🍴	GW ◇ 🛒	GW [1]◇ 🍴	GW [1]◇ 🍴	AW ◇ 🛒	AW B		GW E	GW [1]◇ 🍴	XC [1]◇ 🛒	GW ◇ V	GW [1]◇ 🍴	GW ◇ 🛒	SW [1]◇	GW [1]◇ 🍴	GW [1]◇ 🍴	AW ◇ 🛒	AW B	AW ◇ 🛒
Bath Spa [7]	d						10 08	10 25	10 35		11 00							11 08	11 25	11 35	11 46		12 00			
Oldfield Park	d						10 10											11 10								
Keynsham	d						10 17											11 17								
Bristol Temple Meads [10]	a						10 29	10 39	10 47		11 15							11 29	11 42	11 47	12 05		12 15			
	d			10 21			10 41		10 54						11 21			11 41		11 54						
Filton Abbey Wood	d			10 30			10 48		11 01						11 30			11 48		12 01						
Bristol Parkway [7]	a						10 52											11 52								
	d				10 42					11 07						11 42						12 07				
Patchway	d			10 35											11 35											
Pilning	d																									
Gloucester [7]	d					10 23							10 58				11 23								11 59	
Lydney	d												11 17												12 18	
Chepstow	d												11 27												12 28	
Caldicot	d												11 35												12 36	
Severn Tunnel Jn	d			10 47									11 38		11 46										12 39	
Newport (South Wales)	a			11 02	11 05	11 11			11 26	11 31			11 50		11 58	12 04	12 11			12 24		12 29			12 50	
	d	10 40	10 57	11 03	11 05	11 11			11 27	11 31		11 33	11 52		12 00	12 05	12 11			12 25		12 31		12 33	12 52	12 59
Cardiff Central [7]	a	10 55	11 19	11 22	11 23	11 31			11 44	11 48		11 55	12 10		12 17	12 21	12 31			12 42		12 48		12 54	13 10	13 20

For general notes see front of timetable
For details of catering facilities see Directory of Train Operators

- **A** From Cheltenham Spa (Table 57)
- **B** From Cheltenham Spa (Table 57) to Maesteg (Table 128)
- **C** From Birmingham New Street (Table 57)
- **D** From London Paddington to Swansea (Table 125)
- **E** From Taunton (Table 134)
- **G** From Salisbury (Table 123) to Gloucester (Table 134)
- **H** From Frome (Table 123)
- **J** From Weymouth (Table 123)
- **K** From London Paddington (Table 125)
- **L** From Weston-super-Mare (Table 134)
- **N** From Warminster (Table 123) to Great Malvern (Table 71)
- **Q** From Westbury (Table 123) to Gloucester (Table 134)
- **U** From Southampton Central (Table 123) to Great Malvern (Table 71)
- **V** From Weymouth (Table 123) to Gloucester (Table 134)

Bath Spa, Bristol and Gloucester → Cardiff

Network Diagram - see first page of Table 132

		GW	GW	XC	GW	GW	GW	GW	GW	AW	GW	GW	XC	GW	GW	GW	GW	GW	AW	AW	AW [R]	GW	GW	GW
		[1] ◇		[1] ◇	◇	[1] ◇	◇	[1] ◇	[1] ◇	◇		[1] ◇	[1] ◇	◇	[1] ◇	◇	[1] ◇	[1] ◇	◇					[1] ◇
			A		B						A			C						D		E	A	
		🍴		🛒		🍴	🛒	🍴	🍴	🛒		🍴	🛒		🍴	🛒	🍴	🍴	🛒		🛒			🍴
Bath Spa [7]	d				12 08	12 25	12 35		13 00					13 19	13 25	13 35		14 00				14 08		
Oldfield Park	d				12 10									13 21										
Keynsham	d				12 17									13 28										
Bristol Temple Meads [10]	a				12 29	12 39	12 47		13 15					13 36	13 41	13 47		14 15						
	d		12 21		12 41		12 54				13 21			13 41		13 54							14 21	
Filton Abbey Wood	d		12 30		12 48		13 01				13 30			13 48		14 01						14 29	14 30	
Bristol Parkway [7]	a				12 52									13 52								14 37		
	d	12 42						13 07				13 42					14 07							14 42
Patchway	d		12 35								13 35												14 35	
Pilning	d																							
Gloucester [7]	d			12 23									13 23							13 59				
Lydney	d																			14 18				
Chepstow	d																			14 28				
Caldicot	d																			14 36				
Severn Tunnel Jn	d		12 46								13 46									14 39			14 50	
Newport (South Wales)	a	13 04	13 01	13 11			13 25	13 29			13 58	14 04	14 11			14 24	14 29			14 51			15 03	15 05
	d	13 05	13 01	13 11			13 27	13 31		13 37	14 00	14 05	14 11			14 26	14 31		14 33	14 53	14 59		15 04	15 05
Cardiff Central [7]	a	13 22	13 24	13 31			13 44	13 48		13 54	14 17	14 21	14 31			14 45	14 48		14 54	15 10	15 20		15 24	15 23

		XC	GW	GW	GW	SW	GW	GW	AW [R]	AW	GW	GW	XC	GW	GW	GW	GW	GW	AW [R]	AW	GW	GW	XC	GW
		[1] ◇	◇	[1] ◇	◇	[1] ◇	[1] ◇	[1] ◇				[1] ◇	[1] ◇	◇	[1] ◇	◇	[1] ◇	[1] ◇		◇		[1] ◇	[1] ◇	
			G							D	A			C							A			H
		🛒		🍴	🛒		🍴	🍴	🛒			🍴	🛒		🍴	🛒	🍴	🍴	🛒	🛒		🍴	🛒	
Bath Spa [7]	d		14 15	14 25	14 35	14 46		15 00						15 15	15 25	15 35		16 00						16 08
Oldfield Park	d		14 18											15 17										16 10
Keynsham	d		14 25											15 25										16 17
Bristol Temple Meads [10]	a		14 35	14 39	14 47	15 05		15 15						15 34	15 40	15 47		16 15						16 29
	d		14 41		14 54						15 21			15 41		15 54					16 21			16 41
Filton Abbey Wood	d		14 48		15 01						15 30			15 48		16 01					16 30			16 48
Bristol Parkway [7]	a		14 51											15 52										16 52
	d						15 07					15 42					16 07					16 42		
Patchway	d										15 35										16 35			
Pilning	d																							
Gloucester [7]	d	14 23								14 58			15 23										16 23	
Lydney	d									15 17														
Chepstow	d									15 27														
Caldicot	d									15 35														
Severn Tunnel Jn	d									15 38	15 46										16 46			
Newport (South Wales)	a	15 11			15 25		15 29			15 50	15 58	16 04	16 11			16 24	16 29				17 01	17 05	17 11	
	d	15 11			15 26		15 31		15 33	15 52	16 00	16 05	16 11			16 26	16 31		16 34	16 59	17 02	17 05	17 11	
Cardiff Central [7]	a	15 31			15 43		15 48		15 53	16 10	16 18	16 21	16 31			16 43	16 48		16 54	17 17	17 24	17 22	17 31	

		GW	GW	GW	GW	AW [R]	AW	GW	GW	XC	GW	GW	GW	GW	GW	AW [R]	AW	AW	GW	GW	XC	GW	GW	GW	AW [R]
		[1] ◇	◇	[1] ◇	[1] ◇				[1] ◇	[1] ◇	◇	[1] ◇	◇	[1] ◇	[1] ◇			◇		[1] ◇	[1] ◇		[1] ◇	◇	
							D	A			C						D		A			H			
		🍴	🛒	🍴	🍴	🛒			🍴	🛒		🍴	🛒	🍴	🍴	🛒		🛒		🍴	🛒		🍴	🛒	🛒
Bath Spa [7]	d	16 25	16 35		17 00						17 08	17 25	17 35		18 00							18 08	18 30	18 35	
Oldfield Park	d										17 10											18 10			
Keynsham	d										17 17											18 17			
Bristol Temple Meads [10]	a	16 39	16 47		17 15						17 29	17 41	17 47		18 15							18 28	18 44	18 50	
	d		16 54					17 21			17 41		17 54						18 21			18 41		18 54	
Filton Abbey Wood	d		17 01					17 30			17 48		18 01						18 30			18 48		19 01	
Bristol Parkway [7]	a										17 52											18 52			
	d			17 07					17 42					18 12						18 42					
Patchway	d							17 34											18 34						
Pilning	d																								
Gloucester [7]	d						16 58			17 26							17 59				18 30				
Lydney	d						17 17										18 18								
Chepstow	d						17 27										18 28								
Caldicot	d						17 35										18 36								
Severn Tunnel Jn	d		17 14				17 38	17 45					18 15				18 39		18 50					19 13	
Newport (South Wales)	a		17 27	17 29			17 50	18 00	18 05	18 11			18 27	18 36			18 51		19 05	19 10	19 14			19 27	
	d		17 27	17 31		17 33	17 52	18 00	18 05	18 11			18 27	18 38		18 43	18 53	18 59	19 06	19 10	19 14			19 27	19 33
Cardiff Central [7]	a		17 45	17 48		17 52	18 10	18 19	18 22	18 31			18 45	18 53		18 59	19 09	19 20	19 23	19 27	19 35			19 45	19 49

For general notes see front of timetable
For details of catering facilities see Directory of Train Operators

- **A** From Taunton (Table 134)
- **B** From Brighton (Table 123) to Great Malvern (Table 71)
- **C** From Weymouth (Table 123) to Gloucester (Table 134)
- **D** From Cheltenham Spa (Table 57) to Maesteg (Table 128)
- **E** From Westbury (Table 123)
- **G** From Southampton Central (Table 123) to Worcester Foregate Street (Table 71)
- **H** From Warminster (Table 123) to Great Malvern (Table 71)

Bath Spa, Bristol and Gloucester → Cardiff

Network Diagram - see first page of Table 132

		GW	AW	GW	GW		GW	XC	GW	GW	GW FX	GW FO	GW	AW	GW FX	GW	XC	GW	AW		AW	GW	XC	GW	GW	GW
		[1] ◇		[1] ◇			[1] ◇	[1] ◇		[1] ◇	◇	◇	[1] ◇	[R]		◇	[1] ◇	[1] ◇			◇	[1] ◇	[1] ◇	◇	[1] ◇	◇
			A		B				C								D		A					E		
		☕		☕			☕	🛒		☕	🛒	🛒	☕	🛒				☕			🛒	☕	🛒		☕	🛒
Bath Spa [7]	d			19 00					19 08	19 30	19 35	19 35				19 47		20 00						20 11	20 30	20 35
Oldfield Park	d								19 10							19 50								20 13		
Keynsham	d								19 17							19 58								20 20		
Bristol Temple Meads [10]	a			19 15					19 29	19 43	19 49	19 49				20 05		20 15						20 29	20 44	20 50
	d				19 21				19 41			19 54			20 04		20 15							20 41		20 54
Filton Abbey Wood	d				19 30				19 48			20 01			20 11		20 22							20 48		21 01
Bristol Parkway [7]	a								19 52															20 52		
	d	19 10					19 42						20 07									20 42				
Patchway	d				19 34												20 25									
Pilning	d																									
Gloucester [7]	d		18 58					19 26											19 58				20 23			
Lydney	d		19 17																20 17							
Chepstow	d		19 27																20 27							
Caldicot	d		19 34																20 36							
Severn Tunnel Jn	d		19 37		19 47							20 17			20 28		20 37		20 39							
Newport (South Wales)	a	19 37	19 50		20 01		20 06	20 11				20 28	20 29		20 45		20 47		20 51			21 04	21 11			21 27
	d	19 37	19 52		20 01		20 08	20 11				20 29	20 31	20 44	20 46		20 49		20 52		20 57	21 05	21 11			21 28
Cardiff Central [7]	a	19 53	20 12		20 21		20 27	20 31				20 46	20 48	20 58	21 05		21 07		21 10		21 19	21 21	21 31			21 45

		GW	AW	GW	GW	GW	XC	GW	GW	SW		GW	GW	AW	AW	GW FO	GW FX	GW	GW	GW	AW	AW	GW FO	GW FX
		[1] ◇	◇			[1] ◇	[1] ◇	[1] ◇	◇	[1] ◇		[1] ◇	◇	◇		[1] ◇	[1] ◇	◇		[1] ◇	◇		[1] ◇	[1] ◇
									G						H			G				H		
		☕	🛒			☕	🛒	☕				☕				☕	☕			☕			☕	☕
Bath Spa [7]	d	21 00			21 08			21 30	21 35	21 51		22 15	22 26					22 35	23 02	23 20			23 50	23 56
Oldfield Park	d				21 10								22 28						23 05					
Keynsham	d				21 17					21 59			22 35						23 12					
Bristol Temple Meads [10]	a	21 15			21 29			21 44	21 50	22 06		22 30	22 45					22 47	23 21	23 33			00 03	00 10
	d			21 19					21 54									22 54						
Filton Abbey Wood	d			21 30					22 01									23 01						
Bristol Parkway [7]	a																							
	d					21 42										22 46	22 46							
Patchway	d			21 34					22 06									23 06						
Pilning	d																							
Gloucester [7]	d						21 23								22 00							23 13		
Lydney	d														22 19							23 33		
Chepstow	d														22 29							23 42		
Caldicot	d														22 37							23 51		
Severn Tunnel Jn	d			21 45					22 18						22 40			23 17				23 54		
Newport (South Wales)	a			21 58		22 04	22 11		22 37						22 59	23 15	23 16	23 35				00 13		
	d		21 50	21 59		22 05	22 11		22 38					22 46	23 00	23 18	23 18	23 35			23 48	00 14		
Cardiff Central [7]	a		22 06	22 15		22 25	22 31		22 59					23 04	23 21	23 39	23 39	23 58			00 11	00 35		

Saturdays

		AW	GW	AW	GW	AW	AW	XC	GW	GW	GW	AW	XC	GW	GW		AW	GW	SW	GW	AW	AW	GW	GW	AW	XC
			[1] ◇	◇	[1] ◇			[1] ◇	[1] ◇		[1] ◇	◇	[1] ◇						[1]	[1] ◇	◇				◇	[1] ◇
		H				J	K	L	N		N		L		Q							A	U	V		
			☕		☕			🛒	☕		☕	🛒	🛒							☕	🛒				🛒	🛒
Bath Spa [7]	d				01 13										07 07			07 22	07 34	08 00				08 08		
Oldfield Park	d														07 10			07 25	07 37					08 10		
Keynsham	d														07 17			07 32	07 44					08 17		
Bristol Temple Meads [10]	a				01 27										07 29			07 39	07 52	08 15				08 30		
	d				01 34				06 46	06 50				07 21	07 41			07 54					08 20	08 41		
Filton Abbey Wood	d								06 53	07 02				07 30	07 48			08 01					08 31	08 48		
Bristol Parkway [7]	a								06 57		←				07 52									08 52		
	d		00 17						07 11		07 11															
Patchway	d								→					07 34									08 36			
Pilning	d																									
Gloucester [7]	d	23p13					05 50	06 15					07 01									07 58				08 23
Lydney	d	23p33					06 09	06 34					07 20									08 17				
Chepstow	d	23p42					06 19	06 43					07 29									08 27				
Caldicot	d	23p51					06 27	06 52					07 38									08 35				
Severn Tunnel Jn	d	23p54					06 30	06 55		07 14			07 41	07 46								08 38	08 47			
Newport (South Wales)	a	00 13	00 39		02s03		06 42	07 06		07 26	07 32		07 52	07 58				08 26				08 50	09 00			09 05
	d	00 14	00 40	00 50		06 38	06 44	07 06		07 28	07 34	07 38	07 54	07 59			08 01	08 27			08 37	08 52	09 01		09 01	09 06
Cardiff Central [7]	a	00 35	00 55	01 10	02 22	06 54	07 00	07 25		07 44	07 49	07 55	08 13	08 15			08 19	08 45			08 52	09 10	09 21		09 23	09 25

For general notes see front of timetable
For details of catering facilities see Directory of Train Operators

- **A** From Cheltenham Spa (Table 57) to Maesteg (Table 128)
- **B** From Taunton (Table 134)
- **C** From Westbury (Table 123) to Cheltenham Spa (Table 57)
- **D** From Manchester Piccadilly (Table 51)
- **E** From Brighton (Table 123) to Worcester Shrub Hill (Table 57)
- **G** From Portsmouth Harbour (Table 123)
- **H** From Cheltenham Spa (Table 57)
- **J** To Barry Island (Table 130)
- **K** To Maesteg (Table 128)
- **L** From Birmingham New Street (Table 57)
- **N** To Swansea (Table 125)
- **Q** From Salisbury (Table 123) to Gloucester (Table 134)
- **U** From Weston-super-Mare (Table 134)
- **V** From Warminster (Table 123) to Great Malvern (Table 71)

Bath Spa, Bristol and Gloucester → Cardiff

Network Diagram - see first page of Table 132

		GW	GW	GW	AW	AW	GW		GW	GW	XC	GW	GW	GW	GW	GW	AW	AW	GW	XC	GW	GW		GW	GW	GW
		1 ◇	◇	1 ◇	◇		◇		1		1 ◇	◇	1 ◇	◇	1 ◇	1 ◇	◇	◇		1 ◇		1 ◇		◇	1 ◇	1 ◇
						A	B			C		B							D		E					
		🍴		🍴	🛒				🍴		🛒		🍴		🍴	🍴	🛒	🛒		🛒		🍴			🍴	🍴
Bath Spa 7	d	08 25	08 33				08 47		09 00				09 25	09 35		10 00					10 07	10 25		10 35		11 00
Oldfield Park	d						08 49														10 10					
Keynsham	d						08 57														10 17					
Bristol Temple Meads 10	a	08 39	08 45				09 05		09 15			←	09 39	09 47		10 15					10 29	10 39		10 48		11 15
	d		08 54				09 38			09 21		09 38		09 54					10 21		10 41			10 54		
Filton Abbey Wood	d		09 01				→			09 31		09 45		10 01					10 31		10 48			11 01		
Bristol Parkway 7	a											09 49									10 52					
	d			09 07											10 07										11 07	
Patchway	d									09 35									10 36							
Pilning	d																									
Gloucester 7	d					08 58					09 23									10 23						
Lydney	d					09 17																				
Chepstow	d					09 27																				
Caldicot	d					09 35																				
Severn Tunnel Jn	d					09 38				09 47									10 47							
Newport (South Wales)	a		09 24	09 31		09 50				09 59	10 05			10 23	10 31				11 00	11 05				11 24	11 31	
	d		09 24	09 31	09 33	09 52				10 00	10 06			10 23	10 31		10 37	10 57	11 01	11 06				11 24	11 31	
Cardiff Central 7	a		09 42	09 48	09 54	10 10				10 16	10 25			10 42	10 48		10 53	11 20	11 20	11 25				11 43	11 48	

		AW	AW	GW	XC	GW	GW	GW	SW	GW	GW	AW	AW	AW		GW	XC	GW	GW	GW	GW	GW	AW	GW	XC	GW
		◇			1 ◇	◇	1 ◇	◇	1 ◇	1 ◇	1 ◇	◇		◇			1 ◇	◇	1 ◇	◇	1 ◇	1 ◇	◇		1 ◇	◇
			A	D		B							A			D		G						D		B
		🛒			🛒		🍴			🍴	🍴	🛒		🛒			🛒		🍴		🍴	🍴	🛒		🛒	
Bath Spa 7	d					11 08	11 25	11 35	11 46		12 00							12 08	12 25	12 35		13 00				13 18
Oldfield Park	d					11 10												12 10								13 20
Keynsham	d					11 17												12 17								13 28
Bristol Temple Meads 10	a					11 29	11 39	11 47	12 00		12 15							12 29	12 39	12 47		13 15				13 36
	d			11 21		11 41		11 54								12 21		12 41		12 54				13 21		13 41
Filton Abbey Wood	d			11 31		11 48		12 01								12 31		12 48		13 01				13 31		13 48
Bristol Parkway 7	a					11 52												12 52								13 52
	d									12 07											13 07					
Patchway	d			11 35												12 36								13 35		
Pilning	d																									
Gloucester 7	d		10 58		11 23								11 58				12 23								13 23	
Lydney	d		11 17										12 17													
Chepstow	d		11 27										12 27													
Caldicot	d		11 35										12 35													
Severn Tunnel Jn	d		11 38	11 47									12 38			12 46								13 47		
Newport (South Wales)	a		11 50	11 59	12 05			12 23		12 31			12 50			13 00	13 06			13 25	13 31			13 59	14 05	
	d	11 33	11 52	12 00	12 06			12 23		12 31		12 34	12 52	12 59		13 00	13 06			13 25	13 31		13 33	14 00	14 06	
Cardiff Central 7	a	11 54	12 10	12 16	12 25			12 41		12 48		12 54	13 10	13 20		13 21	13 25			13 42	13 48		13 54	14 16	14 25	

		GW	GW	GW	GW	AW		AW	AW	GW	XC	GW	GW	GW	SW	GW	GW	AW	AW	GW	XC		GW	GW	GW	GW
		1 ◇	◇	1 ◇	1 ◇	◇			◇		1 ◇		1 ◇	◇	1 ◇	1 ◇	1 ◇	R			1 ◇		◇	1 ◇	◇	1 ◇
								A		D		H							A	D			B			
		🍴		🍴	🍴	🛒			🛒		🛒		🍴			🍴	🍴	🛒			🛒			🍴		🍴
Bath Spa 7	d	13 25	13 35		14 00							14 08	14 25	14 35	14 46		15 00						15 18	15 25	15 35	
Oldfield Park	d											14 10											15 21			
Keynsham	d											14 17											15 28			
Bristol Temple Meads 10	a	13 40	13 47		14 15							14 29	14 39	14 47	15 05		15 15						15 35	15 39	15 48	
	d		13 54							14 21		14 41		14 54						15 21			15 41		15 54	
Filton Abbey Wood	d		14 01							14 31		14 48		15 01						15 31			15 48		16 01	
Bristol Parkway 7	a											14 52											15 52			
	d			14 07												15 07										16 07
Patchway	d									14 36										15 35						
Pilning	d																			15 41						
Gloucester 7	d							13 58			14 23								14 58		15 23					
Lydney	d							14 17											15 17							
Chepstow	d							14 27											15 27							
Caldicot	d							14 35											15 35							
Severn Tunnel Jn	d							14 38		14 47									15 38	15 49						
Newport (South Wales)	a		14 23	14 31				14 50		14 59	15 06			15 24		15 31			15 50	16 01	16 05				16 23	16 31
	d		14 23	14 31		14 37		14 52	14 59	15 00	15 06			15 24		15 31		15 33	15 52	16 03	16 06				16 23	16 31
Cardiff Central 7	a		14 43	14 48		14 54		15 09	15 21	15 21	15 25			15 42		15 48		15 54	16 07	16 18	16 25				16 41	16 48

For general notes see front of timetable
For details of catering facilities see Directory of Train Operators

- **A** From Cheltenham Spa (Table 57) to Maesteg (Table 128)
- **B** From Weymouth (Table 123) to Gloucester (Table 134)
- **C** From Weston-super-Mare (Table 134)
- **D** From Taunton (Table 134)
- **E** From Southampton Central (Table 123) to Worcester Foregate Street (Table 71)
- **G** From Brighton (Table 123) to Great Malvern (Table 71)
- **H** From Southampton Central (Table 123) to Great Malvern (Table 71)

Bath Spa, Bristol and Gloucester → Cardiff

Network Diagram - see first page of Table 132

		GW	AW	AW	GW	XC	GW	GW	GW	GW	GW	AW	AW		GW	XC	GW	GW	GW	GW	GW	GW	AW	AW	GW	GW
		1◇	R	R		1◇		1◇	◇	1◇	1◇	R				1◇	◇		1◇	◇	1◇	1◇	R			◇
					A		B						C		A		D	E						C	A	G
		🍴	☕	☕		☕		🍴		🍴	🍴	☕				☕			🍴		🍴	🍴	☕			
Bath Spa 7	d	16 00					16 08	16 25	16 35		17 00						17 08	17 08	17 25	17 35		18 00				18 13
Oldfield Park	d						16 10										17 10	17 10								18 15
Keynsham	d						16 17										17 17	17 17								18 23
Bristol Temple Meads 10	a	16 15					16 30	16 39	16 47		17 15						17 28	17 29	17 39	17 47		18 15				18 35
	d				16 21		16 41		16 54						17 21		17 41	17 41		17 54					18 21	18 41
Filton Abbey Wood	d				16 31		16 48		17 01						17 31		17 48	17 48		18 01					18 31	18 48
Bristol Parkway 7	a						16 52										17 52	17 52								18 52
	d									17 07											18 07					
Patchway	d				16 36										17 35										18 35	
Pilning	d																									
Gloucester 7	d					16 23							16 58			17 23								17 58		
Lydney	d												17 17											18 17		
Chepstow	d												17 27											18 27		
Caldicot	d												17 35											18 35		
Severn Tunnel Jn	d				16 47				17 15				17 38		17 47					18 14				18 38	18 47	
Newport (South Wales)	a				17 00	17 05			17 26	17 31			17 50		17 59	18 05				18 25	18 31			18 50	18 59	
	d		16 33	16 59	17 01	17 06			17 26	17 31		17 33	17 52		18 00	18 06				18 25	18 31		18 39	18 52	19 00	
Cardiff Central 7	a		16 54	17 18	17 20	17 25			17 45	17 48		17 54	18 10		18 16	18 25				18 43	18 48		18 54	19 10	19 16	

		GW	AW	XC	GW		GW	AW	GW	AW	GW	XC	GW	GW	GW	GW	GW	GW	AW	AW		XC	AW	GW	XC	GW
		1◇	◇	1◇	◇		1◇	R	1◇			1◇		1◇	◇	◇	1◇	1◇	R			1◇	◇	1◇	1◇	
										C	A		H							C		J		K		L
		🍴	☕	☕			🍴	☕	🍴			☕		🍴			🍴	🍴	☕			☕	☕	🍴	☕	
Bath Spa 7	d	18 25			18 35		19 00						19 08	19 25	19 35	19 47	20 01									20 18
Oldfield Park	d												19 10			19 49										20 20
Keynsham	d												19 17			19 57										20 28
Bristol Temple Meads 10	a	18 39			18 47		19 15						19 29	19 40	19 47	20 04	20 15									20 35
	d				18 54						19 21		19 41		19 54							20 21				20 41
Filton Abbey Wood	d				19 01						19 28		19 48		20 01							20 28				20 48
Bristol Parkway 7	a												19 52													20 52
	d								19 13									20 07						20 42		
Patchway	d										19 33											20 32				
Pilning	d																									
Gloucester 7	d			18 30						18 58		19 23								19 58					20 23	
Lydney	d									19 17										20 17						
Chepstow	d									19 27										20 27						
Caldicot	d									19 34										20 35						
Severn Tunnel Jn	d									19 37	19 44									20 38		20 45				
Newport (South Wales)	a			19 11	19 23				19 36	19 50	19 56	20 05			20 23			20 31		20 50		20 54		21 04	21 09	
	d		19 04	19 13	19 23			19 30	19 36	19 52	19 57	20 06			20 23			20 31	20 39	20 52		20 56	20 59	21 05	21 11	
Cardiff Central 7	a		19 26	19 32	19 42			19 48	19 53	20 11	20 13	20 25			20 41			20 48	20 54	21 09		21 16	21 20	21 21	21 32	

		GW	GW	GW	GW	GW	AW	GW	XC	GW	GW	SW		AW	GW	AW	GW	GW	GW	GW	GW	AW	GW	AW		
		1◇	◇	1◇	1◇		◇		1◇	1◇	◇	1◇		◇	1◇		1◇	◇	◇	1◇		◇	1◇			
								A			N	Q				U			N			V				
		🍴		🍴	🍴		☕		☕	🍴					🍴		🍴			🍴			🍴			
Bath Spa 7	d	20 25	20 35		21 00	21 08				21 30	21 39	21 51					22 00	22 26	22 35	23 00	23 08					
Oldfield Park	d					21 10												22 28			23 10					
Keynsham	d					21 17						21 59						22 36			23 17					
Bristol Temple Meads 10	a	20 42	20 47		21 15	21 26				21 45	21 51	22 06					22 15	22 45	22 50	23 15	23 28					
	d		20 54					21 28			21 54								22 54							
Filton Abbey Wood	d		21 01					21 36			22 01								23 01							
Bristol Parkway 7	a																									
	d			21 07											22 11								23 29			
Patchway	d							21 40			22 06								23 06							
Pilning	d																									
Gloucester 7	d								21 23							21 58								23 09		
Lydney	d															22 17								23 28		
Chepstow	d															22 27								23 38		
Caldicot	d															22 35								23 46		
Severn Tunnel Jn	d							21 52			22 19					22 38			23 17					23 49		
Newport (South Wales)	a		21 23	21 31				22 09	22 14		22 36				22 46	22 55			23 34				23 58	00 09		
	d		21 24	21 31			21 50	22 10	22 15		22 36			22 42	22 46	22 57			23 35			23 45	23 58	00 10		
Cardiff Central 7	a		21 41	21 48			22 09	22 29	22 39		22 56			23 05	23 06	23 18			23 54			00 08	00 19	00 30		

For general notes see front of timetable
For details of catering facilities see Directory of Train Operators

- **A** From Taunton (Table 134)
- **B** From Warminster (Table 123) to Great Malvern (Table 71)
- **C** From Cheltenham Spa (Table 57) to Maesteg (Table 128)
- **D** From 12 September. From Weymouth (Table 123) to Gloucester (Table 134)
- **E** Until 5 September. From Warminster (Table 123) to Gloucester (Table 134)
- **G** Until 5 September from Weymouth, from 12 September from Warminster (Table 123) to Great Malvern (Table 71)
- **H** From 12 September. From Westbury (Table 123) to Cheltenham Spa (Table 57)
- **J** From Manchester Piccadilly (Table 51)
- **K** From 12 September
- **L** From Brighton (Table 123) to Cheltenham Spa (Table 57)
- **N** From Portsmouth Harbour (Table 123)
- **Q** From London Waterloo (Table 160)
- **U** From Cheltenham Spa (Table 57)
- **V** From 18 July

Table 132

Sundays

until 12 July

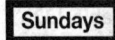

Bath Spa, Bristol and Gloucester → Cardiff

Network Diagram - see first page of Table 132

		AW	AW	GW	GW	GW	GW	GW	GW		GW	AW	AW	AW	GW	XC	GW	GW		GW	AW	XC	AW	GW	AW	GW
				1 ◇	1 ◇	◇	1 ◇	1 ◇			1 ◇		◇		1 ◇	1 ◇	◇	1 ◇		1 ◇	◇	1 ◇		1 ◇	R	1 ◇
						A						B					C						D			
			bus	☕	☕		☕	☕			☕		🛒		☕	🛒	🛒	☕		☕		🛒		☕	🛒	☕
Bath Spa 7	d			00 10	01 08		09 46		10 25		10 41						11 25	11 41						12 41		
Oldfield Park	d								10 28								11 28									
Keynsham	d								10 35								11 35									
Bristol Temple Meads 10	a			00 25	01 21		09 59		10 43		10 56						11 43	11 57						12 54		
	d					09 50											11 48									
Filton Abbey Wood	d					10 00											11 55									
Bristol Parkway 7	a																									
	d							10 17							11 07					12 16						13 16
Patchway	d																12 00									
Pilning	d																									
Gloucester 7	d	23p09												10 33		11 04						12 23	12 33			
Lydney	d	23p28												10 52									12 52			
Chepstow	d	23p38												11 02									13 02			
Caldicot	d	23p46												11 10									13 10			
Severn Tunnel Jn	d	23p49				10 13								11 13			12 11						13 13			
Newport (South Wales)	a	00 09				10 25		10 38						11 25	11 30	11 45	12 24			12 37		13 04	13 25			13 39
	d	00 10	00 22			10 27		10 40				10 56	11 02	11 27	11 32	11 47	12 24			12 39	12 52	13 06	13 27		13 36	13 39
Cardiff Central 7	a	00 30	00 52			10 42		10 55				11 12	11 17	11 45	11 47	12 06	12 39			12 54	13 12	13 25	13 45		13 50	13 56

		XC	GW	GW		AW	GW	XC	AW	GW	AW	GW	SW		GW	AW	XC	GW	GW	AW	GW	XC		GW	GW	GW
						R										R				R						
		1 ◇	◇	1 ◇			1 ◇	1 ◇	◇	◇		1 ◇	1 ◇		1 ◇		1 ◇	◇	1 ◇		1 ◇	1 ◇			◇	1 ◇
											D														C	
		🛒	🛒	☕		🛒	☕	🛒				☕			☕	🛒	🛒	🛒	☕	🛒	☕	🛒			🛒	☕
Bath Spa 7	d		13 26	13 41						14 25		14 41	14 56					15 28	15 41					16 10	16 28	16 41
Oldfield Park	d		13 29							14 27														16 12		
Keynsham	d		13 36							14 35														16 20		
Bristol Temple Meads 10	a		13 43	13 56						14 42		14 55	15 08					15 40	15 55					16 28	16 41	16 55
	d		13 48							14 48								15 48							16 48	
Filton Abbey Wood	d		13 55							14 55								15 55							16 55	
Bristol Parkway 7	a																									
	d						14 16								15 16						16 16					
Patchway	d																								17 00	
Pilning	d																									
Gloucester 7	d	13 23						14 23			14 33						15 23					16 23				
Lydney	d										14 52															
Chepstow	d										15 02															
Caldicot	d										15 10															
Severn Tunnel Jn	d		14 08							15 08	15 13							16 08							17 11	
Newport (South Wales)	a	14 04	14 21				14 39	15 04		15 21	15 25				15 37		16 04	16 21			16 39	17 04			17 24	
	d	14 06	14 21			14 26	14 39	15 06	15 10	15 21	15 27				15 39	15 43	16 06	16 21		16 34	16 39	17 06			17 24	
Cardiff Central 7	a	14 25	14 37			14 46	14 56	15 26	15 30	15 38	15 45				15 54	16 00	16 25	16 39		16 56	16 56	17 25			17 40	

		AW	AW	GW	XC	GW	GW	AW		GW	XC	GW	GW	AW	GW	GW	GW		GW	AW	XC	GW	GW	GW	AW	GW
		R						R												R					R	
				1 ◇	1 ◇	◇	1 ◇			1 ◇	1 ◇		◇		1 ◇	1 ◇	◇		1 ◇		1 ◇	◇	1 ◇	◇		1 ◇
			D											D								C				
		🛒		☕	🛒	🛒	☕	🛒		☕	🛒		🛒		☕	☕			☕	🛒	🛒	🛒	☕		🛒	☕
Bath Spa 7	d					17 26	17 44					18 10	18 25		18 41		19 04		19 14			19 28	19 41	20 02		
Oldfield Park	d					17 29						18 13					19 06							20 04		
Keynsham	d					17 36						18 20					19 14							20 13		
Bristol Temple Meads 10	a					17 43	17 57					18 28	18 38		18 55		19 22		19 28			19 40	19 55	20 20		
	d					17 48							18 48									19 48				
Filton Abbey Wood	d					17 55							18 55									19 55				
Bristol Parkway 7	a																									
	d			17 18						18 18						19 18										20 18
Patchway	d																					20 00				
Pilning	d																									
Gloucester 7	d		16 33		17 23						18 23			18 33							19 28					
Lydney	d		16 52											18 52												
Chepstow	d		17 02											19 02												
Caldicot	d		17 11											19 09												
Severn Tunnel Jn	d		17 14			18 08							19 08	19 12								20 11				
Newport (South Wales)	a		17 31	17 39	18 04	18 21				18 41	19 04		19 21	19 25		19 39					20 09	20 24				20 39
	d	17 29	17 32	17 39	18 06	18 21		18 34		18 41	19 06		19 21	19 27		19 39				19 44	20 11	20 24			20 25	20 41
Cardiff Central 7	a	17 43	17 51	17 56	18 25	18 39		18 55		18 58	19 25		19 38	19 47		19 56				20 05	20 30	20 40			20 49	20 56

For general notes see front of timetable
For details of catering facilities see Directory of Train Operators

A From Exeter St Davids (Table 135)
B To Barry Island (Table 130)
C From Portsmouth Harbour (Table 123)
D From Cheltenham Spa (Table 57)

Table 132

Sundays

until 12 July

Bath Spa, Bristol and Gloucester → Cardiff

Network Diagram - see first page of Table 132

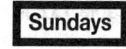

		XC	AW [R]		GW	AW	GW	SW	GW	GW	AW [R]	GW		AW	GW	GW	GW	GW	GW	AW	GW	GW	AW	GW		
		[1] ◇			◇	A	[1] ◇	[1] ◇ B	[1] ◇	◇		[1] ◇		◇	◇ C	[1] ◇	[1] ◇	◇	◇		[1] ◇	[1] ◇	◇	[1] ◇		
		[trolley]			[trolley]		[buffet]		[buffet]		[trolley]	[buffet]			[trolley]	[buffet]	[buffet]		[trolley]		[buffet]	[buffet]		[buffet]		
Bath Spa [7]	d				20 28		20 41	21 00	21 06	21 17					21 28	21 41		22 16	22 28		22 42			23 56		
Oldfield Park	d									21 19								22 18								
Keynsham	d							21 08		21 27								22 27								
Bristol Temple Meads [10]	a				20 40		20 55	21 16	21 22	21 34					21 40	21 55		22 34	22 41		22 58			00 10		
	d				20 48										21 48				22 48							
Filton Abbey Wood	d				20 55										21 57				22 55							
Bristol Parkway [7]	a																									
	d											21 18					22 19					23 18				
Patchway	d														22 02											
Pilning	d																									
Gloucester [7]	d	20 23				20 33														22 33						
Lydney	d					20 52														22 52						
Chepstow	d					21 02														23 02						
Caldicot	d					21 10														23 10						
Severn Tunnel Jn	d				21 08	21 13									22 13				23 10	23 13						
Newport (South Wales)	a	21 04			21 21	21 25						21 44			22 33		22 46		23 28	23 35		23 46				
	d	21 06	21 08		21 21	21 27					21 41	21 45		22 31	22 34		22 47		23 28	23 35		23 47	23 53			
Cardiff Central [7]	a	21 25	21 30		21 38	21 43					22 05	22 04		22 57	22 58		23 07		23 49	23 56		00 06	00 19			

Sundays

19 July to 6 September

		AW	AW	GW	GW	GW	GW	GW	GW		AW	AW	AW	GW	XC	GW	GW	GW		GW	AW	XC	AW	GW	AW [R]	GW
							◇ D	[1] ◇			E	◇		[1] ◇	[1] ◇		◇ C	[1] ◇		[1] ◇	◇	[1] ◇	A	[1] ◇		[1] ◇
				[bus]	[bus]	[bus]		[buffet]				[trolley]		[buffet]	[trolley]	[bus]	[trolley]	[buffet]		[buffet]		[trolley]		[buffet]	[trolley]	[buffet]
Bath Spa [7]	d			00 59	01 53	09 03			10 25							11 10	11 25			12 01				13 01		
Oldfield Park	d								10 28								11 28									
Keynsham	d								10 35								11 35									
Bristol Temple Meads [10]	a			01 29	02 23	09 43			10 43							11 40	11 43			12 16				13 13		
	d						09 50										11 48									
Filton Abbey Wood	d						10 00										11 55									
Bristol Parkway [7]	a																									
	d							10 17						11 07				12 16								13 16
Patchway	d																12 00									
Pilning	d																									
Gloucester [7]	d		23p09										10 33		11 23							12 23	12 33			
Lydney	d		23p28										10 52										12 52			
Chepstow	d		23p38										11 02										13 02			
Caldicot	d		23p46										11 10										13 10			
Severn Tunnel Jn	d		23p49				10 13						11 13				12 11						13 13			
Newport (South Wales)	a		00 09				10 25	10 38					11 25	11 30	12 04		12 24	12 37				13 04	13 25			13 39
	d	00 05	00 10				10 27	10 40			10 56	11 02	11 27	11 32	12 06		12 24	12 39			12 52	13 06	13 27		13 36	13 39
Cardiff Central [7]	a	00 24	00 30				10 42	10 55			11 12	11 17	11 45	11 47	12 25		12 39	12 54			13 12	13 25	13 45		13 50	13 56

		XC	GW	GW		AW [R]	GW	XC	AW	GW	AW	SW	GW		GW	AW [R]	XC	GW	GW	AW [R]	GW	XC		GW	GW	GW
		[1] ◇	◇	[1] ◇			[1] ◇	[1] ◇	◇	◇	A	[1] ◇	[1] ◇		[1] ◇		[1] ◇	◇	[1] ◇		[1] ◇	[1] ◇			◇ C	[1] ◇
		[trolley]	[trolley]	[buffet]		[trolley]	[buffet]	[trolley]					[buffet]		[buffet]	[trolley]	[trolley]	[trolley]	[buffet]	[trolley]	[buffet]	[trolley]			[trolley]	[buffet]
Bath Spa [7]	d		13 26	14 01						14 25		14 56	15 01					15 28	15 41					16 10	16 28	16 41
Oldfield Park	d		13 29							14 27														16 12		
Keynsham	d		13 36							14 35														16 20		
Bristol Temple Meads [10]	a		13 43	14 16						14 42		15 08	15 15					15 40	15 55					16 28	16 41	16 55
	d		13 48							14 48								15 48							16 48	
Filton Abbey Wood	d		13 55							14 55								15 55							16 55	
Bristol Parkway [7]	a																									
	d						14 16								15 16						16 16					
Patchway	d																								17 00	
Pilning	d																									
Gloucester [7]	d	13 23						14 17			14 33						15 23					16 23				
Lydney	d										14 52															
Chepstow	d										15 02															
Caldicot	d										15 10															
Severn Tunnel Jn	d		14 08							15 08	15 13							16 08							17 11	
Newport (South Wales)	a	14 04	14 21				14 39	14 58		15 21	15 25				15 37		16 04	16 21			16 39	17 04			17 24	
	d	14 06	14 21			14 26	14 39	15 00	15 10	15 21	15 27				15 39	15 43	16 06	16 21		16 34	16 39	17 06			17 24	
Cardiff Central [7]	a	14 25	14 37			14 46	14 56	15 19	15 30	15 38	15 45				15 54	16 00	16 25	16 39		16 56	16 56	17 25			17 40	

For general notes see front of timetable
For details of catering facilities see Directory of Train Operators

A From Cheltenham Spa (Table 57)
B From London Waterloo (Table 160)
C From Portsmouth Harbour (Table 123)
D From Exeter St Davids (Table 135)
E To Barry Island (Table 130)

Sundays

19 July to 6 September

Bath Spa, Bristol and Gloucester → Cardiff

Network Diagram - see first page of Table 132

		AW	AW	GW	XC	GW	GW	AW	GW	XC	GW	GW	AW	GW	GW	GW	GW	AW	XC	GW	GW	GW	AW	GW
		[R]		[1] ◇	[1] ◇	◇	[1] ◇	[R]	[1] ◇	[1] ◇		◇		[1] ◇	[1] ◇	◇	[1] ◇	[R]	[1] ◇	◇	[1] ◇	◇	[R]	[1] ◇
			A										A							B				
		T		P	T	T	P	T	P	T		T		P	P		P	T	T	T	P		T	P
Bath Spa 7	d					17 26	17 44				18 10	18 25		18 41		19 04	19 14			19 28	19 41	20 02		
Oldfield Park	d					17 29					18 13					19 06						20 04		
Keynsham	d					17 36					18 20					19 14						20 13		
Bristol Temple Meads 10	a					17 43	17 57				18 28	18 38		18 55		19 22	19 28			19 40	19 55	20 20		
	d					17 48						18 48								19 48				
Filton Abbey Wood	d					17 55						18 55								19 55				
Bristol Parkway 7	a																							
	d			17 18					18 18						19 18									20 18
Patchway	d																			20 00				
Pilning	d																							
Gloucester 7	d		16 33		17 23					18 23			18 33						19 28					
Lydney	d		16 52										18 52											
Chepstow	d		17 02										19 02											
Caldicot	d		17 11										19 09											
Severn Tunnel Jn	d		17 14			18 08						19 08	19 12							20 11				
Newport (South Wales)	a		17 31	17 39	18 04	18 21			18 41	19 04		19 21	19 25		19 39				20 09	20 24				20 39
	d	17 29	17 32	17 39	18 06	18 21		18 34	18 41	19 06		19 21	19 27		19 39			19 44	20 11	20 24			20 25	20 41
Cardiff Central 7	a	17 43	17 51	17 56	18 25	18 39		18 55	18 58	19 25		19 38	19 47		19 56			20 05	20 30	20 40			20 49	20 56

		XC	AW	GW	AW	GW	SW	GW	GW	AW	GW	AW	GW	GW	GW	GW	GW	AW	GW	GW	AW	GW
		[1] ◇	[R]	◇		[1] ◇	[1] ◇	[1] ◇	◇	[R]	[1] ◇	◇	◇	[1] ◇	[1] ◇	◇	◇		[1] ◇	[1] ◇	◇	[1] ◇
					A		C						B									
		T		T		P		P		T	P		T	P	P		T		P	P		P
Bath Spa 7	d			20 28		20 41	21 00	21 06	21 17				21 28	21 41		22 16	22 28		22 42			23 56
Oldfield Park	d								21 19							22 18						
Keynsham	d						21 08		21 27							22 27						
Bristol Temple Meads 10	a			20 40		20 55	21 16	21 22	21 34				21 40	21 55		22 34	22 41		22 58			00 10
	d			20 48									21 48				22 48					
Filton Abbey Wood	d			20 55									21 57				22 55					
Bristol Parkway 7	a																					
	d										21 18				22 19					23 18		
Patchway	d												22 02									
Pilning	d																					
Gloucester 7	d	20 23			20 33													22 33				
Lydney	d				20 52													22 52				
Chepstow	d				21 02													23 02				
Caldicot	d				21 10													23 10				
Severn Tunnel Jn	d			21 08	21 13								22 13				23 10	23 13				
Newport (South Wales)	a	21 04		21 21	21 25						21 44		22 33		22 46		23 28	23 35		23 46		
	d	21 06	21 08	21 21	21 27					21 41	21 45	22 31	22 34		22 47		23 28	23 35		23 47	23 53	
Cardiff Central 7	a	21 25	21 30	21 38	21 43					22 05	22 04	22 57	22 58		23 07		23 49	23 56		00 06	00 19	

Sundays

from 13 September

		AW	AW	GW	GW	AW	GW	GW	GW	GW	AW	AW	XC	GW	GW	AW	XC	GW	XC	GW	GW	AW
				[1] ◇	[1] ◇	◇	◇	[1] ◇	[1] ◇		◇		[1] ◇	[1] ◇	[1] ◇		[1] ◇	◇	[1] ◇	[1] ◇	[1] ◇	◇
							D					E	G			G	E	B	G			
				P	P	T		P	P		T		T	P	P		T	T	T	P	P	
Bath Spa 7	d			00 10	01 08			09 39		10 25				10 44				11 25		11 41		
Oldfield Park	d									10 28								11 28				
Keynsham	d									10 35								11 35				
Bristol Temple Meads 10	a			00 25	01 21			09 52		10 43				10 58				11 43		11 57		
	d						09 50											11 48				
Filton Abbey Wood	d						10 00											11 55				
Bristol Parkway 7	a																					
	d								10 09						11 07						12 13	
Patchway	d																	12 00				
Pilning	d																					
Gloucester 7	d		23p09									10 33	10 40			10 48	11 23		11 40			
Lydney	d		23p28									10 52				11 07						
Chepstow	d		23p38									11 02				11 17						
Caldicot	d		23p46									11 10				11 25						
Severn Tunnel Jn	d		23p49				10 13					11 13				11 28		12 11				
Newport (South Wales)	a		00 09				10 25		10 30			11 25	11 24		11 30	11 40	12 04	12 24	12 28		12 34	
	d	00 05	00 10			09 10	10 27		10 32		11 02	11 27	11 26		11 32	11 42	12 06	12 24	12 29		12 35	12 52
Cardiff Central 7	a	00 24	00 30			09 25	10 42		10 47		11 17	11 45	11 47		11 47	12 00	12 25	12 39	12 49		12 51	13 12

For general notes see front of timetable
For details of catering facilities see Directory of Train Operators

A From Cheltenham Spa (Table 57)
B From Portsmouth Harbour (Table 123)
C From London Waterloo (Table 160)
D From Exeter St Davids (Table 135)
E Until 1 November
G From 8 November

Sundays

from 13 September

Bath Spa, Bristol and Gloucester → Cardiff

Network Diagram - see first page of Table 132

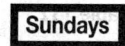

		XC	XC	AW	GW	GW	AW	AW	XC	GW	GW	AW	XC	GW	XC	AW	GW	AW	GW	SW	GW	XC
		1◇	1◇		1◇	1◇	R		1◇	◇	1◇	R	1◇	1◇	1◇	◇	◇		1◇	1◇	1◇	1◇
		A	B	C				D	A				B		A			E				B
		🛒	🛒		☕	☕	🛒		🛒	🛒	☕	🛒		☕	🛒				☕		☕	🛒
Bath Spa 7	d				12 41					13 26	13 41						14 25		14 41	14 56		
Oldfield Park	d									13 29							14 27					
Keynsham	d									13 36							14 35					
Bristol Temple Meads 10	a				12 54					13 43	13 56						14 42		14 55	15 08		
	d									13 48							14 48					
Filton Abbey Wood	d									13 55							14 55					
Bristol Parkway 7	a																					
	d					13 13								14 13							15 13	
Patchway	d																					
Pilning	d																					
Gloucester 7	d	12 23	12 40	12 33				12 53	13 23				13 40		14 24			14 33				14 56
Lydney	d			12 52				13 12										14 52				
Chepstow	d			13 02				13 22										15 02				
Caldicot	d			13 10				13 30										15 10				
Severn Tunnel Jn	d			13 13				13 33		14 08							15 08	15 13				
Newport (South Wales)	a	13 04	13 22	13 25		13 34		13 45	14 04	14 21			14 30	14 34	15 05		15 21	15 25			15 34	15 39
	d	13 06	13 23	13 27		13 35	13 41	13 47	14 06	14 21		14 26	14 31	14 35	15 06	15 10	15 21	15 27			15 35	15 41
Cardiff Central 7	a	13 25	13 44	13 45		13 51	13 57	14 05	14 25	14 40		14 46	14 52	14 51	15 26	15 30	15 38	15 45			15 51	16 00

		AW	XC	GW	GW	GW	AW	GW	XC	XC	GW	AW	XC	GW	AW	AW	GW	AW	XC	GW	GW	AW
		R	1◇	◇	1◇	◇	R	1◇	1◇	1◇	◇	R	1◇	1◇	R		1◇		1◇	◇	1◇	R
			A						B	A	G	A	B		B	C		D	A			
		🛒	🛒	🛒	☕		🛒	☕	🛒	🛒	🛒	🛒	🛒	☕	🛒		☕		🛒	🛒	☕	🛒
Bath Spa 7	d			15 28	15 41	15 58					16 28			16 41						17 26	17 44	
Oldfield Park	d					16 00														17 29		
Keynsham	d					16 08														17 36		
Bristol Temple Meads 10	a			15 40	15 55	16 16					16 41			16 55						17 43	17 57	
	d			15 48							16 48									17 48		
Filton Abbey Wood	d			15 55							16 55									17 55		
Bristol Parkway 7	a																					
	d							16 13									17 13					
Patchway	d										17 00											
Pilning	d																					
Gloucester 7	d		15 23						15 52	16 23			16 39			16 33		16 53	17 23			
Lydney	d															16 52		17 12				
Chepstow	d															17 02		17 22				
Caldicot	d															17 11		17 30				
Severn Tunnel Jn	d			16 08							17 11					17 14		17 33		18 08		
Newport (South Wales)	a		16 04	16 21				16 39	16 44	17 04	17 24		17 28			17 31	17 38	17 45	18 04	18 21		
	d	15 43	16 06	16 21			16 34	16 39	16 46	17 06	17 24	17 29	17 29		17 35	17 32	17 39	17 47	18 06	18 21		18 34
Cardiff Central 7	a	16 00	16 25	16 39			16 56	16 56	17 07	17 25	17 40	17 43	17 49		17 49	17 51	17 54	18 06	18 25	18 39		18 55

		GW	XC	XC	GW	XC	AW	GW	GW	GW	GW	AW	AW	XC	GW	GW	AW	GW	XC	GW	XC	AW
		1◇	1◇	1◇	◇	1◇		1◇	1◇	◇	1◇		R	1◇	◇	1◇	R	1◇	1◇	◇	1◇	R
			B	A		B	C					D		A	G				B		A	
		☕	🛒	🛒	🛒	🛒		☕	☕		☕		🛒	🛒	🛒	☕	🛒	☕	🛒		🛒	🛒
Bath Spa 7	d				18 25			18 41		19 04	19 14				19 28	19 41				20 02		
Oldfield Park	d									19 06										20 04		
Keynsham	d									19 14										20 13		
Bristol Temple Meads 10	a				18 38			18 55		19 22	19 28				19 40	19 55				20 20		
	d				18 48										19 48							
Filton Abbey Wood	d				18 55										19 55							
Bristol Parkway 7	a																					
	d	18 13							19 13									20 13				
Patchway	d														20 00							
Pilning	d																					
Gloucester 7	d		17 48	18 23		18 39	18 33					18 48		19 28					19 52		20 23	
Lydney	d						18 52					19 07										
Chepstow	d						19 02					19 17										
Caldicot	d						19 09					19 27										
Severn Tunnel Jn	d				19 08		19 12					19 30			20 11							
Newport (South Wales)	a	18 39	18 42	19 04	19 21	19 25	19 25		19 37			19 43		20 09	20 24			20 34	20 39		21 04	
	d	18 39	18 44	19 06	19 21	19 26	19 27		19 39			19 44	19 44	20 11	20 24		20 25	20 36	20 41		21 06	21 08
Cardiff Central 7	a	18 57	19 04	19 25	19 38	19 46	19 47		19 54			20 05	20 05	20 30	20 40		20 49	20 51	21 00		21 25	21 30

For general notes see front of timetable
For details of catering facilities see Directory of Train Operators

- **A** Until 1 November
- **B** From 8 November
- **C** Until 1 November. From Cheltenham Spa (Table 57)
- **D** From 8 November. From Cheltenham Spa (Table 57)
- **E** From Cheltenham Spa (Table 57)
- **G** From Portsmouth Harbour (Table 123)

Table 132

Sundays

from 13 September

Bath Spa, Bristol and Gloucester → Cardiff

Network Diagram - see first page of Table 132

		GW	AW	GW	GW	SW	GW	GW	AW	AW	GW	GW	GW	GW	GW	AW	GW	GW	AW	GW
									R											
		◇		1 ◇	1 ◇	1 ◇	1 ◇	◇		◇	◇	1 ◇	1 ◇	◇	◇		1 ◇	1 ◇	◇	1 ◇
			A			B					C									
		🛒		☕	☕		☕		🛒		🛒	☕	☕		🛒		☕	☕		☕
Bath Spa 7	d	20 28		20 41		21 00	21 06	21 17			21 28	21 41		22 16	22 28		22 42			23 56
Oldfield Park	d							21 19						22 18						
Keynsham	d					21 08		21 27						22 27						
Bristol Temple Meads 10	a	20 40		20 55		21 16	21 22	21 34			21 40	21 55		22 34	22 41		22 58			00 10
	d	20 48									21 48				22 48					
Filton Abbey Wood	d	20 55									21 57				22 55					
Bristol Parkway 7	a																			
	d				21 13								22 13					23 18		
Patchway	d										22 02									
Pilning	d																			
Gloucester 7	d		20 33													22 33				
Lydney	d		20 52													22 52				
Chepstow	d		21 02													23 02				
Caldicot	d		21 10													23 10				
Severn Tunnel Jn	d	21 08	21 13								22 13				23 10	23 13				
Newport (South Wales)	a	21 21	21 25		21 34						22 33		22 40		23 28	23 35		23 46		
	d	21 21	21 27		21 36				21 41	22 31	22 34		22 41		23 28	23 35		23 47	23 53	
Cardiff Central 7	a	21 38	21 43		21 51				22 05	22 57	22 58		23 01		23 49	23 56		00 06	00 19	

For general notes see front of timetable
For details of catering facilities see
Directory of Train Operators

A From Cheltenham Spa (Table 57)
B From London Waterloo (Table 160)
C From Portsmouth Harbour (Table 123)

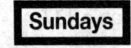

Bristol → Avonmouth and Severn Beach

Network Diagram - see first page of Table 132

Mondays to Fridays

Miles	Station		GW	GW	GW	GW	GW	GW	GW	GW	GW	GW ◇	GW	GW	GW	GW ◇	GW	GW	GW	GW	GW	GW	GW	GW	GW	GW
0	**Bristol Temple Meads** 10	d	05 25	05 49	06 22	06 31	06 50	07 05	07 19	07 46	08 03	08 10	08 36	08 41	08 47	09 10	09 15	09 46	10 03	10 34	10 46	11 16	11 46	12 03	12 34	12 46
1	Lawrence Hill	d	05 28		06 25	06 34	06 54	07 07	07 22	07 50	08 05	08 13	08 38	08a44		09 13	09 17	09 49		10 36	10 49	11 18	11 49		12 36	12 49
1½	Stapleton Road	d	05 30	05 53	06a27	06 36	06a56	07 09	07a24	07a52	08 07	08a15	08 40		08a49	09a15	09 19	09a51	10 07	10 38	10a51	11 20	11a51	12 07	12 38	12a51
2¾	Montpelier	d	05 34	05 56		06 40		07 14			08 12		08 45				09 24		10 11	10 43		11 24		12 11	12 43	
3¼	Redland	d	05 36	05 58		06 42		07 16			08 14		08 47				09 26		10 13	10 45		11 26		12 13	12 45	
4	Clifton Down	d	05 39	06 01		06 46		07 19			08 18		08 52				09 30		10 18	10 49		11 29		12 18	12 49	
6	Sea Mills	d	05 43	06 05		06 50		07 23			08 22		08 56				09 34		10 22	10 53		11 33		12 22	12 53	
7¼	Shirehampton	d	05 46	06 09		06 53		07 26			08 25		08 59				09 37		10 25	10 56		11 37		12 25	12 56	
9	Avonmouth 2	d	05 50	06a14		06 57		07 31			08a31		09a05				09 41		10a31	11a02		11 40		12a31	13a02	
10	St Andrews Road	d	05x53			07x00		07x34									09x44					11x44				
13½	**Severn Beach**	a	06 02			07 08		07 42									09 52					11 53				

Station		GW	GW	GW	GW	GW	GW	GW	GW	GW	GW	GW	GW	GW	GW	GW	GW	GW	GW	GW	GW	GW	GW	GW
Bristol Temple Meads 10	d	13 15	13 46	14 03	14 34	14 46	15 18	15 46	16 03	16 15	16 34	16 46	17 10	17 16	17 46	18 04	18 21	18 48	19 21	19 33	19 46	20 34	21 19	22 15
Lawrence Hill	d	13 18	13 49		14 36	14 49		15 49	16 05	16 17	16 36	16 49	17 12	17 18	17 49	18 07	18 24	18 51	19 23	19 36	19 49	20 37	21 22	22 18
Stapleton Road	d	13 20	13a51	14 07	14 38	14a51		15a51	16 06	16a19	16 38	16a51	17a15	17 20	17a51	18 09	18a26	18 53	19a25	19 38	19a51	20 39	21a24	22 19
Montpelier	d	13 23		14 11	14 43		15 24		16 11		16 43			17 24		18 13		18 57		19 41		20 42		22 23
Redland	d	13 25		14 13	14 45		15 26		16 13		16 45			17 26		18 15		18 59		19 43		20 44		22 25
Clifton Down	d	13 29		14 18	14 49		15 29		16 18		16 49			17 29		18 18		19b08		19 46		20 47		22 29
Sea Mills	d	13 33		14 22	14 53		15 33		16 22		16 53			17 33		18 22		19 12		19 50		20 51		22 33
Shirehampton	d	13 37		14 25	14 56		15 37		16 25		16 56			17 37		18 26		19 16		19 54		20 55		22 36
Avonmouth 2	d	13 40		14a31	15a02		15 40		16a31		17a02			17 40		18 30		19a21		19a59		20 59		22 40
St Andrews Road	d	13x44					15x44							17x44		18x33						21x02		22x43
Severn Beach	a	13 52					15 53							17 53		18 41						21 11		22 52

Saturdays

Station		GW	GW	GW	GW	GW	GW	GW	GW (bus)	GW	GW	GW	GW	GW	GW	GW	GW (bus)	GW
Bristol Temple Meads 10	d	06 03	06 34	06 50	07 16	07 46	08 03	08 20		08 34	08 45	09 16	09 21	09 45	10 03	10 21		10 34
Lawrence Hill	d		06 36	06 53	07 18	07 50	08 05	08 23		08 36	08 48	09 18		09 48				10 36
Stapleton Road	d	06 06	06 38	06a55	07 20	07a52	08 07	08a25		08 38	08a50	09 20	09a24	09a50	10 05	10a25		10 38
Montpelier	d	06 11	06 43		07 24		08 10			08 42		09 24			10 10			10 42
Redland	d	06 13	06 45		07 26		08 12			08 44		09 26			10 12			10 44
Clifton Down	d	06 17	06 49		07 29		08 17			08 48		09 29			10 16			10 48
Sea Mills	d	06 21	06 53		07 33		08 21			08 52		09 33			10 20			10 52
Shirehampton	d	06 25	06 56		07 37		08 25			08 56		09 37			10 24			10 56
Avonmouth 2	d	06a29	07a01		07 40		08a29		08 33	09a00		09 40			10a28		10 33	11a00
St Andrews Road	d				07x44				08x36			09x44					10x36	
Severn Beach	a				07 52				08 48			09 52					10 48	

Station		GW	GW	GW	GW	GW	GW	GW (bus)	GW	GW	GW	GW	GW	GW	GW	GW (bus)	GW	GW
Bristol Temple Meads 10	d	10 45	11 16	11 21	11 45	12 03	12 21		12 34	12 45	13 16	13 21	13 45	14 03	14 21		14 34	14 45
Lawrence Hill	d	10 48	11 18		11 48				12 36	12 48	13 18		13 48				14 36	14 48
Stapleton Road	d	10a50	11 20	11a24	11a50	12 05	12a25		12 38	12a50	13 20	13a24	13a50	14 05	14a25		14 38	14a50
Montpelier	d		11 24			12 10			12 42		13 24			14 10			14 42	
Redland	d		11 26			12 12			12 44		13 26			14 12			14 44	
Clifton Down	d		11 29			12 16			12 48		13 29			14 16			14 48	
Sea Mills	d		11 33			12 20			12 52		13 33			14 20			14 52	
Shirehampton	d		11 37			12 24			12 56		13 37			14 24			14 56	
Avonmouth 2	d		11 40			12a28		12 33	13a00		13 40			14a28		14 33	15a00	
St Andrews Road	d		11x44					12x36			13x44					14x36		
Severn Beach	a		11 52					12 48			13 52					14 48		

Station		GW	GW	GW	GW	GW	GW (bus)	GW	GW	GW	GW	GW	GW	GW	GW	GW	GW	GW	GW
Bristol Temple Meads 10	d	15 16	15 21	15 45	16 03	16 21		16 34	16 45	17 16	17 21	17 45	18 03	18 21	18 45	19 04	19 45	20 34	22 15
Lawrence Hill	d	15 18		15 48				16 36	16 48	17 18		17 48	18 06		18 48	19 07	19 48	20 37	22 18
Stapleton Road	d	15 20	15a24	15a50	16 05	16a25		16 38	16a50	17 20	17a24	17a50	18 08	18a24	18a50	19 09	19a50	20 39	22 20
Montpelier	d	15 24			16 10			16 42		17 24			18 11			19 12		20 42	22 23
Redland	d	15 26			16 12			16 44		17 26			18 13			19 14		20 44	22 25
Clifton Down	d	15 29			16 16			16 48		17 29			18 16			19 17		20 47	22 29
Sea Mills	d	15 33			16 20			16 52		17 33			18 20			19 21		20 51	22 33
Shirehampton	d	15 37			16 24			16 56		17 37			18 24			19 25		20 55	22 36
Avonmouth 2	d	15 40			16a28		16 33	17a00		17 40			18 28			19 29		20 59	22 40
St Andrews Road	d	15x44					16x36			17x44			18x31			19x32		21x02	22x43
Severn Beach	a	15 52					16 48			17 52			18 39			19 40		21 10	22 51

For general notes see front of timetable
For details of catering facilities see Directory of Train Operators

b Arr. 1901

The bus service between Avonmouth and Severn Beach is operated by South Gloucestershire County Council. Valid Rail Tickets are accepted.

Table 133 — Sundays

Bristol → Avonmouth and Severn Beach

Network Diagram - see first page of Table 132

		GW	GW	GW	GW	GW	GW	GW	GW
Bristol Temple Meads 10	d	10 23	11 23	12 23	13 23	14 23	15 23	16 23	17 23
Lawrence Hill	d	10 25	11 25	12 25	13 25	14 25	15 25	16 25	17 25
Stapleton Road	d	10 27	11 27	12 27	13 27	14 27	15 27	16 27	17 27
Montpelier	d	10 31	11 31	12 31	13 31	14 31	15 31	16 31	17 31
Redland	d	10 33	11 33	12 33	13 33	14 33	15 33	16 33	17 33
Clifton Down	d	10 36	11 36	12 36	13 36	14 36	15 36	16 36	17 36
Sea Mills	d	10 40	11 40	12 40	13 40	14 40	15 40	16 40	17 40
Shirehampton	d	10 44	11 44	12 44	13 44	14 44	15 44	16 44	17 44
Avonmouth 2	d	10a49	11a49	12a49	13a49	14a49	15a49	16a49	17a49
St Andrews Road	d								
Severn Beach	a								

For general notes see front of timetable
For details of catering facilities see Directory of Train Operators

The bus service between Avonmouth and Severn Beach is operated by South Gloucestershire County Council. Valid Rail Tickets are accepted.

Severn Beach and Avonmouth → Bristol

Network Diagram - see first page of Table 132

Mondays to Fridays

Miles			GW	GW	GW	GW	GW	GW	GW	GW	GW	GW	GW	GW		GW	GW	GW	GW	GW	GW	GW	GW	GW	GW	GW
											◇							◇							◇	
0	**Severn Beach**	d	06 03				07 20	07 54						09 54						11 54				13 54		
3½	St Andrews Road	d	06x09				07x26	08x00						10x00						12x00				14x00		
4½	Avonmouth 2	d	06 14	06 32			07 31	08 04		08 38		09 17		10 04			10 35		11 15	12 04	12 35		13 15	14 04		14 35
6	Shirehampton	d	06 17	06 35			07 34	08 07		08 41		09 20		10 07			10 38		11 18	12 07	12 38		13 18	14 07		14 38
7½	Sea Mills	d	06 21	06 39			07 38	08 11		08 45		09 24		10 11			10 42		11 22	12 11	12 42		13 22	14 11		14 42
9½	Clifton Down	d	06 26	06 45			07 43	08 17		08 52		09 29		10 16			10 48		11 31	12 16	12 48		13 31	14 16		14 48
10¼	Redland	d	06 29	06 47			07 46	08 19		08 54		09 32		10 19			10 50		11 34	12 19	12 50		13 34	14 19		14 50
10¾	Montpelier	d	06 31	06 49			07 48	08 21		08 56		09 34		10 21			10 52		11 36	12 21	12 52		13 36	14 21		14 52
12	Stapleton Road	d	06 36	06 53	07 07	07 33	07 52	08 26	08 54	09 01	09 28	09 38	09 42	10 25		10 28	10 57	11 28	11 40	12 25	12 56	13 28	13 40	14 25	14 28	14 56
12½	Lawrence Hill	d	06 38	06 56	07 09	07 35	07 55	08 28	08 56	09 03	09 30	09 40				10 30	10 58	11 30	11 42		12 58	13 30	13 42		14 30	14 58
13½	**Bristol Temple Meads 10**	a	06 44	07 02	07 15	07 40	07 58	08 32	09 02	09 09	09 35	09 46	09 50	10 32		10 38	11 06	11 35	11 48	12 32	13 06	13 36	13 48	14 32	14 40	15 05

		GW	GW	GW		GW	GW	GW	GW	GW	GW	GW	GW	GW	GW	GW	GW	GW	GW	GW	GW	GW	GW	GW		
							◇			◇										◇						
Severn Beach	d					15 54									17 54	18 44					21 29		22 54			
St Andrews Road	d					16x00									18x00	18x50					21x35		23x00			
Avonmouth 2	d			15 15		16 04			16 35		17 15				18 04	18 54		19 32	20 02		21 39		23 04			
Shirehampton	d			15 18		16 07			16 38		17 18				18 07	18 58		19 35	20 05		21 43		23 07			
Sea Mills	d			15 22		16 11			16 42		17 22				18 11	19 02		19 39	20 09		21 47		23 11			
Clifton Down	d			15 31		16 16			16 48		17 31				18b29	19c13		19 46	20 14		21 52		23 16			
Redland	d			15 34		16 19			16 50		17 34				18 31	19 15		19 49	20 17		21 54		23 19			
Montpelier	d			15 36		16 21			16 52		17 36				18 33	19 17		19 51	20 19		21 56		23 21			
Stapleton Road	d	14 59	15 28	15 40		16 25	16 28	16 54	17 02	17 28	17 40	17 54	18 18	18 28	18 37	19 22	19 28	19 55	20 24	20 28	22 01	22 18	23 25	23 57		
Lawrence Hill	d	15 01	15 30	15 42			16 30	16 56	17 04	17 30	17 42	17 56	18 20	18 30	18 40	19 24	19 30	19 57	20 26	20 30	22 03	22 20	23 27	23 59		
Bristol Temple Meads 10	a	15 09	15 37	15 49		16 32	16 38	17 02	17 10	17 37	17 48	18 02	18 25	18 37	18 44	19 28	19 36	20 02	20 31	20 38	22 07	22 30	23 32	00 03		

Saturdays

		GW	GW	GW	GW		GW	GW	GW	GW		GW	GW	GW	GW		GW	GW	GW	GW		GW	GW	GW	GW	GW
							Bus	◇						Bus	◇				◇			Bus				◇ Bicycle
Severn Beach	d			07 54			08 55			09 54				10 55				11 54				12 55			13 54	
St Andrews Road	d			08x00			09x07			10x00				11x07				12x00				13x07			14x00	
Avonmouth 2	d	06 35	07 15	08 04	08 35		09a10		09 15	10 04			10 35	11a10			11 15	12 04		12 35		13a10		13 15	14 04	
Shirehampton	d	06 38	07 18	08 07	08 38				09 18	10 07			10 38				11 18	12 07		12 38				13 18	14 07	
Sea Mills	d	06 42	07 22	08 11	08 42				09 22	10 11			10 42				11 22	12 11		12 42				13 22	14 11	
Clifton Down	d	06 48	07e33	08 16	08 47				09 30	10 16			10 47				11 31	12 16		12 47				13 31	14 16	
Redland	d	06 50	07 35	08 19	08 50				09 33	10 19			10 50				11 34	12 19		12 50				13 34	14 19	
Montpelier	d	06 52	07 37	08 21	08 52				09 35	10 21			10 52				11 36	12 21		12 52				13 36	14 21	
Stapleton Road	d	06 55	07 40	08 23	08 54			09 29	09 39	10 23		10 32	10 54		11 29		11 39	12 23	12 32	12 54			13 27	13 39	14 23	14 31
Lawrence Hill	d	06 57	07 42	08 25	08 56			09 31	09 41			10 34	10 56		11 31		11 41		12 34	12 56			13 29	13 41		14 33
Bristol Temple Meads 10	a	07 03	07 48	08 32	09 04			09 35	09 47	10 31		10 39	11 04		11 35		11 48	12 31	12 39	13 04			13 35	13 48	14 31	14 37

		GW		GW	GW	GW	GW		GW	GW	GW	GW		GW	GW	GW	GW		GW	GW	GW	GW		GW		
				Bus					◇		Bus	◇									◇					
Severn Beach	d			14 55			15 54				16 55				17 54				18 54	19 47		21 29		22 54		
St Andrews Road	d			15x07			16x00				17x07				18x00				19x00	19x53		21x35		23x00		
Avonmouth 2	d	14 35		15a10		15 15	16 04			16 35	17a10			17 15	18 04				19 04	19 57		21 39		23 04		
Shirehampton	d	14 38				15 18	16 07			16 38				17 18	18 07				19 07	20 00		21 43		23 07		
Sea Mills	d	14 42				15 22	16 11			16 42				17 22	18 11				19 11	20 04		21 47		23 11		
Clifton Down	d	14 47				15 31	16 16			16 47				17 31	18 17				19f29	20 09		21 52		23 16		
Redland	d	14 50				15 34	16 19			16 50				17 34	18 19				19 31	20 12		21 54		23 19		
Montpelier	d	14 52				15 36	16 21			16 52				17 36	18 21				19 33	20 14		21 56		23 21		
Stapleton Road	d	14 54			15 27	15 39	16 23		16 34	16 54		17 28		17 39	18 23	18 34	19 31		19 40	20 17	20 33	22 01		23 24		
Lawrence Hill	d	14 56			15 29	15 41			16 36	16 56		17 30		17 41	18 26	18 36	19 33		19 42	20 19	20 35	22 03		23 26		
Bristol Temple Meads 10	a	15 04			15 34	15 48	16 31		16 39	17 04		17 35		17 48	18 31	18 39	19 38		19 46	20 25	20 39	22 09		23 32		

Sundays

		GW			GW			GW			GW			GW			GW			GW			GW			
Severn Beach	d																									
St Andrews Road	d																									
Avonmouth 2	d	10 52			11 52			12 52			13 52			14 52			15 52			16 52			17 52			
Shirehampton	d	10 55			11 55			12 55			13 55			14 55			15 55			16 55			17 55			
Sea Mills	d	10 59			11 59			12 59			13 59			14 59			15 59			16 59			17 59			
Clifton Down	d	11 04			12 04			13 04			14 04			15 04			16 04			17 04			18 07			
Redland	d	11 07			12 07			13 07			14 07			15 07			16 07			17 07			18 10			
Montpelier	d	11 09			12 09			13 09			14 09			15 09			16 09			17 09			18 12			
Stapleton Road	d	11 13			12 13			13 13			14 13			15 13			16 13			17 13			18 15			
Lawrence Hill	d	11 15			12 15			13 15			14 15			15 15			16 15			17 15			18 17			
Bristol Temple Meads 10	a	11 20			12 20			13 20			14 20			15 20			16 20			17 19			18 22			

For general notes see front of timetable
For details of catering facilities see Directory of Train Operators

b Arr. 1816
c Arr. 1906
e Arr. 0727
f Arr. 1916

The bus service between Avonmouth and Severn Beach is operated by South Gloucestershire County Council. Valid Rail Tickets are accepted.

Gloucester → Taunton

Network Diagram - see first page of Table 132

Miles			GW MX	XC MX	GW	GW	GW		XC	GW	GW	GW	GW		GW	GW	XC	GW	XC		GW	GW	GW	XC	GW	GW
				1 ◇	◇	1	◇		1 ◇	◇			◇				1 ◇		1 ◇		◇		◇	1 ◇		
			A		B		C			C					D		E	G	H				J			K
									T				T				T		T		T			T		
0	Gloucester 7	d										06 20						07 11					07 50			
13	Cam & Dursley	d										06 35						07 25					08 03			
28	Yate	d										06 48						07 40					08 16			
—	London Paddington 15 ⊖	d																								
—	Bath Spa 7	d																								
34	Bristol Parkway 7	a										06 58						07 48					08 25			
—		d	22p54	00 06								06 58			07 25			07 49	07 58			08 12	08 25	08 28		
35¼	Filton Abbey Wood	d	22p58									07 02	07 09		07 28		07 44	07 53			08 09	08 15	08 28			08 42
38¼	Stapleton Road	d										07 07			07 33											
38¾	Lawrence Hill	d										07 09			07 35											
39¾	Bristol Temple Meads 10	a	23p07	00 20								07 15	07 18		07 40		07 52	08 02	08 08		08 18	08 23	08 37	08 41		08 51
—		d	23p08		05 29	06 03	06 26		06 34		06 48	07 18				07 51			08 11			08 25		08 44		08 55
40¾	Bedminster	d	23b11								06x50					07x53						08x27				
41½	Parson Street	d	23p14								06 53					07 55						08 29				08 58
47¾	Nailsea & Backwell	d	23p23			06 14					07 02	07 28				08 04						08 38				09 06
51¾	Yatton	d	23p29			06 21					07 07	07 34				08 09						08 44			←	09 12
55¾	Worle	d	23p35			06 27					07 12	07 40				08 15						08 50			08 50	09 18
58½	Weston Milton	d	23p40								07 18					08 20						→			08 55	→
59¾	Weston-super-Mare	a	23p43		05 48	06 36	06 47				07 23	07 47				08 26									08 59	
—		d	23p45		05 50		06 51			←		07 50													09 00	
67¼	Highbridge & Burnham	d	23p56		06 01		07 02			07 02		08 01													09 11	
73½	Bridgwater	d	00 04		06 09		→			07 10		08 09													09 19	
85¼	Taunton	a	00 17		06 22				07 06	07 23		08 25							08 42					09 15	09 33	

		GW		GW	XC	GW	GW	GW		GW	XC	GW	GW	XC		GW	GW	GW	XC	GW		XC	GW	GW	GW	XC
				1 ◇	1 ◇	◇				◇	1 ◇			1 ◇		◇			1 ◇			1 ◇	◇		◇	1 ◇
							K			L			K					N		K					L	
				R	T	T					T			T		T			T			T	T			T
Gloucester 7	d									08 42								09 42							10 42	
Cam & Dursley	d									08 57								09 57							10 57	
Yate	d									09 10								10 10							11 10	
London Paddington 15 ⊖	d			07 30																						
Bath Spa 7	d			08 55																						
Bristol Parkway 7	a									09 19								10 18							11 19	
	d	08 46			08 58			09 12		09 19	09 26	09 34		09 58			10 12	10 19	10 28			10 58		11 12	11 19	11 28
Filton Abbey Wood	d	08 49				09 09				09 22		09 37	09 42			10 09	10 15	10 22		10 42			11 09	11 15	11 22	
Stapleton Road	d	08 54								09 28		09 42						10 28							11 28	
Lawrence Hill	d	08 56								09 30								10 30							11 30	
Bristol Temple Meads 10	a	09 02		09 10	09 13	09 18		09 22		09 35	09 41	09 50	09 53	10 13		10 18	10 23	10 38	10 41	10 51		11 13	11 18	11 23	11 35	11 38
	d			09 13				09 25			09 44		09 55				10 25		10 44	10 53		11 15		11 25		11 44
Bedminster	d							09 28									10x27							11x27		
Parson Street	d																10 29							11 29		
Nailsea & Backwell	d							09 38					10 04				10 38			11 03				11 38		
Yatton	d						←	09 44					10 10				10 44			11 08				11 44		
Worle	d						09 18	09 50					10 16				10 50			11 14				11 50		
Weston Milton	d							09 55									10 55							11 55		
Weston-super-Mare	a						09 24	10 03					10 22				11 00			11 21		11 32		12 00		
	d						09 29						10 23							11 23		11 37				
Highbridge & Burnham	d						09 40						10 34							11 34						
Bridgwater	d						09 48						10 42							11 42						
Taunton	a			09 45			10 03				10 16		10 59						11 16	11 59		12 00				12 15

		GW	GW		XC	GW	GW	GW	XC		GW	XC	GW	GW	GW		XC	GW	XC	GW	GW		GW	XC	GW	XC FX
		1 ◇			1 ◇	◇		◇	1 ◇			1 ◇	◇				1 ◇		1 ◇	◇			◇	1 ◇		1 ◇
			K					Q			K				D			K					U			
		Ø			T	T			T			T	T				T		T	T				T		T
Gloucester 7	d							11 42							12 42								13 42			
Cam & Dursley	d							11 57							12 57								13 57			
Yate	d							12 10							13 10								14 10			
London Paddington 15 ⊖	d	10 00																								
Bath Spa 7	d	11 25																								
Bristol Parkway 7	a							12 19							13 19								14 18			
	d				11 58		12 12	12 19	12 28			12 58		13 12	13 19		13 26		13 58		14 12		14 19	14 28	14 47	14 58
Filton Abbey Wood	d		11 42			12 09	12 15	12 22			12 42		13 09	13 15	13 22			13 42		14 09	14 15		14 22		14 50	
Stapleton Road	d														13 28								14 28		14 59	
Lawrence Hill	d														13 30								14 30		15 01	
Bristol Temple Meads 10	a	11 42	11 51		12 13	12 18	12 23	12 35	12 41		12 51	13 13	13 17	13 23	13 36		13 39	13 51	14 13	14 19	14 23		14 40	14 41	15 09	15 13
	d	11 47	11 53				12 25		12 44		12 53			13 25			13 44	13 53			14 25			14 44		
Bedminster	d						12x27							13x27							14x27					
Parson Street	d						12 29							13 29							14 29					
Nailsea & Backwell	d		12 03				12 38				13 03			13 38				14 03			14 38					
Yatton	d		12 08				12 44				13 08			13 44				14 08			14 44					
Worle	d		12 14				12 50				13 14			13 50				14 14			14 50					
Weston Milton	d						12 55							13 55							14 55					
Weston-super-Mare	a	12 06	12 20				13 00				13 21			14 00				14 21			15 00					
	d	12 07	12 21								13 23							14 23								
Highbridge & Burnham	d		12 32								13 34							14 34								
Bridgwater	d		12 40								13 42							14 42								
Taunton	a	12 29	12 57						13 16		13 59						14 15	14 59						15 16		

For general notes see front of timetable
For details of catering facilities see Directory of Train Operators

- **A** From Cardiff Central (Table 132) to Exeter St Davids (Table 135)
- **B** Until 26 June and from 7 September to Penzance, 29 June to 4 September to Newquay (Table 135
- **C** To Penzance (Table 135)
- **D** To Westbury (Table 123)
- **E** To Machester Piccadilly (Table 51)
- **G** From Cheltenham Spa (Table 57)
- **H** From Birmingham New Street (Table 57)
- **J** From Worcester Shrub Hill (Table 57) to Weymouth (Table 123)
- **K** From Cardiff Central (Table 132)
- **L** To Weymouth (Table 123)
- **N** From Great Malvern (Table 71) to Westbury (Table 123)
- **Q** From Great Malvern (Table 71) to Brighton (Table 123)
- **U** From Great Malvern (Table 71) to Weymouth (Table 123)
- **b** Previous night.
- **x** Stops on request, passengers wishing to alight must inform the guard and those wishing to join must give a hand signal to the driver

Gloucester → Taunton

Network Diagram - see first page of Table 132

	XC FO 1◇ 🛒	GW ◇ 🛒	GW A		GW	GW B	XC 1◇ 🛒	GW ◇ 🛒	GW A		XC 1◇ 🛒	GW 1◇ ☕	GW ◇ 🛒	GW	GW ◇ C		XC 1◇ 🛒	GW A	GW B	XC 1◇ 🛒	GW A		GW 1◇ ☕	GW ◇ 🛒	GW
Gloucester 7 d						14 42									15 42										
Cam & Dursley d						14 57									15 57										
Yate d						15 10									16 10										
London Paddington 15 ⊖ d												14 30											15 30		
Bath Spa 7 d								15 35				16 00											17 00		
Bristol Parkway 7 a						15 19									16 18										
d	14 58				15 12	15 19	15 26				15 58			16 12	16 19		16 28		16 46	16 58					17 12
Filton Abbey Wood d		15 09			15 15	15 22		16a01	15 42				16 09	16 15	16 22			16 42	16 49					17 09	17 15
Stapleton Road d						15 28									16 28				16 54						
Lawrence Hill d						15 30									16 30				16 56						
Bristol Temple Meads 10 a	15 13	15 18			15 23	15 37	15 41	15 47	15 51		16 13	16 15	16 18	16 23	16 38		16 41	16 51	17 02	17 13			17 15	17 18	17 23
d	15 13				15 25		15 44		15 53			16 18		16 25			16 44	16 53		17 14			17 19		17 25
Bedminster d					15x27				15x55					16x27				16x55							17x28
Parson Street d					15 29				15 57					16 29				16 57							17 30
Nailsea & Backwell d					15 38				16 06			16 29		16 38				17 06					17 29		17 38
Yatton d			←		15 44				16 11			16 36		16 44				17 11			←		17 35		17 44
Worle d			15 14		15 50				16 17			16 43		16 50				17 17			17 17		17 42		17 50
Weston Milton d					15 55				16 21					16 55				→			17 22				17 55
Weston-super-Mare a			15 25		16 00				16 24			16 52		17 08							17 27		17 52		18 00
d			15 25						16 24												17 28				
Highbridge & Burnham d			15 36						16 37												17 38				
Bridgwater d			15 45						16 45												17 46				
Taunton a	15 44		16 04				16 15		16 59								17 15			17 45	18 01				

	GW ◇ D	XC 1◇ 🛒	GW A	GW B		XC 1◇ 🛒	GW 1◇ ☕	GW ◇ 🛒	GW	GW E		XC 1◇ 🛒	GW 1◇ ☕	GW A	GW 1◇ ☕	GW ◇ 🛒		XC 1◇ 🛒	GW G	XC 1◇ 🛒	GW 1◇ ☕	GW A		XC 1◇ 🛒	GW 1◇ ☕
Gloucester 7 d	16 42									17 42								18 40	18 42						
Cam & Dursley d	16 57									17 57									18 57						
Yate d	17 10									18 10									19 10						
London Paddington 15 ⊖ d							16 30								17 30										18 30
Bath Spa 7 d							18 00								19 00										20 00
Bristol Parkway 7 a	17 19									18 19								19 08	19 19						
d	17 19	17 26		17 46		17 58			18 11	18 19		18 26						19 09	19 19	19 28				19 58	
Filton Abbey Wood d	17 22		17 42	17 49				18 09	18 14	18 22				18 42		19 09			19 22			19 42			
Stapleton Road d	17 28			17 54					18 18	18 28									19 28						
Lawrence Hill d	17 30			17 56					18 20	18 30									19 30						
Bristol Temple Meads 10 a	17 37	17 41	17 51	18 02		18 13	18 15	18 18	18 25	18 37		18 41		18 53	19 15	19 18		19 25	19 36	19 39		19 53		20 13	20 15
d		17 44	17 54				18 21		18 25			18 44		18 55	19 15					19 44		19 55			20 15
Bedminster d			17x56						18x28					18x58								19 58			
Parson Street d			17 57						18 30					19 00								20 01			
Nailsea & Backwell d			18 06				18 32		18 38					19 09	19 26							20 10			20 29
Yatton d			18 11				18 39		18 44					19 14	19 33						←	20 15			20 36
Worle d			18 17				18 46		18 50					19 20	19 40						19 40	20 21			20 44
Weston Milton d			18 22						18 55					19 24	→						19 45	20 25			20 49
Weston-super-Mare a			18 25				18 52		19 00					19 28							19 49	20 29			20 55
d			18 28				18 55							19 29							19 57	20 30			
Highbridge & Burnham d			18 38				19 07						←	19 40								20 41			
Bridgwater d			18 46				19 15						19 15	19 48								20 49			
Taunton a		18 15	19 02				→					19 15	19 30	20 03						20 15	20 23	21 10			

	GW ◇	GW	GW ◇ C	XC 1◇ H 🛒	GW A		XC 1◇ H 🛒	GW A	GW 1◇ ☕	GW ◇	XC 1◇		GW	GW J	XC 1◇	GW A	XC 1◇		GW K	GW 1◇ ☕	GW 1◇ ☕	GW A			
Gloucester 7 d			19 42											21 15							22 49				
Cam & Dursley d			19 57											21 29											
Yate d			20 10											21 43											
London Paddington 15 ⊖ d									19 30											21 45					
Bath Spa 7 d									21 00											23 20					
Bristol Parkway 7 a			20 18											21 52							23 16				
d		20 11	20 19	20 28			20 58				21 27			21 52	22 02		22 25		22 54		23 18				
Filton Abbey Wood d	20 09	20 14	20 22		20 38					21 09				21 57		22 13			22 58			23 50			
Stapleton Road d			20 28													22 18						23 57			
Lawrence Hill d			20 30													22 20						23 59			
Bristol Temple Meads 10 a	20 18	20 25	20 38	20 41	20 48		21 13		21 15	21 19	21 38			22 10	22 19	22 30	22 41		23 07	23 33	23 37	00 03			
d				20 44	20 55		21 13		21 18		21 44		21 55						23 08	23 35					
Bedminster d					20x57								21x57						23x11						
Parson Street d					20 59								21 59						23 14						
Nailsea & Backwell d					21 08				21 27				22 08						23 23	23s46					
Yatton d					21 13			←	21 34				22 14						23 29	23s53					
Worle d					21 19			21 19	21 40				22 20						23 35	23s59					
Weston Milton d					→			21 23					22 24						23 40						
Weston-super-Mare a								21 27	21 50				22 27						23 43	00s06					
d								21 28					22 29						23 45						
Highbridge & Burnham d								21 42					22 40						23 56	00s17					
Bridgwater d								21 50					22 48						00 04	00s25					
Taunton a				21 15			21 44	22 05			22 15		23 03						00 17	00s37					

For general notes see front of timetable
For details of catering facilities see Directory of Train Operators

A From Cardiff Central (Table 132)

B To Westbury (Table 123)

C From Great Malvern (Table 71) to Weymouth (Table 123)

D To Weymouth (Table 123)

E From Cheltenham Spa (Table 57) to Westbury (Table 123)

G To Frome (Table 123)

H 🛒 to Bristol Temple Meads

J From Cheltenham Spa (Table 57)

K From Cariff Central (Table 132) to Exeter St Davids (Table 135)

Gloucester → Taunton

Network Diagram - see first page of Table 132

		GW	XC	GW	GW	XC	GW	GW	GW	GW		GW	XC	GW	XC	GW	GW	GW	XC	GW		XC	GW	GW	GW	GW
			1◇	◇	1◇	1◇						◇	1◇		1◇	◇		◇	1◇			1◇	1	◇		
		A		B									C	D				E		G					G	
				⌶	⊡	⌶							⌶		⌶	⌶			⌶			⌶	⊡	⌶		
Gloucester [7]	d									06 21				07 02				07 40								
Cam & Dursley	d									06 36				07 15				07 55								
Yate	d									06 50				07 30				08 10								
London Paddington [15] ⊖	d																						07 30			
Bath Spa [7]	d																						09 00			
Bristol Parkway [7]	a									07 00				07 39				08 18								
	d	22p54	00 06		05 42					07 00				07 40	07 57		08 12	08 20	08 26			08 58				09 12
Filton Abbey Wood	d	22p58								07 03		07 10	07 41	07 46		08 10	08 15	08 23		08 43				09 09		09 15
Stapleton Road	d																									
Lawrence Hill	d																									
Bristol Temple Meads [10]	a	23p07	00 20		05 53					07 13		07 18	07 51	07 54	08 11	08 18	08 23	08 34	08 38	08 52		09 13	09 15	09 18		09 23
	d	23p08		05 29		06 08	06 18	06 36	06 48	07 22				07 56	08 11		08 25		08 44	08 54			09 17			09 25
Bedminster	d	23b11							06x50								08x27									09x27
Parson Street	d	23p14							06 52								08 29									09 29
Nailsea & Backwell	d	23p23					06 28		07 01	07 33				08 03			08 38			09 03						09 38
Yatton	d	23p29					06 34		07 07	07 38				08 08			08 44			09 08					←	09 44
Worle	d	23p35					06 40		07 13	07 44				08 14			08 50			09 14 →					09 14	09 50
Weston Milton	d	23p40							07 18								08 55									09 55
Weston-super-Mare	a	23p43		05 48			06 45	06 55	07 23	07 51				08 23			09 00								09 22	10 00
	d	23p45		05 50			06 47	06 56		07 52															09 32	
Highbridge & Burnham	d	23p56		06 01			06 58			08 03															09 44	
Bridgwater	d	00 04		06 09			07 06			08 10															09 52	
Taunton	a	00 17		06 22		07 14	07 20	07 24		08 27					08 42				09 15				09 50		10 06	

		GW	XC	GW	XC	GW	GW		GW	XC	GW	GW	XC	GW	GW	GW	XC		GW	XC	GW	GW	GW	GW	XC	GW
		◇	1◇		1◇	◇				1◇	1◇		1◇	◇		◇	1◇			1◇	1◇	◇		◇	1◇	
		H		G					J			G				H			G					K		G
			⌶		⌶	⌶				⌶	⊡		⌶	⌶			⌶			⌶	⊡	⌶			⌶	
Gloucester [7]	d	08 42							09 46							10 42								11 46		
Cam & Dursley	d	08 56							10 02							10 56								12 01		
Yate	d	09 10							10 16							11 10								12 16		
London Paddington [15] ⊖	d										09 00										10 30					
Bath Spa [7]	d										10 25										12 00					
Bristol Parkway [7]	a	09 19							10 24							11 19								12 24		
	d	09 19	09 26		09 58		10 12		10 25	10 28			10 58		11 12	11 19	11 26			11 58			12 12	12 25	12 30	
Filton Abbey Wood	d	09 23		09 42		10 09	10 15		10 28			10 42		11 09	11 15	11 23			11 42			12 09	12 15	12 28		12 42
Stapleton Road	d	09 29							10 32							11 29								12 32		
Lawrence Hill	d	09 31							10 34							11 31								12 34		
Bristol Temple Meads [10]	a	09 35	09 38	09 51	10 13	10 18	10 23		10 39	10 41	10 39	10 52	11 11	11 18	11 23	11 35	11 38		11 52	12 13	12 15	12 18	12 23	12 39	12 41	12 52
	d		09 44	09 53	10 20		10 25			10 44	10 49	10 53	11 13		11 25		11 44		11 53		12 18		12 25		12 44	12 53
Bedminster	d						10x27								11x27								12x27			
Parson Street	d						10 29								11 29								12 29			
Nailsea & Backwell	d			10 03			10 38					11 03			11 38				12 03				12 38			13 03
Yatton	d			10 08			10 44					11 08			11 44				12 08				12 44			13 08
Worle	d			10 14			10 50					11 14			11 50				12 14				12 50			13 14
Weston Milton	d						10 55								11 55								12 55			
Weston-super-Mare	a			10 22			11 00				11 07	11 21	11 31		12 00				12 22		12 36		13 00			13 22
	d			10 23								11 23	11 40						12 23							13 23
Highbridge & Burnham	d			10 34								11 34							12 34							13 34
Bridgwater	d			10 42								11 42							12 42							13 42
Taunton	a		10 16	10 59	11 00					11 15		11 59	12 01				12 15		12 59						13 15	13 59

		XC	GW	GW		GW	XC	GW	XC	GW	GW	GW	GW	XC		GW	XC	GW	GW	GW	GW	XC	GW	XC		GW
		1◇	◇				1◇		1◇	1◇	◇		◇	1◇			1◇	◇				1◇		1◇		1◇
						L		G					N			G			G		L		G			
		⌶	⌶				⌶		⌶	⊡	⌶		⌶	⌶			⌶	⌶				⌶		⌶		⊡
Gloucester [7]	d					12 42							13 42								14 42					
Cam & Dursley	d					12 56							13 57								14 56					
Yate	d					13 10							14 12								15 09					
London Paddington [15] ⊖	d									12 30																14 30
Bath Spa [7]	d									14 00																16 00
Bristol Parkway [7]	a					13 19							14 21								15 18					
	d	12 58		13 12		13 19	13 26		13 58			14 12	14 21	14 28			14 58			15 12	15 18	15 26		15 58		
Filton Abbey Wood	d		13 09	13 15		13 23		13 43			14 09	14 15	14 25			14 42		15 09		15 15	15 22		15 42			
Stapleton Road	d					13 27							14 31								15 27					
Lawrence Hill	d					13 29							14 33								15 29					
Bristol Temple Meads [10]	a	13 13	13 18	13 23		13 35	13 38	13 52	14 13	14 15	14 18	14 23	14 37	14 41		14 53	15 13	15 18		15 23	15 34	15 41	15 52	16 13		16 15
	d			13 25			13 44	13 53		14 18		14 25		14 44		14 53	15 13			15 25		15 44	15 53			16 18
Bedminster	d			13x27								14x27								15x27						
Parson Street	d			13 29								14 29								15 29						
Nailsea & Backwell	d			13 38				14 03				14 38				15 03				15 38			16 03			
Yatton	d			13 44				14 08				14 44				15 08			←	15 44			16 08			
Worle	d			13 50				14 14				14 50				15 14 →			15 14	15 50			16 14			
Weston Milton	d			13 55								14 55								15 55						
Weston-super-Mare	a			14 00				14 22		14 36		15 00							15 23	16 00			16 22			16 36
	d							14 23											15 28				16 23			
Highbridge & Burnham	d							14 34											15 39				16 34			
Bridgwater	d							14 42											15 47				16 42			
Taunton	a						14 15	14 59						15 16			15 44		16 01			16 15	16 59			

For general notes see front of timetable
For details of catering facilities see Directory of Train Operators

- **A** From Cardiff Central (Table 132) to Exeter St Davids (Table 135)
- **B** To Penzance (Table 135)
- **C** To Manchester Piccadilly (Table 51)
- **D** From Cheltenham Spa (Table 57)
- **E** From Worcester Shrub Hill (Table 57) to Weymouth (Table 123)
- **G** From Cardiff Central (Table 132)
- **H** To Weymouth (Table 123)
- **J** From Worcester Shrub Hill (Table 57) to Westbury (Table 123)
- **K** From Great Malvern (Table 71) to Brighton (Table 123)
- **L** To Westbury (Table 123)
- **N** From Worcester Foregate Street (Table 71) to Weymouth (Table 123)
- **b** Previous night.
- **x** Stops on request, passengers wishing to alight must inform the guard and those wishing to join must give a hand signal to the driver

Saturdays

until 5 September

Gloucester → Taunton

Network Diagram - see first page of Table 132

		GW ◇ 🛒	GW	GW ◇ A	XC [1] ◇ 🛒	GW B	XC [1] ◇ 🛒	GW [1] ◇ 🍽	GW ◇ 🛒	GW		GW ◇ C	XC [1] ◇ 🛒	GW B	XC [1] ◇ 🛒	GW [1] ◇ 🍽	GW ◇ 🛒	GW	GW D	XC [1] ◇ 🛒		GW B	GW [1] ◇ 🍽	GW ◇ 🛒	XC [1] ◇ 🛒	GW
Gloucester [7]	d			15 46								16 42							17 46						18 40	
Cam & Dursley	d			16 01								16 56							18 01							
Yate	d			16 15								17 10							18 16							
London Paddington [15] ⊖	d							15 30								16 30							17 30			
Bath Spa [7]	d							17 00								18 00							19 00			
Bristol Parkway [7]	a			16 24								17 19							18 24						19 08	
	d		16 12	16 24	16 28		16 58			17 12		17 19	17 26		17 58			18 12	18 25	18 28					19 09	19 19
Filton Abbey Wood	d	16 09	16 15	16 28		16 42			17 10	17 15		17 23		17 42			18 10	18 14	18 28			18 42		19 09		19 23
Stapleton Road	d			16 34								17 28							18 34							
Lawrence Hill	d			16 36								17 30							18 36							
Bristol Temple Meads [10]	a	16 18	16 23	16 39	16 41	16 52	17 13	17 15	17 18	17 23		17 35	17 38	17 52	18 13	18 15	18 18	18 23	18 39	18 41		18 52	19 15	19 18	19 27	19 31
	d		16 25		16 44	16 53		17 18		17 25			17 44	17 53		18 17		18 25		18 44		18 53	19 17		19 37	
Bedminster	d		16x27							17x27								18x27								
Parson Street	d		16 29							17 29								18 29								
Nailsea & Backwell	d		16 38			17 03				17 38				18 03				18 38				19 03	19 30			
Yatton	d		16 44			17 08				17 44				18 08				18 44				19 08	19 37			
Worle	d		16 50			17 14				17 50				18 14				18 50				19 14	19 43			
Weston Milton	d		16 55							17 55								18 55				19 20				
Weston-super-Mare	a		17 00			17 22		17 36		18 00				18 21		18 36		19 00				19 23	19 52			
	d					17 23								18 23		18 40						19 23				
Highbridge & Burnham	d					17 34								18 34								19 34				
Bridgwater	d					17 42								18 42								19 42				
Taunton	a				17 17	17 59							18 15	18 59		19 06				19 15		19 59			20 08	

		GW E	XC [1] ◇ 🛒	GW B	XC [1] ◇ G 🛒	GW [1] ◇ 🍽	GW ◇ 🛒		GW	GW ◇ A	XC [1] ◇ 🛒	GW [1] ◇ 🍽	GW	XC [1] ◇ 🛒	GW ◇ 🛒	XC [1] ◇ 🛒	GW H		GW J	XC [1] ◇ 🛒	GW [1] ◇ 🍽	XC [1] ◇ 🛒	GW ◇	GW		
Gloucester [7]	d	18 42								19 46									21 16							
Cam & Dursley	d	18 56								19 59									21 30							
Yate	d	19 10								20 14									21 44							
London Paddington [15] ⊖	d					18 30						19 00									20 30					
Bath Spa [7]	d					20 01						20 25									22 00		22 35			
Bristol Parkway [7]	a	19 21								20 23									21 53							
	d	19 21	19 28		19 58				20 17	20 23	20 28			20 58		21 25			21 53	21 58		22 25				
Filton Abbey Wood	d	19 25		19 42			20 09		20 20	20 27			20 38		21 09		21 42						23a01	22 52		
Stapleton Road	d	19 31								20 33																
Lawrence Hill	d	19 33								20 35																
Bristol Temple Meads [10]	a	19 38	19 41	19 52	20 13	20 15	20 18		20 29	20 39	20 41	20 42	20 48	21 13	21 18	21 35	21 50		22 04	22 13	22 15	22 41	22 50	23 00		
	d		19 44	19 53		20 15					20 44	20 55				21 44	21 55				22 17					
Bedminster	d																21x58									
Parson Street	d																22 01									
Nailsea & Backwell	d			20 03								21 04					22 09				22s28					
Yatton	d			20 08								21 11					22 15				22s35					
Worle	d			20 14								21 17					22 21				22s41					
Weston Milton	d			20 19								21 22														
Weston-super-Mare	a			20 23		20 36						21 26					22 27				22s48					
	d			20 23		20 38						21 26					22 28									
Highbridge & Burnham	d			20 34								21 39					22 39				22s59					
Bridgwater	d			20 42								21 46					22 47				23s06					
Taunton	a		20 15	20 59		21 06					21 16	22 00				22 16	23 02				23 18					

Saturdays

from 12 September

		GW H	XC [1] ◇	GW ◇ K 🛒	GW [1] ◇ 🍽	XC [1] ◇ 🛒	GW		GW ◇ 🛒	GW	GW	GW ◇	XC [1] ◇ 🛒	GW J		XC [1] ◇ 🛒	GW ◇ 🛒	GW	GW ◇ L	XC [1] ◇ 🛒	GW B		XC [1] ◇ 🛒	GW [1] ◇ 🍽	GW ◇ 🛒	GW B
Gloucester [7]	d										06 21			07 02					07 40							
Cam & Dursley	d										06 36			07 15					07 55							
Yate	d										06 50			07 30					08 10							
London Paddington [15] ⊖	d																							07 30		
Bath Spa [7]	d																							09 00		
Bristol Parkway [7]	a										07 00			07 39					08 18							
	d	22p54	00 06		05 42						07 00			07 40		07 57		08 12	08 20	08 26			08 58			
Filton Abbey Wood	d	22p58									07 03	07 10	07 41	07 46			08 10	08 15	08 23		08 43				09 09	
Stapleton Road	d																									
Lawrence Hill	d																									
Bristol Temple Meads [10]	a	23p07	00 20		05 53						07 13	07 18	07 51	07 54		08 11	08 18	08 23	08 34	08 38	08 52		09 13	09 15	09 18	
	d	23p08		05 29		06 08	06 18		06 36	06 48	07 22			07 56		08 11		08 25		08 44	08 54			09 17		
Bedminster	d	23b11								06x50								08x27								
Parson Street	d	23p14								06 52								08 29								
Nailsea & Backwell	d	23p23					06 28			07 01	07 33			08 03				08 38			09 03					
Yatton	d	23p29					06 34			07 07	07 38			08 08				08 44			09 08					←
Worle	d	23p35					06 40			07 13	07 44			08 14				08 50			09 14 →					09 14
Weston Milton	d	23p40								07 18								08 55								
Weston-super-Mare	a	23p43		05 48			06 45		06 55	07 23	07 51			08 23				09 00								09 22
	d	23p45		05 50			06 47		06 56		07 52															09 32
Highbridge & Burnham	d	23p56		06 01			06 58				08 03															09 44
Bridgwater	d	00 04		06 09			07 06				08 10															09 52
Taunton	a	00 17		06 22		07 14	07 20		07 24		08 27					08 42				09 15				09 50		10 06

For general notes see front of timetable
For details of catering facilities see Directory of Train Operators

- **A** From Great Malvern (Table 71) to Weymouth (Table 123)
- **B** From Cardiff Central (Table 132)
- **C** To Weymouth (Table 123)
- **D** From Great Malvern (Table 71) to Westbury (Table 123)
- **E** To Frome (Table 123)
- **G** From Manchester Piccadilly (Table 51)
- **H** From Cardiff Central (Table 132) to Exeter St Davids (Table 135)
- **J** From Cheltenham Spa (Table 57)
- **K** To Penzance (Table 135)
- **L** From Worcester Shrub Hill (Table 57) to Weymouth (Table 123)
- **b** Previous night.

Stops on request, passengers wishing to alight must inform the guard and those wishing to join must give a hand signal to the driver

Saturdays

from 12 September

Gloucester → Taunton

Network Diagram - see first page of Table 132

Station		GW	GW ◇ A	XC 1 ◇ ⊼	GW B		XC 1 ◇ ⊼	GW ◇ ⊼	GW	GW C	XC 1 ◇ ⊼	GW B		XC 1 ◇ ⊼	GW ◇ ⊼	GW	GW ◇ A	XC 1 ◇ ⊼	GW B		XC 1 ◇ ⊼	GW ◇ ⊼	GW	GW ◇ D	XC 1 ◇ ⊼	GW B
Gloucester 7	d		08 42							09 46							10 42							11 46		
Cam & Dursley	d		08 56							10 02							10 56							12 01		
Yate	d		09 10							10 16							11 10							12 16		
London Paddington 15 ⊖	d																									
Bath Spa 7	d																									
Bristol Parkway 7	a		09 19							10 24							11 19							12 24		
	d	09 12	09 19	09 26			09 58		10 12	10 25	10 28			10 58		11 12	11 19	11 26			11 58		12 12	12 25	12 30	
Filton Abbey Wood	d	09 15	09 23		09 42			10 09	10 15	10 28		10 42			11 09	11 15	11 23		11 42			12 09	12 15	12 28		12 42
Stapleton Road	d		09 29							10 32							11 29							12 32		
Lawrence Hill	d		09 31							10 34							11 31							12 34		
Bristol Temple Meads 10	a	09 23	09 35	09 38	09 51		10 13	10 18	10 23	10 39	10 41	10 52		11 13	11 18	11 23	11 35	11 38	11 52		12 13	12 18	12 23	12 39	12 41	12 52
	d	09 25		09 44	09 53				10 25		10 44	10 53		11 14		11 25		11 44	11 53				12 25		12 44	12 53
Bedminster	d	09x27							10x27							11x27							12x27			
Parson Street	d	09 29							10 29							11 29							12 29			
Nailsea & Backwell	d	09 38			10 03				10 38			11 03				11 38			12 03				12 38			13 03
Yatton	d	09 44			10 08				10 44			11 08				11 44			12 08				12 44			13 08
Worle	d	09 50			10 14				10 50			11 14				11 50			12 14				12 50			13 14
Weston Milton	d	09 55							10 55							11 55							12 55			
Weston-super-Mare	a	10 00			10 22				11 00			11 21		11 31		12 00			12 22				13 00			13 22
	d				10 23							11 23		11 40					12 23							13 23
Highbridge & Burnham	d				10 34							11 34							12 34							13 34
Bridgwater	d				10 42							11 42							12 42							13 42
Taunton	a			10 16	10 59						11 15	11 59		12 00				12 15	12 59						13 15	13 59

Station		XC 1 ◇ ⊼	GW ◇ ⊼		GW	GW E	XC 1 ◇ ⊼	GW B	XC 1 ◇ ⊼	GW ◇ ⊼		GW	GW ◇ G ⊼	XC 1 ◇ ⊼	GW B	XC 1 ◇ ⊼	GW ◇ ⊼		GW	GW E	XC 1 ◇ ⊼	GW B	XC 1 ◇ ⊼	GW ◇ ⊼		GW
Gloucester 7	d					12 42							13 42							14 42						
Cam & Dursley	d					12 56							13 57							14 56						
Yate	d					13 10							14 12							15 09						
London Paddington 15 ⊖	d																									
Bath Spa 7	d																									
Bristol Parkway 7	a					13 19							14 21							15 18						
	d	12 58			13 12	13 19	13 26		13 58			14 12	14 21	14 28		14 58			15 12	15 18	15 26		15 58			16 12
Filton Abbey Wood	d		13 09		13 15	13 23		13 43		14 09		14 15	14 25		14 42		15 09		15 15	15 22		15 42		16 09		16 15
Stapleton Road	d					13 27							14 31							15 27						
Lawrence Hill	d					13 29							14 33							15 29						
Bristol Temple Meads 10	a	13 13	13 18		13 23	13 35	13 38	13 52	14 13	14 18		14 23	14 37	14 41	14 53	15 13	15 18		15 23	15 34	15 41	15 52	16 13	16 18		16 23
	d				13 25		13 44	13 53				14 25		14 44	14 53				15 25		15 44	15 53				16 25
Bedminster	d				13x27							14x27							15x27							16x27
Parson Street	d				13 29							14 29							15 29							16 29
Nailsea & Backwell	d				13 38			14 03				14 38			15 03				15 38			16 03				16 38
Yatton	d				13 44			14 08				14 44			15 08				15 44			16 08				16 44
Worle	d				13 50			14 14				14 50			15 14				15 50			16 14				16 50
Weston Milton	d				13 55							14 55							15 55							16 55
Weston-super-Mare	a				14 00			14 22				15 00			15 23				16 00			16 22				17 00
	d							14 23							15 28							16 23				
Highbridge & Burnham	d							14 34							15 39							16 34				
Bridgwater	d							14 42							15 47							16 42				
Taunton	a						14 15	14 59						15 17	16 01						16 15	16 59				

Station		GW ◇ H	XC 1 ◇ ⊼	GW B	XC 1 ◇ ⊼	GW ◇ ⊼	GW B		GW	GW ◇ A	XC 1 ◇ ⊼	GW B	XC 1 ◇ ⊼	GW 1 ◇ 🍽		GW ◇ ⊼	GW	GW J	XC 1 ◇ ⊼	GW B	GW 1 ◇ 🍽		GW ◇ ⊼	XC 1 ◇ ⊼	GW	GW K
Gloucester 7	d	15 46								16 42								17 46						18 40		18 42
Cam & Dursley	d	16 01								16 56								18 01								18 56
Yate	d	16 15								17 10								18 16								19 10
London Paddington 15 ⊖	d													16 30							17 30					
Bath Spa 7	d													18 00							19 00					
Bristol Parkway 7	a	16 24								17 19								18 24						19 08		19 21
	d	16 24	16 28		16 58				17 12	17 19	17 26		17 58				18 12	18 25	18 28					19 09	19 19	19 21
Filton Abbey Wood	d	16 28		16 42		17 10			17 15	17 23		17 42				18 10	18 14	18 28		18 42			19 09		19 23	19 25
Stapleton Road	d	16 34								17 28								18 34								19 31
Lawrence Hill	d	16 36								17 30								18 36								19 33
Bristol Temple Meads 10	a	16 39	16 41	16 52	17 11	17 18			17 23	17 35	17 38	17 52	18 13	18 15		18 18	18 23	18 39	18 41	18 52	19 15		19 18	19 27	19 31	19 38
	d		16 44	16 53	17 11				17 25		17 44	17 53		18 17			18 25		18 44	18 53	19 17					
Bedminster	d								17x27								18x27									
Parson Street	d								17 29								18 29									
Nailsea & Backwell	d			17 03					17 38			18 03					18 38			19 03	19 30					
Yatton	d			17 08			←		17 44			18 08					18 44			19 08	19 37					
Worle	d			17 14 →			17 14		17 50			18 14					18 50			19 14	19 43					
Weston Milton	d								17 55								18 55			19 20						
Weston-super-Mare	a						17 22		18 00			18 21		18 36			19 00			19 23	19 52					
	d						17 23					18 23		18 40						19 23						
Highbridge & Burnham	d						17 34					18 34								19 34						
Bridgwater	d						17 42					18 42								19 42						
Taunton	a		17 17		17 42		17 59				18 15	18 59		19 06					19 15	19 59						

For general notes see front of timetable
For details of catering facilities see Directory of Train Operators

A To Weymouth (Table 123)
B From Cardiff Central (Table 132)
C From Worcester Shrub Hill (Table 57) to Westbury (Table 123)
D From Great Malvern (Table 71) to Brighton (Table 123)
E To Westbury (Table 123)
G From Worcester Foregate Street (Table 71) to Weymouth (Table 123)
H From Great Malvern (Table 71) to Weymouth (Table 123)
J From Great Malvern (Table 71) to Westbury (Table 123)
K To Frome (Table 123)

Table 134

Gloucester → Taunton

Saturdays

from 12 September

Network Diagram - see first page of Table 132

Station		XC	GW	XC	GW	GW	GW	GW	XC	GW	GW	XC	GW	GW	XC	GW	GW	XC	GW	XC	GW
		1 ◇ ⊼	A	1 ◇ ⊼	1 ◇ ⊡	◇ ⊼		◇ B	1 ◇ ⊼	1 ◇ ⊡		1 ◇ ⊼	◇ ⊼	1 ◇ ⊡	1 ◇ ⊼	C	D	1 ◇ ⊼	1 ◇ ⊡	1 ◇ ⊼	
Gloucester 7	d							19 46									21 16				
Cam & Dursley	d							19 59									21 30				
Yate	d							20 14									21 44				
London Paddington 15 ⊖	d				18 30					19 00									20 30		
Bath Spa 7	d				20 01					20 25									22 00		
Bristol Parkway 7	a							20 23									21 53				
	d	19 28		19 58			20 17	20 23	20 31			20 58			21 25		21 53	21 58		22 25	
Filton Abbey Wood	d		19 42			20 09	20 20	20 27			20 38		21 09			21 42					22 52
Stapleton Road	d							20 33													
Lawrence Hill	d							20 35													
Bristol Temple Meads 10	a	19 41	19 52	20 13	20 15	20 18	20 29	20 39	20 42	20 42	20 48	21 13	21 18		21 35	21 50	22 04	22 13	22 15	22 41	23 00
	d	19 44	19 53		20 15				20 50	20 55		21 13			21 44	21 55			22 17		
Bedminster	d															21x58					
Parson Street	d															22 01					
Nailsea & Backwell	d		20 03							21 04						22 09			22s28		
Yatton	d		20 08							21 11						22 15			22s35		
Worle	d		20 14							21 17				←		22 21			22s41		
Weston Milton	d		20 19							21 22				21 22							
Weston-super-Mare	a		20 23		20 36					→				21 26		22 27			22s48		
	d		20 23		20 38									21 26		22 28					
Highbridge & Burnham	d		20 34											21 39		22 39			22s59		
Bridgwater	d		20 42											21 46		22 47			23s06		
Taunton	a	20 15	20 59		21 06				21 21			21 44		22 00	22 16	23 02			23 18		

Sundays

until 12 July

Station		GW	GW	GW	GW	XC	GW	GW	GW	XC	GW	GW	XC	GW	GW	XC	GW	GW	GW	XC	GW	GW	GW	XC
		◇ E	◇ E	◇ ⊼	1	1 ◇ ⊼	1 ◇ ⊡	◇ ⊼		1 ◇ ⊼	◇ ⊼	D	1 ◇ ⊼	1 ◇ ⊡	◇ ⊼	1 ◇ ⊼	1 ◇ ⊡	◇ ⊼	D	1 ◇ ⊼	1 ◇ ⊡	◇ ⊼		1 ◇ ⊼
Gloucester 7	d											10 19							12 14					
Cam & Dursley	d											10 32							12 28					
Yate	d											10 46							12 43					
London Paddington 15 ⊖	d						08 00							10 00			11 00				12 00			
Bath Spa 7	d						09 46							11 41			12 41				13 41			
Bristol Parkway 7	a											10 55							12 51					
	d									10 25		10 55	11 30			12 27			12 57	13 25				14 25
Filton Abbey Wood	d			08 54				09 56			10 54	10 59			11 54			12 57	13 01			13 54		
Stapleton Road	d																							
Lawrence Hill	d																							
Bristol Temple Meads 10	a			09 04			09 59	10 06		10 35	11 03	11 08	11 41	11 57	12 04	12 39	12 54	13 05	13 09	13 35	13 56	14 04		14 35
	d	07 45	08 28		09 30	09 44	10 00		10 10	10 44		11 10	11 44	11 57		12 44	12 57			13 44	13 56		14 10	14 44
Bedminster	d								10x13															
Parson Street	d								10 16															
Nailsea & Backwell	d		08 38		09 39				10 24			11 21		12 09			13 07						14 20	
Yatton	d	07 58	08 43		09 46				10 30			11 26		12 15			13 14						14 25	
Worle	d		08 49		09 52				10 36			11 32		12 20			13 20						14 31	
Weston Milton	d																							
Weston-super-Mare	a	08 07	08 55		10 03				10 41			11 38		12 31			13 32						14 37	
	d	08 08	08 56						10 42			11 39											14 38	
Highbridge & Burnham	d		09 07						10 52			11 50											14 49	
Bridgwater	d	08 24	09 15						11 00			11 58											14 57	
Taunton	a	08 37	09 28			10 19	10 33		11 14	11 19		12 12	12 16			13 16				14 15	14 30		15 11	15 15

Station		GW	GW	XC	GW	GW	GW	XC	GW	GW	XC	GW	GW	XC	GW	GW	XC	GW	GW	GW	XC	GW	XC	GW
		◇ ⊼		1 ◇ ⊼		◇ ⊼	G	1 ◇ ⊼		G	1 ◇ ⊼	1 ◇ ⊡	◇ ⊼	1 ◇ ⊼		◇ ⊼	1 ◇ ⊼	◇ ⊼	H	G	1 ◇ ⊼	◇ ⊼	1 ◇ ⊼	
Gloucester 7	d						15 13													17 20				
Cam & Dursley	d						15 27													17 34				
Yate	d						15 41													17 49				
London Paddington 15 ⊖	d											15 00												
Bath Spa 7	d											16 41												
Bristol Parkway 7	a						15 49													17 57				
	d			15 26			15 51	16 00			16 25			16 58			17 25			17 58	18 04		18 25	
Filton Abbey Wood	d	14 55				15 56	15 58						16 55			17 17		17 54		18 02		18 22		
Stapleton Road	d																							
Lawrence Hill	d																							
Bristol Temple Meads 10	a	15 05		15 38		16 06	16 09	16 13		←	16 35	16 55	17 05	17 14		17 25	17 35	18 04		18 14	18 18	18 31	18 37	
	d		15 16	15 44	15 50		16 26	16 14		16 26	16 44	17 02			17 25		17 44		18 07				18 44	19 05
Bedminster	d		15x19		15x53		→								17x28									19x08
Parson Street	d				15 56																			19 10
Nailsea & Backwell	d		15 28		16 04				←	16 36		17 13			17 37				18 17					19 18
Yatton	d		15 34		16 10				16 10	16 41		17 20			17 43				18 23					19 24
Worle	d		15 40		→				16 19	16 47		17 26			17 49				18 29					19 30
Weston Milton	d		15 45							16 53					17 58									19 34
Weston-super-Mare	a		15 48						16 26	16 57		17 36			18 01				18 34					19 37
	d								16 28			17 37							18 36					19 39
Highbridge & Burnham	d								16 40										18 46					19 51
Bridgwater	d								16 48										18 54					19 59
Taunton	a			16 16				16 45	17 03		17 15	18 01					18 19		19 09				19 15	20 14

For general notes see front of timetable
For details of catering facilities see Directory of Train Operators

- **A** From Cardiff Central (Table 132)
- **B** From Great Malvern (Table 71) to Weymouth (Table 123)
- **C** From Cardiff Central (Table 132) to Exeter St Davids (Table 135)
- **D** From Cheltenham Spa (Table 57)
- **E** To Penzance (Table 135)
- **G** From Worcester Shrub Hill (Table 57)
- **H** To Exeter St Davids (Table 135)

Sundays

until 12 July

Gloucester → Taunton

Network Diagram - see first page of Table 132

		GW ◇ 🛒	XC [1] ◇ 🛒	GW [1] ◇ 🍴	XC [1] ◇ 🛒	GW ◇ 🛒	GW A	XC [1] ◇ 🛒	GW	XC [1] ◇ 🛒	GW	GW [1] ◇ B 🍴	GW ◇ 🛒	XC [1] ◇ 🛒	XC [1] ◇ 🛒	GW A	XC [1] ◇ 🛒	GW	XC [1] ◇ 🛒	GW [1] ◇ 🍴	GW ◇ 🛒	XC [1] ◇ 🛒	XC [1] ◇ 🛒
Gloucester [7]	d		18 40				19 18									21 15							
Cam & Dursley	d						19 32									21 31							
Yate	d						19 46									21 45							
London Paddington [15] ⊖	d			17 30								19 00								21 00			
Bath Spa [7]	d			19 14								20 41								22 42			
Bristol Parkway [7]	a		19 08				19 55									21 53							
	d		19 09		19 25		19 55	20 02		20 25				20 58	21 25	21 55	22 00		22 26			22 58	23 26
Filton Abbey Wood	d	18 56				19 52	19 59						20 54			21 58					22 58		
Stapleton Road	d																						
Lawrence Hill	d																						
Bristol Temple Meads [10]	a	19 06	19 25	19 28	19 35	20 02	20 08	20 14		20 35		20 55	21 04	21 14	21 35	22 07	22 14		22 41	22 58	23 07	23 14	23 41
	d			19 30	19 44			20 19	20 25	20 44		20 57			21 44			22 30		22 58			
Bedminster	d								20x28									22x33					
Parson Street	d																	22 35					
Nailsea & Backwell	d			19 41					20 36			21 07						22 43		23 11			
Yatton	d			19 48					20 42		←	21 14						22 49		23 17			
Worle	d			19 54					20 48 →		20 48	21 20						22 55		23 24			
Weston Milton	d																	23 00					
Weston-super-Mare	a			20 02				20 36			20 53	21 27						23 03		23 32			
	d							20 37			20 58	21 29											
Highbridge & Burnham	d										21 09												
Bridgwater	d										21 17												
Taunton	a				20 16			20 58		21 15	21 33	21 50			22 15								

Sundays

19 July to 6 September

		GW ◇ C	GW ◇ C	GW ◇ 🛒	GW [1]	XC [1] ◇ 🛒	GW [1] ◇ 🍴	GW ◇ 🛒	GW	XC [1] ◇ 🛒	GW ◇ 🛒	GW D	XC [1] ◇ 🛒	GW ◇ 🛒	GW [1] ◇ 🍴	XC [1] ◇ 🛒	GW ◇ 🛒	GW D	GW [1] ◇ 🍴	XC [1] ◇ 🛒	GW ◇ 🛒	GW	GW [1] ◇ 🍴	GW	XC [1] ◇ E 🛒
Gloucester [7]	d											10 19						12 14							
Cam & Dursley	d											10 32						12 28							
Yate	d											10 46						12 43							
London Paddington [15] ⊖	d						08 00								10 00				11 00				12 00		
Bath Spa [7]	d														12 01				13 01				14 01		
Bristol Parkway [7]	a											10 55						12 51							
	d									10 25		10 55	11 50			12 25		12 57		13 25					14 27
Filton Abbey Wood	d			08 54				09 56			10 54	10 59		11 54			12 57	13 01			13 54				
Stapleton Road	d																								
Lawrence Hill	d																								
Bristol Temple Meads [10]	a			09 04			09 49	10 06		10 35	11 03	11 08	11 41	12 04	12 16	12 36	13 05	13 09	13 13	13 35	14 04		14 16		14 38
	d	07 45	08 28		09 30	09 44	09 52		10 10	10 44		11 10	11 44		12 17	12 44			13 16	13 44		14 10	14 19		14 44
Bedminster	d								10x13																
Parson Street	d								10 16																
Nailsea & Backwell	d		08 38		09 39				10 24			11 21			12 28				13 26			14 20			
Yatton	d	07 58	08 43		09 46				10 30			11 26			12 35				13 33			14 25		←	
Worle	d		08 49		09 52				10 36			11 32			12 39				13 39			14 31 →		14 31	
Weston Milton	d																								
Weston-super-Mare	a	08 07	08 55		10 03				10 41			11 38			12 50				13 50					14 37	
	d	08 08	08 56						10 42			11 39												14 38	
Highbridge & Burnham	d		09 07						10 52			11 50												14 49	
Bridgwater	d	08 24	09 15						11 00			11 58												14 57	
Taunton	a	08 37	09 28			10 19	10 27		11 14	11 19		12 12	12 16			13 16				14 15			15 00	15 11	15 15

		GW ◇ 🛒	GW	XC [1] ◇ 🛒	GW	GW ◇ 🛒	GW A	XC [1] ◇ 🛒	GW	GW A	XC [1] ◇ 🛒	GW [1] ◇ 🍴	GW ◇ 🛒	XC [1] ◇ 🛒	GW	GW ◇ 🛒	XC [1] ◇ 🛒	GW ◇ 🛒	GW B	GW A	XC [1] ◇ 🛒	GW ◇ 🛒	XC [1] ◇ 🛒	GW
Gloucester [7]	d						15 13													17 20				
Cam & Dursley	d						15 27													17 34				
Yate	d						15 41													17 49				
London Paddington [15] ⊖	d											15 00												
Bath Spa [7]	d											16 41												
Bristol Parkway [7]	a						15 49													17 57				
	d			15 26			15 51	16 00			16 25			16 58			17 25			17 58	18 02		18 25	
Filton Abbey Wood	d	14 55				15 56	15 58						16 55			17 17		17 54		18 01		18 22		
Stapleton Road	d																							
Lawrence Hill	d																							
Bristol Temple Meads [10]	a	15 05		15 38		16 06	16 09	16 13		←	16 35	16 55	17 05	17 14		17 25	17 35	18 04		18 10	18 14	18 31	18 37	
	d		15 16	15 44	15 50		16 26 →	16 14		16 26	16 44	17 02			17 25		17 44		18 07				18 44	19 05
Bedminster	d		15x19		15x53										17x28									19x08
Parson Street	d				15 56																			19 10
Nailsea & Backwell	d		15 28		16 04				←	16 36		17 13			17 37				18 17					19 18
Yatton	d		15 34		16 10 →				16 10	16 41		17 20			17 43				18 23					19 24
Worle	d		15 40						16 19	16 47		17 26			17 49				18 29					19 30
Weston Milton	d		15 45							16 53					17 58									19 34
Weston-super-Mare	a		15 48						16 26	16 57		17 36			18 01				18 34					19 37
	d								16 28			17 37							18 36					19 39
Highbridge & Burnham	d								16 40										18 46					19 51
Bridgwater	d								16 48										18 54					19 59
Taunton	a			16 16				16 45	17 03		17 15	18 01					18 19		19 09				19 15	20 14

For general notes see front of timetable
For details of catering facilities see Directory of Train Operators

A From Worcester Shrub Hill (Table 57)
B To Exeter St Davids (Table 135)
C To Penzance (Table 135)
D From Cheltenham Spa (Table 57)
E From Birmingham New Street (Table 57)

Gloucester → Taunton

Sundays

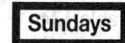

19 July to 6 September

Network Diagram - see first page of Table 132

		GW	XC	GW	XC	GW		GW	XC	GW	XC	GW	GW	GW	XC	XC	GW	XC	GW	XC	GW	GW	XC	XC		
		◇	[1] ◇	[1] ◇	[1] ◇	◇			[1] ◇		[1] ◇		[1] ◇	◇	[1] ◇	[1] ◇		[1] ◇		[1] ◇	[1] ◇	◇	[1] ◇	[1] ◇		
								A					B				A									
		⊤	⊤	⊡	⊤	⊤			⊤		⊤		⊡	⊤	⊤	⊤		⊤		⊤	⊡	⊤	⊤	⊤		
Gloucester [7]	d		18 40					19 18									21 15									
Cam & Dursley	d							19 32									21 31									
Yate	d							19 46									21 45									
London Paddington [15] ⊖	d			17 30									19 00								21 00					
Bath Spa [7]	d			19 14									20 41								22 42					
Bristol Parkway [7]	a		19 08					19 55									21 53									
	d		19 09		19 25			19 55	20 00		20 25				20 58	21 25	21 55	22 00		22 25			22 58	23 25		
Filton Abbey Wood	d	18 56				19 52		19 59						20 54			21 58					22 58				
Stapleton Road	d																									
Lawrence Hill	d																									
Bristol Temple Meads [10]	a	19 06	19 25	19 28	19 35	20 02		20 08	20 14		20 35		20 55	21 04	21 14	21 35	22 07	22 14		22 41	22 58	23 07	23 13	23 41		
	d			19 30	19 44				20 19	20 25	20 44		20 57			21 44			22 30		22 58					
Bedminster	d									20x28									22x33							
Parson Street	d																		22 35							
Nailsea & Backwell	d			19 41						20 36			21 07						22 43		23 11					
Yatton	d			19 48						20 42		←	21 14						22 49		23 17					
Worle	d			19 54						20 48 →		20 48	21 20						22 55		23 24					
Weston Milton	d																		23 00							
Weston-super-Mare	a			20 02					20 36			20 53	21 27						23 03		23 32					
	d								20 37			20 58	21 29													
Highbridge & Burnham	d											21 09														
Bridgwater	d											21 17														
Taunton	a				20 18				20 58		21 15	21 33	21 50			22 15										

Sundays

13 September to 1 November

		GW	XC	GW	GW	GW	XC	GW	GW	GW	XC	GW	GW	XC	GW		GW	XC	GW	GW	GW	XC	GW	GW	GW	XC
		◇	[1] ◇	◇	◇	[1]	[1] ◇	[1] ◇	◇		[1] ◇	◇		[1] ◇	[1] ◇		◇	[1] ◇	[1] ◇	◇		[1] ◇	[1] ◇	◇		[1] ◇
		C		C									D								D					
			⊤		⊤		⊤	⊡	⊤		⊤	⊤		⊤	⊡		⊤	⊤	⊡	⊤		⊤	⊡	⊤		⊤
Gloucester [7]	d												10 19								12 14					
Cam & Dursley	d												10 32								12 28					
Yate	d												10 46								12 43					
London Paddington [15] ⊖	d							08 00							10 03				11 03				12 03			
Bath Spa [7]	d							09 39							11 41				12 41				13 41			
Bristol Parkway [7]	a												10 55								12 51					
	d										10 25		10 55	11 25				12 25			12 57	13 25				14 25
Filton Abbey Wood	d				08 54				09 56			10 54	10 59				11 54			12 57	13 01			13 54		
Stapleton Road	d																									
Lawrence Hill	d																									
Bristol Temple Meads [10]	a				09 04			09 52	10 06		10 35	11 03	11 08	11 37	11 57		12 04	12 37	12 54	13 05	13 09	13 35	13 56	14 04		14 35
	d	07 45	08 25	08 28		09 30	09 44	09 53		10 10	10 44		11 10	11 44	11 57			12 44	12 57			13 44	13 56		14 10	14 44
Bedminster	d									10x13																
Parson Street	d									10 16																
Nailsea & Backwell	d			08 38		09 39				10 24			11 21		12 09				13 07						14 20	
Yatton	d	07 58		08 43		09 46				10 30			11 26		12 15				13 14						14 25	
Worle	d			08 49		09 52				10 36			11 32		12 20				13 20						14 31	
Weston Milton	d																									
Weston-super-Mare	a	08 07		08 55		10 03				10 41			11 38		12 34				13 32						14 37	
	d	08 08		08 56						10 42			11 39												14 38	
Highbridge & Burnham	d			09 07						10 52			11 50												14 49	
Bridgwater	d	08 24		09 15						11 00			11 58												14 57	
Taunton	a	08 37	08 56	09 28			10 19	10 27		11 14	11 19		12 12	12 16				13 16				14 15	14 30		15 11	15 15

		GW	XC	GW	XC	GW	GW		GW	XC	GW	GW	XC	GW	GW	XC	GW	GW	XC	GW	GW	GW		XC	GW	XC
		◇	[1] ◇		[1] ◇		◇			[1] ◇			[1] ◇	[1] ◇	◇	[1] ◇		◇	[1] ◇	◇				[1] ◇	◇	[1] ◇
									A			A									B	A				
		⊤	⊤		⊤		⊤			⊤			⊤	⊡	⊤	⊤		⊤	⊤	⊤				⊤	⊤	⊤
Gloucester [7]	d								15 13													17 20				
Cam & Dursley	d								15 27													17 34				
Yate	d								15 41													17 49				
London Paddington [15] ⊖	d													15 03												
Bath Spa [7]	d													16 41												
Bristol Parkway [7]	a								15 49													17 57				
	d		14 58		15 26				15 51	16 02			16 25			16 58			17 25			17 58		18 02		18 25
Filton Abbey Wood	d	14 55					15 56		15 58						16 55			17 17		17 54		18 01			18 22	
Stapleton Road	d																									
Lawrence Hill	d																									
Bristol Temple Meads [10]	a	15 05	15 14		15 38		16 06		16 09	16 14		←	16 35	16 55	17 05	17 13		17 25	17 35	18 04		18 10		18 14	18 31	18 37
	d			15 16	15 44	15 50			16 26 →	16 14		16 26	16 44	17 02			17 25		17 44		18 07					18 44
Bedminster	d			15x19		15x53											17x28									
Parson Street	d					15 56																				
Nailsea & Backwell	d			15 28		16 04					←	16 36		17 13			17 37				18 17					
Yatton	d			15 34		16 10 →					16 10	16 41		17 20			17 43				18 23					
Worle	d			15 40							16 19	16 47		17 26			17 49				18 29					
Weston Milton	d			15 45								16 53					17 58									
Weston-super-Mare	a			15 48							16 26	16 57		17 36			18 01				18 34					
	d										16 28			17 37							18 36					
Highbridge & Burnham	d										16 40										18 46					
Bridgwater	d										16 48										18 54					
Taunton	a				16 16					16 45	17 03		17 15	18 01					18 19		19 09					19 15

For general notes see front of timetable
For details of catering facilities see Directory of Train Operators

A From Worcester Shrub Hill (Table 57)
B To Exeter St Davids (Table 135)
C To Penzance (Table 135)
D From Cheltenham Spa (Table 57)

Table 134

Sundays

13 September to 1 November

Gloucester → Taunton

Network Diagram - see first page of Table 132

Station		GW	GW ◇ trolley	XC 1◇ trolley	GW 1◇ buffet	XC 1◇ trolley	GW ◇ trolley	GW A	XC 1◇ trolley	GW	XC 1◇ trolley	GW	GW 1◇ B buffet	GW ◇ trolley	XC 1◇ trolley	XC 1◇ trolley	GW A	XC 1◇ trolley	GW	XC 1◇ trolley	GW 1◇ buffet	GW ◇ trolley	XC 1◇ trolley	XC 1◇ trolley
Gloucester [7]	d			18 40				19 18									21 15							
Cam & Dursley	d							19 32									21 31							
Yate	d							19 46									21 45							
London Paddington [15] ⊖	d				17 30								19 03								21 03			
Bath Spa [7]	d				19 14								20 41								22 42			
Bristol Parkway [7]	a			19 08				19 55									21 53							
	d			19 09		19 25		19 55	20 00		20 25				20 58	21 25	21 55	22 00		22 25			22 58	23 26
Filton Abbey Wood	d		18 56				19 52	19 59						20 54			21 58					22 58		
Stapleton Road	d																							
Lawrence Hill	d																							
Bristol Temple Meads [10]	a		19 06	19 25	19 28	19 35	20 02	20 08	20 14		20 35		20 55	21 04	21 14	21 35	22 07	22 14		22 41	22 58	23 07	23 14	23 41
	d	19 05			19 30	19 44			20 19	20 25	20 44		20 57			21 44			22 30		22 58			
Bedminster	d	19x08								20x28									22x33					
Parson Street	d	19 10																	22 35					
Nailsea & Backwell	d	19 18			19 41					20 36			21 07						22 43		23 11			
Yatton	d	19 24			19 48					20 42		←	21 14						22 49		23 17			
Worle	d	19 30			19 54					20 48 →		20 48	21 20						22 55		23 24			
Weston Milton	d	19 34																	23 00					
Weston-super-Mare	a	19 37			20 02				20 36			20 53	21 27						23 03		23 32			
	d	19 39							20 37			20 58	21 29											
Highbridge & Burnham	d	19 51										21 09												
Bridgwater	d	19 59										21 17												
Taunton	a	20 14				20 18			20 58		21 15	21 33	21 50			22 15								

Sundays

from 8 November

Station		GW ◇ C	XC 1◇ trolley	GW ◇ C	GW ◇ trolley	GW 1	XC 1◇ trolley	GW 1◇ buffet	GW ◇ trolley	GW	XC 1◇ trolley	GW ◇ trolley	GW D	XC 1◇ trolley	GW 1◇ buffet	GW ◇ trolley	XC 1◇ trolley	GW 1◇ buffet	GW ◇ trolley	GW D	XC 1◇ trolley	GW 1◇ buffet
Gloucester [7]	d												10 19							12 14		
Cam & Dursley	d												10 32							12 28		
Yate	d												10 46							12 43		
London Paddington [15] ⊖	d							08 00							10 03			11 03				12 03
Bath Spa [7]	d							09 39							11 41			12 41				13 41
Bristol Parkway [7]	a												10 55							12 51		
	d										10 25		10 55	11 25			12 25			12 57	13 25	
Filton Abbey Wood	d				08 54				09 56			10 54	10 59			11 54			12 57	13 01		
Stapleton Road	d																					
Lawrence Hill	d																					
Bristol Temple Meads [10]	a				09 04			09 52	10 06		10 35	11 03	11 08	11 37	11 57	12 04	12 36	12 54	13 05	13 09	13 35	13 56
	d	07 45	08 25	08 28		09 30	09 44	09 53		10 10	10 44		11 10	11 44	11 57		12 44	12 57			13 44	13 56
Bedminster	d									10x13												
Parson Street	d									10 16												
Nailsea & Backwell	d			08 38		09 39				10 24			11 21		12 09			13 07				
Yatton	d	07 58		08 43		09 46				10 30			11 26		12 15			13 14				
Worle	d			08 49		09 52				10 36			11 32		12 20			13 20				
Weston Milton	d																					
Weston-super-Mare	a	08 07		08 55		10 03				10 41			11 38		12 34			13 32				
	d	08 08		08 56						10 42			11 39									
Highbridge & Burnham	d			09 07						10 52			11 50									
Bridgwater	d	08 24		09 15						11 00			11 58									
Taunton	a	08 37	08 56	09 28			10 19	10 27		11 14	11 19		12 12	12 16			13 16				14 15	14 30

Station		GW ◇ trolley	GW	XC 1◇ trolley	GW ◇ trolley	GW	XC 1◇ E trolley	GW	GW ◇ trolley	GW A	XC 1◇ trolley	GW 1◇ buffet	GW ◇ trolley	GW	GW ◇ trolley	XC 1◇ trolley	GW ◇ trolley	GW B	GW A	GW ◇ trolley	XC 1◇ trolley
Gloucester [7]	d									15 13									17 20		
Cam & Dursley	d									15 27									17 34		
Yate	d									15 41									17 49		
London Paddington [15] ⊖	d											15 03									
Bath Spa [7]	d											16 41									
Bristol Parkway [7]	a									15 49									17 57		
	d			14 27			15 25			15 51	16 25					17 25			17 58		18 25
Filton Abbey Wood	d	13 54			14 55				15 56	15 58			16 55		17 17		17 54		18 01	18 22	
Stapleton Road	d																				
Lawrence Hill	d																				
Bristol Temple Meads [10]	a	14 04		14 37	15 05		15 36		16 06	16 09	16 35	16 55	17 05		17 25	17 35	18 04		18 10	18 31	18 35
	d		14 10	14 44		15 16	15 44	15 50		16 26	16 44	17 02		17 25		17 44		18 07			18 44
Bedminster	d					15x19		15x53						17x28							
Parson Street	d							15 56													
Nailsea & Backwell	d		14 20			15 28		16 04		16 36		17 13		17 37				18 17			
Yatton	d		14 25			15 34		16 10		16 41		17 20		17 43				18 23			
Worle	d		14 31			15 40		16 19		16 47		17 26		17 49				18 29			
Weston Milton	d					15 45				16 53				17 58							
Weston-super-Mare	a		14 37			15 48		16 26		16 57		17 36		18 01				18 34			
	d		14 38					16 28				17 37						18 36			
Highbridge & Burnham	d		14 49					16 40										18 46			
Bridgwater	d		14 57					16 48										18 54			
Taunton	a		15 11	15 15			16 16	17 03			17 15	18 01				18 19		19 09			19 15

For general notes see front of timetable
For details of catering facilities see Directory of Train Operators

- **A** From Worcester Shrub Hill (Table 57)
- **B** To Exeter St Davids (Table 135)
- **C** To Penzance (Table 135)
- **D** From Cheltenham Spa (Table 57)
- **E** From Birmingham New Street (Table 57)

Table 134

Sundays

from 8 November

Gloucester → Taunton

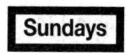

Network Diagram - see first page of Table 132

		GW	GW	GW		XC	GW	GW	GW		XC	GW	GW	GW		XC	GW	GW	XC		GW	GW	XC			
			◇	**1** ◇		**1** ◇	◇				**1** ◇		**1** ◇	◇		**1** ◇			**1** ◇		**1** ◇	◇	**1** ◇			
								A					B				A									
			⊥	⊏P		⊥	⊥				⊥		⊏P	⊥		⊥			⊥		⊏P	⊥	⊥			
Gloucester 7	d							19 18									21 15									
Cam & Dursley	d							19 32									21 31									
Yate	d							19 46									21 45									
London Paddington 15	⊖ d			17 30									19 03								21 03					
Bath Spa 7	d			19 14									20 41								22 42					
Bristol Parkway 7	a							19 55									21 53									
	d					19 25		19 55			20 28					21 25	21 55		22 25				23 25			
Filton Abbey Wood	d		18 56				19 52	19 59						20 54			21 58					22 58				
Stapleton Road	d																									
Lawrence Hill	d																									
Bristol Temple Meads 10	a		19 06	19 28		19 35	20 02	20 08			20 39		20 55	21 04		21 36	22 07		22 40		22 58	23 07	23 40			
	d	19 05		19 30		19 44			20 25		20 44		20 57			21 44		22 30			22 58					
Bedminster	d	19x08							20x28									22x33								
Parson Street	d	19 10																22 35								
Nailsea & Backwell	d	19 18		19 41					20 36				21 07					22 43			23 11					
Yatton	d	19 24		19 48					20 42			←	21 14					22 49			23 17					
Worle	d	19 30		19 54					20 48			20 48	21 20					22 55			23 24					
Weston Milton	d	19 34							→									23 00								
Weston-super-Mare	a	19 37		20 02								20 53	21 27					23 03			23 32					
	d	19 39										20 58	21 29													
Highbridge & Burnham	d	19 51										21 09														
Bridgwater	d	19 59										21 17														
Taunton	a	20 14				20 18					21 15	21 33	21 50			22 15										

For general notes see front of timetable
For details of catering facilities see
Directory of Train Operators

A From Worcester Shrub Hill (Table 57)
B To Exeter St Davids (Table 135)

Table 134

Mondays to Fridays

Taunton → Gloucester

Network Diagram - see first page of Table 132

			GW	XC	GW	GW	GW	GW	XC	GW	GW	GW	GW	XC	GW	GW	GW	GW	XC	GW	GW	GW	GW
				■1 ◇				■1 ◇	■1 ◇	■1 ◇		■1 ◇		■1 ◇				■1 ◇	■1 ◇	◇		■1 ◇	
					A		B				A		C		D	C		C		E	A	G	
Miles				⊼				⊡	⊼	⊡		⊡		⊼				⊡	⊼			⊡	
0	**Taunton**	d				05 30					06 02		06 35	06 51				06 54				07 15	07 28
11¾	Bridgwater	d				05 42					06 14		06 48					07 05				07 25	07 40
18	Highbridge & Burnham	d				05 49					06 21		06 55					07 12				07 33	07 48
25¾	**Weston-super-Mare**	a				06 00					06 32		07 06					07 24				07 43	08 00
—		d				06 01		06 20			06 36	06 49	07 08					07 24			07 37	07 49	08 06
27	Weston Milton	d						06 25			06 39	06 53	07 11			←					07 40	07 53	08 09
29½	Worle	d				06 07		06 30			06 43	06 59	07 16			07 16		07 32			07 44	07 59	08 15
33½	Yatton	d				06 12		06 37			06 49	07 06	→			07 22		07 39			07 49	08 06	→
37½	Nailsea & Backwell	d				06 18		06 44			06 55	07 13				07 28		07 46			07 55	08 13	
43¾	Parson Street	d									07 01					07 34					08 02		
44½	Bedminster	d									07x04					07x37					08x04		
45½	**Bristol Temple Meads** 10	a				06 30		06 55			07 10	07 24		07 26		07 43		07 58			08 10	08 25	
—		d	05 54	06 15	06 22		06 50	07 00	07 00	07 15	07 19	07 30		07 30	07 34	07 46	07 53	08 00	08 00	08 10	08 21	08 30	
46½	Lawrence Hill	d			06 25		06 54				07 22					07 50				08 13			
47	Stapleton Road	d			06 27		06 56				07 24					07 52				08 16			
50	Filton Abbey Wood	d	06a01		06a33		07a02			07a21	07 30				07 44	07 59	08a00			08 21	08a32		
51¼	**Bristol Parkway** 7	a		06 23					07 08		07 33			07 38	07 48	08 05			08 08	08 29			
—		d		06 25											07 48								
—	Bath Spa 7	a						07 11				07 41						08 11				08 41	
—	London Paddington 15	⊖ a						08 44				09 14						09 44				10 14	
57½	Yate	d													07 58								
72¼	Cam & Dursley	d													08 10								
85¼	**Gloucester** 7	a		06 56											08 29								

		XC	GW	GW	GW	XC	GW	GW	GW	XC	GW	GW	GW	GW	XC	GW	GW	XC	GW	GW	GW	XC
		■1 ◇			◇	■1 ◇	◇			■1 ◇			◇	■1 ◇	■1 ◇			■1 ◇	◇		◇	■1 ◇
			H				E	A			J			K		A			L			
		⊼			⊼	⊼				⊼			⊼	⊡	⊼			⊼			⊼	⊼
Taunton	d	07 51				08 11			08 36	08 51				09 05			09 37	09 51				
Bridgwater	d								08 48								09 49					
Highbridge & Burnham	d								08 56								09 57					
Weston-super-Mare	a					08 30			09 09					09 27			10 08					
	d					08 32		08 40	09 10					09 28		09 45	10 10					
Weston Milton	d			←				08 43	09 13			←				09 48	10 13			←		
Worle	d			08 15				08 47	09 18			09 18				09 52	10 18			10 18		
Yatton	d			08 21				08 52	→			09 23		09 39		09 57	→			10 23		
Nailsea & Backwell	d			08 28				08 58				09 30		09 45		10 03				10 29		
Parson Street	d			08 36				09 05				09 36				10 10				10 36		
Bedminster	d			08 40				09x07				09x39				10x12				10x38		
Bristol Temple Meads 10	a	08 27		08 46		08 55		09 16		09 27		09 45		09 56		10 18		10 26		10 44		
	d	08 30	08 41	08 47	08 54	09 00	09 10	09 21		09 30	09 41	09 46	09 54	10 00	10 00	10 21		10 30	10 41	10 46	10 54	11 00
Lawrence Hill	d		08 44				09 13					09 49								10 49		
Stapleton Road	d			08 49			09 15					09 51								10 51		
Filton Abbey Wood	d		08 48	08 57	09a01		09 20	09a30			09 48	09 57	10a01			10a30			10 48	10 57	11a01	
Bristol Parkway 7	a	08 38	08 52	09 05		09 08	09 28			09 38	09 52	10 03			10 08			10 38	10 52	11 03		11 08
	d		08 52								09 52								10 52			
Bath Spa 7	a													10 13								
London Paddington 15	⊖ a													11 40								
Yate	d		09 01								10 01								11 01			
Cam & Dursley	d		09 13								10 13								11 13			
Gloucester 7	a		09 33								10 32								11 34			

		GW	XC	GW	GW	GW	GW	XC	GW	GW	XC	GW	GW	GW	XC	GW	XC	GW	GW	GW	GW	XC
			■1 ◇	◇			◇	■1 ◇	■1 ◇		■1 ◇	◇		◇	■1 ◇		■1 ◇	◇			◇	■1 ◇
		A		E		A				A		N				A		E		A		
			⊼				⊼	⊼	⊡		⊼			⊼	⊼		⊼				⊼	⊼
Taunton	d	10 07	10 51			11 02		11 16	11 26		11 51					12 07	12 51			13 07		13 16
Bridgwater	d	10 19				11 14										12 19				13 19		
Highbridge & Burnham	d	10 27				11 22										12 27				13 27		
Weston-super-Mare	a	10 38				11 34				←						12 38				13 38		
	d	10 40			11 10	11 45				11 45			12 10			12 40			13 10	13 40		
Weston Milton	d				11 13	→							12 13						13 13	→		
Worle	d	10 46			11 18					11 50			12 18			12 46			13 18			
Yatton	d	10 52			11 23					11 57			12 23			12 52			13 23			
Nailsea & Backwell	d	10 58			11 29					12 03			12 29			12 58			13 29			
Parson Street	d				11 36								12 36						13 36			
Bedminster	d				11x38								12x38						13x38			
Bristol Temple Meads 10	a	11 11	11 24		11 44			11 53	11 59	12 17	12 24		12 44			13 10	13 24		13 44			13 56
	d	11 21	11 30	11 41	11 46		11 54	12 00	12 00	12 21	12 30	12 41	12 46	12 54	13 00	13 21	13 30	13 41	13 46		13 54	14 00
Lawrence Hill	d				11 49								12 49						13 49			
Stapleton Road	d				11 51								12 51						13 51			
Filton Abbey Wood	d	11a30		11 48	11 57		12a01			12a29		12 48	12 57	13a01		13a30		13 48	13 57		14a01	
Bristol Parkway 7	a		11 38	11 52	12 03			12 08			12 38	12 52	13 03		13 08		13 38	13 52	14 03			14 08
	d			11 52								12 52						13 52				
Bath Spa 7	a								12 11													
London Paddington 15	⊖ a								13 40													
Yate	d			12 01								13 01						14 01				
Cam & Dursley	d			12 13								13 13						14 13				
Gloucester 7	a			12 31								13 31						14 30				

For general notes see front of timetable
For details of catering facilities see Directory of Train Operators

A To Cardiff Central (Table 132)
B From Westbury to Cardiff Central (Table 123)
C From Exeter St Davids (Table 135)
D From Salisbury (Table 123)
E From Weymouth (Table 123)
G From Plymouth (Table 135)
H From Warminster (Table 123) to Great Malvern (Table 71)
J From Westbury (Table 123)
K From Paignton (Table 135)
L From Southampton Central (Table 123) to Great Malvern (Table 71)
N From Brighton (Table 123) to Great Malvern (Table 71)

Taunton → Gloucester

Network Diagram - see first page of Table 132

		GW	GW	XC		GW	GW	GW	XC	GW		XC	GW	GW	GW	XC		GW	GW	XC	GW	GW		GW	XC	GW
				[1] ◇				◇	[1] ◇			[1] ◇	◇		◇	[1] ◇				[1] ◇				◇	[1] ◇	
		A	B			C				A			D						A		E					
				🛒				🛒	🛒			🛒			🛒	🛒				🛒				🛒	🛒	
Taunton	d			13 53						14 07		14 53				15 12			15 15	15 51						
Bridgwater	d									14 19									15 27							
Highbridge & Burnham	d									14 27									15 34							
Weston-super-Mare	a	←								14 38						15 37			15 45							
	d	13 40					14 10			14 40				15 10		15 38			15 46			16 10				
Weston Milton	d						14 13							15 13								16 13				
Worle	d	13 46					14 18			14 46				15 18					15 52			16 18				
Yatton	d	13 52					14 23			14 52				15 23					15 58			16 23				
Nailsea & Backwell	d	13 58					14 29			14 58				15 29					16 04			16 29				
Parson Street	d						14 36							15 36								16 36				
Bedminster	d						14x38							15x38								16x38				
Bristol Temple Meads [10]	a	14 12		14 27			14 44			15 10		15 27		15 44		15 57			16 17	16 27		16 44				
	d	14 21		14 30		14 41	14 46	14 54	15 00	15 21		15 30	15 41	15 46	15 54	16 00		16 15	16 21	16 30	16 41	16 46		16 54	17 00	17 10
Lawrence Hill	d						14 49							15 49				16 17				16 49				17 12
Stapleton Road	d						14 51							15 51				16 19				16 51				17 15
Filton Abbey Wood	d	14a30	14 29			14 48	14 57	15a01		15a30			15 48	15 57	16a01			16 25	16a30		16 48	16 57		17a01		17 21
Bristol Parkway [7]	a		14 37	14 38		14 51	15 03		15 08			15 38	15 52	16 03		16 08		16 36		16 38	16 52	17 03			17 08	17 27
	d					14 52							15 52								16 52					
Bath Spa [7]	a																									
London Paddington [15] ⊖	a																									
Yate	d					15 01							16 01								17 01					
Cam & Dursley	d					15 13							16 13								17 13					
Gloucester [7]	a					15 32							16 32								17 32					

		GW	GW	XC	GW		GW	GW	GW	GW	XC		XC	GW	XC	GW	GW		GW	GW	XC	GW	XC		GW	GW
											FX		FO													
				[1] ◇	[1] ◇		◇			◇	[1] ◇		[1] ◇		[1] ◇	[1] ◇				◇	[1] ◇		[1] ◇			
			A				D		A					A			E		G			A			H	
				🛒	🍽					🛒	🛒		🛒		🛒	🍽				🛒	🛒		🛒			
Taunton	d		16 16	16 53					17 05				17 21		17 51							18 07	18 53			
Bridgwater	d		16 28						17 17													18 19				
Highbridge & Burnham	d		16 36						17 25													18 27				
Weston-super-Mare	a		16 48						17 36													18 38				
	d	16 38	16 51		17 10			17 16	17 38							18 10			18 15			18 40				19 10
Weston Milton	d								17 41					←								18 43				19 13
Worle	d	16 44						17 21	17 45					17 45					18 21			18 47				19 18
Yatton	d	16 50						17 27	→					17 51					18 26			18 53				19 23
Nailsea & Backwell	d	16 56						17 32						17 57					18 32			18 59				19 29
Parson Street	d													18 04								19 07				19 36
Bedminster	d	17x05												18x06								19x09				19x38
Bristol Temple Meads [10]	a	17 11	17 14	17 27	17 30			17 45					17 54	18 13	18 24	18 29			18 46			19 14	19 27			19 44
	d		17 21	17 30	17 30		17 41	17 46		17 54	18 00		18 00	18 21	18 30	18 30	18 41		18 48	18 54	19 00	19 21	19 30		19 41	19 46
Lawrence Hill	d							17 49						18 24					18 51			19 23				19 49
Stapleton Road	d							17 51						18 26					18a53			19 25				19 51
Filton Abbey Wood	d		17a30				17 48	17 57		18a01				18a30			18 48			19a01		19a30			19 48	19 57
Bristol Parkway [7]	a			17 38			17 52	18 05			18 08		18 08		18 38		18 52				19 08		19 38		19 52	20 04
	d						17 52										18 52								19 52	
Bath Spa [7]	a				17 41											18 41										
London Paddington [15] ⊖	a				19 15											20 14										
Yate	d						18 01										19 01								20 01	
Cam & Dursley	d						18 13										19 13								20 13	
Gloucester [7]	a						18 32										19 30								20 32	

		GW	XC	GW	XC	GW		XC	GW	GW	GW	GW		GW	GW	XC	GW	GW		GW	GW	GW	GW			
		FO		FX																						
		◇	[1] ◇		[1] ◇			[1] ◇	◇	◇				[1] ◇	◇	[1] ◇	[1]			[1] ◇		◇				
								J	K		A															
		🛒						🛒		🛒				🍽						🍽						
Taunton	d					19 12		19 51				20 30		21 12		21 16				21 29	21 47		22 45			
Bridgwater	d					19 24						20 42								21 39			22 57			
Highbridge & Burnham	d					19 32						20 50								21 46			23 05			
Weston-super-Mare	a					19 43						21 00								21 56	22 11		23 15			
	d					19 51						21 02					21 31			21 58	22 13		23 17			
Weston Milton	d											21 05					21 35						23 20			
Worle	d					19 57						21 09					21 40			22 05			23 24			
Yatton	d					20 02						21 14					21 47			22 12			23 30			
Nailsea & Backwell	d					20 08						21 20					21 53			22 18			23 36			
Parson Street	d											21 28											23 43			
Bedminster	d											21x30											23x46			
Bristol Temple Meads [10]	a					20 20		20 24				21 36		21 45		21 51	22 04			22 30	22 34		23 52			
	d	19 54	20 00	20 04	20 15			20 30	20 41	20 54	21 19			21 47	21 54	22 00		22 11		22 33		22 54				
Lawrence Hill	d										21 22															
Stapleton Road	d										21 24															
Filton Abbey Wood	d	20a01		20a11	20a21				20 48	21a01	21a30				22a01			22 18				23a01				
Bristol Parkway [7]	a		20 08					20 38	20 52							22 08		22 22								
	d								20 52									22 22								
Bath Spa [7]	a													21 59						22 44						
London Paddington [15] ⊖	a													23 40						00 33						
Yate	d								21 01									22 31								
Cam & Dursley	d								21 13									22 45								
Gloucester [7]	a								21 30									23 02								

For general notes see front of timetable
For details of catering facilities see Directory of Train Operators

A To Cardiff Central (Table 132)
B From Westbury (Table 123)
C From Southampton Central (Table 123) to Worcester Foregate Street (Table 71)
D From Weymouth (Table 123)
E From Warminster (Table 123) to Great Malvern (Table 71)
G To Avonmouth (Table 133)
H From Westbury (Table 123) to Cheltenham Spa (Table 57)
J 🛒 to Bristol Temple Meads
K From Brighton (Table 123) to Worcester Shrub Hill (Table 57)

Taunton → Gloucester

Network Diagram - see first page of Table 132

		XC 1◇	GW	GW 1◇	GW A	GW 1◇	XC 1◇	GW B	GW	XC 1◇	GW C	GW B	GW	GW 1◇	XC 1◇	GW A	GW	XC 1◇	GW 1◇ B	GW D	GW	GW ◇	XC 1◇	GW 1◇ B
Taunton	d		05 30					06 35		06 51				06 55			07 32	07 51	07 58				08 12	
Bridgwater	d		05 42					06 48						07 05			07 44		08 09					
Highbridge & Burnham	d		05 50					06 55						07 13			07 52		08 16					
Weston-super-Mare	a		06 01					07 06						07 23			08 03		08 26					←
	d		06 03			06 24		07 08						07 25		07 39	08 08		08 29 →					08 29
Weston Milton	d							07 11				←				07 42	08 11				←			
Worle	d		06 08			06 32		07 16 →				07 16		07 32		07 47	08 16 →				08 16			
Yatton	d		06 14			06 39						07 22		07 39		07 52					08 21			08 40
Nailsea & Backwell	d		06 20			06 45						07 28		07 46		07 58					08 27			08 46
Parson Street	d											07 35				08 06					08 35			
Bedminster	d											07x38				08x08					08x37			
Bristol Temple Meads 10	a		06 32			06 56				07 25		07 43		07 58		08 13		08 24			08 41		08 45	08 57
	d	06 15		06 46	06 50	07 00	07 00		07 21	07 30	07 41	07 46	07 54	08 00	08 00	08 20		08 30		08 41	08 45	08 54	09 00	09 00
Lawrence Hill	d				06 53							07 50				08 23					08 48			
Stapleton Road	d				06 56							07 52				08 25					08 50			
Filton Abbey Wood	d			06 53	07a01				07a29		07 48	07 59	08a01			08a31				08 48	08 56	09a01		
Bristol Parkway 7	a	06 23		06 57			07 08			07 38	07 52	08 05			08 08			08 38		08 52	09 03		09 08	
	d	06 25									07 52									08 52				
Bath Spa 7	a					07 11								08 11										09 11
London Paddington 15 ⊖	a					08 44								09 44										10 38
Yate	d										08 02									09 02				
Cam & Dursley	d										08 16									09 16				
Gloucester 7	a	06 55									08 32									09 33				

		GW A	XC 1◇	GW ◇ E	GW	GW ◇	XC 1◇	GW A	XC 1◇	GW G	GW	GW ◇	XC 1◇	GW A	GW 1	XC 1◇	GW ◇ E	GW	GW ◇	GW 1	GW A	XC 1◇	GW A	XC 1◇
Taunton	d		08 51					08 58	09 51				10 07	10 11	10 45	10 51					11 07	11 20		11 51
Bridgwater	d							09 10						10 23							11 19			
Highbridge & Burnham	d							09 18						10 31							11 27			
Weston-super-Mare	a							09 29					10 31	10 42							11 38		←	
	d	08 40			09 10			09 40			10 10		10 33	10 43				11 09		11 33	11 40 →		11 40	
Weston Milton	d				09 13						10 13							11 12						
Worle	d	08 46			09 18			09 46			10 18			10 50				11 17					11 46	
Yatton	d	08 52			09 23			09 51			10 23			10 56				11 22					11 52	
Nailsea & Backwell	d	08 58			09 29			09 57			10 29			11 02				11 28					11 58	
Parson Street	d				09 36						10 36							11 36						
Bedminster	d				09x38						10x38							11x38						
Bristol Temple Meads 10	a	09 13	09 25		09 43			10 10	10 26		10 43		10 51	11 14	11 19	11 26		11 42		11 53		11 57	12 12	12 25
	d	09 21	09 30	09 38	09 45	09 54	10 00	10 21	10 30	10 41	10 45	10 54	11 00	11 21	11 30	11 30	11 41	11 45	11 54	12 00		12 00	12 21	12 30
Lawrence Hill	d				09 48						10 48							11 48						
Stapleton Road	d	09 25			09 50			10 25			10 50			11 25				11 50					12 25	
Filton Abbey Wood	d	09a30		09 45	09 56	10a01		10a31		10 48	10 56	11a01		11a30			11 48	11 56	12a01				12a31	
Bristol Parkway 7	a		09 38	09 49	10 03		10 08		10 38	10 52	11 03		11 08			11 38	11 52	12 03				12 08		12 38
	d			09 49						10 52							11 52							
Bath Spa 7	a														11 41					12 11				
London Paddington 15 ⊖	a														13 22					13 39				
Yate	d			09 59						11 02							12 02							
Cam & Dursley	d			10 11						11 16							12 16							
Gloucester 7	a			10 29						11 32							12 31							

		GW ◇ H	GW	GW ◇	XC 1◇	GW A	GW 1◇	XC 1◇	GW ◇ E	GW	GW ◇	XC 1◇	GW A	XC 1◇	GW J	GW	GW ◇	XC 1◇	GW A	GW 1◇	XC 1◇	GW ◇ E	GW
Taunton	d					12 07		12 54					13 07	13 54					14 07		14 51		
Bridgwater	d					12 19							13 19						14 19				
Highbridge & Burnham	d					12 27							13 27						14 27				
Weston-super-Mare	a					12 38							13 38						14 38				
	d		12 10			12 40	13 01			13 10			13 40			14 10			14 40	15 01			15 10
Weston Milton	d		12 13							13 13						14 13							15 13
Worle	d		12 18			12 46				13 18			13 46			14 18			14 46				15 18
Yatton	d		12 23			12 52				13 23			13 52			14 23			14 52				15 23
Nailsea & Backwell	d		12 29			12 58				13 29			13 58			14 29			14 58				15 29
Parson Street	d		12 36							13 37						14 37							15 37
Bedminster	d		12x38							13x39						14x39							15x39
Bristol Temple Meads 10	a		12 43			13 11	13 19	13 27		13 43			14 13	14 27		14 43			15 11	15 22	15 27		15 43
	d	12 41	12 45	12 54	13 00	13 21	13 30	13 30	13 41	13 45	13 54	14 00	14 21	14 30	14 41	14 45	14 54	15 00	15 21	15 30	15 30	15 41	15 45
Lawrence Hill	d		12 48							13 48						14 48							15 48
Stapleton Road	d		12 50			13 25				13 50			14 25			14 50			15 25				15 50
Filton Abbey Wood	d	12 48	12 56	13a01		13a30			13 48	13 56	14a01		14a31		14 48	14 56	15a01		15a30			15 48	15 56
Bristol Parkway 7	a	12 52	13 03		13 08			13 38	13 52	14 03		14 08		14 38	14 52	15 03		15 08			15 38	15 52	16 03
	d	12 52							13 52						14 52							15 52	
Bath Spa 7	a						13 41													15 41			
London Paddington 15 ⊖	a						15 14													17 14			
Yate	d	13 02							14 02						15 02							16 02	
Cam & Dursley	d	13 16							14 16						15 16							16 16	
Gloucester 7	a	13 34							14 32						15 32							16 32	

For general notes see front of timetable
For details of catering facilities see Directory of Train Operators

A To Cardiff Central (Table 132)
B From Exeter St Davids (Table 135)
C From Salisbury (Table 123)
D From Warminster (Table 123) to Great Malvern (Table 71)
E From Weymouth (Table 123)
G From Southampton Central (Table 123) to Worcester Foregate Street (Table 71)
H From Brighton (Table 123) to Great Malvern (Table 71)
J From Southampton Central (Table 123) to Great Malvern (Table 71)

Table 134

Saturdays

until 5 September

Taunton → Gloucester

Network Diagram - see first page of Table 132

		GW ◇	XC 1◇ 🛒	GW A	XC 1◇ 🛒	GW B	GW	GW ◇	XC 1◇ 🛒	GW A		GW 1◇ ☕	XC 1◇ 🛒	GW ◇ C	GW	GW ◇	XC 1◇ 🛒	GW A	GW 1◇ ☕	XC 1◇ 🛒		GW ◇ D	GW	GW ◇	XC 1◇ 🛒	GW A
Taunton	d		15 04	15 07	15 51					16 07			16 51					17 07		17 51						18 07
Bridgwater	d			15 19						16 19								17 19								18 19
Highbridge & Burnham	d			15 27						16 27								17 27								18 27
Weston-super-Mare	a		15 25	15 38						16 38								17 38								18 38
	d		15 27	15 40			16 10			16 40		17 01			17 10			17 40	18 01				18 10			18 40
Weston Milton	d						16 13								17 13								18 13			
Worle	d			15 46			16 18			16 46					17 18			17 46					18 18			18 46
Yatton	d			15 52			16 23			16 52					17 23			17 52					18 23			18 52
Nailsea & Backwell	d			15 58			16 29			16 58					17 29			17 58					18 29			18 58
Parson Street	d						16 36								17 36								18 37			
Bedminster	d						16x38								17x38								18x39			
Bristol Temple Meads [10]	a		15 47	16 11	16 24		16 43			17 11		17 21	17 25		17 43			18 11	18 21	18 25			18 43			19 10
	d	15 54	16 00	16 21	16 30	16 41	16 45	16 54	17 00	17 21		17 30	17 30	17 41	17 45	17 54	18 00	18 21	18 30	18 30		18 41	18 45	18 54	19 00	19 21
Lawrence Hill	d						16 48								17 48								18 48			
Stapleton Road	d			16 25			16 50			17 25					17 50			18 25					18 50			
Filton Abbey Wood	d	16a01		16a31		16 48	16 56	17a01		17a30				17 48	17 56	18a01		18a30				18 48	18 56	19a01		19a28
Bristol Parkway [7]	a		16 08		16 38	16 52	17 03		17 08				17 38	17 52	18 03		18 08			18 38		18 52	19 03		19 08	
	d					16 52								17 52								18 52				
Bath Spa [7]	a											17 41							18 41							
London Paddington [15] ⊖	a											19 14							20 15							
Yate	d					17 02								18 02								19 01				
Cam & Dursley	d					17 16								18 16								19 13				
Gloucester [7]	a					17 33								18 34								19 33				

		XC 1◇ 🛒	GW E	GW	GW	GW ◇	XC 1◇ 🛒		GW	XC 1◇ 🛒	XC 1◇ 🛒	GW 1◇ ☕	GW G	GW ◇	GW ◇	XC 1◇ 🛒	GW A		GW 1◇ ☕	GW ◇	GW	GW 1◇ ☕	GW	GW ◇		
Taunton	d	18 51			19 06		19 20				19 49					20 14	20 18		21 11			21 30	21 39			
Bridgwater	d				19 18												20 30					21 40	21 51			
Highbridge & Burnham	d				19 26												20 38					21 48	21 59			
Weston-super-Mare	a				19 37				←							20 33	20 50					21 58	22 10			
	d			19 10	19 39				19 39			20 10				20 38	20 51					21 59	22 12			
Weston Milton	d			19 13	→												20 55						22 15			
Worle	d			19 18					19 45								21 00					22 06	22 20			
Yatton	d			19 23					19 50								21 06					22 13	22 26			
Nailsea & Backwell	d			19 29					19 56								21 12					22 18	22 32			
Parson Street	d			19 36													21 19						22 39			
Bedminster	d			19x38													21x22						22x42			
Bristol Temple Meads [10]	a	19 26		19 43			19 55		20 09		20 24	20 30				20 56	21 27		21 44			22 30	22 50			
	d	19 30	19 41	19 45		19 54	20 00			20 21	20 30	20 33	20 41	20 49	20 54	21 00	21 28		21 44	21 54	22 06	22 33		22 54		
Lawrence Hill	d			19 48																						
Stapleton Road	d			19 50																						
Filton Abbey Wood	d		19 48	19 56		20a01				20a27			20 48		21a01		21a35			22a01	22 14			23a01		
Bristol Parkway [7]	a	19 38	19 52	20 03			20 08				20 38		20 52			21 08					22 17					
	d		19 52										20 52	20 23							22 18					
Bath Spa [7]	a											20 44		21 05					21 58			22 44				
London Paddington [15] ⊖	a											22 16							23 38			00 33				
Yate	d		20 02										21 02								22 28					
Cam & Dursley	d		20 16										21 16								22 43					
Gloucester [7]	a		20 33										21 34								23 01					

Saturdays

from 12 September

		XC 1◇ 🛒	GW	GW 1◇ ☕	GW A	GW 1◇ ☕	XC 1◇ 🛒		GW H	GW	XC 1◇ 🛒	GW J	GW H	GW		GW 1◇ ☕	XC 1◇ 🛒	GW A	GW	XC 1◇ 🛒	GW 1◇ H ☕		GW B	GW	GW ◇	XC 1◇ 🛒
Taunton	d		05 30						06 35		06 51					06 55			07 32	07 51	07 58					08 12
Bridgwater	d		05 42						06 48							07 05			07 44		08 09					
Highbridge & Burnham	d		05 50						06 55							07 13			07 52		08 16					
Weston-super-Mare	a		06 01						07 06							07 23			08 03		08 26					
	d		06 03			06 24			07 08							07 25		07 39	08 08		08 29					
Weston Milton	d								07 11				←					07 42	08 11		→			←		
Worle	d		06 08			06 32			07 16				07 16			07 32		07 47	08 16					08 16		
Yatton	d		06 14			06 39			→				07 22			07 39		07 52	→					08 21		
Nailsea & Backwell	d		06 20			06 45							07 28			07 46		07 58						08 27		
Parson Street	d												07 35					08 06						08 35		
Bedminster	d												07x38					08x08						08x37		
Bristol Temple Meads [10]	a		06 32			06 56					07 26		07 43			07 58		08 13		08 24				08 41		08 45
	d	06 15		06 46	06 50	07 00	07 00			07 21	07 30	07 41	07 46	07 54		08 00	08 00	08 20		08 30			08 41	08 45	08 54	09 00
Lawrence Hill	d				06 53								07 50					08 23						08 48		
Stapleton Road	d				06 56								07 52					08 25						08 50		
Filton Abbey Wood	d			06 53	07a01					07a29		07 48	07 59	08a01				08a31					08 48	08 56	09a01	
Bristol Parkway [7]	a	06 23		06 57			07 08				07 38	07 52	08 05				08 08			08 38			08 52	09 03		09 08
	d	06 25										07 52											08 52			
Bath Spa [7]	a					07 11										08 11										
London Paddington [15] ⊖	a					08 44										09 44										
Yate	d											08 02											09 02			
Cam & Dursley	d											08 16											09 16			
Gloucester [7]	a	06 55										08 32											09 33			

For general notes see front of timetable
For details of catering facilities see Directory of Train Operators

- **A** To Cardiff Central (Table 132)
- **B** From Warminster (Table 123) to Great Malvern (Table 71)
- **C** From Warminster (Table 123)
- **D** From Weymouth (Table 123) to Great Malvern (Table 71)
- **E** To Cheltenham Spa (Table 57)
- **G** From Brighton (Table 123) to Cheltenham Spa (Table 57)
- **H** From Exeter St Davids (Table 135)
- **J** From Salisbury (Table 123)

Saturdays

from 12 September

Taunton → Gloucester

Network Diagram - see first page of Table 132

		GW	GW	GW	XC		GW	GW	GW	XC	GW	XC		GW	GW	GW	XC	GW	GW		XC	GW	GW	GW	GW	XC
		1 ◇		1 ◇	1 ◇		◇		◇	1 ◇		1 ◇				◇	1 ◇		◇		1 ◇	◇			◇	1 ◇
		A	B				C				B			D				B				C		B		
		🍽		🍽	🛒					🛒		🛒					🛒		🛒		🛒					🛒
Taunton	d			08 37	08 51						08 58	09 51						10 11			10 51			11 07		11 16
Bridgwater	d										09 10							10 23						11 19		
Highbridge & Burnham	d										09 18							10 31						11 27		
Weston-super-Mare	a	←		08 58							09 29							10 42						11 38		
	d	08 29	08 40	09 02				09 10			09 40				10 10			10 43					11 09	11 40 →		
Weston Milton	d							09 13							10 13								11 12			
Worle	d		08 46					09 18			09 46				10 18			10 50					11 17			
Yatton	d	08 40	08 52					09 23			09 51				10 23			10 56					11 22			
Nailsea & Backwell	d	08 46	08 58					09 29			09 57				10 29			11 02					11 28			
Parson Street	d							09 36							10 36								11 36			
Bedminster	d							09x38							10x38								11x38			
Bristol Temple Meads 10	a	08 57	09 13	09 23	09 25			09 43			10 10	10 26			10 43			11 14			11 26		11 42			11 57
	d	09 00	09 21	09 30	09 30		09 38	09 45	09 54	10 00	10 21	10 30		10 41	10 45	10 54	11 00	11 21	11 22		11 30	11 41	11 45		11 54	12 00
Lawrence Hill	d							09 48							10 48								11 48			
Stapleton Road	d		09 25					09 50			10 25				10 50			11 25					11 50			
Filton Abbey Wood	d		09a30				09 45	09 56	10a01		10a31			10 48	10 56	11a01		11a30	11 09			11 48	11 56		12a01	
Bristol Parkway 7	a				09 38		09 49	10 03		10 08		10 38		10 52	11 03		11 08				11 38	11 52	12 03			12 08
	d						09 49							10 52								11 52				
Bath Spa 7	a	09 11		09 41															11 35							
London Paddington 15	⊖ a	10 38		11 14																						
Yate	d						09 59							11 02								12 02				
Cam & Dursley	d						10 11							11 16								12 16				
Gloucester 7	a						10 29							11 32								12 31				

		GW	XC		GW	GW	GW	XC	GW	XC		GW	GW	GW	GW	XC	GW		XC	GW	GW	GW	XC	GW		XC
			1 ◇		◇		◇	1 ◇		1 ◇		◇			◇	1 ◇			1 ◇			◇	1 ◇			1 ◇
		B			E				B			C		B			B			G				B		
			🛒					🛒		🛒						🛒			🛒				🛒			🛒
Taunton	d		11 51						12 07	12 51				13 07		13 16			13 54					14 07		14 51
Bridgwater	d								12 19					13 19										14 19		
Highbridge & Burnham	d								12 27					13 27										14 27		
Weston-super-Mare	a	←							12 38					13 38			←							14 38		
	d	11 40				12 10			12 40				13 10	13 40 →			13 40				14 10			14 40		
Weston Milton	d					12 13							13 13								14 13					
Worle	d	11 46				12 18			12 46				13 18				13 46				14 18			14 46		
Yatton	d	11 52				12 23			12 52				13 23				13 52				14 23			14 52		
Nailsea & Backwell	d	11 58				12 29			12 58				13 29				13 58				14 29			14 58		
Parson Street	d					12 36							13 37								14 37					
Bedminster	d					12x38							13x39								14x39					
Bristol Temple Meads 10	a	12 12	12 24			12 43			13 11	13 24			13 43			13 56	14 13		14 27		14 43			15 11		15 27
	d	12 21	12 30		12 41	12 45	12 54	13 00	13 21	13 30		13 41	13 45		13 54	14 00	14 21		14 30	14 41	14 45	14 54	15 00	15 21		15 30
Lawrence Hill	d					12 48							13 48								14 48					
Stapleton Road	d	12 25				12 50			13 25				13 50				14 25				14 50			15 25		
Filton Abbey Wood	d	12a31			12 48	12 56	13a01		13a30			13 48	13 56		14a01		14a31			14 48	14 56	15a01		15a30		
Bristol Parkway 7	a		12 38		12 52	13 03		13 08		13 38		13 52	14 03			14 08			14 38	14 52	15 03		15 08			15 38
	d				12 52							13 52								14 52						
Bath Spa 7	a																									
London Paddington 15	⊖ a																									
Yate	d				13 02							14 02								15 02						
Cam & Dursley	d				13 16							14 16								15 16						
Gloucester 7	a				13 34							14 32								15 32						

		GW	GW	GW	XC	GW	XC		GW	GW	GW	XC	GW	XC		GW	GW	GW	XC	GW	XC		GW	GW	GW	XC
		◇		◇	1 ◇		1 ◇				◇	1 ◇		1 ◇		◇		◇	1 ◇		1 ◇				◇	1 ◇
		C				B			H				B			C				B			H			
					🛒		🛒					🛒		🛒					🛒		🛒					🛒
Taunton	d				15 04	15 07	15 51						16 07	16 51						17 07	17 51					
Bridgwater	d					15 19							16 19							17 19						
Highbridge & Burnham	d					15 27							16 27							17 27						
Weston-super-Mare	a				15 25	15 38							16 38							17 38						
	d		15 10		15 29	15 40				16 10			16 40				17 10			17 40				18 10		
Weston Milton	d		15 13							16 13							17 13							18 13		
Worle	d		15 18			15 46				16 18			16 46				17 18			17 46				18 18		
Yatton	d		15 23			15 52				16 23			16 52				17 23			17 52				18 23		
Nailsea & Backwell	d		15 29			15 58				16 29			16 58				17 29			17 58				18 29		
Parson Street	d		15 37							16 36							17 36							18 37		
Bedminster	d		15x39							16x38							17x38							18x39		
Bristol Temple Meads 10	a		15 43		15 48	16 11	16 24			16 43			17 11	17 24			17 43			18 11	18 24			18 43		
	d	15 41	15 45	15 54	16 00	16 21	16 30		16 41	16 45	16 54	17 00	17 21	17 30		17 41	17 45	17 54	18 00	18 21	18 30		18 41	18 45	18 54	19 00
Lawrence Hill	d		15 48							16 48							17 48							18 48		
Stapleton Road	d		15 50			16 25				16 50			17 25				17 50			18 25				18 50		
Filton Abbey Wood	d	15 48	15 56	16a01		16a31			16 48	16 56	17a01		17a30			17 48	17 56	18a01		18a30			18 48	18 56	19a01	
Bristol Parkway 7	a	15 52	16 03		16 08		16 38		16 52	17 03		17 08		17 38		17 52	18 03		18 08		18 38		18 52	19 03		19 08
	d	15 52							16 52							17 52							18 52			
Bath Spa 7	a																									
London Paddington 15	⊖ a																									
Yate	d	16 02							17 02							18 02							19 01			
Cam & Dursley	d	16 16							17 16							18 16							19 15			
Gloucester 7	a	16 32							17 33							18 32							19 33			

For general notes see front of timetable
For details of catering facilities see Directory of Train Operators

- **A** From Exeter St Davids (Table 135)
- **B** To Cardiff Central (Table 132)
- **C** From Weymouth (Table 123)
- **D** From Southampton Central (Table 123) to Worcester Foregate Street (Table 71)
- **E** From Brighton (Table 123) to Great Malvern (Table 71)
- **G** From Southampton Central (Table 123) to Great Malvern (Table 71)
- **H** From Warminster (Table 123) to Great Malvern (Table 71)

Table 134

Saturdays

from 12 September

Taunton → Gloucester

Network Diagram - see first page of Table 132

		GW	XC	GW	GW		GW	XC	GW	XC	XC	GW		GW	GW	GW	GW	GW	GW		GW	GW	GW			
			1◇				◇	1◇		1◇	1◇	1◇			◇		1◇	◇			1◇		◇			
		A		B							C			D		A										
			🛒					🛒		🛒	🛒	🍴					🍴				🍴					
Taunton	d	18 07	18 51						19 06		19 51					20 18	21 11				21 30	21 39				
Bridgwater	d	18 19							19 18							20 30					21 40	21 51				
Highbridge & Burnham	d	18 27							19 26							20 38					21 48	21 59				
Weston-super-Mare	a	18 38							19 37							20 50					21 58	22 10				
	d	18 40			19 10				19 39			20 10				20 51					21 59	22 12				
Weston Milton	d				19 13											20 55						22 15				
Worle	d	18 46			19 18				19 45							21 00					22 06	22 20				
Yatton	d	18 52			19 23				19 50							21 06					22 13	22 26				
Nailsea & Backwell	d	18 58			19 29				19 56							21 12					22 18	22 32				
Parson Street	d				19 36											21 19						22 39				
Bedminster	d				19x38											21x22						22x42				
Bristol Temple Meads 10	a	19 10	19 26		19 43				20 09		20 24	20 30				21 27	21 44				22 30	22 50				
	d	19 21	19 30	19 41	19 45		19 54	20 00		20 21	20 30	20 33		20 41	20 54	21 28	21 44	21 54	22 06		22 33		22 54			
Lawrence Hill	d				19 48																					
Stapleton Road	d				19 50																					
Filton Abbey Wood	d	19a28		19 48	19 56		20a01			20a27				20 48	21a01	21a35		22a01	22 14				23a01			
Bristol Parkway 7	a		19 38	19 52	20 03			20 08			20 38			20 52					22 17							
	d			19 52										20 52					22 18							
Bath Spa 7	a											20 44					21 58				22 44					
London Paddington 15 ⊖	a											22 16					23 36				00 33					
Yate	d			20 02										21 02					22 28							
Cam & Dursley	d			20 16										21 16					22 43							
Gloucester 7	a			20 33										21 34					23 01							

Sundays

until 12 July

		GW	XC	GW	GW	XC	GW	GW		XC	GW	GW	GW	XC	GW	GW		XC	GW	GW	XC	GW	XC	GW		GW
		1◇	1◇		◇	1◇	1◇			1◇		◇	1◇	1◇		1◇		1◇	◇	1◇	1◇		1◇			◇
				E	G			H			H				J							J		J		
		🍴	🛒			🛒	🍴			🛒		🛒	🍴	🛒		🍴		🛒	🛒	🍴	🛒		🛒			
Taunton	d				08 43			10 08		10 23			11 17	11 23	11 35	12 23		12 51			13 25	13 35	13 51			
Bridgwater	d				08 55			10 20							11 47							13 47				
Highbridge & Burnham	d				09 02			10 28							11 54							13 54				
Weston-super-Mare	a				09 12			10 37			←				12 04							14 04		←		
	d	08 26			09 14		10 21	10 51 →			10 51				12 07					13 21		14 09 →		14 09		
Weston Milton	d				09 17										12 10											
Worle	d	08 33			09 21		10 28				10 57				12 15									14 15		
Yatton	d	08 40			09 27		10 35				11 02				12 20					13 32				14 20		
Nailsea & Backwell	d	08 46			09 33		10 41				11 08				12 26					13 38				14 26		
Parson Street	d																									
Bedminster	d														12x37											
Bristol Temple Meads 10	a	08 57			09 45		10 52			10 56	11 20		11 52	11 56	12 40	12 57		13 24		13 49	13 57		14 24	14 38		
	d	09 00	09 00	09 44	09 50	10 10	11 00			11 00		11 48	12 00	12 00	12 44	13 00		13 30	13 48	14 00	14 00		14 30	14 44		14 48
Lawrence Hill	d																									
Stapleton Road	d																									
Filton Abbey Wood	d			09 51	10a00							11a55			12 51				13a55					14 51		14a55
Bristol Parkway 7	a		09 08	09 55		10 21				11 08				12 08	12 55			13 38			14 08		14 38	14 55		
	d		09 10	09 55											12 55									14 56		
Bath Spa 7	a	09 12					11 12						12 12			13 12				14 11						
London Paddington 15 ⊖	a	10 55					12 55						13 55			14 55				15 55						
Yate	d			10 04											13 05									15 06		
Cam & Dursley	d			10 18											13 19									15 20		
Gloucester 7	a		09 39	10 34											13 34									15 41		

		GW	XC	XC	GW	XC	GW	XC		GW	GW	GW	XC	GW	XC	GW		GW	GW	XC	GW	GW	XC	GW		GW
		1◇	1◇	1◇	◇	1◇		1◇			◇		1◇	1◇	1◇	◇		◇	1◇	1◇		1◇	1◇			◇
										J						K			L					J		
		🍴	🛒	🛒	🛒	🛒		🛒			🛒		🛒	🍴	🛒			🛒	🍴	🛒		🍴	🛒			🛒
Taunton	d		14 19	14 53			15 19	15 53					16 01	16 39	16 53				17 03		17 19	17 46	17 53			
Bridgwater	d						15 31														17 30					
Highbridge & Burnham	d						15 38														17 37					
Weston-super-Mare	a						15 48						16 20	17 00					17 24		17 48					
	d	14 21					15 50					16 14	16 30	17 01		17 07			17 24		17 50					
Weston Milton	d						15 53					16 17				17 10										
Worle	d	14 28					15 57					16 21				17 16					17 55					
Yatton	d	14 34					16 02					16 27				17 22			17 36		18 01					
Nailsea & Backwell	d	14 41					16 08					16 33				17 28			17 42		18 07					
Parson Street	d											16 40														
Bedminster	d											16x43				17x38										
Bristol Temple Meads 10	a	14 52	14 56	15 27			16 20	16 27				16 48	16 53	17 22	17 27	17 42			17 53		18 19	18 23	18 27			
	d	15 00	15 00	15 30	15 48	16 00		16 30		16 43	16 48		17 00	17 30	17 30	17 44		17 48	18 00	18 00		18 30	18 30	18 40		18 48
Lawrence Hill	d																									
Stapleton Road	d																									
Filton Abbey Wood	d				15a55					16 50	16a55							17a55						18 47		18a55
Bristol Parkway 7	a		15 08	15 38		16 08		16 38		16 54			17 08		17 38					18 08			18 38	18 51		
	d									16 55														18 51		
Bath Spa 7	a	15 12												17 42		18 00			18 12			18 41				
London Paddington 15 ⊖	a	16 53												19 28					19 55			20 25				
Yate	d									17 05														19 01		
Cam & Dursley	d									17 19														19 15		
Gloucester 7	a									17 34														19 31		

For general notes see front of timetable
For details of catering facilities see Directory of Train Operators

A To Cardiff Central (Table 132)
B From Westbury (Table 123) to Cheltenham Spa (Table 57)
C To Birmingham New Street (Table 57)
D From Brighton (Table 123) to Cheltenham Spa (Table 57)
E To Cheltenham Spa (Table 57)
G From Exeter St Davids (Table 135) to Cardiff Central (Table 132)
H From Exeter St Davids (Table 135)
J To Worcester Shrub Hill (Table 57)
K To Weymouth (Table 123)
L From Paignton (Table 135)

Sundays

until 12 July

Taunton → Gloucester

Network Diagram - see first page of Table 132

		GW	GW	XC	XC	GW	GW	GW	XC	GW	XC	GW	GW	GW	GW	GW	GW	XC	GW	GW	XC	GW
			1 ◇	1 ◇	1 ◇	1 ◇	◇	◇	1 ◇	◇	1 ◇		◇	1 ◇		◇	1 ◇	1 ◇		◇	1 ◇	
							A		B	A		C										
			⊡	ⵜ	ⵜ	⊡	ⵜ	ⵜ	ⵜ	ⵜ	ⵜ		ⵜ	⊡		ⵜ	⊡	ⵜ		ⵜ	ⵜ	
Taunton	d		18 23		18 51		19 04		19 24		19 53				20 20		21 23		21 35		21 51	
Bridgwater	d		18 34				19 16								20 32				21 48			
Highbridge & Burnham	d		18 41				19 24								20 40				21 55			
Weston-super-Mare	a		18 51			←	19 35			←					20 51				22 06			
	d	18 16	18 53 →			18 53	19 43 →			19 43				20 38	20 55				22 08			23 15
Weston Milton	d	18 19													20 58				22 11			23 18
Worle	d	18 24				19 00				19 49					21 03							23 23
Yatton	d	18 29				19 06				19 54					21 08				22 18			23 28
Nailsea & Backwell	d	18 35				19 13				20 00					21 14				22 24			23 34
Parson Street	d	18 43																				
Bedminster	d	18x45													21x25							23x43
Bristol Temple Meads 10	a	18 50			19 25	19 28			19 57	20 12	20 27			20 58	21 28		21 58		22 36		23 06	23 48
	d			19 00	19 30	19 30		19 48	20 00		20 30	20 43	20 48	21 00		21 48	22 05	22 10		22 48		
Lawrence Hill	d																					
Stapleton Road	d																					
Filton Abbey Wood	d							19a55				20 50	20a55			21a57				22a55		
Bristol Parkway 7	a			19 08	19 38				20 08		20 38	20 54						22 18				
	d											20 55										
Bath Spa 7	a					19 42								21 13			22 18					
London Paddington 15 ⊖	a					21 21								23 08			00 06					
Yate	d											21 05										
Cam & Dursley	d											21 19										
Gloucester 7	a											21 35										

Sundays

19 July to 6 September

		GW	XC	GW	GW	XC	GW	GW	XC	GW	GW	GW	XC	GW	XC	GW	XC	XC	GW	GW	XC	GW	XC	GW
		1 ◇	1 ◇		◇	1 ◇	1 ◇		1 ◇	1 ◇	◇		1 ◇		1 ◇	1 ◇	1 ◇	1 ◇	1 ◇	◇	1 ◇		1 ◇	
				C	D			E				G		G								G		G
		⊡	ⵜ			ⵜ	⊡		ⵜ	⊡	ⵜ		ⵜ		ⵜ	⊡	ⵜ	ⵜ	⊡	ⵜ	ⵜ		ⵜ	
Taunton	d				08 43			10 20	10 51	11 07		11 35	11 51		12 00	12 08		12 51			13 25	13 35	13 51	
Bridgwater	d				08 55			10 32				11 47										13 47		
Highbridge & Burnham	d				09 02			10 39				11 54										13 54		
Weston-super-Mare	a				09 12			10 49				12 04			12 20							14 04		←
	d	08 26			09 14		10 12	10 51				12 07		←	12 21				13 15			14 09 →		14 09
Weston Milton	d				09 17							12 10 →		12 10										
Worle	d	08 33			09 21		10 19	10 57						12 15										14 15
Yatton	d	08 40			09 27		10 26	11 02						12 20					13 26					14 20
Nailsea & Backwell	d	08 46			09 33		10 32	11 08						12 26					13 32					14 26
Parson Street	d																							
Bedminster	d													12x37										
Bristol Temple Meads 10	a	08 57			09 45		10 43	11 20	11 27	11 42			12 24	12 40	12 42	12 44	←	13 24	13 43		13 57		14 24	14 38
	d	09 00	09 15	09 44	09 50	10 30	10 45		11 30	11 45	11 48		12 30	12 44	13 00 →	12 45	13 00	13 30	13 45	13 48	14 00		14 30	14 44
Lawrence Hill	d																							
Stapleton Road	d																							
Filton Abbey Wood	d			09 51	10a00						11a55			12 51						13a55				14 51
Bristol Parkway 7	a		09 23	09 55		10 38			11 38				12 38	12 55			13 08	13 38			14 08		14 38	14 55
	d		09 25	09 55										12 55										14 56
Bath Spa 7	a						10 58			11 57						12 58			13 58					
London Paddington 15 ⊖	a	10 55					12 55			13 55						14 55			15 55					
Yate	d			10 04										13 05										15 06
Cam & Dursley	d			10 18										13 19										15 20
Gloucester 7	a		09 54	10 34										13 34										15 41

		GW	GW	XC	XC	GW	XC	GW	XC	GW	GW	GW	XC	GW	XC	GW	GW	GW	XC	GW	GW	XC	GW
		◇	1 ◇	1 ◇	1 ◇	◇	1 ◇		1 ◇		◇		1 ◇	1 ◇	1 ◇	◇	◇	1 ◇	1 ◇		1 ◇	1 ◇	
										G						H		J					G
			⊡	ⵜ	ⵜ	ⵜ	ⵜ		ⵜ		ⵜ		ⵜ	⊡	ⵜ		ⵜ	⊡	ⵜ		⊡	ⵜ	
Taunton	d			14 19	14 53			15 19	15 53				16 01	16 39	16 53			17 03		17 19	17 46	17 51	
Bridgwater	d							15 31												17 30			
Highbridge & Burnham	d							15 38												17 37			
Weston-super-Mare	a							15 48					16 20	17 00				17 24		17 48			
	d		14 21					15 50				16 14	16 30	17 01		17 07		17 24		17 50			
Weston Milton	d							15 53				16 17				17 10							
Worle	d		14 28					15 57				16 21				17 16				17 55			
Yatton	d		14 34					16 02				16 27				17 22		17 36		18 01			
Nailsea & Backwell	d		14 41					16 08				16 33				17 28		17 42		18 07			
Parson Street	d											16 40											
Bedminster	d											16x43				17x38							
Bristol Temple Meads 10	a		14 52	14 56	15 27			16 20	16 27			16 48	16 53	17 22	17 27	17 42		17 53		18 19	18 23	18 27	
	d	14 48	15 00	15 00	15 30	15 48	16 00		16 30	16 43	16 48		17 00	17 30	17 30	17 44	17 48	18 00	18 00		18 30	18 30	18 40
Lawrence Hill	d																						
Stapleton Road	d																						
Filton Abbey Wood	d	14a55				15a55				16 50	16a55						17a55						18 47
Bristol Parkway 7	a			15 08	15 38		16 08		16 38	16 54			17 08		17 38				18 08			18 38	18 51
	d									16 55													18 51
Bath Spa 7	a		15 12											17 42		18 00		18 12			18 41		
London Paddington 15 ⊖	a		16 53											19 28				19 55			20 25		
Yate	d									17 05													19 01
Cam & Dursley	d									17 19													19 15
Gloucester 7	a									17 34													19 31

For general notes see front of timetable
For details of catering facilities see Directory of Train Operators

- **A** From Penzance (Table 135)
- **B** To Birmingham New Street (Table 57)
- **C** To Cheltenham Spa (Table 57)
- **D** From Exeter St Davids (Table 135) to Cardiff Central (Table 132)
- **E** From Exeter St Davids (Table 135)
- **G** To Worcester Shrub Hill (Table 57)
- **H** To Weymouth (Table 123)
- **J** From Paignton (Table 135)

Table 134

Taunton → Gloucester

Sundays

19 July to 6 September

Network Diagram - see first page of Table 132

	GW	GW	GW	XC	XC	GW	GW	GW	XC	GW	XC	GW	GW	GW	GW	GW	GW	XC	GW	GW	XC	GW
	◇		1◇	1◇	1◇	1◇	◇	◇	1◇	◇	1◇		◇	1◇		◇	1◇	1◇		◇	1◇	
							A			A		B										
	☕		🍴	☕	☕	🍴	☕	☕	☕	☕	☕		☕	🍴		☕	🍴	☕		☕	☕	
Taunton d			18 23		18 51		19 04		19 24		19 53				20 20		21 23		21 35		21 51	
Bridgwater d			18 34				19 16								20 32				21 48			
Highbridge & Burnham d			18 41				19 24								20 40				21 55			
Weston-super-Mare a			18 51			←	19 35			←					20 51				22 06			
d		18 16	18 53			18 53	19 43			19 43				20 38	20 55				22 08			23 15
Weston Milton d		18 19	→				→								20 58				22 11			23 18
Worle d		18 24				19 00				19 49					21 03							23 23
Yatton d		18 29				19 06				19 54					21 08				22 18			23 28
Nailsea & Backwell d		18 35				19 13				20 00					21 14				22 24			23 34
Parson Street d		18 43																				
Bedminster d		18x45													21x25							23x43
Bristol Temple Meads 10 a		18 50			19 27	19 25			19 57	20 12	20 27			20 58	21 28		21 58		22 36		23 06	23 48
d	18 48			19 00	19 30	19 30		19 48	20 00		20 30	20 43	20 48	21 00		21 48	22 05	22 10		22 48		
Lawrence Hill d																						
Stapleton Road d																						
Filton Abbey Wood d	18a55							19a55				20 50	20a55			21a57				22a55		
Bristol Parkway 7 a				19 08	19 38				20 08		20 38	20 54						22 18				
d												20 55										
Bath Spa 7 a						19 42								21 13			22 18					
London Paddington 15 ⊖ a						21 21								23 08			00 06					
Yate d												21 05										
Cam & Dursley d												21 19										
Gloucester 7 a												21 35										

Sundays

13 September to 1 November

	GW	XC	GW	GW	XC	GW	GW	XC	GW	GW	GW	XC	GW	XC	GW	XC	GW	GW	XC	GW	XC	GW
	1◇	1◇		◇	1◇	1◇		1◇	◇	1◇		1◇		1◇	1◇	1◇	◇	1◇	1◇		1◇	
			B	C			D				E		E							E		E
	🍴	☕			☕	🍴		☕	☕	🍴		☕		☕	🍴	☕	☕	🍴	☕		☕	
Taunton d				08 43			10 20	10 51		11 22	11 35	11 51		12 00	12 23	12 51			13 25	13 35	13 51	
Bridgwater d				08 55			10 32				11 47									13 47		
Highbridge & Burnham d				09 02			10 39				11 54									13 54		
Weston-super-Mare a				09 12			10 49				12 04			12 20						14 04		←
d	08 26			09 14		10 26	10 51				12 07		←	12 22				13 21		14 09		14 09
Weston Milton d				09 17							12 10 →		12 10							→		
Worle d	08 33			09 21		10 33	10 57						12 15									14 15
Yatton d	08 40			09 27		10 40	11 02						12 20					13 32				14 20
Nailsea & Backwell d	08 46			09 33		10 46	11 08						12 26					13 38				14 26
Parson Street d																						
Bedminster d													12x37									
Bristol Temple Meads 10 a	08 57			09 45		10 57	11 20	11 26		11 57		12 24	12 40	12 45	12 57	13 24		13 49	13 57		14 24	14 38
d	09 00	09 15	09 44	09 50	10 30	11 00		11 30	11 48	12 00		12 30	12 44	13 00	13 00	13 30	13 48	14 00	14 00		14 30	14 44
Lawrence Hill d																						
Stapleton Road d																						
Filton Abbey Wood d			09 51	10a00					11a55				12 51				13a55					14 51
Bristol Parkway 7 a		09 23	09 55		10 38			11 38				12 38	12 55	13 08		13 38			14 08		14 38	14 55
d		09 25	09 55										12 55									14 56
Bath Spa 7 a	09 12					11 12				12 12					13 12			14 11				
London Paddington 15 ⊖ a	10 52					12 53				13 53					14 53			15 53				
Yate d			10 04										13 05									15 06
Cam & Dursley d			10 18										13 19									15 20
Gloucester 7 a		09 54	10 34										13 34									15 38

	GW	GW	XC	XC	GW	XC	GW	XC	GW	GW	GW	XC	GW	XC	GW	GW	GW	XC	GW	GW	XC	GW
	◇	1◇	1◇	1◇	◇	1◇		1◇		◇		1◇	1◇	1◇	◇	◇	1◇	1◇		1◇	1◇	
									E						G		H					E
		🍴	☕	☕	☕	☕		☕		☕		☕	🍴	☕		☕	🍴	☕		🍴	☕	
Taunton d			14 19	14 53			15 19	15 53				16 01	16 39	16 53			17 03		17 19	17 46	17 51	
Bridgwater d							15 31												17 30			
Highbridge & Burnham d							15 38												17 37			
Weston-super-Mare a							15 48					16 20	17 00				17 25		17 48			
d		14 21					15 50				16 14	16 30	17 01		17 07		17 25		17 50			
Weston Milton d							15 53				16 17				17 10							
Worle d		14 28					15 57				16 21				17 16				17 55			
Yatton d		14 34					16 02				16 27				17 22		17 36		18 01			
Nailsea & Backwell d		14 41					16 08				16 33				17 28		17 43		18 07			
Parson Street d											16 40											
Bedminster d											16x43				17x38							
Bristol Temple Meads 10 a		14 52	14 56	15 27			16 20	16 27			16 48	16 53	17 22	17 27	17 42		17 54		18 19	18 23	18 27	
d	14 48	15 00	15 00	15 30	15 48	16 00		16 30	16 43	16 48		17 00	17 30	17 30	17 44	17 48	18 00	18 00		18 30	18 30	18 40
Lawrence Hill d																						
Stapleton Road d																						
Filton Abbey Wood d	14a55				15a55				16 50	16a55						17a55						18 47
Bristol Parkway 7 a			15 08	15 38		16 08		16 38	16 54			17 08		17 38				18 08			18 38	18 51
d									16 55													18 51
Bath Spa 7 a		15 12											17 42		18 00		18 12			18 41		
London Paddington 15 ⊖ a		16 53											19 31				19 53			20 39		
Yate d									17 05													19 01
Cam & Dursley d									17 19													19 15
Gloucester 7 a									17 34													19 31

For general notes see front of timetable
For details of catering facilities see Directory of Train Operators

A From Penzance (Table 135)
B To Cheltenham Spa (Table 57)
C From Exeter St Davids (Table 135) to Cardiff Central (Table 132)
D From Exeter St Davids (Table 135)
E To Worcester Shrub Hill (Table 57)
G To Weymouth (Table 123)
H From Paignton (Table 135)

Table 134

Sundays

13 September to 1 November

Taunton → Gloucester

Network Diagram - see first page of Table 132

		GW ◇	GW	XC 1 ◇	GW 1 ◇	XC 1 ◇	GW ◇	GW ◇		XC 1 ◇	GW ◇	GW ◇	GW	GW ◇	GW 1 ◇	GW		GW ◇	GW 1 ◇	XC 1 ◇	GW	GW ◇	XC 1 ◇	GW ◇		
							A			B		A	C													
Taunton	d				18 23	18 51	19 04			19 24						20 20			21 23		21 35		21 51			
Bridgwater	d				18 34		19 16									20 32					21 48					
Highbridge & Burnham	d				18 41		19 24									20 40					21 55					
Weston-super-Mare	a				18 51		19 35					←				20 51					22 06					
	d		18 16		18 53		19 43 →					19 43			20 38	20 55					22 08					
Weston Milton	d		18 19													20 58					22 11					
Worle	d		18 24		19 00							19 49				21 03										
Yatton	d		18 29		19 06							19 54				21 08					22 18					
Nailsea & Backwell	d		18 35		19 13							20 00				21 14					22 24					
Parson Street	d		18 43																							
Bedminster	d		18x45													21x25										
Bristol Temple Meads 10	a		18 50		19 25	19 27				19 57		20 12			20 58	21 28			21 58		22 36		23 06			
	d	18 48		19 00	19 30	19 30		19 48		20 00	20 10		20 43	20 48	21 00			21 48	22 05	22 10		22 48		23 10		
Lawrence Hill	d																									
Stapleton Road	d																									
Filton Abbey Wood	d	18a55						19a55			19 52		20 50	20a55				21a57				22a55		22 58		
Bristol Parkway 7	a			19 08		19 38				20 08			20 54							22 18						
	d												20 55													
Bath Spa 7	a				19 42						20 21				21 13				22 18					23 21		
London Paddington 15 ⊖	a				21 39										23 08				00 06							
Yate	d												21 05													
Cam & Dursley	d												21 19													
Gloucester 7	a												21 35													

Sundays

from 8 November

		XC 1 ◇	GW 1 ◇	GW		GW ◇	XC 1 ◇	GW 1 ◇		GW	XC 1 ◇	GW ◇		GW 1 ◇	GW	XC 1 ◇		GW	GW 1 ◇	XC 1 ◇		GW ◇	GW 1 ◇	GW		XC 1 ◇
				C		D				E					G			G						G		
Taunton	d					08 43				10 20	10 51			11 22	11 35	11 51			12 23	12 52				13 35		13 43
Bridgwater	d					08 55				10 32					11 47									13 47		
Highbridge & Burnham	d					09 02				10 39					11 54									13 54		
Weston-super-Mare	a					09 12				10 49					12 04			←						14 04		
	d		08 26			09 14		10 26		10 51					12 07								13 21	14 09 →		
Weston Milton	d					09 17									12 10 →			12 10								
Worle	d		08 33			09 21		10 33		10 57								12 15								
Yatton	d		08 40			09 27		10 40		11 02								12 20					13 32			
Nailsea & Backwell	d		08 46			09 33		10 46		11 08								12 26					13 38			
Parson Street	d																									
Bedminster	d																	12x37								
Bristol Temple Meads 10	a		08 57			09 45		10 57		11 20	11 24			11 57		12 24		12 40	12 57	13 25			13 49			14 23
	d	08 45	09 00	09 44		09 50	10 00	11 00			11 30	11 48		12 00		12 30		12 44	13 00	13 30		13 48	14 00			14 30
Lawrence Hill	d																									
Stapleton Road	d																									
Filton Abbey Wood	d			09 51		10a00						11a55						12 51				13a55				
Bristol Parkway 7	a	08 53		09 55			10 08				11 38					12 38		12 55		13 38						14 38
	d	08 55		09 55														12 55								
Bath Spa 7	a		09 12					11 12						12 12					13 12				14 11			
London Paddington 15 ⊖	a		10 52					12 53						13 53					14 53				15 53			
Yate	d			10 04														13 05								
Cam & Dursley	d			10 18														13 19								
Gloucester 7	a	09 24		10 34														13 34								

		GW	GW ◇	GW 1 ◇		XC 1 ◇	GW ◇	GW		XC 1 ◇	GW	GW ◇		GW	GW 1 ◇	XC 1 ◇		GW ◇	GW ◇	GW 1 ◇		GW	GW 1 ◇	XC 1 ◇		GW
		G									G							H		J						G
Taunton	d					14 51		15 19		15 51					16 39	16 51				17 03		17 19	17 46	17 53		
Bridgwater	d							15 31														17 30				
Highbridge & Burnham	d							15 38														17 37				
Weston-super-Mare	a	←						15 48							17 00					17 25		17 48				
	d	14 09		14 21				15 50						16 14	17 01			17 07		17 25		17 50				
Weston Milton	d							15 53						16 17				17 10								
Worle	d	14 15		14 28				15 57						16 21				17 16				17 55				
Yatton	d	14 20		14 34				16 02						16 27				17 22		17 36		18 01				
Nailsea & Backwell	d	14 26		14 41				16 08						16 33				17 28		17 43		18 07				
Parson Street	d													16 40												
Bedminster	d													16x43				17x38								
Bristol Temple Meads 10	a	14 38		14 52		15 24		16 20		16 24				16 48	17 22	17 25		17 42		17 54		18 19	18 23	18 27		
	d	14 44	14 48	15 00		15 30	15 48			16 30	16 43	16 48			17 30	17 30		17 44	17 48	18 00			18 30	18 30		18 40
Lawrence Hill	d																									
Stapleton Road	d																									
Filton Abbey Wood	d	14 51	14a55				15a55				16 50	16a55							17a55							18 47
Bristol Parkway 7	a	14 55				15 38				16 38	16 54					17 38								18 38		18 51
	d	14 56									16 55															18 51
Bath Spa 7	a			15 12											17 42			18 00		18 12			18 41			
London Paddington 15 ⊖	a			16 53											19 31					19 53			20 39			
Yate	d	15 06									17 05															19 01
Cam & Dursley	d	15 20									17 19															19 15
Gloucester 7	a	15 38									17 34															19 31

For general notes see front of timetable
For details of catering facilities see Directory of Train Operators

- **A** From Penzance (Table 135)
- **B** To Birmingham New Street (Table 57)
- **C** To Cheltenham Spa (Table 57)
- **D** From Exeter St Davids (Table 135) to Cardiff Central (Table 132)
- **E** From Exeter St Davids (Table 135)
- **G** To Worcester Shrub Hill (Table 57)
- **H** To Weymouth (Table 123)
- **J** From Paignton (Table 135)

Table 134

Sundays

from 8 November

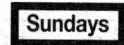

Taunton → Gloucester

Network Diagram - see first page of Table 132

		GW	GW	GW		XC	GW	GW		XC	GW	GW		GW	GW	GW		GW	XC	GW		GW	XC	GW		
		◇		1 ◇		1 ◇	◇	◇		1 ◇		◇		1 ◇		◇		1 ◇	1 ◇			◇	1 ◇			
								A			B															
		⊥		☕		⊥	⊥	⊥		⊥		⊥		☕		⊥		☕	⊥			⊥	⊥			
Taunton	d			18 23		18 51		19 04		19 51					20 20			21 23		21 35			21 53			
Bridgwater	d			18 34				19 16							20 32					21 48						
Highbridge & Burnham	d			18 41				19 24							20 40					21 55						
Weston-super-Mare	a			18 51				19 35							20 51					22 06						
	d		18 16	18 53				19 43						20 38	20 55					22 08				23 15		
Weston Milton	d		18 19												20 58					22 11				23 18		
Worle	d		18 24	19 00				19 49							21 03									23 23		
Yatton	d		18 29	19 06				19 54							21 08					22 18				23 28		
Nailsea & Backwell	d		18 35	19 13				20 00							21 14					22 24				23 34		
Parson Street	d		18 43																							
Bedminster	d		18x45												21x25									23x43		
Bristol Temple Meads [10]	a		18 50	19 25		19 27		20 12		20 24				20 58	21 28			21 58		22 36			23 06	23 48		
	d	18 48		19 30		19 30	19 48			20 30	20 43	20 48		21 00		21 48		22 05	22 10			22 48				
Lawrence Hill	d																									
Stapleton Road	d																									
Filton Abbey Wood	d	18a55					19a55				20 50	20a55				21a57						22a55				
Bristol Parkway [7]	a					19 38				20 38	20 54								22 18							
	d										20 55															
Bath Spa [7]	a			19 42										21 13				22 18								
London Paddington [15] ⊖	a			21 39										23 08				00 06								
Yate	d										21 05															
Cam & Dursley	d										21 19															
Gloucester [7]	a										21 35															

For general notes see front of timetable
For details of catering facilities see Directory of Train Operators

A From Penzance (Table 135)
B To Cheltenham Spa (Table 57)

Route Diagram for Tables 135, 136, 139, 140, 142, 143, 144

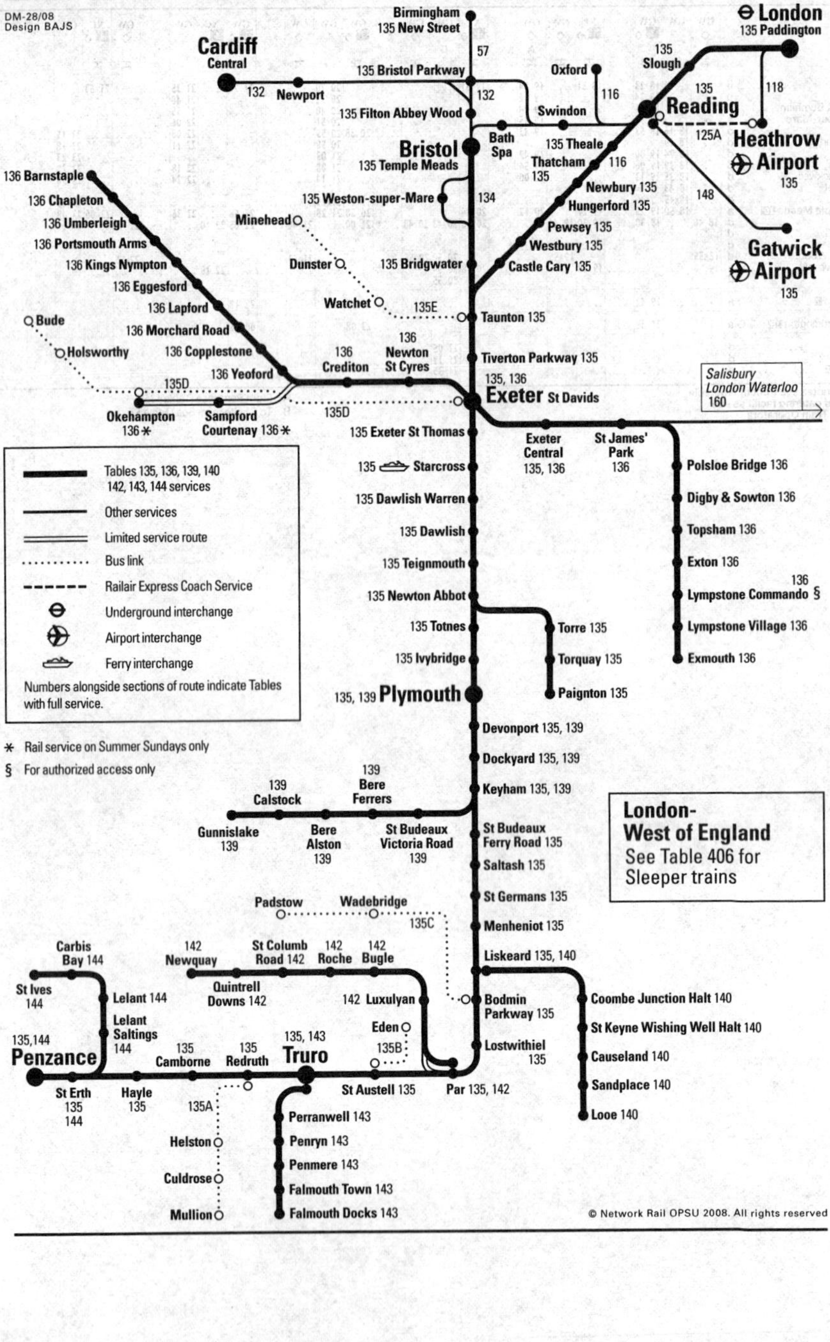

DM-28/08
Design BAJS
Birmingham
135 New Street
57
London
135 Paddington
Cardiff
Central
132
Newport
135 Bristol Parkway
132
Oxford
116
135
Slough
135
Reading
118
135 Filton Abbey Wood
Swindon
Bath Spa
125A
Heathrow Airport
135
Bristol
135 Temple Meads
135 Theale
Thatcham
135
116
Newbury 135
148
Hungerford 135
135 Weston-super-Mare
134
Pewsey 135
Westbury 135
Castle Cary 135
Gatwick Airport
135
136 Barnstaple
136 Chapleton
136 Umberleigh
136 Portsmouth Arms
136 Kings Nympton
136 Eggesford
136 Lapford
136 Morchard Road
136 Copplestone
136 Yeoford
Minehead
Dunster
Watchet
135E
135 Bridgwater
Taunton 135
Bude
Holsworthy
135D
Okehampton
136 *
Sampford
Courtenay 136 *
136
Crediton
136
Newton
St Cyres
Tiverton Parkway 135
135, 136
Exeter St Davids
135D
Salisbury
London Waterloo
160
135 Exeter St Thomas
Exeter Central
135, 136
St James' Park
136
135 Starcross
135 Dawlish Warren
135 Dawlish
135 Teignmouth
135 Newton Abbot
135 Totnes
135 Ivybridge
Polsloe Bridge 136
Digby & Sowton 136
Topsham 136
Exton 136
136
Lympstone Commando §
Lympstone Village 136
Exmouth 136
Torre 135
Torquay 135
Paignton 135
135, 139 Plymouth
Devonport 135, 139
Dockyard 135, 139
Keyham 135, 139
Tables 135, 136, 139, 140
142, 143, 144 services
Other services
Limited service route
Bus link
Railair Express Coach Service
Underground interchange
Airport interchange
Ferry interchange
Numbers alongside sections of route indicate Tables with full service.
* Rail service on Summer Sundays only
§ For authorized access only
139
Calstock
139
Bere
Ferrers
Gunnislake
139
Bere
Alston
139
St Budeaux
Victoria Road
139
St Budeaux
Ferry Road 135
Saltash 135
St Germans 135
Menheniot 135
Liskeard 135, 140
London-
West of England
See Table 406 for
Sleeper trains
Padstow
Wadebridge
135C
Carbis
Bay 144
142
Newquay
St Columb
Road 142
142
Roche
142
Bugle
St Ives
144
Lelant 144
Quintrell
Downs 142
142 Luxulyan
Bodmin
Parkway 135
Coombe Junction Halt 140
Lelant
Saltings
144
Eden
135B
St Keyne Wishing Well Halt 140
135,144
Penzance
135
Camborne
135
Redruth
135, 143
Truro
Lostwithiel
135
Causeland 140
St Erth
135
144
Hayle
135
135A
St Austell 135
Par 135, 142
Sandplace 140
Looe 140
Perranwell 143
Helston
Penryn 143
Penmere 143
Culdrose
Falmouth Town 143
Mullion
Falmouth Docks 143

Sleeper services are published in Table 406

London and Birmingham → Devon and Cornwall

Network Diagram - see first page of Table 135

Miles	Miles		GW	GW	GW	GW	GW	XC	GW		GW	GW	XC	GW	GW	GW	GW		GW	GW	GW	GW	GW	XC
			MX	MX	MX	MX	MO	MO	MX		MX		MX		MO									
			1	1 ◇			◇	1 ◇	◇		◇		1 ◇		◇	1			1	◇	◇		1	1 ◇
				A	B	A			B		A									C	D		C	
			✕	⊒			⊒		⊒		⊒				⊒	⊒								⊼
0	—	**London Paddington** 15 ⊖ d	19p03	20p35			23p50		23p45		23p45													
—	—	**London Waterloo** 15 ⊖ d																						
18½	—	Slough 3 d																						
—	—	Heathrow Central Bus Stn 🚌 d																						
—	—	Gatwick Airport 10 d																						
—	—	Oxford d																						
36	—	**Reading** 7 d	19p32	21p01			00u37		00u37		00u37													
41¼	—	Theale d																						
49¾	—	Thatcham d																						
53	—	Newbury d	19p48	21p18																				
61½	—	Hungerford d																						
75¼	—	Pewsey d		21p38																				
95½	—	Westbury d		21p57																				
115¼	—	Castle Cary d		22p15																				
—	0	**Birmingham New Street** 12 d																						
—	—	Cardiff Central 7 d			22p00	22p00																		
—	—	Newport (South Wales) d			22p17	22p17																		
—	—	Swindon d																						
—	87	Bristol Parkway 7 d			22p54	22p54																		
—	88¼	Filton Abbey Wood d			22p58	22p58																		
—	—	Bath Spa 7 d																						
—	92¾	**Bristol Temple Meads** 10 d			23p08	23p08																05 29	05 29			06 34
—	112¾	Weston-super-Mare d			23p45	23p45																05 50	05 50			
—	126½	Bridgwater d			00 04	00 04																06 09	06 09			
143	138¼	Taunton d	20p53	22p37	00s19	00s32			03b22		03b54											06 23	06 23			07 08
157½	—	Tiverton Parkway d		23p08	00s34	01s05																06 39	06 39			07 20
173¾	—	**Exeter St Davids** 6 a	21p21	23p28	01 08	01 24	04 05		04 14		04 43											06 57	06 57			07 34
—	—	Exeter Central a					*05 13*															*07 14*	*07 14*			*07 51*
—	—	Exmouth a					*06 10*															*07 42*	*07 42*			*08 20*
—	—	Barnstaple a																								
—	—	Exmouth d																				*06 15*	*06 15*	06 46		
—	—	Exeter Central d																				*06 41*	*06 41*	07 13		
—	—	**Exeter St Davids** 6 d	21p22	23p29			04 35		04 17		04 45			05 35			06 11					06 59	06 59	07 20		07 36
174¾	—	Exeter St Thomas d												05 38			06 14					07 02	07 02	07 23		
182¼	—	Starcross d												05 46			06 22					07 11	07 11	07 31		
184¼	—	Dawlish Warren d												05 51			06 27					07 16	07 16	07 36		
185¾	—	Dawlish d												05 55			06 31					07 20	07 20	07 40		
188¾	—	Teignmouth d												06 00			06 36					07 25	07 25	07 45		
193¾	—	Newton Abbot a	21p43	23p49			04 55		04 37		05 05			06 07			06 44					07 32	07 32	07 52		07 56
—	0	Newton Abbot d	21p43	23p50			04 56		04 39		05 07	05 42		06 09			06 45				07 06	07 32	07 32	07 54		07 57
—	5¼	Torre d										05 50		06 17			06 53				07 15			08 02		
—	6	Torquay d										05 53		06 20			06 56				07 20			08 05		
—	8¼	Paignton a										06 00		06 28			07 06				07 29			08 14		
202½	—	Totnes d	21p57	00 02																		07 46	07 46			08 09
214	—	Ivybridge d																				08 02	08 02			
225¾	—	**Plymouth** a	22p25	00 35			05 35		05 18		05 46				←							08 16	08 16			08 39
—	—	d	22p27				06 40 →	05 50	05 50		05 50		06 28		06 40	07 02						08 18	08 20		08 23	
227	—	Devonport d														07 07							08 23		08 28	
227½	—	Dockyard d																								
228	—	Keyham d																								
228¾	—	St Budeaux Ferry Road d																								
230	—	Saltash d	22p36													07 15							08 30		08 36	
235	—	St Germans d	22p43													07 22							08 37		08 43	
240½	—	Menheniot d																				08x37	08x44			
243½	—	Liskeard 8 d	22p55					06 15	06 15		06 15		06 51		07 09	07 34							08 51		08 55	
—	—	Looe a											*07 41*		*07 41*	*09 12*										
252½	—	Bodmin Parkway d	23p10					06 29	06 29		06 29		07 03		07 23	07 46						08 53	09 03			
256	—	Lostwithiel d						06 35	06 35		06 35		07 09		07 29	07 52						08 58	09 08			
260½	—	Par d	23p20					06 42	06 42		06 42		07 15		07 37	07 59						09c12	09 15		09 16	
—	—	Newquay a																				10 04	*10 11*			
265	—	St Austell d	23p28					06 50	06 50		06 50		07 22		07 45	08 07							09 23		09 24	
279½	—	Truro d	23p46					07 09	07 09		07 09		07 39		08 05	08 26							09 41		09 42	
—	—	Falmouth Docks a						*07 41*					*08 13*		*08 45*	*09 15*							*10 15*		*10 15*	
288½	—	Redruth d	23p59					07 23	07 23		07 23		07 50		08 19	08 38							09 54		09 55	
292	—	Camborne d	00 07					07 30	07 30		07 30		07 57		08 26	08 45							10 00		10 02	
298	—	Hayle d						07 39	07 39		07 39		08 05		08 37	08 53							10 07		10 11	
299½	—	St Erth d	00 18					07 44	07 44		07 44		08 12		08 43	08 58							10 11		10 16	
—	—	St Ives a						*08 18*								*09 19*							*10 55*		*10 55*	
305¾	—	**Penzance** a	00 34					08 00	08 00		08 00		08 24		08 59	09 11							10 24		10 29	

For general notes see front of timetable
For details of catering facilities see Directory of Train Operators

A From 8 September
B Until 4 September
C 29 June to 4 September
D Until 26 June and from 7 September

b Arr. 0232
c Arr. 0906

Sleeper services are published in Table 406

London and Birmingham → Devon and Cornwall

Network Diagram - see first page of Table 135

Station	GW	GW ◇	GW		XC 1◇	GW	GW	XC 1◇	GW	GW 1◇	GW		SW 1◇	XC 1◇	SW 1◇	GW	GW 1◇	GW A	GW 1◇ B		GW 1 R A	GW B	XC 1◇	GW
London Paddington 15 ⊖ d										07 30							08 18		09 06		09 06			
London Waterloo 15 ⊖ d													07 10											
Slough 3 d																								
Heathrow Central Bus Stn d										06 57							07 20		08 00		08 00			
Gatwick Airport 10 d										06b00							07 00		07 58		07 58			
Oxford d										07 15							08 15		08 50		08 50			
Reading 7 d										07 57							08 48		09c32		09u32			
Theale d																	08 56							
Thatcham d																	09 04							
Newbury d																	09 12							
Hungerford d																	09 21							
Pewsey d																	09 40							
Westbury d																	09 59							
Castle Cary d																	10 16							
Birmingham New Street 12 d					06 42			07 12						08 12									09 12	
Cardiff Central 7 d																								
Newport (South Wales) d																								
Swindon d										08 25														
Bristol Parkway 7 d					07 58			08 28						09 26									10 28	
Filton Abbey Wood d																								
Bath Spa 7 d										08 55														
Bristol Temple Meads 10 d		06 26			08 11			08 44		09 13				09 44									10 44	
Weston-super-Mare d		06 51																						
Bridgwater d		07 10																						
Taunton d		07 29			08 43			09 17		09 46				10 18			10 38		10 48		10 48		11 18	
Tiverton Parkway d		07 44						09 29						10 30			10 51		11 01		11 01		11 30	
Exeter St Davids 6 a		08 03			09 07			09 43		10 12				10 46			11 12		11 18		11 18		11 46	
Exeter Central a		08 16			09 21			10 13		10 21							11 21		11 51		11 51		12 13	
Exmouth a		08 50			09 50					10 50							11 50		12 18		12 18			
Barnstaple a		09 37			10 35					11 35									12 35		12 35			
Exmouth d	07 15		08 23				08 53		09 23				09 53			10 23							10 53	11 23
Exeter Central d	07 43		08 50				09 25		09 50				10 29			10 50							11 38	11 50
Exeter St Davids 6 d	07 50	08 04	08 56		09 08		09 34	09 45	09 56	10 13			10 37	10 48		10 56			11 19		11 19		11 48	11 56
Exeter St Thomas d	07 53	08 07	08 59						09 59							10 59								11 59
Starcross d	08 01		09 07			←			10 07							11 07								12 07
Dawlish Warren d	08 06		09e21			09 21			10 12				10 49			11 12								→
Dawlish d	08 10	08 20	→			09 25			10 16				10 53			11 16								
Teignmouth d	08 15	08 25				09 30			10 21				10 58			11 21								
Newton Abbot a	08 22	08 32				09 37	09 54	10 03	10 29	10 33	←		11 04	11 08	←	11 29			11 39		11 39		12 08	
Newton Abbot d	08 24	08 32				09 39	09 55	10 04	10 41	10 34	10 41		11 13	11 10	11 13	11 30			11 39		11 39		12 09	
Torre d	08 32					09 47			→		10 49		→			11 38								
Torquay d	08 35				09 37	09 50					10 52				11 23	11 41								
Paignton a	08 44				09 48	09 57					10 59				11 29	11 51								
Totnes d		08 46					10 08	10 17		10 47				11 23					11 53		11 53		12 23	
Ivybridge d		09 02					10 25												12 08		12 08			
Plymouth a		09 16					10 39	10 48		11 15				11 56					12 25		12 25		12 56	
Plymouth d		09 19					10 40			11 18								12 10			12 29	12 39		
Devonport d		09 23																						
Dockyard d																								
Keyham d																								
St Budeaux Ferry Road d							10 46																	
Saltash d		09 30					10 50											12 18			12 39	12 47		
St Germans d		09 37					10 57											12 25			12 46	12 54		
Menheniot d																								
Liskeard 6 d		09 49					11 09			11 41								12 37			12 58	13 06		
Looe a		10 26					11 43			12 43											13 50	13 50		
Bodmin Parkway d		10 01					11 21			11 53								12 49			13 10	13 18		
Lostwithiel d		10 07					11 26											12 54			13 16	13 23		
Par d		10 14					11 33			12 04								13 01			13 26	13 30		
Newquay a							12f28			13g00											14 31			
St Austell d		10 22					11 41			12 12								13 09				13 38		
Truro d		10 41					11 58			12 30								13 26				13 56		
Falmouth Docks a		11 15					12 45			13 15								14 15				14 45		
Redruth d		10 54					12 11			12 42								13 39				14 09		
Camborne d		11 00					12 17			12 50								13 45				14 15		
Hayle d		11 07					12 24											13 53				14 22		
St Erth d		11 12					12 28			13 00								13 56				14 26		
St Ives a		11 55					12 55			13 24								14 24				14 55		
Penzance a		11 27					12 40			13 18								14 11				14 39		

For general notes see front of timetable
For details of catering facilities see Directory of Train Operators

A 29 June to 4 September
B Until 26 June and from 7 September
b Change at Redhill and Reading
c Stops to pick up only until 26 June
e Arr. 0914
f 29 June to 4 September only
g Until 26 June and from 7 September only

Sleeper services are published in Table 406

London and Birmingham → Devon and Cornwall

Network Diagram - see first page of Table 135

		GW	GW	GW	GW	XC		SW	XC	GW	SW	GW	GW	GW		XC	GW	GW	GW	GW	XC	GW		GW	GW
			■1 ◇	■1 ◇		■1 ◇		■1 ◇	■1 ◇		■1 ◇	■1 ◇		■1 ◇		■1 ◇		■1 ◇			■1 ◇			■1 ◇	
		A																							B
			☕	☕		🛒		☕	🛒		☕	☕		☕		🛒		🍴			🛒			☕	
London Paddington 15 ⊖	d		10 00	10 06										11 06				12 06						12 18	
London Waterloo 15 ⊖	d							09 20																	
Slough 3	d																								
Heathrow Central Bus Stn 🚌	d		09 20											10 15				11 15						11 35	
Gatwick Airport 10	d		08b15	09 07										10 03				11 03							
Oxford	d		09 42	10 01										11 01				12 01						12 15	
Reading 7	d		10 27	10c32										11c32				12c32						12 48	
Theale	d																							12 56	
Thatcham	d																							13 04	
Newbury	d																							13 12	
Hungerford	d																							13 21	
Pewsey	d													12 03										13 40	
Westbury	d													12 22										13 59	
Castle Cary	d													12 39										14 23	
Birmingham New Street 12	d					09 42			10 12							11 12					12 12				
Cardiff Central 7	d																								
Newport (South Wales)	d																								
Swindon	d		10 55																						
Bristol Parkway 7	d					10 58			11 28							12 28					13 26				
Filton Abbey Wood	d											←													
Bath Spa 7	d		11 25									11 25													
Bristol Temple Meads 10	d		→			11 15			11 44			11 47				12 44					13 44				
Weston-super-Mare	d					11 37						12 07													
Bridgwater	d																								
Taunton	d					12 02			12 17			12 29		13 02		13 18					14 17			14a46	
Tiverton Parkway	d					12 14			12 29					13 15		13 30					14 29				
Exeter St Davids 6	a			12 09		12 30			12 43			12 55		13 32		13 46		14 09			14 43				
Exeter Central	a			12 21		12 51						13 21		13 51		14 13		14 21			15 21				
Exmouth	a			12 50		13 18						13 50		14 18				14 50			15 50				
Barnstaple	a			13 37								14 37						15 35							
Exmouth	d					11 53							12 23	12 53			13 23				13 53	14 23			
Exeter Central	d					12 17		12 26					12 50	13 17		13 38	13 50				14 17	14 50			
Exeter St Davids 6	d			12 10		12 32		12 38	12 45			12 57	13 01	13 34		13 48	13 56	14 11			14 45	14 56			
Exeter St Thomas	d				←								13 04				13 59		←			14 59			
Starcross	d				12 07						←		13 13				14 07		14 07			15 07			
Dawlish Warren	d				12e23			12f57			12 57		13 18				→		14g23			15 12			
Dawlish	d				12 28	12 44		→			13 01	13 10	13 22						14 28			15 16			
Teignmouth	d				12 33	12 49					13 06	13 16	13 27						14 33			15 21			
Newton Abbot	a			12 30	12 40	12 56			13 03		13 13	13 23	13 34	13 53		14 08		14 30	14 40		15 03	15 29			
	d			12 31	12 41	12 57			13 04		13 13	13 24	13 36	13 54		14 09		14 31	14 41	14 50	15 04	15 30			
Torre	d				12 50								13 44						14 49			15 38			
Torquay	d				12 53	13 09						13 35	13 47						14 52			15 41			
Paignton	a				13 00	13 20						13 48	13 56						15 00			15 49			
Totnes	d								13 17		13 26			14 07		14 23				15 02	15 17				
Ivybridge	d										13 41									15 19					
Plymouth	a			13 09					13 48		13 56			14 39		14 56		15 09		15 36	15 48				
	d			13 11						13 54								15 11							15 57
Devonport	d																								16 00
Dockyard	d																								16x01
Keyham	d																								16x03
St Budeaux Ferry Road	d																								16 06
Saltash	d									14 02															16 11
St Germans	d									14 09															16 18
Menheniot	d																								16x25
Liskeard 6	d			13 34						14 21								15 34							16 32
Looe	a									14 56								16 10							17 11
Bodmin Parkway	d			13 47						14 33								15 47							16 44
Lostwithiel	d									14 38															16 49
Par	d	13 37		13 58						14 45								15 58							16 56
Newquay	a			14h54														17 02							
St Austell	d	13 44		14 06						14 53								16 06							17 05
Truro	d	14 02		14 23						15 11								16 23							17 24
Falmouth Docks	a	14 45		15 15						15 45								17 16							17 52
Redruth	d	14 15		14 36						15 24								16 36							17 37
Camborne	d	14 21		14 44						15 30								16 44							17 43
Hayle	d	14 28		14 54						15 37															17 50
St Erth	d	14 32		14 58						15 42								16 55							17 54
St Ives	a	14 55		15 24						16 24								17 24							18 25
Penzance	a	14 43		15 11						15 54								17 11							18 08

For general notes see front of timetable
For details of catering facilities see Directory of Train Operators

A 29 June to 4 September. From Newquay (Table 142)
B Until 26 June and from 7 September
b Change at Redhill and Reading. Passengers make their own way between Reading and Reading
c Stops to pick up only until 4 September
e Arr. 1212
f Arr. 1249
g Arr. 1412
h Until 26 June and from 7 September only

Sleeper services are published in Table 406

London and Birmingham → Devon and Cornwall

Network Diagram - see first page of Table 135

		GW	GW	GW	XC	SW	GW	XC		GW	GW	GW	XC	GW	GW	GW		GW	GW	GW	XC	SW	XC	GW	GW
								FO																	
			1 ◇	1 ◇	1 ◇	1 ◇		1 ◇			1 ◇		1 ◇						1 ◇		1 ◇	1 ◇	1 ◇	1 ◇	
		A	B	A										C				D			E				
			🍴	🍴	☕	🍴		☕			🍴		☕						🍴		☕	🍴	☕	🍴	
London Paddington 15 ⊖	d		13 06	13 06							14 06								15 06					16 06	
London Waterloo 15 ⊖	d					12 20																14 20			
Slough 3	d																								
Heathrow Central Bus Stn 🚌	d		12 15	12 15							13 15								14 15					15 15	
Gatwick Airport 10	d		12 03	12 03							13 03								14 03					15 03	
Oxford	d		13 01	13 01							14 01								14 42					16 01	
Reading 7	d		13b32	13u32							14c32								15c32					16c32	
Theale	d																								
Thatcham	d																								
Newbury	d																								
Hungerford	d																								
Pewsey	d																		16 03						
Westbury	d																		16 22						
Castle Cary	d																		16 41						
Birmingham New Street 12	d				13 12			13 42					14 12								15 12		15 42		
Cardiff Central 7	d																								
Newport (South Wales)	d																								
Swindon	d																								
Bristol Parkway 7	d				14 28			14 58					15 26								16 28		16 58		
Filton Abbey Wood	d																								
Bath Spa 7	d																								
Bristol Temple Meads 10	d				14 44			15 13					15 44								16 44		17 14		
Weston-super-Mare	d																								
Bridgwater	d																								
Taunton	d		14 51	14 51	15 18			15 46			15 50		16 17						17 05		17 17		17 46	17 50	
Tiverton Parkway	d		15 04	15 04	15 30			15 58			16 03		16 29						17 18		17 29		17 58	18 03	
Exeter St Davids 6	a		15 21	15 21	15 46			16 18			16 19		16 43						17 34		17 43		18 13	18 20	
Exeter Central	a		15 33	15 33	16 13						16 43		16 53						17 43		17 53		18 23	18 32	
Exmouth	a				16 52								17 23								18 23		18 53		
Barnstaple	a		16 35	16 35									18 07								19 13				
Exmouth	d				14 53		15 23					15 53			16 55								17 25		17 55
Exeter Central	d				15 39	15 39	15 50					16 20	16 24	16 46	17 21						17 35	17 35	17 57		18 21
Exeter St Davids 6	d		15 24	15 24	15 48	15 52	15 58				16 22	16 26	16 45	16 56	17 26				17 36		17 45	17 49	18 14	18 21	18 26
Exeter St Thomas	d						16 01					16 29		16 59	17 29					⟵		17 52			18 29
Starcross	d						16 09					16 37		17 07	17 37					17 37		18 00			18 37
Dawlish Warren	d					16 02	16 14					16 42		17 12	⟶					17e49		18 04			18 42
Dawlish	d					16 06	16 18					16 46		17 16						17 53		18 08	18 26		18 46
Teignmouth	d					16 11	16 23					16 51		17 21						17 58		18 13	18 31		18 51
Newton Abbot	a		15 44	15 44	16 08	16 18	16 31				16 41	16 58	17 03	17 29					17 55	18 05	18 10	18 20	18 38	18 42	18 59
	d		15 44	15 44	16 09	16 18	16 32				16 42	17 00	17 04	17 30					17 57	18 09	18 12	18 21	18 40	18 43	19 09
Torre	d						16 41					17 08		17 38						18 17		18 30			⟶
Torquay	d						16 44					17 11		17 41						18 20		18 34	18 51		
Paignton	a						16 53					17 20		17 51						18 28		18 40	19 01		
Totnes	d		15 58	15 58	16 23	16 31					16 55		17 17						18 10		18 24			18 56	
Ivybridge	d					16 46																		19 12	
Plymouth	a		16 29	16 29	16 56	17 01					17 23		17 48						18 38		18 56			19 27	
	d	15 57		16 31						17 06	17 26					17 55		18 17	18 44		19 00			19 31	
Devonport	d	16 00								17 09								18 20							
Dockyard	d	16x01								17x10								18x21							
Keyham	d	16x03								17x12								18x23							
St Budeaux Ferry Road	d	16 06								17 15								18 25							
Saltash	d	16 11								17 20	17 35							18 31						19 40	
St Germans	d	16 18								17 27	17 42							18 38							
Menheniot	d	16x25								17x34								18x45							
Liskeard 6	d	16a33		16 55						17a42	17 54					18 19		18a53	19 07		19 23			19 56	
Looe	a	17 11									18 33								19 46						
Bodmin Parkway	d			17 07							18 06					18 31			19 19		19 35			20 08	
Lostwithiel	d			17 14							18 12					18 36									
Par	d			17 22							18 19					18 43			19 30		19 45			20 19	
Newquay	a										19 21													21 20	
St Austell	d			17 29							18 27					18 51			19 38		19 52			20 27	
Truro	d			17 46							18 46					19 08			19 56		20 10			20 45	
Falmouth Docks	a			18 23							19 25								20 26					21 28	
Redruth	d			17 59							18 57					19 21			20 08		20 25			20 57	
Camborne	d			18 06							19 07					19 27			20 17		20 33			21 06	
Hayle	d			18 15							19 15					19 35									
St Erth	d			18 20							19 20					19 40			20 27		20 44			21 16	
St Ives	a			18 57												19 56			20 55						
Penzance	a			18 37							19 36					19 53			20 44		20 59			21 33	

For general notes see front of timetable
For details of catering facilities see Directory of Train Operators

- A 29 June to 4 September
- B Until 26 June and from 7 September
- C From St James' Park (Table 136)
- D From Gunnislake (Table 139)
- E ☕ to Plymouth
- b Stops to pick up only until 26 June
- c Stops to pick up only until 4 September
- e Arr. 1743

Sleeper services are published in Table 406

London and Birmingham → Devon and Cornwall

Network Diagram - see first page of Table 135

		XC	GW	GW	GW	GW	GW	XC	GW	GW	GW	GW	GW	XC	GW	GW	GW	GW	GW	XC	GW	XC
			FX		FO											FX	FO					
		1◇	1◇		1◇	1◇		1◇		1◇	1◇	1◇	1◇	1◇	1◇	1◇	1◇	1		1◇		1◇
		A						A							B					D		E
		⊼	▭		▭	▭		⊼		▭	▭	✕	▭	⊼	▭	▭	▭	✕		⊼		⊼
London Paddington 15 ⊖	d		16 33		16 33	17 03				17 06	17 33	18 03			18 06	18 36	18 36	19 03				
London Waterloo 15 ⊖	d																					
Slough 3	d		16 48		16 48																	
Heathrow Central Bus Stn 🚌	d					*16 15*					*16 55*	*17 15*				*17 55*	*17 55*	*18 15*				
Gatwick Airport 10	d					*16 03*					*16b08*	*17 03*						*18 03*				
Oxford	d		*16 31*		*16 31*	*16 42*				*17 01*		*17 42*			*18 01*	*18 31*	*18 31*	*18 42*				
Reading 7	d		17 04		17 04	17c31				17 36	18 01	18c31			18 36	19 03	19 03	19 32				
Theale	d									17 45					18 45							
Thatcham	d									17 55					18 55							
Newbury	d		17 20		17 20	17 48				18 01	18 17				19 01	19 19	19 19	19 48				
Hungerford	d		17 30		17 30					18 15					19 15	19 29	19 29					
Pewsey	d		17 45		17 45					18 34	18 41				19 34	19 44	19 44					
Westbury	d		18 05		18 05					18a54	19 01				19a52	20 05	20 05					
Castle Cary	d		18 23		18 23						19 19					20 22	20 22					
Birmingham New Street 12	d	16 12						17 12						18 12						19 12		19 42
Cardiff Central 7	d																					
Newport (South Wales)	d																					
Swindon	d																					
Bristol Parkway 7	d	17 26						18 26						19 28						20 28		20 58
Filton Abbey Wood	d																					
Bath Spa 7	d																					
Bristol Temple Meads 10	d	17 44						18 44						19 44						20 44		21 13
Weston-super-Mare	d																					
Bridgwater	d																					
Taunton	d	18 17	18 45		18 45	18 52		19 17			19 41	19 48		20 17		20 45	20 45	20 53		21 17		21 46
Tiverton Parkway	d	18 29	18 58		18 58	19 05		19 29			19 54			20 29		20 58	20 58			21 29		21 58
Exeter St Davids 6	a	18 43	19 17		19 17	19 21		19 43			20 10	20 13		20 43		21 16	21 16	21 21		21 43		22 12
Exeter Central	a	*18 53*				*19 29*		*20 18*				*20 25*		*21 03*				*21 30*		*22e33*		
Exmouth	a	*19 23*				*19 57*						*20 57*						*21 57*		*23 07*		
Barnstaple	a	*20 10*												*22 13*								
Exmouth	d					*18 28*	18 55					*19 33*		20 01					21 01			
Exeter Central	d					*19 03*	19 21					*19 57*	←	20 32			*20 55*	*20 55*	21 27			21 49
Exeter St Davids 6	d	18 45			19 17	19 23	19 28	19 45			20 19 →	20 16	20 19	20 45			21 16	21 22	21 34	21 45	←	22 14
Exeter St Thomas	d						19 31						20 23						21 37			
Starcross	d						19 39						20 32						21 45 →		21 45	
Dawlish Warren	d						19 44						20 36								21f59	
Dawlish	d						19 48						20 41								22 03	
Teignmouth	d						19 53						20 47								22 08	
Newton Abbot	a	19 04		←	19 37	19 43	20 00	20 04	←			20 35	20 54	21 03			21 36	21 43		22 03	22 15	22 32
	d	19 04		19 09	19 37	19 43	20 09	20 04	20 09			20 36	20 54	21 04			21 37	21 43		22 04	22 16	22 33
Torre	d			19 17			→		20 17				21 04								22 24	
Torquay	d			19 20					20 20				21 07								22 27	
Paignton	a			19 28					20 28				21 20								22 35	
Totnes	d	19 17				19 57		20 17				20 49		21 17				21 57		22 17		22 45
Ivybridge	d																					
Plymouth	a	19 48			20 17	20 25		20 48				21 17		21 48			22 15	22 25		22 48		23 20
	d	19 50				20 28		20 50				21 19						22 27				
Devonport	d																					
Dockyard	d																					
Keyham	d																					
St Budeaux Ferry Road	d																					
Saltash	d					20 38												22 36				
St Germans	d					20 45												22 43				
Menheniot	d																					
Liskeard 6	d	20 13				20 56		21 13				21 43						22 55				
Looe	a																					
Bodmin Parkway	d	20 26				21 08		21 26				21 57						23 10				
Lostwithiel	d							21 31														
Par	d	20 36				21 19		21 38				22 08						23 20				
Newquay	a																					
St Austell	d	20 43				21 27		21 45				22 16						23 28				
Truro	d	21 00				21 44		22 03				22 34						23 46				
Falmouth Docks	a							*22 31*														
Redruth	d	21 15				21 57		22 14				22 46						23 59				
Camborne	d	21 22						22 23										00 07				
Hayle	d					22 09		22 31														
St Erth	d	21 32				22 17		22 35										00 18				
St Ives	a	*21 52*																				
Penzance	a	21 47				22 31		22 50				23 15						00 34				

For general notes see front of timetable
For details of catering facilities see Directory of Train Operators

- **A** ⊼ to Plymouth
- **B** To Frome (Table 123)
- **D** ⊼ to Bristol Temple Meads
- **E** From 7 September. ⊼ to Bristol Temple Meads
- **b** Change at Redhill and Reading
- **c** Stops to pick up only until 4 September
- **e** Fridays arr. 2239
- **f** Arr. 2150

Sleeper services are published in Table 406

London and Birmingham → Devon and Cornwall

Network Diagram - see first page of Table 135

		GW	XC	GW	GW	GW	GW	XC	XC	GW	GW	GW	GW	GW	GW	GW	GW	GW	GW
																FO	FX	FX	FO
		1◇	1◇			1◇		1◇	1◇	1◇	1◇			1◇	1◇	◇	◇	◇	◇
		A	B	C	A	C	C	C	A	C	A	C	A	C	A	C	D	A	E
		🍽	🛒			🍽				🍽	🍽			🍽	🍽	🍽	🍽	🍽	🍽
London Paddington 15 ⊖	d	1945				1945				2035	2035			2145	2145	2345	2345	2345	23p45
London Waterloo 15 ⊖	d																		
Slough 3	d																		
Heathrow Central Bus Stn 🚌	d	*1855*				*1855*				*1940*	*1940*			*2110*	*2110*	*2305*			*2305*
Gatwick Airport 10	d	*1803*				*1803*				*1916*	*1916*			*20b11*	*20b11*	*2222*			*2222*
Oxford	d	*1931*				*1931*				*2015*	*2015*			*2115*	*2115*	*2315*			*2315*
Reading 7	d	2011				2011				2101	2101			2211	2211	00u37	00u37	00u37	00u37
Theale	d																		
Thatcham	d																		
Newbury	d	2027				2027				2118	2118								
Hungerford	d																		
Pewsey	d	2047				2047				2138	2138								
Westbury	d	2105				2105				2157	2157								
Castle Cary	d	2127				2127				2215	2215								
Birmingham New Street 12	d		1942					2012	2012										
Cardiff Central 7	d											2200	2200						
Newport (South Wales)	d											2217	2217						
Swindon	d													2250	2250				
Bristol Parkway 7	d		2058					2127	2127			2254	2254						
Filton Abbey Wood	d											2258	2258						
Bath Spa 7	d													2320	2320				
Bristol Temple Meads 10	d		2113					2144	2144			2308	2308	2335	2335				
Weston-super-Mare	d											2345	2345						
Bridgwater	d											0004	0004						
Taunton	d	2149	2146			2149		2217	2232	2237	2237	00s19	00s32	00s37	00s37	03c22	03e22	03e54	03c54
Tiverton Parkway	d	2202	2158			22f09		2229	2302	2251	2308	00s34	01s05	00s50	01s09				
Exeter St Davids 6	a	2219	2232			2239		2255	2314	2320	2328	0108	0124	0121	0130	0414	0414	0443	0443
Exeter Central	a	*22g33*				*23h00*			*2330*	*2330*						*0513*	*0513*	*0513*	*0513*
Exmouth	a	*2307*							*2357*	*2357*						*0610*	*0610*	*0610*	*0610*
Barnstaple	a																	*0658*	*0658*
Exmouth	d			2204	2204														
Exeter Central	d		*2149*	2230	2230			*22h38*	*22h38*										
Exeter St Davids 6	d	2220	2233	2237	2237	2243	←	2256	2316	2321	2329					0417	0417	0445	0445
Exeter St Thomas	d			2240	2240														
Starcross	d			2248	2248		2248												
Dawlish Warren	d			2253	→		22j59												
Dawlish	d			2257			2303												
Teignmouth	d			2302			2308												
Newton Abbot	a	2241	2252	2309		2306	2315	2321	2334	2341	2349					0437	0437	0505	0505
	d	2241	2253	2310		2307	2316	2322	2335	2342	2350					0439	0439	0507	0507
Torre	d			2318			2324												
Torquay	d			2321			2327												
Paignton	a			2329			2335												
Totnes	d	2255	2304			2320		2334	2348	2354	0002								
Ivybridge	d	2310				2336													
Plymouth	a	2330	2338			2355		0006	0019	0025	0035					0518	0518	0546	0546
	d															0550	0550	0550	0550
Devonport	d																		
Dockyard	d																		
Keyham	d																		
St Budeaux Ferry Road	d																		
Saltash	d																		
St Germans	d																		
Menheniot	d																		
Liskeard 6	d															0615	0615	0615	0615
Looe	a															*0741*	*0741*	*0741*	*0741*
Bodmin Parkway	d															0629	0629	0629	0629
Lostwithiel	d															0635	0635	0635	0635
Par	d															0642	0642	0642	0642
Newquay	a															*0825*			*0744*
St Austell	d															0650	0650	0650	0650
Truro	d															0710	0709	0709	0710
Falmouth Docks	a															*0741*	*0741*	*0741*	*0741*
Redruth	d															0723	0723	0723	0723
Camborne	d															0730	0730	0730	0730
Hayle	d															0739	0739	0739	0739
St Erth	d															0744	0744	0744	0744
St Ives	a															*0813*	*0818*	*0818*	*0813*
Penzance	a															0800	0800	0800	0800

For general notes see front of timetable
For details of catering facilities see Directory of Train Operators

A From 7 September
B Until 4 September. 🛒 to Bristol Temple Meads
C Until 4 September
D Until 3 September
E From 11 September
b Change at Redhill and Reading
c Arr. 0222
e Arr. 0232
f Arr. 2203
g Fridays arr. 2239
h Fridays only
j Arr. 2253

Table 135

Saturdays

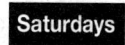

until 5 September

Sleeper services are published in Table 406

London and Birmingham → Devon and Cornwall

Network Diagram - see first page of Table 135

		GW	GW	GW	GW	XC	GW	GW	GW	GW	XC	GW	GW	GW		SW	GW	XC	GW	GW	GW	GW	XC	GW	GW
		[1]		◇		[1] ◇			◇		[1] ◇		[1] ◇			[1]		[1] ◇	[1] ◇				[1] ◇	[1] [R]	[1] [R]
		✕		🛏		🛒			🛒		🛒		🛏					🛒		🛒		🛒	🛒	🛏	🛏
London Paddington [15] ⊖	d	19p03		23p45																				07 30	07 36
London Waterloo [15] ⊖	d																								
Slough [3]	d																								
Heathrow Central Bus Stn 🚌	d																							*06 00*	*07 00*
Gatwick Airport [10]	d																							*06 04*	
Oxford	d																							*07 16*	*07 31*
Reading [7]	d	19p32		00u37																				07 57	08u06
Theale	d																								
Thatcham	d																								
Newbury	d	19p48																							
Hungerford	d																								
Pewsey	d																								
Westbury	d																								
Castle Cary	d																								
Birmingham New Street [12]	d																	06 42					07 12		
Cardiff Central [7]	d		22p00																						
Newport (South Wales)	d		22p17																						
Swindon	d																							08 30	
Bristol Parkway [7]	d		22p54															07 57					08 26		
Filton Abbey Wood	d		22p58																						
Bath Spa [7]	d																							09 00	
Bristol Temple Meads [10]	d		23p08						05 29		06 08			06 36				08 11					08 44	09 17	
Weston-super-Mare	d		23p45						05 50					06 56										→	
Bridgwater	d		00 04						06 09																
Taunton	d	20p53	00s19	03b22					06 23		07 17			07 24				08 43					09 17		
Tiverton Parkway	d		00s34						06 39		07 29			07 41									09 29		
Exeter St Davids [6]	a	21p21	01 08	04 14					06 57		07 43			07 59				09 07					09 43		09 52
Exeter Central	a			*05 13*					*07 14*		*08 03*			*08 21*				*09 21*							*10 13*
Exmouth	a			*06 10*					*07 42*					*08 50*				*09 50*							*10 52*
Barnstaple	a													*09 37*				*10 35*							
Exmouth	d								*06 15*			07 15				*07 53*	08 23						*08 53*		
Exeter Central	d								*06 41*		*07 33*	07 43				08 28	08 50						*09 25*		
Exeter St Davids [6]	d	21p22		04 17	05 18		05 56	06 11	06 59		07 45	07 50		08 05		08 37	08 56	09 08				09 28	09 45		09 53
Exeter St Thomas	d				05 21		05 59	06 14	07 02			07 53					08 59								
Starcross	d				05 29		06 07	06 22	07 10			08 01					09 07				←				
Dawlish Warren	d				05 34		06 12	06 27	07 15			08 06					09c20				09 20				
Dawlish	d				05 38		06 16	06 31	07 19			08 10				08 50	→				09 24				
Teignmouth	d				05 43		06 21	06 36	07 24			08 15				08 55					09 30				
Newton Abbot	a	21p43		04 37	05 50		06 28	06 44	07 31		08 03	08 22		08 26		09 01					09 37	09 48	10 03		
	d	21p43		04 39	05 52		06 30	06 45	07 32	07 39	08 04	08 24		08 27		09 06					09 38	09 49	10 04		
Torre	d				06 00		06 38	06 53		07 47		08 32									09 47				
Torquay	d				06 03		06 41	06 56		07 50		08 35				09 17		09 37			09 50				
Paignton	a				06 11		06 49	07 05		07 58		08 42				09 23		09 49			09 57				
Totnes	d	21p57							07 45		08 17			08 39								10 02	10 17		
Ivybridge	d								08 02					08 55								10 19			
Plymouth	a	22p25		05 18					08 15		08 48			09 09								10 32	10 48		10 51
	d	22p27		05 50		06 30			08 18				08 58						09 26	09 58		10 33			10 51
Devonport	d								08 22											10 01					
Dockyard	d																								
Keyham	d																								
St Budeaux Ferry Road	d																					10 39			
Saltash	d	22p36							08 29											10 08		10 43			
St Germans	d	22p43							08 36											10 15		10 50			
Menheniot	d								08x43											10x22					
Liskeard [6]	d	22p55		06 15		06 53			08 50				09 22						09 49	10 29		11 02			
Looe	a					*07 41*													*10 25*			*11 43*			
Bodmin Parkway	d	23p10		06 29		07 06			09 02				09 34						10 01	10 41		11 14			
Lostwithiel	d			06 35		07 11			09 07										10 08	10 46		11 19			
Par	d	23p20		06 42		07 21			09 14				09 47						10 15	10a53		11 26			11 35
Newquay	a					08 25							11 05												12 45
St Austell	d	23p28		06 50					09 21										10 22			11 37			
Truro	d	23p46		07 09					09 40										10 40			11 55			
Falmouth Docks	a			*07 41*					*10 14*										*11 15*			*12 45*			
Redruth	d	23p59		07 23					09 53										10 52			12 08			
Camborne	d	00 07		07 30					09 59										11 00			12 14			
Hayle	d			07 39					10 06										11 11			12 21			
St Erth	d	00 18		07 44					10 10										11 17			12 24			
St Ives	a			*08 13*					*10 24*										*11 55*			*12 55*			
Penzance	a	00 34		08 00					10 23										11 28			12 37			

For general notes see front of timetable
For details of catering facilities see
Directory of Train Operators

b Arr. 0222
c Arr. 0915

Sleeper services are published in Table 406

London and Birmingham → Devon and Cornwall

Network Diagram - see first page of Table 135

		GW	GW 1	GW	SW 1 ◇	XC 1 ◇	GW	GW 1 R	GW 1 R	XC 1 ◇	XC 1 ◇	GW	GW 1 R	XC 1 ◇	SW 1 ◇	XC 1 ◇	SW 1 ◇	GW	GW 1 R	GW 1 R	XC 1 ◇	GW 1 R A	GW 1 R B
London Paddington 15	⊖ d							08 35	09 06				10 06						10 35	11 06		11 35	11 35
London Waterloo 15	⊖ d				07 10										09 20								
Slough 3	d																						
Heathrow Central Bus Stn	d							08 00	08 30				09 30						10 00	10 30		11 00	11 00
Gatwick Airport 10	d							07b10	08 03				09 03						09b08	10 03		10b08	10b08
Oxford	d							08 31	09 01				10 01						10 31	11 01		11 31	11 31
Reading 7	d							09u04	09u33				10u33						11 04	11u33		12u06	12u06
Theale	d																						
Thatcham	d																						
Newbury	d							09 21															
Hungerford	d																						
Pewsey	d							09 40											11 37				
Westbury	d							09 58											11 55				
Castle Cary	d							10 16											12 13				
Birmingham New Street 12	d					08 12				08 42	09 12			09 42		10 12					11 12		
Cardiff Central 7	d																						
Newport (South Wales)	d																						
Swindon	d																						
Bristol Parkway 7	d					09 26				09 58	10 28			10 58		11 26					12 28		
Filton Abbey Wood	d																						
Bath Spa 7	d		←																				
Bristol Temple Meads 10	d		09 17			09 44				10 20	10 44			11 13		11 44					12 44		
Weston-super-Mare	d													11 40									
Bridgwater	d																						
Taunton	d		09 51			10 17		10 37	10 50	11 02	11 17			12 03		12 17			12 36	12 52	13 17		
Tiverton Parkway	d					10 29			11 03	11 14	11 29			12 15					12 49		13 29		
Exeter St Davids 6	a		10 18			10 46		11 04	11 21	11 30	11 43		12 13	12 31		12 42			13 06	13 19	13 43	13 53	
Exeter Central	a		*10 51*			*11 11*		*11 21*		*11 51*	*12 13*					*12 51*			*13 21*	*13 38*	*14 13*	*14 13*	
Exmouth	a		*11 18*					*11 50*		*12 18*	*12 50*					*13 18*			*13 50*	*14 18*			
Barnstaple	a		*11 35*						*12 35*				*13 37*							*14 37*			
Exmouth	d	09 23			*09 53*		10 23			*10 53*		11 23		*11 53*				12 23			*12 53*		
Exeter Central	d	09 50			10 26		10 50			*11 17*		11 50	*11 58*	*12 20*	12 27			12 50			*13 21*	*13 39*	*13 39*
Exeter St Davids 6	d	09 58	10 19	10 25	10 36	10 49	10 56	11 06	11 23	11 33	11 45	11 56	12 16	12 34	12 39	12 45		12 56	13 09	13 21	13 45	13 56	13u56
Exeter St Thomas	d	10 01					10 59					11 59						12 59					
Starcross	d	10 09					11 07					12 07					←	13 07					
Dawlish Warren	d	10 14			10 47		11 12	11 19				12 13			12c58 →		12 58	13 12					
Dawlish	d	10 19			10 51		11 16	11 25				12 17		12 47			13 02	13 16	13 23				
Teignmouth	d	10 24			10 56		11 21	11 31				12 23		12 54			13 07	13 21	13 29				
Newton Abbot	a	10 32	10 40	10 45	11 03	11 08	11 29	11 38	11 43	11 52	12 03	12 31	12 35	13 00		13 03	13 13	13 29	13 36	13 41	14 03		
	d	10 34	10 40	10 47	11 04	11 10	11 30	11 40	11 44	11 54	12 04	12 32	12 37	13 02		13 04	13 14	13 30	13 38	13 42	14 04		
Torre	d	10 42		10 55			11 38					12 41						13 38					
Torquay	d	10 45		10 58	11 15		11 41	11 52				12 44		13 14				13 41	13 51				
Paignton	a	10 51		11 06	11 22		11 49	12 00				12 51		13 27				13 49	14 00				
Totnes	d		10 54			11 23			11 57		12 17					13 20	13 28			13 55	14 17		
Ivybridge	d																13 43						
Plymouth	a		11 22			11 56			12 26	12 32	12 48		13 14			13 48	13 57			14 23	14 48	14 53	
	d		11 24						12 28	12 39			13 19			13 48				14 26		14 56	14u56
Devonport	d																						
Dockyard	d																						
Keyham	d																						
St Budeaux Ferry Road	d																						
Saltash	d																						
St Germans	d																						
Menheniot	d																						
Liskeard 6	d		11 47						12 51	13 04			13 44			14 12				14 49			
Looe	a		*12 52*							*13 53*						*14 53*							
Bodmin Parkway	d		12 01						13 04	13 17			13 57			14 25				15 02			
Lostwithiel	d								13 10													15 33	15 33
Par	d												14 07			14 35						15 43	15 43
Newquay	a									14 42												16 52	16 52
St Austell	d		12 17						13 21				14 15			14 43				15 17			
Truro	d		12 34						13 39				14 33			15 01				15 35			
Falmouth Docks	a		*13 15*						*14 15*				*15 15*			*15 45*				*16 15*			
Redruth	d		12 47						13 51				14 45			15 13				15 47			
Camborne	d		12 54						13 59				14 53			15 21				15 54			
Hayle	d								14 09				15 03							16 05			
St Erth	d		13 06						14 14				15 08			15 31				16 09			
St Ives	a		*13 24*						*14 55*				*15 24*			*15 55*				*16 24*			
Penzance	a		13 19						14 27				15 21			15 50				16 24			

For general notes see front of timetable
For details of catering facilities see
Directory of Train Operators

A Until 20 June
B From 27 June
b Change at Redhill and Reading
c Arr. 1250

Table 135

Saturdays

until 5 September

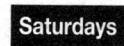

Sleeper services are published in Table 406

London and Birmingham → Devon and Cornwall

Network Diagram - see first page of Table 135

		GW	GW 1 R 🍴	GW	SW 1◇ 🍴	XC 1◇ 🛒	GW	GW 1 R 🍴	GW 🛒	GW 1 R 🍴	XC 1◇ 🛒	SW 1◇ 🍴		GW	XC 1◇ 🛒	GW 1◇ 🍴	XC 1◇ 🛒	GW	GW	GW 🛒	GW 1◇ 🍴	GW	XC 1◇ 🛒	SW 1◇ 🍴	SW 1
London Paddington 15 ⊖	d		12 06					12 35		13 06						14 06					15 06				
London Waterloo 15 ⊖	d				11 20							12 20												14 20	
Slough 3	d																								
Heathrow Central Bus Stn 🚌	d		*11 30*					*12 00*		*12 30*						*13 30*					*14 30*				
Gatwick Airport 10	d		*11 03*					*11b08*		*12 03*						*13 03*					*14 03*				
Oxford	d		*12 01*					*12 31*		*13 01*						*14 01*					*15 01*				
Reading 7	d		12u32					13 04		13u32						14u33					15u33				
Theale	d																								
Thatcham	d																								
Newbury	d							13 21																	
Hungerford	d																								
Pewsey	d							13 42													16 05				
Westbury	d							14 00													16 23				
Castle Cary	d							14 18													16 41				
Birmingham New Street 12	d					12 12					13 12				13 42		14 12						15 12		
Cardiff Central 7	d																								
Newport (South Wales)	d																								
Swindon	d																								
Bristol Parkway 7	d					13 26					14 28				14 58		15 26						16 28		
Filton Abbey Wood	d																								
Bath Spa 7	d																								
Bristol Temple Meads 10	d					13 44					14 44				15 13		15 44						16 44		
Weston-super-Mare	d																								
Bridgwater	d																								
Taunton	d					14 17		14 41		14 49	15 17				15 45	15 49	16 17				17 03		17 19		
Tiverton Parkway	d					14 29				15 02					15 57	16 02	16 29				17 16		17 31		
Exeter St Davids 6	a		14 12			14 43		15 06		15 20	15 43				16 12	16 20	16 43				17 33		17 47		
Exeter Central	a		*14 21*					*15 21*		*15 33*	*16 13*				*16 23*	*16 43*	*16 53*				*17 43*		*18 13*		
Exmouth	a		*14 50*					*15 50*							*16 52*		*17 23*				*18 23*		*18 53*		
Barnstaple	a		*15 35*							*16 35*							*18 07*						*19 13*		
Exmouth	d	13 23			*13 53*		14 23				*14 53*			15 23			*15 53*		16 55						*17 25*
Exeter Central	d	13 50			14 23		14 50				*15 17*	15 39		15 50			*16 25*	16 45	17 21				*17 33*	17 33	17 57
Exeter St Davids 6	d	14 02	14 14	←	14 32	14 45	14 56	15 09		15 21	15 45	15 49		15 57	16 13	16 22	16 45	16 56	17 26		17 35	←	17 49	17 53	18 05
Exeter St Thomas	d	14 05					14 59							16 00				16 59	17 29						
Starcross	d	14 12		14 12			15 07							16 07				17 07	17 37			17 37			
Dawlish Warren	d	→		14c26	14 43		15 12	15 21				15 59		16 12				17 12	→			17e49		18 04	18 16
Dawlish	d			14 30	14 47		15 16	15 27				16 03		16 16				17 16				17 53		18 08	18 20
Teignmouth	d			14 35	14 52		15 21	15 33				16 08		16 21				17 21				17 58		18 13	18 25
Newton Abbot	a		14 33	14 45	14 59	15 03	15 29	15 39		15 44	16 04	16 15		16 29	16 33	16 41	17 03	17 29			17 55	18 05	18 09	18 20	18 32
	d		14 35	14 48	15 00	15 04	15 30	15 41		15 44	16 04	16 15		16 31	16 40	16 43	17 04	17 30			17 57	18 09	18 11	18 21	18 33
Torre	d			14 56	15 09		15 38							16 39				17 38				18 17			
Torquay	d			14 59	15 13		15 41	15 55						16 42	16 52			17 41				18 20			18 44
Paignton	a			15 06	15 19		15 49	16 03						16 51	17 04			17 51				18 28			18 52
Totnes	d					15 17				15 58	16 20	16 28				16 55	17 17				18 10		18 24	18 34	
Ivybridge	d											16 43												18 49	
Plymouth	a		15 11			15 48				16 25	16 47	16 58				17 23	17 48				18 38		18 52	19 03	
	d		15 12						16 03	16 27	16 53									17 52	18 42		19 01	19 11	
Devonport	d																			17 55					
Dockyard	d																			17x57					
Keyham	d																			17x59					
St Budeaux Ferry Road	d																			18 01					
Saltash	d								16 11											18 06				19 19	
St Germans	d								16 18											18 12				19 26	
Menheniot	d								16x25											18x19					
Liskeard 6	d		15 36						16 32	16 50	17 16									18 26	19 06		19 24	19 38	
Looe	a		*16 13*							*17 27*	*18 31*												*19 58*		
Bodmin Parkway	d		15 49						16 44	17 03	17 29									18 38	19 19		19 37	19 50	
Lostwithiel	d								16 50											18 44				19 56	
Par	d		15 59						16a56											18 51	19 30		19 47	20 03	
Newquay	a										18 49														
St Austell	d		16 07							17 18										18 58	19 38		19 55	20 11	
Truro	d		16 24							17 36										19 16	19 58		20 13	20 29	
Falmouth Docks	a		*17 15*							*18 23*											*20 26*				
Redruth	d		16 37							17 48										19 29	20 08		20 25	20 41	
Camborne	d		16 45							17 56										19 35	20 16		20 32	20 47	
Hayle	d									18 07										19 42					
St Erth	d		16 56							18 11										19 46	20 26		20 43		
St Ives	a		*17 26*							*19 13*										*20 04*			*21 00*		
Penzance	a		17 13							18 24										19 57	20 43		20 59	21 05	

For general notes see front of timetable
For details of catering facilities see
Directory of Train Operators

b Change at Redhill and Reading
c Arr. 1418
e Arr. 1743

Sleeper services are published in Table 406

London and Birmingham → Devon and Cornwall

Network Diagram - see first page of Table 135

	GW 1◇	GW	XC 1◇		GW 1◇	GW	GW 1◇	GW 1◇	GW	XC 1◇	GW	GW 1◇	GW	XC 1◇	XC 1◇	GW	GW 1◇	XC 1◇	GW 1◇	XC 1◇	GW	GW 1◇		
London Paddington 15 ⊖ d	16 06				16 30		17 06					18 06					19 06		20 06			20 30		
London Waterloo 15 ⊖ d																								
Slough 3 d																								
Heathrow Central Bus Stn d	*15 30*						*16 30*					*17 30*					*18 30*		*19 20*			*19 50*		
Gatwick Airport 10 d	*15 03*						*16 03*					*17 03*					*18 03*		*19 03*					
Oxford d	*16 01*				*16 16*		*17 01*					*18 01*					*19 01*		*19 43*			*20 16*		
Reading 7 d	16u32				16 57		17u32					18u32					19 32		20 31			20 57		
Theale d																								
Thatcham d																								
Newbury d																	19 49		20 46					
Hungerford d																								
Pewsey d							18 03										20 10		21 05					
Westbury d							18 22										20 28		21 24					
Castle Cary d							18 41										20 45		21 43					
Birmingham New Street 12 d			16 12							17 12				17 42	18 12			19 12		20 12				
Cardiff Central 7 d																					21 00			
Newport (South Wales) d																					21 15			
Swindon d					17 30																	21 30		
Bristol Parkway 7 d			17 26							18 28				19 09	19 28			20 28		21 25				
Filton Abbey Wood d								←													21 42			
Bath Spa 7 d					18 00 →			18 00														22 00		
Bristol Temple Meads 10 d			17 44					18 17		18 44				19 37	19 44			20 44		21 44	21 55	22 17		
Weston-super-Mare d								18 40													22 28			
Bridgwater d																					22 47			
Taunton d	17 48		18 17				19 02	19 06		19 17		19 47		20 09	20 17		21 08	21 17	22 05	22 17	23 02	23 19		
Tiverton Parkway d	18 01		18 29				19 15	19 21		19 29				20 21	20 29		21 21	21 29	22 18	22 29	23 17	23 32		
Exeter St Davids 6 a	18 19		18 43				19 32	19 37		19 43		20 14		20 36	20 43		21 39	21 45	22 36	22 44	23 36	23 53		
Exeter Central a	*18 32*		*18 53*							*20 18*		*20 29*			*21 03*			*22 39*		*23 00*				
Exmouth a			*19 23*									*20 57*			*21 57*			*23 07*		*23 42*				
Barnstaple a			*20 10*												*22 13*									
Exmouth d		17 55				*18 27*	*18 55*				19 33				*20 01*		*21 01*		*22 01*					
Exeter Central d		18 21				*19 03*	*19 21*				19 57				*20 26*		*21 27*		*22 27*					
Exeter St Davids 6 d	18 21	18 26	18 45			19 17	19 34	19 38		19 45	20 06	20 15	←	20 37	20 45	20 56	21 39	21 45	22 38	22 45				
Exeter St Thomas d		18 29				19 20					20 09					20 59								
Starcross d		18 37				19 28					20 17 →		20 17			21 07								
Dawlish Warren d		18 42				19 33							20b32			21 12								
Dawlish d		18 46				19 37							20 36	20 49		21 16			22 50					
Teignmouth d		18 51				19 42							20 41	20 54		21 21			22 56					
Newton Abbot a	18 43	18 59	19 03			19 49	19 53	19 58		20 03		20 37	20 48	21 01	21 03	21 28	22 00	22 06	23 03	23 11				
Newton Abbot d	18 43	19 01	19 04			19 51	19 54	19 59		20 04		20 37	20 49	21 03	21 04	21 30	22 00	22 09	23 04	23 13				
Torre d		19 09				19 59		20 09					20 57			21 38								
Torquay d		19 12				20 02		20 12					21 00	21 15		21 41								
Paignton a		19 21				20 10		20 24					21 08	21 27		21 48								
Totnes d	18 57		19 17				20 07			20 17		20 51			21 17		22 14	22 23	23 17	23 28				
Ivybridge d	19 13																							
Plymouth a	19 28		19 48				20 36			20 48		21 19			21 48		22 42	22 55	23 47	23 59				
Plymouth d	19 29		19 48						20 42	20 58		21 20												
Devonport d																								
Dockyard d																								
Keyham d																								
St Budeaux Ferry Road d																								
Saltash d									20 50															
St Germans d									20 57															
Menheniot d																								
Liskeard 6 d	19 53		20 11						21 09	21 25		21 44												
Looe a			*21 11*																					
Bodmin Parkway d	20 06		20 24						21 21	21 38		21 59												
Lostwithiel d			20 29						21 26															
Par d	20 16		20 36						21 33	21 48		22 09												
Newquay a	*21 13*																							
St Austell d	20 24		20 43						21 44	21 55		22 17												
Truro d	20 42		21 00						22 02	22c19		22 35												
Falmouth Docks a	*21 28*								*22 31*															
Redruth d	20 54		21 12						22 15	22 30		22 47												
Camborne d	21 03		21 18						22 21	22 36		22 56												
Hayle d			21 26						22 28															
St Erth d	21 14		21 30						22 31	22 46		23 09												
St Ives a			*21 58*																					
Penzance a	21 30		21 46						22 43	23 02		23 24												

For general notes see front of timetable
For details of catering facilities see Directory of Train Operators

b Arr. 2022
c Arr. 2211

Saturdays

from 12 September

Sleeper services are published in Table 406

London and Birmingham → Devon and Cornwall

Network Diagram - see first page of Table 135

	GW 1 ✕	GW 1 ◇ 🛏	GW	GW	GW ◇ 🛏	GW	XC 1 ◇ 🛒		GW	GW	GW ◇ 🛒	GW	XC 1 ◇ 🛒	GW	GW ◇ 🛒		SW 1	GW	XC 1 ◇ 🛒	GW 🛒	GW	GW 🛒	XC 1 ◇ 🛒	GW
London Paddington 15 ⊖ d	19p03	20p35			23p45																			
London Waterloo 15 ⊖ d																								
Slough 3 d																								
Heathrow Central Bus Stn 🚌 d																								
Gatwick Airport 10 d																								
Oxford d																								
Reading 7 d	19p32	21p01			00u37																			
Theale d																								
Thatcham d																								
Newbury d	19p48	21p18																						
Hungerford d																								
Pewsey d		21p38																						
Westbury d		21p57																						
Castle Cary d		22p15																						
Birmingham New Street 12 d																			06 42				07 12	
Cardiff Central 7 d			22p00																					
Newport (South Wales) d			22p17																					
Swindon d																								
Bristol Parkway 7 d			22p54																07 57				08 26	
Filton Abbey Wood d			22p58																					
Bath Spa 7 d																								
Bristol Temple Meads 10 d			23p08								05 29		06 08		06 36				08 11				08 44	
Weston-super-Mare d			23p45								05 50				06 56									
Bridgwater d			00 04								06 09													
Taunton d	20p53	22p37	00s32		03b54						06 23		07 17		07 24				08 43				09 17	
Tiverton Parkway d		23p08	01s05								06 39		07 29		07 41								09 29	
Exeter St Davids 6 a	21p21	23p28	01 24		04 43						06 57		07 43		07 59				09 07				09 43	
Exeter Central a					*05 13*						*07 14*		*08 03*		*08 21*				*09 21*				*10 13*	
Exmouth a					*06 10*						*07 42*		*08 50*		*08 50*				*09 50*				*10 50*	
Barnstaple a					*06 58*								*09 37*		*09 37*				*10 35*					
Exmouth d											*06 15*		*06 15*	07 15			*07 53*	08 23					*08 53*	09 23
Exeter Central d											*06 41*		*07 33*	07 43			08 28	08 50					*09 25*	09 50
Exeter St Davids 6 d	21p22	23p29			04 45	05 18			05 56	06 11	06 59		07 45	07 50	08 05		08 37	08 56	09 08			09 28	09 45	09 58
Exeter St Thomas d						05 21			05 59	06 14	07 02			07 53	08 08			08 59						10 01
Starcross d						05 29			06 07	06 22	07 10			08 01				09 07			←			10 08
Dawlish Warren d						05 34			06 12	06 27	07 15			08 06				09c20			09 20			10 13
Dawlish d						05 38			06 16	06 31	07 19			08 10	08 20		08 50	→			09 24			10 17
Teignmouth d						05 43			06 21	06 36	07 24			08 15	08 25		08 55				09 29			10 22
Newton Abbot a	21p43	23p49			05 05	05 50			06 28	06 44	07 31		08 03	08 22	08 32		09 01				09 36	09 48	10 03	10 30
Newton Abbot d	21p43	23p50			05 07	05 52			06 30	06 45	07 32	07 39	08 04	08 24	08 33		09 06				09 38	09 49	10 04	10 33
Torre d						06 00			06 38	06 53		07 47		08 32							09 46			10 41
Torquay d						06 03			06 41	06 56		07 50		08 35			09 17		09 39		09 49			10 44
Paignton a						06 11			06 49	07 05		07 58		08 42			09 23		09 50		09 56			10 50
Totnes d	21p57	00 02									07 45		08 17		08 46							10 02	10 17	
Ivybridge d											08 02				09 03							10 19		
Plymouth a	22p25	00 35			05 46						08 15		08 48		09 17							10 32	10 48	
Plymouth d	22p27				05 50		06 28				08 18				09 20					09 55		10 33		
Devonport d											08 22				09 23					09 58				
Dockyard d																								
Keyham d																								
St Budeaux Ferry Road d																						10 39		
Saltash d	22p36										08 29				09 30					10 05		10 43		
St Germans d	22p43										08 36				09 37					10 12		10 50		
Menheniot d											08x43									10x19				
Liskeard 6 d	22p55				06 15		06 51				08 50				09 49					10 26		11 02		
Looe a							*07 41*								*10 26*							*11 43*		
Bodmin Parkway d	23p10				06 29		07 03				09 02				10 01					10 38		11 14		
Lostwithiel d					06 35		07 09				09 07				10 07					10 43		11 19		
Par d	23p20			06 09	06 42		07 15				09 14				10 14					10 50		11 26		
Newquay a					*07 44*						*10 10*													
St Austell d	23p28			06 16	06 50		07 22				09 21				10 22					10 58		11 37		
Truro d	23p46			06e41	07 09		07 39				09 40				10 41					11f24		11 55		
Falmouth Docks a					*07 41*		*08 13*				*10 15*				*11 15*					*11 45*		*12 45*		
Redruth d	23p59			06 54	07 23		07 50				09 53				10 54					11 37		12 08		
Camborne d	00 07			07 00	07 30		07 57				09 59				11 00					11 43		12 14		
Hayle d				07 07	07 39		08 05				10 06				11 07					11 50		12 21		
St Erth d	00 18			07 10	07 44		08 12				10 10				11 10					11 54		12 24		
St Ives a				*07 26*	*08 13*		*09 19*				*10 24*				*11 55*					*12 24*		*12 55*		
Penzance a	00 34			07 23	08 00		08 24				10 23				11 24					12 06		12 37		

For general notes see front of timetable
For details of catering facilities see Directory of Train Operators

b Arr. 0222
c Arr. 0914
e Arr. 0632
f Arr. 1114

Saturdays

from 12 September

Sleeper services are published in Table 406

London and Birmingham → Devon and Cornwall

Network Diagram - see first page of Table 135

		GW		GW	SW	XC	GW	GW	GW	GW		XC	GW	GW	XC	SW	XC	SW		GW	GW	GW	XC	GW	GW
		1 ◇			1 ◇	1 ◇		1 ◇	1 ◇			1 ◇		1 ◇	1 ◇	1 ◇	1 ◇	1 ◇				1 ◇	1 ◇		1 ◇
		🍽			🍽	🛒		🍽	🍽	🛒		🛒		🍽	🛒	🍽	🛒	🍽			🛒	🍽	🛒		🍽
London Paddington 15	⊖ d	07 30						08 18	09 06					10 06								11 06			12 06
London Waterloo 15	⊖ d				07 10											09 20									
Slough 3	d																								
Heathrow Central Bus Stn	🚌 d	*06 00*						*07 30*	*08 30*					*09 30*								*10 30*			*11 30*
Gatwick Airport 10	d	*06 04*						*07 03*	*08 03*					*09 03*								*10 03*			*11 03*
Oxford	d	*07 16*						*08 16*	*09 01*					*10 01*								*11 01*			*12 01*
Reading 7	d	07 57						08 49	09 32					10 32								11 32			12 32
Theale	d							08 58																	
Thatcham	d							09 07																	
Newbury	d							09 14																	
Hungerford	d							09 23																	
Pewsey	d							09 41														12 03			
Westbury	d							10 00														12 22			
Castle Cary	d							10 18														12 40			
Birmingham New Street 12	d					08 12						09 12			09 42		10 12						11 12		
Cardiff Central 7	d																								
Newport (South Wales)	d																								
Swindon	d	08 30																							
Bristol Parkway 7	d					09 26						10 28			10 58		11 26						12 30		
Filton Abbey Wood	d																								
Bath Spa 7	d	09 00																							
Bristol Temple Meads 10	d	09 17				09 44						10 44			11 14		11 44						12 44		
Weston-super-Mare	d														11 40										
Bridgwater	d																								
Taunton	d	09 51				10 17		10 40	10 48			11 17			12 02		12 17					13 02	13 17		
Tiverton Parkway	d					10 29		10 53	11 01			11 29			12 14		12 29					13 15	13 29		
Exeter St Davids 6	a	10 17				10 46		11 13	11 18			11 43		12 10	12 28		12 43					13 32	13 43		14 10
Exeter Central	a	*10 51*				*11 11*			*11 51*			*12 13*		*12 21*	*12 51*		*13 21*					*13 51*	*14 13*		*14 21*
Exmouth	a	*11 18*				*11 50*			*12 18*					*12 50*	*13 18*		*13 50*					*14 18*			*14 50*
Barnstaple	a	*11 35*							*12 35*					*13 37*			*14 37*								*15 35*
Exmouth	d				*09 53*		10 23					*10 53*	11 23		*11 53*					12 23		*12 53*		13 23	*13 23*
Exeter Central	d				10 26		10 50					*11 17*	11 50	*11 58*	*12 20*	12 27				12 50		*13 21*		13 50	*13 50*
Exeter St Davids 6	d	10 18		10 25	10 36	10 48	10 56		11 18			11 45	11 56	12 10	12 30	12 39	12 45			12 56		13 33	13 45	14 02	14 11
Exeter St Thomas	d						10 59						11 59							12 59				14 05	
Starcross	d						11 07						12 07					←		13 07				14 12	
Dawlish Warren	d				10 47		11 12						12 12			12b58 →		12 58		13 12				→	
Dawlish	d				10 51		11 16						12 16		12 42			13 02		13 16					
Teignmouth	d				10 56		11 21						12 21		12 47			13 07		13 21					
Newton Abbot	a	10 38		10 45	11 03	11 07	11 29		11 39			12 03	12 29	12 31	12 54		13 03	13 13		13 29		13 52	14 03		14 33
	d	10 39		10 47	11 04	11 09	11 30		11 39			12 04	12 30	12 31	12 55		13 04	13 14		13 30		13 54	14 04		14 34
Torre	d			10 55			11 38						12 39							13 38					
Torquay	d			10 58	11 15		11 41						12 42		13 07					13 41					
Paignton	a			11 06	11 22		11 49						12 49		13 16					13 49					
Totnes	d	10 52				11 22			11 53			12 17					13 17	13 28				14 06	14 17		
Ivybridge	d								12 08									13 43							
Plymouth	a	11 19				11 55			12 25			12 48		13 10			13 48	13 57				14 36	14 48		15 09
	d	11 22								12 30				13 10							13 58				15 11
Devonport	d																								
Dockyard	d																								
Keyham	d																								
St Budeaux Ferry Road	d																								
Saltash	d									12 38											14 06				
St Germans	d									12 45											14 13				
Menheniot	d																								
Liskeard 6	d	11 45								12 57				13 34							14 25				15 35
Looe	a	*12 43*								*13 48*				*14 56*							*14 56*				*16 11*
Bodmin Parkway	d	11 57								13 09				13 48							14 37				15 47
Lostwithiel	d									13 14											14 43				
Par	d	12 08								13 21				13 59							14 50				15 58
Newquay	a	*13 05*												*14 48*											*17 02*
St Austell	d	12 16								13 29				14 07							14 57				16 06
Truro	d	12 34								13c54				14 23							15e24				16 23
Falmouth Docks	a	*13 15*								*14 15*				*15 15*							*15 45*				*17 15*
Redruth	d	12 46								14 07				14 37							15 36				16 36
Camborne	d	12 54								14 13				14 43							15 42				16 43
Hayle	d									14 20				14 53							15 50				
St Erth	d	13 04								14 24				14 57							15 52				16 54
St Ives	a	*13 24*								*14 55*				*15 24*							*16 24*				*17 26*
Penzance	a	13 21								14 35				15 13							16 07				17 10

For general notes see front of timetable
For details of catering facilities see Directory of Train Operators

b Arr. 1250
c Arr. 1345
e Arr. 1513

Table 135

Saturdays

from 12 September

Sleeper services are published in Table 406

London and Birmingham → Devon and Cornwall

Network Diagram - see first page of Table 135

		GW	SW	XC		GW	GW	GW	GW	XC	SW	GW		GW	XC	GW	GW	GW	GW	GW		XC	SW	SW	XC
			1 ◇	1 ◇			1 ◇		1 ◇	1 ◇	1 ◇			1 ◇	1 ◇				1 ◇			1 ◇	1 ◇	1	1 ◇
London Paddington 15 ⊖	d						12 18		13 06					14 06					15 06						
London Waterloo 15 ⊖	d		11 20								12 20												14 20		
Slough 3	d																								
Heathrow Central Bus Stn (bus)	d								*12 30*					*13 30*					*14 30*						
Gatwick Airport 10	d								*12 03*					*13 03*					*14 03*						
Oxford	d						*12 16*		*13 01*					*14 01*					*15 01*						
Reading 7	d						12 49		13 32					14 32					15 33						
Theale	d						12 58																		
Thatcham	d						13 07																		
Newbury	d						13 14																		
Hungerford	d						13 23																		
Pewsey	d						13 40												16 05						
Westbury	d						13 59												16 23						
Castle Cary	d						14 21												16 41						
Birmingham New Street 12	d			12 12						13 12					14 12							15 12			15 42
Cardiff Central 7	d																								
Newport (South Wales)	d																								
Swindon	d																								
Bristol Parkway 7	d			13 26						14 28					15 26							16 28			16 58
Filton Abbey Wood	d																								
Bath Spa 7	d																								
Bristol Temple Meads 10	d			13 44						14 44					15 44							16 44			17 11
Weston-super-Mare	d																								
Bridgwater	d																								
Taunton	d			14 17			14a44		14 52	15 17				15 50	16 17				17 03			17 19			17 44
Tiverton Parkway	d			14 29					15 05					16 03	16 29				17 16			17 31			17 56
Exeter St Davids 6	a			14 43					15 22	15 44				16 20	16 43				17 33			17 47			18 10
Exeter Central	a			*15 21*					*15 33*	*16 13*				*16 43*	*16 53*				*17 43*			*18 13*			*18 23*
Exmouth	a			*15 50*					*16 18*	*16 52*					*17 23*				*18 23*						*18 53*
Barnstaple	a			*16 35*											*18 07*							*19 13*			
Exmouth	d		*13 53*			14 23				*14 53*		15 23			*15 53*		16 55							*17 25*	
Exeter Central	d		14 23			14 50				*15 17*	15 39	15 50			*16 25*	16 45	17 21					*17 33*	17 33	17 57	
Exeter St Davids 6	d		14 32	14 45		14 56			15 23	15 45	15 49	15 57		16 22	16 45	16 56	17 26		17 35			17 49	17 53	18 05	18 12
Exeter St Thomas	d	←				14 59						16 00				16 59	17 29			←					
Starcross	d	14 12				15 07						16 07				17 07	17 37			17 37					
Dawlish Warren	d	14c26	14 43			15 12					15 59	16 12				17 12	→			17e49			18 04	18 16	
Dawlish	d	14 30	14 47			15 16					16 03	16 16				17 16				17 53			18 08	18 20	18 27
Teignmouth	d	14 35	14 52			15 21					16 08	16 21				17 21				17 58			18 13	18 25	18 32
Newton Abbot	a	14 45	14 59	15 03		15 29			15 44	16 05	16 15	16 29		16 41	17 03	17 29			17 55	18 05		18 09	18 20	18 32	18 39
	d	14 48	15 00	15 04		15 30			15 44	16 06	16 15	16 31		16 43	17 04	17 30			17 57	18 09		18 11	18 21	18 33	18 40
Torre	d	14 56	15 09			15 38						16 39				17 38				18 17					
Torquay	d	14 59	15 13			15 41						16 42				17 41				18 20				18 44	18 53
Paignton	a	15 06	15 19			15 49						16 51				17 51				18 28				18 52	19 05
Totnes	d			15 17					15 58	16 20	16 28			16 55	17 17				18 10			18 24	18 34		
Ivybridge	d										16 43			17 12									18 49		
Plymouth	a			15 48					16 25	16 52	16 58			17 26	17 48				18 38			18 52	19 03		
	d							16 03	16 27					17 29				17 52	18 42			19 01	19 11		
Devonport	d																	17 55							
Dockyard	d																	17x57							
Keyham	d																	17x59							
St Budeaux Ferry Road	d																	18 01							
Saltash	d							16 12										18 06					19 19		
St Germans	d							16 19										18 12					19 26		
Menheniot	d							16x27										18x19							
Liskeard 6	d							16 33	16 50					17 53				18 26	19 06			19 24	19 38		
Looe	a							*17 14*						*18 33*					*19 46*						
Bodmin Parkway	d							16 45	17 03					18 04				18 38	19 19			19 37	19 50		
Lostwithiel	d							16 50										18 44					19 56		
Par	d							16 57						18 15				18 51	19 30			19 47	20 03		
Newquay	a													*19 12*									*21 07*		
St Austell	d							17 05	17 18					18 23				18 58	19 38			19 55	20 11		
Truro	d							17 24	17 36					18 41				19 16	19 58			20 13	20 29		
Falmouth Docks	a							*17 52*	*18 23*					*19 25*					*20 26*				*21 28*		
Redruth	d							17 37	17 51					18 53				19 29	20 08			20 25	20 41		
Camborne	d							17 43	17 58					19 01				19 35	20 16			20 32	20 47		
Hayle	d							17 50	18 07									19 42							
St Erth	d							17 54	18 12					19 11				19 46	20 26			20 43			
St Ives	a							*18 13*	*19 13*									*20 04*				*21 00*			
Penzance	a							18 08	18 27					19 27				19 57	20 43			20 59	21 05		

For general notes see front of timetable
For details of catering facilities see Directory of Train Operators

c Arr. 1418
e Arr. 1743

Saturdays

from 12 September

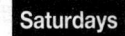

Sleeper services are published in Table 406

London and Birmingham → Devon and Cornwall

Network Diagram - see first page of Table 135

		GW	GW	XC	GW	GW		GW	GW	XC	GW	GW	GW	XC		GW	GW	XC	XC	GW	XC	GW	GW		
		1◇ ⊡		1◇ ⊼	1◇ ⊡			1◇ ⊡	1◇ ⊡	1◇ ⊼		1◇ ⊡		1◇ ⊼			1◇ ⊡	1◇ ⊼	1◇ ⊼	1◇ ⊡	1◇ ⊼		1◇ ⊡		
London Paddington 15 ⊖	d	16 06			16 30			17 06				18 06					19 06			20 06			20 30		
London Waterloo 15 ⊖	d																								
Slough 3	d																								
Heathrow Central Bus Stn 🚌	d	*15 30*						*16 30*				*17 30*					*18 30*			*19 20*			*19 50*		
Gatwick Airport 10	d	*15 03*						*16 03*				*17 03*					*18 03*			*19 03*					
Oxford	d	*16 01*						*17 01*				*18 01*					*19 01*			*20 01*			*20 16*		
Reading 7	d	16 32			16 57			17 32				18 32					19 32			20 32			20 57		
Theale	d																								
Thatcham	d																								
Newbury	d																19 49			20 46					
Hungerford	d																								
Pewsey	d							18 03									20 10			21 06					
Westbury	d							18 22									20 28			21 25					
Castle Cary	d							18 41									20 45			21 43					
Birmingham New Street 12	d			16 12						17 12				18 12				19 12	19 42		20 12				
Cardiff Central 7	d																					21 00			
Newport (South Wales)	d																					21 15			
Swindon	d				17 30																		21 30		
Bristol Parkway 7	d			17 26						18 28				19 28				20 31	20 58		21 25				
Filton Abbey Wood	d								←													21 42			
Bath Spa 7	d				18 00				18 00														22 00		
Bristol Temple Meads 10	d			17 44	→				18 17	18 44				19 44				20 50	21 13		21 44	21 55	22 17		
Weston-super-Mare	d								18 40													22 28			
Bridgwater	d																					22 47			
Taunton	d	17 48		18 17				19 02	19 06	19 17		19 47		20 17			21 08	21 22	21 45	22 06	22 17	23 02	23 19		
Tiverton Parkway	d	18 01		18 29				19 15	19 21	19 29				20 29			21 21	21 34	21 57	22 19	22 29	23 17	23 32		
Exeter St Davids 6	a	18 19		18 43				19 32	19 37	19 43		20 14		20 43			21 39	21 49	22 12	22 37	22 45	23 36	23 53		
Exeter Central	a	*18 32*		*18 53*						*20 18*		*20 29*		*21 03*					*22 39*		*23 00*				
Exmouth	a			*19 23*								*20 57*		*21 57*					*23 07*		*23 42*				
Barnstaple	a			*20 10*										*22 13*											
Exmouth	d		17 55			*18 27*		*18 55*			19 33			*20 01*			*21 01*			*22 01*					
Exeter Central	d		18 21			*19 03*		*19 21*			19 57			*20 26*			*21 27*		*21 48*	*22 27*					
Exeter St Davids 6	d	18 21	18 26	18 45		19 17		19 34	19 38	19 45	20 06	20 15		20 45		20 56	21 39	21 50	22 13	22 38	22 45				
Exeter St Thomas	d		18 29			19 20					20 09		←			20 59									
Starcross	d		18 37			19 28					20 17		20 17			21 07									
Dawlish Warren	d		18 42			19 33					→		20b32			21 12									
Dawlish	d		18 46			19 37							20 36			21 16				22 50					
Teignmouth	d		18 51			19 42							20 41			21 21				22 56					
Newton Abbot	a	18 43	18 59	19 03		19 49		19 53	19 58	20 03		20 37	20 48	21 03		21 28	22 00	22 08	22 31	23 04	23 12				
	d	18 43	19 01	19 04		19 51		19 54	19 59	20 04		20 37	20 49	21 04		21 30	22 00	22 10	22 33	23 04	23 13				
Torre	d		19 09			19 59			20 09				20 57			21 38									
Torquay	d		19 12			20 02			20 12				21 00			21 41									
Paignton	a		19 21			20 10			20 24				21 08			21 48									
Totnes	d	18 57		19 17				20 07		20 17		20 51		21 17			22 14	22 23	22 44	23 18	23 29				
Ivybridge	d	19 13																							
Plymouth	a	19 28		19 48				20 35		20 48		21 19		21 48			22 42	22 55	23 17	23 48	23 59				
	d			19 48				20 39		20 58		21 20													
Devonport	d																								
Dockyard	d																								
Keyham	d																								
St Budeaux Ferry Road	d																								
Saltash	d							20 49																	
St Germans	d							20 57																	
Menheniot	d																								
Liskeard 6	d			20 11				21 08		21 25		21 44													
Looe	a																								
Bodmin Parkway	d			20 24				21 20		21 38		21 59													
Lostwithiel	d			20 29																					
Par	d			20 36				21 31		21 48		22 09													
Newquay	a																								
St Austell	d			20 43				21 42		21 55		22 17													
Truro	d			21 00				22 02		22c19		22 35													
Falmouth Docks	a							*22 31*																	
Redruth	d			21 12				22 12		22 30		22 47													
Camborne	d			21 18						22 36		22 56													
Hayle	d			21 26								23 06													
St Erth	d			21 30				22 28		22 46		23 12													
St Ives	a			*21 58*																					
Penzance	a			21 48				22 42		23 02		23 27													

For general notes see front of timetable
For details of catering facilities see Directory of Train Operators

b Arr. 2022
c Arr. 2211

Table 135

Sundays

until 12 July

Sleeper services are published in Table 406

London and Birmingham → Devon and Cornwall

Network Diagram - see first page of Table 135

	XC	GW	GW	GW	GW	GW	XC	SW	GW	GW	GW	SW	XC	GW	GW	GW	XC	GW	SW	GW	XC
	1	⊼		◇	◇		1 ◇ ⊼	1 ◇	1 ◇ ☕		1 ◇ ☕	1 ◇ ☕	1 ◇ ⊼		1 ◇ ☕		1 ◇ ⊼		1 ◇ ☕	1 ◇ ☕	1 ◇ ⊼
London Paddington 15 ⊖ d									08 00		08 57				09 57					10 57	
London Waterloo 15 ⊖ d												08 15							09 15		
Slough 3 d																					
Heathrow Central Bus Stn (bus) d									*07 30*		*08 30*				*09 30*					*10 30*	
Gatwick Airport 10 d									*06 06*		*07 08*				*08 08*					*09 08*	
Oxford d											*08 38*				*09 38*					*10 38*	
Reading 7 d									08 38		09 32				10 32					11 32	
Theale d																					
Thatcham d																					
Newbury d											09 48										
Hungerford d																					
Pewsey d															11 04						
Westbury d											10 23										
Castle Cary d															11 34						
Birmingham New Street 12 d													08 52				10 12				11 12
Cardiff Central 7 d																					
Newport (South Wales) d																					
Swindon d									09 12												
Bristol Parkway 7 d													10 25				11 30				12 27
Filton Abbey Wood d																					
Bath Spa 7 d									09 46												
Bristol Temple Meads 10 d				07 45	08 28		09 44		10 00				10 44				11 44				12 44
Weston-super-Mare d				08 08	08 56																
Bridgwater d				08 24	09 15																
Taunton d				08 39	09 30		10 21		10 33		10 59		11 21		11 56		12 17			12 47	13 17
Tiverton Parkway d				08 54	09 45		10 33		10 47		11 12		11 34				12 29				13 30
Exeter St Davids 6 a				09 12	10 04		10 47		11 04		11 29		11 48		12 26		12 47			13 14	13 47
Exeter Central a				*09 23*	*10 33*				*11 23*				*12 35*							*13 33*	
Exmouth a				*09 56*	*11 00*				*11 55*				*13 01*							*14 01*	
Barnstaple a				*10 58*									*13 03*								*15 08*
Exmouth d					*09 08*		*10 00*						*11 05*			12 05					*13 10*
Exeter Central d			*08 56*		*09 35*		*10 26*	10 46				11 30	*11 35*			12 31			12 46		*13 36*
Exeter St Davids 6 d			09 05	09 14	10 05	10 08	10 49	10 54	11 06		11 30	11 40	11 50		12 28	12 36	12 49		13 01	13 15	13 49
Exeter St Thomas d			09 08			10 11										12 40		←			
Starcross d			09 16			10 19										12 48		12 48			
Dawlish Warren d			09 21			10 24		11 05								→		13b02			
Dawlish d			09 25	09 30	10 18	10 28		11 09	11 19									13 06	13 14		
Teignmouth d			09 30	09 35	10 23	10 33		11 14	11 25									13 11	13 19		
Newton Abbot a			09 37	09 42	10 30	10 40	11 07	11 21	11 31		11 50	12 00	12 08		12 48		13 08	13 18	13 25	13 35	14 08
d			09 39	09 43	10 31	10 42	11 09	11 23	11 32	11 38	11 52	12 01	12 09	12 30	12 49		13 10	13 20	13 28	13 37	14 10
Torre d			09 47			10 50				11 46				12 38				13 28			
Torquay d			09 50			10 53		11 34		11 49				12 41				13 31	13 39		
Paignton a			09 57			11 01		11 40		11 56				12 48				13 38	13 47		
Totnes d				09 56	10 44		11 21		11 45		12 04	12 14	12 24		13 02		13 23				14 23
Ivybridge d				10 12								12 30									
Plymouth a				10 26	11 12		11 53		12 13		12 32	12 44	12 55		13 33		13 56			14 14	14 53
d	09 05	09 17		10 30	11 14				12 15		12 35		12 55		13 33					14 15	
Devonport d				10 34																	
Dockyard d																					
Keyham d																					
St Budeaux Ferry Road d		09 26																			
Saltash d		09 30		10 44	11 22																
St Germans d		09 37		10 51	11 29																
Menheniot d				10x59	11x38																
Liskeard 6 d	09 30	09 49		11 08	11 44				12 39		12 57		13 18		13 58					14 43	
Looe a		*10 44*		*11 55*					*13 14*						*14 33*					*15 36*	
Bodmin Parkway d	09 43	10 01		11 22	11 56				12 55		13 10		13 30		14 10					14 55	
Lostwithiel d		10 07		11 27	12 01																
Par d		10 14		11 34	12 08				13 07		13 21		13 40		14 24						
Newquay a	11 15			*12 50*											15 30						
St Austell d		10 21		11 42	12 15				13 14		13 28		13 47							15 12	
Truro d		10 40		12 00	12 33				13 31		13 47		14 04							15 28	
Falmouth Docks a		*11 08*		*12 38*					*14 00*				*14 54*							*15 58*	
Redruth d		10 53		12 14	12 47				13 44		13 59		14 16							15 40	
Camborne d		10 59		12 20	12 53				13 51		14 07		14 23							15 47	
Hayle d		11 06		12 27	13 00																
St Erth d		11 10		12 31	13 04				14 04		14 19		14 33							15 58	
St Ives a		*11 24*		*12 55*	*13 24*				*14 24*				*14 55*							*16 24*	
Penzance a		11 24		12 45	13 16				14 18		14 35		14 48							16 11	

For general notes see front of timetable
For details of catering facilities see Directory of Train Operators

b Arr. 1253

Table 135

Sundays

until 12 July

Sleeper services are published in Table 406

London and Birmingham → Devon and Cornwall

Network Diagram - see first page of Table 135

		GW	GW	GW 1 ◇	GW 1 ◇	XC 1 ◇	SW 1 ◇	GW 1 ◇	GW	GW 1 ◇	GW	XC 1 ◇	GW	GW 1 ◇	GW	XC 1 ◇	SW 1 ◇	XC 1 ◇	GW 1 ◇	XC 1 ◇	GW	GW 1 ◇
London Paddington 15 ⊖	d			11 27	11 57			12 00		12 57				13 57					14 57			15 57
London Waterloo 15 ⊖	d						11 15										13 15					
Slough 3	d																					
Heathrow Central Bus Stn 🚌	d			*11 00*	*11 30*					*12 30*				*13 30*					*14 30*			*15 30*
Gatwick Airport 10	d			*10 08*						*11 08*				*12 08*					*13 08*			*14 08*
Oxford	d			*11 16*	*11 38*					*12 47*				*13 43*					*14 47*			*15 50*
Reading 7	d			12 02	12 32			12 37		13 32				14 32					15 32			16 32
Theale	d																					
Thatcham	d																					
Newbury	d				12 48									14 48								16 48
Hungerford	d																					
Pewsey	d			12 43																		
Westbury	d			13 03						14 19												17 24
Castle Cary	d			13 19										15 35								17 41
Birmingham New Street 12	d					12 12						13 12				14 12		14 42		15 12		
Cardiff Central 7	d																					
Newport (South Wales)	d																					
Swindon	d							13 11														
Bristol Parkway 7	d					13 25						14 25				15 26		16 00		16 25		
Filton Abbey Wood	d																					
Bath Spa 7	d							13 41														
Bristol Temple Meads 10	d					13 44		13 56				14 44				15 44		16 14		16 44		
Weston-super-Mare	d																					
Bridgwater	d																					
Taunton	d			13 42	13 50	14 17		14 30		14 55		15 17		15 55		16 17		16 46	16 52	17 17		18 03
Tiverton Parkway	d			13 55	14 05	14 29				15 08		15 29				16 29		16 58	17 05	17 29		18 17
Exeter St Davids 6	a			14 12	14 23	14 44		14 57		15 24		15 44		16 22		16 47		17 13	17 21	17 44		18 37
Exeter Central	a				*14 33*			*15 23*		*15 33*				*16 31*					*17 31*	*18 38*		
Exmouth	a				*15 01*					*16 01*				*16 57*					*18 01*	*19 05*		
Barnstaple	a											*17 14*								*19 12*		
Exmouth	d						*14 10*						*15 10*			*16 10*					*17 10*	
Exeter Central	d						14 43						*15 39*			*16 37*	16 46				*17 37*	
Exeter St Davids 6	d	13 54		14 13	14 24	14 45	14 52	14 57	15 17	15 25		15 45	16 05	16 23		16 49	16 57	17 14	17 23	17 45	17 50	18 38
Exeter St Thomas	d	13 57							15 20				16 07								17 53	
Starcross	d	14 05							15 28		←										18 01	
Dawlish Warren	d	14 10		14 26					15b40		15 40										18 06	
Dawlish	d	14 14		14 30					→		15 44		16 20				17 10	17 26			18 10	
Teignmouth	d	14 19		14 36							15 49		16 25				17 15	17 31			18 15	
Newton Abbot	a	14 26		14 43	14 47	15 03	15 13	15 18		15 46	15 56	16 03	16 31	16 42		17 08	17 22	17 37	17 42	18 03	18 22	18 58
	d	14 29		14 44	14 48	15 04	15 17	15 18		15 46	15 57	16 04	16 31	16 42	16 59	17 10	17 26	17 39	17 43	18 04	18 24	19 00
Torre	d	14 37									16 06				17 07						18 32	
Torquay	d	14 40		14 55			15 28				16 09				17 10		17 37	17 50			18 35	
Paignton	a	14 47		15 04			15 34				16 17				17 17		17 43	18 02			18 42	
Totnes	d				15 01	15 17				16 00		16 17	16 47	16 58		17 23			17 57	18 17		
Ivybridge	d												17 03									
Plymouth	a				15 29	15 48		16 00		16 29		16 48	17 17	17 29		17 56			18 24	18 48		19 38
	d		14 58		15 31					16 35			17 35						18 26	18 55		
Devonport	d																					
Dockyard	d																					
Keyham	d																					
St Budeaux Ferry Road	d																					
Saltash	d		15 06										17 44									
St Germans	d		15 13										17 51									
Menheniot	d												18x00									
Liskeard 6	d		15 25		15 55					16 57			18 06						18 50	19 18		
Looe	a				*16 53*								*18 40*							*20 44*		
Bodmin Parkway	d		15 37		16 07					17 09			18 18						19 02	19 30		
Lostwithiel	d		15 43										18 23									
Par	d		15 50		16 18					17 22			18 30						19 14	19 40		
Newquay	a				*17 30*								*19 37*									
St Austell	d		15 57		16 26					17 28			18 37						19 21	19c51		
Truro	d		16 16		16 43					17 47			18 55						19 38	20 08		
Falmouth Docks	a				*17 23*					*18 33*									*20 26*	*21 27*		
Redruth	d		16 29		16 56					17 59			19 08						19 51	20 19		
Camborne	d		16 35		17 03					18 06			19 14						19 58	20 27		
Hayle	d		16 42										19 21									
St Erth	d		16 46		17 16					18 19			19 25						20 11	20 37		
St Ives	a				*17 39*					*18 39*			*19 45*									
Penzance	a		17 00		17 33					18 35			19 38						20 23	20 52		

For general notes see front of timetable
For details of catering facilities see
Directory of Train Operators

b Arr. 1532
c Arr. 1946

Sundays

until 12 July

Sleeper services are published in Table 406

London and Birmingham → Devon and Cornwall

Network Diagram - see first page of Table 135

		GW	XC	GW	GW		GW	XC	GW	GW	XC	SW		GW	XC	XC	GW	GW	GW		XC	GW	GW		
			1 ◇ ⊼		1 ◇ ⊡			1 ◇ ⊼		1 ◇ ⊡	1 ◇ ⊼	1 ◇ ⊡		1 ◇ ⊡	1 ◇ ⊼	1 ◇ ⊼		1 ◇ ⊡	1 ◇ ⊡		1 ◇ ⊼	1 ◇ ⊡	◇ ⊡		
London Paddington 15 ⊖	d				16 57					17 57				18 57				19 00	19 57			20 57	23 50		
London Waterloo 15 ⊖	d											17 15													
Slough 3	d																								
Heathrow Central Bus Stn (bus)	d				16 30					17 30				18 30					19 20			20 20	23 05		
Gatwick Airport 10	d				15 08					16 08				17 08					18 08			19 08	22 07		
Oxford	d				16 50					17 50				18 40					19 50			20 43	23b00		
Reading 7	d				17 32					18 32				19 32				19 37	20 32			21 32	00u37		
Theale	d																								
Thatcham	d																								
Newbury	d									18 48									20 49						
Hungerford	d																								
Pewsey	d									19 09									21 09						
Westbury	d									19 28									21 28						
Castle Cary	d													20 29					21 46						
Birmingham New Street 12	d		16 12					17 12			18 12				18 42	19 12					20 12				
Cardiff Central 7	d																								
Newport (South Wales)	d																								
Swindon	d																	20 11							
Bristol Parkway 7	d		17 25					18 25			19 25				20 00	20 25					21 25				
Filton Abbey Wood	d																								
Bath Spa 7	d																	20 41							
Bristol Temple Meads 10	d		17 44				18 07	18 44			19 44				20 19	20 44		20 57			21 44				
Weston-super-Mare	d						18 36								20 37			21 29							
Bridgwater	d						18 54																		
Taunton	d		18 21		18 49		19 09	19 17		20 02	20 17			20 51	20 59	21 17		21 52	22 06		22 17	22s49			
Tiverton Parkway	d		18 33		19 01		19 25	19 29		20 16	20 29			21 04	21 12	21 29		22 05	22 19		22 29	23s03			
Exeter St Davids 6	a		18 48		19 18		19 44	19 48		20 33	20 47			21 21	21 26	21 44		22 22	22 37		22 44	23 20	04 05		
Exeter Central	a				*19 38*					*20 43*					*21 38*			*22 34*			*23 13*	*23 29*	*05 13*		
Exmouth	a				*20 05*					*21 12*					*22 04*			*23 03*				*23 55*	*06 10*		
Barnstaple	a							*21 14*																	
Exmouth	d		*18 10*	18 10				*19 10*			*20 10*						21 17								
Exeter Central	d		*18 37*	18 37	*18 43*			*19 36*			*20 36*	20 46					21 43								
Exeter St Davids 6	d		18 49	18 52	19 20			19 49	20 04	20 33	20 48	20 56		21 22	21 30	21 45	21 49		22 37		22 45		04 35		
Exeter St Thomas	d			18 55					20 07								21 53								
Starcross	d			19 03					20 15								22 01								
Dawlish Warren	d			19 08					20 20								22 06								
Dawlish	d			19 12					20 24			21 09		21 36	21 43		22 10								
Teignmouth	d			19 17					20 29			21 14		21 42	21 48		22 15								
Newton Abbot	a		19 07	19 24	19 39			20 07	20 36	20 54	21 06	21 20		21 48	21 54	22 03	22 22		22 58		23 04		04 55		
	d		19 09	19 26	19 40			20 09	20 38	20 55	21 08	21 22		21 49	21 56	22 04	22 24		22 58		23 06		04 56		
Torre	d			19 34					20 46								22 32								
Torquay	d			19 37					20 49			21 33			22 07		22 35								
Paignton	a			19 44					20 56			21 39			22 19		22 42								
Totnes	d		19 21		19 53			20 21		21 10	21 20			22 03		22 17			23 11		23 21				
Ivybridge	d																								
Plymouth	a		19 53		20 21			20 48		21 37	21 52			22 31		22 48			23 44		23 54		05 35		
	d	19 43			20 23			20 50		21 40													06 40		
Devonport	d																								
Dockyard	d																								
Keyham	d																								
St Budeaux Ferry Road	d																								
Saltash	d	19 51																							
St Germans	d	19 58																							
Menheniot	d																								
Liskeard 6	d	20 10			20 47			21 13		22 03													07 09		
Looe	a	*20 44*																					*07 41*		
Bodmin Parkway	d	20 22			21 00			21 25		22 14													07 23		
Lostwithiel	d	20 28																					07 29		
Par	d	20 35			21 11			21 35		22 27													07 37		
Newquay	a																						*10 04*		
St Austell	d	20 42			21 18			21 42		22 35													07 45		
Truro	d	21c09			21 36			21 59		22 51													08 05		
Falmouth Docks	a	*21 27*						*22 26*															*08 45*		
Redruth	d	21 22			21 48			22 10		23 05													08 19		
Camborne	d	21 28			21 56			22 21		23 11													08 26		
Hayle	d	21 35																					08 37		
St Erth	d	21 39			22 08			22 31		23 23													08 43		
St Ives	a																						*09 19*		
Penzance	a	21 51			22 21			22 46		23 38													08 59		

For general notes see front of timetable
For details of catering facilities see Directory of Train Operators

b Change at Didcot Parkway and Reading. By bus to Didcot Parkway

c Arr. 2059

Sleeper services are published in Table 406

London and Birmingham → Devon and Cornwall

Network Diagram - see first page of Table 135

		XC	GW	GW	GW	GW	GW		GW	XC	SW	GW	GW	GW		SW	XC	GW	GW	GW	XC		GW	SW	GW
		1			◇		◇			1 ◇	1 ◇	1 ◇		1 ◇		1 ◇	1 ◇		1 ◇		1 ◇			1 ◇	1 ◇
London Paddington 15 ⊖	d											08 00		08 57					09 57						10 57
London Waterloo 15 ⊖	d															08 15								09 15	
Slough 3	d																								
Heathrow Central Bus Stn	d											07 30		08 30					09 30						10 30
Gatwick Airport 10	d											07 08							08 08						09 08
Oxford	d													08 31					09 38						10 38
Reading 7	d											08 38		09 32					10 32						11 32
Theale	d																								
Thatcham	d																								
Newbury	d													09 48											
Hungerford	d																								
Pewsey	d																		11 04						
Westbury	d													10 23											
Castle Cary	d																		11 34						
Birmingham New Street 12	d																08 52				10 12				
Cardiff Central 7	d																								
Newport (South Wales)	d																								
Swindon	d											09 14													
Bristol Parkway 7	d																10 25				11 30				
Filton Abbey Wood	d																								
Bath Spa 7	d																								
Bristol Temple Meads 10	d				07 45		08 28			09 44		09 52					10 44				11 44				
Weston-super-Mare	d				08 08		08 56																		
Bridgwater	d				08 24		09 15																		
Taunton	d				08 39		09 30			10 21		10 27		10 59			11 21		11 56		12 17				12 47
Tiverton Parkway	d				08 54		09 45			10 33		10 41		11 12			11 34				12 29				
Exeter St Davids 6	a				09 12		10 04			10 47		10 58		11 29			11 48		12 26		12 47				13 14
Exeter Central	a				*09 23*		*10 33*					*11 23*					*12 35*				*13 21*				*13 33*
Exmouth	a				*09 56*		*11 00*					*11 55*					*13 01*								*14 01*
Barnstaple	a				*10 58*												*13 03*								
Exmouth	d						*09 08*			*10 00*							*11 05*			12 05					
Exeter Central	d			*08 56*			*09 35*			*10 26*	10 46					11 30	*11 35*			12 31				12 46	
Exeter St Davids 6	d			09 05	09 14		10 05		10 08	10 49	10 54	11 01		11 30		11 40	11 50		12 28	12 36	12 49			13 01	13 15
Exeter St Thomas	d			09 08					10 11											12 40					
Starcross	d			09 16					10 19											12 48			←		
Dawlish Warren	d			09 21					10 24		11 05									13b02 →			13 02		
Dawlish	d			09 25	09 30		10 18		10 28		11 09	11 15											13 06	13 14	
Teignmouth	d			09 30	09 35		10 23		10 33		11 14	11 21											13 11	13 19	
Newton Abbot	a			09 37	09 42	←	10 30		10 40	11 07	11 21	11 27		11 50		12 00	12 08		12 48		13 08		13 18	13 25	13 35
	d			09 47	09 43	09 47	10 31		10 42	11 09	11 23	11 28	11 38	11 52		12 01	12 09	12 30	12 49		13 10		13 20	13 28	13 37
Torre	d			→		09 55			10 50				11 46					12 38					13 28		
Torquay	d					09 58			10 53		11 34		11 49					12 41					13 31	13 39	
Paignton	a					10 05			11 01		11 40		11 56					12 48					13 38	13 47	
Totnes	d				09 56		10 44			11 21		11 41		12 04		12 14	12 24		13 02		13 23				
Ivybridge	d				10 12											12 30									
Plymouth	a				10 26		11 12			11 53		12 09		12 32		12 44	12 55		13 33		13 56				14 14
	d	09 05	09 17		10 30		11 14					12 13		12 35			12 55		13 33						14 15
Devonport	d				10 34																				
Dockyard	d																								
Keyham	d																								
St Budeaux Ferry Road	d		09 26																						
Saltash	d		09 30		10 44		11 22																		
St Germans	d		09 37		10 51		11 29																		
Menheniot	d				10x59		11x38																		
Liskeard 6	d	09 30	09 49		11 08		11 44					12 37		12 57			13 18		13 58						14 43
Looe	a		*10 44*		*11 55*							*13 14*							*14 33*						*15 36*
Bodmin Parkway	d	09 43	10 01		11 22		11 56					12 49		13 10			13 30		14 10						14 55
Lostwithiel	d		10 07		11 27		12 01																		
Par	d		10 14		11 34		12 08					13 01		13 21			13 40		14 24						
Newquay	a	11 15			*12 50*														15 30						
St Austell	d		10 21		11 42		12 15					13 08		13 28			13 47								15 12
Truro	d		10 40		12 00		12 33					13 25		13 47			14 04								15 28
Falmouth Docks	a		*11 08*		*12 38*							*14 00*					*14 54*								*15 58*
Redruth	d		10 53		12 14		12 47					13 38		13 59			14 16								15 40
Camborne	d		10 59		12 20		12 53					13 45		14 07			14 23								15 47
Hayle	d		11 06		12 27		13 00																		
St Erth	d		11 10		12 31		13 04					13 58		14 19			14 33								15 58
St Ives	a		*11 24*		*12 55*		*13 24*					*14 24*					*14 55*								*16 24*
Penzance	a		11 24		12 45		13 16					14 12		14 35			14 48								16 11

For general notes see front of timetable
For details of catering facilities see
Directory of Train Operators

b Arr. 1253

Table 135

Sundays

19 July to 6 September

Sleeper services are published in Table 406

London and Birmingham → Devon and Cornwall

Network Diagram - see first page of Table 135

		XC	GW	GW	GW	GW	XC	SW	GW	GW	GW	GW	XC	GW	GW	GW	XC	SW	XC	GW	XC	GW
		1 ◇		1 ◇		1 ◇	1 ◇	1 ◇	1 ◇		1 ◇	1 ◇	1 ◇		1 ◇		1 ◇	1 ◇	1 ◇	1 ◇	1 ◇	
London Paddington 15 ⊖	d			11 27		11 57			12 00		12 57				13 57					14 57		
London Waterloo 15 ⊖	d							11 15										13 15				
Slough 3	d																					
Heathrow Central Bus Stn (bus)	d			*11 00*		*11 30*					*12 30*				*13 30*					*14 30*		
Gatwick Airport 10	d			*10 08*							*11 08*				*12 08*					*13 08*		
Oxford	d			*11 16*		*11 38*					*12 47*				*13 43*					*14 47*		
Reading 7	d			12 02		12 32			12 37		13 32				14 32					15 32		
Theale	d																					
Thatcham	d																					
Newbury	d					12 48									14 48							
Hungerford	d																					
Pewsey	d			12 43																		
Westbury	d			13 03							14 19											
Castle Cary	d			13 19											15 35							
Birmingham New Street 12	d	10 45					11 45						12 42				14 12		14 42		15 12	
Cardiff Central 7	d																					
Newport (South Wales)	d																					
Swindon	d								13 21													
Bristol Parkway 7	d	12 25					13 25						14 27				15 26		16 00		16 25	
Filton Abbey Wood	d																					
Bath Spa 7	d								14 01 →			← 14 01										
Bristol Temple Meads 10	d	12 44					13 44					14 19	14 44				15 44		16 14		16 44	
Weston-super-Mare	d																					
Bridgwater	d																					
Taunton	d	13 17		13 42		13 50	14 17				14 55	15 01	15 17		15 55		16 17		16 46	16 52	17 17	
Tiverton Parkway	d	13 30		13 55		14 05	14 29				15 08		15 29				16 29		16 58	17 05	17 29	
Exeter St Davids 6	a	13 47		14 12		14 23	14 43				15 24	15 29	15 43		16 22		16 47		17 13	17 21	17 44	
Exeter Central	a					*14 33*	*15 23*				*15 33*				*16 31*		*17 21*			*17 31*	*18 38*	
Exmouth	a					*15 01*					*16 01*				*16 57*					*18 01*	*19 05*	
Barnstaple	a	*15 08*											*17 14*								*19 12*	
Exmouth	d	*13 10*						*14 10*						*15 10*			*16 10*					*17 10*
Exeter Central	d	*13 36*						*14 43*						*15 39*			*16 37*	16 46				*17 37*
Exeter St Davids 6	d	13 49	13 54	14 13		14 24	14 45	14 52		15 07	15 25	15 30	15 45	16 05	16 23		16 49	16 57	17 14	17 23	17 45	17 50
Exeter St Thomas	d		13 57							15 10				16 07								17 53
Starcross	d		14 05							15 18												18 01
Dawlish Warren	d		14 10	14 26						15 22												18 06
Dawlish	d		14 14	14 30						15 26				16 20				17 10	17 26			18 10
Teignmouth	d		14 19	14 36						15 31				16 25				17 15	17 31			18 15
Newton Abbot	a	14 08	14 26	14 43		14 47	15 03	15 13		15 38	15 46	15 54	16 03	16 31	16 42		17 08	17 22	17 37	17 42	18 03	18 22
	d	14 10	14 29	14 44		14 48	15 04	15 17		15 40	15 46	15 55	16 04	16 31	16 42	16 59	17 10	17 26	17 39	17 43	18 04	18 24
Torre	d		14 37							15 48						17 07						18 32
Torquay	d		14 40	14 55				15 28		15 51						17 10		17 37	17 50			18 35
Paignton	a		14 47	15 04				15 34		15 59						17 17		17 43	18 02			18 42
Totnes	d	14 23				15 01	15 17				16 00		16 17	16 47	16 58		17 23			17 57	18 17	
Ivybridge	d													17 03								
Plymouth	a	14 53				15 29	15 48				16 29	16 39	16 48	17 17	17 29		17 56			18 24	18 48	
	d				14 58	15 31					16 35			17 35						18 26	18 55	
Devonport	d																					
Dockyard	d																					
Keyham	d																					
St Budeaux Ferry Road	d																					
Saltash	d				15 06									17 44								
St Germans	d				15 13									17 51								
Menheniot	d													18x00								
Liskeard 6	d				15 25	15 55					16 57			18 06						18 50	19 18	
Looe	a					*16 53*								*18 40*								
Bodmin Parkway	d				15 37	16 07					17 09			18 18						19 02	19 30	
Lostwithiel	d				15 43									18 23								
Par	d				15 50	16 18					17 22			18 30						19 14	19 40	
Newquay	a					*17 30*								*19 37*								
St Austell	d				15 57	16 26					17 28			18 37						19 21	19b51	
Truro	d				16 16	16 43					17 47			18 55						19 38	20 08	
Falmouth Docks	a					*17 23*					*18 33*									*20 26*		
Redruth	d				16 29	16 56					17 59			19 08						19 51	20 19	
Camborne	d				16 35	17 03					18 06			19 14						19 58	20 27	
Hayle	d				16 42									19 21								
St Erth	d				16 46	17 16					18 19			19 25						20 11	20 37	
St Ives	a					*17 39*					*18 39*			*19 45*								
Penzance	a				17 00	17 33					18 35			19 38						20 23	20 52	

For general notes see front of timetable
For details of catering facilities see Directory of Train Operators

b Arr. 1946

Sundays

19 July to 6 September

Sleeper services are published in Table 406

London and Birmingham → Devon and Cornwall

Network Diagram - see first page of Table 135

		GW	GW	XC	GW	GW	GW	XC	GW	GW	XC	SW	GW	XC	XC	GW	GW	GW	XC	GW	GW
		1 ◇ 🍴		1 ◇ 🛒		1 ◇ 🍴		1 ◇ 🛒		1 ◇ 🍴	1 ◇ 🛒	1 ◇ 🍴	1 ◇ 🍴	1 ◇ 🛒	1 ◇ 🛒		1 ◇ 🍴	1 ◇ 🍴	1 ◇ 🛒	1 ◇ 🍴	◇ 🍴
London Paddington 15 ⊖	d	15 57				16 57				17 57			18 57				19 00	19 57		20 57	23 50
London Waterloo 15 ⊖	d											17 15									
Slough 3	d																				
Heathrow Central Bus Stn (bus)	d	*15 30*				*16 30*				*17 30*			*18 30*					*19 20*		*20 20*	*23 05*
Gatwick Airport 10	d	*14 08*				*15 08*				*16 08*			*17 08*					*18 08*		*19 08*	*22 07*
Oxford	d	*15 50*				*16 50*				*17 50*			*18 40*					*19 50*		*20 43*	*23b00*
Reading 7	d	16 32				17 32				18 32			19 32				19 37	20 32		21 32	00u37
Theale	d																				
Thatcham	d																				
Newbury	d	16 48								18 48								20 49			
Hungerford	d																				
Pewsey	d									19 09								21 09			
Westbury	d	17 24								19 28								21 28			
Castle Cary	d	17 41											20 29					21 46			
Birmingham New Street 12	d			16 12				17 12			18 12			18 42	19 12				20 12		
Cardiff Central 7	d																				
Newport (South Wales)	d																				
Swindon	d																20 11				
Bristol Parkway 7	d			17 25				18 25			19 25			20 00	20 25				21 25		
Filton Abbey Wood	d																				
Bath Spa 7	d																20 41				
Bristol Temple Meads 10	d			17 44			18 07	18 44			19 44			20 19	20 44		20 57		21 44		
Weston-super-Mare	d						18 36							20 37			21 29				
Bridgwater	d						18 54														
Taunton	d	18 03		18 21		18 49	19 09	19 17		20 02	20 20		20 51	20 59	21 17		21 52	22 06	22 17	22s49	
Tiverton Parkway	d	18 17		18 33		19 01	19 25	19 29		20 16	20 29		21 04	21 12	21 29		22 05	22 19	22 29	23s03	
Exeter St Davids 6	a	18 37		18 48		19 18	19 44	19 48		20 33	20 47		21 21	21 26	21 44		22 22	22 37	22 44	23 20	04 05
Exeter Central	a					*19 38*				*20 43*	*21 23*			*21 38*			*22 34*		*23 13*	*23 29*	*05 13*
Exmouth	a					*20 05*				*21 12*				*22 04*			*23 03*			*23 55*	*06 10*
Barnstaple	a							*21 14*													
Exmouth	d			*18 10*	18 10			*19 10*			*20 10*					21 17		*21 17*			
Exeter Central	d			*18 37*	18 37	*18 43*		*19 36*			*20 36*	20 46				21 43		*21 43*			
Exeter St Davids 6	d	18 38		18 49	18 52	19 20		19 49	20 04	20 33	20 48	20 56	21 22	21 30	21 45	21 49		22 37	22 45		04 35
Exeter St Thomas	d				18 55				20 07							21 53					
Starcross	d				19 03				20 15							22 01					
Dawlish Warren	d				19 08				20 20							22 06					
Dawlish	d				19 12				20 24			21 09	21 36	21 43		22 10					
Teignmouth	d				19 17				20 29			21 14	21 42	21 48		22 15					
Newton Abbot	a	18 58		19 07	19 24	19 39		20 07	20 36	20 54	21 06	21 20	21 48	21 54	22 03	22 22		22 58	23 04		04 55
	d	19 00		19 09	19 26	19 40		20 09	20 38	20 55	21 08	21 22	21 49	21 56	22 04	22 24		22 58	23 06		04 56
Torre	d				19 34				20 46							22 32					
Torquay	d				19 37				20 49			21 33		22 07		22 35					
Paignton	a				19 44				20 56			21 39		22 19		22 42					
Totnes	d			19 21		19 53		20 21		21 10	21 20		22 03		22 17			23 11	23 21		
Ivybridge	d																				
Plymouth	a	19 38		19 53		20 21		20 48		21 37	21 52		22 31		22 48			23 44	23 54		05 35
	d		19 43			20 23		20 50		21 40											06 40
Devonport	d																				
Dockyard	d																				
Keyham	d																				
St Budeaux Ferry Road	d																				
Saltash	d		19 51																		
St Germans	d		19 58																		
Menheniot	d																				
Liskeard 6	d		20 10			20 47		21 13		22 03											07 09
Looe	a		*20 44*																		*07 41*
Bodmin Parkway	d		20 22			21 00		21 25		22 14											07 23
Lostwithiel	d		20 28																		07 29
Par	d		20 35			21 11		21 35		22 27											07 37
Newquay	a																				*10 04*
St Austell	d		20 42			21 18		21 42		22 35											07 45
Truro	d		21c09			21 36		21 59		22 51											08 05
Falmouth Docks	a		*21 27*					*22 26*													*08 45*
Redruth	d		21 22			21 48		22 10		23 05											08 19
Camborne	d		21 28			21 56		22 21		23 11											08 26
Hayle	d		21 35																		08 37
St Erth	d		21 39			22 08		22 31		23 23											08 43
St Ives	a																				*09 19*
Penzance	a		21 51			22 21		22 46		23 38											08 59

For general notes see front of timetable
For details of catering facilities see Directory of Train Operators

b Change at Didcot Parkway and Reading. By bus to Didcot Parkway

c Arr. 2059

Sundays

13 September to 1 November

Sleeper services are published in Table 406

London and Birmingham → Devon and Cornwall

Network Diagram - see first page of Table 135

	XC	GW	GW	GW	GW	XC	GW		GW	XC	SW	GW	GW	GW	SW		XC	GW	GW	GW	XC	GW	SW	GW
	1			◇		1 ◇	◇			1 ◇	1 ◇	1 ◇		1 ◇	1 ◇		1 ◇		1 ◇		1 ◇		1 ◇	1 ◇
		trolley				trolley				trolley		restaurant		restaurant	restaurant		trolley		restaurant		trolley		restaurant	restaurant
London Paddington 15 ⊖ d												08 00		08 57					09 57					10 57
London Waterloo 15 ⊖ d															08 15								09 15	
Slough 3 d																								
Heathrow Central Bus Stn (bus) d												*07 30*		*08 30*					*09 30*					*10 30*
Gatwick Airport 10 d												*06 06*		*07 08*					*08 08*					*09 08*
Oxford d														*07b45*					*09 50*					*10 50*
Reading 7 d												08 34		09 32					10 32					11 32
Theale d																								
Thatcham d																								
Newbury d														09 48										
Hungerford d																								
Pewsey d																			11 04					
Westbury d														10 23										
Castle Cary d																			11 34					
Birmingham New Street 12 d																	09 12				10 12			
Cardiff Central 7 d																								
Newport (South Wales) d																								
Swindon d												09 08												
Bristol Parkway 7 d																	10 25				11 25			
Filton Abbey Wood d																								
Bath Spa 7 d												09 39												
Bristol Temple Meads 10 d				07 45		08 25	08 28			09 44		09 53					10 44				11 44			
Weston-super-Mare d				08 08			08 56																	
Bridgwater d				08 24			09 15																	
Taunton d				08 39		08 58	09 30			10 21		10 27		10 59			11 21		11 56		12 18			12 47
Tiverton Parkway d				08 54		09 10	09 45			10 33		10 41		11 12			11 34				12 31			
Exeter St Davids 6 a				09 12		09 24	10 04			10 47		10 58		11 29			11 48		12 26		12 47			13 14
Exeter Central a				*09 23*			*10 33*					*11 23*							*12 35*		*13 21*			*13 33*
Exmouth a				*09 56*			*11 00*					*11 55*							*13 01*					*14 01*
Barnstaple a						*10 58*											*13 03*							
Exmouth d							*09c08*			*10 00*							*11 05*			12 05				
Exeter Central d			*08 56*				*09c35*			*10 26*	10 46				11 30		*11 35*			12 31			12 46	
Exeter St Davids 6 d			09 05	09 14		09 26	10 05		10 08	10 49	10 54	11 01		11 30	11 40		11 50		12 28	12 36	12 49	⟵	13 01	13 15
Exeter St Thomas d			09 08						10 11											12 40				
Starcross d			09 16						10 19											12 48		12 48		
Dawlish Warren d			09 21						10 24		11 05									⟶		13e02		
Dawlish d			09 25	09 30		09 39	10 18		10 28		11 09	11 15										13 06	13 14	
Teignmouth d			09 30	09 35		09 44	10 23		10 33		11 14	11 21										13 11	13 19	
Newton Abbot a			09 37	09 42	⟵	09 50	10 30		10 40	11 07	11 21	11 27		11 50	12 00		12 08		12 48		13 08	13 18	13 25	13 35
Newton Abbot d			09 47	09 43	09 47	09 55	10 31		10 42	11 09	11 23	11 28	11 38	11 52	12 01		12 09	12 30	12 49		13 10	13 20	13 28	13 37
Torre d			⟶		09 55				10 50				11 46					12 38				13 28		
Torquay d					09 58	10 07			10 53		11 34		11 49					12 41				13 31	13 39	
Paignton a					10 05	10 19			11 01		11 40		11 56					12 48				13 38	13 47	
Totnes d				09 56			10 44			11 21		11 41		12 04	12 14		12 24		13 02		13 23			
Ivybridge d				10 12											12 30									
Plymouth a				10 26			11 12			11 53		12 09		12 32	12 44		12 55		13 35		13 56			14 14
Plymouth d	09 05	09 25		10 30			11 14					12 11		12 35			12 55							14 14
Devonport d				10 34																				
Dockyard d																								
Keyham d																								
St Budeaux Ferry Road d																								
Saltash d				10 44			11 22																	
St Germans d				10 51			11 29																	
Menheniot d				10x59			11x38																	
Liskeard 6 d	09 32	09 49		11 08			11 44					12 35		12 57			13 18							14 43
Looe a																								
Bodmin Parkway d	09 44	10 01		11 22			11 56					12 47		13 10			13 30							14 56
Lostwithiel d		10 06		11 27			12 01																	
Par d	09 54	10 13		11 34			12 08					12 59		13 21			13 40							
Newquay a																								
St Austell d	10 01	10 21		11 42			12 15					13 06		13 28			13 47							15 12
Truro d	10 18	10 39		12 00			12 33					13 23		13 47			14 04							15 29
Falmouth Docks a		*11 08*		*12 38*								*14 00*					*14 54*							*15 58*
Redruth d	10 29	10 52		12 14			12 47					13 36		13 59			14 16							15 40
Camborne d	10 36	10 58		12 20			12 53					13 43		14 07			14 23							15 47
Hayle d		11 06		12 27			13 00																	
St Erth d	10 46	11 09		12 31			13 04					13 56		14 19			14 33							15 58
St Ives a		*12 10*		*12 50*			*13 24*					*14 24*					*14 55*							*16 24*
Penzance a	11 00	11 24		12 45			13 18					14 10		14 35			14 43							16 15

For general notes see front of timetable
For details of catering facilities see Directory of Train Operators

b Change at Didcot Parkway and Reading. By bus to Didcot Parkway

c Until 18 October only

e Arr. 1253

Sundays

13 September to 1 November

Sleeper services are published in Table 406

London and Birmingham → Devon and Cornwall

Network Diagram - see first page of Table 135

		XC		GW	GW	GW	GW	XC	SW	GW		GW	GW	GW	XC	GW	GW	GW		XC	SW	XC	GW	XC	GW
London Paddington 15	⊖ d				11 27	11 57				12 03			12 57				13 57						14 57		
London Waterloo 15	⊖ d								11 15												13 15				
Slough 3	d																								
Heathrow Central Bus Stn	d				11 00	11 30							12 30				13 30						14 30		
Gatwick Airport 10	d				10 08								11 08				12 08						13 08		
Oxford	d				11 16	11 50							12 50				13 50						14 50		
Reading 7	d				12 02	12 32				12 37			13 32				14 32						15 32		
Theale	d																								
Thatcham	d																								
Newbury	d					12 48											14 48								
Hungerford	d																								
Pewsey	d				12 40																				
Westbury	d				13 03								14 19												
Castle Cary	d				13 19												15 35								
Birmingham New Street 12	d	11 12						12 12							13 12					14 12		14 42		15 12	
Cardiff Central 7	d																								
Newport (South Wales)	d																								
Swindon	d									13 11															
Bristol Parkway 7	d	12 25						13 25							14 25					15 26		16 02		16 25	
Filton Abbey Wood	d																								
Bath Spa 7	d									13 41															
Bristol Temple Meads 10	d	12 44						13 44		13 56					14 44					15 44		16 14		16 44	
Weston-super-Mare	d																								
Bridgwater	d																								
Taunton	d	13 18			13 42	13 54		14 17		14 30			14 55		15 17		15 55			16 18		16 46	16 50	17 17	
Tiverton Parkway	d	13 31			13 55			14 29					15 08		15 29					16 31		16 58	17 03	17 29	
Exeter St Davids 6	a	13 47			14 12	14 19		14 44		14 57			15 24		15 44		16 22			16 47		17 13	17 19	17 44	
Exeter Central	a					14 33				15 23			15 33				16 31			17 21			17 31	18 38	
Exmouth	a					15 01							16 01				16 57						18 01	19 05	
Barnstaple	a	15 08													17 14									19 12	
Exmouth	d	13 10							14 10							15 10				16 10					17 10
Exeter Central	d	13 36							14 43							15 39				16 37	16 46				17 37
Exeter St Davids 6	d	13 49		13 54	14 13	14 20		14 45	14 52	14 57		15 17	15 25		15 45	16 05	16 23			16 49	16 57	17 14	17 21	17 45	17 50
Exeter St Thomas	d			13 57								15 20				16 07									17 53
Starcross	d			14 05								15 28		←											18 01
Dawlish Warren	d			14 10								15b40 →		15 40											18 06
Dawlish	d			14 14	14 26									15 44		16 20					17 10	17 26			18 10
Teignmouth	d			14 19	14 32									15 49		16 25					17 15	17 31			18 15
Newton Abbot	a	14 08		14 26	14 39	14 43		15 03	15 13	15 18			15 46	15 56	16 03	16 31	16 42			17 08	17 22	17 37	17 40	18 03	18 22
	d	14 10		14 29	14 40	14 45		15 05	15 17	15 18			15 46	15 57	16 05	16 31	16 42	16 59		17 10	17 26	17 39	17 40	18 05	18 24
Torre	d			14 37										16 06				17 07							18 32
Torquay	d			14 40	14 51				15 28					16 09				17 10			17 37	17 50			18 35
Paignton	a			14 47	15 00				15 34					16 17				17 17			17 43	18 02			18 42
Totnes	d	14 23				14 57		15 17					16 00		16 17	16 47	16 58			17 23			17 55	18 17	
Ivybridge	d															17 03									
Plymouth	a	14 56				15 27		15 48		16 00			16 29		16 48	17 17	17 29			17 56			18 22	18 48	
	d						15 35						16 35			17 35							18 23	18 55	
Devonport	d																								
Dockyard	d																								
Keyham	d																								
St Budeaux Ferry Road	d																								
Saltash	d						15 43									17 44									
St Germans	d						15 50									17 51									
Menheniot	d															18x00									
Liskeard 6	d						16 02						16 57			18 06							18 47	19 18	
Looe	a																								
Bodmin Parkway	d						16 14						17 09			18 18							19 00	19 30	
Lostwithiel	d						16 20									18 23									
Par	d						16 27						17 22			18 30							19 11	19 40	
Newquay	a																								
St Austell	d						16 34						17 28			18 37							19 18	19c51	
Truro	d						16 53						17 47			18 55							19 36	20 08	
Falmouth Docks	a						17 23						18 33										20 26		
Redruth	d						17 06						17 59			19 08							19 48	20 19	
Camborne	d						17 12						18 06			19 14							19 56	20 27	
Hayle	d						17 19									19 21									
St Erth	d						17 23						18 19			19 25							20 08	20 37	
St Ives	a						17 55						18 39												
Penzance	a						17 35						18 35			19 38							20 21	20 52	

For general notes see front of timetable
For details of catering facilities see Directory of Train Operators

b Arr. 1532
c Arr. 1946

Table 135

Sundays

13 September to 1 November

Sleeper services are published in Table 406

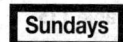

London and Birmingham → Devon and Cornwall

Network Diagram - see first page of Table 135

		GW	GW	XC	GW	GW	GW	XC	GW	GW	XC	SW	GW	XC	XC	GW	GW	GW	XC	GW	GW
		1 ◇ ⊏		1 ◇ ✕		1 ◇ ⊏		1 ◇ ✕		1 ◇ ⊏	1 ◇ ✕	1 ◇ ⊏	1 ◇ ⊏	1 ◇ ✕	1 ◇ ✕		1 ◇ ⊏	1 ◇ ⊏	1 ◇ ✕	1 ◇ ⊏	◇ ⊏
London Paddington 15 ⊖	d	15 57				16 57				17 57			18 57				19 03	19 57		20 57	23 50
London Waterloo 15 ⊖	d											17 15									
Slough 3	d																				
Heathrow Central Bus Stn (bus)	d	*15 30*				*16 30*				*17 30*			*18 30*					*19 20*		*20 20*	*23 05*
Gatwick Airport 10	d	*14 08*				*15 08*				*16 08*			*17 08*					*18 08*		*19 08*	*22 07*
Oxford	d	*15 50*				*16 50*				*17 50*			*18 50*					*19 50*		*20 50*	*23 15*
Reading 7	d	16 32				17 32				18 32			19 32				19 37	20 32		21 32	00u37
Theale	d																				
Thatcham	d																				
Newbury	d	16 48								18 48								20 49			
Hungerford	d																				
Pewsey	d									19 09								21 09			
Westbury	d	17 24								19 28								21 28			
Castle Cary	d	17 41											20 29					21 46			
Birmingham New Street 12	d			16 12				17 12			18 12			18 42	19 12				20 12		
Cardiff Central 7	d																				
Newport (South Wales)	d																				
Swindon	d																20 11				
Bristol Parkway 7	d			17 25				18 25			19 25			20 00	20 25				21 25		
Filton Abbey Wood	d																				
Bath Spa 7	d																20 41				
Bristol Temple Meads 10	d			17 44			18 07	18 44			19 44			20 19	20 44		20 57		21 44		
Weston-super-Mare	d						18 36							20 37			21 29				
Bridgwater	d						18 54														
Taunton	d	18 03		18 21		18 49	19 09	19 17		20 02	20 20		20 51	20 59	21 17		21 52	22 06	22 17	22s48	
Tiverton Parkway	d	18 17		18 33		19 01	19 25	19 31		20 16	20 32		21 04	21 12	21 29		22 05	22 19	22 29	23s02	
Exeter St Davids 6	a	18 37		18 48		19 18	19 44	19 48		20 33	20 47		21 21	21 26	21 44		22 22	22 37	22 44	23 19	04 05
Exeter Central	a			*19 23*		*19 38*				*20 43*	*21 23*			*21 38*			*22 34*		*23 13*	*23 29*	*05 13*
Exmouth	a					*20 05*				*21 12*				*22 04*			*23 03*			*23 55*	*06 10*
Barnstaple	a							*21 14*													
Exmouth	d			*18 10*	18 10			*19 10*			*20 10*					21 17					
Exeter Central	d			*18 37*	18 37	*18 43*		*19 36*			*20 36*	20 46				21 43					
Exeter St Davids 6	d	18 38		18 49	18 52	19 20		19 49	20 04	20 33	20 48	20 56	21 22	21 30	21 45	21 49		22 37	22 45		04 35
Exeter St Thomas	d				18 55				20 07							21 53					
Starcross	d				19 03				20 15							22 01					
Dawlish Warren	d				19 08				20 20							22 06					
Dawlish	d				19 12				20 24			21 09	21 36	21 43		22 10					
Teignmouth	d				19 17				20 29			21 14	21 42	21 48		22 15					
Newton Abbot	a	18 58		19 07	19 24	19 39		20 07	20 36	20 54	21 06	21 20	21 48	21 54	22 03	22 22		22 58	23 04		04 55
	d	19 00		19 09	19 26	19 40		20 09	20 38	20 55	21 08	21 22	21 49	21 56	22 05	22 24		22 58	23 06		04 56
Torre	d				19 34				20 46							22 32					
Torquay	d				19 37				20 49			21 33		22 07		22 35					
Paignton	a				19 44				20 56			21 39		22 19		22 42					
Totnes	d			19 21		19 53		20 21		21 10	21 20		22 03		22 17			23 11	23 21		
Ivybridge	d																				
Plymouth	a	19 38		19 53		20 21		20 48		21 37	21 52		22 31		22 48			23 44	23 54		05 35
	d		19 43			20 23		20 50		21 40											06 40
Devonport	d																				
Dockyard	d																				
Keyham	d																				
St Budeaux Ferry Road	d																				
Saltash	d		19 51																		
St Germans	d		19 58																		
Menheniot	d																				
Liskeard 6	d		20 10			20 47		21 13		22 03											07 09
Looe	a																				*07 41*
Bodmin Parkway	d		20 22			21 00		21 25		22 14											07 23
Lostwithiel	d		20 28																		07 29
Par	d		20 35			21 11		21 35		22 27											07 37
Newquay	a																				
St Austell	d		20 42			21 18		21 42		22 35											07 45
Truro	d		21b09			21 36		21 59		22 51											08 05
Falmouth Docks	a		*21 27*					*22 26*													*08 45*
Redruth	d		21 22			21 48		22 10		23 05											08 19
Camborne	d		21 28			21 56		22 21		23 11											08 26
Hayle	d		21 35																		08 37
St Erth	d		21 39			22 08		22 31		23 23											08 43
St Ives	a																				*09 19*
Penzance	a		21 51			22 21		22 46		23 38											08 59

For general notes see front of timetable
For details of catering facilities see Directory of Train Operators

b Arr. 2059

Sundays

from 8 November

Sleeper services are published in Table 406

London and Birmingham → Devon and Cornwall

Network Diagram - see first page of Table 135

		XC	GW	GW	GW	GW	XC		GW	GW	XC	SW	GW	GW		GW	SW	XC	GW	GW	GW		XC	GW	SW
		1			◇		1 ◇		◇		1 ◇	1 ◇	1 ◇			1 ◇	1 ◇	1 ◇		1 ◇			1 ◇		1 ◇
			🛒				🛒				🛒		🍴			🍴	🍴	🛒		🍴			🛒		🍴
London Paddington [15] ⊖	d												08 00			08 57				09 57					
London Waterloo [15] ⊖	d																08 15								09 15
Slough [3]	d																								
Heathrow Central Bus Stn 🚌	d												*07 30*			*08 30*				*09 30*					
Gatwick Airport [10]	d												*06 06*			*07 08*				*08 08*					
Oxford	d															*07b45*				*09 50*					
Reading [7]	d												08 34			09 32				10 32					
Theale	d																								
Thatcham	d																								
Newbury	d															09 48									
Hungerford	d																								
Pewsey	d																			11 04					
Westbury	d															10 23									
Castle Cary	d																			11 34					
Birmingham New Street [12]	d																	08 42					09 52		
Cardiff Central [7]	d																								
Newport (South Wales)	d																								
Swindon	d												09 08												
Bristol Parkway [7]	d																	10 25					11 25		
Filton Abbey Wood	d																								
Bath Spa [7]	d												09 39												
Bristol Temple Meads [10]	d				07 45		08 25		08 28		09 44		09 53					10 44					11 44		
Weston-super-Mare	d				08 08				08 56																
Bridgwater	d				08 24				09 15																
Taunton	d				08 39		08 58		09 30		10 21		10 27			10 59		11 21		11 56			12 18		
Tiverton Parkway	d				08 54		09 10		09 45		10 33		10 41			11 12		11 34					12 31		
Exeter St Davids [6]	a				09 12		09 24		10 04		10 47		10 58			11 29		11 48		12 26			12 47		
Exeter Central	a				*09 23*				*10 33*				*11 23*							*12 35*					
Exmouth	a				*09 56*				*11 00*				*11 55*							*13 01*					
Barnstaple	a						*10 58*											*13 03*							
Exmouth	d										*10 00*							*11 05*			12 05				
Exeter Central	d			*08 56*							*10 26*	10 46					11 30	*11 35*			12 31				12 46
Exeter St Davids [6]	d			09 05	09 14		09 26		10 05	10 08	10 49	10 54	11 01			11 30	11 40	11 50		12 28	12 36		12 49		13 01
Exeter St Thomas	d			09 08						10 11											12 40				
Starcross	d			09 16						10 19											12 48			←	
Dawlish Warren	d			09 21						10 24		11 05									13c02			13 02	
Dawlish	d			09 25	09 30		09 39		10 18	10 28		11 09	11 15								→			13 06	13 14
Teignmouth	d			09 30	09 35		09 44		10 23	10 33		11 14	11 21											13 11	13 19
Newton Abbot	a			09 37	09 42	←	09 50		10 30	10 40	11 07	11 21	11 27			11 50	12 00	12 08		12 48			13 08	13 18	13 25
	d			09 47	09 43	09 47	09 55		10 31	10 42	11 09	11 23	11 28	11 38		11 52	12 01	12 09	12 30	12 49			13 10	13 20	13 28
Torre	d			→		09 55				10 50				11 46					12 38					13 28	
Torquay	d					09 58	10 07			10 53		11 34		11 49					12 41					13 31	13 39
Paignton	a					10 05	10 19			11 01		11 40		11 56					12 48					13 38	13 47
Totnes	d				09 56				10 44		11 21		11 41			12 04	12 14	12 24		13 02			13 23		
Ivybridge	d				10 12												12 30								
Plymouth	a				10 26				11 12		11 53		12 09			12 32	12 44	12 55		13 35			13 56		
	d	09 05	09 25		10 30				11 14				12 11			12 35		12 55							
Devonport	d				10 34																				
Dockyard	d																								
Keyham	d																								
St Budeaux Ferry Road	d																								
Saltash	d				10 44				11 22																
St Germans	d				10 51				11 29																
Menheniot	d				10x59				11x38																
Liskeard [6]	d	09 32	09 49		11 08				11 44				12 35			12 57		13 18							
Looe	a																								
Bodmin Parkway	d	09 44	10 01		11 22				11 56				12 47			13 10		13 30							
Lostwithiel	d		10 06		11 27				12 01																
Par	d	09 54	10 13		11 34				12 08				12 59			13 21		13 40							
Newquay	a																								
St Austell	d	10 01	10 21		11 42				12 15				13 06			13 28		13 47							
Truro	d	10 18	10 39		12 00				12 33				13 23			13 47		14 04							
Falmouth Docks	a		*11 08*		*12 38*								*14 00*					*14 54*							
Redruth	d	10 29	10 52		12 14				12 47				13 36			13 59		14 16							
Camborne	d	10 36	10 58		12 20				12 53				13 43			14 07		14 23							
Hayle	d		11 06		12 27				13 00																
St Erth	d	10 46	11 09		12 31				13 04				13 56			14 19		14 33							
St Ives	a		*12 10*		*12 50*				*13 24*				*14 24*					*14 55*							
Penzance	a	11 00	11 24		12 45				13 18				14 10			14 35		14 43							

For general notes see front of timetable
For details of catering facilities see
Directory of Train Operators

b Change at Didcot Parkway and Reading. By bus to Didcot Parkway

c Arr. 1253

Table 135

Sundays
from 8 November

Sleeper services are published in Table 406

London and Birmingham → Devon and Cornwall

Network Diagram - see first page of Table 135

		GW 1◇	XC 1◇	GW	GW 1◇	GW 1◇		GW	XC 1◇	SW 1◇	GW 1◇	GW	GW 1◇		GW	XC 1◇	GW	GW 1◇	GW	XC 1◇		SW 1◇	GW 1◇	XC 1◇	GW
London Paddington 15	⊖ d	10 57			11 27	11 57					12 03		12 57					13 57					14 57		
London Waterloo 15	⊖ d									11 15												13 15			
Slough 3	d																								
Heathrow Central Bus Stn	🚌 d	*10 30*			*11 00*	*11 30*							*12 30*					*13 30*					*14 30*		
Gatwick Airport 10	d	*09 08*			*10 08*								*11 08*					*12 08*					*13 08*		
Oxford	d	*10 50*			*11 16*	*11 50*							*12 50*					*13 50*					*14 50*		
Reading 7	d	11 32			12 02	12 32					12 37		13 32					14 32					15 32		
Theale	d																								
Thatcham	d																								
Newbury	d					12 48												14 48							
Hungerford	d																								
Pewsey	d				12 40																				
Westbury	d				13 03								14 19												
Castle Cary	d				13 19													15 35							
Birmingham New Street 12	d		10 46						11 45							12 42				13 42				14 42	
Cardiff Central 7	d																								
Newport (South Wales)	d																								
Swindon	d										13 11														
Bristol Parkway 7	d		12 25						13 25							14 25				15 25				16 25	
Filton Abbey Wood	d																								
Bath Spa 7	d										13 41														
Bristol Temple Meads 10	d		12 44						13 44		13 56					14 44				15 44				16 44	
Weston-super-Mare	d																								
Bridgwater	d																								
Taunton	d	12 47	13 18		13 42	13 54			14 17		14 30		14 55			15 17		15 55		16 18			16 50	17 17	
Tiverton Parkway	d		13 31		13 55				14 29				15 08			15 29				16 31			17 03	17 29	
Exeter St Davids 6	a	13 14	13 47		14 12	14 19			14 44		14 57		15 24			15 44		16 22		16 47			17 19	17 44	
Exeter Central	a	*13 33*				*14 33*					*15 23*		*15 33*					*16 31*		*17 21*			*17 31*	*18 38*	
Exmouth	a	*14 01*				*15 01*							*16 01*					*16 57*					*18 01*	*19 05*	
Barnstaple	a		*15 08*													*17 14*								*19 12*	
Exmouth	d		*13 10*							*14 10*							*15 10*			*16 10*					*17 10*
Exeter Central	d		*13 36*							14 43							*15 39*			*16 37*		16 46			*17 37*
Exeter St Davids 6	d	13 15	13 49	13 54	14 13	14 20			14 45	14 52	14 57	15 17	15 25			15 45	16 05	16 23		16 49		16 57	17 21	17 45	17 50
Exeter St Thomas	d			13 57								15 20					16 07								17 53
Starcross	d			14 05								15 28			←										18 01
Dawlish Warren	d			14 10								15b40 →			15 40										18 06
Dawlish	d			14 14	14 26										15 44		16 20					17 10			18 10
Teignmouth	d			14 19	14 32										15 49		16 25					17 15			18 15
Newton Abbot	a	13 35	14 08	14 26	14 39	14 43			15 03	15 13	15 18		15 46		15 56	16 03	16 31	16 42		17 08		17 22	17 40	18 03	18 22
	d	13 37	14 10	14 29	14 40	14 45			15 04	15 17	15 18		15 46		15 57	16 05	16 31	16 42	16 59	17 10		17 26	17 40	18 05	18 24
Torre	d			14 37											16 06				17 07						18 32
Torquay	d			14 40	14 51					15 28					16 09				17 10			17 37			18 35
Paignton	a			14 47	15 00					15 34					16 17				17 17			17 43			18 42
Totnes	d		14 23			14 57			15 17				16 00			16 17	16 47	16 58		17 23			17 55	18 17	
Ivybridge	d																17 03								
Plymouth	a	14 14	14 56			15 27			15 49		16 00		16 29			16 49	17 17	17 29		17 56			18 22	18 44	
	d	14 14						15 35					16 35				17 35						18 23	18 55	
Devonport	d																								
Dockyard	d																								
Keyham	d																								
St Budeaux Ferry Road	d																								
Saltash	d							15 43									17 44								
St Germans	d							15 50									17 51								
Menheniot	d																18x00								
Liskeard 6	d	14 43						16 02					16 57				18 06						18 47	19 18	
Looe	a																								
Bodmin Parkway	d	14 56						16 14					17 09				18 18						19 00	19 30	
Lostwithiel	d							16 20									18 23								
Par	d							16 27					17 22				18 30						19 11	19 40	
Newquay	a																								
St Austell	d	15 12						16 34					17 28				18 37						19 18	19c51	
Truro	d	15 29						16 53					17 47				18 55						19 36	20 08	
Falmouth Docks	a	*15 58*						*17 23*					*18 33*										*20 26*		
Redruth	d	15 40						17 06					17 59				19 08						19 48	20 19	
Camborne	d	15 47						17 12					18 06				19 14						19 56	20 27	
Hayle	d							17 19									19 21								
St Erth	d	15 58						17 23					18 19				19 25						20 08	20 37	
St Ives	a	*16 24*						*17 55*					*18 39*												
Penzance	a	16 15						17 35					18 35				19 38						20 21	20 52	

For general notes see front of timetable
For details of catering facilities see Directory of Train Operators

b Arr. 1532
c Arr. 1946

Table 135

Sundays

from 8 November

Sleeper services are published in Table 406

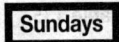

London and Birmingham → Devon and Cornwall

Network Diagram - see first page of Table 135

	GW	GW	XC	GW	GW	GW	XC	GW	GW	XC	SW	GW	XC	GW	GW	GW	XC	GW	GW
	1 ◇ ⊡		1 ◇ ⊼		1 ◇ ⊡		1 ◇ ⊼		1 ◇ ⊡	1 ◇ ⊼	1 ◇ ⊡	1 ◇ ⊡	1 ◇ ⊼		1 ◇ ⊡	1 ◇ ⊡	1 ◇ ⊼	1 ◇ ⊡	◇ ⊡
London Paddington 15 ⊖ d	15 57				16 57				17 57			18 57			19 03	19 57		20 57	23 50
London Waterloo 15 ⊖ d											17 15								
Slough 3 d																			
Heathrow Central Bus Stn 🚌 d	15 30				16 30				17 30			18 30				19 20		20 20	23 05
Gatwick Airport 10 d	14 08				15 08				16 08			17 08				18 08		19 08	22 07
Oxford d	15 50				16 50				17 50			18 50				19 50		20 50	23 15
Reading 7 d	16 32				17 32				18 32			19 32			19 37	20 32		21 32	00u37
Theale d																			
Thatcham d																			
Newbury d	16 48								18 48							20 49			
Hungerford d																			
Pewsey d									19 09							21 09			
Westbury d	17 24								19 28							21 28			
Castle Cary d	17 41											20 29				21 46			
Birmingham New Street 12 d			15 42				16 42			17 42			18 42				19 42		
Cardiff Central 7 d																			
Newport (South Wales) d																			
Swindon d															20 11				
Bristol Parkway 7 d			17 25				18 25			19 25			20 28				21 25		
Filton Abbey Wood d																			
Bath Spa 7 d															20 41				
Bristol Temple Meads 10 d			17 44			18 07	18 44			19 44			20 44		20 57		21 44		
Weston-super-Mare d						18 36									21 29				
Bridgwater d						18 54													
Taunton d	18 03		18 21		18 49	19 09	19 17		20 02	20 20		20 51	21 17		21 52	22 06	22 17	22s48	
Tiverton Parkway d	18 17		18 33		19 01	19 25	19 31		20 16	20 32		21 04	21 29		22 05	22 19	22 29	23s02	
Exeter St Davids 6 a	18 37		18 48		19 18	19 44	19 48		20 33	20 46		21 21	21 43		22 22	22 37	22 44	23 19	04 05
Exeter Central a			*19 23*		*19 38*				*20 43*	*21 23*		*21 38*			*22 34*		*23 13*	*23 29*	*05 13*
Exmouth a					*20 05*				*21 12*			*22 04*			*23 03*			*23 55*	*06 10*
Barnstaple a							*21 14*												
Exmouth d			*18 10*	18 10			*19 10*			*20 10*				21 17					
Exeter Central d			*18 37*	18 37	*18 43*		*19 36*			*20 36*	20 46			21 43					
Exeter St Davids 6 d	18 38		18 49	18 52	19 20		19 49	20 04	20 33	20 48	20 56	21 22	21 45	21 49		22 37	22 45		04 35
Exeter St Thomas d				18 55				20 07						21 53					
Starcross d				19 03				20 15						22 01					
Dawlish Warren d				19 08				20 20						22 06					
Dawlish d				19 12				20 24			21 09	21 36		22 10					
Teignmouth d				19 17				20 29			21 14	21 42		22 15					
Newton Abbot a	18 58		19 07	19 24	19 39		20 07	20 36	20 54	21 06	21 20	21 48	22 03	22 22		22 58	23 04		04 55
Newton Abbot d	19 00		19 09	19 26	19 40		20 09	20 38	20 55	21 07	21 22	21 49	22 04	22 24		22 58	23 06		04 56
Torre d				19 34				20 46						22 32					
Torquay d				19 37				20 49			21 33			22 35					
Paignton a				19 44				20 56			21 39			22 42					
Totnes d			19 21		19 53		20 21		21 10	21 20		22 03	22 17			23 11	23 21		
Ivybridge d																			
Plymouth a	19 38		19 53		20 21		20 48		21 37	21 51		22 31	22 48			23 44	23 54		05 35
Plymouth d		19 43			20 23		20 50		21 40										06 40
Devonport d																			
Dockyard d																			
Keyham d																			
St Budeaux Ferry Road d																			
Saltash d		19 51																	
St Germans d		19 58																	
Menheniot d																			
Liskeard 6 d		20 10			20 47		21 13		22 03										07 09
Looe a																			*07 41*
Bodmin Parkway d		20 22			21 00		21 25		22 14										07 23
Lostwithiel d		20 28																	07 29
Par d		20 35			21 11		21 35		22 27										07 37
Newquay a																			
St Austell d		20 42			21 18		21 42		22 35										07 45
Truro d		21b09			21 36		21 59		22 51										08 05
Falmouth Docks a		*21 27*					*22 26*												*08 45*
Redruth d		21 22			21 48		22 10		23 05										08 19
Camborne d		21 28			21 56		22 21		23 11										08 26
Hayle d		21 35																	08 37
St Erth d		21 39			22 08		22 31		23 23										08 43
St Ives a																			*09 19*
Penzance a		21 51			22 21		22 46		23 38										08 59

For general notes see front of timetable
For details of catering facilities see Directory of Train Operators

b Arr. 2059

Sleeper services are published in Table 406

Cornwall and Devon → Birmingham and London

Network Diagram - see first page of Table 135

Miles	Miles			GW MX	GW MO ◇ ☕	GW MX ◇ ☕	GW 1◇ ☕	GW 1◇ A ☕		GW 1◇ ☕	GW	XC 1◇ 🛒	GW 1◇ ☕	GW 1◇ ☕		GW 1◇ ☕	GW	GW 1◇ ☕	GW	GW		GW 1◇ ☕	GW 1◇ ☕	XC 1◇ 🛒	GW
0	—	**Penzance**	d		21p15	21p45																			
—	—	St Ives	d																						
5¾	—	St Erth	d		21p25	21p55																			
7¼	—	Hayle	d																						
13½	—	Camborne	d		21p37	22p07																			
16¾	—	Redruth	d		21p44	22p14																			
—	—	Falmouth Docks	d																						
25¾	—	Truro	d		21p59	22p27																			
40¼	—	St Austell	d		22p17	22p45																			
—	—	Newquay	d																						
44¾	—	Par	d			22p53																			
49¼	—	Lostwithiel	d																						
52¾	—	Bodmin Parkway	d		22p34	23p05																			
—	—	Looe	d																						
61¾	—	Liskeard 3	d		22p49	23p20																			
65	—	Menheniot	d																						
70¼	—	St Germans	d																						
75¼	—	Saltash	d																						
76½	—	St Budeaux Ferry Road	d																						
77¼	—	Keyham	d																						
77¾	—	Dockyard	d																						
78¼	—	Devonport	d																						
79½	—	**Plymouth**	a		23p15	23p47																			
—	—		d		23p20	23p51						05 20		05 30		05 41		06 00						06 25	
90¼	—	Ivybridge	d																						
102¾	—	Totnes	d		23p48	00 19						05 45		05 57		06 08								06 50	
—	0	Paignton	d	23p40													06 07			06 34					
—	2¼	Torquay	d	23p45													06 12			06 39					
—	3	Torre	d	23p48													06 15			06 42					
111½	8¼	Newton Abbot	a	23p57	23p59	00 31						05 56		06 08		06 20	06 23	06 34		06 50				07 01	
—	—		d	23p58	00 01	00 32						06 02		06 10		06 22	06 25	06 35		06 52				07 03	
116½	—	Teignmouth	d	00 05										06 17			06 32			06 58					
119¾	—	Dawlish	d	00 09										06 23			06 37		←	07 03					←
121	—	Dawlish Warren	d	00 15													06b48		06 48	07c14					07 14
123	—	Starcross	d	00 19													→		06 52	→					07 18
130½	—	Exeter St Thomas	d	00 28															07 02						07 27
131½	—	**Exeter St Davids 5**	a	00 34	00 36	00 54						06 21		06 36		06 43		06 54	07 06					07 21	07 33
—	—	Exeter Central	a									*06 32*		*06 45*					07 14						07 51
—	—	Exmouth	a									*07 11*							07 42						08 20
—	—	Barnstaple	d																						
—	—	Exmouth	d			*00 01*												*06 15*						*06 46*	
—	—	Exeter Central	d		*00 24*	*00 27*										*06 32*		*06 41*						*07 13*	
—	—	**Exeter St Davids 5**	d		01 27	01 02				05 46	06 00	06 23	06 30	06 38		06 45		06 55						07 23	
148	—	Tiverton Parkway	d							06 02	06 18	06 37		06 53		07 00								07 37	
162¼	—	Taunton	d			02e33				06 17	06 35	06 51	06 54	07 08		07 15		07 19						07 51	
—	11¾	Bridgwater	a								06 47		07 05			07 24									
—	25¾	Weston-super-Mare	a								07 06		07 24			07 43									
—	45½	**Bristol Temple Meads 10**	a								07 43	07 26	07 58			08 25								08 27	
—	—	Bath Spa 7	a										08 11			08 41									
—	—	Filton Abbey Wood	a								07 58					→									
—	51¼	Bristol Parkway 7	a								08 05	07 38											←	08 38	
—	—	Swindon	a										08 40										08 40		
—	—	Newport (South Wales)	a										→												
—	—	Cardiff Central 7	a																						
—	138¼	**Birmingham New Street 12**	a									08 56												09 56	
190	—	Castle Cary	d							06 38				07 30								←			
209¾	—	Westbury	d				06 08	06 18		07 05				07 51								07 51			
230	—	Pewsey	d				06 25	06 35		07 22				→								08 09			
243¾	—	Hungerford	a				06 38	06 53		07 35															
252¼	—	Newbury	a				06 49	07 08		07 46												08 30			
255¾	—	Thatcham	a				06 56	07 15																	
264½	—	Theale	a				07 06	07 25																	
269¼	—	**Reading 7**	a		04s17	04s27	07 20	07 38		08 07								08 33				08 51	09 14		
—	—	Oxford	a		*06 22*		*08f00*	*08 19*		*08 48*								*09 04*				*09 34*			
—	—	Gatwick Airport 10	a		*05 52*		*09 01*	*09g53*		*09 58*												*10g39*			
—	—	Heathrow Terminal 1 Bus	a		*05 50*		*08 49*	*09 09*		*09 49*								*09 59*				*10 19*			
286¾	—	Slough 3	a																						
—	—	**London Waterloo 15**	⊖ a																						
305¼	—	**London Paddington 15**	⊖ a		05 05	05 43	07 52	08 09		08 38								09 00				09 21	09 44		

For general notes see front of timetable
For details of catering facilities see Directory of Train Operators

- **A** From Frome (Table 123)
- **b** Arr. 0641
- **c** Arr. 0708
- **e** Arr. 0213
- **f** Change at Reading and Didcot Parkway
- **g** Change at Reading and Redhill

Sleeper services are published in Table 406

Cornwall and Devon → Birmingham and London

Network Diagram - see first page of Table 135

		XC	GW	GW	GW	GW	GW	GW	XC	GW	GW	GW	GW	GW	XC	GW	GW	GW	XC	XC	GW
		1◇		1◇			1◇	1◇	1◇	1◇	1◇	1◇			1◇		1◇		1◇	1◇	1◇
			A			A															B
		🛒		✕			☕	☕	🛒	☕	☕	☕			🛒		☕		🛒	🛒	☕
Penzance	d			05 05	05 21						05 41			06 00	06 28		06 48				07 37
St Ives	d																				07 28
St Erth	d													06 08	06 36		06 59				07 47
Hayle	d				05 31									06 11							07 51
Camborne	d				05 40						06 00			06 22	06 46		07 10				08 01
Redruth	d			05 26							06 07			06 28	06 52		07 17				08 08
Falmouth Docks	d																06 37				07 48
Truro	d			05 39	05a55						06 19			06 40	07 04		07 29				08 21
St Austell	d			05 56							06 37			06 57	07 20		07 47				08 38
Newquay	d																06 57				
Par	d										06 44			07 04	07 28		07 55				08 46
Lostwithiel	d										06 51			07 11			08 02				08 53
Bodmin Parkway	d			06 12							06 58			07 17	07 39		08 08				09 00
Looe	d										06 37						07 47				
Liskeard 6	d			06 24							07 11			07 30	07 51		08 21				09 13
Menheniot	d										07 16			07x34							
St Germans	d													07 42			08 32				09 24
Saltash	d										07 31			07 49			08 39				09 31
St Budeaux Ferry Road	d													07 53							
Keyham	d													07x55							
Dockyard	d													07x57							
Devonport	d													07 59							
Plymouth	a			06 49							07 42			08 05	08 20		08 51				09 42
	d			06 55					07 25		07 47			08 07	08 25		08 55		09 25		09 45
Ivybridge	d													08 22							10 00
Totnes	d								07 50		08 14			08 36	08 50		09 22		09 50		10 14
Paignton	d	07 00	07 07				07 38						08 23			09 13				10 05	
Torquay	d	07 06	07 14				07 44						08 28			09 18				10 11	
Torre	d		07 17				07 48						08 31			09 21					
Newton Abbot	a	07 16	07 25	07 29		←	07 58		08 01	←	08 25		08 39	08 48	09 01	09 29	09 33	←	10 01	10 21	10 26
	d	07 17	07 34	07 30		07 34	08 06		08 03	08 06	08 27		08 41	08 50	09 03	09 39	09 35	09 39	10 03	10 22	10 27
Teignmouth	d	07 24	→			07 41	→			08 13			08 48	08 57		→		09 46		10 29	
Dawlish	d	07 29				07 46				08 19			08 53	09 02				09 51		10 34	
Dawlish Warren	d					07 51							08 58					09 56			
Starcross	d					07 55				08 25			09 02					10 00			
Exeter St Thomas	d					08 05				08 34			09 11					10 09			
Exeter St Davids 6	a	07 41		07 50		08 10			08 21	08 39	08 47		09 15	09 21	09 21		09 55	10 17	10 21	10 46	10 50
Exeter Central	a	*07 51*		*08 03*		08 16				*08 51*	*09 06*		09 21		*09 51*		*10 13*	10 21	*10 51*		
Exmouth	a	*08 20*				*08 50*				*09 20*			09 50		*10 18*			10 50	*11 18*		
Barnstaple	d									*07 09*							*08 43*				*09 43*
Exmouth	d			*07 15*						*07 53*					*08 23*		*08 53*		*09 23*	*09 53*	
Exeter Central	d	*07 33*		*07 43*					*08 12*	*08 19*	*08 36*				*09 08*		*09 25*		*09 50*	*10 29*	
Exeter St Davids 6	d	07 43		07 52					08 23	08 40	08 49				09 23		09 57		10 23	10 48	10 56
Tiverton Parkway	d	07 56							08 37		09 04				09 37		10 12		10 37	11 02	11 11
Taunton	d	08 11		08 17					08 51	09 05	09 19				09 51		10 27		10 51	11 16	11 26
Bridgwater	a																				
Weston-super-Mare	a	08 30								09 27		←									
Bristol Temple Meads 10	a	08 55						←	09 27	09 56		09 56			10 26				11 24	11 53	11 59
Bath Spa 7	a							08 41		→		10 13									12 11
Filton Abbey Wood	a																				
Bristol Parkway 7	a	09 08							09 38						10 38				11 38	12 08	
Swindon	a							09 10				10 41									12 40
Newport (South Wales)	a																				
Cardiff Central 7	a																				
Birmingham New Street 12	a	10 26							10 56						11 56				12 56	13 26	
Castle Cary	d										09 40										
Westbury	d										09 59						11 03				
Pewsey	d										10 15										
Hungerford	a																				
Newbury	a																				
Thatcham	a																				
Theale	a																				
Reading 7	a			09 33				09 44			10 51	11 11					11 51				13 11
Oxford	a			*10 04*							*11 34*						*12 34*				*13 51*
Gatwick Airport 10	a							*11b39*			*12b39*						*13b39*				
Heathrow Terminal 1 Bus	a							*10 59*			*12 19*						*13 19*				
Slough 3	a																				
London Waterloo 15	⊖ a																				
London Paddington 15	⊖ a			10 02				10 14			11 23	11 40					12 25				13 40

For general notes see front of timetable
For details of catering facilities see
Directory of Train Operators

A To St James' Park (Table 136)
B From 7 September
b Change at Reading and Redhill

Sleeper services are published in Table 406

Cornwall and Devon → Birmingham and London

Network Diagram - see first page of Table 135

		GW	GW	XC	GW	GW	GW	XC	XC	GW	GW	GW	SW	XC	GW	SW	GW	GW	GW	GW	XC	XC
		1 ◇		1 ◇	1	1 ◇		1 ◇	1 ◇		1		1 ◇	1 ◇		1 ◇		1 ◇	1 ◇		1 ◇	1 ◇
		A													B			B	C			
		☕		🛒	☕	☕		🛒	🛒		✕		☕	🛒		☕		✕	✕		🛒	🛒
Penzance	d	07 37		08 28	08 44				09 40		10 00				10 46				10 49			
St Ives	d	*07 28*		*08 19*					*09 22*		*09 53*				*10 25*				*10 25*			
St Erth	d	07 47		08 36	08 55				09 48		10 11				10 54				10 59			
Hayle	d	07 51							09 52						10 57				11 03			
Camborne	d	08 01		08 46	09 07				10 01		10 22				11 07				11 13			
Redruth	d	08 08		08 52	09 14				10 08		10 29				11 13				11 20			
Falmouth Docks	d	*07 48*		*08 20*	*08 50*				*09 20*		*09 50*				*10 50*				*10 50*			
Truro	d	08 21		09 04	09 26				10 19		10 41				11 25				11 33			
St Austell	d	08 38		09 20	09 44				10 35		10 59				11 42				11 50			
Newquay	d										*10 13*											
Par	d	08 46		09 28	09 51				10 43		11 07				11 50				11 58			
Lostwithiel	d	08 53							10 50						11 56							
Bodmin Parkway	d	09 00		09 39	10 03				10 57		11 18				12 02				12 10			
Looe	d			*09 15*					*10 31*						*11 44*				*11 44*			
Liskeard 6	d	09 13		09 51	10 16				11 09		11 31				12 15				12 23			
Menheniot	d																					
St Germans	d	09 24													12 26				12 34			
Saltash	d	09 31													12 34				12 43			
St Budeaux Ferry Road	d																					
Keyham	d																					
Dockyard	d																					
Devonport	d																					
Plymouth	a	09 42		10 15	10 40				11 37		11 56				12 46				12 52			
	d	09 45		10 25	10 44			11 25	11 50		12 00			12 21				12 55	12 55		13 21	
Ivybridge	d	10 00									12 15											
Totnes	d	10 14		10 50				11 50	12 15		12 29			12 48				13 22	13 22		13 48	
Paignton	d		10 23				11 23			12 13			12 35				13 13					14 01
Torquay	d		10 28				11 28			12 18			12 41				13 18					14 07
Torre	d		10 31				11 31			12 21							13 21					
Newton Abbot	a	10 26	10 39	11 01			11 39	12 01	12 26	12 30	12 41		12 51	13 00			13 30	13 33	13 33	←	14 00	14 17
	d	10 27	10 41	11 03			11 41	12 03	12 28	12 32	12 42		12 53	13 01			13 41	13 35	13 35	13 41	14 01	14 18
Teignmouth	d	10 35	10 48				11 48			12 39			13 00			←	→			13 48		14 25
Dawlish	d	10 41	10 53				11 53			12 44		←	13 05			13 05				13 53		14 30
Dawlish Warren	d		10 58				11 58			12b55		12 55	→			13c16				13 58		
Starcross	d		11 02				12 02			→		12 59								14 02		
Exeter St Thomas	d		11 11				12 11					13 08								14 11		
Exeter St Davids 6	a	10 54	11 17	11 21	11 37		12 16	12 21	12 46		13 02	13 13		13 21		13 26		13 55	13 55	14 16	14 21	14 42
Exeter Central	a		11 21		*11 51*		12 21	*12 51*				13 21				13 38		*14 13*	*14 13*	14 21		*14 51*
Exmouth	a		11 50		*12 18*		12 50	*13 18*				13 50				*14 18*				14 50		*15 18*
Barnstaple	d	*09 43*				*10 43*					*11 43*							*12 43*	*12 43*			
Exmouth	d			*10 23*	*10 53*			*11 23*	*11 53*		*12 23*							*12 53*	*12 53*		*13 23*	*13 53*
Exeter Central	d			*10 50*	*11 17*	*11 38*		*11 50*	*12 26*		*12 50*							*13 38*	*13 38*		*13 50*	*14 17*
Exeter St Davids 6	d	10 56		11 23	11 39	11 55		12 23	12 48		13 04			13 23				13 57	13 57		14 23	14 44
Tiverton Parkway	d	11 11		11 37		12 09		12 37	13 02		13 19			13 38							14 38	14 57
Taunton	d	11 26		11 51		12 24		12 51	13 16		13 34			13 53				14 23	14 23		14 53	15 12
Bridgwater	a																					
Weston-super-Mare	a																					15 37
Bristol Temple Meads 10	a	11 59		12 24				13 24	13 56					14 27							15 27	15 57
Bath Spa 7	a	12 11																				
Filton Abbey Wood	a																					
Bristol Parkway 7	a			12 38				13 38	14 08					14 38							15 38	16 08
Swindon	a	12 40																				
Newport (South Wales)	a																					
Cardiff Central 7	a																					
Birmingham New Street 12	a			13 56				14 56	15 26					15 56							16 56	17 26
Castle Cary	d					12 45												14 44	14 44			
Westbury	d					13 05												15 03	15 03			
Pewsey	d					13 21																
Hungerford	a					13 39																
Newbury	a					13 49																
Thatcham	a					13 56																
Theale	a					14 05																
Reading 7	a	13 11			13 17	14 17					14 51							15 51	15 51			
Oxford	a	*13 51*			*14 04*	*15 04*					*15 34*							*16 34*	*16 34*			
Gatwick Airport 10	a				*14 50*	*15 50*					*16e55*							*17e49*	*17e49*			
Heathrow Terminal 1 Bus	a				*14 39*	*15 39*					*16 19*							*17 19*	*17 19*			
Slough 3	a																					
London Waterloo 15 ⊖	a															16 49						
London Paddington 15 ⊖	a	13 40			13 44	14 44					15 23							16 21	16 21			

For general notes see front of timetable
For details of catering facilities see Directory of Train Operators

A Until 4 September
B Until 26 June and from 7 September
C 29 June to 4 September
b Arr. 1248
c Arr. 1309
e Change at Reading and Redhill

Sleeper services are published in Table 406

Cornwall and Devon → Birmingham and London

Network Diagram - see first page of Table 135

		GW	GW	GW	GW	XC	SW	GW	GW	GW	GW	GW	XC	GW	XC	GW	GW	XC	GW	GW	GW
															FO						
		◇	1◇	1◇		1◇	1◇			1◇	1◇		1◇		1◇	1◇		1◇			
								A											B	C	
			🍴	🍴		☕	🍴			🍴	🍴		☕		☕	🍴		☕			
Penzance	d	11 45						12 54								14 00			14 49	14 53	
St Ives	d	*11 25*						*12 25*								*13 55*			*14 25*	*14 25*	
St Erth	d	11 53						13 02								14 11			14 57	15 01	
Hayle	d	11 57						13 05											15 01	15 05	
Camborne	d	12 06						13 15								14 22			15 10	15 14	
Redruth	d	12 12						13 21								14 29			15 16	15 20	
Falmouth Docks	d	*11 50*						*12 50*								*13 50*			*14 50*	*14 50*	
Truro	d	12 24						13 33								14 41			15 27	15 31	
St Austell	d	12 41						13 50								14 59			15 44	15 48	
Newquay	d							*13b03*											*14 58*		
Par	d	12 49						13 57								15 06			15 52	15a55	
Lostwithiel	d	12 55						14 04											15 58		
Bodmin Parkway	d	13 01						14 10								15 18			16 04		
Looe	d							*13 51*								*14 58*					
Liskeard 6	d	13 14						14 23								15 32			16 17		
Menheniot	d	13x19																	16x21		
St Germans	d	13 27						14 34											16 30		
Saltash	d	13 34						14 41											16 37		
St Budeaux Ferry Road	d																		16 41		
Keyham	d																		16x43		
Dockyard	d																		16x45		
Devonport	d																		16 47		
Plymouth	a	13 44						14 51								15 57			16 52		
	d	13 46				14 25	14 47				15 00		15 21			16 00		16 25			
Ivybridge	d	14 01					15 02														
Totnes	d	14 15				14 50	15 16				15 27		15 48			16 27		16 50			
Paignton	d			14 15	14 22				15 19					16 12							16 55
Torquay	d			14 21	14 27				15 24					16 17							17 00
Torre	d				14 30				15 27					16 20							17 03
Newton Abbot	a	14 28		14 31	14 38	15 01	15 27		15 35		15 38	←	16 00	16 28		16 38		17 01			17 11
	d			14 33	14 40	15 03	15 29		15 43 →		15 40	15 43	16 01	16 30		16 40		17 03			17 13
Teignmouth	d			14 40	14 47		15 36					15 51		16 37							17 20
Dawlish	d			14 46	14 52		15 41					15 56		16 42			←				17 25
Dawlish Warren	d				14 57		15 45					16 00		16c53 →			16 53				17 30
Starcross	d				15 01							16 04					16 57				17 34
Exeter St Thomas	d				15 10							16 14					17 06				17 43
Exeter St Davids 6	a			14 59	15 15	15 21	15 56				16 00	16 18	16 21			17 00	17 11	17 21			17 48
Exeter Central	a				15 21	*15 33*	16 13				*16 13*	16 23	*16 43*				17 23	*17 43*			17 53
Exmouth	a				15 50	*16 18*						16 52	*17 23*				17 53				18 23
Barnstaple	d			*13 43*							*14 43*					*15 43*					
Exmouth	d			*14 23*							*14 53*		*15 23*		*15 53*			*16 25*			
Exeter Central	d			*14 50*							*15 39*		*15 50*		*16 24*	*16 46*		*16 53*			
Exeter St Davids 6	d			15 00		15 23					16 00		16 23		16 53	17 00		17 23			
Tiverton Parkway	d			15 16		15 37					16 16		16 37		17 07	17 16		17 37			
Taunton	d		15 19	15 30		15 51					16 30		16 53		17 21	17 30		17 51			
Bridgwater	a																				
Weston-super-Mare	a																				
Bristol Temple Meads 10	a					16 27							17 27		17 54			18 24			
Bath Spa 7	a																				
Filton Abbey Wood	a																				
Bristol Parkway 7	a					16 38							17 38		18 08			18 38			
Swindon	a																				
Newport (South Wales)	a																				
Cardiff Central 7	a																				
Birmingham New Street 12	a					17 56							18 56		19 26			19 56			
Castle Cary	d		15 41																		
Westbury	d		16 09							←											
Pewsey	d		16 26 →							16 26											
Hungerford	a									16 39											
Newbury	a									16 49											
Thatcham	a									16 56											
Theale	a									17 05											
Reading 7	a			16 51						17 17	17 51					18 51					
Oxford	a			*17 34*						*18 04*	*18 34*					*19 34*					
Gatwick Airport 10	a			*18e50*						*19 00*	*19 53*					*20 50*					
Heathrow Terminal 1 Bus 🚌	a			*18 19*						*18 39*	*19 29*					*20 29*					
Slough 3	a									17 31											
London Waterloo 15 ⊖	a						19 49														
London Paddington 15 ⊖	a			17 24						17 54	18 21					19 24					

For general notes see front of timetable
For details of catering facilities see Directory of Train Operators

A To Gunnislake (Table 139)
B Until 26 June and from 7 September
C 29 June to 4 September
b 29 June to 4 September dep. 1240
c Arr. 1646
e Change at Reading and Redhill

Sleeper services are published in Table 406

Cornwall and Devon → Birmingham and London

Network Diagram - see first page of Table 135

		GW	GW	GW	GW	XC	GW	SW	GW	GW	GW	GW	XC	GW	GW	GW	GW	GW	SW	GW	GW
															FX	FO	FX	FO			FO
		1 ◇	1			1 ◇		1 ◇	1 ◇	1 ◇			1 ◇		◇	◇	1 ◇	1 ◇	1 ◇		1 ◇
		A	B	B							C		D								
		☕	☕			🍴			☕	☕			🍴				☕	☕			☕
Penzance	d									16 00					16 44	16 44					17 38
St Ives	d									*15 55*					*16 25*	*16 25*					*17 25*
St Erth	d									16 11					16 52	16 52					17 48
Hayle	d														16 56	16 56					17 52
Camborne	d									16 23					17 05	17 05					18 03
Redruth	d									16 30					17 11	17 11					18 10
Falmouth Docks	d									*15 50*					*16 50*	*16 50*					*17 27*
Truro	d									16 42					17 24	17 24					18 23
St Austell	d									17 00					17 41	17 41					18 40
Newquay	d		15 00																		*17 22*
Par	d		16 00							17 08					17 48	17 48					18 48
Lostwithiel	d		16 08							17 15					17 55	17 55					
Bodmin Parkway	d		16 15							17 22					18 01	18 01					18 59
Looe	d			*16 11*						*16 11*	*17 15*										*18 34*
Liskeard 6	d		16 28	16 43						17 36	17 49				18 14	18 14					19 12
Menheniot	d			16x47																	
St Germans	d			16 55							18 00				18 25	18 25					
Saltash	d			17 02							18 07				18 32	18 32					
St Budeaux Ferry Road	d			17 06							18 12										
Keyham	d			17x08																	
Dockyard	d			17x10																	
Devonport	d			17 12																	
Plymouth	a		16 53	17 18						17 59	18 18				18 42	18 42					19 37
	d	16 57	16 57			17 21		17 52		18 00			18 25		18 43	18 43					19 40
Ivybridge	d	17 12	17 12					18 07							18 59	18 59					
Totnes	d	17 27	17 27			17 48		18 21		18 30			18 50		19 13	19 13					20 07
Paignton	d				17 25		17 52					18 35							19 12	19 31	
Torquay	d				17 30		17 57					18 40							19 18	19 36	
Torre	d				17 33		18 00					18 43								19 39	
Newton Abbot	a	17 38	17 38		17 41	18 00	18 08	18 32		18 42		18 50	19 01		19 25	19 25			19 29	19 48	20 18
	d	17 40	17 40		17 43	18 01	18 10	18 33		18 43		18 53	19 03		19 25	19 25			19 31	19 49	20 20
Teignmouth	d				17 50		18 17	18 40				19 00							19 38	19 57	
Dawlish	d				17 55		18 22	18 45				19 05		←					19 43	20 02	
Dawlish Warren	d				18 00		18 27	18 49				19b16		19 16					19 47	20 06	
Starcross	d				18 04		18 31					→		19 20						20 10	
Exeter St Thomas	d				18 13		18 40							19 29						20 20	
Exeter St Davids 6	a	18 00	18 00		18 18	18 21	18 46	18 59		19 03			19 21	19 35	19 48	19 48			19 59	20 24	20 40
Exeter Central	a	*18 13*	*18 13*		18 23		18 53	19 13		*19 13*			*19 29*						20 18	20 29	
Exmouth	a				18 53		19 23						*19 57*							20 57	
Barnstaple	d									*17 09*						*18 13*	*18 13*				*19 16*
Exmouth	d	*16 55*	*16 55*			*17 25*				*18 28*						*18 55*	*18 55*				*20 01*
Exeter Central	d	*17 35*	*17 35*			*17 57*				*18 51*			*19 03*			*19 21*	*19 21*				*20 27*
Exeter St Davids 6	d	18 00	18 00			18 23				19 05			19 23			19 48	19 54				20 42
Tiverton Parkway	d	18 16	18 16			18 38				19 20			19 37			20 05	20 09				20 57
Taunton	d	18 30	18 30			18 53				19 35			19 51			20a21	20 24	20 26			21 12
Bridgwater	a																				
Weston-super-Mare	a																				
Bristol Temple Meads 10	a					19 27							20 24								21 45
Bath Spa 7	a																				21 59
Filton Abbey Wood	a																				
Bristol Parkway 7	a					19 38							20 38								
Swindon	a																				
Newport (South Wales)	a																				22 27
Cardiff Central 7	a																				
Birmingham New Street 12	a					20 56							22 06								
Castle Cary	d	18 53	18 53														20 45	20 45			
Westbury	d	19 11	19 11						19 17								21 04	21 04			
Pewsey	d								19 34								21 21	21 21			
Hungerford	a								19 51												
Newbury	a	19 45	19 45						20 06								21 42	21 42			
Thatcham	a								20 12												
Theale	a								20 21												
Reading 7	a	20 07	20 07						20 33	20 51							22 00	22 00			23 03
Oxford	a	*20 49*	*20 49*						*21 16*	*21 34*							*22 51*	*22 51*			*23 49*
Gatwick Airport 10	a	*22 04*	*22 04*							*23 04*							*00c10*	*00c10*			*01 02*
Heathrow Terminal 1 Bus	a	*21 25*	*21 25*						*21 55*	*22 55*							*23 55*	*23 55*			
Slough 3	a																				
London Waterloo 15	⊖ a							22 57													
London Paddington 15	⊖ a	20 39	20 39						21 01	21 21							22 30	22 32			23 38

For general notes see front of timetable
For details of catering facilities see Directory of Train Operators

A Until 26 June and from 7 September
B 29 June to 4 September
C To Gunnislake (Table 139)
D 🍴 to Bristol Temple Meads

b Arr. 1909
c Change at Reading and Redhill

Sleeper services are published in Table 406

Cornwall and Devon → Birmingham and London

Network Diagram - see first page of Table 135

		GW	XC	GW	GW	GW	GW	GW	GW	GW	GW	GW	GW	GW	GW	GW	GW	GW	XC
		FX													FO	FX	FO	FX	
		[1] ◇	[1] ◇		[1]	[1] ◇			[1]			[1]			◇	◇	◇	◇	[1] ◇
				A	B						B				C	D	E	G	
		☕				☕						☕			☕	☕	☕	☕	
Penzance	d	17 38		19 13	19 13							20 14			21 45	21 45	21 45	21 45	22 08
St Ives	d	17 25		18 58	18 58							19 55			20 55	20 55	20 55	20 55	21 54
St Erth	d	17 48		19 21	19 23							20 25			21 55	21 55	21 55	21 55	22 16
Hayle	d	17 52		19 24	19 27							20 29							22 20
Camborne	d	18 03		19 34	19 38							20 40			22 07	22 07	22 07	22 07	22 30
Redruth	d	18 10		19 40	19 45							20 47			22 14	22 14	22 14	22 14	22 36
Falmouth Docks	d	17 27		19 00	19 00							20 29			21 30	21 30	21 30	21 30	
Truro	d	18 23		19 52	19 58							21 00			22 27	22 27	22 27	22 27	22 48
St Austell	d	18 40		20 09	20 15							21 17			22 45	22 45	22 45	22 45	23 04
Newquay	d	17 22		19 25	19 25										21 26	21 26	21 26	21 26	
Par	d	18 48		20 16	20 23										22 53	22 53	22 53	22 53	23 12
Lostwithiel	d			20 23	20 30							21 31							23 19
Bodmin Parkway	d	18 59		20 29	20 37							21 37			23 05	23 05	23 05	23 05	23 26
Looe	d	18 34		19 49	19 49														
Liskeard [6]	d	19 12		20 43	20 50						21 09	21 50			23 20	23 20	23 20	23 20	23 39
Menheniot	d			20x47							21x13								
St Germans	d			20 56							21 21								
Saltash	d			21 03							21 28								
St Budeaux Ferry Road	d			21 07							21 32								
Keyham	d			21x09							21x34								
Dockyard	d			21x11							21x36								
Devonport	d			21 13							21 38								
Plymouth	a	19 37		21 18	21 18						21 44	22 17			23 47	23 47	23 47	23 47	00 08
	d	19 40								21 23					23 51	23 51	23 51	23 51	
Ivybridge	d									21 38									
Totnes	d	20 07								21 52					00 19	00 19	00 19	00 19	
Paignton	d		20 10					20 32	21 31				22 40	23 40					
Torquay	d		20 16					20 37	21 37				22 45	23 45					
Torre	d							20 40	21 41				22 48	23 48					
Newton Abbot	a	20 18	20 26					20 48	21 52	22 04			22 56	23 57	00 31	00 31	00 31	00 31	
	d	20 20	20 27					20 50		22 04			22 58	23 58	00 32	00 32	00 32	00 32	
Teignmouth	d							20 57		22 11			23 05	00 05					
Dawlish	d							21 02		22 16			23 10	00 09					
Dawlish Warren	d							21 07		22 21			23 15	00 15					
Starcross	d							21 11		22 25			23 19	00 19					
Exeter St Thomas	d							21 20		22 34			23 28	00 28					
Exeter St Davids [6]	a	20 40	20 46					21 27		22 38			23 34	00 34	00 54	00 54	00 54	00 54	
Exeter Central	a		21 03					21 33		23b30									
Exmouth	a		21 57					22 00		23 57									
Barnstaple	d	19 16													22 18	22 18	22 18	22 18	
Exmouth	d	20 01													00 01	00 01	00 01	00 01	
Exeter Central	d	20 27	20 32				20 55								00 27	00 27	00 27	00 27	
Exeter St Davids [6]	d	20 42	20 48				21 11								01 02	01 02	01 14	01 14	
Tiverton Parkway	d	20 57	21 01				21 28												
Taunton	d	21 12	21 16			21 29	21 47								02c33	02c33	02 33	02 33	
Bridgwater	a					21 38													
Weston-super-Mare	a					21 56	22 11												
Bristol Temple Meads [10]	a	21 45	21 51			22 30	22 34												
Bath Spa [7]	a	21 59				22 44													
Filton Abbey Wood	a																		
Bristol Parkway [7]	a		22 08																
Swindon	a	22 27				23 14													
Newport (South Wales)	a																		
Cardiff Central [7]	a																		
Birmingham New Street [12]	a		23 44																
Castle Cary	d																		
Westbury	d																		
Pewsey	d																		
Hungerford	a																		
Newbury	a																		
Thatcham	a																		
Theale	a																		
Reading [7]	a	23 03				23 55									04s17	04s27	04s17	04s27	
Oxford	a	23 39				00e33													
Gatwick Airport [10]	a	01 02													05 58	05 52	05 58	05 52	
Heathrow Terminal 1 Bus	a																		
Slough [3]	a																		
London Waterloo [15] ⊖	a																		
London Paddington [15] ⊖	a	23 42				00 33									05 43	05 43	05 43	05 43	

For general notes see front of timetable
For details of catering facilities see Directory of Train Operators

A Until 26 June and from 7 September
B 29 June to 4 September
C From 11 September
D From 7 September
E Until 4 September
G Until 3 September
b Fridays arr. 2300
c Arr. 0213
e Saturday mornings arr. 0106

Saturdays

until 5 September

Sleeper services are published in Table 406

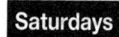

Cornwall and Devon → Birmingham and London

Network Diagram - see first page of Table 135

		GW	GW	GW	XC	GW	GW	GW	XC	GW	GW	XC	GW	GW	GW	XC	GW	GW	GW	XC	XC
			◇ ☕		1 ◇ 🛒		1 ◇ ☕		1 ◇ 🛒	1 ◇ ☕		1 ◇ 🛒		1 ◇ ☕	1 ◇ ☕	1 ◇ 🛒	1 ◇ ☕			1 ◇ 🛒	1 ◇ 🛒
Penzance	d		21p45			05 22													06 01	06 30	
St Ives	d																				
St Erth	d		21p55																06 08	06 38	
Hayle	d																		06 11	06 41	
Camborne	d		22p07			05 39													06 21	06 51	
Redruth	d		22p14			05 45													06 27	06 57	
Falmouth Docks	d																				
Truro	d		22p27			05a56													06 39	07 09	
St Austell	d		22p45																06 56	07 25	
Newquay	d																				
Par	d		22p53																07 03	07 32	
Lostwithiel	d																		07 10	07 39	
Bodmin Parkway	d		23p05																07 16	07 46	
Looe	d																		*06 37*		
Liskeard 6	d		23p20																07 30	07 58	
Menheniot	d																		07x35		
St Germans	d																		07 42		
Saltash	d																		07 49		
St Budeaux Ferry Road	d																		07 53		
Keyham	d																		07x55		
Dockyard	d																		07x57		
Devonport	d																		07 59		
Plymouth	a		23p47																08 05	08 22	
	d		23p51		05 25		05 40		06 25					06 55		07 25	07 47		08 06	08 25	08 40
Ivybridge	d																		08 21		
Totnes	d		00 19		05 50		06 07		06 50							07 50	08 14		08 35	08 50	09 05
Paignton	d	23p40						06 13			06 51	07 00	07 08					08 11			
Torquay	d	23p45						06 18			06 56	07 06	07 14					08 16			
Torre	d	23p48						06 21			06 59		07 17					08 19			
Newton Abbot	a	23p57	00 31		06 01		06 18	06 29	07 01		07 07	07 16	07 25	07 30		08 01	08 26	08 27	08 47	09 01	09 16
	d	23p58	00 32		06 03		06 20	06 31	07 03		07 09	07 18		07 31		08 03	08 27	08 37	08 48	09 03	09 18
Teignmouth	d	00 05						06 38			07 16	07 25						08 44	08 55		
Dawlish	d	00 09						06 43			07 21	07 30						08 49	09 00		
Dawlish Warren	d	00 15						06 48			07 26							08 54			
Starcross	d	00 19						06 52			07 30							08 58			
Exeter St Thomas	d	00 28						07 01			07 39							09 07			
Exeter St Davids 6	a	00 34	00 54		06 21		06 40	07 05	07 21		07 44	07 46		07 51		08 21	08 47	09 12	09 16	09 21	09 36
Exeter Central	a				*06 32*			07 14			07 51			*08 03*		*08 51*		09 21			*09 51*
Exmouth	a				*07 06*			07 42			08 20			*08 50*		*09 20*		09 50			*10 20*
Barnstaple	d																*07 09*				
Exmouth	d								*06 15*					*07 15*			*07 53*			*08 23*	*08 53*
Exeter Central	d						*06 32*		*06 41*			*07 33*		*07 43*			*08 28*			*08 50*	*09 25*
Exeter St Davids 6	d		01 14	06 00	06 23		06 41		07 23	07 28		07 48		07 53		08 23	08 49			09 23	09 39
Tiverton Parkway	d			06 18	06 37		06 56		07 37	07 43						08 37	09 04			09 37	09 52
Taunton	d		02 33	06 35	06 51		07 11		07 51	07 58		08 12		08 19		08 51	09 19			09 51	10 07
Bridgwater	a			06 47						08 08					←						
Weston-super-Mare	a			07 06						08 26 →					08 26						10 31
Bristol Temple Meads 10	a			07 43	07 25				08 24			08 45			08 57	09 25				10 26	10 51
Bath Spa 7	a														09 11						
Filton Abbey Wood	a			07 58																	
Bristol Parkway 7	a			08 05	07 38				08 38			09 08				09 38				10 38	11 08
Swindon	a														09 39						
Newport (South Wales)	a																				
Cardiff Central 7	a																				
Birmingham New Street 12	a				08 56				09 56			10 26				10 56				11 56	12 26
Castle Cary	d						07 33										09 40				
Westbury	d						07b56										09 59				
Pewsey	d						08 13										10 16				
Hungerford	a																				
Newbury	a						08 33														
Thatcham	a																				
Theale	a																				
Reading 7	a		04s17				08 52							09 35	10 09		10 51				
Oxford	a						*09 34*							*10 20*			*11 34*				
Gatwick Airport 10	a						*10c39*							*11c39*			*12c39*				
Heathrow Terminal 1 Bus 🚌	a						*10 09*							*11 09*			*12 09*				
Slough 3	a																				
London Waterloo 15 ⊖	a																				
London Paddington 15 ⊖	a		05 43				09 21							10 08	10 38		11 24				

For general notes see front of timetable
For details of catering facilities see Directory of Train Operators

b Arr. 0751
c Change at Reading and Redhill

Saturdays

until 5 September

Sleeper services are published in Table 406

Cornwall and Devon → Birmingham and London

Network Diagram - see first page of Table 135

		GW	GW	GW	GW	XC	GW	GW	XC	SW	GW	XC	GW	GW	GW	XC	GW	GW	GW	SW
			1 R ⊡		1 R ⊡	1 ◇ ⌶	1 R ⊡	1 R ⊡	1 ◇ ⌶	1 ◇ ⊡		1 ◇ ⌶	1 R ⊡			1 ◇ ⌶		1 R ⊡		1 ◇ ⊡
Penzance	d		06 50				07 22					08 25	08 42					09 55		
St Ives	d						*07 00*					*08 15*						*09 22*		
St Erth	d		07 01				07 34					08 33	08 54					10 07		
Hayle	d						07 38											10 11		
Camborne	d		07 12				07 48					08 43	09 05					10 21		
Redruth	d		07 19				07 55					08 49	09 12					10 28		
Falmouth Docks	d		*06 37*				*07 17*					*08 20*	*08 50*					*09 50*		
Truro	d		07 31				08 09					09 02	09 26					10 42		
St Austell	d		07 49				08 26					09 18	09 43					10 59		
Newquay	d															09 30				
Par	d		07 56				08 34					09 26	09 51					11 07		
Lostwithiel	d		08 03				08 41													
Bodmin Parkway	d		08 10				08 47					09 37	10 02					11 19		
Looe	d		*07 44*									*09 16*						*10 41*		
Liskeard 6	d		08 23				09 00					09 49	10 15					11 33		
Menheniot	d																			
St Germans	d						09 11													
Saltash	d						09 20													
St Budeaux Ferry Road	d																			
Keyham	d																			
Dockyard	d																			
Devonport	d																			
Plymouth	a		08 48				09 30					10 18	10 39			11 18		11 59		
	d		08 52			09 25	09 34					10 25	10 43			11 21		11 59		
Ivybridge	d																	12 14		
Totnes	d		09 19			09 50	10 01					10 50				11 48		12 29		
Paignton	d	09 04			09 20				10 05	10 14	10 23			10 55	11 23		12 13			12 34
Torquay	d	09 09			09 27				10 12	10 20	10 28			11 00	11 28		12 18			12 40
Torre	d	09 12								10 23	10 31			11 03	11 31		12 21			
Newton Abbot	a	09 20	09 31		09 37	10 01	10 13		10 21	10 31	10 38	11 01		11 11	11 39	12 00	12 30	12 40		12 50
	d	09 22	09 32		09 39	10 03	10 14		10 23	10 33	10 41	11 03		11 23	11 41	12 01	12 32	12 42		12 52
Teignmouth	d	09 29			09 48				10 32	10 40	10 48			11 30	11 48		12 39			12 59
Dawlish	d	09 34		←	09 55				10 38	10 45	10 53			11 35	11 53		12 44		←	13 04 →
Dawlish Warren	d	09b50 →		09 50	10 01					10 49	10 58			11 40	11 58		12c55 →		12 55	
Starcross	d			09 54							11 02			11 44	12 02				12 59	
Exeter St Thomas	d			10 03							11 12			11 53	12 11				13 08	
Exeter St Davids 6	a		09 52	10 08	10 13	10 21	10 34		10 50	11 00	11 15	11 21	11 36	11 57	12 16	12 21		13 02	13 13	
Exeter Central	a		*10 13*	10 21			*10 51*			11 11	11 21		*11 51*	*12 13*	12 21	*12 51*			13 21	
Exmouth	a			10 52			*11 18*				11 50		*12 18*		12 50	*13 18*			13 50	
Barnstaple	d		*08 43*									*09 43*				*10 43*		*11 43*		
Exmouth	d				*09 23*		*09 53*					*10 23*	*10 53*			*11 23*		*12 23*		
Exeter Central	d				*09 50*		*10 26*					*10 50*	*11 17*			*11 58*		*12 50*		
Exeter St Davids 6	d		09 54		10 15	10 23	10 37		10 52			11 23	11 39			12 23		13 04		
Tiverton Parkway	d		10 09		10 30	10 37			11 06			11 37				12 39		13 19		
Taunton	d		10 24		10 45	10 51	11 02		11 20			11 51				12 54		13 34		
Bridgwater	a																			
Weston-super-Mare	a																			
Bristol Temple Meads 10	a				11 19 →	11 26		← 11 19	11 57			12 25				13 27				
Bath Spa 7	a							11 41												
Filton Abbey Wood	a																			
Bristol Parkway 7	a					11 38			12 08			12 38				13 38				
Swindon	a							12 09												
Newport (South Wales)	a																			
Cardiff Central 7	a																			
Birmingham New Street 12	a					12 56			13 26			13 56				14 56				
Castle Cary	d						11 23													
Westbury	d		11 02				11 43													
Pewsey	d						12 00													
Hungerford	a																			
Newbury	a																			
Thatcham	a																			
Theale	a																			
Reading 7	a		11 51				12 41	12 48					13 17					14 51		
Oxford	a		*12 34*				*13 19*						*14 04*					*15 34*		
Gatwick Airport 10	a		*13e39*					*14e39*					*14 50*					*16e39*		
Heathrow Terminal 1 Bus	🚌 a		*13 09*					*14 09*					*14 39*					*16 09*		
Slough 3	a																			
London Waterloo 15	⊖ a									14 49										
London Paddington 15	⊖ a		12 23				13 14	13 22					13 54					15 23		

For general notes see front of timetable
For details of catering facilities see
Directory of Train Operators

b Arr. 0938
c Arr. 1248
e Change at Reading and Redhill

Table 135

Saturdays

until 5 September

Sleeper services are published in Table 406

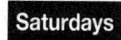

Cornwall and Devon → Birmingham and London

Network Diagram - see first page of Table 135

		XC	SW	GW	GW	GW	GW	GW	GW	GW	XC	XC	GW	GW	GW	GW	XC	GW	SW	GW	GW
		1 ◇	1 ◇		R	1 R	1 R	1 R	1 R	1 R	1 ◇	1 ◇	1	1 R		1 R	1 ◇	1 R	1 ◇		1 R
									A	B											
Penzance	d						11 00							11 58							
St Ives	d						*10 55*							*11 25*							
St Erth	d						11 12							12 10							
Hayle	d						11 16							12 14							
Camborne	d						11 26							12 24							
Redruth	d						11 33							12 31							
Falmouth Docks	d						*10 50*							*11 50*							
Truro	d						11 47							12 45							
St Austell	d						12 04							13 02							
Newquay	d								11 22	11 22											13 14
Par	d			11 32					12 27	12 27											14 16
Lostwithiel	d			11 39																	
Bodmin Parkway	d			11 45			12 21							13 19							
Looe	d						*11 54*							*12 53*							
Liskeard 6	d			11 58			12 34							13 32							
Menheniot	d			12x02																	
St Germans	d			12 11																	
Saltash	d			12 20																	
St Budeaux Ferry Road	d																				
Keyham	d																				
Dockyard	d																				
Devonport	d																				
Plymouth	a			12 29			12 59		13 11	13s11				13 57							15 03
	d	12 21		12 29			13 01		13 12		13 25			13 59			14 25		14 48		15 05
Ivybridge	d			12 45															15 03		
Totnes	d	12 48		12 59			13 29				13 50						14 50		15 17		
Paignton	d				12 58	13 07						13 47			14 22	14 30				15 13	
Torquay	d				13 03	13 14						13 54			14 27	14 36				15 18	
Torre	d				13 06										14 30					15 21	
Newton Abbot	a	13 00		13 11	13 14	13 25	13 40				14 01	14 04		14 35	14 38	14 47	15 01		15 28	15 29	15 42
	d	13 01		13 11	13 21	13 26	13 42				14 03	14 06		14 36	14 40	14 50	15 03		15 30	15 34	15 44
Teignmouth	d		⟵		13 28	13 35		⟵				14 15			14 47	14 58		⟵	15 37	15 42	
Dawlish	d		13 04		13 33	13b43		13 43				14 23			14 52	15 04		15 04	15 42	15 47	
Dawlish Warren	d		13c15		13 38	⟶		13e55							14 57	⟶		15f17	15 46	16g00	
Starcross	d				13 42										15 01					⟶	
Exeter St Thomas	d				13 51										15 10						
Exeter St Davids 6	a	13 21	13 25	13 33	14 00		14 02	14 08	14 15	14s15	14 21	14 36		14 55	15 15		15 21	15 28	16 00		16 05
Exeter Central	a		13 38	*13 51*	14 21		*14 13*	*14 21*				*14 51*			15 21		*15 33*	*15 51*	16 13		
Exmouth	a			*14 18*	14 50			*14 50*				*15 18*			15 50			*16 18*			
Barnstaple	d						*12 43*							*13 43*							*14 43*
Exmouth	d						*13 23*					*13 53*					*14 23*	*14 53*			*15 23*
Exeter Central	d						*13 50*					*14 23*					*14 50*	*15 17*			*15 50*
Exeter St Davids 6	d	13 23					14 05	14 11	14 18		14 23	14 38		14 59			15 23	15 32			16 07
Tiverton Parkway	d	13 39									14 37			15 14			15 37				
Taunton	d	13 54					14 30	14h44			14 51	15 04		15 29			15 51	15 57			16 32
Bridgwater	a																				
Weston-super-Mare	a											15 25									
Bristol Temple Meads 10	a	14 27									15 27	15 48					16 24				
Bath Spa 7	a																				
Filton Abbey Wood	a																				
Bristol Parkway 7	a	14 38									15 38	16 08					16 38				
Swindon	a																				
Newport (South Wales)	a																				
Cardiff Central 7	a																				
Birmingham New Street 12	a	15 56									16 56	17 26	⟵				17 56				
Castle Cary	d							15 08					15 08					16 18			
Westbury	d							⟶					15 28					16 38			
Pewsey	d												15 45					16 53			
Hungerford	a																				
Newbury	a												16 05								
Thatcham	a																				
Theale	a																				
Reading 7	a						15 49		15 59	15 59			16 28	16 49				17 35			17 51
Oxford	a								*16 34*	*16 34*			*17 04*	*17 34*				*18 18*			*18 34*
Gatwick Airport 10	a						*17j39*		*17 50*	*17 50*				*18j39*							*19j39*
Heathrow Terminal 1 Bus	a								*17 09*	*17 09*			*17 39*	*18 09*							*19 09*
Slough 3	a																				
London Waterloo 15 ⊖	a		16 49																19 49		
London Paddington 15 ⊖	a						16 21		16 29	16 29			16 59	17 21				18 08			18 21

For general notes see front of timetable
For details of catering facilities see Directory of Train Operators

- **A** Until 20 June
- **B** From 27 June
- **b** Arr. 1340
- **c** Arr. 1307
- **e** Arr. 1347
- **f** Arr. 1509
- **g** Arr. 1551
- **h** Arr. 1435
- **j** Change at Reading and Redhill

Table 135

Saturdays

until 5 September

Sleeper services are published in Table 406

Cornwall and Devon → Birmingham and London

Network Diagram - see first page of Table 135

		GW	GW	XC 1◇	SW 1	GW	GW 1◇	GW	XC 1◇	GW	GW 1◇	GW	XC 1◇	GW	XC 1◇	SW 1◇	GW 1◇	SW 1◇	XC 1◇	XC 1◇
Penzance	d	13 00					14 00			14 49							15 53		16 25	
St Ives	d	12 55					13 55			14 25							15 25			
St Erth	d	13 11					14 11			14 57							16 04		16 38	
Hayle	d	13 14								15 01										
Camborne	d	13 23					14 22			15 10							16 15		16 47	
Redruth	d	13 29					14 29			15 16							16 22		16 54	
Falmouth Docks	d	12 50					13 50			14 50							15 50			
Truro	d	13 41					14 41			15 28							16 34		17 06	
St Austell	d	13 57					14 59			15 45							16 52		17 24	
Newquay	d												15 20							
Par	d	14b24					15 06			15 53							16 59			
Lostwithiel	d	14 32								16 00							17 06			
Bodmin Parkway	d	14 38					15 18			16 06			16 36				17 13		17 40	
Looe	d	13 58					14 54						16 16							
Liskeard 6	d	14 51					15 34			16 19			16 50				17 26		17 53	
Menheniot	d									16x23										
St Germans	d	15 02								16 31										
Saltash	d	15 09								16 38										
St Budeaux Ferry Road	d																			
Keyham	d																			
Dockyard	d																			
Devonport	d	15 16																		
Plymouth	a	15 21					15 57			16 48			17 15				17 51		18 18	
	d			15 25			16 00		16 25				17 21			17 42	17 54		18 21	18 32
Ivybridge	d															17 57				
Totnes	d			15 50			16 27		16 50				17 48			18 11	18 21		18 48	18 57
Paignton	d				15 52	16 12					17 03	17 23		17 52	18 03					
Torquay	d				15 58	16 17					17 10	17 28		17 57	18 10					
Torre	d					16 20						17 31		18 00						
Newton Abbot	a			16 01	16 08	16 28	16 39		17 01		17 21	17 39	17 59	18 08	18 20	18 24	18 32		19 00	19 08
	d			16 03	16 10	16 30	16 40		17 03		17 22	17 41	18 01	18 10	18 22	18 25	18 34		19 01	19 10
Teignmouth	d				16 17	16 38					17 30	17 49		18 17		18 32		←		19 17
Dawlish	d		←		16 22	16 43		←			17 37	17 54		18 22		18 36 →		18 36		19 22
Dawlish Warren	d		16 00			16c55 →		16 55			17 42	17 59		18 27				18e48		
Starcross	d		16 04					16 59				18 04		18 31						
Exeter St Thomas	d		16 14					17 09				18 13		18 40						
Exeter St Davids 6	a		16 17	16 21	16 35		17 00	17 12	17 21		17 54	18 17	18 21	18 43	18 47		18 54	19 00	19 21	19 32
Exeter Central	a		16 23		16 43			17 23	*17 43*		*18 13*	18 23		18 53				19 13		
Exmouth	a		16 52		*17 23*			17 53	*18 23*			18 53		19 23				*19 57*		
Barnstaple	d						*15 43*								*17 09*					*18 13*
Exmouth	d						*15 53*		*16 25*		*17 25*				*17 55*					*18 55*
Exeter Central	d						*16 45*		*16 53*		*17 51*		*17 57*		*18 35*					*19 21*
Exeter St Davids 6	d			16 23			17 01		17 23		18 02		18 23		18 52		18 56		19 23	19 45
Tiverton Parkway	d			16 37			17 17		17 37		18 17		18 37		19 05		19 11			19 58
Taunton	d			16 51			17 31		17 51		18 32		18 51		19 20		19 26		19 49	20 14
Bridgwater	a																			20 33
Weston-super-Mare	a																			
Bristol Temple Meads 10	a			17 25					18 25				19 26		19 55				20 24	20 56
Bath Spa 7	a																			
Filton Abbey Wood	a																			
Bristol Parkway 7	a			17 38					18 38				19 38		20 08				20 38	21 08
Swindon	a																			
Newport (South Wales)	a																			
Cardiff Central 7	a																			
Birmingham New Street 12	a			18 56					19 56				20 56		21 41				21 56	22 27
Castle Cary	d										18 53						19 47			
Westbury	d										19 12						20 06			
Pewsey	d																20 23			
Hungerford	a																			
Newbury	a										19 48									
Thatcham	a																			
Theale	a																			
Reading 7	a						18 49				20 06						20 58			
Oxford	a						*19 34*				*20 47*						*21 34*			
Gatwick Airport 10	a						*20f38*				*21 59*						*23 03*			
Heathrow Terminal 1 Bus	a						*20 09*				*21 19*									
Slough 3	a																			
London Waterloo 15	⊖ a																	22 57		
London Paddington 15	⊖ a						19 22				20 45						21 32			

For general notes see front of timetable
For details of catering facilities see Directory of Train Operators

b Arr. 1404
c Arr. 1647
e Arr. 1840
f Change at Reading and Redhill

Table 135

Saturdays

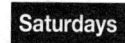

until 5 September

Sleeper services are published in Table 406

Cornwall and Devon → Birmingham and London

Network Diagram - see first page of Table 135

		GW	GW ◇ ✠	GW 1	SW 1 ◇	GW	GW 1 ◇ 🛏	GW	GW 1 ◇ 🛏	GW	GW	GW 1 ◇ 🛏	GW	GW ◇ ✠	XC 1 ◇	GW	GW	GW	XC 1 ◇ ✠
Penzance	d			16 45					17 37					19 06					21 32
St Ives	d			*16 25*					*17 27*					*18 17*					*21 12*
St Erth	d			16 54					17 48					19 14					21 40
Hayle	d			16 58					17 52					19 17					
Camborne	d			17 08					18 02					19 27					21 51
Redruth	d			17 15					18 09					19 33					21 58
Falmouth Docks	d			*16 50*					*17 27*					*19 00*					*21 30*
Truro	d			17 27					18 22					19 45					22 09
St Austell	d			17 45					18 39					20 02					22 26
Newquay	d						17 18								19 58			21 20	
Par	d			17 51			18 21		18 47	18 59				20 09				22 06	22 33
Lostwithiel	d			17 58						19 06				20 16				22 15	
Bodmin Parkway	d			18 04			18 33		18 58	19 12				20 22	21 08			22 21	22 44
Looe	d			*17 29*					*18 34*					*20 01*			*21 12*		
Liskeard 6	d			18 17			18 46		19 11	19 25				20 35	21 21		21 53	22 34	22 57
Menheniot	d													20x39				22x38	
St Germans	d			18 31						19 36				20 48				22 46	
Saltash	d			18 39						19 45				20 56				22 53	
St Budeaux Ferry Road	d													21 00				22 57	
Keyham	d													21x02				22x59	
Dockyard	d													21x04				23x00	
Devonport	d													21 06				23 02	
Plymouth	a			18 51			19 11		19 36	19 54				21 10	21 51		22 17	23 09	23 26
	d		18 42				19 12		19 39					21 15					
Ivybridge	d		18 59											21 30					
Totnes	d		19 13						20 06					21 44					
Paignton	d	18 53			19 14	19 23					20 13		21 13			21 53			
Torquay	d	18 58			19 20	19 28					20 18		21 18			21 58			
Torre	d	19 01				19 31					20 21		21 21			22 01			
Newton Abbot	a	19 09	19 25		19 30	19 39	19 49		20 17		20 29		21 29	21 56		22 09			
	d	19 14	19 26		19 32	19 41	19 50		20 19		20 31		21 31	21 56		22 11			
Teignmouth	d	19 22	19 33		19 39	19 48					20 38		21 38	22 03		22 18			
Dawlish	d	19 27	19 39		19 44	19 53		←			20 43		21 43	22 08		22 23			
Dawlish Warren	d	19 31			19 49	20b05 →		20 05			20 48		21 48	22 13		22 28			
Starcross	d	19 35						20 09			20 52		21 52	22 17		22 32			
Exeter St Thomas	d	19 45						20 19			21 01		22 01	22 26		22 41			
Exeter St Davids 6	a	19 48	19 52		20 03		20 09	20 22	20 38		21 05		22 05	22 30		22 45			
Exeter Central	a				20 18		*20 18*	20 29	*21 03*		*21 30*			*22 39*		*23 00*			
Exmouth	a							20 57			*21 57*			*23 07*		*23 42*			
Barnstaple	d								*19 16*										
Exmouth	d						*19 33*		*20 01*										
Exeter Central	d						*19 57*		*20 26*										
Exeter St Davids 6	d						20 11		20 40										
Tiverton Parkway	d								20 57										
Taunton	d						20 38		21 11			21 30							
Bridgwater	a											21 39							
Weston-super-Mare	a											21 58							
Bristol Temple Meads 10	a								21 44			22 30							
Bath Spa 7	a								21 58			22 44							
Filton Abbey Wood	a																		
Bristol Parkway 7	a																		
Swindon	a								22 27			23 13							
Newport (South Wales)	a																		
Cardiff Central 7	a																		
Birmingham New Street 12	a																		
Castle Cary	d																		
Westbury	d																		
Pewsey	d																		
Hungerford	a																		
Newbury	a																		
Thatcham	a																		
Theale	a																		
Reading 7	a						21 58		23 01			23 52							
Oxford	a						*22 49*		*00 04*			*00 38*							
Gatwick Airport 10	a								*01c02*										
Heathrow Terminal 1 Bus 🚌	a						*23 55*												
Slough 3	a																		
London Waterloo 15 ⊖	a																		
London Paddington 15 ⊖	a						22 26		23 38			00 33							

For general notes see front of timetable
For details of catering facilities see Directory of Train Operators

b Arr. 1957
c Change at Reading and Redhill

Sleeper services are published in Table 406

Cornwall and Devon → Birmingham and London

Network Diagram - see first page of Table 135

		GW	GW ◇ 🍴	GW	XC 1 ◇ 🛒	GW	GW 1 ◇ 🍴	GW	XC 1 ◇ 🛒	GW 1 ◇ 🍴		GW	XC 1 ◇ 🛒	GW	GW 1 ◇ 🍴	GW 1 ◇ 🍴	GW 1 ◇ 🍴	XC 1 ◇ 🛒	GW 1 ◇ 🍴	GW		GW	XC 1 ◇ 🛒	GW	GW 1 R 🍴
Penzance	d		21p45			05 22																06 01	06 30		06 50
St Ives	d																								
St Erth	d		21p55																			06 08	06 38		07 01
Hayle	d																					06 11	06 41		
Camborne	d		22p07			05 39																06 21	06 51		07 12
Redruth	d		22p14			05 45																06 27	06 57		07 19
Falmouth Docks	d																								*06 37*
Truro	d		22p27			05a56																06 39	07 09		07 31
St Austell	d		22p45																			06 56	07 25		07 49
Newquay	d																								
Par	d		22p53																			07 03	07 32		07 56
Lostwithiel	d																					07 10	07 39		08 03
Bodmin Parkway	d		23p05																			07 16	07 46		08 10
Looe	d																					*06 37*			*07 44*
Liskeard 6	d		23p20																			07 30	07 58		08 23
Menheniot	d																					07x35			
St Germans	d																					07 42			
Saltash	d																					07 49			
St Budeaux Ferry Road	d																					07 53			
Keyham	d																					07x55			
Dockyard	d																					07x57			
Devonport	d																					07 59			
Plymouth	a		23p47																			08 05	08 22		08 48
	d		23p51		05 25		05 40		06 25						06 55			07 25	07 47			08 06	08 25		08 52
Ivybridge	d																					08 21			
Totnes	d		00 19		05 50		06 07		06 50									07 50	08 14			08 35	08 50		09 19
Paignton	d	23p40						06 13				06 51	07 00	07 08			07 20			08 11				09 11	
Torquay	d	23p45						06 18				06 56	07 06	07 14			07 26			08 16				09 16	
Torre	d	23p48						06 21				06 59		07 17			07 30			08 19				09 19	
Newton Abbot	a	23p57	00 31		06 01		06 18	06 29	07 01			07 07	07 16	07 25	07 30		07 38	08 01	08 26	08 27		08 47	09 01	09 27	09 31
	d	23p58	00 32		06 03		06 20	06 31	07 03			07 09	07 18		07 31		07 40	08 03	08 27	08 37		08 48	09 03	09 37 →	09 32
Teignmouth	d	00 05						06 38				07 16	07 25				07 47			08 44		08 55			
Dawlish	d	00 09						06 43				07 21	07 30				07 53			08 49		09 00			
Dawlish Warren	d	00 15						06 48				07 26								08 54					
Starcross	d	00 19						06 52				07 30								08 58					
Exeter St Thomas	d	00 28						07 01				07 39								09 07					
Exeter St Davids 6	a	00 34	00 54		06 21		06 40	07 05	07 21			07 44	07 46		07 51		08 05	08 21	08 47	09 12		09 16	09 21		09 52
Exeter Central	a				*06 32*			07 14				07 51			*08 03*			*08 51*		09 21			*09 51*		*10 13*
Exmouth	a				*07 06*			07 42				08 20						*09 20*		09 50			*10 20*		
Barnstaple	d																		*07 09*						*08 43*
Exmouth	d		*00 01*						*06 15*						*07 15*				*07 53*				*08 23*		*08 53*
Exeter Central	d		*00 27*				*06 32*		*06 41*				*07 33*		*07 43*				*08 28*				*08 50*		*09 25*
Exeter St Davids 6	d		01 02	06 00	06 23		06 41		07 23	07 28			07 48		07 53		08 07	08 23	08 49				09 23		09 54
Tiverton Parkway	d			06 18	06 37		06 56		07 37	07 43							08 22	08 37	09 04				09 37		10 09
Taunton	d		02b33	06 35	06 51		07 11		07 51	07 58			08 12		08 19		08 37	08 51	09 19				09 51		10 24
Bridgwater	a			06 47						08 08						←									
Weston-super-Mare	a			07 06						08 26						08 26	08 58								
Bristol Temple Meads 10	a			07 43	07 26				08 24	→			08 45			08 57	09 23	09 25					10 26		
Bath Spa 7	a															09 11	09 41								
Filton Abbey Wood	a			07 58																					
Bristol Parkway 7	a			08 05	07 38				08 38				09 08					09 38					10 38		
Swindon	a															09 39	10 09								
Newport (South Wales)	a																								
Cardiff Central 7	a																								
Birmingham New Street 12	a				08 56				09 56				10 26					10 56					11 56		
Castle Cary	d						07 33												09 40						
Westbury	d						07c56												09 59						11 02
Pewsey	d						08 13												10 16						
Hungerford	a																								
Newbury	a						08 33																		
Thatcham	a																								
Theale	a																								
Reading 7	a		04s17				08 52								09 35	10 09	10 45		10 51						11 51
Oxford	a						*09 34*								*10 20*		*11 19*		*11 34*						*12 34*
Gatwick Airport 10	a		*05 58*				*10e39*								*11e39*				*12e39*						*13e39*
Heathrow Terminal 1 Bus 🚌	a						*10 09*								*11 09*				*12 09*						*13 09*
Slough 3	a																								
London Waterloo 15 ⊖	a																								
London Paddington 15 ⊖	a		05 43				09 21								10 08	10 42	11 14		11 24						12 23

For general notes see front of timetable
For details of catering facilities see Directory of Train Operators

b Arr. 0213
c Arr. 0751
e Change at Reading and Redhill

Table 135

Saturdays

from 12 September

Sleeper services are published in Table 406

Cornwall and Devon → Birmingham and London

Network Diagram - see first page of Table 135

Station		GW	XC 1◇	GW	XC 1◇	SW 1◇	GW	GW 1◇		GW	XC 1◇	GW 1◇	GW 1◇	GW	GW	XC 1◇	XC 1◇	GW		GW 1◇	GW	SW 1◇	XC 1◇	GW	SW 1◇
Penzance	d			07 35				08 00			08 28	08 45					09 43			10 00				10 36	
St Ives	d			07 28							08 15						09 22			09 52				10 25	
St Erth	d			07 47				08 10			08 36	08 56					09 51			10 11				10 44	
Hayle	d			07 51				08 14																10 47	
Camborne	d			08 01				08 24			08 46	09 07					10 01			10 22				10 57	
Redruth	d			08 08				08 31			08 52	09 14					10 07			10 29				11 03	
Falmouth Docks	d			07 48							08 20	08 50					09 20			09 50				10 20	
Truro	d			08 21				08 44			09 04	09 26					10 19			10 41				11 15	
St Austell	d			08 36				09 01			09 20	09 44					10 35			10 59				11 32	
Newquay	d			07 48																10 12					
Par	d			08 45				09 09			09 28	09 51					10 42			11 07				11 39	
Lostwithiel	d			08 52													10 49							11 46	
Bodmin Parkway	d			08 58				09 20			09 39	10 03					10 56			11 18				11 52	
Looe	d			07 44							09 15						10 31								
Liskeard 6	d			09 11				09 33			09 51	10 16					11 08			11 31				12 06	
Menheniot	d																							12x11	
St Germans	d			09 22																				12 18	
Saltash	d			09 30																				12 24	
St Budeaux Ferry Road	d																								
Keyham	d																								
Dockyard	d																								
Devonport	d																								
Plymouth	a			09 40				09 58			10 18	10 40					11 45			11 58				12 37	
	d		09 25					10 01			10 25	10 43				11 25	11 48			12 00			12 21		
Ivybridge	d							10 16												12 15					
Totnes	d		09 50					10 30			10 50					11 50	12 13			12 29			12 48		
Paignton	d				10 05	10 14	10 23							10 54	11 23			12 13				12 34			
Torquay	d				10 11	10 20	10 28							10 59	11 28			12 18				12 40			
Torre	d					10 23	10 31							11 02	11 31			12 21							
Newton Abbot	a	←	10 01		10 21	10 31	10 38	10 42		←	11 01			11 11	11 39	12 01	12 24	12 30		12 41		12 50	13 00		
	d	09 37	10 03		10 22	10 33	10 47	10 43		10 47	11 03			11 23	11 41	12 03	12 25	12 32		12 42		12 52	13 01		
Teignmouth	d	09 46			10 29	10 40	→			10 54				11 30	11 48			12 39				12 59			←
Dawlish	d	09 51			10 34	10 45				10 59				11 35	11 53			12 44			←	13 04			13 04
Dawlish Warren	d	09 56				10 49				11 04				11 40	11 58			12b55			12 55	→			13c15
Starcross	d	10 00												11 44	12 02			→			12 59				
Exeter St Thomas	d	10 09												11 53	12 11						13 08				
Exeter St Davids 6	a	10 17	10 21		10 46	11 00		11 04		11 15	11 21	11 37		11 57	12 16	12 21	12 44			13 02	13 13		13 21		13 25
Exeter Central	a	10 21	*10 51*			11 11				11 21		*11 51*		*12 13*	12 21	*12 51*					13 21				13 38
Exmouth	a	10 50	*11 18*							11 50		*12 18*			12 50	*13 18*					13 50				*14 18*
Barnstaple	d							*09 43*					*10 43*							*11 43*					
Exmouth	d		*09 23*		*09 53*			*10 23*				*10 53*				*11 23*	*11 53*			*12 23*					
Exeter Central	d		*09 50*		*10 26*			*10 50*				*11 17*				*11 58*	*12 27*			*12 50*					
Exeter St Davids 6	d		10 23		10 48			11 06			11 23	11 39	11 54			12 23	12 48			13 04			13 23		
Tiverton Parkway	d		10 37		11 02			11 21			11 37		12 09			12 37	13 02			13 19			13 39		
Taunton	d		10 51		11 16			11 36			11 51		12 24			12 51	13 16			13 34			13 54		
Bridgwater	a																								
Weston-super-Mare	a																								
Bristol Temple Meads 10	a		11 26		11 57						12 24					13 24	13 56						14 27		
Bath Spa 7	a																								
Filton Abbey Wood	a																								
Bristol Parkway 7	a		11 38		12 08						12 38					13 38	14 08						14 38		
Swindon	a																								
Newport (South Wales)	a																								
Cardiff Central 7	a																								
Birmingham New Street 12	a		12 56		13 26						13 56					14 56	15 26						15 56		
Castle Cary	d												12 45												
Westbury	d												13 05												
Pewsey	d												13 22												
Hungerford	a												13 39												
Newbury	a												13 49												
Thatcham	a												13 56												
Theale	a												14 05												
Reading 7	a							12 52				13 17	14 19							14 51					
Oxford	a							*13 34*				*14 04*	*15 04*							*15 34*					
Gatwick Airport 10	a							*14e39*				*14 50*	*15 50*							*16e39*					
Heathrow Terminal 1 Bus	a							*14 09*				*14 39*	*15 39*							*16 09*					
Slough 3	a																								
London Waterloo 15 ⊖	a					14 49																			16 49
London Paddington 15 ⊖	a							13 21				13 46	14 45							15 22					

For general notes see front of timetable
For details of catering facilities see
Directory of Train Operators

b Arr. 1248
c Arr. 1307
e Change at Reading and Redhill

Sleeper services are published in Table 406

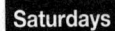

Cornwall and Devon → Birmingham and London

Network Diagram - see first page of Table 135

		GW	GW	XC	GW	XC		GW	GW	GW	XC	SW	GW	GW	GW	GW		XC	SW	GW	GW	XC	GW	GW	GW
		1 ◇ 🍴		1 ◇ 🛒	🛒	1 ◇ 🛒		1 ◇ 🍴		1 ◇ 🍴	1 ◇ 🛒	1 ◇ 🍴	🛒		1 ◇ 🍴			1 ◇ 🛒	1	1 ◇ 🍴		1 ◇ 🛒	🛒		1 ◇ 🍴
Penzance	d	11 00			11 44								13 00							14 00			14 49		
St Ives	d				11 25								12 25							13 55			14 25		
St Erth	d	11 10			11 52								13 08							14 11			14 57		
Hayle	d				11 56								13 11										15 01		
Camborne	d	11 21			12 05								13 21							14 22			15 10		
Redruth	d	11 28			12 11								13 27							14 29			15 16		
Falmouth Docks	d	10 50			11 50								12 50							13 50			14 50		
Truro	d	11 41			12 23								13 39							14 41			15 28		
St Austell	d	11 58			12 40								13 55							14 59			15 45		
Newquay	d												13 07										14 59		
Par	d				12 48								14 01							15 06			15 53		
Lostwithiel	d				12 54								14 09										16 00		
Bodmin Parkway	d	12 15			13 00								14 15							15 18			16 06		
Looe	d	11 44											13 52							14 58					
Liskeard 6	d	12 28			13 14								14 28							15 32			16 19		
Menheniot	d				13x19																		16x23		
St Germans	d				13 27								14 39										16 31		
Saltash	d				13 36								14 46										16 38		
St Budeaux Ferry Road	d																								
Keyham	d																								
Dockyard	d																								
Devonport	d												14 53												
Plymouth	a	12 53			13 45								14 59							15 56			16 48		
	d	12 54		13 25				14 00			14 25	14 48			15 04			15 25		16 00		16 25			16 57
Ivybridge	d											15 03													17 12
Totnes	d	13 21		13 50							14 50	15 17			15 31			15 50		16 27		16 50			17 27
Paignton	d		13 23			13 53			14 22					15 13					15 52		16 23			17 11	
Torquay	d		13 28			13 59			14 27					15 18					15 58		16 28			17 16	
Torre	d		13 31						14 30					15 21							16 31			17 19	
Newton Abbot	a	13 34	13 39	14 01		14 09		14 35	14 38		15 01	15 28		15 29	15 42			16 01	16 08	16 39	16 39	17 01		17 27	17 38
	d	13 35	13 41	14 03		14 10		14 36	14 40		15 03	15 30		15 34	15 44			16 03	16 10	16 40	16 43	17 03		17 29	17 40
Teignmouth	d		13 48			14 17			14 47			15 37		15 42					16 17		16 51			17 36	
Dawlish	d		13 53			14 22			14 52			15 42		15 47		←			16 22		16 56			17 41	
Dawlish Warren	d		13 58						14 57			15 46		16b00 →		16 00					17 00			17c57 →	
Starcross	d		14 02						15 01							16 04					17 04				
Exeter St Thomas	d		14 11						15 10							16 14					17 14				
Exeter St Davids 6	a	13 54	14 16	14 21		14 34		14 56	15 15		15 21	16 00			16 04	16 17		16 21	16 35	17 00	17 17	17 21			18 00
Exeter Central	a	14 13	14 21			14 51			15 21		15 33	16 13			16 13	16 23			16 43		17 23	17 43			
Exmouth	a		14 50			15 18			15 50		16 18					16 52			17 23		17 53	18 23			
Barnstaple	d	12 43						13 43							14 43					15 43					
Exmouth	d	12 53		13 23		13 53					14 23				15 23					15 53		16 25			17 25
Exeter Central	d	13 39		13 50		14 23					14 50				15 50					16 45		16 53			17 51
Exeter St Davids 6	d	13 56		14 23		14 36		14 58			15 23				16 06			16 23		17 01		17 23			18 02
Tiverton Parkway	d			14 37		14 49		15 13			15 37				16 21			16 37		17 17		17 37			18 17
Taunton	d	14 23		14 51		15 04		15 28		15 34	15 51				16 36			16 51		17 31		17 51			18 32
Bridgwater	a																								
Weston-super-Mare	a					15 25																			
Bristol Temple Meads 10	a			15 27		15 48					16 24							17 24				18 24			
Bath Spa 7	a																								
Filton Abbey Wood	a																								
Bristol Parkway 7	a			15 38		16 08					16 38							17 38				18 38			
Swindon	a																								
Newport (South Wales)	a																								
Cardiff Central 7	a																								
Birmingham New Street 12	a			16 56		17 26					17 56							18 56				19 56			
Castle Cary	d	14 44								16 00															18 53
Westbury	d	15 03								16 25															19 12
Pewsey	d									16 42															
Hungerford	a									16 59															
Newbury	a									17 09															19 49
Thatcham	a									17 16															
Theale	a									17 25															
Reading 7	a	15 51						16 50		17 39					17 53					18 49					20 07
Oxford	a	16 34						17 34		18 18					18 34					19 34					20 47
Gatwick Airport 10	a	17e39						18e39							19e39					20e38					21 59
Heathrow Terminal 1 Bus	a	17 09						18 09							19 09					20 09					21 19
Slough 3	a																								
London Waterloo 15 ⊖	a											19 49													
London Paddington 15 ⊖	a	16 23						17 21		18 08					18 21					19 22					20 37

For general notes see front of timetable
For details of catering facilities see
Directory of Train Operators

b Arr. 1551
c Arr. 1745
e Change at Reading and Redhill

Saturdays

from 12 September

Sleeper services are published in Table 406

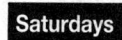

Cornwall and Devon → Birmingham and London

Network Diagram - see first page of Table 135

		GW	XC	GW		SW	GW	SW	XC	GW	GW	SW	GW	GW		GW	GW	GW	GW	GW	GW	GW	XC		
			1 ◇ ⊼			1 ◇	1 ◇ ⊏⊐	1 ◇	1 ◇ ⊼		◇ ⊼	1 ◇		1 ◇ ⊏⊐			1 ⊏⊐	1 ◇ ⊏⊐		◇ ⊼			1 ◇ ⊼		
Penzance	d						15 53				16 43			17 37						19 06			21 32		
St Ives	d						15 25				16 25			17 27						18 17			21 12		
St Erth	d						16 04				16 51			17 48						19 14			21 42		
Hayle	d										16 55			17 52						19 17					
Camborne	d						16 15				17 04			18 02						19 27			21 53		
Redruth	d						16 22				17 10			18 09						19 33			22 00		
Falmouth Docks	d						15 50				16 50			17 27						19 00			21 30		
Truro	d						16 34				17 24			18 22						19 45			22 13		
St Austell	d						16 52				17 39			18 39						20 03			22 30		
Newquay	d													17 22						19 21		21 15			
Par	d						16 59				17 46			18 47						20 11		22 06	22 38		
Lostwithiel	d						17 06				17 52									20 17		22 15			
Bodmin Parkway	d						17 13				17 58			18 58						20 23		22 21	22 49		
Looe	d						16 12				17 15			18 34						19 49					
Liskeard 6	d						17 26				18 11			19 11						20 36		22 34	23 02		
Menheniot	d																			20x41		22x38			
St Germans	d										18 24									20 49		22 46			
Saltash	d										18 31									20 57		22 53			
St Budeaux Ferry Road	d																			21 01		22 57			
Keyham	d																			21x03		22x59			
Dockyard	d																			21x05		23x00			
Devonport	d																			21 07		23 02			
Plymouth	a						17 51				18 41			19 36						21 12		23 09	23 32		
	d		17 21			17 42	17 54		18 25		18 43			19 39						21 15					
Ivybridge	d					17 57					18 58									21 30					
Totnes	d		17 48			18 11	18 21		18 50		19 12			20 06						21 44					
Paignton	d			17 52						18 53		19 14	19 23			20 13	20 46		21 13		21 53				
Torquay	d			17 57						18 58		19 20	19 28			20 18	20 52		21 18		21 58				
Torre	d			18 00						19 01			19 31			20 21			21 21		22 01				
Newton Abbot	a		17 59	18 08		18 24	18 32		19 01	19 09	19 24	19 30	19 39	20 17		20 29	21 02		21 29	21 56	22 09				
	d		18 01	18 10		18 25	18 34		19 03	19 11	19 25	19 32	19 41	20 19		20 31	21 04		21 31	21 56	22 11				
Teignmouth	d			18 17		18 32				19 18	19 32	19 39	19 48			20 38			21 38	22 03	22 18				
Dawlish	d	←		18 22		18 36		← 18 36		19 23	19 37	19 44	19 53			20 43			21 43	22 08	22 23				
Dawlish Warren	d	17 57		18 27		→		18b48		19 28		19 49	19 58			20 48			21 48	22 13	22 28				
Starcross	d	18 01		18 31						19 32			20 02			20 52			21 52	22 17	22 32				
Exeter St Thomas	d	18 10		18 40						19 41			20 11			21 01			22 01	22 26	22 41				
Exeter St Davids 6	a	18 15	18 21	18 43			18 54	19 00	19 21	19 44	19 49	20 03	20 23	20 38		21 05	21 24		22 05	22 30	22 45				
Exeter Central	a	18 23		18 53				19 13				20 18	20 29	21 03		21 30	21 40			22 39	23 00				
Exmouth	a	18 53		19 23				19 57					20 57			21 57				23 07	23 42				
Barnstaple	d						17 09							19 16											
Exmouth	d						17 55		18 27					20 01											
Exeter Central	d		17 57				18 35		19 03					20 26											
Exeter St Davids 6	d		18 23				18 56		19 23					20 40											
Tiverton Parkway	d		18 37				19 11		19 37					20 57											
Taunton	d		18 51				19 26		19 51					21 11				21 30							
Bridgwater	a																	21 39							
Weston-super-Mare	a																	21 58							
Bristol Temple Meads 10	a		19 26						20 24					21 44				22 30							
Bath Spa 7	a													21 58				22 44							
Filton Abbey Wood	a																								
Bristol Parkway 7	a		19 38						20 38																
Swindon	a													22 27				23 13							
Newport (South Wales)	a																								
Cardiff Central 7	a																								
Birmingham New Street 12	a		20 56						21 58																
Castle Cary	d						19 47																		
Westbury	d						20 06																		
Pewsey	d						20 23																		
Hungerford	a																								
Newbury	a																								
Thatcham	a																								
Theale	a																								
Reading 7	a						20 58							23 01				23 52							
Oxford	a						21 34							00c23				00 38							
Gatwick Airport 10	a						23 03							01e02											
Heathrow Terminal 1 Bus	a																								
Slough 3	a																								
London Waterloo 15 ⊖	a							22 57																	
London Paddington 15 ⊖	a						21 32							23 36				00 33							

For general notes see front of timetable
For details of catering facilities see Directory of Train Operators

b Arr. 1840

c Change at Reading and Didcot Parkway. By bus from Didcot Parkway

e Change at Reading and Redhill

Sundays

until 12 July

Sleeper services are published in Table 406

Cornwall and Devon → Birmingham and London

Network Diagram - see first page of Table 135

		GW ◇	GW 1 ◇	GW	GW 1 ◇	XC 1 ◇	GW	GW 1 ◇	XC 1 ◇		GW	GW	GW 1 ◇	GW 1 ◇	XC 1 ◇	GW	GW 1 ◇	XC 1 ◇		SW 1 ◇	XC 1 ◇	GW	XC 1 ◇	GW 1 ◇	XC 1 ◇
			🍽		🍽	🛒		🍽	🛒				🍽	🍽	🛒		🍽	🛒		🍽	🛒		🛒	🍽	🛒
Penzance	d												08 37		09 30		09 50							11 00	
St Ives	d														*09 15*		*09 45*							*10 50*	
St Erth	d												08 47		09 38		10 02							11 10	
Hayle	d												08 52												
Camborne	d												09 02		09 48		10 13							11 22	
Redruth	d												09 08		09 54		10 19							11 28	
Falmouth Docks	d																							*11 12*	
Truro	d												09 21		10 06		10 31							11 42	
St Austell	d												09 38		10 24		10 49							11 58	
Newquay	d																*09 54*								11 30
Par	d												09 46		10 31		10 56							12 06	
Lostwithiel	d																								
Bodmin Parkway	d												09 58		10 42		11 09							12 18	12 41
Looe	d																*10 47*							*11 58*	
Liskeard 6	d												10 11		10 54		11 22							12 32	12 54
Menheniot	d																								
St Germans	d												10 22												
Saltash	d												10 31												
St Budeaux Ferry Road	d																								
Keyham	d																								
Dockyard	d																								
Devonport	d																								
Plymouth	a												10 40		11 17		11 45							12 57	13 17
	d				08 40	08 55		09 45	09 55				10 40	10 54	11 25		11 45	12 00			12 25			13 00	13 21
Ivybridge	d																								
Totnes	d				09 08	09 20		10 13	10 20				11 10		11 50		12 16				12 50			13 27	13 48
Paignton	d						10 05					11 04				12 08				12 25		12 52	13 08		
Torquay	d						10 10					11 09				12 13				12 31		12 57	13 14		
Torre	d						10 13					11 12				12 16						13 00			
Newton Abbot	a				09 20	09 31	10 21	10 24	10 33		⟵	11 20	11 22	11 30	12 01	12 24	12 28	12 34		12 41	13 01	13 09	13 24	13 39	14 00
	d				09 21	09 33	10 39 ⟶	10 26	10 33		10 39		11 25	11 32	12 03		12 30	12 36		12 44	13 03	13 10	13 26	13 40	14 01
Teignmouth	d				09 28						10 46									12 51		13 18	13 33		
Dawlish	d				09 34						10 51									12 56		13 23	13 38		
Dawlish Warren	d										10 56											13 27			
Starcross	d										11 00											13 31			
Exeter St Thomas	d										11 09											13 41			
Exeter St Davids 6	a				09 48	09 53		10 46	10 53		11 14		11 45	11 52	12 21		12 50	12 55		13 09	13 21	13 45	13 49	14 00	14 21
Exeter Central	a					*10 33*			*11 23*		11 28				*12 35*					13 21	*13 33*				*14 33*
Exmouth	a					*11 00*					11 55				*13 01*						*14 01*				*15 01*
Barnstaple	d																*11 10*								
Exmouth	d				*09 08*			*10 00*					*11 05*				*12 05*						*13 10*		
Exeter Central	d			*09 06*	*09 35*			*10 26*	*10 46*				*11 35*				*12 31*	*12 46*					*13 36*		
Exeter St Davids 6	d	08 10	08 38	09 34	09 49	09 55		10 48	10 55				11 47	11 54	12 23		12 51	12 57			13 23		13 51	14 02	14 23
Tiverton Parkway	d	08 27	08 53	09 51		10 09		11 02	11 09					12 09	12 37			13 10			13 37		14 05	14 16	14 37
Taunton	d	08 43	09 08	10 08	10 15	10 23		11 17	11 23				12 13	12 23	12 51		13 17	13 25			13 51		14 19	14 31	14 53
Bridgwater	a	08 54		10 20																					
Weston-super-Mare	a	09 12		10 37																					
Bristol Temple Meads 10	a	09 45		11 20		10 56		11 52	11 56					12 57	13 24			13 57			14 24		14 56		15 27
Bath Spa 7	a							12 12						13 12											
Filton Abbey Wood	a	10 00																							
Bristol Parkway 7	a					11 08			12 08						13 38			14 08			14 38		15 08		15 38
Swindon	a							12 40						13 40											
Newport (South Wales)	a	10 25																							
Cardiff Central 7	a	10 42																							
Birmingham New Street 12	a					12 50			13 50						14 50			15 26			15 50		16 26		16 50
Castle Cary	d		09 29										12 34												
Westbury	d		09 49		10 53								12 53				13 57								
Pewsey	d		10 06										13 10												
Hungerford	a																								
Newbury	a		10 26		11 26								13 30												
Thatcham	a																								
Theale	a																								
Reading 7	a		10 44		11 47			13 13					13 48	14 13			14 43							15 48	
Oxford	a		*11 35*		*12 35*			*13 50*					*14 35*	*14 50*			*15 35*							*16 35*	
Gatwick Airport 10	a		*12 27*		*13 32*								*15 32*				*16 25*							*17 32*	
Heathrow Terminal 1 Bus 🚌	a		*12 09*		*13 09*			*14 39*					*15 09*	*15 39*			*16 09*							*17 09*	
Slough 3	a																								
London Waterloo 15 ⊖	a																			16 58					
London Paddington 15 ⊖	a		11 22		12 32			13 55					14 24	14 55			15 25							16 24	

For general notes see front of timetable
For details of catering facilities see
Directory of Train Operators

Sundays

until 12 July

Sleeper services are published in Table 406

Cornwall and Devon → Birmingham and London

Network Diagram - see first page of Table 135

		GW	GW	GW	SW		GW	XC	XC	GW	GW	GW	SW	XC		GW	GW	SW	SW	GW	GW	GW	XC		GW
			1 ◇		1 ◇			1 ◇	1 ◇		1 ◇	1 ◇	1 ◇	1 ◇		1 ◇	1 ◇	1 ◇	1 ◇		1 ◇	1 ◇	1 ◇		1 ◇
Penzance	d		11 42				12 15		12 30		12 55								13 50						14 45
St Ives	d		*11 25*				*11 56*				*12 25*								*13 25*						*14 25*
St Erth	d		11 53				12 22		12 40		13 06								14 00						14 56
Hayle	d								12 44										14 03						
Camborne	d		12 04				12 34		12 55		13 17								14 13						15 07
Redruth	d		12 11				12 40		13 01		13 23								14 19						15 14
Falmouth Docks	d								*12 44*										*14 03*						*14 57*
Truro	d		12 24				12 52		13 13		13 35								14 32						15 26
St Austell	d		12 41				13 10		13 30		13 54								14 48						15 44
Newquay	d										*13 00*														
Par	d		12 49				13 18		13 37		14 00								14 56						15 51
Lostwithiel	d						13 25		13 44										15 03						
Bodmin Parkway	d		13 00				13 32		13 51		14 13								15 08						16 03
Looe	d								*13 24*										*14 36*						*15 39*
Liskeard 6	d		13 15				13 46		14 03		14 27								15 22						16 16
Menheniot	d																		15x29						
St Germans	d						13 57												15 37						
Saltash	d						14 06												15 45						
St Budeaux Ferry Road	d																								
Keyham	d																								
Dockyard	d																								
Devonport	d																								
Plymouth	a		13 40				14 15		14 27		14 52								15 53						16 41
	d		13 44		14 06			14 21	14 35		14 55	15 05		15 21			15 43		16 02			16 10	16 25		16 45
Ivybridge	d				14 21														16 17						
Totnes	d		14 11		14 35			14 48	15 00		15 22	15 34		15 48			16 11		16 31			16 42	16 50		17 12
Paignton	d	14 04								15 00			15 30			15 45		16 10		16 31					
Torquay	d	14 09								15 05			15 36			15 51		16 16		16 36					
Torre	d	14 12								15 08						15 56				16 39					
Newton Abbot	a	14 20	14 23	←	14 46			15 00	15 11	15 16	15 34	15 46	15 46	16 00		16 04	16 22	16 28	16 42	16 47		16 53	17 01		17 24
	d	14 35	14 25	14 35	14 47			15 01	15 12	15 18	15 35	15 47	15 51	16 01		16 05	16 24	16 30	16 43			16 55	17 03		17 25
Teignmouth	d	→		14 42	14 54					15 25			15 58			16 13									
Dawlish	d			14 47	14 59					15 30			16 03			16 18									
Dawlish Warren	d			14 52						15 35			16 07			16 25									
Starcross	d			14 56						15 39															
Exeter St Thomas	d			15 05						15 48															
Exeter St Davids 6	a		14 45	15 10	15 15			15 21	15 31	15 52	15 55	16 07	16 18	16 21		16 36	16 44	16 53	17 05			17 15	17 21		17 45
Exeter Central	a			15 33	15 23			*15 33*					16 36	*16 31*				17 21					*17 31*		
Exmouth	a			16 01				*16 01*						*16 57*									*18 01*		
Barnstaple	d		*13 17*																						
Exmouth	d		*14 10*								*15 10*											*16 10*			*17 10*
Exeter Central	d		*14 36*								*15 39*											*17 06*			*17 37*
Exeter St Davids 6	d		14 46					15 23	15 33		15 58	16 09		16 23		16 38	16 45					17 17	17 23		17 47
Tiverton Parkway	d							15 38	15 46		16 13	16 24		16 38			17 01					17 32	17 38		18 02
Taunton	d		15 11					15 53	16 01		16 28	16 39		16 53		17 03	17 15					17 46	17 51		18 17
Bridgwater	a																								
Weston-super-Mare	a								16 20			17 00				17 24					←				
Bristol Temple Meads 10	a							16 27	16 53			17 22		17 27		17 53					17 53	18 23	18 27		
Bath Spa 7	a											17 42				→					18 12	18 41			
Filton Abbey Wood	a																								
Bristol Parkway 7	a							16 38	17 08					17 38									18 38		
Swindon	a											18 10									18 40	19 11			
Newport (South Wales)	a																								
Cardiff Central 7	a																								
Birmingham New Street 12	a							17 50	18 27					18 56									19 50		
Castle Cary	d		15 33														17 37								
Westbury	d		15 51														17 57								18b58
Pewsey	d		16 09														18 14								
Hungerford	a																								
Newbury	a		16 29														18 34								
Thatcham	a																								
Theale	a																								
Reading 7	a		16 47								17 48	18 44					18 53				19 15	19 43			19 43
Oxford	a		*17 35*								*18 35*						*19 35*								*20 35*
Gatwick Airport 10	a		*18 27*								*19 32*						*20 27*								*21 32*
Heathrow Terminal 1 Bus	a		*18 09*								*19 09*						*20 09*								*21 19*
Slough 3	a																								
London Waterloo 15 ⊖	a				18 58								20 04					20 58							
London Paddington 15 ⊖	a		17 28								18 26	19 28					19 42				19 55	20 25			20 23

For general notes see front of timetable
For details of catering facilities see Directory of Train Operators

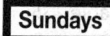

b Arr. 1852

Table 135

Sundays

until 12 July

Sleeper services are published in Table 406

Cornwall and Devon → Birmingham and London

Network Diagram - see first page of Table 135

		GW	GW	XC	GW	GW	XC	SW	GW	XC	GW	GW	GW	GW	GW	XC	GW	GW	GW	SW	GW	GW
			◇	1 ◇	◇	1 ◇	1 ◇	1 ◇	1 ◇	1 ◇		1 ◇			1 ◇	1 ◇		◇		1		◇
			🛒	🛒	🛒	🍴	🛒	🍴	🍴	🛒		🍴			🍴	🛒			🛒			🍴
Penzance	d		15 06	15 30		15 45						17 20	17 50					19 00	20 00			21 15
St Ives	d		*14 56*			*15 25*						*16 56*	*17 40*					*18 40*	*19 46*			
St Erth	d		15 15	15 38		15 57						17 30	17 59					19 08	20 09			21 25
Hayle	d		15 18										18 02						20 12			
Camborne	d		15 28	15 48		16 08						17 42	18 11					19 19	20 21			21 37
Redruth	d		15 34	15 54		16 15						17 49	18 17					19 25	20 27			21 44
Falmouth Docks	d					*16 00*						*17 30*						*18 43*				*21 30*
Truro	d		15 46	16 06		16 28						18 00	18 29					19 37	20 40			21 59
St Austell	d		16 03	16 22		16 45						18 19	18 46					19 54	20 57			22 17
Newquay	d								16 15			*17 32*							*19 40*			
Par	d		16 10	16 30		16 52			17 15			18 26	18 54					20 02	21 04			
Lostwithiel	d		16 17						17 23				19 00					20 08				
Bodmin Parkway	d		16 23	16 41		17 04			17 30			18 38	19 06					20 14	21 16			22 34
Looe	d								*17 05*				*18 43*						*20 51*			
Liskeard 6	d		16 36	16 53		17 17			17 43			18 51	19 22					20 27	21 30			22 49
Menheniot	d		16x41															20x32				
St Germans	d		16 48															20 39				
Saltash	d		16 56															20 47				
St Budeaux Ferry Road	d																					
Keyham	d																					
Dockyard	d																					
Devonport	d												19 43					20 54				
Plymouth	a		17 04	17 17		17 42			18 09			19 15	19 46					20 58	21 59			23 15
	d		17 08	17 25		17 45			18 10	18 21		19 15			19 55	20 25		21 15				23 20
Ivybridge	d		17 23																			
Totnes	d		17 38	17 50		18 12			18 39	18 48		19 46				20 50		21 42				23 48
Paignton	d	17 20					18 17	18 24			18 55			19 55			21 00			22 10	23 00	
Torquay	d	17 25					18 23	18 30			19 00			20 00			21 05			22 16	23 05	
Torre	d	17 28									19 03			20 03			21 08				23 08	
Newton Abbot	a	17 36	17 50	18 01		18 23	18 33	18 40	18 50	19 00	19 11	19 57		20 11	20 31	21 01	21 16	21 54		22 28	23 16	23 59
	d	17 38	17 51	18 03		18 25	18 36	18 42	18 51	19 01	19 13	19 59		20 13	20 32	21 03	21 18	21 55		22 30	23 18	00 01
Teignmouth	d	17 45	17 59					18 49			19 20			20 20			21 25	22 02		22 37	23 25	
Dawlish	d	17 50	18 04					18 54			19 25			20 25			21 30	22 07		22 42	23 30	
Dawlish Warren	d	17 55						18 58			19 30			20 30			21 35			22 46	23 35	
Starcross	d	17 59									19 34			20 34			21 39				23 39	
Exeter St Thomas	d	18 08									19 43			20 43			21 48				23 48	
Exeter St Davids 6	a	18 13	18 18	18 21		18 45	18 54	19 09	19 12	19 21	19 50	20 19		20 47	20 53	21 21	21 52	22 21		22 57	23 52	00 36
Exeter Central	a			*18 38*		*19 01*		19 23	*19 23*	*19 38*		*20 43*			*21 23*	*21 38*		*22 34*		*23 13*		
Exmouth	a			*19 05*						*20 05*		*21 12*				*22 04*		*23 03*		*23 55*		
Barnstaple	d					*17 20*									*19 17*							
Exmouth	d					*18 10*						*19 10*			*20 10*							*23 59*
Exeter Central	d				←	*18 37*	*18 43*					*19 36*			*20 46*							*00 24*
Exeter St Davids 6	d		18 33 →	18 23	18 33	18 47	18 56		19 14	19 23		20 20			20 55	21 23						01 27
Tiverton Parkway	d			18 37			19 10		19 29	19 38		20 36			21 10	21 37						
Taunton	d			18 51	19 04	19 11	19 24		19 43	19 53		20 49			21 23	21 51						
Bridgwater	a				19 15																	
Weston-super-Mare	a				19 35																	
Bristol Temple Meads 10	a			19 27	20 12		19 57			20 27					21 58	23 06						
Bath Spa 7	a														22 18							
Filton Abbey Wood	a																					
Bristol Parkway 7	a			19 38			20 08			20 38												
Swindon	a														22 46							
Newport (South Wales)	a																					
Cardiff Central 7	a																					
Birmingham New Street 12	a			20 50			21 31			21 56												
Castle Cary	d								20 05			21 12										
Westbury	d								20 25			21 30										
Pewsey	d											21 48										
Hungerford	a																					
Newbury	a					20 15						22 08										
Thatcham	a																					
Theale	a																					
Reading 7	a					20 34			21 12			22 28			23 26							04s17
Oxford	a					*21 27*			*21 51*			*23b55*			*00c38*							*06 22*
Gatwick Airport 10	a					*22 25*			*23 33*			*00e59*										*05 52*
Heathrow Terminal 1 Bus	🚌 a					*21 49*			*22 55*			*23 55*										*05 50*
Slough 3	a																					
London Waterloo 15	⊖ a							22 58														
London Paddington 15	⊖ a					21 13			21 56			23 17			00 06							05 05

For general notes see front of timetable
For details of catering facilities see Directory of Train Operators

b Change at Reading and Didcot Parkway. By bus from Didcot Parkway

c Change at Reading and Didcot Parkway

e Change at Reading and Redhill

Table 135

Sundays

19 July to 6 September

Sleeper services are published in Table 406

Cornwall and Devon → Birmingham and London

Network Diagram - see first page of Table 135

		GW	GW	GW	GW	GW	XC	GW	GW	XC	XC	GW		GW	GW	GW	XC	GW	GW	XC	SW	XC	GW	XC	GW
		◇	1 ◇ ⊡		1 ◇ ⊡		1 ◇ ⊼	1 ◇ ⊡		1 ◇ ⊼	1 ◇ ⊼	1 ◇ ⊡			1 ◇ ⊡	1 ◇ ⊡	1 ◇ ⊼		1 ◇ ⊡	1 ◇ ⊼	1 ◇ ⊡	1 ◇ ⊼		1 ◇ ⊼	1 ◇ ⊡
Penzance	d														08 37		09 30		09 50						11 00
St Ives	d																*09 15*		*09 45*						*10 50*
St Erth	d														08 47		09 38		10 02						11 10
Hayle	d														08 52										
Camborne	d														09 02		09 48		10 13						11 22
Redruth	d														09 08		09 54		10 19						11 28
Falmouth Docks	d																								*11 12*
Truro	d														09 21		10 06		10 31						11 42
St Austell	d														09 38		10 24		10 49						11 58
Newquay	d																		*09 54*						
Par	d														09 46		10 31		10 56						12 06
Lostwithiel	d																								
Bodmin Parkway	d														09 58		10 42		11 09						12 18
Looe	d																		*10 47*						*11 58*
Liskeard 6	d														10 11		10 54		11 22						12 32
Menheniot	d																								
St Germans	d														10 22										
Saltash	d														10 31										
St Budeaux Ferry Road	d																								
Keyham	d																								
Dockyard	d																								
Devonport	d																								
Plymouth	a														10 40		11 17		11 45						12 57
	d				08 40		09 25	09 35		10 25		10 35			10 42		11 25		11 45	12 00		12 25			13 00
Ivybridge	d																								
Totnes	d				09 08		09 50	10 03		10 50					11 10		11 50		12 16			12 50			13 27
Paignton	d								10 10		10 50			11 04				12 08			12 25		12 52	13 08	
Torquay	d								10 15		10 56			11 09				12 13			12 31		12 57	13 14	
Torre	d								10 18					11 12				12 16					13 00		
Newton Abbot	a				09 20		10 01	10 14	10 26	11 01	11 06	11 12		11 20	11 24		12 01	12 24	12 28	12 34	12 41	13 01	13 09	13 24	13 39
	d				09 21		10 03	10 16	10 39	11 03	11 08	11 14			11 25		12 03		12 30	12 36	12 44	13 03	13 10	13 26	13 40
Teignmouth	d				09 28				10 46		11 15										12 51		13 18	13 33	
Dawlish	d				09 34				10 51		11 20										12 56		13 23	13 38	
Dawlish Warren	d								10 56														13 27		
Starcross	d								11 00														13 31		
Exeter St Thomas	d								11 09														13 41		
Exeter St Davids 6	a				09 48		10 21	10 36	11 14	11 21	11 30	11 37			11 45		12 21		12 50	12 55	13 09	13 21	13 45	13 49	14 00
Exeter Central	a						*10 33*	*10 49*	11 28								*12 35*				13 21	*13 33*			
Exmouth	a						*11 00*		11 55								*13 01*					*14 01*			
Barnstaple	d																		*11 10*						
Exmouth	d				*09 08*			*10 00*							*11 05*				*12 05*					*13 10*	
Exeter Central	d			*09 06*	*09 35*			*10 26*		*11 06*		*11 30*			*11 35*				*12 31*	*12 46*				*13 36*	
Exeter St Davids 6	d	08 10	08 38	09 34	09 49	←	10 23	10 38		11 23	11 32	11 39			11 47		12 23		12 51	12 57		13 23		13 51	14 02
Tiverton Parkway	d	08 27	08 53	09 51			10 37	10 52		11 37	11 46	11 54					12 37			13 10		13 37		14 05	14 16
Taunton	d	08 43	09 08	10b20	10 15	10 20	10 51	11 07		11 51	12 00	12 08			12 13		12 51		13 17	13 25		13 51		14 19	14 31
Bridgwater	a	08 54		→		10 31																			
Weston-super-Mare	a	09 12				10 49					12 20					←									
Bristol Temple Meads 10	a	09 45				11 20	11 27	11 42		12 24	12 42	12 44 →				12 44	13 24			13 57		14 24		14 56	
Bath Spa 7	a							11 57								12 58									
Filton Abbey Wood	a	10 00																							
Bristol Parkway 7	a						11 38			12 38	13 08						13 38			14 08		14 38		15 08	
Swindon	a							12 33								13 39									
Newport (South Wales)	a	10 25																							
Cardiff Central 7	a	10 42																							
Birmingham New Street 12	a						12 50			13 50	14 26						14 50			15 26		15 50		16 26	
Castle Cary	d		09 29												12 34										
Westbury	d		09 49		10 53										12 53				13 57						
Pewsey	d		10 06												13 10										
Hungerford	a																								
Newbury	a		10 26		11 26										13 30										
Thatcham	a																								
Theale	a																								
Reading 7	a		10 44		11 47			13 13							13 48	14 13			14 43						15 48
Oxford	a		*11 35*		*12 35*			*13 50*							*14 35*				*15 35*						*16 35*
Gatwick Airport 10	a		*12 27*		*13 32*										*15 32*				*16 25*						*17 32*
Heathrow Terminal 1 Bus	🚌 a		*12 09*		*13 09*			*14 39*							*15 09*				*16 09*						*17 09*
Slough 3	a																								
London Waterloo 15	⊖ a																				16 58				
London Paddington 15	⊖ a		11 22		12 27			13 55							14 24	14 55			15 25						16 24

For general notes see front of timetable
For details of catering facilities see Directory of Train Operators

b Arr. 1007

Sundays

19 July to 6 September

Sleeper services are published in Table 406

Cornwall and Devon → Birmingham and London

Network Diagram - see first page of Table 135

		XC		GW	GW	GW	SW	GW	XC	XC	GW	GW	GW	SW		XC	GW	GW	SW	SW	GW	GW	GW	XC	GW
		1 ◇			1 ◇		1 ◇		1 ◇	1 ◇		1 ◇	1 ◇	1 ◇		1 ◇	1 ◇	1 ◇	1 ◇	1 ◇		1 ◇	1 ◇	1 ◇	1 ◇
		🛒			☕		☕		🛒	🛒		☕	☕	☕		🛒	☕	☕		☕		☕	☕	🛒	☕
Penzance	d				11 42			12 15		12 30		12 55								13 50					14 45
St Ives	d				*11 25*			*11 56*				*12 25*								*13 25*					*14 25*
St Erth	d				11 53			12 22		12 40		13 06								14 00					14 56
Hayle	d									12 44										14 03					
Camborne	d				12 04			12 34		12 55		13 17								14 13					15 07
Redruth	d				12 11			12 40		13 01		13 23								14 19					15 14
Falmouth Docks	d									*12 44*										*14 03*					*14 57*
Truro	d				12 24			12 52		13 13		13 35								14 32					15 26
St Austell	d				12 41			13 10		13 30		13 54								14 48					15 44
Newquay	d	11 30										*13 00*													
Par	d				12 49			13 18		13 37		14 00								14 56					15 51
Lostwithiel	d							13 25		13 44										15 03					
Bodmin Parkway	d	12 41			13 00			13 32		13 51		14 13								15 08					16 03
Looe	d									*13 24*										*14 36*					*15 39*
Liskeard 6	d	12 54			13 15			13 46		14 03		14 27								15 22					16 16
Menheniot	d																			15x29					
St Germans	d							13 57												15 37					
Saltash	d							14 06												15 45					
St Budeaux Ferry Road	d																								
Keyham	d																								
Dockyard	d																								
Devonport	d																								
Plymouth	a	13 17			13 40			14 15		14 27		14 52								15 53					16 41
	d	13 21			13 44		14 06		14 21	14 35		14 55	15 05			15 21		15 43		16 02			16 10	16 25	16 45
Ivybridge	d						14 21													16 17					
Totnes	d	13 48			14 11		14 35		14 48	15 00		15 22	15 34			15 48		16 11		16 31			16 42	16 50	17 12
Paignton	d			14 04							15 00			15 30			15 45		16 10		16 31				
Torquay	d			14 09							15 05			15 36			15 51		16 16		16 36				
Torre	d			14 12							15 08						15 56				16 39				
Newton Abbot	a	14 00		14 20	14 23	←	14 46		15 00	15 11	15 16	15 34	15 46	15 46		16 00	16 04	16 22	16 28	16 42	16 47		16 53	17 01	17 24
	d	14 01		14 35 →	14 25	14 35	14 47		15 01	15 12	15 18	15 35	15 47	15 51		16 01	16 05	16 24	16 30	16 43			16 55	17 03	17 25
Teignmouth	d					14 42	14 54				15 25			15 58			16 13								
Dawlish	d					14 47	14 59				15 30			16 03			16 18								
Dawlish Warren	d					14 52					15 35			16 07			16 25								
Starcross	d					14 56					15 39														
Exeter St Thomas	d					15 05					15 48														
Exeter St Davids 6	a	14 21			14 45	15 10	15 15		15 21	15 31	15 52	15 55	16 07	16 18		16 22	16 36	16 44	16 53	17 05			17 15	17 21	17 45
Exeter Central	a	*14 33*				15 33	15 23		*15 33*					16 36		*16 31*			17 21					*17 31*	
Exmouth	a	*15 01*				16 01			*16 01*							*16 57*								*18 01*	
Barnstaple	d				*13 17*																				
Exmouth	d				*14 10*							*15 10*											*16 10*		*17 10*
Exeter Central	d				*14 36*							*15 39*											*17 06*		*17 37*
Exeter St Davids 6	d	14 23			14 46				15 23	15 33		15 58	16 09			16 23	16 38	16 45					17 17	17 23	17 47
Tiverton Parkway	d	14 37							15 37	15 46		16 13	16 24			16 37		17 01					17 32	17 37	18 02
Taunton	d	14 53			15 11				15 53	16 01		16 28	16 39			16 53	17 03	17 15					17 46	17 51	18 17
Bridgwater	a																					←			
Weston-super-Mare	a									16 20			17 00				17 24								
Bristol Temple Meads 10	a	15 27							16 27	16 53			17 22			17 27	17 53 →					17 53	18 23	18 27	
Bath Spa 7	a												17 42									18 12	18 41		
Filton Abbey Wood	a																								
Bristol Parkway 7	a	15 38							16 38	17 08						17 38								18 38	
Swindon	a												18 10									18 40	19 11		
Newport (South Wales)	a																								
Cardiff Central 7	a																								
Birmingham New Street 12	a	16 50							17 50	18 27						18 56								19 50	
Castle Cary	d				15 33													17 37							
Westbury	d				15 51													17 57							18b58
Pewsey	d				16 09													18 14							
Hungerford	a																								
Newbury	a				16 29													18 34							
Thatcham	a																								
Theale	a																								
Reading 7	a				16 47							17 48	18 44					18 53				19 15	19 43		19 43
Oxford	a				*17 35*							*18 35*						*19 35*							*20 35*
Gatwick Airport 10	a				*18 27*							*19 32*						*20 27*							*21 32*
Heathrow Terminal 1 Bus	🚌 a				*18 09*							*19 09*						*20 09*							*21 19*
Slough 3	a																								
London Waterloo 15	⊖ a						18 58							20 04						20 58					
London Paddington 15	⊖ a				17 28							18 26	19 28					19 42				19 55	20 25		20 23

For general notes see front of timetable
For details of catering facilities see Directory of Train Operators

b Arr. 1852

Table 135

Sundays

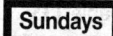

19 July to 6 September

Sleeper services are published in Table 406

Cornwall and Devon → Birmingham and London

Network Diagram - see first page of Table 135

		GW	GW ◇ 🛒	XC 1 ◇ 🛒		GW ◇ 🛒	GW 1 ◇ ☕	XC 1 ◇ 🛒	SW 1 ◇ ☕	GW 1 ◇ ☕	XC 1 ◇ 🛒	GW	GW 1 ◇ ☕	GW	GW	GW 1 ◇ ☕	XC 1 ◇ 🛒	GW	GW ◇	GW 🛒	SW 1	GW	GW ◇ ☕		
Penzance	d		15 06	15 30			15 45						17 20	17 50					19 00	20 00			21 15		
St Ives	d		14 56				15 25						16 56	17 40					18 40	19 46					
St Erth	d		15 15	15 38			15 57						17 30	17 59					19 08	20 09			21 25		
Hayle	d		15 18											18 02						20 12					
Camborne	d		15 28	15 48			16 08						17 42	18 11					19 19	20 21			21 37		
Redruth	d		15 34	15 54			16 15						17 49	18 17					19 25	20 27			21 44		
Falmouth Docks	d						16 00						17 30						18 43				21 30		
Truro	d		15 46	16 06			16 28						18 00	18 29					19 37	20 40			21 59		
St Austell	d		16 03	16 22			16 45						18 19	18 46					19 54	20 57			22 17		
Newquay	d									16 15			17 32							19 40					
Par	d		16 10	16 30			16 52			17 15			18 26	18 54					20 02	21 04					
Lostwithiel	d		16 17							17 23				19 00					20 08						
Bodmin Parkway	d		16 23	16 41			17 04			17 30			18 38	19 06					20 14	21 16			22 34		
Looe	d									17 05				18 43						20 51					
Liskeard 6	d		16 36	16 53			17 17			17 43			18 51	19 22					20 27	21 30			22 49		
Menheniot	d		16x41																20x32						
St Germans	d		16 48																20 39						
Saltash	d		16 56																20 47						
St Budeaux Ferry Road	d																								
Keyham	d																								
Dockyard	d																								
Devonport	d													19 43					20 54						
Plymouth	a		17 04	17 17			17 42			18 09			19 15	19 46					20 58	21 59			23 15		
	d		17 08	17 25			17 45			18 10	18 21		19 15			19 55	20 25		21 15				23 20		
Ivybridge	d		17 23																						
Totnes	d		17 38	17 50			18 12			18 39	18 48		19 46				20 50		21 42				23 48		
Paignton	d	17 20						18 17	18 24			18 55			19 55			21 00			22 10	23 00			
Torquay	d	17 25						18 23	18 30			19 00			20 00			21 05			22 16	23 05			
Torre	d	17 28										19 03			20 03			21 08				23 08			
Newton Abbot	a	17 36	17 50	18 01			18 23	18 33	18 40	18 50	19 00	19 11	19 57		20 11	20 31	21 01	21 16	21 54		22 28	23 16	23 59		
	d	17 38	17 51	18 03			18 25	18 36	18 42	18 51	19 01	19 13	19 59		20 13	20 32	21 03	21 18	21 55		22 30	23 18	00 01		
Teignmouth	d	17 45	17 59						18 49			19 20			20 20			21 25	22 02		22 37	23 25			
Dawlish	d	17 50	18 04						18 54			19 25			20 25			21 30	22 07		22 42	23 30			
Dawlish Warren	d	17 55							18 58			19 30			20 30			21 35			22 46	23 35			
Starcross	d	17 59										19 34			20 34			21 39				23 39			
Exeter St Thomas	d	18 08										19 43			20 43			21 48				23 48			
Exeter St Davids 6	a	18 13	18 18	18 21			18 45	18 54	19 09	19 12	19 21	19 50	20 19		20 47	20 53	21 21	21 52	22 21		22 57	23 52	00 36		
Exeter Central	a			18 38			19 01		19 23	19 23	19 38		20 43			21 23	21 38		22 34		23 13				
Exmouth	a			19 05							20 05		21 12				22 04		23 03		23 55				
Barnstaple	d						17 20									19 17									
Exmouth	d						18 10						19 10			20 10							23 59		
Exeter Central	d					⟵	18 37	18 43					19 36			20 46							00 24		
Exeter St Davids 6	d		18 33 ⟶	18 23		18 33	18 47	18 56		19 14	19 23		20 20			20 55	21 23						01 27		
Tiverton Parkway	d			18 37				19 10		19 29	19 37		20 36			21 10	21 37								
Taunton	d			18 51		19 04	19 11	19 24		19 43	19 53		20 49			21 23	21 51								
Bridgwater	a					19 15																			
Weston-super-Mare	a					19 35																			
Bristol Temple Meads 10	a			19 27		20 12		19 57			20 27					21 58	23 06								
Bath Spa 7	a															22 18									
Filton Abbey Wood	a																								
Bristol Parkway 7	a			19 38				20 08			20 38														
Swindon	a															22 46									
Newport (South Wales)	a																								
Cardiff Central 7	a																								
Birmingham New Street 12	a			20 50				21 31			21 56														
Castle Cary	d									20 05			21 12												
Westbury	d									20 25			21 30												
Pewsey	d												21 48												
Hungerford	a																								
Newbury	a						20 15						22 08												
Thatcham	a																								
Theale	a																								
Reading 7	a						20 34			21 12			22 28			23 26							04s17		
Oxford	a						21 27			21 51			23b55			00 34							06 22		
Gatwick Airport 10	a						22 25			23 33			00c59										05 52		
Heathrow Terminal 1 Bus	a						21 49			22 55			23 55										05 50		
Slough 3	a																								
London Waterloo 15	⊖ a								22 58																
London Paddington 15	⊖ a						21 13			21 56			23 17			00 06							05 05		

For general notes see front of timetable
For details of catering facilities see Directory of Train Operators

b Change at Reading and Didcot Parkway. By bus from Didcot Parkway

c Change at Reading and Redhill

Sundays

13 September to 1 November

Sleeper services are published in Table 406

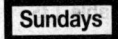

Cornwall and Devon → Birmingham and London

Network Diagram - see first page of Table 135

		GW	GW	GW	GW	GW	XC	GW	GW	GW	XC	XC	GW	GW		GW	XC	GW	GW	XC	SW	XC	GW	XC	GW
		◇	1 ◇ ⊡		1 ◇ ⊡		1 ◇ ⊼		1 ◇ ⊡		1 ◇ ⊼	1 ◇ ⊼		1 ◇ ⊡		1 ◇ ⊡	1 ◇ ⊼		1 ◇ ⊡	1 ◇ ⊼	1 ◇ ⊡	1 ◇ ⊼		1 ◇ ⊼	1 ◇ ⊡
Penzance	d													08 37			09 30		09 50						11 00
St Ives	d																								
St Erth	d													08 47			09 38		10 02						11 10
Hayle	d													08 52											
Camborne	d													09 02			09 48		10 13						11 22
Redruth	d													09 08			09 54		10 19						11 28
Falmouth Docks	d																								11 12
Truro	d													09 21			10 06		10 31						11 42
St Austell	d													09 38			10 24		10 49						11 58
Newquay	d																								
Par	d													09 46			10 31		10 56						12 06
Lostwithiel	d																								
Bodmin Parkway	d													09 58			10 42		11 09						12 18
Looe	d																								
Liskeard 6	d													10 11			10 54		11 22						12 32
Menheniot	d																								
St Germans	d													10 22											
Saltash	d													10 31											
St Budeaux Ferry Road	d																								
Keyham	d																								
Dockyard	d																								
Devonport	d																								
Plymouth	a													10 40			11 17		11 45						12 57
	d				08 40		09 25		09 50		10 25			10 40		10 54	11 25		11 45	12 00		12 25			13 00
Ivybridge	d																								
Totnes	d				09 08		09 50		10 18		10 50			11 10			11 50		12 16			12 50			13 27
Paignton	d							10 10				10 50	11 04					12 08			12 25		12 52	13 08	
Torquay	d							10 15				10 56	11 09					12 13			12 31		12 57	13 14	
Torre	d							10 18					11 12					12 16					13 00		
Newton Abbot	a				09 20		10 01	10 26	10 29	←	11 01	11 06	11 20	11 22		11 30	12 01	12 24	12 28	12 34	12 41	13 01	13 09	13 24	13 39
	d				09 21		10 03	10 39	10 31	10 39	11 03	11 08		11 25		11 32	12 03		12 30	12 36	12 44	13 03	13 10	13 26	13 40
Teignmouth	d				09 28			→		10 46		11 15									12 51		13 18	13 33	
Dawlish	d				09 34					10 51		11 20									12 56		13 23	13 38	
Dawlish Warren	d									10 56													13 27		
Starcross	d									11 00													13 31		
Exeter St Thomas	d									11 09													13 41		
Exeter St Davids 6	a				09 48		10 21		10 51	11 14	11 21	11 30		11 45		11 52	12 21		12 50	12 55	13 09	13 21	13 45	13 49	14 00
Exeter Central	a						10 33		11 23	11 28							12 35				13 21	13 33			
Exmouth	a						11 00			11 55							13 01					14 01			
Barnstaple	d																		11 10						
Exmouth	d				09b08				10 00					11 05					12 05					13 10	
Exeter Central	d			08 56	09b35				10 26		10 46			11 35					12 31	12 46				13 36	
Exeter St Davids 6	d	08 10	08 38	09 34	09 49		10 23		10 53		11 23	11 32		11 47		11 54	12 23		12 51	12 57		13 23		13 51	14 02
Tiverton Parkway	d	08 27	08 53	09 51		←	10 37		11 07		11 37	11 46				12 09	12 37			13 10		13 37		14 05	14 16
Taunton	d	08 43	09 07	10c20	10 15	10 20	10 51		11 22		11 51	12 00		12 13		12 23	12 51		13 17	13 25		13 51		14 19	14 31
Bridgwater	a	08 54		→		10 31																			
Weston-super-Mare	a	09 12				10 49						12 20													
Bristol Temple Meads 10	a	09 45				11 20	11 26		11 57		12 24	12 45				12 57	13 24			13 57		14 24		14 56	
Bath Spa 7	a								12 12							13 12									
Filton Abbey Wood	a	10 00																							
Bristol Parkway 7	a						11 38				12 38	13 08					13 38			14 08		14 38		15 08	
Swindon	a								12 40							13 40									
Newport (South Wales)	a	10 25																							
Cardiff Central 7	a	10 42																							
Birmingham New Street 12	a						12 50				13 50	14 26					14 50			15 26		15 50		16 26	
Castle Cary	d		09 29											12 34											
Westbury	d		09 49		10 53									12 53					13 57						
Pewsey	d		10 06											13 10											
Hungerford	a																								
Newbury	a		10 26		11 26									13 30											
Thatcham	a																								
Theale	a																								
Reading 7	a		10 44		11 47				13 13					13 48		14 13			14 43						15 48
Oxford	a		11 35		12 35				13 49					14 35		14 49			15 35						16 35
Gatwick Airport 10	a		12 31		13 31									15 31					16 31						17 31
Heathrow Terminal 1 Bus	🚌 a		12 09		13 09				14 39					15 09		15 39			16 09						17 09
Slough 3	a																								
London Waterloo 15	⊖ a																				16 58				
London Paddington 15	⊖ a		11 30		12 32				13 53					14 29		14 53			15 30						16 29

For general notes see front of timetable
For details of catering facilities see
Directory of Train Operators

b Until 18 October only
c Arr. 1007

Sundays

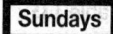

13 September to 1 November

Sleeper services are published in Table 406

Cornwall and Devon → Birmingham and London

Network Diagram - see first page of Table 135

		XC	GW	GW	GW	SW		GW	XC	XC	GW	GW	GW	SW	XC	GW	GW	GW	SW	SW		GW	GW	XC	GW
		1◇ 🛒		1◇ ☕		1◇ ☕			1◇ 🛒	1◇ 🛒		1◇ ☕	1◇ ☕	1◇ ☕	1◇ 🛒	1◇ ☕	1◇ ☕	1◇ ☕	1◇	1◇ ☕			1◇ ☕	1◇ 🛒	1◇ ☕
Penzance	d	11 23						12 15		12 30		12 55								13 50					14 45
St Ives	d									*12 11*		*12 50*								*13 25*					*14 25*
St Erth	d	11 33						12 22		12 40		13 06								14 00					14 56
Hayle	d									12 44										14 03					
Camborne	d	11 45						12 34		12 55		13 17								14 13					15 07
Redruth	d	11 51						12 40		13 01		13 23								14 19					15 14
Falmouth Docks	d									*12 44*										*14 03*					*14 57*
Truro	d	12 04						12 52		13 13		13 35								14 32					15 26
St Austell	d	12 23						13 10		13 30		13 54								14 48					15 44
Newquay	d																								
Par	d	12 30						13 18		13 37		14 00								14 56					15 51
Lostwithiel	d							13 25		13 44										15 03					
Bodmin Parkway	d	12 42						13 32		13 51		14 13								15 08					16 03
Looe	d																								
Liskeard 6	d	12 55						13 46		14 03		14 26								15 22					16 16
Menheniot	d																			15x29					
St Germans	d							13 57												15 37					
Saltash	d							14 06												15 45					
St Budeaux Ferry Road	d																								
Keyham	d																								
Dockyard	d																								
Devonport	d																								
Plymouth	a	13 18						14 15		14 27		14 51								15 53					16 41
	d	13 21		13 44		14 06			14 21	14 35		14 55	15 05		15 21		15 43			16 02			16 10	16 25	16 45
Ivybridge	d					14 21														16 17					
Totnes	d	13 48		14 11		14 35			14 48	15 00		15 22	15 34		15 48		16 11			16 31			16 42	16 50	17 12
Paignton	d		14 04								15 00			15 30		15 45			16 10			16 31			
Torquay	d		14 09								15 05			15 36		15 51			16 16			16 36			
Torre	d		14 12								15 08					15 56						16 39			
Newton Abbot	a	14 00	14 20	14 23	←	14 46			15 00	15 11	15 16	15 34	15 46	15 46	16 00	16 04	16 22		16 28	16 42		16 47	16 53	17 03	17 24
	d	14 01	14 35	14 25	14 35	14 47			15 01	15 12	15 18	15 35	15 47	15 51	16 01	16 05	16 24		16 30	16 43			16 55	17 03	17 25
Teignmouth	d		→		14 42	14 54					15 25			15 58		16 13									
Dawlish	d				14 47	14 59					15 30			16 03		16 18									
Dawlish Warren	d				14 52						15 35			16 07											
Starcross	d				14 56						15 39														
Exeter St Thomas	d				15 05						15 48														
Exeter St Davids 6	a	14 21		14 45	15 10	15 15			15 21	15 31	15 52	15 55	16 07	16 18	16 22	16 32	16 44		16 53	17 05			17 15	17 21	17 45
Exeter Central	a	*14 33*			15 33	15 23			*15 33*					16 36	*16 31*				17 21					*17 31*	
Exmouth	a	*15 01*			16 01				*16 01*						*16 57*									*18 01*	
Barnstaple	d			*13 17*																					
Exmouth	d			*14 10*								*15 10*											*16 10*		*17 10*
Exeter Central	d			*14 36*								*15 39*											*16 46*		*17 37*
Exeter St Davids 6	d	14 23		14 46					15 23	15 33		15 58	16 09		16 23	16 34	16 45						17 17	17 23	17 47
Tiverton Parkway	d	14 38							15 38	15 46		16 13	16 24		16 38	16 49	17 01						17 32	17 37	18 02
Taunton	d	14 53		15 11					15 53	16 01		16 28	16 39		16 53	17 03	17 15						17 46	17 51	18 17
Bridgwater	a																								
Weston-super-Mare	a									16 20			17 00			17 25		←							
Bristol Temple Meads 10	a	15 27							16 27	16 53			17 22		17 27	17 54		17 54					18 23	18 27	
Bath Spa 7	a												17 42			→		18 12					18 41		
Filton Abbey Wood	a																						→		
Bristol Parkway 7	a	15 38							16 38	17 08					17 38									18 38	
Swindon	a												18 10					18 40							
Newport (South Wales)	a																								
Cardiff Central 7	a																								
Birmingham New Street 12	a	16 50							17 50	18 27					18 50									19 50	
Castle Cary	d			15 33													17 37								
Westbury	d			15 51													17 57								18b58
Pewsey	d			16 09													18 14								
Hungerford	a																								
Newbury	a			16 30													18 34								
Thatcham	a																								
Theale	a																								
Reading 7	a			16 48								17 44	18 44				18 52	19 15							19 43
Oxford	a			*17 35*								*18 35*					*19 35*								
Gatwick Airport 10	a			*18 31*								*19 31*					*20 31*								
Heathrow Terminal 1 Bus	🚌 a			*18 09*								*19 09*					*20 09*								
Slough 3	a																								
London Waterloo 15	⊖ a					18 58								20 04					20 58						
London Paddington 15	⊖ a			17 33								18 29	19 31				19 43	19 53							20 29

For general notes see front of timetable
For details of catering facilities see
Directory of Train Operators

b Arr. 1852

Sundays

13 September to 1 November

Sleeper services are published in Table 406

Cornwall and Devon → Birmingham and London

Network Diagram - see first page of Table 135

		GW	GW ◇	GW 1 ◇	XC 1 ◇	GW ◇	GW 1 ◇	XC 1 ◇	SW 1 ◇	GW 1 ◇	XC 1 ◇	GW	GW 1 ◇	GW	GW 1 ◇	XC 1 ◇	GW	GW ◇	GW	SW 1	GW	GW ◇	XC 1 ◇
Penzance	d		15 06		15 30					16 13			17 20					19 00	20 00			21 15	21 41
St Ives	d		14 56							15 56			16 56					18 40	19 46				
St Erth	d		15 15		15 38					16 24			17 30					19 08	20 09			21 25	21 49
Hayle	d		15 18																20 12				
Camborne	d		15 28		15 48					16 35			17 42					19 19	20 21			21 37	22 01
Redruth	d		15 34		15 54					16 42			17 49					19 25	20 27			21 44	22 07
Falmouth Docks	d									16 00			17 30					18 43				21 30	
Truro	d		15 46		16 06					16 54			18 00					19 37	20 40			21 59	22 19
St Austell	d		16 03		16 24					17 12			18 19					19 54	20 57			22 17	22 35
Newquay	d																						
Par	d		16 10		16 31					17 18			18 26					20 02	21 04				22 42
Lostwithiel	d		16 17															20 08					
Bodmin Parkway	d		16 23		16 42					17 30			18 38					20 14	21 16			22 34	22 53
Looe	d																						
Liskeard 6	d		16 36		16 54					17 43			18 51					20 27	21 30			22 49	23 05
Menheniot	d		16x41															20x32					
St Germans	d		16 48															20 39					
Saltash	d		16 56															20 47					
St Budeaux Ferry Road	d																						
Keyham	d																						
Dockyard	d																						
Devonport	d																	20 54					
Plymouth	a		17 04		17 17					18 09			19 15					20 58	21 59			23 15	23 33
	d		17 08		17 25		17 45			18 10	18 21		19 15		19 55	20 25		21 15				23 20	
Ivybridge	d		17 23																				
Totnes	d		17 38		17 50		18 12			18 39	18 48		19 46			20 50		21 42				23 48	
Paignton	d	17 20						18 17	18 24			18 55		19 55			21 00			22 10	23 00		
Torquay	d	17 25						18 23	18 30			19 00		20 00			21 05			22 16	23 05		
Torre	d	17 28										19 03		20 03			21 08				23 08		
Newton Abbot	a	17 36	17 50		18 01		18 24	18 33	18 40	18 50	19 00	19 11	19 57	20 11	20 31	21 01	21 16	21 54		22 28	23 16	23 59	
	d	17 38	17 51		18 03		18 25	18 36	18 42	18 51	19 01	19 13	19 59	20 13	20 32	21 03	21 18	21 55		22 30	23 18	00 01	
Teignmouth	d	17 45	17 59						18 49			19 20		20 20			21 25	22 02		22 37	23 25		
Dawlish	d	17 50	18 04						18 54			19 25		20 25			21 30	22 07		22 42	23 30		
Dawlish Warren	d	17 55							18 58			19 30		20 30			21 35			22 46	23 35		
Starcross	d	17 59										19 34		20 34			21 39				23 39		
Exeter St Thomas	d	18 08										19 43		20 43			21 48				23 48		
Exeter St Davids 6	a	18 13	18 18		18 21		18 46	18 54	19 09	19 12	19 21	19 50	20 19	20 47	20 53	21 21	21 52	22 21		22 57	23 52	00 36	
Exeter Central	a				18 38				19 23	19 23	19 38		20 43		21 23	21 38		22 34		23 13			
Exmouth	a				19 05						20 05		21 12			22 04		23 03		23 55			
Barnstaple	d						17 20								19 17								
Exmouth	d						18 10						19 10		20 10							23 59	
Exeter Central	d					⟵	18 37	18 43					19 36		20 46							00 24	
Exeter St Davids 6	d		18 33 ⟶		18 23	18 33	18 49	18 56		19 14	19 23		20 20		20 55	21 23						01 27	
Tiverton Parkway	d				18 37			19 10		19 29	19 38		20 36		21 10	21 37							
Taunton	d				18 51	19 04	19 11	19 24		19 43	19 53		20 49		21 23	21 51							
Bridgwater	a					19 15																	
Weston-super-Mare	a					19 35																	
Bristol Temple Meads 10	a			⟵	19 27	20 12		19 57			20 27				21 58	23 06							
Bath Spa 7	a			18 41											22 18								
Filton Abbey Wood	a																						
Bristol Parkway 7	a				19 38			20 08			20 38												
Swindon	a			19 11											22 46								
Newport (South Wales)	a																						
Cardiff Central 7	a																						
Birmingham New Street 12	a				20 55			21 31			21 50												
Castle Cary	d									20 05			21 12										
Westbury	d									20 25			21 30										
Pewsey	d												21 48										
Hungerford	a																						
Newbury	a						20 20						22 08										
Thatcham	a																						
Theale	a																						
Reading 7	a			19 46			20 43			21 12			22 28		23 26							04s17	
Oxford	a			20 35			21 35			21 51			23 35		00 34							06 22	
Gatwick Airport 10	a			21 31			22 31			23 31			00b59									05 52	
Heathrow Terminal 1 Bus	a			21 19			21 55			22 55			23 55									05 50	
Slough 3	a																						
London Waterloo 15	⊖ a								22 58														
London Paddington 15	⊖ a			20 39			21 29			21 53			23 17		00 06							05 05	

For general notes see front of timetable
For details of catering facilities see
Directory of Train Operators

b Change at Reading and Redhill

Table 135

Sundays
from 8 November

Sleeper services are published in Table 406

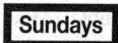

Cornwall and Devon → Birmingham and London

Network Diagram - see first page of Table 135

		GW	GW	GW	GW	GW	XC		GW	GW	GW	XC	GW	GW		GW	XC	GW	GW	SW	XC		GW	GW	XC
		◇	1 ◇		1 ◇		1 ◇			1 ◇		1 ◇		1 ◇		1 ◇	1 ◇		1 ◇	1 ◇	1 ◇			1 ◇	1 ◇
			🍴		🍴		🛒			🍴		🛒		🍴		🍴	🛒		🍴	🍴	🛒			🍴	🛒
Penzance	d													08 37			09 30		09 50					11 00	11 25
St Ives	d																								
St Erth	d													08 47			09 38		10 02					11 10	11 33
Hayle	d													08 52											
Camborne	d													09 02			09 48		10 13					11 22	11 45
Redruth	d													09 08			09 54		10 19					11 28	11 51
Falmouth Docks	d																							*11 12*	
Truro	d													09 21			10 06		10 31					11 42	12 03
St Austell	d													09 38			10 24		10 49					11 58	12 21
Newquay	d																								
Par	d													09 46			10 31		10 56					12 06	12 28
Lostwithiel	d																								
Bodmin Parkway	d													09 58			10 42		11 09					12 18	12 40
Looe	d																								
Liskeard 6	d													10 11			10 54		11 22					12 32	12 52
Menheniot	d																								
St Germans	d													10 22											
Saltash	d													10 31											
St Budeaux Ferry Road	d																								
Keyham	d																								
Dockyard	d																								
Devonport	d																								
Plymouth	a													10 40			11 17		11 45					12 57	13 14
	d				08 40		09 25			09 50		10 25		10 40		10 54	11 25		11 45					13 00	13 25
Ivybridge	d																								
Totnes	d				09 08		09 50			10 18		10 50		11 10			11 51		12 16					13 27	13 50
Paignton	d								10 10				11 04					12 08		12 25	12 32		12 52		
Torquay	d								10 15				11 09					12 13		12 31	12 38		12 57		
Torre	d								10 18				11 12					12 16					13 00		
Newton Abbot	a				09 20		10 01		10 26	10 29	←	11 01	11 20	11 22		11 30	12 01	12 24	12 28	12 41	12 48		13 09	13 39	14 01
	d				09 21		10 03		10 39 →	10 31	10 39	11 03		11 25		11 32	12 03		12 30	12 44	12 50		13 10	13 40	14 03
Teignmouth	d				09 28						10 46									12 51			13 18		
Dawlish	d				09 34						10 51									12 56			13 23		
Dawlish Warren	d										10 56												13 27		
Starcross	d										11 00												13 31		
Exeter St Thomas	d										11 09												13 41		
Exeter St Davids 6	a				09 48		10 21			10 51	11 14	11 21		11 45		11 52	12 22		12 50	13 09	13 13		13 45	14 00	14 21
Exeter Central	a						*10 33*			*11 23*	11 28						*12 35*			13 21	*13 33*				*14 33*
Exmouth	a						*11 00*				11 55						*13 01*				*14 01*				*15 01*
Barnstaple	d																		*11 10*						
Exmouth	d									*10 00*				*11 05*					*12 05*					*13 10*	
Exeter Central	d			*08 56*						*10 26*		*10 46*		*11 35*					*12 31*		*12 46*			*13 36*	
Exeter St Davids 6	d	08 10	08 38	09 34	09 49		10 23			10 53		11 23		11 47		11 54	12 24		12 51		13 15			14 02	14 23
Tiverton Parkway	d	08 27	08 53	09 51		←	10 37			11 07		11 37				12 09	12 38				13 28			14 16	14 37
Taunton	d	08 43	09 07	10b20	10 15	10 20	10 51			11 22		11 51		12 13		12 23	12 52		13 17		13 43			14 31	14 51
Bridgwater	a	08 54		→		10 31																			
Weston-super-Mare	a	09 12				10 49																			
Bristol Temple Meads 10	a	09 45				11 20	11 24			11 57		12 24				12 57	13 25				14 23				15 24
Bath Spa 7	a									12 12						13 12									
Filton Abbey Wood	a	10 00																							
Bristol Parkway 7	a						11 38					12 38					13 38				14 38				15 38
Swindon	a									12 40						13 40									
Newport (South Wales)	a	10 25																							
Cardiff Central 7	a	10 42																							
Birmingham New Street 12	a						13 20					14 20					15 20				16 19				17 25
Castle Cary	d		09 29											12 34											
Westbury	d		09 49		10 53									12 53					13 57						
Pewsey	d		10 06											13 10											
Hungerford	a																								
Newbury	a		10 26		11 26									13 30											
Thatcham	a																								
Theale	a																								
Reading 7	a		10 44		11 47					13 13				13 48		14 13			14 43					15 48	
Oxford	a		*11 35*		*12 35*					*13 49*				*14 35*		*14 49*			*15 35*					*16 35*	
Gatwick Airport 10	a		*12 31*		*13 31*									*15 31*					*16 31*					*17 31*	
Heathrow Terminal 1 Bus	a		*12 09*		*13 09*					*14 39*				*15 09*		*15 39*			*16 09*					*17 09*	
Slough 3	a																								
London Waterloo 15 ⊖	a																			16 58					
London Paddington 15 ⊖	a		11 30		12 32					13 53				14 29		14 53			15 30					16 29	

For general notes see front of timetable
For details of catering facilities see Directory of Train Operators

b Arr. 1007

Sleeper services are published in Table 406

Cornwall and Devon → Birmingham and London

Network Diagram - see first page of Table 135

Station		GW	GW 1◇	GW	SW 1◇	GW	XC 1◇	GW	GW 1◇	GW 1◇	SW 1◇	XC 1◇	GW 1◇	GW 1◇	GW 1◇	SW 1◇	SW 1◇	GW	GW 1◇	XC 1◇	GW 1◇	GW
Penzance	d					12 15			12 55								13 50				14 45	
St Ives	d								*12 50*								*13 25*				*14 25*	
St Erth	d					12 22			13 06								14 00				14 56	
Hayle	d																14 03					
Camborne	d					12 34			13 17								14 13				15 07	
Redruth	d					12 40			13 23								14 19				15 14	
Falmouth Docks	d								*12 44*								*14 03*				*14 57*	
Truro	d					12 52			13 35								14 32				15 26	
St Austell	d					13 10			13 54								14 48				15 44	
Newquay	d																					
Par	d					13 18			14 00								14 56				15 51	
Lostwithiel	d					13 25											15 03					
Bodmin Parkway	d					13 32			14 13								15 08				16 03	
Looe	d																					
Liskeard 6	d					13 46			14 26								15 22				16 16	
Menheniot	d																15x29					
St Germans	d					13 57											15 37					
Saltash	d					14 06											15 45					
St Budeaux Ferry Road	d																					
Keyham	d																					
Dockyard	d																					
Devonport	d																					
Plymouth	a					14 15			14 51								15 53				16 41	
	d		13 44		14 06		14 25		14 55	15 05		15 25		15 43			16 02		16 10	16 25	16 45	
Ivybridge	d				14 21												16 17					
Totnes	d		14 11		14 35		14 50		15 22	15 34		15 50		16 11			16 31		16 42	16 52	17 12	
Paignton	d	14 04						15 00			15 30		15 45			16 10		16 31				17 20
Torquay	d	14 09						15 05			15 36		15 51			16 16		16 36				17 25
Torre	d	14 12						15 08					15 56					16 39				17 28
Newton Abbot	a	14 20	14 23	⟵	14 46		15 01	15 16	15 34	15 46	15 46	16 01	16 04	16 22		16 28	16 42	16 47	16 53	17 03	17 24	17 36
	d	14 35	14 25	14 35	14 47		15 02	15 18	15 35	15 47	15 51	16 03	16 05	16 24		16 30	16 43		16 55	17 05	17 25	17 38
Teignmouth	d	⟶		14 42	14 54			15 25			15 58		16 13									17 45
Dawlish	d			14 47	14 59			15 30			16 03		16 18									17 50
Dawlish Warren	d			14 52				15 35			16 07											17 55
Starcross	d			14 56				15 39														17 59
Exeter St Thomas	d			15 05				15 48														18 08
Exeter St Davids 6	a		14 45	15 10	15 15		15 21	15 52	15 55	16 07	16 18	16 22	16 32	16 44		16 53	17 05		17 15	17 23	17 45	18 13
Exeter Central	a			15 33	15 23		*15 33*				16 36	*16 31*					17 21			*17 31*		
Exmouth	a			16 01			*16 01*					*16 57*								*18 01*		
Barnstaple	d		*13 17*									*15 14*										
Exmouth	d		*14 10*						*15 10*										*16 10*		*17 10*	
Exeter Central	d		*14 36*						*15 39*										*16 46*		*17 37*	
Exeter St Davids 6	d		14 46				15 23		15 58	16 09		16 23	16 34	16 45					17 17	17 25	17 47	
Tiverton Parkway	d						15 36		16 13	16 24		16 37	16 49	17 01					17 32	17 39	18 02	
Taunton	d		15 11				15 51		16 28	16 39		16 51	17 03	17 15					17 46	17 53	18 17	
Bridgwater	a																					
Weston-super-Mare	a									17 00			17 25		⟵							
Bristol Temple Meads 10	a						16 24			17 22		17 25	17 54		17 54				18 23	18 27		
Bath Spa 7	a									17 42			⟶		18 12				18 41			
Filton Abbey Wood	a																		⟶			
Bristol Parkway 7	a						16 38					17 38								18 38		
Swindon	a									18 10					18 40							
Newport (South Wales)	a																					
Cardiff Central 7	a																					
Birmingham New Street 12	a						18 20					19 25								20 20		
Castle Cary	d		15 33											17 37								
Westbury	d		15 51											17 57							18b58	
Pewsey	d		16 09											18 14								
Hungerford	a																					
Newbury	a		16 30											18 34								
Thatcham	a																					
Theale	a																					
Reading 7	a		16 48						17 44	18 44				18 52	19 15						19 43	
Oxford	a		*17 35*						*18 35*					*19 35*								
Gatwick Airport 10	a		*18 31*						*19 31*					*20 31*								
Heathrow Terminal 1 Bus	a		*18 09*						*19 09*					*20 09*								
Slough 3	a																					
London Waterloo 15	⊖ a				18 58						20 04						20 58					
London Paddington 15	⊖ a		17 33						18 29	19 31				19 43	19 53						20 29	

b Arr. 1852

For general notes see front of timetable
For details of catering facilities see
Directory of Train Operators

Sundays

from 8 November

Sleeper services are published in Table 406

Cornwall and Devon → Birmingham and London

Network Diagram - see first page of Table 135

		GW	GW	XC	GW		GW	SW	GW	XC	GW	GW		GW	GW	XC	GW	GW	GW	SW	GW	GW	XC
		◇ 🛒	1 ◇ 🍴	1 ◇ 🛒	◇ 🛒		1 ◇ 🍴	1 ◇ 🍴	1 ◇ 🍴	1 ◇ 🛒		1 ◇ 🍴			1 ◇ 🍴	1 ◇ 🛒		◇	🛒	1		◇ 🍴	1 ◇ 🛒
Penzance	d	15 06		15 30					16 13			17 20						19 00	20 00			21 15	21 41
St Ives	d	14 56							15 56			16 56						18 40	19 46				
St Erth	d	15 15		15 38					16 24			17 30						19 08	20 09			21 25	21 49
Hayle	d	15 18																	20 12				
Camborne	d	15 28		15 49					16 35			17 42						19 19	20 21			21 37	22 01
Redruth	d	15 34		15 55					16 42			17 49						19 25	20 27			21 44	22 07
Falmouth Docks	d								16 00			17 30						18 43				21 30	
Truro	d	15 46		16 07					16 54			18 00						19 37	20 40			21 59	22 19
St Austell	d	16 03		16 25					17 12			18 19						19 54	20 57			22 17	22 35
Newquay	d																						
Par	d	16 10		16 32					17 18			18 26						20 02	21 04				22 42
Lostwithiel	d	16 17																20 08					
Bodmin Parkway	d	16 23		16 43					17 30			18 38						20 14	21 16			22 34	22 53
Looe	d																						
Liskeard 6	d	16 36		16 55					17 43			18 51						20 27	21 30			22 49	23 05
Menheniot	d	16x41																20x32					
St Germans	d	16 48																20 39					
Saltash	d	16 56																20 47					
St Budeaux Ferry Road	d																						
Keyham	d																						
Dockyard	d																						
Devonport	d																	20 54					
Plymouth	a	17 04		17 18					18 09			19 15						20 58	21 59			23 15	23 33
	d	17 08		17 25			17 45		18 10	18 25		19 15			19 55	20 25		21 15				23 20	
Ivybridge	d	17 23																					
Totnes	d	17 38		17 50			18 12		18 39	18 50		19 46				20 50		21 42				23 48	
Paignton	d							18 24			18 55			19 55			21 00			22 10	23 00		
Torquay	d							18 30			19 00			20 00			21 05			22 16	23 05		
Torre	d										19 03			20 03			21 08				23 08		
Newton Abbot	a	17 50		18 01			18 24	18 40	18 50	19 01	19 11	19 57		20 11	20 31	21 01	21 16	21 54		22 28	23 16	23 59	
	d	17 51		18 03			18 25	18 42	18 51	19 03	19 13	19 59		20 13	20 32	21 03	21 18	21 55		22 30	23 18	00 01	
Teignmouth	d	17 59						18 49			19 20			20 20			21 25	22 02		22 37	23 25		
Dawlish	d	18 04						18 54			19 25			20 25			21 30	22 07		22 42	23 30		
Dawlish Warren	d							18 58			19 30			20 30			21 35			22 46	23 35		
Starcross	d										19 34			20 34			21 39				23 39		
Exeter St Thomas	d										19 43			20 43			21 48				23 48		
Exeter St Davids 6	a	18 18		18 21			18 46	19 09	19 12	19 21	19 50	20 19		20 47	20 53	21 21	21 52	22 21		22 57	23 52	00 36	
Exeter Central	a			18 38				19 23	19 23	19 38		20 43			21 23	21 38		22 34		23 13			
Exmouth	a			19 05						20 05		21 12				22 04		23 03		23 55			
Barnstaple	d						17 20								19 17								
Exmouth	d						18 10					19 10			20 10							23 59	
Exeter Central	d				←		18 37		18 43			19 36			20 46							00 24	
Exeter St Davids 6	d	18 33		18 23	18 33		18 49		19 14	19 23		20 20			20 55	21 23						01 27	
Tiverton Parkway	d	→		18 37					19 29	19 37		20 36			21 10	21 37							
Taunton	d			18 51	19 04		19 11		19 43	19 51		20 49			21 23	21 51							
Bridgwater	a				19 15																		
Weston-super-Mare	a				19 35																		
Bristol Temple Meads 10	a		←	19 27	20 12					20 24					21 58	23 06							
Bath Spa 7	a		18 41												22 18								
Filton Abbey Wood	a																						
Bristol Parkway 7	a			19 38						20 38													
Swindon	a		19 11												22 46								
Newport (South Wales)	a																						
Cardiff Central 7	a																						
Birmingham New Street 12	a			21 39						22 17													
Castle Cary	d								20 05			21 12											
Westbury	d								20 25			21 30											
Pewsey	d											21 48											
Hungerford	a																						
Newbury	a						20 20					22 08											
Thatcham	a																						
Theale	a																						
Reading 7	a		19 46				20 43		21 12			22 28			23 26							04s17	
Oxford	a		20 35				21 35		21 51			23 35			00 34							06 22	
Gatwick Airport 10	a		21 31				22 31		23 31			00b59										05 52	
Heathrow Terminal 1 Bus	a		21 19				21 55		22 55			23 55										05 50	
Slough 3	a																						
London Waterloo 15 ⊖	a							22 58															
London Paddington 15 ⊖	a		20 39				21 29		21 53			23 17			00 06							05 05	

For general notes see front of timetable
For details of catering facilities see Directory of Train Operators

b Change at Reading and Redhill

Table 135A

Mondays to Fridays

Redruth — Helston and Culdrose

Bus Service

		GW	GW	GW	GW	GW	GW	GW	GW	GW	GW	GW	GW	GW	GW
Redruth	d	08 00	09 15	10 15	11 15	12 15	13 15	14 15	15 15	16 15	17 00	18 15	19 15	21 15	23 15
Helston (Woolworths)	a	08 47	09 47	10 47	11 47	12 47	13 47	14 47	15 47	16 47	17 32	18 47	19 47	21 47	23 41
Culdrose (R.N.A.S.)	a	08x56	10x00	11 00	12x00	13 00	14x00	15x00	16x00	17 00	17 50	18 55	19x55	21x55	
Mullion Holiday Park	a														

Saturdays

		GW	GW	GW	GW	GW	GW	GW	GW	GW	GW	GW	GW	GW	GW
Redruth	d	08 15	09 15	10 15	11 15	12 15	13 15	14 15	15 15	16 15	17 15	18 15	19 15	21 15	23 15
Helston (Woolworths)	a	08 47	09 47	10 47	11 47	12 47	13 47	14 47	15 47	16 47	17 47	18 47	19 47	21 47	23 41
Culdrose (R.N.A.S.)	a	08x55	10x00	11 00	12 00	13 00	14 00	15 00	16 00	17 00	18 00	18 55	19 55	21 55	
Mullion Holiday Park	a														

Sundays

		GW	GW	GW	GW	GW	GW
Redruth	d	09 50	11 50	13 50	15 50	17 50	23 00
Helston (Woolworths)	a	10 19	12 19	14 19	16 19	18s19	23s29
Culdrose (R.N.A.S.)	a	10 35	12 35	14x35	16 35	18 35	23 45
Mullion Holiday Park	a						

Mondays to Fridays

		GW	GW	GW	GW	GW	GW	GW	GW	GW	GW	GW	GW	GW	GW	GW
Mullion Holiday Park	d															
Culdrose (R.N.A.S.)	d	06 55	08 01	09 21	10 14	11 14	12 14	13 00	14 14	15 09	16 14	17 14	17 14	18 14	18 14	19 39
Helston (Woolworths)	d	07 05	08 06	09 27	10 27	11 27	12 27	13 10	14 27	15 15	16 27	17 27	17 27	18 27	18 27	19 47
Redruth	a	07 39	08 55	10 01	11 01	12 01	13 01	13 40	15 01	16 01	17 01	18 01	18 01	18 59	18 59	20 19

Saturdays

		GW	GW	GW	GW	GW	GW	GW	GW	GW	GW	GW	GW
Mullion Holiday Park	d												
Culdrose (R.N.A.S.)	d	07 19	08 19	09 19	10 14	11 14	12 14	13 14	14 14	15 14	16 14	18 14	19 39
Helston (Woolworths)	d	07 27	08 27	09 27	10 27	11 27	12 27	13 27	14 27	15 27	16 27	18 27	19 47
Redruth	a	08 01	09 01	10 01	11 01	12 01	13 01	14 01	15 01	16 01	17 01	18 59	20 19

Sundays

		GW	GW	GW	GW	GW
Mullion Holiday Park	d					
Culdrose (R.N.A.S.)	d		10 35	12 35	14 35	16 35
Helston (Woolworths)	d	08 50	10 50	12 50	14 50	16 50
Redruth	a	09 21	11 21	13 21	15 21	17 21

For general notes see front of timetable
For details of catering facilities see
Directory of Train Operators

Table 135B

Mondays to Fridays

St. Austell — Eden Project
Bus Service

		GW	GW	GW	GW	GW	GW	GW	GW	GW	GW	GW	GW	GW	GW	GW	GW	GW	GW	GW	GW	GW
St Austell	d	08 35	08 50	09 30	09 35	10 30	10 35	10 55	11 35	11 40	12 35	12 40	13 10	13 35	13 50	14 35	15 15	15 35	15 50	16 35	16 50	17 30
Eden Project	a	08 57	09 10	09 50	09 57	10 50	10 57	11 15	11 57	12 00	12 57	13 00	13 30	13 57	14 10	14 57	15 35	15 57	16 10	16 57	17 10	17 50

Saturdays

		GW	GW	GW	GW	GW	GW	GW	GW	GW	GW	GW	GW	GW	GW
St Austell	d	08 50	09 30	10 30	11 40	12 40	12 50	13 50	15 35	15 50	15 55	16 35	16 50	17 20	17 30
Eden Project	a	09 10	09 50	10 50	12 00	13 00	13 10	14 10	15 55	16 10	16 15	16 55	17 10	17 40	17 50

Sundays

		GW	GW	GW	GW	GW	GW	GW	GW	GW	GW	GW	GW	GW
St Austell	d	08 50	10 00	10 40	11 35	12 30	13 35	15 00	15 20	15 40	16 30	16 35	17 20	17 35
Eden Project	a	09 10	10 20	11 00	11 55	12 50	13 55	15 20	15 40	16 00	16 50	16 55	17 40	17 55

Mondays to Fridays

		GW	GW	GW	GW	GW	GW	GW	GW	GW	GW	GW	GW	GW	GW	GW	GW	GW
Eden Project	d	09 00	09 10	09 50	10 00	11 00	12 00	12 10	13 00	13 10	14 00	15 00	15 05	16 00	16 30	17 00	17 10	18 00
St Austell	a	09 20	09 30	10 10	10 20	11 20	12 20	12 30	13 20	13 30	14 20	15 20	15 25	16 20	16 50	17 20	17 30	18 20

Saturdays

		GW	GW	GW	GW	GW	GW	GW	GW	GW	GW	GW
Eden Project	d	09 10	09 50	11 00	12 10	13 10	14 20	15 05	16 30	17 00	17 10	18 00
St Austell	a	09 30	10 10	11 20	12 30	13 30	14 40	15 25	16 50	17 20	17 30	18 20

Sundays

		GW	GW	GW	GW	GW	GW	GW	GW	GW	GW	GW	GW	GW
Eden Project	d	10 10	10 20	11 00	11 55	12 50	14 40	15 20	16 15	16 35	17 00	17 10	17 50	18 00
St Austell	a	10 30	10 40	11 20	12 15	13 10	15 00	15 40	16 35	16 55	17 20	17 30	18 10	18 20

For general notes see front of timetable
For details of catering facilities see
Directory of Train Operators

Table 135C

Mondays to Saturdays

Bodmin — Wadebridge and Padstow

Bus Service

		GW Bus	GW Bus	GW Bus	GW Bus	GW Bus	GW Bus	GW Bus	GW Bus	GW Bus	GW SX Bus	GW Bus	GW Bus	GW Bus	GW Bus
Bodmin Parkway	d	07 25	08 30	09 30	10 30	11 30	12 30	13 30	14 30	15 30	16 30	17 30	18 30	19 30	22 00
Bodmin Mount Folly	a	07 35	08 40	09 40	10 40	11 40	12 40	13 40	14 40	15 40	16 40	17 40	18 40	19 40	22 10
Wadebridge Bus Station	a	07 55	09 00	10 00	11 00	12 00	13 00	14 00	15 00	16 00	17 00	18 00	19 00	20 00	22 30
Padstow Old Rly Station	a	08 27	09 27	10 27	11 27	12 27	13 27	14 27	15 27	16 27	17 27	18 27	19 27	20 27	22 57

Sundays

		GW Bus	GW Bus	GW Bus	GW Bus	GW Bus	GW Bus
Bodmin Parkway	d	09 30	11 30	13 30	15 30	17 30	19 30
Bodmin Mount Folly	a	09 40	11 40	13 40	15 40	17 40	19 40
Wadebridge Bus Station	a	10 00	12 00	14 00	16 00	18 00	20 00
Padstow Old Rly Station	a	10 27	12 27	14 27	16 27	18 27	20 27

Mondays to Saturdays

		GW Bus	GW Bus	GW Bus	GW Bus	GW Bus	GW Bus	GW Bus	GW Bus	GW Bus	GW Bus	GW Bus	GW Bus	GW Bus	GW Bus
Padstow Old Rly Station	d	06 30	07 30	08 30	09 30	10 30	11 30	12 30	13 30	14 30	15 30	16 30	17 30	18 30	20 30
Wadebridge Bus Station	d	06 55	07 55	08 55	09 55	10 55	11 55	12 55	13 55	14 55	15 55	16 55	17 55	18 55	20 55
Bodmin Tsb Bus Stop	d	07 17	08 17	09 17	10 17	11 17	12 17	13 17	14 17	15 17	16 17	17 17	18 17	19 17	21 17
Bodmin Parkway	a	07 25	08 25	09 25	10 25	11 25	12 25	13 25	14 25	15 25	16 25	17 25	18 25	19 25	21 25

Sundays

		GW Bus	GW Bus	GW Bus	GW Bus	GW Bus	GW Bus
Padstow Old Rly Station	d	08 30	10 30	12 30	14 30	16 30	18 30
Wadebridge Bus Station	d	08 55	10 55	12 55	14 55	16 55	18 55
Bodmin Tsb Bus Stop	d	09 17	11 17	13 17	15 17	17 17	19 17
Bodmin Parkway	a	09 25	11 25	13 25	15 25	17 25	19 25

For general notes see front of timetable
For details of catering facilities see Directory of Train Operators

Table 135D

Mondays to Fridays

Exeter — Okehampton, Holsworthy and Bude
Bus Service

		GW	GW	GW	GW	GW	GW	GW	GW	GW	GW FO
		🚌	🚌	🚌	🚌	🚌	🚌	🚌	🚌	🚌	🚌
Exeter St Davids	d	08 42	09 50	11 22	11 50	13 22	13 50	15 22	15 40	17 55	20 40
Okehampton West Street	a	09 26	10 25	12 15	12 25	14 06	14 25	16 15	16 25	18 30	21 30
Holsworthy Church	a		10 58		12 58		14 58		16 58	19 03	22 02
Bude Strand	a		11 20		13 20		15 20		17 20	19 25	22 29

Saturdays

		GW	GW	GW	GW	GW	GW	GW	GW	GW	GW	GW	GW	GW	GW	GW	GW
		🚌	🚌	🚌	🚌	🚌	🚌	🚌	🚌	🚌	🚌	🚌	🚌	🚌	🚌	🚌	🚌
Exeter St Davids	d	09 25	10 25	11 25	12 25	13 25	13 55	14 25	15 25	15 55	16 25	16 55	17 25	17 55	18 25	19 40	20 40
Okehampton West Street	a	10 00	11 10	12 00	13 10	14 00	14 40	15 00	16 10	16 30	17 00	17 45	18 15	18 45	19 15	20 30	21 30
Holsworthy Church	a	10 33		12 33		14 33					17 33		18 48		19 48	21 03	22 03
Bude Strand	a	10 55		12 55		14 55					17 55		19 10	20 00	20 10	21 25	22 25

Sundays

		GW	GW
		🚌	🚌
Exeter St Davids	d	12 25	17 25
Okehampton West Street	a	13 15	18 15
Holsworthy Church	a	13 48	18 48
Bude Strand	a	14 10	19 10

Mondays to Fridays

		GW	GW	GW	GW	GW	GW	GW	GW	GW	GW	GW
		🚌	🚌	🚌	🚌	🚌	🚌	🚌	🚌	🚌	🚌	🚌
Bude Strand	d	06 40			09 00		11 30		13 30		15 25	15 30
Holsworthy Church	d	07 02			09 22		11 52		13 52		15 57	15 57
Okehampton West Street	d	07 40	09 35	09 45	10 00	11 45	12 30	14 15	14 30	15 45	16 35	16 35
Exeter St Davids	a	08 15	10 10	10 35	10 35	12 35	13 05	15 05	15 05	16 35	17 15	17 15

Saturdays

		GW	GW	GW	GW	GW	GW	GW	GW	GW	GW	GW	GW	GW	GW	GW
		🚌	🚌	🚌	🚌	🚌	🚌	🚌	🚌	🚌	🚌	🚌	🚌	🚌	🚌	🚌
Bude Strand	d	05 45	06 40	08 15	09 15			11 15		13 15				15 30	17 15	17 30
Holsworthy Church	d		07 02	08 37	09 37			11 37		13 37				15 57	17 37	17 52
Okehampton West Street	d	07 00	07 40	09 15	10 15	10 45	11 15	12 15	13 15	14 15	14 45	15 15	16 15	16 35	18 10	18 25
Exeter St Davids	a	07 40	08 20	10 00	10 50	11 20	12 00	12 50	14 00	14 50	15 30	15 50	17 00	17 10	18 50	19 07

Sundays

		GW	GW
		🚌	🚌
Bude Strand	d	10 10	15 10
Holsworthy Church	d	10 32	15 32
Okehampton West Street	d	11 10	16 10
Exeter St Davids	a	12 00	17 00

For general notes see front of timetable
For details of catering facilities see Directory of Train Operators

Taunton — Watchet, Dunster and Minehead
Bus Service

		GW	GW	GW	GW	GW	GW	GW	GW	GW	GW	GW	GW	GW	GW	GW	GW	GW
Taunton	d	05 41	07 14	07 44	08 14	08 44	09 14	09 44	10 14	10 44	11 14	11 44	12 14	12 44	13 14	13 44	14 14	14 44
Watchet (West Somerset Ry)	a	06 25	07 58	08 28	08 58	09 32	10 02	10 32	11 02	11 32	12 02	12 32	13 02	13 32	14 02	14 32	15 02	15 32
Dunster Steep	a	06 39	08 15	08 45	09 15	09 49	10 19	10 49	11 19	11 49	12 19	12 49	13 19	13 49	14 19	14 49	15 19	15 49
Minehead Parade	a	06 47	08 23	08 53	09 23	09 57	10 27	10 57	11 27	11 57	12 27	12 57	13 27	13 57	14 27	14 57	15 27	15 57

		GW	GW	GW	GW	GW SX	GW SO	GW	GW	GW	GW	GW	GW	GW	GW SX	GW SO
Taunton	d	15 14	15 44	16 14	16 44	17 09	17 09	17 29	17 59	18 29	19 16	20 16	21 16	22 16	23 15	23 16
Watchet (West Somerset Ry)	a	16 02	16 32	16 58	17 28	17 51	17 53	18 13	18 43	19 13	20 00	21 00	22 00	23 00	23 58	23 59
Dunster Steep	a	16 19	16 49	17 15	17 45	18 08	18 10	18 30	19 00	19 30	20 14	21 14	22 14	23 14	00 12	00 14
Minehead Parade	a	16 27	16 57	17 23	17 53	18 16	18 18	18 38	19 08	19 38	20 22	21 22	22 22	23 22	00 20	00 22

Sundays

		GW	GW	GW	GW	GW	GW	GW	GW	GW	GW
Taunton	d	09 35	11 35	12 35	13 35	14 35	15 35	16 35	17 35	19 35	23 15
Watchet (West Somerset Ry)	a	10 18	12 18	13 18	14 18	15 18	16 18	17 18	18 18	20 18	23 58
Dunster Steep	a	10 32	12 32	13 32	14 32	15 32	16 32	17 32	18 32	20 32	00 12
Minehead Parade	a	10 40	12 40	13 40	14 40	15 40	16 40	17 40	18 40	20 40	00 20

Mondays to Saturdays

		GW	GW SX	GW SO	GW SX	GW SO	GW	GW	GW	GW	GW	GW	GW	GW	GW	GW	GW	GW
Minehead Bancks Street	d	05 50	07 00	07 10	07 20	07 42	08 17	08 47	09 17	09 47	10 17	10 47	11 17	11 47	12 17	12 47	13 17	13 47
Dunster Steep	d	05 58	07 08	07 18	07 28	07 50	08 25	08 55	09 25	09 55	10 25	10 55	11 25	11 55	12 25	12 55	13 25	13 55
Watchet (West Somerset Ry)	d	06 13	07 26	07 36	07 46	08 08	08 43	09 13	09 43	10 13	10 43	11 13	11 43	12 13	12 43	13 13	13 43	14 13
Taunton	a	06 55	08 14	08 18	08 33	08 50	09 25	09 55	10 25	10 55	11 25	11 59	12 29	12 59	13 29	14 00	14 29	14 59

		GW	GW	GW	GW	GW	GW	GW	GW	GW SX	GW SO	GW	GW	GW	GW	GW
Minehead Bancks Street	d	14 17	14 47	15 17	15 47	16 17	16 47	17 17	17 47	18 17	18 17	18 45	19 45	20 35	21 35	22 35
Dunster Steep	d	14 25	14 55	15 25	15 55	16 25	16 55	17 25	17 55	18 25	18 25	18 53	19 53	20 43	21 43	22 43
Watchet (West Somerset Ry)	d	14 43	15 13	15 43	16 13	16 43	17 13	17 43	18 13	18 43	18 43	19 08	20 08	20 58	21 58	22 58
Taunton	a	15 29	15 59	16 29	16 59	17 29	17 59	18 29	19 00	19 25	19 29	19 50	20 50	21 40	22 40	23 40

Sundays

		GW	GW	GW	GW	GW	GW	GW	GW	GW
Minehead Bancks Street	d	08 55	10 55	12 55	13 55	14 55	15 55	16 55	17 55	18 55
Dunster Steep	d	09 03	11 03	13 03	14 03	15 03	16 03	17 03	18 03	19 03
Watchet (West Somerset Ry)	d	09 18	11 18	13 18	14 18	15 18	16 18	17 18	18 18	19 18
Taunton	a	10 00	12 00	14 00	15 00	16 00	17 00	18 00	19 00	20 00

For general notes see front of timetable
For details of catering facilities see Directory of Train Operators

Table 136

Mondays to Fridays

Exmouth → Exeter → Barnstaple

Network Diagram - see first page of Table 135

Miles	Miles	Station		GW MO	GW MX	GW	SW ■1	GW	GW A	SW ■1	GW A	SW ■1	GW	GW	GW A	GW	GW	SW ■1	GW A	GW	SW ■1 ◇ ☕	GW A
0	—	**Exmouth**	d	23p59	00 01			06 15	06 46		07 15		07 53		08 23		08 53		09 23	09 53		10 23
2	—	Lympstone Village	d	00 03	00 05			06 19	06 50		07 19		07 57		08 27		08 57		09 27	09 57		10 27
3	—	Lympstone Commando	d	00x04	00x06			06x20	06x53		07x21		07x58		08x29		08x58		09x28			10x28
3½	—	Exton	d	00x06	00x08			06x22	06x54		07x22		08x00		08x30		09x00		09x30			10x30
5	—	Topsham	d	00 11	00 13			06 27	06 59		07 29		08 05		08 35		09 05		09 35	10 05		10 35
7	—	Digby & Sowton	d	00 15	00 18			06 32	07 04		07 33		08 10		08 40		09 10		09 40	10 10		10 40
9	—	Polsloe Bridge	d	00 19	00 21			06 35	07 07		07 37		08 13		08 44		09 13		09 44			10 44
10	—	St James' Park	d	00 21	00 24			06 38	07 10		07 40		08 16	08 33	08 47		09 16		09 47			10 47
10½	—	**Exeter Central**	a	00 24	00 26			06 40	07 12		07 42		08 18	08 35	08 49		09 18		09 49	10 16		10 49
—	—		d	00 24	00 27		06 32	06 41	07 13	07 33	07 43	08 12	08 19	08 36	08 50	09 08	09 19	09 25	09 50	10 17	10 29	10 50
11¼	—	**Exeter St Davids** 5	a	00 27	00 33		06 36	06 44	07 16	07 36	07 46	08 15	08 24	08 41	08 54	09 13	09 24	09 28	09 54	10 21	10 32	10 54
—	—		d			05 56		06 50					08 27				09 27			10 27		
15½	—	Newton St Cyres	d																			
18¼	0	Crediton	d			06 07		07 01					08 38				09 38			10 38		
21¾	3½	Yeoford	d			06 13		07 07					08 44				09 44			10 44		
—	14¼	Sampford Courtenay	d																			
—	18	Okehampton	a																			
24½	—	Copplestone	d			06x18		07x12					08x49				09x49			10x49		
26¼	—	Morchard Road	d					07x15					08x52				09x52			10x52		
28¾	—	Lapford	d					07x19														
32½	—	Eggesford	d			06 32		07b40					09 08				10 08			11 08		
36¼	—	Kings Nympton	d					07x45					09x14									
39¼	—	Portsmouth Arms	d					07x50														
43½	—	Umberleigh	d			06x47		07x56					09x23				10x23			11x23		
45¾	—	Chapelton	d					08x00														
50¼	—	**Barnstaple**	a			06 58		08 09					09 37				10 35			11 35		

Station		GW	SW ■1 ◇ ☕	GW A	GW	SW ■1 ◇ ☕	GW A	GW	SW ■1 ◇ ☕	GW A	GW	GW A	GW	SW ■1 ◇ ☕	GW A	GW A	SW ■1	GW A	GW	GW A	SW ■1 ◇ ☕
Exmouth	d	10 53		11 23	11 53		12 23	12 53		13 23	13 53	14 23	14 53		15 23	15 53			16 25	16 55	
Lympstone Village	d	10 57		11 27	11 57		12 27	12 57		13 27	13 57	14 27	14 57		15 27	15 57			16 29	16 59	
Lympstone Commando	d			11x28			12x28			13x28		14x28			15x28	15x58			16x30	17x00	
Exton	d			11x30			12x30			13x30		14x30			15x30	16x00			16x32	17x02	
Topsham	d	11 05		11 35	12 05		12 35	13 05		13 35	14 05	14 35	15 05		15 35	16 05			16 39	17 07	
Digby & Sowton	d	11 10		11 40	12 10		12 40	13 10		13 40	14 10	14 40	15 10		15 40	16 10			16 43	17 12	
Polsloe Bridge	d			11 44			12 44			13 44		14 44			15 44	16 14			16 47	17 15	
St James' Park	d			11 47			12 47			13 47		14 47			15 47	16 16		16 43	16 49	17 18	
Exeter Central	a	11 16		11 49	12 16		12 49	13 16		13 49	14 16	14 49	15 16		15 49	16 19		16 45	16 52	17 20	
	d	11 17	11 38	11 50	12 17	12 26	12 50	13 17	13 38	13 50	14 17	14 50	15 17	15 39	15 50	16 20	16 24	16 46	16 53	17 21	17 35
Exeter St Davids 6	a	11 21	11 42	11 54	12 24	12 29	12 54	13 21	13 41	13 54	14 21	14 54	15 21	15 42	15 56	16 23	16 27	16 49	16 56	17 24	17 38
	d	11 27			12 27			13 27			14 27		15 27						16 57		
Newton St Cyres	d																				
Crediton	d	11 38			12 38			13 38			14 38		15 38						17 08		
Yeoford	d	11 44			12 44			13 44			14 44		15 44						17 15		
Sampford Courtenay	d																				
Okehampton	a																				
Copplestone	d	11x49			12x49			13x49			14x49		15x49						17x19		
Morchard Road	d	11x52			12x52			13x52			14x52		15x52						17x22		
Lapford	d																		17x27		
Eggesford	d	12 08			13 08			14 08			15 08		16 08						17 38		
Kings Nympton	d							14x15											17x45		
Portsmouth Arms	d																				
Umberleigh	d	12x23			13x23			14x23			15x23		16x23						17x55		
Chapelton	d																				
Barnstaple	a	12 35			13 37			14 37			15 35		16 35						18 07		

Station		GW	SW ■1	GW A	GW	GW	SW ■1	GW A	SW ■1 ◇ ☕	GW	GW	SW ■1 ◇ ☕	GW	GW A	GW	SW ■1 ◇ ☕	GW A	SW FO ■1 ◇ ☕	GW	SW FO ■1 ◇ ☕	SW FX ■1 ◇ ☕
Exmouth	d	17 25		17 55		18 28		18 55		19 33	20 01			21 01			22 04		23 10		
Lympstone Village	d	17 29		17 59		18 31		18 59		19 37	20 05			21 05			22 08		23 14		
Lympstone Commando	d	17x30		18x00				19x00			20x06			21x06			22x09		23x15		
Exton	d	17x32		18x02				19x02			20x08			21x08			22x11		23x17		
Topsham	d	17 37		18 07		18 37		19 07		19 43	20 13			21 13			22 16		23 22		
Digby & Sowton	d	17 42		18 12		18 42		19 12		19 48	20 18			21 18			22 27		23 27		
Polsloe Bridge	d	17 45		18 15				19 15			20 21			21 21			22 21		23 30		
St James' Park	d	17 48		18 18				19 18			20 24			21 24			22 27		23 33		
Exeter Central	a	17 50		18 20		18 48		19 20		19 56	20 26			21 26			22 29		23 35		
	d	17 51	17 57	18 21	18 35	18 51	19 03	19 21	19 52	19 57	20 27	20 32	20 55	21 27	21 42	21 49	22 30	22 38	23 36	23 51	23 58
Exeter St Davids 6	a	17 55	18 00	18 24	18 39	18 55	19 06	19 25	19 57	20 04	20 33	20 36	20 58	21 31	21 47	21 54	22 33	22 41	23 42	23 54	00 01
	d	17 57				18 57							21 00								
Newton St Cyres	d	18x04				19x04							21x07								
Crediton	d	18 11				19 11							21 14								
Yeoford	d	18 17				19 18							21 20								
Sampford Courtenay	d																				
Okehampton	a																				
Copplestone	d	18x22				19x22							21x26								
Morchard Road	d	18x25				19x25							21x29								
Lapford	d	18x29											21x33								
Eggesford	d	18 41				19 43							21 43								
Kings Nympton	d	18x48											21x48								
Portsmouth Arms	d	18x52											21x53								
Umberleigh	d	18x59				19x57							21x59								
Chapelton	d	19x03											22x03								
Barnstaple	a	19 13				20 10							22 13								

For general notes see front of timetable
For details of catering facilities see Directory of Train Operators

A To Paignton (Table 135)
b Arr. 0728

Table 136

Saturdays

Exmouth → Exeter → Barnstaple

Network Diagram - see first page of Table 135

		GW	GW	SW 1	GW	SW 1	GW A	GW	SW 1	GW A	GW	SW 1	GW A	GW	SW 1 ◇ (catering)	GW A	GW	GW A
Exmouth	d	00 01			06 15		07 15	07 53		08 23	08 53		09 23	09 53		10 23	10 53	11 23
Lympstone Village	d	00 05			06 19		07 19	07 57		08 27	08 57		09 27	09 57		10 27	10 57	11 27
Lympstone Commando	d	00x06			06x20		07x21	07x58		08x29	08x58		09x28	09x58		10x28	10x58	11x28
Exton	d	00x08			06x22		07x22	08x00		08x30	09x00		09x30			10x30		11x30
Topsham	d	00 13			06 27		07 29	08 05		08 35	09 05		09 35	10 05		10 35	11 05	11 35
Digby & Sowton	d	00 18			06 32		07 33	08 10		08 40	09 10		09 40	10 10		10 40	11 10	11 40
Polsloe Bridge	d	00 21			06 35		07 37	08 13		08 44	09 13		09 44			10 44		11 44
St James' Park	d	00 24			06 38		07 40	08 16		08 47	09 16		09 47			10 47		11 47
Exeter Central	a	00 26			06 40		07 42	08 18		08 49	09 18		09 49	10 16		10 49	11 16	11 49
	d	00 27		06 32	06 41	07 33	07 43	08 19	08 28	08 50	09 19	09 25	09 50	10 17	10 26	10 50	11 17	11 50
Exeter St Davids 6	a	00 33		06 35	06 44	07 36	07 46	08 24	08 31	08 54	09 24	09 28	09 54	10 21	10 29	10 54	11 21	11 54
	d		05 56		06 50			08 27			09 27			10 27			11 27	
Newton St Cyres	d																	
Crediton	d		06 07		07 01			08 38			09 38			10 38			11 38	
Yeoford	d		06 13		07 07			08 44			09 44			10 44			11 44	
Sampford Courtenay	d																	
Okehampton	a																	
Copplestone	d		06x18		07x12			08x49			09x49			10x49			11x49	
Morchard Road	d				07x15			08x52			09x52			10x52			11x52	
Lapford	d				07x19													
Eggesford	d		06 32		07b40			09 08			10 08			11 08			12 08	
Kings Nympton	d				07x45			09x14										
Portsmouth Arms	d				07x50													
Umberleigh	d		06x47		07x56			09x23			10x23			11x23			12x23	
Chapelton	d				08x00													
Barnstaple	a		06 58		08 09			09 37			10 35			11 35			12 35	

		SW 1 ◇ (catering)	GW	SW 1 ◇ (catering)	GW A	GW	SW 1 ◇ (catering)	GW A	GW	SW 1 ◇ (catering)	GW A	GW	SW 1 ◇ (catering)	GW A	GW	SW 1	GW	GW
Exmouth	d		11 53		12 23	12 53		13 23	13 53		14 23	14 53		15 23	15 53			16 25
Lympstone Village	d		11 57		12 27	12 57		13 27	13 57		14 27	14 57		15 27	15 57			16 29
Lympstone Commando	d		11x58		12x28	12x58		13x28	13x58		14x28	14x58		15x28	15x58			16x30
Exton	d				12x30			13x30			14x30			15x30	16x00			16x32
Topsham	d		12 05		12 35	13 05		13 35	14 05		14 35	15 05		15 35	16 05			16 39
Digby & Sowton	d		12 10		12 40	13 10		13 40	14 10		14 40	15 10		15 40	16 10			16 43
Polsloe Bridge	d				12 44			13 44			14 44			15 44	16 14			16 47
St James' Park	d				12 47			13 47			14 47			15 47	16 16			16 49
Exeter Central	a		12 16		12 49	13 16		13 49	14 18		14 49	15 16		15 49	16 19			16 52
	d	11 58	12 20	12 27	12 50	13 21	13 39	13 50	14 19	14 23	14 50	15 17	15 39	15 50	16 20	16 25	16 45	16 53
Exeter St Davids 6	a	12 01	12 24	12 30	12 54	13 25	13 42	13 54	14 23	14 26	14 54	15 21	15 42	15 54	16 23	16 28	16 48	16 56
	d		12 27			13 27			14 27			15 27						16 57
Newton St Cyres	d																	
Crediton	d		12 38			13 38			14 38			15 38						17 08
Yeoford	d		12 44			13 44			14 44			15 44						17 15
Sampford Courtenay	d																	
Okehampton	a																	
Copplestone	d		12x49			13x49			14x49			15x49						17x19
Morchard Road	d		12x52			13x52			14x52			15x52						17x22
Lapford	d																	17x27
Eggesford	d		13 08			14 08			15 08			16 08						17 38
Kings Nympton	d					14x15												17x45
Portsmouth Arms	d																	
Umberleigh	d		13x23			14x23			15x23			16x23						17x55
Chapelton	d																	
Barnstaple	a		13 37			14 37			15 35			16 35						18 07

		GW A	SW 1 ◇ (catering)	GW	SW 1	GW A	GW	GW	SW 1	GW	SW 1 ◇ (catering)	GW A	GW	GW	GW	SW 1 ◇ (catering)	GW	SW 1 ◇ (catering)	GW	GW
Exmouth	d	16 55		17 25		17 55		18 27		18 55		19 33	20 01		21 01		22 01		23 13	23 43
Lympstone Village	d	16 59		17 29		17 59		18 31		18 59		19 37	20 05		21 05		22 05		23 17	23 47
Lympstone Commando	d	17x00		17x30		18x00				19x00			20x06		21x06		22x06		23x18	23x48
Exton	d	17x02		17x32		18x02				19x02			20x08		21x08		22x08		23x20	23x50
Topsham	d	17 07		17 37		18 07		18 37		19 07		19 43	20 13		21 13		22 13		23 27	23 55
Digby & Sowton	d	17 12		17 42		18 12		18 42		19 12		19 48	20 18		21 18		22 18		23 32	23 59
Polsloe Bridge	d	17 15		17 45		18 15				19 15			20 21		21 21		22 21		23 35	00 03
St James' Park	d	17 18		17 48		18 18				19 18			20 24		21 24		22 24		23 38	00 06
Exeter Central	a	17 20		17 50		18 20		18 48		19 20		19 56	20 26		21 26		22 26		23 40	00 08
	d	17 21	17 33	17 51	17 57	18 21	18 35	18 49	19 03	19 21	19 52	19 57	20 26	20 55	21 27	21 48	22 27	22 39	23 41	00 09
Exeter St Davids 6	a	17 24	17 36	17 55	18 00	18 24	18 40	18 52	19 06	19 25	19 57	20 04	20 32	20 58	21 31	21 53	22 31	22 42	23 45	00 14
	d			17 57				18 57						21 00						
Newton St Cyres	d			18x04				19x04						21x07						
Crediton	d			18 11				19 11						21 14						
Yeoford	d			18 17				19 18						21 20						
Sampford Courtenay	d																			
Okehampton	a																			
Copplestone	d			18x22				19x22						21x26						
Morchard Road	d			18x25				19x25						21x29						
Lapford	d			18x29										21x33						
Eggesford	d			18 41				19 43						21 43						
Kings Nympton	d			18x48										21x48						
Portsmouth Arms	d			18x52										21x53						
Umberleigh	d			18x59				19x57						21x59						
Chapelton	d			19x03										22x03						
Barnstaple	a			19 13				20 10						22 13						

For general notes see front of timetable
For details of catering facilities see
Directory of Train Operators

A To Paignton (Table 135)
b Arr. 0728

Table 136

Sundays

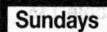

Exmouth → Exeter → Barnstaple

Network Diagram - see first page of Table 135

		GW	SW 1	GW A	GW B	GW	SW 1 ◇	SW 1 ◇ ☕	GW	GW C	SW 1 ◇ ☕	GW	GW	SW 1 ◇ ☕
Exmouth	d	23p43		09§08		10 00			11 05	12 05		13 10	14 10	
Lympstone Village	d	23p47		09§12		10 04			11 09	12 09		13 14	14 14	
Lympstone Commando	d	23b48		09x13		10x05			11x10	12x10		13x15	14x15	
Exton	d	23b50		09x15		10x07			11x12	12x12		13x17	14x17	
Topsham	d	23p55		09§21		10 12			11 18	12 17		13 22	14 22	
Digby & Sowton	d	23p59		09§26		10 17			11 23	12 22		13 27	14 27	
Polsloe Bridge	d	00 03		09§29		10 20			11 26	12 25		13 30	14 30	
St James' Park	d	00 06		09§32		10 23			11 31	12 28		13 33	14 33	
Exeter Central	a	00 08		09§34		10 25			11 34	12 30		13 35	14 35	
	d	00 09	08 56	09§35		10 26	10 46	11 30	11 35	12 31	12 46	13 36	14 36	14 43
Exeter St Davids 6	a	00 14	08 59	09§38		10 30	10 49	11 33	11 38	12 34	12 49	13 39	14 40	14 46
	d			09§40	09§40				11 58			13 54		
Newton St Cyres	d			09x47	09x47							14x01		
Crediton	d			10c00	10c00				12 10			14e10		
Yeoford	d			10§07	10§07				12 17			14 17		
Sampford Courtenay	d													
Okehampton	a													
Copplestone	d			10x11	10x11				12x21			14x21		
Morchard Road	d			10x14	10x14				12x24			14x24		
Lapford	d			10x18	10x18							14x28		
Eggesford	d			10§28	10§28				12 37			14 38		
Kings Nympton	d			10x34	10x34							14x44		
Portsmouth Arms	d			10x38	10x38							14x48		
Umberleigh	d			10x45	10x45				12x51			14x55		
Chapelton	d			10x49	10x49							14x59		
Barnstaple	a			10§58	10§58				13 03			15 08		

		GW	GW	SW 1 ◇ ☕	GW	GW C	SW 1 ◇ ☕	GW	GW	SW 1 ◇ ☕	GW C	GW	SW 1 ◇ ☕	GW	GW
Exmouth	d	15 10	16 10		17 10	18 10		19 10	20 10		21 17	22 10		23 07	23 59
Lympstone Village	d	15 14	16 14		17 14	18 14		19 14	20 14		21 21	22 14		23 11	00 03
Lympstone Commando	d	15x15	16x15		17x15	18x15		19x15	20x15		21x22	22x15		23x12	00x04
Exton	d	15x17	16x17		17x17	18x17		19x17	20x17		21x24	22x17		23x14	00x06
Topsham	d	15 22	16 22		17 23	18 21		19 22	20 22		21 29	22 23		23 19	00 11
Digby & Sowton	d	15 27	16 27		17 28	18 26		19 27	20 27		21 34	22 28		23 24	00 15
Polsloe Bridge	d	15 30	16 30		17 31	18 29		19 30	20 30		21 37	22 31		23 27	00 19
St James' Park	d	15 33	16 33		17 34	18 32		19 33	20 33		21 40	22 34		23 30	00 21
Exeter Central	a	15 38	16 36		17 36	18 34		19 35	20 35		21 42	22 36		23 33	00 24
	d	15 39	16 37	16 46	17 37	18 37	18 43	19 36	20 36	20 46	21 43	22 37	22 46	23 34	00 24
Exeter St Davids 6	a	15 42	16 40	16 49	17 40	18 41	18 46	19 39	20 39	20 49	21 46	22 40	22 49	23 37	00 27
	d	16 01			18 00			19 58							
Newton St Cyres	d	16x09						20x05							
Crediton	d	16 16			18f16			20g15							
Yeoford	d	16 23			18 23			20 21							
Sampford Courtenay	d														
Okehampton	a														
Copplestone	d	16x28			18x28			20x26							
Morchard Road	d	16x31			18x31			20x29							
Lapford	d	16x35			18x36			20x33							
Eggesford	d	16 42			18 45			20 43							
Kings Nympton	d	16x50			18x51			20x49							
Portsmouth Arms	d	16x53			18x56			20x53							
Umberleigh	d	17x01			19x01			21x00							
Chapelton	d	17x05						21x04							
Barnstaple	a	17 14			19 12			21 14							

For general notes see front of timetable
For details of catering facilities see Directory of Train Operators

A Until 18 October

B From 25 October

C To Paignton (Table 135)

b Previous night.

x Stops on request, passengers wishing to alight must inform the guard and those wishing to join must give a hand signal to the driver

c Arr. 0953

e Arr. 1407

f Arr. 1811

g Arr. 2011

Barnstaple → Exeter → Exmouth

Network Diagram - see first page of Table 135

Miles	Miles			SW 1◇ ☕	GW	GW	GW	SW 1◇ ☕	GW A	GW A	SW 1	GW A	GW	SW 1◇ ☕	GW	GW	GW A	GW	SW 1◇ ☕	GW A	GW
0	—	**Barnstaple**	d										07x09					08 43			09 43
4¼	—	Chapelton	d										07x14								
6¾	—	Umberleigh	d										07x18					08x51			09x51
10¾	—	Portsmouth Arms	d										07x25								
13¾	—	Kings Nympton	d										07x30					09x03			
17½	—	Eggesford	d										07 39					09 07			10 07
21½	—	Lapford	d										07x45								
23¾	—	Morchard Road	d										07x49					09x16			10x16
25½	—	Copplestone	d										07x52					09x20			10x20
—	0	Okehampton	d																		
—	3¾	Sampford Courtenay	d																		
28½	14½	Yeoford	d										07 58					09 24			10 24
32	18	Crediton	d										08 05					09c37			10c37
34¾	—	Newton St Cyres	d										08x08								
39	—	**Exeter St Davids 6**	a										08 17					09 48			10 48
—	—		d	05 10	05 44	06 09	06 29	06 42	07 11	07 48	08 00	08 12	08 18	08 25	08 48	09 01	09 18	09 48	10 10	10 18	10 48
39¾	—	**Exeter Central**	a	05 13	05 47	06 12	06 32	06 45	07 14	07 51	08 03	08 16	08 21	08 29	08 51	09 06	09 21	09 51	10 13	10 21	10 51
—	—		d		05 48	06 13	06 39		07 15	07 52		08 17	08 22		08 52		09 22	09 52		10 22	10 52
40½	—	St James' Park	d			06 15	06 41		07 17	07 54		08a21	08 24		08 54		09 24			10 24	
41¼	—	Polsloe Bridge	d			06 18	06 44		07 20	07 57			08 27		08 57		09 27			10 27	
43¼	—	Digby & Sowton	d		05 54	06 22	06 48		07 24	08 01			08 31		09 01		09 31	10 01		10 31	11 01
45¼	—	Topsham	d		05 58	06 28	06e58		07 28	08 05			08 35		09 05		09 35	10 05		10 35	11 05
46¾	—	Exton	d			06x30	07x01		07x31	08x07			08x38		09x08		09x38			10x38	
47¼	—	Lympstone Commando	d			06x32	07x03		07x33	08x09			08x40		09x10		09x40			10x40	
48¼	—	Lympstone Village	d		06 03	06 34	07 06		07 36	08 13			08 43		09 13		09 43	10 10		10 43	11 10
50¼	—	**Exmouth**	a		06 10	06 40	07 11		07 42	08 20			08 50		09 20		09 50	10 18		10 50	11 18

		GW A	GW	SW 1◇ ☕	GW A	GW	GW A	SW 1◇ ☕	GW	SW 1◇ ☕	GW A	GW	GW A	SW 1	GW	SW 1◇ ☕	GW A	SW 1	GW	GW A
Barnstaple	d		10 43			11 43			12 43			13 43			14 43				15 43	
Chapelton	d																			
Umberleigh	d		10x51			11x51			12x51			13x51			14x51				15x51	
Portsmouth Arms	d																			
Kings Nympton	d								13x02											
Eggesford	d		11 07			12 07			13 07			14 07			15 07				16 07	
Lapford	d																			
Morchard Road	d		11x16			12x16			13x16			14x16			15x16				16x16	
Copplestone	d		11x20			12x20			13x20			14x20			15x20				16x20	
Okehampton	d																			
Sampford Courtenay	d																			
Yeoford	d		11 24			12 24			13 24			14 24			15 24				16 24	
Crediton	d		11c37			12c37			13c37			14c37			15c37				16c37	
Newton St Cyres	d																			
Exeter St Davids 6	a		11 48			12 48			13 48			14 48			15 48				16 48	
	d	11 18	11 48	12 10	12 18	12 48	13 18	13 35	13 48	14 10	14 18	14 48	15 18	15 30	15 48	16 10	16 20	16 40	16 50	17 20
Exeter Central	a	11 21	11 51	12 13	12 21	12 51	13 21	13 38	13 51	14 13	14 21	14 51	15 21	15 33	15 51	16 13	16 23	16 43	16 53	17 23
	d	11 22	11 52		12 22	12 52	13 22		13 52		14 22	14 52	15 22		15 52		16 24		16 54	17 24
St James' Park	d	11 24			12 24		13 24				14 24		15 24				16 26		16 56	17 26
Polsloe Bridge	d	11 27			12 27		13 27				14 27		15 27				16 29		16 59	17 29
Digby & Sowton	d	11 31	12 01		12 31	13 01	13 31		14 01		14 31	15 01	15 31		16 01		16 33		17 03	17 33
Topsham	d	11 35	12 05		12 35	13 05	13 35		14 05		14 35	15 05	15 35		16 05		16 37		17 07	17 37
Exton	d	11x38			12x38		13x38				14x38		15x38				16x40		17x10	17x40
Lympstone Commando	d	11x40			12x40		13x40				14x40		15x40				16x42		17x12	17x42
Lympstone Village	d	11 43	12 10		12 43	13 10	13 43		14 10		14 43	15 10	15 43		16 10		16 45		17 15	17 45
Exmouth	a	11 50	12 18		12 50	13 18	13 50		14 18		14 50	15 18	15 50		16 18		16 52		17 23	17 53

		SW 1	GW A	SW 1◇ ☕	GW A	GW	GW	SW 1◇	GW	SW 1◇	GW	GW A	SW 1	GW A	GW	SW FX 1	GW	SW FO 1	GW
Barnstaple	d					17 09			18 13		19 16				20 23				22 18
Chapelton	d																		22x23
Umberleigh	d					17x17			18x21		19x24				20x31				22x27
Portsmouth Arms	d								18x28		19x31								22x34
Kings Nympton	d					17 28			18x33										22x39
Eggesford	d					17 38			18 40		19 42				20 48				22 47
Lapford	d					17 46			18x47						20x54				22x52
Morchard Road	d					17x48			18x51						20x59				22x57
Copplestone	d					17x51			18x55		19x52				21x01				23x00
Okehampton	d																		
Sampford Courtenay	d																		
Yeoford	d					17 56			18 59		19 57				21 07				23 06
Crediton	d					18 11			19 11		20 05				21 14				23 13
Newton St Cyres	d								19x16		20x09				21x17				23x16
Exeter St Davids 6	a					18 24			19 25		20 18				21 31				23 26
	d	17 40	17 50	18 10	18 20	18 26	18 50	19 10	19 27	20 15	20 20	20 27	21 00	21 30	21 33	22 30	22 36	22 57	23 27
Exeter Central	a	17 43	17 53	18 13	18 23	18 32	18 53	19 13	19 29	20 18	20 25	20 29	21 03	21 33	21 40	22 33	22 39	23 00	23 30
	d		17 54		18 24		18 54		19 30			20 30		21 34			22 40		23 31
St James' Park	d		17 56		18 26		18 56		19 32			20 32		21 36			22 42		23 33
Polsloe Bridge	d		17 59		18 29		18 59		19 35			20 35		21 39			22 45		23 36
Digby & Sowton	d		18 03		18 33		19 03		19 39			20 39		21 44			22 49		23 40
Topsham	d		18 07		18 37		19 07		19 43			20 43		21 47			22 53		23 44
Exton	d		18x10		18x40		19x10		19x46			20x46		21x49			22x56		23x46
Lympstone Commando	d		18x12		18x42		19x12		19x48			20x48		21x51			22x58		23x48
Lympstone Village	d		18 15		18 45		19 15		19 51			20 51		21 55			23 01		23 51
Exmouth	a		18 23		18 53		19 23		19 57			20 57		22 00			23 07		23 57

For general notes see front of timetable
For details of catering facilities see Directory of Train Operators

A From Paignton (Table 135)
c Arr. 5 minutes earlier
e Arr. 0652

Table 136

Barnstaple → Exeter → Exmouth

Network Diagram - see first page of Table 135

		SW 1 ◇ ☕	GW	GW	SW 1 ◇ ☕	GW A	GW A	SW 1	GW	SW 1 ◇ ☕	GW	GW A	GW	SW 1 ◇ ☕	GW B	GW C	GW	SW 1 ◇ ☕	GW A	GW
Barnstaple	d								07 09				08 43				09 43			10 43
Chapelton	d								07x14											
Umberleigh	d								07x18				08x51				09x51			10x51
Portsmouth Arms	d								07x25											
Kings Nympton	d								07x30				09x03							
Eggesford	d								07 39				09 07				10 07			11 07
Lapford	d								07x45											
Morchard Road	d								07x49				09x16				10x16			11x16
Copplestone	d								07x52				09x20				10x20			11x20
Okehampton	d																			
Sampford Courtenay	d																			
Yeoford	d								07 58				09 24				10 24			11 24
Crediton	d								08 05				09b37				10b37			11b37
Newton St Cyres	d								08x08											
Exeter St Davids 6	a								08 18				09 48				10 48			11 48
	d	05 10	05 44	06 29	06 41	07 11	07 48	08 00	08 18	08 25	08 48	09 18	09 48	10 10	10 18	10 18	10 48	11 08	11 18	11 48
Exeter Central	a	05 13	05 47	06 32	06 44	07 14	07 51	08 03	08 21	08 29	08 51	09 21	09 51	10 13	10 21	10 21	10 51	11 11	11 21	11 51
	d		05 48	06 39		07 15	07 52		08 22		08 52	09 22	09 52		10 22	10 22	10 52		11 22	11 52
St James' Park	d			06 41		07 17	07 54		08 24		08 54	09 24	09 55		10 24	10 24			11 24	
Polsloe Bridge	d			06 44		07 20	07 57		08 27		08 57	09 27	09 58		10 27	10 27			11 27	
Digby & Sowton	d		05 54	06 48		07 24	08 01		08 31		09 01	09 31	10 01		10 31	10 31	11 01		11 31	12 01
Topsham	d		05 58	06 52		07 28	08 05		08 35		09 05	09 35	10 05		10 35	10 36	11 05		11 35	12 05
Exton	d			06x54		07x31	08x07		08x38		09x08	09x38	10x09		10x38	10x39			11x38	
Lympstone Commando	d			06x56		07x33	08x09		08x40		09x10	09x40	10x11		10x40	10x41	11x08		11x40	12x08
Lympstone Village	d		06 03	06 59		07 36	08 13		08 43		09 13	09 43	10 13		10 43	10 44	11 10		11 43	12 10
Exmouth	a		06 10	07 06		07 42	08 20		08 50		09 20	09 50	10 20		10 50	10 52	11 18		11 50	12 18

		SW 1 ◇ ☕	GW A	GW	GW A	SW 1 ◇ ☕	GW	SW 1 ◇ ☕	GW A	GW	GW A	SW 1	GW	SW 1 ◇ ☕	GW A	SW 1	GW	GW A	SW 1	GW
Barnstaple	d			11 43			12 43			13 43			14 43				15 43			
Chapelton	d																			
Umberleigh	d			11x51			12x51			13x51			14x51				15x51			
Portsmouth Arms	d																			
Kings Nympton	d						13x02													
Eggesford	d			12 07			13 07			14 07			15 07				16 07			
Lapford	d																			
Morchard Road	d			12x16			13x16			14x16			15x16				16x16			
Copplestone	d			12x20			13x20			14x20			15x20				16x20			
Okehampton	d																			
Sampford Courtenay	d																			
Yeoford	d			12 24			13 24			14 24			15 24				16 24			
Crediton	d			12b37			13b37			14b37			15b37				16b37			
Newton St Cyres	d																			
Exeter St Davids 6	a			12 48			13 48			14 48			15 48				16 48			
	d	12 10	12 18	12 48	13 18	13 35	13 48	14 10	14 18	14 48	15 18	15 30	15 48	16 10	16 20	16 40	16 50	17 20	17 40	17 50
Exeter Central	a	12 13	12 21	12 51	13 21	13 38	13 51	14 13	14 21	14 51	15 21	15 33	15 51	16 13	16 23	16 43	16 53	17 23	17 43	17 53
	d		12 22	12 52	13 22		13 52		14 22	14 52	15 22		15 52		16 24		16 54	17 24		17 54
St James' Park	d		12 24		13 24				14 24		15 24		15 55		16 26		16 56	17 26		17 56
Polsloe Bridge	d		12 27		13 27				14 27		15 27				16 29		16 59	17 29		17 59
Digby & Sowton	d		12 31	13 01	13 31		14 01		14 31	15 01	15 31		16 01		16 33		17 03	17 33		18 03
Topsham	d		12 35	13 05	13 35		14 05		14 35	15 05	15 35		16 05		16 37		17 07	17 37		18 07
Exton	d		12x38		13x38				14x38		15x38				16x40		17x10	17x40		18x10
Lympstone Commando	d		12x40	13x08	13x40		14x08		14x40	15x08	15x40		16x08		16x42		17x12	17x42		18x12
Lympstone Village	d		12 43	13 10	13 43		14 10		14 43	15 10	15 43		16 10		16 45		17 15	17 45		18 15
Exmouth	a		12 50	13 18	13 50		14 18		14 50	15 18	15 50		16 18		16 52		17 23	17 53		18 23

		SW 1 ◇ ☕	GW A	GW	GW A	SW 1 ◇	GW	SW 1 ◇	GW A	GW	SW 1	GW	GW	GW	SW 1	GW	GW
Barnstaple	d			17 09			18 13			19 16			20 23				22 18
Chapelton	d																22x23
Umberleigh	d			17x17			18x21			19x24			20x31				22x27
Portsmouth Arms	d						18x28			19x31							22x34
Kings Nympton	d			17x28			18x33										22x39
Eggesford	d			17 38			18 40			19 42			20 48				22 47
Lapford	d			17x46			18x47						20x54				22x52
Morchard Road	d			17x48			18x51						20x59				22x57
Copplestone	d			17x51			18x55			19x52			21x01				23x00
Okehampton	d																
Sampford Courtenay	d																
Yeoford	d			17 56			18 59			19 57			21 07				23 06
Crediton	d			18 11			19 11			20 05			21 14				23 13
Newton St Cyres	d						19x16			20x09			21x17				23x16
Exeter St Davids 6	a			18 24			19 25			20 20			21 31				23 26
	d	18 10	18 20	18 26	18 50	19 10	19 26	20 15	20 26	20 35	21 00	21 27	21 33	22 36	22 57	23 10	
Exeter Central	a	18 13	18 23	18 32	18 53	19 13	19 29	20 18	20 29	20 40	21 03	21 30	21 40	22 39	23 00	23 12	
	d		18 24		18 54		19 30		20 30			21 31		22 40		23 13	
St James' Park	d		18 26		18 56		19 32		20 32			21 33		22 42		23 15	
Polsloe Bridge	d		18 29		18 59		19 35		20 35			21 36		22 45		23 18	
Digby & Sowton	d		18 33		19 03		19 39		20 39			21 40		22 49		23 22	
Topsham	d		18 37		19 07		19 43		20 43			21 44		22 53		23 26	
Exton	d		18x40		19x10		19x46		20x46			21x46		22x56		23x28	
Lympstone Commando	d		18x42		19x12		19x48		20x48			21x48		22x58		23x30	
Lympstone Village	d		18 45		19 15		19 51		20 51			21 52		23 01		23 33	
Exmouth	a		18 53		19 23		19 57		20 57			21 57		23 07		23 42	

For general notes see front of timetable
For details of catering facilities see Directory of Train Operators

- **A** From Paignton (Table 135)
- **B** From 12 September. From Paignton (Table 135)
- **C** Until 5 September. From Paignton (Table 135)
- **b** Arr. 5 minutes earlier

Table 136

Sundays

Barnstaple → Exeter → Exmouth

Network Diagram - see first page of Table 135

		GW	SW	GW	GW	SW	GW	GW	SW	GW	GW	SW	GW	GW	SW	SW	GW	GW	SW	GW	GW	SW	GW	GW	SW	GW
			1 ◇			1 ◇			1 ◇			1 ◇			1 ◇	1 ◇			1 ◇			1			1	
		A					B						B													
			☕			☕			☕			☕			☕	☕			☕							
Barnstaple	d							11 10			13 17			15 14				17 20			19 17			21 30		
Chapelton	d							11x15						15x19				17x25			19x22					
Umberleigh	d							11x19			13x25			15x23				17x29			19x26			21x38		
Portsmouth Arms	d							11x26						15x30				17x36			19x33					
Kings Nympton	d							11x31						15x35				17x41			19x38					
Eggesford	d							11 41			13 42			15 44				17 50			19 48			21 55		
Lapford	d							11x46						15x49				17x55			19x53					
Morchard Road	d							11x51			13x50			15x54				18x00			19x58					
Copplestone	d							11x54			13x54			15x57				18x03			20x01			22 06		
Okehampton	d																									
Sampford Courtenay	d																									
Yeoford	d							12 00			13 59			16 03				18 09			20 07			22 10		
Crediton	d							12 08			14 08			16 14				18 18			20 16			22 18		
Newton St Cyres	d							12x11						16x18				18x22			20x19					
Exeter St Davids 6	a							12 23			14 23			16 27				18 33			20 30			22 30		
	d	08 25	09 20	09 26	10 30	11 20	11 25	12 32	13 18	13 30	14 30	15 20	15 30	16 28	16 33	17 18	17 30	18 35	19 20	19 35	20 40	21 20	21 35	22 30	23 10	23 26
Exeter Central	a	08 28	09 23	09 29	10 33	11 23	11 28	12 35	13 21	13 33	14 33	15 23	15 33	16 31	16 36	17 21	17 31	18 38	19 23	19 38	20 43	21 23	21 38	22 34	23 13	23 29
	d	08 29		09 30	10 34		11 29	12 36		13 34	14 34		15 34	16 32			17 32	18 39		19 39	20 44		21 39	22 35		23 30
St James' Park	d	08 31		09 32	10 36		11 31	12 38		13 36	14 36		15 36	16 34			17 34	18 41		19 41	20 46		21 41	22 37		23 32
Polsloe Bridge	d	08 34		09 35	10 39		11 34	12 41		13 39	14 39		15 39	16 37			17 39	18 44		19 44	20 49		21 44	22 40		23 35
Digby & Sowton	d	08 38		09 39	10 43		11 38	12 45		13 43	14 43		15 43	16 41			17 43	18 48		19 48	20 53		21 48	22 44		23 39
Topsham	d	08 43		09 44	10 48		11 43	12 49		13 48	14 48		15 48	16 45			17 48	18 53		19 53	20 58		21 52	22 49		23 43
Exton	d	08x45		09x46	10x50		11x45	12x51		13x50	14x50		15x50	16x47			17x50	18x55		19x55	21x00		21x54	22x51		23x45
Lympstone Commando	d	08x47		09x48	10x52		11x47	12x53		13x52	14x52		15x52	16x49			17x52	18x57		19x58	21x02		21x56	22x53		23x47
Lympstone Village	d	08 50		09 51	10 55		11 50	12 57		13 56	14 55		15 55	16 53			17 55	19 00		20 00	21 06		22 00	22 57		23 51
Exmouth	a	08 55		09 56	11 00		11 55	13 01		14 01	15 01		16 01	16 57			18 01	19 05		20 05	21 12		22 04	23 03		23 55

For general notes see front of timetable
For details of catering facilities see Directory of Train Operators

A Until 18 October
B From Paignton (Table 135)

Plymouth → Gunnislake

Network Diagram - see first page of Table 135

Mondays to Fridays

Miles			GW	GW	GW 1 ☕	GW ◇ A	GW 1 B	GW	GW ◇	GW	GW	GW	GW C	GW	GW	GW	GW	GW D	GW
0	**Plymouth**	d	05 12	06 44	07 02	08§20	08§23	08 57	09 19	10 40	10 46	12 55	14 55	15 57	16 42	17 06	18 17	18 23	21 30
1¼	Devonport	d		06 47	07a06	08a23	08a27	09 00	09a23		10 49	12 58	14 58	16 00	16 45	17 09	18 20	18 26	21 33
1¾	Dockyard	d		06x48				09x01			10x50	12x59	14x59	16x01	16x46	17x10	18x21	18x27	21x34
2¼	Keyham	d		06x50				09x03			10x52	13x01	15x01	16x03	16x48	17x12	18x23	18x29	21x36
—	St Budeaux Ferry Road	a								10 46				16 06		17 15	18 25		
3¼	St Budeaux Victoria Road	d	05 17	06 53				09 06			10 55	13 04	15 04		16 51			18 32	21 39
7½	Bere Ferrers	d		07x01				09x14			11x03	13x12	15x12		16x59			18x40	21x47
10¼	Bere Alston	a	05 30	07 08				09 21			11 10	13 19	15 19		17 06			18 47	21 54
—		d	05 33	07 10				09 23			11 12	13 21	15 21		17 08			18 49	21 56
12	Calstock	d	05x38	07x16				09x29			11x18	13x27	15x27		17x14			18x55	22x02
15	**Gunnislake**	a	05 52	07 29				09 43			11 31	13 40	15 40		17 27			19 08	22 15

Saturdays

		GW	GW ◇ 🚲	GW	GW ◇ E 🚲	GW E 🚲	GW G 🚲	GW 🚲	GW	GW	GW	GW	GW 🚲	GW	GW
Plymouth	d	06 44	08 18	08 50	09§20	09§55	09§58	10 33	10 45	12 55	14 47	16 39	17 52	18 21	21 30
Devonport	d	06 47	08a22	08 53	09a23	09a58	10a01		10 48	12 58	14 50	16 42	17 55	18 24	21 33
Dockyard	d	06x49		08x55					10x50	13x00	14x52	16x44	17x57	18x26	21x35
Keyham	d	06x51		08x57					10x52	13x02	14x54	16x46	17x59	18x28	21x37
St Budeaux Ferry Road	a							10 39					18 00		
St Budeaux Victoria Road	d	06 54		09 00					10 55	13 05	14 57	16 49		18 31	21 40
Bere Ferrers	d	07x02		09x08					11x02	13x13	15x05	16x57		18x39	21x48
Bere Alston	a	07 08		09 14					11 08	13 19	15 11	17 03		18 45	21 54
	d	07 10		09 16					11 10	13 21	15 13	17 05		18 47	21 56
Calstock	d	07x17		09x23					11x18	13x28	15x20	17x12		18x54	22x03
Gunnislake	a	07 29		09 36					11 30	13 40	15 32	17 24		19 06	22 15

Sundays until 20 September

		GW	GW H 🚲	GW ◇	GW	GW	GW	GW
Plymouth	d	09 12	09§17	10 30	11 17	13 13	15 17	17 41
Devonport	d	09 15		10a33	11 20	13 16	15 20	17 44
Dockyard	d	09x17			11x22	13x18	15x22	17x46
Keyham	d	09x19			11x24	13x20	15x24	17x48
St Budeaux Ferry Road	a		09§25					
St Budeaux Victoria Road	d	09 22			11 27	13 23	15 27	17 51
Bere Ferrers	d	09x30			11x35	13x31	15x35	17x59
Bere Alston	a	09 36			11 41	13 37	15 41	18 05
	d	09 39			11 44	13 40	15 44	18 08
Calstock	d	09x46			11x51	13x47	15x51	18x15
Gunnislake	a	09 58			12 03	13 59	16 03	18 27

Sundays from 27 September

		GW	GW ◇	GW	GW	GW	GW
Plymouth	d	09 30	10 30	11 40	13 45	15 40	17 45
Devonport	d	09 33	10a33	11 43	13 48	15 43	17 48
Dockyard	d	09x35		11x45	13x50	15x45	17x50
Keyham	d	09x37		11x47	13x52	15x47	17x52
St Budeaux Ferry Road	a						
St Budeaux Victoria Road	d	09 40		11 50	13 55	15 53	17 55
Bere Ferrers	d	09x48		11x58	14x03	16x01	18x03
Bere Alston	a	09 54		12 04	14 09	16 07	18 09
	d	09 57		12 07	14 12	16 10	18 12
Calstock	d	10x04		12x14	14x19	16x17	18x19
Gunnislake	a	10 16		12 26	14 31	16 29	18 31

For general notes see front of timetable
For details of catering facilities see Directory of Train Operators

- **A** Until 26 June and from 7 September
- **B** 29 June to 4 September
- **C** From Penzance (Table 135)
- **D** From Liskeard (Table 135)
- **E** From 12 September
- **G** Until 5 September
- **H** Until 6 September

Table 139

Mondays to Fridays

Gunnislake → Plymouth

Network Diagram - see first page of Table 135

Miles			GW	GW	GW	GW	GW	GW	GW	GW	GW	GW	GW	GW	GW	GW	GW
										A	B	C			A	B	
0	**Gunnislake**	d	05 56		07 32	09 45	11 35	13 45	15 45			17 30		19 15			22 19
3	Calstock	d	06x07		07x43	09x57	11x47	13x57	15x56			17x41		19x26			22x30
4¾	Bere Alston	a	06 14		07 50	10 03	11 53	14 03	16 03			17 48		19 33			22 37
—		d	06 17		07 52	10 06	11 56	14 06	16 05			17 50		19 35			22 39
7½	Bere Ferrers	d	06x21		07x57	10x10	12x00	14x10	16x10			17x54		19x40			22x44
11¾	St Budeaux Victoria Road	d	06 29		08 05	10 19	12 09	14 19	16 18			18 03		19 48			22 52
—	St Budeaux Ferry Road	d		07 53						16∫41	17∫06		18 12		21∫07	21∫32	
12¾	Keyham	d	06x31	07x55	08x08	10x21	12x11	14x21	16x21	16x43	17x08	18x05		19x51	21x09	21x34	22x55
13¼	Dockyard	d	06x33	07x57	08x10	10x23	12x13	14x23	16x23	16x45	17x10	18x07		19x53	21x11	21x36	22x57
13¾	Devonport	d	06 35	07 59	08 12	10 25	12 15	14 25	16 25	16∫47	17∫12	18 09		19 55	21∫13	21∫38	22 59
15	**Plymouth**	a	06 39	08 05	08 17	10 30	12 20	14 30	16 30	16∫52	17∫18	18 14	18 18	20 00	21∫18	21∫44	23 04

Saturdays

		GW	GW	GW	GW	GW	GW	GW	GW	GW	GW	GW	GW	GW	GW
							D (bus)	E (bus)				◇ E (bus)	◇ D (bus)		G
Gunnislake	d		07 32	09 45	11 35	13 45			15 45	17 29	19 16			22 19	
Calstock	d		07x43	09x57	11x47	13x57			15x56	17x41	19x27			22x30	
Bere Alston	a		07 50	10 03	11 53	14 03			16 03	17 48	19 34			22 37	
	d		07 52	10 06	11 55	14 05			16 05	17 50	19 36			22 39	
Bere Ferrers	d		07x58	10x11	12x00	14x10			16x11	17x55	19x42			22x45	
St Budeaux Victoria Road	d		08 06	10 20	12 09	14 19			16 19	18 04	19 50			22 53	
St Budeaux Ferry Road	d	07 53										21∫00	21∫01		22 57
Keyham	d	07x55	08x09	10x22	12x12	14x22			16x22	18x06	19x53	21x02	21x03	22x56	22x59
Dockyard	d	07x57	08x11	10x24	12x14	14x24			16x24	18x08	19x55	21x04	21x05	22x58	23x00
Devonport	d	07 59	08 13	10 26	12 16	14 26	14∫53	15∫16	16 26	18 10	19 57	21∫06	21∫07	23 00	23 02
Plymouth	a	08 05	08 16	10 30	12 20	14 30	14∫59	15∫21	16 29	18 14	20 00	21∫10	21∫12	23 03	23 09

Sundays

until 20 September

		GW	GW	GW	GW	GW	GW	GW
							H	◇
Gunnislake	d	10 18	12 07	14 02	16 07	18 37		
Calstock	d	10x30	12x19	14x14	16x19	18x49		
Bere Alston	a	10 36	12 25	14 20	16 25	18 55		
	d	10 38	12 27	14 22	16 27	18 57		
Bere Ferrers	d	10x44	12x33	14x28	16x33	19x03		
St Budeaux Victoria Road	d	10 52	12 41	14 36	16 41	19 11		
St Budeaux Ferry Road	d							
Keyham	d	10x55	12x44	14x39	16x44	19x14		
Dockyard	d	10x57	12x46	14x41	16x46	19x16		
Devonport	d	10 59	12 48	14 43	16 48	19 18	19∫43	20 54
Plymouth	a	11 03	12 52	14 47	16 52	19 22	19∫46	20 58

Sundays

from 27 September

		GW	GW	GW	GW	GW	GW
							◇
Gunnislake	d	10 25	12 45	14 45	16 54	18 37	
Calstock	d	10x37	12x57	14x57	17x06	18x49	
Bere Alston	a	10 43	13 03	15 03	17 12	18 55	
	d	10 45	13 05	15 05	17 14	18 57	
Bere Ferrers	d	10x51	13x11	15x11	17x20	19x03	
St Budeaux Victoria Road	d	10 59	13 19	15 19	17 28	19 11	
St Budeaux Ferry Road	d						
Keyham	d	11x02	13x22	15x22	17x31	19x14	
Dockyard	d	11x04	13x24	15x24	17x33	19x16	
Devonport	d	11 06	13 26	15 26	17 35	19 18	20 54
Plymouth	a	11 10	13 30	15 30	17 39	19 22	20 58

For general notes see front of timetable
For details of catering facilities see Directory of Train Operators

- **A** Until 26 June and from 7 September
- **B** 29 June to 4 September
- **C** To Liskeard (Table 135)
- **D** From 12 September
- **E** Until 5 September
- **G** From Newquay (Table 142)
- **H** Until 6 September

Mondays to Fridays

Liskeard → Looe

Network Diagram - see first page of Table 135

Miles			GW	GW	GW	GW	GW	GW	GW	GW	GW	GW	GW	GW
0	**Liskeard**	d	06 04	07 10	08 41	09 55	11 15	12 12	13 19	14 28	15 39	16 40	18 02	19 15
2	Coombe Junction Halt	a				10 01								19 21
—		d				10 04								19 24
3¾	St Keyne Wishing Well Halt	d	06x17	07x23	08x54	10x10		12x25	13x32		15x52	16x53	18x15	19x30
5	Causeland	d	06x20	07x26	08x57	10x14		12x28	13x35		15x55	16x56	18x18	19x34
6½	Sandplace	d	06x24	07x30	09x01	10x18		12x32	13x39		15x59	17x00	18x22	19x38
8¾	**Looe**	a	06 35	07 41	09 12	10 26	11 43	12 43	13 50	14 56	16 10	17 11	18 33	19 46

Saturdays
until 5 September

		GW	GW	GW	GW	GW	GW	GW	GW	GW	GW	GW	GW	GW
Liskeard	d	06 04	07 10	08 41	09 54	11 15	12 21	13 24	14 25	15 42	16 56	18 00	19 29	20 40
Coombe Junction Halt	a				10 00							18 06		
	d				10 03							18 09		
St Keyne Wishing Well Halt	d	06x17	07x23	08x54	10x09		12x34	13x37		15x55	17x09	18x15	19x41	20x53
Causeland	d	06x20	07x26	08x57	10x13		12x37	13x40		15x58	17x12	18x19	19x44	20x56
Sandplace	d	06x24	07x30	09x01	10x17		12x41	13x44		16x02	17x16	18x23	19x49	21x00
Looe	a	06 35	07 41	09 12	10 25	11 43	12 52	13 53	14 53	16 13	17 27	18 31	19 58	21 11

Saturdays
from 12 September

		GW	GW	GW	GW	GW	GW	GW	GW	GW	GW	GW	GW
Liskeard	d	06 04	07 10	08 41	09 55	11 15	12 12	13 19	14 28	15 40	16 43	18 02	19 15
Coombe Junction Halt	a				10 01								19 21
	d				10 04								19 24
St Keyne Wishing Well Halt	d	06x17	07x23	08x54	10x10		12x25	13x32		15x53	16x56	18x15	19x30
Causeland	d	06x20	07x26	08x57	10x14		12x28	13x35		15x56	16x59	18x18	19x34
Sandplace	d	06x24	07x30	09x01	10x18		12x32	13x39		16x00	17x03	18x22	19x38
Looe	a	06 35	07 41	09 12	10 26	11 43	12 43	13 48	14 56	16 11	17 14	18 33	19 46

Sundays
until 6 September

		GW	GW	GW	GW	GW	GW	GW	GW
Liskeard	d	10 15	11 26	12 45	14 04	15 07	16 24	18 11	20 15
Coombe Junction Halt	a								
	d								
St Keyne Wishing Well Halt	d	10x28	11x39	12x58	14x17	15x20	16x37	18x24	20x28
Causeland	d	10x31	11x42	13x01	14x20	15x23	16x40	18x27	20x31
Sandplace	d	10x35	11x46	13x05	14x24	15x27	16x44	18x31	20x35
Looe	a	10 44	11 55	13 14	14 33	15 36	16 53	18 40	20 44

For general notes see front of timetable
For details of catering facilities see Directory of Train Operators

No Sunday Service from 13 September

Mondays to Fridays

Looe → Liskeard

Network Diagram - see first page of Table 135

Miles			GW	GW	GW	GW	GW	GW	GW	GW	GW	GW	GW	GW
0	**Looe**	d	06 37	07 47	09 15	10 31	11 44	12 44	13 51	14 58	16 11	17 15	18 34	19 49
2¼	Sandplace	d	06x42	07x52	09x20	10x36		12x49		15x03		17x20	18x39	19x54
3¾	Causeland	d	06x46	07x56	09x24	10x40		12x53		15x07		17x24	18x43	19x58
5	St Keyne Wishing Well Halt	d	06x50	08x00	09x28	10x44		12x57		15x11		17x28	18x47	20x02
6¾	Coombe Junction Halt	a				10 49								20 10
—		d				10 51								20 12
8¾	**Liskeard** 3	a	07 05	08 15	09 43	11 02	12 09	13 14	14 15	15 26	16 37	17 43	19 02	20 20

Saturdays

until 5 September

		GW	GW	GW	GW	GW	GW	GW	GW	GW	GW	GW	GW	GW
Looe	d	06 37	07 44	09 16	10 41	11 54	12 53	13 58	14 54	16 16	17 29	18 34	20 01	21 12
Sandplace	d	06x42	07x49	09x21	10x46		12x58		14x59	16x21	17x34	18x39	20x06	21x17
Causeland	d	06x46	07x53	09x25	10x50		13x02		15x03	16x25	17x38	18x43	20x10	21x21
St Keyne Wishing Well Halt	d	06x50	07x57	09x29	10x54		13x06		15x07	16x29	17x42	18x47	20x14	21x25
Coombe Junction Halt	a				10 59							18 52		
	d				11 01							18 54		
Liskeard 6	a	07 07	08 14	09 45	11 12	12 18	13 23	14 23	15 22	16 46	17 59	19 05	20 29	21 40

Saturdays

from 12 September

		GW	GW	GW	GW	GW	GW	GW	GW	GW	GW	GW	GW
Looe	d	06 37	07 44	09 15	10 31	11 44	12 44	13 52	14 58	16 12	17 15	18 34	19 49
Sandplace	d	06x42	07x49	09x20	10x36		12x49		15x03	16x17	17x20	18x39	19x54
Causeland	d	06x46	07x53	09x24	10x40		12x53		15x07	16x21	17x24	18x43	19x58
St Keyne Wishing Well Halt	d	06x50	07x57	09x28	10x44		12x57		15x11	16x25	17x28	18x47	20x02
Coombe Junction Halt	a				10 49								20 07
	d				10 51								20 09
Liskeard 6	a	07 07	08 14	09 44	11 02	12 08	13 14	14 17	15 26	16 42	17 45	19 02	20 20

Sundays

until 6 September

		GW	GW	GW	GW	GW	GW	GW	GW
Looe	d	10 47	11 58	13 24	14 36	15 39	17 05	18 43	20 51
Sandplace	d	10x52	12x03	13x29	14x41	15x44	17x10	18x48	20x56
Causeland	d	10x56	12x07	13x33	14x45	15x48	17x14	18x52	21x00
St Keyne Wishing Well Halt	d	11x00	12x11	13x37	14x49	15x52	17x18	18x56	21x04
Coombe Junction Halt	a								
	d								
Liskeard 6	a	11 15	12 26	13 52	15 04	16 07	17 33	19 11	21 19

For general notes see front of timetable
For details of catering facilities see Directory of Train Operators

No Sunday Service from 13 September

Par → Newquay

Network Diagram - see first page of Table 135

Miles			GW	GW	GW	GW	GW	GW	GW	GW	GW	GW
				◇				1 R				
				A	B	C	B	C	B			
								🍴				
0	**Par**	d	06 01	09§12	09§19	11§38	12§10	13§26	14§02	16 10	18 29	20 28
4¼	Luxulyan	d	06x12	09x23	09x30				14x13	16x21	18x40	20x39
6¼	Bugle	d	06x18	09x29	09x36				14x19	16x27	18x46	20x45
8¾	Roche	d	06x23	09x34	09x41				14x24	16x32	18x51	20x50
14½	St Columb Road	d	06x34	09x45	09x52				14x35	16x43	19x02	21x01
18¼	Quintrell Downs	d	06x42	09x53	10x00	12x17	12x49		14§43	16x51	19x10	21x09
20¾	**Newquay**	a	06 53	10§04	10§11	12§28	13§00	14§31	14§54	17 02	19 21	21 20

Saturdays

until 5 September

		XC	GW	GW	GW	GW
		1 ◇	1 ◇	1 R	1 R	
		🍴	🍴	🍴	🍴	
Par	d	07 21	09 47	11 35	15 43	20 21
Luxulyan	d					
Bugle	d					
Roche	d					
St Columb Road	d					
Quintrell Downs	d					
Newquay	a	08 25	11 05	12 45	16 52	21 13

Saturdays

from 12 September

		GW	GW	GW	GW	GW	GW	GW
Par	d	06 52	09 18	12 13	14 02	16 10	18 20	20 15
Luxulyan	d	07x03	09x29	12x24		16x21	18x31	20x26
Bugle	d	07x09	09x35	12x30		16x27	18x37	20x32
Roche	d	07x14	09x40	12x35		16x32	18x42	20x37
St Columb Road	d	07x25	09x51	12x46		16x43	18x53	20x48
Quintrell Downs	d	07x33	09x59	12x54		16x51	19x01	20x56
Newquay	a	07 44	10 10	13 05	14 48	17 02	19 12	21 07

Sundays

until 6 September

		GW	GW	GW	GW	GW
				1 ◇		
				🍴		
Par	d	09 00	11 52	14 24	16 36	18 45
Luxulyan	d	09x11	12x03			18x56
Bugle	d	09x17	12x16			19x02
Roche	d	09x22	12x21			19x07
St Columb Road	d	09x33	12x32			19x18
Quintrell Downs	d	09x41	12x40			19x26
Newquay	a	09 52	12 50	15 30	17 30	19 37

For general notes see front of timetable
For details of catering facilities see Directory of Train Operators

A 29 June to 4 September. From Bristol Temple Meads (Table 135)
B Until 26 June and from 7 September
C 29 June to 4 September

No Sunday Service from 13 September

Newquay → Par

Network Diagram - see first page of Table 135

Mondays to Fridays

Miles	Station		GW	GW	GW	GW	GW	GW	GW	GW	GW
								[1] [R]			
					A	B	B	C ⊐P			
0	**Newquay**	d	06 57	10 13	12s40	13s03	14s58	15s00	17 22	19 25	21 26
2½	Quintrell Downs	d	07 03	10 19	12s46	13s09	15s04	|	17 28	19 31	21 32
6½	St Columb Road	d	07x11	10x27	12x54	13x17	15x12	|	17x36		21x40
12	Roche	d	07x22	10x38	13x05	13x28	15x23	|	17x47		21x51
14½	Bugle	d	07x27	10x43	13x10	13x33	15x28	|	17x52		21x56
16½	Luxulyan	d	07x32	10x48	13x15	13x38	15x33	|	17x57		22x01
20¾	**Par**	a	07 48	11 02	13s34	13s52	15s47	15s58	18 13	20 11	22 16

Saturdays
until 5 September

Station		GW	GW	GW	GW
		[1] [R] ⊐P	[1] [R] ⊐P	[1] ◇ ⊐P	
Newquay	d	11 22	13 14	17 18	21 20
Quintrell Downs	d				
St Columb Road	d				
Roche	d				
Bugle	d				
Luxulyan	d				
Par	a	12 23	14 15	18 19	22 04

Saturdays
from 12 September

Station		GW	GW	GW	GW	GW	GW	GW
								D
Newquay	d	07 48	10 12	13 07	14 59	17 22	19 21	21 15
Quintrell Downs	d	07 54	10 18	13x13	15x05	17x28	19x27	21x21
St Columb Road	d	08x02	10x26	13x21	15x13	17x36		21x29
Roche	d	08x13	10x37	13x32	15x24	17x47		21x40
Bugle	d	08x18	10x42	13x37	15x29	17x52		21x45
Luxulyan	d	08x23	10x47	13x42	15x34	17x57		21x50
Par	a	08 39	11 02	13 58	15 49	18 12	20 07	22 04

Sundays
until 6 September

Station		GW	GW	GW	GW	GW
				[1] ◇ ⊐P		
Newquay	d	09 54	13 00	16 15	17 32	19 40
Quintrell Downs	d	10x00	13x06		17x38	19x46
St Columb Road	d	10x08	13x14		17x46	19x54
Roche	d	10x19	13x25		17x57	20x05
Bugle	d	10x24	13x30		18x02	20x10
Luxulyan	d	10x35	13x35		18x07	20x15
Par	a	10 49	13 50	17 13	18 21	20 30

For general notes see front of timetable
For details of catering facilities see Directory of Train Operators

A 29 June to 4 September. To Penzance (Table 135)
B Until 26 June and from 7 September
C 29 June to 4 September
D To Plymouth (Table 135)

No Sunday Service from 13 September

Truro → Falmouth

Network Diagram - see first page of Table 135

Mondays to Fridays

Miles			GW	GW	GW	GW	GW	GW	GW	GW	GW	GW	GW	GW	GW
0	**Truro**	d	06 10	06 37	07 16	07 48	08 20	08 50	09 20	09 50	10 20	10 50	11 20	11 50	12 20
4¼	Perranwell	d	06x16	06x43	07x22	07x54	08x26		09 26		10x26		11x26		12x26
8¼	Penryn	d	06 24	06 51	07 30	08 02	08 34	09 04	09 34	10 04	10 34	11 04	11 34	12 04	12 34
10¼	Penmere	d	06 29	06 56	07 35	08 07	08 39	09 09	09 39	10 09	10 39	11 09	11 39	12 09	12 39
11¾	Falmouth Town	d	06 32	06 59	07 38	08 10	08 42	09 12	09 42	10 12	10 42	11 12	11 42	12 12	12 42
12¼	**Falmouth Docks**	a	06 35	07 02	07 41	08 13	08 45	09 15	09 45	10 15	10 45	11 15	11 45	12 15	12 45

		GW	GW	GW	GW	GW	GW	GW	GW	GW	GW	GW	GW	GW	GW	GW	GW
Truro	d	12 50	13 20	13 50	14 20	14 50	15 20	15 50	16 20	16 50	17 27	17 58	18 29	19 00	20 01	21 03	22 06
Perranwell	d		13x26		14x26		15x26		16x26	16x57	17x33	18x04	18x35	19x06	20x07	21x09	22x12
Penryn	d	13 04	13 34	14 04	14 34	15 04	15 34	16 04	16 34	17 05	17 41	18 12	18 43	19 14	20 15	21 17	22 20
Penmere	d	13 09	13 39	14 09	14 39	15 09	15 39	16 09	16 39	17 10	17 46	18 17	18 48	19 19	20 20	21 22	22 25
Falmouth Town	d	13 12	13 42	14 12	14 42	15 12	15 42	16 12	16 42	17 13	17 49	18 20	18 51	19 22	20 23	21 25	22 28
Falmouth Docks	a	13 15	13 45	14 15	14 45	15 15	15 45	16 15	16 45	17 16	17 52	18 23	18 54	19 25	20 26	21 28	22 31

Saturdays

		GW	GW	GW	GW	GW	GW	GW	GW	GW	GW	GW	GW	GW	GW
Truro	d	06 10	06 37	07 16	07 48	08 20	08 50	09 20	09 50	10 20	10 50	11 20	11 50	12 20	12 50
Perranwell	d		06x43	07x22	07x54	08 26		09x26		10x26		11x26		12x26	
Penryn	d	06 24	06 51	07 30	08 02	08 34	09 04	09 34	10 04	10 34	11 04	11 34	12 04	12 34	13 04
Penmere	d	06 29	06 56	07 35	08 07	08 39	09 09	09 39	10 09	10 39	11 09	11 39	12 09	12 39	13 09
Falmouth Town	d	06 32	06 59	07 38	08 10	08 42	09 12	09 42	10 12	10 42	11 12	11 42	12 12	12 42	13 12
Falmouth Docks	a	06 35	07 02	07 41	08 13	08 45	09 15	09 45	10 15	10 45	11 15	11 45	12 15	12 45	13 15

		GW	GW	GW	GW	GW	GW	GW	GW	GW	GW	GW	GW	GW	GW	GW
Truro	d	13 20	13 50	14 20	14 50	15 20	15 50	16 20	16 50	17 27	17 58	18 29	19 00	20 01	21 03	22 06
Perranwell	d	13x26		14x26		15x26		16x26	16x57	17x33	18x04	18x35	19x06	20x07	21x09	22x12
Penryn	d	13 34	14 04	14 34	15 04	15 34	16 04	16 34	17 05	17 41	18 12	18 43	19 14	20 15	21 17	22 20
Penmere	d	13 39	14 09	14 39	15 09	15 39	16 09	16 39	17 10	17 46	18 17	18 48	19 19	20 20	21 22	22 25
Falmouth Town	d	13 42	14 12	14 42	15 12	15 42	16 12	16 42	17 13	17 49	18 20	18 51	19 22	20 23	21 25	22 28
Falmouth Docks	a	13 45	14 15	14 45	15 15	15 45	16 15	16 45	17 15	17 52	18 23	18 54	19 25	20 26	21 28	22 31

Sundays

		GW	GW	GW	GW	GW	GW	GW	GW	GW	GW
Truro	d	10 45	12 15	13 37	14 31	15 35	17 00	18 10	20 03	21 04	22 03
Perranwell	d	10 52	12 22	13 44	14 38	15 42	17 07	18 17	20 10	21 11	22 10
Penryn	d	10 59	12 29	13 51	14 45	15 49	17 14	18 24	20 17	21 18	22 17
Penmere	d	11 03	12 33	13 55	14 49	15 52	17 18	18 28	20 21	21 22	22 21
Falmouth Town	d	11 05	12 35	13 57	14 51	15 55	17 20	18 30	20 23	21 24	22 23
Falmouth Docks	a	11 08	12 38	14 00	14 54	15 58	17 23	18 33	20 26	21 27	22 26

For general notes see front of timetable
For details of catering facilities see Directory of Train Operators

Falmouth → Truro

Network Diagram - see first page of Table 135

Miles			GW	GW	GW	GW	GW	GW	GW	GW	GW	GW	GW	GW	GW
0	**Falmouth Docks**	d	06 37	07 17	07 48	08 20	08 50	09 20	09 50	10 20	10 50	11 20	11 50	12 20	12 50
½	Falmouth Town	d	06 40	07 20	07 51	08 23	08 53	09 23	09 53	10 23	10 53	11 23	11 53	12 23	12 53
2	Penmere	d	06 43	07 23	07 54	08 26	08 56	09 26	09 56	10 26	10 56	11 26	11 56	12 26	12 56
4	Penryn	d	06 51	07 31	08 02	08 34	09 04	09 34	10 04	10 34	11 04	11 34	12 04	12 34	13 04
8	Perranwell	d	06x57	07x37	08x08	08x40		09x40		10x40		11x40		12x40	
12¼	**Truro**	a	07 05	07 46	08 16	08 49	09 18	09 49	10 18	10 49	11 18	11 49	12 18	12 49	13 18

		GW	GW	GW	GW	GW	GW	GW	GW	GW	GW	GW	GW	GW	GW	GW	GW
Falmouth Docks	d	13 20	13 50	14 20	14 50	15 20	15 50	16 20	16 50	17 27	17 58	18 29	19 00	19 27	20 29	21 30	22 33
Falmouth Town	d	13 23	13 53	14 23	14 53	15 23	15 53	16 23	16 53	17 30	18 01	18 32	19 03	19 30	20 32	21 33	22 36
Penmere	d	13 26	13 56	14 26	14 56	15 26	15 56	16 26	16 56	17 33	18 04	18 35	19 06	19 33	20 35	21 36	22 39
Penryn	d	13 34	14 04	14 34	15 04	15 34	16 04	16 34	17 04	17x40	18 12	18 43	19 14	19 38	20 40	21 41	22 44
Perranwell	d	13x40		14x40		15x40		16x40	17x11	17 48	18x18	18x49	19x20	19x44	20x46	21x48	22x50
Truro	a	13 49	14 18	14 49	15 18	15 49	16 18	16 49	17 19	17 56	18 27	18 58	19 29	19 54	20 55	21 58	23 00

Saturdays

		GW	GW	GW	GW	GW	GW	GW	GW	GW	GW	GW	GW	GW	GW
Falmouth Docks	d	06 37	07 17	07 48	08 20	08 50	09 20	09 50	10 20	10 50	11 20	11 50	12 20	12 50	13 20
Falmouth Town	d	06 40	07 20	07 51	08 23	08 53	09 23	09 53	10 23	10 53	11 23	11 53	12 23	12 53	13 23
Penmere	d	06 43	07 23	07 54	08 26	08 56	09 26	09 56	10 26	10 56	11 26	11 56	12 26	12 56	13 26
Penryn	d	06 51	07 31	08 02	08 34	09 04	09 34	10 04	10 34	11 04	11 34	12 04	12 34	13 04	13 34
Perranwell	d	06x57	07x37	08x08	08x40		09x40		10x40		11x40		12x40		13x40
Truro	a	07 05	07 46	08 16	08 49	09 18	09 49	10 18	10 49	11 18	11 49	12 18	12 49	13 18	13 49

		GW	GW	GW	GW	GW	GW	GW	GW	GW	GW	GW	GW	GW	GW	GW
Falmouth Docks	d	13 50	14 20	14 50	15 20	15 50	16 20	16 50	17 27	17 58	18 29	19 00	19 27	20 29	21 30	22 33
Falmouth Town	d	13 53	14 23	14 53	15 23	15 53	16 23	16 53	17 30	18 01	18 32	19 03	19 30	20 32	21 33	22 36
Penmere	d	13 56	14 26	14 56	15 26	15 56	16 26	16 56	17 33	18 04	18 35	19 06	19 33	20 35	21 36	22 39
Penryn	d	14 04	14 34	15 04	15 34	16 04	16 34	17 04	17 40	18 12	18 43	19 14	19 38	20 40	21 41	22 44
Perranwell	d		14x40		15x40		16x40	17x11	17x48	18x18	18x49	19x20	19x44	20x46	21x48	22x50
Truro	a	14 18	14 49	15 18	15 49	16 18	16 49	17 19	17 56	18 27	18 58	19 29	19 53	20 55	21 57	23 00

Sundays

		GW	GW	GW	GW	GW	GW	GW	GW	GW	GW
Falmouth Docks	d	11 12	12 44	14 03	14 57	16 00	17 30	18 43	20 30	21 30	22 35
Falmouth Town	d	11 14	12 46	14 05	14 59	16 02	17 32	18 45	20 32	21 32	22 37
Penmere	d	11 17	12 49	14 08	15 02	16 05	17 35	18 48	20 35	21 35	22 40
Penryn	d	11 22	12 54	14 13	15 07	16 09	17 40	18 53	20 40	21 40	22 45
Perranwell	d	11 29	13 01	14 20	15 14	16 16	17 47	19 00	20 47	21 47	22 52
Truro	a	11 36	13 08	14 27	15 21	16 23	17 54	19 07	20 54	21 54	22 59

For general notes see front of timetable
For details of catering facilities see Directory of Train Operators

St. Erth → St. Ives

Network Diagram - see first page of Table 135

Miles		GW	GW	GW	GW	GW	GW	GW	GW	GW	GW	GW	GW	GW	GW
—	Penzance d	06 37	06 48	07 37	08 57		09 40	10 00	10b46		11 45		12 54		
0	**St Erth** d	06 45	07 14	08 05	09 05	09 38	10 11	10 41	11 11	11 41	12 11	12 41	13 11	13 41	14 11
¾	Lelant Saltings d				09 08	09 41	10 14	10 44	11 14	11 44	12 14	12 44	13 14	13 44	14 14
1	Lelant d	06x48	07x17	08x08	09x10										
3	Carbis Bay d	06 53	07 22	08 13	09 15	09 47		10 50		11 50		12 50		13 50	
4¼	**St Ives** a	06 58	07 27	08 18	09 19	09 52	10 25	10 55	11 24	11 55	12 24	12 55	13 24	13 55	14 24

	GW	GW	GW	GW	GW	GW	GW	GW	GW	GW	GW	GW	GW	GW
Penzance d	14 00	14c49			16 00	16 44		17 37			19 13		20 14	
St Erth d	14 41	15 11	15 41	16 11	16 41	17 11	17 41	18 11	18 41	19 11	19 41	20 11	20 41	21 38
Lelant Saltings d	14 44	15 14	15 44	16 14		17 14		18 14		19 14		20 14		21 41
Lelant d					16x44		17x44	18x15	18x44		19x44		20x44	21x43
Carbis Bay d	14 50		15 50		16 49		17 49	18 20	18 49		19 49		20 49	21 48
St Ives a	14 55	15 24	15 55	16 24	16 55	17 24	17 55	18 25	18 57	19 25	19 56	20 24	20 55	21 52

Saturdays

	GW	GW	GW	GW	GW	GW	GW	GW	GW	GW	GW	GW	GW
Penzance d	06 37	06 50	07e22	08 57		09f55		11 00		11g58		13 00	
St Erth d	06 45	07 14	08 01	09 05	09 38	10 11	10 41	11 11	11 41	12 11	12 41	13 11	13 41
Lelant Saltings d				09 08	09 41	10 14	10 44	11 14	11 44	12 14	12 44	13 14	13 44
Lelant d	06x48	07x17	08x04	09x10									
Carbis Bay d	06 53	07 22	08 09	09 15	09 47		10 50		11 50		12 50		13 50
St Ives a	06 58	07 26	08 13	09 19	09 52	10 24	10 55	11 24	11 55	12 24	12 55	13 24	13 55

	GW	GW	GW	GW	GW	GW	GW	GW	GW	GW	GW	GW
Penzance d	14 00		14 49		15 53		16h45	17 37	18 50	19 06		21 32
St Erth d	14 11	14 41	15 11	15 41	16 11	16 41	17 12	17 59	18 58	19 50	20 46	21 46
Lelant Saltings d	14 14	14 44	15 14	15 44	16 14	16 44	17 15	18 02	19 01	19 53	20 49	21 47
Lelant d						16x46		18x04	19x03	19x55	20x51	21x49
Carbis Bay d		14 50		15 50		16 51	17 21	18 09	19 08	20 00	20 56	21 54
St Ives a	14 24	14 55	15 24	15 55	16 24	16 55	17 26	18 13	19 13	20 04	21 00	21 58

Sundays

until 6 September

	GW	GW	GW	GW	GW	GW	GW	GW	GW	GW
Penzance d	08 50		09 30	09 50	11 00		11 42	12 30	12 55	
St Erth d	08 59	09 30	10 00	10 30	11 11	11 41	12 11	12 41	13 11	13 41
Lelant Saltings d	09 02	09 34	10 03	10 33	11 14	11 44	12 14	12 44	13 14	13 44
Lelant d	09x03									
Carbis Bay d	09 09		10 09	10 39		11 50		12 50		13 50
St Ives a	09 14	09 44	10 14	10 45	11 24	11 55	12 25	12 55	13 24	13 56

	GW	GW	GW	GW	GW	GW	GW	GW	GW
Penzance d	13 50		14 45	15 30	15 45			17 50	19 00
St Erth d	14 11	14 41	15 11	15 41	16 11	16 41	17 24	18 24	19 30
Lelant Saltings d	14 14	14 44	15 14	15 44	16 14	16 44	17 27	18 27	19 33
Lelant d							17 29	18 29	19 35
Carbis Bay d		14 50		15 50		16 50	17 34	18 34	19 40
St Ives a	14 24	14 55	15 24	15 55	16 24	16 55	17 39	18 39	19 45

Sundays

from 13 September

	GW	GW	GW	GW	GW	GW	GW	GW	GW	GW	GW	GW	GW	GW
Penzance d	11 45	12 15	12 55		13 50		14 45	15 30		16 13		17 20		19 00
St Erth d	11 55	12 35	13 11	13 41	14 11	14 41	15 11	15 41	16 11	16 41	17 11	17 41	18 24	19 20
Lelant Saltings d	11 58	12 38	13 14	13 44	14 13	14 44	15 14	15 44	16 14	16 44	17 14	17 44	18 27	19 23
Lelant d	12x00												18x29	19x25
Carbis Bay d	12 05	12 44		13 50		14 50		15 50		16 50		17 50	18 34	19 30
St Ives a	12 10	12 50	13 24	13 55	14 24	14 55	15 24	15 55	16 24	16 55	17 24	17 55	18 39	19 35

For general notes see front of timetable
For details of catering facilities see Directory of Train Operators

- **b** 29 June to 4 September dep. 1049
- **c** 29 June to 4 September dep. 1453
- **e** From 12 September dep. 0735
- **f** From 12 September dep. 1000
- **g** From 12 September dep. 1144
- **h** From 12 September dep. 1643

St. Ives → St. Erth

Network Diagram - see first page of Table 135

Mondays to Fridays

Miles			GW	GW	GW	GW	GW	GW	GW	GW	GW	GW	GW	GW	GW	GW
0	St Ives	d	06 59	07 28	08 19	09 22	09 53	10 25	10 55	11 25	11 55	12 25	12 55	13 25	13 55	14 25
1¼	Carbis Bay	d	07 02	07 31	08 22	09 25	.	10 28	.	11 28	.	12 28	.	13 28	.	14 28
3¼	Lelant	d	07x07	07x36	08x27	09x30										
3½	Lelant Saltings	d	.	.	.	09 33	10 02	10 35	11 05	11 35	12 05	12 35	13 05	13 35	14 05	14 35
4¼	St Erth	a	07 12	07 41	08 30	09 35	10 06	10 40	11 08	11 39	12 09	12 39	13 09	13 39	14 09	14 39
—	Penzance	a	.	08 00	08 42	.	10b24	.	11 27	.	12 40	13 18	.	14c11	14e39	15 11

		GW	GW	GW	GW	GW	GW	GW	GW	GW	GW	GW	GW	GW	GW
St Ives	d	14 55	15 25	15 55	16 25	16 55	17 25	17 55	18 25	18 58	19 25	19 55	20 25	20 55	21 54
Carbis Bay	d	.	15 28	.	16 28	.	17 28	.	18 28	.	19 28	.	20 28	.	21 57
Lelant	d						17x33		18x33		19x33		20x33	21x03	22x02
Lelant Saltings	d	15 05	15 35	16 05	16 35	17 05	17 36	18 05	18 36	.	19 36	20 05	20 36	21 06	22 05
St Erth	a	15 09	15 39	16 09	16 39	17 09	17 39	18 09	18 41	19 10	19 39	20 10	20 39	21 09	22 08
Penzance	a	.	15 54	.	17 11	.	.	18c37	.	19 36	.	20 44	20 59	21 33	22 19

Saturdays

		GW	GW	GW	GW	GW	GW	GW	GW	GW	GW	GW	GW	GW	GW	GW	GW	GW	GW	GW	GW	GW	GW	GW	GW	GW
St Ives	d	07 00	07 28	08 15	09 22	09 52	10 25	10 55	11 25	11 55	12 25	12 55	13 25	13 55	14 25	14 56	15 25	15 55	16 25	16 57	17 27	18 17	19 28	20 10	21 12	22 02
Carbis Bay	d	07 03	07 31	08 18	09 25	.	10 28	.	11 28	.	12 28	.	13 28	.	14 28	.	15 28	.	16 28	17 00	17 30	18 20	19 31	20 13	21 15	22 05
Lelant	d	07x08	07x36	08x23	09x30																17x35	18x25	19x36	20 18	21x20	22x10
Lelant Saltings	d	.	.	.	09 33	10 02	10 35	11 05	11 35	12 05	12 35	13 05	13 35	14 05	14 35	15 05	15 35	16 05	16 35	17 07	17 38	18 28	19 39	20 21	21 23	22 13
St Erth	a	07 12	07 40	08 26	09 35	10 06	10 39	11 09	11 39	12 09	12 39	13 09	13 39	14 09	14 39	15 09	15 39	16 09	16 39	17 10	17 41	18 30	19 42	20 24	21 26	22 15
Penzance	a	.	08 00	08 36	.	10 23	11f24	11g28	12f06	12 37	13h19	.	.	14j27	15k21	15g45	16m24	.	17n13	.	18q24	18 42	19 57	20 43	21r46	22 27

Sundays until 6 September

		GW	GW	GW	GW	GW	GW	GW	GW	GW	GW	GW	GW	GW	GW	GW	GW	GW	GW	GW
St Ives	d	09 15	09 45	10 15	10 50	11 25	11 56	12 25	12 56	13 25	13 56	14 25	14 56	15 25	15 56	16 25	16 56	17 40	18 40	19 46
Carbis Bay	d	09 18	.	10 18	.	11 28	.	12 28	.	13 28	.	14 28	.	15 28	.	16 28	.	17 43	18 43	19 49
Lelant	d	09x23																17 48	18 48	19x54
Lelant Saltings	d	09 26	09 54	10 25	10 59	11 35	12 05	12 35	13 05	13 35	14 05	14 35	15 05	15 35	16 05	16 35	17 05	17 51	18 51	19 57
St Erth	a	09 30	09 58	10 29	11 03	11 39	12 09	12 37	13 09	13 39	14 09	14 39	15 09	15 39	16 09	16 38	17 09	17 54	18 55	19 59
Penzance	a	.	.	.	11 24	.	12 45	13 16	.	14t18	14 35	.	.	16 11	.	17 00	17 33	18 35	19 38	20 12

Sundays from 13 September

		GW	GW	GW	GW	GW	GW	GW	GW	GW	GW	GW	GW	GW	GW
St Ives	d	12 11	12 50	13 25	13 56	14 25	14 56	15 25	15 56	16 25	16 56	17 25	17 56	18 40	19 46
Carbis Bay	d	12 14	.	13 28	.	14 28	.	15 28	.	16 28	.	17 28	.	18 43	19 49
Lelant	d	12x19												18x48	19x54
Lelant Saltings	d	12 22	12 59	13 35	14 05	14 35	15 05	15 35	16 05	16 35	17 05	17 35	18 05	18 51	19 57
St Erth	a	12 25	13 03	13 39	14 09	14 39	15 09	15 37	16 09	16 39	17 09	17 39	18 09	18 55	19 59
Penzance	a	12 45	.	14 10	14 35	.	.	16 15	.	.	17 35	.	18 35	19 38	20 12

For general notes see front of timetable
For details of catering facilities see Directory of Train Operators

b Tuesdays to Fridays 30 June to 4 September arr. 1029
c 29 June to 4 September only
e 29 June to 4 September arr. 1443
f From 12 September only
g Until 5 September only
h From 12 September arr. 1321
j From 12 September arr. 1435
k From 12 September arr. 1513
m From 12 September arr. 1607
n From 12 September arr. 1710
q From 12 September arr. 1808
r From 12 September arr. 2148
t From 19 July arr. 1412

Network Diagram for Tables 148, 149

DM-11/09
Design BAJS

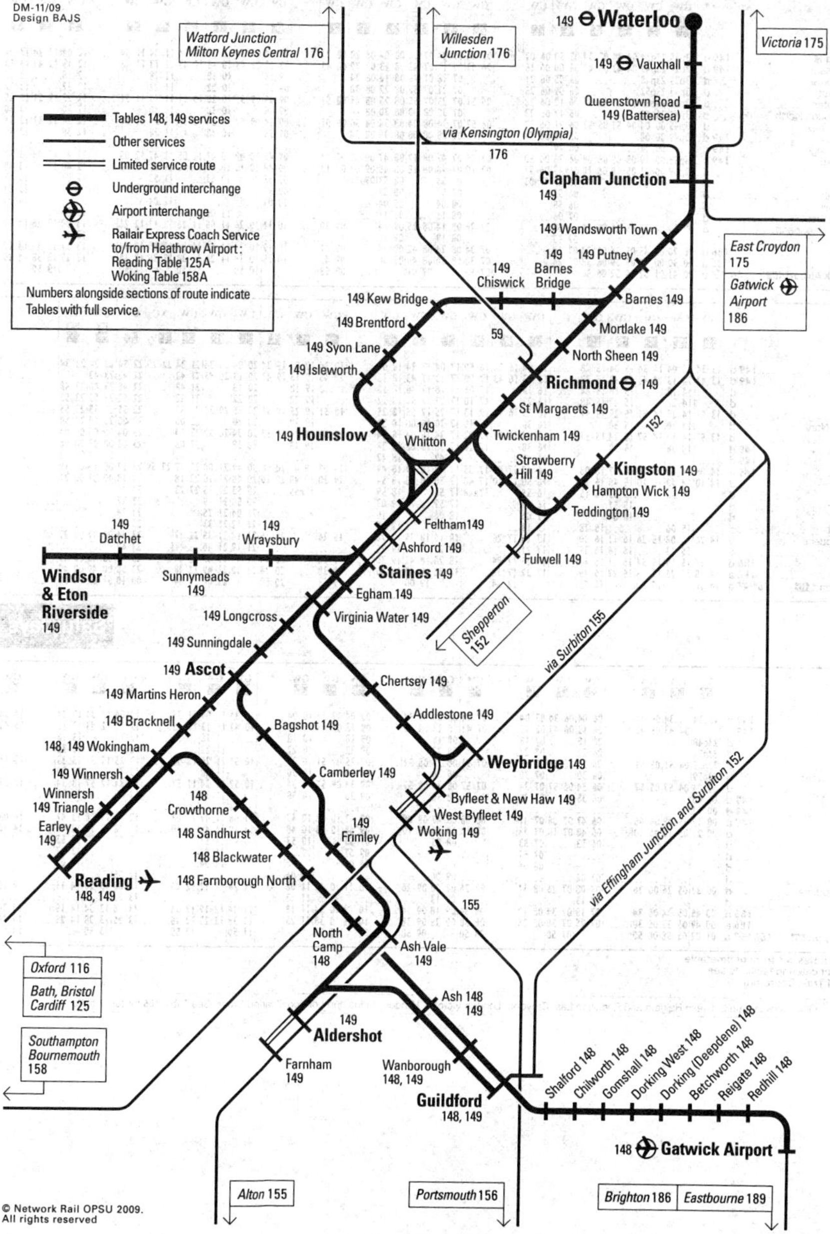
Tables 148, 149 services
Other services
Limited service route
Underground interchange
Airport interchange
Railair Express Coach Service to/from Heathrow Airport: Reading Table 125A Woking Table 158A
Numbers alongside sections of route indicate Tables with full service.
Watford Junction Milton Keynes Central 176
Willesden Junction 176
Victoria 175
149 Waterloo
149 Vauxhall
Queenstown Road 149 (Battersea)
via Kensington (Olympia)
176
Clapham Junction 149
149 Wandsworth Town
149 Putney
149 Barnes Bridge
149 Chiswick
East Croydon 175
Gatwick Airport 186
149 Kew Bridge
Barnes 149
149 Brentford
Mortlake 149
59
149 Syon Lane
North Sheen 149
149 Isleworth
Richmond 149
St Margarets 149
152
149 Hounslow
149 Whitton
Twickenham 149
Strawberry Hill 149
Kingston 149
Hampton Wick 149
Teddington 149
149 Datchet
149 Wraysbury
Feltham 149
Ashford 149
Fulwell 149
Windsor & Eton Riverside 149
Sunnymeads 149
Staines 149
Egham 149
149 Longcross
Virginia Water 149
149 Sunningdale
Shepperton 152
149 Ascot
via Surbiton 155
Chertsey 149
149 Martins Heron
149 Bracknell
Bagshot 149
Addlestone 149
148, 149 Wokingham
Weybridge 149
149 Winnersh
Camberley 149
via Effingham Junction and Surbiton 152
Winnersh 149 Triangle
148 Crowthorne
Byfleet & New Haw 149
West Byfleet 149
Earley 149
148 Sandhurst
149 Frimley
Woking 149
148 Blackwater
Reading 148, 149
148 Farnborough North
155
North Camp 148
Ash Vale 149
Oxford 116
Bath, Bristol Cardiff 125
Ash 148 149
149 Aldershot
Southampton Bournemouth 158
Farnham 149
Wanborough 148, 149
Guildford 148, 149
Shalford 148
Chilworth 148
Gomshall 148
Dorking West 148
Dorking (Deepdene) 148
Betchworth 148
Reigate 148
Redhill 148
148 Gatwick Airport
Alton 155
Portsmouth 156
Brighton 186
Eastbourne 189

Reading → Guildford, Redhill, and Gatwick Airport

Network Diagram - see first page of Table 148

Mondays to Fridays

Miles	Station		GW MO 1	GW MX 1	GW 1	GW 1	GW 1	GW 1	GW 1	GW 1	GW 1	GW 1	GW 1	GW 1
0	**Reading 7**	149 d	23p15	23p34	04 34	05 34	05 50	06 07	06 34	07 04	07 34	08 04	08 20	08 34
6¾	Wokingham	149 d	23p24	23p43	04 43	05 43	06 00	06 16	06 43	07 13	07 43	08 13	08 29	08 43
10	Crowthorne	d	23p29	23p48			06 05	06 21		07 18	07 48	08 18	08 34	
11½	Sandhurst	d	23p33	23p52			06 09	06 25		07 22	07 52	08 22	08 38	
13½	Blackwater	d	23p36	23p55	04 51	05 51	06 12	06 28	06 51	07 25	07 55	08 25	08 41	08 51
15½	Farnborough North	d	23p41	23p59			06 17	06 33		07 30	08 00	08 30	08 46	
17½	North Camp	d	23p45	00 04	04 57	05 57	06 21	06 37	06 57	07 34	08 04	08 34	08 50	09 01
19½	Ash 3	149 d	23p49	00 08			06 25	06 41		07 38	08 08	08 38	08 54	
21½	Wanborough	149 d		00 12			06 29							
25¾	**Guildford**	149 a	23p58	00 19	05 08	06 08	06 36	06 50	07 08	07 47	08 17	08 47	09 03	09 13
—		d	23p59	00 21	05 10	06 10	06 43	06 57	07 10	07 48	08 18	08 48	09 04	09 13
27¾	Shalford	d					06 48	07a03		07 53		08 53	09a11	
29¾	Chilworth	d					06 52			07 57		08 57		
33½	Gomshall	d					06 58			08 04		09 04		
38¼	Dorking West	d					07 06			08 11		09 11		
39	Dorking Deepdene	d	00 19	00 37	05 26	06 26	07 08		07 26	08 14	08 35	09 14		09 30
41¾	Betchworth	d					07 13			08 19		09 19		
44½	Reigate	186 d	00 26	00 45	05 34	06 34	07 18		07 34	08 24	08 42	09 24		09 37
46½	**Redhill**	186 a	00 30	00 49	05 39	06 38	07 24		07 38	08 30	08 46	09 30		09 42
52¼	**Gatwick Airport 10**	186 ✈ a	00 41	01 02	05 52	06 56			07 50		09 01			09 58

Station		GW 1	GW 1	GW 1	GW 1	GW 1	GW 1	GW 1	GW 1	GW 1
Reading 7	149 d	09 04	09 34	10 04	10 34	11 04	11 34	12 04	12 34	13 04
Wokingham	149 d	09 13	09 43	10 13	10 43	11 13	11 43	12 13	12 43	13 13
Crowthorne	d	09 18		10 18		11 18		12 18		13 18
Sandhurst	d	09 22		10 22		11 22		12 22		13 22
Blackwater	d	09 25	09 51	10 25	10 51	11 25	11 51	12 25	12 51	13 25
Farnborough North	d	09 30		10 30		11 30		12 30		13 30
North Camp	d	09 34	09 57	10 34	10 57	11 34	11 57	12 34	12 57	13 34
Ash 3	149 d	09 38		10 38		11 38		12 38		13 38
Wanborough	149 d									
Guildford	149 a	09 47	10 09	10 47	11 08	11 47	12 08	12 47	13 08	13 47
	d	09 48	10 10	10 48	11 10	11 48	12 10	12 48	13 10	13 48
Shalford	d	09 53		10 53		11 53		12 53		13 53
Chilworth	d	09 57				11 57				13 57
Gomshall	d	10 04				12 04				14 04
Dorking West	d			11 06				13 06		
Dorking Deepdene	d	10 11	10 26	11 08	11 26	12 11	12 26	13 08	13 26	14 11
Betchworth	d			11 13				13 13		
Reigate	186 d	10 19	10 34	11 19	11 34	12 19	12 34	13 19	13 34	14 19
Redhill	186 a	10 25	10 38	11 25	11 38	12 25	12 38	13 25	13 38	14 25
Gatwick Airport 10	186 ✈ a		10 50		11 50		12 50		13 50	

Station		GW 1	GW 1	GW 1	GW 1	GW 1	GW 1	GW 1	GW 1	GW 1	GW 1	GW 1
Reading 7	149 d	13 34	14 04	14 34	15 04	15 28	16 04	16 34	16 50	17 04	17 34	18 04
Wokingham	149 d	13 43	14 13	14 43	15 13	15 39	16 13	16 43	17 00	17 13	17 43	18 13
Crowthorne	d		14 18		15 18	15 44	16 18		17 06	17 18	17 48	18 18
Sandhurst	d		14 22		15 22	15 48	16 22		17 10	17 22	17 52	18 22
Blackwater	d	13 51	14 25	14 51	15 25	15 51	16 25	16 51	17 13	17 25	17 55	18 25
Farnborough North	d		14 30		15 30		16 30		17 18	17 30	18 00	18 30
North Camp	d	13 57	14 34	14 57	15 34	15 57	16 34	16 57	17 22	17 34	18 04	18 34
Ash 3	149 d		14 38		15 38		16 38		17 26	17 38	18 08	18 38
Wanborough	149 d						16 42			17 42		18 42
Guildford	149 a	14 08	14 47	15 08	15 47	16 08	16 49	17 08	17 35	17 49	18 17	18 49
	d	14 10	14 48	15 10	15 48	16 10	16 50	17 10	17 40	17 50	18 18	18 54
Shalford	d		14 53		15 53	16 15	16 55		17a48	17 55		18 59
Chilworth	d				15 57		16 59			17 59		19 03
Gomshall	d				16 04		17 06			18 06		19 10
Dorking West	d		15 06			16 28	17 13			18 13		19 17
Dorking Deepdene	d	14 26	15 08	15 26	16 11	16 30	17 16	17 26		18 16	18 35	19 20
Betchworth	d		15 13		16 16	16 35	17 21			18 21		19 25
Reigate	186 d	14 34	15 19	15 34	16 21	16 40	17 26	17 34		18 26	18 42	19 30
Redhill	186 a	14 38	15 25	15 38	16 27	16 45	17 32	17 38		18 32	18 47	19 36
Gatwick Airport 10	186 ✈ a	14 50		15 50		16 58		17 54			19 00	

Station		GW 1	GW 1	GW 1	GW 1	GW 1	GW 1	XC 1 ◊	GW 1	GW FX 1	GW FO 1
Reading 7	149 d	18 34	19 04	19 34	20 04	20 34	21 34	22 20	22 34	23 34	23 34
Wokingham	149 d	18 43	19 13	19 43	20 13	20 43	21 43		22 43	23 43	
Crowthorne	d		19 18		20 18		21 48		22 48	23 48	23 48
Sandhurst	d		19 22		20 22		21 52		22 52	23 52	23 52
Blackwater	d	18 51	19 25	19 51	20 25	20 51	21 55		22 55	23 55	23 55
Farnborough North	d		19 30		20 30		22 00		23 00	23 59	23 59
North Camp	d	18 57	19 34	19 57	20 34	20 57	22 04		23 04	00 04	00 04
Ash 3	149 d		19 38		20 38		22 08		23 08	00 08	00 08
Wanborough	149 d									00 12	00 12
Guildford	149 a	19 08	19 47	20 08	20 47	21 08	22 17	22 59	23 17	00 19	00 19
	d	19 10	19 48	20 10	20 48	21 10	22 18		23 18	00 21	00 21
Shalford	d		19a55		20 53	21 15	22 23		23 23		
Chilworth	d				20 58	21 19			23 27		
Gomshall	d				21 04	21 25			23 34		
Dorking West	d				21 12	21 33			23 41		
Dorking Deepdene	d	19 26		20 26	21 14	21 35	22 37		23 44	00 37	00 37
Betchworth	d				21 19	21 40			23 49		
Reigate	186 d	19 34		20 34	21 24	21 45	22 44		23 54	00 45	00 45
Redhill	186 a	19 38		20 38	21 30	21 49	22 48		23 58	00 49	00 49
Gatwick Airport 10	186 ✈ a	19 53		20 50		22 04	23 04		00 10	01 02	01 02

Saturdays

Station		GW 1	GW 1	GW 1	GW 1	GW 1	GW 1	GW 1	GW 1	GW 1
Reading 7	149 d	23p34	04 34	05 34	06 04	06 34	07 04	07 34	08 04	08 34
Wokingham	149 d		04 43	05 43	06 13	06 43	07 13	07 43	08 13	08 43
Crowthorne	d	23p48			06 18		07 18		08 18	
Sandhurst	d	23p52			06 22		07 22		08 22	
Blackwater	d	23p55	04 51	05 51	06 25	06 51	07 25	07 51	08 25	08 51
Farnborough North	d	23p59			06 30		07 30		08 30	
North Camp	d	00 04	04 57	05 57	06 34	06 57	07 34	07 57	08 34	08 57
Ash 3	149 d	00 08			06 38		07 38		08 38	
Wanborough	149 d	00 12								
Guildford	149 a	00 19	05 08	06 08	06 47	07 08	07 47	08 08	08 47	09 08
	d	00 21	05 10	06 10	06 48	07 10	07 48	08 10	08 48	09 10
Shalford	d				06 53		07 53		08 53	
Chilworth	d						07 57			
Gomshall	d						08 04			
Dorking West	d				07 06				09 06	
Dorking Deepdene	d	00 37	05 26	06 26	07 08	07 26	08 11	08 26	09 08	09 26
Betchworth	d				07 13				09 13	
Reigate	186 d	00 45	05 34	06 34	07 18	07 34	08 19	08 34	09 18	09 34
Redhill	186 a	00 49	05 38	06 38	07 25	07 38	08 25	08 38	09 25	09 38
Gatwick Airport 10	186 ✈ a	01 02	05 58	06 50		07 50		08 50		09 50

Station		GW 1	GW 1	GW 1	GW 1	GW 1	GW 1	GW 1	GW 1	GW 1	GW 1
Reading 7	149 d	09 04	09 34	10 04	10 34	11 04	11 34	12 04	12 34	13 04	13 34
Wokingham	149 d	09 13	09 43	10 13	10 43	11 13	11 43	12 13	12 43	13 13	13 43
Crowthorne	d	09 18		10 18		11 18		12 18		13 18	
Sandhurst	d	09 22		10 22		11 22		12 22		13 22	
Blackwater	d	09 25	09 51	10 25	10 51	11 25	11 51	12 25	12 51	13 25	13 51
Farnborough North	d	09 30		10 30		11 30		12 30		13 30	
North Camp	d	09 34	09 57	10 34	10 57	11 34	11 57	12 34	12 57	13 34	13 57
Ash 3	149 d	09 38		10 38		11 38		12 38		13 38	
Wanborough	149 d										
Guildford	149 a	09 47	10 08	10 47	11 08	11 47	12 08	12 47	13 08	13 47	14 08
	d	09 48	10 10	10 48	11 10	11 48	12 10	12 48	13 10	13 48	14 10
Shalford	d	09 53		10 53		11 53		12 53		13 53	
Chilworth	d	09 57				11 57				13 57	
Gomshall	d	10 04				12 04				14 04	
Dorking West	d			11 06				13 06			
Dorking Deepdene	d	10 11	10 26	11 08	11 26	12 11	12 26	13 08	13 26	14 11	14 26
Betchworth	d			11 13				13 13			
Reigate	186 d	10 19	10 34	11 18	11 34	12 19	12 34	13 18	13 34	14 19	14 34
Redhill	186 a	10 25	10 38	11 25	11 38	12 25	12 38	13 25	13 38	14 25	14 38
Gatwick Airport 10	186 ✈ a		10 50		11 50		12 50		13 50		14 50

For general notes see front of timetable
For details of catering facilities see
Directory of Train Operators

Other services run between Reigate and Redhill to East Croydon, London Victoria, London Bridge and London Charing Cross. See Table 186 for full details.

Table 148

Saturdays

Reading → Guildford, Redhill, and Gatwick Airport

Network Diagram - see first page of Table 148

		GW 1	GW 1	GW 1	GW 1	GW 1	GW 1	GW 1	GW 1	GW 1	GW 1	GW 1	GW 1	GW 1	GW 1	GW 1	XC 1 ◇	GW 1	GW 1
Reading 7	149 d	14 04	14 34	15 04	15 34	16 04	16 34	17 04	17 34	18 04	18 34	19 04	19 34	20 04	20 34	21 34	22 15	22 34	23 34
Wokingham	149 d	14 13	14 43	15 13	15 43	16 13	16 43	17 13	17 43	18 13	18 43	19 13	19 43	20 13	20 43	21 43		22 43	
Crowthorne	d	14 18		15 18		16 18		17 18		18 18		19 18		20 18		21 48		22 48	23 48
Sandhurst	d	14 22		15 22		16 22		17 22		18 22		19 22		20 22		21 52		22 52	23 52
Blackwater	d	14 25	14 51	15 25	15 51	16 25	16 51	17 25	17 51	18 25	18 51	19 25	19 51	20 25	20 51	21 55		22 55	23 55
Farnborough North	d	14 30		15 30		16 30		17 30		18 30		19 30		20 30		22 00		23 00	23 59
North Camp	d	14 34	14 57	15 34	15 57	16 34	16 57	17 34	17 57	18 34	18 57	19 34	19 57	20 34	20 57	22 04		23 04	00 04
Ash 3	149 d	14 38		15 38		16 38		17 38		18 38		19 38		20 38		22 08		23 08	00 08
Wanborough	149 d																		00 12
Guildford	149 a	14 47	15 08	15 47	16 08	16 47	17 08	17 47	18 08	18 47	19 08	19 47	20 08	20 47	21 08	22 17	22 59	23 17	00 19
	d	14 48	15 10	15 48	16 10	16 48	17 10	17 48	18 10	18 48	19 10	19 48	20 10	20 48	21 10	22 18		23 18	00 21
Shalford	d	14 53		15 53		16 53		17 53		18 53		19 53		20 53	21 15	22 23		23 23	
Chilworth	d			15 57				17 57				19 57			21 19			23 27	
Gomshall	d			16 04				18 04				20 04			21 25			23 34	
Dorking West	d	15 06				17 06				19 06				21 06		22 36		23 41	
Dorking Deepdene	d	15 08	15 26	16 11	16 26	17 08	17 26	18 11	18 26	19 08	19 26	20 11	20 26	21 08	21 33	22 38		23 44	00 37
Betchworth	d	15 13				17 13				19 13				21 13		22 43		23 49	
Reigate	186 d	15 18	15 34	16 19	16 34	17 18	17 34	18 19	18 34	19 18	19 34	20 19	20 34	21 18	21 40	22 48		23 54	00 45
Redhill	186 a	15 25	15 38	16 25	16 38	17 25	17 38	18 25	18 38	19 25	19 38	20 25	20 38	21 25	21 44	22 52		23 58	00 49
Gatwick Airport 10	186 ✈ a		15 50		16 50		17 50		18 50		19 50		20 50		21 59	23 03		00 10	01 02

Sundays

		GW 1	GW 1	GW 1 A	GW 1 B	GW 1	GW 1	GW 1	GW 1 A	GW 1 B	GW 1	GW 1 A	GW 1 B	GW 1
Reading 7	149 d	23p34	06 03	07 03	07 03	08 03	09 03	10 03	11 03	11 03	12 03	13 03	13 03	14 03
Wokingham	149 d		06 11	07 11	07 11	08 11	09 11	10 11	11 11	11 11	12 11	13 11	13 11	14 11
Crowthorne	d	23p48		07 17	07 17		09 17		11 17	11 17		13 17	13 17	
Sandhurst	d	23p52		07 21	07 21		09 21		11 21	11 21		13 21	13 21	
Blackwater	d	23p55	06 20	07 24	07 24	08 19	09 24	10 19	11 24	11 24	12 19	13 24	13 24	14 19
Farnborough North	d	23p59		07 29	07 29		09 29		11 29	11 29		13 29	13 29	
North Camp	d	00 04	06 26	07 33	07 33	08 26	09 33	10 26	11 33	11 33	12 26	13 33	13 33	14 26
Ash 3	149 d	00 08		07 37	07 37		09 37		11 37	11 37		13 37	13 37	
Wanborough	149 d	00 12												
Guildford	149 a	00 19	06 37	07 46	07 46	08 37	09 46	10 37	11 46	11 46	12 37	13 46	13 46	14 37
	d	00 21	06 40	07 47	07 47	08 39	09 49	10 39	11 47	11 47	12 39	13 47	13 47	14 39
Shalford	d					08 44		10 44			12 44			14 44
Chilworth	d					08 48		10 48			12 48			14 48
Gomshall	d					08 54		10 54			12 54			14 54
Dorking West	d					09 02		11 02			13 02			15 02
Dorking Deepdene	d	00 37	06 57	08 04	08 04	09 04	10 04	11 04	12 04	12 04	13 04	14 04	14 04	15 04
Betchworth	d					09 09		11 09			13 09			15 09
Reigate	186 d	00 45	07 05	08 11	08 11	09 13	10 13	11 13	12 11	12 13	13 13	14 11	14 13	15 13
Redhill	186 a	00 49	07 09	08 15	08 17	09 18	10 17	11 18	12 15	12 17	13 18	14 15	14 17	15 18
Gatwick Airport 10	186 ✈ a	01 02	07 27	08 25	08 30	09b32	10b31	11b32	12 27	12 31	13b32	14 25	14 31	15b32

		GW 1 A	GW 1 B	GW 1	GW 1 A	GW 1 B	GW 1	GW 1 A	GW 1 B	GW 1	GW 1 A	GW 1 B	GW 1 B	GW 1 A	GW 1
Reading 7	149 d	15 03	15 03	16 03	17 03	17 03	18 03	19 03	19 03	20 03	21 03	21 03	22 03	22 03	23 15
Wokingham	149 d	15 11	15 11	16 11	17 11	17 11	18 11	19 11	19 11	20 11	21 11	21 11	22 11	22 11	23 24
Crowthorne	d	15 17	15 17		17 17	17 17		19 17	19 17		21 17	21 17			23 29
Sandhurst	d	15 21	15 21		17 21	17 21		19 21	19 21		21 21	21 21			23 33
Blackwater	d	15 24	15 24	16 19	17 24	17 24	18 19	19 24	19 24	20 19	21 24	21 24	22 19	22 19	23 36
Farnborough North	d	15 29	15 29		17 29	17 29		19 29	19 29		21 29	21 29			23 41
North Camp	d	15 33	15 33	16 26	17 33	17 33	18 26	19 33	19 33	20 26	21 33	21 33	22 26	22 26	23 45
Ash 3	149 d	15 37	15 37		17 37	17 37		19 37	19 37		21 37	21 37			23 49
Wanborough	149 d														
Guildford	149 a	15 46	15 46	16 37	17 46	17 46	18 37	19 46	19 46	20 37	21 46	21 46	22 37	22 37	23 58
	d	15 47	15 47	16 39	17 47	17 47	18 39	19 47	19 47	20 39	21 47	21 47	22 39	22 39	23 59
Shalford	d			16 44			18 44			20 44			22 44	22 44	
Chilworth	d			16 48			18 48			20 48			22 48	22 48	
Gomshall	d			16 54			18 54			20 54			22 54	22 54	
Dorking West	d			17 02			19 02			21 02			23 02	23 02	
Dorking Deepdene	d	16 04	16 04	17 04	18 04	18 04	19 04	20 04	20 04	21 04	22 04	22 04	23 04	23 04	00 19
Betchworth	d			17 09			19 09			21 09			23 09	23 09	
Reigate	186 d	16 11	16 13	17 13	18 12	18 13	19 13	20 11	20 13	21 13	22 11	22 13	23 13	23 13	00 26
Redhill	186 a	16 15	16 17	17 18	18 16	18 17	19 18	20 16	20 17	21 18	22 15	22 18	23 18	23 18	00 30
Gatwick Airport 10	186 ✈ a	16 25	16 31	17b32	18 27	18 31	19b32	20 27	20 31	21b32	22 25	22 31	23 31	23 33	00 41

For general notes see front of timetable
For details of catering facilities see Directory of Train Operators

A Until 6 September
B From 13 September
b From 13 September arr 1 minute earlier

Other services run between Reigate and Redhill to East Croydon, London Victoria, London Bridge and London Charing Cross. See Table 186 for full details.

Gatwick Airport, Redhill and Guildford → Reading

Network Diagram - see first page of Table 148

Mondays to Fridays

Miles	Station		GW MO 1	GW MX 1	XC 1 ◊ ✠	GW 1	GW 1	GW 1	GW 1	GW 1	GW 1	GW 1	GW 1	GW 1	GW 1	GW 1	GW 1	GW 1	GW 1	GW 1	GW 1	GW 1	GW 1
0	**Gatwick Airport 10**	186 ✈ d	23p07	23p18		05 31	05 56			07 00		07 58			09 07		10 03		11 03		12 03		13 03
5¾	**Redhill**	186 d	23p20	23p29		05 44	06 14	06 24		07 11	07 28	08 09	08 33		09 24	09 34	10 14	10 34	11 14	11 34	12 14	12 34	13 14
7¾	Reigate	186 d	23p24	23p33		05 49	06 18	06 28		07 15	07 32	08 13	08 37		09 28	09 38	10 18	10 38	11 18	11 38	12 18	12 38	13 18
10½	Betchworth	d						06 33			07 37		08 42			09 43		10 43				12 43	
13½	Dorking Deepdene	d	23p31	23p40		05 56	06 25	06 37		07 22	07 41	08 20	08 46		09 35	09 47	10 25	10 47	11 25	11 45	12 25	12 47	13 25
14	Dorking West	d						06 40			07 44		08 49			09 50		10 50				12 50	
18¾	Gomshall	d						06 48		07 30	07 52		08 57			09 58				11 53			
22½	Chilworth	d						06 54			07 58		09 03			10 04				11 59			
24½	Shalford	d						06 58	07 21		08 02		09 07	09 31		10 08		11 03		12 03		13 03	
26½	**Guildford**	a	23p49	23p59		06 11	06 41	07 02	07 25	07 40	08 06	08 36	09 11	09 35	09 52	10 12	10 42	11 07	11 42	12 07	12 42	13 07	13 42
—		d	23p51	00 01	06 00	06 12	06 42	07 04	07 26	07 42	08 12	08 37	09 12	09 36	09 54	10 13	10 43	11 09	11 43	12 09	12 43	13 09	13 43
30¾	Wanborough	149 d				06 20		07 11			08 20		09 20										
32¾	Ash 3	149 d	23p59			06 24	06 52	07 16	07 36	07 52	08 24		09 24	09 46		10 23		11 18		12 18		13 18	
34¾	North Camp	d	00 04	00 13		06 28	06 56	07 20	07 41	07 56	08 28	08 49	09 28	09 50		10 27	10 55	11 22	11 55	12 22	12 55	13 22	13 55
36¾	Farnborough North	d	00 08			06 32	07 00	07 24	07 45	08 00	08 32		09 32			10 31		11 26		12 26		13 26	
38¾	Blackwater	d	00 13	00 20		06 37	07 04	07 28	07 49	08 04	08 37	08 56	09 37	09 56		10 35	11 02	11 31	12 02	12 31	13 02	13 31	14 02
40¾	Sandhurst	d	00 16			06 40	07 08	07 32	07 53	08 08	08 40		09 40			10 39		11 34		12 34		13 34	
42¼	Crowthorne	d	00 20			06 44	07 12	07 36	07 57	08 12	08 44		09 44			10 43		11 38		12 38		13 38	
45½	Wokingham	149 d	00 25	00 28		06 49	07 17	07 41	08 02	08 17	08 49	09 04	09 51	10 04		10 48	11 10	11 43	12 10	12 43	13 10	13 43	14 10
52¼	**Reading 7**	149 a	00 37	00 38	06 35	06 58	07 29	07 51	08 17	08 28	09 00	09 16	10 01	10 17	10 23	10 58	11 19	11 54	12 19	12 54	13 19	13 54	14 19

Station		GW 1	GW 1	GW 1	GW 1	GW 1	GW 1	GW 1	GW 1	GW 1	GW 1	GW 1	GW 1	GW 1	GW 1	GW 1	GW 1	GW 1	GW 1	GW 1	GW 1
Gatwick Airport 10	186 ✈ d		14 03		15 03		16 03		17 03			18 03		19 16		20 03		21 03		22 22	23 18
Redhill	186 d	13 34	14 14	14 34	15 14	15 29	16 14	16 32	17 14		17 44	18 14	18 43	19 27		20 14	20 34	21 14	21 35	22 33	23 29
Reigate	186 d	13 38	14 18	14 38	15 18	15 34	16 18	16 36	17 18		17 49	18 18	18 47	19 31		20 18	20 40	21 18	21 39	22 38	23 33
Betchworth	d			14 43		15 38		16 41			17 53		18 52				20 45		21 44	22 43	
Dorking Deepdene	d	13 45	14 25	14 47	15 25	15 43	16 25	16 45	17 25		17 58	18 25	18 56	19 38		20 25	20 49	21 25	21 48	22 47	23 40
Dorking West	d			14 50		15 45					18 00		18 59				20 52		21 51	22 50	
Gomshall	d	13 53				15 53		16 53			18 08		19 07				21 00		21 59	22 58	
Chilworth	d	13 59				15 59		16 59			18 14		19 13				21 06		22 05	23 04	
Shalford	d	14 03		15 03		16 03		17 03		18 08	18 18		19 17		20 08		21 10		22 09	23 08	
Guildford	a	14 07	14 42	15 07	15 42	16 07	16 42	17 07	17 43	18 12	18 22	18 42	19 21	19 54	20 12	20 42	21 14	21 42	22 13	23 12	23 59
	d	14 09	14 43	15 09	15 43	16 14	16 43	17 09	17 43	18 13	18 24	18 49	19 36	19 55	20 13	20 43	21 15	21 43	22 14	23 14	00 01
Wanborough	149 d																			23 21	
Ash 3	149 d	14 18		15 18		16 23		17 18	17 54	18 23	18 33		19 45		20 23		21 25		22 23	23 26	
North Camp	d	14 22	14 55	15 22	15 55	16 27	16 55	17 22	17 58	18 27	18 38	19 01	19 49	20 07	20 27	20 55	21 29	21 55	22 27	23 30	00 13
Farnborough North	d	14 26		15 26		16 31		17 26	18 02	18 31	18 42		19 53		20 31		21 33		22 31	23 34	
Blackwater	d	14 31	15 02	15 31	16 02	16 36	17 02	17 31	18 07	18 35	18 46	19 06	19 58	20 14	20 35	21 02	21 37	22 02	22 35	23 38	00 20
Sandhurst	d	14 34		15 34		16 39		17 34		18 39	18 51		20 01		20 39		21 41		22 39	23 42	
Crowthorne	d	14 38		15 38		16 43		17 38		18 43	18 59		20 05		20 43		21 45		22 43	23 46	
Wokingham	149 d	14 43	15 10	15 43	16 10	16 48	17 10	17 43	18 15	18 51	19 04	19 15	20 10	20 22	20 48	21 10	21 50	22 10	22 48	23 51	00 28
Reading 7	149 a	14 55	15 19	15 55	16 23	17 00	17 19	17 54	18 24	19 02	19 17	19 25	20 21	20 32	20 59	21 19	22 01	22 19	23 01	00 01	00 38

Saturdays

Station		GW 1	XC 1 ◊ ✠	GW 1	GW 1	GW 1	GW 1	GW 1	GW 1	GW 1	GW 1	GW 1	GW 1	GW 1	GW 1	GW 1	GW 1	GW 1	GW 1	GW 1
Gatwick Airport 10	186 ✈ d	23p18		05 31	06 04		07 03		08 03		09 03		10 03		11 03		12 03		13 03	
Redhill	186 d	23p29		05 42	06 14	06 34	07 14	07 34	08 14	08 34	09 14	09 34	10 14	10 34	11 14	11 34	12 14	12 34	13 14	13 34
Reigate	186 d	23p33		05 47	06 18	06 38	07 18	07 38	08 18	08 38	09 18	09 38	10 18	10 38	11 18	11 38	12 18	12 38	13 18	13 38
Betchworth	d					06 43				08 43				10 43				12 43		
Dorking Deepdene	d	23p40		05 54	06 25	06 47	07 25	07 45	08 25	08 47	09 25	09 45	10 25	10 47	11 25	11 45	12 25	12 47	13 25	13 45
Dorking West	d					06 50				08 50				10 50				12 50		
Gomshall	d							07 53				09 53				11 53				13 53
Chilworth	d							07 59				09 59				11 59				13 59
Shalford	d					07 03		08 03		09 03		10 03		11 03		12 03		13 03		14 03
Guildford	a	23p59		06 11	06 42	07 07	07 41	08 07	08 42	09 07	09 42	10 07	10 42	11 07	11 42	12 07	12 42	13 07	13 42	14 07
	d	00 01	06 09	06 12	06 44	07 09	07 43	08 09	08 43	09 09	09 43	10 09	10 43	11 09	11 43	12 09	12 43	13 09	13 43	14 09
Wanborough	149 d			06 20																
Ash 3	149 d			06 24		07 18		08 18		09 18		10 18		11 18		12 18		13 18		14 18
North Camp	d	00 13		06 28	06 56	07 22	07 55	08 22	08 55	09 22	09 55	10 22	10 55	11 22	11 55	12 22	12 55	13 22	13 55	14 22
Farnborough North	d			06 32		07 26		08 26		09 26		10 26		11 26		12 26		13 26		14 26
Blackwater	d	00 20		06 37	07 02	07 31	08 02	08 31	09 02	09 31	10 02	10 31	11 02	11 31	12 02	12 31	13 02	13 31	14 02	14 31
Sandhurst	d			06 40		07 34		08 34		09 34		10 34		11 34		12 34		13 34		14 34
Crowthorne	d			06 44		07 38		08 38		09 38		10 38		11 38		12 38		13 38		14 38
Wokingham	149 d	00 28		06 49	07 10	07 43	08 10	08 43	09 10	09 43	10 10	10 43	11 10	11 43	12 10	12 43	13 10	13 43	14 10	14 43
Reading 7	149 a	00 38	06 44	07 03	07 19	07 53	08 19	08 53	09 21	09 53	10 19	10 53	11 19	11 53	12 19	12 53	13 19	13 53	14 19	14 53

For general notes see front of timetable
For details of catering facilities see
Directory of Train Operators

Other services run between Redhill and Reigate from London Charing Cross, London Bridge, London Victoria and East Croydon. See Table 186 for full details.

Table 148

Saturdays

Gatwick Airport, Redhill and Guildford → Reading

Network Diagram - see first page of Table 148

		GW 1	GW 1	GW 1	GW 1	GW 1	GW 1	GW 1	GW 1	GW 1	GW 1	GW 1	GW 1	GW 1	GW 1	GW 1	GW 1	GW 1	GW 1
Gatwick Airport 10	186 ✈ d	14 03		15 03		16 03		17 03		18 03		19 03		20 03		21 03		22 22	23 18
Redhill	186 d	14 14	14 34	15 14	15 34	16 14	16 34	17 14	17 34	18 14	18 34	19 14	19 34	20 14	20 34	21 14	21 36	22 33	23 29
Reigate	186 d	14 18	14 38	15 18	15 38	16 18	16 38	17 18	17 38	18 18	18 38	19 18	19 38	20 18	20 38	21 18	21 40	22 38	23 33
Betchworth	d		14 43				16 43				18 43				20 43			22 43	
Dorking Deepdene	d	14 25	14 47	15 25	15 45	16 25	16 47	17 25	17 45	18 25	18 47	19 25	19 45	20 25	20 47	21 25	21 47	22 47	23 40
Dorking West	d		14 50				16 50				18 50				20 50			22 50	
Gomshall	d				15 53				17 53				19 53				21 55	22 58	
Chilworth	d				15 59				17 59				19 59				22 01	23 04	
Shalford	d		15 03		16 03		17 03		18 03		19 03		20 03		21 03		22 05	23 08	
Guildford	a	14 42	15 07	15 42	16 07	16 42	17 07	17 42	18 07	18 42	19 07	19 42	20 07	20 42	21 07	21 42	22 12	23 12	23 59
	d	14 43	15 09	15 43	16 09	16 43	17 09	17 43	18 09	18 43	19 09	19 43	20 09	20 43	21 09	21 44	22 14	23 14	00 01
Wanborough	149 d																	23 21	
Ash 3	149 d		15 18		16 18		17 18		18 18		19 18		20 18		21 18		22 23	23 26	
North Camp	d	14 55	15 22	15 55	16 22	16 55	17 22	17 55	18 22	18 55	19 22	19 55	20 22	20 55	21 22	21 56	22 27	23 30	00 13
Farnborough North	d		15 26		16 26		17 26		18 26		19 26		20 26		21 26		22 31	23 34	
Blackwater	d	15 02	15 31	16 02	16 31	17 02	17 31	18 02	18 31	19 02	19 31	20 02	20 31	21 02	21 31	22 02	22 36	23 38	00 20
Sandhurst	d		15 34		16 34		17 34		18 34		19 34		20 34		21 34		22 39	23 42	
Crowthorne	d		15 38		16 38		17 38		18 38		19 38		20 38		21 38		22 43	23 46	
Wokingham	149 d	15 10	15 43	16 10	16 43	17 10	17 43	18 10	18 43	19 10	19 43	20 10	20 43	21 10	21 43	22 10	22 48	23 51	00 28
Reading 7	149 a	15 19	15 53	16 19	16 53	17 19	17 54	18 19	18 53	19 19	19 53	20 19	20 53	21 19	21 53	22 19	22 57	23 59	00 37

Sundays

		GW 1	GW 1	GW 1	GW 1	GW 1	GW 1	GW 1	XC 1 ◇	GW 1	GW 1	GW 1	GW 1	GW 1	GW 1	GW 1	GW 1	GW 1	GW 1	GW 1	GW 1
Gatwick Airport 10	186 ✈ d	23p18	06 06	07 08	08 08	09 08	10 08	11 08		12 08	13 08	14 08	15 08	16 08	17 08	18 08	19 08	20 08	21 08	22 07	23 07
Redhill	186 d	23p29	06 19	07 19	08 19	09 19	10 19	11 19		12 19	13 19	14 19	15 19	16 19	17 19	18 19	19 19	20 19	21 20	22 20	23 20
Reigate	186 d	23p33	06 23	07 23	08 23	09 23	10 23	11 23		12 23	13 23	14 23	15 23	16 23	17 23	18 23	19 23	20 23	21 25	22 24	23 24
Betchworth	d				08 28		10 28			12 28		14 28		16 28		18 28		20 28		22 29	
Dorking Deepdene	d	23p40	06 31	07 31	08 31	09 31	10 31	11 31		12 31	13 31	14 31	15 31	16 31	17 31	18 31	19 31	20 31	21 32	22 33	23 31
Dorking West	d				08 35		10 35			12 35		14 35		16 35		18 35		20 35		22 36	
Gomshall	d				08 43		10 43			12 43		14 43		16 43		18 43		20 43		22 44	
Chilworth	d				08 49		10 49			12 49		14 49		16 49		18 49		20 49		22 50	
Shalford	d				08 53		10 53			12 53		14 53		16 53		18 53		20 53		22 54	
Guildford	a	23p59	06 47	07 48	08 57	09 48	10 57	11 49		12 57	13 49	14 57	15 49	16 57	17 49	18 57	19 48	20 57	21 49	22 58	23 49
	d	00 01	06 49	07 50	08 58	09 51	10 58	11 51	12 14	12 58	13 51	14 58	15 51	16 58	17 51	18 58	19 51	20 57	21 51	22 59	23 51
Wanborough	149 d																				
Ash 3	149 d			07 59		10 00		12 00			14 00		16 00		18 00		20 01		22 00		23 59
North Camp	d	00 13	07 01	08 03	09 10	10 04	11 11	12 04		13 10	14 04	15 10	16 04	17 10	18 04	19 10	20 05	21 10	22 04	23 11	00 04
Farnborough North	d			08 07		10 08		12 08			14 08		16 08		18 08		20 08		22 08		00 08
Blackwater	d	00 20	07 07	08 12	09 17	10 13	11 18	12 13		13 17	14 13	15 17	16 13	17 17	18 13	19 17	20 13	21 17	22 13	23 18	00 13
Sandhurst	d			08 15		10 16		12 16			14 16		16 16		18 16		20 16		22 16		00 16
Crowthorne	d			08 19		10 20		12 20			14 20		16 20		18 20		20 20		22 20		00 20
Wokingham	149 d	00 28	07 15	08 24	09 25	10 25	11 26	12 25		13 25	14 25	15 25	16 25	17 25	18 25	19 25	20 25	21 25	22 25	23 26	00 25
Reading 7	149 a	00 37	07 24	08 34	09 34	10 34	11 35	12 34	12 50	13 34	14 34	15 34	16 34	17 34	18 34	19 34	20 35	21 34	22 37	23 37	00 37

For general notes see front of timetable
For details of catering facilities see
Directory of Train Operators

Other services run between Redhill and Reigate from London Charing Cross, London Bridge, London Victoria and East Croydon. See Table 186 for full details.

South West Trains
A Stagecoach Company

These notes apply to Tables 149 to 156, 158, 160, 165 and 167

Spring Holiday

Saturday 23 May — A normal Saturday service will operate
Sunday 24 May — A normal Sunday service will operate
Monday 25 May — A normal Saturday service will operate

Engineering Works
No significant Engineering Works are taking place on this weekend.

Late Summer Holiday

Saturday 29 August — A normal Saturday service will operate
Sunday 30 August — A normal Sunday service will operate
Monday 31 August — A normal Saturday service will operate

Engineering Works will be taking place between Barnes and Hounslow on Sunday.

For details of Bank Holiday service alterations, please see first page of this Table

London → Hounslow, Richmond, Kingston, Windsor, Weybridge, Ascot, Guildford and Reading

Network Diagram - see first page of Table 148

Miles	Miles	Miles			SW MX 1	SW MO	SW MX	SW MO 1	SW MX	SW MX 1	SW MX	SW MX	SW MX	SW MX 1	SW MX	SW MO 1	SW MX	SW MO	SW MO	SW MX	SW MX	SW MX	SW	SW A	SW 1
0	—	0	**London Waterloo 15** ⊖	d	22p50	22p50	22p52	23p09	23p13	23p20	23p22	23p35	23p37			23p39			23p44	23p52	23p58		00 18		
1¼	—	1¼	Vauxhall ⊖	d		22p54	22p56	23p13	23p17		23p26		23p41			23p43			23p48	23p56	00 02		00 22		
2¾	—	2¾	Queenstown Rd.(Battersea)	d		22p57	22p59				23p29		23p44						23p51	23p59			00 25		
4	—	4	**Clapham Junction 10**	d	22p58	23p00	23p02	23p19	23p23	23p28	23p32	23p43	23p47			23p49			23p54	00 02	00 08		00 28		
4¾	—	4¾	Wandsworth Town	d		23p03	23p05				23p35		23p50						23p57	00 05			00 31		
5¾	—	5¾	Putney	d		23p06	23p08	23p23	23p27		23p38		23p53			23p53	←		23p59	00 08	00 12		00 34		
7	0	7	Barnes	d		23p09	23p12				23p42		23p56				23p56		00 03	00 12			00 37		
—	½	—	Barnes Bridge	d		23p11	23p14				23p44		↦		←					00 14					
—	1½	—	Chiswick	d		23p13	23p17				23p47				23p47					00 17		←			
—	2½	—	Kew Bridge	d		23p16	23p20				↦				23p50					00 20		00 20			
—	3½	—	Brentford	d		23p19	23p23								23p53					↦		00 23			
—	4¼	—	Syon Lane	d		23p21	23p25								23p55							00 25			
—	5	—	Isleworth	d		23p23	23p27								23p57							00 27			
—	6½	—	**Hounslow**	d		23p27	23p31								00 01							00 31			
8¼	—	8¼	Mortlake	d													23p58		00 05				00 39		
9	—	9	North Sheen	d													00 01		00 07				00 41		
9¾	—	9¾	**Richmond** ⊖	d	23p06			23p29	23p33	23p36		23p51				23p59	00 03		00 10		00 18		00 44		
10¾	—	10¾	St Margarets	d													00 06		00 12				00 46		
11¼	—	11¼	Twickenham	a	23p10			23p32	23p36	23p40		23p55				00 02	00 08		00 14		00 21		00 48		
—	—	—		d	23p10			23p33	23p37	23p40		23p55				00 03	00 08		00 15		00 22		00 49	04 52	
12¼	—	—	Strawberry Hill	d													00 12						00s52	04 55	
12½	—	—	Fulwell	a																					
13½	—	—	Teddington	a													00 15						00s55	04 58	
14¾	—	—	Hampton Wick	a													00 17						00s58	05 01	
15¼	—	—	**Kingston**	a													00 19						01 00	05 03	
—	—	12½	Whitton	d					23p40										00 18		00 25				
—	—	14¾	Feltham	d	23p16	23p33	23p36	23p39	23p44	23p48		00 01			00 06	00 09			00 22		00 29	00 36			
—	—	17½	Ashford (Surrey)	d		23p37	23p40		23p48						00 10				00 26		00 33	00 40			
0	—	19	**Staines**	d	23p23	23p41	23p45	23p45	23p52	23p56		00 08			00 15	00 15		00 21	00a30		00a37	00a46			05 23
2½	—	—	Wraysbury	d					23p56																
3¾	—	—	Sunnymeads	d					23p59																
4¾	—	—	Datchet	d					00 02																
6¾	—	—	**Windsor & Eton Riverside**	a					00 06																
—	—	21	Egham	d	23p27	23p45	23p50	23p50		00 01		00 12			00 20	00 20		00s25							05 27
0	—	23¼	Virginia Water	a	23p31	23p49	23p54	23p54		00 05		00 16			00 24	00 24		00s29							05 31
—	—	—		d	23p31	23p49	23p54	23p54		00 05		00 16			00 24	00 24									05 31
2½	—	—	Chertsey §	d		23p55	23p59								00 29			00s34							
4	—	—	Addlestone §	d		23p58	00 02								00 32			00s38							
5¾	—	—	**Weybridge**	a											00 37										
7¼	—	—	Byfleet & New Haw	d		00 02	00 07																		
8½	—	—	West Byfleet	d		00 05	00 10																		
11	—	—	Woking	a		00 10	00 18											00 50							
—	—	25¼	Longcross	d																					
—	—	27	Sunningdale	d	23p37			23p59		00 10		00 22				00 29									05 37
—	0	29	**Ascot 3**	d	23p43			00 04		00 15		00 27		00 29		00 34									05 43
—	3¼	—	Bagshot	d										00 35											
—	6½	—	Camberley	a										00 41											
—	—	—		d										00 41											
—	8¾	—	Frimley	d										00 45											
—	12	—	Ash Vale	d										00 52											
—	14½	—	**Aldershot**	a										00 57											
—	—	—		d																					
—	17¼	—	Ash 3	d																					
—	19¼	—	Wanborough	d																					
—	23½	—	**Guildford**	a																					
—	—	31¼	Martins Heron	d	23p47			00 08		00 19		00 31				00 38									05 47
—	—	32¼	Bracknell	d	23p50			00 11		00 23		00 34				00 41									05 50
—	—	36¾	**Wokingham**	d	23p57			00 18		00 32		00 41				00 48									05 57
—	—	38¾	Winnersh	d	00 01			00 21		00 36						00 51									06 00
—	—	39¼	Winnersh Triangle	d	00 02			00 23		00 38						00 53									06 02
—	—	40½	Earley	d	00 05			00 26		00 40						00 56									06 05
—	—	43½	**Reading 7**	a	00 10			00 31		00 45		00 49				01 01									06 10

For general notes see front of timetable
For details of catering facilities see Directory of Train Operators

A To London Waterloo (Table 152)

§ Passengers to/from London may travel via Weybridge. See Table 155.

From 28 September due to seasonal difficulties a large number of trains on this table will have minor retimings that could mean slightly earlier departure or later arrival times at certain stations. For further details see local publicity or contact National Rail Enquiries 08457 48 49 50

For details of Bank Holiday service alterations, please see first page of this Table

London → Hounslow, Richmond, Kingston, Windsor, Weybridge, Ascot, Guildford and Reading

Network Diagram - see first page of Table 148

		SW	SW	SW	SW		SW	SW	SW	SW	SW	SW	SW	SW	SW	SW	SW	SW	SW	SW	SW	SW	SW	SW	SW
			1	1					1	1	1						1	1							
							A					B		A	B					B		A	B	B	
London Waterloo 15 ⊖	d			05 05			05 33				05 50		05 58	06 03	06 15			06 20	06 22		06 28	06 33	06 45		
Vauxhall ⊖	d			05 09			05 37						06 02	06 07	06 19				06 26		06 32	06 37	06 49		
Queenstown Rd.(Battersea)	d			05 12			05 40							06 10	06 22				06 29			06 40	06 52		
Clapham Junction 10	d			05 15			05 43				05 58		06 08	06 13	06 25			06 28	06 32		06 38	06 43	06 55		
Wandsworth Town	d			05 18			05 46							06 16	06 28				06 35			06 46	06 58		
Putney	d			05 21			05 49						06 12	06 19	06 31				06 38	←	06 42	06 49	07 01		
Barnes	d			05 24			05 52							06 22	06 35				06 42	06 35		06 52	07 05		
Barnes Bridge	d														↳				06 44				→		
Chiswick	d																		06 47						←
Kew Bridge	d																		06 50						06 50
Brentford	d																		↳						06 53
Syon Lane	d																								06 55
Isleworth	d																								06 57
Hounslow	d																							06 48	07 01
Mortlake	d			05 26			05 54							06 24						06 37		06 54			
North Sheen	d			05 28			05 56							06 26						06 39		06 56			
Richmond ⊖	d			05 31			05 59				06 06		06 18	06 29				06 36		06 42	06 48	06 59			
St Margarets	d			05 33			06 01							06 31						06 44		07 01			
Twickenham	a			05 35			06 03				06 10		06 21	06 33				06 40		06 46	06 51	07 03			
	d			05 36	05 51		06 04				06 10	06 17	06 22	06 34				06 40		06 47	06 52	07 04			
Strawberry Hill	d						06 07							06 37								07 07			
Fulwell	a																								
Teddington	a						06 11							06 40								07 10			
Hampton Wick	a						06 14							06 44								07 14			
Kingston	a						06 16							06 46								07 16			
Whitton	d			05 39	05 54							06a20	06 25							06a50	06 55			06a53	
Feltham	d			05 43	05 58						06 16		06 29					06 46			06 59				07 06
Ashford (Surrey)	d			05 47	06 02								06 33								07 03				07 10
Staines	d	05 45		05 53	06 06			06 15			06 23		06 37			06 45		06 53			07 07				07 15
Wraysbury	d				06 10								06 41								07 11				
Sunnymeads	d				06 13								06 44								07 14				
Datchet	d				06 16								06 47								07 17				
Windsor & Eton Riverside	a				06 23								06 51								07 21				
Egham	d	05 50		05 57				06 20			06 27					06 50		06 57							07 20
Virginia Water	a	05 54		06 01				06 24			06 31					06 54		07 01							07 24
	d	05 54		06 01				06 24			06 31					06 54		07 01							07 24
Chertsey §	d	05 59						06 29								06 59									07 29
Addlestone §	d	06 02						06 32								07 02									07 32
Weybridge	a	06 07						06 37								07 07									07 37
Byfleet & New Haw	d																								
West Byfleet	d																								
Woking	a																								
Longcross	d										06 35							07 05							
Sunningdale	d			06 07							06 37							07 07							
Ascot 3	d			06 13						06 23	06 43						06 53	07 13							
Bagshot	d									06 29							06 59								
Camberley	a									06 35							07 05								
	d									06 39							07 09								
Frimley	d									06 43							07 13								
Ash Vale	d									06 49							07 19								
Aldershot	a									06 56							07 26								
	d		06 08						06 38	07 08							07 38								
Ash 3	d		06 15						06 45	07 15							07 45								
Wanborough	d		06 18						06 48	07 18							07 48								
Guildford	a		06 25						06 55	07 25							07 55								
Martins Heron	d			06 17							06 47							07 17							
Bracknell	d			06 20							06 50							07 20							
Wokingham	d			06 27							06 57							07 27							
Winnersh	d			06 30							07 00							07 30							
Winnersh Triangle	d			06 32							07 02							07 32							
Earley	d			06 35							07 05							07 35							
Reading 7	a			06 40							07 10							07 40							

For general notes see front of timetable
For details of catering facilities see Directory of Train Operators

A To London Waterloo (Table 152)
B To London Waterloo

§ Passengers to/from London may travel via Weybridge. See Table 155.

From 28 September due to seasonal difficulties a large number of trains on this table will have minor retimings that could mean slightly earlier departure or later arrival times at certain stations. For further details see local publicity or contact National Rail Enquiries 08457 48 49 50

For details of Bank Holiday service alterations, please see first page of this Table

London → Hounslow, Richmond, Kingston, Windsor, Weybridge, Ascot, Guildford and Reading

Network Diagram - see first page of Table 148

		SW 1	SW 1	SW	GW 1	SW 1	SW		SW	SW	SW	SW	SW	SW 1	SW	SW	SW	SW 1	SW	SW	SW	SW	SW	SW 1	SW
					A		B			C		B	C			B			C			B	C		
London Waterloo 15 ⊖	d		06 50	06 52					06 58	07 03		07 15		07 20	07 22		07 28		07 33		07 37	07 45		07 50	07 52
Vauxhall ⊖	d			06 56					07 02	07 07		07 19			07 26		07 32		07 37		07 41	07 49			07 56
Queenstown Rd.(Battersea)	d			06 59						07 10		07 22			07 29				07 40		07 44	07 52			07 59
Clapham Junction 10	d		06 58	07 02					07 08	07 13		07 25		07 28	07 32		07 38		07 43		07 47	07 55		07 58	08 02
Wandsworth Town	d			07 05						07 16		07 28			07 35				07 46		07 50	07 58			08 05
Putney	d			07 08			←		07 12	07 19		07 31			07 38	←	07 42		07 49		07 53	08 01			08 08
Barnes	d			07 12			07 05			07 22		07 35			07 42	07 35			07 52		07 57	08 05			08 12
Barnes Bridge	d			07 14								→			07 44						07 59	→			08 14
Chiswick	d			07 17							←				07 47					←	08 02				08 17
Kew Bridge	d			07 20							07 20				07 50					07 50	08 05				08 20
Brentford	d			→							07 23				→					07 53	08 08				→
Syon Lane	d										07 25									07 55	08 10				
Isleworth	d										07 27									07 57	08 12				
Hounslow	d										07 31									08 01	08a18				
Mortlake	d						07 07			07 24						07 37			07 54						
North Sheen	d						07 09			07 26						07 39			07 56						
Richmond ⊖	d		07 06				07 12		07 18	07 29				07 36		07 42	07 48	07 54	07 59					08 06	
St Margarets	d						07 14			07 31						07 44			08 01						
Twickenham	a		07 10				07 16		07 21	07 33				07 40		07 46	07 51	07 57	08 03					08 10	
	d		07 10				07 17		07 22	07 34			07 37	07 40		07 47	07 52	07 58	08 04				08 07	08 10	
Strawberry Hill	d									07 37			07b47						08 07				08c17		
Fulwell	a																								
Teddington	a									07 40			07 50						08 10				08 20		
Hampton Wick	a									07 44			07 52						08 14				08 22		
Kingston	a									07 46			07 54						08 16				08 24		
Whitton	d						07a20		07 25							07a50	07 55								
Feltham	d		07 16						07 29		07 36			07 46			07 59	08 04		08 06				08 16	
Ashford (Surrey)	d								07 33		07 40						08 03	08 08		08 10					
Staines	d		07 23						07 37		07 45			07 53			08 07	08 12		08 15				08 23	
Wraysbury	d								07 41								08 11								
Sunnymeads	d								07 44								08 14								
Datchet	d								07 47								08 17								
Windsor & Eton Riverside	a								07 51								08 21								
Egham	d		07 27								07 50			07 57				08 16		08 20				08 27	
Virginia Water	a		07 31								07 54			08 01						08 24				08 31	
	d		07 31								07 54			08 01						08 24				08 31	
Chertsey §	d										07 59									08 29					
Addlestone §	d										08 02									08 32					
Weybridge	a										08 07									08 38					
Byfleet & New Haw	d																								
West Byfleet	d																								
Woking	a																								
Longcross	d		07 35											08 05										08 35	
Sunningdale	d		07 37											08 07										08 37	
Ascot 3	d	07 23	07 43			07 53								08 13				08 26						08 43	
Bagshot	d	07 29				07 59												08 32							
Camberley	a	07 35				08 05												08 38							
	d	07 39				08 09												08 39							
Frimley	d	07 43				08 13												08 43							
Ash Vale	d	07 49				08 19												08 49							
Aldershot	a	07 54				08 24												08 54							
	d	08 08				08 38												09 08							
Ash 3	d	08 15				08 45												09 15							
Wanborough	d	08 18				08 48												09 18							
Guildford	a	08 25				08 55												09 25							
Martins Heron	d		07 47											08 17										08 47	
Bracknell	d		07 50											08 20										08 50	
Wokingham	d		07 57		08 17									08 27										08 57	
Winnersh	d		08 00		08 21									08 30										09 00	
Winnersh Triangle	d		08 02											08 32										09 02	
Earley	d		08 05											08 35										09 05	
Reading 7	a		08 10		08 28									08 40										09 10	

For general notes see front of timetable
For details of catering facilities see Directory of Train Operators

§ Passengers to/from London may travel via Weybridge. See Table 155.

A From Gatwick Airport (Table 148)
B To London Waterloo
C To London Waterloo (Table 152)

b Arr. 0740
c Arr. 0810

From 28 September due to seasonal difficulties a large number of trains on this table will have minor retimings that could mean slightly earlier departure or later arrival times at certain stations. For further details see local publicity or contact National Rail Enquiries 08457 48 49 50

For details of Bank Holiday service alterations, please see first page of this Table

London → Hounslow, Richmond, Kingston, Windsor, Weybridge, Ascot, Guildford and Reading

Network Diagram - see first page of Table 148

		SW 1	SW	SW	SW	SW 1	SW	SW	SW		SW	SW 1	SW	SW 1	SW	SW	SW	SW 1	SW	SW	SW	SW	SW 1	SW	SW 1
			A		B		B		A		A				A		B		B		A	A			
London Waterloo 15 ⊖	d			07 58	08 03	08 07			08 10		08 15	08 20	08 22			08 28	08 33	08 37			08 40	08 43	08 50	08 52	
Vauxhall ⊖	d			08 02	08 07				08 14		08 19		08 26			08 32	08 37				08 44	08 47		08 56	
Queenstown Rd.(Battersea)	d				08 10				08 17		08 22		08 29				08 40				08 47	08 50		08 59	
Clapham Junction 10	d			08 08	08 13	08 16			08 20		08 25	08 28	08 32			08 38	08 43	08 45			08 50	08 55	08 58	09 02	
Wandsworth Town	d				08 16				08 23		08 28		08 35				08 46				08 53	08 58		09 05	
Putney	d		←	08 12	08 19		←		08 26		08 31		08 38		←	08 42	08 49		←		08 56	09 01		09 08	
Barnes	d		08 05		08 23		08 23		08 27		08 35		08 42		08 35		08 52		08 52		08 57	09 05		09 12	
Barnes Bridge	d				→				08 29		→		08 44				→				08 59	→		09 14	
Chiswick	d							←	08 32				08 47							←	09 02			09 17	
Kew Bridge	d							08 20	08 35				08 50							08 50	09 05			09 20	
Brentford	d							08 23	08 38				→							08 53	09 08			→	
Syon Lane	d							08 25	08 40											08 55	09 10				
Isleworth	d							08 27	08 42											08 57	09 12				
Hounslow	d							08 31	08 48											09 01	09 18				
Mortlake	d		08 07				08 25								08 37				08 54						
North Sheen	d		08 09				08 27								08 39				08 56						
Richmond ⊖	d		08 12	08 18		08 24	08 30					08 36			08 42	08 48		08 53	08 59				09 06		
St Margarets	d		08 14				08 32								08 44				09 01						
Twickenham	a		08 16	08 21		08 28	08 34					08 40			08 46	08 51		08 57	09 03				09 10		
	d		08 17	08 22		08 28	08 35					08 40			08 47	08 52		08 57	09 04				09 10		
Strawberry Hill	d						08 38												09 07						
Fulwell	a																								
Teddington	a						08 41												09 10						
Hampton Wick	a						08 44												09 14						
Kingston	a						08 46												09 16						
Whitton	d		08a20	08 25					08a53						08a50	08 55					09a23				
Feltham	d			08 29		08 34		08 36				08 46				08 59		09 03		09 06			09 16		
Ashford (Surrey)	d			08 33		08 38		08 40								09 03		09 07		09 10					
Staines	d			08 37		08 42		08 45				08 53				09 07		09 11		09 15			09 23		
Wraysbury	d			08 41												09 11									
Sunnymeads	d			08 44												09 14									
Datchet	d			08 47												09 17									
Windsor & Eton Riverside	a			08 51												09 21									
Egham	d					08 47		08 50				08 57						09 16		09 20			09 27		
Virginia Water	a					08 51		08 54				09 01						09 20		09 24			09 31		
	d					08 51		08 54				09 01						09 20		09 24			09 31		
Chertsey §	d							08 59												09 29					
Addlestone §	d							09 02												09 32					
Weybridge	a							09 07												09 37					
Byfleet & New Haw	d																								
West Byfleet	d																								
Woking	a																								
Longcross	d					08 54																			
Sunningdale	d					08 58						09 07						09 25					09 37		
Ascot 3	d	08 53				09 02						09 13		09 23				09 30					09 43		09 53
Bagshot	d	08 59												09 29											09 59
Camberley	a	09 05												09 35											10 05
	d	09 09												09 39											10 09
Frimley	d	09 13												09 43											10 13
Ash Vale	d	09 19												09 49											10 19
Aldershot	a	09 25												09 54											10 24
	d	09 38												10 08											10 38
Ash 3	d	09 45												10 15											10 45
Wanborough	d	09 48												10 18											10 48
Guildford	a	09 55												10 25											10 55
Martins Heron	d					09 06						09 17						09 34					09 47		
Bracknell	d					09 10						09 20						09 37					09 50		
Wokingham	d					09 17						09 27						09 46					09 57		
Winnersh	d					09 20						09 30											10 00		
Winnersh Triangle	d					09 22						09 32											10 02		
Earley	d					09 25						09 35											10 05		
Reading 7	a					09 30						09 40						09 55					10 10		

For general notes see front of timetable
For details of catering facilities see Directory of Train Operators

A To London Waterloo
B To London Waterloo (Table 152)

§ Passengers to/from London may travel via Weybridge. See Table 155.

From 28 September due to seasonal difficulties a large number of trains on this table will have minor retimings that could mean slightly earlier departure or later arrival times at certain stations. For further details see local publicity or contact National Rail Enquiries 08457 48 49 50

For details of Bank Holiday service alterations, please see first page of this Table

London → Hounslow, Richmond, Kingston, Windsor, Weybridge, Ascot, Guildford and Reading

Network Diagram - see first page of Table 148

Station		SW	SW	SW	SW	SW	SW	SW	SW	SW	SW	SW	SW	SW	SW	SW	SW	SW	SW	SW	SW	SW	SW
								1		1							1		1				
		A		B		A	A				A		B		A	A				A		B	
London Waterloo 15	⊖ d		08 58	09 03		09 07	09 15	09 20	09 22			09 28	09 33		09 37	09 45	09 50	09 52			09 58	10 03	
Vauxhall	⊖ d		09 02	09 07		09 11	09 19		09 26			09 32	09 37		09 41	09 49		09 56			10 02	10 07	
Queenstown Rd.(Battersea)	d			09 10		09 14	09 22		09 29				09 40		09 44	09 52		09 59				10 10	
Clapham Junction 10	d		09 08	09 13		09 17	09 25	09 28	09 32			09 38	09 43		09 47	09 55	09 58	10 02			10 08	10 13	
Wandsworth Town	d			09 16		09 20	09 28		09 35				09 46		09 50	09 58		10 05				10 16	
Putney	d	←	09 12	09 19		09 23	09 31		09 38		←	09 42	09 49		09 53	10 01		10 08		←	10 12	10 19	
Barnes	d	09 05		09 22		09 27	09 35		09 42		09 35		09 52		09 57	10 05		10 12		10 05		10 22	
Barnes Bridge	d					09 29	→		09 44						09 59	→		10 14					
Chiswick	d				←	09 32			09 47					←	10 02			10 17					←
Kew Bridge	d				09 20	09 35			09 50					09 50	10 05			10 20					10 20
Brentford	d				09 23	09 38			→					09 53	10 08			→					10 23
Syon Lane	d				09 25	09 40								09 55	10 10								10 25
Isleworth	d				09 27	09 42								09 57	10 12								10 27
Hounslow	d				09 31	09b48								10 01	10c18								10 31
Mortlake	d	09 07		09 24							09 37		09 54							10 07		10 24	
North Sheen	d	09 09		09 26							09 39		09 56							10 09		10 26	
Richmond	⊖ d	09 12	09 18	09 29				09 36			09 42	09 48	09 59				10 06			10 12	10 18	10 29	
St Margarets	d	09 14		09 31							09 44		10 01							10 14		10 31	
Twickenham	a	09 16	09 21	09 33				09 40			09 46	09 51	10 03				10 10			10 16	10 21	10 33	
	d	09 17	09 22	09 34				09 40			09 47	09 52	10 04				10 10			10 17	10 22	10 34	
Strawberry Hill	d			09 37									10 07									10 37	
Fulwell	a																						
Teddington	a			09 40									10 10									10 40	
Hampton Wick	a			09 44									10 14									10 44	
Kingston	a			09 46									10 16									10 46	
Whitton	d	09a20	09 25			09a53					09a50	09 55			10a26					10a20	10 25		
Feltham	d		09 29		09 36			09 46				09 59		10 06			10 16				10 29		10 36
Ashford (Surrey)	d		09 33		09 40							10 03		10 10							10 33		10 40
Staines	d		09 37		09 45			09 53				10 07		10 15			10 23				10 37		10 45
Wraysbury	d		09 41									10 11									10 41		
Sunnymeads	d		09 44									10 14									10 44		
Datchet	d		09 47									10 17									10 47		
Windsor & Eton Riverside	a		09 51									10 21									10 51		
Egham	d				09 50			09 57						10 20			10 27						10 50
Virginia Water	a				09 54			10 01						10 24			10 31						10 54
	d				09 54			10 01						10 24			10 31						10 54
Chertsey §	d				09 59									10 29									10 59
Addlestone §	d				10 02									10 32									11 02
Weybridge	a				10 07									10 37									11 07
Byfleet & New Haw	d																						
West Byfleet	d																						
Woking	a																						
Longcross	d																						
Sunningdale	d							10 07									10 37						
Ascot 3	d							10 13		10 23							10 43		10 53				
Bagshot	d									10 29									10 59				
Camberley	a									10 35									11 05				
	d									10 39									11 09				
Frimley	d									10 43									11 13				
Ash Vale	d									10 49									11 19				
Aldershot	a									10 54									11 24				
	d									11 08									11 38				
Ash 3	d									11 15									11 45				
Wanborough	d									11 18									11 48				
Guildford	a									11 25									11 55				
Martins Heron	d							10 17									10 47						
Bracknell	d							10 20									10 50						
Wokingham	d							10 27									10 57						
Winnersh	d							10 30									11 00						
Winnersh Triangle	d							10 32									11 02						
Earley	d							10 35									11 05						
Reading 7	a							10 40									11 10						

For general notes see front of timetable
For details of catering facilities see Directory of Train Operators

§ Passengers to/from London may travel via Weybridge. See Table 155.

A To London Waterloo
B To London Waterloo (Table 152)
b Arr. 0945
c Arr. 1015

From 28 September due to seasonal difficulties a large number of trains on this table will have minor retimings that could mean slightly earlier departure or later arrival times at certain stations. For further details see local publicity or contact National Rail Enquiries 08457 48 49 50

For details of Bank Holiday service alterations, please see first page of this Table

London → Hounslow, Richmond, Kingston, Windsor, Weybridge, Ascot, Guildford and Reading

Network Diagram - see first page of Table 148

		SW	SW	SW 1	SW	SW 1	SW	SW	SW	SW	SW	SW	SW 1	SW	SW 1	SW	SW	SW	SW		SW	SW
		A	A				A		B		A	A				A		B		C	A	A
London Waterloo 15	⊖ d	10 07	10 15	10 20	10 22			10 28	10 33		10 37	10 45	10 50	10 52			10 58	11 03			15 07	15 15
Vauxhall	⊖ d	10 11	10 19		10 26			10 32	10 37		10 41	10 49		10 56			11 02	11 07			15 11	15 19
Queenstown Rd.(Battersea)	d	10 14	10 22		10 29				10 40		10 44	10 52		10 59				11 10			15 14	15 22
Clapham Junction 10	d	10 17	10 25	10 28	10 32			10 38	10 43		10 47	10 55	10 58	11 02			11 08	11 13			15 17	15 25
Wandsworth Town	d	10 20	10 28		10 35				10 46		10 50	10 58		11 05				11 16			15 20	15 28
Putney	d	10 23	10 31		10 38		←	10 42	10 49		10 53	11 01		11 08		←	11 12	11 19			15 23	15 31
Barnes	d	10 27	10 35		10 42		10 35		10 52		10 57	11 05		11 12		11 05		11 22			15 27	15 35
Barnes Bridge	d	10 29	→		10 44						10 59	→		11 14							15 29	→
Chiswick	d	10 32			10 47					←	11 02			11 17					←		15 32	
Kew Bridge	d	10 35			10 50					10 50	11 05			11 20					11 20		15 35	
Brentford	d	10 38			→					10 53	11 08			→					11 23		15 38	
Syon Lane	d	10 40								10 55	11 10								11 25		15 40	
Isleworth	d	10 42								10 57	11 12								11 27		15 42	
Hounslow	d	10b48								11 01	11c18								11 31		15e48	
Mortlake	d						10 37		10 54							11 07		11 24				
North Sheen	d						10 39		10 56							11 09		11 26				
Richmond	⊖ d			10 36			10 42	10 48	10 59				11 06			11 12	11 18	11 29				
St Margarets	d						10 44		11 01							11 14		11 31				
Twickenham	a			10 40			10 46	10 51	11 03				11 10			11 16	11 21	11 33				
	d			10 40			10 47	10 52	11 04				11 10			11 17	11 22	11 34				
Strawberry Hill	d								11 07									11 37				
Fulwell	a																					
Teddington	a								11 10									11 40				
Hampton Wick	a								11 14									11 44				
Kingston	a								11 16									11 46				
Whitton	d	10a56					10a50	10 55			11a23					11a20	11 25				15a53	
Feltham	d			10 46				10 59		11 06			11 16				11 29		11 36			
Ashford (Surrey)	d							11 03		11 10							11 33		11 40			
Staines	d			10 53				11 07		11 15			11 23				11 37		11 45			
Wraysbury	d							11 11									11 41					
Sunnymeads	d							11 14									11 44					
Datchet	d							11 17									11 47					
Windsor & Eton Riverside	a							11 21									11 51					
Egham	d			10 57						11 20			11 27						11 50			
Virginia Water	a			11 01						11 24			11 31						11 54			
	d			11 01						11 24			11 31						11 54			
Chertsey §	d									11 29									11 59			
Addlestone §	d									11 32									12 02			
Weybridge	a									11 37									12 07			
Byfleet & New Haw	d																					
West Byfleet	d																					
Woking	a																					
Longcross	d																					
Sunningdale	d			11 07									11 37									
Ascot 3	d			11 13		11 23							11 43		11 53							
Bagshot	d					11 29									11 59							
Camberley	a					11 35									12 05							
	d					11 39									12 09							
Frimley	d					11 43									12 13							
Ash Vale	d					11 49									12 19							
Aldershot	a					11 54									12 24							
	d					12 08									12 38							
Ash 3	d					12 15									12 45							
Wanborough	d					12 18									12 48							
Guildford	a					12 25									12 55							
Martins Heron	d			11 17									11 47									
Bracknell	d			11 20									11 50									
Wokingham	d			11 27									11 57									
Winnersh	d			11 30									12 00									
Winnersh Triangle	d			11 32									12 02									
Earley	d			11 35									12 05									
Reading 7	a			11 40									12 10									

For general notes see front of timetable
For details of catering facilities see Directory of Train Operators

§ Passengers to/from London may travel via Weybridge. See Table 155.

A To London Waterloo
B To London Waterloo (Table 152)
C 1250 from Waterloo calls Longcross 1335
b Arr. 1045
c Arr. 1115
e Arr. 1545

From 28 September due to seasonal difficulties a large number of trains on this table will have minor retimings that could mean slightly earlier departure or later arrival times at certain stations. For further details see local publicity or contact National Rail Enquiries 08457 48 49 50

London → Hounslow, Richmond, Kingston, Windsor, Weybridge, Ascot, Guildford and Reading

For details of Bank Holiday service alterations, please see first page of this Table

Network Diagram - see first page of Table 148

		SW	SW	SW	SW	SW	SW	SW	SW	SW	SW	SW	SW	SW	SW	SW	SW	SW	SW	SW	SW	SW	SW	SW	SW
		1		1							1		1				1					1		1	
					A		B		A	A				A		B		B		A	A				A
London Waterloo 15	⊖ d	15 20	15 22			15 28	15 33		15 37	15 45	15 50	15 52			15 58	16 01	16 05			16 07	16 15	16 20	16 22		
Vauxhall	⊖ d		15 26			15 32	15 37		15 41	15 49		15 56			16 02	16 05	16 09			16 11	16 19		16 26		
Queenstown Rd.(Battersea)	d		15 29				15 40		15 44	15 52		15 59				16 08				16 14	16 22		16 29		
Clapham Junction 10	d	15 28	15 32			15 38	15 43		15 47	15 55	15 58	16 02			16 08	16 11	16 15			16 17	16 25	16 28	16 32		
Wandsworth Town	d		15 35				15 46		15 50	15 58		16 05				16 14				16 20	16 28		16 35		
Putney	d		15 38		←	15 42	15 49		15 53	16 01		16 08		←	16 12	16 17		←		16 23	16 31		16 38		←
Barnes	d		15 42		15 35		15 52		15 57	16 05		16 12		16 05		16 22		16 22		16 27	16 35		16 42		16 35
Barnes Bridge	d		15 44						15 59	→		16 14				→				16 29	→		16 44		
Chiswick	d		15 47					←	16 02			16 17							←	16 32			16 47		
Kew Bridge	d		15 50					15 50	16 05			16 20							16 20	16 35			16 50		
Brentford	d		→					15 53	16 08			→							16 23	16 38			→		
Syon Lane	d							15 55	16 10										16 25	16 40					
Isleworth	d							15 57	16 12										16 27	16 42					
Hounslow	d							16 01	16b18										16 31	16c48					
Mortlake	d				15 37		15 54							16 07				16 24							16 37
North Sheen	d				15 39		15 56							16 09				16 26							16 39
Richmond	⊖ d	15 36			15 42	15 48	15 59				16 06			16 12	16 18		16 23	16 29				16 36			16 42
St Margarets	d				15 44		16 01							16 14				16 31							16 44
Twickenham	a	15 40			15 46	15 51	16 03				16 10			16 16	16 21		16 27	16 33				16 40			16 46
	d	15 40			15 47	15 52	16 04				16 10			16 17	16 22		16 27	16 34				16 40			16 47
Strawberry Hill	d						16 07											16 37							
Fulwell	a																								
Teddington	a						16 10											16 42							
Hampton Wick	a						16 14											16 46							
Kingston	a						16 16											16 48							
Whitton	d				15a50	15 55			16a23					16a20	16 25					16a53					16a50
Feltham	d	15 46				15 59		16 06			16 16				16 29		16 33		16 36			16 46			
Ashford (Surrey)	d					16 03		16 10							16 33		16 37		16 40						
Staines	d	15 53				16 07		16 15			16 23				16 37		16 41		16 45			16 53			
Wraysbury	d					16 11									16 41										
Sunnymeads	d					16 14									16 44										
Datchet	d					16 17									16 47										
Windsor & Eton Riverside	a					16 21									16 51										
Egham	d	15 57						16 20			16 27						16 46		16 50			16 57			
Virginia Water	a	16 01						16 24			16 31						16 50		16 54			17 01			
	d	16 01						16 24			16 31						16 50		16 54			17 01			
Chertsey §	d							16 29											16 59						
Addlestone §	d							16 32											17 02						
Weybridge	a							16 37											17 07						
Byfleet & New Haw	d																								
West Byfleet	d																								
Woking	a																								
Longcross	d																								
Sunningdale	d	16 07									16 37						16 55					17 07			
Ascot 3	d	16 13		16 23							16 43		16 53				17 00					17 13		17 23	
Bagshot	d			16 29									16 59											17 29	
Camberley	a			16 35									17 05											17 35	
	d			16 39									17 09											17 39	
Frimley	d			16 43									17 13											17 43	
Ash Vale	d			16 49									17 19											17 49	
Aldershot	a			16 54									17 24											17 54	
	d			17 08									17 38											18 08	
Ash 3	d			17 15									17 45											18 15	
Wanborough	d			17 18									17 48											18 18	
Guildford	a			17 25									17 55											18 25	
Martins Heron	d	16 17									16 47						17 04					17 17			
Bracknell	d	16 20									16 50						17 07					17 20			
Wokingham	d	16 27									16 57						17 17					17 27			
Winnersh	d	16 30									17 00											17 30			
Winnersh Triangle	d	16 32									17 02											17 32			
Earley	d	16 35									17 05											17 35			
Reading 7	a	16 40									17 10						17 27					17 42			

For general notes see front of timetable
For details of catering facilities see Directory of Train Operators

§ Passengers to/from London may travel via Weybridge. See Table 155.

A To London Waterloo
B To London Waterloo (Table 152)
b Arr. 1615
c Arr. 1645

From 28 September due to seasonal difficulties a large number of trains on this table will have minor retimings that could mean slightly earlier departure or later arrival times at certain stations. For further details see local publicity or contact National Rail Enquiries 08457 48 49 50

For details of Bank Holiday service alterations, please see first page of this Table

London → Hounslow, Richmond, Kingston, Windsor, Weybridge, Ascot, Guildford and Reading

Network Diagram - see first page of Table 148

		SW		SW	SW	SW	SW	SW	SW	SW 1	SW	SW	SW	SW	SW 1	SW	SW	SW 1	SW	SW	SW	SW 1	SW	SW 1	SW
				A		A		B	B			B		A		A			B	A	B				B
London Waterloo 15	⊖ d	16 28		16 31	16 35			16 37	16 45	16 50	16 52		16 58	17 01	17 05				17 07	17 13	17 15	17 20	17 22		
Vauxhall	⊖ d	16 32		16 35	16 39			16 41	16 49		16 56		17 02	17 05	17 09				17 11	17 17	17 19		17 26		
Queenstown Rd.(Battersea)	d			16 38				16 44	16 52		16 59			17 08					17 14		17 22		17 29		
Clapham Junction 10	d	16 38		16 41	16 45			16 47	16 55	16 58	17 02		17 08	17 11	17 15				17 17	17 23	17 25	17 28	17 32		
Wandsworth Town	d			16 44				16 50	16 58		17 05			17 14					17 20		17 28		17 35		
Putney	d	16 42		16 47		←		16 53	17 01		17 08	←	17 12	17 17		←			17 23	17 27	17 31		17 38		←
Barnes	d			16 52		16 52		16 57	17 05		17 12	17 05		17 22		17 22			17 27		17 35		17 42		17 35
Barnes Bridge	d			→				16 59	→		17 14			→					17 29		→		17 44		
Chiswick	d						←	17 02			17 17						←		17 32				17 47		
Kew Bridge	d						16 50	17 05			17 20						17 20		17 35				17 50		
Brentford	d						16 53	17 08			→						17 23		17 38				→		
Syon Lane	d						16 55	17 10									17 25		17 40						
Isleworth	d						16 57	17 12									17 27		17 42						
Hounslow	d						17 01	17b18									17 31		17c48						
Mortlake	d					16 54						17 07				17 24									17 37
North Sheen	d					16 56						17 09				17 26									17 39
Richmond	⊖ d	16 48			16 53	16 59				17 06		17 12	17 18		17 23	17 29				17 33		17 36			17 42
St Margarets	d					17 01						17 14				17 31									17 44
Twickenham	a	16 51			16 57	17 03				17 10		17 16	17 21		17 27	17 33				17 37		17 40			17 46
	d	16 52			16 57	17 04				17 10		17 17	17 22		17 27	17 34				17 37		17 40			17 47
Strawberry Hill	d					17 07										17 37				17 41					
Fulwell	a																								
Teddington	a					17 12										17 42				17 46					
Hampton Wick	a					17 16										17 46				17 54					
Kingston	a					17 18										17 48				17 56					
Whitton	d	16 55						17a23				17a20	17 25						17a53						17a50
Feltham	d	16 59			17 03		17 06			17 16			17 29		17 33		17 36					17 46			
Ashford (Surrey)	d	17 03			17 07		17 10						17 33		17 37		17 40								
Staines	d	17 07			17 11		17 15			17 23			17 37		17 41		17 45					17 53			
Wraysbury	d	17 11											17 41												
Sunnymeads	d	17 14											17 44												
Datchet	d	17 17											17 47												
Windsor & Eton Riverside	a	17 23											17 53												
Egham	d				17 16		17 20			17 27					17 46		17 50					17 57			
Virginia Water	a				17 20		17 24			17 31					17 50		17 54					18 01			
	d				17 20		17 24			17 31					17 50		17 54					18 01			
Chertsey §	d						17 29										17 59								
Addlestone §	d						17 32										18 02								
Weybridge	a						17 40										18 10								
Byfleet & New Haw	d																								
West Byfleet	d																								
Woking	a																								
Longcross	d				17 23																				
Sunningdale	d				17 27					17 37					17 55							18 07			
Ascot 3	d				17 31					17 43					18 00							18 13		18 23	
Bagshot	d														18 06									18 29	
Camberley	a														18 12									18 35	
	d														18 13									18 39	
Frimley	d														18 17									18 43	
Ash Vale	d														18 24									18 49	
Aldershot	a														18 31									18 54	
	d																	18 38						19 08	
Ash 3	d																	18 45						19 15	
Wanborough	d																	18 48						19 18	
Guildford	a																	18 55						19 25	
Martins Heron	d				17 35					17 47												18 17			
Bracknell	d				17 39					17 50												18 20			
Wokingham	d				17 47					17 57												18 27			
Winnersh	d									18 00												18 30			
Winnersh Triangle	d									18 02												18 32			
Earley	d									18 05												18 35			
Reading 7	a				17 58					18 12												18 43			

For general notes see front of timetable
For details of catering facilities see Directory of Train Operators

§ Passengers to/from London may travel via Weybridge. See Table 155.

A To London Waterloo (Table 152)
B To London Waterloo
b Arr. 1715
c Arr. 1745

From 28 September due to seasonal difficulties a large number of trains on this table will have minor retimings that could mean slightly earlier departure or later arrival times at certain stations. For further details see local publicity or contact National Rail Enquiries 08457 48 49 50

London → Hounslow, Richmond, Kingston, Windsor, Weybridge, Ascot, Guildford and Reading

For details of Bank Holiday service alterations, please see first page of this Table

Network Diagram - see first page of Table 148

		SW	SW	SW		SW	SW	SW	SW	SW	SW	SW	SW	SW	SW	SW	SW	SW	SW	SW	SW	SW	SW	SW	SW
				1							1					1			1				1		1
			A			A		B	C	B			B		A		A			B	C	B			
London Waterloo 15	⊖ d	17 28	17 31	17 35				17 37	17 43	17 45	17 50	17 52		17 58	18 01	18 05				18 07	18 13	18 15	18 20	18 22	
Vauxhall	⊖ d	17 32	17 35	17 39				17 41	17 47	17 49		17 56		18 02	18 05	18 09				18 11	18 17	18 19		18 26	
Queenstown Rd.(Battersea)	d		17 38					17 44		17 52		17 59			18 08					18 14		18 22		18 29	
Clapham Junction 10	d	17 38	17 41	17 45				17 47	17 53	17 55	17 58	18 02		18 08	18 11	18 15				18 17	18 23	18 25	18 28	18 32	
Wandsworth Town	d		17 44					17 50		17 58		18 05			18 14					18 20		18 28		18 35	
Putney	d	17 42	17 47			←		17 53	17 57	18 01		18 08	←	18 12	18 17		←			18 23	18 27	18 31		18 38	
Barnes	d		17 52			17 52		17 57		18 05		18 12	18 05		18 22		18 22			18 27		18 35		18 42	
Barnes Bridge	d		→					17 59		→		18 14			→					18 29		→		18 44	
Chiswick	d						←	18 02				18 17						←		18 32				18 47	
Kew Bridge	d						17 50	18 05				18 20						18 20		18 35				18 50	
Brentford	d						17 53	18 08				→						18 23		18 38				→	
Syon Lane	d						17 55	18 10										18 25		18 40					
Isleworth	d						17 57	18 12										18 27		18 42					
Hounslow	d						18 01	18b18										18 31		18c48					
Mortlake	d					17 54							18 07				18 24								
North Sheen	d					17 56							18 09				18 26								
Richmond	⊖ d	17 48		17 53		17 59			18 03		18 06		18 12	18 18		18 23	18 29				18 33		18 36		
St Margarets	d					18 01							18 14				18 31								
Twickenham	a	17 51		17 57		18 03			18 07		18 10		18 16	18 21		18 27	18 33				18 37		18 40		
	d	17 52		17 57		18 04			18 07		18 10		18 17	18 22		18 27	18 34				18 37		18 40		
Strawberry Hill	d					18 07			18 11								18 37				18 41				
Fulwell	a								18 13												18 43				
Teddington	a					18 12											18 42								
Hampton Wick	a					18 16											18 46								
Kingston	a					18 18											18 48								
Whitton	d	17 55						18a23					18a20	18 25						18a53					
Feltham	d	17 59		18 03			18 06				18 16			18 29		18 33		18 36					18 46		
Ashford (Surrey)	d	18 03		18 07			18 10							18 33		18 37		18 40							
Staines	d	18 07		18 11			18 15				18 23			18 37		18 41		18 45					18 53		
Wraysbury	d	18 11												18 41											
Sunnymeads	d	18 14												18 44											
Datchet	d	18 17												18 47											
Windsor & Eton Riverside	a	18 23												18 53											
Egham	d			18 16			18 20				18 27					18 46		18 50					18 57		
Virginia Water	a			18 20			18 24				18 31					18 50		18 54					19 01		
	d			18 20			18 24				18 31					18 50		18 54					19 01		
Chertsey §	d						18 29											18 59							
Addlestone §	d						18 32											19 02							
Weybridge	a						18 40											19 10							
Byfleet & New Haw	d																								
West Byfleet	d																								
Woking	a																								
Longcross	d										18 35														
Sunningdale	d			18 25							18 37					18 55							19 07		
Ascot 3	d			18 30							18 43					19 02							19 13		19 23
Bagshot	d															19 08									19 29
Camberley	a															19 14									19 35
	d															19 15									19 39
Frimley	d															19 19									19 43
Ash Vale	d															19 26									19 49
Aldershot	a															19 35									19 54
	d																		19 38						20 08
Ash 3	d																		19 45						20 15
Wanborough	d																		19 48						20 18
Guildford	a																		19 55						20 25
Martins Heron	d			18 34							18 47												19 17		
Bracknell	d			18 37							18 50												19 20		
Wokingham	d			18 47							18 57												19 27		
Winnersh	d										19 00												19 30		
Winnersh Triangle	d										19 02												19 32		
Earley	d										19 05												19 35		
Reading 7	a			18 57							19 12												19 42		

For general notes see front of timetable
For details of catering facilities see Directory of Train Operators

§ Passengers to/from London may travel via Weybridge. See Table 155.

A To London Waterloo (Table 152)
B To London Waterloo
C To Shepperton (Table 152)

b Arr. 1815
c Arr. 1845

From 28 September due to seasonal difficulties a large number of trains on this table will have minor retimings that could mean slightly earlier departure or later arrival times at certain stations. For further details see local publicity or contact National Rail Enquiries 08457 48 49 50

For details of Bank Holiday service alterations, please see first page of this Table

London → Hounslow, Richmond, Kingston, Windsor, Weybridge, Ascot, Guildford and Reading

Network Diagram - see first page of Table 148

Station		SW	SW	SW	SW 1	SW		SW	SW	SW	SW	SW 1	SW	SW 1	SW	SW	SW	SW 1	SW	SW	SW	SW	SW 1	SW	SW 1
		A		B		B			A	C	A				A		B		B		A	A			
London Waterloo 15 ⊖	d		18 28	18 31	18 35				18 37	18 43	18 45	18 50	18 52			18 58	19 01	19 05			19 07	19 15	19 20	19 22	
Vauxhall ⊖	d		18 32	18 35	18 39				18 41	18 47	18 49		18 56			19 02	19 05	19 09			19 11	19 19		19 26	
Queenstown Rd.(Battersea)	d			18 38					18 44		18 52		18 59				19 08				19 14	19 22		19 29	
Clapham Junction 10	d		18 38	18 41	18 45				18 47	18 53	18 55	18 58	19 02			19 08	19 11	19 15			19 17	19 25	19 28	19 32	
Wandsworth Town	d			18 44					18 50		18 58		19 05				19 14				19 20	19 28		19 35	
Putney	d	←	18 42	18 47		←			18 53	18 57	19 01		19 08		←	19 12	19 17		←		19 23	19 31		19 38	
Barnes	d	18 35		18 52		18 52			18 57		19 05		19 12		19 05		19 22		19 22		19 27	19 35		19 42	
Barnes Bridge	d			→					18 59		→		19 14				→				19 29	→		19 44	
Chiswick	d							←	19 02				19 17							←	19 32			19 47	
Kew Bridge	d							18 50	19 05				19 20							19 20	19 35			19 50	
Brentford	d							18 53	19 08				→							19 23	19 38			→	
Syon Lane	d							18 55	19 10											19 25	19 40				
Isleworth	d							18 57	19 12											19 27	19 42				
Hounslow	d							19 01	19b18											19 31	19c48				
Mortlake	d	18 37				18 54									19 07				19 24						
North Sheen	d	18 39				18 56									19 09				19 26						
Richmond ⊖	d	18 42	18 48		18 53	18 59				19 03		19 06			19 12	19 18		19 23	19 29				19 36		
St Margarets	d	18 44				19 01									19 14				19 31						
Twickenham	a	18 46	18 51		18 57	19 03				19 07		19 10			19 16	19 21		19 27	19 33				19 40		
	d	18 47	18 52		18 57	19 04				19 07		19 10			19 17	19 22		19 27	19 34				19 40		
Strawberry Hill	d					19 07				19 11									19 37						
Fulwell	a									19 13															
Teddington	a					19 12													19 42						
Hampton Wick	a					19 16													19 46						
Kingston	a					19 18													19 48						
Whitton	d	18a50	18 55						19a23						19a20	19 25					19a53				
Feltham	d		18 59		19 03			19 06				19 16				19 29		19 33		19 36			19 46		
Ashford (Surrey)	d		19 03		19 07			19 10								19 33		19 37		19 40					
Staines	d		19 07		19 11			19 15				19 23				19 37		19 41		19 45			19 53		
Wraysbury	d		19 11													19 41									
Sunnymeads	d		19 14													19 44									
Datchet	d		19 17													19 47									
Windsor & Eton Riverside	a		19 23													19 53									
Egham	d				19 16			19 20				19 27						19 46		19 50			19 57		
Virginia Water	a				19 20			19 24				19 31						19 50		19 54			20 01		
	d				19 20			19 24				19 31						19 50		19 54			20 01		
Chertsey §	d							19 29												19 59					
Addlestone §	d							19 32												20 02					
Weybridge	a							19 40												20 10					
Byfleet & New Haw	d																								
West Byfleet	d																								
Woking	a																								
Longcross	d																								
Sunningdale	d				19 25							19 37						19 55					20 07		
Ascot 3	d				19 30							19 43		19 53				20 00					20 13		20 23
Bagshot	d													19 59											20 29
Camberley	a													20 05											20 35
	d													20 09											20 39
Frimley	d													20 13											20 43
Ash Vale	d													20 19											20 49
Aldershot	a													20 24											20 54
	d													20 38											21 08
Ash 3	d													20 45											21 15
Wanborough	d													20 48											21 18
Guildford	a													20 55											21 25
Martins Heron	d				19 34							19 47						20 04					20 17		
Bracknell	d				19 37							19 50						20 07					20 20		
Wokingham	d				19 47							19 57						20 17					20 27		
Winnersh	d											20 00											20 30		
Winnersh Triangle	d											20 02											20 32		
Earley	d											20 05											20 35		
Reading 7	a				19 57							20 12						20 25					20 40		

For general notes see front of timetable
For details of catering facilities see Directory of Train Operators

§ Passengers to/from London may travel via Weybridge. See Table 155.

A To London Waterloo
B To London Waterloo (Table 152)
C To Shepperton (Table 152)

b Arr. 1915
c Arr. 1945

From 28 September due to seasonal difficulties a large number of trains on this table will have minor retimings that could mean slightly earlier departure or later arrival times at certain stations. For further details see local publicity or contact National Rail Enquiries 08457 48 49 50

For details of Bank Holiday service alterations, please see first page of this Table

London → Hounslow, Richmond, Kingston, Windsor, Weybridge, Ascot, Guildford and Reading

Network Diagram - see first page of Table 148

		SW	SW	SW	SW	SW	SW	SW		SW	SW	SW	SW	SW	SW	SW	SW	SW	SW	SW	SW	SW	SW	SW	SW
								1			1							1		1	1				
		A		B		A	A					A		B		A	A					A		B	
London Waterloo 15	⊖ d		19 28	19 33		19 37	19 45	19 50		19 52			19 58	20 03		20 07	20 15	20 20	20 22				20 28	20 33	
Vauxhall	⊖ d		19 32	19 37		19 41	19 49			19 56			20 02	20 07		20 11	20 19		20 26				20 32	20 37	
Queenstown Rd.(Battersea)	d			19 40		19 44	19 52			19 59				20 10		20 14	20 22		20 29					20 40	
Clapham Junction 10	d		19 38	19 43		19 47	19 55	19 58		20 02			20 08	20 13		20 17	20 25	20 28	20 32				20 38	20 43	
Wandsworth Town	d			19 46		19 50	19 58			20 05				20 16		20 20	20 28		20 35					20 46	
Putney	d	←	19 42	19 49		19 53	20 01			20 08		←	20 12	20 19		20 23	20 31		20 38			←	20 42	20 49	
Barnes	d	19 35		19 52		19 57	20 05			20 12		20 05		20 22		20 27	20 35		20 42			20 35		20 52	
Barnes Bridge	d					19 59	→			20 14						20 29	→		20 44						
Chiswick	d				←	20 02				20 17					←	20 32			20 47						←
Kew Bridge	d				19 50	20 05				20 20					20 20	20 35			20 50						20 50
Brentford	d				19 53	20 08				→					20 23	20 38			→						20 53
Syon Lane	d				19 55	20 10									20 25	20 40									20 55
Isleworth	d				19 57	20 12									20 27	20 42									20 57
Hounslow	d				20 01	20b18									20 31	20c48									21 01
Mortlake	d	19 37		19 54								20 07		20 24								20 37		20 54	
North Sheen	d	19 39		19 56								20 09		20 26								20 39		20 56	
Richmond	⊖ d	19 42	19 48	19 59				20 06				20 12	20 18	20 29				20 36				20 42	20 48	20 59	
St Margarets	d	19 44		20 01								20 14		20 31								20 44		21 01	
Twickenham	a	19 46	19 51	20 03				20 10				20 16	20 21	20 33				20 40				20 46	20 51	21 03	
	d	19 47	19 52	20 04				20 10				20 17	20 22	20 34				20 40				20 47	20 52	21 04	
Strawberry Hill	d			20 07										20 37										21 07	
Fulwell	a																								
Teddington	a			20 10										20 40										21 10	
Hampton Wick	a			20 14										20 44										21 14	
Kingston	a			20 16										20 46										21 16	
Whitton	d	19a50	19 55			20a23						20a20	20 25			20a53						20a50	20 55		
Feltham	d		19 59		20 06			20 16					20 29		20 36			20 46					20 59		21 06
Ashford (Surrey)	d		20 03		20 10								20 33		20 40								21 03		21 10
Staines	d		20 07		20 15			20 23					20 37		20 45			20 53					21 07		21 15
Wraysbury	d		20 11										20 41										21 11		
Sunnymeads	d		20 14										20 44										21 14		
Datchet	d		20 17										20 47										21 17		
Windsor & Eton Riverside	a		20 21										20 51										21 21		
Egham	d				20 20			20 27							20 50			20 57							21 20
Virginia Water	a				20 24			20 31							20 54			21 01							21 24
	d				20 24			20 31							20 54			21 01							21 24
Chertsey §	d				20 29										20 59										21 29
Addlestone §	d				20 32										21 02										21 32
Weybridge	a				20 37										21 07										21 37
Byfleet & New Haw	d																								
West Byfleet	d																								
Woking	a																								
Longcross	d																								
Sunningdale	d							20 37										21 07							
Ascot 3	d							20 43			20 53							21 13		21 23					
Bagshot	d										20 59									21 29					
Camberley	a										21 05									21 35					
	d										21 09									21 39					
Frimley	d										21 13									21 43					
Ash Vale	d										21 19									21 49					
Aldershot	a										21 24									21 54					
	d										21 38									22 08	22 38				
Ash 3	d										21 45									22 15	22 45				
Wanborough	d										21 48									22 18	22 48				
Guildford	a										21 55									22 25	22 55				
Martins Heron	d							20 47										21 17							
Bracknell	d							20 50										21 20							
Wokingham	d							20 57										21 27							
Winnersh	d							21 00										21 30							
Winnersh Triangle	d							21 02										21 32							
Earley	d							21 05										21 35							
Reading 7	a							21 10										21 40							

For general notes see front of timetable
For details of catering facilities see Directory of Train Operators

§ Passengers to/from London may travel via Weybridge. See Table 155.

A To London Waterloo
B To London Waterloo (Table 152)
b Arr. 2015
c Arr. 2045

From 28 September due to seasonal difficulties a large number of trains on this table will have minor retimings that could mean slightly earlier departure or later arrival times at certain stations. For further details see local publicity or contact National Rail Enquiries 08457 48 49 50

For details of Bank Holiday service alterations, please see first page of this Table

London → Hounslow, Richmond, Kingston, Windsor, Weybridge, Ascot, Guildford and Reading

Network Diagram - see first page of Table 148

		SW	SW	SW	SW	SW	SW	SW	SW	SW		SW	SW	SW	SW	SW	SW	SW	SW	SW	SW	SW	SW	SW	SW
				1									1		1							1			
		A	A			A		B		A		A				A		B		A					
London Waterloo 15 ⊖	d	20 37	20 45	20 50	20 52		20 58	21 03		21 07		21 15	21 20	21 22			21 28	21 33		21 37	21 45	21 50		21 52	21 58
Vauxhall ⊖	d	20 41	20 49		20 56		21 02	21 07		21 11		21 19		21 26			21 32	21 37		21 41	21 49			21 56	22 02
Queenstown Rd.(Battersea)	d	20 44	20 52		20 59			21 10		21 14		21 22		21 29				21 40		21 44	21 52			21 59	
Clapham Junction 10	d	20 47	20 55	20 58	21 02		21 08	21 13		21 17		21 25	21 28	21 32			21 38	21 43		21 47	21 55	21 58		22 02	22 08
Wandsworth Town	d	20 50	20 58		21 05			21 16		21 20		21 28		21 35				21 46		21 50	21 58			22 05	
Putney	d	20 53	21 01		21 08	←	21 12	21 19		21 23		21 31		21 38		←	21 42	21 49		21 53	22 01		←	22 08	22 12
Barnes	d	20 57	21 05		21 12	21 05		21 22		21 27		21 35		21 42		21 35		21 52		21 57	22 05		22 05	22 12	
Barnes Bridge	d	20 59	→		21 14					21 29		→		21 44						21 59	→			22 14	
Chiswick	d	21 02			21 17				←	21 32				21 47					←	22 02				22 17	
Kew Bridge	d	21 05			21 20				21 20	21 35				21 50					21 50	22 05				22 20	
Brentford	d	21 08			→				21 23	21 38				→					21 53	22 08				→	
Syon Lane	d	21 10							21 25	21 40									21 55	22 10					
Isleworth	d	21 12							21 27	21 42									21 57	22 12					
Hounslow	d	21b18							21 31	21c48									22 01	22e18					
Mortlake	d					21 07		21 24								21 37		21 54					22 07		
North Sheen	d					21 09		21 26								21 39		21 56					22 09		
Richmond ⊖	d			21 06		21 12	21 18	21 29					21 36			21 42	21 48	21 59				22 06	22 12		22 18
St Margarets	d					21 14		21 31								21 44		22 01					22 14		
Twickenham	a			21 10		21 16	21 21	21 33					21 40			21 46	21 51	22 03				22 10	22 16		22 21
	d			21 10		21 17	21 22	21 34					21 40			21 47	21 52	22 04				22 10			22 22
Strawberry Hill	d							21 37										22 07							
Fulwell	a																								
Teddington	a							21 40										22 10							
Hampton Wick	a							21 44										22 14							
Kingston	a							21 46										22 16							
Whitton	d	21a23				21a20	21 25			21a53						21a50	21 55			22a23					22 25
Feltham	d			21 16			21 29		21 36				21 46				21 59		22 06			22 16			22 29
Ashford (Surrey)	d						21 33		21 40								22 03		22 10						22 33
Staines	d			21 23			21 37		21 45				21 53				22 07		22 15			22 23			22 37
Wraysbury	d						21 41										22 11								22 41
Sunnymeads	d						21 44										22 14								22 44
Datchet	d						21 47										22 17								22 47
Windsor & Eton Riverside	a						21 51										22 21								22 51
Egham	d			21 27					21 50				21 57						22 20			22 27			
Virginia Water	a			21 31					21 54				22 01						22 24			22 31			
	d			21 31					21 54				22 01						22 24			22 31			
Chertsey §	d								21 59										22 29						
Addlestone §	d								22 02										22 32						
Weybridge	a								22 07										22 37						
Byfleet & New Haw	d																								
West Byfleet	d																								
Woking	a																								
Longcross	d																								
Sunningdale	d			21 37									22 07									22 37			
Ascot 3	d			21 43									22 13		22 23							22 43			
Bagshot	d														22 29										
Camberley	a														22 35										
	d														22 39										
Frimley	d														22 43										
Ash Vale	d														22 49										
Aldershot	a														22 54										
	d														23 08										
Ash 3	d														23 15										
Wanborough	d														23 18										
Guildford	a														23 25										
Martins Heron	d			21 47									22 17									22 47			
Bracknell	d			21 50									22 20									22 50			
Wokingham	d			21 57									22 27									22 57			
Winnersh	d			22 00									22 30									23 00			
Winnersh Triangle	d			22 02									22 32									23 02			
Earley	d			22 05									22 35									23 05			
Reading 7	a			22 10									22 40									23 10			

For general notes see front of timetable
For details of catering facilities see Directory of Train Operators

§ Passengers to/from London may travel via Weybridge. See Table 155.

A To London Waterloo
B To London Waterloo (Table 152)
b Arr. 2115
c Arr. 2145
e Arr. 2215

From 28 September due to seasonal difficulties a large number of trains on this table will have minor retimings that could mean slightly earlier departure or later arrival times at certain stations. For further details see local publicity or contact National Rail Enquiries 08457 48 49 50

London → Hounslow, Richmond, Kingston, Windsor, Weybridge, Ascot, Guildford and Reading

For details of Bank Holiday service alterations, please see first page of this Table

Network Diagram - see first page of Table 148

Station		SW	SW	SW	SW	SW	SW	SW	SW	SW	SW	SW	SW	SW	SW	SW	SW	SW	SW	SW	SW	SW	SW
		A		1			A	1 B		1			A			1							
London Waterloo 15 ⊖	d	22 03		22 20	22 22	22 28	22 33			22 50	22 52	22 58	23 03		23 13	23 20	23 22	23 35		23 37	23 52	23 58	
Vauxhall ⊖	d	22 07			22 26	22 32	22 37				22 56	23 02	23 07		23 17		23 26			23 41	23 56	00 02	
Queenstown Rd.(Battersea)	d	22 10			22 29		22 40				22 59		23 10				23 29			23 44	23 59		
Clapham Junction 10	d	22 13		22 28	22 32	22 38	22 43			22 58	23 02	23 08	23 13		23 23	23 28	23 32	23 43		23 47	00 02	00 08	
Wandsworth Town	d	22 16			22 35		22 46				23 05		23 16				23 35			23 50	00 05		
Putney	d	22 19			22 38	22 42	22 49				23 08	23 12	23 19		23 27		23 38			23 53	00 08	00 12	
Barnes	d	22 22			22 42		22 52				23 12		23 22				23 42			23 56	00 12		
Barnes Bridge	d				22 44						23 14						23 44		←		00 14		
Chiswick	d		←		22 47				←		23 17			←			23 47		23 47		00 17		←
Kew Bridge	d		22 20		22 50				22 50		23 20			23 20			→		23 50		00 20		00 20
Brentford	d		22 23		→				22 53		→			23 23					23 53		→		00 23
Syon Lane	d		22 25						22 55					23 25					23 55				00 25
Isleworth	d		22 27						22 57					23 27					23 57				00 27
Hounslow	d		22 31						23 01					23 31					00 01				00 31
Mortlake	d	22 24					22 54						23 24							23 58			
North Sheen	d	22 26					22 56						23 26							00 01			
Richmond ⊖	d	22 29		22 36		22 48	22 59			23 06		23 18	23 29		23 33	23 36		23 51		00 03		00 18	
St Margarets	d	22 31					23 01						23 31							00 06			
Twickenham	a	22 33		22 40		22 51	23 03			23 10		23 21	23 33		23 36	23 40		23 55		00 08		00 21	
	d	22 34		22 40		22 52	23 04			23 10		23 22	23 34		23 37	23 40		23 55		00 08		00 22	
Strawberry Hill	d	22 37					23 07						23 37							00 12			
Fulwell	a																						
Teddington	a	22 40					23 10						23 40							00 15			
Hampton Wick	a	22 44					23 14						23 44							00 17			
Kingston	a	22 46					23 16						23 46							00 19			
Whitton	d					22 55						23 25			23 40							00 25	
Feltham	d		22 36	22 46		22 59			23 06	23 16		23 29		23 36	23 44	23 48		00 01	00 06			00 29	00 36
Ashford (Surrey)	d		22 40			23 03			23 10			23 33		23 40	23 48				00 10			00 33	00 40
Staines	d		22 45	22 53		23 07			23 15	23 23		23 37		23 45	23 52	23 56		00 08	00 15			00a37	00a46
Wraysbury	d					23 11						23 41			23 56								
Sunnymeads	d					23 14						23 44			23 59								
Datchet	d					23 17						23 47			00 02								
Windsor & Eton Riverside	a					23 21						23 51			00 06								
Egham	d		22 50	22 57					23 20	23 27				23 50		00 01		00 12	00 20				
Virginia Water	a		22 54	23 01					23 24	23 31				23 54		00 05		00 16	00 24				
	d		22 54	23 01					23 24	23 31				23 54		00 05		00 16	00 24				
Chertsey §	d		22 59						23 29					23 59					00 29				
Addlestone §	d		23 02						23 32					00 02					00 32				
Weybridge	a		23 07						23 37										00 37				
Byfleet & New Haw	d													00 07									
West Byfleet	d													00 10									
Woking	a													00 18									
Longcross	d																						
Sunningdale	d			23 07						23 37						00 10		00 22					
Ascot 3	d			23 13				23 23		23 43						00 15		00 27					
Bagshot	d							23 29															
Camberley	a							23 35															
	d							23 39															
Frimley	d							23 43															
Ash Vale	d							23 49															
Aldershot	a							23 54															
	d																						
Ash 3	d																						
Wanborough	d																						
Guildford	a																						
Martins Heron	d			23 17						23 47						00 19		00 31					
Bracknell	d			23 20						23 50						00 23		00 34					
Wokingham	d			23 27						23 57						00 32		00 41					
Winnersh	d			23 30						00 01						00 36							
Winnersh Triangle	d			23 32						00 02						00 38							
Earley	d			23 35						00 05						00 40							
Reading 7	a			23 40						00 10						00 45		00 49					

For general notes see front of timetable
For details of catering facilities see Directory of Train Operators

A To London Waterloo (Table 152)
B To Farnham (Table 155)

§ Passengers to/from London may travel via Weybridge. See Table 155.

From 28 September due to seasonal difficulties a large number of trains on this table will have minor retimings that could mean slightly earlier departure or later arrival times at certain stations. For further details see local publicity or contact National Rail Enquiries 08457 48 49 50

London → Hounslow, Richmond, Kingston, Windsor, Weybridge, Ascot, Guildford and Reading

Network Diagram - see first page of Table 148

		SW 1	SW	SW	SW 1	SW	SW	SW	SW 1		SW	SW	SW	SW	SW	SW	SW 1	SW		SW 1	SW	SW 1	SW	SW	SW 1
																A					B			A	
London Waterloo 15	⊖ d	22p50	22p52	23p13	23p20	23p22	23p35	23p37				23p52	23p58		00 18					05 05				05 33	
Vauxhall	⊖ d		22p56	23p17		23p26		23p41				23p56	00 02		00 22					05 09				05 37	
Queenstown Rd.(Battersea)	d		22p59			23p29		23p44				23p59			00 25					05 12				05 40	
Clapham Junction 10	d	22p58	23p02	23p23	23p28	23p32	23p43	23p47				00 02	00 08		00 28					05 15				05 43	
Wandsworth Town	d		23p05			23p35		23p50				00 05			00 31					05 18				05 46	
Putney	d		23p08	23p27		23p38		23p53				00 08	00 12		00 34					05 21				05 49	
Barnes	d		23p12			23p42		23p56				00 12			00 37					05 24				05 52	
Barnes Bridge	d		23p14			23p44					←	00 14													
Chiswick	d		23p17			23p47					23p47	00 17		←											
Kew Bridge	d		23p20			→					23p50	00 20		00 20											
Brentford	d		23p23								23p53	→		00 23											
Syon Lane	d		23p25								23p55			00 25											
Isleworth	d		23p27								23p57			00 27											
Hounslow	d		23p31								00 01			00 31											
Mortlake	d							23p58							00 39					05 26				05 54	
North Sheen	d							00 01							00 41					05 28				05 56	
Richmond	⊖ d	23p06		23p33	23p36		23p51	00 03					00 18		00 44					05 31				05 59	
St Margarets	d							00 06							00 46					05 33				06 01	
Twickenham	a	23p10		23p36	23p40		23p55	00 08					00 21		00 48					05 35				06 03	
	d	23p10		23p37	23p40		23p55	00 08					00 22		00 49	04 52				05 36	05 38		05 52	06 04	
Strawberry Hill	d							00 12							00s52	04 55								06 07	
Fulwell	a																								
Teddington	a							00 15							00s55	04 58								06 10	
Hampton Wick	a							00 17							00s58	05 01								06 14	
Kingston	a							00 19							01 00	05 03								06 16	
Whitton	d			23p40									00 25							05 39	05a41		05 55		
Feltham	d	23p16	23p36	23p44	23p48		00 01				00 06		00 29	00 36						05 43			05 59		
Ashford (Surrey)	d		23p40	23p48							00 10		00 33	00 40						05 47			06 03		
Staines	d	23p23	23p45	23p52	23p56		00 08				00 15		00a37	00a46			05 23	05 45		05 53			06 07		
Wraysbury	d			23p56																			06 11		
Sunnymeads	d			23p59																			06 14		
Datchet	d			00 02																			06 17		
Windsor & Eton Riverside	a			00 06																			06 24		
Egham	d	23p27	23p50		00 01		00 12				00 20						05 27	05 50		05 57					
Virginia Water	a	23p31	23p54		00 05		00 16				00 24						05 31	05 54		06 01					
	d	23p31	23p54		00 05		00 16				00 24						05 31	05 54		06 01					
Chertsey §	d		23p59								00 29							05 59							
Addlestone §	d		00 02								00 32							06 02							
Weybridge	a										00 37							06 07							
Byfleet & New Haw	d		00 07																						
West Byfleet	d		00 10																						
Woking	a		00 18																						
Longcross	d																								
Sunningdale	d	23p37			00 10		00 22										05 37			06 07					
Ascot 3	d	23p43			00 15		00 27		00 29								05 43			06 13					
Bagshot	d								00 35																
Camberley	a								00 41																
	d								00 41																
Frimley	d								00 45																
Ash Vale	d								00 52																
Aldershot	a								00 57																
	d																					06 08			06 38
Ash 3	d																					06 15			06 45
Wanborough	d																					06 18			06 48
Guildford	a																					06 25			06 55
Martins Heron	d	23p47			00 19		00 31										05 47			06 17					
Bracknell	d	23p50			00 23		00 34										05 50			06 20					
Wokingham	d	23p57			00 32		00 41										05 57			06 27					
Winnersh	d	00 01			00 36												06 00			06 30					
Winnersh Triangle	d	00 02			00 38												06 02			06 32					
Earley	d	00 05			00 40												06 05			06 35					
Reading 7	a	00 10			00 45		00 49										06 10			06 40					

For general notes see front of timetable
For details of catering facilities see Directory of Train Operators

§ Passengers to/from London may travel via Weybridge. See Table 155.

A To London Waterloo (Table 152)
B To London Waterloo

From 3 October due to seasonal difficulties a large number of trains on this table will have minor retimings that could mean slightly earlier departure or later arrival times at certain stations. For further details see local publicity or contact National Rail Enquiries 08457 48 49 50.

Table 149

London → Hounslow, Richmond, Kingston, Windsor, Weybridge, Ascot, Guildford and Reading

Network Diagram - see first page of Table 148

		SW	SW 1	SW	SW		SW	SW 1	SW 1	SW 1	SW	SW	SW	SW		SW 1	SW	SW	SW	SW	SW	SW 1	SW 1		SW 1
					A								A						A	B					
London Waterloo 15	⊖ d		05 50	05 58	06 03					06 20	06 22	06 28	06 33			06 50	06 52	06 58	07 03	07 15					07 20
Vauxhall	⊖ d			06 02	06 07						06 26	06 32	06 37				06 56	07 02	07 07	07 19					
Queenstown Rd.(Battersea)	d				06 10						06 29		06 40				06 59		07 10	07 22					
Clapham Junction 10	d		05 58	06 08	06 13					06 28	06 32	06 38	06 43			06 58	07 02	07 08	07 13	07 25					07 28
Wandsworth Town	d				06 16						06 35		06 46				07 05		07 16	07 28					
Putney	d			06 12	06 19						06 38	06 42	06 49				07 08	07 12	07 19	07 31					
Barnes	d				06 22						06 42		06 52				07 12		07 22	07 35					
Barnes Bridge	d										06 44						07 14			↳					
Chiswick	d										06 47			←			07 17				←				
Kew Bridge	d										06 50 →			06 50			07 20 →				07 20				
Brentford	d													06 53							07 23				
Syon Lane	d													06 55							07 25				
Isleworth	d													06 57							07 27				
Hounslow	d													07 01							07 31				
Mortlake	d				06 24								06 54						07 24						
North Sheen	d				06 26								06 56						07 26						
Richmond	⊖ d		06 06	06 18	06 29					06 36		06 48	06 59			07 06		07 18	07 29						07 36
St Margarets	d				06 31								07 01						07 31						
Twickenham	a		06 10	06 21	06 33					06 40		06 51	07 03			07 10		07 21	07 33						07 40
	d		06 10	06 22	06 34					06 40		06 52	07 04			07 10		07 22	07 34						07 40
Strawberry Hill	d				06 37								07 07						07 37						
Fulwell	a																								
Teddington	a				06 40								07 10						07 40						
Hampton Wick	a				06 44								07 14						07 44						
Kingston	a				06 46								07 16						07 46						
Whitton	d			06 25								06 55						07 25							
Feltham	d		06 16	06 29						06 46		06 59		07 06		07 16		07 29			07 36				07 46
Ashford (Surrey)	d			06 33								07 03		07 10				07 33			07 40				
Staines	d	06 16	06 23	06 37			06 45			06 53		07 07		07 15		07 23		07 37			07 45				07 53
Wraysbury	d			06 41								07 11						07 41							
Sunnymeads	d			06 44								07 14						07 44							
Datchet	d			06 47								07 17						07 47							
Windsor & Eton Riverside	a			06 51								07 21						07 51							
Egham	d	06 21	06 27				06 50			06 57				07 20		07 27					07 50				07 57
Virginia Water	a	06 25	06 31				06 54			07 01				07 24		07 31					07 54				08 01
	d	06 25	06 31				06 54			07 01				07 24		07 31					07 54				08 01
Chertsey §	d	06 30					06 59							07 29							07 59				
Addlestone §	d	06 33					07 02							07 32							08 02				
Weybridge	a	06 38					07 07							07 37							08 07				
Byfleet & New Haw	d																								
West Byfleet	d																								
Woking	a																								
Longcross	d																								
Sunningdale	d		06 37							07 07						07 37									08 07
Ascot 3	d		06 43						06 53	07 13						07 43							07 53		08 13
Bagshot	d								06 59														07 59		
Camberley	a								07 05														08 05		
	d								07 09														08 09		
Frimley	d								07 13														08 13		
Ash Vale	d								07 19														08 19		
Aldershot	a								07 24														08 24		
	d							07 08	07 38													08 08	08 38		
Ash 3	d							07 15	07 45													08 15	08 45		
Wanborough	d							07 18	07 48													08 18	08 48		
Guildford	a							07 25	07 55													08 25	08 55		
Martins Heron	d		06 47							07 17						07 47									08 17
Bracknell	d		06 50							07 20						07 50									08 20
Wokingham	d		06 57							07 27						07 57									08 27
Winnersh	d		07 00							07 30						08 00									08 30
Winnersh Triangle	d		07 02							07 32						08 02									08 32
Earley	d		07 05							07 35						08 05									08 35
Reading 7	a		07 10							07 40						08 10									08 40

For general notes see front of timetable
For details of catering facilities see Directory of Train Operators

§ Passengers to/from London may travel via Weybridge. See Table 155.

A To London Waterloo (Table 152)
B To London Waterloo

From 3 October due to seasonal difficulties a large number of trains on this table will have minor retimings that could mean slightly earlier departure or later arrival times at certain stations. For further details see local publicity or contact National Rail Enquiries 08457 48 49 50.

Table 149

Saturdays

London → Hounslow, Richmond, Kingston, Windsor, Weybridge, Ascot, Guildford and Reading

Network Diagram - see first page of Table 148

		SW	SW 1	SW	SW	SW	SW	SW	SW		SW 1	SW	SW 1	SW	SW	SW	SW	SW		SW	SW 1	SW	SW 1	SW	SW
				A		B		A	A					A		B		A		A				A	
London Waterloo 15 ⊖	d	07 22			07 28	07 33		07 37	07 45		07 50	07 52			07 58	08 03		08 07		08 15	08 20	08 22			08 28
Vauxhall ⊖	d	07 26			07 32	07 37		07 41	07 49			07 56			08 02	08 07		08 11		08 19		08 26			08 32
Queenstown Rd.(Battersea)	d	07 29				07 40		07 44	07 52			07 59				08 10		08 14		08 22		08 29			
Clapham Junction 10	d	07 32			07 38	07 43		07 47	07 55		07 58	08 02			08 08	08 13		08 17		08 25	08 28	08 32			08 38
Wandsworth Town	d	07 35				07 46		07 50	07 58			08 05				08 16		08 20		08 28		08 35			
Putney	d	07 38		←	07 42	07 49		07 53	08 01			08 08		←	08 12	08 19		08 23		08 31		08 38		←	08 42
Barnes	d	07 42		07 35		07 52		07 57	08 05			08 12		08 05		08 22		08 27		08 35		08 42		08 35	
Barnes Bridge	d	07 44						07 59	→			08 14						08 29		→		08 44			
Chiswick	d	07 47					←	08 02				08 17					←	08 32				08 47			
Kew Bridge	d	07 50					07 50	08 05				08 20					08 20	08 35				08 50			
Brentford	d	→					07 53	08 08				→					08 23	08 38				→			
Syon Lane	d						07 55	08 10									08 25	08 40							
Isleworth	d						07 57	08 12									08 27	08 42							
Hounslow	d						08 01	08b18									08 31	08c48							
Mortlake	d			07 37		07 54								08 07		08 24								08 37	
North Sheen	d			07 39		07 56								08 09		08 26								08 39	
Richmond ⊖	d			07 42	07 48	07 59					08 06			08 12	08 18	08 29					08 36			08 42	08 48
St Margarets	d			07 44		08 01								08 14		08 31								08 44	
Twickenham	a			07 46	07 51	08 03					08 10			08 16	08 21	08 33					08 40			08 46	08 51
	d			07 47	07 52	08 04					08 10			08 17	08 22	08 34					08 40			08 47	08 52
Strawberry Hill	d					08 07										08 37									
Fulwell	a																								
Teddington	a					08 10										08 40									
Hampton Wick	a					08 14										08 44									
Kingston	a					08 16										08 46									
Whitton	d			07a50	07 55			08a23						08a20	08 25			08a53						08a50	08 55
Feltham	d				07 59		08 06				08 16				08 29		08 36				08 46				08 59
Ashford (Surrey)	d				08 03		08 10								08 33		08 40								09 03
Staines	d				08 07		08 15				08 23				08 37		08 45				08 53				09 07
Wraysbury	d				08 11										08 41										09 11
Sunnymeads	d				08 14										08 44										09 14
Datchet	d				08 17										08 47										09 17
Windsor & Eton Riverside	a				08 21										08 51										09 21
Egham	d						08 20				08 27						08 50				08 57				
Virginia Water	a						08 24				08 31						08 54				09 01				
	d						08 24				08 31						08 54				09 01				
Chertsey §	d						08 29										08 59								
Addlestone §	d						08 32										09 02								
Weybridge	a						08 37										09 07								
Byfleet & New Haw	d																								
West Byfleet	d																								
Woking	a																								
Longcross	d																								
Sunningdale	d										08 37										09 07				
Ascot 3	d		08 23								08 43		08 53								09 13		09 23		
Bagshot	d		08 29										08 59										09 29		
Camberley	a		08 35										09 05										09 35		
	d		08 39										09 09										09 39		
Frimley	d		08 43										09 13										09 43		
Ash Vale	d		08 49										09 19										09 49		
Aldershot	a		08 54										09 24										09 54		
	d		09 08										09 38										10 08		
Ash 3	d		09 15										09 45										10 15		
Wanborough	d		09 18										09 48										10 18		
Guildford	a		09 25										09 55										10 25		
Martins Heron	d										08 47										09 17				
Bracknell	d										08 50										09 20				
Wokingham	d										08 57										09 27				
Winnersh	d										09 00										09 30				
Winnersh Triangle	d										09 02										09 32				
Earley	d										09 05										09 35				
Reading 7	a										09 10										09 40				

For general notes see front of timetable
For details of catering facilities see Directory of Train Operators

§ Passengers to/from London may travel via Weybridge. See Table 155.

A To London Waterloo
B To London Waterloo (Table 152)
b Arr. 0815
c Arr. 0845

From 3 October due to seasonal difficulties a large number of trains on this table will have minor retimings that could mean slightly earlier departure or later arrival times at certain stations. For further details see local publicity or contact National Rail Enquiries 08457 48 49 50.

London → Hounslow, Richmond, Kingston, Windsor, Weybridge, Ascot, Guildford and Reading

Network Diagram - see first page of Table 148

Station		SW	SW	SW	SW	SW	SW	SW	SW	SW
						1		1		
		A		B	B				B	
London Waterloo 15	⊖ d	08 33		08 37	08 45	08 50	08 52			08 58
Vauxhall	⊖ d	08 37		08 41	08 49		08 56			09 02
Queenstown Rd.(Battersea)	d	08 40		08 44	08 52		08 59			
Clapham Junction 10	d	08 43		08 47	08 55	08 58	09 02			09 08
Wandsworth Town	d	08 46		08 50	08 58		09 05			
Putney	d	08 49		08 53	09 01		09 08		←	09 12
Barnes	d	08 52		08 57	09 05		09 12		09 05	
Barnes Bridge	d			08 59	→		09 14			
Chiswick	d		←	09 02			09 17			
Kew Bridge	d		08 50	09 05			09 20			
Brentford	d		08 53	09 08			→			
Syon Lane	d		08 55	09 10						
Isleworth	d		08 57	09 12						
Hounslow	d		09 01	09b18						
Mortlake	d	08 54							09 07	
North Sheen	d	08 56							09 09	
Richmond	⊖ d	08 59				09 06			09 12	09 18
St Margarets	d	09 01							09 14	
Twickenham	a	09 03				09 10			09 16	09 21
	d	09 04				09 10			09 17	09 22
Strawberry Hill	d	09 07								
Fulwell	a									
Teddington	a	09 10								
Hampton Wick	a	09 14								
Kingston	a	09 16								
Whitton	d			09a23					09a20	09 25
Feltham	d		09 06			09 16				09 29
Ashford (Surrey)	d		09 10							09 33
Staines	d		09 15			09 23				09 37
Wraysbury	d									09 41
Sunnymeads	d									09 44
Datchet	d									09 47
Windsor & Eton Riverside	a									09 51
Egham	d		09 20			09 27				
Virginia Water	a		09 24			09 31				
	d		09 24			09 31				
Chertsey §	d		09 29							
Addlestone §	d		09 32							
Weybridge	a		09 37							
Byfleet & New Haw	d									
West Byfleet	d									
Woking	a									
Longcross	d									
Sunningdale	d					09 37				
Ascot 3	d					09 43		09 53		
Bagshot	d							09 59		
Camberley	a							10 05		
	d							10 09		
Frimley	d							10 13		
Ash Vale	d							10 19		
Aldershot	a							10 24		
	d							10 38		
Ash 3	d							10 45		
Wanborough	d							10 48		
Guildford	a							10 55		
Martins Heron	d					09 47				
Bracknell	d					09 50				
Wokingham	d					09 57				
Winnersh	d					10 00				
Winnersh Triangle	d					10 02				
Earley	d					10 05				
Reading 7	a					10 10				

Station		SW	SW	SW	SW	SW	SW	SW	SW	SW	SW	SW	SW	SW
						1		1						
		A		B	B				B		A		B	B
London Waterloo 15	⊖ d	09 03		09 07	09 15	09 20	09 22			09 28	09 33		09 37	09 45
Vauxhall	⊖ d	09 07		09 11	09 19		09 26			09 32	09 37		09 41	09 49
Queenstown Rd.(Battersea)	d	09 10		09 14	09 22		09 29				09 40		09 44	09 52
Clapham Junction 10	d	09 13		09 17	09 25	09 28	09 32			09 38	09 43		09 47	09 55
Wandsworth Town	d	09 16		09 20	09 28		09 35				09 46		09 50	09 58
Putney	d	09 19		09 23	09 31		09 38		←	09 42	09 49		09 53	10 01
Barnes	d	09 22		09 27	09 35		09 42		09 35		09 52		09 57	10 05
Barnes Bridge	d			09 29	→		09 44						09 59	→
Chiswick	d		←	09 32			09 47					←	10 02	
Kew Bridge	d		09 20	09 35			09 50					09 50	10 05	
Brentford	d		09 23	09 38			→					09 53	10 08	
Syon Lane	d		09 25	09 40								09 55	10 10	
Isleworth	d		09 27	09 42								09 57	10 12	
Hounslow	d		09 31	09c48								10 01	10e18	
Mortlake	d	09 24							09 37		09 54			
North Sheen	d	09 26							09 39		09 56			
Richmond	⊖ d	09 29				09 36			09 42	09 48	09 59			
St Margarets	d	09 31							09 44		10 01			
Twickenham	a	09 33				09 40			09 46	09 51	10 03			
	d	09 34				09 40			09 47	09 52	10 04			
Strawberry Hill	d	09 37									10 07			
Fulwell	a													
Teddington	a	09 40									10 10			
Hampton Wick	a	09 44									10 14			
Kingston	a	09 46									10 16			
Whitton	d			09a53					09a50	09 55			10a23	
Feltham	d		09 36			09 46				09 59		10 06		
Ashford (Surrey)	d		09 40							10 03		10 10		
Staines	d		09 45			09 53				10 07		10 15		
Wraysbury	d									10 11				
Sunnymeads	d									10 14				
Datchet	d									10 17				
Windsor & Eton Riverside	a									10 21				
Egham	d		09 50			09 57						10 20		
Virginia Water	a		09 54			10 01						10 24		
	d		09 54			10 01						10 24		
Chertsey §	d		09 59									10 29		
Addlestone §	d		10 02									10 32		
Weybridge	a		10 07									10 37		
Byfleet & New Haw	d													
West Byfleet	d													
Woking	a													
Longcross	d													
Sunningdale	d					10 07								
Ascot 3	d					10 13		10 23						
Bagshot	d							10 29						
Camberley	a							10 35						
	d							10 39						
Frimley	d							10 43						
Ash Vale	d							10 49						
Aldershot	a							10 54						
	d							11 08						
Ash 3	d							11 15						
Wanborough	d							11 18						
Guildford	a							11 25						
Martins Heron	d					10 17								
Bracknell	d					10 20								
Wokingham	d					10 27								
Winnersh	d					10 30								
Winnersh Triangle	d					10 32								
Earley	d					10 35								
Reading 7	a					10 40								

For general notes see front of timetable
For details of catering facilities see Directory of Train Operators

§ Passengers to/from London may travel via Weybridge. See Table 155.

A To London Waterloo (Table 152)
B To London Waterloo
b Arr. 0915
c Arr. 0945
e Arr. 1015

From 3 October due to seasonal difficulties a large number of trains on this table will have minor retimings that could mean slightly earlier departure or later arrival times at certain stations. For further details see local publicity or contact National Rail Enquiries 08457 48 49 50.

London → Hounslow, Richmond, Kingston, Windsor, Weybridge, Ascot, Guildford and Reading

Network Diagram - see first page of Table 148

		SW 1	SW	SW 1	SW A	SW			SW B	SW	SW A	SW A	SW 1	SW	SW 1	SW A		SW	SW B	SW	SW A	SW A	SW 1	SW
London Waterloo 15	⊖ d	09 50	09 52			09 58			19 03		19 07	19 15	19 20	19 22				19 28	19 33		19 37	19 45	19 50	19 52
Vauxhall	⊖ d		09 56			10 02			19 07		19 11	19 19		19 26				19 32	19 37		19 41	19 49		19 56
Queenstown Rd.(Battersea)	d		09 59						19 10		19 14	19 22		19 29					19 40		19 44	19 52		19 59
Clapham Junction 10	d	09 58	10 02			10 08			19 13		19 17	19 25	19 28	19 32				19 38	19 43		19 47	19 55	19 58	20 02
Wandsworth Town	d		10 05						19 16		19 20	19 28		19 35					19 46		19 50	19 58		20 05
Putney	d		10 08		⟵	10 12			19 19		19 23	19 31		19 38		⟵		19 42	19 49		19 53	20 01		20 08
Barnes	d		10 12		10 05				19 22		19 27	19 35		19 42		19 35			19 52		19 57	20 05		20 12
Barnes Bridge	d		10 14								19 29	⟶		19 44							19 59	⟶		20 14
Chiswick	d		10 17							⟵	19 32			19 47						⟵	20 02			20 17
Kew Bridge	d		10 20							19 20	19 35			19 50						19 50	20 05			20 20
Brentford	d		⟶							19 23	19 38			⟶						19 53	20 08			⟶
Syon Lane	d									19 25	19 40									19 55	20 10			
Isleworth	d									19 27	19 42									19 57	20 12			
Hounslow	d									19 31	19b48									20 01	20c18			
Mortlake	d				10 07				19 24							19 37			19 54					
North Sheen	d				10 09				19 26							19 39			19 56					
Richmond	⊖ d	10 06			10 12	10 18			19 29				19 36			19 42		19 48	19 59				20 06	
St Margarets	d				10 14				19 31							19 44			20 01					
Twickenham	a	10 10			10 16	10 21			19 33				19 40			19 46		19 51	20 03				20 10	
	d	10 10			10 17	10 22			19 34				19 40			19 47		19 52	20 04				20 10	
Strawberry Hill	d								19 37										20 07					
Fulwell	a																							
Teddington	a								19 40										20 10					
Hampton Wick	a								19 44										20 14					
Kingston	a						and at		19 46										20 16					
Whitton	d				10a20	10 25					19a53					19a50		19 55			20a23			
Feltham	d	10 16				10 29	the same			19 36			19 46					19 59		20 06			20 16	
Ashford (Surrey)	d					10 33				19 40								20 03		20 10				
Staines	d	10 23				10 37	minutes			19 45			19 53					20 07		20 15			20 23	
Wraysbury	d					10 41	past											20 11						
Sunnymeads	d					10 44												20 14						
Datchet	d					10 47	each											20 17						
Windsor & Eton Riverside	a					10 51	hour until											20 21						
Egham	d	10 27								19 50			19 57							20 20			20 27	
Virginia Water	a	10 31								19 54			20 01							20 24			20 31	
	d	10 31								19 54			20 01							20 24			20 31	
Chertsey §	d									19 59										20 29				
Addlestone §	d									20 02										20 32				
Weybridge	a									20 07										20 37				
Byfleet & New Haw	d																							
West Byfleet	d																							
Woking	a																							
Longcross	d																							
Sunningdale	d	10 37											20 07										20 37	
Ascot 3	d	10 43		10 53									20 13		20 23								20 43	
Bagshot	d			10 59											20 29									
Camberley	a			11 05											20 35									
	d			11 09											20 39									
Frimley	d			11 13											20 43									
Ash Vale	d			11 19											20 49									
Aldershot	a			11 24											20 54									
	d			11 38											21 08									
Ash 3	d			11 45											21 15									
Wanborough	d			11 48											21 18									
Guildford	a			11 55											21 25									
Martins Heron	d	10 47											20 17										20 47	
Bracknell	d	10 50											20 20										20 50	
Wokingham	d	10 57											20 27										20 57	
Winnersh	d	11 00											20 30										21 00	
Winnersh Triangle	d	11 02											20 32										21 02	
Earley	d	11 05											20 35										21 05	
Reading 7	a	11 10											20 40										21 10	

For general notes see front of timetable
For details of catering facilities see
Directory of Train Operators

§ Passengers to/from London may travel via Weybridge. See Table 155.

A To London Waterloo
B To London Waterloo (Table 152)
b Arr. 1945
c Arr. 2015

From 3 October due to seasonal difficulties a large number of trains on this table will have minor retimings that could mean slightly earlier departure or later arrival times at certain stations. For further details see local publicity or contact National Rail Enquiries 08457 48 49 50.

London → Hounslow, Richmond, Kingston, Windsor, Weybridge, Ascot, Guildford and Reading

Network Diagram - see first page of Table 148

		SW 1	SW	SW	SW	SW	SW	SW	SW 1	SW	SW 1	SW 1	SW	SW	SW	SW	SW	SW	SW 1	SW	SW	SW
			A		B		A	A					A		B		A	A			A	
London Waterloo 15	⊖ d			19 58	20 03		20 07	20 15	20 20	20 22				20 28	20 33		20 37	20 45	20 50	20 52		20 58
Vauxhall	⊖ d			20 02	20 07		20 11	20 19		20 26				20 32	20 37		20 41	20 49		20 56		21 02
Queenstown Rd.(Battersea)	d				20 10		20 14	20 22		20 29					20 40		20 44	20 52		20 59		
Clapham Junction 10	d			20 08	20 13		20 17	20 25	20 28	20 32				20 38	20 43		20 47	20 55	20 58	21 02		21 08
Wandsworth Town	d				20 16		20 20	20 28		20 35					20 46		20 50	20 58		21 05		
Putney	d		←	20 12	20 19		20 23	20 31		20 38			←	20 42	20 49		20 53	21 01		21 08	←	21 12
Barnes	d		20 05		20 22		20 27	20 35		20 42			20 35		20 52		20 57	21 05		21 12	21 05	
Barnes Bridge	d						20 29	→		20 44							20 59	→		21 14		
Chiswick	d					←	20 32			20 47						←	21 02			21 17		
Kew Bridge	d					20 20	20 35			20 50						20 50	21 05			21 20		
Brentford	d					20 23	20 38			→						20 53	21 08			→		
Syon Lane	d					20 25	20 40									20 55	21 10					
Isleworth	d					20 27	20 42									20 57	21 12					
Hounslow	d					20 31	20b48									21 01	21c18					
Mortlake	d		20 07		20 24		21a08						20 37		20 54						21 07	
North Sheen	d		20 09		20 26								20 39		20 56						21 09	
Richmond	⊖ d		20 12	20 18	20 29				20 36				20 42	20 48	20 59				21 06		21 12	21 18
St Margarets	d		20 14		20 31								20 44		21 01						21 14	
Twickenham	a		20 16	20 21	20 33				20 40				20 46	20 51	21 03				21 10		21 16	21 21
	d		20 17	20 22	20 34				20 40				20 47	20 52	21 04				21 10		21 17	21 22
Strawberry Hill	d				20 37										21 07							
Fulwell	a																					
Teddington	a				20 40										21 10							
Hampton Wick	a				20 44										21 14							
Kingston	a				20 46										21 16							
Whitton	d		20a20	20 25			20a53						20a50	20 55			21a23				21a20	21 25
Feltham	d			20 29		20 36			20 46					20 59		21 06			21 16			21 29
Ashford (Surrey)	d			20 33		20 40								21 03		21 10						21 33
Staines	d			20 37		20 45			20 53					21 07		21 15			21 23			21 37
Wraysbury	d			20 41										21 11								21 41
Sunnymeads	d			20 44										21 14								21 44
Datchet	d			20 47										21 17								21 47
Windsor & Eton Riverside	a			20 51										21 21								21 51
Egham	d					20 50			20 57							21 20			21 27			
Virginia Water	a					20 54			21 01							21 24			21 31			
	d					20 54			21 01							21 24			21 31			
Chertsey §	d					20 59										21 29						
Addlestone §	d					21 02										21 32						
Weybridge	a					21 07										21 37						
Byfleet & New Haw	d																					
West Byfleet	d																					
Woking	a																					
Longcross	d																					
Sunningdale	d								21 07										21 37			
Ascot 3	d	20 53							21 13		21 23								21 43			
Bagshot	d	20 59									21 29											
Camberley	a	21 05									21 35											
	d	21 09									21 39											
Frimley	d	21 13									21 43											
Ash Vale	d	21 19									21 49											
Aldershot	a	21 24									21 54											
	d	21 38									22 08	22 38										
Ash 3	d	21 45									22 15	22 45										
Wanborough	d	21 48									22 18	22 48										
Guildford	a	21 55									22 25	22 55										
Martins Heron	d								21 17										21 47			
Bracknell	d								21 20										21 50			
Wokingham	d								21 27										21 57			
Winnersh	d								21 30										22 00			
Winnersh Triangle	d								21 32										22 02			
Earley	d								21 35										22 05			
Reading 7	a								21 40										22 10			

For general notes see front of timetable
For details of catering facilities see Directory of Train Operators

§ Passengers to/from London may travel via Weybridge. See Table 155.

A To London Waterloo
B To London Waterloo (Table 152)
b Arr. 2045
c Arr. 2115

From 3 October due to seasonal difficulties a large number of trains on this table will have minor retimings that could mean slightly earlier departure or later arrival times at certain stations. For further details see local publicity or contact National Rail Enquiries 08457 48 49 50.

London → Hounslow, Richmond, Kingston, Windsor, Weybridge, Ascot, Guildford and Reading

Network Diagram - see first page of Table 148

		SW	SW	SW	SW	SW	SW	SW	SW	SW	SW	SW	SW	SW	SW	SW	SW	SW	SW	SW	SW	SW	SW
						1		1							1						1		
		A		B	B				B		A		B						A				
London Waterloo 15	⊖ d	21 03		21 07	21 15	21 20	21 22			21 28	21 33		21 37	21 45	21 50		21 52	21 58	22 03		22 20	22 22	22 28
Vauxhall	⊖ d	21 07		21 11	21 19		21 26			21 32	21 37		21 41	21 49			21 56	22 02	22 07			22 26	22 32
Queenstown Rd.(Battersea)	d	21 10		21 14	21 22		21 29				21 40		21 44	21 52			21 59		22 10			22 29	
Clapham Junction 10	d	21 13		21 17	21 25	21 28	21 32			21 38	21 43		21 47	21 55	21 58		22 02	22 08	22 13		22 28	22 32	22 38
Wandsworth Town	d	21 16		21 20	21 28		21 35				21 46		21 50	21 58			22 05		22 16			22 35	
Putney	d	21 19		21 23	21 31		21 38		←	21 42	21 49		21 53	22 01		←	22 08	22 12	22 19			22 38	22 42
Barnes	d	21 22		21 27	21 35		21 42		21 35		21 52		21 57	22 05		22 05	22 12		22 22			22 42	
Barnes Bridge	d			21 29	→		21 44						21 59	→			22 14					22 44	
Chiswick	d		←	21 32			21 47					←	22 02				22 17			←		22 47	
Kew Bridge	d		21 20	21 35			21 50					21 50	22 05				22 20			22 20		22 50	
Brentford	d		21 23	21 38			→					21 53	22 08				→			22 23		→	
Syon Lane	d		21 25	21 40								21 55	22 10							22 25			
Isleworth	d		21 27	21 42								21 57	22 12							22 27			
Hounslow	d		21 31	21b48								22 01	22c18							22 31			
Mortlake	d	21 24		22a08					21 37		21 54					22 07			22 24				
North Sheen	d	21 26							21 39		21 56					22 09			22 26				
Richmond	⊖ d	21 29				21 36			21 42	21 48	21 59				22 06	22 12		22 18	22 29		22 36		22 48
St Margarets	d	21 31							21 44		22 01					22 14			22 31				
Twickenham	a	21 33				21 40			21 46	21 51	22 03				22 10	22 16		22 21	22 33		22 40		22 51
	d	21 34				21 40			21 47	21 52	22 04				22 10			22 22	22 34		22 40		22 52
Strawberry Hill	d	21 37									22 07								22 37				
Fulwell	a																						
Teddington	a	21 40									22 10								22 40				
Hampton Wick	a	21 44									22 14								22 44				
Kingston	a	21 46									22 16								22 46				
Whitton	d			21a53					21a50	21 55			22a23					22 25					22 55
Feltham	d		21 36			21 46				21 59		22 06			22 16			22 29		22 36	22 46		22 59
Ashford (Surrey)	d		21 40							22 03		22 10						22 33		22 40			23 03
Staines	d		21 45			21 53				22 07		22 15			22 23			22 37		22 45	22 53		23 07
Wraysbury	d									22 11								22 41					23 11
Sunnymeads	d									22 14								22 44					23 14
Datchet	d									22 17								22 47					23 17
Windsor & Eton Riverside	a									22 21								22 51					23 21
Egham	d		21 50			21 57						22 20			22 27					22 50	22 57		
Virginia Water	a		21 54			22 01						22 24			22 31					22 54	23 01		
	d		21 54			22 01						22 24			22 31					22 54	23 01		
Chertsey §	d		21 59									22 29								22 59			
Addlestone §	d		22 02									22 32								23 02			
Weybridge	a		22 07									22 37								23 07			
Byfleet & New Haw	d																						
West Byfleet	d																						
Woking	a																						
Longcross	d																						
Sunningdale	d					22 07									22 37						23 07		
Ascot 3	d					22 13		22 23							22 43						23 13		
Bagshot	d							22 29															
Camberley	a							22 35															
	d							22 39															
Frimley	d							22 43															
Ash Vale	d							22 49															
Aldershot	a							22 54															
	d							23 08															
Ash 3	d							23 15															
Wanborough	d							23 18															
Guildford	a							23 25															
Martins Heron	d					22 17									22 47						23 17		
Bracknell	d					22 20									22 50						23 20		
Wokingham	d					22 27									22 57						23 27		
Winnersh	d					22 30									23 00						23 30		
Winnersh Triangle	d					22 32									23 02						23 32		
Earley	d					22 35									23 05						23 35		
Reading 7	a					22 40									23 10						23 40		

For general notes see front of timetable
For details of catering facilities see Directory of Train Operators

§ Passengers to/from London may travel via Weybridge. See Table 155.

A To London Waterloo (Table 152)
B To London Waterloo
b Arr. 2145
c Arr. 2215

From 3 October due to seasonal difficulties a large number of trains on this table will have minor retimings that could mean slightly earlier departure or later arrival times at certain stations. For further details see local publicity or contact National Rail Enquiries 08457 48 49 50.

London → Hounslow, Richmond, Kingston, Windsor, Weybridge, Ascot, Guildford and Reading

Network Diagram - see first page of Table 148

		SW	SW	SW	SW		SW	SW	SW	SW	SW	SW	SW	SW		SW	SW	SW	SW	SW
		A	1		1				A			1		1						
London Waterloo 15 ⊖	d	22 33			22 50		22 52	22 58	23 03		23 13	23 20	23 22	23 35			23 37	23 52	23 58	
Vauxhall ⊖	d	22 37					22 56	23 02	23 07		23 17		23 26				23 41	23 56	00 02	
Queenstown Rd.(Battersea)	d	22 40					22 59		23 10				23 29				23 44	23 59		
Clapham Junction 10	d	22 43			22 58		23 02	23 08	23 13		23 23	23 28	23 32	23 43			23 47	00 02	00 08	
Wandsworth Town	d	22 46					23 05		23 16				23 35				23 50	00 05		
Putney	d	22 49					23 08	23 12	23 19		23 27		23 38				23 53	00 08	00 12	
Barnes	d	22 52					23 12		23 22				23 42				23 56	00 12		
Barnes Bridge	d						23 14						23 44			←		00 14		
Chiswick	d			←			23 17			←			23 47			23 47		00 17		←
Kew Bridge	d			22 50			23 20			23 20			→			23 50		00 20		00 20
Brentford	d			22 53			→			23 23						23 53		→		00 23
Syon Lane	d			22 55						23 25						23 55				00 25
Isleworth	d			22 57						23 27						23 57				00 27
Hounslow	d			23 01						23 31						00 01				00 31
Mortlake	d	22 54							23 24								23 58			
North Sheen	d	22 56							23 26								00 01			
Richmond ⊖	d	22 59			23 06			23 18	23 29		23 33	23 36		23 51			00 03		00 18	
St Margarets	d	23 01							23 31								00 06			
Twickenham	a	23 03			23 10			23 21	23 33		23 36	23 40		23 55			00 08		00 21	
	d	23 04			23 10			23 22	23 34		23 37	23 40		23 55			00 08		00 22	
Strawberry Hill	d	23 07							23 37								00 12			
Fulwell	a																			
Teddington	a	23 10							23 40								00 15			
Hampton Wick	a	23 14							23 44								00 17			
Kingston	a	23 16							23 46								00 19			
Whitton	d							23 25			23 40								00 25	
Feltham	d			23 06	23 16			23 29		23 36	23 44	23 48		00 01		00 06			00 29	00 36
Ashford (Surrey)	d			23 10				23 33		23 40	23 48					00 10			00 33	00 40
Staines	d			23 15	23 23			23 37		23 45	23 52	23 56		00 08		00 15			00a37	00a46
Wraysbury	d							23 41			23 56									
Sunnymeads	d							23 44			23 59									
Datchet	d							23 47			00 02									
Windsor & Eton Riverside	a							23 51			00 06									
Egham	d			23 20	23 27					23 50		00 01		00 12		00 20				
Virginia Water	a			23 24	23 31					23 54		00 05		00 16		00 24				
	d			23 24	23 31					23 54		00 05		00 16		00 24				
Chertsey §	d			23 29						23 59						00 29				
Addlestone §	d			23 32						00 02						00 32				
Weybridge	a			23 37												00 37				
Byfleet & New Haw	d									00 07										
West Byfleet	d									00 10										
Woking	a									00 20										
Longcross	d																			
Sunningdale	d				23 37							00 10		00 22						
Ascot 3	d		23 23		23 43							00 15		00 27						
Bagshot	d		23 29																	
Camberley	a		23 35																	
	d		23 39																	
Frimley	d		23 43																	
Ash Vale	d		23 49																	
Aldershot	a		23 54																	
	d																			
Ash 3	d																			
Wanborough	d																			
Guildford	a																			
Martins Heron	d				23 47							00 19		00 31						
Bracknell	d				23 50							00 23		00 34						
Wokingham	d				23 57							00 31		00 41						
Winnersh	d				00 01							00 35								
Winnersh Triangle	d				00 02							00 37								
Earley	d				00 05							00 39								
Reading 7	a				00 10							00 44		00 49						

For general notes see front of timetable
For details of catering facilities see Directory of Train Operators

A To London Waterloo (Table 152)

§ Passengers to/from London may travel via Weybridge. See Table 155.

From 3 October due to seasonal difficulties a large number of trains on this table will have minor retimings that could mean slightly earlier departure or later arrival times at certain stations. For further details see local publicity or contact National Rail Enquiries 08457 48 49 50.

Table 149

Sundays

London → Hounslow, Richmond, Kingston, Windsor, Weybridge, Ascot, Guildford and Reading

Network Diagram - see first page of Table 148

		SW [1]	SW	SW	SW [1]	SW	SW [1]	SW	SW [1]	SW	SW	SW	SW	SW	SW [1]	SW	SW	SW [1]	SW	SW [1]	SW	SW [1]
																A					A	
London Waterloo [15]	⊖ d	22p50	22p52	23p13	23p20	23p22	23p35	23p37			23p52	23p58		00 18		06 14	06 44			07 09	07 14	
Vauxhall	⊖ d		22p56	23p17		23p26		23p41			23p56	00 02		00 22		06 18	06 48			07 13	07 18	
Queenstown Rd.(Battersea)	d		22p59			23p29		23p44			23p59			00 25		06 21	06 51				07 21	
Clapham Junction [10]	d	22p58	23p02	23p23	23p28	23p32	23p43	23p47			00 02	00 08		00 28		06 24	06 54			07 19	07 24	
Wandsworth Town	d		23p05			23p35		23p50			00 05			00 31		06 27	06 57				07 27	
Putney	d		23p08	23p27		23p38		23p53			00 08	00 12		00 34		06 30	07 00			07 23	07 30	
Barnes	d		23p12			23p42		23p56			00 12			00 37		06 33	07 03				07 33	
Barnes Bridge	d		23p14			23p44				←	00 14											
Chiswick	d		23p17			23p47				23p47	00 17		←									
Kew Bridge	d		23p20			→				23p50	00 20		00 20									
Brentford	d		23p23							23p53	→		00 23									
Syon Lane	d		23p25							23p55			00 25									
Isleworth	d		23p27							23p57			00 27									
Hounslow	d		23p31							00 01			00 31									
Mortlake	d							23p58						00 39		06 35	07 05				07 35	
North Sheen	d							00 01						00 41		06 37	07 07				07 37	
Richmond	⊖ d	23p06		23p33	23p36		23p51	00 03				00 18		00 44		06 40	07 10			07 29	07 40	
St Margarets	d							00 06						00 46		06 42	07 12				07 42	
Twickenham	a	23p10		23p36	23p40		23p55	00 08				00 21		00 48		06 44	07 14			07 32	07 44	
	d	23p10		23p37	23p40		23p55	00 08				00 22		00 49		06 45	07 15			07 33	07 45	
Strawberry Hill	d							00 12						00s52		06 49					07 49	
Fulwell	a																					
Teddington	a							00 15						00s55		06 52					07 52	
Hampton Wick	a							00 17						00s58		06 57					07 57	
Kingston	a							00 19						01 00		06 59					07 59	
Whitton	d			23p40								00 25					07 18					
Feltham	d	23p16	23p36	23p44	23p48		00 01			00 06		00 29	00 36				07 22			07 39		
Ashford (Surrey)	d		23p40	23p48						00 10		00 33	00 40				07 26					
Staines	d	23p23	23p45	23p52	23p56		00 08			00 15		00a37	00a46		06 32		07 30		07 41	07 45		
Wraysbury	d			23p56													07 34					
Sunnymeads	d			23p59													07 37					
Datchet	d			00 02													07 40					
Windsor & Eton Riverside	a			00 06													07 44					
Egham	d	23p27	23p50		00 01		00 12			00 20					06 37				07 45	07 50		
Virginia Water	a	23p31	23p54		00 05		00 16			00 24					06 41				07 49	07 54		
	d	23p31	23p54		00 05		00 16			00 24					06 41				07 49	07 54		
Chertsey §	d		23p59							00 29					06 46				07 55			
Addlestone §	d		00 02							00 32					06 49				07 58			
Weybridge	a									00 37					06 53							
Byfleet & New Haw	d		00 07																08 02			
West Byfleet	d		00 10																08 05			
Woking	a		00 20																08 10			
Longcross	d																					
Sunningdale	d	23p37			00 10		00 22													07 59		
Ascot [3]	d	23p43			00 15		00 27		00 29											08 04		08 13
Bagshot	d								00 35													08 19
Camberley	a								00 41													08 25
	d								00 41													08 25
Frimley	d								00 45													08 29
Ash Vale	d								00 52													08 36
Aldershot	a								00 57													08 41
	d																	07 48				08 48
Ash [3]	d																	07 55				08 55
Wanborough	d																	07 58				08 58
Guildford	a																	08 05				09 05
Martins Heron	d	23p47			00 19		00 31													08 08		
Bracknell	d	23p50			00 23		00 34													08 11		
Wokingham	d	23p57			00 31		00 41													08 18		
Winnersh	d	00 01			00 35															08 21		
Winnersh Triangle	d	00 02			00 37															08 23		
Earley	d	00 05			00 39															08 26		
Reading [7]	a	00 10			00 44		00 49													08 31		

For general notes see front of timetable
For details of catering facilities see Directory of Train Operators

A To London Waterloo (Table 152)

§ Passengers to/from London may travel via Weybridge. See Table 155.

From 27 September due to seasonal difficulties a large number of trains on this table will have minor retimings that could mean slightly earlier departure or later arrival times at certain stations. For further details see local publicity or contact National Rail Enquiries 08457 48 49 50.

Sundays

London → Hounslow, Richmond, Kingston, Windsor, Weybridge, Ascot, Guildford and Reading

Network Diagram - see first page of Table 148

		SW 1	SW	SW	SW 1	SW A	SW 1	SW 1	SW	SW	SW 1	SW A	SW 1	SW	SW 1	SW	SW	SW 1	SW A	SW 1	SW	SW 1
London Waterloo 15	⊖ d		07 44	07 50	08 09	08 14		08 39	08 44	08 50	09 09	09 14		09 25	09 39	09 44	09 50	10 09	10 14		10 25	10 39
Vauxhall	⊖ d		07 48	07 54	08 13	08 18		08 43	08 48	08 54	09 13	09 18		09 29	09 43	09 48	09 54	10 13	10 18		10 29	10 43
Queenstown Rd.(Battersea)	d		07 51	07 57		08 21			08 51	08 57		09 21				09 51	09 57		10 21			
Clapham Junction 10	d		07 54	08 00	08 19	08 24		08 49	08 54	09 00	09 19	09 24		09 35	09 49	09 54	10 00	10 19	10 24		10 35	10 49
Wandsworth Town	d		07 57	08 03		08 27			08 57	09 03		09 27				09 57	10 03		10 27			
Putney	d		08 00	08 06	08 23	08 30		08 53	09 00	09 06	09 23	09 30		09 39	09 53	10 00	10 06	10 23	10 30		10 39	10 53
Barnes	d		08 03	08 09		08 33			09 03	09 09		09 33				10 03	10 09		10 33			
Barnes Bridge	d			08 11						09 11							10 11					
Chiswick	d			08 13						09 13							10 13					
Kew Bridge	d			08 16						09 16							10 16					
Brentford	d			08 19						09 19							10 19					
Syon Lane	d			08 21						09 21							10 21					
Isleworth	d			08 23						09 23							10 23					
Hounslow	d			08 27						09 27							10 27					
Mortlake	d		08 05			08 35			09 05			09 35				10 05			10 35			
North Sheen	d		08 07			08 37			09 07			09 37				10 07			10 37			
Richmond	⊖ d		08 10		08 29	08 40		08 59	09 10		09 29	09 40		09 45	09 59	10 10		10 29	10 40		10 45	10 59
St Margarets	d		08 12			08 42			09 12			09 42				10 12			10 42			
Twickenham	a		08 14		08 32	08 44		09 02	09 14		09 32	09 44		09 48	10 02	10 14		10 32	10 44		10 48	11 02
	d		08 15		08 33	08 45		09 03	09 15		09 33	09 45		09 49	10 03	10 15		10 33	10 45		10 49	11 03
Strawberry Hill	d					08 49						09 49							10 49			
Fulwell	a																					
Teddington	a					08 52						09 52							10 52			
Hampton Wick	a					08 57						09 57							10 57			
Kingston	a					08 59						09 59							10 59			
Whitton	d		08 18						09 18					09 52		10 18					10 52	
Feltham	d		08 22	08 33	08 39			09 09	09 22	09 33	09 39			09 56	10 09	10 22	10 33	10 39			10 56	11 09
Ashford (Surrey)	d		08 26	08 37					09 26	09 37				10 00		10 26	10 37				11 00	
Staines	d	08 15	08 30	08 41	08 45			09 15	09 30	09 41	09 45			10 04	10 15	10 30	10 41	10 45			11 04	11 15
Wraysbury	d		08 34						09 34							10 34						
Sunnymeads	d		08 37						09 37							10 37						
Datchet	d		08 40						09 40					10 12		10 40					11 12	
Windsor & Eton Riverside	a		08 44						09 44					10 16		10 44					11 16	
Egham	d	08 20		08 45	08 50			09 20		09 45	09 50				10 20		10 45	10 50				11 20
Virginia Water	a	08 24		08 49	08 54			09 24		09 49	09 54				10 24		10 49	10 54				11 24
	d	08 24		08 49	08 54			09 24		09 49	09 54				10 24		10 49	10 54				11 24
Chertsey §	d			08 55						09 55							10 55					
Addlestone §	d			08 58						09 58							10 58					
Weybridge	a																					
Byfleet & New Haw	d			09 02						10 02							11 02					
West Byfleet	d			09 05						10 05							11 05					
Woking	a			09 10						10 10							11 10					
Longcross	d																					
Sunningdale	d	08 29			08 59			09 29			09 59				10 29			10 59				11 29
Ascot 3	d	08 34			09 04		09 13	09 34			10 04		10 13		10 34			11 04		11 13		11 34
Bagshot	d						09 19						10 19							11 19		
Camberley	a						09 25						10 25							11 25		
	d						09 25						10 25							11 25		
Frimley	d						09 29						10 29							11 29		
Ash Vale	d						09 36						10 36							11 36		
Aldershot	a						09 41						10 41							11 41		
	d						09 48						10 48							11 48		
Ash 3	d						09 55						10 55							11 55		
Wanborough	d						09 58						10 58							11 58		
Guildford	a						10 05						11 05							12 05		
Martins Heron	d	08 38			09 08			09 38			10 08				10 38			11 08				11 38
Bracknell	d	08 41			09 11			09 41			10 11				10 41			11 11				11 41
Wokingham	d	08 48			09 18			09 48			10 18				10 48			11 18				11 48
Winnersh	d	08 51			09 21			09 51			10 21				10 51			11 21				11 51
Winnersh Triangle	d	08 53			09 23			09 53			10 23				10 53			11 23				11 53
Earley	d	08 56			09 26			09 56			10 26				10 56			11 26				11 56
Reading 7	a	09 01			09 31			10 01			10 31				11 01			11 31				12 01

For general notes see front of timetable
For details of catering facilities see
Directory of Train Operators

A To London Waterloo (Table 152)

§ Passengers to/from London may travel via Weybridge. See Table 155.

From 27 September due to seasonal difficulties a large number of trains on this table will have minor retimings that could mean slightly earlier departure or later arrival times at certain stations. For further details see local publicity or contact National Rail Enquiries 08457 48 49 50.

Sundays

London → Hounslow, Richmond, Kingston, Windsor, Weybridge, Ascot, Guildford and Reading

Network Diagram - see first page of Table 148

		SW	SW	SW [1]	SW	SW [1]	SW	SW [1]	SW	SW	SW [1]	SW	SW [1]	SW	SW [1]	SW	SW	SW [1]	SW	SW [1]	SW	SW [1]
					A							A							A			
London Waterloo [15]	⊖ d	10 44	10 50	11 09	11 14		11 25	11 39	11 44	11 50	12 09	12 14		12 25	12 39	12 44	12 50	13 09	13 14		13 25	13 39
Vauxhall	⊖ d	10 48	10 54	11 13	11 18		11 29	11 43	11 48	11 54	12 13	12 18		12 29	12 43	12 48	12 54	13 13	13 18		13 29	13 43
Queenstown Rd.(Battersea)	d	10 51	10 57		11 21				11 51	11 57		12 21				12 51	12 57		13 21			
Clapham Junction [10]	d	10 54	11 00	11 19	11 24		11 35	11 49	11 54	12 00	12 19	12 24		12 35	12 49	12 54	13 00	13 19	13 24		13 35	13 49
Wandsworth Town	d	10 57	11 03		11 27				11 57	12 03		12 27				12 57	13 03		13 27			
Putney	d	11 00	11 06	11 23	11 30		11 39	11 53	12 00	12 06	12 23	12 30		12 39	12 53	13 00	13 06	13 23	13 30		13 39	13 53
Barnes	d	11 03	11 09		11 33				12 03	12 09		12 33				13 03	13 09		13 33			
Barnes Bridge	d		11 11							12 11							13 11					
Chiswick	d		11 13							12 13							13 13					
Kew Bridge	d		11 16							12 16							13 16					
Brentford	d		11 19							12 19							13 19					
Syon Lane	d		11 21							12 21							13 21					
Isleworth	d		11 23							12 23							13 23					
Hounslow	d		11 27							12 27							13 27					
Mortlake	d	11 05			11 35				12 05			12 35				13 05			13 35			
North Sheen	d	11 07			11 37				12 07			12 37				13 07			13 37			
Richmond	⊖ d	11 10		11 29	11 40		11 45	11 59	12 10		12 29	12 40		12 45	12 59	13 10		13 29	13 40		13 45	13 59
St Margarets	d	11 12			11 42				12 12			12 42				13 12			13 42			
Twickenham	a	11 14		11 32	11 44		11 48	12 02	12 14		12 32	12 44		12 48	13 02	13 14		13 32	13 44		13 48	14 02
	d	11 15		11 33	11 45		11 49	12 03	12 15		12 33	12 45		12 49	13 03	13 15		13 33	13 45		13 49	14 03
Strawberry Hill	d				11 49							12 49							13 49			
Fulwell	a																					
Teddington	a				11 52							12 52							13 52			
Hampton Wick	a				11 57							12 57							13 57			
Kingston	a				11 59							12 59							13 59			
Whitton	d	11 18					11 52		12 18					12 52		13 18					13 52	
Feltham	d	11 22	11 33	11 39			11 56	12 09	12 22	12 33	12 39			12 56	13 09	13 22	13 33	13 39			13 56	14 09
Ashford (Surrey)	d	11 26	11 37				12 00		12 26	12 37				13 00		13 26	13 37				14 00	
Staines	d	11 30	11 41	11 45			12 04	12 15	12 30	12 41	12 45			13 04	13 15	13 30	13 41	13 45			14 04	14 15
Wraysbury	d	11 34							12 34							13 34						
Sunnymeads	d	11 37							12 37							13 37						
Datchet	d	11 40					12 12		12 40					13 12		13 40					14 12	
Windsor & Eton Riverside	a	11 44					12 16		12 44					13 16		13 44					14 16	
Egham	d		11 45	11 50				12 20		12 45	12 50				13 20		13 45	13 50				14 20
Virginia Water	a		11 49	11 54				12 24		12 49	12 54				13 24		13 49	13 54				14 24
	d		11 49	11 54				12 24		12 49	12 54				13 24		13 49	13 54				14 24
Chertsey §	d		11 55							12 55							13 55					
Addlestone §	d		11 58							12 58							13 58					
Weybridge	a																					
Byfleet & New Haw	d		12 02							13 02							14 02					
West Byfleet	d		12 05							13 05							14 05					
Woking	a		12 10							13 10							14 10					
Longcross	d																					
Sunningdale	d			11 59				12 29			12 59				13 29			13 59				14 29
Ascot [3]	d			12 04		12 13		12 34			13 04		13 13		13 34			14 04		14 13		14 34
Bagshot	d					12 19							13 19							14 19		
Camberley	a					12 25							13 25							14 25		
	d					12 25							13 25							14 25		
Frimley	d					12 29							13 29							14 29		
Ash Vale	d					12 36							13 36							14 36		
Aldershot	a					12 41							13 41							14 41		
	d					12 48							13 48							14 48		
Ash [3]	d					12 55							13 55							14 55		
Wanborough	d					12 58							13 58							14 58		
Guildford	a					13 05							14 05							15 05		
Martins Heron	d			12 08				12 38			13 08				13 38			14 08				14 38
Bracknell	d			12 11				12 41			13 11				13 41			14 11				14 41
Wokingham	d			12 18				12 48			13 18				13 48			14 18				14 48
Winnersh	d			12 21				12 51			13 21				13 51			14 21				14 51
Winnersh Triangle	d			12 23				12 53			13 23				13 53			14 23				14 53
Earley	d			12 26				12 56			13 26				13 56			14 26				14 56
Reading [7]	a			12 31				13 01			13 31				14 01			14 31				15 01

For general notes see front of timetable
For details of catering facilities see Directory of Train Operators

A To London Waterloo (Table 152)

§ Passengers to/from London may travel via Weybridge. See Table 155.

From 27 September due to seasonal difficulties a large number of trains on this table will have minor retimings that could mean slightly earlier departure or later arrival times at certain stations. For further details see local publicity or contact National Rail Enquiries 08457 48 49 50.

Table 149

Sundays

London → Hounslow, Richmond, Kingston, Windsor, Weybridge, Ascot, Guildford and Reading

Network Diagram - see first page of Table 148

		SW	SW	SW			SW 1	SW A	SW 1	SW	SW 1	SW	SW	SW			SW 1	SW A	SW 1	SW 1	SW	SW		SW
London Waterloo 15 ⊖	d	13 44	13 50	13 56			14 09	14 14		14 25	14 39	14 44	14 50	14 56	and at the same minutes past each hour until		20 09	20 14		20 39	20 44	20 50		20 56
Vauxhall ⊖	d	13 48	13 54	14 00			14 13	14 18		14 29	14 43	14 48	14 54	15 00			20 13	20 18		20 43	20 48	20 54		21 00
Queenstown Rd.(Battersea)	d	13 51	13 57	14 03				14 21				14 51	14 57	15 03				20 21			20 51	20 57		21 03
Clapham Junction 10	d	13 54	14 00	14 06			14 19	14 24		14 35	14 49	14 54	15 00	15 06			20 19	20 24		20 49	20 54	21 00		21 06
Wandsworth Town	d	13 57	14 03	14 09				14 27				14 57	15 03	15 09				20 27			20 57	21 03		21 09
Putney	d	14 00	14 06	14 12			14 23	14 30		14 39	14 53	15 00	15 06	15 12			20 23	20 30		20 53	21 00	21 06		21 12
Barnes	d	14 03	14 09	14 15				14 33				15 03	15 09	15 15				20 33			21 03	21 09		21 15
Barnes Bridge	d		14 11										15 11									21 11		
Chiswick	d		14 13										15 13									21 13		
Kew Bridge	d		14 16										15 16									21 16		
Brentford	d		14 19										15 19									21 19		
Syon Lane	d		14 21										15 21									21 21		
Isleworth	d		14 23										15 23									21 23		
Hounslow	d		14 27										15 27									21 27		
Mortlake	d	14 05		14 17				14 35				15 05		15 17				20 35			21 05			21 17
North Sheen	d	14 07		14 19				14 37				15 07		15 19				20 37			21 07			21 19
Richmond ⊖	d	14 10		14 22			14 29	14 40		14 45	14 59	15 10		15 22			20 29	20 40		20 59	21 10			21 22
St Margarets	d	14 12		14 24				14 42				15 12		15 24				20 42			21 12			21 24
Twickenham	a	14 14		14 26			14 32	14 44		14 48	15 02	15 14		15 26			20 32	20 44		21 02	21 14			21 26
	d	14 15		14 27			14 33	14 45		14 49	15 03	15 15		15 27			20 33	20 45		21 03	21 15			21 27
Strawberry Hill	d			14 30				14 49						15 30				20 49						21 30
Fulwell	a																							
Teddington	a			14 33				14 52						15 33				20 52						21 33
Hampton Wick	a			14 36				14 57						15 36				20 57						21 36
Kingston	a			14 38				14 59						15 38				20 59						21 38
Whitton	d	14 18								14 52		15 18									21 18			
Feltham	d	14 22	14 33				14 39			14 56	15 09	15 22	15 33				20 39			21 09	21 22	21 33		
Ashford (Surrey)	d	14 26	14 37							15 00		15 26	15 37								21 26	21 37		
Staines	d	14 30	14 41				14 45			15 04	15 15	15 30	15 41				20 45			21 15	21 30	21 41		
Wraysbury	d	14 34										15 34									21 34			
Sunnymeads	d	14 37										15 37									21 37			
Datchet	d	14 40								15 12		15 40									21 40			
Windsor & Eton Riverside	a	14 44								15 16		15 44									21 44			
Egham	d		14 45				14 50				15 20		15 45				20 50			21 20		21 45		
Virginia Water	a		14 49				14 54				15 24		15 49				20 54			21 24		21 49		
	d		14 49				14 54				15 24		15 49				20 54			21 24		21 49		
Chertsey §	d		14 55										15 55									21 55		
Addlestone §	d		14 58										15 58									21 58		
Weybridge	a																							
Byfleet & New Haw	d		15 02										16 02									22 02		
West Byfleet	d		15 05										16 05									22 05		
Woking	a		15 10										16 10									22 10		
Longcross	d																							
Sunningdale	d						14 59				15 29						20 59			21 29				
Ascot 3	d						15 04		15 13		15 34						21 04		21 13	21 34				
Bagshot	d								15 19										21 19					
Camberley	a								15 25										21 25					
	d								15 25										21 25					
Frimley	d								15 29										21 29					
Ash Vale	d								15 36										21 36					
Aldershot	a								15 41										21 41					
	d								15 48										21 48					
Ash 3	d								15 55										21 55					
Wanborough	d								15 58										21 58					
Guildford	a								16 05										22 05					
Martins Heron	d						15 08				15 38						21 08			21 38				
Bracknell	d						15 11				15 41						21 11			21 41				
Wokingham	d						15 18				15 48						21 18			21 48				
Winnersh	d						15 21				15 51						21 21			21 51				
Winnersh Triangle	d						15 23				15 53						21 23			21 53				
Earley	d						15 26				15 56						21 26			21 56				
Reading 7	a						15 31				16 01						21 31			22 01				

For general notes see front of timetable
For details of catering facilities see
Directory of Train Operators

A To London Waterloo (Table 152)

§ Passengers to/from London may travel via Weybridge. See Table 155.

From 27 September due to seasonal difficulties a large number of trains on this table will have minor retimings that could mean slightly earlier departure or later arrival times at certain stations. For further details see local publicity or contact National Rail Enquiries 08457 48 49 50.

London → Hounslow, Richmond, Kingston, Windsor, Weybridge, Ascot, Guildford and Reading

Network Diagram - see first page of Table 148

		SW 1	SW	SW 1	SW 1	SW	SW	SW	SW 1	SW	SW 1	SW 1	SW	SW	SW	SW 1	SW	SW 1	SW
			A							A	B								
London Waterloo 15	⊖ d	21 09	21 14		21 39	21 44	21 50	21 56	22 09	22 14		22 39	22 44	22 50	22 56	23 09	23 14	23 39	23 44
Vauxhall	⊖ d	21 13	21 18		21 43	21 48	21 54	22 00	22 13	22 18		22 43	22 48	22 54	23 00	23 13	23 18	23 43	23 48
Queenstown Rd.(Battersea)	d		21 21			21 51	21 57	22 03		22 21			22 51	22 57	23 03		23 21		23 51
Clapham Junction 10	d	21 19	21 24		21 49	21 54	22 00	22 06	22 19	22 24		22 49	22 54	23 00	23 06	23 19	23 24	23 49	23 54
Wandsworth Town	d		21 27			21 57	22 03	22 09		22 27			22 57	23 03	23 09		23 27		23 57
Putney	d	21 23	21 30		21 53	22 00	22 06	22 12	22 23	22 30		22 53	23 00	23 06	23 12	23 23	23 30	23 53	23 59
Barnes	d		21 33			22 03	22 09	22 15		22 33			23 03	23 09	23 15		23 33		00 03
Barnes Bridge	d						22 11							23 11					
Chiswick	d						22 13							23 13					
Kew Bridge	d						22 16							23 16					
Brentford	d						22 19							23 19					
Syon Lane	d						22 21							23 21					
Isleworth	d						22 23							23 23					
Hounslow	d						22 27							23 27					
Mortlake	d		21 35			22 05		22 17		22 35			23 05		23 17		23 35		00 05
North Sheen	d		21 37			22 07		22 19		22 37			23 07		23 19		23 37		00 07
Richmond	⊖ d	21 29	21 40		21 59	22 10		22 22	22 29	22 40		22 59	23 10		23 22	23 29	23 40	23 59	00 10
St Margarets	d		21 42			22 12		22 24		22 42			23 12		23 24		23 42		00 12
Twickenham	a	21 32	21 44		22 02	22 14		22 26	22 32	22 44		23 02	23 14		23 26	23 32	23 44	00 02	00 14
	d	21 33	21 45		22 03	22 15		22 27	22 33	22 45		23 03	23 15		23 27	23 33	23 45	00 03	00 15
Strawberry Hill	d		21 49					22 30		22 49					23 30		23 48		
Fulwell	a																		
Teddington	a		21 52					22 33		22 52					23 33		23 51		
Hampton Wick	a		21 57					22 36		22 57					23 36		23 54		
Kingston	a		21 59					22 38		22 59					23 38		23 56		
Whitton	d					22 18							23 18						00 18
Feltham	d	21 39			22 09	22 22	22 33		22 39			23 09	23 22	23 33		23 39		00 09	00 22
Ashford (Surrey)	d					22 26	22 37						23 26	23 37					00 26
Staines	d	21 45			22 15	22 30	22 41		22 45			23 15	23 30	23 41		23 45		00 15	00a30
Wraysbury	d					22 34							23 34						
Sunnymeads	d					22 37							23 37						
Datchet	d					22 40							23 40						
Windsor & Eton Riverside	a					22 44							23 44						
Egham	d	21 50			22 20		22 45		22 50			23 20		23 45		23 50		00 20	
Virginia Water	a	21 54			22 24		22 49		22 54			23 24		23 49		23 54		00 24	
	d	21 54			22 24		22 49		22 54			23 24		23 49		23 54		00 24	
Chertsey §	d						22 55							23 55					
Addlestone §	d						22 58							23 58					
Weybridge	a																		
Byfleet & New Haw	d						23 02							00 02					
West Byfleet	d						23 05							00 05					
Woking	a						23 10							00 10					
Longcross	d																		
Sunningdale	d	21 59			22 29				22 59			23 29				23 59		00 29	
Ascot 3	d	22 04		22 13	22 34				23 04		23 13	23 34				00 04		00 34	
Bagshot	d			22 19							23 19								
Camberley	a			22 25							23 25								
	d			22 25							23 25								
Frimley	d			22 29							23 29								
Ash Vale	d			22 36							23 36								
Aldershot	a			22 41							23 41								
	d			22 48															
Ash 3	d			22 55															
Wanborough	d			22 58															
Guildford	a			23 05															
Martins Heron	d	22 08			22 38				23 08			23 38				00 08		00 38	
Bracknell	d	22 11			22 41				23 11			23 41				00 11		00 41	
Wokingham	d	22 18			22 48				23 18			23 48				00 18		00 48	
Winnersh	d	22 21			22 51				23 21			23 51				00 21		00 51	
Winnersh Triangle	d	22 23			22 53				23 23			23 53				00 23		00 53	
Earley	d	22 26			22 56				23 26			23 56				00 26		00 56	
Reading 7	a	22 31			23 01				23 31			00 01				00 31		01 01	

For general notes see front of timetable
For details of catering facilities see Directory of Train Operators

A To London Waterloo (Table 152)
B To Farnham (Table 155)

§ Passengers to/from London may travel via Weybridge. See Table 155.

From 27 September due to seasonal difficulties a large number of trains on this table will have minor retimings that could mean slightly earlier departure or later arrival times at certain stations. For further details see local publicity or contact National Rail Enquiries 08457 48 49 50.

Reading, Guildford, Ascot, Weybridge, Windsor, Kingston, Richmond and Hounslow → London

Network Diagram - see first page of Table 148

Miles	Miles	Miles	Miles			SW MO	SW MO	SW MX A	SW MO 1	SW MX A	SW MX 1	SW	SW	SW B	SW	SW	SW	SW	SW	SW	SW 1	SW		SW C	SW
—	—	0	—	**Reading** 7	d				22p54		23p12										05 42				
—	—	3	—	Earley	d				22p59		23p17										05 47				
—	—	4½	—	Winnersh Triangle	d				23p01		23p19										05 49				
—	—	4¾	—	Winnersh	d				23p03		23p21										05 51				
—	—	6¾	—	**Wokingham**	d				23p08		23p26										05 56				
—	—	11¼	—	Bracknell	d				23p14		23p32										06 02				
—	—	12¼	—	Martins Heron	d				23p17		23p35										06 05				
—	0	—	—	**Guildford**	d																				
—	4¼	—	—	Wanborough	d																				
—	6¼	—	—	Ash 3	d																				
—	9	—	—	**Aldershot**	a																				
—	—	—	—		d																				
—	11½	—	—	Ash Vale	d																				
—	14¾	—	—	Frimley	d																				
—	17	—	—	Camberley	a																				
—	—	—	—		d																				
—	20¼	—	—	Bagshot	d																				
—	23½	14½	—	**Ascot** 3	d				23p22		23p40										06 10				
—	—	16½	—	Sunningdale	d				23p25		23p43										06 13				
—	—	18¼	—	Longcross	d																				
0	—	—	—	Woking	d		22p52											05 25							
2½	—	—	—	West Byfleet	d		22p56											05 30							
3¾	—	—	—	Byfleet & New Haw	d		23p00											05 33							
5¼	—	—	—	**Weybridge**	d																				
7	—	—	—	Addlestone §	d		23p04											05 37							
8½	—	—	—	Chertsey §	d		23p07											05 40							
11	—	20¼	—	Virginia Water	a		23p12		23p30		23p49							05 45			06 19				
—	—	—	—		d		23p12		23p30		23p49							05 54			06 19				
—	—	22½	—	Egham	d		23p16		23p34		23p53							05 57			06 23				
—	—	—	0	**Windsor & Eton Riverside**	d	23p01													05 53						
—	—	—	2	Datchet	d	23p04													05 56						
—	—	—	3	Sunnymeads	d	23p07													05 59						
—	—	—	4¼	Wraysbury	d	23p10													06 02						
—	—	24½	6¾	**Staines**	d	23p16	23p21		23p39		23p59	04 58			05 37			06 03	06 08		06 29				06 33
—	—	26	—	Ashford (Surrey)	d	23p19	23p24					05 01			05 40			06 06	06 11						06 36
—	—	28¾	—	Feltham	d	23p24	23p29		23p46		00 05	05 06			05 45			06 11	06 16		06 35				06 41
—	—	31	—	Whitton	d	23p28						05 10			05 49				06 20			06 20			
0	—	—	—	**Kingston**	d			23p29		23p55							05 59							06 29	
½	—	—	—	Hampton Wick	d			23p31		23p57							06 01							06 31	
1¾	—	—	—	Teddington	d			23p35		23p59							06 05							06 35	
2¾	—	—	—	Fulwell	d									05 36											
3	—	—	—	Strawberry Hill	d			23p38		00 03				05 38			06 08							06 38	
4	—	32¼	—	Twickenham	a	23p31		23p42	23p51	00 07	00 10	05 13		05 42	05 52		06 12		06 23		06 40			06 42	
—	—	—	—		d	23p32		23p43	23p51		00 11	05 13		05 43	05 53		06 13		06 23		06 41			06 43	
4½	—	32¾	—	St Margarets	d	23p34		23p45				05 15		05 45			06 15							06 45	
5½	—	33¾	—	**Richmond**	⊖ d	23p37		23p49	23p56		00 15	05 19		05 49	05 58		06 19		06 28		06 45			06 49	
6¼	—	34½	—	North Sheen	d	23p39		23p51				05 21		05 51			06 21							06 51	
7	—	35¼	—	Mortlake	d	23p42		23p53				05 23		05 53			06 23							06 53	
—	0	—	—	**Hounslow**	d		23p35						05 31			06 01		06 16				06 31			06 46
—	—	—	—	Isleworth	d		23p38						05 34			06 04		06 19				06 34			06 49
—	2¼	—	—	Syon Lane	d		23p40						05 36			06 06		06 21		←		06 36			06 51
—	3	—	—	Brentford	d		23p42						05 39			06 09		06 24		06 24		06 39			06 54
—	4	—	—	Kew Bridge	d		23p45						05 41			06 11		→		06 26		06 41			→
—	5	—	—	Chiswick	d		23p47						05 44			06 14				06 29		06 44			
—	6	—	—	Barnes Bridge	d		23p50						05 46			06 16				06 31		06 46			
8¼	6½	36½	—	Barnes	d	23p45	23p53	23p56				05 26	05 49	05 56		06 19	06 26			06 34		06 49		06 56	
9½	—	37¾	—	Putney	d	23p48	23p56	23p59	00 02			05 29	05 52	05 59	06 04	06 22	06 29		06 34	06 37	06 52	06 52		06 59	
10½	—	38¾	—	Wandsworth Town	d	23p51	23p59	00 02				05 32	05 55	06 02		06 25	06 32			06 40		06 55		07 02	
11¼	—	39½	—	**Clapham Junction** 10	d	23p54	00 02	00 05	00 07		00 24	05 35	05 58	06 05	06 09	06 28	06 35		06 39	06 43	06 56	06 58		07 05	
12½	—	41¾	—	Queenstown Rd.(Battersea)	d	23p57	00 05	00 08				05 38	06 01	06 08		06 31	06 38			06 46		07 01		07 08	
14	—	42¼	—	Vauxhall	⊖ d	00 01	00 08	00 12	00 12			05 42	06 05	06 12	06 15	06 35	06 42		06 45	06 50		07 05		07 12	
15¼	—	43½	—	**London Waterloo** 15	⊖ a	00 05	00 13	00 16	00 17		00 32	05 46	06 09	06 16	06 19	06 39	06 46		06 49	06 56	07 07	07 11		07 18	

For general notes see front of timetable
For details of catering facilities see Directory of Train Operators

§ Passengers to/from London may travel via Weybridge. See Table 155.

A From London Waterloo (Table 152)
B From Shepperton (Table 152)
C From Wimbledon (Table 152)

From 28 September due to seasonal difficulties a large number of trains on this table will have minor retimings that could mean slightly earlier departure or later arrival times at certain stations. For further details see local publicity or contact National Rail Enquiries 08457 48 49 50.

Reading, Guildford, Ascot, Weybridge, Windsor, Kingston, Richmond and Hounslow → London

Network Diagram - see first page of Table 148

		SW	SW 1	SW	SW	SW 1	SW	SW	SW A	SW	SW	SW B	SW 1	SW 1	SW B	SW 1	SW	SW		SW A	SW	SW	SW B	SW 1	SW 1
Reading 7	d					06 12										06 42									
Earley	d					06 17										06 47									
Winnersh Triangle	d					06 19										06 49									
Winnersh	d					06 21										06 51									
Wokingham	d					06 26										06 56									
Bracknell	d					06 32										07 02									
Martins Heron	d					06 35										07 05									
Guildford	d													06 30											07 00
Wanborough	d													06 36											07 06
Ash 3	d													06 40											07 10
Aldershot	a													06 47											07 17
	d		05 58										06 28											07 00	
Ash Vale	d		06 02										06 32											07 04	
Frimley	d		06 10										06 40											07 10	
Camberley	a		06 14										06 44											07 14	
	d		06 18										06 47											07 17	
Bagshot	d		06 23										06 52											07 22	
Ascot 3	d		06a30			06 40							06 59			07 10								07 29	
Sunningdale	d					06 43							07 02			07 13								07 32	
Longcross	d																								
Woking	d																								
West Byfleet	d																								
Byfleet & New Haw	d																								
Weybridge	d							06 33										07 03							
Addlestone §	d							06 37										07 07							
Chertsey §	d							06 40										07 10							
Virginia Water	a					06 49		06 46					07 08			07 19		07 15						07 38	
	d					06 49		06 54					07 08			07 19		07 24						07 38	
Egham	d					06 53		06 57					07 12			07 23		07 27						07 42	
Windsor & Eton Riverside	d	06 23								06 53											07 23				
Datchet	d	06 26								06 56											07 26				
Sunnymeads	d	06 29								06 59											07 29				
Wraysbury	d	06 32								07 02											07 32				
Staines	d	06 38				06 59		07 03		07 08			07 18			07 29		07 33			07 38			07 48	
Ashford (Surrey)	d	06 41						07 06		07 11			07 21					07 36			07 41			07 51	
Feltham	d	06 46				07 05		07 11		07 16			07 26			07 35		07 41			07 46			07 56	
Whitton	d	06 50			06 53		06 50			07 20			07 30				07 20				07 50			08 00	
Kingston	d								06 59											07 29					
Hampton Wick	d								07 01											07 31					
Teddington	d								07 05											07 35					
Fulwell	d											07 12											07 42		
Strawberry Hill	d								07 08			07 14								07 38			07 44		
Twickenham	a	06 53			06 56	07 10			07 12	07 23		07 18	07 33			07 40				07 42	07 53		07 48	08 03	
	d	06 53			06 58	07 11			07 13	07 23		07 27	07 33			07 41				07 43	07 53		07 57	08 03	
St Margarets	d				07 00				07 15			07 29								07 45			07 59		
Richmond	⊖ d	06 58			07 04	07 15			07 19	07 28		07 32	07 38			07 45				07 49	07 58		08 02	08 08	
North Sheen	d				07 06				07 21			07 34								07 51			08 04		
Mortlake	d				07 08				07 23			07 37								07 53			08 07		
Hounslow	d						07 01	07 16									07 31	07 46							
Isleworth	d						07 04	07 19									07 34	07 49							
Syon Lane	d			←			07 06	07 21			←						07 36	07 51				←			
Brentford	d			06 54			07 09	07 24			07 24						07 39	07 54				07 54			
Kew Bridge	d			06 56			07 11	→			07 26						07 41	→				07 56			
Chiswick	d			06 59			07 14				07 29						07 44					07 59			
Barnes Bridge	d			07 01			07 16				07 31				←		07 46					08 01			
Barnes	d			07 04	07 11		07 19		07 26		07 34	07 40			07 40		07 49			07 56		08 04	08 10		
Putney	d	07 04		07 07	07 14	07 22	07 22		07 29	07 34	07 37	→			07 43		07 52			07 59	08 04	08 07	→		
Wandsworth Town	d			07 10	07 17		07 25		07 32		07 40				07 46		07 55			08 02		08 10			
Clapham Junction 10	d	07 09		07 13	07 20	07 26	07 28		07 35	07 39	07 43		07 47		07 49	07 54	07 58			08 05	08 09	08 13		08 17	
Queenstown Rd.(Battersea)	d			07 16	07 23		07 31		07 38		07 46				07 52		08 01			08 08		08 16			
Vauxhall	⊖ d	07 15		07 20	07 27		07 35		07 42	07 45	07 50		07 53		07 56		08 05			08 12	08 15	08 20		08 23	
London Waterloo 15	⊖ a	07 21		07 28	07 34	07 37	07 43		07 48	07 51	07 58		07 59		08 04	08 06	08 11			08 18	08 21	08 28		08 29	

For general notes see front of timetable
For details of catering facilities see
Directory of Train Operators

A From London Waterloo (Table 152)
B From Shepperton (Table 152)

§ Passengers to/from London may travel via Weybridge. See Table 155.

From 28 September due to seasonal difficulties a large number of trains on this table will have minor retimings that could mean slightly earlier departure or later arrival times at certain stations. For further details see local publicity or contact National Rail Enquiries 08457 48 49 50.

Reading, Guildford, Ascot, Weybridge, Windsor, Kingston, Richmond and Hounslow → London

Network Diagram - see first page of Table 148

	SW A	SW 1	SW	SW	SW B	SW 1	SW B	SW	SW	SW A	SW 1	SW A	SW 1		SW	SW B	SW	SW	SW	SW	SW 1	SW 1	SW	SW B
Reading 7 d		07 12				07 24							07 42									08 12		
Earley d		07 17											07 47									08 17		
Winnersh Triangle d		07 19											07 49									08 19		
Winnersh d		07 21											07 51									08 21		
Wokingham d		07 26				07 33							07 56									08 26		
Bracknell d		07 32				07 39							08 02									08 32		
Martins Heron d		07 35				07 42							08 05									08 35		
Guildford d																					07 30			
Wanborough d																					07 36			
Ash 3 d																					07 40			
Aldershot a																					07 47			
d											07 30										08 00			
Ash Vale d											07 34										08 04			
Frimley d											07 40										08 10			
Camberley a											07 44										08 14			
d											07 47										08 18			
Bagshot d											07 52										08 23			
Ascot 3 d		07 40				07 47					07 59		08 10								08a30	08 40		
Sunningdale d		07 43				07 50					08 02		08 13									08 43		
Longcross d													08 16									08 46		
Woking d																								
West Byfleet d																								
Byfleet & New Haw d																								
Weybridge d				07 33													08 03							
Addlestone § d				07 37													08 07							
Chertsey § d				07 40													08 10							
Virginia Water a				07 45		07 55					08 08		08 19				08 15					08 49		
d				07 51		07 55					08 08		08 19				08 24					08 49		
Egham d		07 50		07 54		07 58					08 12		08 23				08 27					08 53		
Windsor & Eton Riverside d								07 53										08 23						
Datchet d								07 56										08 26						
Sunnymeads d								07 59										08 29						
Wraysbury d								08 02										08 32						
Staines d		07 56		08 00		08 04		08 08			08 18		08 29				08 33	08 38				08 59		
Ashford (Surrey) d				08 03				08 11			08 21						08 36	08 41						
Feltham d		08 03		08 08		08 12		08 16			08 26		08 35				08 41	08 46				09 05		
Whitton d			07 50					08 20			08 30				08 20			08 50		08 53			08 50	
Kingston d					07 59											08 29								08 59
Hampton Wick d					08 01											08 31								09 01
Teddington d					08 05											08 35								09 05
Fulwell d										08 12														
Strawberry Hill d					08 08					08 14						08 38								09 08
Twickenham a		08 09			08 12	08 17		08 23		08 18	08 33		08 40			08 42		08 53		08 56		09 10		09 12
d		08 09			08 13	08 18		08 23		08 27	08 33		08 41			08 43		08 53		08 58		09 11		09 13
St Margarets d					08 15					08 29						08 45				09 00				09 15
Richmond ⊖ d		08 14			08 19	08 24		08 28		08 32	08 38		08 45			08 49		08 58		09 04		09 15		09 19
North Sheen d					08 21					08 34						08 51				09 06				09 21
Mortlake d					08 23					08 37						08 53				09 08				09 23
Hounslow d			08 01	08 16											08 31		08 46						09 01	
Isleworth d			08 04	08 19											08 34		08 49						09 04	
Syon Lane d			08 06	08 21											08 36		08 51		←				09 06	
Brentford d			08 09	08 24					←						08 39		08 54		08 54				09 09	
Kew Bridge d			08 11	08 26					08 26						08 41		→		08 56				09 11	
Chiswick d			08 14	→					08 29						08 44				08 59				09 14	
Barnes Bridge d	←		08 16				←		08 31			←			08 46				09 01				09 16	
Barnes d	08 10		08 19		08 26		08 26		08 34	08 40		08 40			08 49	08 56			09 04	09 11			09 19	09 26
Putney d	08 13		08 22		→		08 29	08 34	08 37	→		08 43			08 52	08 59		09 04	09 07	09 14			09 22	09 29
Wandsworth Town d	08 16		08 25				08 32		08 40			08 46			08 55	09 02			09 10	09 17			09 25	09 32
Clapham Junction 10 d	08 19	08 22	08 28			08 33	08 35	08 39	08 43		08 47	08 49	08 54		08 58	09 05		09 09	09 13	09 20		09 24	09 28	09 35
Queenstown Rd.(Battersea) d	08 22		08 31				08 38		08 46			08 52			09 01	09 08			09 16	09 23			09 31	09 38
Vauxhall ⊖ d	08 26		08 35			08 38	08 42	08 45	08 50		08 53	08 56			09 05	09 12		09 15	09 20	09 27			09 35	09 42
London Waterloo 15 ⊖ a	08 34	08 38	08 43			08 46	08 49	08 51	08 58		09 00	09 04	09 06		09 13	09 18		09 21	09 28	09 34		09 34	09 43	09 48

For general notes see front of timetable
For details of catering facilities see Directory of Train Operators

A From Shepperton (Table 152)
B From London Waterloo (Table 152)

§ Passengers to/from London may travel via Weybridge. See Table 155.

From 28 September due to seasonal difficulties a large number of trains on this table will have minor retimings that could mean slightly earlier departure or later arrival times at certain stations. For further details see local publicity or contact National Rail Enquiries 08457 48 49 50.

Reading, Guildford, Ascot, Weybridge, Windsor, Kingston, Richmond and Hounslow → London

Network Diagram - see first page of Table 148

		SW	SW	SW	SW	SW	SW	SW	SW	SW	SW	SW	SW	SW	SW	SW	SW	SW	SW	SW	SW	SW	SW	SW
						1	1							1	1					1			1	1
									A								A							
Reading 7	d						08 42								09 12					09 25				09 42
Earley	d						08 47								09 17					09 30				09 47
Winnersh Triangle	d						08 49								09 19					09 32				09 49
Winnersh	d						08 51								09 21					09 34				09 51
Wokingham	d						08 56								09 26					09 39				09 56
Bracknell	d						09 02								09 32					09 46				10 02
Martins Heron	d						09 05								09 35					09 49				10 05
Guildford	d					08 00								08 30									09 00	
Wanborough	d					08 06								08 36									09 06	
Ash 3	d					08 10								08 40									09 10	
Aldershot	a					08 17								08 47									09 17	
	d					08 30								09 00									09 30	
Ash Vale	d					08 34								09 04									09 34	
Frimley	d					08 40								09 10									09 40	
Camberley	a					08 44								09 14									09 44	
	d					08 48								09 18									09 48	
Bagshot	d					08 53								09 23									09 53	
Ascot 3	d					09a00	09 10							09a30	09 40					09 55			10a00	10 10
Sunningdale	d						09 13								09 43					09 58				10 13
Longcross	d						09 16																	
Woking	d																							
West Byfleet	d																							
Byfleet & New Haw	d																							
Weybridge	d	08 33								09 03								09 33						
Addlestone §	d	08 37								09 07								09 37						
Chertsey §	d	08 40								09 10								09 40						
Virginia Water	a	08 45					09 19			09 15					09 49			09 45		10 03				10 19
	d	08 54					09 19			09 24					09 49			09 54		10 03				10 19
Egham	d	08 57					09 23			09 27					09 53			09 57		10 06				10 23
Windsor & Eton Riverside	d		08 53								09 23								09 53					
Datchet	d		08 56								09 26								09 56					
Sunnymeads	d		08 59								09 29								09 59					
Wraysbury	d		09 02								09 32								10 02					
Staines	d	09 03	09 08				09 29			09 33	09 38				09 59			10 03	10 08	10 14				10 29
Ashford (Surrey)	d	09 06	09 11							09 36	09 41							10 06	10 11					
Feltham	d	09 11	09 16				09 35			09 41	09 46				10 05			10 11	10 16	10 20				10 35
Whitton	d		09 20		09 23			09 20			09 50		09 53			09 50			10 20			10 26		
Kingston	d								09 29								09 59							
Hampton Wick	d								09 31								10 01							
Teddington	d								09 35								10 05							
Fulwell	d																							
Strawberry Hill	d								09 38								10 08							
Twickenham	a		09 23		09 26		09 40		09 42		09 53		09 56		10 10		10 12		10 23	10 27		10 28		10 40
	d		09 23		09 28		09 41		09 43		09 53		09 58		10 11		10 13		10 23	10 27		10 28		10 41
St Margarets	d				09 30				09 45				10 00				10 15					10 30		
Richmond	⊖ d		09 28		09 34		09 45		09 49		09 58		10 04		10 15		10 19		10 28	10 32		10 34		10 45
North Sheen	d				09 36				09 51				10 06				10 21					10 36		
Mortlake	d				09 38				09 53				10 08				10 23					10 38		
Hounslow	d	09 16						09 31		09 46						10 01		10 16						
Isleworth	d	09 19						09 34		09 49						10 04		10 19						
Syon Lane	d	09 21		←				09 36		09 51		←				10 06		10 21						
Brentford	d	09 24		09 24				09 39		09 54		09 54				10 09		10 24			←			
Kew Bridge	d	→		09 26				09 41		→		09 56				10 11		10 26			10 26			
Chiswick	d			09 29				09 44				09 59				10 14		→			10 29			
Barnes Bridge	d			09 31				09 46				10 01				10 16					10 31			
Barnes	d			09 34	09 41			09 49	09 56			10 04	10 11			10 19	10 26				10 34	10 41		
Putney	d		09 34	09 37	09 44			09 52	09 59		10 04	10 07	10 14			10 22	10 29		10 34		10 37	10 44		
Wandsworth Town	d			09 40	09 47			09 55	10 02			10 10	10 17			10 25	10 32				10 40	10 47		
Clapham Junction 10	d		09 39	09 43	09 50		09 54	09 58	10 05		10 09	10 13	10 20		10 24	10 28	10 35		10 39	10 42	10 43	10 50		10 54
Queenstown Rd.(Battersea)	d			09 46	09 53			10 01	10 08			10 16	10 23			10 31	10 38				10 46	10 53		
Vauxhall	⊖ d		09 45	09 50	09 57			10 05	10 12		10 15	10 20	10 27			10 35	10 42		10 45		10 50	10 57		
London Waterloo 15	⊖ a		09 51	09 58	10 02		10 04	10 11	10 16		10 19	10 26	10 32		10 34	10 41	10 46		10 49	10 53	10 56	11 02		11 04

For general notes see front of timetable
For details of catering facilities see
Directory of Train Operators

A From London Waterloo (Table 152)

§ Passengers to/from London may travel via Weybridge. See Table 155.

From 28 September due to seasonal difficulties a large number of trains on this table will have minor retimings that could mean slightly earlier departure or later arrival times at certain stations. For further details see local publicity or contact National Rail Enquiries 08457 48 49 50.

Reading, Guildford, Ascot, Weybridge, Windsor, Kingston, Richmond and Hounslow → London

Network Diagram - see first page of Table 148

		SW	SW	SW	SW	SW		SW	SW	SW		SW	SW	SW	SW	SW	SW	SW	SW	SW	SW	SW	SW	SW	SW
						1				1		1							1	1					
			A											A								A			
Reading 7	d					09 56						10 12								10 42					
Earley	d					10 01						10 17								10 47					
Winnersh Triangle	d					10 03						10 19								10 49					
Winnersh	d					10 05						10 21								10 51					
Wokingham	d					10 10						10 26								10 56					
Bracknell	d					10 16						10 32								11 02					
Martins Heron	d					10 19						10 35								11 05					
Guildford	d									09 30									10 00						
Wanborough	d									09 36									10 06						
Ash 3	d									09 40									10 10						
Aldershot	a									09 47									10 17						
	d									10 00									10 30						
Ash Vale	d									10 04									10 34						
Frimley	d									10 10									10 40						
Camberley	a									10 14									10 44						
	d									10 18									10 48						
Bagshot	d									10 23									10 53						
Ascot 3	d					10 25				10a30		10 40							11a00	11 10					
Sunningdale	d					10 28						10 43								11 13					
Longcross	d																								
Woking	d																								
West Byfleet	d																								
Byfleet & New Haw	d																								
Weybridge	d			10 03											10 33								11 03		
Addlestone §	d			10 07											10 37								11 07		
Chertsey §	d			10 10											10 40								11 10		
Virginia Water	a			10 15		10 33						10 49			10 45					11 19			11 15		
	d			10 24		10 33						10 49			10 54					11 19			11 24		
Egham	d			10 27		10 36						10 53			10 57					11 23			11 27		
Windsor & Eton Riverside	d				10 23											10 53								11 23	
Datchet	d				10 26											10 56								11 26	
Sunnymeads	d				10 29											10 59								11 29	
Wraysbury	d				10 32											11 02								11 32	
Staines	d			10 33	10 38	10 44						10 59			11 03	11 08				11 29			11 33	11 38	
Ashford (Surrey)	d			10 36	10 41										11 06	11 11							11 36	11 41	
Feltham	d			10 41	10 46	10 50						11 05			11 11	11 16				11 35			11 41	11 46	
Whitton	d	10 20			10 50				10 56				10 50			11 20		11 23			11 20			11 50	
Kingston	d		10 29											10 59								11 29			
Hampton Wick	d		10 31											11 01								11 31			
Teddington	d		10 35											11 05								11 35			
Fulwell	d																								
Strawberry Hill	d		10 38											11 08								11 38			
Twickenham	a		10 42		10 53	10 57			10 58			11 10		11 12		11 23		11 26		11 40		11 42		11 53	
	d		10 43		10 53	10 57			10 58			11 11		11 13		11 23		11 28		11 41		11 43		11 53	
St Margarets	d		10 45						11 00					11 15				11 30				11 45			
Richmond ⊖	d		10 49		10 58	11 02			11 04			11 15		11 19		11 28		11 34		11 45		11 49		11 58	
North Sheen	d		10 51						11 06					11 21				11 36				11 51			
Mortlake	d		10 53						11 08					11 23				11 38				11 53			
Hounslow	d	10 31		10 46									11 01		11 16						11 31		11 46		
Isleworth	d	10 34		10 49									11 04		11 19						11 34		11 49		
Syon Lane	d	10 36		10 51									11 06		11 21		←				11 36		11 51		←
Brentford	d	10 39		10 54				←					11 09		11 24		11 24				11 39		11 54		11 54
Kew Bridge	d	10 41		10 56				10 56					11 11		→		11 26				11 41		→		11 56
Chiswick	d	10 44		→				10 59					11 14				11 29				11 44				11 59
Barnes Bridge	d	10 46						11 01					11 16				11 31				11 46				12 01
Barnes	d	10 49	10 56					11 04	11 11				11 19	11 26			11 34	11 41			11 49	11 56			12 04
Putney	d	10 52	10 59		11 04			11 07	11 14				11 22	11 29		11 34	11 37	11 44			11 52	11 59		12 04	12 07
Wandsworth Town	d	10 55	11 02					11 10	11 17				11 25	11 32			11 40	11 47			11 55	12 02			12 10
Clapham Junction 10	d	10 58	11 05		11 09	11 12		11 13	11 20			11 24	11 28	11 35		11 39	11 43	11 50		11 54	11 58	12 05		12 09	12 13
Queenstown Rd.(Battersea)	d	11 01	11 08					11 16	11 23				11 31	11 38			11 46	11 53			12 01	12 08			12 16
Vauxhall ⊖	d	11 05	11 12		11 15			11 20	11 27				11 35	11 42		11 45	11 50	11 57			12 05	12 12		12 15	12 20
London Waterloo 15 ⊖	a	11 11	11 16		11 19	11 25		11 27	11 32			11 34	11 41	11 46		11 49	11 56	12 02		12 04	12 11	12 16		12 19	12 26

For general notes see front of timetable
For details of catering facilities see
Directory of Train Operators

A From London Waterloo (Table 152)

§ Passengers to/from London may travel via Weybridge. See Table 155.

From 28 September due to seasonal difficulties a large number of trains on this table will have minor retimings that could mean slightly earlier departure or later arrival times at certain stations. For further details see local publicity or contact National Rail Enquiries 08457 48 49 50.

Reading, Guildford, Ascot, Weybridge, Windsor, Kingston, Richmond and Hounslow → London

Network Diagram - see first page of Table 148

		SW	SW [1]		SW [1]	SW	SW	SW	SW	SW [1]	GW [1]	SW	SW	SW [1]	SW	SW	SW	SW	SW	SW	SW [1]		SW [1]
				A				B			C					B							
Reading [7]	d				15 12						15 28			15 42									16 12
Earley	d				15 17									15 47									16 17
Winnersh Triangle	d				15 19									15 49									16 19
Winnersh	d				15 21						15 35			15 51									16 21
Wokingham	d				15 26						15a38			15 56									16 26
Bracknell	d				15 32									16 02									16 32
Martins Heron	d				15 35									16 05									16 35
Guildford	d		10 30							15 00											15 30		
Wanborough	d		10 36							15 06											15 36		
Ash [3]	d		10 40							15 10											15 40		
Aldershot	a		10 47							15 17											15 47		
	d		11 00							15 30											16 00		
Ash Vale	d		11 04							15 34											16 04		
Frimley	d		11 10							15 40											16 10		
Camberley	a		11 14							15 44											16 14		
	d		11 18							15 48											16 18		
Bagshot	d		11 23							15 53											16 23		
Ascot [3]	d		11a30		15 40					16a00				16 10							16a30		16 40
Sunningdale	d				15 43									16 13									16 43
Longcross	d																						
Woking	d																						
West Byfleet	d																						
Byfleet & New Haw	d																						
Weybridge	d						15 33										16 03						
Addlestone §	d			and at			15 37										16 07						
Chertsey §	d						15 40										16 10						
Virginia Water	a			the same	15 49		15 45							16 19			16 15						16 49
	d			minutes	15 49		15 54							16 19			16 24						16 49
Egham	d				15 53		15 57							16 23			16 27						16 53
Windsor & Eton Riverside	d			past					15 53									16 23					
Datchet	d								15 56									16 26					
Sunnymeads	d			each					15 59									16 29					
Wraysbury	d			hour until					16 02									16 32					
Staines	d				15 59		16 03		16 08					16 29			16 33	16 38					16 59
Ashford (Surrey)	d						16 06		16 11								16 36	16 41					
Feltham	d				16 05		16 11		16 16					16 35			16 41	16 46					17 05
Whitton	d	11 53				15 50			16 20				16 23		16 20			16 50		16 53			
Kingston	d							15 59								16 29							
Hampton Wick	d							16 01								16 31							
Teddington	d							16 05								16 35							
Fulwell	d																						
Strawberry Hill	d							16 08								16 38							
Twickenham	a	11 56			16 10			16 12	16 23				16 26	16 40		16 42		16 53		16 56			17 10
	d	11 58			16 11			16 13	16 23				16 28	16 41		16 43		16 53		16 58			17 11
St Margarets	d	12 00						16 15					16 30			16 45				17 00			
Richmond	⊖ d	12 04			16 15			16 19	16 28				16 34	16 45		16 49		16 58		17 04			17 15
North Sheen	d	12 06						16 21					16 36			16 51				17 06			
Mortlake	d	12 08						16 23					16 38			16 53				17 08			
Hounslow	d					16 01	16 16								16 31		16 46						
Isleworth	d					16 04	16 19								16 34		16 49						
Syon Lane	d					16 06	16 21					←			16 36		16 51		←				
Brentford	d					16 09	16 24					16 24			16 39		16 54		16 54				
Kew Bridge	d					16 11	→					16 26			16 41		→		16 56				
Chiswick	d					16 14						16 29			16 44				16 59				
Barnes Bridge	d					16 16						16 31			16 46				17 01				
Barnes	d	12 11				16 19		16 26				16 34	16 41		16 49	16 56			17 04	17 11			
Putney	d	12 14				16 22		16 29	16 34			16 37	16 44		16 52	16 59		17 04	17 07	17 14			
Wandsworth Town	d	12 17				16 25		16 32				16 40	16 47		16 55	17 02			17 10	17 17			
Clapham Junction [10]	d	12 20			16 24	16 28		16 35	16 39			16 43	16 50	16 54	16 58	17 05		17 09	17 13	17 20			17 24
Queenstown Rd.(Battersea)	d	12 23				16 31		16 38				16 46	16 53		17 01	17 08			17 16	17 23			
Vauxhall	⊖ d	12 27				16 35		16 42	16 45			16 50	16 57		17 05	17 12		17 15	17 20	17 27			
London Waterloo [15]	⊖ a	12 32			16 34	16 41		16 49	16 49			16 56	17 02	17 04	17 11	17 19		17 19	17 26	17 32			17 34

For general notes see front of timetable
For details of catering facilities see Directory of Train Operators

§ Passengers to/from London may travel via Weybridge. See Table 155.

A 1242 Reading to Waterloo calls at Longcross 1316
B From London Waterloo (Table 152)
C To Gatwick Airport (Table 148)

From 28 September due to seasonal difficulties a large number of trains on this table will have minor retimings that could mean slightly earlier departure or later arrival times at certain stations. For further details see local publicity or contact National Rail Enquiries 08457 48 49 50.

Reading, Guildford, Ascot, Weybridge, Windsor, Kingston, Richmond and Hounslow → London

Network Diagram - see first page of Table 148

Station		SW	SW A	SW	SW	SW	SW	SW 1	SW 1	SW	SW A	SW	SW	SW	SW	SW 1	SW 1	SW		SW A	SW	SW	SW	SW 1	SW
Reading 7	d								16 42								17 12							17 22	
Earley	d								16 47								17 17							17 27	
Winnersh Triangle	d								16 49								17 19							17 29	
Winnersh	d								16 51								17 21							17 31	
Wokingham	d								16 56								17 26							17 36	
Bracknell	d								17 02								17 32							17 42	
Martins Heron	d								17 05								17 35							17 45	
Guildford	d							16 00								16 30									
Wanborough	d							16 06								16 36									
Ash 3	d							16 10								16 40									
Aldershot	a							16 17								16 47									
	d							16 30								17 00									
Ash Vale	d							16 34								17 04									
Frimley	d							16 40								17 10									
Camberley	a							16 44								17 14									
	d							16 48								17 18									
Bagshot	d							16 53								17 23									
Ascot 3	d							17a00	17 10							17a30	17 40							17b55	
Sunningdale	d								17 13								17 43							17 58	
Longcross	d								17 16																
Woking	d																								
West Byfleet	d																								
Byfleet & New Haw	d																								
Weybridge	d			16 33								17 03									17 37				
Addlestone §	d			16 37								17 07									17 41				
Chertsey §	d			16 40								17 10									17 44				
Virginia Water	a			16 45					17 19			17 15					17 49				17 49			18 03	
	d			16 54					17 19			17 24					17 49				17 54			18 03	
Egham	d			16 57					17 23			17 27					17 53				17 57			18 06	
Windsor & Eton Riverside	d				16 53								17 23									17 53			
Datchet	d				16 56								17 26									17 56			
Sunnymeads	d				16 59								17 29									17 59			
Wraysbury	d				17 02								17 32									18 02			
Staines	d			17 03	17 08				17 29			17 33	17 38				17 59				18 03	18 08		18 14	
Ashford (Surrey)	d			17 06	17 11							17 36	17 41								18 06	18 11			
Feltham	d			17 11	17 16				17 35			17 41	17 46				18 05				18 11	18 16		18 20	
Whitton	d	16 50			17 20		17 23			17 20			17 50		17 53			17 50				18 20			18 23
Kingston	d		16 59								17 29									17 59					
Hampton Wick	d		17 01								17 31									18 01					
Teddington	d		17 05								17 35									18 05					
Fulwell	d																								
Strawberry Hill	d		17 08								17 38									18 08					
Twickenham	a		17 12		17 23		17 26		17 40		17 42		17 53		17 56		18 10			18 12		18 23			18 26
	d		17 13		17 23		17 28		17 41		17 43		17 53		17 58		18 11			18 13		18 23			18 28
St Margarets	d		17 15				17 30				17 45				18 00					18 15					18 30
Richmond	⊖ d		17 19		17 28		17 34		17 45		17 49		17 58		18 04		18 15			18 19		18 28			18 34
North Sheen	d		17 21				17 36				17 51				18 06					18 21					18 36
Mortlake	d		17 23				17 38				17 53				18 08					18 23					18 38
Hounslow	d	17 01		17 16						17 31		17 46						18 01			18 16			18 26	
Isleworth	d	17 04		17 19						17 34		17 49						18 04			18 19				
Syon Lane	d	17 06		17 21		←				17 36		17 51		←				18 06			18 21		←		
Brentford	d	17 09		17 24 →		17 24				17 39		17 54 →		17 54				18 09			18 24 →		18 24	18 31	
Kew Bridge	d	17 11				17 26				17 41				17 56				18 11					18 26		
Chiswick	d	17 14				17 29				17 44				17 59				18 14					18 29		
Barnes Bridge	d	17 16				17 31				17 46				18 01				18 16					18 31		
Barnes	d	17 19	17 26			17 34	17 41			17 49	17 56			18 04	18 11			18 19		18 26			18 34		18 41
Putney	d	17 22	17 29		17 34	17 37	17 44			17 52	17 59		18 04	18 07	18 14			18 22		18 29		18 34	18 37	18 39	18 44
Wandsworth Town	d	17 25	17 32			17 40	17 47			17 55	18 02			18 10	18 17			18 25		18 32			18 40		18 47
Clapham Junction 10	d	17 28	17 35		17 39	17 43	17 50		17 54	17 58	18 05		18 09	18 13	18 20		18 24	18 28		18 35		18 39	18 43	18 44	18 50
Queenstown Rd.(Battersea)	d	17 31	17 38			17 46	17 53			18 01	18 08			18 16	18 23			18 31		18 38			18 46		18 53
Vauxhall	⊖ d	17 35	17 42		17 45	17 50	17 57			18 05	18 12		18 15	18 20	18 27			18 35		18 42		18 45	18 50		18 57
London Waterloo 15	⊖ a	17 41	17 49		17 49	17 56	18 02		18 04	18 11	18 19		18 19	18 26	18 32		18 34	18 41		18 49		18 49	18 56	18 56	19 02

For general notes see front of timetable
For details of catering facilities see Directory of Train Operators

A From London Waterloo (Table 152)
b Arr. 1749

§ Passengers to/from London may travel via Weybridge. See Table 155.

From 28 September due to seasonal difficulties a large number of trains on this table will have minor retimings that could mean slightly earlier departure or later arrival times at certain stations. For further details see local publicity or contact National Rail Enquiries 08457 48 49 50.

Reading, Guildford, Ascot, Weybridge, Windsor, Kingston, Richmond and Hounslow → London

Network Diagram - see first page of Table 148

		SW 1	SW 1	SW	SW	SW	SW	SW	SW 1	SW	SW 1	SW	SW	SW		SW	SW	SW 1	SW	SW	SW 1	SW	SW	SW 1	SW
					A									A											A
Reading 7	d		17 42						17 53			18 12									18 42			18 52	
Earley	d		17 47						17 58			18 17									18 47			18 57	
Winnersh Triangle	d		17 49						18 00			18 19									18 49			18 59	
Winnersh	d		17 51						18 02			18 21									18 51			19 01	
Wokingham	d		17 56						18 07			18 26									18 56			19 06	
Bracknell	d		18 02						18 13			18 32									19 02			19 12	
Martins Heron	d		18 05						18 16			18 35									19 05			19 15	
Guildford	d	17 00									17 30							18 00							
Wanborough	d	17 06									17 36							18 06							
Ash 3	d	17 10									17 40							18 10							
Aldershot	a	17 18									17 47							18 17							
	d	17 30									18 00							18 30							
Ash Vale	d	17 34									18 04							18 34							
Frimley	d	17 40									18 10							18 40							
Camberley	a	17 44									18 14							18 44							
	d	17 48									18 18							18 48							
Bagshot	d	17 53									18 23							18 53							
Ascot 3	d	18a00	18 10						18b25		18a30	18 40						19a00			19 10			19a19	
Sunningdale	d		18 13						18 28			18 43									19 13				
Longcross	d		18 16									18 46									19 16				
Woking	d																								
West Byfleet	d																								
Byfleet & New Haw	d																								
Weybridge	d					18 07										18 37							19 07		
Addlestone §	d					18 11										18 41							19 11		
Chertsey §	d					18 14										18 44							19 14		
Virginia Water	a		18 19			18 19			18 33			18 49				18 49					19 19		19 19		
	d		18 19			18 24			18 33			18 49				18 54					19 19		19 24		
Egham	d		18 23			18 27			18 37			18 53				18 57					19 23		19 27		
Windsor & Eton Riverside	d						18 23										18 53								
Datchet	d						18 26										18 56								
Sunnymeads	d						18 29										18 59								
Wraysbury	d						18 32										19 02								
Staines	d		18 29			18 33	18 38		18 44			18 59				19 03	19 08				19 29		19 33		
Ashford (Surrey)	d					18 36	18 41									19 06	19 11						19 36		
Feltham	d		18 35			18 41	18 46		18 50			19 05				19 11	19 16				19 35		19 41		
Whitton	d			18 20			18 50			18 53			18 50				19 20			19 23		19 20			
Kingston	d				18 29									18 59											19 29
Hampton Wick	d				18 31									19 01											19 31
Teddington	d				18 35									19 05											19 35
Fulwell	d																								
Strawberry Hill	d				18 38									19 08											19 38
Twickenham	a		18 40		18 42		18 53			18 56		19 10		19 12			19 23			19 26	19 40				19 42
	d		18 41		18 43		18 53			18 58		19 11		19 13			19 23			19 28	19 41				19 43
St Margarets	d				18 45					19 00				19 15						19 30					19 45
Richmond	⊖ d		18 45		18 49		18 58			19 04		19 15		19 19			19 28			19 34	19 45				19 49
North Sheen	d				18 51					19 06				19 21						19 36					19 51
Mortlake	d				18 53					19 08				19 23						19 38					19 53
Hounslow	d			18 31		18 46			18 56				19 01			19 16						19 31	19 46		
Isleworth	d			18 34		18 49							19 04			19 19						19 34	19 49		
Syon Lane	d			18 36		18 51		←					19 06			19 21			←			19 36	19 51		
Brentford	d			18 39		18 54		18 54	19 01				19 09			19 24			19 24			19 39	19 54		
Kew Bridge	d			18 41		→		18 56					19 11			→			19 26			19 41	→		
Chiswick	d			18 44				18 59					19 14						19 29			19 44			
Barnes Bridge	d			18 46				19 01					19 16						19 31			19 46			
Barnes	d			18 49	18 56			19 04		19 11			19 19	19 26					19 34	19 41		19 49			19 56
Putney	d			18 52	18 59		19 04	19 07	19 09	19 14			19 22	19 29			19 34		19 37	19 44		19 52			19 59
Wandsworth Town	d			18 55	19 02			19 10		19 17			19 25	19 32					19 40	19 47		19 55			20 02
Clapham Junction 10	d		18 54	18 58	19 05		19 09	19 13	19 14	19 20		19 24	19 28	19 35			19 39		19 43	19 50	19 54	19 58			20 05
Queenstown Rd.(Battersea)	d			19 01	19 08			19 16		19 23			19 31	19 38					19 46	19 53		20 01			20 08
Vauxhall	⊖ d			19 05	19 12		19 15	19 20		19 27			19 35	19 42			19 45		19 50	19 57		20 05			20 12
London Waterloo 15	⊖ a		19 04	19 11	19 16		19 19	19 26	19 28	19 32		19 34	19 41	19 46			19 49		19 56	20 02	20 04	20 09			20 16

For general notes see front of timetable
For details of catering facilities see Directory of Train Operators

A From London Waterloo (Table 152)
b Arr. 1820

§ Passengers to/from London may travel via Weybridge. See Table 155.

From 28 September due to seasonal difficulties a large number of trains on this table will have minor retimings that could mean slightly earlier departure or later arrival times at certain stations. For further details see local publicity or contact National Rail Enquiries 08457 48 49 50.

Reading, Guildford, Ascot, Weybridge, Windsor, Kingston, Richmond and Hounslow → London

Network Diagram - see first page of Table 148

		SW	SW	SW	SW 1	SW 1	SW	SW	SW	SW		SW	SW	SW 1	SW 1	SW	SW	SW	SW	SW 1	SW	SW	SW 1	SW	SW
								A									A								
Reading 7	d					19 12									19 42								20 12		
Earley	d					19 17									19 47								20 17		
Winnersh Triangle	d					19 19									19 49								20 19		
Winnersh	d					19 21									19 51								20 21		
Wokingham	d					19 26									19 56								20 26		
Bracknell	d					19 32									20 02								20 32		
Martins Heron	d					19 35									20 05								20 35		
Guildford	d				18 30									19 00						19 30					
Wanborough	d				18 36									19 06						19 36					
Ash 3	d				18 40									19 10						19 40					
Aldershot	a				18 47									19 17						19 47					
	d				19 00									19 30						20 00					
Ash Vale	d				19 04									19 34						20 04					
Frimley	d				19 10									19 40						20 10					
Camberley	a				19 14									19 44						20 14					
	d				19 18									19 48						20 18					
Bagshot	d				19 23									19 53						20 23					
Ascot 3	d				19a30	19 40								20a00	20 10					20a30			20 40		
Sunningdale	d					19 43									20 13								20 43		
Longcross	d					19 46									20 16								20 46		
Woking	d																								
West Byfleet	d																								
Byfleet & New Haw	d																								
Weybridge	d								19 37									20 03							20 33
Addlestone §	d								19 41									20 07							20 37
Chertsey §	d								19 44									20 10							20 40
Virginia Water	a					19 49			19 49						20 19			20 15					20 49		20 45
	d					19 49			19 54						20 19			20 24					20 49		20 54
Egham	d					19 53			19 57						20 23			20 27					20 53		20 57
Windsor & Eton Riverside	d	19 23								19 53									20 23						
Datchet	d	19 26								19 56									20 26						
Sunnymeads	d	19 29								19 59									20 29						
Wraysbury	d	19 32								20 02									20 32						
Staines	d	19 38				19 59			20 03	20 08					20 29			20 33	20 38				20 59		21 03
Ashford (Surrey)	d	19 41							20 06	20 11								20 36	20 41						21 06
Feltham	d	19 46				20 05			20 11	20 16					20 35			20 41	20 46				21 05		21 11
Whitton	d	19 50		19 53			19 50			20 20			20 23			20 20			20 50			20 53		20 50	
Kingston	d							19 59									20 29								
Hampton Wick	d							20 01									20 31								
Teddington	d							20 05									20 35								
Fulwell	d																								
Strawberry Hill	d							20 08									20 38								
Twickenham	a	19 53		19 56		20 10		20 12		20 23			20 26		20 40		20 42		20 53			20 56	21 10		
	d	19 53		19 58		20 11		20 13		20 23			20 28		20 41		20 43		20 53			20 58	21 11		
St Margarets	d			20 00				20 15					20 30				20 45					21 00			
Richmond ⊖	d	19 58		20 04		20 15		20 19		20 28			20 34		20 45		20 49		20 58			21 04	21 15		
North Sheen	d			20 06				20 21					20 36				20 51					21 06			
Mortlake	d			20 08				20 23					20 38				20 53					21 08			
Hounslow	d						20 01		20 16							20 31		20 46						21 01	21 16
Isleworth	d						20 04		20 19							20 34		20 49						21 04	21 19
Syon Lane	d		←				20 06		20 21			←				20 36		20 51			←			21 06	21 21
Brentford	d		19 54				20 09		20 24			20 24				20 39		20 54			20 54			21 09	21 24
Kew Bridge	d		19 56				20 11		→			20 26				20 41		→			20 56			21 11	→
Chiswick	d		19 59				20 14					20 29				20 44					20 59			21 14	
Barnes Bridge	d		20 01				20 16					20 31				20 46					21 01			21 16	
Barnes	d		20 04	20 11			20 19	20 26				20 34	20 41			20 49	20 56				21 04	21 11		21 19	
Putney	d	20 04	20 07	20 14			20 22	20 29		20 34		20 37	20 44			20 52	20 59		21 04		21 07	21 14		21 22	
Wandsworth Town	d		20 10	20 17			20 25	20 32				20 40	20 47			20 55	21 02				21 10	21 17		21 25	
Clapham Junction 10	d	20 09	20 13	20 20		20 24	20 28	20 35		20 39		20 43	20 50		20 54	20 58	21 05		21 09		21 13	21 20	21 24	21 28	
Queenstown Rd.(Battersea)	d		20 16	20 23			20 31	20 38				20 46	20 53			21 01	21 08				21 16	21 23		21 31	
Vauxhall ⊖	d	20 15	20 20	20 27			20 35	20 42		20 45		20 50	20 57			21 05	21 12		21 15		21 20	21 27		21 35	
London Waterloo 15 ⊖	a	20 19	20 26	20 32		20 34	20 41	20 46		20 49		20 56	21 02		21 04	21 11	21 16		21 19		21 26	21 32	21 34	21 41	

For general notes see front of timetable
For details of catering facilities see Directory of Train Operators

A From London Waterloo (Table 152)

§ Passengers to/from London may travel via Weybridge. See Table 155.

From 28 September due to seasonal difficulties a large number of trains on this table will have minor retimings that could mean slightly earlier departure or later arrival times at certain stations. For further details see local publicity or contact National Rail Enquiries 08457 48 49 50.

Reading, Guildford, Ascot, Weybridge, Windsor, Kingston, Richmond and Hounslow → London

Network Diagram - see first page of Table 148

		SW A	SW	SW 1	SW 1	SW		SW	SW 1	SW	SW A	SW	SW	SW	SW	SW 1	SW	SW	SW A	SW	SW 1	SW 1	SW	SW	SW 1
Reading 7	d								20 42							21 12									21 42
Earley	d								20 47							21 17									21 47
Winnersh Triangle	d								20 49							21 19									21 49
Winnersh	d								20 51							21 21									21 51
Wokingham	d								20 56							21 26									21 56
Bracknell	d								21 02							21 32									22 02
Martins Heron	d								21 05							21 35									22 05
Guildford	d			20 00	20 30																21 00	21 30			
Wanborough	d			20 06	20 36																21 06	21 36			
Ash 3	d			20 10	20 40																21 10	21 40			
Aldershot	a			20 17	20 47																21 17	21 47			
	d			20 30																	21 30				
Ash Vale	d			20 34																	21 34				
Frimley	d			20 40																	21 40				
Camberley	a			20 44																	21 44				
	d			20 48																	21 48				
Bagshot	d			20 53																	21 53				
Ascot 3	d			21a00					21 10							21 40					22a00				22 10
Sunningdale	d								21 13							21 43									22 13
Longcross	d																								
Woking	d																								
West Byfleet	d																								
Byfleet & New Haw	d																								
Weybridge	d											21 03						21 33							
Addlestone §	d											21 07						21 37							
Chertsey §	d											21 10						21 40							
Virginia Water	a								21 19			21 15				21 49		21 45							22 19
	d								21 19			21 24				21 49		21 54							22 19
Egham	d								21 23			21 27				21 53		21 57							22 23
Windsor & Eton Riverside	d		20 53										21 23							21 53					
Datchet	d		20 56										21 26							21 56					
Sunnymeads	d		20 59										21 29							21 59					
Wraysbury	d		21 02										21 32							22 02					
Staines	d		21 08						21 29			21 33	21 38			21 59		22 03		22 08					22 29
Ashford (Surrey)	d		21 11									21 36	21 41					22 06		22 11					
Feltham	d		21 16						21 35			21 41	21 46			22 05		22 11		22 16					22 35
Whitton	d		21 20					21 23		21 20			21 50		21 53		21 50			22 20				22 23	
Kingston	d	20 59									21 29								21 59						
Hampton Wick	d	21 01									21 31								22 01						
Teddington	d	21 05									21 35								22 05						
Fulwell	d																								
Strawberry Hill	d	21 08									21 38								22 08						
Twickenham	a	21 12	21 23					21 26	21 40		21 42		21 53		21 56	22 10			22 12	22 23				22 26	22 40
	d	21 13	21 23					21 28	21 41		21 43		21 53		21 58	22 11			22 13	22 23				22 28	22 41
St Margarets	d	21 15						21 30			21 45				22 00				22 15					22 30	
Richmond	⊖ d	21 19	21 28					21 34	21 45		21 49		21 58		22 04	22 15			22 19	22 28				22 34	22 45
North Sheen	d	21 21						21 36			21 51				22 06				22 21					22 36	
Mortlake	d	21 23						21 38			21 53				22 08				22 23					22 38	
Hounslow	d									21 31		21 46					22 01	22 16							
Isleworth	d									21 34		21 49					22 04	22 19							
Syon Lane	d					←				21 36		21 51		←			22 06	22 21					←		
Brentford	d					21 24				21 39		21 54 →		21 54			22 09	22 24 →					22 24		
Kew Bridge	d					21 26				21 41				21 56			22 11						22 26		
Chiswick	d					21 29				21 44				21 59			22 14						22 29		
Barnes Bridge	d					21 31				21 46				22 01			22 16						22 31		
Barnes	d	21 26				21 34		21 41		21 49	21 56			22 04	22 11		22 19		22 26				22 34	22 41	
Putney	d	21 29	21 34			21 37		21 44		21 52	21 59		22 04	22 07	22 14		22 22		22 29	22 34			22 37	22 44	
Wandsworth Town	d	21 32				21 40		21 47		21 55	22 02			22 10	22 17		22 25		22 32				22 40	22 47	
Clapham Junction 10	d	21 35	21 39			21 43		21 50	21 54	21 58	22 05		22 09	22 13	22 20	22 24	22 28		22 35	22 39			22 43	22 50	22 54
Queenstown Rd.(Battersea)	d	21 38				21 46		20 44		22 01	22 08			22 16	21 14		22 31		22 38				22 46	22 53	
Vauxhall	⊖ d	21 42	21 45			21 50		21 57		22 05	22 12		22 15	22 20	22 27		22 35		22 42	22 45			22 50	22 57	
London Waterloo 15	⊖ a	21 46	21 49			21 56		22 02	22 04	22 11	22 16		22 19	22 26	22 32	22 34	22 41		22 46	22 49			22 56	23 02	23 04

For general notes see front of timetable
For details of catering facilities see
Directory of Train Operators

A From London Waterloo (Table 152)

§ Passengers to/from London may travel via Weybridge. See Table 155.

From 28 September due to seasonal difficulties a large number of trains on this table will have minor retimings that could mean slightly earlier departure or later arrival times at certain stations. For further details see local publicity or contact National Rail Enquiries 08457 48 49 50.

Reading, Guildford, Ascot, Weybridge, Windsor, Kingston, Richmond and Hounslow → London

Network Diagram - see first page of Table 148

		SW A	SW	SW	SW	SW 1	SW	SW A	SW 1	SW 1	SW	SW	SW 1	SW A	SW	SW	SW A	SW 1	SW	SW 1	SW 1
Reading 7	d					22 12							22 42					23 12			
Earley	d					22 17							22 47					23 17			
Winnersh Triangle	d					22 19							22 49					23 19			
Winnersh	d					22 21							22 51					23 21			
Wokingham	d					22 26							22 56					23 26			
Bracknell	d					22 32							23 02					23 32			
Martins Heron	d					22 35							23 05					23 35			
Guildford	d								22 00	22 30										23 00	23 30
Wanborough	d								22 06	22 36										23 06	23 36
Ash 3	d								22 10	22 40										23 10	23 40
Aldershot	a								22 17	22 47										23 17	23 47
	d								22 30											23 30	
Ash Vale	d								22 34											23 34	
Frimley	d								22 40											23 40	
Camberley	a								22 44											23 44	
	d								22 48											23 48	
Bagshot	d								22 53											23 53	
Ascot 3	d					22 40			23a00				23 10					23 40		00a01	
Sunningdale	d					22 43							23 13					23 43			
Longcross	d																				
Woking	d																				
West Byfleet	d																				
Byfleet & New Haw	d																				
Weybridge	d		22 03				22 33								23 03				23 33		
Addlestone §	d		22 07				22 37								23 07				23 37		
Chertsey §	d		22 10				22 40								23 10				23 40		
Virginia Water	a		22 15			22 49	22 45						23 19		23 15			23 49	23 45		
	d		22 24			22 49	22 54						23 19		23 24			23 49	23 54		
Egham	d		22 27			22 53	22 57						23 23		23 27			23 53	23 57		
Windsor & Eton Riverside	d			22 23							22 53					23 23					
Datchet	d			22 26							22 56					23 26					
Sunnymeads	d			22 29							22 59					23 29					
Wraysbury	d			22 32							23 02					23 32					
Staines	d		22 33	22 38		22 59	23 03				23 08		23 29		23a32	23a37		23 59	00a02		
Ashford (Surrey)	d		22 36	22 41			23 06				23 11										
Feltham	d		22 41	22 46		23 05	23 11				23 16		23 35					00 05			
Whitton	d			22 50							23 20										
Kingston	d	22 29						22 59						23 29			23 55				
Hampton Wick	d	22 31						23 01						23 31			23 57				
Teddington	d	22 35						23 05						23 35			23 59				
Fulwell	d																				
Strawberry Hill	d	22 38						23 08						23 38			00 03				
Twickenham	a	22 42		22 53		23 10		23 12			23 23		23 40	23 42			00 07	00 10			
	d	22 43		22 53		23 11		23 13			23 23		23 41	23 43				00 11			
St Margarets	d	22 45						23 15						23 45							
Richmond ⊖	d	22 49		22 58		23 15		23 19			23 28		23 45	23 49				00 15			
North Sheen	d	22 51						23 21						23 51							
Mortlake	d	22 53						23 23						23 53							
Hounslow	d		22 46				23 16														
Isleworth	d		22 49				23 19														
Syon Lane	d		22 51		←		23 21					←									
Brentford	d		22 54		22 54		23 24					23 24									
Kew Bridge	d		→		22 56		→					23 26									
Chiswick	d				22 59							23 29									
Barnes Bridge	d				23 01							23 31									
Barnes	d	22 56			23 04			23 26				23 34		23 56							
Putney	d	22 59		23 04	23 07			23 29			23 34	23 37		23 59							
Wandsworth Town	d	23 02			23 10			23 32				23 40		00 02							
Clapham Junction 10	d	23 05		23 09	23 13	23 24		23 35			23 39	23 43	23 54	00 05				00 24			
Queenstown Rd.(Battersea)	d	23 08			23 16			23 38				23 46		00 08							
Vauxhall ⊖	d	23 12		23 15	23 20			23 42			23 45	23 50		00 12							
London Waterloo 15 ⊖	a	23 16		23 19	23 26	23 34		23 46			23 49	23 56	00 04	00 16				00 32			

For general notes see front of timetable
For details of catering facilities see Directory of Train Operators

A From London Waterloo (Table 152)

§ Passengers to/from London may travel via Weybridge. See Table 155.

From 28 September due to seasonal difficulties a large number of trains on this table will have minor retimings that could mean slightly earlier departure or later arrival times at certain stations. For further details see local publicity or contact National Rail Enquiries 08457 48 49 50.

Table 149

Saturdays

Reading, Guildford, Ascot, Weybridge, Windsor, Kingston, Richmond and Hounslow → London

Network Diagram - see first page of Table 148

		SW	SW	SW [1]	SW	SW	SW	SW	SW	SW	SW	SW	SW [1]	SW	SW [1]	SW	SW	SW	SW [1]	SW	SW	SW	SW	SW [1]	SW
		A	A											B						A					
Reading [7]	d			23p12									05 42						06 12					06 42	
Earley	d			23p17									05 47						06 17					06 47	
Winnersh Triangle	d			23p19									05 49						06 19					06 49	
Winnersh	d			23p21									05 51						06 21					06 51	
Wokingham	d			23p26									05 56						06 26					06 56	
Bracknell	d			23p32									06 02						06 32					07 02	
Martins Heron	d			23p35									06 05						06 35					07 05	
Guildford	d																								
Wanborough	d																								
Ash [3]	d																								
Aldershot	a																								
	d														06 00										
Ash Vale	d														06 04										
Frimley	d														06 10										
Camberley	a														06 14										
	d														06 18										
Bagshot	d														06 23										
Ascot [3]	d			23p40									06 10		06a30				06 40					07 10	
Sunningdale	d			23p43									06 13						06 43					07 13	
Longcross	d																								
Woking	d									05 25															
West Byfleet	d									05 30															
Byfleet & New Haw	d									05 33															
Weybridge	d																				06 33				
Addlestone §	d									05 37											06 37				
Chertsey §	d									05 40											06 40				
Virginia Water	a			23p49						05 45			06 19						06 49		06 45			07 19	
	d			23p49						05 54			06 19						06 49		06 54			07 19	
Egham	d			23p53						05 57			06 23						06 53		06 57			07 23	
Windsor & Eton Riverside	d										05 53						06 23					06 53			
Datchet	d										05 56						06 26					06 56			
Sunnymeads	d										05 59						06 29					06 59			
Wraysbury	d										06 02						06 32					07 02			
Staines	d			23p59	04 58		05 37			06 03	06 08		06 29			06 33	06 38		06 59		07 03	07 08		07 29	
Ashford (Surrey)	d				05 01		05 40			06 06	06 11					06 36	06 41				07 06	07 11			
Feltham	d			00 05	05 06		05 45			06 11	06 16		06 35			06 41	06 46		07 05		07 11	07 16		07 35	
Whitton	d				05 10		05 49	05 41			06 20						06 50					07 20			
Kingston	d	23p29	23p55						05 59					06 29						06 59					
Hampton Wick	d	23p31	23p57						06 01					06 31						07 01					
Teddington	d	23p35	23p59						06 05					06 35						07 05					
Fulwell	d																								
Strawberry Hill	d	23p38	00 03			05 38			06 08					06 38						07 08					
Twickenham	a	23p42	00 07	00 10	05 13	05 41	05 52		06 12		06 23		06 40	06 42			06 53		07 10	07 12		07 23		07 40	
	d	23p43		00 11	05 13	05 43	05 53	05 38	06 13		06 23		06 41	06 43			06 53		07 11	07 13		07 23		07 41	
St Margarets	d	23p45			05 15	05 45			06 15					06 45						07 15					
Richmond	⊖ d	23p49		00 15	05 19	05 49	05 58		06 19		06 28		06 45	06 49			06 58		07 15	07 19		07 28		07 45	
North Sheen	d	23p51			05 21	05 51			06 21					06 51						07 21					
Mortlake	d	23p53			05 23	05 53			06 23					06 53						07 23					
Hounslow	d							05 46		06 16						06 46					07 16				07 31
Isleworth	d							05 49		06 19						06 49					07 19				07 34
Syon Lane	d							05 51		06 21		←				06 51		←			07 21		←		07 36
Brentford	d							05 54		06 24		06 24				06 54		06 54			07 24		07 24		07 39
Kew Bridge	d							05 56		→		06 26				→		06 56			→		07 26		07 41
Chiswick	d							05 59				06 29						06 59					07 29		07 44
Barnes Bridge	d							06 01				06 31						07 01					07 31		07 46
Barnes	d	23p56			05 26	05 56		06 04	06 26			06 34		06 56				07 04		07 26			07 34		07 49
Putney	d	23p59			05 29	05 59	06 04	06 07	06 29		06 34	06 37		06 59			07 04	07 07		07 29		07 34	07 37		07 52
Wandsworth Town	d	00 02			05 32	06 02		06 10	06 32			06 40		07 02				07 10		07 32			07 40		07 55
Clapham Junction [10]	d	00 05		00 24	05 35	06 05	06 09	06 13	06 35		06 39	06 43	06 54	07 05			07 09	07 13	07 24	07 35		07 39	07 43	07 54	07 58
Queenstown Rd.(Battersea)	d	00 08			05 38	06 08		06 16	06 38			06 46		07 08				07 16		07 38			07 46		08 01
Vauxhall	⊖ d	00 12			05 42	06 12	06 15	06 20	06 42		06 45	06 50		07 12			07 15	07 20		07 42		07 45	07 50		08 05
London Waterloo [15]	⊖ a	00 16		00 32	05 46	06 16	06 19	06 26	06 46		06 49	06 56	07 04	07 16			07 19	07 26	07 34	07 46		07 49	07 56	08 04	08 11

For general notes see front of timetable
For details of catering facilities see Directory of Train Operators

A From London Waterloo (Table 152)
B From Wimbledon (Table 152)

§ Passengers to/from London may travel via Weybridge. See Table 155.

From 3 October due to seasonal difficulties a large number of trains on this table will have minor retimings that could mean slightly earlier departure or later arrival times at certain stations. For further details see local publicity or contact National Rail Enquiries 08457 48 49 50.

Table 149

Saturdays

Reading, Guildford, Ascot, Weybridge, Windsor, Kingston, Richmond and Hounslow → London

Network Diagram - see first page of Table 148

		SW	SW	SW	SW	SW	SW	SW	SW	SW	SW	SW	SW	SW	SW	SW	SW	SW	SW	SW	SW	SW	SW	SW	SW
					1			1							1	1							1	1	
		A								A								A							
Reading 7	d							07 12								07 42								08 12	
Earley	d							07 17								07 47								08 17	
Winnersh Triangle	d							07 19								07 49								08 19	
Winnersh	d							07 21								07 51								08 21	
Wokingham	d							07 26								07 56								08 26	
Bracknell	d							07 32								08 02								08 32	
Martins Heron	d							07 35								08 05								08 35	
Guildford	d				06 30										07 00								07 30		
Wanborough	d				06 36										07 06								07 36		
Ash 3	d				06 40										07 10								07 40		
Aldershot	a				06 47										07 17								07 47		
	d				07 00										07 30								08 00		
Ash Vale	d				07 04										07 34								08 04		
Frimley	d				07 10										07 40								08 10		
Camberley	a				07 14										07 44								08 14		
	d				07 18										07 48								08 18		
Bagshot	d				07 23										07 53								08 23		
Ascot 3	d				07a30			07 40							08a00	08 10							08a30	08 40	
Sunningdale	d							07 43								08 13								08 43	
Longcross	d																								
Woking	d																								
West Byfleet	d																								
Byfleet & New Haw	d																								
Weybridge	d		07 03								07 33								08 03						
Addlestone §	d		07 07								07 37								08 07						
Chertsey §	d		07 10								07 40								08 10						
Virginia Water	a		07 15					07 49			07 45					08 19			08 15					08 49	
	d		07 24					07 49			07 54					08 19			08 24					08 49	
Egham	d		07 27					07 53			07 57					08 23			08 27					08 53	
Windsor & Eton Riverside	d			07 23								07 53								08 23					
Datchet	d			07 26								07 56								08 26					
Sunnymeads	d			07 29								07 59								08 29					
Wraysbury	d			07 32								08 02								08 32					
Staines	d		07 33	07 38				07 59			08 03	08 08				08 29			08 33	08 38				08 59	
Ashford (Surrey)	d		07 36	07 41							08 06	08 11							08 36	08 41					
Feltham	d		07 41	07 46				08 05			08 11	08 16				08 35			08 41	08 46				09 05	
Whitton	d			07 50					07 50			08 20		08 23			08 20			08 50		08 53			08 50
Kingston	d	07 29								07 59								08 29							
Hampton Wick	d	07 31								08 01								08 31							
Teddington	d	07 35								08 05								08 35							
Fulwell	d																								
Strawberry Hill	d	07 38								08 08								08 38							
Twickenham	a	07 42		07 53				08 10		08 12		08 23		08 26		08 40		08 42		08 53		08 56		09 10	
	d	07 43		07 53			07 58	08 11		08 13		08 23		08 28		08 41		08 43		08 53		08 58		09 11	
St Margarets	d	07 45					08 00			08 15				08 30				08 45				09 00			
Richmond	⊖ d	07 49		07 58			08 04	08 15		08 19		08 28		08 34		08 45		08 49		08 58		09 04		09 15	
North Sheen	d	07 51					08 06			08 21				08 36				08 51				09 06			
Mortlake	d	07 53					08 08			08 23				08 38				08 53				09 08			
Hounslow	d		07 46						08 01		08 16						08 31		08 46						09 01
Isleworth	d		07 49						08 04		08 19						08 34		08 49						09 04
Syon Lane	d		07 51			←			08 06		08 21		←				08 36		08 51		←				09 06
Brentford	d		07 54 →			07 54			08 09		08 24 →		08 24				08 39		08 54 →		08 54				09 09
Kew Bridge	d					07 56			08 11				08 26				08 41				08 56				09 11
Chiswick	d					07 59			08 14				08 29				08 44				08 59				09 14
Barnes Bridge	d					08 01			08 16				08 31				08 46				09 01				09 16
Barnes	d	07 56				08 04	08 11		08 19	08 26			08 34	08 41			08 49	08 56			09 04	09 11			09 19
Putney	d	07 59		08 04		08 07	08 14		08 22	08 29		08 34	08 37	08 44			08 52	08 59		09 04	09 07	09 14			09 22
Wandsworth Town	d	08 02				08 10	08 17		08 25	08 32			08 40	08 47			08 55	09 02			09 10	09 17			09 25
Clapham Junction 10	d	08 05		08 09		08 13	08 20	08 24	08 28	08 35		08 39	08 43	08 50		08 54	08 58	09 05		09 09	09 13	09 20		09 24	09 28
Queenstown Rd.(Battersea)	d	08 08				08 16	08 23		08 31	08 38			08 46	08 53			09 01	09 08			09 16	09 23			09 31
Vauxhall	⊖ d	08 12		08 15		08 20	08 27		08 35	08 42		08 45	08 50	08 57			09 05	09 12		09 15	09 20	09 27			09 35
London Waterloo 15	⊖ a	08 16		08 19		08 26	08 32	08 34	08 41	08 46		08 49	08 56	09 02		09 04	09 11	09 16		09 19	09 26	09 32		09 34	09 41

For general notes see front of timetable
For details of catering facilities see
Directory of Train Operators

A From London Waterloo (Table 152)

§ Passengers to/from London may travel via Weybridge. See Table 155.

From 3 October due to seasonal difficulties a large number of trains on this table will have minor retimings that could mean slightly earlier departure or later arrival times at certain stations. For further details see local publicity or contact National Rail Enquiries 08457 48 49 50.

Reading, Guildford, Ascot, Weybridge, Windsor, Kingston, Richmond and Hounslow → London

Network Diagram - see first page of Table 148

		SW	SW	SW	SW	SW	SW	SW	SW	SW	SW	SW	SW	SW	SW	SW	SW	SW	SW	SW	SW	SW	SW
		A					1	1		A					1	1		A					1	1
Reading 7	d							08 42								09 12								09 42
Earley	d							08 47								09 17								09 47
Winnersh Triangle	d							08 49								09 19								09 49
Winnersh	d							08 51								09 21								09 51
Wokingham	d							08 56								09 26								09 56
Bracknell	d							09 02								09 32								10 02
Martins Heron	d							09 05								09 35								10 05
Guildford	d						08 00								08 30								09 00	
Wanborough	d						08 06								08 36								09 06	
Ash 3	d						08 10								08 40								09 10	
Aldershot	a						08 17								08 47								09 17	
	d						08 30								09 00								09 30	
Ash Vale	d						08 34								09 04								09 34	
Frimley	d						08 40								09 10								09 40	
Camberley	a						08 44								09 14								09 44	
	d						08 48								09 18								09 48	
Bagshot	d						08 53								09 23								09 53	
Ascot 3	d						09a00	09 10							09a30	09 40							10a00	10 10
Sunningdale	d							09 13								09 43								10 13
Longcross	d																							
Woking	d																							
West Byfleet	d																							
Byfleet & New Haw	d																							
Weybridge	d		08 33								09 03								09 33					
Addlestone §	d		08 37								09 07								09 37					
Chertsey §	d		08 40								09 10								09 40					
Virginia Water	a		08 45					09 19			09 15					09 49			09 45					10 19
	d		08 54					09 19			09 24					09 49			09 54					10 19
Egham	d		08 57					09 23			09 27					09 53			09 57					10 23
Windsor & Eton Riverside	d			08 53								09 23								09 53				
Datchet	d			08 56								09 26								09 56				
Sunnymeads	d			08 59								09 29								09 59				
Wraysbury	d			09 02								09 32								10 02				
Staines	d		09 03	09 08				09 29			09 33	09 38				09 59			10 03	10 08				10 29
Ashford (Surrey)	d		09 06	09 11							09 36	09 41							10 06	10 11				
Feltham	d		09 11	09 16				09 35			09 41	09 46				10 05			10 11	10 16				10 35
Whitton	d			09 20		09 23			09 20			09 50		09 53			09 50			10 20		10 23		
Kingston	d	08 59								09 29								09 59						
Hampton Wick	d	09 01								09 31								10 01						
Teddington	d	09 05								09 35								10 05						
Fulwell	d																							
Strawberry Hill	d	09 08								09 38								10 08						
Twickenham	a	09 12		09 23		09 26		09 40		09 42		09 53		09 56		10 10		10 12		10 23		10 26		10 40
	d	09 13		09 23		09 28		09 41		09 43		09 53		09 58		10 11		10 13		10 23		10 28		10 41
St Margarets	d	09 15				09 30				09 45				10 00				10 15				10 30		
Richmond	⊖ d	09 19		09 28		09 34		09 45		09 49		09 58		10 04		10 15		10 19		10 28		10 34		10 45
North Sheen	d	09 21				09 36				09 51				10 06				10 21				10 36		
Mortlake	d	09 23				09 38				09 53				10 08				10 23				10 38		
Hounslow	d		09 16						09 31		09 46						10 01		10 16					
Isleworth	d		09 19						09 34		09 49						10 04		10 19					
Syon Lane	d		09 21		←				09 36		09 51		←				10 06		10 21		←			
Brentford	d		09 24 →		09 24				09 39		09 54 →		09 54				10 09		10 24 →		10 24			
Kew Bridge	d				09 26				09 41				09 56				10 11				10 26			
Chiswick	d				09 29				09 44				09 59				10 14				10 29			
Barnes Bridge	d				09 31				09 46				10 01				10 16				10 31			
Barnes	d	09 26			09 34	09 41			09 49	09 56			10 04	10 11			10 19	10 26			10 34	10 41		
Putney	d	09 29		09 34	09 37	09 44			09 52	09 59		10 04	10 07	10 14			10 22	10 29		10 34	10 37	10 44		
Wandsworth Town	d	09 32			09 40	09 47			09 55	10 02			10 10	10 17			10 25	10 32			10 40	10 47		
Clapham Junction 10	d	09 35		09 39	09 43	09 50		09 54	09 58	10 05		10 09	10 13	10 20		10 24	10 28	10 35		10 39	10 43	10 50		10 54
Queenstown Rd.(Battersea)	d	09 38			09 46	09 53			10 01	10 08			10 16	10 23			10 31	10 38			10 46	10 53		
Vauxhall	⊖ d	09 42		09 45	09 50	09 57			10 05	10 12		10 15	10 20	10 27			10 35	10 42		10 45	10 50	10 57		
London Waterloo 15	⊖ a	09 46		09 49	09 56	10 02		10 04	10 11	10 16		10 19	10 26	10 32		10 34	10 41	10 46		10 49	10 56	11 02		11 04

For general notes see front of timetable
For details of catering facilities see Directory of Train Operators

A From London Waterloo (Table 152)

§ Passengers to/from London may travel via Weybridge. See Table 155.

From 3 October due to seasonal difficulties a large number of trains on this table will have minor retimings that could mean slightly earlier departure or later arrival times at certain stations. For further details see local publicity or contact National Rail Enquiries 08457 48 49 50.

Table 149

Saturdays

Reading, Guildford, Ascot, Weybridge, Windsor, Kingston, Richmond and Hounslow → London

Network Diagram - see first page of Table 148

		SW	SW A	SW	SW	SW	SW		SW 1	SW 1	SW	SW A	SW	SW	SW	SW	SW 1	SW 1	SW	SW A	SW	SW	SW 1	SW
Reading 7	d									19 12								19 42						
Earley	d									19 17								19 47						
Winnersh Triangle	d									19 19								19 49						
Winnersh	d									19 21								19 51						
Wokingham	d									19 26								19 56						
Bracknell	d									19 32								20 02						
Martins Heron	d									19 35								20 05						
Guildford	d								18 30								19 00						19 30	
Wanborough	d								18 36								19 06						19 36	
Ash 3	d								18 40								19 10						19 40	
Aldershot	a								18 47								19 17						19 47	
	d								19 00								19 30						20 00	
Ash Vale	d								19 04								19 34						20 04	
Frimley	d								19 10								19 40						20 10	
Camberley	a								19 14								19 44						20 14	
	d								19 18								19 48						20 18	
Bagshot	d								19 23								19 53						20 23	
Ascot 3	d								19a30	19 40							20a00	20 10					20a30	
Sunningdale	d									19 43								20 13						
Longcross	d																							
Woking	d																							
West Byfleet	d																							
Byfleet & New Haw	d																							
Weybridge	d			10 03									19 33								20 03			
Addlestone §	d			10 07									19 37								20 07			
Chertsey §	d			10 10				and at					19 40								20 10			
Virginia Water	a			10 15				the same		19 49			19 45					20 19			20 15			
	d			10 24						19 49			19 54					20 19			20 24			
Egham	d			10 27				minutes		19 53			19 57					20 23			20 27			
Windsor & Eton Riverside	d				10 23			past						19 53								20 23		
Datchet	d				10 26			each						19 56								20 26		
Sunnymeads	d				10 29			hour until						19 59								20 29		
Wraysbury	d				10 32									20 02								20 32		
Staines	d			10 33	10 38					19 59			20 03	20 08				20 29			20 33	20 38		
Ashford (Surrey)	d			10 36	10 41								20 06	20 11							20 36	20 41		
Feltham	d			10 41	10 46					20 05			20 11	20 16				20 35			20 41	20 46		
Whitton	d	10 20			10 50		10 53				19 50			20 20		20 23			20 20			20 50		
Kingston	d		10 29									19 59								20 29				
Hampton Wick	d		10 31									20 01								20 31				
Teddington	d		10 35									20 05								20 35				
Fulwell	d																							
Strawberry Hill	d		10 38									20 08								20 38				
Twickenham	a		10 42		10 53		10 56			20 10		20 12		20 23		20 26		20 40		20 42		20 53		
	d		10 43		10 53		10 58			20 11		20 13		20 23		20 28		20 41		20 43		20 53		
St Margarets	d		10 45				11 00					20 15				20 30				20 45				
Richmond	⊖ d		10 49		10 58		11 04			20 15		20 19		20 28		20 34		20 45		20 49		20 58		
North Sheen	d		10 51				11 06					20 21				20 36				20 51				
Mortlake	d		10 53				11 08					20 23				20 38				20 53				
Hounslow	d	10 31		10 46							20 01		20 16						20 31		20 46			
Isleworth	d	10 34		10 49							20 04		20 19						20 34		20 49			
Syon Lane	d	10 36		10 51		←					20 06		20 21		←				20 36		20 51			←
Brentford	d	10 39		10 54 →		10 54					20 09		20 24 →		20 24				20 39		20 54 →			20 54
Kew Bridge	d	10 41				10 56					20 11				20 26				20 41					20 56
Chiswick	d	10 44				10 59					20 14				20 29				20 44					20 59
Barnes Bridge	d	10 46				11 01	10 29				20 16				20 31				20 46					21 01
Barnes	d	10 49	10 56			11 04	11 11				20 19	20 26			20 34	20 41			20 49	20 56				21 04
Putney	d	10 52	10 59		11 04	11 07	11 14				20 22	20 29		20 34	20 37	20 44			20 52	20 59		21 04		21 07
Wandsworth Town	d	10 55	11 02			11 10	11 17				20 25	20 32			20 40	20 47			20 55	21 02				21 10
Clapham Junction 10	d	10 58	11 05		11 09	11 13	11 20			20 24	20 28	20 35		20 39	20 43	20 50		20 54	20 58	21 05		21 09		21 13
Queenstown Rd.(Battersea)	d	11 01	11 08			11 16	10 14				20 31	20 38			20 46	20 53			21 01	21 08				21 16
Vauxhall	⊖ d	11 05	11 12		11 15	11 20	11 27				20 35	20 42		20 45	20 50	20 57			21 05	21 12		21 15		21 20
London Waterloo 15	⊖ a	11 11	11 16		11 19	11 26	11 32			20 34	20 41	20 46		20 49	20 56	21 02		21 04	21 11	21 16		21 19		21 26

For general notes see front of timetable
For details of catering facilities see
Directory of Train Operators

A From London Waterloo (Table 152)

§ Passengers to/from London may travel via Weybridge. See Table 155.

From 3 October due to seasonal difficulties a large number of trains on this table will have minor retimings that could mean slightly earlier departure or later arrival times at certain stations. For further details see local publicity or contact National Rail Enquiries 08457 48 49 50.

Table 149

Saturdays

Reading, Guildford, Ascot, Weybridge, Windsor, Kingston, Richmond and Hounslow → London

Network Diagram - see first page of Table 148

		SW	SW 1	SW	SW	SW	SW	SW 1	SW 1	SW	SW	SW 1	SW	SW	SW	SW	SW	SW	SW 1	SW	SW	SW	SW	SW 1	SW 1
						A								A								A			
Reading 7	d		20 12									20 42							21 12						
Earley	d		20 17									20 47							21 17						
Winnersh Triangle	d		20 19									20 49							21 19						
Winnersh	d		20 21									20 51							21 21						
Wokingham	d		20 26									20 56							21 26						
Bracknell	d		20 32									21 02							21 32						
Martins Heron	d		20 35									21 05							21 35						
Guildford	d							20 00	20 30															21 00	21 30
Wanborough	d							20 06	20 36															21 06	21 36
Ash 3	d							20 10	20 40															21 10	21 40
Aldershot	a							20 17	20 47															21 17	21 47
	d							20 30																21 30	
Ash Vale	d							20 34																21 34	
Frimley	d							20 40																21 40	
Camberley	a							20 44																21 44	
	d							20 48																21 48	
Bagshot	d							20 53																21 53	
Ascot 3	d		20 40					21a00				21 10							21 40					22a00	
Sunningdale	d		20 43									21 13							21 43						
Longcross	d																								
Woking	d																								
West Byfleet	d																								
Byfleet & New Haw	d																								
Weybridge	d				20 33										21 03						21 33				
Addlestone §	d				20 37										21 07						21 37				
Chertsey §	d				20 40										21 10						21 40				
Virginia Water	a		20 49		20 45							21 19			21 15				21 49		21 45				
	d		20 49		20 54							21 19			21 24				21 49		21 54				
Egham	d		20 53		20 57							21 23			21 27				21 53		21 57				
Windsor & Eton Riverside	d						20 53									21 23							21 53		
Datchet	d						20 56									21 26							21 56		
Sunnymeads	d						20 59									21 29							21 59		
Wraysbury	d						21 02									21 32							22 02		
Staines	d		20 59		21 03		21 08					21 29			21 33	21 38			21 59		22 03		22 08		
Ashford (Surrey)	d				21 06		21 11								21 36	21 41					22 06		22 11		
Feltham	d		21 05		21 11		21 16					21 35			21 41	21 46			22 05		22 11		22 16		
Whitton	d	20 53		20 50			21 20				21 23		21 20			21 50		21 53		21 50			22 20		
Kingston	d					20 59								21 29								21 59			
Hampton Wick	d					21 01								21 31								22 01			
Teddington	d					21 05								21 35								22 05			
Fulwell	d																								
Strawberry Hill	d					21 08								21 38								22 08			
Twickenham	a	20 56	21 10			21 12	21 23				21 26	21 40		21 42		21 53		21 56	22 10			22 12	22 23		
	d	20 58	21 11			21 13	21 23				21 28	21 41		21 43		21 53		21 58	22 11			22 13	22 23		
St Margarets	d	21 00				21 15					21 30			21 45				22 00				22 15			
Richmond	⊖ d	21 04	21 15			21 19	21 28				21 34	21 45		21 49		21 58		22 04	22 15			22 19	22 28		
North Sheen	d	21 06				21 21					21 36			21 51				22 06				22 21			
Mortlake	d	21 08				21 23					21 38			21 53				22 08				22 23			
Hounslow	d			21 01	21 16								21 31		21 46					22 01	22 16				
Isleworth	d			21 04	21 19								21 34		21 49					22 04	22 19				
Syon Lane	d			21 06	21 21					←			21 36		21 51		←			22 06	22 21				
Brentford	d			21 09	21 24					21 24			21 39		21 54		21 54			22 09	22 24				
Kew Bridge	d			21 11	→					21 26			21 41		→		21 56			22 11	→				
Chiswick	d			21 14						21 29			21 44				21 59			22 14					
Barnes Bridge	d			21 16						21 31			21 46				22 01			22 16					
Barnes	d	21 11		21 19		21 26				21 34	21 41		21 49	21 56			22 04	22 11		22 19		22 26			
Putney	d	21 14		21 22		21 29	21 34			21 37	21 44		21 52	21 59		22 04	22 07	22 14		22 22		22 29	22 34		
Wandsworth Town	d	21 17		21 25		21 32				21 40	21 47		21 55	22 02			22 10	22 17		22 25		22 32			
Clapham Junction 10	d	21 20	21 24	21 28		21 35	21 39			21 43	21 50	21 54	21 58	22 05		22 09	22 13	22 20	22 24	22 28		22 35	22 39		
Queenstown Rd.(Battersea)	d	21 23		21 31		21 38				21 46	21 53		22 01	22 08			22 16	22 23		22 31		22 38			
Vauxhall	⊖ d	21 27		21 35		21 42	21 45			21 50	21 57		22 05	22 12		22 15	22 20	22 27		22 35		22 42	22 45		
London Waterloo 15	⊖ a	21 32	21 34	21 41		21 46	21 49			21 56	22 02	22 04	22 11	22 16		22 19	22 26	22 32	22 34	22 41		22 46	22 49		

For general notes see front of timetable
For details of catering facilities see Directory of Train Operators

A From London Waterloo (Table 152)

§ Passengers to/from London may travel via Weybridge. See Table 155.

From 3 October due to seasonal difficulties a large number of trains on this table will have minor retimings that could mean slightly earlier departure or later arrival times at certain stations. For further details see local publicity or contact National Rail Enquiries 08457 48 49 50.

Saturdays

Reading, Guildford, Ascot, Weybridge, Windsor, Kingston, Richmond and Hounslow → London

Network Diagram - see first page of Table 148

	SW	SW	SW 1	SW A	SW	SW	SW	SW 1	SW	SW A	SW 1	SW 1	SW	SW	SW 1	SW A	SW	SW	SW A	SW 1	SW	SW 1	SW 1 B
Reading 7 d			21 42					22 12							22 42					23 12			
Earley d			21 47					22 17							22 47					23 17			
Winnersh Triangle d			21 49					22 19							22 49					23 19			
Winnersh d			21 51					22 21							22 51					23 21			
Wokingham d			21 56					22 26							22 56					23 26			
Bracknell d			22 02					22 32							23 02					23 32			
Martins Heron d			22 05					22 35							23 05					23 35			
Guildford d											22 00	22 30										23 00	23 30
Wanborough d											22 06	22 36										23 06	23 36
Ash 3 d											22 10	22 40										23 10	23 40
Aldershot a											22 17	22 47										23 17	23 47
d											22 30											23 30	
Ash Vale d											22 34											23 34	
Frimley d											22 40											23 40	
Camberley a											22 44											23 44	
d											22 48											23 48	
Bagshot d											22 53											23 53	
Ascot 3 d			22 10					22 40			23a00				23 10					23 40		00a01	
Sunningdale d			22 13					22 43							23 13					23 43			
Longcross d																							
Woking d																							
West Byfleet d																							
Byfleet & New Haw d																							
Weybridge d					22 03				22 33								23 03				23 33		
Addlestone § d					22 07				22 37								23 07				23 37		
Chertsey § d					22 10				22 40								23 10				23 40		
Virginia Water a			22 19		22 15			22 49	22 45						23 19		23 15			23 49	23 45		
d			22 19		22 24			22 49	22 54						23 19		23 24			23 49	23 54		
Egham d			22 23		22 27			22 53	22 57						23 23		23 27			23 53	23 57		
Windsor & Eton Riverside d						22 23							22 53					23 23					
Datchet d						22 26							22 56					23 26					
Sunnymeads d						22 29							22 59					23 29					
Wraysbury d						22 32							23 02					23 32					
Staines d			22 29		22 33	22 38		22 59	23 03				23 08		23 29		23a32	23a37		23 59	00a02		
Ashford (Surrey) d					22 36	22 41			23 06				23 11										
Feltham d			22 35		22 41	22 46		23 05	23 11				23 16		23 35					00 05			
Whitton d		22 23				22 50							23 20										
Kingston d				22 29						22 59						23 29			23 55				
Hampton Wick d				22 31						23 01						23 31			23 57				
Teddington d				22 35						23 05						23 35			23 59				
Fulwell d																							
Strawberry Hill d				22 38						23 08						23 38			00 03				
Twickenham a		22 26	22 40	22 42		22 53		23 10		23 12			23 23		23 40	23 42			00 07	00 10			
d		22 28	22 41	22 43		22 53		23 11		23 13			23 23		23 41	23 43				00 11			
St Margarets d		22 30		22 45						23 15						23 45							
Richmond ⊖ d		22 34	22 45	22 49		22 58		23 15		23 19			23 28		23 45	23 49				00 15			
North Sheen d		22 36		22 51						23 21						23 51							
Mortlake d		22 38		22 53						23 23						23 53							
Hounslow d					22 46				23 16														
Isleworth d					22 49				23 19														
Syon Lane d	←				22 51		←		23 21					←									
Brentford d	22 24				22 54 →		22 54		23 24 →					23 24									
Kew Bridge d	22 26						22 56							23 26									
Chiswick d	22 29						22 59							23 29									
Barnes Bridge d	22 31						23 01							23 31									
Barnes d	22 34	22 41		22 56			23 04			23 26				23 34		23 56							
Putney d	22 37	22 44		22 59		23 04	23 07			23 29			23 34	23 37		23 59							
Wandsworth Town d	22 40	22 47		23 02			23 10			23 32				23 40		00 02							
Clapham Junction 10 d	22 43	22 50	22 54	23 05		23 09	23 13	23 24		23 35			23 39	23 43	23 54	00 05				00 24			
Queenstown Rd.(Battersea) d	22 46	22 53		23 08			23 16			23 38				23 46		00 08							
Vauxhall ⊖ d	22 50	22 57		23 12		23 15	23 20			23 42			23 45	23 50		00 12							
London Waterloo 15 ⊖ a	22 56	23 02	23 04	23 16		23 19	23 26	23 34		23 46			23 49	23 56	00 02	00 16				00 33			

For general notes see front of timetable
For details of catering facilities see Directory of Train Operators

A From London Waterloo (Table 152)
B To Farnham (Table 155)

§ Passengers to/from London may travel via Weybridge. See Table 155.

From 3 October due to seasonal difficulties a large number of trains on this table will have minor retimings that could mean slightly earlier departure or later arrival times at certain stations. For further details see local publicity or contact National Rail Enquiries 08457 48 49 50.

Reading, Guildford, Ascot, Weybridge, Windsor, Kingston, Richmond and Hounslow → London

Network Diagram - see first page of Table 148

		SW	SW	SW	SW	SW	SW	SW		SW	SW	SW	SW	SW	SW	SW		SW	SW	SW	SW	SW	SW	SW	SW
				1									1	1		1				1	1		1		
		A	A		A	A				A					A							A			
Reading 7	d			23p12										07 54		08 24					08 54		09 24		
Earley	d			23p17										07 59		08 29					08 59		09 29		
Winnersh Triangle	d			23p19										08 01		08 31					09 01		09 31		
Winnersh	d			23p21										08 03		08 33					09 03		09 33		
Wokingham	d			23p26										08 08		08 38					09 08		09 38		
Bracknell	d			23p32										08 14		08 44					09 14		09 44		
Martins Heron	d			23p35										08 17		08 47					09 17		09 47		
Guildford	d												07 17							08 17					
Wanborough	d												07 23							08 23					
Ash 3	d												07 27							08 27					
Aldershot	a												07 34							08 34					
	d												07 40							08 40					
Ash Vale	d												07 45							08 45					
Frimley	d												07 51							08 51					
Camberley	a												07 55							08 55					
	d												07 55							08 55					
Bagshot	d												08 01							09 01					
Ascot 3	d			23p40									08a07	08 22		08 52				09a07	09 22		09 52		
Sunningdale	d			23p43										08 25		08 55					09 25		09 55		
Longcross	d																								
Woking	d											07 52							08 52						09 52
West Byfleet	d											07 56							08 56						09 56
Byfleet & New Haw	d											08 00							09 00						10 00
Weybridge	d							07 00																	
Addlestone §	d							07 04				08 04							09 04						10 04
Chertsey §	d							07 07				08 07							09 07						10 07
Virginia Water	a			23p49				07 12				08 12		08 30		09 00			09 12		09 30		10 00		10 12
	d			23p49				07 12				08 12		08 30		09 00			09 12		09 30		10 00		10 12
Egham	d			23p53				07 16				08 16		08 34		09 04			09 16		09 34		10 04		10 16
Windsor & Eton Riverside	d						07 01				08 01							09 01						10 01	
Datchet	d						07 04				08 04							09 04						10 04	
Sunnymeads	d						07 07				08 07							09 07						10 07	
Wraysbury	d						07 10				08 10							09 10						10 10	
Staines	d			23p59			07 16	07 21			08 16	08 21		08 39		09 09		09 16	09 21		09 39		10 09	10 16	10 21
Ashford (Surrey)	d						07 19	07 24			08 19	08 24						09 19	09 24					10 19	10 24
Feltham	d			00 05			07 24	07 29			08 24	08 29		08 46		09 16		09 24	09 29		09 46		10 16	10 24	10 29
Whitton	d						07 28				08 28							09 28						10 28	
Kingston	d	23p29	23p55		02 09	06 49				07 49					08 49							09 49			
Hampton Wick	d	23p31	23p57			06 51				07 51					08 51							09 51			
Teddington	d	23p35	23p59			06 56				07 56					08 56							09 56			
Fulwell	d																								
Strawberry Hill	d	23p38	00 03		02s16	06 59				07 59					08 59							09 59			
Twickenham	a	23p42	00 07	00 10	02 20	07 02	07 31			08 02	08 31			08 51	09 02	09 21		09 31			09 51	10 02	10 21	10 31	
	d	23p43		00 11		07 03	07 32			08 03	08 32			08 51	09 03	09 21		09 32			09 51	10 03	10 21	10 32	
St Margarets	d	23p45				07 05	07 34			08 05	08 34				09 05			09 34				10 05		10 34	
Richmond	⊖ d	23p49		00 15		07 09	07 37			08 09	08 37			08 56	09 09	09 26		09 37			09 56	10 09	10 26	10 37	
North Sheen	d	23p51				07 11	07 39			08 11	08 39				09 11			09 39				10 11		10 39	
Mortlake	d	23p53				07 13	07 42			08 13	08 42				09 13			09 42				10 13		10 42	
Hounslow	d							07 35				08 35							09 35						10 35
Isleworth	d							07 38				08 38							09 38						10 38
Syon Lane	d							07 40				08 40							09 40						10 40
Brentford	d							07 42				08 42							09 42						10 42
Kew Bridge	d							07 45				08 45							09 45						10 45
Chiswick	d							07 47				08 47							09 47						10 47
Barnes Bridge	d							07 50				08 50							09 50						10 50
Barnes	d	23p56				07 16	07 45	07 53		08 16	08 45	08 53			09 16			09 45	09 53			10 16		10 45	10 53
Putney	d	23p59				07 19	07 48	07 56		08 19	08 48	08 56		09 02	09 19	09 32		09 48	09 56		10 02	10 19	10 32	10 48	10 56
Wandsworth Town	d	00 02				07 22	07 51	07 59		08 22	08 51	08 59			09 22			09 51	09 59			10 22		10 51	10 59
Clapham Junction 10	d	00 05		00 24		07 25	07 54	08 02		08 25	08 54	09 02		09 07	09 25	09 37		09 54	10 02		10 07	10 25	10 37	10 54	11 04
Queenstown Rd.(Battersea)	d	00 08				07 28	07 57	08 05		08 28	08 57	09 05			09 28			09 57	10 05			10 28		10 58	11 09
Vauxhall	⊖ d	00 12				07 32	08 00	08 08		08 32	09 00	09 08		09 12	09 32	09 42		10 00	10 08		10 12	10 32	10 42	11 02	11 13
London Waterloo 15	⊖ a	00 16		00 33		07 41	08 11	08 13		08 41	09 10	09 13		09 23	09 41	09 53		10 10	10 13		10 23	10 41	10 53	11 10	11 19

For general notes see front of timetable
For details of catering facilities see
Directory of Train Operators

A From London Waterloo (Table 152)

§ Passengers to/from London may travel via Weybridge. See Table 155.

From 27 September due to seasonal difficulties a large number of trains on this table will have minor retimings that could mean slightly earlier departure or later arrival times at certain stations. For further details see local publicity or contact National Rail Enquiries 08457 48 49 50.

Reading, Guildford, Ascot, Weybridge, Windsor, Kingston, Richmond and Hounslow → London

Network Diagram - see first page of Table 148

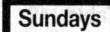

		SW 1	SW 1	SW	SW	SW 1	SW	SW	SW 1	SW 1	SW	SW	SW 1	SW	SW	SW 1	SW 1	SW	SW	SW 1	SW	SW
					A							A							A			
Reading 7	d		09 54			10 24				10 54			11 24				11 54			12 24		
Earley	d		09 59			10 29				10 59			11 29				11 59			12 29		
Winnersh Triangle	d		10 01			10 31				11 01			11 31				12 01			12 31		
Winnersh	d		10 03			10 33				11 03			11 33				12 03			12 33		
Wokingham	d		10 08			10 38				11 08			11 38				12 08			12 38		
Bracknell	d		10 14			10 44				11 14			11 44				12 14			12 44		
Martins Heron	d		10 17			10 47				11 17			11 47				12 17			12 47		
Guildford	d	09 17							10 17							11 17						
Wanborough	d	09 23							10 23							11 23						
Ash 3	d	09 27							10 27							11 27						
Aldershot	a	09 34							10 34							11 34						
	d	09 40							10 40							11 40						
Ash Vale	d	09 45							10 45							11 45						
Frimley	d	09 51							10 51							11 51						
Camberley	a	09 55							10 55							11 55						
	d	09 55							10 55							11 55						
Bagshot	d	10 01							11 01							12 01						
Ascot 3	d	10a07	10 22			10 52			11a07	11 22			11 52			12a07	12 22			12 52		
Sunningdale	d		10 25			10 55				11 25			11 55				12 25			12 55		
Longcross	d																					
Woking	d							10 52							11 52							
West Byfleet	d							10 56							11 56							
Byfleet & New Haw	d							11 00							12 00							
Weybridge	d																					
Addlestone §	d							11 04							12 04							
Chertsey §	d							11 07							12 07							
Virginia Water	a		10 30			11 00		11 12		11 30			12 00		12 12		12 30			13 00		
	d		10 30			11 00		11 12		11 30			12 00		12 12		12 30			13 00		
Egham	d		10 34			11 04		11 16		11 34			12 04		12 16		12 34			13 04		
Windsor & Eton Riverside	d			10 34			11 01				11 34			12 01				12 34				13 01
Datchet	d			10 37			11 04				11 37			12 04				12 37				13 04
Sunnymeads	d						11 07							12 07								13 07
Wraysbury	d						11 10							12 10								13 10
Staines	d		10 39	10 45		11 09	11 16	11 21		11 39	11 45		12 09	12 16	12 21		12 39	12 45		13 09		13 16
Ashford (Surrey)	d			10 48			11 19	11 24			11 48			12 19	12 24			12 48				13 19
Feltham	d		10 46	10 53		11 16	11 24	11 29		11 46	11 53		12 16	12 24	12 29		12 46	12 53		13 16		13 24
Whitton	d			10 57			11 28				11 57			12 28				12 57				13 28
Kingston	d				10 49							11 49							12 49		13 11	
Hampton Wick	d				10 51							11 51							12 51		13 13	
Teddington	d				10 56							11 56							12 56		13 16	
Fulwell	d																					
Strawberry Hill	d				10 59							11 59							12 59		13 19	
Twickenham	a		10 51	11 00	11 02	11 21	11 31			11 51	12 00	12 02	12 21	12 31			12 51	13 00	13 02	13 21	13 22	13 31
	d		10 51	11 01	11 03	11 21	11 32			11 51	12 01	12 03	12 21	12 32			12 51	13 01	13 03	13 21	13 23	13 32
St Margarets	d				11 05		11 34					12 05		12 34					13 05		13 25	13 34
Richmond	⊖ d		10 56	11 05	11 09	11 26	11 37			11 56	12 05	12 09	12 26	12 37			12 56	13 05	13 09	13 26	13 29	13 37
North Sheen	d				11 11		11 39					12 11		12 39					13 11		13 31	13 39
Mortlake	d				11 13		11 42					12 13		12 42					13 13		13 33	13 42
Hounslow	d							11 35							12 35							
Isleworth	d							11 38							12 38							
Syon Lane	d							11 40							12 40							
Brentford	d							11 42							12 42							
Kew Bridge	d							11 45							12 45							
Chiswick	d							11 47							12 47							
Barnes Bridge	d							11 50							12 50							
Barnes	d				11 16		11 45	11 53				12 16		12 45	12 53				13 16		13 36	13 45
Putney	d		11 02	11 14	11 19	11 32	11 48	11 56		12 02	12 14	12 19	12 32	12 48	12 56		13 02	13 14	13 19	13 32	13 39	13 48
Wandsworth Town	d				11 22		11 51	11 59				12 22		12 51	12 59				13 22		13 42	13 51
Clapham Junction 10	d		11 07	11 18	11 25	11 37	11 54	12 04		12 07	12 18	12 25	12 37	12 54	13 02		13 07	13 18	13 25	13 37	13 45	13 54
Queenstown Rd.(Battersea)	d				11 33		11 58	12 09				12 33		12 58	13 05				13 28		13 48	13 57
Vauxhall	⊖ d		11 16	11 26	11 37	11 45	12 02	12 13		12 16	12 26	12 37	12 45	13 02	13 08		13 12	13 24	13 32	13 42	13 52	14 00
London Waterloo 15	⊖ a		11 23	11 34	11 41	11 53	12 10	12 19		12 23	12 34	12 41	12 53	13 10	13 13		13 23	13 34	13 41	13 53	14 00	14 10

For general notes see front of timetable
For details of catering facilities see Directory of Train Operators

A From London Waterloo (Table 152)

§ Passengers to/from London may travel via Weybridge. See Table 155.

From 27 September due to seasonal difficulties a large number of trains on this table will have minor retimings that could mean slightly earlier departure or later arrival times at certain stations. For further details see local publicity or contact National Rail Enquiries 08457 48 49 50.

Table 149

Sundays

Reading, Guildford, Ascot, Weybridge, Windsor, Kingston, Richmond and Hounslow → London

Network Diagram - see first page of Table 148

		SW	SW 1	SW 1		SW	SW A	SW 1	SW	SW	SW	SW 1		SW 1	SW	SW A	SW 1	SW	SW	SW		SW 1	SW 1	SW	SW A
Reading 7	d			12 54				13 24						13 54			14 24						14 54		
Earley	d			12 59				13 29						13 59			14 29						14 59		
Winnersh Triangle	d			13 01				13 31						14 01			14 31						15 01		
Winnersh	d			13 03				13 33						14 03			14 33						15 03		
Wokingham	d			13 08				13 38						14 08			14 38						15 08		
Bracknell	d			13 14				13 44						14 14			14 44						15 14		
Martins Heron	d			13 17				13 47						14 17			14 47						15 17		
Guildford	d		12 17									13 17										14 17			
Wanborough	d		12 23									13 23										14 23			
Ash 3	d		12 27									13 27										14 27			
Aldershot	a		12 34									13 34										14 34			
	d		12 40									13 40										14 40			
Ash Vale	d		12 45									13 45										14 45			
Frimley	d		12 51									13 51										14 51			
Camberley	a		12 55									13 55										14 55			
	d		12 55									13 55										14 55			
Bagshot	d		13 01									14 01										15 01			
Ascot 3	d		13a07	13 22				13 52				14a07		14 22			14 52					15a07	15 22		
Sunningdale	d			13 25				13 55						14 25			14 55						15 25		
Longcross	d																								
Woking	d	12 52									13 52									14 52					
West Byfleet	d	12 56									13 56									14 56					
Byfleet & New Haw	d	13 00									14 00									15 00					
Weybridge	d																								
Addlestone §	d	13 04									14 04									15 04					
Chertsey §	d	13 07									14 07									15 07					
Virginia Water	a	13 12		13 30				14 00			14 12			14 30			15 00			15 12			15 30		
	d	13 12		13 30				14 00			14 12			14 30			15 00			15 12			15 30		
Egham	d	13 16		13 34				14 04			14 16			14 34			15 04			15 16			15 34		
Windsor & Eton Riverside	d					13 34				14 01					14 34				15 01					15 34	
Datchet	d					13 37				14 04					14 37				15 04					15 37	
Sunnymeads	d									14 07									15 07						
Wraysbury	d									14 10									15 10						
Staines	d	13 21		13 39		13 45		14 09		14 16	14 21			14 39	14 45		15 09		15 16	15 21			15 39	15 45	
Ashford (Surrey)	d	13 24				13 48				14 19	14 24				14 48				15 19	15 24				15 48	
Feltham	d	13 29		13 46		13 53		14 16		14 24	14 29			14 46	14 53		15 16		15 24	15 29			15 46	15 53	
Whitton	d					13 57				14 28					14 57				15 28					15 57	
Kingston	d						13 49		14 11							14 49		15 11							15 49
Hampton Wick	d						13 51		14 13							14 51		15 13							15 51
Teddington	d						13 56		14 16							14 56		15 16							15 56
Fulwell	d																								
Strawberry Hill	d						13 59		14 19							14 59		15 19							15 59
Twickenham	a			13 51		14 00	14 02	14 21	14 22	14 31				14 51	15 00	15 02	15 21	15 22	15 31				15 51	16 00	16 02
	d			13 51		14 01	14 03	14 21	14 23	14 32				14 51	15 01	15 03	15 21	15 23	15 32				15 51	16 01	16 03
St Margarets	d						14 05		14 25	14 34						15 05		15 25	15 34						16 05
Richmond	⊖ d			13 56		14 05	14 09	14 26	14 29	14 37				14 56	15 05	15 09	15 26	15 29	15 37				15 56	16 05	16 09
North Sheen	d						14 11		14 31	14 39						15 11		15 31	15 39						16 11
Mortlake	d						14 13		14 33	14 42						15 13		15 33	15 42						16 13
Hounslow	d	13 35									14 35									15 35					
Isleworth	d	13 38									14 38									15 38					
Syon Lane	d	13 40									14 40									15 40					
Brentford	d	13 42									14 42									15 42					
Kew Bridge	d	13 45									14 45									15 45					
Chiswick	d	13 47									14 47									15 47					
Barnes Bridge	d	13 50									14 50									15 50					
Barnes	d	13 53					14 16		14 36	14 45	14 53					15 16		15 36	15 45	15 53					16 16
Putney	d	13 56		14 02		14 14	14 19	14 32	14 39	14 48	14 56			15 02	15 14	15 19	15 32	15 39	15 48	15 56			16 02	16 14	16 19
Wandsworth Town	d	13 59					14 22		14 42	14 51	14 59					15 22		15 42	15 51	15 59					16 22
Clapham Junction 10	d	14 02		14 07		14 18	14 25	14 37	14 45	14 54	15 02			15 07	15 18	15 25	15 37	15 45	15 54	16 02			16 07	16 18	16 25
Queenstown Rd.(Battersea)	d	14 05					14 28		14 48	14 57	15 05					15 28		15 48	15 57	16 05					16 28
Vauxhall	⊖ d	14 08		14 12		14 24	14 32	14 42	14 52	15 00	15 08			15 12	15 24	15 32	15 42	15 52	16 00	16 08			16 12	16 24	16 32
London Waterloo 15	⊖ a	14 13		14 23		14 29	14 36	14 48	15 00	15 05	15 13			15 18	15 29	15 36	15 48	16 00	16 05	16 13			16 18	16 29	16 36

For general notes see front of timetable
For details of catering facilities see
Directory of Train Operators

A From London Waterloo (Table 152)

§ Passengers to/from London may travel via Weybridge. See Table 155.

From 27 September due to seasonal difficulties a large number of trains on this table will have minor retimings that could mean slightly earlier departure or later arrival times at certain stations. For further details see local publicity or contact National Rail Enquiries 08457 48 49 50.

Table 149

Sundays

Reading, Guildford, Ascot, Weybridge, Windsor, Kingston, Richmond and Hounslow → London

Network Diagram - see first page of Table 148

		SW [1]	SW	SW	SW	SW [1]		SW [1]	SW	SW	SW [1]	SW	SW	SW		SW [1]	SW [1]	SW	SW	SW [1]	SW	SW		SW	SW [1]
										A									A						
Reading [7]	d	15 24						15 54			16 24						16 54			17 24					
Earley	d	15 29						15 59			16 29						16 59			17 29					
Winnersh Triangle	d	15 31						16 01			16 31						17 01			17 31					
Winnersh	d	15 33						16 03			16 33						17 03			17 33					
Wokingham	d	15 38						16 08			16 38						17 08			17 38					
Bracknell	d	15 44						16 14			16 44						17 14			17 44					
Martins Heron	d	15 47						16 17			16 47						17 17			17 47					
Guildford	d					15 17										16 17									17 17
Wanborough	d					15 23										16 23									17 23
Ash [3]	d					15 27										16 27									17 27
Aldershot	a					15 34										16 34									17 34
	d					15 40										16 40									17 40
Ash Vale	d					15 45										16 45									17 45
Frimley	d					15 51										16 51									17 51
Camberley	a					15 55										16 55									17 55
	d					15 55										16 55									17 55
Bagshot	d					16 01										17 01									18 01
Ascot [3]	d	15 52				16a07		16 22			16 52					17a07	17 22			17 52					18a07
Sunningdale	d	15 55						16 25			16 55						17 25			17 55					
Longcross	d																								
Woking	d				15 52									16 52										17 52	
West Byfleet	d				15 56									16 56										17 56	
Byfleet & New Haw	d				16 00									17 00										18 00	
Weybridge	d																								
Addlestone §	d				16 04									17 04										18 04	
Chertsey §	d				16 07									17 07										18 07	
Virginia Water	a	16 00			16 12			16 30			17 00			17 12			17 30			18 00				18 12	
	d	16 00			16 12			16 30			17 00			17 12			17 30			18 00				18 12	
Egham	d	16 04			16 16			16 34			17 04			17 16			17 34			18 04				18 16	
Windsor & Eton Riverside	d			16 01					16 34				17 01					17 34				18 01			
Datchet	d			16 04					16 37				17 04					17 37				18 04			
Sunnymeads	d			16 07									17 07									18 07			
Wraysbury	d			16 10									17 10									18 10			
Staines	d	16 09		16 16	16 21			16 39	16 45		17 09		17 16	17 21			17 39	17 45		18 09		18 16		18 21	
Ashford (Surrey)	d			16 19	16 24				16 48				17 19	17 24				17 48				18 19		18 24	
Feltham	d	16 16		16 24	16 29			16 46	16 53		17 16		17 24	17 29			17 46	17 53		18 16		18 24		18 29	
Whitton	d			16 28					16 57				17 28					17 57				18 28			
Kingston	d		16 11							16 49		17 11							17 49		18 11				
Hampton Wick	d		16 13							16 51		17 13							17 51		18 13				
Teddington	d		16 16							16 56		17 16							17 56		18 16				
Fulwell	d																								
Strawberry Hill	d		16 19							16 59		17 19							17 59		18 19				
Twickenham	a	16 21	16 22	16 31				16 51	17 00	17 02	17 21	17 22	17 31				17 51	18 00	18 02	18 21	18 22	18 31			
	d	16 21	16 23	16 32				16 51	17 01	17 03	17 21	17 23	17 32				17 51	18 01	18 03	18 21	18 23	18 32			
St Margarets	d		16 25	16 34						17 05		17 25	17 34						18 05		18 25	18 34			
Richmond ⊖	d	16 26	16 29	16 37				16 56	17 05	17 09	17 26	17 29	17 37				17 56	18 05	18 09	18 26	18 29	18 37			
North Sheen	d		16 31	16 39						17 11		17 31	17 39						18 11		18 31	18 39			
Mortlake	d		16 33	16 42						17 13		17 33	17 42						18 13		18 33	18 42			
Hounslow	d				16 35									17 35										18 35	
Isleworth	d				16 38									17 38										18 38	
Syon Lane	d				16 40									17 40										18 40	
Brentford	d				16 42									17 42										18 42	
Kew Bridge	d				16 45									17 45										18 45	
Chiswick	d				16 47									17 47										18 47	
Barnes Bridge	d				16 50									17 50										18 50	
Barnes	d		16 36	16 45	16 53					17 16		17 36	17 45	17 53					18 16		18 36	18 45		18 53	
Putney	d	16 32	16 39	16 48	16 56			17 02	17 14	17 19	17 32	17 39	17 48	17 56			18 02	18 14	18 19	18 32	18 39	18 48		18 56	
Wandsworth Town	d		16 42	16 51	16 59					17 22		17 42	17 51	17 59					18 22		18 42	18 51		18 59	
Clapham Junction [10]	d	16 37	16 45	16 54	17 02			17 07	17 18	17 25	17 37	17 45	17 54	18 02			18 07	18 18	18 25	18 37	18 45	18 54		19 02	
Queenstown Rd.(Battersea)	d		16 48	16 57	17 05					17 28		17 48	17 57	18 05					18 28		18 48	18 57		19 05	
Vauxhall ⊖	d	16 42	16 52	17 00	17 08			17 12	17 24	17 32	17 42	17 52	18 00	18 08			18 12	18 24	18 32	18 42	18 52	19 00		19 08	
London Waterloo [15] ⊖	a	16 48	17 00	17 05	17 13			17 18	17 29	17 36	17 48	18 00	18 05	18 13			18 18	18 29	18 36	18 48	19 00	19 05		19 13	

For general notes see front of timetable
For details of catering facilities see Directory of Train Operators

A From London Waterloo (Table 152)

§ Passengers to/from London may travel via Weybridge. See Table 155.

From 27 September due to seasonal difficulties a large number of trains on this table will have minor retimings that could mean slightly earlier departure or later arrival times at certain stations. For further details see local publicity or contact National Rail Enquiries 08457 48 49 50.

Reading, Guildford, Ascot, Weybridge, Windsor, Kingston, Richmond and Hounslow → London

Network Diagram - see first page of Table 148

		SW 1	SW	SW	SW 1	SW	SW	SW		SW 1	SW 1	SW	SW	SW 1	SW	SW		SW	SW 1	SW 1	SW	SW	SW 1	SW	SW
				A									A									A			
Reading 7	d	17 54			18 24						18 54			19 24						19 54			20 24		
Earley	d	17 59			18 29						18 59			19 29						19 59			20 29		
Winnersh Triangle	d	18 01			18 31						19 01			19 31						20 01			20 31		
Winnersh	d	18 03			18 33						19 03			19 33						20 03			20 33		
Wokingham	d	18 08			18 38						19 08			19 38						20 08			20 38		
Bracknell	d	18 14			18 44						19 14			19 44						20 14			20 44		
Martins Heron	d	18 17			18 47						19 17			19 47						20 17			20 47		
Guildford	d									18 17									19 17						
Wanborough	d									18 23									19 23						
Ash 3	d									18 27									19 27						
Aldershot	a									18 34									19 34						
	d									18 40									19 40						
Ash Vale	d									18 45									19 45						
Frimley	d									18 51									19 51						
Camberley	a									18 55									19 55						
	d									18 55									19 55						
Bagshot	d									19 01									20 01						
Ascot 3	d	18 22			18 52					19a07	19 22			19 52					20a07	20 22			20 52		
Sunningdale	d	18 25			18 55						19 25			19 55						20 25			20 55		
Longcross	d																								
Woking	d							18 52										19 52							
West Byfleet	d							18 56										19 56							
Byfleet & New Haw	d							19 00										20 00							
Weybridge	d																								
Addlestone §	d							19 04										20 04							
Chertsey §	d							19 07										20 07							
Virginia Water	a	18 30			19 00			19 12			19 30			20 00				20 12		20 30			21 00		
	d	18 30			19 00			19 12			19 30			20 00				20 12		20 30			21 00		
Egham	d	18 34			19 04			19 16			19 34			20 04				20 16		20 34			21 04		
Windsor & Eton Riverside	d		18 34				19 01					19 34				20 01					20 34				21 01
Datchet	d		18 37				19 04					19 37				20 04					20 37				21 04
Sunnymeads	d						19 07									20 07									21 07
Wraysbury	d						19 10									20 10									21 10
Staines	d	18 39	18 45		19 09		19 16	19 21			19 39	19 45		20 09		20 16		20 21		20 39	20 45		21 09		21 16
Ashford (Surrey)	d		18 48				19 19	19 24				19 48				20 19		20 24			20 48				21 19
Feltham	d	18 46	18 53		19 16		19 24	19 29			19 46	19 53		20 16		20 24		20 29		20 46	20 53		21 16		21 24
Whitton	d		18 57				19 28					19 57				20 28					20 57				21 28
Kingston	d			18 49		19 11							19 49		20 11							20 49		21 11	
Hampton Wick	d			18 51		19 13							19 51		20 13							20 51		21 13	
Teddington	d			18 56		19 16							19 56		20 16							20 56		21 16	
Fulwell	d																								
Strawberry Hill	d			18 59		19 19							19 59		20 19							20 59		21 19	
Twickenham	a	18 51	19 00	19 02	19 21	19 22	19 31				19 51	20 00	20 02	20 21	20 22	20 31				20 51	21 00	21 02	21 21	21 22	21 31
	d	18 51	19 01	19 03	19 21	19 23	19 32				19 51	20 01	20 03	20 21	20 23	20 32				20 51	21 01	21 03	21 21	21 23	21 32
St Margarets	d			19 05		19 25	19 34						20 05		20 25	20 34						21 05		21 25	21 34
Richmond	⊖ d	18 56	19 05	19 09	19 26	19 29	19 37				19 56	20 05	20 09	20 26	20 29	20 37				20 56	21 05	21 09	21 26	21 29	21 37
North Sheen	d			19 11		19 31	19 39						20 11		20 31	20 39						21 11		21 31	21 39
Mortlake	d			19 13		19 33	19 42						20 13		20 33	20 42						21 13		21 33	21 42
Hounslow	d							19 35										20 35							
Isleworth	d							19 38										20 38							
Syon Lane	d							19 40										20 40							
Brentford	d							19 42										20 42							
Kew Bridge	d							19 45										20 45							
Chiswick	d							19 47										20 47							
Barnes Bridge	d							19 50										20 50							
Barnes	d			19 16		19 36	19 45	19 53					20 16		20 36	20 45		20 53				21 16		21 36	21 45
Putney	d	19 02	19 14	19 19	19 32	19 39	19 48	19 56			20 02	20 14	20 19	20 32	20 39	20 48		20 56		21 02	21 14	21 19	21 32	21 39	21 48
Wandsworth Town	d			19 22		19 42	19 51	19 59					20 22		20 42	20 51		20 59				21 22		21 42	21 51
Clapham Junction 10	d	19 07	19 18	19 25	19 37	19 45	19 54	20 02			20 07	20 18	20 25	20 37	20 45	20 54		21 02		21 07	21 18	21 25	21 37	21 45	21 54
Queenstown Rd.(Battersea)	d			19 28		19 48	19 57	20 05					20 28		20 48	20 57		21 05				21 28		21 48	21 57
Vauxhall	⊖ d	19 12	19 24	19 32	19 42	19 52	20 00	20 08			20 12	20 24	20 32	20 42	20 52	21 00		21 08		21 12	21 24	21 32	21 42	21 52	22 00
London Waterloo 15	⊖ a	19 18	19 29	19 36	19 48	20 00	20 05	20 13			20 18	20 29	20 36	20 48	21 00	21 05		21 13		21 18	21 29	21 36	21 48	22 00	22 05

For general notes see front of timetable
For details of catering facilities see Directory of Train Operators

A From London Waterloo (Table 152)

§ Passengers to/from London may travel via Weybridge. See Table 155.

From 27 September due to seasonal difficulties a large number of trains on this table will have minor retimings that could mean slightly earlier departure or later arrival times at certain stations. For further details see local publicity or contact National Rail Enquiries 08457 48 49 50.

Sundays

Reading, Guildford, Ascot, Weybridge, Windsor, Kingston, Richmond and Hounslow → London

Network Diagram - see first page of Table 148

		SW		SW 1	SW 1	SW	SW 1	SW	SW	SW		SW 1	SW 1	SW	SW 1	SW	SW	SW		SW 1	SW 1	SW 1			
						A								A											
Reading 7	d				20 54		21 24						21 54		22 24							22 54			
Earley	d				20 59		21 29						21 59		22 29							22 59			
Winnersh Triangle	d				21 01		21 31						22 01		22 31							23 01			
Winnersh	d				21 03		21 33						22 03		22 33							23 03			
Wokingham	d				21 08		21 38						22 08		22 38							23 08			
Bracknell	d				21 14		21 44						22 14		22 44							23 14			
Martins Heron	d				21 17		21 47						22 17		22 47							23 17			
Guildford	d			20 17								21 17								22 17	23 17				
Wanborough	d			20 23								21 23								22 23	23 23				
Ash 3	d			20 27								21 27								22 27	23 27				
Aldershot	a			20 34								21 34								22 34	23 34				
	d			20 40								21 40								22 40					
Ash Vale	d			20 45								21 45								22 45					
Frimley	d			20 51								21 51								22 51					
Camberley	a			20 55								21 55								22 55					
	d			20 55								21 55								22 55					
Bagshot	d			21 01								22 01								23 01					
Ascot 3	d			21a07	21 22		21 52					22a07	22 22		22 52					23a07		23 22			
Sunningdale	d				21 25		21 55						22 25		22 55							23 25			
Longcross	d																								
Woking	d	20 52								21 52								22 52							
West Byfleet	d	20 56								21 56								22 56							
Byfleet & New Haw	d	21 00								22 00								23 00							
Weybridge	d																								
Addlestone §	d	21 04								22 04								23 04							
Chertsey §	d	21 07								22 07								23 07							
Virginia Water	a	21 12			21 30		22 00			22 12			22 30		23 00			23 12				23 30			
	d	21 12			21 30		22 00			22 12			22 30		23 00			23 12				23 30			
Egham	d	21 16			21 34		22 04			22 16			22 34		23 04			23 16				23 34			
Windsor & Eton Riverside	d								22 01								23 01								
Datchet	d								22 04								23 04								
Sunnymeads	d								22 07								23 07								
Wraysbury	d								22 10								23 10								
Staines	d	21 21			21 39		22 09		22 16	22 21			22 39		23 09		23 16	23 21				23 39			
Ashford (Surrey)	d	21 24							22 19	22 24							23 19	23 24							
Feltham	d	21 29			21 46		22 16		22 24	22 29			22 46		23 16		23 24	23 29				23 46			
Whitton	d								22 28								23 28								
Kingston	d					21 49		22 11						22 49		23 11									
Hampton Wick	d					21 51		22 13						22 51		23 13									
Teddington	d					21 56		22 16						22 56		23 16									
Fulwell	d																								
Strawberry Hill	d					21 59		22 19						22 59		23 19									
Twickenham	a				21 51	22 02	22 21	22 22	22 31				22 51	23 02	23 21	23 22	23 31					23 51			
	d				21 51	22 03	22 21	22 23	22 32				22 51	23 03	23 21	23 23	23 32					23 51			
St Margarets	d					22 05		22 25	22 34					23 05		23 25	23 34								
Richmond	⊖ d				21 56	22 09	22 26	22 29	22 37				22 56	23 09	23 26	23 29	23 37					23 56			
North Sheen	d					22 11		22 31	22 39					23 11		23 31	23 39								
Mortlake	d					22 13		22 33	22 42					23 13		23 33	23 42								
Hounslow	d	21 35								22 35								23 35							
Isleworth	d	21 38								22 38								23 38							
Syon Lane	d	21 40								22 40								23 40							
Brentford	d	21 42								22 42								23 42							
Kew Bridge	d	21 45								22 45								23 45							
Chiswick	d	21 47								22 47								23 47							
Barnes Bridge	d	21 50								22 50								23 50							
Barnes	d	21 53				22 16		22 36	22 45	22 53				23 16		23 36	23 45	23 53							
Putney	d	21 56			22 02	22 19	22 32	22 39	22 48	22 56			23 02	23 19	23 32	23 39	23 48	23 56				00 02			
Wandsworth Town	d	21 59				22 22		22 42	22 51	22 59				23 22		23 42	23 51	23 59							
Clapham Junction 10	d	22 02			22 07	22 25	22 37	22 45	22 54	23 02			23 07	23 25	23 37	23 45	23 54	00 02				00 07			
Queenstown Rd.(Battersea)	d	22 05				22 28		22 48	22 57	23 05				23 28		23 48	23 57	00 05							
Vauxhall	⊖ d	22 08			22 12	22 32	22 42	22 52	23 00	23 08			23 12	23 32	23 42	23 52	00 01	00 08				00 12			
London Waterloo 15	⊖ a	22 13			22 18	22 36	22 48	23 00	23 05	23 13			23 18	23 36	23 48	23 59	00 05	00 13				00 17			

For general notes see front of timetable
For details of catering facilities see Directory of Train Operators

A From London Waterloo (Table 152)

§ Passengers to/from London may travel via Weybridge. See Table 155.

From 27 September due to seasonal difficulties a large number of trains on this table will have minor retimings that could mean slightly earlier departure or later arrival times at certain stations. For further details see local publicity or contact National Rail Enquiries 08457 48 49 50.

Network Diagram for Table 152

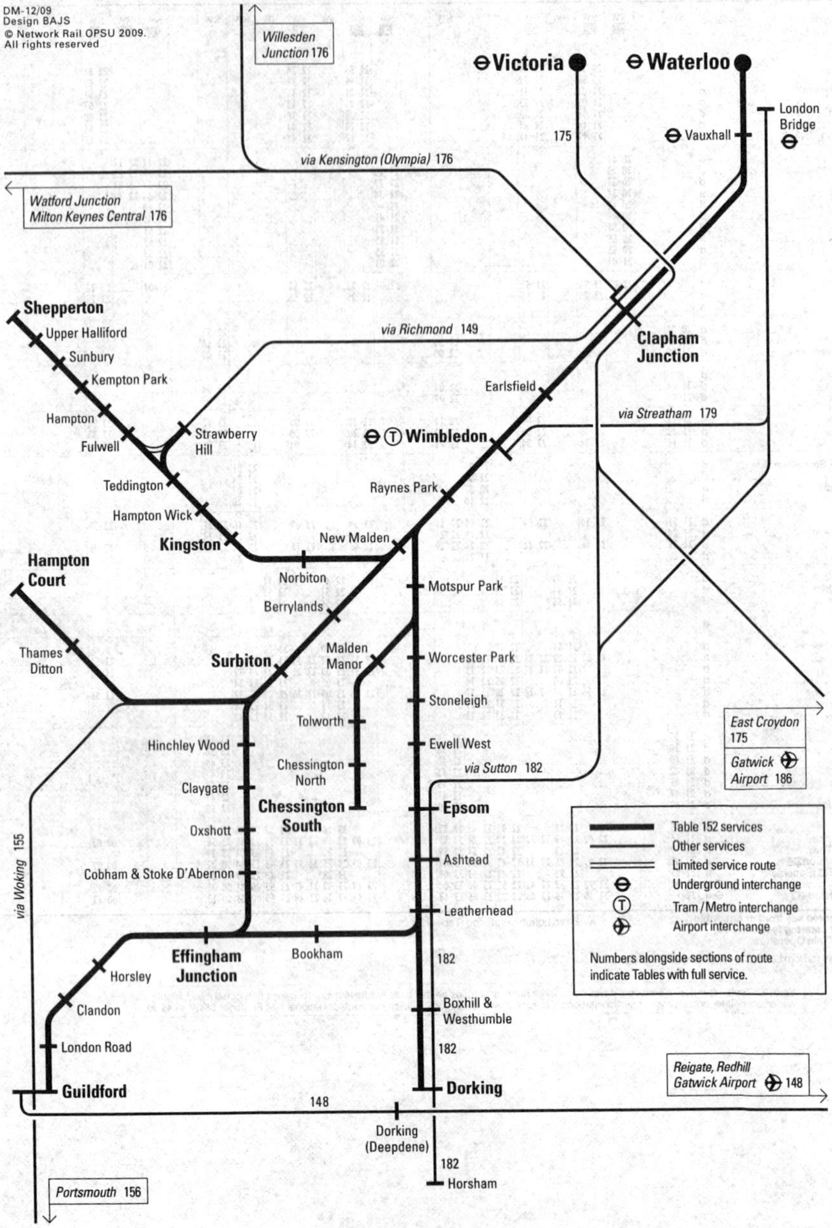
Willesden Junction 176
Victoria
Waterloo
London Bridge
Vauxhall
175
via Kensington (Olympia) 176
Watford Junction
Milton Keynes Central 176
Shepperton
Upper Halliford
Sunbury
Kempton Park
Hampton
Fulwell
Strawberry Hill
Teddington
Hampton Wick
Kingston
via Richmond 149
Clapham Junction
Earlsfield
via Streatham 179
Wimbledon
Raynes Park
New Malden
Norbiton
Hampton Court
Berrylands
Thames Ditton
Surbiton
Malden Manor
Motspur Park
Worcester Park
Stoneleigh
Ewell West
via Sutton 182
Tolworth
Hinchley Wood
Chessington North
Claygate
Chessington South
Oxshott
Cobham & Stoke D'Abernon
Epsom
Ashtead
Leatherhead
via Woking 155
East Croydon 175
Gatwick Airport 186
Table 152 services
Other services
Limited service route
Underground interchange
Tram / Metro interchange
Airport interchange
Numbers alongside sections of route indicate Tables with full service.
Effingham Junction
Bookham
Horsley
Clandon
182
Boxhill & Westhumble
182
London Road
Guildford
Dorking
Reigate, Redhill
Gatwick Airport 148
148
Dorking (Deepdene)
182
Horsham
Portsmouth 156

For details of Bank Holiday service alterations, please see first page of Table 149

London → Chessington South, Dorking, Guildford Shepperton and Hampton Court

Network Diagram - see first page of Table 152

Miles	Miles	Miles	Miles	Miles	Station		SW MO	SW MX	SW MO	SW MO 1 A	SW MX	SW MX	SW MX	SW MX	SW MO	SW MX	SW MX	SW MX	SW	SW 1 B	SW 1 C	SW	SW 1 D	SW	SW E	SW
0	—	—	—	0	**London Waterloo 15** ⊖	d	23p00	23p30	23p32	23p40	23p42	23p50	23p57	.	00 01	00 09	00 15	00 27	00 42	01 05	05 00	05 12	05 20	.	.	05 47
1¼	—	—	—	1¼	Vauxhall ⊖	d	23p04	23p34	23p36	23p44	23p46	23p54	00 01	.	00 04	00 13	00 19	00 31	00 46	01 09	05 04	05 16	05 24	.	.	05 51
4	—	—	—	4	**Clapham Junction 10**	d	23p09	23p39	23p41	23p49	23p51	23p59	00 06	.	00 09	00 18	00 24	00 36	00 51	01 14	05 09	05 21	05 29	.	.	05 56
5½	—	—	—	5½	Earlsfield	d	23p12	23p42	23p44	23p52	23p54	00 02	00 09	.	00 12	00 21	00 27	00s39	.	.	05 12	05 24	05 32	.	.	05 59
7¼	—	—	—	7¼	**Wimbledon 6** ⊖	d	23p16	23p46	23p48	23p56	23p58	00 06	00 13	.	00 16	00 25	00 31	00 43	01 05	01 20	05 16	05 28	05 36	05 49	.	06 03
8¾	—	0	0	8¾	Raynes Park 6	d	.	23p49	23p52	.	00 01	.	00 16	.	00 19	.	00 34	00 46	01 08	.	.	05 31	.	.	.	06 06
—	—	1	1	—	Motspur Park	d	.	.	23p55	.	00 04	.	.	.	.	.	00 37	.	.	.	.	.	.	.	.	06 09
—	—	—	2½	—	Malden Manor	d	.	.	.	.	.	.	.	.	.	.	.	.	.	.	.	.	.	.	.	.
—	—	—	3¾	—	Tolworth	d	.	.	.	.	.	.	.	.	.	.	.	.	.	.	.	.	.	.	.	.
—	—	—	4½	—	Chessington North	d	.	.	.	.	.	.	.	.	.	.	.	.	.	.	.	.	.	.	.	.
—	—	—	5¼	—	**Chessington South**	a	.	.	.	.	.	.	.	.	.	.	.	.	.	.	.	.	.	.	.	.
—	—	2	—	—	Worcester Park	d	.	.	23p57	.	00 06	.	.	.	.	.	00 39	.	.	.	.	.	.	.	.	06 11
—	—	3¼	—	—	Stoneleigh	d	.	.	23p59	.	00 09	.	.	←	.	.	00 42	.	.	.	.	.	.	.	.	06 14
—	—	4¼	—	—	Ewell West	d	.	.	00 03	.	00 12	.	.	00 12	.	.	00 45	.	.	.	.	.	.	.	.	06 17
—	—	5½	—	—	**Epsom 3**	a	.	.	00 06	.	→	.	.	00 15	.	.	00 48	.	.	.	.	.	.	.	.	06 20
—	—	—	—	—		d	.	.	.	.	.	.	.	00 19	.	.	.	.	.	.	.	.	.	.	.	06 21
—	—	7½	—	—	Ashtead	d	.	.	.	.	.	.	.	00 23	.	.	.	.	.	.	.	.	.	.	.	06 25
—	0	9¼	—	—	Leatherhead	d	.	.	.	.	.	.	.	00 26	.	.	.	.	.	.	.	.	.	.	.	06 28
—	—	12¼	—	—	Boxhill & Westhumble	d	.	.	.	.	.	.	.	.	.	.	.	.	.	.	.	.	.	.	.	.
—	—	13¼	—	—	**Dorking 4**	a	.	.	.	.	.	.	.	.	.	.	.	.	.	.	.	.	.	.	.	.
9¾	—	—	—	9¾	New Malden 6	d	.	23p52	.	.	.	.	00 19	.	00 22	.	.	00 49	01 11	.	.	05 34	.	.	.	.
—	—	—	—	11¼	Norbiton	d	.	.	.	.	.	.	00 22	.	.	.	.	.	01 14	.	.	05 37	.	.	.	.
—	—	—	—	12	Kingston	a	.	.	.	.	.	.	00 25	.	.	.	.	.	01 17	.	.	05 40	.	.	.	.
—	—	—	—	—		d	.	.	.	.	.	.	00 25	.	.	.	.	.	01 17	.	.	05 40	.	.	05 59	.
—	—	—	—	12¾	Hampton Wick	d	.	.	.	.	.	.	00 27	.	.	.	.	.	01s22	.	.	05 42	.	.	06 01	.
—	—	—	—	13¾	Teddington	d	.	.	.	.	.	.	00 30	.	.	.	.	.	01s25	.	.	05 45	.	.	06 05	.
—	—	—	—	—	Strawberry Hill	a	.	.	.	.	.	.	.	.	.	.	.	.	01 28	.	.	.	.	.	06 08	.
—	—	—	—	14¾	Fulwell	d	.	.	.	.	.	.	00 34	.	.	.	.	.	.	.	.	05 49	.	.	.	.
—	—	—	—	16½	Hampton	d	.	.	.	.	.	.	00 38	.	.	.	.	.	.	.	.	05 53	.	.	.	.
—	—	—	—	18¼	Kempton Park	d	.	.	.	.	.	.	00 41	.	.	.	.	.	.	.	.	.	.	.	.	.
—	—	—	—	18¾	Sunbury	d	.	.	.	.	.	.	00 43	.	.	.	.	.	.	.	.	05 58	.	.	.	.
—	—	—	—	19¼	Upper Halliford	d	.	.	.	.	.	.	00 45	.	.	.	.	.	.	.	.	06 00	.	.	.	.
—	—	—	—	20¾	**Shepperton**	a	.	.	.	.	.	.	00 48	.	.	.	.	.	.	.	.	06 03	.	.	.	.
11	—	—	—	—	Berrylands	d	.	23p54	.	.	.	.	.	.	00 25	.	.	00s51	.	.	.	.	.	.	.	.
12	—	—	0	—	**Surbiton 6**	d	23b32	23p59	.	00 05	.	00 14	.	.	00 31	00 33	.	00a55	.	01 29	05 24	.	05 44	05 57	.	.
—	—	—	2	—	Thames Ditton	d	.	00 03	.	.	.	.	.	.	.	.	.	.	.	.	.	.	.	.	.	.
—	—	—	3	—	**Hampton Court**	a	.	00 06	.	.	.	.	.	.	.	.	.	.	.	.	.	.	.	.	.	.
14	—	—	—	—	Hinchley Wood	d	23p36	.	.	.	.	00 18	.	.	00 35	.	.	.	.	.	.	.	.	06 01	.	.
15¼	—	—	—	—	Claygate	d	23p39	.	.	.	.	00 21	.	.	00 38	.	.	.	.	.	.	.	.	06 04	.	.
17	—	—	—	—	Oxshott	d	23p42	.	.	.	.	00 24	.	.	00 41	.	.	.	.	.	.	.	.	06 07	.	.
19	—	—	—	—	Cobham & Stoke d'Abernon	d	23p46	.	.	.	.	00 28	.	.	00 45	.	.	.	.	.	.	.	.	06 11	.	.
—	2½	—	—	—	Bookham	d	.	.	.	.	.	.	.	00 31	.	.	.	.	.	.	.	.	.	.	.	06 33
21¼	4¼	—	—	—	Effingham Junction 6	d	23p50	.	.	.	.	00 32	.	00 36	00 49	.	.	.	.	.	.	.	.	06 15	.	06 37
22¼	—	—	—	—	Horsley	d	23p53	.	.	.	.	00 35	.	00 39	00 52	.	.	.	.	.	.	.	.	06 18	.	.
25½	—	—	—	—	Clandon	d	23p58	.	.	.	.	00 40	.	00 44	00 57	.	.	.	.	.	.	.	.	06 23	.	.
28¾	—	—	—	—	London Road (Guildford)	d	00 03	.	.	.	.	00 45	.	00 49	01 02	.	.	.	.	.	.	.	.	06 28	.	06 46
30	—	—	—	—	**Guildford**	a	00 07	.	.	.	.	00 49	.	00 54	01 06	01 06	.	.	.	.	05 59	.	06 21	06 32	.	06 50

For general notes see front of timetable
For details of catering facilities see Directory of Train Operators

- **A** To Farnham (Table 155)
- **B** To Southampton Central (Table 158)
- **C** To Portsmouth Harbour (Table 156)
- **D** To Portsmouth & Southsea (Table 156)
- **E** To London Waterloo (Table 149)
- **b** Previous night. Arr. 2328

From 28 September due to seasonal difficulties a large number of trains on this table will have minor retimings that could mean slightly earlier departure or later arrival times at certain stations. For further details see local publicity or contact National Rail Enquiries 08457 48 49 50.

For details of Bank Holiday service alterations, please see first page of Table 149

London → Chessington South, Dorking, Guildford Shepperton and Hampton Court

Network Diagram - see first page of Table 152

		SW	SW	SW	SW	SW	SW	SW	SN	SW		SW	SW	SW	SW	SW	SW	SW	SW	SW	SW	SW	SW	SW	SN	SW
															1											
		A	B						C				B		D							B			E	
London Waterloo 15 ⊖	d	05 50			06 03	06 06	06 12	06 16		06 20		06 24	06 27	06 33	06 42	06 36	06 39	06 42	06 46	06 50	06 54	06 57	07 03	07 06		07 09
Vauxhall ⊖	d	05 54			06 07	06 10	06 16	06 20		06 24		06 28	06 31	06 37		06 40	06 43	06 46	06 50	06 54	06 58	07 01	07 07	07 10		07 13
Clapham Junction 10	d	05 59			06 12	06 15	06 21	06 25		06 29		06 33	06 36	06 42	06u49	06 45	06 48	06 51	06 55	06 59	07 03	07 06	07 12	07 15		07 18
Earlsfield	d	06 02			06 15	06 18	06 24	06 28		06 32		06 36	06 39	06 45		06 48	06 51	06 54	06 58	07 02	07 06	07 09	07 15	07 18		07 21
Wimbledon 6 ⊖	d	06 06	06 13	06 16	06 19	06 22	06 28	06 32		06 36		06 40	06 43	06 49		06 52	06 55	06 58	07 02	07 06	07 10	07 13	07 19	07 22		07 25
Raynes Park 6	d		06 16	06 19		06 25	06 31	06 35				06 43	06 46			06 55		07 01	07 05		07 13	07 16		07 25		07 28
Motspur Park	d			06 21				06 38				06 46							07 08		07 16					07 31
Malden Manor	d			06 25				06 41											07 11							
Tolworth	d			06 27				06 44											07 14							
Chessington North	d			06 30				06 47											07 17							
Chessington South	a			06 32				06 49											07 19							
Worcester Park	d											06 48					07 01				07 18					07 33
Stoneleigh	d											06 51									07 21					07 36
Ewell West	d											06 54									07 24					07 39
Epsom 3	a											06 57					07 08				07 27					07 42
	d								06 50			06 58					07 08				07 28				07 36	
Ashtead	d											07 02					07 12				07 32				07 40	
Leatherhead	d								06 56			07 05					07 15				07 35				07 45	
Boxhill & Westhumble	d																									
Dorking 4	a											07 11									07 41					
New Malden 6	d		06 19			06 28	06 34						06 49			06 58		07 04				07 19		07 28		
Norbiton	d		06 22				06 37						06 52					07 07				07 22				
Kingston	a		06 25				06 40						06 55					07 10				07 25				
	d		06 29				06 40						06 59					07 10				07 29				
Hampton Wick	d		06 31				06 42						07 01					07 12				07 31				
Teddington	d		06 35				06 45						07 05					07 15				07 35				
Strawberry Hill	a		06 38										07 08									07 38				
Fulwell	d						06 49											07 19								
Hampton	d						06 53											07 23								
Kempton Park	d																									
Sunbury	d						06 58											07 28								
Upper Halliford	d						07 00											07 30								
Shepperton	a						07 03											07 33								
Berrylands	d					06 30										07 00								07 30		
Surbiton 6	d	06 14			06 27	06 35				06 44				06 57	07 00	07 05				07 14			07 27	07 35		
Thames Ditton	d					06 39										07 09								07 39		
Hampton Court	a					06 42										07 12								07 42		
Hinchley Wood	d				06 31									07 01									07 31			
Claygate	d				06 34									07 04									07 34			
Oxshott	d				06 37									07 07									07 37			
Cobham & Stoke d'Abernon	d				06 41									07 11									07 41			
Bookham	d								07 01								07 21								07 50	
Effingham Junction 6	d				06 45				07 05					07 15			07a24						07 45		07 54	
Horsley	d				06 48									07 18									07 48			
Clandon	d				06 53									07 23									07 53			
London Road (Guildford)	d				06 58									07 28									07 58		08 03	
Guildford	a				07 02				07 17	07 20				07 32						07 47			08 02		08 07	

For general notes see front of timetable
For details of catering facilities see Directory of Train Operators

A To Woking (Table 155)
B To London Waterloo (Table 149)
C From Sutton (Surrey) (Table 182)
D To Portsmouth Harbour (Table 158)
E From London Bridge (Table 178)

From 28 September due to seasonal difficulties a large number of trains on this table will have minor retimings that could mean slightly earlier departure or later arrival times at certain stations. For further details see local publicity or contact National Rail Enquiries 08457 48 49 50.

For details of Bank Holiday service alterations, please see first page of Table 149

London → Chessington South, Dorking, Guildford Shepperton and Hampton Court

Network Diagram - see first page of Table 152

		SW	SW	SW	SW	SW	SW	SW	SW	SW	SW	SW	SW	SW	SW	SW 1	SW	SW	SW	SW	SW	SW	SW	SW	SW
				A		B								B		C					A		B		
London Waterloo 15 ⊖	d	07 12	07 16	07 20	07 24	07 27	07 33	07 36	07 39	07 42	07 46	07 50	07 54	07 57	08 03	08 12	08 06	08 09	08 12	08 16	08 20	08 24	08 27	08 33	08 36
Vauxhall ⊖	d	07 16	07 20	07 24	07 28	07 31	07 37	07 40	07 43	07 46	07 50	07 54	07 58	08 01	08 07		08 10	08 13	08 16	08 20	08 24	08 28	08 31	08 37	08 40
Clapham Junction 10	d	07 21	07 25	07 29	07 33	07 36	07 42	07 45	07 48	07 51	07 55	07 59	08 03	08 06	08 12	08u19	08 15	08 18	08 21	08 25	08 29	08 33	08 36	08 42	08 45
Earlsfield	d	07 24	07 28	07 32	07 36	07 39	07 45	07 48	07 51	07 54	07 58	08 02	08 06	08 09	08 15		08 18	08 21	08 24	08 28	08 32	08 36	08 39	08 45	08 48
Wimbledon 6 ⊖	d	07 28	07 32	07 36	07 40	07 43	07 49	07 52	07 55	07 58	08 02	08 06	08 10	08 13	08 19		08 22	08 25	08 28	08 32	08 36	08 40	08 43	08 49	08 52
Raynes Park 6	d	07 31	07 35		07 43	07 46		07 55	07 58	08 01	08 05		08 13	08 16			08 25	08 28	08 31	08 35		08 43	08 46		08 55
Motspur Park	d		07 38		07 46				08 01		08 08		08 16					08 31		08 38		08 46			
Malden Manor	d		07 41								08 11									08 41					
Tolworth	d		07 44								08 14									08 44					
Chessington North	d		07 47								08 17									08 47					
Chessington South	a		07 49								08 19									08 49					
Worcester Park	d				07 48				08 03				08 18					08 33				08 48			
Stoneleigh	d				07 51				08 06				08 21					08 36				08 51			
Ewell West	d				07 54				08 09				08 24					08 39				08 54			
Epsom 3	a				07 58				08 13				08 27					08 42				08 57			
	d				07 58				08 17				08 28					08 47				08 58			
Ashtead	d				08 02				08 21				08 32					08 51				09 02			
Leatherhead	d				08 05				08 24				08 35					08 54				09 05			
Boxhill & Westhumble	d																								
Dorking 4	a				08 12								08 41									09 11			
New Malden 6	d	07 34				07 49		07 58		08 04				08 19			08 28		08 34				08 49		08 58
Norbiton	d	07 37				07 52				08 07				08 22					08 37				08 52		
Kingston	a	07 40				07 55				08 10				08 25					08 40				08 55		
	d	07 40				07 59				08 10				08 29					08 40				08 59		
Hampton Wick	d	07 42				08 01				08 12				08 31					08 42				09 01		
Teddington	d	07 45				08 05				08 15				08 35					08 45				09 05		
Strawberry Hill	a					08 08								08 38									09 08		
Fulwell	d	07 49								08 19									08 49						
Hampton	d	07 53								08 23									08 53						
Kempton Park	d	07 56								08 26									08 56						
Sunbury	d	07 58								08 28									08 58						
Upper Halliford	d	08 00								08 30									09 00						
Shepperton	a	08 03								08 33									09 03						
Berrylands	d							08 00									08 30								09 00
Surbiton 6	d			07 44			07 57	08 05				08 14			08 27	08 30	08 35				08 44			08 57	09 05
Thames Ditton	d							08 09									08 39								09 09
Hampton Court	a							08 12									08 42								09 12
Hinchley Wood	d						08 01								08 31									09 01	
Claygate	d						08 04								08 34									09 04	
Oxshott	d						08 07								08 37									09 07	
Cobham & Stoke d'Abernon	d						08 11								08 41									09 11	
Bookham	d								08 29									08 59							
Effingham Junction 6	d						08 15		08 33						08 45			09 03						09 15	
Horsley	d						08 18		08 36						08 48			09 06						09 18	
Clandon	d						08 23		08 41						08 53			09 11						09 23	
London Road (Guildford)	d						08 28		08 46						08 58			09 16						09 28	
Guildford	a						08 32		08 50			08 50			09 04			09 20						09 32	

For general notes see front of timetable
For details of catering facilities see Directory of Train Operators

A To Woking (Table 155)
B To London Waterloo (Table 149)
C To Basingstoke (Table 155)

From 28 September due to seasonal difficulties a large number of trains on this table will have minor retimings that could mean slightly earlier departure or later arrival times at certain stations. For further details see local publicity or contact National Rail Enquiries 08457 48 49 50.

For details of Bank Holiday service alterations, please see first page of Table 149

London → Chessington South, Dorking, Guildford Shepperton and Hampton Court

Network Diagram - see first page of Table 152

		SW	SW	SW	SW	SW	SW	SW	SW	SW	SW	SW	SW	SW	SW	SW	SW	SW	SW	SW	SW	SW	SW	SW	SW
					A		B						A		B						A		B		
London Waterloo 15 ⊖	d	08 39	08 42	08 46	08 50	08 54	08 57	09 03	09 06	09 09	09 12	09 16	09 20	09 24	09 27	09 33	09 36	09 39	09 42	09 46	09 50	09 54	09 57	10 03	10 06
Vauxhall ⊖	d	08 43	08 46	08 50	08 54	08 58	09 01	09 07	09 10	09 13	09 16	09 20	09 24	09 28	09 31	09 37	09 40	09 43	09 46	09 50	09 54	09 58	10 01	10 07	10 10
Clapham Junction 10	d	08 48	08 51	08 55	08 59	09 03	09 06	09 12	09 15	09 18	09 21	09 25	09 29	09 33	09 36	09 42	09 45	09 48	09 51	09 55	09 59	10 03	10 06	10 12	10 15
Earlsfield	d	08 51	08 54	08 58	09 02	09 06	09 09	09 15	09 18	09 21	09 24	09 28	09 32	09 36	09 39	09 45	09 48	09 51	09 54	09 58	10 02	10 06	10 09	10 15	10 18
Wimbledon 6 ⊖	d	08 55	08 58	09 02	09 06	09 10	09 13	09 19	09 22	09 25	09 28	09 32	09 36	09 40	09 43	09 49	09 52	09 55	09 58	10 02	10 06	10 10	10 13	10 19	10 22
Raynes Park 6	d	08 58	09 01	09 05		09 13	09 16		09 25	09 28	09 31	09 35		09 43	09 46		09 55	09 58	10 01	10 05		10 13	10 16		10 25
Motspur Park	d	09 01		09 08		09 16				09 31		09 38		09 46				10 01		10 08		10 16			
Malden Manor	d			09 11								09 41								10 11					
Tolworth	d			09 14								09 44								10 14					
Chessington North	d			09 17								09 47								10 17					
Chessington South	a			09 19								09 49								10 19					
Worcester Park	d	09 03				09 18				09 33				09 48				10 03				10 18			
Stoneleigh	d	09 06				09 21				09 36				09 51				10 06				10 21			
Ewell West	d	09 09				09 24				09 39				09 54				10 09				10 24			
Epsom 3	a	09 16				09 27				09 42				09 57				10 16				10 27			
	d	09 17				09 28				09 47				09 58				10 17				10 28			
Ashtead	d	09 21				09 32				09 51				10 02				10 21				10 32			
Leatherhead	d	09 24				09 35				09 54				10 05				10 24				10 35			
Boxhill & Westhumble	d																								
Dorking 4	a					09 41								10 11								10 41			
New Malden 6	d		09 04				09 19		09 28		09 34				09 49		09 58		10 04				10 19		10 28
Norbiton	d		09 07				09 22				09 37				09 52				10 07				10 22		
Kingston	a		09 10				09 25				09 40				09 55				10 10				10 25		
	d		09 10				09 29				09 40				09 59				10 10				10 29		
Hampton Wick	d		09 12				09 31				09 42				10 01				10 12				10 31		
Teddington	d		09 15				09 35				09 45				10 05				10 15				10 35		
Strawberry Hill	a						09 38								10 08								10 38		
Fulwell	d		09 19								09 49								10 19						
Hampton	d		09 23								09 53								10 23						
Kempton Park	d		09 26								09 56								10 26						
Sunbury	d		09 28								09 58								10 28						
Upper Halliford	d		09 30								10 00								10 30						
Shepperton	a		09 33								10 03								10 33						
Berrylands	d								09 30								10 00								10 30
Surbiton 6	d				09 14			09 27	09 35				09 44			09 57	10 05				10 14			10 28	10 35
Thames Ditton	d								09 39								10 09								10 39
Hampton Court	a								09 42								10 12								10 42
Hinchley Wood	d							09 31								10 01								10 31	
Claygate	d							09 34								10 04								10 34	
Oxshott	d							09 37								10 07								10 37	
Cobham & Stoke d'Abernon	d							09 41								10 11								10 41	
Bookham	d	09 29								09 59								10 29							
Effingham Junction 6	d	09 33						09 45		10 03						10 15		10 33						10 45	
Horsley	d	09 36						09 48		10 06						10 18		10 36						10 48	
Clandon	d	09 41						09 53		10 11						10 23		10 41						10 53	
London Road (Guildford)	d	09 46						09 58		10 16						10 28		10 46						10 58	
Guildford	a	09 50						10 02		10 20						10 32		10 50						11 02	

For general notes see front of timetable
For details of catering facilities see
Directory of Train Operators

A To Woking (Table 155)
B To London Waterloo (Table 149)

From 28 September due to seasonal difficulties a large number of trains on this table will have minor retimings that could mean slightly earlier departure or later arrival times at certain stations. For further details see local publicity or contact National Rail Enquiries 08457 48 49 50.

For details of Bank Holiday service alterations, please see first page of Table 149

London → Chessington South, Dorking, Guildford Shepperton and Hampton Court

Network Diagram - see first page of Table 152

Station		SW	SW	SW	SW A	SW	SW B	SW	
London Waterloo [15] ⊖	d	10 09	10 12	10 16	10 20	10 24	10 27	10 33	
Vauxhall ⊖	d	10 13	10 16	10 20	10 24	10 28	10 31	10 37	
Clapham Junction [10]	d	10 18	10 21	10 25	10 29	10 33	10 36	10 42	
Earlsfield	d	10 21	10 24	10 28	10 32	10 36	10 39	10 45	
Wimbledon [6] ⊖	d	10 25	10 28	10 32	10 36	10 40	10 43	10 49	
Raynes Park [6]	d	10 28	10 31	10 35		10 43	10 46		
Motspur Park	d	10 31		10 38		10 46			
Malden Manor	d			10 41					
Tolworth	d			10 44					
Chessington North	d			10 47					
Chessington South	a			10 49					
Worcester Park	d	10 33				10 48			
Stoneleigh	d	10 36				10 51			
Ewell West	d	10 39				10 54			
Epsom [3]	a	10 46				10 57			
	d	10 47				10 58			
Ashtead	d	10 51				11 02			
Leatherhead	d	10 54				11 05			
Boxhill & Westhumble	d								
Dorking [4]	a					11 11			and at
New Malden [6]	d		10 34				10 49		the same
Norbiton	d		10 37				10 52		minutes
Kingston	a		10 40				10 55		
	d		10 40				10 59		past
Hampton Wick	d		10 42				11 01		
Teddington	d		10 45				11 05		each
Strawberry Hill	a						11 08		hour until
Fulwell	d		10 49						
Hampton	d		10 53						
Kempton Park	d		10 56						
Sunbury	d		10 58						
Upper Halliford	d		11 00						
Shepperton	a		11 03						
Berrylands	d								
Surbiton [6]	d				10 44			10 57	
Thames Ditton	d								
Hampton Court	a								
Hinchley Wood	d							11 01	
Claygate	d							11 04	
Oxshott	d							11 07	
Cobham & Stoke d'Abernon	d							11 11	
Bookham	d	10 59							
Effingham Junction [6]	d	11 03						11 15	
Horsley	d	11 06						11 18	
Clandon	d	11 11						11 23	
London Road (Guildford)	d	11 16						11 28	
Guildford	a	11 20						11 32	

Station		SW	SW	SW	SW	SW A	SW	SW B	SW	SW	SW	SW	SW	SW A	SW	SW B
London Waterloo [15] ⊖	d	15 36	15 39	15 42	15 46	15 50	15 54	15 57	16 03	16 06	16 09	16 12	16 16	16 20	16 24	16 27
Vauxhall ⊖	d	15 40	15 43	15 46	15 50	15 54	15 58	16 01	16 07	16 10	16 13	16 16	16 20	16 24	16 28	16 31
Clapham Junction [10]	d	15 45	15 48	15 51	15 55	15 59	16 03	16 06	16 12	16 15	16 18	16 21	16 25	16 29	16 33	16 36
Earlsfield	d	15 48	15 51	15 54	15 58	16 02	16 06	16 09	16 15	16 18	16 21	16 24	16 28	16 32	16 36	16 39
Wimbledon [6] ⊖	d	15 52	15 55	15 58	16 02	16 06	16 10	16 13	16 19	16 22	16 25	16 28	16 32	16 36	16 40	16 43
Raynes Park [6]	d	15 55	15 58	16 01	16 05		16 13	16 16		16 25	16 28	16 31	16 35		16 43	16 46
Motspur Park	d		16 01		16 08		16 16				16 31		16 38		16 46	
Malden Manor	d				16 11								16 41			
Tolworth	d				16 14								16 44			
Chessington North	d				16 17								16 47			
Chessington South	a				16 19								16 51			
Worcester Park	d		16 03				16 18				16 33				16 48	
Stoneleigh	d		16 06				16 21				16 36				16 51	
Ewell West	d		16 09				16 24				16 39				16 54	
Epsom [3]	a		16 16				16 27				16 46				16 57	
	d		16 17				16 28				16 47				16 58	
Ashtead	d		16 21				16 32				16 51				17 02	
Leatherhead	d		16 24				16 35				16 54				17 05	
Boxhill & Westhumble	d														17 10	
Dorking [4]	a						16 41								17 14	
New Malden [6]	d	15 58		16 04				16 19		16 28		16 34				16 49
Norbiton	d			16 07				16 22				16 37				16 52
Kingston	a			16 10				16 25				16 40				16 55
	d			16 10				16 29				16 40				16 59
Hampton Wick	d			16 12				16 31				16 42				17 01
Teddington	d			16 15				16 35				16 45				17 05
Strawberry Hill	a							16 38								17 08
Fulwell	d			16 19								16 49				
Hampton	d			16 23								16 53				
Kempton Park	d			16 26								16 56				
Sunbury	d			16 28								16 58				
Upper Halliford	d			16 30								17 00				
Shepperton	a			16 33								17 05				
Berrylands	d	16 00								16 30						
Surbiton [6]	d	16 05				16 14			16 27	16 35				16 44		
Thames Ditton	d	16 09								16 39						
Hampton Court	a	16 12								16 44						
Hinchley Wood	d								16 31							
Claygate	d								16 34							
Oxshott	d								16 37							
Cobham & Stoke d'Abernon	d								16 41							
Bookham	d		16 29								16 59					
Effingham Junction [6]	d		16 33						16 45		17 03					
Horsley	d		16 36						16 48		17 06					
Clandon	d		16 41						16 53		17 11					
London Road (Guildford)	d		16 46						16 58		17 16					
Guildford	a		16 50						17 04		17 22					

For general notes see front of timetable
For details of catering facilities see Directory of Train Operators

A To Woking (Table 155)
B To London Waterloo (Table 149)

From 28 September due to seasonal difficulties a large number of trains on this table will have minor retimings that could mean slightly earlier departure or later arrival times at certain stations. For further details see local publicity or contact National Rail Enquiries 08457 48 49 50.

For details of Bank Holiday service alterations, please see first page of Table 149

London → Chessington South, Dorking, Guildford Shepperton and Hampton Court

Network Diagram - see first page of Table 152

		SW	SW	SN A	SW	SW	SW	SW B	SW	SW C	SW	SW	SN A	SW	SW	SW	SW B	SW	SW C	SW	SW	SW	SN A	SW	SW
London Waterloo 15 ⊖	d	16 33	16 36		16 39	16 42	16 46	16 50	16 54	16 57	17 02	17 06		17 09	17 12	17 16	17 20	17 24	17 27	17 30	17 32	17 36		17 39	17 43
Vauxhall ⊖	d	16 37	16 40		16 43	16 46	16 50	16 54	16 58	17 01	17 07	17 10		17 13	17 16	17 20	17 24	17 28	17 31	17 34	17 37	17 40		17 43	17 47
Clapham Junction 10	d	16 42	16 45		16 48	16 51	16 55	16 59	17 03	17 06	17 12	17 15		17 18	17 22	17 25	17 29	17 33	17 36	17 39	17 42	17 45		17 48	17 53
Earlsfield	d	16 45	16 48		16 51	16 54	16 58	17 02	17 06	17 09	17 15	17 18		17 21	17 25	17 28	17 32	17 36	17 39	17 42	17 45	17 48		17 51	
Wimbledon 6 ⊖	d	16 49	16 52		16 55	16 58	17 02	17 06	17 10	17 13	17 19	17 22		17 25	17 29	17 32	17 36	17 40	17 43	17 46	17 49	17 52		17 55	
Raynes Park 6	d		16 55		16 58	17 01	17 05		17 13	17 16		17 25		17 28	17 32	17 35		17 43	17 46	17 49		17 55		17 58	
Motspur Park	d				17 01		17 08		17 16					17 31		17 38				17 52				18 01	
Malden Manor	d						17 11									17 41									
Tolworth	d						17 14									17 44									
Chessington North	d						17 17									17 47									
Chessington South	a						17 21									17 51									
Worcester Park	d				17 03				17 18					17 33				17 47		17 54				18 03	
Stoneleigh	d				17 06				17 21					17 36						17 57				18 06	
Ewell West	d				17 09				17 24					17 39						18 00				18 09	
Epsom 3	a				17 12				17 27					17 42				17 54		18 06				18 20	
	d			17 08	17 17				17 28				17 38	17 47				17 54					18 11	18 20	
Ashtead	d			17 12	17 21				17 32				17 42	17 51				17 58					18 15	18 24	
Leatherhead	d			17 15	17 24				17 35				17 45	17 54				18 01					18 18	18 28	
Boxhill & Westhumble	d								17 40									18 06							
Dorking 4	a								17 44									18 11							
New Malden 6	d		16 58			17 04				17 19		17 28			17 35				17 49			17 58			
Norbiton	d					17 07				17 22					17 38				17 52						
Kingston	a					17 10				17 25					17 41				17 55						
	d					17 10				17 29					17 41				17 59						
Hampton Wick	d					17 12				17 31					17 43				18 01						
Teddington	d					17 15				17 35					17 46				18 05						
Strawberry Hill	a									17 38									18 08						18 11
Fulwell	d					17 19									17 50										18 13
Hampton	d					17 23									17 54										18 17
Kempton Park	d					17 26									17 57										
Sunbury	d					17 28									17 59										18 21
Upper Halliford	d					17 30									18 01										18 23
Shepperton	a					17 35									18 06										18 28
Berrylands	d		17 00									17 30										18 00			
Surbiton 6	d	16 57	17 05					17 14			17 27	17 35					17 44				17 57	18 05			
Thames Ditton	d		17 09									17 39										18 09			
Hampton Court	a		17 14									17 44										18 14			
Hinchley Wood	d	17 01									17 31										18 05				
Claygate	d	17 04									17 34										18 08				
Oxshott	d	17 07									17 37										18 11				
Cobham & Stoke d'Abernon	d	17 11									17 41										18 15				
Bookham	d			17 21	17 29								17 51	17 59									18 23	18 33	
Effingham Junction 6	d	17 15		17 24	17 33						17 45		17 54	18a05							18 20		18 27	18a44	
Horsley	d	17 18			17 36						17 48		17 57								18 22		18 29		
Clandon	d	17 23			17 41						17 53		18 02								18 27		18 34		
London Road (Guildford)	d	17 28			17 46						17 58		18 07								18 32		18 39		
Guildford	a	17 34		17 39	17 52						18 04		18 13								18 38		18 45		

For general notes see front of timetable
For details of catering facilities see Directory of Train Operators

A From London Bridge (Table 182)
B To Woking (Table 155)
C To London Waterloo (Table 149)

From 28 September due to seasonal difficulties a large number of trains on this table will have minor retimings that could mean slightly earlier departure or later arrival times at certain stations. For further details see local publicity or contact National Rail Enquiries 08457 48 49 50.

For details of Bank Holiday service alterations, please see first page of Table 149

London → Chessington South, Dorking, Guildford Shepperton and Hampton Court

Network Diagram - see first page of Table 152

		SW	SW	SW A	SW	SW B	SW	SW	SW	SW	SW	SW	SW	SW A	SW	SW B	SW	SW	SW	SW		SW	SW	SW	SW A	SW
London Waterloo 15 ⊖	d	17 42	17 46	17 50	17 54	17 57	18 00	18 02	18 06	18 09	18 13	18 12	18 16	18 20	18 24	18 27	18 30	18 32	18 36	18 43		18 39	18 42	18 46	18 50	18 54
Vauxhall ⊖	d	17 46	17 50	17 54	17 58	18 01	18 04	18 07	18 10	18 13	18 17	18 16	18 20	18 24	18 28	18 31	18 34	18 37	18 40	18 47		18 43	18 46	18 50	18 54	18 58
Clapham Junction 10	d	17 52	17 55	17 59	18 03	18 06	18 09	18 12	18 15	18 18	18 23	18 22	18 25	18 29	18 33	18 36	18 39	18 42	18 45	18 53		18 48	18 52	18 55	18 59	19 03
Earlsfield	d	17 55	17 58	18 02	18 06	18 09	18 12	18 15	18 18	18 21		18 25	18 28	18 32	18 36	18 39	18 42	18 45	18 48			18 51	18 55	18 58	19 02	19 06
Wimbledon 6 ⊖	d	17 59	18 02	18 06	18 10	18 13	18 16	18 19	18 22	18 25		18 29	18 32	18 36	18 40	18 43	18 46	18 49	18 52			18 55	18 59	19 02	19 06	19 10
Raynes Park 6	d	18 02	18 05		18 13	18 16	18 19		18 25	18 28		18 32	18 35		18 43	18 46	18 49		18 55			18 58	19 02	19 05		19 13
Motspur Park	d		18 08				18 22			18 31			18 38				18 52					19 01		19 08		
Malden Manor	d		18 11										18 41											19 11		
Tolworth	d		18 14										18 44											19 14		
Chessington North	d		18 17										18 47											19 17		
Chessington South	a		18 21										18 51											19 21		
Worcester Park	d				18 17		18 24			18 33					18 47		18 54					19 03				19 17
Stoneleigh	d						18 27			18 36							18 57					19 06				
Ewell West	d						18 30			18 39							19 00					19 09				
Epsom 3	a				18 24		18 35			18 43					18 54		19 05					19 13				19 24
	d				18 24					18 47					18 54							19 17				19 24
Ashtead	d				18 28					18 51					18 58							19 21				19 28
Leatherhead	d				18 31					18 54					19 01							19 24				19 31
Boxhill & Westhumble	d				18 36										19 06											19 36
Dorking 4	a				18 41										19 11											19 43
New Malden 6	d	18 05				18 19			18 28			18 35				18 49			18 58				19 05			
Norbiton	d	18 08				18 22						18 38				18 52							19 08			
Kingston	a	18 11				18 25						18 41				18 55							19 11			
	d	18 11				18 29						18 41				18 59							19 11			
Hampton Wick	d	18 13				18 31						18 43				19 01							19 13			
Teddington	d	18 16				18 35						18 46				19 05							19 16			
Strawberry Hill	a					18 38					18 41					19 08				19 11						
Fulwell	d	18 20									18 43	18 50								19 13			19 20			
Hampton	d	18 24									18 47	18 54								19 17			19 24			
Kempton Park	d	18 27										18 57											19 27			
Sunbury	d	18 29									18 51	18 59								19 21			19 29			
Upper Halliford	d	18 31									18 53	19 01								19 23			19 31			
Shepperton	a	18 40									18 58	19 10								19 28			19 37			
Berrylands	d								18 30										19 00							
Surbiton 6	d			18 14				18 27	18 35					18 44				18 57	19 05						19 14	
Thames Ditton	d								18 39										19 09							
Hampton Court	a								18 44										19 14							
Hinchley Wood	d							18 35										19 01								
Claygate	d							18 38										19 04								
Oxshott	d							18 41										19 07								
Cobham & Stoke d'Abernon	d							18 45										19 11								
Bookham	d									18 59												19 29				
Effingham Junction 6	d							18 50		19 03								19 15				19 33				
Horsley	d							18 52		19 06								19 18				19 36				
Clandon	d							18 57		19 11								19 23				19 41				
London Road (Guildford)	d							19 02		19 16								19 28				19 46				
Guildford	a							19 08		19 22								19 34				19 52				

For general notes see front of timetable
For details of catering facilities see Directory of Train Operators

A To Woking (Table 155)
B To London Waterloo (Table 149)

From 28 September due to seasonal difficulties a large number of trains on this table will have minor retimings that could mean slightly earlier departure or later arrival times at certain stations. For further details see local publicity or contact National Rail Enquiries 08457 48 49 50.

For details of Bank Holiday service alterations, please see first page of Table 149

London → Chessington South, Dorking, Guildford Shepperton and Hampton Court

Network Diagram - see first page of Table 152

	SW A	SW	SW	SW	SW	SW	SW	SW B	SW	SW A	SW	SW	SW	SW	SW	SW B	SW	SW A	SW	SW	SW	SW	SW	SW B	SW
London Waterloo 15 ⊖ d	18 57	19 00	19 02	19 06	19 09	19 12	19 16	19 20	19 24	19 27	19 33	19 36	19 39	19 42	19 46	19 50	19 54	19 57	20 03	20 06	20 09	20 12	20 16	20 20	20 24
Vauxhall ⊖ d	19 01	19 04	19 07	19 10	19 13	19 16	19 20	19 24	19 28	19 31	19 37	19 40	19 43	19 46	19 50	19 54	19 58	20 01	20 07	20 10	20 13	20 16	20 20	20 24	20 28
Clapham Junction 10 d	19 06	19 09	19 12	19 15	19 18	19 22	19 25	19 29	19 33	19 36	19 42	19 45	19 48	19 51	19 55	19 59	20 03	20 06	20 12	20 15	20 18	20 21	20 25	20 29	20 33
Earlsfield d	19 09	19 12	19 15	19 18	19 21	19 25	19 28	19 32	19 36	19 39	19 45	19 48	19 51	19 54	19 58	20 02	20 06	20 09	20 15	20 18	20 21	20 24	20 28	20 32	20 36
Wimbledon 6 ⊖ d	19 13	19 16	19 19	19 22	19 25	19 29	19 32	19 36	19 40	19 43	19 49	19 52	19 55	19 58	20 02	20 06	20 10	20 13	20 19	20 22	20 25	20 28	20 32	20 36	20 40
Raynes Park 6 d	19 16	19 19		19 25	19 28	19 32	19 35		19 43	19 46		19 55	19 58	20 01	20 05		20 13	20 16		20 25	20 28	20 31	20 35		20 43
Motspur Park d		19 22			19 31		19 38		19 46				20 01		20 08		20 16				20 31		20 38		20 46
Malden Manor d							19 41								20 11								20 41		
Tolworth d							19 44								20 14								20 44		
Chessington North d							19 47								20 17								20 47		
Chessington South a							19 49								20 19								20 49		
Worcester Park d		19 24			19 33				19 48				20 03				20 18				20 33				20 48
Stoneleigh d		19 27			19 36				19 51				20 06				20 21				20 36				20 51
Ewell West d		19 30			19 39				19 54				20 09				20 24				20 39				20 54
Epsom 3 a		19 33			19 43				19 57				20 12				20 27				20 42				20 57
d					19 47				19 58				20 17								20 47				
Ashtead d					19 51				20 02				20 21								20 51				
Leatherhead d					19 54				20 05				20 24								20 54				
Boxhill & Westhumble d									20 10												20 59				
Dorking 4 a									20 12												21 01				
New Malden 6 d	19 19			19 28		19 35				19 49		19 58		20 04				20 19		20 28		20 34			
Norbiton d	19 22					19 38				19 52				20 07				20 22				20 37			
Kingston a	19 25					19 41				19 55				20 10				20 25				20 40			
d	19 29					19 41				19 59				20 10				20 29				20 40			
Hampton Wick d	19 31					19 43				20 01				20 12				20 31				20 42			
Teddington d	19 35					19 46				20 05				20 15				20 35				20 45			
Strawberry Hill a	19 38									20 08								20 38							
Fulwell d						19 50								20 19								20 49			
Hampton d						19 54								20 23								20 53			
Kempton Park d						19 57								20 26								20 56			
Sunbury d						19 59								20 28								20 58			
Upper Halliford d						20 01								20 30								21 00			
Shepperton a						20 04								20 33								21 03			
Berrylands d				19 30								20 00								20 30					
Surbiton 6 d			19 27	19 35				19 44			19 57	20 05				20 14			20 27	20 35				20 44	
Thames Ditton d				19 39								20 09								20 39					
Hampton Court a				19 42								20 12								20 42					
Hinchley Wood d			19 31								20 01								20 31						
Claygate d			19 34								20 04								20 34						
Oxshott d			19 37								20 07								20 37						
Cobham & Stoke d'Abernon d			19 41								20 11								20 41						
Bookham d					19 59								20 29												
Effingham Junction 6 d			19 45		20 03						20 15		20 33						20 45						
Horsley d			19 48		20 06						20 18		20 36						20 48						
Clandon d			19 53		20 11						20 23		20 41						20 53						
London Road (Guildford) d			19 58		20 16						20 28		20 46						20 58						
Guildford a			20 02		20 20						20 32		20 50						21 02						

For general notes see front of timetable
For details of catering facilities see Directory of Train Operators

A To London Waterloo (Table 149)
B To Woking (Table 155)

From 28 September due to seasonal difficulties a large number of trains on this table will have minor retimings that could mean slightly earlier departure or later arrival times at certain stations. For further details see local publicity or contact National Rail Enquiries 08457 48 49 50.

For details of Bank Holiday service alterations, please see first page of Table 149

London → Chessington South, Dorking, Guildford Shepperton and Hampton Court

Network Diagram - see first page of Table 152

		SW A		SW	SW	SW	SW	SW	SW B	SW	SW A	SW	SW	SW	SW B	SW	SW A	SW	SW	SW	SW	SW	SW	SW	SW A	SW
London Waterloo [15] ⊖	d	20 27		20 33	20 36	20 39	20 42	20 46	20 50	20 54	20 57	21 03	21 09	21 12	21 20	21 24	21 27	21 33	21 36	21 39	21 42	21 46	21 50	21 54	21 57	22 03
Vauxhall ⊖	d	20 31		20 37	20 40	20 43	20 46	20 50	20 54	20 58	21 01	21 07	21 13	21 16	21 24	21 28	21 31	21 37	21 40	21 43	21 46	21 50	21 54	21 58	22 01	22 07
Clapham Junction [10]	d	20 36		20 42	20 45	20 48	20 51	20 55	20 59	21 03	21 06	21 12	21 18	21 21	21 29	21 33	21 36	21 42	21 45	21 48	21 51	21 55	21 59	22 03	22 06	22 12
Earlsfield	d	20 39		20 45	20 48	20 51	20 54	20 58	21 02	21 06	21 09	21 15	21 21	21 24	21 32	21 36	21 39	21 45	21 48	21 51	21 54	21 58	22 02	22 06	22 09	22 15
Wimbledon [6] ⊖	d	20 43		20 49	20 52	20 55	20 58	21 02	21 06	21 10	21 13	21 19	21 25	21 28	21 36	21 40	21 43	21 49	21 52	21 55	21 58	22 02	22 06	22 10	22 13	22 19
Raynes Park [6]	d	20 46			20 55	20 58	21 01	21 05		21 13	21 16		21 28	21 31		21 43	21 46		21 55	21 58	22 01	22 05		22 13	22 16	
Motspur Park	d					21 01		21 08		21 16			21 31			21 46				22 01		22 08		22 16		
Malden Manor	d							21 11														22 11				
Tolworth	d							21 14														22 14				
Chessington North	d							21 17														22 17				
Chessington South	a							21 19														22 19				
Worcester Park	d					21 03				21 18			21 33			21 48				22 03				22 18		
Stoneleigh	d					21 06				21 21			21 36			21 51				22 06				22 21		
Ewell West	d					21 09				21 24			21 39			21 54				22 09				22 24		
Epsom [3]	a					21 12				21 27			21 42			21 57				22 12				22 27		
	d					21 17							21 47							22 17						
Ashtead	d					21 21							21 51							22 21						
Leatherhead	d					21 24							21 54							22 24						
Boxhill & Westhumble	d												21 59													
Dorking [4]	a												22 01													
New Malden [6]	d	20 49			20 58		21 04				21 19			21 34			21 49		21 58		22 04				22 19	
Norbiton	d	20 52					21 07				21 22			21 37			21 52				22 07				22 22	
Kingston	a	20 55					21 10				21 25			21 40			21 55				22 10				22 25	
	d	20 59					21 10				21 29			21 40			21 59				22 10				22 29	
Hampton Wick	d	21 01					21 12				21 31			21 42			22 01				22 12				22 31	
Teddington	d	21 05					21 15				21 35			21 45			22 05				22 15				22 35	
Strawberry Hill	a	21 08									21 38						22 08								22 38	
Fulwell	d						21 19							21 49							22 19					
Hampton	d						21 23							21 53							22 23					
Kempton Park	d						21 26							21 56							22 26					
Sunbury	d						21 28							21 58							22 28					
Upper Halliford	d						21 30							22 00							22 30					
Shepperton	a						21 33							22 03							22 33					
Berrylands	d				21 00														22 00							
Surbiton [6]	d			20 57	21 05				21 14			21 27			21 44			21 57	22 05				22 14			22 27
Thames Ditton	d				21 09														22 09							
Hampton Court	a				21 12														22 12							
Hinchley Wood	d			21 01								21 31						22 01								22 31
Claygate	d			21 04								21 34						22 04								22 34
Oxshott	d			21 07								21 37						22 07								22 37
Cobham & Stoke d'Abernon	d			21 11								21 41						22 11								22 41
Bookham	d					21 29														22 29						
Effingham Junction [6]	d			21 15		21 33						21 45						22 15		22 33						22 45
Horsley	d			21 18		21 36						21 48						22 18		22 36						22 48
Clandon	d			21 23		21 41						21 53						22 23		22 41						22 53
London Road (Guildford)	d			21 28		21 46						21 58						22 28		22 46						22 58
Guildford	a			21 32		21 50						22 02						22 32		22 50			22 47			23 06

For general notes see front of timetable
For details of catering facilities see Directory of Train Operators

A To London Waterloo (Table 149)
B To Woking (Table 155)

From 28 September due to seasonal difficulties a large number of trains on this table will have minor retimings that could mean slightly earlier departure or later arrival times at certain stations. For further details see local publicity or contact National Rail Enquiries 08457 48 49 50.

For details of Bank Holiday service alterations, please see first page of Table 149

London → Chessington South, Dorking, Guildford Shepperton and Hampton Court

Network Diagram - see first page of Table 152

	SW	SW	SW	SW	SW	SW		SW	SW	SW	SW	SW	SW	SW	SW	SW	SW	SW	SW	SW	SW	SW	SW
			A	B						A	B					A	C						
London Waterloo 15 ⊖ d	22 09	22 12	22 20	22 27	22 33	22 36		22 39	22 42	22 50	22 57	23 00	23 03	23 09	23 12	23 20	23 27	23 30	23 37	23 42	23 50	23 57	
Vauxhall ⊖ d	22 13	22 16	22 24	22 31	22 37	22 40		22 43	22 46	22 54	23 01	23 04	23 07	23 13	23 16	23 24	23 31	23 34	23 41	23 46	23 54	00 01	
Clapham Junction 10 d	22 18	22 21	22 29	22 36	22 42	22 45		22 48	22 51	22 59	23 06	23 09	23 12	23 18	23 21	23 29	23 36	23 39	23 47	23 51	23 59	00 06	
Earlsfield d	22 21	22 24	22 32	22 39	22 45	22 48		22 51	22 54	23 02	23 09	23 12	23 15	23 21	23 24	23 32	23 39	23 42		23 54	00 02	00 09	
Wimbledon 6 ⊖ d	22 25	22 28	22 36	22 43	22 49	22 52		22 55	22 59	23 06	23 13	23 16	23 19	23 25	23 28	23 36	23 43	23 46		23 58	00 06	00 13	
Raynes Park 6 d	22 28	22 31		22 46		22 55		22 58	23 02		23 16	23 19		23 28	23 31		23 46	23 49		00 01		00 16	
Motspur Park d	22 31							23 01				23 22		23 31						00 04			
Malden Manor d												23 25											
Tolworth d												23 28											
Chessington North d												23 31											
Chessington South a												23 33											
Worcester Park d	22 33							23 03						23 33						00 06			
Stoneleigh d	22 36							23 06						23 36						00 09			←
Ewell West d	22 39							23 09						23 39						00 12 →			00 12
Epsom 3 a	22 42							23 12						23 42									00 15
d	22 47							23 17						23 47									00 19
Ashtead d	22 51							23 21						23 51									00 23
Leatherhead d	22 54							23 24						23 54									00 26
Boxhill & Westhumble d	22 59													23 59									
Dorking 4 a	23 01													00 01									
New Malden 6 d		22 34		22 49		22 58			23 05		23 19				23 34		23 49	23 52				00 19	
Norbiton d		22 37		22 52					23 08		23 22				23 37		23 52					00 22	
Kingston a		22 40		22 55					23 11		23 25				23 40		23 55		00 19			00 25	
d		22 40		22 59					23 11		23 29				23 40		23 55					00 25	
Hampton Wick d		22 42		23 01					23 13		23 31				23 42		23 57					00 27	
Teddington d		22 45		23 05					23 16		23 35				23 45		23 59					00 30	
Strawberry Hill a				23 08							23 38						00 03		00 12				
Fulwell d		22 49							23 20						23 49							00 34	
Hampton d		22 53							23 24						23 53							00 38	
Kempton Park d		22 56							23 27						23 56							00 41	
Sunbury d		22 58							23 29						23 58							00 43	
Upper Halliford d		23 00							23 31						23 59							00 45	
Shepperton a		23 03							23 34						00 03							00 48	
Berrylands d						23 00												23 54					
Surbiton 6 d			22 44		22 57	23 05				23 14			23 27			23 44		23 59			00 14		
Thames Ditton d						23 09												00 03					
Hampton Court a						23 12												00 06					
Hinchley Wood d					23 01								23 31								00 18		
Claygate d					23 04								23 34								00 21		
Oxshott d					23 07								23 37								00 24		
Cobham & Stoke d'Abernon d					23 11								23 41								00 28		
Bookham d								23 29															00 31
Effingham Junction 6 d					23 15			23 33					23 45								00 32		00 36
Horsley d					23 18			23 36					23 48								00 35		00 39
Clandon d					23 23			23 41					23 53								00 40		00 44
London Road (Guildford) d					23 28			23 46					23 58								00 45		00 49
Guildford a					23 32			23 54					00 02								00 49		00 54

For general notes see front of timetable
For details of catering facilities see Directory of Train Operators

A To Woking (Table 155)
B To London Waterloo (Table 149)
C To Twickenham (Table 149)

From 28 September due to seasonal difficulties a large number of trains on this table will have minor retimings that could mean slightly earlier departure or later arrival times at certain stations. For further details see local publicity or contact National Rail Enquiries 08457 48 49 50.

Table 152

Saturdays

For details of Bank Holiday service alterations, please see first page of Table 149

London → Chessington South, Dorking, Guildford Shepperton and Hampton Court

Network Diagram - see first page of Table 152

Station		SW	SW	SW	SW	SW	SW	SW	SW		SW	SW 1 A	SW 1 B	SW	SW 1 C	SW D	SW E	SW D		SW 1 G	SW	SW	SW	SW E	SW D	SW
London Waterloo 15 ⊖	d	23p30	23p42	23p50	23p57		00 09	00 15	00 27		00 42	01 05	05 00	05 12	05 20		05 50			06 12	06 06	06 12	06 16	06 20	06 27	06 33
Vauxhall ⊖	d	23p34	23p46	23p54	00 01		00 13	00 19	00 31		00 46	01 09	05 04	05 16	05 24		05 54				06 10	06 16	06 20	06 24	06 31	06 37
Clapham Junction 10	d	23p39	23p51	23p59	00 06		00 18	00 24	00 36		00 51	01 14	05 09	05 21	05 29		05 59			06u19	06 15	06 21	06 25	06 29	06 36	06 42
Earlsfield	d	23p42	23p54	00 02	00 09		00 21	00 27	00s39				05 12	05 24	05 32		06 02				06 18	06 24	06 28	06 32	06 39	06 45
Wimbledon 6 ⊖	d	23p46	23p58	00 06	00 13		00 25	00 31	00 43		01 05	01 20	05 16	05 28	05 36		06 06	06 13			06 22	06 28	06 32	06 36	06 43	06 49
Raynes Park 6	d	23p49	00 01		00 16			00 34	00 46		01 08			05 31				06 16			06 25	06 31	06 35		06 46	
Motspur Park	d		00 04					00 37															06 38			
Malden Manor	d																						06 41			
Tolworth	d																						06 44			
Chessington North	d																						06 47			
Chessington South	a																						06 49			
Worcester Park	d		00 06					00 39																		
Stoneleigh	d		00 09			←		00 42																		
Ewell West	d		00 12 →			00 12		00 45																		
Epsom 3	a					00 15		00 48																		
	d					00 19																				
Ashtead	d					00 23																				
Leatherhead	d					00 26																				
Boxhill & Westhumble	d																									
Dorking 4	a																									
New Malden 6	d	23p52			00 19				00 49		01 11			05 34				06 19			06 28	06 34			06 49	
Norbiton	d				00 22						01 14			05 37				06 22				06 37			06 52	
Kingston	a				00 25						01 17			05 40				06 25				06 40			06 55	
	d				00 25						01 17			05 40		05 59		06 29				06 40			06 59	
Hampton Wick	d				00 27						01s22			05 42		06 01		06 31				06 42			07 01	
Teddington	d				00 30						01s25			05 45		06 05		06 35				06 45			07 05	
Strawberry Hill	a										01 28					06 08		06 38							07 08	
Fulwell	d				00 34									05 49								06 49				
Hampton	d				00 38									05 53								06 53				
Kempton Park	d				00 41									05 56								06 56				
Sunbury	d				00 43									05 58								06 58				
Upper Halliford	d				00 45									06 00								07 00				
Shepperton	a				00 48									06 03								07 03				
Berrylands	d	23p54							00s51												06 30					
Surbiton 6	d	23p59		00 14			00 33		00a55			01 29	05 24		05 44		06 14			06 30	06 35			06 44		06 57
Thames Ditton	d	00 03																			06 39					
Hampton Court	a	00 06																			06 42					
Hinchley Wood	d			00 18																						07 01
Claygate	d			00 21																						07 04
Oxshott	d			00 24																						07 07
Cobham & Stoke d'Abernon	d			00 28																						07 11
Bookham	d					00 31																				
Effingham Junction 6	d			00 32		00 36																				07 15
Horsley	d			00 35		00 39																				07 18
Clandon	d			00 40		00 44																				07 23
London Road (Guildford)	d			00 45		00 49																				07 28
Guildford	a			00 49		00 54	01 06						05 59		06 23											07 32

For general notes see front of timetable
For details of catering facilities see Directory of Train Operators

- **A** To Southampton Central (Table 158)
- **B** To Haslemere (Table 156)
- **C** To Portsmouth Harbour (Table 156)
- **D** To London Waterloo (Table 149)
- **E** To Woking (Table 155)
- **G** To Basingstoke (Table 155)

From 3 October due to seasonal difficulties a large number of trains on this table will have minor retimings that could mean slightly earlier departure or later arrival times at certain stations. For further details see local publicity or contact National Rail Enquiries 08457 48 49 50.

For details of Bank Holiday service alterations, please see first page of Table 149

London → Chessington South, Dorking, Guildford Shepperton and Hampton Court

Network Diagram - see first page of Table 152

Station		SW	SW	SW	SW	SW A	SW B	SW	SW C	SW	SW	SW	SW	SW A	SW	SW B	SW	SW	SW	SW	SW	SW A	SW
London Waterloo 15 ⊖	d	06 36	06 39	06 42	06 46	06 50	06 57	07 03	07 03	07 06	07 09	07 12	07 16	07 20	07 24	07 27	07 33	07 36	07 39	07 42	07 46	07 50	07 54
Vauxhall ⊖	d	06 40	06 43	06 46	06 50	06 54	07 01	07 07	07 07	07 10	07 13	07 16	07 20	07 24	07 28	07 31	07 37	07 40	07 43	07 46	07 50	07 54	07 58
Clapham Junction 10	d	06 45	06 48	06 51	06 55	06 59	07 06	07 12	07 13	07 15	07 18	07 21	07 25	07 29	07 33	07 36	07 42	07 45	07 48	07 51	07 55	07 59	08 03
Earlsfield	d	06 48	06 51	06 54	06 58	07 02	07 09	07 15	08a05	07 18	07 21	07 24	07 28	07 32	07 36	07 39	07 45	07 48	07 51	07 54	07 58	08 02	08 06
Wimbledon 6 ⊖	d	06 52	06 55	06 58	07 02	07 06	07 13	07 19		07 22	07 25	07 28	07 32	07 36	07 40	07 43	07 49	07 52	07 55	07 58	08 02	08 06	08 10
Raynes Park 6	d	06 55	06 58	07 01	07 05		07 16			07 25	07 28	07 31	07 35		07 43	07 46		07 55	07 58	08 01	08 05		08 13
Motspur Park	d		07 01		07 08						07 31		07 38		07 46				08 01		08 08		08 16
Malden Manor	d				07 11								07 41								08 11		
Tolworth	d				07 14								07 44								08 14		
Chessington North	d				07 17								07 47								08 17		
Chessington South	a				07 19								07 49								08 19		
Worcester Park	d		07 03								07 33				07 48				08 03				08 18
Stoneleigh	d		07 06								07 36				07 51				08 06				08 21
Ewell West	d		07 09								07 39				07 54				08 09				08 24
Epsom 3	a		07 16								07 46				07 57				08 16				08 27
	d		07 17								07 47				07 58				08 17				08 28
Ashtead	d		07 21								07 51				08 02				08 21				08 32
Leatherhead	d		07 24								07 54				08 05				08 24				08 35
Boxhill & Westhumble	d																						
Dorking 4	a														08 11								08 41
New Malden 6	d	06 58		07 04			07 19			07 28		07 34				07 49		07 58		08 04			
Norbiton	d			07 07			07 22					07 37				07 52				08 07			
Kingston	a			07 10			07 25					07 40				07 55				08 10			
	d			07 10			07 29					07 40				07 59				08 10			
Hampton Wick	d			07 12			07 31					07 42				08 01				08 12			
Teddington	d			07 15			07 35					07 45				08 05				08 15			
Strawberry Hill	a						07 38		07 37							08 08							
Fulwell	d			07 19								07 49								08 19			
Hampton	d			07 23								07 53								08 23			
Kempton Park	d			07 26								07 56								08 26			
Sunbury	d			07 28								07 58								08 28			
Upper Halliford	d			07 30								08 00								08 30			
Shepperton	a			07 33								08 03								08 33			
Berrylands	d	07 00								07 30								08 00					
Surbiton 6	d	07 05				07 14		07 27		07 35				07 44			07 57	08 05				08 14	
Thames Ditton	d	07 09								07 39								08 09					
Hampton Court	a	07 12								07 42								08 12					
Hinchley Wood	d							07 31									08 01						
Claygate	d							07 34									08 04						
Oxshott	d							07 37									08 07						
Cobham & Stoke d'Abernon	d							07 41									08 11						
Bookham	d		07 29								07 59								08 29				
Effingham Junction 6	d		07 33					07 45			08 03						08 15		08 33				
Horsley	d		07 36					07 48			08 06						08 18		08 36				
Clandon	d		07 41					07 53			08 11						08 23		08 41				
London Road (Guildford)	d		07 46					07 58			08 16						08 28		08 46				
Guildford	a		07 50					08 02			08 20						08 32		08 50				

For general notes see front of timetable
For details of catering facilities see Directory of Train Operators

A To Woking (Table 155)
B To London Waterloo (Table 149)
C To London Waterloo

From 3 October due to seasonal difficulties a large number of trains on this table will have minor retimings that could mean slightly earlier departure or later arrival times at certain stations. For further details see local publicity or contact National Rail Enquiries 08457 48 49 50.

London → Chessington South, Dorking, Guildford Shepperton and Hampton Court

For details of Bank Holiday service alterations, please see first page of Table 149

Network Diagram - see first page of Table 152

		SW A	SW	SW	SW	SW	SW	SW B	SW	SW A	SW	SW	SW	SW	SW	SW B	SW	SW A		SW	SW	SW	SW
London Waterloo 15 ⊖	d	07 57	08 03	08 06	08 09	08 12	08 16	08 20	08 24	08 27	08 33	08 36	08 39	08 42	08 46	08 50	08 54	08 57		19 03	19 06	19 09	19 12
Vauxhall ⊖	d	08 01	08 07	08 10	08 13	08 16	08 20	08 24	08 28	08 31	08 37	08 40	08 43	08 46	08 50	08 54	08 58	09 01		19 07	19 10	19 13	19 16
Clapham Junction 10	d	08 06	08 12	08 15	08 18	08 21	08 25	08 29	08 33	08 36	08 42	08 45	08 48	08 51	08 55	08 59	09 03	09 06		19 12	19 15	19 18	19 21
Earlsfield	d	08 09	08 15	08 18	08 21	08 24	08 28	08 32	08 36	08 39	08 45	08 48	08 51	08 54	08 58	09 02	09 06	09 09		19 15	19 18	19 21	19 24
Wimbledon 6 ⊖	d	08 13	08 19	08 22	08 25	08 28	08 32	08 36	08 40	08 43	08 49	08 52	08 55	08 58	09 02	09 06	09 10	09 13		19 19	19 22	19 25	19 28
Raynes Park 6	d	08 16		08 25	08 28	08 31	08 35		08 43	08 46		08 55	08 58	09 01	09 05		09 13	09 16			19 25	19 28	19 31
Motspur Park	d				08 31		08 38		08 46				09 01		09 08		09 16					19 31	
Malden Manor	d						08 41								09 11								
Tolworth	d						08 44								09 14								
Chessington North	d						08 47								09 17								
Chessington South	a						08 49								09 19								
Worcester Park	d				08 33				08 48				09 03				09 18					19 33	
Stoneleigh	d				08 36				08 51				09 06				09 21					19 36	
Ewell West	d				08 39				08 54				09 09				09 24					19 39	
Epsom 3	a				08 46				08 57				09 16				09 27					19 42	
	d				08 47				08 58				09 17				09 28					19 47	
Ashtead	d				08 51				09 02				09 21				09 32					19 51	
Leatherhead	d				08 54				09 05				09 24				09 35					19 54	
Boxhill & Westhumble	d																						
Dorking 4	a								09 11								09 41		and at				
New Malden 6	d	08 19		08 28		08 34				08 49		08 58		09 04				09 19	the same		19 28		19 34
Norbiton	d	08 22				08 37				08 52				09 07				09 22	minutes				19 37
Kingston	a	08 25				08 40				08 55				09 10				09 25					19 40
	d	08 29				08 40				08 59				09 10				09 29	past				19 40
Hampton Wick	d	08 31				08 42				09 01				09 12				09 31					19 42
Teddington	d	08 35				08 45				09 05				09 15				09 35	each				19 45
Strawberry Hill	a	08 38								09 08								09 38	hour until				
Fulwell	d					08 49								09 19									19 49
Hampton	d					08 53								09 23									19 53
Kempton Park	d					08 56								09 26									19 56
Sunbury	d					08 58								09 28									19 58
Upper Halliford	d					09 00								09 30									20 00
Shepperton	a					09 03								09 33									20 03
Berrylands	d			08 30								09 00									19 30		
Surbiton 6	d		08 27	08 35				08 44			08 57	09 05				09 14				19 27	19 35		
Thames Ditton	d			08 39								09 09									19 39		
Hampton Court	a			08 42								09 12									19 42		
Hinchley Wood	d		08 31								09 01									19 31			
Claygate	d		08 34								09 04									19 34			
Oxshott	d		08 37								09 07									19 37			
Cobham & Stoke d'Abernon	d		08 41								09 11									19 41			
Bookham	d				08 59								09 29									19 59	
Effingham Junction 6	d		08 45		09 03						09 15		09 33							19 45		20 03	
Horsley	d		08 48		09 06						09 18		09 36							19 48		20 06	
Clandon	d		08 53		09 11						09 23		09 41							19 53		20 11	
London Road (Guildford)	d		08 58		09 16						09 28		09 46							19 58		20 16	
Guildford	a		09 02		09 20						09 32		09 50							20 02		20 20	

For general notes see front of timetable
For details of catering facilities see Directory of Train Operators

A To London Waterloo (Table 149)
B To Woking (Table 155)

From 3 October due to seasonal difficulties a large number of trains on this table will have minor retimings that could mean slightly earlier departure or later arrival times at certain stations. For further details see local publicity or contact National Rail Enquiries 08457 48 49 50.

For details of Bank Holiday service alterations, please see first page of Table 149

London → Chessington South, Dorking, Guildford Shepperton and Hampton Court

Network Diagram - see first page of Table 152

		SW	SW A	SW	SW B	SW	SW	SW	SW	SW	SW A	SW	SW B	SW	SW	SW	SW	SW	SW A	SW	SW B	SW	SW	SW
London Waterloo 15 ⊖	d	19 16	19 20	19 24	19 27	19 33	19 36	19 39	19 42	19 46	19 50	19 54	19 57	20 03	20 06	20 09	20 12	20 16	20 20	20 24	20 27	20 33	20 36	20 39
Vauxhall ⊖	d	19 20	19 24	19 28	19 31	19 37	19 40	19 43	19 46	19 50	19 54	19 58	20 01	20 07	20 10	20 13	20 16	20 20	20 24	20 28	20 31	20 37	20 40	20 43
Clapham Junction 10	d	19 25	19 29	19 33	19 36	19 42	19 45	19 48	19 51	19 55	19 59	20 03	20 06	20 12	20 15	20 18	20 21	20 25	20 29	20 33	20 36	20 42	20 45	20 48
Earlsfield	d	19 28	19 32	19 36	19 39	19 45	19 48	19 51	19 54	19 58	20 02	20 06	20 09	20 15	20 18	20 21	20 24	20 28	20 32	20 36	20 39	20 45	20 48	20 51
Wimbledon 6 ⊖ 🚋	d	19 32	19 36	19 40	19 43	19 49	19 52	19 55	19 58	20 02	20 06	20 10	20 13	20 19	20 22	20 25	20 28	20 32	20 36	20 40	20 43	20 49	20 52	20 55
Raynes Park 6	d	19 35		19 43	19 46		19 55	19 58	20 01	20 05		20 13	20 16		20 25	20 28	20 31	20 35		20 43	20 46		20 55	20 58
Motspur Park	d	19 38		19 46				20 01		20 08		20 16				20 31		20 38		20 46				21 01
Malden Manor	d	19 41								20 11								20 41						
Tolworth	d	19 44								20 14								20 44						
Chessington North	d	19 47								20 17								20 47						
Chessington South	a	19 49								20 19								20 49						
Worcester Park	d			19 48				20 03				20 18				20 33				20 48				21 03
Stoneleigh	d			19 51				20 06				20 21				20 36				20 51				21 06
Ewell West	d			19 54				20 09				20 24				20 39				20 54				21 09
Epsom 3	a			19 57				20 12				20 27				20 42				20 57				21 12
	d			19 58				20 17								20 47								21 17
Ashtead	d			20 02				20 21								20 51								21 21
Leatherhead	d			20 05				20 24								20 54								21 24
Boxhill & Westhumble	d																							
Dorking 4	a			20 11												21 00								
New Malden 6	d				19 49		19 58		20 04				20 19		20 28		20 34				20 49		20 58	
Norbiton	d				19 52				20 07				20 22				20 37				20 52			
Kingston	a				19 55				20 10				20 25				20 40				20 55			
	d				19 59				20 10				20 29				20 40				20 59			
Hampton Wick	d				20 01				20 12				20 31				20 42				21 01			
Teddington	d				20 05				20 15				20 35				20 45				21 05			
Strawberry Hill	a				20 08								20 38								21 08			
Fulwell	d								20 19								20 49							
Hampton	d								20 23								20 53							
Kempton Park	d								20 26								20 56							
Sunbury	d								20 28								20 58							
Upper Halliford	d								20 30								21 00							
Shepperton	a								20 33								21 03							
Berrylands	d						20 00								20 30								21 00	
Surbiton 6	d		19 44			19 57	20 05				20 14			20 27	20 35				20 44			20 57	21 05	
Thames Ditton	d						20 09								20 39								21 09	
Hampton Court	a						20 12								20 42								21 12	
Hinchley Wood	d					20 01								20 31								21 01		
Claygate	d					20 04								20 34								21 04		
Oxshott	d					20 07								20 37								21 07		
Cobham & Stoke d'Abernon	d					20 11								20 41								21 11		
Bookham	d							20 29																21 29
Effingham Junction 6	d					20 15		20 33						20 45								21 15		21 33
Horsley	d					20 18		20 36						20 48								21 18		21 36
Clandon	d					20 23		20 41						20 53								21 23		21 41
London Road (Guildford)	d					20 28		20 46						20 58								21 28		21 46
Guildford	a					20 32		20 50						21 02								21 32		21 50

For general notes see front of timetable
For details of catering facilities see Directory of Train Operators

A To Woking (Table 155)
B To London Waterloo (Table 149)

From 3 October due to seasonal difficulties a large number of trains on this table will have minor retimings that could mean slightly earlier departure or later arrival times at certain stations. For further details see local publicity or contact National Rail Enquiries 08457 48 49 50.

London → Chessington South, Dorking, Guildford Shepperton and Hampton Court

For details of Bank Holiday service alterations, please see first page of Table 149

Network Diagram - see first page of Table 152

	SW		SW	SW A	SW	SW B	SW	SW	SW	SW A		SW	SW B	SW	SW	SW	SW	SW	SW		SW	SW B	SW	SW	SW
London Waterloo 15 ⊖ d	20 42		20 46	20 50	20 54	20 57	21 03	21 09	21 12	21 20		21 24	21 27	21 33	21 36	21 39	21 42	21 46	21 50		21 54	21 57	22 03	22 09	22 12
Vauxhall ⊖ d	20 46		20 50	20 54	20 58	21 01	21 07	21 13	21 16	21 24		21 28	21 31	21 37	21 40	21 43	21 46	21 50	21 54		21 58	22 01	22 07	22 13	22 16
Clapham Junction 10 d	20 51		20 55	20 59	21 03	21 06	21 12	21 18	21 21	21 29		21 33	21 36	21 42	21 45	21 48	21 51	21 55	21 59		22 03	22 06	22 12	22 18	22 21
Earlsfield d	20 54		20 58	21 02	21 06	21 09	21 15	21 21	21 24	21 32		21 36	21 39	21 45	21 48	21 51	21 54	21 58	22 02		22 06	22 09	22 15	22 21	22 24
Wimbledon 6 ⊖ d	20 58		21 02	21 06	21 10	21 13	21 19	21 25	21 28	21 36		21 40	21 43	21 49	21 52	21 55	21 58	22 02	22 06		22 10	22 13	22 19	22 25	22 28
Raynes Park 6 d	21 01		21 05		21 13	21 16		21 28	21 31			21 43	21 46		21 55	21 58	22 01	22 05			22 13	22 16		22 28	22 31
Motspur Park d			21 08		21 16			21 31				21 46				22 01		22 08			22 16			22 31	
Malden Manor d			21 11															22 11							
Tolworth d			21 14															22 14							
Chessington North d			21 17															22 17							
Chessington South a			21 19															22 19							
Worcester Park d					21 18			21 33				21 48				22 03					22 18			22 33	
Stoneleigh d					21 21			21 36				21 51				22 06					22 21			22 36	
Ewell West d					21 24			21 39				21 54				22 09					22 24			22 39	
Epsom 3 a					21 27			21 42				21 57				22 12					22 27			22 42	
d								21 47								22 17								22 47	
Ashtead d								21 51								22 21								22 51	
Leatherhead d								21 54								22 24								22 54	
Boxhill & Westhumble d																									
Dorking 4 a								22 00																23 00	
New Malden 6 d	21 04					21 19			21 34				21 49		21 58		22 04					22 19			22 34
Norbiton d	21 07					21 22			21 37				21 52				22 07					22 22			22 37
Kingston a	21 10					21 25			21 40				21 55				22 10					22 25			22 40
d	21 10					21 29			21 40				21 59				22 10					22 29			22 40
Hampton Wick d	21 12					21 31			21 42				22 01				22 12					22 31			22 42
Teddington d	21 15					21 35			21 45				22 05				22 15					22 35			22 45
Strawberry Hill a						21 38							22 08									22 38			
Fulwell d	21 19								21 49								22 19								22 49
Hampton d	21 23								21 53								22 23								22 53
Kempton Park d	21 26								21 56								22 26								22 56
Sunbury d	21 28								21 58								22 28								22 58
Upper Halliford d	21 30								22 00								22 30								23 00
Shepperton a	21 33								22 03								22 33								23 03
Berrylands d															22 00										
Surbiton 6 d				21 14			21 27			21 44				21 57	22 05				22 14				22 27		
Thames Ditton d															22 09										
Hampton Court a															22 12										
Hinchley Wood d							21 31							22 01									22 31		
Claygate d							21 34							22 04									22 34		
Oxshott d							21 37							22 07									22 37		
Cobham & Stoke d'Abernon d							21 41							22 11									22 41		
Bookham d																22 29									
Effingham Junction 6 d							21 45							22 15		22 33							22 45		
Horsley d							21 48							22 18		22 36							22 48		
Clandon d							21 53							22 23		22 41							22 53		
London Road (Guildford) d							21 58							22 28		22 46							22 58		
Guildford a							22 02							22 32		22 50			22 47				23 02		

For general notes see front of timetable
For details of catering facilities see Directory of Train Operators

A To Woking (Table 155)
B To London Waterloo (Table 149)

From 3 October due to seasonal difficulties a large number of trains on this table will have minor retimings that could mean slightly earlier departure or later arrival times at certain stations. For further details see local publicity or contact National Rail Enquiries 08457 48 49 50.

For details of Bank Holiday service alterations, please see first page of Table 149

London → Chessington South, Dorking, Guildford Shepperton and Hampton Court

Network Diagram - see first page of Table 152

		SW	SW	SW	SW	SW	SW	SW	SW	SW	SW	SW	SW	SW	SW	SW	SW	SW	SW	SW
		A	B					A	B					A	C					
London Waterloo 15 ⊖	d	22 20	22 27	22 33	22 36	22 39	22 42	22 50	22 57	23 00	23 03	23 09	23 12	23 20	23 27	23 30	23 42	23 50	23 57	
Vauxhall ⊖	d	22 24	22 31	22 37	22 40	22 43	22 46	22 54	23 01	23 04	23 07	23 13	23 16	23 24	23 31	23 34	23 46	23 54	00 01	
Clapham Junction 10	d	22 29	22 36	22 42	22 45	22 48	22 51	22 59	23 06	23 09	23 12	23 18	23 21	23 29	23 36	23 39	23 51	23 58	00 06	
Earlsfield	d	22 32	22 39	22 45	22 48	22 51	22 54	23 02	23 09	23 12	23 15	23 21	23 24	23 32	23 39	23 42	23 54	00 02	00 09	
Wimbledon 6 ⊖	d	22 36	22 43	22 49	22 52	22 55	22 58	23 06	23 13	23 16	23 19	23 25	23 28	23 36	23 43	23 46	23 58	00 06	00 13	
Raynes Park 6	d		22 46		22 55	22 58	23 01		23 16	23 19		23 28	23 31		23 46	23 49	00 01		00 16	
Motspur Park	d					23 01				23 22		23 31					00 04			
Malden Manor	d									23 25										
Tolworth	d									23 28										
Chessington North	d									23 31										
Chessington South	a									23 33										
Worcester Park	d					23 03						23 33					00 06			←
Stoneleigh	d					23 06						23 36					00 09			
Ewell West	d					23 09						23 39					00 12 →			00 12
Epsom 3	a					23 12						23 42								00 15
	d					23 17						23 47								00 19
Ashtead	d					23 21						23 51								00 23
Leatherhead	d					23 24						23 54								00 26
Boxhill & Westhumble	d																			
Dorking 4	a											00 01								
New Malden 6	d		22 49		22 58		23 04		23 19				23 34		23 49	23 52			00 19	
Norbiton	d		22 52				23 07		23 22				23 37		23 52				00 22	
Kingston	a		22 55				23 10		23 25				23 40		23 55				00 25	
	d		22 59				23 10		23 29				23 40		23 55				00 25	
Hampton Wick	d		23 01				23 12		23 31				23 42		23 57				00 27	
Teddington	d		23 05				23 15		23 35				23 45		23 59				00 30	
Strawberry Hill	a		23 08						23 38						00 03					
Fulwell	d						23 19						23 49						00 34	
Hampton	d						23 23						23 53						00 38	
Kempton Park	d						23 26						23 56						00 41	
Sunbury	d						23 28						23 58						00 43	
Upper Halliford	d						23 30						23 59						00 45	
Shepperton	a						23 33						00 03						00 48	
Berrylands	d				23 00											23 54				
Surbiton 6	d	22 44		22 57	23 05			23 14			23 27			23 44		23 59		00 14		
Thames Ditton	d				23 09											00 03				
Hampton Court	a				23 12											00 06				
Hinchley Wood	d			23 01							23 31							00 18		
Claygate	d			23 04							23 34							00 21		
Oxshott	d			23 07							23 37							00 24		
Cobham & Stoke d'Abernon	d			23 11							23 41							00 28		
Bookham	d					23 29														00 31
Effingham Junction 6	d			23 15		23 33					23 45							00 32		00 36
Horsley	d			23 18		23 36					23 48							00 35		00 39
Clandon	d			23 23		23 41					23 53							00 40		00 44
London Road (Guildford)	d			23 28		23 46					23 58							00 45		00 49
Guildford	a			23 32		23 54					00 02							00 49		00 53

For general notes see front of timetable
For details of catering facilities see Directory of Train Operators

A To Woking (Table 155)
B To London Waterloo (Table 149)
C To Twickenham (Table 149)

From 3 October due to seasonal difficulties a large number of trains on this table will have minor retimings that could mean slightly earlier departure or later arrival times at certain stations. For further details see local publicity or contact National Rail Enquiries 08457 48 49 50.

Table 152

Sundays

For details of Bank Holiday service alterations, please see first page of Table 149

London → Chessington South, Dorking, Guildford Shepperton and Hampton Court

Network Diagram - see first page of Table 152

Station		SW	SW	SW	SW	SW	SW	SW	SW	SW	SW 1	SW	SW	SW	SW	SW	SW	SW	SW	SW	SW	SW	SW
											A	B	C	D						D			
London Waterloo 15 ⊖	d	23p30	23p42	23p50	23p57		00 09	00 15	00 27	00 42	01 05	01 42	06 14	06 18		06 57			07 10	07 18		07 27	
Vauxhall ⊖	d	23p34	23p46	23p54	00 01		00 13	00 19	00 31	00 46	01 09	01 46	06 18	06 22		07 01			07 14	07 22		07 31	
Clapham Junction 10	d	23p39	23p51	23p58	00 06		00 18	00 24	00 36	00 51	01 14	01 51	06 24	06 27		07 06			07 19	07 27		07 36	
Earlsfield	d	23p42	23p54	00 02	00 09		00 21	00 27	00s39				07a22			07 09			07 22	07 30		07 39	
Wimbledon 6 ⊖	d	23p46	23p58	00 06	00 13		00 25	00 31	00 43	01 05	01 20	01 57		06 34	06 48	07 13	07 16	07 18	07 26	07 34	07 37	07 43	07 48
Raynes Park 6	d	23p49	00 01		00 16			00 34	00 46	01 08		02 00		06 37	06 52	07 16		07 22		07 37	07 40	07 46	07 52
Motspur Park	d		00 04					00 37							06 55			07 25			07 43		07 55
Malden Manor	d																				07 46		
Tolworth	d																				07 49		
Chessington North	d																				07 52		
Chessington South	a																				07 54		
Worcester Park	d		00 06					00 39							06 57			07 27					07 57
Stoneleigh	d		00 09			←		00 42							07 00			07 30					08 00
Ewell West	d		00 12			00 12		00 45							07 03			07 33					08 03
Epsom 3	a		→			00 15		00 48							07 06			07 37					08 06
	d					00 19																	08 08
Ashtead	d					00 23																	08 12
Leatherhead	d					00 26																	08 15
Boxhill & Westhumble	d																						
Dorking 4	a																						
New Malden 6	d	23p52			00 19				00 49	01 11		02 02		06 40		07 19				07 40		07 49	
Norbiton	d				00 22					01 14		02 06		06 43						07 43			
Kingston	a				00 25					01 17		02 08		06 46						07 46			
	d				00 25					01 17		02 09		06 49						07 49			
Hampton Wick	d				00 27					01s22		02s11		06 51						07 51			
Teddington	d				00 30					01s25		02s13		06 56						07 56			
Strawberry Hill	a									01 28		02s16	06 48	06 59						07 59			
Fulwell	d				00 34																		
Hampton	d				00 38																		
Kempton Park	d				00 41																		
Sunbury	d				00 43																		
Upper Halliford	d				00 45																		
Shepperton	a				00 48																		
Berrylands	d	23p54							00s51							07 21						07 51	
Surbiton 6	d	23p59		00 14			00 33		00a55		01 29					07 25	07b32		07 35			07 55	
Thames Ditton	d	00 03														07 30						08 00	
Hampton Court	a	00 06														07 33						08 03	
Hinchley Wood	d			00 18													07 36						
Claygate	d			00 21													07 39						
Oxshott	d			00 24													07 42						
Cobham & Stoke d'Abernon	d			00 28													07 46						
Bookham	d					00 31																	08 20
Effingham Junction 6	d			00 32		00 36											07 50						08 24
Horsley	d			00 35		00 39											07 53						08 27
Clandon	d			00 40		00 44											07 58						08 32
London Road (Guildford)	d			00 45		00 49											08 03						08 37
Guildford	a			00 49		00 53	01 06										08 07		08 14				08 41

For general notes see front of timetable
For details of catering facilities see Directory of Train Operators

A To Southampton Central (Table 158)
B To Twickenham (Table 149)
C To London Waterloo
D To London Waterloo (Table 149)
b Arr. 0728

From 27 September due to seasonal difficulties a large number of trains on this table will have minor retimings that could mean slightly earlier departure or later arrival times at certain stations. For further details see local publicity or contact National Rail Enquiries 08457 48 49 50.

For details of Bank Holiday service alterations, please see first page of Table 149

London → Chessington South, Dorking, Guildford Shepperton and Hampton Court

Network Diagram - see first page of Table 152

Station		SW	SW	SW	SW		SW	SW	SW	SW	SW A	SW	SW	SW	SW	SW	SW	SW			SW	SW	SW	SW	SW B
London Waterloo 15 ⊖	d	07 40	07 48		07 57			08 02		08 10	08 18	08 21	08 27	08 32	08 40	08 48	08 51	08 57				12 02		12 10	12 14
Vauxhall ⊖	d	07 44	07 52		08 01			08 06		08 14	08 22	08 25	08 31	08 36	08 44	08 52	08 55	09 01				12 06		12 14	12 18
Clapham Junction 10	d	07 49	07 57		08 06			08 11		08 19	08 27	08 30	08 36	08 41	08 49	08 57	09 00	09 06				12 11		12 19	12 24
Earlsfield	d	07 52	08 00		08 09			08 14		08 22	08 30	08 33	08 39	08 44	08 52	09 00	09 03	09 09				12 14		12 22	13a20
Wimbledon 6 ⊖	d	07 56	08 04	08 07	08 13		08 16	08 18		08 26	08 34	08 37	08 43	08 48	08 56	09 04	09 07	09 13			12 16	12 18		12 26	
Raynes Park 6	d		08 07	08 10	08 16			08 22			08 37	08 40	08 46	08 52		09 07	09 10	09 16				12 22			
Motspur Park	d			08 13				08 25				08 43		08 55			09 13					12 25			
Malden Manor	d			08 16								08 46					09 16								
Tolworth	d			08 19								08 49					09 19								
Chessington North	d			08 22								08 52					09 22								
Chessington South	a			08 24								08 54					09 24								
Worcester Park	d							08 27						08 57								12 27			
Stoneleigh	d							08 30						09 00								12 30			
Ewell West	d							08 33						09 03								12 33			
Epsom 3	a							08 36						09 06								12 36			
	d							08 38						09 08								12 38			
Ashtead	d							08 42						09 12								12 42			
Leatherhead	d							08 45						09 15								12 45			
Boxhill & Westhumble	d																								
Dorking 4	a							08 51											and at the same minutes past each hour until			12 51			
New Malden 6	d		08 10		08 19						08 40		08 49			09 10		09 19							
Norbiton	d		08 13								08 43					09 13									
Kingston	a		08 16								08 46					09 16									
	d		08 16								08 49					09 16									
Hampton Wick	d		08 18								08 51					09 18									
Teddington	d		08 21								08 56					09 21									
Strawberry Hill	a										08 59														12 48
Fulwell	d		08 25													09 25									
Hampton	d		08 29													09 29									
Kempton Park	d		08 32													09 32									
Sunbury	d		08 34													09 34									
Upper Halliford	d		08 36													09 36									
Shepperton	a		08 39													09 39									
Berrylands	d				08 21				←				08 51					09 21					←		
Surbiton 6	d	08 05			08 25		08b32		08 32	08 35			08 55		09 05			09 25			12c32		12 32	12 35	
Thames Ditton	d				08 30		→						09 00					09 30			→				
Hampton Court	a				08 33								09 03					09 33							
Hinchley Wood	d								08 36														12 36		
Claygate	d								08 39														12 39		
Oxshott	d								08 42														12 42		
Cobham & Stoke d'Abernon	d								08 46														12 46		
Bookham	d													09 20											
Effingham Junction 6	d								08 50					09 24									12 50		
Horsley	d								08 53					09 27									12 53		
Clandon	d								08 58					09 32									12 58		
London Road (Guildford)	d								09 03					09 37									13 03		
Guildford	a	08 40							09 07	09 10				09 41	09 40								13 07	13 14	

For general notes see front of timetable
For details of catering facilities see Directory of Train Operators

A To London Waterloo (Table 149)
B To London Waterloo
b Arr. 0828
c Arr. 1228

From 27 September due to seasonal difficulties a large number of trains on this table will have minor retimings that could mean slightly earlier departure or later arrival times at certain stations. For further details see local publicity or contact National Rail Enquiries 08457 48 49 50.

Sundays

For details of Bank Holiday service alterations, please see first page of Table 149

London → Chessington South, Dorking, Guildford Shepperton and Hampton Court

Network Diagram - see first page of Table 152

		SW A	SW	SW	SW		SW	SW A	SW	SW	SW	SW	SW		SW	SW	SW B	SW A	SW	SW	SW		SW	SW A	SW	SW
London Waterloo 15 ⊖	d	12 18	12 21	12 27	12 32		12 40		12 48	12 51	12 57	13 00	13 02			13 10	13 14	13 18	13 21	13 27	13 32		13 40		13 48	13 51
Vauxhall ⊖	d	12 22	12 25	12 31	12 36		12 44		12 52	12 55	13 01	13 04	13 06			13 14	13 18	13 22	13 25	13 31	13 36		13 44		13 52	13 55
Clapham Junction 10	d	12 27	12 30	12 36	12 41		12 49		12 57	13 00	13 06	13 09	13 11			13 19	13 24	13 27	13 30	13 36	13 41		13 49		13 57	14 00
Earlsfield	d	12 30	12 33	12 39	12 44		12 52		13 00	13 03	13 09	13 12	13 14			13 22	14a20	13 30	13 33	13 39	13 44		13 52		14 00	14 03
Wimbledon 6 ⊖	d	12 34	12 37	12 43	12 48		12 56		13 04	13 07	13 13	13 16	13 18			13 26		13 34	13 37	13 43	13 48		13 56		14 04	14 07
Raynes Park 6	d	12 37	12 40	12 46	12 52				13 07	13 10	13 16		13 22					13 37	13 40	13 46	13 52				14 07	14 10
Motspur Park	d		12 43		12 55					13 13			13 25						13 43		13 55					14 13
Malden Manor	d		12 46							13 16									13 46							14 16
Tolworth	d		12 49							13 19									13 49							14 19
Chessington North	d		12 52							13 22									13 52							14 22
Chessington South	a		12 54							13 24									13 54							14 24
Worcester Park	d				12 57								13 27								13 57					
Stoneleigh	d				13 00								13 30								14 00					
Ewell West	d				13 03								13 33								14 03					
Epsom 3	a				13 06								13 36								14 06					
	d				13 08								13 38								14 08					
Ashtead	d				13 12								13 42								14 12					
Leatherhead	d				13 15								13 45								14 15					
Boxhill & Westhumble	d																									
Dorking 4	a												13 51													
New Malden 6	d	12 40		12 49					13 10		13 19							13 40		13 49					14 10	
Norbiton	d	12 43							13 13									13 43							14 13	
Kingston	a	12 46							13 16									13 46							14 16	
	d	12 49						13 11	13 16									13 49						14 11	14 16	
Hampton Wick	d	12 51						13 13	13 18									13 51						14 13	14 18	
Teddington	d	12 56						13 16	13 21									13 56						14 16	14 21	
Strawberry Hill	a	12 59						13 19									13 48	13 59						14 19		
Fulwell	d								13 25																14 25	
Hampton	d								13 29																14 29	
Kempton Park	d								13 32																14 32	
Sunbury	d								13 34																14 34	
Upper Halliford	d								13 36																14 36	
Shepperton	a								13 39																14 39	
Berrylands	d			12 51							13 21				←					13 51						
Surbiton 6	d			12 55			13 05				13 25	13b32			13 32	13 35				13 55			14 05			
Thames Ditton	d			13 00							13 30	→								14 00						
Hampton Court	a			13 03							13 33									14 03						
Hinchley Wood	d														13 36											
Claygate	d														13 39											
Oxshott	d														13 42											
Cobham & Stoke d'Abernon	d														13 46											
Bookham	d				13 20																14 20					
Effingham Junction 6	d				13 24										13 50						14 24					
Horsley	d				13 27										13 53						14 27					
Clandon	d				13 32										13 58						14 32					
London Road (Guildford)	d				13 37										14 03						14 37					
Guildford	a				13 41		13 44								14 07	14 14					14 41		14 44			

For general notes see front of timetable
For details of catering facilities see Directory of Train Operators

A To London Waterloo (Table 149)
B To London Waterloo
b Arr. 1328

From 27 September due to seasonal difficulties a large number of trains on this table will have minor retimings that could mean slightly earlier departure or later arrival times at certain stations. For further details see local publicity or contact National Rail Enquiries 08457 48 49 50.

Sundays

For details of Bank Holiday service alterations, please see first page of Table 149

London → Chessington South, Dorking, Guildford Shepperton and Hampton Court

Network Diagram - see first page of Table 152

		SW	SW	SW	SW	SW	SW	SW	SW	SW	SW	SW	SW	SW	SW	SW	SW	SW	SW	SW	SW	SW	SW
							A					A									A		
London Waterloo 15 ⊖	d	13 57	14 00	14 02		14 10	14 18	14 21	14 27	14 32	14 40		14 48	14 51	14 56	14 57	15 00	15 02		15 10	15 18	15 21	15 27
Vauxhall ⊖	d	14 01	14 04	14 06		14 14	14 22	14 25	14 31	14 36	14 44		14 52	14 55	15 00	15 01	15 04	15 06		15 14	15 22	15 25	15 31
Clapham Junction 10	d	14 06	14 09	14 11		14 19	14 27	14 30	14 36	14 41	14 49		14 57	15 00	15 06	15 06	15 09	15 11		15 19	15 27	15 30	15 36
Earlsfield	d	14 09	14 12	14 14		14 22	14 30	14 33	14 39	14 44	14 52		15 00	15 03		15 09	15 12	15 14		15 22	15 30	15 33	15 39
Wimbledon 6 ⊖	d	14 13	14 16	14 18		14 26	14 34	14 37	14 43	14 48	14 56		15 04	15 07		15 13	15 16	15 18		15 26	15 34	15 37	15 43
Raynes Park 6	d	14 16		14 22			14 37	14 40	14 46	14 52			15 07	15 10		15 16		15 22			15 37	15 40	15 46
Motspur Park	d			14 25				14 43		14 55				15 13				15 25				15 43	
Malden Manor	d							14 46						15 16								15 46	
Tolworth	d							14 49						15 19								15 49	
Chessington North	d							14 52						15 22								15 52	
Chessington South	a							14 54						15 24								15 54	
Worcester Park	d			14 27						14 57								15 27					
Stoneleigh	d			14 30						15 00								15 30					
Ewell West	d			14 33						15 03								15 33					
Epsom 3	a			14 36						15 06								15 36					
	d			14 38						15 08								15 38					
Ashtead	d			14 42						15 12								15 42					
Leatherhead	d			14 45						15 15								15 45					
Boxhill & Westhumble	d																						
Dorking 4	a			14 51														15 51					
New Malden 6	d	14 19					14 40		14 49				15 10			15 19					15 40		15 49
Norbiton	d						14 43						15 13								15 43		
Kingston	a						14 46						15 16		15 38						15 46		
	d						14 49					15 11	15 16								15 49		
Hampton Wick	d						14 51					15 13	15 18								15 51		
Teddington	d						14 56					15 16	15 21								15 56		
Strawberry Hill	a						14 59					15 19			15 30						15 59		
Fulwell	d												15 25										
Hampton	d												15 29										
Kempton Park	d												15 32										
Sunbury	d												15 34										
Upper Halliford	d												15 36										
Shepperton	a												15 39										
Berrylands	d	14 21			⟵				14 51							15 21			⟵				15 51
Surbiton 6	d	14 25	14b32		14 32	14 35			14 55		15 05					15 25	15c32		15 32	15 35			15 55
Thames Ditton	d	14 30	⟶						15 00							15 30	⟶						16 00
Hampton Court	a	14 33							15 03							15 33							16 03
Hinchley Wood	d				14 36														15 36				
Claygate	d				14 39														15 39				
Oxshott	d				14 42														15 42				
Cobham & Stoke d'Abernon	d				14 46														15 46				
Bookham	d									15 20													
Effingham Junction 6	d				14 50					15 24									15 50				
Horsley	d				14 53					15 27									15 53				
Clandon	d				14 58					15 32									15 58				
London Road (Guildford)	d				15 03					15 37									16 03				
Guildford	a				15 07	15 14				15 41	15 44								16 07	16 14			

For general notes see front of timetable
For details of catering facilities see Directory of Train Operators

A To London Waterloo (Table 149)
b Arr. 1428
c Arr. 1528

From 27 September due to seasonal difficulties a large number of trains on this table will have minor retimings that could mean slightly earlier departure or later arrival times at certain stations. For further details see local publicity or contact National Rail Enquiries 08457 48 49 50.

Sundays

For details of Bank Holiday service alterations, please see first page of Table 149

London → Chessington South, Dorking, Guildford Shepperton and Hampton Court

Network Diagram - see first page of Table 152

		SW	SW	SW A	SW	SW	SW		SW	SW	SW	SW	SW A	SW	SW	SW	SW	SW A	SW	SW	SW	SW	SW
London Waterloo 15 ⊖	d	15 32	15 40		15 48	15 51	15 57		19 00	19 02		19 10	19 18	19 21	19 27	19 32	19 40		19 48	19 57	20 00	20 02	
Vauxhall ⊖	d	15 36	15 44		15 52	15 55	16 01		19 04	19 06		19 14	19 22	19 25	19 31	19 36	19 44		19 52	20 01	20 04	20 06	
Clapham Junction 10	d	15 41	15 49		15 57	16 00	16 06		19 09	19 11		19 19	19 27	19 30	19 36	19 41	19 49		19 57	20 06	20 09	20 11	
Earlsfield	d	15 44	15 52		16 00	16 03	16 09		19 12	19 14		19 22	19 30	19 33	19 39	19 44	19 52		20 00	20 09	20 12	20 14	
Wimbledon 6 ⊖	d	15 48	15 56		16 04	16 07	16 13		19 16	19 18		19 26	19 34	19 37	19 43	19 48	19 56		20 04	20 13	20 16	20 18	
Raynes Park 6	d	15 52			16 07	16 10	16 16			19 22			19 37	19 40	19 46	19 52			20 07	20 16		20 22	
Motspur Park	d	15 55				16 13				19 25				19 43		19 55						20 25	
Malden Manor	d					16 16								19 46									
Tolworth	d					16 19								19 49									
Chessington North	d					16 22								19 52									
Chessington South	a					16 24								19 54									
Worcester Park	d	15 57								19 27						19 57						20 27	
Stoneleigh	d	16 00								19 30						20 00						20 30	
Ewell West	d	16 03								19 33						20 03						20 33	
Epsom 3	a	16 06								19 36						20 06						20 36	
	d	16 08								19 38						20 08						20 38	
Ashtead	d	16 12								19 42						20 12						20 42	
Leatherhead	d	16 15								19 45						20 15						20 45	
Boxhill & Westhumble	d																						
Dorking 4	a							and at		19 51												20 51	
New Malden 6	d				16 10		16 19	the same					19 40		19 49				20 10	20 19			
Norbiton	d				16 13			minutes					19 43						20 13				
Kingston	a				16 16								19 46						20 16				
	d			16 11	16 16			past					19 49					20 11	20 16				
Hampton Wick	d			16 13	16 18								19 51					20 13	20 18				
Teddington	d			16 16	16 21			each					19 56					20 16	20 21				
Strawberry Hill	a			16 19				hour until					19 59					20 19					
Fulwell	d				16 25														20 25				
Hampton	d				16 29														20 29				
Kempton Park	d				16 32														20 32				
Sunbury	d				16 34														20 34				
Upper Halliford	d				16 36														20 36				
Shepperton	a				16 39														20 39				
Berrylands	d						16 21								19 51					20 21			
Surbiton 6	d		16 05				16 25		19b32		← 19 32	19 35			19 55		20 05			20 25	20c32		← 20 32
Thames Ditton	d						16 30		→						20 00					20 30	→		
Hampton Court	a						16 33								20 03					20 33			
Hinchley Wood	d										19 36												20 36
Claygate	d										19 39												20 39
Oxshott	d										19 42												20 42
Cobham & Stoke d'Abernon	d										19 46												20 46
Bookham	d	16 20														20 20							
Effingham Junction 6	d	16 24									19 50					20 24							20 50
Horsley	d	16 27									19 53					20 27							20 53
Clandon	d	16 32									19 58					20 32							20 58
London Road (Guildford)	d	16 37									20 03					20 37							21 03
Guildford	a	16 41	16 44								20 07	20 14				20 41	20 44						21 07

For general notes see front of timetable
For details of catering facilities see Directory of Train Operators

A To London Waterloo (Table 149)
b Arr. 1928
c Arr. 2028

From 27 September due to seasonal difficulties a large number of trains on this table will have minor retimings that could mean slightly earlier departure or later arrival times at certain stations. For further details see local publicity or contact National Rail Enquiries 08457 48 49 50.

For details of Bank Holiday service alterations, please see first page of Table 149

London → Chessington South, Dorking, Guildford Shepperton and Hampton Court

Network Diagram - see first page of Table 152

		SW		SW	SW	SW	SW	SW	SW	SW		SW	SW	SW	SW	SW	SW	SW		SW	SW	SW	SW	SW	SW	SW
				A					A								A					A				
London Waterloo 15 ⊖	d	20 10		20 18	20 21	20 27	20 32	20 40		20 48		20 57	21 00	21 02		21 10	21 18	21 21		21 32	21 40		21 48	21 57	22 00	22 02
Vauxhall ⊖	d	20 14		20 22	20 25	20 31	20 36	20 44		20 52		21 01	21 04	21 06		21 14	21 22	21 25		21 36	21 44		21 52	22 01	22 04	22 06
Clapham Junction 10	d	20 19		20 27	20 30	20 36	20 41	20 49		20 57		21 06	21 09	21 11		21 19	21 27	21 30		21 41	21 49		21 57	22 06	22 09	22 11
Earlsfield	d	20 22		20 30	20 33	20 39	20 44	20 52		21 00		21 09	21 12	21 14		21 22	21 30	21 33		21 44	21 52		22 00	22 09	22 12	22 14
Wimbledon 6 ⊖ 🚋	d	20 26		20 34	20 37	20 43	20 48	20 56		21 04		21 13	21 16	21 18		21 26	21 34	21 37		21 48	21 56		22 04	22 13	22 16	22 18
Raynes Park 6	d			20 37	20 40	20 46	20 52			21 07		21 16		21 22			21 37	21 40		21 52			22 07	22 16		22 22
Motspur Park	d				20 43		20 55							21 25				21 43		21 55						22 25
Malden Manor	d				20 46													21 46								
Tolworth	d				20 49													21 49								
Chessington North	d				20 52													21 52								
Chessington South	a				20 54													21 54								
Worcester Park	d						20 57							21 27						21 57						22 27
Stoneleigh	d						21 00							21 30						22 00						22 30
Ewell West	d						21 03							21 33						22 03						22 33
Epsom 3	a						21 06							21 36						22 06						22 36
	d						21 08							21 38						22 08						22 38
Ashtead	d						21 12							21 42						22 12						22 42
Leatherhead	d						21 15							21 45						22 15						22 45
Boxhill & Westhumble	d																									
Dorking 4	a													21 51												22 51
New Malden 6	d			20 40		20 49				21 10		21 19					21 40						22 10	22 19		
Norbiton	d			20 43						21 13							21 43						22 13			
Kingston	a			20 46						21 16							21 46						22 16			
	d			20 49					21 11	21 16							21 49					22 11	22 16			
Hampton Wick	d			20 51					21 13	21 18							21 51					22 13	22 18			
Teddington	d			20 56					21 16	21 21							21 56					22 16	22 21			
Strawberry Hill	a			20 59					21 19								21 59					22 19				
Fulwell	d									21 25													22 25			
Hampton	d									21 29													22 29			
Kempton Park	d									21 32													22 32			
Sunbury	d									21 34													22 34			
Upper Halliford	d									21 36													22 36			
Shepperton	a									21 39													22 39			
Berrylands	d					20 51						21 21			←									22 21		
Surbiton 6	d	20 35				20 55		21 05				21 25	21b32		21 32	21 35					22 05			22 25	22c32	
Thames Ditton	d					21 00						21 30	→											22 30	→	
Hampton Court	a					21 03						21 33												22 33		
Hinchley Wood	d														21 36											
Claygate	d														21 39											
Oxshott	d														21 42											
Cobham & Stoke d'Abernon	d														21 46											
Bookham	d						21 20													22 20						
Effingham Junction 6	d						21 24								21 50					22 24						
Horsley	d						21 27								21 53					22 27						
Clandon	d						21 32								21 58					22 32						
London Road (Guildford)	d						21 37								22 03					22 37						
Guildford	a	21 14					21 41	21 44							22 07	22 14				22 41	22 44					

For general notes see front of timetable
For details of catering facilities see Directory of Train Operators

A To London Waterloo (Table 149)
b Arr. 2128
c Arr. 2228

From 27 September due to seasonal difficulties a large number of trains on this table will have minor retimings that could mean slightly earlier departure or later arrival times at certain stations. For further details see local publicity or contact National Rail Enquiries 08457 48 49 50.

Table 152

Sundays

For details of Bank Holiday service alterations, please see first page of Table 149

London → Chessington South, Dorking, Guildford Shepperton and Hampton Court

Network Diagram - see first page of Table 152

		SW	SW	SW	SW	SW	SW	SW	SW	SW	SW	SW	SW	SW	SW	SW	SW	SW
																		1
				A				A										B
London Waterloo 15 ⊖	d		22 10	22 18	22 21	22 32	22 40		22 48	22 51	22 57	23 00	23 02		23 10	23 18	23 32	23 40
Vauxhall ⊖	d		22 14	22 22	22 25	22 36	22 44		22 52	22 55	23 01	23 04	23 06		23 14	23 22	23 36	23 44
Clapham Junction 10	d		22 19	22 27	22 30	22 41	22 49		22 57	23 00	23 06	23 09	23 11		23 19	23 27	23 41	23 49
Earlsfield	d		22 22	22 30	22 33	22 44	22 52		23 00	23 03	23 09	23 12	23 14		23 22	23 30	23 44	23 52
Wimbledon 6 ⊖ ⛴	d		22 26	22 34	22 37	22 48	22 56		23 04	23 07	23 13	23 16	23 18		23 26	23 34	23 48	23 56
Raynes Park 6	d			22 37	22 40	22 52			23 07	23 10	23 16		23 22			23 37	23 52	
Motspur Park	d				22 43	22 55				23 13			23 25				23 55	
Malden Manor	d				22 46					23 16								
Tolworth	d				22 49					23 19								
Chessington North	d				22 52					23 22								
Chessington South	a				22 54					23 24								
Worcester Park	d					22 57							23 27				23 57	
Stoneleigh	d					23 00							23 30				23 59	
Ewell West	d					23 03							23 33				00 03	
Epsom 3	a					23 06							23 36				00 06	
	d					23 08												
Ashtead	d					23 12												
Leatherhead	d					23 15												
Boxhill & Westhumble	d																	
Dorking 4	a																	
New Malden 6	d			22 40					23 10		23 19					23 40		
Norbiton	d			22 43					23 13							23 43		
Kingston	a			22 46					23 16							23 46		
	d			22 49				23 11	23 16							23 47		
Hampton Wick	d			22 51				23 13	23 18							23 49		
Teddington	d			22 56				23 16	23 21							23 51		
Strawberry Hill	a			22 59				23 19								23 54		
Fulwell	d								23 25									
Hampton	d								23 29									
Kempton Park	d								23 32									
Sunbury	d								23 34									
Upper Halliford	d								23 36									
Shepperton	a								23 39									
Berrylands	d	←									23 21			←				
Surbiton 6	d	22 32	22 35				23 05				23 25	23b32		23 32	23 35			00 05
Thames Ditton	d										23 30	↪						
Hampton Court	a										23 33							
Hinchley Wood	d	22 36												23 36				
Claygate	d	22 39												23 39				
Oxshott	d	22 42												23 42				
Cobham & Stoke d'Abernon	d	22 46												23 46				
Bookham	d					23 20												
Effingham Junction 6	d	22 50				23 24								23 50				
Horsley	d	22 53				23 27								23 53				
Clandon	d	22 58				23 32								23 58				
London Road (Guildford)	d	23 03				23 37								00 03				
Guildford	a	23 07	23 13			23 41	23 45							00 07	00 13			

For general notes see front of timetable
For details of catering facilities see Directory of Train Operators

A To London Waterloo (Table 149)
B To Farnham (Table 155)
b Arr. 2328

From 27 September due to seasonal difficulties a large number of trains on this table will have minor retimings that could mean slightly earlier departure or later arrival times at certain stations. For further details see local publicity or contact National Rail Enquiries 08457 48 49 50.

For details of Bank Holiday service alterations, please see first page of Table 149

Hampton Court, Shepperton, Guildford, Dorking and Chessington South → London

Network Diagram - see first page of Table 152

Miles	Miles	Miles	Miles	Miles			SW MX	SW MX A	SW MX	SW MO	SW MX A	SW MX A	SW B	SW	SW	SW	SW	SW	SW	SW A	SW	SW	SW	SW	SW	SW
0	—	—	—	—	**Guildford**	d			23p08					04 58				05 38				05 58			06 07	
1¼	—	—	—	—	London Road (Guildford)	d			23p12					05 02				05 42				06 02			06 11	
4½	—	—	—	—	Clandon	d			23p17					05 07				05 47				06 07			06 16	
7¾	—	—	—	—	Horsley	d			23p21					05 11				05 51				06 11			06 20	
8¾	0	—	—	—	Effingham Junction 6	d			23p24					05 16				05 54				06 16			06 24	
—	1¾	—	—	—	Bookham	d								05 19								06 19				
11	—	—	—	—	Cobham & Stoke d'Abernon	d			23p28									05 58							06 27	
13	—	—	—	—	Oxshott	d			23p31									06 01							06 31	
14¾	—	—	—	—	Claygate	d			23p34									06 04							06 34	
16	—	—	—	—	Hinchley Wood	d			23p37									06 07							06 37	
—	—	—	0	—	**Hampton Court**	d				23p45							05 54						06 24			
—	—	—	1	—	Thames Ditton	d				23p47							05 56						06 26			
18	—	—	3	—	**Surbiton** 6	d			23p42	23p53							06 02	06 12					06 32		06 42	
19	—	—	—	—	Berrylands	d				23p55							06 04						06 34			
—	—	—	—	0	**Shepperton**	d	23p11								05 23									06 11		
—	—	—	—	1½	Upper Halliford	d	23p14								05 26									06 14		
—	—	—	—	2	Sunbury	d	23p16								05 28									06 16		
—	—	—	—	2½	Kempton Park	d	23p18																			
—	—	—	—	4¼	Hampton	d	23p21								05 33									06 21		
—	—	—	—	6	Fulwell	d	23p24								05 36									06 24		
—	—	—	0	—	Strawberry Hill	d		23p37				00 12	04 55		05 38					06 08						
—	—	—	1¼	7	Teddington	d	23p29	23p41				00 15	04 59			05 44				06 11				06 29		
—	—	—	—	8½	Hampton Wick	d	23p31	23p44				00 17	05 01			05 46				06 14				06 31		
—	—	—	—	8¾	Kingston	a	23p33	23p46				00 19	05 03			05 48				06 16				06 33		
—	—	—	—	—		d	23p34	23p49					05 04			05 49				06 19				06 34		
—	—	—	—	9½	Norbiton	d	23p36	23p51					05 06			05 51				06 21				06 36		
20	—	—	—	11	New Malden 6	d	23p40	23p55		23p58			05 10			05 55	06 07			06 25			06 37	06 40		
—	—	0	—	—	**Dorking** 4	d													05 48							
—	—	¾	—	—	Boxhill & Westhumble	d													05 50							
—	4¼	4	—	—	Leatherhead	d								05 24					05 56			06 24				
—	—	5¾	—	—	Ashtead	d								05 28					05 59			06 28				
—	—	7¾	—	—	**Epsom** 3	a								05 32					06 04			06 32				
—	—	—	—	—		d								05 34					06 04		06 18	06 33				←
—	—	9	—	—	Ewell West	d								05 37					06 07		06 21	06 36 →				06 36
—	—	10	—	—	Stoneleigh	d								05 40					06 10		06 24					06 38
—	—	11¼	—	—	Worcester Park	d								05 42					06 12		06 27					06 41
—	0	—	—	—	**Chessington South**	d																				
—	¾	—	—	—	Chessington North	d																				
—	1¾	—	—	—	Tolworth	d																				
—	2¾	—	—	—	Malden Manor	d																				
—	3¾	12¼	—	—	Motspur Park	d					←			05 46					06 16		06 30					06 46
21½	5½	13½	—	12	Raynes Park 6	d	23p43	23p58		00 01	23p58		05 13	05 49		05 58	06 10		06 19	06 28	06 34		06 40	06 43		06 49
22¾	6¾	14¾	—	13½	**Wimbledon** 6 ⊖	d	23p52	→	23p55	00a04	00 05		05 17	05 53		06 02	06 14	06 20	06 23	06 32	06 38		06 44	06 47	06 50	06 53
24½	8½	16½	—	15¼	Earlsfield	d	23p55		23p58		00 08		05 21	05 57		06 05	06 17	06 24	06 27	06 35	06 42		06 47	06 50	06 54	06 57
26	10	18	—	16¾	**Clapham Junction** 10	d	23p59		00 02		23p13		05 25	06 01	06 05	06 09	06 21	06 28	06 31	05 43	06 46		06 51	06 54	06 58	07 01
28¾	12¾	20¾	—	19¼	Vauxhall ⊖	d	00 04		00 07		00 17		05 30	06 06	06 12	06 14	06 26	06 33	06 36	06 44	06 51		06 56	06 59	07 03	07 06
30	14	22	—	20¾	**London Waterloo** 15 ⊖	a	00 11		00 14		00 23		05 35	06 11	06 16	06 19	06 31	06 37	06 40	06 49	06 55		07 03	07 06	07 09	07 12

For general notes see front of timetable
For details of catering facilities see Directory of Train Operators

A From London Waterloo (Table 149)
B From Twickenham (Table 149)

From 28 September due to seasonal difficulties a large number of trains on this table will have minor retimings that could mean slightly earlier departure or later arrival times at certain stations. For further details see local publicity or contact National Rail Enquiries 08457 48 49 50.

For details of Bank Holiday service alterations, please see first page of Table 149

Hampton Court, Shepperton, Guildford, Dorking and Chessington South → London

Network Diagram - see first page of Table 152

		SW	SW A	SW	SW	SW	SW	SW	SW	SW	SW A	SW	SW	SW	SW	SW	SW	SW	SW	SW	SW	SW	SW A	SW	SW B	SW
Guildford	d						06 28	06 37							06 58				07 07	07 17						
London Road (Guildford)	d						06 32	06 41							07 02				07 11	07 21						
Clandon	d						06 37	06 46							07 07				07 16	07 26						
Horsley	d						06 41	06 50							07 11				07 20	07 30						
Effingham Junction 6	d						06b48	06 54							07 16				07 24	07 34						
Bookham	d						06 51								07 19											
Cobham & Stoke d'Abernon	d							06 57											07 27	07 37						
Oxshott	d							07 01											07 31	07 41						
Claygate	d							07 04											07 34	07 44						
Hinchley Wood	d							07 07											07 37	07 47						
Hampton Court	d				06 54												07 24									
Thames Ditton	d				06 56												07 26									
Surbiton 6	d				07 02			07 12									07 32		07 42	07 53						
Berrylands	d				07 04												07 34									
Shepperton	d					06 41										07 00		07 11								
Upper Halliford	d					06 44										07 03		07 14								
Sunbury	d					06 46										07 05		07 16								
Kempton Park	d																									
Hampton	d					06 51										07 09		07 21								
Fulwell	d					06 54										07 12		07 24								
Strawberry Hill	d		06 37								07 07					07 14							07 37		07 47	
Teddington	d		06 41			06 59					07 11		07 20					07 29					07 41		07 50	
Hampton Wick	d		06 44			07 01					07 14		07 22					07 31					07 44		07 52	
Kingston	a		06 46			07 03					07 16		07 24					07 33					07 46		07 54	
	d		06 49			07 04					07 19		07 26					07 34					07 49		07 56	
Norbiton	d		06 51			07 06					07 21		07 28					07 36					07 51		07 58	
New Malden 6	d		06 55		07 07	07 10					07 25		07 32				07 37	07 40	07 46				07 55		08 02	
Dorking 4	d			06 32								07 02												07 32		
Boxhill & Westhumble	d			06 34								07 04												07 34		
Leatherhead	d			06 39			06 56					07 09			07 25									07 39		
Ashtead	d			06 43			06 59					07 13			07 28									07 43		
Epsom 3	a			06 47			07 04					07 17			07 33									07 47		
	d			06 48			07 04		←			07 18		07 22	07 34						←			07 48		07 52
Ewell West	d			06 51			07 07		07 07					07 25	07 37						07 37					07 55
Stoneleigh	d			06 53			→		07 10					07 27	→						07 40					07 57
Worcester Park	d			06 56					07 12			07 25		07 30							07 43			07 55		08 00
Chessington South	d	06 40								07 10												07 40				
Chessington North	d	06 42								07 12												07 42				
Tolworth	d	06 44								07 14												07 44				
Malden Manor	d	06 47								07 17												07 47				
Motspur Park	d	06 50		07 00					07 16	07 20				07 34							07 46	07 50				08 04
Raynes Park 6	d	06 54	06 58	07 04	07 10	07 13			07 19	07 24	07 28	07 31	07 34	07 37			07 40	07 43			07 50	07 54	07 58	08 01	08 04	08 07
Wimbledon 6 ⊖ ⛴	d	06 58	07 02	07 08	07 14	07 17		07 20	07 23	07 28	07 32	07 35	07 38	07 41			07 44	07 47	07 51		07 54	07 58	08 02	08 05	08 08	08 11
Earlsfield	d	07 01	07 05	07 11	07 17	07 20		07 24	07 27	07 31	07 35	07 38	07 42	07 45			07 48	07 51	07 54		07 58	08 01	08 05	08 08	08 12	08 15
Clapham Junction 10	d	07 05	07 08	07 15	07 21	07 24		07 28	07 31	07 35	07 38	07 42	07 46	07 49		07 49	07 52	07 55	07 58		08 02	08 05	08 08	08 12	08 16	08 19
Vauxhall ⊖	d	07 10	07 14	07 20	07 26	07 29		07 33	07 36	07 40	07 44	07 47	07 51	07 54		07 56	07 57	08 00	08 03		08 07	08 10	08 14	08 17	08 21	08 24
London Waterloo 15 ⊖	a	07 17	07 21	07 27	07 33	07 36		07 39	07 42	07 47	07 51	07 54	07 57	08 00		08 04	08 04	08 06	08 11	08 13	08 13	08 17	08 21	08 24	08 27	08 30

For general notes see front of timetable
For details of catering facilities see Directory of Train Operators

A From London Waterloo (Table 149)
B From Twickenham (Table 149)
b Arr. 0644

From 28 September due to seasonal difficulties a large number of trains on this table will have minor retimings that could mean slightly earlier departure or later arrival times at certain stations. For further details see local publicity or contact National Rail Enquiries 08457 48 49 50.

For details of Bank Holiday service alterations, please see first page of Table 149

Hampton Court, Shepperton, Guildford, Dorking and Chessington South → London

Network Diagram - see first page of Table 152

		SN	SW	SW	SW	SW	SW	SW	SW	SW	SW	SW	SW	SW	SW	SW	SW	SW	SW	SW 1	SW	SW	SN	SW	SW 1	SW
		A								B		C								D	B		E		G	
Guildford	d	07 26					07 37										07 58	08 07					08 16			
London Road (Guildford)	d	07 29					07 41										08 02	08 11					08 19			
Clandon	d						07 46										08 07	08 16					08 24			
Horsley	d						07 50										08 11	08 20					08 29			
Effingham Junction 6	d	07 38	07 46				07 54										08 15	08 24					08 32	08 48		
Bookham	d	07 41	07 49														08 18						08 35	08 51		
Cobham & Stoke d'Abernon	d						07 57											08 27								
Oxshott	d						08 01											08 31								
Claygate	d						08 04											08 34								
Hinchley Wood	d						08 07											08 37								
Hampton Court	d				07 54									08 24												08 54
Thames Ditton	d				07 56									08 26												08 56
Surbiton 6	d				08 02		08 12							08 32				08 42								09 02
Berrylands	d				08 04									08 34												09 04
Shepperton	d			07 30		07 41									08 00	08 11										
Upper Halliford	d			07 33		07 44									08 03	08 14										
Sunbury	d			07 35		07 46									08 05	08 16										
Kempton Park	d																									
Hampton	d			07 39		07 51									08 09	08 21										
Fulwell	d			07 42		07 54									08 12	08 24										
Strawberry Hill	d			07 44						08 07		08 17			08 14						08 38					
Teddington	d					07 59				08 11		08 20				08 29					08 41					
Hampton Wick	d					08 01				08 14		08 22				08 31					08 44					
Kingston	a					08 03				08 16		08 24				08 33					08 46					
	d					08 04				08 19		08 26				08 34					08 49					
Norbiton	d					08 06				08 21		08 28				08 36					08 51					
New Malden 6	d				08 07	08 10	08 16			08 25		08 32		08 37		08 40					08 55					09 07
Dorking 4	d										08 02											08 31				
Boxhill & Westhumble	d										08 04											08 33				
Leatherhead	d	07 46	07 54								08 09						08 25					08 38	08 41	08 56		
Ashtead	d	07 50	07 57								08 13						08 28					08 42	08 45	08 59		
Epsom 3	a	07 54	08 02								08 17						08 33					08 46	08 49	09 04		
	d		08 04					←			08 18		08 22				08 34					08 48		09 04		
Ewell West	d		08 07					08 07					08 25				08 37					08 51		09 07		
Stoneleigh	d		→					08 10					08 27				08 40					08 54		→		
Worcester Park	d							08 13			08 25		08 30				08 42					08 57				
Chessington South	d								08 10										08 40							
Chessington North	d								08 12										08 42							
Tolworth	d								08 14										08 44							
Malden Manor	d								08 17										08 47							
Motspur Park	d							08 16	08 20				08 34				08 46		08 50			09 00				
Raynes Park 6	d				08 10	08 13		08 20	08 24	08 28	08 31	08 34	08 37	08 40		08 43	08 49		08 54		08 58	09 04				09 10
Wimbledon 6	⊖ d				08 14	08 17	08 21	08 24	08 28	08 32	08 35	08 38	08 41	08 44		08 47	08 53		08 58		09 02	09 08				09 14
Earlsfield	d				08 18	08 21	08 24	08 28	08 31	08 35	08 38	08 42	08 45	08 48		08 51	08 57		09 01		09 05	09 12				09 17
Clapham Junction 10	d			08 19	08 22	08 25	08 28	08 32	08 35	08 38	08 42	08 46	08 49	08 52	08 49	08 55	09 01		09 05		09 08	09 16				09 21
Vauxhall	⊖ d			08 26	08 27	08 30	08 33	08 37	08 40	08 44	08 47	08 51	08 54	08 57	08 56	09 00	09 06		09 10		09 14	09 21				09 26
London Waterloo 15	⊖ a			08 34	08 33	08 36	08 40	08 43	08 47	08 51	08 54	08 57	09 00	09 03	09 04	09 06	09 12	09 01	09 17	09 10	09 21	09 27			09 21	09 33

For general notes see front of timetable
For details of catering facilities see Directory of Train Operators

A To London Bridge (Table 182)
B From London Waterloo (Table 149)
C From Twickenham (Table 149)
D From Southampton Central (Table 158)
E To London Bridge (Table 178)
G From Alton (Table 155)

From 28 September due to seasonal difficulties a large number of trains on this table will have minor retimings that could mean slightly earlier departure or later arrival times at certain stations. For further details see local publicity or contact National Rail Enquiries 08457 48 49 50.

For details of Bank Holiday service alterations, please see first page of Table 149

Hampton Court, Shepperton, Guildford, Dorking and Chessington South → London

Network Diagram - see first page of Table 152

	SW	SW	SW	SW	SW A	SW	SW	SW	SW	SW	SW	SW	SW A	SW	SW	SW	SW	SW	SW	SW	SW A	SW	SW	SW	SW
Guildford d		08 37					08 58			09 08					09 28			09 38					09 58		
London Road (Guildford) d		08 41					09 02			09 12					09 32			09 42					10 02		
Clandon d		08 46					09 07			09 17					09 37			09 47					10 07		
Horsley d		08 50					09 11			09 21					09 41			09 51					10 11		
Effingham Junction 6 d		08 54					09 16			09 24					09 46			09 54					10 16		
Bookham d							09 19								09 49								10 19		
Cobham & Stoke d'Abernon d		08 57								09 28								09 58							
Oxshott d		09 01								09 31								10 01							
Claygate d		09 04								09 34								10 04							
Hinchley Wood d		09 07								09 37								10 07							
Hampton Court d								09 24								09 54								10 24	
Thames Ditton d								09 26								09 56								10 26	
Surbiton 6 d		09 12						09 32		09 42						10 02		10 12						10 32	
Berrylands d								09 34								10 04								10 34	
Shepperton d	08 41								09 11								09 41								10 11
Upper Halliford d	08 44								09 14								09 44								10 14
Sunbury d	08 46								09 16								09 46								10 16
Kempton Park d									09 18								09 48								10 18
Hampton d	08 51								09 21								09 51								10 21
Fulwell d	08 54								09 24								09 54								10 24
Strawberry Hill d					09 07								09 37								10 07				
Teddington d	08 59				09 11				09 29				09 41				09 59				10 11				10 29
Hampton Wick d	09 01				09 14				09 31				09 44				10 01				10 14				10 31
Kingston a	09 03				09 16				09 33				09 46				10 03				10 16				10 33
d	09 04				09 19				09 34				09 49				10 04				10 19				10 34
Norbiton d	09 06				09 21				09 36				09 51				10 06				10 21				10 36
New Malden 6 d	09 10				09 25			09 37	09 40				09 55			10 07	10 10				10 25			10 37	10 40
Dorking 4 d						09 02								09 35								10 05			
Boxhill & Westhumble d						09 04																			
Leatherhead d						09 09	09 24							09 41	09 54							10 11	10 24		
Ashtead d						09 13	09 28							09 45	09 58							10 14	10 28		
Epsom 3 a						09 17	09 32							09 49	10 02							10 19	10 32		
d			←			09 18	09 35				←			09 50	10 05				←			10 20	10 35		
Ewell West d			09 07			09 21	09 38				09 38			09 53	10 08				10 08			10 23	10 38		
Stoneleigh d			09 10			09 24	→				09 40			09 55	→				10 10			10 25	→		
Worcester Park d			09 12			09 27					09 43			09 58					10 13			10 28			
Chessington South d				09 10								09 40								10 10					
Chessington North d				09 12								09 42								10 12					
Tolworth d				09 14								09 44								10 14					
Malden Manor d				09 17								09 47								10 17					
Motspur Park d			09 16	09 20		09 30					09 46	09 50		10 01					10 16	10 20		10 31			
Raynes Park 6 d	09 13		09 19	09 24	09 28	09 34		09 40	09 43		09 49	09 53	09 58	10 04		10 10	10 13		10 19	10 23	10 28	10 34		10 40	10 43
Wimbledon 6 ⊖ ⛴ d	09 17	09 20	09 23	09 28	09 32	09 38		09 44	09 47	09 50	09 53	09 57	10 02	10 08		10 14	10 17	10 20	10 23	10 27	10 32	10 38		10 44	10 47
Earlsfield d	09 20	09 24	09 27	09 31	09 35	09 42		09 47	09 50	09 54	09 57	10 01	10 05	10 12		10 17	10 20	10 24	10 27	10 31	10 35	10 42		10 47	10 50
Clapham Junction 10 d	09 24	09 28	09 31	09 35	09 38	09 46		09 51	09 54	09 58	10 01	10 05	10 08	10 16		10 21	10 24	10 28	10 31	10 35	10 38	10 46		10 51	10 54
Vauxhall ⊖ d	09 29	09 33	09 36	09 40	09 44	09 51		09 56	09 59	10 03	10 06	10 10	10 14	10 21		10 26	10 29	10 33	10 36	10 40	10 44	10 51		10 56	10 59
London Waterloo 15 ⊖ a	09 36	09 39	09 42	09 47	09 51	09 57		10 01	10 04	10 07	10 10	10 15	10 19	10 25		10 31	10 34	10 37	10 40	10 45	10 49	10 55		11 01	11 04

For general notes see front of timetable
For details of catering facilities see Directory of Train Operators

A From London Waterloo (Table 149)

From 28 September due to seasonal difficulties a large number of trains on this table will have minor retimings that could mean slightly earlier departure or later arrival times at certain stations. For further details see local publicity or contact National Rail Enquiries 08457 48 49 50.

For details of Bank Holiday service alterations, please see first page of Table 149

Hampton Court, Shepperton, Guildford, Dorking and Chessington South → London

Network Diagram - see first page of Table 152

Station		SW	SW		SW	SW A	SW	SW	SW	SW	SW	SW	SW	SW A	SW	SW	SW	SW	SW	SW		SW	SW A	SW	SW
Guildford	d	10 08						10 28			10 38					10 58			11 08						16 28
London Road (Guildford)	d	10 12						10 32			10 42					11 02			11 12						16 32
Clandon	d	10 17						10 37			10 47					11 07			11 17						16 37
Horsley	d	10 21						10 41			10 51					11 11			11 21						16 41
Effingham Junction 6	d	10 24						10 46			10 54					11 16			11 24						16 46
Bookham	d							10 49								11 19									16 49
Cobham & Stoke d'Abernon	d	10 28									10 58								11 28						
Oxshott	d	10 31									11 01								11 31						
Claygate	d	10 34									11 04								11 34						
Hinchley Wood	d	10 37									11 07								11 37						
Hampton Court	d								10 54								11 24								
Thames Ditton	d								10 56								11 26								
Surbiton 6	d	10 42							11 02		11 12						11 32		11 42						
Berrylands	d								11 04								11 34								
Shepperton	d									10 41								11 11							
Upper Halliford	d									10 44								11 14							
Sunbury	d									10 46								11 16							
Kempton Park	d									10 48								11 18			and at				
Hampton	d									10 51								11 21							
Fulwell	d									10 54								11 24			the same				
Strawberry Hill	d					10 37								11 07							minutes		16 37		
Teddington	d					10 41				10 59				11 11				11 29			past		16 43		
Hampton Wick	d					10 44				11 01				11 14				11 31					16 46		
Kingston	a					10 46				11 03				11 16				11 33			each		16 48		
	d					10 49				11 04				11 19				11 34					16 49		
Norbiton	d					10 51				11 06				11 21				11 36			hour until		16 51		
New Malden 6	d					10 55			11 07	11 10				11 25			11 37	11 40					16 55		
Dorking 4	d						10 35								11 05									16 35	
Boxhill & Westhumble	d																								
Leatherhead	d						10 41	10 54							11 11	11 24								16 41	16 54
Ashtead	d						10 44	10 58							11 14	11 28								16 44	16 58
Epsom 3	a						10 49	11 02							11 19	11 32								16 49	17 02
	d		←				10 50	11 05				←			11 20	11 35				←				16 50	17 05
Ewell West	d		10 38				10 53	11 08				11 08			11 23	11 38				11 38				16 53	17 08
Stoneleigh	d		10 40				10 55	→				11 10			11 25	→				11 40				16 55	→
Worcester Park	d		10 43				10 58					11 13			11 28					11 43				16 58	
Chessington South	d				10 40								11 10									16 40			
Chessington North	d				10 42								11 12									16 42			
Tolworth	d				10 44								11 14									16 44			
Malden Manor	d				10 47								11 17									16 47			
Motspur Park	d		10 46		10 50		11 01					11 16	11 20		11 31					11 46		16 50		17 01	
Raynes Park 6	d		10 49		10 53	10 58	11 04		11 10	11 13		11 19	11 23	11 28	11 34		11 40	11 43		11 49		16 53	16 58	17 04	
Wimbledon 6 ⊖	d	10 50	10 53		10 57	11 02	11 08		11 14	11 17	11 20	11 23	11 27	11 32	11 38		11 44	11 47	11 50	11 53		16 57	17 02	17 08	
Earlsfield	d	10 54	10 57		11 01	11 05	11 12		11 17	11 20	11 24	11 27	11 31	11 35	11 42		11 47	11 50	11 54	11 57		17 01	17 05	17 12	
Clapham Junction 10	d	10 58	11 01		11 05	11 08	11 16		11 21	11 24	11 28	11 31	11 35	11 38	11 46		11 51	11 54	11 58	12 01		17 05	17 08	17 16	
Vauxhall ⊖	d	11 03	11 06		11 10	11 14	11 21		11 26	11 29	11 33	11 36	11 40	11 44	11 51		11 56	11 59	12 03	12 06		17 10	17 14	17 21	
London Waterloo 15 ⊖	a	11 07	11 10		11 15	11 19	11 25		11 31	11 34	11 37	11 40	11 45	11 49	11 55		12 01	12 04	12 08	12 11		17 16	17 19	17 25	

For general notes see front of timetable
For details of catering facilities see Directory of Train Operators

A From London Waterloo (Table 149)

From 28 September due to seasonal difficulties a large number of trains on this table will have minor retimings that could mean slightly earlier departure or later arrival times at certain stations. For further details see local publicity or contact National Rail Enquiries 08457 48 49 50.

For details of Bank Holiday service alterations, please see first page of Table 149

Hampton Court, Shepperton, Guildford, Dorking and Chessington South → London

Network Diagram - see first page of Table 152

		SW	SW	SW	SW	SW	SW	SW	SW	SW	SW	SW	SW	SW	SW	SW	SW	SW	SW	SW	SW	SN	SW	SW	SW	SW
							A								A			A				B			A	
Guildford	d			16 38					16 58			17 08					17 28				17 34	17 42				
London Road (Guildford)	d			16 42					17 02			17 12					17 32				17 38					
Clandon	d			16 47					17 07			17 17					17 37				17 43					
Horsley	d			16 51					17 11			17 21					17 41				17 47					
Effingham Junction 6	d			16 54					17 16			17 24					17 46				17 50	17 55				
Bookham	d								17 19								17 49									
Cobham & Stoke d'Abernon	d			16 58								17 28									17 54					
Oxshott	d			17 01								17 31									17 57					
Claygate	d			17 04								17 34									18 00					
Hinchley Wood	d			17 07								17 37									18 03					
Hampton Court	d	16 54								17 24									17 54							
Thames Ditton	d	16 56								17 26									17 56							
Surbiton 6	d	17 02		17 12						17 32		17 42							18 02		18 12					
Berrylands	d	17 04								17 34									18 04							
Shepperton	d		16 41								17 11									17 41						
Upper Halliford	d		16 44								17 14									17 44						
Sunbury	d		16 46								17 16									17 46						
Kempton Park	d		16 48								17 18									17 48						
Hampton	d		16 51								17 21									17 51						
Fulwell	d		16 54								17 24									17 54						
Strawberry Hill	d						17 07								17 37			17 41							18 07	
Teddington	d		16 59				17 13				17 29				17 43			17b52		17 59					18 13	
Hampton Wick	d		17 01				17 16				17 31				17 46			17 54		18 01					18 16	
Kingston	a		17 03				17 18				17 33				17 48			17 56		18 03					18 18	
	d		17 04				17 19				17 34				17 49			17 58		18 04					18 19	
Norbiton	d		17 06				17 21				17 36				17 51			18 00		18 06					18 21	
New Malden 6	d	17 07	17 10				17 25			17 37	17 40				17 55			18 04	18 07	18 10					18 25	
Dorking 4	d							17 05								17 35										18 05
Boxhill & Westhumble	d																									
Leatherhead	d							17 11	17 24							17 41	17 54					18 02				18 11
Ashtead	d							17 14	17 28							17 44	17 58					18 06				18 14
Epsom 3	a							17 19	17 32							17 49	18 02					18 10				18 19
	d				←			17 20	17 35				←			17 50	18 05						←			18 20
Ewell West	d				17 08			17 23	17 38				17 38			17 53	18 08						18 08			18 23
Stoneleigh	d				17 10			17 25	→				17 40			17 55	→						18 10			18 25
Worcester Park	d				17 13			17 28					17 43			17 58							18 13			18 28
Chessington South	d					17 10								17 40										18 10		
Chessington North	d					17 12								17 42										18 12		
Tolworth	d					17 14								17 44										18 14		
Malden Manor	d					17 17								17 47										18 17		
Motspur Park	d				17 16	17 20		17 31					17 46	17 50		18 01							18 16	18 20		18 31
Raynes Park 6	d	17 10	17 13		17 19	17 23	17 28	17 34		17 40	17 43		17 49	17 53	17 58	18 04		18 07	18 10	18 13			18 19	18 23	18 28	18 34
Wimbledon 6 ⊖	d	17 14	17 17	17 20	17 23	17 27	17 32	17 38		17 44	17 47	17 50	17 53	17 57	18 02	18 08		18 11	18 14	18 17	18 20		18 23	18 27	18 32	18 38
Earlsfield	d	17 17	17 20	17 24	17 27	17 31	17 35	17 42		17 47	17 50	17 54	17 57	18 01	18 05	18 12		18 15	18 17	18 20	18 24		18 27	18 31	18 35	18 42
Clapham Junction 10	d	17 21	17 24	17 28	17 31	17 35	17 38	17 46		17 51	17 54	17 58	18 01	18 05	18 08	18 16		18 18	18 21	18 24	18 28		18 31	18 35	18 38	18 46
Vauxhall ⊖	d	17 26	17 29	17 33	17 36	17 40	17 44	17 51		17 56	17 59	18 03	18 06	18 10	18 14	18 21		18 24	18 26	18 29	18 33		18 36	18 40	18 44	18 51
London Waterloo 15 ⊖	a	17 31	17 35	17 37	17 40	17 45	17 49	17 55		18 01	18 05	18 07	18 10	18 15	18 19	18 25		18 29	18 31	18 35	18 37		18 40	18 47	18 49	18 55

For general notes see front of timetable
For details of catering facilities see Directory of Train Operators

A From London Waterloo (Table 149)
B To London Victoria (Table 182)
b Arr. 1746

From 28 September due to seasonal difficulties a large number of trains on this table will have minor retimings that could mean slightly earlier departure or later arrival times at certain stations. For further details see local publicity or contact National Rail Enquiries 08457 48 49 50.

For details of Bank Holiday service alterations, please see first page of Table 149

Hampton Court, Shepperton, Guildford, Dorking and Chessington South → London

Network Diagram - see first page of Table 152

		SW	SW	SW	SW	SW	SW	SW	SW	SN	SW	SW	SW	SW	SW	SW	SW	SN	SW	SW 1	SW	SW	SW	SW	SW	SW
								A		B						A		C		D					A	
Guildford	d	17 58			18 08					18 22			18 38					18 52				19 08				
London Road (Guildford)	d	18 02			18 12					18 25			18 42					18 55				19 12				
Clandon	d	18 07			18 17					18 30			18 47					19 00				19 17				
Horsley	d	18 11			18 21					18 35			18 51					19 05				19 21				
Effingham Junction 6	d	18 16			18 24					18 39			18 54				18 59	19 08				19 24				
Bookham	d	18 19								18 42							19 02	19 11								
Cobham & Stoke d'Abernon	d				18 28								18 58									19 28				
Oxshott	d				18 31								19 01									19 31				
Claygate	d				18 34								19 04									19 34				
Hinchley Wood	d				18 37								19 07									19 37				
Hampton Court	d		18 24								18 54								19 24							
Thames Ditton	d		18 26								18 56								19 26							
Surbiton 6	d		18 32		18 42						19 02		19 12						19 32	19 38		19 42				
Berrylands	d		18 34								19 04								19 34							
Shepperton	d			18 11								18 36									19 06					
Upper Halliford	d			18 14								18 39									19 09					
Sunbury	d			18 16								18 41									19 11					
Kempton Park	d			18 18								18 43									19 13					
Hampton	d			18 21								18b51									19c21					
Fulwell	d			18 24								18 54									19 24					
Strawberry Hill	d							18 37								19 07									19 37	
Teddington	d			18 29				18 43				18 59				19 13					19 29				19 43	
Hampton Wick	d			18 31				18 46				19 01				19 16					19 31				19 46	
Kingston	a			18 33				18 48				19 03				19 18					19 33				19 48	
	d			18 34				18 49				19 04				19 19					19 34				19 49	
Norbiton	d			18 36				18 51				19 06				19 21					19 36				19 51	
New Malden 6	d		18 37	18 40				18 55			19 07	19 10				19 25			19 37		19 40				19 55	
Dorking 4	d								18 35					18 50												19 33
Boxhill & Westhumble	d																									
Leatherhead	d	18 24							18 41	18 47				18 56			19 08	19 16								19 39
Ashtead	d	18 28							18 44	18 50				18 59			19 12	19 20								19 42
Epsom 3	a	18 32							18 50	18 58				19 04			19 16	19 24								19 47
	d	18 35				←			18 50					19 05			19 20						19 35			19 50
Ewell West	d	18 38				18 38			18 53					19 08			19 23						19 38			19 53
Stoneleigh	d	→				18 40			18 55					19 10			19 25						19 40			19 55
Worcester Park	d					18 43			18 58					19 13			19 28						19 43			19 58
Chessington South	d						18 40								19 10									19 40		
Chessington North	d						18 42								19 12									19 42		
Tolworth	d						18 44								19 14									19 44		
Malden Manor	d						18 47								19 17									19 47		
Motspur Park	d					18 46	18 50		19 01					19 16	19 20		19 31						19 46	19 50		20 01
Raynes Park 6	d		18 40	18 43		18 49	18 53	18 58	19 04		19 10	19 13		19 19	19 23	19 28	19 34		19 40		19 43		19 49	19 53	19 58	20 04
Wimbledon 6 ⊖ ⛴	d		18 44	18 47	18 50	18 53	18 57	19 02	19 08		19 14	19 17	19 20	19 23	19 27	19 32	19 38		19 44		19 47	19 50	19 53	19 57	20 02	20 08
Earlsfield	d		18 47	18 50	18 54	18 57	19 01	19 05	19 12		19 17	19 20	19 24	19 27	19 31	19 35	19 42		19 47		19 50	19 54	19 57	20 01	20 05	20 12
Clapham Junction 10	d		18 51	18 54	18 58	19 01	19 05	19 08	19 16		19 21	19 24	19 28	19 31	19 35	19 38	19 46		19 51	19 49	19 54	19 58	20 01	20 05	20 08	20 16
Vauxhall ⊖	d		18 56	18 59	19 03	19 06	19 10	19 14	19 21		19 26	19 29	19 33	19 36	19 40	19 44	19 51		19 56		19 59	20 03	20 06	20 10	20 14	20 21
London Waterloo 15 ⊖	a		19 01	19 05	19 07	19 10	19 14	19 19	19 27		19 31	19 34	19 37	19 41	19 45	19 49	19 55		20 01	19 57	20 04	20 07	20 10	20 15	20 19	20 25

For general notes see front of timetable
For details of catering facilities see Directory of Train Operators

A From London Waterloo (Table 149)
B To London Bridge (Table 182)
C To London Bridge (Table 178)
D From Alton (Table 155)
b Arr. 1846
c Arr. 1916

From 28 September due to seasonal difficulties a large number of trains on this table will have minor retimings that could mean slightly earlier departure or later arrival times at certain stations. For further details see local publicity or contact National Rail Enquiries 08457 48 49 50.

For details of Bank Holiday service alterations, please see first page of Table 149

Hampton Court, Shepperton, Guildford, Dorking and Chessington South → London

Network Diagram - see first page of Table 152

Station		SW	SW	SW	SW	SW	SW	SW A	SW	SW	SW	SW	SW	SW	SW	SW A	SW	SW	SW	SW	SW	SW	SW A	SW	SW	SW
Guildford	d	19 28			19 38					19 58			20 08							20 38				20 46		
London Road (Guildford)	d	19 32			19 42					20 02			20 12							20 42				20 50		
Clandon	d	19 37			19 47					20 07			20 17							20 47				20 55		
Horsley	d	19 41			19 51					20 11			20 21							20 51				20 59		
Effingham Junction 6	d	19 46			19 54					20 16			20 24							20 54				21 03		
Bookham	d	19 49								20 19														21 06		
Cobham & Stoke d'Abernon	d				19 58								20 28							20 58						
Oxshott	d				20 01								20 31							21 01						
Claygate	d				20 04								20 34							21 04						
Hinchley Wood	d				20 07								20 37							21 07						
Hampton Court	d		19 54								20 24							20 54							21 24	
Thames Ditton	d		19 56								20 26							20 56							21 26	
Surbiton 6	d		20 02		20 12						20 32		20 42					21 02		21 12					21 32	
Berrylands	d		20 04								20 34							21 04							21 34	
Shepperton	d			19 41								20 11							20 41							21 11
Upper Halliford	d			19 44								20 14							20 44							21 14
Sunbury	d			19 46								20 16							20 46							21 16
Kempton Park	d			19 48								20 18							20 48							21 18
Hampton	d			19 51								20 21							20 51							21 21
Fulwell	d			19 54								20 24							20 54							21 24
Strawberry Hill	d							20 07								20 37							21 07			
Teddington	d			19 59				20 11				20 29				20 41			20 59				21 11			21 29
Hampton Wick	d			20 01				20 14				20 31				20 44			21 01				21 14			21 31
Kingston	a			20 04				20 16				20 33				20 46			21 03				21 16			21 33
	d			20 04				20 19				20 34				20 49			21 04				21 19			21 34
Norbiton	d			20 06				20 21				20 36				20 51			21 06				21 21			21 36
New Malden 6	d		20 07	20 10				20 25			20 37	20 40				20 55		21 07	21 10				21 25		21 37	21 40
Dorking 4	d								20 05								20 35									
Boxhill & Westhumble	d																									
Leatherhead	d	19 54							20 11	20 24							20 41							21 11		
Ashtead	d	19 58							20 14	20 28							20 44							21 14		
Epsom 3	a	20 02							20 19	20 32							20 49							21 19		
	d	20 05				←			20 20	20 35				←			20 50				21 05			21 20		
Ewell West	d	20 08				20 08			20 23	20 38				20 38			20 53				21 08			21 23		
Stoneleigh	d	→				20 10			20 25	→				20 40			20 55				21 10			21 25		
Worcester Park	d					20 13			20 28					20 43			20 58				21 13			21 28		
Chessington South	d						20 10								20 40							21 10				
Chessington North	d						20 12								20 42							21 12				
Tolworth	d						20 14								20 44							21 14				
Malden Manor	d						20 17								20 47							21 17				
Motspur Park	d					20 16	20 20		20 31					20 46	20 50		21 01				21 16	21 20		21 31		
Raynes Park 6	d		20 10	20 13		20 19	20 23	20 28	20 34		20 40	20 43		20 49	20 53	20 58	21 04	21 10	21 13		21 19	21 23	21 28	21 34	21 40	21 43
Wimbledon 6 ⊖	d		20 14	20 17	20 20	20 23	20 27	20 32	20 38		20 44	20 47	20 50	20 53	20 57	21 02	21 08	21 14	21 17	21 20	21 23	21 27	21 32	21 38	21 44	21 47
Earlsfield	d		20 17	20 20	20 24	20 27	20 31	20 35	20 42		20 47	20 50	20 54	20 57	21 01	21 05	21 12	21 17	21 20	21 24	21 27	21 31	21 35	21 42	21 47	21 50
Clapham Junction 10	d		20 21	20 24	20 28	20 31	20 35	20 38	20 46		20 51	20 54	20 58	21 01	21 05	21 08	21 16	21 21	21 24	21 28	21 31	21 35	21 38	21 46	21 51	21 54
Vauxhall ⊖	d		20 26	20 29	20 33	20 36	20 40	20 44	20 51		20 56	20 59	21 03	21 06	21 10	21 14	21 21	21 26	21 29	21 33	21 36	21 40	21 44	21 51	21 56	21 59
London Waterloo 15 ⊖	a		20 31	20 35	20 38	20 41	20 46	20 49	20 55		21 01	21 04	21 07	21 10	21 15	21 19	21 25	21 31	21 34	21 37	21 40	21 45	21 49	21 55	22 01	22 04

For general notes see front of timetable
For details of catering facilities see Directory of Train Operators

A From London Waterloo (Table 149)

From 28 September due to seasonal difficulties a large number of trains on this table will have minor retimings that could mean slightly earlier departure or later arrival times at certain stations. For further details see local publicity or contact National Rail Enquiries 08457 48 49 50.

For details of Bank Holiday service alterations, please see first page of Table 149

Hampton Court, Shepperton, Guildford, Dorking and Chessington South → London

Network Diagram - see first page of Table 152

		SW	SW	SW	SW	SW	SW	SW	SW	SW	SW	SW	SW	SW	SW	SW	SW	SW	SW	SW	SW	SW	SW	SW	SW
					A				A						A				A						A
Guildford	d	21 08						21 38		21 46			22 08					22 38		22 46			23 08		
London Road (Guildford)	d	21 12						21 42		21 50			22 12					22 42		22 50			23 12		
Clandon	d	21 17						21 47		21 55			22 17					22 47		22 55			23 17		
Horsley	d	21 21						21 51		21 59			22 21					22 51		22 59			23 21		
Effingham Junction 6	d	21 24						21 54		22 03			22 24					22 54		23 03			23 24		
Bookham	d									22 06										23 06					
Cobham & Stoke d'Abernon	d	21 28						21 58					22 28					22 58					23 28		
Oxshott	d	21 31						22 01					22 31					23 01					23 31		
Claygate	d	21 34						22 04					22 34					23 04					23 34		
Hinchley Wood	d	21 37						22 07					22 37					23 07					23 37		
Hampton Court	d										22 24										23 24				
Thames Ditton	d										22 26										23 26				
Surbiton 6	d	21 42						22 12			22 32		22 42					23 12			23 32		23 42		
Berrylands	d										22 34										23 34				
Shepperton	d						21 41					22 11					22 41					23 11			
Upper Halliford	d						21 44					22 14					22 44					23 14			
Sunbury	d						21 46					22 16					22 46					23 16			
Kempton Park	d						21 48					22 18					22 48					23 18			
Hampton	d						21 51					22 21					22 51					23 21			
Fulwell	d						21 54					22 24					22 54					23 24			
Strawberry Hill	d				21 37				22 07						22 37				23 07						23 37
Teddington	d				21 41		21 59		22 11			22 29			22 41		22 59		23 11			23 29			23 41
Hampton Wick	d				21 44		22 01		22 14			22 31			22 44		23 01		23 14			23 31			23 44
Kingston	a				21 46		22 03		22 16			22 33			22 46		23 03		23 16			23 33			23 46
	d				21 49		22 04		22 19			22 34			22 49		23 04		23 19			23 34			23 49
Norbiton	d				21 51		22 06		22 21			22 36			22 51		23 06		23 21			23 36			23 51
New Malden 6	d				21 55		22 10		22 25		22 37	22 40			22 55		23 10		23 25		23 37	23 40			23 55
Dorking 4	d					21 35										22 35									
Boxhill & Westhumble	d																								
Leatherhead	d					21 41				22 11						22 41				23 11					
Ashtead	d					21 44				22 14						22 44				23 14					
Epsom 3	a					21 49				22 19						22 49				23 19					
	d		21 35			21 50				22 20						22 50				23 20					
Ewell West	d		21 38			21 53				22 23						22 53				23 23					
Stoneleigh	d		21 40			21 55				22 25						22 55				23 25					
Worcester Park	d		21 43			21 58				22 28						22 58				23 28					
Chessington South	d			21 40										22 40										23 40	
Chessington North	d			21 42										22 42										23 42	
Tolworth	d			21 44										22 44										23 44	
Malden Manor	d			21 47										22 47										23 47	
Motspur Park	d		21 46	21 50		22 01				22 31				22 50		23 01				23 31				23 50	
Raynes Park 6	d		21 49	21 53	21 58	22 04	22 13		22 28	22 34	22 40	22 43		22 53	22 58	23 04	23 13		23 28	23b37	23 40	23 43		23 54	23 58
Wimbledon 6 ⊖	d	21 50	21 53	21 57	22 02	22 08	22 17	22 20	22 32	22 38	22 44	22 47	22 50	22 57	23 02	23 08	23 17	23 20	23 32	23 41	23a45	23 52	23 55	00a01	00 05
Earlsfield	d	21 54	21 57	22 01	22 05	22 12	22 20	22 24	22 35	22 42	22 47	22 50	22 54	23 01	23 05	23 12	23 20	23 24	23 35	23 44		23 55	23 58		00 08
Clapham Junction 10	d	21 58	22 01	22 05	22 08	22 16	22 24	22 28	22 38	22 46	22 51	22 54	22 58	23 05	23 08	23 16	23 24	23 28	22 43	23 48		23 59	00 02		00 11
Vauxhall ⊖	d	22 03	22 06	22 10	22 14	22 21	22 29	22 33	22 44	22 51	22 56	22 59	23 03	23 10	23 14	23 21	23 29	23 33	23 44	23 53		00 04	00 07		00 17
London Waterloo 15 ⊖	a	22 07	22 10	22 16	22 19	22 25	22 34	22 39	22 49	22 55	23 01	23 04	23 07	23 15	23 19	23 25	23 34	23 37	23 49	23 58		00 11	00 14		00 23

For general notes see front of timetable
For details of catering facilities see Directory of Train Operators

A From London Waterloo (Table 149)
b Arr. 2334

From 28 September due to seasonal difficulties a large number of trains on this table will have minor retimings that could mean slightly earlier departure or later arrival times at certain stations. For further details see local publicity or contact National Rail Enquiries 08457 48 49 50.

Table 152

Saturdays

Hampton Court, Shepperton, Guildford, Dorking and Chessington South → London

For details of Bank Holiday service alterations, please see first page of Table 149

Network Diagram - see first page of Table 152

		SW	SW	SW A	SW A	SW B	SW	SW	SW	SW	SW A	SW	SW	SW	SW	SW A	SW	SW	SW	SW	SW	SW	SW A	SW	SW	SW
Guildford	d		23p08														06 28			06 38				06 58		
London Road (Guildford)	d		23p12														06 32			06 42				07 02		
Clandon	d		23p17														06 37			06 47				07 07		
Horsley	d		23p21														06 41			06 51				07 11		
Effingham Junction 6	d		23p24														06 46			06 54				07 16		
Bookham	d																06 49							07 19		
Cobham & Stoke d'Abernon	d		23p28																	06 58						
Oxshott	d		23p31																	07 01						
Claygate	d		23p34																	07 04						
Hinchley Wood	d		23p37																	07 07						
Hampton Court	d								05 54			06 24						06 54							07 24	
Thames Ditton	d								05 56			06 26						06 56							07 26	
Surbiton 6	d		23p42						06 02			06 32						07 02		07 12					07 32	
Berrylands	d								06 04			06 34						07 04							07 34	
Shepperton	d	23p11											06 11						06 41							07 11
Upper Halliford	d	23p14											06 14						06 44							07 14
Sunbury	d	23p16											06 16						06 46							07 16
Kempton Park	d	23p18											06 18						06 48							07 18
Hampton	d	23p21											06 21						06 51							07 21
Fulwell	d	23p24											06 24						06 54							07 24
Strawberry Hill	d			23p37	00 12	04 55					06 07					06 37							07 07			
Teddington	d	23p29		23p41	00 15	04 59		05 44			06 11		06 29			06 41			06 59				07 11			07 29
Hampton Wick	d	23p31		23p44	00 17	05 01		05 46			06 14		06 31			06 44			07 01				07 14			07 31
Kingston	a	23p33		23p46	00 19	05 03		05 48			06 16		06 33			06 46			07 03				07 16			07 33
	d	23p34		23p49		05 04		05 49			06 19		06 34			06 49			07 04				07 19			07 34
Norbiton	d	23p36		23p51		05 06		05 51			06 21		06 36			06 51			07 06				07 21			07 36
New Malden 6	d	23p40		23p55		05 10		05 55	06 07		06 25	06 37	06 40			06 55		07 07	07 10				07 25		07 37	07 40
Dorking 4	d																									
Boxhill & Westhumble	d																									
Leatherhead	d																06 54							07 24		
Ashtead	d																06 58							07 28		
Epsom 3	a																07 02							07 32		
	d						05 35			06 05				06 35			07 05				←			07 35		
Ewell West	d						05 38			06 08				06 38			07 08 →				07 08			07 38 →		
Stoneleigh	d						05 40			06 10				06 40							07 10					
Worcester Park	d						05 43			06 13				06 43							07 13					
Chessington South	d														06 40							07 10				
Chessington North	d														06 42							07 12				
Tolworth	d														06 44							07 14				
Malden Manor	d														06 47							07 17				
Motspur Park	d						05 46			06 16				06 46	06 50						07 16	07 20				
Raynes Park 6	d	23p43		23p58		05 13	05 49	05 58	06 10	06 19	06 28	06 40	06 43	06 49	06 53	06 58		07 10	07 13		07 19	07 23	07 28		07 40	07 43
Wimbledon 6 ⊖ ⇌	d	23p52	23p55	00 05		05 17	05 53	06 02	06 14	06 23	06 32	06 44	06 47	06 53	06 57	07 02		07 14	07 17	07 20	07 23	07 27	07 32		07 44	07 47
Earlsfield	d	23p55	23p58	00 08		05 21	05 57	06 05	06 17	06 27	06 35	06 47	06 50	06 57	07 01	07 05		07 17	07 20	07 24	07 27	07 31	07 35		07 47	07 50
Clapham Junction 10	d	23p59	00 02	23p13		05 25	06 01	06 09	06 21	06 31	06 38	06 51	06 54	07 01	07 05	07 08		07 21	07 24	07 28	07 31	07 35	07 38		07 51	07 54
Vauxhall ⊖	d	00 04	00 07	00 17		05 30	06 06	06 14	06 26	06 36	06 44	06 56	06 59	07 06	07 10	07 14		07 26	07 29	07 33	07 36	07 40	07 44		07 56	07 59
London Waterloo 15 ⊖	a	00 11	00 14	00 23		05 35	06 11	06 19	06 31	06 40	06 49	07 01	07 04	07 10	07 15	07 19		07 31	07 34	07 37	07 40	07 45	07 49		08 01	08 04

For general notes see front of timetable
For details of catering facilities see Directory of Train Operators

A From London Waterloo (Table 149)
B From Twickenham (Table 149)

From 3 October due to seasonal difficulties a large number of trains on this table will have minor retimings that could mean slightly earlier departure or later arrival times at certain stations. For further details see local publicity or contact National Rail Enquiries 08457 48 49 50.

For details of Bank Holiday service alterations, please see first page of Table 149

Hampton Court, Shepperton, Guildford, Dorking and Chessington South → London

Network Diagram - see first page of Table 152

Station		SW	SW	SW	SW A	SW	SW	SW	SW	SW	SW	SW A	SW
Guildford	d	07 08				07 28			07 38				
London Road (Guildford)	d	07 12				07 32			07 42				
Clandon	d	07 17				07 37			07 47				
Horsley	d	07 21				07 41			07 51				
Effingham Junction 6	d	07 24				07 46			07 54				
Bookham	d					07 49							
Cobham & Stoke d'Abernon	d	07 28							07 58				
Oxshott	d	07 31							08 01				
Claygate	d	07 34							08 04				
Hinchley Wood	d	07 37							08 07				
Hampton Court	d						07 54						
Thames Ditton	d						07 56						
Surbiton 6	d	07 42					08 02		08 12				
Berrylands	d						08 04						
Shepperton	d							07 41					
Upper Halliford	d							07 44					
Sunbury	d							07 46					
Kempton Park	d							07 48					
Hampton	d							07 51					
Fulwell	d							07 54					
Strawberry Hill	d				07 37							08 07	
Teddington	d				07 41			07 59				08 11	
Hampton Wick	d				07 44			08 01				08 14	
Kingston	a				07 46			08 03				08 16	
	d				07 49			08 04				08 19	
Norbiton	d				07 51			08 06				08 21	
New Malden 6	d				07 55		08 07	08 10				08 25	
Dorking 4	d												08 05
Boxhill & Westhumble	d												
Leatherhead	d					07 54							08 11
Ashtead	d					07 58							08 14
Epsom 3	a					08 02							08 19
	d		←			08 05				←			08 20
Ewell West	d		07 38			08 08				08 08			08 23
Stoneleigh	d		07 40			→				08 10			08 25
Worcester Park	d		07 43							08 13			08 28
Chessington South	d			07 40							08 10		
Chessington North	d			07 42							08 12		
Tolworth	d			07 44							08 14		
Malden Manor	d			07 47							08 17		
Motspur Park	d		07 46	07 50						08 16	08 20		08 31
Raynes Park 6	d		07 49	07 53	07 58		08 10	08 13		08 19	08 23	08 28	08 34
Wimbledon 6	⊖ d	07 50	07 53	07 57	08 02		08 14	08 17	08 20	08 23	08 27	08 32	08 38
Earlsfield	d	07 54	07 57	08 01	08 05		08 17	08 20	08 24	08 27	08 31	08 35	08 42
Clapham Junction 10	d	07 58	08 01	08 05	08 08		08 21	08 24	08 28	08 31	08 35	08 38	08 46
Vauxhall	⊖ d	08 03	08 06	08 10	08 14		08 26	08 29	08 33	08 36	08 40	08 44	08 51
London Waterloo 15	⊖ a	08 07	08 10	08 15	08 19		08 31	08 34	08 37	08 40	08 45	08 49	08 55

Station		SW	SW	SW	SW	SW	SW	SW A	SW	SW	SW	SW	SW
Guildford	d	07 58			08 08					08 28			08 38
London Road (Guildford)	d	08 02			08 12					08 32			08 42
Clandon	d	08 07			08 17					08 37			08 47
Horsley	d	08 11			08 21					08 41			08 51
Effingham Junction 6	d	08 16			08 24					08 46			08 54
Bookham	d	08 19								08 49			
Cobham & Stoke d'Abernon	d				08 28								08 58
Oxshott	d				08 31								09 01
Claygate	d				08 34								09 04
Hinchley Wood	d				08 37								09 07
Hampton Court	d		08 24								08 54		
Thames Ditton	d		08 26								08 56		
Surbiton 6	d		08 32		08 42						09 02		09 12
Berrylands	d		08 34								09 04		
Shepperton	d			08 11								08 41	
Upper Halliford	d			08 14								08 44	
Sunbury	d			08 16								08 46	
Kempton Park	d			08 18								08 48	
Hampton	d			08 21								08 51	
Fulwell	d			08 24								08 54	
Strawberry Hill	d							08 37					
Teddington	d			08 29				08 41				08 59	
Hampton Wick	d			08 31				08 44				09 01	
Kingston	a			08 33				08 46				09 03	
	d			08 34				08 49				09 04	
Norbiton	d			08 36				08 51				09 06	
New Malden 6	d		08 37	08 40				08 55			09 07	09 10	
Dorking 4	d								08 35				
Boxhill & Westhumble	d												
Leatherhead	d	08 24							08 41	08 54			
Ashtead	d	08 28							08 44	08 58			
Epsom 3	a	08 32							08 49	09 02			
	d	08 35				←			08 50	09 05			
Ewell West	d	08 38				08 38			08 53	09 08			
Stoneleigh	d	→				08 40			08 55	→			
Worcester Park	d					08 43			08 58				
Chessington South	d						08 40						
Chessington North	d						08 42						
Tolworth	d						08 44						
Malden Manor	d						08 47						
Motspur Park	d					08 46	08 50		09 01				
Raynes Park 6	d		08 40	08 43		08 49	08 53	08 58	09 04		09 10	09 13	
Wimbledon 6	⊖ d		08 44	08 47	08 50	08 53	08 57	09 02	09 08		09 14	09 17	09 20
Earlsfield	d		08 47	08 50	08 54	08 57	09 01	09 05	09 12		09 17	09 20	09 24
Clapham Junction 10	d		08 51	08 54	08 58	09 01	09 05	09 08	09 16		09 21	09 24	09 28
Vauxhall	⊖ d		08 56	08 59	09 03	09 06	09 10	09 14	09 21		09 26	09 29	09 33
London Waterloo 15	⊖ a		09 01	09 04	09 07	09 10	09 15	09 19	09 25		09 31	09 34	09 37

For general notes see front of timetable
For details of catering facilities see Directory of Train Operators

A From London Waterloo (Table 149)

From 3 October due to seasonal difficulties a large number of trains on this table will have minor retimings that could mean slightly earlier departure or later arrival times at certain stations. For further details see local publicity or contact National Rail Enquiries 08457 48 49 50.

For details of Bank Holiday service alterations, please see first page of Table 149

Hampton Court, Shepperton, Guildford, Dorking and Chessington South → London

Network Diagram - see first page of Table 152

		SW	SW	SW A	SW	SW	SW	SW	SW	SW
Guildford	d					08 58			09 08	
London Road (Guildford)	d					09 02			09 12	
Clandon	d					09 07			09 17	
Horsley	d					09 11			09 21	
Effingham Junction 6	d					09 16			09 24	
Bookham	d					09 19				
Cobham & Stoke d'Abernon	d								09 28	
Oxshott	d								09 31	
Claygate	d								09 34	
Hinchley Wood	d								09 37	
Hampton Court	d						09 24			
Thames Ditton	d						09 26			
Surbiton 6	d						09 32		09 42	
Berrylands	d						09 34			
Shepperton	d							09 11		
Upper Halliford	d							09 14		
Sunbury	d							09 16		
Kempton Park	d							09 18		
Hampton	d							09 21		
Fulwell	d							09 24		
Strawberry Hill	d			09 07						
Teddington	d			09 11				09 29		
Hampton Wick	d			09 14				09 31		
Kingston	a			09 16				09 33		
	d			09 19				09 34		
Norbiton	d			09 21				09 36		
New Malden 6	d			09 25			09 37	09 40		
Dorking 4	d				09 05					
Boxhill & Westhumble	d									
Leatherhead	d				09 11	09 24				
Ashtead	d				09 14	09 28				
Epsom 3	a				09 19	09 32				
	d	←			09 20	09 35				←
Ewell West	d	09 08			09 23	09 38				09 38
Stoneleigh	d	09 10			09 25	→				09 40
Worcester Park	d	09 13			09 28					09 43
Chessington South	d		09 10							
Chessington North	d		09 12							
Tolworth	d		09 14							
Malden Manor	d		09 17							
Motspur Park	d	09 16	09 20		09 31					09 46
Raynes Park 6	d	09 19	09 23	09 28	09 34		09 40	09 43		09 49
Wimbledon 6 ⊖ ⛴	d	09 23	09 27	09 32	09 38		09 44	09 47	09 50	09 53
Earlsfield	d	09 27	09 31	09 35	09 42		09 47	09 50	09 54	09 57
Clapham Junction 10	d	09 31	09 35	09 38	09 46		09 51	09 54	09 58	10 01
Vauxhall ⊖	d	09 36	09 40	09 44	09 51		09 56	09 59	10 03	10 06
London Waterloo 15 ⊖	a	09 40	09 45	09 49	09 55		10 01	10 04	10 07	10 10

and at the same minutes past each hour until

		SW	SW A	SW	SW	SW	SW	SW	SW	SW A	SW	SW	SW	SW	SW
Guildford	d						20 38				20 46			21 08	
London Road (Guildford)	d						20 42				20 50			21 12	
Clandon	d						20 47				20 55			21 17	
Horsley	d						20 51				20 59			21 21	
Effingham Junction 6	d						20 54				21 03			21 24	
Bookham	d										21 06				
Cobham & Stoke d'Abernon	d						20 58							21 28	
Oxshott	d						21 01							21 31	
Claygate	d						21 04							21 34	
Hinchley Wood	d						21 07							21 37	
Hampton Court	d				20 54							21 24			
Thames Ditton	d				20 56							21 26			
Surbiton 6	d				21 02		21 12					21 32		21 42	
Berrylands	d				21 04							21 34			
Shepperton	d					20 41							21 11		
Upper Halliford	d					20 44							21 14		
Sunbury	d					20 46							21 16		
Kempton Park	d					20 48							21 18		
Hampton	d					20 51							21 21		
Fulwell	d					20 54							21 24		
Strawberry Hill	d		20 37							21 07					
Teddington	d		20 41			20 59				21 11			21 29		
Hampton Wick	d		20 44			21 01				21 14			21 31		
Kingston	a		20 46			21 03				21 16			21 33		
	d		20 49			21 04				21 19			21 34		
Norbiton	d		20 51			21 06				21 21			21 36		
New Malden 6	d		20 55		21 07	21 10				21 25		21 37	21 40		
Dorking 4	d			20 35											
Boxhill & Westhumble	d														
Leatherhead	d			20 41							21 11				
Ashtead	d			20 44							21 14				
Epsom 3	a			20 49							21 19				
	d			20 50				21 05			21 20				21 35
Ewell West	d			20 53				21 08			21 23				21 38
Stoneleigh	d			20 55				21 10			21 25				21 40
Worcester Park	d			20 58				21 13			21 28				21 43
Chessington South	d	20 40							21 10						
Chessington North	d	20 42							21 12						
Tolworth	d	20 44							21 14						
Malden Manor	d	20 47							21 17						
Motspur Park	d	20 50		21 01				21 16	21 20		21 31				21 46
Raynes Park 6	d	20 53	20 58	21 04	21 10	21 13		21 19	21 23	21 28	21 34	21 40	21 43		21 49
Wimbledon 6 ⊖ ⛴	d	20 57	21 02	21 08	21 14	21 17	21 20	21 23	21 27	21 32	21 38	21 44	21 47	21 50	21 53
Earlsfield	d	21 01	21 05	21 12	21 17	21 20	21 24	21 27	21 31	21 35	21 42	21 47	21 50	21 54	21 57
Clapham Junction 10	d	21 05	21 08	21 16	21 21	21 24	21 28	21 31	21 35	21 38	21 46	21 51	21 54	21 58	22 01
Vauxhall ⊖	d	21 10	21 14	21 21	21 26	21 29	21 33	21 36	21 40	21 44	21 51	21 56	21 59	22 03	22 06
London Waterloo 15 ⊖	a	21 15	21 19	21 25	21 31	21 34	21 37	21 40	21 45	21 49	21 55	22 01	22 04	22 07	22 10

For general notes see front of timetable
For details of catering facilities see
Directory of Train Operators

A From London Waterloo (Table 149)

From 3 October due to seasonal difficulties a large number of trains on this table will have minor retimings that could mean slightly earlier departure or later arrival times at certain stations. For further details see local publicity or contact National Rail Enquiries 08457 48 49 50.

For details of Bank Holiday service alterations, please see first page of Table 149

Hampton Court, Shepperton, Guildford, Dorking and Chessington South → London

Network Diagram - see first page of Table 152

		SW	SW	SW	SW	SW	SW	SW	SW	SW	SW	SW	SW	SW	SW	SW	SW	SW	SW	SW	SW	SW	SW	SW
								1																
			A				A	B						A				A						A
Guildford	d					21 38			21 46			22 08					22 38		22 46			23 08		
London Road (Guildford)	d					21 42			21 50			22 12					22 42		22 50			23 12		
Clandon	d					21 47			21 55			22 17					22 47		22 55			23 17		
Horsley	d					21 51			21 59			22 21					22 51		22 59			23 21		
Effingham Junction 6	d					21 54			22 03			22 24					22 54		23 03			23 24		
Bookham	d								22 06										23 06					
Cobham & Stoke d'Abernon	d					21 58						22 28					22 58					23 28		
Oxshott	d					22 01						22 31					23 01					23 31		
Claygate	d					22 04						22 34					23 04					23 34		
Hinchley Wood	d					22 07						22 37					23 07					23 37		
Hampton Court	d									22 24										23 24				
Thames Ditton	d									22 26										23 26				
Surbiton 6	d					22 12				22 32		22 42					23 12			23 32		23 42		
Berrylands	d									22 34										23 34				
Shepperton	d				21 41						22 11					22 41					23 11			
Upper Halliford	d				21 44						22 14					22 44					23 14			
Sunbury	d				21 46						22 16					22 46					23 16			
Kempton Park	d				21 48						22 18					22 48					23 18			
Hampton	d				21 51						22 21					22 51					23 21			
Fulwell	d				21 54						22 24					22 54					23 24			
Strawberry Hill	d		21 37				22 07							22 37				23 07						23 37
Teddington	d		21 41		21 59		22 11				22 29			22 41		22 59		23 11			23 29			23 41
Hampton Wick	d		21 44		22 01		22 14				22 31			22 44		23 01		23 14			23 31			23 44
Kingston	a		21 46		22 03		22 16				22 33			22 46		23 03		23 16			23 33			23 46
	d		21 49		22 04		22 19				22 34			22 49		23 04		23 19			23 34			23 49
Norbiton	d		21 51		22 06		22 21				22 36			22 51		23 06		23 21			23 36			23 51
New Malden 6	d		21 55		22 10		22 25			22 37	22 40			22 55		23 10		23 25		23 37	23 41			23 55
Dorking 4	d			21 35											22 35									
Boxhill & Westhumble	d																							
Leatherhead	d			21 41					22 11						22 41				23 11					
Ashtead	d			21 44					22 14						22 44				23 14					
Epsom 3	a			21 49					22 19						22 49				23 19					
	d			21 50					22 20						22 50				23 20					
Ewell West	d			21 53					22 23						22 53				23 23					
Stoneleigh	d			21 55					22 25						22 55				23 25					
Worcester Park	d			21 58					22 28						22 58				23 28					
Chessington South	d	21 40											22 40										23 40	
Chessington North	d	21 42											22 42										23 42	
Tolworth	d	21 44											22 44										23 44	
Malden Manor	d	21 47											22 47										23 47	
Motspur Park	d	21 50		22 01					22 31				22 50		23 01				23 31				23 50	
Raynes Park 6	d	21 53	21 58	22 04	22 13		22 28		22 34	22 40	22 43		22 53	22 58	23 04	23 13		23 28	23b37	23 40	23 43		23 54	23 58
Wimbledon 6 ⊖	d	21 57	22 02	22 08	22 17	22 20	22 32		22 38	22 44	22 47	22 50	22 57	23 02	23 08	23 17	23 20	23 32	23 41	23 44	23 52	23 58	00a02	00 07
Earlsfield	d	22 01	22 05	22 12	22 20	22 24	22 35		22 42	22 47	22 50	22 54	23 01	23 05	23 12	23 20	23 24	23 35	23 44	23 47	23 55	00 01		00 10
Clapham Junction 10	d	22 05	22 08	22 16	22 24	22 28	22 38		22 46	22 51	22 54	22 58	23 05	23 08	23 16	23 24	23 28	23 38	23 48	23 51	00 04	00 07		00 13
Vauxhall ⊖	d	22 10	22 14	22 21	22 29	22 33	22 44		22 51	22 56	22 59	23 03	23 10	23 14	23 21	23 29	23 33	23 44	23 53	23 57	00 09	00 12		00 19
London Waterloo 15 ⊖	a	22 15	22 19	22 25	22 34	22 39	22 49	22 49	22 55	23 01	23 04	23 07	23 15	23 19	23 25	23 34	23 37	23 49	23 58	00 02	00 13	00 16		00 24

For general notes see front of timetable
For details of catering facilities see Directory of Train Operators

A From London Waterloo (Table 149)
B From Southampton Central (Table 158)
b Arr. 2334

From 3 October due to seasonal difficulties a large number of trains on this table will have minor retimings that could mean slightly earlier departure or later arrival times at certain stations. For further details see local publicity or contact National Rail Enquiries 08457 48 49 50.

Table 152

Sundays

For details of Bank Holiday service alterations, please see first page of Table 149

Hampton Court, Shepperton, Guildford, Dorking and Chessington South → London

Network Diagram - see first page of Table 152

		SW	SW	SW A	SW A	SW A	SW	SW	SW	SW		SW A	SW	SW	SW	SW	SW	SW	SW	SW		SW A	SW	SW	SW	SW
Guildford	d		23p08												07 50					08 20					08 50	
London Road (Guildford)	d		23p12												07 54					08 24					08 54	
Clandon	d		23p17												07 59					08 29					08 59	
Horsley	d		23p21												08 03					08 33					09 03	
Effingham Junction 6	d		23p24												08 06					08 36					09 06	
Bookham	d																			08 39						
Cobham & Stoke d'Abernon	d		23p28												08 10										09 10	
Oxshott	d		23p31												08 13										09 13	
Claygate	d		23p34												08 16										09 16	
Hinchley Wood	d		23p37												08 19										09 19	
Hampton Court	d								07 35				08 05					08 35					09 05			
Thames Ditton	d								07 37				08 07					08 37					09 07			
Surbiton 6	d		23p42						07 43				08 13		08 24			08 43					09 13		09 24	
Berrylands	d								07 45				08 15					08 45					09 15			
Shepperton	d	23p11						07 11									08 11									
Upper Halliford	d	23p14						07 14									08 14									
Sunbury	d	23p16						07 16									08 16									
Kempton Park	d	23p18						07 18									08 18									
Hampton	d	23p21						07 21									08 21									
Fulwell	d	23p24						07 24									08 24									
Strawberry Hill	d			23p37	00 12	06 49						07 49										08 49				
Teddington	d	23p29		23p41	00 15	06b55		07 29				07c55					08 29					08e55				
Hampton Wick	d	23p31		23p44	00 17	06 57		07 31				07 57					08 31					08 57				
Kingston	a	23p33		23p46	00 19	06 59		07 33				07 59					08 33					08 59				
	d	23p34		23p49		07 04		07 34				08 04					08 34					09 04				
Norbiton	d	23p36		23p51		07 06		07 36				08 06					08 36					09 06				
New Malden 6	d	23p41		23p55		07 10		07 40	07 48			08 10	08 18				08 40	08 48				09 10	09 18			
Dorking 4	d																									09 08
Boxhill & Westhumble	d																									
Leatherhead	d																			08 45						09 15
Ashtead	d																			08 48						09 18
Epsom 3	a																			08 53						09 23
	d						07 24			07 54						08 24				08 54						09 24
Ewell West	d						07 27			07 57						08 27				08 57						09 27
Stoneleigh	d						07 29			07 59						08 29				08 59						09 29
Worcester Park	d						07 32			08 02						08 32				09 02						09 32
Chessington South	d													08 10					08 40					09 10		
Chessington North	d													08 12					08 42					09 12		
Tolworth	d													08 14					08 44					09 14		
Malden Manor	d													08 17					08 47					09 17		
Motspur Park	d						07 35			08 05				08 20		08 35			08 50	09 05				09 20		09 35
Raynes Park 6	d	23p43		23p58		07 13	07 38	07 43	07 51	08 08		08 13	08 21	08 24		08 38	08 43	08 51	08 54	09 08		09 13	09 21	09 24		09 38
Wimbledon 6 ⊖ ⛴	d	23p52	23p58	00 07		07f19	07 42	07 47	07 55	08 12		08 17	08 25	08 28	08a33	08 42	08 47	08 55	08 58	09 12		09 17	09 25	09 28	09a33	09 42
Earlsfield	d	23p55	00 01	00 10		07 22	07 46	07 50	07 58	08 16		08 20	08 28	08 31		08 46	08 50	08 58	09 01	09 16		09 20	09 28	09 31		09 46
Clapham Junction 10	d	00 04	00 07	00 13		07 25	07 50	07 54	08 02	08 20		08 23	08 34	08 37		08 50	08 54	09 02	09 09	09 20		09 23	09 32	09 36		09 50
Vauxhall ⊖	d	00 09	00 12	00 19		07 31	07 55	07 59	08 07	08 25		08 29	08 39	08 42		08 55	08 59	09 07	09 14	09 25		09 29	09 37	09 41		09 55
London Waterloo 15 ⊖	a	00 13	00 16	00 24		07 41	08 04	08 07	08 17	08 34		08 39	08 47	08 50		09 04	09 07	09 17	09 20	09 34		09 39	09 47	09 50		10 04

For general notes see front of timetable
For details of catering facilities see Directory of Train Operators

A From London Waterloo (Table 149)
b Arr. 0652
c Arr. 0752
e Arr. 0852
f Arr. 0716

From 27 September due to seasonal difficulties a large number of trains on this table will have minor retimings that could mean slightly earlier departure or later arrival times at certain stations. For further details see local publicity or contact National Rail Enquiries 08457 48 49 50.

Table 152

Sundays

For details of Bank Holiday service alterations, please see first page of Table 149

Hampton Court, Shepperton, Guildford, Dorking and Chessington South → London

Network Diagram - see first page of Table 152

		SW	SW	SW	SW	SW A	SW		SW	SW	SW	SW	SW	SW	SW	SW A	SW		SW	SW	SW	SW	SW	SW	SW	SW A
Guildford	d				09 20					09 50					10 20					10 50					11 20	
London Road (Guildford)	d				09 24					09 54					10 24					10 54					11 24	
Clandon	d				09 29					09 59					10 29					10 59					11 29	
Horsley	d				09 33					10 03					10 33					11 03					11 33	
Effingham Junction (6)	d				09 36					10 06					10 36					11 06					11 36	
Bookham	d				09 39										10 39										11 39	
Cobham & Stoke d'Abernon	d									10 10										11 10						
Oxshott	d									10 13										11 13						
Claygate	d									10 16										11 16						
Hinchley Wood	d									10 19										11 19						
Hampton Court	d		09 35				10 05						10 35				11 05						11 35			
Thames Ditton	d		09 37				10 07						10 37				11 07						11 37			
Surbiton (6)	d		09 43				10 13			10 24			10 43				11 13			11 24			11 43			
Berrylands	d		09 45				10 15						10 45				11 15						11 45			
Shepperton	d	09 11										10 11										11 11				
Upper Halliford	d	09 14										10 14										11 14				
Sunbury	d	09 16										10 16										11 16				
Kempton Park	d	09 18										10 18										11 18				
Hampton	d	09 21										10 21										11 21				
Fulwell	d	09 24										10 24										11 24				
Strawberry Hill	d					09 49										10 49										11 49
Teddington	d	09 29				09b55						10 29				10c55						11 29				11e55
Hampton Wick	d	09 31				09 57						10 31				10 57						11 31				11 57
Kingston	a	09 33				09 59						10 33				10 59						11 33				11 59
	d	09 34				10 04						10 34				11 04						11 34				12 04
Norbiton	d	09 36				10 06						10 36				11 06						11 36				12 06
New Malden (6)	d	09 40	09 48			10 10	10 18					10 40	10 48			11 10	11 18					11 40	11 48			12 10
Dorking (4)	d										10 08										11 08					
Boxhill & Westhumble	d																									
Leatherhead	d				09 45						10 15				10 45						11 15				11 45	
Ashtead	d				09 48						10 18				10 48						11 18				11 48	
Epsom (3)	a				09 53						10 23				10 53						11 23				11 53	
	d				09 54						10 24				10 54						11 24				11 54	
Ewell West	d				09 57						10 27				10 57						11 27				11 57	
Stoneleigh	d				09 59						10 29				10 59						11 29				11 59	
Worcester Park	d				10 02						10 32				11 02						11 32				12 02	
Chessington South	d			09 40					10 10					10 40					11 10					11 40		
Chessington North	d			09 42					10 12					10 42					11 12					11 42		
Tolworth	d			09 44					10 14					10 44					11 14					11 44		
Malden Manor	d			09 47					10 17					10 47					11 17					11 47		
Motspur Park	d			09 50	10 05				10 20		10 35			10 50	11 05				11 20		11 35			11 50	12 05	
Raynes Park (6)	d	09 43	09 51	09 54	10 08	10 13	10 21		10 24		10 38	10 43	10 51	10 54	11 08	11 13	11 21		11 24		11 38	11 43	11 51	11 54	12 08	12 13
Wimbledon (6) ⊖	d	09 47	09 55	09 58	10 12	10 17	10 25		10 28	10a33	10 42	10 47	10 55	10 58	11 12	11 17	11 25		11 28	11a33	11 42	11 47	11 55	11 58	12 12	12 17
Earlsfield	d	09 50	09 58	10 01	10 16	10 20	10 28		10 31		10 46	10 50	10 58	11 01	11 16	11 20	11 28		11 31		11 46	11 50	11 58	12 01	12 16	12 20
Clapham Junction (10)	d	09 54	10 02	10 05	10 20	10 23	10 32		10 36		10 50	10 54	11 02	11 05	11 20	11 23	11 32		11 35		11 50	11 54	12 02	12 05	12 20	12 23
Vauxhall ⊖	d	09 59	10 07	10 10	10 25	10 29	10 37		10 41		10 55	10 59	11 07	11 10	11 25	11 29	11 37		11 40		11 55	11 59	12 07	12 10	12 25	12 29
London Waterloo (15) ⊖	a	10 07	10 17	10 20	10 34	10 39	10 47		10 50		11 04	11 07	11 17	11 20	11 34	11 39	11 47		11 50		12 04	12 07	12 17	12 20	12 34	12 39

For general notes see front of timetable
For details of catering facilities see Directory of Train Operators

A From London Waterloo (Table 149)
b Arr. 0952
c Arr. 1052
e Arr. 1152

From 27 September due to seasonal difficulties a large number of trains on this table will have minor retimings that could mean slightly earlier departure or later arrival times at certain stations. For further details see local publicity or contact National Rail Enquiries 08457 48 49 50.

Table 152

Sundays

For details of Bank Holiday service alterations, please see first page of Table 149

Hampton Court, Shepperton, Guildford, Dorking and Chessington South → London

Network Diagram - see first page of Table 152

		SW	SW	SW		SW	SW	SW	SW	SW	SW A	SW	SW	SW		SW	SW	SW	SW	SW	SW A	SW	SW		SW	SW
Guildford	d			11 50						12 20				12 50						13 20					13 50	
London Road (Guildford)	d			11 54						12 24				12 54						13 24					13 54	
Clandon	d			11 59						12 29				12 59						13 29					13 59	
Horsley	d			12 03						12 33				13 03						13 33					14 03	
Effingham Junction 6	d			12 06						12 36				13 06						13 36					14 06	
Bookham	d									12 39										13 39						
Cobham & Stoke d'Abernon	d			12 10										13 10											14 10	
Oxshott	d			12 13										13 13											14 13	
Claygate	d			12 16										13 16											14 16	
Hinchley Wood	d			12 19										13 19											14 19	
Hampton Court	d	12 05						12 35				13 05						13 35				14 05				
Thames Ditton	d	12 07						12 37				13 07						13 37				14 07				
Surbiton 6	d	12 13		12 24				12 43				13 13		13 24				13 43				14 13			14 24	
Berrylands	d	12 15						12 45				13 15						13 45				14 15				
Shepperton	d						12 11										13 11									
Upper Halliford	d						12 14										13 14									
Sunbury	d						12 16										13 16									
Kempton Park	d						12 18										13 18									
Hampton	d						12 21										13 21									
Fulwell	d						12 24										13 24									
Strawberry Hill	d										12 49										13 49					
Teddington	d						12 29				12b55						13 29				13c55					
Hampton Wick	d						12 31				12 57						13 31				13 57					
Kingston	a						12 33				12 59						13 33				13 59					
	d						12 34				13 04						13 34				14 04					
Norbiton	d						12 36				13 06						13 36				14 06					
New Malden 6	d	12 18					12 40	12 48			13 10	13 18					13 40	13 48			14 10	14 18				
Dorking 4	d					12 08										13 08										14 08
Boxhill & Westhumble	d																									
Leatherhead	d					12 15				12 45						13 15				13 45						14 15
Ashtead	d					12 18				12 48						13 18				13 48						14 18
Epsom 3	a					12 23				12 53						13 23				13 53						14 23
	d					12 24				12 54						13 24				13 54						14 24
Ewell West	d					12 27				12 57						13 27				13 57						14 27
Stoneleigh	d					12 29				12 59						13 29				13 59						14 29
Worcester Park	d					12 32				13 02						13 32				14 02						14 32
Chessington South	d		12 10						12 40				13 10						13 40				14 10			
Chessington North	d		12 12						12 42				13 12						13 42				14 12			
Tolworth	d		12 14						12 44				13 14						13 44				14 14			
Malden Manor	d		12 17						12 47				13 17						13 47				14 17			
Motspur Park	d		12 20			12 35			12 50	13 05			13 20			13 35			13 50	14 05			14 20			14 35
Raynes Park 6	d	12 21	12 24			12 38	12 43	12 51	12 54	13 08	13 13	13 21	13 24			13 38	13 43	13 51	13 54	14 08	14 13	14 21	14 24			14 38
Wimbledon 6 ⊖	d	12 25	12 28	12 31		12 42	12 47	12 55	12 58	13 12	13 17	13 25	13 28	13 31		13 42	13 47	13 55	13 58	14 12	14 17	14 25	14 28		14 31	14 42
Earlsfield	d	12 28	12 31	12 35		12 46	12 50	12 58	13 01	13 16	13 20	13 28	13 31	13 35		13 46	13 50	13 58	14 01	14 16	14 20	14 28	14 31		14 35	14 46
Clapham Junction 10	d	12 32	12 35	12 39		12 50	12 54	13 02	13 05	13 20	13 23	13 32	13 35	13 39		13 50	13 54	14 02	14 05	14 20	14 23	14 32	14 35		14 39	14 50
Vauxhall ⊖	d	12 37	12 40	12 44		12 55	12 59	13 07	13 10	13 25	13 29	13 37	13 40	13 44		13 55	13 59	14 07	14 10	14 25	14 29	14 37	14 40		14 44	14 55
London Waterloo 15 ⊖	a	12 47	12 50	12 53		13 04	13 07	13 17	13 20	13 34	13 39	13 47	13 50	13 53		14 04	14 07	14 17	14 20	14 34	14 34	14 42	14 45		14 48	14 59

For general notes see front of timetable
For details of catering facilities see Directory of Train Operators

A From London Waterloo (Table 149)
b Arr. 1252
c Arr. 1352

From 27 September due to seasonal difficulties a large number of trains on this table will have minor retimings that could mean slightly earlier departure or later arrival times at certain stations. For further details see local publicity or contact National Rail Enquiries 08457 48 49 50.

Table 152

Sundays

For details of Bank Holiday service alterations, please see first page of Table 149

Hampton Court, Shepperton, Guildford, Dorking and Chessington South → London

Network Diagram - see first page of Table 152

Station		SW	SW A	SW	SW	SW	SW A	SW	SW		SW	SW	SW	SW A	SW	SW	SW A	SW	SW	SW	SW	SW	SW A
Guildford	d					14 20				and at the same minutes past each hour until	19 50					20 20				20 50			
London Road (Guildford)	d					14 24					19 54					20 24				20 54			
Clandon	d					14 29					19 59					20 29				20 59			
Horsley	d					14 33					20 03					20 33				21 03			
Effingham Junction 6	d					14 36					20 06					20 36				21 06			
Bookham	d					14 39										20 39							
Cobham & Stoke d'Abernon	d										20 10									21 10			
Oxshott	d										20 13									21 13			
Claygate	d										20 16									21 16			
Hinchley Wood	d										20 19									21 19			
Hampton Court	d			14 35				15 05							20 35			21 05					
Thames Ditton	d			14 37				15 07							20 37			21 07					
Surbiton 6	d			14 43				15 13			20 24				20 43			21 13		21 24			
Berrylands	d			14 45				15 15							20 45			21 15					
Shepperton	d	14 11											20 11									21 11	
Upper Halliford	d	14 14											20 14									21 14	
Sunbury	d	14 16											20 16									21 16	
Kempton Park	d	14 18											20 18									21 18	
Hampton	d	14 21											20 21									21 21	
Fulwell	d	14 24											20 24									21 24	
Strawberry Hill	d		14 30				14 49							20 30			20 49						21 30
Teddington	d	14 29	14 33				14b55						20 29	20 33			20c55					21 29	21 33
Hampton Wick	d	14 31	14 36				14 57						20 31	20 36			20 57					21 31	21 36
Kingston	a	14 33	14 38				14 59						20 33	20 38			20 59					21 33	21 38
	d	14 34					15 04						20 34				21 04					21 34	
Norbiton	d	14 36					15 06						20 36				21 06					21 36	
New Malden 6	d	14 40		14 48			15 10	15 18					20 40		20 48		21 10	21 18				21 40	
Dorking 4	d											20 08									21 08		
Boxhill & Westhumble	d																						
Leatherhead	d					14 45						20 15				20 45					21 15		
Ashtead	d					14 48						20 18				20 48					21 18		
Epsom 3	a					14 53						20 23				20 53					21 23		
	d					14 54						20 24				20 54					21 24		
Ewell West	d					14 57						20 27				20 57					21 27		
Stoneleigh	d					14 59						20 29				20 59					21 29		
Worcester Park	d					15 02						20 32				21 02					21 32		
Chessington South	d				14 40				15 10										21 10				
Chessington North	d				14 42				15 12										21 12				
Tolworth	d				14 44				15 14										21 14				
Malden Manor	d				14 47				15 17										21 17				
Motspur Park	d				14 50	15 05			15 20			20 35				21 05			21 20		21 35		
Raynes Park 6	d	14 43		14 51	14 54	15 08	15 13	15 21	15 24			20 38	20 43		20 51	21 08	21 13	21 21	21 24		21 38	21 43	
Wimbledon 6 ⊖	d	14 47		14 55	14 58	15 12	15 17	15 25	15 28		20 31	20 42	20 47		20 55	21 12	21 17	21 25	21 28	21 31	21 42	21 47	
Earlsfield	d	14 50		14 58	15 01	15 16	15 20	15 28	15 31		20 35	20 46	20 50		20 58	21 16	21 20	21 28	21 31	21 35	21 46	21 50	
Clapham Junction 10	d	14 54		15 02	15 05	15 20	15 23	15 32	15 35		20 39	20 50	20 54		21 02	21 20	21 23	21 32	21 35	21 39	21 50	21 54	
Vauxhall ⊖	d	14 59		15 07	15 10	15 25	15 29	15 37	15 40		20 44	20 55	20 59		21 07	21 25	21 29	21 37	21 40	21 44	21 55	21 59	
London Waterloo 15 ⊖	a	15 04		15 12	15 15	15 29	15 34	15 42	15 45		20 48	21 00	21 04		21 13	21 29	21 35	21 42	21 45	21 48	22 00	22 04	

For general notes see front of timetable
For details of catering facilities see Directory of Train Operators

A From London Waterloo (Table 149)
b Arr. 1452
c Arr. 2052

From 27 September due to seasonal difficulties a large number of trains on this table will have minor retimings that could mean slightly earlier departure or later arrival times at certain stations. For further details see local publicity or contact National Rail Enquiries 08457 48 49 50.

Sundays

For details of Bank Holiday service alterations, please see first page of Table 149

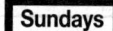

Hampton Court, Shepperton, Guildford, Dorking and Chessington South → London

Network Diagram - see first page of Table 152

		SW	SW	SW A	SW	SW	SW	SW		SW	SW A	SW	SW A	SW	SW	SW	SW	SW		SW A	SW	SW A	SW			
Guildford	d		21 20				21 50					22 20				22 50										
London Road (Guildford)	d		21 24				21 54					22 24				22 54										
Clandon	d		21 29				21 59					22 29				22 59										
Horsley	d		21 33				22 03					22 33				23 03										
Effingham Junction 6	d		21 36				22 06					22 36				23 06										
Bookham	d		21 39									22 39														
Cobham & Stoke d'Abernon	d						22 10									23 10										
Oxshott	d						22 13									23 13										
Claygate	d						22 16									23 16										
Hinchley Wood	d						22 19									23 19										
Hampton Court	d	21 35			22 05									23 05									23 45			
Thames Ditton	d	21 37			22 07									23 07									23 47			
Surbiton 6	d	21 43			22 13		22 24							23 13		23 24							23 53			
Berrylands	d	21 45			22 15									23 15									23 55			
Shepperton	d									22 11								23 11								
Upper Halliford	d									22 14								23 14								
Sunbury	d									22 16								23 16								
Kempton Park	d									22 18								23 18								
Hampton	d									22 21								23 21								
Fulwell	d									22 24								23 24								
Strawberry Hill	d			21 49							22 30		22 49							23 30		23 48				
Teddington	d			21b55						22 29	22 33		22c55					23 29		23 33		23 51				
Hampton Wick	d			21 57						22 31	22 36		22 57					23 31		23 36		23 54				
Kingston	a			21 59						22 33	22 38		22 59					23 33		23 38		23 56				
	d			22 04						22 34			23 04					23 34								
Norbiton	d			22 06						22 36			23 06					23 36								
New Malden 6	d	21 48		22 10	22 18					22 40			23 10	23 18				23 40					23 58			
Dorking 4	d	↳						22 08									23 08									
Boxhill & Westhumble	d																									
Leatherhead	d		21 45					22 15				22 45					23 15									
Ashtead	d		21 48					22 18				22 48					23 18									
Epsom 3	a		21 53					22 23				22 53					23 23									
	d		21 54					22 24				22 54					23 24									
Ewell West	d		21 57					22 27				22 57					23 27									
Stoneleigh	d		21 59					22 29				22 59					23 29									
Worcester Park	d		22 02					22 32				23 02					23 32									
Chessington South	d					22 10									23 10						23 40					
Chessington North	d					22 12									23 12						23 42					
Tolworth	d					22 14									23 14						23 44					
Malden Manor	d					22 17									23 17						23 47					
Motspur Park	d		22 05			22 20		22 35				23 05			23 20		23 35				23 50					
Raynes Park 6	d		22 08	22 13	22 21	22 24		22 38		22 43		23 08	23 13	23 21	23 24		23 38	23 43			23 53		00 01			
Wimbledon 6	d		22 12	22 17	22 25	22 28	22 31	22 42		22 47		23 12	23 17	23 25	23 28	23 31	23 42	23 47			23a59		00a04			
Earlsfield	d		22 16	22 20	22 28	22 31	22 35	22 46		22 50		23 16	23 20	23 28	23 31	23 35	23 46	23 50								
Clapham Junction 10	d		22 20	22 23	22 32	22 35	22 39	22 50		22 54		23 20	23 23	23 32	23 35	23 39	23 50	23 54								
Vauxhall	d		22 25	22 29	22 37	22 40	22 44	22 55		22 59		23 25	23 29	23 37	23 40	23 44	23 55	23 59								
London Waterloo 15	a		22 29	22 35	22 42	22 45	22 48	23 00		23 04		23 29	23 34	23 42	23 45	23 48	23 59	00 04								

For general notes see front of timetable
For details of catering facilities see Directory of Train Operators

A From London Waterloo (Table 149)
b Arr. 2152
c Arr. 2252

From 27 September due to seasonal difficulties a large number of trains on this table will have minor retimings that could mean slightly earlier departure or later arrival times at certain stations. For further details see local publicity or contact National Rail Enquiries 08457 48 49 50.

Network Diagram for Tables 155, 156, 157

DM-13/09
Design BAJS

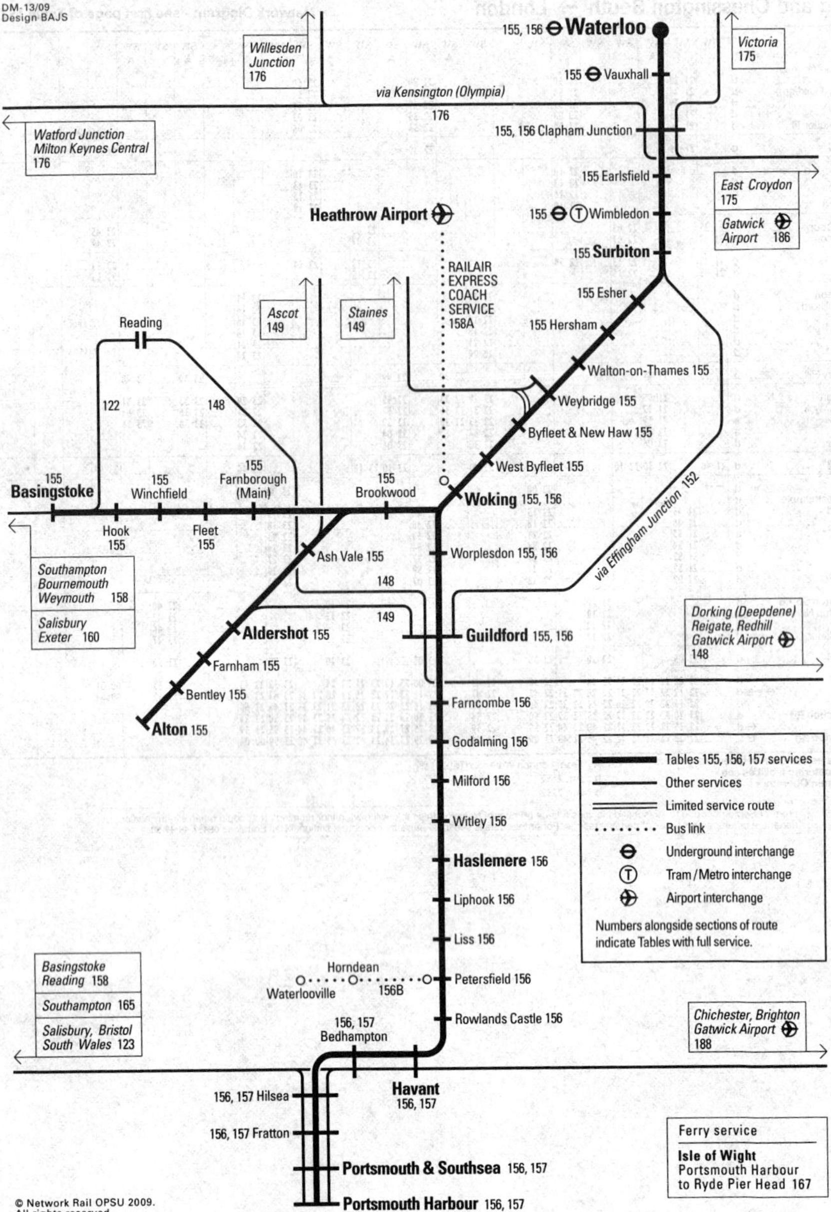

155, 156 Waterloo
155 Vauxhall
155, 156 Clapham Junction
155 Earlsfield
155 Wimbledon
155 Surbiton
155 Esher
155 Hersham
Walton-on-Thames 155
Weybridge 155
Byfleet & New Haw 155
West Byfleet 155
Woking 155, 156
Worplesdon 155, 156
Guildford 155, 156
Farncombe 156
Godalming 156
Milford 156
Witley 156
Haslemere 156
Liphook 156
Liss 156
Petersfield 156
Rowlands Castle 156
156, 157 Bedhampton
Havant 156, 157
156, 157 Hilsea
156, 157 Fratton
Portsmouth & Southsea 156, 157
Portsmouth Harbour 156, 157
Horndean
Waterlooville
156B
155 Basingstoke
Hook 155
155 Winchfield
Fleet 155
155 Farnborough (Main)
155 Brookwood
Ash Vale 155
Aldershot 155
Farnham 155
Bentley 155
Alton 155
Reading
122
148
149
Willesden Junction 176
via Kensington (Olympia)
176
Watford Junction Milton Keynes Central 176
Victoria 175
East Croydon 175
Gatwick Airport 186
Heathrow Airport
RAILAIR EXPRESS COACH SERVICE 158A
Ascot 149
Staines 149
via Effingham Junction 152
Southampton Bournemouth Weymouth 158
Salisbury Exeter 160
Dorking (Deepdene) Reigate, Redhill Gatwick Airport 148
Basingstoke Reading 158
Southampton 165
Salisbury, Bristol South Wales 123
Chichester, Brighton Gatwick Airport 188
Tables 155, 156, 157 services
Other services
Limited service route
Bus link
Underground interchange
Tram / Metro interchange
Airport interchange
Numbers alongside sections of route indicate Tables with full service.
Ferry service
Isle of Wight
Portsmouth Harbour to Ryde Pier Head 167

For details of Bank Holiday service alterations, please see first page of Table 149

London → Woking, Guildford, Alton and Basingstoke

Network Diagram - see first page of Table 155

Miles	Miles	Miles			SW MX 1	SW MO 1		SW MX 1	SW MO	SW MO	SW MX	SW MX 1	SW MO 1	SW MX 1	SW MO	SW MO 1 A	SW MX 1	SW MX	SW MO	SW MO 1 A	SW MO 1	SW MX 1	SW MX	SW MO 1	SW MX 1	SW MO 1	SW MX 1 B
0	—	—	**London Waterloo** 15 ⊖	d	22p53	23p07		23p12		23p10	23p20	23p23	23p30	23p35		23p35	23p39				23p40	23p45			23p48		00 05
1¼	—	—	Vauxhall ⊖	d						23p14	23p24										23p44						
4	—	—	Clapham Junction 10	d	23b00	23p15		23b19		23p19	23p29	23b30	23b39	23b42		23b44	23b46	←			23p49	23b52			23b56		00u12
5½	—	—	Earlsfield	d						23p22	23p32							23p32			23p52						
7¼	—	—	Wimbledon 6 ⊖	d		23p22				23p26	→							23p36			23p56						00u18
12	—	—	**Surbiton** 6	d	23p11	23p30		23p30		23p35		23p41						23p44			00 05				00 10		
14½	—	—	Esher	d						23p39								23p48			00 09						
16	—	—	Hersham	d					←	23p42								23p51			00 12			←			
17	—	—	Walton-on-Thames	d				23p37	23p45	23p45								23p54			00 15			00 15	00 17		
19	—	—	Weybridge	d				23p41	23p49	→								23p58			→			00 19	00 21	←	
20½	—	—	Byfleet & New Haw	d					23p51									00 01	00 02				00 07	00 21		00 21	
21¾	—	—	West Byfleet	d	23p21				23p54			23p51						00 03	00 05				00 10	→		00 24	
24¼	0	—	**Woking**	a	23p28	23p42		23p48	23p59			23p59	00 01	00 02	←	00 07	00 07	00 08	00 10	←		00 16	00 18		00 27	00 30	00 35
—	—	—		d	23p30	23p46	23p49	23p49	00 05			00 01	00 02	00 03	00 05	00 08	00 08			00 08		00 17			00 29	00 35	00 36
—	2½	—	Worplesdon	d					→							→						00 22					
—	6	—	**Guildford**	a									00 10		00 13							00 28					
28	—	0	Brookwood	d	23p36	23p52	23p56	23p55				00 06													00 35	00 41	
—	—	4½	Ash Vale	d	23p44		00 04					00 14														00 48	
—	—	7	**Aldershot**	d	23p50		00 09					00 20														00 54	
—	—	10	Farnham	a	23p56		00 15					00 25														00 59	
—	—	—		d	23p57		00 15					00 26															
—	—	14	Bentley	d	00 03		00 23					00 33															
—	—	18¾	**Alton**	a	00 11		00 30					00 41															
33¼	—	—	Farnborough (Main)	d		23p59		00 03									00 18			00 18					00 42		
36½	—	—	Fleet	d		00 05		00 08									00 23			00 24					00 48		
40	—	—	Winchfield	d		00 10		00 14																	00s53		
42¼	—	—	Hook	d		00 15		00 18																	00s58		
47¾	—	—	**Basingstoke**	a		00 22		00 25						00 23			00 34			00 39					01 07		00 55

		SW MX 1	SW MX 1	SW MX	SW MO 1	SW 1 C	SW 1 D	SW 1 E	SW 1◊ G	SW 1	SW 1 E	SW 1 H	SW 1	SW	SW 1 G	SW 1	SW	SW 1	SW 1 G	SW 1◊	SW 1 H	SW 1	SW	SW 1	SW	SW 1 H	SW 1
London Waterloo 15 ⊖	d			00 09	00 50	01 05	05 00	05 20	05 30					05 50	06 12	06 15	06 20			06 30	06 42			06 45	06 50		
Vauxhall ⊖	d			00 13		01 09	05 04	05 24						05 54			06 24								06 54		
Clapham Junction 10	d			00 18	00u57	01 14	05 09	05 29	05u37					05 59	06u19	06u22	06 29			06u37	06u49			06u52	06 59		
Earlsfield	d			00 21			05 12	05 32						06 02			06 32								07 02		
Wimbledon 6 ⊖	d			00 25		01 20	05 16	05 36	05 43					06 06			06 36								→		
Surbiton 6	d			00 33		01 29	05 24	05 44						06 14	06 30		06 44				07 00						
Esher	d			00s37			05 28	05 48						06 18			06 48										
Hersham	d			00s40			05 32	05 51			←			06 21			06 51		←				←			←	
Walton-on-Thames	d			00s43			05 35	05 54			05 54			06 24	06 37		06 54		06 37		07 07		06 54			07 07	
Weybridge	d			00s46			05 39	→			05 58			06 28	→		→		06 41		→		06 58			07 11	
Byfleet & New Haw	d			00s49			05 42				06 00			06 30									07 00				
West Byfleet	d			00s52			05 45				06 03			06 33									07 03				
Woking	a			00 57	01 16	01 42	05 50		05 59		06 08			06 38		06 41			06 48	06 56			07 08	07 11		07 18	
	d		00 40	00 58	01 18	01 42	05 51		06 01	06 02	06 11	06 19	06 30			06 43			06 50	06 57		06 58	07 10	07 13		07 19	
Worplesdon	d										06 16					06 48								07 18			
Guildford	a			01 06	01s26		05 59				06 21					06 53							07 20	07 23			
Brookwood	d		00 45							06 08		06 25	06 36						06 56			07c06				07 25	
Ash Vale	d	00 52	00 56							06 16			06 44					06 49				07 14					07 19
Aldershot	d	00a57	01 02							06 21			06 50					06a56				07 20					07a26
Farnham	a		01 07							06 27			06 55									07 25					
	d		01 08							06 27			06 57									07 26					
Bentley	d		01s14							06 34			07 03									07 32					
Alton	a		01 21							06 41			07 10									07 40					
Farnborough (Main)	d					01s58						06 33							07 04							07 33	
Fleet	d											06 38							07 09							07 38	
Winchfield	d											06 44							07 15							07 44	
Hook	d											06 48							07 19							07 48	
Basingstoke	a					02s12			06 20			06 58							07 28	07 16						07 56	

For general notes see front of timetable
For details of catering facilities see Directory of Train Operators

A To Salisbury (Table 160)
B To Bournemouth (Table 158)
C To Southampton Central (Table 158)
D To Portsmouth Harbour (Table 156)
E To Portsmouth & Southsea (Table 156)
G To Weymouth (Table 158)
H To Portsmouth Harbour (Table 158)
b Previous night.
Stops to pick up only
c Arr. 0703

For details of Bank Holiday service alterations, please see first page of Table 149

London → Woking, Guildford, Alton and Basingstoke

Network Diagram - see first page of Table 155

Station		SW 1	SW 1◇ ☕	SW	SW 1	SW 1	SW	SW 1	SW 1	SW 1 ☕	SW 1◇ ☕	SW 1	SW	SW 1	SW 1	SW 1	SW 1◇ ☕	SW	SW 1	SW 1	SW 1	SW 1◇ ☕	SW 1	SW	SW 1	SW 1	SW 1◇ ☕
London Waterloo 15 ⊖	d	06 53	07 10		07 12	07 15	07 20			07 30	07 35	07 23		07 39	07 45		07 50	07 50	07 42	08 00	07 53	08 05	08 09		08 12	08 15	08 20
Vauxhall ⊖	d						07 24											07 54									
Clapham Junction 10	d	07u00	07u17	←	07u20	07u22	07 29					07u30	←	07u46	07u52		07u57	07 59			08u00	08u12		←	08u19	08u22	08u27
Earlsfield	d			07 02			07 32						07 32					08 02						08 02			
Wimbledon 6 ⊖	d			07 06			→						07 36					→						08 06			
Surbiton 6	d	07 11		07 14	07 30							07 41	07 44						08 00		08 11			08 14	08 30		
Esher	d			07 18									07 48											08 18			
Hersham	d			07 21				←					07 51											08 21			
Walton-on-Thames	d			07 24	07 37			07 37					07 54						08 07					08 24	08 37		
Weybridge	d			07 28	→			07 41					07 58						08 11					08 28	→		
Byfleet & New Haw	d			07 30									08 00											08 30			
West Byfleet	d	07 21		07 33								07 51	08 03								08 21			08 33			
Woking	a	07 26	07 35	07 38		07 42		07 48		07 55	07 58	07 59	08 08		08 12		08 15		08 18	08 24	08 29		08 34	08 38		08 42	08 45
	d	07 30	07 36	07 39		07 44		07 49		07 55	08 00	08 00			08 14		08 16		08 19	08 25	08 30		08 35	08 39		08 44	08 46
Worplesdon	d					07 49									08 19											08 49	
Guildford	a			07 47		07 54				08 04					08 24					08 35				08 50		08 54	
Brookwood	d	07 36						07 55				08 06							08 25		08 36						
Ash Vale	d	07 44							07 49			08 14				08 19					08 44						
Aldershot	d	07 50							07a54			08 20				08a24					08 50						
Farnham	a	07 55										08 26									08 55						
	d	07 57										08 26									08 57						
Bentley	d	08 03										08 32									09 03						
Alton	a	08 10										08 40									09 10						
Farnborough (Main)	d							08 03						08 13					08 33				08 45				
Fleet	d							08 08						08 19					08 38								
Winchfield	d							08 14											08 44								
Hook	d							08 18											08 48								
Basingstoke	a		07 55					08 25			08 19			08 34			08 35		08 58			08 48	08 59				09 06

Station		SW 1	SW 1	SW 1 ☕	SW 1◇ ☕	SW 1	SW	SW 1	SW 1		SW 1	SW 1◇ ☕	SW	SW 1	SW 1 ☕	SW 1	SW 1◇ ☕	SW 1	SW	SW 1	SW 1	SW 1◇ A ☕	SW 1	SW 1	SW 1 ☕	SW 1◇ ☕	SW 1 B
London Waterloo 15 ⊖	d			08 30	08 35	08 23	08 20	08 39			08 45	08 50	08 50	08 42	09 00	08 53	09 05	09 09		09 12	09 15	09 20			09 30	09 35	09 23
Vauxhall ⊖	d						08 24						08 54														
Clapham Junction 10	d						08 29	08u46			08u52		08 59			09u00	09u12		←	09u19	09u22	09u27					
Earlsfield	d						08 32						09 02						09 02								
Wimbledon 6 ⊖	d						08 36						→						09 06								
Surbiton 6	d					08 41	08 44							09 00		09 11			09 14	09 30							09 41
Esher	d						08 48												09 18								
Hersham	d	←					08 51												09 21				←				
Walton-on-Thames	d	08 37					08 54							09 07					09 24	09 37			09 37				
Weybridge	d	08 41					08 58							09 11					09 28	→			09 41				
Byfleet & New Haw	d						09 00												09 30								
West Byfleet	d					08 51	09 03									09 21			09 33								09 51
Woking	a	08 49		08 55	08 58	09 00	09 08				09 11	09 15		09 18	09 24	09 29		09 33	09 38		09 42	09 45	09 48		09 54	09 58	09 59
	d	08 49		08 55	09 00	09 00					09 13	09 16		09 19	09 25	09 30		09 35			09 43	09 46	09 49		09 55	10 00	10 00
Worplesdon	d										09 18																
Guildford	a			09 05							09 23				09 33						09 52				10 03		
Brookwood	d	08 55				09 06								09 25		09 36							09 55				10 06
Ash Vale	d		08 49			09 14			09 19							09 44								09 49			10 14
Aldershot	d		08a54			09 20			09a24							09 50								09a54			10 20
Farnham	a					09 26										09 55											10 25
	d					09 26										09 57											10 26
Bentley	d															10 03											
Alton	a					09 39										10 10											10 38
Farnborough (Main)	d	09 03						09 13						09 33				09 45					10 03				
Fleet	d	09 08						09 19						09 38									10 08				
Winchfield	d	09 14												09 44									10 14				
Hook	d	09 18												09 48									10 18				
Basingstoke	a	09 28						09 34				09 35		09 58			09 48	09 58				10 05	10 28				

For general notes see front of timetable
For details of catering facilities see Directory of Train Operators

A To Bristol Temple Meads (Table 123)
B Until 2 October

For details of Bank Holiday service alterations, please see first page of Table 149

London → Woking, Guildford, Alton and Basingstoke

Network Diagram - see first page of Table 155

	SW	SW	SW	SW	SW	SW	SW	SW	SW	SW	SW	SW	SW	SW	SW	SW	SW	SW	SW	SW	SW	SW	SW	SW	SW	SW
	1 A		1	1	1	1 ◇ ☕		1	1 ☕	1	1 ◇ ☕	1		1	1	1 ◇ ☕	1	1	1 ☕	1 ◇ ☕	1		1	1	1	1 ◇ ☕
London Waterloo 15 ⊖ d	09 23	09 20	09 39	09 45		09 50	09 50	09 42	10 00	09 53	10 05	10 09		10 12	10 15	10 20			10 30	10 35	10 23	10 20	10 39	10 45		10 50
Vauxhall ⊖ d		09 24					09 54															10 24				
Clapham Junction 10 d		09 29	09u46	09u52			09 59			10u00	10u12		←	10u19	10u22	10u27						10 29	10u46	10u52		
Earlsfield d		09 32					10 02						10 02									10 32				
Wimbledon 6 ⊖ d		09 36					→						10 06									10 36				
Surbiton 6 d	09 41	09 44						10 00		10 11			10 14	10 30							10 41	10 44				
Esher d		09 48											10 18									10 48				
Hersham d		09 51											10 21				←					10 51				
Walton-on-Thames d		09 54						10 07					10 24	10 37			10 37					10 54				
Weybridge d		09 58						10 11					10 28	→			10 41					10 58				
Byfleet & New Haw d		10 00											10 30									11 00				
West Byfleet d	09 51	10 03								10 21			10 33								10 51	11 03				
Woking a	09 59	10 08		10 11		10 14		10 18	10 24	10 29		10 33	10 38		10 41	10 45	10 48		10 54	10 58	10 59	11 08		11 11		11 14
d	10 00			10 13		10 16		10 19	10 25	10 30		10 35			10 43	10 46	10 49		10 55	11 00	11 00			11 13		11 16
Worplesdon d				10 18																				11 18		
Guildford a				10 23					10 33						10 50				11 03					11 23		
Brookwood d	10 06							10 25		10 36							10 55				11 06					
Ash Vale d	10 14				10 19					10 44								10 49			11 14				11 19	
Aldershot d	10 20				10a24					10 50								10a54			11 20				11a24	
Farnham a	10 25									10 55											11 25					
d	10 26									10 57																
Bentley d										11 03																
Alton a	10 58									11 10																
Farnborough (Main) d			10 13					10 33				10 45					11 03						11 13			
Fleet d			10 19					10 38									11 08						11 19			
Winchfield d								10 44									11 14									
Hook d								10 48									11 18									
Basingstoke a			10 34			10 35		10 58			10 48	10 58				11 05	11 28						11 34			11 35

	SW	SW	SW	SW	SW	SW	SW	SW	SW	SW	SW	SW	SW	SW	SW	SW	SW	SW	SW	SW	SW	SW	SW	SW	SW	SW
		1	1 ☕	1	1 ◇ ☕	1		1	1	1 ◇ ☕	1	1	1 ☕	1 ◇ ☕	1		1	1	1	1 ◇ ☕		1	1 ☕	1	1 ◇ ☕	1
London Waterloo 15 ⊖ d	10 50	10 42	11 00	10 53	11 05	11 09		11 12	11 15	11 20			11 30	11 35	11 23	11 20	11 39	11 45		11 50	11 50	11 42	12 00	11 53	12 05	12 09
Vauxhall ⊖ d	10 54															11 24					11 54					
Clapham Junction 10 d	10 59			11u00	11u12		←	11u19	11u22	11u27						11 29	11u46	11u52			11 59			12u00	12u12	
Earlsfield d	11 02						11 02									11 32					12 02					
Wimbledon 6 ⊖ d	→						11 06									11 36					→					
Surbiton 6 d		11 00		11 11			11 14	11 30							11 41	11 44						12 00		12 11		
Esher d							11 18									11 48										
Hersham d							11 21				←					11 51										
Walton-on-Thames d		11 07					11 24	11 37			11 37					11 54						12 07				
Weybridge d		11 11					11 28	→			11 41					11 58						12 11				
Byfleet & New Haw d							11 30									12 00										
West Byfleet d				11 21			11 33								11 51	12 03								12 21		
Woking a		11 18	11 24	11 29		11 33	11 38		11 41	11 45	11 48		11 54	11 58	11 59	12 08		12 11		12 14		12 18	12 24	12 29		12 33
d		11 19	11 25	11 30		11 35			11 43	11 46	11 49		11 55	12 00	12 00			12 13		12 16		12 19	12 25	12 30		12 35
Worplesdon d																		12 18								
Guildford a			11 33						11 50				12 03					12 23					12 33			
Brookwood d		11 25		11 36							11 55				12 06							12 25		12 36		
Ash Vale d				11 44								11 49			12 14				12 19					12 44		
Aldershot d				11 50								11a54			12 20				12a24					12 50		
Farnham a				11 55											12 25									12 55		
d				11 57											12 26									12 57		
Bentley d				12 03																				13 03		
Alton a				12 10											12 37									13 10		
Farnborough (Main) d		11 33				11 45					12 03						12 13					12 33				12 45
Fleet d		11 38									12 08						12 19					12 38				
Winchfield d		11 44									12 14											12 44				
Hook d		11 48									12 18											12 48				
Basingstoke a		11 58			11 48	11 58				12 05	12 28						12 34			12 35		12 58			12 48	12 58

For general notes see front of timetable
For details of catering facilities see
Directory of Train Operators

A From 5 October

For details of Bank Holiday service alterations, please see first page of Table 149

London → Woking, Guildford, Alton and Basingstoke

Network Diagram - see first page of Table 155

		SW	SW 1	SW 1	SW 1 ◇ A ☕	SW 1	SW 1	SW 1 ☕	SW 1 ◇ ☕	SW 1	SW	SW 1	SW 1	SW 1
London Waterloo 15 ⊖	d		12 12	12 15	12 20			12 30	12 35	12 23	12 20	12 39	12 45	
Vauxhall ⊖	d										12 24			
Clapham Junction 10	d	←	12u19	12u22	12u27						12 29	12u46	12u52	
Earlsfield	d	12 02									12 32			
Wimbledon 6 ⊖	d	12 06									12 36			
Surbiton 6	d	12 14	12 30							12 41	12 44			
Esher	d	12 18									12 48			
Hersham	d	12 21				←					12 51			
Walton-on-Thames	d	12 24	12 37			12 37					12 54			
Weybridge	d	12 28	→			12 41					12 58			
Byfleet & New Haw	d	12 30									13 00			
West Byfleet	d	12 33								12 51	13 03			
Woking	a	12 38		12 41	12 45	12 48		12 54	12 58	12 59	13 08		13 11	
	d			12 43	12 46	12 49		12 55	13 00	13 00			13 13	
Worplesdon	d												13 18	
Guildford	a			12 50				13 03					13 23	
Brookwood	d					12 55				13 06				
Ash Vale	d						12 49			13 14				13 19
Aldershot	d						12a54			13 20				13a24
Farnham	a									13 25				
	d									13 26				
Bentley	d													
Alton	a									13 37				
Farnborough (Main)	d					13 03						13 13		
Fleet	d					13 08						13 19		
Winchfield	d					13 14								
Hook	d					13 18								
Basingstoke	a				13 05	13 28						13 34		

		SW 1 ◇ ☕		SW	SW 1	SW 1 ☕	SW 1	SW 1 ◇ ☕	SW 1	SW	SW 1	SW 1	SW 1 ◇ ☕	SW 1
London Waterloo 15 ⊖	d	12 50		12 50	12 42	13 00	12 53	13 05	13 09		13 12	13 15	13 20	
Vauxhall ⊖	d			12 54										
Clapham Junction 10	d			12 59			13u00	13u12		←	13u19	13u22	13u27	
Earlsfield	d			13 02 →						13 02				
Wimbledon 6 ⊖	d									13 06				
Surbiton 6	d				13 00		13 11			13 14	13 30			
Esher	d									13 18				
Hersham	d									13 21				←
Walton-on-Thames	d				13 07					13 24	13 37			13 37
Weybridge	d				13 11					13 28	→			13 41
Byfleet & New Haw	d									13 30				
West Byfleet	d						13 21			13 33				
Woking	a	13 14			13 18	13 24	13 29		13 33	13 38		13 41	13 45	13 48
	d	13 16			13 19	13 25	13 30		13 35			13 43	13 46	13 49
Worplesdon	d													
Guildford	a					13 33						13 50		
Brookwood	d				13 25		13 36							13 55
Ash Vale	d						13 44							
Aldershot	d						13 50							
Farnham	a						13 55							
	d						13 57							
Bentley	d						14 03							
Alton	a						14 11							
Farnborough (Main)	d				13 33				13 45					14 03
Fleet	d				13 38									14 08
Winchfield	d				13 44									14 14
Hook	d				13 48									14 18
Basingstoke	a	13 35			13 58			13 48	13 59				14 05	14 28

		SW 1	SW 1 ☕	SW 1 ◇ ☕	SW 1	SW	SW 1	SW 1	SW 1	SW 1 ◇ ☕	SW	SW 1	SW 1 ☕	SW 1
London Waterloo 15 ⊖	d		13 30	13 35	13 23	13 20	13 39	13 45		13 50	13 50	13 42	14 00	13 53
Vauxhall ⊖	d					13 24					13 54			
Clapham Junction 10	d					13 29	13u46	13u52			13 59			14u00
Earlsfield	d					13 32					14 02 →			
Wimbledon 6 ⊖	d					13 36								
Surbiton 6	d				13 41	13 44						14 00		14 11
Esher	d					13 48								
Hersham	d					13 51								
Walton-on-Thames	d					13 54						14 07		
Weybridge	d					13 58						14 11		
Byfleet & New Haw	d					14 00								
West Byfleet	d				13 51	14 03								14 21
Woking	a		13 54	13 58	13 59	14 08		14 11		14 14		14 18	14 24	14 29
	d		13 55	14 00	14 00			14 13		14 16		14 19	14 25	14 30
Worplesdon	d							14 18						
Guildford	a		14 03					14 23					14 33	
Brookwood	d				14 06							14 25		14 36
Ash Vale	d	13 49			14 14				14 19					14 44
Aldershot	d	13a54			14 20				14a24					14 50
Farnham	a				14 25									14 55
	d				14 26									14 57
Bentley	d													15 03
Alton	a				14 37									15 10
Farnborough (Main)	d						14 13					14 33		
Fleet	d						14 19					14 38		
Winchfield	d											14 44		
Hook	d											14 48		
Basingstoke	a						14 34			14 35		14 58		

		SW 1 ◇ ☕	SW 1	SW	SW 1	SW 1	SW 1 ◇ ☕	SW 1	SW 1	SW 1 ☕	SW 1 ◇ ☕	SW 1	SW	SW 1
London Waterloo 15 ⊖	d	14 05	14 09		14 12	14 15	14 20			14 30	14 35	14 23	14 20	14 39
Vauxhall ⊖	d												14 24	
Clapham Junction 10	d	14u12		←	14u19	14u22	14u27						14 29	14u46
Earlsfield	d			14 02									14 32	
Wimbledon 6 ⊖	d			14 06									14 36	
Surbiton 6	d			14 14	14 30							14 41	14 44	
Esher	d			14 18									14 48	
Hersham	d			14 21				←					14 51	
Walton-on-Thames	d			14 24	14 37			14 37					14 54	
Weybridge	d			14 28	→			14 41					14 58	
Byfleet & New Haw	d			14 30									15 00	
West Byfleet	d			14 33								14 51	15 03	
Woking	a		14 33	14 38		14 41	14 45	14 48		14 54	14 58	14 59	15 08	
	d		14 35			14 43	14 46	14 49		14 55	15 00	15 00		
Worplesdon	d													
Guildford	a					14 50				15 03				
Brookwood	d							14 55				15 06		
Ash Vale	d								14 49			15 14		
Aldershot	d								14a54			15 20		
Farnham	a											15 25		
	d											15 26		
Bentley	d													
Alton	a											15 37		
Farnborough (Main)	d		14 45					15 03						15 13
Fleet	d							15 08						15 19
Winchfield	d							15 14						
Hook	d							15 18						
Basingstoke	a	14 48	14 58				15 05	15 28						15 34

For general notes see front of timetable
For details of catering facilities see
Directory of Train Operators

A To Bristol Temple Meads (Table 123)

For details of Bank Holiday service alterations, please see first page of Table 149

London → Woking, Guildford, Alton and Basingstoke

Network Diagram - see first page of Table 155

	SW 1	SW 1	SW 1◇ ☕	SW	SW 1	SW 1 ☕	SW 1	SW 1◇ ☕	SW 1	SW	SW 1	SW 1	SW 1◇ ☕	SW 1	SW 1	SW 1 ☕	SW 1◇ ☕	SW 1	SW	SW 1	SW 1	SW 1	SW 1◇ ☕	SW	SW 1	SW 1 ☕
London Waterloo 15 ⊖ d	14 45		14 50	14 50	14 42	15 00	14 53	15 05	15 09		15 12	15 15	15 20			15 30	15 35	15 23	15 20	15 39	15 45		15 50	15 50	15 42	16 00
Vauxhall ⊖ d				14 54															15 24					15 54		
Clapham Junction 10 d	14u52			14 59			15u00	15u12		←	15u19	15u22	15u27						15 29	15u46	15u52		15u57	15 59		
Earlsfield d				15 02						15 02									15 32					16 02		
Wimbledon 6 ⊖ d				→						15 06									15 36					→		
Surbiton 6 d					15 00		15 11			15 14	15 30							15 41	15 44						16 00	
Esher d										15 18									15 48							
Hersham d										15 21				←					15 51							
Walton-on-Thames d					15 07					15 24	15 37			15 37					15 54						16 07	
Weybridge d					15 11					15 28	→			15 41					15 58						16 11	
Byfleet & New Haw d										15 30									16 00							
West Byfleet d							15 21			15 33								15 51	16 03							
Woking a	15 11		15 14		15 18	15 23	15 29		15 33	15 38		15 41	15 45	15 48		15 54	15 58	15 59	16 08		16 11		16 15		16 18	16 24
d	15 13		15 16		15 19	15 25	15 30		15 35			15 43	15 46	15 49		15 55	16 00	16 00			16 13		16 16		16 19	16 25
Worplesdon d	15 18											15 48														
Guildford a	15 23					15 32						15 53				16 03					16 20					16 33
Brookwood d					15 25		15 36							15 55				16 06							16 25	
Ash Vale d		15 19					15 44								15 49			16 14				16 19				
Aldershot d		15a24					15 50								15a54			16 20				16a24				
Farnham a							15 55											16 25								
d							15 57											16 26								
Bentley d							16 03																			
Alton a							16 10											16 37								
Farnborough (Main) d					15 33				15 45					16 03						16 13					16 33	
Fleet d					15 38									16 08						16 19					16 38	
Winchfield d					15 44									16 14											16 44	
Hook d					15 48									16 18											16 48	
Basingstoke a			15 35		15 58			15 48	15 58				16 05	16 28						16 34			16 35		16 58	

	SW 1	SW 1◇ ☕	SW 1	SW	SW 1	SW 1	SW 1◇ ☕	SW 1	SW 1	SW 1 ☕	SW 1	SW 1	SW 1◇	SW	SW 1	SW 1	SW 1◇ ☕	SW 1	SW	SW 1 ☕		SW 1	SW 1	SW 1	SW 1	SW 1
London Waterloo 15 ⊖ d	15 53	16 05	16 09		16 12	16 15	16 20			16 30	16 25		16 35	16 20	16 39	16 45	16 50	16 42	16 50	17 00		16 55		17 09	17 12	17 15
Vauxhall ⊖ d														16 24					16 54							
Clapham Junction 10 d	16u00	16u12		←	16u19	16u22	16u27							16 29	16u46	16u52	16u57		16 59			17u02				
Earlsfield d				16 02										16 32					17 02							
Wimbledon 6 ⊖ d				16 06										16 36					17 06							
Surbiton 6 d	16 11			16 14	16 30						16 41			16 44				17 00	17 14							
Esher d				16 18										16 48					17 18							
Hersham d				16 21				←						16 51					17 21							
Walton-on-Thames d				16 24	16 37			16 37						16 54				17 07	→							
Weybridge d				16 28	→			16 41						16 58				17 11								
Byfleet & New Haw d				16 30										17 00												
West Byfleet d	16 21			16 33							16 51			17 03								17 21				
Woking a	16 29		16 33	16 38		16 41	16 45	16 48		16 54	16 59			17 10		17 11		17 18		17 24		17 29		17 32	17 36	17 38
d	16 30		16 35			16 43	16 46	16 49		16 55	17 00		17u00			17 13	17u16	17 19		17 25		17 30		17 34	17 37	17 40
Worplesdon d						16 48														17 30						17 45
Guildford a						16 53				17 03						17 20				17 36						17 51
Brookwood d	16 36							16 55			17 06							17 25				17 36			17 43	
Ash Vale d	16 44								16 49		17 14	17 19										17 44	17 49			
Aldershot d	16 50								16a54		17 21	17a24										17 50	17a54			
Farnham a	16 55										17 26											17 55				
d	16 57										17 27											17 57				
Bentley d	17 03										17 33											18 03				
Alton a	17 10										17 42											18 12				
Farnborough (Main) d			16 45					17 03							17 13			17 33							17 51	
Fleet d								17 08							17 19			17 38							17 56	
Winchfield d								17 14										17 44							18 02	
Hook d								17 18										17 48							18 06	
Basingstoke a		16 48	16 58				17 05	17 30							17 34		17 35	18 00						17 53	18 16	

For general notes see front of timetable
For details of catering facilities see
Directory of Train Operators

For details of Bank Holiday service alterations, please see first page of Table 149

London → Woking, Guildford, Alton and Basingstoke

Network Diagram - see first page of Table 155

	SW	SW 1	SW 1 ◇ ☕	SW 1	SW 1	SW 1	SW 1 ☕	SW 1	SW	SW 1	SW 1	SW 1	SW 1	SW 1 ◇ ☕	SW 1	SW 1	SW 1	SW 1 ☕	SW 1	SW	SW 1	SW 1	SW 1	SW 1 ◇ ☕	SW 1	SW 1
London Waterloo 15 ⊖ d		17 02	17 20	17 25	17 05	17 23	17 30	17 39	17 20	17 41	17 45	17 48	17 32	17 50	17 55	17 53		18 00	18 09	17 50	18 12	18 15	18 18	18 20	18 02	18 23
Vauxhall ⊖ d					17 09				17 24											17 54						
Clapham Junction 10 d					17 15				17 29											17 59				18u27		
Earlsfield d									17 32											18 02						
Wimbledon 6 ⊖ d									17 36											18 06						
Surbiton 6 d		17 18				17 39			17 44				17 48			18 09				18 14					18 18	18 40
Esher d	←	17 22							17 48				17 52							18 18					18 22	→
Hersham d	17 21	17 25							17 51				17 55							18 21					18 25	
Walton-on-Thames d	17 24	17 29							17 54				17 59							18 24					18 29	
Weybridge d	17 28	17 33							17 58				18 03							18 28					18 33	
Byfleet & New Haw d	17 30	17 36							18 00				18 06							18 30					18 36	
West Byfleet d	17 33	17 39							18 03				18 09			18 19				18 33					18 39	
Woking a	17 43	17 44		17 50		17 51	17 54	18 02	18 10			18 11	18 14		18 20	18 23			18 33	18 40			18 42	18 45	18 48	
d		17 46	17u46	17 51		17 52	17 56	18 04				18 13	18 16		18 21	18 26			18 35				18 43	18 46		
Worplesdon d							18 00						18 21										18 48			
Guildford a		17 56					18 06				18 21		18 29					18 31				18 50	18 54			
Brookwood d						18 00				18 11					18 27						18 41					
Ash Vale d				18 03	18 24										18 35		18 49									
Aldershot d				18 09	18a31										18 41		18a54									
Farnham a				18 14											18 46											
d				18 15											18 48											
Bentley d				18 24											18 54											
Alton a				18 32											19 03											
Farnborough (Main) d						18 08				18 19						18 38					18 48					
Fleet d						18 13				18 24						18 44					18 54					
Winchfield d						18 19				18 30						18 49					18 59					
Hook d						18 23				18 34						18 54					19 04					
Basingstoke a			18 05			18 32		18 23		18 45		18 32		18 37		19 03			18 54		19 16			19 05		

	SW	SW 1	SW 1	SW 1	SW 1 ☕	SW 1	SW	SW 1 A	SW 1 ◇ ☕	SW 1	SW 1	SW	SW 1	SW 1 ☕	SW 1	SW 1 ◇ ☕	SW 1	SW 1	SW	SW 1	SW 1 ◇ ☕	SW 1	SW	SW 1 ☕	SW 1 ◇ ☕	SW 1
London Waterloo 15 ⊖ d	18 20	18 25	18 05		18 30	18 39		18 45	18 50	18 41	18 32	18 50	18 55	19 00		19 05	19 09	19 12		19 15	19 20	19 02	19 20	19 30	19 35	19 25
Vauxhall ⊖ d	18 24		18 09									18 54											19 24			
Clapham Junction 10 d	18 29	18u33	18 15			18u46						18 59	19u02			19u12		19u19		19u22	19u27		19 29			19u32
Earlsfield d	18 32											19 02											19 32			
Wimbledon 6 ⊖ d	18 36			←								19 06											19 36			
Surbiton 6 d	18 44			18 40							18 48	19 14										19 18	19 44			
Esher d	18 48										18 52	19 18										19 22	19 48			
Hersham d	18 51						←				18 55	19 21							←			19 25	19 51			
Walton-on-Thames d	18 54						18 54				18 59	19 24							19 24			19 29	→			
Weybridge d	→						18 58				19 03	→							19 28			19 33				
Byfleet & New Haw d							19 00				19 06								19 30			19 36				
West Byfleet d							19 03	19 08			19 09								19 33			19 39				19 51
Woking a		18 52		18 52	18 57	19 05	19 12	19 13	19 17		19 18		19 21	19 24			19 33	19 38	19 42	19 43	19 45	19 48		19 54	19 58	19 59
d		18 53		18 54	18 58	19 06		19 14	19 18		19 20		19 23	19 25			19 35	19 39		19 45	19 46			19 55	20 00	20 00
Worplesdon d														19 30												
Guildford a					19 06			19 23						19 36						19 52				20 03		
Brookwood d				19 02						19 13			19 30					19 45								20 06
Ash Vale d		19 05	19 26										19 37		19 49											20 14
Aldershot d		19 11	19a35										19 43		19a54											20 20
Farnham a		19 16											19 48													20 25
d		19 18											19 49													20 26
Bentley d		19 24											19 55													20 32
Alton a		19 33											20 04													20 39
Farnborough (Main) d				19 10						19 20	19 31						19 45	19 53								
Fleet d				19 15						19 26	19 37							19 58								
Winchfield d				19 21						19 31	19 42							20 04								
Hook d				19 25						19 36	19 47							20 08								
Basingstoke a				19 34		19 28			19 37	19 47	20 00					19 48	19 58	20 15			20 06					

For general notes see front of timetable
For details of catering facilities see
Directory of Train Operators

A To Portsmouth Harbour (Table 156)

For details of Bank Holiday service alterations, please see first page of Table 149

London → Woking, Guildford, Alton and Basingstoke

Network Diagram - see first page of Table 155

Station		SW 1	SW	SW 1	SW 1 ◇ ☕	SW	SW 1	SW 1 ☕	SW 1	SW 1	SW 1 ◇ ☕	SW 1	SW	SW 1
London Waterloo 15 ⊖	d	19 39		19 45	19 50	19 50	19 42	20 00		19 53	20 05	20 09		20 12
Vauxhall ⊖	d					19 54								
Clapham Junction 10	d	19u46		19u52		19 59				20u00	20u12		←	20u19
Earlsfield	d					20 02							20 02	
Wimbledon 6 ⊖	d					→							20 06	
Surbiton 6	d						20 00			20 11			20 14	20 30
Esher	d		←										20 18	
Hersham	d		19 51										20 21	
Walton-on-Thames	d		19 54				20 07						20 24	20 37
Weybridge	d		19 58				20 11						20 28	→
Byfleet & New Haw	d		20 00										20 30	
West Byfleet	d		20 03							20 21			20 33	
Woking	a		20 08	20 11	20 14		20 18	20 24		20 29		20 33	20 38	
	d			20 13	20 16		20 19	20 25		20 30		20 35		
Worplesdon	d			20 18										
Guildford	a			20 23				20 33						
Brookwood	d						20 25			20 36				
Ash Vale	d								20 19	20 44				
Aldershot	d								20a24	20 50				
Farnham	a									20 55				
	d									20 57				
Bentley	d									21 03				
Alton	a									21 17				
Farnborough (Main)	d	20 13					20 33					20 45		
Fleet	d	20 19					20 38							
Winchfield	d						20 44							
Hook	d						20 48							
Basingstoke	a	20 34			20 35		20 58				20 48	20 58		

Station		SW 1	SW 1 ◇ ☕	SW 1	SW 1	SW 1 ☕	SW 1 ◇ ☕	SW 1	SW	SW 1	SW 1	SW 1	SW	SW 1
London Waterloo 15 ⊖	d	20 15	20 20			20 30	20 35	20 23	20 20	20 39	20 45	20 42	20 50	
Vauxhall ⊖	d								20 24				20 54	
Clapham Junction 10	d	20u22	20u27						20 29	20u46	20u52		20 59	
Earlsfield	d								20 32				21 02	
Wimbledon 6 ⊖	d								20 36				→	
Surbiton 6	d							20 41	20 44			21 00		
Esher	d								20 48					
Hersham	d				←				20 51					
Walton-on-Thames	d				20 37				20 54			21 07		
Weybridge	d				20 41				20 58			21 11		
Byfleet & New Haw	d								21 00					
West Byfleet	d							20 51	21 03					
Woking	a	20 41	20 45		20 48	20 54	20 58	20 59	21 08		21 11	21 18		
	d	20 43	20 46		20 49	20 55	21 00	21 00			21 13	21 19		
Worplesdon	d										21 18			
Guildford	a	20 50				21 03					21 23			
Brookwood	d				20 55			21 06				21 25		
Ash Vale	d			20 49				21 14						21 19
Aldershot	d			20a54				21 20						21a24
Farnham	a							21 25						
	d							21 26						
Bentley	d							21 32						
Alton	a							21 42						
Farnborough (Main)	d				21 03					21 13		21 33		
Fleet	d				21 08					21 19		21 38		
Winchfield	d				21 14							→		
Hook	d				21 18									
Basingstoke	a		21 05		21 28					21 34				

Station		SW 1 ☕	SW 1	SW 1 ◇ ☕	SW	SW 1	SW 1	SW 1 ◇ ☕	SW 1	SW 1	SW 1	SW 1 ◇ ☕	SW 1	SW
London Waterloo 15 ⊖	d	21 00	20 53	21 05		21 12		21 20			21 30	21 35	21 23	21 20
Vauxhall ⊖	d													21 24
Clapham Junction 10	d		21u00	21u12	←	21u19		21u27						21 29
Earlsfield	d				21 02									21 32
Wimbledon 6 ⊖	d				21 06									21 36
Surbiton 6	d		21 11		21 14	21 30							21 41	21 44
Esher	d				21 18									21 48
Hersham	d				21 21					←				21 51
Walton-on-Thames	d				21 24	21 37				21 37				21 54
Weybridge	d				21 28	→				21 41				21 58
Byfleet & New Haw	d				21 30									22 00
West Byfleet	d		21 21		21 33								21 51	22 03
Woking	a	21 24	21 29	21 31	21 38			21 45		21 48	21 54	21 58	21 59	22 08
	d	21 25	21 30	21 32				21 49		21 49	21 55	22 00	22 00	
Worplesdon	d													
Guildford	a	21 33									22 03			
Brookwood	d		21 36							21 55			22 06	
Ash Vale	d		21 44						21 49				22 14	
Aldershot	d		21 50						21a54				22 20	
Farnham	a		21 55										22 25	
	d		21 57										22 26	
Bentley	d		22 03										22 32	
Alton	a		22 10										22 39	
Farnborough (Main)	d						←			22 03				
Fleet	d						21 38			22 08				
Winchfield	d						21 44			22 14				
Hook	d						21 48			22 18				
Basingstoke	a			21 51			21 58	22 08		22 28				

Station		SW 1	SW 1	SW 1 A	SW	SW 1	SW 1	SW 1 ◇ ☕	SW	SW 1	SW 1 ☕	SW	SW 1	SW 1
London Waterloo 15 ⊖	d	21 39	21 45	21 42	21 50	22 00	21 53	22 05		22 12	22 20	22 20		
Vauxhall ⊖	d				21 54							22 24		
Clapham Junction 10	d	21u46	21u52		21 59		22u00	22u12	←	22u19	22u27	22 29		
Earlsfield	d				22 02				22 02			22 32		
Wimbledon 6 ⊖	d				→				22 06			→		
Surbiton 6	d			22 00			22 11		22 14	22 30				
Esher	d								22 18					
Hersham	d								22 21					←
Walton-on-Thames	d			22 07					22 24	22 37				22 37
Weybridge	d			22 11					22 28	→				22 41
Byfleet & New Haw	d								22 30					
West Byfleet	d						22 21		22 33					
Woking	a		22 11	22 18		22 24	22 29	22 31	22 38		22 45			22 48
	d		22 13	22 19		22 25	22 30	22 32	22 39		22 49			22 49
Worplesdon	d		22 18											
Guildford	a		22 23			22 33			22 47					
Brookwood	d			22 25			22 36							22 55
Ash Vale	d						22 44						22 49	
Aldershot	d						22 50						22a54	
Farnham	a						22 56							
	d						22 57							
Bentley	d						23 03							
Alton	a						23 10							
Farnborough (Main)	d	22 13		22 33										23 03
Fleet	d	22 19		22 38										23 08
Winchfield	d			22 44										23 14
Hook	d			22 48										23 18
Basingstoke	a	22 34		22 58				22 51			23 10			23 27

For general notes see front of timetable
For details of catering facilities see
Directory of Train Operators

A To Portsmouth Harbour (Table 158)

For details of Bank Holiday service alterations, please see first page of Table 149

London → Woking, Guildford, Alton and Basingstoke

Network Diagram - see first page of Table 155

	SW 1	SW 1 ◇	SW 1	SW	SW 1	SW 1	SW 1	SW 1	SW	SW 1	SW 1 A	SW 1 ◇	SW	SW 1	SW 1	SW 1	SW	SW 1	SW 1	SW 1	SW	SW 1	SW	SW 1
London Waterloo 15 ⊖ d	22 30	22 35	22 23		22 39	22 42	22 45		22 50	22 53		23 05		23 12	23 15		23 20	23 23	23 35	23 39		23 45		23 48
Vauxhall ⊖ d									22 54								23 24							
Clapham Junction 10 d			22u30	←	22u46	22u49	22u52		22 59	23u00		23u12	←	23u19	23u22		23 29	23u30	23u42	23u46	←	23u52		23u56
Earlsfield d				22 32					23 02 →				23 02				23 32 →				23 32			
Wimbledon 6 ⊖ d				22 36									23 06								23 36			
Surbiton 6 d			22 41	22 44		23 00				23 11			23 14	23 30				23 41			23 44			00 10
Esher d				22 48									23 18								23 48			
Hersham d				22 51				←					23 21			←					23 51			
Walton-on-Thames d				22 54		23 07 →		23 07					23 24	23 37 →		23 37					23 54			00 17
Weybridge d				22 58				23 11					23 28			23 41					23 58			00 21
Byfleet & New Haw d				23 00									23 30								00 01		00 07	
West Byfleet d			22 51	23 03						23 21			23 33					23 51			00 03		00 10	
Woking a	22 54	22 58	22 59	23 08			23 11	23 18		23 28		23 31	23 38		23 41	23 48		23 59	00 02	00 07	00 08	00 16	00 18	00 27
d	22 55	23 00	23 00				23 13	23 19		23 30		23 32			23 43	23 49		00 01	00 03	00 08		00 17		00 29
Worplesdon d							23 18															00 22		
Guildford a	23 03						23 23								23 51							00 28		
Brookwood d			23 06					23 25		23 36						23 55		00 06						00 35
Ash Vale d			23 14							23 44	23 49							00 14						
Aldershot d			23 20							23 50	23 55							00 20						
Farnham a			23 25							23 56	00 03							00 25						
d			23 26							23 57								00 26						
Bentley d			23 32							00 03								00 33						
Alton a			23 39							00 11								00 41						
Farnborough (Main) d					23 13			23 33								00 03				00 18				00 42
Fleet d					23 19			23 38								00 08				00 23				00 48
Winchfield d								23 44								00 14								00s53
Hook d								23 48								00 18								00s58
Basingstoke a					23 33			23 57				23 52				00 25			00 23	00 34				01 07

Saturdays

	SW 1	SW 1	SW	SW 1	SW 1	SW 1	SW	SW 1	SW	SW 1	SW 1 B	SW 1	SW 1	SW	SW 1 C	SW 1 D	SW 1 E	SW 1 ◇ G	SW 1	SW 1 E	SW 1 H	SW 1	SW	SW 1	SW 1
London Waterloo 15 ⊖ d	22p53	23p12	23p20	23p23	23p35	23p39		23p45		23p48	00 05			00 09	01 05	05 00	05 20	05 30					05 50	06 12	06 15
Vauxhall ⊖ d			23p24											00 13	01 09	05 04	05 24						05 54		
Clapham Junction 10 d	23b00	23b19	23p29	23b30	23b42	23b46	←	23b52		23b56	00u12			00 18	01 14	05 09	05 29	05u37					05 59	06u19	06u22
Earlsfield d			23p32 →				23p32							00 21		05 12	05 32						06 02		
Wimbledon 6 ⊖ d							23p36				00u18			00 25	01 20	05 16	05 36	05 43					06 06		
Surbiton 6 d	23p11	23p30		23p41			23p44			00 10				00 33	01 29	05 24	05 44						06 14	06 30	
Esher d							23p48							00s37		05 28	05 48						06 18		
Hersham d							23p51							00s40		05 32	05 51			←			06 21		
Walton-on-Thames d		23p37					23p54			00 17				00s43		05 35	05 54 →			05 54			06 24	06 37 →	
Weybridge d		23p41					23p58			00 21				00s46		05 39				05 58			06 28		
Byfleet & New Haw d							00 01		00 07					00s49		05 42				06 00			06 30		
West Byfleet d	23p21			23p51			00 03		00 10					00s52		05 45				06 03			06 33		
Woking a	23p28	23p48		23p59	00 02	00 07	00 08	00 16	00 18	00 27	00 35			00 57	01 42	05 50		05 59		06 08			06 38		06 41
d	23p30	23p49		00 01	00 03	00 08		00 17		00 29	00 36		00 40	00 58	01 42	05 51		06 01	06 02	06 13	06 19	06 30			06 43
Worplesdon d								00 22												06 18					
Guildford a								00 28						01 06		05 59				06 23					06 50
Brookwood d	23p36	23p55		00 06						00 35			00 45						06 08		06 25	06 36			
Ash Vale d	23p44			00 14								00 52	00 56						06 16			06 44			
Aldershot d	23p50			00 20								00a57	01 02						06 21			06 50			
Farnham a	23p56			00 25									01 07						06 27			06 55			
d	23p57			00 26									01 08						06 27			06 57			
Bentley d	00 03			00 33									01s14						06 34			07 03			
Alton a	00 11			00 41									01 21						06 41			07 10			
Farnborough (Main) d		00 03				00 18				00 42					01s58						06 33				
Fleet d		00 08				00 23				00 48											06 38				
Winchfield d		00 14								00s53											06 43				
Hook d		00 18								00 58											06 48				
Basingstoke a		00 25			00 23	00 34				01 07	00 55				02s12			06 20			06 58				

For general notes see front of timetable
For details of catering facilities see Directory of Train Operators

A From Ascot (Table 149)
B To Bournemouth (Table 158)
C To Southampton Central (Table 158)
D To Haslemere (Table 156)
E To Portsmouth Harbour (Table 156)
G To Weymouth (Table 158)
H To Portsmouth Harbour (Table 158)
b Previous night. Stops to pick up only

London → Woking, Guildford, Alton and Basingstoke

Network Diagram - see first page of Table 155

Station		SW		SW 1	SW 1◇	SW 1 A	SW 1	SW	SW 1	SW	SW 1	SW 1 A	SW 1	SW 1◇	SW		SW 1	SW 1	SW	SW 1	SW 1	SW 1◇	SW 1	SW	SW 1	SW 1	SW 1
London Waterloo 15 ⊖	d	06 20			06 30	06 42			06 45	06 50			06 53	07 10			07 12	07 15	07 20		07 30	07 35	07 23		07 39	07 45	
Vauxhall ⊖	d	06 24								06 54									07 24								
Clapham Junction 10	d	06 29			06u37	06u49			06u52	06 59			07u00	07u17	←		07u19	07u22	07 29				07u30	←	07u46	07u52	
Earlsfield	d	06 32								07 02 →					07 02				07 32 →					07 32			
Wimbledon 6 ⊖	d	06 36													07 06									07 36			
Surbiton 6	d	06 44				07 00							07 11		07 14		07 30						07 41	07 44			
Esher	d	06 48													07 18									07 48			
Hersham	d	06 51		←				←				←			07 21					←				07 51			
Walton-on-Thames	d	06 54 →		06 37		07 07 →		06 54				07 07			07 24		07 37 →			07 37				07 54			
Weybridge	d			06 41				06 58				07 11			07 28					07 41				07 58			
Byfleet & New Haw	d							07 00							07 30									08 00			
West Byfleet	d							07 03					07 21		07 33								07 51	08 03			
Woking	a			06 48	06 56			07 08	07 11			07 18	07 26	07 35	07 38			07 41		07 48	07 54	07 58	07 59	08 08		08 11	
	d			06 49	06 57		07 00		07 13			07 19	07 30	07 36				07 43		07 49	07 55	08 00	08 00			08 13	
Worplesdon	d								07 18																	08 18	
Guildford	a								07 23									07 50			08 03					08 23	
Brookwood	d			06 55			07 06					07 25	07 36							07 55			08 06				
Ash Vale	d						07 14				07 19		07 44										08 14				08 19
Aldershot	d						07 20				07a24		07 50										08 20				08a24
Farnham	a						07 25						07 55										08 25				
	d						07 26						07 57										08 26				
Bentley	d						07 32						08 03										08 32				
Alton	a						07 40						08 10										08 40				
Farnborough (Main)	d			07 03								07 33								08 03					08 13		
Fleet	d			07 08								07 38								08 08					08 19		
Winchfield	d			07 14								07 44								08 14							
Hook	d			07 18								07 48								08 18							
Basingstoke	a			07 28	07 16							07 58		07 57						08 28		08 20			08 34		

Station		SW 1◇	SW 1	SW 1		SW 1	SW 1	SW	SW 1◇	SW 1	SW 1	SW 1◇	SW 1	SW 1	SW 1	SW 1◇	SW 1		SW	SW 1	SW 1	SW 1	SW 1◇	SW	SW 1	SW 1	SW 1 B
London Waterloo 15 ⊖	d	07 50	07 42	08 00		07 52	08 09	07 50	08 05	08 12	08 15	08 20			08 30	08 35	08 23		08 20	08 39	08 45		08 50	08 50	08 42	09 00	08 53
Vauxhall ⊖	d							07 54											08 24					08 54			
Clapham Junction 10	d	07u57				07u59		07 59	08u12	08u19	08u22	08u27							08 29	08u46	08u52			08 59			09u00
Earlsfield	d							08 02											08 32					09 02 →			
Wimbledon 6 ⊖	d							08 06											08 36								
Surbiton 6	d		08 00			08 11		08 14		08 30							08 41		08 44						09 00		09 11
Esher	d							08 18											08 48								
Hersham	d							08 21					←						08 51								
Walton-on-Thames	d		08 07					08 24		08 37 →			08 37						08 54						09 07		
Weybridge	d		08 11					08 28					08 41						08 58						09 11		
Byfleet & New Haw	d							08 30											09 00								
West Byfleet	d					08 21		08 33									08 51		09 03								09 21
Woking	a	08 15	08 18	08 24		08 29	08 33	08 38			08 41	08 45	08 48		08 54	08 58	08 59		09 08		09 11		09 14		09 18	09 24	09 29
	d	08 16	08 19	08 25		08 30	08 35				08 43	08 46	08 49		08 55	09 00	09 00				09 13		09 16		09 19	09 25	09 30
Worplesdon	d																				09 18						
Guildford	a			08 33							08 50				09 03						09 23					09 33	
Brookwood	d		08 25			08 36							08 55				09 06								09 25		09 36
Ash Vale	d					08 44								08 49			09 14					09 19					09 44
Aldershot	d					08 50								08a54			09 20					09a24					09 50
Farnham	a					08 55											09 25										09 55
	d					08 57											09 26										09 57
Bentley	d					09 03																					10 03
Alton	a					09 10											09 38										10 10
Farnborough (Main)	d		08 33				08 45						09 03							09 13					09 33		
Fleet	d		08 38										09 08							09 19					09 38		
Winchfield	d		08 44										09 14												09 44		
Hook	d		08 48										09 18												09 48		
Basingstoke	a	08 35	08 58				08 58		08 48			09 05	09 28							09 34			09 35		09 58		

Station		SW 1 C	SW 1◇	SW 1	SW	SW 1		SW 1	SW 1◇ D	SW 1	SW 1	SW 1	SW 1◇	SW 1	SW	SW 1	SW 1	SW 1	SW 1◇		SW 1		SW	SW 1	SW 1	SW 1◇	SW 1
London Waterloo 15 ⊖	d	08 53	09 05	09 09		09 12		09 15	09 20			09 30	09 35	09 23	09 20	09 39	09 45		09 50		09 42		09 50	10 00	09 53	10 05	10 09
Vauxhall ⊖	d														09 24								09 54				
Clapham Junction 10	d	09u00	09u12		←	09u19		09u22	09u27						09 29	09u46	09u52						09 59		10u00	10u12	
Earlsfield	d				09 02										09 32								10 02 →				
Wimbledon 6 ⊖	d				09 06										09 36												
Surbiton 6	d	09 11			09 14	09 30								09 41	09 44						10 00				10 11		
Esher	d				09 18										09 48												
Hersham	d				09 21					←					09 51												
Walton-on-Thames	d				09 24	09 37 →				09 37					09 54						10 07						
Weybridge	d				09 28					09 41					09 58						10 11						
Byfleet & New Haw	d				09 30										10 00												
West Byfleet	d	09 21			09 33									09 51	10 03										10 21		
Woking	a	09 29		09 33	09 38			09 41	09 45	09 48		09 54	09 58	09 59	10 08		10 11		10 14		10 18			10 24	10 29		10 33
	d	09 30		09 35				09 43	09 46	09 49		09 55	10 00	10 00			10 13		10 16		10 19			10 25	10 30		10 35
Worplesdon	d																10 18										
Guildford	a							09 50				10 03					10 23							10 33			
Brookwood	d	09 36								09 55				10 06							10 25				10 36		
Ash Vale	d	09 44									09 49			10 14				10 19							10 44		
Aldershot	d	09 50									09a54			10 20				10a24							10 50		
Farnham	a	09 55												10 25											10 55		
	d	09 57												10 26											10 57		
Bentley	d	10 03																							11 03		
Alton	a	10 29												10 38											11 10		
Farnborough (Main)	d			09 45						10 03						10 13					10 33						10 45
Fleet	d									10 08						10 19					10 38						
Winchfield	d									10 14											10 44						
Hook	d									10 18											10 48						
Basingstoke	a		09 48	09 58					10 05	10 28						10 34			10 35		10 58					10 48	10 58

For general notes see front of timetable
For details of catering facilities see
Directory of Train Operators

A To Portsmouth Harbour (Table 158)
B Until 26 September
C From 3 October
D To Bristol Temple Meads (Table 123)

London → Woking, Guildford, Alton and Basingstoke

Network Diagram - see first page of Table 155

	SW	SW 1	SW 1	SW 1 ◇ ☕	SW 1	SW 1	SW 1 ☕	SW 1 ◇ ☕	SW 1	SW	SW 1	SW 1	SW 1	SW 1 ◇ ☕	SW 1	and at the same minutes past each hour until		SW	SW 1 ☕	SW 1	SW 1 ◇ ☕	SW 1	SW	SW 1	SW 1
London Waterloo 15 ⊖ d		10 12	10 15	10 20			10 30	10 35	10 23	10 20	10 39	10 45		10 50	10 42			15 50	16 00	15 53	16 05	16 09		16 12	16 15
Vauxhall ⊖ d										10 24								15 54							
Clapham Junction 10 d	←	10u19	10u22	10u27						10 29	10u46	10u52						15 59		16u00	16u12		←	16u19	16u22
Earlsfield d	10 02									10 32								16 02 →					16 02		
Wimbledon 6 ⊖ d	10 06									10 36													16 06		
Surbiton 6 d	10 14	10 30							10 41	10 44					11 00					16 11			16 14	16 30	
Esher d	10 18									10 48													16 18		
Hersham d	10 21				←					10 51													16 21		
Walton-on-Thames d	10 24	10 37 →			10 37					10 54					11 07								16 24	16 37 →	
Weybridge d	10 28				10 41					10 58					11 11								16 28		
Byfleet & New Haw d	10 30									11 00													16 30		
West Byfleet d	10 33								10 51	11 03										16 21			16 33		
Woking a	10 38		10 41	10 45	10 48		10 54	10 58	10 59	11 08		11 11		11 14	11 18				16 24	16 29		16 33	16 38		16 41
Woking d			10 43	10 46	10 49		10 55	11 00	11 00			11 13		11 16	11 19				16 25	16 30		16 35			16 43
Worplesdon d												11 18													
Guildford a			10 50				11 03					11 23							16 33						16 50
Brookwood d					10 55				11 06						11 25					16 36					
Ash Vale d						10 49			11 14				11 19							16 44					
Aldershot d						10a54			11 20				11a24							16 50					
Farnham a									11 25											16 55					
Farnham d									11 27											16 57					
Bentley d																				17 03					
Alton a									11 38											17 17					
Farnborough (Main) d					11 03						11 13				11 33							16 45			
Fleet d					11 08						11 19				11 38										
Winchfield d					11 14										11 44										
Hook d					11 18										11 48										
Basingstoke a				11 05	11 28						11 34			11 35	11 58						16 48	16 58			

	SW 1 ◇ ☕	SW 1	SW 1	SW 1 ☕	SW 1 ◇ ☕	SW 1		SW	SW 1	SW 1	SW 1	SW 1 ◇ ☕	SW	SW 1	SW 1 ☕	SW 1	SW 1 ◇ ☕	SW 1	SW		SW 1	SW 1	SW 1 ◇ ☕	SW 1	SW 1	SW 1 ☕
London Waterloo 15 ⊖ d	16 20			16 30	16 35	16 23		16 20	16 39	16 45		16 50	16 50	16 42	17 00	16 53	17 05	17 09			17 12	17 15	17 20			17 30
Vauxhall ⊖ d								16 24					16 54													
Clapham Junction 10 d	16u27							16 29	16u46	16u52			16 59			17u00	17u12		←		17u19	17u22	17u27			
Earlsfield d								16 32					17 02 →						17 02							
Wimbledon 6 ⊖ d								16 36											17 06							
Surbiton 6 d						16 41		16 44						17 00		17 11			17 14		17 30					
Esher d								16 48											17 18							
Hersham d		←						16 51											17 21					←		
Walton-on-Thames d		16 37						16 54						17 07					17 24		17 37 →			17 37		
Weybridge d		16 41						16 58						17 11					17 28					17 41		
Byfleet & New Haw d								17 00											17 30							
West Byfleet d						16 51		17 03								17 21			17 33							
Woking a	16 45	16 48		16 54	16 58	16 59		17 08		17 11		17 14		17 18	17 24	17 29		17 33	17 38			17 41	17 45	17 48		17 54
Woking d	16 46	16 49		16 55	17 00	17 00				17 13		17 16		17 19	17 25	17 30		17 35				17 43	17 46	17 49		17 55
Worplesdon d										17 18																
Guildford a				17 03						17 23					17 33							17 50				18 03
Brookwood d		16 55				17 06								17 25		17 36								17 55		
Ash Vale d			16 49			17 14					17 19					17 44									17 49	
Aldershot d			16a54			17 20					17a24					17 50									17a54	
Farnham a						17 25										17 55										
Farnham d						17 26										17 57										
Bentley d						17 32										18 03										
Alton a						17 42										18 10										
Farnborough (Main) d		17 03							17 13					17 33				17 45						18 03		
Fleet d		17 08							17 19					17 38										18 08		
Winchfield d		17 14												17 44										18 14		
Hook d		17 18												17 48										18 18		
Basingstoke a	17 05	17 28							17 34			17 35		17 58			17 48	17 58					18 05	18 28		

	SW 1 ◇ ☕	SW 1	SW	SW 1	SW 1	SW 1	SW 1 ◇ ☕	SW		SW 1	SW 1 ☕	SW 1	SW 1 ◇ ☕	SW 1	SW	SW 1	SW 1	SW 1 ◇ ☕	SW 1	SW 1	SW 1 ☕		SW 1 ◇ ☕	SW 1	SW	SW 1
London Waterloo 15 ⊖ d	17 35	17 23	17 20	17 39	17 45		17 50	17 50		17 42	18 00	17 53	18 05	18 09		18 12	18 15	18 20			18 30		18 35	18 23	18 20	18 39
Vauxhall ⊖ d			17 24					17 54																	18 24	
Clapham Junction 10 d			17 29	17u46	17u52			17 59				18u00	18u12		←	18u19	18u22	18u27							18 29	18u46
Earlsfield d			17 32					18 02 →							18 02										18 32	
Wimbledon 6 ⊖ d			17 36												18 06										18 36	
Surbiton 6 d		17 41	17 44							18 00		18 11			18 14	18 30								18 41	18 44	
Esher d			17 48												18 18										18 48	
Hersham d			17 51												18 21				←						18 51	
Walton-on-Thames d			17 54							18 07					18 24	18 37 →			18 37						18 54	
Weybridge d			17 58							18 11					18 28				18 41						18 58	
Byfleet & New Haw d			18 00												18 30										19 00	
West Byfleet d		17 51	18 03									18 21			18 33									18 51	19 03	
Woking a	17 58	17 59	18 08		18 11		18 14			18 18	18 24	18 29		18 33	18 38		18 41	18 45	18 48		18 54		18 58	18 59	19 08	
Woking d	18 00	18 00			18 13		18 16			18 19	18 25	18 30		18 35			18 43	18 46	18 49		18 55		19 00	19 00		
Worplesdon d					18 18																					
Guildford a					18 23						18 33						18 50				19 03					
Brookwood d		18 06								18 25		18 36							18 55					19 06		
Ash Vale d		18 14				18 19						18 44								18 49				19 14		
Aldershot d		18 20				18a24						18 50								18a54				19 20		
Farnham a		18 26										18 55												19 25		
Farnham d		18 26										18 57												19 26		
Bentley d		18 32										19 03												19 32		
Alton a		18 40										19 10												19 39		
Farnborough (Main) d				18 13						18 33				18 45					19 03							19 13
Fleet d				18 19						18 38									19 08							19 19
Winchfield d										18 44									19 14							
Hook d										18 48									19 18							
Basingstoke a				18 34			18 35			18 58			18 48	18 58				19 05	19 28							19 34

For general notes see front of timetable
For details of catering facilities see
Directory of Train Operators

London → Woking, Guildford, Alton and Basingstoke

Network Diagram - see first page of Table 155

		SW 1	SW 1	SW 1◇	SW	SW 1	SW 1	SW 1	SW 1◇	SW 1	SW		SW 1	SW 1	SW 1◇	SW 1	SW 1	SW 1	SW 1◇	SW 1	SW	SW 1	SW 1	SW 1		SW 1◇	SW
															A												
				☕			☕		☕						☕			☕	☕							☕	
London Waterloo 15	⊖ d	18 45		18 50	18 50	18 42	19 00	18 53	19 05	19 09			19 12	19 15	19 20			19 30	19 35	19 23	19 20	19 39	19 45			19 50	19 50
Vauxhall	⊖ d				18 54																19 24						19 54
Clapham Junction 10	d	18u52			18 59			19u00	19u12		←		19u19	19u22	19u27						19 29	19u46	19u52				19 59
Earlsfield	d				19 02						19 02										19 32						20 02
Wimbledon 6	⊖ d				→						19 06										19 36						→
Surbiton 6	d					19 00		19 11			19 14		19 30							19 41	19 44						
Esher	d										19 18										19 48						
Hersham	d										19 21					←					19 51						
Walton-on-Thames	d					19 07					19 24		19 37			19 37					19 54						
Weybridge	d					19 11					19 28		→			19 41					19 58						
Byfleet & New Haw	d										19 30										20 00						
West Byfleet	d							19 21			19 33									19 51	20 03						
Woking	a	19 11		19 15		19 18	19 24	19 29		19 33	19 38			19 41	19 45	19 48		19 54	19 58	19 59	20 08		20 11			20 14	
	d	19 13		19 16		19 19	19 25	19 30		19 35				19 43	19 46	19 49		19 55	20 00	20 00			20 13			20 16	
Worplesdon	d	19 18																					20 18				
Guildford	a	19 23					19 33							19 50				20 03					20 23				
Brookwood	d					19 25		19 36								19 55				20 06							
Ash Vale	d		19 19					19 44									19 49			20 14				20 19			
Aldershot	d		19a24					19 50									19a54			20 20				20a24			
Farnham	a							19 55												20 25							
	d							19 57												20 26							
Bentley	d							20 03												20 32							
Alton	a							20 10												20 39							
Farnborough (Main)	d					19 33				19 45						20 03						20 13					
Fleet	d					19 38										20 08						20 19					
Winchfield	d					19 44										20 14											
Hook	d					19 48										20 18											
Basingstoke	a			19 35		19 58			19 48	19 58					20 05	20 28						20 34				20 35	

		SW 1	SW 1	SW 1	SW 1◇	SW 1	SW	SW 1	SW 1	SW 1◇	SW 1	SW 1	SW 1		SW 1◇	SW 1	SW	SW 1	SW 1	SW 1	SW	SW 1	SW 1	SW 1	SW 1◇	SW	SW 1
																				B							
					☕					☕					☕										☕		
London Waterloo 15	⊖ d	19 42	20 00	19 53	20 05	20 09		20 12	20 15	20 20			20 30		20 35	20 23	20 20	20 39	20 45	20 42	20 50		21 00	20 53	21 05		21 12
Vauxhall	⊖ d																20 24				20 54						
Clapham Junction 10	d			20u00	20u12		←	20u19	20u22	20u27							20 29	20u46	20u52		20 59			21u00	21u12	←	21u19
Earlsfield	d						20 02										20 32				21 02					21 02	
Wimbledon 6	⊖ d						20 06										20 36				→					21 06	
Surbiton 6	d	20 00		20 11			20 14	20 30								20 41	20 44			21 00				21 11		21 14	21 30
Esher	d						20 18										20 48									21 18	
Hersham	d						20 21				←						20 51									21 21	
Walton-on-Thames	d	20 07					20 24	20 37			20 37						20 54			21 07						21 24	21 37
Weybridge	d	20 11					20 28	→			20 41						20 58			21 11						21 28	→
Byfleet & New Haw	d						20 30										21 00									21 30	
West Byfleet	d			20 21			20 33									20 51	21 03							21 21		21 33	
Woking	a	20 18	20 24	20 29		20 33	20 38		20 41	20 45	20 48		20 54		20 58	20 59	21 08		21 11	21 18			21 24	21 29	21 31	21 38	
	d	20 19	20 25	20 30		20 35			20 43	20 46	20 49		20 55		21 00	21 00			21 13	21 19			21 25	21 30	21 32		
Worplesdon	d																		21 18								
Guildford	a		20 33						20 50				21 03						21 23				21 33				
Brookwood	d	20 25		20 36							20 55					21 06				21 25				21 36			
Ash Vale	d			20 44								20 49				21 14						21 19		21 44			
Aldershot	d			20 50								20a54				21 20						21a24		21 50			
Farnham	a			20 55												21 25								21 55			
	d			20 57												21 26								21 57			
Bentley	d			21 03												21 32								22 03			
Alton	a			21 10												21 39								22 10			
Farnborough (Main)	d	20 33				20 45					21 03							21 13		21 33							
Fleet	d	20 38									21 08							21 19		21 38							
Winchfield	d	20 44									21 14									21 44							
Hook	d	20 48									21 18									21 48							
Basingstoke	a	20 58			20 48	20 58				21 05	21 28							21 34		21 58					21 51		

		SW 1◇		SW 1	SW 1	SW 1	SW 1◇	SW 1	SW	SW 1	SW 1	SW 1	SW	SW 1	SW 1		SW 1◇	SW	SW 1	SW 1	SW	SW 1	SW 1	SW 1	SW 1◇	SW 1	SW
												B															
		☕					☕										☕			☕					☕		
London Waterloo 15	⊖ d	21 20				21 30	21 35	21 23	21 20	21 39	21 45	21 42	21 50	22 00	21 53		22 05		22 12	22 20	22 20			22 30	22 35	22 23	
Vauxhall	⊖ d								21 24				21 54								22 24						
Clapham Junction 10	d	21u27							21 29	21u46	21u52		21 59		22u00		22u12	←	22u19	22u27	22 29					22u30	←
Earlsfield	d								21 32				22 02					22 02			22 32						22 32
Wimbledon 6	⊖ d								21 36				→					22 06			→						22 36
Surbiton 6	d							21 41	21 44			22 00			22 11			22 14	22 30							22 41	22 44
Esher	d								21 48									22 18									22 48
Hersham	d			←					21 51									22 21				←					22 51
Walton-on-Thames	d			21 37					21 54			22 07						22 24	22 37			22 37					22 54
Weybridge	d			21 41					21 58			22 11						22 28	→			22 41					22 58
Byfleet & New Haw	d								22 00									22 30									23 00
West Byfleet	d							21 51	22 03						22 21			22 33								22 51	23 03
Woking	a	21 45		21 48		21 54	21 58	21 59	22 08		22 11	22 18		22 24	22 29		22 31	22 38		22 45		22 48		22 54	22 58	22 59	23 08
	d	21 49		21 49		21 55	22 00	22 00			22 13	22 19		22 25	22 30		22 32	22 39		22 49		22 49		22 55	23 00	23 00	
Worplesdon	d										22 18																
Guildford	a					22 03					22 23			22 33				22 47						23 03			
Brookwood	d			21 55				22 06				22 25			22 36							22 55				23 06	
Ash Vale	d				21 49			22 14							22 44								22 49			23 14	
Aldershot	d				21a54			22 20							22 50								22a54			23 20	
Farnham	a							22 25							22 56											23 25	
	d							22 26							22 57											23 26	
Bentley	d							22 32							23 03											23 32	
Alton	a							22 39							23 10											23 39	
Farnborough (Main)	d			22 03						22 13		22 33										23 03					
Fleet	d			22 08						22 19		22 38										23 08					
Winchfield	d			22 14								22 44										23 14					
Hook	d			22 18								22 48										23 18					
Basingstoke	a	22 10		22 25						22 34		22 58					22 51			23 08		23 25					

For general notes see front of timetable
For details of catering facilities see
Directory of Train Operators

A To Bristol Temple Meads (Table 123)
B To Portsmouth Harbour (Table 158)

Saturdays

London → Woking, Guildford, Alton and Basingstoke

Network Diagram - see first page of Table 155

		SW 1	SW 1	SW 1		SW 1	SW	SW 1	SW 1	SW 1 A	SW 1 ◇	SW	SW 1	SW 1	SW 1	SW	SW 1		SW 1	SW 1	SW	SW 1	SW	SW 1			
London Waterloo 15 ⊖	d	22 39	22 42	22 45			22 50	22 53			23 05		23 12	23 15		23 20	23 23		23 35	23 39		23 45		23 48			
Vauxhall ⊖	d						22 54									23 24											
Clapham Junction 10	d	22u46	22u49	22u52			22 59	23u00			23u12	←	23u19	23u22		23 29	23u30		23u42	23u46	←	23u52		23u56			
Earlsfield	d						23 02					23 02				23 32					23 32						
Wimbledon 6 ⊖	d						→					23 06				→					23 36						
Surbiton 6	d		23 00					23 11				23 14	23 30				23 41				23 44			00 10			
Esher	d											23 18									23 48						
Hersham	d					←						23 21			←						23 51						
Walton-on-Thames	d		23 07			23 07						23 24	23 37		23 37						23 54			00 17			
Weybridge	d		→			23 11						23 28	→		23 41						23 58			00 21			
Byfleet & New Haw	d											23 30									23 59		00 07				
West Byfleet	d							23 21				23 33					23 56				00 03		00 10				
Woking	a			23 11		23 18		23 29			23 31	23 38		23 41	23 48		23 58		00 01	00 07	00 08	00 16	00 20	00 27			
	d			23 13		23 19		23 30			23 32			23 43	23 49		00 01		00 03	00 08		00 17		00 29			
Worplesdon	d			23 18																		00 22					
Guildford	a			23 23										23 51								00 28					
Brookwood	d					23 25		23 36							23 55		00 06							00 35			
Ash Vale	d							23 44	23 49								00 14										
Aldershot	d							23 50	23a54	23 58							00 20										
Farnham	a							23 55		00 03							00 25										
	d							23 57									00 26										
Bentley	d							00 04									00 33										
Alton	a							00 11									00 41										
Farnborough (Main)	d	23 13				23 33									00 03					00 18				00 42			
Fleet	d	23 19				23 38									00 08					00 23				00 48			
Winchfield	d					23 44									00 14									00s53			
Hook	d					23 48									00 18									00s58			
Basingstoke	a	23 34				23 55					23 51				00 25				00 23	00 34				01 07			

Sundays

		SW 1	SW 1	SW	SW 1	SW 1	SW 1	SW	SW 1	SW	SW 1	SW 1 B	SW 1	SW 1	SW	SW 1 C	SW 1	SW 1	SW 1	SW	SW	SW D	SW 1 ◇	SW	SW 1	SW 1	
London Waterloo 15 ⊖	d	22p53	23p12	23p20	23p23	23p35	23p39		23p45		23p48	00 05			00 09	01 05				07 10	07 40		07 54			08 00	
Vauxhall ⊖	d			23p24											00 13	01 09				07 14	07 44						
Clapham Junction 10	d	23b00	23b19	23p29	23b30	23b42	23b46	←	23b52		23b56	00u12			00 18	01 14				07 19	07 49		08u03			08u09	
Earlsfield	d			23p32				23p32							00 21					07 22	07 52						
Wimbledon 6 ⊖	d			→				23p36				00u18			00 25	01 20				07 26	07 56						
Surbiton 6	d	23p11	23p30		23p41			23p44			00 10				00 33	01 29				07 35	08 05						
Esher	d							23p48							00s37					07 39	08 09						
Hersham	d							23p51							00s40					07 42	08 12			←			
Walton-on-Thames	d		23p37					23p54			00 17				00s43					07 45	08 15			08 15			
Weybridge	d		23p41					23p58			00 21				00s46					07 49	→			08 19			
Byfleet & New Haw	d							23p59		00 07					00s49					07 51		08 02		08 21			
West Byfleet	d	23p21			23p56			00 03		00 10					00s52					07 54		08 05		08 24			
Woking	a	23p29	23p48		23p58	00 01	00 07	00 08	00 16	00 20	00 27	00 35			00 57	01 42				07 59		08 10	08 27	08 29		08 34	
	d	23p30	23p49		00 01	00 03	00 08		00 17		00 29	00 36		00 40	00 58	01 42	07 32	07 46	07 49	08 05			08 28	08 32		08 35	
Worplesdon	d								00 22																		
Guildford	a								00 28						01 06		07 40			08 14				08 40		08 43	
Brookwood	d	23p36	23p55		00 06						00 35			00 45				07 52	07 56								
Ash Vale	d	23p44			00 14								00 52	00 56					08 04						08 36		
Aldershot	d	23p50			00 20								00a57	01 02					08 09						08a41		
Farnham	a	23p55			00 25									01 07					08 15								
	d	23p57			00 26									01 08					08 15								
Bentley	d	00 04			00 33									01s14					08 24								
Alton	a	00 11			00 41									01 21					08 31								
Farnborough (Main)	d		00 03				00 18				00 42					01s58		07 59									
Fleet	d		00 08				00 23				00 48							08 05									
Winchfield	d		00 14								00s53							08 10									
Hook	d		00 18								00s58							08 15									
Basingstoke	a		00 25			00 23	00 34				01 07	00 55				02s12		08 22					08 46				

For general notes see front of timetable
For details of catering facilities see
Directory of Train Operators

A From Guildford (Table 149)
B To Bournemouth (Table 158)
C To Southampton Central (Table 158)
D From Staines (Table 149)

b Previous night.
Stops to pick up only

Sundays

London → Woking, Guildford, Alton and Basingstoke

Network Diagram - see first page of Table 155

		SW 1		SW	SW 1 ◇ ☕	SW 1	SW	SW 1	SW 1	SW 1 ◇	SW	SW	SW 1 ◇	SW	SW 1	SW 1		SW	SW 1 ◇ ☕	SW 1	SW	SW 1	SW 1	SW 1 ◇	SW
London Waterloo 15 ⊖	d	08 07		08 10	08 15				08 30	08 35		08 40	08 54		09 00	09 07		09 10	09 15				09 30	09 35	
Vauxhall ⊖	d			08 14								08 44						09 14							
Clapham Junction 10	d	08 15		08 19	08u22				08u39	08u42		08 49	09u03		09u09	09 15		09 19	09u22				09u39	09u42	
Earlsfield	d			08 22								08 52						09 22							
Wimbledon 6 ⊖	d	08 22		08 26								08 56				09 22		09 26							
Surbiton 6	d	08 30		08 35								09 05				09 30		09 35							
Esher	d			08 39								09 09						09 39							
Hersham	d			08 42			←					09 12		←				09 43			←				
Walton-on-Thames	d			08 45			08 45					09 15		09 15				09 45			09 45				
Weybridge	d			→			08 49					→		09 19				→			09 49				
Byfleet & New Haw	d						08 51				09 02			09 21							09 51				10 02
West Byfleet	d						08 54				09 05			09 24							09 54				10 05
Woking	a	08 42			08 46	←	08 59		09 03	09 08	09 10		09 27	09 29	09 34	09 42			09 46	←	09 59		10 03	10 08	10 10
	d	08 46	08 49		08 47	08 49	09 02		09 04	09 09			09 28	09 32	09 35	09 46	09 49		09 47	09 49	10 02		10 04	10 09	
Worplesdon	d		→														→								
Guildford	a						09 10		09 12					09 40	09 43						10 10		10 12		
Brookwood	d	08 52				08 56										09 52				09 56					
Ash Vale	d					09 04		09 36												10 04		10 36			
Aldershot	d					09 09		09a41												10 09		10a41			
Farnham	a					09 15														10 15					
	d					09 15														10 15					
Bentley	d					09 24														10 24					
Alton	a					09 31														10 31					
Farnborough (Main)	d	08 59														09 59									
Fleet	d	09 05														10 05									
Winchfield	d	09 10														10 10									
Hook	d	09 15														10 15									
Basingstoke	a	09 22			09 06					09 28			09 47			10 22			10 06					10 28	

		SW	SW 1 ◇	SW	SW 1	SW	SW 1		SW	SW 1 ◇ ☕	SW 1	SW	SW 1	SW 1	SW	SW 1 ◇ ☕	SW		SW	SW 1 ◇	SW	SW 1	SW
London Waterloo 15 ⊖	d	09 40	09 54		10 00		10 07		10 10	10 15				10 30		10 35		and at the same minutes past each hour until	14 40	14 54		15 00	
Vauxhall ⊖	d	09 44							10 14										14 44				
Clapham Junction 10	d	09 49	10u03		10u09		10 15		10 19	10u22				10u39		10u42			14 49	15u03		15u09	
Earlsfield	d	09 52							10 22										14 52				
Wimbledon 6 ⊖	d	09 56					10 22		10 26										14 56				
Surbiton 6	d	10 05					10 30		10 35										15 05				
Esher	d	10 09							10 39										15 09				
Hersham	d	10 12		←					10 42			←							15 12		←		
Walton-on-Thames	d	10 15		10 15					10 45			10 45							15 15		15 15		
Weybridge	d	→		10 19					→			10 49							→		15 19		
Byfleet & New Haw	d			10 21								10 51					11 02				15 21		
West Byfleet	d			10 24								10 54					11 05				15 24		
Woking	a		10 26	10 29	10 31	←	10 42			10 45	←	10 59		11 01	←	11 06	11 10			15 26	15 29	15 31	←
	d		10 28	10 35	10 32	10 35	10 46	10 49		10 46	10 49	11 05		11 02	11 05	11 07				15 28	15 35	15 32	15 35
Worplesdon	d			→				→				→									→		
Guildford	a				10 40	10 44								11 10	11 14							15 40	15 44
Brookwood	d						10 52				10 56												
Ash Vale	d										11 04		11 36										
Aldershot	d										11 09		11a41										
Farnham	a										11 15												
	d										11 15												
Bentley	d										11 24												
Alton	a										11 31												
Farnborough (Main)	d						10 59																
Fleet	d						11 05																
Winchfield	d						11 10																
Hook	d						11 15																
Basingstoke	a		10 47				11 22			11 05						11 26				15 47			

For general notes see front of timetable
For details of catering facilities see Directory of Train Operators

Table 155

Sundays

London → Woking, Guildford, Alton and Basingstoke

Network Diagram - see first page of Table 155

	SW 1		SW	SW 1 ◇ ☕	SW 1	SW	SW 1	SW 1 ☕	SW	SW 1 ◇ ☕	SW	SW 1		SW	SW 1 ◇	SW	SW 1	SW	SW 1		SW		SW 1 ◇ ☕	SW 1	SW	SW 1
London Waterloo 15 ⊖ d	15 07		15 10	15 15				15 30		15 35		15 37		15 40	15 54		16 00		16 07		16 10		16 15			
Vauxhall ⊖ d			15 14											15 44							16 14					
Clapham Junction 10 d	15 15		15 19	15u22				15u39		15u42		15 46		15 49	16u03		16u09		16 15		16 19		16u22			
Earlsfield d			15 22											15 52							16 22					
Wimbledon 6 ⊖ 🚋 d	15 22		15 26									15 53		15 56					16 22		16 26					
Surbiton 6 d	15 30		15 35									16 02		16 05					16 30		16 35					
Esher d			15 39											16 09							16 39					
Hersham d			15 42			←								16 12		←					16 42				←	
Walton-on-Thames d			15 45			15 45						16 09		16 15		16 15					16 45				16 45	
Weybridge d			→			15 49						16 13		→		16 19					→				16 49	
Byfleet & New Haw d						15 51					16 02					16 21									16 51	
West Byfleet d						15 54					16 05					16 24									16 54	
Woking a	15 42			15 45	←	15 59		16 01	←	16 06	16 10	16 19			16 26	16 29	16 31	←	16 42				16 45	←	16 59	
d	15 46	15 49		15 46	15 49	16 05		16 02	16 05	16 07		16 23	16 26		16 28	16 35	16 32	16 35	16 46	16 49			16 46	16 49	17 05	
Worplesdon d		→				→										→				→					→	
Guildford a								16 10	16 14								16 40	16 44								
Brookwood d	15 52				15 56							16 29	16 33						16 52					16 56		
Ash Vale d					16 04		16 36						16 41											17 04		17 36
Aldershot d					16 09		16a41						16 46											17 09		17a41
Farnham a					16 15								16 52											17 15		
d					16 15								16 56											17 15		
Bentley d					16 24																			17 24		
Alton a					16 31								17 07											17 31		
Farnborough (Main) d	15 59											16 36							16 59							
Fleet d	16 05											16 42							17 05							
Winchfield d	16 10																		17 10							
Hook d	16 15																		17 15							
Basingstoke a	16 22			16 05						16 26		16 54			16 47				17 22				17 05			

	SW 1 ☕	SW	SW 1 ◇ ☕	SW	SW 1		SW	SW 1 ◇	SW	SW 1	SW	SW 1		SW	SW 1 ◇ ☕	SW 1	SW	SW 1	SW 1 ☕	SW	SW 1 ◇ ☕	SW	SW 1			SW
London Waterloo 15 ⊖ d	16 30		16 35		16 37		16 40	16 54		17 00		17 07		17 10	17 15				17 30		17 35		17 37			17 40
Vauxhall ⊖ d							16 44							17 14												17 44
Clapham Junction 10 d	16u39		16u42		16 46		16 49	17u03		17u09		17 15		17 19	17u22				17u39		17u42		17 46			17 49
Earlsfield d							16 52							17 22												17 52
Wimbledon 6 ⊖ 🚋 d					16 53		16 56					17 22		17 26									17 53			17 56
Surbiton 6 d					17 02		17 05					17 30		17 35									18 02			18 05
Esher d							17 09							17 39												18 09
Hersham d							17 12		←					17 42			←									18 12
Walton-on-Thames d					17 09		17 15		17 15					17 45			17 45						18 09			18 15
Weybridge d					17 13		→		17 19					→			17 49						18 13			→
Byfleet & New Haw d				17 02					17 21								17 51					18 02				
West Byfleet d				17 05					17 24								17 54					18 05				
Woking a	17 01	←	17 06	17 10	17 19			17 26	17 29	17 31	←	17 42			17 45	←	17 59		18 01	←	18 06	18 10	18 19			
d	17 02	17 05	17 07		17 23	17 26		17 28	17 35	17 32	17 35	17 46	17 49		17 46	17 49	18 05		18 02	18 05	18 07		18 23	18 26		
Worplesdon d									→				→				→									
Guildford a	17 10	17 14								17 40	17 44								18 10	18 14						
Brookwood d					17 29	17 33						17 52				17 56							18 29	18 33		
Ash Vale d						17 41										18 04		18 36						18 41		
Aldershot d						17 46										18 09		18a41						18 46		
Farnham a						17 52										18 15								18 52		
d						17 56										18 15								18 56		
Bentley d																18 24										
Alton a						18 07										18 31								19 07		
Farnborough (Main) d					17 36							17 59											18 36			
Fleet d					17 42							18 05											18 42			
Winchfield d												18 10														
Hook d												18 15														
Basingstoke a			17 26		17 54			17 47				18 22			18 05						18 26		18 54			

For general notes see front of timetable
For details of catering facilities see
Directory of Train Operators

Sundays

London → Woking, Guildford, Alton and Basingstoke

Network Diagram - see first page of Table 155

		SW 1 ◇	SW	SW 1	SW	SW 1		SW	SW 1 ◇ A ☕	SW 1	SW	SW 1	SW 1 ☕	SW	SW 1 ◇ ☕	SW	SW 1		SW	SW 1 ◇	SW	SW 1	SW	SW 1		SW	SW 1 ◇ ☕
London Waterloo 15 ⊖	d	17 54		18 00		18 07		18 10	18 15				18 30		18 35		18 37		18 40	18 54		19 00		19 07		19 10	19 15
Vauxhall ⊖	d							18 14											18 44							19 14	
Clapham Junction 10	d	18u03		18u09		18 15		18 19	18u22				18u39		18u42		18 46		18 49	19u03		19u09		19 15		19 19	19u22
Earlsfield	d							18 22											18 52							19 22	
Wimbledon 6 ⊖	d					18 22		18 26									18 53		18 56					19 22		19 26	
Surbiton 6	d					18 30		18 35									19 02		19 05					19 30		19 35	
Esher	d							18 39											19 09							19 39	
Hersham	d		←					18 42			←								19 12		←					19 42	
Walton-on-Thames	d		18 15					18 45 →			18 45						19 09		19 15 →		19 15					19 45 →	
Weybridge	d		18 19								18 49						19 13				19 19						
Byfleet & New Haw	d		18 21								18 51					19 02					19 21						
West Byfleet	d		18 24								18 54					19 05					19 24						
Woking	a	18 26	18 29	18 31	←	18 42			18 45	←	18 59		19 01	←	19 06	19 10	19 19			19 26	19 29	19 31	←	19 42			19 45
	d	18 28	18 35	18 32	18 35	18 46	18 49		18 46	18 49	19 05		19 02	19 05	19 07		19 23	19 26		19 28	19 35	19 32	19 35	19 46	19 49		19 46
Worplesdon	d		→				→				→										→				→		
Guildford	a			18 40	18 44								19 10	19 14								19 40	19 44				
Brookwood	d					18 52				18 56							19 29	19 33						19 52			
Ash Vale	d									19 04		19 36						19 41									
Aldershot	d									19 09		19a41						19 46									
Farnham	a									19 15								19 52									
	d									19 15								19 56									
Bentley	d									19 24																	
Alton	a									19 31								20 07									
Farnborough (Main)	d					18 59											19 36							19 59			
Fleet	d					19 05											19 42							20 05			
Winchfield	d					19 10																		20 10			
Hook	d					19 15																		20 15			
Basingstoke	a	18 47				19 22			19 05						19 26		19 54			19 47				20 22			20 05

		SW 1		SW	SW 1	SW 1 ☕	SW	SW 1 ◇ ☕	SW	SW 1		SW	SW 1 ◇	SW	SW 1	SW	SW 1		SW	SW 1 ◇ ☕	SW 1	SW	SW 1	SW 1 ☕	SW	SW 1 ◇ ☕	SW
London Waterloo 15 ⊖	d					19 30		19 35		19 37		19 40	19 54		20 00		20 07		20 10	20 15				20 30		20 35	
Vauxhall ⊖	d											19 44							20 14								
Clapham Junction 10	d					19u39		19u42		19 46		19 49	20u03		20u09		20 15		20 19	20u22				20u39		20u42	
Earlsfield	d											19 52							20 22								
Wimbledon 6 ⊖	d									19 53		19 56					20 22		20 26								
Surbiton 6	d									20 02		20 05					20 30		20 35								
Esher	d											20 09							20 39								
Hersham	d			←								20 12		←					20 42			←					
Walton-on-Thames	d			19 45						20 09		20 15 →		20 15					20 45 →			20 45					
Weybridge	d			19 49						20 13				20 19								20 49					
Byfleet & New Haw	d			19 51					20 02					20 21								20 51					21 02
West Byfleet	d			19 54					20 05					20 24								20 54					21 05
Woking	a	←		19 59		20 01	←	20 06	20 10	20 19			20 26	20 29	20 31	←	20 42			20 45	←	20 59		21 01	←	21 06	21 10
	d	19 49		20 05		20 02	20 05	20 07		20 23	20 26		20 28	20 35	20 32	20 35	20 46	20 49		20 46	20 49	21 05		21 02	21 05	21 07	
Worplesdon	d			→										→				→				→					
Guildford	a					20 10	20 14								20 40	20 44								21 10	21 14		
Brookwood	d	19 56								20 29	20 33						20 52				20 56						
Ash Vale	d	20 04			20 36						20 41										21 04		21 36				
Aldershot	d	20 09			20a41						20 46										21 09		21a41				
Farnham	a	20 15									20 52										21 15						
	d	20 15									20 56										21 15						
Bentley	d	20 24																			21 24						
Alton	a	20 31									21 07										21 31						
Farnborough (Main)	d									20 36							20 59										
Fleet	d									20 42							21 05										
Winchfield	d																21 10										
Hook	d																21 15										
Basingstoke	a							20 26		20 54			20 47				21 22			21 05						21 26	

For general notes see front of timetable
For details of catering facilities see
Directory of Train Operators

A To Bristol Temple Meads (Table 123)

London → Woking, Guildford, Alton and Basingstoke

Network Diagram - see first page of Table 155

	SW 1		SW		SW 1 ◇	SW	SW 1	SW	SW 1		SW 1	SW	SW 1 ◇ ☕	SW 1	SW	SW 1	SW	SW 1 ◇ ☕	SW	SW 1		SW	SW A	SW 1 ◇	SW	SW 1
London Waterloo 15 ⊖ d	20 37		20 40		20 54		21 00		21 07			21 10	21 15			21 30		21 35		21 37		21 40	21 48	21 54		22 00
Vauxhall ⊖ d			20 44									21 14										21 44	21a51			
Clapham Junction 10 d	20 46		20 49		21u03		21u09		21 15			21 19	21u22			21u39		21u42		21 46		21 49		22u03		22u09
Earlsfield d			20 52									21 22										21 52				
Wimbledon 6 ⊖ d	20 53		20 56						21 22			21 26								21 53		21 56				
Surbiton 6 d	21 02		21 05						21 30			21 35								22 02		22 05				
Esher d			21 09									21 39										22 09				
Hersham d			21 12			←						21 42			←							22 12			←	
Walton-on-Thames d	21 09		21 15 →			21 15						21 45 →			21 45					22 09		22 15 →			22 15	
Weybridge d	21 13					21 19									21 49					22 13					22 19	
Byfleet & New Haw d						21 21									21 51				22 02						22 21	
West Byfleet d						21 24									21 54				22 05						22 24	
Woking a	21 19				21 26	21 29	21 31	←	21 42				21 45	←	21 59	22 01	←	22 06	22 10	22 19				22 26	22 29	22 31
Woking d	21 23	21 26			21 28	21 35	21 32	21 35	21 46	21 49			21 46	21 49	22 05	22 02	22 05	22 07		22 23	22 26			22 28	22 35	22 32
Worplesdon d						→				→					→										→	
Guildford a							21 40	21 44								22 10	22 14									22 40
Brookwood d	21 29	21 33							21 52					21 56						22 29	22 33					
Ash Vale d		21 41									22 36			22 04							22 41					
Aldershot d		21 46									22a41			22 09							22 46					
Farnham a		21 52												22 15							22 52					
Farnham d		21 56												22 15							22 56					
Bentley d														22 24												
Alton a		22 07												22 31							23 07					
Farnborough (Main) d	21 36								21 59											22 36						
Fleet d	21 42								22 05											22 42						
Winchfield d									22 10																	
Hook d									22 15																	
Basingstoke a	21 54				21 47				22 22				22 05					22 26		22 54				22 47		

	SW	SW 1		SW	SW 1 ☕		SW 1	SW	SW 1 B	SW 1	SW	SW	SW 1		SW	SW 1 ◇ ☕	SW	SW 1	SW	SW 1		SW	SW 1	SW	SW 1 C	SW
London Waterloo 15 ⊖ d		22 07		22 10	22 15					22 30			22 37		22 40	22 54		23 00		23 07		23 10	23 30		23 35	
Vauxhall ⊖ d				22 14											22 44							23 14				
Clapham Junction 10 d		22 15		22 19	22u22					22u39			22 46		22 49	23u03		23u09		23 15		23 19	23u39		23u44	
Earlsfield d				22 22											22 52							23 22				
Wimbledon 6 ⊖ d		22 22		22 26									22 53		22 56					23 22		23 26				
Surbiton 6 d		22 30		22 35									23 02		23 05					23 30		23 35				
Esher d				22 39											23 09							23 39				
Hersham d				22 42				←							23 12		←					23 42				
Walton-on-Thames d				22 45 →				22 45					23 09		23 15 →		23 15					23 45				
Weybridge d								22 49					23 13				23 19					23 49				
Byfleet & New Haw d								22 51				23 02					23 21					23 51				00 02
West Byfleet d								22 54				23 05					23 24					23 54				00 05
Woking a	←	22 42			22 45		←	22 59		23 01	←	23 10	23 19			23 26	23 29	23 31	←	23 42		23 59	00 01	←	00 07	00 10
Woking d	22 35	22 46	22 49		22 46		22 49	23 05		23 02	23 05		23 23	23 26		23 28	23 35	23 32	23 35	23 46	23 49	00 05	00 02	00 05	00 08	
Worplesdon d			→					→									→					→				
Guildford a	22 44									23 10	23 13							23 40	23 45				00 10	00 13		
Brookwood d		22 52					22 56						23 29	23 33						23 52	23 56					
Ash Vale d							23 04		23 36					23 41							00 04					
Aldershot d							23 09		23 42					23 47							00 09					
Farnham a							23 15		23 47					23 54							00 15					
Farnham d							23 15							23 56							00 15					
Bentley d							23 24														00 23					
Alton a							23 31							00 07							00 30					
Farnborough (Main) d		22 59											23 36							23 59					00 18	
Fleet d		23 05											23 42							00 05					00 24	
Winchfield d		23 10																		00 10						
Hook d		23 15																		00 15						
Basingstoke a		23 22			23 05								23 54			23 47				00 22					00 39	

For general notes see front of timetable
For details of catering facilities see Directory of Train Operators

A From 27 September to Shepperton
B From Ascot (Table 149)
C To Salisbury (Table 160)

Table 155

Sundays

London → Woking, Guildford, Alton and Basingstoke

Network Diagram - see first page of Table 155

		SW 1
London Waterloo 15 ⊖	d	23 40
Vauxhall ⊖	d	23 44
Clapham Junction 10	d	23 49
Earlsfield	d	23 52
Wimbledon 6 ⊖	d	23 56
Surbiton 6	d	00 05
Esher	d	00 09
Hersham	d	00 12
Walton-on-Thames	d	00 15
Weybridge	d	00 19
Byfleet & New Haw	d	00 21
West Byfleet	d	00 24
Woking	a	00 30
	d	00 35
Worplesdon	d	
Guildford	a	
Brookwood	d	00 41
Ash Vale	d	00 48
Aldershot	d	00 54
Farnham	a	00 59
	d	
Bentley	d	
Alton	a	
Farnborough (Main)	d	
Fleet	d	
Winchfield	d	
Hook	d	
Basingstoke	a	

For general notes see front of timetable
For details of catering facilities see Directory of Train Operators

For details of Bank Holiday service alterations, please see first page of Table 149

Basingstoke, Alton, Guildford and Woking → Waterloo

Network Diagram - see first page of Table 155

Miles	Miles	Miles			SW MO	SW MX 1	SW MO 1	SW MX 1	SW MX 1	SW MO 1 ◇	SW MO 1	SW MX 1 A	SW	SW	SW 1	SW	SW 1 B	SW 1 C	SW	SW	SW 1	SW	SW 1	SW 1	SW 1 ◇ ☕	SW	SW 1 B
0	—	—	**Basingstoke**	d		22p54				23p44		23p44					04 54	04 54					05 39	05 54	05 59		
5½	—	—	Hook	d		23p01						23p51					05 01	05 01						06 01			
7¾	—	—	Winchfield	d		23p05						23p55					05 05	05 05						06 05			
11¼	—	—	Fleet	d		23p10						00 01					05 10	05 10					05 50	06 10			
14½	—	—	Farnborough (Main)	d		23p16						00 06					05 16	05 16					05 56	→			
—	0	—	**Alton**	d																							05 42
—	4¾	—	Bentley	d																							05 49
—	8¾	—	Farnham	a																							05 54
—	—	—		d																							05 56
—	11¾	—	**Aldershot**	d											05 58												06 02
—	14¾	—	Ash Vale	d											06a02												06 07
19¾	18¾	—	Brookwood	d		23p23						00 13					05 23	05 23									06 14
—	—	0	**Guildford**	d			23p35		23p39		00 05		04 00	05 12							05 50						
—	—	3½	Worplesdon	d					23p44					05 17							05 55						
23½	—	6	**Woking**	a		23p28	23p42		23p49	00 02	00 13	00 18	04 08	05 22			05 28	05 28	←		06 00		06 05		06 18		06 19
—	—	—		d	22p52	23p33	23p45		23p56	00 04		00 20	04 10	05 33		05 25	05 29	05 29	05 33	05 43	06 01	06 04	06 06		06 19		06 20
26	—	—	West Byfleet	d	22p56	23p37						00 25		→		05 30			05 37	05 47		06 08					06 25
27¼	—	—	Byfleet & New Haw	d	23p00	23p40										05 33			05 40			06 11					
28¾	—	—	Weybridge	d		23p43		←				00 29							05 43	05 51		06 14				←	
30¾	—	—	Walton-on-Thames	d		23p47		23p47				00 34							05 47	05 55		06 18				06 18	
31¾	—	—	Hersham	d		→		23p49											05 49			→				06 20	
33¼	—	—	Esher	d				23p52											05 52							06 23	
35¾	—	—	**Surbiton** 6	a				23p57				00 40	04 24				05 40	05 40	05 56	06 01						06 27	06 35
40½	—	—	Wimbledon 6 ⊖	a				00 07				00 48	04 31				05 48	05 48	06 04							06 35	
42¼	—	—	Earlsfield	a				00 11											06 08							06 39	
43¾	—	—	Clapham Junction 10	a	00 01		00 04	00 15	00 21	00 23		00 54	04 43			06 43	06 00	06 00	06 12		06 20		06 25		06 38	06 42	06 46
46½	—	—	Vauxhall ⊖	a	00 08			00 20								06 49	06 07	06 07	06 17							06 47	
47¾	—	—	**London Waterloo** 15 ⊖	a	00 13		00 14	00 28	00 30	00 33		01 02	04 53			06 56	06 12	06 15	06 22	06 20	06 29		06 34		06 49	06 52	06 57

		SW 1 C	SW 1	SW	SW 1	SW 1 ☕	SW 1		SW 1	SW	SW 1	SW 1 ◇ ☕	SW 1	SW	SW 1 ◇ ☕	SW 1	SW 1	SW 1	SW 1	SW 1	SW 1 ◇ ☕	SW 1	SW 1 C	SW 1 B	SW 1	SW 1 ☕	SW 1
Basingstoke	d						06 23					06 27			06 35					06 42	06 51						06 54
Hook	d						06 31																				07 01
Winchfield	d		←				06 35									←											07 05
Fleet	d		06 10				06 40									06 40				06 54							07 10
Farnborough (Main)	d		06 16				→									06 46				07 00							07 16
Alton	d	05 42											06 12												06 44		
Bentley	d	05 49											06 19												06 51		
Farnham	a	05 54											06 24												06 56		
	d	05 56											06 26												06 58		
Aldershot	d	06 02							06 28				06 32										06 59	07 00	07 04		
Ash Vale	d	06 07							06 32				06 37										07 03	07 04	07 09		
Brookwood	d	06 14	06 23										06 44			06 53									07 16		07 23
Guildford	d				06 24	06 31												06 53				07 07				07 17	
Worplesdon	d				06 30													06 59									
Woking	a	06 19	06 28		06 35	06 39						06 46	06 49		06 53	06 58		07 03		07 10		07 15			07 21	07 25	07 28
	d	06 20	06 29	06 32	06 37	06 41					06 41	06 47	06 50		06 55	06 59	07 02	07 05	07 07	07 11		07 17			07 22	07 26	07 29
West Byfleet	d	06 25		06 36							06 46						07 07		07b16								
Byfleet & New Haw	d			06 39							06 49								07 19								
Weybridge	d			06 43						←	06 52						07 11		07 22								
Walton-on-Thames	d			06 47						06 47	06 57						07 16		07 27								
Hersham	d			→						06 49	07 00						07 19		07 30								
Esher	d									06 52	07 03						07 22		07 33								
Surbiton 6	a	06 35	06 40							06 56	07 07						07 26		07 37								
Wimbledon 6 ⊖	a		06 47							07 04				←													
Earlsfield	a									07 08				07 08													
Clapham Junction 10	a	06 46	06 54		06 58	07 02			07 46	→			07 09	07 12	07 14	07 20		07 24			07 28		08 16	08 16			
Vauxhall ⊖	a								07 52					07 17									08 22	08 22			
London Waterloo 15 ⊖	a	06 59	07 04		07 08	07 12			07 59		07 26	07 14	07 20	07 24	07 24	07 31	07 49	07 36	07 56	07 41	07 39	07 45	08 29	08 29	07 51	07 54	07 59

For general notes see front of timetable
For details of catering facilities see Directory of Train Operators

A From Weymouth (Table 158)
B Until 25 September
C From 28 September

b Arr. 0711

For details of Bank Holiday service alterations, please see first page of Table 149

Basingstoke, Alton, Guildford and Woking → Waterloo

Network Diagram - see first page of Table 155

Station		SW 1	SW 1	SW 1	SW 1	SW 1 ◊	SW 1	SW 1	SW 1	SW 1	SW 1		SW 1	SW 1	SW 1 ◊	SW 1	SW 1	SW 1	SW 1	SW 1	SW 1	SW 1	SW 1	SW 1	SW	SW 1 ◊	SW 1
									A	B									C		C						
															⊡	⊡										⊡	
Basingstoke	d	07 06	07 17											07 24	07 29				07 36	07 47				07 52		07 59	
Hook	d	07 13												07 31					07 43		←			07 59			
Winchfield	d	07 17												07 35					07 47		07 47			08 04			
Fleet	d	07 22												07 40					→		07 52			08 09			
Farnborough (Main)	d	07 28												07 46							07 58			→			
Alton	d										07 14																07 44
Bentley	d										07 21																07 51
Farnham	a										07 26																07 56
	d										07 28							07 39									07 58
Aldershot	d								07 29	07 30	07 34							07 46					08 00				08 04
Ash Vale	d								07 33	07 34	07 39							07 50					08a04				08 09
Brookwood	d										07 46			07 53				07 57									08 16
Guildford	d			07 32									07 45			07 54						08 03					
Worplesdon	d			07 40									07 50														
Woking	a					07 38					07 51		07 54	07 58				08 03		08 05	08 08	08 11				08 18	08 21
	d				07 32	07 40		07 47			07 52		07 56	07 59			08 02	08 05		08 06	08 09	08 12			08 17	08 19	08 23
West Byfleet	d				07 37		07 46	07b54									08 06	08c16							08e26		
Byfleet & New Haw	d						07 49	07 57										08 19							08 29		
Weybridge	d				07 41		07 52	08 01									08 11	08 22							08 32		
Walton-on-Thames	d				07 46		07 57	08 06									08 15	08 27							08 36		
Hersham	d				07 49		08 00	08 09									08 17	08 30							08 39		
Esher	d				07 52		08 03	08 13									08 20	08 33							08 43		
Surbiton 6	a				07 56		08 07	08 18									08 24	08 37							08 47		
Wimbledon 6 ⊖	a																										
Earlsfield	a																										
Clapham Junction 10	a								08 46	08 46																	
Vauxhall ⊖	a								08 52	08 52																	
London Waterloo 15 ⊖	a	08 06	08 01	08 11	08 19	08 08	08 26	08 36	09 00	09 00	08 22		08 24	08 29	08 14	08 32	08 46	08 59		08 34	08 39	08 41			09 06	08 46	08 52

Station		SW 1	SW 1	SW	SW 1	SW 1	SW 1	SW 1	SW 1	SW 1	SW 1	SW 1 ◊	SW 1	SW	SW 1 ◊		SW 1	SW 1	SW 1	SW 1	SW	SW 1	SW 1	SW 1 ◊	SW 1	SW	SW 1
					C		C			C							C										
		⊡										⊡			⊡							⊡		⊡			
Basingstoke	d				08 05	08 16				08 24		08 29			08 35			08 42	08 54					08 59			
Hook	d				08 12		←			08 31									09 01								
Winchfield	d		←		08 16		08 16			08 35							←		09 05								
Fleet	d		08 09		→		08 22			08 40							08 40	08 54	09 10								
Farnborough (Main)	d		08 16				08 28			→							08 46	08 59	→								
Alton	d												08 14														08 44
Bentley	d												08 21														08 51
Farnham	a												08 26														08 56
	d												08 28														08 58
Aldershot	d								08 30				08 34												09 00		09 04
Ash Vale	d								08a34				08 39												09a04		09 09
Brookwood	d		08 23										08 46				08 53										09 16
Guildford	d	08 15		08 20				08 31													08 46	08 54	09 03				
Worplesdon	d	08 20						08 37													08 51						
Woking	a	08 26	08 28	08 30		08 34	08 38	08 41				08 48	08 51		08 53		08 58				08 59		09 11	09 18			09 21
	d	08 27	08 29	08 32		08 36	08 39	08 43			08 47	08 49	08 52		08 55		08 59				09 02		09 13	09 19			09 22
West Byfleet	d			08 36							08f54										09 06						09 27
Byfleet & New Haw	d			08 39							08 57									←	09 09						→
Weybridge	d			08 43							09 02			←						09 02	09 13					←	
Walton-on-Thames	d			08 47							→			08 47						09 07	09 17					09 17	
Hersham	d			→										08 49						09 10	→					09 19	
Esher	d													08 52						09 13						09 22	
Surbiton 6	a													08 56			09 10			09 18						09 26	
Wimbledon 6 ⊖	a													09 04												09 34	
Earlsfield	a													09 08												09 38	
Clapham Junction 10	a							09 03						09 12	09 14			09 26					09 32	09 38		09 42	
Vauxhall ⊖	a													09 17												09 47	
London Waterloo 15 ⊖	a	08 55	09 00			09 03	09 10	09 13				09 17	09 21	09 24	09 25		09 29	09 38		09 40		09 31	09 43	09 51		09 54	

For general notes see front of timetable
For details of catering facilities see Directory of Train Operators

- **A** From 28 September
- **B** Until 25 September
- **C** From Southampton Central (Table 158)
- **b** Arr. 0751
- **c** Arr. 0809
- **e** Arr. 0821
- **f** Arr. 0851

For details of Bank Holiday service alterations, please see first page of Table 149

Basingstoke, Alton, Guildford and Woking → Waterloo

Network Diagram - see first page of Table 155

		SW 1◇ ☕	SW 1 ☕	SW 1	SW 1	SW	SW 1	SW 1	SW 1	SW 1	SW 1◇ ☕	SW	SW 1	SW 1◇ ☕
Basingstoke	d							09 17		09 24	09 31			09 36
Hook	d									09 31				
Winchfield	d				←					09 35				
Fleet	d				09 10					09 40				
Farnborough (Main)	d				09 16			09 31		→				
Alton	d												09 14	
Bentley	d												09 21	
Farnham	a												09 26	
	d												09 28	
Aldershot	d						09 30						09 34	
Ash Vale	d						09a34						09 39	
Brookwood	d				09 23								09 46	
Guildford	d		09 17						09 32					
Worplesdon	d								09 40					
Woking	a	09 22	09 27		09 28			09 40	09 44		09 49		09 51	09 54
	d	09 24	09 28	←	09 29	09 33		09 41	09 46		09 51		09 52	09 55
West Byfleet	d			09 27		09 37							09 57	
Byfleet & New Haw	d					09 40								
Weybridge	d				09 36	09 43						←		
Walton-on-Thames	d				09 41	09 47 →						09 47		
Hersham	d											09 49		
Esher	d											09 52		
Surbiton 6	a			09 37	09 47							09 56	10 07	
Wimbledon 6 ⊖	a											10 04		
Earlsfield	a											10 08		
Clapham Junction 10	a	09 43		09 50	09 58				10 05		10 10	10 12		10 14
Vauxhall ⊖	a											10 17		
London Waterloo 15 ⊖	a	09 53	09 55	09 59	10 06			10 08	10 13		10 19	10 22	10 25	10 23

		SW 1	SW 1 ☕	SW 1	SW	SW 1		SW 1	SW 1	SW 1◇ ☕	SW 1◇ ☕	SW	SW 1	SW 1 ☕
Basingstoke	d			09 41					09 54	09 57				
Hook	d								10 01					
Winchfield	d	←							10 05					
Fleet	d	09 40		09 53					10 10					
Farnborough (Main)	d	09 46		09 58					→					
Alton	d												09 44	
Bentley	d												09 51	
Farnham	a												09 56	
	d												09 58	
Aldershot	d							10 00					10 04	
Ash Vale	d							10a04					10 09	
Brookwood	d	09 53											10 16	
Guildford	d		09 47			10 02								10 17
Worplesdon	d													
Woking	a	09 58	09 59			10 11				10 15	10 20		10 21	10 25
	d	09 59	09 59		10 03	10 12				10 17	10 21		10 22	10 26
West Byfleet	d				10 07								10 27	
Byfleet & New Haw	d				10 10									
Weybridge	d	10 06			10 13							←		
Walton-on-Thames	d	10 11			10 17 →							10 17		
Hersham	d											10 19		
Esher	d											10 22		
Surbiton 6	a	10 17										10 26	10 37	
Wimbledon 6 ⊖	a											10 34		
Earlsfield	a											10 38		
Clapham Junction 10	a			10 24		10 31				10 36		10 42	10 48	
Vauxhall ⊖	a											10 47		
London Waterloo 15 ⊖	a	10 35	10 27	10 34		10 40				10 49	10 49	10 52	10 57	10 51

		SW 1	SW	SW 1	SW 1	SW 1	SW 1	SW 1◇ ☕	SW 1◇ ☕	SW	SW 1	SW 1 ☕	SW 1	SW 1
Basingstoke	d				10 17		10 24	10 31	10 36					10 41
Hook	d						10 31							
Winchfield	d	←					10 35						←	
Fleet	d	10 10					10 40						10 40	10 53
Farnborough (Main)	d	10 16			10 31		→						10 46	10 58
Alton	d										10 14			
Bentley	d										10 21			
Farnham	a										10 26			
	d										10 28			
Aldershot	d			10 30							10 34			
Ash Vale	d			10a34							10 39			
Brookwood	d	10 23									10 46		10 53	
Guildford	d					10 32						10 47		
Worplesdon	d					10 40								
Woking	a	10 28			10 40	10 44		10 49			10 51	10 57	10 58	
	d	10 29	10 33		10 41	10 46		10 51			10 52	10 59	10 59	
West Byfleet	d		10 37								10 57			
Byfleet & New Haw	d		10 40											
Weybridge	d	10 36	10 43							←			11 06	
Walton-on-Thames	d	10 41	10 47 →							10 47			11 11	
Hersham	d									10 49				
Esher	d									10 52				
Surbiton 6	a	10 47								10 56	11 07		11 17	
Wimbledon 6 ⊖	a									11 04				
Earlsfield	a									11 08				
Clapham Junction 10	a	10 58				11 05			11 12	11 12				11 24
Vauxhall ⊖	a									11 17				
London Waterloo 15 ⊖	a	11 06			11 08	11 13		11 19	11 20	11 22	11 27	11 24	11 36	11 34

		SW	SW 1	SW 1	SW 1	SW 1◇ ☕	SW 1◇ ☕	SW	SW 1	SW 1 ☕		SW 1	SW	SW 1
Basingstoke	d				10 54	10 57								
Hook	d				11 01									
Winchfield	d				11 05							←		
Fleet	d				11 10							11 10		
Farnborough (Main)	d				→							11 16		
Alton	d								10 44					
Bentley	d								10 51					
Farnham	a								10 56					
	d								10 58					
Aldershot	d			11 00					11 04					11 30
Ash Vale	d			11a04					11 09					11a34
Brookwood	d								11 16			11 23		
Guildford	d		11 02							11 17				
Worplesdon	d													
Woking	a		11 11			11 15	11 19		11 21	11 25		11 28		
	d	11 03	11 12			11 17	11 21		11 22	11 26		11 29	11 33	
West Byfleet	d	11 07							11 27				11 37	
Byfleet & New Haw	d	11 10											11 40	
Weybridge	d	11 13						←				11 36	11 43	
Walton-on-Thames	d	11 17 →						11 17				11 41	11 47 →	
Hersham	d							11 19						
Esher	d							11 22						
Surbiton 6	a							11 26	11 37			11 47		
Wimbledon 6 ⊖	a							11 34						
Earlsfield	a							11 38						
Clapham Junction 10	a		11 31			11 36		11 42	11 48			11 58		
Vauxhall ⊖	a							11 47						
London Waterloo 15 ⊖	a		11 40			11 49	11 49	11 52	11 57	11 51		12 06		

For general notes see front of timetable
For details of catering facilities see Directory of Train Operators

For details of Bank Holiday service alterations, please see first page of Table 149

Basingstoke, Alton, Guildford and Woking → Waterloo

Network Diagram - see first page of Table 155

		SW 1	SW 1	SW 1	SW 1◇ ☕	SW 1◇ ☕	SW	SW 1	SW 1 ☕	SW 1	SW 1	SW	SW 1	SW 1	SW 1	SW 1◇ ☕	SW 1◇ ☕	SW	SW 1	SW 1 ☕	SW 1	SW	SW 1	SW 1	SW 1	SW 1	SW 1◇ ☕
Basingstoke	d	11 17		11 24	11 31	11 36					11 41				11 54	11 57								12 17		12 24	12 31
Hook	d			11 31											12 01											12 31	
Winchfield	d			11 35						←					12 05						←					12 35	
Fleet	d			11 40						11 40	11 53				12 10						12 10					12 40	
Farnborough (Main)	d	11 31		→						11 46	11 58				→						12 16			12 31		→	
Alton	d							11 15											11 44								
Bentley	d																		11 51								
Farnham	a							11 25											11 56								
	d							11 28											11 58								
Aldershot	d							11 34						12 00					12 04				12 30				
Ash Vale	d							11 39						12a04					12 09				12a34				
Brookwood	d							11 46		11 53									12 16		12 23						
Guildford	d		11 32						11 47				12 02							12 17					12 32		
Worplesdon	d		11 40																						12 40		
Woking	a	11 40	11 44		11 49			11 51	11 57	11 58			12 11			12 15	12 19		12 21	12 25	12 28			12 40	12 44		12 49
	d	11 41	11 46		11 51			11 52	11 59	11 59		12 03	12 12			12 17	12 21		12 22	12 26	12 29	12 33		12 41	12 46		12 51
West Byfleet	d							11 57				12 07							12 27			12 37					
Byfleet & New Haw	d											12 10										12 40					
Weybridge	d						←			12 06		12 13						←			12 36	12 43					
Walton-on-Thames	d						11 47			12 11		12 17						12 17			12 41	12 47					
Hersham	d						11 49					→						12 19				→					
Esher	d						11 52											12 22									
Surbiton 6	a						11 56	12 07		12 17								12 26	12 37		12 47						
Wimbledon 6 ⊖	a						12 04											12 34									
Earlsfield	a						12 08											12 38									
Clapham Junction 10	a		12 05			12 12	12 12				12 24		12 31			12 36		12 42	12 48		12 58				13 05		
Vauxhall ⊖	a						12 17											12 47									
London Waterloo 15 ⊖	a	12 08	12 13		12 19	12 20	12 22	12 27	12 23	12 36	12 34		12 40			12 49	12 49	12 52	12 57	12 51	13 06			13 08	13 13		13 19

		SW 1◇ ☕	SW		SW 1	SW 1 ☕	SW 1	SW 1	SW	SW 1	SW 1	SW 1	SW 1◇ ☕	SW 1◇ ☕	SW	SW 1	SW 1 ☕	SW 1	SW	SW 1	SW 1	SW 1	SW 1	SW 1◇ ☕	SW 1◇ ☕	SW	SW 1
Basingstoke	d	12 36						12 41				12 54	12 57								13 17		13 24	13 31	13 36		
Hook	d											13 01											13 31				
Winchfield	d						←					13 05						←					13 35				
Fleet	d						12 40	12 53				13 10						13 10					13 40				
Farnborough (Main)	d						12 46	12 58				→						13 16			13 31		→				
Alton	d															12 44											13 15
Bentley	d															12 51											
Farnham	a															12 56											13 25
	d				12 28											12 58											13 28
Aldershot	d				12 34						13 00					13 04				13 30							13 34
Ash Vale	d				12 39						13a04					13 09				13a34							13 39
Brookwood	d				12 46		12 53									13 16		13 23									13 46
Guildford	d					12 47				13 02							13 17					13 32					
Worplesdon	d																					13 40					
Woking	a				12 51	12 57	12 58			13 11			13 15	13 19		13 21	13 25	13 28			13 40	13 44		13 49			13 51
	d				12 52	12 59	12 59		13 03	13 12			13 17	13 21		13 22	13 26	13 29	13 33		13 41	13 46		13 51			13 52
West Byfleet	d				12 57				13 07							13 27			13 37								13 57
Byfleet & New Haw	d								13 10										13 40								
Weybridge	d		←				13 06		13 13						←			13 36	13 43							←	
Walton-on-Thames	d		12 47				13 11		13 17						13 17			13 41	13 47							13 47	
Hersham	d		12 49						→						13 19				→							13 49	
Esher	d		12 52												13 22											13 52	
Surbiton 6	a		12 56		13 07		13 17								13 26	13 37		13 47								13 56	14 07
Wimbledon 6 ⊖	a		13 04												13 34											14 04	
Earlsfield	a		13 08												13 38											14 08	
Clapham Junction 10	a	13 12	13 12					13 24		13 31			13 36		13 42	13 48		13 58				14 05			14 12	14 12	
Vauxhall ⊖	a		13 17												13 47											14 17	
London Waterloo 15 ⊖	a	13 20	13 22		13 25	13 23	13 35	13 34		13 40			13 49	13 49	13 52	13 57	13 51	14 06			14 08	14 13		14 19	14 20	14 22	14 25

For general notes see front of timetable
For details of catering facilities see
Directory of Train Operators

For details of Bank Holiday service alterations, please see first page of Table 149

Basingstoke, Alton, Guildford and Woking → Waterloo

Network Diagram - see first page of Table 155

		SW 1 ☕	SW 1	SW 1	SW	SW 1	SW 1		SW 1	SW 1 ◇ ☕	SW 1 ◇ ☕	SW	SW 1	SW 1 ☕	SW 1	SW	SW 1	SW 1	SW 1	SW 1	SW 1 ◇ ☕	SW 1 ◇ ☕	SW	SW 1	SW 1 ☕	SW 1	SW 1
Basingstoke	d			13 41					13 54	13 57								14 17		14 24	14 31	14 36					14 41
Hook	d								14 01											14 31							
Winchfield	d		←						14 05						←					14 35						←	
Fleet	d		13 40	13 53					14 10						14 10					14 40						14 40	14 53
Farnborough (Main)	d		13 46	13 58					→						14 16			14 31		→						14 46	14 58
Alton	d												13 44											14 15			
Bentley	d												13 51														
Farnham	a												13 56											14 25			
	d												13 58											14 28			
Aldershot	d						14 00						14 04				14 30							14 34			
Ash Vale	d						14a04						14 09				14a34							14 39			
Brookwood	d		13 53										14 16		14 23									14 46		14 53	
Guildford	d	13 47				14 02								14 17					14 32						14 47		
Worplesdon	d																		14 40								
Woking	a	13 57	13 58			14 11				14 15	14 19		14 21	14 25	14 28			14 40	14 44		14 49			14 51	14 57	14 58	
	d	13 59	13 59		14 03	14 12				14 17	14 21		14 22	14 26	14 29	14 33		14 41	14 46		14 51			14 52	14 59	14 59	
West Byfleet	d				14 07								14 27			14 37								14 57			
Byfleet & New Haw	d				14 10											14 40											
Weybridge	d		14 06		14 13							←			14 36	14 43							←			15 06	
Walton-on-Thames	d		14 11		14 17							14 17			14 41	14 47							14 47			15 11	
Hersham	d				→							14 19				→							14 49				
Esher	d											14 22											14 52				
Surbiton 6	a		14 17									14 26	14 37		14 47								14 56	15 07		15 17	
Wimbledon 6 ⊖	a											14 34											15 04				
Earlsfield	a											14 38											15 08				
Clapham Junction 10	a			14 24		14 31				14 36		14 42	14 48		14 58				15 05			15 12	15 12				15 24
Vauxhall ⊖	a											14 47											15 17				
London Waterloo 15 ⊖	a	14 23	14 35	14 34		14 40				14 49	14 49	14 52	14 57	14 51	15 06			15 08	15 13		15 19	15 20	15 22	15 25	15 23	15 35	15 32

		SW	SW 1	SW 1	SW 1	SW 1 ◇ ☕	SW 1 ◇ ☕	SW	SW 1	SW 1 ☕	SW 1		SW	SW 1	SW 1	SW 1	SW 1	SW 1 ◇ ☕	SW 1 ◇ ☕	SW	SW 1	SW 1 ☕	SW 1	SW 1	SW	SW 1	SW 1
Basingstoke	d				14 54	14 57									15 17		15 24	15 31	15 36					15 41			
Hook	d				15 01												15 31										
Winchfield	d				15 05						←						15 35						←				
Fleet	d				15 10						15 10						15 40						15 40	15 53			
Farnborough (Main)	d				→						15 16				15 31		→						15 46	15 58			
Alton	d								14 44												15 15						
Bentley	d								14 51																		
Farnham	a								14 56												15 25						
	d								14 58												15 28						
Aldershot	d			15 00					15 04					15 30							15 34						16 00
Ash Vale	d			15a04					15 09					15a34							15 39						16a04
Brookwood	d								15 16		15 23										15 46		15 53				
Guildford	d		15 02							15 17						15 32						15 47				16 00	
Worplesdon	d															15 40										16 06	
Woking	a		15 11			15 15	15 19		15 21	15 25	15 28				15 40	15 44		15 49			15 51	15 57	15 58			16 11	
	d	15 03	15 12			15 17	15 21		15 22	15 26	15 29		15 33		15 41	15 46		15 51			15 52	15 59	15 59		16 03	16 12	
West Byfleet	d	15 07							15 27				15 37								15 57				16 07		
Byfleet & New Haw	d	15 10											15 40												16 10		
Weybridge	d	15 13						←			15 36		15 43							←			16 06		16 13		
Walton-on-Thames	d	15 17						15 17			15 41		15 47							15 47			16 11		16 17		
Hersham	d	→						15 19					→							15 49					→		
Esher	d							15 22												15 52							
Surbiton 6	a							15 26	15 37		15 47									15 56	16 07		16 17				
Wimbledon 6 ⊖	a							15 34												16 04							
Earlsfield	a							15 38												16 08							
Clapham Junction 10	a		15 31			15 36		15 42	15 48		15 58					16 05			16 12	16 12				16 24		16 31	
Vauxhall ⊖	a							15 47												16 17							
London Waterloo 15 ⊖	a		15 43			15 49	15 49	15 52	15 58	15 51	16 06				16 08	16 13		16 19	16 20	16 22	16 29	16 24	16 36	16 34		16 40	

For general notes see front of timetable
For details of catering facilities see
Directory of Train Operators

For details of Bank Holiday service alterations, please see first page of Table 149

Basingstoke, Alton, Guildford and Woking → Waterloo

Network Diagram - see first page of Table 155

		SW [1]	SW [1] ◇ ☕	SW [1] ◇ ☕	SW	SW [1]	SW [1] ☕	SW [1]	SW	SW [1]	SW [1]	SW [1]	SW [1]	SW [1] ◇ ☕	SW [1] ◇ ☕		SW	SW [1]	SW [1]	SW [1]	SW [1]	SW	SW [1] ☕	SW [1]	SW [1]	SW [1] ◇ ☕	SW [1] ◇ ☕
Basingstoke	d	15 54	15 57								16 17		16 24	16 31	16 36						16 41				16 54	16 57	
Hook	d	16 01											16 31												17 01		
Winchfield	d	16 05						←					16 35							←					17 05		
Fleet	d	16 10						16 10					16 40							16 40	16 53				17 10		
Farnborough (Main)	d	→						16 16			16 31		→							16 46	16 58				→		
Alton	d					15 44												16 15									
Bentley	d					15 51																					
Farnham	a					15 56												16 25									
	d					15 58												16 28									
Aldershot	d					16 04				16 30								16 34						17 00			
Ash Vale	d					16 09				16a34								16 39						17a04			
Brookwood	d					16 16		16 23										16 46		16 53							
Guildford	d						16 17					16 32							16 47				17 00				
Worplesdon	d											16 40											17 06				
Woking	a		16 15	16 19		16 21	16 25	16 28			16 40	16 44		16 49				16 51	16 57	16 58			17 11			17 15	17 20
	d		16 17	16 21		16 22	16 26	16 29	16 33		16 41	16 46		16 51				16 52	16 59	16 59		17 03	17 12			17 17	17 21
West Byfleet	d					16 27			16 37									16 57				17 07					
Byfleet & New Haw	d								16 40													17 10					
Weybridge	d				←			16 36	16 43								←			17 06		17 13					
Walton-on-Thames	d				16 17			16 41	16 47								16 47			17 11		17 17					
Hersham	d				16 19				→								16 49					→					
Esher	d				16 22												16 52										
Surbiton [6]	a				16 26	16 37		16 47									16 56	17 07		17 17							
Wimbledon [6] ⊖ 🚊	a				16 35												17 04										
Earlsfield	a				16 38												17 08										
Clapham Junction [10]	a		16 36		16 42	16 48		16 58				17 05			17 12		17 12				17 24		17 31			17 36	
Vauxhall ⊖	a				16 47												17 17										
London Waterloo [15] ⊖	a		16 49	16 49	16 53	16 59	16 51	17 08			17 08	17 14		17 19	17 20		17 22	17 29	17 24	17 34	17 36		17 43			17 44	17 50

		SW	SW [1]	SW [1] ☕	SW [1]	SW	SW [1]	SW [1]	SW [1]	SW [1]	SW [1] ◇ ☕	SW	SW [1] ◇ ☕	SW [1]	SW [1]	SW [1]	SW [1]	SW	SW [1] ☕		SW [1]	SW [1]	SW [1] ◇ ☕	SW [1] ◇ ☕	SW	SW [1]	SW [1] ☕
Basingstoke	d							17 17		17 24	17 31		17 36				17 41					17 54	17 57				
Hook	d									17 31												18 01					
Winchfield	d				←					17 35						←						18 05					
Fleet	d				17 10					17 40						17 40	17 53					18 10					
Farnborough (Main)	d				17 16			17 31		→						17 46	17 58					→					
Alton	d		16 44											17 14												17 44	
Bentley	d		16 51											17 21												17 51	
Farnham	a		16 56											17 26												17 56	
	d		16 58											17 28												17 58	
Aldershot	d		17 04				17 30							17 34							18 00					18 04	
Ash Vale	d		17 09				17a34							17 39							18a04					18 09	
Brookwood	d		17 16		17 23									17 46		17 53										18 16	
Guildford	d			17 17					17 32						17 47				18 00								18 17
Worplesdon	d								17 40										18 06								
Woking	a		17 21	17 25	17 28			17 40	17 44		17 49			17 51	17 58	17 58			18 11				18 15	18 19		18 21	
	d		17 22	17 26	17 29	17 33		17 41	17 46		17 51			17 52	17 59	17 59		18 03	18 12				18 17	18 21		18 22	
West Byfleet	d		17 27			17 37								17 57				18 07								18 27	
Byfleet & New Haw	d					17 40												18 10									
Weybridge	d	←			17 36	17 43						←				18 06		18 13							←		
Walton-on-Thames	d	17 17			17 41	17 47						17 47				18 11		18 17							18 17		
Hersham	d	17 19				→						17 49						→							18 19		
Esher	d	17 22										17 52													18 22		
Surbiton [6]	a	17 26	17 37		17 47							17 56		18 07		18 17									18 26	18 37	
Wimbledon [6] ⊖ 🚊	a	17 34										18 04													18 34		
Earlsfield	a	17 38										18 08													18 38		
Clapham Junction [10]	a	17 42	17 48		17 58				18 05			18 12	18 12				18 24		18 31				18 36		18 42	18 48	
Vauxhall ⊖	a	17 47										18 17													18 47		
London Waterloo [15] ⊖	a	17 52	17 59	17 54	18 09			18 08	18 14		18 21	18 23	18 23	18 29	18 27	18 39	18 34		18 43				18 45	18 47	18 52	18 57	18 59

For general notes see front of timetable
For details of catering facilities see Directory of Train Operators

For details of Bank Holiday service alterations, please see first page of Table 149

Basingstoke, Alton, Guildford and Woking → Waterloo

Network Diagram - see first page of Table 155

		SW 1	SW	SW 1	SW 1	SW 1	SW 1	SW 1 ◇ 🍴	SW 1 ◇ 🍴	SW	SW 1	SW 1	SW	SW 1 🍴	SW 1	SW 1	SW 1	SW 1 ◇ 🍴	SW	SW 1	SW 1 ◇ 🍴	SW 1	SW 1 🍴		SW	SW 1	SW 1
Basingstoke	d			18 17			18 24	18 31	18 36						18 41		18 54	19 01								19 17	
Hook	d						18 31										19 01										
Winchfield	d	←					18 35					←					19 05					←					
Fleet	d	18 10					18 40					18 40			18 53		19 10					19 10					
Farnborough (Main)	d	18 16		18 31			→					18 46			18 58		→					19 16				19 31	
Alton	d										18 14									18 35							
Bentley	d										18b23									18 42							
Farnham	a										18 28									18 47							
	d										18 28									18 58							
Aldershot	d					18 30					18 34					19 00				19 04							
Ash Vale	d					18a34					18 39					19a04				19 09							
Brookwood	d	18 23									18 46	18 53								19 16		19 23					
Guildford	d				18 32									18 55									19 21				19 32
Worplesdon	d				18 40																						19 40
Woking	a	18 28		18 40	18 44			18 49			18 52	18 58		19 03				19 19		19 21	19 24	19 28	19 28			19 40	19 45
	d	18 29	18 33	18 41	18 46			18 51			18 52	18 59	19 03	19 05				19 21		19 22	19 25	19 29	19 30		19 33	19 41	19 46
West Byfleet	d		18 37								18 57		19 07							19 27					19 37		
Byfleet & New Haw	d		18 40										19 10												19 40		
Weybridge	d	18 36	18 43							←		19 06	19 13						←			19 36			19 43		
Walton-on-Thames	d	18 41	18 47							18 47		19 11	19 17						19 17			19 41			19 47		
Hersham	d		→							18 49			→						19 19						→		
Esher	d									18 52									19 22								
Surbiton 6	a	18 47								18 56	19 08	19 17							19 26	19 37		19 47					
Wimbledon 6 ⊖ 🚊	a									19 05									19 34								
Earlsfield	a									19 08									19 38								
Clapham Junction 10	a	18 58			19 05				19 12	19 12					19 26			19 40	19 42	19 48		19 58					20 05
Vauxhall ⊖	a									19 17									19 47								
London Waterloo 15 ⊖	a	19 06		19 08	19 14			19 19	19 20	19 23	19 25	19 39		19 29	19 38			19 49	19 52	19 57	19 51	20 06	19 59			20 08	20 14

		SW 1	SW 1	SW 1 ◇ 🍴	SW 1 ◇ 🍴	SW	SW 1	SW 1 🍴	SW 1	SW 1	SW	SW 1	SW 1 ◇ 🍴	SW 1	SW	SW 1	SW 1	SW 1	SW 1 ◇ 🍴	SW 1	SW 1	SW	SW 1	SW 1	SW 1	SW 1	SW 1
Basingstoke	d		19 24	19 31	19 36					19 41								19 54	20 09				20 17				20 24
Hook	d		19 31															20 01									20 31
Winchfield	d		19 35						←									20 05									20 35
Fleet	d		19 40						19 40	19 53								20 10									20 40
Farnborough (Main)	d		→						19 46	19 58								20 16					20 31				20 46
Alton	d						19 07									19 35								20 15			
Bentley	d															19 42											
Farnham	a						19 17									19 47								20 25			
	d						19 28									19 58								20 28			
Aldershot	d	19 30					19 34							20 00		20 04				20 30				20 34			
Ash Vale	d	19a34					19 39							20a04		20 09				20a34				20 39			
Brookwood	d						19 46		19 53							20 16		20 23						20 46			20 53
Guildford	d							19 47				20 02					20 17								20 39	20 47	
Worplesdon	d																								20 44		
Woking	a			19 49			19 51	19 57	19 58			20 11	20 19			20 21	20 25	20 28	20 29				20 40	20 51	20 52	20 57	20 58
	d			19 51			19 52	19 59	19 59		20 03	20 12	20 21			20 22	20 26	20 29	20 30			20 33	20 41	20 52	20 53	20 59	20 59
West Byfleet	d						19 57				20 07					20 27						20 37		20 57			
Byfleet & New Haw	d										20 10										←	20 40					
Weybridge	d					←			20 06		20 13				←			20 36			20 36	20 43					21 06
Walton-on-Thames	d					19 47			20 11		20 17				20 17			→			20 41	20 47					21 11
Hersham	d					19 49					→				20 19							20 49					
Esher	d					19 52									20 22							20 52					
Surbiton 6	a					19 56	20 07		20 17						20 26	20 37					20 47	20 56		21 07			21 17
Wimbledon 6 ⊖ 🚊	a					20 04									20 35							21 05					
Earlsfield	a					20 08									20 38							21 08					
Clapham Junction 10	a				20 12	20 12				20 25		20 31			20 41	20 48			20 52		20 58	21 11			21 12		
Vauxhall ⊖	a					20 17									20 46							21 16					
London Waterloo 15 ⊖	a			20 19	20 20	20 22	20 25	20 23	20 36	20 34		20 40	20 49		20 52	20 57	20 50		21 00		21 06	21 22	21 08	21 29	21 21	21 27	21 34

For general notes see front of timetable
For details of catering facilities see
Directory of Train Operators

b Arr. 1820

For details of Bank Holiday service alterations, please see first page of Table 149

Basingstoke, Alton, Guildford and Woking → Waterloo

Network Diagram - see first page of Table 155

		SW 1 ◇ ☕	SW		SW 1	SW 1 ◇ ☕	SW	SW 1	SW 1	SW 1	SW 1 ◇ ☕	SW 1	SW 1	SW
Basingstoke	d	20 36			20 41					20 54	21 09			
Hook	d									21 01				
Winchfield	d									21 05				
Fleet	d				20 53					21 10				
Farnborough (Main)	d				20 58					21 16				
Alton	d							20 44						
Bentley	d							20 51						
Farnham	a							20 56						
	d							20 58						
Aldershot	d							21 04				21 30		
Ash Vale	d							21 09				21a34		
Brookwood	d							21 16		21 23				
Guildford	d								21 17					
Worplesdon	d													
Woking	a				21 07	21 19		21 21	21 25	21 28	21 29			
	d		21 03		21 09	21 21		21 22	21 26	21 29	21 30			21 33
West Byfleet	d		21 07					21 27						21 37
Byfleet & New Haw	d		21 10										←	21 40
Weybridge	d		21 13				←			21 36			21 36	21 43
Walton-on-Thames	d		21 17				21 17			→			21 41	21 47
Hersham	d		→				21 19							→
Esher	d						21 22							
Surbiton 6	a						21 26	21 37					21 47	
Wimbledon 6 ⊖	a						21 34							
Earlsfield	a						21 38							
Clapham Junction 10	a	21 16			21 33		21 42	21 48			21 52		21 58	
Vauxhall ⊖	a						21 47							
London Waterloo 15 ⊖	a	21 24			21 43	21 49	21 52	21 57	21 50		22 04		22 06	

		SW 1	SW	SW 1	SW 1	SW 1 A	SW 1 ◇	SW	SW 1	SW 1	SW	SW 1	SW 1	SW 1 ◇
Basingstoke	d					21 24	21 36		21 41				21 54	22 09
Hook	d					21 31							22 01	
Winchfield	d					21 35							22 05	
Fleet	d					21 40			21 53				22 10	
Farnborough (Main)	d					21 46			21 58				22 16	
Alton	d			21 15								21 44		
Bentley	d											21 51		
Farnham	a			21 28								21 56		
	d			21 28								21 58		
Aldershot	d			21 34								22 04		
Ash Vale	d			21 39								22 09		
Brookwood	d			21 46		21 53						22 16	22 23	
Guildford	d	21 39			21 47								→	
Worplesdon	d	21 44												
Woking	a	21 49		21 51	21 57	21 58			22 07	22 19		22 21		22 28
	d	21 50		21 52	21 59	21 59		22 03	22 09	22 21		22 22		22 29
West Byfleet	d			21 57				22 07				22 27		
Byfleet & New Haw	d							22 10				→		
Weybridge	d		←			22 06		22 13			←			
Walton-on-Thames	d		21 47			22 11		22 17			22 17			
Hersham	d		21 49					→			22 19			
Esher	d		21 52								22 22			
Surbiton 6	a		21 56	22 07		22 17					22 26			
Wimbledon 6 ⊖	a		22 04								22 34			
Earlsfield	a		22 08								22 38			
Clapham Junction 10	a	22 09	22 12				22 14		22 30		22 42			22 48
Vauxhall ⊖	a		22 17								22 47			
London Waterloo 15 ⊖	a	22 18	22 22	22 26	22 27	22 34	22 22		22 38	22 49	22 52			22 57

		SW 1	SW 1	SW	SW 1	SW 1	SW		SW 1	SW 1 A	SW 1 ◇	SW 1 A	SW	SW 1
Basingstoke	d									22 24	22 36			22 41
Hook	d									22 31				
Winchfield	d									22 35		←		
Fleet	d									22 40		22 40		22 53
Farnborough (Main)	d									→		22 46		22 58
Alton	d								22 15					
Bentley	d													
Farnham	a								22 25					
	d								22 28					
Aldershot	d				22 30				22 34					
Ash Vale	d		←		22a34				22 39					
Brookwood	d		22 23						22 46			22 53		
Guildford	d			22 20		22 39							22 55	
Worplesdon	d					22 44								
Woking	a		22 28	22 32		22 49			22 51		22 54	22 58	23 05	23 07
	d	←	22 29	22 33		22 50			22 52		22 55	22 59	23 06	23 09
West Byfleet	d	22 27		22 37					22 57				23 10	
Byfleet & New Haw	d			22 40									23 13	
Weybridge	d		22 36	22 43			←					23 06	23 16	
Walton-on-Thames	d		22 41	22 47			22 47					23 11	23 20	
Hersham	d			→			22 49						→	
Esher	d						22 52							
Surbiton 6	a	22 37	22 47				22 56		23 07			23 17		
Wimbledon 6 ⊖	a						23 04							
Earlsfield	a						23 08							
Clapham Junction 10	a	22 52	22 58			23 09	23 12				23 14			
Vauxhall ⊖	a						23 17							
London Waterloo 15 ⊖	a	23 01	23 08			23 19	23 23		23 27		23 23	23 39		

		SW	SW 1	SW 1	SW 1	SW 1	SW 1	SW 1	SW 1	SW 1	SW 1	SW 1 B		
Basingstoke	d				22 54	23 13						23 44		
Hook	d				23 01							23 51		
Winchfield	d				23 05							23 55		
Fleet	d				23 10							00 01		
Farnborough (Main)	d				23 16							00 06		
Alton	d		22 44							23 15	23 44			
Bentley	d		22 51								23 51			
Farnham	a		22 56							23 25	23 56			
	d		22 58							23 28				
Aldershot	d		23 04	23 08			23 30			23 34				
Ash Vale	d		23 09	22 49			23a34			23 39				
Brookwood	d		23 16		23 23					23 46		00 13		
Guildford	d			23a25					23 39					
Worplesdon	d								23 44					
Woking	a		23 21		23 28	23 33			23 49	23 51		00 18		
	d		23 22		23 33	23 34			23 56			00 20		
West Byfleet	d		23 27		23 37							00 25		
Byfleet & New Haw	d				23 40									
Weybridge	d	←			23 43			←				00 29		
Walton-on-Thames	d	23 20			23 47			23 47				00 34		
Hersham	d	23 22			→			23 49						
Esher	d	23 25						23 52						
Surbiton 6	a	23 29	23 37					23 57				00 40		
Wimbledon 6 ⊖	a	23 37						00 07				00 48		
Earlsfield	a	23 41						00 11						
Clapham Junction 10	a	23 44	23 50			23 56		00 15	00 21			00 54		
Vauxhall ⊖	a	23 49						00 20						
London Waterloo 15 ⊖	a	23 54	00 03			00 06		00 28	00 30			01 02		

For general notes see front of timetable
For details of catering facilities see Directory of Train Operators

A From Portsmouth Harbour (Table 158)
B From Weymouth (Table 158)

Basingstoke, Alton, Guildford and Woking → Waterloo

Network Diagram - see first page of Table 155

	SW 1	SW 1	SW 1	SW	SW	SW 1	SW	SW 1	SW 1	SW	SW	SW 1	SW 1	SW 1	SW 1 ◇	SW	SW 1	SW 1	SW	SW 1		SW 1	SW 1 ◇	SW	SW 1	SW 1
			A					B	C				D	E			D	E				G			B	C
															☕								☕			
Basingstoke d	22p54		23p44					04 54	04 54				05 54	05 54	05 59							06 24	06 31			
Hook d	23p01		23p51					05 01	05 01				06 01	06 01								06 31				
Winchfield d	23p05		23p55					05 05	05 05				06 05	06 05			←	←				06 35				
Fleet d	23p10		00 01					05 10	05 10				06 10 →	06 10 →			06 10	06 10				06 40 →				
Farnborough (Main) d	23p16		00 06					05 16	05 16								06 16	06 16								
Alton d																									06 14	06 14
Bentley d																									06 21	06 21
Farnham a																									06 26	06 26
Farnham d																									06 28	06 28
Aldershot d						06 00																			06 34	06 34
Ash Vale d						06a04																			06 39	06 39
Brookwood d	23p23		00 13					05 23	05 23								06 23	06 23							06 46	06 46
Guildford d		23p39		04 00	05 12							06 02								06 32						
Worplesdon d		23p44			05 17															06 40						
Woking a	23p28	23p49	00 18	04 08	05 22			05 28	05 28	←		06 11			06 18		06 28	06 28		06 44			06 49		06 51	06 51
Woking d	23p33	23p56	00 20	04 10	05 33 →		05 25	05 29	05 29	05 33	06 03	06 13			06 19		06 29	06 29	06 33	06 46			06 51		06 52	06 52
West Byfleet d	23p37		00 25				05 30			05 37	06 07								06 37						06 57	06 57
Byfleet & New Haw d	23p40						05 33			05 40	06 10								06 40							
Weybridge d	23p43		00 29							05 43	06 13					←	06 36	06 36	06 43					←		
Walton-on-Thames d	23p47		00 34							05 47	06 17 →					06 17	06 41	06 41	06 47 →					06 47		
Hersham d	23p49									05 49						06 19								06 49		
Esher d	23p52									05 52						06 22								06 52		
Surbiton 6 a	23p57		00 40	04 24				05 40	05 40	05 56						06 26	06 47	06 47						06 56	07 07	07 07
Wimbledon 6 ⊖ a	00 07		00 48	04 31				05 48	05 48	06 04						06 34								07 04		
Earlsfield a	00 11									06 08						06 38								07 08		
Clapham Junction 10 a	00 15	00 21	00 54	04 43			06 43	06 00	06 00	06 12		06 32			06 38	06 42	06 58	06 58		07 05				07 12	07 18	07 18
Vauxhall ⊖ a	00 20						06 49	06 07	06 07	06 17						06 47								07 17		
London Waterloo 15 ⊖ a	00 28	00 30	01 02	04 53			06 56	06 12	06 15	06 22		06 40			06 49	06 52	07 06	07 09		07 13			07 19	07 22	07 27	07 30

	SW 1	SW 1	SW	SW 1	SW 1	SW 1	SW 1 ◇	SW	SW 1	SW 1 ◇	SW 1	SW	SW 1	SW 1	SW 1	SW 1 ◇	SW		SW 1	SW 1	SW 1	SW	SW 1	SW 1	SW 1	SW 1
	G														H						H					
							☕			☕						☕				☕						
Basingstoke d		06 40				06 54	06 57			07 09					07 24	07 31							07 42			07 54
Hook d						07 01									07 31											08 01
Winchfield d	←					07 05					←				07 35						←					08 05
Fleet d	06 40					07 10 →					07 10				07 40 →						07 40		07 53			08 10 →
Farnborough (Main) d	06 46										07 16										07 46		07 59			
Alton d									06 44										07 14							
Bentley d									06 51										07 21							
Farnham a									06 56										07 26							
Farnham d									06 58										07 28							
Aldershot d					07 00				07 04					07 30					07 34						08 00	
Ash Vale d					07a04				07 09					07a34					07 39						08a04	
Brookwood d	06 53								07 16		07 23								07 46		07 53					
Guildford d				07 02									07 32							07 47				08 02		
Worplesdon d													07 40													
Woking a	06 58	06 58		07 11			07 15		07 21	07 27	07 28		07 44			07 49			07 51	07 57	07 58		08 08	08 12		
Woking d	06 59	07 00	07 03	07 12			07 17		07 22	07 29	07 29	07 33	07 46			07 51			07 52	07 59	07 59	08 03	08 09	08 14		
West Byfleet d			07 07						07 27			07 37							07 57			08 07				
Byfleet & New Haw d			07 10									07 40										08 10				
Weybridge d	07 06		07 13					←			07 36	07 43					←				08 06	08 13				
Walton-on-Thames d	07 11		07 17 →					07 17			07 41	07 47 →					07 47				08 11	08 17 →				
Hersham d								07 19									07 49									
Esher d								07 22									07 52									
Surbiton 6 a	07 17							07 27	07 37		07 47						07 56		08 07		08 17					
Wimbledon 6 ⊖ a								07 35									08 04									
Earlsfield a								07 38									08 08									
Clapham Junction 10 a		07 23		07 31			07 36	07 42	07 50		07 58		08 05				08 12						08 30	08 33		
Vauxhall ⊖ a								07 47									08 17									
London Waterloo 15 ⊖ a	07 33	07 31		07 40			07 49	07 52	07 58	07 53	08 06		08 13			08 19	08 22		08 25	08 23	08 34		08 38	08 42		

	SW 1 ◇	SW	SW 1	SW 1 ◇	SW 1	SW 1	SW	SW 1	SW 1	SW 1	SW 1	SW 1 ◇	SW 1 ◇	SW		SW 1	SW 1	SW 1	SW 1	SW	SW 1	SW 1	SW 1	SW 1 ◇	SW 1 ◇	SW
	☕			☕	☕							☕	☕				☕							☕	☕	
Basingstoke d	07 57							08 17			08 24	08 28	08 36						08 41				08 54	08 57		
Hook d											08 31												09 01			
Winchfield d						←					08 35							←					09 05			
Fleet d						08 10					08 40 →							08 40	08 53				09 10 →			
Farnborough (Main) d						08 16		08 31										08 46	08 58							
Alton d			07 44													08 14										
Bentley d			07 51													08 21										
Farnham a			07 56													08 26										
Farnham d			07 58													08 28										
Aldershot d			08 04							08 30						08 34						09 00				
Ash Vale d			08 09							08a34						08 39						09a04				
Brookwood d			08 16			08 23										08 46		08 53								
Guildford d					08 17				08 32								08 47				09 02					
Worplesdon d									08 40																	
Woking a	08 17		08 21	08 21	08 26	08 28		08 40	08 44			08 49				08 51	08 57	08 58			09 11			09 15	09 19	
Woking d	08 18		08 22	08 23	08 27	08 29	08 33	08 41	08 46			08 51				08 52	08 59	08 59		09 03	09 12			09 17	09 21	
West Byfleet d			08 27				08 37									08 57				09 07						
Byfleet & New Haw d							08 40													09 10						
Weybridge d		←				08 36	08 43							←				09 06		09 13						←
Walton-on-Thames d		00 17				08 41	08 47 →							08 47				09 11		09 17 →						09 17
Hersham d		08 19												08 49												09 19
Esher d		08 22												08 52												09 22
Surbiton 6 a		08 26	08 37			08 47								08 56		09 07		09 17								09 26
Wimbledon 6 ⊖ a		08 34												09 04												09 34
Earlsfield a		08 38												09 08												09 38
Clapham Junction 10 a	08 37	08 42	08 49			08 58			09 05				09 12	09 12					09 24		09 31			09 36		09 42
Vauxhall ⊖ a		08 47												09 17												09 47
London Waterloo 15 ⊖ a	08 49	08 52	08 58	08 49	08 51	09 06		09 08	09 13			09 19	09 20	09 22		09 25	09 23	09 35	09 34		09 40			09 49	09 49	09 52

For general notes see front of timetable
For details of catering facilities see Directory of Train Operators

- **A** From Weymouth (Table 158)
- **B** Until 26 September
- **C** From 3 October
- **D** Until 26 September. From Southampton Central (Table 158)
- **E** From 3 October. From Southampton Central (Table 158)
- **G** From Southampton Central (Table 158)
- **H** From Portsmouth Harbour (Table 158)

Table 155

Saturdays

Basingstoke, Alton, Guildford and Woking → Waterloo

Network Diagram - see first page of Table 155

		SW 1	SW 1 ☕	SW 1	SW	SW 1	SW 1	SW 1	SW 1	SW 1 ◇ ☕	SW 1 ◇ ☕	SW
Basingstoke	d						09 17		09 24	09 31	09 36	
Hook	d								09 31			
Winchfield	d			←					09 35			
Fleet	d			09 10					09 40			
Farnborough (Main)	d			09 16			09 31		→			
Alton	d	08 44										
Bentley	d	08 51										
Farnham	a	08 56										
	d	08 58										
Aldershot	d	09 04				09 30						
Ash Vale	d	09 09				09a34						
Brookwood	d	09 16		09 23								
Guildford	d		09 17					09 32				
Worplesdon	d							09 40				
Woking	a	09 21	09 25	09 28			09 40	09 44		09 49		
	d	09 22	09 26	09 29	09 33		09 41	09 46		09 51		
West Byfleet	d	09 27			09 37							
Byfleet & New Haw	d				09 40							
Weybridge	d			09 36	09 43							←
Walton-on-Thames	d			09 41	09 47							09 47
Hersham	d				→							09 49
Esher	d											09 52
Surbiton 6	a	09 37		09 47								09 56
Wimbledon 6 ⊖ 🚊	a											10 04
Earlsfield	a											10 08
Clapham Junction 10	a	09 48		09 58				10 05			10 12	10 12
Vauxhall ⊖	a											10 17
London Waterloo 15 ⊖	a	09 57	09 51	10 06			10 08	10 13		10 19	10 20	10 22

		SW 1	SW 1 ☕	SW 1	SW 1	SW	SW 1	SW 1	SW 1	SW 1 ◇ ☕	SW 1 ◇ ☕	SW	SW 1	SW 1 ☕	SW 1
Basingstoke	d				09 41				09 54	09 57					
Hook	d								10 01						
Winchfield	d			←					10 05						←
Fleet	d			09 40	09 53				10 10						10 10
Farnborough (Main)	d			09 46	09 58				→						10 16
Alton	d	09 14											09 44		
Bentley	d	09 21											09 51		
Farnham	a	09 26											09 56		
	d	09 28											09 58		
Aldershot	d	09 34						10 00					10 04		
Ash Vale	d	09 39						10a04					10 09		
Brookwood	d	09 46		09 53									10 16		10 23
Guildford	d		09 47				10 02							10 17	
Worplesdon	d														
Woking	a	09 51	09 57	09 58			10 11			10 15	10 19		10 21	10 25	10 28
	d	09 52	09 59	09 59		10 03	10 12			10 17	10 21		10 22	10 26	10 29
West Byfleet	d	09 57				10 07							10 27		
Byfleet & New Haw	d					10 10									
Weybridge	d			10 06		10 13						←			10 36
Walton-on-Thames	d			10 11		10 17						10 17			10 41
Hersham	d					→						10 19			
Esher	d											10 22			
Surbiton 6	a	10 07		10 17								10 26	10 37		10 47
Wimbledon 6 ⊖ 🚊	a											10 34			
Earlsfield	a											10 38			
Clapham Junction 10	a				10 24		10 31			10 36		10 42	10 48		10 58
Vauxhall ⊖	a											10 47			
London Waterloo 15 ⊖	a	10 25	10 23	10 35	10 34		10 40			10 49	10 49	10 52	10 57	10 51	11 06

		SW	SW 1	SW 1	SW 1	SW 1	SW 1 ◇ ☕	SW 1 ◇ ☕	SW	SW 1	SW 1 ☕	SW 1	SW 1
Basingstoke	d			10 17		10 24	10 31	10 36					10 41
Hook	d					10 31							
Winchfield	d					10 35						←	
Fleet	d					10 40						10 40	10 53
Farnborough (Main)	d			10 31		→						10 46	10 58
Alton	d									10 14			
Bentley	d									10 21			
Farnham	a									10 26			
	d									10 28			
Aldershot	d		10 30							10 34			
Ash Vale	d		10a34							10 39			
Brookwood	d									10 46		10 53	
Guildford	d				10 32						10 47		
Worplesdon	d				10 40								
Woking	a			10 40	10 44		10 49			10 51	10 57	10 58	
	d	10 33		10 41	10 46		10 51			10 52	10 59	10 59	
West Byfleet	d	10 37								10 57			
Byfleet & New Haw	d	10 40											
Weybridge	d	10 43							←			11 06	
Walton-on-Thames	d	10 47							10 47			11 11	
Hersham	d	→							10 49				
Esher	d								10 52				
Surbiton 6	a								10 56	11 07		11 17	
Wimbledon 6 ⊖ 🚊	a								11 04				
Earlsfield	a								11 08				
Clapham Junction 10	a				11 05			11 12	11 12				11 24
Vauxhall ⊖	a								11 17				
London Waterloo 15 ⊖	a			11 08	11 13		11 19	11 20	11 22	11 25	11 23	11 35	11 34

		SW	SW 1	SW 1	SW 1	SW 1 ◇ ☕	SW 1 ◇ ☕	SW	SW 1	SW 1 ☕	SW 1	SW	SW 1
Basingstoke	d				10 54	10 57							
Hook	d				11 01								
Winchfield	d				11 05						←		
Fleet	d				11 10						11 10		
Farnborough (Main)	d				→						11 16		
Alton	d								10 44				
Bentley	d								10 51				
Farnham	a								10 56				
	d								10 58				
Aldershot	d			11 00					11 04				11 30
Ash Vale	d			11a04					11 09				11a34
Brookwood	d								11 16		11 23		
Guildford	d		11 02							11 17			
Worplesdon	d												
Woking	a		11 11			11 15	11 19		11 21	11 25	11 28		
	d	11 03	11 12			11 17	11 21		11 22	11 26	11 29	11 33	
West Byfleet	d	11 07							11 27			11 37	
Byfleet & New Haw	d	11 10										11 40	
Weybridge	d	11 13						←			11 36	11 43	
Walton-on-Thames	d	11 17						11 17			11 41	11 47	
Hersham	d	→						11 19				→	
Esher	d							11 22					
Surbiton 6	a							11 26	11 37		11 47		
Wimbledon 6 ⊖ 🚊	a							11 34					
Earlsfield	a							11 38					
Clapham Junction 10	a		11 31			11 36		11 42	11 48		11 58		
Vauxhall ⊖	a							11 47					
London Waterloo 15 ⊖	a		11 40			11 49	11 49	11 52	11 57	11 51	12 06		

		SW 1	SW 1	SW 1	SW 1 ◇ ☕	SW 1 ◇ ☕	SW	SW 1	SW 1 ☕	SW 1	SW 1	
Basingstoke	d	11 17		11 24	11 31	11 36					11 41	
Hook	d			11 31								
Winchfield	d			11 35						←		
Fleet	d			11 40						11 40	11 53	
Farnborough (Main)	d	11 31		→						11 46	11 58	
Alton	d							11 15				
Bentley	d											and at
Farnham	a							11 25				
	d							11 28				the same
Aldershot	d							11 34				
Ash Vale	d							11 39				minutes
Brookwood	d							11 46		11 53		
Guildford	d		11 32						11 47			past
Worplesdon	d		11 40									
Woking	a	11 40	11 44		11 49			11 51	11 57	11 58		each
	d	11 41	11 46		11 51			11 52	11 59	11 59		
West Byfleet	d							11 57				hour until
Byfleet & New Haw	d											
Weybridge	d						←			12 06		
Walton-on-Thames	d						11 47			12 11		
Hersham	d						11 49					
Esher	d						11 52					
Surbiton 6	a						11 56	12 07		12 17		
Wimbledon 6 ⊖ 🚊	a						12 04					
Earlsfield	a						12 08					
Clapham Junction 10	a		12 05			12 12	12 12				12 24	
Vauxhall ⊖	a						12 17					
London Waterloo 15 ⊖	a	12 08	12 13		12 19	12 20	12 22	12 27	12 23	12 35	12 34	

		SW	SW 1	SW 1	SW 1	SW 1 ◇ ☕	SW 1 ◇ ☕	SW	SW 1	SW 1	SW 1	SW	SW 1	SW 1
Basingstoke	d				18 54	18 57								19 17
Hook	d				19 01									
Winchfield	d				19 05						←			
Fleet	d				19 10						19 10			
Farnborough (Main)	d				→						19 16			19 31
Alton	d								18 44					
Bentley	d								18 51					
Farnham	a								18 56					
	d								18 58					
Aldershot	d			19 00					19 04				19 30	
Ash Vale	d			19a04					19 09				19a34	
Brookwood	d								19 16		19 23			
Guildford	d		19 02							19 17				
Worplesdon	d													
Woking	a		19 11			19 15	19 19		19 21	19 25	19 28			19 40
	d	19 03	19 12			19 17	19 21		19 22	19 26	19 29	19 33		19 41
West Byfleet	d	19 07							19 27			19 37		
Byfleet & New Haw	d	19 10										19 40		
Weybridge	d	19 13						←			19 36	19 43		
Walton-on-Thames	d	19 17						19 17			19 41	19 47		
Hersham	d	→						19 19				→		
Esher	d							19 22						
Surbiton 6	a							19 26	19 37		19 47			
Wimbledon 6 ⊖ 🚊	a							19 34						
Earlsfield	a							19 38						
Clapham Junction 10	a		19 31			19 36		19 42	19 48		19 58			
Vauxhall ⊖	a							19 47						
London Waterloo 15 ⊖	a		19 40			19 49	19 49	19 52	19 57	19 51	20 06			20 08

For general notes see front of timetable
For details of catering facilities see Directory of Train Operators

Table 155

Saturdays

Basingstoke, Alton, Guildford and Woking → Waterloo

Network Diagram - see first page of Table 155

		SW 1	SW 1	SW 1 ◇	SW 1 ◇	SW	SW 1	SW 1	SW 1	SW 1		SW	SW 1	SW 1 ◇	SW 1	SW	SW 1	SW 1	SW 1	SW 1 ◇	SW 1	SW 1	SW	SW 1	SW 1	SW 1	SW 1
				☕	☕									☕						☕							
Basingstoke	d		19 24	19 31	19 36					19 41									19 54	20 09				20 17			
Hook	d		19 31																20 01								
Winchfield	d		19 35						←										20 05								
Fleet	d		19 40						19 40	19 53									20 10								
Farnborough (Main)	d		→						19 46	19 58									20 16					20 31			
Alton	d						19 15										19 44								20 15		
Bentley	d																19 51										
Farnham	a						19 25										19 56								20 25		
	d						19 28										19 58								20 28		
Aldershot	d						19 34								20 00		20 04				20 30				20 34		
Ash Vale	d						19 39								20a04		20 09				20a34				20 39		
Brookwood	d						19 46		19 53								20 16		20 23						20 46		
Guildford	d	19 32						19 47					20 02					20 17								20 39	20 47
Worplesdon	d	19 40																								20 44	
Woking	a	19 44		19 49			19 51	19 57	19 58				20 11	20 19			20 21	20 25	20 28	20 29				20 40	20 51	20 52	20 57
	d	19 46		19 51			19 52	19 59	19 59			20 03	20 12	20 21			20 22	20 26	20 29	20 30			20 33	20 41	20 52	20 53	20 59
West Byfleet	d						19 57					20 07					20 27						20 37		20 57		
Byfleet & New Haw	d											20 10										←	20 40				
Weybridge	d					←			20 06			20 13				←			20 36			20 36	20 43				
Walton-on-Thames	d					19 47			20 11			20 17				20 17			→			20 41	20 47				
Hersham	d					19 49						→				20 19							20 49				
Esher	d					19 52										20 22							20 52				
Surbiton 6	a					19 56	20 07		20 17							20 26	20 37					20 47	20 56		21 07		
Wimbledon 6 ⊖	a					20 04										20 34							21 04				
Earlsfield	a					20 08										20 38							21 08				
Clapham Junction 10	a	20 05			20 12	20 12				20 24			20 31			20 42	20 48			20 52		20 58	21 12			21 12	
Vauxhall ⊖	a					20 17										20 47							21 17				
London Waterloo 15 ⊖	a	20 13		20 19	20 20	20 22	20 25	20 23	20 35	20 34			20 40	20 49		20 52	20 57	20 50		21 04		21 06	21 23	21 08	21 29	21 21	21 27

		SW 1	SW 1 ◇	SW	SW 1	SW 1 ◇	SW		SW 1	SW 1	SW 1	SW 1 ◇	SW 1	SW 1	SW	SW 1	SW	SW 1	SW 1	SW 1	SW 1 ◇	SW	SW 1	SW 1	SW	SW 1	SW 1
			☕			☕						☕								A							
Basingstoke	d	20 24	20 36		20 41						20 54	21 09								21 24	21 36		21 41				21 54
Hook	d	20 31									21 01									21 31							22 01
Winchfield	d	20 35									21 05									21 35							22 05
Fleet	d	20 40			20 53						21 10									21 40			21 53				22 10
Farnborough (Main)	d	20 46			20 58						21 16									21 46			21 58				22 16
Alton	d								20 44									21 15								21 44	
Bentley	d								20 51																	21 51	
Farnham	a								20 56									21 25								21 56	
	d								20 58									21 28								21 58	
Aldershot	d								21 04				21 30					21 34								22 04	
Ash Vale	d								21 09				21a34					21 39								22 09	
Brookwood	d	20 53							21 16		21 23							21 46		21 53						22 16	22 23 →
Guildford	d									21 17						21 39			21 49								
Worplesdon	d															21 44											
Woking	a	20 58			21 07	21 19			21 21	21 25	21 28	21 29				21 49		21 51	21 57	21 58			22 07	22 19		22 21	
	d	20 59		21 03	21 09	21 21			21 22	21 26	21 29	21 30			21 33	21 50		21 52	21 59	21 59		22 03	22 09	22 21		22 22	
West Byfleet	d			21 07					21 27						21 37			21 57				22 07				22 27	
Byfleet & New Haw	d			21 10										←	21 40							22 10				→	
Weybridge	d	21 06		21 13			←				21 36			21 36	21 43		←			22 06		22 13			←		
Walton-on-Thames	d	21 11		21 17			21 17				→			21 41	21 47		21 47			22 11		22 17			22 17		
Hersham	d			→			21 19								→		21 49					→			22 19		
Esher	d						21 22										21 52								22 22		
Surbiton 6	a	21 17					21 26		21 37					21 47			21 56	22 07		22 17					22 26		
Wimbledon 6 ⊖	a						21 34										22 04								22 34		
Earlsfield	a						21 38										22 08								22 38		
Clapham Junction 10	a		21 16		21 30		21 42		21 48			21 52		21 58		22 09	22 12				22 14		22 30		22 42		
Vauxhall ⊖	a						21 47										22 17								22 47		
London Waterloo 15 ⊖	a	21 34	21 24		21 39	21 49	21 52		21 57	21 50		22 04		22 07		22 18	22 22	22 27	22 24	22 34	22 22		22 38	22 49	22 52		

		SW 1 ◇	SW 1	SW 1		SW	SW 1	SW 1	SW	SW 1	SW 1	SW 1 ◇	SW 1	SW	SW 1	SW	SW 1	SW 1	SW 1	SW 1	SW 1	SW 1	SW 1	SW 1	SW 1		
											A		A												B		
Basingstoke	d	22 09									22 24	22 36			22 41			22 54	23 14						23 44		
Hook	d										22 31							23 01							23 51		
Winchfield	d										22 35		←					23 05							23 55		
Fleet	d										22 40		22 40		22 53			23 10							00 01		
Farnborough (Main)	d										→		22 46		22 58			23 16							00 06		
Alton	d									22 15							22 44						23 15	23 44			
Bentley	d																22 51							23 51			
Farnham	a									22 25							22 56						23 25	23 56			
	d									22 28							22 58						23 28				
Aldershot	d						22 30			22 34							23 04			23 30			23 34				
Ash Vale	d			←			22a34			22 39							23 09			23a34			23 39				
Brookwood	d			22 23						22 46			22 53				23 16	23 23					23 46		00 13		
Guildford	d					22 20		22 39						22 55								23 39					
Worplesdon	d							22 44														23 44					
Woking	a	22 28		22 28		22 32		22 49		22 51		22 54	22 58	23 05	23 07		23 21	23 28	23 32			23 49	23 51		00 18		
	d	22 29	←	22 29		22 33		22 50		22 52		22 56	22 59	23 06	23 09		23 22	23 33	23 33			23 56			00 20		
West Byfleet	d		22 27			22 37				22 57				23 10			23 27	23 37							00 25		
Byfleet & New Haw	d					22 40								23 13				23 40									
Weybridge	d			22 36		22 43			←				23 06	23 16		←		23 43			←				00 29		
Walton-on-Thames	d			22 41		22 47			22 47				23 11	23 20		23 20		23 47			23 47				00 34		
Hersham	d					→			22 49					→		23 22		→			23 49						
Esher	d								22 52							23 25					23 52						
Surbiton 6	a		22 37	22 47					22 56	23 07			23 17			23 29	23 37				23 57				00 40		
Wimbledon 6 ⊖	a								23 04							23 37					00 08				00 48		
Earlsfield	a								23 08							23 41					00 10						
Clapham Junction 10	a	22 48	22 52	22 58				23 09	23 12			23 15			23 33	23 44	23 55		23 58		00 14	00 20			00 54		
Vauxhall ⊖	a								23 17							23 49					00 19						
London Waterloo 15 ⊖	a	22 57	23 01	23 06				23 18	23 22	23 28		23 23	23 39		23 43	23 54	00 04		00 10		00 31	00 32			01 02		

For general notes see front of timetable
For details of catering facilities see
Directory of Train Operators

A From Portsmouth Harbour (Table 158)
B From Weymouth (Table 158)

Table 155

Sundays

Basingstoke, Alton, Guildford and Woking → Waterloo

Network Diagram - see first page of Table 155

		SW 1	SW 1	SW 1	SW	SW	SW	SW 1	SW 1	SW 1 ◇	SW	SW	SW 1	SW 1	SW 1	SW 1	SW 1	SW 1	SW 1	SW	SW 1	SW	SW 1 ◇	SW	SW 1	SW	SW
				A				B	C				C	B	B	C	C										
										☕													☕				
Basingstoke	d	22p54		23p44				07 16	07 16	07 20									07 44				08 05				
Hook	d	23p01		23p51				07 23	07 23																		
Winchfield	d	23p05		23p55				07 27	07 27				←	←													
Fleet	d	23p10		00 01				07 32 →	07 32 →				07 32	07 32													
Farnborough (Main)	d	23p16		00 06									07 38	07 38													
Alton	d																										
Bentley	d																										
Farnham	a																										
	d														07 30		07 30										
Aldershot	d														07 36		07 36	07 40									
Ash Vale	d														07 41	←	07 41	07a44									
Brookwood	d	23p23		00 13									07 45	07 45	07 48	07 45	07 48										
Guildford	d		23p39			06 57	07 27						→							07 57	08 05			08 27	08 35		
Worplesdon	d		23p44																								
Woking	a	23p28	23p49	00 18		07 05	07 35			07 39				07 50	07 54	07 50	07 54		08 02	08 05	08 13		08 23	08 35	08 42		
	d	23p33	23p56	00 20	06 36	07 06	07 36			07 40		07 52		07 58		07 58			08 04	08 06	08 15		08 25	08 36	08 45		08 52
West Byfleet	d	23p37		00 25	06 40	07 10	07 40					07 56								08 10				08 40			08 56
Byfleet & New Haw	d	23p40			06 43	07 13	07 43					08 00								08 13				08 43			09 00
Weybridge	d	23p43		00 29	06 46	07 16	07 46				←									08 16		←		08 46		←	
Walton-on-Thames	d	23p47		00 34	06 50	07 20	07 50				07 50									08 20		08 20		08 50		08 50	
Hersham	d	23p49			06 52	07 22	→				07 52									→		08 22		→		08 52	
Esher	d	23p52			06 55	07 25					07 55											08 25				08 55	
Surbiton 6	a	23p57		00 40	06 59	07 29					07 59			08 09		08 09						08 29				08 59	
Wimbledon 6 ⊖	a	00 08		00 48	07 07	07 37					08 07			08 16		08 16						08 37				09 07	
Earlsfield	a	00 10			07 11	07 41					08 11											08 41				09 11	
Clapham Junction 10	a	00 14	00 20	00 54	07 15	07 45				08 03	08 15			08 23		08 23			08 27		08 37	08 45	08 55		09 06	09 15	
Vauxhall ⊖	a	00 19			07 20	07 50					08 20											08 50				09 20	
London Waterloo 15 ⊖	a	00 31	00 32	01 02	07 30	08 00				08 19	08 30			08 39		08 42			08 42		08 49	09 00	09 09		09 19	09 30	

		SW 1	SW 1	SW 1	SW 1	SW 1	SW 1	SW 1 ◇	SW	SW 1	SW	SW 1 ◇	SW	SW 1	SW	SW	SW 1	SW 1	SW 1	SW 1 ◇	SW	SW 1	SW 1 ◇	SW 1 ◇	SW	SW	SW 1
		C	B	B	C	C																					
								☕				☕											☕	☕			☕
Basingstoke	d	08 16	08 16					08 44				09 11					09 16			09 44			10 00	10 05			
Hook	d	08 23	08 23														09 23										
Winchfield	d	08 27	08 27														09 27										
Fleet	d	08 32	08 32														09 32										
Farnborough (Main)	d	08 38	08 38														09 38										
Alton	d			08 15		08 15												09 15									
Bentley	d			08b24		08b24												09c24									
Farnham	a			08 29		08 29												09 29									
	d			08 30		08 30												09 30									
Aldershot	d			08 36		08 36	08 40											09 36	09 40								
Ash Vale	d			08 41	←	08 41	08a44											09 41	09a44								
Brookwood	d	08 45	08 45	08 48	08 45	08 48											09 45	09 48									
Guildford	d	→							08 57	09 05			09 27	09 35							09 57	10 05				10 27	10 35
Worplesdon	d																										
Woking	a		08 50	08 54	08 50	08 54		09 02	09 05	09 15		09 30	09 35	09 42			09 50	09 54		10 02	10 05	10 15	10 19	10 23		10 35	10 42
	d		08 58		08 58			09 04	09 06	09 15		09 31	09 36	09 45		09 52	09 58			10 04	10 06	10 15	10 20	10 25		10 36	10 45
West Byfleet	d								09 10				09 40			09 56					10 10					10 40	
Byfleet & New Haw	d								09 13				09 43			10 00					10 13					10 43	
Weybridge	d								09 16		←		09 46		←						10 16				←	10 46	
Walton-on-Thames	d								09 20		09 20		09 50		09 50						10 20				10 20	10 50	
Hersham	d								→		09 22		→		09 52						→				10 22	→	
Esher	d										09 25				09 55										10 25		
Surbiton 6	a		09 09		09 09						09 29				09 59		10 09								10 29		
Wimbledon 6 ⊖	a		09 16		09 16						09 37				10 07		10 17								10 37		
Earlsfield	a										09 41				10 11										10 41		
Clapham Junction 10	a		09 24		09 24			09 27		09 35	09 45	09 55		10 06	10 15		10 22			10 27		10 35	10 39	10 44	10 45		11 04
Vauxhall ⊖	a										09 50				10 20										10 50		
London Waterloo 15 ⊖	a		09 39		09 42			09 42		09 49	10 00	10 08		10 21	10 30		10 39			10 42		10 49	10 54	11 03	11 00		11 19

For general notes see front of timetable
For details of catering facilities see Directory of Train Operators

A From Weymouth (Table 158)
B Until 20 September
C From 27 September

b Arr. 0821
c Arr. 0921

Sundays

Basingstoke, Alton, Guildford and Woking → Waterloo

Network Diagram - see first page of Table 155

		SW	SW	SW 1	SW 1	SW 1	SW 1 ◇	SW	SW 1	SW 1 ◇ ☕	SW	SW 1 ◇ ☕	SW	SW 1 ☕	SW	SW	SW 1	SW 1		SW 1	SW 1 ◇	SW	SW 1	SW 1 ◇ ☕	SW 1 ◇ ☕	SW	SW
Basingstoke	d			10 16			10 44			11 00		11 11					11 16				11 44			12 00	12 05		
Hook	d			10 23													11 23										
Winchfield	d			10 27													11 27										
Fleet	d			10 32													11 32										
Farnborough (Main)	d			10 38													11 38										
Alton	d				10 15													11 15									
Bentley	d				10b24													11c24									
Farnham	a				10 29													11 29									
	d				10 30													11 30									
Aldershot	d				10 36	10 40												11 36		11 40							
Ash Vale	d				10 41	10a44												11 41		11a44							
Brookwood	d			10 45	10 48												11 45	11 48									
Guildford	d							10 57	11 05				11 27	11 35								11 57	12 05				12 27
Worplesdon	d																										
Woking	a			10 50	10 54		11 02	11 05	11 13	11 18		11 30	11 35	11 42			11 50	11 54			12 02	12 05	12 13	12 18	12 23		12 35
	d		10 52	10 58			11 04	11 06	11 15	11 20		11 31	11 36	11 45		11 52	11 58				12 04	12 06	12 15	12 20	12 25		12 36
West Byfleet	d		10 56					11 10					11 40			11 56						12 10					12 40
Byfleet & New Haw	d		11 00					11 13					11 43			12 00						12 13					12 43
Weybridge	d	←						11 16			←		11 46		←							12 16				←	12 46
Walton-on-Thames	d	10 50						11 20 →			11 20		11 50 →		11 50							12 20 →				12 20	12 50 →
Hersham	d	10 52									11 22				11 52											12 22	
Esher	d	10 55									11 25				11 55											12 25	
Surbiton 6	a	10 59		11 09							11 29				11 59		12 09									12 29	
Wimbledon 6 ⊖	a	11 07		11 16							11 37				12 07		12 17									12 37	
Earlsfield	a	11 11									11 41				12 11											12 41	
Clapham Junction 10	a	11 15		11 22			11 27		11 34	11 39	11 45	11 50		12 04	12 15		12 23				12 27		12 34	12 39	12 44	12 45	
Vauxhall ⊖	a	11 20									11 50				12 20											12 50	
London Waterloo 15 ⊖	a	11 30		11 39			11 40		11 49	11 52	12 00	12 03		12 19	12 30		12 39				12 40		12 49	12 52	13 03	13 00	

		SW 1 ☕	SW	SW	SW 1	SW 1	SW 1	SW 1 ◇	SW	SW 1	SW 1 ◇ ☕	SW	SW 1 ◇ ☕	SW	SW 1 ☕	SW	SW	SW 1	SW 1	SW 1	SW 1 ◇	SW	SW 1	SW 1	SW 1 ◇ ☕	SW 1	SW 1 ◇ ☕
Basingstoke	d				12 16			12 44			13 00		13 11					13 16			13 44			13 50	14 00		14 05
Hook	d				12 23													13 23									
Winchfield	d				12 27													13 27									
Fleet	d				12 32													13 32						14 02		←	
Farnborough (Main)	d				12 38													13 38						14 08		14 08	
Alton	d					12 15													13 15					→			
Bentley	d					12e24													13f24								
Farnham	a					12 29													13 29								
	d					12 30													13 30								
Aldershot	d					12 36	12 40												13 36	13 40							
Ash Vale	d					12 41	12a44												13 41	13a44							
Brookwood	d				12 45	12 48												13 45	13 48							14 15	
Guildford	d	12 35							12 57	13 05				13 27	13 35							13 57	14 05				
Worplesdon	d																										
Woking	a	12 42			12 50	12 54		13 02	13 05	13 13	13 18		13 30	13 35	13 42			13 50	13 54		14 02	14 05	14 13		14 18	14 20 →	14 23
	d	12 45		12 52	12 58			13 04	13 06	13 15	13 20		13 31	13 36	13 45		13 52	13 58			14 04	14 06	14 15		14 20		14 25
West Byfleet	d			12 56					13 10					13 40			13 56					14 10					
Byfleet & New Haw	d			13 00					13 13					13 43			14 00					14 13					
Weybridge	d		←						13 16			←		13 46		←						14 16					
Walton-on-Thames	d		12 50						13 20 →			13 20		13 50 →		13 50						14 20 →					
Hersham	d		12 52									13 22				13 52											
Esher	d		12 55									13 25				13 55											
Surbiton 6	a		12 59		13 09							13 29				13 59		14 09									
Wimbledon 6 ⊖	a		13 07		13 17							13 37				14 07		14 17									
Earlsfield	a		13 11									13 41				14 11											
Clapham Junction 10	a	13 04	13 15		13 23			13 27		13 34	13 39	13 45	13 50		14 04	14 15		14 23			14 27		14 34		14 39		14 44
Vauxhall ⊖	a		13 20									13 50				14 20											
London Waterloo 15 ⊖	a	13 14	13 30		13 39			13 40		13 44	13 49	14 00	14 04		14 14	14 30		14 34			14 37		14 44		14 49		14 58

For general notes see front of timetable
For details of catering facilities see Directory of Train Operators

b Arr. 1021
c Arr. 1121
e Arr. 1221
f Arr. 1321

Sundays

Basingstoke, Alton, Guildford and Woking → Waterloo

Network Diagram - see first page of Table 155

	SW	SW 1	SW 1	SW	SW 1 ☕	SW	SW	SW 1	SW 1	SW 1	SW 1 ◇	SW	SW 1	SW 1	SW 1 ◇ ☕	SW	SW 1	SW 1	SW 1 ◇ ☕	SW	SW 1	SW 1 ☕	SW	SW	SW 1	SW 1
Basingstoke d								14 16			14 44			14 50	15 00				15 11						15 16	
Hook d								14 23																	15 23	
Winchfield d								14 27																	15 27	
Fleet d								14 32						15 02			←								15 32	
Farnborough (Main) d								14 38						15 08			15 08								15 38	
Alton d			13 45						14 15					→				14 45								15 15
Bentley d									14b24																	15c24
Farnham a			13 55						14 29									14 55								15 29
Farnham d			14 00						14 30									15 00								15 30
Aldershot d			14 06						14 36	14 40								15 06								15 36
Ash Vale d			14 11						14 41	14a44								15 11								15 41
Brookwood d			14 18					14 45	14 48								15 15	15 18							15 45	15 48
Guildford d				14 27	14 35							14 57	15 05							15 27		15 35				
Worplesdon d		←																								
Woking a		14 20	14 24	14 35	14 42			14 50	14 54		15 02	15 05	15 13		15 18		15 20	15 24	15 30	15 35		15 42			15 50	15 54
Woking d		14 28		14 36	14 45		14 52	14 58			15 04	15 06	15 15		15 20		15 28		15 31	15 36		15 45		15 52	15 58	
West Byfleet d				14 40			14 56					15 10								15 40				15 56		
Byfleet & New Haw d				14 43			15 00					15 13								15 43				16 00		
Weybridge d	←	14 35		14 46		←						15 16				←	15 35			15 46			←			
Walton-on-Thames d	14 20	14 39		14 50 →		14 50						15 20 →				15 20	15 39			15 50 →			15 50			
Hersham d	14 22					14 52										15 22							15 52			
Esher d	14 25					14 55										15 25					←		15 55			
Surbiton 6 a	14 29	14 45				14 59		15 09								15 29	15 45 →				15 45		15 59		16 09	
Wimbledon 6 ⊖ a	14 37	14 53				15 07		15 17								15 37					15 53		16 07		16 17	
Earlsfield a	14 41					15 11										15 41							16 11			
Clapham Junction 10 a	14 45	14 59			15 04	15 15		15 23			15 27		15 34		15 39	15 45			15 50		15 59	16 04	16 15		16 23	
Vauxhall ⊖ a	14 50					15 20										15 50							16 20			
London Waterloo 15 ⊖ a	14 55	15 10			15 14	15 25		15 34			15 37		15 44		15 49	15 55			16 04		16 10	16 14	16 25		16 34	

	SW 1	SW 1 ◇	SW	SW 1	SW 1	SW 1 ◇ ☕	SW 1	SW 1 ◇ ☕	SW	SW 1	SW 1		SW	SW 1 ☕	SW	SW	SW 1	SW 1	SW 1	SW 1 ◇	SW	SW 1	SW 1	SW 1 ◇ ☕	SW	
Basingstoke d		15 44			15 50	16 00		16 05									16 16			16 44			16 50	17 00		
Hook d																	16 23									
Winchfield d																	16 27									
Fleet d					16 02		←										16 32						17 02			
Farnborough (Main) d					16 08		16 08										16 38						17 08			
Alton d					→						15 45							16 15					→			
Bentley d																		16e24								
Farnham a											15 55							16 29								
Farnham d											16 00							16 30								
Aldershot d	15 40										16 06							16 36	16 40							
Ash Vale d	15a44										16 11							16 41	16a44							
Brookwood d							16 15				16 18						16 45	16 48								
Guildford d			15 57	16 05									16 27	16 35							16 57	17 05				
Worplesdon d										←																
Woking a		16 02	16 05	16 13		16 18	16 20 →	16 23		16 20	16 24		16 35	16 42			16 50	16 54		17 02	17 05	17 13		17 18		
Woking d		16 04	16 06	16 15		16 20		16 25		16 28			16 36	16 45		16 52	16 58			17 04	17 06	17 15		17 20		
West Byfleet d			16 10										16 40			16 56					17 10					
Byfleet & New Haw d			16 13										16 43			17 00					17 13					
Weybridge d			16 16						←	16 35			16 46		←						17 16				←	
Walton-on-Thames d			16 20 →						16 20	16 39			16 50 →		16 50						17 20 →				17 20	
Hersham d									16 22						16 52										17 22	
Esher d									16 25						16 55										17 25	
Surbiton 6 a									16 29	16 45					16 59		17 09								17 29	
Wimbledon 6 ⊖ a									16 37	16 53					17 07		17 17								17 37	
Earlsfield a									16 41						17 11										17 41	
Clapham Junction 10 a		16 27		16 34		16 39		16 44	16 45	16 59				17 04	17 15		17 23			17 27		17 34		17 39	17 45	
Vauxhall ⊖ a									16 50						17 20										17 50	
London Waterloo 15 ⊖ a		16 37		16 44		16 49		16 58	16 55	17 10				17 14	17 25		17 34			17 37		17 44		17 49	17 55	

For general notes see front of timetable
For details of catering facilities see Directory of Train Operators

b Arr. 1421
c Arr. 1521
e Arr. 1621

Sundays

Basingstoke, Alton, Guildford and Woking → Waterloo

Network Diagram - see first page of Table 155

		SW 1	SW 1	SW 1 ◇ ☕	SW	SW 1	SW 1 ☕	SW	SW	SW 1	SW 1	SW 1	SW 1 ◇	SW	SW 1	SW 1	SW 1 ◇ ☕	SW 1	SW 1 ◇ ☕	SW	SW 1	SW 1	SW	SW 1 ☕	SW	SW	
Basingstoke	d			17 11						17 16			17 44			17 50	18 00		18 05								
Hook	d									17 23																	
Winchfield	d									17 27																	
Fleet	d	←								17 32						18 02		←									
Farnborough (Main)	d	17 08								17 38						18 08		18 08									
Alton	d		16 45								17 15					→						17 45					
Bentley	d										17b24																
Farnham	a		16 55								17 29											17 55					
	d		17 00								17 30											18 00					
Aldershot	d		17 06								17 36	17 40										18 06					
Ash Vale	d		17 11								17 41	17a44										18 11					
Brookwood	d	17 15	17 18							17 45	17 48							18 15				18 18					
Guildford	d				17 27		17 35							17 57	18 05						←		18 27	18 35			
Worplesdon	d																										
Woking	a	17 20	17 24	17 30	17 35		17 42			17 50	17 54		18 02	18 05	18 13		18 18	18 20 →	18 23		18 20	18 24	18 35	18 42			
	d	17 28		17 31	17 36		17 45		17 52	17 58			18 04	18 06	18 15		18 20		18 25		18 28		18 36	18 45		18 52	
West Byfleet	d				17 40				17 56					18 10									18 40			18 56	
Byfleet & New Haw	d				17 43				18 00					18 13									18 43			19 00	
Weybridge	d	17 35			17 46			←						18 16						←	18 35		18 46		←		
Walton-on-Thames	d	17 39			17 50 →			17 50						18 20 →						18 20	18 39		18 50 →		18 50		
Hersham	d							17 52												18 22					18 52		
Esher	d					←		17 55												18 25					18 55		
Surbiton 6	a	17 45 →				17 45		17 59		18 09										18 29	18 45				18 59		
Wimbledon 6 ⊖	a					17 53		18 07		18 17										18 37	18 53				19 07		
Earlsfield	a							18 11												18 41					19 11		
Clapham Junction 10	a			17 50		17 59	18 04	18 15		18 23			18 27		18 34		18 39		18 44	18 45	18 59			19 04	19 15		
Vauxhall ⊖	a							18 20												18 50					19 20		
London Waterloo 15 ⊖	a			18 04		18 10	18 14	18 25		18 34			18 37		18 44		18 49		18 58	18 55	19 10			19 14	19 25		

		SW 1	SW 1	SW 1	SW 1 ◇	SW	SW 1	SW 1	SW 1 ◇ ☕	SW	SW 1	SW 1	SW 1 ◇ ☕	SW	SW 1	SW 1 ☕	SW	SW	SW 1	SW 1	SW 1	SW 1 ◇	SW	SW 1	SW 1	SW 1 ◇ ☕	SW 1
Basingstoke	d	18 16			18 44			18 50	19 00				19 11						19 16			19 44			19 50	20 00	
Hook	d	18 23																	19 23								
Winchfield	d	18 27																	19 27								
Fleet	d	18 32						19 02			←								19 32						20 02		←
Farnborough (Main)	d	18 38						19 08			19 08								19 38						20 08		20 08
Alton	d		18 15					→				18 45								19 15					→		
Bentley	d		18c24																	19e24							
Farnham	a		18 29									18 55								19 29							
	d		18 30									19 00								19 30							
Aldershot	d		18 36	18 40								19 06								19 36	19 40						
Ash Vale	d		18 41	18a44								19 11								19 41	19a44						
Brookwood	d	18 45	18 48								19 15	19 18							19 45	19 48							20 15
Guildford	d					18 57	19 05							19 27		19 35							19 57	20 05			
Worplesdon	d																										
Woking	a	18 50	18 54		19 02	19 05	19 13		19 18		19 20	19 24	19 30	19 35		19 42			19 50	19 54		20 02	20 05	20 13		20 18	20 20 →
	d	18 58			19 04	19 06	19 15		19 20		19 28		19 31	19 36		19 45		19 52	19 58			20 04	20 06	20 15		20 20	
West Byfleet	d					19 10								19 40				19 56					20 10				
Byfleet & New Haw	d					19 13								19 43				20 00					20 13				
Weybridge	d					19 16				←	19 35			19 46			←						20 16				
Walton-on-Thames	d					19 20 →				19 20	19 39			19 50 →			19 50						20 20 →				
Hersham	d									19 22							19 52										
Esher	d									19 25					←		19 55										
Surbiton 6	a	19 09								19 29	19 45 →				19 45		19 59		20 09								
Wimbledon 6 ⊖	a	19 17								19 37					19 53		20 07		20 17								
Earlsfield	a									19 41							20 11										
Clapham Junction 10	a	19 23			19 27		19 34		19 39	19 45			19 50		19 59	20 04	20 15		20 23			20 27		20 34		20 39	
Vauxhall ⊖	a									19 50							20 20										
London Waterloo 15 ⊖	a	19 34			19 37		19 44		19 49	19 55			20 04		20 10	20 14	20 25		20 34			20 37		20 44		20 49	

For general notes see front of timetable
For details of catering facilities see Directory of Train Operators

b Arr. 1721
c Arr. 1821
e Arr. 1921

Table 155

Sundays

Basingstoke, Alton, Guildford and Woking → Waterloo

Network Diagram - see first page of Table 155

	SW 1◇ A ☕	SW	SW 1	SW 1	SW	SW 1	SW	SW	SW 1	SW 1	SW 1	SW 1◇	SW	SW 1	SW 1	SW 1◇ ☕	SW	SW 1	SW 1	SW 1◇ ☕	SW	SW 1	SW 1	SW	SW
Basingstoke d	20 05								20 16			20 44			20 50	21 00				21 11					
Hook d									20 23																
Winchfield d									20 27																
Fleet d									20 32						21 02			←							
Farnborough (Main) d									20 38						21 08			21 08							
Alton d				19 45						20 15					→				20 45						
Bentley d										20b24															
Farnham a				19 55						20 29									20 55						
Farnham d				20 00						20 30									21 00						
Aldershot d				20 06						20 36	20 40								21 06						
Ash Vale d				20 11						20 41	20a44								21 11						
Brookwood d				20 18					20 45	20 48								21 15	21 18						
Guildford d					20 27	20 35							20 57	21 05							21 27		21 35		
Worplesdon d			←																						
Woking a	20 23		20 20	20 24	20 35	20 42			20 50	20 54		21 02	21 05	21 13		21 18		21 20	21 24	21 30	21 35		21 42		
Woking d	20 25		20 28		20 36	20 45		20 52	20 58			21 04	21 06	21 15		21 20		21 28		21 31	21 36		21 45		21 52
West Byfleet d					20 40			20 56					21 10								21 40				21 56
Byfleet & New Haw d					20 43			21 00					21 13								21 43				22 00
Weybridge d		←	20 35		20 46		←						21 16				←	21 35			21 46			←	
Walton-on-Thames d		20 20	20 39		20 50 →		20 50						21 20 →				21 20	21 39			21 50 →			21 50	
Hersham d		20 22					20 52										21 22							21 52	
Esher d		20 25					20 55										21 25					←		21 55	
Surbiton 6 a		20 29	20 45				20 59		21 09								21 29	21 45 →				21 45		21 59	
Wimbledon 6 ⊖ a		20 37	20 53				21 07		21 17								21 37					21 53		22 07	
Earlsfield a		20 41					21 11										21 41							22 11	
Clapham Junction 10 a	20 44	20 45	20 59			21 04	21 15		21 23			21 27		21 34		21 39	21 45			21 50		21 59	22 04	22 15	
Vauxhall ⊖ a		20 50					21 20										21 50							22 20	
London Waterloo 15 ⊖ a	20 58	20 55	21 10			21 14	21 25		21 34			21 37		21 44		21 49	21 55			22 04		22 10	22 14	22 25	

	SW 1	SW 1	SW 1	SW 1◇	SW	SW 1	SW 1	SW 1◇ ☕	SW	SW 1	SW 1	SW	SW 1	SW	SW	SW 1	SW 1	SW 1	SW 1◇	SW	SW 1	SW	SW 1	SW 1	SW 1	SW 1
Basingstoke d	21 16			21 44			21 50	22 05								22 16			22 44						23 16	
Hook d	21 23															22 23									23 23	
Winchfield d	21 27															22 27									23 27	
Fleet d	21 32						22 02									22 32									23 32	
Farnborough (Main) d	21 38						22 08									22 38									23 38	
Alton d		21 15									21 45						22 15						22 45			23 15
Bentley d		21c24															22e24									23f24
Farnham a		21 29									21 55						22 29						22 55			23 29
Farnham d		21 30									22 00						22 30						23 00			23 30
Aldershot d		21 36	21 40								22 06						22 36	22 40					23 06			23 36
Ash Vale d		21 41	21a44								22 11						22 41	22a44					23 11			23 41
Brookwood d	21 45	21 48					22 15				22 18					22 45	22 48						23 18		23 45	23 48
Guildford d					21 57	22 05						22 27	22 35							22 57	23 05			23 35		
Worplesdon d										←																
Woking a	21 50	21 54		22 02	22 05	22 13	22 21 →	22 23		22 21	22 24	22 35	22 42			22 50	22 54		23 02	23 05	23 13		23 24	23 42	23 50	23 54
Woking d	21 58			22 04	22 06	22 15		22 25		22 28		22 36	22 45		22 52	22 58			23 04	23 06	23 15		23 28	23 45		
West Byfleet d					22 10							22 40			22 56					23 10						
Byfleet & New Haw d					22 13							22 43			23 00					23 13						
Weybridge d					22 16				←	22 35		22 46		←						23 16		←	23 35			
Walton-on-Thames d					22 20 →				22 20	22 39		22 50 →		22 50						23 20 →		23 20	23 39			
Hersham d									22 22					22 52								23 22				
Esher d									22 25					22 55								23 25				
Surbiton 6 a	22 09								22 29	22 45				22 59		23 09						23 29	23 45			
Wimbledon 6 ⊖ a	22 17								22 37	22 53				23 07		23 17						23 37	23 53			
Earlsfield a									22 41					23 11								23 41				
Clapham Junction 10 a	22 23			22 27		22 34		22 44	22 45	22 59			23 04	23 15		23 23			23 27		23 34	23 45	23 58	00 04		
Vauxhall ⊖ a									22 50					23 20								23 50				
London Waterloo 15 ⊖ a	22 34			22 37		22 44		22 58	22 55	23 11			23 14	23 25		23 34			23 37		23 44	23 55	00 10	00 14		

For general notes see front of timetable
For details of catering facilities see Directory of Train Operators

A From Penzance (Table 135)
b Arr. 2021
c Arr. 2121
e Arr. 2221
f Arr. 2321

Basingstoke, Alton, Guildford and Woking → Waterloo

Network Diagram - see first page of Table 155

		SW 1 ◇
Basingstoke	d	23 44
Hook	d	
Winchfield	d	
Fleet	d	
Farnborough (Main)	d	
Alton	d	
Bentley	d	
Farnham	a	
	d	
Aldershot	d	
Ash Vale	d	
Brookwood	d	
Guildford	d	
Worplesdon	d	
Woking	a	00 02
	d	00 04
West Byfleet	d	
Byfleet & New Haw	d	
Weybridge	d	
Walton-on-Thames	d	
Hersham	d	
Esher	d	
Surbiton 6	a	
Wimbledon 6 ⊖	a	
Earlsfield	a	
Clapham Junction 10	a	00 23
Vauxhall ⊖	a	
London Waterloo 15 ⊖	a	00 33

For general notes see front of timetable
For details of catering facilities see Directory of Train Operators

London → Guildford, Haslemere and Portsmouth

Network Diagram - see first page of Table 155

Miles	Station		SW MX 1	SW MO 1	SW MX 1	SW MO 1	SW MX 1		SW MO 1	SW MO 1	SW MX 1	SW MO 1	SW 1		SW 1	SW 1	SW 1	SW 1	SW 1		SW 1 ☕	SW 1	SW 1	SW 1	SW 1	SW 1
0	**London Waterloo** 15 ⊖	d	22p30	22p30	22p45	23p00	23p15			23p30	23p45	00 50			05 00	05 20	06 15	06 45	07 15		07 30		07 45	08 00		08 15
4	Clapham Junction 10	d		22b39	22b52	23b09	23b22			23b39	23b52	00u57			05 09	05 29	06u22	06u52	07u22				07u52			08u22
24¼	**Woking**	a	22p54	23p01	23p11	23p31	23p41			00 01	00 16	01 16			05 50	06 08	06 41	07 11	07 42		07 55		08 12	08 24		08 42
—		d	22p55	23p02	23p13	23p32	23p43			00 02	00 17	01 18			05 51	06 11	06 43	07 13	07 44		07 55		08 14	08 25		08 44
26¾	Worplesdon	d			23p18						00 22					06 16	06 48	07 18	07 49				08 19			08 49
30¼	**Guildford**	a	23p03	23p10	23p23	23p40	23p51			00 10	00 28	01s26			05 59	06 21	06 53	07 23	07 54		08 04		08 24	08 35		08 54
—		d	23p04	23p12	23p25	23p42	23p52			00 12	00 30		05 15		06 00	06 25	06 55	07 25	07 56		08 04		08 26	08 39		08 56
33½	Farncombe	d	23p10		23p31	23p48	23p58				00 36				06 06	06 31	07 01	07 31	08 02				08 32			09 02
34½	Godalming	d	23p13		23p34	23p51	00 01				00 39				06 09	06 34	07 04	07 34	08 05				08 35			09 05
36¼	Milford (Surrey)	d			23p38	23p55					00s43				06 13	06 38	07 08	07 38	08 09				08 39			09 09
38½	Witley	d			23p42	23p59					00s47				06 18	06 42	07 12	07 42	08 13				08 43			09 13
43	**Haslemere** 4	a	23p24	23p26	23p49	00 06	00 12			00 26	00 54		05 29		06 24	06 49	07 19	07 49	08 20		08 24	←	08 50	08 54	←	09 20
—		d	23p25	23p27	23p50	00 07	00 13			00 27	00 54		05 30		06 25	06 55	07 20	07 55	08 30		08 25	08 30	08 58	08 55	08 58	
46¾	Liphook	d			23p55	00 12					00s59		05 35		06 30	07 00	07 25	08 00	→			08 35	→		09 03	
51½	Liss	d			00 01	00 18					01s05		05 41		06 36	07 06	07 31	08 06				08 41			09 09	
55	Petersfield	d	23p36	23p38	00 06	00 23	00 24		←	00 38	01 11		05 46		06 41	07 11	07 36	08 11			08 36	08 46		09 06	09 15	
63¼	Rowlands Castle	d			00 16	00 33			00 33		01s20		05 56		06 51	07 21	07 46	08 21				08 56			09 24	
66½	**Havant**	a	23p48	23p50	00 21	→	00 36		00 38	00 50	01 25	02s00	06 01		06 57	07 27	07 51	08 26			08 49	09 04		09 19	09 29	
66½		d	23p49	23p51	00 22		00 37		00 39	00 51	01 26		06 02		06 58	07 28	07 52	08 27			08 50	09 05		09 20	09 30	
67¼	Bedhampton	a			00 24				00 41		01s29		06 04		07 00	07 30	07 54	08 29				09 07			09 32	
70½	Hilsea	a			00 30						01s34		06 10		07 07	07 37	08 00	08 35				09 13			09 38	
72¾	Fratton	a	23p58	23p59	00 34		00 46		00 49	01 00	01s38	02s10	06 14		07 11	07 41	08 04	08 39			08 58	09 17		09 28	09 42	
73¾	**Portsmouth & Southsea**	a	00 02	00 04	00 38		00 50		00 53	01 04	01 42	02s14	06 18		07 16	07 46	08 07	08 43			09 02	09 20		09 32	09 46	
74½	**Portsmouth Harbour**	a	00 07	00 09			00 55		00 58	01 09		02 19	06 22		07 20		08 12	08 48			09 07	09 26		09 37		

Station		SW 1 ☕		SW 1	SW 1 ☕	SW 1	SW 1	SW 1 ☕			SW 1	SW 1 ☕	SW 1	SW 1	SW 1 ☕			SW 1	SW 1 ☕	SW 1	SW 1	SW 1 ☕		SW 1	SW 1
London Waterloo 15 ⊖	d	08 30		08 45	09 00		09 15	09 30			09 45	10 00		10 15	10 30			14 45	15 00		15 15	15 30			15 45
Clapham Junction 10	d			08u52			09u22				09u52			10u22				14u52			15u22				15u52
Woking	a	08 55		09 11	09 24		09 42	09 54			10 11	10 24		10 41	10 54			15 11	15 23		15 41	15 54			16 11
	d	08 55		09 13	09 25		09 43	09 55			10 13	10 25		10 43	10 55			15 13	15 25		15 43	15 55			16 13
Worplesdon	d			09 18							10 18							15 18			15 48				
Guildford	a	09 05		09 23	09 33		09 52	10 03			10 23	10 33		10 50	11 03	and at		15 23	15 32		15 53	16 03			16 20
	d	09 07		09 25	09 34		09 54	10 04			10 25	10 34		10 52	11 04	the same		15 25	15 34		15 55	16 04			16 22
Farncombe	d			09 31			10 00				10 31			10 58				15 31			16 01				16 28
Godalming	d			09 34			10 03				10 34			11 01		minutes		15 34			16 04				16 31
Milford (Surrey)	d						10 07							11 05							16 08				16 35
Witley	d						10 11							11 09		past					16 12				16 39
Haslemere 4	a	09 24		09 45	09 49	←	10 19	10 22			10 45	10 49	←	11 16	11 20			15 45	15 49	←	16 19	16 23		←	16 46
	d	09 25		09 55	09 50	09 55		10 23			10 55	10 50	10 55		11 21	each		15 55	15 50	15 55	16 29	16 24		16 29	16 55
Liphook	d			→		10 00					→		11 00					→		16 00	→			16 34	→
Liss	d					10 06							11 06			hour until				16 06				16 40	
Petersfield	d	09 36			10 01	10 11		10 34				11 01	11 11		11 32				16 01	16 11		16 35		16 45	
Rowlands Castle	d					10 21							11 21							16 21				16 55	
Havant	a	09 49			10 15	10 26		10 49				11 14	11 26		11 49				16 15	16 26		16 49		17 03	
	d	09 50			10 16	10 27		10 50				11 16	11 27		11 50				16 16	16 27		16 50		17 04	
Bedhampton	a					10 29							11 29							16 29				17 06	
Hilsea	a					10 36							11 36							16 36				17 11	
Fratton	a	09 59			10 24	10 40		10 59				11 24	11 40		11 59				16 24	16 40		16 59		17 15	
Portsmouth & Southsea	a	10 02			10 28	10 44		11 02				11 28	11 44		12 02				16 28	16 44		17 02		17 20	
Portsmouth Harbour	a	10 07			10 33			11 07				11 33			12 07				16 33	16 49		17 07		17 25	

Station		SW 1 ☕	SW 1	SW 1	SW 1 ☕	SW 1		SW 1	SW 1 ☕	SW 1	SW 1	SW 1 ☕		SW 1	SW 1	SW 1 ☕	SW 1	SW 1		SW 1	SW 1 ☕	SW 1	SW 1 ☕	SW 1		SW 1
London Waterloo 15 ⊖	d	16 00		16 15	16 30			16 45	17 00		17 15	17 30			17 45	18 00		18 15		18 18	18 30	18 45	19 00			19 15
Clapham Junction 10	d			16u22				16u52																		19u22
Woking	a	16 24		16 41	16 54			17 11	17 24		17 38	17 54								18 42	18 57	19 13	19 24			19 43
	d	16 25		16 43	16 55			17 13	17 25		17 40	17 56								18 43	18 58	19 14	19 25			19 45
Worplesdon	d			16 48					17 30		17 45	18 00								18 48			19 30			
Guildford	a	16 33		16 53	17 03			17 20	17 36		17 51	18 06			18 21	18 31		18 50		18 54	19 06	19 23	19 36			19 52
	d	16 34		16 55	17 04			17 22	17 37		17 54	18 08			18 23	18 33		18 51		18 57	19 08	19 24	19 37			19 54
Farncombe	d			17 01				17 28			18 00				18 29					19 03		19 30				20 00
Godalming	d			17 04				17 31			18 03	18 15			18 32	18 39				19 06	19 14	19 33				20 03
Milford (Surrey)	d			17 08				17 35			18 07				18 36					19 10		19 37				20 07
Witley	d			17 12				17 39			18 11				18 40					19 14		19 41				20 11
Haslemere 4	a	16 50	←	17 19	17 23	←		17 46	17 51	←	18 18	18 25		←	18 49	18 51	←	19 05		19 23	19 25	19 49	19 52	←		20 18
	d	16 51	16 55	17 29	17 24	17 29		17 56	17 52	17 56	18 31	18 26		18 31	18 56	18 52	18 56	19 06			19 26	19 57	19 53	19 57		20 27
Liphook	d		17 00	→		17 34		→		18 01	→			18 36	→		19 01	19 11				→		20 02		→
Liss	d		17 06			17 40				18 07				18 42			19 07	19 17						20 08		
Petersfield	d	17 02	17 11		17 35	17 45			18 03	18 12		18 37		18 47		19 03	19 12	19 23			19 37		20 04	20 13		
Rowlands Castle	d		17 21			17 55				18 22				18 57			19 22	19 32						20 23		
Havant	a	17 15	17 26		17 49	18 03			18 18	18 29		18 50		19 02		19 16	19 29	19 40			19 50		20 18	20 28		
	d	17 16	17 27		17 50	18 04			18 19	18 30		18 51		19 03		19 17		19 41			19 51		20 18	20 29		
Bedhampton	a		17 29			18 07				18 32				19 06				19 44						20 31		
Hilsea	a		17 36			18 12				18 39				19 11				19 49						20 37		
Fratton	a	17 24	17 40		17 59	18 16			18 28	18 43		18 59		19 15		19 25		19 55			19 59		20 28	20 41		
Portsmouth & Southsea	a	17 28	17 44		18 02	18 20			18 32	18 46		19 03				19 29					20 03		20 32	20 44		
Portsmouth Harbour	a	17 35			18 09	18 28			18 39			19 10				19 36					20 10		20 37	20 52		

For general notes see front of timetable
For details of catering facilities see
Directory of Train Operators

b Previous night.
Stops to pick up only

London → Guildford, Haslemere and Portsmouth

Network Diagram - see first page of Table 155

Mondays to Fridays

	SW	SW	SW	SW	SW	SW	SW	SW	SW	SW	SW	SW	SW	SW	SW	SW	SW	SW
	1	1	1	1	1	1	1	1	1	1	1	1	1	1	1	1	1	1
	☕			☕			☕		☕									
London Waterloo 15 ⊖ d	19 30		19 45	20 00		20 15	20 30	20 45	21 00		21 30	21 45	22 00		22 30	22 45	23 15	23 45
Clapham Junction 10 d			19u52			20u22		20u52				21u52				22u52	23u22	23u52
Woking a	19 54		20 11	20 24		20 41	20 54	21 11	21 24		21 54	22 11	22 24		22 54	23 11	23 41	00 16
d	19 55		20 13	20 25		20 43	20 55	21 13	21 25		21 55	22 13	22 25		22 55	23 13	23 43	00 17
Worplesdon d			20 18					21 18				22 18				23 18		00 22
Guildford a	20 03		20 23	20 33		20 50	21 03	21 23	21 33		22 03	22 23	22 33		23 03	23 23	23 51	00 28
d	20 04		20 25	20 34		20 52	21 04	21 25	21 34		22 04	22 25	22 34		23 04	23 25	23 52	00 30
Farncombe d			20 31	20 40		20 58		21 31	21 40		22 10	22 31	22 40		23 10	23 31	23 58	00 36
Godalming d	20 11		20 34	20 43		21 01	21 11	21 34	21 43		22 13	22 34	22 43		23 13	23 34	00 01	00 39
Milford (Surrey) d			20 38			21 05		21 38				22 38				23 38		00s43
Witley d			20 42			21 09		21 42				22 42				23 42		00s47
Haslemere 4 a	20 22	←	20 49	20 54	←	21 16	21 21	21 49	21 54	←	22 24	22 49	22 54	←	23 24	23 49	00 12	00 54
d	20 22	20 27	20 59	20 55	20 59		21 22	21 59	21 55	21 59	22 25	22 59	22 55	22 59	23 25	23 50	00 13	00 54
Liphook d		20 32	→		21 04			→		22 04		→		23 04		23 55		00s59
Liss d		20 38			21 10					22 10				23 10		00 01		01s05
Petersfield d	20 33	20 43		21 06	21 16		21 33		22 06	22 16	22 36		23 06	23 15	23 36	00 06	00 24	01 11
Rowlands Castle d		20 53			21 25					22 25				23 25		00 16		01s20
Havant a	20 48	21 00		21 18	21 30		21 46		22 18	22 30	22 48		23 18	23 30	23 48	00 21	00 36	01 25
d	20 49			21 19	21 31		21 46		22 19	22 31	22 49		23 19	23 31	23 49	00 22	00 37	01 26
Bedhampton a					21 34					22 34				23 33		00 24		01s29
Hilsea a					21 41					22 39				23 39		00 30		01s34
Fratton a	20 57			21 28	21 45		21 55		22 28	22 43	22 59		23 28	23 43	23 58	00 34	00 46	01s38
Portsmouth & Southsea a	21 01			21 32	21 48		21 58		22 32	22 47	23 04		23 32	23 47	00 02	00 38	00 50	01 42
Portsmouth Harbour a	21 06			21 37			22 02		22 37		23 08		23 37		00 07		00 55	

Saturdays

	SW	SW	SW	SW	SW	SW	SW	SW	SW	SW	SW	SW	SW	SW		SW	SW	SW	SW	SW
	1	1	1	1	1	1	1	1	1	1	1	1	1	1		1	1	1	1	1
																	☕		☕	
London Waterloo 15 ⊖ d	22p30	22p45	23p15	23p45		05 00	05 20	06 15	06 45	07 15	07 30	07 45	08 00			18 15	18 30	18 45	19 00	
Clapham Junction 10 d		22b52	23b22	23b52		05 09	05 29	06u22	06u52	07u22		07u52				18u22		18u52		
Woking a	22p54	23p11	23p41	00 16		05 50	06 08	06 41	07 11	07 41	07 54	08 11	08 24			18 41	18 54	19 11	19 24	
d	22p55	23p13	23p43	00 17		05 51	06 13	06 43	07 13	07 43	07 55	08 13	08 25			18 43	18 55	19 13	19 25	
Worplesdon d		23p18		00 22			06 18		07 18			08 18						19 18		
Guildford a	23p03	23p23	23p51	00 28		05 59	06 23	06 50	07 23	07 50	08 03	08 23	08 33		and at the same minutes past each hour until	18 50	19 03	19 23	19 33	
d	23p04	23p25	23p52	00 30	05 15	06 00	06 25	06 52	07 25	07 52	08 04	08 25	08 34			18 52	19 04	19 25	19 34	
Farncombe d	23p10	23p31	23p58	00 36		06 06	06 31	06 58	07 31	07 58		08 31				18 58		19 31		
Godalming d	23p13	23p34	00 01	00 39		06 09	06 34	07 01	07 34	08 01		08 34				19 01		19 34		
Milford (Surrey) d		23p38		00s43		06 13		07 05		08 05						19 05				
Witley d		23p42		00s47		06 18		07 09		08 09						19 09				
Haslemere 4 a	23p24	23p49	00 12	00 54	05 29	06 25	06 44	07 16	07 44	08 16	08 20	08 45	08 49	←		19 16	19 20	19 45	19 49	←
d	23p25	23p50	00 13	00 54	05 29		06 45		07 45		08 21	08 55	08 50	08 55			19 21	19 55	19 50	19 55
Liphook d		23p55		00s59	05 34		06 50		07 50			→		09 00				→		20 00
Liss d		00 01		01s05	05 40		06 56		07 56					09 06						20 06
Petersfield d	23p36	00 06	00 24	01 11	05 46		07 01		08 01		08 32		09 01	09 11			19 32		20 01	20 11
Rowlands Castle d		00 16		01s20	05 55		07 11		08 11					09 21						20 21
Havant a	23p48	00 21	00 36	01 25	06 00		07 19		08 16		08 49		09 15	09 26			19 49		20 15	20 29
d	23p49	00 22	00 37	01 26	06 01		07 20		08 17		08 50		09 16	09 27			19 50		20 16	20 30
Bedhampton a		00 24		01s29	06 03		07 22		08 19					09 29						20 32
Hilsea a		00 30		01s34	06 09		07 27		08 25					09 36						20 41
Fratton a	23p58	00 34	00 46	01s38	06 13		07 31		08 29		08 59		09 24	09 40			19 59		20 24	20 45
Portsmouth & Southsea a	00 02	00 38	00 50	01 42	06 17		07 35		08 32		09 02		09 28	09 44			20 02		20 28	20 48
Portsmouth Harbour a	00 07		00 55		06 22		07 40		08 37		09 07		09 33				20 07		20 33	

	SW	SW	SW	SW	SW	SW	SW	SW	SW	SW	SW	SW	SW	SW	SW	SW	SW	SW
	1	1	1	1	1	1	1	1	1	1	1	1	1	1	1	1	1	1
		☕																
London Waterloo 15 ⊖ d	19 15	19 30	19 45	20 00		20 15	20 30	20 45	21 00		21 30	21 45	22 00		22 30	22 45	23 15	23 45
Clapham Junction 10 d	19u22		19u52			20u22		20u52				21u52				22u52	23u22	23u52
Woking a	19 41	19 54	20 11	20 24		20 41	20 54	21 11	21 24		21 54	22 11	22 24		22 54	23 11	23 41	00 16
d	19 43	19 55	20 13	20 25		20 43	20 55	21 13	21 25		21 55	22 13	22 25		22 55	23 13	23 43	00 17
Worplesdon d			20 18					21 18				22 18				23 18		00 22
Guildford a	19 50	20 03	20 23	20 33		20 50	21 03	21 23	21 33		22 03	22 23	22 33		23 03	23 23	23 51	00 28
d	19 52	20 04	20 25	20 34		20 52	21 04	21 25	21 34		22 04	22 25	22 34		23 04	23 25	23 52	00 29
Farncombe d	19 58		20 31			20 58		21 31	21 40		22 10	22 31	22 40		23 10	23 31	23 58	00 35
Godalming d	20 01		20 34			21 01		21 34	21 43		22 13	22 34	22 43		23 13	23 34	00 01	00 38
Milford (Surrey) d	20 05					21 05		21 38				22 38				23 38		00s42
Witley d	20 09					21 09		21 42				22 42				23 42		00s47
Haslemere 4 a	20 16	20 20	20 45	20 49	←	21 16	21 20	21 49	21 54	←	22 24	22 49	22 54	←	23 24	23 49	00 12	00 53
d		20 21	20 55	20 50	20 55		21 21	21 59	21 55	21 59	22 25	22 59	22 55	22 59	23 25	23 50	00 13	00 54
Liphook d			→		21 00			→		22 04		→		23 04		23 55		00s59
Liss d					21 06					22 10				23 10		00 01		01s05
Petersfield d		20 32		21 01	21 11		21 32		22 06	22 15	22 36		23 06	23 15	23 36	00 06	00 24	01 10
Rowlands Castle d					21 21					22 25				23 25		00 16		01s20
Havant a		20 49		21 15	21 26		21 45		22 18	22 30	22 48		23 18	23 30	23 48	00 21	00 36	01 25
d		20 50		21 16	21 27		21 46		22 19	22 31	22 49		23 19	23 31	23 49	00 22	00 37	01 26
Bedhampton a					21 29					22 33				23 33		00 24		01s28
Hilsea a					21 36					22 41				23 41		00 30		01s34
Fratton a		20 59		21 24	21 40		21 54		22 28	22 45	22 58		23 28	23 45	23 58	00 34	00 46	01s38
Portsmouth & Southsea a		21 02		21 28	21 44		21 58		22 32	22 49	23 02		23 32	23 48	00 02	00 38	00 50	01 42
Portsmouth Harbour a		21 07		21 33			22 03		22 36	22 53	23 08		23 37	23 53	00 07		00 55	

For general notes see front of timetable
For details of catering facilities see Directory of Train Operators

b Previous night.
Stops to pick up only

Table 156

Sundays

London → Guildford, Haslemere and Portsmouth

Network Diagram - see first page of Table 155

		SW 1	SW 1	SW 1	SW 1	SW 1	SW 1	SW 1	SW 1	SW 1	SW 1	SW 1	SW 1 A	SW 1 B
London Waterloo 15 ⊖	d	22p30	22p45	23p15	23p45		08 00	08 30	09 00	09 30	10 00	10 30	11 00	11 00
Clapham Junction 10	d	.	22b52	23b22	23b52	.	08u09	08u39	09u09	09u39	10u09	10u39	11u09	11u09
Woking	a	22p54	23p11	23p41	00 16		08 34	09 03	09 34	10 03	10 31	11 01	11 31	11 31
	d	22p55	23p13	23p43	00 17	07 32	08 35	09 04	09 35	10 04	10 32	11 02	11 32	11 32
Worplesdon	d		23p18		00 22									
Guildford	a	23p03	23p23	23p51	00 28	07 40	08 43	09 12	09 43	10 12	10 40	11 10	11 40	11 40
	d	23p04	23p25	23p52	00 29	07 42	08 45	09 14	09 45	10 14	10 42	11 12	11 42	11 42
Farncombe	d	23p10	23p31	23p58	00 35	07 48	08 53	.	09 53	.	10 48	.	11 48	11 48
Godalming	d	23p13	23p34	00 01	00 38	07 51	08 56		09 56		10 51		11 51	11 51
Milford (Surrey)	d	.	23p38	.	00s42	07 55	09 00	.	10 00	.	10 55	.	11 55	11 55
Witley	d		23p42		00s47	07 59	09 04		10 04		10 59		11 59	11 59
Haslemere 4	a	23p24	23p49	00 12	00 53	08 06	09 11	09 28	10 11	10 28	11 06	11 26	12 06	12 06
	d	23p25	23p50	00 13	00 54	08 07	09 12	09 29	10 12	10 29	11 07	11 27	12 07	12 07
Liphook	d		23p55	.	00s59	08 12	09 17	.	10 17	.	11 12	.	12 12	12 12
Liss	d		00 01		01s05	08 18	09 23		10 23		11 18		12 18	12 18
Petersfield	d	23p36	00 06	00 24	01 10	08 23	09 28	09 40	10 28	10 40	11 23	11 38	12 23	12 23
Rowlands Castle	d		00 16		01s20	08 33	09 38		10 38		11 33		12 33	12 33
Havant	a	23p48	00 21	00 36	01 25	08 38	09 44	09 52	10 44	10 52	11 38	11 50	12 38	12 38
	d	23p49	00 22	00 37	01 26	08 39	09 45	09 53	10 45	10 53	11 39	11 51	12 39	12 39
Bedhampton	a	.	00 24	.	01s28	08 41	09 47	.	10 47	.	11 41	.	12 41	12 41
Hilsea	a		00 30		01s34									
Fratton	a	23p58	00 34	00 46	01s38	08 49	09 55	10 01	10 55	11 01	11 49	12 00	12 49	12 49
Portsmouth & Southsea	a	00 02	00 38	00 50	01 42	08 53	09 59	10 06	10 59	11 05	11 53	12 04	12 53	12 54
Portsmouth Harbour	a	00 07	.	00 55	.	08 57	10 04	10 11	11 04	11 11	11 58	12 09	12 58	12 59

		SW 1 ☕	SW 1		SW 1 ☕	SW 1	SW 1 ☕	SW 1	SW 1	SW 1	SW 1	SW 1	SW 1
London Waterloo 15 ⊖	d	11 30	12 00		19 30	20 00	20 30	21 00	21 30	22 00	22 30	23 00	23 30
Clapham Junction 10	d	11u39	12u09		19u39	20u09	20u39	21u09	21u39	22u09	22u39	23u09	23u39
Woking	a	12 01	12 31		20 01	20 31	21 01	21 31	22 01	22 31	23 01	23 31	00 01
	d	12 02	12 32		20 02	20 32	21 02	21 32	22 02	22 32	23 02	23 32	00 02
Worplesdon	d												
Guildford	a	12 10	12 40	and at	20 10	20 40	21 10	21 40	22 10	22 40	23 10	23 40	00 10
	d	12 12	12 42	the same	20 12	20 42	21 12	21 42	22 12	22 42	23 12	23 42	00 12
Farncombe	d	.	12 48		.	20 48	.	21 48	.	22 48	.	23 48	.
Godalming	d		12 51	minutes		20 51		21 51		22 51		23 51	
Milford (Surrey)	d	.	12 55		.	20 55	.	21 55	.	22 55	.	23 55	.
Witley	d		12 59	past		20 59		21 59		22 59		23 59	
Haslemere 4	a	12 26	13 06		20 26	21 06	21 26	22 06	22 26	23 06	23 26	00 06	00 26
	d	12 27	13 07	each	20 27	21 07	21 27	22 07	22 27	23 07	23 27	00 07	00 27
Liphook	d	.	13 12		.	21 12	.	22 12	.	23 12	.	00 12	.
Liss	d		13 18	hour until		21 18		22 18		23 18		00 18	
Petersfield	d	12 38	13 23		20 38	21 23	21 38	22 23	22 38	23 23	23 38	00 23	00 38
Rowlands Castle	d		13 33			21 33		22 33		23 33		00 33	
Havant	a	12 50	13 38		20 50	21 38	21 50	22 38	22 50	23 38	23 50	00 38	00 50
	d	12 51	13 39		20 51	21 39	21 51	22 39	22 51	23 39	23 51	00 39	00 51
Bedhampton	a	.	13 41		.	21 41	.	22 41	.	23 41	.	00 41	.
Hilsea	a												
Fratton	a	13 00	13 49		21 00	21 49	22 00	22 49	23 00	23 49	23 59	00 49	01 00
Portsmouth & Southsea	a	13 04	13 53		21 04	21 53	22 04	22 53	23 04	23 53	00 04	00 53	01 04
Portsmouth Harbour	a	13 11	13 58		21 09	21 58	22 11	22 58	23 09	23 58	00 09	00 58	01 09

For general notes see front of timetable
For details of catering facilities see
Directory of Train Operators

A From 13 September
B Until 6 September

b Previous night.
Stops to pick up only

Portsmouth, Haslemere and Guildford → London

Network diagram - see first page of Table 155

Miles	Station		SW	SW	SW	SW	SW	SW	SW	SW	SW	SW	SW	SW		SW	SW	SW	SW	SW	SW	SW	SW	SW	SW	SW
			MX	MO	MX	MO	MX																			
			1	1	1	1	1	1	1	1	1	1	1	1		1	1	1	1	1	1	1	1	1	1	1
								A	B	A	B	A	B	A		B										
												☕	☕					☕			☕			☕		
0	Portsmouth Harbour	d	22p18	22p32		22p48	23p18	04 25	04 30			05 14	05 19				05 50	06 15			06 42		06 55	07 13		07 29
¾	Portsmouth & Southsea	d	22p24	22p37		22p53	23p24	04 30	04 35			05 19	05 24				05 55	06 20			06 47		07 00	07 18		07 33
1¾	Fratton	d	22p28	22p41		22p57	23p28	04 34	04 39			05 23	05 28				05 59	06 24			06 51		07 04	07 22		07 37
4	Hilsea	d	22p32				23p32	04 38	04 43			05 27	05 32				06 03			06 42			07 08			07 41
7¼	Bedhampton	d	22p37			23p04	23p37	04 43	04 48			05 32	05 37				06 08			06 47			07 13			07 48
8	Havant	a	22p39	22p49		23p07	23p39	04 45	04 50			05 35	05 40				06 10	06 33		06 49	06 59		07 15	07 30		07 50
—		d	22p40	22p50		23p07	23p40	04 46	04 51			05 36	05 41				06 11	06 34		06 50	07 00	07 11	07 16	07 32		07 52
11¼	Rowlands Castle	d	22p46			23p13	23p46	04 52	04 57			05 41	05 46				06 16			06 56			07 22			07 57
19½	Petersfield	d	22p57	23p04		23p24	23p57	05 03	05 08			05 52	05 57				06 29	06 48		07 07	07 14	07 25	07 33	07 46		08 08
23	Liss	d	23p02			23p29	00 02	05 08	05 13			05 57	06 02				06 34			07 12	07 20		07 38			08 13
27¾	Liphook	d	23p09			23p36	00 09	05 15	05 20			06 04	06 09				06 41			07 19	07 27		07 45			08 20
31½	Haslemere 4	a	23p15	23p16		23p41	00 15	05 20	05 25			06 10	06 15				06 46	07 01		07 25	07 33	07 38	07 51	07 59	←	08 26
—		d	23p15	23p17		23p42	00 15	05 21	05 26	05 57	06 00	06 11	06 16	06 27		06 30	06 47	07 02	07 10	07 26	07 35	07 40	08 07	08 00	08 07	08 39
36	Witley	d	23p21		←	23p48	00 21	05 27	05 32	06 03	06 06			06 33		06 36			07 16			07 46	→		08 13	→
38¼	Milford (Surrey)	d	23p25		23p25	23p52	00 25	05 31	05 36	06 08	06 11			06 37		06 40			07 21			07 50			08 17	
40	Godalming	d	→		23p29	23p56	00 29	05 35	05 40	06 12	06 15			06 41		06 44	06 57		07 25	07 35	07 45	07 54			08 21	
41	Farncombe	d			23p32	23p59	00 32	05 38	05 43	06 15	06 18			06 44		06 47	07 00		07 28	07 38		07 57			08 25	
44¼	Guildford	a		23p31	23p37	00 04	00 37	05 48	05 48	06 23	06 23	06 29	06 29	06 52		06 52	07 05	07 15	07 32	07 43	07 52	08 02		08 13	08 30	
—		d		23p35	23p39	00 05		05 50	05 50	06 24	06 24	06 31	06 31	06 53		06 53	07 07	07 17	07 32	07 45	07 54	08 03		08 15	08 31	
47¾	Worplesdon	d			23p44			05 55	05 55	06 30	06 30			06 59		06 59			07 40	07 50				08 20	08 37	
50½	Woking	a		23p42	23p49	00 13		06 00	06 00	06 35	06 35	06 39	06 39	07 03		07 03	07 15	07 25		07 54		08 11		08 26	08 41	
—		d		23p45	23p56			06 01	06 01	06 37	06 37	06 41	06 41	07 05		07 05	07 17	07 26		07 56		08 12		08 27	08 43	
70½	Clapham Junction 10	a		00 04	00 21			06 20	06 20	06 58	06 58	07 02	07 02	07 24		07 24									09 03	
74½	London Waterloo 15 ⊖	a		00 14	00 30			06 29	06 29	07 08	07 08	07 12	07 12	07 36		07 36	07 45	07 54	08 11	08 24	08 32	08 41		08 55	09 13	

Station		SW	SW	SW		SW	SW	SW	SW	SW	SW	SW		SW	SW	SW	SW		SW		SW	SW	SW	SW	SW
		1	1	1		1	1	1	1	1	1	1		1	1	1	1		1		1	1	1	1	1
		☕		☕			☕		☕		☕			☕		☕			☕			☕		☕	
Portsmouth Harbour	d	07 45		08 15			08 45		09 15	09 19	09 45			10 15		10 45			14 15			14 45		15 15	
Portsmouth & Southsea	d	07 50		08 20		08 24	08 50		09 20	09 24	09 50			10 20	10 24	10 50			14 20		14 24	14 50		15 20	15 24
Fratton	d	07 54		08 24		08 28	08 54		09 24	09 28	09 54			10 24	10 28	10 54			14 24		14 28	14 54		15 24	15 28
Hilsea	d					08 32				09 32					10 32						14 32				15 32
Bedhampton	d					08 37				09 37					10 37						14 37				15 37
Havant	a	08 03		08 32		08 40	09 03		09 33	09 39	10 03			10 33	10 39	11 03		and at the same minutes past each hour until	14 33		14 39	15 03		15 33	15 39
	d	08 04		08 34		08 40	09 04		09 34	09 40	10 04			10 34	10 40	11 04			14 34		14 40	15 04		15 34	15 40
Rowlands Castle	d					08 46				09 46					10 46						14 46				15 46
Petersfield	d	08 18		08 48		08 57	09 18		09 48	09 57	10 18			10 48	10 57	11 18			14 48		14 57	15 18		15 48	15 57
Liss	d					09 02				10 02					11 02						15 02				16 02
Liphook	d					09 09				10 09					11 09						15 09				16 09
Haslemere 4	a	08 31	←	09 01		09 15	09 31		10 01	10 15	10 31			11 01	11 15	11 31			15 01		15 15	15 31		16 01	16 15
	d	08 32	08 39	09 02		09 15	09 32	09 39	10 02	10 15	10 32	10 39		11 02	11 15	11 32	11 39		15 02		15 15	15 32	15 37	16 02	16 15
Witley	d		08 45					09 45				10 45					11 45						15 43		
Milford (Surrey)	d		08 49					09 49				10 49					11 49						15 47		
Godalming	d		08 53			09 25		09 53		10 25		10 53			11 25		11 53				15 25		15 51		16 25
Farncombe	d		08 57			09 28		09 56		10 28		10 56			11 28		11 56				15 28		15 54		16 28
Guildford	a	08 46	09 02	09 15		09 32	09 45	10 01	10 15	10 32	10 46	11 01		11 15	11 32	11 45	12 01		15 15		15 32	15 45	15 59	16 15	16 32
	d	08 54	09 03	09 17		09 32	09 47	10 02	10 17	10 32	10 47	11 02		11 17	11 32	11 47	12 02		15 17		15 32	15 47	16 00	16 17	16 32
Worplesdon	d					09 40				10 40					11 40						15 40		16 06		16 40
Woking	a		09 11	09 27		09 44	09 59	10 11	10 25	10 44	10 57	11 11		11 25	11 44	11 57	12 11		15 25		15 44	15 57	16 11	16 25	16 44
	d		09 13	09 28		09 46	09 59	10 12	10 26	10 46	10 59	11 12		11 26	11 46	11 59	12 12		15 26		15 46	15 59	16 12	16 26	16 46
Clapham Junction 10	a		09 32			10 05		10 31		11 05		11 31			12 05		12 31				16 05		16 31		17 05
London Waterloo 15 ⊖	a	09 31	09 43	09 55		10 13	10 27	10 40	10 51	11 13	11 24	11 40		11 51	12 13	12 23	12 40		15 51		16 13	16 24	16 40	16 51	17 14

Station		SW	SW	SW	SW	SW	SW	SW	SW	SW		SW	SW	SW	SW	SW	SW	SW	SW	SW	SW	SW	SW	SW		
		1	1	1	1	1	1	1	1	1		1	1	1	1	1	1	1	1	1	1	1	1	1		
			☕	☕			☕	☕		☕		☕		☕												
Portsmouth Harbour	d		15 45	16 15			16 45	17 15	17 17	17 45		18 15		18 45		19 15		19 45	20 15	20 18	20 45	21 18	22 18	23 18		
Portsmouth & Southsea	d		15 50	16 20	16 24		16 50	17 20	17 24	17 50		18 20	18 24	18 50		19 20	19 24	19 50	20 20	20 24	20 50	21 24	22 24	23 24		
Fratton	d		15 54	16 24	16 28		16 54	17 24	17 28	17 54		18 24	18 28	18 54		19 24	19 28	19 54	20 24	20 28	20 54	21 28	22 28	23 28		
Hilsea	d				16 32				17 32				18 32				19 32			20 32		21 32	22 32	23 32		
Bedhampton	d				16 37				17 37				18 37				19 37			20 37		21 37	22 37	23 37		
Havant	a		16 03	16 33	16 39		17 03	17 33	17 39	18 03		18 32	18 39	19 03		19 33	19 39	20 03	20 33	20 39	21 03	21 39	22 39	23 39		
	d	15 54	16 04	16 34	16 40	16 56	17 04	17 34	17 40	18 04		18 34	18 40	19 04		19 34	19 40	20 04	20 34	20 40	21 04	21 40	22 40	23 40		
Rowlands Castle	d				16 46				17 46				18 46				19 46			20 46		21 46	22 46	23 46		
Petersfield	d	16b10	16 18	16 48	16 57	17 10	17 18	17 48	17 57	18 18		18 48	18 57	19 18		19 48	19 57	20 18	20 48	20 57	21 18	21 57	22 57	23 57		
Liss	d		16 23		17 02		17 23		18 02				19 02				20 02			21 02		22 02	23 02	00 02		
Liphook	d		16 30		17 09		17 30		18 09				19 09				20 09			21 09		22 09	23 09	00 09		
Haslemere 4	a	16 23	16 36	17 01	17 15	17 23	17 36	18 01	18 15	18 31		19 01	19 15	19 31		20 01	20 15	20 31	21 01	21 15	21 31	22 15	23 15	00 15		
	d	16 24	16 37	17 02	17 15	17 32	17 37	18 02	18 15	18 32		19 02	19 15	19 32	19 39	20 02	20 15	20 32	21 02	21 15	21 32	22 15	23 15	00 15		
Witley	d	16 30	16 43				17 43			18 38					19 45		20 21			21 21		22 21	23 21	00 21		
Milford (Surrey)	d	16 34	16 47				17 47			18 42					19 49		20 25			21 25		22 25	23 25	00 25		
Godalming	d	16 38	16 51		17 25		17 51		18 25	18 46		19 11	19 25		19 53		20 29			21 29		22 29	23 29	00 29		
Farncombe	d	16 41	16 54		17 28		17 54		18 28	18 49		19 14	19 28		19 56		20 32			21 32		22 32	23 32	00 32		
Guildford	a	16 46	16 59	17 15	17 32	17 45	17 59	18 15	18 32	18 54		19 19	19 32	19 47	20 01	20 15	20 37	20 45	21 16	21 37	21 45	22 37	23 37	00 37		
	d	16 47	17 00	17 17	17 32	17 47	18 00	18 17	18 32	18 55		19 21	19 32	19 47	20 02	20 17	20 39	20 47	21 17	21 39	21 47	22 39	23 39			
Worplesdon	d		17 06		17 40		18 06		18 40				19 40				20 44			21 44		22 44	23 44			
Woking	a	16 57	17 11	17 25	17 44	17 58	18 11		18 44	19 03		19 28	19 45	19 57	20 11	20 25	20 52	20 57	21 25	21 49	21 57	22 49	23 49			
	d	16 59	17 12	17 26	17 46	17 59	18 12		18 46	19 05		19 30	19 46	19 59	20 12	20 26	20 53	20 59	21 26	21 50	21 59	22 50	23 56			
Clapham Junction 10	a		17 31		18 05		18 31		19 05				20 05		20 31		21 12			22 09		23 09	00 21			
London Waterloo 15 ⊖	a	17 24	17 43	17 54	18 14	18 27	18 43	18 59	19 14	19 29		19 59	20 14	20 23	20 40	20 50	21 21	21 27	21 50	22 18	22 27	23 19	00 30			

For general notes see front of timetable
For details of catering facilities see Directory of Train Operators

- **A** From 28 September
- **B** Until 25 September
- **b** Arr. 1607

Saturdays

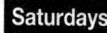

Portsmouth, Haslemere and Guildford → London

Network diagram - see first page of Table 155

		SW 1	SW 1	SW 1 A	SW 1 B	SW 1 A	SW 1 B	SW 1	SW 1	SW 1 (catering)	SW 1	SW 1 (catering)	SW 1	SW 1 (catering)	SW 1	SW 1 (catering)	SW 1	SW 1 (catering)	SW 1		SW 1 (catering)
Portsmouth Harbour	d	22p18	23p18	04 38	04 43	05 14	05 19		06 19	06 45		07 15		07 45		08 15		08 45			16 15
Portsmouth & Southsea	d	22p24	23p24	04 43	04 48	05 19	05 24		06 24	06 50		07 20	07 24	07 50		08 20	08 24	08 50			16 20
Fratton	d	22p28	23p28	04 47	04 52	05 23	05 28		06 28	06 54		07 24	07 28	07 54		08 24	08 28	08 54			16 24
Hilsea	d	22p32	23p32	04 51	04 56	05 27	05 32		06 32				07 32				08 32				
Bedhampton	d	22p37	23p37	04 56	05 01	05 32	05 37		06 37				07 37				08 37				
Havant	a	22p39	23p39	04 58	05 03	05 34	05 39		06 39	07 03		07 33	07 39	08 03		08 33	08 39	09 03		and at	16 33
	d	22p40	23p40	04 59	05 04	05 35	05 40		06 40	07 04		07 34	07 40	08 04		08 34	08 40	09 04		the same	16 34
Rowlands Castle	d	22p46	23p46	05 04	05 09	05 41	05 46		06 46				07 46				08 46				
Petersfield	d	22p57	23p57	05 15	05 20	05 52	05 57		06 57	07 18		07 48	07 57	08 18		08 48	08 57	09 18		minutes	16 48
Liss	d	23p02	00 02	05 20	05 25	05 57	06 02		07 02				08 02				09 02				
Liphook	d	23p09	00 09	05 27	05 32	06 04	06 09		07 09				08 09				09 09			past	
Haslemere 4	a	23p15	00 15	05 33	05 38	06 10	06 15		07 15	07 31		08 01	08 15	08 31		09 01	09 15	09 31			17 01
	d	23p15	00 15	05 34	05 39	06 10	06 15	06 39	07 15	07 32	07 39	08 02	08 15	08 32	08 39	09 02	09 15	09 32	09 39	each	17 02
Witley	d	23p21	00 21	05 40	05 45			06 45			07 45				08 45				09 45	hour until	
Milford (Surrey)	d	23p25	00 25	05 44	05 49			06 49			07 49				08 49				09 49		
Godalming	d	23p29	00 29	05 48	05 53	06 20	06 25	06 53	07 25		07 53		08 25		08 53		09 25		09 53		
Farncombe	d	23p32	00 32	05 51	05 56	06 23	06 28	06 56	07 28		07 56		08 28		08 56		09 28		09 56		
Guildford	a	23p37	00 37	06 01	06 01	06 32	06 32	07 01	07 32	07 45	08 01	08 15	08 32	08 45	09 01	09 15	09 32	09 45	10 01		17 15
	d	23p39		06 02	06 02	06 32	06 32	07 02	07 32	07 47	08 02	08 17	08 32	08 47	09 02	09 17	09 32	09 47	10 02		17 17
Worplesdon	d	23p44				06 40	06 40		07 40				08 40				09 40				
Woking	a	23p49		06 11	06 11	06 44	06 44	07 11	07 44	07 57	08 12	08 26	08 44	08 57	09 11	09 25	09 44	09 57	10 11		17 25
	d	23p56		06 13	06 13	06 46	06 46	07 12	07 46	07 59	08 14	08 27	08 46	08 59	09 12	09 26	09 46	09 59	10 12		17 26
Clapham Junction 10	a	00 21		06 32	06 32	07 05	07 05	07 31	08 05		08 33		09 05		09 31		10 05		10 31		
London Waterloo 15	⊖ a	00 30		06 40	06 40	07 13	07 13	07 40	08 13	08 23	08 42	08 51	09 13	09 23	09 40	09 51	10 13	10 23	10 40		17 51

		SW 1	SW 1 (catering)	SW 1	SW 1	SW 1	SW 1 (catering)	SW 1	SW 1	SW 1	SW 1	SW 1	SW 1	SW 1	SW 1	SW 1	SW 1	SW 1	SW 1	SW 1	SW 1
Portsmouth Harbour	d		16 45			17 17	17 45		18 15		18 45		19 15		19 45	20 15		20 45	21 18	22 18	23 18
Portsmouth & Southsea	d	16 24	16 50		17 10	17 24	17 50		18 20	18 24	18 50		19 20	19 24	19 50	20 20	20 24	20 50	21 24	22 24	23 24
Fratton	d	16 28	16 54		17 14	17 28	17 54		18 24	18 28	18 54		19 24	19 28	19 54	20 24	20 28	20 54	21 28	22 28	23 28
Hilsea	d	16 32			17 18	17 32				18 32				19 32			20 32		21 32	22 32	23 32
Bedhampton	d	16 37			17 23	17 37				18 37				19 37			20 37		21 37	22 37	23 37
Havant	a	16 39	17 03		17 25	17 39	18 03		18 33	18 39	19 03		19 33	19 39	20 03	20 33	20 39	21 03	21 39	22 39	23 39
	d	16 40	17 04		17 26	17 40	18 04		18 34	18 40	19 04		19 34	19 40	20 04	20 34	20 40	21 04	21 40	22 40	23 40
Rowlands Castle	d	16 46			17 32	17 46				18 46				19 46			20 46		21 46	22 46	23 46
Petersfield	d	16 57	17 18		17 43	17 57	18 18		18 48	18 57	19 18		19 48	19 57	20 18	20 48	20 57	21 18	21 57	22 57	23 57
Liss	d	17 02			17 48	18 02				19 02				20 02			21 02		22 02	23 02	00 02
Liphook	d	17 09			17 55	18 09				19 09				20 09			21 09		22 09	23 09	00 09
Haslemere 4	a	17 15	17 31		18 01	18 15	18 31		19 01	19 15	19 31		20 01	20 15	20 31	21 01	21 15	21 31	22 15	23 15	00 15
	d	17 15	17 32	17 39	18 02	18 15	18 32	18 39	19 02	19 15	19 32	19 39	20 02	20 15	20 32	21 02	21 15	21 32	22 15	23 15	00 15
Witley	d			17 45				18 45				19 45		20 21			21 21		22 21	23 21	00 21
Milford (Surrey)	d			17 49				18 49				19 49		20 25			21 25		22 25	23 25	00 25
Godalming	d	17 25		17 53		18 25		18 53		19 25		19 53		20 29			21 29		22 29	23 29	00 29
Farncombe	d	17 28		17 56		18 28		18 56		19 28		19 56		20 32			21 32		22 32	23 32	00 32
Guildford	a	17 32	17 45	18 01	18 15	18 32	18 45	19 01	19 15	19 32	19 45	20 01	20 15	20 37	20 45	21 15	21 37	21 47	22 37	23 37	00 37
	d	17 32	17 47	18 02	18 17	18 32	18 47	19 02	19 17	19 32	19 47	20 02	20 17	20 39	20 47	21 17	21 39	21 49	22 39	23 39	
Worplesdon	d	17 40				18 40				19 40				20 44			21 44		22 44	23 44	
Woking	a	17 44	17 57	18 11	18 25	18 44	18 57	19 11	19 25	19 44	19 57	20 11	20 25	20 52	20 57	21 25	21 49	21 57	22 49	23 49	
	d	17 46	17 59	18 12	18 26	18 46	18 59	19 12	19 26	19 46	19 59	20 12	20 26	20 53	20 59	21 26	21 50	21 59	22 50	23 56	
Clapham Junction 10	a	18 05		18 31		19 05		19 31		20 05		20 31		21 12			22 09		23 09	00 20	
London Waterloo 15	⊖ a	18 13	18 23	18 40	18 51	19 13	19 23	19 40	19 51	20 13	20 23	20 40	20 50	21 21	21 27	21 50	22 18	22 24	23 18	00 32	

Sundays

		SW 1	SW 1	SW 1 C	SW 1 D	SW 1 C	SW 1 D	SW 1	SW 1 C	SW 1 D	SW 1	SW 1 (catering)	SW 1	SW 1 (catering)	SW 1		SW 1	SW 1
Portsmouth Harbour	d	22p18	23p18	06 43	06 48	07 29	07 32	07 48	08 29	08 32	08 48	09 32	09 48	10 32	10 48		22 32	22 48
Portsmouth & Southsea	d	22p24	23p24	06 48	06 53	07 34	07 37	07 53	08 34	08 37	08 53	09 37	09 53	10 37	10 53		22 37	22 53
Fratton	d	22p28	23p28	06 52	06 57	07 38	07 41	07 57	08 38	08 41	08 57	09 41	09 57	10 41	10 57		22 41	22 57
Hilsea	d	22p32	23p32															
Bedhampton	d	22p37	23p37	06 59	07 04			08 04			09 04		10 04		11 04			23 04
Havant	a	22p39	23p39	07 02	07 07	07 46	07 49	08 07	08 46	08 49	09 07	09 49	10 06	10 49	11 06	and at	22 49	23 07
	d	22p40	23p40	07 02	07 07	07 47	07 50	08 07	08 47	08 50	09 07	09 50	10 07	10 50	11 07	the same	22 50	23 07
Rowlands Castle	d	22p46	23p46	07 08	07 13			08 13			09 13		10 13		11 13			23 13
Petersfield	d	22p57	23p57	07 19	07 24	08 01	08 04	08 24	09 01	09 04	09 24	10 04	10 24	11 04	11 24	minutes	23 04	23 24
Liss	d	23p02	00 02	07 24	07 29			08 29			09 29		10 29		11 29			23 29
Liphook	d	23p09	00 09	07 31	07 36			08 36			09 36		10 36		11 36	past		23 36
Haslemere 4	a	23p15	00 15	07 36	07 41	08 13	08 16	08 41	09 13	09 16	09 41	10 16	10 41	11 16	11 41		23 16	23 41
	d	23p15	00 15	07 37	07 42	08 14	08 17	08 42	09 14	09 17	09 42	10 17	10 42	11 17	11 42	each	23 17	23 42
Witley	d	23p21	00 21	07 43	07 48			08 48			09 48		10 48		11 48	hour until		23 48
Milford (Surrey)	d	23p25	00 25	07 47	07 52			08 52			09 52		10 52		11 52			23 52
Godalming	d	23p29	00 29	07 51	07 56			08 56			09 56		10 56		11 56			23 56
Farncombe	d	23p32	00 32	07 54	07 59			08 59			09 59		10 59		11 59			23 59
Guildford	a	23p37	00 37	08 04	08 04	08 31	08 31	09 04	09 31	09 31	10 04	10 31	11 04	11 31	12 04		23 31	00 04
	d	23p39		08 05	08 05	08 35	08 35	09 05	09 35	09 35	10 05	10 35	11 05	11 35	12 05		23 35	00 05
Worplesdon	d	23p44																
Woking	a	23p49		08 13	08 13	08 42	08 42	09 15	09 42	09 42	10 15	10 42	11 13	11 42	12 13		23 42	00 13
	d	23p56		08 15	08 15	08 45	08 45	09 15	09 45	09 45	10 15	10 45	11 15	11 45	12 15		23 45	
Clapham Junction 10	a	00 20		08 37	08 37	09 06	09 06	09 35	10 06	10 06	10 35	11 04	11 34	12 04	12 34		00 04	
London Waterloo 15	⊖ a	00 32		08 49	08 49	09 19	09 19	09 49	10 21	10 21	10 49	11 19	11 49	12 19	12 49		00 14	

For general notes see front of timetable
For details of catering facilities see Directory of Train Operators

A From 3 October
B Until 26 September
C From 27 September
D Until 20 September

Petersfield—Waterlooville
Bus Service

		SW	SW	SW	SW	SW	SW	SW	SW	SW	SW	SW	SW	SW	SW	SW
London Waterloo 15 ⊖	156 d	05 00	06 15	07 30	08 30	09 30	10 30	11 30	12 30	13 30	14 30	15 30	16 30	17 30	18 30	19 30
Woking	156 d	05 51	06 43	07 55	08 55	09 55	10 55	11 55	12 55	13 55	14 55	15 55	16 55	17 56	18 58	19 55
Guildford	156 d	06 00	06 55	08 04	09 04	10 04	11 04	12 04	13 04	14 04	15 04	16 04	17 04	18 08	19 08	20 04
Haslemere	156 d	06 25	07 20	08 25	09 25	10 23	11 21	12 21	13 21	14 21	15 21	16 21	17 21	18 26	19 26	20 22
Petersfield	d	06 42	07 40	08 45	09 45	10 42	11 42	12 42	13 42	14 42	15 42	16 42	17 42	18 42	19 45	20 45
Horndean Precinct	d	06 57	07 55	09 00	10 00	10 57	11 57	12 57	13 57	14 57	15 57	16 57	17 57	18 57	20 00	21 00
Cowplain (Shops)	d	07 01	07 59	09 04	10 04	11 01	12 01	13 01	14 01	15 01	16 01	17 01	18 01	19 01	20 04	21 04
Waterlooville (Precinct)	a	07 06	08 04	09 09	10 09	11 06	12 06	13 06	14 06	15 06	16 06	17 06	18 06	19 06	20 09	21 09

Saturdays

Network Diagram - see first page of Table 155

		SW	SW	SW	SW	SW	SW	SW	SW	SW	SW	SW	SW	SW	SW
London Waterloo 15 ⊖	156 d	05 20	07 30	08 30	09 30	10 30	11 30	12 30	13 30	14 30	15 30	16 30	17 30	18 30	19 30
Woking	156 d	06 13	07 55	08 55	09 55	10 55	11 55	12 55	13 55	14 55	15 55	16 55	17 55	18 55	19 55
Guildford	156 d	06 25	08 04	09 04	10 04	11 04	12 04	13 04	14 04	15 04	16 04	17 04	18 04	19 04	20 04
Haslemere	156 d	06 45	08 21	09 21	10 21	11 21	12 21	13 21	14 21	15 21	16 21	17 21	18 21	19 21	20 21
Petersfield	d	07 42	08 45	09 45	10 42	11 42	12 42	13 42	14 42	15 42	16 42	17 42	18 42	19 42	20 42
Horndean Precinct	d	07 57	09 00	10 00	10 57	11 57	12 57	13 57	14 57	15 57	16 57	17 57	18 57	19 57	20 57
Cowplain (Shops)	d	08 01	09 04	10 04	11 01	12 01	13 01	14 01	15 01	16 01	17 01	18 01	19 01	20 01	21 01
Waterlooville (Precinct)	a	08 06	09 09	10 09	11 06	12 06	13 06	14 06	15 06	16 06	17 06	18 06	19 06	20 06	21 06

Mondays to Fridays

		SW	SW	SW	SW	SW	SW	SW	SW	SW	SW	SW	SW	SW	SW	SW
Waterlooville (Precinct)	d	06 15	07 10	08 05	09 15	10 15	11 15	12 15	13 15	14 15	15 15	16 15	17 15	18 15	19 15	20 15
Cowplain (Shops)	d	06 20	07 15	08 10	09 20	10 20	11 20	12 20	13 20	14 20	15 20	16 20	17 20	18 20	19 20	20 20
Horndean Precinct	d	06 24	07 19	08 14	09 24	10 24	11 24	12 24	13 24	14 24	15 24	16 24	17 24	18 24	19 24	20 24
Petersfield	a	06 39	07 34	08 39	09 39	10 39	11 39	12 39	13 39	14 39	15 39	16 39	17 39	18 39	19 39	20 39
Haslemere	156 a	07 01	07 59	09 01	10 01	11 01	12 01	13 01	14 01	15 01	16 01	17 01	18 01	19 01	20 01	21 01
Guildford	156 a	07 15	08 13	09 15	10 15	11 15	12 15	13 15	14 15	15 15	16 15	17 15	18 15	19 19	20 15	21 16
Woking	156 a	07 25	08 26	09 27	10 25	11 25	12 25	13 25	14 25	15 25	16 25	17 25	18 44	19 28	20 25	21 25
London Waterloo 15 ⊖	156 a	07 54	08 55	09 55	10 51	11 51	12 51	13 51	14 51	15 51	16 51	17 52	18 59	19 59	20 50	21 50

Saturdays

		SW	SW	SW	SW	SW	SW	SW	SW	SW	SW	SW	SW	SW	SW
Waterlooville (Precinct)	d	07 15	08 15	09 15	10 15	11 15	12 15	13 15	14 15	15 15	16 15	17 15	18 15	19 15	20 15
Cowplain (Shops)	d	07 20	08 20	09 20	10 20	11 20	12 20	13 20	14 20	15 20	16 20	17 20	18 20	19 20	20 20
Horndean Precinct	d	07 24	08 24	09 24	10 24	11 24	12 24	13 24	14 24	15 24	16 24	17 24	18 24	19 24	20 24
Petersfield	a	07 39	08 39	09 39	10 39	11 39	12 39	13 39	14 39	15 39	16 39	17 39	18 39	19 39	20 39
Haslemere	156 a	08 01	09 01	10 01	11 01	12 01	13 01	14 01	15 01	16 01	17 01	18 01	19 01	20 01	21 01
Guildford	156 a	08 16	09 16	10 15	11 15	12 15	13 15	14 15	15 15	16 15	17 15	18 15	19 15	20 15	21 15
Woking	156 a	08 26	09 26	10 25	11 25	12 25	13 25	14 25	15 25	16 25	17 25	18 25	19 25	20 25	21 25
London Waterloo 15 ⊖	156 a	08 51	09 52	10 51	11 51	12 52	13 31	14 51	15 51	16 51	17 51	18 51	19 51	20 50	21 50

For general notes see front of timetable
For details of catering facilities see
Directory of Train Operators

No Sunday Service

Havant → Portsmouth Harbour
(Complete service)

Network Diagram - see first page of Table 155

		SW MX 1	SW MO 1	SW MO 1	SW MX 1	SW MX 1	SW MX 1	SW MO 1	SW MO 1	SW MX 1	SW 1	SN 1	SN 1	SW 1	SN 1	SW 1	SN 1	SW 1	SW 1	SW 1	GW	SW 1	SW 1
Havant	d	23p49	23p51			00 22	00 37	00 39	00 51	01 26	04 40	05 21	05 39	06 02	06 13		06 53		06 58				07 28
Bedhampton	d					00 25		00 41		01s29	04 43			06 05	06 15		06 56		07 01				07 31
Hilsea	d			23p59	00 04	00 30				01s34	04 48			06 10	06 20	06 33	07 01	07 05	07 07	07 13		07 35	07 37
Fratton	d	23p59	00 01	00 04	00 08	00 34	00 47	00 50	01 01	01s38	04 52	05 30	05 48	06 15	06 25	06 38	07 05	07 09	07 12	07 17	07 35	07 39	07 42
Portsmouth & Southsea	a	00 02	00 04	00 08	00 11	00 38	00 50	00 53	01 04	01 42	04 55	05 33	05 51	06 18	06 28	06 44	07 08	07 12	07 16	07 22	07 38	07 42	07 46
	d	00 03	00 05	00 09	00 13		00 51	00 54	01 05		04 56	05 33	05 51	06 19	06 28	06 45	07 09	07 13	07 17		07 39	07 43	
Portsmouth Harbour	a	00 07	00 09	00 13	00 16		00 55	00 58	01 09		04 59	05 37	05 55	06 22	06 32	06 49	07 12	07 17	07 20		07 45	07 48	

		SN 1	SN 1	SW 1	SW 1	SN 1	SW 1	GW ◇	SN 1	SW 1	SW 1	SN 1	SW 1 ☕	SW 1	SN 1	SW 1	SW 1	SW 1	GW ◇ 🍴	SW 1	SN 1	SN 1	SW 1 ☕
Havant	d	07 35	07 41	07 52		07 58			08 22	08 27		08 44	08 50		09 01	09 05	09 20			09 30	09 33	09 46	09 50
Bedhampton	d	07 37		07 55		08 00			08 25	08 30						09 08				09 33	09 36		
Hilsea	d	07 42		08 00	08 03	08 05	08 09		08 30	08 35	08 45			09 05		09 13		09 33		09 38	09 42		
Fratton	d	07 47	07 50	08 04	08 07	08 10	08 13	08 21	08 34	08 40	08 49	08 53	08 59	09 10	09 13	09 17	09 29	09 38	09 41	09 43	09 47	09 55	09 59
Portsmouth & Southsea	a	07 50	07 53	08 07	08 11	08 15	08 18	08 24	08 37	08 43	08 52	08 56	09 02	09 13	09 17	09 20	09 32	09 42	09 45	09 46	09 50	09 58	10 02
	d		07 53	08 09	08 13	08 16	08 20	08 25	08 38	08 45	08 54	08 57	09 04	09 14	09 18	09 22	09 34		09 45			09 58	10 04
Portsmouth Harbour	a		07 58	08 12	08 16	08 19	08 23	08 30	08 41	08 48	08 58	09 00	09 07	09 18	09 21	09 26	09 37		09 54			10 02	10 07

		SW 1	SN 1	SW 1 ☕	SW 1	SW 1	GW ◇ 🍴	SN 1	SN 1	SW 1 ☕	SW 1	SN 1	SW 1 ☕	SW 1	SW 1	GW ◇ 🍴	SN 1	SN 1	SW 1 ☕	SW 1	SN 1	SW 1 ☕	SW 1
Havant	d		10 07	10 16		10 27		10 32	10 46	10 50		11 05	11 16		11 27		11 32	11 46	11 50		12 05	12 16	
Bedhampton	d					10 30		10 34							11 30		11 34						
Hilsea	d	10 03			10 33	10 36		10 42			11 03			11 33	11 36		11 42			12 03			12 33
Fratton	d	10 08	10 16	10 25	10 37	10 40	10 41	10 47	10 55	10 59	11 08	11 14	11 25	11 37	11 40	11 41	11 47	11 55	11 59	12 08	12 14	12 25	12 37
Portsmouth & Southsea	a	10 11	10 19	10 28	10 42	10 44	10 45	10 50	10 58	11 02	11 11	11 17	11 28	11 42	11 44	11 45	11 50	11 58	12 02	12 11	12 17	12 28	12 42
	d	10 12	10 20	10 29			10 45		10 58	11 04	11 12	11 17	11 29			11 45		11 58	12 04	12 12	12 17	12 29	
Portsmouth Harbour	a	10 18	10 23	10 33			10 54		11 02	11 07	11 18	11 21	11 33			11 54		12 02	12 07	12 18	12 21	12 33	

		SW 1	GW ◇ 🍴	SN 1	SN 1	SW 1 ☕	SW 1	SN 1	SW 1 ☕	SW 1	SW 1	GW ◇ 🍴	SN 1	SN 1	SW 1 ☕	SW 1	SN 1	SW 1 ☕	SW 1	SW 1	GW ◇ 🍴	SN 1	SN 1
Havant	d	12 27		12 32	12 46	12 50		13 05	13 16		13 27		13 32	13 46	13 50		14 05	14 16		14 27		14 32	14 47
Bedhampton	d	12 30		12 34							13 30		13 34							14 30		14 34	
Hilsea	d	12 36		12 42			13 03			13 33	13 36		13 42			14 03			14 33	14 36		14 42	
Fratton	d	12 40	12 41	12 47	12 55	12 59	13 08	13 14	13 25	13 37	13 40	13 41	13 47	13 55	13 59	14 08	14 14	14 25	14 37	14 40	14 41	14 47	14 56
Portsmouth & Southsea	a	12 44	12 45	12 50	12 58	13 02	13 11	13 17	13 28	13 42	13 44	13 45	13 50	13 58	14 02	14 11	14 17	14 28	14 42	14 44	14 45	14 50	14 59
	d		12 45		12 58	13 04	13 12	13 17	13 29			13 45		13 58	14 04	14 12	14 17	14 29			14 45		14 59
Portsmouth Harbour	a		12 54		13 02	13 07	13 18	13 21	13 33			13 54		14 02	14 07	14 18	14 21	14 33			14 54		15 04

		SW 1 ☕	SW 1	SN 1	SW 1 ☕	SW 1	SW 1	GW ◇ 🍴	SN 1	SN 1	SW 1 ☕	SW 1	SN 1	SN 1	SW 1 ☕	SW 1	SW 1	GW ◇ 🍴	SN 1	SN 1	SW 1 ☕	SW 1	SN 1
Havant	d	14 50		15 05	15 16		15 27		15 32	15 46	15 50		16 02	16 09	16 16		16 27		16 32	16 46	16 50		17 00
Bedhampton	d						15 30		15 34				16 04				16 30		16 34				17 02
Hilsea	d		15 03			15 33	15 36		15 42			16 03				16 33	16 36		16 42			17 03	17 07
Fratton	d	14 59	15 08	15 14	15 25	15 37	15 40	15 41	15 47	15 55	15 59	16 08	16 12	16 18	16 25	16 37	16 40	16 41	16 47	16 55	16 59	17 08	17 12
Portsmouth & Southsea	a	15 02	15 11	15 17	15 28	15 42	15 44	15 45	15 50	15 58	16 02	16 11	16 15	16 21	16 28	16 40	16 44	16 45	16 50	16 58	17 02	17 11	17 16
	d	15 04	15 12	15 17	15 29			15 45		15 58	16 04	16 12	16 16	16 22	16 29	16 41	16 45	16 45		16 58	17 04	17 12	17 16
Portsmouth Harbour	a	15 07	15 18	15 21	15 33			15 54		16 02	16 07	16 18	16 21	16 25	16 33	16 44	16 49	16 54		17 02	17 07	17 18	17 20

		SW 1	SN 1	SW 1 ☕	SW 1	SW 1	SW 1	GW ◇ 🍴	SN 1	SW 1 ☕	SN 1	SW 1	SW 1	SN 1	SW 1 ☕	SW 1	SW 1	SW 1	SN 1	GW ◇ 🍴	SW 1 ☕	SN 1	SW 1
Havant	d	17 04	17 09	17 16			17 27		17 32	17 50	17 54		18 04	18 13	18 19			18 30	18 34		18 51	18 54	
Bedhampton	d	17 06					17 30		17 34		17 56		18 07					18 33	18 36			18 57	
Hilsea	d	17 11				17 33	17 36		17 42		18 01	18 03	18 12			18 33		18 39	18 41			19 02	19 05
Fratton	d	17 16	17 19	17 25	17 27	17 37	17 40	17 41	17 47	17 59	18 06	18 09	18 17	18 22	18 29	18 37	18 40	18 43	18 46	18 48	19 00	19 06	19 09
Portsmouth & Southsea	a	17 20	17 22	17 28	17 33	17 42	17 44	17 45	17 50	18 02	18 09	18 11	18 20	18 25	18 32	18 42	18 43	18 46	18 49	18 52	19 03	19 09	19 12
	d	17 21		17 30	17 34			17 45		18 04	18 09	18 13	18 22	18 26	18 33		18 45			18 52	19 05		19 14
Portsmouth Harbour	a	17 25		17 35	17 38			17 54		18 09	18 15	18 20	18 28	18 31	18 39		18 51			18 58	19 10		19 20

		SW 1	SN 1	SW 1 ☕	SW 1	SW 1	GW ◇ 🍴	SN 1	SW 1	SN 1	SW 1 ☕	SW 1	SN 1	SW 1 ☕	SW 1	GW ◇ 🍴	SW 1	SW 1 ☕	SN 1	SW 1	SN 1	SW 1 ☕	SW 1
Havant	d	19 03	19 08	19 17				19 33	19 41	19 46	19 51		20 07	20 18			20 29	20 49	20 52		21 10	21 19	
Bedhampton	d	19 06						19 35	19 44								20 32						
Hilsea	d	19 11			19 28	19 33		19 43	19 49			20 02			20 33		20 37			21 03			21 33
Fratton	d	19a15	19 18	19 26	19 33	19 37	19 41	19 47	19a55	19 57	20 00	20b13	20 16	20 29	20 37	20 41	20 41	20 58	21 02	21 08	21 19	21 29	21 37
Portsmouth & Southsea	a		19 21	19 29	19 36	19 42	19 45	19 50		20 01	20 03	20 16	20 20	20 32	20 42	20 45	20 44	21 01	21 06	21 11	21 23	21 32	21 42
	d		19 21	19 31	19 38		19 45			20 01	20 05	20 17		20 34		20 45	20 46	21 03		21 13	21 23	21 33	
Portsmouth Harbour	a		19 25	19 36	19 43		19 54			20 07	20 10	20 23		20 37		20 54	20 52	21 06		21 16	21 27	21 37	

For general notes see front of timetable
For details of catering facilities see
Directory of Train Operators

b Arr. 2006

Table 157 **Mondays to Fridays**

Havant → Portsmouth Harbour
(Complete service)

Network Diagram - see first page of Table 155

		GW	SW	SW	SN	SW	SN	SW		SW	SW	SN	GW	SW	SW	SN		SW	SW	SW	GW	SW	SN	SW	
		◇	1	1	1	1	1	1		1	1	1	◇	1	1	1		1	1	1	◇	1	1	1	
		trolley		buffet	trolley			buffet																	
Havant	d	...	21 31	21 46	21 49	...	22 10	22 19	...	...	22 31	22 43	...	22 49	22 59	23 11	...	23 19	...	...	...	23 31	23 34	23 49	...
Bedhampton	d	.	21 34	.	.	.	.	.	.	.	22 34	.	.	.	23a01	.	.	.	.	.	.	23 34	.	.	.
Hilsea	d	...	21 41	...	...	22 03	...	...	...	22 33	22 39	...	...	...	...	...	...	...	23 24	23 33	...	23 39	...	...	...
Fratton	d	21 42	21 45	21 55	21 58	22 08	22 19	22 29	.	22 37	22 44	22 52	22 56	23 00	...	23 20	.	23 29	23 33	23 37	23 40	23 44	23 47	23 59	.
Portsmouth & Southsea	a	21 45	21 48	21 58	22 01	22 11	22 22	22 32	...	22 42	22 47	22 55	22 59	23 04	...	23 23	...	23 32	23 36	23 40	23 44	23 47	23 51	00 02	...
	d	21 46	.	21 59	22 02	22 13	22 22	22 33	.	.	.	22 56	22 59	23 05	.	23 24	.	23 33	23 36	.	23 44	.	.	00 03	.
Portsmouth Harbour	a	21 52	...	22 02	22 05	22 16	22 26	22 37	...	...	...	22 59	23 04	23 08	...	23 27	...	23 37	23 40	...	23 53	...	...	00 07	...

Saturdays

		SW	SW	SW	SW	SW	SW	SN	SN	SN		SW	SW	SN	SN	SW	SN	SW	SW	SN		SN	SW	SN	SW	SW
		1	1	1	1	1	1	1	1	1		1	1	1	1	1	1	1	1	1		1	1	1	1	1
Havant	d	23p49	...	00 22	00 37	01 26	04 40	05 34	05 49	05 57	...	06 01	...	06 32	06 46	...	07 04	07 20	...	07 32	...	07 46	...	08 04	08 17	...
Bedhampton	d	.	.	00 25	.	01s29	04 43	.	.	.	.	06 04	.	06 34	.	.	.	07 22	.	07 34	.	.	.	.	08 20	.
Hilsea	d	...	00 04	00 30	...	01s34	04 48	...	...	...	...	06 09	06 33	06 42	...	07 03	...	07 27	07 33	07 42	...	...	08 03	...	08 25	08 33
Fratton	d	23p59	00 08	00 34	00 47	01s38	04 52	05 43	05 58	06 06	.	06 14	06 37	06 47	06 55	07 08	07 13	07 32	07 37	07 47	.	07 55	08 08	08 13	08 29	08 37
Portsmouth & Southsea	a	00 02	00 11	00 38	00 50	01 42	04 55	05 46	06 01	06 09	...	06 17	06 42	06 50	06 58	07 11	07 16	07 35	07 42	07 50	...	07 58	08 11	08 16	08 32	08 42
	d	00 03	00 13	.	00 51	.	04 57	.	06 01	06 09	.	06 18	.	.	06 58	07 12	07 16	07 36	.	.	.	07 59	08 12	08 16	08 34	.
Portsmouth Harbour	a	00 07	00 16	...	00 55	...	05 00	...	06 05	06 16	...	06 22	...	...	07 02	07 16	07 20	07 40	...	...	...	08 02	08 18	08 20	08 37	...

		GW	SN	SN	SW	SW	SN		SW	SW	SW	GW	SN	SN	SW	SW	SN		SW	SW	SW	GW	SN	SN	SW	SW
		◇	1	1	1	1	1		1	1	1	◇	1	1	1	1	1		1	1	1	◇	1	1	1	1
																			buffet			trolley			buffet	
Havant	d	...	08 32	08 46	08 50	...	09 04	...	09 16	...	09 27	...	09 32	09 46	09 50	...	10 07	...	10 16	...	10 27	...	10 32	10 46	10 50	...
Bedhampton	d	.	08 34	.	.	.	.	.	.	.	09 30	.	09 34	.	.	.	.	.	.	.	10 30	.	10 34	.	.	.
Hilsea	d	...	08 42	...	...	09 03	...	...	...	09 33	09 36	...	09 42	...	...	10 03	...	...	...	10 33	10 36	...	10 43	...	...	11 03
Fratton	d	08 42	08 47	08 55	08 59	09 08	09 13	.	09 25	09 37	09 40	09 42	09 47	09 55	09 59	10 08	10 16	.	10 25	10 37	10 40	10 43	10 47	10 55	10 59	11 08
Portsmouth & Southsea	a	08 46	08 50	08 58	09 02	09 11	09 16	...	09 28	09 42	09 44	09 46	09 50	09 58	10 02	10 11	10 19	...	10 28	10 42	10 44	10 46	10 50	10 58	11 02	11 11
	d	08 46	.	08 59	09 04	09 12	09 16	.	09 29	.	.	09 46	.	09 58	10 04	10 12	10 20	.	10 29	.	.	10 46	.	10 58	11 04	11 12
Portsmouth Harbour	a	08 52	...	09 02	09 07	09 18	09 20	...	09 33	...	...	09 52	...	10 02	10 07	10 18	10 23	...	10 33	...	...	10 53	...	11 02	11 07	11 18

		SN	SW	SW		SW	GW	SN	SN	SW	SW	SN	SW	SW		SW	GW	SN	SN	SW	SW	SN	SW	SW		SW
		1	1	1		1	◇	1	1	1	1	1	1	1		1	◇	1	1	1	1	1	1	1		1
			buffet				trolley			buffet			buffet				trolley			buffet			buffet			
Havant	d	11 05	11 16	...	...	11 27	...	11 32	11 46	11 50	...	12 05	12 16	...	...	12 27	...	12 32	12 46	12 50	...	13 05	13 16	...	...	13 27
Bedhampton	d	.	.	.	.	11 30	.	11 34	.	.	.	.	.	.	.	12 30	.	12 34	.	.	.	.	.	.	.	13 30
Hilsea	d	...	...	11 33	...	11 36	...	11 42	...	...	12 03	...	...	12 33	...	12 36	...	12 42	...	...	13 03	...	...	13 33	...	13 36
Fratton	d	11 14	11 25	11 37	.	11 40	11 42	11 47	11 55	11 59	12 08	12 14	12 25	12 37	.	12 40	12 42	12 47	12 55	12 59	13 08	13 14	13 25	13 37	.	13 40
Portsmouth & Southsea	a	11 17	11 28	11 42	...	11 44	11 46	11 50	11 58	12 02	12 11	12 17	12 28	12 42	...	12 44	12 46	12 50	12 58	13 02	13 11	13 17	13 28	13 42	...	13 44
	d	11 17	11 29	.	.	.	11 46	.	11 58	12 04	12 12	12 17	12 29	.	.	.	12 46	.	12 58	13 04	13 12	13 17	13 29	.	.	.
Portsmouth Harbour	a	11 21	11 33	...	...	...	11 52	...	12 02	12 07	12 18	12 21	12 33	...	...	...	12 52	...	13 02	13 07	13 18	13 21	13 33	...	...	...

		GW	SN	SN	SW	SW	SN	SW	SW	SW		GW	SN	SN	SW	SW	SN	SW	SW	SW		GW	SN	SN	SW	SW
		◇	1	1	1	1	1	1	1	1		◇	1	1	1	1	1	1	1	1		◇	1	1	1	1
		trolley			buffet			buffet				trolley			buffet			buffet				trolley			buffet	
Havant	d	...	13 32	13 46	13 50	...	14 05	14 16	...	14 27	...	...	14 32	14 46	14 50	...	15 05	15 16	...	15 27	...	...	15 32	15 46	15 50	...
Bedhampton	d	.	13 34	.	.	.	.	.	.	14 30	.	.	14 34	.	.	.	.	.	.	15 30	.	.	15 34	.	.	.
Hilsea	d	...	13 42	...	...	14 03	...	...	14 33	14 36	...	...	14 42	...	...	15 03	...	...	15 33	15 36	...	...	15 42	...	...	16 03
Fratton	d	13 42	13 47	13 55	13 59	14 08	14 14	14 25	14 37	14 40	.	14 42	14 47	14 55	14 59	15 08	15 14	15 25	15 37	15 40	.	15 42	15 47	15 55	15 59	16 08
Portsmouth & Southsea	a	13 46	13 50	13 58	14 02	14 11	14 17	14 28	14 42	14 44	...	14 46	14 50	14 58	15 02	15 11	15 17	15 28	15 42	15 44	...	15 46	15 50	15 58	16 02	16 11
	d	13 46	.	13 58	14 04	14 12	14 17	14 29	.	.	.	14 46	.	14 58	15 04	15 12	15 17	15 29	.	.	.	15 46	.	15 58	16 04	16 12
Portsmouth Harbour	a	13 52	...	14 02	14 07	14 18	14 21	14 33	...	...	...	14 52	...	15 02	15 07	15 18	15 21	15 33	...	...	...	15 52	...	16 02	16 07	16 18

		SN	SW	SW	SW	GW	SN		SN	SW	SW	SN	SW	SW	SW	GW	SN		SN	SW	SW	SN	SW	SW	SW	GW
		1	1	1	1	◇	1		1	1	1	1	1	1	1	◇	1		1	1	1	1	1	1	1	◇
			buffet			trolley				buffet			buffet			trolley				buffet			buffet			trolley
Havant	d	16 05	16 16	...	16 27	...	16 32	...	16 46	16 50	...	17 05	17 16	...	17 27	...	17 32	...	17 46	17 50	...	18 06	18 16	...	18 27	...
Bedhampton	d	.	.	.	16 30	.	16 34	.	.	.	.	.	.	.	17 30	.	17 34	.	.	.	.	.	.	.	18 30	.
Hilsea	d	...	...	16 33	16 36	...	16 42	...	...	...	17 03	...	...	17 33	17 36	...	17 42	...	...	...	18 03	...	...	18 33	18 36	...
Fratton	d	16 14	16 25	16 37	16 40	16 42	16 47	.	16 55	16 59	17 08	17 14	17 25	17 37	17 40	17 42	17 47	.	17 55	17 59	18 08	18 15	18 25	18 37	18 40	18 43
Portsmouth & Southsea	a	16 17	16 28	16 40	16 44	16 46	16 50	...	16 58	17 02	17 11	17 17	17 28	17 42	17 44	17 46	17 50	...	17 58	18 02	18 11	18 18	18 28	18 42	18 44	18 47
	d	16 17	16 29	16 41	.	16 46	.	.	16 58	17 04	17 12	17 17	17 29	.	.	17 46	.	.	17 58	18 04	18 12	18 19	18 29	.	.	18 47
Portsmouth Harbour	a	16 21	16 33	16 44	...	16 52	...	...	17 02	17 07	17 18	17 21	17 33	...	...	17 52	...	...	18 02	18 07	18 18	18 22	18 33	...	...	18 52

		SN	SN	SW		SW	SN	SW	SW	SW	GW	SN	SN	SW		SW	SN	SW	SW	GW	SW	SN	SW	SW		SN
		1	1	1		1	1	1	1	1	◇	1	1	1		1	1	1	1	◇	1	1	1	1		1
				buffet				buffet			trolley			buffet				buffet		trolley			buffet			
Havant	d	18 32	18 46	18 50	...	...	19 05	19 16	...	19 27	...	19 32	19 46	19 50	...	...	20 10	20 16	...	...	20 30	20 46	20 50	...	...	21 10
Bedhampton	d	18 34	.	.	.	.	.	.	.	19 30	.	19 34	.	.	.	.	.	.	.	.	20 33	.	.	.	.	.
Hilsea	d	18 42	...	...	...	19 03	...	...	19 33	19 36	...	19 42	...	...	...	20 03	...	...	20 33	...	20 41	...	...	21 03	...	...
Fratton	d	18 47	18 55	18 59	.	19 08	19 14	19 25	19 37	19 40	19 43	19 47	19 55	19 59	.	20 08	20 19	20 25	20 37	20 42	20 45	20 55	20 59	21 08	.	21 19
Portsmouth & Southsea	a	18 50	18 58	19 02	...	19 11	19 17	19 28	19 42	19 44	19 46	19 50	19 58	20 02	...	20 11	20 22	20 28	20 42	20 45	20 48	20 58	21 02	21 11	...	21 22
	d	.	18 58	19 04	.	19 12	19 17	19 29	.	.	19 47	.	19 58	20 04	.	20 12	20 22	20 29	.	20 46	.	20 58	21 04	21 12	.	21 22
Portsmouth Harbour	a	...	19 02	19 07	...	19 18	19 21	19 33	...	...	19 52	...	20 02	20 07	...	20 18	20 26	20 33	...	20 51	...	21 02	21 07	21 18	...	21 26

For general notes see front of timetable
For details of catering facilities see
Directory of Train Operators

Table 157

Saturdays

Havant → Portsmouth Harbour
(Complete service)

Network Diagram - see first page of Table 155

		SW 1	SW 1	SW 1	GW ◇ ⊼	SW 1	SN 1	SW 1	SN 1	SW 1		SW 1	GW ◇ ⊼	SW 1	SN 1	SW 1	SW 1	SN 1	SW 1	SW 1	GW ◇ ⊼	SW 1	SN 1	SW 1		
Havant	d	21 16	.....	21 27	.....	21 46	21 49	.....	22 10	22 19	.....	.....	.....	22 31	22 43	22 49	.....	23 10	23 19	.....	.....	23 31	23 36	23 49	.....	.....
Bedhampton	d	.	.	21 30	.	.	.	.	.	.	.	.	.	22 34	.	.	.	.	.	.	.	23 34	.	.	.	.
Hilsea	d	.....	21 33	21 36	.....	.....	.....	22 03	.....	.....	.....	22 33	.....	22 41	.....	.....	23 03	.....	.....	23 33	.....	23 41	.....	.....	.....	.....
Fratton	d	21 25	21 37	21 40	21 43	21 55	21 59	22 08	22 19	22 29	.	22 37	22 41	22 45	22 52	22 59	23 08	23 19	23 29	23 37	23 42	23 45	23 48	23 59	.	.
Portsmouth & Southsea	a	21 28	21 42	21 44	21 46	21 58	22 02	22 11	22 22	22 32	.....	22 40	22 44	22 49	22 55	23 02	23 11	23 22	23 32	23 40	23 45	23 48	23 51	00 02	.....	.....
	d	21 29	.	.	21 47	22 00	22 03	22 12	22 22	22 33	.	22 41	22 45	22 50	22 56	23 03	23 12	23 22	23 33	.	23 46	23 50	.	00 03	.	.
Portsmouth Harbour	a	21 33	.....	.....	21 52	22 03	22 06	22 18	22 26	22 36	.....	22 47	22 52	22 53	22 59	23 08	23 18	23 26	23 37	.....	23 49	23 53	.....	00 07	.....	.....

Sundays

		SW 1	SW 1	SW 1	SW 1	SW 1	SN 1	SW 1		SW 1	SN 1 A	SN 1 B	SW 1	SN 1 A	SW 1	SN 1 B		SW 1	SN 1 A	SN 1 B	SW 1	SN 1 A	SW 1	SN 1 B		SW 1
Havant	d	23p49	.....	00 22	00 37	01 26	07 10	.....	.....	.....	08 09	08 11	.....	08 35	08 39	08 49	.....	.....	09 09	09 11	.....	09 35	09 45	09 49	.....	09 53
Bedhampton	d	.	.	00 25	.	01s28	.	.	.	.	⌇	⌇	.	08 37	08 41	08 51	.	.	⌇	⌇	.	09 37	09 47	09 51	.	.
Hilsea	d	.....	00 03	00 30	.....	01s34	.....	07 26	.....	08 00	⌇	⌇	08 26	⌇	.....	⌇	.....	09 00	⌇	⌇	09 26	⌇	.....	⌇	.....	.....
Fratton	d	23p59	00 07	00 34	00 47	01s38	07 19	07 30	.	08 05	08 18	08 20	08 30	08 45	08 50	08 59	.	09 05	09 18	09 20	09 30	09 45	09 56	09 59	.	10 02
Portsmouth & Southsea	a	00 02	00 11	00 38	00 50	01 42	07 22	07 33	.....	08 08	08 21	08 23	08 33	08 48	08 53	09 03	.....	09 08	09 21	09 23	09 33	09 48	09 59	10 03	.....	10 06
	d	00 03	00 12	.	00 51	.	07 22	.	.	08 09	08 21	08 23	.	08 49	08 54	09 04	.	09 09	09 21	09 23	.	09 49	10 00	10 04	.	10 08
Portsmouth Harbour	a	00 07	00 16	.....	00 55	.....	07 26	.....	.....	08 13	08 25	08 27	.....	08 52	08 57	09 07	.....	09 13	09 25	09 27	.....	09 52	10 04	10 07	.....	10 11

		SW 1	SN 1 A	SN 1 B	SW 1	SN 1 A	SN 1 B	SW 1		SW 1	SW 1	SN 1 A	SN 1 B	SW 1	GW ◇ ⊼	SN 1 A		SW 1	SN 1 B	SW 1	SW 1	SN 1 A	SN 1 B	SW 1		GW ◇ ⊼
Havant	d	.....	10 12	10 17	.....	10 35	10 41	10 45	.....	10 53	.....	11 12	11 17	.....	.....	11 35	.....	11 39	11 44	11 51	.....	12 12	12 17	.....	.....	.....
Bedhampton	d	.	⌇	⌇	.	10 37	10 43	10 47	.	.	.	⌇	⌇	.	.	11 37	.	11 41	11 46	.	.	⌇	⌇	.	.	.
Hilsea	d	10 00	⌇	⌇	10 26	⌇	⌇	.....	.....	.....	11 00	⌇	⌇	11 26	.....	⌇	.....	.....	⌇	.....	12 00	⌇	⌇	12 26	.....	.....
Fratton	d	10 05	10 21	10 26	10 30	10 45	10 51	10 56	.	11 02	11 05	11 21	11 26	11 30	11 41	11 45	.	11 50	11 54	12 01	12 04	12 21	12 26	12 30	.	12 44
Portsmouth & Southsea	a	10 10	10 24	10 29	10 33	10 50	10 54	10 59	.....	11 05	11 08	11 24	11 29	11 33	11 44	11 48	.....	11 53	11 57	12 04	12 08	12 24	12 29	12 33	.....	12 47
	d	10 12	10 25	10 30	.	10 51	10 55	11 00	.	11 07	11 09	11 25	11 30	.	11 44	11 49	.	11 54	11 58	12 05	12 09	12 25	12 30	.	.	12 48
Portsmouth Harbour	a	10 15	10 28	10 35	.....	10 54	10 58	11 04	.....	11 11	11 14	11 28	11 35	.....	11 53	11 53	.....	11 58	12 01	12 09	12 13	12 28	12 35	.....	.....	12 53

		SN 1 A	SW 1 B	SW 1 A	SN 1 B	SW 1 ⊏	SW 1	SN 1 A		SN 1 B	SW 1	SN 1 A	SW 1	SN 1 B	SW 1 ⊏	SW 1		SN 1 A	SN 1 B	SW 1	GW ◇ ⊼	SN 1 A	SW 1	SN 1 B		SW 1 ⊏
Havant	d	12 35	12 39	12 39	12 44	12 51	.....	13 12	.....	13 17	.....	13 35	13 39	13 44	13 51	.....	.....	14 12	14 17	.....	.....	14 35	14 39	14 44	.....	14 51
Bedhampton	d	12 37	12 41	12 41	12 46	.	.	⌇	.	⌇	.	13 37	13 41	13 46	.	.	.	⌇	⌇	.	.	14 37	14 41	14 46	.	.
Hilsea	d	⌇	⌇	⌇	⌇	.....	13 00	⌇	.....	⌇	13 26	⌇	.....	⌇	.....	14 00	.....	⌇	⌇	14 26	.....	⌇	.....	⌇	.....	.....
Fratton	d	12 46	12 50	12 50	12 54	13 01	13 04	13 21	.	13 26	13 30	13 45	13 50	13 54	14 01	14 04	.	14 21	14 26	14 30	14 38	14 45	14 50	14 54	.	15 01
Portsmouth & Southsea	a	12 51	12 53	12 54	12 57	13 04	13 08	13 24	.....	13 29	13 33	13 48	13 53	13 57	14 04	14 08	.....	14 24	14 29	14 33	14 41	14 48	14 53	14 57	.....	15 04
	d	12 51	12 54	12 56	12 58	13 05	13 09	13 25	.	13 30	.	13 49	13 54	13 58	14 05	14 09	.	14 25	14 30	.	14 42	14 49	14 54	14 58	.	15 05
Portsmouth Harbour	a	12 55	12 58	12 59	13 01	13 11	13 13	13 28	.....	13 35	.....	13 52	13 58	14 01	14 11	14 13	.....	14 28	14 35	.....	14 48	14 52	14 58	15 01	.....	15 11

		SW 1	SN 1 A	SN 1 B	SW 1	SN 1 A	SW 1	SN 1 B		SW 1 ⊏	SW 1	SN 1 A	SN 1 B	SW 1	GW ◇ ⊼	SN 1 A		SW 1 B	SW 1 A	SN 1 B	SW 1 ⊏	SW 1	SN 1 A	SN 1 B		SW 1
Havant	d	.....	15 12	15 17	.....	15 35	15 39	15 44	.....	15 51	.....	16 12	16 17	.....	.....	16 35	.....	16 39	16 39	16 44	16 51	.....	17 12	17 17	.....	.....
Bedhampton	d	.	⌇	⌇	.	15 37	15 41	15 46	.	.	.	⌇	⌇	.	.	16 37	.	16 41	16 41	16 46	.	.	⌇	⌇	.	.
Hilsea	d	15 00	⌇	⌇	15 26	⌇	.....	⌇	.....	.....	16 00	⌇	⌇	16 26	.....	⌇	.....	⌇	⌇	⌇	.....	17 00	⌇	⌇	.....	17 26
Fratton	d	15 04	15 21	15 26	15 30	15 45	15 50	15 54	.	16 01	16 04	16 23	16 26	16 30	16 44	16 46	.	16 50	16 50	16 54	17 01	17 05	17 21	17 26	.	17 30
Portsmouth & Southsea	a	15 08	15 24	15 29	15 33	15 48	15 53	15 57	.....	16 04	16 08	16 26	16 29	16 33	16 47	16 51	.....	16 53	16 54	16 57	17 04	17 08	17 24	17 29	.....	17 33
	d	15 09	15 25	15 30	.	15 49	15 54	15 58	.	16 05	16 09	16 27	16 30	.	16 48	16 51	.	16 54	16 56	16 58	17 05	17 09	17 25	17 30	.	.
Portsmouth Harbour	a	15 13	15 28	15 35	.....	15 52	15 58	16 01	.....	16 11	16 13	16 30	16 35	.....	16 53	16 55	.....	16 58	16 59	17 01	17 11	17 13	17 28	17 35	.....	.....

		GW ◇ ⊼	SN 1 A	SW 1 B	SW 1 A	SN 1 B	SW 1 ⊏	SW 1		SN 1 A	SN 1 B	SW 1	GW ◇ ⊼	SN 1 A	SW 1 B	SW 1 A		SN 1 B	SW 1 ⊏	SW 1	SN 1 A	SN 1 B	SW 1	GW ◇ ⊼		SN 1 A
Havant	d	.....	17 35	17 39	17 39	17 44	17 51	.....	.....	18 12	18 17	.....	.....	18 35	18 39	18 39	.....	18 44	18 51	.....	19 12	19 17	.....	.....	.....	19 35
Bedhampton	d	.	17 37	17 41	17 41	17 46	.	.	.	⌇	⌇	.	.	18 37	18 41	18 41	.	18 46	.	.	⌇	⌇	.	.	.	19 37
Hilsea	d	.....	⌇	⌇	⌇	⌇	.....	18 00	.....	⌇	⌇	18 26	.....	⌇	⌇	⌇	.....	⌇	.....	19 00	⌇	⌇	19 26	.....	.....	⌇
Fratton	d	17 44	17 46	17 50	17 50	17 54	18 01	18 04	.	18 21	18 26	18 30	18 44	18 46	18 50	18 50	.	18 54	19 01	19 05	19 21	19 26	19 30	19 44	.	19 46
Portsmouth & Southsea	a	17 47	17 51	17 53	17 54	17 57	18 04	18 08	.....	18 24	18 29	18 33	18 47	18 51	18 53	18 54	.....	18 57	19 04	19 08	19 24	19 29	19 33	19 47	.....	19 51
	d	17 48	17 51	17 54	17 56	17 58	18 05	18 09	.	18 25	18 30	.	18 48	18 51	18 54	18 56	.	18 58	19 05	19 09	19 25	19 30	.	19 48	.	19 51
Portsmouth Harbour	a	17 53	17 55	17 58	17 59	18 01	18 11	18 13	.....	18 28	18 35	.....	18 51	18 55	18 58	18 59	.....	19 01	19 11	19 13	19 28	19 35	.....	19 53	.....	19 55

		SW 1 B	SW 1 A	SN 1 B	SW 1 ⊏	SW 1	SN 1 A	SN 1 B		SW 1	GW ◇ ⊼	SN 1 A	SW 1	SN 1 B	SW 1 ⊏	SW 1		GW ◇ ⊼	SN 1 A	SN 1 B	SW 1	GW ◇ ⊼	SN 1 A	SW 1		SN 1 B
Havant	d	19 39	19 39	19 44	19 51	.....	20 12	20 17	.....	.....	.....	20 35	20 39	20 44	20 51	.....	.....	.....	21 12	21 17	.....	.....	21 35	21 39	.....	21 44
Bedhampton	d	19 41	19 41	19 46	.	.	⌇	⌇	.	.	.	20 37	20 41	20 46	.	.	.	.	⌇	⌇	.	.	21 37	21 41	.	21 46
Hilsea	d	⌇	⌇	⌇	.....	20 00	⌇	⌇	.....	20 26	.....	⌇	.....	⌇	.....	21 00	.....	.....	⌇	⌇	21 26	.....	⌇	.....	.....	⌇
Fratton	d	19 50	19 50	19 54	20 01	20 04	20 21	20 26	.	20 30	20 39	20 45	20 50	20 54	21 01	21 04	.	21 10	21 21	21 26	21 30	21 36	21 45	21 50	.	21 54
Portsmouth & Southsea	a	19 53	19 54	19 57	20 04	20 08	20 24	20 29	.....	20 33	20 43	20 48	20 53	20 57	21 04	21 08	.....	21 15	21 24	21 29	21 33	21 39	21 48	21 53	.....	21 57
	d	19 54	19 56	19 58	20 05	20 09	20 25	20 30	.	.	20 44	20 49	20 54	20 58	21 05	21 09	.	21 15	21 25	21 30	.	21 40	21 49	21 54	.	21 58
Portsmouth Harbour	a	19 58	19 59	20 01	20 11	20 13	20 28	20 35	.....	.....	20 47	20 52	20 58	21 01	21 09	21 13	.....	21 24	21 28	21 35	.....	21 48	21 52	21 58	.....	22 01

For general notes see front of timetable
For details of catering facilities see
Directory of Train Operators

A Until 6 September
B From 13 September

Table 157

Sundays

Havant → Portsmouth Harbour
(Complete service)

Network Diagram - see first page of Table 155

		SW	SW	SN	SN	SW	GW	SN		SW	GW	SN	GW	SW	SW	SW		SN	SN	GW	SW	SW	SW			
		1	1	1	1	1	◇	1		1	1	1	1	1	1	1		1	1	◇	1	1	1			
				A	B			A			A	B	B					A	B							
		⊡					⊼													⊼						
Havant	d	21 51		22 12	22 17			22 35		22 39	22 42	22 44	22 47	22 51				23 21	23 27		23 39	23 51				
Bedhampton	d							22 37		22 41		22 46									23 41					
Hilsea	d		22 00			22 26									23 00	23 24							23 59			
Fratton	d	22 01	22 04	22 21	22 26	22 30	22 36	22 45		22 50	22 54	22 54	22 57	23 01	23 04	23 29		23 31	23 37	23 37	23 50	00 01	00 04			
Portsmouth & Southsea	a	22 04	22 08	22 24	22 29	22 33	22 39	22 48		22 53	22 57	22 57	23 00	23 04	23 08	23 32		23 34	23 40	23 40	23 53	00 04	00 08			
	d	22 05	22 09	22 25	22 30		22 40	22 49		22 54	22 57	22 58	23 01	23 05	23 09			23 35	23 41	23 41	23 54	00 05	00 09			
Portsmouth Harbour	a	22 11	22 13	22 28	22 35		22 46	22 52		22 58	23 01	23 01	23 04	23 09	23 13			23 38	23 44	23 48	23 58	00 09	00 13			

For general notes see front of timetable
For details of catering facilities see
Directory of Train Operators

A Until 6 September
B From 13 September

Portsmouth Harbour → Havant
(Complete service)

Network Diagram - see first page of Table 155

		SW 1 A	SW 1 B	SW 1	SW 1	SW 1 A ⊏P	SW 1 B ⊏P	SN 1	SW 1	SN 1	SW 1	GW ◇ ⚲	SN 1	SW 1 ⊏P	SW 1	SW 1	SW 1	SW 1	SN 1		SW 1 ⊏P	SN 1	GW ◇ ⚲	SW 1	GW	SW 1 ⊏P
Portsmouth Harbour	d	04 25	04 30	05 00	...	05 14	05 19	05 34	05 43	05 47	05 50	06 00	06 04	06 15	...	06 23	...	06 38	...	...	06 42	06 46	06 51	06 55	07 01	07 13
Portsmouth & Southsea	a	04 28	04 33	05 03	.	05 17	05 22	05 37	05 46	05 50	05 53	06 03	06 07	06 18	.	06 26	.	06 41	.	.	06 45	06 49	06 54	06 58	07 04	07 16
	d	04 30	04 35	05 05	05 16	05 19	05 24	05 38	05 48	05 51	05 55	06 04	06 08	06 20	06 23	06 28	...	06 43	...	...	06 47	06 50	06 55	07 00	07 05	07 18
Fratton	d	04 34	04 39	05 09	05 20	05 23	05 28	05 42	05 52	05 55	05 59	06a07	06 12	06 24	06 27	06 32	.	06 47	.	.	06 51	06 54	06a59	07 04	07 10	07 22
Hilsea	d	04 38	04 43	05a13	05a24	05 27	05 32	05 46	05a56	05 59	06 03	...	...	...	06a31	06a36	06 42	06a51	...	...	...	06 58	...	07 08	...	...
Bedhampton	d	04 43	04 48	.	.	05 32	05 37	05 51	.	06 04	06 08	.	.	.	.	.	06 47	.	06 34	.	.	07 03	.	07 13	.	.
Havant	a	04 45	04 50	...	...	05 35	05 40	05 53	...	06 06	06 10	...	06 20	06 33	...	...	06 49	...	06 37	...	06 59	07 05	...	07 15	07 19	07 30

		SN 1	SW 1	SW 1	SW 1	SW 1 ⊏P	SW 1	SN 1	SW 1	SN 1	SW 1 ⊏P	SW 1	GW ◇ ⚲	SN 1	SW 1		SW 1 ⊏P	SN 1	SW 1	SN 1	SW 1 ⊏P	SW 1	GW ◇ ⚲	SN 1	SW 1	SW 1 ⊏P
Portsmouth Harbour	d	07 20	07 24	07 29	...	07 45	07 55	...	08 05	08 10	08 15	...	08 22	08 29	08 33	...	08 45	08 52	08 55	09 12	09 15	09 19	09 22	09 29	09 33	09 45
Portsmouth & Southsea	a	07 23	07 27	07 32	.	07 48	07 58	.	08 08	08 13	08 18	.	08 26	08 32	08 36	.	08 48	08 55	08 58	09 15	09 18	09 22	09 26	09 32	09 36	09 48
	d	07 24	07 29	07 33	07 38	07 50	08 00	08 03	08 10	08 14	08 20	08 24	08 27	08 33	08 38	...	08 50	08 56	09 00	09 16	09 20	09 24	09 27	09 33	09 38	09 50
Fratton	d	07 28	07 33	07 37	07 43	07 54	08 04	08 07	08 14	08 18	08 24	08 28	08a31	08 37	08 43	.	08 54	09 00	09 04	09 20	09 24	09 28	09a31	09 37	09 43	09 54
Hilsea	d	...	07a37	07 41	07a47	...	08a08	08 11	08a18	...	...	08 32	...	...	08a47	...	...	09 04	09a08	...	...	09 32	...	...	09a47	...
Bedhampton	d	.	.	07 48	.	.	.	08 16	.	.	.	08 37	.	.	.	.	.	09 13	.	.	.	09 37	.	.	.	.
Havant	a	07 36	...	07 50	...	08 03	...	08 18	...	08 26	08 32	08 40	...	08 45	...	...	09 03	09 15	...	09 29	09 33	09 39	...	09 45	...	10 03

		SN 1	SW 1	SN 1	SW 1 ⊏P	SW 1	GW ◇ ⚲	SN 1	SW 1	SW 1 ⊏P	SN 1		SW 1	SN 1	SW 1 ⊏P	SW 1	GW ◇ ⚲	SN 1	SW 1	SW 1 ⊏P	SN 1	SW 1	SN 1	SW 1 ⊏P	SW 1	GW ◇ ⚲
Portsmouth Harbour	d	...	09 55	10 12	10 15	...	10 22	10 29	10 33	10 45	...	...	10 55	11 12	11 15	...	11 22	11 29	...	11 45	...	11 55	12 12	12 15	...	12 22
Portsmouth & Southsea	a	.	09 58	10 15	10 18	.	10 26	10 32	10 36	10 48	.	.	10 58	11 15	11 18	.	11 26	11 32	.	11 48	.	11 58	12 15	12 18	.	12 26
	d	09 56	10 00	10 16	10 20	10 24	10 27	10 33	10 38	10 50	10 56	...	11 00	11 16	11 20	11 24	11 27	11 33	11 38	11 50	11 56	12 00	12 16	12 20	12 24	12 27
Fratton	d	10 01	10 04	10 20	10 24	10 28	10a31	10 37	10 43	10 54	11 01	.	11 04	11 20	11 24	11 28	11a31	11 37	11 43	11 54	12 01	12 04	12 20	12 24	12 28	12a31
Hilsea	d	10 05	10a08	...	...	10 32	...	...	10a47	...	11 05	...	11a08	...	...	11 32	...	...	11a47	...	12 05	12a08	...	...	12 32	...
Bedhampton	d	10 13	.	.	.	10 37	.	.	.	.	11 13	.	.	.	.	11 37	.	.	.	.	12 13	.	.	.	12 37	.
Havant	a	10 15	...	10 29	10 33	10 39	...	10 45	...	11 03	11 15	...	...	11 29	11 33	11 39	...	11 45	...	12 03	12 15	...	12 29	12 33	12 39	...

		SN 1	SW 1	SW 1 ⊏P	SN 1	SW 1	SN 1		SW 1 ⊏P	SW 1	GW ◇ ⚲	SN 1	SW 1	SW 1 ⊏P	SN 1	SW 1	SN 1	SW 1 ⊏P	SW 1	GW ◇ ⚲	SN 1	SW 1	SW 1 ⊏P	SN 1	SW 1	SN 1
Portsmouth Harbour	d	12 29	...	12 45	...	12 55	13 12	...	13 15	...	13 22	13 29	...	13 45	...	13 55	14 12	14 15	...	14 22	14 29	...	14 45	...	14 55	15 12
Portsmouth & Southsea	a	12 32	.	12 48	.	12 58	13 15	.	13 18	.	13 26	13 32	.	13 48	.	13 58	14 15	14 18	.	14 26	14 32	.	14 48	.	14 58	15 15
	d	12 33	12 38	12 50	12 56	13 00	13 16	...	13 20	13 24	13 27	13 33	13 38	13 50	13 56	14 00	14 16	14 20	14 24	14 27	14 33	14 38	14 50	14 56	15 00	15 16
Fratton	d	12 37	12 43	12 54	13 01	13 04	13 20	.	13 24	13 28	13a31	13 37	13 43	13 54	14 01	14 04	14 20	14 24	14 28	14a31	14 37	14 43	14 54	15 01	15 04	15 20
Hilsea	d	...	12a47	...	13 05	13a08	...	...	...	13 32	...	...	13a47	...	14 05	14a08	...	...	14 32	...	...	14a47	...	15 05	15a08	...
Bedhampton	d	.	.	.	13 13	.	.	.	.	13 37	.	.	.	.	14 13	.	.	.	14 37	.	.	.	.	15 14	.	.
Havant	a	12 45	...	13 03	13 15	...	13 29	...	13 33	13 39	...	13 45	...	14 03	14 15	...	14 29	14 33	14 39	...	14 45	...	15 03	15 17	...	15 29

		SW 1 ⊏P	SW 1		GW ◇ ⚲	SN 1	SW 1	SW 1 ⊏P	SN 1	SW 1	SN 1	SW 1 ⊏P	SW 1	GW ◇ ⚲	SN 1	SW 1	SN 1	SW 1 ⊏P	SN 1	SW 1	SW 1	SN 1		SW 1 ⊏P	SW 1	GW ◇ ⚲
Portsmouth Harbour	d	15 15	...	...	15 22	15 29	...	15 45	...	15 55	16 12	16 15	...	16 22	16 29	...	16 40	16 45	...	16 55	17 03	17 12	...	17 15	17 17	17 22
Portsmouth & Southsea	a	15 18	.	.	15 26	15 32	.	15 48	.	15 58	16 15	16 18	.	16 26	16 32	.	16 44	16 48	.	16 58	17 06	17 15	.	17 18	17 22	17 26
	d	15 20	15 24	...	15 27	15 33	15 38	15 50	15 56	16 00	16 16	16 20	16 24	16 27	16 33	16 38	16 46	16 50	16 56	17 00	17 07	17 16	...	17 20	17 24	17 27
Fratton	d	15 24	15 28	.	15a31	15 37	15 43	15 54	16 01	16 04	16 20	16 24	16 28	16a31	16 37	16 43	16 50	16 54	17 01	17 04	17 11	17 20	.	17 24	17 28	17a31
Hilsea	d	...	15 32	...	...	...	15a47	...	16 05	16a08	...	...	16 32	...	...	16a47	16 54	...	17 05	17a08	17a15	...	...	...	17 32	...
Bedhampton	d	.	15 37	.	.	.	.	.	16 13	.	.	.	16 37	.	.	.	.	.	17 13	.	.	.	.	.	17 37	.
Havant	a	15 33	15 39	...	...	15 45	...	16 03	16 15	...	16 29	16 33	16 39	...	16 45	...	16 59	17 03	17 15	...	...	17 29	...	17 33	17 39	...

		SN 1	SW 1	SN 1	SW 1 ⊏P	SN 1	SW 1	SW 1 ⊏P	SW 1	GW ◇ ⚲	SN 1	SW 1	SN 1	SW 1 ⊏P	SN 1	SW 1	SW 1	SW 1		GW ◇	SN 1	SW 1	SN 1	SW 1	SN 1	SW 1
Portsmouth Harbour	d	17 29	17 33	...	17 45	...	17 55	18 15	...	18 22	18 28	...	18 37	18 45	...	18 55	19 15	...	...	19 22	...	...	19 40	19 45	...	19 55
Portsmouth & Southsea	a	17 32	17 36	.	17 48	.	17 58	18 18	.	18 26	18 31	.	18 40	18 48	.	18 58	19 18	.	.	19 26	.	.	19 43	19 48	.	19 58
	d	17 33	17 38	17 46	17 50	17 56	18 00	18 20	18 24	18 27	18 32	18 38	18 42	18 50	18 56	19 00	19 20	19 24	...	19 27	19 32	19 38	19 44	19 50	19 56	20 00
Fratton	d	17 37	17 43	17 50	17 54	18 01	18 04	18 24	18 28	18a31	18 36	18 43	18 46	18 54	19 01	19 04	19 24	19 28	.	19a31	19 36	19 43	19 48	19 54	20 01	20 04
Hilsea	d	...	17a47	17 54	...	18 05	18a08	...	18 32	...	...	18a47	18 50	...	19 05	19a08	...	19 32	...	...	...	19a47	...	...	20 05	20a08
Bedhampton	d	.	.	.	.	18 13	.	.	18 37	.	.	.	.	.	19 13	.	.	19 37	.	.	.	.	.	.	20 14	.
Havant	a	17 45	...	17 59	18 03	18 15	...	18 32	18 39	...	18 44	...	18 56	19 03	19 15	...	19 33	19 39	...	...	19 44	...	19 56	20 03	20 16	...

		SW 1	SW 1	GW ◇	SN 1	SW 1	SN 1	SW 1	SW 1	SN 1	SW 1	GW	SW 1	SW 1	SN 1	SW 1	SN 1	SW 1	SW 1	SW 1	SN 1	SN 1	SW 1	SW 1		
Portsmouth Harbour	d	20 15	20 18	20 22	...	...	20 40	20 45	20 55	...	21 18	21 22	21 28	...	21 40	21 55	22 15	22 18	22 28	...	22 44	23 15	23 18	23 24	...	...
Portsmouth & Southsea	a	20 18	20 22	20 26	.	.	20 43	20 48	20 58	.	21 21	21 26	21 31	.	21 43	21 58	22 18	22 21	22 31	.	22 47	23 18	23 21	23 27	.	.
	d	20 20	20 24	20 27	20 32	20 38	20 44	20 50	21 00	21 15	21 24	21 27	21 33	21 38	21 44	22 00	22 19	22 24	22 33	22 38	22 48	23 19	23 24	23 29	...	...
Fratton	d	20 24	20 28	20a31	20 36	20 43	20 48	20 54	21 04	21 19	21 28	21a31	21 37	21 43	21 48	22 04	22 23	22 28	22 37	22 43	22 52	23 23	23 28	23 33	.	.
Hilsea	d	...	20 32	...	...	20a47	...	...	21a08	21 23	21 32	...	21 41	21a47	21 52	22a08	22 27	22 32	22 41	22a47	22 56	23 27	23 32	23a37	...	...
Bedhampton	d	.	20 37	.	.	.	.	.	.	21 28	21 37	.	21 47	.	21 57	.	22 32	22 37	22 46	.	23 01	23 33	23 37	.	.	.
Havant	a	20 33	20 39	...	20 44	...	20 56	21 03	...	21 30	21 39	...	21 51	...	21 59	...	22 34	22 39	22 53	...	23 05	23 36	23 39	...	...	...

For general notes see front of timetable
For details of catering facilities see
Directory of Train Operators

A From 28 September
B Until 25 September

Table 157

Portsmouth Harbour → Havant
(Complete service)

Network Diagram - see first page of Table 155

	SW 1 A	SW 1 B	SN 1	SW 1	SW 1 A	SW 1 B	SN 1	SW 1	GW ◇	SN 1	SW 1	SN 1	SW 1	SW 1 (trolley)	GW	SN 1	SW 1	GW ◇	SN 1	SW 1 (trolley)	SW 1	SN 1
Portsmouth Harbour d	04 38	04 43			05 14	05 19		05 55	06 00	06 12	06 19	06 29		06 45	06 48		06 55	07 05	07 12	07 15		07 29
Portsmouth & Southsea a	04 41	04 46			05 17	05 22		05 58	06 03	06 15	06 22	06 32		06 48	06 53		06 58	07 08	07 15	07 18		07 32
Portsmouth & Southsea d	04 43	04 48	04 56	05 16	05 19	05 24	05 56	06 00	06 04	06 16	06 24	06 33	06 38	06 50	06 54	06 56	07 00	07 09	07 16	07 20	07 24	07 33
Fratton d	04 47	04 52	05 00	05 20	05 23	05 28	06 01	06 04	06a07	06 20	06 28	06 37	06 43	06 54	06 58	07 01	07 04	07a13	07 20	07 24	07 28	07 37
Hilsea d	04 51	04 56		05a24	05 27	05 32	06 05	06a08			06 32		06a47			07 05	07a08				07 32	
Bedhampton d	04 56	05 01			05 32	05 37	06 13				06 37					07 13					07 37	
Havant a	04 58	05 03	05 08		05 34	05 39	06 15			06 29	06 39	06 45		07 03	07 08	07 15			07 29	07 33	07 39	07 45

	SW 1	SW 1 (trolley)	SN 1	SW 1	SN 1	SW 1 (trolley)	SW 1	GW ◇	SN 1	SW 1	SW 1 (trolley)	SN 1	SW 1	SN 1	SW 1 (trolley)	SW 1	GW ◇	SN 1	SW 1	SW 1 (trolley)	SN 1	SW 1
Portsmouth Harbour d		07 45		07 55	08 12	08 15		08 22	08 29		08 45		08 55	09 12	09 15		09 22	09 29		09 45		09 55
Portsmouth & Southsea a		07 48		07 58	08 15	08 18		08 25	08 32		08 48		08 58	09 15	09 18		09 25	09 32		09 48		09 58
Portsmouth & Southsea d	07 38	07 50	07 56	08 00	08 16	08 20	08 24	08 27	08 33	08 38	08 50	08 56	09 00	09 16	09 20	09 24	09 27	09 33	09 38	09 50	09 56	10 00
Fratton d	07 43	07 54	08 01	08 04	08 20	08 24	08 28	08a30	08 37	08 43	08 54	09 01	09 04	09 20	09 24	09 28	09a30	09 37	09 43	09 54	10 01	10 04
Hilsea d	07a47		08 05	08a08			08 32			08a47		09 05	09a08			09 32			09a47		10 05	10a08
Bedhampton d			08 13				08 37					09 13				09 37					10 13	
Havant a		08 03	08 15		08 29	08 33	08 39		08 45		09 03	09 15		09 29	09 33	09 39		09 45		10 03	10 15	

	SN 1	SW 1 (trolley)	SW 1	GW ◇	SN 1	SW 1	SW 1 (trolley)	SN 1	SW 1	SN 1	SW 1 (trolley)	SW 1	GW ◇	SN 1	SW 1	SW 1 (trolley)	SN 1	SW 1	SN 1	SW 1 (trolley)	SW 1	GW ◇
Portsmouth Harbour d	10 12	10 15		10 22	10 29		10 45		10 55	11 12	11 15		11 22	11 29		11 45		11 55	12 12	12 15		12 22
Portsmouth & Southsea a	10 15	10 18		10 25	10 32		10 48		10 58	11 15	11 18		11 25	11 32		11 48		11 58	12 15	12 18		12 25
Portsmouth & Southsea d	10 16	10 20	10 24	10 27	10 33	10 38	10 50	10 56	11 00	11 16	11 20	11 24	11 27	11 33	11 38	11 50	11 56	12 00	12 16	12 20	12 24	12 27
Fratton d	10 20	10 24	10 28	10a30	10 37	10 43	10 54	11 01	11 04	11 20	11 24	11 28	11a30	11 37	11 43	11 54	12 01	12 04	12 20	12 24	12 28	12a30
Hilsea d			10 32			10a47		11 05	11a08			11 32			11a47		12 05	12a08			12 32	
Bedhampton d			10 37					11 13				11 37					12 13				12 37	
Havant a	10 29	10 33	10 39		10 45		11 03	11 15		11 29	11 33	11 39		11 45		12 03	12 15		12 29	12 33	12 39	

	SN 1	SW 1	SW 1 (trolley)	SN 1	SW 1	SN 1	SW 1 (trolley)	SW 1	GW ◇	SN 1	SW 1	SW 1 (trolley)	SN 1	SW 1	SN 1	SW 1 (trolley)	SW 1	GW ◇	SN 1	SW 1	SW 1 (trolley)	SN 1
Portsmouth Harbour d	12 29		12 45		12 55	13 12	13 15		13 22	13 29		13 45		13 55	14 12	14 15		14 22	14 29		14 45	
Portsmouth & Southsea a	12 32		12 48		12 58	13 15	13 18		13 25	13 32		13 48		13 58	14 15	14 18		14 25	14 32		14 48	
Portsmouth & Southsea d	12 33	12 38	12 50	12 56	13 00	13 16	13 20	13 24	13 27	13 33	13 38	13 50	13 56	14 00	14 16	14 20	14 24	14 27	14 33	14 38	14 50	14 56
Fratton d	12 37	12 43	12 54	13 01	13 04	13 20	13 24	13 28	13a30	13 37	13 43	13 54	14 01	14 04	14 20	14 24	14 28	14a30	14 37	14 43	14 54	15 01
Hilsea d		12a47		13 05	13a08			13 32			13a47		14 05	14a08			14 32			14a47		15 05
Bedhampton d				13 13				13 37					14 13				14 37					15 14
Havant a	12 45		13 03	13 15		13 29	13 33	13 39		13 45		14 03	14 15		14 29	14 33	14 39		14 45		15 03	15 17

	SW 1	SN 1	SW 1 (trolley)	SW 1	GW ◇	SN 1	SW 1	SW 1 (trolley)	SN 1	SW 1	SN 1	SW 1 (trolley)	SW 1	GW ◇	SN 1	SW 1	SW 1 (trolley)	SN 1	SW 1	SW 1	SN 1	SW 1
Portsmouth Harbour d	14 55	15 12	15 15		15 22	15 29		15 45		15 55	16 12	16 15		16 22	16 29		16 45		16 55		17 12	17 17
Portsmouth & Southsea a	14 58	15 15	15 18		15 25	15 32		15 48		15 58	16 15	16 18		16 25	16 32		16 48		16 58		17 15	17 22
Portsmouth & Southsea d	15 00	15 16	15 20	15 24	15 27	15 33	15 38	15 50	15 56	16 00	16 16	16 20	16 24	16 27	16 33	16 38	16 50	16 56	17 00	17 10	17 16	17 24
Fratton d	15 04	15 20	15 24	15 28	15a30	15 37	15 43	15 54	16 01	16 04	16 20	16 24	16 28	16a31	16 37	16 43	16 54	17 01	17 04	17 14	17 20	17 28
Hilsea d	15a08			15 32			15a47		16 05	16a08			16 32			16a47		17 05	17a08	17 18		17 32
Bedhampton d				15 37					16 13				16 37					17 13		17 23		17 37
Havant a		15 29	15 33	15 39		15 45		16 03	16 15		16 29	16 33	16 39		16 45		17 03	17 15		17 25	17 29	17 39

	GW ◇	SN 1	SW 1	SW 1 (trolley)	SN 1	SW 1	SN 1	SW 1	SW 1	GW ◇	SN 1	SW 1	SW 1	SN 1	SW 1	SN 1	SW 1	SW 1	GW ◇	SN 1	SW 1	SW 1
Portsmouth Harbour d	17 22	17 29	17 33	17 45		17 55	18 12	18 15		18 22	18 29		18 45		18 55	19 12	19 15		19 22	19 29		19 45
Portsmouth & Southsea a	17 26	17 32	17 36	17 48		17 58	18 15	18 18		18 26	18 32		18 48		18 58	19 15	19 18		19 25	19 32		19 48
Portsmouth & Southsea d	17 27	17 33	17 38	17 50	17 56	18 00	18 16	18 20	18 24	18 27	18 33	18 38	18 50	18 56	19 00	19 16	19 20	19 24	19 27	19 33	19 38	19 50
Fratton d	17a31	17 37	17 43	17 54	18 01	18 04	18 20	18 24	18 28	18a31	18 37	18 43	18 54	19 01	19 04	19 20	19 24	19 28	19a30	19 37	19 43	19 54
Hilsea d			17a47		18 05	18a08			18 32			18a47		19 05	19a08			19 32			19a47	
Bedhampton d					18 13				18 37					19 13				19 37				
Havant a		17 45		18 03	18 15		18 29	18 33	18 39		18 45		19 03	19 15		19 29	19 33	19 39		19 46		20 03

	SN 1	SW 1	SW 1	SW 1	GW ◇	SN 1	SW 1	SN 1	SW 1	SW 1	SN 1	SW 1	SW 1	SN 1	SW 1	SN 1	SW 1	SW 1	SN 1	SN 1	SW 1	SW 1
Portsmouth Harbour d		19 55	20 15		20 22	20 28		20 40	20 45	20 55	21 11	21 18		21 40	21 55	22 15	22 18		22 44	23 15	23 18	23 24
Portsmouth & Southsea a		19 58	20 18		20 25	20 31		20 43	20 48	20 58	21 14	21 21		21 43	21 58	22 18	22 21		22 47	23 18	23 22	23 28
Portsmouth & Southsea d	19 56	20 00	20 20	20 24	20 27	20 32	20 38	20 44	20 50	21 00	21 15	21 24	21 38	21 44	22 00	22 19	22 24	22 38	22 48	23 19	23 24	23 29
Fratton d	20 01	20 04	20 24	20 28	20a30	20 36	20 43	20 48	20 54	21 04	21 19	21 28	21 43	21 48	22 04	22 23	22 28	22 43	22 52	23 23	23 28	23 33
Hilsea d	20 05	20a08		20 32			20a47			21a08	21 23	21 32	21a47	21 52	22a08	22 27	22 32	22a47	22 56	23 27	23 32	23a37
Bedhampton d	20 13			20 37							21 28	21 37		21 57		22 32	22 37		23 01	23 33	23 37	
Havant a	20 15		20 33	20 39		20 44		20 56	21 03		21 30	21 39		21 59		22 34	22 39		23 05	23 36	23 39	

For general notes see front of timetable
For details of catering facilities see Directory of Train Operators

A From 3 October
B Until 26 September

Sundays

Portsmouth Harbour → Havant
(Complete service)

Network Diagram - see first page of Table 155

		SW 1	SW 1 A	SW 1 B	SN 1 C	GW 1	SN 1 D		SW 1	SW 1 A	SW 1 B	SW 1	SN 1	SW 1		SN 1 C	SN 1 D	SW 1	SW 1 A	SW 1 B	SW 1		SN 1	SW 1	SN 1 C	GW ◇
Portsmouth Harbour	d	06 37	06 43	06 48	07 05	07 08	07 14	.....	07 17	07 29	07 32	.....	07 43	07 48	.....	08 05	08 14	08 17	08 29	08 32	.....	.....	08 43	08 48	09 05	09 08
Portsmouth & Southsea	a	06 40	06 46	06 51	07 08	07 11	07 17	.	07 20	07 32	07 35	.	07 46	07 51	.	08 08	08 17	08 20	08 32	08 35	.	.	08 46	08 51	09 08	09 11
	d	06 42	06 48	06 53	07 09	07 12	07 18	.....	07 22	07 34	07 37	07 42	07 47	07 53	.....	08 09	08 18	08 22	08 34	08 37	08 42	.....	08 47	08 53	09 09	09 12
Fratton	d	06 46	06 52	06 57	07 13	07a15	07 22	.	07 26	07 38	07 41	07 46	07 51	07 57	.	08 13	08 22	08 26	08 38	08 41	08 46	.	08 51	08 57	09 13	09a15
Hilsea	d	06a50				.....		.....	07a30			07a50	.....	.....	.....			08a30			08a50	.....	.....	.....		.....
Bedhampton	d	.	06 59	07 04	07 20	.	07 30	.	.			.	.	08 04	.	08 20	08 30	.			.	.	.	09 04	09 20	.
Havant	a	.....	07 02	07 07	07 23	.....	07 32	.....	.....	07 46	07 49	.....	07 59	08 07	.....	08 23	08 32	.....	08 46	08 49	.....	.....	08 59	09 07	09 23	.....

		SN 1 D	SW 1	SW 1	SW 1		SN 1	SW 1	SN 1 C	SN 1 D	SW 1	SW 1		SW 1	SN 1	SW 1	SN 1 C	GW ◇	SN 1 D		SW 1	SW 1	SW 1	SN 1	SW 1	SN 1 C
Portsmouth Harbour	d	09 14	09 17	09 32	.....	.....	09 43	09 48	10 05	10 14	10 17	10 32	.....	.....	10 43	10 48	11 05	11 08	11 14	.....	11 17	11 32	.....	11 43	11 48	12 05
Portsmouth & Southsea	a	09 17	09 20	09 35	.	.	09 46	09 51	10 08	10 17	10 20	10 35	.	.	10 46	10 51	11 08	11 11	11 17	.	11 20	11 35	.	11 46	11 51	12 08
	d	09 18	09 22	09 37	09 42	.....	09 47	09 53	10 09	10 18	10 22	10 37	.....	10 42	10 47	10 53	11 09	11 12	11 18	.....	11 22	11 37	11 42	11 47	11 53	12 09
Fratton	d	09 22	09 26	09 41	09 46	.	09 51	09 57	10 13	10 22	10 26	10 41	.	10 46	10 51	10 57	11 13	11a15	11 22	.	11 26	11 41	11 46	11 51	11 57	12 13
Hilsea	d		09a30	.....	09a50	.....	.....	.....			10a30	.....	.....	10a50	.....	.....		.....		.....	11a30	.....	11a50	.....	.....	
Bedhampton	d	09 30	.	.	.	.	.	10 04	10 20	10 30	.	.	.	.	.	11 04	11 20	.	11 30	.	.	.	.	.	12 04	12 20
Havant	a	09 32	.....	09 49	.....	.....	09 59	10 06	10 23	10 32	.....	10 49	.....	.....	10 59	11 06	11 23	.....	11 32	.....	.....	11 49	.....	11 59	12 07	12 23

		SN 1 D	SW 1		SW 1	SW 1	SN 1	SW 1	SN 1 C	GW ◇		SN 1 D	SW 1	SW 1	SW 1	SN 1	SW 1		SN 1 C	GW ◇	SN 1 D	SW 1	SW 1	SW 1		SN 1
Portsmouth Harbour	d	12 14	12 17	.....	12 32	.....	12 43	12 48	13 05	13 08	.....	13 14	13 17	13 32	.....	13 43	13 48	.....	14 05	14 08	14 14	14 17	14 32	.....	.....	14 43
Portsmouth & Southsea	a	12 17	12 20	.	12 35	.	12 46	12 51	13 08	13 11	.	13 17	13 20	13 35	.	13 46	13 51	.	14 08	14 11	14 17	14 20	14 35	.	.	14 46
	d	12 18	12 22	.....	12 37	12 42	12 47	12 53	13 09	13 12	.....	13 18	13 22	13 37	13 42	13 47	13 53	.....	14 09	14 12	14 18	14 22	14 37	14 42	.....	14 47
Fratton	d	12 22	12 26	.	12 41	12 46	12 51	12 57	13 13	13a15	.	13 22	13 26	13 41	13 46	13 51	13 57	.	14 13	14a15	14 22	14 26	14 41	14 46	.	14 51
Hilsea	d		12a30	.....	.....	12a50	.....	.....		.....	.....		13a30	.....	13a50	.....	.....	.....		.....		14a30	.....	14a50	.....	.....
Bedhampton	d	12 30	.	.	.	.	.	13 04	13 20	.	.	13 30	.	.	.	.	14 04	.	14 20	.	14 30	.	.	.	.	.
Havant	a	12 32	.....	.....	12 49	.....	12 59	13 07	13 23	.....	.....	13 32	.....	13 49	.....	13 59	14 07	.....	14 23	.....	14 32	.....	14 49	.....	.....	14 59

		SW 1	SN 1 C	GW ◇	SN 1 D	SW 1	SW 1		SW 1	SN 1	SW 1	SN 1 C	GW ◇	SN 1 D		SW 1	SW 1	SW 1	SN 1	SW 1	SN 1 C		GW ◇	SN 1 D	SW 1	SW 1
Portsmouth Harbour	d	14 48	15 05	15 08	15 14	15 17	15 32	.....	.....	15 43	15 48	16 05	16 08	16 14	.....	16 17	16 32	.....	16 43	16 48	17 05	.....	17 08	17 14	17 17	17 32
Portsmouth & Southsea	a	14 51	15 08	15 11	15 17	15 20	15 35	.	.	15 46	15 51	16 08	16 11	16 17	.	16 20	16 35	.	16 46	16 51	17 08	.	17 11	17 17	17 20	17 35
	d	14 53	15 09	15 12	15 18	15 22	15 37	.....	15 42	15 47	15 53	16 09	16 12	16 18	.....	16 22	16 37	16 42	16 47	16 53	17 09	.....	17 12	17 18	17 22	17 37
Fratton	d	14 57	15 13	15a15	15 22	15 26	15 41	.	15 46	15 51	15 57	16 13	16a15	16 22	.	16 26	16 41	16 46	16 51	16 57	17 13	.	17a15	17 22	17 26	17 41
Hilsea	d	.....		.....		15a30	.....	.....	15a50	.....	.....		.....		.....	16a30	.....	16a50	.....	.....		.....	.....		17a30	.....
Bedhampton	d	15 04	15 20	.	15 30	.	.	.	.	.	16 04	16 20	.	16 30	.	.	.	.	.	17 04	17 20	.	.	17 30	.	.
Havant	a	15 07	15 23	.....	15 32	.....	15 49	.....	.....	15 59	16 07	16 23	.....	16 32	.....	.....	16 49	.....	16 59	17 07	17 23	.....	.....	17 32	.....	17 49

		SW 1	SN 1	SW 1	SN 1 C		GW ◇	SN 1 D	SW 1	SW 1	SW 1	SN 1		SW 1	SN 1 C	GW ◇	SN 1 D	SW 1	SW 1		SW 1	SN 1	SW 1	SN 1 C	GW ◇	SN 1 D
Portsmouth Harbour	d	.....	17 43	17 48	18 05	.....	18 08	18 14	18 17	18 32	.....	18 43	.....	18 48	19 05	19 08	19 14	19 17	19 32	.....	.....	19 43	19 48	20 05	20 08	20 14
Portsmouth & Southsea	a	.	17 46	17 51	18 08	.	18 11	18 17	18 20	18 35	.	18 46	.	18 51	19 08	19 11	19 17	19 20	19 35	.	.	19 46	19 51	20 08	20 11	20 17
	d	17 42	17 47	17 53	18 09	.....	18 12	18 18	18 22	18 37	18 42	18 47	.....	18 53	19 09	19 12	19 18	19 22	19 37	.....	19 42	19 47	19 53	20 09	20 12	20 18
Fratton	d	17 46	17 51	17 57	18 13	.	18a15	18 22	18 26	18 41	18 46	18 51	.	18 57	19 13	19a15	19 22	19 26	19 41	.	19 46	19 51	19 57	20 13	20a15	20 22
Hilsea	d	17a50	.....	.....		.....	.....		18a30	.....	18a50	.....	.....	.....		.....		19a30	.....	.....	19a50	.....	.....		.....	
Bedhampton	d	.	.	18 04	18 20	.	.	18 30	.	.	.	.	.	19 04	19 20	.	19 30	.	.	.	.	.	20 04	20 20	.	20 30
Havant	a	.....	17 59	18 07	18 23	.....	.....	18 32	.....	18 49	.....	18 59	.....	19 07	19 23	.....	19 32	.....	19 49	.....	.....	19 59	20 07	20 23	.....	20 32

		SW 1	SW 1		SW 1	SN 1	SW 1	SN 1 C	SN 1 D	SW 1		SW 1	SW 1	SN 1	SW 1	GW ◇	SN 1		SW 1	SW 1	SW 1	SN 1	SW 1	SW 1		
Portsmouth Harbour	d	20 17	20 32	.....	.....	20 43	20 48	21 05	21 14	21 17	.....	21 32	.....	21 43	21 48	22 03	22 14	.....	22 17	22 32	.....	22 43	22 48	23 17	.....	.....
Portsmouth & Southsea	a	20 20	20 35	.	.	20 46	20 51	21 08	21 17	21 20	.	21 35	.	21 46	21 51	22 11	22 17	.	22 20	22 35	.	22 46	22 51	23 20	.	.
	d	20 22	20 37	.....	20 42	20 47	20 53	21 09	21 18	21 22	.....	21 37	21 42	21 47	21 53	22 12	22 18	.....	22 22	22 37	22 42	22 47	22 53	23 22	.....	.....
Fratton	d	20 26	20 41	.	20 46	20 51	20 57	21 13	21 22	21 26	.	21 41	21 46	21 51	21 57	22a15	22 22	.	22 26	22 41	22 46	22 51	22 57	23 26	.	.
Hilsea	d	20a30	.....	.....	20a50	.....	.....			21a30	.....	.....	21a50	.....	.....	.....	.....	.....	22a30	.....	22a50	.....	.....	23a30	.....	.....
Bedhampton	d	.	.	.	.	.	21 04	21 20	21 30	.	.	.	.	.	22 04	.	22 30	.	.	.	.	.	23 04	.	.	.
Havant	a	.....	20 49	.....	.....	20 59	21 07	21 23	21 32	.....	.....	21 49	.....	21 59	22 07	.....	22 32	.....	.....	22 49	.....	22 59	23 07	.....	.....	.....

For general notes see front of timetable
For details of catering facilities see Directory of Train Operators

A From 27 September
B Until 20 September
C Until 6 September
D From 13 September

Network Diagram for Table 158

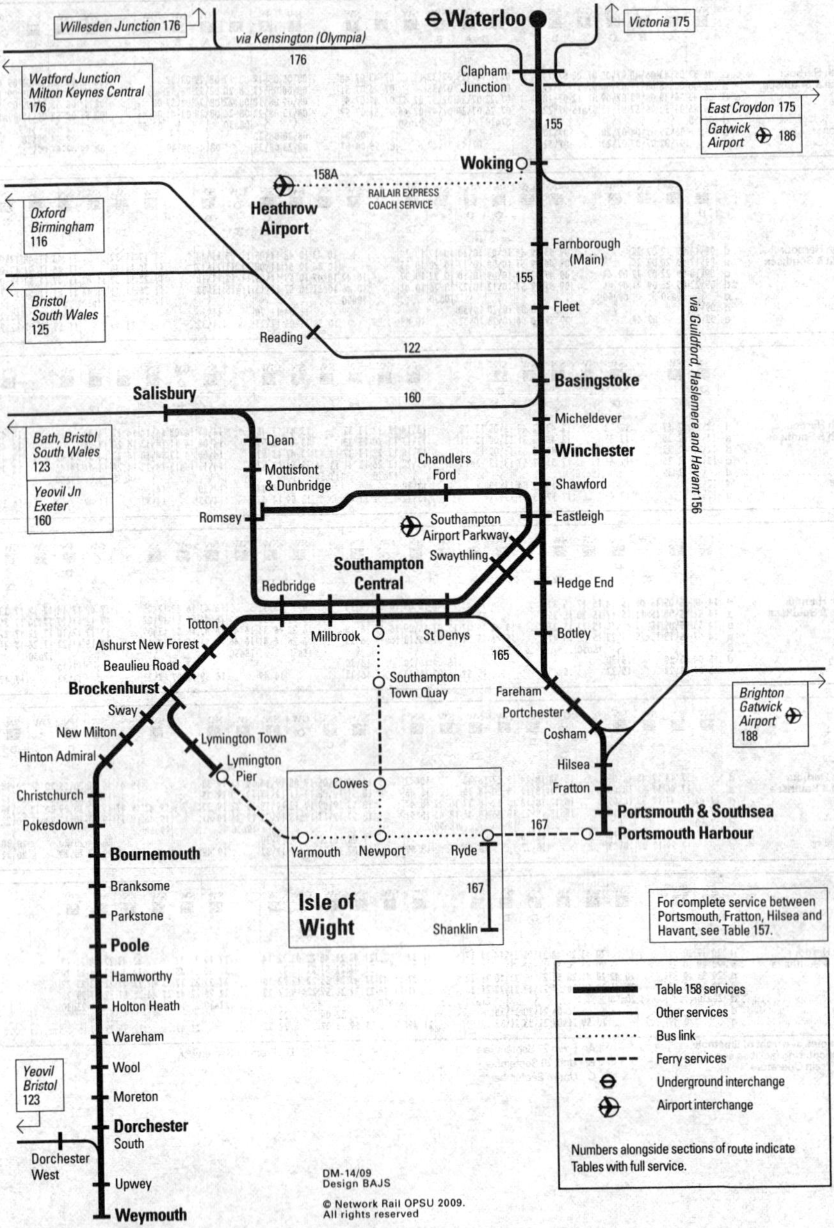
Willesden Junction 176
via Kensington (Olympia)
176
Waterloo
Victoria 175
Clapham Junction
Watford Junction
Milton Keynes Central
176
East Croydon 175
Gatwick Airport 186
155
Woking
158A
RAILAIR EXPRESS COACH SERVICE
Heathrow Airport
Oxford
Birmingham
116
Farnborough (Main)
155
Bristol
South Wales
125
Fleet
Reading
122
via Guildford, Haslemere and Havant 156
Basingstoke
Salisbury
160
Micheldever
Bath, Bristol
South Wales
123
Yeovil Jn
Exeter
160
Dean
Winchester
Mottisfont & Dunbridge
Chandlers Ford
Shawford
Romsey
Eastleigh
Southampton Airport Parkway
Swaythling
Southampton Central
Redbridge
Hedge End
Totton
Millbrook
St Denys
Botley
Ashurst New Forest
165
Beaulieu Road
Southampton Town Quay
Fareham
Brockenhurst
Brighton
Gatwick Airport
188
Sway
Portchester
New Milton
Lymington Town
Cosham
Hinton Admiral
Lymington Pier
Hilsea
Cowes
Fratton
Christchurch
Portsmouth & Southsea
Pokesdown
167
Portsmouth Harbour
Yarmouth
Newport
Ryde
Bournemouth
167
Branksome
Isle of Wight
Shanklin
For complete service between Portsmouth, Fratton, Hilsea and Havant, see Table 157.
Parkstone
Poole
Table 158 services
Hamworthy
Other services
Holton Heath
Bus link
Wareham
Ferry services
Wool
Underground interchange
Yeovil
Bristol
123
Moreton
Airport interchange
Dorchester South
Numbers alongside sections of route indicate Tables with full service.
Dorchester West
Upwey
DM-14/09
Design BAJS
Weymouth

For details of Bank Holiday service alterations, please see first page of Table 149

London → Basingstoke, Southampton, Romsey Lymington, Bournemouth and Weymouth

Network Diagram - see first page of Table 158

Miles	Miles			SW MX 1 ◇	SW MO 1 ◇	SW MO 1 ◇	SW MX 1 ◇	SW MO 1 ◇		SW MX 1	SW MO 1	SW MX 1	SW MX 1 ◇	SW MX 1	SW MO 1 ◇		SW MX 1 ◇	SW MO 1 ◇	SW MO 1	SW MX 1	SW MX 1	SW MX 1	SW 1	SW 1	SW 1
							trolley						trolley		A trolley			trolley							
0	—	**London Waterloo** 15 ⊖	d	21p35	21p35	21p54	22p05					21p42	22p35	22p39	22p54		23p05				23p39	00 05	01 05		
4	—	Clapham Junction 10	d		21b42	22b03	22b12							22b46	23b03		23b12				23b46	00u12	01 14		
24¼	—	**Woking**	d	22p00	22p07	22p28	22p32					22p19	23p00		23p28		23p32				00 08	00 36	01 42		
33¼	—	Farnborough (Main)	d									22p33		23p13							00 18		01s58		
36½	—	Fleet	d									22p38		23p19							00 23				
—	—	Reading 7	d																		23c34				
47¾	—	**Basingstoke**	a		22p26	22p47	22p51					22p58		23p33	23p47		23p52				00 34	00 55	02s12		
—	—		d		22p28	22p48	22p53					23p00		23p34	23p48		23p53				00 36	00 57			
58	—	Micheldever	d			22p58		←				23p10			23p58		00 03								
66½	—	**Winchester**	d	22p33	22p44	23p08	23p09	23p08				23p19	23p33	23p51	00 08		00 12				00 53	01 13	02s29		
69¾	—	Shawford	d			→						23p24		23p55											
—	0	**Romsey**	d							23p07															
—	5¼	Chandlers Ford	d							23p14															
73½	—	Eastleigh 3	a				23p17	23p17		23p22	←	23p30		00 01	00 18		00 20	←	←		01 00	01 21	02s38		
—	0		d				23p18	23p26	23p22	23p22	23p26	23p30		00 02	00 30	00 22	00 21	00 22	00 30	00 30	01 01	01 22		05 05	
—	4½	Hedge End	d					→			23p32	23p36			→	→			00s36	00s36					
—	5½	Botley	d								23p36	23p40							00s39	00s39					
—	11	Fareham	d								23p44	23p48							00s47	00s47					
—	14¼	Portchester	d								23p49	23p53							00s53	00s53					
—	16¾	Cosham	d								23p54	23p59							00s57	00s57					
—	18¼	Hilsea	a								23p59	00 04													
—	20½	Fratton	a								00 04	00 08							01s05	01s05					
—	21½	**Portsmouth & Southsea**	a								00 08	00 11							01s08	01s08					
—	22¼	**Portsmouth Harbour**	a								00 13	00 16							01 12	01 12					
75	—	**Southampton Airport Parkwy** ✈	d	22p42	22p53		23p23		23p27	23p26			23p42	00 06			00 26	00 27			01 07	01 27	02s43	05 09	
75¾	—	Swaythling	d							23p28														05 12	
77¼	—	St Denys	d							23p31							00s30	00s31					02s48	05 15	
79¼	—	**Southampton Central**	a	22p49	23p00		23p30		23p34	23p37			23p49	00 13			00 35	00 36			01 15	01 36	02 53	05 20	
—	—		d	22p51	23p03		23p31		23p35	23p38			23p51				00 36	00 37				01 37			
80¼	—	Millbrook (Hants)	d							23p40															
82	0	Redbridge	d							23p44															
—	6	**Romsey**	d							23p56															
—	9¾	Mottisfont & Dunbridge	d							00 01															
—	13½	Dean	d							00 06															
—	22½	**Salisbury**	a							00 19															
82½	—	Totton	d				23p37		23p41								00s41	00s42				01s42			
85½	—	Ashurst New Forest	d				23p41		23p45																
88	—	Beaulieu Road	d																						
92¾	—	**Brockenhurst** 3	a	23p04	23p16		23p49		23p53				00 04				00s52	00s53				01s53			
—	0		d	23p05	23p17		23p50		23p54				00 05												05 59
—	4¾	Lymington Town	d																						06 07
—	5¼	**Lymington Pier**	a																						06 09
—	—	Yarmouth (I.O.W.) ⛴	a																						
95½	—	Sway	d				23p55		23p59																
98½	—	New Milton	d		23p24		23p59		00 04								01s00	01s01				02s01			
101	—	Hinton Admiral	d				00 04		00 08																
104½	—	Christchurch	d				00 09		00 13								01s07	01s08				02s08			
106¼	—	Pokesdown	d				00 12		00 16								01s11	01s12				02s12			
108	—	**Bournemouth**	a	23p25	23p35		00 16		00 21				00 22				01 15	01 16				02 16			
—	—		d	23p29	23p40		00 18		00 22				00 24				01 16	01 18							
110¾	—	Branksome	d	23p35	23p45		00 23		00 28				00 29				01s21	01s23							
112	—	Parkstone (Dorset)	d	23p38	23p48		00 26		00 31				00 32				01s24	01s26							
113¾	—	**Poole** 3	a	23p41	23p51		00 30		00 35				00 36				01 30	01 30							
—	—		d	23p42	23p52																				
116	—	Hamworthy	d	23p47	23p57																				
118¾	—	Holton Heath	d																						
120¾	—	Wareham	d	23p54	00 04																				
125¾	—	Wool	d	00 01	00 11																				
130¼	—	Moreton (Dorset)	d	00 07	00 17																				
135¾	—	**Dorchester South**	d	00 15	00 25																				
—	—	Dorchester West	d																						
140½	—	Upwey	d	00 21	00 32																				
142¾	—	**Weymouth**	a	00 26	00 36																				

For general notes see front of timetable
For details of catering facilities see Directory of Train Operators

A trolley to Eastleigh
b Previous night.
Stops to pick up only
c Tuesdays to Fridays

During July and August ferry connection times to and from Yarmouth IOW are subject to alteration, please contact www.wightliink.co.uk or 0871 376 1000 for further details.

For details of Bank Holiday service alterations, please see first page of Table 149

London → Basingstoke, Southampton, Romsey Lymington, Bournemouth and Weymouth

Network Diagram - see first page of Table 158

		SW	SW	SW	SW	SW	SW	SW	SW	SW	GW	SW	GW	SW		SW	SW	SW	SW	SW	SW	GW	SW	SW	SW
		1	1	1	1	1	1	1	1	1	◇	1	◇	1 ◇		1	1	1	1	1	1	◇	1	1 ◇	1
		A	B				A	B		C															
London Waterloo 15 ⊖	d													05 30										06 30	
Clapham Junction 10	d													05u37										06u37	
Woking	d													06 01									06 19	06 57	
Farnborough (Main)	d																						06 33		
Fleet	d																						06 38		
Reading 7	d													*05 39*							*06 07*			*06 39*	
Basingstoke	a													06 20									06 58	07 16	
	d						05 40	05 40						06 21							06 55		07 00	07 18	
Micheldever	d						05 50	05 50															07 10		
Winchester	d						05 59	05 59				06 18		06 38							07 11		07 19	07 34	
Shawford	d											06 23									07 16				
Romsey	d									05 58										07 07					
Chandlers Ford	d									06 06										07 14					
Eastleigh 3	a						06 07	06 07		06 11		06 28		06 47						07 20	07 22		07 29	07 43	
	d					06 00	06 08	06 08		06 13		06 30		06 48					07 02	07 21	07 24		07 30	07 44	
Hedge End	d					06 06						06 36							07 08				07 36		
Botley	d					06 10						06 40							07 12				07 40		
Fareham	d					06 18					06 24	06 50							07 20			07 18	07 48		
Portchester	d					06 23						06 55							07 25				07 53		
Cosham	d					06 28					06 15	07 00							07 29				07 58		
Hilsea	a					06 33						07 05							07 35				08 03		
Fratton	a					06 38						07 09							07 39				08 07		
Portsmouth & Southsea	a					06 44						07 12							07 42				08 11		
Portsmouth Harbour	a					06 49						07 17							07 48				08 16		
Southampton Airport Parkwy ✈	d						06 13	06 13		06 17				06 53						07 25	07 29			07 49	
Swaythling	d						06 15	06 15		06 20										07 28	07 31				
St Denys	d						06 18	06 18		06 24										07 31	07 34				
Southampton Central	a						06 23	06 23		06 29	06 45			07 00						07 36	07 39	07 45		07 57	
	d						06 25	06 25		06 30	06 46			07 01			07 18			07 38		07 47		08 00	
Millbrook (Hants)	d									06 33							07 20			07 40					
Redbridge	d									06 36							07 24			07 44					
Romsey	d									06 44	07 00									07 52		08 00			
Mottisfont & Dunbridge	d									06 49										07 57					
Dean	d									06 55										08 02					
Salisbury	a									07 07	07 18									08 15		08 20			
Totton	d						06 30	06 30						07 07			07 27							08 05	
Ashurst New Forest	d						06 35	06 35									07 31								
Beaulieu Road	d																07 36								
Brockenhurst 3	a						06 43	06 43						07 17			07 42							08 16	
	d			06 16	06 29		06 44	06 44	06 59					07 18		07 29	07 44	07 59						08 17	08 29
Lymington Town	d				06 37				07 07							07 37		08 07							08 37
Lymington Pier	a				06 39				07 09							07 39		08 09							08 39
Yarmouth (I.O.W.) ⛴	a				*07b15*				*07b45*									*08b45*							*09b30*
Sway	d			06 20			06 48	06 48						07 23			07 48							08 21	
New Milton	d			06 25			06 53	06 53						07 28			07 53							08 26	
Hinton Admiral	d			06 29			06 57	06 57						07 32			07 57							08 30	
Christchurch	d			06 34			07 02	07 02						07 37			08 02							08 35	
Pokesdown	d			06 38			07 06	07 06						07 40			08 06							08 39	
Bournemouth	a			06 42			07 10	07 10						07 44			08 10							08 43	
	d	06 11	06 11	06 44			07 11	07 11						07 46			08 11							08 44	
Branksome	d	06 16	06 16	06 49			07 16	07 16						07 51			08 16							08 49	
Parkstone (Dorset)	d	06 19	06 19	06 52			07 19	07 19						07 54			08 19							08 52	
Poole 4	a	06 23	06 23	06 55			07 23	07 23						07 57			08 23							08 56	
	d	06 24	06 24	06 57			07 24	07 24						07 58			08 24							08 57	
Hamworthy	d	06 29	06 29	07 02			07 29	07 29						08 03			08 29							09 02	
Holton Heath	d	06 33	06 33	07 06			07 33	07 33						08 07			08 33								
Wareham	d	06 38	06 38	07 11			07 38	07 38						08 12			08 38							09 09	
Wool	d	06 44	06 44	07 17			07 44	07 44						08 19			08 44							09 15	
Moreton (Dorset)	d	06 50	06 50	07 23			07 50	07 50						08 25			08 50							09 21	
Dorchester South	d	06 58	06 58	07 31			07 58	07 58						08 33			08 58							09 29	
Dorchester West	d												08 08												
Upwey	d	07 05	07 05	07 38			08 05	08 05					08 15	08 40			09 05							09 36	
Weymouth	a	07 09	07 14	07 42			08 09	08 14					08 21	08 44			09 09							09 40	

For general notes see front of timetable
For details of catering facilities see Directory of Train Operators

A Until 25 September
B From 28 September
C From Salisbury
b By ship

During July and August ferry connection times to and from Yarmouth IOW are subject to alteration, please contact www.wightliink.co.uk or 0871 376 1000 for further details.

London → Basingstoke, Southampton, Romsey Lymington, Bournemouth and Weymouth

For details of Bank Holiday service alterations, please see first page of Table 149

Network Diagram - see first page of Table 158

Station		SW	GW	SW	SW	XC	SW	SW	GW	SW	SW	GW	SW
		1	◇	1	1	1 ◇ A	1	1 ◇	◇	1	1	◇ B	1 ◇ C
London Waterloo 15 ⊖	d	06 12			06 42			07 35		07 39			08 05
Clapham Junction 10	d	06u19			06u49					07u46			08u12
Woking	d	06 50			07 19			08 00					
Farnborough (Main)	d	07 04			07 33					08 13			
Fleet	d	07 09			07 38					08 19			
Reading 7	d				*07 07*	07 45				*08 07*			
Basingstoke	a	07 28			07 56	08 08		08 19		08 34			08 48
	d	07 30			08 00	08 10		08 20		08 36			08 50
Micheldever	d	07 41			08 10								
Winchester	d	07 50			08 19	08 25		08 37		08 52			09 06
Shawford	d	07 55			08 24					08 57			
Romsey	d			08 07									
Chandlers Ford	d			08 14									
Eastleigh 3	a	08 00		08 20	08 31			08 46		09 02			
	d	08 02		08 21	08 31			08 47		09 03			
Hedge End	d				08 36								
Botley	d				08 41								
Fareham	d				08 50				08 47				
Portchester	d				08 55								
Cosham	d				09 00								
Hilsea	a				09 05								
Fratton	a				09 09								
Portsmouth & Southsea	a				09 13								
Portsmouth Harbour	a				09 18								
Southampton Airport Parkwy ✈	d	08 06		08 25		08 33		08 51		09 08			09 15
Swaythling	d	08 09		08 28									
St Denys	d	08 12		08 31									
Southampton Central	a	08 17		08 36		08 43		08 58	09 08	09 16			09 22
	d	08 19	08 23	08 38		08 43		09 00	09 10	09 30 →			09 24
Millbrook (Hants)	d	08 21		08 40									
Redbridge	d	08 25		08 44									
Romsey	d		08 35	08 52					09 21				
Mottisfont & Dunbridge	d			08 57									
Dean	d			09 02									
Salisbury	a		09 00	09 15					09 40				
Totton	d	08 28						09 05					
Ashurst New Forest	d	08 32											
Beaulieu Road	d	08 37											
Brockenhurst 3	a	08 43				08 57		09 16					09 37
	d	08 44				08 57	08 59	09 17			09 29		09 38
Lymington Town	d						09 07				09 37		
Lymington Pier	a						09 09				09 39		
Yarmouth (I.O.W.) ⛴	a										*10b15*		
Sway	d	08 48						09 21					
New Milton	d	08 53						09 26					09 45
Hinton Admiral	d	08 57						09 30					
Christchurch	d	09 02						09 35					09 52
Pokesdown	d	09 06						09 39					09 56
Bournemouth	a	09 10				09 15		09 43					10 00
	d	09 11						09 44					10 04
Branksome	d	09 16						09 49					
Parkstone (Dorset)	d	09 19						09 52					
Poole 4	a	09 23						09 56					10 13
	d	09 24						09 57					10 14
Hamworthy	d	09 29						10 02					10 20
Holton Heath	d	09 33											10 27
Wareham	d	09 38						10 09					10c35
Wool	d	09 44											10 42
Moreton (Dorset)	d	09 50											10 48
Dorchester South	d	09 58						10 27					10 56
Dorchester West	d											10 42	
Upwey	d	10 05										10 49	11 02
Weymouth	a	10 09						10 35				10 56	11 07

Station		SW	SW	SW	XC	SW	SW	SW	GW	SW	SW	SW	SW
		1	1	1	1 ◇	1	1 ◇ C	1	◇	1	1	1 ◇ C	1
London Waterloo 15 ⊖	d			08 09			08 35			08 39		09 05	
Clapham Junction 10	d									08u46		09u12	
Woking	d												
Farnborough (Main)	d			08 35			09 00			09 13			
Fleet	d			08 45						09 19			
Reading 7	d				08 45							*09 07*	
Basingstoke	a			08 59	09 08					09 34		09 48	
	d			09 00	09 10					09 36		09 50	
Micheldever	d			09 10									
Winchester	d			09 19	09 25		09 33			09 52		10 06	
Shawford	d									09 57			
Romsey	d		09 07										
Chandlers Ford	d		09 14										
Eastleigh 3	a		09 20	09 29						10 02			
	d		09 21	09 30						10 03			
Hedge End	d			09 36									
Botley	d			09 40									
Fareham	d			09 48									
Portchester	d			09 53					09 47				
Cosham	d			09 58									
Hilsea	a			10 03									
Fratton	a			10 07									
Portsmouth & Southsea	a			10 11									
Portsmouth Harbour	a			10 18									
Southampton Airport Parkwy ✈	d		09 25		09 33		09 42			10 08		10 15	
Swaythling	d		09 28										
St Denys	d		09 31										
Southampton Central	a	←	09 36		09 43		09 49		10 08	10 17		10 22	←
	d	09 30	09 38		09 43		09 51		10 10	10 30 →		10 24	10 30
Millbrook (Hants)	d		09 40										
Redbridge	d		09 44										
Romsey	d		09 52						10 21				
Mottisfont & Dunbridge	d		09 57										
Dean	d		10 02										
Salisbury	a		10 15						10 40				
Totton	d	09 35											10 35
Ashurst New Forest	d	09 40											10 40
Beaulieu Road	d												10 44
Brockenhurst 3	a	09 49			09 57		10 04	←				10 37	10 51
	d	10 16			09 57	09 59	10 05	10 16			10 29	10 38	11 16
Lymington Town	d	→				10 07					10 37		→
Lymington Pier	a					10 09					10 39		
Yarmouth (I.O.W.) ⛴	a					*11b00*							
Sway	d							10 20					
New Milton	d							10 25				10 45	
Hinton Admiral	d							10 29					
Christchurch	d							10 34				10 52	
Pokesdown	d							10 38				10 56	
Bournemouth	a				10 15		10 20	10 42				11 00	
	d						10 24	10 43				11 04	
Branksome	d						10 29	10 48					
Parkstone (Dorset)	d						10 32	10 51					
Poole 4	a						10 36	10 55				11 13	
	d						10 37					11 14	
Hamworthy	d						10 42					11 19	
Holton Heath	d											11 23	
Wareham	d						10 49					11 28	
Wool	d											11 35	
Moreton (Dorset)	d											11 41	
Dorchester South	d						11 05					11 49	
Dorchester West	d												
Upwey	d											11 55	
Weymouth	a						11 13					12 00	

For general notes see front of timetable
For details of catering facilities see Directory of Train Operators

A From Birmingham New Street (Table 116)
B From Worcester Shrub Hill (Table 57)
C ⊡ to Bournemouth

b By ship
c Arr. 1031

During July and August ferry connection times to and from Yarmouth IOW are subject to alteration, please contact www.wightliink.co.uk or 0871 376 1000 for further details.

For details of Bank Holiday service alterations, please see first page of Table 149

London → Basingstoke, Southampton, Romsey Lymington, Bournemouth and Weymouth

Network Diagram - see first page of Table 158

		SW	GW	GW	SW	XC	SW	SW	XC	SW	SW	GW	SW	SW	SW	SW	SW	SW	SW	XC	SW	SW	SW	GW
		1	◇ A	◇ B	1	R 1 C 🛒	1	1	R 1 🛒	1 ◇ D 🚌	1	◇ 🛒	1	1	1 ◇ D 🚌	1	1	1	1	1 ◇ 🛒	1	1 ◇ D 🚌	1	◇ 🛒
London Waterloo 15 ⊖	d				09 09					09 35			09 39		10 05				10 09			10 35		
Clapham Junction 10	d												09u46		10u12									
Woking	d				09 35					10 00									10 35			11 00		
Farnborough (Main)	d				09 45								10 13						10 45					
Fleet	d												10 19											
Reading 7	d					09 45			09 45				*09 45*		*10 07*					10 45				
Basingstoke	a				09 58	10 08			10 08				10 34		10 48				10 58	11 08				
	d				10 00	10 10			10 10				10 36		10 50				11 00	11 10				
Micheldever	d				10 10														11 10					
Winchester	d				10 19	10 25			10 25	10 33			10 52		11 06				11 19	11 25		11 33		
Shawford	d												10 57											
Romsey	d	10 07															11 07	11 11						
Chandlers Ford	d	10 14															11 14	11a55						
Eastleigh 3	a	10 20			10 29								11 02				11 20		11 29					
	d	10 21			10 30								11 03				11 21		11 30					
Hedge End	d				10 36														11 36					
Botley	d				10 40														11 40					
Fareham	d		10 14		10 48							10 47							11 48					11 47
Portchester	d				10 53														11 53					
Cosham	d				10 58							10 39							11 58					
Hilsea	a				11 03														12 03					
Fratton	a				11 07														12 07					
Portsmouth & Southsea	a				11 11														12 11					
Portsmouth Harbour	a				11 18														12 18					
Southampton Airport Parkwy ✈	d	10 25				10 33			10 33	10 42			11 08		11 15		11 25			11 33		11 42		
Swaythling	d	10 28															11 28							
St Denys	d	10 31															11 31							
Southampton Central	a	10 36	10 41			10 43		←	10 43	10 49		11 08	11 17		11 22	←	11 36			11 43		11 49		12 08
	d	10 44 →	10 42			10 43		10 44	10 45	10 51		11 10	11 30 →		11 24	11 30	11 38			11 43		11 51		12 10
Millbrook (Hants)	d							10 48									11 40							
Redbridge	d							10 51									11 44	11a19						
Romsey	d		10 54					10 59				11 21					11 52							12 21
Mottisfont & Dunbridge	d							11 04									11 57							
Dean	d							11 10									12 02							
Salisbury	a		11 13					11 22				11 40					12 15							12 40
Totton	d															11 35								
Ashurst New Forest	d															11 40								
Beaulieu Road	d															11 44								
Brockenhurst 3	a					10 57			10 57	11 04	←				11 37	11 51				11 57		12 04	←	
	d					10 57	10 59		10 57	11 05	11 16			11 29	11 38	12 16				11 57	11 59	12 05	12 16	
Lymington Town	d						11 07							11 37		→					12 07			
Lymington Pier	a						11 09							11 39							12 09			
Yarmouth (I.O.W.) ⛴	a						*11b45*														*12b45*			
Sway	d										11 20												12 20	
New Milton	d										11 25				11 45								12 25	
Hinton Admiral	d										11 29												12 29	
Christchurch	d										11 34				11 52								12 34	
Pokesdown	d										11 38				11 56								12 38	
Bournemouth	a					11 15			11 15	11 20	11 42				12 00					12 15		12 20	12 42	
	d									11 24	11 43				12 04							12 24	12 43	
Branksome	d									11 29	11 48											12 29	12 48	
Parkstone (Dorset)	d									11 32	11 51											12 32	12 51	
Poole 4	a									11 36	11 55				12 13							12 36	12 55	
	d									11 37					12 14							12 37		
Hamworthy	d									11 42					12 19							12 42		
Holton Heath	d														12 23									
Wareham	d									11 49					12 28							12 49		
Wool	d														12 35									
Moreton (Dorset)	d														12 41									
Dorchester South	d									12 05					12 49							13 05		
Dorchester West	d			11 51																				
Upwey	d			12 02											12 55									
Weymouth	a			12 08						12 13					13 00							13 13		

For general notes see front of timetable
For details of catering facilities see Directory of Train Operators

A To Great Malvern (Table 71)
B From Gloucester (Table 134)
C Until 4 September
D 🚌 to Bournemouth
b By ship

During July and August ferry connection times to and from Yarmouth IOW are subject to alteration, please contact www.wightliink.co.uk or 0871 376 1000 for further details.

For details of Bank Holiday service alterations, please see first page of Table 149

London → Basingstoke, Southampton, Romsey Lymington, Bournemouth and Weymouth

Network Diagram - see first page of Table 158

		SW	SW	SW	GW	SW	SW	GW	SW	XC	SW	SW	SW	GW	SW	SW		SW	SW	SW	SW	XC	SW	SW	SW
		1	1	1 ◇	◇	1	1	◇	1	1 ◇	1	1 ◇	1	◇	1	1		1 ◇	1	1	1	1 ◇	1	1 ◇	1
				A ☕				B		🛒		A ☕		🛒				A ☕				🛒		A ☕	
London Waterloo 15 ⊖	d	10 39		11 05					11 09			11 35			11 39			12 05			12 09			12 35	
Clapham Junction 10	d	10u46		11u12											11u46			12u12							
Woking	d								11 35			12 00									12 35			13 00	
Farnborough (Main)	d	11 13							11 45						12 13						12 45				
Fleet	d	11 19													12 19										
Reading 7	d	*11 07*								11 45								*12 07*				12 45			
Basingstoke	a	11 34		11 48					11 58	12 08					12 34			12 48			12 58	13 08			
	d	11 36		11 50					12 00	12 10					12 36			12 50			13 00	13 10			
Micheldever	d								12 10												13 10				
Winchester	d	11 52		12 06					12 19	12 25		12 33			12 52			13 06			13 19	13 25		13 33	
Shawford	d	11 57													12 57										
Romsey	d						12 07													13 07					
Chandlers Ford	d						12 14													13 14					
Eastleigh 3	a	12 02					12 20		12 29						13 02					13 20	13 29				
	d	12 03					12 21		12 30						13 03					13 21	13 30				
Hedge End	d								12 36												13 36				
Botley	d								12 40												13 40				
Fareham	d								12 48					12 47							13 48				
Portchester	d								12 53												13 53				
Cosham	d								12 58												13 58				
Hilsea	a								13 03												14 03				
Fratton	a								13 07												14 07				
Portsmouth & Southsea	a								13 11												14 11				
Portsmouth Harbour	a								13 18												14 18				
Southampton Airport Parkwy ✈	d	12 08		12 15			12 25			12 33		12 42			13 08			13 15		13 25		13 33		13 42	
Swaythling	d						12 28													13 28					
St Denys	d						12 31													13 31					
Southampton Central	a	12 17		12 22		←	12 36			12 41		12 49		13 08	13 17			13 22	←	13 36		13 41		13 49	
	d	12 30 →		12 24	12 26	12 30	12 38			12 43		12 51		13 10	13 30 →			13 24	13 30	13 38		13 43		13 51	
Millbrook (Hants)	d						12 40													13 40					
Redbridge	d						12 44													13 44					
Romsey	d				12 39		12 52							13 21						13 52					
Mottisfont & Dunbridge	d						12 57													13 57					
Dean	d						13 02													14 02					
Salisbury	a				13 02		13 15							13 40						14 15					
Totton	d					12 35													13 35						
Ashurst New Forest	d					12 40													13 40						
Beaulieu Road	d																								
Brockenhurst 3	a			12 37		12 51				12 56		13 04	←					13 37	13 51			13 56		14 04	←
	d		12 29	12 38		13 16				12 57	12 59	13 05	13 16			13 29		13 38	14 16			13 57	13 59	14 05	14 16
Lymington Town	d		12 37			→					13 07					13 37			→				14 07		
Lymington Pier	a		12 39								13 09					13 39							14 09		
Yarmouth (I.O.W.) ⛴	a										*13b45*					*14b30*							*15c15*		
Sway	d												13 20												14 20
New Milton	d			12 45									13 25					13 45							14 25
Hinton Admiral	d												13 29												14 29
Christchurch	d			12 52									13 34					13 52							14 34
Pokesdown	d			12 56									13 38					13 56							14 38
Bournemouth	a			13 00						13 15		13 20	13 42					14 00				14 15		14 20	14 42
	d			13 04								13 24	13 43					14 04						14 24	14 43
Branksome	d											13 29	13 48											14 29	14 48
Parkstone (Dorset)	d											13 32	13 51											14 32	14 51
Poole 4	a			13 13								13 36	13 55					14 13						14 36	14 55
	d			13 14								13 37						14 14						14 37	
Hamworthy	d			13 19								13 42						14 19						14 42	
Holton Heath	d			13 23														14 23							
Wareham	d			13 28								13 49						14 28						14 49	
Wool	d			13 35														14 35							
Moreton (Dorset)	d			13 41														14 41							
Dorchester South	d			13 49								14 05						14 49						15 05	
Dorchester West	d							13 54																	
Upwey	d			13 55				14 02										14 55							
Weymouth	a			14 00				14 09				14 13						15 00						15 13	

For general notes see front of timetable
For details of catering facilities see Directory of Train Operators

A ☕ to Bournemouth
B From Gloucester (Table 134)
b By ship
c Mondays, Tuesdays, Thursdays and Fridays only. By ship

During July and August ferry connection times to and from Yarmouth IOW are subject to alteration, please contact www.wightliink.co.uk or 0871 376 1000 for further details.

For details of Bank Holiday service alterations, please see first page of Table 149

London → Basingstoke, Southampton, Romsey Lymington, Bournemouth and Weymouth

Network Diagram - see first page of Table 158

		GW	SW	SW	SW	SW	SW	SW	XC	SW	SW	SW	GW	SN	SW	SW	SW	SW	SW	GW	SW	XC	SW	SW	SW
		◇	1	1	1 ◇	1	1	1	1 ◇	1	1 ◇	1	◇	1	1	1	1 ◇	1	1	◇	1	1 ◇	1	1 ◇	1
					A						A			B			A			C				A	
		🛒			🍽				🛒		🍽		🛒				🍽					🛒		🍽	
London Waterloo 15 ⊖	d		12 39		13 05			13 09			13 35				13 39		14 05				14 09			14 35	
Clapham Junction 10	d		12u46		13u12										13u46		14u12								
Woking	d							13 35			14 00										14 35			15 00	
Farnborough (Main)	d		13 13					13 45							14 13						14 45				
Fleet	d		13 19												14 19										
Reading 7	d		*13 07*						13 45						*14 07*							14 45			
Basingstoke	a		13 34		13 48			13 59	14 08						14 34		14 48				14 58	15 07			
	d		13 36		13 50			14 00	14 10						14 36		14 50				15 00	15 10			
Micheldever	d							14 10													15 10				
Winchester	d		13 52		14 06			14 20	14 25		14 33				14 52		15 06				15 19	15 25		15 33	
Shawford	d		13 57												14 57										
Romsey	d						14 07												15 07						
Chandlers Ford	d						14 14												15 14						
Eastleigh 3	a		14 02				14 20	14 29							15 02				15 20		15 29				
	d		14 03				14 21	14 30						14 43	15 03				15 21		15 30				
Hedge End	d							14 36													15 36				
Botley	d							14 40													15 40				
Fareham	d	13 47						14 48					14 47	14a59							15 48				
Portchester	d							14 53													15 53				
Cosham	d							14 58													15 58				
Hilsea	a							15 03													16 03				
Fratton	a							15 07													16 07				
Portsmouth & Southsea	a							15 11													16 11				
Portsmouth Harbour	a							15 18													16 18				
Southampton Airport Parkwy ✈	d		14 08		14 15		14 25		14 33		14 42				15 08		15 15		15 25			15 33		15 42	
Swaythling	d						14 28												15 28						
St Denys	d						14 31												15 31						
Southampton Central	a	14 08	14 17		14 22	←	14 36		14 40		14 49		15 08		15 17		15 22	←	15 36			15 41		15 49	
	d	14 10	14 30 →		14 24	14 30	14 38		14 43		14 51		15 10		15 30 →		15 24	15 30	15 38			15 43		15 51	
Millbrook (Hants)	d						14 40												15 40						
Redbridge	d						14 44												15 44						
Romsey	d	14 21					14 52						15 21						15 52						
Mottisfont & Dunbridge	d						14 57												15 57						
Dean	d						15 02												16 02						
Salisbury	a	14 40					15 15						15 40						16 15						
Totton	d					14 35												15 35							
Ashurst New Forest	d					14 40												15 40							
Beaulieu Road	d																								
Brockenhurst 3	a				14 37	14 51			14 56		15 04	←					15 37	15 51				15 56		16 04	←
	d			14 29	14 38	15 16			14 57	14 59	15 05	15 16				15 29	15 38	16 28				15 57	15 59	16 05	16 28
Lymington Town	d			14 37		→				15 07						15 37		→					16 07		
Lymington Pier	a			14 39						15 09						15 39							16 09		
Yarmouth (I.O.W.) ⛴	a			*15b15*						*16c00*													*16c45*		
Sway	d											15 20													16 32
New Milton	d				14 45							15 25					15 45								16 37
Hinton Admiral	d											15 29													16 41
Christchurch	d				14 52							15 34					15 52								16 46
Pokesdown	d				14 56							15 38					15 56								16 50
Bournemouth	a				15 00				15 15		15 20	15 42					16 00					16 15		16 20	16 54
	d				15 04						15 24	15 43					16 04							16 24	16 55
Branksome	d										15 29	15 48												16 29	17 00
Parkstone (Dorset)	d										15 32	15 51												16 32	17 03
Poole 4	a				15 13						15 36	15 55					16 13							16 36	17 07
	d				15 14						15 37						16 14							16 37	
Hamworthy	d				15 19						15 42						16 19							16 42	
Holton Heath	d				15 23												16 23								
Wareham	d				15 28						15 49						16 28							16 49	
Wool	d				15 35												16 35								
Moreton (Dorset)	d				15 41												16 41								
Dorchester South	d				15 49						16 05						16 49							17 05	
Dorchester West	d																			16 57					
Upwey	d				15 55												16 55			17 03					
Weymouth	a				16 00						16 13						17 00			17 10				17 13	

For general notes see front of timetable
For details of catering facilities see Directory of Train Operators

A 🍽 to Bournemouth
B To Brighton (Table 188)
C From Great Malvern (Table 71)

b By ship. Wednesdays arr. 1600
c By ship

During July and August ferry connection times to and from Yarmouth IOW are subject to alteration, please contact www.wightliink.co.uk or 0871 376 1000 for further details.

For details of Bank Holiday service alterations, please see first page of Table 149

London → Basingstoke, Southampton, Romsey Lymington, Bournemouth and Weymouth

Network Diagram - see first page of Table 158

	GW	SW	SW	SW	SW		SW	SW	XC	SW	SW		SW	GW	SW	SW	SW	SW	SW	SW	GW	SW	XC	SW
	◇	1	1	1 ◇	1		1	1	1 ◇	1	1 ◇		1	◇	1	1	1	1 ◇	1	1	◇	1	1 ◇	1
				A							A										B			
	⊼			⌸					⊼		⌸			⊼				⌸					⊼	
London Waterloo 15 ⊖ d		14 39		15 05				15 09			15 35					15 39		16 05				16 09		
Clapham Junction 10 d		14u46		15u12												15u46		16u12						
Woking d								15 35			16 00											16 35		
Farnborough (Main) d		15 13						15 45								16 13						16 45		
Fleet d		15 19														16 19								
Reading 7 d		*15 07*							15 45							*16 07*							16 45	
Basingstoke a		15 34		15 48				15 58	16 08							16 34		16 48				16 58	17 08	
d		15 36		15 50				16 00	16 10						16 24	16 36		16 50				17 00	17 10	
Micheldever d								16 10														17 10		
Winchester d		15 52		16 06				16 19	16 25		16 33		16 38		16 43	16 52		17 06				17 19	17 25	
Shawford d		15 57											16 42			16 57								
Romsey d							16 07													17 07				
Chandlers Ford d							16 14													17 14				
Eastleigh 8 a		16 02					16 20	16 29					16 48		16 51	17 02				17 20		17 29		
d		16 03					16 21	16 30					16 49		16 52	17 03				17 21		17 30		
Hedge End d								16 36							16 58							17 36		
Botley d								16 40							17 02							17 40		
Fareham d	15 47							16 48						16 47	17 10							17 48		
Portchester d								16 53							17 15							17 53		
Cosham d								16 58						16 39	17 20							17 58		
Hilsea a								17 03														18 03		
Fratton a								17 07							17 27							18 08		
Portsmouth & Southsea a								17 11							17 33							18 11		
Portsmouth Harbour a								17 18							17 38							18 20		
Southampton Airport Parkway ✈ d		16 08		16 15			16 25		16 33		16 42		16 53			17 08		17 15		17 25			17 33	
Swaythling d							16 28						16 56							17 28				
St Denys d							16 31						16 59							17 31				
Southampton Central a	16 08	16 17		16 22	⟵		16 36		16 41		16 49		17 04	17 08		17 17		17 22	⟵	17 36			17 41	
d	16 10	16 30 ⟶		16 24	16 30		16 38		16 43		16 54	16 56	17 06	17 10		17 30 ⟶		17 24	17 30	17 38			17 43	
Millbrook (Hants) d							16 40													17 40				
Redbridge d							16 44													17 44				
Romsey d	16 21						16 52							17 21						17 52				
Mottisfont & Dunbridge d							16 57													17 57				
Dean d							17 02													18 02				
Salisbury a	16 40						17 15							17 40						18 15				
Totton d					16 35							17 01	17a11						17 35					
Ashurst New Forest d					16 40							17 06							17 40					
Beaulieu Road d					16 44														17 44					
Brockenhurst 3 a				16 37	16 51				16 56		17 06	17 14						17 37	17 51				17 56	
d			16 29	16 38					16 57	16 59	17 08	17 16					17 29	17 38					17 57	17 59
Lymington Town d			16 37							17 07							17 37							18 07
Lymington Pier a			16 39							17 09							17 39							18 09
Yarmouth (I.O.W.) ⛴ a			*17b30*														*18b15*							*19b00*
Sway d				16 43								17 20						17 43						
New Milton d				16 48								17 25						17 48						
Hinton Admiral d				16 52								17 29						17 52						
Christchurch d				16 57								17 34						17 57						
Pokesdown d				17 00								17 38						18 00						
Bournemouth a				17 04					17 15		17 23	17 42						18 04					18 15	
d				17 06							17 24	17 43						18 09						
Branksome d											17 29	17 48												
Parkstone (Dorset) d											17 32	17 51												
Poole 4 a				17 15							17 36	17 55						18 18						
d				17 16							17 37							18 19						
Hamworthy d				17 21							17 42							18 24						
Holton Heath d				17 25														18 28						
Wareham d				17 30							17 49							18 33						
Wool d				17 36							17 55							18 39						
Moreton (Dorset) d				17 42														18 45						
Dorchester South d				17 50							18 06							18 53						
Dorchester West d																					18 58			
Upwey d				17 57														19 00			19 05			
Weymouth a				18 02							18 15							19 06			19 12			

For general notes see front of timetable
For details of catering facilities see Directory of Train Operators

A ⌸ to Bournemouth
B From Great Malvern (Table 71)
b By ship

During July and August ferry connection times to and from Yarmouth IOW are subject to alteration, please contact www.wightlink.co.uk or 0871 376 1000 for further details.

For details of Bank Holiday service alterations, please see first page of Table 149

London → Basingstoke, Southampton, Romsey Lymington, Bournemouth and Weymouth

Network Diagram - see first page of Table 158

		SW 1 ◇ A 🛒		GW ◇ 🍴	SW 1	SW 1	SW 1	SW 1 ◇ B 🛒		SW 1	GW ◇ C	SW 1	XC 1 ◇ 🍴	SW 1	GW ◇ D	SW 1 ◇ B 🛒		GW ◇ 🍴	SW 1	SW 1	SW 1	SW 1 ◇ A 🛒	SW 1	SW 1
London Waterloo 15 ⊖	d	16 35					16 39	17 05				17 09				17 35			17 39	17 48		18 05		
Clapham Junction 10	d						16u46												18 04	18 13				
Woking	d	17u00										17 34												
Farnborough (Main)	d						17 13																	
Fleet	d						17 19																	
Reading 7	d											*17 07*	17 45											
Basingstoke	a						17 34					17 53	18 08						18 23	18 32				
	d				17 24		17 36					17 54	18 10						18 24	18 33				
Micheldever	d				17 34							18 04							18 34					
Winchester	d	17 33			17 44		17 52	18 01				18 14	18 25			18 31			18 44	18 50		19b01	19 05	
Shawford	d				17 48							18 18							18 49				19 09	
Romsey	d									18 07														19 07
Chandlers Ford	d									18 14														19 14
Eastleigh 3	a				17 53		18 00			18 20		18 24							18 54	18 58			19 15	19 20
	d				17 54		18 01			18 21		18 25							18 55	18 59			19 16	19 21
Hedge End	d						18 07					18 31							19 01					
Botley	d						18 11					18 35							19 05					
Fareham	d			17 47			18 23				18 13	18 45						18 47	19 14					
Portchester	d						18 28					18 50							19 19					
Cosham	d						18 33					18 55							19 24					
Hilsea	a											19 05							19 28					
Fratton	a						18 40					19 09							19 32					
Portsmouth & Southsea	a						18 43					19 12							19 36					
Portsmouth Harbour	a						18 51					19 20							19 43					
Southampton Airport Parkwy ✈	d	17 42			17 59			18 10		18 26			18 34			18 40				19 03		19 10	19 20	19 25
Swaythling	d				18 01					18 28										19 06			19 23	19 28
St Denys	d				18 04					18 31										19 09			19 26	19 31
Southampton Central	a	17 49		18 08	18 10			18 17		18 36	18 41		18 41			18 48		19 08		19 18		19 18	19 33	19 36
	d	17 53	17 56	18 10				18 22	18 25	18 38	18 42		18 43			18 52	18 55	19 10				19 19		19 38
Millbrook (Hants)	d									18 40														19 40
Redbridge	d									18 44														19 44
Romsey	d			18 21						19 00	18 54							19 21						19 52
Mottisfont & Dunbridge	d									19 05														19 57
Dean	d									19 10														20 02
Salisbury	a			18 40						19 23	19 12							19 40						20 15
Totton	d		18 01						18 30								19 00					19 25		
Ashurst New Forest	d		18 06						18 35								19 05							
Beaulieu Road	d																							
Brockenhurst 3	a	18 07	18 14						18 43				18 56				19 13					19 35		
	d	18 08	18 16			18 29			18 44				18 57	18 59			19 14				19 29	19 36		
Lymington Town	d					18 37								19 07							19 37			
Lymington Pier	a					18 39								19 09							19 39			
Yarmouth (I.O.W.) ⛴	a													*19c45*										
Sway	d		18 20						18 48								19 18					19 41		
New Milton	d		18 25						18 53								19 23					19 46		
Hinton Admiral	d		18 29						18 58								19 26					19 50		
Christchurch	d		18 34						19 02								19 32					19 55		
Pokesdown	d		18 38						19 06								19 36					19 58		
Bournemouth	a	18 22	18 44					18 49	19 10				19 15			19 20	19 40					20 02		
	d	18 24						18 50	19 11							19 21	19 41					20 07		
Branksome	d	18 29						18 55	19 16							19 26	19 46					20 12		
Parkstone (Dorset)	d	18 32						18 58	19 19							19 29	19 49					20 15		
Poole 4	a	18 36						19 02	19 26							19 33	19 56					20 18		
	d	18 37						19 03								19 34						20 19		
Hamworthy	d	18 42						19 08								19 39						20 24		
Holton Heath	d							19 12														20 28		
Wareham	d	18 49						19 17								19 46						20 33		
Wool	d							19 23														20 40		
Moreton (Dorset)	d							19 30														20 46		
Dorchester South	d	19 05						19 38								20 02						20 54		
Dorchester West	d														19 55									
Upwey	d							19 45							20 02							21 00		
Weymouth	a	19 17						19 51							20 08	20 15						21 07		

For general notes see front of timetable
For details of catering facilities see Directory of Train Operators

A 🛒 to Bournemouth
B 🛒 and 🛒 to Bournemouth
C To Worcester Shrub Hill (Table 57)
D From Gloucester (Table 134)
b Arr. 1858
c By ship

During July and August ferry connection times to and from Yarmouth IOW are subject to alteration, please contact www.wightliink.co.uk or 0871 376 1000 for further details.

For details of Bank Holiday service alterations, please see first page of Table 149

London → Basingstoke, Southampton, Romsey Lymington, Bournemouth and Weymouth

Network Diagram - see first page of Table 158

		SW	XC	SW	SW	SW	GW	SW	SW	SW	SW	SW	SW	SW	XC	SW	SW	SW	GW	SW	SW	GW	SW	SW	GW
		[1]	[1] ◇	[1]	[1] ◇	[1] ◇	◇	[1]	[1]	[1]	[1] ◇	[1]	[1]	[1]	[1] ◇	[1]	[1] ◇	[1]	◇	[1]	[1]		[1] ◇	[1]	◇
					A	A					B						B								C
			[trolley]		[buffet]	[buffet]					[buffet]				[trolley]		[buffet]						[buffet]		
London Waterloo [15] ⊖	d	18 09			18 35				18 39		19 05			19 09			19 35			19 39			20 05		
Clapham Junction [10]	d								18u46		19u12									19u46			20u12		
Woking	d	18 35							19 06					19 35			20 00								
Farnborough (Main)	d													19 45						20 13					
Fleet	d																			20 19					
Reading [7]	d	18 07	18 45								19 07				19 45					20 07					
Basingstoke	a	18 54	19 08						19 28		19 48			19 58	20 09					20 34			20 48		
	d	18 55	19 10					19 24	19 30		19 50			20 00	20 10					20 36			20 50		
Micheldever	d	19 05							19 40					20 10											
Winchester	d	19 15	19 25		19 31			19 40	19 49		20 06			20 19	20 25		20 33			20 52			21 06		
Shawford	d	19 19						19 45	19 54					20 24						20 57					
Romsey	d												20 07											21 07	
Chandlers Ford	d												20 14											21 14	
Eastleigh [3]	a	19 25						19 50	19 59				20 20	20 30						21 02				21 20	
	d	19 26						19 51	20 00				20 21	20 30						21 03				21 21	
Hedge End	d	19 32						19 57						20 36											
Botley	d	19 36						20 01						20 40											
Fareham	d	19 45					19 47	20a09						20 48					20 47						
Portchester	d	19 50												20 53											
Cosham	d	19 55												20 58											
Hilsea	a	20 02												21 03											
Fratton	a	20 06												21 08											
Portsmouth & Southsea	a	20 16												21 11											
Portsmouth Harbour	a	20 23												21 16											
Southampton Airport Parkway ✈	d		19 34		19 40				20 05		20 15		20 25		20 34		20 42			21 08			21 15	21 25	
Swaythling	d												20 28											21 28	
St Denys	d												20 31											21 31	
Southampton Central	a		19 41		19 47		20 08		20 16		20 22	←	20 36		20 41		20 49		21 08	21 17			21 22	21 36	
	d		19 43		19 52	19 55	20 10		20 30 →		20 24	20 30	20 38		20 43		20 51		21 10			21 20	21 22	21 38	
Millbrook (Hants)	d												20 40											21 40	
Redbridge	d												20 44											21 44	
Romsey	d						20 21						20 52						21 21			21 31		21 52	
Mottisfont & Dunbridge	d												20 57											21 57	
Dean	d												21 02											22 02	
Salisbury	a						20 40						21 15						21 40			21 51		22 17	
Totton	d					20 00						20 35					20 56						21 29		
Ashurst New Forest	d					20 05						20 40											21 34		
Beaulieu Road	d											20 44													
Brockenhurst [3]	a		19 56			20 13					20 37	20 51			20 56		21 07	←					21 42		
	d		19 57	19 59		20 14				20 29	20 38	21 16			20 57	20 59	21 08	21 16			21 29		21 43		
Lymington Town	d			20 07						20 37		→				21 07					21 37				
Lymington Pier	a			20 09						20 39						21 09					21 39				
Yarmouth (I.O.W.) ⛴	a			20b45						21b30															
Sway	d					20 18												21 20					21 47		
New Milton	d					20 23					20 45							21 25					21 52		
Hinton Admiral	d					20 27												21 29					21 56		
Christchurch	d					20 32					20 52							21 34					22 02		
Pokesdown	d					20 36					20 56							21 38					22 05		
Bournemouth	a		20 15		20 20	20 40					21 00				21 15		21 22	21 42					22 09		
	d				20 21	20 41					21 04						21 27	21 43					22 10		
Branksome	d				20 26	20 46											21 32	21 48					22 15		
Parkstone (Dorset)	d				20 29	20 49											21 35	21 51					22 18		
Poole [4]	a				20 33	20 56					21 13						21 38	21 57					22 23		
	d				20 34						21 14						21 39								
Hamworthy	d				20 39						21 19						21 44								
Holton Heath	d																								
Wareham	d				20 46						21 26						21 51								
Wool	d										21 32						21 58								
Moreton (Dorset)	d										21 38						22 04								
Dorchester South	d				21 02						21 47						22 12								
Dorchester West	d																								22 53
Upwey	d										21 53						22 18								23 00
Weymouth	a				21 13						21 58						22 23								23 07

For general notes see front of timetable
For details of catering facilities see Directory of Train Operators

A [buffet] and [buffet] to Bournemouth
B [buffet] to Bournemouth
C From Great Malvern (Table 71)
b By ship

During July and August ferry connection times to and from Yarmouth IOW are subject to alteration, please contact www.wightliink.co.uk or 0871 376 1000 for further details.

For details of Bank Holiday service alterations, please see first page of Table 149

London → Basingstoke, Southampton, Romsey Lymington, Bournemouth and Weymouth

Network Diagram - see first page of Table 158

		SW	XC	SW	SW	SW	XC	GW	SW	SW	XC	SW	SW	SW	SW	SW	SW	XC	SW	XC	SW	SW	SW
		1	1 ◇	1	1 ◇	1	1 ◇		1 ◇	1	1 ◇	1 ◇	1	1	1 ◇	1	1	1 ◇	1 ◇	1 ◇	1	1 ◇	1
					A ⊡				⊡			A ⊡			⊡				⊡				
London Waterloo 15 ⊖	d	20 09			20 35	20 39			21 05			21 35		21 39	22 05		21 42		22 35		22 39	23 05	23 39
Clapham Junction 10	d					20u46			21u12					21u46	22u12						22u46	23u12	23u46
Woking	d	20 35			21 00				21 32			22 00			22 32		22 19		23 00			23 32	00 08
Farnborough (Main)	d	20 45				21 13								22 13			22 33				23 13		00 18
Fleet	d					21 19								22 19			22 38				23 19		00 23
Reading 7	d		20 45			*21 07*					21 45				*22 10*			22 45			*22 52*		23b34
Basingstoke	a	20 58	21 08			21 34			21 51		22 08			22 34	22 51		22 58	23 12			23 33	23 52	00 34
	d	21 00	21 10			21 36			21 53		22 10		22 21	22 36	22 53		23 00	23 14			23 34	23 53	00 36
Micheldever	d	21 10				21 46							22 31	22s46			23 10					00 03	
Winchester	d	21 19	21 25		21 33	21 55			22 09		22 25	22 33	22 40	22 55	23 09		23 19	23 29	23 33		23 51	00 12	00 53
Shawford	d	21 24				22 00							22 45	23 00			23 24				23 55		
Romsey	d									22 07						23 07							
Chandlers Ford	d									22 14						23 14							
Eastleigh 3	a	21 30				22 05			22 17	22 21			22 50	23 05	23 17	23 22	23 30				00 01	00 20	01 00
	d	21 30				22 06			22 18	22 22			22 51	23 06	23 18	23 22	23 30				00 02	00 21	01 01
Hedge End	d	21 36											22 57				23 36						
Botley	d	21 40											23 01				23 40						
Fareham	d	21 48						21 47					23 10				23 48						
Portchester	d	21 53											23 15				23 53						
Cosham	d	21 58											23 20				23 59						
Hilsea	a	22 03											23 24				00 04						
Fratton	a	22 08											23 32				00 08						
Portsmouth & Southsea	a	22 11											23 36				00 11			⟵			
Portsmouth Harbour	a	22 16											23 40				00 16						
Southampton Airport Parkwy ✈	d		21 34		21 42	22 11			22 23	22 26	22 33	22 42		23 11	23 23	23 26		23 38 ⟶	23 42	23 38	00 06	00 26	01 07
Swaythling	d									22 28						23 28							
St Denys	d									22 31						23 31						00s30	
Southampton Central	a		21 41		21 49	22 18		22 20	22 31	22 36	22 41	22 49		23 18	23 30	23 37			23 49	23 52	00 13	00 35	01 15
	d		21 43		21 51			22 22	22 32	22 38	22 43	22 51			23 31	23 38			23 51			00 36	
Millbrook (Hants)	d									22 40						23 40							
Redbridge	d									22 44						23 44							
Romsey	d							22 33		22a52						23 56							
Mottisfont & Dunbridge	d															00 01							
Dean	d															00 06							
Salisbury	a							22 58								00 19							
Totton	d								22 38						23 37							00s41	
Ashurst New Forest	d								22 42						23 41								
Beaulieu Road	d																						
Brockenhurst 3	a		21 56		22 04		⟵		22 50		22 56	23 04			23 49				00 04			00s52	
	d		21 57	21 59	22 05		21 57		22 51		22 57	23 05			23 50				00 05				
Lymington Town	d		⟶	22 07																			
Lymington Pier	a			22 09																			
Yarmouth (I.O.W.) ⛴	a			*23c00*																			
Sway	d								22 56						23 55								
New Milton	d								23 01						23 59							01s00	
Hinton Admiral	d								23 05						00 04								
Christchurch	d								23 10						00 09							01s07	
Pokesdown	d								23 13						00 12							01s11	
Bournemouth	a				22 20		22 21		23 17		23 21	23 25			00 16				00 22			01 15	
	d				22 24				23 19			23 29			00 18				00 24			01 16	
Branksome	d				22 29				23 24			23 35			00 23				00 29			01s21	
Parkstone (Dorset)	d				22 32				23 27			23 38			00 26				00 32			01s24	
Poole 4	a				22 36				23 30			23 41			00 30				00 36			01 30	
	d				22 37							23 42											
Hamworthy	d				22 42							23 47											
Holton Heath	d																						
Wareham	d				22 49							23 54											
Wool	d				22 55							00 01											
Moreton (Dorset)	d				23 01							00 07											
Dorchester South	d				23 09							00 15											
Dorchester West	d																						
Upwey	d				23 16							00 21											
Weymouth	a				23 20							00 26											

For general notes see front of timetable
For details of catering facilities see Directory of Train Operators

A ⊡ to Bournemouth
b Tuesdays to Saturdays only
c By ship

During July and August ferry connection times to and from Yarmouth IOW are subject to alteration, please contact www.wightliink.co.uk or 0871 376 1000 for further details.

London → Basingstoke, Southampton, Romsey Lymington, Bournemouth and Weymouth

Network Diagram - see first page of Table 158

		SW	SW	SW	SW	SW	SW	SW	SW	SW	SW	SW	SW	SW	SW	SW	SW	SW	SW	GW	SW	GW	SW	SW	SW
		1 ◇	1 ◇	1	1	1 ◇	1	1 ◇	1	1	1	1	1	1	1	1	1	1	1	◇	1		1 ◇	1	1
			☕			☕													A						
London Waterloo 15 ⊖	d	21p35	22p05		21p42	22p35	22p39	23p05		23p39	00 05	01 05											05 30		
Clapham Junction 10	d		22b12				22b46	23b12		23b46	00u12	01 14											05u37		
Woking	d	22p00	22p32		22p19	23p00		23p32		00 08	00 36	01 42											06 01		
Farnborough (Main)	d				22p33		23p13			00 18		01s58													
Fleet	d				22p38		23p19			00 23															
Reading 7	d									23c34															
Basingstoke	a		22p51		22p58		23p33	23p52		00 34	00 55	02s12											06 20		
	d		22p53		23p00		23p34	23p53		00 36	00 57												06 21		
Micheldever	d				23p10			00 03															06 31		
Winchester	d	22p33	23p09		23p19	23p33	23p51	00 12		00 53	01 13	02s29											06 41		
Shawford	d				23p24		23p55																		
Romsey	d			23p07															05 58						
Chandlers Ford	d			23p14															06 06						
Eastleigh 3	a		23p17	23p22	23p30		00 01	00 20		01 00	01 21	02s38							06 11				06 50		
	d		23p18	23p22	23p30		00 02	00 21	00 30	01 01	01 22								06 13		06 30		06 51		
Hedge End	d				23p36				00s36												06 36				
Botley	d				23p40				00s39												06 40				
Fareham	d				23p48				00s47											06 28	06 48				
Portchester	d				23p53				00s53												06 53				
Cosham	d				23p59				00s57												06 58				
Hilsea	a				00 04																07 03				
Fratton	a				00 08				01s05												07 07				
Portsmouth & Southsea	a				00 11				01s08												07 11				
Portsmouth Harbour	a				00 16				01 12												07 16				
Southampton Airport Parkwy ✈	d	22p42	23p23	23p26		23p42	00 06	00 26		01 07	01 27	02s43							06 17				06 56		
Swaythling	d			23p28															06 20						
St Denys	d			23p31				00s30				02s48							06 23						
Southampton Central	a	22p49	23p30	23p37		23p49	00 13	00 35		01 15	01 36	02 53							06 28	06 49			07 03		
	d	22p51	23p31	23p38		23p51		00 36			01 37						06 25		06 30	06 52			07 05		07 25
Millbrook (Hants)	d			23p40															06 32						
Redbridge	d			23p44															06 36						
Romsey	d			23p56															06 44	07 11					
Mottisfont & Dunbridge	d			00 01															06 49						
Dean	d			00 06															06 54						
Salisbury	a			00 19															07 07	07 29					
Totton	d		23p37					00s41			01s42						06 30						07 10		07 30
Ashurst New Forest	d		23p41														06 35								07 35
Beaulieu Road	d																								
Brockenhurst 3	a	23p04	23p49			00 04		00s52			01s53						06 43						07 21		07 43
	d	23p05	23p50			00 05							05 59		06 16	06 29	06 44	06 59					07 22	07 29	07 44
Lymington Town	d												06 07			06 37		07 07						07 37	
Lymington Pier	a												06 09			06 39		07 09						07 39	
Yarmouth (I.O.W.) ⛴	a															07e15		07e45							
Sway	d		23p55												06 20		06 48						07 26		07 48
New Milton	d		23p59					01s00			02s01				06 25		06 53						07 31		07 53
Hinton Admiral	d		00 04												06 29		06 57						07 35		07 57
Christchurch	d		00 09					01s07			02s08				06 34		07 02						07 40		08 02
Pokesdown	d		00 12					01s11			02s12				06 38		07 06						07 44		08 06
Bournemouth	a	23p25	00 16			00 22		01 15			02 16				06 42		07 10						07 48		08 10
	d	23p29	00 18			00 24		01 16						06 11	06 44		07 11						07 49		08 11
Branksome	d	23p35	00 23			00 29		01s21						06 16	06 49		07 16						07 54		08 16
Parkstone (Dorset)	d	23p38	00 26			00 32		01s24						06 19	06 52		07 19						07 57		08 19
Poole 4	a	23p41	00 30			00 36		01 30						06 23	06 55		07 23						08 01		08 23
	d	23p42												06 24	06 57		07 24						08 02		08 24
Hamworthy	d	23p47												06 29	07 02		07 29						08 07		08 29
Holton Heath	d													06 33	07 06		07 33								08 33
Wareham	d	23p54												06 38	07 11		07 38						08 14		08 38
Wool	d	00 01												06 44	07 17		07 44						08 20		08 44
Moreton (Dorset)	d	00 07												06 50	07 23		07 50						08 26		08 50
Dorchester South	d	00 15												06 58	07 31		07 58						08 34		08 58
Dorchester West	d																					08 14			
Upwey	d	00 21												07 05	07 38		08 05					08 20	08 41		09 05
Weymouth	a	00 26												07 09	07 42		08 09					08 26	08 45		09 09

For general notes see front of timetable
For details of catering facilities see Directory of Train Operators

A From Salisbury
b Previous night. Stops to pick up only
c Saturdays
e By ship

During July and August ferry connection times to and from Yarmouth IOW are subject to alteration, please contact www.wightlink.co.uk or 0871 376 1000 for further details.

London → Basingstoke, Southampton, Romsey Lymington, Bournemouth and Weymouth

Network Diagram - see first page of Table 158

		SW	SW	GW	SW	SW	SW	SW	GW	SW	SW	XC	SW	SW	GW	SW	SW	GW	SW	SW	SW	SW	XC	SW
		1	1	◇	1	1 ◇	1	1		1	1	1 ◇	1	1 ◇	◇	1	1	◇	1 ◇	1	1	1	1 ◇	1
												A ✠						B					✠	
London Waterloo 15 ⊖	d					06 30					06 42			07 35		07 39			08 05			08 09		
Clapham Junction 10	d					06u37					06u49					07u46			08u12					
Woking	d				06 19	06 57					07 19			08 00								08 35		
Farnborough (Main)	d				06 33						07 33					08 13						08 45		
Fleet	d				06 38						07 38					08 19								
Reading 7	d				*06 07*	*06 39*					*07 07*	07 45				*08 07*							08 45	
Basingstoke	a				06 58	07 16					07 58	08 08		08 20		08 34			08 48			08 58	09 08	
	d				07 00	07 18					08 00	08 10		08 21		08 36			08 50			09 00	09 10	
Micheldever	d				07 10						08 10											09 10		
Winchester	d				07 19	07 34					08 19	08 25		08 38		08 52			09 06			09 19	09 25	
Shawford	d				07 24						08 24					08 57								
Romsey	d	07 07								08 07											09 07			
Chandlers Ford	d	07 14								08 14											09 14			
Eastleigh 3	a	07 20			07 30	07 42				08 20	08 30			08 46		09 02					09 20	09 29		
	d	07 21			07 30	07 43				08 21	08 30			08 47		09 03					09 21	09 30		
Hedge End	d				07 36						08 36											09 36		
Botley	d				07 40						08 40											09 40		
Fareham	d			07 30	07 48						08 48				08 47							09 48		
Portchester	d				07 53						08 53											09 53		
Cosham	d				07 58						08 58											09 58		
Hilsea	a				08 03						09 03											10 03		
Fratton	a				08 07						09 07											10 07		
Portsmouth & Southsea	a				08 11						09 11											10 11		
Portsmouth Harbour	a				08 18						09 18											10 18		
Southampton Airport Parkwy ✈	d	07 25				07 48				08 25		08 33		08 51		09 08			09 15		09 25		09 33	
Swaythling	d	07 28								08 28											09 28			
St Denys	d	07 31								08 31											09 31			
Southampton Central	a	07 36		07 51		07 56				08 36		08 41		08 58	09 08	09 17			09 22	←	09 36		09 40	
	d	07 38		07 54		08 00		08 22	08 27	08 38		08 43		09 00	09 10	09 30			09 24	09 30	09 38		09 43	
Millbrook (Hants)	d	07 40								08 40						→					09 40			
Redbridge	d	07 44								08 44											09 44			
Romsey	d	07 52		08 12					08 38	08 52					09 21						09 52			
Mottisfont & Dunbridge	d	07 57								08 57											09 57			
Dean	d	08 02								09 02											10 02			
Salisbury	a	08 15		08 30					09 03	09 15					09 40						10 15			
Totton	d					08 05		08 27						09 05						09 35				
Ashurst New Forest	d							08 31												09 40				
Beaulieu Road	d							08 36												09 44				
Brockenhurst 3	a					08 16		08 42				08 57		09 16					09 37	09 51			09 57	
	d		07 59			08 17	08 29	08 44				08 57	08 59	09 16			09 29		09 38	10 16			09 58	09 59
Lymington Town	d		08 07				08 37						09 07				09 37			→				10 07
Lymington Pier	a		08 09				08 39						09 09				09 39							10 09
Yarmouth (I.O.W.) ⛴	a		*08b45*				*09b30*										*10b15*							*11b00*
Sway	d					08 21		08 48						09 20										
New Milton	d					08 26		08 53						09 25					09 45					
Hinton Admiral	d					08 30		08 57						09 29										
Christchurch	d					08 35		09 02						09 34					09 52					
Pokesdown	d					08 39		09 06						09 38					09 56					
Bournemouth	a					08 43		09 10				09 15		09 43					10 00				10 15	
	d					08 44		09 11						09 43					10 04					
Branksome	d					08 49		09 16						09 48										
Parkstone (Dorset)	d					08 52		09 19						09 51										
Poole 4	a					08 56		09 23						09 56					10 13					
	d					08 57		09 24						09 56					10 14					
Hamworthy	d					09 02		09 29						10 02					10 19					
Holton Heath	d							09 33											10 23					
Wareham	d					09 09		09 38						10 11					10 28					
Wool	d					09 15		09 44											10 35					
Moreton (Dorset)	d					09 21		09 50											10 41					
Dorchester South	d					09 29		09 58						10 27					10 49					
Dorchester West	d																	10 40						
Upwey	d					09 36		10 05										10 50	10 55					
Weymouth	a					09 40		10 09						10 35				10 55	11 00					

For general notes see front of timetable
For details of catering facilities see Directory of Train Operators

A From Birmingham New Street (Table 116)
B From Worcester Shrub Hill (Table 57)
b By ship

During July and August ferry connection times to and from Yarmouth IOW are subject to alteration, please contact www.wightliink.co.uk or 0871 376 1000 for further details.

Saturdays

London → Basingstoke, Southampton, Romsey Lymington, Bournemouth and Weymouth

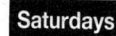

Network Diagram - see first page of Table 158

		SW	SW	GW	SW	SW	GW	SW	SW	SW		GW	GW	SW	XC	SW	SW	SW	GW	SW	SW	SW	SW	SW	SW
		1 ◇ A ⊡	1	◇	1	1	B	1 ◇ A ⊡	1	1		◇ C	◇ D	1	R 1 ✕	1	1 ◇ A ⊡	1	◇	1	1	1 ◇ A ⊡	1	1	1
London Waterloo 15 ⊖	d	08 35			08 39			09 05						09 09			09 35			09 39		10 05			10 09
Clapham Junction 10	d				08u46			09u12												09u46		10u12			
Woking	d	09 00												09 35			10 00								10 35
Farnborough (Main)	d				09 13									09 45						10 13					10 45
Fleet	d				09 19															10 19					
Reading 7	d				*09 07*										09 45					*10 07*					
Basingstoke	a				09 34			09 48						09 58	10 08					10 34		10 48			10 58
	d				09 36			09 50						10 00	10 10					10 36		10 50			11 00
Micheldever	d													10 10											11 10
Winchester	d	09 33			09 52			10 06						10 19	10 25		10 33			10 52		11 06			11 19
Shawford	d				09 57															10 57					
Romsey	d									10 07														11 07	
Chandlers Ford	d									10 14														11 14	
Eastleigh 3	a				10 02					10 20				10 29						11 02				11 20	11 29
	d				10 03					10 21				10 30						11 03				11 21	11 30
Hedge End	d													10 36											11 36
Botley	d													10 40											11 40
Fareham	d			09 47								10 16		10 48					10 47						11 48
Portchester	d													10 53											11 53
Cosham	d													10 58											11 58
Hilsea	a													11 03											12 03
Fratton	a													11 07											12 07
Portsmouth & Southsea	a													11 11											12 11
Portsmouth Harbour	a													11 18											12 18
Southampton Airport Parkwy ✈	d	09 42			10 08			10 15		10 25					10 33		10 42			11 08		11 15		11 25	
Swaythling	d									10 28														11 28	
St Denys	d									10 31														11 31	
Southampton Central	a	09 49		10 08	10 15			10 22	⟵	10 36		10 40			10 40		10 49		11 08	11 17		11 22	⟵	11 36	
	d	09 51		10 10	10 30 ↪			10 24	10 30	10 38		10 42			10 43		10 51		11 10	11 30 ↪		11 24	11 30	11 38	
Millbrook (Hants)	d									10 40														11 40	
Redbridge	d									10 44														11 44	
Romsey	d			10 21						10 59		10 53							11 21					11 52	
Mottisfont & Dunbridge	d									11 04														11 57	
Dean	d									11 10														12 02	
Salisbury	a			10 40						11 22		11 13							11 40					12 15	
Totton	d								10 35														11 35		
Ashurst New Forest	d								10 40														11 40		
Beaulieu Road	d																						11 44		
Brockenhurst 3	a	10 04	⟵					10 37	10 51						10 57		11 04	⟵				11 37	11 51		
	d	10 05	10 16			10 29		10 38	11 16						10 58	10 59	11 05	11 16			11 29	11 38	12 16		
Lymington Town	d					10 37			↪							11 07					11 37		↪		
Lymington Pier	a					10 39										11 09					11 39				
Yarmouth (I.O.W.) ⛴	a															11b45									
Sway	d		10 20															11 20							
New Milton	d		10 25					10 45										11 25				11 45			
Hinton Admiral	d		10 29															11 29							
Christchurch	d		10 34					10 52										11 34				11 52			
Pokesdown	d		10 38					10 56										11 38				11 56			
Bournemouth	a	10 20	10 42					11 00							11 15		11 20	11 42				12 00			
	d	10 24	10 43					11 04									11 24	11 43				12 04			
Branksome	d	10 29	10 49														11 29	11 48							
Parkstone (Dorset)	d	10 32	10 52														11 32	11 51							
Poole 4	a	10 36	10 55					11 13									11 36	11 55				12 13			
	d	10 37						11 14									11 37					12 14			
Hamworthy	d	10 42						11 19									11 42					12 19			
Holton Heath	d							11 23														12 23			
Wareham	d	10 49						11 28									11 49					12 28			
Wool	d							11 35														12 35			
Moreton (Dorset)	d							11 41														12 41			
Dorchester South	d	11 05						11 49									12 05					12 49			
Dorchester West	d						11 30						11 56												
Upwey	d							11 55					12 03									12 55			
Weymouth	a	11 13					11 42	12 00					12 08				12 13					13 00			

For general notes see front of timetable
For details of catering facilities see Directory of Train Operators

A ⊡ to Bournemouth
B Until 5 September
C To Great Malvern (Table 71)
D From Gloucester (Table 134)
b By ship

During July and August ferry connection times to and from Yarmouth IOW are subject to alteration, please contact www.wightliink.co.uk or 0871 376 1000 for further details.

Table 158

London → Basingstoke, Southampton, Romsey Lymington, Bournemouth and Weymouth

Network Diagram - see first page of Table 158

		XC	SW	SW	SW	GW	SW	SW	SW	GW	SW	SW	GW	SW	XC		SW	SW	SW	GW	SW	SW	SW	SW	SW
		1 ◇	1	1 ◇	1	◇	1	1	1 ◇		1	1	◇	1	1 ◇		1	1 ◇	1	◇	1	1	1 ◇	1	1
				A					A				B					A					A		
		⊥o		⊥P					⊥P						⊥o			⊥P					⊥P		
London Waterloo 15 ⊖	d			10 35			10 39		11 05					11 09				11 35			11 39		12 05		
Clapham Junction 10	d						10u46		11u12												11u46		12u12		
Woking	d			11 00										11 35				12 00							
Farnborough (Main)	d						11 13							11 45							12 13				
Fleet	d						11 19														12 19				
Reading 7	d	10 45					*11 07*								11 45						*11b45*		*12b10*		
Basingstoke	a	11 08					11 34		11 48					11 58	12 08						12 34		12 48		
	d	11 10					11 36		11 50					12 00	12 10						12 36		12 50		
Micheldever	d													12 10											
Winchester	d	11 25		11 33			11 52		12 06					12 19	12 25			12 33			12 52		13 06		
Shawford	d						11 57														12 57				
Romsey	d											12 07													13 07
Chandlers Ford	d											12 14													13 14
Eastleigh 3	a						12 02					12 20		12 29							13 02				13 20
	d						12 03					12 21		12 30							13 03				13 21
Hedge End	d													12 36											
Botley	d													12 40											
Fareham	d					11 47								12 48						12 47					
Portchester	d													12 53											
Cosham	d													12 58											
Hilsea	a													13 03											
Fratton	a													13 07											
Portsmouth & Southsea	a													13 11											
Portsmouth Harbour	a													13 18											
Southampton Airport Parkwy ✈	d	11 33		11 42			12 08		12 15			12 25			12 33			12 42			13 08		13 15		13 25
Swaythling	d											12 28													13 28
St Denys	d											12 31													13 31
Southampton Central	a	11 41		11 49		12 08	12 17		12 22		←	12 36			12 41			12 49		13 08	13 17		13 22	←	13 36
	d	11 43		11 51		12 10	12 30 →		12 24	12 27	12 30	12 38			12 43			12 51		13 10	13 30 →		13 24	13 30	13 38
Millbrook (Hants)	d											12 40													13 40
Redbridge	d											12 44													13 44
Romsey	d					12 21				12 38		12 52								13 21					13 52
Mottisfont & Dunbridge	d											12 57													13 57
Dean	d											13 02													14 02
Salisbury	a					12 40				13 03		13 15								13 40					14 15
Totton	d										12 35													13 35	
Ashurst New Forest	d										12 40													13 40	
Beaulieu Road	d																							13 44	
Brockenhurst 3	a	11 57		12 04	←				12 37		12 51				12 57			13 04	←				13 37	13 51	
	d	11 58	11 59	12 05	12 16			12 29	12 38		13 16				12 58		12 59	13 05	13 16			13 29	13 38	14 16	
Lymington Town	d		12 07					12 37			→						13 07					13 37		→	
Lymington Pier	a		12 09					12 39									13 09					13 39			
Yarmouth (I.O.W.) ⛴	a		*12c45*														*13c45*					*14c30*			
Sway	d				12 20														13 20						
New Milton	d				12 25				12 45										13 25				13 45		
Hinton Admiral	d				12 29														13 29						
Christchurch	d				12 34				12 52										13 34				13 52		
Pokesdown	d				12 38				12 56										13 38				13 56		
Bournemouth	a	12 15		12 20	12 42				13 00						13 15			13 20	13 42				14 00		
	d			12 24	12 43				13 04									13 24	13 43				14 04		
Branksome	d			12 29	12 48													13 29	13 48						
Parkstone (Dorset)	d			12 32	12 51													13 32	13 51						
Poole 4	a			12 36	12 55				13 13									13 36	13 55				14 13		
	d			12 37					13 14									13 37					14 14		
Hamworthy	d			12 42					13 19									13 42					14 19		
Holton Heath	d								13 23														14 23		
Wareham	d			12 49					13 28									13 49					14 28		
Wool	d								13 35														14 35		
Moreton (Dorset)	d								13 41														14 41		
Dorchester South	d			13 05					13 49									14 05					14 49		
Dorchester West	d												13 55												
Upwey	d								13 55				14 03										14 55		
Weymouth	a			13 13					14 00				14 08					14 13					15 00		

For general notes see front of timetable
For details of catering facilities see Directory of Train Operators

A ⊥P to Bournemouth
B From Gloucester (Table 134)
b From 12 September dep. 1207
c By ship

During July and August ferry connection times to and from Yarmouth IOW are subject to alteration, please contact www.wightliink.co.uk or 0871 376 1000 for further details.

London → Basingstoke, Southampton, Romsey Lymington, Bournemouth and Weymouth

Network Diagram - see first page of Table 158

		SW 1	XC 1 ◇	SW 1	SW 1 ◇	SW 1	GW ◇	SW 1	SW 1	SW 1 ◇	SW 1	SW 1	SW 1	XC 1 ◇	SW 1	SW 1 ◇	SW 1	GW ◇	SN 1	SW 1		SW 1	SW 1 ◇	SW 1	SW 1
			🛒		A 🍴					A 🍴				🛒		A 🍴			B				🍴		
London Waterloo 15 ⊖	d	12 09			12 35			12 39		13 05			13 09			13 35				13 39			14 05		
Clapham Junction 10	d							12u46		13u12										13u46			14u12		
Woking	d	12 35			13 00								13 35			14 00									
Farnborough (Main)	d	12 45						13 13					13 45							14 13					
Fleet	d							13 19												14 19					
Reading 7	d		12 45					12b45		13 07				13 45						14 07					
Basingstoke	a	12 58	13 08					13 34		13 48			13 58	14 08						14 34			14 48		
	d	13 00	13 10					13 36		13 50			14 00	14 10						14 36			14 50		
Micheldever	d	13 10											14 10												
Winchester	d	13 19	13 25		13 33			13 52		14 06			14 19	14 25		14 33				14 52			15 06		
Shawford	d							13 57												14 57					
Romsey	d											14 07													15 07
Chandlers Ford	d											14 14													15 14
Eastleigh 3	a	13 29						14 02				14 20	14 29							15 02					15 20
	d	13 30						14 03				14 21	14 30						14 43	15 03					15 21
Hedge End	d	13 36											14 36												
Botley	d	13 40											14 40												
Fareham	d	13 48					13 47						14 48					14 47	14a59						
Portchester	d	13 53											14 53												
Cosham	d	13 58											14 58												
Hilsea	a	14 03											15 03												
Fratton	a	14 07											15 07												
Portsmouth & Southsea	a	14 11											15 11												
Portsmouth Harbour	a	14 18											15 18												
Southampton Airport Parkwy ✈	d		13 33		13 42			14 08		14 15		14 25		14 34		14 42				15 08			15 15		15 25
Swaythling	d											14 28													15 28
St Denys	d											14 31													15 31
Southampton Central	a		13 41		13 49		14 08	14 17		14 22	←	14 36		14 41		14 49		15 08		15 17			15 22	←	15 36
	d		13 43		13 51		14 10	14 30		14 24	14 30	14 38		14 43		14 51		15 10		15 30			15 24	15 30	15 38
Millbrook (Hants)	d							→				14 40								→					15 40
Redbridge	d											14 44													15 44
Romsey	d						14 21					14 52						15 21							15 52
Mottisfont & Dunbridge	d											14 57													15 57
Dean	d											15 02													16 02
Salisbury	a						14 40					15 15						15 40							16 15
Totton	d										14 35													15 35	
Ashurst New Forest	d										14 40													15 40	
Beaulieu Road	d																							15 44	
Brockenhurst 3	a		13 57		14 04	←				14 37	14 51			14 57		15 04	←						15 37	15 51	
	d		13 58	13 59	14 05	14 16			14 29	14 38	15 16			14 58	14 59	15 05	15 16					15 29	15 38	16 16	
Lymington Town	d			14 07					14 37		→				15 07							15 37		→	
Lymington Pier	a			14 09					14 39						15 09							15 39			
Yarmouth (I.O.W.) ⛴	a								*15c15*						*16c00*										
Sway	d					14 20											15 20								
New Milton	d					14 25				14 45							15 25						15 45		
Hinton Admiral	d					14 29											15 29								
Christchurch	d					14 34				14 52							15 34						15 52		
Pokesdown	d					14 38				14 56							15 38						15 56		
Bournemouth	a		14 15		14 20	14 42				15 00				15 15		15 20	15 42						16 00		
	d				14 24	14 43				15 04						15 24	15 43						16 04		
Branksome	d				14 29	14 48										15 29	15 48								
Parkstone (Dorset)	d				14 32	14 51										15 32	15 51								
Poole 4	a				14 36	14 55				15 13						15 36	15 55						16 13		
	d				14 37					15 14						15 37							16 14		
Hamworthy	d				14 42					15 19						15 42							16 19		
Holton Heath	d									15 23													16 23		
Wareham	d				14 49					15 28						15 49							16 28		
Wool	d									15 35													16 35		
Moreton (Dorset)	d									15 41													16 41		
Dorchester South	d				15 05					15 49						16 05							16 49		
Dorchester West	d																								
Upwey	d									15 55													16 55		
Weymouth	a				15 13					16 00						16 13							17 00		

For general notes see front of timetable
For details of catering facilities see Directory of Train Operators

A 🍴 to Bournemouth
B To Brighton (Table 188)
b From 12 September dep. 1307
c By ship

During July and August ferry connection times to and from Yarmouth IOW are subject to alteration, please contact www.wightliink.co.uk or 0871 376 1000 for further details.

Table 158

Saturdays

London → Basingstoke, Southampton, Romsey Lymington, Bournemouth and Weymouth

Network Diagram - see first page of Table 158

		GW	GW	SW	XC	SW	SW	SW	GW	SW	SW	SW	SW	SW	SW	XC	SW	SW	SW	GW	SW	SW	SW	SW	SW
		◇ A 🛒	◇ B 🛒	1	1 ◇ 🛒	1	1 ◇ C 🍽	1	◇	1	1	1 ◇ C 🍽	1	1	1	1 ◇ 🛒	1	1 ◇ C 🍽	1	◇	1	1	1 ◇ C 🍽	1	1
London Waterloo 15 ⊖	d			14 09			14 35			14 39		15 05			15 09			15 35			15 39		16 05		
Clapham Junction 10	d									14u46		15u12									15u46		16u12		
Woking	d			14 35			15 00								15 35			16 00							
Farnborough (Main)	d			14 45						15 13					15 45						16 13				
Fleet	d									15 19											16 19				
Reading 7	d				14 45					*15 07*						15 45					*16 07*				
Basingstoke	a			14 58	15 08					15 34		15 48			15 58	16 08					16 34		16 48		
	d			15 00	15 10					15 36		15 50			16 00	16 10					16 36		16 50		
Micheldever	d			15 10											16 10										
Winchester	d			15 19	15 25		15 33			15 52		16 06			16 19	16 25		16 33			16 52		17 06		
Shawford	d									15 57											16 57				
Romsey	d													16 07											17 07
Chandlers Ford	d													16 14											17 14
Eastleigh 3	a			15 29						16 02				16 20	16 29						17 02				17 20
	d			15 30						16 03				16 21	16 30						17 03				17 21
Hedge End	d			15 36											16 36										
Botley	d			15 40											16 40										
Fareham	d			15 48					15 47						16 48					16 47					
Portchester	d			15 53											16 53										
Cosham	d			15 58											16 58										
Hilsea	a			16 03											17 03										
Fratton	a			16 07											17 07										
Portsmouth & Southsea	a			16 11											17 11										
Portsmouth Harbour	a			16 18											17 18										
Southampton Airport Parkwy ✈	d				15 33		15 42			16 08		16 15		16 25		16 33		16 42			17 08		17 15		17 25
Swaythling	d													16 28											17 28
St Denys	d													16 31											17 31
Southampton Central	a				15 41		15 49		16 08	16 17		16 22	←	16 36		16 41		16 49		17 08	17 17		17 22	←	17 36
	d				15 43		15 51		16 10	16 30		16 24	16 30	16 38		16 43		16 51		17 10	17 30		17 24	17 30	17 38
Millbrook (Hants)	d									→				16 40							→				17 40
Redbridge	d													16 44											17 44
Romsey	d								16 21					16 52						17 21					17 52
Mottisfont & Dunbridge	d													16 57											17 57
Dean	d													17 02											18 02
Salisbury	a								16 40					17 15						17 40					18 15
Totton	d												16 35											17 35	
Ashurst New Forest	d												16 40											17 40	
Beaulieu Road	d																							17 44	
Brockenhurst 3	a				15 57		16 04	←				16 37	16 51			16 57		17 04	←				17 37	17 51	
	d				15 58	15 59	16 05	16 16			16 29	16 38	17 16			16 58	16 59	17 05	17 16			17 29	17 38	18 16	
Lymington Town	d					16 07					16 37		→				17 07					17 37		→	
Lymington Pier	a					16 09					16 39						17 09					17 39			
Yarmouth (I.O.W.) ⛴	a					*16b45*					*17b30*											*18b15*			
Sway	d							16 20											17 20						
New Milton	d							16 25				16 45							17 25				17 45		
Hinton Admiral	d							16 29											17 29						
Christchurch	d							16 34				16 52							17 34				17 52		
Pokesdown	d							16 38				16 56							17 38				17 56		
Bournemouth	a				16 15		16 20	16 42				17 00				17 15		17 20	17 42				18 00		
	d						16 24	16 43				17 04						17 24	17 43				18 04		
Branksome	d						16 29	16 48										17 29	17 48						
Parkstone (Dorset)	d						16 32	16 51										17 32	17 51						
Poole 4	a						16 36	16 55				17 13						17 36	17 55				18 13		
	d						16 37					17 14						17 37					18 14		
Hamworthy	d						16 42					17 19						17 42					18 19		
Holton Heath	d											17 23											18 23		
Wareham	d						16 49					17 28						17 49					18 28		
Wool	d											17 35											18 35		
Moreton (Dorset)	d											17 41											18 41		
Dorchester South	d						17 05					17 49						18 05					18 49		
Dorchester West	d	16 56	16 56																						
Upwey	d	17 02	17 03									17 55											18 55		
Weymouth	a	17 07	17 07				17 13					18 00						18 13					19 00		

For general notes see front of timetable
For details of catering facilities see Directory of Train Operators

A Until 5 September. From Worcester Foregate Street (Table 71)
B From 12 September. From Worcester Foregate Street (Table 71)
C 🍽 to Bournemouth
b By ship

During July and August ferry connection times to and from Yarmouth IOW are subject to alteration, please contact www.wightliink.co.uk or 0871 376 1000 for further details.

Table 158

Saturdays

London → Basingstoke, Southampton, Romsey Lymington, Bournemouth and Weymouth

Network Diagram - see first page of Table 158

		SW	XC		SW	SW	SW	GW	SW	SW	SW	GW	SW	SW	SW	GW	SW	XC	SW	GW	SW	SW	GW	SW	SW
		1	1◇		1	1◇	1	◇	1	1	1	◇	1◇	1	1	◇	1	1◇	1		1◇	1	◇	1	1
						A						B	A			C				D	A				
			⊼			⊏P							⊏P					⊼			⊏P				
London Waterloo 15 ⊖	d	16 09				16 35				16 39			17 05				17 09				17 35			17 39	
Clapham Junction 10	d									16u46			17u12											17u46	
Woking	d	16 35				17 00											17 35				18 00				
Farnborough (Main)	d	16 45								17 13							17 45							18 13	
Fleet	d									17 19														18 19	
Reading 7	d		16 45							*17 07*								17 45						*18 07*	
Basingstoke	a	16 58	17 08							17 34			17 48				17 58	18 08						18 34	
	d	17 00	17 10						17 24	17 36			17 50				18 00	18 10						18 36	
Micheldever	d	17 10							17 34								18 10								
Winchester	d	17 19	17 25			17 33			17 43	17 52			18 06				18 19	18 25			18 33			18 52	
Shawford	d								17 48	17 57														18 57	
Romsey	d														18 07										
Chandlers Ford	d														18 14										
Eastleigh 3	a	17 29							17 53	18 02					18 20		18 29							19 02	
	d	17 30							17 54	18 03					18 21		18 30							19 03	
Hedge End	d	17 36															18 36								
Botley	d	17 40															18 40								
Fareham	d	17 48						17 47									18 48			18 15			18 47		
Portchester	d	17 53															18 53								
Cosham	d	17 58															18 58								
Hilsea	a	18 03															19 03								
Fratton	a	18 07															19 07								
Portsmouth & Southsea	a	18 11															19 11								
Portsmouth Harbour	a	18 18															19 18								
Southampton Airport Parkwy ✈	d		17 33			17 42			17 59	18 08			18 15		18 25			18 33			18 42			19 08	
Swaythling	d								18 01						18 28										
St Denys	d								18 04						18 31										
Southampton Central	a		17 41			17 49		18 08	18 10	18 17			18 22	←	18 36			18 40		18 43	18 49		19 08	19 17	
	d		17 43			17 51		18 10		18 30			18 24	18 30	18 38			18 43		18 45	18 51		19 10	19 30	
Millbrook (Hants)	d									→					18 40									→	
Redbridge	d														18 44										
Romsey	d							18 21							19 00					18 56			19 21		
Mottisfont & Dunbridge	d														19 05										
Dean	d														19 10										
Salisbury	a							18 40							19 23					19 15			19 40		
Totton	d													18 35											
Ashurst New Forest	d													18 40											
Beaulieu Road	d																								
Brockenhurst 3	a		17 57			18 04	←						18 37	18 51				18 57			19 04	←			
	d		17 58		17 59	18 05	18 16				18 29		18 38	19 16				18 58	18 59		19 05	19 16			19 29
Lymington Town	d				18 07						18 37			→					19 07						19 37
Lymington Pier	a				18 09						18 39								19 09						19 39
Yarmouth (I.O.W.) ⛴	a				*19b00*														*19b45*						
Sway	d						18 20															19 20			
New Milton	d						18 25						18 45									19 25			
Hinton Admiral	d						18 29															19 29			
Christchurch	d						18 34						18 52									19 34			
Pokesdown	d						18 38						18 56									19 38			
Bournemouth	a		18 15			18 20	18 42						19 00					19 15			19 20	19 42			
	d					18 24	18 43						19 04								19 24	19 43			
Branksome	d					18 29	18 48														19 29	19 48			
Parkstone (Dorset)	d					18 32	18 51														19 32	19 51			
Poole 4	a					18 36	18 55						19 13								19 36	19 55			
	d					18 37							19 14								19 37				
Hamworthy	d					18 42							19 19								19 42				
Holton Heath	d												19 23												
Wareham	d					18 49							19 28								19 49				
Wool	d												19 35												
Moreton (Dorset)	d												19 41												
Dorchester South	d					19 05							19 49								20 05				
Dorchester West	d											19 12				19 54									
Upwey	d											19 21	19 55			20 02									
Weymouth	a					19 13						19 26	20 01			20 08					20 13				

For general notes see front of timetable
For details of catering facilities see Directory of Train Operators

A ⊏P to Bournemouth
B From Great Malvern (Table 71)
C From Gloucester (Table 134)
D To Cheltenham Spa (Table 57)
b By ship

During July and August ferry connection times to and from Yarmouth IOW are subject to alteration, please contact www.wightliink.co.uk or 0871 376 1000 for further details.

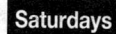

London → Basingstoke, Southampton, Romsey Lymington, Bournemouth and Weymouth

Network Diagram - see first page of Table 158

		SW	SW	SW	SW	XC	SW	SW	SW	GW	SW	SW	SW	SW	SW	SW	XC	SW	SW	SW	GW	SW	SW	SW
		1 ◇	1	1	1	1 ◇	1	1 ◇	1	◇	1	1	1 ◇	1	1	1	1 ◇	1	1 ◇	1	◇	1	1	1 ◇
		A						A					A						A					
		🛒				🍴		🛒					🛒				🍴		🛒					🛒
London Waterloo 15 ⊖	d	18 05			18 09			18 35			18 39		19 05			19 09			19 35			19 39		20 05
Clapham Junction 10	d	18u12									18u46		19u12									19u46		20u12
Woking	d				18 35			19 00								19 35			20 00					
Farnborough (Main)	d				18 45						19 13					19 45						20 13		
Fleet	d										19 19											20 19		
Reading 7	d					18 45					*19 07*						19 45					*20 07*		
Basingstoke	a	18 48			18 58	19 08					19 34		19 48			19 58	20 08					20 34		20 48
	d	18 50			19 00	19 10					19 36		19 50			20 00	20 10					20 36		20 50
Micheldever	d				19 10											20 10								
Winchester	d	19 06			19 19	19 25		19 33			19 52		20 06			20 19	20 25		20 33			20 52		21 06
Shawford	d										19 57											20 57		
Romsey	d			19 07											20 07									
Chandlers Ford	d			19 14											20 14									
Eastleigh 3	a			19 20	19 29						20 02				20 20	20 29						21 02		
	d			19 21	19 30						20 03				20 21	20 30						21 03		
Hedge End	d				19 36											20 36								
Botley	d				19 40											20 40								
Fareham	d				19 48					19 47						20 48					20 48			
Portchester	d				19 53											20 53								
Cosham	d				19 58											20 58								
Hilsea	a				20 03											21 03								
Fratton	a				20 07											21 07								
Portsmouth & Southsea	a				20 11											21 11								
Portsmouth Harbour	a				20 18											21 18								
Southampton Airport Parkwy ✈	d	19 15		19 25		19 33		19 42			20 08		20 15		20 25		20 33		20 42			21 08		21 15
Swaythling	d			19 28											20 28									
St Denys	d			19 31											20 31									
Southampton Central	a	19 22	⟵	19 36		19 41		19 49		20 09	20 17		20 22	⟵	20 36		20 41		20 49		21 10	21 17		21 22
	d	19 24	19 30	19 38		19 43		19 51		20 10	20 30 ⟶		20 24	20 30	20 38		20 43		20 51		21 12			21 24
Millbrook (Hants)	d			19 40											20 40									
Redbridge	d			19 44											20 44									
Romsey	d			19 52						20 21					20 52						21 23			
Mottisfont & Dunbridge	d			19 57											20 57									
Dean	d			20 02											21 02									
Salisbury	a			20 15						20 40					21 15						21 42			
Totton	d		19 35											20 35										21 29
Ashurst New Forest	d		19 40											20 40										21 34
Beaulieu Road	d		19 44																					
Brockenhurst 3	a	19 37	19 51			19 57		20 04	⟵				20 37	20 51			20 57		21 04	⟵				21 42
	d	19 38	20 16			19 58	19 59	20 05	20 16			20 29	20 38	21 16			20 58	20 59	21 05	21 16			21 29	21 43
Lymington Town	d		⟶				20 07					20 37		⟶				21 07					21 37	
Lymington Pier	a						20 09					20 39						21 09					21 39	
Yarmouth (I.O.W.) ⛴	a						20b45					21b30												
Sway	d								20 20											21 20				21 47
New Milton	d	19 45							20 25				20 45							21 25				21 52
Hinton Admiral	d								20 29											21 29				21 56
Christchurch	d	19 52							20 34				20 52							21 34				22 01
Pokesdown	d	19 56							20 38				20 56							21 38				22 05
Bournemouth	a	20 00				20 15		20 20	20 42				21 00				21 15		21 20	21 42				22 09
	d	20 04						20 24	20 43				21 04						21 24	21 43				22 10
Branksome	d							20 29	20 48										21 29	21 48				22 15
Parkstone (Dorset)	d							20 32	20 51										21 32	21 51				22 18
Poole 4	a	20 13						20 36	20 55				21 11						21 36	21 55				22 23
	d	20 14						20 37					21 14						21 37					
Hamworthy	d	20 19						20 42					21 19						21 42					
Holton Heath	d	20 23																						
Wareham	d	20 28						20 49					21 26						21 49					
Wool	d	20 35											21 32						21 55					
Moreton (Dorset)	d	20 41											21 38						22 01					
Dorchester South	d	20 49						21 05					21 47						22 10					
Dorchester West	d																							
Upwey	d	20 55											21 53						22 16					
Weymouth	a	21 00						21 13					21 59						22 21					

For general notes see front of timetable
For details of catering facilities see Directory of Train Operators

A 🛒 to Bournemouth
b By ship

During July and August ferry connection times to and from Yarmouth IOW are subject to alteration, please contact www.wightliink.co.uk or 0871 376 1000 for further details.

Table 158

Saturdays

London → Basingstoke, Southampton, Romsey Lymington, Bournemouth and Weymouth

Network Diagram - see first page of Table 158

		GW	SW	SW	XC	SW	GW	SW	SW	SW	SW	SW	XC	SW	SW	SW	SW	SW	XC	SW	SW	SW	SW
			[1]	[1]	[1] ◇	[1]	◇	[1] ◇	[1]	[1] ◇	[1]	[1]	[1] ◇	[1] ◇	[1]	[1] ◇	[1]	[1]	[1] ◇	[1] ◇	[1]	[1] ◇	[1]
							A	B						B									
					🍴			☕		☕			🍴	☕		☕			🍴	☕			
London Waterloo [15] ⊖	d			20 09				20 35	20 39	21 05		20 42		21 35	21 39	22 05		21 42		22 35	22 39	23 05	23 39
Clapham Junction [10]	d								20u46	21u12					21u46	22u12					22u46	23u12	23u46
Woking	d			20 35				21 00		21 32		21 19		22 00		22 32		22 19		23 00		23 32	00 08
Farnborough (Main)	d			20 45					21 13			21 33			22 13			22 33			23 13		00 18
Fleet	d								21 19			21 38			22 19			22 38			23 19		00 23
Reading [7]	d				20 45				*21 07*				21 45		*22 07*				22 45		*23 07*		
Basingstoke	a			20 58	21 08				21 34	21 51		21 58	22 08		22 34	22 51		22 58	23 11		23 34	23 51	00 34
	d			21 00	21 10				21 36	21 53		22 00	22 10		22 36	22 53		23 00	23 13		23 36	23 53	00 36
Micheldever	d			21 10					21 46			22 10			22s46			23 10				00 03	
Winchester	d			21 19	21 25			21 33	21 55	22 09		22 19	22 25	22 33	22 56	23 09		23 19	23 28	23 33	23 52	00 12	00 53
Shawford	d								22 00						23 00						23 57		
Romsey	d		21 07								22 07						23 09						
Chandlers Ford	d		21 14								22 14						23 16						
Eastleigh [3]	a		21 20	21 29					22 05	22 17	22 21	22 29			23 06	23 17	23 22	23 29			00 02	00 20	01 01
	d		21 21	21 30					22 06	22 18	22 22	22 30			23 07	23 18	23 23	23 30			00 03	00 21	01 02
Hedge End	d			21 36								22 36						23 36					
Botley	d			21 40								22 40						23 40					
Fareham	d			21 48								22 48						23 48					
Portchester	d			21 53								22 53						23 53					
Cosham	d			21 58								22 58						23 58					
Hilsea	a			22 03								23 03						00 03					
Fratton	a			22 07								23 07						00 07					
Portsmouth & Southsea	a			22 11								23 11						00 11					
Portsmouth Harbour	a			22 18								23 18						00 16					
Southampton Airport Parkwy ✈	d		21 25		21 33			21 42	22 11	22 23	22 26		22 33	22 42	23 11	23 23	23 27		23 36	23 42	00 08	00 26	01 06
Swaythling	d		21 28								22 29						23 30						
St Denys	d		21 31								22 32						23 33					00s30	
Southampton Central	a		21 36		21 41			21 49	22 18	22 30	22 36		22 41	22 49	23 18	23 30	23 38		23 48	23 49	00 15	00 35	01 15
	d	21 27	21 38		21 43			21 51		22 31	22 38		22 43	22 51		23 31	23 40			23 51		00 36	
Millbrook (Hants)	d		21 40								22 41						23 42						
Redbridge	d		21 44								22 45						23 46						
Romsey	d	21 38	21 52								22a52						23 57						
Mottisfont & Dunbridge	d		21 57														00 02						
Dean	d		22 02														00 08						
Salisbury	a	22 03	22 15														00 20						
Totton	d									22 37						23 37							
Ashurst New Forest	d									22 41						23 41						00s41	
Beaulieu Road	d																						
Brockenhurst [3]	a				21 57			22 04		22 49			22 57	23 04		23 49				00 04		00s52	
	d				21 58	21 59		22 05		22 50			22 58	23 05		23 50				00 05			
Lymington Town	d					22 07																	
Lymington Pier	a					22 09																	
Yarmouth (I.O.W.) ⛴	a					23b00																	
Sway	d									22 55						23 55							
New Milton	d									23 00						23 59							
Hinton Admiral	d									23 04						00 04						01s00	
Christchurch	d									23 09						00 09							
Pokesdown	d									23 12						00 12						01s07	
Bournemouth	a				22 15			22 20		23 16			23 21	23 25		00 16				00 22		01s11	
	d							22 24		23 18				23 29		00 18				00 24		01 15	
Branksome	d							22 29		23 23				23 35		00 23				00 29		01 16	
Parkstone (Dorset)	d							22 32		23 26				23 38		00 26				00 32		01s21	
Poole [4]	a							22 36		23 30				23 41		00 30				00 36		01s24	
	d							22 37						23 42								01 29	
Hamworthy	d							22 42						23 47									
Holton Heath	d																						
Wareham	d							22 49						23 54									
Wool	d							22 55						00 01									
Moreton (Dorset)	d							23 01						00 07									
Dorchester South	d							23 09						00 15									
Dorchester West	d						22 53																
Upwey	d						23 00	23 16						00 21									
Weymouth	a						23 05	23 20						00 26									

For general notes see front of timetable
For details of catering facilities see
Directory of Train Operators

A From Great Malvern (Table 71)
B ☕ to Bournemouth
b By ship

During July and August ferry connection times to and from Yarmouth IOW are subject to alteration, please contact www.wightlink.co.uk or 0871 376 1000 for further details.

Table 158

Sundays

London → Basingstoke, Southampton, Romsey Lymington, Bournemouth and Weymouth

Network Diagram - see first page of Table 158

		SW	SW	SW	SW	SW	SW	SW	SW	SW	SW	SW	GW	SW	SW		SW	GW	SW	SW	SW	SW		SW	GW
		1◇	1◇	1	1	1◇	1	1◇	1	1	1	1	1	1	1		1	◇	1	1	1	1◇		1	◇
													A					B		C					
			⊏P			⊏P							⊥												⊥
London Waterloo 15 ⊖	d	21p35	22p05		21p42	22p35	22p39	23p05		23p39	00 05	01 05										07 54			
Clapham Junction 10	d		22b12				22b46	23b12		23b46	00u12	01 14										08u03			
Woking	d	22p00	22p32		22p19	23p00		23p32		00 08	00 36	01 42										08 28			
Farnborough (Main)	d				22p33		23p13			00 18		01s58													
Fleet	d				22p38		23p19			00 23															
Reading 7	d																					07 37			
Basingstoke	a		22p51		22p58		23p34	23p51		00 34	00 55	02s12										08 46			
	d		22p53		23p00		23p36	23p53		00 36	00 57				07 48							08 48			
Micheldever	d				23p10			00 03							07 58							08 58			
Winchester	d	22p33	23p09		23p19	23p33	23p52	00 12		00 53	01 13	02s29			08 08							09 08			
Shawford	d						23p57								08 12										
Romsey	d			23p09																08 35					
Chandlers Ford	d			23p16																08 42					
Eastleigh 3	a		23p17	23p22	23p29		00 02	00 20		01 01	01 21	02s38			08 18					08 47		09 18			
	d		23p18	23p23	23p30		00 03	00 21	00 30	01 02	01 22				08 22	08 26				08 54		09 22	09 26		
Hedge End	d				23p36				00s36							08 32							09 32		
Botley	d				23p40				00s39							08 36							09 36		
Fareham	d				23p48				00s47				07 32			08 44							09 44		09 32
Portchester	d				23p53				00s53							08 49							09 49		
Cosham	d				23p58				00s57							08 54							09 54		
Hilsea	a				00 03											09 00							10 00		
Fratton	a				00 07				01s05							09 04							10 04		
Portsmouth & Southsea	a				00 11				01s08							09 08							10 10		
Portsmouth Harbour	a				00 16				01 12							09 13							10 15		
Southampton Airport Parkwy ✈	d	22p42	23p23	23p27		23p42	00 08	00 26		01 06	01 27	02s43			08 27					08 58		09 27			
Swaythling	d			23p30																09 01					
St Denys	d			23p33				00s30				02s48								09 04					
Southampton Central	a	22p49	23p30	23p38		23p49	00 15	00 35		01 15	01 36	02 53	07 53		08 34					09 09		09 34			09 53
	d	22p51	23p31	23p40		23p51		00 36			01 37		07 54		08 35				09 04	09 10		09 35			09 54
Millbrook (Hants)	d			23p42																09 13					
Redbridge	d			23p46																09 16					
Romsey	d			23p57									08a05							09 24					10 05
Mottisfont & Dunbridge	d			00 02																09 29					
Dean	d			00 08																09 35					
Salisbury	a			00 20																09 47					10 24
Totton	d		23p37					00s41			01s42				08 41							09 41			
Ashurst New Forest	d		23p41												08 45							09 45			
Beaulieu Road	d														08 50							09 50			
Brockenhurst 3	a	23p04	23p49			00 04		00s52			01s53				08 56				09 17			09 56			
	d	23p05	23p50			00 05									08 57		08 59		09 18		09 29	09 57		09 59	
Lymington Town	d																09 07				09 37			10 07	
Lymington Pier	a																09 09				09 39			10 09	
Yarmouth (I.O.W.) ⛴	a																				*10c15*			*11c00*	
Sway	d		23p55												09 01							10 01			
New Milton	d		23p59					01s00			02s01				09 06				09 25			10 06			
Hinton Admiral	d		00 04												09 10							10 10			
Christchurch	d		00 09					01s07			02s08				09 15							10 15			
Pokesdown	d		00 12					01s11			02s12				09 19							10 19			
Bournemouth	a	23p25	00 16			00 22		01 15			02 16				09 23				09 35			10 23			
	d	23p29	00 18			00 24		01 16						08 40	09 25				09 40			10 25			
Branksome	d	23p35	00 23			00 29		01s21						08 45					09 45						
Parkstone (Dorset)	d	23p38	00 26			00 32		01s24						08 48					09 48						
Poole 4	a	23p41	00 30			00 36		01 29						08 51	09 34				09 51			10 34			
	d	23p42												08 52					09 52						
Hamworthy	d	23p47												08 57					09 57						
Holton Heath	d																								
Wareham	d	23p54												09 04					10 04						
Wool	d	00 01												09 11					10 11						
Moreton (Dorset)	d	00 07												09 17					10 17						
Dorchester South	d	00 15												09 25					10 25						
Dorchester West	d																	10 13							
Upwey	d	00 21												09 32				10 20	10 32						
Weymouth	a	00 26												09 36				10 25	10 36						

For general notes see front of timetable
For details of catering facilities see Directory of Train Operators

A From Portsmouth Harbour (Table 165)
B Until 6 September
C From Salisbury

b Previous night.
Stops to pick up only
c By ship

During July and August ferry connection times to and from Yarmouth IOW are subject to alteration, please contact www.wightliink.co.uk or 0871 376 1000 for further details.

Sundays

London → Basingstoke, Southampton, Romsey Lymington, Bournemouth and Weymouth

Network Diagram - see first page of Table 158

		GW	SW	SW	SW	SW			SW	XC	SW	SW	SW	SW		SW	XC	GW	SW	SW	SW	SW		SW	XC
		◇ A	1 ◇	1	1	1 ◇			1	R 1	1 ◇	1	1	1 ◇		1	1 ◇ B	◇	1 ◇ C	1	1	1 ◇		1	1 ◇
London Waterloo 15 ⊖	d		08 35			08 54					09 35			09 54					10 35			10 54			
Clapham Junction 10	d		08u42			09u03					09u42			10u03					10u42			11u03			
Woking	d		09 09			09 28					10 09			10 28					11 07			11 28			
Farnborough (Main)	d																								
Fleet	d																								
Reading 7	d		*08 37*							09 51	*09 51*						10 50								11 51
Basingstoke	a		09 28			09 47				10 09	10 28			10 47			11 09		11 26			11 47			12 09
	d		09 30			09 48				10 11	10 30			10 48			11 10		11 28			11 48			12 10
Micheldever	d					09 58								10 58								11 58			
Winchester	d		09 46			10 08				10 26	10 46			11 08			11 25		11 44			12 08			12 25
Shawford	d					10 12																12 12			
Romsey	d				09 35								10 35								11 35				
Chandlers Ford	d				09 42								10 42								11 42				
Eastleigh 3	a				09 48	10 18							10 48	11 18							11 48	12 18			
	d				09 54	10 22	10 26						10 54	11 22	11 26						11 54	12 22	12 26		
Hedge End	d						10 32								11 32								12 32		
Botley	d						10 36								11 36								12 36		
Fareham	d						10 44								11 44			11 32					12 44		
Portchester	d						10 49								11 49								12 49		
Cosham	d						10 54								11 54								12 54		
Hilsea	a						11 00								12 00								13 00		
Fratton	a						11 04								12 04								13 04		
Portsmouth & Southsea	a						11 08								12 08								13 08		
Portsmouth Harbour	a						11 14								12 13								13 13		
Southampton Airport Parkwy ✈	d		09 55		09 58	10 27				10 34	10 55		10 58	11 27			11 34		11 53		11 58	12 27			12 34
Swaythling	d				10 01								11 01								12 01				
St Denys	d				10 04								11 04								12 04				
Southampton Central	a		10 02		10 09	10 34				10 42	11 02		11 09	11 34			11 42	11 53	12 00		12 09	12 34			12 42
	d		10 04		10 10	10 35				10 45	11 04		11 10	11 35			11 45	11 54	12 03		12 10	12 35			12 45
Millbrook (Hants)	d				10 13								11 13								12 13				
Redbridge	d				10 16								11 16								12 16				
Romsey	d				10 24								11 24					12 06			12 24				
Mottisfont & Dunbridge	d												11 29												
Dean	d												11 35												
Salisbury	a				10 44								11 50					12 24			12 43				
Totton	d					10 41								11 41								12 41			
Ashurst New Forest	d					10 45								11 45								12 45			
Beaulieu Road	d					10 50								11 50								12 50			
Brockenhurst 3	a		10 17			10 56				11 02	11 17			11 56			12 01		12 16			12 56			13 01
	d		10 18	10 29		10 57			10 59	11 03	11 18	11 29		11 57		11 59	12 02		12 17	12 29		12 57		12 59	13 02
Lymington Town	d			10 37					11 07			11 37				12 07				12 37				13 07	
Lymington Pier	a			10 39					11 09			11 39				12 09				12 39				13 09	
Yarmouth (I.O.W.) ⛴	a								*11b45*							*12b45*								*13b45*	
Sway	d					11 01								12 01								13 01			
New Milton	d		10 25			11 06					11 25			12 06					12 24			13 06			
Hinton Admiral	d					11 10								12 10								13 10			
Christchurch	d					11 15								12 15								13 15			
Pokesdown	d					11 19								12 19								13 19			
Bournemouth	a		10 35			11 23				11 27	11 35			12 23			12 27		12 35			13 23			13 27
	d		10 40			11 25					11 40			12 25					12 40			13 25			
Branksome	d		10 45								11 45								12 45						
Parkstone (Dorset)	d		10 48								11 48								12 48						
Poole 4	a		10 51			11 34					11 51			12 34					12 51			13 34			
	d		10 52								11 52								12 52						
Hamworthy	d		10 57								11 57								12 57						
Holton Heath	d																								
Wareham	d		11 04								12 04								13 04						
Wool	d		11 11								12 11								13 11						
Moreton (Dorset)	d		11 17								12 17								13 17						
Dorchester South	d		11 25								12 25								13 25						
Dorchester West	d	11 16																							
Upwey	d	11 23	11 32								12 32								13 32						
Weymouth	a	11 27	11 36								12 36								13 36						

For general notes see front of timetable
For details of catering facilities see Directory of Train Operators

A Until 6 September
B From Birmingham New Street (Table 116)
C to Bournemouth
b By ship

During July and August ferry connection times to and from Yarmouth IOW are subject to alteration, please contact www.wightliink.co.uk or 0871 376 1000 for further details.

London → Basingstoke, Southampton, Romsey Lymington, Bournemouth and Weymouth

Network Diagram - see first page of Table 158

		GW	SW	SW	SW	SW		SW	XC	GW	SW	SW	SW	SW		SW	GW	GW	XC	GW	SW	SW	SW
		◇	■1 ◇	■1	■1	■1 ◇		■1	■1 ◇	◇	■1 ◇	■1	■1	■1 ◇		■1	◇	◇	■1 ◇	◇	■1 ◇	■1	■1
			A								A						B	C			A		
			⊡						⊡	⊡	⊡								⊡	⊡	⊡		
London Waterloo 15 ⊖	d		11 35			11 54					12 35			12 54							13 35		
Clapham Junction 10	d		11u42			12u03					12u42			13u03							13u42		
Woking	d		12 07			12 28					13 07			13 28							14 07		
Farnborough (Main)	d																						
Fleet	d																						
Reading 7	d								12 51										13 51				
Basingstoke	a		12 26			12 47			13 09		13 26			13 47					14 09		14 26		
	d		12 28			12 48			13 10		13 28			13 48					14 10		14 28		
Micheldever	d					12 58								13 58									
Winchester	d		12 44			13 08			13 25		13 44			14 08					14 25		14 44		
Shawford	d													14 12									
Romsey	d				12 35								13 35										14 35
Chandlers Ford	d				12 42								13 42										14 42
Eastleigh 3	a				12 48	13 18							13 48	14 18									14 48
	d				12 54	13 22	13 26						13 54	14 22	14 26								14 54
Hedge End	d						13 32								14 32								
Botley	d						13 36								14 36								
Fareham	d	12 32					13 44			13 32					14 44					14 32			
Portchester	d						13 49								14 49								
Cosham	d						13 54								14 54								
Hilsea	a						14 00								15 00								
Fratton	a						14 04								15 04								
Portsmouth & Southsea	a						14 08								15 08								
Portsmouth Harbour	a						14 13								15 13								
Southampton Airport Parkwy ✈	d		12 53		12 58	13 27			13 34		13 53		13 58	14 27					14 34		14 53		14 58
Swaythling	d				13 01								14 01										15 01
St Denys	d				13 04								14 04										15 04
Southampton Central	a	12 53	13 00		13 09	13 34			13 42	13 53	14 00		14 09	14 34					14 42	14 53	15 00		15 09
	d	12 54	13 03		13 10	13 35			13 45	13 54	14 03		14 10	14 35					14 45	14 54	15 03		15 10
Millbrook (Hants)	d				13 13								14 13										15 13
Redbridge	d				13 16								14 16										15 16
Romsey	d	13 06			13 24					14 06			14 24							15 06			15 24
Mottisfont & Dunbridge	d				13 29																		15 29
Dean	d				13 35																		15 35
Salisbury	a	13 24			13 50					14 24			14 43							15 24			15 50
Totton	d					13 41								14 41									
Ashurst New Forest	d					13 45								14 45									
Beaulieu Road	d					13 50								14 50									
Brockenhurst 3	a		13 16			13 56			14 01		14 16			14 56					15 01		15 16		
	d		13 17	13 29		13 57		13 59	14 02		14 17	14 29		14 57		14 59			15 02		15 17	15 29	
Lymington Town	d			13 37				14 07				14 37				15 07						15 37	
Lymington Pier	a			13 39				14 09				14 39				15 09						15 39	
Yarmouth (I.O.W.) ⛴	a			*14b30*								*15b15*				*16b00*							
Sway	d					14 01								15 01									
New Milton	d		13 24			14 06					14 24			15 06							15 24		
Hinton Admiral	d					14 10								15 10									
Christchurch	d					14 15								15 15									
Pokesdown	d					14 19								15 19									
Bournemouth	a		13 35			14 23			14 27		14 35			15 23					15 27		15 35		
	d		13 40			14 25					14 40			15 25							15 40		
Branksome	d		13 45								14 45										15 45		
Parkstone (Dorset)	d		13 48								14 48										15 48		
Poole 4	a		13 51			14 34					14 51			15 34							15 51		
	d		13 52								14 52										15 52		
Hamworthy	d		13 57								14 57										15 57		
Holton Heath	d																						
Wareham	d		14 04								15 04										16 04		
Wool	d		14 11								15 11										16 11		
Moreton (Dorset)	d		14 17								15 17										16 17		
Dorchester South	d		14 25								15 25										16 25		
Dorchester West	d																15 33	15 53					
Upwey	d		14 32								15 32						15 40	16 00			16 32		
Weymouth	a		14 36								15 36						15 45	16 05			16 36		

For general notes see front of timetable
For details of catering facilities see Directory of Train Operators

A ⊡ to Bournemouth
B Until 6 September
C From 13 September
b By ship

During July and August ferry connection times to and from Yarmouth IOW are subject to alteration, please contact www.wightlink.co.uk or 0871 376 1000 for further details.

Table 158

Sundays

London → Basingstoke, Southampton, Romsey Lymington, Bournemouth and Weymouth

Network Diagram - see first page of Table 158

		SW 1 ◇		SW 1	XC 1 ◇	GW ◇	SW 1 ◇	SW 1	SW 1	SW 1 ◇		SW 1	XC 1 ◇	GW ◇	SW 1 ◇	SW 1	SW 1	GW ◇	SW 1 ◇		SW 1	XC 1 ◇		GW ◇	SW 1 ◇
							A								A										A
					🛒	🛒	🍽						🛒	🛒	🍽							🛒		🛒	🍽
London Waterloo 15 ⊖	d	13 54					14 35			14 54					15 35				15 54						16 35
Clapham Junction 10	d	14u03					14u42			15u03					15u42				16u03						16u42
Woking	d	14 28					15 07			15 28					16 07				16 28						17 07
Farnborough (Main)	d																								
Fleet	d																								
Reading 7	d				14 51								15 51									16 51			
Basingstoke	a	14 47			15 09		15 26			15 47			16 09		16 26				16 47			17 09			17 26
	d	14 48			15 10		15 28			15 48			16 10		16 28				16 48			17 10			17 28
Micheldever	d	14 58								15 58									16 58						
Winchester	d	15 08			15 25		15 44			16 08			16 25		16 44				17 08			17 25			17 44
Shawford	d									16 12															
Romsey	d								15 35								16 35								
Chandlers Ford	d								15 42								16 42								
Eastleigh 3	a	15 18							15 48	16 18							16 48		17 18						
	d	15 22	15 26						15 54	16 22	16 26						16 54		17 22	17 26					
Hedge End	d		15 32								16 32									17 32					
Botley	d		15 36								16 36									17 36					
Fareham	d		15 44			15 32					16 44			16 32				17 03		17 44				17 32	
Portchester	d		15 49								16 49									17 49					
Cosham	d		15 54								16 54			16 23						17 54					
Hilsea	a		16 00								17 00									18 00					
Fratton	a		16 04								17 04									18 04					
Portsmouth & Southsea	a		16 08								17 08									18 08					
Portsmouth Harbour	a		16 13								17 13									18 13					
Southampton Airport Parkwy ✈	d	15 27			15 34		15 53		15 58	16 27			16 34		16 53		16 58		17 27			17 34			17 53
Swaythling	d								16 01								17 01								
St Denys	d								16 04								17 04								
Southampton Central	a	15 34			15 42	15 53	16 00		16 09	16 34			16 42	16 53	17 00		17 09	17 24	17 34			17 40		17 53	18 00
	d	15 35			15 45	15 54	16 03		16 10	16 35			16 45	16 54	17 03		17 10	17 26	17 35			17 45		17 54	18 03
Millbrook (Hants)	d								16 13								17 13								
Redbridge	d								16 16								17 16								
Romsey	d					16 06			16 24					17 06			17 24	17 39						18 06	
Mottisfont & Dunbridge	d																17 29								
Dean	d																17 35								
Salisbury	a					16 24			16 43					17 24			17 50	18 01						18 24	
Totton	d	15 41								16 41									17 41						
Ashurst New Forest	d	15 45								16 45									17 45						
Beaulieu Road	d	15 50								16 50									17 50						
Brockenhurst 3	a	15 56			16 01		16 16			16 56			17 01		17 16				17 56			18 01			18 16
	d	15 57		15 59	16 02		16 17	16 29		16 57		16 59	17 02		17 17	17 29			17 57		17 59	18 02			18 17
Lymington Town	d			16 07				16 37				17 07				17 37					18 07				
Lymington Pier	a			16 09				16 39				17 09				17 39					18 09				
Yarmouth (I.O.W.) ⛴	a			*16b45*				*17b30*								*18b15*					*19b00*				
Sway	d	16 01								17 01									18 01						
New Milton	d	16 06					16 24			17 06					17 24				18 06						18 24
Hinton Admiral	d	16 10								17 10									18 10						
Christchurch	d	16 15								17 15									18 15						
Pokesdown	d	16 19								17 19									18 19						
Bournemouth	a	16 23			16 27		16 35			17 23			17 27		17 35				18 23			18 27			18 35
	d	16 25					16 40			17 25					17 40				18 25						18 40
Branksome	d						16 45								17 45										18 45
Parkstone (Dorset)	d						16 48								17 48										18 48
Poole 4	a	16 34					16 51			17 34					17 51				18 34						18 51
	d						16 52								17 52										18 52
Hamworthy	d						16 57								17 57										18 57
Holton Heath	d																								
Wareham	d						17 04								18 04										19 04
Wool	d						17 11								18 11										19 11
Moreton (Dorset)	d						17 17								18 17										19 17
Dorchester South	d						17 25								18 25										19 25
Dorchester West	d																								
Upwey	d						17 32								18 32										19 32
Weymouth	a						17 36								18 36										19 36

For general notes see front of timetable
For details of catering facilities see Directory of Train Operators

A 🍽 to Bournemouth
b By ship

During July and August ferry connection times to and from Yarmouth IOW are subject to alteration, please contact www.wightliink.co.uk or 0871 376 1000 for further details.

London → Basingstoke, Southampton, Romsey Lymington, Bournemouth and Weymouth

Network Diagram - see first page of Table 158

	SW 1	SW 1	SW 1 ◇		SW 1	GW ◇	XC 1 ◇	GW ◇	SW 1 ◇	SW 1	SW 1	GW ◇	SW 1 ◇		SW 1	XC 1 ◇	GW ◇	SW 1 ◇	SW 1	SW 1	SW 1 ◇		SW 1	XC 1 ◇
						A			B									B						
							⊥	⊥	⊡							⊥	⊥	⊡						⊥
London Waterloo 15 ⊖ d			16 54						17 35				17 54					18 35			18 54			
Clapham Junction 10 d			17u03						17u42				18u03					18u42			19u03			
Woking d			17 28						18 07				18 28					19 07			19 28			
Farnborough (Main) d																								
Fleet d																								
Reading 7 d							17 51									18 51								19 51
Basingstoke a			17 47				18 09		18 26				18 47			19 09		19 26			19 47			20 09
d			17 48				18 10		18 28				18 48			19 10		19 28			19 48			20 10
Micheldever d			17 58										18 58								19 58			
Winchester d			18 08				18 25		18 44				19 08			19 25		19 44			20 08			20 25
Shawford d			18 12																		20 12			
Romsey d		17 35									18 35									19 35				
Chandlers Ford d		17 42									18 42									19 42				
Eastleigh 3 a		17 48	18 18								18 48		19 18							19 48	20 18			
d		17 54	18 22	18 26							18 54		19 22	19 26						19 54	20 22	20 26		
Hedge End d				18 32										19 32								20 32		
Botley d				18 36										19 36								20 36		
Fareham d				18 44				18 32				19 03		19 44			19 32					20 44		
Portchester d				18 49										19 49								20 49		
Cosham d				18 54										19 54								20 54		
Hilsea a				19 00										20 00								21 00		
Fratton a				19 04										20 04								21 04		
Portsmouth & Southsea a				19 08										20 08								21 08		
Portsmouth Harbour a				19 13										20 13								21 13		
Southampton Airport Parkwy ✈ d		17 58	18 27				18 34		18 53		18 58		19 27			19 34		19 53		19 58	20 27			20 34
Swaythling d		18 01									19 01									20 01				
St Denys d		18 04									19 04									20 04				
Southampton Central a		18 09	18 34				18 42	18 53	19 00		19 09	19 24	19 34			19 40	19 53	20 00		20 09	20 34			20 42
d		18 10	18 35				18 45	18 54	19 03		19 10	19 30	19 35			19 45	19 54	20 03		20 10	20 35			20 45
Millbrook (Hants) d		18 13									19 13									20 13				
Redbridge d		18 16									19 16									20 16				
Romsey d		18 24						19 06			19 24	19 42					20 06			20 24				
Mottisfont & Dunbridge d											19 29													
Dean d											19 35													
Salisbury a		18 43						19 24			19 50	20 00					20 24			20 43				
Totton d			18 41										19 41								20 41			
Ashurst New Forest d			18 45										19 45								20 45			
Beaulieu Road d			18 50										19 50								20 50			
Brockenhurst 3 a			18 56				19 01		19 16				19 56			20 01		20 16			20 56			21 01
d	18 29		18 57		18 59		19 02		19 17	19 29			19 57		19 59	20 02		20 17	20 29		20 57		20 59	21 02
Lymington Town d	18 37				19 07					19 37					20 07				20 37				21 07	
Lymington Pier a	18 39				19 09					19 39					20 09				20 39				21 09	
Yarmouth (I.O.W.) ⛴ a					19b45										20b45				21b30					
Sway d			19 01										20 01								21 01			
New Milton d			19 06						19 24				20 06					20 24			21 06			
Hinton Admiral d			19 10										20 10								21 10			
Christchurch d			19 15										20 15								21 15			
Pokesdown d			19 19										20 19								21 19			
Bournemouth a			19 23				19 27		19 35				20 23			20 27		20 35			21 23			21 27
d			19 25						19 40				20 25					20 40			21 25			
Branksome d									19 45									20 45						
Parkstone (Dorset) d									19 48									20 48						
Poole 4 a			19 34						19 51				20 34					20 51			21 34			
d									19 52									20 52						
Hamworthy d									19 57									20 57						
Holton Heath d																								
Wareham d									20 04									21 04						
Wool d									20 11									21 11						
Moreton (Dorset) d									20 17									21 17						
Dorchester South d									20 25									21 25						
Dorchester West d						19 48																		
Upwey d						19 55			20 32									21 32						
Weymouth a						20 01			20 36									21 36						

For general notes see front of timetable
For details of catering facilities see Directory of Train Operators

A From Weston-super-Mare (Table 134)
B ⊡ to Bournemouth
b By ship

During July and August ferry connection times to and from Yarmouth IOW are subject to alteration, please contact www.wightliink.co.uk or 0871 376 1000 for further details.

Sundays

London → Basingstoke, Southampton, Romsey Lymington, Bournemouth and Weymouth

Network Diagram - see first page of Table 158

Station		GW	SW	SW	SW	SW		SW	XC	GW	SW	SW	GW	SW		XC	SW	XC	SW	SW		XC	SW	
		◇	1 ◇	1	1	1 ◇		1	1 ◇	◇	1 ◇	1	◇	1 ◇		1 ◇	1 ◇	1 ◇	1	1 ◇		1 ◇	1 ◇	
			A								A						A						B	
		⌶	⊡						⌶		⊡		⌶			⌶	⊡	⌶				⌶	⊡	
London Waterloo 15 ⊖	d		19 35			19 54					20 35			20 54			21 35			21 54			22 54	
Clapham Junction 10	d		19u42			20u03					20u42			21u03			21u42			22u03			23u03	
Woking	d		20 07			20 28					21 07			21 28			22 07			22 28			23 28	
Farnborough (Main)	d																							
Fleet	d																							
Reading 7	d								20 51							21 51		22 12		22 12			22 37	
Basingstoke	a		20 26			20 47			21 09		21 26			21 47		22 11	22 26	22 30		22 47		←	23 47	
	d		20 28			20 48			21 10		21 28			21 48		22 12	22 28	22 32		22 48		22 32	23 48	
Micheldever	d					20 58								21 58				→		22 58			23 58	
Winchester	d		20 44			21 08			21 25		21 44			22 08		22 27	22 44			23 08			00 08	
Shawford	d													22 12										
Romsey	d				20 35							21 35							22 35					
Chandlers Ford	d				20 42							21 42							22 42					
Eastleigh 3	a				20 48	21 18						21 48		22 18					22 48	23 17			00 18	
	d				20 54	21 22	21 26					21 54		22 22	22 26				22 54	23 22	23 26		00 22	00 30
Hedge End	d						21 32								22 32						23 32			00s36
Botley	d						21 36								22 36						23 36			00s39
Fareham	d	20 32					21 44						22 32		22 44						23 44			00s47
Portchester	d						21 49								22 49						23 49			00s53
Cosham	d						21 54								22 54						23 54			00s57
Hilsea	a						22 00								23 00						23 59			
Fratton	a						22 04								23 04						00 04			01s05
Portsmouth & Southsea	a						22 08								23 08						00 08			01s08
Portsmouth Harbour	a						22 13								23 13						00 13			01 12
Southampton Airport Parkway ✈	d		20 53		20 58	21 27			21 34		21 53	21 58		22 27		22 36	22 53		22 58	23 27		23 36	00 27	
Swaythling	d				21 01							22 01							23 01					
St Denys	d				21 04							22 04							23 04				00s31	
Southampton Central	a	20 53	21 00		21 09	21 34			21 42		22 00	22 09		22 34		22 47	23 00		23 09	23 34		23 47	00 36	
	d	20 54	21 03		21 10	21 35			21 45		22 03	22 10		22 35			23 03		23 10	23 35			00 37	
Millbrook (Hants)	d				21 13							22 13							23 13					
Redbridge	d				21 16							22 16							23 16					
Romsey	d	21 06			21 24							22a24	23 09						23 24					
Mottisfont & Dunbridge	d				21 29														23 29					
Dean	d				21 35														23 35					
Salisbury	a	21 24			21 50								23 27						23 50					
Totton	d					21 41								22 41						23 41			00s42	
Ashurst New Forest	d					21 45								22 45						23 45				
Beaulieu Road	d					21 50								22 50										
Brockenhurst 3	a		21 16			21 56			22 01		22 16			22 56			23 16			23 53			00s53	
	d		21 17	21 29		21 57		21 59	22 02		22 17			22 57			23 17			23 54				
Lymington Town	d			21 37				22 07																
Lymington Pier	a			21 39				22 09																
Yarmouth (I.O.W.) ⛴	a							23b00																
Sway	d					22 01								23 01						23 59				
New Milton	d		21 24			22 06					22 24			23 06			23 24			00 04			01s01	
Hinton Admiral	d					22 10								23 10						00 08				
Christchurch	d					22 15								23 15						00 13			01s08	
Pokesdown	d					22 19								23 19						00 16			01s12	
Bournemouth	a		21 35			22 23			22 27		22 35			23 23			23 35			00 21			01 16	
	d		21 40			22 25					22 40			23 25			23 40			00 22			01 18	
Branksome	d		21 45								22 45						23 45			00 28			01s23	
Parkstone (Dorset)	d		21 48								22 48						23 48			00 31			01s26	
Poole 4	a		21 51			22 34					22 51			23 34			23 51			00 35			01 30	
	d		21 52								22 52						23 52							
Hamworthy	d		21 57								22 57						23 57							
Holton Heath	d																							
Wareham	d		22 04								23 04						00 04							
Wool	d		22 11								23 11						00 11							
Moreton (Dorset)	d		22 17								23 17						00 17							
Dorchester South	d		22 25								23 25						00 25							
Dorchester West	d									22 52														
Upwey	d		22 32							22 59	23 32						00 32							
Weymouth	a		22 36							23 03	23 36						00 36							

For general notes see front of timetable
For details of catering facilities see Directory of Train Operators

A ⊡ to Bournemouth
B ⊡ to Poole
b By ship

During July and August ferry connection times to and from Yarmouth IOW are subject to alteration, please contact www.wightlink.co.uk or 0871 376 1000 for further details.

For details of Bank Holiday service alterations, please see first page of Table 149

Weymouth, Bournemouth, Lymington, Romsey, Southampton and Basingstoke → London

Network Diagram - see first page of Table 158

Miles	Miles			SW	SW	SW	SW	SW	SW	XC	SW	SW	SW	SW	SW	SW	XC	SW	SW	SW	SW	GW	SW	SW	SW
				MO	MX	MX	MX																		
				■1 ◇	■1	■1	■1 ◇	■1	■1	■1 ◇	■1	■1	■1 ◇	■1 ◇	■1	■1	■1 ◇	■1	■1 ◇	■1 ◇	■1	◇	■1	■1	■1
													A	B	A	B			A	B		C	D		
										(catering)			(catering)	(catering)			(catering)		(catering)	(catering)					
0	—	**Weymouth**	d	20p58	21p10		22p10															05 35			
2¼	—	Upwey	d	21p02	21p14		22p14															05 40			
—	—	Dorchester West	a																			05 48			
7	—	**Dorchester South**	d	21p10	21p22		22p22																		
12½	—	Moreton (Dorset)	d	21p17	21p28		22p28																		
17	—	Wool	d	21p23	21p34		22p34																		
22	—	Wareham	d	21p30	21p42		22p42																		
24	—	Holton Heath	d																						
26¾	—	Hamworthy	d	21p37	21p48		22p48																		
29	—	**Poole** 4	a	21p41	21p53		22p53																		
—	—		d	21p50	21p54		22p54						04 57	05 00	05 23	05 26			05 42	05 45					
30¾	—	Parkstone (Dorset)	d	21p54	21p58		22p58						05 01	05 04	05 27	05 30									
32	—	Branksome	d	21p57	22p01		23p01						05 04	05 07	05 30	05 33									
34¾	—	**Bournemouth**	a	22p03	22p07		23p07						05 09	05 12	05 36	05 38			05 51	05 54					
—	—		d	22p06	22p12		23p12						05 12	05 15	05 38	05 40			05 54	05 57					
36½	—	Pokesdown	d	22p10	22p16		23p16						05 16	05 19	05 42	05 44									
38½	—	Christchurch	d	22p14	22p20		23p20						05 20	05 23	05 46	05 48									
41¾	—	Hinton Admiral	d	22p19	22p25		23p25								05 51	05 53									
44½	—	New Milton	d	22p23	22p29		23p29						05 27	05 30	05 55	05 57									
47¼	—	Sway	d	22p28	22p34		23p34								06 00	06 02									
—	—	Yarmouth (I.O.W.) ⛴	d																						06 14
—	0	**Lymington Pier** ⛴	d																						06 16
—	½	Lymington Town	d																						
50	5¼	**Brockenhurst** 3	a	22p33	22p39		23p39						05 37	05 37	06 07	06 07			06 12	06 12					06 24
—	—		d	22p34	22p40		23p40						05 38	05 38					06 14	06 14					
54¾	—	Beaulieu Road	d	22p39																					
57¼	—	Ashurst New Forest	d	22p43	22p47		23p47																		
60¼	—	Totton	d	22p48	22p52		23p52						05 49	05 49				06 12							
—	0	**Salisbury**	d																				05 35		
—	9	Dean	d																				05 47		
—	12¾	Mottisfont & Dunbridge	d																				05 53		
—	16½	**Romsey**	d																				05 58		
60¾	22½	Redbridge	d															06 14					06 36		
62½	—	Millbrook (Hants)	d															06 17							
63½	—	**Southampton Central**	a	22p53	22p57		23p57						05 54	05 54				06 24	06 27	06 27				←	
—	—		d	22p55	23p00		23p59	04 40	04 55	05 15		05 42	05 55	05 55			06 15	06 35 →	06 30	06 30				06 35	
65½	—	St Denys	d				00 04	04 45				05 47												06 40	
67	—	Swaythling	d				00 07	04 48				05 50												06 43	
67¾	—	**Southampton Airport Parkwy** ✈	d	23p03	23p08		00 10	04 51	05 02	05 22		05 53	06 03	06 03			06 22		06 38	06 38				06 46	
—	0	**Portsmouth Harbour**	d			23p24					05 00										05 43				
—	¾	**Portsmouth & Southsea**	d			23p29					05 05										05 48				
—	1¾	Fratton	d			23p33					05 09										05 52				
—	4	Hilsea	d			23p37					05 13										05 56				
—	5½	Cosham	d			23p42					05 18										06 03				
—	8	Portchester	d			23p47					05 23										06 08				
—	11½	Fareham	d			23p53					05 29										06 19				
—	16¾	Botley	d			23p59					05 36										06 27				
—	17¾	Hedge End	d			00 05					05 40										06 31				
69¼	22¼	Eastleigh 3	a	23p09	23p11	00 11	00 14	04 56	05 06		05 48	05 56	06 07	06 07							06 37			06 49	
—	—		d	23p11	23p11	00 19			05 06		05 49		06 08	06 08							06 43			06 50	
—	24¼	Chandlers Ford	d																				06 06	06 55	
—	29½	**Romsey**	a																				06 44	07 03	
73	—	Shawford	d		23p17				05 12		05 55										06 49				
76½	—	**Winchester**	d	23p23	23p24	00a28			05 18	05 31	06 01		06 18	06 18			06 31		06 48	06 48	06 55				
84¾	—	Micheldever	d	23p32	23p33				05 27		06 10										07 04				
95	—	**Basingstoke**	a	23p42	23p43				05 37	05 46	06 21		06 34	06 34			06 46				07 14				
—	—		d	23p44	23p44				05 39	05 47			06 35	06 35			06 47				07 17				
—	—	Reading 7	a	*00 30*						06 05	*07 00*						07 05								
106¼	—	Fleet	d		00 01				05 50																
109½	—	Farnborough (Main)	d		00 06				05 56																
118½	—	**Woking**	a	00 02	00 18				06 05				06 53	06 53											
138¾	—	Clapham Junction 10	a	00 23	00 54				06 25				07 14	07 14											
142¾	—	**London Waterloo** 15 ⊖	a	00 33	01 02				06 34				07 24	07 24					07 47	07 47	08 01				

For general notes see front of timetable
For details of catering facilities see Directory of Train Operators

A From 28 September
B Until 25 September
C To Bristol Parkway (Table 132)
D To Salisbury

During July and August ferry connection times to and from Yarmouth IOW are subject to alteration, please contact www.wightliink.co.uk or 0871 376 1000 for further details.

For details of Bank Holiday service alterations, please see first page of Table 149

Weymouth, Bournemouth, Lymington, Romsey, Southampton and Basingstoke → London

Network Diagram - see first page of Table 158

		SW	SW	GW	SW	SW	SW	SW	SW	SW	SW	XC	SW	SW	SW	SW	SW	SW	SW	SW	SW	SW	GW	SW	SW
		1◇	1		1◇	1◇	1◇	1◇	1◇	1	1	1◇	1	1	1◇	1◇	1◇	1◇	1◇	1	1	1	◇	1	1◇
					A	B	B	A	A						A	B	C	A	D						A
					⊡	⊡	⊡	⊡	⊡			✕			⊡	⊡	⊡	⊡	⊡						⊡
Weymouth	d																05 50		05 55						
Upwey	d																05 54		05 59						
Dorchester West	a																								
Dorchester South	d																06 02		06 07						
Moreton (Dorset)	d																06 09		06 14						
Wool	d																06 15		06 20						
Wareham	d																06 22		06 27						
Holton Heath	d																06 26		06 31						
Hamworthy	d																06 31		06 36						
Poole 4	a																06 35		06 40						
	d						06 08		06 11								06 36		06 41						
Parkstone (Dorset)	d						06 12		06 15								06 40		06 45						
Branksome	d						06 15		06 18								06 46		06 49						
Bournemouth	a						06 23		06 23								06 54		06 54						
	d				06 04	06 04	06 25		06 25			06 30			06 34	06 34	06 56		06 56						07 04
Pokesdown	d				06 08	06 08									06 38	06 38									07 08
Christchurch	d				06 12	06 12									06 42	06 42									07 12
Hinton Admiral	d				06 17	06 17									06 47	06 47									07 17
New Milton	d				06 21	06 21									06 51	06 51									07 21
Sway	d				06 26	06 26									06 56	06 56									07 26
Yarmouth (I.O.W.) ⛴	d												*06b00*											*06b30*	
Lymington Pier ⛴	d												06 44											07 14	
Lymington Town	d												06 46											07 16	
Brockenhurst 3	a				06 31	06 31						06 46	06 54		07 01	07 01								07 24	07 31
	d				06 32	06 32						06 49			07 02	07 02									07 32
Beaulieu Road	d																								
Ashurst New Forest	d				06 40	06 40		←							07 10	07 10		←							07 40
Totton	d				06 45	06 45		06 45							07 15	07 15		07 15							07 45
Salisbury	d			06 20	↪										↪						06 50		07 11		↪
Dean	d																				07 02				
Mottisfont & Dunbridge	d																				07 08				
Romsey	d			06 38																	07 13		07 30		
Redbridge	d																				07 21				
Millbrook (Hants)	d																				07 23				
Southampton Central	a			06 49		06 51	06 55	06 51	06 55			07 01				07 20	07 25	07 20	07 25		07 29		07 41		
	d		06 43			07 00		07 00			07 10	07 15				07 30		07 30			07 35	07 38			
St Denys	d		06 48																		07 40	07 43			
Swaythling	d		06 51																		07 43	07 46			
Southampton Airport Parkwy ✈	d	06 50	06 54			07 08		07 08			07 18	07 22				07 38		07 38			07 46	07 49			
Portsmouth Harbour	d									06 23										06 38					
Portsmouth & Southsea	d									06 28										06 43					
Fratton	d									06 32										06 47					
Hilsea	d									06 36										06 51					
Cosham	d									06 42										06 58					
Portchester	d									06 46										07 03					
Fareham	d									06 53										07 11					
Botley	d									07 01										07 25					
Hedge End	d									07 05										07 29					
Eastleigh 3	a	06 53	06 58							07 11	07 21			←						07 35	07 49	07 53			
	d	06 54	06 59							07 13	07 30			07 30						07 43	07 50	07 54			
Chandlers Ford	d										↪										07 55				
Romsey	a																				08 03				
Shawford	d		07 05											07 36						07 49		08 00			
Winchester	d	07 05	07 11			07 18		07 18		07 22		07 31		07 42		07 48		07 48		07 55		08 06			
Micheldever	d									07 31										08 02					
Basingstoke	a		07 27							07 41		07 46		07 58						08 14		08 22			
	d		07 36							07 47		07 47		08 05						08 16		08 24			
Reading 7	a		*08 00*									08 05		*08 30*								*09 00*			
Fleet	d		07 52											08 22								08 40			
Farnborough (Main)	d		07 58											08 28								08 46			
Woking	a	07 38	08 08							08 05				08 38								08 58			
Clapham Junction 10	a																			08 34					
London Waterloo 15 ⊖	a	08 08	08 39			08 16		08 16		08 34				09 10		08 50		08 50		09 03		09 29			

For general notes see front of timetable
For details of catering facilities see Directory of Train Operators

- **A** Until 25 September
- **B** From 28 September
- **C** From 28 September. ⊡ from Bournemouth
- **D** Until 25 September. ⊡ from Bournemouth
- **b** By ship

During July and August ferry connection times to and from Yarmouth IOW are subject to alteration, please contact www.wightliink.co.uk or 0871 376 1000 for further details.

For details of Bank Holiday service alterations, please see first page of Table 149

Weymouth, Bournemouth, Lymington, Romsey, Southampton and Basingstoke → London

Network Diagram - see first page of Table 158

		SW	SW	SW	SW	GW	SW	XC	GW	SW	XC	SW	GW	SW	SW	SW	SW	SW	SW	SW	SW	SW	GW	SW	SW
		1 ◇	1 ◇	1 ◇	1 ◇	◇	1	1 ◇		1	1 ◇	1		1	1 ◇	1 ◇	1	1	1	1	1	1 ◇	◇	1	1
		A	B	C	D	E									B	D									
		⊡	⊡	⊡	⊡			⌶			⌶				⊡	⊡						⊡	⌶		
Weymouth	d		06 20		06 25	06 40									06 50	06 55								07 25	
Upwey	d		06 24		06 29	06 45									06 54	06 59								07 29	
Dorchester West	a					06 53																			
Dorchester South	d		06 32		06 37										07 02	07 07								07 37	
Moreton (Dorset)	d		06 39		06 44										07 09	07 14								07 44	
Wool	d		06 45		06 50										07 15	07 20								07 50	
Wareham	d		06 52		06 57										07 22	07 27								07 57	
Holton Heath	d														07 26	07 31								08 01	
Hamworthy	d		06 59		07 04										07 31	07 36								08 06	
Poole 4	a		07 03		07 08										07 35	07 40								08 10	
	d		07 06		07 11							07 20			07 36	07 41						07 55		08 11	
Parkstone (Dorset)	d		07 10		07 15							07 24			07 40	07 45						07 59		08 15	
Branksome	d		07 14		07 19							07 27			07 46	07 49						08 02		08 19	
Bournemouth	a		07 24		07 24							07 32			07 54	07 54						08 07		08 24	
	d	07 04	07 26		07 26			07 30				07 34			07 59	07 59						08 10		08 26	
Pokesdown	d	07 08										07 38										08 14		08 30	
Christchurch	d	07 12										07 42										08 18		08 34	
Hinton Admiral	d	07 17										07 47										08 24		08 39	
New Milton	d	07 21										07 51										08 29		08 43	
Sway	d	07 26										07 56										08 34		08 48	
Yarmouth (I.O.W.) ⛴	d																	07b30							08b00
Lymington Pier ⛴	d									07 44								08 14							08 44
Lymington Town	d									07 46								08 16							08 46
Brockenhurst 3	a	07 31						07 46		07 54		08 01			08 14	08 14		08 24				08 39		08 53	08 54
	d	07 32						07 49				08 02			08 15	08 15						08 41			
Beaulieu Road	d											08 08													
Ashurst New Forest	d	07 40		←								08 12										08 48			
Totton	d	07 45		07 45								08 17										08 53			
Salisbury	d								07 36					07 48									08 32		
Dean	d													08 00											
Mottisfont & Dunbridge	d													08 06											
Romsey	d								07 56					08 11									08 50		
Redbridge	d													08 21											
Millbrook (Hants)	d													08 24											
Southampton Central	a	07 50	07 55	07 50	07 55			08 03	08 09		←	08 22		08 27	08 28	08 28			←		←	08 58	09 04		
	d		08 00		08 00			08 15 →			08 15	08 48 →	08 23	08 35 →	08 30	08 30			08 35		08 48	09 00			
St Denys	d																		08 40		08 53				
Swaythling	d																		08 43		08 56				
Southampton Airport Parkwy ✈	d		08 08		08 08						08 22				08 38	08 38			08 46		08 59	09 08			
Portsmouth Harbour	d						07 24										07 55			08 05					
Portsmouth & Southsea	d						07 29										08 00			08 10					
Fratton	d						07 33										08 04			08 14					
Hilsea	d						07 37										08 08			08 18					
Cosham	d						07 43										08 13			08 23					
Portchester	d						07 48										08 18			08 28					
Fareham	d						07 54										08 24			08 34					
Botley	d						08 01										08 31			08 42					
Hedge End	d						08 06										08 36			08 46					
Eastleigh 3	a						08 12										08 42		08 49	08 52	09 03				
	d						08 13										08 43		08 50	08 54	09 11				
Chandlers Ford	d																		08 55		→				
Romsey	a												08 34						09 03						
Shawford	d						08 19										08 49								
Winchester	d		08 18		08 18		08 25				08 31				08 48	08 48	08 54			09 03		09 18			
Micheldever	d																09 02								
Basingstoke	a		08 34		08 34		08 41				08 46						09 15			09 19		09 35			
	d		08 35		08 35		08 42				08 47						09 17					09 36			
Reading 7	a										09 05									10 00					
Fleet	d						08 54																		
Farnborough (Main)	d						08 59										09 31								
Woking	a		08 53		08 53										09 22	09 22	09 40					09 54			
Clapham Junction 10	a		09 14		09 14		09 26								09 43	09 43						10 14			
London Waterloo 15 ⊖	a		09 25		09 25		09 38								09 53	09 53	10 08					10 23			

For general notes see front of timetable
For details of catering facilities see Directory of Train Operators

A From 28 September
B From 28 September. ⊡ from Bournemouth
C Until 25 September
D Until 25 September. ⊡ from Bournemouth
E To Bristol Parkway (Table 132)
b By ship

During July and August ferry connection times to and from Yarmouth IOW are subject to alteration, please contact www.wightlink.co.uk or 0871 376 1000 for further details.

For details of Bank Holiday service alterations, please see first page of Table 149

Weymouth, Bournemouth, Lymington, Romsey, Southampton and Basingstoke → London

Network Diagram - see first page of Table 158

Station		SW	XC	SW	SW	SW	SW	SW	SW	SW	GW	GW	SW	SW	SW	XC	SW	SW	SW	SW	SW	SW	SW	GW	SW
		1	1 ◇	1	1 ◇	1	1	1	1	1 ◇	◇	◇	1	1	1	1 ◇	1	1 ◇	1	1	1	1	1 ◇	◇	1
					A					A	B							A					A		
			🛒		🍴					🍴		🛒				🛒		🍴					🍴	🛒	
Weymouth	d				07 55					08 20	08 50							09 03					09 20		
Upwey	d				07 59					08 24	08 55												09 24		
Dorchester West	a										09 03														
Dorchester South	d				08 07					08 33								09 13					09 33		
Moreton (Dorset)	d				08 14					08 39													09 39		
Wool	d				08 20					08 45													09 45		
Wareham	d				08 27					08 53								09 28					09 53		
Holton Heath	d				08 31					08 56													09 56		
Hamworthy	d				08 36					09 01								09 35					10 01		
Poole 4	a				08 40					09 06								09 39					10 06		
	d				08 41				08 50	09 07			09 13					09 40				09 50	10 07		
Parkstone (Dorset)	d				08 45				08 54				09 17					09 44				09 54			
Branksome	d				08 49				08 57				09 20					09 48				09 57			
Bournemouth	a				08 54				09 02	09 16			09 25					09 53				10 02	10 17		
	d		08 45		08 59				09 05	09 18			09 27			09 45		09 55				10 05	10 22		
Pokesdown	d								09 09	09 22			09 30									10 09	10 26		
Christchurch	d								09 13	09 26			09 34									10 13	10 30		
Hinton Admiral	d								09 18				09 39									10 18			
New Milton	d								09 22	09 33			09 44									10 22	10 37		
Sway	d								09 27				09 48									10 27			
Yarmouth (I.O.W.) ⛴	d													09b00											09b45
Lymington Pier ⛴	d						09 14							09 44						10 14					10 44
Lymington Town	d						09 16							09 46						10 16					10 46
Brockenhurst 3	a		08 58		09 14		09 24		09 32	09 40			09 53	09 54		09 58		10 10		10 24		10 32	10 44		10 54
	d		09 00		09 15				09 33	09 41			09 54			10 00		10 11				10 33	10 45		
Beaulieu Road	d																								
Ashurst New Forest	d								09 40													10 40			
Totton	d								09 45													10 45			
Salisbury	d			08 48								09 32					09 48							10 30	
Dean	d			09 00													10 00								
Mottisfont & Dunbridge	d			09 06													10 06								
Romsey	d			09 11								09 50					10 11							10 48	
Redbridge	d			09 19													10 19								
Millbrook (Hants)	d			09 22													10 22								
Southampton Central	a		09 12	09 25	09 28			←	09 52	09 55		10 04	10 09			10 12	10 25	10 26			←	10 53	10 58	11 04	
	d		09 15	09 35 →	09 30			09 35	09 55	10 00						10 15	10 35 →	10 30			10 35	10 55	11 00		
St Denys	d							09 40													10 40				
Swaythling	d							09 43													10 43				
Southampton Airport Parkwy ✈	d		09 22		09 38			09 46	10 03	10 08						10 22		10 38			10 46	11 03	11 08		
Portsmouth Harbour	d					08 55													09 55						
Portsmouth & Southsea	d					09 00													10 00						
Fratton	d					09 04													10 04						
Hilsea	d					09 08													10 08						
Cosham	d					09 13													10 13						
Portchester	d					09 18													10 18						
Fareham	d					09 24													10 24						
Botley	d					09 31													10 31						
Hedge End	d					09 36													10 36						
Eastleigh 3	a	←				09 42		09 49	10 06						←				10 42		10 49	11 06			
	d	09 11				09 43		09 50	10 11						10 11				10 43		10 50	11 11			
Chandlers Ford	d							09 55	→												10 55	→			
Romsey	a							10 03													11 03				
Shawford	d	09 17													10 17										
Winchester	d	09 24	09 31		09 48	09 54				10 18					10 24	10 31		10 48	10 54				11 18		
Micheldever	d					10 02													11 02						
Basingstoke	a	09 40	09 46			10 15				10 34					10 40	10 46			11 15				11 34		
	d	09 41	09 47			10 17				10 36					10 41	10 47			11 17				11 36		
Reading 7	a		10 05			*11 00*										11 05			*12 00*						
Fleet	d	09 53													10 53										
Farnborough (Main)	d	09 58				10 31									10 58				11 31						
Woking	a				10 20	10 40												11 19	11 40						
Clapham Junction 10	a	10 24								11 12					11 24								12 12		
London Waterloo 15 ⊖	a	10 34			10 49	11 08				11 20					11 34			11 49	12 08				12 20		

For general notes see front of timetable
For details of catering facilities see Directory of Train Operators

A 🍴 from Bournemouth
B To Gloucester (Table 134)
b By ship

During July and August ferry connection times to and from Yarmouth IOW are subject to alteration, please contact www.wightliink.co.uk or 0871 376 1000 for further details.

For details of Bank Holiday service alterations, please see first page of Table 149

Weymouth, Bournemouth, Lymington, Romsey, Southampton and Basingstoke → London

Network Diagram - see first page of Table 158

		SW	XC	SW	SW	SW	SW	SW	SW	GW	SW	SW	XC	GW	SW	GW	SW	GW	SW	SW	SW	SW	SW	GW	SW
		1	1 ◇	1 ◇	1	1	1	1	1 ◇	◇	1	1	1 ◇		1		1 ◇	◇	1	1	1	1	1 ◇	◇	1
				A					A								A	B					A		
			⊼	⊡					⊡	⊼			⊼				⊡						⊡	⊼	
Weymouth	d			10 03					10 20								11 03	11 10					11 20		
Upwey	d								10 24									11 16					11 24		
Dorchester West	a																	11 23							
Dorchester South	d			10 13					10 33								11 13						11 33		
Moreton (Dorset)	d								10 39														11 39		
Wool	d								10 45														11 45		
Wareham	d			10 28					10 53								11 28						11 53		
Holton Heath	d								10 56														11 56		
Hamworthy	d			10 35					11 01								11 35						12 01		
Poole 4	a			10 39					11 06								11 39						12 06		
	d			10 40				10 50	11 07								11 40					11 50	12 07		
Parkstone (Dorset)	d			10 44				10 54									11 44					11 54			
Branksome	d			10 48				10 57									11 48					11 57			
Bournemouth	a			10 54				11 02	11 17								11 54					12 02	12 17		
	d		10 45	10 59				11 05	11 22				11 45				11 59					12 05	12 22		
Pokesdown	d							11 09	11 26													12 09	12 26		
Christchurch	d							11 13	11 30													12 13	12 30		
Hinton Admiral	d							11 18														12 18			
New Milton	d							11 22	11 37													12 22	12 37		
Sway	d							11 27														12 27			
Yarmouth (I.O.W.) ⛴	d						*10b30*													*11b15*					
Lymington Pier ⛴	d						11 14					11 44								12 14					12 44
Lymington Town	d						11 16					11 46								12 16					12 46
Brockenhurst 3	a		10 58	11 14			11 24	11 32	11 44			11 54	11 58				12 14			12 24		12 32	12 44		12 54
	d		11 00	11 15				11 33	11 45				12 00				12 15					12 33	12 45		
Beaulieu Road	d							11 38														12 40			
Ashurst New Forest	d							11 42														12 45			
Totton	d							11 47																	
Salisbury	d					10 48				11 32				11 39	11 48									12 32	
Dean	d					11 00									12 00										
Mottisfont & Dunbridge	d					11 06									12 06										
Romsey	d					11 11				11 50				12 00	12 11									12 50	
Redbridge	d					11 19									12 19										
Millbrook (Hants)	d					11 22									12 22										
Southampton Central	a		11 12	11 28		11 28		11 53	11 58	12 04			12 12	12 19	12 25		12 28				←	12 52	12 58	13 04	
	d		11 15	11 30		11 35		11 55	12 00				12 15		12 35 →	12 26	12 30				12 35	12 55	13 00		
St Denys	d					11 40															12 40				
Swaythling	d					11 43															12 43				
Southampton Airport Parkwy ✈	d		11 22	11 38		11 46		12 03	12 08				12 22				12 38				12 46	13 03	13 08		
Portsmouth Harbour	d				10 55														11 55						
Portsmouth & Southsea	d				11 00														12 00						
Fratton	d				11 04														12 04						
Hilsea	d				11 08														12 08						
Cosham	d				11 13														12 13						
Portchester	d				11 18														12 18						
Fareham	d				11 24														12 24						
Botley	d				11 31														12 31						
Hedge End	d				11 36														12 36						
Eastleigh 3	a	←			11 42	11 49		12 06			←								12 42		12 49	13 06			
	d	11 11			11 43	11 50		12 11			12 11								12 43		12 50	13 11			
Chandlers Ford	d					11 55		→													12 55	→			
Romsey	a					12 03										12 38					13 03				
Shawford	d	11 17									12 17														
Winchester	d	11 24	11 31	11 48	11 54				12 18		12 24		12 31				12 48		12 54				13 18		
Micheldever	d				12 02														13 02						
Basingstoke	a	11 40	11 46		12 15				12 34		12 40		12 46						13 15				13 34		
	d	11 41	11 47		12 17				12 36		12 41		12 47						13 17				13 36		
Reading 7	a		12 05		*13 00*								13 05						*14 00*						
Fleet	d	11 53									12 53														
Farnborough (Main)	d	11 58			12 31						12 58								13 31						
Woking	a			12 19	12 40												13 19		13 40						
Clapham Junction 10	a	12 24							13 12		13 24												14 12		
London Waterloo 15 ⊖	a	12 34		12 49	13 08				13 20		13 34						13 49		14 08				14 20		

For general notes see front of timetable
For details of catering facilities see Directory of Train Operators

A ⊡ from Bournemouth
B To Gloucester (Table 134)
b By ship

During July and August ferry connection times to and from Yarmouth IOW are subject to alteration, please contact www.wightliink.co.uk or 0871 376 1000 for further details.

For details of Bank Holiday service alterations, please see first page of Table 149

Weymouth, Bournemouth, Lymington, Romsey, Southampton and Basingstoke → London

Network Diagram - see first page of Table 158

		SW	XC	SW	SW	SW	SW	SW	SW	SW	GW	SW	SW	XC	SW	SN	SW	GW	SW	GW	SW	SW	SW	SW	GW
		1	1 ◇	1	1 ◇	1	1	1	1	1 ◇	◇	1	1	1 ◇	1	1	1 ◇	◇	1	◇	1	1	1	1 ◇	◇
					A					A							A	B						A	
			⊥		⊡					⊡	⊥			⊥			⊡							⊡	⊥
Weymouth	d				12 03					12 20							13 03	13 10						13 20	
Upwey	d									12 24								13 16						13 24	
Dorchester West	a																	13 24							
Dorchester South	d				12 13					12 33							13 13							13 33	
Moreton (Dorset)	d									12 39														13 39	
Wool	d									12 45														13 45	
Wareham	d				12 28					12 53							13 28							13 53	
Holton Heath	d									12 56														13 56	
Hamworthy	d				12 35					13 01							13 35							14 01	
Poole 4	a				12 39					13 06							13 39							14 06	
	d				12 40				12 50	13 07							13 40						13 50	14 07	
Parkstone (Dorset)	d				12 44				12 54								13 44						13 54		
Branksome	d				12 48				12 57								13 48						13 57		
Bournemouth	a				12 54				13 02	13 17							13 54						14 02	14 17	
	d		12 45		12 59				13 05	13 22				13 45			13 59						14 05	14 22	
Pokesdown	d								13 09	13 26													14 09	14 26	
Christchurch	d								13 13	13 30													14 13	14 30	
Hinton Admiral	d								13 18														14 18		
New Milton	d								13 22	13 37													14 22	14 37	
Sway	d								13 27														14 27		
Yarmouth (I.O.W.) ⛴	d						*12b15*					*13b00*													
Lymington Pier ⛴	d						13 14					13 44									14 14				
Lymington Town	d						13 16					13 46									14 16				
Brockenhurst 3	a		12 58		13 14		13 24		13 32	13 44		13 54		13 58			14 14				14 24		14 32	14 44	
	d		13 00		13 15				13 33	13 45				14 00			14 15						14 33	14 45	
Beaulieu Road	d																								
Ashurst New Forest	d								13 40														14 40		
Totton	d								13 45														14 45		
Salisbury	d			12 48							13 32				13 48					13 59					14 32
Dean	d			13 00											14 00										
Mottisfont & Dunbridge	d			13 06											14 06										
Romsey	d			13 11							13 50				14 11					14 20					14 50
Redbridge	d			13 19											14 19										
Millbrook (Hants)	d			13 22											14 22										
Southampton Central	a		13 12	13 25	13 28			←	13 53	13 58	14 04			14 12	14 25		14 28			14 32		←	14 52	14 58	15 04
	d		13 15	13 35 →	13 30			13 35	13 55	14 00				14 15	14 35 →	14 27	14 30					14 35	14 55	15 00	
St Denys	d							13 40														14 40			
Swaythling	d							13 43														14 43			
Southampton Airport Parkwy ✈	d		13 22		13 38			13 46	14 03	14 08				14 22			14 38					14 46	15 03	15 08	
Portsmouth Harbour	d					12 55													13 55						
Portsmouth & Southsea	d					13 00													14 00						
Fratton	d					13 04													14 04						
Hilsea	d					13 08													14 08						
Cosham	d					13 13													14 13						
Portchester	d					13 18													14 18						
Fareham	d					13 24													14 24						
Botley	d					13 31													14 31						
Hedge End	d					13 36													14 36						
Eastleigh 3	a	←				13 42		13 49	14 09				←			14 37			14 42			14 49	15 06		
	d	13 11				13 43		13 50	14 11				14 11						14 43			14 50	15 11		
Chandlers Ford	d							13 55	→													14 55	→		
Romsey	a							14 03														15 04			
Shawford	d	13 17											14 17												
Winchester	d	13 24	13 31		13 48	13 54				14 18			14 24	14 31			14 48		14 54					15 18	
Micheldever	d					14 02													15 02						
Basingstoke	a	13 40	13 46			14 15				14 34			14 40	14 46					15 15					15 34	
	d	13 41	13 47			14 17				14 36			14 41	14 47					15 17					15 36	
Reading 7	a		14 05			*15 00*								15 05					*16 00*						
Fleet	d	13 53											14 53												
Farnborough (Main)	d	13 58				14 31							14 58						15 31						
Woking	a				14 19	14 40											15 19		15 40						
Clapham Junction 10	a	14 24								15 12			15 24											16 12	
London Waterloo 15 ⊖	a	14 34			14 49	15 08				15 20			15 32				15 49		16 08					16 20	

For general notes see front of timetable
For details of catering facilities see Directory of Train Operators

A ⊡ from Bournemouth
B To Gloucester (Table 134)
b By ship

During July and August ferry connection times to and from Yarmouth IOW are subject to alteration, please contact www.wightliink.co.uk or 0871 376 1000 for further details.

For details of Bank Holiday service alterations, please see first page of Table 149

Weymouth, Bournemouth, Lymington, Romsey, Southampton and Basingstoke → London

Network Diagram - see first page of Table 158

		SW	SW	XC	SW	SW	SW	SW	SW	SW	SW	GW	SW	SW	XC	SW	SW	GW	SW	SW	SW	SW	SN	SW	GW
		1	1	1 ◇	1	1 ◇	1	1	1	1	1 ◇	◇	1	1	1 ◇	1	1 ◇	◇	1	1	1	1	1	1 ◇	◇
						A					A						A	B					C	A	
				🛒		🚌					🚌	🛒			🛒		🚌							🚌	🛒
Weymouth	d					14 03					14 20						15 03	15 10						15 20	
Upwey	d										14 24							15 16						15 24	
Dorchester West	a																	15 24							
Dorchester South	d					14 13					14 33						15 13							15 33	
Moreton (Dorset)	d										14 39													15 39	
Wool	d										14 45													15 45	
Wareham	d					14 28					14 53						15 28							15 53	
Holton Heath	d										14 56													15 56	
Hamworthy	d					14 35					15 01						15 35							16 01	
Poole 4	a					14 39					15 06						15 39							16 06	
	d					14 40				14 50	15 07						15 40					15 50		16 07	
Parkstone (Dorset)	d					14 44				14 54							15 44					15 54			
Branksome	d					14 48				14 57							15 48					15 57			
Bournemouth	a					14 54				15 02	15 17						15 54					16 02		16 17	
	d			14 45		14 59				15 05	15 22				15 45		15 59					16 05		16 22	
Pokesdown	d									15 09	15 26											16 09		16 26	
Christchurch	d									15 13	15 30											16 13		16 30	
Hinton Admiral	d									15 18												16 18			
New Milton	d									15 22	15 37											16 22		16 37	
Sway	d									15 27												16 27			
Yarmouth (I.O.W.) ⛴	d	*14b00*											*14b45*							*15c30*					
Lymington Pier ⛴	d	14 44						15 14					15 44							16 14					
Lymington Town	d	14 46						15 16					15 46							16 16					
Brockenhurst 3	a	14 54		14 58		15 14		15 24		15 32	15 44		15 54		15 58		16 14			16 24		16 32		16 44	
	d			15 00		15 15				15 33	15 45				16 00		16 15					16 33		16 45	
Beaulieu Road	d																								
Ashurst New Forest	d									15 40												16 40			
Totton	d									15 45												16 45			
Salisbury	d				14 48							15 32				15 48									16 32
Dean	d				15 00											16 00									
Mottisfont & Dunbridge	d				15 06											16 06									
Romsey	d				15 11							15 50				16 11									16 50
Redbridge	d				15 19											16 19									
Millbrook (Hants)	d				15 22											16 22									
Southampton Central	a			15 12	15 25	15 28			←	15 51	15 58	16 04			16 12	16 25	16 28				←	16 51		16 58	17 04
	d			15 15	15 35 →	15 30			15 35	15 55	16 00				16 15	16 35 →	16 30				16 35	16 52		17 00	
St Denys	d								15 40												16 40	16 57			
Swaythling	d								15 43												16 43	17 00			
Southampton Airport Parkwy ✈	d			15 22		15 38			15 46	16 03	16 08				16 22		16 38				16 46	17 04		17 08	
Portsmouth Harbour	d						14 55												15 55						
Portsmouth & Southsea	d						15 00												16 00						
Fratton	d						15 04												16 04						
Hilsea	d						15 08												16 08						
Cosham	d						15 13												16 13				16 46		
Portchester	d						15 18												16 18						
Fareham	d						15 24												16 24				16 54		
Botley	d						15 31												16 31						
Hedge End	d						15 36												16 36						
Eastleigh 3	a		←				15 42		15 49	16 07				←					16 42		16 49	17 07	17 07		
	d		15 11				15 43		15 50	16 11				16 11					16 43		16 50	17 11			
Chandlers Ford	d								15 55	→											16 55	→			
Romsey	a								16 03												17 03				
Shawford	d		15 17											16 17											
Winchester	d		15 24	15 31		15 48	15 54				16 18			16 24	16 31		16 48		16 54					17 18	
Micheldever	d						16 02												17 02						
Basingstoke	a		15 40	15 46			16 15				16 34			16 40	16 46				17 15					17 34	
	d		15 41	15 47			16 17				16 36			16 41	16 47				17 17					17 36	
Reading 7	a			16 05			*17 00*								17 05				*18 00*						
Fleet	d		15 53											16 53											
Farnborough (Main)	d		15 58				16 31							16 58					17 31						
Woking	a					16 19	16 40										17 20		17 40						
Clapham Junction 10	a		16 24								17 12			17 24										18 12	
London Waterloo 15 ⊖	a		16 34			16 49	17 08				17 20			17 36			17 50		18 08					18 23	

For general notes see front of timetable
For details of catering facilities see Directory of Train Operators

- **A** 🚌 from Bournemouth
- **B** To Gloucester (Table 134)
- **C** From Brighton (Table 188)
- **b** By ship
- **c** By ship. Wednesdays dep. 1445

During July and August ferry connection times to and from Yarmouth IOW are subject to alteration, please contact www.wightlink.co.uk or 0871 376 1000 for further details.

For details of Bank Holiday service alterations, please see first page of Table 149

Weymouth, Bournemouth, Lymington, Romsey, Southampton and Basingstoke → London

Network Diagram - see first page of Table 158

Station		SW	SW	XC	SW	SW	SW	SW	SW	SW	SW	SW	GW	SW	SW	XC	SW	SW	SW	SW	SW	SW	SW	SW	GW
		1	1	1 ◇	1	1 ◇	1	1	1	1	1	1 ◇	◇	1	1	1 ◇	1	1	1 ◇	1	1	1	1	1 ◇	◇
				🛒		A 🍴						A 🍴	🛒			🛒			A 🍴					A 🍴	
Weymouth	d					16 03						16 20							17 03					17 20	17 30
Upwey	d											16 24												17 24	17 35
Dorchester West	a																								17 43
Dorchester South	d					16 13						16 33							17 13					17 33	
Moreton (Dorset)	d											16 39												17 39	
Wool	d											16 45												17 45	
Wareham	d					16 28						16 53							17 28					17 53	
Holton Heath	d											16 56												17 56	
Hamworthy	d					16 35						17 01							17 35					18 01	
Poole 4	a					16 39						17 06							17 39					18 06	
	d					16 40					16 50	17 07							17 40				17 50	18 07	
Parkstone (Dorset)	d					16 44					16 54								17 44				17 54		
Branksome	d					16 48					16 57								17 48				17 57		
Bournemouth	a					16 54					17 02	17 17							17 54				18 02	18 17	
	d			16 45		16 59					17 05	17 22				17 45			17 59				18 05	18 22	
Pokesdown	d										17 09	17 26											18 09	18 26	
Christchurch	d										17 13	17 30											18 13	18 30	
Hinton Admiral	d										17 18												18 18		
New Milton	d										17 22	17 37											18 22	18 37	
Sway	d										17 27												18 27		
Yarmouth (I.O.W.) ⛴	d	15b30								16c15				17c00											
Lymington Pier ⛴	d	16 44								17 14				17 44							18 14				
Lymington Town	d	16 46								17 16				17 46							18 16				
Brockenhurst 3	a	16 54		16 58		17 14				17 24	17 32	17 44		17 54		17 58			18 14		18 24		18 32	18 44	
	d			17 00		17 15			17 20		17 33	17 45				18 00			18 15				18 33	18 45	
Beaulieu Road	d																						18 38		
Ashurst New Forest	d								17 27		17 40												18 42		
Totton	d								17 32		17 45												18 47		
Salisbury	d				16 48								17 32					17 48							
Dean	d				17 00													18 00							
Mottisfont & Dunbridge	d				17 06													18 06							
Romsey	d				17 11								17 50					18 11							
Redbridge	d				17 19													18 19							
Millbrook (Hants)	d				17 22													18 22							
Southampton Central	a			17 12	17 25	17 28			17 41		17 53	17 58	18 04			18 12		18 25	18 28				18 53	18 58	
	d			17 15	17 35 →	17 30		← 17 35			17 55	18 00				18 15	18 17	18 35 →	18 30			← 18 35	18 55	19 00	
St Denys	d							17 40									18 22					18 40			
Swaythling	d							17 43									18 25					18 43			
Southampton Airport Parkwy ✈	d			17 22		17 38		17 46			18 03	18 08				18 22	18 28		18 38			18 46	19 03	19 08	
Portsmouth Harbour	d						16 55													17 55					
Portsmouth & Southsea	d						17 00													18 00					
Fratton	d						17 04													18 04					
Hilsea	d						17 08													18 08					
Cosham	d						17 13													18 13					
Portchester	d						17 18													18 18					
Fareham	d						17 24													18 24					
Botley	d						17 31													18 31					
Hedge End	d						17 36													18 36					
Eastleigh 3	a		←				17 42	17 49			18 06				←		18 32			18 42		18 49	19 06		
	d		17 11				17 43	17 50			18 11				18 11		18 33			18 43		18 50	19 11		
Chandlers Ford	d							17 55			→											18 55	→		
Romsey	a							18 03														19 04			
Shawford	d		17 17												18 17										
Winchester	d		17 24	17 31		17 48	17 54					18 18			18 24	18 31	18a41		18 48	18 54				19 18	
Micheldever	d						18 02													19 02					
Basingstoke	a		17 40	17 46			18 15					18 34			18 40	18 46				19 15				19 34	
	d		17 41	17 47			18 17					18 36			18 41	18 47				19 17				19 36	
Reading 7	a			18 05			*19 00*									19 05				*20 00*					
Fleet	d		17 53												18 53										
Farnborough (Main)	d		17 58				18 31								18 58					19 31					
Woking	a					18 19	18 40												19 24	19 40					
Clapham Junction 10	a		18 24									19 12			19 26									20 12	
London Waterloo 15 ⊖	a		18 34			18 47	19 08					19 20			19 38				19 51	20 08				20 20	

For general notes see front of timetable
For details of catering facilities see Directory of Train Operators

A 🍴 from Bournemouth
b Mondays, Tuesdays, Thursdays and Fridays only. By ship
c By ship

During July and August ferry connection times to and from Yarmouth IOW are subject to alteration, please contact www.wightliink.co.uk or 0871 376 1000 for further details.

For details of Bank Holiday service alterations, please see first page of Table 149

Weymouth, Bournemouth, Lymington, Romsey, Southampton and Basingstoke → London

Network Diagram - see first page of Table 158

		GW	SW	SW	XC	SW	SW	SW	SW	SW	SW	SW	GW	SW	SW	XC	SW	SW	SW	SW	SW	GW	SW	SW	GW
		◇	1	1	1 ◇	1	1 ◇	1	1	1	1	1 ◇	◇	1	1	1 ◇	1	1 ◇	1	1	1		1	1 ◇	◇
							A					A				B		A							
		⊼			⊼		Ꝓ					Ꝓ	⊼					Ꝓ							⊼
Weymouth	d						18 04					18 20						19 06						19 20	
Upwey	d											18 24												19 24	
Dorchester West	a																								
Dorchester South	d						18 14					18 33						19 16						19b38	
Moreton (Dorset)	d											18 39												19 44	
Wool	d											18 45												19 50	
Wareham	d						18 29					18 53						19 31						19 57	
Holton Heath	d											18 56													
Hamworthy	d						18 36					19 01						19 38						20 04	
Poole 4	a						18 40					19 06						19 42						20 08	
	d						18 41				18 50	19 07						19 43					19 50	20 09	
Parkstone (Dorset)	d						18 45				18 54							19 47					19 54		
Branksome	d						18 49				18 57							19 51					19 57		
Bournemouth	a						18 54				19 02	19 17						19 56					20 02	20 18	
	d				18 45		18 59				19 05	19 22				19 45		19 59					20 05	20 22	
Pokesdown	d										19 09	19 26											20 09	20 26	
Christchurch	d										19 13	19 30											20 13	20 30	
Hinton Admiral	d										19 18												20 18		
New Milton	d										19 22	19 37											20 22	20 37	
Sway	d										19 27												20 27		
Yarmouth (I.O.W.) ⛴	d		17c45						18c30											19c15					
Lymington Pier ⛴	d		18 44						19 14					19 44						20 14					
Lymington Town	d		18 46						19 16					19 46						20 16					
Brockenhurst 3	a		18 54		18 58		19 14		19 24		19 32	19 44		19 54		19 58		20 14		20 24			20 32	20 44	
	d				19 00		19 15				19 33	19 45				20 00		20 15					20 33	20 45	
Beaulieu Road	d																								
Ashurst New Forest	d										19 40												20 40		
Totton	d										19 45												20 45		
Salisbury	d	18 32				18 48							19 32				19 48					20 13			20 32
Dean	d					19 00											20 00								
Mottisfont & Dunbridge	d					19 06											20 06								
Romsey	d	18 50				19 11							19 50				20 11					20 35			20 50
Redbridge	d					19 19											20 19								
Millbrook (Hants)	d					19 22											20 22								
Southampton Central	a	19 04			19 12	19 25	19 28			←	19 51	19 58	20 04			20 12	20 26	20 28			←	20 48	20 51	20 58	21 04
	d				19 15	19 35 →	19 30			19 35	19 55	20 00				20 15	20 35 →	20 30			20 35		20 55	21 00	
St Denys	d									19 40											20 40				
Swaythling	d									19 43											20 43				
Southampton Airport Parkwy ✈	d				19 22		19 38			19 46	20 03	20 08				20 22		20 38			20 46		21 03	21 08	
Portsmouth Harbour	d							18 55											19 55						
Portsmouth & Southsea	d							19 00											20 00						
Fratton	d							19 04											20 04						
Hilsea	d							19 08											20 08						
Cosham	d							19 13											20 13						
Portchester	d							19 18											20 18						
Fareham	d							19 24											20 24						
Botley	d							19 31											20 31						
Hedge End	d							19 36											20 36						
Eastleigh 3	a			←				19 42		19 49	20 06				←				20 42		20 49		21 06		
	d			19 11				19 43		19 50	20 11				20 11				20 43		20 50		21 11		
Chandlers Ford	d									19 55	→										20 55		→		
Romsey	a									20 03											21 03				
Shawford	d			19 17											20 17				20 49						
Winchester	d			19 24	19 31		19 48	19 54				20 18			20 24	20 31		20 48	20 54					21 18	
Micheldever	d							20 02											21 04						
Basingstoke	a			19 40	19 46			20 15				20 34			20 40	20 46			21 20					21 34	
	d			19 41	19 47			20 17				20 36			20 41	20 47			21 24					21 36	
Reading 7	a				20 05			*21 01*								21 05								*22 05*	
Fleet	d			19 53											20 53				21 40						
Farnborough (Main)	d			19 58				20 31							20 58				21 46						
Woking	a						20 19	20 40							21 07			21 19	21 58						
Clapham Junction 10	a			20 25								21 16			21 33									22 14	
London Waterloo 15 ⊖	a			20 34			20 49	21 08				21 24			21 43			21 49	22 34					22 22	

For general notes see front of timetable
For details of catering facilities see Directory of Train Operators

A Ꝓ from Bournemouth
B To Birmingham New Street (Table 116)
b Arr. 1931
c By ship

During July and August ferry connection times to and from Yarmouth IOW are subject to alteration, please contact www.wightliink.co.uk or 0871 376 1000 for further details.

Weymouth, Bournemouth, Lymington, Romsey, Southampton and Basingstoke → London

For details of Bank Holiday service alterations, please see first page of Table 149

Network Diagram - see first page of Table 158

		SW 1	SW 1	GW	SW 1	SW 1	SW 1	SW 1	SW 1	SW 1 ◇	GW ◇	GW ◇	SW 1	SW 1	SW 1	SW 1	SW 1	SW 1	SW 1	GW ◇	SW 1	SW 1	SW 1 ◇	SW 1
Weymouth	d									20 10	20 24								21 10				22 10	23 10
Upwey	d									20 14	20 29								21 14				22 14	23 14
Dorchester West	a										20 37													
Dorchester South	d									20 22									21 22				22 22	23 22
Moreton (Dorset)	d									20 28									21 28				22 28	23 28
Wool	d									20 34									21 34				22 34	23 34
Wareham	d									20 42									21 42				22 42	23 42
Holton Heath	d																							
Hamworthy	d									20 48									21 48				22 48	23 48
Poole 4	a									20 53									21 53				22 53	23 53
	d									20 54									21 54				22 54	23 54
Parkstone (Dorset)	d									20 58									21 58				22 58	
Branksome	d									21 01									22 01				23 01	
Bournemouth	a									21 07									22 07				23 07	00 03
	d									21 12									22 12				23 12	
Pokesdown	d									21 16									22 16				23 16	
Christchurch	d									21 20									22 20				23 20	
Hinton Admiral	d									21 25									22 25				23 25	
New Milton	d									21 29									22 29				23 29	
Sway	d									21 34									22 34				23 34	
Yarmouth (I.O.W.) ⛴	d							20b15										21b15						
Lymington Pier ⛴	d	20 44						21 14					21 44					22 14						
Lymington Town	d	20 46						21 16					21 46					22 16						
Brockenhurst 3	a	20 54						21 24		21 39			21 54					22 24	22 39				23 39	
	d									21 40									22 40				23 40	
Beaulieu Road	d																							
Ashurst New Forest	d									21 47									22 47				23 47	
Totton	d									21 52									22 52				23 52	
Salisbury	d						20 48					21 32					21 48			22 32				
Dean	d						21 00										22 00							
Mottisfont & Dunbridge	d						21 06										22 06							
Romsey	d						21 11					21 50					22 11			22 50	22 58			
Redbridge	d						21 19										22 19				23 05			
Millbrook (Hants)	d						21 22										22 22				23 09			
Southampton Central	a						21 25			21 57		22 02					22 25		22 57	23 03	23 11		23 57	
	d			21 20	21 30		21 35		21 55	22 00					22 30		22 35		23 00		23 20		23 59	
St Denys	d						21 40										22 40				23 25		00 04	
Swaythling	d						21 43										22 43				23 28		00 07	
Southampton Airport Parkwy ✈	d				21 38		21 46		22 03	22 08					22 38		22 46		23 08		23 31		00 10	
Portsmouth Harbour	d					20 55										21 55						23 24		
Portsmouth & Southsea	d					21 00										22 00						23 29		
Fratton	d					21 04										22 04						23 33		
Hilsea	d					21 08										22 08						23 37		
Cosham	d					21 13										22 13						23 42		
Portchester	d					21 18										22 18						23 47		
Fareham	d					21 24										22 24						23 53		
Botley	d					21 31										22 31						23 59		
Hedge End	d					21 36										22 36						00 05		
Eastleigh 3	a		←			21 42	21 49		22 06					←	22 41	22 43	22 49		23 11		23 34	00 11	00 14	
	d		21 11			21 43	21 50		22 11					22 11	22 46		22 50		23 11		23 36	00 19		
Chandlers Ford	d						21 55		→								22 55				23 41			
Romsey	a			21 31			22 03										23 03				23 48			
Shawford	d		21 17											22 17					23 17					
Winchester	d		21 24		21 48	21c54				22 18				22 24	22 54				23 24			00a28		
Micheldever	d					22 02													23 33					
Basingstoke	a		21 40			22 15				22 34				22 40	23 11				23 43					
	d		21 41			22 24				22 36				22 41	23 13				23 44					
Reading 7	a					22 47								23 18	23 53				00 26					
Fleet	d		21 53			22 40								22 53					00 01					
Farnborough (Main)	d		21 58			22 46								22 58					00 06					
Woking	a		22 07		22 19	22 58				22 54				23 07	23 33				00 18					
Clapham Junction 10	a		22 29							23 14				23 33	23 56				00 54					
London Waterloo 15 ⊖	a		22 38		22 49	23 39				23 23				23 43	00 06				01 02					

For general notes see front of timetable
For details of catering facilities see Directory of Train Operators

b By ship
c Arr. 2151

During July and August ferry connection times to and from Yarmouth IOW are subject to alteration, please contact www.wightliink.co.uk or 0871 376 1000 for further details.

Weymouth, Bournemouth, Lymington, Romsey, Southampton and Basingstoke → London

Network Diagram - see first page of Table 158

		SW	SW	SW	XC	SW	SW	SW	SW	SW	XC	SW	SW	SW	SW	SW	SW	XC	SW	XC	SW	SW	SW	SW	GW
		1	1	1 ◇	1 ◇	1	1	1	1	1	1 ◇	1	1 ◇	1	1	1	1	1 ◇	1	1 ◇	1	1	1 ◇	1	◇
						A	B								C										D
Weymouth	d	21p10		22p10																					06 40
Upwey	d	21p14		22p14																					06 45
Dorchester West	a																								06 53
Dorchester South	d	21p22		22p22																					
Moreton (Dorset)	d	21p28		22p28																					
Wool	d	21p34		22p34																					
Wareham	d	21p42		22p42																					
Holton Heath	d																								
Hamworthy	d	21p48		22p48																					
Poole 4	a	21p53		22p53																					
	d	21p54		22p54									05 28										06 28		
Parkstone (Dorset)	d	21p58		22p58									05 32										06 32		
Branksome	d	22p01		23p01									05 35										06 35		
Bournemouth	a	22p07		23p07									05 40										06 40		
	d	22p12		23p12									05 42					06 25		06 37			06 42		
Pokesdown	d	22p16		23p16									05 46										06 46		
Christchurch	d	22p20		23p20									05 50										06 50		
Hinton Admiral	d	22p25		23p25									05 55										06 55		
New Milton	d	22p29		23p29									05 59										06 59		
Sway	d	22p34		23p34									06 04										07 04		
Yarmouth (I.O.W.) ⛴	d																				06b00				
Lymington Pier ⛴	d															06 14					06 44				
Lymington Town	d															06 16					06 46				
Brockenhurst 3	a	22p39		23p39									06 09			06 24		06 38		06 52	06 54		07 09		
	d	22p40		23p40									06 10					06 39		06 55			07 10		
Beaulieu Road	d																								
Ashurst New Forest	d	22p47		23p47									06 17										07 17		
Totton	d	22p52		23p52								06 12	06 22										07 22		
Salisbury	d														05 35							06 48			
Dean	d														05 47							07 00			
Mottisfont & Dunbridge	d														05 53							07 06			
Romsey	d														05 58							07 11			
Redbridge	d											06 14			06 36							07 19			
Millbrook (Hants)	d											06 18										07 22			
Southampton Central	a	22p57		23p57								06 21	06 27				←	06 52		07 07		07 25	07 27		
	d	23p00		23p59	05 09	05 12	05 12		05 30	06 00	06 15	06 35 →	06 30				06 35	06 53	07 00	07 15		07 35 →	07 30		
St Denys	d			00 04					05 35								06 40								
Swaythling	d			00 07					05 38								06 43								
Southampton Airport Parkwy ✈	d	23p08		00 10	05 16	05 20	05 20		05 41	06 08	06 22		06 38				06 46	07 01	07 08	07 22			07 38		
Portsmouth Harbour	d		23p24											05 55										06 55	
Portsmouth & Southsea	d		23p29											06 00										07 00	
Fratton	d		23p33											06 04										07 04	
Hilsea	d		23p37											06 08										07 08	
Cosham	d		23p42					05 09						06 13										07 13	
Portchester	d		23p47					05 14						06 18										07 18	
Fareham	d		23p53					05 20						06 24										07 24	
Botley	d		23p59					05 27						06 31										07 31	
Hedge End	d		00 05					05 32						06 36										07 36	
Eastleigh 3	a	23p11	00 11	00 14		05 23	05 23	05 38	05 45	06 11			06 41	06 42			06 49		07 11					07 42	
	d	23p11	00 19			05 24	05 24		05 46	06 13			06 42	06 46			06 50		07 12					07 43	
Chandlers Ford	d														06 06		06 55								
Romsey	a														06 43		07 03								
Shawford	d	23p17							05 52					06 52					07 18						
Winchester	d	23p24	00a28		05 25	05 34	05 34		06c00	06 23	06 31		06 52	07 00				07 09	07 24	07 31			07 48	07 54	
Micheldever	d	23p33							06 08					07 08										08 02	
Basingstoke	a	23p43			05 40	05 50	05 50		06 19	06 39	06 46		07 08	07 19				07 24	07 40	07 46				08 15	
	d	23p44			05 41	05 54	05 54		06 24	06 40	06 47		07 09	07 24				07 25	07 42	07 47				08 17	
Reading 7	a	*00 26*			05 59				*07 00*		07 04							07 41		08 04				*09 00*	
Fleet	d	00 01				06 10	06 10		06 40					07 40					07 53						
Farnborough (Main)	d	00 06				06 16	06 16		06 46					07 46					07 59					08 31	
Woking	a	00 18				06 28	06 28		06 58	06 58			07 27	07 58					08 08				08 21	08 40	
Clapham Junction 10	a	00 54				06 58	06 58			07 23									08 30						
London Waterloo 15 ⊖	a	01 02				07 06	07 09		07 33	07 31			07 53	08 34					08 38				08 49	09 08	

For general notes see front of timetable
For details of catering facilities see Directory of Train Operators

A Until 26 September
B From 3 October
C To Salisbury
D To Gloucester (Table 134)
b By ship
c Arr. 0557

During July and August ferry connection times to and from Yarmouth IOW are subject to alteration, please contact www.wightlink.co.uk or 0871 376 1000 for further details.

Weymouth, Bournemouth, Lymington, Romsey, Southampton and Basingstoke → London

Network Diagram - see first page of Table 158

Station		SW	SW	SW	SW	GW	GW	SW	SW	XC	SW	GW	SW	SW	SW	SW	SW	SW	SW	SW	SW	GW	SW	SW	XC
		1	1	1	1 ◇	◇		1	1	1 ◇	1		1 ◇	1 ◇	1	1	1	1	1	1 ◇	1 ◇	◇	1	1	1 ◇
					A ☕					🍴			B ☕	C ☕						B ☕	C ☕				🍴
Weymouth	d												06 50	06 55						07 17	07 20				
Upwey	d												06 54	06 59						07 21	07 24				
Dorchester West	a																								
Dorchester South	d												07 02	07 07						07 33	07 33				
Moreton (Dorset)	d												07 09	07 14						07 39	07 39				
Wool	d												07 15	07 20						07 45	07 45				
Wareham	d				06 53								07 22	07 27						07 53	07 53				
Holton Heath	d				06 56								07 26	07 31						07 56	07 56				
Hamworthy	d				07 01								07 31	07 36						08 01	08 01				
Poole 4	a				07 06								07 35	07 40						08 06	08 06				
	d			06 50	07 07								07 36	07 41					07 50	08 07	08 07				
Parkstone (Dorset)	d			06 54									07 40	07 45					07 54						
Branksome	d			06 57									07 44	07 49					07 57						
Bournemouth	a			07 02	07 17								07 54	07 54					08 02	08 17	08 17				
	d			07 05	07 22					07 45			07 59	07 59					08 05	08 22	08 22				08 45
Pokesdown	d			07 09	07 26														08 09	08 26	08 26				
Christchurch	d			07 13	07 30														08 13	08 30	08 30				
Hinton Admiral	d			07 18															08 18						
New Milton	d			07 22	07 37														08 22	08 37	08 37				
Sway	d			07 27															08 27						
Yarmouth (I.O.W.) ⛴	d	06b30														07b30							08b00		
Lymington Pier ⛴	d	07 14						07 44								08 14							08 44		
Lymington Town	d	07 16						07 46								08 16							08 46		
Brockenhurst 3	a	07 24		07 32	07 44			07 54		07 58			08 14	08 14		08 24			08 32	08 44	08 44		08 54		08 58
	d			07 33	07 45					08 00			08 15	08 15					08 33	08 45	08 45				09 00
Beaulieu Road	d																								
Ashurst New Forest	d			07 40															08 40						
Totton	d			07 45															08 45						
Salisbury	d					07 24	07 37				07 48											08 33			
Dean	d										08 00														
Mottisfont & Dunbridge	d										08 06														
Romsey	d					07 44	07 56				08 11											08 51			
Redbridge	d										08 19														
Millbrook (Hants)	d										08 22														
Southampton Central	a		←	07 51	07 58	08 02	08 07			08 12	08 25		08 28	08 28		←			08 52	08 58	08 58	09 02			09 12
	d		07 35	07 55	08 00					08 15	08 35 →	08 27	08 30	08 30		08 35	08 44		08 55	09 00	09 00				09 15
St Denys	d		07 40													08 40	08a49								
Swaythling	d		07 43													08 43									
Southampton Airport Parkwy ✈	d		07 46	08 03	08 08					08 22			08 38	08 38		08 46			09 03	09 08	09 08				09 22
Portsmouth Harbour	d														07 55										
Portsmouth & Southsea	d														08 00										
Fratton	d														08 04										
Hilsea	d														08 08										
Cosham	d														08 13										
Portchester	d														08 18										
Fareham	d														08 24										
Botley	d														08 31										
Hedge End	d														08 36										
Eastleigh 3	a		07 49	08 06				←							08 42	08 49			09 06					←	
	d		07 50	08 11				08 11							08 43	08 50			09 11					09 11	
Chandlers Ford	d		07 55	→												08 55			→						
Romsey	a		08 03									08 38				09 03									
Shawford	d							08 17																09 17	
Winchester	d				08 18			08 24	08 31				08 48	08 48	08 54					09 18	09 18			09 24	09 31
Micheldever	d														09 02										
Basingstoke	a				08 34			08 40	08 46						09 15					09 34	09 34			09 40	09 46
	d				08 36			08 41	08 47						09 17					09 36	09 36			09 41	09 47
Reading 7	a								09 04						*10 00*										10 04
Fleet	d							08 53																09 53	
Farnborough (Main)	d							08 58							09 31									09 58	
Woking	a												09 19	09 19	09 40										
Clapham Junction 10	a				09 12			09 24												10 12	10 12			10 24	
London Waterloo 15 ⊖	a				09 20			09 34					09 49	09 49	10 08					10 20	10 20			10 34	

For general notes see front of timetable
For details of catering facilities see Directory of Train Operators

A ☕ from Bournemouth
B From 3 October. ☕ from Bournemouth
C Until 26 September. ☕ from Bournemouth
b By ship

During July and August ferry connection times to and from Yarmouth IOW are subject to alteration, please contact www.wightliink.co.uk or 0871 376 1000 for further details.

Weymouth, Bournemouth, Lymington, Romsey, Southampton and Basingstoke → London

Network Diagram - see first page of Table 158

		SW	SW	SW	SW	SW	SW	SW	SW	GW	GW	SW	SW	XC	SW	SW	SW	SW	SW	SW	SW	GW	SW	SW	XC
		1	1 ◇	1 ◇	1	1	1	1	1 ◇	◇	◇	1	1	1 ◇	1	1 ◇	1	1	1	1	1 ◇	◇	1	1	1 ◇
			A	B					C	D						C					C				
			🍽	🍽					🍽		🛒			🛒		🍽					🍽	🛒			🛒
Weymouth	d		07 58	08 03					08 20	08 52						09 03					09 20				
Upwey	d								08 24	08 57											09 24				
Dorchester West	a									09 05															
Dorchester South	d		08 08	08 13					08 33							09 13					09 33				
Moreton (Dorset)	d								08 39												09 39				
Wool	d								08 45												09 45				
Wareham	d		08 23	08 28					08 53							09 28					09 53				
Holton Heath	d								08 56												09 56				
Hamworthy	d		08 30	08 35					09 01							09 35					10 01				
Poole 4	a		08 34	08 39					09 06							09 39					10 06				
	d		08 35	08 40				08 50	09 06							09 40				09 50	10 07				
Parkstone (Dorset)	d		08 39	08 44				08 54								09 44				09 54					
Branksome	d		08 43	08 48				08 57								09 48				09 57					
Bournemouth	a		08 54	08 54				09 02	09 17							09 54				10 02	10 17				
	d		08 59	08 59				09 05	09 22					09 45		09 59				10 05	10 22				10 45
Pokesdown	d							09 09	09 26											10 09	10 26				
Christchurch	d							09 13	09 30											10 13	10 30				
Hinton Admiral	d							09 18												10 18					
New Milton	d							09 22	09 37											10 22	10 37				
Sway	d							09 27												10 27					
Yarmouth (I.O.W.) ⛴	d											*09b00*											*09b45*		
Lymington Pier ⛴	d					09 14						09 44						10 14					10 44		
Lymington Town	d					09 16						09 46						10 16					10 46		
Brockenhurst 3	a		09 14	09 14		09 24		09 32	09 44			09 54		09 58		10 14		10 24		10 32	10 44		10 54		10 58
	d		09 15	09 15				09 33	09 45					10 00		10 15				10 33	10 45				11 00
Beaulieu Road	d							09 38																	
Ashurst New Forest	d							09 42												10 40					
Totton	d							09 47												10 45					
Salisbury	d	08 48									09 33				09 48							10 32			
Dean	d	09 00													10 00										
Mottisfont & Dunbridge	d	09 06													10 06										
Romsey	d	09 11									09 51				10 11							10 50			
Redbridge	d	09 19													10 19										
Millbrook (Hants)	d	09 22													10 22										
Southampton Central	a	09 25	09 28	09 28			⟵	09 53	09 58		10 02			10 12	10 25	10 28			⟵	10 53	10 58	11 02			11 12
	d	09 35	09 30	09 30			09 35	09 55	10 00					10 15	10 35	10 30			10 35	10 55	11 00				11 15
		⟶													⟶										
St Denys	d						09 40												10 40						
Swaythling	d						09 43												10 43						
Southampton Airport Parkwy ✈	d		09 38	09 38			09 46	10 03	10 08					10 22		10 38			10 46	11 03	11 08				11 22
Portsmouth Harbour	d				08 55												09 55								
Portsmouth & Southsea	d				09 00												10 00								
Fratton	d				09 04												10 04								
Hilsea	d				09 08												10 08								
Cosham	d				09 13												10 13								
Portchester	d				09 18												10 18								
Fareham	d				09 24												10 24								
Botley	d				09 31												10 31								
Hedge End	d				09 36												10 36								
Eastleigh 3	a				09 42		09 49	10 06					⟵				10 42		10 49	11 06				⟵	
	d				09 43		09 50	10 11					10 11				10 43		10 50	11 11				11 11	
Chandlers Ford	d						09 55	⟶											10 55	⟶					
Romsey	a						10 03												11 03						
Shawford	d												10 17											11 17	
Winchester	d		09 48	09 48	09 54				10 18				10 24	10 31		10 48	10 54				11 18			11 24	11 31
Micheldever	d				10 02												11 02								
Basingstoke	a				10 15				10 34				10 40	10 46			11 15				11 34			11 40	11 46
	d				10 17				10 36				10 41	10 47			11 17				11 36			11 41	11 47
Reading 7	a				*11 00*									11 04			*12 00*								12 04
Fleet	d												10 53											11 53	
Farnborough (Main)	d				10 31								10 58				11 31							11 58	
Woking	a		10 19	10 19	10 40											11 19	11 40								
Clapham Junction 10	a								11 12				11 24								12 12			12 24	
London Waterloo 15 ⊖	a		10 49	10 49	11 08				11 20				11 34			11 49	12 08				12 20			12 34	

For general notes see front of timetable
For details of catering facilities see Directory of Train Operators

A From 3 October. 🍽 from Bournemouth
B Until 26 September. 🍽 from Bournemouth
C 🍽 from Bournemouth
D To Gloucester (Table 134)
b By ship

During July and August ferry connection times to and from Yarmouth IOW are subject to alteration, please contact www.wightliink.co.uk or 0871 376 1000 for further details.

Table 158

Saturdays

Weymouth, Bournemouth, Lymington, Romsey, Southampton and Basingstoke → London

Network Diagram - see first page of Table 158

		SW	SW	SW	SW	SW		SW	SW	GW	SW	SW	XC	GW	SW	SW	GW	SW	GW	SW	SW	SW	SW	GW	SW
		1	1 ◇	1	1	1		1	1 ◇	◇	1	1	1 ◇		1	1		1 ◇	◇	1	1	1	1 ◇	◇	1
			A ⊐P						A ⊐P	⊼			⊼					A ⊐P	B				A ⊐P	⊼	
Weymouth	d		10 03						10 20									11 03	11 10				11 20		
Upwey	d								10 24										11 15				11 24		
Dorchester West	a																		11 23						
Dorchester South	d		10 13						10 33									11 13					11 33		
Moreton (Dorset)	d								10 39														11 39		
Wool	d								10 45														11 45		
Wareham	d		10 28						10 53									11 28					11 53		
Holton Heath	d								10 56														11 56		
Hamworthy	d		10 35						11 01									11 35					12 01		
Poole 4	a		10 39						11 06									11 39					12 06		
	d		10 40					10 50	11 07									11 40				11 50	12 07		
Parkstone (Dorset)	d		10 44					10 54										11 44				11 54			
Branksome	d		10 48					10 57										11 48				11 57			
Bournemouth	a		10 54					11 03	11 17									11 54				12 02	12 17		
	d		10 59					11 05	11 22				11 45					11 59				12 05	12 22		
Pokesdown	d							11 09	11 26													12 09	12 26		
Christchurch	d							11 12	11 30													12 13	12 30		
Hinton Admiral	d							11 18														12 18			
New Milton	d							11 22	11 37													12 22	12 37		
Sway	d							11 27														12 27			
Yarmouth (I.O.W.) ⛴	d				*10b30*															*11b15*					
Lymington Pier ⛴	d				11 14							11 44								12 14					12 44
Lymington Town	d				11 16							11 46								12 16					12 46
Brockenhurst 3	a		11 14		11 24			11 32	11 44			11 54	11 58					12 14		12 24		12 32	12 44		12 54
	d		11 15					11 33	11 45				12 00					12 15				12 33	12 45		
Beaulieu Road	d							11 38																	
Ashurst New Forest	d							11 42														12 40			
Totton	d							11 47														12 45			
Salisbury	d	10 48								11 33				11 39		11 48								12 33	
Dean	d	11 00														12 00									
Mottisfont & Dunbridge	d	11 06														12 06									
Romsey	d	11 11								11 51				12 00		12 11								12 51	
Redbridge	d	11 19														12 19									
Millbrook (Hants)	d	11 22														12 22									
Southampton Central	a	11 25	11 28			←		11 53	11 58	12 02			12 12	12 20		12 25		12 28			←	12 51	12 58	13 02	
	d	11 35	11 30			11 35		11 55	12 00				12 15			12 35	12 27	12 30			12 35	12 55	13 00		
St Denys	d	→				11 40										→					12 40				
Swaythling	d					11 43															12 43				
Southampton Airport Parkwy ✈	d		11 38			11 46		12 03	12 08				12 22					12 38			12 46	13 03	13 08		
Portsmouth Harbour	d			10 55											11 55										
Portsmouth & Southsea	d			11 00											12 00										
Fratton	d			11 04											12 04										
Hilsea	d			11 08											12 08										
Cosham	d			11 13											12 13										
Portchester	d			11 18											12 18										
Fareham	d			11 24											12 24										
Botley	d			11 31											12 31										
Hedge End	d			11 36											12 36										
Eastleigh 3	a			11 42		11 49		12 07							12 42						12 49	13 06			
	d			11 43		11 50		12 11			← 12 11				12 43						12 50	13 11			
Chandlers Ford	d					11 55		→													12 55	→			
Romsey	a					12 03											12 38				13 03				
Shawford	d										12 17														
Winchester	d		11 48	11 54					12 18		12 24		12 31		12 54			12 48					13 18		
Micheldever	d			12 02											13 02										
Basingstoke	a			12 15					12 34		12 40		12 46		13 15								13 34		
	d			12 17					12 36		12 41		12 47		13 17								13 36		
Reading 7	a			*13 00*									13 04		*14 00*										
Fleet	d										12 53														
Farnborough (Main)	d			12 31							12 58				13 31										
Woking	a		12 19	12 40											13 40			13 19							
Clapham Junction 10	a								13 12		13 24												14 12		
London Waterloo 15 ⊖	a		12 49	13 08					13 20		13 34				14 08			13 49					14 20		

For general notes see front of timetable
For details of catering facilities see Directory of Train Operators

A ⊐P from Bournemouth
B To Gloucester (Table 134)
b By ship

During July and August ferry connection times to and from Yarmouth IOW are subject to alteration, please contact www.wightlink.co.uk or 0871 376 1000 for further details.

Table 158

Saturdays

Weymouth, Bournemouth, Lymington, Romsey, Southampton and Basingstoke → London

Network Diagram - see first page of Table 158

Station		SW	XC	SW	SW	SW	SW	SW	SW	SW	GW	SW	SW
		1	1 ◇	1	1 ◇	1	1	1	1	1 ◇	◇	1	1
					A					A			
			🛒		🍽					🍽	🛒		
Weymouth	d				12 03					12 20			
Upwey	d									12 24			
Dorchester West	a												
Dorchester South	d				12 13					12 33			
Moreton (Dorset)	d									12 39			
Wool	d									12 45			
Wareham	d				12 28					12 53			
Holton Heath	d									12 56			
Hamworthy	d				12 35					13 01			
Poole 4	a				12 39					13 06			
	d				12 40				12 50	13 07			
Parkstone (Dorset)	d				12 44				12 54				
Branksome	d				12 48				12 57				
Bournemouth	a				12 54				13 02	13 17			
	d		12 45		12 59				13 05	13 22			
Pokesdown	d								13 09	13 26			
Christchurch	d								13 13	13 30			
Hinton Admiral	d								13 18				
New Milton	d								13 22	13 37			
Sway	d								13 27				
Yarmouth (I.O.W.) ⛴	d						*12b15*					*13b00*	
Lymington Pier ⛴	d						13 14					13 44	
Lymington Town	d						13 16					13 46	
Brockenhurst 3	a		12 58		13 14		13 24		13 32	13 44		13 54	
	d		13 00		13 15				13 33	13 45			
Beaulieu Road	d								13 38				
Ashurst New Forest	d								13 42				
Totton	d								13 47				
Salisbury	d			12 48							13 33		
Dean	d			13 00									
Mottisfont & Dunbridge	d			13 06									
Romsey	d			13 11							13 51		
Redbridge	d			13 19									
Millbrook (Hants)	d			13 22									
Southampton Central	a		13 12	13 25	13 28			←	13 53	13 58	14 02		
	d		13 15	13 35 →	13 30			13 35	13 55	14 00			
St Denys	d							13 40					
Swaythling	d							13 43					
Southampton Airport Parkwy ✈	d		13 22		13 38			13 46	14 03	14 08			
Portsmouth Harbour	d					12 55							
Portsmouth & Southsea	d					13 00							
Fratton	d					13 04							
Hilsea	d					13 08							
Cosham	d					13 13							
Portchester	d					13 18							
Fareham	d					13 24							
Botley	d					13 31							
Hedge End	d					13 36							
Eastleigh 3	a	←				13 42		13 49	14 06				←
	d	13 11				13 43		13 50	14 11				14 11
Chandlers Ford	d							13 55	→				
Romsey	a							14 03					
Shawford	d	13 17											14 17
Winchester	d	13 24	13 31		13 48	13 54				14 18			14 24
Micheldever	d					14 02							
Basingstoke	a	13 40	13 46			14 15				14 34			14 40
	d	13 41	13 47			14 17				14 36			14 41
Reading 7	a		14 04			*15 00*							
Fleet	d	13 53											14 53
Farnborough (Main)	d	13 58				14 31							14 58
Woking	a				14 19	14 40							
Clapham Junction 10	a	14 24								15 12			15 24
London Waterloo 15 ⊖	a	14 34			14 49	15 08				15 20			15 34

Station		XC	SW	SN	SW	GW	SW	GW	SW	SW	SW	SW	GW
		1 ◇	1	1	1 ◇	◇	1	◇	1	1	1	1 ◇	◇
					A	B						A	
		🛒			🍽							🍽	🛒
Weymouth	d				13 03	13 10						13 20	
Upwey	d					13 15						13 24	
Dorchester West	a					13 23							
Dorchester South	d				13 13							13 33	
Moreton (Dorset)	d											13 39	
Wool	d											13 45	
Wareham	d				13 28							13 53	
Holton Heath	d											13 56	
Hamworthy	d				13 35							14 01	
Poole 4	a				13 39							14 06	
	d				13 40						13 50	14 07	
Parkstone (Dorset)	d				13 44						13 54		
Branksome	d				13 48						13 57		
Bournemouth	a				13 54						14 02	14 17	
	d	13 45			13 59						14 05	14 22	
Pokesdown	d										14 09	14 26	
Christchurch	d										14 13	14 30	
Hinton Admiral	d										14 18		
New Milton	d										14 22	14 37	
Sway	d										14 27		
Yarmouth (I.O.W.) ⛴	d												
Lymington Pier ⛴	d								14 14				
Lymington Town	d								14 16				
Brockenhurst 3	a	13 58			14 14				14 24		14 32	14 44	
	d	14 00			14 15						14 33	14 45	
Beaulieu Road	d												
Ashurst New Forest	d										14 40		
Totton	d										14 45		
Salisbury	d		13 48					13 59					14 33
Dean	d		14 00										
Mottisfont & Dunbridge	d		14 06										
Romsey	d		14 11					14 19					14 51
Redbridge	d		14 19										
Millbrook (Hants)	d		14 22										
Southampton Central	a	14 12	14 25		14 28			14 32		←	14 51	14 58	15 02
	d	14 15	14 35 →	14 27	14 30					14 35	14 55	15 00	
St Denys	d									14 40			
Swaythling	d									14 43			
Southampton Airport Parkwy ✈	d	14 22			14 38					14 46	15 03	15 08	
Portsmouth Harbour	d						13 55						
Portsmouth & Southsea	d						14 00						
Fratton	d						14 04						
Hilsea	d						14 08						
Cosham	d						14 13						
Portchester	d						14 18						
Fareham	d						14 24						
Botley	d						14 31						
Hedge End	d						14 36						
Eastleigh 3	a			14 36			14 42			14 50	15 06		
	d						14 43			14 50	15 11		
Chandlers Ford	d									14 55	→		
Romsey	a									15 04			
Shawford	d												
Winchester	d	14 31			14 48		14 54					15 18	
Micheldever	d						15 02						
Basingstoke	a	14 46					15 15					15 34	
	d	14 47					15 17					15 36	
Reading 7	a	15 04					*16c02*						
Fleet	d												
Farnborough (Main)	d						15 31						
Woking	a				15 19		15 40						
Clapham Junction 10	a											16 12	
London Waterloo 15 ⊖	a				15 49		16 08					16 20	

For general notes see front of timetable
For details of catering facilities see Directory of Train Operators

A 🍽 from Bournemouth
B To Gloucester (Table 134)
b By ship
c From 12 September arr. 1600

During July and August ferry connection times to and from Yarmouth IOW are subject to alteration, please contact www.wightliink.co.uk or 0871 376 1000 for further details.

Weymouth, Bournemouth, Lymington, Romsey, Southampton and Basingstoke → London

Network Diagram - see first page of Table 158

		SW	SW	XC	SW	SW	SW	SW	SW	SW	SW	GW	SW	SW	XC	SW	SW	SW	GW	SW	SW	SW	SW	SW	GW
		1	1	1◇	1	1◇	1	1	1	1	1◇	◇	1	1	1◇	1	1	1◇	◇	1	1	1	1	1◇	◇
						A					A							A	B					A	
				⊼		🍴					🍴	⊼			⊼			🍴						🍴	⊼
Weymouth	d					14 03					14 20							15 03	15 09					15 20	
Upwey	d										14 24								15 14					15 24	
Dorchester West	a																		15 22						
Dorchester South	d					14 13					14 33							15 13						15 33	
Moreton (Dorset)	d										14 39													15 39	
Wool	d										14 45													15 45	
Wareham	d					14 28					14 53							15 28						15 53	
Holton Heath	d										14 56													15 56	
Hamworthy	d					14 35					15 01							15 35						16 01	
Poole 4	a					14 39					15 06							15 39						16 06	
	d					14 40				14 50	15 07							15 40					15 50	16 07	
Parkstone (Dorset)	d					14 44				14 54								15 44					15 54		
Branksome	d					14 48				14 57								15 48					15 57		
Bournemouth	a					14 54				15 02	15 17							15 54					16 02	16 17	
	d			14 45		14 59				15 05	15 22				15 45			15 59					16 05	16 22	
Pokesdown	d									15 09	15 26												16 09	16 26	
Christchurch	d									15 13	15 30												16 13	16 30	
Hinton Admiral	d									15 18													16 18		
New Milton	d									15 22	15 37												16 22	16 37	
Sway	d									15 27													16 27		
Yarmouth (I.O.W.) ⛴	d	14b00											14b45								15b30				
Lymington Pier ⛴	d	14 44						15 14					15 44								16 14				
Lymington Town	d	14 46						15 16					15 46								16 16				
Brockenhurst 3	a	14 54		14 58		15 14		15 24		15 32	15 44		15 54		15 58			16 14			16 24		16 32	16 44	
	d			15 00		15 15				15 33	15 45				16 00			16 15					16 33	16 45	
Beaulieu Road	d									15 38															
Ashurst New Forest	d									15 42													16 40		
Totton	d									15 47													16 45		
Salisbury	d				14 48							15 33					15 48								16 33
Dean	d				15 00												16 00								
Mottisfont & Dunbridge	d				15 06												16 06								
Romsey	d				15 11							15 51				16 07	16 11								16 51
Redbridge	d				15 19											16 44	16 19								
Millbrook (Hants)	d				15 22												16 22								
Southampton Central	a			15 12	15 25	15 28			←	15 53	15 58	16 02			16 12		16 25	16 28				←	16 51	16 58	17 02
	d			15 15	15 35	15 30			15 35	15 55	16 00				16 15		16 35	16 30				16 35	16 55	17 00	
St Denys	d				→				15 40								→					16 40			
Swaythling	d								15 43													16 43			
Southampton Airport Parkwy ✈	d			15 22		15 38			15 46	16 03	16 08				16 22			16 38				16 46	17 03	17 08	
Portsmouth Harbour	d						14 55													15 55					
Portsmouth & Southsea	d						15 00													16 00					
Fratton	d						15 04													16 04					
Hilsea	d						15 08													16 08					
Cosham	d						15 13													16 13					
Portchester	d						15 18													16 18					
Fareham	d						15 24													16 24					
Botley	d						15 31													16 31					
Hedge End	d						15 36													16 36					
Eastleigh 3	a		←				15 42		15 49	16 06				←						16 42		16 49	17 06		
	d		15 11				15 43		15 50	16 11				16 11						16 43		16 50	17 11		
Chandlers Ford	d								15 55	→						16 14						16 55	→		
Romsey	a								16 03							16 51						17 03			
Shawford	d		15 17											16 17											
Winchester	d		15 24	15 31		15 48	15 54				16 18			16 24	16 31			16 48		16 54				17 18	
Micheldever	d						16 02													17 02					
Basingstoke	a		15 40	15 46			16 15				16 34			16 40	16 46					17 15				17 34	
	d		15 41	15 47			16 17				16 36			16 41	16 47					17 17				17 36	
Reading 7	a			16 04			*17 00*								17 04					*18 00*					
Fleet	d		15 53											16 53											
Farnborough (Main)	d		15 58				16 31							16 58						17 31					
Woking	a					16 19	16 40											17 19		17 40					
Clapham Junction 10	a		16 24								17 12			17 24										18 12	
London Waterloo 15 ⊖	a		16 34			16 49	17 08				17 20			17 34				17 49		18 08				18 20	

For general notes see front of timetable
For details of catering facilities see Directory of Train Operators

A 🍴 from Bournemouth
B From 12 September. To Gloucester (Table 134)
b By ship

During July and August ferry connection times to and from Yarmouth IOW are subject to alteration, please contact www.wightliink.co.uk or 0871 376 1000 for further details.

Weymouth, Bournemouth, Lymington, Romsey, Southampton and Basingstoke → London

Network Diagram - see first page of Table 158

		SW	SW	XC	SW	SW	GW	SW	SW	SW	SW	SW	GW	SW	SW	XC	SW	SW	SW	SW	SW	SW	SW	GW	GW
		1	1	1 ◇	1	1 ◇	◇	1	1	1	1	1 ◇	◇	1	1	1 ◇	1	1 ◇	1	1	1	1	1 ◇	◇	◇
						A	B					A						A					A		
				[trolley]		[restaurant]						[restaurant]	[trolley]			[trolley]		[restaurant]					[restaurant]		[trolley]
Weymouth	d					16 03	16 10					16 20						17 03					17 20	17 30	
Upwey	d						16 15					16 24											17 24	17 35	
Dorchester West	a						16 23																	17 43	
Dorchester South	d					16 13						16 33						17 13					17 33		
Moreton (Dorset)	d											16 39											17 39		
Wool	d											16 45											17 45		
Wareham	d					16 28						16 53						17 28					17 53		
Holton Heath	d											16 56											17 56		
Hamworthy	d					16 35						17 01						17 35					18 01		
Poole 4	a					16 39						17 06						17 39					18 06		
	d					16 40					16 50	17 07						17 40				17 50	18 07		
Parkstone (Dorset)	d					16 44					16 54							17 44				17 54			
Branksome	d					16 48					16 57							17 48				17 57			
Bournemouth	a					16 54					17 02	17 17						17 54				18 02	18 17		
	d			16 45		16 59					17 05	17 22				17 45		17 59				18 05	18 22		
Pokesdown	d										17 09	17 26										18 09	18 26		
Christchurch	d										17 13	17 30										18 13	18 30		
Hinton Admiral	d										17 18											18 18			
New Milton	d										17 22	17 37										18 22	18 37		
Sway	d										17 27											18 27			
Yarmouth (I.O.W.) [ship]	d								16b15					17b00											
Lymington Pier [ship]	d	16 44							17 14					17 44						18 14					
Lymington Town	d	16 46							17 16					17 46						18 16					
Brockenhurst 3	a	16 54		16 58		17 14			17 24		17 32	17 44		17 54		17 58		18 14		18 24		18 32	18 44		
	d			17 00		17 15					17 33	17 45				18 00		18 15				18 33	18 45		
Beaulieu Road	d										17 38														
Ashurst New Forest	d										17 42											18 40			
Totton	d										17 47											18 45			
Salisbury	d				16 48								17 33				17 48								18 33
Dean	d				17 00												18 00								
Mottisfont & Dunbridge	d				17 06												18 06								
Romsey	d				17 11								17 51				18 11								18 51
Redbridge	d				17 19												18 19								
Millbrook (Hants)	d				17 22												18 22								
Southampton Central	a			17 12	17 25	17 28				←	17 53	17 58	18 02			18 12	18 25	18 28			←	18 51	18 58		19 02
	d			17 15	17 35 →	17 30				17 35	17 55	18 00				18 15	18 35 →	18 30			18 35	18 55	19 00		
St Denys	d									17 40											18 40				
Swaythling	d									17 43											18 43				
Southampton Airport Parkwy [plane]	d			17 22		17 38				17 46	18 03	18 08				18 22		18 38			18 46	19 03	19 08		
Portsmouth Harbour	d							16 55											17 55						
Portsmouth & Southsea	d							17 00											18 00						
Fratton	d							17 04											18 04						
Hilsea	d							17 08											18 08						
Cosham	d							17 13											18 13						
Portchester	d							17 18											18 18						
Fareham	d							17 24											18 24						
Botley	d							17 31											18 31						
Hedge End	d							17 36											18 36						
Eastleigh 3	a		←					17 42		17 49	18 06				←				18 42		18 49	19 06			
	d		17 11					17 43		17 50	18 11				18 11				18 43		18 50	19 11			
Chandlers Ford	d									17 55	→										18 55	→			
Romsey	a									18 03											19 04				
Shawford	d		17 17												18 17										
Winchester	d		17 24	17 31		17 48		17 54				18 18			18 24	18 31		18 48	18 54				19 18		
Micheldever	d							18 02											19 02						
Basingstoke	a		17 40	17 46				18 15				18 34			18 40	18 46			19 15				19 34		
	d		17 41	17 47				18 17				18 36			18 41	18 47			19 17				19 36		
Reading 7	a			18 04				*19 00*								19 04			*20 01*						
Fleet	d		17 53												18 53										
Farnborough (Main)	d		17 58					18 31							18 58				19 31						
Woking	a					18 19		18 40										19 19	19 40						
Clapham Junction 10	a		18 24									19 12			19 24								20 12		
London Waterloo 15 [Underground]	a		18 34			18 49		19 08				19 20			19 34			19 49	20 08				20 20		

For general notes see front of timetable
For details of catering facilities see Directory of Train Operators

A [restaurant] from Bournemouth
B Until 5 September. To Great Malvern (Table 71)
b By ship

During July and August ferry connection times to and from Yarmouth IOW are subject to alteration, please contact www.wightliink.co.uk or 0871 376 1000 for further details.

Weymouth, Bournemouth, Lymington, Romsey, Southampton and Basingstoke → London

Network Diagram - see first page of Table 158

		SW	SW	XC	SW	SW	SW	SW	SW	SW	SW	GW	SW	SW	XC	GW	SW	SW	SW	SW	SW	SW	SW	GW	SW
		1	1	1 ◇	1	1 ◇	1	1	1	1	1 ◇	◇	1	1	1 ◇		1	1 ◇	1	1	1	1	1 ◇	◇	1
						A					A				B			A							
				🍴		⊐P					⊐P	🍴			🍴			⊐P						🍴	
Weymouth	d					18 03					18 20							19 03					19 20		
Upwey	d										18 24												19 24		
Dorchester West	a																								
Dorchester South	d					18 13					18 33							19 13					19 33		
Moreton (Dorset)	d										18 39												19 39		
Wool	d										18 45												19 45		
Wareham	d					18 28					18 53							19 28					19 53		
Holton Heath	d										18 56														
Hamworthy	d					18 35					19 01							19 35					20 01		
Poole 4	a					18 39					19 06							19 39					20 06		
	d					18 40				18 50	19 07							19 40				19 50	20 07		
Parkstone (Dorset)	d					18 44				18 54								19 44				19 54			
Branksome	d					18 48				18 57								19 48				19 57			
Bournemouth	a					18 54				19 02	19 17							19 54				20 02	20 17		
	d			18 45		18 59				19 05	19 22				19 45			19 59				20 05	20 22		
Pokesdown	d									19 09	19 26											20 09	20 26		
Christchurch	d									19 13	19 30											20 13	20 30		
Hinton Admiral	d									19 18												20 18			
New Milton	d									19 22	19 37											20 22	20 37		
Sway	d									19 27												20 27			
Yarmouth (I.O.W.) ⛴	d	*17b45*						*18b30*												*19b15*					
Lymington Pier ⛴	d	18 44						19 14						19 44						20 14					20 44
Lymington Town	d	18 46						19 16						19 46						20 16					20 46
Brockenhurst 3	a	18 54		18 58		19 14		19 24		19 32	19 44			19 54	19 58			20 14		20 24		20 32	20 44		20 54
	d			19 00		19 15				19 33	19 45				20 00			20 15				20 33	20 45		
Beaulieu Road	d																								
Ashurst New Forest	d									19 40												20 40			
Totton	d									19 45												20 45			
Salisbury	d				18 48							19 33				19 41	19 48							20 33	
Dean	d				19 00												20 00								
Mottisfont & Dunbridge	d				19 06												20 06								
Romsey	d				19 11							19 51				20 02	20 11							20 51	
Redbridge	d				19 19												20 19								
Millbrook (Hants)	d				19 22												20 22								
Southampton Central	a			19 12	19 25	19 28			⟵	19 51	19 58	20 02			20 12	20 18	20 25	20 28			⟵	20 51	20 58	21 02	
	d			19 15	19 35 ⟶	19 30			19 35	19 55	20 00				20 15		20 35 ⟶	20 30			20 35	20 55	21 00		
St Denys	d								19 40												20 40				
Swaythling	d								19 43												20 43				
Southampton Airport Parkwy ✈	d			19 22		19 38			19 46	20 03	20 08				20 22			20 38			20 46	21 03	21 08		
Portsmouth Harbour	d						18 55												19 55						
Portsmouth & Southsea	d						19 00												20 00						
Fratton	d						19 04												20 04						
Hilsea	d						19 08												20 08						
Cosham	d						19 13												20 13						
Portchester	d						19 18												20 18						
Fareham	d						19 24												20 24						
Botley	d						19 31												20 31						
Hedge End	d						19 36												20 36						
Eastleigh 3	a		⟵				19 42		19 49	20 06			⟵						20 42		20 49	21 06			
	d		19 11				19 43		19 50	20 11			20 11						20 43		20 50	21 11			
Chandlers Ford	d								19 55	⟶											20 55	⟶			
Romsey	a								20 03												21 03				
Shawford	d		19 17										20 17												
Winchester	d		19 24	19 31		19 48	19 54				20 18		20 24		20 31			20 48	20 54				21 18		
Micheldever	d						20 02												21 02						
Basingstoke	a		19 40	19 46			20 15				20 34		20 40		20 46				21 16				21 34		
	d		19 41	19 47			20 17				20 36		20 41		20 47				21 24				21 36		
Reading 7	a			20 04			*21 00*								21 04				*22 00*						
Fleet	d		19 53										20 53						21 40						
Farnborough (Main)	d		19 58				20 31						20 58						21 46						
Woking	a					20 19	20 40						21 07					21 19	21 58						
Clapham Junction 10	a		20 24								21 16		21 30										22 14		
London Waterloo 15 ⊖	a		20 34			20 49	21 08				21 24		21 39					21 49	22 34				22 22		

For general notes see front of timetable
For details of catering facilities see Directory of Train Operators

A ⊐P from Bournemouth
B To Birmingham New Street (Table 116)
b By ship

During July and August ferry connection times to and from Yarmouth IOW are subject to alteration, please contact www.wightlink.co.uk or 0871 376 1000 for further details.

Table 158

Saturdays

Weymouth, Bournemouth, Lymington, Romsey, Southampton and Basingstoke → London

Network Diagram - see first page of Table 158

		SW	GW	SW	SW	SW	SW	SW	SW	GW	GW	SW	SW	SW	SW	SW	SW	SW	GW	SW	SW	SW	SW
		1		**1**	**1**	**1**	**1**	**1**	**1** ◇	◇	◇ (catering)	**1**	**1**	**1**	**1**	**1**	**1**	**1**	◇ (catering)	**1**	**1**	**1**	**1**
Weymouth	d								20 10	20 24								21 10				22 10	23 10
Upwey	d								20 14	20 29								21 14				22 14	23 14
Dorchester West	a									20 36													
Dorchester South	d								20 22									21 22				22 22	23 22
Moreton (Dorset)	d								20 28									21 28				22 28	23 28
Wool	d								20 34									21 34				22 34	23 34
Wareham	d								20 42									21 42				22 42	23 42
Holton Heath	d																						
Hamworthy	d								20 48									21 48				22 48	23 48
Poole 4	a								20 53									21 53				22 53	23 53
	d								20 54									21 54				22 54	23 54
Parkstone (Dorset)	d								20 58									21 58				22 58	
Branksome	d								21 01									22 01				23 01	
Bournemouth	a								21 07									22 07				23 07	00 03
	d								21 12									22 12				23 12	
Pokesdown	d								21 16									22 16				23 16	
Christchurch	d								21 20									22 20				23 20	
Hinton Admiral	d								21 25									22 25				23 25	
New Milton	d								21 29									22 29				23 29	
Sway	d								21 34									22 34				23 34	
Yarmouth (I.O.W.)	d						20b15										21b15						
Lymington Pier	d						21 14					21 44					22 14						
Lymington Town	d						21 16					21 46					22 16						
Brockenhurst 3	a						21 24		21 39			21 54					22 24	22 39				23 39	
	d								21 40									22 40				23 40	
Beaulieu Road	d																						
Ashurst New Forest	d								21 47									22 47				23 47	
Totton	d								21 52									22 52				23 52	
Salisbury	d					20 48					21 33					21 48			22 32				
Dean	d					21 00										22 00							
Mottisfont & Dunbridge	d					21 06										22 06							
Romsey	d					21 11					21 51					22 11			22 52	23 00			
Redbridge	d					21 19										22 19				23 08			
Millbrook (Hants)	d					21 22										22 22				23 12			
Southampton Central	a					21 25			21 57		22 02					22 25		22 57	23 02	23 15		23 57	
	d		21 27	21 30		21 35		21 55	22 00					22 30		22 35		23 00		23 21		23 59	
St Denys	d					21 40										22 40				23 26		00 04	
Swaythling	d					21 43										22 43				23 29		00 07	
Southampton Airport Parkwy	d			21 38		21 46		22 03	22 08					22 38		22 46		23 08		23 32		00 10	
Portsmouth Harbour	d				20 55										21 55						23 24		
Portsmouth & Southsea	d				21 00										22 00						23 29		
Fratton	d				21 04										22 04						23 33		
Hilsea	d				21 08										22 08						23 37		
Cosham	d				21 13										22 13						23 42		
Portchester	d				21 18										22 18						23 47		
Fareham	d				21 24										22 24						23 53		
Botley	d				21 31										22 31						23 59		
Hedge End	d				21 36										22 36						00 05		
Eastleigh 3	a	←			21 42	21 49		22 06					←	22 41	22 42	22 49		23 11		23 35	00 11	00 14	
	d	21 11			21 43	21 50		22 11					22 11	22 45		22 50		23 12		23 37	00 21		
Chandlers Ford	d					21 55		→								22 55				23 42			
Romsey	a		21 38			22 03										23 03				23 49			
Shawford	d	21 17											22 17					23 18					
Winchester	d	21 24		21 48	21 54				22 18				22 24	22 54				23 24			00a30		
Micheldever	d				22 02													23 33					
Basingstoke	a	21 40			22 15				22 34				22 40	23 10				23 43					
	d	21 41			22 24				22 36				22 41	23 14				23 44					
Reading 7	a	*22 31*			*23 00*								*23 31*	*00 01*									
Fleet	d	21 53			22 40								22 53					00 01					
Farnborough (Main)	d	21 58			22 46								22 58					00 06					
Woking	a	22 07		22 19	22 58				22 54				23 07	23 32				00 18					
Clapham Junction 10	a	22 30							23 15				23 33	23 58				00 54					
London Waterloo 15 ⊖	a	22 38		22 49	23 39				23 23				23 43	00 10				01 02					

For general notes see front of timetable
For details of catering facilities see Directory of Train Operators

b By ship

During July and August ferry connection times to and from Yarmouth IOW are subject to alteration, please contact www.wightliink.co.uk or 0871 376 1000 for further details.

Table 158

Sundays

Weymouth, Bournemouth, Lymington, Romsey, Southampton and Basingstoke → London

Network Diagram - see first page of Table 158

		SW	SW	SW	SW	SW	SW	GW	SW	SW	SW	SW	SW	XC	SW	SW	SW	SW	SW	SW	SW	XC
		1	1	1	1	1 ◇	1 ◇	1	1	1	1 ◇	1 ◇	1	1 ◇	1 ◇	1 ◇	1	1	1 ◇	1 ◇	1	1 ◇
								A	B						C	D						
							🍴	🛒						🛒	🍴	🍴						🛒
Weymouth	d	21p10		22p10											07 43	07 48						
Upwey	d	21p14		22p14											07 47	07 52						
Dorchester West	a																					
Dorchester South	d	21p22		22p22											07 55	08 00						
Moreton (Dorset)	d	21p28		22p28											08 02	08 07						
Wool	d	21p34		22p34											08 08	08 13						
Wareham	d	21p42		22p42											08 15	08 20						
Holton Heath	d																					
Hamworthy	d	21p48		22p48											08 22	08 27						
Poole 4	a	21p53		22p53											08 26	08 31						
	d	21p54		22p54			06 50					07 50			08 27	08 32				08 55		
Parkstone (Dorset)	d	21p58		22p58			06 54					07 54			08 31	08 36						
Branksome	d	22p01		23p01			06 57					07 57			08 35	08 40						
Bournemouth	a	22p07		23p07			07 02					08 02			08 46	08 46				09 04		
	d	22p12		23p12			07 06					08 06			08 50	08 50				09 06		09 40
Pokesdown	d	22p16		23p16			07 10					08 10								09 10		
Christchurch	d	22p20		23p20			07 14					08 14								09 14		
Hinton Admiral	d	22p25		23p25			07 19					08 19								09 19		
New Milton	d	22p29		23p29			07 23					08 23			09 01	09 01				09 23		
Sway	d	22p34		23p34			07 28					08 28								09 28		
Yarmouth (I.O.W.) ⛴	d																*08b00*					
Lymington Pier ⛴	d																09 14					
Lymington Town	d																09 16					
Brockenhurst 3	a	22p39		23p39			07 33					08 33			09 08	09 08	09 24			09 33		09 53
	d	22p40		23p40			07 34					08 34			09 09	09 09				09 34		09 57
Beaulieu Road	d											08 39								09 39		
Ashurst New Forest	d	22p47		23p47			07 43					08 43								09 43		
Totton	d	22p52		23p52			07 48					08 48								09 48		
Salisbury	d								08 08	08 20								09 08				
Dean	d								08 20									09 20				
Mottisfont & Dunbridge	d								08 26									09 26				
Romsey	d							08 19	08c35	08 39								09 32				
Redbridge	d								09 16	08 46								09 39				
Millbrook (Hants)	d									08 50								09 43				
Southampton Central	a	22p57		23p57			07 53	08 29		08 52		08 53	←		09 23	09 23		09 45		09 53	←	10 10
	d	23p00		23p59	06 55		07 55			08 59 →		08 55	08 59	09 15	09 25	09 25		09 59 →		09 55	09 59	10 15
St Denys	d			00 04									09 04								10 04	
Swaythling	d			00 07									09 07								10 07	
Southampton Airport Parkwy ✈	d	23p08		00 10	07 03		08 03					09 03	09 10	09 22	09 33	09 33				10 03	10 10	10 22
Portsmouth Harbour	d		23p24			07 17					08 17								09 17			
Portsmouth & Southsea	d		23p29			07 22					08 22								09 22			
Fratton	d		23p33			07 26					08 26								09 26			
Hilsea	d		23p37			07 30					08 30								09 30			
Cosham	d		23p42			07 35					08 35								09 35			
Portchester	d		23p47			07 40					08 40								09 40			
Fareham	d		23p53			07 46					08 46								09 46			
Botley	d		23p59			07 54					08 54								09 54			
Hedge End	d		00 05			07 58					08 58								09 58			
Eastleigh 3	a	23p11	00 11	00 14	07 07	08 04	08 07				09 04	09 07	09 13						10 04	10 07	10 13	
	d	23p12	00 21		07 11	08 11					09 11		09 15						10 11		10 15	
Chandlers Ford	d								08 42				09 20								10 20	
Romsey	a								09 24				09 28								10 28	
Shawford	d	23p18									09 17											
Winchester	d	23p24	00a30		07 23	08 23					09 23			09 31	09 42	09 42			10 23			10 31
Micheldever	d	23p33			07 32	08 32					09 32								10 32			
Basingstoke	a	23p43			07 42	08 42					09 42			09 46	09 58	09 58			10 42			10 46
	d	23p44			07 44	08 44					09 44			09 47	10 00	10 00			10 44			10 47
Reading 7	a				*08 30*	*09 30*								10 04	*10 30*	*10e31*						11 04
Fleet	d	00 01																				
Farnborough (Main)	d	00 06																				
Woking	a	00 18			08 02	09 02					10 02				10 19	10 19			11 02			
Clapham Junction 10	a	00 54			08 27	09 27					10 27				10 39	10 39			11 27			
London Waterloo 15 ⊖	a	01 02			08 42	09 42					10 42				10 54	10 54			11 40			

For general notes see front of timetable
For details of catering facilities see Directory of Train Operators

- **A** To Brighton (Table 188)
- **B** To Salisbury
- **C** From 27 September. 🍴 from Bournemouth
- **D** Until 20 September. 🍴 from Bournemouth
- **b** By ship
- **c** Arr. 0831
- **e** 13 and 20 September arr. 1030

During July and August ferry connection times to and from Yarmouth IOW are subject to alteration, please contact www.wightlink.co.uk or 0871 376 1000 for further details.

Sundays

Weymouth, Bournemouth, Lymington, Romsey, Southampton and Basingstoke → London

Network Diagram - see first page of Table 158

		SW	SW	SW	SW	SW	SW	SW		SW	GW	XC	SW	SW	SW		SW	SW	SW	SW	GW	XC		SW	SW
		1	1◇	1◇	1	1	1◇	1◇		1	◇	1◇	1	1◇	1		1	1◇	1◇	1	◇	1◇		1	1◇
			A	B										C											C
			🍴	🍴							🛒	🛒		🍴							🛒	🛒			🍴
Weymouth	d		08 43	08 48										09 48											10 48
Upwey	d		08 47	08 52										09 52											10 52
Dorchester West	a																								
Dorchester South	d		08 55	09 00										10 00											11 00
Moreton (Dorset)	d		09 02	09 07										10 07											11 07
Wool	d		09 08	09 13										10 13											11 13
Wareham	d		09 15	09 20										10 20											11 20
Holton Heath	d																								
Hamworthy	d		09 22	09 27										10 27											11 27
Poole 4	a		09 26	09 31										10 31											11 31
	d		09 27	09 32				09 55						10 32					10 55						11 32
Parkstone (Dorset)	d		09 31	09 36										10 36											11 36
Branksome	d		09 35	09 40										10 40											11 40
Bournemouth	a		09 46	09 46				10 04						10 46					11 04						11 46
	d		09 50	09 50				10 06				10 40		10 50					11 06			11 40			11 50
Pokesdown	d							10 10											11 10						
Christchurch	d							10 14											11 14						
Hinton Admiral	d							10 19											11 19						
New Milton	d		10 01	10 01				10 23						11 01					11 23						12 01
Sway	d							10 28											11 28						
Yarmouth (I.O.W.) ⛴	d	*09b00*											*09b45*		*10b30*										
Lymington Pier ⛴	d	09 44			10 14								10 44		11 14									11 44	
Lymington Town	d	09 46			10 16								10 46		11 16									11 46	
Brockenhurst 3	a	09 54	10 08	10 08	10 24			10 33				10 53	10 54	11 08	11 24				11 33			11 53		11 54	12 08
	d		10 09	10 09				10 34				10 57		11 09					11 34			11 57			12 09
Beaulieu Road	d							10 39											11 39						
Ashurst New Forest	d							10 43											11 43						
Totton	d							10 48											11 48						
Salisbury	d					10 13					10 31						11 08				11 31				
Dean	d																11 20								
Mottisfont & Dunbridge	d																11 26								
Romsey	d					10 32					10 50						11 32				11 49				
Redbridge	d					10 39											11 39								
Millbrook (Hants)	d					10 43											11 43								
Southampton Central	a		10 23	10 23		10 45		10 53		←	11 00	11 10		11 23			11 45		11 53	←	12 04	12 10			12 23
	d		10 25	10 25		10 59 →		10 55		10 59		11 15		11 25			11 59 →		11 55	11 59		12 15			12 25
St Denys	d									11 04										12 04					
Swaythling	d									11 07										12 07					
Southampton Airport Parkwy ✈	d		10 33	10 33				11 03		11 10		11 22		11 33					12 03	12 10		12 22			12 33
Portsmouth Harbour	d						10 17											11 17							
Portsmouth & Southsea	d						10 22											11 22							
Fratton	d						10 26											11 26							
Hilsea	d						10 30											11 30							
Cosham	d						10 35											11 35							
Portchester	d						10 40											11 40							
Fareham	d						10 46											11 46							
Botley	d						10 54											11 54							
Hedge End	d						10 58											11 58							
Eastleigh 3	a						11 04	11 07		11 13								12 04	12 07	12 13					
	d							11 11		11 15									12 11	12 15					
Chandlers Ford	d									11 20										12 20					
Romsey	a									11 28										12 28					
Shawford	d							11 17																	
Winchester	d		10 42	10 42				11 23				11 31		11 42					12 23			12 31			12 42
Micheldever	d							11 32											12 32						
Basingstoke	a		10 58	10 58				11 42				11 46		11 58					12 42			12 46			12 58
	d		11 00	11 00				11 44				11 47		12 00					12 44			12 47			13 00
Reading 7	a		*11 30*	*11 30*								12 04		*12 30*								13 04			*13 30*
Fleet	d																								
Farnborough (Main)	d																								
Woking	a		11 18	11 18				12 02						12 18					13 02						13 18
Clapham Junction 10	a		11 39	11 39				12 27						12 39					13 27						13 39
London Waterloo 15 ⊖	a		11 52	11 52				12 40						12 52					13 40						13 49

For general notes see front of timetable
For details of catering facilities see Directory of Train Operators

A From 27 September. 🍴 from Bournemouth
B Until 20 September. 🍴 from Bournemouth
C 🍴 from Bournemouth
b By ship

During July and August ferry connection times to and from Yarmouth IOW are subject to alteration, please contact www.wightliink.co.uk or 0871 376 1000 for further details.

Table 158

Sundays

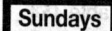

Weymouth, Bournemouth, Lymington, Romsey, Southampton and Basingstoke → London

Network Diagram - see first page of Table 158

		GW	SW	SW	SW	SW	SW	GW	XC	SW	SW	SW	SW	SW	SW	GW	SW	XC	SW	SW	SW	SW
			1	1	1 ◇	1 ◇	1	◇	1 ◇	1	1 ◇	1	1	1 ◇	1 ◇	◇	1	1 ◇	1	1 ◇	1	1
		A									B									B		
		🚲						🚲	🚲		🍴					🚲		🚲		🍴		
Weymouth	d	11 11									11 48									12 48		
Upwey	d	11 16									11 52									12 52		
Dorchester West	a	11 24																				
Dorchester South	d										12 00									13 00		
Moreton (Dorset)	d										12 07									13 07		
Wool	d										12 13									13 13		
Wareham	d										12 20									13 20		
Holton Heath	d																					
Hamworthy	d										12 27									13 27		
Poole 4	a										12 31									13 31		
	d					11 55					12 32				12 55					13 32		
Parkstone (Dorset)	d										12 36									13 36		
Branksome	d										12 40									13 40		
Bournemouth	a					12 04					12 46				13 04					13 46		
	d					12 06			12 40		12 50				13 06			13 40		13 50		
Pokesdown	d					12 10									13 10							
Christchurch	d					12 14									13 14							
Hinton Admiral	d					12 19									13 19							
New Milton	d					12 23					13 01				13 23					14 01		
Sway	d					12 28									13 28							
Yarmouth (I.O.W.) ⛴	d		*11b15*									*12b15*							*13b00*			
Lymington Pier ⛴	d		12 14							12 44		13 14							13 44		14 14	
Lymington Town	d		12 16							12 46		13 16							13 46		14 16	
Brockenhurst 3	a		12 24			12 33			12 53	12 54	13 08	13 24			13 33			13 53	13 54	14 08	14 24	
	d					12 34			12 57		13 09				13 34			13 57		14 09		
Beaulieu Road	d					12 39									13 39							
Ashurst New Forest	d					12 43									13 43							
Totton	d					12 48									13 48							
Salisbury	d			12 13				12 36					13 08			13 29						14 13
Dean	d												13 20									
Mottisfont & Dunbridge	d												13 26									
Romsey	d			12 32				12 56					13 32			13 47						14 32
Redbridge	d			12 39									13 39									14 39
Millbrook (Hants)	d			12 43									13 43									14 43
Southampton Central	a			12 45		12 53	←	13 06	13 10		13 23		13 45		13 53	13 58	←	14 10		14 23		14 45
	d			12 59		12 55	12 59		13 15		13 25		13 59		13 55		13 59	14 15		14 25		14 59
St Denys	d			→			13 04						→				14 04					→
Swaythling	d						13 07										14 07					
Southampton Airport Parkwy ✈	d					13 03	13 10		13 22		13 33				14 03		14 10	14 22		14 33		
Portsmouth Harbour	d				12 17									13 17								
Portsmouth & Southsea	d				12 22									13 22								
Fratton	d				12 26									13 26								
Hilsea	d				12 30									13 30								
Cosham	d				12 35									13 35								
Portchester	d				12 40									13 40								
Fareham	d				12 46									13 46								
Botley	d				12 54									13 54								
Hedge End	d				12 58									13 58								
Eastleigh 3	a				13 04	13 07	13 13							14 04	14 07		14 13					
	d				13 11		13 15							14 11			14 15					
Chandlers Ford	d						13 20										14 20					
Romsey	a						13 28										14 28					
Shawford	d				13 17																	
Winchester	d				13 23				13 31		13 42			14 23				14 31		14 42		
Micheldever	d				13 32									14 32								
Basingstoke	a				13 42				13 46		13 58			14 42				14 46		14 58		
	d				13 44				13 47		14 00			14 44				14 47		15 00		
Reading 7	a								14 04		*14 30*							15 04		*15 30*		
Fleet	d																					
Farnborough (Main)	d																					
Woking	a				14 02						14 18			15 02						15 18		
Clapham Junction 10	a				14 27						14 39			15 27						15 39		
London Waterloo 15 ⊖	a				14 37						14 49			15 37						15 49		

For general notes see front of timetable
For details of catering facilities see Directory of Train Operators

A Until 6 September
B 🍴 from Bournemouth
b By ship

During July and August ferry connection times to and from Yarmouth IOW are subject to alteration, please contact www.wightliink.co.uk or 0871 376 1000 for further details.

Sundays

Weymouth, Bournemouth, Lymington, Romsey, Southampton and Basingstoke → London

Network Diagram - see first page of Table 158

		SW	SW	SW	XC	SW	GW	SW	GW	GW	SW	SW	SW	SW	SW	GW	XC	SW	SW	SW	SW
		1 ◇	1 ◇	1	1 ◇	1	◇	1 ◇	◇		1	1	1 ◇	1 ◇	1	◇	1 ◇	1	1 ◇	1	1
								A	B	C									A		
Weymouth	d							13 48	14 00	14 10									14 48		
Upwey	d							13 52	14 05	14 15									14 52		
Dorchester West	a								14 13	14 23											
Dorchester South	d							14 00											15 00		
Moreton (Dorset)	d							14 07											15 07		
Wool	d							14 13											15 13		
Wareham	d							14 20											15 20		
Holton Heath	d																				
Hamworthy	d							14 27											15 27		
Poole 4	a							14 31											15 31		
	d		13 55					14 32						14 55					15 32		
Parkstone (Dorset)	d							14 36											15 36		
Branksome	d							14 40											15 40		
Bournemouth	a		14 04					14 46						15 04					15 46		
	d		14 06		14 40			14 50						15 06			15 40		15 50		
Pokesdown	d		14 10											15 10							
Christchurch	d		14 14											15 14							
Hinton Admiral	d		14 19											15 19							
New Milton	d		14 23					15 01						15 23					16 01		
Sway	d		14 28											15 28							
Yarmouth (I.O.W.) ⛴	d					*14b00*												*14b45*		*15b30*	
Lymington Pier ⛴	d					14 44					15 14							15 44		16 14	
Lymington Town	d					14 46					15 16							15 46		16 16	
Brockenhurst 3	a		14 33		14 53	14 54		15 08			15 24			15 33			15 53	15 54	16 08	16 24	
	d		14 34		14 57			15 09						15 34			15 57		16 09		
Beaulieu Road	d		14 39											15 39							
Ashurst New Forest	d		14 43											15 43							
Totton	d		14 48											15 48							
Salisbury	d						14 48					15 08				15 31					16 13
Dean	d											15 20									
Mottisfont & Dunbridge	d											15 26									
Romsey	d						15 10					15 32				15 51					16 32
Redbridge	d											15 39									16 39
Millbrook (Hants)	d											15 43									16 43
Southampton Central	a		14 53	←	15 10		15 20	15 23				15 45		15 53	←	16 05	16 10		16 23		16 45
	d		14 55	14 59	15 15			15 25				15 59 →		15 55	15 59		16 15		16 25		16 59 →
St Denys	d			15 04											16 04						
Swaythling	d			15 07											16 07						
Southampton Airport Parkwy ✈	d		15 03	15 10	15 22			15 33						16 03	16 10		16 22		16 33		
Portsmouth Harbour	d	14 17											15 17								
Portsmouth & Southsea	d	14 22											15 22								
Fratton	d	14 26											15 26								
Hilsea	d	14 30											15 30								
Cosham	d	14 35											15 35								
Portchester	d	14 40											15 40								
Fareham	d	14 46											15 46								
Botley	d	14 54											15 54								
Hedge End	d	14 58											15 58								
Eastleigh 3	a	15 04	15 07	15 13									16 04	16 07	16 13						
	d		15 11	15 15										16 11	16 15						
Chandlers Ford	d			15 20											16 20						
Romsey	a			15 28											16 28						
Shawford	d		15 17																		
Winchester	d		15 23		15 31			15 42						16 23			16 31		16 42		
Micheldever	d		15 32											16 32							
Basingstoke	a		15 42		15 46			15 58						16 42			16 46		16 58		
	d		15 44		15 47			16 00						16 44			16 47		17 00		
Reading 7	a				16 04			*16 30*									17 04		*17 30*		
Fleet	d																				
Farnborough (Main)	d																				
Woking	a		16 02					16 18						17 02					17 18		
Clapham Junction 10	a		16 27					16 39						17 27					17 39		
London Waterloo 15 ⊖	a		16 37					16 49						17 37					17 49		

For general notes see front of timetable
For details of catering facilities see Directory of Train Operators

A from Bournemouth
B From 13 September
C Until 6 September
b By ship

During July and August ferry connection times to and from Yarmouth IOW are subject to alteration, please contact www.wightlink.co.uk or 0871 376 1000 for further details.

Table 158

Sundays

Weymouth, Bournemouth, Lymington, Romsey, Southampton and Basingstoke → London

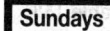

Network Diagram - see first page of Table 158

		SW	SW	SW	GW	XC	SW	SW	GW	SW	SW	SW	SW	SW	GW	XC	SW	SW	SW	SW	SW	SW
		1 ◇	1 ◇	1	◇	1 ◇	1	1 ◇		1	1	1 ◇	1 ◇	1	◇	1 ◇	1	1 ◇	1	1	1 ◇	1 ◇
								A	B									A				
Weymouth	d							15 48	16 13									16 48				
Upwey	d							15 52	16 18									16 52				
Dorchester West	a								16 26													
Dorchester South	d							16 00										17 00				
Moreton (Dorset)	d							16 07										17 07				
Wool	d							16 13										17 13				
Wareham	d							16 20										17 20				
Holton Heath	d																					
Hamworthy	d							16 27										17 27				
Poole 4	a							16 31										17 31				
	d		15 55					16 32					16 55					17 32				17 55
Parkstone (Dorset)	d							16 36										17 36				
Branksome	d							16 40										17 40				
Bournemouth	a		16 04					16 46					17 04					17 46				18 04
	d		16 06			16 40		16 50					17 06			17 40		17 50				18 06
Pokesdown	d		16 10										17 10									18 10
Christchurch	d		16 14										17 14									18 14
Hinton Admiral	d		16 19										17 19									18 19
New Milton	d		16 23					17 01					17 23					18 01				18 23
Sway	d		16 28										17 28									18 28
Yarmouth (I.O.W.) ⛴	d									*16b15*							*17b00*					
Lymington Pier ⛴	d						16 44			17 14							17 44		18 14			
Lymington Town	d						16 46			17 16							17 46		18 16			
Brockenhurst 3	a		16 33			16 53	16 54	17 08		17 24			17 33			17 53	17 54	18 08	18 24			18 33
	d		16 34			16 57		17 09					17 34			17 57		18 09				18 34
Beaulieu Road	d		16 39										17 39									18 39
Ashurst New Forest	d		16 43										17 43									18 43
Totton	d		16 48										17 48									18 48
Salisbury	d				16 31						17 08				17 31					18 13		
Dean	d										17 20											
Mottisfont & Dunbridge	d										17 26											
Romsey	d				16 49						17 32				17 49					18 32		
Redbridge	d										17 39									18 39		
Millbrook (Hants)	d										17 43									18 43		
Southampton Central	a		16 53	←	17 04	17 10		17 23			17 45		17 53	←	18 04	18 10		18 23		18 45		18 53
	d		16 55	16 59		17 15		17 25			17 59		17 55	17 59		18 15		18 25		18 59		18 55
St Denys	d			17 04							→			18 04						→		
Swaythling	d			17 07										18 07								
Southampton Airport Parkwy ✈	d		17 03	17 10		17 22		17 33					18 03	18 10		18 22		18 33				19 03
Portsmouth Harbour	d	16 17										17 17									18 17	
Portsmouth & Southsea	d	16 22										17 22									18 22	
Fratton	d	16 26										17 26									18 26	
Hilsea	d	16 30										17 30									18 30	
Cosham	d	16 35										17 35									18 35	
Portchester	d	16 40										17 40									18 40	
Fareham	d	16 46										17 46									18 46	
Botley	d	16 54										17 54									18 54	
Hedge End	d	16 58										17 58									18 58	
Eastleigh 3	a	17 04	17 07	17 13								18 04	18 07	18 13							19 04	19 07
	d	17 11		17 15								18 11		18 15							19 11	
Chandlers Ford	d			17 20										18 20								
Romsey	a			17 28										18 28								
Shawford	d	17 17																			19 17	
Winchester	d	17 23				17 31		17 42				18 23				18 31		18 42			19 23	
Micheldever	d	17 32										18 32									19 32	
Basingstoke	a	17 42				17 46		17 58				18 42				18 46		18 58			19 42	
	d	17 44				17 47		18 00				18 44				18 47		19 00			19 44	
Reading 7	a					18 04		*18 30*								19 04		*19 30*				
Fleet	d																					
Farnborough (Main)	d																					
Woking	a	18 02						18 18				19 02						19 18			20 02	
Clapham Junction 10	a	18 27						18 39				19 27						19 39			20 27	
London Waterloo 15 ⊖	a	18 37						18 49				19 37						19 49			20 37	

For general notes see front of timetable
For details of catering facilities see Directory of Train Operators

A from Bournemouth
B Until 6 September
b By ship

During July and August ferry connection times to and from Yarmouth IOW are subject to alteration, please contact www.wightliink.co.uk or 0871 376 1000 for further details.

Weymouth, Bournemouth, Lymington, Romsey, Southampton and Basingstoke → London

Network Diagram - see first page of Table 158

		SW	GW	XC	SW	SW	GW	GW	SW	SW	SW	SW	GW	SW	XC	SW	SW	GW	SW	SW	SW	SW
		1	◇	1 ◇	1	1 ◇	◇	◇	1	1	1 ◇	1 ◇	◇	1	1 ◇	1	1 ◇	◇	1	1	1 ◇	1 ◇
						A									B		A					
Weymouth	d					17 48	18 00										18 48					
Upwey	d					17 52	18 05										18 52					
Dorchester West	a						18 13															
Dorchester South	d					18 00											19 00					
Moreton (Dorset)	d					18 07											19 07					
Wool	d					18 13											19 13					
Wareham	d					18 20											19 20					
Holton Heath	d																					
Hamworthy	d					18 27											19 27					
Poole 4	a					18 31											19 31					
	d					18 32						18 55					19 32					19 55
Parkstone (Dorset)	d					18 36											19 36					
Branksome	d					18 40											19 40					
Bournemouth	a					18 46						19 04					19 46					20 04
	d			18 40		18 50						19 06			19 40		19 50					20 06
Pokesdown	d											19 10										20 10
Christchurch	d											19 14										20 14
Hinton Admiral	d											19 19										20 19
New Milton	d					19 01						19 23					20 01					20 23
Sway	d											19 28										20 28
Yarmouth (I.O.W.) ⛴	d				17b45				18b30										19b15			
Lymington Pier ⛴	d				18 44				19 14							19 44			20 14			
Lymington Town	d				18 46				19 16							19 46			20 16			
Brockenhurst 3	a			18 53	18 54	19 08			19 24			19 33			19 53	19 54	20 08		20 24			20 33
	d			18 57		19 09						19 34			19 57		20 09					20 34
Beaulieu Road	d											19 39										20 39
Ashurst New Forest	d											19 43										20 43
Totton	d											19 48										20 48
Salisbury	d		18 31					18 57		19 08			19 29					20 00		20 13		
Dean	d									19 20												
Mottisfont & Dunbridge	d									19 26												
Romsey	d		18 49					19 15		19 32			19 47					20 19		20 32		
Redbridge	d									19 39										20 39		
Millbrook (Hants)	d									19 43										20 43		
Southampton Central	a	←	19 04	19 10		19 23		19 26		19 45		19 53	19 57	←	20 10		20 23	20 29		20 45		20 53
	d	18 59		19 15		19 25				19 59 →		19 55		19 59	20 15		20 25			20 59 →		20 55
St Denys	d	19 04												20 04								
Swaythling	d	19 07												20 07								
Southampton Airport Parkwy ✈	d	19 10		19 22		19 33						20 03		20 10	20 22		20 33					21 03
Portsmouth Harbour	d										19 17										20 17	
Portsmouth & Southsea	d										19 22										20 22	
Fratton	d										19 26										20 26	
Hilsea	d										19 30										20 30	
Cosham	d										19 35										20 35	
Portchester	d										19 40										20 40	
Fareham	d										19 46										20 46	
Botley	d										19 54										20 54	
Hedge End	d										19 58										20 58	
Eastleigh 3	a	19 13									20 04	20 07		20 13							21 04	21 07
	d	19 15									20 11			20 15							21 11	
Chandlers Ford	d	19 20												20 20								
Romsey	a	19 28												20 28								
Shawford	d																				21 17	
Winchester	d			19 31		19 42					20 23				20 31		20 42				21 23	
Micheldever	d										20 32										21 32	
Basingstoke	a			19 46		19 58					20 42				20 46		20 58				21 42	
	d			19 47		20 00					20 44				20 47		21 00				21 44	
Reading 7	a			20 04		*20 30*									21 04		*21 30*				22 33	
Fleet	d																					
Farnborough (Main)	d																					
Woking	a					20 18					21 02						21 18				22 02	
Clapham Junction 10	a					20 39					21 27						21 39				22 27	
London Waterloo 15 ⊖	a					20 49					21 37						21 49				22 37	

For general notes see front of timetable
For details of catering facilities see Directory of Train Operators

A from Bournemouth
B To Birmingham New Street (Table 116)
b By ship

During July and August ferry connection times to and from Yarmouth IOW are subject to alteration, please contact www.wightliink.co.uk or 0871 376 1000 for further details.

Table 158

Sundays

Weymouth, Bournemouth, Lymington, Romsey, Southampton and Basingstoke → London

Network Diagram - see first page of Table 158

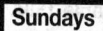

Station		SW 1	SW 1	GW ◇ 🚌	SW 1	SW 1	SW 1	SW 1 ◇	GW ◇	GW ◇ 🚌	SW 1	SW 1	SW 1	SW 1	SW 1	SW 1 ◇	GW ◇ 🚌	SW 1	SW 1	SW 1	SW 1
Weymouth	d							19 58	20 09							20 58				21 58	22 58
Upwey	d							20 02	20 14							21 02				22 02	23 02
Dorchester West	a								20 22												
Dorchester South	d							20 10								21 10				22 10	23 10
Moreton (Dorset)	d							20 17								21 17				22 17	23 17
Wool	d							20 23								21 23				22 23	23 23
Wareham	d							20 30								21 30				22 30	23 30
Holton Heath	d																				
Hamworthy	d							20 37								21 37				22 37	23 37
Poole 4	a							20 41								21 41				22 41	23 41
	d							20 50								21 50				22 50	23 50
Parkstone (Dorset)	d							20 54								21 54				22 54	23 54
Branksome	d							20 57								21 57				22 57	23 57
Bournemouth	a							21 03								22 03				23 03	00 03
	d							21 06								22 06				23 06	
Pokesdown	d							21 10								22 10				23 10	
Christchurch	d							21 14								22 14				23 14	
Hinton Admiral	d							21 19								22 19				23 19	
New Milton	d							21 23								22 23				23 23	
Sway	d							21 28								22 28				23 28	
Yarmouth (I.O.W.) ⛴	d				20b15									21b15							
Lymington Pier ⛴	d	20 44			21 14						21 44			22 14							
Lymington Town	d	20 46			21 16						21 46			22 16							
Brockenhurst 3	a	20 54			21 24			21 33			21 54			22 24		22 33				23 33	
	d							21 34								22 34				23 34	
Beaulieu Road	d							21 39								22 39					
Ashurst New Forest	d							21 43								22 43				23 43	
Totton	d							21 48								22 48				23 48	
Salisbury	d			20 30		21 08				21 29							22 29				
Dean	d					21 20															
Mottisfont & Dunbridge	d					21 26															
Romsey	d			20 48		21 32				21 47					22 28		22 48				
Redbridge	d					21 39									22 35						
Millbrook (Hants)	d					21 43									22 39						
Southampton Central	a		←	20 59		21 45		21 53		21 58		←			22 41	22 53	22 59	←		23 53	
	d		20 59			21 59 →		21 55				21 59			23 05 →	22 55		23 05			
St Denys	d		21 04									22 04						23 10			
Swaythling	d		21 07									22 07						23 13			
Southampton Airport Parkwy ✈	d		21 10					22 03				22 10				23 03		23 16			
Portsmouth Harbour	d						21 17						22 17						23 17		
Portsmouth & Southsea	d						21 22						22 22						23 22		
Fratton	d						21 26						22 26						23 26		
Hilsea	d						21 30						22 30						23 30		
Cosham	d						21 35						22 35						23 35		
Portchester	d						21 40						22 40						23 40		
Fareham	d						21 46						22 46						23 46		
Botley	d						21 54						22 54						23 54		
Hedge End	d						21 58						22 58						23 58		
Eastleigh 3	a		21 13				22 04	22 07				22 13	23 04			23 09		23 19	00 04		
	d		21 15				22 11					22 15				23 11		23 21			
Chandlers Ford	d		21 20									22 20						23 26			
Romsey	a		21 28									22 31						23 33			
Shawford	d																				
Winchester	d						22 23									23 23					
Micheldever	d						22 32									23 32					
Basingstoke	a						22 42									23 42					
	d						22 44									23 44					
Reading 7	a						23 30									00 30					
Fleet	d																				
Farnborough (Main)	d																				
Woking	a						23 02									00 02					
Clapham Junction 10	a						23 27									00 23					
London Waterloo 15 ⊖	a						23 37									00 33					

For general notes see front of timetable
For details of catering facilities see Directory of Train Operators

b By ship

During July and August ferry connection times to and from Yarmouth IOW are subject to alteration, please contact www.wightliink.co.uk or 0871 376 1000 for further details.

Woking → Heathrow Railair

Express Coach Service

Mondays to Saturdays

	SW SX	SW SX	SW SX	SW SX	SW	SW		SW	SW SO	SW SX	SW	SW SO	SW SX		SW	SW SO	SW SX	SW	SW SO	SW SX		SW	SW SO	SW SX	SW
Woking § d		05 20		05 50		06 20			06 50	06 50		07 20	07 20			07 50	07 50		08 20	08 20			08 50	08 50	
Heathrow Terminal 5 Bus d		05 45		06 15		06 45			07 15	07 25		07 45	08 05			08 15	08 35		08 45	09 05			09 15	09 35	
Heathrow Central Bus Stn a		06 00		06 30		07 00			07 30	07 40		08 00	08 20			08 30	08 50		09 00	09 20			09 30	09 50	
d	05 45		06 15		06 45			07 15			07 45				08 30			09 00				09 30			10 00
Heathrow Terminal 5 Bus a	06 00		06 30		07 00			07 30			08 00				08 45			09 15				09 45			10 15
Woking a	06 30		07 00		07 30			08 05			08 40				09 25			09 55				10 25			10 50

	SW SO	SW SX	SW	SW		SW	SW	SW	SW	SW	SW		SW	SW	SW	SW	SW	SW		SW	SW	SW	SW	SW	SW
Woking § d	09 35	09 35		10 05			10 35		11 05		11 35			12 05		12 35		13 05			13 35		14 05		14 35
Heathrow Terminal 5 Bus d	10 00	10 10		10 30			11 00		11 30		12 00			12 30		13 00		13 30			14 00		14 30		15 00
Heathrow Central Bus Stn a	10 15	10 25		10 45			11 15		11 45		12 15			12 45		13 15		13 45			14 15		14 45		15 15
d			10 30			11 00		11 30		12 00			12 30		13 00		13 30			14 00		14 30		15 00	
Heathrow Terminal 5 Bus a			10 45			11 15		11 45		12 15			12 45		13 15		13 45			14 15		14 45		15 15	
Woking a			11 15			11 45		12 15		12 45			13 15		13 45		14 15			14 45		15 15		15 45	

	SW	SW		SW	SW	SW	SW SO	SW SX	SW		SW SO	SW SX	SW	SW SO	SW SX	SW		SW SO	SW SX	SW	SW SO	SW SX	SW		SW
Woking § d		15 05			15 35		16 05	16 05			16 35	16 35		17 05	17 05			17 35	17 35		18 05	18 05			18 35
Heathrow Terminal 5 Bus d		15 30			16 00		16 30	16 35			17 00	17 10		17 30	17 40			18 00	18 10		18 30	18 40			19 00
Heathrow Central Bus Stn a		15 45			16 15		16 45	16 50			17 15	17 25		17 45	17 55			18 15	18 25		18 45	18 55			19 15
d	15 30			16 00		16 30			17 00				17 30			18 00				18 30			19 00		
Heathrow Terminal 5 Bus a	15 45			16 15		16 45			17 15				17 45			18 15				18 45			19 15		
Woking a	16 15			16 45		17 25			18 05				18 35			19 05				19 35			19 55		

	SW	SW SO	SW SX	SW	SW SO	SW SX		SW	SW SO	SW SX	SW	SW SO	SW SX		SW SO	SW SX	SW SO	SW SX	SW SO	SW SX		SW SO	SW SX		
Woking § d		19 05	19 05		19 35	19 35			20 05	20 05		20 35	20 35		21 05	21 05			22 05	22 05					
Heathrow Terminal 5 Bus d		19 30	19 35		20 00	20 05			20 30	20 35		21 00	21 05		21 30	21 35			22 30	22 35					
Heathrow Central Bus Stn a		19 45	19 45		20 15	20 15			20 45	20 45		21 15	21 15		21 45	21 45			22 45	22 45					
d	19 30			20 00				20 30			21 15						22 15	22 15				23 15	23 15		
Heathrow Terminal 5 Bus a	19 45			20 15				20 45			21 30						22 30	22 30				23 30	23 30		
Woking a	20 15			20 45				21 15			22 00						22 55	23 00				23 55	23 59		

Sundays

	SW	SW	SW	SW	SW		SW	SW	SW	SW	SW		SW	SW	SW	SW	SW		SW	SW	SW	SW	SW		SW
Woking § d		06 20		06 50			07 20		07 50		08 20			08 50		09 35			10 05		10 35		11 05		
Heathrow Terminal 5 Bus d		06 45		07 15			07 45		08 15		08 45			09 15		10 00			10 30		11 00		11 30		
Heathrow Central Bus Stn a		07 00		07 30			08 00		08 30		09 00			09 30		10 15			10 45		11 15		11 45		
d	06 45		07 15		07 45			08 30		09 00			09 30		10 00		10 30			11 00		11 30			12 00
Heathrow Terminal 5 Bus a	07 00		07 30		08 00			08 45		09 15			09 45		10 15		10 45			11 15		11 45			12 15
Woking a	07 30		08 00		08 25			09 15		09 45			10 15		10 45		11 15			11 45		12 15			12 45

	SW	SW	SW	SW	SW		SW	SW	SW	SW	SW		SW	SW	SW	SW	SW		SW	SW	SW	SW	SW		SW
Woking § d	11 35		12 05		12 35			13 05		13 35			14 05		14 35		15 05			15 35		16 05			16 35
Heathrow Terminal 5 Bus d	12 00		12 30		13 00			13 30		14 00			14 30		15 00		15 30			16 00		16 30			17 00
Heathrow Central Bus Stn a	12 15		12 45		13 15			13 45		14 15			14 45		15 15		15 45			16 15		16 45			17 15
d		12 30		13 00			13 30		14 00		14 30			15 00		15 30			16 00		16 30		17 00		
Heathrow Terminal 5 Bus a		12 45		13 15			13 45		14 15		14 45			15 15		15 45			16 15		16 45		17 15		
Woking a		13 15		13 45			14 15		14 45		15 15			15 45		16 15			16 45		17 15		17 45		

	SW	SW	SW	SW	SW		SW	SW	SW	SW	SW		SW	SW	SW	SW	SW		SW	SW	SW	SW	SW		
Woking § d		17 05		17 35			18 05		18 35		19 05			19 35		20 05			20 35	21 05		22 05			
Heathrow Terminal 5 Bus d		17 30		18 00			18 30		19 00		19 30			20 00		20 30			21 00	21 30		22 30			
Heathrow Central Bus Stn a		17 45		18 15			18 45		19 15		19 45			20 15		20 45			21 15	21 45		22 45			
d	17 30		18 00		18 30			19 00		19 30			20 00		20 30		21 15				22 15		23 15		
Heathrow Terminal 5 Bus a	17 45		18 15		18 45			19 15		19 45			20 15		20 45		21 30				22 30		23 30		
Woking a	18 15		18 45		19 15			19 45		20 15			20 45		21 15		22 00				23 00		23 59		

For general notes see front of timetable
For details of catering facilities see
Directory of Train Operators

§ On arrival at Woking passengers should proceed to the exit on platform 5, the coach leaves from immediately outside the station.

Network Diagram for Table 160

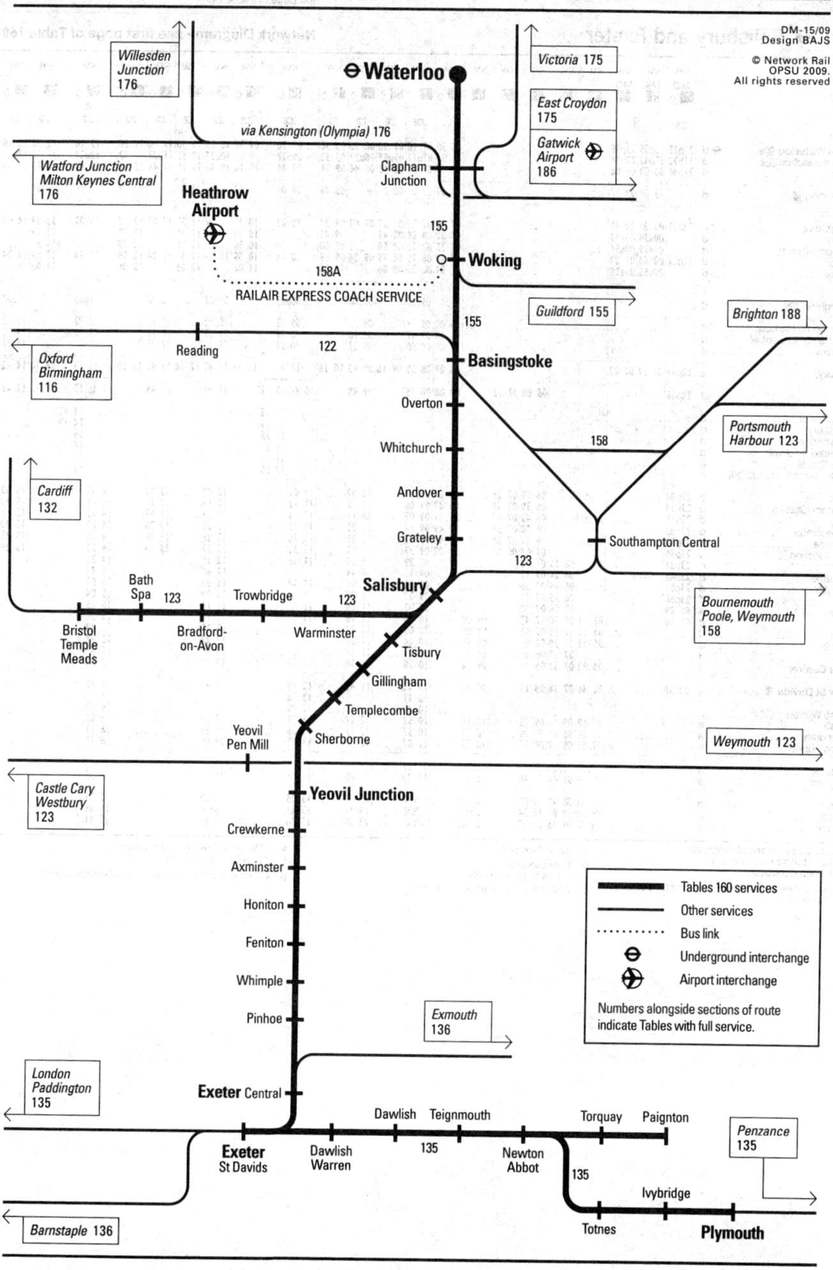

DM-15/09
Design BAJS
© Network Rail
OPSU 2009.
All rights reserved
Willesden Junction 176
Waterloo
Victoria 175
East Croydon 175
Gatwick Airport 186
via Kensington (Olympia) 176
Watford Junction Milton Keynes Central 176
Clapham Junction
Heathrow Airport
155
Woking
158A
RAILAIR EXPRESS COACH SERVICE
Guildford 155
155
Brighton 188
Reading
122
Oxford Birmingham 116
Basingstoke
Overton
Whitchurch
158
Portsmouth Harbour 123
Andover
Cardiff 132
Grateley
Southampton Central
123
Bath Spa
123
Trowbridge
123
Salisbury
Bristol Temple Meads
Bradford-on-Avon
Warminster
Bournemouth Poole, Weymouth 158
Tisbury
Gillingham
Templecombe
Yeovil Pen Mill
Sherborne
Weymouth 123
Castle Cary Westbury 123
Yeovil Junction
Crewkerne
Axminster
Honiton
Feniton
Whimple
Pinhoe
Tables 160 services
Other services
Bus link
Underground interchange
Airport interchange
Numbers alongside sections of route indicate Tables with full service.
Exmouth 136
London Paddington 135
Exeter Central
Dawlish
Teignmouth
Torquay
Paignton
Exeter St Davids
Dawlish Warren
135
Newton Abbot
Penzance 135
135
Ivybridge
Barnstaple 136
Totnes
Plymouth

For details of Bank Holiday service alterations, please see first page of Table 149

London → Salisbury and Exeter

Network Diagram - see first page of Table 160

Miles	Station		SW MO [1] ◇ [trolley]	SW MX [1]	SW MO [1]	SW [1]	SW [1]	SW [1]	SW [1]	SW [1]	SW [1] ◇	SW [1] ◇ [trolley]	SW [1] ◇ [trolley]	SW [1] ◇ [trolley]	SW [1] ◇ [trolley]	SW [1] ◇ A [trolley]		SW [1] ◇ [trolley]	SW [1] ◇ [trolley]	SW [1] ◇ [trolley]	SW [1] ◇ [trolley]	SW [1] ◇ [trolley]	SW [1] ◇ A [trolley]		SW [1] ◇ [trolley]	SW [1] ◇ [trolley]
0	**London Waterloo** [15] ⊖	d	21p15	23p35	23p35						06 30	07 10	07 50	08 20	08 50	09 20		09 50	10 20	10 50	11 20	11 50	12 20		12 50	13 20
4	Clapham Junction [10]	d	21b22	23b42	23b44						06 37	07u17	07u57	08u27	08 52	09u27		09 52	10u27	10 52	11u27	11 52	12u27		12 52	13u27
24¼	Woking	d	21p46	00 03	00 08						06 57	07 36	08 16	08 46	09 16	09 46		10 16	10 46	11 16	11 46	12 16	12 46		13 16	13 46
—	Reading [7]	d		23 34	23 37						06 39	07 07	08 07		08 45	09 07		10 07		11 07		12 07			13 07	
47¾	**Basingstoke**	d	22p07	00 24	00 40						07 22	07 57	08 37	09 07	09 37	10 07		10 37	11 07	11 37	12 07	12 37	13 07		13 37	14 07
55½	Overton	d		00s34	00s49						07 30	08 05	08 45		09 45			10 45		11 45		12 45			13 45	
59¼	Whitchurch (Hants)	d		00s39	00s54						07 35	08 10	08 50		09 50			10 50		11 50		12 50			13 50	
66½	Andover	d	22p24	00 46	01 02						07 44	08 19	08 59	09 24	09 59	10 24		10 59	11 24	11 59	12 24	12 59	13 24		13 59	14 24
72¾	Grateley	d		00s55	01s10						07 51	08 26	09 06		10 06			11 06		12 06		13 06			14 06	
—	Brighton [10]	d										05c30		07c06		08e03			09e03		10e03		11e03			12e03
—	Portsmouth Harbour	d									06 00	06 51		08 22		09 22			10 22		11 22		12 22			13 22
—	Southampton Central	d									06 46	07 47		09 10		10 10			11 10		12 10		13 10			14 10
—	Romsey	d									07 00	08 00		09 21		10 21			11 21		12 21		13 21			14 21
83¾	**Salisbury**	a	22p44	01 07	01 22						08 03	08 39	09 18	09 43	10 18	10 42		11 18	11 42	12 18	12 42	13 19	13 43		14 20	14 42
—		d	22p48					06 08	07 12		08 08	08 45		09 48		10 48	10 52		11 48		12 48		13 48	13 52		14 48
—	Warminster	d															11 12							14 12		
—	Westbury	d															11 19							14 19		
—	Trowbridge	d															11 25							14 25		
—	Bradford-on-Avon	d															11 31							14 31		
—	Bath Spa [7]	a															11 45							14 45		
—	Bristol Temple Meads [10]	a															12 05							15 05		
96¼	Tisbury	d	23p04					06 29	07 31		08 27			10 02		11 02			12 02		13 02		14 02			15 02
105¼	Gillingham (Dorset)	a	23p14					06 39	07 41		08 37	09 06		10 12		11 12			12 12		13 12		14 12			15 12
—		d	23p15					06 42	07 43		08 41	09 07		10 13		11 13			12 13		13 13		14 13			15 13
112¼	Templecombe	d	23p22					06 50	07 51		08 49	09 14		10 20		11 20			12 20		13 20		14 20			15 20
118¼	Sherborne	d	23p30					06 57	07 58		08 56	09 22		10 28		11 28			12 28		13 28		14 28			15 28
122¾	Yeovil Junction	a	23p35					07 03	08 04		09 02	09 27		10 33		11 33			12 33		13 34		14 33			15 34
—		d	23p37				06 15	07 08				09 29		10 35		11 35			12 35				14 35			
131¾	Crewkerne	d	23p46				06 24	07 17				09 38		10 44					12 44				14 44			
144¾	Axminster	a	23p58				06 44	07 36				09 51		11 04		11 54			13 03				15 03			
—		d	23p58				06 55	07 37				09 52		11 04		11 55			13 04				15 04			
155	Honiton	a	00 09				07 06	07 48				10 03		11 16		12 06			13 15				15 15			
—		d	00 10			06 13	07 10	07 49		09 00		10 04		11 16		12 07			13 16				15 16			
159½	Feniton	d				06 18	07 15	07 55		09 05		10 09		11 22					13 22				15 22			
163¼	Whimple	d				06 23	07 20	08 01		09 10		10 14		11 27					13 27				15 27			
169	Pinhoe	d					07 27	08 07		09 17		10 21		11 33					13 33				15 33			
171¾	**Exeter Central**	a				06 32	07 31	08 12		09 24		10 28		11 38		12 24			13 38				15 38			
172½	**Exeter St Davids** [3]	a	00 30			06 36	07 36	08 15		09 28		10 32		11 42		12 29			13 41				15 42			
—		d										10 37				12 38							15 52			
—	Dawlish Warren	a										10 48				12 49							16 02			
—	Dawlish	a				07 19	08 10	09 25		10 16		10 52		12 27		13 01			14 28				16 06			
—	Teignmouth	a				07 24	08 15	09 30		10 21		10 57		12 32		13 06			14 33				16 11			
—	Newton Abbot	a				07 32	08 22	09 37		10 03		11 04		12 30		13 13			14 08				16 18			
—	Torquay	a										11 22														
—	Paignton	a				08 14	08 44	09 48		10 59		11 29		13 00		13 48			15 00				16 53			
—	Totnes	a				07 45	08 45	10 08		10 17		11f22		13 16		13 25			14 22				16 31			
—	Ivybridge	a				08 02	09 02	10 24		12g08		12f08		13 41		13 41			15g18				16 46			
—	Plymouth	a				08 16	09 16	10 39		10 48		11f56		13 09		13 56			14 56				17 01			

For general notes see front of timetable
For details of catering facilities see Directory of Train Operators

For full service between Salisbury and Bristol Temple Meads see Table 123

A [trolley] to Plymouth
b Previous night. Stops to pick up only
c Change at Fareham and Salisbury
e Change at Fratton and Salisbury
f Change at Newton Abbot
g Change at Exeter St Davids and Newton Abbot

For details of Bank Holiday service alterations, please see first page of Table 149

London → Salisbury and Exeter

Network Diagram - see first page of Table 160

		SW	SW	SW	SW	SW	SW	SW	SW	SW	SW	SW	SW	SW	SW	SW		SW		SW	SW	SW	SW	SW	SW
																FX		FO			FO	FX			
		1 ◇	1	1 ◇	1 ◇	1	1 ◇	1 ◇	1	1 ◇	1 ◇	1 ◇	1 ◇	1 ◇	1 ◇	1 ◇		1 ◇		1 ◇	1 ◇	1 ◇	1 ◇	1	1
London Waterloo 15 ⊖	d	13 50		14 20	14 50		15 20	15 50		16 20	16 50	17 20	17 50	18 20	18 50	19 20		19 20		19 50	20 20	20 20	21 20	22 20	23 35
Clapham Junction 10	d	13 52		14u27	14 52		15u27	15u57		16u27	16u57	17 02		18u27	18 46	19u27		19u27		19 52	20u27	20u27	21u27	22u27	23u42
Woking	d	14 16		14 46	15 16		15 46	16 16		16 46	17u16	17u46	18 13	18 46	19 18	19 46		19 46		20 16	20 46	20 46	21 49	22 49	00 03
Reading 7	d	14 07			15 07			16 07			17 07		18 07		19 07					20 07	20 37	20 37	21 39	22 10	23 34
Basingstoke	d	14 37		15 07	15 37		16 07	16 37		17 07	17 37	18 07	18 38	19 07	19 39	20 07		20 07		20 37	21 07	21 07	22 10	23 10	00 24
Overton	d	14 45			15 45			16 45		17 15	17 45	18 15	18 47	19 15	19 47	20 15		20 15		20 45	21 15	21 15	22 18	23 18	00s34
Whitchurch (Hants)	d	14 50			15 50			16 50		17 20	17 50	18 20	18 52	19 20	19 52	20 20		20 20		20 50	21 20	21 20	22 23	23 23	00s39
Andover	d	14 59		15 24	15 59		16 24	16 59		17 29	17 59	18 29	19 00	19 29	20 01	20 29		20 29		20 59	21 29	21 29	22 32	23 32	00 46
Grateley	d	15 06			16 06			17 06		17 36	18 06	18 36	19 08	19 36	20 08	20 36		20 36		21 06	21 36	21 36	22 39	23 39	00s55
Brighton 10	d			13b03			14b03			15b03		16b03	17 00	17b03		18b00		18b00			19b00	19b00	20c30		
Portsmouth Harbour	d			14 22			15 22			16 22		17 22		18 22		19 22		19 22			20 22	20 22	21 22		
Southampton Central	d			15 10			16 10			17 10		18 10	18 42	19 10		20 10		20 10			21 20	21 20	22 22		
Romsey	d			15 21			16 21			17 21		18 21	18 54	19 21		20 21		20 21			21 31	21 31	22 33		
Salisbury	a	15 18		15 42	16 18		16 42	17 18		17 48	18 18	18 48	19 20	19 48	20 22	20 49		20 49		21 18	21 48	21 48	22 55	23 53	01 07
	d	15 21		15 48			16 48	17 23		17 53	18 23	18 53	19 23	19 53		20 53	20 57	20 53	20 57		22 04	22 04	23 04		
Warminster	d																21 17		21 17						
Westbury	d																21 24		21 24						
Trowbridge	d																21 30		21 30						
Bradford-on-Avon	d																21 36		21 36						
Bath Spa 7	a																21 51		21 51						
Bristol Temple Meads 10	a																22 06		22 06						
Tisbury	d			16 02			17 02	17 37		18 07	18 37	19 07	19 37	20 07		21 07		21 07			22 18	22 18	23s19		
Gillingham (Dorset)	a	15 44		16 12			17 12	17 47		18 17	18 47	19 17	19 47	20 17		21 17		21 17			22 28	22 28	23s30		
	d			16 13			17 13			18 18	18 48	19 18	19 48	20 18		21 18		21 18			22 29	22 29			
Templecombe	d			16 20			17 20			18 25	18 55	19 25	19 55	20 25		21 25		21 25			22 36	22 36	23s38		
Sherborne	d			16 28			17 28			18 33	19 03	19 33	20 03	20 33		21 33		21 33			22 44	22 44	23s45		
Yeovil Junction	a			16 33			17 34			18 38	19 11	19 38	20 12	20 38		21 38		21 38			22 49	22 49	23 52		
	d			16 37						18 40		19 40		20 40		21 40		21 40			22 51	22 51			
Crewkerne	d			16 46						18 49		19 49		20 49		21 49		21 49			23 00	23 00			
Axminster	a			17 05						19 04		20 02		21 10		22 02		22 02			23 13	23 22			
	d			17 06					18 23	19 05		20 03		21 11		22 03		22 03			23 14	23 23			
Honiton	a			17 17					18 34	19 16		20 14		21 22		22 14		22 14			23 27	23 34			
	d		16 01	17 18		17 32			18 38	19 30		20 15		21 23				22 15			23 28	23 35			
Feniton	d		16 06			17 37			18 44	19 36				21 29				22 20			23 33	23 41			
Whimple	d		16 11			17 42			18 49	19 41				21 34				22 25			23 38	23 46			
Pinhoe	d		16 18			17 49			18 55	19 47				21 40				22 32			23 45	23 52			
Exeter Central	a		16 23	17 33		17 56			19 02	19 52		20 31		21 48				22 36			23 49	23 57			
Exeter St Davids 6	a		16 27	17 38		18 00			19 06	19 57		20 36		21 54				22 41			23 54	00 01			
	d			17 49																					
Dawlish Warren	a			18 04																					
Dawlish	a		17 16	18 08		18 25			19 48	20 41		22 03		23 03											
Teignmouth	a		17 21	18 13		18 30			19 53	20 47		22 08		23 08											
Newton Abbot	a		17 03	18 20		18 38			19 43	20 35		21 03		22 52				23 21							
Torquay	a			18 32																					
Paignton	a		17 51	18 40		19 01			20 21	21 20		22 35		23 35											
Totnes	a		17 16	18e23		18 56			19 57	20 49		21 16		23 04				23 34							
Ivybridge	a			19f12		19 12								23 36											
Plymouth	a		17 48	18e56		19 27			20 25	21 17		21 48		23 38				00 06							

For general notes see front of timetable
For details of catering facilities see Directory of Train Operators

For full service between Salisbury and Bristol Temple Meads see Table 123

b Change at Fratton and Salisbury
c Change at Southampton Central and Salisbury
e Change at Exeter St Davids
f Change at Newton Abbot

London → Salisbury and Exeter

Network Diagram - see first page of Table 160

		SW	SW	SW	SW	SW	SW		SW	SW	SW	SW	SW	SW			SW	SW	SW	SW	SW	SW			SW	SW
		■1	■1	■1	■1	■1	■1		■1 ◇	■1 ◇	■1 ◇	■1 ◇	■1 ◇	■1 ◇			■1 ◇	■1 ◇	■1 ◇	■1 ◇	■1 ◇	■1 ◇			■1 ◇	■1 ◇
														A								A				
										🍴	🍴	🍴	🍴	🍴			🍴	🍴	🍴	🍴	🍴	🍴			🍴	🍴
London Waterloo 15 ⊖	d	23p35							06 30	07 10	07 50	08 20	08 50	09 20			09 50	10 20	10 50	11 20	11 50	12 20			12 50	13 20
Clapham Junction 10	d	23b42							06 37	07u17	07u57	08u27	08 52	09u27			09 52	10u27	10 52	11u27	11 52	12u27			12 52	13u27
Woking	d	00 03							06 57	07 36	08 16	08 46	09 16	09 46			10 16	10 46	11 16	11 46	12 16	12 46			13 16	13 46
Reading 7	d	23c34							06 39	07 07	08 07		09 07				10 07		11 07		11e45	12e10			12f45	13 07
Basingstoke	d	00 24							07 22	07 59	08 37	09 07	09 37	10 07			10 37	11 07	11 37	12 07	12 37	13 07			13 37	14 07
Overton	d	00s34							07 30	08 07	08 45		09 45				10 45		11 45		12 45				13 45	
Whitchurch (Hants)	d	00s39							07 35	08 12	08 50		09 50				10 50		11 50		12 50				13 50	
Andover	d	00 46							07 44	08 21	08 59	09 24	09 59	10 24			10 59	11 24	11 59	12 24	12 59	13 24			13 59	14 24
Grateley	d	00s55							07 51	08 28	09 06		10 06				11 06		12 06		13 06				14 06	
Brighton 10	d									05g27		07h03		08h03				09h03		10h03		11h03				12h03
Portsmouth Harbour	d								06 00	07 05		08 22		09 22				10 22		11 22		12 22				13 22
Southampton Central	d								06 52	07 54		09 10		10 10				11 10		12 10		13 10				14 10
Romsey	d								07 11	08 12		09 21		10 21				11 21		12 21		13 21				14 21
Salisbury	a	01 07							08 03	08 42	09 18	09 42	10 18	10 42			11 18	11 42	12 18	12 42	13 18	13 42			14 18	14 42
	d				06 15	07 12			08 08	08 45		09 48		10 48	10 52			11 48		12 48		13 48	13 52			14 48
Warminster	d														11 12								14 12			
Westbury	d														11 19								14 19			
Trowbridge	d														11 25								14 25			
Bradford-on-Avon	d														11 31								14 31			
Bath Spa 7	a														11 45								14 45			
Bristol Temple Meads 10	a														12 00								15 05			
Tisbury	d				06 29	07 31			08 27			10 02		11 02				12 02				14 02				15 02
Gillingham (Dorset)	a				06 39	07 41			08 37	09 06		10 12		11 12				12 12		13 09		14 12				15 12
	d				06 42	07 43			08 41	09 07		10 13		11 13				12 13		13 10		14 13				15 13
Templecombe	d				06 50	07 51			08 49	09 14		10 20		11 20				12 20				14 20				15 20
Sherborne	d				06 57	07 58			08 56	09 22		10 28		11 28				12 28				14 28				15 28
Yeovil Junction	a				07 03	08 04			09 02	09 27		10 33		11 33				12 33		13 27		14 33				15 34
	d			06 15	07 08					09 29		10 35		11 35				12 35		13 28		14 35				
Crewkerne	d			06 24	07 17					09 38		10 44						12 44				14 44				
Axminster	a			06 44	07 36					09 51		11 04		11 54				13 03				15 03				
	d			06 55	07 37					09 52		11 05		11 55				13 04				15 04				
Honiton	a			07 06	07 48					10 03		11 16		12 06				13 15		13 56		15 15				
	d		06 13	07 10	07 49		09 00			10 04		11 30		12 07				13 16		14 00		15 16				
Feniton	d		06 18	07 15	07 55		09 05			10 09		11 35						13 22				15 22				
Whimple	d		06 23	07 20	08 01		09 10			10 14		11 40						13 27				15 27				
Pinhoe	d			07 27	08j16		09 17			10 21		11 47						13 33				15 33				
Exeter Central	a		06 32	07 31	08 24		09 24			10 25		11 55		12 25				13 38		14 22		15 38				
Exeter St Davids 6	a		06 35	07 36	08 31		09 28			10 29		12 01		12 30				13 42		14 26		15 42				
	d				08 37					10 36				12 39						14 32		15 49				
Dawlish Warren	a									10 47				12 50						14 43		15 59				
Dawlish	a		07 19	08 10	08 49		10 19			10 51		12 46		13 01				14 30		14 47		16 03				
Teignmouth	a		07 24	08 15	08 54		10 24			10 56		12 52		13 06				14 35		14 52		16 08				
Newton Abbot	a		07 31	08 03	09 01		10 04			11 03		12 35		13 13				14 33		14 59		16 15				
Torquay	a				09 15					11 14										15 11						
Paignton	a		07k58	08 42	09 23		10 51			11 22		13 27		13 49				15 06		15 19		16 51				
Totnes	a		07 45	08 16	10m02		10 16			11m22		13 19		13 26				15n17		15m17		16 28				
Ivybridge	a		08 01	08 55	10m18					12q08		13 43		13 43				16r43				16 43				
Plymouth	a		08 15	08 48	10m32		10 48			11m56		13 14		13 57				15t09		15m48		16 58				

For general notes see front of timetable
For details of catering facilities see Directory of Train Operators

For full service between Salisbury and Bristol Temple Meads see Table 123

A 🍴 to Plymouth
b Previous night.
Stops to pick up only
c Saturdays
e From 12 September dep. 1207
f From 12 September dep. 1307
g Change at Fareham and Salisbury
h Change at Fratton and Salisbury
j Arr. 0807
k Change at Exeter St Davids and Newton Abbot
m Change at Newton Abbot
n From 12 September arr. 1516
q From 12 September only. Change at Newton Abbot
r Until 5 September only. Change at Exeter St Davids and Dawlish
t Until 20 June arr. 1453

Table 160

Saturdays

London → Salisbury and Exeter

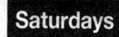

Network Diagram - see first page of Table 160

		SW	SW	SW	SW	SW	SW	SW	SW	SW	SW	SW	SW	SW	SW	SW	SW	SW	SW	SW	SW	SW
		1 ◇	1	1 ◇	1 ◇	1 ◇	1 ◇	1	1	1 ◇	1 ◇	1 ◇	1 ◇	1 ◇	1 ◇	1 ◇	1 ◇	1 ◇	1 ◇	1 ◇	1	1
				A												B	B					
		☕		☕	☕	☕	☕			☕	☕	☕	☕	☕	☕	☕	☕	☕	☕	☕	☕	
London Waterloo 15 ⊖	d	13 50		14 20	14 50	15 20	15 50			16 20	16 50	17 20	17 50	18 20	18 50	19 20		19 50	20 20	21 20	22 20	23 35
Clapham Junction 10	d	13 52		14u27	14 52	15u27	15 52			16u27	16 52	17u27	17 52	18u27	18 52	19u27		19 52	20u27	21u27	22u27	23u42
Woking	d	14 16		14 46	15 16	15 46	16 16			16 46	17 16	17 46	18 16	18 46	19 16	19 46		20 16	20 46	21 49	22 49	00 03
Reading 7	d	14 07			15 07		16 07				17 07		18 07		19 07			20 07		21 39	22 39	23 07
Basingstoke	d	14 37		15 07	15 37	16 07	16 37			17 07	17 37	18 07	18 37	19 07	19 37	20 07		20 37	21 07	22 12	23 12	00 24
Overton	d	14 45			15 45		16 45				17 45		18 45		19 45			20 45	21 15	22 20	23 20	00s34
Whitchurch (Hants)	d	14 50			15 50		16 50				17 50		18 50		19 50			20 50	21 20	22 25	23 25	00s39
Andover	d	14 59		15 24	15 59	16 24	16 59			17 24	17 59	18 24	18 59	19 24	19 59	20 24		20 59	21 29	22 34	23 34	00 46
Grateley	d	15 06			16 06		17 06				18 06		19 06		20 06			21 06	21 36	22 41	23 41	00s55
Brighton 10	d			13b03		14b03				15b03		16b03		17b03		18b03			19b03	19c29		
Portsmouth Harbour	d			14 22		15 22				16 22		17 22		18 22		19 22			20 22			
Southampton Central	d			15 10		16 10				17 10		18 10		19 10		20 10			21 12	21 27		
Romsey	d			15 21		16 21				17 21		18 21		19 21		20 21			21 23	21 38		
Salisbury	a	15 18		15 42	16 18	16 42	17 18			17 42	18 18	18 43	19 18	19 45	20 18	20 42		21 18	21 48	22 53	23 53	01 07
	d			15 48		16 48				17 48		18 53		19 53		20 53	20 57		22 00	23 04		
Warminster	d																21 17					
Westbury	d																21 24					
Trowbridge	d																21 30					
Bradford-on-Avon	d																21 36					
Bath Spa 7	a																21 50					
Bristol Temple Meads 10	a																22 06					
Tisbury	d			16 02		17 02				18 02		19 07		20 07		21 07			22 15	23s18		
Gillingham (Dorset)	a			16 12		17 12				18 12		19 17		20 17		21 17			22 25	23s29		
	d			16 13		17 13				18 13		19 18		20 18		21 18			22 26			
Templecombe	d			16 20		17 20				18 20		19 25		20 25		21 25			22 33	23s37		
Sherborne	d			16 28		17 28				18 28		19 33		20 33		21 33			22 41	23s44		
Yeovil Junction	a			16 33		17 34				18 33		19 39		20 38		21 38			22 47	23 51		
	d			16 35						18 35				20 40		21 40						
Crewkerne	d			16 44						18 44				20 49		21 49						
Axminster	a			17 03						19 03				21 10		22 02						
	d			17 04					18 23	19 04				21 11		22 03						
Honiton	a			17 15					18 34	19 15				21 22		22 14						
	d		16 01	17 16				17 30	18 38	19 30				21 23		22 15						
Feniton	d		16 06					17 35	18 43	19 35				21 29		22 20						
Whimple	d		16 11					17 40	18 48	19 40				21 34		22 25						
Pinhoe	d		16 18					17 47	18 55	19 47				21 40		22 32						
Exeter Central	a		16 24	17 32				17 56	19 02	19 51				21 48		22 38						
Exeter St Davids 6	a		16 28	17 36				18 00	19 06	19 57				21 53		22 42						
	d			17 53				18 05														
Dawlish Warren	a			18 04				18 16														
Dawlish	a		17 16	18 08				18 20	19 37	20 35				22 50								
Teignmouth	a		17 21	18 13				18 25	19 42	20 40				22 56								
Newton Abbot	a		17 03	18 20				18 32	19 49	20 37				23e03								
Torquay	a							18 43														
Paignton	a		17 51					18 52	20 10	21 08												
Totnes	a		17 16	18 33				18f57	20 08	20 51				23g17								
Ivybridge	a		18 49	18 49				19f12														
Plymouth	a		17 48	19 03				19f28	20 36	21 19				23h47								

For general notes see front of timetable
For details of catering facilities see Directory of Train Operators

For full service between Salisbury and Bristol Temple Meads see Table 123

- **A** To Penzance (Table 135)
- **B** ☕ to Exeter St Davids
- **b** Change at Fratton and Salisbury
- **c** Change at Southampton Central and Salisbury
- **e** From 12 September arr. 2231
- **f** Change at Newton Abbot
- **g** From 12 September arr. 2243
- **h** From 12 September arr. 2317

Table 160

Sundays

London → Salisbury and Exeter

Network Diagram - see first page of Table 160

		SW 1	SW 1	SW 1 ◇	SW 1 ◇ ☕	SW 1 ◇ ☕		SW 1 ◇ ☕	SW 1 ◇ ☕	SW 1 ◇ ☕		SW 1 ◇ ☕		SW 1 ◇ ☕	SW 1 ◇ ☕	SW 1 ◇ ☕	SW 1 ◇ ☕	SW 1 ◇ ☕		SW 1 ◇ ☕	SW 1 ◇ ☕	SW 1 ◇ ☕	SW 1 ☕	SW 1		
London Waterloo 15 ⊖	d	23p35			08 15	09 15		10 15	11 15	12 15		13 15		14 15	15 15	16 15	17 15	18 15		19 15	20 15	21 15	22 15	23 35		
Clapham Junction 10	d	23b42			08u22	09u22		10u22	11u22	12u22		13u22		14u22	15u22	16u22	17u22	18u22		19u22	20u22	21u22	22u22	23u44		
Woking	d	00 03			08 47	09 47		10 46	11 46	12 46		13 46		14 46	15 46	16 46	17 46	18 46		19 46	20 46	21 46	22 46	00 08		
Reading 7	d	23c07		07 37	08 37	09 37		10 37	11 37	12 37		13 37		14 37	15 37	16 37	17 37	18 37		19 37	20 37	21 37	22 37	23 37		
Basingstoke	d	00 24		08 08	09 08	10 08		11 07	12 07	13 07		14 07		15 07	16 07	17 07	18 07	19 07		20 07	21 07	22 07	23 07	00 40		
Overton	d	00s34		08 16	09 16			11 15		13 15				15 15		17 15		19 15			21 15		23 15	00s49		
Whitchurch (Hants)	d	00s39		08 21	09 21			11 20		13 20				15 20		17 20		19 20			21 20		23 20	00s54		
Andover	d	00 46		08 30	09 30	10 25		11 29	12 24	13 29		14 24		15 29	16 24	17 29	18 24	19 29		20 24	21 29	22 24	23 29	01 02		
Grateley	d	00s55		08 37	09 37			11 36		13 36				15 36		17 36		19 36			21 36		23 36	01s10		
Brighton 10	d					07e18			09e12	11f08		11g12		12g12	13g12	14g12	15 45	16g12		17 45	18g12					
Portsmouth Harbour	d					09 08			11 08			13 08		14 08	15 08	16 08	17 08	18 08		19 08	20 08					
Southampton Central	d					09 54			11 54	12 54		13 54		14 54	15 54	16 54	17 54	18 54		19 54	20 54					
Romsey	d					10 05			12 06	13 06		14 06		15 06	16 06	17 06	18 06	19 06		20 06	21 06					
Salisbury	a	01 07		08 49	09 50	10 41		11 48	12 40	13 48		14 40		15 48	16 40	17 48	18 40	19 48		20 40	21 48	22 44	23 48	01 22		
	d		07 10	08 54	09 54	10 50		11 54	12 50	13 54	13 58	14 50		15 54	16 54	17 54	18 50	19 54	19 58	20 54	21 54	22 48				
Warminster	d										14 18								20 18							
Westbury	d										14 25								20 31							
Trowbridge	d										14 32								20 37							
Bradford-on-Avon	d										14 38								20 43							
Bath Spa 7	a										14 54								20 59							
Bristol Temple Meads 10	a										15 08								21 16							
Tisbury	d		07 24	09 08	10 08	11 04		12 08	13 04	14 08		15 04		16 08	17 08	18 08	19 04	20 08		21 08	22 08	23 04				
Gillingham (Dorset)	a		07 34	09 18	10 18	11 14		12 18	13 14	14 18		15 14		16 18	17 18	18 18	19 14	20 18		21 18	22 18	23 14				
	d		07 35	09 19	10 19	11 15		12 19	13 15	14 19		15 15		16 19	17 19	18 19	19 15	20 19		21 19	22 19	23 15				
Templecombe	d		07 42	09 26	10 26	11 22		12 26	13 22	14 26		15 22		16 26	17 26	18 26	19 22	20 26		21 26	22 26	23 22				
Sherborne	d		07 50	09 34	10 34	11 30		12 34	13 30	14 34		15 30		16 34	17 34	18 34	19 30	20 34		21 34	22 34	23 30				
Yeovil Junction	a		07 55	09 39	10 39	11 35		12 40	13 35	14 40		15 35		16 40	17 39	18 40	19 35	20 40		21 40	22 40	23 35				
	d		07 57	09 41	10 41	11 40			13 40			15 40			17 40		19 40			21 40		23 37				
Crewkerne	d		08 06	09 50		11 49			13 49			15 49			17 49		19 49			21 49		23 46				
Axminster	a		08 19	10 10	11 00	12 10			14 10			16 10			18 10		20 12			22 10		23 58				
	d		08 20	10 11	11 01	12 11			14 11			16 11			18 11		20 13			22 11		23 58				
Honiton	a		08 31	10 22	11 12	12 22			14 22			16 22			18 22		20 24			22 22		00 09				
	d		08 35	10 23	11 13	12 23			14 23			16 23			18 23		20 25			22 23		00 10				
Feniton	d		08 41	10 28		12 28			14 28			16 28			18 28		20 31			22 28						
Whimple	d		08 46	10 33		12 33			14 33			16 33			18 33		20 36			22 33						
Pinhoe	d			10 40		12 40																				
Exeter Central	a		08 54	10 44	11 29	12 44			14 42			16 45			18 42		20 44			22 45						
Exeter St Davids 6	a		08 59	10 49	11 33	12 49			14 46			16 49			18 46		20 49			22 49		00 30				
	d			10 54	11 40	13 01			14 52			16 57					20 56									
Dawlish Warren	a			11 05																						
Dawlish	a		09 30	11 09	13 06	13 13			15h43			17 09			20 24		21 08									
Teignmouth	a		09 35	11 14	13 11	13 18			15j48			17 14			20 29		21 13									
Newton Abbot	a		09 42	11 21	12 00	13 25			15 13			17 22			19 39		21 20									
Torquay	a			11 32		13 37			15 26			17 35					21 31									
Paignton	a		11k01	11 40	12 48	13 47			15 34			17 43			20 56		21 39									
Totnes	a		09 55	11m41	12 14	14n22			16m00			17m56			19 53		22m02									
Ivybridge	a		10 12		12 29				17m03																	
Plymouth	a		10 26	12m09	12 44	14m14			16q00			18m24			20 21		22m31									

For general notes see front of timetable
For details of catering facilities see Directory of Train Operators

For full service between Salisbury and Bristol Temple Meads see Table 123

b Previous night. Stops to pick up only
c Sundays
e Change at Fratton and Salisbury
f From 13 September dep. 1110
g Change at Fratton and Salisbury. From 13 September dep. 5 minutes later
h 19 July to 6 September arr. 1526
j 19 July to 6 September arr. 1531
k From 19 July arr. 1005, change at Exeter St Davids and Newton Abbot
m Change at Newton Abbot
n Change at Newton Abbot. 19 July to 6 September arr. 1347
q Change at Newton Abbot. 19 July to 6 September arr. 1629

For details of Bank Holiday service alterations, please see first page of Table 149

Exeter and Salisbury → London

Network Diagram - see first page of Table 160

Miles			SW	SW	SW	SW	SW	SW	SW	SW	SW	SW	SW	SW	SW	SW	SW	SW	SW		SW	SW	SW	SW	SW	SW
			MO 1	1◇	1◇	1◇	1◇	1◇	1◇	1◇	1◇	1◇	1◇	1◇	1◇	1	1◇	1◇	1◇		1◇	1◇	1◇	1◇	1◇	1◇
				A	B	A	B	A	B																	
				☕	☕	☕	☕	☕	☕	☕	☕	☕	☕	☕	☕		☕		☕		☕	☕	☕	☕	☕	☕
—	Plymouth	d												05 20		06 55								08 55		
—	Ivybridge	d																						08 22		
—	Totnes	d												05 45		06 50								09 22		
—	Paignton	d	22p10													07b07								09b13		
—	Torquay	d	22p16													07b14								09b18		
—	Newton Abbot	d	22p30											06 02		07 30			07 34					09 35		
—	Teignmouth	d	22p37													07 24								08 57		
—	Dawlish	d	22p42													07 29								09 02		
—	Dawlish Warren	d	22p46																							
0	**Exeter St Davids 3**	a	22p57																							
—		d	23p10								05 10			06 42		08 00			08 25					10 10		
¾	**Exeter Central**	d	23p14								05 14			06 45		08 05			08 30					10 14		
3½	Pinhoe	d									05 19			06 50		08 11								10 21		
9¼	Whimple	d									05 26			06 57		08 18								10 28		
13	Feniton	d									05 31			07 02		08 23								10 33		
17½	Honiton	a	23c29								05 37			07 09		08 29			08 45					10 39		
—		d									05 38	06 20		07 12					08 46					10 40		
27¾	Axminster	a	23c40								05 48	06 30		07 22					08 56					10 50		
—		d									05 49	06 31		07 23					08 57					10 51		
40¾	Crewkerne	d	00s04								06 02	06 44		07 36					09 10					11 04		
49¾	Yeovil Junction	a	00s13								06 11	06 52		07 45					09 19					11 13		
—		d						05 12	05 15	05 50	06 20	06 54	07 20	07 50	08 20				09 20			10 20		11 20		12 20
54¼	Sherborne	d						05 18	05 21	05 56	06 26	07 00	07 26	07 56	08 26				09 26			10 26		11 26		12 26
60¼	Templecombe	d						05 26	05 29	06 04	06 34	07 08	07 34	08 04	08 34				09 34			10 34		11 34		12 34
67¼	Gillingham (Dorset)	a						05 33	05 36	06 11	06 41	07 15	07 43	08 11	08 41				09 41			10 41		11 41		12 41
—		d						05 34	05 37	06 12	06 42	07 16	07 44	08 12	08 42				09 42			10 42		11 42		12 42
76¼	Tisbury	d						05 44	05 47	06 24	06 52	07 26	07 54	08 22	08 52				09 52			10 52		11 52		12 52
—	Bristol Temple Meads 10	d																08 50								
—	Bath Spa 7	d																09 07								
—	Bradford-on-Avon	d																09 20								
—	Trowbridge	d																09 27								
—	Westbury	d																09 39								
—	Warminster	d																09 46								
88¾	**Salisbury**	a	00 50					05 59	06 02	06 39	07 07	07 40	08 09	08 37	09 15			10 09	10 15			11 15		12 15		13 15
—		d		05 12	05 15	05 40	05 43	06 03	06 06	06 45	07 15	07 45	08 15	08 45	09 20		09 45		10 20		10 45	11 20	11 45	12 20	12 45	13 20
—	Romsey	a						06 38	06 38	07 30	07 56		08 50		09 50				10 52			11 50		12 50		13 50
—	Southampton Central	a						06 49	06 49	07 41	08 09		09 04		10 04				11 04			12 04		13 04		14 04
—	Portsmouth Harbour	a						07 45	07 45	08 30			09 54		10 54				11 54			12 54		13 54		14 54
—	Brighton 10	a						09e18	09e18	09f48	10g18		11e18		12e18				13e18			14e18		15e18		16 14
99¾	Grateley	d		05 24	05 27	05 52	05 55	06 16	06 19	06 57	07 27	07 57	08 27	08 57			09 57				10 57		11 57		12 57	
106	Andover	d		05 32	05 35	06 00	06 03	06 23	06 26	07 05	07 35	08 05	08 35	09 04	09 37		10 04		10 37		11 04	11 37	12 04	12 37	13 04	13 37
113¼	Whitchurch (Hants)	d		05 40	05 43	06 08	06 11	06 32	06 35	07 13	07 43	08 13	08 43	09 12			10 12				11 12		12 12		13 12	
117	Overton	d		05 46	05 49	06 14	06 17	06 38	06 41	07 19	07 49	08 19	08 49	09 18			10 18				11 18		12 18		13 18	
124¾	**Basingstoke**	a		05 58	05 58	06 26	06 26	06 49	06 49	07 28	07 58	08 28	08 58	09 27	09 54		10 27		10 55		11 27	11 54	12 27	12 54	13 27	13 54
—	Reading 7	a		06 32	06 32	07 00	07 00	07 31	07 31	08 00	08 30	09 00	09 30	10 00	10 30		11 00		11 30			12 30	13 00	13 30	14 00	14 30
148¼	Woking	a		06 18	06 18	06 46	06 46	07 28	07 28	08 05	08 18	08 48	09 18	09 49	10 15		10 49		11 15		11 49	12 15	12 49	13 15	13 49	14 15
168¼	Clapham Junction 10	a		06 38	06 38	07 14	07 14	07 28	07 28	09 14	09 03	09 14	09 38	10 10	10 36		11h12		11 36			12 36	13h12	13 36	14h12	14 36
172½	**London Waterloo 15** ⊖	a		06 49	06 49	07 14	07 14	07 39	07 39	08 14	08 46	09 17	09 51	10 19	10 49		11 19		11 49		12 19	12 49	13 19	13 49	14 19	14 49

For general notes see front of timetable
For details of catering facilities see Directory of Train Operators

For full service between Bristol Temple Meads and Salisbury see Table 123

- A From 28 September
- B Until 25 September
- b Change at Newton Abbot and Exeter St Davids
- c Previous night. Stops to set down only
- e Change at Salisbury and Fareham
- f Change at Salisbury and Fratton
- g Change at Salisbury and Southampton Central
- h Change at Basingstoke

For details of Bank Holiday service alterations, please see first page of Table 149

Exeter and Salisbury → London

Network Diagram - see first page of Table 160

		SW	SW	SW	SW	SW	SW	SW	SW	SW	SW	SW	SW	SW	SW	SW	SW	SW	SW	SW	SW	SW	SW FX	SW FO
		1 ◇ ☕	1 ◇ ☕	1 ◇	1 ◇ ☕	1 ◇ ☕	1 ◇ ☕	1 ◇ ☕	1	1 ◇ ☕	1 ◇	1 ◇ ☕	1 ◇ ☕	1 ◇ ☕	1	1	1 ◇ ☕	1 ◇ ☕	1 ◇ ☕	1 ◇	1 ◇	1	1	1
Plymouth	d		10 44			12b21		12 55	14 25					14 47	15 21	16 25			16 57	17 52	18c43	19 38		21 23
Ivybridge	d		10 00			12c15		12 15	14e01					15 02	15 02				17 12	18 07	18c59	18 59		21 38
Totnes	d		10 50			12b48		13 22	14 50					15 16	15 48	16 50			17 27	18 21	19c13	20 05		21 52
Paignton	d		10 23			12 35		13e13	14 22					15e19		16 12			16 55	17 52	19 12	20 10	20 28	21e31
Torquay	d		10 28			12 41		13e18	14 27					15e24		16 17			17 00	17 57	19 18	20 16	20 33	21e37
Newton Abbot	d		11 03			12 53		13 35	15 03					15 29	16 01	17 03			17 40	18 33	19 31	20 27	20 46	22 04
Teignmouth	d		10 48			13 00			14 47					15 36	15 51	16 37			17 20	18 40	19 38	19 57	20 53	22 11
Dawlish	d		10 53			13 05			14 52					15 41	15 56	16 42			17 25	18 45	19 43	20 02	20 58	22 16
Dawlish Warren	d					13 16								15 45						18 49	19 47			
Exeter St Davids 6	a					13 26								15 56						18 59	19 59			
	d		12 10			13 35		14 10	15 30					16 10	16 40	17 40			18 10	19 10	20 15	21 00	22 30	22 57
Exeter Central	d		12 14			13 39		14 14	15 34					16 14	16 44	17 44			18 14	19 14	20 19	21 04	22 34	23 01
Pinhoe	d		12 19					14 19	15 39					16 19	16 49	17 49			18 19		20f27		22 39	23 06
Whimple	d		12 26					14 26	15 46					16 26	16 56	17 56			18 26		20 34		22 46	23 13
Feniton	d		12 31					14 31	15 51					16 31	17 01	18 01			18 31		20 39		22 51	23 18
Honiton	a		12 37			13 54		14 37	15 57					16 37	17 07	18 07			18 38	19 30	20 45	21 20	22 57	23 25
	d		12 38			13 57		14 38						16 38		18 08			18 39	19 31	20 46	21 23	22 58	23 27
Axminster	a		12 48			14 07		14 48						16 48		18 18			18 49	19 41	20 56	21 33	23 08	23 37
	d		12 49			14 08		14 49						16 49					18 50	19 42	20 57	21 45	23 09	23 38
Crewkerne	d		13 03					15 03						17 05					19 10	20 08	21 10	22 08	23 22	23 51
Yeovil Junction	a		13 12			14 27		15 12						17 14					19 18	20 16	21 19	22 16	23 31	23 59
	d		13 20		13 50	14 28		15 20				16 20		17 24				18 20	19 20	20 20	21 20	22 24	23 34	00 01
Sherborne	d		13 26		13 56			15 26				16 26		17 31				18 26	19 26	20 26	21 26	22 30		
Templecombe	d		13 34					15 34				16 34		17 38				18 34	19 34	20 34	21 34	22 41		
Gillingham (Dorset)	a		13 41		14 09	14 44		15 41				16 41		17 45				18 41	19 41	20 41	21 41	22 48		
	d		13 42		14 13	14 45		15 45		16 15		16 42		17 48				18 48	19 48	20 42	21 42	22 49		
Tisbury	d		13 52			14 55		15 55		16 25		16 52		17 58				18 58	19 59	20 52	21 52	22 59		
Bristol Temple Meads 10	d			13 10							15 52													
Bath Spa 7	d			13 22							16 07													
Bradford-on-Avon	d			13 35							16 22													
Trowbridge	d			13 42							16 28													
Westbury	d			13 53							16 39													
Warminster	d			14 00							16 47													
Salisbury	a		14 15	14 25	14 35	15 15		16 15		16 40	17 09	17 15		18 20				19 23	20 20	21 20	22 09	23 13	00 28	00 35
	d	13 45	14 20		14 45	15 20	15 45	16 20		16 45		17 20	17 45	18 25			18 45	19 25	20 25	21 25	22 25			
Romsey	a				14 50	15 50		16 50				17 50		18 50				19 50	20 50	21 50	22 50			
Southampton Central	a				15 04	16 04		17 04				18 04		19 04				20 04	21 04	22 02	23 03			
Portsmouth Harbour	a				15 54	16 54		17 54				18 58		19 54				20 54	21 52	23 04	23 53			
Brighton 10	a				17g18	18h09		19g18				20g18		21g18				22j21	23j18					
Grateley	d	13 57			14 57		15 57	16 32		16 57			17 57				18 57	19 37	20 37	21 37	22 37			
Andover	d	14 04	14 37		15 04	15 37	16 04	16 39		17 04		17 37	18 04	18 42			19 04	19 44	20 44	21 44	22 44			
Whitchurch (Hants)	d	14 12			15 12		16 12			17 12			18 12				19 12	19 52	20 52	21 52	22 52			
Overton	d	14 18			15 18		16 18			17 18			18 18				19 18	19 58	20 58	21 58	22 58			
Basingstoke	a	14 27	14 54		15 27	15 54	16 28	16 55		17 27		17 54	18 27	18 59			19 28	20 08	21 08	22 08	23 07			
Reading 7	a	15 00	15 30		16 00	16 30	17 00	17 30		18 00		18 31	19 00	19 31			20 00	21 01	22 05	22 47	23 53			
Woking	a	14 49	15 15		15 49	16 15	16 49	17 15		17 49		18 15	18 49	19 19			19 49	20 29	21 29	22 28	23 33			
Clapham Junction 10	a	15k12	15 36		16k12	16 36	17k12	17 36		18k12		18 36	19k12	19 40			20k12	20 52	21 52	22 48	23 56			
London Waterloo 15 ⊖	a	15 19	15 49		16 19	16 49	17 19	17 44		18 21		18 45	19 19	19 49			20 19	21 00	22 04	22 57	00 06			

For general notes see front of timetable
For details of catering facilities see Directory of Train Operators
For full service between Bristol Temple Meads and Salisbury see Table 123

- **b** Change at Exeter St Davids
- **c** Change at Newton Abbot
- **e** Change at Newton Abbot and Exeter St Davids
- **f** Arr. 2024
- **g** Change at Salisbury and Fareham
- **h** Change at Salisbury and Fratton
- **j** Change at Salisbury and Southampton Central
- **k** Change at Basingstoke

Table 160

Saturdays

Exeter and Salisbury → London

Network Diagram - see first page of Table 160

		SW	SW	SW	SW	SW	SW	SW	SW	SW	SW	SW	SW	SW	SW	SW	SW	SW	SW	SW	SW	SW	SW
		1	1 ◇	1 ◇	1 ◇	1 ◇	1 ◇	1 ◇	1 ◇	1 ◇	1 ◇	1 ◇	1 ◇	1 ◇	1	1 ◇	1 ◇	1 ◇	1 ◇	1 ◇	1 ◇	1 ◇	1 ◇
			A	B	A	B	A	B															
			☕	☕	☕	☕	☕	☕	☕	☕	☕	☕	☕	☕		☕		☕	☕	☕	☕	☕	☕
Plymouth	d												05 25		06 55							08 52	
Ivybridge	d																					08 21	
Totnes	d												05 50		06 50							09 19	
Paignton	d														07b08			07c20				09b04	
Torquay	d														07b14							09b09	
Newton Abbot	d												06 03		07 31							09 32	
Teignmouth	d														07 25							08 55	
Dawlish	d														07 30							09 00	
Dawlish Warren	d																						
Exeter St Davids 6	a																						
	d	22p57								05 10			06 41		08 00			08 25				10 10	
Exeter Central	d	23p01								05 14			06 45		08 08			08 30				10 14	
Pinhoe	d	23p06								05 19			06 50		08 13							10 21	
Whimple	d	23p13								05 26			06 57		08 20							10 28	
Feniton	d	23p18								05 31			07 02		08 25							10 33	
Honiton	a	23p25								05 37			07 08		08 31			08 45				10 39	
	d	23p27								05 38	06 20		07 12					08 46				10 40	
Axminster	a	23p37								05 48	06 30		07 22					08 56				10 50	
	d	23p38								05 49	06 31		07 23					08 57				10 51	
Crewkerne	d	23p51								06 02	06 44		07 36					09 10				11 04	
Yeovil Junction	a	23p59								06 11	06 52		07 45					09 19				11 13	
	d	00 01								06 20	06 54		07 50	08 20				09 20		10 20		11 20	
Sherborne	d									06 26	07 00		07 56	08 26				09 26		10 26		11 26	
Templecombe	d									06 34	07 08		08 04	08 34				09 34		10 34		11 34	
Gillingham (Dorset)	a									06 41	07 15		08 11	08 41				09 41		10 41		11 41	
	d									06 42	07 16		08 12	08 42				09 42		10 42		11 42	
Tisbury	d									06 52	07 26		08 22	08 52				09 52		10 52		11 52	
Bristol Temple Meads 10	d																08 50						
Bath Spa 7	d																09 07						
Bradford-on-Avon	d																09 20						
Trowbridge	d																09 27						
Westbury	d																09 39						
Warminster	d																09 46						
Salisbury	a	00 35								07 10	07 40		08 37	09 15			10 09	10 15		11 15		12 15	
	d		05 12	05 15	05 42	05 45	06 17	06 20	06 45	07 20	07 45	08 20	08 45	09 20		09 45	10 20		10 45	11 20	11 45	12 20	12 45
Romsey	a									07 42	08 51			09 51			10 50			11 51		12 51	
Southampton Central	a									08 02	09 02			10 02			11 02			12 02		13 02	
Portsmouth Harbour	a									08 52	09 52			10 53			11 52			12 52		13 52	
Brighton 10	a									10e18	11e18			12e18			13e18			14e18		15e18	
Grateley	d		05 24	05 27	05 54	05 57			06 57		07 57		08 57			09 57			10 57		11 57		12 57
Andover	d		05 32	05 35	06 01	06 04	06 34	06 37	07 04	07 37	08 04	08 37	09 04	09 37		10 04	10 37		11 04	11 37	12 04	12 37	13 04
Whitchurch (Hants)	d		05 40	05 43	06 09	06 12			07 12		08 12		09 12			10 12			11 12		12 12		13 12
Overton	d		05 46	05 49	06 15	06 18			07 18		08 18		09 18			10 18			11 18		12 18		13 18
Basingstoke	a		05 58	05 58	06 27	06 27	06 54	06 54	07 27	07 54	08 27	08 54	09 27	09 54		10 27	10 55		11 27	11 54	12 27	12 54	13 27
Reading 7	a				07 00	07 00	07 31	07 31	08 00	08 31	09 00	09 31	10 00	10 31		11 00	11 31			12 31	13 00	13 31	14 00
Woking	a		06 18	06 18	06 49	06 49	07 15	07 15	07 49	08 17	08 49	09 15	09 49	10 15		10 49	11 15		11 49	12 15	12 49	13 15	13 49
Clapham Junction 10	a		06 38	06 38	07 23	07 23	07 36	07 36	08 30	08 37	09f12	09 36	10f12	10 36		11f12	11 36			12 36	13f12	13 36	14f12
London Waterloo 15 ⊖	a		06 49	06 49	07 19	07 19	07 49	07 49	08 19	08 49	09 19	09 49	10 19	10 49		11 19	11 49		12 19	12 49	13 19	13 49	14 19

For general notes see front of timetable
For details of catering facilities see Directory of Train Operators

For full service between Bristol Temple Meads and Salisbury see Table 123

A From 3 October
B Until 26 September
b Change at Newton Abbot and Exeter St Davids
c From 12 September only
e Change at Salisbury and Fareham
f Change at Basingstoke

Exeter and Salisbury → London

Network Diagram - see first page of Table 160

		SW	SW	SW	SW	SW	SW	SW		SW	SW	SW	SW	SW	SW	SW	SW	SW	SW	SW	SW	SW	SW	SW
		1◇	1◇	1◇	1◇	1◇	1◇	1◇		1	1◇	1◇	1◇	1◇	1◇	1	1	1◇	1◇	1◇	1◇	1◇	1	1
		[trolley]	[trolley]	[trolley]		[trolley]	[trolley]	[trolley]			[trolley]		[trolley]	[trolley]	[trolley]			[trolley]	[trolley]	[trolley]				
Plymouth	d	09b34		10 43		12c21		13e01		14 25					14 48	15f25	16 25			16g25	17 42	18f42	19 39	21 15
Ivybridge	d	08h21				12f14		12j45							15 03		15 03				17 57	18f58	18 58	21 30
Totnes	d	10k01		10 50		12c48		13m29		14 50					15 17	15f50	16 50			16n50	18 11	19f12	20 06	21 44
Paignton	d	10 14		10 54		12 34		13q07		14r30					14r30	15 52	16t12			17v03	18w03	19 14	19 23	21 53
Torquay	d	10 20		10 59		12 40		13y14		14z36					14z36	15 58	16A17			17B10	18C10	19 20	19 28	21 58
Newton Abbot	d	10 33		11 23		12 52		13D42		15 03					15 30	16 10	17 03			17E22	18 25	19 32	20 19	22 11
Teignmouth	d	10 40		11 30		12 59		13G28		14 47					15 37	16 17	16H38			17H30	18 32	19 39	19 48	22 18
Dawlish	d	10 45		11 35		13 04		13J33		14 52					15 42	16 22	16K43			17K37	18 36	19 44	19 53	22 23
Dawlish Warren	d	10 49				13 15									15 46						18 48	19 49		
Exeter St Davids 6	a	11 00				13 25									16 00	16 35					19 00	20 03		
	d	11 08		12 10		13 35		14 10		15 30					16 10	16 40	17 40			18 10	19 10	20 15	21 00	22 57
Exeter Central	d	11 12		12 14		13 39		14 14		15 34					16 14	16 44	17 44			18 14	19 14	20 19	21 04	23 01
Pinhoe	d			12 19				14 19		15 39					16 19	16 49	17 49			18 19		20L27		23 06
Whimple	d			12 26				14 26		15 46					16 26	16 56	17 56			18 26		20 34		23 13
Feniton	d			12 31				14 31		15 51					16 31	17 01	18 01			18 31		20 39		23 18
Honiton	a	11 27		12 37		13 54		14 37		15 57					16 37	17 07	18 07			18 37	19 29	20 45	21 19	23 24
	d	11 28		12 38		13 57		14 38							16 38		18 08			18 38	19 30	20 46	21 23	23 28
Axminster	a	11 38		12 48		14 07		14 48							16 48		18 18			18 48	19 40	20 56	21 33	23 38
	d	11 39		12 49		14 08		14 49							16 49					18 49	19 41	20 57	21 46	23 39
Crewkerne	d	12 00		13 03				15 03							17 03					19 03	19 54	21 10	22 09	23 52
Yeovil Junction	a	12 09		13 12		14 27		15 12							17 12					19 12	20 03	21 19	22 17	00 01
	d	12 20		13 20		14 28		15 20					16 20		17 20				18 20	19 20	20 20	21 20	22 24	00 02
Sherborne	d	12 26		13 26				15 26					16 26		17 26				18 26	19 26	20 26	21 26	22 30	
Templecombe	d	12 34		13 34				15 34					16 34		17 34				18 34	19 34	20 34	21 34	22 38	
Gillingham (Dorset)	a	12 41		13 41		14 44		15 41					16 41		17 41				18 41	19 41	20 41	21 41	22 45	
	d	12 42		13 42		14 45		15 42					16 42		17 42				18 42	19 42	20 42	21 42	22 46	
Tisbury	d	12 52		13 52		14 55		15 52					16 52		17 52				18 52	19 52	20 52	21 52	22 56	
Bristol Temple Meads 10	d				13 15							15 52												
Bath Spa 7	d				13 27							16 07												
Bradford-on-Avon	d				13 40							16 24												
Trowbridge	d				13 47							16 30												
Westbury	d				13 54							16 39												
Warminster	d				14 02							16 47												
Salisbury	a	13 15		14 15	14 25	15 15		16 15				17 09	17 15		18 15				19 21	20 20	21 20	22 07	23 12	00 36
	d	13 20	13 45	14 20	14 45	15 20	15 45	16 20			16 45	17 20		17 45	18 20			18 45	19 25	20 25	21 25	22 25		
Romsey	a	13 51			14 51	15 51		16 51				17 51			18 51				19 51	20 51	21 51	22 51		
Southampton Central	a	14 02			15 02	16 02		17 02				18 02			19 02				20 02	21 02	22 02	23 02		
Portsmouth Harbour	a	14 52			15 52	16 52		17 52				18 52			19 52				20 51	21 52	22 52	23 49		
Brighton 10	a	16 14			17N18	18N18		19N18				20N19			21N18				22Q21	23Q18	00U25			
Grateley	d		13 57		14 57		15 57				16 57			17 57				18 57	19 37	20 37	21 37	22 37		
Andover	d	13 37	14 04	14 37	15 04	15 37	16 04	16 37			17 04	17 37		18 04	18 37			19 04	19 44	20 44	21 44	22 44		
Whitchurch (Hants)	d		14 12		15 12		16 12				17 12			18 12				19 12	19 52	20 52	21 52	22 52		
Overton	d		14 18		15 18		16 18				17 18			18 18				19 18	19 58	20 58	21 58	22 58		
Basingstoke	a	13 54	14 27	14 54	15 27	15 54	16 27	16 54			17 27	17 54		18 27	18 54			19 27	20 06	21 06	22 06	23 07		
Reading 7	a	14 31	15 00	15 31	16 02	16 31	17 00	17 31			18 00	18 31		19 00	19 31			20 01	21 00	22 00	23 00	00 01		
Woking	a	14 15	14 49	15 15	15 49	16 15	16 49	17 15			17 49	18 15		18 49	19 15			19 49	20 29	21 29	22 28	23 32		
Clapham Junction 10	a	14 36	15V12	15 36	16V12	16 36	17V12	17 36			18V12	18 36		19V12	19 36			20V12	20 52	21 52	22 48	23 58		
London Waterloo 15 ⊖	a	14 49	15 19	15 49	16 19	16 49	17 19	17 49			18 19	18 49		19 19	19 49			20 19	21 04	22 04	22 57	00 10		

For general notes see front of timetable
For details of catering facilities see Directory of Train Operators
For full service between Bristol Temple Meads and Salisbury see Table 123

- **A** From 12 September dep. 1628
- **B** From 12 September dep. 1716
- **C** From 12 September dep. 1757
- **D** From 12 September dep. 1335
- **E** From 12 September dep. 1740
- **G** From 12 September dep. 1259
- **H** From 12 September dep. 1651
- **J** From 12 September dep. 1304
- **K** From 12 September dep. 1656
- **L** Arr. 2024
- **N** Change at Salisbury and Fareham
- **Q** Change at Salisbury and Southampton Central
- **U** Change at Salisbury and Fratton
- **V** Change at Basingstoke
- **b** Change at Newton Abbot. From 12 September dep. 0925
- **c** Change at Exeter St Davids
- **e** From 12 September dep. 1254
- **f** Change at Newton Abbot
- **g** From 12 September dep. 1657
- **h** Change at Newton Abbot and Teignmouth
- **j** From 12 September dep. 1215
- **k** Change at Newton Abbot. From 12 September dep. 0950
- **m** From 12 September dep. 1321
- **n** From 12 September dep. 1727
- **q** From 12 September dep. 1234
- **r** From 12 September dep. 1422
- **t** From 12 September dep. 1623
- **v** From 12 September dep. 1711
- **w** From 12 September dep. 1752
- **y** From 12 September dep. 1240
- **z** From 12 September dep. 1427

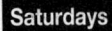

Table 160

Sundays

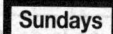

Exeter and Salisbury → London

Network Diagram - see first page of Table 160

		SW	SW	SW	SW	SW	SW	SW	SW	SW	SW	SW	SW	SW	SW	SW	SW	SW	SW	SW	SW	SW	SW	SW	SW
		1	1 ◇	1 ◇	1 ◇	1 ◇	1 ◇	1 ◇	1 ◇	1 ◇	1 ◇	1 ◇	1 ◇	1 ◇	1 ◇	1 ◇	1 ◇	1 ◇	1 ◇	1 ◇	1 ◇	1 ◇	1 ◇	1	1
			A	B	A	B														C					
			☕	☕	☕	☕	☕	☕	☕	☕	☕	☕	☕	☕		☕	☕		☕	☕	☕				
Plymouth	d											09b50		12c00			14 06	15e25		16 02		18f10		19 55	21g15
Ivybridge	d																14 21		16f17	16 17		17g23		17h23	
Totnes	d											10j18		12g16			14 35		16g11	16 31		18f39		19 46	21g42
Paignton	d											10k10		12 25			14 04	15 30	16 10			18 24		19 55	22 10
Torquay	d											10m15		12 31				15 36	16 16			18 30		20 00	22 16
Newton Abbot	d											10n31		12 44			14 47	15 51	16 30	16 43		18 42		20 32	22 30
Teignmouth	d											09 28		12 51			14 54	15 58	16 13			18 49		20 20	22 37
Dawlish	d											09 34		12 56			14 59	16 03	16 18			18 54		20 25	22 42
Dawlish Warren	d																	16 07				18 58			22 46
Exeter St Davids 6	a													13 09			15 15	16 18	16 53	17 05		19 09			22 57
	d	22p57								09 20		11 20		13 18			15 20	16 33	17 18			19 20		21 20	23 10
Exeter Central	d	23p01								09 24		11 24		13 22			15 24	16 37	17 23			19 24		21 24	23 14
Pinhoe	d	23p06																16 42				19 29			
Whimple	d	23p13								09 33		11 33		13 33			15 33		17 33			19 36		21 33	
Feniton	d	23p18								09 39		11 39		13 39			15 39		17 39			19 41		21 39	
Honiton	a	23p24								09 45		11 45		13 45			15 45	16 54	17 45			19 47		21 45	23s29
	d	23p28							08 46	09 46		11 46		13 46			15 46	16 55	17 46			19 48		21 46	
Axminster	a	23p38							08 56	09 56		11 56		13 56			15 56	17 05	17 56			19 58		21 56	23s40
	d	23p39							08 57	09 57		11 57		13 57			15 57	17 06	17 57			19 59		21 57	
Crewkerne	d	23p52							09 10	10 10		12 10		14 10			16 10	17 19	18 10			20 12		22 10	00s04
Yeovil Junction	a	00 01							09 18	10 18		12 18		14 18			16 18	17 28	18 18			20 21		22 18	00s13
	d	00 02					07 32		09 25	10 25	11 25	12 25	13 25	14 25	15 25		16 25	17 29	18 25		19 25	20 25	21 25	22 25	
Sherborne	d						07 38		09 31	10 31	11 31	12 31	13 31	14 31	15 31		16 31	17 36	18 31		19 31	20 31	21 31	22 31	
Templecombe	d						07 47		09 39	10 39	11 39	12 39	13 39	14 39	15 39		16 39	17 43	18 39		19 39	20 39	21 39	22 39	
Gillingham (Dorset)	a						07 54		09 46	10 46	11 46	12 46	13 46	14 46	15 46		16 46	17 50	18 46		19 46	20 46	21 46	22 46	
	d						07 55		09 47	10 47	11 47	12 47	13 47	14 47	15 47		16 47	17 51	18 47		19 47	20 47	21 47	22 47	
Tisbury	d						08 05		09 57	10 57	11 57	12 57	13 57	14 57	15 57		16 57	18 02	18 57		19 57	20 57	21 57	22 57	
Bristol Temple Meads 10	d															16 04									
Bath Spa 7	d															16 20									
Bradford-on-Avon	d															16 31									
Trowbridge	d															16 37									
Westbury	d															16 46									
Warminster	d															16 53									
Salisbury	a	00 36					08 20		10 21	11 17	12 21	13 17	14 21	15 18	16 21	17 16	17 21	18 22	19 17		20 21	21 21	22 21	23 17	00 50
	d		06 42	06 45	07 23	07 26	08 26	09 26	10 26	11 26	12 26	13 26	14 26	15 26	16 26	17 26		18 26	19 26		20 26	21 26	22 26		
Romsey	a								10 49	11 49	12 55	13 47	15 09	15 50	16 49	17 49			19 47		20 48	21 47	22 48		
Southampton Central	a								11 00	12 04	13 06	13 58	15 20	16 05	17 04	18 04			19 57		20 59	21 58	22 59		
Portsmouth Harbour	a								11 53	12 53		14 48		16 53	17 53	18 51			20 47		21 48	22 46	23 48		
Brighton 10	a								13q49	14r49	15 04	16t49	17 05	18v49	19w49	20y49			22z27		23z29				
Grateley	d						08 38		10 38		12 38		14 38		16 38			18 38			20 38		22 38		
Andover	d		06 59	07 02	07 40	07 43	08 46	09 43	10 46	11 43	12 46	13 43	14 46	15 43	16 46	17 43		18 46	19 43		20 46	21 43	22 46		
Whitchurch (Hants)	d				07 48	07 51	08 54		10 54		12 54		14 54		16 54			18 54			20 54		22 54		
Overton	d						08 59		10 59		12 59		14 59		16 59			18 59			20 59		22 59		
Basingstoke	a		07 19	07 19	08 03	08 03	09 08	10 00	11 08	12 00	13 08	14 00	15 08	16 00	17 08	18 00		19 08	20 00		21 08	22 00	23 08		
Reading 7	a		08 30	08 30	09 30	09 30	10 04	10 31	12 04	12 30	14 04	14 30	16 04	16 30	18 04	18 30			20 30			22 33	00 30		
Woking	a		07 39	07 39	08 23	08 23	09 30	10 23	11 30	12 23	13 30	14 23	15 30	16 23	17 30	18 23		19 30	20 23		21 30	22 23	23 50		
Clapham Junction 10	a		08 03	08 03	08 55	08 55	09 55	10 44	11 50	12 44	13 50	14 44	15 50	16 44	17 50	18 44		19 50	20 44		21 50	22 44	00 23		
London Waterloo 15 ⊖	a		08 19	08 19	09 09	09 09	10 08	11 03	12 03	13 03	14 04	14 58	16 04	16 58	18 04	18 58		20 04	20 58		22 04	22 58	00 33		

For general notes see front of timetable
For details of catering facilities see Directory of Train Operators

For full service between Bristol Temple Meads and Salisbury see Table 123

- **A** From 27 September
- **B** Until 20 September
- **C** From Penzance (Table 135)
- **b** Until 12 July dep. 0955. 19 July to 6 September dep. 0935
- **c** Change at Newton Abbot. From 8 November dep. 1145
- **e** From 8 November only. Change at Exeter St Davids
- **f** Change at Exeter St Davids
- **g** Change at Newton Abbot
- **h** Change at Newton Abbot and Exeter St Davids
- **j** Until 12 July dep. 1022. 19 July to 6 September dep. 1003
- **k** Until 12 July and from 13 September only. Change at Newton Abbot and Exeter St Davids. Until 12 July dep. 1005
- **m** Until 12 July and from 13 September only. Change at Newton Abbot and Exeter St Davids. Until 12 July dep. 1010
- **n** Until 12 July dep. 1035. 19 July to 6 September dep. 1016
- **q** Change at Salisbury and Fratton. From 13 September arr. 1400
- **r** Change at Salisbury and Fratton. From 13 September arr. 1459
- **t** Change at Salisbury and Fratton. From 13 September arr. 1700
- **v** Change at Salisbury and Fratton. From 13 September arr. 1900
- **w** Change at Salisbury and Fratton. From 13 September arr. 2000
- **y** Change at Salisbury and Fratton. From 13 September arr. 2100
- **z** Change at Salisbury and Fratton

Network Diagram for Tables 165, 167

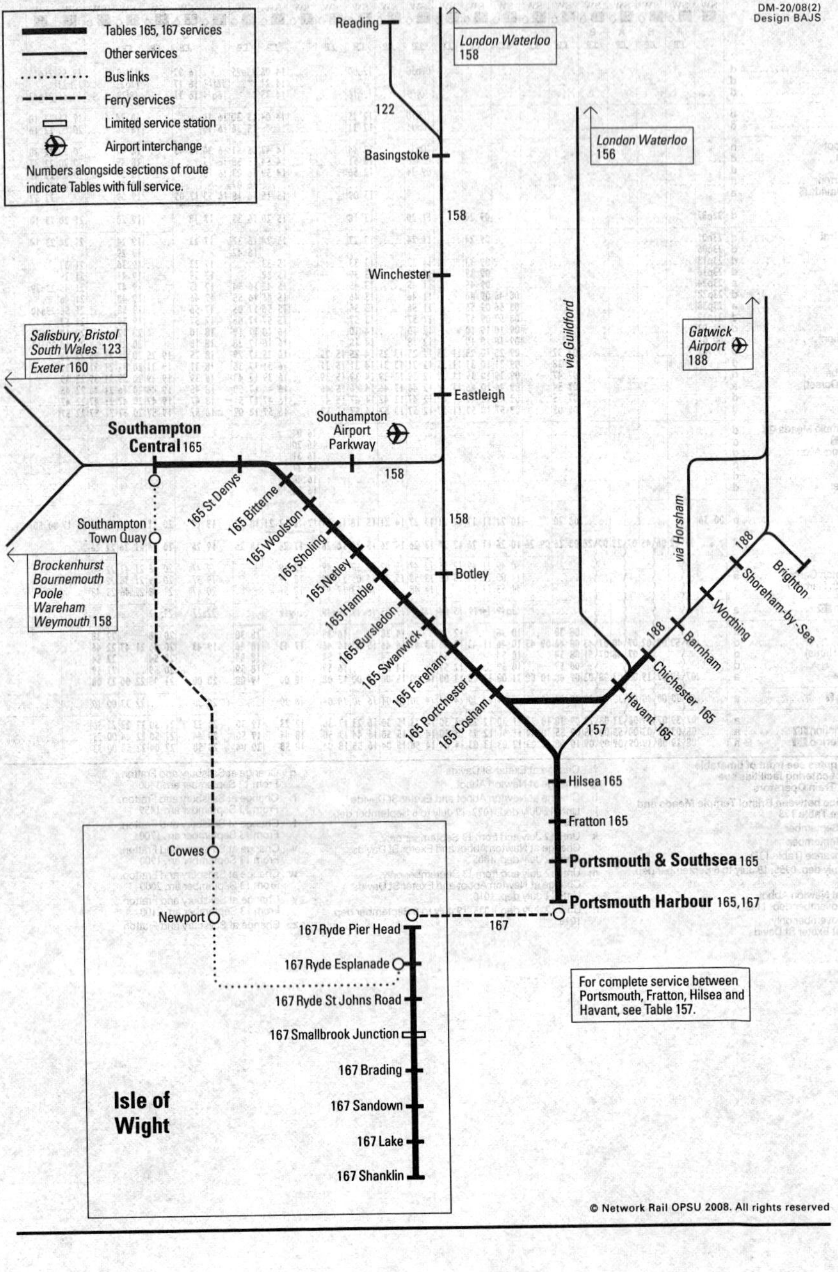

For details of Bank Holiday service alterations, please see first page of Table 149

Southampton → Fareham and Portsmouth

Network Diagram - see first page of Table 165

Miles	Miles			SW MO 1	SW MX 1	SN 1 A	SW 1	SN 1 B	SW 1	SW 1	GW	SW 1	SN 1 C	SW 1	SW 1	SN 1	GW ◇	SW 1	SN 1 C	SW 1	SN 1	SW 1	GW ◇ 🛒	SN 1	SW 1	SN 1
0	—	**Southampton Central**	d			05 48		06 10		06 21	06 53		07 06		07 17	07 33	07 42	07 51	08 10		08 33	08 44	09 06	09 10		09 33
2	—	St Denys	d							06 28					07 23			07 57	08 15			08 49				
2½	—	Bitterne	d							06 30					07 25			08 00				08 52				
4¼	—	Woolston	d			05 57		06 19		06 34			07 15		07 29			08 03				08 55				
5	—	Sholing	d							06 36					07 31			08 06				08 58				
6¾	—	Netley	d							06 40					07 35			08 10				09 02				
7½	—	Hamble	d							06 42					07 37			08 12				09 04				
8¾	—	Bursledon	d							06 45					07 40			08 15				09 07				
10¾	—	Swanwick	d			06 06		06 27		06 49			07 24		07 44	07 51		08 20	08 28		08 50	09 11		09 28		09 50
14½	—	**Fareham**	a			06 12		06 33		06 57	07 14		07 30		07 52	07 58	08 05	08 27	08 34		08 56	09 17	09 27	09 36		09 56
—	—		d	23p44	23p48	06 13	06 18	06 34	06 50	06 58	07 15	07 20	07 31	07 48	07 53	07 58	08 06	08 28	08 35	08 50	08 57	09 18	09 27	09 37	09 48	09 56
17¾	—	Portchester	d	23p49	23p53	06 18	06 23	06 40	06 55	07 03		07 25	07 36	07 53	07 58			08 33	08 40	08 55		09 23		09 42	09 53	
20¼	0	Cosham	d	23p54	23p59	06 23	06 28	06 44	07 00	07 08	07 23	07 29	07 40	07 58	08 03	08 07	08 14	08 39	08 44	09 00	09 05	09 28	09 35	09 46	09 58	10 05
—	4	Havant	a			06 37		06 53					07 46			08 13			08 50		09 11			09 53		10 11
—	12¾	Chichester 4	a			06 58		07 07					08 08			08 27			09 11		09 24			10 10		10 23
21¾	—	Hilsea	a	23p59	00 04		06 33		07 05	07 13		07 35		08 03	08 09			08 45		09 05		09 33			10 03	
24	—	Fratton	a	00 04	00 08		06 38		07 09	07 17	07 34	07 39		08 07	08 13		08 21	08 49		09 09		09 37	09 41		10 07	
25	—	**Portsmouth & Southsea**	a	00 08	00 11		06 44		07 12	07 22	07 38	07 42		08 11	08 18		08 24	08 52		09 13		09 42	09 45		10 11	
25¾	—	**Portsmouth Harbour**	a	00 13	00 16		06 49		07 17		07 45	07 48		08 16	08 23		08 30	08 58		09 18			09 54		10 18	

		SW 1	GW ◇ 🛒	SN 1	SW 1	SN 1	SW 1	GW ◇ 🛒	SN 1	SW 1	SN 1	SW 1		GW ◇ 🛒	SN 1	SW 1	SN 1	SW 1	GW ◇ 🛒	SN 1	SW 1	SN 1	SW 1	GW ◇ 🛒	SN 1	SW 1
Southampton Central	d	09 44	10 06	10 10		10 33	10 44	11 06	11 13		11 33	11 44		12 06	12 13		12 33	12 44	13 06	13 13		13 33	13 44	14 06	14 13	
St Denys	d	09 49					10 49					11 49						12 49					13 49			
Bitterne	d	09 52					10 52					11 52						12 52					13 52			
Woolston	d	09 55					10 55					11 55						12 55					13 55			
Sholing	d	09 58					10 58					11 58						12 58					13 58			
Netley	d	10 02					11 02					12 02						13 02					14 02			
Hamble	d	10 04					11 04					12 04						13 04					14 04			
Bursledon	d	10 07					11 07					12 07						13 07					14 07			
Swanwick	d	10 11		10 28		10 50	11 11		11 33		11 50	12 11			12 33		12 50	13 11		13 33		13 50	14 11		14 33	
Fareham	a	10 17	10 27	10 36		10 56	11 17	11 27	11 39		11 56	12 17		12 27	12 39		12 56	13 17	13 27	13 39		13 56	14 17	14 27	14 39	
	d	10 18	10 27	10 37	10 48	10 56	11 18	11 27	11 40	11 48	11 57	12 18		12 27	12 40	12 48	12 56	13 18	13 27	13 40	13 48	13 56	14 18	14 27	14 40	14 48
Portchester	d	10 23		10 42	10 53		11 23		11 45	11 53		12 23			12 45	12 53		13 23		13 45	13 53		14 23		14 45	14 53
Cosham	d	10 28	10 35	10 46	10 58	11 05	11 28	11 35	11 49	11 58	12 05	12 28		12 35	12 49	12 58	13 05	13 28	13 35	13 49	13 58	14 05	14 28	14 35	14 49	14 58
Havant	a			10 53		11 11			11 55		12 11				12 55		13 11			13 55		14 11			14 55	
Chichester 4	a			11 10		11 24			12 10		12 24				13 10		13 23			14 10		14 23			15 10	
Hilsea	a	10 33			11 03		11 33			12 03		12 33				13 03		13 33			14 03		14 33			15 03
Fratton	a	10 37	10 41		11 07		11 37	11 41		12 07		12 37		12 41		13 07		13 37	13 41		14 07		14 37	14 41		15 07
Portsmouth & Southsea	a	10 42	10 45		11 11		11 42	11 45		12 11		12 42		12 45		13 11		13 42	13 45		14 11		14 42	14 45		15 11
Portsmouth Harbour	a		10 54		11 18			11 54		12 18				12 54		13 18			13 54		14 18			14 54		15 18

		GW ◇ D	SN 1	SW 1	GW ◇ 🛒	SN 1	SW 1	SN 1	SW 1	GW ◇ 🛒	SN 1	SW 1	SN 1	SW 1	SW 1	GW ◇ 🛒	SN 1	SW 1	SN 1	SW 1	SW 1	GW ◇ 🛒	SN 1	SW 1	SN 1	SW 1
Southampton Central	d	14 34	14 27	14 44	15 06	15 13		15 33	15 44	16 06	16 12		16 33		16 44	17 06	17 13		17 33	17 44		18 05	18 11		18 33	
St Denys	d			14 49					15 49						16 49					17 49						
Bitterne	d			14 52					15 52						16 52					17 52						
Woolston	d			14 55					15 55						16 55					17 55						
Sholing	d			14 58					15 58						16 58					17 58						
Netley	d			15 02					16 02						17 02					18 02						
Hamble	d			15 04					16 04						17 04					18 04						
Bursledon	d			15 07					16 07						17 07					18 07						
Swanwick	d			15 11		15 33		15 50	16 11		16 29		16 50		17 11		17 33		17 50	18 11			18 28		18 50	
Fareham	a	14 55	14 59	15 17	15 27	15 39		15 56	16 17	16 27	16 35		16 56		17 17	17 27	17 39		17 56	18 17		18 27	18 34		18 56	
	d	14 56	15 00	15 18	15 27	15 40	15 48	15 57	16 18	16 27	16 36	16 48	16 56	17 10	17 18	17 27	17 40	17 48	17 56	18 18	18 23	18 27	18 35	18 45	18 56	19 14
Portchester	d			15 23		15 45	15 53		16 23		16 41	16 53		17 15	17 23		17 45	17 53		18 23	18 28		18 40	18 50		19 19
Cosham	d	15 04		15 28	15 35	15 49	15 58	16 05	16 28	16 35	16 45	16 58	17 05	17 20	17 28	17 35	17 49	17 58	18 05	18 28	18 33	18 35	18 44	18 55	19 05	19 24
Havant	a	15 10	15 14			15 57		16 11			16 51		17 11				17 55		18 11				18 50		19 11	
Chichester 4	a	15 21	15 25			16 12		16 24			17 06		17 24				18 10		18 24				19 05		19 22	
Hilsea	a			15 33			16 03		16 33			17 03			17 33			18 03		18 33				19 05		19 28
Fratton	a			15 37	15 41		16 07		16 37	16 41		17 07		17 27	17 37	17 41		18 08		18 37	18 40	18 48		19 09		19 32
Portsmouth & Southsea	a			15 42	15 45		16 11		16 40	16 45		17 11		17 33	17 42	17 45		18 11		18 42	18 43	18 52		19 12		19 36
Portsmouth Harbour	a				15 54		16 18		16 44	16 54		17 18		17 38		17 54		18 20			18 51	18 58		19 20		19 43

For general notes see front of timetable
For details of catering facilities see Directory of Train Operators

A To London Bridge (Table 188)
B To Brighton (Table 188)
C To London Victoria (Table 188)
D From Great Malvern (Table 71)

For details of Bank Holiday service alterations, please see first page of Table 149

Southampton → Fareham and Portsmouth

Network Diagram - see first page of Table 165

		SW 1	GW ◇ ⊼	SN 1	SW 1	SN 1	SW 1	GW ◇ ⊼	SN 1	SW 1	SN 1	SW 1	GW ◇ ⊼	SN 1	SW 1	SN 1	SW 1	SN 1	GW ◇	SN 1	SW 1	SW 1	GW ◇	SW 1
Southampton Central	d	18 44	19 06	19 12		19 33	19 44	20 06	20 11		20 33	20 44	21 06	21 13		21 32	21 44	22 13	22 04	22 22		22 44	23 03	
St Denys	d	18 49					19 49					20 49					21 49					22 49		
Bitterne	d	18 52					19 52					20 52					21 52					22 52		
Woolston	d	18 55					19 55					20 55					21 55					22 55		
Sholing	d	18 58					19 58					20 58					21 58					22 58		
Netley	d	19 02					20 02					21 02					22 02					23 02		
Hamble	d	19 04					20 04					21 04					22 04					23 04		
Bursledon	d	19 07					20 07					21 07					22 07					23 07		
Swanwick	d	19 11		19 29		19 51	20 11		20 28		20 50	21 11		21 33		21 51	22 11	22 30				23 11		
Fareham	a	19 17	19 27	19 35		19 57	20 17	20 27	20 34		20 56	21 17	21 27	21 39		21 57	22 17	22 36	22 42	22 58		23 17	23 25	
	d	19 18	19 27	19 36	19 45	19 57	20 18	20 27	20 35	20 48	20 57	21 18	21 27	21 40	21 48	21 58	22 18	22 37	22 42	23 00	23 10	23 18	23 25	23 48
Portchester	d	19 23		19 41	19 50		20 23		20 40	20 53		21 23		21 45	21 53	22 03	22 23	22 42			23 15	23 23		23 53
Cosham	d	19 28	19 35	19 46	19 55	20 06	20 28		20 44	20 58	21 06	21 28		21 49	21 58	22 07	22 28	22 47		23 08	23 20	23 28		23 59
Havant	a			19 52		20 12			20 50		21 12			21 55		22 13		22 56		23 14				
Chichester 4	a			20 06		20 24			21 05		21 24			22 06		22 34		23 11		23 25				
Hilsea	a	19 33			20 02		20 33			21 03		21 33			22 03		22 33				23 24	23 33		00 04
Fratton	a	19 37	19 41		20 06		20 37	20 41		21 08		21 37	21 41		22 08		22 37		22 56		23 32	23 37	23 40	00 08
Portsmouth & Southsea	a	19 42	19 45		20 16		20 42	20 45		21 11		21 42	21 45		22 11		22 42		22 59		23 36	23 40	23 44	00 11
Portsmouth Harbour	a		19 54		20 23			20 54		21 16			21 52		22 16				23 04		23 40		23 53	00 16

Saturdays

		SW 1	SW 1	SN 1	SW 1	SN 1	SW 1	SN 1	SW 1	SN 1	SW 1	GW ◇	SN 1	SW 1	SN 1	SW 1	GW ◇	SN 1	SW 1	SN 1	SW 1	GW ◇ ⊼	SN 1
Southampton Central	d		05 44	06 13		06 33	06 44	07 13		07 33	07 44	08 05	08 13		08 33	08 44	09 05	09 13		09 33	09 44	10 03	10 13
St Denys	d		05 49				06 49				07 49					08 49					09 49		
Bitterne	d		05 52				06 52				07 52					08 52					09 52		
Woolston	d		05 55				06 55				07 55					08 55					09 55		
Sholing	d		05 58				06 58				07 58					08 58					09 58		
Netley	d		06 02				07 02				08 02					09 02					10 02		
Hamble	d		06 04				07 04				08 04					09 04					10 04		
Bursledon	d		06 07				07 07				08 07					09 07					10 07		
Swanwick	d		06 11	06 33		06 50	07 11	07 33		07 50	08 11		08 33		08 50	09 11		09 33		09 50	10 11		10 33
Fareham	a		06 17	06 39		06 56	07 17	07 39		07 56	08 17	08 27	08 39		08 56	09 17	09 27	09 39		09 56	10 17	10 27	10 39
	d	23p48	06 18	06 40	06 48	06 56	07 18	07 40	07 48	07 56	08 18	08 27	08 40	08 48	08 56	09 18	09 27	09 40	09 48	09 56	10 18	10 27	10 40
Portchester	d	23p53	06 23	06 45	06 53		07 23	07 45	07 53		08 23		08 45	08 53		09 23		09 45	09 53		10 23		10 45
Cosham	d	23p59	06 28	06 49	06 58	07 05	07 28	07 49	07 58	08 05	08 28	08 35	08 49	08 58	09 05	09 28	09 35	09 49	09 58	10 05	10 28	10 35	10 49
Havant	a			06 55		07 11		07 55		08 11			08 55		09 11			09 55		10 11			10 55
Chichester 4	a			07 10		07 23		08 10		08 23			09 10		09 23			10 10		10 23			11 10
Hilsea	a	00 04	06 33		07 03		07 33		08 03		08 33			09 03		09 33			10 03		10 33		
Fratton	a	00 08	06 37		07 07		07 37		08 07		08 37	08 42		09 07		09 37	09 42		10 07		10 37	10 43	
Portsmouth & Southsea	a	00 11	06 42		07 11		07 42		08 11		08 42	08 46		09 11		09 42	09 46		10 11		10 42	10 46	
Portsmouth Harbour	a	00 16			07 16				08 18			08 52		09 18			09 52		10 18			10 53	

		SW 1	SN 1	SW 1	GW ◇ ⊼	SN 1	SW 1	SN 1	SW 1	GW ◇ ⊼	SN 1	SW 1	SN 1	SW 1	GW ◇ ⊼	SN 1	SW 1	SN 1	SW 1	GW ◇ ⊼	SN 1	SW 1	GW ◇ A
Southampton Central	d		10 33	10 44	11 05	11 13		11 33	11 44	12 05	12 13		12 33	12 44	13 05	13 13		13 33	13 44	14 05	14 13		14 34
St Denys	d			10 49					11 49					12 49					13 49				
Bitterne	d			10 52					11 52					12 52					13 52				
Woolston	d			10 55					11 55					12 55					13 55				
Sholing	d			10 58					11 58					12 58					13 58				
Netley	d			11 02					12 02					13 02					14 02				
Hamble	d			11 04					12 04					13 04					14 04				
Bursledon	d			11 07					12 07					13 07					14 07				
Swanwick	d		10 50	11 11		11 33		11 50	12 11		12 33		12 50	13 11		13 33		13 50	14 11		14 33		
Fareham	a		10 56	11 17	11 27	11 39		11 56	12 17	12 27	12 39		12 56	13 17	13 27	13 39		13 56	14 17	14 27	14 39		14 54
	d	10 48	10 56	11 18	11 27	11 40	11 48	11 56	12 18	12 27	12 40	12 48	12 56	13 18	13 27	13 40	13 48	13 56	14 18	14 27	14 40	14 48	14 55
Portchester	d	10 53		11 23		11 45	11 53		12 23		12 45	12 53		13 23		13 45	13 53		14 23		14 45	14 53	
Cosham	d	10 58	11 05	11 28	11 35	11 49	11 58	12 05	12 28	12 35	12 49	12 58	13 05	13 28	13 35	13 49	13 58	14 05	14 28	14 35	14 49	14 58	15 03
Havant	a		11 11			11 55		12 11			12 55		13 11			13 55		14 11			14 55		15 10
Chichester 4	a		11 23			12 10		12 23			13 10		13 23			14 10		14 23			15 10		15 21
Hilsea	a	11 03		11 33			12 03		12 33			13 03		13 33			14 03		14 33			15 03	
Fratton	a	11 07		11 37	11 42		12 07		12 37	12 42		13 07		13 37	13 42		14 07		14 37	14 42		15 07	
Portsmouth & Southsea	a	11 11		11 42	11 46		12 11		12 42	12 46		13 11		13 42	13 46		14 11		14 42	14 46		15 11	
Portsmouth Harbour	a	11 18			11 52		12 18			12 52		13 18			13 52		14 18			14 52		15 18	

For general notes see front of timetable
For details of catering facilities see Directory of Train Operators

A From Great Malvern (Table 71)

Table 165

Southampton → Fareham and Portsmouth

Network Diagram - see first page of Table 165

		SN 1	SW 1	GW ◇ 🍴	SN 1	SW 1	SN 1	SW 1		GW ◇ 🍴	SN 1	SW 1	SN 1	SW 1	GW ◇ 🍴	SN 1		SW 1	SN 1	SW 1	GW ◇ 🍴	SN 1	SW 1	SN 1		SW 1
Southampton Central	d	14 27	14 44	15 05	15 13		15 33	15 44		16 05	16 13		16 33	16 44	17 05	17 13			17 33	17 44	18 05	18 11		18 33		18 44
St Denys	d		14 49					15 49						16 49						17 49						18 49
Bitterne	d		14 52					15 52						16 52						17 52						18 52
Woolston	d		14 55					15 55						16 55						17 55						18 55
Sholing	d		14 58					15 58						16 58						17 58						18 58
Netley	d		15 02					16 02						17 02						18 02						19 02
Hamble	d		15 04					16 04						17 04						18 04						19 04
Bursledon	d		15 07					16 07						17 07						18 07						19 07
Swanwick	d		15 11		15 33		15 50	16 11			16 33		16 50	17 11		17 33			17 50	18 11		18 28		18 50		19 11
Fareham	a	14 59	15 17	15 27	15 39		15 56	16 17		16 27	16 39		16 56	17 17	17 27	17 39			17 56	18 17	18 27	18 34		18 56		19 17
	d	15 00	15 18	15 27	15 40	15 48	15 56	16 18		16 27	16 40	16 48	16 56	17 18	17 27	17 40		17 48	17 56	18 18	18 27	18 35	18 48	18 56		19 18
Portchester	d		15 23		15 45	15 53		16 23			16 45	16 53		17 23		17 45		17 53		18 23		18 40	18 53			19 23
Cosham	d		15 28	15 35	15 49	15 58	16 05	16 28		16 35	16 49	16 58	17 05	17 28	17 35	17 49		17 58	18 05	18 28	18 35	18 44	18 58	19 05		19 28
Havant	a	15 14			15 55		16 11				16 55		17 11			17 55			18 11			18 50		19 11		
Chichester 4	a	15 25			16 10		16 23				17 10		17 23			18 10			18 23			19 05		19 23		
Hilsea	a		15 33			16 03		16 33				17 03		17 33				18 03		18 33			19 03			19 33
Fratton	a		15 37	15 42		16 07		16 37		16 42		17 07		17 37	17 42			18 07		18 37	18 43		19 07			19 37
Portsmouth & Southsea	a		15 42	15 46		16 11		16 40		16 46		17 11		17 42	17 46			18 11		18 42	18 47		19 11			19 42
Portsmouth Harbour	a			15 52		16 18		16 44		16 52		17 18			17 52			18 18			18 52		19 18			

		GW ◇ 🍴	SN 1	SW 1	SN 1	SW 1	GW ◇ 🍴	SN 1		SW 1	SN 1	SW 1	GW ◇ 🍴	SN 1	SW 1	SN 1 A	SW 1	GW ◇ 🍴	SN 1	SW 1	SN 1	SW 1	GW ◇ 🍴	SW 1		
Southampton Central	d	19 05	19 11		19 33	19 44	20 03	20 11			20 33	20 44	21 05	21 13		21 23	21 44	22 05	22 13		22 33	22 44	23 06			
St Denys	d					19 49						20 49				21 28	21 49					22 49				
Bitterne	d					19 52						20 52					21 52					22 52				
Woolston	d					19 55						20 55				21 33	21 55					22 55				
Sholing	d					19 58						20 58					21 58					22 58				
Netley	d					20 02						21 02				21 37	22 02					23 02				
Hamble	d					20 04						21 04					22 04					23 04				
Bursledon	d					20 07						21 07					22 07					23 07				
Swanwick	d		19 28		19 50	20 11		20 28			20 50	21 11		21 33		21 45	22 11		22 31		22 50	23 11				
Fareham	a	19 27	19 34		19 56	20 17	20 27	20 34			20 56	21 17	21 27	21 39		21 54	22 17	22 26	22 38		22 56	23 17	23 27			
	d	19 27	19 35	19 48	19 56	20 18	20 27	20 35		20 48	20 56	21 18	21 27	21 40	21 48	21 56	22 18	22 26	22 39	22 48	23 00	23 18	23 28	23 48		
Portchester	d		19 40	19 53		20 23		20 40		20 53		21 23		21 45	21 53	22 01	22 23		22 44	22 53		23 23		23 53		
Cosham	d	19 35	19 44	19 58	20 05	20 28		20 44		20 58	21 05	21 28		21 49	21 58	22 06	22 28		22 48	22 58	23 08	23 28		23 58		
Havant	a		19 51		20 11			20 50			21 11			21 55		22 12			22 54		23 14					
Chichester 4	a		20 06		20 23			21 05			21 23			22 06		22 33			23 09		23 25					
Hilsea	a			20 03		20 33				21 03		21 33			22 03		22 33			23 03		23 33		00 03		
Fratton	a	19 43		20 07		20 37	20 41			21 07		21 37	21 43		22 07		22 37	22 40		23 07		23 37	23 41	00 07		
Portsmouth & Southsea	a	19 46		20 11		20 42	20 45			21 11		21 42	21 46		22 11		22 40	22 44		23 11		23 40	23 45	00 11		
Portsmouth Harbour	a	19 52		20 18			20 51			21 18			21 52		22 18		22 47	22 52		23 18			23 49	00 16		

Sundays

		SW 1	SW 1		SW 1	SW 1		SW 1	GW 1 B 🍴		SW 1	SW 1		SW 1	SW 1		SW 1	GW ◇ 🍴		SW 1	SW 1		GW ◇ 🍴	SW 1		SW 1
Southampton Central	d		06 35			07 35			08 31		08 35			09 35			10 35	11 04			11 35		12 07			12 35
St Denys	d		06 41			07 41					08 41			09 41			10 41				11 41					12 41
Bitterne	d		06 43			07 43					08 43			09 43			10 43				11 43					12 43
Woolston	d		06 47			07 47					08 47			09 47			10 47				11 47					12 47
Sholing	d		06 49			07 49					08 49			09 49			10 49				11 49					12 49
Netley	d		06 53			07 53					08 53			09 53			10 53				11 53					12 53
Hamble	d		06 55			07 55					08 55			09 55			10 55				11 55					12 55
Bursledon	d		06 58			07 58					08 58			09 58			10 58				11 58					12 58
Swanwick	d		07 02			08 02					09 02			10 02			11 02				12 02					13 02
Fareham	a		07 09			08 09			08 51		09 09			10 09			11 09	11 25			12 09		12 28			13 09
	d	23p48	07 10		07 44	08 10		08 44	08 52		09 10	09 44		10 10	10 44		11 10	11 26		11 44	12 10		12 29	12 44		13 10
Portchester	d	23p53	07 15		07 49	08 15		08 49			09 15	09 49		10 15	10 49		11 15			11 49	12 15			12 49		13 15
Cosham	d	23p58	07 20		07 54	08 20		08 54	09 00		09 20	09 54		10 20	10 54		11 20	11 34		11 54	12 20		12 37	12 54		13 20
Havant	a								09 11																	
Chichester 4	a								09 22																	
Hilsea	a	00 03	07 26		08 00	08 26		09 00			09 26	10 00		10 26	11 00		11 26			12 00	12 26			13 00		13 26
Fratton	a	00 07	07 30		08 04	08 30		09 04			09 30	10 04		10 30	11 04		11 30	11 40		12 04	12 30		12 44	13 04		13 30
Portsmouth & Southsea	a	00 11	07 33		08 08	08 33		09 08			09 33	10 10		10 33	11 08		11 33	11 44		12 08	12 33		12 47	13 08		13 33
Portsmouth Harbour	a	00 16			08 13			09 13				10 15			11 14			11 53		12 13			12 53	13 13		

For general notes see front of timetable
For details of catering facilities see Directory of Train Operators

A To Barnham (Table 188)
B From Romsey (Table 158)

Table 165

Sundays

Southampton → Fareham and Portsmouth

Network Diagram - see first page of Table 165

		GW ◇	SW 1	SW 1	GW ◇	SW 1	SW 1	SW 1	GW ◇	SW 1	GW ◇	SW 1	SW 1	GW ◇	SW 1	SW 1	GW ◇	SW 1
Southampton Central	d	13 08		13 35	14 01		14 35		15 22	15 35	16 07		16 35	17 07		17 35	18 07	
St Denys	d			13 41			14 41			15 41			16 41			17 41		
Bitterne	d			13 43			14 43			15 43			16 43			17 43		
Woolston	d			13 47			14 47			15 47			16 47			17 47		
Sholing	d			13 49			14 49			15 49			16 49			17 49		
Netley	d			13 53			14 53			15 53			16 53			17 53		
Hamble	d			13 55			14 55			15 55			16 55			17 55		
Bursledon	d			13 58			14 58			15 58			16 58			17 58		
Swanwick	d			14 02			15 02			16 02			17 02			18 02		
Fareham	a	13 33		14 09	14 22		15 09		15 50	16 09	16 28		17 09	17 28		18 09	18 28	
	d	13 34	13 44	14 10	14 23	14 44	15 10	15 44	15 51	16 10	16 29	16 44	17 10	17 29	17 44	18 10	18 29	18 44
Portchester	d		13 49	14 15		14 49	15 15	15 49		16 15		16 49	17 15		17 49	18 15		18 49
Cosham	d	13 42	13 54	14 20	14 31	14 54	15 20	15 54	16 01	16 20	16 37	16 54	17 20	17 37	17 54	18 20	18 37	18 54
Havant	a	14 03							16 11									
Chichester 4	a	14 19							16 22									
Hilsea	a		14 00	14 26		15 00	15 26	16 00		16 26		17 00	17 26		18 00	18 26		19 00
Fratton	a		14 04	14 30	14 38	15 04	15 30	16 04		16 30	16 44	17 04	17 30	17 44	18 04	18 30	18 44	19 04
Portsmouth & Southsea	a		14 08	14 33	14 41	15 08	15 33	16 08		16 33	16 47	17 08	17 33	17 47	18 08	18 33	18 47	19 08
Portsmouth Harbour	a		14 13		14 48	15 13		16 13			16 53	17 13		17 53	18 13		18 51	19 13

		SW 1	GW ◇	SW 1	GW ◇	SW 1	GW ◇	SW 1	GW ◇	SW 1	GW ◇	SW 1	SW 1	GW ◇	SW 1	SW 1	GW ◇	SW 1
Southampton Central	d	18 35	19 07		19 27	19 35	20 01		20 31	20 35	21 01		21 35	22 01		22 35	23 00	
St Denys	d	18 41				19 41				20 41			21 41			22 41		
Bitterne	d	18 43				19 43				20 43			21 43			22 43		
Woolston	d	18 47				19 47				20 47			21 47			22 47		
Sholing	d	18 49				19 49				20 49			21 49			22 49		
Netley	d	18 53				19 53				20 53			21 53			22 53		
Hamble	d	18 55				19 55				20 55			21 55			22 55		
Bursledon	d	18 58				19 58				20 58			21 58			22 58		
Swanwick	d	19 02				20 02				21 02			22 02			23 02		
Fareham	a	19 09	19 28		19 48	20 09	20 23		20 54	21 09	21 22		22 09	22 22		23 09	23 21	
	d	19 10	19 29	19 44	19 49	20 10	20 24	20 44	20 55	21 10	21 23	21 44	22 10	22 23	22 44	23 10	23 22	23 44
Portchester	d	19 15		19 49		20 15		20 49		21 15		21 49	22 15		22 49	23 15		23 49
Cosham	d	19 20	19 37	19 54	19 59	20 20		20 54		21 20		21 54	22 20		22 54	23 20		23 54
Havant	a				20 10													
Chichester 4	a				20 21													
Hilsea	a	19 26		20 00		20 26		21 00		21 26		22 00	22 26		23 00	23 24		23 59
Fratton	a	19 30	19 44	20 04		20 30	20 39	21 04	21 09	21 30	21 36	22 04	22 30	22 36	23 04	23 28	23 37	00 04
Portsmouth & Southsea	a	19 33	19 47	20 08		20 33	20 43	21 08	21 15	21 33	21 39	22 08	22 33	22 39	23 08	23 32	23 40	00 08
Portsmouth Harbour	a		19 53	20 13			20 47	21 13	21 24		21 48	22 13		22 46	23 13		23 48	00 13

For general notes see front of timetable
For details of catering facilities see
Directory of Train Operators

For details of Bank Holiday service alterations, please see first page of Table 149

Portsmouth and Fareham → Southampton

Network Diagram - see first page of Table 165

Miles	Miles			SW 1	SN 1 A	SW 1	SW 1	GW ◇ ⊼	SN 1	SW 1	SW 1	SN 1	SW 1	GW ◇ ⊼	SN 1 B	SN 1 C	SW 1	SW 1	SN 1 C	SW 1	SW 1	GW ◇ ⊼	SN 1	SW 1	SW 1	SN 1
0	—	**Portsmouth Harbour**	d	05 00			05 43	06 00			06 23		06 38	06 51			07 24			07 55	08 05	08 22		08 33	08 55	
¾	—	**Portsmouth & Southsea**	d	05 05		05 16	05 48	06 04		06 23	06 28		06 43	06 55			07 29	07 38		08 00	08 10	08 27		08 38	09 00	
1¾	—	Fratton	d	05 09		05 20	05 52	06 08		06 27	06 32		06 47	06 59			07 33	07 43		08 04	08 14	08 31		08 43	09 04	
4	—	Hilsea	d	05 13		05 24	05 56			06 31	06 36		06 51				07 37	07 47		08 08	08 18			08 47	09 08	
—	0	Chichester 4	d		05 06				06 09			06 26			07 08	07 13			07 52				08 22			09 08
—	8¾	Havant	d		05 17				06 20			06 40			07 19	07 31			08 03				08 37			09 23
5½	12¾	Cosham	d	05 18	05 24	05 30	06 03	06 15	06 27	06 36	06 42	06 50	06 58	07 07	07 26	07 38	07 43	07 52	08 09	08 13	08 23	08 39	08 45	08 52	09 13	09 30
8	—	Portchester	d	05 23	05 28	05 35	06 08			06 41	06 46	06 54	07 03		07 30		07 48	07 57	08 13	08 18	08 28		08 49	08 57	09 18	
11¼	—	**Fareham**	a	05 28	05 33	05 40	06 13	06 23	06 36	06 46	06 51	06 59	07 08	07 17	07 35	07 46	07 53	08 02	08 18	08 23	08 33	08 46	08 54	09 02	09 23	09 37
—	—		d		05 34	05 41		06 24	06 37	06 47		07 00		07 18	07 36	07 47		08 03	08 19			08 47	08 55	09 03		09 38
15	—	Swanwick	d		05 40	05 47			06 43	06 53		07 06			07 42	07 53		08 09	08 26				09 01	09 09		09 44
17	—	Bursledon	d			05 51				06 57								08 13	08 29					09 13		
18¼	—	Hamble	d			05 54				07 00								08 16	08 32					09 16		
19	—	Netley	d		05 46	05 56				07 02					07 48	07 59		08 18	08 34					09 18		
20¾	—	Sholing	d			06 00				07 06								08 22	08 38					09 22		
21½	—	Woolston	d		05 50	06 02				07 08					07 52	08 04		08 24	08 40					09 24		
23½	—	Bitterne	d			06 06				07 12								08 28	08 43					09 28		
23¾	—	St Denys	d			06 09				07 15						08 08		08 31	08 46					09 31		
25¾	—	**Southampton Central**	a		05 59	06 14		06 45	07 02	07 21		07 24		07 45	08 01	08 13		08 38	08 52			09 08	09 19	09 38		10 01

		GW ◇ ⊼	SN 1	SW 1	GW ◇ D	SW 1	SN 1	GW ◇ ⊼	SN 1	SW 1	SW 1	SN 1		GW ◇ ⊼	SN 1	SW 1	SW 1	SN 1	GW ◇ ⊼	SN 1	SW 1	SW 1	SN 1	GW ◇ ⊼	SN 1	SW 1
Portsmouth Harbour	d	09 22		09 33		09 55		10 22		10 33	10 55			11 22			11 55		12 22			12 55		13 22		
Portsmouth & Southsea	d	09 27		09 38		10 00		10 27		10 38	11 00			11 27		11 38	12 00		12 27		12 38	13 00		13 27		13 38
Fratton	d	09 31		09 43		10 04		10 31		10 43	11 04			11 31		11 43	12 04		12 31		12 43	13 04		13 31		13 43
Hilsea	d			09 47		10 08				10 47	11 08					11 47	12 08				12 47	13 08				13 47
Chichester 4	d		09 24		09 47		10 06		10 25			11 05			11 25			12 05		12 25			13 05		13 25	
Havant	d		09 38		09 59		10 20		10 37			11 19			11 37			12 19		12 37			13 19		13 37	
Cosham	d	09 39	09 46	09 52	10 05	10 13	10 28	10 39	10 46	10 52	11 13	11 26		11 39	11 46	11 52	12 13	12 26	12 39	12 46	12 52	13 13	13 26	13 39	13 46	13 52
Portchester	d			09 57		10 18	10 32			10 57	11 18	11 30				11 57	12 18	12 30			12 57	13 18	13 30			13 57
Fareham	a	09 46	09 53	10 02	10 14	10 23	10 37	10 46	10 53	11 02	11 23	11 35		11 46	11 53	12 02	12 23	12 35	12 46	12 53	13 02	13 23	13 35	13 46	13 53	14 02
	d	09 47	09 54	10 03	10 14		10 38	10 47	10 54	11 03		11 36		11 47	11 54	12 03		12 36	12 47	12 54	13 03		13 36	13 47	13 54	14 03
Swanwick	d		10 00	10 09			10 44		11 00	11 09		11 42			12 00	12 09		12 42		13 00	13 09		13 42		14 00	14 09
Bursledon	d			10 13						11 13						12 13					13 13					14 13
Hamble	d			10 16						11 16						12 16					13 16					14 16
Netley	d			10 18						11 18						12 18					13 18					14 18
Sholing	d			10 22						11 22						12 22					13 22					14 22
Woolston	d			10 24						11 24						12 24					13 24					14 24
Bitterne	d			10 28						11 28						12 29					13 28					14 28
St Denys	d			10 31						11 31						12 31					13 31					14 31
Southampton Central	a	10 08	10 19	10 38	10 41		11 01	11 08	11 19	11 38		12 01		12 08	12 19	12 38		12 59	13 08	13 19	13 38		13 59	14 08	14 19	14 39

		SW 1	SN 1	GW ◇ ⊼	SN 1	SW 1	SW 1	SN 1	GW ◇ ⊼	SN 1	SW 1	SW 1	SN 1	GW ◇ ⊼	SN 1	SW 1	SW 1	SW 1	SN 1 ◇ E	GW ◇ ⊼	SN 1	SW 1	GW ◇ G	SW 1	SN 1 ⊼	GW ◇ ⊼
Portsmouth Harbour	d	13 55		14 22			14 55		15 22			15 55		16 22			16 55	17 03		17 22		17 33		17 55		18 22
Portsmouth & Southsea	d	14 00		14 27		14 38	15 00		15 27		15 38	16 00		16 27		16 38	17 00	17 07		17 27		17 38		18 00		18 27
Fratton	d	14 04		14 31		14 43	15 04		15 31		15 43	16 04		16 31		16 43	17 04	17 11		17 31		17 43		18 04		18 31
Hilsea	d	14 08				14 47	15 08				15 47	16 08				16 47	17 08	17 15				17 47		18 08		
Chichester 4	d		14 05		14 25			15 05		15 25			16 05		16 25				17 05		17 25		17 47		18 05	
Havant	d		14 19		14 37			15 19		15 37			16 19		16 37				17 19		17 37		17 58		18 22	
Cosham	d	14 13	14 26	14 39	14 46	14 52	15 13	15 26	15 39	15 46	15 52	16 13	16 26	16 39	16 46	16 52	17 13	17 20	17 26	17 39	17 46	17 52	18 05	18 13	18 29	18 39
Portchester	d	14 18	14 30			14 57	15 18	15 30			15 57	16 18	16 30			16 57	17 18	17 25	17 30			17 57		18 18	18 33	
Fareham	a	14 23	14 35	14 46	14 53	15 02	15 23	15 35	15 46	15 53	16 02	16 23	16 35	16 46	16 53	17 02	17 23	17 30	17 35	17 46	17 53	18 02	18 12	18 23	18 38	18 46
	d		14 36	14 47	14 54	15 03		15 36	15 47	15 54	16 03		16 36	16 47	16 54	17 03			17 36	17 47	17 54	18 03	18 13		18 39	18 47
Swanwick	d		14 42		15 00	15 09		15 42		16 00	16 09		16 42			17 09			17 42		18 00	18 09			18 45	
Bursledon	d					15 13					16 13					17 13						18 13				
Hamble	d					15 16					16 16					17 16						18 16				
Netley	d					15 18					16 18					17 18			17 48			18 18				
Sholing	d					15 22					16 22					17 22						18 22				
Woolston	d					15 24					16 24					17 24			17 52			18 24				
Bitterne	d					15 28					16 28					17 28						18 28				
St Denys	d					15 31					16 31					17 31			17 57			18 31				
Southampton Central	a		14 59	15 08	15 19	15 38		15 59	16 08	16 19	16 38		17 01	17 08	17 28	17 38			18 03	18 08	18 19	18 38	18 41		19 04	19 08

		SN 1	SW 1	SW 1	SN 1	GW ◇	SN 1	SW 1	SW 1	SN 1	GW ◇	SN 1	SW 1	SW 1 H	SN 1 J ⊼	GW	SN 1	SW 1	SW 1	SW 1	SN 1	SW 1	SW 1	SW 1
Portsmouth Harbour	d			18 55		19 22			19 55		20 22			20 55		21 22				21 55				23 24
Portsmouth & Southsea	d		18 38	19 00		19 27		19 38	20 00		20 27		20 38	21 00		21 27		21 38		22 00		22 38		23 29
Fratton	d		18 43	19 04		19 31		19 43	20 04		20 31		20 43	21 04		21 31		21 43		22 04		22 43		23 33
Hilsea	d		18 47	19 08				19 47	20 08				20 47	21 08				21 47		22 08		22 47		23 37
Chichester 4	d	18 25			19 02		19 20			20 01		20 26			21 05		21 26				22 05			
Havant	d	18 37			19 20		19 36			20 22		20 37			21 26		21 37		21 58		22 26		22 59	
Cosham	d	18 44	18 52	19 13	19 27	19 39	19 44	19 52	20 13	20 29		20 44	20 52	21 13	21 34		21 44	21 52	22 04	22 13	22 34	22 52	23 08	23 42
Portchester	d		18 57	19 18	19 31			19 57	20 18			20 48	20 57	21 18	21 38			21 57		22 18		22 57	23 13	23 47
Fareham	a	18 52	19 02	19 23	19 36	19 46	19 52	20 02	20 23	20 36	20 46	20 53	21 02	21 23	21 43	21 46	21 51	22 02	22 12	22 23	22 42	23 02	23 18	23 52
	d	18 53	19 03		19 37	19 47	19 53	20 03		20 37	20 47	20 54	21 03		21 44	21 47	21 52	22 03			22 43	23 03		
Swanwick	d	18 59	19 09		19 43		19 59	20 09		20 44		21 00	21 09		21 50		21 58	22 09			22 49	23 09		
Bursledon	d		19 13					20 13					21 13					22 13				23 13		
Hamble	d		19 16					20 16					21 16					22 16				23 16		
Netley	d		19 18					20 18					21 18					22 18				23 18		
Sholing	d		19 22					20 22					21 22					22 22				23 22		
Woolston	d		19 24					20 24					21 24		21 58			22 24				23 24		
Bitterne	d		19 28					20 28					21 28					22 28				23 28		
St Denys	d		19 31					20 31					21 31		22 03			22 31				23 31		
Southampton Central	a	19 20	19 38		20 03	20 08	20 18	20 38		21 03	21 08	21 19	21 38		22 08	22 20	22 16	22 39			23 07	23 39		

For general notes see front of timetable
For details of catering facilities see Directory of Train Operators

A From Barnham (Table 188)
B From Gatwick Airport (Table 188)
C From Brighton (Table 188)
D To Great Malvern (Table 71)
E From London Victoria (Table 188)
G To Worcester Shrub Hill (Table 57)
H To London Waterloo (Table 155)
J From London Victoria (Table 188). ⊼ to Horsham

Portsmouth and Fareham → Southampton

Network Diagram - see first page of Table 165

		SW 1	SN 1 A	SW 1	SN 1	SW 1	GW ◇	SN 1	SN 1		SW 1	SW 1	GW ◇	SN 1	SN 1	SW 1	SW 1	SN 1		GW ◇	SN 1	SW 1	SW 1	SN 1	GW ◇	SN 1
Portsmouth Harbour	d					05 55	06 00					06 55	07 05				07 55			08 22			08 55		09 22	
Portsmouth & Southsea	d			05 16		06 00	06 04				06 38	07 00	07 09			07 38	08 00			08 27		08 38	09 00		09 27	
Fratton	d			05 20		06 04	06 08				06 43	07 04	07 14			07 43	08 04			08 31		08 43	09 04		09 31	
Hilsea	d			05 24		06 08					06 47	07 08				07 47	08 08					08 47	09 08			
Chichester 4	d		05 05		05 28			06 06	06 23					07 07	07 25			08 05			08 25			09 05		09 25
Havant	d		05 16		05 39			06 24	06 37					07 23	07 37			08 20			08 37			09 19		09 37
Cosham	d	05 09	05 23	05 31	05 49	06 13	06 19	06 30	06 46		06 52	07 13	07 21	07 30	07 46	07 52	08 13	08 28		08 39	08 46	08 52	09 13	09 26	09 39	09 46
Portchester	d	05 14	05 27	05 35		06 18		06 34			06 57	07 18		07 34		07 57	08 18	08 32				08 57	09 18	09 30		
Fareham	a	05 19	05 32	05 40	05 57	06 23	06 27	06 39	06 53		07 02	07 23	07 29	07 39	07 53	08 02	08 23	08 37		08 46	08 53	09 02	09 23	09 35	09 46	09 53
	d		05 33	05 41	05 58		06 28	06 40	06 54		07 03		07 30	07 39	07 54	08 03		08 38		08 47	08 54	09 03		09 36	09 47	09 54
Swanwick	d		05 39	05 48	06 04			06 46	07 00		07 09			07 45	08 00	08 09		08 44			09 00	09 09		09 42		10 00
Bursledon	d			05 51							07 13					08 13						09 13				
Hamble	d			05 55							07 16					08 16						09 16				
Netley	d		05 45	05 57							07 18					08 18						09 18				
Sholing	d			06 01							07 22					08 22						09 22				
Woolston	d		05 49	06 03							07 24					08 24						09 24				
Bitterne	d			06 06							07 28					08 28						09 28				
St Denys	d			06 09							07 31					08 31						09 31				
Southampton Central	a		05 59	06 14	06 24		06 49	07 05	07 18		07 38		07 51	08 03	08 17	08 38		09 01		09 08	09 19	09 38		09 59	10 08	10 17

		SW 1	GW ◇ B	SW 1		SN 1	GW ◇	SN 1	SW 1	SW 1	SN 1	GW ◇	SN 1		SW 1	SW 1	SN 1	GW ◇	SN 1	SW 1	SW 1	SN 1		GW ◇	SN 1	SW 1
Portsmouth Harbour	d			09 55			10 22			10 55		11 22				11 55		12 22			12 55			13 22		
Portsmouth & Southsea	d	09 38		10 00			10 27		10 38	11 00		11 27			11 38	12 00		12 27		12 38	13 00			13 27		13 38
Fratton	d	09 43		10 04			10 31		10 43	11 04		11 31			11 43	12 04		12 31		12 43	13 04			13 31		13 43
Hilsea	d	09 47		10 08					10 47	11 08					11 47	12 08				12 47	13 08					13 47
Chichester 4	d		09 49			10 05		10 25			11 05		11 25				12 05		12 25			13 05			13 25	
Havant	d		10 00			10 19		10 37			11 19		11 37				12 19		12 37			13 19			13 37	
Cosham	d	09 52	10 06	10 13		10 26	10 39	10 46	10 52	11 13	11 26	11 39	11 46		11 52	12 13	12 26	12 39	12 46	12 52	13 13	13 26		13 39	13 46	13 52
Portchester	d	09 57		10 18		10 30			10 57	11 18	11 30				11 57	12 18	12 30			12 57	13 18	13 30				13 57
Fareham	a	10 02	10 15	10 23		10 35	10 46	10 53	11 02	11 23	11 35	11 46	11 53		12 02	12 23	12 35	12 46	12 53	13 02	13 23	13 35		13 46	13 53	14 02
	d	10 03	10 16			10 36	10 47	10 54	11 03		11 36	11 47	11 54		12 03		12 36	12 47	12 54	13 03		13 36		13 47	13 54	14 03
Swanwick	d	10 09				10 42		11 00	11 09		11 42		12 00		12 09		12 42		13 00	13 09		13 42			14 00	14 09
Bursledon	d	10 13							11 13						12 13					13 13						14 13
Hamble	d	10 16							11 16						12 16					13 16						14 16
Netley	d	10 18							11 18						12 18					13 18						14 18
Sholing	d	10 22							11 22						12 22					13 22						14 22
Woolston	d	10 24							11 24						12 24					13 24						14 24
Bitterne	d	10 28							11 28						12 28					13 28						14 28
St Denys	d	10 31							11 31						12 31					13 31						14 31
Southampton Central	a	10 38	10 40			10 59	11 08	11 19	11 38		11 59	12 08	12 19		12 38		12 59	13 08	13 19	13 38		13 59		14 08	14 19	14 39

		SW 1	SN 1	GW ◇	SN 1	SW 1	SW 1	SN 1		GW ◇	SN 1	SW 1	SW 1	SN 1	GW ◇	SN 1	SW 1		SW 1	SN 1	GW ◇	SN 1	SW 1	GW C	SW 1	SN 1
Portsmouth Harbour	d	13 55		14 22			14 55			15 22			15 55		16 22				16 55		17 22		17 33		17 55	
Portsmouth & Southsea	d	14 00		14 27		14 38	15 00			15 27		15 38	16 00		16 27		16 38		17 00		17 27		17 38		18 00	
Fratton	d	14 04		14 31		14 43	15 04			15 31		15 43	16 04		16 31		16 43		17 04		17 31		17 43		18 04	
Hilsea	d	14 08				14 47	15 08					15 47	16 08				16 47		17 08				17 47		18 08	
Chichester 4	d		14 05		14 25			15 05			15 25			16 05		16 25				17 05		17 25		17 46		18 05
Havant	d		14 19		14 37			15 19			15 37			16 19		16 37				17 19		17 37		18 00		18 19
Cosham	d	14 13	14 26	14 39	14 46	14 52	15 13	15 26		15 39	15 46	15 52	16 13	16 26	16 39	16 46	16 52		17 13	17 26	17 39	17 46	17 52	18 06	18 13	18 26
Portchester	d	14 18	14 30			14 57	15 18	15 30				15 57	16 18	16 30			16 57		17 18	17 30			17 57		18 18	18 30
Fareham	a	14 23	14 35	14 46	14 53	15 02	15 23	15 35		15 46	15 53	16 02	16 23	16 35	16 46	16 53	17 02		17 23	17 35	17 46	17 53	18 02	18 14	18 23	18 35
	d		14 36	14 47	14 54	15 03		15 36		15 47	15 54	16 03		16 36	16 47	16 54	17 03			17 36	17 47	17 54	18 03	18 15		18 36
Swanwick	d		14 42		15 00	15 09		15 42			16 00	16 09		16 42		17 00	17 09			17 42		18 00	18 09			18 42
Bursledon	d					15 13						16 13					17 13						18 13			
Hamble	d					15 16						16 16					17 16						18 16			
Netley	d					15 18						16 18					17 18						18 18			
Sholing	d					15 22						16 22					17 22						18 22			
Woolston	d					15 24						16 24					17 24						18 24			
Bitterne	d					15 28						16 28					17 28						18 28			
St Denys	d					15 31						16 31					17 31						18 31			
Southampton Central	a		14 59	15 08	15 19	15 38		15 59		16 08	16 19	16 38		16 59	17 08	17 19	17 38			17 59	18 08	18 19	18 38	18 43		18 59

For general notes see front of timetable
For details of catering facilities see
Directory of Train Operators

A From Barnham (Table 188)
B To Great Malvern (Table 71)
C To Cheltenham Spa (Table 57)

Table 165

Saturdays

Portsmouth and Fareham → Southampton

Network Diagram - see first page of Table 165

		GW ◇	SN 1	SW 1	SW 1	SN 1	GW ◇	SN 1	SW 1	SW 1 A	SN 1	GW ◇
Portsmouth Harbour	d	18 22			18 55		19 22			19 55		20 22
Portsmouth & Southsea	d	18 27		18 38	19 00		19 27		19 38	20 00		20 27
Fratton	d	18 31		18 43	19 04		19 31		19 43	20 04		20 31
Hilsea	d			18 47	19 08				19 47	20 08		
Chichester 4	d		18 25			19 05		19 25			20 05	
Havant	d		18 37			19 19		19 37			20 26	
Cosham	d	18 39	18 46	18 52	19 13	19 26	19 39	19 46	19 52	20 13	20 32	
Portchester	d			18 57	19 18	19 30			19 57	20 18	20 36	
Fareham	a	18 46	18 53	19 02	19 23	19 35	19 46	19 53	20 02	20 23	20 41	20 44
	d	18 47	18 54	19 03		19 36	19 47	19 54	20 03		20 42	20 48
Swanwick	d		19 00	19 09		19 42		20 00	20 09		20 48	
Bursledon	d			19 13					20 13			
Hamble	d			19 16					20 16			
Netley	d			19 18					20 18			
Sholing	d			19 22					20 22			
Woolston	d			19 24					20 24			
Bitterne	d			19 28					20 28			
St Denys	d			19 31					20 31			
Southampton Central	a	19 08	19 19	19 38		19 59	20 09	20 19	20 38		21 05	21 10

		SN 1	SW 1	SW 1 A	SN 1	SN 1	SW 1	SW 1	SN 1	SW 1	SW 1
Portsmouth Harbour	d			20 55				21 55			23 24
Portsmouth & Southsea	d		20 38	21 00			21 38	22 00		22 38	23 29
Fratton	d		20 43	21 04			21 43	22 04		22 43	23 33
Hilsea	d		20 47	21 08			21 47	22 08		22 47	23 37
Chichester 4	d	20 25			21 05	21 28			22 05		
Havant	d	20 37			21 23	21 40			22 26		
Cosham	d	20 46	20 52	21 13	21 29	21 47	21 52	22 13	22 34	22 52	23 42
Portchester	d		20 57	21 18	21 33		21 57	22 18		22 57	23 47
Fareham	a	20 53	21 02	21 23	21 38	21 54	22 02	22 23	22 41	23 02	23 52
	d	20 54	21 03		21 39	21 55	22 03		22 42	23 03	
Swanwick	d	21 00	21 09		21 45	22 01	22 09		22 48	23 09	
Bursledon	d		21 13				22 13			23 13	
Hamble	d		21 16				22 16			23 16	
Netley	d		21 18				22 18			23 18	
Sholing	d		21 22				22 22			23 22	
Woolston	d		21 24				22 24			23 24	
Bitterne	d		21 28				22 28			23 28	
St Denys	d		21 31				22 31			23 31	
Southampton Central	a	21 19	21 38		22 02	22 20	22 39		23 05	23 36	

Sundays

		SW 1	GW 1 B ⌶	SW 1	SW 1	SW 1	SW 1	GW ◇ ⌶	SW 1	SW 1
Portsmouth Harbour	d	06 37	07 08	07 17		08 17		09 08	09 17	
Portsmouth & Southsea	d	06 42	07 12	07 22	07 42	08 22	08 42	09 12	09 22	09 42
Fratton	d	06 46	07 16	07 26	07 46	08 26	08 46	09 16	09 26	09 46
Hilsea	d	06 50		07 30	07 50	08 30	08 50		09 30	09 50
Chichester 4	d									
Havant	d									
Cosham	d	06 55	07 23	07 35	07 55	08 35	08 55	09 23	09 35	09 55
Portchester	d	07 00		07 40	08 00	08 40	09 00		09 40	10 00
Fareham	a	07 05	07 31	07 45	08 05	08 45	09 05	09 31	09 45	10 05
	d	07 06	07 32		08 06		09 06	09 32		10 06
Swanwick	d	07 12			08 12		09 12			10 12
Bursledon	d	07 16			08 16		09 16			10 16
Hamble	d	07 19			08 19		09 19			10 19
Netley	d	07 21			08 21		09 21			10 21
Sholing	d	07 25			08 25		09 25			10 25
Woolston	d	07 27			08 27		09 27			10 27
Bitterne	d	07 31			08 31		09 31			10 31
St Denys	d	07 34			08 34		09 34			10 34
Southampton Central	a	07 40	07 53		08 40		09 40	09 53		10 40

		SW 1	SW 1	GW ◇ ⌶	SW 1	SW 1	GW ◇ C	GW ◇ D	SW 1
Portsmouth Harbour	d	10 17		11 08	11 17				12 17
Portsmouth & Southsea	d	10 22	10 42	11 12	11 22	11 42			12 22
Fratton	d	10 26	10 46	11 16	11 26	11 46			12 26
Hilsea	d	10 30	10 50		11 30	11 50			12 30
Chichester 4	d						11 55	11 58	
Havant	d						12 10	12 10	
Cosham	d	10 35	10 55	11 23	11 35	11 55	12b23	12b23	12 35
Portchester	d	10 40	11 00		11 40	12 00			12 40
Fareham	a	10 45	11 05	11 31	11 45	12 05	12 31	12 31	12 45
	d		11 06	11 32		12 06	12 32	12 32	
Swanwick	d		11 12			12 12			
Bursledon	d		11 16			12 16			
Hamble	d		11 19			12 19			
Netley	d		11 21			12 21			
Sholing	d		11 25			12 25			
Woolston	d		11 27			12 27			
Bitterne	d		11 31			12 31			
St Denys	d		11 34			12 34			
Southampton Central	a		11 40	11 53		12 40	12 53	12 53	

		SW 1	GW ◇ ⌶	SW 1	SW 1	GW ◇ ⌶	SW 1	SW 1	GW ◇ ⌶	SW 1
Portsmouth Harbour	d		13 08	13 17		14 08	14 17		15 08	15 17
Portsmouth & Southsea	d	12 42	13 12	13 22	13 42	14 12	14 22	14 42	15 12	15 22
Fratton	d	12 46	13 16	13 26	13 46	14 16	14 26	14 46	15 16	15 26
Hilsea	d	12 50		13 30	13 50		14 30	14 50		15 30
Chichester 4	d									
Havant	d									
Cosham	d	12 55	13 23	13 35	13 55	14 23	14 35	14 55	15 23	15 35
Portchester	d	13 00		13 40	14 00		14 40	15 00		15 40
Fareham	a	13 05	13 31	13 45	14 05	14 31	14 45	15 05	15 31	15 45
	d	13 06	13 32		14 06	14 32		15 06	15 32	
Swanwick	d	13 12			14 12			15 12		
Bursledon	d	13 16			14 16			15 16		
Hamble	d	13 19			14 19			15 19		
Netley	d	13 21			14 21			15 21		
Sholing	d	13 25			14 25			15 25		
Woolston	d	13 27			14 27			15 27		
Bitterne	d	13 31			14 31			15 31		
St Denys	d	13 34			14 34			15 34		
Southampton Central	a	13 40	13 53		14 40	14 53		15 40	15 53	

		SW 1	GW ◇ ⌶	SW 1	GW ◇	SW 1	GW ◇ ⌶	SW 1	SW 1
Portsmouth Harbour	d		16 08	16 17			17 08	17 17	
Portsmouth & Southsea	d	15 42	16 12	16 22		16 42	17 12	17 22	17 42
Fratton	d	15 46	16 16	16 26		16 46	17 16	17 26	17 46
Hilsea	d	15 50		16 30		16 50		17 30	17 50
Chichester 4	d				16 34				
Havant	d				16 48				
Cosham	d	15 55	16 23	16 35	16 55	16 58	17 23	17 35	17 55
Portchester	d	16 00		16 40		17 02		17 40	18 00
Fareham	a	16 05	16 31	16 45	17 02	17 07	17 31	17 45	18 05
	d	16 06	16 32		17 03	17 08	17 32		18 06
Swanwick	d	16 12				17 12			18 12
Bursledon	d	16 16				17 16			18 16
Hamble	d	16 19				17 19			18 19
Netley	d	16 21				17 21			18 21
Sholing	d	16 25				17 25			18 25
Woolston	d	16 27				17 27			18 27
Bitterne	d	16 31				17 31			18 31
St Denys	d	16 34				17 34			18 34
Southampton Central	a	16 40	16 53		17 24	17 42	17 53		18 40

For general notes see front of timetable
For details of catering facilities see
Directory of Train Operators

A To London Waterloo (Table 155)
B To Romsey (Table 158)
C Until 6 September
D From 13 September
b Arr. 1216

Table 165

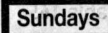

Portsmouth and Fareham → Southampton

Network Diagram - see first page of Table 165

		GW ◇ 🛒	SW 1	GW ◇	SW 1	GW ◇ 🛒	SW 1	SW 1	GW ◇ 🛒	SW 1	SW 1	SW 1	SW 1	GW ◇ 🛒	SW 1	SW 1	SW 1
Portsmouth Harbour	d	18 08	18 17	.	.	19 08	19 17	.	20 08	20 17	.	21 17	.	22 03	22 17	.	23 17
Portsmouth & Southsea	d	18 12	18 22	.	18 42	19 12	19 22	19 42	20 12	20 22	20 42	21 22	21 42	22 12	22 22	22 42	23 22
Fratton	d	18 16	18 26	.	18 46	19 16	19 26	19 46	20 16	20 26	20 46	21 26	21 46	22 16	22 26	22 46	23 26
Hilsea	d	.	18 30	.	18 50	.	19 30	19 50	.	20 30	20 50	21 30	21 50	.	22 30	22 50	23 30
Chichester 4	d	.	.	18 34	.	.	.	.	.	.	.	.	.	.	.	.	.
Havant	d	.	.	18 48	.	.	.	.	.	.	.	.	.	.	.	.	.
Cosham	d	18 23	18 35	18 55	18 58	19 23	19 35	19 55	20 23	20 35	20 55	21 35	21 55	22 23	22 35	22 55	23 35
Portchester	d	.	18 40	.	19 02	.	19 40	20 00	.	20 40	21 00	21 40	22 00	.	22 40	23 00	23 40
Fareham	a	18 31	18 45	19 02	19 07	19 31	19 45	20 05	20 31	20 45	21 05	21 45	22 05	22 31	22 45	23 05	23 45
	d	18 32	.	19 03	19 08	19 32	.	20 06	20 32	.	21 06	.	22 06	.	.	23 06	.
Swanwick	d	.	.	.	19 12	.	.	20 12	.	.	21 12	.	22 12	.	.	23 12	.
Bursledon	d	.	.	.	19 16	.	.	20 16	.	.	21 16	.	22 16	.	.	23 16	.
Hamble	d	.	.	.	19 19	.	.	20 19	.	.	21 19	.	22 19	.	.	23 19	.
Netley	d	.	.	.	19 21	.	.	20 21	.	.	21 21	.	22 21	.	.	23 21	.
Sholing	d	.	.	.	19 25	.	.	20 25	.	.	21 25	.	22 25	.	.	23 25	.
Woolston	d	.	.	.	19 27	.	.	20 27	.	.	21 27	.	22 27	.	.	23 27	.
Bitterne	d	.	.	.	19 31	.	.	20 31	.	.	21 31	.	22 31	.	.	23 31	.
St Denys	d	.	.	.	19 34	.	.	20 34	.	.	21 34	.	22 34	.	.	23 34	.
Southampton Central	a	18 53	.	19 24	19 42	19 53	.	20 40	20 53	.	21 40	.	22 40	.	.	23 40	.

For general notes see front of timetable
For details of catering facilities see Directory of Train Operators

Table 167

Mondays to Fridays

To and from the Isle of Wight via Portsmouth and Ryde

Network Diagram - see first page of Table 165

Miles			IL	IL	IL	IL	IL	IL	IL	IL	IL	IL	IL	IL	IL	IL	IL	IL	IL
—	**Portsmouth Harbour** ⛴	d	05b15	05b45	06b15	06b45	07b15	07b45	08b15	08b45	09b15	09b45	10b15	10b45	11b15	11b45		12b45	
0	**Ryde Pier Head**	d	05 49	06 08	06 49	07 08	07 49	08 08	08 49	09 08	09 49	10 08	10 49	11 08	11 49	12 08	12 49	13 08	13 49
—	**Ryde Esplanade**	d	05 51	06 10	06 51	07 10	07 51	08 10	08 51	09 10	09 51	10 10	10 51	11 10	11 51	12 10	12 51	13 10	13 51
1¼	Ryde St Johns Road	d	05 54	06 13	06 54	07 13	07 54	08 13	08 54	09 13	09 54	10 13	10 54	11 13	11 54	12 13	12 54	13 13	13 54
2¼	Smallbrook Junction §	d											10 57	11 16	11 57	12 16	12 57	13 16	13 57
4¾	Brading	d	06 02	06 21	07 02	07 21	08 02	08 21	09 02	09 21	10 02	10 21	11 02	11 21	12 02	12 21	13 02	13 21	14 02
6½	Sandown	d	06 06	06 25	07 06	07 25	08 06	08 25	09 06	09 25	10 06	10 25	11 06	11 25	12 06	12 25	13 06	13 25	14 06
7¼	Lake	d	06 09	06 28	07 09	07 28	08 09	08 28	09 09	09 28	10 09	10 28	11 09	11 28	12 09	12 28	13 09	13 28	14 09
8½	**Shanklin**	a	06 13	06 32	07 13	07 32	08 13	08 32	09 13	09 32	10 13	10 32	11 13	11 32	12 13	12 32	13 13	13 32	14 13

		IL	IL	IL	IL	IL	IL	IL	IL	IL	IL	IL	IL	IL	IL	IL	IL	IL	IL
Portsmouth Harbour ⛴	d	13b45		14b45		15b45	16b15	16b45	17b15	17b45	18b15	18b45	19b15	19b45	20b15	20b45	21b45	22b45
Ryde Pier Head	d	14 08	14 49	15 08	15 49	16 08	16 49	17 08	17 49	18 08	18 49	19 08	19 49	20 08	20 45	21 08	22 08	23 08
Ryde Esplanade	d	14 10	14 51	15 10	15 51	16 10	16 51	17 10	17 51	18 10	18 51	19 10	19 51	20 10	20 47	21 10	22 10	23 10
Ryde St Johns Road	d	14 13	14 54	15 13	15 54	16 13	16 54	17 13	17 54	18 13	18 54	19 13	19 54	20 13	20a50	21 13	22 13	23a13
Smallbrook Junction §	d	14 16	14 57	15 16	15 57	16 16	16 57											
Brading	d	14 21	15 02	15 21	16 02	16 21	17 02	17 21	18 02	18 21	19 02	19 21	20 02	20 21		21 21	22 21	
Sandown	d	14 25	15 06	15 25	16 06	16 25	17 06	17 25	18 06	18 25	19 06	19 25	20 06	20 25		21 25	22 25	
Lake	d	14 28	15 09	15 28	16 09	16 28	17 09	17 28	18 09	18 28	19 09	19 28	20 09	20 28		21 28	22 28	
Shanklin	a	14 32	15 13	15 32	16 13	16 32	17 13	17 32	18 13	18 32	19 13	19 32	20 13	20 32		21 32	22 32	

Saturdays

		IL	IL	IL	IL	IL	IL	IL	IL	IL	IL	IL	IL	IL	IL	IL	IL	IL
Portsmouth Harbour ⛴	d	05b15		06b15	06b45	07b15	07b45	08b15	08b45	09b15	09b45	10b15	10b45	11b15	11b45	12b15	12b45	
Ryde Pier Head	d	05 49	06 08	06 49	07 08	07 49	08 08	08 49	09 08	09 49	10 08	10 49	11 08	11 49	12 08	12 49	13 08	13 49
Ryde Esplanade	d	05 51	06 10	06 51	07 10	07 51	08 10	08 51	09 10	09 51	10 10	10 51	11 10	11 51	12 10	12 51	13 10	13 51
Ryde St Johns Road	d	05 54	06 13	06 54	07 13	07 54	08 13	08 54	09 13	09 54	10 13	10 54	11 13	11 54	12 13	12 54	13 13	13 54
Smallbrook Junction §	d											10 57		11 57			13 16	13 57
Brading	d	06 02	06 21	07 02	07 21	08 02	08 21	09 02	09 21	10 02	10 21	11 02	11 21	12 02	12 21	13 02	13 21	14 02
Sandown	d	06 06	06 25	07 06	07 25	08 06	08 25	09 06	09 25	10 06	10 25	11 06	11 25	12 06	12 25	13 06	13 25	14 06
Lake	d	06 09	06 28	07 09	07 28	08 09	08 28	09 09	09 28	10 09	10 28	11 09	11 28	12 09	12 28	13 09	13 28	14 09
Shanklin	a	06 13	06 32	07 13	07 32	08 13	08 32	09 13	09 32	10 13	10 32	11 13	11 32	12 13	12 32	13 13	13 32	14 13

		IL	IL	IL	IL	IL	IL	IL	IL	IL	IL	IL	IL	IL	IL	IL	IL
Portsmouth Harbour ⛴	d	13b45		14b45	15b15	15b45	16b15	16b45	17b15	17b45	18b15	18b45		19b45	20b45	21b45	22b45
Ryde Pier Head	d	14 08	14 49	15 08	15 49	16 08	16 49	17 08	17 49	18 08	18 49	19 08	19 49	20 08	21 08	22 08	23 08
Ryde Esplanade	d	14 10	14 51	15 10	15 51	16 10	16 51	17 10	17 51	18 10	18 51	19 10	19 51	20 10	21 10	22 10	23 10
Ryde St Johns Road	d	14 13	14 54	15 13	15 54	16 13	16 54	17 13	17 54	18 13	18 54	19 13	19 54	20 13	21 13	22 13	23a13
Smallbrook Junction §	d	14 16	14 57		15 57	16 16											
Brading	d	14 21	15 02	15 21	16 02	16 21	17 02	17 21	18 02	18 21	19 02	19 21	20 02	20 21	21 21	22 21	
Sandown	d	14 25	15 06	15 25	16 06	16 25	17 06	17 25	18 06	18 25	19 06	19 25	20 06	20 25	21 25	22 25	
Lake	d	14 28	15 09	15 28	16 09	16 28	17 09	17 28	18 09	18 28	19 09	19 28	20 09	20 28	21 28	22 28	
Shanklin	a	14 32	15 13	15 32	16 13	16 32	17 13	17 32	18 13	18 32	19 13	19 32	20 13	20 32	21 32	22 32	

Sundays

		IL	IL	IL	IL	IL	IL	IL	IL	IL	IL	IL	IL	IL	IL	IL	IL	IL
				A		A		A		A		A		A		A		
Portsmouth Harbour ⛴	d	06b15	07b15		08b15		09b15		10b15		11b15		12b15		13b15		14b15	14b45
Ryde Pier Head	d	06 49	07 49		08 49	09⌇08	09 49	10⌇08	10 49	11⌇08	11 49	12⌇08	12 49	13⌇08	13 49	14⌇08	14 49	15 08
Ryde Esplanade	d	06 51	07 51		08 51	09⌇10	09 51	10⌇10	10 51	11⌇10	11 51	12⌇10	12 51	13⌇10	13 51	14⌇10	14 51	15 10
Ryde St Johns Road	d	06 54	07 54	08⌇13	08 54	09⌇13	09 54	10⌇13	10 54	11⌇13	11 54	12⌇13	12 54	13⌇13	13 54	14⌇13	14 54	15 13
Smallbrook Junction §	d			⌇		⌇		⌇	10 57	⌇	11 57	⌇		13⌇16	13 57	14⌇16	14 57	
Brading	d	07 02	08 02	08⌇21	09 02	09⌇21	10 02	10⌇21	11 02	11⌇21	12 02	12⌇21	13 02	13⌇21	14 02	14⌇21	15 02	15 21
Sandown	d	07 06	08 06	08⌇25	09 06	09⌇25	10 06	10⌇25	11 06	11⌇25	12 06	12⌇25	13 06	13⌇25	14 06	14⌇25	15 06	15 25
Lake	d	07 09	08 09	08⌇28	09 09	09⌇28	10 09	10⌇28	11 09	11⌇28	12 09	12⌇28	13 09	13⌇28	14 09	14⌇28	15 09	15 28
Shanklin	a	07 13	08 14	08⌇32	09 13	09⌇32	10 13	10⌇32	11 13	11⌇32	12 13	12⌇32	13 13	13⌇32	14 13	14⌇32	15 13	15 32

		IL	IL	IL	IL	IL	IL	IL	IL	IL	IL	IL	IL	IL
Portsmouth Harbour ⛴	d	15b15	15b45	16b15	16b45	17b15	17b45	18b15	18b45	19b15	19b45	20b15	21b15	22b15
Ryde Pier Head	d	15 49	16 08	16 49	17 08	17 49	18 08	18 49	19 08	19 49	20 08	20 49	21 49	22 46
Ryde Esplanade	d	15 51	16 10	16 51	17 10	17 51	18 10	18 51	19 10	19 51	20 10	20 51	21 51	22 48
Ryde St Johns Road	d	15 54	16 13	16 54	17 13	17 54	18 13	18 54	19 13	19 54	20a13	20 54	21 54	22a51
Smallbrook Junction §	d	15 57	16 16											
Brading	d	16 02	16 21	17 02	17 21	18 02	18 21	19 02	19 21	20 02		21 02	22 02	
Sandown	d	16 06	16 25	17 06	17 25	18 06	18 25	19 06	19 25	20 06		21 06	22 06	
Lake	d	16 09	16 28	17 09	17 28	18 09	18 28	19 09	19 28	20 09		21 09	22 09	
Shanklin	a	16 13	16 32	17 13	17 32	18 13	18 32	19 13	19 32	20 13		21 13	22 13	

For general notes see front of timetable
For details of catering facilities see Directory of Train Operators

A Until 20 September
b By ship

§ Smallbrook Jn is only open for access to The I.O.W. Steam Railway. For days of operation please enquire locally.

From September due to amended ferry timings some trains on this table will be subject to alteration, please contact www.wightlink.co.uk or 0871 376 1000 for further details.

To and from the Isle of Wight via Portsmouth and Ryde

Network Diagram - see first page of Table 165

Mondays to Fridays

Miles			IL	IL	IL	IL	IL	IL	IL	IL	IL	IL	IL	IL	IL	IL	IL	IL	IL
0	**Shanklin**	d			06 17	06 36	07 17	07 36	08 17	08 36	09 17	09 36	10 17	10 36	11 17	11 36	12 17	12 36	13 17
1¼	Lake	d			06 21	06 40	07 21	07 40	08 21	08 40	09 21	09 40	10 21	10 40	11 21	11 40	12 21	12 40	13 21
2	Sandown	d			06 24	06 43	07 24	07 43	08 24	08 43	09 24	09 43	10 24	10 43	11 24	11 43	12 24	12 43	13 24
3¾	Brading	d			06 28	06 47	07 28	07 47	08 28	08 47	09 28	09 47	10 28	10 47	11 28	11 47	12 28	12 47	13 28
6¼	Smallbrook Junction §	d											10 33	10 52	11 33	11 52	12 33	12 52	13 33
7¼	Ryde St Johns Road	d	05 36	05 55	06 36	06 55	07 36	07 55	08 36	08 55	09 36	09 55	10 36	10 55	11 36	11 55	12 36	12 55	13 36
8¼	**Ryde Esplanade**	d	05 39	05 58	06 39	06 58	07 39	07 58	08 39	08 58	09 39	09 58	10 39	10 58	11 39	11 58	12 39	12 58	13 39
8½	**Ryde Pier Head**	a	05 41	06 00	06 42	07 01	07 42	08 01	08 42	09 01	09 42	10 01	10 42	11 01	11 42	12 01	12 42	13 01	13 42
—	**Portsmouth Harbour** ⛴	a	06b03	06b33	07b03	07b33	08b03	08b33	09b03	09b33	10b03	10b33	11b03	11b33	12b03	12b33		13b33	

		IL	IL	IL	IL	IL	IL	IL	IL	IL	IL	IL	IL	IL	IL	IL	IL	IL
Shanklin	d	13 36	14 17	14 36	15 17	15 36	16 17	16 36	17 17	17 36	18 17	18 36	19 17	19 36	20 17	20 36	21 36	22 36
Lake	d	13 40	14 21	14 40	15 21	15 40	16 21	16 40	17 21	17 40	18 21	18 40	19 21	19 40	20 21	20 40	21 40	22 40
Sandown	d	13 43	14 24	14 43	15 24	15 43	16 24	16 43	17 24	17 43	18 24	18 43	19 24	19 43	20 24	20 43	21 43	22 43
Brading	d	13 47	14 28	14 47	15 28	15 47	16 28	16 47	17 28	17 47	18 28	18 47	19 28	19 47	20 28	20 47	21 47	22 47
Smallbrook Junction §	d	13 52	14 33	14 52	15 33	15 52	16 33	16 52										
Ryde St Johns Road	d	13 55	14 36	14 55	15 36	15 55	16 36	16 55	17 36	17 55	18 36	18 55	19 36	19 55	20 36	20 55	21 55	22 55
Ryde Esplanade	d	13 58	14 39	14 58	15 39	15 58	16 39	16 58	17 39	17 58	18 39	18 58	19 39	19 58	20 39	20 58	21 58	22 58
Ryde Pier Head	a	14 01	14 42	15 01	15 42	16 01	16 42	17 01	17 42	18 01	18 42	19 01	19 42	20 01	20 42	21 01	22 01	23 01
Portsmouth Harbour ⛴	a	14b33		15b33		16b33	17b03	17b33	18b03	18b33	19b03	19b33	20b03	20b33	21b03	21b33	22b33	23b33

Saturdays

		IL	IL	IL	IL	IL	IL	IL	IL	IL	IL	IL	IL	IL	IL	IL	IL	IL
Shanklin	d			06 17	06 36	07 17	07 36	08 17	08 36	09 17	09 36	10 17	10 36	11 17	11 36	12 17	12 36	13 17
Lake	d			06 21	06 40	07 21	07 40	08 21	08 40	09 21	09 40	10 21	10 40	11 21	11 40	12 21	12 40	13 21
Sandown	d			06 24	06 43	07 24	07 43	08 24	08 43	09 24	09 43	10 24	10 43	11 24	11 43	12 24	12 43	13 24
Brading	d			06 28	06 47	07 28	07 47	08 28	08 47	09 28	09 47	10 28	10 47	11 28	11 47	12 28	12 47	13 28
Smallbrook Junction §	d												10 52		11 52		12 52	
Ryde St Johns Road	d	05 36	05 55	06 36	06 55	07 36	07 55	08 36	08 55	09 36	09 55	10 36	10 55	11 36	11 55	12 36	12 55	13 36
Ryde Esplanade	d	05 39	05 58	06 39	06 58	07 39	07 58	08 39	08 58	09 39	09 58	10 39	10 58	11 39	11 58	12 39	12 58	13 39
Ryde Pier Head	a	05 41	06 01	06 42	07 01	07 42	08 01	08 42	09 01	09 42	10 01	10 42	11 01	11 42	12 01	12 42	13 01	13 42
Portsmouth Harbour ⛴	a	06b03		07b03	07b33	08b03	08b33	09b03	09b33	10b03	10b33	11b03	11b33	12b03	12b33	13b03	13b33	

		IL	IL	IL	IL	IL	IL	IL	IL	IL	IL	IL	IL	IL	IL	IL	IL	IL
Shanklin	d	13 36	14 17	14 36	15 17	15 36	16 17	16 36	17 17	17 36	18 17	18 36	19 17	19 36	20 17	20 36	21 36	22 36
Lake	d	13 40	14 21	14 40	15 21	15 40	16 21	16 40	17 21	17 40	18 21	18 40	19 21	19 40	20 21	20 40	21 40	22 40
Sandown	d	13 43	14 24	14 43	15 24	15 43	16 24	16 43	17 24	17 43	18 24	18 43	19 24	19 43	20 24	20 43	21 43	22 43
Brading	d	13 47	14 28	14 47	15 28	15 47	16 28	16 47	17 28	17 47	18 28	18 47	19 28	19 47	20 28	20 47	21 47	22 47
Smallbrook Junction §	d					15 52												
Ryde St Johns Road	d	13 55	14 36	14 55	15 36	15 55	16 36	16 55	17 36	17 55	18 36	18 55	19 36	19 55	20a36	20 55	21 55	22 55
Ryde Esplanade	d	13 58	14 39	14 58	15 39	15 58	16 39	16 58	17 39	17 58	18 39	18 58	19 39	19 58		20 58	21 58	22 58
Ryde Pier Head	a	14 01	14 42	15 01	15 42	16 01	16 42	17 01	17 42	18 01	18 42	19 01	19 42	20 01		21 01	22 01	23 01
Portsmouth Harbour ⛴	a	14b33		15b33	16b03	16b33	17b03	17b33	18b03	18b33	19b03	19b33		20b33		21b33	22b33	23b33

Sundays

		IL	IL	IL	IL A	IL	IL A	IL	IL A	IL	IL A	IL	IL A	IL	IL A	IL	IL A	IL A
Shanklin	d		07 17	08 17	08 36	09 17	09 36	10 17	10 36	11 17	11 36	12 17	12 36	13 17	13 36	14 17	14 36	
Lake	d		07 21	08 21	08 40	09 21	09 40	10 21	10 40	11 21	11 40	12 21	12 40	13 21	13 40	14 21	14 40	
Sandown	d		07 24	08 24	08 43	09 24	09 43	10 24	10 43	11 24	11 43	12 24	12 43	13 24	13 43	14 24	14 43	
Brading	d		07 28	08 28	08 47	09 28	09 47	10 28	10 47	11 28	11 47	12 28	12 47	13 28	13 47	14 28	14 47	
Smallbrook Junction §	d								10 52		11 52		12 52				14 52	
Ryde St Johns Road	d	06 36	07 36	08 36	08 55	09 36	09 55	10 36	10 55	11 36	11 55	12 36	12 55	13 36	13 55	14 36	14 55	14 55
Ryde Esplanade	d	06 39	07 39	08 39	08 58	09 39	09 58	10 39	10 58	11 39	11 58	12 39	12 58	13 39	13 58	14 39	14 58	14 58
Ryde Pier Head	a	06 42	07 42	08 42	09 01	09 42	10 01	10 42	11 01	11 42	12 01	12 42	13 01	13 42	14 01	14 42	15 01	15 01
Portsmouth Harbour ⛴	a	07b03	08b03	09b03		10b03		11b03		12b03		13b03		14b03		15b03		15b33

		IL	IL	IL	IL	IL	IL	IL	IL	IL	IL	IL	IL	IL
Shanklin	d	15 17	15 36	16 17	16 36	17 17	17 36	18 17	18 36	19 17	19 36	20 17	21 17	22 17
Lake	d	15 21	15 40	16 21	16 40	17 21	17 40	18 21	18 40	19 21	19 40	20 21	21 21	22 21
Sandown	d	15 24	15 43	16 24	16 43	17 24	17 43	18 24	18 43	19 24	19 43	20 24	21 24	22 24
Brading	d	15 28	15 47	16 28	16 47	17 28	17 47	18 28	18 47	19 28	19 47	20 28	21 28	22 28
Smallbrook Junction §	d		15 52											
Ryde St Johns Road	d	15 36	15 55	16 36	16 55	17 36	17 55	18 36	18 55	19 36	19 55	20 36	21 36	22 36
Ryde Esplanade	d	15 39	15 58	16 39	16 58	17 39	17 58	18 39	18 58	19 39	19 58	20 39	21 39	22 39
Ryde Pier Head	a	15 42	16 01	16 42	17 01	17 42	18 01	18 42	19 01	19 42	20 01	20 42	21 42	22 42
Portsmouth Harbour ⛴	a	16b03	16b33	17b03	17b33	18b03	18b33	19b03	19b33	20b03	20b33	21b03	22b03	23b03

For general notes see front of timetable
For details of catering facilities see Directory of Train Operators

§ Smallbrook Jn is only open for access to the I.O.W. Steam Railway. For days of operation please enquire locally.

A Until 20 September
b By ship

From September due to amended ferry timings some trains on this table will be subject to alteration, please contact www.wightlink.co.uk or 0871 376 1000 for further details.

Table 175

Mondays to Fridays

London → East Croydon and Purley
COMPLETE SERVICE

	SN MX 1	SN MO	SN MX	SN MO 1	SN MX 1	FC	SN 1	SN	SN MX	FC	SN	SN 1 ◇	FC 1	FC 1	SN 1	FC 1	SN 1	FC	FC 1	SN 1 ◇	FC 1	FC 1	SN 1 ◇	FC 1
London Victoria 15 ⊖ d	23p47				00 05		00 14	00 17			00 42	01 00			02 00		03 00			04 00			05 02	
Clapham Junction 10 d	23p53			00 02	00 11		00 20	00 23			00 50	01 08			02 08		03 08			04 08			05 08	
London Charing Cross 4 ⊖ d		23p34	23p45						00 12															
London Waterloo (East) 4 ⊖ d		23p37	23p48						00 15															
St Pancras International 15 ⊖ d																								04 52
Farringdon 3 ⊖ d																								04 57
City Thameslink 3 d																								
London Blackfriars 3 ⊖ d																								05 04
London Bridge 4 ⊖ d		23p44	23p53			00 11			00 26	00 41			01 05	01 35		02 05		03 05	03 35		04 05	04 35		
Norwood Junction 2 a		00 09	00 16						00 49															
East Croydon a	00 05	00 13	00 20	00 22	00 24	00 26	00 32	00 43	00 53	00 56	01 10	01 21	01 32	02 02	02 21	02 30	03 21	03 30	04 00	04 21	04 30	05 00	05 20	05 30
South Croydon 4 a		00 16	00 23																					
Purley Oaks a		00 19	00 26																					
Purley 4 a	00 12	00 22	00 29				00 38					01 27			02 27		03 27			04 27			05 25	

	SN 1		FC 1	SN 1	FC 1	SN 1	SN 1	SN	FC 1	SN 1 ◇	SN	SN	SN 1	SN 1 ◇	FC 1	SN	SN 1	SN 1	SN 1	SN	FC 1	SN	SN 1	SN 1
London Victoria 15 ⊖ d	05 32			05 23			06 02	06 17		06 21		06 15		06 32			06 47	06 51		06 44			07 02	07 07
Clapham Junction 10 d	05 38			05 33			06 08	06 23		06 27		06 23		06 38			06 53	06 57		06 50			07 08	07 13
London Charing Cross 4 ⊖ d											06 05													
London Waterloo (East) 4 ⊖ d											06 08													
St Pancras International 15 ⊖ d			05 12		05 32				06 02						06 20						06 40			
Farringdon 3 ⊖ d			05 17		05 37				06 07						06 25						06 45			
City Thameslink 3 d			05 21		05 41				06 11						06 27						06 47			
London Blackfriars 3 ⊖ d			05 24		05 44				06 14						06 34						06 50			
London Bridge 4 ⊖ d			05 31		05 51	05 55			06 21		06 13		06 30		06 43	06 35			06 56		07 01	06 52		
Norwood Junction 2 a				05 49							06 37		06 44			06 55						07 13		
East Croydon a	05 48		05 51	05 53	06 04	06 09	06 17	06 34	06 35	06 37	06 41	06 45	06 48	06 48	06 56	06 59	07 03	07 06	07 09	07 11	07 15	07 17	07 18	07 24
South Croydon 4 a				05 56							06 45					07 02						07 20		
Purley Oaks a											06 48					07 05						07 23		
Purley 4 a	05 54						06 23			06 42	06 51	06 56		06 54		07 08						07 26	07 24	

	FC 1	SN	SN 1		SN 1	SN 1	SN 1	SN	SN 1	SN 1	FC 1	SN	SN	SN	SN 1	SN 1	SN 1	SN 1	SN	SN 1	SN 1 [trolley]	SN 1	SN 1 ◇	FC 1
London Victoria 15 ⊖ d		07 17			07 23			07 20		07 36					07 47		07 52		07 45		08 02		08 07	
Clapham Junction 10 d		07 23			07 29			07 28		07 42					07 53		07 58		07 51		08 08		08 13	
London Charing Cross 4 ⊖ d																								
London Waterloo (East) 4 ⊖ d																								
St Pancras International 15 ⊖ d	07 00										07 20													07 48
Farringdon 3 ⊖ d	07 05										07 25													07 53
City Thameslink 3 d	07 07										07 29													07 57
London Blackfriars 3 ⊖ d	07 10										07 32													08 00
London Bridge 4 ⊖ d	07 16		07 20			07 28	07 33		07 35		07 40	07 25	07 46	07 39		07 53		07 56		08 00		08 06		
Norwood Junction 2 a			07 32			07 41			07 48			07 48		07 59				08 07		08 12				
East Croydon a	07 31	07 33	07 36		07 41	07 45	07 48	07 49	07 52	07 52	07 55	07 55	08 00	08 03	08 03	08 06	08 09	08 11	08 13	08 16	08 18	08 21	08 22	08 25
South Croydon 4 a								07 52						08 06					08 16					
Purley Oaks a								07 55						08 09					08 19					
Purley 4 a								07 58		07 57		08 01		08 12					08 22	08 24				

	SN 1	SN	SN	SN 1	FC 1		SN 1	SN 1 ◇	SN 1	SN	SN 1 ◇	SN	SN 1 [trolley]	SN 1	SN 1 ◇ [trolley]	SN	SN 1 ◇	SN	SN 1 [trolley]	SN 1	FC 1	SN	SN 1	SN
London Victoria 15 ⊖ d	08 11			08 17				08 21		08 15	08 26		08 32		08 36		08 40		08 47				08 53	08 43
Clapham Junction 10 d				08 23				08 27		08 23	08 32		08 38		08 43		08 46		08 53				08 59	08 51
London Charing Cross 4 ⊖ d																								
London Waterloo (East) 4 ⊖ d																								
St Pancras International 15 ⊖ d					08 00																08 20			
Farringdon 3 ⊖ d					08 05																08 25			
City Thameslink 3 d					08 09																08 29			
London Blackfriars 3 ⊖ d					08 12																08 32			
London Bridge 4 ⊖ d		08 03	08 09		08 19		08 23		08 25			08 27		08 30		08 21		08 36		08 48		08 52		
Norwood Junction 2 a		08 25	08 26						08 36					08 44		08 49		08 56						
East Croydon a	08 25	08 29	08 33	08 33	08 36		08 37	08 39	08 40	08 43	08 43	08 45	08 48	08 49	08 52	08 53	08 56	09 00	09 03	09 03	09 06	09 07	09 09	09 12
South Croydon 4 a		08 32							08 44	08 47								09 03						09 15
Purley Oaks a		08 35								08 50								09 06						09 18
Purley 4 a		08 38	08 41							08 53				08 55				09 09		09 11		09 14		09 21

	SN 1 [trolley]	SN 1	SN 1 ◇ [trolley]	FC 1	SN 1	SN	SN 1		SN 1 [trolley]	SN	SN 1 ◇	FC 1	SN 1	SN	SN 1	SN 1 [trolley]	SN 1 ◇	FC 1	SN 1	SN	SN 1	SN 1 [trolley]	SN	SN 1
London Victoria 15 ⊖ d	09 02		09 06						09 17		09 21		09 23	09 13		09 32	09 36					09 47		09 53
Clapham Junction 10 d	09 08		09 12						09 23				09 29	09 21		09 38	09 42		09 35			09 53		09 59
London Charing Cross 4 ⊖ d																								
London Waterloo (East) 4 ⊖ d																								
St Pancras International 15 ⊖ d				08 48								09 04						09 20						
Farringdon 3 ⊖ d				08 53								09 09						09 25						
City Thameslink 3 d				08 56								09 13						09 29						
London Blackfriars 3 ⊖ d				08 59								09 16						09 34						
London Bridge 4 ⊖ d		09 03		09 06	09 09	09 05	09 18			09 21		09 25			09 30			09 42		09 35	09 46		09 52	
Norwood Junction 2 a		09 14				09 26									09 44					09 55				
East Croydon a	09 18	09 18	09 22	09 23	09 24	09 29	09 32		09 33	09 36	09 37	09 39	09 39	09 42	09 48	09 48	09 52	09 54	09 57	09 59	10 02	10 03	10 06	10 09
South Croydon 4 a						09 32								09 45						10 02				
Purley Oaks a						09 35								09 48						10 05				
Purley 4 a		09 26				09 38	09 40			09 43				09 51	09 56					10 08	10 10		10 13	

For general notes see front of timetable
For details of catering facilities see
Directory of Train Operators

London → East Croydon and Purley
COMPLETE SERVICE

	FC 1	SN	SN 1 (trolley)	SN 1	SN 1 ◊ (trolley)	SN 1	FC 1	SN	SN 1		SN 1 (trolley)	SN	SN 1 ◊		FC 1	SN 1	SN	SN 1 (trolley)	SN 1	SN 1 ◊	FC 1	SN 1	SN	SN 1
London Victoria 15 ⊖ d		09 43	10 02		10 06						10 17		10 21			10 23	10 13	10 32		10 36				
Clapham Junction 10 d		09 51	10 08		10 12						10 23					10 29	10 21	10 38		10 42		10 34		
London Charing Cross 4 ⊖ d																								10 40
London Waterloo (East) 4 ⊖ d																								10 43
St Pancras International 15 ⊖ d	09 39						09 54								10 09						10 24			
Farringdon 3 ⊖ d	09 44						09 59								10 14						10 29			
City Thameslink 3 d	09 48						10 02								10 17						10 32			
London Blackfriars 3 ⊖ d	09 50						10 05								10 20						10 35			
London Bridge 4 ⊖ d	09 58			10 03		10 08	10 11	10 05	10 19			10 22			10 26				10 33		10 41		10 35	10 48
Norwood Junction 2 a				10 14				10 25											10 44				10 55	
East Croydon a	10 10	10 12	10 18	10 18	10 22	10 22	10 24	10 29	10 32		10 33	10 36	10 37		10 39	10 39	10 42	10 48	10 48	10 52	10 54	10 57	10 59	11 02
South Croydon 4 a		10 15						10 32									10 45						11 02	
Purley Oaks a		10 18						10 35									10 48						11 05	
Purley 4 a		10 21		10 26				10 38	10 40			10 43					10 51		10 56				11 08	11 10

	SN 1	SN 1 (trolley)	SN	FC 1	SN 1	SN	SN 1	SN 1	SN 1 ◊	SN 1	FC 1	SN	SN 1	SN 1 (trolley)	SN	SN 1 ◊			FC 1	SN 1	SN	SN 1 ◊	SN 1
London Victoria 15 ⊖ d		10 47			10 53	10 43	11 02		11 06					11 17		11 21	and at the same minutes past each hour until			15 23	15 13	15 32	
Clapham Junction 10 d		10 53			10 59	10 51	11 08		11 12					11 23						15 29	15 21	15 38	
London Charing Cross 4 ⊖ d	10 40												11 10										
London Waterloo (East) 4 ⊖ d	10 43												11 13										
St Pancras International 15 ⊖ d				10 39							10 54								15 09				
Farringdon 3 ⊖ d				10 44							10 59								15 14				
City Thameslink 3 d				10 47							11 02								15 17				
London Blackfriars 3 ⊖ d				10 50							11 05								15 20				
London Bridge 4 ⊖ d	10 48		10 52	10 56				11 03		11 08	11 11	11 05	11 18		11 22				15 26				15 33
Norwood Junction 2 a								11 14				11 25											15 44
East Croydon a	11 02	11 03	11 06	11 09	11 10	11 12	11 18	11 18	11 22	11 23	11 24	11 29	11 32	11 33	11 36	11 37			15 39	15 40	15 43	15 48	15 48
South Croydon 4 a						11 15						11 32								15 43	15 46		
Purley Oaks a						11 18						11 35									15 49		
Purley 4 a	11 10		11 13			11 21		11 26				11 38	11 40		11 43						15 52		15 56

	SN 1 ◊ (trolley)	SN 1	FC 1	SN 1	SN	SN 1	SN 1 (trolley)	SN	FC 1	SN 1	SN	SN 1	SN 1	SN 1 (trolley)	SN 1	FC 1	SN	SN 1	SN 1 (trolley)	SN 1		SN	SN 1	FC 1
London Victoria 15 ⊖ d	15 36						15 47			15 53	15 43	16 02		16 06					16 17	16 19			16 23	
Clapham Junction 10 d	15 42			15 34			15 53			15 59	15 51	16 08		16 12					16 23	16 26			16 29	
London Charing Cross 4 ⊖ d						15 40												16 08						
London Waterloo (East) 4 ⊖ d						15 43												16 11						
St Pancras International 15 ⊖ d			15 24						15 39							15 54								16 09
Farringdon 3 ⊖ d			15 29						15 44							15 59								16 14
City Thameslink 3 d			15 32						15 47							16 02								16 17
London Blackfriars 3 ⊖ d			15 35						15 50							16 05								16 20
London Bridge 4 ⊖ d		15 38	15 41		15 35	15 48		15 52	15 56				16 03		16 08	16 11	16 05	16 16				16 22		16 26
Norwood Junction 2 a					15 55								16 14				16 25	16 28						
East Croydon a	15 52	15 52	15 54	15 57	15 59	16 02	16 03	16 06	16 09	16 09	16 12	16 18	16 18	16 22	16 23	16 24	16 29	16 32	16 33	16 36		16 36	16 39	16 40
South Croydon 4 a					16 02					16 12	16 15						16 32						16 42	
Purley Oaks a					16 05						16 18						16 35							
Purley 4 a					16 08	16 10		16 13			16 21		16 26				16 38	16 40				16 43		

	SN	SN 1 (trolley)	SN 1	SN 1 (trolley)	SN 1	SN	FC 1	SN 1	SN 1 (trolley)	SN	SN 1	SN 1	SN 1	SN	SN 1	SN 1	SN 1	SN 1	FC 1	SN	SN 1	SN 1		SN
London Victoria 15 ⊖ d	16 13	16 32		16 36		16 39			16 47		16 49	16 53		16 43		17 02	17 06			17 09		17 17		
Clapham Junction 10 d	16 21	16 38		16 42		16 45		16 34	16 53		16 56	16 59		16 51		17 08	17 12			17 15		17 23		
London Charing Cross 4 ⊖ d																								
London Waterloo (East) 4 ⊖ d																								
St Pancras International 15 ⊖ d							16 24																	
Farringdon 3 ⊖ d							16 29																	
City Thameslink 3 d							16 33																	
London Blackfriars 3 ⊖ d							16 36																	
London Bridge 4 ⊖ d			16 33		16 38		16 46			16 48			16 57		16 59			17 07	17 11		17 15			17 17
Norwood Junction 2 a			16 44							17 01					17 10									17 30
East Croydon a	16 42	16 47	16 48	16 52	16 52	16 55	16 59	16 59	17 03	17 05	17 06	17 09	17 09	17 12	17 14	17 17	17 21	17 22	17 24	17 27	17 29	17 32		17 34
South Croydon 4 a	16 45					16 58				17 08		17 12		17 19						17 30	17 32			17 37
Purley Oaks a	16 48					17 01				17 11				17 22						17 33				17 40
Purley 4 a	16 51		16 55			17 04				17 14				17 25	17 20					17 36				17 44

	SN 1	SN 1	SN 1	SN 1	FC 1	SN 1	SN 1 (trolley)	SN 1	SN	SN 1	SN 1	SN 1	SN 1	SN	SN 1	FC 1	SN 1	SN 1	SN 1	SN 1	SN 1	SN 1 (trolley)	FC 1	SN 1
London Victoria 15 ⊖ d		17 21	17 23			17 32	17 36		17 39				17 47		17 49		17 53			18 02		18 06		
Clapham Junction 10 d		17 27	17 30			17 38	17 42		17 45		17 33		17 53		17 56		18 00			18 08		18 12		
London Charing Cross 4 ⊖ d																								
London Waterloo (East) 4 ⊖ d																								
St Pancras International 15 ⊖ d					17 10											17 34							17 42	
Farringdon 3 ⊖ d					17 15											17 39							17 47	
City Thameslink 3 d					17 19											17 43							17 51	
London Blackfriars 3 ⊖ d					17 22											17 46							17 54	
London Bridge 4 ⊖ d	17 23			17 29	17 32			17 42		17 44		17 47		17 49		17 52		17 57	17 59		18 08			18 12
Norwood Junction 2 a				17 40										18 01					18 11					
East Croydon a	17 35	17 36	17 40	17 44	17 45	17 48	17 51	17 54	17 55	17 58	17 59	17 59	18 02	18 05	18 05	18 08	18 10	18 11	18 15	18 17	18 21	18 22	18 24	18 24
South Croydon 4 a									17 58	18 01				18 08										
Purley Oaks a									18 01					18 11										
Purley 4 a				17 50					18 03					18 14					18 20					

For general notes see front of timetable
For details of catering facilities see
Directory of Train Operators

Table 175

London → East Croydon and Purley
COMPLETE SERVICE

Station																								
	SN		SN [1]	SN	SN [1]	SN	SN [1]	SN [1]	FC [1]	SN [1]	SN [1]	SN [1]	SN [1]	FC [1]	SN	SN [1]	SN [1]	SN [1] 🛒	SN	SN [1]	FC [1]	SN [1]	SN	SN [1] 🛒
London Victoria [15] ⊖ d	18 09				18 17			18 19		18 23		18 32	18 36		18 39			18 47		18 51		18 53		19 02
Clapham Junction [10] d	18 15			18 02	18 23			18 26		18 30		18 38	18 42		18 45		18 34	18 53		18 57		19 00		19 08
London Charing Cross [4] ⊖ d																								
London Waterloo (East) [4] ⊖ d																								
St Pancras International [15] ⊖ d									18 08												18 38			
Farringdon [3] ⊖ d									18 13												18 43			
City Thameslink [3] d									18 17												18 47			
London Blackfriars [3] ⊖ d									18 20												18 50			
London Bridge [4] ⊖ d			18 15			18 18	18 22		18 26		18 29			18 42		18 47			18 49		18 56		18 59	
Norwood Junction [2] a						18 30					18 41								19 01					
East Croydon 🚊 a	18 27		18 30	18 32	18 33	18 34	18 36	18 37	18 40	18 40	18 45	18 48	18 52	18 54	18 57	19 00	19 02	19 02	19 05	19 07	19 10	19 10	19 13	19 18
South Croydon [4] a	18 30		18 33			18 39									19 00	19 03			19 08				19 16	
Purley Oaks a	18 33					18 45									19 03				19 11				19 19	
Purley [4] a	18 36			18 40		18 48		18 42			18 50				19 06				19 14				19 22	

Station																								
	SN [1]	SN [1] 🛒	SN [1]		FC [1]	SN [1]	SN	SN [1] 🛒	FC [1]	SN [1]	SN	SN [1] 🛒	SN [1]	FC [1]	SN [1]	SN	SN [1] 🛒	SN [1]	SN [1]	SN	FC [1]	SN [1] 🛒	SN [1]	SN [1] ◇
London Victoria [15] ⊖ d		19 06				19 10	19 00	19 17		19 23		19 32	19 36		19 40	19 30	19 47		19 53			20 02		20 06
Clapham Junction [10] d		19 12				19 16	19 08	19 23		19 29		19 38	19 42		19 46	19 38	19 53		19 59			20 08		20 12
London Charing Cross [4] ⊖ d																				19 37				
London Waterloo (East) [4] ⊖ d																				19 40				
St Pancras International [15] ⊖ d					18 53				19 08					19 22							19 42			
Farringdon [3] ⊖ d					18 57				19 13					19 27							19 47			
City Thameslink [3] d					19 01				19 17					19 31							19 51			
London Blackfriars [3] ⊖ d					19 04				19 20					19 34							19 54			
London Bridge [4] ⊖ d	19 03		19 08		19 12				19 27		19 14			19 41				19 52		19 45	20 01		20 05	
Norwood Junction [2] a	19 14										19 37							20 03		20 08			20 16	
East Croydon 🚊 a	19 18	19 22	19 22		19 24	19 28	19 30	19 33	19 39	19 39	19 41	19 48	19 52	19 54	19 58	20 00	20 03	20 06	20 09	20 12	20 14	20 19	20 19	20 22
South Croydon [4] a							19 34				19 45					20 03				20 15				
Purley Oaks a							19 37				19 48					20 06				20 18				
Purley [4] a	19 24					19 33	19 40				19 51				20 03	20 09		20 11		20 21				

Station																								
	FC [1]	SN [1]	SN	SN [1]	SN [1]		SN [1]	SN	SN [1]	SN [1]	SN [1] ◇	FC [1]	SN [1]	SN	SN [1]	SN [1]	SN [1]	SN	SN [1]	SN [1]	SN [1] ◇	FC [1]	SN [1]	SN
London Victoria [15] ⊖ d		20 10	20 00	20 17	20 23				20 32		20 36		20 40	20 30	20 47	20 53			21 02		21 06		21 10	21 00
Clapham Junction [10] d		20 16	20 08	20 23	20 29				20 38		20 42		20 46	20 38	20 53	20 59			21 08		21 12		21 16	21 08
London Charing Cross [4] ⊖ d								20 07										20 37						
London Waterloo (East) [4] ⊖ d								20 10										20 40						
St Pancras International [15] ⊖ d	19 52											20 22										20 52		
Farringdon [3] ⊖ d	19 57											20 27										20 57		
City Thameslink [3] d	20 01											20 31										21 01		
London Blackfriars [3] ⊖ d	20 04											20 34										21 04		
London Bridge [4] ⊖ d	20 11						20 28	20 15		20 35		20 41					20 58	20 45		21 05		21 11		
Norwood Junction [2] a								20 38		20 46								21 08		21 16				
East Croydon 🚊 a	20 24	20 28	20 29	20 33	20 39		20 40	20 42	20 48	20 49	20 52	20 54	20 58	20 59	21 03	21 09	21 10	21 12	21 18	21 19	21 22	21 24	21 28	21 29
South Croydon [4] a			20 32					20 45						21 02				21 15						21 32
Purley Oaks a			20 36					20 48						21 05				21 18						21 35
Purley [4] a		20 33	20 39					20 51					21 03	21 08				21 21					21 33	21 38

Station																								
	SN [1]	SN [1]	SN	SN [1]	SN [1]	SN [1] ◇	FC [1]		SN [1]	SN	SN [1]	SN [1]	SN	SN [1] ◇	SN [1]	SN [1] ◇	FC [1]	SN [1]	SN	SN [1]	SN [1]	SN	SN	SN [1]
London Victoria [15] ⊖ d	21 17	21 23			21 32	21 36			21 40	21 30	21 47	21 53		22 02		22 06		22 10	22 00	22 17	22 23			22 32
Clapham Junction [10] d	21 23	21 29			21 38	21 42			21 46	21 38	21 53	21 59		22 08		22 12		22 16	22 08	22 23	22 29			22 38
London Charing Cross [4] ⊖ d			21 07										21 37									22 07		
London Waterloo (East) [4] ⊖ d			21 10										21 40									22 10		
St Pancras International [15] ⊖ d							21 22										21 52							
Farringdon [3] ⊖ d							21 27										21 57							
City Thameslink [3] d							21 31										22 01							
London Blackfriars [3] ⊖ d							21 34										22 04							
London Bridge [4] ⊖ d			21 15	21 28			21 41						21 45		22 05		22 11					22 15	22 28	
Norwood Junction [2] a			21 38	21 39									22 08		22 16							22 38	22 40	
East Croydon 🚊 a	21 33	21 39	21 42	21 44	21 48	21 52	21 54		21 58	21 59	22 03	22 09	22 12	22 18	22 19	22 22	22 24	22 28	22 29	22 33	22 39	22 42	22 44	22 48
South Croydon [4] a			21 45							22 02			22 15						22 32			22 45		
Purley Oaks a			21 48							22 05			22 18						22 35			22 48		
Purley [4] a			21 51						22 03	22 08			22 21					22 33	22 38			22 51		

Station																								
	SN [1]	FC [1]	SN [1]	SN	SN [1]	SN [1]	SN	SN [1]	SN [1] ◇		SN [1] ◇	FC [1]	SN [1]	SN	SN [1]	SN [1]	SN	SN [1] ◇	FC [1]	SN [1]	SN [1]	SN		
London Victoria [15] ⊖ d	22 36		22 40	22 30	22 47	22 53			23 02		23 06		23 10	23 00	23 17	23 24		23 32		23 47	23 49			
Clapham Junction [10] d	22 42		22 46	22 38	22 53	22 59			23 08		23 12		23 16	23 08	23 23	23 30		23 38		23 53	23 56			
London Charing Cross [4] ⊖ d							22 37										23 07					23 45		
London Waterloo (East) [4] ⊖ d							22 40										23 10					23 48		
St Pancras International [15] ⊖ d																								
Farringdon [3] ⊖ d																								
City Thameslink [3] d																								
London Blackfriars [3] ⊖ d																								
London Bridge [4] ⊖ d		22 41					22 45	22 58				23 11					23 15		23 41			23 53		
Norwood Junction [2] a							23 08	23 09									23 38					00 16		
East Croydon 🚊 a	22 52	22 53	22 58	22 59	23 03	23 09	23 12	23 14	23 19		23 22	23 24	23 28	23 29	23 33	23 40	23 42	23 51	23 56	00 05	00 09	00 20		
South Croydon [4] a				23 02			23 15							23 32			23 45					00 23		
Purley Oaks a				23 05			23 18							23 35			23 48					00 26		
Purley [4] a			23 03	23 08			23 21						23 33	23 38			23 51			00 12		00 29		

For general notes see front of timetable
For details of catering facilities see
Directory of Train Operators

Table 175

London → East Croydon and Purley
COMPLETE SERVICE

		SN 1	SN	SN 1	FC 1	SN 1	SN	SN	FC 1	SN	SN 1 ◇	FC 1	FC 1	SN 1	FC 1	SN 1		FC 1	FC 1	SN 1 ◇	FC 1	FC 1	SN 1 ◇	FC 1	SN 1 ◇
London Victoria 15	⊖ d	23p47		00 05		00 14	00 17			00 42	01 00			02 00		03 00				04 00			05 02		05 32
Clapham Junction 10	d	23p53		00 11		00 20	00 23			00 50	01 08			02 08		03 08				04 08			05 08		05 38
London Charing Cross 4	⊖ d		23p45					00 12																	
London Waterloo (East) 4	⊖ d		23p48					00 15																	
St Pancras International 15	⊖ d																								
Farringdon 3	⊖ d																								
City Thameslink 3	d																								
London Blackfriars 3	⊖ d																								
London Bridge 4	⊖ d		23p53		00 11			00 26	00 41			01 05	01 35		02 05			03 05	03 35		04 05	04 35		05 05	
Norwood Junction 2	a		00 16					00 49																	
East Croydon	a	00 05	00 20	00 24	00 26	00 32	00 43	00 53	00 56	01 10	01 21	01 32	02 02	02 21	02 30	03 21		03 30	04 00	04 21	04 30	05 00	05 21	05 32	05 48
South Croydon 4	a		00 23																						
Purley Oaks	a		00 26																						
Purley 4	a	00 12	00 29			00 38					01 27			02 27		03 27				04 27			05 26		05 53

		SN 1	FC 1	SN 1	SN 1	SN 1	FC 1	SN 1	FC 1	SN 1		SN	SN	SN 1	FC 1	SN	SN 1	SN 1 ◇	SN 1	FC 1	SN	SN	SN 1 ◇	SN 1	FC 1
London Victoria 15	⊖ d	05 25		06 02		06 23		06 32						06 53		06 43		07 06					07 21	07 23	
Clapham Junction 10	d	05 31		06 08		06 29		06 38		06 34				06 59		06 51		07 12						07 29	
London Charing Cross 4	⊖ d																								
London Waterloo (East) 4	⊖ d																								
St Pancras International 15	⊖ d																								
Farringdon 3	⊖ d																								
City Thameslink 3	d																								
London Blackfriars 3	⊖ d																								
London Bridge 4	⊖ d		05 51		06 08		06 27		06 41			06 35	06 50		06 56		07 03		07 08	07 11	07 05	07 22			07 26
Norwood Junction 2	a	05 47										06 55	07 02				07 14				07 25				
East Croydon	a	05 51	06 04	06 18	06 22	06 39	06 39	06 48	06 54	06 57		06 59	07 06	07 09	07 09	07 12	07 18	07 22	07 22	07 24	07 29	07 36	07 37	07 39	07 39
South Croydon 4	a	05 54										07 02				07 15					07 32				
Purley Oaks	a											07 05				07 18					07 35				
Purley 4	a			06 23				06 53				07 08	07 13			07 21	07 26				07 38	07 43			

		SN	SN 1	SN 1		SN 1 ◇	FC 1	SN 1	SN	SN 1	SN 1	SN	SN 1	FC 1	SN	SN 1	SN 1	SN 1 ◇	SN 1	FC 1		SN	SN 1	SN 1	SN
London Victoria 15	⊖ d	07 13	07 32			07 36					07 47		07 53		07 43	08 02		08 06						08 17	
Clapham Junction 10	d	07 21	07 38			07 42		07 34			07 53		07 59		07 51	08 08		08 12						08 23	
London Charing Cross 4	⊖ d									07 40													08 10		
London Waterloo (East) 4	⊖ d									07 43													08 13		
St Pancras International 15	⊖ d																								
Farringdon 3	⊖ d																								
City Thameslink 3	d																								
London Blackfriars 3	⊖ d																								
London Bridge 4	⊖ d			07 33			07 41		07 35	07 48		07 52		07 56			08 03		08 08	08 11		08 05	08 18		08 22
Norwood Junction 2	a			07 44					07 55								08 14					08 25			
East Croydon	a	07 42	07 48	07 48		07 52	07 54	07 57	07 59	08 02	08 03	08 06	08 09	08 09	08 12	08 18	08 18	08 22	08 22	08 24		08 29	08 32	08 33	08 36
South Croydon 4	a	07 45							08 02						08 15							08 32			
Purley Oaks	a	07 48							08 05						08 18							08 35			
Purley 4	a	07 51		07 56					08 08	08 10		08 13			08 21		08 26					08 38	08 40		08 43

		SN 1 ◇	SN 1	FC 1	SN	SN 1	SN 1	SN 1 ◇	FC 1	SN 1	SN	SN 1	SN 1	SN		SN 1	FC 1	SN	SN 1	SN 1	SN 1 ◇ 🛒	SN 1	FC 1	SN	SN 1
London Victoria 15	⊖ d	08 21	08 23		08 13	08 32		08 36					08 47			08 53		08 43	09 02		09 06				
Clapham Junction 10	d		08 29		08 21	08 38		08 42		08 34			08 53			08 59		08 51	09 08		09 12				
London Charing Cross 4	⊖ d											08 40													09 10
London Waterloo (East) 4	⊖ d											08 43													09 13
St Pancras International 15	⊖ d																								
Farringdon 3	⊖ d																								
City Thameslink 3	d																								
London Blackfriars 3	⊖ d																								
London Bridge 4	⊖ d			08 26			08 33		08 41		08 35	08 48		08 52			08 56			09 03		09 08	09 11	09 05	09 18
Norwood Junction 2	a						08 44				08 55									09 14				09 25	
East Croydon	a	08 37	08 39	08 39	08 42	08 48	08 48	08 52	08 54	08 57	08 59	09 02	09 03	09 06		09 09	09 09	09 12	09 18	09 18	09 22	09 22	09 24	09 29	09 32
South Croydon 4	a				08 45						09 02							09 15						09 32	
Purley Oaks	a				08 48						09 05							09 18						09 35	
Purley 4	a				08 51		08 56				09 08	09 10		09 13				09 21		09 26				09 38	09 40

		SN 1	SN	SN 1 ◇		SN 1	FC 1	SN	SN 1	SN 1	SN 1 ◇ 🛒	FC 1	SN 1	SN	SN 1	SN 1	SN	SN 1	FC 1	SN	SN 1 🛒	SN 1	SN 1 ◇ 🛒	SN 1	FC 1
London Victoria 15	⊖ d	09 17		09 21		09 23		09 13	09 32		09 36					09 47		09 53		09 43	10 02		10 06		
Clapham Junction 10	d	09 23				09 29		09 21	09 38		09 42		09 34			09 53		09 59		09 51	10 08		10 12		
London Charing Cross 4	⊖ d														09 40										
London Waterloo (East) 4	⊖ d														09 43										
St Pancras International 15	⊖ d																								
Farringdon 3	⊖ d																								
City Thameslink 3	d																								
London Blackfriars 3	⊖ d																								
London Bridge 4	⊖ d		09 22				09 26			09 33		09 41		09 35	09 48		09 52		09 56			10 03		10 08	10 11
Norwood Junction 2	a									09 44				09 55								10 14			
East Croydon	a	09 33	09 36	09 37		09 39	09 39	09 42	09 48	09 48	09 52	09 54	09 57	09 59	10 02	10 03	10 06	10 09	10 09	10 12	10 18	10 18	10 22	10 22	10 24
South Croydon 4	a							09 45						10 02						10 15					
Purley Oaks	a							09 48						10 05						10 18					
Purley 4	a		09 43					09 51		09 56				10 08	10 10		10 13			10 21		10 26			

For general notes see front of timetable
For details of catering facilities see Directory of Train Operators

London → East Croydon and Purley
COMPLETE SERVICE

Station		SN	SN 1	SN 1	SN	SN 1 ◇			SN 1	FC 1	SN	SN 1	SN 1	SN 1 ◇ 🛒	FC 1	SN 1	SN	SN 1	SN 1	SN	SN 1	FC 1	SN	SN 1 🛒
London Victoria 15	⊖ d			10 17		10 21	and at the same minutes past each hour until		18 23		18 13	18 32		18 36					18 47		18 53			19 02
Clapham Junction 10	d			10 23					18 29		18 21	18 38		18 42		18 34			18 53		18 59			19 08
London Charing Cross 4	⊖ d		10 10															18 40						
London Waterloo (East) 4	⊖ d		10 13															18 43						
St Pancras International 15	⊖ d																							
Farringdon 3	⊖ d																							
City Thameslink 3	d																							
London Blackfriars 3	⊖ d																							
London Bridge 4	⊖ d	10 05	10 18		10 22					18 26			18 33		18 41		18 35	18 48		18 52		18 56	18 44	
Norwood Junction 2	a	10 25											18 44				18 55						19 10	
East Croydon	a	10 29	10 32	10 33	10 36	10 37			18 39	18 39	18 42	18 48	18 48	18 52	18 54	18 57	18 59	19 02	19 03	19 06	19 09	19 09	19 14	19 18
South Croydon 4	a	10 32									18 45						19 02						19 17	
Purley Oaks	a	10 35									18 48						19 05						19 20	
Purley 4	a	10 38	10 40		10 43						18 51		18 56				19 08	19 10		19 13			19 23	

Station		SN 1		SN 1 ◇ 🛒	SN 1	FC 1	SN	SN 1	SN 1 ◇	SN 1	FC 1	SN	SN 1	SN 1	SN 1 ◇	FC 1	SN 1	SN		SN 1	SN 1	FC 1	SN	SN 1 🛒	SN 1 ◇
London Victoria 15	⊖ d			19 06			19 00	19 17	19 21	19 23			19 32		19 36			19 30		19 47	19 53			20 02	20 06
Clapham Junction 10	d			19 12			19 08	19 23		19 29			19 38		19 42		19 35	19 38		19 53	19 59			20 08	20 12
London Charing Cross 4	⊖ d											19 07											19 37		
London Waterloo (East) 4	⊖ d											19 10											19 40		
St Pancras International 15	⊖ d																								
Farringdon 3	⊖ d																								
City Thameslink 3	d																								
London Blackfriars 3	⊖ d																								
London Bridge 4	⊖ d	19 03			19 08	19 11					19 26	19 15		19 33		19 41						19 56	19 45		
Norwood Junction 2	a	19 14										19 38		19 44									20 08		
East Croydon	a	19 18		19 22	19 22	19 24	19 29	19 33	19 37	19 39	19 39	19 42	19 48	19 49	19 52	19 54	19 57	20 00		20 03	20 09	20 09	20 12	20 19	20 22
South Croydon 4	a						19 32					19 45						20 03					20 15		
Purley Oaks	a						19 35					19 48						20 06					20 18		
Purley 4	a	19 26					19 38					19 51		19 57				20 09					20 21		

Station		SN 1	FC 1	SN 1	SN	SN 1	SN 1 ◇	SN 1	SN	SN 1	SN 1 ◇	FC 1		SN 1	SN 1	SN	SN 1	SN 1	SN	SN 1 ◇	SN 1 ◇	SN 1	FC 1	SN 1	SN
London Victoria 15	⊖ d			20 10	20 00	20 17	20 21	20 23		20 32	20 36				20 40	20 30	20 47	20 53		21 02	21 06			21 10	21 00
Clapham Junction 10	d			20 16	20 08	20 23		20 29		20 38	20 42			20 34	20 46	20 38	20 53	20 59		21 08	21 12			21 16	21 08
London Charing Cross 4	⊖ d								20 07										20 37						
London Waterloo (East) 4	⊖ d								20 10										20 40						
St Pancras International 15	⊖ d																								
Farringdon 3	⊖ d																								
City Thameslink 3	d																								
London Blackfriars 3	⊖ d																								
London Bridge 4	⊖ d	20 08	20 11						20 15			20 41							20 45			21 08	21 11		
Norwood Junction 2	a	20 19							20 38										21 08			21 19			
East Croydon	a	20 22	20 24	20 28	20 29	20 33	20 37	20 39	20 42	20 48	20 52	20 54		20 57	20 58	21 00	21 03	21 09	21 12	21 18	21 22	21 22	21 24	21 28	21 29
South Croydon 4	a				20 32				20 45							21 03			21 15						21 32
Purley Oaks	a				20 35				20 48							21 06			21 18						21 35
Purley 4	a			20 33	20 38				20 51						21 03	21 09			21 21					21 33	21 38

Station		SN 1	SN 1	SN	SN 1	SN 1 ◇		FC 1	SN 1	SN	SN 1	SN 1	SN	SN 1 ◇	SN 1 ◇	SN 1	FC 1	SN 1	SN	SN 1	SN 1	SN		SN 1	SN 1 ◇
London Victoria 15	⊖ d	21 17	21 23		21 32	21 36			21 40	21 30	21 47	21 53		22 02	22 06			22 10	22 00	22 17	22 23			22 32	22 36
Clapham Junction 10	d	21 23	21 29		21 38	21 42			21 46	21 38	21 53	21 59		22 08	22 12			22 16	22 08	22 23	22 29			22 38	22 42
London Charing Cross 4	⊖ d			21 07									21 37									22 07			
London Waterloo (East) 4	⊖ d			21 10									21 40									22 10			
St Pancras International 15	⊖ d																								
Farringdon 3	⊖ d																								
City Thameslink 3	d																								
London Blackfriars 3	⊖ d																								
London Bridge 4	⊖ d			21 15				21 41					21 45			22 08	22 11					22 15			
Norwood Junction 2	a			21 38									22 08			22 19						22 38			
East Croydon	a	21 33	21 39	21 42	21 48	21 52		21 54	21 58	21 59	22 03	22 09	22 12	22 18	22 22	22 22	22 24	22 28	22 29	22 33	22 39	22 42		22 48	22 52
South Croydon 4	a			21 45						22 02			22 15						22 32			22 45			
Purley Oaks	a			21 48						22 05			22 18						22 35			22 48			
Purley 4	a			21 51					22 03	22 08			22 21					22 33	22 38			22 51			

Station		FC 1	SN 1	SN	SN 1	SN 1	SN	SN	SN 1 ◇	SN 1 ◇	FC 1	SN 1	SN	SN 1	SN 1	SN		SN 1	FC 1	SN 1	SN 1	SN			
London Victoria 15	⊖ d		22 40	22 30	22 47	22 53			23 02	23 06		23 10	23 00	23 17	23 24			23 32		23 47	23 49				
Clapham Junction 10	d		22 46	22 38	22 53	22 59			23 08	23 12		23 16	23 08	23 23	23 30			23 38		23 53	23 56				
London Charing Cross 4	⊖ d						22 37									23 07						23 45			
London Waterloo (East) 4	⊖ d						22 40									23 10						23 48			
St Pancras International 15	⊖ d																								
Farringdon 3	⊖ d																								
City Thameslink 3	d																								
London Blackfriars 3	⊖ d																								
London Bridge 4	⊖ d	22 41					22 45	22 58			23 11					23 15			23 41			23 53			
Norwood Junction 2	a						23 08	23 09								23 38						00 16			
East Croydon	a	22 54	22 58	22 59	23 03	23 09	23 12	23 14	23 18	23 22	23 24	23 28	23 29	23 33	23 41	23 42		23 52	23 56	00 06	00 09	00 20			
South Croydon 4	a			23 02			23 15						23 32			23 45						00 23			
Purley Oaks	a			23 05			23 18						23 35			23 48						00 26			
Purley 4	a		23 03	23 08			23 21					23 33	23 38			23 51				00 12		00 29			

For general notes see front of timetable
For details of catering facilities see
Directory of Train Operators

London → East Croydon and Purley

COMPLETE SERVICE

	SN 1	SN	SN 1	FC 1	SN 1	SN	SN		FC 1	SN	SN 1	FC 1	SN 1	SN 1	SN 1		SN 1	SN 1◇	SN 1◇	SN 1 A	SN 1 A	SN 1 B	FC 1 A	FC 1 B
London Victoria 15 ⊖ d	23p47		00 05		00 14	00 17				00 42	01 00		02 00	03 00	04 00		05 02	05 47	06 32	07 02		07 02		
Clapham Junction 10 d	23p53		00 11		00 20	00 23				00 49	01 08		02 08	03 08	04 08		05 08	05 53	06 38	07 08		07 08		
London Charing Cross 4 ⊖ d		23p45					00 12																	
London Waterloo (East) 4 ⊖ d		23p48					00 15																	
St Pancras International 15 ⊖ d																								
Farringdon 3 ⊖ d																								
City Thameslink 3 d																								
London Blackfriars 3 ⊖ d																								
London Bridge 4 ⊖ d		23p53		00 11			00 26		00 41			01 05									07 05		07 11	07 11
Norwood Junction 2 a		00 16					00 49														07 16			
East Croydon a	00 06	00 20	00 24	00 27	00 32	00 42	00 53		00 56	01 10	01 21	01 32	02 21	03 21	04 21		05 22	06 05	06 51	07 19	07 20	07 23	07 25	07 26
South Croydon 4 a		00 23																						
Purley Oaks a		00 26																						
Purley 4 a	00 12	00 29			00 38						01 27		02 27	03 27	04 27		05 28		06 56	07 25	07 27	07 28		

	SN 1◇ A		SN 1 B	SN 1 A	SN 1 A	SN 1◇ B	SN 1 B	FC 1 A	FC 1 B		SN	SN 1 A	SN 1 A	SN 1 B	FC 1 A	FC 1 B	SN 1 A		SN 1 B	SN	SN 1◇ A	SN 1 B	SN 1 A	SN 1 A
London Victoria 15 ⊖ d	07 21		07 22	07 25	07 32	07 32	07 34					08 02		08 04			08 17		08 17		08 21	08 22	08 25	08 32
Clapham Junction 10 d	07 27		07 28	07 31	07 38	07 38	07 40					08 08		08 10			08 23		08 23		08 27	08 28	08 31	08 38
London Charing Cross 4 ⊖ d											07 34									08 04				
London Waterloo (East) 4 ⊖ d											07 37									08 07				
St Pancras International 15 ⊖ d																								
Farringdon 3 ⊖ d																								
City Thameslink 3 d																								
London Blackfriars 3 ⊖ d																								
London Bridge 4 ⊖ d								07 41	07 41		07 44		08 05		08 11	08 11				08 14				
Norwood Junction 2 a											08 04		08 16							08 34				
East Croydon a	07 38		07 42	07 42	07 49	07 50	07 53	07 55	07 56		08 08	08 17	08 20	08 24	08 25	08 27	08 32		08 37	08 38	08 38	08 42	08 42	08 47
South Croydon 4 a											08 11									08 41				
Purley Oaks a											08 14									08 44				
Purley 4 a					07 55		07 59				08 17	08 23	08 26	08 30						08 47				08 53

	SN 1◇ B	SN 1 B	FC 1 A		FC 1 B	SN 1 A	SN 1 B	SN		SN 1 A	SN 1 A	SN 1◇ B	SN 1◇ A	SN 1 B	FC 1 A	FC 1 B	SN 1 A	SN 1 B	SN	SN 1◇ A	SN 1 B	SN 1 A	SN 1 A	SN 1◇ B
London Victoria 15 ⊖ d	08 32	08 34				08 47	08 47			09 02		09 02	09 06	09 04			09 17	09 17		09 21	09 22	09 25	09 32	09 32
Clapham Junction 10 d	08 38	08 40				08 53	08 53			09 08		09 08	09 12	09 10			09 23	09 23		09 27	09 28	09 31	09 38	09 38
London Charing Cross 4 ⊖ d								08 34											09 04					
London Waterloo (East) 4 ⊖ d								08 37											09 07					
St Pancras International 15 ⊖ d																								
Farringdon 3 ⊖ d																								
City Thameslink 3 d																								
London Blackfriars 3 ⊖ d																								
London Bridge 4 ⊖ d			08 41		08 41			08 44			09 05				09 11	09 11			09 14					
Norwood Junction 2 a								09 04			09 16								09 34					
East Croydon a	08 50	08 53	08 55		08 56	09 02	09 07	09 08		09 17	09 20	09 21	09 22	09 24	09 25	09 27	09 32	09 37	09 38	09 38	09 42	09 42	09 47	09 50
South Croydon 4 a								09 11											09 41					
Purley Oaks a								09 14											09 44					
Purley 4 a		08 59						09 17		09 23	09 26			09 30					09 47				09 53	

	SN 1◇ A	SN 1 B	FC 1 A	FC 1 B	SN 1 A	SN 1 B	SN	and at the same minutes past each hour until		SN 1 A	SN 1 A	SN 1◇ B	SN 1◇ A	SN 1 B	FC 1 A	FC 1 B		SN 1 A	SN 1 B	SN	SN 1◇ A	SN 1 B	SN 1 A
London Victoria 15 ⊖ d	09 36	09 34			09 47	09 47				21 02		21 02	21 06	21 04				21 17	21 17		21 21	21 22	21 25
Clapham Junction 10 d	09 42	09 40			09 53	09 53				21 08		21 08	21 12	21 10				21 23	21 23		21 27	21 28	21 31
London Charing Cross 4 ⊖ d							09 34													21 04			
London Waterloo (East) 4 ⊖ d							09 37													21 07			
St Pancras International 15 ⊖ d																							
Farringdon 3 ⊖ d																							
City Thameslink 3 d																							
London Blackfriars 3 ⊖ d																							
London Bridge 4 ⊖ d			09 41	09 41			09 44				21 05				21 11	21 11				21 14			
Norwood Junction 2 a							10 04				21 16									21 34			
East Croydon a	09 52	09 53	09 55	09 56	10 02	10 07	10 08			21 17	21 20	21 21	21 22	21 24	21 25	21 27		21 32	21 36	21 38	21 38	21 42	21 42
South Croydon 4 a							10 11													21 41			
Purley Oaks a							10 14													21 44			
Purley 4 a		09 59					10 17			21 23	21 26			21 30						21 47			

For general notes see front of timetable
For details of catering facilities see Directory of Train Operators

A Until 6 September
B From 13 September

Table 175

London → East Croydon and Purley
COMPLETE SERVICE

Station		SN 1 A	SN 1 ◊ B	SN 1 B		FC 1 A	FC 1 B	SN 1 A	SN 1 B	SN	SN 1 A	SN 1 A		FC 1 A	SN 1 B	FC 1 B	SN 1 A	SN 1 B	SN 1 ◊ A	SN		SN 1 A	SN 1 B	SN 1 A	SN 1 ◊ B
London Victoria 15	⊖ d	21 32	21 32	21 34				21 47	21 47		22 02				22 04		22 17	22 17	22 21			22 25	22 22	22 32	22 32
Clapham Junction 10	d	21 38	21 38	21 40				21 53	21 53		22 08				22 10		22 23	22 23	22 27			22 31	22 28	22 38	22 38
London Charing Cross 4	⊖ d									21 34										22 04					
London Waterloo (East) 4	⊖ d									21 37										22 07					
St Pancras International 15	⊖ d																								
Farringdon 3	⊖ d																								
City Thameslink 3	d																								
London Blackfriars 3	⊖ d																								
London Bridge 4	⊖ d					21 41	21 41			21 44		22 05		22 11		22 11				22 14					
Norwood Junction 2	a									22 04		22 16								22 37					
East Croydon	a	21 47	21 50	21 53		21 55	21 56	22 02	22 07	22 08	22 17	22 20		22 24	22 24	22 27	22 32	22 36	22 38	22 42		22 42	22 43	22 47	22 50
South Croydon 4	a									22 11										22 45					
Purley Oaks	a									22 14										22 48					
Purley 4	a	21 53		21 59						22 17	22 23	22 26			22 30					22 51				22 53	

Station		SN 1 B	FC 1 A	FC 1 B	SN 1 A	SN 1 B		SN	SN 1	FC 1 A	FC 1 B	SN 1	SN	SN 1 ◊		FC 1	SN	SN	SN
London Victoria 15	⊖ d	22 34			22 47	22 47			23 04			23 17		23 32			23 47		23 49
Clapham Junction 10	d	22 40			22 53	22 53			23 10			23 23		23 38			23 53		23 56
London Charing Cross 4	⊖ d							22 34					23 04					23 34	
London Waterloo (East) 4	⊖ d							22 37					23 07					23 37	
St Pancras International 15	⊖ d																		
Farringdon 3	⊖ d																		
City Thameslink 3	d																		
London Blackfriars 3	⊖ d																		
London Bridge 4	⊖ d		22 41	22 41				22 44		23 11	23 11		23 14			23 41		23 44	
Norwood Junction 2	a							23 07					23 37					00 09	
East Croydon	a	22 53	22 55	22 56	23 02	23 07		23 12	23 23	23 25	23 26	23 37	23 42	23 52		23 56	00 06	00 13	00 16
South Croydon 4	a							23 15					23 45					00 16	
Purley Oaks	a							23 18					23 48					00 19	
Purley 4	a	22 59						23 21	23 28				23 51					00 22	

For general notes see front of timetable
For details of catering facilities see Directory of Train Operators

A Until 6 September
B From 13 September

Purley and East Croydon → London
COMPLETE SERVICE

		SN	SN	FC	FC	FC	SN	FC	SN	SN	SN	FC	SN	FC	SN	FC		SN	FC	SN	SN	SN	SN	FC	SN
		MO 1	MX 1	MO 1	MX 1	MX 1	1 ◊	1		1	1	1	1	1	1				1	1				1	1
Purley 4	d	23p50	23p49				00 11			01 22	02 22		03 22		04 22			05 07		05 23		05 39			06 00
Purley Oaks	d																					05 42			
South Croydon 4	d																					05 45			
East Croydon	d	23p56	23b58	00 01	00 04	00 04	00 17	00 36	00 49	01 28	02 28	02 47	03 28	03 47	04 28	04 47		05 13	05 17	05 29	05 34	05 48	05 51	06 02	06 07
Norwood Junction 2	d																	05 17			05 38		05 55		
London Bridge 4	⊖ a			00 14	00 19	00 19		00 52				03 12		04 12				05 41	05 34				06 24	06 15	
London Blackfriars 3	⊖ a															05 14			05 43					06 24	
City Thameslink 3	a															05 16			05 46					06 26	
Farringdon 3	⊖ a															05 20			05 50					06 30	
St Pancras International 15	⊖ a															05 23			05 53					06 33	
London Waterloo (East) 4	⊖ a																	05 46							
London Charing Cross 4	⊖ a																	05 49							
Clapham Junction 10	a	00 10	00 11				00 29		01 02	01 40	02 40		03 40		04 47					05 48	05 58	06 09			06 18
London Victoria 15	⊖ a	00 18	00 18				00 37		01 09	01 49	02 49		03 49		04 54					05 58	06 07	06 18			06 25

		SN	SN	SN	SN	SN	SN	SN	SN	FC		SN	SN	FC	SN	SN	SN	SN	FC	SN	SN	SN	SN	SN	SN
		1		1		1	1		1	1			1	1		1	1	1	1		1	1		1	
Purley 4	d		06 03					06 22	06 26			06 31						06 57				07 05	07 03		
Purley Oaks	d		06 06					06 25				06 34											07 06		
South Croydon 4	d		06 09					06 28				06 37			06 42								07 09		
East Croydon	d	06 11	06 12	06 15	06 17	06 23	06 27	06 31	06 31	06 32		06 40	06 42	06 44	06 45	06 57	06 59	07 02	07 02	07 05	07 08	07 10	07 12	07 15	07 17
Norwood Junction 2	d		06 17					06 35				06 45											07 17		
London Bridge 4	⊖ a		06 35			06 40		06 56		06 46		07 02		06 58			07 14	07 21	07 16	07 43	07 25		07 33		
London Blackfriars 3	⊖ a									06 53				07 06					07 23						
City Thameslink 3	a									06 56				07 08					07 25						
Farringdon 3	⊖ a									07 00				07 11					07 28						
St Pancras International 15	⊖ a									07 03				07 15					07 32						
London Waterloo (East) 4	⊖ a																								
London Charing Cross 4	⊖ a																								
Clapham Junction 10	a	06 21		06 25	06 37		06 38		06 41				06 51		07 05	07 07						07 19		07 24	07 37
London Victoria 15	⊖ a	06 28		06 32	06 45		06 45		06 48				07 00		07 16	07 17						07 28		07 33	07 47

		SN	SN	FC		SN	SN	SN	SN	SN	SN	SN	SN	SN	SN	SN	SN	FC	SN	SN		SN	SN	SN	SN
		1		1		1		1	1		1 ⚲	1	1	1	1			1	1			1	1	1 ⚲	1
Purley 4	d		07 12				07 23			07 27		07 34					07 43			07 48			07 55		
Purley Oaks	d		07 15							07 30							07 46			07 51					
South Croydon 4	d		07 18							07 33							07 49			07 54					
East Croydon	d	07 21	07 22	07 24		07 26	07 29	07 29	07 32	07 36	07 39	07 40	07 44	07 44	07 47	07 47	07 52	07 54	07 54	07 57		07 57	08 00	08 01	08 03
Norwood Junction 2	d									07 41										08 01					
London Bridge 4	⊖ a	07 38				07 44		07 46	07 48	08 01					08 04				08 11	08 16			08 18		08 20
London Blackfriars 3	⊖ a			07 53														08 22							
City Thameslink 3	a			07 56														08 24							
Farringdon 3	⊖ a			08 00														08 28							
St Pancras International 15	⊖ a			08 03														08 31							
London Waterloo (East) 4	⊖ a																								
London Charing Cross 4	⊖ a																								
Clapham Junction 10	a		07 31				07 39				07 48	07 51	07 54	07 57		08 08	08 02					08 06		08 10	
London Victoria 15	⊖ a		07 41				07 48				07 57	08 00	08 03	08 06			08 12					08 16		08 19	

		SN	SN	SN	SN	SN	SN	SN	SN	SN	SN	SN	SN	SN		FC	SN	SN	SN	SN	SN	FC	SN	SN	SN
		1	1	1	1		1 ⚲	1			1	1 ⚲	1	1		1	1	1	1		1	1	1	1 ⚲	
Purley 4	d					08 03			08 07		08 15									08 25	08 31				08 36
Purley Oaks	d					08 06			08 10											08 28					08 39
South Croydon 4	d	08 01				08 09			08 13				08 22							08 31			08 37		08 42
East Croydon	d	08 04	08 07	08 09	08 11	08 12	08 14	08 16	08 17	08 18	08 21	08 24	08 26	08 27		08 28	08 30	08 30	08 33	08 34	08 37	08 38	08 40	08 44	08 45
Norwood Junction 2	d					08 17														08 40					08 49
London Bridge 4	⊖ a		08 24	08 26		08 31		08 35			08 41	08 43		08 45			08 53		08 50	08 57			09 00		09 05
London Blackfriars 3	⊖ a															08 54						09 08			
City Thameslink 3	a															08 56						09 10			
Farringdon 3	⊖ a															09 00						09 14			
St Pancras International 15	⊖ a															09 03						09 17			
London Waterloo (East) 4	⊖ a																								
London Charing Cross 4	⊖ a																								
Clapham Junction 10	a	08 16			08 20		08 23		08 26	08 40			08 36					08 40			08 47			08 53	
London Victoria 15	⊖ a	08 26			08 29		08 32		08 35	08 51			08 45					08 48			08 57			09 02	

		SN	SN	SN	SN	FC	SN	SN		SN	SN	SN	FC	SN	SN	SN	SN	SN	SN	SN	SN	SN	FC	SN	SN
		1 ⚲	1		1	1	1	1		1			1	1	1 ⚲	1			1 ⚲	1 ⚲	1		1	1	1
Purley 4	d						08 50					08 56		09 05			09 08	09 14				09 22			09 32
Purley Oaks	d											08 59					09 11					09 25			
South Croydon 4	d				08 49							09 02					09 14					09 28			
East Croydon	d	08 47	08 48	08 50	08 53	08 54	08 56	09 00		09 01	09 02	09 05	09 08	09 11	09 14	09 14	09 17	09 20	09 22	09 26	09 29	09 31	09 32	09 33	09 37
Norwood Junction 2	d											09 09						09 25				09 35			09 42
London Bridge 4	⊖ a		09 08			09 10	09 15	09 19			09 43	09 24						09 42				09 59	09 45	09 51	09 56
London Blackfriars 3	⊖ a					09 20							09 38										09 54		
City Thameslink 3	a					09 22							09 40										09 56		
Farringdon 3	⊖ a					09 28							09 44										10 00		
St Pancras International 15	⊖ a					09 31							09 47										10 03		
London Waterloo (East) 4	⊖ a																								
London Charing Cross 4	⊖ a																								
Clapham Junction 10	a	08 56		09 12	09 04					09 10				09 20	09 23	09 26	09 38		09 32	09 35	09 38				
London Victoria 15	⊖ a	09 05		09 22	09 14					09 19				09 29	09 32	09 37	09 48		09 41	09 44	09 48				

For general notes see front of timetable
For details of catering facilities see
Directory of Train Operators

b Previous night.
Arr. 2355

Table 175

Mondays to Fridays

Purley and East Croydon → London

COMPLETE SERVICE

		SN 1 🛒		SN 1	SN 1	SN	FC 1	SN	SN 1	SN 1 ◇ 🛒	SN	SN 1 🛒	FC 1	SN 1	SN 1	SN 1 🛒	SN 1	SN		FC 1	SN	SN 1 ◇ 🛒	SN 1	SN 1	SN
Purley 4	d					09 38		09 45	09 49		09 51			10 02				10 08			10 15		10 19		10 21
Purley Oaks	d					09 41					09 54							10 11							10 24
South Croydon 4	d					09 44					09 57							10 14							10 27
East Croydon	d	09 39		09 43	09 44	09 47	09 47	09 51	09 55	09 55	10 00	10 00	10 02	10 08	10 10	10 11	10 14	10 17		10 17	10 21	10 24	10 25	10 29	10 30
Norwood Junction 2	d								09 59		10 05												10 29		10 35
London Bridge 4	⊖ a						10 01	10 10	10 12		10 26		10 16	10 22						10 30	10 38		10 42		10 57
London Blackfriars 3	⊖ a						10 07						10 24							10 37					
City Thameslink 3	a						10 10						10 26							10 40					
Farringdon 3	⊖ a						10 14						10 30							10 44					
St Pancras International 15	⊖ a						10 17						10 33							10 47					
London Waterloo (East) 4	⊖ a													10 27											
London Charing Cross 4	⊖ a													10 30											
Clapham Junction 10	a	09 48		09 52	09 55	10 07				10 04		10 09			10 35	10 20	10 25	10 37				10 33		10 38	
London Victoria 15	⊖ a	09 58		10 00	10 05	10 16				10 11		10 16				10 27	10 32	10 46				10 40		10 45	

		FC 1	SN 1	SN 1	SN 1 🛒	SN 1		SN	FC 1	SN	SN 1 ◇	SN 1	SN 1 ◇ 🛒	SN	SN 1	FC 1	SN 1	SN 1	SN 1 🛒	SN 1	SN	FC 1	SN	SN 1 ◇ 🛒	SN 1
Purley 4	d			10 32				10 38		10 45		10 49		10 51			11 01				11 08		11 15		11 19
Purley Oaks	d							10 41						10 54							11 11				
South Croydon 4	d							10 44						10 57							11 14				
East Croydon	d	10 32	10 33	10 37	10 41	10 44		10 47	10 47	10 51	10 53	10 55	10 56	11 00	11 00	11 02	11 07	11 10	11 11	11 14	11 17	11 17	11 21	11 24	11 25
Norwood Junction 2	d											10 59		11 05											11 29
London Bridge 4	⊖ a	10 45	10 49	10 52					11 00	11 08		11 12		11 26		11 15	11 22					11 30	11 38		11 42
London Blackfriars 3	⊖ a	10 54							11 07							11 23						11 37			
City Thameslink 3	a	10 56							11 10							11 26						11 40			
Farringdon 3	⊖ a	11 00							11 14							11 30						11 44			
St Pancras International 15	⊖ a	11 03							11 17							11 33						11 47			
London Waterloo (East) 4	⊖ a			10 56													11 26								
London Charing Cross 4	⊖ a			11 00													11 30								
Clapham Junction 10	a				10 50	10 55		11 07			11 02		11 05		11 09			11 33	11 20	11 25	11 37			11 33	
London Victoria 15	⊖ a				10 57	11 05		11 16			11 09		11 12		11 16				11 27	11 35	11 46			11 40	

		SN 1 🛒	SN	FC 1	SN 1	SN 1	SN 1 🛒	SN 1			SN	FC 1	SN	SN 1 ◇	SN 1	SN 1 ◇ 🛒	SN	SN 1 🛒	FC 1	SN 1	SN 1 🛒	SN 1	SN	FC 1
Purley 4	d		11 21			11 31			and at		15 38		15 45		15 49		15 51			16 02			16 08	
Purley Oaks	d		11 24						the same		15 41						15 54						16 11	
South Croydon 4	d		11 27								15 44						15 57						16 14	
East Croydon	d	11 28	11 30	11 32	11 33	11 37	11 41	11 44	minutes		15 47	15 47	15 51	15 53	15 55	15 56	16 00	16 00	16 02	16 07	16 11	16 14	16 17	16 17
Norwood Junction 2	d		11 35												15 59		16 05			16 12				
London Bridge 4	⊖ a		11 56	11 45	11 49	11 52			past			16 00	16 08		16 12		16 29		16 15	16 25				
London Blackfriars 3	⊖ a			11 53								16 07							16 25					16 48
City Thameslink 3	a			11 56					each			16 10							16 28					16 52
Farringdon 3	⊖ a			12 00								16 13							16 31					16 57
St Pancras International 15	⊖ a			12 03					hour until			16 17							16 35					17 01
London Waterloo (East) 4	⊖ a					11 56																		
London Charing Cross 4	⊖ a					12 00																		
Clapham Junction 10	a	11 37					11 50	11 55			16 07			16 02		16 05		16 09			16 20	16 25	16 37	
London Victoria 15	⊖ a	11 44					11 57	12 02			16 16			16 09		16 12		16 20			16 28	16 32	16 46	

		SN	SN 1 ◇ 🛒	SN 1		FC 1	SN	SN 1 🛒	SN 1	SN 1	SN 1 🛒	SN 1	SN	FC 1	SN	SN 1 ◇	SN 1	SN 1 🛒	FC 1	SN		SN 1	SN 1	FC 1	SN 1
Purley 4	d	16 15		16 19			16 21			16 34			16 38		16 45		16 49			16 51			17 02		
Purley Oaks	d						16 24						16 41							16 54					
South Croydon 4	d						16 27						16 44							16 57					
East Croydon	d	16 21	16 24	16 25		16 27	16 30	16 30	16 33	16 40	16 41	16 44	16 47	16 47	16 51	16 53	16 55	16 56	16 57	17 00		17 01	17 07	17 09	17 10
Norwood Junction 2	d			16 29			16 35			16 45							16 59			17 05			17 12		
London Bridge 4	⊖ a	16 39		16 47		16 42	16 56		16 53	17 00				17 02	17 10		17 12			17 28			17 26	17 28	
London Blackfriars 3	⊖ a					16 53													17 25					17 36	
City Thameslink 3	a					16 56													17 28					17 38	
Farringdon 3	⊖ a					17 01													17 31					17 41	
St Pancras International 15	⊖ a					17 05													17 35					17 45	
London Waterloo (East) 4	⊖ a																								
London Charing Cross 4	⊖ a																								
Clapham Junction 10	a		16 33					16 39			16 50	16 55	17 07			17 02		17 05				17 10			17 34
London Victoria 15	⊖ a		16 42					16 46			16 58	17 05	17 16			17 09		17 12				17 20			

		SN 1 🛒	SN 1	SN	SN	SN 1	SN 1 🛒	FC 1	SN 1 🛒	SN	SN 1	SN 1	SN 1 🛒	SN 1		SN 1	SN	FC 1	SN	SN 1	SN	SN 1 🛒	FC 1	SN 1 🛒	SN 1
Purley 4	d			17 08	17 15	17 19				17 23							17 38		17 45		17 49				
Purley Oaks	d			17 11						17 26							17 41								
South Croydon 4	d			17 14						17 29							17 44								
East Croydon	d	17 12	17 14	17 17	17 21	17 25	17 25	17 28	17 30	17 32	17 36	17 38	17 41	17 41		17 44	17 47	17 47	17 51	17 53	17 55	17 56	18 01	18 02	18 08
Norwood Junction 2	d				17 25	17 29				17 37				17 45							17 59				
London Bridge 4	⊖ a				17 38	17 42				17 58	17 50			18 00				18 11	18 11		18 15		18 17		
London Blackfriars 3	⊖ a							17 55										18 21							
City Thameslink 3	a							17 58										18 24							
Farringdon 3	⊖ a							18 01										18 27							
St Pancras International 15	⊖ a							18 05										18 31							
London Waterloo (East) 4	⊖ a																								
London Charing Cross 4	⊖ a																								
Clapham Junction 10	a	17 21	17 25	17 37			17 34		17 40			17 47	17 50			17 55	18 07			18 02		18 05		18 13	18 18
London Victoria 15	⊖ a	17 28	17 35	17 48			17 42		17 50			17 54	17 58			18 05	18 16			18 09		18 12		18 20	18 26

For general notes see front of timetable
For details of catering facilities see
Directory of Train Operators

Purley and East Croydon → London
COMPLETE SERVICE

	SN	SN [1] 🛒	SN [1]	SN	FC [1]	SN	SN [1] 🛒		SN [1]	SN [1] 🛒	SN	FC [1]	SN [1]	SN [1]	SN [1] 🛒	SN [1]	SN	FC [1]	SN [1]	SN [1]	SN [1]	SN [1]	SN [1]	FC [1]
Purley [4] d	17 59			18 08		18 15			18 19		18 23						18 37			18 49				
Purley Oaks d	18 02			18 11							18 26						18 40							
South Croydon [4] d	18 05			18 14							18 29						18 44							
East Croydon d	18 11	18 12	18 14	18 17	18 17	18 21	18 25		18 26	18 30	18 32	18 32	18 38	18 40	18 43	18 44	18 47	18 47	18 53	18 55	18 57	18 57	19 00	19 02
Norwood Junction [2] d	18 15					18 29					18 36											19 02		
London Bridge [4] ⊖ a	18 28					18 42					18 58	18 45	18 54					19 00				19 15		19 16
London Blackfriars [3] ⊖ a					18 48							18 53						19 07						19 23
City Thameslink [3] a					18 52							18 58						19 14						19 26
Farringdon [3] ⊖ a					18 57							19 01						19 17						19 29
St Pancras International [15] ⊖ a					19 01							19 05						19 21						19 33
London Waterloo (East) [4] ⊖ a																								
London Charing Cross [4] ⊖ a																								
Clapham Junction [10] a		18 21	18 25	18 39			18 34		18 37	18 40				18 49	18 52	18 55	19 08		19 02	19 05	19 08		19 11	
London Victoria [15] ⊖ a		18 29	18 35	18 46			18 41		18 44	18 47				18 56	18 59	19 05	19 15		19 09	19 12	19 15		19 18	

	SN [1]		SN [1]	SN	SN [1] 🛒	SN [1]	SN	FC [1]	SN [1] ◇	SN [1]	SN [1] ◇ 🛒	FC [1]	SN [1]	SN	SN [1]	SN [1]	SN [1]		SN	FC [1]	SN [1] ◇	SN [1]	SN [1] ◇	FC [1]
Purley [4] d				19 01			19 08			19 19				19 29					19 38			19 51		
Purley Oaks d				19 04			19 11							19 32					19 41					
South Croydon [4] d				19 07			19 14							19 35					19 44					
East Croydon d	19 07		19 09	19 10	19 12	19 14	19 17	19 17	19 24	19 25	19 29	19 32	19 33	19 40	19 40	19 43	19 44		19 47	19 47	19 54	19 57	20 00	20 02
Norwood Junction [2] d				19 15										19 44										
London Bridge [4] ⊖ a			19 24	19 39				19 30				19 45	19 51	20 11						20 00				20 15
London Blackfriars [3] ⊖ a								19 37				19 53								20 07				20 23
City Thameslink [3] a								19 40				19 56								20 10				20 26
Farringdon [3] ⊖ a								19 44				20 00								20 13				20 30
St Pancras International [15] ⊖ a								19 47				20 03								20 17				20 33
London Waterloo (East) [4] ⊖ a				19 45										20 16										
London Charing Cross [4] ⊖ a				19 49										20 20										
Clapham Junction [10] a	19 34				19 21	19 25	19 37		19 33	19 36	19 40				19 49	19 52	19 55		20 07		20 03	20 07	20 10	
London Victoria [15] ⊖ a					19 29	19 35	19 48		19 40	19 43	19 47				19 56	19 59	20 05		20 18		20 10	20 14	20 20	

	SN [1]	SN	SN [1]	SN [1]	SN	FC [1]	SN [1] ◇	SN [1]	SN	SN [1]	FC [1]		SN [1]	SN	SN [1]	SN [1]	SN	FC [1]	SN [1] ◇	SN [1]	SN [1]	SN [1] ◇	FC [1]	SN
Purley [4] d		19 59			20 08			20 20	20 23					20 29			20 38				20 49			20 59
Purley Oaks d		20 02			20 11									20 32			20 41							21 02
South Croydon [4] d		20 05			20 14									20 35			20 44							21 05
East Croydon d	20 07	20 10	20 11	20 14	20 17	20 17	20 24	20 26	20 29	20 30	20 32		20 32	20 40	20 41	20 44	20 47	20 47	20 54	20 54	20 57	21 00	21 02	21 10
Norwood Junction [2] d		20 14							20 34					20 44										21 14
London Bridge [4] ⊖ a	20 21	20 41				20 30			21 01		20 45		20 49	21 11				21 00		21 11			21 15	21 41
London Blackfriars [3] ⊖ a						20 37					20 53							21 07					21 23	
City Thameslink [3] a						20 40					20 56							21 10					21 26	
Farringdon [3] ⊖ a						20 43					21 00							21 13					21 30	
St Pancras International [15] ⊖ a						20 47					21 03							21 17					21 33	
London Waterloo (East) [4] ⊖ a		20 46												21 16										21 46
London Charing Cross [4] ⊖ a		20 50												21 20										21 50
Clapham Junction [10] a			20 20	20 25	20 37		20 33	20 37		20 40					20 50	20 55	21 07		21 03		21 07	21 11		
London Victoria [15] ⊖ a			20 28	20 35	20 46		20 43	20 45		20 48					20 58	21 05	21 16		21 10		21 14	21 20		

	SN [1]	SN [1]	SN	FC [1]	SN [1] ◇		SN [1]	SN [1]	FC [1]	SN [1]	SN	SN [1]	SN [1]	SN	SN [1] ◇	SN [1]	SN [1] ◇	FC [1]	SN	SN [1]	SN [1]		SN	SN [1]
Purley [4] d			21 08				21 19				21 29			21 38		21 49			21 59				22 08	
Purley Oaks d			21 11								21 32			21 41					22 02				22 11	
South Croydon [4] d			21 14								21 35			21 44					22 05				22 14	
East Croydon d	21 10	21 14	21 17	21 17	21 25		21 26	21 30	21 32	21 33	21 40	21 41	21 44	21 47	21 53	21b57	22 00	22 02	22 10	22 10	22 14		22 17	22 17
Norwood Junction [2] d											21 44								22 14					
London Bridge [4] ⊖ a				21 30					21 45	21 49	22 11							22 17	22 41					22 32
London Blackfriars [3] ⊖ a				21 37					21 53															
City Thameslink [3] a				21 40					21 56															
Farringdon [3] ⊖ a				21 43					22 00															
St Pancras International [15] ⊖ a				21 47					22 03															
London Waterloo (East) [4] ⊖ a											22 16								22 46					
London Charing Cross [4] ⊖ a											22 20								22 50					
Clapham Junction [10] a	21 19	21 25	21 37		21 34		21 37	21 40				21 50	21 55	22 07	22 02	22 07	22 10			22 19	22 25		22 37	
London Victoria [15] ⊖ a	21 27	21 35	21 46		21 41		21 45	21 50				21 57	22 05	22 16	22 10	22 14	22 20			22 27	22 35		22 46	

	SN [1] ◇	SN [1]	SN [1]	FC [1]	SN [1]	SN	SN [1]	SN [1]	SN	SN [1]	SN [1] ◇	FC [1]	SN	SN [1]	SN		SN [1]	FC [1]	SN	SN [1]				
Purley [4] d		22 20				22 29			22 38	22 52			22 59		23 08				23 34	23 49				
Purley Oaks d						22 32			22 41				23 02		23 11				23 37					
South Croydon [4] d						22 35			22 44				23 05		23 14				23 40					
East Croydon d	22 24	22 26	22 30	22 32	22 34	22 40	22 40	22 44	22 47	22 58	23 00	23 02	23 10	23 14	23 17		23 30	23 32	23a42	23c58				
Norwood Junction [2] d						22 44							23 14											
London Bridge [4] ⊖ a				22 47	22 49	23 11						23 17	23 38					23 47						
London Blackfriars [3] ⊖ a																								
City Thameslink [3] a																								
Farringdon [3] ⊖ a																								
St Pancras International [15] ⊖ a																								
London Waterloo (East) [4] ⊖ a						23 16							23 43											
London Charing Cross [4] ⊖ a						23 20							23 48											
Clapham Junction [10] a	22 33	22 37	22 40				22 49	22 55	23 07	23 07	23 10			23 25	23 37		23 42			00 11				
London Victoria [15] ⊖ a	22 40	22 44	22 50				22 57	23 05	23 16	23 15	23 20			23 35	23 46		23 52			00 18				

For general notes see front of timetable
For details of catering facilities see Directory of Train Operators

b Arr. 2154
c Arr. 2355

Table 175

Saturdays

Purley and East Croydon → London
COMPLETE SERVICE

		SN 1	FC 1	SN 1 ◇	FC 1	SN	SN 1	SN 1	FC 1	SN 1	FC 1	SN 1	FC 1	FC 1	SN 1	FC 1	SN 1 ◇	SN 1 ◇	FC 1	SN 1	SN	SN 1 ◇	SN	SN	FC 1
Purley 4	d	23p49		00 11			01 22	02 22		03 22		04 22			05 24		05 58			06 19	06 21			06 38	
Purley Oaks	d																				06 24			06 41	
South Croydon 4	d																				06 27			06 44	
East Croydon	d	23b58	00 04	00 17	00 36	00 49	01 28	02 28	02 47	03 28	03 47	04 28	04 47	05 17	05 29	05 42	06c07	06 11	06 17	06 25	06 30	06 41	06 43	06 47	06 47
Norwood Junction 2	d																			06 29	06 35		06 49		
London Bridge 4	⊖ a		00 19		00 52				03 12		04 12		05 12	05 42		05 57			06 31	06 42	06 56		07 14		07 02
London Blackfriars 3	⊖ a																								
City Thameslink 3	a																								
Farringdon 3	⊖ a																								
St Pancras International 15	⊖ a																								
London Waterloo (East) 4	⊖ a																								
London Charing Cross 4	⊖ a																								
Clapham Junction 10	a	00 11		00 29		01 02	01 40	02 40		03 40		04 41			05 49		06 18	06 21				06 50		07 07	
London Victoria 15	⊖ a	00 18		00 37		01 09	01 49	02 49		03 49		04 49			05 58		06 26	06 30				06 57		07 16	

		SN 1 ◇	SN 1	SN	SN 1	SN 1 ◇	SN 1		SN	FC 1	SN 1 ◇	SN 1	SN	SN 1	FC 1	SN 1	SN 1	SN 1	SN 1	SN	FC 1	SN	SN 1 ◇	SN 1	SN 1 ◇
Purley 4	d		06 49	06 51	07 02				07 08			07 19	07 21				07 32			07 38		07 45		07 49	
Purley Oaks	d			06 54					07 11				07 24							07 41					
South Croydon 4	d			06 57					07 14				07 27							07 44					
East Croydon	d	06 53	06 55	07 00	07 07	07 11	07 14		07 17	07 17	07 24	07 25	07 30	07 30	07 32	07 33	07 37	07 41	07 44	07 47	07 47	07 51	07 53	07 55	07 56
Norwood Junction 2	d		06 59	07 05								07 29	07 35											07 59	
London Bridge 4	⊖ a		07 12	07 26	07 24					07 31		07 42	07 56		07 47	07 49	07 52				08 02	08 08		08 12	
London Blackfriars 3	⊖ a																								
City Thameslink 3	a																								
Farringdon 3	⊖ a																								
St Pancras International 15	⊖ a																								
London Waterloo (East) 4	⊖ a				07 28												07 57								
London Charing Cross 4	⊖ a				07 32												08 00								
Clapham Junction 10	a	07 02				07 20	07 25		07 37		07 33			07 39				07 50	07 55	08 07			08 02		08 05
London Victoria 15	⊖ a	07 09				07 27	07 32		07 46		07 40			07 46				07 57	08 02	08 16			08 09		08 12

		SN	SN 1	FC 1	SN 1	SN 1	SN 1 ☕	SN 1	SN	FC 1	SN	SN 1 ◇ ☕	SN 1	SN 1		SN	FC 1	SN 1	SN 1	SN 1	SN 1	SN	FC 1	SN	SN 1 ◇
Purley 4	d	07 51			08 02				08 08		08 15		08 19			08 21			08 32			08 38		08 45	
Purley Oaks	d	07 54							08 11							08 24						08 41			
South Croydon 4	d	07 57							08 14							08 27						08 44			
East Croydon	d	08 00	08 00	08 02	08 07	08 10	08 11	08 14	08 17	08 17	08 21	08 24	08 25	08 28		08 30	08 32	08 33	08 37	08 41	08 44	08 47	08 47	08 51	08 53
Norwood Junction 2	d	08 05											08 29			08 35									
London Bridge 4	⊖ a	08 26		08 17	08 22					08 32	08 38		08 42			08 56	08 47	08 49	08 52				09 02	09 08	
London Blackfriars 3	⊖ a																								
City Thameslink 3	a																								
Farringdon 3	⊖ a																								
St Pancras International 15	⊖ a																								
London Waterloo (East) 4	⊖ a				08 26														08 56						
London Charing Cross 4	⊖ a				08 30														09 00						
Clapham Junction 10	a		08 09			08 34	08 20	08 25	08 37			08 33		08 37						08 50	08 55	09 07			09 02
London Victoria 15	⊖ a		08 16				08 27	08 32	08 46			08 40		08 44						08 57	09 02	09 16			09 09

		SN 1	SN 1 ◇ ☕	SN	SN 1	FC 1	SN 1	SN 1 ☕	SN 1	SN	FC 1	SN	SN 1 ◇ ☕	SN 1	SN 1 ☕	SN	FC 1	SN 1	SN 1	SN 1	SN 1		SN	FC 1	SN
Purley 4	d	08 49		08 51			09 02			09 08		09 15		09 19		09 21			09 32				09 38		09 45
Purley Oaks	d			08 54						09 11						09 24							09 41		
South Croydon 4	d			08 57						09 14						09 27							09 44		
East Croydon	d	08 55	08 56	09 00	09 00	09 02	09 07	09 11	09 14	09 17	09 17	09 21	09 24	09 25	09 28	09 30	09 32	09 33	09 37	09 42	09 44		09 47	09 47	09 51
Norwood Junction 2	d	08 59		09 05										09 29		09 35									
London Bridge 4	⊖ a	09 12		09 26		09 17	09 22				09 32	09 38		09 42		09 56	09 47	09 49	09 52					10 02	10 08
London Blackfriars 3	⊖ a																								
City Thameslink 3	a																								
Farringdon 3	⊖ a																								
St Pancras International 15	⊖ a																								
London Waterloo (East) 4	⊖ a						09 26												09 56						
London Charing Cross 4	⊖ a						09 30												10 00						
Clapham Junction 10	a		09 05		09 09			09 20	09 25	09 37			09 33		09 37					09 51	09 55		10 07		
London Victoria 15	⊖ a		09 12		09 16			09 27	09 32	09 46			09 40		09 44					09 58	10 02		10 16		

		SN 1 ◇	SN 1	SN 1 ◇ ☕	SN	SN 1	FC 1	SN 1	SN 1 ☕	SN 1	SN	FC 1	SN	SN 1 ◇ ☕	SN 1	SN 1 ☕	SN	FC 1	SN 1	SN 1	SN 1	SN 1	SN 1	SN	FC 1
Purley 4	d		09 49		09 51			10 02			10 08		10 15		10 19		10 21			10 32				10 38	
Purley Oaks	d				09 54						10 11						10 24							10 41	
South Croydon 4	d				09 57						10 14						10 27							10 44	
East Croydon	d	09 53	09 55	09 56	10 00	10 00	10 02	10 07	10 11	10 14	10 17	10 17	10 21	10 24	10 25	10 28	10 30	10 32	10 33	10 37	10 38	10 42	10 44	10 47	10 47
Norwood Junction 2	d		09 59		10 05										10 29		10 35								
London Bridge 4	⊖ a		10 12		10 26		10 17	10 22				10 32	10 38		10 42		10 56	10 47	10 49	10 52					11 02
London Blackfriars 3	⊖ a																								
City Thameslink 3	a																								
Farringdon 3	⊖ a																								
St Pancras International 15	⊖ a																								
London Waterloo (East) 4	⊖ a							10 26												10 56					
London Charing Cross 4	⊖ a							10 30												11 00					
Clapham Junction 10	a	10 02		10 05		10 09			10 20	10 25	10 37			10 33		10 37					10 47	10 51	10 55	11 07	
London Victoria 15	⊖ a	10 09		10 12		10 16			10 27	10 32	10 46			10 40		10 44					10 56	10 59	11 02	11 16	

For general notes see front of timetable
For details of catering facilities see
Directory of Train Operators

b Previous night. Arr. 2355

c Arr. 0602

Purley and East Croydon → London
COMPLETE SERVICE

		SN	SN 1◇	SN 1	SN 1◇ (trolley)	SN		SN 1	FC 1		SN 1	SN 1 (trolley)	SN 1	SN	FC 1	SN	SN 1◇ (trolley)	SN 1	SN 1 (trolley)	SN	FC 1	SN 1	SN 1	SN 1	SN 1
Purley 4	d	10 45		10 49		10 51					11 02			11 08		11 15		11 19		11 21			11 32		
Purley Oaks	d					10 54								11 11						11 24					
South Croydon 4	d					10 57								11 14						11 27					
East Croydon	d	10 51	10 53	10 55	10 56	11 00		11 00	11 02		11 07	11 11	11 14	11 17	11 17	11 21	11 24	11 25	11 28	11 30	11 32	11 33	11 37	11 41	11 44
Norwood Junction 2	d			10 59		11 05												11 29		11 35					
London Bridge 4	⊖ a	11 08		11 12		11 26			11 17		11 22				11 32	11 38		11 42		11 56	11 47	11 49	11 52		
London Blackfriars 3	⊖ a																								
City Thameslink 3	a																								
Farringdon 3	⊖ a																								
St Pancras International 15	⊖ a																								
London Waterloo (East) 4	⊖ a										11 26												11 56		
London Charing Cross 4	⊖ a										11 30												12 00		
Clapham Junction 10	a		11 02		11 05			11 09				11 20	11 25	11 37			11 33		11 37					11 50	11 55
London Victoria 15	⊖ a		11 09		11 12			11 16				11 27	11 32	11 46			11 40		11 44					11 57	12 02

		SN	FC 1	SN	SN 1◇	SN 1	SN 1◇ (trolley)	SN	SN 1	FC 1		SN 1	SN 1 (trolley)	SN 1	SN		FC 1	SN	SN 1◇ (trolley)	SN 1	SN 1 (trolley)	SN	FC 1	SN 1
Purley 4	d	11 38		11 45		11 49		11 51			and at the same minutes past each hour until	18 02			18 08			18 15		18 19		18 21		
Purley Oaks	d	11 41						11 54							18 11							18 24		
South Croydon 4	d	11 44						11 57							18 14							18 27		
East Croydon	d	11 47	11 47	11 51	11 53	11 55	11 56	12 00	12 00	12 02		18 07	18 11	18 14	18 17		18 17	18 21	18 24	18 25	18 28	18 30	18 32	18 33
Norwood Junction 2	d					11 59		12 05												18 29		18 35		
London Bridge 4	⊖ a		12 02	12 08		12 12		12 26		12 17		18 22					18 32	18 38		18 42		18 56	18 47	18 49
London Blackfriars 3	⊖ a																							
City Thameslink 3	a																							
Farringdon 3	⊖ a																							
St Pancras International 15	⊖ a																							
London Waterloo (East) 4	⊖ a											18 26												
London Charing Cross 4	⊖ a											18 30												
Clapham Junction 10	a	12 07			12 02		12 05		12 09				18 20	18 25	18 37				18 33		18 37			
London Victoria 15	⊖ a	12 16			12 09		12 12		12 16				18 27	18 32	18 46				18 40		18 44			

		SN 1	SN 1	SN 1	SN	SN	SN 1◇	SN 1	SN 1◇	SN	SN 1	FC 1	SN 1	SN	SN 1 (trolley)	SN 1	SN	FC 1	SN 1◇	SN 1	SN 1	FC 1	SN 1		SN
Purley 4	d	18 32			18 38	18 45		18 49		18 54				19 01			19 08			19 20					19 29
Purley Oaks	d				18 41									19 04			19 11								19 32
South Croydon 4	d				18 44									19 07			19 14								19 35
East Croydon	d	18 37	18 41	18 44	18 47	18 51	18 53	18 55	18 56	19 00	19 00	19 02	19 05	19 10	19 11	19 14	19 17	19 17	19 24	19 25	19 29	19 32	19 33		19 40
Norwood Junction 2	d							18 59		19 04			19 09	19 14											19 44
London Bridge 4	⊖ a	18 52				19 08		19 12		19 28		19 17	19 23	19 41				19 32				19 47	19 49		20 11
London Blackfriars 3	⊖ a																								
City Thameslink 3	a																								
Farringdon 3	⊖ a																								
St Pancras International 15	⊖ a																								
London Waterloo (East) 4	⊖ a	18 56											19 28	19 48											20 18
London Charing Cross 4	⊖ a	19 00											19 31	19 51											20 21
Clapham Junction 10	a		18 50	18 55	19 07		19 02		19 05		19 09				19 20	19 25	19 37		19 33	19 37	19 40				
London Victoria 15	⊖ a		18 57	19 02	19 16		19 09		19 12		19 16				19 27	19 32	19 46		19 40	19 44	19 47				

		SN 1	SN 1	SN	FC 1	SN 1◇	SN 1◇	SN 1	SN 1	FC 1	SN	SN 1	SN 1	SN	FC 1	SN 1◇	SN 1	SN 1	FC 1	SN 1	SN	SN 1	SN 1	SN	FC 1
Purley 4	d			19 38				19 49			19 59			20 08			20 19				20 29			20 38	
Purley Oaks	d			19 41							20 02			20 11							20 32			20 41	
South Croydon 4	d			19 44							20 05			20 14							20 35			20 44	
East Croydon	d	19 41	19 44	19 47	19 47	19 53	19 56	19b57	20 00	20 02	20 10	20 11	20 14	20 17	20 17	20 24	20 25	20 30	20 32	20 33	20 40	20 41	20 44	20 47	20 47
Norwood Junction 2	d										20 14										20 44				
London Bridge 4	⊖ a				20 02					20 17	20 41				20 32				20 47	20 49	21 11				21 02
London Blackfriars 3	⊖ a																								
City Thameslink 3	a																								
Farringdon 3	⊖ a																								
St Pancras International 15	⊖ a																								
London Waterloo (East) 4	⊖ a										20 48										21 18				
London Charing Cross 4	⊖ a										20 51										21 21				
Clapham Junction 10	a	19 50	19 55	20 07		20 02	20 05	20 08	20 11			20 20	20 25	20 37		20 33	20 37	20 40				20 50	20 55	21 07	
London Victoria 15	⊖ a	19 57	20 02	20 16		20 09	20 12	20 15	20 20			20 27	20 32	20 46		20 40	20 44	20 50				20 57	21 02	21 16	

		SN 1◇	SN 1	SN 1◇	FC 1	SN	SN 1		SN 1	SN	FC 1	SN 1◇	SN 1	SN 1	FC 1	SN 1	SN	SN 1	SN 1	SN	SN 1◇	SN 1	SN 1◇	FC 1	SN
Purley 4	d		20 51			20 59				21 08			21 19				21 29			21 38		21 49			21 59
Purley Oaks	d					21 02				21 11							21 32			21 41					22 02
South Croydon 4	d					21 05				21 14							21 35			21 44					22 05
East Croydon	d	20 54	20 57	21 00	21 02	21 10	21 11		21 14	21 17	21 17	21 24	21 25	21 30	21 32	21 33	21 40	21 41	21 44	21 47	21 54	21 55	22 00	22 02	22 10
Norwood Junction 2	d					21 14											21 44								22 14
London Bridge 4	⊖ a				21 17	21 41					21 32				21 47	21 49	22 11							22 17	22 41
London Blackfriars 3	⊖ a																								
City Thameslink 3	a																								
Farringdon 3	⊖ a																								
St Pancras International 15	⊖ a																								
London Waterloo (East) 4	⊖ a					21 48											22 18								22 48
London Charing Cross 4	⊖ a					21 51											22 21								22 51
Clapham Junction 10	a	21 03	21 07	21 10			21 20		21 25	21 37		21 33	21 37	21 40				21 50	21 55	22 07	22 03	22 07	22 10		
London Victoria 15	⊖ a	21 10	21 14	21 17			21 27		21 32	21 46		21 40	21 44	21 47				21 57	22 02	22 16	22 10	22 14	22 20		

For general notes see front of timetable
For details of catering facilities see Directory of Train Operators

b Arr. 1954

Table 175

Saturdays

Purley and East Croydon → London
COMPLETE SERVICE

		SN 1	SN 1	SN	SN 1◇	SN 1	SN 1	FC 1	SN 1	SN	SN 1	SN 1	SN	SN 1	SN 1◇	FC 1	SN	SN 1	SN	SN 1	FC 1	SN	SN 1		
Purley 4	d			22 08		22 19				22 29			22 38	22 52			22 59		23 08			23 34	23 49		
Purley Oaks	d			22 11						22 32			22 41				23 02		23 11			23 37			
South Croydon 4	d			22 14						22 35			22 44				23 05		23 14			23 40			
East Croydon	d	22 11	22 14	22 17	22 24	22 25	22 30	22 32	22 33	22 40	22 40	22 44	22 47	22 58	23 00	23 02	23 10	23 14	23 17	23 30	23 32	23a42	23 56		
Norwood Junction 2	d									22 44							23 14								
London Bridge 4	⊖ a							22 47	22 49	23 11						23 17	23 38				23 47				
London Blackfriars 3	⊖ a																								
City Thameslink 3	a																								
Farringdon 3	⊖ a																								
St Pancras International 15	⊖ a																								
London Waterloo (East) 4	⊖ a									23 16							23 43								
London Charing Cross 4	⊖ a									23 20							23 48								
Clapham Junction 10	a	22 20	22 25	22 37	22 33	22 37	22 40				22 49	22 55	23 07	23 07	23 10			23 25	23 37	23 42			00 11		
London Victoria 15	⊖ a	22 27	22 32	22 46	22 40	22 44	22 50				22 58	23 02	23 18	23 14	23 17			23 32	23 46	23 52			00 18		

Sundays

		SN 1	FC 1	SN 1◇	FC 1	SN	SN 1	SN 1	SN 1	SN 1	SN 1◇ A	SN 1◇ B	FC 1	SN 1	FC 1	SN	SN	FC 1	SN 1 B	SN 1◇ A	SN	SN	SN 1	FC 1 A	FC 1 B
Purley 4	d	23p49		00 11			01 37	02 33	03 33	04 33	05 22	05 22		05 56			06 35						07 20		
Purley Oaks	d																06 38								
South Croydon 4	d																06 41						07 24		
East Croydon	d	23p56	00 04	00 17	00 36	00 49	01 43	02 40	03 40	04 40	05 28	05 28	05 32	06 02	06 32	06 40	06 44	07 02	07 10	07 10	07 12	07 14	07 27	07 32	07 33
Norwood Junction 2	d																06 48				07 18				
London Bridge 4	⊖ a		00 19		00 52								05 59		06 59		07 12	07 17			07 42	07 48		07 47	07 47
London Blackfriars 3	⊖ a																								
City Thameslink 3	a																								
Farringdon 3	⊖ a																								
St Pancras International 15	⊖ a																								
London Waterloo (East) 4	⊖ a																07 17				07 47				
London Charing Cross 4	⊖ a																07 20				07 50				
Clapham Junction 10	a	00 11		00 28		01 02	01 53	02 52	03 52	04 52	05 47	05 48		06 14		07 00			07 19	07 24			07 40		
London Victoria 15	⊖ a	00 18		00 36		01 09	02 05	03 05	04 05	05 05	05 56	05 58		06 22		07 08			07 26	07 31			07 48		

		SN	SN 1 B	SN 1 A	SN 1◇ B	SN 1◇ A		FC 1 A	FC 1 B	SN 1 B ⊼	SN 1 A ⊼	SN	SN 1 B	SN 1 A	SN 1	FC 1 A	FC 1 B	SN 1 B	SN 1 B	SN 1 A	SN 1◇ B	SN	SN 1 B	SN 1 A	SN 1◇ B
Purley 4	d	07 38	07 50	07 49								08 08	08 14	08 18				08 27				08 38	08 50	08 49	
Purley Oaks	d	07 41										08 11										08 41			
South Croydon 4	d	07 44										08 14										08 44			
East Croydon	d	07 47	07 56	07b58	08 00	08 00		08 02	08 03	08 09	08 10	08 17	08 21	08 26	08 29	08 32	08 33	08 34	08 39	08 40	08 46	08 47	08 56	08c58	09 00
Norwood Junction 2	d	07 51										08 21						08 38				08 51			
London Bridge 4	⊖ a	08 12						08 17	08 17			08 42				08 47	08 47	08 51				09 12			
London Blackfriars 3	⊖ a																								
City Thameslink 3	a																								
Farringdon 3	⊖ a																								
St Pancras International 15	⊖ a																								
London Waterloo (East) 4	⊖ a	08 17										08 47										09 17			
London Charing Cross 4	⊖ a	08 20										08 50										09 20			
Clapham Junction 10	a		08 06	08 08	08 10	08 11				08 18	08 24		08 31	08 37	08 41				08 48	08 54	08 55		09 06	09 08	09 10
London Victoria 15	⊖ a		08 13	08 16	08 17	08 18				08 25	08 31		08 39	08 46	08 48				08 55	09 01	09 02		09 13	09 16	09 17

		SN 1◇ A ⊼	FC 1 A	FC 1 B	SN 1 B ⊼	SN 1 A ⊼	SN	SN 1◇ B	SN 1 B	SN 1 A ⊼	SN 1	FC 1 A		FC 1 B	SN 1 B	SN 1◇ A	SN 1 B	SN 1 A	SN 1◇ B	SN	SN 1 B	SN 1 A	SN 1◇ B	SN 1◇ A ⊼	FC 1 A
Purley 4	d						09 08		09 14	09 18					09 27					09 38	09 50	09 49			
Purley Oaks	d						09 11													09 41					
South Croydon 4	d						09 14													09 44					
East Croydon	d	09 00	09 02	09 03	09 09	09 10	09 17	09 17	09 21	09 25	09 29	09 32		09 33	09 34	09 35	09 39	09 40	09 46	09 47	09 56	09e58	10 00	10 00	10 02
Norwood Junction 2	d						09 21								09 38					09 51					
London Bridge 4	⊖ a		09 17	09 17			09 42					09 47		09 47	09 51					10 12					10 17
London Blackfriars 3	⊖ a																								
City Thameslink 3	a																								
Farringdon 3	⊖ a																								
St Pancras International 15	⊖ a																								
London Waterloo (East) 4	⊖ a						09 47													10 17					
London Charing Cross 4	⊖ a						09 50													10 20					
Clapham Junction 10	a	09 11			09 18	09 24		09 26	09 31	09 37	09 41					09 47	09 48	09 54	09 55		10 06	10 08	10 10	10 11	
London Victoria 15	⊖ a	09 18			09 25	09 31		09 33	09 39	09 46	09 48					09 53	09 55	10 01	10 02		10 13	10 16	10 17	10 18	

For general notes see front of timetable
For details of catering facilities see
Directory of Train Operators

A From 13 September
B Until 6 September
b Arr. 0754
c Arr. 0854
e Arr. 0954

Table 175

Purley and East Croydon → London
COMPLETE SERVICE

	FC	SN	SN	SN	SN	SN	SN	SN	FC	FC	SN	SN	SN	SN	SN	SN	SN		SN	SN	SN	FC	FC	SN
	1	1	1		1 ◇	1	1	1	1	1	1	1 ◇	1	1	1 ◇		1		1	1 ◇	1 ◇	1	1	1
	A	A	B		A	A	B		B	A	A	B	A	B	A		A		B	A	B	B	A	A
		🛒	🛒				🛒														🛒			🛒
Purley [4] d				10 08		10 14	10 18				10 27					10 38	10 50		10 49					
Purley Oaks d				10 11												10 41								
South Croydon [4] d				10 14												10 44								
East Croydon d	10 03	10 09	10 10	10 17	10 17	10 21	10 25	10 29	10 32	10 33	10 34	10 35	10 39	10 40	10 46	10 47	10 56		10b58	11 00	11 00	11 02	11 03	11 09
Norwood Junction [2] d				10 21							10 38					10 51								
London Bridge [4] ⊖ a	10 17			10 42					10 47	10 47	10 51					11 12						11 17	11 17	
London Blackfriars [3] ⊖ a																								
City Thameslink [3] a																								
Farringdon [3] ⊖ a																								
St Pancras International [15] ⊖ a																								
London Waterloo (East) [4] ⊖ a				10 47												11 17								
London Charing Cross [4] ⊖ a				10 50												11 20								
Clapham Junction [10] a		10 18	10 24		10 26	10 31	10 37	10 41				10 47	10 48	10 54	10 55		11 06		11 08	11 10	11 11			11 18
London Victoria [15] ⊖ a		10 25	10 31		10 33	10 39	10 46	10 48				10 53	10 55	11 01	11 02		11 13		11 16	11 17	11 18			11 25

	SN	SN	SN	SN	SN	SN	FC	FC	SN	SN	SN	SN	SN	SN	SN	SN	SN	SN	FC	FC	SN	SN	SN	SN
	1		1 ◇	1	1	1	1	1	1	1 ◇	1	1	1 ◇		1	1	1 ◇	1 ◇	1	1	1	1		1 ◇
	B		A	A	B		B	A	A	B	A	B	A		A	B	A	B	B	A	A	B		A
	🛒			🛒	🛒													🛒			🛒	🛒		
Purley [4] d		11 08		11 14	11 18				11 27					11 38	11 50	11 49							12 08	
Purley Oaks d		11 11												11 41									12 11	
South Croydon [4] d		11 14												11 44									12 14	
East Croydon d	11 10	11 17	11 17	11 21	11 25	11 29	11 32	11 33	11 34	11 35	11 39	11 40	11 46	11 47	11 56	11c58	12 00	12 00	12 02	12 03	12 09	12 10	12 17	12 17
Norwood Junction [2] d		11 21							11 38					11 51									12 21	
London Bridge [4] ⊖ a		11 42					11 47	11 47	11 51					12 12					12 17	12 17			12 42	
London Blackfriars [3] ⊖ a																								
City Thameslink [3] a																								
Farringdon [3] ⊖ a																								
St Pancras International [15] ⊖ a																								
London Waterloo (East) [4] ⊖ a		11 47												12 17									12 47	
London Charing Cross [4] ⊖ a		11 50												12 20									12 50	
Clapham Junction [10] a	11 24		11 26	11 31	11 37	11 41				11 47	11 48	11 54	11 55		12 06	12 08	12 10	12 11			12 18	12 24		12 26
London Victoria [15] ⊖ a	11 31		11 33	11 39	11 46	11 48				11 53	11 55	12 01	12 02		12 13	12 16	12 17	12 18			12 25	12 31		12 33

	SN		SN	SN	FC	FC	SN	SN	SN	SN	SN	SN	SN	SN	SN	SN	FC	FC	SN	SN	SN	SN	SN	SN
	1		1	1	1	1	1	1 ◇	1	1	1 ◇		1	1	1 ◇	1 ◇	1	1	1	1		1 ◇	1	1
	A		B		B	A	A	B	A	B	A		A	B	A	B	B	A	A	B		A	A	B
	🛒		🛒													🛒			🛒	🛒			🛒	🛒
Purley [4] d	12 14		12 18				12 27					12 38	12 50	12 49							13 08		13 14	13 18
Purley Oaks d												12 41									13 11			
South Croydon [4] d												12 44									13 14			
East Croydon d	12 21		12 25	12 29	12 32	12 33	12 34	12 35	12 39	12 40	12 46	12 47	12 56	12e58	13 00	13 00	13 02	13 03	13 09	13 10	13 17	13 17	13 21	13 25
Norwood Junction [2] d							12 38					12 51									13 21			
London Bridge [4] ⊖ a					12 47	12 47	12 51					13 12					13 17	13 17			13 42			
London Blackfriars [3] ⊖ a																								
City Thameslink [3] a																								
Farringdon [3] ⊖ a																								
St Pancras International [15] ⊖ a																								
London Waterloo (East) [4] ⊖ a												13 17									13 47			
London Charing Cross [4] ⊖ a												13 20									13 50			
Clapham Junction [10] a	12 31		12 37	12 41				12 47	12 48	12 54	12 55		13 06	13 08	13 10	13 11			13 18	13 24		13 26	13 31	13 37
London Victoria [15] ⊖ a	12 39		12 46	12 48				12 53	12 55	13 01	13 02		13 13	13 16	13 17	13 18			13 25	13 31		13 33	13 39	13 46

	SN	FC	FC	SN	SN	SN	SN		SN	SN	SN	SN	SN	SN	FC	FC	SN	SN	SN	SN	SN	SN	SN	FC
	1	1	1	1	1 ◇	1	1		1 ◇		1	1	1 ◇	1 ◇	1	1	1	1		1 ◇	1	1	1	1
		B	A	A	B	A	B		A		A	B	A	B	B	A	A	B		A	A	B		B
														🛒			🛒	🛒			🛒	🛒		
Purley [4] d				13 27						13 38	13 50	13 49							14 08		14 14	14 18		
Purley Oaks d										13 41									14 11					
South Croydon [4] d										13 44									14 14					
East Croydon d	13 29	13 32	13 33	13 34	13 35	13 39	13 40		13 46	13 47	13 56	13f58	14 00	14 00	14 02	14 03	14 09	14 10	14 17	14 17	14 21	14 25	14 29	14 32
Norwood Junction [2] d				13 38						13 51									14 21					
London Bridge [4] ⊖ a		13 47	13 47	13 51						14 12					14 17	14 17			14 42					14 47
London Blackfriars [3] ⊖ a																								
City Thameslink [3] a																								
Farringdon [3] ⊖ a																								
St Pancras International [15] ⊖ a																								
London Waterloo (East) [4] ⊖ a										14 17									14 47					
London Charing Cross [4] ⊖ a										14 20									14 50					
Clapham Junction [10] a	13 41				13 47	13 48	13 54		13 55		14 06	14 08	14 10	14 11			14 18	14 24		14 26	14 31	14 37	14 41	
London Victoria [15] ⊖ a	13 48				13 53	13 55	14 01		14 02		14 13	14 16	14 17	14 18			14 25	14 31		14 33	14 39	14 46	14 48	

	FC	SN	SN	SN	SN	SN	SN	SN	SN	SN	SN	FC	FC		SN	SN	SN	SN	SN	SN	SN	FC	FC	SN
	1	1	1 ◇	1	1	1 ◇		1	1	1 ◇	1 ◇	1	1		1	1		1 ◇	1	1	1	1	1	1
	A	A	B	A	B	A		A	B	A	B	B	A		A	B		A	A	B		B	A	A
											🛒				🛒	🛒			🛒	🛒				
Purley [4] d		14 27					14 38	14 50	14 49								15 08		15 14	15 18				15 27
Purley Oaks d							14 41										15 11							
South Croydon [4] d							14 44										15 14							
East Croydon d	14 33	14 34	14 35	14 39	14 40	14 46	14 47	14 56	14g58	15 00	15 00	15 02	15 03		15 09	15 10	15 17	15 17	15 21	15 25	15 29	15 32	15 33	15 34
Norwood Junction [2] d		14 38					14 51										15 21							15 38
London Bridge [4] ⊖ a	14 47	14 51					15 12					15 17	15 17				15 42					15 47	15 47	15 51
London Blackfriars [3] ⊖ a																								
City Thameslink [3] a																								
Farringdon [3] ⊖ a																								
St Pancras International [15] ⊖ a																								
London Waterloo (East) [4] ⊖ a							15 17										15 47							
London Charing Cross [4] ⊖ a							15 20										15 50							
Clapham Junction [10] a			14 47	14 48	14 54	14 55		15 06	15 08	15 10	15 11				15 18	15 24		15 26	15 31	15 37	15 41			
London Victoria [15] ⊖ a			14 53	14 55	15 01	15 02		15 13	15 16	15 17	15 18				15 25	15 31		15 33	15 39	15 46	15 48			

For general notes see front of timetable
For details of catering facilities see Directory of Train Operators

- A Until 6 September
- B From 13 September
- b Arr. 1054
- c Arr. 1154
- e Arr. 1254
- f Arr. 1354
- g Arr. 1454

Table 175

Sundays

Purley and East Croydon → London

COMPLETE SERVICE

Station		SN	SN	SN	SN	SN	SN	SN	SN	SN	FC	FC	SN	SN	SN	SN	SN	SN	SN	FC		FC	SN	SN	SN
		1◇	1	1	1◇		1	1	1◇	1◇	1	1	1	1		1◇	1	1	1	1		1	1	1◇	1
		A	B	A	B		B	A	B	A	A	B	B	A		B	B	A		A		B	B	A	B
										🛒			🛒	🛒			🛒	🛒							
Purley 4	d					15 38	15 50	15 49							16 08		16 14	16 18					16 27		
Purley Oaks	d					15 41									16 11										
South Croydon 4	d					15 44									16 14										
East Croydon	d	15 35	15 39	15 40	15 46	15 47	15 56	15b58	16 00	16 00	16 02	16 03	16 09	16 10	16 17	16 17	16 21	16 25	16 29	16 32		16 33	16 34	16 35	16 39
Norwood Junction 2	d					15 51									16 21								16 38		
London Bridge 4	⊖ a					16 12					16 17	16 17			16 42					16 47		16 47	16 51		
London Blackfriars 3	⊖ a																								
City Thameslink 3	a																								
Farringdon 3	⊖ a																								
St Pancras International 15	⊖ a																								
London Waterloo (East) 4	⊖ a					16 17									16 47										
London Charing Cross 4	⊖ a					16 20									16 50										
Clapham Junction 10	a	15 47	15 48	15 54	15 55		16 06	16 08	16 10	16 11			16 18	16 24		16 26	16 31	16 37	16 41					16 47	16 48
London Victoria 15	⊖ a	15 53	15 55	16 01	16 02		16 13	16 16	16 17	16 18			16 25	16 31		16 33	16 39	16 46	16 48					16 53	16 55

Station		SN	SN	SN	SN	SN	SN	SN	FC	FC	SN	SN	SN	SN	SN	SN	SN	FC	FC	SN	SN	SN	SN	SN	SN
		1	1◇		1	1	1◇	1◇	1	1	1	1		1◇	1	1	1	1	1	1	1◇	1	1	1◇	
		A	B		B	A	B	A	A	B	B	A		B	B	A		A	B	B	A	B	A	B	
								🛒			🛒	🛒			🛒	🛒									
Purley 4	d			16 38	16 50	16 49							17 08		17 14	17 18				17 27					17 38
Purley Oaks	d			16 41									17 11												17 41
South Croydon 4	d			16 44									17 14												17 44
East Croydon	d	16 40	16 46	16 47	16 56	16c58	17 00	17 00	17 02	17 03	17 09	17 10	17 17	17 17	17 21	17 25	17 29	17 32	17 33	17 34	17 35	17 39	17 40	17 46	17 47
Norwood Junction 2	d			16 51									17 21							17 38					17 51
London Bridge 4	⊖ a			17 12					17 17	17 17			17 42					17 47	17 47	17 51					18 12
London Blackfriars 3	⊖ a																								
City Thameslink 3	a																								
Farringdon 3	⊖ a																								
St Pancras International 15	⊖ a																								
London Waterloo (East) 4	⊖ a			17 17									17 47												18 17
London Charing Cross 4	⊖ a			17 20									17 50												18 20
Clapham Junction 10	a	16 54	16 55		17 06	17 08	17 10	17 11			17 18	17 24		17 26	17 31	17 37	17 41				17 47	17 48	17 54	17 55	
London Victoria 15	⊖ a	17 01	17 02		17 13	17 16	17 17	17 18			17 25	17 31		17 33	17 39	17 46	17 48				17 53	17 55	18 01	18 02	

Station		SN	SN	SN		SN	FC	FC	SN	SN	SN	SN	SN	SN	SN	FC	FC	SN	SN	SN	SN	SN	SN	SN	SN
		1	1	1◇		1◇	1	1	1	1		1◇	1	1	1	1	1	1	1◇	1	1	1◇		1	1
		B	A	B		A	A	B	B	A		B	B	A		A	B	B	A	B	A	B		B	A
						🛒			🛒	🛒			🛒	🛒											
Purley 4	d	17 50	17 49								18 08		18 14	18 18				18 27					18 38	18 50	18 49
Purley Oaks	d										18 11												18 41		
South Croydon 4	d										18 14												18 44		
East Croydon	d	17 56	17e58	18 00		18 00	18 02	18 03	18 09	18 10	18 17	18 17	18 21	18 25	18 29	18 32	18 33	18 34	18 35	18 39	18 40	18 46	18 47	18 56	18f58
Norwood Junction 2	d										18 21							18 38					18 51		
London Bridge 4	⊖ a						18 17	18 17			18 42					18 47	18 47	18 51					19 12		
London Blackfriars 3	⊖ a																								
City Thameslink 3	a																								
Farringdon 3	⊖ a																								
St Pancras International 15	⊖ a																								
London Waterloo (East) 4	⊖ a										18 47												19 17		
London Charing Cross 4	⊖ a										18 50												19 20		
Clapham Junction 10	a	18 06	18 08	18 10		18 11			18 18	18 24		18 26	18 31	18 37	18 41				18 47	18 48	18 54	18 55		19 06	19 08
London Victoria 15	⊖ a	18 13	18 16	18 17		18 18			18 25	18 31		18 33	18 39	18 46	18 48				18 53	18 55	19 01	19 02		19 13	19 16

Station		SN	SN	FC	FC	SN	SN	SN	SN	SN		SN	SN	FC	FC	SN	SN	SN	SN	SN	SN	SN	SN	SN	SN
		1◇	1◇	1	1	1	1		1◇	1		1	1	1	1	1	1◇	1	1	1◇		1	1	1◇	1◇
		B	A	A	B	B	A		B	B		A		A	B	B	A	B	A	B		B	A	B	A
						🛒	🛒																		
Purley 4	d							19 08		19 14		19 18				19 27					19 38	19 50	19 49		
Purley Oaks	d							19 11													19 41				
South Croydon 4	d							19 14													19 44				
East Croydon	d	19 00	19 00	19 02	19 03	19 09	19 10	19 17	19 17	19 21		19 25	19 29	19 32	19 33	19 34	19 35	19 39	19 40	19 46	19 47	19 56	19g58	20 00	20 00
Norwood Junction 2	d							19 21								19 38					19 51				
London Bridge 4	⊖ a			19 17	19 17			19 42						19 47	19 47	19 51					20 12				
London Blackfriars 3	⊖ a																								
City Thameslink 3	a																								
Farringdon 3	⊖ a																								
St Pancras International 15	⊖ a																								
London Waterloo (East) 4	⊖ a							19 47													20 17				
London Charing Cross 4	⊖ a							19 50													20 20				
Clapham Junction 10	a	19 10	19 11			19 18	19 24		19 26	19 31		19 37	19 41				19 47	19 48	19 54	19 55		20 06	20 08	20 10	20 11
London Victoria 15	⊖ a	19 17	19 18			19 25	19 31		19 33	19 39		19 46	19 48				19 53	19 55	20 01	20 02		20 13	20 16	20 17	20 18

Station		FC	FC	SN	SN	SN	SN	SN	SN	SN	FC	FC	SN	SN	SN	SN		SN	SN	SN	SN	SN	SN	FC	FC
		1	1	1	1		1◇	1	1	1	1	1	1	1◇	1	1		1◇		1	1	1◇	1◇	1	1
		A	B	B	A		B	B	A		A	B	B	A	B	A		B		B	A	B	A	A	B
Purley 4	d					20 08		20 14	20 18				20 27						20 38	20 50	20 49				
Purley Oaks	d					20 11													20 41						
South Croydon 4	d					20 14													20 44						
East Croydon	d	20 02	20 03	20 09	20 10	20 17	20 17	20 21	20 25	20 29	20 32	20 33	20 34	20 35	20 39	20 40		20 46	20 47	20 56	20h58	21 00	21 00	21 02	21 03
Norwood Junction 2	d					20 21							20 38						20 51						
London Bridge 4	⊖ a	20 17	20 17			20 42					20 47	20 47	20 51						21 12					21 17	21 17
London Blackfriars 3	⊖ a																								
City Thameslink 3	a																								
Farringdon 3	⊖ a																								
St Pancras International 15	⊖ a																								
London Waterloo (East) 4	⊖ a					20 47													21 17						
London Charing Cross 4	⊖ a					20 50													21 20						
Clapham Junction 10	a			20 18	20 24		20 26	20 31	20 37	20 41				20 47	20 48	20 54		20 55		21 06	21 08	21 10	21 11		
London Victoria 15	⊖ a			20 25	20 31		20 33	20 39	20 46	20 48				20 53	20 55	21 01		21 02		21 13	21 16	21 17	21 18		

For general notes see front of timetable
For details of catering facilities see Directory of Train Operators

- **A** From 13 September
- **B** Until 6 September
- **b** Arr. 1554
- **c** Arr. 1654
- **e** Arr. 1754
- **f** Arr. 1854
- **g** Arr. 1954
- **h** Arr. 2054

Purley and East Croydon → London
COMPLETE SERVICE

		SN	SN	SN	SN	SN	SN	SN	FC	FC	SN	SN	SN	SN	SN	SN	SN	SN	SN	FC	FC	SN		SN	SN
		1	1		1 ◇	1	1	1	1	1	1	1 ◇	1	1		1	1	1 ◇	1 ◇	1	1	1		1	
		A	B		A	A	B		B	A	A	B	A	B		A	B	A	B	B	A	A		B	
Purley 4	d			21 08		21 14	21 19				21 27				21 38	21 50	21 49								22 08
Purley Oaks	d			21 11											21 41										22 11
South Croydon 4	d			21 14											21 44										22 14
East Croydon	d	21 09	21 10	21 17	21 17	21 21	21 25	21 29	21 32	21 33	21 34	21 35	21 39	21 40	21 47	21 56	21b58	22 00	22 00	22 02	22 03	22 09		22 10	22 17
Norwood Junction 2	d			21 21							21 38				21 51										22 21
London Bridge 4	⊖ a			21 42					21 47	21 47	21 51				22 12					22 17	22 17				22 42
London Blackfriars 3	⊖ a																								
City Thameslink 3	a																								
Farringdon 3	⊖ a																								
St Pancras International 15	⊖ a																								
London Waterloo (East) 4	⊖ a			21 47											22 17										22 47
London Charing Cross 4	⊖ a			21 50											22 20										22 50
Clapham Junction 10	a	21 18	21 24		21 26	21 31	21 37	21 41				21 47	21 48	21 54		22 06	22 08	22 10	22 11			22 18		22 24	
London Victoria 15	⊖ a	21 25	21 31		21 33	21 39	21 46	21 48				21 53	21 55	22 01		22 13	22 16	22 17	22 18			22 25		22 31	

		SN	SN	SN	FC	FC	SN	SN	SN	SN	SN	SN	SN	FC	FC	SN	SN	SN	SN	SN	FC	FC	SN		
		1	1	1	1	1	1			1	1	1 ◇	1 ◇	1	1		1	1	1		1	1	1		
		A	B		B	A	A			A	B	A	B	B	A		A	B			B	A			
Purley 4	d	22 14	22 18				22 27		22 38	22 50	22 49					23 08	23 14	23 18		23 23			23 50		
Purley Oaks	d								22 41							23 11				23 26					
South Croydon 4	d								22 44							23 14				23 29					
East Croydon	d	22 21	22 25	22 29	22 32	22 33	22 34	22 44	22 47	22 56	22c58	23 00	23 00	23 02	23 03	23a16	23 21	23 25	23 29	23a31	23 32	23 33	23 56		
Norwood Junction 2	d						22 38		22 51																
London Bridge 4	⊖ a				22 47	22 47	22 51	23 19	23 12					23 17	23 17						23 47	23 47			
London Blackfriars 3	⊖ a																								
City Thameslink 3	a																								
Farringdon 3	⊖ a																								
St Pancras International 15	⊖ a																								
London Waterloo (East) 4	⊖ a								23 17																
London Charing Cross 4	⊖ a								23 20																
Clapham Junction 10	a	22 31	22 37	22 41						23 07	23 10	23 10	23 12				23 31	23 37	23 41				00 10		
London Victoria 15	⊖ a	22 39	22 46	22 48						23 14	23 16	23 17	23 20				23 38	23 46	23 51				00 18		

For general notes see front of timetable
For details of catering facilities see Directory of Train Operators

A Until 6 September
B From 13 September
b Arr. 2154
c Arr. 2254

Network Diagram for Table 176

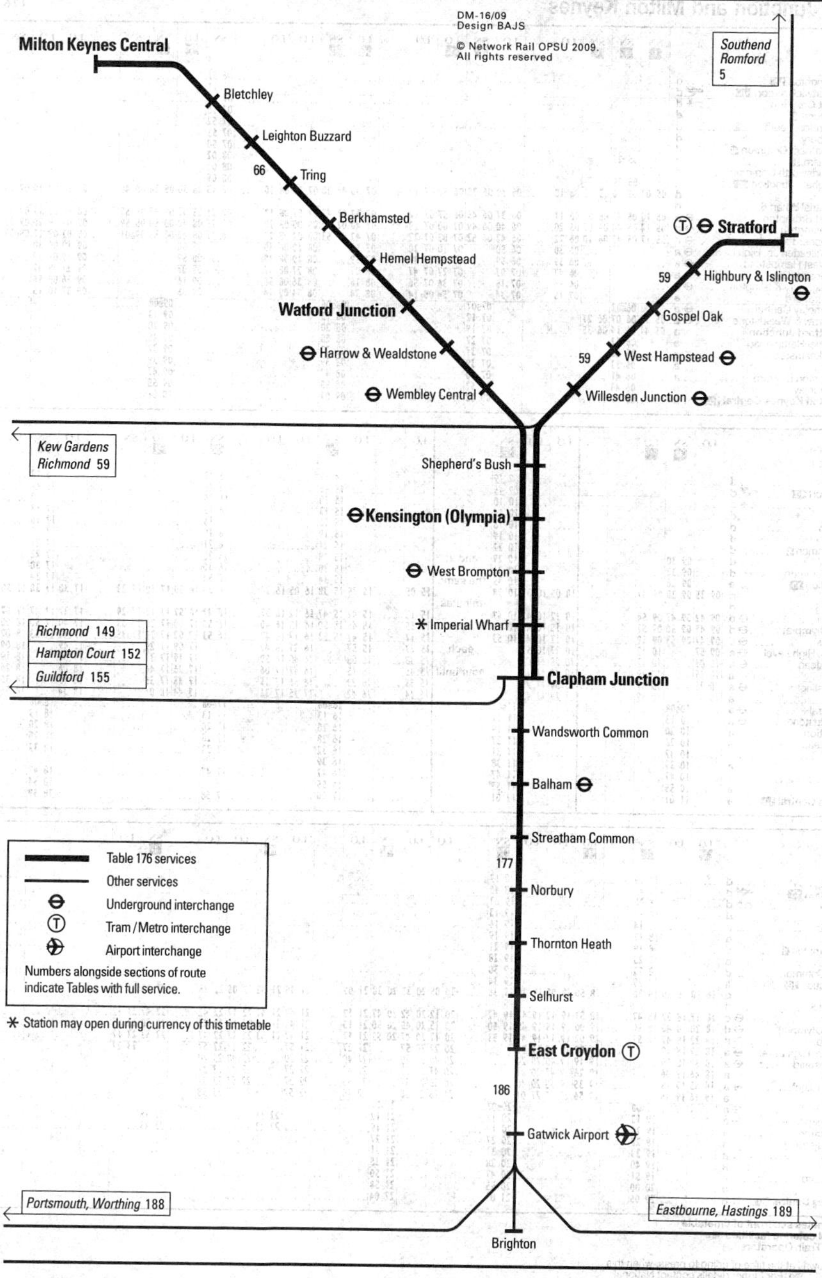

DM-16/09
Design BAJS
© Network Rail OPSU 2009. All rights reserved
Milton Keynes Central
Bletchley
Leighton Buzzard
66
Tring
Berkhamsted
Hemel Hempstead
Watford Junction
Harrow & Wealdstone
Wembley Central
Southend
Romford
5
Stratford
59
Highbury & Islington
Gospel Oak
59
West Hampstead
Willesden Junction
Kew Gardens
Richmond 59
Shepherd's Bush
Kensington (Olympia)
West Brompton
* Imperial Wharf
Richmond 149
Hampton Court 152
Guildford 155
Clapham Junction
Wandsworth Common
Balham
Streatham Common
177
Norbury
Thornton Heath
Selhurst
East Croydon
186
Gatwick Airport
Portsmouth, Worthing 188
Eastbourne, Hastings 189
Brighton
Table 176 services
Other services
Underground interchange
Tram / Metro interchange
Airport interchange
Numbers alongside sections of route indicate Tables with full service.
* Station may open during currency of this timetable

East Croydon, Clapham Junction, Kensington Olympia → Watford Junction and Milton Keynes

Network Diagram - see first page of Table 176

Miles	Miles	Station		SN 1	SN 1	SN 1	LO	LO	SN 1	LO 1	LO	LO 1	SN 1	LO	LO	SN	LO 1	SN 1	SN	LO	LO	SN
—	—	Brighton 10	d													06 51						
—	—	Gatwick Airport 10 ✈	d													07 11						
0	—	**East Croydon**	d													07 47						
1	—	Selhurst 4	d													07 50						
1¾	—	Thornton Heath	d													07 52						
3	—	Norbury	d													07 55						
4	—	Streatham Common 4	d													07 58						
5¾	—	Balham 4	d		05 25											08 02						
6½	—	Wandsworth Common	d													08 04						
7¾	—	Clapham Junction 10	a		05 29											08 08						
—	—		d	05 03	05 30	05 55	06 10	06 30	06 38	06 50	07 10	07 30	07 38	07 50	08 10	08 13	08 30	08 38	08 48	08 50	09 10	09 24
8¾	—	Imperial Wharf §	d																			
9½	—	West Brompton ⊖	d	05 10	05 40	06 03	06 17	06 37	06 45	06 57	07 17	07 37	07 47	07 57	08 17	08 21	08 37	08 47	08 55	08 57	09 17	09 31
11½	—	**Kensington (Olympia)** ⊖	d	05 14	05 44	06 07	06 20	06 40	06 49	07 00	07 20	07 40	07 50	08 00	08 20	08 25	08 40	08 50	08 59	09 00	09 20	09 35
12¾	0	Shepherd's Bush ⊖	d	05 17	05 47	06 10	06 22	06 42	06 52	07 02	07 22	07 42	07 53	08 02	08 22	08a27	08 42	08 53	09a01	09 02	09 22	09a37
—	1½	Willesden Jn. High Level ⊖	a				06 30	06 50		07 10	07 30	07 50		08 10	08 30		08 50			09 10	09 30	
—	4	West Hampstead ⊖	a				06 39	06 59		07 19	07 39	07 59		08 19	08 39		08 59			09 19	09 39	
—	6	Gospel Oak	a				06 47	07 07		07 27	07 47	08 07		08 27	08 47		09 07			09 27	09 47	
—	8¾	Highbury & Islington ⊖	a				06 56	07 16		07 36	07 56	08 16		08 36	08 56		09 16			09 36	09 56	
907	13½	Stratford	a				07 15	07 34		07 54	08 14	08 34		08 54	09 14		09 35			09 57	10 15	
17	—	Wembley Central ⊖	a		06s02				07s07				08s08					09s08				
20½	—	Harrow & Wealdstone ⊖	a	05 33	06 07	06 27			07 12				08 13					09 13				
25	—	**Watford Junction**	a	05 41	06 14	06 35			07 19				08 20					09 20				
32	—	Hemel Hempstead	a		06 22				07 27				08 28					09 28				
35½	—	Berkhamsted	a		06 26				07 31				08 32					09 32				
39¼	—	Tring	a		06 33				07 39				08 39					09 39				
47¾	—	Leighton Buzzard	a		06 41				07 50				08 47					09 47				
54¼	—	Bletchley	a		06 48				07 57				08 55					09 55				
57¼	—	**Milton Keynes Central 10**	a		06 55				08 03				09 01					10 01				

Station		LO	SN 1	LO 1	LO	LO	SN 1		LO	LO	SN 1	LO	LO	SN 1	LO	LO 1	SN	LO	SN 1	LO
Brighton 10	d						09 19				14 19			15 19					16 19	
Gatwick Airport 10 ✈	d						09 46				14 46			15 46					16 41	
East Croydon	d						10 10				15 10			16 10					17 10	
Selhurst 4	d						10 14				15 13			16 13					17 13	
Thornton Heath	d						10 16				15 16			16 16					17 16	
Norbury	d						10 19				15 19			16 19					17 19	
Streatham Common 4	d						10 22				15 21			16 21					17 21	
Balham 4	d		09 30				10 29	and at			15 28			16 28					17 28	
Wandsworth Common	d		09 32				10 31				15 30			16 30					17 30	
Clapham Junction 10	a		09 36				10 35	the same			15 34			16 34					17 34	
	d	09 35	09 38	09 47	10 05	10 35	10 38		15 05	15 35	15 38	16 05	16 30	16 38	16 50	17 10	17 23	17 30	17 38	17 50
Imperial Wharf §	d							minutes												
West Brompton ⊖	d	09 42	09 47	09 54	10 12	10 42	10 47		15 12	15 42	15 47	16 12	16 37	16 47	16 57	17 17	17 29	17 37	17 47	17 57
Kensington (Olympia) ⊖	d	09 45	09 50	09 57	10 15	10 45	10 50	past	15 15	15 45	15 50	16 15	16 40	16 50	17 00	17 20	17 33	17 40	17 50	18 00
Shepherd's Bush ⊖	d	09 47	09 53	09 59	10 17	10 47	10 53		15 17	15 47	15 53	16 17	16 42	16 53	17 02	17 22	17a35	17 42	17 53	18 02
Willesden Jn. High Level ⊖	a	09 57		10 12	10 27	10 57		each	15 27	15 57		16 27	16 49		17 09	17 29		17 49		18 09
West Hampstead ⊖	a	10 08		10 22	10 38	11 08			15 38	16 08		16 40	16 59		17 19	17 39		17 59		18 19
Gospel Oak	a	10 15		10 29	10 45	11 15		hour until	15 45	16 15		16 47	17 06		17 26	17 46		18 06		18 26
Highbury & Islington ⊖	a	10 25		10 39	10 54	11 25			15 55	16 23		16 56	17 15		17 35	17 55		18 15		18 35
Stratford	a	10 45		10 59	11 14	11 45			16 14	16 42		17 15	17 36		17 44	18 04		18 34		18 56
Wembley Central ⊖	a		10s08				11s07				16s08			17s08					18s08	
Harrow & Wealdstone ⊖	a		10 13				11 12				16 13			17 13					18 13	
Watford Junction	a		10 20				11 19				16 20			17 20					18 20	
Hemel Hempstead	a		10 28				11 27				16 28			17 28					18 28	
Berkhamsted	a		10 32				11 31				16 32			17 33					18 32	
Tring	a		10 39				11 38				16 39									
Leighton Buzzard	a		10 47				11 47				16 47			17 47					18 47	
Bletchley	a		10 55				11 55				16 55								18 54	
Milton Keynes Central 10	a		11 01				12 01				17 00			17 58					18 59	

Station		LO 1	LO	SN 1	LO 1	LO	LO	SN 1	LO	LO	SN 1	LO	LO	SN 1	LO	LO	SN 1	LO
Brighton 10	d			17 19				18 19										
Gatwick Airport 10 ✈	d			17 46				18 46										
East Croydon	d			18 08				19 07										
Selhurst 4	d			18 11				19 13										
Thornton Heath	d			18 14				19 16										
Norbury	d			18 17				19 19										
Streatham Common 4	d			18 19				19 21										
Balham 4	d			18 23				19 28										
Wandsworth Common	d			18 25				19 30										
Clapham Junction 10	a			18 29				19 34										
	d	18 10	18 30	18 38	18 50	19 05	19 35	19 38	20 05	20 35	20 38	21 05	21 35	21 38	22 05	22 35	22 38	23 05
Imperial Wharf §	d																	
West Brompton ⊖	d	18 17	18 37	18 47	18 57	19 12	19 42	19 47	20 12	20 42	20 47	21 12	21 42	21 47	22 12	22 42	22 47	23 12
Kensington (Olympia) ⊖	d	18 20	18 40	18 50	19 00	19 15	19 45	19 50	20 15	20 45	20 50	21 15	21 45	21 50	22 15	22 45	22 50	23 15
Shepherd's Bush ⊖	d	18 22	18 42	18 53	19 02	19 17	19 47	19 53	20 17	20 47	20 53	21 17	21 47	21 53	22 17	22 47	22 53	23 17
Willesden Jn. High Level ⊖	a	18 29	18 49		19 09	19 27	19 57		20 27	20 57		21 27	21 57		22 27	22 57		23 27
West Hampstead ⊖	a	18 39	18 59		19 19	19 40	20 24		20 40	21 20		21 40	22 20		22 40	23 20		
Gospel Oak	a	18 46	19 06		19 26	19 47	20 31		20 47	21 27		21 47	22 27		22 47	23 27		
Highbury & Islington ⊖	a	18 55	19 15		19 35	19 58	20 40		20 56	21 37		21 56	22 37		22 57	23 37		
Stratford	a	19 16	19 36		19 56	20 17	21 01		21 16	21 58		22 16	22 57		23 17	23 58		
Wembley Central ⊖	a			19s08				20s07			21s07							
Harrow & Wealdstone ⊖	a			19 13				20 12			21 12			22 16			23 16	
Watford Junction	a			19 20				20 19			21 19			22 23			23 23	
Hemel Hempstead	a			19 28				20 27			21 27							
Berkhamsted	a			19 33				20 31			21 31							
Tring	a			19 40				20 38			21 38							
Leighton Buzzard	a			19 51				20 47			21 50							
Bletchley	a			20 00				20 55			21 58							
Milton Keynes Central 10	a			20 06				21 01			22 04							

For general notes see front of timetable
For details of catering facilities see Directory of Train Operators

§ It is unknown , at the time of going to press, when this station will open. For further details contact National rail Enquiries 08457-484950 or see local publicity

Table 176

Saturdays

East Croydon, Clapham Junction, Kensington Olympia → Watford Junction and Milton Keynes

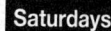

Network Diagram - see first page of Table 176

		SN 1	SN 1	LO	SN 1		LO	SN 1	LO	LO		SN 1	LO	LO	SN 1			LO	LO	SN 1		LO		LO	SN 1
Brighton 10	d							03 50				06 04			07 19					08 19					15 19
Gatwick Airport 10 ✈	d							05 38				06 38			07 46					08 46					15 46
East Croydon	d							06 10				07 10			08 10					09 10					16 10
Selhurst 4	d							06 13				07 13			08 13					09 13					16 13
Thornton Heath	d							06 16				07 16			08 16					09 16					16 16
Norbury	d							06 19				07 19			08 19					09 19					16 19
Streatham Common 4	d							06 21				07 21			08 21					09 21					16 21
Balham 4	d		05 33					06 28				07 28			08 28					09 28					16 28
Wandsworth Common	d							06 30				07 30			08 30					09 30					16 30
Clapham Junction 10	a		05 37					06 34				07 34			08 34					09 34					16 34
	d	05 08	05 38	06 05	06 08		06 35	06 38	07 05	07 35		07 38	08 05	08 35	08 38			09 05	09 35	09 38		16 05		16 35	16 38
Imperial Wharf §	d																								
West Brompton	⊖ d	05 15	05 45	06 12	06 18		06 42	06 47	07 12	07 42		07 47	08 12	08 42	08 47			09 12	09 42	09 47	and at the same minutes past each hour until	16 12		16 42	16 47
Kensington (Olympia)	⊖ d	05 19	05 49	06 15	06 22		06 45	06 50	07 15	07 45		07 50	08 15	08 45	08 50			09 15	09 45	09 50		16 15		16 45	16 50
Shepherd's Bush	⊖ d	05 22	05 52	06 17	06 25		06 47	06 53	07 17	07 47		07 53	08 17	08 47	08 53			09 17	09 47	09 53		16 17		16 47	16 53
Willesden Jn. High Level	⊖ a			06 27			06 57		07 28	07 57			08 27	08 57				09 27	09 57			16 27		16 57	
West Hampstead	⊖ a			06 37			07 07		07 52	08 07			08 37	09 07				09 37	10 07			16 37		17 07	
Gospel Oak	a			06 44			07 14		07 59	08 14			08 44	09 14				09 44	10 14			16 44		17 14	
Highbury & Islington	⊖ a			06 54			07 23		08 08	08 23			08 54	09 23				09 54	10 23			16 54		17 23	
Stratford	a			07 14			07 43		08 28	08 43			09 15	09 43				10 13	10 43			17 13		17 43	
Wembley Central	⊖ a		06s07					07s07				08s07			09s07					10s07					17s07
Harrow & Wealdstone	⊖ a	05 40	06 12		06 41			07 12				08 12			09 12					10 12					17 12
Watford Junction	a	05 47	06 19		06 50			07 19				08 19			09 19					10 19					17 19
Hemel Hempstead	a		06 27					07 27				08 27			09 27					10 27					17 27
Berkhamsted	a		06 31					07 32				08 31			09 33					10 31					17 31
Tring	a		06 37					07 39				08 37			09 38					10 37					17 37
Leighton Buzzard	a		06 46					07 47				08 46			09 47					10 47					17 46
Bletchley	a		06 54					07 54				08 54			09 54					10 54					17 54
Milton Keynes Central 10	a		07 00					08 00				09 00			10 00					11 00					18 00

		LO	LO	SN 1	LO		LO	SN 1	LO	LO		SN 1	LO	SN 1	LO		LO	LO	SN 1	LO		LO	SN 1	LO		
Brighton 10	d			16 19				17 19				18 19														
Gatwick Airport 10 ✈	d			16 46				17 46				18 46														
East Croydon	d			17 10				18 10				19 07														
Selhurst 4	d			17 16				18 13				19 13														
Thornton Heath	d			17 18				18 16				19 16														
Norbury	d			17 21				18 19				19 19														
Streatham Common 4	d			17 24				18 21				19 21														
Balham 4	d			17 28				18 28				19 28														
Wandsworth Common	d			17 30				18 30				19 30														
Clapham Junction 10	a			17 34				18 34				19 35														
	d	17 05	17 35	17 38	18 05		18 35	18 38	19 05	19 35		19 38	20 05	20 25	20 35		21 05	21 35	21 38	22 05		22 35	22 38	23 05		
Imperial Wharf §	d																									
West Brompton	⊖ d	17 12	17 42	17 47	18 12		18 42	18 47	19 12	19 42		19 45	20 12	20 32	20 42		21 12	21 42	21 53	22 12		22 42	22 47	23 12		
Kensington (Olympia)	⊖ d	17 15	17 45	17 50	18 15		18 45	18 50	19 15	19 45		19 48	20 15	20 36	20 45		21 15	21 45	21 57	22 15		22 45	22 50	23 15		
Shepherd's Bush	⊖ d	17 17	17 47	17 53	18 17		18 47	18 52	19 17	19 47		19 50	20 17	20 39	20 47		21 17	21 47	22 00	22 17		22 47	22 53	23 17		
Willesden Jn. High Level	⊖ a	17 27	17 57		18 27		19 01		19 27	19 57			20 27		20 57		21 27	21 57		22 27		22 57		23 29		
West Hampstead	⊖ a	17 37	18 07		18 37		19 21		19 41	20 08			20 41		21 21		21 41	22 21		22 41		23 21				
Gospel Oak	a	17 44	18 14		18 44		19 28		19 48	20 15			20 48		21 28		21 48	22 28		22 48		23 28				
Highbury & Islington	⊖ a	17 54	18 23		18 54		19 37		19 57	20 23			20 57		21 37		21 57	22 37		22 57		23 37				
Stratford	a	18 13	18 43		19 13		19 59		20 16	20 42			21 19		21 59		22 16	22 56		23 17		23 58				
Wembley Central	⊖ a			18s07																						
Harrow & Wealdstone	⊖ a			18 12				19 12				20 08		20 59					22 20				23 12			
Watford Junction	a			18 19				19 21				20 15		21 06					22 27				23 19			
Hemel Hempstead	a			18 27																						
Berkhamsted	a			18 31																						
Tring	a			18 37																						
Leighton Buzzard	a			18 46																						
Bletchley	a			18 54																						
Milton Keynes Central 10	a			19 00																						

For general notes see front of timetable
For details of catering facilities see Directory of Train Operators

§ It is unknown , at the time of going to press, when this station will open. For further details contact National rail Enquiries 08457-484950 or see local publicity

East Croydon, Clapham Junction, Kensington Olympia → Watford Junction and Milton Keynes

Network Diagram - see first page of Table 176

		SN 1	SN 1	LO	SN 1	LO	LO	SN 1	LO	LO	SN 1	LO	LO
Brighton 10	d												
Gatwick Airport 10 ✈	d												
East Croydon	d												
Selhurst 4	d												
Thornton Heath	d												
Norbury	d												
Streatham Common 4	d												
Balham 4	d												
Wandsworth Common	d												
Clapham Junction 10	a												
	d	07 25	08 15	08 48	09 15	09 18	09 48	10 15	10 18	10 48	11 15	11 18	11 48
Imperial Wharf §	d												
West Brompton	⊖ d	07 30	08 22	08 55	09 22	09 25	09 55	10 22	10 25	10 55	11 22	11 25	11 55
Kensington (Olympia)	⊖ d	07 34	08 26	08 58	09 26	09 28	09 58	10 26	10 28	10 58	11 26	11 28	11 58
Shepherd's Bush	⊖ d	07a36	08 29	09 00	09 29	09 30	10 00	10 29	10 30	11 00	11 29	11 30	12 00
Willesden Jn. High Level	⊖ a			09 08		09 41	10 08		10 41	11 08		11 41	12 08
West Hampstead	⊖ a			09 33		10 03	10 33		11 03	11 33		12 03	12 33
Gospel Oak	a			09 40		10 10	10 40		11 10	11 40		12 10	12 40
Highbury & Islington	⊖ a			09 49		10 19	10 49		11 19	11 49		12 19	12 49
Stratford	a			10 09		10 39	11 09		11 39	12 09		12 39	13 09
Wembley Central	⊖ a												
Harrow & Wealdstone	⊖ a		08 48		09 48			10 48			11 48		
Watford Junction	a		08 58		09 58			10 58			11 58		
Hemel Hempstead	a												
Berkhamsted	a												
Tring	a												
Leighton Buzzard	a												
Bletchley	a												
Milton Keynes Central 10	a												

		SN 1	LO	LO		SN 1	LO	LO	SN 1 A	SN 1 B	LO	LO	SN 1	LO	LO	LO
Brighton 10	d															
Gatwick Airport 10 ✈	d															
East Croydon	d															
Selhurst 4	d															
Thornton Heath	d															
Norbury	d															
Streatham Common 4	d															
Balham 4	d				and at											
Wandsworth Common	d															
Clapham Junction 10	a				the same											
	d	12 05	12 18	12 48	minutes	20 05	20 18	20 48	21 15	21 15	21 18	21 48	22 15	22 18	22 48	23 18
Imperial Wharf §	d															
West Brompton	⊖ d	12 12	12 25	12 55	past	20 12	20 25	20 55	21 22	21 22	21 25	21 55	22 22	22 25	22 55	23 25
Kensington (Olympia)	⊖ d	12 16	12 28	12 58		20 16	20 28	20 58	21 26	21 26	21 28	21 58	22 26	22 28	22 58	23 28
Shepherd's Bush	⊖ d	12 19	12 30	13 00	each	20 19	20 30	21 00	21 29	21 29	21 30	22 00	22 29	22 30	23 00	23 30
Willesden Jn. High Level	⊖ a		12 38	13 08	hour until		20 40	21 08			21 42	22 08		22 42	23 08	23 38
West Hampstead	⊖ a		13 03	13 33			21 03	21 33			22 03	22 33		23 03		
Gospel Oak	a		13 10	13 40			21 10	21 40			22 10	22 40		23 10		
Highbury & Islington	⊖ a		13 19	13 49			21 19	21 49			22 19	22 49		23 19		
Stratford	a		13 39	14 09			21 39	22 09			22 39	23 09		23 39		
Wembley Central	⊖ a															
Harrow & Wealdstone	⊖ a	12 36				20 36			21 48	21 49			22 48			
Watford Junction	a	12 46				20 46			21 57	21 58			22 58			
Hemel Hempstead	a															
Berkhamsted	a															
Tring	a															
Leighton Buzzard	a															
Bletchley	a															
Milton Keynes Central 10	a															

For general notes see front of timetable
For details of catering facilities see Directory of Train Operators

§ It is unknown , at the time of going to press, when this station will open. For further details contact National rail Enquiries 08457-484950 or see local publicity

A From 19 July
B Until 12 July

Milton Keynes, Watford Junction, Kensington Olympia → Clapham Junction and East Croydon

Network Diagram - see first page of Table 176

Miles	Miles			SN MO [1]	LO	SN [1]	LO	LO [1]	SN [1]	LO	LO	SN [1]	LO [1]	LO	SN	LO	SN	LO	SN [1]	LO [1]	SN	LO
0	—	**Milton Keynes Central [10]**	d									07 01							08 13			
3	—	Bletchley	d									07 05							08 17			
9½	—	Leighton Buzzard	d									07 13							08 24			
18	—	Tring	d									07 22							08 34			
21¾	—	Berkhamsted	d									07 26							08 39			
25¼	—	Hemel Hempstead	d									07 31							08 43			
32¼	—	**Watford Junction**	d	23p17		05 54			06 53			07 38							08 51			
36¾	—	Harrow & Wealdstone	⊖ d	23p23		06 00			06 59			07 45							08 58			
40¼	—	Wembley Central	⊖ d			06 05			07 04			07u49							09u05			
—	0	Stratford [7]	⊖ d					06 19		06 39	06 59		07 19	07 37		07 59		08 19		08 39		08 59
—	4¾	Highbury & Islington	⊖ d					06 33		06 53	07 13		07 33	07 51		08 13		08 33		08 53		09 13
—	7½	Gospel Oak	d					06 46		07 06	07 26		07 46	08 05		08 26		08 48		09 05		09 27
—	9½	West Hampstead	⊖ d					06 52		07 12	07 32		07 52	08 11		08 32		08 54		09 14		09 33
—	12	Willesden Jn. High Level	⊖ d		06 08		06 38	06 58		07 18	07 38		07 56	08 18		08 38		09 01		09 21		09 40
44½	13½	Shepherd's Bush	⊖ d	23p45	06 15	06 19	06 45	07 09	07 19	07 29	07 49	08 04	08 09	08 27	08 32	08 49	09 06	09 11	09 23	09 30	09 42	09 49
45¾	—	**Kensington (Olympia)**	⊖ d	23p48	06 17	06 22	06 47	07 11	07 22	07 31	07 51	08 07	08 11	08 29	08 34	08 51	09 09	09 13	09 25	09 32	09 45	09 51
47¾	—	West Brompton	⊖ d	23p50	06 19	06 25	06 49	07 14	07 25	07 34	07 54	08 10	08 14	08 32	08 37	08 54	09 12	09 16	09 28	09 35	09 48	09 54
48½	—	Imperial Wharf §	d																			
49½	—	**Clapham Junction [10]**	a	23p58	06 28	06 32	06 59	07 23	07 32	07 41	08 01	08 17	08 21	08 39	08 44	09 01	09 19	09 23	09 35	09 42	09 55	10 01
—	—		d	00 02															09 35			
50¾	—	Wandsworth Common	a																09 38			
51½	—	Balham [4]	a																09 41			
53¼	—	Streatham Common [4]	a																09 45			
54¼	—	Norbury	a																09 48			
55½	—	Thornton Heath	a																09 51			
56¼	—	Selhurst [4]	a																09 53			
57¼	—	**East Croydon**	a	00 22															09 57			
—	—	Gatwick Airport [10]	✈ a	00 49															10 18			
—	—	Brighton [10]	a	02 23															10 54			

		LO	SN [1]	LO	LO	SN [1]		LO	LO	SN [1]	LO	LO [1]	SN [1]	LO	SN	LO	LO [1]	SN [1]	LO	LO
Milton Keynes Central [10]	d		09 13			10 13				15 13			16 13					17 13		
Bletchley	d		09 17			10 17				15 17			16 17					17 17		
Leighton Buzzard	d		09 24			10 24				15 24			16 24					17 24		
Tring	d		09 34			10 34				15 34			16 34					17 34		
Berkhamsted	d		09 39			10 39				15 39			16 39					17 39		
Hemel Hempstead	d		09 43			10 43				15 43			16 43					17 43		
Watford Junction	d		09 51			10 51				15 51			16 51					17 51		
Harrow & Wealdstone	⊖ d		09 58			10 59	and at			15 59			16 59					17 59		
Wembley Central	⊖ d		10u05			11u04				16u05			17u05					18u05		
Stratford [7]	⊖ d	09 22		09 52	10 22		the same	14 52	15 22		15 52	16 19		16 39		16 59	17 19		17 39	17 59
Highbury & Islington	⊖ d	09 38		10 08	10 38			15 08	15 38		16 08	16 33		16 53		17 13	17 33		17 53	18 13
Gospel Oak	d	09 49		10 19	10 49		minutes	15 19	15 49		16 19	16 46		17 06		17 26	17 46		18 06	18 26
West Hampstead	⊖ d	09 54		10 24	10 54			15 24	15 54		16 24	16 52		17 12		17 32	17 52		18 12	18 32
Willesden Jn. High Level	⊖ d	10 08		10 38	11 08		past	15 38	16 08		16 38	16 58		17 18		17 38	17 58		18 18	18 38
Shepherd's Bush	⊖ d	10 15	10 23	10 45	11 15	11 18		15 45	16 15	16 19	16 45	17 09	17 19	17 29	17 48	17 54	18 09	18 19	18 29	18 49
Kensington (Olympia)	⊖ d	10 17	10 25	10 47	11 17	11 20	each	15 47	16 17	16 22	16 47	17 11	17 22	17 31	17 50	17 56	18 11	18 22	18 31	18 51
West Brompton	⊖ d	10 19	10 27	10 49	11 19	11 23		15 49	16 19	16 25	16 49	17 14	17 25	17 34	17 53	17 59	18 14	18 25	18 34	18 54
Imperial Wharf §	d						hour until													
Clapham Junction [10]	a	10 28	10 33	10 58	11 28	11 30		15 58	16 28	16 32	16 58	17 21	17 32	17 41	18 00	18 06	18 21	18 32	18 41	19 01
	d		10 34			11 34				16 34			17 33		18 02			18 34		
Wandsworth Common	a		10 37			11 37				16 37			17 36		18 05			18 37		
Balham [4]	a		10 40			11 40				16 40			17 39		18 08			18 40		
Streatham Common [4]	a		10 45			11 45				16 45			17 44		18 15			18 44		
Norbury	a		10 48			11 48				16 48			17 47		18 18			18 47		
Thornton Heath	a		10 51			11 51				16 51			17 50		18 21			18 50		
Selhurst [4]	a		10 53			11 53				16 55			17 53		18 24			18 54		
East Croydon	a		10 57			11 57				16 59			17 59		18 32			19 02		
Gatwick Airport [10]	✈ a		11 18			12 18				17 39			18 24		18 56			19 26		
Brighton [10]	a		11 54			12 54				18 10			19 04		19 34			20 00		

		LO	SN [1]	LO	LO	LO	SN [1]	LO	LO	SN [1]	LO	LO	SN [1]	LO	SN [1]	LO	SN [1]	SN [1]
Milton Keynes Central [10]	d		18 13				19 13			20 13			21 13				22 11	
Bletchley	d		18 17				19 17			20 17			21 17				22 15	
Leighton Buzzard	d		18 24				19 24			20 24			21 24				22 22	
Tring	d		18 34				19 34			20 34			21 34				22 34	
Berkhamsted	d		18 39				19 39			20 39			21 39				22 39	
Hemel Hempstead	d		18 43				19 44			20 43			21 43				22 43	
Watford Junction	d		18 51				19 53			20 51			21 51		22 27		22 53	23 29
Harrow & Wealdstone	⊖ d		18 59				20 01			20 59			21 59		22 33		23 00	23 35
Wembley Central	⊖ d		19u05				20u06			21u04								
Stratford [7]	⊖ d	18 19		18 39	18 52	19 23		19 52	20 12		20 52	21 12		21 52		22 12		
Highbury & Islington	⊖ d	18 33		18 53	19 08	19 40		20 08	20 28		21 08	21 28		22 08		22 28		
Gospel Oak	d	18 46		19 08	19 19	19 51		20 18	20 38		21 18	21 38		22 18		22 38		
West Hampstead	⊖ d	18 52		19 14	19 25	19 57		20 23	20 43		21 23	21 43		22 23		22 43		
Willesden Jn. High Level	⊖ d	18 58		19 21	19 38	20 08		20 38	21 08		21 38	22 08		22 38		23 08		
Shepherd's Bush	⊖ d	19 10	19 18	19 30	19 45	20 15	20 21	20 45	21 15	21 23	21 45	22 15	22 23	22 45	22 49	23 15	23 21	23 54
Kensington (Olympia)	⊖ d	19 12	19 20	19 32	19 47	20 17	20 23	20 47	21 17	21 25	21 47	22 17	22 25	22 47	22 51	23 17	23 23	23 56
West Brompton	⊖ d	19 15	19 23	19 35	19 49	20 19	20 25	20 49	21 19	21 27	21 49	22 19	22 27	22 49	22 54	23 19	23 26	23 59
Imperial Wharf §	d																	
Clapham Junction [10]	a	19 22	19 30	19 42	19 58	20 28	20 32	20 58	21 28	21 34	21 58	22 28	22 34	22 58	23 01	23 28	23 33	00 07
	d		19 34														23 40	
Wandsworth Common	a		19 37															
Balham [4]	a		19 40														23 44	
Streatham Common [4]	a		19 45														23 48	
Norbury	a		19 47														23 51	
Thornton Heath	a		19 50														23 54	
Selhurst [4]	a		19 53														23 56	
East Croydon	a																	
Gatwick Airport [10]	✈ a																	
Brighton [10]	a																	

For general notes see front of timetable
For details of catering facilities see Directory of Train Operators

§ It is unknown , at the time of going to press, when this station will open. For further details contact National rail Enquiries 08457-484950 or see local publicity

Table 176

Saturdays

Milton Keynes, Watford Junction, Kensington Olympia → Clapham Junction and East Croydon

Network Diagram - see first page of Table 176

	LO	SN 1	LO		LO	SN 1	LO		LO	SN 1	LO		LO	SN 1		LO	LO	SN 1			LO	LO	SN 1	LO
Milton Keynes Central 10 d										07 13				08 13				09 13					17 13	
Bletchley d										07 17				08 17				09 17					17 17	
Leighton Buzzard d										07 24				08 24				09 24					17 24	
Tring d										07 34				08 34				09 34					17 34	
Berkhamsted d										07 39				08 39				09 39					17 39	
Hemel Hempstead d										07 43				08 43				09 43					17 43	
Watford Junction d		05 51				06 55				07 52				08 51				09 52					17 51	
Harrow & Wealdstone ⊖ d		05 58				07 01				07 59				08 58				09 59					17 58	
Wembley Central ⊖ d						07 06				08u04				09u03				10u04	and at				18u03	
Stratford 7 ⊖ d					06 22		06 52		07 22		07 52		08 22			08 52	09 22		the same		16 52	17 22		17 52
Highbury & Islington ⊖ d					06 38		07 08		07 38		08 08		08 38			09 08	09 38		minutes		17 08	17 38		18 08
Gospel Oak d					06 49		07 19		07 49		08 19		08 49			09 19	09 49		past		17 19	17 49		18 19
West Hampstead ⊖ d					06 54		07 25		07 54		08 25		08 54			09 25	09 54		each		17 25	17 54		18 25
Willesden Jn. High Level ⊖ d	06 08		06 38		07 08		07 38		08 08		08 38		09 08			09 38	10 08		hour until		17 38	18 08		18 38
Shepherd's Bush ⊖ d	06 15	06 19	06 45		07 15	07 19	07 45		08 15	08 19	08 45		09 15	09 19		09 45	10 15	10 19			17 45	18 15	18 19	18 45
Kensington (Olympia) ⊖ d	06 17	06 22	06 47		07 17	07 22	07 47		08 17	08 22	08 47		09 17	09 22		09 47	10 17	10 22			17 47	18 17	18 22	18 47
West Brompton ⊖ d	06 19	06 25	06 49		07 19	07 25	07 49		08 19	08 25	08 49		09 19	09 25		09 49	10 19	10 25			17 49	18 19	18 25	18 49
Imperial Wharf § d																								
Clapham Junction 10 a	06 29	06 33	06 59		07 29	07 33	07 59		08 29	08 33	08 59		09 29	09 33		09 59	10 29	10 33			17 59	18 29	18 33	18 59
d		06 34				07 34				08 34				09 34				10 34					18 34	
Wandsworth Common a		06 37				07 37				08 37				09 37				10 37					18 37	
Balham 4 a		06 40				07 40				08 40				09 40				10 40					18 40	
Streatham Common 4 a		06 45				07 45				08 45				09 45				10 45					18 45	
Norbury a		06 48				07 48				08 48				09 48				10 48					18 48	
Thornton Heath a		06 51				07 51				08 51				09 51				10 51					18 51	
Selhurst 4 a		06 53				07 53				08 53				09 53				10 53					18 53	
East Croydon a		06 57				07 57				08 57				09 57				10 57					18 57	
Gatwick Airport 10 ✈ a		07 25				08 18				09 18				10 18				11 18					19 18	
Brighton 10 a		07 54				08 54				09 54				10 54				11 54					19 54	

	LO		SN 1	LO	SN 1		LO	SN 1	LO		SN 1	LO	LO		SN 1	LO	LO		SN 1	LO	SN 1				
Milton Keynes Central 10 d			18 13					19 13																	
Bletchley d			18 17					19 17																	
Leighton Buzzard d			18 24					19 24																	
Tring d			18 34					19 34																	
Berkhamsted d			18 39					19 39																	
Hemel Hempstead d			18 43					19 43																	
Watford Junction d			18 51		19 31			19 51			20 43				21 43				22 48		23 25				
Harrow & Wealdstone ⊖ d			18 58		19 38			19 58			20 50				21 50				22 55		23 31				
Wembley Central ⊖ d			19u03		19 43																				
Stratford 7 ⊖ d	18 22			18 52			19 22		19 52			20 12	20 52			21 12	21 52			22 12					
Highbury & Islington ⊖ d	18 38			19 08			19 38		20 08			20 28	21 08			21 28	22 08			22 28					
Gospel Oak d	18 49			19 19			19 49		20 18			20 39	21 19			21 39	22 19			22 39					
West Hampstead ⊖ d	18 55			19 25			19 55		20 24			20 44	21 24			21 44	22 24			22 44					
Willesden Jn. High Level ⊖ d	19 08			19 38			20 08		20 38			21 08	21 38			22 08	22 38			23 08					
Shepherd's Bush ⊖ d	19 15		19 19	19 45	19 57		20 15	20 19	20 45		21 08	21 15	21 45		22 08	22 15	22 45		23 13	23 15	23 49				
Kensington (Olympia) ⊖ d	19 17		19 22	19 47	20 00		20 17	20 22	20 47		21 11	21 17	21 47		22 11	22 17	22 47		23 16	23 17	23 51				
West Brompton ⊖ d	19 19		19 25	19 49	20 03		20 19	20 25	20 49		21 14	21 19	21 49		22 14	22 19	22 49		23 19	23 19	23 54				
Imperial Wharf § d																									
Clapham Junction 10 a	19 29		19 33	19 59	20 10		20 29	20 33	21 00		21 21	21 29	21 59		22 21	22 29	22 59		23 26	23 29	00 02				
d			19 35					20 34																	
Wandsworth Common a			19 38					20 37																	
Balham 4 a			19 41					20 40																	
Streatham Common 4 a			19 45					20 45																	
Norbury a			19 48					20 48																	
Thornton Heath a			19 51					20 51																	
Selhurst 4 a			19 53					20 53																	
East Croydon a			19 57					20 57																	
Gatwick Airport 10 ✈ a			20 18					21 18																	
Brighton 10 a			20 54					22 00																	

For general notes see front of timetable
For details of catering facilities see Directory of Train Operators

§ It is unknown , at the time of going to press, when this station will open. For further details contact National rail Enquiries 08457-484950 or see local publicity

Sundays

Milton Keynes, Watford Junction, Kensington Olympia → Clapham Junction and East Croydon

Network Diagram - see first page of Table 176

		SN 1	SN 1	LO	LO	SN 1	LO	LO	SN 1	LO	LO	SN 1	LO	LO
Milton Keynes Central 10	d													
Bletchley	d													
Leighton Buzzard	d													
Tring	d													
Berkhamsted	d													
Hemel Hempstead	d													
Watford Junction	d					09 17			10 17			11 17		
Harrow & Wealdstone ⊖	d					09 23			10 23			11 23		
Wembley Central ⊖	d													
Stratford 7 ⊖	d						08 49	09 19		09 49	10 19		10 49	11 19
Highbury & Islington ⊖	d						09 05	09 35		10 05	10 35		11 05	11 35
Gospel Oak	d						09 16	09 46		10 16	10 46		11 16	11 46
West Hampstead ⊖	d						09 22	09 52		10 22	10 52		11 22	11 52
Willesden Jn. High Level ⊖	d			08 51	09 21		09 51	10 21		10 51	11 21		11 51	12 21
Shepherd's Bush ⊖	d	07 48	08 50	08 58	09 28	09 45	09 58	10 28	10 45	10 58	11 28	11 45	11 58	12 28
Kensington (Olympia) ⊖	d	07 50	08 53	09 00	09 30	09 48	10 00	10 30	10 48	11 00	11 30	11 48	12 00	12 30
West Brompton ⊖	d	07 52	08 56	09 02	09 32	09 50	10 02	10 32	10 50	11 02	11 32	11 50	12 02	12 32
Imperial Wharf §	d													
Clapham Junction 10	a	07 58	09 03	09 11	09 41	09 58	10 11	10 41	10 58	11 11	11 41	11 58	12 11	12 41
	d													
Wandsworth Common	a													
Balham 4	a													
Streatham Common 4	a													
Norbury	a													
Thornton Heath	a													
Selhurst 4	a													
East Croydon	a													
Gatwick Airport 10 ✈	a													
Brighton 10	a													

		SN 1		LO	LO	SN 1	LO	LO	SN 1	LO	LO	SN 1	LO	LO	SN 1
Milton Keynes Central 10	d														
Bletchley	d														
Leighton Buzzard	d														
Tring	d														
Berkhamsted	d														
Hemel Hempstead	d														
Watford Junction	d	12 22				20 22			21 17			22 17			23 17
Harrow & Wealdstone ⊖	d	12 29				20 28			21 23			22 23			23 23
Wembley Central ⊖	d		and at												
Stratford 7 ⊖	d		the same	18 49	19 19		19 49	20 19		20 49	21 19		21 49	22 19	
Highbury & Islington ⊖	d			19 05	19 35		20 05	20 35		21 05	21 35		22 05	22 35	
Gospel Oak	d		minutes	19 16	19 46		20 16	20 46		21 16	21 46		22 16	22 46	
West Hampstead ⊖	d			19 22	19 52		20 22	20 52		21 22	21 52		22 22	22 52	
Willesden Jn. High Level ⊖	d		past	19 51	20 21		20 51	21 21		21 51	22 21		22 51	23 21	
Shepherd's Bush ⊖	d	12 45	each	19 58	20 28	20 45	20 58	21 28	21 45	21 58	22 28	22 45	22 58	23 28	23 45
Kensington (Olympia) ⊖	d	12 48		20 00	20 30	20 48	21 00	21 30	21 48	22 00	22 30	22 48	23 00	23 30	23 48
West Brompton ⊖	d	12 50	hour until	20 02	20 32	20 50	21 02	21 32	21 50	22 02	22 32	22 50	23 02	23 32	23 50
Imperial Wharf §	d														
Clapham Junction 10	a	12 58		20 11	20 43	20 58	21 11	21 41	21 58	22 11	22 41	22 58	23 11	23 41	23 58
	d														00 02
Wandsworth Common	a														
Balham 4	a														
Streatham Common 4	a														
Norbury	a														
Thornton Heath	a														
Selhurst 4	a														
East Croydon	a														00 22
Gatwick Airport 10 ✈	a														00 49
Brighton 10	a														02 23

For general notes see front of timetable
For details of catering facilities see Directory of Train Operators

§ It is unknown , at the time of going to press, when this station will open. For further details contact National rail Enquiries 08457-484950 or see local publicity

Network Diagram for Tables 177, 178, 179, 181, 182 also 175★

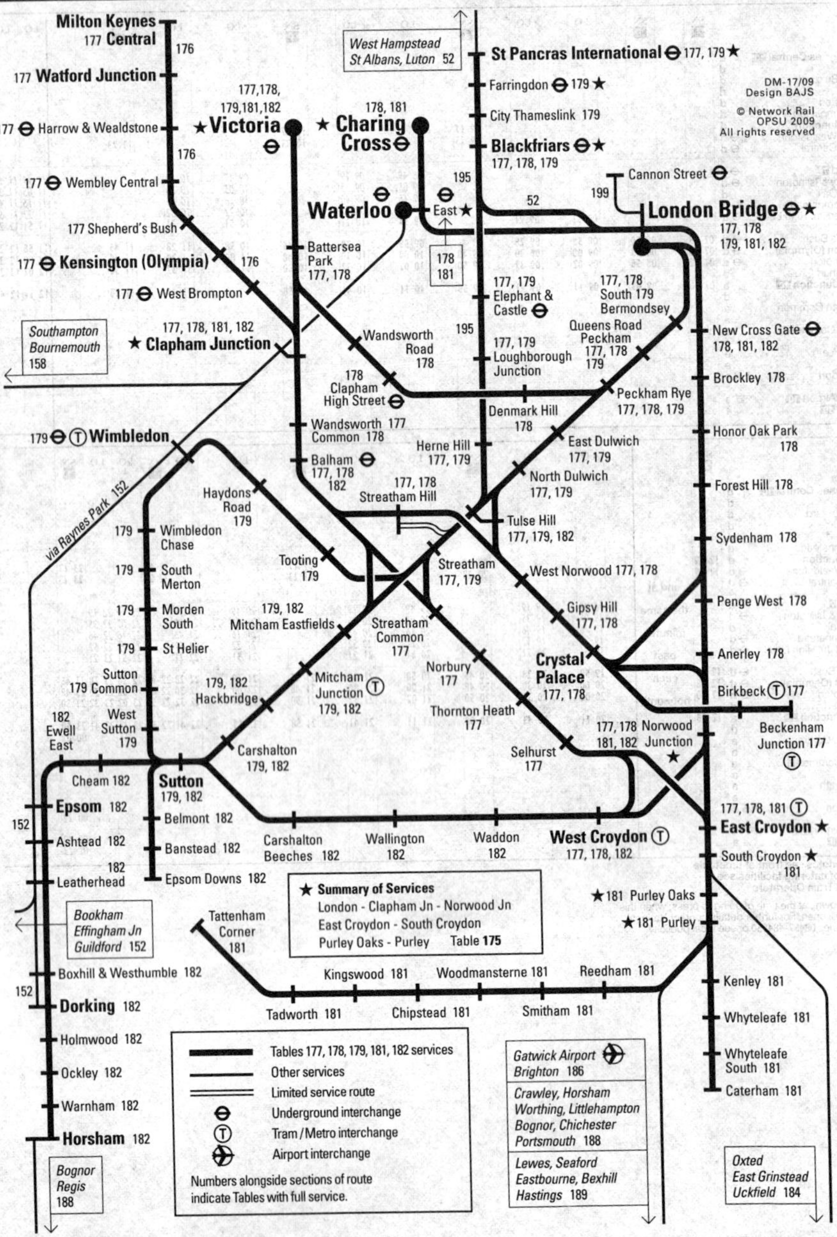

Milton Keynes
177 Central
176
177 Watford Junction
177 Harrow & Wealdstone
176
177 Wembley Central
177 Shepherd's Bush
177 Kensington (Olympia)
176
177 West Brompton
177,178,
179,181,182
★ Victoria
178, 181
★ Charing
Cross
195
Waterloo
East ★
178
181
West Hampstead
St Albans, Luton 52
St Pancras International 177, 179★
Farringdon 179 ★
City Thameslink 179
Blackfriars ★
177, 178, 179
DM-17/09
Design BAJS
© Network Rail
OPSU 2009
All rights reserved
Cannon Street
199
52
London Bridge ★
177, 178
179, 181, 182
Battersea
Park
177, 178
Southampton
Bournemouth
158
177, 178, 181, 182
★ Clapham Junction
Wandsworth
Road
178
178
Clapham
High Street
195
177, 179
Elephant &
Castle
177, 179
Loughborough
Junction
177, 178
South 179
Bermondsey
Queens Road
Peckham
177, 178
179
New Cross Gate
178, 181, 182
Brockley 178
Peckham Rye
177, 178, 179
Denmark Hill
178
Wandsworth 177
Common 178
179 Wimbledon
Balham
177, 178
182
Herne Hill
177, 179
East Dulwich
177, 179
Honor Oak Park
178
North Dulwich
177, 179
177, 178
Streatham Hill
Forest Hill 178
Haydons
Road
179
via Raynes Park 152
179 Wimbledon
Chase
179 South
Merton
179 Morden
South
179 St Helier
Sutton
179 Common
182
Ewell
East
West
Sutton
179
Tooting
179
179, 182
Mitcham Eastfields
Streatham
177, 179
Tulse Hill
177, 179, 182
West Norwood 177, 178
Sydenham 178
Gipsy Hill
177, 178
Penge West 178
Streatham
Common
177
179, 182
Hackbridge
Mitcham
Junction
179, 182
Norbury
177
Crystal
Palace
177, 178
Anerley 178
Birkbeck 177
Thornton Heath
177
Beckenham
Junction 177
177, 178 Norwood
181, 182 Junction ★
Carshalton
179, 182
Selhurst
177
Cheam 182
Sutton
179, 182
Epsom 182
152
Ashtead 182
182
Leatherhead
Belmont 182
Banstead 182
Epsom Downs 182
Carshalton
Beeches 182
Wallington
182
Waddon
182
West Croydon
177, 178, 182
177, 178, 181
East Croydon ★
South Croydon ★
181
★181 Purley Oaks
★181 Purley
★ Summary of Services
London - Clapham Jn - Norwood Jn
East Croydon - South Croydon
Purley Oaks - Purley Table 175
Bookham
Effingham Jn
Guildford 152
Tattenham
Corner
181
Boxhill & Westhumble 182
152
Dorking 182
Kingswood 181
Woodmansterne 181
Reedham 181
Kenley 181
Tadworth 181
Chipstead 181
Smitham 181
Whyteleafe 181
Whyteleafe
South 181
Caterham 181
Holmwood 182
Ockley 182
Warnham 182
Horsham 182
Tables 177, 178, 179, 181, 182 services
Other services
Limited service route
Underground interchange
Tram / Metro interchange
Airport interchange
Numbers alongside sections of route
indicate Tables with full service.
Gatwick Airport
Brighton 186
Crawley, Horsham
Worthing, Littlehampton
Bognor, Chichester
Portsmouth 188
Lewes, Seaford
Eastbourne, Bexhill
Hastings 189
Bognor
Regis
188
Oxted
East Grinstead
Uckfield 184

Luton, Milton Keynes and London → East and West Croydon via Tulse Hill → Crystal Palace → Norbury

Local Services

Network Diagram - see first page of Table 177

Miles	Miles	Miles	Miles	Miles			SN MX	SN MO	SN MO	SN MO	SN MX A	SN MX	SN MX	FC MX	SN	SN MX	SN	SN [1]	SN [1]	SN	SN	SN [1]	SN	SN B	SN
—	0	—	—	0	**London Bridge [4]**	⊖ d			23p44			23p53	23p48	23p58		00 26					05 45				06 00
—	1¾	—	—	1¾	South Bermondsey	d							23p52												06 04
—	2¾	—	—	2¾	Queens Rd Peckham	d							23p54												06 06
—	3½	—	—	3½	Peckham Rye [4]	d							23p57												06 09
—	4¼	—	—	4¼	East Dulwich	d							00 01												06 12
—	4¾	—	—	4¾	North Dulwich	d							00 03												06 14
—	—	—	—	—	**Luton [10]**	d																			
—	—	—	—	—	Luton Airport Parkway [7]	✈ d																			
—	—	—	—	—	St Pancras International [15]	⊖ d																			
—	—	—	—	—	City Thameslink [3]	d																			
—	—	—	—	—	London Blackfriars [3]	⊖ d																			
—	—	—	—	—	Elephant & Castle	⊖ d																			
—	—	—	—	—	Loughborough Jn	d																			
—	—	—	—	—	Herne Hill [4]	d																			
—	6	—	—	6	Tulse Hill [3]	d							00 06	00 10											06 17
—	7½	—	—	—	Streatham [4]	d								00a13											06a21
0	—	0	0	—	**London Victoria [15]**	⊖ d	23p37	23p38		23p49	23p51				00 17		00 42	05 02	05 23				05 57	06 00	
1¼	—	1¼	1¼	—	Battersea Park [4]	d	23p41	23p42		23p53	23p55						00 46							06 04	
—	—	—	—	—	Milton Keynes Central	d																			
—	—	—	—	—	Watford Junction	d																			
—	—	—	—	—	Harrow & Wealdstone	⊖ d																			
—	—	—	—	—	Wembley Central	⊖ d																			
—	—	—	—	—	Shepherd's Bush	⊖ d									23b54										
—	—	—	—	—	Kensington (Olympia)	⊖ d									23c56										
—	—	—	—	—	West Brompton	⊖ d									23e59										
2¾	—	2¾	2¾	—	Clapham Junction [10]	d	23p45	23p45		23p56	23p59				00 23		00 50	05 08	05 33				06 03	06 08	
4	—	4	4	—	Wandsworth Common	d	23p48	23p48		23p59	00 02						00 53							06 11	
4¾	—	4¾	4¾	—	Balham [4]	⊖ d	23p51	23p51		00 01	00 04				00 28		00 55						06 08	06 13	
5¾	—	5¾	—	—	Streatham Hill	d	23p54	23p54																	
7	—	7	—	6½	West Norwood [4]	d	23p57	23p57					00 09												
8	—	8	—	7½	Gipsy Hill	d	23p59	23p59					00 12												
8¾	—	8¾	—	8¼	**Crystal Palace [4]**	d	00 03	00 03					00 15												
—	—	10¼	—	—	Birkbeck	🚊 d																			
—	—	11¾	—	—	Beckenham Junction [4]	🚊 a																			
—	—	—	—	—	Bromley South [4]	a																			
—	8	—	6½	—	Streatham Common [4]	d				00 05	00 08				00 32		00 59							06 17	
—	9	—	7½	—	Norbury	d				00 08	00 11				00 34		01 02							06 20	
—	10¼	—	8¾	—	Thornton Heath	d				00 11	00 14				00 37		01 05							06 23	
—	11	—	9½	—	Selhurst [4]	d				00 13	00 17				00 40		01 07	05 17						06 26	
10¼	—	—	—	9¾	Norwood Junction [2]	a	00 07	00 07	00 09			00 16	00 19			00 49			05 49		06 08				
—	—	—	—	—		d	00 07		00 10			00 16				00 50			05 50	05 54	06 09	06 10			
—	12	—	—	—	**West Croydon [4]**	🚊 a	00 13				00 21									05 58	06 13			06 30	
11½	—	—	10½	11	**East Croydon**	🚊 a			00 13	00 16		00 20			00 43	00 53	01 10	05 20	05 53			06 13			

		FC	SN	SN C	SN D	SN	SN		SN	SN B	SN	SN [1]	SN	SN	SN	SN	SN	FC	SN	SN	SN E	SN	SN B	SN	SN
London Bridge [4]	⊖ d		06 13				06 11		06 20		06 30	06 30	06 35				06 38		06 41	06 46	06 48			06 52	07 00
South Bermondsey	d						06 15		06 24		06 34						06 42		06 45		06 52				07 04
Queens Rd Peckham	d						06 18		06 26		06 36						06 44		06 48		06 54				07 06
Peckham Rye [4]	d						06 20		06 29		06 39						06 47		06 50		06 57				07 09
East Dulwich	d								06 32		06 42						06 50				07 00				07 12
North Dulwich	d								06 34		06 44						06 52				07 02				07 14
Luton [10]	d																	05 48							
Luton Airport Parkway [7]	✈ d																	05 50							
St Pancras International [15]	⊖ d	05 56																06 34							
City Thameslink [3]	d	06 03																06 43							
London Blackfriars [3]	⊖ d	06 06																06 46							
Elephant & Castle	⊖ d	06 09																06 49							
Loughborough Jn	d	06 13																06 53							
Herne Hill [4]	d	06 20																06 58							
Tulse Hill [3]	d	06 26							06 37		06 47						06f58	07 03			07 05				07 17
Streatham [4]	d	06 30							06 41		06a51						07 01	07 06							07a21
London Victoria [15]	⊖ d			06 07	06 15	06 25				06 28				06 37	06 41	06 44						06 52	07 00		
Battersea Park [4]	d			06 11	06 19					06 34				06 41	06a45							06 56	07 04		
Milton Keynes Central	d																								
Watford Junction	d																								
Harrow & Wealdstone	⊖ d																								
Wembley Central	⊖ d																								
Shepherd's Bush	⊖ d									06 19															
Kensington (Olympia)	⊖ d									06 22															
West Brompton	⊖ d									06 25															
Clapham Junction [10]	d			06 15	06 23	06 31				06 38				06 45		06 50						07 00	07 08		
Wandsworth Common	d			06 18	06 26					06 41				06 48		06 53						07 03	07 11		
Balham [4]	⊖ d			06 20	06 28	06 36				06 44				06 50		06 56						07 05	07 13		
Streatham Hill	d			06 23										06 53								07 08			
West Norwood [4]	d			06 27										06 57							07 08	07 12			
Gipsy Hill	d			06 30										07 00							07 11	07 15			
Crystal Palace [4]	d			06 32										07 02							07a14	07 17			
Birkbeck	🚊 d																					07 21			
Beckenham Junction [4]	🚊 a																					07 25			
Bromley South [4]	a																					08 04			
Streatham Common [4]	d				06 32				06 44	06 48						07 00	07 04						07 18		
Norbury	d				06 35				06 46	06 50						07 02	07 07						07 21		
Thornton Heath	d				06 38				06 49	06 53						07 05	07 10						07 24		
Selhurst [4]	d				06 41				06 52	06 56						07 08	07 13						07 27		
Norwood Junction [2]	a		06 37	06 37								06 44	06 55	07 07						07 10				07 13	
	d		06 38	06 39								06 44	06 56	07 07						07 10				07 14	
West Croydon [4]	🚊 a			06 43						07 00				07 12			07 22			07 15			07 31		
East Croydon	🚊 a		06 41		06 45				06 55			06 48	06 59			07 11								07 17	

For general notes see front of timetable
For details of catering facilities see Directory of Train Operators

A To Sutton (Surrey) (Table 182)

B To Epsom Downs (Table 182)
C To Epsom (Table 182)
D To Tattenham Corner (Table 181)
E To London Bridge (Table 178)
b Mondays to Fridays. Mondays dep. 2345

c Mondays to Fridays. Mondays dep. 2348
e Mondays to Fridays. Mondays dep. 2350
f Arr. 0655

Luton, Milton Keynes and London → East and West Croydon via Tulse Hill → Crystal Palace → Norbury

Local Services

Network Diagram - see first page of Table 177

		SN	FC	FC 1	SN 1	SN	SN	SN	SN A		SN	SN	SN	SN 1	SN B	SN	SN 1	SN	SN	SN	SN	SN	FC	SN C	SN D
London Bridge 4	⊖ d	07 08			07 20						07 11	07 15	07 22	07 28			07 35	07 25	07 31	07 39					
South Bermondsey	d	07 12									07 15		07 26						07 35						
Queens Rd Peckham	d	07 14									07 17		07 28						07 37						
Peckham Rye 4	d	07 17									07 20		07 31						07 40						
East Dulwich	d	07 20											07 34						07 43						
North Dulwich	d	07 22											07 36						07 45						
Luton 10	d		06 18	06 36																			06 56		
Luton Airport Parkway 7	✈ d		06 20																						
St Pancras International 15	⊖ d		07 04	07 08																			07 28		
City Thameslink 3	d		07 13	07 17																			07 37		
London Blackfriars 3	⊖ d		07 16	07 20																			07 40		
Elephant & Castle	⊖ d		07 19	07 23																			07 43		
Loughborough Jn	d		07 23	07 27																			07 47		
Herne Hill 4	d		07 28	07 34																			07 52		
Tulse Hill 3	d	07 26	07 32	07 38									07 40						07 48				07 56		
Streatham 4	d	07 30	07 36	07a42															07a52				07 59		
London Victoria 15	⊖ d					07 06	07 11	07 15	07 20						07 30						07 36	07 41		07 45	07 47
Battersea Park 4	d					07 10	07a15		07 24						07 34						07 40	07a45			07 51
Milton Keynes Central	d																								
Watford Junction	d																								
Harrow & Wealdstone	⊖ d																								
Wembley Central	⊖ d																								
Shepherd's Bush	⊖ d														*07 19*										
Kensington (Olympia)	⊖ d														*07 22*										
West Brompton	⊖ d														*07 25*										
Clapham Junction 10	d					07 14		07 21	07 28						07 38						07 44			07 51	07 55
Wandsworth Common	d					07 17			07 31						07 41						07 47			07 54	07 58
Balham 4	⊖ d					07 19		07 26	07 33						07 44						07 49			07 57	08 00
Streatham Hill	d					07 22										07 45					07 52				
West Norwood 4	d					07 26							07 43			07 48					07 56				
Gipsy Hill	d					07 29							07 46			07 51					07 59				
Crystal Palace 4	d					07 31							07 49			07a54					08 01				
Birkbeck	d												07 53												
Beckenham Junction 4	a												07 56												
Bromley South 4	a																								
Streatham Common 4	d	07 33							07 37						07 48									08 01	
Norbury	d	07 35							07 40						07 50									08 03	
Thornton Heath	d	07 38							07 43						07 53									08 06	
Selhurst 4	d	07 41							07 46						07 56									08 09	
Norwood Junction 2	a				07 32	07 36						07 38		07 41			07 48	07 48		07 59	08 06				
	d				07 32	07 36						07 39		07 42			07 48	07 51		08 00	08 06				
West Croydon 4	a	07 49				07 41						07 44			08 02						08 11				
East Croydon	a				07 36				07 49					07 45			07 52	07 55		08 03				08 13	

		SN	SN	SN	SN	SN 1	SN	SN B	SN 1	FC 1	SN		SN	SN	SN	FC	SN	SN 1	SN	SN	SN C	SN	SN	SN	SN 1
London Bridge 4	⊖ d	07 47	07 41	07 53		07 56	07 48		08 00				08 02	08 03	08 09		08 17	08 25					08 10	08 19	08 30
South Bermondsey	d		07 45										08 06										08 14		
Queens Rd Peckham	d		07 48										08 08										08 16		
Peckham Rye 4	d	07 53	07 50	07 59									08 11										08 19		
East Dulwich	d	07 56											08 14												
North Dulwich	d	07 58											08 16												
Luton 10	d									07 16						07 08									
Luton Airport Parkway 7	✈ d															07 10									
St Pancras International 15	⊖ d									07 48						07 56									
City Thameslink 3	d									07 57						08 05									
London Blackfriars 3	⊖ d									08 00						08 08									
Elephant & Castle	⊖ d															08 11									
Loughborough Jn	d															08 15									
Herne Hill 4	d									08 09						08 22									
Tulse Hill 3	d	08 02		08 05						08 13			08 19			08 26									
Streatham 4	d	08 05											08a23			08 29									
London Victoria 15	⊖ d				07 51			08 03											08 07	08 11	08 15	08 20			
Battersea Park 4	d				07 55			08 07											08 11	08a15	08 19		08a32		
Milton Keynes Central	d																								
Watford Junction	d																								
Harrow & Wealdstone	⊖ d																								
Wembley Central	⊖ d																					*08 04*			
Shepherd's Bush	⊖ d																					*08 07*			
Kensington (Olympia)	⊖ d																					*08 10*			
West Brompton	⊖ d																								
Clapham Junction 10	d				07 59			08 11											08 15		08 23	08 26			
Wandsworth Common	d				08 02			08 14											08 18		08 26				
Balham 4	⊖ d				08 04			08 16											08 20		08 28	08 31			
Streatham Hill	d				08 07						08 14								08 23						
West Norwood 4	d			08 08	08 11						08 17								08 27						
Gipsy Hill	d			08 11	08 14						08 20								08 30						
Crystal Palace 4	d			08 14	08a16						08a23						08a36		08 32						
Birkbeck	d			08 18																					
Beckenham Junction 4	a			08 21																					
Bromley South 4	a			*08 32*																					
Streatham Common 4	d	08 08						08 20													08 32				
Norbury	d	08 11						08 23													08 35				
Thornton Heath	d	08 14						08 26													08 38				
Selhurst 4	d	08 17						08b32													08 40				
Norwood Junction 2	a					08 07	08 11		08 12					08 25	08 26			08 36	08 37					08 44	08 44
	d					08 07	08 11		08 12					08 26	08 27			08 37	08 37					08 44	08 45
West Croydon 4	a	08 22					08 16	08 36											08 42					08 49	
East Croydon	a					08 11			08 16	08 25				08 29	08 33			08 40			08 43				08 49

For general notes see front of timetable
For details of catering facilities see Directory of Train Operators

- **A** To Tattenham Corner (Table 181)
- **B** To Epsom Downs (Table 182)
- **C** To Caterham (Table 181)
- **D** To Sutton (Surrey) (Table 182)
- **b** Arr. 0828

Luton, Milton Keynes and London → East and West Croydon via Tulse Hill → Crystal Palace → Norbury

Local Services

Network Diagram - see first page of Table 177

Station		SN	SN	SN A	SN	SN B	SN	FC 1	SN	FC 1	SN	SN	SN
London Bridge 4	⊖ d	08 21					08 24		08 36		08 31		
South Bermondsey	d						08 28				08 35		
Queens Rd Peckham	d						08 30				08 37		
Peckham Rye 4	d	08 27					08 33				08 40		
East Dulwich	d	08 30									08 43		
North Dulwich	d	08 32									08 45		
Luton 10	d							07 40		07 48			
Luton Airport Parkway 7	✈ d							07 42					
St Pancras International 15	⊖ d							08 16		08 20			
City Thameslink 3	d							08 25		08 29			
London Blackfriars 3	⊖ d							08 28		08 32			
Elephant & Castle	⊖ d							08 31					
Loughborough Jn	d							08 35					
Herne Hill 4	d							08 39		08 43			
Tulse Hill 3	d	08 36					08 38	08 43		08 47	08 50		
Streatham 4	d						08a42	08 47					
London Victoria 15	⊖ d		08 22	08 28	08 30	08 32						08 36	08 41
Battersea Park 4	d		08 26			08 36						08 40	08a45
Milton Keynes Central	d												
Watford Junction	d												
Harrow & Wealdstone	⊖ d												
Wembley Central	⊖ d												
Shepherd's Bush	⊖ d												
Kensington (Olympia)	⊖ d												
West Brompton	⊖ d												
Clapham Junction 10	d		08 30	08 35		08 40						08 44	
Wandsworth Common	d		08 33	08 38		08 43						08 47	
Balham 4	⊖ d		08 35	08 42		08 45						08 50	
Streatham Hill	d		08 38									08 53	
West Norwood 4	d	08 39	08 42								08 53	08 57	
Gipsy Hill	d	08 42	08 45								08 56	09 00	
Crystal Palace 4	d	08 44	08a47								08 59	09 02	
Birkbeck	d										09 03		
Beckenham Junction 4	a										09 06		
Bromley South 4	a										*09 32*		
Streatham Common 4	d			08 46		08 50							
Norbury	d			08 48		08 52							
Thornton Heath	d			08 51		08 55							
Selhurst 4	d			08 54		09 00							
Norwood Junction 2	a	08 49							08 56			09 07	
	d	08 49							08 57			09 07	
West Croydon 4	a			08 58	08 52	09 05						09 12	
East Croydon	a	08 53							09 00	09 06			

Station			SN C	SN	SN	FC	SN A	SN	SN	SN	SN D	SN 1	FC
London Bridge 4	⊖ d							08 41	08 43	08 48		09 03	
South Bermondsey	d							08 45		08 52			
Queens Rd Peckham	d							08 48		08 54			
Peckham Rye 4	d							08 50		08 57			
East Dulwich	d									09 00			
North Dulwich	d									09 02			
Luton 10	d					07 36							
Luton Airport Parkway 7	✈ d					07 38							
St Pancras International 15	⊖ d					08 24							08 40
City Thameslink 3	d					08 33							08 49
London Blackfriars 3	⊖ d					08 36							08 52
Elephant & Castle	⊖ d					08 39							08 55
Loughborough Jn	d					08 43							08 59
Herne Hill 4	d					08 48							09 06
Tulse Hill 3	d					08b57				09 05			09c16
Streatham 4	d					09a00				09 09			09 19
London Victoria 15	⊖ d		08 43	08 47	08 49		08 52				09 03		
Battersea Park 4	d		08 47		08 53		08 56				09 07		
Milton Keynes Central	d												
Watford Junction	d												
Harrow & Wealdstone	⊖ d												
Wembley Central	⊖ d												
Shepherd's Bush	⊖ d		*08 33*										
Kensington (Olympia)	⊖ d		*08 35*										
West Brompton	⊖ d		*08 37*										
Clapham Junction 10	d		08 51	08 54	08 57		09 00				09 11		
Wandsworth Common	d		08 54		09 00		09 03				09 14		
Balham 4	⊖ d		08 56	09 00	09 02		09 05				09 16		
Streatham Hill	d				09 05								
West Norwood 4	d				09 09								
Gipsy Hill	d				09 12								
Crystal Palace 4	d				09a14								
Birkbeck	d												
Beckenham Junction 4	a												
Bromley South 4	a												
Streatham Common 4	d		09 00				09 09			09 13	09 20		
Norbury	d		09 03				09 12			09 15	09 23		
Thornton Heath	d		09 06				09 15			09 18	09 26		
Selhurst 4	d		09 09				09 17			09 21	09 29		
Norwood Junction 2	a								09 10			09 14	
	d								09 10			09 15	
West Croydon 4	a						09 22		09 15	09 25	09 33		
East Croydon	a		09 12									09 18	

Station		FC	SN	SN	SN	SN	SN C	SN	SN	FC	SN	SN	SN B
London Bridge 4	⊖ d		09 03	09 05							09 11	09 14	
South Bermondsey	d		09 07								09 15		
Queens Rd Peckham	d		09 09								09 18		
Peckham Rye 4	d		09 12								09 20		
East Dulwich	d		09 15										
North Dulwich	d		09 17										
Luton 10	d	08 20											
Luton Airport Parkway 7	✈ d												
St Pancras International 15	⊖ d	08 52								08 56			
City Thameslink 3	d	09 01								09 05			
London Blackfriars 3	⊖ d	09 04								09 08			
Elephant & Castle	⊖ d	09 07								09 11			
Loughborough Jn	d	09 11								09 15			
Herne Hill 4	d	09 15								09 22			
Tulse Hill 3	d	09 20	09 20							09 28			
Streatham 4	d	09a23								09a31			
London Victoria 15	⊖ d				09 07	09 11	09 13	09 17	09 19				09 23
Battersea Park 4	d				09 11	09a15	09 17		09 23				
Milton Keynes Central	d												
Watford Junction	d												
Harrow & Wealdstone	⊖ d												
Wembley Central	⊖ d												
Shepherd's Bush	⊖ d							*09 06*					
Kensington (Olympia)	⊖ d							*09 09*					
West Brompton	⊖ d							*09 12*					
Clapham Junction 10	d				09 15		09 21	09 24	09 27				09 30
Wandsworth Common	d				09 18		09 24		09 30				09 33
Balham 4	⊖ d				09 20		09 26	09 30	09 32				09 35
Streatham Hill	d				09 23				09 35				
West Norwood 4	d		09 23		09 27				09 39				
Gipsy Hill	d		09 26		09 30				09 42				
Crystal Palace 4	d		09 29		09 32				09a44				
Birkbeck	d		09 33										
Beckenham Junction 4	a		09 36										
Bromley South 4	a		*09 47*										
Streatham Common 4	d						09 30						09 39
Norbury	d						09 33						09 42
Thornton Heath	d						09 36						09 45
Selhurst 4	d						09 39						09 47
Norwood Junction 2	a			09 26	09 37							09 40	
	d			09 26	09 37							09 40	
West Croydon 4	a				09 42							09 45	09 52
East Croydon	a			09 29			09 42						

Station		SN	FC		SN 1	SN D	SN	SN 1	SN	FC	SN	SN	SN
London Bridge 4	⊖ d	09 18					09 24	09 30	09 33		09 35		
South Bermondsey	d	09 22							09 37				
Queens Rd Peckham	d	09 24							09 39				
Peckham Rye 4	d	09 27							09 42				
East Dulwich	d	09 30							09 45				
North Dulwich	d	09 32							09 47				
Luton 10	d									08 54			
Luton Airport Parkway 7	✈ d									08 56			
St Pancras International 15	⊖ d		09 16							09 34			
City Thameslink 3	d		09 25							09 43			
London Blackfriars 3	⊖ d		09 28							09 46			
Elephant & Castle	⊖ d		09 31							09 49			
Loughborough Jn	d		09 35							09 53			
Herne Hill 4	d		09 42							09 57			
Tulse Hill 3	d	09 35	09 46						09 50	10 02			
Streatham 4	d	09 39	09 49							10a05			
London Victoria 15	⊖ d					09 33						09 36	09 41
Battersea Park 4	d					09 37						09 40	09a45
Milton Keynes Central	d				08 13								
Watford Junction	d				08 51								
Harrow & Wealdstone	⊖ d				08 58								
Wembley Central	⊖ d				09u05								
Shepherd's Bush	⊖ d				09 23								
Kensington (Olympia)	⊖ d				09 25								
West Brompton	⊖ d				09 28								
Clapham Junction 10	d				09 35	09 41						09 44	
Wandsworth Common	d				09 38	09 44						09 47	
Balham 4	⊖ d				09 41	09 46						09 50	
Streatham Hill	d											09 53	
West Norwood 4	d								09 53			09 57	
Gipsy Hill	d								09 56			10 00	
Crystal Palace 4	d						09a43		09 59			10 02	
Birkbeck	d								10 03				
Beckenham Junction 4	a								10 06				
Bromley South 4	a								*10 17*				
Streatham Common 4	d	09 42			09 45	09 50							
Norbury	d	09 45			09 48	09 53							
Thornton Heath	d	09 48			09 51	09 56							
Selhurst 4	d	09 51			09 54	09 59							
Norwood Junction 2	a							09 44			09 55	10 07	
	d							09 45			09 56	10 07	
West Croydon 4	a	09 55				10 03						10 12	
East Croydon	a				09 57			09 48			09 59		

For general notes see front of timetable
For details of catering facilities see Directory of Train Operators

A To Epsom (Table 182)
B To Epsom Downs (Table 182)
C To Caterham (Table 181)
D To Sutton (Surrey) (Table 182)
b Arr. 0852
c Arr. 0910

Luton, Milton Keynes and London → East and West Croydon via Tulse Hill → Crystal Palace → Norbury

Local Services

Network Diagram - see first page of Table 177

Station		SN	SN	SN	SN	SN	SN	SN	SN	SN	FC	SN	SN	FC	SN	SN	SN		SN	SN	SN	SN	SN	SN	SN
		A					B		C			1							A					D	
London Bridge 4 ⊖	d				09 41	09 45		09 48		09 54		10 03	10 03		10 05							10 11	10 15		10 18
South Bermondsey	d				09 45			09 52					10 07									10 15			10 22
Queens Rd Peckham	d				09 48			09 54					10 09									10 18			10 24
Peckham Rye 4	d				09 50			09 57					10 12									10 20			10 27
East Dulwich	d							10 00					10 15												10 30
North Dulwich	d							10 02					10 17												10 32
Luton 10	d													09 14											
Luton Airport Parkway 7 ✈	d													09 16											
St Pancras International 15 ⊖	d										09 48			10 04											
City Thameslink 3	d										09 57			10 13											
London Blackfriars 3 ⊖	d										10 00			10 16											
Elephant & Castle ⊖	d										10 03			10 19											
Loughborough Jn	d										10 07			10 23											
Herne Hill 4	d										10 12			10 27											
Tulse Hill 3	d							10 05			10 16		10 20	10 32											10 35
Streatham 4	d							10 09			10 19			10a35											10 39
London Victoria 15 ⊖	d	09 43	09 47	09 49			09 53		10 03							10 06	10 11		10 13	10 17	10 19			10 23	
Battersea Park 4	d	09 47		09 53					10 07							10 10	10a15		10 17		10 23				
Milton Keynes Central	d																								
Watford Junction	d																								
Harrow & Wealdstone ⊖	d																								
Wembley Central ⊖	d																								
Shepherd's Bush ⊖	d						*09 42*																		
Kensington (Olympia) ⊖	d						*09 45*																		
West Brompton ⊖	d						*09 48*																		
Clapham Junction 10	d	09 51	09 54	09 57			10 00		10 11							10 14			10 21	10 24	10 27			10 30	
Wandsworth Common	d	09 54		10 00			10 03		10 14							10 17			10 24		10 30			10 33	
Balham 4 ⊖	d	09 56	10 00	10 02			10 05		10 16							10 20			10 26	10 30	10 32			10 35	
Streatham Hill	d			10 05												10 23					10 35				
West Norwood 4	d			10 10									10 23			10 27					10 39				
Gipsy Hill	d			10 13									10 26			10 30					10 42				
Crystal Palace 4	d			10a15						10a14			10 29			10 32					10a45				
Birkbeck	d												10 33												
Beckenham Junction 4	a												10 36												
Bromley South 4	a												*10 47*												
Streatham Common 4	d	10 00					10 09	10 12	10 20										10 30					10 39	10 42
Norbury	d	10 03					10 12	10 15	10 23										10 33					10 42	10 45
Thornton Heath	d	10 06					10 15	10 18	10 26										10 36					10 45	10 48
Selhurst 4	d	10 09					10 17	10 21	10 29										10 39					10 47	10 51
Norwood Junction 2	a					10 10						10 14			10 25	10 37							10 40		
	d					10 10						10 15			10 26	10 37							10 40		
West Croydon 4	a					10 15	10 22	10 25	10 33							10 42							10 45	10 51	10 55
East Croydon	a	10 12										10 18			10 29				10 42						

Station		FC	SN	SN	SN	SN	SN	FC	SN	SN	SN	SN	SN	SN	SN	SN	SN	SN		SN	FC	SN	SN	SN	FC
			1	C		1						A					B			C			1		
London Bridge 4 ⊖	d				10 24	10 33	10 33		10 35						10 41	10 45		10 48				10 54	11 03	11 03	
South Bermondsey	d						10 37								10 45			10 52						11 07	
Queens Rd Peckham	d						10 39								10 48			10 54						11 09	
Peckham Rye 4	d						10 42								10 50			10 57						11 12	
East Dulwich	d						10 45											11 00						11 15	
North Dulwich	d						10 47											11 02						11 17	
Luton 10	d							09 44																	10 14
Luton Airport Parkway 7 ✈	d							09 46																	10 16
St Pancras International 15 ⊖	d	10 18						10 34													10 48				11 04
City Thameslink 3	d	10 27						10 43													10 57				11 13
London Blackfriars 3 ⊖	d	10 30						10 46													11 00				11 16
Elephant & Castle ⊖	d	10 33						10 49													11 03				11 19
Loughborough Jn	d	10 37						10 53													11 07				11 23
Herne Hill 4	d	10 42						10 57													11 12				11 27
Tulse Hill 3	d	10 46					10 50	11 02										11 05			11 16			11 20	11 32
Streatham 4	d	10 49						11a05										11 09			11 19				11a35
London Victoria 15 ⊖	d			10 33						10 36	10 41	10 43	10 47	10 49			10 53			11 03					
Battersea Park 4	d			10 37						10 40	10a45	10 47		10 53						11 07					
Milton Keynes Central	d		09 13																						
Watford Junction	d		09 51																						
Harrow & Wealdstone ⊖	d		09 58																						
Wembley Central ⊖	d		10u05																						
Shepherd's Bush ⊖	d		10 23																						
Kensington (Olympia) ⊖	d		10 25																						
West Brompton ⊖	d		10 27																						
Clapham Junction 10	d		10 34	10 41						10 44		10 51	10 54	10 57			11 00			11 11					
Wandsworth Common	d		10 37	10 44						10 47		10 54		11 00			11 03			11 14					
Balham 4 ⊖	d		10 40	10 46						10 50		10 56	11 00	11 02			11 05			11 16					
Streatham Hill	d									10 53				11 05											
West Norwood 4	d						10 53			10 57				11 09										11 23	
Gipsy Hill	d						10 56			11 00				11 12										11 26	
Crystal Palace 4	d				10a43		10 59			11 02				11a15								11a13		11 29	
Birkbeck	d						11 03																	11 33	
Beckenham Junction 4	a						11 06																	11 36	
Bromley South 4	a						*11 17*																	*11 47*	
Streatham Common 4	d		10 45	10 50								11 00					11 09	11 12		11 20					
Norbury	d		10 48	10 53								11 03					11 12	11 15		11 23					
Thornton Heath	d		10 51	10 56								11 06					11 15	11 18		11 26					
Selhurst 4	d		10 54	10 59								11 09					11 17	11 21		11 29					
Norwood Junction 2	a					10 44			10 55	11 07						11 10							11 14		
	d					10 45			10 56	11 07						11 10							11 15		
West Croydon 4	a			11 03						11 12						11 15	11 22	11 25		11 33					
East Croydon	a		10 57			10 48			10 59			11 12											11 18		

For general notes see front of timetable
For details of catering facilities see
Directory of Train Operators

A To Caterham (Table 181)
B To Epsom (Table 182)
C To Sutton (Surrey) (Table 182)
D To Epsom Downs (Table 182)

Table 177

Mondays to Fridays

Luton, Milton Keynes and London → East and West Croydon via Tulse Hill → Crystal Palace → Norbury

Local Services

Network Diagram - see first page of Table 177

Station		SN	SN	SN	SN A	SN	SN	SN	SN	SN B	SN	FC	SN 1
London Bridge 4 ⊖	d	11 05						11 11	11 15		11 18		
South Bermondsey	d							11 15			11 22		
Queens Rd Peckham	d							11 18			11 24		
Peckham Rye 4	d							11 20			11 27		
East Dulwich	d										11 30		
North Dulwich	d										11 32		
Luton 10	d												
Luton Airport Parkway 7 ✈	d												
St Pancras International 15 ⊖	d											11 18	
City Thameslink 3	d											11 27	
London Blackfriars 3 ⊖	d											11 30	
Elephant & Castle ⊖	d											11 33	
Loughborough Jn	d											11 37	
Herne Hill 4	d											11 42	
Tulse Hill 3	d										11 35	11 46	
Streatham 4	d										11 39	11 49	
London Victoria 15 ⊖	d		11 06	11 11	11 13	11 17	11 19			11 23			
Battersea Park 4	d		11 10	11a15	11 17		11 23						
Milton Keynes Central	d												10 13
Watford Junction	d												10 51
Harrow & Wealdstone ⊖	d												10 59
Wembley Central ⊖	d												11u04
Shepherd's Bush ⊖	d												11 18
Kensington (Olympia) ⊖	d												11 20
West Brompton ⊖	d												11 23
Clapham Junction 10	d		11 14		11 21	11 24	11 27			11 30			11b34
Wandsworth Common	d		11 17		11 24		11 30			11 33			11 37
Balham 4 ⊖	d		11 20		11 26	11 30	11 32			11 35			11 40
Streatham Hill	d		11 23				11 35						
West Norwood 4	d		11 27				11 39						
Gipsy Hill	d		11 30				11 42						
Crystal Palace 4	d		11 32				11a45						
Birkbeck 🚊	d												
Beckenham Junction 4 🚊	a												
Bromley South 4	a												
Streatham Common 4	d				11 30					11 39	11 42		11 45
Norbury	d				11 33					11 42	11 45		11 48
Thornton Heath	d				11 36					11 45	11 48		11 51
Selhurst 4	d				11 39					11 47	11 51		11 54
Norwood Junction 2	a	11 25	11 37						11 40				
	d	11 26	11 37						11 40				
West Croydon 4 🚊	a		11 42						11 45	11 52	11 55		
East Croydon 🚊	a	11 29			11 42								11 57

Station		SN C	SN	SN 1	SN	SN	FC	SN	SN	SN A	SN	SN	SN
London Bridge 4 ⊖	d		11 24	11 33		11 33		11 35					11 41
South Bermondsey	d					11 37							11 45
Queens Rd Peckham	d					11 39							11 48
Peckham Rye 4	d					11 42							11 50
East Dulwich	d					11 45							
North Dulwich	d					11 47							
Luton 10	d						10 44						
Luton Airport Parkway 7 ✈	d						10 46						
St Pancras International 15 ⊖	d						11 34						
City Thameslink 3	d						11 43						
London Blackfriars 3 ⊖	d						11 46						
Elephant & Castle ⊖	d						11 49						
Loughborough Jn	d						11 53						
Herne Hill 4	d						11 57						
Tulse Hill 3	d					11 50	12 02						
Streatham 4	d						12a05						
London Victoria 15 ⊖	d	11 33			11 41				11 36	11 43	11 47	11 49	
Battersea Park 4	d	11 37			11a45				11 40	11 47		11 53	
Milton Keynes Central	d												
Watford Junction	d												
Harrow & Wealdstone ⊖	d												
Wembley Central ⊖	d												
Shepherd's Bush ⊖	d												
Kensington (Olympia) ⊖	d												
West Brompton ⊖	d												
Clapham Junction 10	d	11 41							11 44	11 51	11 54	11 57	
Wandsworth Common	d	11 44							11 47	11 54		12 00	
Balham 4 ⊖	d	11 46							11 50	11 56	12 00	12 02	
Streatham Hill	d								11 53			12 05	
West Norwood 4	d					11 53			11 57			12 09	
Gipsy Hill	d					11 56			12 00			12 12	
Crystal Palace 4	d		11a43			11 59			12 02			12a14	
Birkbeck 🚊	d					12 03							
Beckenham Junction 4 🚊	a					12 06							
Bromley South 4	a					12 17							
Streatham Common 4	d	11 50								12 00			
Norbury	d	11 53								12 03			
Thornton Heath	d	11 56								12 06			
Selhurst 4	d	11 59								12 09			
Norwood Junction 2	a			11 44				11 55	12 07				
	d			11 45				11 56	12 07				
West Croydon 4 🚊	a	12 03							12 12				
East Croydon 🚊	a			11 48				11 59		12 12			

Station		SN	SN D	SN		SN C	FC	SN	SN 1	SN	FC	SN
London Bridge 4 ⊖	d	11 45		11 48	and at the same minutes past each hour until			14 54	15 03	15 03		15 05
South Bermondsey	d			11 52						15 07		
Queens Rd Peckham	d			11 54						15 09		
Peckham Rye 4	d			11 57						15 12		
East Dulwich	d			12 00						15 15		
North Dulwich	d			12 02						15 17		
Luton 10	d										14 14	
Luton Airport Parkway 7 ✈	d										14 16	
St Pancras International 15 ⊖	d						14 48				15 04	
City Thameslink 3	d						14 57				15 13	
London Blackfriars 3 ⊖	d						15 00				15 16	
Elephant & Castle ⊖	d						15 03				15 19	
Loughborough Jn	d						15 07				15 23	
Herne Hill 4	d						15 12				15 27	
Tulse Hill 3	d			12 05			15 16			15 20	15 32	
Streatham 4	d			12 09			15 19				15a35	
London Victoria 15 ⊖	d		11 53			15 03						
Battersea Park 4	d					15 07						
Milton Keynes Central	d											
Watford Junction	d											
Harrow & Wealdstone ⊖	d											
Wembley Central ⊖	d											
Shepherd's Bush ⊖	d											
Kensington (Olympia) ⊖	d											
West Brompton ⊖	d											
Clapham Junction 10	d		12 00			15 11						
Wandsworth Common	d		12 03			15 14						
Balham 4 ⊖	d		12 05			15 16						
Streatham Hill	d											
West Norwood 4	d									15 23		
Gipsy Hill	d									15 26		
Crystal Palace 4	d							15a13		15 29		
Birkbeck 🚊	d									15 33		
Beckenham Junction 4 🚊	a									15 36		
Bromley South 4	a									15 47		
Streatham Common 4	d		12 09	12 12		15 20						
Norbury	d		12 12	12 15		15 23						
Thornton Heath	d		12 15	12 18		15 26						
Selhurst 4	d		12 17	12 21		15 29						
Norwood Junction 2	a	12 10							15 14			15 25
	d	12 10							15 15			15 26
West Croydon 4 🚊	a	12 15	12 22	12 25		15 33						
East Croydon 🚊	a								15 18			15 29

Station		SN	SN	SN A	SN	SN	SN	SN	SN B	SN	FC	SN 1
London Bridge 4 ⊖	d						15 11	15 15		15 18		
South Bermondsey	d						15 15			15 22		
Queens Rd Peckham	d						15 18			15 24		
Peckham Rye 4	d						15 20			15 27		
East Dulwich	d									15 30		
North Dulwich	d									15 32		
Luton 10	d											
Luton Airport Parkway 7 ✈	d											
St Pancras International 15 ⊖	d										15 18	
City Thameslink 3	d										15 27	
London Blackfriars 3 ⊖	d										15 30	
Elephant & Castle ⊖	d										15 33	
Loughborough Jn	d										15 37	
Herne Hill 4	d										15 42	
Tulse Hill 3	d									15 35	15 46	
Streatham 4	d									15 39	15 49	
London Victoria 15 ⊖	d	15 06	15 11	15 13	15 17	15 19			15 23			
Battersea Park 4	d	15 10	15a15	15 17		15 23						
Milton Keynes Central	d											14 13
Watford Junction	d											14 51
Harrow & Wealdstone ⊖	d											14 59
Wembley Central ⊖	d											15u04
Shepherd's Bush ⊖	d											15 23
Kensington (Olympia) ⊖	d											15 25
West Brompton ⊖	d											15 27
Clapham Junction 10	d	15 14		15 21	15 24	15 27			15 30			15 34
Wandsworth Common	d	15 17		15 24		15 30			15 33			15 37
Balham 4 ⊖	d	15 20		15 26	15 30	15 32			15 35			15 40
Streatham Hill	d	15 23				15 35						
West Norwood 4	d	15 27				15 39						
Gipsy Hill	d	15 30				15 42						
Crystal Palace 4	d	15 32				15a45						
Birkbeck 🚊	d											
Beckenham Junction 4 🚊	a											
Bromley South 4	a											
Streatham Common 4	d			15 30					15 39	15 42		15 45
Norbury	d			15 33					15 42	15 45		15 48
Thornton Heath	d			15 36					15 45	15 48		15 51
Selhurst 4	d			15 39					15 47	15 51		15 54
Norwood Junction 2	a	15 37						15 40				
	d	15 37						15 40				
West Croydon 4 🚊	a	15 42						15 45	15 52	15 55		
East Croydon 🚊	a			15 43								15 57

For general notes see front of timetable
For details of catering facilities see Directory of Train Operators

A To Caterham (Table 181)
B To Epsom Downs (Table 182)
C To Sutton (Surrey) (Table 182)
D To Epsom (Table 182)
b Arr. 1130

Luton, Milton Keynes and London → East and West Croydon via Tulse Hill → Crystal Palace → Norbury

Local Services

Network Diagram - see first page of Table 177

Station		SN A	SN	SN 1	SN	FC	SN	SN	SN	SN B	SN	SN
London Bridge 4	⊖ d		15 24	15 33	15 33		15 35					
South Bermondsey	d				15 37							
Queens Rd Peckham	d				15 39							
Peckham Rye 4	d				15 42							
East Dulwich	d				15 45							
North Dulwich	d				15 47							
Luton 10	d					14 44						
Luton Airport Parkway 7	✈ d					14 46						
St Pancras International 15	⊖ d					15 34						
City Thameslink 3	d					15 43						
London Blackfriars 3	⊖ d					15 46						
Elephant & Castle	⊖ d					15 49						
Loughborough Jn	d					15 53						
Herne Hill 4	d					15 57						
Tulse Hill 3	d				15 50	16 02						
Streatham 4	d					16a06						
London Victoria 15	⊖ d	15 33						15 36	15 41	15 43	15 47	15 49
Battersea Park 4	d	15 37						15 40	15a45	15 47		15 53
Milton Keynes Central	d											
Watford Junction	d											
Harrow & Wealdstone	⊖ d											
Wembley Central	⊖ d											
Shepherd's Bush	⊖ d											
Kensington (Olympia)	⊖ d											
West Brompton	⊖ d											
Clapham Junction 10	d	15 41						15 44		15 51	15 54	15 57
Wandsworth Common	d	15 44						15 47		15 54		16 00
Balham 4	⊖ d	15 46						15 50		15 56	16 00	16 02
Streatham Hill	d							15 53				16 05
West Norwood 4	d				15 53			15 57				16 09
Gipsy Hill	d				15 56			16 00				16 12
Crystal Palace 4	d		15a43		15 59			16 02				16a15
Birkbeck	🚊 d				16 03							
Beckenham Junction 4	🚊 a				16 06							
Bromley South 4	a				*16 17*							
Streatham Common 4	d	15 50								16 00		
Norbury	d	15 53								16 03		
Thornton Heath	d	15 56								16 06		
Selhurst 4	d	15 59								16 09		
Norwood Junction 2	a			15 44			15 55	16 07				
	d			15 45			15 56	16 07				
West Croydon 4	🚊 a	16 03						16 12				
East Croydon	🚊 a			15 48			15 59			16 12		

Station		SN	SN	SN C	SN	SN A	FC	SN	SN 1	SN	FC	SN	SN 1
London Bridge 4	⊖ d	15 41	15 45		15 48			15 54	16 03	16 03		16 05	16 16
South Bermondsey	d	15 45			15 52					16 07			
Queens Rd Peckham	d	15 48			15 54					16 09			
Peckham Rye 4	d	15 50			15 57					16 12			
East Dulwich	d				16 00					16 15			
North Dulwich	d				16 02					16 17			
Luton 10	d										15 14		
Luton Airport Parkway 7	✈ d										15 16		
St Pancras International 15	⊖ d						15 48				16 04		
City Thameslink 3	d						15 57				16 13		
London Blackfriars 3	⊖ d						16 00				16 16		
Elephant & Castle	⊖ d						16 03				16 19		
Loughborough Jn	d						16 07				16 23		
Herne Hill 4	d						16 12				16 27		
Tulse Hill 3	d				16 05		16 16			16 20	16 32		
Streatham 4	d				16 09		16 19				16a35		
London Victoria 15	⊖ d			15 53		16 03							
Battersea Park 4	d					16 07							
Milton Keynes Central	d												
Watford Junction	d												
Harrow & Wealdstone	⊖ d												
Wembley Central	⊖ d												
Shepherd's Bush	⊖ d												
Kensington (Olympia)	⊖ d												
West Brompton	⊖ d												
Clapham Junction 10	d			16 00		16 11							
Wandsworth Common	d			16 03		16 14							
Balham 4	⊖ d			16 05		16 16							
Streatham Hill	d									16 23			
West Norwood 4	d									16 26			
Gipsy Hill	d									16 29			
Crystal Palace 4	d							16a13		16 33			
Birkbeck	🚊 d									16 38			
Beckenham Junction 4	🚊 a									*16 52*			
Bromley South 4	a												
Streatham Common 4	d			16 09	16 12	16 20							
Norbury	d			16 12	16 15	16 23							
Thornton Heath	d			16 15	16 18	16 26							
Selhurst 4	d			16 18	16 21	16 29							
Norwood Junction 2	a		16 10						16 14			16 25	16 28
	d		16 10						16 15			16 26	16 29
West Croydon 4	🚊 a		16 15	16 22	16 25	16 33			16 18			16 29	16 32
East Croydon	🚊 a												

Station		SN	SN	SN B	SN	SN	SN	SN	SN	FC	SN 1	SN C
London Bridge 4	⊖ d						16 11	16 15	16 18			
South Bermondsey	d						16 15		16 22			
Queens Rd Peckham	d						16 18		16 24			
Peckham Rye 4	d						16 20		16 27			
East Dulwich	d								16 30			
North Dulwich	d								16 32			
Luton 10	d											
Luton Airport Parkway 7	✈ d											
St Pancras International 15	⊖ d									16 18		
City Thameslink 3	d									16 27		
London Blackfriars 3	⊖ d									16 30		
Elephant & Castle	⊖ d									16 33		
Loughborough Jn	d									16 37		
Herne Hill 4	d									16 42		
Tulse Hill 3	d								16 35	16b50		
Streatham 4	d								16 39	16 54		
London Victoria 15	⊖ d	16 07	16 11	16 13	16 17	16 19						16 33
Battersea Park 4	d	16 11	16a15	16 17		16 23						16 37
Milton Keynes Central	d										15 13	
Watford Junction	d										15 51	
Harrow & Wealdstone	⊖ d										15 59	
Wembley Central	⊖ d										16u05	
Shepherd's Bush	⊖ d										16 19	
Kensington (Olympia)	⊖ d										16 22	
West Brompton	⊖ d										16 25	
Clapham Junction 10	d	16 15		16 21	16 24	16 27					16 34	16 41
Wandsworth Common	d	16 18		16 24		16 30					16 37	16 44
Balham 4	⊖ d	16 20		16 26	16 30	16 32					16 40	16 46
Streatham Hill	d	16 23				16 35						
West Norwood 4	d	16 27				16 39						
Gipsy Hill	d	16 30				16 42						
Crystal Palace 4	d	16 32				16a45						
Birkbeck	🚊 d											
Beckenham Junction 4	🚊 a											
Bromley South 4	a											
Streatham Common 4	d			16 30					16 42		16 45	16 50
Norbury	d			16 33					16 45		16 48	16 53
Thornton Heath	d			16 36					16 48		16 51	16 56
Selhurst 4	d			16 39					16a52		16 56	16 59
Norwood Junction 2	a	16 37						16 40				
	d	16 37						16 40				
West Croydon 4	🚊 a	16 44						16 45				17 05
East Croydon	🚊 a			16 42							16 59	

Station		SN	SN 1	SN	FC	SN	SN	SN	SN	SN B	SN	SN	SN
London Bridge 4	⊖ d	16 24	16 33	16 33		16 35	16 48						16 41
South Bermondsey	d			16 37									16 45
Queens Rd Peckham	d			16 39									16 48
Peckham Rye 4	d			16 42									16 50
East Dulwich	d			16 45									
North Dulwich	d			16 47									
Luton 10	d				15 44								
Luton Airport Parkway 7	✈ d				15 46								
St Pancras International 15	⊖ d				16 34								
City Thameslink 3	d				16 43								
London Blackfriars 3	⊖ d				16 46								
Elephant & Castle	⊖ d				16 50								
Loughborough Jn	d				16 54								
Herne Hill 4	d				16 58								
Tulse Hill 3	d			16 50	17 02								
Streatham 4	d				17a05								
London Victoria 15	⊖ d							16 37	16 41	16 43	16 50	16 52	
Battersea Park 4	d							16 41	16a45	16 47		16 56	
Milton Keynes Central	d												
Watford Junction	d												
Harrow & Wealdstone	⊖ d												
Wembley Central	⊖ d												
Shepherd's Bush	⊖ d												
Kensington (Olympia)	⊖ d												
West Brompton	⊖ d												
Clapham Junction 10	d							16 45		16 51	16 56	17 00	
Wandsworth Common	d							16 48		16 54		17 03	
Balham 4	⊖ d							16 50		16 56	17 01	17 05	
Streatham Hill	d							16 53				17 08	
West Norwood 4	d			16 53				16 57				17 13	
Gipsy Hill	d			16 56				17 00				17 16	
Crystal Palace 4	d	16a43		16 59				17 02				17a18	
Birkbeck	🚊 d			17 03									
Beckenham Junction 4	🚊 a			17 08									
Bromley South 4	a												
Streatham Common 4	d									17 00			
Norbury	d									17 03			
Thornton Heath	d									17 06			
Selhurst 4	d									17 09			
Norwood Junction 2	a		16 44			16 58	17 01	17 07					
	d		16 45			16 59	17 02	17 07					
West Croydon 4	🚊 a					17 05		17 14					
East Croydon	🚊 a		16 48				17 05			17 12			

For general notes see front of timetable
For details of catering facilities see Directory of Train Operators

A To Sutton (Surrey) (Table 182)
B To Caterham (Table 181)
C To Epsom Downs (Table 182)
b Arr. 1646

Luton, Milton Keynes and London → East and West Croydon via Tulse Hill → Crystal Palace → Norbury

Local Services

Network Diagram - see first page of Table 177

	SN	SN	SN A	SN	SN	FC	SN 1	SN	SN	FC	SN		SN	SN	SN B	SN	SN	SN	SN	SN	SN 1	SN	SN A	FC
London Bridge 4 ⊖ d	16 44	16 48		16 54	16 58		16 59	17 05	17 05		17 17							17 11	17 18	17 19				
South Bermondsey d		16 52			17 02				17 09									17 15	17 22					
Queens Rd Peckham d		16 54			17 04				17 11									17 18	17 24					
Peckham Rye 4 d		16 57			17 07				17 14									17 20	17 27					
East Dulwich d		17 00			17 10				17 17										17 30					
North Dulwich d		17 02			17 12				17 19										17 32					
Luton 10 d										16 14														
Luton Airport Parkway 7 ✈ d										16 16														
St Pancras International 15 ⊖ d						16 46				17 02														17 18
City Thameslink 3 d						16 55				17 11														17 27
London Blackfriars 3 ⊖ d						16 58				17 14														17 30
Elephant & Castle ⊖ d						17 02				17 18														17 34
Loughborough Jn d						17 06				17 22														17 38
Herne Hill 4 d						17 10				17 26														17 42
Tulse Hill 3 d		17 05			17 15	17 16			17 23	17 32									17 35					17 46
Streatham 4 d		17 09				17 20			17 26	17a35									17 39					17 50
London Victoria 15 ⊖ d			17 01										17 07	17 11	17 13	17 20	17 22					17 31	17 33	
Battersea Park 4 d			17 05											17a15	17 17		17 26						17 37	
Milton Keynes Central d																					16 13			
Watford Junction d																					16 51			
Harrow & Wealdstone ⊖ d																					16 59			
Wembley Central ⊖ d																					17u05			
Shepherd's Bush ⊖ d																					17 19			
Kensington (Olympia) ⊖ d																					17 22			
West Brompton ⊖ d																					17 25			
Clapham Junction 10 d			17 09										17 13		17 21	17 26	17 30				17 33	17 37	17 41	
Wandsworth Common d			17 12										17 16		17 24		17 33				17 36		17 44	
Balham 4 ⊖ d			17 14										17 19		17 26	17 32	17 35				17 39	17 42	17 46	
Streatham Hill d													17 22				17 38							
West Norwood 4 d					17 18								17 26				17 42							
Gipsy Hill d					17 21								17 29				17 45							
Crystal Palace 4 d				17a13	17 24								17 31				17a47							
Birkbeck 🚋 d					17 28																			
Beckenham Junction 4 🚋 a					17 33																			
Bromley South 4 a					*17 51*																			
Streatham Common 4 d		17 12	17 18												17 30				17 42		17 44		17 50	
Norbury d		17 15	17 21												17 33				17 44		17 47		17 53	
Thornton Heath d		17 18	17 24												17 36				17 47		17 50		17 56	
Selhurst 4 d		17a22	17 27												17 39				17a52		17 54		17 59	
Norwood Junction 2 a	17 10						17 10	17 28			17 30		17 36							17 40				
d	17 10						17 11	17 29			17 31		17 36							17 40				
West Croydon 4 🚋 a	17 15		17 31					17 35					17 41		17 43					17 46			18 05	
East Croydon 🚋 a							17 14				17 34										17 59			

	SN	SN	SN 1	SN	SN	FC	FC 1	SN	SN	SN	SN	SN	SN		SN	SN	SN C	SN	SN A	SN 1	SN	SN	SN	FC
London Bridge 4 ⊖ d	17 25	17 28	17 29	17 35	17 35			17 49							17 41	17 48				17 59	17 51	17 55	17 58	
South Bermondsey d		17 32			17 39										17 45	17 52							18 02	
Queens Rd Peckham d		17 35			17 41										17 48	17 54							18 04	
Peckham Rye 4 d		17 37			17 44										17 50	17 57							18 07	
East Dulwich d		17 40			17 47											18 00							18 10	
North Dulwich d		17 42			17 49											18 02							18 12	
Luton 10 d						16 44																		
Luton Airport Parkway 7 ✈ d						16 46																		
St Pancras International 15 ⊖ d						17 30	17 42																	17 50
City Thameslink 3 d						17 39	17 51																	17 59
London Blackfriars 3 ⊖ d						17 42	17 54																	18 02
Elephant & Castle ⊖ d						17 46																		18 06
Loughborough Jn d						17 50																		18 10
Herne Hill 4 d						17 54	18 07																	18 14
Tulse Hill 3 d		17 46			17 52	17 58										18 05							18 15	18 18
Streatham 4 d					17 56	18a01										18 09								18 22
London Victoria 15 ⊖ d									17 37	17 41	17 45	17 50	17 52					18 01	18 03					
Battersea Park 4 d									17 41	17a45	17 49		17 56						18 07					
Milton Keynes Central d																								
Watford Junction d																								
Harrow & Wealdstone ⊖ d																								
Wembley Central ⊖ d																								
Shepherd's Bush ⊖ d																	17 50							
Kensington (Olympia) ⊖ d																	17 52							
West Brompton ⊖ d																	17 55							
Clapham Junction 10 d									17 45		17 53	17 56	18 00				18 02	18 08	18 11					
Wandsworth Common d									17 48		17 56		18 03				18 05		18 14					
Balham 4 ⊖ d									17 50		17 58	18 02	18 05				18 08	18 12	18 16					
Streatham Hill d									17 53				18 08											
West Norwood 4 d		17 49							17 57				18 15										18 18	
Gipsy Hill d		17 52							18 00				18 18										18 21	
Crystal Palace 4 d	17a44	17 54							18 02				18a20									18a15	18 24	
Birkbeck 🚋 d		17 58																					18 28	
Beckenham Junction 4 🚋 a		18 04																					18 33	
Bromley South 4 a		*18 20*																					*18 48*	
Streatham Common 4 d											18 02					18 12	18 15		18 20					
Norbury d											18 05					18 14	18 18		18 23					
Thornton Heath d											18 08					18 17	18 21		18 26					
Selhurst 4 d											18a12					18a22	18 26		18 29					
Norwood Junction 2 a			17 40	17 58			18 01	18 07												18 11	18 12			
d			17 41	17 59			18 02	18 07												18 11	18 12			
West Croydon 4 🚋 a				18 05				18 14											18 36		18 17			
East Croydon 🚋 a			17 44			18 24	18 05										18 32			18 15				

For general notes see front of timetable
For details of catering facilities see Directory of Train Operators

- **A** To Epsom Downs (Table 182)
- **B** To Sutton (Surrey) (Table 182)
- **C** To Purley (Table 175)

Luton, Milton Keynes and London → East and West Croydon via Tulse Hill → Crystal Palace → Norbury

Local Services

Network Diagram - see first page of Table 177

	SN	SN	FC	SN	SN	SN	SN	SN	SN	SN	SN	SN	SN 1	SN	SN		SN	FC	SN 1	SN	SN	FC	SN	SN
														A										
London Bridge 4 ⊖ d	18 05	18 07		18 18						18 11	18 18	18 20			18 24		18 28		18 29	18 34	18 38		18 48	18 49
South Bermondsey d		18 11								18 15	18 22						18 32				18 42		18 52	
Queens Rd Peckham d		18 13								18 18	18 24						18 34				18 44		18 54	
Peckham Rye 4 d		18 16								18 20	18 27						18 37				18 47		18 57	
East Dulwich d		18 19									18 30						18 40				18 50		19 00	
North Dulwich d		18 21									18 32						18 42				18 52		19 02	
Luton 10 d			17 18																					
Luton Airport Parkway 7 ✈ d			17 20																					
St Pancras International 15 ⊖ d			18 04															18 16				18 34		
City Thameslink 3 d			18 13															18 25				18 43		
London Blackfriars 3 ⊖ d			18 16															18 30				18 46		
Elephant & Castle ⊖ d			18 20															18 34				18 49		
Loughborough Jn d			18 24															18 38				18 53		
Herne Hill 4 d			18 28															18 44				18 57		
Tulse Hill 3 d		18 24	18 32								18 35						18 45	18 48			18 55	19 02	19 05	
Streatham 4 d		18 28	18a35								18 39							18 52			18 59	19a05	19 09	
London Victoria 15 ⊖ d					18 06	18 11	18 13	18 20	18 23					18 32										
Battersea Park 4 d					18 10	18a15	18 17		18 27					18 36										
Milton Keynes Central d													17 13											
Watford Junction d													17 51											
Harrow & Wealdstone ⊖ d													17 59											
Wembley Central ⊖ d													18u05											
Shepherd's Bush ⊖ d													18 19											
Kensington (Olympia) ⊖ d													18 22											
West Brompton ⊖ d													18 25											
Clapham Junction 10 d					18 14		18 21	18 26	18 31				18 34	18 40										
Wandsworth Common d					18 17		18 24		18 34				18 37	18 43										
Balham 4 ⊖ d					18 19		18 26	18 32	18 36				18 40	18 45										
Streatham Hill d					18 22				18 39															
West Norwood 4 d					18 26				18 43								18 48							
Gipsy Hill d					18 29				18 46								18 51							
Crystal Palace 4 d					18 31				18a48						18a43		18 54							
Birkbeck 🚋 d																	18 58							
Beckenham Junction 4 🚋 a																	19 03							
Bromley South 4 a																	*19 17*							
Streatham Common 4 d							18 30				18 42		18 44	18 49									19 12	
Norbury d							18 33				18 44		18 47	18 52									19 15	
Thornton Heath d							18 36				18 47		18 50	18 55									19 18	
Selhurst 4 d							18a40				18a52		18 56	19 00									19a22	
Norwood Junction 2 a	18 28			18 30	18 36							18 40							18 41	18 58				19 01
d	18 29			18 31	18 36							18 41							18 41	18 59				19 02
West Croydon 4 🚋 a	18 35				18 44							18 45		19 06						19 05				
East Croydon 🚋 a				18 34									19 02						18 45					19 05

	SN	SN	SN	SN	SN	SN	FC	SN 1	SN	SN	SN	SN	SN	SN	SN	SN	SN		SN	FC	SN 1	SN	SN	SN
			B							C						A								
London Bridge 4 ⊖ d					18 41	18 58		19 03			19 05	18 51							19 08			19 14	19 18	19 11
South Bermondsey d					18 45	19 02													19 12				19 22	19 15
Queens Rd Peckham d					18 48	19 04													19 14				19 24	19 18
Peckham Rye 4 d					18 50	19 07													19 17				19 27	19 20
East Dulwich d						19 10													19 20				19 30	
North Dulwich d						19 12													19 22				19 32	
Luton 10 d							18 02													18 24				
Luton Airport Parkway 7 ✈ d							18 04													18 26				
St Pancras International 15 ⊖ d							18 48													19 04				
City Thameslink 3 d							18 57													19 13				
London Blackfriars 3 ⊖ d							19 00													19 16				
Elephant & Castle ⊖ d							19 04													19 19				
Loughborough Jn d							19 08													19 23				
Herne Hill 4 d							19 12						←							19 27				
Tulse Hill 3 d						19 17	19 16						19 17						19 26	19 32			19 35	
Streatham 4 d						→	19 19													19a35			19 39	
London Victoria 15 ⊖ d	18 36	18 41	18 43	18 50					18 52	19 00				19 06	19 11	19 15	19 20							
Battersea Park 4 d	18 40	18a45	18 47						18 56	19 04				19 10	19a15	19 19								
Milton Keynes Central d																					18 13			
Watford Junction d																					18 51			
Harrow & Wealdstone ⊖ d																					18 59			
Wembley Central ⊖ d																					19u05			
Shepherd's Bush ⊖ d																					19 18			
Kensington (Olympia) ⊖ d																					19 20			
West Brompton ⊖ d																					19 23			
Clapham Junction 10 d	18 44		18 51	18 56					19 00	19 08				19 14		19 23	19 26				19b34			
Wandsworth Common d	18 47		18 54						19 03	19 11				19 17		19 26					19 37			
Balham 4 ⊖ d	18 49		18 56	19 02					19 05	19 14				19 19		19 28	19 32				19 40			
Streatham Hill d	18 52								19 08					19 22										
West Norwood 4 d	18 56								19 12				19 20	19 26					19 29					
Gipsy Hill d	18 59								19 15				19 23	19 29					19 32					
Crystal Palace 4 d	19 01								19 17			19a12	19 26	19a31					19 35					
Birkbeck 🚋 d																			19 39					
Beckenham Junction 4 🚋 a																			19 42					
Bromley South 4 a																			*20 03*					
Streatham Common 4 d			19 00							19 18						19 32					19 45		19 42	
Norbury d			19 03							19 20						19 35					19 47		19 44	
Thornton Heath d			19 06							19 23						19 38					19 50		19 47	
Selhurst 4 d			19 09							19 26						19 41					19a53		19 50	
Norwood Junction 2 a	19 06							19 14	19 22		19 28		19 30									19 37		
d	19 06							19 15	19 22		19 28		19 35									19 38		
West Croydon 4 🚋 a	19 14		19 14						19 29		19 33		19 41			19 45							19 56	
East Croydon 🚋 a								19 18		19 30												19 41		

For general notes see front of timetable
For details of catering facilities see Directory of Train Operators

A To Epsom Downs (Table 182)
B To Epsom (Table 182)
C To Tattenham Corner (Table 181) and to Caterham (Table 181)
b Arr. 1930

Table 177

Mondays to Fridays

Luton, Milton Keynes and London → East and West Croydon via Tulse Hill → Crystal Palace → Norbury

Local Services

Network Diagram - see first page of Table 177

Station		SN	SN	SN A	SN B	SN	SN	SN	SN C	FC	SN	SN	SN	FC	SN	SN 1	FC	SN	SN	SN 1		SN A	SN B	SN	SN
London Bridge 4	⊖ d	19 31	19 24			19 28						19 45	19 38		19 48	19 52		19 54	19 41	20 05					
South Bermondsey	d					19 32							19 42		19 52				19 45						
Queens Rd Peckham	d					19 34							19 44		19 54				19 48						
Peckham Rye 4	d					19 37							19 47		19 57				19 50						
East Dulwich	d					19 40							19 50		20 00										
North Dulwich	d					19 42							19 52		20 02										
Luton 10	d													18 54											
Luton Airport Parkway 7	d													18 56											
St Pancras International 15	⊖ d									19 18				19 34			19 48								
City Thameslink 3	d									19 27				19 43			19 57								
London Blackfriars 3	⊖ d									19 30				19 46			20 00								
Elephant & Castle	⊖ d									19 33				19 49			20 03								
Loughborough Jn	d									19 37				19 53			20 07								
Herne Hill 4	d									19 42				19 57			20 12								
Tulse Hill 3	d					19 46				19 46			19 56	20 02	20 05		20 16								
Streatham 4	d									19 49				20a05	20 09		20 19								
London Victoria 15	⊖ d			19 23	19 30		19 36	19 41	19 45		19 50											19 53	20 00	20 06	20 11
Battersea Park 4	d			19 27	19 34		19 40	19a45	19 49													19 57	20 04	20 10	20a15
Milton Keynes Central	d																								
Watford Junction	d																								
Harrow & Wealdstone	⊖ d																								
Wembley Central	⊖ d																								
Shepherd's Bush	⊖ d																								
Kensington (Olympia)	⊖ d																								
West Brompton	⊖ d																								
Clapham Junction 10	d			19 31	19 38		19 44		19 53		19 56											20 01	20 08	20 14	
Wandsworth Common	d			19 34	19 41		19 47		19 56													20 04	20 11	20 17	
Balham 4	⊖ d			19 36	19 43		19 49		19 58		20 02											20 06	20 14	20 19	
Streatham Hill	d			19 39			19 52															20 09		20 22	
West Norwood 4	d			19 43		19 49	19 56						19 59									20 13		20 26	
Gipsy Hill	d			19 46		19 52	19 59						20 02									20 16		20 29	
Crystal Palace 4	d		19a43	19 48		19 58	20a01						20 05					20a13				20 18		20a31	
Birkbeck	d												20 09												
Beckenham Junction 4	a												20 12												
Bromley South 4	a												*20 36*												
Streatham Common 4	d				19 48				20 02						20 12								20 18		
Norbury	d				19 50				20 05						20 15								20 20		
Thornton Heath	d				19 53				20 08						20 18								20 23		
Selhurst 4	d				19 57				20 11						20 21								20 26		
Norwood Junction 2	a	19 43		19 53		20 03						20 08				20 03				20 16		20 23			
	d	19 44		19 54		20 05						20 09				20 03				20 16		20 24			
West Croydon 4	a	19 48		19 59		20 10			20 15						20 26							20 29			
East Croydon	a				20 00							20 12				20 06				20 19			20 29		

Station		SN	SN D	SN	SN	FC	SN	FC	FC	SN	SN	SN 1	SN A	SN B	SN	SN	SN C	SN	SN	SN	SN	FC		SN	SN 1
London Bridge 4	⊖ d	20 15			20 03		20 18			20 11	20 24	20 35							20 45	20 41	20 48			20 54	21 05
South Bermondsey	d				20 07		20 22			20 15										20 45	20 52				
Queens Rd Peckham	d				20 09		20 24			20 18										20 48	20 54				
Peckham Rye 4	d				20 12		20 27			20 20										20 50	20 57				
East Dulwich	d				20 15		20 30														21 00				
North Dulwich	d				20 17		20 32														21 02				
Luton 10	d					19 18			19 48													20 18			
Luton Airport Parkway 7	d					19 20			19 50													20 20			
St Pancras International 15	⊖ d					20 04		20 18	20 34													21 04			
City Thameslink 3	d					20 13		20 27	20 43													21 13			
London Blackfriars 3	⊖ d					20 16		20 30	20 46													21 16			
Elephant & Castle	⊖ d					20 19		20 33	20 49													21 19			
Loughborough Jn	d					20 23		20 37	20 53													21 23			
Herne Hill 4	d					20 27		20 42	20 57													21 27			
Tulse Hill 3	d				20 20	20 32	20 35	20 46	21 02												21 05	21 32			
Streatham 4	d				20 24	20a35	20 39	20 49	21a05												21 09	21a35			
London Victoria 15	⊖ d		20 15	20 20									20 23	20 30	20 36	20 41	20 45	20 50							
Battersea Park 4	d		20 19										20 27	20 34	20 40	20a45	20 49								
Milton Keynes Central	d																								
Watford Junction	d																								
Harrow & Wealdstone	⊖ d																								
Wembley Central	⊖ d																								
Shepherd's Bush	⊖ d													*20 19*											
Kensington (Olympia)	⊖ d													*20 21*											
West Brompton	⊖ d													*20 24*											
Clapham Junction 10	d		20 23	20 26									20 31	20 38	20 44		20 53	20 56							
Wandsworth Common	d		20 26										20 34	20 41	20 47		20 56								
Balham 4	⊖ d		20 28	20 31									20 36	20 44	20 49		20 58	21 02							
Streatham Hill	d												20 39		20 52										
West Norwood 4	d												20 43		20 56										
Gipsy Hill	d												20 46		20 59										
Crystal Palace 4	d										20a43		20 48		21a01									21a13	
Birkbeck	d																								
Beckenham Junction 4	a																								
Bromley South 4	a																								
Streatham Common 4	d		20 32		20 27		20 42							20 48			21 02				21 12				
Norbury	d		20 35		20 29		20 44							20 50			21 05				21 15				
Thornton Heath	d		20 38		20 32		20 47							20 53			21 08				21 18				
Selhurst 4	d		20 41		20a35		20 51							20 56			21 11				21 21				
Norwood Junction 2	a	20 38										20 46	20 53						21 08						21 16
	d	20 39										20 46	20 54						21 09						21 16
West Croydon 4	a		20 45				20 56						20 59				21 15				21 26				
East Croydon	a	20 42										20 49		20 59					21 12						21 19

For general notes see front of timetable
For details of catering facilities see Directory of Train Operators

A To Sutton (Surrey) (Table 182)
B To Tattenham Corner (Table 181)
C To Epsom Downs (Table 182)
D To Epsom (Table 182)

Luton, Milton Keynes and London → East and West Croydon via Tulse Hill → Crystal Palace → Norbury

Local Services

Network Diagram - see first page of Table 177

Station		SN A	SN B	SN	SN	SN C	SN	SN	SN	SN	FC	SN	SN 1	SN A	SN B	SN	SN	SN D	SN	SN	SN	SN	FC	SN	SN 1
London Bridge 4 ⊖	d							21 15	21 11	21 18		21 24	21 28							21 45	21 41	21 48		21 54	22 05
South Bermondsey	d								21 15	21 22											21 45	21 52			
Queens Rd Peckham	d								21 18	21 24											21 48	21 54			
Peckham Rye 4	d								21 20	21 27											21 50	21 57			
East Dulwich	d									21 30												22 00			
North Dulwich	d									21 32												22 02			
Luton 10	d										20 48												21 18		
Luton Airport Parkway 7 ✈	d										20 50												21 20		
St Pancras International 15 ⊖	d										21 34												22 04		
City Thameslink 3	d										21 43												22 13		
London Blackfriars 3 ⊖	d										21 46												22 16		
Elephant & Castle ⊖	d										21 49												22 19		
Loughborough Jn	d										21 53												22 23		
Herne Hill 4	d										21 57												22 27		
Tulse Hill 3	d									21 35	22 02											22 05	22 32		
Streatham 4	d									21 39	22a05											22 09	22a35		
London Victoria 15 ⊖	d	20 53	21 00	21 06	21 11	21 15	21 20							21 23	21 30	21 36	21 41	21 45	21 50						
Battersea Park 4	d	20 57	21 04	21 10	21a15	21 19								21 27	21 34	21 40	21a45	21 49							
Milton Keynes Central	d																								
Watford Junction	d																								
Harrow & Wealdstone ⊖	d																								
Wembley Central ⊖	d															21 23									
Shepherd's Bush ⊖	d															21 25									
Kensington (Olympia) ⊖	d															21 27									
West Brompton ⊖	d																								
Clapham Junction 10	d	21 01	21 08	21 14		21 23	21 26							21 31	21 38	21 44		21 53	21 56						
Wandsworth Common	d	21 04	21 11	21 17		21 26								21 34	21 41	21 47		21 56							
Balham 4 ⊖	d	21 06	21 14	21 19		21 28	21 31							21 36	21 44	21 49		21 58	22 02						
Streatham Hill	d	21 09		21 22										21 39		21 52									
West Norwood 4	d	21 13		21 26										21 43		21 56									
Gipsy Hill	d	21 16		21 29										21 46		21 59									
Crystal Palace 4	d	21 18		21a31								21a43		21 48		22a01								22a13	
Birkbeck	d																								
Beckenham Junction 4	a																								
Bromley South 4	a																								
Streatham Common 4	d		21 18			21 32				21 42					21 48			22 02				22 12			
Norbury	d		21 20			21 35				21 45					21 50			22 05				22 15			
Thornton Heath	d		21 23			21 38				21 48					21 53			22 08				22 18			
Selhurst 4	d		21 26			21 41				21 51					21 56			22 11				22 21			
Norwood Junction 2	a	21 23						21 38					21 39	21 53						22 08					22 16
	d	21 24						21 39					21 40	21 54						22 09					22 16
West Croydon 4	a	21 29				21 45				21 56				21 59				22 15				22 26			
East Croydon	a		21 29					21 42					21 44		21 59					22 12					22 19

Station		SN A		SN B	SN	SN	SN C	SN	SN	SN	SN	SN	SN	SN A	SN B	SN	SN	SN D	SN	SN	SN	SN	FC	SN	SN 1
London Bridge 4 ⊖	d								22 15	22 11	22 18	22 24	22 28							22 45	22 41	22 48	22 58	22 54	22 58
South Bermondsey	d									22 15	22 22										22 45	22 52			
Queens Rd Peckham	d									22 18	22 24										22 48	22 54			
Peckham Rye 4	d									22 20	22 27										22 50	22 57			
East Dulwich	d										22 30											23 00			
North Dulwich	d										22 32											23 02			
Luton 10	d																								
Luton Airport Parkway 7 ✈	d																								
St Pancras International 15 ⊖	d																								
City Thameslink 3	d																								
London Blackfriars 3 ⊖	d																								
Elephant & Castle ⊖	d																								
Loughborough Jn	d																								
Herne Hill 4	d																								
Tulse Hill 3	d										22 35											23 05	23 10		
Streatham 4	d										22 39											23 09	23a13		
London Victoria 15 ⊖	d	21 53		22 00	22 06	22 11	22 15	22 20						22 23	22 30	22 36	22 41	22 45	22 50						
Battersea Park 4	d	21 57		22 04	22 10	22a15	22 19							22 27	22 34	22 40	22a45	22 49							
Milton Keynes Central	d																								
Watford Junction	d																								
Harrow & Wealdstone ⊖	d																								
Wembley Central ⊖	d															22 23									
Shepherd's Bush ⊖	d															22 25									
Kensington (Olympia) ⊖	d															22 27									
West Brompton ⊖	d																								
Clapham Junction 10	d	22 01		22 08	22 14		22 23	22 27						22 31	22 38	22 44		22 53	22 56						
Wandsworth Common	d	22 04		22 11	22 17		22 26							22 34	22 41	22 47		22 56							
Balham 4 ⊖	d	22 06		22 14	22 19		22 28	22 32						22 36	22 44	22 49		22 58	23 01						
Streatham Hill	d	22 09			22 22									22 39		22 52									
West Norwood 4	d	22 13			22 26									22 43		22 56									
Gipsy Hill	d	22 16			22 29									22 46		22 59									
Crystal Palace 4	d	22 18			22a31							22a43		22 48		23a01								23a13	
Birkbeck	d																								
Beckenham Junction 4	a																								
Bromley South 4	a																								
Streatham Common 4	d			22 18			22 32				22 42				22 48			23 02				23 12			
Norbury	d			22 20			22 35				22 45				22 50			23 05				23 15			
Thornton Heath	d			22 23			22 38				22 48				22 53			23 08				23 18			
Selhurst 4	d			22 26			22 41				22 51				22 56			23 11				23 21			
Norwood Junction 2	a	22 23							22 38				22 40	22 53						23 08					23 09
	d	22 24							22 39				22 40	22 54						23 09					23 10
West Croydon 4	a	22 29					22 47				22 56			22 59				23 15				23 26			
East Croydon	a			22 29					22 42				22 44		22 59					23 12					23 14

For general notes see front of timetable
For details of catering facilities see
Directory of Train Operators

A To Sutton (Surrey) (Table 182)
B To Tattenham Corner (Table 181)
C To Epsom (Table 182)
D To Epsom Downs (Table 182)

Table 177

Luton, Milton Keynes and London → East and West Croydon via Tulse Hill → Crystal Palace → Norbury

Local Services

Network Diagram - see first page of Table 177

	SN	SN	SN		SN	SN	SN	SN	SN	SN	SN	SN	SN	SN	SN	SN	FC	SN	SN	FC				
	A	B				C		C				1			C									
London Bridge 4 ⊖ d							23 15		23 11		23 18					23 24	23 28	23 53	23 48	23 58				
South Bermondsey d									23 15		23 22								23 52					
Queens Rd Peckham d									23 18		23 24								23 54					
Peckham Rye 4 d									23 20		23 27								23 57					
East Dulwich d											23 30								00 01					
North Dulwich d											23 32								00 03					
Luton 10 d																								
Luton Airport Parkway 7 ✈ d																								
St Pancras International 15 ⊖ d																								
City Thameslink 3 d																								
London Blackfriars 3 ⊖ d																								
Elephant & Castle ⊖ d																								
Loughborough Jn d																								
Herne Hill 4 d																								
Tulse Hill 3 d											23 35						23 40		00 06	00 10				
Streatham 4 d											23 39						23a43			00a13				
London Victoria 15 ⊖ d	22 53	23 00	23 06		23 11	23 15		23 23		23 26			23 34	23 37	23 51									
Battersea Park 4 d	22 57	23 04	23 10		23a15	23 19		23 27					23 38	23 41	23 55									
Milton Keynes Central d												22 11												
Watford Junction d												22 53												
Harrow & Wealdstone ⊖ d												23 00												
Wembley Central ⊖ d																								
Shepherd's Bush ⊖ d		22 49										23 21												
Kensington (Olympia) ⊖ d		22 51										23 23												
West Brompton ⊖ d		22 54										23 26												
Clapham Junction 10 d	23 01	23 08	23 14			23 23		23 31		23 34		23b40	23 42	23 45	23 59									
Wandsworth Common d	23 04	23 11	23 17			23 26		23 34					23 45	23 48	00 02									
Balham 4 ⊖ d	23 06	23 14	23 19			23 28		23 36		23 40		23 44	23 47	23 51	00 04									
Streatham Hill d	23 09		23 22					23 39						23 54										
West Norwood 4 d	23 13		23 26					23 43						23 57					00 09					
Gipsy Hill d	23 16		23 29					23 46						23 59					00 12					
Crystal Palace 4 d	23 18		23a31					23 48						00 03		23a43			00 15					
Birkbeck 🚊 d																								
Beckenham Junction 4 🚊 a																								
Bromley South 4 a																								
Streatham Common 4 d		23 18				23 32					23 42	23 48	23 51		00 08									
Norbury d		23 20				23 35					23 45	23 51	23 54		00 11									
Thornton Heath d		23 23				23 38					23 48	23 54	23 57		00 14									
Selhurst 4 d		23 26				23 41					23 51	23a56	23a59		00 17									
Norwood Junction 2 a	23 23						23 38	23 53						00 07				00 16	00 19					
d	23 24						23 39	23 54						00 07				00 16						
West Croydon 4 🚊 a	23 29					23 45		23 58			23 55			00 13	00 21									
East Croydon 🚊 a		23 29					23 42											00 20						

For general notes see front of timetable
For details of catering facilities see Directory of Train Operators

A To Epsom (Table 182)
B To Tattenham Corner (Table 181)
C To Sutton (Surrey) (Table 182)

b Arr. 2333

Luton, Milton Keynes and London → East and West Croydon via Tulse Hill → Crystal Palace → Norbury

Local Services

Network Diagram - see first page of Table 177

	SN	SN	SN	SN	FC	SN	SN	SN	SN 1	SN	SN	SN 1	SN	FC	SN	SN	FC	SN	SN	SN	FC	SN	SN	SN
		A									B							C					A	D
London Bridge 4 ⊖ d			23p53	23p48	23p58		00 26						06 11	06 21	06 35					06 41	06 45	06 50		
South Bermondsey d				23p52									06 15							06 45				
Queens Rd Peckham d				23p54									06 18							06 48				
Peckham Rye 4 d				23p57									06 20							06 50				
East Dulwich d				00 01																				
North Dulwich d				00 03																				
Luton 10 d																								
Luton Airport Parkway 7 ✈ d																								
St Pancras International 15 ⊖ d																								
City Thameslink 3 d																								
London Blackfriars 3 ⊖ d																								
Elephant & Castle ⊖ d																								
Loughborough Jn d																	06 42							
Herne Hill 4 d														06 32			06 46				07b02			
Tulse Hill 3 d				00 06	00 10									06a35			06 49				07a05			
Streatham 4 d					00a13																			
London Victoria 15 ⊖ d	23p37	23p51				00 17		00 42	05 25		06 23					06 41		06 43	06 47					06 53
Battersea Park 4 d	23p41	23p55						00 46								06a45		06 47						
Milton Keynes Central d																								
Watford Junction d												05 51												
Harrow & Wealdstone ⊖ d												05 58												
Wembley Central ⊖ d																								
Shepherd's Bush ⊖ d						23c54						06 19												
Kensington (Olympia) ⊖ d						23c56						06 22												
West Brompton ⊖ d						23c59						06 25												
Clapham Junction 10 d	23p45	23p59				00 23		00 50	05 31		06 30	06 34						06 51	06 54					07 00
Wandsworth Common d	23p48	00 02						00 53			06 33	06 37						06 54						07 03
Balham 4 ⊖ d	23p51	00 04				00 28		00 55			06 35	06 40						06 56	07 00					07 05
Streatham Hill d	23p54																						06 53	
West Norwood 4 d	23p57			00 09																			06 56	
Gipsy Hill d	23p59			00 12																			06 59	
Crystal Palace 4 d	00 03			00 15																			07 02	
Birkbeck 🚋 d																								
Beckenham Junction 4 🚋 a																								
Bromley South 4 a																								
Streatham Common 4 d		00 08				00 32		00 59			06 39	06 45						07 00						07 09
Norbury d		00 11				00 34		01 02			06 42	06 48						07 03						07 12
Thornton Heath d		00 14				00 37		01 05			06 45	06 51						07 06						07 15
Selhurst 4 d		00 17				00 40		01 07			06 47	06 54						07 09						07 17
Norwood Junction 2 a	00 07		00 16	00 19			00 49		05 47						06 55							07 02	07 06	
Norwood Junction d	00 07		00 16				00 49		05 48	06 31					06 56							07 03	07 06	
West Croydon 4 🚋 a	00 13	00 21									06 52												07 11	07 22
East Croydon 🚋 a			00 20			00 43	00 53	01 10	05 51	06 36		06 57			06 59			07 12				07 06		

For general notes see front of timetable
For details of catering facilities see Directory of Train Operators

A To Sutton (Surrey) (Table 182)
B To Epsom Downs (Table 182)
C To Caterham (Table 181)
D To Epsom (Table 182)

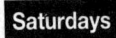

b Arr. 0658
c Saturdays

Table 177

Saturdays

Luton, Milton Keynes and London → East and West Croydon via Tulse Hill → Crystal Palace → Norbury

Local Services

Network Diagram - see first page of Table 177

		SN	SN	SN	SN	SN	SN	FC	SN	SN	SN	SN	FC	SN	SN	SN	SN		FC	SN	SN	SN	SN	SN	SN
			1												1	1									
							A					B					C							A	
London Bridge 4	⊖ d	06 48	07 03	07 05						07 11	07 14		07 15	07 18	07 33					07 33	07 35				
South Bermondsey	d	06 52								07 15				07 22						07 37					
Queens Rd Peckham	d	06 54								07 18				07 24						07 39					
Peckham Rye 4	d	06 57								07 20				07 27						07 42					
East Dulwich	d	07 00												07 30						07 45					
North Dulwich	d	07 02												07 32						07 47					
Luton 10	d																								
Luton Airport Parkway 7	✈ d																								
St Pancras International 15	⊖ d																								
City Thameslink 3	d																								
London Blackfriars 3	⊖ d																								
Elephant & Castle	⊖ d																								
Loughborough Jn	d																								
Herne Hill 4	d							07 12											07 42						
Tulse Hill 3	d	07 05						07 16					07b32	07 35					07 46	07 50					
Streatham 4	d	07 09						07 19					07a35	07 39					07 49						
London Victoria 15	⊖ d				07 06	07 11	07 13		07 17			07 23					07 33					07 36	07 41	07 43	07 47
Battersea Park 4	d				07 10	07a15	07 17										07 37					07 40	07a45	07 47	
Milton Keynes Central	d																								
Watford Junction	d															06 55									
Harrow & Wealdstone	⊖ d															07 01									
Wembley Central	⊖ d															07 06									
Shepherd's Bush	⊖ d															07 19									
Kensington (Olympia)	⊖ d															07 22									
West Brompton	⊖ d															07 25									
Clapham Junction 10	d				07 14		07 21		07 24			07 30				07 34	07 41					07 44		07 51	07 54
Wandsworth Common	d				07 17		07 24					07 33				07 37	07 44					07 47		07 54	
Balham 4	⊖ d				07 20		07 26		07 30			07 35				07 40	07 46					07 50		07 56	08 00
Streatham Hill	d				07 23																	07 53			
West Norwood 4	d				07 27															07 53		07 57			
Gipsy Hill	d				07 30															07 56		08 00			
Crystal Palace 4	d				07 32															07 59		08 02			
Birkbeck	🚊 d																			08 03					
Beckenham Junction 4	🚊 a																			08 06					
Bromley South 4	a																			*08 17*					
Streatham Common 4	d	07 12					07 30					07 39		07 42		07 45	07 50							08 00	
Norbury	d	07 15					07 33					07 42		07 45		07 48	07 53							08 03	
Thornton Heath	d	07 18					07 36					07 45		07 48		07 51	07 56							08 06	
Selhurst 4	d	07 21					07 39					07 47		07 51		07 54	07 59							08 09	
Norwood Junction 2	a		07 14	07 25	07 37						07 40				07 44						07 55	08 07			
	d		07 15	07 26	07 37						07 40				07 45						07 56	08 07			
West Croydon 4	🚊 a	07 25			07 42						07 45	07 52		07 55			08 03					08 12			
East Croydon	🚊 a		07 18	07 29			07 42								07 48	07 57					07 59			08 12	

		SN	SN	SN	SN	FC	SN	SN	SN	FC	SN	SN	SN	SN	SN	SN	SN	SN	SN	SN	FC	SN	FC	SN	SN
									1															1	
					D			C							A					B					C
London Bridge 4	⊖ d		07 41	07 44		07 45	07 48		08 03		08 03	08 05						08 11	08 14		08 15	08 18			
South Bermondsey	d		07 45				07 52				08 07							08 15				08 22			
Queens Rd Peckham	d		07 48				07 54				08 09							08 18				08 24			
Peckham Rye 4	d		07 50				07 57				08 12							08 20				08 27			
East Dulwich	d						08 00				08 15											08 30			
North Dulwich	d						08 02				08 17											08 32			
Luton 10	d																								
Luton Airport Parkway 7	✈ d																								
St Pancras International 15	⊖ d																								
City Thameslink 3	d																								
London Blackfriars 3	⊖ d																								
Elephant & Castle	⊖ d																								
Loughborough Jn	d																								
Herne Hill 4	d									08 12													08 42		
Tulse Hill 3	d					08c02	08 05			08 16	08 20										08e32	08 35	08 46		
Streatham 4	d					08a05	08 09			08 19											08a35	08 39	08 49		
London Victoria 15	⊖ d	07 49			07 53			08 03					08 06	08 11	08 13	08 17	08 19			08 23					08 33
Battersea Park 4	d	07 53						08 07					08 10	08a15	08 17		08 23								08 37
Milton Keynes Central	d																							07 13	
Watford Junction	d																							07 52	
Harrow & Wealdstone	⊖ d																							07 59	
Wembley Central	⊖ d																							08u04	
Shepherd's Bush	⊖ d																							08 19	
Kensington (Olympia)	⊖ d																							08 22	
West Brompton	⊖ d																							08 25	
Clapham Junction 10	d	07 57			08 00			08 11					08 14		08 21	08 24	08 27			08 30				08 34	08 41
Wandsworth Common	d	08 00			08 03			08 14					08 17		08 24		08 30			08 33				08 37	08 44
Balham 4	⊖ d	08 02			08 05			08 16					08 20		08 26	08 30	08 32			08 35				08 40	08 46
Streatham Hill	d	08 05											08 23				08 35								
West Norwood 4	d	08 09									08 23		08 27				08 39								
Gipsy Hill	d	08 12									08 26		08 30				08 42								
Crystal Palace 4	d	08a14									08 29		08 32				08a45								
Birkbeck	🚊 d										08 33														
Beckenham Junction 4	🚊 a										08 36														
Bromley South 4	a										*08 47*														
Streatham Common 4	d				08 09		08 12	08 20							08 30					08 39		08 42		08 45	08 50
Norbury	d				08 12		08 15	08 23							08 33					08 42		08 45		08 48	08 53
Thornton Heath	d				08 15		08 18	08 26							08 36					08 45		08 48		08 51	08 56
Selhurst 4	d				08 17		08 21	08 29							08 39					08 47		08 51		08 54	08 59
Norwood Junction 2	a			08 10					08 14			08 25	08 37						08 40						
	d			08 10					08 15			08 26	08 37						08 40						
West Croydon 4	🚊 a			08 15	08 22		08 25	08 33					08 42						08 45	08 52		08 55			09 03
East Croydon	🚊 a								08 18			08 29			08 42									08 57	

For general notes see front of timetable
For details of catering facilities see
Directory of Train Operators

A To Caterham (Table 181)
B To Epsom Downs (Table 182)
C To Sutton (Surrey) (Table 182)
D To Epsom (Table 182)

b Arr. 0728
c Arr. 0758
e Arr. 0828

Luton, Milton Keynes and London → East and West Croydon via Tulse Hill → Crystal Palace → Norbury

Local Services

Network Diagram - see first page of Table 177

Station		SN	SN	SN	SN	SN	SN	SN	SN	SN	SN	SN		SN	FC	SN	SN		FC	SN	SN	SN	SN	SN	SN
			1																		1				
								A						B			C								
London Bridge 4	⊖ d	08 24	08 33	08 33	08 35						08 41	08 44			08 45	08 48				08 54	09 03	09 03	09 05		
South Bermondsey	d			08 37							08 45					08 52						09 07			
Queens Rd Peckham	d			08 39							08 48					08 54						09 09			
Peckham Rye 4	d			08 42							08 50					08 57						09 12			
East Dulwich	d			08 45												09 00						09 15			
North Dulwich	d			08 47												09 02						09 17			
Luton 10	d																								
Luton Airport Parkway 7	✈ d																								
St Pancras International 15	⊖ d																								
City Thameslink 3	d																								
London Blackfriars 3	⊖ d																								
Elephant & Castle	⊖ d																								
Loughborough Jn	d																		09 12						
Herne Hill 4	d														09b02	09 05			09 16			09 20			
Tulse Hill 3	d			08 50											09a05	09 09			09 19						
Streatham 4	d																								
London Victoria 15	⊖ d					08 36	08 41	08 43	08 47	08 49				08 53			09 03							09 06	09 11
Battersea Park 4	d					08 40	08a45	08 47		08 53							09 07							09 10	09a15
Milton Keynes Central	d																								
Watford Junction	d																								
Harrow & Wealdstone	⊖ d																								
Wembley Central	⊖ d																								
Shepherd's Bush	⊖ d																								
Kensington (Olympia)	⊖ d																								
West Brompton	⊖ d																								
Clapham Junction 10	d					08 44		08 51	08 54	08 57				09 00			09 11							09 14	
Wandsworth Common	d					08 47		08 54		09 00				09 03			09 14							09 17	
Balham 4	⊖ d					08 50		08 56	09 00	09 02				09 05			09 16							09 20	
Streatham Hill	d					08 53				09 05														09 23	
West Norwood 4	d			08 53		08 57				09 09												09 23		09 27	
Gipsy Hill	d			08 56		09 00				09 12												09 26		09 30	
Crystal Palace 4	d	08a43		08 59		09 02				09a15										09a13		09 29		09 32	
Birkbeck	🚋 d			09 03																		09 33			
Beckenham Junction 4	🚋 a			09 06																		09 36			
Bromley South 4	a			*09 17*																		*09 47*			
Streatham Common 4	d							09 00						09 09		09 12	09 20								
Norbury	d							09 03						09 12		09 15	09 23								
Thornton Heath	d							09 06						09 15		09 18	09 26								
Selhurst 4	d							09 09						09 17		09 21	09 29								
Norwood Junction 2	a		08 44		08 55	09 07						09 10									09 14		09 25	09 37	
	d		08 45		08 56	09 07						09 10									09 15		09 26	09 37	
West Croydon 4	🚋 a					09 12						09 15		09 22		09 25	09 33							09 42	
East Croydon	🚋 a		08 48		08 59			09 12													09 18		09 29		

Station		SN	SN	SN	SN	SN	SN	FC	SN	FC	SN	SN	SN	SN	SN	SN	SN	SN	SN	SN	SN	SN	SN	SN	FC
											1			1											
		A					D					C							A					B	
London Bridge 4	⊖ d				09 11	09 14		09 15	09 18				09 24	09 33	09 33	09 35						09 41	09 44		09 45
South Bermondsey	d				09 15				09 22						09 37							09 45			
Queens Rd Peckham	d				09 18				09 24						09 39							09 48			
Peckham Rye 4	d				09 20				09 27						09 42							09 50			
East Dulwich	d								09 30						09 45										
North Dulwich	d								09 32						09 47										
Luton 10	d																								
Luton Airport Parkway 7	✈ d																								
St Pancras International 15	⊖ d																								
City Thameslink 3	d																								
London Blackfriars 3	⊖ d																								
Elephant & Castle	⊖ d																								
Loughborough Jn	d									09 42															
Herne Hill 4	d							09c32	09 35	09 46					09 50										10e02
Tulse Hill 3	d							09a35	09 39	09 49															10a05
Streatham 4	d																								
London Victoria 15	⊖ d	09 13	09 17	09 19			09 23					09 33					09 36	09 41	09 43	09 47	09 49			09 53	
Battersea Park 4	d	09 17		09 23								09 37					09 40	09a45	09 47		09 53				
Milton Keynes Central	d										08 13														
Watford Junction	d										08 51														
Harrow & Wealdstone	⊖ d										08 58														
Wembley Central	⊖ d										09u03														
Shepherd's Bush	⊖ d										09 19														
Kensington (Olympia)	⊖ d										09 22														
West Brompton	⊖ d										09 25														
Clapham Junction 10	d	09 21	09 24	09 27			09 30				09 34	09 41					09 44		09 51	09 54	09 57			10 00	
Wandsworth Common	d	09 24		09 30			09 33				09 37	09 44					09 47		09 54		10 00			10 03	
Balham 4	⊖ d	09 26	09 30	09 32			09 35				09 40	09 46					09 50		09 56	10 00	10 02			10 05	
Streatham Hill	d			09 35													09 53				10 05				
West Norwood 4	d			09 39											09 53		09 57				10 09				
Gipsy Hill	d			09 42											09 56		10 00				10 12				
Crystal Palace 4	d			09a45									09a43		09 59		10 02				10a15				
Birkbeck	🚋 d														10 03										
Beckenham Junction 4	🚋 a														10 06										
Bromley South 4	a														*10 17*										
Streatham Common 4	d	09 30					09 39		09 42		09 45	09 50							10 00					10 09	
Norbury	d	09 33					09 42		09 45		09 48	09 53							10 03					10 12	
Thornton Heath	d	09 36					09 45		09 48		09 51	09 56							10 06					10 15	
Selhurst 4	d	09 39					09 47		09 51		09 54	09 59							10 09					10 17	
Norwood Junction 2	a					09 40								09 44		09 55	10 07						10 10		
	d					09 40								09 45		09 56	10 07						10 10		
West Croydon 4	🚋 a					09 45	09 52		09 55			10 03					10 12						10 15	10 22	
East Croydon	🚋 a	09 42									09 57			09 48		09 59			10 12						

For general notes see front of timetable
For details of catering facilities see
Directory of Train Operators

- **A** To Caterham (Table 181)
- **B** To Epsom (Table 182)
- **C** To Sutton (Surrey) (Table 182)
- **D** To Epsom Downs (Table 182)
- **b** Arr. 0858
- **c** Arr. 0928
- **e** Arr. 0958

Table 177

Luton, Milton Keynes and London → East and West Croydon via Tulse Hill → Crystal Palace → Norbury

Local Services

Network Diagram - see first page of Table 177

Station		SN	SN		FC	SN	SN	SN	SN		SN	SN	SN	SN	SN	SN	SN	SN	FC	SN	FC	SN	SN	SN
						1																1		
			A										B					C					A	
London Bridge 4	⊖ d	09 48				17 03	16 54	17 03	17 05							17 11	17 14		17 15	17 18				17 24
South Bermondsey	d	09 52						17 07								17 15				17 22				
Queens Rd Peckham	d	09 54						17 09								17 18				17 24				
Peckham Rye 4	d	09 57						17 12								17 20				17 27				
East Dulwich	d	10 00						17 15												17 30				
North Dulwich	d	10 02						17 17												17 32				
Luton 10	d																							
Luton Airport Parkway 7	✈ d																							
St Pancras International 15	⊖ d																							
City Thameslink 3	d																							
London Blackfriars 3	⊖ d																							
Elephant & Castle	⊖ d																							
Loughborough Jn	d																							
Herne Hill 4	d				17 12																17 42			
Tulse Hill 3	d	10 05		and at	17 16			17 20											17b32	17 35	17 46			
Streatham 4	d	10 09			17 19														17a35	17 39	17 49			
London Victoria 15	⊖ d		10 03	the same							17 06	17 11	17 13	17 17	17 19			17 23					17 33	
Battersea Park 4	d		10 07								17 10	17a15	17 17		17 23								17 37	
Milton Keynes Central	d			minutes																		16 13		
Watford Junction	d																					16 51		
Harrow & Wealdstone	⊖ d			past																		16 58		
Wembley Central	⊖ d																					17u03		
Shepherd's Bush	⊖ d			each																		17 19		
Kensington (Olympia)	⊖ d																					17 22		
West Brompton	⊖ d			hour until																		17 25		
Clapham Junction 10	d		10 11								17 14		17 21	17 24	17 27			17 30				17 34	17 41	
Wandsworth Common	d		10 14								17 17		17 24		17 30			17 33				17 37	17 44	
Balham 4	⊖ d		10 16								17 20		17 26	17 30	17 32			17 35				17 40	17 46	
Streatham Hill	d										17 23				17 35									
West Norwood 4	d							17 23			17 27				17 39									
Gipsy Hill	d							17 26			17 30				17 42									
Crystal Palace 4	d						17a13	17 29			17 32				17a45									17a43
Birkbeck	🚊 d							17 33																
Beckenham Junction 4	🚊 a							17 36																
Bromley South 4	a							*17 47*																
Streatham Common 4	d	10 12	10 20										17 30					17 39		17 42		17 45	17 50	
Norbury	d	10 15	10 23										17 33					17 42		17 45		17 48	17 53	
Thornton Heath	d	10 18	10 26										17 36					17 45		17 48		17 51	17 56	
Selhurst 4	d	10 21	10 29										17 39					17 47		17 51		17 54	17 59	
Norwood Junction 2	a					17 14			17 25		17 37						17 40							
	d					17 15			17 26		17 37						17 40							
West Croydon 4	🚊 a	10 25	10 33								17 42						17 45	17 52		17 55			18 03	
East Croydon	🚊 a					17 18			17 29				17 42									17 57		

Station		SN	SN	SN	SN	SN	SN	SN	SN	SN	SN	SN	FC	SN	SN	FC	SN	SN	SN	SN	SN	SN	SN	SN	SN
		1																1							
							B					D											B		
London Bridge 4	⊖ d	17 33	17 33	17 35						17 41	17 44		17 45	17 48			17 54	18 03	18 03	18 05					
South Bermondsey	d		17 37							17 45				17 52					18 07						
Queens Rd Peckham	d		17 39							17 48				17 54					18 09						
Peckham Rye 4	d		17 42							17 50				17 57					18 12						
East Dulwich	d		17 45											18 00					18 15						
North Dulwich	d		17 47											18 02					18 17						
Luton 10	d																								
Luton Airport Parkway 7	✈ d																								
St Pancras International 15	⊖ d																								
City Thameslink 3	d																								
London Blackfriars 3	⊖ d																								
Elephant & Castle	⊖ d																								
Loughborough Jn	d																								
Herne Hill 4	d															18 12									
Tulse Hill 3	d		17 50										18c02	18 05		18 16			18 20						
Streatham 4	d												18a05	18 09		18 19									
London Victoria 15	⊖ d				17 36	17 41	17 43	17 47	17 49			17 53			18 03						18 06	18 11	18 13	18 17	18 19
Battersea Park 4	d				17 40	17a45	17 47		17 53						18 07						18 10	18a15	18 17		18 23
Milton Keynes Central	d																								
Watford Junction	d																								
Harrow & Wealdstone	⊖ d																								
Wembley Central	⊖ d																								
Shepherd's Bush	⊖ d																								
Kensington (Olympia)	⊖ d																								
West Brompton	⊖ d																								
Clapham Junction 10	d				17 44		17 51	17 54	17 57			18 00			18 11						18 14		18 21	18 24	18 27
Wandsworth Common	d				17 47		17 54		18 00			18 03			18 14						18 17		18 24		18 30
Balham 4	⊖ d				17 50		17 56	18 00	18 02			18 05			18 16						18 20		18 26	18 30	18 32
Streatham Hill	d				17 53				18 05												18 23				18 35
West Norwood 4	d		17 53		17 57				18 09										18 23		18 27				18 39
Gipsy Hill	d		17 56		18 00				18 12										18 26		18 30				18 42
Crystal Palace 4	d		17 59		18 02				18a15								18a13		18 29		18 32				18a45
Birkbeck	🚊 d		18 03																18 33						
Beckenham Junction 4	🚊 a		18 06																18 36						
Bromley South 4	a		*18 17*																*18 47*						
Streatham Common 4	d						18 00					18 09		18 12	18 20								18 30		
Norbury	d						18 03					18 12		18 15	18 23								18 33		
Thornton Heath	d						18 06					18 15		18 18	18 26								18 36		
Selhurst 4	d						18 09					18 17		18 21	18a28								18 39		
Norwood Junction 2	a	17 44		17 55	18 07						18 10							18 14		18 25	18 37				
	d	17 45		17 56	18 07						18 10							18 15		18 26	18 37				
West Croydon 4	🚊 a				18 12						18 15	18 22		18 25							18 42				
East Croydon	🚊 a	17 48		17 59			18 12											18 18		18 29			18 42		

For general notes see front of timetable
For details of catering facilities see Directory of Train Operators

A To Sutton (Surrey) (Table 182)
B To Caterham (Table 181)
C To Epsom Downs (Table 182)
D To Epsom (Table 182)

b Arr. 1728
c Arr. 1758

Luton, Milton Keynes and London → East and West Croydon via Tulse Hill → Crystal Palace → Norbury

Local Services

Network Diagram - see first page of Table 177

		SN	SN	SN	FC		SN	FC	SN 1	SN	SN	SN 1	SN	SN	SN	SN	SN	SN	SN	SN	FC	SN	FC	SN	SN 1
				A													B								
London Bridge 4 Θ	d	18 11	18 14		18 15		18 18				18 24	18 33	18 33	18 35					18 44	18 41	18 45	18 48		18 54	19 03
South Bermondsey	d	18 15					18 22						18 37							18 45		18 52			
Queens Rd Peckham	d	18 18					18 24						18 39							18 48		18 54			
Peckham Rye 4	d	18 20					18 27						18 42							18 50		18 57			
East Dulwich	d						18 30						18 45									19 00			
North Dulwich	d						18 32						18 47									19 02			
Luton 10	d																								
Luton Airport Parkway 7 ✈	d																								
St Pancras International 15 Θ	d																								
City Thameslink 3	d																								
London Blackfriars 3 Θ	d																								
Elephant & Castle Θ	d																								
Loughborough Jn	d																								
Herne Hill 4	d							18 42															19 12		
Tulse Hill 3	d				18b32		18 35	18 46					18 50								19c02	19 05	19 16		
Streatham 4	d				18a35		18 39	18 49													19a05	19 09	19 19		
London Victoria 15 Θ	d			18 23						18 33					18 36	18 41	18 45	18 50							
Battersea Park 4	d									18 37					18 40	18a45	18 49								
Milton Keynes Central	d								17 13																
Watford Junction	d								17 51																
Harrow & Wealdstone Θ	d								17 58																
Wembley Central Θ	d								18u03																
Shepherd's Bush Θ	d								18 19																
Kensington (Olympia) Θ	d								18 22																
West Brompton Θ	d								18 25																
Clapham Junction 10	d			18 30					18 34	18 41					18 44		18 53	18 57							
Wandsworth Common	d			18 33					18 37	18 44					18 47		18 56								
Balham 4 Θ	d			18 35					18 40	18 46					18 50		18 58	19 01							
Streatham Hill	d														18 53										
West Norwood 4	d												18 53		18 57										
Gipsy Hill	d												18 56		19 00										
Crystal Palace 4	d										18a43		18 59		19 02									19a13	
Birkbeck 🚊	d												19 03												
Beckenham Junction 4 🚊	a												19 06												
Bromley South 4	a												*19 17*												
Streatham Common 4	d			18 39			18 42		18 45	18 50							19 02					19 12			
Norbury	d			18 42			18 45		18 48	18 53							19 05					19 15			
Thornton Heath	d			18 45			18 48		18 51	18 56							19 08					19 18			
Selhurst 4	d			18 47			18 51		18 54	18a58							19 11					19 21			
Norwood Junction 2	a		18 40									18 44		18 55	19 07				19 10						19 14
	d		18 40									18 45		18 56	19 07				19 10						19 15
West Croydon 4 🚊	a		18 45	18 52			18 55								19 12		19 15					19 25			
East Croydon 🚊	a								18 57			18 48		18 59					19 14						19 18

		SN	SN	SN	SN	SN	SN	SN	SN	SN	FC	SN	FC	SN	SN 1	SN	SN 1	SN	SN	SN	SN	SN		SN	SN
		A	C					D								A		C						B	
London Bridge 4 Θ	d			19 15	19 03					19 11	19 15	19 18		19 24	19 33				19 45	19 33					
South Bermondsey	d				19 07					19 15		19 22								19 37					
Queens Rd Peckham	d				19 09					19 18		19 24								19 39					
Peckham Rye 4	d				19 12					19 20		19 27								19 42					
East Dulwich	d				19 15							19 30								19 45					
North Dulwich	d				19 17							19 32								19 47					
Luton 10	d																								
Luton Airport Parkway 7 ✈	d																								
St Pancras International 15 Θ	d																								
City Thameslink 3	d																								
London Blackfriars 3 Θ	d																								
Elephant & Castle Θ	d																								
Loughborough Jn	d																								
Herne Hill 4	d												19 42												
Tulse Hill 3	d				19 20						19e32	19 35	19 46							19 50					
Streatham 4	d										19a35	19 39	19 49												
London Victoria 15 Θ	d	18 53	19 00			19 06	19 11	19 15	19 20							19 23		19 30			19 36	19 41		19 45	19 50
Battersea Park 4	d	18 57	19 04			19 10	19a15	19 19								19 27		19 34			19 40	19a45		19 49	
Milton Keynes Central	d																18 13								
Watford Junction	d																18 51								
Harrow & Wealdstone Θ	d																18 58								
Wembley Central Θ	d																19u03								
Shepherd's Bush Θ	d																19 19								
Kensington (Olympia) Θ	d																19 22								
West Brompton Θ	d																19 25								
Clapham Junction 10	d	19 01	19 08			19 14		19 23	19 26							19 31	19 35	19 38			19 44			19 53	19 56
Wandsworth Common	d	19 04	19 11			19 17		19 26								19 34	19 38	19 41			19 47			19 56	
Balham 4 Θ	d	19 06	19 14			19 19		19 28	19 32							19 36	19 41	19 44			19 49			19 58	20 02
Streatham Hill	d	19 09				19 22										19 39					19 52				
West Norwood 4	d	19 13			19 23	19 27										19 43				19 53	19 57				
Gipsy Hill	d	19 16			19 26	19 30										19 46				19 56	20 00				
Crystal Palace 4	d	19 18			19 29	19a32								19a43		19 48				19 59	20a02				
Birkbeck 🚊	d				19 33															20 03					
Beckenham Junction 4 🚊	a				19 36															20 06					
Bromley South 4	a				*19 47*															*20 17*					
Streatham Common 4	d		19 18					19 32				19 42					19 45	19 48						20 02	
Norbury	d		19 20					19 35				19 45					19 48	19 51						20 05	
Thornton Heath	d		19 23					19 38				19 48					19 51	19 54						20 08	
Selhurst 4	d		19 26					19 41				19 51					19 54	19 57						20 11	
Norwood Junction 2	a	19 23		19 38											19 44	19 53			20 08						
	d	19 24		19 39											19 45	19 54			20 09						
West Croydon 4 🚊	a	19 29						19 45				19 55				19 59								20 15	
East Croydon 🚊	a		19 29	19 42											19 49		19 57	20 00	20 12						

For general notes see front of timetable
For details of catering facilities see Directory of Train Operators

A To Sutton (Surrey) (Table 182)
B To Epsom Downs (Table 182)
C To Tattenham Corner (Table 181)
D To Epsom (Table 182)

b Arr. 1828
c Arr. 1858
e Arr. 1928

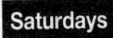

Table 177

Saturdays

Luton, Milton Keynes and London → East and West Croydon via Tulse Hill → Crystal Palace → Norbury

Local Services

Network Diagram - see first page of Table 177

Station		SN	FC	SN	SN	SN	SN	SN	SN	SN	SN	SN	SN	SN	SN	SN	FC	SN	SN	SN	SN	SN	SN	SN	SN
						1										1									
							A	B			C				A					B			D		
London Bridge 4	⊖ d	19 41	19 45	19 48	19 54	20 08							20 11	20 15			20 15	20 18	20 24						20 45
South Bermondsey	d	19 45		19 52									20 15					20 22							
Queens Rd Peckham	d	19 48		19 54									20 18					20 24							
Peckham Rye 4	d	19 50		19 57									20 20					20 27							
East Dulwich	d			20 00														20 30							
North Dulwich	d			20 02														20 32							
Luton 10	d																								
Luton Airport Parkway 7	✈ d																								
St Pancras International 15	⊖ d																								
City Thameslink 3	d																								
London Blackfriars 3	⊖ d																								
Elephant & Castle	⊖ d																								
Loughborough Jn	d																								
Herne Hill 4	d																								
Tulse Hill 3	d		20b02	20 05													20c32	20 35							
Streatham 4	d		20a05	20 09													20a35	20 39							
London Victoria 15	⊖ d						19 53	20 00	20 06	20 11	20 15	20 20			20 23					20 30	20 36	20 41	20 45	20 50	
Battersea Park 4	d						19 57	20 04	20 10	20a15	20 19				20 27					20 34	20 40	20a45	20 49		
Milton Keynes Central	d															19 13									
Watford Junction	d															19 51									
Harrow & Wealdstone	⊖ d															19 58									
Wembley Central	⊖ d																								
Shepherd's Bush	⊖ d										19 57					20 19									
Kensington (Olympia)	⊖ d										20 00					20 22									
West Brompton	⊖ d										20 03					20 25									
Clapham Junction 10	d						20 01	20 08	20 14		20 23	20 26			20 31	20 34				20 38	20 44		20 53	20 56	
Wandsworth Common	d						20 04	20 11	20 17		20 26				20 34	20 37				20 41	20 47		20 56		
Balham 4	⊖ d						20 06	20 14	20 19		20 28	20 32			20 36	20 40				20 44	20 49		20 58	21 02	
Streatham Hill	d						20 09		20 22						20 39						20 52				
West Norwood 4	d						20 13		20 26						20 43						20 56				
Gipsy Hill	d						20 16		20 29						20 46						20 59				
Crystal Palace 4	d				20a13		20 18		20a31						20 48				20a43		21a01				
Birkbeck	🚋 d																								
Beckenham Junction 4	🚋 a																								
Bromley South 4	a																								
Streatham Common 4	d			20 12				20 18			20 32					20 45		20 42		20 48			21 02		
Norbury	d			20 15				20 20			20 35					20 48		20 45		20 51			21 05		
Thornton Heath	d			20 18				20 23			20 38					20 51		20 48		20 54			21 08		
Selhurst 4	d			20 21				20 26			20 41					20 54		20 51		20 57			21 11		
Norwood Junction 2	a					20 19	20 23							20 38	20 53										21 08
	d					20 19	20 24							20 39	20 54										21 09
West Croydon 4	🚋 a			20 26			20 29				20 45				20 59			20 56					21 15		
East Croydon	🚋 a					20 22		20 29						20 42		20 57				21 00					21 12

Station		SN	FC	SN	SN	SN	SN	SN	SN	SN	SN	SN	SN	SN	SN	FC	SN		SN	SN	SN	SN	SN	SN	SN
						1																			
							A	B			C			A						B			D		
London Bridge 4	⊖ d	20 41	20 45	20 48	20 54	21 08							21 15		21 11	21 15	21 24		21 18						21 45
South Bermondsey	d	20 45		20 52											21 15				21 22						
Queens Rd Peckham	d	20 48		20 54											21 18				21 24						
Peckham Rye 4	d	20 50		20 57											21 20				21 27						
East Dulwich	d			21 00															21 30						
North Dulwich	d			21 02															21 32						
Luton 10	d																								
Luton Airport Parkway 7	✈ d																								
St Pancras International 15	⊖ d																								
City Thameslink 3	d																								
London Blackfriars 3	⊖ d																								
Elephant & Castle	⊖ d																								
Loughborough Jn	d																								
Herne Hill 4	d																								
Tulse Hill 3	d		21e02	21 05												21f32			21 35						
Streatham 4	d		21a05	21 09												21a35			21 39						
London Victoria 15	⊖ d						20 53	21 00	21 06	21 11	21 15	21 20		21 23						21 30	21 36	21 41	21 45	21 50	
Battersea Park 4	d						20 57	21 04	21 10	21a15	21 19			21 27						21 34	21 40	21a45	21 49		
Milton Keynes Central	d																								
Watford Junction	d																								
Harrow & Wealdstone	⊖ d																								
Wembley Central	⊖ d																								
Shepherd's Bush	⊖ d											21 08													
Kensington (Olympia)	⊖ d											21 11													
West Brompton	⊖ d											21 14													
Clapham Junction 10	d						21 01	21 08	21 14		21 23	21 26		21 31						21 38	21 44		21 53	21 56	
Wandsworth Common	d						21 04	21 11	21 17		21 26			21 34						21 41	21 47		21 56		
Balham 4	⊖ d						21 06	21 14	21 19		21 28	21 32		21 36						21 44	21 49		21 58	22 02	
Streatham Hill	d						21 09		21 22					21 39							21 52				
West Norwood 4	d						21 13		21 26					21 43							21 56				
Gipsy Hill	d						21 16		21 29					21 46							21 59				
Crystal Palace 4	d				21a13		21 18		21a31					21 48			21a43				22a01				
Birkbeck	🚋 d																								
Beckenham Junction 4	🚋 a																								
Bromley South 4	a																								
Streatham Common 4	d			21 12				21 18			21 32								21 42	21 48			22 02		
Norbury	d			21 15				21 20			21 35								21 45	21 50			22 05		
Thornton Heath	d			21 18				21 23			21 38								21 48	21 53			22 08		
Selhurst 4	d			21 21				21 26			21 41								21 51	21 56			22 11		
Norwood Junction 2	a					21 19	21 23						21 38	21 53											22 08
	d					21 19	21 24						21 39	21 54											22 09
West Croydon 4	🚋 a			21 26			21 29				21 45			21 59					21 56				22 15		
East Croydon	🚋 a					21 22		21 29					21 42							21 59					22 12

For general notes see front of timetable
For details of catering facilities see Directory of Train Operators

A To Sutton (Surrey) (Table 182)
B To Tattenham Corner (Table 181)
C To Epsom (Table 182)
D To Epsom Downs (Table 182)

b Arr. 1958
c Arr. 2028
e Arr. 2058
f Arr. 2128

Table 177

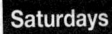

Luton, Milton Keynes and London → East and West Croydon via Tulse Hill → Crystal Palace → Norbury

Local Services

Network Diagram - see first page of Table 177

	SN	FC	SN	SN	SN	SN	SN	SN	SN	SN	SN	SN	SN	SN	FC	SN	SN	SN	SN	SN	SN	SN	SN	SN
					1	A	B			C			A					B			D			
London Bridge 4 ⊖ d	21 41	21 45	21 48	21 54	22 08							22 15		22 11	22 15	22 18	22 24						22 41	22 45
South Bermondsey d	21 45		21 52											22 15		22 22							22 45	
Queens Rd Peckham d	21 48		21 54											22 18		22 24							22 48	
Peckham Rye 4 d	21 50		21 57											22 20		22 27							22 50	
East Dulwich d			22 00													22 30								
North Dulwich d			22 02													22 32								
Luton 10 d																								
Luton Airport Parkway 7 ✈ d																								
St Pancras International 15 ⊖ d																								
City Thameslink 3 d																								
London Blackfriars 3 ⊖ d																								
Elephant & Castle ⊖ d																								
Loughborough Jn d																								
Herne Hill 4 d																								
Tulse Hill 3 d		22b02	22 05												22c32	22 35								
Streatham 4 d		22a05	22 09												22a35	22 39								
London Victoria 15 ⊖ d						21 53	22 00	22 06	22 11	22 15	22 20		22 23					22 30	22 36	22 41	22 45	22 50		
Battersea Park 4 d						21 57	22 04	22 10	22a15	22 19			22 27					22 34	22 40	22a45	22 49			
Milton Keynes Central d																								
Watford Junction d																								
Harrow & Wealdstone ⊖ d																								
Wembley Central ⊖ d																								
Shepherd's Bush ⊖ d											22 08													
Kensington (Olympia) ⊖ d											22 11													
West Brompton ⊖ d											22 14													
Clapham Junction 10 d						22 01	22 08	22 14		22 23	22 26		22 31					22 38	22 44		22 53	22 56		
Wandsworth Common d						22 04	22 11	22 17		22 26			22 34					22 41	22 47		22 56			
Balham 4 ⊖ d						22 06	22 14	22 19		22 28	22 32		22 36					22 43	22 49		22 58	23 01		
Streatham Hill d						22 09		22 22					22 39						22 52					
West Norwood 4 d						22 13		22 26					22 43						22 56					
Gipsy Hill d						22 16		22 29					22 46						22 59					
Crystal Palace 4 d						22 18		22a31					22 48				22a43		23a01					
Birkbeck 🚊 d																								
Beckenham Junction 4 🚊 a																								
Bromley South 4 a																								
Streatham Common 4 d			22 12				22 18			22 32						22 42		22 47			23 02			
Norbury d			22 15				22 20			22 35						22 45		22 50			23 05			
Thornton Heath d			22 18				22 23			22 38						22 48		22 53			23 08			
Selhurst 4 d			22 21				22 26			22 41						22 51		22 55			23 11			
Norwood Junction 2 a					22 19	22 23						22 38	22 53											23 08
Norwood Junction 2 d					22 19	22 24						22 39	22 54											23 09
West Croydon 4 🚊 a			22 26			22 29				22 45			22 59			22 56					23 15			
East Croydon 🚊 a					22 22		22 29					22 42						22 59						23 12

	FC	SN	SN	SN	SN	SN	SN	SN	SN	SN	SN	SN	SN	FC	SN	SN	SN	SN	SN	FC	SN	SN		
					C	B			A			A						A						
London Bridge 4 ⊖ d	22 45	22 54	22 48	22 58						23 11	23 15			23 15	23 18				23 24	23 45	23 53	23 48		
South Bermondsey d			22 52							23 15					23 22							23 52		
Queens Rd Peckham d			22 54							23 18					23 24							23 54		
Peckham Rye 4 d			22 57							23 20					23 27							23 57		
East Dulwich d			23 00												23 30							00 01		
North Dulwich d			23 02												23 32							00 03		
Luton 10 d																								
Luton Airport Parkway 7 ✈ d																								
St Pancras International 15 ⊖ d																								
City Thameslink 3 d																								
London Blackfriars 3 ⊖ d																								
Elephant & Castle ⊖ d																								
Loughborough Jn d																								
Herne Hill 4 d																								
Tulse Hill 3 d	23e02		23 05											23f32	23 35					00g02		00 06		
Streatham 4 d	23a05		23 09											23a35	23 39					00a05				
London Victoria 15 ⊖ d					22 53	23 00	23 06	23 11	23 15			23 23	23 26			23 34	23 37	23 51						
Battersea Park 4 d					22 57	23 04	23 10	23a15	23 19			23 27				23 38	23 41	23 55						
Milton Keynes Central d																								
Watford Junction d																								
Harrow & Wealdstone ⊖ d																								
Wembley Central ⊖ d																								
Shepherd's Bush ⊖ d												23 13												
Kensington (Olympia) ⊖ d												23 16												
West Brompton ⊖ d												23 19												
Clapham Junction 10 d					23 01	23 08	23 14		23 23			23 31	23 33			23 42	23 45	23 59						
Wandsworth Common d					23 04	23 11	23 17		23 26			23 34				23 45	23 48	00 02						
Balham 4 ⊖ d					23 06	23 14	23 19		23 28			23 36	23 38			23 47	23 51	00 04						
Streatham Hill d					23 09		23 22					23 39					23 54							
West Norwood 4 d					23 13		23 26					23 43					23 57					00 09		
Gipsy Hill d					23 16		23 29					23 46					23 59					00 12		
Crystal Palace 4 d		23a13			23 18		23a31					23 48					00 03		23a43			00 15		
Birkbeck 🚊 d																								
Beckenham Junction 4 🚊 a																								
Bromley South 4 a																								
Streatham Common 4 d			23 12			23 18			23 32						23 42	23 51		00 08						
Norbury d			23 15			23 20			23 35						23 45	23 54		00 11						
Thornton Heath d			23 18			23 23			23 38						23 48	23 57		00 14						
Selhurst 4 d			23 21			23 26			23 41						23 51	23a59		00 17						
Norwood Junction 2 a				23 09	23 23						23 38	23 53					00 07				00 16	00 19		
Norwood Junction 2 d				23 10	23 24						23 39	23 54					00 07				00 16			
West Croydon 4 🚊 a			23 26		23 29				23 45			23 58			23 55		00 13	00 21						
East Croydon 🚊 a				23 14		23 29					23 42										00 20			

For general notes see front of timetable
For details of catering facilities see Directory of Train Operators

- A To Sutton (Surrey) (Table 182)
- B To Tattenham Corner (Table 181)
- C To Epsom (Table 182)
- D To Epsom Downs (Table 182)
- b Arr. 2158
- c Arr. 2228
- e Arr. 2258
- f Arr. 2328
- g Arr. 2358

Table 177

Sundays

Luton, Milton Keynes and London → East and West Croydon via Tulse Hill → Crystal Palace → Norbury

Local Services

Network Diagram - see first page of Table 177

		SN	SN A	SN	FC	SN	SN	SN		SN	SN B	SN [1] C	SN [1] D	SN [1] E	SN B	SN		SN [1] G	SN [1] H	SN	SN A	SN	SN A	SN	SN
London Bridge [4]	⊖ d			23p53	23p45	23p48		00 26					07 05			07 11				07 25				07 41	07 44
South Bermondsey	d					23p52										07 15				07 29				07 45	
Queens Rd Peckham	d					23p54										07 18				07 31				07 48	
Peckham Rye [4]	d					23p57										07 20				07 34				07 50	
East Dulwich	d					00 01														07 37					
North Dulwich	d					00 03														07 39					
Luton [10]	d																								
Luton Airport Parkway [7]	✈ d																								
St Pancras International [15]	⊖ d																								
City Thameslink [3]	d																								
London Blackfriars [3]	⊖ d																								
Elephant & Castle	⊖ d																								
Loughborough Jn	d																								
Herne Hill [4]	d																								
Tulse Hill [3]	d				00b02	00 06														07 42					
Streatham [4]	d				00a05															07 46					
London Victoria [15]	⊖ d	23p37	23p51				00 17			00 42	06 49	07 02		07 02	07 19			07 32	07 34		07 38	07 41	07 49		
Battersea Park [4]	d	23p41	23p55							00 46	06 53				07 23						07 42	07a45	07 53		
Milton Keynes Central	d																								
Watford Junction	d																								
Harrow & Wealdstone	⊖ d																								
Wembley Central	⊖ d																								
Shepherd's Bush	⊖ d						23c49																		
Kensington (Olympia)	⊖ d						23c51																		
West Brompton	⊖ d						23c54																		
Clapham Junction [10]	d	23p45	23p59				00 23			00 49	06 56	07 08		07 08	07 26			07 38	07 40		07 45		07 56		
Wandsworth Common	d	23p48	00 02							00 52	06 59				07 29						07 48		07 59		
Balham [4]	⊖ d	23p51	00 04				00 27			00 55	07 02				07 32						07 51		08 02		
Streatham Hill	d	23p54																							
West Norwood [4]	d	23p57				00 09															07 54				
Gipsy Hill	d	23p59				00 12															07 57				
Crystal Palace [4]	d	00 03				00 15															08 00				
Birkbeck	d																				08 03				
Beckenham Junction [4]	a																								
Bromley South [4]	a																								
Streatham Common [4]	d		00 08				00 31			00 59	07 06				07 36					07 49			08 06		
Norbury	d		00 11				00 34			01 01	07 08				07 38					07 51			08 08		
Thornton Heath	d		00 14				00 37			01 04	07 11				07 41					07 54			08 11		
Selhurst [4]	d		00 17				00 39			01 07	07 14	07 16		07 18	07 44			07 46	07 50	07 58			08 14		
Norwood Junction [2]	a	00 07		00 16		00 19		00 49					07 16								08 07				08 04
	d	00 07		00 16				00 49					07 16								08 07				08 04
West Croydon [4]	a	00 13	00 21								07 18				07 48						08 12		08 18		
East Croydon	a			00 20			00 42	00 53		01 10		07 19	07 20	07 23				07 49	07 53	08 02					08 08

For general notes see front of timetable
For details of catering facilities see Directory of Train Operators

- **A** To Sutton (Surrey) (Table 182)
- **B** To Dorking (Table 182)
- **C** Until 6 September. To Bognor Regis (Table 188)
- **D** Until 6 September
- **E** From 13 September. To Bognor Regis (Table 188)
- **G** Until 6 September. To Horsham (Table 186)
- **H** From 13 September. To Horsham (Table 186)
- **b** Arr. 2358
- **c** Sundays

Sundays

Luton, Milton Keynes and London → East and West Croydon via Tulse Hill → Crystal Palace → Norbury

Local Services

Network Diagram - see first page of Table 177

Station		SN		SN	SN 1	SN	SN	SN	SN	SN		SN	SN	SN	SN	SN	SN	SN		SN	SN	SN	SN	SN 1	SN
					A		B		B							B		B						A	
London Bridge 4 ⊖	d			07 55	08 05	07 58				08 11		08 14		08 25	08 28					08 41	08 44		08 55	09 05	08 58
South Bermondsey	d			07 59						08 15				08 29						08 45			08 59		
Queens Rd Peckham	d			08 01						08 18				08 31						08 48			09 01		
Peckham Rye 4	d			08 04						08 20				08 34						08 50			09 04		
East Dulwich	d			08 07										08 37									09 07		
North Dulwich	d			08 09										08 39									09 09		
Luton 10	d																								
Luton Airport Parkway 7 ✈	d																								
St Pancras International 15 ⊖	d																								
City Thameslink 3	d																								
London Blackfriars 3 ⊖	d																								
Elephant & Castle ⊖	d																								
Loughborough Jn	d																								
Herne Hill 4	d																								
Tulse Hill 3	d			08 12										08 42									09 12		
Streatham 4	d			08 16										08 46									09 16		
London Victoria 15 ⊖	d	08 06					08 08	08 11	08 19				08 36			08 38	08 41	08 49				09 06			
Battersea Park 4	d						08 12	08a15	08 23							08 42	08a45	08 53		09a02					
Milton Keynes Central	d																								
Watford Junction	d																								
Harrow & Wealdstone ⊖	d																								
Wembley Central ⊖	d																								
Shepherd's Bush ⊖	d	07 48																				08 50			
Kensington (Olympia) ⊖	d	07 50																				08 53			
West Brompton ⊖	d	07 52																				08 56			
Clapham Junction 10	d	08 12					08 15		08 26				08 42			08 45		08 56				09 12			
Wandsworth Common	d						08 18		08 29							08 48		08 59							
Balham 4 ⊖	d	08 16					08 21		08 32				08 46			08 51		09 02				09 16			
Streatham Hill	d						08 24									08 54									
West Norwood 4	d						08 27									08 57									
Gipsy Hill	d						08 30									09 00									
Crystal Palace 4	d						08 33									09 03									
Birkbeck (tram)	d																								
Beckenham Junction 4 (tram)	a																								
Bromley South 4	a																								
Streatham Common 4	d			08 19					08 36					08 49				09 06					09 19		
Norbury	d			08 21					08 38					08 51				09 08					09 21		
Thornton Heath	d			08 24					08 41					08 54				09 11					09 24		
Selhurst 4	d			08 27					08 44					08 57				09 14					09 27		
Norwood Junction 2	a				08 16	08 21	08 37					08 34			08 51	09 07					09 04			09 16	09 21
	d				08 16	08 21	08 37					08 34			08 51	09 07					09 04			09 16	09 21
West Croydon 4 (tram)	a					08 26	08 42		08 48						08 56	09 12		09 18							09 26
East Croydon (tram)	a			08 32	08 20							08 38		09 00							09 08		09 32	09 20	

Station		SN	SN	SN			SN	SN	FC	SN	SN	SN	SN	SN	SN	SN	SN	FC	SN	SN	SN 1	SN	SN	SN	
		B		B									B		B						A		B		
London Bridge 4 ⊖	d						09 11	09 14	09 21		09 25	09 28				09 41	09 44	09 51		09 55	10 05	09 58			
South Bermondsey	d						09 15				09 29					09 45				09 59					
Queens Rd Peckham	d						09 18				09 31					09 48				10 01					
Peckham Rye 4	d						09 20				09 34					09 50				10 04					
East Dulwich	d										09 37									10 07					
North Dulwich	d										09 39									10 09					
Luton 10	d																								
Luton Airport Parkway 7 ✈	d																								
St Pancras International 15 ⊖	d																								
City Thameslink 3	d																								
London Blackfriars 3 ⊖	d																								
Elephant & Castle ⊖	d																								
Loughborough Jn	d																								
Herne Hill 4	d																								
Tulse Hill 3	d								09 32		09 42							10 02		10 12					
Streatham 4	d								09a35		09 46							10a05		10 16					
London Victoria 15 ⊖	d	09 08	09 11	09 19						09 36			09 38	09 41	09 49				10 06				10 08	10 11	
Battersea Park 4	d	09 12	09a15	09 23									09 42	09a45	09 53								10 12	10a15	
Milton Keynes Central	d																								
Watford Junction	d																								
Harrow & Wealdstone ⊖	d																								
Wembley Central ⊖	d																								
Shepherd's Bush ⊖	d																		09 45						
Kensington (Olympia) ⊖	d																		09 48						
West Brompton ⊖	d																		09 50						
Clapham Junction 10	d	09 15		09 26						09 42			09 45		09 56				10 12				10 15		
Wandsworth Common	d	09 18		09 29									09 48		09 59								10 18		
Balham 4 ⊖	d	09 21		09 32						09 46			09 51		10 02				10 16				10 21		
Streatham Hill	d	09 24											09 54										10 24		
West Norwood 4	d	09 27											09 57										10 27		
Gipsy Hill	d	09 30											10 00										10 30		
Crystal Palace 4	d	09 33											10 03										10 33		
Birkbeck (tram)	d																								
Beckenham Junction 4 (tram)	a																								
Bromley South 4	a																								
Streatham Common 4	d			09 36							09 49				10 06					10 19					
Norbury	d			09 38							09 51				10 08					10 21					
Thornton Heath	d			09 41							09 54				10 11					10 24					
Selhurst 4	d			09 44							09 57				10 14					10 27					
Norwood Junction 2	a	09 37						09 34				09 51	10 07				10 04				10 16	10 21	10 37		
	d	09 37						09 34				09 51	10 07				10 04				10 16	10 21	10 37		
West Croydon 4 (tram)	a	09 42		09 48								09 56	10 12		10 18							10 26	10 42		
East Croydon (tram)	a							09 38			10 02						10 08			10 32	10 20				

For general notes see front of timetable
For details of catering facilities see Directory of Train Operators

A Until 6 September
B To Sutton (Surrey) (Table 182)

Table 177

Sundays

Luton, Milton Keynes and London → East and West Croydon via Tulse Hill → Crystal Palace → Norbury

Local Services

Network Diagram - see first page of Table 177

		SN	and at the same minutes past each hour until	SN	SN	FC	SN	SN	SN	SN	SN	SN	SN	SN	FC	SN	SN	SN	SN	SN	SN
		A								A		A						1 B		A	
London Bridge 4	⊖ d			20 11	20 14	20 21		20 25	20 28				20 41	20 44	20 51		20 55	21 05	20 58		
South Bermondsey	d			20 15				20 29					20 45				20 59				
Queens Rd Peckham	d			20 18				20 31					20 48				21 01				
Peckham Rye 4	d			20 20				20 34					20 50				21 04				
East Dulwich	d							20 37									21 07				
North Dulwich	d							20 39									21 09				
Luton 10	d																				
Luton Airport Parkway 7	✈ d																				
St Pancras International 15	⊖ d																				
City Thameslink 3	d																				
London Blackfriars 3	⊖ d																				
Elephant & Castle	⊖ d																				
Loughborough Jn	d																				
Herne Hill 4	d																				
Tulse Hill 3	d					20 32		20 42							21 02		21 12				
Streatham 4	d					20a35		20 46							21a05		21 16				
London Victoria 15	⊖ d	10 19					20 36			20 38	20 41	20 49				21 06				21 08	21 11
Battersea Park 4	d	10 23								20 42	20a45	20 53								21 12	21a15
Milton Keynes Central	d																				
Watford Junction	d																				
Harrow & Wealdstone	⊖ d																				
Wembley Central	⊖ d																				
Shepherd's Bush	⊖ d															20 45					
Kensington (Olympia)	⊖ d															20 48					
West Brompton	⊖ d															20 50					
Clapham Junction 10	d	10 26					20 42			20 45		20 56				21 12				21 15	
Wandsworth Common	d	10 29								20 48		20 59								21 18	
Balham 4	⊖ d	10 32					20 46			20 51		21 02				21 16				21 21	
Streatham Hill	d									20 54										21 24	
West Norwood 4	d									20 57										21 27	
Gipsy Hill	d									21 00										21 30	
Crystal Palace 4	d									21 03										21 33	
Birkbeck	🚊 d																				
Beckenham Junction 4	🚊 a																				
Bromley South 4	a																				
Streatham Common 4	d	10 36						20 49				21 06					21 19				
Norbury	d	10 38						20 51				21 08					21 21				
Thornton Heath	d	10 41						20 54				21 11					21 24				
Selhurst 4	d	10 44						20 57				21 14					21 27				
Norwood Junction 2	a				20 34				20 51	21 07				21 04				21 16	21 21	21 37	
	d				20 34				20 51	21 07				21 04				21 16	21 21	21 37	
West Croydon 4	🚊 a	10 48							20 56	21 12		21 18							21 26	21 42	
East Croydon	🚊 a				20 38			21 02						21 08			21 32	21 20			

		SN	SN	SN	SN	SN	SN	SN	SN	SN	SN	SN	SN	SN	SN	SN	SN	SN	SN	SN	SN	SN	SN
		A						A		A					1 B		A		A			
London Bridge 4	⊖ d		21 11	21 14		21 25	21 28				21 41	21 44		21 55	22 05	21 58				22 11	22 14	
South Bermondsey	d		21 15			21 29					21 45			21 59						22 15		
Queens Rd Peckham	d		21 18			21 31					21 48			22 01						22 18		
Peckham Rye 4	d		21 20			21 34					21 50			22 04						22 20		
East Dulwich	d					21 37								22 07								
North Dulwich	d					21 39								22 09								
Luton 10	d																					
Luton Airport Parkway 7	✈ d																					
St Pancras International 15	⊖ d																					
City Thameslink 3	d																					
London Blackfriars 3	⊖ d																					
Elephant & Castle	⊖ d																					
Loughborough Jn	d																					
Herne Hill 4	d																					
Tulse Hill 3	d					21 42								22 12								
Streatham 4	d					21 46								22 16								
London Victoria 15	⊖ d	21 19			21 36			21 38	21 41	21 49			22 06				22 08	22 11	22 19			22 36
Battersea Park 4	d	21 23						21 42	21a45	21 53							22 12	22a15	22 23	22a32		
Milton Keynes Central	d																					
Watford Junction	d																					
Harrow & Wealdstone	⊖ d																					
Wembley Central	⊖ d																					
Shepherd's Bush	⊖ d												21 45									
Kensington (Olympia)	⊖ d												21 48									
West Brompton	⊖ d												21 50									
Clapham Junction 10	d	21 26			21 42			21 45		21 56			22 12				22 15		22 26			22 42
Wandsworth Common	d	21 29						21 48		21 59							22 18		22 29			
Balham 4	⊖ d	21 32			21 46			21 51		22 02			22 16				22 21		22 32			22 46
Streatham Hill	d							21 54									22 24					
West Norwood 4	d							21 57									22 27					
Gipsy Hill	d							22 00									22 30					
Crystal Palace 4	d							22 03									22 33					
Birkbeck	🚊 d																					
Beckenham Junction 4	🚊 a																					
Bromley South 4	a																					
Streatham Common 4	d	21 36				21 49				22 06				22 19					22 36			
Norbury	d	21 38				21 51				22 08				22 21					22 38			
Thornton Heath	d	21 41				21 54				22 11				22 24					22 41			
Selhurst 4	d	21 44				21 57				22 14				22 27					22 44			
Norwood Junction 2	a			21 34			21 51	22 07				22 04			22 16	22 21	22 37				22 37	
	d			21 34			21 51	22 07				22 04			22 16	22 21	22 39				22 39	
West Croydon 4	🚊 a	21 48					21 56	22 12		22 18						22 26	22 43		22 48			
East Croydon	🚊 a			21 38		22 00						22 08		22 32	22 20						22 42	

For general notes see front of timetable
For details of catering facilities see Directory of Train Operators

A To Sutton (Surrey) (Table 182)
B Until 6 September

Luton, Milton Keynes and London → East and West Croydon via Tulse Hill → Crystal Palace → Norbury

Local Services

Network Diagram - see first page of Table 177

		SN	SN	SN	SN	SN	SN	SN		SN	SN	SN	SN	SN	SN	SN		SN	SN	SN	SN
																1 ◇					
		A			A								B			C					
London Bridge 4	⊖ d			22 25		22 41	22 44					22 55		23 11	23 14				23 25	23 44	
South Bermondsey	d			22 29		22 45						22 59		23 15					23 29		
Queens Rd Peckham	d			22 31		22 48						23 01		23 18					23 31		
Peckham Rye 4	d			22 34		22 50						23 04		23 20					23 34		
East Dulwich	d			22 37								23 07							23 37		
North Dulwich	d			22 39								23 09							23 39		
Luton 10	d																				
Luton Airport Parkway 7	✈ d																				
St Pancras International 15	⊖ d																				
City Thameslink 3	d																				
London Blackfriars 3	⊖ d																				
Elephant & Castle	⊖ d																				
Loughborough Jn	d																				
Herne Hill 4	d																				
Tulse Hill 3	d			22 42								23 12							23 42		
Streatham 4	d			22 46								23 16							23 46		
London Victoria 15	⊖ d	22 38	22 41		22 49			23 06		23 08	23 11		23 19			23 32		23 38			23 49
Battersea Park 4	d	22 42	22a45		22 53	23a02				23 12	23a15		23 23	23a32				23 42			23 53
Milton Keynes Central	d																				
Watford Junction	d																				
Harrow & Wealdstone	⊖ d																				
Wembley Central	⊖ d																				
Shepherd's Bush	⊖ d							22 45								22 45					
Kensington (Olympia)	⊖ d							22 48								22 48					
West Brompton	⊖ d							22 50								22 50					
Clapham Junction 10	d	22 45			22 56			23 12		23 15			23 26			23 38		23 45			23 56
Wandsworth Common	d	22 48			22 59					23 18			23 29					23 48			23 59
Balham 4	⊖ d	22 51			23 02			23 16		23 21			23 32					23 51			00 01
Streatham Hill	d	22 54								23 24								23 54			
West Norwood 4	d	22 57								23 27								23 57			
Gipsy Hill	d	23 00								23 30								23 59			
Crystal Palace 4	d	23 03								23 33								00 03			
Birkbeck	🚋 d																				
Beckenham Junction 4	🚋 a																				
Bromley South 4	a																				
Streatham Common 4	d			22 49	23 06							23 19	23 36						23 49		00 05
Norbury	d			22 51	23 08							23 21	23 38						23 51		00 08
Thornton Heath	d			22 54	23 11							23 24	23 41						23 54		00 11
Selhurst 4	d			22 57	23 14							23 27	23 44			23 48			23 57		00 13
Norwood Junction 2	a	23 07					23 07			23 37					23 37			00 07		00 09	
	d	23 07					23 09			23 37					23 39					00 10	
West Croydon 4	🚋 a	23 12			23 18					23 42			23 48								
East Croydon	🚋 a			23 00			23 12					23 32			23 42	23 52			00 01	00 13	00 16

For general notes see front of timetable
For details of catering facilities see
Directory of Train Operators

A To Sutton (Surrey) (Table 182)
B To Epsom (Table 182)
C To Brighton (Table 186)

East and West Croydon, London → Milton Keynes and Luton via Norbury → Crystal Palace → Tulse Hill

Local Services

Network Diagram - see first page of Table 177

Miles	Miles	Miles	Miles	Miles	Station		SN	SN	SN	SN	FC	SN	SN	SN	SN	SN	FC	SN	SN	SN	SN	SN	SN	SN	FC
							MX	MO																	
								1		1								1							
								A		B	C				D		C	A	E						
0	—	—	0	0	**East Croydon**	d		23p56	05 13	05 29			05 34		05 48	05 51		06 07		06 12					
—	0	—	—	—	**West Croydon** [4]	d								05 45					06 01		06 15				
1¼	—	—	—	1¼	Norwood Junction [2]	a			05 17				05 38	05 50		05 54				06 16	06 19				
—	—	—	—	—		d			05 17				05 38	05 50		05 55				06 17	06 19				
—	1	—	1	—	Selhurst [4]	d		00 01		05 32	05 36				05 52		05 56	06 10	06 06						
—	1¾	—	1¾	—	Thornton Heath	d				05 35	05 38				05 54		05 58		06 08						
—	3	—	3	—	Norbury	d				05 38	05 40				05 57		06 00		06 11						
—	4	—	4	—	Streatham Common [4]	d				05 40	05 43				05 59		06 03		06 13						
—	—	—	—	—	Bromley South [4]	d																			
—	—	0	—	—	Beckenham Junction [4]	d																			
—	—	1½	—	—	Birkbeck	d																			
2¾	—	3	—	2¾	**Crystal Palace** [4]	d	23p43						05 42			05 59									
3½	—	3¾	—	3½	Gipsy Hill	d	23p46						05 44			06 01									
4½	—	4¾	—	4½	West Norwood [4]	d	23p49						05 47			06 04									
5¾	—	6	—	—	Streatham Hill	d	23p52						05 51												
6¾	—	7	5¾	—	Balham [4] ⊖	d	23p55			05 44			05 54		06 03				06 17				06 27		
7½	—	7¾	6½	—	Wandsworth Common	d	23p57								06 05				06 19						
8¾	—	9	7¾	—	Clapham Junction [10]	d	00 01	00 11		05 49			05 59		06 09			06 18	06 23				06 31		
—	—	—	—	—	West Brompton ⊖	d												*06 45*					*06 45*		
—	—	—	—	—	Kensington (Olympia) ⊖	d												*06 48*					*06 48*		
—	—	—	—	—	Shepherd's Bush ⊖	d												*06 51*					*06 51*		
—	—	—	—	—	Wembley Central ⊖	d																			
—	—	—	—	—	Harrow & Wealdstone ⊖	d																			
—	—	—	—	—	Watford Junction	d																			
—	—	—	—	—	Milton Keynes Central [10]	a																			
10¼	—	10½	9¼	—	Battersea Park [4]	d	00 04			05 52			06 02		06 13				06 27			06 32			
11½	—	11¾	10½	—	**London Victoria** [15] ⊖	a	00 12	00 18		05 58			06 07		06 18			06 25	06 31			06 36	06 38		
—	4½	—	—	—	Streatham [4]	d					05 46	05 53					06 06							06 30	06 34
—	6	—	—	5	Tulse Hill [3]	d					05 50	05 57				06 07	06 10							06 34	06 38
—	—	—	—	—	Herne Hill [4]	a					05 53						06 13								06 42
—	—	—	—	—	Loughborough Jn	a											06 17								06 45
—	—	—	—	—	Elephant & Castle ⊖	a					06 00						06 22								06 49
—	—	—	—	—	London Blackfriars [3] ⊖	a					06 04						06 28								06 58
—	—	—	—	—	City Thameslink [3]	a					06 06						06 32								07 00
—	—	—	—	—	St Pancras International [15] ⊖	a					06 13						06 39								07 07
—	—	—	—	—	Luton Airport Parkway [7] ✈	a					06 59						07 25								07 46
—	—	—	—	—	**Luton** [10]	a					07 02						07 28								07 50
—	7¼	—	—	6¼	North Dulwich	d										06 10								06 37	
—	7¾	—	—	6¾	East Dulwich	d										06 12								06 39	
—	8½	—	—	7½	Peckham Rye [4]	d						06 02				06 15								06 42	
—	9¼	—	—	8¼	Queens Rd Peckham	d										06 17								06 44	
—	10¼	—	—	9¼	South Bermondsey	d										06 20								06 47	
—	12	—	—	11	**London Bridge** [4] ⊖	a			05 41			06 08		06 14		06 24				06 35	06 44			06 51	

Station		SN		SN	SN	SN	FC	SN	SN	SN	SN	SN	SN	SN	SN	SN	SN	SN	FC	SN	SN		SN	SN	SN
								G								H				J					
East Croydon	d	06 17			06 31					06 40						06 45					07 12				07 05
West Croydon [4]	d							06 29				06 45								06 59					
Norwood Junction [2]	a				06 35					06 44		06 49									07 16				
	d			06 23	06 35				06 42	06 45		06 50					06 53	07 02			07 17				
Selhurst [4]	d	06 20				06 30		06 33								06 48				07 04					07 09
Thornton Heath	d	06 22				06 32		06 35								06 50				07 06					07 11
Norbury	d	06 25				06 35		06 38								06 53				07 09					07 14
Streatham Common [4]	d	06 27				06 37		06 41								06 56				07 11					07 16
Bromley South [4]	d																								
Beckenham Junction [4]	d																								
Birkbeck	d																								
Crystal Palace [4]	d			06 27					06 46								06 57	07 06					07 15		
Gipsy Hill	d			06 29					06 48								06 59	07 08							
West Norwood [4]	d			06 32					06 51								07 02	07 11							
Streatham Hill	d			06 36													07 06								
Balham [4] ⊖	d	06 31		06 39				06 45						06 57		07 00	07 09			07 15					
Wandsworth Common	d	06 33		06 41				06 47								07 02	07 11			07 17					
Clapham Junction [10]	d	06 37		06 45				06 51						07 01		07 06	07 15			07 21					
West Brompton ⊖	d																								
Kensington (Olympia) ⊖	d																								
Shepherd's Bush ⊖	d																								
Wembley Central ⊖	d																								
Harrow & Wealdstone ⊖	d																								
Watford Junction	d																								
Milton Keynes Central [10]	a																								
Battersea Park [4]	d	06 41		06 48				06 54					07 02			07 09	07 18			07 25					
London Victoria [15] ⊖	a	06 45		06 53				07 01					07 08	07 10		07 16	07 25			07 31					
Streatham [4]	d					06 41	06 50								07 06				07 16						07 20
Tulse Hill [3]	d					06 46	06 56		06b58						07 09			07 14	07 20						07 24
Herne Hill [4]	a						07 00												07 24						
Loughborough Jn	a						07 03												07 27						
Elephant & Castle ⊖	a						07 07												07 31						
London Blackfriars [3] ⊖	a						07 11												07 35						
City Thameslink [3]	a						07 14												07 38						
St Pancras International [15] ⊖	a						07 21												07 47						
Luton Airport Parkway [7] ✈	a																		08 23						
Luton [10]	a																		08 26						
North Dulwich	d					06 49			07 01						07 12			07 17							07 27
East Dulwich	d					06 51			07 03						07 14			07 19							07 29
Peckham Rye [4]	d					06 53			07 05		06 56				07 17			07 22						07 26	07 31
Queens Rd Peckham	d					06 56			07 08		06 59							07 24						07 29	07 34
South Bermondsey	d					06 58			07 10		07 01							07 27					06 52	07 31	07 36
London Bridge [4] ⊖	a				06 56	07 05			07 18	07 02	07 08	07 16			07 25			07 33			07 33		07 36	07 38	07 43

For general notes see front of timetable
For details of catering facilities see Directory of Train Operators

A From Horsham (Table 186)
B From Brighton (Table 186)
C To Bedford (Table 52)
D From Redhill (Table 186)
E From Epsom (Table 182)
G From Sutton (Surrey) (Table 182)
H From Sanderstead (Table 184)
J From Epsom Downs (Table 182)
b Arr. 0654

East and West Croydon, London → Milton Keynes and Luton via Norbury → Crystal Palace → Tulse Hill

Local Services

Network Diagram - see first page of Table 177

		SN	SN	SN	SN	SN	SN	SN	SN	SN	SN	FC	SN	SN	SN	SN	SN	SN		SN	SN	SN	SN	SN	SN
													A												
East Croydon	d				07 17				07 36											07 47					
West Croydon 4	d	07 16				07 19	07 28						07 30		07 43									07 46	07 56
Norwood Junction 2	a	07 21				07 23	07 32		07 40						07 48									07 50	08 00
	d	07 21				07 24	07 33		07 41						07 48									07 51	08 01
Selhurst 4	d				07 20								07 35	07 40						07 50			07 53		
Thornton Heath	d				07 22								07 37	07 42						07 52			07 55		
Norbury	d				07 25								07 40	07 45						07 55			07 58		
Streatham Common 4	d				07 27								07 42	07 47						07 58			08 01		
Bromley South 4	d																*07 16*								
Beckenham Junction 4	d																07 36								
Birkbeck	d																07 39								
Crystal Palace 4	d					07 28											07 43				07 51	07 54		07 55	
Gipsy Hill	d					07 30											07 45				07 53			07 57	
West Norwood 4	d					07 33											07 48				07 56			08 00	
Streatham Hill	d					07 37											07 52							08 04	
Balham 4 ⊖	d			07 29	07 31	07 40		07 42					07 46	07 51			07 55	08 00		08 02			08 05	08 09	
Wandsworth Common	d				07 33	07 42							07 48				07 57			08 04			08 07	08 11	
Clapham Junction 10	d			07 34	07 37	07 46		07 49					07 52	07 56			08 01	08 04		08 13			08 11	08 15	
West Brompton ⊖	d			*07 46*																08 21					
Kensington (Olympia) ⊖	d			*07 50*																08 25					
Shepherd's Bush ⊖	d			*07 53*																08a27					
Wembley Central ⊖	d																								
Harrow & Wealdstone ⊖	d																								
Watford Junction	d																								
Milton Keynes Central 10	a																								
Battersea Park 4	d		07 32		07 41	07 49							07 56			08 02	08 04						08 14	08 19	
London Victoria 15 ⊖	a		07 38	07 43	07 47	07 56		07 58					08 02	08 05		08 08	08 11	08 13					08 21	08 27	
Streatham 4	d									07 42		07 52									08 00				
Tulse Hill 3	d									07 46		07 56													
Herne Hill 4	a											08 00													
Loughborough Jn	a											08 04													
Elephant & Castle ⊖	a											08 08													
London Blackfriars 3 ⊖	a											08 14													
City Thameslink 3	a											08 16													
St Pancras International 15 ⊖	a											08 23													
Luton Airport Parkway 7 ✈	a											09 02													
Luton 10	a											09 06													
North Dulwich	d									07 49											08 03				
East Dulwich	d									07 51											08 05				
Peckham Rye 4	d									07 53	07 56										08 08				
Queens Rd Peckham	d										07 59										08 10				
South Bermondsey	d										08 01										08 13				
London Bridge 4 ⊖	a	07 48					07 59		08 01	08 02	08 08				08 08						08 21	08 16			08 27

		SN	SN	FC	FC	SN	SN	SN	SN	SN	SN	SN	SN	SN	SN		SN	SN	SN	FC 1	SN	SN	SN	SN	SN
								B	A	C										D			C		
East Croydon	d	07 57				08 12											08 09	08 18		08 28					08 34
West Croydon 4	d								08 01	08 07	08 16										08 19	08 23		08 28	
Norwood Junction 2	a	08 01				08 16					08 20										08 24	08 28		08 32	08 39
	d	08 01				08 17					08 20										08 25	08 28		08 33	08 40
Selhurst 4	d								08 05	08 11							08 16	08 21							
Thornton Heath	d								08 07	08 13							08 18	08 23							
Norbury	d								08 10	08 16							08 21	08 26							
Streatham Common 4	d								08 12	08 19							08 23	08 28							
Bromley South 4	d												*07 37*												
Beckenham Junction 4	d												08 05												
Birkbeck	d												08 08												
Crystal Palace 4	d												08 12	08 16	08 23						08 29				
Gipsy Hill	d												08 14								08 31				
West Norwood 4	d												08 17								08 34				
Streatham Hill	d												08 21						08 32		08 38				
Balham 4 ⊖	d							08 14	08 17	08 23			08 25					08 35			08 41		08 44		
Wandsworth Common	d								08 19				08 27					08 37			08 43		08 46		
Clapham Junction 10	d							08 19	08 23	08 27			08 31					08 41			08 47		08 50		
West Brompton ⊖	d												*08 46*					*08 55*							
Kensington (Olympia) ⊖	d												*08 50*					*08 58*							
Shepherd's Bush ⊖	d												*08 53*					*09 01*							
Wembley Central ⊖	d																								
Harrow & Wealdstone ⊖	d																								
Watford Junction	d																								
Milton Keynes Central 10	a																								
Battersea Park 4	d							08 22	08 26			08 32	08 35					08 44			08 50				
London Victoria 15 ⊖	a							08 29	08 33	08 37		08 39	08 41					08 51			08 57		09 01		
Streatham 4	d		08 05	08 10	08 22												08 26								
Tulse Hill 3	d		08 09	08 14	08 26												08 30		08 36	08 39					
Herne Hill 4	a			08 19	08 30															08 43					
Loughborough Jn	a			08 25	08 34																				
Elephant & Castle ⊖	a			08 31	08 39															08 54					
London Blackfriars 3 ⊖	a			08 38	08 46															08 56					
City Thameslink 3	a			08 40	08 49															09 03					
St Pancras International 15 ⊖	a			08 47	08 56															09 37					
Luton Airport Parkway 7 ✈	a			09 30																09 40					
Luton 10	a			09 34																					
North Dulwich	d		08 12														08 33		08 39						
East Dulwich	d		08 14														08 35		08 41						
Peckham Rye 4	d		08 16				08 26										08 38		08 43						
Queens Rd Peckham	d		08 19				08 29										08 40		08 46						
South Bermondsey	d		08 21				08 31										08 43		08 48						
London Bridge 4 ⊖	a	08 16	08 30			08 31	08 38				08 42			08 38	08 46		08 49		08 57			08 48		09 00	08 57

For general notes see front of timetable
For details of catering facilities see
Directory of Train Operators

A From Epsom Downs (Table 182)
B From Epsom (Table 182)
C From Sutton (Surrey) (Table 182)
D From Brighton (Table 52)

East and West Croydon, London → Milton Keynes and Luton via Norbury → Crystal Palace → Tulse Hill

Local Services

Network Diagram - see first page of Table 177

		SN	FC	SN	FC	SN	SN	SN	SN	SN	SN	SN		SN	SN	SN	SN	SN	FC	SN	SN	SN	SN	SN	SN
		A	1 B				C														D				
East Croydon	d		08 38	08 45										08 50									09 02	09 05	
West Croydon 4	d						08 32			08 44					08 50	08 59					08 57				
Norwood Junction 2	a			08 49						08 49					08 54	09 03								09 09	
	d			08 49						08 49					08 55	09 04								09 09	
Selhurst 4	d						08 36							08 53							09 01		09 05		
Thornton Heath	d						08 38							08 55							09 03		09 07		
Norbury	d						08 41							08 58							09 06		09 10		
Streatham Common 4	d						08 43							09 01							09 09		09 13		
Bromley South 4	d							*08 21*																	
Beckenham Junction 4	d							08 32																	
Birkbeck	d							08 35																	
Crystal Palace 4	d	08 36						08 39	08 48						08 59		09 03			09 14					
Gipsy Hill	d	08 38						08 41							09 01		09 05								
West Norwood 4	d	08 42						08 44							09 04		09 08								
Streatham Hill	d							08 48							09 08										
Balham 4	d						08 47	08 51				09 04		09 06	09 11						09 13	09 23			
Wandsworth Common	d						08 49	08 53						09 08	09 13						09 15				
Clapham Junction 10	d						08 53	08 57				09 08		09 12	09 17						09 20	09 28			
West Brompton	d																				*09 31*				
Kensington (Olympia)	d																				*09 34*				
Shepherd's Bush	d																				*09 37*				
Wembley Central	d																								
Harrow & Wealdstone	d																								
Watford Junction	d																								
Milton Keynes Central 10	a																								
Battersea Park 4	d						08 57				09 02			09 16	09 20						09 23				
London Victoria 15	a						09 03	09 06			09 08	09 18		09 22	09 27						09 30	09 37			
Streatham 4	d				08 52													09 10	09 15				09 18		
Tulse Hill 3	d	08b51	08 54		08 58												09 11	09 15	09 19				09 22		
Herne Hill 4	a		08 57		09 02														09 22						
Loughborough Jn	a				09 05														09 26						
Elephant & Castle	a				09 09														09 30						
London Blackfriars 3	a		09 08		09 14														09 34						
City Thameslink 3	a		09 10		09 16														09 36						
St Pancras International 15	a		09 17		09 23														09 43						
Luton Airport Parkway 7	a		09 52																10 29						
Luton 10	a		09 56																10 34						
North Dulwich	d	08 54															09 14	09 18					09 25		
East Dulwich	d	08 56															09 16	09 20					09 27		
Peckham Rye 4	d	09 01				08 56											09 19	09 23					09 30		09 26
Queens Rd Peckham	d	09 03				08 59											09 21	09 25					09 33		09 29
South Bermondsey	d	09 06				09 01											09 24	09 28					09 35		09 31
London Bridge 4	a	09 12		09 05		09 08			09 12	09 18						09 30	09 30	09 34		09 38			09 43	09 24	09 38

		SN	SN	SN	SN	SN	FC	SN	SN		SN	SN	SN	SN	SN	SN	SN	SN	FC	SN	SN	SN	SN	SN	SN
					1			E					1			C				D					E
East Croydon	d							09 17			09 20	09 31	09 37												09 47
West Croydon 4	d	09 15							09 18							09 27		09 31		09 35	09 46				
Norwood Junction 2	a	09 19							09 23		09 24	09 35	09 41								09 50				
	d	09 20							09 23		09 25	09 35	09 42								09 51				
Selhurst 4	d							09 21								09 31		09 35		09 39					09 50
Thornton Heath	d							09 23								09 33		09 37		09 41					09 52
Norbury	d							09 26								09 36		09 40		09 44					09 55
Streatham Common 4	d							09 28								09 39		09 43		09 47					09 58
Bromley South 4	d					*09 03*																			
Beckenham Junction 4	d					09 16																			
Birkbeck	d					09 19																			
Crystal Palace 4	d			09 13		09 23			09 27					09 33									09 43	09 44	
Gipsy Hill	d			09 15		09 25			09 30					09 35									09 46		
West Norwood 4	d			09 18		09 28			09 33					09 39									09 49		
Streatham Hill	d			09 22					09 36														09 52		
Balham 4	d			09 27	09 30			09 32	09 41							09 43	09 49			09 52			09 56		10 02
Wandsworth Common	d			09 29	09 32			09 34	09 43							09 46				09 54			09 58		10 04
Clapham Junction 10	d			09 33	09 38			09 38	09 47							09 50	09 54			09 58			10 02		10 08
West Brompton	d				09 47																				
Kensington (Olympia)	d				09 50																				
Shepherd's Bush	d				09 53																				
Wembley Central	d																								
Harrow & Wealdstone	d				10 13																				
Watford Junction	d				10 20																				
Milton Keynes Central 10	a				11 01																				
Battersea Park 4	d		09 33					09 42	09 50							09 53						10 03	10 05		10 11
London Victoria 15	a		09 39	09 42				09 48	09 58							10 00	10 01			10 05		10 07	10 11		10 16
Streatham 4	d						09 34											09 46	09 53						
Tulse Hill 3	d					09 33	09 38							09 42				09c54	09 57						
Herne Hill 4	a						09 42												10 01						
Loughborough Jn	a						09 45												10 04						
Elephant & Castle	a						09 49												10 09						
London Blackfriars 3	a						09 58												10 14						
City Thameslink 3	a						10 00												10 16						
St Pancras International 15	a						10 07												10 23						
Luton Airport Parkway 7	a						10 56																		
Luton 10	a						11 00																		
North Dulwich	d					09 36								09 45				09 57							
East Dulwich	d					09 38								09 47				09 59							
Peckham Rye 4	d					09 40								09 49	09 56			10 01							
Queens Rd Peckham	d					09 43								09 52	09 59			10 04							
South Bermondsey	d					09 45								09 54	10 01			10 06							
London Bridge 4	a	09 46				09 52					09 42	09 59	09 56	09 59	10 06			10 11			10 16			10 08	

For general notes see front of timetable
For details of catering facilities see Directory of Train Operators

- **A** From London Bridge (Table 178)
- **B** From Brighton (Table 52)
- **C** From Wimbledon (Table 52)
- **D** From Epsom Downs (Table 182)
- **E** From Caterham (Table 181)
- **b** Arr. 0846
- **c** Arr. 0950

East and West Croydon, London → Milton Keynes and Luton via Norbury → Crystal Palace → Tulse Hill

Local Services

Network Diagram - see first page of Table 177

Station		SN	SN 1	SN	SN	FC		SN	SN A	SN	SN	FC	SN B	SN	SN 1	SN	SN	SN	SN C	SN	SN 1	SN	FC	SN	SN
East Croydon	d		09 55	10 00											10 10				10 17		10 25			10 30	
West Croydon 4	d	09 49							09 56		10 01		10 05	10 15						10 18					
Norwood Junction 2	a	09 53	09 59	10 04										10 19						10 23	10 29			10 34	
	d	09 53	09 59	10 05										10 20						10 23	10 29			10 35	
Selhurst 4	d								10 01		10 05		10 09		10 14				10 20						
Thornton Heath	d								10 03		10 07		10 11		10 16				10 22						
Norbury	d								10 06		10 10		10 14		10 19				10 25						
Streatham Common 4	d								10 08		10 13		10 17		10 22				10 28						
Bromley South 4	d				09 33																	10 03			
Beckenham Junction 4	d				09 53																	10 23			
Birkbeck	d				09 56																	10 26			
Crystal Palace 4	d	09 57			10 00												10 14	10 15		10 27		10 30			
Gipsy Hill	d	10 00			10 03												10 16			10 30		10 33			
West Norwood 4	d	10 03			10 06												10 19			10 33		10 36			
Streatham Hill	d	10 06															10 23			10 36					
Balham 4	⊖ d	10 09							10 12	10 18			10 21		10 29		10 26		10 32	10 39					
Wandsworth Common	d	10 11							10 14				10 23		10 31		10 28		10 34						
Clapham Junction 10	d	10 16							10 18	10 22			10 27		10b38		10 32		10 38	10 45					
West Brompton	⊖ d														10 47		10 47								
Kensington (Olympia)	⊖ d														10 50		10 50								
Shepherd's Bush	⊖ d														10 53		10 53								
Wembley Central	⊖ d																								
Harrow & Wealdstone	⊖ d														11 12										
Watford Junction	d														11 19										
Milton Keynes Central 10	a														12 01										
Battersea Park 4	d	10 19						10 15	10 22							10 32	10 35		10 41	10 48					
London Victoria 15	⊖ a	10 24							10 26	10 29			10 34			10 36	10 40		10 46	10 53					
Streatham 4	d					10 06					10 16	10 23											10 36		
Tulse Hill 3	d				10 09	10 12					10c24	10 27										10 39	10 42		
Herne Hill 4	a					10 15						10 30											10 45		
Loughborough Jn	a					10 19						10 34											10 49		
Elephant & Castle	⊖ a					10 23						10 38											10 53		
London Blackfriars 3	⊖ a					10 28						10 44											10 57		
City Thameslink 3	a					10 30						10 46											11 00		
St Pancras International 15	⊖ a					10 37						10 53											11 07		
Luton Airport Parkway 7	✈ a					11 26																	11 56		
Luton 10	a					11 30																	12 00		
North Dulwich	d				10 12						10 27											10 42			
East Dulwich	d				10 14						10 29											10 44			
Peckham Rye 4	d				10 17			10 26			10 31											10 47			10 56
Queens Rd Peckham	d				10 19			10 29			10 34											10 49			10 59
South Bermondsey	d				10 22			10 31			10 36											10 52			11 01
London Bridge 4	⊖ a		10 12	10 26	10 27			10 36			10 41			10 44				10 35			10 42	10 56		10 57	11 06

Station		SN		SN D	SN	FC	SN B	SN	SN	SN	SN	SN C	SN	SN 1	SN	FC	SN	SN	SN	SN A	SN	FC	SN B	SN	SN
East Croydon	d											10 47		10 55			11 00								
West Croydon 4	d			10 26	10 31		10 35	10 45					10 48							10 56	11 01		11 05		
Norwood Junction 2	a							10 49					10 53	10 59			11 04								
	d							10 50					10 53	10 59			11 05								
Selhurst 4	d			10 31	10 35		10 39					10 50								11 01	11 05		11 09		
Thornton Heath	d			10 33	10 37		10 41					10 52								11 03	11 07		11 11		
Norbury	d			10 36	10 40		10 44					10 55								11 06	11 10		11 14		
Streatham Common 4	d			10 38	10 43		10 47					10 58								11 08	11 13		11 17		
Bromley South 4	d														10 33										
Beckenham Junction 4	d														10 53										
Birkbeck	d														10 56										
Crystal Palace 4	d									10 43	10 45		10 57		11 00									11 13	11 14
Gipsy Hill	d									10 46			11 00		11 03									11 16	
West Norwood 4	d									10 49			11 03		11 06									11 19	
Streatham Hill	d									10 52			11 06											11 22	
Balham 4	⊖ d	10 48		10 42			10 51			10 55		11 02	11 09						11 18	11 12			11 21	11 25	
Wandsworth Common	d			10 44			10 53			10 57		11 04								11 14			11 23	11 27	
Clapham Junction 10	d	10 52		10 48			10 57			11 01		11 08	11 15						11 22	11 18			11 27	11 31	
West Brompton	⊖ d																								
Kensington (Olympia)	⊖ d																								
Shepherd's Bush	⊖ d																								
Wembley Central	⊖ d																								
Harrow & Wealdstone	⊖ d																								
Watford Junction	d																								
Milton Keynes Central 10	a																								
Battersea Park 4	d			10 52					11 02	11 05		11 11	11 18							11 22				11 35	
London Victoria 15	⊖ a	10 59		10 56			11 04		11 06	11 09		11 16	11 23						11 29	11 26			11 34	11 40	
Streatham 4	d				10 46	10 53										11 06					11 16	11 23			
Tulse Hill 3	d				10e54	10 57									11 09	11 12					11f24	11 27			
Herne Hill 4	a					11 00										11 15						11 30			
Loughborough Jn	a					11 04										11 19						11 34			
Elephant & Castle	⊖ a					11 08										11 23						11 38			
London Blackfriars 3	⊖ a					11 14										11 27						11 44			
City Thameslink 3	a					11 16										11 30						11 46			
St Pancras International 15	⊖ a					11 23										11 37						11 53			
Luton Airport Parkway 7	✈ a															12 26									
Luton 10	a															12 30									
North Dulwich	d				10 57										11 12						11 27				
East Dulwich	d				10 59										11 14						11 29				
Peckham Rye 4	d				11 01										11 17			11 26			11 31				
Queens Rd Peckham	d				11 04										11 19			11 29			11 34				
South Bermondsey	d				11 06										11 22			11 31			11 36				
London Bridge 4	⊖ a				11 11			11 14			11 06			11 12	11 26		11 26	11 36			11 41				11 35

For general notes see front of timetable
For details of catering facilities see Directory of Train Operators

A From Epsom Downs (Table 182)
B From Sutton (Surrey) (Table 182)
C From Caterham (Table 181)
D From Epsom (Table 182)

b Arr. 1035
c Arr. 1019
e Arr. 1049
f Arr. 1120

East and West Croydon, London → Milton Keynes and Luton via Norbury → Crystal Palace → Tulse Hill

Local Services

Network Diagram - see first page of Table 177

Station		SN	SN	SN	SN	SN	SN	SN	FC	SN	SN			SN	SN	SN	FC	SN	SN	SN	SN	SN	SN	SN
			1				1																	
					A									B				C						A
East Croydon	d		11 10		11 17		11 25			11 30		and at the same minutes past each hour until												15 47
West Croydon 4	d	11 15				11 18								15 26		15 31		15 35	15 45					
Norwood Junction 2	a	11 19				11 23	11 29			11 34									15 49					
	d	11 20				11 23	11 29			11 35									15 50					
Selhurst 4	d		11 16		11 20									15 31		15 35		15 39						15 50
Thornton Heath	d		11 18		11 22									15 33		15 37		15 41						15 52
Norbury	d		11 21		11 25									15 36		15 40		15 44						15 55
Streatham Common 4	d		11 24		11 28									15 38		15 43		15 47						15 58
Bromley South 4	d							11 03																
Beckenham Junction 4	d							11 23																
Birkbeck	d							11 26																
Crystal Palace 4	d					11 27		11 30													15 43	15 45		
Gipsy Hill	d					11 30		11 33													15 46			
West Norwood 4	d					11 33		11 36													15 49			
Streatham Hill	d					11 36															15 52		15 49	
Balham 4	⊖ d		11 28		11 32	11 39								15 42	15 48			15 51			15 55			16 02
Wandsworth Common	d		11 30		11 34									15 44				15 53			15 57			16 04
Clapham Junction 10	d		11b38		11 38	11 44								15 48	15 52			15 57			16 01			16 08
West Brompton	⊖ d		11 47																					
Kensington (Olympia)	⊖ d		11 50																					
Shepherd's Bush	⊖ d		11 53																					
Wembley Central	⊖ d																							
Harrow & Wealdstone	⊖ d		12 12																					
Watford Junction	d		12 19																					
Milton Keynes Central 10	a		13 01																					
Battersea Park 4	d			11 32	11 41	11 48								15 52						16 02	16 05			16 11
London Victoria 15	⊖ a			11 36	11 46	11 53								15 56	15 59			16 04		16 06	16 10			16 16
Streatham 4	d								11 36							15 46	15 53							
Tulse Hill 3	d							11 39	11 42							15 50	15 57						16 00	
Herne Hill 4	a								11 45								16 00							
Loughborough Jn	a								11 49								16 04							
Elephant & Castle	⊖ a								11 53								16 08							
London Blackfriars 3	⊖ a								11 57								16 14							
City Thameslink 3	a								12 00								16 16							
St Pancras International 15	⊖ a								12 07								16 23							
Luton Airport Parkway 7	a								12 56															
Luton 10	a								13 00															
North Dulwich	d							11 42								15 53							16 03	
East Dulwich	d							11 44								15 55							16 05	
Peckham Rye 4	d							11 47			11 56					16 00							16 07	
Queens Rd Peckham	d							11 49			11 59					16 02							16 10	
South Bermondsey	d							11 52			12 01					16 05							16 12	
London Bridge 4	⊖ a	11 44					11 42	11 56		11 56	12 06					16 10			16 14			16 07	16 17	

Station		SN	SN	SN	FC	SN	SN	SN	SN	SN		SN	FC	SN	SN	FC	SN	SN	SN	SN	SN	SN	SN	SN	FC
			1				1									1	1						1		
									D					C		E					A				
East Croydon	d		15 55			16 00	16 07									16 17	16 10				16 17		16 25		
West Croydon 4	d	15 48							15 56			16 01		16 05	16 15							16 18			
Norwood Junction 2	a	15 53	15 59			16 04	16 11								16 19							16 23	16 29		
	d	15 53	15 59			16 05	16 12								16 21							16 23	16 29		
Selhurst 4	d								16 01			16 05		16 09			16 13				16 20				
Thornton Heath	d								16 03			16 07		16 11			16 16				16 22				
Norbury	d								16 06			16 10		16 14			16 19				16 25				
Streatham Common 4	d								16 08			16 13		16 17			16 21				16 28				
Bromley South 4	d			15 33																				16 03	
Beckenham Junction 4	d			15 53																				16 23	
Birkbeck	d			15 56																				16 26	
Crystal Palace 4	d	15 57		16 00															16 13	16 15		16 27		16 30	
Gipsy Hill	d	16 00		16 03															16 16			16 30		16 33	
West Norwood 4	d	16 03		16 06															16 19			16 33		16 36	
Streatham Hill	d	16 06																	16 22			16 36			
Balham 4	⊖ d	16 09							16 12	16 18				16 21			16 28		16 25		16 32	16 39			
Wandsworth Common	d								16 14					16 23			16 30		16 27		16 34	16 41			
Clapham Junction 10	d	16 15							16 18	16 22				16 27			16c38		16 31		16 38	16 45			
West Brompton	⊖ d																16 47		16 46						
Kensington (Olympia)	⊖ d																16 50		16 50						
Shepherd's Bush	⊖ d																16 53		16 53						
Wembley Central	⊖ d																								
Harrow & Wealdstone	⊖ d																17 13								
Watford Junction	d																17 21								
Milton Keynes Central 10	a																17 58								
Battersea Park 4	d	16 18							16 22									16 32	16 35		16 41	16 49			
London Victoria 15	⊖ a	16 23							16 26	16 29				16 34				16 38	16 40		16 46	16 55			
Streatham 4	d				16 06							16 16	16 23												16 38
Tulse Hill 3	d			16 09	16 12							16e24	16 27			16 34								16 39	16 42
Herne Hill 4	a				16 15								16 30			16 37									16 46
Loughborough Jn	a				16 19								16 34												16 49
Elephant & Castle	⊖ a				16 23								16 39			16 44									16 53
London Blackfriars 3	⊖ a				16 29								16 44			16 48									16 59
City Thameslink 3	a				16 32								16 46			16 52									17 02
St Pancras International 15	⊖ a				16 39								16 53			17 01									17 09
Luton Airport Parkway 7	a																								17 50
Luton 10	a															17 34									17 54
North Dulwich	d			16 12								16 27												16 42	
East Dulwich	d			16 14								16 29												16 44	
Peckham Rye 4	d			16 17				16 26				16 31												16 47	
Queens Rd Peckham	d			16 19				16 29				16 34												16 49	
South Bermondsey	d			16 22				16 31				16 36												16 52	
London Bridge 4	⊖ a		16 12	16 27		16 29	16 25	16 38				16 41			16 45					16 36			16 47	16 56	

For general notes see front of timetable
For details of catering facilities see Directory of Train Operators

- **A** From Caterham (Table 181)
- **B** From Epsom (Table 182)
- **C** From Sutton (Surrey) (Table 182)
- **D** From Epsom Downs (Table 182)
- **E** From Brighton (Table 52)
- **b** Arr. 1133
- **c** Arr. 1634
- **e** Arr. 1619

East and West Croydon, London → Milton Keynes and Luton via Norbury → Crystal Palace → Tulse Hill

Local Services

Network Diagram - see first page of Table 177

		SN	SN 1	SN	SN A	SN	SN		FC	SN B	SN	SN	SN	SN	SN C	SN	SN 1	SN	FC	SN	SN 1	SN	SN D	SN	SN B
East Croydon	d	16 30	16 40												16 47		16 55			17 00	17 07				
West Croydon 4	d				16 26		16 31			16 35	16 45					16 48							16 56		17 05
Norwood Junction 2	a	16 34	16 44								16 49					16 52	16 59			17 04	17 11				
	d	16 35	16 45								16 50					16 53	16 59			17 05	17 12				
Selhurst 4	d				16 31		16 35			16 39					16 50								17 01		17 09
Thornton Heath	d				16 33		16 37			16 41					16 52								17 03		17 11
Norbury	d				16 36		16 40			16 44					16 55								17 06		17 14
Streatham Common 4	d				16 38		16 43			16 47					16 58								17 08		17 17
Bromley South 4	d																	16 19							
Beckenham Junction 4	d																	16 53							
Birkbeck	d																	16 56							
Crystal Palace 4	d												16 43	16 45		16 57		17 00							
Gipsy Hill	d												16 46			16 59		17 02							
West Norwood 4	d												16 49			17 02		17 05							
Streatham Hill	d												16 52			17 06									
Balham 4 ⊖	d				16 42	16 48				16 51			16 55		17 02	17 09							17 12	17 18	17 21
Wandsworth Common	d				16 44					16 53			16 57		17 04	17 11							17 14		17 23
Clapham Junction 10	d				16 48	16 52				16 57			17 01		17 08	17 15							17 18	17 23	17 27
West Brompton ⊖	d																						17 29		
Kensington (Olympia) ⊖	d																						17 32		
Shepherd's Bush ⊖	d																						17 35		
Wembley Central ⊖	d																								
Harrow & Wealdstone ⊖	d																								
Watford Junction	d																								
Milton Keynes Central 10	a																								
Battersea Park 4	d				16 52							17 02	17 05		17 11	17 18							17 22		
London Victoria 15 ⊖	a				16 57	16 59				17 04		17 08	17 10		17 16	17 23							17 26	17 30	17 34
Streatham 4	d						16 46		16 53										17 06						
Tulse Hill 3	d						16b53		16 57									17 09	17c14						
Herne Hill 4	a								17 00										17 18						
Loughborough Jn	a																		17 21						
Elephant & Castle ⊖	a								17 07										17 25						
London Blackfriars 3 ⊖	a								17 12										17 29						
City Thameslink 3	a								17 14										17 34						
St Pancras International 15 ⊖	a								17 21										17 41						
Luton Airport Parkway 7 ✈	a								17 55										18 27						
Luton 10	a								17 58										18 32						
North Dulwich	d						16 56											17 12							
East Dulwich	d						16 58											17 14							
Peckham Rye 4	d			16 56			17 00											17 16				17 26			
Queens Rd Peckham	d			16 59			17 03											17 19				17 29			
South Bermondsey	d			17 01			17 05											17 21				17 31			
London Bridge 4 ⊖	a	16 56	17 00	17 08			17 10				17 14			17 10			17 12	17 26		17 28	17 26	17 38			

		SN 1	SN	SN		SN	SN	SN	FC	SN	SN E	SN	SN	SN 1	SN	FC	SN	SN 1	SN	SN D	SN	SN	FC		SN
East Croydon	d	17 10									17 17		17 21	17 25			17 32	17 41							
West Croydon 4	d		17 14							17 09		17 18								17 26		17 38			17 47
Norwood Junction 2	a		17 18									17 22	17 25	17 29			17 36	17 45							17 52
	d		17 19									17 23	17 25	17 29	17 34		17 37	17 45							17 52
Selhurst 4	d	17 13								17 16	17 20									17 31		17 43			
Thornton Heath	d	17 16								17 18	17 22									17 33		17 45			
Norbury	d	17 19								17 21	17 25									17 36		17 48			
Streatham Common 4	d	17 21								17 24	17 28									17 38		17 51			
Bromley South 4	d							16 47																	
Beckenham Junction 4	d							17 11																	
Birkbeck	d							17 14																	
Crystal Palace 4	d					17 13	17 18	17 18				17 27			17 38										
Gipsy Hill	d					17 16		17 20				17 29			17 40										
West Norwood 4	d					17 19		17 23				17 32			17 43										
Streatham Hill	d					17 22						17 36													
Balham 4 ⊖	d	17 28				17 25					17 32	17 39								17 42	17 47				
Wandsworth Common	d	17 30				17 27					17 34	17 41								17 44					
Clapham Junction 10	d	17e38				17 31					17 38	17 45								17 49	17 52				
West Brompton ⊖	d	17 47				17 46																			
Kensington (Olympia) ⊖	d	17 50				17 50																			
Shepherd's Bush ⊖	d	17 53				17 53																			
Wembley Central ⊖	d																								
Harrow & Wealdstone ⊖	d	18 13																							
Watford Junction	d	18 20																							
Milton Keynes Central 10	a	18 58																							
Battersea Park 4	d			17 32		17 35					17 41	17 48								17 52					
London Victoria 15 ⊖	a			17 38		17 42					17 48	17 55								17 57	17 59				
Streatham 4	d								17 23	17 30						17 42						17 54	17 57		
Tulse Hill 3	d							17 27	17f30	17 34					17 46	17 48						17 58	18 02		
Herne Hill 4	a								17 33							17 51							18 05		
Loughborough Jn	a								17 39							17 57							18 09		
Elephant & Castle ⊖	a								17 43							18 01							18 13		
London Blackfriars 3 ⊖	a								17 48							18 05							18 18		
City Thameslink 3	a								17 50							18 08							18 20		
St Pancras International 15 ⊖	a								17 57							18 15							18 27		
Luton Airport Parkway 7 ✈	a															18 50									
Luton 10	a															18 53									
North Dulwich	d							17 30		17 37					17 49							18 01			
East Dulwich	d							17 32		17 39					17 51							18 03			
Peckham Rye 4	d							17 34		17 41					17 54				17 57			18 05			
Queens Rd Peckham	d							17 37		17 44					17 56				17 59			18 08			
South Bermondsey	d							17 39		17 46					17 59				18 02			18 10			
London Bridge 4 ⊖	a		17 44				17 40	17 44		17 54			17 38	17 42	18 03		17 58	18 00	18 08			18 15			18 20

For general notes see front of timetable
For details of catering facilities see Directory of Train Operators

- **A** From Epsom (Table 182)
- **B** From Sutton (Surrey) (Table 182)
- **C** From Caterham (Table 181)
- **D** From Epsom Downs (Table 182)
- **E** From Caterham (Table 181) and from Tattenham Corner (Table 181)
- **b** Arr. 1649
- **c** Arr. 1710
- **e** Arr. 1734
- **f** Arr. 1727

East and West Croydon, London → Milton Keynes and Luton via Norbury → Crystal Palace → Tulse Hill

Local Services

Network Diagram - see first page of Table 177

		SN	SN	SN	SN	FC	SN	SN	SN	SN	SN	FC	SN	SN	SN	SN	SN	SN	SN		SN	SN	FC	SN	SN
							A								B		1						1 C		
East Croydon	d						17 47		17 55				18 11				18 08						18 17		
West Croydon 4	d							17 50							17 56									18 09	18 15
Norwood Junction 2	a							17 54	17 59				18 15												18 19
	d							17 55	17 59	18 04			18 15												18 20
Selhurst 4	d						17 50								18 01		18 11							18 14	
Thornton Heath	d						17 52								18 03		18 14							18 17	
Norbury	d						17 55								18 06		18 17							18 20	
Streatham Common 4	d						17 58								18 08		18 19							18 22	
Bromley South 4	d				17 17																17 47				
Beckenham Junction 4	d				17 49																18 11				
Birkbeck	d				17 52																18 14				
Crystal Palace 4	d		17 44	17 48	17 56			17 59											18 15		18 18	18 20			
Gipsy Hill	d		17 46		17 58			18 01											18 17		18 20				
West Norwood 4	d		17 49		18 01			18 04											18 20		18 23				
Streatham Hill	d		17 53					18 08											18 24						
Balham 4	⊖ d		17 56				18 02	18 11							18 13	18 18	18 23		18 29						
Wandsworth Common	d		17 58				18 04	18 13							18 16		18 25		18 31						
Clapham Junction 10	d		18 02				18 08	18 17							18 20	18 23	18b38		18 35						
West Brompton	⊖ d																18 47								
Kensington (Olympia)	⊖ d																18 50								
Shepherd's Bush	⊖ d																18 53								
Wembley Central	⊖ d																								
Harrow & Wealdstone	⊖ d																19 13								
Watford Junction	d																19 21								
Milton Keynes Central 10	a																20 06								
Battersea Park 4	d	18 02	18 06				18 11	18 20							18 23			18 32	18 39						
London Victoria 15	⊖ a	18 08	18 12				18 16	18 25							18 28	18 31		18 39	18 45						
Streatham 4	d					18 06					18 13	18 23												18 27	
Tulse Hill 3	d				18 05	18 12					18 17	18 27									18 27		18 31	18 34	
Herne Hill 4	a					18 16						18 30											18 36		
Loughborough Jn	a					18 21						18 34													
Elephant & Castle	⊖ a					18 25						18 38											18 44		
London Blackfriars 3	⊖ a					18 30						18 44											18 48		
City Thameslink 3	a					18 34						18 48											18 52		
St Pancras International 15	⊖ a					18 41						18 55											19 01		
Luton Airport Parkway 7	✈ a					19 29																			
Luton 10	a					19 34																	19 34		
North Dulwich	d				18 08						18 20										18 30			18 37	
East Dulwich	d				18 10						18 22										18 32			18 39	
Peckham Rye 4	d				18 12						18 24			18 27							18 35			18 41	
Queens Rd Peckham	d				18 15									18 30							18 37			18 44	
South Bermondsey	d				18 17									18 32							18 40			18 46	
London Bridge 4	⊖ a			18 10	18 22				18 15	18 25	18 31		18 28	18 39							18 44	18 42		18 51	18 45

		FC	SN	SN	SN	SN	SN	SN	SN	SN	FC	SN	SN	SN	SN	SN		SN	SN	SN	FC	SN	SN	SN	SN
			A	B					D										E				1		
East Croydon	d		18 17			18 21		18 32											18 47				18 57		
West Croydon 4	d			18 24	18 18				18 36				18 39	18 48								18 51			
Norwood Junction 2	a				18 23	18 28		18 36						18 52								18 55	19 01		
	d				18 24	18 29		18 36						18 53								18 56	19 02	19 06	
Selhurst 4	d		18 20	18 28					18 40				18 43						18 51						
Thornton Heath	d		18 22						18 42				18 45						18 53						
Norbury	d		18 25						18 45				18 48						18 56						
Streatham Common 4	d		18 28	18 33					18 47				18 51						18 58						
Bromley South 4	d																			18 17					
Beckenham Junction 4	d																			18 49					
Birkbeck	d																			18 52					
Crystal Palace 4	d				18 28											18 43		18 48		18 56		19 00			
Gipsy Hill	d				18 30											18 46				18 58		19 02			
West Norwood 4	d				18 33											18 49				19 01		19 05			
Streatham Hill	d				18 37											18 52						19 09			
Balham 4	⊖ d		18 33	18 37	18 40		18 48		18 51							18 55			19 02			19 12			19 17
Wandsworth Common	d		18 35		18 42				18 53							18 57			19 04			19 14			
Clapham Junction 10	d		18 39	18 42	18 46		18 52		18 57							19 01			19 08			19 18			19 22
West Brompton	⊖ d																								
Kensington (Olympia)	⊖ d																								
Shepherd's Bush	⊖ d																								
Wembley Central	⊖ d																								
Harrow & Wealdstone	⊖ d																								
Watford Junction	d																								
Milton Keynes Central 10	a																								
Battersea Park 4	d				18 49										19 02	19 05						19 21			
London Victoria 15	⊖ a		18 46	18 49	18 55		19 01		19 04						19 09	19 12			19 15			19 26			19 30
Streatham 4	d	18 36								18 45	18 49		18 54								19 08				
Tulse Hill 3	d	18 42								18 50	18c57		18 58							19 05	19 14				
Herne Hill 4	a	18 46									19 00										19 18				
Loughborough Jn	a	18 51									19 04										19 21				
Elephant & Castle	⊖ a	18 55									19 08										19 25				
London Blackfriars 3	⊖ a	19 00									19 15										19 30				
City Thameslink 3	a	19 02									19 18										19 34				
St Pancras International 15	⊖ a	19 09									19 25										19 41				
Luton Airport Parkway 7	✈ a	19 54									20 11										20 26				
Luton 10	a	19 58									20 14										20 30				
North Dulwich	d									18 53			19 01							19 08					
East Dulwich	d									18 55			19 03							19 10					
Peckham Rye 4	d									19 00		18 56	19 05							19 12					
Queens Rd Peckham	d									19 03		18 59	19 08							19 15					
South Bermondsey	d									19 05		19 01	19 10							19 17					
London Bridge 4	⊖ a					18 42		18 58		19 10		19 08	19 15	19 18				19 10		19 22			19 15	19 27	

For general notes see front of timetable
For details of catering facilities see Directory of Train Operators

A From Caterham (Table 181)
B From Epsom Downs (Table 182)
C From Brighton (Table 52)
D From Guildford (Table 182)
E From Tattenham Corner (Table 181)
b Arr. 1829
c Arr. 1853

East and West Croydon, London → Milton Keynes and Luton via Norbury → Crystal Palace → Tulse Hill

Local Services

Network Diagram - see first page of Table 177

Station		SN	SN	FC	SN	SN	SN	SN	SN	SN 1	SN	SN	SN		SN	SN	FC	SN	SN	SN	SN	SN	FC 1	FC	SN
					A						B										A				
East Croydon	d						19 10			19 07	19 17								19 40						
West Croydon 4	d				19 01	19 09						19 18	19 22								19 28	19 36			
Norwood Junction 2	a						19 14					19 22	19 27						19 44						
	d						19 15					19 23	19 27						19 44						
Selhurst 4	d				19 06	19 16				19 13	19 20										19 32	19 40			
Thornton Heath	d				19 08	19 18				19 16	19 22										19 34	19 42			
Norbury	d				19 11	19 21				19 19	19 25										19 37	19 45			
Streatham Common 4	d				19 13	19 24				19 21	19 28										19 40	19 48			
Bromley South 4	d															*18 47*									
Beckenham Junction 4	d															19 25									
Birkbeck	d															19 28									
Crystal Palace 4	d								19 13			19 27			19 32	19 32									
Gipsy Hill	d								19 16			19 29				19 34									
West Norwood 4	d								19 19			19 32				19 37									
Streatham Hill	d								19 22			19 36													
Balham 4	⊖ d				19 19				19 25	19 28	19 32	19 39						19 44			19 47				
Wandsworth Common	d				19 21				19 27	19 30	19 34	19 41									19 49				
Clapham Junction 10	d				19 25				19 31	19b38	19 38	19 45						19 49			19 53				
West Brompton	⊖ d									19 47															
Kensington (Olympia)	⊖ d									19 50															
Shepherd's Bush	⊖ d									19 53															
Wembley Central	⊖ d																								
Harrow & Wealdstone	⊖ d									20 12															
Watford Junction	d									20 19															
Milton Keynes Central 10	a									21 01															
Battersea Park 4	d				19 29			19 32	19 35		19 41	19 48									19 56				20 02
London Victoria 15	⊖ a				19 33			19 36	19 42		19 48	19 53						19 56			20 03				20 06
Streatham 4	d		19 16	19 23		19 27											19 38					19 52	19 56	20 06	
Tulse Hill 3	d		19 20	19 27		19 31										19 41	19 44					19 56	19 59	20 10	
Herne Hill 4	a			19 30													19 48						20 03	20 14	
Loughborough Jn	a			19 35													19 51						20 07	20 19	
Elephant & Castle	⊖ a			19 39													19 55						20 11	20 23	
London Blackfriars 3	⊖ a			19 46													19 59						20 15	20 27	
City Thameslink 3	a			19 48													20 02						20 18	20 32	
St Pancras International 15	⊖ a			19 55													20 09						20 25	20 39	
Luton Airport Parkway 7	✈ a			20 41													20 56							21 26	
Luton 10	a			20 44													21 00							21 30	
North Dulwich	d		19 23			19 34										19 44						19 59			
East Dulwich	d		19 25			19 36										19 46						20 01			
Peckham Rye 4	d	19 26	19 30			19 38										19 48				19 56		20 03			
Queens Rd Peckham	d	19 29	19 33			19 41										19 51				19 59		20 06			
South Bermondsey	d	19 31	19 35			19 43										19 53				20 01		20 08			
London Bridge 4	⊖ a	19 36	19 40			19 48	19 39						19 49		19 53	19 58			20 11	20 06		20 14			

Station		SN	SN	SN	SN	SN	SN	SN	SN	SN		SN	SN	FC 1	SN	SN	SN	SN	SN	SN	FC	SN	SN	SN	SN
			B									A					B	C							
East Croydon	d		19 47						20 10								20 17							20 29	20 40
West Croydon 4	d			19 47	19 49							20 01	20 06					20 18							
Norwood Junction 2	a			19 51	19 54				20 14									20 22						20 34	20 44
	d			19 52	19 55				20 14									20 23						20 34	20 44
Selhurst 4	d		19 50									20 05	20 10				20 20								
Thornton Heath	d		19 52									20 07	20 12				20 22								
Norbury	d		19 55									20 10	20 15				20 25								
Streatham Common 4	d		19 58									20 12	20 18				20 28								
Bromley South 4	d					*19 33*													*20 03*						
Beckenham Junction 4	d					19 54													20 24						
Birkbeck	d					19 57													20 27						
Crystal Palace 4	d	19 43		19 56		20 01		20 02								20 13		20 27	20 31	20 32					
Gipsy Hill	d	19 46		19 58		20 03										20 16		20 29	20 33						
West Norwood 4	d	19 49		20 01		20 06										20 19		20 32	20 36						
Streatham Hill	d	19 52		20 05												20 22		20 36							
Balham 4	⊖ d	19 55	20 02	20 08			20 14					20 17				20 25	20 32	20 39					20 44		
Wandsworth Common	d	19 57	20 04	20 10								20 19				20 27	20 34	20 41							
Clapham Junction 10	d	20 01	20 08	20 14			20 19					20 23				20 31	20 38	20 45					20 49		
West Brompton	⊖ d															*20 46*									
Kensington (Olympia)	⊖ d															*20 50*									
Shepherd's Bush	⊖ d															*20 53*									
Wembley Central	⊖ d																								
Harrow & Wealdstone	⊖ d																								
Watford Junction	d																								
Milton Keynes Central 10	a																								
Battersea Park 4	d	20 05	20 11	20 17								20 27			20 32	20 35	20 41	20 48		20 10					
London Victoria 15	⊖ a	20 09	20 18	20 26			20 28					20 33			20 36	20 39	20 46	20 53					20 56		
Streatham 4	d												20 22	20 26							20 36	←			
Tulse Hill 3	d					20 11							20 26	20 29					20 41 →		20 40	20 41			
Herne Hill 4	a													20 33							20 44				
Loughborough Jn	a													20 37							20 49				
Elephant & Castle	⊖ a													20 41							20 53				
London Blackfriars 3	⊖ a													20 45							20 57				
City Thameslink 3	a													20 48							21 02				
St Pancras International 15	⊖ a													20 55							21 09				
Luton Airport Parkway 7	✈ a																				21 56				
Luton 10	a																				22 00				
North Dulwich	d					20 14							20 29									20 44			
East Dulwich	d					20 16							20 31									20 46			
Peckham Rye 4	d					20 18				20 26			20 33									20 48			
Queens Rd Peckham	d					20 21				20 29			20 36									20 51			
South Bermondsey	d					20 23				20 31			20 38									20 53			
London Bridge 4	⊖ a				20 20	20 28		20 23	20 41	20 36			20 43							20 53		20 58		21 01	21 11

For general notes see front of timetable
For details of catering facilities see Directory of Train Operators

A From Epsom Downs (Table 182)
B From Tattenham Corner (Table 181)
C From Epsom (Table 182)

b Arr. 1934

East and West Croydon, London → Milton Keynes and Luton via Norbury → Crystal Palace → Tulse Hill

Local Services

Network Diagram - see first page of Table 177

Station		SN	SN	SN	FC	FC	SN		SN	SN	SN	SN	SN
			A		1					B	C		
East Croydon	d									20 47			
West Croydon 4	d		20 31	20 36							20 48		
Norwood Junction 2	a										20 52		
	d										20 53		
Selhurst 4	d		20 36	20 41						20 50			
Thornton Heath	d		20 38	20 43						20 52			
Norbury	d		20 41	20 46						20 55			
Streatham Common 4	d		20 44	20 49						20 58			
Bromley South 4	d												
Beckenham Junction 4	d												
Birkbeck	d												
Crystal Palace 4	d								20 43		20 57		21 02
Gipsy Hill	d								20 46		20 59		
West Norwood 4	d								20 49		21 02		
Streatham Hill	d								20 52		21 06		
Balham 4	⊖ d		20 48						20 55	21 02	21 09	21 14	
Wandsworth Common	d		20 50						20 57	21 04	21 11		
Clapham Junction 10	d		20 54						21 01	21 08	21 15	21 19	
West Brompton	⊖ d												
Kensington (Olympia)	⊖ d												
Shepherd's Bush	⊖ d												
Wembley Central	⊖ d												
Harrow & Wealdstone	⊖ d												
Watford Junction	d												
Milton Keynes Central 10	a												
Battersea Park 4	d		20 57				21 02		21 05	21 11	21 18		
London Victoria 15	⊖ a		21 03				21 06		21 09	21 16	21 23	21 26	
Streatham 4	d			20 52	20 56	21 06							
Tulse Hill 3	d			20 56	20 59	21 10							
Herne Hill 4	a				21 03	21 15							
Loughborough Jn	a				21 07	21 19							
Elephant & Castle	⊖ a				21 11	21 23							
London Blackfriars 3	⊖ a				21 15	21 27							
City Thameslink 3	a				21 18	21 32							
St Pancras International 15	⊖ a				21 25	21 39							
Luton Airport Parkway 7	✈ a					22 26							
Luton 10	a					22 30							
North Dulwich	d			20 59									
East Dulwich	d			21 01									
Peckham Rye 4	d	20 56		21 04									
Queens Rd Peckham	d	20 59		21 06									
South Bermondsey	d	21 01		21 09									
London Bridge 4	⊖ a	21 08		21 14									21 22

Station		SN	SN	SN	SN	FC	FC	SN	SN	SN	SN	SN	SN
				A		1				B	D		
East Croydon	d	21 10								21 17			
West Croydon 4	d			21 01	21 06						21 18		
Norwood Junction 2	a	21 14									21 22		
	d	21 14									21 23		
Selhurst 4	d			21 06	21 10					21 20			
Thornton Heath	d			21 08	21 12					21 22			
Norbury	d			21 11	21 15					21 25			
Streatham Common 4	d			21 14	21 18					21 28			
Bromley South 4	d												
Beckenham Junction 4	d												
Birkbeck	d												
Crystal Palace 4	d								21 13		21 27		21 32
Gipsy Hill	d								21 16		21 29		
West Norwood 4	d								21 19		21 32		
Streatham Hill	d								21 22		21 36		
Balham 4	⊖ d			21 18					21 25	21 32	21 39	21 44	
Wandsworth Common	d			21 20					21 27	21 34	21 41		
Clapham Junction 10	d			21 24					21 31	21 38	21 45	21 49	
West Brompton	⊖ d								21 46				
Kensington (Olympia)	⊖ d								21 50				
Shepherd's Bush	⊖ d								21 53				
Wembley Central	⊖ d												
Harrow & Wealdstone	⊖ d												
Watford Junction	d												
Milton Keynes Central 10	a												
Battersea Park 4	d			21 27				21 32	21 35	21 41	21 48		
London Victoria 15	⊖ a			21 33				21 36	21 39	21 46	21 53	21 56	
Streatham 4	d				21 21	21 26	21 46						
Tulse Hill 3	d				21 25	21 29	21 50						
Herne Hill 4	a					21 33	21 54						
Loughborough Jn	a					21 37	21 57						
Elephant & Castle	⊖ a					21 41	22 01						
London Blackfriars 3	⊖ a					21 45	22 05						
City Thameslink 3	a					21 48	22 08						
St Pancras International 15	⊖ a					21 55	22 15						
Luton Airport Parkway 7	✈ a						22 59						
Luton 10	a						23 02						
North Dulwich	d				21 28								
East Dulwich	d				21 30								
Peckham Rye 4	d		21 26		21 32								
Queens Rd Peckham	d		21 29		21 35								
South Bermondsey	d		21 31		21 37								
London Bridge 4	⊖ a	21 41	21 36		21 42								21 52

Station		SN	SN	SN		SN	SN	SN	SN	SN	SN	SN	SN
				A					B	C			
East Croydon	d	21 40							21 47				22 10
West Croydon 4	d			21 31		21 36				21 48			
Norwood Junction 2	a	21 44								21 52			22 14
	d	21 44								21 53			22 14
Selhurst 4	d			21 36		21 40			21 50				
Thornton Heath	d			21 38		21 42			21 52				
Norbury	d			21 41		21 45			21 55				
Streatham Common 4	d			21 44		21 48			21 58				
Bromley South 4	d												
Beckenham Junction 4	d												
Birkbeck	d												
Crystal Palace 4	d							21 43		21 57		22 02	
Gipsy Hill	d							21 46		21 59			
West Norwood 4	d							21 49		22 02			
Streatham Hill	d							21 52		22 06			
Balham 4	⊖ d			21 48				21 55	22 02	22 09	22 14		
Wandsworth Common	d			21 50				21 57	22 04	22 11			
Clapham Junction 10	d			21 54				22 01	22 08	22 15	22 19		
West Brompton	⊖ d												
Kensington (Olympia)	⊖ d												
Shepherd's Bush	⊖ d												
Wembley Central	⊖ d												
Harrow & Wealdstone	⊖ d												
Watford Junction	d												
Milton Keynes Central 10	a												
Battersea Park 4	d			21 57			22 02	22 05	22 11	22 18			
London Victoria 15	⊖ a			22 03			22 06	22 09	22 16	22 23	22 27		
Streatham 4	d					21 51							
Tulse Hill 3	d					21 55							
Herne Hill 4	a												
Loughborough Jn	a												
Elephant & Castle	⊖ a												
London Blackfriars 3	⊖ a												
City Thameslink 3	a												
St Pancras International 15	⊖ a												
Luton Airport Parkway 7	✈ a												
Luton 10	a												
North Dulwich	d					21 58							
East Dulwich	d					22 00							
Peckham Rye 4	d		21 56			22 02							
Queens Rd Peckham	d		21 59			22 05							
South Bermondsey	d		22 01			22 07							
London Bridge 4	⊖ a	22 11	22 07			22 12						22 22	22 41

Station		SN	SN	SN	FC	SN	SN	SN	SN	SN	SN		SN
			A					B	D				
East Croydon	d							22 17					22 40
West Croydon 4	d		22 01	22 06					22 18				
Norwood Junction 2	a								22 22				22 44
	d								22 23				22 44
Selhurst 4	d		22 06	22 10				22 20					
Thornton Heath	d		22 08	22 12				22 22					
Norbury	d		22 11	22 15				22 25					
Streatham Common 4	d		22 14	22 18				22 28					
Bromley South 4	d												
Beckenham Junction 4	d												
Birkbeck	d												
Crystal Palace 4	d						22 13		22 27		22 32		
Gipsy Hill	d						22 16		22 29				
West Norwood 4	d						22 19		22 32				
Streatham Hill	d						22 22		22 36				
Balham 4	⊖ d		22 18				22 25	22 32	22 39	22 44			
Wandsworth Common	d		22 20				22 27	22 34	22 41				
Clapham Junction 10	d		22 24				22 31	22 38	22 45	22 49			
West Brompton	⊖ d						22 46						
Kensington (Olympia)	⊖ d						22 50						
Shepherd's Bush	⊖ d						22 53						
Wembley Central	⊖ d												
Harrow & Wealdstone	⊖ d												
Watford Junction	d												
Milton Keynes Central 10	a												
Battersea Park 4	d		22 27			22 32	22 35	22 41	22 48				
London Victoria 15	⊖ a		22 33			22 36	22 39	22 46	22 53	22 56			
Streatham 4	d			22 21	22 36								
Tulse Hill 3	d			22 25	22 40								
Herne Hill 4	a												
Loughborough Jn	a												
Elephant & Castle	⊖ a												
London Blackfriars 3	⊖ a												
City Thameslink 3	a												
St Pancras International 15	⊖ a												
Luton Airport Parkway 7	✈ a												
Luton 10	a												
North Dulwich	d			22 28									
East Dulwich	d			22 30									
Peckham Rye 4	d	22 26		22 32									
Queens Rd Peckham	d	22 29		22 35									
South Bermondsey	d	22 31		22 37									
London Bridge 4	⊖ a	22 36		22 42	22 52						22 52		23 11

For general notes see front of timetable
For details of catering facilities see Directory of Train Operators

A From Sutton (Surrey) (Table 182)
B From Tattenham Corner (Table 181)
C From Epsom (Table 182)
D From Epsom Downs (Table 182)

East and West Croydon, London → Milton Keynes and Luton via Norbury → Crystal Palace → Tulse Hill

Local Services

Network Diagram - see first page of Table 177

		SN	SN A	SN	SN	SN	SN B	SN C	SN	SN	SN	SN	SN A	SN	SN	SN	SN B	SN D	SN		SN				
East Croydon	d						22 47				23 10						23 17								
West Croydon 4	d		22 31	22 36				22 48					23 01	23 06				23 18							
Norwood Junction 2	a							22 52			23 14							23 22							
	d							22 53			23 14							23 23							
Selhurst 4	d		22 36	22 40			22 50						23 05	23 10			23 20								
Thornton Heath	d		22 38	22 42			22 52						23 07	23 12			23 22								
Norbury	d		22 41	22 45			22 55						23 10	23 15			23 25								
Streatham Common 4	d		22 44	22 48			22 58						23 13	23 18			23 28								
Bromley South 4	d																								
Beckenham Junction 4	d																								
Birkbeck	d																								
Crystal Palace 4	d					22 43		22 57		23 02						23 13		23 27	23 32		23 43				
Gipsy Hill	d					22 46		22 59								23 16		23 29			23 46				
West Norwood 4	d					22 49		23 02								23 19		23 32			23 49				
Streatham Hill	d					22 52		23 06								23 22		23 36			23 52				
Balham 4	⊖ d		22 48			22 55	23 02	23 09	23 14				23 17			23 25	23 32	23 40			23 55				
Wandsworth Common	d		22 50			22 57	23 04	23 11					23 19			23 27	23 34	23 42			23 57				
Clapham Junction 10	d		22 54			23 01	23 08	23 15	23 19				23 23			23 31	23 38	23 46			00 01				
West Brompton	⊖ d																								
Kensington (Olympia)	⊖ d																								
Shepherd's Bush	⊖ d																								
Wembley Central	⊖ d																								
Harrow & Wealdstone	⊖ d																								
Watford Junction	d																								
Milton Keynes Central 10	a																								
Battersea Park 4	d		22 57		23 02	23 05	23 11	23 19					23 26		23 32	23 35	23 41	23 49			00 04				
London Victoria 15	⊖ a		23 03		23 06	23 10	23 16	23 23	23 26				23 31		23 37	23 40	23 46	23 54			00 12				
Streatham 4	d			22 51										23 21											
Tulse Hill 3	d			22 55										23 25											
Herne Hill 4	a																								
Loughborough Jn	a																								
Elephant & Castle	⊖ a																								
London Blackfriars 3	⊖ a																								
City Thameslink 3	a																								
St Pancras International 15	⊖ a																								
Luton Airport Parkway 7	✈ a																								
Luton 10	a																								
North Dulwich	d			22 58										23 28											
East Dulwich	d			23 00										23 30											
Peckham Rye 4	d	22 56		23 02								23 26		23 32											
Queens Rd Peckham	d	22 59		23 05								23 29		23 35											
South Bermondsey	d	23 01		23 07								23 31		23 37											
London Bridge 4	⊖ a	23 06		23 12						23 22	23 38	23 36		23 42					23 52						

For general notes see front of timetable
For details of catering facilities see Directory of Train Operators

A From Sutton (Surrey) (Table 182)
B From Tattenham Corner (Table 181)
C From Epsom (Table 182)
D From Epsom Downs (Table 182)

Table 177

Saturdays

East and West Croydon, London → Milton Keynes and Luton via Norbury → Crystal Palace → Tulse Hill

Local Services

Network Diagram - see first page of Table 177

		SN	FC	SN 1	SN	SN	FC	SN	SN 1	FC	SN	SN 1	SN	SN	SN	SN	SN	FC	SN	SN	SN	SN 1	SN	FC	SN
																				A					
East Croydon	d								06 10			06 25	06 30				06 43			06 47		06 55	07 00		
West Croydon 4	d										06 18										06 48				
Norwood Junction 2	a										06 22	06 29	06 34				06 48				06 53	06 59	07 04		
	d				05 53						06 23	06 29	06 35	06 42	06 46		06 49				06 53	06 59	07 05		
Selhurst 4	d		05 39			06 01	06 09		06 13	06 39										06 50					
Thornton Heath	d		05 41			06 03	06 11		06 16	06 41										06 52					
Norbury	d		05 43			06 06	06 13		06 19	06 43										06 55					
Streatham Common 4	d		05 46			06 08	06 16		06 21	06 46										06 58					
Bromley South 4	d																								
Beckenham Junction 4	d																								
Birkbeck	d																								
Crystal Palace 4	d	23p43			05 57						06 27			06 46							06 57				
Gipsy Hill	d	23p46			05 59						06 29			06 48							07 00				
West Norwood 4	d	23p49			06 02						06 32			06 51							07 03				
Streatham Hill	d	23p52			06 06						06 36										07 06				
Balham 4	⊖ d	23p55		05 33	06 09	06 12			06 28		06 39									07 02	07 09				
Wandsworth Common	d	23p57			06 11	06 14			06 30		06 41									07 04					
Clapham Junction 10	d	00 01		05 38	06 15	06 18			06b38		06 45									07 08	07 15				
West Brompton	⊖ d			05 45					06 47																
Kensington (Olympia)	⊖ d			05 49					06 50																
Shepherd's Bush	⊖ d			05 52					06 53																
Wembley Central	⊖ d			06s07																					
Harrow & Wealdstone	⊖ d			06 12					07 12																
Watford Junction	d			06 19					07 19																
Milton Keynes Central 10	a			07 00					08 00																
Battersea Park 4	d	00 04			06 18	06 22		06 32			06 48								07 02	07 11	07 18				
London Victoria 15	⊖ a	00 12			06 23	06 26		06 36			06 53								07 06	07 16	07 23				
Streatham 4	d		05 49				06 19			06 49								←						07 10	
Tulse Hill 3	d		05 55				06 23			06c57 →				06 54				06 57						07e17	
Herne Hill 4	a																	07 01							
Loughborough Jn	a																								
Elephant & Castle	⊖ a																								
London Blackfriars 3	⊖ a																								
City Thameslink 3	a																								
St Pancras International 15	⊖ a																								
Luton Airport Parkway 7	✈ a																								
Luton 10	a																								
North Dulwich	d													06 57											
East Dulwich	d													06 59											
Peckham Rye 4	d													07 02		06 56									07 26
Queens Rd Peckham	d													07 04		06 59									07 29
South Bermondsey	d													07 07		07 01									07 31
London Bridge 4	⊖ a		06 09				06 35					06 42	06 56	07 14	07 00	07 06	07 14					07 12	07 26	07 30	07 36

For general notes see front of timetable
For details of catering facilities see Directory of Train Operators

A From Tattenham Corner (Table 181)
b Arr. 0634
c Arr. 0653
e Arr. 0714

East and West Croydon, London → Milton Keynes and Luton via Norbury → Crystal Palace → Tulse Hill

Local Services

Network Diagram - see first page of Table 177

Station		SN		SN	SN	FC	SN	SN	SN	SN	SN	SN	SN	FC	SN	SN	SN	SN	FC	SN	SN	SN	SN	SN	SN
		A							1	B		1				C								D	
East Croydon	d								07 10	07 17		07 25	07 30											07 47	
West Croydon 4	d	06 56			07 01		07 15				07 18					07 26		07 31			07 45				07 48
Norwood Junction 2	a						07 19				07 23	07 29	07 34								07 49				07 53
	d						07 20				07 23	07 29	07 35								07 50				07 53
Selhurst 4	d	07 01			07 05				07 13	07 20						07 31		07 35		07 39				07 50	
Thornton Heath	d	07 03			07 07				07 16	07 22						07 33		07 37		07 41				07 52	
Norbury	d	07 06			07 10				07 19	07 25						07 36		07 40		07 44				07 55	
Streatham Common 4	d	07 08			07 13				07 21	07 28						07 38		07 43		07 47				07 58	
Bromley South 4	d																								
Beckenham Junction 4	d																								
Birkbeck	d																								
Crystal Palace 4	d										07 27												07 43		07 57
Gipsy Hill	d										07 30												07 46		08 00
West Norwood 4	d										07 33												07 49		08 03
Streatham Hill	d										07 36												07 52		08 06
Balham 4 ⊖	d	07 12		07 17					07 28	07 32	07 39					07 42	07 48			07 51			07 55	08 02	08 09
Wandsworth Common	d	07 14							07 30	07 34						07 44				07 53			07 57	08 04	
Clapham Junction 10	d	07 18		07 22					07b38	07 38	07 45					07 48	07 52			07 57			08 01	08 08	08 15
West Brompton ⊖	d								07 47																
Kensington (Olympia) ⊖	d								07 50																
Shepherd's Bush ⊖	d								07 53																
Wembley Central ⊖	d								08s07																
Harrow & Wealdstone ⊖	d								08 12																
Watford Junction	d								08 19																
Milton Keynes Central 10	a								09 00																
Battersea Park 4	d	07 22						07 32		07 41	07 48				07 45	07 52						08 02	08 05	08 11	08 18
London Victoria 15 ⊖	a	07 26		07 29				07 36		07 46	07 53					07 56	07 59			08 04		08 06	08 09	08 16	08 23
Streatham 4	d				07 16	07 23								07 40				07 46	07 53						
Tulse Hill 3	d				07c24	07 27								07e47				07f54	07 57						
Herne Hill 4	a					07 31													08 01						
Loughborough Jn	a																								
Elephant & Castle ⊖	a																								
London Blackfriars 3 ⊖	a																								
City Thameslink 3	a																								
St Pancras International 15 ⊖	a																								
Luton Airport Parkway 7 ✈	a																								
Luton 10	a																								
North Dulwich	d				07 27													07 57							
East Dulwich	d				07 29													07 59							
Peckham Rye 4	d				07 31										07 56			08 01							
Queens Rd Peckham	d				07 34										07 59			08 04							
South Bermondsey	d				07 36										08 01			08 06							
London Bridge 4 ⊖	a				07 41		07 44					07 42	07 56	08 00	08 06			08 11			08 14				

Station		SN	SN	FC		SN	SN	SN	SN	FC	SN	SN	SN	SN	SN	SN	SN	SN	SN	SN	SN	FC	SN	SN	SN
		1					E						1				D		1					C	
East Croydon	d	07 55	08 00										08 10				08 17		08 25		08 30				
West Croydon 4	d						07 56		08 01			08 15						08 18						08 26	
Norwood Junction 2	a	07 59	08 04									08 19						08 23	08 29		08 34				
	d	07 59	08 05									08 20						08 23	08 29		08 35				
Selhurst 4	d						08 01		08 05		08 09		08 13				08 20							08 31	
Thornton Heath	d						08 03		08 07		08 11		08 16				08 22							08 33	
Norbury	d						08 06		08 10		08 14		08 19				08 25							08 36	
Streatham Common 4	d						08 08		08 13		08 17		08 21				08 28							08 38	
Bromley South 4	d																			07 48					
Beckenham Junction 4	d																			08 23					
Birkbeck	d																			08 26					
Crystal Palace 4	d														08 13	08 14		08 27		08 30					
Gipsy Hill	d														08 16			08 30		08 33					
West Norwood 4	d														08 19			08 33		08 36					
Streatham Hill	d														08 22			08 36							
Balham 4 ⊖	d						08 12	08 18			08 21		08 28		08 25		08 32	08 39						08 42	08 48
Wandsworth Common	d						08 14				08 23		08 30		08 27		08 34							08 44	
Clapham Junction 10	d						08 18	08 22			08 27		08g38		08 31		08 38	08 45						08 48	08 52
West Brompton ⊖	d												08 47		08 46										
Kensington (Olympia) ⊖	d												08 50		08 50										
Shepherd's Bush ⊖	d												08 53		08 53										
Wembley Central ⊖	d																								
Harrow & Wealdstone ⊖	d												09 12												
Watford Junction	d												09 19												
Milton Keynes Central 10	a												10 00												
Battersea Park 4	d						08 22							08 32	08 35		08 41	08 48						08 52	
London Victoria 15 ⊖	a						08 26	08 29			08 34			08 36	08 39		08 46	08 53						08 56	08 59
Streatham 4	d			08 10					08 16	08 23												08 40			
Tulse Hill 3	d			08h17					08j24	08 27										08 39		08k47			
Herne Hill 4	a									08 31															
Loughborough Jn	a																								
Elephant & Castle ⊖	a																								
London Blackfriars 3 ⊖	a																								
City Thameslink 3	a																								
St Pancras International 15 ⊖	a																								
Luton Airport Parkway 7 ✈	a																								
Luton 10	a																								
North Dulwich	d								08 27											08 42					
East Dulwich	d								08 29											08 44					
Peckham Rye 4	d					08 26			08 31											08 47			08 56		
Queens Rd Peckham	d					08 29			08 34											08 49			08 59		
South Bermondsey	d					08 31			08 36											08 52			09 01		
London Bridge 4 ⊖	a	08 12	08 26	08 30		08 36			08 41			08 44				08 35			08 42	08 56	08 56	09 00	09 06		

For general notes see front of timetable
For details of catering facilities see Directory of Train Operators

- **A** From Sutton (Surrey) (Table 182)
- **B** From Tattenham Corner (Table 181)
- **C** From Epsom (Table 182)
- **D** From Caterham (Table 181)
- **E** From Epsom Downs (Table 182)
- **b** Arr. 0734
- **c** Arr. 0719
- **e** Arr. 0744
- **f** Arr. 0749
- **g** Arr. 0834
- **h** Arr. 0814
- **j** Arr. 0819
- **k** Arr. 0844

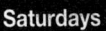

Table 177

Saturdays

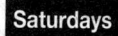

East and West Croydon, London → Milton Keynes and Luton via Norbury → Crystal Palace → Tulse Hill

Local Services

Network Diagram - see first page of Table 177

		SN	FC	SN	SN	SN		SN	SN	SN	SN	SN	SN	SN	FC	SN	SN	SN	SN	FC	SN	SN	SN	SN	SN
				A						B		1					C				A		1		
East Croydon	d									08 47		08 55		09 00									09 10		
West Croydon 4	d	08 31		08 35	08 45						08 48						08 56		09 01		09 05	09 15			
Norwood Junction 2	a				08 49						08 53	08 59		09 04								09 19			
	d				08 50						08 53	08 59		09 05								09 20			
Selhurst 4	d	08 35		08 39						08 50							09 01		09 05		09 09		09 13		
Thornton Heath	d	08 37		08 41						08 52							09 03		09 07		09 11		09 16		
Norbury	d	08 40		08 44						08 55							09 06		09 10		09 14		09 19		
Streatham Common 4	d	08 43		08 47						08 58							09 08		09 13		09 17		09 21		
Bromley South 4	d												*08 33*												
Beckenham Junction 4	d												08 53												
Birkbeck	d												08 56												
Crystal Palace 4	d							08 43	08 45		08 57		09 00												09 13
Gipsy Hill	d							08 46			09 00		09 03												09 16
West Norwood 4	d							08 49			09 03		09 06												09 19
Streatham Hill	d							08 52			09 06														09 22
Balham 4	⊖ d			08 51				08 55		09 02	09 09						09 12	09 18			09 21		09 28		09 25
Wandsworth Common	d			08 53				08 57		09 04							09 14				09 23		09 30		09 27
Clapham Junction 10	d			08 57				09 01		09 08	09 15						09 18	09 22			09 27		09b38		09 31
West Brompton	⊖ d																						09 47		*09 46*
Kensington (Olympia)	⊖ d																						09 50		*09 50*
Shepherd's Bush	⊖ d																						09 53		*09 53*
Wembley Central	⊖ d																								
Harrow & Wealdstone	⊖ d																						10 12		
Watford Junction	d																						10 19		
Milton Keynes Central 10	a																						11 00		
Battersea Park 4	d					09 02		09 05		09 11	09 18						09 22							09 32	09 35
London Victoria 15	⊖ a			09 04		09 06		09 09		09 16	09 23						09 26	09 29			09 34			09 36	09 39
Streatham 4	d	08 46	08 53												09 10				09 16	09 23					
Tulse Hill 3	d	08c54	08 57										09 09		09e17				09f24	09 27					
Herne Hill 4	a		09 01																	09 31					
Loughborough Jn	a																								
Elephant & Castle	⊖ a																								
London Blackfriars 3	⊖ a																								
City Thameslink 3	a																								
St Pancras International 15	⊖ a																								
Luton Airport Parkway 7	✈ a																								
Luton 10	a																								
North Dulwich	d	08 57											09 12						09 27						
East Dulwich	d	08 59											09 14						09 29						
Peckham Rye 4	d	09 01											09 17			09 26			09 31						
Queens Rd Peckham	d	09 04											09 19			09 29			09 34						
South Bermondsey	d	09 06											09 22			09 31			09 36						
London Bridge 4	⊖ a	09 11			09 14				09 05			09 12	09 26	09 26	09 30	09 36			09 41			09 44			

		SN	SN	SN	SN	SN	SN	FC		SN	SN	SN	SN	FC	SN	SN	SN	SN	SN	SN	SN	SN	SN		
			B		1						D				A					B		1			
East Croydon	d		09 17		09 25		09 30													09 47		09 55			
West Croydon 4	d			09 18							09 26		09 31		09 35	09 45					09 48				
Norwood Junction 2	a			09 23	09 29		09 34									09 49					09 53	09 59			
	d			09 23	09 29		09 35									09 50					09 53	09 59			
Selhurst 4	d		09 20								09 31		09 35		09 39					09 50					
Thornton Heath	d		09 22								09 33		09 37		09 41					09 52					
Norbury	d		09 25								09 36		09 40		09 44					09 55					
Streatham Common 4	d		09 28								09 38		09 43		09 47					09 58					
Bromley South 4	d					*09 03*																	*09 33*		
Beckenham Junction 4	d					09 23																	09 53		
Birkbeck	d					09 26																	09 56		
Crystal Palace 4	d	09 15		09 27		09 30												09 43	09 45		09 57		10 00		
Gipsy Hill	d			09 30		09 33												09 46			10 00		10 03		
West Norwood 4	d			09 33		09 36												09 49			10 03		10 06		
Streatham Hill	d			09 36														09 52			10 06				
Balham 4	⊖ d		09 32	09 39							09 42	09 48			09 51			09 55		10 02	10 09				
Wandsworth Common	d		09 34								09 44				09 53			09 57		10 04					
Clapham Junction 10	d		09 38	09 45							09 48	09 52			09 57			10 01		10 08	10 15				
West Brompton	⊖ d																								
Kensington (Olympia)	⊖ d																								
Shepherd's Bush	⊖ d																								
Wembley Central	⊖ d																								
Harrow & Wealdstone	⊖ d																								
Watford Junction	d																								
Milton Keynes Central 10	a																								
Battersea Park 4	d		09 41	09 48							09 52						10 02	10 05		10 11	10 18				
London Victoria 15	⊖ a		09 46	09 53							09 56	09 59			10 04		10 06	10 09		10 16	10 23				
Streatham 4	d							09 40					09 46	09 53											
Tulse Hill 3	d					09 39		09g47					09h54	09 57									10 09		
Herne Hill 4	a													10 01											
Loughborough Jn	a																								
Elephant & Castle	⊖ a																								
London Blackfriars 3	⊖ a																								
City Thameslink 3	a																								
St Pancras International 15	⊖ a																								
Luton Airport Parkway 7	✈ a																								
Luton 10	a																								
North Dulwich	d					09 42							09 57										10 12		
East Dulwich	d					09 44							09 59										10 14		
Peckham Rye 4	d					09 47				09 56			10 01										10 17		
Queens Rd Peckham	d					09 49				09 59			10 04										10 19		
South Bermondsey	d					09 52				10 01			10 06										10 22		
London Bridge 4	⊖ a	09 35			09 42	09 56	09 56	10 00		10 06			10 11			10 14			10 05			10 12	10 26		

For general notes see front of timetable
For details of catering facilities see Directory of Train Operators

A From Sutton (Surrey) (Table 182)
B From Caterham (Table 181)
C From Epsom Downs (Table 182)
D From Epsom (Table 182)
b Arr. 0934
c Arr. 0849
e Arr. 0914
f Arr. 0919
g Arr. 0944
h Arr. 0949

Table 177

Saturdays

East and West Croydon, London → Milton Keynes and Luton via Norbury → Crystal Palace → Tulse Hill

Local Services

Network Diagram - see first page of Table 177

		SN	FC	SN	SN	SN	SN	FC	SN	SN	SN 1	SN	SN	SN	SN	SN	SN 1	SN	SN	FC	SN	SN	SN	SN
					A				B						C							D		
East Croydon	d	10 00									10 10				10 17		10 25		10 30					
West Croydon 4	d				09 56		10 01		10 05	10 15						10 18						10 26		10 31
Norwood Junction 2	a	10 04								10 19						10 23	10 29		10 34					
	d	10 05								10 20						10 23	10 29		10 35					
Selhurst 4	d				10 01		10 05		10 09		10 13				10 20							10 31		10 35
Thornton Heath	d				10 03		10 07		10 11		10 16				10 22							10 33		10 37
Norbury	d				10 06		10 10		10 14		10 19				10 25							10 36		10 40
Streatham Common 4	d				10 08		10 13		10 17		10 21				10 28							10 38		10 43
Bromley South 4	d																	*10 03*						
Beckenham Junction 4	d																	10 23						
Birkbeck	d																	10 26						
Crystal Palace 4	d												10 13	10 15		10 27		10 30						
Gipsy Hill	d												10 16			10 30		10 33						
West Norwood 4	d												10 19			10 33		10 36						
Streatham Hill	d												10 22			10 36								
Balham 4	⊖ d				10 12	10 18			10 21		10 28		10 25		10 32	10 39						10 42	10 48	
Wandsworth Common	d				10 14				10 23		10 30		10 27		10 34							10 44		
Clapham Junction 10	d				10 18	10 22			10 27		10b38		10 31		10 38	10 45						10 48	10 52	
West Brompton	⊖ d										10 47		*10 47*											
Kensington (Olympia)	⊖ d										10 50		*10 50*											
Shepherd's Bush	⊖ d										10 53		*10 53*											
Wembley Central	⊖ d																							
Harrow & Wealdstone	⊖ d										11 13													
Watford Junction	d										11 20													
Milton Keynes Central 10	a										12 00													
Battersea Park 4	d				10 22							10 32	10 35		10 41	10 48						10 52		
London Victoria 15	⊖ a				10 26	10 29			10 34			10 36	10 39		10 46	10 53						10 56	10 59	
Streatham 4	d		10 10				10 16	10 23												10 40				10 46
Tulse Hill 3	d		10c17				10e24	10 27										10 39		10f47				10g54
Herne Hill 4	a							10 31																
Loughborough Jn	a																							
Elephant & Castle	⊖ a																							
London Blackfriars 3	⊖ a																							
City Thameslink 3	a																							
St Pancras International 15	⊖ a																							
Luton Airport Parkway 7	✈ a																							
Luton 10	a																							
North Dulwich	d						10 27											10 42						10 57
East Dulwich	d						10 29											10 44						10 59
Peckham Rye 4	d			10 26			10 31											10 47			10 56			11 01
Queens Rd Peckham	d			10 29			10 34											10 49			10 59			11 04
South Bermondsey	d			10 31			10 36											10 52			11 01			11 06
London Bridge 4	⊖ a	10 26	10 30	10 36			10 41			10 44				10 35			10 42	10 56	10 56	11 00	11 06			11 11

		FC	SN	SN	SN	SN	SN	SN	SN	SN 1	SN		SN	FC	SN	SN	SN	SN	FC	SN	SN	SN 1	SN
			B					C								A				B			
East Croydon	d							10 47		10 55			17 00									17 10	
West Croydon 4	d		10 35	10 45					10 48							16 56		17 01		17 05	17 15		
Norwood Junction 2	a			10 49					10 53	10 59			17 04								17 19		
	d			10 50					10 53	10 59			17 05								17 20		
Selhurst 4	d		10 39					10 50								17 01		17 05		17 09		17 16	
Thornton Heath	d		10 41					10 52								17 03		17 07		17 11		17 18	
Norbury	d		10 44					10 55								17 06		17 10		17 14		17 21	
Streatham Common 4	d		10 47					10 58								17 08		17 13		17 17		17 24	
Bromley South 4	d										*10 33*												
Beckenham Junction 4	d										10 53												
Birkbeck	d										10 56												
Crystal Palace 4	d					10 43	10 45		10 57		11 00												
Gipsy Hill	d					10 46			11 00		11 03												
West Norwood 4	d					10 49			11 03		11 06	and at											
Streatham Hill	d					10 52			11 06														
Balham 4	⊖ d		10 51			10 55		11 02	11 09			the same				17 12	17 18			17 21		17 28	
Wandsworth Common	d		10 53			10 57		11 04								17 14				17 23		17 30	
Clapham Junction 10	d		10 57			11 01		11 08	11 15			minutes				17 18	17 22			17 27		17h38	
West Brompton	⊖ d																					17 47	
Kensington (Olympia)	⊖ d											past										17 50	
Shepherd's Bush	⊖ d																					17 53	
Wembley Central	⊖ d											each											
Harrow & Wealdstone	⊖ d																					18 12	
Watford Junction	d											hour until										18 19	
Milton Keynes Central 10	a																					19 00	
Battersea Park 4	d				11 02	11 05		11 11	11 18							17 22							17 32
London Victoria 15	⊖ a		11 04		11 06	11 09		11 16	11 23							17 26	17 29			17 34			17 36
Streatham 4	d	10 53												17 10				17 16	17 23				
Tulse Hill 3	d	10 57									11 09			17j17				17k24	17 27				
Herne Hill 4	a	11 01																	17 31				
Loughborough Jn	a																						
Elephant & Castle	⊖ a																						
London Blackfriars 3	⊖ a																						
City Thameslink 3	a																						
St Pancras International 15	⊖ a																						
Luton Airport Parkway 7	✈ a																						
Luton 10	a																						
North Dulwich	d										11 12							17 27					
East Dulwich	d										11 14							17 29					
Peckham Rye 4	d										11 17				17 26			17 31					
Queens Rd Peckham	d										11 19				17 29			17 34					
South Bermondsey	d										11 22				17 31			17 36					
London Bridge 4	⊖ a			11 14			11 05			11 12	11 26		17 26	17 30	17 36			17 41			17 44		

For general notes see front of timetable
For details of catering facilities see Directory of Train Operators

A From Epsom Downs (Table 182)
B From Sutton (Surrey) (Table 182)
C From Caterham (Table 181)
D From Epsom (Table 182)
b Arr. 1034
c Arr. 1014
e Arr. 1019
f Arr. 1044
g Arr. 1049
h Arr. 1734
j Arr. 1714
k Arr. 1719

Table 177

Saturdays

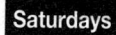

East and West Croydon, London → Milton Keynes and Luton via Norbury → Crystal Palace → Tulse Hill

Local Services

Network Diagram - see first page of Table 177

		SN	SN	SN	SN	SN	SN	SN	FC	SN	SN	SN	SN	FC	SN		SN	SN	SN	SN	SN	SN	SN	SN	SN
				A		1					B				C						A		1		
East Croydon 🚊	d			17 17		17 25		17 30													17 47		17 55		18 00
West Croydon 4 🚊	d				17 18						17 26		17 31		17 35		17 45					17 48			
Norwood Junction 2	a				17 23	17 29		17 34									17 49					17 53	17 59		18 04
	d				17 23	17 29		17 35									17 50					17 53	17 59		18 05
Selhurst 4	d			17 20							17 31		17 35		17 39						17 50				
Thornton Heath	d			17 22							17 33		17 37		17 41						17 52				
Norbury	d			17 25							17 36		17 40		17 44						17 55				
Streatham Common 4	d			17 28							17 38		17 43		17 47						17 58				
Bromley South 4	d						17 03																	17 33	
Beckenham Junction 4 🚊	d						17 23																	17 53	
Birkbeck 🚊	d						17 26																	17 56	
Crystal Palace 4	d	17 13	17 15		17 27		17 30												17 43	17 45		17 57		18 00	
Gipsy Hill	d	17 16			17 30		17 33												17 46			18 00		18 03	
West Norwood 4	d	17 19			17 33		17 36												17 49			18 03		18 06	
Streatham Hill	d	17 22			17 36														17 52			18 06			
Balham 4	⊖ d	17 25		17 32	17 39						17 42	17 48			17 51				17 55		18 02	18 09			
Wandsworth Common	d	17 27		17 34							17 44				17 53				17 57		18 04				
Clapham Junction 10	d	17 32		17 38	17 45						17 48	17 52			17 57				18 01		18 08	18 15			
West Brompton	⊖ d	17 46																							
Kensington (Olympia)	⊖ d	17 50																							
Shepherd's Bush	⊖ d	17 53																							
Wembley Central	⊖ d																								
Harrow & Wealdstone	⊖ d																								
Watford Junction	d																								
Milton Keynes Central 10	a																								
Battersea Park 4	d	17 36		17 41	17 48						17 52							18 02	18 05		18 11	18 18			
London Victoria 15	⊖ a	17 40		17 46	17 53						17 56	17 59			18 04			18 06	18 09		18 16	18 23			
Streatham 4	d								17 40				17 46	17 53											
Tulse Hill 3	d						17 39		17b47				17c54	17 57										18 09	
Herne Hill 4	a													18 01											
Loughborough Jn	a																								
Elephant & Castle	⊖ a																								
London Blackfriars 3	⊖ a																								
City Thameslink 3	a																								
St Pancras International 15	⊖ a																								
Luton Airport Parkway 7	✈ a																								
Luton 10	a																								
North Dulwich	d						17 42						17 57											18 12	
East Dulwich	d						17 44						17 59											18 14	
Peckham Rye 4	d						17 47			17 56			18 01											18 17	
Queens Rd Peckham	d						17 49			17 59			18 04											18 19	
South Bermondsey	d						17 52			18 01			18 06											18 22	
London Bridge 4	⊖ a		17 35			17 42	17 56	17 56	18 00	18 06			18 11				18 14			18 05			18 12	18 26	18 26

		FC	SN	SN	SN	SN	FC	SN	SN	SN	SN	SN	SN	SN	SN	SN	SN		SN	FC	SN	SN	SN	SN	FC
				D				C		1				A		1						B			
East Croydon 🚊	d									18 10				18 17		18 25			18 30						
West Croydon 4 🚊	d			17 56		18 01		18 05	18 15						18 18							18 26		18 31	
Norwood Junction 2	a								18 19						18 23	18 29			18 34						
	d								18 20						18 23	18 29			18 35						
Selhurst 4	d			18 01		18 05		18 09		18 13				18 20								18 31		18 35	
Thornton Heath	d			18 03		18 07		18 11		18 16				18 22								18 33		18 37	
Norbury	d			18 06		18 10		18 14		18 19				18 25								18 36		18 40	
Streatham Common 4	d			18 08		18 13		18 17		18 21				18 28								18 38		18 43	
Bromley South 4	d																18 03								
Beckenham Junction 4 🚊	d																18 23								
Birkbeck 🚊	d																18 26								
Crystal Palace 4	d											18 13	18 15		18 27		18 30								
Gipsy Hill	d											18 16			18 30		18 33								
West Norwood 4	d											18 19			18 33		18 36								
Streatham Hill	d											18 22			18 36										
Balham 4	⊖ d			18 12	18 18			18 21		18 28		18 25		18 32	18 39							18 42	18 48		
Wandsworth Common	d			18 14				18 23		18 30		18 27		18 34								18 44			
Clapham Junction 10	d			18 18	18 22			18 27		18e38		18 31		18 38	18 45							18 48	18 52		
West Brompton	⊖ d									18 47		18 47													
Kensington (Olympia)	⊖ d									18 50		18 50													
Shepherd's Bush	⊖ d									18a52		18 52													
Wembley Central	⊖ d																								
Harrow & Wealdstone	⊖ d																								
Watford Junction	d																								
Milton Keynes Central 10	a																								
Battersea Park 4	d			18 22							18 32	18 35	17 53	18 41	18 48							18 52			
London Victoria 15	⊖ a			18 26	18 29			18 34			18 36	18 39		18 46	18 53							18 56	18 59		
Streatham 4	d	18 10				18 16	18 23													18 40				18 46	18 53
Tulse Hill 3	d	18f17				18g24	18 27										18 39			18h47				18j54	18 57
Herne Hill 4	a						18 31																		19 01
Loughborough Jn	a																								
Elephant & Castle	⊖ a																								
London Blackfriars 3	⊖ a																								
City Thameslink 3	a																								
St Pancras International 15	⊖ a																								
Luton Airport Parkway 7	✈ a																								
Luton 10	a																								
North Dulwich	d					18 27											18 42							18 57	
East Dulwich	d					18 29											18 44							18 59	
Peckham Rye 4	d		18 26			18 31											18 47				18 56			19 01	
Queens Rd Peckham	d		18 29			18 34											18 49				18 59			19 04	
South Bermondsey	d		18 31			18 36											18 52				19 01			19 06	
London Bridge 4	⊖ a	18 30	18 36			18 41			18 44				18 35			18 42	18 56		18 56	19 00	19 06			19 11	

For general notes see front of timetable
For details of catering facilities see Directory of Train Operators

- **A** From Caterham (Table 181)
- **B** From Epsom (Table 182)
- **C** From Sutton (Surrey) (Table 182)
- **D** From Epsom Downs (Table 182)
- **b** Arr. 1744
- **c** Arr. 1749
- **e** Arr. 1834
- **f** Arr. 1814
- **g** Arr. 1819
- **h** Arr. 1844
- **j** Arr. 1849

East and West Croydon, London → Milton Keynes and Luton via Norbury → Crystal Palace → Tulse Hill

Local Services

Network Diagram - see first page of Table 177

	SN	SN	SN	SN	SN	SN	SN	SN	SN	SN	FC	SN	SN	SN	SN	SN	FC	SN		SN	SN	SN	SN	SN
								1				1									1			
	A					B								C									D	
East Croydon d						18 47		18 55		19 00		19 05									19 07	19 10	19 17	
West Croydon 4 d	18 35	18 45					18 48							18 56		19 01								19 18
Norwood Junction 2 a		18 49					18 53	18 59		19 04		19 09										19 14		19 22
d		18 50					18 53	18 59		19 04		19 09										19 14		19 23
Selhurst 4 d	18 39					18 50								19 01		19 05					19 13		19 20	
Thornton Heath d	18 41					18 52								19 03		19 07					19 16		19 22	
Norbury d	18 44					18 55								19 06		19 10					19 19		19 25	
Streatham Common 4 d	18 47					18 58								19 08		19 13					19 21		19 28	
Bromley South 4 d									18 33															
Beckenham Junction 4 d									18 53															
Birkbeck d									18 56															
Crystal Palace 4 d				18 43	18 45		18 57		19 00											19 13				19 27
Gipsy Hill d				18 46			19 00		19 03											19 16				19 29
West Norwood 4 d				18 49			19 03		19 06											19 19				19 32
Streatham Hill d				18 52			19 06													19 22				19 36
Balham 4 d	18 51			18 55		19 02	19 09							19 12	19 18					19 25	19 28		19 32	19 39
Wandsworth Common d	18 53			18 57		19 04								19 14						19 27	19 30		19 34	19 41
Clapham Junction 10 d	18 57			19 01		19 08	19 15							19 18	19 22					19 31	19b38		19 38	19 45
West Brompton d																					19 45			
Kensington (Olympia) d																					19 48			
Shepherd's Bush d																					19a50			
Wembley Central d																								
Harrow & Wealdstone d																								
Watford Junction d																								
Milton Keynes Central 10 a																								
Battersea Park 4 d			19 02	19 05		19 11	19 18							19 22				19 32		19 35			19 41	19 48
London Victoria 15 a	19 04		19 06	19 09		19 16	19 23							19 26	19 29			19 36		19 39			19 46	19 53
Streatham 4 d											19 10					19 16	19 23							
Tulse Hill 3 d									19 10		19c17					19e24	19 27							
Herne Hill 4 a																	19 31							
Loughborough Jn a																								
Elephant & Castle a																								
London Blackfriars 3 a																								
City Thameslink 3 a																								
St Pancras International 15 a																								
Luton Airport Parkway 7 a																								
Luton 10 a																								
North Dulwich d									19 13							19 27								
East Dulwich d									19 15							19 29								
Peckham Rye 4 d									19 18				19 26			19 31								
Queens Rd Peckham d									19 20				19 29			19 34								
South Bermondsey d									19 23				19 31			19 36								
London Bridge 4 a		19 14			19 05			19 12	19 27	19 28	19 30	19 23	19 36			19 41						19 41		

	SN	SN	FC	SN	SN	SN	SN	SN	SN	SN	SN	SN	SN	SN	FC	SN	SN	SN	SN	SN		SN	SN	SN
						A					D	E							A					D
East Croydon d				19 40							19 47						20 10							20 17
West Croydon 4 d						19 26		19 36				19 48							20 01	20 06				
Norwood Junction 2 a				19 44								19 52					20 14							
d				19 44								19 53					20 14							
Selhurst 4 d						19 31		19 40			19 50								20 05	20 10				20 20
Thornton Heath d						19 33		19 42			19 52								20 07	20 12				20 22
Norbury d						19 36		19 45			19 55								20 10	20 15				20 25
Streatham Common 4 d						19 38		19 48			19 58								20 13	20 18				20 28
Bromley South 4 d	19 03												19 33											
Beckenham Junction 4 d	19 23												19 53											
Birkbeck d	19 26												19 56											
Crystal Palace 4 d	19 30	19 33								19 43		19 57	20 00	20 03									20 13	
Gipsy Hill d	19 32									19 46		19 59	20 02										20 16	
West Norwood 4 d	19 35									19 49		20 02	20 05										20 19	
Streatham Hill d										19 52		20 06											20 22	
Balham 4 d						19 42	19 48			19 55	20 02	20 09				20 15			20 17				20 25	20 32
Wandsworth Common d						19 44				19 57	20 04	20 11							20 19				20 27	20 34
Clapham Junction 10 d						19 48	19 52			20 01	20 08	20 15				20 19			20 23				20 31	20 38
West Brompton d																20 32								
Kensington (Olympia) d																20 35								
Shepherd's Bush d																20 38								
Wembley Central d																								
Harrow & Wealdstone d																								
Watford Junction d																								
Milton Keynes Central 10 a																								
Battersea Park 4 d						19 52			20 02	20 05	20 11	20 18							20 26			20 32	20 35	20 41
London Victoria 15 a						19 56	19 59		20 06	20 09	20 16	20 23				20 26			20 33			20 36	20 39	20 46
Streatham 4 d			19 40					19 51							20 10					20 21				
Tulse Hill 3 d	19 40		19f47					19 55					20 10		20g17					20 25				
Herne Hill 4 a																								
Loughborough Jn a																								
Elephant & Castle a																								
London Blackfriars 3 a																								
City Thameslink 3 a																								
St Pancras International 15 a																								
Luton Airport Parkway 7 a																								
Luton 10 a																								
North Dulwich d	19 43							19 58					20 13							20 28				
East Dulwich d	19 45							20 00					20 15							20 30				
Peckham Rye 4 d	19 47				19 56			20 02					20 17					20 26		20 32				
Queens Rd Peckham d	19 50				19 59			20 05					20 20					20 29		20 35				
South Bermondsey d	19 52				20 01			20 07					20 22					20 31		20 37				
London Bridge 4 a	19 57	19 52	20 00	20 11	20 06			20 12					20 27	20 22	20 30		20 41	20 36		20 42				

For general notes see front of timetable
For details of catering facilities see Directory of Train Operators

A From Sutton (Surrey) (Table 182)
B From Caterham (Table 181)
C From Epsom Downs (Table 182)
D From Tattenham Corner (Table 181)
E From Epsom (Table 182)
b Arr. 1935
c Arr. 1914
e Arr. 1921
f Arr. 1944
g Arr. 2014

Saturdays

East and West Croydon, London → Milton Keynes and Luton via Norbury → Crystal Palace → Tulse Hill

Local Services

Network Diagram - see first page of Table 177

		SN A	SN	SN	FC	SN	SN	SN	SN B	SN	SN	SN	FC	SN C	SN D	SN	SN	SN	SN	SN B	SN	SN	SN		FC
East Croydon	d						20 40							20 47				21 10							
West Croydon 4	d	20 18							20 31	20 36					20 48					21 01	21 06				
Norwood Junction 2	a	20 22					20 44								20 52			21 14							
	d	20 23					20 44								20 53			21 14							
Selhurst 4	d								20 35	20 40				20 50						21 06	21 10				
Thornton Heath	d								20 37	20 42				20 52						21 08	21 12				
Norbury	d								20 40	20 45				20 55						21 11	21 15				
Streatham Common 4	d								20 43	20 48				20 58						21 14	21 18				
Bromley South 4	d		20 03																						
Beckenham Junction 4	d		20 23																						
Birkbeck	d		20 26																						
Crystal Palace 4	d	20 27	20 30	20 32								20 43			20 57		21 02						21 13		
Gipsy Hill	d	20 29	20 32									20 46			20 59								21 16		
West Norwood 4	d	20 32	20 35									20 49			21 02								21 19		
Streatham Hill	d	20 36										20 52			21 06								21 22		
Balham 4	d	20 39				20 44			20 47			20 55		21 02	21 09	21 14				21 18			21 25		
Wandsworth Common	d	20 41							20 49			20 57		21 04	21 11					21 20			21 27		
Clapham Junction 10	d	20 45				20 49			20 53			21 01		21 08	21 15	21 19				21 24			21 31		
West Brompton	d																						21 53		
Kensington (Olympia)	d																						21 56		
Shepherd's Bush	d																						21 59		
Wembley Central	d																								
Harrow & Wealdstone	d																								
Watford Junction	d																								
Milton Keynes Central 10	a																								
Battersea Park 4	d	20 48							20 56		21 02	21 05		21 11	21 18				21 15	21 27		21 32	21 35		
London Victoria 15	a	20 53				20 56			21 03		21 06	21 09		21 16	21 23	21 26				21 33		21 36	21 39		
Streatham 4	d				20 40					20 51			21 10								21 21				21 40
Tulse Hill 3	d		20 40		20b47					20 55			21c17								21 25				21e47
Herne Hill 4	a																								
Loughborough Jn	a																								
Elephant & Castle	a																								
London Blackfriars 3	a																								
City Thameslink 3	a																								
St Pancras International 15	a																								
Luton Airport Parkway 7	a																								
Luton 10	a																								
North Dulwich	d		20 43							20 58											21 28				
East Dulwich	d		20 45							21 00											21 30				
Peckham Rye 4	d		20 47					20 56		21 02									21 26		21 32				
Queens Rd Peckham	d		20 50					20 59		21 05									21 29		21 35				
South Bermondsey	d		20 52					21 01		21 07									21 31		21 37				
London Bridge 4	a		20 57	20 52	21 00		21 11	21 06		21 12			21 30				21 22	21 41	21 36		21 42				22 00

		SN C	SN A	SN	SN	SN	SN	SN B	SN	SN	SN	FC	SN C	SN D	SN	SN	SN	SN	SN B	SN	SN	SN	FC	SN C	SN A
East Croydon	d	21 17				21 40							21 47				22 10							22 17	
West Croydon 4	d		21 18					21 31	21 36					21 48					22 01	22 06					22 18
Norwood Junction 2	a		21 22			21 44								21 52			22 14								22 22
	d		21 23			21 44								21 53			22 14								22 23
Selhurst 4	d	21 20						21 36	21 40				21 50						22 06	22 10				22 20	
Thornton Heath	d	21 22						21 38	21 42				21 52						22 08	22 12				22 22	
Norbury	d	21 25						21 41	21 45				21 55						22 11	22 15				22 25	
Streatham Common 4	d	21 28						21 44	21 48				21 58						22 14	22 18				22 28	
Bromley South 4	d																								
Beckenham Junction 4	d																								
Birkbeck	d																								
Crystal Palace 4	d		21 27		21 32						21 43			21 57		22 02						22 13			22 27
Gipsy Hill	d		21 29								21 46			21 59								22 16			22 29
West Norwood 4	d		21 32								21 49			22 02								22 19			22 32
Streatham Hill	d		21 36								21 52			22 06								22 22			22 36
Balham 4	d	21 32	21 39	21 44				21 48			21 55		22 02	22 09	22 14				22 18			22 25		22 32	22 39
Wandsworth Common	d	21 34	21 41					21 50			21 57		22 04	22 11					22 20			22 27		22 34	22 41
Clapham Junction 10	d	21 38	21 45	21 49				21 54			22 01		22 08	22 15	22 19				22 24			22 31		22 38	22 45
West Brompton	d																					22 46			
Kensington (Olympia)	d																					22 50			
Shepherd's Bush	d																					22 53			
Wembley Central	d																								
Harrow & Wealdstone	d																								
Watford Junction	d																								
Milton Keynes Central 10	a																								
Battersea Park 4	d	21 41	21 48					21 57		22 02	22 05		22 11	22 18					22 27		22 32	22 35		22 41	22 48
London Victoria 15	a	21 46	21 53	21 56				22 03		22 06	22 09		22 16	22 23	22 26				22 33		22 36	22 39		22 46	22 53
Streatham 4	d								21 51			22 10								22 21			22 40		
Tulse Hill 3	d								21 55			22f17								22 25			22g47		
Herne Hill 4	a																								
Loughborough Jn	a																								
Elephant & Castle	a																								
London Blackfriars 3	a																								
City Thameslink 3	a																								
St Pancras International 15	a																								
Luton Airport Parkway 7	a																								
Luton 10	a																								
North Dulwich	d								21 58											22 28					
East Dulwich	d								22 00											22 30					
Peckham Rye 4	d						21 56		22 02									22 26		22 32					
Queens Rd Peckham	d						21 59		22 05									22 29		22 35					
South Bermondsey	d						22 01		22 07									22 31		22 37					
London Bridge 4	a				21 52	22 11	22 06		22 12			22 30				22 22	22 41	22 36		22 42			23 00		

For general notes see front of timetable
For details of catering facilities see Directory of Train Operators

A From Epsom Downs (Table 182)
B From Sutton (Surrey) (Table 182)
C From Tattenham Corner (Table 181)
D From Epsom (Table 182)
b Arr. 2044
c Arr. 2114
e Arr. 2144
f Arr. 2214
g Arr. 2244

Table 177

Saturdays

East and West Croydon, London → Milton Keynes and Luton via Norbury → Crystal Palace → Tulse Hill

Local Services

Network Diagram - see first page of Table 177

		SN		SN	SN	SN	SN A	SN	SN	SN	SN B	SN C	SN	SN	SN	SN	SN A	SN	SN	SN	SN B	SN D	SN	SN	
East Croydon	d				22 40						22 47				23 10						23 17				
West Croydon 4	d						22 31	22 36				22 48					23 01	23 06				23 18			
Norwood Junction 2	a				22 44							22 52			23 14							23 22			
	d				22 44							22 53			23 14							23 23			
Selhurst 4	d						22 36	22 40			22 50						23 05	23 10			23 20				
Thornton Heath	d						22 38	22 42			22 52						23 07	23 12			23 22				
Norbury	d						22 41	22 45			22 55						23 10	23 15			23 25				
Streatham Common 4	d						22 44	22 48			22 58						23 13	23 18			23 28				
Bromley South 4	d																								
Beckenham Junction 4	d																								
Birkbeck	d																								
Crystal Palace 4	d			22 32						22 43		22 57		23 02						23 13		23 27	23 32	23 43	
Gipsy Hill	d									22 46		22 59								23 16		23 29		23 46	
West Norwood 4	d									22 49		23 02								23 19		23 32		23 49	
Streatham Hill	d									22 52		23 06								23 22		23 36		23 52	
Balham 4	d	22 44					22 48			22 55	23 02	23 09	23 14				23 17			23 25	23 32	23 40		23 55	
Wandsworth Common	d						22 50			22 57	23 04	23 11					23 19			23 27	23 34	23 42		23 57	
Clapham Junction 10	d	22 49					22 54			23 01	23 08	23 15	23 19				23 23			23 31	23 38	23 46		00 01	
West Brompton	d																								
Kensington (Olympia)	d																								
Shepherd's Bush	d																								
Wembley Central	d																								
Harrow & Wealdstone	d																								
Watford Junction	d																								
Milton Keynes Central 10	a																								
Battersea Park 4	d						22 57		23 02	23 05	23 11	23 18					23 26		23 32	23 35	23 41	23 49	23 10	00 05	
London Victoria 15	a	22 56					23 03		23 06	23 10	23 18	23 23	23 26				23 31		23 37	23 40	23 46	23 54		00 10	
Streatham 4	d							22 51										23 21							
Tulse Hill 3	d							22 55										23 25							
Herne Hill 4	a																								
Loughborough Jn	a																								
Elephant & Castle	a																								
London Blackfriars 3	a																								
City Thameslink 3	a																								
St Pancras International 15	a																								
Luton Airport Parkway 7	a																								
Luton 10	a																								
North Dulwich	d							22 58										23 28							
East Dulwich	d							23 00										23 30							
Peckham Rye 4	d					22 56		23 02								23 26		23 32							
Queens Rd Peckham	d					22 59		23 05								23 29		23 35							
South Bermondsey	d					23 01		23 07								23 31		23 37							
London Bridge 4	a			22 52	23 11	23 06		23 12						23 22	23 38	23 36		23 42					23 52		

For general notes see front of timetable
For details of catering facilities see
Directory of Train Operators

A From Sutton (Surrey) (Table 182)
B From Tattenham Corner (Table 181)
C From Epsom (Table 182)
D From Epsom Downs (Table 182)

Table 177

Sundays

East and West Croydon, London → Milton Keynes and Luton via Norbury → Crystal Palace → Tulse Hill

Local Services

Network Diagram - see first page of Table 177

		SN	SN	SN	SN	SN	SN	SN	SN	SN	SN 1	SN	SN	SN	SN	SN	SN	SN	SN	SN	SN	SN	SN	SN	SN
									A		B					C								C	
East Croydon	d		06 40		06 44		07 12			07 14	07 27						07 44	07 47							08 14
West Croydon 4	d								07 09				07 18			07 39			07 48	08 01				08 09	
Norwood Junction 2	a				06 48		07 17						07 23					07 51	07 53	08 05					
	d				06 48	06 54	07 18						07 24					07 51	07 54	08 05					
Selhurst 4	d		06 43	06 47					07 14	07 17	07 31					07 44	07 47							08 14	08 17
Thornton Heath	d		06 45	06 49					07 16	07 19						07 46	07 49							08 16	08 19
Norbury	d		06 48	06 52					07 19	07 22						07 49	07 52							08 19	08 22
Streatham Common 4	d		06 51	06 54					07 21	07 24						07 51	07 54							08 21	08 24
Bromley South 4	d																								
Beckenham Junction 4	d																								
Birkbeck	d																								
Crystal Palace 4	d	23p43				06 58							07 28						07 58						
Gipsy Hill	d	23p46				07 00							07 30						08 00						
West Norwood 4	d	23p49				07 03							07 33						08 03						
Streatham Hill	d	23p52				07 07							07 37						08 07						
Balham 4	d	23p55	06 55			07 10			07 25				07 40	07 48		07 55			08 10			08 18		08 25	
Wandsworth Common	d	23p57	06 57			07 12			07 27				07 42			07 57			08 12					08 27	
Clapham Junction 10	d	00 01	07 00			07 15			07 31		07 41		07 45	07 52		08 01			08 15			08 22		08 31	
West Brompton	d					*07 30*					*08 22*					*08 22*									
Kensington (Olympia)	d					*07 33*					*08 25*					*08 25*									
Shepherd's Bush	d					*07 36*					*08 28*					*08 28*									
Wembley Central	d																								
Harrow & Wealdstone	d																								
Watford Junction	d																								
Milton Keynes Central 10	a																								
Battersea Park 4	d	00 05	07 04			07 19		07 32	07 35				07 49		08 02	08 05			08 19				08 32	08 35	
London Victoria 15	a	00 10	07 08			07 23		07 36	07 39		07 48		07 53	07 59	08 06	08 09			08 23			08 29	08 36	08 39	
Streatham 4	d			06 57						07 27							07 57								08 27
Tulse Hill 3	d			07 01						07 31							08 01								08 31
Herne Hill 4	a																								
Loughborough Jn	a																								
Elephant & Castle	a																								
London Blackfriars 3	a																								
City Thameslink 3	a																								
St Pancras International 15	a																								
Luton Airport Parkway 7	a																								
Luton 10	a																								
North Dulwich	d			07 04						07 34							08 04								08 34
East Dulwich	d			07 06						07 36							08 06								08 36
Peckham Rye 4	d			07 08						07 38		07 56					08 08				08 26				08 38
Queens Rd Peckham	d			07 11						07 41		07 59					08 11				08 29				08 41
South Bermondsey	d			07 13						07 43		08 01					08 13				08 31				08 43
London Bridge 4	a			07 18	07 12		07 42			07 48		08 06					08 18	08 12		08 31	08 36				08 48

For general notes see front of timetable
For details of catering facilities see Directory of Train Operators

A From Epsom (Table 182)
B From Horsham (Table 186)
C From Sutton (Surrey) (Table 182)

Sundays

East and West Croydon, London → Milton Keynes and Luton via Norbury → Crystal Palace → Tulse Hill

Local Services

Network Diagram - see first page of Table 177

		SN	SN	SN	SN		SN	SN	SN	SN	SN	SN	SN	SN	SN	SN	SN	SN	SN	SN	SN	SN	SN	SN	SN
			1 A					1 B			C			C					C			1 A	C		
East Croydon	d	08 17	08 29					08 34				08 44	08 47							09 14	09 17	09 29			
West Croydon 4	d			08 18	08 31						08 39			08 48	09 01				09 09				09 18	09 31	
Norwood Junction 2	a	08 21		08 23	08 35			08 38					08 51	08 53	09 05						09 21		09 23	09 35	
	d	08 21		08 24	08 35			08 38					08 51	08 54	09 05						09 21		09 24	09 35	
Selhurst 4	d		08 33								08 44	08 47							09 14	09 17		09 33			
Thornton Heath	d										08 46	08 49							09 16	09 19					
Norbury	d										08 49	08 52							09 19	09 22					
Streatham Common 4	d										08 51	08 54							09 21	09 24					
Bromley South 4	d																								
Beckenham Junction 4	d																								
Birkbeck	d																								
Crystal Palace 4	d			08 28										08 58									09 28		
Gipsy Hill	d			08 30										09 00									09 30		
West Norwood 4	d			08 33										09 03									09 33		
Streatham Hill	d			08 37										09 07									09 37		
Balham 4	⊖ d			08 40			08 48				08 55			09 10			09 18		09 25				09 40		09 48
Wandsworth Common	d			08 42							08 57			09 12					09 27				09 42		
Clapham Junction 10	d		08 41	08 45			08 52				09 01			09 15			09 22		09 31			09 41	09 45		09 52
West Brompton	⊖ d		*09 22*								*09 22*											*10 22*			
Kensington (Olympia)	⊖ d		*09 25*								*09 25*											*10 25*			
Shepherd's Bush	⊖ d		*09 28*								*09 28*											*10 28*			
Wembley Central	⊖ d																								
Harrow & Wealdstone	⊖ d																								
Watford Junction	d																								
Milton Keynes Central 10	a																								
Battersea Park 4	d			08 49						09 02	09 05			09 19				09 32	09 35				09 49		
London Victoria 15	⊖ a		08 48	08 53			08 59			09 06	09 09			09 23			09 29	09 36	09 39			09 48	09 53		09 59
Streatham 4	d											08 57								09 27					
Tulse Hill 3	d											09 01								09 31					
Herne Hill 4	a																								
Loughborough Jn	a																								
Elephant & Castle	⊖ a																								
London Blackfriars 3	⊖ a																								
City Thameslink 3	a																								
St Pancras International 15	⊖ a																								
Luton Airport Parkway 7	✈ a																								
Luton 10	a																								
North Dulwich	d											09 04								09 34					
East Dulwich	d											09 06								09 36					
Peckham Rye 4	d								08 56			09 08				09 26				09 38					
Queens Rd Peckham	d								08 59			09 11				09 29				09 41					
South Bermondsey	d								09 01			09 13				09 31				09 43					
London Bridge 4	⊖ a	08 42			09 01			08 51	09 06			09 18	09 12		09 31	09 36				09 48	09 42			10 01	

		SN	SN	SN	SN	SN	SN	SN		SN	SN	SN	SN	SN	SN	SN	SN	FC	SN	SN	SN	SN	SN	SN	SN
		1 B			C			C						C			1 A		C			1 B			C
East Croydon	d	09 34				09 44	09 47								10 14	10 17	10 29					10 34			
West Croydon 4	d				09 39			09 48		10 01				10 09					10 18	10 31					10 39
Norwood Junction 2	a	09 38					09 51	09 53		10 05						10 21			10 23	10 35		10 38			
	d	09 38					09 51	09 54		10 05						10 21			10 24	10 35		10 38			
Selhurst 4	d				09 44	09 47								10 14	10 17		10 33								10 44
Thornton Heath	d				09 46	09 49								10 16	10 19										10 46
Norbury	d				09 49	09 52								10 19	10 22										10 49
Streatham Common 4	d				09 51	09 54								10 21	10 24										10 51
Bromley South 4	d																								
Beckenham Junction 4	d																								
Birkbeck	d																								
Crystal Palace 4	d							09 58											10 28						
Gipsy Hill	d							10 00											10 30						
West Norwood 4	d							10 03											10 33						
Streatham Hill	d							10 07											10 37						
Balham 4	⊖ d				09 55			10 10				10 18		10 25					10 40		10 48				10 55
Wandsworth Common	d				09 57			10 12						10 27					10 42						10 57
Clapham Junction 10	d				10 01			10 15				10 22		10 31			10 41		10 45		10 52				11 01
West Brompton	⊖ d				*10 22*												*11 22*								*11 22*
Kensington (Olympia)	⊖ d				*10 25*												*11 25*								*11 25*
Shepherd's Bush	⊖ d				*10 28*												*11 28*								*11 28*
Wembley Central	⊖ d																								
Harrow & Wealdstone	⊖ d																								
Watford Junction	d																								
Milton Keynes Central 10	a																								
Battersea Park 4	d			10 02	10 05			10 19					10 32	10 35					10 49					11 02	11 05
London Victoria 15	⊖ a			10 06	10 09			10 23				10 29	10 36	10 39			10 48		10 53		10 59			11 06	11 09
Streatham 4	d					09 57									10 27			10 43							
Tulse Hill 3	d					10 01									10 31			10 47							
Herne Hill 4	a																								
Loughborough Jn	a																								
Elephant & Castle	⊖ a																								
London Blackfriars 3	⊖ a																								
City Thameslink 3	a																								
St Pancras International 15	⊖ a																								
Luton Airport Parkway 7	✈ a																								
Luton 10	a																								
North Dulwich	d					10 04									10 34										
East Dulwich	d					10 06									10 36										
Peckham Rye 4	d		09 56			10 08					10 26				10 38								10 56		
Queens Rd Peckham	d		09 59			10 11					10 29				10 41								10 59		
South Bermondsey	d		10 01			10 13					10 31				10 43								11 01		
London Bridge 4	⊖ a	09 51	10 06			10 18	10 12			10 31	10 36				10 48	10 42		10 59		11 01		10 51	11 06		

For general notes see front of timetable
For details of catering facilities see Directory of Train Operators

A From East Grinstead (Table 184)
B Until 6 September
C From Sutton (Surrey) (Table 182)

Table 177

Sundays

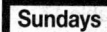

East and West Croydon, London → Milton Keynes and Luton via Norbury → Crystal Palace → Tulse Hill

Local Services

Network Diagram - see first page of Table 177

		SN	SN	FC	SN		SN	SN	SN	SN	SN	SN	SN	SN	FC	SN	SN	SN	SN	SN	SN	SN	SN
														1					1				
					A						A			B		A			C			A	
East Croydon	d	10 44	10 47			and at the same minutes past each hour until						18 14	18 17	18 29					18 34				18 44
West Croydon 4	d				10 48		18 01				18 09					18 18	18 31					18 39	
Norwood Junction 2	a		10 51		10 53		18 05						18 21			18 23	18 35		18 38				
	d		10 51		10 54		18 05						18 21			18 24	18 35		18 38				
Selhurst 4	d	10 47									18 14	18 17		18 33								18 44	18 47
Thornton Heath	d	10 49									18 16	18 19										18 46	18 49
Norbury	d	10 52									18 19	18 22										18 49	18 52
Streatham Common 4	d	10 54									18 21	18 24										18 51	18 54
Bromley South 4	d																						
Beckenham Junction 4	d																						
Birkbeck	d																						
Crystal Palace 4	d				10 58											18 28							
Gipsy Hill	d				11 00											18 30							
West Norwood 4	d				11 03											18 33							
Streatham Hill	d				11 07											18 37							
Balham 4	⊖ d				11 10				18 18		18 25					18 40		18 48				18 55	
Wandsworth Common	d				11 12						18 27					18 42						18 57	
Clapham Junction 10	d				11 15				18 22		18 31			18 41		18 45		18 52				19 01	
West Brompton	⊖ d													*19 12*				*19 12*					
Kensington (Olympia)	⊖ d													*19 15*				*19 15*					
Shepherd's Bush	⊖ d													*19 18*				*19 18*					
Wembley Central	⊖ d																						
Harrow & Wealdstone	⊖ d																						
Watford Junction	d																						
Milton Keynes Central 10	a																						
Battersea Park 4	d				11 19			18 15		18 32	18 35					18 49					19 02	19 05	
London Victoria 15	⊖ a				11 23				18 29	18 36	18 39			18 48		18 53		18 59			19 06	19 09	
Streatham 4	d	10 57		11 13								18 27			18 43								18 57
Tulse Hill 3	d	11 01		11 17								18 31			18 47								19 01
Herne Hill 4	a																						
Loughborough Jn	a																						
Elephant & Castle	⊖ a																						
London Blackfriars 3	⊖ a																						
City Thameslink 3	a																						
St Pancras International 15	⊖ a																						
Luton Airport Parkway 7	✈ a																						
Luton 10	a																						
North Dulwich	d	11 04										18 34											19 04
East Dulwich	d	11 06										18 36											19 06
Peckham Rye 4	d	11 08						18 26				18 38								18 56			19 08
Queens Rd Peckham	d	11 11						18 29				18 41								18 59			19 11
South Bermondsey	d	11 13						18 31				18 43								19 01			19 13
London Bridge 4	⊖ a	11 18	11 12	11 29			18 31	18 36				18 48	18 42		18 59		19 01		18 51	19 06			19 18

		SN	FC	SN	SN	SN	SN	SN	SN	SN	SN	SN	FC	SN	SN	SN	SN	SN	SN	SN	SN	SN	FC	SN
												1					1							
				A					A			B		A			C			A				A
East Croydon	d	18 47								19 14	19 17	19 29					19 34				19 44	19 47		
West Croydon 4	d			18 48	19 01				19 09					19 18	19 31					19 39				19 48
Norwood Junction 2	a	18 51		18 53	19 05						19 21			19 23	19 35		19 38					19 51		19 53
	d	18 51		18 54	19 05						19 21			19 24	19 35		19 38					19 51		19 54
Selhurst 4	d								19 14	19 17		19 33								19 44	19 47			
Thornton Heath	d								19 16	19 19										19 46	19 49			
Norbury	d								19 19	19 22										19 49	19 52			
Streatham Common 4	d								19 21	19 24										19 51	19 54			
Bromley South 4	d																							
Beckenham Junction 4	d																							
Birkbeck	d																							
Crystal Palace 4	d			18 58										19 28										19 58
Gipsy Hill	d			19 00										19 30										20 00
West Norwood 4	d			19 03										19 33										20 03
Streatham Hill	d			19 07										19 37										20 07
Balham 4	⊖ d			19 10			19 18		19 25					19 40		19 48				19 55				20 10
Wandsworth Common	d			19 12					19 27					19 42						19 57				20 12
Clapham Junction 10	d			19 15			19 22		19 31			19 41		19 45		19 52				20 01				20 15
West Brompton	⊖ d											*20 12*				*20 12*								
Kensington (Olympia)	⊖ d											*20 15*				*20 15*								
Shepherd's Bush	⊖ d											*20 18*				*20 18*								
Wembley Central	⊖ d																							
Harrow & Wealdstone	⊖ d																							
Watford Junction	d																							
Milton Keynes Central 10	a																							
Battersea Park 4	d			19 19				19 32	19 35					19 49					20 02	20 05				20 19
London Victoria 15	⊖ a			19 23			19 29	19 36	19 39			19 48		19 53		19 59			20 06	20 09				20 23
Streatham 4	d		19 13							19 27			19 43								19 57		20 13	
Tulse Hill 3	d		19 17							19 31			19 47								20 01		20 17	
Herne Hill 4	a																							
Loughborough Jn	a																							
Elephant & Castle	⊖ a																							
London Blackfriars 3	⊖ a																							
City Thameslink 3	a																							
St Pancras International 15	⊖ a																							
Luton Airport Parkway 7	✈ a																							
Luton 10	a																							
North Dulwich	d									19 34											20 04			
East Dulwich	d									19 36											20 06			
Peckham Rye 4	d					19 26				19 38								19 56			20 08			
Queens Rd Peckham	d					19 29				19 41								19 59			20 11			
South Bermondsey	d					19 31				19 43								20 01			20 13			
London Bridge 4	⊖ a	19 12	19 29		19 31	19 36				19 48	19 42		19 59		20 01		19 51	20 06			20 18	20 12	20 29	

For general notes see front of timetable
For details of catering facilities see Directory of Train Operators

A From Sutton (Surrey) (Table 182)
B From East Grinstead (Table 184)
C Until 6 September

Table 177

Sundays

East and West Croydon, London → Milton Keynes and Luton via Norbury → Crystal Palace → Tulse Hill

Local Services

Network Diagram - see first page of Table 177

		SN	SN	SN	SN	SN	SN	SN	SN	FC	SN	SN	SN	SN	SN	SN	SN		SN	SN	FC	SN	SN	SN	SN
									1					1											
						A			B		A			C			A					A			
East Croydon	d						20 14	20 17	20 29					20 34					20 44	20 47					
West Croydon 4	d	20 01				20 09					20 18	20 31		20 38			20 39					20 48	21 01		
Norwood Junction 2	a	20 05						20 21			20 23	20 35		20 38						20 51		20 53	21 05		
	d	20 05						20 21			20 24	20 35		20 38						20 51		20 54	21 05		
Selhurst 4	d					20 14	20 17		20 33								20 44		20 47						
Thornton Heath	d					20 16	20 19										20 46		20 49						
Norbury	d					20 19	20 22										20 49		20 52						
Streatham Common 4	d					20 21	20 24										20 51		20 54						
Bromley South 4	d																								
Beckenham Junction 4	d																								
Birkbeck	d																								
Crystal Palace 4	d										20 28											20 58			
Gipsy Hill	d										20 30											21 00			
West Norwood 4	d										20 33											21 03			
Streatham Hill	d										20 37											21 07			
Balham 4	⊖ d			20 18		20 25					20 40		20 48				20 55					21 10			21 18
Wandsworth Common	d					20 27					20 42						20 57					21 12			
Clapham Junction 10	d			20 22		20 31			20 41		20 45		20 52				21 01					21 15			21 22
West Brompton	⊖ d								21 22								21 22								
Kensington (Olympia)	⊖ d								21 25								21 25								
Shepherd's Bush	⊖ d								21 28								21 28								
Wembley Central	⊖ d																								
Harrow & Wealdstone	⊖ d																								
Watford Junction	d																								
Milton Keynes Central 10	a																								
Battersea Park 4	d				20 32	20 35					20 49					21 02	21 05					21 19			
London Victoria 15	⊖ a			20 29	20 36	20 39			20 48		20 53		20 59			21 06	21 09					21 23			21 29
Streatham 4	d						20 27			20 43									20 57		21 13				
Tulse Hill 3	d						20 31			20 47									21 01		21 17				
Herne Hill 4	a																								
Loughborough Jn	a																								
Elephant & Castle	⊖ a																								
London Blackfriars 3	⊖ a																								
City Thameslink 3	a																								
St Pancras International 15	⊖ a																								
Luton Airport Parkway 7	✈ a																								
Luton 10	a																								
North Dulwich	d						20 34												21 04						
East Dulwich	d						20 36												21 06						
Peckham Rye 4	d		20 26				20 38								20 56				21 08					21 26	
Queens Rd Peckham	d		20 29				20 41								20 59				21 11					21 29	
South Bermondsey	d		20 31				20 43								21 01				21 13					21 31	
London Bridge 4	⊖ a	20 31	20 36				20 48	20 42		20 59		21 01		20 51	21 06				21 18	21 12	21 29		21 31	21 36	

		SN	SN	SN	SN	SN	FC	SN	SN	SN	SN	SN	SN	SN	SN	SN	SN	SN	SN	SN	SN	SN		SN	SN
						1					1														
			A			B		A			C			A			A					A			
East Croydon	d			21 14	21 17	21 29					21 34				21 44	21 47								22 14	22 17
West Croydon 4	d		21 09					21 18	21 31		21 38			21 39			21 48	22 01				22 09			
Norwood Junction 2	a				21 21			21 23	21 35		21 38					21 51	21 53	22 05							22 21
	d				21 21			21 24	21 35		21 38					21 51	21 54	22 05							22 21
Selhurst 4	d		21 14	21 17		21 33								21 44	21 47							22 14		22 17	
Thornton Heath	d		21 16	21 19										21 46	21 49							22 16		22 19	
Norbury	d		21 19	21 22										21 49	21 52							22 19		22 22	
Streatham Common 4	d		21 21	21 24										21 51	21 54							22 21		22 24	
Bromley South 4	d																								
Beckenham Junction 4	d																								
Birkbeck	d																								
Crystal Palace 4	d							21 28									21 58								
Gipsy Hill	d							21 30									22 00								
West Norwood 4	d							21 33									22 03								
Streatham Hill	d							21 37									22 07								
Balham 4	⊖ d		21 25					21 40		21 48				21 55			22 10			22 18		22 25			
Wandsworth Common	d		21 27					21 42						21 57			22 12					22 27			
Clapham Junction 10	d		21 31			21 41		21 45		21 52				22 01			22 15			22 22		22 31			
West Brompton	⊖ d					22 22								22 22											
Kensington (Olympia)	⊖ d					22 25								22 25											
Shepherd's Bush	⊖ d					22 28								22 28											
Wembley Central	⊖ d																								
Harrow & Wealdstone	⊖ d																								
Watford Junction	d																								
Milton Keynes Central 10	a																								
Battersea Park 4	d	21 32	21 35					21 49					22 02	22 05			22 19				22 32	22 35			
London Victoria 15	⊖ a	21 36	21 39			21 48		21 53		21 59			22 06	22 09			22 23			22 29	22 36	22 39			
Streatham 4	d			21 27			21 43								21 57									22 27	
Tulse Hill 3	d			21 31			21 47								22 01									22 31	
Herne Hill 4	a																								
Loughborough Jn	a																								
Elephant & Castle	⊖ a																								
London Blackfriars 3	⊖ a																								
City Thameslink 3	a																								
St Pancras International 15	⊖ a																								
Luton Airport Parkway 7	✈ a																								
Luton 10	a																								
North Dulwich	d			21 34											22 04									22 34	
East Dulwich	d			21 36											22 06									22 36	
Peckham Rye 4	d			21 38								21 56			22 08				22 26					22 38	
Queens Rd Peckham	d			21 41								21 59			22 11				22 29					22 41	
South Bermondsey	d			21 43								22 01			22 13				22 31					22 43	
London Bridge 4	⊖ a			21 48	21 42		21 59		22 01		21 51	22 06			22 18	22 12		22 31	22 36					22 48	22 42

For general notes see front of timetable
For details of catering facilities see
Directory of Train Operators

A From Sutton (Surrey) (Table 182)
B From East Grinstead (Table 184)
C Until 6 September

Table 177

Sundays

East and West Croydon, London → Milton Keynes and Luton via Norbury → Crystal Palace → Tulse Hill

Local Services

Network Diagram - see first page of Table 177

		SN 1 A	SN B	SN	SN	SN 1 C	SN	SN	SN B	SN	SN	SN 1 D	SN 1 E	SN	SN B	SN	SN	SN B	SN 1 A	SN B	SN	SN B	SN 1 G
East Croydon	d	22 29				22 34				22 44	22 47	22 56	22 58						23 29				23 56
West Croydon 4	d		22 18	22 31					22 39						22 48			23 09		23 18		23 40	
Norwood Junction 2	a		22 23	22 35		22 38					22 51				22 53					23 23			
	d		22 24	22 35		22 38					22 51				22 54					23 26			
Selhurst 4	d	22 33							22 44	22 47		22 59	23 02					23 14	23 33			23a44	00 01
Thornton Heath	d								22 46	22 49								23 16					
Norbury	d								22 49	22 52								23 19					
Streatham Common 4	d								22 51	22 54								23 21					
Bromley South 4	d																						
Beckenham Junction 4	d																						
Birkbeck	d																						
Crystal Palace 4	d		22 28												22 58					23 30			
Gipsy Hill	d		22 30												23 00					23 32			
West Norwood 4	d		22 33												23 03					23 35			
Streatham Hill	d		22 37												23 07					23 39			
Balham 4	⊖ d		22 40		22 48				22 55						23 10	23 18		23 25		23 42	23 48		
Wandsworth Common	d		22 42						22 57						23 12			23 27		23 44			
Clapham Junction 10	d	22 41	22 45		22 52				23 01			23 07	23 10		23 15	23 22		23 31	23 41	23 47	23 52		00 11
West Brompton	⊖ d																						
Kensington (Olympia)	⊖ d																						
Shepherd's Bush	⊖ d																						
Wembley Central	⊖ d																						
Harrow & Wealdstone	⊖ d																						
Watford Junction	d																						
Milton Keynes Central 10	a																						
Battersea Park 4	d		22 49					23 02	23 05						23 19		23 32	23 35		23 51			
London Victoria 15	⊖ a	22 48	22 53		22 59			23 06	23 09			23 14	23 16		23 23	23 29	23 37	23 39	23 51	23 55	23 59		00 18
Streatham 4	d									22 57													
Tulse Hill 3	d									23 01													
Herne Hill 4	a																						
Loughborough Jn	a																						
Elephant & Castle	⊖ a																						
London Blackfriars 3	⊖ a																						
City Thameslink 3	a																						
St Pancras International 15	⊖ a																						
Luton Airport Parkway 7	✈ a																						
Luton 10	a																						
North Dulwich	d									23 04													
East Dulwich	d									23 06													
Peckham Rye 4	d						22 56			23 08				23 26									
Queens Rd Peckham	d						22 59			23 11				23 29									
South Bermondsey	d						23 01			23 13				23 31									
London Bridge 4	⊖ a			23 01		22 51	23 06			23 19	23 12			23 36									

For general notes see front of timetable
For details of catering facilities see Directory of Train Operators

A From East Grinstead (Table 184)
B From Sutton (Surrey) (Table 182)
C Until 6 September
D Until 6 September. From Horsham (Table 186)
E From 13 September. From Horsham (Table 186)
G From Horsham (Table 186)

Charing Cross and London Bridge → London Victoria and Croydon

Network Diagram - see first page of Table 177

Miles	Miles	Miles	Miles	Miles	Station		SN MX	SN MO A	SN MX A	SN MX	SE	SN B	SE	SN	SN A	SE	SN 1 C	SN A	SN	SE	SN D	SN E	SN	SN G	SN A	SN 1 H
—	—	0	—	—	**London Charing Cross** 4	⊖ d		23p34	23p45	00 12					06 05											
—	—	¾	—	—	London Waterloo (East) 4	⊖ d		23p37	23p48	00 15					06 08											
0	0	1¾	—	—	**London Bridge** 4	⊖ d	23p24	23p44	23p53	00 26		05 45		06 11	06 13		06 30	06 35	06 41		06 46	06 52	07 11	07 15	07 25	07 28
—	2¾	4½	—	—	New Cross Gate 4	⊖ d	23p30	23p49	23p58	00 31		05 50			06 19		06 35	06 40			06 51	06 58		07 20	07 30	07 33
—	3¾	5½	—	—	Brockley	d	23p32	23p52	00 01	00 34		05 53			06 22			06 43			06 54	07 01		07 23	07 33	
—	4¾	6½	—	—	Honor Oak Park	d	23p35	23p55	00 04	00 37		05 56			06 25			06 46			06 57	07 04		07 26	07 36	
—	5¾	7½	—	—	Forest Hill 4	d	23p38	23p57	00 06	00 39		05 58			06 27			06 48			06 59	07 06		07 28	07 38	
—	6½	8¼	—	—	Sydenham	d	23p40	23p59	00 09	00 42		06 01			06 30			06 51			07 02	07 09		07 31	07 41	
—	7¾	—	—	—	**Crystal Palace** 4	d	23p43																			
—	8½	—	—	—	Gipsy Hill	d	23p46																			
—	9½	—	—	—	West Norwood 4	d	23p49																			
—	10¾	—	—	—	Streatham Hill	d	23p52																			
—	11¾	—	—	—	Balham 4	⊖ d	23p55																			
—	12½	—	—	—	Wandsworth Common	d	23p57																			
—	13¾	—	—	—	Clapham Junction 10	d	00 01																			
1¾	—	—	—	—	South Bermondsey	d								06 15					06 45				07 15			
2¾	—	—	—	—	Queens Rd Peckham	d								06 18					06 48				07 17			
3½	—	—	0	0	Peckham Rye 4	d					05 04		06 04	06 20		06 33			06 50	07 02			07 20			
4¼	—	—	¾	¾	Denmark Hill 4	d					05 06		06 07	06 23		06 35			06 53	07 05			07 23			
—	—	—	—	4½	**London Blackfriars** 3	⊖ a					05 17		06 16			06 44				07 16						
6¼	—	—	—	—	Clapham High Street	⊖ d								06 28					06 58				07 28			
6¾	—	—	—	—	Wandsworth Road	d								06 29					06 59				07 29			
7½	15¼	—	—	—	Battersea Park 4	d	00 04							06 32					07 02				07 32			
8¾	16½	—	5	—	**London Victoria** 15	⊖ a	00 12							06 36					07 08				07 38			
—	—	9	—	—	Penge West	d		00 02	00 11	00 44		06 03			06 32						07 04			07 33	07 43	
—	—	9¼	—	—	Anerley	d		00 04	00 13	00 46		06 05			06 34						07 06			07 35	07 45	
—	—	10½	—	0	Norwood Junction 2	d		00 10	00 16	00 50		06 09			06 38		06 44	06 56			07 10	07 14		07 39	07b51	07 42
—	—	—	—	1¾	**West Croydon** 4	a						06 13									07 15			07 44		
—	—	11¾	—	—	**East Croydon**	a		00 13	00 20	00 53					06 41		06 48	06 59				07 17			07 55	07 45

Station		SE	SN E	SN	SE J	SE K	SE	SN L	SE 1	SE J	SE K	SE	SN A	SN	SE	SE	SN N	SE J	SE K	SE	SE 1	SE	SN B	SN 1	SN A	SN
London Charing Cross 4	⊖ d																									
London Waterloo (East) 4	⊖ d																									
London Bridge 4	⊖ d		07 39	07 41				07 48					08 03	08 10			08 17						08 19	08 27	08 36	08 41
New Cross Gate 4	⊖ d		07 44					07 53					08 08				08 22						08 26	08 32	08 41	
Brockley	d		07 47					07 56					08 11				08 25						08 29		08 44	
Honor Oak Park	d		07 50					07 59					08 14				08 28						08 32		08 47	
Forest Hill 4	d		07 52					08 01					08 16				08 30						08 34		08 49	
Sydenham	d		07 55					08 04					08 19				08 33						08 37		08 52	
Crystal Palace 4	d																08 36									
Gipsy Hill	d																08 38									
West Norwood 4	d																08a42									
Streatham Hill	d																									
Balham 4	⊖ d																									
Wandsworth Common	d																									
Clapham Junction 10	d																									
South Bermondsey	d			07 45										08 14												08 45
Queens Rd Peckham	d			07 48										08 16												08 48
Peckham Rye 4	d	07 34		07 50	07 55	07 55	08 00			08 11	08 11	08 15		08 19				08 32	08 32	08 35		08 44				08 50
Denmark Hill 4	d	07 37		07 53	07 59	07 59	08 02		08 06	08 14	08 14	08 18		08 22	08 26	08 29		08 35	08 35	08 37	08 40	08 47				08 53
London Blackfriars 3	⊖ a	07 48					08 18					08 30			08 41					08 50		08 58				
Clapham High Street	⊖ d			07 58										08 27												08 58
Wandsworth Road	d			07 59										08 29												08 59
Battersea Park 4	d			08 02										08 32												09 02
London Victoria 15	⊖ a			08 08	08 11	08 12			08 17	08 28	08 29			08 39		08 41		08 46	08 47		08 52					09 08
Penge West	d							08 06															08 39			
Anerley	d							08 08															08 41			
Norwood Junction 2	d		08 00					08 11					08 26										08 44		08 57	
West Croydon 4	a							08 16															08 49			
East Croydon	a		08 03										08 29											08 45	09 00	

For general notes see front of timetable
For details of catering facilities see Directory of Train Operators

- **A** To Caterham (Table 181)
- **B** To Sutton (Surrey) (Table 182)
- **C** To East Grinstead (Table 184)
- **D** To Guildford (Table 182)
- **E** To Tattenham Corner (Table 181) and to Caterham (Table 181)
- **G** To Epsom (Table 182)
- **H** To Tonbridge (Table 186)
- **J** Until 9 October
- **K** From 12 October
- **L** To Dorking (Table 182)
- **N** To London Bridge (Table 177)
- **b** Arr. 0748

Charing Cross and London Bridge → London Victoria and Croydon

Network Diagram - see first page of Table 177

		SE A	SE B		SE	SN C	SE	SE	SE A	SE B	SN	SN D	SN	SE	SN C	SN	SN D	SN	SE A	SE B	SE	SN C	SN	SN D	SN	SE
London Charing Cross 4	⊖ d																									
London Waterloo (East) 4	⊖ d																									
London Bridge 4	⊖ d					08 43					08 54	09 05	09 11		09 14	09 24	09 35	09 41				09 45	09 54	10 05	10 11	
New Cross Gate 4	⊖ d					08 48					08 59	09 11			09 20	09 30	09 40					09 50	10 00	10 10		
Brockley	d					08 51					09 02	09 13			09 23	09 32	09 43					09 53	10 03	10 13		
Honor Oak Park	d					08 54					09 05	09 16			09 26	09 35	09 46					09 56	10 06	10 16		
Forest Hill 4	d					08 56					09 07	09 19			09 28	09 38	09 48					09 58	10 08	10 18		
Sydenham	d					08 59					09 10	09 21			09 31	09 40	09 51					10 01	10 11	10 21		
Crystal Palace 4	d										09 13					09 43							10 14			
Gipsy Hill	d										09 15					09 46							10 16			
West Norwood 4	d										09 18					09 49							10 19			
Streatham Hill	d										09 22					09 52							10 23			
Balham 4	⊖ d										09 27					09 56							10 26			
Wandsworth Common	d										09 29					09 58							10 28			
Clapham Junction 10	d										09 33					10 02							10 32			
South Bermondsey	d												09 15					09 45							10 15	
Queens Rd Peckham	d												09 18					09 48							10 18	
Peckham Rye 4	d	08{55	08{55		09 04		09 08	09 16	09{18	09{18			09 20	09 28				09 50	09{58	09{58	10 01				10 20	10 22
Denmark Hill 4	d	08{59	08{59		09 07		09 11	09 19	09{20	09{20			09 23	09 31				09 53	10{01	10{01	10 04				10 23	10 25
London Blackfriars 3	⊖ a				09 18		09 26	09 30						09 44							10 17					10 34
Clapham High Street	⊖ d												09 28					09 58							10 28	
Wandsworth Road	d												09 29					09 59							10 29	
Battersea Park 4	d												09 33			10 05		10 03					10 35		10 32	
London Victoria 15	⊖ a	09{11	09{12						09{32	09{33	09 42		09 39			10 11		10 07	10{12	10{14			10 40		10 36	
Penge West	d					09 01									09 33							10 03				
Anerley	d					09 03									09 35							10 05				
Norwood Junction 2	d					09 10						09 26			09 40		09 56					10 10		10 26		
West Croydon 4	a					09 15									09 45							10 15				
East Croydon	a											09 29					09 59							10 29		

		SE		SN C	SN	SN D	SN	SE	SE	SN C	SN	SN D	SN	SE	SE	and at the same minutes past each hour until	SN C	SN	SN D	SN	SE	SE	SN C	SN	SN D
London Charing Cross 4	⊖ d																								
London Waterloo (East) 4	⊖ d																								
London Bridge 4	⊖ d			10 15	10 24	10 35	10 41			10 45	10 54	11 05	11 11				15 15	15 24	15 35	15 41			15 45	15 54	16 05
New Cross Gate 4	⊖ d			10 20	10 30	10 40				10 50	11 00	11 10					15 20	15 30	15 40				15 50	16 00	16 10
Brockley	d			10 23	10 32	10 43				10 53	11 02	11 13					15 23	15 32	15 43				15 53	16 02	16 13
Honor Oak Park	d			10 26	10 35	10 46				10 56	11 05	11 16					15 26	15 35	15 46				15 56	16 05	16 16
Forest Hill 4	d			10 28	10 38	10 48				10 58	11 08	11 18					15 28	15 38	15 48				15 58	16 08	16 18
Sydenham	d			10 31	10 40	10 51				11 01	11 10	11 21					15 31	15 40	15 51				16 01	16 10	16 21
Crystal Palace 4	d				10 43						11 13							15 43						16 13	
Gipsy Hill	d				10 46						11 16							15 46						16 16	
West Norwood 4	d				10 49						11 19							15 49						16 19	
Streatham Hill	d				10 52						11 22							15 52						16 22	
Balham 4	⊖ d				10 55						11 25							15 55						16 25	
Wandsworth Common	d				10 57						11 27							15 57						16 27	
Clapham Junction 10	d				11 01						11 31							16 01						16 31	
South Bermondsey	d						10 45						11 15							15 45					
Queens Rd Peckham	d						10 48						11 18							15 48					
Peckham Rye 4	d	10 28					10 50	10 52	10 58				11 20	11 22	11 28					15 50	15 52	15 58			
Denmark Hill 4	d	10 31					10 53	10 55	11 01				11 23	11 25	11 31					15 53	15 55	16 01			
London Blackfriars 3	⊖ a							11 04						11 34							16 04				
Clapham High Street	⊖ d						10 58						11 28							15 58					
Wandsworth Road	d						10 59						11 29							15 59					
Battersea Park 4	d				11 05		11 02				11 35		11 32					16 05		16 02				16 35	
London Victoria 15	⊖ a	10 42			11 09		11 06		11 12		11 40		11 36		11 42			16 10		16 06		16 12		16 40	
Penge West	d			10 33						11 03							15 33						16 03		
Anerley	d			10 35						11 05							15 35						16 05		
Norwood Junction 2	d			10 40		10 56				11 10		11 26					15 40		15 56				16 10		16 26
West Croydon 4	a			10 45						11 15							15 45						16 15		
East Croydon	a					10 59						11 29							15 59						16 29

For general notes see front of timetable
For details of catering facilities see Directory of Train Operators

A Until 9 October
B From 12 October
C To Sutton (Surrey) (Table 182)
D To Caterham (Table 181)

Charing Cross and London Bridge → London Victoria and Croydon

Network Diagram - see first page of Table 177

	SN	SE	SN		SE	SN	SN	SN	SE	SN	SE	SN	SN	SN	SE	SN	SN	SN	SN	SE	SE	SN	SN	SN	SN
		1	A						1	A						A						B			
London Charing Cross 4 ⊖ d																									
London Waterloo (East) 4 ⊖ d																									
London Bridge 4 ⊖ d	16 11		16 15			16 24	16 35	16 41		16 44		16 54	17 05	17 11		17 19	17 25	17 35	17 41			17 51	17 55	18 05	18 11
New Cross Gate 4 ⊖ d			16 20			16 30	16 40			16 49		17 00	17 10			17 25	17 30	17 40				17 57	18 01	18 10	
Brockley d			16 23			16 32	16 43			16 52		17 02	17 13			17 27	17 33	17 43				17 59	18 04	18 13	
Honor Oak Park d			16 26			16 35	16 46			16 55		17 05	17 16			17 30	17 36	17 46				18 02	18 07	18 16	
Forest Hill 4 d			16 28			16 38	16 48			16 57		17 08	17 18			17 33	17 38	17 48				18 05	18 09	18 18	
Sydenham d			16 31			16 40	16 51			17 00		17 10	17 21			17 35	17 41	17 51				18 07	18 12	18 21	
Crystal Palace 4 d						16 43						17 13					17 44						18 15		
Gipsy Hill d						16 46						17 16					17 46						18 17		
West Norwood 4 d						16 49						17 19					17 49						18 20		
Streatham Hill d						16 52						17 22					17 53						18 24		
Balham 4 ⊖ d						16 55						17 25					17 56						18 29		
Wandsworth Common d						16 57						17 27					17 58						18 31		
Clapham Junction 10 d						17 01						17 31					18 02						18 35		
South Bermondsey d	16 15							16 45						17 15					17 45						18 15
Queens Rd Peckham d	16 18							16 48						17 18					17 48						18 18
Peckham Rye 4 d	16 20	16 22			16 42			16 50	16 53		17 15			17 20	17 24				17 50	17 54	18 03				18 20
Denmark Hill 4 d	16 23	16 25			16 46			16 53	16 56		17 18			17 23	17 26				17 53	17 57	18 06				18 23
London Blackfriars 3 ⊖ a		16 34							17 07						17 39					18 09					
Clapham High Street ⊖ d	16 28							16 58						17 28					17 58						18 28
Wandsworth Road d	16 29							16 59						17 29					17 59						18 29
Battersea Park 4 d	16 32					17 05		17 02				17 35		17 32			18 06		18 02				18 39		18 32
London Victoria 15 ⊖ a	16 38				17 03	17 10		17 08			17 28	17 42		17 38			18 12		18 08		18 16		18 45		18 39
Penge West d			16 33				16 53			17 02			17 23					17 53						18 23	
Anerley d			16 35				16 55			17 04			17 25					17 55						18 25	
Norwood Junction 2 d			16 40				16 59			17 10			17 29			17 40		17 59				18 12		18 29	
West Croydon 4 a			16 45				17 05			17 15			17 35			17 46		18 05				18 17		18 35	
East Croydon a																									

	SE	SN	SE	SN	SN	SN	SE	SE	SN	SN	SN	SE	SN	SN	SN	SN	SE	SN	SN	SN	SE	SN	SN	SN	SE
	1	B					1			C			D					D				D			
London Charing Cross 4 ⊖ d																		19 37				20 07			
London Waterloo (East) 4 ⊖ d																		19 40				20 10			
London Bridge 4 ⊖ d		18 20		18 24	18 34	18 41			18 51	19 05	19 11		19 14	19 24	19 35	19 41		19 45	19 54	20 11		20 15	20 24	20 41	
New Cross Gate 4 ⊖ d		18 25		18 30	18 40				18 56	19 10			19 19	19 30	19 40			19 50	20 00			20 20	20 30		
Brockley d		18 28		18 32	18 43				18 59	19 13			19 22	19 32	19 43			19 53	20 02			20 23	20 32		
Honor Oak Park d		18 31		18 35	18 46				19 02	19 16			19 25	19 35	19 46			19 56	20 05			20 26	20 35		
Forest Hill 4 d		18 33		18 38	18 48				19 04	19 18			19 27	19 38	19 48			19 58	20 08			20 28	20 38		
Sydenham d		18 36		18 40	18 51				19 07	19 21			19 30	19 40	19 51			20 01	20 10			20 31	20 40		
Crystal Palace 4 d				18 43					19 13					19 43					20 13				20 43		
Gipsy Hill d				18 46					19 16					19 46					20 16				20 46		
West Norwood 4 d				18 49					19 19					19 49					20 19				20 49		
Streatham Hill d				18 52					19 22					19 52					20 22				20 52		
Balham 4 ⊖ d				18 55					19 25					19 55					20 25				20 55		
Wandsworth Common d				18 57					19 27					19 57					20 27				20 57		
Clapham Junction 10 d				19 01					19 31					20 01					20 31				21 01		
South Bermondsey d						18 45					19 15					19 45				20 15				20 45	
Queens Rd Peckham d						18 48					19 18					19 48				20 18				20 48	
Peckham Rye 4 d	18 23		18 47			18 50	18 52	19 12			19 20	19 28				19 50	19 53			20 20	20 22			20 50	20 52
Denmark Hill 4 d	18 25		18 50			18 53	18 55	19 15			19 23	19 31				19 53	19 55			20 23	20 25			20 53	20 55
London Blackfriars 3 ⊖ a	18 35						19 05					19 41					20 03				20 33				21 03
Clapham High Street ⊖ d						18 58					19 28					19 58				20 28				20 58	
Wandsworth Road d						18 59					19 29					19 59				20 29				20 59	
Battersea Park 4 d				19 05		19 02			19 35		19 32			20 05		20 02			20 35	20 32			21 05	21 02	
London Victoria 15 ⊖ a			19 01	19 12		19 09		19 25	19 42		19 36			20 09		20 06			20 39	20 36			21 09	21 06	
Penge West d					18 53					19 23			19 32		19 53			20 03				20 33			
Anerley d					18 55					19 25			19 34		19 55			20 05				20 35			
Norwood Junction 2 d		18 41			18 59					19 28			19 38		19a58			20 09				20 39			
West Croydon 4 a		18 45			19 05					19 33			19 41					20 12				20 42			
East Croydon a																									

For general notes see front of timetable
For details of catering facilities see Directory of Train Operators

A To Guildford (Table 182)
B To Dorking (Table 182)
C To Epsom (Table 182)
D To Caterham (Table 181)

Charing Cross and London Bridge → London Victoria and Croydon

Network Diagram - see first page of Table 177

Mondays to Fridays

		SN A	SN	SN	SE	SN A	SN	SN	SE	SN A	SN	SN	SE	SN A	SN	SN	SE	SN A	SN	SN	SE	SN A	SN	SN A
London Charing Cross 4 ⊖	d	20 37				21 07				21 37				22 07				22 37				23 07		23 45
London Waterloo (East) 4 ⊖	d	20 40				21 10				21 40				22 10				22 40				23 10		23 48
London Bridge 4 ⊖	d	20 45	20 54	21 11		21 15	21 24	21 41		21 45	21 54	22 11		22 15	22 24	22 41		22 45	22 54	23 11		23 15	23 24	23 53
New Cross Gate 4 ⊖	d	20 50	21 00			21 20	21 30			21 50	22 00			22 20	22 30			22 50	23 00			23 20	23 30	23 58
Brockley	d	20 53	21 02			21 23	21 32			21 53	22 02			22 23	22 32			22 53	23 02			23 23	23 32	00 01
Honor Oak Park	d	20 56	21 05			21 26	21 35			21 56	22 05			22 26	22 35			22 56	23 05			23 26	23 35	00 04
Forest Hill 4	d	20 58	21 08			21 28	21 38			21 58	22 08			22 28	22 38			22 58	23 08			23 28	23 38	00 06
Sydenham	d	21 01	21 10			21 31	21 40			22 01	22 10			22 31	22 40			23 01	23 10			23 31	23 40	00 09
Crystal Palace 4	d		21 13				21 43				22 13				22 43				23 13				23 43	
Gipsy Hill	d		21 16				21 46				22 16				22 46				23 16				23 46	
West Norwood 4	d		21 19				21 49				22 19				22 49				23 19				23 49	
Streatham Hill	d		21 22				21 52				22 22				22 52				23 22				23 52	
Balham 4 ⊖	d		21 25				21 55				22 25				22 55				23 25				23 55	
Wandsworth Common	d		21 27				21 57				22 27				22 57				23 27				23 57	
Clapham Junction 10	d		21 31				22 01				22 31				23 01				23 31				00 01	
South Bermondsey	d			21 15				21 45				22 15				22 45				23 15				
Queens Rd Peckham	d			21 18				21 48				22 18				22 48				23 18				
Peckham Rye 4	d			21 20	21 22			21 50	21 52			22 20	22 22			22 50	22 52			23 20	23 22			
Denmark Hill 4	d			21 23	21 24			21 53	21 54			22 23	22 24			22 53	22 54			23 23	23 24			
London Blackfriars 3 ⊖	a																							
Clapham High Street ⊖	d			21 28				21 58				22 28				22 58				23 28				
Wandsworth Road	d			21 29				21 59				22 29				22 59				23 29				
Battersea Park 4	d		21 35	21 32			22 05	22 02			22 35	22 32			23 05	23 02			23 35	23 32			00 04	
London Victoria 15 ⊖	a		21 39	21 36	21 33		22 09	22 06	22 03		22 39	22 36	22 37		23 10	23 06	23 03		23 40	23 37	23 33		00 12	
Penge West	d	21 03				21 33				22 03				22 33				23 03				23 33		00 11
Anerley	d	21 05				21 35				22 05				22 35				23 05				23 35		00 13
Norwood Junction 2	d	21 09				21 39				22 09				22 39				23 09				23 39		00 16
West Croydon 4 🚋	a																							
East Croydon 🚋	a	21 12				21 42				22 12				22 42				23 12				23 42		00 20

Saturdays

		SN	SN A	SN	SN	SE		SN A	SN	SE	SN A	SN		SE	SE	SN B	SN A	SN		SE	SE	SN B	SN A	SN		SE
London Charing Cross 4 ⊖	d		23p45	00 12																						
London Waterloo (East) 4 ⊖	d		23p48	00 15																						
London Bridge 4 ⊖	d	23p24	23p53	00 26	06 11			06 35	06 41		07 05	07 11				07 14	07 35	07 41				07 44	08 05	08 11		
New Cross Gate 4 ⊖	d	23p30	23p58	00 31				06 40			07 10					07 20	07 40					07 50	08 10			
Brockley	d	23p32	00 01	00 34				06 43			07 13					07 22	07 43					07 52	08 13			
Honor Oak Park	d	23p35	00 04	00 37				06 46			07 16					07 25	07 46					07 55	08 16			
Forest Hill 4	d	23p38	00 06	00 39				06 48			07 18					07 28	07 48					07 58	08 18			
Sydenham	d	23p40	00 09	00 42				06 51			07 21					07 30	07 51					08 00	08 21			
Crystal Palace 4	d	23p43																								
Gipsy Hill	d	23p46																								
West Norwood 4	d	23p49																								
Streatham Hill	d	23p52																								
Balham 4 ⊖	d	23p55																								
Wandsworth Common	d	23p57																								
Clapham Junction 10	d	00 01																								
South Bermondsey	d				06 15				06 45			07 15						07 45						08 15		
Queens Rd Peckham	d				06 18				06 48			07 18						07 48						08 18		
Peckham Rye 4	d				06 20	06 22			06 50	06 52		07 20		07 22	07 28			07 50		07 52	07 58			08 20		08 22
Denmark Hill 4	d				06 23	06 25			06 53	06 55		07 23		07 25	07 31			07 53		07 55	08 01			08 23		08 25
London Blackfriars 3 ⊖	a																									
Clapham High Street ⊖	d				06 28				06 58			07 28						07 58						08 28		
Wandsworth Road	d				06 29				06 59			07 29						07 59						08 29		
Battersea Park 4	d	00 04			06 32				07 02			07 32						08 02						08 32		
London Victoria 15 ⊖	a	00 12			06 36	06 35			07 06	07 06		07 36		07 36	07 41			08 06		08 06	08 12			08 36		08 36
Penge West	d		00 11	00 44												07 33						08 03				
Anerley	d		00 13	00 46												07 35						08 05				
Norwood Junction 2	d		00 16	00 49				06 56			07 26					07 40	07 56					08 10	08 26			
West Croydon 4 🚋	a															07 45						08 15				
East Croydon 🚋	a		00 20	00 53				06 59			07 29						07 59						08 29			

For general notes see front of timetable
For details of catering facilities see Directory of Train Operators

A To Caterham (Table 181)
B To Sutton (Surrey) (Table 182)

Table 178

Saturdays

Charing Cross and London Bridge → London Victoria and Croydon

Network Diagram - see first page of Table 177

	SE		SN A	SN	SN B	SN	SE	SE	SN A	SN	SN B	SN	SE	SE			SN C	SN	SN B	SN	SE		SE	SN B
London Charing Cross 4 ⊖ d																								
London Waterloo (East) 4 ⊖ d																								
London Bridge 4 ⊖ d			08 14	08 24	08 35	08 41			08 44	08 54	09 05	09 11					18 14	18 24	18 35	18 41				18 44
New Cross Gate 4 ⊖ d			08 20	08 30	08 40				08 50	09 00	09 10						18 20	18 30	18 40					18 50
Brockley d			08 22	08 32	08 43				08 52	09 02	09 13						18 22	18 32	18 43					18 52
Honor Oak Park d			08 25	08 35	08 46				08 55	09 05	09 16						18 25	18 35	18 46					18 55
Forest Hill 4 d			08 28	08 38	08 48				08 58	09 08	09 18						18 28	18 38	18 48					18 58
Sydenham d			08 30	08 40	08 51				09 00	09 10	09 21				and at		18 30	18 40	18 51					19 00
Crystal Palace 4 d				08 43						09 13								18 43						
Gipsy Hill d				08 46						09 16					the same			18 46						
West Norwood 4 d				08 49						09 19								18 49						
Streatham Hill d				08 52						09 22					minutes			18 52						
Balham 4 ⊖ d				08 55						09 25								18 55						
Wandsworth Common d				08 57						09 27					past			18 57						
Clapham Junction 10 d				09 01						09 31								19 01						
South Bermondsey d						08 45						09 15			each					18 45				
Queens Rd Peckham d						08 48						09 18								18 48				
Peckham Rye 4 d	08 28					08 50	08 52	08 58				09 20	09 22	09 28	hour until					18 50	18 52		18 58	
Denmark Hill 4 d	08 31					08 53	08 55	09 01				09 23	09 25	09 31						18 53	18 55		19 01	
London Blackfriars 3 ⊖ a																								
Clapham High Street ⊖ d						08 58						09 28								18 58				
Wandsworth Road d						08 59						09 29								18 59				
Battersea Park 4 d				09 05		09 02				09 35		09 32						19 05		19 02				
London Victoria 15 ⊖ a	08 42			09 09		09 06	09 06	09 12		09 39		09 36	09 36	09 42				19 09		19 06	19 06		19 12	
Penge West d			08 33						09 03								18 33							19 03
Anerley d			08 35						09 05								18 35							19 05
Norwood Junction 2 d			08 40		08 56				09 10		09 26						18 40		18 56					19 10
West Croydon 4 a			08 45						09 15								18 45							
East Croydon a					08 59						09 29								18 59					19 14

	SN	SN	SE	SN B	SN		SN	SE	SN B	SN	SN		SE	SN B	SN	SN	SE		SN B	SN	SN	SE	SN B		SN
London Charing Cross 4 ⊖ d				19 07					19 37					20 07					20 37				21 07		
London Waterloo (East) 4 ⊖ d				19 10					19 40					20 10					20 40				21 10		
London Bridge 4 ⊖ d	18 54	19 11		19 15	19 24		19 41		19 45	19 54	20 11			20 15	20 24	20 41			20 45	20 54	21 11		21 15		21 24
New Cross Gate 4 ⊖ d	19 00			19 20	19 30				19 50	20 00				20 20	20 30				20 50	21 00			21 20		21 30
Brockley d	19 02			19 23	19 32				19 53	20 02				20 23	20 32				20 53	21 02			21 23		21 32
Honor Oak Park d	19 05			19 26	19 35				19 56	20 05				20 26	20 35				20 56	21 05			21 26		21 35
Forest Hill 4 d	19 08			19 28	19 38				19 58	20 08				20 28	20 38				20 58	21 08			21 28		21 38
Sydenham d	19 10			19 31	19 40				20 01	20 10				20 31	20 40				21 01	21 10			21 31		21 40
Crystal Palace 4 d	19 13				19 43					20 13					20 43					21 13					21 43
Gipsy Hill d	19 16				19 46					20 16					20 46					21 16					21 46
West Norwood 4 d	19 19				19 49					20 19					20 49					21 19					21 49
Streatham Hill d	19 22				19 52					20 22					20 52					21 22					21 52
Balham 4 ⊖ d	19 25				19 55					20 25					20 55					21 25					21 55
Wandsworth Common d	19 27				19 57					20 27					20 57					21 27					21 57
Clapham Junction 10 d	19 31				20 01					20 31					21 01					21 31					22 01
South Bermondsey d		19 15					19 45				20 15					20 45					21 15				
Queens Rd Peckham d		19 18					19 48				20 18					20 48					21 18				
Peckham Rye 4 d		19 20	19 22				19 50	19 52			20 20		20 22			20 50	20 52				21 20	21 22			
Denmark Hill 4 d		19 23	19 25				19 53	19 55			20 23		20 25			20 53	20 55				21 23	21 25			
London Blackfriars 3 ⊖ a																									
Clapham High Street ⊖ d		19 28					19 58				20 28					20 58					21 28				
Wandsworth Road d		19 29					19 59				20 29					20 59					21 29				
Battersea Park 4 d	19 35	19 32			20 05		20 02			20 35	20 32				21 05	21 02				21 35	21 32				22 05
London Victoria 15 ⊖ a	19 39	19 36	19 36		20 09		20 06	20 06		20 39	20 36		20 36		21 09	21 06	21 06			21 39	21 36	21 36			22 09
Penge West d				19 33					20 03					20 33					21 03				21 33		
Anerley d				19 35					20 05					20 35					21 05				21 35		
Norwood Junction 2 d				19 39					20 09					20 39					21 09				21 39		
West Croydon 4 a																									
East Croydon a				19 42					20 12					20 42					21 12				21 42		

	SN	SE	SN B	SN	SN		SE	SN B	SN	SN	SE		SN B	SN	SN	SE	SN B		SN	SN B					
London Charing Cross 4 ⊖ d			21 37					22 07					22 37				23 07			23 45					
London Waterloo (East) 4 ⊖ d			21 40					22 10					22 40				23 10			23 48					
London Bridge 4 ⊖ d	21 41		21 45	21 54	22 11			22 15	22 24	22 41			22 45	22 54	23 11		23 15		23 24	23 53					
New Cross Gate 4 ⊖ d			21 50	22 00				22 20	22 30				22 50	23 00			23 20		23 30	23 58					
Brockley d			21 53	22 02				22 23	22 32				22 53	23 02			23 23		23 32	00 01					
Honor Oak Park d			21 56	22 05				22 26	22 35				22 56	23 05			23 26		23 35	00 04					
Forest Hill 4 d			21 58	22 08				22 28	22 38				22 58	23 08			23 28		23 38	00 06					
Sydenham d			22 01	22 10				22 31	22 40				23 01	23 10			23 31		23 40	00 09					
Crystal Palace 4 d				22 13					22 43					23 13					23 43						
Gipsy Hill d				22 16					22 46					23 16					23 46						
West Norwood 4 d				22 19					22 49					23 19					23 49						
Streatham Hill d				22 22					22 52					23 22					23 52						
Balham 4 ⊖ d				22 25					22 55					23 25					23 55						
Wandsworth Common d				22 27					22 57					23 27					23 57						
Clapham Junction 10 d				22 31					23 01					23 31					00 01						
South Bermondsey d	21 45				22 15					22 45					23 15										
Queens Rd Peckham d	21 48				22 18					22 48					23 18										
Peckham Rye 4 d	21 50	21 52			22 20		22 22			22 50	22 52				23 20	23 22									
Denmark Hill 4 d	21 53	21 55			22 23		22 25			22 53	22 55				23 23	23 25									
London Blackfriars 3 ⊖ a																									
Clapham High Street ⊖ d	21 58				22 28					22 58					23 28										
Wandsworth Road d	21 59				22 29					22 59					23 29										
Battersea Park 4 d	22 02			22 35	22 32				23 05	23 02				23 35	23 32				00 05						
London Victoria 15 ⊖ a	22 06	22 06		22 39	22 36		22 36		23 10	23 06	23 06			23 40	23 37	23 36			00 10						
Penge West d			22 03					22 33					23 03				23 33			00 11					
Anerley d			22 05					22 35					23 05				23 35			00 13					
Norwood Junction 2 d			22 09					22 39					23 09				23 39			00 16					
West Croydon 4 a																									
East Croydon a			22 12					22 42					23 12				23 42			00 20					

For general notes see front of timetable
For details of catering facilities see Directory of Train Operators

A To Sutton (Surrey) (Table 182)
B To Caterham (Table 181)
C To Epsom Downs (Table 182)

Table 178

Sundays

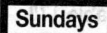

Charing Cross and London Bridge → London Victoria and Croydon

Network Diagram - see first page of Table 177

		SN	SN		SN	SE		SN	SE		SN		SN	SE	SN	SN	SN	SE	SN	SN			SN	SE	SN
			A										B				A						B		
London Charing Cross 4	⊖ d		23p45		00 12								07 34				08 04						21 34		
London Waterloo (East) 4	⊖ d		23p48		00 15								07 37				08 07						21 37		
London Bridge 4	⊖ d	23p24	23p53		00 26			07 11			07 41		07 44		07 58	08 11	08 14		08 28	08 41			21 44		21 58
New Cross Gate 4	⊖ d	23p30	23p58		00 31								07 49		08 03		08 19		08 33				21 49		22 03
Brockley	d	23p32	00 01		00 34								07 52		08 06		08 22		08 36				21 52		22 06
Honor Oak Park	d	23p35	00 04		00 37								07 55		08 09		08 25		08 39				21 55		22 09
Forest Hill 4	d	23p38	00 06		00 39								07 57		08 11		08 27		08 41				21 57		22 11
Sydenham	d	23p40	00 09		00 42								08 00		08 14		08 30		08 44				22 00		22 14
Crystal Palace 4	d	23p43																			and at				
Gipsy Hill	d	23p46																							
West Norwood 4	d	23p49																			the same				
Streatham Hill	d	23p52																							
Balham 4	⊖ d	23p55																			minutes				
Wandsworth Common	d	23p57																							
Clapham Junction 10	d	00 01																			past				
South Bermondsey	d							07 15			07 45					08 15				08 45	each				
Queens Rd Peckham	d							07 18			07 48					08 18				08 48					
Peckham Rye 4	d					07 12		07 20	07 42		07 50			08 12		08 20		08 42		08 50				22 12	
Denmark Hill 4	d					07 14		07 23	07 44		07 53			08 14		08 23		08 44		08 53	hour until			22 14	
London Blackfriars 3	⊖ a																								
Clapham High Street	⊖ d							07 28			07 58					08 28				08 58					
Wandsworth Road	d							07 29			07 59					08 29				08 59					
Battersea Park 4	d	00 05						07 32			08 02					08 32				09 02					
London Victoria 15	⊖ a	00 10				07 23		07 36	07 54		08 06			08 24		08 36		08 54		09 06				22 24	
Penge West	d		00 11		00 44										08 16				08 46						22 16
Anerley	d		00 13		00 46										08 18				08 48						22 18
Norwood Junction 2	d		00 16		00 49								08 04		08 21		08 34		08 51				22 04		22 21
West Croydon 4	🚋 a														08 26				08 56						22 26
East Croydon	🚋 a		00 20		00 53								08 08				08 38						22 08		

		SN		SN	SE		SN	SN		SE	SN		SN	SE		SN
				A				B					A			A
London Charing Cross 4	⊖ d			22 04				22 34					23 04			23 34
London Waterloo (East) 4	⊖ d			22 07				22 37					23 07			23 37
London Bridge 4	⊖ d	22 11		22 14			22 41	22 44			23 11		23 14			23 44
New Cross Gate 4	⊖ d			22 19				22 49					23 19			23 49
Brockley	d			22 22				22 52					23 22			23 52
Honor Oak Park	d			22 25				22 55					23 25			23 55
Forest Hill 4	d			22 27				22 57					23 27			23 57
Sydenham	d			22 30				23 00					23 30			23 59
Crystal Palace 4	d															
Gipsy Hill	d															
West Norwood 4	d															
Streatham Hill	d															
Balham 4	⊖ d															
Wandsworth Common	d															
Clapham Junction 10	d															
South Bermondsey	d	22 15					22 45				23 15					
Queens Rd Peckham	d	22 18					22 48				23 18					
Peckham Rye 4	d	22 20			22 42		22 50			23 12	23 20			23 42		
Denmark Hill 4	d	22 23			22 44		22 53			23 14	23 23			23 44		
London Blackfriars 3	⊖ a															
Clapham High Street	⊖ d	22 28					22 58				23 28					
Wandsworth Road	d	22 29					22 59				23 29					
Battersea Park 4	d	22 32					23 02				23 32					
London Victoria 15	⊖ a	22 36			22 54		23 06			23 24	23 37			23 53		
Penge West	d			22 32				23 02					23 32			00 02
Anerley	d			22 34				23 04					23 34			00 04
Norwood Junction 2	d			22 39				23 09					23 39			00 10
West Croydon 4	🚋 a															
East Croydon	🚋 a			22 42				23 12					23 42			00 13

For general notes see front of timetable
For details of catering facilities see Directory of Train Operators

A To Caterham (Table 181)
B To Tattenham Corner (Table 181)

Croydon and London Victoria → London Bridge and Charing Cross

Network Diagram - see first page of Table 177

Miles	Miles	Miles	Miles	Miles			SN	SE	SN	SE	SN	SN	SN	SE	SN	SN	SN	FC 1	SN	SN	SN	FC 1	SN		SN	SN
							A		B		C	D	E				D			G			B			C
—	—	0	—	—	**East Croydon**	d	05 13				06 12		06 31		06 40				07 12							07 36
—	—	—	—	0	**West Croydon 4**	d			05 45			06 15					06 45						07 16		07 28	
—	—	1¼	—	1¾	Norwood Junction 2	d	05 17		05 50		06 17	06 19	06 35		06 45		06 50		07 17				07 21		07 33	07 41
—	—	2½	—	—	Anerley	d	05 20		05 53			06 22					06 53						07 24		07 36	
—	—	2¾	—	—	Penge West	d	05 22		05 55			06 24					06 55						07 26		07 38	
0	0	—	0	—	**London Victoria 15**	⊖ d										06 41					07 11					
1¼	1¼	—	—	—	Battersea Park 4	d										06 45					07 15					
2	—	—	—	—	Wandsworth Road	d										06 47					07 17					
2½	—	—	—	—	Clapham High Street	⊖ d										06 49					07 19					
—	—	—	—	0	**London Blackfriars 3**	⊖ d		05 28		06 10				06 40				07 06				07 24				
4½	—	—	4¼	3¾	Denmark Hill 4	d		05 37		06 20				06 50		06 54		07 15			07 24	07 34				
5¼	—	—	5	4½	Peckham Rye 4	d		05a39		06a23				06a52		06 56		07a20		06 57	07 26	07a36				
6	—	—	—	—	Queens Rd Peckham	d										06 59					07 29					
7	—	—	—	—	South Bermondsey	d										07 01				06 52	07 31					
—	2¾	—	—	—	Clapham Junction 10	d																				
—	4	—	—	—	Wandsworth Common	d																				
—	4¾	—	—	—	Balham 4	⊖ d																				
—	5¾	—	—	—	Streatham Hill	d																				
—	7	—	—	—	West Norwood 4	d														07 08						
—	8	—	—	—	Gipsy Hill	d														07 11						
—	8¾	—	—	—	**Crystal Palace 4**	d														07 15						
—	10	3½	—	—	Sydenham	d	05 24		05 58		06 21	06 27	06 40				06 57			07 18			07 29		07 40	07 45
—	10¾	4¼	—	—	Forest Hill 4	d	05 27		06 00		06 24	06 29	06 42				07 00			07 20			07 31		07 43	07 48
—	11¾	5¼	—	—	Honor Oak Park	d	05 29		06 03			06 32	06 45				07 02			07 23			07 34		07 45	
—	12¾	6¼	—	—	Brockley	d	05 32		06 05			06 34	06 47				07 05			07 25			07 36		07 48	
—	13¾	7¼	—	—	New Cross Gate 4	⊖ d	05 34		06 08		06 28	06 37	06 50		06 53		07 07		07 24	07 28			07 39		07 50	07 53
8¾	16½	10	—	—	**London Bridge 4**	⊖ a	05 41		06 14		06 35	06 44	06 56		07 02	07 08	07 16		07 33	07 36	07 38		07 48		07 59	08 01
—	—	11	—	—	London Waterloo (East) 4	⊖ a	05 46																			
—	—	11¾	—	—	**London Charing Cross 4**	⊖ a	05 49																			

		FC	SN	SN	SN	FC	FC	SN	SN	SN	SN	SE	FC	SN	SN	FC	SN	SN		SN	SN	FC	SN	SN	SE	FC
				B										H							B					
East Croydon	d																08 45									
West Croydon 4	d			07 43				07 56						08 23	08 28						08 44		08 59			
Norwood Junction 2	d			07 48				08 01						08 28	08 33		08 49				08 49		09 04			
Anerley	d							08 04							08 36						08 52		09 07			
Penge West	d							08 06							08 38						08 54		09 09			
London Victoria 15	⊖ d		07 41						07 51	08 11		08 21						08 41		08 22				08 49	09 01	
Battersea Park 4	d		07 45						07 55	08 15								08 45		08 26				08 53		
Wandsworth Road	d		07 47							08 17								08 47								
Clapham High Street	⊖ d		07 49							08 19								08 49								
London Blackfriars 3	⊖ d	07 44				07 52	07 56						08 24			08 44						08 56				09 12
Denmark Hill 4	d	07 53	07 54			08 01	08 06			08 24		08 31	08 35			08 52		08 54				09 07			09 12	09 22
Peckham Rye 4	d	07a56	07 56			08a04	08a08			08 26		08a35	08a37			08a55		08 56				09a10			09a14	09a24
Queens Rd Peckham	d		07 59							08 29								08 59								
South Bermondsey	d		08 01							08 31								09 01								
Clapham Junction 10	d								07 59											08 30				08 57		
Wandsworth Common	d								08 02											08 33				09 00		
Balham 4	⊖ d								08 04											08 35				09 02		
Streatham Hill	d				07 45				08 07		08 14									08 38				09 05		
West Norwood 4	d				07 48				08 11		08 17									08 42				09 09		
Gipsy Hill	d				07 51				08 14		08 20									08 45				09 12		
Crystal Palace 4	d				07 54				08 16		08 23									08 48				09 14		
Sydenham	d			07 53	07 57			08 08	08 19		08 26			08 33	08 40					08 51	08 57		09 11	09 17		
Forest Hill 4	d			07 55	07 59			08 11	08 22		08 29			08 35	08 43					08 53	08 59		09 14	09 20		
Honor Oak Park	d				08 02			08 13	08 24		08 31				08 45					08 56	09 02		09 16	09 22		
Brockley	d				08 04			08 16	08 27		08 34				08 48					08 58	09 04		09 19	09 25		
New Cross Gate 4	⊖ d			08 00	08 07			08 18	08 29		08 36				08 50		08 57			09 01	09 07		09 21	09 27		
London Bridge 4	⊖ a		08 08	08 08	08 16			08 27	08 38	08 38	08 46			08 48	09 00		09 05	09 08		09 12	09 18		09 30	09 38		
London Waterloo (East) 4	⊖ a																									
London Charing Cross 4	⊖ a																									

		SN	SN	SN	SE	SN	FC	SN	SN	SN		SN	SN	SE	FC	SN	SN	SN	SN	SE	FC	SN	SN		SN
				J		C				B		C					D	C					D		C
East Croydon	d		09 20			09 31						10 00						10 30							15 00
West Croydon 4	d			09 15						09 46							10 15						10 45		
Norwood Junction 2	d		09 25	09 20		09 35				09 51		10 05					10 20	10 35					10 50		15 05
Anerley	d			09 23						09 54							10 23						10 53		
Penge West	d			09 25						09 56							10 25						10 55		
London Victoria 15	⊖ d	09 11			09 31			09 41	09 19				09 49	10 01		10 11			10 19	10 31		10 41			
Battersea Park 4	d	09 15						09 45	09 23				09 53			10 15			10 23			10 45		and at	
Wandsworth Road	d	09 17						09 47								10 17						10 47		the same	
Clapham High Street	⊖ d	09 19						09 49								10 19						10 49		minutes	
London Blackfriars 3	⊖ d						09 42								10 12						10 42			past	
Denmark Hill 4	d	09 24			09 42		09 52	09 54						10 12	10 22	10 24				10 42	10 52	10 54		each	
Peckham Rye 4	d	09 26			09a44		09a54	09 56						10a14	10a24	10 26				10a44	10a54	10 56		hour until	
Queens Rd Peckham	d	09 29						09 59								10 29						10 59			
South Bermondsey	d	09 31						10 01								10 31						11 01			
Clapham Junction 10	d								09 27				09 57						10 27						
Wandsworth Common	d								09 30				10 00						10 30						
Balham 4	⊖ d								09 32				10 02						10 32						
Streatham Hill	d								09 35				10 05						10 35						
West Norwood 4	d								09 39				10 10						10 39						
Gipsy Hill	d								09 42				10 13						10 42						
Crystal Palace 4	d								09 44				10 15						10 45						
Sydenham	d			09 27		09 40			09 47	09 58		10 09	10 18				10 27	10 39	10 48				10 57		15 09
Forest Hill 4	d			09 30		09 42			09 50	10 01		10 12	10 21				10 30	10 42	10 50				11 00		15 12
Honor Oak Park	d			09 32		09 45			09 52	10 03		10 14	10 23				10 32	10 44	10 53				11 02		15 14
Brockley	d			09 35		09 47			09 55	10 06		10 17	10 26				10 35	10 47	10 55				11 05		15 17
New Cross Gate 4	⊖ d		09 33	09 37		09 50			09 57	10 08		10 19	10 28				10 37	10 49	10 58				11 07		15 19
London Bridge 4	⊖ a	09 38	09 42	09 46		09 59		10 06	10 08	10 16		10 26	10 35			10 36	10 44	10 57	11 06			11 06	11 14		15 26
London Waterloo (East) 4	⊖ a																								
London Charing Cross 4	⊖ a																								

For general notes see front of timetable
For details of catering facilities see Directory of Train Operators

- **A** From Purley (Table 175)
- **B** From Epsom (Table 182)
- **C** From Caterham (Table 181)
- **D** From Sutton (Surrey) (Table 182)
- **E** From Tattenham Corner (Table 181)
- **G** From London Bridge (Table 177)
- **H** From Epsom Downs (Table 182)
- **J** From Guildford (Table 182)

Table 178

Mondays to Fridays

Croydon and London Victoria → London Bridge and Charing Cross

Network Diagram - see first page of Table 177

		SN		SE	FC	SN	SN	SN	SE	FC	SN	SN	SN	SN	SN	FC	SN	SE	SN	FC		SN	FC	SN	SN	SN
							A	B					A	B					A			B				A
East Croydon	d							15 30						16 00								16 30				
West Croydon 4	d						15 15						15 45						16 15							16 45
Norwood Junction 2	d						15 20	15 35					15 50	16 05					16 21			16 35				16 50
Anerley	d						15 23						15 53						16 24							16 53
Penge West	d						15 25						15 55						16 26							16 55
London Victoria 15	⊖ d	14 49		15 01		15 11			15 31		15 41	15 19			15 49		16 11	16 14						16 41	16 19	
Battersea Park 4	d	14 53				15 15					15 45	15 23			15 53		16 15							16 45	16 23	
Wandsworth Road	d					15 17					15 47						16 17							16 47		
Clapham High Street	⊖ d					15 19					15 49						16 19							16 49		
London Blackfriars 3	⊖ d				15 12					15 42						16 12				16 26			16 42			
Denmark Hill 4	d			15 12	15 22	15 24			15 42	15 52	15 54					16 22	16 24	16 27		16 36			16 52	16 54		
Peckham Rye 4	d			15a14	15a24	15 26			15a44	15a54	15 56					16a24	16 26	16a29		16a40			16a54	16 56		
Queens Rd Peckham	d					15 29					15 59						16 29							16 59		
South Bermondsey	d					15 31					16 01						16 31							17 01		
Clapham Junction 10	d	14 57										15 27			15 57										16 27	
Wandsworth Common	d	15 00										15 30			16 00										16 30	
Balham 4	⊖ d	15 02										15 32			16 02										16 32	
Streatham Hill	d	15 05										15 35			16 05										16 35	
West Norwood 4	d	15 09										15 39			16 09										16 39	
Gipsy Hill	d	15 12										15 42			16 12										16 42	
Crystal Palace 4	d	15 15										15 45			16 15										16 45	
Sydenham	d	15 18					15 27	15 39				15 48	15 57	16 09	16 18				16 28			16 39			16 48	16 57
Forest Hill 4	d	15 20					15 30	15 42				15 50	16 00	16 12	16 20				16 31			16 42			16 51	17 00
Honor Oak Park	d	15 23					15 32	15 44				15 53	16 02	16 14	16 23				16 33			16 44			16 53	17 02
Brockley	d	15 25					15 35	15 47				15 55	16 05	16 17	16 25				16 36			16 47			16 56	17 05
New Cross Gate 4	⊖ d	15 28					15 37	15 49				15 58	16 07	16 19	16 28				16 38			16 49			16 58	17 07
London Bridge 4	⊖ a	15 35				15 36	15 44	15 58			16 06	16 07	16 14	16 29	16 36		16 38		16 45			16 56		17 08	17 10	17 14
London Waterloo (East) 4	⊖ a																									
London Charing Cross 4	⊖ a																									

		SE	SN	FC	SN	SN	SE	SN	SN	FC	SE	SN	SN	SN	SN		SE	FC	SN	SN	FC	SN	SN	FC	SN	SN
			B	1				C	B					C								A	B	1		
East Croydon	d		17 00						17 32														18 32			
West Croydon 4	d							17 14						17 47								18 15				
Norwood Junction 2	d		17 05					17 19	17 37					17 52	18 04							18 20	18 36			
Anerley	d							17 22						17 55								18 23				
Penge West	d							17 24						17 57								18 25				
London Victoria 15	⊖ d	17 00			17 11	16 52	17 19				17 41	17 41	17 22				18 08		18 11	17 52					18 41	18 23
Battersea Park 4	d				17 15	16 56						17 45	17 26						18 15	17 56					18 45	18 27
Wandsworth Road	d				17 17							17 47							18 17						18 47	
Clapham High Street	⊖ d				17 19							17 49							18 19						18 49	
London Blackfriars 3	⊖ d			17 10						17 36								18 06			18 24			18 42		
Denmark Hill 4	d	17 09		17 20	17 24		17 28			17 45	17 51	17 54					18 17	18b20	18 24		18 34			18 52	18 54	
Peckham Rye 4	d	17a12		17a23	17 26		17a31			17a47	17a54	17 57					18a20	18a23	18 27		18a37			18a54	18 56	
Queens Rd Peckham	d				17 29							17 59							18 30						18 59	
South Bermondsey	d				17 31							18 02							18 32						19 01	
Clapham Junction 10	d					17 00							17 30							18 00						18 31
Wandsworth Common	d					17 03							17 33							18 03						18 34
Balham 4	⊖ d					17 05							17 35							18 05						18 36
Streatham Hill	d					17 08							17 38							18 08						18 39
West Norwood 4	d					17 13							17 42							18 15						18 43
Gipsy Hill	d					17 16							17 45							18 18						18 46
Crystal Palace 4	d					17 18							17 48							18 20						18 48
Sydenham	d		17 09			17 21		17 26	17 41				17 51	18 00	18 08					18 23		18 27	18 41			18 51
Forest Hill 4	d		17 12			17 24		17 29	17 44				17 54	18 02	18 11					18 26		18 30	18 43			18 54
Honor Oak Park	d		17 14			17 26		17 31	17 46				17 56	18 05	18 13					18 28		18 32	18 46			18 56
Brockley	d		17 17			17 29		17 34	17 49				17 59	18 07	18 16					18 31		18 35	18 48			18 59
New Cross Gate 4	⊖ d		17 19			17 31		17 36	17 51				18 01	18 10	18 18					18 33		18 37	18 51			19 01
London Bridge 4	⊖ a		17 28		17 38	17 40		17 44	17 58			18 08	18 10	18 20	18 25				18 39	18 42		18 45	18 58		19 08	19 10
London Waterloo (East) 4	⊖ a																									
London Charing Cross 4	⊖ a																									

		SE	SN	SN	FC	SN	SN	SE	SN	SN		FC	SN	SN	SE	SN	SN	FC	SN	SN	SN	SN	FC	SN	SN	SN
			C				B		D					B		D				B		E			B	
East Croydon	d						19 10							19 40						20 10		20 29			20 40	
West Croydon 4	d		18 48						19 22							19 49										
Norwood Junction 2	d		18 53	19 06			19 15		19 27					19 44		19 55				20 14		20 34			20 44	
Anerley	d		18 56				19 18							19 47		19 58				20 17		20 37			20 47	
Penge West	d		18 58				19 20							19 49		20 00				20 19		20 39			20 49	
London Victoria 15	⊖ d	18 46				19 11		19 16		19 06			19 41		19 46		19 36		20 11		20 06			20 41		20 36
Battersea Park 4	d					19 15				19 10			19 45				19 40		20 15		20 10			20 45		20 40
Wandsworth Road	d					19 17							19 47						20 17					20 47		
Clapham High Street	⊖ d					19 19							19 49						20 19					20 49		
London Blackfriars 3	⊖ d				19 12							19 42						20 12					20 42			
Denmark Hill 4	d	18 57			19 22	19 24		19 27				19 52	19 54		19 57			20 22	20 24				20 52	20 54		
Peckham Rye 4	d	19a00			19a25	19 26		19a31				19a55	19 56		20a01			20a25	20 26				20a55	20 56		
Queens Rd Peckham	d					19 29							19 59						20 29					20 59		
South Bermondsey	d					19 31							20 01						20 31					21 01		
Clapham Junction 10	d									19 14							19 44				20 14					20 44
Wandsworth Common	d									19 17							19 47				20 17					20 47
Balham 4	⊖ d									19 19							19 49				20 19					20 49
Streatham Hill	d									19 22							19 52				20 22					20 52
West Norwood 4	d									19 26							19 56				20 26					20 56
Gipsy Hill	d									19 29							19 59				20 29					20 59
Crystal Palace 4	d									19 32							20 02				20 32					21 02
Sydenham	d		19 01	19 10			19 22		19 32	19 35				19 52		20 02	20 05			20 22	20 35	20 42			20 52	21 05
Forest Hill 4	d		19 03	19 13			19 25		19 34	19 37				19 54		20 05	20 08			20 24	20 37	20 44			20 54	21 07
Honor Oak Park	d		19 06	19 15			19 27		19 37	19 40				19 57		20 07	20 10			20 27	20 40	20 47			20 57	21 10
Brockley	d		19 08	19 18			19 30		19 39	19 42				19 59		20 10	20 13			20 29	20 42	20 49			20 59	21 12
New Cross Gate 4	⊖ d		19 11	19 20			19 32		19 42	19 45				20 02		20 12	20 15			20 32	20 45	20 52			21 02	21 15
London Bridge 4	⊖ a		19 18	19 27		19 36	19 39		19 49	19 53			20 06	20 11		20 20	20 23		20 36	20 41	20 53	21 01		21 08	21 11	21 22
London Waterloo (East) 4	⊖ a						19 45							20 16						20 46					21 16	
London Charing Cross 4	⊖ a						19 49							20 20						20 50					21 20	

For general notes see front of timetable
For details of catering facilities see Directory of Train Operators

A From Sutton (Surrey) (Table 182)
B From Caterham (Table 181)
C From Epsom (Table 182)
D From Guildford (Table 182)
E From Tattenham Corner (Table 181)
b Arr. 1816

Croydon and London Victoria → London Bridge and Charing Cross

Network Diagram - see first page of Table 177

		FC	SN	SN A	SN		SE	SN	SN A	SN	SE	SN	SN A	SN	SE	SN	SN A	SN	SE	SN	SN A	SN	SE			
East Croydon	d			21 10					21 40				22 10				22 40				23 10					
West Croydon	d																									
Norwood Junction	d			21 14					21 44				22 14				22 44				23 14					
Anerley	d			21 17					21 47				22 17				22 47				23 17					
Penge West	d			21 19					21 49				22 19				22 49				23 19					
London Victoria	d		21 11		21 06		21 42	21 41		21 36	22 12	22 11		22 06	22 42	22 41		22 36	23 12	23 11		23 06	23 42			
Battersea Park	d		21 15		21 10			21 45		21 40		22 15		22 10		22 45		22 40		23 15		23 10				
Wandsworth Road	d		21 17					21 47				22 17				22 47				23 17						
Clapham High Street	d		21 19					21 49				22 19				22 49				23 19						
London Blackfriars	d	21 12																								
Denmark Hill	d	21 22	21 24				21 52	21 54			22 22	22 24			22 52	22 54			23 22	23 24			23 52			
Peckham Rye	d	21a25	21 26				21a55	21 56			22a25	22 26			22a55	22 56			23a25	23 26			23a55			
Queens Rd Peckham	d		21 29					21 59				22 29				22 59				23 29						
South Bermondsey	d		21 31					22 01				22 31				23 01				23 31						
Clapham Junction	d				21 14					21 44				22 14				22 44				23 14				
Wandsworth Common	d				21 17					21 47				22 17				22 47				23 17				
Balham	d				21 19					21 49				22 19				22 49				23 19				
Streatham Hill	d				21 22					21 52				22 22				22 52				23 22				
West Norwood	d				21 26					21 56				22 26				22 56				23 26				
Gipsy Hill	d				21 29					21 59				22 29				22 59				23 29				
Crystal Palace	d				21 32					22 02				22 32				23 02				23 32				
Sydenham	d			21 22	21 35				21 52	22 05			22 22	22 35			22 52	23 05			23 22	23 35				
Forest Hill	d			21 24	21 37				21 54	22 07			22 24	22 37			22 54	23 07			23 24	23 37				
Honor Oak Park	d			21 27	21 40				21 57	22 10			22 27	22 40			22 57	23 10			23 27	23 40				
Brockley	d			21 29	21 42				21 59	22 12			22 29	22 42			22 59	23 12			23 29	23 42				
New Cross Gate	d			21 32	21 45				22 02	22 15			22 32	22 45			23 02	23 15			23 32	23 45				
London Bridge	a		21 36	21 41	21 52			22 07	22 11	22 22		22 36	22 41	22 52		23 06	23 11	23 22		23 36	23 38	23 52				
London Waterloo (East)	a			21 46					22 16				22 46				23 16				23 43					
London Charing Cross	a			21 50					22 20				22 50				23 20				23 48					

Saturdays

		SE	SN A	SE	SN	SN		SN A	SE	SN	SN B	SN A		SE	SN	SN B	SN A	SN		SE	SE	SN	SN B	SN A		SN
East Croydon	d		06 30			06 43		07 00				07 30					08 00							08 30		
West Croydon	d										07 15					07 45							08 15			
Norwood Junction	d		06 35			06 49		07 05			07 20	07 35				07 50	08 05						08 20	08 35		
Anerley	d					06 52					07 23					07 53							08 23			
Penge West	d					06 54					07 25					07 55							08 25			
London Victoria	d	06 13		06 42	06 41				07 12	07 11				07 42	07 41			07 49		08 01	08 12	08 11				08 19
Battersea Park	d				06 45					07 15					07 45			07 53				08 15				08 23
Wandsworth Road	d				06 47					07 17					07 47							08 17				
Clapham High Street	d				06 49					07 19					07 49							08 19				
London Blackfriars	d																									
Denmark Hill	d	06 22		06 52	06 54				07 22	07 24				07 52	07 54					08 12	08 22	08 24				
Peckham Rye	d	06a25		06a55	06 56				07a25	07 26				07a55	07 56					08a14	08a25	08 26				
Queens Rd Peckham	d				06 59					07 29					07 59							08 29				
South Bermondsey	d				07 01					07 31					08 01							08 31				
Clapham Junction	d																	07 57								08 27
Wandsworth Common	d																	08 00								08 30
Balham	d																	08 02								08 32
Streatham Hill	d																	08 05								08 35
West Norwood	d																	08 09								08 39
Gipsy Hill	d																	08 12								08 42
Crystal Palace	d																	08 14								08 45
Sydenham	d		06 39			06 57		07 09			07 27	07 39				07 57	08 09	08 17					08 27	08 39		08 48
Forest Hill	d		06 42			06 59		07 12			07 30	07 42				08 00	08 12	08 20					08 30	08 42		08 50
Honor Oak Park	d		06 44			07 02		07 14			07 32	07 44				08 02	08 14	08 22					08 32	08 44		08 53
Brockley	d		06 47			07 04		07 17			07 35	07 47				08 05	08 17	08 25					08 35	08 47		08 55
New Cross Gate	d		06 49			07 07		07 19			07 37	07 49				08 07	08 19	08 27					08 37	08 49		08 58
London Bridge	a		06 56		07 06	07 14		07 26		07 36	07 44	07 56			08 06	08 14	08 26	08 35				08 36	08 44	08 56		09 05
London Waterloo (East)	a																									
London Charing Cross	a																									

For general notes see front of timetable
For details of catering facilities see
Directory of Train Operators

A From Caterham (Table 181)
B From Sutton (Surrey) (Table 182)

Table 178

Saturdays

Croydon and London Victoria → London Bridge and Charing Cross

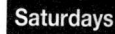

Network Diagram - see first page of Table 177

		SE	SE	SN	SN A	SN B	SN	SE	SE	SN	SN A	SN B	SN	SE	SE	SN	SN A	SN B	SN	SE	SE	SN
East Croydon	d					09 00						09 30						10 00				
West Croydon 4	d				08 45						09 15						09 45					
Norwood Junction 2	d				08 50	09 05					09 20	09 35					09 50	10 05				
Anerley	d				08 53						09 23						09 53					
Penge West	d				08 55						09 25						09 55					
London Victoria 15	⊖ d	08 31	08 42	08 41			08 49	09 01	09 12	09 11			09 19	09 31	09 42	09 41			09 49	10 01	10 12	10 11
Battersea Park 4	d			08 45			08 53			09 15			09 23			09 45			09 53			10 15
Wandsworth Road	d			08 47						09 17						09 47						10 17
Clapham High Street	⊖ d			08 49						09 19						09 49						10 19
London Blackfriars 3	⊖ d																					
Denmark Hill 4	d	08 42	08 52	08 54				09 12	09 22	09 24				09 42	09 52	09 54				10 12	10 22	10 24
Peckham Rye 4	d	08a44	08a55	08 56				09a14	09a25	09 26				09a44	09a55	09 56				10a14	10a25	10 26
Queens Rd Peckham	d			08 59						09 29						09 59						10 29
South Bermondsey	d			09 01						09 31						10 01						10 31
Clapham Junction 10	d						08 57						09 27						09 57			
Wandsworth Common	d						09 00						09 30						10 00			
Balham 4	⊖ d						09 02						09 32						10 02			
Streatham Hill	d						09 05						09 35						10 05			
West Norwood 4	d						09 09						09 39						10 09			
Gipsy Hill	d						09 12						09 42						10 12			
Crystal Palace 4	d						09 15						09 45						10 15			
Sydenham	d				08 57	09 09	09 18				09 27	09 39	09 48				09 57	10 09	10 18			
Forest Hill 4	d				09 00	09 12	09 20				09 30	09 42	09 50				10 00	10 12	10 20			
Honor Oak Park	d				09 02	09 14	09 23				09 32	09 44	09 53				10 02	10 14	10 23			
Brockley	d				09 05	09 17	09 25				09 35	09 47	09 55				10 05	10 17	10 25			
New Cross Gate 4	⊖ d				09 07	09 19	09 28				09 37	09 49	09 58				10 07	10 19	10 28			
London Bridge 4	⊖ a			09 06	09 14	09 26	09 35			09 36	09 44	09 56	10 05			10 06	10 14	10 26	10 35			10 36
London Waterloo (East) 4	⊖ a																					
London Charing Cross 4	⊖ a																					

		SN A	SN B	SN	SE	SE	SN	SN A		SN B	SN	SE	SE	SN	SN A	SN B	SN	SE	SE	SN	SN A	SE
East Croydon	d		10 30							18 00						18 30						
West Croydon 4	d	10 15						10 45							18 15						18 45	
Norwood Junction 2	d	10 20	10 35					10 50		18 05					18 20	18 35					18 50	
Anerley	d	10 23						10 53							18 23						18 53	
Penge West	d	10 25						10 55							18 25						18 55	
London Victoria 15	⊖ d			10 19	10 31	10 42	10 41				17 49	18 01	18 12	18 11			18 19	18 31	18 42	18 41		19 01
Battersea Park 4	d			10 23			10 45				17 53			18 15			18 23			18 45		
Wandsworth Road	d						10 47		and at					18 17						18 47		
Clapham High Street	⊖ d						10 49							18 19						18 49		
London Blackfriars 3	⊖ d								the same													
Denmark Hill 4	d				10 42	10 52	10 54					18 12	18 22	18 24				18 42	18 52	18 54		19 12
Peckham Rye 4	d				10a44	10a55	10 56		minutes			18a14	18a25	18 26				18a44	18a55	18 56		19a14
Queens Rd Peckham	d						10 59							18 29						18 59		
South Bermondsey	d						11 01		past					18 31						19 01		
Clapham Junction 10	d			10 27							17 57						18 27					
Wandsworth Common	d			10 30					each		18 00						18 30					
Balham 4	⊖ d			10 32							18 02						18 32					
Streatham Hill	d			10 35					hour until		18 05						18 35					
West Norwood 4	d			10 39							18 09						18 39					
Gipsy Hill	d			10 42							18 12						18 42					
Crystal Palace 4	d			10 45							18 15						18 45					
Sydenham	d	10 27	10 39	10 48				10 57		18 09	18 18				18 27	18 39	18 48				18 57	
Forest Hill 4	d	10 30	10 42	10 50				11 00		18 12	18 20				18 30	18 42	18 50				19 00	
Honor Oak Park	d	10 32	10 44	10 53				11 02		18 14	18 23				18 32	18 44	18 53				19 02	
Brockley	d	10 35	10 47	10 55				11 05		18 17	18 25				18 35	18 47	18 55				19 05	
New Cross Gate 4	⊖ d	10 37	10 49	10 58				11 07		18 19	18 28				18 37	18 49	18 58				19 07	
London Bridge 4	⊖ a	10 44	10 56	11 05			11 06	11 14		18 26	18 35			18 36	18 44	18 56	19 05			19 06	19 14	
London Waterloo (East) 4	⊖ a																					
London Charing Cross 4	⊖ a																					

		SN C	SE	SN	SN B	SN	SE	SE	SN	SN B	SN	SE	SN	SN B	SN	SE	SN	SN B	SN	SE	SN	SN B
East Croydon	d	19 00			19 10					19 40				20 10				20 40				21 10
West Croydon 4	d																					
Norwood Junction 2	d	19 04			19 14					19 44				20 14				20 44				21 14
Anerley	d	19 07			19 17					19 47				20 17				20 47				21 17
Penge West	d	19 09			19 19					19 49				20 19				20 49				21 19
London Victoria 15	⊖ d		19 12	19 11		19 06	19 31	19 42	19 41		19 36	20 12	20 11		20 06	20 42	20 41		20 36	21 12	21 11	
Battersea Park 4	d			19 15		19 10			19 45		19 40		20 15		20 10		20 45		20 40		21 15	
Wandsworth Road	d			19 17					19 47				20 17				20 47				21 17	
Clapham High Street	⊖ d			19 19					19 49				20 19				20 49				21 19	
London Blackfriars 3	⊖ d																					
Denmark Hill 4	d		19 22	19 24			19 42	19 52	19 54			20 22	20 24			20 52	20 54			21 22	21 24	
Peckham Rye 4	d		19a25	19 26			19a44	19a55	19 56			20a25	20 26			20a55	20 56			21a25	21 26	
Queens Rd Peckham	d			19 29					19 59				20 29				20 59				21 29	
South Bermondsey	d			19 31					20 01				20 31				21 01				21 31	
Clapham Junction 10	d					19 14					19 44				20 14				20 44			
Wandsworth Common	d					19 17					19 47				20 17				20 47			
Balham 4	⊖ d					19 19					19 49				20 19				20 49			
Streatham Hill	d					19 22					19 52				20 22				20 52			
West Norwood 4	d					19 27					19 57				20 26				20 56			
Gipsy Hill	d					19 30					20 00				20 29				20 59			
Crystal Palace 4	d					19 33					20 03				20 32				21 02			
Sydenham	d	19 11			19 22	19 36				19 52	20 06			20 22	20 35			20 52	21 05			21 22
Forest Hill 4	d	19 14			19 24	19 38				19 54	20 08			20 24	20 37			20 54	21 07			21 24
Honor Oak Park	d	19 16			19 27	19 41				19 57	20 11			20 27	20 40			20 57	21 10			21 27
Brockley	d	19 19			19 29	19 43				19 59	20 13			20 29	20 42			20 59	21 12			21 29
New Cross Gate 4	⊖ d	19 21			19 32	19 46				20 02	20 16			20 32	20 45			21 02	21 15			21 32
London Bridge 4	⊖ a	19 28		19 36	19 41	19 52			20 06	20 11	20 22		20 36	20 41	20 52		21 06	21 11	21 22		21 36	21 41
London Waterloo (East) 4	⊖ a				19 48					20 18				20 48				21 18				21 48
London Charing Cross 4	⊖ a				19 51					20 21				20 51				21 21				21 51

For general notes see front of timetable
For details of catering facilities see Directory of Train Operators

A From Sutton (Surrey) (Table 182)
B From Caterham (Table 181)
C From Tattenham Corner (Table 181)

Croydon and London Victoria → London Bridge and Charing Cross

Network Diagram - see first page of Table 177

		SN	SE	SN	SN A	SN		SE	SN	SN A	SN	SE		SN	SN A	SN	SE	SN		SN A	SN	SE				
East Croydon	d				21 40					22 10					22 40					23 10						
West Croydon 4	d																									
Norwood Junction 2	d				21 44					22 14					22 44					23 14						
Anerley	d				21 47					22 17					22 47					23 17						
Penge West	d				21 49					22 19					22 49					23 19						
London Victoria 15	⊖ d	21 06	21 42	21 41		21 36		22 12	22 11		22 06	22 42		22 41		22 36	23 12	23 11			23 06	23 42				
Battersea Park 4	d	21 10		21 45		21 40			22 15		22 10			22 45		22 40		23 15			23 10					
Wandsworth Road	d			21 47					22 17					22 47				23 17								
Clapham High Street	⊖ d			21 49					22 19					22 49				23 19								
London Blackfriars 3	⊖ d																									
Denmark Hill 4	d		21 52	21 54				22 22	22 24			22 52		22 54			23 22	23 24				23 52				
Peckham Rye 4	d		21a55	21 56				22a25	22 26			22a55		22 56			23a25	23 26				23a55				
Queens Rd Peckham	d			21 59					22 29					22 59				23 29								
South Bermondsey	d			22 01					22 31					23 01				23 31								
Clapham Junction 10	d	21 14				21 44					22 14					22 44					23 14					
Wandsworth Common	d	21 17				21 47					22 17					22 47					23 17					
Balham 4	⊖ d	21 19				21 49					22 19					22 49					23 19					
Streatham Hill	d	21 22				21 52					22 22					22 52					23 22					
West Norwood 4	d	21 26				21 56					22 26					22 56					23 26					
Gipsy Hill	d	21 29				21 59					22 29					22 59					23 29					
Crystal Palace 4	d	21 32				22 02					22 32					23 02					23 32					
Sydenham	d	21 35			21 52	22 05				22 22	22 35				22 52	23 05				23 22	23 35					
Forest Hill 4	d	21 37			21 54	22 07				22 24	22 37				22 54	23 07				23 24	23 37					
Honor Oak Park	d	21 40			21 57	22 10				22 27	22 40				22 57	23 10				23 27	23 40					
Brockley	d	21 42			21 59	22 12				22 29	22 42				22 59	23 12				23 29	23 42					
New Cross Gate 4	⊖ d	21 45			22 02	22 15				22 32	22 45				23 02	23 15				23 32	23 45					
London Bridge 4	⊖ a	21 52		22 06	22 11	22 22			22 36	22 41	22 52			23 06	23 11	23 22		23 36		23 38	23 52					
London Waterloo (East) 4	⊖ a				22 18					22 48					23 16					23 43						
London Charing Cross 4	⊖ a				22 21					22 51					23 20					23 48						

Sundays

		SN B		SN		SE		SN		SN A		SE		SN		SN		SN C		SE			SN	SN	SN A	SE
East Croydon	d	06 44		07 12						07 47								08 17							08 47	
West Croydon 4	d													08 01									08 31			
Norwood Junction 2	d	06 48		07 18						07 51				08 05				08 21					08 35		08 51	
Anerley	d	06 51		07 21										08 08									08 38			
Penge West	d	06 53		07 23										08 10									08 40			
London Victoria 15	⊖ d					07 38		07 41				08 08				08 11				08 38				08 41		09 08
Battersea Park 4	d							07 45								08 15								08 45		
Wandsworth Road	d							07 47								08 17								08 47		
Clapham High Street	⊖ d							07 49								08 19								08 49		
London Blackfriars 3	⊖ d																									
Denmark Hill 4	d					07 47		07 54				08 17				08 24				08 47				08 54		09 17
Peckham Rye 4	d					07a49		07 56				08a19				08 26				08a49				08 56		09a19
Queens Rd Peckham	d							07 59								08 29								08 59		
South Bermondsey	d							08 01								08 31								09 01		
Clapham Junction 10	d																									
Wandsworth Common	d																									
Balham 4	⊖ d																									
Streatham Hill	d																									
West Norwood 4	d																									
Gipsy Hill	d																									
Crystal Palace 4	d																									
Sydenham	d	06 55		07 25						07 55				08 13				08 25					08 43		08 55	
Forest Hill 4	d	06 58		07 28						07 58				08 15				08 28					08 45		08 58	
Honor Oak Park	d	07 00		07 30						08 00				08 18				08 30					08 48		09 00	
Brockley	d	07 03		07 33						08 03				08 20				08 33					08 50		09 03	
New Cross Gate 4	⊖ d	07 05		07 35						08 05				08 23				08 35					08 53		09 05	
London Bridge 4	⊖ a	07 12		07 42				08 06		08 12				08 31		08 36		08 42					09 01	09 06	09 12	
London Waterloo (East) 4	⊖ a	07 17		07 47						08 17								08 47							09 17	
London Charing Cross 4	⊖ a	07 20		07 50						08 20								08 50							09 20	

For general notes see front of timetable
For details of catering facilities see Directory of Train Operators

A From Caterham (Table 181)
B From Purley (Table 175)
C From Tattenham Corner (Table 181)

Table 178

Sundays

Croydon and London Victoria → London Bridge and Charing Cross

Network Diagram - see first page of Table 177

		SN	SN	SN A	SE		SN	SN	SN B	SE	SN
East Croydon	d			09 17					22 47		
West Croydon 4	d	09 01					22 31				
Norwood Junction 2	d	09 05		09 21			22 35		22 51		
Anerley	d	09 08					22 38				
Penge West	d	09 10					22 40				
London Victoria 15	⊖ d		09 11		09 38			22 41		23 08	23 11
Battersea Park 4	d		09 15					22 45			23 15
Wandsworth Road	d		09 17					22 47			23 17
Clapham High Street	⊖ d		09 19			and at		22 49			23 19
London Blackfriars 3	⊖ d					the same					
Denmark Hill 4	d		09 24		09 47	minutes		22 54		23 17	23 24
Peckham Rye 4	d		09 26		09a49	past		22 56		23a19	23 26
Queens Rd Peckham	d		09 29			each		22 59			23 29
South Bermondsey	d		09 31			hour until		23 01			23 31
Clapham Junction 10	d										
Wandsworth Common	d										
Balham 4	⊖ d										
Streatham Hill	d										
West Norwood 4	d										
Gipsy Hill	d										
Crystal Palace 4	d										
Sydenham	d	09 13		09 25			22 43		22 55		
Forest Hill 4	d	09 15		09 28			22 45		22 58		
Honor Oak Park	d	09 18		09 30			22 48		23 00		
Brockley	d	09 20		09 33			22 50		23 03		
New Cross Gate 4	⊖ d	09 23		09 35			22 53		23 05		
London Bridge 4	⊖ a	09 31	09 36	09 42			23 01	23 06	23 12		23 36
London Waterloo (East) 4	⊖ a			09 47					23 17		
London Charing Cross 4	⊖ a			09 50					23 20		

For general notes see front of timetable
For details of catering facilities see Directory of Train Operators

A From Tattenham Corner (Table 181)
B From Caterham (Table 181)

Luton and London → Wimbledon and Sutton via Streatham

Network Diagram - see first page of Table 177

Miles	Miles	Station		FC MX	FC MX	SN	SN	FC	SN	FC	SN	FC	FC 1 A	SN B	FC A		SN C	FC	SN B	FC 1 A	FC	FC D	FC A	FC D	FC D	FC
—	—	Luton 10	d					04 44		05 48		06 18	06 36		06 56			07 08		07 40	07 36	08 04	08 20		08 28	08 54
—	—	Luton Airport Parkway 7 ✈	d					04 46		05 50		06 20	06 26		06 46			07 10		07 42	07 38	07 58	08 14		08 30	08 56
—	—	St Pancras International 15 ⊖	d					05 56		06 34		07 04	07 08		07 28			07 56		08 16	08 24	08 40	08 52	08 56	09 16	09 34
—	—	Farringdon 3 ⊖	d					06 01		06 39		07 09	07 13		07 33			08 01		08 21	08 29	08 45	08 57	09 01	09 21	09 39
—	0	City Thameslink 3	d					06 03		06 43		07 13	07 17		07 37			08 05		08 25	08 33	08 49	09 01	09 05	09 25	09 43
—	½	**London Blackfriars 3** ⊖	d					06 06		06 46		07 16	07 20		07 40			08 08		08 28	08 36	08 52	09 04	09 08	09 28	09 46
—	1½	Elephant & Castle ⊖	d					06 09		06 49		07 19	07 23		07 43			08 11		08 31	08 39	08 55	09 07	09 11	09 31	09 49
—	3½	Loughborough Jn	d					06 13		06 53		07 23	07 27		07 47			08 15		08 35	08 43	08 59	09 11	09 15	09 35	09 53
—	4½	Herne Hill 4	d					06b20		06 58		07 28	07 34		07 52			08c22		08 39	08 48	09e06	09 15	09 22	09f42	09 57
0	—	**London Bridge 4** ⊖	d	23p28	23p58		06 00	06 00	06 30	06 38	07 00	07 08	07 08	07 31	07 31		08 02	08 02	08 24	08 24	08 31	08 48		09 03	09 18	09 33
1¾	—	South Bermondsey	d		23 22		06 04	06 04	06 34	06 42	07 04	07 12	07 12	07 35	07 35		08 06	08 06	08 28	08 28	08 35	08 52		09 07	09 22	09 37
2¾	—	Queens Rd Peckham	d		23 54		06 06	06 06	06 36	06 44	07 06	07 14	07 14	07 37	07 37		08 08	08 08	08 30	08 30	08 37	08 54		09 09	09 24	09 39
3½	—	Peckham Rye 4	d		23 57		06 09	06 09	06 39	06 47	07 09	07 17	07 17	07 40	07 40		08 11	08 11	08 33	08 33	08 40	08 57		09 12	09 27	09 42
4¼	—	East Dulwich	d		00 01		06 12	06 12	06 42	06 50	07 12	07 20	07 20	07 43	07 43		08 14	08 14		08 30	08 43	09 00		09 15	09 30	09 45
4¾	—	North Dulwich	d		00 03		06 14		06 44	06 52	07 14	07 22	07 22	07 45			08 16			08 32	08 45	09 02		09 17	09 32	09 47
6	5½	Tulse Hill 3	d	23p40	00 10		06 17	06 26	06 47	07 03	07 17	07 32	07 38	07 48	07 56		08 19	08 26	08 38	08 43	08g57	09h16	09 20	09 28	09 46	10 02
7½	7	Streatham 4	d	23p43	00 13		06 21	06 30	06 51	07 06	07 21	07 36	07 42	07 52	07 59		08 23	08 29	08 42	08 47	09 00	09 19	09 23	09 31	09 49	10 05
—	8	Mitcham Eastfields	d					06 34		07 10		07 40			08 03			08 33		08 51		09 23			09 53	
—	9	Mitcham Junction 🚋	d					06 38		07 14		07 44			08 07			08 37		08 55		09 27			09 57	
—	11	Hackbridge	d					06 41		07 17		07 47			08 10			08 40		08 58		09 30			10 00	
—	11¾	Carshalton	d					06 44		07 20		07 50			08 13			08 43		09 01		09 33			10 03	
9	—	Tooting	d	23p48	00 18		06 27		06 56		07 25		07 46	07 56			08 27		08 46		09 06		09 27	09 36		10 10
10¼	—	Haydons Road	d	23p51	00 21		06 30		06 59		07 28		07 49	07 59			08 30		08 49		09 09		09 30	09 39		10 13
11½	—	**Wimbledon 6** ⊖ 🚋	a	23p54	00 24		06 32		07 02		07 31		07 52	08 01			08 32		08 51		09 11		09 33	09 44		10 16
—	—		d	23p54	00 25	05 56	06 33		07 02		07 32			08 02			08 33		08 55		09 17			09 47		10 17
12½	—	Wimbledon Chase	d	23p57	00 28	05 59	06 36		07 10		07 35			08 05			08 36		08 58		09 20			09 50		10 20
13	—	South Merton	d	23p59	00 30	06 01	06 38		07 12		07 37			08 07			08 38		09 00		09 22			09 52		10 22
13½	—	Morden South	d	00 01	00 32	06 03	06 40		07 14		07 39			08 09			08 40		09 02		09 24			09 54		10 24
14	—	St Helier	d	00 03	00 34	06 05	06 42		07 16		07 41			08 11			08 42		09 04		09 26			09 56		10 26
15	—	Sutton Common	d	00 05	00 36	06 07	06 44		07 18		07 43			08 13			08 44		09 06		09 28			09 58		10 28
16	—	West Sutton	d	00 08	00 39	06 10	06 47		07 21		07 46			08 16			08 47		09 09		09 31			10 01		10 31
17	13	**Sutton (Surrey) 4**	a	00 12	00 43	06 13	06 50	06 47	07 25	07 23	07 49	07 53		08 19	08 16		08 50	08 46	09 13	09 05	09 37	09 36		10 05	10 07	10 35

Station		FC D	FC	FC D	FC		FC D	FC	FC D		FC	FC D	FC	FC D		FC	FC D	FC	FC D	FC		FC D	SN	FC	FC D
Luton 10	d	09 04	09 14	09 40	09 44		10 10	10 14	10 40		10 44	11 04	11 14	11 34		14 44	15 04	15 14	15 34	15 44		16 04		16 14	16 46
Luton Airport Parkway 7 ✈	d	09 06	09 16	09 36	09 46		10 06	10 16	10 36		10 46	11 06	11 16	11 36		14 46	15 06	15 16	15 36	15 46		16 06		16 16	16 36
St Pancras International 15 ⊖	d	09 48	10 04	10 18	10 34		10 48	11 04	11 18		11 34	11 48	12 04	12 18		15 34	15 48	16 04	16 18	16 34		16 46		17 02	17 18
Farringdon 3 ⊖	d	09 53	10 09	10 23	10 39		10 53	11 09	11 23		11 39	11 53	12 09	12 23		15 39	15 53	16 09	16 23	16 39		16 51		17 07	17 23
City Thameslink 3	d	09 57	10 13	10 27	10 43		10 57	11 13	11 27		11 43	11 57	12 13	12 27		15 43	15 57	16 13	16 27	16 43		16 55		17 11	17 27
London Blackfriars 3 ⊖	d	10 00	10 16	10 30	10 46		11 00	11 16	11 30		11 46	12 00	12 16	12 30		15 46	16 00	16 16	16 30	16 46		16 58		17 14	17 30
Elephant & Castle ⊖	d	10 03	10 19	10 33	10 49		11 03	11 19	11 33		11 49	12 03	12 19	12 33		15 49	16 03	16 19	16 33	16 50		17 02		17 18	17 34
Loughborough Jn	d	10 07	10 23	10 37	10 53		11 07	11 23	11 37		11 53	12 07	12 23	12 37		15 53	16 07	16 23	16 37	16 54		17 06		17 22	17 38
Herne Hill 4	d	10 12	10 27	10 42	10 57		11 12	11 27	11 42		11 57	12 12	12 27	12 42		15 57	16 12	16 27	16 42	16 58		17 10		17 26	17 42
London Bridge 4 ⊖	d	09 48	10 03	10 18	10 33		10 48	11 03	11 18		11 33	11 48	12 03	12 18	and at	15 33	15 48	16 03	16 18	16 33		16 48	17 05	17 05	17 18
South Bermondsey	d	09 52	10 07	10 22	10 37		10 52	11 07	11 22		11 37	11 52	12 07	12 22		15 37	15 52	16 07	16 22	16 37		16 52	17 09	17 09	17 22
Queens Rd Peckham	d	09 54	10 09	10 24	10 39		10 54	11 09	11 24		11 39	11 54	12 09	12 24	the same	15 39	15 54	16 09	16 24	16 39		16 54	17 11	17 11	17 24
Peckham Rye 4	d	09 57	10 12	10 27	10 42		10 57	11 12	11 27		11 42	11 57	12 12	12 27		15 42	15 57	16 12	16 27	16 42		16 57	17 14	17 14	17 27
East Dulwich	d	10 00	10 15	10 30	10 45		11 00	11 15	11 30		11 45	12 00	12 15	12 30	minutes	15 45	16 00	16 15	16 30	16 45		17 00	17 17	17 17	17 30
North Dulwich	d	10 02	10 17	10 32	10 47		11 02	11 17	11 32		11 47	12 02	12 17	12 32		15 47	16 02	16 17	16 32	16 47		17 02	17 19		17 32
Tulse Hill 3	d	10 16	10 32	10 46	11 02		11 16	11 32	11 46		12 02	12 16	12 32	12 46	past	16 02	16 16	16 32	16j50	17 02		17 16	17 23	17 32	17 46
Streatham 4	d	10 19	10 35	10 49	11 05		11 19	11 35	11 49		12 05	12 19	12 35	12 49		16 06	16 19	16 35	16 54	17 05		17 20	17 26	17 35	17 50
Mitcham Eastfields	d	10 23		10 53			11 23		11 53			12 23		12 53	each		16 23		16 58			17 24	17 31		17 54
Mitcham Junction 🚋	d	10 27		10 57			11 27		11 57			12 27		12 57	hour until		16 27		17 02			17 28	17 34		17 58
Hackbridge	d	10 30		11 00			11 30		12 00			12 30		13 00			16 30		17 05			17 31	17 38		18 01
Carshalton	d	10 33		11 03			11 33		12 03			12 33		13 03			16 33		17 08			17 34	17 40		18 04
Tooting	d		10 40		11 10			11 40			12 10		12 40			16 11		16 41		17 10				17 40	
Haydons Road	d		10 43		11 13			11 43			12 13		12 43			16 14		16 44		17 13				17 43	
Wimbledon 6 ⊖ 🚋	a		10 46		11 16			11 46			12 16		12 46			16 17		16 47		17 16				17 46	
	d		10 47		11 17			11 47			12 17		12 47			16 17		16 47		17 19				17 47	
Wimbledon Chase	d		10 50		11 20			11 50			12 20		12 50			16 20		16 50		17 22				17 50	
South Merton	d		10 52		11 22			11 52			12 22		12 52			16 22		16 52		17 24				17 52	
Morden South	d		10 54		11 24			11 54			12 24		12 54			16 24		16 54		17 26				17 54	
St Helier	d		10 56		11 26			11 56			12 26		12 56			16 26		16 56		17 28				17 56	
Sutton Common	d		10 58		11 28			11 58			12 28		12 58			16 29		16 59		17 30				17 58	
West Sutton	d		11 01		11 31			12 01			12 31		13 01			16 31		17 01		17 33				18 01	
Sutton (Surrey) 4	a	10 36	11 05	11 06	11 35		11 36	12 05	12 06		12 35	12 36	13 05	13 06		16 36	16 36	17 06	17 12	17 39		17 38	17 44	18 05	18 08

For general notes see front of timetable
For details of catering facilities see Directory of Train Operators

A From Bedford (Table 52)
B To London Victoria (Table 177)
C To London Bridge
D From St Albans City (Table 52)
b Arr. 0617
c Arr. 0819
e Arr. 0903
f Arr. 0939
g Arr. 0852
h Arr. 0910
j Arr. 1646

Luton and London → Wimbledon and Sutton via Streatham

Network Diagram - see first page of Table 177

		SN	FC	FC A	SN	FC	FC A	SN B	FC A	FC	FC C	FC A	FC C	FC A	FC	FC A	FC	FC	FC	FC	FC	FC	FC
Luton 10	d		16 44	17 10		17 18	17 34		17 44	18 02	18 24	18 34	18 54	19 06	19 18		19 48	20 18	20 48	21 18			
Luton Airport Parkway 7	d		16 46	17 12		17 20	17 36		17 46	18 04	18 26	18 36	18 56	19 08	19 20		19 50	20 20	20 50	21 20			
St Pancras International 15	d		17 30	17 50		18 04	18 16		18 34	18 48	19 04	19 18	19 34	19 48	20 04	20 18	20 34	21 04	21 34	22 04			
Farringdon 3	d		17 35	17 55		18 09	18 21		18 39	18 53	19 09	19 23	19 39	19 53	20 09	20 23	20 39	21 09	21 39	22 09			
City Thameslink 3	d		17 39	17 59		18 13	18 25		18 43	18 57	19 13	19 27	19 43	19 57	20 13	20 27	20 43	21 13	21 43	22 13			
London Blackfriars 3	d		17 42	18 02		18 16	18b30		18 46	19 00	19 16	19 30	19 46	20 00	20 16	20 30	20 46	21 16	21 46	22 16			
Elephant & Castle	d		17 46	18 06		18 20	18 34		18 49	19 04	19 19	19 33	19 49	20 03	20 19	20 33	20 49	21 19	21 49	22 19			
Loughborough Jn	d		17 50	18 10		18 24	18 38		18 53	19 08	19 23	19 37	19 53	20 07	20 23	20 37	20 53	21 23	21 53	22 23			
Herne Hill 4	d		17 54	18 14		18 28	18c44		18 57	19 12	19 27	19 42	19 57	20 12	20 27	20 42	20 57	21 27	21 57	22 27			
London Bridge 4	d	17 35	17 35	17 58	18 07	18 07	18 28	18 38	18 38	18 48	19 08	19 18	19 38	19 48	20 03	20 18		20 48	21 18	21 48	22 58	23 28	23 58
South Bermondsey	d	17 39	17 39	18 02	18 11	18 11	18 32	18 42	18 42	18 52	19 12	19 22	19 42	19 52	20 07	20 22		20 52	21 22	21 52	22 52	23 22	23 22
Queens Rd Peckham	d	17 41	17 41	18 04	18 13	18 13	18 34	18 44	18 44	18 54	19 14	19 24	19 44	19 54	20 09	20 24		20 54	21 24	21 54	22 54	23 24	23 54
Peckham Rye 4	d	17 44	17 44	18 07	18 16	18 16	18 37	18 47	18 47	18 57	19 17	19 27	19 47	19 57	20 12	20 27		20 57	21 27	21 57	22 57	23 27	23 57
East Dulwich	d	17 47	17 47	18 10	18 19	18 19	18 40	18 50	18 50	19 00	19 20	19 30	19 50	20 00	20 15	20 30		21 00	21 30	22 00	23 00	23 30	00 01
North Dulwich	d	17 49		18 12	18 21		18 42	18 52		19 02	19 22	19 32	19 52	20 02	20 17	20 32		21 02	21 32	22 02	23 02	23 32	00 03
Tulse Hill 3	d	17 52	17 58	18 18	18 24	18 32	18 48	18 55	19 02	19 16	19 32	19 46	20 02	20 16	20 32	20 46	21 02	21 32	22 02	22 32	23 10	23 40	00 10
Streatham 4	d	17 56	18 01	18 22	18 28	18 35	18 52	18 59	19 05	19 19	19 35	19 49	20 05	20 19	20 35	20 49	21 05	21 35	22 05	22 35	23 13	23 43	00 13
Mitcham Eastfields	d	18 00		18 26	18 32		18 56	19 03		19 23		19 53		20 23		20 53							
Mitcham Junction	d	18 04		18 30	18 36		18 59	19 07		19 27		19 57		20 27		20 57							
Hackbridge	d	18 07		18 33	18 39		19 03	19 10		19 30		20 00		20 30		21 00							
Carshalton	d	18 10		18 36	18 42		19 05	19 13		19 33		20 03		20 33		21 03							
Tooting	d		18 06			18 40			19 10		19 40		20 10		20 40		21 10	21 40	22 10	22 40	23 18	23 48	00 18
Haydons Road	d		18 09			18 43			19 13		19 43		20 13		20 43		21 13	21 43	22 13	22 43	23 21	23 51	00 21
Wimbledon 6	a		18 12			18 46			19 16		19 46		20 16		20 46		21 16	21 46	22 16	22 46	23 24	23 54	00 24
	d		18 13			18 47			19 19		19 49		20 17		20 47		21 17	21 47	22 17	22 47	23 25	23 54	00 25
Wimbledon Chase	d		18 16			18 50			19 22		19 52		20 20		20 50		21 20	21 50	22 20	22 50	23 28	23 57	00 28
South Merton	d		18 18			18 52			19 24		19 54		20 22		20 52		21 22	21 52	22 22	22 52	23 30	23 59	00 30
Morden South	d		18 20			18 54			19 26		19 56		20 24		20 54		21 24	21 54	22 24	22 54	23 32	00 01	00 32
St Helier	d		18 22			18 56			19 28		19 58		20 26		20 56		21 26	21 56	22 26	22 56	23 34	00 03	00 34
Sutton Common	d		18 24			18 58			19 30		20 00		20 28		20 58		21 28	21 58	22 28	22 58	23 36	00 05	00 36
West Sutton	d		18 27			19 01			19 33		20 03		20 31		21 01		21 31	22 01	22 31	23 01	23 39	00 08	00 39
Sutton (Surrey) 4	a	18 13	18 31	18 39	18 45	19 05	19 09	19 16	19 39	19 36	20 09	20 06	20 35	20 36	21 05	21 06	21 39	22 07	22 40	23 05	23 43	00 12	00 43

Saturdays

		FC	FC	FC	FC	FC	FC	FC	FC	FC	FC	FC	FC
Luton 10	d												
Luton Airport Parkway 7	d												
St Pancras International 15	d												
Farringdon 3	d												
City Thameslink 3	d												
London Blackfriars 3	d												
Elephant & Castle	d												
Loughborough Jn	d												
Herne Hill 4	d				06 42		07 12		07 42		08 12		08 42
London Bridge 4	d	23p28	23p58	06 21		06 45	06 48	07 15	07 18	07 45	07 48	08 15	08 18
South Bermondsey	d		23e22				06 52		07 22	07 37	07 52	08 07	08 22
Queens Rd Peckham	d		23e54				06 54		07 24	07 39	07 54	08 09	08 24
Peckham Rye 4	d		23e57				06 57		07 27	07 42	07 57	08 12	08 27
East Dulwich	d		00 01				07 00		07 30	07 45	08 00	08 15	08 30
North Dulwich	d		00 03				07 02		07 32	07 47	08 02	08 17	08 32
Tulse Hill 3	d	23p40	00 10	06 32	06 46	07f02	07 16	07g32	07 46	08h02	08 16	08j32	08 46
Streatham 4	d	23p43	00 13	06 35	06 49	07 05	07 19	07 35	07 49	08 05	08 19	08 35	08 49
Mitcham Eastfields	d				06 53		07 23		07 53		08 23		08 53
Mitcham Junction	d				06 57		07 27		07 57		08 27		08 57
Hackbridge	d				07 00		07 30		08 00		08 30		09 00
Carshalton	d				07 03		07 33		08 03		08 33		09 03
Tooting	d	23p48	00 18	06 40		07 10		07 40		08 10		08 40	
Haydons Road	d	23p51	00 21	06 43		07 13		07 43		08 13		08 43	
Wimbledon 6	a	23p54	00 24	06 46		07 16		07 46		08 16		08 46	
	d	23p54	00 25	06 47		07 17		07 47		08 17		08 47	
Wimbledon Chase	d	23p57	00 28	06 50		07 20		07 50		08 20		08 50	
South Merton	d	23p59	00 30	06 52		07 22		07 52		08 22		08 52	
Morden South	d	00 01	00 32	06 54		07 24		07 54		08 24		08 54	
St Helier	d	00 03	00 34	06 56		07 26		07 56		08 26		08 56	
Sutton Common	d	00 05	00 36	06 58		07 28		07 58		08 28		08 58	
West Sutton	d	00 08	00 39	07 01		07 31		08 01		08 31		09 01	
Sutton (Surrey) 4	a	00 12	00 43	07 05	07 06	07 35	07 36	08 05	08 06	08 35	08 36	09 05	09 06

For general notes see front of timetable
For details of catering facilities see Directory of Train Operators

A From St Albans City (Table 52)

B To Epsom (Table 182)
C From Bedford (Table 52)
b Arr. 1827
c Arr. 1841
e Saturdays

f Arr. 0658
g Arr. 0728
h Arr. 0758
j Arr. 0828

Luton and London → Wimbledon and Sutton via Streatham

Network Diagram - see first page of Table 177

		FC		FC	FC	FC	FC	FC	FC	FC	FC	FC	FC	FC
Luton 10	d													
Luton Airport Parkway 7 ✈	d													
St Pancras International 15 ⊖	d													
Farringdon 3 ⊖	d													
City Thameslink 3	d													
London Blackfriars 3 ⊖	d													
Elephant & Castle ⊖	d													
Loughborough Jn	d													
Herne Hill 4	d			19 12		19 42								
London Bridge 4 ⊖	d	08 45	and at	18 48	19 15	19 18	19 45	20 15	20 45	21 15	21 45	22 15	22 45	23 15
South Bermondsey	d	08 37		18 52	19 07	19 22	19 37	19 52	20 22	20 52	21 22	21 52	22 22	22 52
Queens Rd Peckham	d	08 39		18 54	19 09	19 24	19 39	19 54	20 24	20 54	21 24	21 54	22 24	22 54
Peckham Rye 4	d	08 42	the same	18 57	19 12	19 27	19 42	19 57	20 27	20 57	21 27	21 57	22 27	22 57
East Dulwich	d	08 45		19 00	19 15	19 30	19 45	20 00	20 30	21 00	21 30	22 00	22 30	23 00
North Dulwich	d	08 47	minutes	19 02	19 17	19 32	19 47	20 02	20 32	21 02	21 32	22 02	22 32	23 02
Tulse Hill 3	d	09b02		19 16	19c32	19 46	20e02	20f32	21g02	21h32	22j02	22k32	23m02	23n32
Streatham 4	d	09 05	past	19 19	19 35	19 49	20 05	20 35	21 05	21 35	22 05	22 35	23 05	23 35
Mitcham Eastfields	d		each	19 23		19 53								
Mitcham Junction 🚊	d			19 27		19 57								
Hackbridge	d		hour until	19 30		20 00								
Carshalton	d			19 33		20 03								
Tooting	d	09 10			19 40		20 10	20 40	21 10	21 40	22 10	22 40	23 10	23 40
Haydons Road	d	09 13			19 43		20 13	20 43	21 13	21 43	22 13	22 43	23 13	23 43
Wimbledon 6 ⊖ 🚊	a	09 16			19 46		20 16	20 46	21 16	21 46	22 16	22 46	23 16	23 46
	d	09 17			19 47		20 17	20 47	21 17	21 47	22 17	22 47	23 17	23 47
Wimbledon Chase	d	09 20			19 50		20 20	20 50	21 20	21 50	22 20	22 50	23 20	23 50
South Merton	d	09 22			19 52		20 22	20 52	21 22	21 52	22 22	22 52	23 22	23 52
Morden South	d	09 24			19 54		20 24	20 54	21 24	21 54	22 24	22 54	23 24	23 54
St Helier	d	09 26			19 56		20 26	20 56	21 26	21 56	22 26	22 56	23 26	23 56
Sutton Common	d	09 28			19 58		20 28	20 58	21 28	21 58	22 28	22 58	23 28	23 58
West Sutton	d	09 31			20 01		20 31	21 01	21 31	22 01	22 31	23 01	23 31	00 01
Sutton (Surrey) 4	a	09 35		19 36	20 05	20 06	20 39	21 05	21 39	22 05	22 39	23 05	23 35	00 05

		FC
Luton 10	d	
Luton Airport Parkway 7 ✈	d	
St Pancras International 15 ⊖	d	
Farringdon 3 ⊖	d	
City Thameslink 3	d	
London Blackfriars 3 ⊖	d	
Elephant & Castle ⊖	d	
Loughborough Jn	d	
Herne Hill 4	d	
London Bridge 4 ⊖	d	23 45
South Bermondsey	d	23 22
Queens Rd Peckham	d	23 24
Peckham Rye 4	d	23 27
East Dulwich	d	23 30
North Dulwich	d	23 32
Tulse Hill 3	d	00q02
Streatham 4	d	00 05
Mitcham Eastfields	d	
Mitcham Junction 🚊	d	
Hackbridge	d	
Carshalton	d	
Tooting	d	00 10
Haydons Road	d	00 13
Wimbledon 6 ⊖ 🚊	a	00 16
	d	00 17
Wimbledon Chase	d	00 20
South Merton	d	00 22
Morden South	d	00 24
St Helier	d	00 26
Sutton Common	d	00 28
West Sutton	d	00 31
Sutton (Surrey) 4	a	00 35

For general notes see front of timetable
For details of catering facilities see Directory of Train Operators

b Arr. 0858
c Arr. 1928
e Arr. 1958
f Arr. 2028
g Arr. 2058
h Arr. 2128
j Arr. 2158
k Arr. 2228
m Arr. 2258
n Arr. 2328
q Arr. 2358

Table 179

Sundays

Luton and London → Wimbledon and Sutton via Streatham

Network Diagram - see first page of Table 177

		FC		FC		FC		FC			FC	FC			FC		FC
Luton 10	d																
Luton Airport Parkway 7 ✈	d																
St Pancras International 15 ⊖	d																
Farringdon 3 ⊖	d																
City Thameslink 3	d																
London Blackfriars 3 ⊖	d																
Elephant & Castle ⊖	d																
Loughborough Jn	d																
Herne Hill 4	d																
London Bridge 4 ⊖	d	23p15		23p45		09 21		09 51			10 21	10 51			20 21		20 51
South Bermondsey	d			23p22		08 59		09 29			09 59	10 29	and at		19 59		20 29
Queens Rd Peckham	d			23p24		09 01		09 31			10 01	10 31			20 01		20 31
Peckham Rye 4	d			23p27		09 04		09 34			10 04	10 34	the same		20 04		20 34
East Dulwich	d			23p30		09 07		09 37			10 07	10 37			20 07		20 37
North Dulwich	d			23p32		09 09		09 39			10 09	10 39	minutes		20 09		20 39
Tulse Hill 3	d	23b32		00c02		09 32		10 02			10 32	11 02			20 32		21 02
Streatham 4	d	23p35		00 05		09 35		10 05			10 35	11 05	past		20 35		21 05
Mitcham Eastfields	d																
Mitcham Junction 🚋	d												each				
Hackbridge	d																
Carshalton	d												hour until				
Tooting	d	23p40		00 10		09 40		10 10			10 40	11 10			20 40		21 10
Haydons Road	d	23p43		00 13		09 43		10 13			10 43	11 13			20 43		21 13
Wimbledon 6 ⊖ 🚋	a	23p46		00 16		09 46		10 16			10 46	11 16			20 46		21 16
	d	23p47		00 17		09 47		10 17			10 47	11 17			20 47		21 17
Wimbledon Chase	d	23p50		00 20		09 50		10 20			10 50	11 20			20 50		21 20
South Merton	d	23p52		00 22		09 52		10 22			10 52	11 22			20 52		21 22
Morden South	d	23p54		00 24		09 54		10 24			10 54	11 24			20 54		21 24
St Helier	d	23p56		00 26		09 56		10 26			10 56	11 26			20 56		21 26
Sutton Common	d	23p58		00 28		09 58		10 28			10 58	11 28			20 58		21 28
West Sutton	d	00 01		00 31		10 01		10 31			11 01	11 31			21 01		21 31
Sutton (Surrey) 4	a	00 05		00 35		10 05		10 35			11 05	11 35			21 05		21 35

For general notes see front of timetable
For details of catering facilities see Directory of Train Operators

b Previous night. Arr.2328

c Arr. 2358

Sutton and Wimbledon → London and Luton via Streatham

Network Diagram - see first page of Table 177

Miles	Miles	Station		SN	SN	FC	FC A	SN	FC B	SN	FC	SN	FC B	FC A	FC A	SN	FC	FC	FC A	FC	FC A
0	0	**Sutton (Surrey)** 4	d	05 37	06 14		06 22	06 51	06 48	07 25	07 24	07 50		07 54	08 20	08 51	08 47	09 06	09 38	09 37	10 06
1	—	West Sutton	d				06 25		06 51		07 27			07 57	08 23		08 50	09 09		09 40	
2	—	Sutton Common	d				06 27		06 53		07 29			07 59	08 25		08 52	09 11		09 42	
3	—	St Helier	d				06 30		06 56		07 32			08 02	08 28		08 55	09 14		09 45	
3½	—	Morden South	d				06 32		06 58		07 34			08 04	08 30		08 57	09 16		09 47	
4	—	South Merton	d				06 34		07 00		07 36			08 06	08 32		08 59	09 18		09 49	
4½	—	Wimbledon Chase	d				06 36		07 02		07 38			08 08	08 34		09 01	09 20		09 51	
5½	—	**Wimbledon** 3 ⊖	a				06 39		07 05		07 41			08 11	08 37		09 04	09 23		09 55	
—	—		d		05 56	06 24	06 40		07 06		07 42		07 58	08 12	08 42		09 05	09 24		09 56	
6¾	—	Haydons Road	d			06 26	06 42		07 08		07 44		08 00	08 14	08 44		09 07	09 26		09 58	
8	—	Tooting	d			06 29	06 45		07 11		07 47		08 03	08 17	08 47		09 10	09 29		10 01	
—	1¼	Carshalton	d	05 40	06 17			06 54		07 28		07 53				08 54			09 41		10 09
—	2	Hackbridge	d	05 42	06 19			06 56		07 31		07 55				08 56			09 43		10 11
—	4	Mitcham Junction	d	05 46	06 23			07 00		07 34		07 59				09 00			09 46		10 14
—	5	Mitcham Eastfields	d	05 49	06 26					07 38						09 03			09 50		10 18
9½	6	Streatham 4	d	05 53	06 30	06 34	06 50	07 06	07 16	07 42	07 52	08 05	08 10	08 22	08 52	09 10	09 15	09 34	09 53	10 06	10 23
11	7½	Tulse Hill 3	d	05 57	06 34	06 38	06 56	07 09	07 20	07 46	07 56	08 09	08 14	08 26	08 58	09 15	09 19	09 38	09 57	10 12	10 27
12¼	—	North Dulwich	d	06 10	06 37	06 49	07 01	07 12	07 27	07 49	08 03	08 12		08 33	09 14	09 18	09 25	09 45	10 12	10 27	10 42
12½	—	East Dulwich	d	06 12	06 39	06 51	07 03	07 14	07 29	07 51	08 05	08 14		08 35	09 16	09 20	09 27	09 47	10 14	10 29	10 44
13¼	—	Peckham Rye 4	d	06 02	06 42	06 53	07 05	07 17	07 31	07 53	08 07	08 16		08 38	09 19	09 23	09 30	09 49	10 17	10 31	10 47
14¼	—	Queens Rd Peckham	d	06 17	06 44	06 56	07 08	07 24	07 34	08 10	08 10	08 19		08 40	09 21	09 25	09 33	09 52	10 19	10 34	10 49
15¼	—	South Bermondsey	d	06 20	06 47	06 58	07 10	07 27	07 36	08 13	08 13	08 21		08 43	09 24	09 28	09 35	09 54	10 22	10 36	10 52
17	—	**London Bridge** 4 ⊖	a	06 08	06 51	07 05	07 18	07 25	07 43	08 02	08 21	08 30		08 49	09 30	09 34	09 43	09 59	10 27	10 41	10 56
—	8½	Herne Hill 4	d			06 42	07 00		07 24		08 01		08b22	08 31	09 02		09 23	09 42	10 01	10 16	10 31
—	9½	Loughborough Jn	d			06 45	07 03		07 27		08 04		08 25	08 34	09 05		09 26	09 45	10 04	10 19	10 34
—	11½	Elephant & Castle ⊖	d			06 50	07 08		07 32		08 09		08 32	08 41	09 10		09 30	09 50	10 09	10 24	10 39
—	12½	**London Blackfriars** 3 ⊖	a			06 58	07 11		07 35		08 14		08 38	08 46	09 14		09 34	09 58	10 14	10 28	10 44
—	13	City Thameslink 3	a			07 00	07 14		07 38		08 16		08 40	08 49	09 16		09 36	10 00	10 16	10 30	10 46
—	—	Farringdon 3 ⊖	a			07 04	07 17		07 42		08 20		08 44	08 53	09 20		09 40	10 04	10 20	10 34	10 50
—	—	St Pancras International 15 ⊖	a			07 07	07 21		07 47		08 23		08 47	08 56	09 23		09 43	10 07	10 23	10 37	10 53
—	—	Luton Airport Parkway 7 ✈	a			07 46	08 05		08 23		09 02		09 30	09 29	10 00		10 29	10 56	11 06	11 26	11 37
—	—	**Luton** 10	a			07 50	08 08		08 26		09 06		09 34	09 32	10 04		10 34	11 00	11 09	11 30	11 40

Station		FC	FC A	FC	FC A	FC	FC A		FC A	FC A	FC	FC B	FC	FC A	FC B	FC A	FC	SN	FC A
Sutton (Surrey) 4	d	10 07	10 36	10 37	11 06	11 07	11 36		15 37	16 06	16 07	16 36	16 37	17 06	17 12	17 40	17 38	17 46	18 06
West Sutton	d	10 10		10 40		11 10			15 40		16 10		16 40		17 15		17 41	17 49	
Sutton Common	d	10 12		10 42		11 12			15 42		16 12		16 42		17 17		17 43	17 52	
St Helier	d	10 15		10 45		11 15			15 45		16 15		16 45		17 20		17 46	17 54	
Morden South	d	10 17		10 47		11 17			15 47		16 17		16 47		17 22		17 48	17 56	
South Merton	d	10 19		10 49		11 19			15 49		16 19		16 49		17 24		17 50	17 58	
Wimbledon Chase	d	10 21		10 51		11 21			15 51		16 21		16 51		17 26		17 52	18 00	
Wimbledon 6 ⊖	a	10 25		10 55		11 25			15 55		16 25		16 55		17 31		17 55	18 04	
	d	10 26		10 56		11 26			15 56		16 28		16 56		17 32		17 56	18 04	
Haydons Road	d	10 28		10 58		11 28		and at	15 58		16 30		16 58		17 34		17 58	18 06	
Tooting	d	10 31		11 01		11 31			16 01		16 33		17 01		17 37		18 01	18 09	
Carshalton	d		10 39		11 09		11 39	the same		16 09		16 39		17 09		17 43			18 09
Hackbridge	d		10 41		11 11		11 41	minutes		16 11		16 41		17 11		17 45			18 11
Mitcham Junction	d		10 44		11 14		11 44			16 14		16 44		17 14		17 48			18 14
Mitcham Eastfields	d		10 48		11 18		11 48	past		16 18		16 48		17 18		17 52			18 18
Streatham 4	d	10 36	10 53	11 06	11 23	11 36	11 53	each	16 06	16 23	16 38	16 53	17 06	17 23	17 42	17 57	18 06	18 13	18 23
Tulse Hill 3	d	10 42	10 57	11 12	11 27	11 42	11 57		16 12	16 27	16 42	16 57	17c14	17e30	17 48	18 02	18 12	18 17	18 27
North Dulwich	d	10 57	11 12	11 27	11 42	11 57	12 12	hour until	16 27	16 42	16 56	17 12	17 30	17 37	18 01	18 08		18 20	18 37
East Dulwich	d	10 59	11 14	11 29	11 44	11 59	12 14		16 29	16 44	16 58	17 14	17 32	17 39	18 03	18 10	18 22	18 22	18 39
Peckham Rye 4	d	11 01	11 17	11 31	11 47	12 01	12 17		16 31	16 47	17 00	17 16	17 34	17 41	18 05	18 12	18 24	18 24	18 41
Queens Rd Peckham	d	11 04	11 19	11 34	11 49	12 04	12 19		16 34	16 49	17 03	17 19	17 37	17 44	18 08	18 15	18 37	18 37	18 44
South Bermondsey	d	11 06	11 22	11 36	11 52	12 06	12 22		16 36	16 52	17 05	17 21	17 39	17 46	18 10	18 17	18 40	18 40	18 46
London Bridge 4 ⊖	a	11 11	11 26	11 41	11 56	12 11	12 27		16 41	16 56	17 10	17 26	17 44	17 54	18 15	18 22	18 31	18 31	18 51
Herne Hill 4	d	10 46	11 01	11 16	11 31	11 46	12 01		16 16	16 31	16 46	17 01	17 18	17f36	17g54	18 06	18 18		18 31
Loughborough Jn	d	10 49	11 04	11 19	11 34	11 49	12 04		16 19	16 34	16 49		17 21	17 39	17 57	18 09	18 21		18 34
Elephant & Castle ⊖	d	10 54	11 09	11 24	11 39	11 54	12 09		16 24	16 39	16 54	17 08	17 26	17 44	18 02	18 14	18 26		18 39
London Blackfriars 3 ⊖	a	10 57	11 14	11 27	11 44	11 57	12 14		16 29	16 44	16 59	17 12	17 29	17 48	18 05	18 18	18 30		18 44
City Thameslink 3	a	11 00	11 16	11 30	11 46	12 00	12 16		16 32	16 46	17 02	17 14	17 34	17 50	18 08	18 20	18 34		18 48
Farringdon 3 ⊖	a	11 04	11 20	11 34	11 50	12 04	12 20		16 35	16 49	17 05	17 17	17 37	17 53	18 11	18 23	18 37		18 51
St Pancras International 15 ⊖	a	11 07	11 23	11 37	11 53	12 07	12 23		16 39	16 53	17 09	17 21	17 41	17 57	18 15	18 27	18 41		18 55
Luton Airport Parkway 7 ✈	a	11 56	12 07	12 26	12 37	12 56	13 07		17 19	17 39	17 50	17 55	18 27	18 39	18 50	19 09	19 29		19 39
Luton 10	a	12 00	12 10	12 30	12 40	13 00	13 10		17 22	17 34	17 54	17 58	18 32	18 34	18 53	19 04	19 34		19 34

For general notes see front of timetable
For details of catering facilities see Directory of Train Operators

A To St Albans City (Table 52)
B To Bedford (Table 52)
b Arr. 0819
c Arr. 1710
e Arr. 1727
f Arr. 1733
g Arr. 1751

Sutton and Wimbledon → London and Luton via Streatham

Network Diagram - see first page of Table 177

		FC	SN	FC	FC	SN	FC	FC	FC	FC	FC	FC	FC	FC	FC	FC	FC
									1		1		1		1		
				A			A		B		B		B		B	A	
Sutton (Surrey) 4	d	18 08	18 16	18 32	18 40	18 47	19 06	19 10	19 40	19 37	20 10	20 07	20 40	20 37	21 10	21 07	22 07
West Sutton	d	18 11	18 19		18 43	18 51		19 13		19 40		20 10		20 40		21 10	22 10
Sutton Common	d	18 13	18 22		18 45	18 53		19 15		19 42		20 12		20 42		21 12	22 12
St Helier	d	18 16	18 24		18 48	18 56		19 18		19 45		20 15		20 45		21 15	22 15
Morden South	d	18 18	18 26		18 50	18 58		19 20		19 47		20 17		20 47		21 17	22 17
South Merton	d	18 20	18 28		18 52	19 00		19 22		19 49		20 19		20 49		21 19	22 19
Wimbledon Chase	d	18 22	18 30		18 54	19 02		19 24		19 51		20 21		20 51		21 21	22 21
Wimbledon 6 ⊖	a	18 25	18 34		18 57	19 06		19 27		19 55		20 25		20 55		21 25	22 24
	d	18 26	18 34		18 58	19 06		19 28		19 56		20 26		20 56		21 36	22 26
Haydons Road	d	18 28	18 36		19 00	19 08		19 30		19 58		20 28		20 58		21 38	22 28
Tooting	d	18 31	18 39		19 03	19 11		19 33		20 01		20 31		21 01		21 41	22 31
Carshalton	d			18 35			19 09		19 43		20 13		20 43		21 13		
Hackbridge	d			18 37			19 11		19 45		20 15		20 45		21 15		
Mitcham Junction	d			18 40			19 14		19 48		20 18		20 48		21 18		
Mitcham Eastfields	d			18 44			19 18		19 52		20 22		20 52		21 22		
Streatham 4	d	18 36	18 45	18 49	19 08	19 16	19 23	19 38	19 56	20 06	20 26	20 36	20 56	21 06	21 26	21 46	22 36
Tulse Hill 3	d	18 42	18 50	18b57	19 14	19 20	19 27	19 44	19 59	20 10	20 29	20 40	20 59	21 10	21 29	21 50	22 40
North Dulwich	d		18 53	*19 01*		19 23	*19 34*	*19 59*	*20 14*	*20 29*	*20 44*	*20 59*	*21 28*	*21 28*	*21 58*	*21 58*	*22 58*
East Dulwich	d	*18 55*	18 55	*19 03*	*19 25*	19 25	*19 36*	*20 01*	*20 16*	*20 31*	*20 46*	*21 01*	*21 30*	*21 30*	*22 00*	*22 00*	*23 00*
Peckham Rye 4	d	*19 00*	19 00	*19 05*	*19 30*	19 30	*19 38*	*20 03*	*20 18*	*20 33*	*20 48*	*21 04*	*21 32*	*21 32*	*22 02*	*22 02*	*23 02*
Queens Rd Peckham	d	*19 03*	19 03	*19 08*	*19 33*	19 33	*19 41*	*20 06*	*20 21*	*20 36*	*20 51*	*21 06*	*21 35*	*21 35*	*22 05*	*22 05*	*23 05*
South Bermondsey	d	*19 05*	19 05	*19 10*	*19 35*	19 35	*19 43*	*20 08*	*20 23*	*20 38*	*20 53*	*21 09*	*21 37*	*21 37*	*22 07*	*22 07*	*23 07*
London Bridge 4 ⊖	a	*19 10*	19 10	*19 15*	*19 40*	19 40	*19 48*	*20 14*	*20 28*	*20 43*	*20 58*	*21 14*	*21 42*	*21 42*	*22 12*	*22 12*	22 52
Herne Hill 4	d	18 48		19 01	19 18		19 32	19 48	20 03	20 16	20 33	20 46	21 03	21 16	21 33	21 54	
Loughborough Jn	d	18 51		19 04	19 21		19 35	19 51	20 07	20 19	20 37	20 49	21 07	21 19	21 37	21 57	
Elephant & Castle ⊖	d	18 56		19 09	19 26		19 40	19 56	20 11	20 24	20 41	20 54	21 11	21 24	21 41	22 02	
London Blackfriars 3 ⊖	a	19 00		19 15	19 30		19 46	19 59	20 15	20 27	20 45	20 57	21 15	21 27	21 45	22 05	
City Thameslink 3	a	19 02		19 18	19 34		19 48	20 02	20 18	20 32	20 48	21 02	21 18	21 32	21 48	22 08	
Farringdon 3 ⊖	a	19 05		19 21	19 38		19 51	20 05	20 21	20 35	20 51	21 05	21 21	21 35	21 51	22 11	
St Pancras International 15 ⊖	a	19 09		19 25	19 41		19 55	20 09	20 25	20 39	20 55	21 09	21 25	21 39	21 55	22 15	
Luton Airport Parkway 7 ✈	a	19 54		20 11	20 26		20 41	20 56	*21 07*	21 26	*21 37*	21 56	*22 07*	22 26	*22 37*	22 59	
Luton 10	a	19 58		20 14	20 30		20 44	21 00	*21 10*	21 30	*21 40*	22 00	*22 10*	22 30	*22 40*	23 02	

Saturdays

		FC	FC	FC	FC	FC	FC	FC	FC	FC	FC	FC	FC		FC	FC	FC	FC
Sutton (Surrey) 4	d		07 06	07 07	07 36	07 37	08 06	08 07	08 36	08 37	09 06	09 07	09 36		16 37	17 06	17 07	17 36
West Sutton	d			07 10		07 40		08 10		08 40		09 10			16 40		17 10	
Sutton Common	d			07 12		07 42		08 12		08 42		09 12			16 42		17 12	
St Helier	d			07 15		07 45		08 15		08 45		09 15			16 45		17 15	
Morden South	d			07 17		07 47		08 17		08 47		09 17			16 47		17 17	
South Merton	d			07 19		07 49		08 19		08 49		09 19			16 49		17 19	
Wimbledon Chase	d			07 21		07 51		08 21		08 51		09 21			16 51		17 21	
Wimbledon 6 ⊖	a			07 25		07 55		08 25		08 55		09 25			16 55		17 25	
	d	07 00		07 30		08 00		08 30		09 00		09 30			17 00		17 30	
Haydons Road	d	07 02		07 32		08 02		08 32		09 02		09 32			17 02		17 32	
Tooting	d	07 05		07 35		08 05		08 35		09 05		09 35		and at	17 05		17 35	
Carshalton	d		07 09		07 39		08 09		08 39		09 09		09 39	the same		17 09		17 39
Hackbridge	d		07 11		07 41		08 11		08 41		09 11		09 41			17 11		17 41
Mitcham Junction	d		07 14		07 44		08 14		08 44		09 14		09 44	minutes		17 14		17 44
Mitcham Eastfields	d		07 18		07 48		08 18		08 48		09 18		09 48			17 18		17 48
Streatham 4	d	07 10	07 23	07 40	07 53	08 10	08 23	08 40	08 53	09 10	09 23	09 40	09 53	past	17 10	17 23	17 40	17 53
Tulse Hill 3	d	07c17	07 27	07e47	07 57	08f17	08 27	08g47	08 57	09h17	09 27	09j47	09 57	each	17k17	17 27	17m47	17 57
North Dulwich	d	*07 27*		*07 57*		*08 27*	*08 42*	*08 57*	*09 12*	*09 27*	*09 42*	*09 57*	*10 12*		*17 27*	*17 42*	*17 57*	*18 12*
East Dulwich	d	*07 29*		*07 59*		*08 29*	*08 44*	*08 59*	*09 14*	*09 29*	*09 44*	*09 59*	*10 14*	hour until	*17 29*	*17 44*	*17 59*	*18 14*
Peckham Rye 4	d	*07 31*		*08 01*		*08 31*	*08 47*	*09 01*	*09 17*	*09 31*	*09 47*	*10 01*	*10 17*		*17 31*	*17 47*	*18 01*	*18 17*
Queens Rd Peckham	d	*07 34*		*08 04*		*08 34*	*08 49*	*09 04*	*09 19*	*09 34*	*09 49*	*10 04*	*10 19*		*17 34*	*17 49*	*18 04*	*18 19*
South Bermondsey	d	*07 36*		*08 06*		*08 36*	*08 52*	*09 06*	*09 22*	*09 36*	*09 52*	*10 06*	*10 22*		*17 36*	*17 52*	*18 06*	*18 22*
London Bridge 4 ⊖	a	07 30		08 00		08 30	*08 56*	09 00	*09 26*	09 30	*09 56*	10 00	*10 26*		17 30	*17 56*	18 00	*18 26*
Herne Hill 4	d		07a31		08a01		08a31		09a01		09a31		10a01			17a31		18a01
Loughborough Jn	d																	
Elephant & Castle ⊖	d																	
London Blackfriars 3 ⊖	a																	
City Thameslink 3	a																	
Farringdon 3 ⊖	a																	
St Pancras International 15 ⊖	a																	
Luton Airport Parkway 7 ✈	a																	
Luton 10	a																	

For general notes see front of timetable
For details of catering facilities see Directory of Train Operators

A To Bedford (Table 52)

B To St Albans City (Table 52)
b Arr. 1853
c Arr. 0714
e Arr. 0744
f Arr. 0814
g Arr. 0844
h Arr. 0914
j Arr. 0944
k Arr. 1714
m Arr. 1744

Saturdays

Sutton and Wimbledon → London and Luton via Streatham

Network Diagram - see first page of Table 177

Station		FC	FC	FC	FC	FC	FC	FC	FC	FC	FC	FC	FC	FC
Sutton (Surrey) 4	d	17 37	18 06	18 07	18 36	18 37	19 06	19 07	19 37	20 07	20 37	21 07	21 37	22 07
West Sutton	d	17 40		18 10		18 40		19 10	19 40	20 10	20 40	21 10	21 40	22 10
Sutton Common	d	17 42		18 12		18 42		19 12	19 42	20 12	20 42	21 12	21 42	22 12
St Helier	d	17 45		18 15		18 45		19 15	19 45	20 15	20 45	21 15	21 45	22 15
Morden South	d	17 47		18 17		18 47		19 17	19 47	20 17	20 47	21 17	21 47	22 17
South Merton	d	17 49		18 19		18 49		19 19	19 49	20 19	20 49	21 19	21 49	22 19
Wimbledon Chase	d	17 51		18 21		18 51		19 21	19 51	20 21	20 51	21 21	21 51	22 21
Wimbledon 6 ⊖	a	17 55		18 25		18 55		19 25	19 55	20 25	20 55	21 25	21 55	22 25
	d	18 00		18 30		19 00		19 30	20 00	20 30	21 00	21 30	22 00	22 30
Haydons Road	d	18 02		18 32		19 02		19 32	20 02	20 32	21 02	21 32	22 02	22 32
Tooting	d	18 05		18 35		19 05		19 35	20 05	20 35	21 05	21 35	22 05	22 35
Carshalton	d		18 09		18 39		19 09							
Hackbridge	d		18 11		18 41		19 11							
Mitcham Junction	d		18 14		18 44		19 14							
Mitcham Eastfields	d		18 18		18 48		19 18							
Streatham 4	d	18 10	18 23	18 40	18 53	19 10	19 23	19 40	20 10	20 40	21 10	21 40	22 10	22 40
Tulse Hill 3	d	18b17	18 27	18c47	18 57	19e17	19 27	19f47	20g17	20h47	21j17	21k47	22m17	22n47
North Dulwich	d	*18 27*	*18 42*	*18 57*	*19 13*	*19 27*	*19 43*	*19 58*	*20 28*	*20 58*	*21 28*	*21 58*	*22 28*	*22 58*
East Dulwich	d	*18 29*	*18 44*	*18 59*	*19 15*	*19 29*	*19 45*	*20 00*	*20 30*	*21 00*	*21 30*	*22 00*	*22 30*	*23 00*
Peckham Rye 4	d	*18 31*	*18 47*	*19 01*	*19 18*	*19 31*	*19 47*	*20 02*	*20 32*	*21 02*	*21 32*	*22 02*	*22 32*	*23 02*
Queens Rd Peckham	d	*18 34*	*18 49*	*19 04*	*19 20*	*19 34*	*19 50*	*20 05*	*20 35*	*21 05*	*21 35*	*22 05*	*22 35*	*23 05*
South Bermondsey	d	*18 36*	*18 52*	*19 06*	*19 23*	*19 36*	*19 52*	*20 07*	*20 37*	*21 07*	*21 37*	*22 07*	*22 37*	*23 07*
London Bridge 4 ⊖	a	18 30	*18 56*	19 00	*19 27*	19 30	*19 57*	20 00	20 30	21 00	21 30	22 00	22 30	23 00
Herne Hill 4	d		18a31		19a01		19a31							
Loughborough Jn	d													
Elephant & Castle ⊖	d													
London Blackfriars 3 ⊖	a													
City Thameslink 3	a													
Farringdon 3 ⊖	a													
St Pancras International 15 ⊖	a													
Luton Airport Parkway 7 ✈	a													
Luton 10	a													

Sundays

Station		FC	FC	FC	FC		FC	FC	FC
Sutton (Surrey) 4	d	10 15	10 45	11 15	11 45		20 15	20 45	21 15
West Sutton	d	10 18	10 48	11 18	11 48		20 18	20 48	21 18
Sutton Common	d	10 20	10 50	11 20	11 50		20 20	20 50	21 20
St Helier	d	10 23	10 53	11 23	11 53		20 23	20 53	21 23
Morden South	d	10 25	10 55	11 25	11 55		20 25	20 55	21 25
South Merton	d	10 27	10 57	11 27	11 57		20 27	20 57	21 27
Wimbledon Chase	d	10 29	10 59	11 29	11 59		20 29	20 59	21 29
Wimbledon 6 ⊖	a	10 32	11 02	11 32	12 02		20 32	21 02	21 32
	d	10 33	11 03	11 33	12 03		20 33	21 03	21 33
Haydons Road	d	10 35	11 05	11 35	12 05		20 35	21 05	21 35
Tooting	d	10 38	11 08	11 38	12 08	and at	20 38	21 08	21 38
Carshalton	d					the same			
Hackbridge	d								
Mitcham Junction	d					minutes			
Mitcham Eastfields	d					past			
Streatham 4	d	10 43	11 13	11 43	12 13		20 43	21 13	21 43
Tulse Hill 3	d	10 47	11 17	11 47	12 17	each	20 47	21 17	21 47
North Dulwich	d	*11 04*	*11 34*	*12 04*	*12 34*		*21 04*	*21 34*	*22 04*
East Dulwich	d	*11 06*	*11 36*	*12 06*	*12 36*	hour until	*21 06*	*21 36*	*22 06*
Peckham Rye 4	d	*11 08*	*11 38*	*12 08*	*12 38*		*21 08*	*21 38*	*22 08*
Queens Rd Peckham	d	*11 11*	*11 41*	*12 11*	*12 41*		*21 11*	*21 41*	*22 11*
South Bermondsey	d	*11 13*	*11 43*	*12 13*	*12 43*		*21 13*	*21 43*	*22 13*
London Bridge 4 ⊖	a	10 59	11 29	11 59	12 29		20 59	21 29	21 59
Herne Hill 4	d								
Loughborough Jn	d								
Elephant & Castle ⊖	d								
London Blackfriars 3 ⊖	a								
City Thameslink 3	a								
Farringdon 3 ⊖	a								
St Pancras International 15 ⊖	a								
Luton Airport Parkway 7 ✈	a								
Luton 10	a								

For general notes see front of timetable
For details of catering facilities see Directory of Train Operators

b Arr. 1814
c Arr. 1844
e Arr. 1914
f Arr. 1944
g Arr. 2014
h Arr. 2044
j Arr. 2114
k Arr. 2144
m Arr. 2214
n Arr. 2244

London and Croydon → Caterham and Tattenham Corner

Network Diagram - see first page of Table 177

Miles	Miles			SN	SN	SN	SN	SN	SN	SN	SN		SN		SN	SN	SN		SN	SN		SN	SN	SN	SN
				MX	MX	MX	MO	MX																	
0	—	**London Victoria** 15	⊖ d	23p00						06 15					07 20				07 45				08 15		
2¾	—	Clapham Junction 10	d	23p08						06 23					07 28				07 51				08 23		
—	0	**London Charing Cross** 4	⊖ d		23p07		23p34	23p45	06 05																
—	¾	**London Waterloo (East)** 4	⊖ d		23p10		23p37	23p48	06 08																
—	1½	**London Bridge** 4	⊖ d		23p15		23p44	23p53	06 13		06 35		06 52			07 25	07 39			08 03		08 09		08 36	08 52
—	4½	New Cross Gate 4	⊖ d		23p20		23p49	23p58	06 19		06 40		06 58			07 30	07 44			08 08				08 41	
—	10½	Norwood Junction 2	d		23p39		00 10	00 16	06 38		06 56		07 14			07b51	08 00			08 26		08 27		08 57	
10½	11¾	**East Croydon**	d	23p30	23p43		00 14	00 20	06 42	06c49	07 00		07 18		07 49	07 55	08 04		08 13	08 30		08 34	08 44	09 01	09 07
11½	12¾	South Croydon 4	d	23p32	23p45		00 16	00 23	06 45		07 02		07 20		07 52		08 06		08 16	08 32			08 47	09 03	
12½	13¾	Purley Oaks	d	23p35	23p48		00 19	00 26	06 48		07 05		07 23		07 55		08 09		08 19	08 35			08 50	09 06	
13½	14¾	Purley 4	a	23p38	23p51	←	00 22	00 29	06 51	06 56	07 08		07 26		07 58	08 01	08 12		08 22	08 38		08 41	08 53	09 09	09 14
—	—		d	23p55	23p52	23p55	00 22	00 31	06 53	07 00	07 09		07 29	07 32	07 59	08 01	08 16	08 20	08 24	08 39		08 44	08 53	09 12	09 17
—	16	Kenley	d	→	23p55		00 25	00 34	06 56		07 12		07 32			08 04	08 19		08 27	08 42			08 56	09 15	
—	17¼	Whyteleafe	d		23p58		00 29	00 38	07 00		07 15		07 35			08 08	08 22		08 30	08 45			09 00	09 18	
—	17¾	Whyteleafe South	d		00 01		00 31	00 40	07 02		07 17		07 37			08 10	08 24		08 32	08 47			09 02	09 20	
—	19½	**Caterham**	a		00 06		00 35	00 44	07 06		07 22		07 42			08 14	08 29		08 37	08 52			09 06	09 25	
14¼	—	Reedham	d			23p57				07 02				07 34	08 01			08 22				08 46			09 19
15	—	Smitham	d			00 01				07 05				07 37	08 04			08 25				08 49			09 22
15¾	—	Woodmansterne	d			00 04				07 08				07 40	08 07			08 28				08 52			09 25
16¾	—	Chipstead	d			00 07				07 11				07 43	08 10			08 31				08 55			09 28
19¼	—	Kingswood	d			00 12				07 16				07 48	08 15			08 36				09 00			09 33
20½	—	Tadworth	d			00 16				07 20				07 52	08 19			08 40				09 04			09 37
21¾	—	**Tattenham Corner**	a			00 19				07 23				07 55	08 22			08 43				09 07			09 40

		SN	SN	SN	SN	SN	SN		SN	SN	SN	SN		SN	SN	SN	SN	SN	SN	SN			SN	SN
London Victoria 15	⊖ d	08 43			09 13					09 43				10 13				10 43					16 13	16 39
Clapham Junction 10	d	08 51			09 21					09 51				10 21				10 51					16 21	16 45
London Charing Cross 4	⊖ d																							
London Waterloo (East) 4	⊖ d																							
London Bridge 4	⊖ d		09 05	09 21			09 35		09 52		10 05	10 22				10 35	10 52		11 05	11 22	and at			
New Cross Gate 4	⊖ d		09 11				09 40				10 10					10 40			11 10					
Norwood Junction 2	d		09 26				09 56				10 26					10 56			11 26					
East Croydon	d	09 13	09 30	09 37	09 43		10 00		10 07	10 13	10 30	10 37		10 43		11 00	11 07	11 13	11 30	11 37	the same		16 43	16 56
South Croydon 4	d	09 15	09 32		09 45		10 02			10 15	10 32			10 45		11 02		11 15	11 32				16 45	16 58
Purley Oaks	d	09 18	09 35		09 48		10 05			10 18	10 35			10 48		11 05		11 18	11 35		minutes		16 48	17 01
Purley 4	a	09 21	09 38	09 43	09 51		10 08		10 13	10 21	10 38	10 43		10 51		11 08	11 13	11 21	11 38	11 43			16 51	17 04
	d	09 22	09 39	09 43	09 52	10 02	10 09		10 13	10 22	10 39	10 43		10 52	11 02	11 09	11 13	11 22	11 39	11 43	past		16 52	17 05
Kenley	d	09 25	09 42		09 55		10 12			10 25	10 42			10 55		11 12		11 25	11 42		each		16 55	17 08
Whyteleafe	d	09 28	09 45		09 58		10 15			10 28	10 45			10 58		11 15		11 28	11 45				16 58	17 11
Whyteleafe South	d	09 30	09 47		10 00		10 17			10 30	10 47			11 00		11 17		11 30	11 47		hour until		17 00	17 13
Caterham	a	09 35	09 52		10 05		10 22			10 35	10 52			11 05		11 22		11 35	11 52				17 07	17 20
Reedham	d			09 46		10 04			10 16			10 46			11 04		11 16			11 46				
Smitham	d			09 48		10 07			10 18			10 48			11 07		11 18			11 48				
Woodmansterne	d			09 51		10 10			10 21			10 51			11 10		11 21			11 51				
Chipstead	d			09 54		10 13			10 24			10 54			11 13		11 24			11 54				
Kingswood	d			10 00		10 18			10 30			11 00			11 18		11 30			12 00				
Tadworth	d			10 03		10 22			10 33			11 03			11 22		11 33			12 03				
Tattenham Corner	a			10 07		10 25			10 37			11 07			11 25		11 37			12 07				

		SN		SN	SN		SN		SN			SN		SN		SN		SN			SN		SN	SN	
London Victoria 15	⊖ d			16 43	17 09				17 39					18 09				18 39						19 00	
Clapham Junction 10	d			16 51	17 15				17 45					18 15				18 45						19 08	
London Charing Cross 4	⊖ d																								
London Waterloo (East) 4	⊖ d																								
London Bridge 4	⊖ d	16 48					17 17					17 49				18 18					18 49		18 59		
New Cross Gate 4	⊖ d																								
Norwood Junction 2	d	17 02					17 31					18 02				18 31					19 02				
East Croydon	d	17 06		17e17	17 27		17 35		17 56			18 06		18 28		18f37		18 57			19 06		19 14	19 32	
South Croydon 4	d	17 08		17 19	17 30		17 37		17 58			18 08		18 30		18g42		19 00			19 08		19 16	19 34	
Purley Oaks	d	17 11		17 22	17 33		17 40		18 01			18 11		18 33		18 45		19 03			19 11		19 19	19 37	
Purley 4	a	17 14		17 25	17 36		17 44		18 03			18 14		18 36		18 48		19 06			19 14		19 22	19 40	
	d	17 18	17 22	17 28	17 40	17 42	17 48	17 50	18 07	18 09		18 18	18 20	18 40	18 42	18 52	18 54	19 10	19 12		19 18	19 20	19 28	19 43	19 45
Kenley	d	17 21		17 31	17 43		17 51		18 10			18 21		18 43		18 55		19 13			19 21			19 46	
Whyteleafe	d	17 24		17 34	17 46		17 54		18 13			18 24		18 46		18 58		19 16			19 24			19 49	
Whyteleafe South	d	17 26		17 36	17 48		17 56		18 15			18 26		18 48		19 00		19 18			19 26			19 51	
Caterham	a	17 33		17 43	17 55		18 03		18 22			18 33		18 55		19 07		19 25			19 33			19 56	
Reedham	d		17 24			17 44		17 52		18 11			18 22		18 44		18 56		19 14			19 22	19 30		19 47
Smitham	d		17 27			17 47		17 55		18 14			18 25		18 47		18 59		19 17			19 25	19a35		19 50
Woodmansterne	d		17 30			17 50		17 58		18 17			18 28		18 50		19 02		19 20			19 28			19 53
Chipstead	d		17 33			17 53		18 01		18 20			18 31		18 53		19 05		19 23			19 31			19 56
Kingswood	d		17 38			17 58		18 06		18 25			18 36		18 58		19 10		19 28			19 36			20 01
Tadworth	d		17 42			18 02		18 10		18 29			18 40		19 02		19 14		19 32			19 40			20 05
Tattenham Corner	a		17 47			18 07		18 15		18 34			18 45		19 07		19 19		19 37			19 45			20 08

For general notes see front of timetable
For details of catering facilities see Directory of Train Operators

b Arr. 0748
c Arr. 0645
e Arr. 1712
f Arr. 1834
g Arr. 1839

London and Croydon → Caterham and Tattenham Corner

Network Diagram - see first page of Table 177

		SN	SN	SN	SN	SN		SN	SN	SN	SN	SN	SN	SN	SN		SN	SN	SN	SN	SN	SN			
London Victoria 15	⊖ d		19 30		20 00			20 30		21 00		21 30		22 00			22 30		23 00						
Clapham Junction 10	d		19 38		20 08			20 38		21 08		21 38		22 08			22 38		23 08						
London Charing Cross 4	⊖ d			19 37		20 07			20 37		21 07		21 37		22 07			22 37		23 07		23 45			
London Waterloo (East) 4	⊖ d			19 40		20 10			20 40		21 10		21 40		22 10			22 40		23 10		23 48			
London Bridge 4	⊖ d	19 14		19 45		20 15			20 45		21 15		21 45		22 15			22 45		23 15		23 53			
New Cross Gate 4	⊖ d	19 19		19 50		20 20			20 50		21 20		21 50		22 20			22 50		23 20		23 58			
Norwood Junction 2	d	19 38		20 09		20 39			21 09		21 39		22 09		22 39			23 09		23 39		00 16			
East Croydon	d	19 43	20 00	20 13	20 30	20 43		21 00	21 13	21 30	21 43	22 00	22 13	22 30	22 43		23 00	23 13	23 30	23 43		00 20			
South Croydon 4	d	19 45	20 03	20 15	20 32	20 45		21 02	21 15	21 32	21 45	22 02	22 15	22 32	22 45		23 02	23 15	23 32	23 45		00 23			
Purley Oaks	d	19 48	20 06	20 18	20 36	20 48		21 05	21 18	21 35	21 48	22 05	22 18	22 35	22 48		23 05	23 18	23 35	23 48		00 26			
Purley 4	a	19 51	20 09	20 21	20 39	20 51		21 08	21 21	21 38	21 51	22 08	22 21	22 38	22 51		23 08	23 21	23 38	23 51	⟵	00 29			
	d	19 54	20 11	20 24	20 39	20 54		21 09	21 24	21 39	21 54	22 09	22 24	22 39	22 54		23 11	23 24	23 55	23 52	23 55	00 31			
Kenley	d	19 57		20 27		20 57			21 27		21 57		22 27		22 57			23 27	⟶	23 55		00 34			
Whyteleafe	d	20 00		20 30		21 00			21 30		22 00		22 30		23 00			23 30		23 58		00 38			
Whyteleafe South	d	20 02		20 32		21 02			21 32		22 02		22 32		23 02			23 32		00 01		00 40			
Caterham	a	20 07		20 37		21 07			21 37		22 07		22 37		23 07			23 37		00 06		00 44			
Reedham	d		20 14		20 42			21 11		21 41		22 11		22 41			23 13				23 57				
Smitham	d		20 16		20 44			21 14		21 44		22 14		22 44			23 16				00 01				
Woodmansterne	d		20 19		20 47			21 17		21 47		22 17		22 47			23 19				00 04				
Chipstead	d		20 22		20 50			21 20		21 50		22 20		22 50			23 22				00 07				
Kingswood	d		20 28		20 56			21 25		21 55		22 25		22 55			23 27				00 12				
Tadworth	d		20 31		20 59			21 29		21 59		22 29		22 59			23 31				00 16				
Tattenham Corner	a		20 35		21 03			21 32		22 02		22 32		23 02			23 34				00 19				

Saturdays

		SN	SN		SN	SN		SN	SN		SN	SN		SN	SN		SN	SN		SN	SN		SN	SN	SN
London Victoria 15	⊖ d	23p00										06 43					07 13						07 43		
Clapham Junction 10	d	23p08										06 51					07 21						07 51		
London Charing Cross 4	⊖ d		23p07			23p45																			
London Waterloo (East) 4	⊖ d		23p10			23p48																			
London Bridge 4	⊖ d		23p15			23p53			06 35		06 50			07 05	07 22					07 35	07 52			08 05	08 22
New Cross Gate 4	⊖ d		23p20			23p58			06 40					07 10						07 40				08 10	
Norwood Junction 2	d		23p39			00 16		06 31	06 56		07 03			07 26						07 56				08 26	
East Croydon	d	23p30	23p43			00 20		06 37	07 00		07 07	07 13		07 30	07 37		07 43			08 00	08 07		08 13	08 30	08 37
South Croydon 4	d	23p32	23p45			00 23			07 02			07 15		07 32			07 45			08 02			08 15	08 32	
Purley Oaks	d	23p35	23p48			00 26			07 05			07 18		07 35			07 48			08 05			08 18	08 35	
Purley 4	a	23p38	23p51		⟵	00 29		06 43	07 08		07 13	07 21		07 38	07 43		07 51			08 08	08 13		08 21	08 38	08 43
	d	23p55	23p52		23p55	00 31		06 43	07 09		07 13	07 22		07 39	07 43		07 52	08 02		08 09	08 13		08 22	08 39	08 43
Kenley	d	⟶	23p55			00 34			07 12			07 25		07 42			07 55			08 12			08 25	08 42	
Whyteleafe	d		23p58			00 38			07 15			07 28		07 45			07 58			08 15			08 28	08 45	
Whyteleafe South	d		00 01			00 40			07 17			07 30		07 47			08 00			08 17			08 30	08 47	
Caterham	a		00 06			00 44			07 22			07 35		07 52			08 05			08 22			08 35	08 52	
Reedham	d				23p57			06 46			07 16				07 46			08 04			08 16				08 46
Smitham	d				00 01			06 48			07 18				07 48			08 07			08 18				08 48
Woodmansterne	d				00 04			06 51			07 21				07 51			08 10			08 21				08 51
Chipstead	d				00 07			06 54			07 24				07 54			08 13			08 24				08 54
Kingswood	d				00 12			07 00			07 30				08 00			08 18			08 30				09 00
Tadworth	d				00 16			07 03			07 33				08 03			08 22			08 33				09 03
Tattenham Corner	a				00 19			07 07			07 37				08 07			08 25			08 37				09 07

			SN	SN	SN	SN	SN	SN	SN			SN	SN		SN	SN		SN	SN		SN	SN		SN
London Victoria 15	⊖ d		08 13				08 43					18 13						19 00			19 30			20 00
Clapham Junction 10	d		08 21				08 51					18 21						19 08			19 38			20 08
London Charing Cross 4	⊖ d																		19 07			19 37		
London Waterloo (East) 4	⊖ d																		19 10			19 40		
London Bridge 4	⊖ d				08 35	08 52		09 05	09 22				18 35		18 52	18 44			19 15			19 45		
New Cross Gate 4	⊖ d				08 40			09 10		and at			18 40			18 50			19 20			19 50		
Norwood Junction 2	d				08 56			09 26					18 56			19 10			19 39			20 09		
East Croydon	d		08 43		09 00	09 07	09 13	09 30	09 37	the same		18 43	19 00		19 07	19 14		19 30	19 43		20 00	20 13		20 30
South Croydon 4	d		08 45		09 02		09 15	09 32		minutes		18 45	19 02			19 17		19 32	19 45		20 03	20 15		20 32
Purley Oaks	d		08 48		09 05		09 18	09 35				18 48	19 05			19 20		19 35	19 48		20 06	20 18		20 35
Purley 4	a		08 51		09 08	09 13	09 21	09 38	09 43	past		18 51	19 08		19 13	19 23		19 38	19 51		20 09	20 21		20 38
	d		08 52	09 02	09 09	09 13	09 22	09 39	09 43			18 52	19 11		19 13	19 23		19 39	19 54		20 09	20 24		20 41
Kenley	d		08 55		09 12		09 25	09 42		each		18 55	19 14			19 26			19 57			20 27		
Whyteleafe	d		08 58		09 15		09 28	09 45				18 58	19 17			19 30			20 00			20 30		
Whyteleafe South	d		09 00		09 17		09 30	09 47		hour until		19 00	19 19			19 32			20 02			20 32		
Caterham	a		09 05		09 22		09 35	09 52				19 05	19 24			19 36			20 07			20 37		
Reedham	d			09 04		09 16			09 46						19 16			19 41			20 12			20 43
Smitham	d			09 07		09 18			09 48						19 18			19 44			20 14			20 46
Woodmansterne	d			09 10		09 21			09 51						19 21			19 47			20 17			20 49
Chipstead	d			09 13		09 24			09 54						19 24			19 50			20 20			20 52
Kingswood	d			09 18		09 30			10 00						19 30			19 55			20 26			20 57
Tadworth	d			09 22		09 33			10 03						19 33			19 59			20 29			21 01
Tattenham Corner	a			09 25		09 37			10 07						19 37			20 02			20 33			21 04

For general notes see front of timetable
For details of catering facilities see
Directory of Train Operators

Table 181

Saturdays

London and Croydon → Caterham and Tattenham Corner

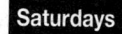

Network Diagram - see first page of Table 177

		SN	SN	SN	SN	SN	SN	SN	SN	SN	SN	SN	SN	SN	SN	SN
London Victoria 15	⊖ d		20 30		21 00		21 30		22 00		22 30		23 00			
Clapham Junction 10	d		20 38		21 08		21 38		22 08		22 38		23 08			
London Charing Cross 4	⊖ d	20 07		20 37		21 07		21 37		22 07		22 37		23 07		23 45
London Waterloo (East) 4	⊖ d	20 10		20 40		21 10		21 40		22 10		22 40		23 10		23 48
London Bridge 4	⊖ d	20 15		20 45		21 15		21 45		22 15		22 45		23 15		23 53
New Cross Gate 4	⊖ d	20 20		20 50		21 20		21 50		22 20		22 50		23 20		23 58
Norwood Junction 2	d	20 39		21 09		21 39		22 09		22 39		23 09		23 39		00 16
East Croydon	d	20 43	21 00	21 13	21 30	21 43	22 00	22 13	22 30	22 43	22 59	23 13	23 30	23 43		00 20
South Croydon 4	d	20 45	21 03	21 15	21 32	21 45	22 02	22 15	22 32	22 45	23 02	23 15	23 32	23 45		00 23
Purley Oaks	d	20 48	21 06	21 18	21 35	21 48	22 05	22 18	22 35	22 48	23 05	23 18	23 35	23 48		00 26
Purley 4	a	20 51	21 09	21 21	21 38	21 51	22 08	22 21	22 38	22 51	23 08	23 21	23 38	23 51	←	00 29
	d	20 54	21 09	21 24	21 39	21 54	22 09	22 24	22 39	22 54	23 08	23 24	23 55	23 52	23 55	00 31
Kenley	d	20 57		21 27		21 57		22 27		22 57		23 27	→	23 55		00 34
Whyteleafe	d	21 00		21 30		22 00		22 30		23 00		23 30		23 58		00 38
Whyteleafe South	d	21 02		21 32		22 02		22 32		23 02		23 32		00 01		00 40
Caterham	a	21 07		21 37		22 07		22 37		23 07		23 37		00 06		00 44
Reedham	d		21 12		21 41		22 11		22 41		23 10				23 57	
Smitham	d		21 14		21 44		22 14		22 44		23 13				00 01	
Woodmansterne	d		21 17		21 47		22 17		22 47		23 16				00 04	
Chipstead	d		21 20		21 50		22 20		22 50		23 19				00 07	
Kingswood	d		21 26		21 55		22 25		22 55		23 24				00 12	
Tadworth	d		21 29		21 59		22 29		22 59		23 28				00 16	
Tattenham Corner	a		21 33		22 02		22 32		23 02		23 31				00 19	

Sundays

		SN	SN	SN	SN	SN	SN		SN	SN	SN	SN	SN
London Victoria 15	⊖ d	23p00											
Clapham Junction 10	d	23p08											
London Charing Cross 4	⊖ d		23p07		23p45	07 34	08 04		21 34	22 04	22 34	23 04	23 34
London Waterloo (East) 4	⊖ d		23p10		23p48	07 37	08 07		21 37	22 07	22 37	23 07	23 37
London Bridge 4	⊖ d		23p15		23p53	07 44	08 14		21 44	22 14	22 44	23 14	23 44
New Cross Gate 4	⊖ d		23p20		23p58	07 49	08 19		21 49	22 19	22 49	23 19	23 49
Norwood Junction 2	d		23p39		00 16	08 04	08 34	and at	22 04	22 39	23 09	23 39	00 10
East Croydon	d	23p30	23p43		00 20	08 09	08 39	the same	22 09	22 43	23 13	23 43	00 14
South Croydon 4	d	23p32	23p45		00 23	08 11	08 41	minutes	22 11	22 45	23 15	23 45	00 16
Purley Oaks	d	23p35	23p48		00 26	08 14	08 44		22 14	22 48	23 18	23 48	00 19
Purley 4	a	23p38	23p51	←	00 29	08 17	08 47	past	22 17	22 51	23 21	23 51	00 22
	d	23p55	23p52	23p55	00 31	08 17	08 47		22 17	22 51	23 32	23 51	00 22
Kenley	d	→	23p55		00 34		08 50	each		22 54		23 54	00 25
Whyteleafe	d		23p58		00 38		08 54			22 58		23 58	00 29
Whyteleafe South	d		00 01		00 40		08 56	hour until		23 00		23 59	00 31
Caterham	a		00 06		00 44		09 00			23 04		00 04	00 35
Reedham	d			23p57		08 20			22 20		23 34		
Smitham	d			00 01		08 22			22 22		23 37		
Woodmansterne	d			00 04		08 25			22 25		23 40		
Chipstead	d			00 07		08 28			22 28		23 43		
Kingswood	d			00 12		08 34			22 34		23 48		
Tadworth	d			00 16		08 37			22 37		23 52		
Tattenham Corner	a			00 19		08 41			22 41		23 55		

For general notes see front of timetable
For details of catering facilities see Directory of Train Operators

Tattenham Corner and Caterham → Croydon and London

Network Diagram - see first page of Table 177

Miles	Miles	Station		SN	SN	SN	SN	SN	SN	SN	SN	SN	SN	SN	SN	SN	SN	SN	SN	SN
0	—	**Tattenham Corner**	d		05 56		06 33			06 58		07 17		07 33		07 42		07 58		08 08
1¼	—	Tadworth	d		05 59		06 36			07 01		07 20		07 36		07 45		08 01		08 11
2½	—	Kingswood	d		06 02		06 39			07 04		07 23		07 39		07 48		08 04		08 14
5	—	Chipstead	d		06 08		06 45			07 10		07 29		07 45		07 54		08 10		08 20
6	—	Woodmansterne	d		06 11		06 48			07 13		07 32		07 48		07 57		08 13		08 23
6¾	—	Smitham	d		06 14		06 51			07 16		07 35		07 51		08 00		08 16		08 26
7½	—	Reedham	d		06 16		06 53			07 18		07 37		07 53		08 02		08 18		08 28
—	0	**Caterham**	d	05 52		06 20		06 47	07 00		07 14		07 36		07 47		08 08		08 19	
—	1¾	Whyteleafe South	d	05 55		06 23		06 50	07 03		07 17		07 39		07 50		08 11		08 22	
—	2¼	Whyteleafe	d	05 57		06 25		06 52	07 05		07 19		07 41		07 52		08 13		08 24	
—	3½	Kenley	d	06 00		06 28		06 55	07 08		07 22		07 44		07 55		08 16		08 27	
8¼	4¾	Purley 4	a	06 03	06 19	06 31	06 56	06 59	07 11	07 21	07 26	07 40	07 47	07 56	07 58	08 05	08 19	08 21	08 30	08 32
—	—		d	06 03	06 22	06 31	07 03		07 12	07 23	07 27	07 43	07 48	08 03		08 07	08 25		08 36	
9¼	5¾	Purley Oaks	d	06 06	06 25	06 34	07 06		07 15		07 30	07 46	07 51	08 06		08 10	08 28		08 39	
10¼	6¾	South Croydon 4	d	06 09	06 28	06 37	07 09		07 18		07 33	07 49	07 54	08 09		08 13	08 31		08 42	
11¼	7¾	**East Croydon**	d	06 12	06 31	06 40	07 12		07 22	07 29	07 36	07 52	07 57	08 12		08 17	08 34		08 45	
—	9	Norwood Junction 2	d	06 17	06 35	06 45	07 17				07 41		08 01	08 17			08 40		08 49	
—	15	New Cross Gate 4	⊖ a	06 28	06 50	06 53	07 24				07 53								08 57	
—	17¾	**London Bridge 4**	⊖ a	06 35	06 56	07 02	07 33				08 01		08 16	08 31			08 57		09 05	
—	18¾	**London Waterloo (East) 4**	⊖ a																	
—	19½	**London Charing Cross 4**	⊖ a																	
19	—	Clapham Junction 10	a						07 31	07 39		08 02				08 26				
21¾	—	**London Victoria 15**	⊖ a						07 41	07 48		08 12				08 35				

Station		SN	SN	SN	SN	SN	SN	SN	SN	SN	SN	SN	SN	SN	SN	SN	SN	SN	SN	SN
Tattenham Corner	d	08 27			08 51			09 21		09 33		09 49			10 21		10 33		10 51	
Tadworth	d	08 30			08 54			09 24		09 36		09 52			10 24		10 36		10 54	
Kingswood	d	08 33			08 57			09 27		09 39		09 55			10 27		10 39		10 57	
Chipstead	d	08 39			09 03			09 33		09 45		10 01			10 33		10 45		11 03	
Woodmansterne	d	08 42			09 06			09 36		09 48		10 04			10 36		10 48		11 06	
Smitham	d	08 45			09 09			09 39		09 51		10 07			10 39		10 51		11 09	
Reedham	d	08 47			09 11			09 41		09 53		10 09			10 41		10 53		11 11	
Caterham	d		08 40	08 56		09 10	09 26		09 37		09 56		10 09	10 26		10 39		10 56		11 09
Whyteleafe South	d		08 43	08 59		09 13	09 29		09 40		09 59		10 12	10 29		10 42		10 59		11 12
Whyteleafe	d		08 45	09 01		09 15	09 31		09 42		10 01		10 14	10 31		10 44		11 01		11 14
Kenley	d		08 48	09 04		09 18	09 34		09 45		10 04		10 17	10 34		10 47		11 04		11 17
Purley 4	a	08 50	08 52	09 07	09 14	09 21	09 37	09 44	09 48	09 56	10 07	10 12	10 20	10 37	10 44	10 50	10 56	11 07	11 14	11 20
	d	08 56		09 08	09 14	09 22	09 38	09 45	09 51		10 08	10 15	10 21	10 38	10 45	10 51		11 08	11 15	11 21
Purley Oaks	d	08 59		09 11		09 25	09 41		09 54		10 11		10 24	10 41		10 54		11 11		11 24
South Croydon 4	d	09 02		09 14		09 28	09 44		09 57		10 14		10 27	10 44		10 57		11 14		11 27
East Croydon	d	09 05		09 17	09 20	09 31	09 47	09 51	10 00		10 17	10 21	10 30	10 47	10 51	11 00		11 17	11 21	11 30
Norwood Junction 2	d	09 09			09 25	09 35			10 05				10 35			11 05				11 35
New Cross Gate 4	⊖ a				09 32	09 50			10 19				10 49			11 19				11 49
London Bridge 4	⊖ a	09 24			09 42	09 59		10 10	10 26			10 38	10 57		11 08	11 26			11 38	11 56
London Waterloo (East) 4	⊖ a																			
London Charing Cross 4	⊖ a																			
Clapham Junction 10	a			09 38			10 07				10 37			11 07				11 37		
London Victoria 15	⊖ a			09 48			10 16				10 46			11 16				11 46		

Station		SN		SN	SN	SN	SN	SN	SN	SN	SN	SN	SN	SN	SN	SN	SN	SN	SN	SN
Tattenham Corner	d			16 21		16 33		16 51			17 19			17 51		18 12		18 42		19 14
Tadworth	d			16 24		16 36		16 54			17 22			17 54		18 15		18 45		19 17
Kingswood	d			16 27		16 39		16 57			17 25			17 57		18 18		18 48		19 20
Chipstead	d			16 33		16 45		17 03			17 31			18 03		18 24		18 54		19 26
Woodmansterne	d			16 36		16 48		17 06			17 34			18 06		18 27		18 57		19 29
Smitham	d			16 39		16 51		17 09			17 37			18 09		18 30		19 00		19 32
Reedham	d			16 41		16 53		17 11			17 39			18 11		18 32		19 02		19 34
Caterham	d	11 26	and at		16 39		16 52		17 10	17 26		17 45	17 56		18 11		18 49		19 15	
Whyteleafe South	d	11 29	the same		16 42		16 55		17 13	17 29		17 48	17 59		18 14		18 52		19 18	
Whyteleafe	d	11 31			16 44		16 57		17 15	17 31		17 50	18 01		18 16		18 54		19 20	
Kenley	d	11 34	minutes		16 47		17 00		17 18	17 34		17 53	18 04		18 19		18 57		19 23	
Purley 4	a	11 37	past	16 44	16 50	16 56	17 04	17 14	17 21	17 37	17 42	17 56	18 07	18 14	18 22	18 35	19 00	19 05	19 26	19 37
	d	11 38	each	16 45	16 51	17 08		17 15	17 23	17 38	17 45	17 59	18 08	18 15	18 23	18 37	19 01	19 08	19 29	19 38
Purley Oaks	d	11 41			16 54	17 11			17 26	17 41		18 02	18 11		18 26	18 40	19 04	19 11	19 32	19 41
South Croydon 4	d	11 44	hour until		16 57	17 14			17 29	17 44		18 05	18 14		18 29	18 44	19 07	19 14	19 35	19 44
East Croydon	d	11 47		16 51	17 00	17 17		17 21	17 32	17 47	17 51	18 11	18 17	18 21	18 32	18 47	19 10	19 17	19 40	19 47
Norwood Junction 2	d				17 05			17 25	17 37			18 15		18 29	18 36		19 15		19 44	
New Cross Gate 4	⊖ a				17 19				17 51						18 51		19 32		20 02	
London Bridge 4	⊖ a			17 10	17 28			17 38	17 58		18 11	18 28		18 42	18 58		19 39		20 11	
London Waterloo (East) 4	⊖ a																19 45		20 16	
London Charing Cross 4	⊖ a																19 49		20 20	
Clapham Junction 10	a	12 07				17 37				18 07			18 39			19 08		19 37		20 07
London Victoria 15	⊖ a	12 16				17 48				18 16			18 46			19 15		19 48		20 18

For general notes see front of timetable
For details of catering facilities see Directory of Train Operators

Table 181

Mondays to Fridays

Tattenham Corner and Caterham → Croydon and London

Network Diagram - see first page of Table 177

		SN		SN	SN	SN	SN		SN	SN	SN	SN		SN	SN	SN	SN		SN	SN	SN				
Tattenham Corner	d			19 42	19 57		20 12			20 42		21 12			21 42		22 12			22 42					
Tadworth	d			19 45	20 00		20 15			20 45		21 15			21 45		22 15			22 45					
Kingswood	d			19 48	20 03		20 18			20 48		21 18			21 48		22 18			22 48					
Chipstead	d			19 54	20 09		20 24			20 54		21 24			21 54		22 24			22 54					
Woodmansterne	d			19 57	20 12		20 27			20 57		21 27			21 57		22 27			22 57					
Smitham	d			20 00	20 15		20 30			21 00		21 30			22 00		22 30			23 00					
Reedham	d			20 02	20 17		20 32			21 02		21 32			22 02		22 32			23 02					
Caterham	d	19 45				20 15			20 45		21 15			21 45		22 15			22 45		23 17				
Whyteleafe South	d	19 48				20 18			20 48		21 18			21 48		22 18			22 48		23 20				
Whyteleafe	d	19 50				20 20			20 50		21 20			21 50		22 20			22 50		23 22				
Kenley	d	19 53				20 23			20 53		21 23			21 53		22 23			22 53		23 25				
Purley 4	a	19 56		20 05	20 20	20 26	20 35		20 56	21 05	21 26	21 35		21 56	22 05	22 26	22 35		22 56	23 05	23 28				
	d	19 59		20 08	20 23	20 29	20 38		20 59	21 08	21 29	21 38		21 59	22 08	22 29	22 38		22 59	23 08	23 34				
Purley Oaks	d	20 02		20 11		20 32	20 41		21 02	21 11	21 32	21 41		22 02	22 11	22 32	22 41		23 02	23 11	23 37				
South Croydon 4	d	20 05		20 14		20 35	20 44		21 05	21 14	21 35	21 44		22 05	22 14	22 35	22 44		23 05	23 14	23 40				
East Croydon	d	20 10		20 17	20 29	20 40	20 47		21 10	21 17	21 40	21 47		22 10	22 17	22 40	22 47		23 10	23 17	23 43				
Norwood Junction 2	d	20 14			20 34	20 44			21 14		21 44			22 14		22 44			23 14		23a47				
New Cross Gate 4	⊖ a	20 32			20 52	21 02			21 32		22 02			22 32		23 02			23 32						
London Bridge 4	⊖ a	20 41			21 01	21 11			21 41		22 11			22 41		23 11			23 38						
London Waterloo (East) 4	⊖ a	20 46				21 16			21 46		22 16			22 46		23 16			23 43						
London Charing Cross 4	⊖ a	20 50				21 20			21 50		22 20			22 50		23 20			23 48						
Clapham Junction 10	a			20 37			21 07			21 37		22 07			22 37		23 07			23 37					
London Victoria 15	⊖ a			20 46			21 16			21 46		22 16			22 46		23 16			23 46					

Saturdays

		SN	SN		SN	SN		SN	SN		SN	SN		SN	SN		SN	SN		SN	SN		SN	SN	
Tattenham Corner	d		06 12			06 42					07 21				07 51					08 21			08 33		
Tadworth	d		06 15			06 45					07 24				07 54					08 24			08 36		
Kingswood	d		06 18			06 48					07 27				07 57					08 27			08 39		
Chipstead	d		06 24			06 54					07 33				08 03					08 33			08 45		
Woodmansterne	d		06 27			06 57					07 36				08 06					08 36			08 48		
Smitham	d		06 30			07 00					07 39				08 09					08 39			08 51		
Reedham	d		06 32			07 02					07 41				08 11					08 41			08 53		
Caterham	d	06 07			06 39			07 09	07 26			07 39		07 56			08 09	08 26			08 39			08 56	
Whyteleafe South	d	06 10			06 42			07 12	07 29			07 42		07 59			08 12	08 29			08 42			08 59	
Whyteleafe	d	06 12			06 44			07 14	07 31			07 44		08 01			08 14	08 31			08 44			09 01	
Kenley	d	06 15			06 47			07 17	07 34			07 47		08 04			08 17	08 34			08 47			09 04	
Purley 4	a	06 18	06 35		06 50	07 05		07 20	07 37		07 44	07 50		08 07	08 14		08 20	08 37		08 44	08 50		08 56	09 07	
	d	06 21	06 38		06 51	07 08		07 21	07 38		07 45	07 51		08 08	08 15		08 21	08 38		08 45	08 51			09 08	
Purley Oaks	d	06 24	06 41		06 54	07 11		07 24	07 41			07 54		08 11			08 24	08 41			08 54			09 11	
South Croydon 4	d	06 27	06 44		06 57	07 14		07 27	07 44			07 57		08 14			08 27	08 44			08 57			09 14	
East Croydon	d	06 30	06 47		07 00	07 17		07 30	07 47		07 51	08 00		08 17	08 21		08 30	08 47		08 51	09 00			09 17	
Norwood Junction 2	d	06 35			07 05			07 35				08 05					08 35				09 05				
New Cross Gate 4	⊖ a	06 49			07 19			07 49				08 19					08 49				09 19				
London Bridge 4	⊖ a	06 56			07 26			07 56			08 08	08 26			08 38		08 56			09 08	09 26				
London Waterloo (East) 4	⊖ a																								
London Charing Cross 4	⊖ a																								
Clapham Junction 10	a		07 07			07 37			08 07					08 37				09 07						09 37	
London Victoria 15	⊖ a		07 16			07 46			08 16					08 46				09 16						09 46	

			SN	SN	SN	SN	SN	SN	SN			SN	SN		SN	SN		SN	SN		SN	SN		SN
Tattenham Corner	d		08 51			09 21		09 33				17 51				18 21		18 30			18 42			19 12
Tadworth	d		08 54			09 24		09 36				17 54				18 24		18 33			18 45			19 15
Kingswood	d		08 57			09 27		09 39				17 57				18 27		18 36			18 48			19 18
Chipstead	d		09 03			09 33		09 45				18 03				18 33		18 42			18 54			19 24
Woodmansterne	d		09 06			09 36		09 48				18 06				18 36		18 45			18 57			19 27
Smitham	d		09 09			09 39		09 51				18 09				18 39		18 48			19 00			19 30
Reedham	d		09 11			09 41		09 53		and at		18 11				18 41		18 50			19 02			19 32
Caterham	d			09 09	09 26		09 39		09 56	the same			18 09		18 26				18 45			19 15		
Whyteleafe South	d			09 12	09 29		09 42		09 59				18 12		18 29				18 48			19 18		
Whyteleafe	d			09 14	09 31		09 44		10 01	minutes			18 14		18 31				18 50			19 20		
Kenley	d			09 17	09 34		09 47		10 04				18 17		18 34				18 53			19 23		
Purley 4	a		09 14	09 20	09 37	09 44	09 50	09 56	10 07	past		18 14	18 20		18 37	18 44		18 53	18 56		19 05	19 26		19 35
	d		09 15	09 21	09 38	09 45	09 51		10 08			18 15	18 21		18 38	18 45		18 54	19 01		19 08	19 29		19 38
Purley Oaks	d			09 24	09 41		09 54		10 11	each			18 24		18 41				19 04		19 11	19 32		19 41
South Croydon 4	d			09 27	09 44		09 57		10 14				18 27		18 44				19 07		19 14	19 35		19 44
East Croydon	d		09 21	09 30	09 47	09 51	10 00		10 17	hour until		18 21	18 30		18 47	18 51		19 00	19 10		19 17	19 40		19 47
Norwood Junction 2	d			09 35			10 05						18 35					19 04	19 14			19 44		
New Cross Gate 4	⊖ a			09 49			10 19						18 49					19 21	19 32			20 02		
London Bridge 4	⊖ a		09 38	09 56		10 08	10 26					18 38	18 56			19 08		19 28	19 41			20 11		
London Waterloo (East) 4	⊖ a																		19 48			20 18		
London Charing Cross 4	⊖ a																		19 51			20 21		
Clapham Junction 10	a				10 07				10 37						19 07						19 37			20 07
London Victoria 15	⊖ a				10 16				10 46						19 16						19 46			20 16

For general notes see front of timetable
For details of catering facilities see Directory of Train Operators

Table 181

Saturdays

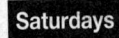

Tattenham Corner and Caterham → Croydon and London

Network Diagram - see first page of Table 177

		SN	SN		SN	SN		SN	SN		SN	SN		SN	SN		SN	SN		SN	SN		SN		
Tattenham Corner	d		19 42			20 12			20 42			21 12			21 42			22 12			22 42				
Tadworth	d		19 45			20 15			20 45			21 15			21 45			22 15			22 45				
Kingswood	d		19 48			20 18			20 48			21 18			21 48			22 18			22 48				
Chipstead	d		19 54			20 24			20 54			21 24			21 54			22 24			22 54				
Woodmansterne	d		19 57			20 27			20 57			21 27			21 57			22 27			22 57				
Smitham	d		20 00			20 30			21 00			21 30			22 00			22 30			23 00				
Reedham	d		20 02			20 32			21 02			21 32			22 02			22 32			23 02				
Caterham	d	19 45			20 15			20 45			21 15			21 45			22 15			22 45			23 17		
Whyteleafe South	d	19 48			20 18			20 48			21 18			21 48			22 18			22 48			23 20		
Whyteleafe	d	19 50			20 20			20 50			21 20			21 50			22 20			22 50			23 22		
Kenley	d	19 53			20 23			20 53			21 23			21 53			22 23			22 53			23 25		
Purley 4	a	19 56	20 05		20 26	20 35		20 56	21 05		21 26	21 35		21 56	22 05		22 26	22 35		22 56	23 05		23 28		
	d	19 59	20 08		20 29	20 38		20 59	21 08		21 29	21 38		21 59	22 08		22 29	22 38		22 59	23 08		23 34		
Purley Oaks	d	20 02	20 11		20 32	20 41		21 02	21 11		21 32	21 41		22 02	22 11		22 32	22 41		23 02	23 11		23 37		
South Croydon 4	d	20 05	20 14		20 35	20 44		21 05	21 14		21 35	21 44		22 05	22 14		22 35	22 44		23 05	23 14		23 40		
East Croydon	d	20 10	20 17		20 40	20 47		21 10	21 17		21 40	21 47		22 10	22 17		22 40	22 47		23 10	23 17		23 43		
Norwood Junction 2	d	20 14			20 44			21 14			21 44			22 14			22 44			23 14			23a47		
New Cross Gate 4	⊖ a	20 32			21 02			21 32			22 02			22 32			23 02			23 32					
London Bridge 4	⊖ a	20 41			21 11			21 41			22 11			22 41			23 11			23 38					
London Waterloo (East) 4	⊖ a	20 48			21 18			21 48			22 18			22 48			23 16			23 43					
London Charing Cross 4	⊖ a	20 51			21 21			21 51			22 21			22 51			23 20			23 48					
Clapham Junction 10	a		20 37			21 07			21 37			22 07			22 37			23 07			23 37				
London Victoria 15	⊖ a		20 46			21 16			21 46			22 16			22 46			23 18			23 46				

Sundays

			SN	SN			SN		SN		SN
Tattenham Corner	d			07 46					22 46		
Tadworth	d			07 49					22 49		
Kingswood	d			07 52					22 52		
Chipstead	d			07 57					22 57		
Woodmansterne	d			08 00					23 00		
Smitham	d			08 03					23 03		
Reedham	d			08 05	and at				23 05		
Caterham	d		07 26		the same		22 26				23 10
Whyteleafe South	d		07 29				22 29				23 13
Whyteleafe	d		07 31		minutes		22 31				23 15
Kenley	d		07 34				22 34				23 18
Purley 4	a		07 37	08 08	past		22 37		23 08		23 21
	d		07 38	08 08			22 38		23 08		23 23
Purley Oaks	d		07 41	08 11	each		22 41		23 11		23 26
South Croydon 4	d		07 44	08 14			22 44		23 14		23 29
East Croydon	d		07 47	08 17	hour until		22 47		23 17		23a31
Norwood Junction 2	d		07 51	08 21			22 51		23a21		
New Cross Gate 4	⊖ a		08 05	08 35			23 05				
London Bridge 4	⊖ a		08 12	08 42			23 12				
London Waterloo (East) 4	⊖ a		08 17	08 47			23 17				
London Charing Cross 4	⊖ a		08 20	08 50			23 20				
Clapham Junction 10	a										
London Victoria 15	⊖ a										

For general notes see front of timetable
For details of catering facilities see
Directory of Train Operators

London → Sutton, Epsom, Guildford, Dorking and Horsham

Network Diagram - see first page of Table 177

Miles	Miles	Miles	Station		SN MO	SN MX	SN MX	SN MO	SW MX	SN MX	SN MX	SW MX	SN		SN	SW	FC A	SN	SN	SN	SN	FC B	SW		SN	SW
—	0	—	London Victoria 15 ⊖	d	23p19	23p23	23p26				23p51								05 57		06 00				06 07	
—	—	—	London Waterloo 15 ⊖	d					23p42			00 15				05 47							06 24			06 39
—	2¾	—	Clapham Junction 10	d	23p26	23p31	23p34		23p51		23p59	00 24				05 56			06 03		06 08		06 33		06 15	06 48
—	4¾	—	Balham 4 ⊖	d	23p32	23p36	23p40				00 04								06 08		06 13				06 20	
0	—	0	London Bridge 4 ⊖	d														05 45								
—	—	6	Tulse Hill 3	d																		06 26				
2¾	—	—	New Cross Gate 4 ⊖	d														05 50								
8¾	—	—	Norwood Junction 2	d		23p54									05 54			06 09							06 39	
10½	—	12	West Croydon 4	d	23p50	00b01		←		←	00 21		05 46		05 59			06 14			06 30				06 44	
11½	—	—	Waddon	d	23p52	00 03		23p52		00 03	00 24		05 48		06 02			06 16			06 33				06 46	
13	—	—	Wallington	d	→	→		23p56		00 07	00 27		05 52		06 05			06 20			06 36				06 50	
13¾	—	—	Carshalton Beeches	d				23p58		00 09	00 30		05 54		06 08			06 22			06 39				06 52	
—	8	—	Mitcham Eastfields	d			23p47												06 15			06 34				
—	9	—	Mitcham Junction	d			23p50												06 18			06 38				
—	9¾	—	Hackbridge	d			23p54												06 22			06 41				
—	10¾	—	Carshalton	d			23p56												06 24			06 44				
14¾	12	0	Sutton (Surrey) 4	a			00 01	00 02		00 13	00 33		05 58		06 11			06 26	06 29		06 42	06 47			06 56	
—	—	—		d			00 02	00 04							06 18		06 22		06 30	06 42	06 48	06 48			06 56	
—	—	1	West Sutton	a													06 25					06 51				
—	—	5½	Wimbledon 6 ⊖	a													06 39					07 05				
—	13	—	Belmont	d											06 21						06 51					
—	14½	—	Banstead	d											06 25						06 55					
—	16	—	Epsom Downs	a											06 28						06 58					
15¾	—	—	Cheam	d			00 04	00 06											06 32						06 59	
17¼	—	—	Ewell East	d			00 08	00 10											06 36						07 02	
18¾	—	—	Epsom 3	a			00 12	00 14	00 15			00 48				06 20			06 40	06 49			06 57		07 06	07 08
—	—	—		d			00 12		00 19							06 21			06 40	06 50			06 58			07 08
20½	—	—	Ashtead	d			00 16		00 23							06 25			06 44				07 02			07 12
22½	—	0	Leatherhead	d			00 19		00 26							06 28			06 47	06 56			07 05			07 15
25	—	—	Bookham	d					00 31							06 33				07 01						07 21
26¾	—	—	Effingham Junction 6	d					00 36							06 37				07 05						07a24
35	—	—	Guildford	a					00 54							06 50				07 17						
—	—	3¼	Boxhill & Westhumble	d			00 24												06 52							
—	—	4	Dorking 4	a			00 27												06 55				07 11			
—	—	—		d			00 27												06 56							
—	—	9	Holmwood	d			00s34												07 03							
—	—	11¼	Ockley	d			00s38												07 07							
—	—	15¾	Warnham	d			00s44												07 13							
—	—	17¾	Horsham 4	a			00 48												07 17							

Station		SN	SN	FC C	SW	SN	SN	SW	SN	SW		SN	FC C	SN	SN	SW	FC D	SN	SW	SN		SN	SW	FC C	SN	SW
London Victoria 15 ⊖	d	06 25	06 28				07 00		07 15						07 30			07 47		07 55					08 03	
London Waterloo 15 ⊖	d				06 54			07 09		07 24						07 39			07 54				08 09			08 24
Clapham Junction 10	d	06 31	06 38		07 03		07 08	07 18	07 21	07 33					07 38	07 48		07 55	08 03	08 03			08 18		08 11	08 33
Balham 4 ⊖	d	06 36	06 44				07 13		07 26						07 44			08 00							08 16	
London Bridge 4 ⊖	d					06 46								07 15								07 48				
Tulse Hill 3	d			07 03									07 32				07 56							08 26		
New Cross Gate 4 ⊖	d					06 51								07 20								07 53				
Norwood Junction 2	d					07 10								07 39								08 11				
West Croydon 4	d		07 01			07 15	07 31					←		07 45	08 03							08 16			08 36	
Waddon	d		07 03			07 18	07 34					07 34		07 47	08 05							08 19			08 39	
Wallington	d		07 07			07 21	→					07 37		07 51	08 09							08 22			08 42	
Carshalton Beeches	d		07 09			07 24						07 40		07 53	08 11							08 25			08 45	
Mitcham Eastfields	d	06 43		07 10									07 40				08 03			08 13				08 33		
Mitcham Junction	d	06 46		07 14					07 34				07 44				08 07	08 10						08 37		
Hackbridge	d	06 50		07 17					07 37				07 47				08 10	08 13						08 40		
Carshalton	d	06 52		07 20					07 40				07 50				08 13	08 16						08 43		
Sutton (Surrey) 4	a	07 00	07 13	07 23		07 27			07 43			07 43	07 53	07 58	08 15		08 16	08 19		08 23		08 28		08 46	08 48	
	d	07 00	07 18	07 24		07 28			07 44			07 45	07 54	07 58	08 16		08 20			08 23		08 29		08 47	08 53	
West Sutton	a			07 27									07 57				08 23							08 50	→	
Wimbledon 6 ⊖	a			07 41									08 11				08 37							09 04		
Belmont	d		07 21									07 48			08 19											
Banstead	d		07 25									07 52			08 23											
Epsom Downs	a		07 28									07 55			08 26											
Cheam	d	07 03				07 30			07 46					08 01						08 26		08 31				
Ewell East	d	07 06							07 50					08 04						08 29		08 35				
Epsom 3	a	07 10			07 27	07 36		07 42	07 54	07 58				08 08		08 13			08 27	08 33		08 39	08 42			08 57
	d	07 11			07 28	07 36			07 54	07 58						08 17			08 28	08 34		08 39	08 47			08 58
Ashtead	d	07 15			07 32	07 40			07 58	08 02						08 21			08 32	08 38			08 51			09 02
Leatherhead	d	07 18			07 35	07 45			08 01	08 05						08 24			08 35	08 41		08 45	08 54			09 05
Bookham	d					07 50										08 29							08 59			
Effingham Junction 6	d					07 54										08 33							09 03			
Guildford	a					08 07										08 50							09 20			
Boxhill & Westhumble	d								08 06													08 50				
Dorking 4	a	07 24			07 41				08 09	08 12									08 41	08 47		08 52				09 11
	d	07 24							08 09											08 47						
Holmwood	d	07 32							08 17																	
Ockley	d	07 36							08 21																	
Warnham	d	07 41							08 26																	
Horsham 4	a	07 45							08 30											09 03						

For general notes see front of timetable
For details of catering facilities see Directory of Train Operators

- **A** To St Albans City (Table 52)
- **B** From St Pancras International (Table 52)
- **C** From Luton (Table 52)
- **D** From Bedford (Table 52)
- **b** Arr. 2358

From 28 September due to seasonal difficulties a large number of trains on this table will have minor retimings that could mean slightly earlier departure or later arrival times at certain stations. For further details see local publicity or contact National Rail Enquiries 08457 48 49 50.

London → Sutton, Epsom, Guildford, Dorking and Horsham

Network Diagram - see first page of Table 177

	SN	SN	SN	FC A	SW	SN		SN	SW	SN	SN	SN	SN	FC B	SW	SN		SN	SW	SN	SN	SN	SN	SN	FC B
London Victoria 15 ⊖ d	08 20					08 28		08 32		08 47		08 52	09 01					09 03		09 17		09 23	09 31		
London Waterloo 15 ⊖ d					08 39				08 54						09 09				09 24						
Clapham Junction 10 d	08 26				08 48	08 35		08 40	09 03	08 54		09 00	09 08		09 18			09 11	09 33	09 24		09 30	09 38		
Balham 4 ⊖ d	08 31					08 42		08 45		09 00		09 05						09 16		09 30		09 35			
London Bridge 4 ⊖ d			08 19								08 43										09 14				
Tulse Hill 3 d				08 43										09 16											09 46
New Cross Gate 4 ⊖ d			08 26								08 48										09 20				
Norwood Junction 2 d			08 44								09 10										09 40				
West Croydon 4 d			08 49			08 59		09 06			09 15	09b27				←		09 33			09 45	09 54		←	
Waddon d			08 52			09 01		09 08			09 18	09 29				09 29		09 36			09 48	09 56		09 56	
Wallington d			08 55			09 05		09 12			09 21	→				09 33		09 39			09 51	→		10 00	
Carshalton Beeches d			08 58			09 07		09 14			09 24					09 35		09 42			09 54			10 02	
Mitcham Eastfields d	08 38			08 51						09 09				09 23						09 40					09 53
Mitcham Junction d	08 41			08 55						09 12				09 27						09 43					09 57
Hackbridge d	08 45			08 58						09 16				09 30						09 47					10 00
Carshalton d	08 47			09 01						09 18				09 33						09 49					10 03
Sutton (Surrey) 4 a	08 51	←	09 01	09 05		09 11		09 18		09 22	09 27		09 28	09 36		09 40		09 45		09 53	09 57		09 58	10 06	10 07
d	08 51	08 53		09 06		09 11		09 19		09 22			09 29	09 37		09 41				09 53			09 59	10 07	10 07
West Sutton a				09 09										09 40											10 10
Wimbledon 6 ⊖ a				09 23										09 55											10 25
Belmont d		08 56						09 22																10 10	
Banstead d		09 00						09 26																10 14	
Epsom Downs a		09 03						09 29																10 17	
Cheam d	08 54									09 25			09 31			09 43				09 56			10 01		
Ewell East d	08 57									09 28						09 47				09 59			10 05		
Epsom 3 a	09 01				09 16	09 18			09 27	09 32			09 37		09 42	09 51			09 57	10 03			10 09		
d	09 02				09 17				09 28				09 38		09 47				09 58				10 09		
Ashtead d	09 06				09 21				09 32				09 42		09 51				10 02				10 13		
Leatherhead d	09 09				09 24				09 35				09 45		09 54				10 05				10 16		
Bookham d					09 29										09 59										
Effingham Junction 6 d					09 33										10 03										
Guildford a					09 50										10 20										
Boxhill & Westhumble d	09 14												09 50										10 21		
Dorking 4 a	09 16								09 41				09 52						10 11				10 24		
d	09 17																						10 24		
Holmwood d	09 24																						10 32		
Ockley d	09 28																						10 36		
Warnham d	09 34																						10 41		
Horsham 4 a	09 38																						10 45		

	SN	SW	SW		SN	SN	SN	SN	FC B	SW	SN	SN	SW		SN	SN	SN	SN	FC B	SN	SN	SW	SW		SN
London Victoria 15 ⊖ d	09 33				09 47		09 53	10 01				10 03			10 17		10 23	10 31			10 33				10 47
London Waterloo 15 ⊖ d		09 39	09 54							10 09			10 24									10 39	10 54		
Clapham Junction 10 d	09 41	09 48	10 03		09 54		10 00	10 08		10 18		10 11	10 33		10 24		10 30	10 38			10 41	10 48	11 03		10 54
Balham 4 ⊖ d	09 46				10 00		10 05					10 16			10 30		10 35				10 46				11 00
London Bridge 4 ⊖ d						09 45										10 15									
Tulse Hill 3 d									10 16										10 46						
New Cross Gate 4 ⊖ d						09 50										10 20									
Norwood Junction 2 d						10 10										10 40									
West Croydon 4 d	10 03					10 15	10c26				←	10 33				10 45	10e54			←	11 03				
Waddon d	10 06					10 18	10 28				10 28	10 36				10 48	10 56			10 56	11 06				
Wallington d	10 09					10 21	→				10 32	10 39				10 51	→			11 00	11 09				
Carshalton Beeches d	10 12					10 24					10 34	10 42				10 54				11 02	11 12				
Mitcham Eastfields d					10 09				10 23						10 39				10 53						11 09
Mitcham Junction d					10 12				10 27						10 42				10 57						11 12
Hackbridge d					10 16				10 30						10 46				11 00						11 16
Carshalton d					10 18				10 33						10 48				11 03						11 18
Sutton (Surrey) 4 a	10 15				10 22	10 27		10 28	10 36		10 39	10 45			10 52	10 57		10 58	11 06	11 06	11 15				11 22
d					10 22			10 29	10 37		10 40				10 52			10 59	11 07	11 07					11 22
West Sutton a									10 40										11 10						
Wimbledon 6 ⊖ a									10 55										11 25						
Belmont d																				11 10					
Banstead d																				11 14					
Epsom Downs a																				11 17					
Cheam d					10 25			10 31			10 42				10 55			11 01							11 25
Ewell East d					10 28						10 46				10 58			11 05							11 28
Epsom 3 a		10 16	10 27		10 32			10 38		10 46	10 50		10 57		11 02			11 09				11 16	11 27		11 32
d		10 17	10 28					10 38		10 47			10 58					11 09				11 17	11 28		
Ashtead d		10 21	10 32					10 42		10 51			11 02					11 13				11 21	11 32		
Leatherhead d		10 24	10 35					10 45		10 54			11 05					11 16				11 24	11 35		
Bookham d		10 29								10 59												11 29			
Effingham Junction 6 d		10 33								11 03												11 33			
Guildford a		10 50								11 20												11 50			
Boxhill & Westhumble d																		11 21							
Dorking 4 a			10 41					10 51					11 11					11 24					11 41		
d																		11 24							
Holmwood d																		11 32							
Ockley d																		11 36							
Warnham d																		11 41							
Horsham 4 a																		11 45							

For general notes see front of timetable
For details of catering facilities see Directory of Train Operators

A From Bedford (Table 52)
B From St Albans City (Table 52)
b Arr. 0922
c Arr. 1022
e Arr. 1051

From 28 September due to seasonal difficulties a large number of trains on this table will have minor retimings that could mean slightly earlier departure or later arrival times at certain stations. For further details see local publicity or contact National Rail Enquiries 08457 48 49 50.

Table 182

Mondays to Fridays

London → Sutton, Epsom, Guildford, Dorking and Horsham

Network Diagram - see first page of Table 177

Station		SN	SN	SN	FC A	SW	SN	SN	SW	SN	SN	SN	SN	FC A	SN	SN	SW	SW	SN		SN	SN	SN
London Victoria 15 ⊖	d		10 53	11 01				11 03		11 17		11 23	11 31			11 33			11 47			15 53	16 01
London Waterloo 15 ⊖	d					11 09			11 24								11 39	11 54					
Clapham Junction 10	d		11 00	11 08		11 18		11 11	11 33	11 24		11 30	11 38			11 41	11 48	12 03	11 54			16 00	16 08
Balham 4 ⊖	d		11 05					11 16		11 30		11 35				11 46			12 00			16 05	
London Bridge 4 ⊖	d	10 45									11 15										15 45		
Tulse Hill 3	d				11 16									11 46									
New Cross Gate 4 ⊖	d	10 50									11 20										15 50		
Norwood Junction 2	d	11 10									11 40										16 10		
West Croydon 4	d	11 15	11b26				←	11 33			11 45	11 54			←	12 03					16 15	16 24	
Waddon	d	11 18	11 28				11 28	11 36			11 48	11 56			11 56	12 06					16 18	16 26	
Wallington	d	11 21	→				11 32	11 39			11 51	→			12 00	12 09					16 21	→	
Carshalton Beeches	d	11 24					11 34	11 42			11 54				12 02	12 12					16 24		
Mitcham Eastfields	d				11 23					11 39				11 53					12 09				
Mitcham Junction	d				11 27					11 42				11 57					12 12				16 22
Hackbridge	d				11 30					11 46				12 00					12 16	and at			
Carshalton	d				11 33					11 48				12 03					12 18				
Sutton (Surrey) 4	a	11 27		11 28	11 36		11 39	11 45		11 52	11 57		11 58	12 06	12 06	12 15			12 22	the same	16 27		16 29
	d			11 29	11 37		11 40			11 52			11 59	12 07	12 07				12 22				16 30
West Sutton	a				11 40									12 10						minutes			
Wimbledon 6 ⊖	a				11 55									12 25						past			
Belmont	d														12 10								
Banstead	d														12 14					each			
Epsom Downs	a														12 17					hour until			
Cheam	d			11 31			11 42			11 55			12 01						12 25				16 32
Ewell East	d						11 46			11 58			12 05						12 28				16 36
Epsom 3	a			11 38		11 46	11 50		11 57	12 02			12 09				12 16	12 27	12 32				16 40
	d			11 38		11 47			11 58				12 09				12 17	12 28					16 40
Ashtead	d			11 42		11 51			12 02				12 13				12 21	12 32					16 44
Leatherhead	d			11 45		11 54			12 05				12 16				12 24	12 35					16 47
Bookham	d					11 59											12 29						
Effingham Junction 6	d					12 03											12 33						
Guildford	a					12 20											12 50						
Boxhill & Westhumble	d												12 21										16 52
Dorking 4	a			11 51					12 11				12 24					12 41					16 57
	d												12 24										
Holmwood	d												12 32										
Ockley	d												12 36										
Warnham	d												12 41										
Horsham 4	a												12 45										

Station		FC A	SW	SN	SN	SW	SN	SN	SW	SN	FC A	SN	SW	SN	SN	FC A	SN	SN	SW	SN	SW	SN	SW	SN
London Victoria 15 ⊖	d				16 03		16 17			16 31		16 33		16 50			17 01			17 13		17 20		
London Waterloo 15 ⊖	d		16 09			16 24			16 39				16 54						17 09		17 24		17 30	
Clapham Junction 10	d		16 18		16 11	16 33	16 24		16 48	16 38		16 41	17 03	16 56			17 09		17 18	17 21	17 33	17 26	17 39	
Balham 4 ⊖	d				16 16		16 30					16 46		17 01			17 14			17 26		17 32		
London Bridge 4 ⊖	d							16 15							16 44			17 05						
Tulse Hill 3	d	16 16									16 50					17 16		17 23						
New Cross Gate 4 ⊖	d							16 20							16 49									
Norwood Junction 2	d							16 40							17 10									
West Croydon 4	d			←	16 33			16 45				17 06			17 15		17 31			17 44				←
Waddon	d			16 26	16 36			16 48				17 08			17 18		17 34			17 46				17 46
Wallington	d			16 30	16 39			16 51				17 12			17 21		17 37			→				17 50
Carshalton Beeches	d			16 32	16 42			16 54				17 14			17 24		17 40							17 52
Mitcham Eastfields	d	16 23					16 39			16 51	16 58			17 09		17 24		17 31				17 39		
Mitcham Junction	d	16 27					16 43			16 55	17 02			17 12		17 28		17 34				17 42		
Hackbridge	d	16 30					16 46			16 58	17 05			17 16		17 31		17 38				17 46		
Carshalton	d	16 33					16 49			17 01	17 08			17 18		17 34		17 40				17 48		
Sutton (Surrey) 4	a	16 36		16 36	16 47		16 52	16 57		17 05	17 12	17 18		17 22	17 27	17 38	17 43	17 44				17 52		17 58
	d	16 37		16 37			16 53	16 58		17 06	17 12	17 19		17 22	17 28	17 38	17 45	17 46				17 52		
West Sutton	a	16 40									17 15					17 41		17 49						
Wimbledon 6 ⊖	a	16 55									17 31					17 55		18 05						
Belmont	d			16 40								17 22					17 48							
Banstead	d			16 44								17 26					17 52							
Epsom Downs	a			16 47								17 31					17 57							
Cheam	d						16 55	17 00		17 08				17 25	17 30							17 55		
Ewell East	d						16 59	17 04		17 12				17 28	17 34							17 58		
Epsom 3	a		16 46			16 57	17 03	17 08	17 12	17 18			17 27	17 32	17 38				17 42		17 54	18 02	18 06	
	d		16 47			16 58	17 03	17 08	17 17				17 28	17 33	17 38				17 47		17 54	18 04		
Ashtead	d		16 51			17 02	17 07	17 12	17 21				17 32	17 37	17 42				17 51		17 58	18 08		
Leatherhead	d		16 54			17 05	17 10	17 15	17 24				17 35	17 40	17 45				17 54		18 01	18 11		
Bookham	d		16 59					17 21	17 29						17 51				17 59					
Effingham Junction 6	d		17 03					17 24	17 33						17 54				18a05					
Guildford	a		17 22					17 39	17 52						18 13									
Boxhill & Westhumble	d					17 10	17 15						17 40	17 45							18 06	18 16		
Dorking 4	a					17 14	17 18						17 44	17 47							18 11	18 18		
	d						17 20							17 50								18 21		
Holmwood	d						17 28							17 57								18 28		
Ockley	d						17 32							18 01								18 32		
Warnham	d						17 37							18 07								18 38		
Horsham 4	a						17 43							18 13								18 43		

For general notes see front of timetable
For details of catering facilities see Directory of Train Operators

A From St Albans City (Table 52)
b Arr. 1122

From 28 September due to seasonal difficulties a large number of trains on this table will have minor retimings that could mean slightly earlier departure or later arrival times at certain stations. For further details see local publicity or contact National Rail Enquiries 08457 48 49 50.

London → Sutton, Epsom, Guildford, Dorking and Horsham

Network Diagram - see first page of Table 177

		SN	SN	FC A	SN	SN		SW	SW	SN	SW	SN	SW	SN	FC A	SN		SN	SW	SN	SW	SN	FC A	SW	SW	SN
London Victoria 15	⊖ d		17 31			17 33				17 50				18 01				18 03		18 20				18 39	18 54	
London Waterloo 15	⊖ d							17 39	17 54		18 00		18 09						18 24		18 30					
Clapham Junction 10	d		17 37			17 41		17 48	18 03	17 56	18 09		18 18	18 08				18 11	18 33	18 26	18 39			18 48	19 03	
Balham 4	⊖ d		17 42			17 46				18 02				18 12				18 16		18 32						
London Bridge 4	⊖ d	17 19			17 35							17 51				18 07						18 20				18 38
Tulse Hill 3	d			17 46	17 52										18 18	18 24							18 48			18 55
New Cross Gate 4	⊖ d	17 25										17 57										18 25				
Norwood Junction 2	d	17 40										18 12										18 41				
West Croydon 4	d	17 47				18 06						18 17						18 37				18 46				
Waddon	d	17 49				18 08						18 20						18 39				18 48				
Wallington	d	17 53				18 12						18 23						18 43				18 52				
Carshalton Beeches	d	17 55				18 14						18 26						18 45				18 54				
Mitcham Eastfields	d		17 49	17 54	18 00					18 09				18 19	18 26	18 32				18 39			18 56			19 03
Mitcham Junction	d		17 52	17 58	18 04					18 12				18 23	18 30	18 36				18 42			18 59			19 07
Hackbridge	d		17 56	18 01	18 07					18 16				18 26	18 33	18 39				18 46			19 03			19 10
Carshalton	d		17 58	18 04	18 10					18 18				18 29	18 36	18 42				18 48			19 05			19 13
Sutton (Surrey) 4	a	17 59	18 02	18 08	18 13	18 18				18 22		18 29		18 32	18 39	18 45		18 49		18 52		18 58	19 09			19 16
	d	18 00	18 05	18 08	18 16	18 19				18 22		18 30		18 33	18 40	18 47		18 50		18 52		18 58	19 10			19 17
West Sutton	a			18 11	18 19										18 43	18 51							19 13			
Wimbledon 6	⊖ a			18 25	18 35										18 57	19 07							19 27			
Belmont	d					18 22												18 53								
Banstead	d					18 26												18 57								
Epsom Downs	a					18 31												19 02								
Cheam	d	18 02	18 07							18 25		18 32		18 35						18 55		19 01				19 19
Ewell East	d	18 06	18 11							18 28		18 36		18 39						18 58		19 04				19 23
Epsom 3	a	18 10	18 17					18 20	18 24	18 32	18 35	18 40	18 43	18 45					18 54	19 02	19 05	19 08		19 13	19 24	19 29
	d	18 11						18 20	18 24	18 34		18 41	18 47						18 54	19 04		19 10		19 17	19 24	
Ashtead	d	18 15						18 24	18 28	18 38		18 45	18 51						18 58	19 08		19 14		19 21	19 28	
Leatherhead	d	18 18						18 28	18 31	18 41		18 48	18 54						19 01	19 11		19 17		19 24	19 31	
Bookham	d	18 23						18 33					18 59											19 29		
Effingham Junction 6	d	18 27						18a44					19 03											19 33		
Guildford	a	18 45											19 22											19 52		
Boxhill & Westhumble	d								18 36	18 46		18 53							19 06	19 16		19 22			19 36	
Dorking 4	a								18 41	18 48		18 57							19 11	19 18		19 27			19 43	
	d									18 51										19 21						
Holmwood	d									18 58										19 28						
Ockley	d									19 02										19 32						
Warnham	d									19 08										19 38						
Horsham 4	a									19 13										19 43						

		SN	SN		SN	SW	SN	FC B	SW	SN	SN	SW	SN		SN	SN	FC A	SN	SW	SN	SW	SN	SN		FC A	SN
London Victoria 15	⊖ d	18 32	18 43		18 50						19 15		19 20					19 23		19 45		19 50				19 53
London Waterloo 15	⊖ d					19 00			19 09			19 24							19 39		19 54					
Clapham Junction 10	d	18 40	18 51		18 56	19 09			19 18		19 23	19 33	19 26					19 31	19 48	19 53	20 03	19 56				20 01
Balham 4	⊖ d	18 45	18 56		19 02						19 28		19 32					19 36		19 58		20 02				20 06
London Bridge 4	⊖ d									19 05						19 31										
Tulse Hill 3	d							19 16									19 46								20 16	
New Cross Gate 4	⊖ d									19 10																
Norwood Junction 2	d									19 28						19 44		19 54								20 24
West Croydon 4	d	19 07	19 15				←			19 33	19 45				←	19 49		20 00		20 15			←			20 30
Waddon	d	19 09	19 17				19 17			19 36	19 48				19 48	19 51		20 02		20 18			20 18			20 32
Wallington	d	19 13	→				19 21			19 39	→				19 51	19 55		20 06		→			20 21			20 36
Carshalton Beeches	d	19 15					19 23			19 42					19 54	19 57		20 08					20 24			20 38
Mitcham Eastfields	d				19 09			19 23					19 39				19 53					20 09			20 23	
Mitcham Junction	d				19 12			19 27					19 42				19 57					20 12			20 27	
Hackbridge	d				19 16			19 30					19 46				20 00					20 16			20 30	
Carshalton	d				19 18			19 33					19 48				20 03					20 18			20 33	
Sutton (Surrey) 4	a	19 19			19 22		19 27	19 36		19 45			19 52		19 57	20 01	20 06	20 12				20 22	20 27		20 36	20 42
	d	19 20			19 22		19 28	19 37		19 46			19 52		19 58	20 02	20 07					20 22	20 28		20 37	
West Sutton	a							19 40									20 10								20 40	
Wimbledon 6	⊖ a							19 55									20 25								20 55	
Belmont	d	19 23													20 01								20 31			
Banstead	d	19 27													20 05								20 35			
Epsom Downs	a	19 32													20 08								20 38			
Cheam	d				19 25		19 30			19 48			19 55			20 04						20 25				
Ewell East	d				19 28		19 34			19 52			19 58			20 08						20 28				
Epsom 3	a				19 32	19 33	19 40		19 43	19 56		19 57	20 02			20 12			20 12		20 27	20 32				
	d				19 34				19 47			19 58	20 03			20 13			20 17			20 33				
Ashtead	d				19 38				19 51			20 02	20 07						20 21			20 37				
Leatherhead	d				19 41				19 54			20 05	20 10			20 19			20 24			20 40				
Bookham	d								19 59										20 29							
Effingham Junction 6	d								20 03										20 33							
Guildford	a								20 20										20 50							
Boxhill & Westhumble	d				19 46							20 10	20 15									20 45				
Dorking 4	a				19 49							20 12	20 17			20 25						20 47				
	d												20 18													
Holmwood	d												20 25													
Ockley	d												20 29													
Warnham	d												20 35													
Horsham 4	a												20 39													

For general notes see front of timetable
For details of catering facilities see
Directory of Train Operators

A From St Albans City (Table 52)
B From Luton (Table 52)

From 28 September due to seasonal difficulties a large number of trains on this table will have minor retimings that could mean slightly earlier departure or later arrival times at certain stations. For further details see local publicity or contact National Rail Enquiries 08457 48 49 50.

London → Sutton, Epsom, Guildford, Dorking and Horsham

Network Diagram - see first page of Table 177

Station		SW	SN	SW	SN	SN	FC A	SN	SW	SN		SW	SN	SN	SN	SW	SN	SW	SN	SN		SW	FC B	SN	SN	SW
London Victoria 15 ⊖	d		20 15		20 20			20 23		20 45			20 50		20 53		21 15		21 20					21 23	21 45	
London Waterloo 15 ⊖	d	20 09		20 24					20 39			20 54				21 09		21 24				21 39				21 54
Clapham Junction 10	d	20 18	20 23	20 33	20 26			20 31	20 48	20 53		21 03	20 56		21 01	21 18	21 23	21 33	21 26			21 48		21 31	21 53	22 03
Balham 4 ⊖	d		20 28		20 31			20 36		20 58			21 02		21 06		21 28		21 31					21 36	21 58	
London Bridge 4 ⊖	d																									
Tulse Hill 3	d						20 46																			
New Cross Gate 4 ⊖	d																									
Norwood Junction 2	d							20 54							21 24									21 54		
West Croydon 4 (tram)	d		20 45			←		21 00		21 15				←	21 30		21 45			←				22 00	22 15	
Waddon	d		20 48			20 48		21 02		21 18				21 18	21 32		21 48			21 48				22 02	22 18	
Wallington	d		→			20 51		21 06		→				21 21	21 36		→			21 51				22 06	→	
Carshalton Beeches	d					20 54		21 08						21 24	21 38					21 54				22 08		
Mitcham Eastfields	d				20 39		20 53						21 09						21 39							
Mitcham Junction (tram)	d				20 42		20 57						21 12						21 42							
Hackbridge	d				20 46		21 00						21 16						21 46							
Carshalton	d				20 48		21 03						21 18						21 48							
Sutton (Surrey) 4	a				20 52	20 57	21 06	21 12					21 22	21 27	21 42				21 52	21 57				22 12		
	d				20 52	20 58	21 07						21 22	21 28					21 52	21 58			22 07			
West Sutton	a						21 10																22 10			
Wimbledon 6 ⊖ (tram)	a						21 25																22 24			
Belmont	d													21 31												
Banstead	d													21 35												
Epsom Downs	a													21 38												
Cheam	d				20 55	21 00							21 25						21 55	22 00						
Ewell East	d				20 58	21 04							21 28						21 58	22 04						
Epsom 3	a	20 42		20 57	21 02	21 08			21 12			21 27	21 32			21 42		21 57	22 02	22 08		22 12				22 27
	d	20 47			21 03				21 17				21 33			21 47			22 03			22 17				
Ashtead	d	20 51			21 07				21 21				21 37			21 51			22 07			22 21				
Leatherhead	d	20 54			21 10				21 24				21 40			21 54			22 10			22 24				
Bookham	d								21 29													22 29				
Effingham Junction 6	d								21 33													22 33				
Guildford	a								21 50													22 50				
Boxhill & Westhumble	d	20 59			21 15								21 45			21 59										
Dorking 4	a	21 01			21 17								21 47			22 01			22 16							
	d																									
Holmwood	d																									
Ockley	d																									
Warnham	d																									
Horsham 4	a																									

Station		SN	SN	SN	SW	SN	SN		SN	SN	SW	SN	SN	SW	SN	SN	SN		SN	SN	SW	SN	SN			
London Victoria 15 ⊖	d	21 50		21 53		22 15	22 20			22 23		22 45	22 50			22 53	23 15		23 23	23 26			23 51			
London Waterloo 15 ⊖	d				22 09						22 39			23 09							23 42					
Clapham Junction 10	d	21 56		22 01	22 18	22 23	22 27			22 31	22 48	22 53	22 56	23 18		23 01	23 23		23 31	23 34	23 51		23 59			
Balham 4 ⊖	d	22 02		22 06		22 28	22 32			22 36		22 58	23 01			23 06	23 28		23 36	23 40			00 04			
London Bridge 4 ⊖	d																									
Tulse Hill 3	d																									
New Cross Gate 4 ⊖	d																									
Norwood Junction 2	d			22 24						22 54						23 24			23 54							
West Croydon 4 (tram)	d		←	22 30		22 47			←	23 00		23 15			←	23 30	23 45		00b01			←	00 21			
Waddon	d		22 18	22 32		22 50			22 50	23 02		23 18			23 18	23 32	23 48		00 03			00 03	00 24			
Wallington	d		22 21	22 36		→			22 53	23 06		→			23 21	23 36	23 51		→			00 07	00 27			
Carshalton Beeches	d		22 24	22 38					22 56	23 08					23 24	23 38	23 54					00 09	00 30			
Mitcham Eastfields	d	22 09					22 39						23 08							23 47						
Mitcham Junction (tram)	d	22 12					22 42						23 11							23 50						
Hackbridge	d	22 16					22 46						23 15							23 54						
Carshalton	d	22 18					22 48						23 17							23 56						
Sutton (Surrey) 4	a	22 22	22 27	22 42			22 52		22 59	23 12			23 21		23 27	23 42	23 57			00 01		00 13	00 33			
	d	22 22	22 28				22 52		23 00				23 21		23 28	23 42				00 02						
West Sutton	a																									
Wimbledon 6 ⊖ (tram)	a																									
Belmont	d		22 31												23 31											
Banstead	d		22 35												23 35											
Epsom Downs	a		22 38												23 38											
Cheam	d	22 25					22 55		23 02				23 24			23 45				00 04						
Ewell East	d	22 28					22 58		23 06				23 27			23 48				00 08						
Epsom 3	a	22 32			22 42		23 02		23 10		23 12		23 31	23 42		23 52				00 12	00 15					
	d	22 33			22 47		23 03				23 17		23 32	23 47						00 12	00 19					
Ashtead	d	22 37			22 51		23 07				23 21		23 36	23 51						00 16	00 23					
Leatherhead	d	22 40			22 54		23 10				23 24		23 39	23 54						00 19	00 26					
Bookham	d										23 29										00 31					
Effingham Junction 6	d										23 33										00 36					
Guildford	a										23 54										00 54					
Boxhill & Westhumble	d	22 45			22 59								23 44	23 59						00 24						
Dorking 4	a	22 47			23 01		23 16						23 46	00 01						00 27						
	d																			00 27						
Holmwood	d																			00s34						
Ockley	d																			00s38						
Warnham	d																			00s44						
Horsham 4	a																			00 48						

For general notes see front of timetable
For details of catering facilities see Directory of Train Operators

A From St Albans City (Table 52)
B To London Bridge (Table 179)
b Arr. 2358

From 28 September due to seasonal difficulties a large number of trains on this table will have minor retimings that could mean slightly earlier departure or later arrival times at certain stations. For further details see local publicity or contact National Rail Enquiries 08457 48 49 50.

London → Sutton, Epsom, Guildford, Dorking and Horsham

Network Diagram - see first page of Table 177

Station		SN	SN	SW	SN	SN	SW	SN	SN	FC A	SW	SN	SN B
London Victoria 15	⊖ d	23p23	23p26			23p51			06 23			06 47	
London Waterloo 15	⊖ d			23p42			00 15				06 39		
Clapham Junction 10	d	23p31	23p34	23p51		23p59	00 24		06 30		06 48	06 54	
Balham 4	⊖ d	23p36	23p40			00 04			06 35			07 00	
London Bridge 4	⊖ d												
Tulse Hill 3	d									06 46			
New Cross Gate 4	⊖ d												
Norwood Junction 2	d	23p54											07 06
West Croydon 4	d	00b01			←	00 21		06 45	06 54				07c14
Waddon	d	00 03			00 03	00 24		06 47	06 56				07 17
Wallington	d	→			00 07	00 27		06 51	07 00				07 20
Carshalton Beeches	d				00 09	00 30		06 53	07 02				07 23
Mitcham Eastfields	d		23p47							06 53		07 09	
Mitcham Junction	d		23p50							06 57		07 12	
Hackbridge	d		23p54							07 00		07 16	
Carshalton	d		23p56							07 03		07 18	
Sutton (Surrey) 4	a		00 01		00 13	00 33		06 57	07 06	07 06		07 22	07 26
	d		00 02					06 57	07 07	07 07		07 22	
West Sutton	a									07 10			
Wimbledon 6	⊖ a									07 25			
Belmont	d								07 10				
Banstead	d								07 14				
Epsom Downs	a								07 17				
Cheam	d		00 04					07 00				07 25	
Ewell East	d		00 08					07 03				07 28	
Epsom 3	a		00 12	00 15			00 48	07 07			07 16	07 32	
	d		00 12	00 19				07 08			07 17	07 33	
Ashtead	d		00 16	00 23				07 12			07 21	07 37	
Leatherhead	d		00 19	00 26				07 15			07 24	07 40	
Bookham	d			00 31							07 29		
Effingham Junction 6	d			00 36							07 33		
Guildford	a			00 54							07 50		
Boxhill & Westhumble	d		00 24									07 45	
Dorking 4	a		00 27					07 21				07 47	
	d		00 27										
Holmwood	d		00s34										
Ockley	d		00s38										
Warnham	d		00s44										
Horsham 4	a		00 48										

Station		FC A	SW	SN	SW	SN	SN	SN	SN	FC A	SN		SN	SW
London Victoria 15	⊖ d			06 53		07 17		07 23	07 31				07 33	
London Waterloo 15	⊖ d		07 09		07 24									07 39
Clapham Junction 10	d		07 18	07 00	07 33	07 24		07 30	07 38				07 41	07 48
Balham 4	⊖ d			07 05		07 30		07 35					07 46	
London Bridge 4	⊖ d						07 14							
Tulse Hill 3	d	07 16								07 46				
New Cross Gate 4	⊖ d						07 20							
Norwood Junction 2	d						07 40							
West Croydon 4	d			07e26			07 45	07 54			←		08 03	
Waddon	d			07 28			07 48	07 56			07 56		08 06	
Wallington	d			07 32			07 51	→			08 00		08 09	
Carshalton Beeches	d			07 34			07 54				08 02		08 12	
Mitcham Eastfields	d	07 23				07 39				07 53				
Mitcham Junction	d	07 27				07 42				07 57				
Hackbridge	d	07 30				07 46				08 00				
Carshalton	d	07 33				07 48				08 03				
Sutton (Surrey) 4	a	07 36		07 39		07 52	07 57		07 58	08 06	08 06		08 15	
	d	07 37		07 40		07 52			07 59	08 07	08 07			
West Sutton	a	07 40								08 10				
Wimbledon 6	⊖ a	07 55								08 25				
Belmont	d										08 10			
Banstead	d										08 14			
Epsom Downs	a										08 17			
Cheam	d			07 42		07 55			08 01					
Ewell East	d			07 46		07 58			08 05					
Epsom 3	a		07 46	07 50	07 57	08 02			08 09					08 16
	d		07 47		07 58				08 09					08 17
Ashtead	d		07 51		08 02				08 13					08 21
Leatherhead	d		07 54		08 05				08 16					08 24
Bookham	d		07 59											08 29
Effingham Junction 6	d		08 03											08 33
Guildford	a		08 20											08 50
Boxhill & Westhumble	d								08 21					
Dorking 4	a				08 11				08 24					
	d								08 24					
Holmwood	d								08 32					
Ockley	d								08 36					
Warnham	d								08 41					
Horsham 4	a								08 45					

Station		SW	SN	SN	SN	SN	FC A	SW	SN	SN	SW	SN	SN
London Victoria 15	⊖ d		07 47		07 53	08 01				08 03		08 17	
London Waterloo 15	⊖ d	07 54						08 09			08 24		
Clapham Junction 10	d	08 03	07 54		08 00	08 08		08 18		08 11	08 33	08 24	
Balham 4	⊖ d		08 00		08 05					08 16		08 30	
London Bridge 4	⊖ d			07 44									08 14
Tulse Hill 3	d						08 16						
New Cross Gate 4	⊖ d			07 50									08 20
Norwood Junction 2	d			08 10									08 40
West Croydon 4	d			08 15	08f26				←	08 33			08 45
Waddon	d			08 18	08 28				08 28	08 36			08 48
Wallington	d			08 21	→				08 32	08 39			08 51
Carshalton Beeches	d			08 24					08 34	08 42			08 54
Mitcham Eastfields	d		08 09				08 23					08 39	
Mitcham Junction	d		08 12				08 27					08 42	
Hackbridge	d		08 16				08 30					08 46	
Carshalton	d		08 18				08 33					08 48	
Sutton (Surrey) 4	a		08 22	08 27		08 28	08 36		08 39	08 45		08 52	08 57
	d		08 22			08 29	08 37		08 40			08 52	
West Sutton	a						08 40						
Wimbledon 6	⊖ a						08 55						
Belmont	d												
Banstead	d												
Epsom Downs	a												
Cheam	d		08 25			08 31			08 42			08 55	
Ewell East	d		08 28						08 46			08 58	
Epsom 3	a	08 27	08 32			08 38		08 46	08 50		08 57	09 02	
	d	08 28				08 38		08 47			08 58		
Ashtead	d	08 32				08 42		08 51			09 02		
Leatherhead	d	08 35				08 45		08 54			09 05		
Bookham	d							08 59					
Effingham Junction 6	d							09 03					
Guildford	a							09 20					
Boxhill & Westhumble	d												
Dorking 4	a	08 41				08 51					09 11		
	d												
Holmwood	d												
Ockley	d												
Warnham	d												
Horsham 4	a												

Station		SN	SN	FC A	SN		SN	SW	SW	SN	SN	SN	SN
London Victoria 15	⊖ d	08 23	08 31				17 33			17 47		17 53	18 01
London Waterloo 15	⊖ d							17 39	17 54				
Clapham Junction 10	d	08 30	08 38				17 41	17 48	18 03	17 54		18 00	18 08
Balham 4	⊖ d	08 35					17 46			18 00		18 05	
London Bridge 4	⊖ d										17 44		
Tulse Hill 3	d			08 46									
New Cross Gate 4	⊖ d										17 50		
Norwood Junction 2	d										18 10		
West Croydon 4	d	08 54			←		18 03				18 15	18g26	
Waddon	d	08 56			08 56		18 06				18 18	18 28	
Wallington	d	→			09 00		18 09				18 21	→	
Carshalton Beeches	d				09 02	and at	18 12				18 24		
Mitcham Eastfields	d			08 53						18 09			
Mitcham Junction	d			08 57		the same				18 12			
Hackbridge	d			09 00						18 16			
Carshalton	d			09 03		minutes				18 18			
Sutton (Surrey) 4	a		08 58	09 06	09 06		18 15			18 22	18 27		18 28
	d		08 59	09 07	09 07	past				18 22			18 29
West Sutton	a			09 10									
Wimbledon 6	⊖ a			09 25		each							
Belmont	d				09 10								
Banstead	d				09 14	hour until							
Epsom Downs	a				09 17								
Cheam	d		09 01							18 25			18 31
Ewell East	d		09 05							18 28			
Epsom 3	a		09 09					18 16	18 27	18 32			18 38
	d		09 09					18 17	18 28				18 38
Ashtead	d		09 13					18 21	18 32				18 42
Leatherhead	d		09 16					18 24	18 35				18 45
Bookham	d							18 29					
Effingham Junction 6	d							18 33					
Guildford	a							18 50					
Boxhill & Westhumble	d		09 21										
Dorking 4	a		09 24						18 41				18 51
	d		09 24										
Holmwood	d		09 32										
Ockley	d		09 36										
Warnham	d		09 41										
Horsham 4	a		09 45										

For general notes see front of timetable
For details of catering facilities see Directory of Train Operators

- **A** From Herne Hill (Table 52)
- **B** From Streatham Hill (Table 177)
- **b** Arr. 2358
- **c** Arr. 0711
- **e** Arr. 0722
- **f** Arr. 0822
- **g** Arr. 1822

From 3 October due to seasonal difficulties a large number of trains on this table will have minor retimings that could mean slightly earlier departure or later arrival times at certain stations. For further details see local publicity or contact National Rail Enquiries 08457 48 49 50.

London → Sutton, Epsom, Guildford, Dorking and Horsham

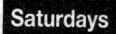

Network Diagram - see first page of Table 177

Station		FC A	SW	SN	SW	SN	SN	FC A	SN	SW	SN	SW	SN	SN	FC A	SN	SW	SN	SW	SN	SN	FC A	SN	SW	SN	SW
London Victoria 15 ⊖	d					18 17			18 23		18 45		18 50			18 53		19 15		19 20			19 23		19 45	
London Waterloo 15 ⊖	d		18 09		18 24					18 39		18 54					19 09		19 24					19 39		19 54
Clapham Junction 10	d		18 18		18 33	18 24			18 30	18 48	18 53	19 03	18 57			19 01	19 18	19 23	19 33	19 26			19 31	19 48	19 53	20 03
Balham 4 ⊖	d					18 30			18 35		18 58		19 01			19 06		19 28		19 32			19 36		19 58	
London Bridge 4 ⊖	d						18 14																			
Tulse Hill 3	d	18 16						18 46							19 16							19 46				
New Cross Gate 4 ⊖	d						18 20																			
Norwood Junction 2	d						18 40									19 24							19 54			
West Croydon 4 🚋	d			←			18 45		18b56		19 15			←		19 30		19 45			←		20 00		20 15	
Waddon	d			18 28			18 48		18 58		19 18			19 18		19 32		19 48			19 48		20 02		20 18	
Wallington	d			18 32			18 51		19 02		→			19 21		19 36		→			19 51		20 06		→	
Carshalton Beeches	d			18 34			18 54		19 04					19 24		19 38					19 54		20 08			
Mitcham Eastfields	d	18 23				18 39		18 53					19 09		19 23					19 39		19 53				
Mitcham Junction 🚋	d	18 27				18 42		18 57					19 12		19 27					19 42		19 57				
Hackbridge	d	18 30				18 46		19 00					19 16		19 30					19 46		20 00				
Carshalton	d	18 33				18 48		19 03					19 18		19 33					19 48		20 03				
Sutton (Surrey) 4	a	18 36		18 39		18 52	18 57	19 06	19 08				19 22	19 27	19 36	19 42				19 52	19 57	20 06	20 12			
	d	18 37		18 40		18 52	18 58	19 07					19 22	19 28	19 37					19 52	19 58	20 07				
West Sutton	a	18 40						19 10							19 40							20 10				
Wimbledon 6 ⊖ 🚋	a	18 55						19 25							19 55							20 25				
Belmont	d						19 01							19 31												
Banstead	d						19 05							19 35												
Epsom Downs	a						19 08							19 38												
Cheam	d			18 42		18 55							19 25							19 55	20 00					
Ewell East	d			18 46		18 58							19 28							19 58	20 04					
Epsom 3	a		18 46	18 50	18 57	19 02				19 12		19 27	19 32				19 42		19 57	20 02	20 08			20 12		20 27
	d		18 47		18 58	19 03				19 17		19 28	19 33				19 47		19 58	20 03				20 17		
Ashtead	d		18 51		19 02	19 07				19 21		19 32	19 37				19 51		20 02	20 07				20 21		
Leatherhead	d		18 54		19 05	19 10				19 24		19 35	19 40				19 54		20 05	20 10				20 24		
Bookham	d		18 59							19 29							19 59							20 29		
Effingham Junction 6	d		19 03							19 33							20 03							20 33		
Guildford	a		19 20							19 50							20 20							20 50		
Boxhill & Westhumble	d					19 15							19 45													
Dorking 4	a				19 11	19 17						19 41	19 47						20 11	20 16						
	d																									
Holmwood	d																									
Ockley	d																									
Warnham	d																									
Horsham 4	a																									

Station		SN	SN	FC B	SN	SW	SN	SW	SN	SN	SW	FC B	SN	SN	SW	SN	SN	FC B	SN	SW	SN	SW	SN	SN	SW	FC B
London Victoria 15 ⊖	d	19 50			19 53		20 15		20 20				20 23	20 45		20 50			20 53		21 15		21 20			
London Waterloo 15 ⊖	d					20 09		20 24			20 39				20 54					21 09		21 24			21 39	
Clapham Junction 10	d	19 56			20 01	20 18	20 23	20 33	20 26		20 48		20 31	20 53	21 03	20 56			21 01	21 18	21 23	21 33	21 26		21 48	
Balham 4 ⊖	d	20 02			20 06		20 28		20 32				20 36	20 58		21 02			21 06		21 28		21 32			
London Bridge 4 ⊖	d																									
Tulse Hill 3	d																									
New Cross Gate 4 ⊖	d																									
Norwood Junction 2	d				20 24								20 54						21 24							
West Croydon 4 🚋	d		←		20 30		20 45			←			21 00	21 15			←		21 30		21 45			←		
Waddon	d		20 18		20 32		20 48			20 48			21 02	21 18			21 18		21 32		21 48			21 48		
Wallington	d		20 21		20 36		→			20 51			21 06	→			21 21		21 36		→			21 51		
Carshalton Beeches	d		20 24		20 38					20 54			21 08				21 24		21 38					21 54		
Mitcham Eastfields	d	20 09							20 39							21 09							21 39			
Mitcham Junction 🚋	d	20 12							20 42							21 12							21 42			
Hackbridge	d	20 16							20 46							21 16							21 46			
Carshalton	d	20 18							20 48							21 18							21 48			
Sutton (Surrey) 4	a	20 22	20 27		20 42				20 52	20 57			21 12			21 22	21 27		21 42				21 52	21 57		
	d	20 22	20 28	20 37					20 52	20 58		21 07				21 22	21 28	21 37					21 52	21 58		22 07
West Sutton	a			20 40								21 10						21 40								22 10
Wimbledon 6 ⊖ 🚋	a			20 55								21 25						21 55								22 25
Belmont	d		20 31														21 31									
Banstead	d		20 35														21 35									
Epsom Downs	a		20 38														21 38									
Cheam	d	20 25							20 55	21 00						21 25							21 55	22 00		
Ewell East	d	20 28							20 58	21 04						21 28							21 58	22 04		
Epsom 3	a	20 32				20 42		20 57	21 02	21 08	21 12				21 27	21 32				21 42		21 57	22 02	22 08	22 12	
	d	20 33				20 47			21 03		21 17					21 33				21 47			22 03		22 17	
Ashtead	d	20 37				20 51			21 07		21 21					21 37				21 51			22 07		22 21	
Leatherhead	d	20 40				20 54			21 10		21 24					21 40				21 54			22 10		22 24	
Bookham	d										21 29														22 29	
Effingham Junction 6	d										21 33														22 33	
Guildford	a										21 50														22 50	
Boxhill & Westhumble	d	20 45														21 45										
Dorking 4	a	20 47				21 00			21 16							21 47				22 00			22 16			
	d																									
Holmwood	d																									
Ockley	d																									
Warnham	d																									
Horsham 4	a																									

For general notes see front of timetable
For details of catering facilities see Directory of Train Operators

- **A** From Herne Hill (Table 52)
- **B** To London Bridge (Table 179)
- **b** Arr. 1852

From 3 October due to seasonal difficulties a large number of trains on this table will have minor retimings that could mean slightly earlier departure or later arrival times at certain stations. For further details see local publicity or contact National Rail Enquiries 08457 48 49 50.

Table 182

Saturdays

London → Sutton, Epsom, Guildford, Dorking and Horsham

Network Diagram - see first page of Table 177

		SN	SN	SW	SN	SN	SN	SW	SN	SN	SN	SN	SW	SN	SN	SN	SW	SN	SN	SN	SN	SW	SN	SN
London Victoria 15 ⊖	d	21 23	21 45		21 50		21 53		22 15	22 20		22 23		22 45	22 50			22 53	23 15	23 23	23 26			23 51
London Waterloo 15 ⊖	d			21 54				22 09					22 39				23 09					23 42		
Clapham Junction 10	d	21 31	21 53	22 03	21 56		22 01	22 18	22 23	22 26		22 31	22 48	22 53	22 56		23 18	23 01	23 23	23 31	23 33	23 51		23 59
Balham 4 ⊖	d	21 36	21 58		22 02		22 06		22 28	22 32		22 36		22 58	23 01			23 06	23 28	23 36	23 38			00 04
London Bridge 4 ⊖	d																							
Tulse Hill 3	d																							
New Cross Gate 4 ⊖	d																							
Norwood Junction 2	d	21 54					22 24					22 54						23 24		23 54				
West Croydon 4	d	22 00	22 15			←	22 30		22 45		←	23 00		23 15		←		23 30	23 45	00b01			←	00 21
Waddon	d	22 02	22 18			22 18	22 32		22 48		22 48	23 02		23 18		23 18		23 32	23 48	00 03			00 03	00 24
Wallington	d	22 06	→			22 21	22 36		→		22 51	23 06		→		23 21		23 36	23 51	→			00 07	00 27
Carshalton Beeches	d	22 08				22 24	22 38				22 54	23 08				23 24		23 38	23 54				00 09	00 30
Mitcham Eastfields	d				22 09					22 39					23 08						23 45			
Mitcham Junction	d				22 12					22 42					23 11						23 48			
Hackbridge	d				22 16					22 46					23 15						23 52			
Carshalton	d				22 18					22 48					23 17						23 54			
Sutton (Surrey) 4	a	22 12			22 22	22 27	22 42			22 52	22 57	23 12			23 21	23 27		23 42	23 57		23 58		00 13	00 33
	d				22 22	22 28				22 52	22 58				23 21	23 28		23 42			00 02			
West Sutton	a																							
Wimbledon 6 ⊖	a																							
Belmont	d					22 31										23 31								
Banstead	d					22 35										23 35								
Epsom Downs	a					22 38										23 38								
Cheam	d				22 25					22 55	23 00				23 24			23 45			00 04			
Ewell East	d				22 28					22 58	23 04				23 27			23 48			00 08			
Epsom 3	a			22 27	22 32			22 42		23 02	23 08		23 12		23 31		23 42	23 52			00 12	00 15		
	d				22 33			22 47		23 03			23 17		23 32		23 47				00 12	00 19		
Ashtead	d				22 37			22 51		23 07			23 21		23 36		23 51				00 16	00 23		
Leatherhead	d				22 40			22 54		23 10			23 24		23 39		23 54				00 19	00 26		
Bookham	d												23 29									00 31		
Effingham Junction 6	d												23 33									00 36		
Guildford	a												23 54									00 53		
Boxhill & Westhumble	d				22 45										23 44						00 24			
Dorking 4	a				22 47			23 00		23 16					23 46		00 01				00 27			
	d																							
Holmwood	d																							
Ockley	d																							
Warnham	d																							
Horsham 4	a																							

Sundays

		SN	SN	SW	SN		SN	SW	SN	SW A		SN	SN	SN	SW		SN	SN	SN	SW		SN	SN	SN	SW	SN
London Victoria 15 ⊖	d	23p23	23p26				23p51		06 49			07 19	07 38	07 49			08 06	08 08	08 19			08 36	08 38	08 49		09 06
London Waterloo 15 ⊖	d			23p42				00 15							08 02					08 32					09 02	
Clapham Junction 10	d	23p31	23p33	23p51			23p59	00 24	06 56			07 26	07 45	07 56	08 11		08 12	08 15	08 26	08 41		08 42	08 45	08 56	09 11	09 12
Balham 4 ⊖	d	23p36	23p38				00 04		07 02			07 32	07 51	08 02			08 16	08 21	08 32			08 46	08 51	09 02		09 16
London Bridge 4 ⊖	d																									
Tulse Hill 3	d																									
New Cross Gate 4 ⊖	d																									
Norwood Junction 2	d	23p54											08 07					08 37					09 07			
West Croydon 4	d	00b01			←		00 21		07 20			07 50	08 13	08 20				08 43	08 50				09 13	09 20		
Waddon	d	00 03			00 03		00 24		07 22			07 52		08 22					08 52					09 22		
Wallington	d	→			00 07		00 27		07 26			07 56	08 18	08 26				08 48	08 56				09 18	09 26		
Carshalton Beeches	d				00 09		00 30		07 28			07 58		08 28					08 58					09 28		
Mitcham Eastfields	d		23p45														08 23					08 53				09 23
Mitcham Junction	d		23p48														08 27					08 57				09 27
Hackbridge	d		23p52														08 30					09 00				09 30
Carshalton	d		23p54														08 33					09 03				09 33
Sutton (Surrey) 4	a		23p58		00 13		00 33		07 32			08 02	08 22	08 32			08 36	08 52	09 02			09 06	09 22	09 32		09 36
	d		00 02						07 37			08 07					08 37					09 07				09 37
West Sutton	a																									
Wimbledon 6 ⊖	a																									
Belmont	d																									
Banstead	d																									
Epsom Downs	a																									
Cheam	d		00 04						07 39			08 09					08 39					09 09				09 39
Ewell East	d		00 08						07 43			08 13					08 43					09 13				09 43
Epsom 3	a		00 12	00 15				00 48	07 47	08 06		08 17			08 36		08 47			09 06		09 17			09 36	09 47
	d		00 12	00 19					07 47	08 08		08 17			08 38		08 47			09 08		09 17			09 38	09 47
Ashtead	d		00 16	00 23					07 51	08 12		08 21			08 42		08 51			09 12		09 21			09 42	09 51
Leatherhead	d		00 19	00 26					07 54	08 15		08 24			08 45		08 54			09 15		09 24			09 45	09 54
Bookham	d			00 31						08 20										09 20						
Effingham Junction 6	d			00 36						08 24										09 24						
Guildford	a			00 53						08 41										09 41						
Boxhill & Westhumble	d		00 24						07 59			08 29					08 59					09 29				09 59
Dorking 4	a		00 27						08 02			08 32			08 51		09 02					09 32			09 51	10 02
	d																									
Holmwood	d																									
Ockley	d																									
Warnham	d																									
Horsham 4	a																									

For general notes see front of timetable
For details of catering facilities see Directory of Train Operators

A From Wimbledon (Table 152)
b Arr. 2358

From 3 October due to seasonal difficulties a large number of trains on this table will have minor retimings that could mean slightly earlier departure or later arrival times at certain stations. For further details see local publicity or contact National Rail Enquiries 08457 48 49 50.

From 27 September due to seasonal difficulties a large number of trains on this table will have minor retimings that could mean slightly earlier departure or later arrival times at certain stations. For further details see local publicity or contact National Rail Enquiries 08457 48 49 50.

London → Sutton, Epsom, Guildford, Dorking and Horsham

Sundays

Network Diagram - see first page of Table 177

	SN		SN	SW	SN		FC A	SN	SN	SW	SN	FC A	SN	SN	SW	SN			FC A	SN	SN	SW		SN
London Victoria 15 ⊖ d	09 08		09 19		09 36			09 38	09 49		10 06		10 08	10 19		10 36	and at the same minutes past each hour until			20 38	20 49			21 06
London Waterloo 15 ⊖ d				09 32						10 02					10 32							21 02		
Clapham Junction 10 d	09 15		09 26	09 41	09 42			09 45	09 56	10 11	10 12		10 15	10 26	10 41	10 42				20 45	20 56	21 11		21 12
Balham 4 ⊖ d	09 21		09 32		09 46			09 51	10 02		10 16		10 21	10 32		10 46				20 51	21 02			21 16
London Bridge 4 ⊖ d																								
Tulse Hill 3 d																								
New Cross Gate 4 ⊖ d																								
Norwood Junction 2 d	09 37							10 07					10 37							21 07				
West Croydon 4 d	09 43		09 50					10 13	10 20				10 43	10 50						21 13	21 20			
Waddon d			09 52						10 22					10 52							21 22			
Wallington d	09 48		09 56					10 18	10 26				10 48	10 56						21 18	21 26			
Carshalton Beeches d			09 58						10 28					10 58							21 28			
Mitcham Eastfields d					09 53						10 23					10 53								21 23
Mitcham Junction d					09 57						10 27					10 57								21 27
Hackbridge d					10 00						10 30					11 00								21 30
Carshalton d					10 03						10 33					11 03								21 33
Sutton (Surrey) 4 a	09 52		10 02		10 06			10 22	10 32		10 36		10 52	11 02		11 06				21 22	21 32			21 36
d					10 07		10 15				10 37	10 45				11 07			21 15					21 37
West Sutton a							10 18					10 48							21 18					
Wimbledon 6 ⊖ a							10 32					11 02							21 32					
Belmont d																								
Banstead d																								
Epsom Downs a																								
Cheam d					10 09						10 39					11 09								21 39
Ewell East d					10 13						10 43					11 13								21 43
Epsom 3 a				10 06	10 17					10 36	10 47				11 06	11 17						21 36		21 47
d				10 08	10 17					10 38	10 47				11 08	11 17						21 38		21 47
Ashtead d				10 12	10 21					10 42	10 51				11 12	11 21						21 42		21 51
Leatherhead d				10 15	10 24					10 45	10 54				11 15	11 24						21 45		21 54
Bookham d				10 20											11 20									
Effingham Junction 6 d				10 24											11 24									
Guildford a				10 41											11 41									
Boxhill & Westhumble d					10 29						10 59					11 29								21 59
Dorking 4 a					10 32					10 51	11 02					11 32						21 51		22 02
d																								
Holmwood d																								
Ockley d																								
Warnham d																								
Horsham 4 a																								

	SN	SN	SW	SN		SN	SN	SW	SN		SN	SN	SW	SN		SN	SN	SW	SN		SW	SN			
London Victoria 15 ⊖ d	21 08	21 19		21 36		21 38	21 49		22 06		22 08	22 19		22 36		22 38	22 49		23 06			23 19			
London Waterloo 15 ⊖ d			21 32					22 02					22 32					23 02			23 32				
Clapham Junction 10 d	21 15	21 26	21 41	21 42		21 45	21 56	22 11	22 12		22 15	22 26	22 41	22 42		22 45	22 56	23 11	23 12		23 41	23 26			
Balham 4 ⊖ d	21 21	21 32		21 46		21 51	22 02		22 16		22 21	22 32		22 46		22 51	23 02		23 16			23 32			
London Bridge 4 ⊖ d																									
Tulse Hill 3 d																									
New Cross Gate 4 ⊖ d																									
Norwood Junction 2 d	21 37					22 07					22 39					23 07									
West Croydon 4 d	21 43	21 50				22 13	22 20				22 43	22 50				23 13	23 20					23 50			
Waddon d		21 52					22 22					22 52					23 22					23 52			
Wallington d	21 48	21 56				22 18	22 26				22 48	22 56				23 18	23 26					23 56			
Carshalton Beeches d		21 58					22 28					22 58					23 28					23 58			
Mitcham Eastfields d				21 53					22 23					22 53					23 23						
Mitcham Junction d				21 57					22 27					22 57					23 27						
Hackbridge d				22 00					22 30					23 00					23 30						
Carshalton d				22 03					22 33					23 03					23 33						
Sutton (Surrey) 4 a	21 52	22 02		22 06		22 22	22 32		22 36		22 53	23 02		23 06		23 22	23 32		23 36			00 02			
d				22 07					22 37					23 07					23 37			00 04			
West Sutton a																									
Wimbledon 6 ⊖ a																									
Belmont d																									
Banstead d																									
Epsom Downs a																									
Cheam d				22 09					22 39					23 09					23 39			00 06			
Ewell East d				22 13					22 43					23 13					23 43			00 10			
Epsom 3 a			22 06	22 17				22 36	22 47				23 06	23 17				23 36	23 47		00 06	00 14			
d			22 08	22 17				22 38	22 47				23 08	23 17					23 47						
Ashtead d			22 12	22 21				22 42	22 51				23 12	23 21					23 51						
Leatherhead d			22 15	22 24				22 45	22 54				23 15	23 24					23 54						
Bookham d			22 20										23 20												
Effingham Junction 6 d			22 24										23 24												
Guildford a			22 41										23 41												
Boxhill & Westhumble d				22 29					22 59					23 29					23 59						
Dorking 4 a				22 32				22 51	23 02					23 32					00 02						
d																									
Holmwood d																									
Ockley d																									
Warnham d																									
Horsham 4 a																									

For general notes see front of timetable
For details of catering facilities see
Directory of Train Operators

A To London Bridge (Table 179)

From 27 September due to seasonal difficulties a large number of trains on this table will have minor retimings that could mean slightly earlier departure or later arrival times at certain stations. For further details see local publicity or contact National Rail Enquiries 08457 48 49 50.

Horsham, Dorking, Guildford, Epsom and Sutton → London

Network Diagram - see first page of Table 177

Miles	Miles	Miles			SN MX	FC MX A	FC MX A	SN	SN	SW	SN	SN	SN	SN	SW	SN	SW	SN	SN	SN	SN	SW	SW	SN	SN
—	—	0	**Horsham 4**	d															05 49						06 20
—	—	2	Warnham	d															05 53						06 24
—	—	6½	Ockley	d															06 00						06 31
—	—	8¾	Holmwood	d															06 04						06 35
—	—	13¾	**Dorking 4**	a															06 10						06 41
—	—	—		d											05 48				06 11				06 32		06 44
—	—	14½	Boxhill & Westhumble	d											05 50				06 13				06 34		06 46
0	—	—	**Guildford**	d						04 58												05 58			
8¼	—	—	Effingham Junction 6	d						05 16												06 16			
10	—	—	Bookham	d						05 19												06 19			
12½	—	17¾	Leatherhead	d						05 24					05 56				06 18			06 24	06 39		06 51
14½	—	—	Ashtead	d						05 28					05 59				06 22			06 28	06 43		06 55
16¼	—	—	**Epsom 3**	a						05 32					06 04				06 26			06 32	06 47		06 59
—	—	—		d				05 23		05 34	05 39		05 57		06 04		06 18		06 27			06 33	06 48	06 54	07 00
17¾	—	—	Ewell East	d				05 27			05 43		06 01						06 31					06 58	07 04
19¼	—	—	Cheam	d				05 30			05 46		06 04						06 34					07 01	07 07
—	0	—	**Epsom Downs**	d	23p44															06 37					
—	1½	—	Banstead	d	23p47															06 40					
—	3	—	Belmont	d	23p50															06 43					
—	—	0	Wimbledon 6 ⊖	d		23p54	00 25							05 56							06 33				
—	—	4½	West Sutton	d		00 08	00 39							06 10							06 47				
20¼	4	5½	**Sutton (Surrey) 4**	a	23p53	00 12	00 43	05 33			05 49		06 07	06 13					06 37	06 46	06 50			07 04	07 10
—	—	—		d	23p54			05 33	05 37		05 49	06 03	06 07	06 14		06 17		06 33	06 37	06 47	06 51			07 04	07 10
—	5¼	—	Carshalton	d					05 40				06 10	06 17					06 40		06 54				07 13
—	6¼	—	Hackbridge	d					05 42				06 13	06 19					06 43		06 56				07 16
—	7	—	Mitcham Junction	d					05 46				06 16	06 23					06 46		07 00				07 19
—	8	—	Mitcham Eastfields	d					05 49				06 20	06 26					06 50						07 23
21¼	—	—	Carshalton Beeches	d	23p57			05 36			05 52	06 06				06 20		06 36		06 50				07 07	
22	—	—	Wallington	d	23p59			05 39			05 55	06 08				06 22		06 38		06 53				07 10	
23½	—	—	Waddon	d	00 02			05 42			05 58	06 11				06 25		06 41		06 56				07 13	
24½	—	0	**West Croydon 4**	d	00a05			05 45			06 01	06 15				06 29		06 45		06 59				07 16	
26½	—	—	Norwood Junction 2	d				05 50				06 19						06 50						07 21	
32¼	—	—	New Cross Gate 4 ⊖	d				06 08				06 37						07 07						07 39	
—	—	6	Tulse Hill 3	d					05 57					06 34							07 09				
35	—	12	**London Bridge 4** ⊖	a				06 14	06 08			06 44		06 51				07 16			07 25			07 48	
—	11¼	—	Balham 4 ⊖	d							06 17		06 27			06 45			06 57	07 15					07 29
—	13¼	—	Clapham Junction 10	a						06 00	06 23		06 31		06 30	06 50	06 45		07 01	07 21		07 00	07 15		07 33
—	—	—	**London Waterloo 15** ⊖	a						06 11					06 40		06 55					07 12	07 27		
—	16	—	**London Victoria 15** ⊖	a							06 31		06 38			07 01			07 10	07 31					07 43

		SN	SW	SN	SN	SW	SN	SW	SN	SN	SN	SW	SN	SN	SW	SW	SN	SN	SW	SN	SN	SN	SW
Horsham 4	d								06 50											07 28			
Warnham	d								06 54											07 32			
Ockley	d								07 01											07 39			
Holmwood	d								07 05											07 43			
Dorking 4	a								07 11											07 49			
	d			06 52		07 02			07 16						07 32					07 50			08 02
Boxhill & Westhumble	d			06 57		07 04									07 34								08 04
Guildford	d		06 28									06 58					07 26						
Effingham Junction 6	d		06b48									07 16					07 38		07 46				
Bookham	d		06 51									07 19					07 41		07 49				
Leatherhead	d		06 56	07 02		07 09			07 22			07 25			07 39		07 46		07 54	07 56			08 09
Ashtead	d		06 59	07 06		07 13			07 25			07 28			07 43		07 50		07 57	08 00			08 13
Epsom 3	a		07 04	07 10		07 17			07 30			07 33			07 47		07 54		08 02	08 04			08 17
	d		07 04	07 11		07 18	07 21	07 22	07 33			07 34	07 44		07 48	07 52	07 55		08 04	08 05			08 18
Ewell East	d			07 15			07 25						07 48				07 59			08 09			
Cheam	d			07 18			07 28		07 38				07 51				08 02			08 12			
Epsom Downs	d	07 08								07 34								08 00					
Banstead	d	07 11								07 37								08 03					
Belmont	d	07 14								07 40								08 06					
Wimbledon 6 ⊖	d				07 02						07 32										08 02		
West Sutton	d				07 21						07 46										08 16		
Sutton (Surrey) 4	a	07 17		07 21	07 25		07 31		07 41	07 43	07 49		07 54				08 05	08 09		08 15	08 19		
	d	07 18		07 21	07 25		07 31		07 42	07 48	07 50		07 54	07 55			08 05	08 10		08 15	08 20	08 25	
Carshalton	d			07 24	07 28				07 45		07 53		07 57							08 18		08 28	
Hackbridge	d			07 27	07 31						07 55		08 00							08 21		08 30	
Mitcham Junction	d			07 30	07 34				07 49		07 59		08 03							08 24		08 34	
Mitcham Eastfields	d			07 34	07 38				07 53				08 07									08 37	
Carshalton Beeches	d	07 21					07 34			07 51				07 58			08 08	08 13			08 23		
Wallington	d	07 23					07 37			07 53				08 00			08 11	08 15			08 25		
Waddon	d	07 26					07 40			07 56				08 03				08 18			08 28		
West Croydon 4	d	07 30					07 43			08 01				08 07			08 16	08 23			08 32		
Norwood Junction 2	d						07 48										08 20	08 28					
New Cross Gate 4 ⊖	d						08 00																
Tulse Hill 3	d				07 46						08 09												
London Bridge 4 ⊖	a				08 02		08 08				08 30						08 42	08 48					
Balham 4 ⊖	d	07 46		07 42					08 00	08 17			08 14	08 23							08 47	08 44	
Clapham Junction 10	a	07 52	07 30	07 48		07 42		07 48	08 04	08 22		08 01	08 18	08 27	08 12	08 18			08 31	08 36	08 53	08 49	08 42
London Waterloo 15 ⊖	a		07 42			07 54		08 00				08 13			08 24	08 30			08 43				08 54
London Victoria 15 ⊖	a	08 02		07 58					08 13	08 33			08 29	08 37						08 46	09 03	09 01	

For general notes see front of timetable
For details of catering facilities see
Directory of Train Operators

A From London Bridge (Table 52)
b Arr. 0644

From 28 September due to seasonal difficulties a large number of trains on this table will have minor retimings that could mean slightly earlier departure or later arrival times at certain stations. For further details see local publicity or contact National Rail Enquiries 08457 48 49 50.

Table 182

Horsham, Dorking, Guildford, Epsom and Sutton → London

Mondays to Fridays

Network Diagram - see first page of Table 177

		SN	SW	SN	SN	SW	SN	SN	SW	SN	SN		SN	SN	SW	SN	SW	SN	SN	FC A	SN	SW		SN	SN	SN
Horsham 4	d				07 53																					09 09
Warnham	d				07 57																					09 13
Ockley	d				08 04																					09 20
Holmwood	d				08 08																					09 24
Dorking 4	a				08 14																					09 30
	d				08 15				08 31							08 57	09 02									09 31
Boxhill & Westhumble	d				08 17				08 33							08 59	09 04									09 33
Guildford	d					07 58				08 16												08 58				
Effingham Junction 6	d					08 15				08 32					08 48							09 16				
Bookham	d					08 18				08 35					08 51							09 19				
Leatherhead	d				08 22	08 25			08 38	08 41					08 56	09 04	09 09					09 24				09 38
Ashtead	d				08 26	08 28			08 42	08 45					08 59	09 08	09 13					09 28				09 42
Epsom 3	a				08 30	08 33			08 46	08 49					09 04	09 12	09 17					09 32				09 46
	d	08 22	08 22		08 33	08 34			08 48	08 50					09 04	09 13	09 18		09 23			09 35		09 42		09 47
Ewell East	d	08 26			08 37					08 54						09 17			09 27					09 46		09 51
Cheam	d	08 29			08 40					08 57						09 20			09 30					09 49		09 54
Epsom Downs	d			08 32										09 09							09 34					
Banstead	d			08 35										09 12							09 37					
Belmont	d			08 38										09 15							09 40					
Wimbledon 6 ⊖	d							08 33					08 55							09 17						
West Sutton	d							08 47					09 09							09 31						
Sutton (Surrey) 4	a	08 32		08 41	08 43		←	08 50		09 00			09 13	09 18		09 23			09 33	09 37	09 43			09 52		09 57
	d	08 32		08 45 →	08 44		08 45	08 51		09 02	09 06		09 15	09 23		09 23		09 32	09 34	09 38	09 44			09 52	09 53	09 57
Carshalton	d				08 47			08 54			09 09							09 35		09 41						10 00
Hackbridge	d				08 50			08 56			09 11							09 37		09 43						10 03
Mitcham Junction	d				08 53			09 00			09 15							09 41		09 46						10 06
Mitcham Eastfields	d				08 57			09 03								09 32				09 50						10 10
Carshalton Beeches	d	08 35					08 48			09 05			09 18	09 26					09 37		09 47				09 56	
Wallington	d	08 38					08 50			09 07			09 20	09 28					09 39		09 50				09 58	
Waddon	d	08 41					08 53			09 10			09 23	09 31					09 42		09 53				10 01	
West Croydon 4	d	08 44					08 57			09 15			09 27	09 35					09 46		09 56				10 05	
Norwood Junction 2	d	08 49								09 20									09 51							
New Cross Gate 4 ⊖	d	09 07								09 37									10 08							
Tulse Hill 3	d							09 15												09a57						
London Bridge 4 ⊖	a	09 18						09 34		09 46									10 16							
Balham 4 ⊖	d				09 04		09 13				09 23		09 43	09 52				09 49			10 12				10 21	10 18
Clapham Junction 10	a		08 48		09 08	09 00	09 19		09 15		09 27		09 49	09 57	09 30	09 42	09 45	09 53			10 18	10 00		10 10	10 26	10 22
London Waterloo 15 ⊖	a		09 00			09 12			09 27						09 42		09 57					10 10				
London Victoria 15 ⊖	a				09 18		09 30				09 37		10 00	10 05		09 54		10 01			10 26			10 20	10 34	10 29

		SW	SN	FC A	SN	SW	SN	SN	SN	SW		SN	FC A	SN	SW	SN	SN	SN	SW	SN	FC A			SN	SW	SN
Horsham 4	d															10 04										
Warnham	d															10 08										
Ockley	d															10 15										
Holmwood	d															10 19										
Dorking 4	a															10 25										
	d	09 35					09 56			10 05						10 26			10 35							10 58
Boxhill & Westhumble	d						09 58									10 28										
Guildford	d					09 28									09 58										10 28	
Effingham Junction 6	d					09 46									10 16										10 46	
Bookham	d					09 49									10 19										10 49	
Leatherhead	d	09 41				09 54	10 03			10 11					10 24	10 33			10 41						10 54	11 04
Ashtead	d	09 45				09 58	10 07			10 14					10 28	10 37			10 44						10 58	11 07
Epsom 3	a	09 49				10 02	10 11			10 19					10 32	10 41			10 49						11 02	11 12
	d	09 50			10 04	10 05	10 12		10 17	10 20					10 35	10 42		10 47	10 50					11 04	11 05	11 12
Ewell East	d				10 08		10 16		10 21							10 46		10 51						11 08		
Cheam	d				10 11		10 19		10 24							10 49		10 54						11 11		11 18
Epsom Downs	d													10 34												
Banstead	d													10 37												
Belmont	d													10 40												
Wimbledon 6 ⊖	d			09 47									10 17								10 47					
West Sutton	d			10 01									10 31								11 01					
Sutton (Surrey) 4	a			10 05	10 14		10 22		10 27				10 35	10 43		10 52		10 57			11 05			11 14		11 22
	d		10 03	10 06	10 14		10 22	10 23	10 27			10 33	10 36	10 44		10 52	10 53	10 57		11 03	11 06			11 14		11 22
Carshalton	d			10 09					10 30				10 39					11 00			11 09					
Hackbridge	d			10 11					10 33				10 41					11 03			11 11					
Mitcham Junction	d			10 14					10 36				10 44					11 06			11 14					
Mitcham Eastfields	d			10 18					10 40				10 48					11 10			11 18					
Carshalton Beeches	d		10 06		10 17			10 26				10 36		10 47			10 56			11 06				11 17		
Wallington	d		10 08		10 20			10 28				10 38		10 50			10 58			11 08				11 20		
Waddon	d		10 11		10 23			10 31				10 41		10 53			11 01			11 11				11 23		
West Croydon 4	d		10 15		10 26			10 35				10 45		10 56			11 05			11 15				11 26		
Norwood Junction 2	d		10 20									10 50								11 20						
New Cross Gate 4 ⊖	d		10 37									11 07								11 37						
Tulse Hill 3	d			10a27									10a57								11a27					
London Bridge 4 ⊖	a		10 44									11 14								11 44						
Balham 4 ⊖	d				10 42			10 51	10 48					11 12			11 21	11 18						11 42		
Clapham Junction 10	a	10 15			10 48	10 30	10 40	10 56	10 52	10 45				11 18	11 00	11 10	11 26	11 22	11 15					11 48	11 30	11 40
London Waterloo 15 ⊖	a	10 25				10 40				10 55					11 10				11 25						11 40	
London Victoria 15 ⊖	a				10 56		10 48	11 04	10 59					11 26		11 18	11 34	11 29						11 56		11 48

For general notes see front of timetable
For details of catering facilities see Directory of Train Operators

A To St Albans City (Table 52)

From 28 September due to seasonal difficulties a large number of trains on this table will have minor retimings that could mean slightly earlier departure or later arrival times at certain stations. For further details see local publicity or contact National Rail Enquiries 08457 48 49 50.

Horsham, Dorking, Guildford, Epsom and Sutton → London

Network Diagram - see first page of Table 177

		SN	SN	SW	SN	FC A	SN	SW	SN	SN	SN	SW	SN	FC A		SN	SW	SN	SN	SN	SN	SW	SW	FC B
Horsham 4	d								11 04						and at									
Warnham	d								11 08						the same									
Ockley	d								11 15						minutes									
Holmwood	d								11 19						past									
Dorking 4	a								11 25						each									
	d			11 05					11 26			11 35			hour until			15 56				16 05		
Boxhill & Westhumble	d								11 28									15 58						
Guildford	d							10 58									15 28						15 58	
Effingham Junction 6	d							11 16									15 46						16 16	
Bookham	d							11 19									15 49						16 19	
Leatherhead	d			11 11				11 24	11 33			11 41					15 54	16 03				16 11	16 24	
Ashtead	d			11 14				11 28	11 37			11 44					15 58	16 07				16 14	16 28	
Epsom 3	a			11 19				11 32	11 41			11 49					16 02	16 11				16 19	16 32	
	d		11 17	11 20				11 35	11 42		11 47	11 50				16 04	16 05	16 12		16 17		16 20	16 35	
Ewell East	d		11 21						11 46		11 51					16 08		16 16		16 21				
Cheam	d		11 24						11 49		11 54					16 11		16 19		16 24				
Epsom Downs	d						11 34																	
Banstead	d						11 37																	
Belmont	d						11 40																	
Wimbledon 6	⊖ d					11 17								11 47										16 17
West Sutton	d					11 31								12 01										16 31
Sutton (Surrey) 4	a		11 28			11 35	11 43		11 52		11 57			12 05		16 14		16 22		16 27				16 36
	d	11 23	11 28		11 33	11 36	11 44		11 52	11 53	11 57		12 03	12 06		16 14		16 22	16 23	16 27	16 33			16 36
Carshalton	d		11 31			11 39					12 00			12 09						16 30				16 39
Hackbridge	d		11 34			11 41					12 03			12 11						16 33				16 41
Mitcham Junction	d		11 37			11 44					12 06			12 14						16 36				16 44
Mitcham Eastfields	d		11 41			11 48					12 10			12 18						16 40				16 48
Carshalton Beeches	d	11 26			11 36		11 47			11 56			12 06			16 17			16 26		16 36			
Wallington	d	11 28			11 38		11 50			11 58			12 08			16 20			16 28		16 38			
Waddon	d	11 31			11 41		11 53			12 01			12 11			16 23			16 31		16 41			
West Croydon 4	d	11 35			11 45		11 56			12 05			12 15			16 26			16 35		16 45			
Norwood Junction 2	d				11 50								12 20								16 50			
New Cross Gate 4	⊖ d				12 07								12 37								17 07			
Tulse Hill 3	d					11a57								12a27										16a57
London Bridge 4	⊖ a				12 14								12 44								17 14			
Balham 4	⊖ d	11 51	11 48				12 12			12 21	12 18					16 42			16 51	16 48				
Clapham Junction 10	a	11 56	11 52	11 45			12 18	12 01	12 10	12 26	12 22	12 15				16 48	16 30	16 40	16 56	16 52		16 45	17 00	
London Waterloo 15	⊖ a			11 55				12 11				12 25					16 40					16 55	17 10	
London Victoria 15	⊖ a	12 04	11 59				12 26		12 18	12 34	12 29					16 57		16 48	17 04	16 59				

		SN	SN	SN	SN	SW	SN	SW	FC A	SN	SN	SW	SN	FC A	SN	SW	SN	SW	SW	SN	FC A	SN	SN	SN
Horsham 4	d		16 04														17 04							17 34
Warnham	d		16 08														17 08							17 38
Ockley	d		16 15														17 15							17 45
Holmwood	d		16 19														17 19							17 49
Dorking 4	a		16 25														17 25							17 55
	d		16 26			16 35					17 00	17 05					17 28	17 35						17 58
Boxhill & Westhumble	d		16 28								17 02						17 30							18 00
Guildford	d							16 28								16 58			17 28				17 42	
Effingham Junction 6	d							16 46								17 16			17 46				17 55	
Bookham	d							16 49								17 19			17 49					
Leatherhead	d		16 33			16 41		16 54			17 07	17 11				17 24	17 35	17 41	17 54				18 02	18 06
Ashtead	d		16 37			16 44		16 58			17 11	17 14				17 28	17 39	17 44	17 58				18 06	18 10
Epsom 3	a		16 41			16 49		17 02			17 15	17 19				17 32	17 44	17 49	18 02				18 10	18 14
	d		16 42		16 47	16 50	16 53	17 05			17 17	17 20	17 25			17 35	17 47	17 50	18 05				18 11	18 17
Ewell East	d		16 46		16 51						17 21		17 29				17 51						18 15	18 21
Cheam	d		16 49		16 54		16 58				17 24		17 32				17 54						18 18	18 24
Epsom Downs	d	16 26								17 02					17 34							18 02		
Banstead	d	16 29								17 05					17 37							18 05		
Belmont	d	16 32								17 08					17 40							18 08		
Wimbledon 6	⊖ d								16 47					17 19							17 47			
West Sutton	d								17 01					17 33							18 01			
Sutton (Surrey) 4	a	16 35	16 52		16 57		17 01		17 06	17 11	17 27		17 35	17 39	17 43		17 57				18 05	18 11	18 21	18 27
	d	16 44	16 52	16 53	16 57		17 02		17 06	17 14	17 27		17 35	17 40	17 44		17 57			18 03	18 06	18 12	18 23	18 27
Carshalton	d				17 00				17 09		17 30			17 43			18 00				18 09			18 30
Hackbridge	d				17 03				17 11		17 33			17 45			18 03				18 11			18 33
Mitcham Junction	d				17 06				17 14		17 36			17 48			18 06				18 14			18 36
Mitcham Eastfields	d				17 10				17 18		17 40			17 52			18 10				18 18			18 40
Carshalton Beeches	d	16 47		16 56			17 05			17 17			17 38		17 47					18 06		18 15	18 26	
Wallington	d	16 50		16 58			17 07			17 20			17 41		17 50					18 08		18 17	18 28	
Waddon	d	16 53		17 01			17 10			17 23			17 44		17 53					18 11		18 20	18 31	
West Croydon 4	d	16 56		17 05			17 14			17 26			17 47		17 56					18 15		18 24	18 36	
Norwood Junction 2	d						17 19						17 52							18 20				
New Cross Gate 4	⊖ d						17 36						18 10							18 37				
Tulse Hill 3	d								17a27					18a01							18a27			
London Bridge 4	⊖ a						17 44						18 20							18 45				
Balham 4	⊖ d	17 12		17 21	17 18					17 42	17 47				18 13		18 18					18 37	18 51	18 48
Clapham Junction 10	a	17 18	17 10	17 26	17 22	17 15		17 30		17 48	17 51	17 45			18 19	18 00	18 22	18 15	18 30			18 42	18 57	18 52
London Waterloo 15	⊖ a					17 25		17 40				17 55				18 10		18 25	18 40					
London Victoria 15	⊖ a	17 26	17 18	17 34	17 30					17 57	17 59				18 28		18 31					18 49	19 04	19 01

For general notes see front of timetable
For details of catering facilities see Directory of Train Operators

A To St Albans City (Table 52)
B To Bedford (Table 52)

From 28 September due to seasonal difficulties a large number of trains on this table will have minor retimings that could mean slightly earlier departure or later arrival times at certain stations. For further details see local publicity or contact National Rail Enquiries 08457 48 49 50.

Horsham, Dorking, Guildford, Epsom and Sutton → London

Network Diagram - see first page of Table 177

Station		SW	FC A		SN	SN	SW	SN	SW	FC A	SN	SN	SW	SN		SW	SN	FC [1] B	SN	SW	SN	SW	SN	FC [1] B	SW	SN
Horsham [4]	d							18 04						18 34							19 04					
Warnham	d							18 08						18 38							19 08					
Ockley	d							18 15						18 45							19 15					
Holmwood	d							18 19						18 49							19 19					
Dorking [4]	a							18 25						18 55							19 25					
	d	18 05						18 28	18 35				18 50	18 58							19 28	19 33				
Boxhill & Westhumble	d							18 30						19 00							19 30					
Guildford	d						17 58				18 22						18 52								19 28	
Effingham Junction [6]	d						18 16				18 39					18 59	19 08								19 46	
Bookham	d						18 19				18 42					19 02	19 11								19 49	
Leatherhead	d	18 11					18 24	18 35	18 41		18 47		18 56	19 05		19 08	19 16				19 35	19 39			19 54	
Ashtead	d	18 14					18 28	18 39	18 44		18 50		18 59	19 09		19 12	19 20				19 39	19 42			19 58	
Epsom [3]	a	18 19					18 32	18 45	18 50		18 58		19 04	19 14		19 16	19 24				19 44	19 47			20 02	
	d	18 20			18 27		18 35	18 47	18 50		18 58		19 05	19 15		19 20	19 25			19 35	19 45	19 50	19 52		20 05	
Ewell East	d							18 51			19 02			19 19			19 29				19 49		19 56			
Cheam	d				18 32			18 54			19 05			19 22			19 32				19 52		19 59			
Epsom Downs	d					18 35						19 06							19 39							
Banstead	d					18 38						19 09							19 42							
Belmont	d					18 41						19 12							19 45							
Wimbledon [6] ⊖ (tram)	d		18 13							18 47								19 19						19 49		
West Sutton	d		18 27							19 01								19 33						20 03		
Sutton (Surrey) [4]	a		18 31		18 35	18 44		18 57		19 05	19 09	19 15		19 25			19 35	19 39	19 48		19 55		20 02	20 09		
	d		18 32		18 36	18 49		18 57		19 06	19 10	19 16		19 25			19 37	19 40	19 49		19 55		20 03	20 10		20 19
Carshalton	d		18 35					19 00		19 09				19 28				19 43			19 58			20 13		
Hackbridge	d		18 37					19 03		19 11				19 31				19 45			20 01			20 15		
Mitcham Junction (tram)	d		18 40					19 06		19 14				19 34				19 48			20 04			20 18		
Mitcham Eastfields	d		18 44					19 10		19 18				19 38				19 52			20 08			20 22		
Carshalton Beeches	d				18 39	18 52					19 13	19 19					19 40		19 52				20 06			20 22
Wallington	d				18 41	18 54					19 15	19 21					19 42		19 54				20 08			20 24
Waddon	d				18 44	18 57					19 18	19 24					19 45		19 57				20 11			20 27
West Croydon [4] (tram)	d				18 48	19 01					19 22	19 28					19 49		20 01				20b18			20 31
Norwood Junction [2]	d				18 53						19 27						19 55						20 23			
New Cross Gate [4] ⊖	d				19 11						19 42						20 12									
Tulse Hill [3]	d		18a53							19a27								19a59						20a29		
London Bridge [4] ⊖	a				19 18						19 49						20 20									
Balham [4] ⊖	d					19 19		19 17				19 47		19 44					20 17		20 14		20 39			20 48
Clapham Junction [10]	a	18 45				19 25	19 00	19 21	19 16			19 52	19 30	19 48		19 45			20 23	20 00	20 18	20 15	20 44		20 30	20 53
London Waterloo [15] ⊖	a	18 55					19 10		19 27				19 41			19 55				20 10		20 25			20 41	
London Victoria [15] ⊖	a					19 33		19 30				20 03		19 56					20 33		20 28		20 53			21 03

Station		SN		SN	SN	SW	SN	FC [1] B	SW	SN	SN	SN	SW		FC [1] B	SW	SN	SN	SW	SN	FC C	SW	SN	SN		SN
Horsham [4]	d										20 06															
Warnham	d										20 10															
Ockley	d										20 17															
Holmwood	d										20 21															
Dorking [4]	a										20 27															
	d			19 59		20 05					20 30		20 35					20 59						21 30		
Boxhill & Westhumble	d			20 01														21 01								
Guildford	d								19 58										20 46							
Effingham Junction [6]	d								20 16										21 03							
Bookham	d								20 19										21 06							
Leatherhead	d			20 06		20 11			20 24		20 36		20 41					21 06	21 11					21 36		
Ashtead	d			20 10		20 14			20 28		20 39		20 44					21 10	21 14					21 40		
Epsom [3]	a			20 14		20 19			20 32		20 44		20 49					21 14	21 19					21 44		
	d			20 15		20 20	20 22		20 35		20 45		20 50			21 05		21 15	21 20	21 25		21 35		21 45		
Ewell East	d			20 19			20 26				20 49							21 19		21 29				21 49		
Cheam	d			20 22			20 29				20 52							21 22		21 32				21 52		
Epsom Downs	d	20 15										20 54														21 54
Banstead	d	20 18										20 57														21 57
Belmont	d	20 21										21 00														22 00
Wimbledon [6] ⊖ (tram)	d							20 17							20 47						21 17					
West Sutton	d							20 31							21 01						21 31					
Sutton (Surrey) [4]	a	20 24		20 25	←		20 32	20 35			20 55	21 03			21 05			21 25		21 35	21 39			21 55		22 03
	d	20 28		20 25	20 28		20 33	20 40		20 49	20 55	21 06			21 10		21 19	21 25		21 36			21 49	21 55		22 06
Carshalton	d	→		20 28				20 43			20 58				21 13			21 28						21 58		
Hackbridge	d			20 31				20 45			21 01				21 15			21 31						22 01		
Mitcham Junction (tram)	d			20 34				20 48			21 04				21 18			21 34						22 04		
Mitcham Eastfields	d			20 38				20 52			21 08				21 22			21 38						22 08		
Carshalton Beeches	d				20 31		20 36			20 52		21 09					21 22			21 39			21 52			22 09
Wallington	d				20 33		20 38			20 54		21 11					21 24			21 41			21 54			22 11
Waddon	d				20 36		20 41			20 57		21 14					21 27			21 44			21 57			22 14
West Croydon [4] (tram)	d				20a39		20c48			21 01		21 18					21 31			21 48			22 01			22 18
Norwood Junction [2]	d						20 53					21 23								21 53						22 23
New Cross Gate [4] ⊖	d																									
Tulse Hill [3]	d							20a59							21a29											
London Bridge [4] ⊖	a																									
Balham [4] ⊖	d			20 44			21 09			21 18	21 14	21 39					21 48	21 44		22 09			22 18	22 14		22 39
Clapham Junction [10]	a			20 48		20 45	21 14		21 00	21 23	21 18	21 44	21 15			21 30	21 53	21 48	21 45	22 14		22 00	22 23	22 18		22 44
London Waterloo [15] ⊖	a					20 55			21 10				21 25			21 40			21 55			22 10				
London Victoria [15] ⊖	a			20 56			21 23			21 33	21 26	21 53					22 03	21 56		22 23			22 33	22 27		22 53

For general notes see front of timetable
For details of catering facilities see Directory of Train Operators

A To Bedford (Table 52)
B To St Albans City (Table 52)
C From Luton (Table 52)
b Arr. 2014
c Arr. 2044

From 28 September due to seasonal difficulties a large number of trains on this table will have minor retimings that could mean slightly earlier departure or later arrival times at certain stations. For further details see local publicity or contact National Rail Enquiries 08457 48 49 50.

Horsham, Dorking, Guildford, Epsom and Sutton → London

Network Diagram - see first page of Table 177

Mondays to Fridays

Station		SW	FC A	SN	SN	SW	SN	FC A	SN	SN	SN		FC A	SW	SN	SN	SW	SN	FC B	SN	SN	FC B
Horsham 4	d																					
Warnham	d																					
Ockley	d																					
Holmwood	d																					
Dorking 4	a																					
	d	21 35			21 59					22 30				22 35		23 00					23 30	
Boxhill & Westhumble	d				22 01											23 02						
Guildford	d					21 46											22 46					
Effingham Junction 6	d					22 03											23 03					
Bookham	d					22 06											23 06					
Leatherhead	d	21 41			22 06	22 11				22 36				22 41		23 07	23 11				23 36	
Ashtead	d	21 44			22 10	22 14				22 40				22 44		23 11	23 14				23 39	
Epsom 3	a	21 49			22 14	22 19				22 44				22 49		23 15	23 19				23 45	
	d	21 50			22 15	22 20	22 25			22 45				22 50		23 16	23 20	23 25				
Ewell East	d				22 19		22 29			22 49						23 20		23 29				
Cheam	d				22 22		22 32			22 52						23 23		23 32				
Epsom Downs	d										22 54									23 44		
Banstead	d										22 57									23 47		
Belmont	d										23 00									23 50		
Wimbledon 6 ⊖	d		21 47					22 17					22 47						23 25			23 54
West Sutton	d		22 01					22 31					23 01						23 39			00 08
Sutton (Surrey) 4	a		22 07		22 25		22 35	22 40		22 55	23 03		23 05			23 26		23 35	23 43	23 53		00 12
	d			22 19	22 25		22 36		22 49	22 55	23 06				23 19	23 27		23 40		23 54		
Carshalton	d				22 28					22 58												
Hackbridge	d				22 31					23 01												
Mitcham Junction	d				22 34					23 04												
Mitcham Eastfields	d				22 38					23 08												
Carshalton Beeches	d			22 22			22 39		22 52		23 09				23 22	23 30		23 43		23 57		
Wallington	d			22 24			22 41		22 54		23 11				23 24	23 32		23 45		23 59		
Waddon	d			22 27			22 44		22 57		23 14				23 27	23 35		23 48		00 02		
West Croydon 4	d			22 31			22 48		23 01		23 18				23a30	23a38		23a51		00a05		
Norwood Junction 2	d						22 53				23 23											
New Cross Gate 4 ⊖	d																					
Tulse Hill 3	d																					
London Bridge 4 ⊖	a																					
Balham 4 ⊖	d			22 48	22 44		23 09		23 17	23 14	23 40											
Clapham Junction 10	a	22 15		22 53	22 48	22 45	23 15		23 22	23 18	23 45			23 15			23 48					
London Waterloo 15 ⊖	a	22 25				22 55								23 25			23 58					
London Victoria 15 ⊖	a			23 03	22 56		23 23		23 31	23 26	23 54											

Saturdays

Station		SN	FC B	FC B	SW	SW	SW		SN	SN	SN	SN	FC C	SN		SW	SN	SN	SW	SN	FC C		SN	SN	SN	SN
Horsham 4	d																									
Warnham	d																									
Ockley	d																									
Holmwood	d																									
Dorking 4	a																									
	d									06 26							06 57							07 26		
Boxhill & Westhumble	d																06 59							07 28		
Guildford	d															06 28			06 58							
Effingham Junction 6	d															06 46			07 16							
Bookham	d															06 49			07 19							
Leatherhead	d									06 33						06 54	07 04		07 24					07 33		
Ashtead	d									06 37						06 58	07 08		07 28					07 37		
Epsom 3	a									06 41						07 02	07 12		07 32					07 41		
	d				05 35	06 05	06 35			06 42	06 47			07 04		07 05	07 13	07 17	07 35					07 42	07 47	
Ewell East	d									06 46	06 51			07 08				07 21						07 46	07 51	
Cheam	d									06 49	06 54			07 11			07 18	07 24						07 49	07 54	
Epsom Downs	d	23p44																					07 34			
Banstead	d	23p47																					07 37			
Belmont	d	23p50																					07 40			
Wimbledon 6 ⊖	d		23p54	00 25									06 47								07 17					
West Sutton	d		00 08	00 39									07 01								07 31					
Sutton (Surrey) 4	a	23p53	00 12	00 43						06 52	06 57		07 05	07 14			07 22	07 27			07 35		07 43	07 52	07 57	
	d	23p54							06 44	06 52	06 57	07 03	07 06	07 14			07 22	07 27		07 33	07 36		07 44	07 52	07 57	08 03
Carshalton	d										07 00		07 09					07 30			07 39				08 00	
Hackbridge	d										07 03		07 11					07 33			07 41				08 03	
Mitcham Junction	d										07 06		07 14					07 36			07 44				08 06	
Mitcham Eastfields	d										07 10		07 18					07 40			07 48				08 10	
Carshalton Beeches	d	23p57							06 47			07 06		07 17						07 36			07 47			08 06
Wallington	d	23p59							06 50			07 08		07 20						07 38			07 50			08 08
Waddon	d	00 02							06 53			07 11		07 23						07 41			07 53			08 11
West Croydon 4	d	00a05							06 56			07 15		07 26						07 45			07 56			08 15
Norwood Junction 2	d											07 20								07 50						08 20
New Cross Gate 4 ⊖	d											07 37								08 07						08 37
Tulse Hill 3	d												07a27								07a57					
London Bridge 4 ⊖	a											07 44								08 14						08 44
Balham 4 ⊖	d								07 12		07 17			07 42				07 48					08 12		08 18	
Clapham Junction 10	a				06 01	06 30	07 00		07 18	07 10	07 21			07 48		07 30	07 40	07 52	08 00				08 18	08 10	08 22	
London Waterloo 15 ⊖	a				06 11	06 40	07 10									07 40			08 10							
London Victoria 15 ⊖	a								07 26	07 18	07 29			07 56			07 50	07 59					08 26	08 18	08 29	

For general notes see front of timetable
For details of catering facilities see
Directory of Train Operators

A From Luton (Table 52)
B From London Bridge (Table 52)
C To Herne Hill (Table 177)

From 28 September due to seasonal difficulties a large number of trains on this table will have minor retimings that could mean slightly earlier departure or later arrival times at certain stations. For further details see local publicity or contact National Rail Enquiries 08457 48 49 50.

From 3 October due to seasonal difficulties a large number of trains on this table will have minor retimings that could mean slightly earlier departure or later arrival times at certain stations. For further details see local publicity or contact National Rail Enquiries 08457 48 49 50.

Table 182

Horsham, Dorking, Guildford, Epsom and Sutton → London

Saturdays

Network Diagram - see first page of Table 177

		FC A	SN	SW	SN		SN	SN	SW	SW	SN	FC A		SN	SN	SN	SN	SW	SN		FC A	SN	SW		SN	SN
Horsham 4	d														08 04											
Warnham	d														08 08											
Ockley	d														08 15											
Holmwood	d														08 19											
Dorking 4	a														08 25											
	d				07 58				08 05						08 26			08 35							08 58	
Boxhill & Westhumble	d														08 28											
Guildford	d			07 28						07 58													08 28			
Effingham Junction 6	d			07 46						08 16													08 46			
Bookham	d			07 49						08 19													08 49			
Leatherhead	d			07 54	08 04				08 11	08 24					08 33			08 41					08 54		09 04	
Ashtead	d			07 58	08 07				08 14	08 28					08 37			08 44					08 58		09 07	
Epsom 3	a			08 02	08 12				08 19	08 32					08 41			08 49					09 02		09 12	
	d		08 04	08 05	08 12			08 17	08 20	08 35					08 42		08 47	08 50				09 04	09 05		09 12	
Ewell East	d		08 08					08 21							08 46		08 51					09 08				
Cheam	d		08 11		08 18			08 24							08 49		08 54					09 11			09 18	
Epsom Downs	d													08 34												
Banstead	d													08 37												
Belmont	d													08 40												
Wimbledon 6 ⊖	d	07 47										08 17									08 47					
West Sutton	d	08 01										08 31									09 01					
Sutton (Surrey) 4	a	08 05	08 14		08 22			08 27				08 35		08 43	08 52		08 57				09 05	09 14			09 22	
	d	08 06	08 14		08 22		08 23	08 27			08 33	08 36		08 44	08 52	08 53	08 57		09 03		09 06	09 14			09 22	09 23
Carshalton	d	08 09						08 30				08 39					09 00				09 09					
Hackbridge	d	08 11						08 33				08 41					09 03				09 11					
Mitcham Junction	d	08 14						08 36				08 44					09 06				09 14					
Mitcham Eastfields	d	08 18						08 40				08 48					09 10				09 18					
Carshalton Beeches	d		08 17				08 26				08 36			08 47		08 56			09 06			09 17				09 26
Wallington	d		08 20				08 28				08 38			08 50		08 58			09 08			09 20				09 28
Waddon	d		08 23				08 31				08 41			08 53		09 01			09 11			09 23				09 31
West Croydon 4	d		08 26				08 35				08 45			08 56		09 05			09 15			09 26				09 35
Norwood Junction 2	d										08 50								09 20							
New Cross Gate 4 ⊖	d										09 07								09 37							
Tulse Hill 3	d	08a27										08a57									09a27					
London Bridge 4 ⊖	a										09 14								09 44							
Balham 4 ⊖	d		08 42				08 51	08 48						09 12		09 21	09 18					09 42				09 51
Clapham Junction 10	a		08 48	08 30	08 40		08 56	08 52	08 45	09 00				09 18	09 10	09 26	09 22	09 15				09 48	09 30		09 40	09 56
London Waterloo 15 ⊖	a			08 40					08 55	09 10								09 25					09 40			
London Victoria 15 ⊖	a		08 56		08 48		09 04	08 59						09 26	09 18	09 34	09 29					09 56			09 48	10 04

		SN	SW	SW	SN	FC A	SN	SN	SN	SN	SW	SN	FC A	SN	SW			SN	SN	SN	SW	SW	SN		FC A
Horsham 4	d							09 04																	
Warnham	d							09 08																	
Ockley	d							09 15																	
Holmwood	d							09 19																	
Dorking 4	a							09 25																	
	d		09 05					09 26			09 35							17 58			18 05				
Boxhill & Westhumble	d							09 28																	
Guildford	d			08 58											09 28							17 58			
Effingham Junction 6	d			09 16											09 46							18 16			
Bookham	d			09 19											09 49							18 19			
Leatherhead	d		09 11	09 24				09 33			09 41				09 54			18 04			18 11	18 24			
Ashtead	d		09 14	09 28				09 37			09 44				09 58			18 07			18 14	18 28			
Epsom 3	a		09 19	09 32				09 41			09 49				10 02			18 12			18 19	18 32			
	d	09 17	09 20	09 35				09 42		09 47	09 50			10 04	10 05			18 12		18 17	18 20	18 35			
Ewell East	d	09 21						09 46		09 51				10 08		and at				18 21					
Cheam	d	09 24						09 49		09 54				10 11		the same		18 18		18 24					
Epsom Downs	d						09 34									minutes									
Banstead	d						09 37																		
Belmont	d						09 40									past									
Wimbledon 6 ⊖	d					09 17							09 47			each									18 17
West Sutton	d					09 31							10 01												18 31
Sutton (Surrey) 4	a	09 27				09 35	09 43	09 52		09 57			10 05	10 14		hour until		18 22		18 27					18 35
	d	09 27			09 33	09 36	09 44	09 52	09 53	09 57		10 03	10 06	10 14				18 22	18 23	18 27			18 33		18 36
Carshalton	d	09 30				09 39				10 00			10 09							18 30					18 39
Hackbridge	d	09 33				09 41				10 03			10 11							18 33					18 41
Mitcham Junction	d	09 36				09 44				10 06			10 14							18 36					18 44
Mitcham Eastfields	d	09 40				09 48				10 10			10 18							18 40					18 48
Carshalton Beeches	d				09 36		09 47		09 56			10 06		10 17					18 26				18 36		
Wallington	d				09 38		09 50		09 58			10 08		10 20					18 28				18 38		
Waddon	d				09 41		09 53		10 01			10 11		10 23					18 31				18 41		
West Croydon 4	d				09 45		09 56		10 05			10 15		10 26					18 35				18 45		
Norwood Junction 2	d				09 50							10 20											18 50		
New Cross Gate 4 ⊖	d				10 07							10 37											19 07		
Tulse Hill 3	d					09a57							10a27												18a57
London Bridge 4 ⊖	a				10 14							10 44											19 14		
Balham 4 ⊖	d	09 48					10 12		10 21	10 18				10 42					18 51	18 48					
Clapham Junction 10	a	09 52	09 45	10 00			10 18	10 10	10 26	10 22	10 15			10 48	10 30			18 40	18 56	18 52	18 45	19 00			
London Waterloo 15 ⊖	a		09 55	10 10							10 25				10 40						18 55	19 10			
London Victoria 15 ⊖	a	09 59					10 26	10 18	10 34	10 29				10 56				18 48	19 04	18 59					

For general notes see front of timetable
For details of catering facilities see Directory of Train Operators

A To Herne Hill (Table 177)

From 3 October due to seasonal difficulties a large number of trains on this table will have minor retimings that could mean slightly earlier departure or later arrival times at certain stations. For further details see local publicity or contact National Rail Enquiries 08457 48 49 50.

Horsham, Dorking, Guildford, Epsom and Sutton → London

Network Diagram - see first page of Table 177

		SN	SN	SN	SW	FC A	SW		SN	SN	SN	SW	SN	FC B		SW	SN	SN	SN	FC B	SW		SW	SN	SN	SW
Horsham 4	d		18 04																							
Warnham	d		18 08																							
Ockley	d		18 15																							
Holmwood	d		18 19																							
Dorking 4	a		18 25																							
	d		18 26		18 35						19 00	19 05						19 30			19 35				19 59	20 05
Boxhill & Westhumble	d		18 28								19 02														20 01	
Guildford	d						18 28									18 58							19 28			
Effingham Junction 6	d						18 46									19 16							19 46			
Bookham	d						18 49									19 19							19 49			
Leatherhead	d		18 33		18 41		18 54				19 07	19 11				19 24		19 36			19 41		19 54		20 06	20 11
Ashtead	d		18 37		18 44		18 58				19 11	19 14				19 28		19 40			19 44		19 58		20 10	20 14
Epsom 3	a		18 41		18 49		19 02				19 15	19 19				19 32		19 44			19 49		20 02		20 14	20 19
	d		18 42	18 47	18 50		19 05				19 17	19 20	19 25			19 35		19 45			19 50		20 05		20 15	20 20
Ewell East	d		18 46	18 51							19 21		19 29					19 49							20 19	
Cheam	d		18 49	18 54							19 24		19 32					19 52							20 22	
Epsom Downs	d	18 34								19 15									19 54							
Banstead	d	18 37								19 18									19 57							
Belmont	d	18 40								19 21									20 00							
Wimbledon 6 ⊖	d					18 47								19 17						19 47						
West Sutton	d					19 01								19 31						20 01						
Sutton (Surrey) 4	a	18 43	18 52	18 57		19 05				19 24	19 27		19 35	19 39				19 55	20 03	20 05					20 25	
	d	18 44	18 52	18 57		19 06			19 14	19 25	19 27		19 36				19 49	19 55	20 06					20 19	20 25	
Carshalton	d			19 00		19 09					19 30							19 58							20 28	
Hackbridge	d			19 03		19 11					19 33							20 01							20 31	
Mitcham Junction	d			19 06		19 14					19 36							20 04							20 34	
Mitcham Eastfields	d			19 10		19 18					19 40							20 08							20 38	
Carshalton Beeches	d	18 47							19 17	19 28			19 39				19 52		20 09					20 22		
Wallington	d	18 50							19 20	19 30			19 41				19 54		20 11					20 24		
Waddon	d	18 53							19 23	19 33			19 44				19 57		20 14					20 27		
West Croydon 4	d	18 56							19 26	19a36			19 48				20 01		20 18					20 31		
Norwood Junction 2	d												19 53						20 23							
New Cross Gate 4 ⊖	d																									
Tulse Hill 3	d					19a27																				
London Bridge 4 ⊖	a																									
Balham 4 ⊖	d	19 12		19 18					19 42		19 48		20 09				20 17	20 15	20 39					20 47	20 44	
Clapham Junction 10	a	19 18	19 10	19 22	19 15		19 30		19 48		19 52	19 45	20 14			20 00	20 22	20 19	20 44		20 15		20 30	20 52	20 48	20 45
London Waterloo 15 ⊖	a				19 25		19 40					19 55				20 10					20 25		20 40			20 55
London Victoria 15 ⊖	a	19 26	19 18	19 29					19 56		19 59		20 23				20 33	20 26	20 53					21 03	20 56	

		SN	SW	FC B	SN		SN	SN	FC B	SW	SW	SN		SN	SW	SN	FC B	SW	SN		SN	SN	FC B	SW	SN	SN
Horsham 4	d																									
Warnham	d																									
Ockley	d																									
Holmwood	d																									
Dorking 4	a																									
	d						20 30			20 35				20 59							21 30			21 35		21 59
Boxhill & Westhumble	d													21 01												22 01
Guildford	d		19 58												20 46											
Effingham Junction 6	d		20 16												21 03											
Bookham	d		20 19												21 06											
Leatherhead	d		20 24				20 36			20 41				21 06	21 11						21 36			21 41		22 06
Ashtead	d		20 28				20 40			20 44				21 10	21 14						21 40			21 44		22 10
Epsom 3	a		20 32				20 44			20 49				21 14	21 19						21 44			21 49		22 14
	d	20 25	20 35				20 45			20 50	21 05			21 15	21 20	21 25		21 35			21 45			21 50		22 15
Ewell East	d	20 29					20 49							21 19		21 29					21 49					22 19
Cheam	d	20 32					20 52							21 22		21 32					21 52					22 22
Epsom Downs	d							20 54														21 54				
Banstead	d							20 57														21 57				
Belmont	d							21 00														22 00				
Wimbledon 6 ⊖	d			20 17					20 47								21 17						21 47			
West Sutton	d			20 31					21 01								21 31						22 01			
Sutton (Surrey) 4	a	20 35		20 39			20 55	21 03	21 05					21 25		21 35	21 39				21 55	22 03	22 05			22 25
	d	20 36			20 49		20 55	21 06				21 19		21 25		21 36			21 49		21 55	22 06			22 19	22 25
Carshalton	d						20 58							21 28							21 58					22 28
Hackbridge	d						21 01							21 31							22 01					22 31
Mitcham Junction	d						21 04							21 34							22 04					22 34
Mitcham Eastfields	d						21 08							21 38							22 08					22 38
Carshalton Beeches	d	20 39			20 52			21 09				21 22				21 39			21 52			22 09			22 22	
Wallington	d	20 41			20 54			21 11				21 24				21 41			21 54			22 11			22 24	
Waddon	d	20 44			20 57			21 14				21 27				21 44			21 57			22 14			22 27	
West Croydon 4	d	20 48			21 01			21 18				21 31				21 48			22 01			22 18			22 31	
Norwood Junction 2	d	20 53						21 23								21 53						22 23				
New Cross Gate 4 ⊖	d																									
Tulse Hill 3	d																									
London Bridge 4 ⊖	a																									
Balham 4 ⊖	d	21 09			21 18		21 14	21 39				21 48		21 44		22 09			22 18		22 14	22 39			22 48	22 44
Clapham Junction 10	a	21 14	21 00		21 23		21 18	21 44		21 15	21 30	21 53		21 48	21 45	22 14		22 00	22 23		22 18	22 44		22 15	22 53	22 48
London Waterloo 15 ⊖	a		21 10							21 25	21 40				21 55			22 10						22 25		
London Victoria 15 ⊖	a	21 23			21 33		21 26	21 53				22 03		21 56		22 23			22 33		22 26	22 53			23 03	22 56

For general notes see front of timetable
For details of catering facilities see
Directory of Train Operators

A To Herne Hill (Table 177)
B From London Bridge (Table 52)

From 3 October due to seasonal difficulties a large number of trains on this table will have minor retimings that could mean slightly earlier departure or later arrival times at certain stations. For further details see local publicity or contact National Rail Enquiries 08457 48 49 50.

Table 182

Saturdays

Horsham, Dorking, Guildford, Epsom and Sutton → London

Network Diagram - see first page of Table 177

		SW	SN		FC A	SN	SN	SN	FC A	SW		SN	SN	FC A	SW	SN	SN		SN	FC A						
Horsham 4	d																									
Warnham	d																									
Ockley	d																									
Holmwood	d																									
Dorking 4	a																									
	d						22 30			22 35			23 00						23 30							
Boxhill & Westhumble	d												23 02													
Guildford	d	21 46													22 46											
Effingham Junction 6	d	22 03													23 03											
Bookham	d	22 06													23 06											
Leatherhead	d	22 11					22 36			22 41			23 07		23 11				23 36							
Ashtead	d	22 14					22 40			22 44			23 11		23 14				23 39							
Epsom 3	a	22 19					22 44			22 49			23 15		23 19				23 45							
	d	22 20	22 25				22 45			22 50			23 16		23 20	23 25										
Ewell East	d		22 29				22 49						23 20			23 29										
Cheam	d		22 32				22 52						23 23			23 32										
Epsom Downs	d							22 54									23 44									
Banstead	d							22 57									23 47									
Belmont	d							23 00									23 50									
Wimbledon 6 ⊖	d				22 17				22 47					23 17						23 47						
West Sutton	d				22 31				23 01					23 31						00 01						
Sutton (Surrey) 4	a		22 35		22 39		22 55	23 03	23 05				23 26	23 35		23 39	23 53			00 05						
	d		22 36			22 49	22 55	23 06				23 19	23 27			23 40	23 54									
Carshalton	d						22 58																			
Hackbridge	d						23 01																			
Mitcham Junction	d						23 04																			
Mitcham Eastfields	d						23 08																			
Carshalton Beeches	d		22 39			22 52		23 09				23 22	23 30			23 43	23 57									
Wallington	d		22 41			22 54		23 11				23 24	23 32			23 45	23 59									
Waddon	d		22 44			22 57		23 14				23 27	23 35			23 48	00 02									
West Croydon 4	d		22 48			23 01		23 18				23a30	23a38			23a51	00a05									
Norwood Junction 2	d		22 53					23 23																		
New Cross Gate 4 ⊖	d																									
Tulse Hill 3	d																									
London Bridge 4 ⊖	a																									
Balham 4 ⊖	d		23 09			23 17	23 14	23 40																		
Clapham Junction 10	a	22 45	23 14			23 22	23 18	23 45		23 15					23 48											
London Waterloo 15 ⊖	a	22 55								23 25					23 58											
London Victoria 15 ⊖	a		23 23			23 31	23 26	23 54																		

Sundays

		SN	FC A	FC A	SN		SN	SN	SW	SN		SN	SW	SN	SN		SW	SN	SN	SN		SW	SN	SN	SN	SW
Horsham 4	d																									
Warnham	d																									
Ockley	d																									
Holmwood	d																									
Dorking 4	a																									
	d							06 56				07 26			07 56					08 26					08 56	09 08
Boxhill & Westhumble	d							06 58				07 28			07 58					08 28					08 58	
Guildford	d																					08 20				
Effingham Junction 6	d																					08 36				
Bookham	d																					08 39				
Leatherhead	d							07 03				07 33			08 03					08 33		08 45			09 03	09 15
Ashtead	d							07 07				07 37			08 07					08 37		08 48			09 07	09 18
Epsom 3	a							07 11				07 41			08 11					08 41		08 53			09 11	09 23
	d				06 47			07 12	07 24			07 42	07 54		08 12		08 24			08 42		08 54			09 12	09 24
Ewell East	d				06 51			07 16				07 46			08 16					08 46					09 16	
Cheam	d				06 54			07 19				07 49			08 19					08 49					09 19	
Epsom Downs	d	23p44																								
Banstead	d	23p47																								
Belmont	d	23p50																								
Wimbledon 6 ⊖	d		23p47	00 17																						
West Sutton	d		00 01	00 31																						
Sutton (Surrey) 4	a	23p53	00 05	00 35	06 57			07 22				07 52			08 22					08 52					09 22	
	d	23p54			06 57		07 28	07 29		07 58		07 59		08 27	08 29			08 39	08 57	08 59			09 09	09 27	09 29	
Carshalton	d							07 32				08 02			08 32					09 02					09 32	
Hackbridge	d							07 34				08 04			08 34					09 04					09 34	
Mitcham Junction	d							07 38				08 08			08 38					09 08					09 38	
Mitcham Eastfields	d							07 41				08 11			08 41					09 11					09 41	
Carshalton Beeches	d	23p57			07 00		07 31			08 01				08 30					09 00					09 30		
Wallington	d	23p59			07 02		07 33			08 03				08 32				08 43	09 02				09 13	09 32		
Waddon	d	00 02			07 05		07 36			08 06				08 35					09 05					09 35		
West Croydon 4	d	00a05			07 09		07 39			08 09				08 39				08 48	09 09				09 18	09 39		
Norwood Junction 2	d																	08 54					09 24			
New Cross Gate 4 ⊖	d																									
Tulse Hill 3	d																									
London Bridge 4 ⊖	a																									
Balham 4 ⊖	d				07 25		07 55	07 48		08 25		08 18		08 55	08 48			09 10	09 25	09 18			09 40	09 55	09 48	
Clapham Junction 10	a				07 31		08 01	07 52	07 49	08 31		08 22	08 19	09 01	08 52		08 49	09 15	09 31	09 22		09 19	09 45	10 01	09 52	09 49
London Waterloo 15 ⊖	a								08 04				08 34				09 04					09 34				10 04
London Victoria 15 ⊖	a				07 39		08 09	07 59		08 39		08 29		09 09	08 59			09 23	09 39	09 29			09 53	10 09	09 59	

For general notes see front of timetable
For details of catering facilities see Directory of Train Operators

A From London Bridge (Table 52)

From 3 October due to seasonal difficulties a large number of trains on this table will have minor retimings that could mean slightly earlier departure or later arrival times at certain stations. For further details see local publicity or contact National Rail Enquiries 08457 48 49 50.

From 27 September due to seasonal difficulties a large number of trains on this table will have minor retimings that could mean slightly earlier departure or later arrival times at certain stations. For further details see local publicity or contact National Rail Enquiries 08457 48 49 50.

Table 182

Sundays

Horsham, Dorking, Guildford, Epsom and Sutton → London

Network Diagram - see first page of Table 177

Station		SN		SN	SN		FC A	SW	SN	SN	SN	FC A	SW	SN	SN	SN			FC A	SW	SN	SN		SN	FC A
Horsham 4	d																								
Warnham	d																								
Ockley	d																								
Holmwood	d																								
Dorking 4	a																								
	d				09 26						09 56		10 08			10 26								20 56	
Boxhill & Westhumble	d				09 28						09 58					10 28								20 58	
Guildford	d							09 20												20 20					
Effingham Junction 6	d							09 36												20 36					
Bookham	d							09 39												20 39					
Leatherhead	d				09 33			09 45			10 03		10 15			10 33				20 45				21 03	
Ashtead	d				09 37			09 48			10 07		10 18			10 37				20 48				21 07	
Epsom 3	a				09 41			09 53			10 11		10 23			10 41				20 53				21 11	
	d				09 42			09 54			10 12		10 24			10 42	and at			20 54				21 12	
Ewell East	d				09 46						10 16					10 46								21 16	
Cheam	d				09 49						10 19					10 49	the same							21 19	
Epsom Downs	d																minutes								
Banstead	d																								
Belmont	d																past								
Wimbledon 6 ⊖	d						09 47					10 17					each		20 47						21 17
West Sutton	d						10 01					10 31							21 01						21 31
Sutton (Surrey) 4	a				09 52		10 05				10 22	10 35				10 52	hour until		21 05					21 22	21 35
	d	09 39		09 57	09 59				10 09	10 27	10 29			10 39	10 57	10 59					21 09	21 27		21 29	
Carshalton	d				10 02						10 32					11 02								21 32	
Hackbridge	d				10 04						10 34					11 04								21 34	
Mitcham Junction	d				10 08						10 38					11 08								21 38	
Mitcham Eastfields	d				10 11						10 41					11 11								21 41	
Carshalton Beeches	d			10 00						10 30					11 00							21 30			
Wallington	d	09 43		10 02					10 13	10 32				10 43	11 02						21 13	21 32			
Waddon	d			10 05						10 35					11 05							21 35			
West Croydon 4	d	09 48		10 09					10 18	10 39				10 48	11 09						21 18	21 39			
Norwood Junction 2	d	09 54							10 24					10 54							21 24				
New Cross Gate 4 ⊖	d																								
Tulse Hill 3	d																								
London Bridge 4 ⊖	a																								
Balham 4 ⊖	d	10 10		10 25	10 18				10 40	10 55	10 48			11 10	11 25	11 18					21 40	21 55		21 48	
Clapham Junction 10	a	10 15		10 31	10 22			10 19	10 45	11 01	10 52		10 49	11 15	11 31	11 22				21 19	21 45	22 01		21 52	
London Waterloo 15 ⊖	a							10 34					11 04							21 29					
London Victoria 15 ⊖	a	10 23		10 39	10 29				10 53	11 09	10 59			11 23	11 39	11 29					21 53	22 09		21 59	

Station		SW	SN	SN	SN		SW	SN	SN	SN		SW	SN	SN	SN		SW	SN	SN B	SN		SW	SN			
Horsham 4	d																									
Warnham	d																									
Ockley	d																									
Holmwood	d																									
Dorking 4	a																									
	d	21 08			21 26					21 56		22 08			22 26					22 56		23 08				
Boxhill & Westhumble	d				21 28					21 58					22 28					22 58						
Guildford	d						21 20										22 20									
Effingham Junction 6	d						21 36										22 36									
Bookham	d						21 39										22 39									
Leatherhead	d	21 15			21 33		21 45			22 03		22 15			22 33		22 45			23 03		23 15				
Ashtead	d	21 18			21 37		21 48			22 07		22 18			22 37		22 48			23 07		23 18				
Epsom 3	a	21 23			21 41		21 53			22 11		22 23			22 41		22 53			23 11		23 23				
	d	21 24			21 42		21 54			22 12		22 24			22 42		22 54			23 12		23 24				
Ewell East	d				21 46					22 16					22 46					23 16						
Cheam	d				21 49					22 19					22 49					23 19						
Epsom Downs	d																									
Banstead	d																									
Belmont	d																									
Wimbledon 6 ⊖	d																									
West Sutton	d																									
Sutton (Surrey) 4	a				21 52					22 22					22 52					23 22						
	d		21 39	21 57	21 59			22 09	22 27	22 29			22 39	22 57	22 59			23 09	23 27	23 29			23 39			
Carshalton	d				22 02					22 32					23 02					23 32						
Hackbridge	d				22 04					22 34					23 04					23 34						
Mitcham Junction	d				22 08					22 38					23 08					23 38						
Mitcham Eastfields	d				22 11					22 41					23 11					23 41						
Carshalton Beeches	d			22 00					22 30					23 00					23 30				23 42			
Wallington	d		21 43	22 02				22 13	22 32				22 43	23 02				23 13	23 32				23 44			
Waddon	d			22 05					22 35					23 05					23 35				23 47			
West Croydon 4	d		21 48	22 09				22 18	22 39				22 48	23 09				23 18	23a38				23a50			
Norwood Junction 2	d		21 54					22 24					22 54					23b26								
New Cross Gate 4 ⊖	d																									
Tulse Hill 3	d																									
London Bridge 4 ⊖	a																									
Balham 4 ⊖	d		22 10	22 25	22 18			22 40	22 55	22 48			23 10	23 25	23 18			23 42		23 48						
Clapham Junction 10	a	21 49	22 15	22 31	22 22		22 19	22 45	23 01	22 52		22 49	23 15	23 31	23 22		23 19	23 47		23 52		23 49				
London Waterloo 15 ⊖	a	22 00					22 29					23 00					23 29					23 59				
London Victoria 15 ⊖	a		22 23	22 39	22 29			22 53	23 09	22 59			23 23	23 39	23 29			23 55		23 59						

For general notes see front of timetable
For details of catering facilities see Directory of Train Operators

A From London Bridge (Table 52)
B To Selhurst (Table 177)
b Arr. 2323

From 27 September due to seasonal difficulties a large number of trains on this table will have minor retimings that could mean slightly earlier departure or later arrival times at certain stations. For further details see local publicity or contact National Rail Enquiries 08457 48 49 50.

Network Diagram for Tables 184, 189

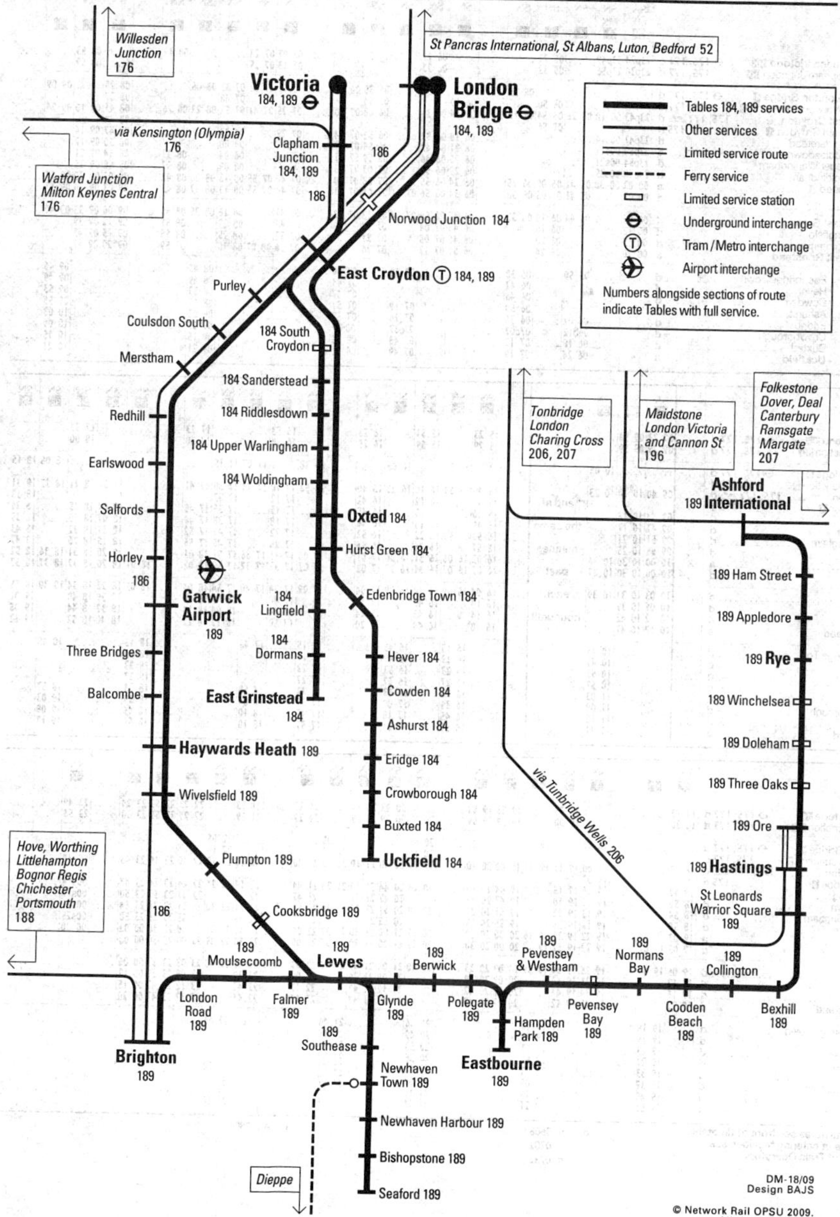

Willesden Junction 176
St Pancras International, St Albans, Luton, Bedford 52
Victoria 184, 189
London Bridge 184, 189
Tables 184, 189 services
Other services
Limited service route
Ferry service
Limited service station
Underground interchange
Tram / Metro interchange
Airport interchange
Numbers alongside sections of route indicate Tables with full service.
via Kensington (Olympia) 176
Watford Junction Milton Keynes Central 176
Clapham Junction 184, 189
186
Norwood Junction 184
East Croydon 184, 189
Purley
Coulsdon South
Merstham
184 South Croydon
184 Sanderstead
184 Riddlesdown
184 Upper Warlingham
184 Woldingham
Redhill
Earlswood
Salfords
Horley
Oxted 184
Hurst Green 184
Edenbridge Town 184
Gatwick Airport 189
184 Lingfield
184 Dormans
Three Bridges
Balcombe
East Grinstead 184
Hever 184
Cowden 184
Ashurst 184
Eridge 184
Crowborough 184
Buxted 184
Uckfield 184
Haywards Heath 189
Wivelsfield 189
Plumpton 189
Cooksbridge 189
Hove, Worthing Littlehampton Bognor Regis Chichester Portsmouth 188
Tonbridge London Charing Cross 206, 207
Maidstone London Victoria and Cannon St 196
Folkestone Dover, Deal Canterbury Ramsgate Margate 207
Ashford 189 International
189 Ham Street
189 Appledore
189 Rye
189 Winchelsea
189 Doleham
189 Three Oaks
189 Ore
189 Hastings
St Leonards Warrior Square 189
via Tunbridge Wells 206
189 Moulsecoomb
189 Lewes
189 Berwick
189 Pevensey & Westham
189 Normans Bay
189 Collington
London Road 189
Falmer 189
Glynde 189
Polegate 189
Hampden Park 189
Pevensey Bay 189
Cooden Beach 189
Bexhill 189
Brighton 189
189 Southease
Eastbourne 189
Newhaven Town 189
Newhaven Harbour 189
Bishopstone 189
Seaford 189
Dieppe

DM-18/09
Design BAJS

London → Oxted, East Grinstead and Uckfield

Network Diagram - see first page of Table 184

Miles	Miles	Station		SN MX 1	SN MX 1	SN 1	SN 1	SN 1		SN 1	SN 1	SN 1	SN 1	SN 1		SN 1	SN 1	SN 1	SN 1	SN 1		SN 1	SN 1	SN 1	
0	—	**London Victoria** 15	⊖ 175, 177 d	23p24	23p49		05 23				06 17					07 07	07 23			08 11			08 53		
2¾	—	Clapham Junction 10	175, 177 d	23p30	23p56		05 33				06 23					07 13	07 29						08 59		
—	0	**London Bridge** 4	⊖ 175, 177 d					05 55					06 30	06 56				07 35	08 06			08 25		09 09	
—	8¾	Norwood Junction 2	175, 177 d				05 50			06 10			06 44					07 48				08 37			
10½	10¼	**East Croydon**	175, 177 d	23p43	00 10	05 26	05 54	06 10		06 14	06 35		06 48	07 10		07 25	07 41	07 52	08 22	08 26		08 41	09 10	09 24	
11½	—	South Croydon 4	175 d				05 56															08 44			
12½	—	Sanderstead	d	23p47	00s14					06 18	06 39		06 52	07 14		07 29		07 57				08 47	09 14		
13¾	—	Riddlesdown	d	23p50	00s17					06 21	06 42		06 55	07 17				08 00				08 50	09 17		
15½	—	Upper Warlingham	d	23p54	00s21					06 25	06 46		06 59	07 21				08 04		08 33		08 54	09 21		
17¼	—	Woldingham	d	23p58	00s25					06 29	06 50		07 03	07 25				08 08		08 37		08 58	09 25		
20½	—	**Oxted** 3	a	00 03	00 30	05 41	06 08	06 25		06 34	06 55		07 08	07 30		07 40	07 55	08 13	08 36	08 42		09 03	09 30	09 37	
—	—		d	00 03		05 41	06 08	06 30		06 34	06 56	07 01	07 08	07 31		07 40	07 55	08 13	08 37	08 43		09 03	09 30	09 37	
21½	0	Hurst Green	d	00 06		05 44	06 10	06 32		06 37	06 58	07 04	07 12	07 33		07 42		08 16	08 39	08 45		09 06	09 33	09 40	
26¼	—	Lingfield	d	00 12			06 16			06 43	07 04		07 18			07 48		08 22		08 51		09 12	09 39		
28	—	Dormans	d	00 15			06 20			06 46	07 08		07 21			07 52		08 25		08 55		09 15	09 42		
30¼	—	**East Grinstead**	a	00 20			06 24			06 51	07 12		07 26			07 56	08 07	08 30		08 59		09 20	09 47		
—	4¼	Edenbridge Town	d			05 50		06 38				07 10		07 39					08 45					09 46	
—	6	Hever	d					06 42						07 43					08 49					09 49	
—	8	Cowden	d					06 46						07 47					08 53					09 53	
—	10¾	Ashurst	d					06 50				07 19		07 51					08 57					09 58	
—	14½	Eridge	d			06 02		06 56				07 26		07 58					09 03					10 03	
—	17¾	Crowborough	d			06b12		07c07				07e37		08f09					09 09					10 09	
—	22½	Buxted	d			06 18		07 13				07 43		08 15					09 15					10 15	
—	25	**Uckfield**	a			06 24		07 19				07 49		08 21					09 21					10 21	

Station			SN 1	SN 1	SN 1			SN 1	SN 1	SN 1	SN 1	SN 1		SN 1	SN 1	SN 1	SN 1	SN 1		SN 1	SN 1	SN 1	SN 1	SN 1
London Victoria 15	⊖ 175, 177 d		09 23	09 53		and at the same minutes past each hour until		15 23		15 53		16 23			16 53			17 23				17 53		
Clapham Junction 10	175, 177 d		09 29	09 59				15 29		15 59		16 29			16 59			17 30				18 00		
London Bridge 4	⊖ 175, 177 d				10 08				15 38		16 08			16 38		17 07	17 15				17 44		18 08	18 15
Norwood Junction 2	175, 177 d																							
East Croydon	175, 177 d		09 40	10 10	10 23			15 40	15 53	16 10	16 23	16 40		16 53	17 10	17 23	17 30	17 41			17 58	18 11	18 22	18 31
South Croydon 4	175 d							15 43		16 12		16 42			17 12		17 32				18 01			18 33
Sanderstead	d		09 44	10 14				15 46		16 15		16 45			17 15		17 35	17 45			18 04	18 15		18 36
Riddlesdown	d		09 47	10 17				15 49		16 18		16 48			17 18		17 38	17 48			18 07	18 18		18 39
Upper Warlingham	d		09 51	10 21				15 53		16 22		16 52			17 22		17 42	17 52			18 11	18 22		18 43
Woldingham	d		09 55	10 25				15 57		16 26		16 56			17 26		17 46	17 56			18 15	18 26		18 47
Oxted 3	a		10 00	10 30	10 36			16 02	16 06	16 31	16 36	17 01		17 06	17 31	17 36	17 51	18 01			18 20	18 31	18 36	18 52
	d		10 00	10 30	10 37			16 02	16 07	16 31	16 37	17 02		17 07	17 32	17 37	17 52	18 02		18 07	18 20	18 32	18 37	18 53
Hurst Green	d		10 03	10 33	10 39			16 04	16 09	16 34	16 39	17 04		17 09	17 34	17 40	17 54	18 04		18 09	18 23	18 34	18 39	18 55
Lingfield	d		10 09	10 39				16 10		16 40		17 10			17 40		18 00	18 10			18 29	18 40		19 01
Dormans	d		10 12	10 42				16 14		16 43		17 14			17 44		18 04	18 14			18 32	18 44		19 05
East Grinstead	a		10 17	10 47				16 18		16 48		17 20			17 50		18 12	18 22			18 40	18 52		19 12
Edenbridge Town	d				10 45				16 15		16 45			17 15		17 46				18 15			18 45	
Hever	d				10 49				16 19		16 49			17 19						18 19				
Cowden	d				10 53				16 23		16 53			17 23						18 23				
Ashurst	d				10 57				16 27		16 57			17 27						18 27				
Eridge	d				11 03				16 33		17 03			17 33		17 58				18 33			18 57	
Crowborough	d				11 09				16 39		17 09			17 39		18 04				18 39			19 03	
Buxted	d				11 15				16 45		17 15			17 45		18 10				18 45			19 09	
Uckfield	a				11 21				16 51		17 21			17 51		18 18				18 51			19 17	

Station		SN 1	SN 1		SN 1	SN 1	SN 1	SN 1	SN 1		SN 1	SN 1	SN 1	SN 1	SN 1		SN 1	SN 1	SN 1	SN 1	SN 1		SN 1		
London Victoria 15	⊖ 175, 177 d	18 23				18 53		19 23	19 53			20 23	20 53		21 23		21 53		22 23	22 53	23 24		23 49		
Clapham Junction 10	175, 177 d	18 30				19 00		19 29	19 59			20 29	20 59		21 29		21 59		22 29	22 59	23 30		23 56		
London Bridge 4	⊖ 175, 177 d				18 47		19 08				20 05			21 05				22 05							
Norwood Junction 2	175, 177 d										20 16			21 16				22 16							
East Croydon	175, 177 d	18 42			19 00	19 11	19 23	19 40	20 10		20 20	20 40	21 10	21 20	21 40		22 10	22 20	22 40	23 10	23 43		00 10		
South Croydon 4	175 d				19 03																				
Sanderstead	d	18 47			19 06	19 15		19 44	20 14		20 24	20 44	21 14	21 24	21 44		22 14	22 24	22 44	23 14	23 47		00s14		
Riddlesdown	d	18 50			19 09	19 18		19 47	20 17			20 47	21 17		21 47		22 17		22 47	23 17	23 50		00s17		
Upper Warlingham	d	18 54			19 13	19 22		19 51	20 21		20 30	20 51	21 21	21 30	21 51		22 21	22 30	22 51	23 21	23 54		00s21		
Woldingham	d	18 58			19 17	19 26		19 55	20 25			20 55	21 25		21 55		22 25		22 55	23 25	23 58		00s25		
Oxted 3	a	19 03			19 22	19 31	19 36	20 00	20 30		20 37	21 00	21 30	21 37	22 00		22 30	22 37	23 00	23 30	00 03		00 30		
	d	19 03	19 07		19 22	19 32	19 37	20 00	20 30		20 37	21 00	21 30	21 37	22 00		22 30	22 37	23 00	23 30	00 03				
Hurst Green	d	19 06	19 09		19 25	19 34	19 39	20 03	20 33		20 40	21 03	21 33	21 40	22 03		22 33	22 40	23 03	23 33	00 06				
Lingfield	d	19 12			19 31	19 40		20 09	20 39			21 09	21 39		22 09		22 39		23 09	23 39	00 12				
Dormans	d	19 15			19 34	19 44		20 12	20 42			21 12	21 42		22 12		22 42		23 12	23 42	00 15				
East Grinstead	a	19 22			19 42	19 52		20 17	20 47			21 17	21 47		22 17		22 47		23 17	23 47	00 20				
Edenbridge Town	d		19 15				19 45				20 46			21 46				22 46							
Hever	d		19 19				19 49				20 49			21 49											
Cowden	d		19 23				19 53				20 53			21 53											
Ashurst	d		19 27				19 57				20 58			21 58											
Eridge	d		19 33				20 03				21 03			22 03				22 58							
Crowborough	d		19 39				20 09				21 09			22 09				23 04							
Buxted	d		19 45				20 15				21 15			22 15				23 10							
Uckfield	a		19 51				20 21				21 21			22 21				23 16							

For general notes see front of timetable
For details of catering facilities see Directory of Train Operators

b Arr. 0608
c Arr. 0702
e Arr. 0732
f Arr. 0804

Table 184

London → Oxted, East Grinstead and Uckfield

Saturdays

Network Diagram - see first page of Table 184

		SN 1	SN 1	SN 1	SN 1	SN 1	SN 1	SN 1	SN 1	SN 1	SN 1		SN 1	SN 1
London Victoria 15	⊖ 175, 177 d	23p24	23p49	05 25		06 23	06 53		07 23	07 53		and at the same minutes past each hour until	19 23	19 53
Clapham Junction 10	175, 177 d	23p30	23p56	05 31		06 29	06 59		07 29	07 59			19 29	19 59
London Bridge 4	⊖ 175, 177 d				06 08			07 08			08 08			
Norwood Junction 2	175, 177 d			05 48										
East Croydon	175, 177 d	23p43	00 10	05 52	06 23	06 40	07 10	07 23	07 40	08 10	08 23		19 40	20 10
South Croydon 4	175 d			05 54										
Sanderstead	d	23p47	00s14			06 44	07 14		07 44	08 14			19 44	20 14
Riddlesdown	d	23p50	00s17			06 47	07 17		07 47	08 17			19 47	20 17
Upper Warlingham	d	23p54	00s21			06 51	07 21		07 51	08 21			19 51	20 21
Woldingham	d	23p58	00s25			06 55	07 25		07 55	08 25			19 55	20 25
Oxted 3	a	00 03	00 30	06 06	06 36	07 00	07 30	07 36	08 00	08 30	08 36		20 00	20 30
	d	00 03		06 06	06 37	07 00	07 30	07 37	08 00	08 30	08 37		20 00	20 30
Hurst Green	d	00 06		06 09	06 39	07 03	07 33	07 39	08 03	08 33	08 39		20 03	20 33
Lingfield	d	00 12		06 15		07 09	07 39		08 09	08 39			20 09	20 39
Dormans	d	00 15		06 18		07 12	07 42		08 12	08 42			20 12	20 42
East Grinstead	a	00 20		06 23		07 17	07 47		08 17	08 47			20 17	20 47
Edenbridge Town	d				06 45			07 45			08 45			
Hever	d				06 49			07 49			08 49			
Cowden	d				06 53			07 53			08 53			
Ashurst	d				06 57			07 57			08 57			
Eridge	d				07 03			08 03			09 03			
Crowborough	d				07 09			08 09			09 09			
Buxted	d				07 15			08 15			09 15			
Uckfield	a				07 21			08 21			09 21			

		SN 1	SN 1	SN 1	SN 1	SN 1	SN 1	SN 1	SN 1	SN 1	SN 1	SN 1
London Victoria 15	⊖ 175, 177 d		20 23	20 53		21 23	21 53		22 23	22 53	23 24	23 49
Clapham Junction 10	175, 177 d		20 29	20 59		21 29	21 59		22 29	22 59	23 30	23 56
London Bridge 4	⊖ 175, 177 d	20 08			21 08			22 08				
Norwood Junction 2	175, 177 d	20 19			21 19			22 19				
East Croydon	175, 177 d	20 23	20 40	21 10	21 23	21 40	22 10	22 23	22 40	23 10	23 43	00 10
South Croydon 4	175 d											
Sanderstead	d		20 44	21 14		21 44	22 14		22 44	23 14	23 47	00s14
Riddlesdown	d		20 47	21 17		21 47	22 17		22 47	23 17	23 50	00s17
Upper Warlingham	d		20 51	21 21		21 51	22 21		22 51	23 21	23 54	00s21
Woldingham	d		20 55	21 25		21 55	22 25		22 55	23 25	23 58	00s25
Oxted 3	a	20 36	21 00	21 30	21 36	22 00	22 30	22 36	23 00	23 30	00 03	00 30
	d	20 37	21 00	21 30	21 37	22 00	22 30	22 37	23 00	23 30	00 03	
Hurst Green	d	20 39	21 03	21 33	21 39	22 03	22 33	22 39	23 03	23 33	00 06	
Lingfield	d		21 09	21 39		22 09	22 39		23 09	23 39	00 12	
Dormans	d		21 12	21 42		22 12	22 42		23 12	23 42	00 15	
East Grinstead	a		21 17	21 47		22 17	22 47		23 17	23 47	00 20	
Edenbridge Town	d	20 45			21 45			22 45				
Hever	d	20 49			21 49							
Cowden	d	20 53			21 53							
Ashurst	d	20 57			21 57							
Eridge	d	21 03			22 03			22 57				
Crowborough	d	21 09			22 09			23 03				
Buxted	d	21 15			22 15			23 09				
Uckfield	a	21 21			22 21			23 15				

Sundays

		SN 1	SN 1	SN 1 A	SN 1 B	SN 1 A	SN 1 B	SN 1	SN 1 A	SN 1 B	SN 1	SN 1 A	SN 1 B	SN 1		SN 1 A	SN 1 B	SN 1	SN 1 B	SN 1 A
London Victoria 15	⊖ 175, 177 d	23p24	23p49	07 22	07 25	08 22	08 25		09 22	09 25		10 22	10 25		and at the same minutes past each hour until	21 22	21 25		22 25	22 22
Clapham Junction 10	175, 177 d	23p30	23p56	07 28	07 31	08 28	08 31		09 28	09 31		10 28	10 31			21 28	21 31		22 31	22 28
London Bridge 4	⊖ 175, 177 d																			
Norwood Junction 2	175, 177 d																			
East Croydon	175, 177 d	23p43	00 10	07 43	07 43	08 43	08 43	09 05	09 43	09 43	10 05	10 43	10 43			21 43	21 43		22 43	22 44
South Croydon 4	175 d																			
Sanderstead	d	23p47	00s14	07 47	07 47	08 47	08 47		09 47	09 47		10 47	10 47			21 47	21 47		22 47	22 48
Riddlesdown	d	23p50	00s17	07 50	07 50	08 50	08 50		09 50	09 50		10 50	10 50			21 50	21 50		22 50	22 51
Upper Warlingham	d	23p54	00s21	07 54	07 54	08 54	08 54		09 54	09 54		10 54	10 54			21 54	21 54		22 54	22 55
Woldingham	d	23p58	00s25	07 58	07 58	08 58	08 58		09 58	09 58		10 58	10 58			21 58	21 58		22 58	22 59
Oxted 3	a	00 03	00 30	08 03	08 03	09 03	09 03	09 17	10 03	10 03	10 17	11 03	11 03			22 03	22 03		23 03	23 04
	d	00 03		08 03	08 03	09 03	09 03	09 18	10 03	10 03	10 18	11 03	11 03	11 18		22 03	22 03	22 18	23 03	23 04
Hurst Green	d	00 06		08 06	08 06	09 06	09 06	09 21	10 06	10 06	10 21	11 06	11 06	11 21		22 06	22 06	22 21	23 06	23 07
Lingfield	d	00 12		08 12	08 12	09 12	09 12		10 12	10 12		11 12	11 12			22 12	22 12		23 12	23 13
Dormans	d	00 15		08 15	08 15	09 15	09 15		10 15	10 15		11 15	11 15			22 15	22 15		23 15	23 16
East Grinstead	a	00 20		08 20	08 20	09 20	09 20		10 20	10 20		11 20	11 20			22 20	22 20		23 20	23 21
Edenbridge Town	d							09 27			10 27			11 27				22 27		
Hever	d							09 31			10 31			11 31				22 31		
Cowden	d							09 35			10 35			11 35				22 35		
Ashurst	d							09 39			10 39			11 39				22 39		
Eridge	d							09 45			10 45			11 45				22 45		
Crowborough	d							09 51			10 51			11 51				22 51		
Buxted	d							09 57			10 57			11 57				22 57		
Uckfield	a							10 03			11 03			12 03				23 03		

For general notes see front of timetable
For details of catering facilities see Directory of Train Operators

A From 13 September
B Until 6 September

Uckfield, East Grinstead and Oxted → London

Network Diagram - see first page of Table 184

Miles	Miles	Station		SN 1	SN 1	SN	SN 1	SN 1	SN 1	SN 1	SN 1	SN 1	SN 1	SN 1		SN 1	SN 1	SN 1	SN 1	SN 1	SN 1	SN 1	SN 1	SN 1	SN 1
—	0	**Uckfield**	d					06 00			06 30		06 57						07 30			08 02		08 34	
—	2½	Buxted	d					06 05			06 35		07 02						07 35			08 07		08 39	
—	7¼	Crowborough	d					06 12			06 42		07 09						07 42			08 14		08 46	
—	10½	Eridge	d					06 17			06 47		07 14						07 47			08 19		08 51	
—	14¼	Ashurst	d					06 22			06 52								07 52			08 24		08 56	
—	17	Cowden	d					06 27			06 57								07 57			08 29		09 01	
—	19	Hever	d					06 31			07 01								08 01			08 33		09 05	
—	20¾	Edenbridge Town	d					06 34			07 04		07 27						08 04			08 36		09 08	
0	—	**East Grinstead**	d		05 58		06 20		06 36	06 44		07 06		07 23		07 31	07 39	07 47		08 02	08 14		08 37		09 07
2¼	—	Dormans	d		06 02		06 24		06 40	06 48		07 10		07 27			07 43	07 51		08 06	08 18		08 41		09 11
4	—	Lingfield	d		06 05		06 27		06 43	06 51		07 13		07 30			07 46	07 54		08 09	08 21		08 44		09 14
8¾	—	Hurst Green	d	06 00	06 12		06 34	06 41	06 50	06 58	07 11	07 20	07 34	07 38		07 43	07 55	08 01	08 11	08 16	08 28	08 43	08 51	09 15	09 21
9¾	25	**Oxted 3**	a	06 02	06 14		06 36	06 44	06 52	07 00	07 13	07 22	07 37	07 41		07 46	07 57	08 03	08 13	08 18	08 30	08 45	08 53	09 18	09 23
—	—		d	06 03	06 15		06 36		06 52	07 00	07 14	07 23	07 37	07 41		07 46	07 58	08 03	08 15	08 18	08 31	08 46	08 53	09 19	09 23
13	—	Woldingham	d	06 08			06 42			07 06		07 28		07 47		07 52		08 09		08 24	08 36		08 59		09 29
14¾	—	Upper Warlingham	d	06 12			06 45			07 09		07 32		07 50		07 55		08 12		08 27	08 40		09 02		09 32
16½	—	Riddlesdown	d	06 15			06 49			07 13		07 35		07 54		07 59		08 16		08 31	08 43		09 06		09 36
17¾	—	Sanderstead	d	06 18		06 38	06 52		07 03	07 16		07 39		07 57		08 02	08 08	08 19		08 34	08 46		09 09		09 39
18¾	—	South Croydon 4	175 d			06 42								08 01				08 22		08 37	08 49				
19¾	0	**East Croydon**	175, 177 a	06 23	06 27	06 44	06 56		07 08	07 20	07 25	07 43	07 53	08 03		08 06	08 15	08 24	08 29	08 39	08 52	08 59	09 13	09 32	09 43
—	1½	Norwood Junction 2	175, 177 a																						
—	10¼	**London Bridge 4**	⊖ 175, 177 a	06 40					07 25	07 38	07 44		08 11			08 24	08 35		08 53	09 00		09 19		09 51	
27½	—	Clapham Junction 10	175, 177 a		06 38	07 05	07 07					07 57		08 16				08 36			09 04		09 26		09 55
30¼	—	**London Victoria 15**	⊖ 175, 177 a		06 45	07 16	07 17					08 06		08 26				08 45			09 14		09 37		10 05

Station		SN 1	SN 1	SN 1		SN 1		SN 1	SN 1	SN 1		SN 1	SN 1	SN 1	SN 1	SN 1	SN 1	SN 1		SN 1	SN 1	SN 1	SN 1	SN 1
Uckfield	d		09 34					10 34			and at the same minutes past each hour until	14 34			15 34			16 33			17 03		17 32	
Buxted	d		09 39					10 39				14 39			15 39			16 38			17 08		17 37	
Crowborough	d		09 46					10 46				14 46			15 46			16 46			17 16		17 44	
Eridge	d		09 51					10 51				14 51			15 51			16 51			17 21		17 49	
Ashurst	d		09 56					10 56				14 56			15 56			16 56			17 26		17 54	
Cowden	d		10 01					11 01				15 01			16 01			17 01			17 31		17 59	
Hever	d		10 05					11 05				15 05			16 05			17 05			17 35		18 03	
Edenbridge Town	d		10 08					11 08				15 08			16 08			17 08			17 38		18 06	
East Grinstead	d	09 37		10 07		10 37			11 07	11 37			15 07	15 37		16 07	16 37			17 07		17 37		18 07
Dormans	d	09 41		10 11		10 41			11 11	11 41			15 11	15 41		16 11	16 41			17 11		17 41		18 11
Lingfield	d	09 44		10 14		10 44			11 14	11 44			15 14	15 44		16 14	16 44			17 14		17 44		18 14
Hurst Green	d	09 51	10 15	10 21		10 51		11 15	11 21	11 51		15 15	15 21	15 51	16 15	16 21	16 51	17 15		17 21	17 45	17 51	18 13	18 21
Oxted 3	a	09 53	10 17	10 23		10 53		11 17	11 23	11 53		15 17	15 23	15 53	16 17	16 23	16 53	17 17		17 23	17 48	17 53	18 15	18 23
	d	09 53	10 18	10 23		10 53		11 18	11 23	11 53		15 18	15 23	15 53	16 18	16 23	16 53	17 18		17 23		17 53	18 20	18 23
Woldingham	d	09 59		10 29		10 59			11 29	11 59			15 29	15 59		16 29	16 59			17 29		17 59		18 29
Upper Warlingham	d	10 02		10 32		11 02			11 32	12 02			15 32	16 02		16 32	17 02			17 32		18 02		18 32
Riddlesdown	d	10 06		10 36		11 06			11 36	12 06			15 36	16 06		16 36	17 06			17 36		18 06		18 36
Sanderstead	d	10 09		10 39		11 09			11 39	12 09			15 39	16 09		16 39	17 09			17 39		18 09		18 39
South Croydon 4	175 d																							
East Croydon	175, 177 a	10 13	10 32	10 43		11 13		11 32	11 43	12 13		15 32	15 43	16 13	16 32	16 43	17 13	17 35		17 43		18 13	18 38	18 43
Norwood Junction 2	175, 177 a																							
London Bridge 4	⊖ 175, 177 a		10 49					11 49				15 49			16 53			17 50					18 54	
Clapham Junction 10	175, 177 a	10 25		10 55		11 25			11 55	12 25			15 55	16 25		16 55	17 25			17 55		18 25		18 55
London Victoria 15	⊖ 175, 177 a	10 32		11 05		11 35			12 02	12 32			16 02	16 32		17 05	17 35			18 05		18 35		19 05

Station		SN 1	SN 1	SN 1	SN 1	SN 1	SN 1	SN 1	SN 1		SN 1	SN 1	SN 1	SN 1	SN 1	SN 1	SN 1	SN 1	SN 1	SN 1	SN 1	SN 1	SN 1		
Uckfield	d		17 58			18 30			18 57				19 33		20 04		20 34			21 34			22 32		
Buxted	d		18 03			18 35			19 02				19 38		20 09		20 39			21 39			22 37		
Crowborough	d		18b16			18 43			19c16				19 46		20 16		20 46			21 46			22 44		
Eridge	d		18 21			18 48			19 21				19 51		20 21		20 51			21 51			22 49		
Ashurst	d		18 26						19 26				19 56				20 56			21 56					
Cowden	d		18 31						19 31				20 01				21 01			22 01					
Hever	d		18 35			19 00			19 35				20 05				21 05			22 05					
Edenbridge Town	d		18 38			19 03			19 38				20 08		20 33		21 08			22 08			23 01		
East Grinstead	d	18 17		18 37	18 47		19 07	19 17			19 37	19 47		20 07		20 37		21 07	21 37		22 07	22 37			
Dormans	d	18 21		18 41	18 51		19 11	19 21			19 41	19 51		20 11		20 41		21 11	21 41		22 11	22 41			
Lingfield	d	18 24		18 44	18 54		19 14	19 24			19 44	19 54		20 14		20 44		21 14	21 44		22 14	22 44			
Hurst Green	d	18 31	18 45	18 51	19 01	19 10	19 21	19 31	19 45		19 51	20 01	20 15	20 21	20 39	20 51	21 15	21 21	21 51	22 15	22 21	22 51	23 08		
Oxted 3	a	18 33	18 47	18 53	19 03	19 12	19 23	19 33	19 47		19 53	20 03	20 17	20 23	20 42	20 53	21 17	21 23	21 53	22 17	22 23	22 53	23 10		
	d	18 34		18 53	19 04	19 13	19 23	19 34	19 48		19 53	20 04	20 18	20 23	20 42	20 53	21 18	21 23	21 53	22 18	22 23	22 53	23 11		
Woldingham	d	18 39		18 59	19 09		19 29	19 39			19 59	20 09		20 29		20 59		21 29	21 59		22 29	22 59			
Upper Warlingham	d	18 43		19 02	19 13		19 32	19 43			20 02	20 13		20 32		21 02		21 32	22 02		22 32	23 02			
Riddlesdown	d	18 46		19 06	19 16		19 36	19 46			20 06	20 16		20 36		21 06		21 36	22 06		22 36	23 06			
Sanderstead	d	18 49		19 09	19 19		19 39	19 49			20 09	20 19		20 39		21 09		21 39	22 09		22 39	23 09			
South Croydon 4	175 d																								
East Croydon	175, 177 a	18 56		19 13	19 25	19 31	19 43	19 55	20 06		20 13	20 25	20 31	20 43	20 54	21 13	21 31	21 43	22 13	22 33	22 43	23 13	23 28		
Norwood Junction 2	175, 177 a	19 01																							
London Bridge 4	⊖ 175, 177 a	19 15				19 51			20 21				20 49		21 11		21 49			22 49					
Clapham Junction 10	175, 177 a			19 25			19 55				20 25			20 55		21 25		21 55	22 25		22 55	23 25			
London Victoria 15	⊖ 175, 177 a			19 35			20 05				20 35			21 05		21 35		22 05	22 35		23 05	23 35			

For general notes see front of timetable
For details of catering facilities see Directory of Train Operators

b Arr. 1810
c Arr. 1909

Table 184

Saturdays

Uckfield, East Grinstead and Oxted → London

Network Diagram - see first page of Table 184

Station		SN 1	SN 1	SN 1	SN 1	SN 1		SN 1	SN 1	SN 1
Uckfield	d		06 34			07 34	and at			22 32
Buxted	d		06 39			07 39	the same			22 37
Crowborough	d		06 46			07 46	minutes			22 44
Eridge	d		06 51			07 51	past			22 49
Ashurst	d		06 56			07 56	each			
Cowden	d		07 01			08 01	hour until			
Hever	d		07 05			08 05				
Edenbridge Town	d		07 08			08 08				23 01
East Grinstead	d	06 37		07 07	07 37			22 07	22 37	
Dormans	d	06 41		07 11	07 41			22 11	22 41	
Lingfield	d	06 44		07 14	07 44			22 14	22 44	
Hurst Green	d	06 51	07 15	07 21	07 51	08 15		22 21	22 51	23 08
Oxted 3	a	06 53	07 18	07 23	07 53	08 18		22 23	22 53	23 10
	d	06 53	07 19	07 23	07 53	08 19		22 23	22 53	23 11
Woldingham	d	06 59		07 29	07 59			22 29	22 59	
Upper Warlingham	d	07 02		07 32	08 02			22 32	23 02	
Riddlesdown	d	07 06		07 36	08 06			22 36	23 06	
Sanderstead	d	07 09		07 39	08 09			22 39	23 09	
South Croydon 4	175 d									
East Croydon	175, 177 ⇌ a	07 13	07 33	07 43	08 13	08 32		22 43	23 13	23 26
Norwood Junction 2	175, 177 a									
London Bridge 4	⊖ 175, 177 a		07 49			08 49				
Clapham Junction 10	175, 177 a	07 25		07 55	08 25			22 55	23 25	
London Victoria 15	⊖ 175, 177 a	07 32		08 02	08 32			23 02	23 32	

Sundays

Station		SN 1	SN 1	SN 1	SN 1	SN 1		SN 1	SN 1	SN 1	SN 1
Uckfield	d				10 17		and at	21 17		22 17	
Buxted	d				10 22		the same	21 22		22 22	
Crowborough	d				10 29		minutes	21 29		22 29	
Eridge	d				10 34		past	21 34		22 34	
Ashurst	d				10 39		each	21 39		22 39	
Cowden	d				10 44		hour until	21 44		22 44	
Hever	d				10 48			21 48		22 48	
Edenbridge Town	d				10 51			21 51		22 51	
East Grinstead	d	07 52	08 52	09 52		10 52			21 52		22 52
Dormans	d	07 56	08 56	09 56		10 56			21 56		22 56
Lingfield	d	07 59	08 59	09 59		10 59			21 59		22 59
Hurst Green	d	08 06	09 06	10 06	10 58	11 06		21 58	22 06	22 58	23 06
Oxted 3	a	08 08	09 08	10 08	11 01	11 08		22 01	22 08	23 01	23 08
	d	08 08	09 08	10 08		11 08			22 08	23 02	23 08
Woldingham	d	08 14	09 14	10 14		11 14			22 14		23 14
Upper Warlingham	d	08 17	09 17	10 17		11 17			22 17		23 17
Riddlesdown	d	08 21	09 21	10 21		11 21			22 21		23 21
Sanderstead	d	08 24	09 24	10 24		11 24			22 24		23 24
South Croydon 4	175 d										
East Croydon	175, 177 ⇌ a	08 28	09 28	10 28		11 28			22 28	23 14	23 28
Norwood Junction 2	175, 177 a										
London Bridge 4	⊖ 175, 177 a										
Clapham Junction 10	175, 177 a	08 41	09 41	10 41		11 41			22 41		23 41
London Victoria 15	⊖ 175, 177 a	08 48	09 48	10 48		11 48			22 48		23 51

For general notes see front of timetable
For details of catering facilities see Directory of Train Operators

Network Diagram for Tables 186, 188

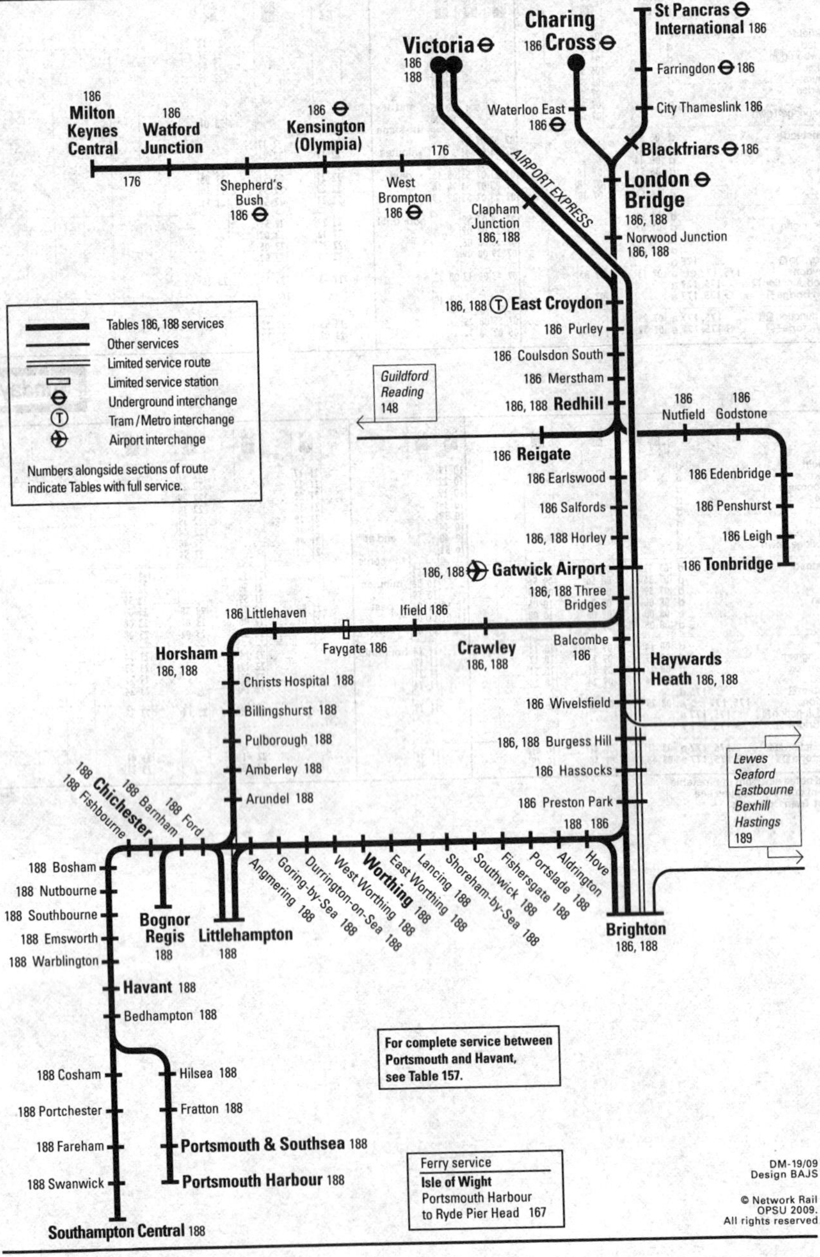

St Pancras International 186
Charing Cross 186
Victoria 186 188
Farringdon 186
City Thameslink 186
Waterloo East 186
Blackfriars 186
London Bridge 186, 188
186 Milton Keynes Central
186 Watford Junction
186 Kensington (Olympia)
176
176
Shepherd's Bush 186
West Brompton 186
Clapham Junction 186, 188
AIRPORT EXPRESS
Norwood Junction 186, 188
186, 188 East Croydon
186 Purley
186 Coulsdon South
186 Merstham
186, 188 Redhill
Guildford
Reading
148
186 Nutfield
186 Godstone
186 Reigate
186 Earlswood
186 Salfords
186, 188 Horley
186, 188 Gatwick Airport
186, 188 Three Bridges
186 Edenbridge
186 Penshurst
186 Leigh
186 Tonbridge
Tables 186, 188 services
Other services
Limited service route
Limited service station
Underground interchange
Tram / Metro interchange
Airport interchange
Numbers alongside sections of route indicate Tables with full service.
186 Littlehaven
Ifield 186
Faygate 186
Crawley 186, 188
Balcombe 186
Horsham 186, 188
Haywards Heath 186, 188
Christs Hospital 188
Billingshurst 188
Pulborough 188
Amberley 188
Arundel 188
186 Wivelsfield
186, 188 Burgess Hill
186 Hassocks
186 Preston Park
Lewes
Seaford
Eastbourne
Bexhill
Hastings
189
188 Fishbourne
188 Chichester
188 Barnham
188 Ford
188 186
188 Bosham
188 Nutbourne
188 Southbourne
188 Emsworth
188 Warblington
Bognor Regis 188
Littlehampton 188
Angmering 188
Goring-by-Sea 188
Durrington-on-Sea 188
West Worthing 188
Worthing 188
East Worthing 188
Lancing 188
Shoreham-by-Sea 188
Southwick 188
Fishersgate 188
Portslade 188
Aldrington 188
Hove
Brighton 186, 188
Havant 188
Bedhampton 188
For complete service between Portsmouth and Havant, see Table 157.
188 Cosham
Hilsea 188
188 Portchester
Fratton 188
188 Fareham
Portsmouth & Southsea 188
188 Swanwick
Portsmouth Harbour 188
Southampton Central 188
Ferry service
Isle of Wight
Portsmouth Harbour to Ryde Pier Head 167

DM-19/09
Design BAJS

Table 186

Bedford and London → Brighton

Network Diagram - see first page of Table 186

Miles	Miles	Miles	Station		SN MX 1◇	SN MO 1	FC MX 1	FC MO 1 A	SN MX 1◇	FC MX 1	FC MO 1 B	SN 1	SN MO 1	SN MX 1	SN MX 1	SN MO 1	SN MX 1	SN MX 1	SN MO 1	GW MX 1	SN MX 1◇	SN MO 1◇	FC 1	SN MX 1	GX 1
0	—	—	**London Victoria** 15 ⊖	d	23p02	23p04								23p10	23p17				23p17		23p32	23p32		23p47	00 01
—	0	—	Milton Keynes Central 10	d																					
—	32¼	—	Watford Junction	d																					
—	—	1½	Shepherd's Bush ⊖	d																					
—	47½	2¾	Kensington (Olympia) ⊖	d																					
—	48¾	3¼	West Brompton ⊖	d																					
2¾	50¾	6¼	Clapham Junction 10	d	23p08	23p10								23p16	23p23				23p23		23p38	23p38		23p53	
—	—	—	**Bedford** 7	d																					
—	—	—	Luton 10	d																					
—	—	—	Luton Airport Parkway 7 ✈	d																					
—	—	—	St Albans City	d																					
—	—	—	St Pancras International 15 ⊖	d																					
—	—	—	Farringdon 3 ⊖	d																					
—	—	—	City Thameslink 3	d																					
—	—	—	**London Blackfriars** 3 ⊖	d																					
—	—	—	**London Charing Cross** 4 ⊖	d																					
—	—	—	**London Waterloo (East)** 4 ⊖	d																					
—	0	—	**London Bridge** 4 ⊖	d			23p11	23p11			23p11														
—	9	—	Norwood Junction 2	d																			23p41	*23 41*	
10½	10¼	—	**East Croydon**	a	23p19	23p23	23p24	23p25			23p26			23p28	23p33				23p37		23p51	23p52	23p56	00 05	
—	—	—		d	23p20	23p23	23p24	23p25			23p27			23p28	23p33				23p38		23p52	23p53	23p57	00 06	
13½	—	—	Purley 4	d		23p29								23p33										00 12	
15½	—	—	Coulsdon South	d		23p33							←	23p37										00 15	
19	—	—	Merstham	d		23p38							23p38	23p42										00 21	
21	0	0	**Redhill** 5	a	23p31	→							23p42	23p46			←				00 03	00 05		00 24	
—	—	—		d	23p31								23p42	23p46			23p46	23p55		00 03	00 05	00 05		00 25	
—	1¾	—	**Reigate**	a										→											
—	—	2	Nutfield	d																					
—	—	5¾	Godstone	d																					
—	—	10½	Edenbridge	d																					
—	—	15½	Penshurst	d														00 06							
—	—	17¼	Leigh (Kent)	d																					
—	—	19¾	**Tonbridge** 4	a														00 15							
21¾	—	—	Earlswood (Surrey)	d													23p49								
23¾	—	—	Salfords	d												←	23p52								
26	—	—	Horley 4	d												23p50	23p56							00 31	
26¾	—	—	**Gatwick Airport** 10 ✈	a	23p38		23p41	23p41			23p48		23p50 →		23p50	23p54	23p58		23p59	00 10	00 14	00 14	00 17	00 33	00 35
—	—	—		d	23p39		23p41	23p42			23p50				23p51	23p55	23p59		00 01		00 15	00 15	00 18	00 34	
29½	0	—	Three Bridges 15	a	23p44		23p47	23p47		←	23p54				23p55	00 01	00 04		00 05		00 19	00 19	00 25	00 39	
—	—	—		d	23p44		23p47 →	23p47		23p47	23p54	07 05			23p56	00 01	00 04		00 06		00 20	00 20		00 39	
—	1½	—	Crawley	d								07 08				00 05	00 07							00 42	
—	2¾	—	Ifield	d								07 11				00 07	00 10							00 45	
—	5¼	—	Faygate	d								07 15													
—	7½	—	Littlehaven	d								07 19				00 14	00 16							00 51	
—	8½	—	**Horsham** 4	a								07 22				00 17	00 19							00 54	
34	—	—	Balcombe	d						23p53											00 26	00 26			
38	—	—	**Haywards Heath** 3	a	23p52			23p56		23p58	00 03			00 04					00 14		00 31	00 31			
—	—	—		d	23p53			23p56		23p58	00 03			00 05					00 15		00 31	00 31			
41	0	—	Wivelsfield 4	d	23p57					00 02											00 35	00 35			
—	9¼	—	Lewes 4	a																					
41¾	—	—	Burgess Hill 4	d	23p59			00 01	←	00 04	00 08			00 10							00 37	00 37			
43¾	—	—	Hassocks 4	d	00 02				00 02	00 08											00 41	00 41			
49½	0	—	Preston Park	d	→				00 09	00 15											00 48	00 48			
—	1½	—	Hove 2	a										00 21					00 28						
51	—	—	**Brighton** 10	a				00 12	00 15	00 20	00 22										00 52	00 52			

For general notes see front of timetable
For details of catering facilities see Directory of Train Operators

A Until 7 September
B From 14 September

Bedford and London → Brighton

Network Diagram - see first page of Table 186

Station		GW	SN	FC	SN	GW	GX	FC	SN	FC	FC	SN	FC	SN	FC	GX	FC	SN	FC	GX	FC	GX	SN	SN
		MO	MX			MX																		
		1	1		1	1	1		1 ◇	1	1	1	1	1		1	1	1 ◇	1	1	1	1	1	1 ◇
			A																					
London Victoria 15 ⊖	d		00 05	23 49	00 14		00 32	00b17	01 00			02 00		03 00		03 30		04 00		04 30		05 00		05 02
Milton Keynes Central 10	d		22 11																					
Watford Junction	d		22 53		23 29																			
Shepherd's Bush ⊖	d		23 21		23 54																			
Kensington (Olympia) ⊖	d		23 23		23 56																			
West Brompton ⊖	d		23 26		23 59																			
Clapham Junction 10	d		00 11	23 56	00 20			00b23	01 08			02 08		03 08				04 08						05 08
Bedford 7	d																							
Luton 10	d																							
Luton Airport Parkway 7 ✈	d																							
St Albans City	d																							
St Pancras International 15 ⊖	d																							
Farringdon 3 ⊖	d																							
City Thameslink 3	d																							
London Blackfriars 3 ⊖	d																							
London Charing Cross 4 ⊖	d																							
London Waterloo (East) 4 ⊖	d																							
London Bridge 4 ⊖	d		23 53	00 11	00 11			00 41	00 41	01 05	01 35		02 05		03 05		03 35		04 05		04 35			
Norwood Junction 2	d																							
East Croydon	a		00 24	00 26	00 32			00 56	01 21	01 32	02 02	02 21	02 30	03 21	03 30		04 00	04 21	04 30		05 00			05 20
	d		00 25	00 27	00 33			00 57	01 22	01 32	02 02	02 22	02 32	03 22	03 32		04 02	04 22	04 32		05 02			05 20
Purley 4	d				00 38				01 27			02 27		03 27				04 27						05 25
Coulsdon South	d				00 41																			05 28
Merstham	d				00 47																			05 34
Redhill 5	a				00 50																			05 37
	d	00 34			00 51	00 53																	05 36	05 38
Reigate	a																							
Nutfield	d																						05 40	
Godstone	d																						05 46	
Edenbridge	d																						05 51	
Penshurst	d																						05 58	
Leigh (Kent)	d																						06 01	
Tonbridge 4	a																						06 06	
Earlswood (Surrey)	d																							
Salfords	d																							
Horley 4	d				00 57				01 42			02 42		03 42				04 43						05 44
Gatwick Airport 10 ✈	a	00 41	00 42	00 49	00 59	01 02	01 05	01 16	01 44	01 51	02 21	02 44	02 51	03 44	03 51	04 05	04 24	04 45	04 51	05 05	05 21	05 35		05 46
	d		00 43	00 50				01 17	01 46	01 52	02 22	02 46	02 52	03 46	03 52		04 24	04 47	04 52		05 22			05 47
Three Bridges 15	a		00 48	00 55				01 24	01 50	01 58	02 28	02 50	02 58	03 50	03 58		04 30	04 51	04 58		05 26			05 52
	d		00 48						01 52									04 52	04 58		05 26			05 52
Crawley	d																							
Ifield	d																							
Faygate	d																							
Littlehaven	d																							
Horsham 4	a																							
Balcombe	d																							05 58
Haywards Heath 3	a		01 00						02 06									05 00	05 08		05 36			06 03
	d		01 03	01 06					02 06									05 01	05 08		05 36			06 04
Wivelsfield 4	d																				05 40			06 08
Lewes 4	a			01 20																				
Burgess Hill 4	d																				05 42			06 10
Hassocks 4	d																				05 46			06 13
Preston Park	d																				05 53			06 20
Hove 2	a		01s25																					
Brighton 10	a		01s17						02 23									05 16	05 29		05 59			06 25

For general notes see front of timetable
For details of catering facilities see
Directory of Train Operators

A To Eastbourne (Table 189)
b Change at East Croydon

Bedford and London → Brighton

Network Diagram - see first page of Table 186

		GX	GW	FC	GW	SN	GX	SN	SN	SN	FC	GX	SN	FC	GX	GW	GW		SN		GX	FC	SN	SN	GW
		1	1	1	1	1	1	1	1	1	1	1	1	1	1	1	1		1		1	1	1	1	1
						A				B			B						C				C		
London Victoria [15]	⊖ d	05 15					05 30			05 32		05 45			06 00				06 02		06 15				
Milton Keynes Central [10]	d																								
Watford Junction	d																								
Shepherd's Bush	⊖ d																								
Kensington (Olympia)	⊖ d																								
West Brompton	⊖ d																								
Clapham Junction [10]	d									05 38									06 08						
Bedford [7]	d			03 40							04 10			04 20								04 50			
Luton [10]	d			04 04							04 34			04 44								05 14			
Luton Airport Parkway [7]	✈ d			04 06							04 36			04 46								05 16			
St Albans City	d			04 18							04 48			04 58								05 28			
St Pancras International [15]	⊖ d			04 52							05 12			05 32								06 02			
Farringdon [3]	⊖ d			04 57							05 17			05 37								06 07			
City Thameslink [3]	d										05 21			05 41								06 11			
London Blackfriars [3]	⊖ d			05 04							05 24			05 44								06 14			
London Charing Cross [4]	⊖ d																								
London Waterloo (East) [4]	⊖ d																								
London Bridge [4]	⊖ d										05 31			05 51					*05 55*			06 21			
Norwood Junction [2]	d																								
East Croydon	a			05 30						05 48	05 51			06 04					06 17			06 35			
	d			05 32						05 49	05 52			06 04					06 18			06 36			
Purley [4]	d									05 54									06 23						
Coulsdon South	d									05 58									06 27						
Merstham	d									06 03									06 33						
Redhill [5]	a									06 07			←						06 36				←		
	d		05 44		05 44				05 56	06 07			06 07			06 14	06 24		06 40	06 42			06 40	06 42	06 46
Reigate	a				05 48					↪						06 18	06 28		↪					06 46	
Nutfield	d								06 00											06 46					
Godstone	d								06 06											06 52					
Edenbridge	d								06 11											06 57					
Penshurst	d								06 18											07 04					
Leigh (Kent)	d								06 21											07 07					
Tonbridge [4]	a								06 26											07 15					
Earlswood (Surrey)	d												06 10										06 42		
Salfords	d												06 13										06 46		
Horley [4]	d												06 17										06 49		
Gatwick Airport [10]	✈ a	05 50	05 52	05 53			06 00				06 08	06 15	06 19	06 20	06 30						06 45	06 51	06 53		06 56
	d			05 54		05 59					06 08		06 20	06 20								06 52	06 54		
Three Bridges [15]	a			05 59		06 03					06 14		06 25	06 26								06 56	06 59		
	d			06 00		06 04					06 14		06 25	06 26								06 56	07 00		
Crawley	d					06 07																	07 03		
Ifield	d					06 10																			
Faygate	d																								
Littlehaven	d					06 16																			
Horsham [4]	a					06 19																	07 11		
Balcombe	d										06 20			06 33											
Haywards Heath [3]	a			06 09							06 25		06 33	06 38								07 05			
	d			06 10				06 13			06 25		06 34	06 38								07 06			
Wivelsfield [4]	d			06 14				06 17			06 29		06 38	06 42								07 10			
Lewes [4]	a							06 28					06 49												
Burgess Hill [4]	d			06 16							06 32			06 44								07 12			
Hassocks [4]	d			06 19							06 35			06 47								07 15			
Preston Park	d			06 26							06 42			06 54								07 22			
Hove [2]	a																								
Brighton [10]	a			06 33							06 47			06 59								07 29			

For general notes see front of timetable
For details of catering facilities see Directory of Train Operators

A To Southampton Central (Table 188) and to Bognor Regis (Table 188)
B To Ore (Table 189)
C To Bognor Regis (Table 188)

Bedford and London → Brighton

Network Diagram - see first page of Table 186

Station		SN 1	GX 1	SN 1 ◇		SN 1	SN 1	SN 1 ◇	FC 1	GX 1	SN 1	SN 1 ◇		GW 1	SN 1		GW 1	SN 1	GX 1	FC 1	SN 1	SN 1	GX 1	FC 1	GW 1
								A			B	A													
London Victoria 15 ⊖	d		06 30	06 21				06 32		06 45	06 47				06 51				07 00			07 02	07 15	07b07	
Milton Keynes Central 10	d																								
Watford Junction	d							*05 54*																	
Shepherd's Bush ⊖	d							*06 19*																	
Kensington (Olympia) ⊖	d							*06 22*																	
West Brompton ⊖	d							*06 25*																	
Clapham Junction 10	d			06 27				06 38			06 53				06 57							07 08		07b13	
Bedford 7	d								05 20											05 40				06 00	
Luton 10	d								05 44											06 04				06 24	
Luton Airport Parkway 7 ✈	d								05 46											06 06				06 26	
St Albans City	d								05 58											06 18				06 38	
St Pancras International 15 ⊖	d								06 20											06 40				07 00	
Farringdon 3 ⊖	d								06 25											06 45				07 05	
City Thameslink 3	d								06 27											06 47				07 07	
London Blackfriars 3 ⊖	d								06 34											06 50				07 10	
London Charing Cross 4 ⊖	d																								
London Waterloo (East) 4 ⊖	d																								
London Bridge 4 ⊖	d								06 43											07 01		*06 56*		07 16	
Norwood Junction 2	d																								
East Croydon	a			06 37				06 48	06 56		07 03				07 06					07 15		07 18		07 31	
	d			06 38				06 49	06 56		07 03				07 07					07 16		07 19		07 32	
Purley 4	d			06 43				06 54														07 24			
Coulsdon South	d							06 57							07 13							07 27			
Merstham	d							07 03							07 19							07 33			
Redhill 5	a			06 51			←	07 06				←			07 22			←			←	07 36			
	d			06 55	07 03	07 00	07 03	07 07				07 07		07 11	07 27	07 29	07 28	07 29			07 27	07 37			07 41
Reigate	a				→	07 04		→						07 15	→	→	07 32					07 44			
Nutfield	d						07 07											07 33							
Godstone	d						07 13											07 39							
Edenbridge	d						07 18											07 44							
Penshurst	d						07 25											07 51							
Leigh (Kent)	d						07 28											07 54							
Tonbridge 4	a						07 33											08 02							
Earlswood (Surrey)	d											07 09									07 29				
Salfords	d											07 13									07 33				
Horley 4	d			07 01								07 16									07 36				
Gatwick Airport 10 ✈	a		07 00	07 03					07 11	07 15	07 18	07 19							07 30	07 31	07 39		07 45	07 48	07 50
	d			07 04					07 12		07 19	07 20								07 32	07 40			07 50	
Three Bridges 15	a			07 09					07 17		07 24	07 24								07 37	07 44			07 54	
	d			07 09					07 18		07 24	07 28	07 30							07 38	07 45			07 54	
Crawley	d												07 34								07 49				
Ifield	d												07 36								07 51				
Faygate	d																								
Littlehaven	d												07 43								07 58				
Horsham 4	a												07 46								08 01				
Balcombe	d			07 15								07 35												08 00	
Haywards Heath 3	a			07 20					07 27		07 32	07 40								07 47				08 06	
	d	07 10		07 21					07 28		07 33	07 40								07 48				08 06	
Wivelsfield 4	d	07 14		07 25					07 32		07 37	07 44												08 10	
Lewes 4	a	07 29									07 52														
Burgess Hill 4	d			07 27					07 34			07 46								07 54				08 12	
Hassocks 4	d			07 30					07 37			07 50												08 15	
Preston Park	d			07 37					07 44			07 57												08 22	
Hove 2	a																								
Brighton 10	a			07 42					07 49			08 02								08 07				08 27	

For general notes see front of timetable
For details of catering facilities see
Directory of Train Operators

A To Chichester (Table 188)
B To Ore (Table 189)
b Change at East Croydon

Bedford and London → Brighton

Network Diagram - see first page of Table 186

		SN 1	GX 1	SN 1	SN 1	SN 1	GW 1	SN 1	FC 1	GX 1	SN 1	SN 1	SN 1	SN 1		SN 1	SN 1	SN 1	GX 1	SN 1	SN 1 ◇	FC 1	GX 1	SN 1	
		A																							
London Victoria 15	⊖ d	07 17	07 30		07b23			07 36		07 45	07 47					07 52			08 00	08 02	08 07		08 15	08 17	
Milton Keynes Central 10	d																								
Watford Junction	d							06 53																	
Shepherd's Bush	⊖ d							07 19																	
Kensington (Olympia)	⊖ d							07 22																	
West Brompton	⊖ d							07 25																	
Clapham Junction 10	d	07 23			07b29			07 42			07 53					07 58				08 08	08 13			08 23	
Bedford 7	d								06 20													06 56			
Luton 10	d								06 44													07 16			
Luton Airport Parkway 7	✈ d								06 46																
St Albans City	d								06 58													07 28			
St Pancras International 15	⊖ d								07 20													07 48			
Farringdon 3	⊖ d								07 25													07 53			
City Thameslink 3	d								07 29													07 57			
London Blackfriars 3	⊖ d								07 32													08 00			
London Charing Cross 4	⊖ d																								
London Waterloo (East) 4	⊖ d																								
London Bridge 4	⊖ d				07 28	07 33			07 40					07 53		07 46	08 00			07 56		08 06			
Norwood Junction 2	d				07 42												08 12								
East Croydon	a	07 33			07 45	07 48		07 52	07 55		08 03			08 06		08 09	08 16			08 18	08 22	08 25		08 33	
	d	07 34			07 46	07 49		07 52	07 56		08 03			08 06		08 09	08 17			08 18	08 23	08 26		08 33	
Purley 4	d							07 57									08 25								
Coulsdon South	d				07 52			08 01									08 28 →								
Merstham	d				07 58			08 07																	
Redhill 5	a	07 45			08 01			08 10						08 17						08 31					
	d	07 46		07 59	08 02		08 09	08 11				← 08 11	08 16	08 21	08 23			← 08 21		08 32					
Reigate	a			08 03			08 13 →						08 20 →												
Nutfield	d				08 06										08 27										
Godstone	d				08 12										08 33										
Edenbridge	d				08 17										08 38										
Penshurst	d				08 24										08 45										
Leigh (Kent)	d				08 27										08 48										
Tonbridge 4	a				08 32										08 53										
Earlswood (Surrey)	d	07 48										08 13													
Salfords	d	07 52										08 17													
Horley 4	d	07 55										08 21													
Gatwick Airport 10	✈ a	07 58	08 02			08 04			08 11	08 15	08 18	08 24				08 24		08 28	08 31	08 39		08 40	08 45	08 48	
	d	07 59				08 05			08 12		08 19	08 25				08 25		08 29		08 40		08 42		08 49	
Three Bridges 15	a	08 04				08 09			08 16			08 30						08 33		08 44	08 41	08 46			
	d	08 05				08 10			08 16			08 31						08 34		08 45	08 42	08 46			
Crawley	d	08 09										08 34								08 48					
Ifield	d	08 11										08 37													
Faygate	d	08 15										08 41													
Littlehaven	d	08 19										08 45													
Horsham 4	a	08 22										08 49								08 56					
Balcombe	d								08 22													08 52			
Haywards Heath 3	a					08 19			08 27		08 30					08 36		08 42			08 50	08 57		09 00	
	d					08 19			08 28		08 32					08 37		08 43			08 51	08 58		09 13 →	09 04
Wivelsfield 4	d								08 32		08 36							08 47				09 02			
Lewes 4	a										08 51														
Burgess Hill 4	d					08 25			08 34									08 49				09 04			09 09
Hassocks 4	d								08 37									08 52				09 07			
Preston Park	d								08 44									08 59				09 14			
Hove 2	a															08 53									09 21
Brighton 10	a					08 36			08 49									09 04			09 07	09 19			

For general notes see front of timetable
For details of catering facilities see Directory of Train Operators

A To Southampton Central (Table 188)
b Change at East Croydon

Bedford and London → Brighton

Network Diagram - see first page of Table 186

		GW	FC	SN	SN	GW	SN		SN	SN	SN	GW	GX	SN	SN	SN	SN	SN	GX	SN		SN	SN	FC
		1	1	1	1	1	1		1 ◊	1	1 ◊	1	1	1	1	1 ◊	1 ◊	1 ◊	1	1		1	1	1
														🛒		🛒				A 🛒				
London Victoria [15] ⊖	d		*08b11*						08 21		08 26		08 30	08 32		08 36		08 40	08 45	08 47				
Milton Keynes Central [10]	d								*07 01*															
Watford Junction	d								*07 38*															
Shepherd's Bush ⊖	d								*08 06*											08 32				
Kensington (Olympia) ⊖	d								*08 09*											08 34				
West Brompton ⊖	d								*08 12*											08 37				
Clapham Junction [10]	d								08 27		08 32			08 38		08 43		08 46		08 53				
Bedford [7]	d		07 00																					07 28
Luton [10]	d		07 24																					07 48
Luton Airport Parkway [7] ✈	d		07 26																					
St Albans City	d		07 38																					08 00
St Pancras International [15] ⊖	d		08 00																					08 20
Farringdon [3] ⊖	d		08 05																					08 25
City Thameslink [3]	d		08 09																					08 29
London Blackfriars [3] ⊖	d		08 12																					08 32
London Charing Cross [4] ⊖	d																							
London Waterloo (East) [4] ⊖	d																							
London Bridge [4] ⊖	d		08 19				08 23		*08 09*					*08 25*	08 30	*08 27*							08 48	*08 36*
Norwood Junction [2]	d														08 45									
East Croydon	a		08 36				08 37		08 39		08 43			08 48	08 49	08 52		08 56		09 03			09 03	09 06
	d		08 36				08 38		08 39		08 44			08 48	08 50	08 53		08 57		09 03			09 04	09 06
Purley [4]	d			←											08 56								09 12	
Coulsdon South	d			08 28			08 46								09 00								09 15	
Merstham	d			08 34											09 06									
Redhill [5]	a			08 37	←		08 53					←		09 02	09 10							←	09 22	
	d	08 33		08 41	08 41	08 51	08 57	08 59				08 51		09 03	09 11							09 11	09 23	
Reigate	a	08 37		→		→		09 03							→									
Nutfield	d						09 01																09 27	
Godstone	d						09 07																09 33	
Edenbridge	d						09 12																09 38	
Penshurst	d						09 19																09 45	
Leigh (Kent)	d						09 22																09 48	
Tonbridge [4]	a						09 27																09 53	
Earlswood (Surrey)	d				08 43																	09 13		
Salfords	d				08 47																	09 17		
Horley [4]	d				08 50																	09 21		
Gatwick Airport [10] ✈	a		08 51		08 53				08 55		08 58	09 01	09 02	09 10				09 12	09 15	09 18		09 23		09 24
	d		08 52		08 54				08 56		09 00			09 11				09 14		09 19		09 25		09 26
Three Bridges [15]	a		08 57		08 59						09 04			09 16				09 18				09 29		09 30
	d		08 57		08 59						09 05			09 16				09 19				09 30		09 30
Crawley	d				09 03									09 19								09 33		
Ifield	d				09 06																	09 36		
Faygate	d				09 10																			
Littlehaven	d				09 14																	09 42		
Horsham [4]	a				09 17									09 27								09 46		
Balcombe	d																							
Haywards Heath [3]	a		09 06						09 09	←	09 14							09 27		09 30				09 39
	d		09 07						09 10	09 13	09 17						←	09 28		09 34	09 37			09 40
Wivelsfield [4]	d									09 17	09 21						09 21	09 34						
Lewes [4]	a									09 28	→									09 52				
Burgess Hill [4]	d																09 23	09 36						
Hassocks [4]	d																09 27	09 39						
Preston Park	d																09 34							
Hove [2]	a																				09 51			
Brighton [10]	a		09 23						09 26							09 30	09 40	09 49						09 54

For general notes see front of timetable
For details of catering facilities see
Directory of Train Operators

A 🛒 to Lewes
b Change at East Croydon

Bedford and London → Brighton

Network Diagram - see first page of Table 186

	GX	GW	SN	GW	SN	SN	FC	GX	GW	SN	SN	SN	SN	FC	GW	GX	SN	SN	SN	SN	FC	GX	GW
	1	1	1	1	1	1 ◇	1	1	1	1	1	1 ◇	1	1	1	1	1	1	1 ◇	1 ◇	1	1	1
											A												
			⊼			⊼					⊼						⊼						
London Victoria 15 ⊖ d	09 00		09 02		08b53	09 06		09 15			09 17	09 21				09 30	09 32	09b23	09 36			09 45	
Milton Keynes Central 10 d																			08 13				
Watford Junction d																			08 51				
Shepherd's Bush ⊖ d																	09 06		09 23				
Kensington (Olympia) ⊖ d																	09 09		09 25				
West Brompton ⊖ d																	09 12		09 28				
Clapham Junction 10 d			09 08		08b59	09 12					09 23						09 38	09b29	09 42				
Bedford 7 d							07 48							08 04							08 20		
Luton 10 d							08 12							08 28							08 44		
Luton Airport Parkway 7 ✈ d							08 14							08 30							08 46		
St Albans City d							08 26							08 44							09 00		
St Pancras International 15 ⊖ d							08 48							09 04							09 20		
Farringdon 3 ⊖ d							08 53							09 09							09 25		
City Thameslink 3 d							08 56							09 13							09 29		
London Blackfriars 3 ⊖ d							08 59							09 16							09 34		
London Charing Cross 4 ⊖ d																							
London Waterloo (East) 4 ⊖ d																							
London Bridge 4 ⊖ d			08 52		09 03		09 06			09 18	09 09			09 25				09 30			09 42		
Norwood Junction 2 d					09 15													09 45					
East Croydon a			09 18		09 18	09 22	09 23			09 32	09 33	09 37		09 39			09 48	09 48	09 52		09 54		
East Croydon d			09 18		09 21	09 22	09 24			09 33	09 33	09 37		09 39			09 48	09 51	09 52		09 54		
Purley 4 d					09 27					09 41								09 57					
Coulsdon South d					09 30					09 44								10 00					
Merstham d					09 36													10 06					
Redhill 5 a			09 30		09 39					09 51							10 00	10 09					
Redhill d		09 24	09 30	09 34	09 40				09 51	09 53			← 09 40		← 09 51		10 00	10 10					10 14
Reigate a		09 28		09 38	↪				↪	09 57								↪					10 18
Nutfield d																							
Godstone d																							
Edenbridge d																							
Penshurst d																							
Leigh (Kent) d																							
Tonbridge 4 a																							
Earlswood (Surrey) d													09 42										
Salfords d													09 46										
Horley 4 d			09 36										09 50										
Gatwick Airport 10 ✈ a	09 30		09 39				09 40	09 45			09 48	09 52	09 53	09 56	09 58	10 00	10 08				10 10	10 15	
Gatwick Airport d			09 40				09 41				09 49	09 53	09 54	09 57			10 09				10 11		
Three Bridges 15 a			09 44				09 45					09 58	09 59	10 01			10 14				10 15		
Three Bridges d			09 45				09 45					09 58	10 00	10 02			10 14				10 15		
Crawley d			09 48										10 03				10 18						
Ifield d													10 06										
Faygate d																							
Littlehaven d													10 12										
Horsham 4 a			09 56										10 15				10 26						
Balcombe d							09 51														10 21		
Haywards Heath 3 a							09 56				10 00	10 08		10 10							10 26		
Haywards Heath d							09 57				10 04 / 10 07	10 18 →		10 10						← 10 18	10 27		
Wivelsfield 4 d							10 01				10 11									10 22	10 31		
Lewes 4 a											10 22												
Burgess Hill 4 d							10 03				10 09									10 24	10 33		
Hassocks 4 d							10 06													10 27	10 36		
Preston Park d							10 13													10 34	10 43		
Hove 2 a											10 21												
Brighton 10 a						09 58	10 19							10 24					10 27	10 40	10 49		

For general notes see front of timetable
For details of catering facilities see Directory of Train Operators

A ⊼ to Lewes
b Change at East Croydon

Bedford and London → Brighton

Network Diagram - see first page of Table 186

	SN 1	SN 1 A 🍴		SN 1	FC 1	GX 1	SN 1 🍴	SN 1	SN 1 ◇ 🍴	FC 1	GX 1	GW 1	GW 1	SN 1	SN 1	SN 1 A 🍴		GW 1	SN 1 ◇	FC 1	SN 1	SN 1 ◇		GX 1
London Victoria 15 ⊖ d		09 47				10 00	10 02	09b53	10 06		10 15					10 17			10 21					10 30
Milton Keynes Central 10 d																								
Watford Junction d																								
Shepherd's Bush ⊖ d							*09 42*																	
Kensington (Olympia) ⊖ d							*09 45*																	
West Brompton ⊖ d							*09 48*																	
Clapham Junction 10 d		09 53					10 08	09b59	10 12							10 23								
Bedford 7 d					08 40					08 54										09 10				
Luton 10 d					09 04					09 18										09 34				
Luton Airport Parkway 7 ✈ d					09 06					09 20										09 36				
St Albans City d					09 18					09 34										09 48				
St Pancras International 15 ⊖ d					09 39					09 54										10 09				
Farringdon 3 ⊖ d					09 44					09 59										10 14				
City Thameslink 3 d					09 48					10 02										10 17				
London Blackfriars 3 ⊖ d					09 50					10 05										10 20				
London Charing Cross 4 ⊖ d																								
London Waterloo (East) 4 ⊖ d																								
London Bridge 4 ⊖ d	09 46				09 58			10 03		10 11					10 19					10 26				
Norwood Junction 2 d								10 15																
East Croydon 🚌 a	10 02	10 03			10 10		10 18	10 18	10 22	10 24					10 32	10 33			10 37	10 39				
East Croydon d	10 03	10 03			10 10		10 18	10 21	10 22	10 24					10 33	10 33			10 37	10 39				
Purley 4 d	10 11							10 27							10 41									
Coulsdon South d	10 14							10 30						←	10 44									
Merstham d								10 36						10 36										
Redhill 5 a	10 21			←			10 30	→						10 39	10 51			←						
Redhill d	10 22			10 10			10 30					10 34	10 41	10 44	10 52			10 41						
Reigate a												10 38	→		10 56									
Nutfield d	10 26																							
Godstone d	10 32																							
Edenbridge d	10 37																							
Penshurst d	10 44																							
Leigh (Kent) d	10 47																							
Tonbridge 4 a	10 52																							
Earlswood (Surrey) d				10 12																				
Salfords d				10 16																	←			
Horley 4 d				10 19			10 36							10 51 →							10 51			
Gatwick Airport 10 ✈ a		10 18		10 23	10 26	10 30	10 39			10 40	10 45					10 48		10 50	10 52	10 55	10 55	←		11 00
Gatwick Airport d		10 19		10 24	10 26		10 40			10 41						10 49			10 58 →	10 56	10 56	10 58		
Three Bridges 15 a				10 29			10 44			10 45											11 01	11 03		
Three Bridges d				10 30			10 45			10 45											11 01	11 03		
Crawley d				10 33			10 48														11 05			
Ifield d				10 36																	11 07			
Faygate d																								
Littlehaven d				10 42																	11 14			
Horsham 4 a				10 45			10 56														11 17			
Balcombe d																								
Haywards Heath 3 a		10 30			10 39					10 54						11 00				11 06		11 12		
Haywards Heath d		10 34	10 37		10 40					10 55						11 04	11 07			11 08		11 17		
Wivelsfield 4 d										10 59							11 11					11 21		
Lewes 4 a		10 51															11 22							
Burgess Hill 4 d										11 01						11 09						11 23		
Hassocks 4 d										11 04												11 26		
Preston Park d										11 11												11 33		
Hove 2 a			10 51													11 21						→		
Brighton 10 a					10 54				10 58	11 17										11 24				

For general notes see front of timetable
For details of catering facilities see
Directory of Train Operators

A 🍴 to Lewes
b Change at East Croydon

Bedford and London → Brighton

Network Diagram - see first page of Table 186

		SN 1 ✠	SN 1	SN 1 ◇	SN 1 ◇	FC 1	GX 1	GW 1	SN 1	SN 1 A ✠	SN 1	FC 1	GX 1	SN 1	SN 1	SN 1 ◇	FC 1	GX 1	GW 1	GW 1	SN 1	SN 1	SN 1 A ✠
London Victoria 15 ⊖	d	10 32	10b23	10 36			10 45			10 47			11 00	11 02	10b53	11 06		11 15					11 17
Milton Keynes Central 10	d	09 13																					
Watford Junction	d	09 51																					
Shepherd's Bush ⊖	d	10 23																					
Kensington (Olympia) ⊖	d	10 25																					
West Brompton ⊖	d	10 27																					
Clapham Junction 10	d	10 38	10b29	10 42						10 53				11 08	10b59	11 12							11 23
Bedford 7	d					09 24						09 40					09 54						
Luton 10	d					09 48						10 04					10 18						
Luton Airport Parkway 7 ✈	d					09 50						10 06					10 20						
St Albans City	d					10 03						10 18					10 34						
St Pancras International 15 ⊖	d					10 24						10 39					10 54						
Farringdon 3 ⊖	d					10 29						10 44					10 59						
City Thameslink 3	d					10 32						10 47					11 02						
London Blackfriars 3 ⊖	d					10 35						10 50					11 05						
London Charing Cross 4 ⊖	d								10 40													11 10	
London Waterloo (East) 4 ⊖	d								10 43													11 13	
London Bridge 4 ⊖	d		10 33			10 41			10 48			10 56			11 03		11 11					11 18	
Norwood Junction 2	d		10 45												11 15								
East Croydon 🚊	a	10 48	10 48	10 52		10 54			11 02	11 03		11 09		11 18	11 18	11 22	11 24					11 32	11 33
	d	10 48	10 51	10 52		10 54			11 03	11 03		11 09		11 18	11 21	11 22	11 24					11 33	11 33
Purley 4	d		10 57						11 11						11 27							11 41	
Coulsdon South	d		11 00						11 14						11 30						←	11 44	
Merstham	d		11 06												11 36						11 36		
Redhill 5	a	11 00	11 09						11 21		←			11 30	→						11 39	11 51	
	d	11 00	11 09					11 14	11 22		11 09			11 30					11 34	11 41	11 44	11 52	
Reigate	a		→					11 18											11 38	→		11 56	
Nutfield	d								11 26														
Godstone	d								11 32														
Edenbridge	d								11 37														
Penshurst	d								11 44														
Leigh (Kent)	d								11 47														
Tonbridge 4	a								11 52														
Earlswood (Surrey)	d										11 12												
Salfords	d										11 15												
Horley 4	d										11 19			11 36									
Gatwick Airport 10 ✈	a	11 08				11 10	11 15			11 18	11 23	11 25	11 30	11 39			11 40	11 45			11 51 →		11 48
	d	11 09				11 11				11 19	11 24	11 26		11 40			11 41						11 49
Three Bridges 15	a	11 14				11 15					11 29			11 44			11 45						
	d	11 14				11 15					11 30			11 45			11 45						
Crawley	d	11 18									11 33			11 48									
Ifield	d										11 36												
Faygate	d																						
Littlehaven	d										11 42												
Horsham 4	a	11 26									11 45			11 56									
Balcombe	d					11 21																	
Haywards Heath 3	a					11 26				11 30		11 36					11 54						12 00
	d					11 27				11 34 / 11 37		11 38					11 55						12 04 / 12 07
Wivelsfield 4	d					11 31											11 59						12 11
Lewes 4	a									11 48													12 22
Burgess Hill 4	d					11 33											12 01						12 09
Hassocks 4	d				←	11 36											12 04						
Preston Park	d				11 33	11 43											12 11						
Hove 2	a									11 51													12 21
Brighton 10	a			11 27	11 40	11 49						11 54				11 58	12 17						

For general notes see front of timetable
For details of catering facilities see
Directory of Train Operators

A ✠ to Lewes
b Change at East Croydon

Bedford and London → Brighton

Network Diagram - see first page of Table 186

		GW	SN	FC	SN	SN	GX	SN	SN	SN	SN	FC	GX	GW	SN	SN	SN	FC	GX	SN	SN	SN	FC	GX
		[1]	[1] ◇	[1]	[1]	[1] ◇	[1]	[1]	[1]	[1] ◇	[1] ◇	[1]	[1]	[1]	[1]	[1]	[1]	[1]	[1]	[1]	[1]	[1] ◇	[1]	[1]
																A								
										⌶						⌶				⌶		⌶		
London Victoria [15]	⊖ d		11 21				11 30	11 32	11b23	11 36			11 45			11 47			12 00	12 02	11b53	12 06		12 15
Milton Keynes Central [10]	d							10 13																
Watford Junction	d							10 51																
Shepherd's Bush	⊖ d							11 18																
Kensington (Olympia)	⊖ d							11 20																
West Brompton	⊖ d							11 23																
Clapham Junction [10]	d							11 38	11b29	11 42						11 53				12 08	11b59	12 12		
Bedford [7]	d			10 10								10 24						10 40					10 54	
Luton [10]	d			10 34								10 48						11 04					11 18	
Luton Airport Parkway [7]	✈ d			10 36								10 50						11 06					11 20	
St Albans City	d			10 48								11 03						11 18					11 34	
St Pancras International [15]	⊖ d			11 09								11 24						11 39					11 54	
Farringdon [3]	⊖ d			11 14								11 29						11 44					11 59	
City Thameslink [3]	d			11 17								11 32						11 47					12 02	
London Blackfriars [3]	⊖ d			11 20								11 35						11 50					12 05	
London Charing Cross [4]	⊖ d														11 40									
London Waterloo (East) [4]	⊖ d														11 43									
London Bridge [4]	⊖ d			11 26					11 33			11 41			11 48			11 56			12 03		12 11	
Norwood Junction [2]	d								11 45												12 15			
East Croydon	🚋 a		11 37	11 39				11 48	11 48	11 52		11 54			12 02	12 03		12 09		12 18	12 18	12 22	12 24	
	d		11 37	11 39				11 48	11 51	11 52		11 54			12 03	12 03		12 09		12 18	12 21	12 22	12 24	
Purley [4]	d								11 57						12 11						12 27			
Coulsdon South	d								12 00						12 14						12 30			
Merstham	d								12 06												12 36 →			
Redhill [5]	a							12 00	12 09						12 21					12 30				
	d	← 11 41						12 00	12 10					12 14	12 22		← 12 10			12 30				
Reigate	a								→					12 18										
Nutfield	d														12 26									
Godstone	d														12 32									
Edenbridge	d														12 37									
Penshurst	d														12 44									
Leigh (Kent)	d														12 47									
Tonbridge [4]	a														12 52									
Earlswood (Surrey)	d																12 12							
Salfords	d																12 16							
Horley [4]	d				← 11 51												12 19			12 36				
Gatwick Airport [10]	✈ a	11 50	11 52	11 55	11 55	←	12 00	12 08				12 10	12 15			12 18	12 23	12 25	12 30	12 39			12 40	12 45
	d		11 58 →	11 56	11 56	11 58		12 09				12 11				12 19	12 24	12 26		12 40			12 41	
Three Bridges [15]	a				12 01	12 03		12 14				12 15					12 29			12 44			12 45	
	d				12 01	12 03		12 14				12 15					12 30			12 45			12 45	
Crawley	d				12 05			12 18									12 33			12 48				
Ifield	d				12 07												12 36							
Faygate	d				12 11																			
Littlehaven	d				12 15												12 42							
Horsham [4]	a				12 18			12 26									12 45			12 56				
Balcombe	d											12 21												
Haywards Heath [3]	a			12 06		12 12						12 26				12 30		12 36					12 54	
	d			12 08		12 17						12 27				12 34 / 12 37		12 38					12 55	
Wivelsfield [4]	d					12 21						12 31											12 59	
Lewes [4]	a															12 51								
Burgess Hill [4]	d					12 23						12 33											13 01	
Hassocks [4]	d					12 26						12 36											13 04	
Preston Park	d					12 33					← 12 33	12 43											13 11	
Hove [2]	a					→										12 51								
Brighton [10]	a			12 24						12 27	12 40	12 49						12 54				12 58	13 17	

For general notes see front of timetable
For details of catering facilities see Directory of Train Operators

A ⌶ to Lewes
b Change at East Croydon

Bedford and London → Brighton

Network Diagram - see first page of Table 186

		GW [1]	GW [1]	SN [1]	SN [1]	SN [1] A (trolley)		GW [1]	SN [1] ◇	FC [1]	SN [1]	SN [1] ◇	GX [1]	SN [1]	SN [1]	SN [1] ◇ (trolley)	SN [1] ◇	FC [1]	GX [1]	GW [1]	SN [1]	SN [1] A (trolley)		SN [1]
London Victoria [15] ⊖	d					12 17			12 21				12 30	12 32	12b23	12 36			12 45			12 47		
Milton Keynes Central [10]	d													*11 13*										
Watford Junction	d													*11 51*										
Shepherd's Bush ⊖	d													*12 19*										
Kensington (Olympia) ⊖	d													*12 22*										
West Brompton ⊖	d													*12 25*										
Clapham Junction [10]	d					12 23								12 38	12b29	12 42						12 53		
Bedford [7]	d									11 10								11 24						
Luton [10]	d									11 34								11 48						
Luton Airport Parkway [7] ✈	d									11 36								11 50						
St Albans City	d									11 48								12 04						
St Pancras International [15] ⊖	d									12 09								12 24						
Farringdon [3] ⊖	d									12 14								12 29						
City Thameslink [3]	d									12 17								12 32						
London Blackfriars [3] ⊖	d									12 20								12 35						
London Charing Cross [4] ⊖	d				12 10																12 40			
London Waterloo (East) [4] ⊖	d				12 13																12 43			
London Bridge [4] ⊖	d				12 18					12 26					12 33			12 41			12 48			
Norwood Junction [2]	d														12 47									
East Croydon (tram)	a				12 32	12 33			12 37	12 39				12 48	12 50	12 52		12 54			13 02	13 03		
	d				12 33	12 34			12 37	12 39				12 48	12 51	12 52		12 54			13 03	13 03		
Purley [4]	d				12 41										12 57						13 11			
Coulsdon South	d			←	12 44										13 00						13 14			
Merstham	d			12 36											13 06									
Redhill [5]	a			12 39	12 51			←						13 00	13 09						13 21			←
	d	12 34	12 41	12 44	12 52			12 41						13 00	13 10					13 14	13 22			13 10
Reigate	a	12 38	→		12 56										→					13 18				
Nutfield	d																				13 26			
Godstone	d																				13 32			
Edenbridge	d																				13 37			
Penshurst	d																				13 44			
Leigh (Kent)	d																				13 47			
Tonbridge [4]	a																				13 52			
Earlswood (Surrey)	d																							13 12
Salfords	d										←													13 16
Horley [4]	d			12 51							12 51													13 19
Gatwick Airport [10] ✈	a			→		12 49		12 50	12 52	12 55	12 55	←	13 00	13 08				13 10	13 15			13 18		13 23
	d					12 50			12 58	12 56	12 56	12 58		13 09				13 11				13 19		13 24
Three Bridges [15]	a								→		13 01	13 03		13 14				13 15						13 29
	d										13 01	13 03		13 14				13 15						13 30
Crawley	d										13 05			13 18										13 33
Ifield	d										13 07													13 36
Faygate	d																							
Littlehaven	d										13 14													13 42
Horsham [4]	a										13 17			13 26										13 45
Balcombe	d																	13 21						
Haywards Heath [3]	a					13 01				13 06		13 12						13 26				13 30		
	d					13 04	13 07			13 08		13 17						13 27				13 34	13 37	
Wivelsfield [4]	d						13 11					13 21						13 31						
Lewes [4]	a						13 22															13 48		
Burgess Hill [4]	d					13 10						13 23						13 33						
Hassocks [4]	d											13 26					←	13 36						
Preston Park	d											13 33					13 33	13 43						
Hove [2]	a					13 21						→											13 51	
Brighton [10]	a									13 24						13 27	13 40	13 49						

For general notes see front of timetable
For details of catering facilities see
Directory of Train Operators

A (trolley) to Lewes
b Change at East Croydon

Bedford and London → Brighton

Network Diagram - see first page of Table 186

		FC 1	GX 1	SN 1	SN 1	SN 1 ◇	FC 1	GX 1	GW 1	GW 1	SN 1	SN 1	SN 1		GW 1	SN 1 ◇	FC 1	SN 1	SN 1 ◇	GX 1	SN 1	SN 1	SN 1 ◇	SN 1 ◇	FC 1
													A												
				🛒		🛒							🛒								🛒		🛒		
London Victoria 15	⊖ d		13 00	13 02	12b53	13 06		13 15					13 17			13 21				13 30	13 32	13b23	13 36		
Milton Keynes Central 10	d																				12 13				
Watford Junction	d																				12 51				
Shepherd's Bush	⊖ d																				13 19				
Kensington (Olympia)	⊖ d																				13 22				
West Brompton	⊖ d																				13 25				
Clapham Junction 10	d			13 08	12b59	13 12							13 23								13 38	13b29	13 42		
Bedford 7	d	11 40					11 54										12 10								12 24
Luton 10	d	12 04					12 18										12 34								12 48
Luton Airport Parkway 7	✈ d	12 06					12 20										12 36								12 50
St Albans City	d	12 18					12 34										12 48								13 04
St Pancras International 15	⊖ d	12 39					12 54										13 09								13 24
Farringdon 3	⊖ d	12 44					12 59										13 14								13 29
City Thameslink 3	d	12 47					13 02										13 17								13 32
London Blackfriars 3	⊖ d	12 50					13 05										13 20								13 35
London Charing Cross 4	⊖ d											13 10													
London Waterloo (East) 4	⊖ d											13 13													
London Bridge 4	⊖ d	12 56			13 03		13 11					13 18					13 26					13 33			13 41
Norwood Junction 2	d				13 15																	13 45			
East Croydon	a	13 09		13 18	13 18	13 22	13 24					13 32	13 33			13 37	13 39				13 48	13 48	13 52		13 54
	d	13 09		13 18	13 21	13 22	13 24					13 33	13 33			13 37	13 39				13 48	13 51	13 52		13 54
Purley 4	d				13 27							13 41										13 57			
Coulsdon South	d				13 30						←	13 44										14 00			
Merstham	d				13 36						13 36											14 06			
Redhill 5	a			13 30	→						13 39	13 51			←						14 00	14 09			
	d			13 30					13 34	13 41	13 44	13 52			13 41						14 00	14 10			
Reigate	a								13 38	→		13 56										→			
Nutfield	d																								
Godstone	d																								
Edenbridge	d																								
Penshurst	d																								
Leigh (Kent)	d																								
Tonbridge 4	a																								
Earlswood (Surrey)	d																								
Salfords	d										13 51							←							
Horley 4	d			13 36							→							13 51							
Gatwick Airport 10	✈ a	13 25	13 30	13 39			13 40	13 45					13 48		13 50	13 52	13 55	13 55	←	14 00	14 08				14 10
	d	13 26		13 40			13 41						13 49			13 58	13 56	13 56	13 58		14 09				14 11
Three Bridges 15	a			13 44			13 45									→		14 01	14 03		14 14				14 15
	d			13 45			13 45											14 01	14 03		14 14				14 15
Crawley	d			13 48														14 05			14 18				
Ifield	d																	14 07							
Faygate	d																								
Littlehaven	d																	14 14							
Horsham 4	a			13 56														14 17			14 26				
Balcombe	d																								14 21
Haywards Heath 3	a	13 36					13 54						14 00				14 06		14 12						14 26
	d	13 38					13 55						14 04	14 07			14 08		14 17						14 27
Wivelsfield 4	d						13 59							14 11					14 21						14 31
Lewes 4	a													14 22											
Burgess Hill 4	d						14 01						14 09						14 23						14 33
Hassocks 4	d						14 04												14 26					←	14 36
Preston Park	d						14 11												14 33					14 33	14 43
Hove 2	a												14 21						→						
Brighton 10	a	13 54				13 58	14 17										14 25						14 27	14 40	14 49

For general notes see front of timetable
For details of catering facilities see
Directory of Train Operators

A 🛒 to Lewes
b Change at East Croydon

Bedford and London → Brighton

Network Diagram - see first page of Table 186

	GX 1	GW 1	SN 1	SN 1 A ⌶		SN 1	FC 1	GX 1	SN 1 ⌶	SN 1	SN 1 ◇ ⌶	FC 1	GX 1	GW 1	GW 1	SN 1	SN 1	SN 1 A ⌶		GW 1	SN 1 ◇	FC 1	SN 1	SN 1 ◇
London Victoria 15 ⊖ d	13 45			13 47				14 00	14 02	13b53	14 06		14 15					14 17			14 21			
Milton Keynes Central 10 d																								
Watford Junction d																								
Shepherd's Bush ⊖ d																								
Kensington (Olympia) ⊖ d																								
West Brompton ⊖ d																								
Clapham Junction 10 d				13 53					14 08	13b59	14 12							14 23						
Bedford 7 d							12 40					12 54										13 10		
Luton 10 d							13 04					13 18										13 34		
Luton Airport Parkway 7 ✈ d							13 06					13 20										13 36		
St Albans City d							13 18					13 34										13 48		
St Pancras International 15 ⊖ d							13 39					13 54										14 09		
Farringdon 3 ⊖ d							13 44					13 59										14 14		
City Thameslink 3 d							13 47					14 02										14 17		
London Blackfriars 3 ⊖ d							13 50					14 05										14 20		
London Charing Cross 4 ⊖ d			13 40														14 10							
London Waterloo (East) 4 ⊖ d			13 43														14 13							
London Bridge 4 ⊖ d			13 48				13 56			14 03		14 11					14 18					14 26		
Norwood Junction 2 d										14 15														
East Croydon a			14 02	14 03			14 09		14 18	14 18	14 22	14 24					14 32	14 33			14 37	14 39		
d			14 03	14 03			14 09		14 18	14 21	14 22	14 24					14 33	14 33			14 37	14 39		
Purley 4 d			14 11							14 27							14 41							
Coulsdon South d			14 14							14 30						←	14 44							
Merstham d										14 36						14 36								
Redhill 5 a			14 21			←			14 30	→						14 39	14 51			←				
d		14 14	14 22			14 10			14 30					14 34	14 41	14 44	14 52			14 41				
Reigate a		14 18												14 38	→		14 56							
Nutfield d			14 26																					
Godstone d			14 32																					
Edenbridge d			14 37																					
Penshurst d			14 44																					
Leigh (Kent) d			14 47																					
Tonbridge 4 a			14 52																					
Earlswood (Surrey) d						14 12																		
Salfords d						14 16																	←	
Horley 4 d						14 19			14 36														14 51	
Gatwick Airport 10 ✈ a	14 15			14 18		14 23	14 25	14 30	14 39		14 40	14 45				14 51 →		14 48		14 50	14 52	14 55	14 55	←
d				14 19		14 24	14 26		14 40		14 41							14 49			14 58 →	14 56	14 56	14 58
Three Bridges 15 a						14 29			14 44		14 45												15 01	15 03
d						14 30			14 45		14 45												15 01	15 03
Crawley d						14 33			14 48														15 05	
Ifield d						14 36																	15 07	
Faygate d																								
Littlehaven d						14 42																	15 14	
Horsham 4 a						14 45			14 56														15 17	
Balcombe d																								
Haywards Heath 3 a				14 30			14 36				14 54							15 00			15 06			15 12
d				14 34	14 37		14 38				14 55							15 04	15 07		15 08			15 17
Wivelsfield 4 d											14 59								15 11					15 21
Lewes 4 a				14 48															15 22					
Burgess Hill 4 d											15 01							15 09						15 23
Hassocks 4 d											15 04													15 26
Preston Park d											15 11													15 33
Hove 2 a					14 51													15 21						→
Brighton 10 a							14 54			14 58	15 17										15 24			

For general notes see front of timetable
For details of catering facilities see Directory of Train Operators

A ⌶ to Lewes
b Change at East Croydon

Table 186

Mondays to Fridays

Bedford and London → Brighton

Network Diagram - see first page of Table 186

		GX	SN	SN	SN	SN	FC	GX	GW	SN	SN		SN	FC	GX	GW	SN	GW	SN	SN	FC	GX	SN
		1	1	1	1 ◇	1 ◇	1	1	1	1	1		1	1	1	1	1	1	1	1 ◇	1	1	1
											A												
			🛒		🛒						🛒						🛒			🛒			
London Victoria 15	⊖ d	14 30	14 32	14b23	14 36			14 45			14 47				15 00		15 02		14b53	15 06		15 15	
Milton Keynes Central 10	d		13 13																				
Watford Junction	d		13 51																				
Shepherd's Bush	⊖ d		14 19																				
Kensington (Olympia)	⊖ d		14 22																				
West Brompton	⊖ d		14 25																				
Clapham Junction 10	d		14 38	14b29	14 42						14 53						15 08		14b59	15 12			
Bedford 7	d						13 24							13 40							13 54		
Luton 10	d						13 48							14 04							14 18		
Luton Airport Parkway 7	✈ d						13 50							14 06							14 20		
St Albans City	d						14 04							14 18							14 34		
St Pancras International 15	⊖ d						14 24							14 39							14 54		
Farringdon 3	⊖ d						14 29							14 44							14 59		
City Thameslink 3	d						14 32							14 47							15 02		
London Blackfriars 3	⊖ d						14 35							14 50							15 05		
London Charing Cross 4	⊖ d									14 40													15 10
London Waterloo (East) 4	⊖ d									14 43													15 13
London Bridge 4	⊖ d			14 33			14 41			14 48				14 56					15 03		15 11		15 18
Norwood Junction 2	d			14 45															15 15				
East Croydon	⇌ a		14 48	14 48	14 52		14 54			15 02	15 03			15 09			15 18		15 18	15 22	15 24		15 32
	d		14 48	14 51	14 52		14 54			15 03	15 03			15 09			15 18		15 21	15 22	15 24		15 33
Purley 4	d			14 57						15 11									15 27				15 41
Coulsdon South	d			15 00						15 14									15 30				15 44
Merstham	d			15 06															15 36				
Redhill 5	a		15 00	15 09						15 21			←				15 30		15 39				15 51
	d		15 00	15 10					15 14	15 22			15 10			15 29	15 30	15 41	15 44				15 52
Reigate	a			→					15 18							15 33		→	→				15 56
Nutfield	d									15 26													
Godstone	d									15 32													
Edenbridge	d									15 37													
Penshurst	d									15 44													
Leigh (Kent)	d									15 47													
Tonbridge 4	a									15 52													
Earlswood (Surrey)	d												15 12										
Salfords	d												15 16										
Horley 4	d												15 19				15 36						
Gatwick Airport 10	✈ a	15 00	15 08				15 10	15 15			15 18		15 23	15 25	15 30		15 39				15 40	15 45	
	d		15 09				15 11				15 19		15 24	15 26			15 40				15 41		
Three Bridges 15	a		15 14				15 15						15 29				15 44				15 45		
	d		15 14				15 15						15 30				15 45				15 45		
Crawley	d		15 18										15 33				15 48						
Ifield	d												15 36										
Faygate	d																						
Littlehaven	d												15 42										
Horsham 4	a		15 26										15 48				15 56						
Balcombe	d						15 21																
Haywards Heath 3	a						15 26				15 30			15 36							15 54		
	d						15 27				15 34	15 37		15 38							15 55		
Wivelsfield 4	d						15 31				15 38										15 59		
Lewes 4	a										15 51												
Burgess Hill 4	d						15 33														16 01		
Hassocks 4	d					←	15 36														16 04		
Preston Park	d					15 33	15 43														16 11		
Hove 2	a											15 51											
Brighton 10	a				15 28	15 40	15 49							15 54						15 58	16 17		

For general notes see front of timetable
For details of catering facilities see Directory of Train Operators

A 🛒 to Lewes
b Change at East Croydon

Bedford and London → Brighton

Network Diagram - see first page of Table 186

	SN		GW	SN	FC	SN	GX	SN	SN	SN	SN	FC	GX	GW	SN	SN		SN	FC	GX	SN	GW	SN	
	1 A 🛒		1	1 ◇	1	1	1	1 ◇	1	1 ◇ 🛒	1 ◇	1	1	1	1	1 A 🛒		1	1	1	1	1	1	
London Victoria 15 ⊖ d	15 17			15 21			15 30	15 32	15b23	15 36			15 45			15 47				16 00	16 02		15b53	
Milton Keynes Central 10 d								14 13																
Watford Junction d								14 51																
Shepherd's Bush ⊖ d								15 23																
Kensington (Olympia) ⊖ d								15 25																
West Brompton ⊖ d								15 27																
Clapham Junction 10 d	15 23							15 38	15b29	15 42						15 53					16 08		15b59	
Bedford 7 d					14 10							14 24							14 40					
Luton 10 d					14 34							14 48							15 04					
Luton Airport Parkway 7 ✈ d					14 36							14 50							15 06					
St Albans City d					14 48							15 04							15 18					
St Pancras International 15 ⊖ d					15 09							15 24							15 39					
Farringdon 3 ⊖ d					15 14							15 29							15 44					
City Thameslink 3 d					15 17							15 32							15 47					
London Blackfriars 3 ⊖ d					15 20							15 35							15 50					
London Charing Cross 4 ⊖ d															15 40									
London Waterloo (East) 4 ⊖ d															15 43									
London Bridge 4 ⊖ d					15 26				15 33			15 41			15 48				15 56				16 03	
Norwood Junction 2 d									15 45														16 15	
East Croydon a	15 33			15 36	15 39			15 48	15 48	15 52		15 54			16 02	16 03			16 09		16 18		16 18	
East Croydon d	15 33			15 37	15 39			15 48	15 51	15 52		15 54			16 03	16 03			16 09		16 18		16 21	
Purley 4 d									15 57						16 11								16 27	
Coulsdon South d									16 00						16 14								16 30	
Merstham d									16 06														16 36	
Redhill 5 a			←			←		16 00	16 09						16 21			←			16 30		16 39	
Redhill d			15 41			15 44		16 00	16 10					16 14	16 22			16 10			16 30	16 32	16 43	16 45
Reigate a									→					16 18								16 36	→	
Nutfield d															16 26									16 49
Godstone d															16 32									16 55
Edenbridge d															16 37									17 00
Penshurst d															16 44									17 07
Leigh (Kent) d															16 47									17 10
Tonbridge 4 a															16 52									17 17
Earlswood (Surrey) d						15 46												16 12						
Salfords d						15 50												16 16						
Horley 4 d						15 53												16 19			16 36			
Gatwick Airport 10 ✈ a	15 48		15 50	15 52	15 56	15 56	16 00	16 08				16 10	16 15			16 18		16 23	16 25	16 30	16 39			
Gatwick Airport d	15 49			15 53	15 57	15 57		16 09				16 11				16 19		16 24	16 26		16 40			
Three Bridges 15 a				15 57	16 01	16 01		16 14				16 15						16 29	16 30		16 44			
Three Bridges d				15 57	16 02	16 02		16 14				16 15						16 30	16 30		16 45			
Crawley d						16 06		16 18										16 34			16 48			
Ifield d						16 08												16 36						
Faygate d						16 12												16 40						
Littlehaven d						16 16												16 44						
Horsham 4 a						16 19		16 26										16 47			16 56			
Balcombe d												16 21												
Haywards Heath 3 a	16 00			16 09	16 11						←	16 26				16 30			16 40					
Haywards Heath d	16 04	16 07		16 17	16 11						16 17	16 27				16 33	16 37		16 40					
Wivelsfield 4 d		16 11		→							16 21	16 31				16 37								
Lewes 4 a		16 22														16 52								
Burgess Hill 4 d	16 09										16 23	16 33												
Hassocks 4 d											16 26	16 36												
Preston Park d											16 33	16 43												
Hove 2 a	16 21																16 51							
Brighton 10 a					16 25					16 27	16 40	16 49							16 55					

For general notes see front of timetable
For details of catering facilities see Directory of Train Operators

A 🛒 to Lewes
b Change at East Croydon

Table 186

Mondays to Fridays

Bedford and London → Brighton

Network Diagram - see first page of Table 186

Station		SN 1	FC 1	GX 1	GW 1	SN 1	SN 1 A		SN 1	FC 1	SN 1	GW 1	GX 1	SN 1 B		SN 1	SN 1 C		FC 1	GX 1	SN 1 D	SN 1	SN 1	GW 1
		🛒					🛒							🛒			🛒				🛒			
London Victoria 15	⊖ d	16 06		16 15			16 17		16 19				16 30	16 32		16b23	16 36		16b39	16 45	16 47			
Milton Keynes Central 10	d													15 13										
Watford Junction	d													15 51										
Shepherd's Bush	⊖ d													16 19										
Kensington (Olympia)	⊖ d													16 22										
West Brompton	⊖ d													16 25										
Clapham Junction 10	d	16 12					16 23		16 26					16 38		16b29	16 42		16b45		16 53			
Bedford 7	d		14 54							15 10									15 24					
Luton 10	d		15 18							15 34									15 48					
Luton Airport Parkway 7	✈ d		15 20							15 36									15 50					
St Albans City	d		15 34							15 48									16 04					
St Pancras International 15	⊖ d		15 54							16 09									16 24					
Farringdon 3	⊖ d		15 59							16 14									16 29					
City Thameslink 3	d		16 02							16 17									16 33					
London Blackfriars 3	⊖ d		16 05							16 20									16 36					
London Charing Cross 4	⊖ d					16 08																		
London Waterloo (East) 4	⊖ d					16 11																		
London Bridge 4	⊖ d		16 11			16 16				16 26						16 33			16 46		16 38			
Norwood Junction 2	d					16 29										16 45								
East Croydon	🚌 a	16 22	16 24			16 32	16 33		16 36	16 40				16 47		16 48	16 52		16 59		17 03			
	d	16 22	16 24			16 33	16 33		16 36	16 40				16 48		16 49	16 52		17 00		17 03			
Purley 4	d					16 41										16 55								
Coulsdon South	d					16 44										16 59								
Merstham	d					16 50										17 04								
Redhill 5	a					16 53					←	←		16 59		17 08						←		
	d				16 51	16 54					16 43	16 51		17 00		17 08						17 08	17 12	17 14
Reigate	a				↪	17 00										↪								17 18
Nutfield	d																						17 16	
Godstone	d																						17 22	
Edenbridge	d																						17 27	
Penshurst	d																						17 34	
Leigh (Kent)	d																						17 37	
Tonbridge 4	a																						17 42	
Earlswood (Surrey)	d										16 45											17 11		
Salfords	d										16 49											17 14		
Horley 4	d										16 52			17 06								17 18		
Gatwick Airport 10	✈ a		16 40	16 43			16 48		16 52	16 55	16 55	16 58	17 00	17 08					17 15	17 15	17 19	17 20		
	d		16 41	16 46			16 49		16 53	16 56	16 56			17 09					17 16		17 20	17 21		
Three Bridges 15	a		16 45						16 57	17 00	17 00			17 14			17 10		17 21		17 25	17 26		
	d		16 45						16 58	17 00	17 02			17 18	17 20		17 10		17 21		17 25	17 26		
Crawley	d								17 02		17 06			17 22	17 26							17 30		
Ifield	d										17 08				17 28							17 33		
Faygate	d										17 12											17 37		
Littlehaven	d										17 16				17 35							17 41		
Horsham 4	a								17 12		17 21			17 30	17 38							17 46		
Balcombe	d																		17 27					
Haywards Heath 3	a		16 54	16 57			17 00			17 10							17 19		17 32		17 35			
	d		16 55				17 04	17 06		17 10							17 23	17 26	17 33		17 36			
Wivelsfield 4	d		16 59					17 10										17 30	17 37		17 41			
Lewes 4	a							17 21													17 56			
Burgess Hill 4	d		17 01				17 09											17 32	17 40					
Hassocks 4	d		17 04															17 35	17 44					
Preston Park	d		17 11															17 42	17 51					
Hove 2	a						17 20																	
Brighton 10	a	17 00	17 17							17 27							17 39	17 49	17 57					

For general notes see front of timetable
For details of catering facilities see Directory of Train Operators

A 🛒 to Lewes
B To Bognor Regis (Table 188). 🛒 to Horsham
C 🛒 to Brighton
D To Ore (Table 189). 🛒 to Lewes
b Change at East Croydon

Bedford and London → Brighton

Network Diagram - see first page of Table 186

		GX [1]	SN [1]	SN [1]	SN [1] A	SN [1]	SN [1]	SN [1]	SN [1]	FC [1]	GX [1]	SN [1] A	SN [1]	SN [1] B
London Victoria [15]	⊖ d	17 00	16 49			16b53		17 02	17 06		17 15	17 17		17b09
Milton Keynes Central [10]	d													
Watford Junction	d													
Shepherd's Bush	⊖ d													
Kensington (Olympia)	⊖ d													
West Brompton	⊖ d													
Clapham Junction [10]	d		16 56			16b59		17 08	17 12			17 23		17b15
Bedford [7]	d													
Luton [10]	d													
Luton Airport Parkway [7]	✈ d													
St Albans City	d													
St Pancras International [15]	⊖ d													
Farringdon [3]	⊖ d													
City Thameslink [3]	d													
London Blackfriars [3]	⊖ d													
London Charing Cross [4]	⊖ d													
London Waterloo (East) [4]	⊖ d													
London Bridge [4]	⊖ d				16 57	16 59				17 11				17 23
Norwood Junction [2]	d					17 11								
East Croydon	🚊 a		17 06		17 09	17 14		17 17	17 21	17 24		17 32		17 35
	d		17 07		17 10	17 15		17 18	17 22	17 25		17 33		17 36
Purley [4]	d					17 21								
Coulsdon South	d		17 13			17 24								
Merstham	d		17 19			17 30								
Redhill [5]	a		17 22			17 33								
	d		17 27	17 29		17 37	17 39						← 17 37	
Reigate	a			17 35		→								
Nutfield	d						17 43							
Godstone	d						17 49							
Edenbridge	d						17 54							
Penshurst	d						18 01							
Leigh (Kent)	d						18 04							
Tonbridge [4]	a						18 11							
Earlswood (Surrey)	d		17 29										17 39	
Salfords	d		17 33										17 43	
Horley [4]	d		17 36										17 46	17 50
Gatwick Airport [10]	✈ a	17 30	17 39							17 40	17 45	17 47	17 49	
	d		17 40							17 41		17 48	17 50	
Three Bridges [15]	a		17 46		17 29			17 36		17 45			17 54	17 55
	d				17 29			17 37		17 46			17 55	17 56
Crawley	d							17 41					17 59	
Ifield	d												18 01	
Faygate	d													
Littlehaven	d												18 08	
Horsham [4]	a							17 49					18 13	
Balcombe	d									17 52				
Haywards Heath [3]	a				17 38				17 45	17 57		18 00		18 04
	d				17 39				17 46	17 57		18 00		18 05
Wivelsfield [4]	d								17 50					18 09
Lewes [4]	a													18 20
Burgess Hill [4]	d				17 46				17 53	18 03		18 07		
Hassocks [4]	d				17 49				17 57	18 07		18 11		
Preston Park	d				17 56				18 04	18 14				
Hove [2]	a				18 00							18 21		
Brighton [10]	a								18 10	18 20				

		GW [1]	GW [1]	SN [1]	SN [1]	FC [1]	GX [1] [trolley]	SN [1] C	SN [1] [trolley]	SN [1] A	SN [1]	FC [1]
London Victoria [15]	⊖ d			17 21	17b23		17 30	17 32	17 36			
Milton Keynes Central [10]	d							16 13				
Watford Junction	d							16 51				
Shepherd's Bush	⊖ d							17 19				
Kensington (Olympia)	⊖ d							17 22				
West Brompton	⊖ d							17 25				
Clapham Junction [10]	d			17 27	17b30			17 38	17 42			
Bedford [7]	d					16 10						
Luton [10]	d					16 34						
Luton Airport Parkway [7]	✈ d					16 36						
St Albans City	d					16 48						
St Pancras International [15]	⊖ d					17 10						
Farringdon [3]	⊖ d					17 15						
City Thameslink [3]	d					17 19						
London Blackfriars [3]	⊖ d					17 22						
London Charing Cross [4]	⊖ d											
London Waterloo (East) [4]	⊖ d											
London Bridge [4]	⊖ d			17 15	17 29	17 32				17 42		
Norwood Junction [2]	d				17 41							
East Croydon	🚊 a			17 36	17 44	17 45		17 48	17 51	17 54		
	d			17 38	17 45	17 46		17 49	17 52	17 55		
Purley [4]	d				17 51							
Coulsdon South	d			17 44	17 54							
Merstham	d			17 50	→							
Redhill [5]	a			17 53		18 00						
	d	17 41	17 44	17 55		18 00					← 17 55	← 18 00
Reigate	a		17 48	→		→						
Nutfield	d											
Godstone	d											
Edenbridge	d											
Penshurst	d											
Leigh (Kent)	d											
Tonbridge [4]	a											
Earlswood (Surrey)	d										17 57	
Salfords	d										18 01	
Horley [4]	d										18 04	
Gatwick Airport [10]	✈ a	17 54					17 57		18 06		18 08	18 12
	d						18 00		18 07		18 10	18 12
Three Bridges [15]	a							18 06			18 16	18 18
	d							18 07				18 18 →
Crawley	d							18 11				
Ifield	d											
Faygate	d											
Littlehaven	d							18 19				
Horsham [4]	a							18 22				
Balcombe	d											
Haywards Heath [3]	a						18 11		18 18	18 21		
	d						18 12		18 18	18 22		
Wivelsfield [4]	d								18 23			
Lewes [4]	a								18 38			
Burgess Hill [4]	d						18 18			18 27		
Hassocks [4]	d						18 22			18 31		
Preston Park	d									18 39		
Hove [2]	a									18 43		
Brighton [10]	a						18 34					

For general notes see front of timetable
For details of catering facilities see Directory of Train Operators

A To Littlehampton (Table 188)
B To Eastbourne (Table 189)
C To Southampton Central (Table 188) and to Bognor Regis (Table 188)
b Change at East Croydon

Bedford and London → Brighton

Network Diagram - see first page of Table 186

Station		GX	SN	FC	SN	SN		SN	GW	SN		FC	SN	GX	SN	SN	SN	SN	SN	SN	FC	GX	SN	SN	SN
		1	1	1	1	1		1	1	1		1	1	1	1	1	1	1	1	1	1	1	1	1	1
			A		B														B					B	C
London Victoria 15 ⊖	d	17 45	17b39		17 47					17 49				18 00		17b53	18 02	18 06				18 15		18 17	18b09
Milton Keynes Central 10	d																								
Watford Junction	d																								
Shepherd's Bush ⊖	d																17 48								
Kensington (Olympia) ⊖	d																17 50								
West Brompton ⊖	d																17 53								
Clapham Junction 10	d		17b45		17 53					17 56						18b00	18 08	18 12						18 23	18b15
Bedford 7	d											16 32													
Luton 10	d											16 56													
Luton Airport Parkway 7 ✈	d											16 58													
St Albans City	d											17 10													
St Pancras International 15 ⊖	d											17 34									17 42				
Farringdon 3 ⊖	d											17 39									17 47				
City Thameslink 3	d											17 43									17 51				
London Blackfriars 3 ⊖	d											17 46									17 54				
London Charing Cross 4 ⊖	d																								
London Waterloo (East) 4 ⊖	d																								
London Bridge 4 ⊖	d		17 47		17 44							17 52	17 57			17 59			18 12						18 22
Norwood Junction 2	d															18 11									
East Croydon	a		17 59		18 02					18 05		18 08	18 11			18 15	18 17	18 22	18 24		18 24			18 33	18 36
	d		18 00		18 03					18 06		18 09	18 12			18 15	18 18	18 22	18 25		18 25			18 33	18 37
Purley 4	d					←										18 21									
Coulsdon South	d					17 54				18 12						18 24									
Merstham	d					18 00				18 18						18 30									
Redhill 5	a					18 03				18 21						18 33				←	18 37		←		
	d					18 07	18 09	18 12	18 14	18 25	18 27				18 32	18 34				18 25	18 38		18 34		
Reigate	a					18 13			18 18	→	18 33					→					→				
Nutfield	d							18 16							18 36										
Godstone	d							18 22							18 42										
Edenbridge	d							18 27							18 47										
Penshurst	d							18 34							18 54										
Leigh (Kent)	d							18 37							18 57										
Tonbridge 4	a							18 42							19 02										
Earlswood (Surrey)	d						18 11													18 27			18 36		
Salfords	d						18 15													18 31			18 40		
Horley 4	d				18 18		18 18													18 34			18 43		
Gatwick Airport 10 ✈	a	18 12					18 21					18 24		18 30				18 37		18 37		18 43	18 46	18 48	
	d	18 14					18 22					18 25		18 35				18 38		18 38		18 46	18 47	18 49	
Three Bridges 15	a		18 21	←	18 23		18 26						18 31				18 36		18 44	18 44			18 51		18 55
	d		18 22	18 18	18 24		18 27						18 32				18 37		18 45				18 52		18 56
Crawley	d		18 26				18 31										18 41						18 56		
Ifield	d		18 28				18 33																18 58		
Faygate	d						18 37																		
Littlehaven	d		18 35				18 41										18 49						19 05		
Horsham 4	a		18 38				18 47																19 10		
Balcombe	d			18 24								18 35	18 40	18 46				18 49	18 54			18 57		18 57	
Haywards Heath 3	a	18 25		18 29	18 33							18 36	18 41	18 47				18 50	18 54			18 58		19 02	19 05
	d	18 26		18 30	18 33							18 40						18 54						19 03	19 06
Wivelsfield 4	d			18 34																					19 11
Lewes 4	a																	19 09							19 27
Burgess Hill 4	d			18 37	18 41							18 45	18 49	18 53					19 00					19 08	
Hassocks 4	d			18 41	18 45							18 49	18 53	18 57					19 04					19 12	
Preston Park	d	18 43		18 48	18 53							18 57	19 01						19 11			19 15			
Hove 2	a				18 57														19 17					19 22	
Brighton 10	a	18 50		18 54								19 04	19 07	19 10								19 22			

For general notes see front of timetable
For details of catering facilities see Directory of Train Operators

A To Bognor Regis (Table 188)
B To Littlehampton (Table 188)
C To Eastbourne (Table 189)

b Change at East Croydon

Bedford and London → Brighton

Network Diagram - see first page of Table 186

	FC [1]	GW [1]	GW [1]	SN [1]	SN [1]		FC [1]	GX [1]	GW [1]	SN [1]			SN [1]	SN [1]	FC [1]	SN [1]	GX [1]	FC [1]	SN [1]		SN [1]	SN [1]	FC [1]	GX [1]
								⚒					A				⚒		B ⚒					
London Victoria [15] ⊖ d					18 19			18 30		18b23			18 32	18 36			18 45		18 47			18 51		19 00
Milton Keynes Central [10] d													17 13											
Watford Junction d													17 51											
Shepherd's Bush ⊖ d													18 19											
Kensington (Olympia) ⊖ d													18 22											
West Brompton ⊖ d													18 25											
Clapham Junction [10] d					18 26					18b30			18 38	18 42					18 53			18 57		
Bedford [7] d							17 10																17 34	
Luton [10] d							17 34																17 58	
Luton Airport Parkway [7] ✈ d							17 36																18 00	
St Albans City d							17 48																18 12	
St Pancras International [15] ⊖ d							18 08																18 38	
Farringdon [3] ⊖ d							18 13																18 43	
City Thameslink [3] d							18 17																18 47	
London Blackfriars [3] ⊖ d							18 20																18 50	
London Charing Cross [4] ⊖ d																								
London Waterloo (East) [4] ⊖ d																								
London Bridge [4] ⊖ d					*18 15*		18 26			18 29					18 42							*18 47*	18 56	
Norwood Junction [2] d										18 41														
East Croydon a					18 37		18 40			18 45			18 48	18 52	18 54				19 02			19 07	19 10	
East Croydon d					18 38		18 40			18 45			18 48	18 52	18 54				19 03			19 08	19 10	
Purley [4] d					18 43					18 51														
Coulsdon South d					18 46					18 54												19 14		
Merstham d					18 52					19 00												19 20		
Redhill [5] a					18 55					19 03												19 23		
Redhill d	← 18 38	18 43	18 51	18 54	18 59	19 01			← 18 51	19 07	19 09					← 18 59					← 19 07	19 24		
Reigate a		18 47	→	18 58	→					→	19 15											→		
Nutfield d						19 05																		
Godstone d						19 11																		
Edenbridge d						19 16																		
Penshurst d						19 23																		
Leigh (Kent) d						19 26																		
Tonbridge [4] a						19 34																		
Earlswood (Surrey) d																19 01					19 09			
Salfords d																19 05					19 13			
Horley [4] d																19 08					19 16			
Gatwick Airport [10] ✈ a	18 50						18 56	19 00	19 00						19 10	19 13	19 14		19 19		19 19		19 26	19 30
Gatwick Airport d	18 51						18 56	19 05							19 11	19 14	19 16		19 20		19 20		19 27	
Three Bridges [15] a	18 56						19 01						19 06			19 19					19 24		19 31	
Three Bridges d							19 02						19 07			19 19					19 25		19 32	
Crawley d													19 11			19 23					19 29			
Ifield d																19 26					19 31			
Faygate d																					19 35			
Littlehaven d													19 19			19 32					19 39			
Horsham [4] a													19 22			19 37					19 45			
Balcombe d							19 08								19 19									
Haywards Heath [3] a							19 12	19 16						19 18	19 24		19 27		19 31				19 40	
Haywards Heath d							19 12	19 17						19 20	19 31		19 28	← 19 31	19 34	19 37			19 41	
Wivelsfield [4] d														19 24	→				19 38					
Lewes [4] a																			19 53					
Burgess Hill [4] d							19 17	19 23										19 36		19 42			19 46	
Hassocks [4] d							19 21	19 27										19 40		19 46			19 49	
Preston Park d																	19 41	19 48						
Hove [2] a																				19 56				
Brighton [10] a							19 34	19 39						19 42			19 47	19 52					20 00	

For general notes see front of timetable
For details of catering facilities see Directory of Train Operators

A To Southampton Central (Table 188) and to Bognor Regis (Table 188)

B To Littlehampton (Table 188). ⚒ to Lewes

b Change at East Croydon

Bedford and London → Brighton

Network Diagram - see first page of Table 186

		SN	GW	SN	SN	SN	SN	FC	GX	GW	SN	SN		SN	GW	FC	SN	GX	SN	SN	SN	FC	SN	GW	SN
		1	1	1	1	1	1	1	1	1	1	1		1	1	1	1	1	1	1	1	1	1	1	1
				⌶			⌶					A ⌶								⌶					
London Victoria 15 ⊖	d			19 02		18b53	19 06		19 15		19 10	19 17						19 30		19 32	19 36				19 40
Milton Keynes Central 10	d																			18 13					
Watford Junction	d																			18 51					
Shepherd's Bush ⊖	d																			19 18					
Kensington (Olympia) ⊖	d																			19 20					
West Brompton ⊖	d																			19 23					
Clapham Junction 10	d			19 08		19b00	19 12				19 16	19 23								19 38	19 42				19 46
Bedford 7	d							17 54								18 10						18 24			
Luton 10	d							18 18								18 34						18 48			
Luton Airport Parkway 7 ✈	d							18 20								18 36						18 50			
St Albans City	d							18 32								18 48						19 02			
St Pancras International 15 ⊖	d							18 53								19 08						19 22			
Farringdon 3 ⊖	d							18 57								19 13						19 27			
City Thameslink 3	d							19 01								19 17						19 31			
London Blackfriars 3 ⊖	d							19 04								19 20						19 34			
London Charing Cross 4 ⊖	d																								
London Waterloo (East) 4 ⊖	d																								
London Bridge 4 ⊖	d			18 59		19 03		19 12			19 08					19 27						19 41			
Norwood Junction 2	d					19 15																			
East Croydon ⇌	a			19 18		19 18	19 22	19 24			19 28	19 33				19 39				19 48	19 52	19 54			19 58
	d			19 18		19 19	19 22	19 24			19 28	19 33				19 39				19 48	19 52	19 54			19 58
Purley 4	d					19 24					19 33														20 03
Coulsdon South	d					19 28					19 37														20 06
Merstham	d					19 33					19 42														20 12
Redhill 5	a			19 30		19 37					19 46									20 00					20 15
	d	← 19 24	19 27	19 31	19 36	19 37				19 43	19 46			← 19 37	← 19 43		← 19 46		19 51	20 00			20 05	20 14	20 16
Reigate	a		19 31		19 40	→				→	→												20 10	20 18	→
Nutfield	d																		19 55						
Godstone	d																		20 01						
Edenbridge	d																		20 06						
Penshurst	d																		20 13						
Leigh (Kent)	d																		20 16						
Tonbridge 4	a																		20 21						
Earlswood (Surrey)	d	19 26												19 40			19 49								
Salfords	d	19 30												19 43			19 52								
Horley 4	d	19 33												19 47			19 56								
Gatwick Airport 10 ✈	a	19 36		19 39				19 40	19 45			19 48		19 49	19 53	19 56	19 58	20 00		20 08		20 10			
	d	19 37		19 40				19 41				19 49		19 50		19 56	19 59			20 09		20 11			
Three Bridges 15	a	19 43		19 45				19 45						19 55		20 01	20 04			20 14		20 15			
	d			19 45				19 45						19 55		20 02	20 04			20 14		20 15			
Crawley	d			19 49										19 59			20 08			20 18					
Ifield	d													20 02			20 11								
Faygate	d																20 15								
Littlehaven	d													20 08			20 19								
Horsham 4	a			19 57										20 13			20 22			20 26					
Balcombe	d							19 51																	
Haywards Heath 3	a						19 45	19 56				20 00				20 10					20 16	20 25			
	d						19 45	19 57				20 04	20 07			20 10					20 17	20 26			
Wivelsfield 4	d							20 01					20 11									20 30			
Lewes 4	a												20 22												
Burgess Hill 4	d							20 03				20 09				20 16						20 32			
Hassocks 4	d							20 06								20 20						20 35			
Preston Park	d							20 13														20 42			
Hove 2	a											20 21													
Brighton 10	a						20 02	20 18								20 30					20 33	20 46			

For general notes see front of timetable
For details of catering facilities see Directory of Train Operators

A ⌶ to Lewes
b Change at East Croydon

Bedford and London → Brighton

Network Diagram - see first page of Table 186

Station		GX 1	SN 1 A ✠		SN 1	SN 1	GX 1	FC 1	SN 1 ✠	SN 1 ◇	FC 1	SN 1	GX 1	SN 1		GW 1	GW 1	SN 1	SN 1	GX 1	SN 1	SN 1	SN 1 ◇	FC 1	SN 1
London Victoria 15 ⊖	d	19 45	19 47				20 00	19b53	20 02	20 06		20 10	20 15	20 17						20 30		20 32	20 36		
Milton Keynes Central 10	d																					19 13			
Watford Junction	d																					19 53			
Shepherd's Bush ⊖	d																					20 19			
Kensington (Olympia) ⊖	d																					20 21			
West Brompton ⊖	d																					20 24			
Clapham Junction 10	d		19 53					19b59	20 08	20 12		20 16		20 23								20 38	20 42		
Bedford 7	d							18 42			18 54													19 20	
Luton 10	d							19 06			19 18													19 44	
Luton Airport Parkway 7 ✈	d							19 08			19 20													19 46	
St Albans City	d							19 20			19 33													19 58	
St Pancras International 15 ⊖	d							19 42			19 52													20 22	
Farringdon 3 ⊖	d							19 47			19 57													20 27	
City Thameslink 3	d							19 51			20 01													20 31	
London Blackfriars 3 ⊖	d							19 54			20 04													20 34	
London Charing Cross 4 ⊖	d																								
London Waterloo (East) 4 ⊖	d																								
London Bridge 4 ⊖	d					19 52		20 01			20 11							20 28						20 41	
Norwood Junction 2	d					20 03																			
East Croydon	a		20 03			20 06		20 14	20 19	20 22	20 24	20 28		20 33				20 40				20 48	20 52	20 54	
	d		20 03			20 07		20 14	20 19	20 22	20 24	20 29		20 33				20 40				20 48	20 52	20 54	
Purley 4	d					20 12						20 33													
Coulsdon South	d					20 15						20 37							←						
Merstham	d					20 21						20 42							20 42						
Redhill 5	a				←	20 24			20 30			→							20 46			21 00			
	d				20 16	20 25			20 31							20 34	20 41		20 46		20 51	21 00			21 05
Reigate	a					20 30										20 38									21 09
Nutfield	d																				20 55				
Godstone	d																				21 01				
Edenbridge	d																				21 06				
Penshurst	d																				21 13				
Leigh (Kent)	d																				21 16				
Tonbridge 4	a																				21 21				
Earlswood (Surrey)	d				20 18														20 49						
Salfords	d				20 22																				
Horley 4	d				20 25														20 54						
Gatwick Airport 10 ✈	a	20 15	20 18		20 28		20 30	20 31	20 38		20 40		20 45	20 48			20 50	20 55	20 57	21 00		21 08		21 10	
	d		20 19		20 29			20 31	20 39		20 41			20 49				20 56	20 58			21 09		21 11	
Three Bridges 15	a				20 34				20 44		20 45							21 01	21 02			21 14		21 15	
	d				20 34				20 44		20 45							21 01	21 06			21 14		21 15	
Crawley	d				20 38				20 48										21 09			21 18			
Ifield	d				20 40														21 12						
Faygate	d																								
Littlehaven	d				20 47														21 18						
Horsham 4	a				20 50				20 56										21 21			21 26			
Balcombe	d										20 51														
Haywards Heath 3	a		20 30					20 42		20 47	20 56			21 00				21 10					21 15	21 24	
	d		20 34	20 36				20 42		20 47	20 57			21 04	21 07			21 11					21 15	21 26	
Wivelsfield 4	d			20 40							21 01				21 11									21 30	
Lewes 4	a			20 55											21 22										
Burgess Hill 4	d		20 39								21 03			21 09										21 32	
Hassocks 4	d		20 42								21 06													21 35	
Preston Park	d		20 49								21 13													21 42	
Hove 2	a		20 53											21 21											
Brighton 10	a							20 58		21 01	21 18							21 26					21 30	21 48	

For general notes see front of timetable
For details of catering facilities see Directory of Train Operators

A To Littlehampton (Table 188).
✠ to Lewes
b Change at East Croydon

Bedford and London → Brighton

Network Diagram - see first page of Table 186

Station		GW 1	SN 1	GX 1	SN 1 A		SN 1	SN 1	GX 1	SN 1	SN 1	SN 1 ◇	SN 1	FC 1	SN 1	GX 1	SN 1 B		GW 1	SN 1	GX 1	GW 1	SN 1	SN 1
London Victoria 15 ⊖	d		20 40	20 45	20 47				21 00		21 02	21 06			21 10	21 15	21 17				21 30			21 32
Milton Keynes Central 10	d																							
Watford Junction	d																							
Shepherd's Bush ⊖	d																							
Kensington (Olympia) ⊖	d																							
West Brompton ⊖	d																							
Clapham Junction 10	d		20 46		20 53						21 08	21 12			21 16		21 23							21 38
Bedford 7	d													19 50										
Luton 10	d													20 14										
Luton Airport Parkway 7 ✈	d													20 16										
St Albans City	d													20 28										
St Pancras International 15 ⊖	d													20 52										
Farringdon 3 ⊖	d													20 57										
City Thameslink 3	d													21 01										
London Blackfriars 3 ⊖	d													21 04										
London Charing Cross 4 ⊖	d																							
London Waterloo (East) 4 ⊖	d																							
London Bridge 4 ⊖	d		*20 35*				20 58							21 11	*21 05*									*21b15*
Norwood Junction 2	d																							
East Croydon	a		20 58		21 03		21 10				21 18	21 22		21 24	21 28		21 33							21 48
	d		20 58		21 04		21 11				21 18	21 22		21 24	21 28		21 33							21 48
Purley 4	d		21 03												21 33					←				
Coulsdon South	d		21 06												21 37									
Merstham	d		21 12												21 42 →					21 42				
Redhill 5	a		21 15								21 30									21 46				21 59
	d	21 14	21 16					← 21 16		21 22	21 31								21 35	21 46		21 53	21 55	22 00
Reigate	a	21 18	→							21 26									21 39					
Nutfield	d																						21 59	
Godstone	d																						22 05	
Edenbridge	d																						22 10	
Penshurst	d																						22 17	
Leigh (Kent)	d																						22 20	
Tonbridge 4	a																						22 25	
Earlswood (Surrey)	d							21 18												21 49				
Salfords	d							21 22																
Horley 4	d							21 25												21 54				
Gatwick Airport 10 ✈	a			21 15	21 18		21 26	21 28	21 30		21 38		←	21 41		21 45	21 48			21 57	22 00	22 04		22 08
	d				21 19		21 27	21 29			21 39 →		21 39	21 41			21 49			21 58				22 09
Three Bridges 15	a						21 31	21 33					21 44	21 45			21 53			22 02				22 14
	d						21 32	21 36					21 44	21 45			21 53			22 03				22 14
Crawley	d							21 39												22 06				22 18
Ifield	d							21 42												22 09				
Faygate	d																							
Littlehaven	d							21 48												22 15				
Horsham 4	a							21 52												22 18				22 26
Balcombe	d													21 51										
Haywards Heath 3	a				21 30		21 40					21 45	21 52	21 58			22 02							
	d				21 34	21 37	21 41					21 45	21 53	21 58			22 06	22 08						
Wivelsfield 4	d					21 41							21 57	22 02				22 12						
Lewes 4	a					21 54												22 23						
Burgess Hill 4	d				21 39								21 59	22 04			22 11							
Hassocks 4	d				21 42								22 02	22 08										
Preston Park	d				21 49								22 09	22 15										
Hove 2	a				21 53												22 22							
Brighton 10	a						21 55					22 00	22 15	22 20										

For general notes see front of timetable
For details of catering facilities see Directory of Train Operators

A To Littlehampton (Table 188)
B To Eastbourne (Table 189)
b London Bridge

Bedford and London → Brighton

Network Diagram - see first page of Table 186

		SN	FC	SN	SN	GX	SN		SN	GX	SN	SN	SN	SN	FC	SN	GX	SN	GW	SN	GX	GW	SN	SN	SN
		1◇	1	1	1	1	1		1	1	1	1◇	1◇	1◇	1	1	1	1	1	1	1	1	1	1	1
London Victoria 15 ⊖	d	21 36			21 40	21 45	21 47			22 00		22 02	22 06			22 10	22 15	22 17			22 30			22 32	22 36
Milton Keynes Central 10	d	*20 13*																							*21 13*
Watford Junction	d	*20 51*																							*21 51*
Shepherd's Bush ⊖	d	*21 23*																							*22 23*
Kensington (Olympia) ⊖	d	*21 25*																							*22 25*
West Brompton ⊖	d	*21 27*																							*22 27*
Clapham Junction 10	d	21 42			21 46		21 53					22 08	22 12			22 16		22 23						22 38	22 42
Bedford 7	d		20 20																						
Luton 10	d		20 44												20 50										
Luton Airport Parkway 7 ✈	d		20 46												21 14										
St Albans City	d		20 58												21 16										
St Pancras International 15 ⊖	d		21 22												21 28										
Farringdon 3 ⊖	d		21 27												21 52										
City Thameslink 3	d		21 31												21 57										
London Blackfriars 3 ⊖	d		21 34												22 01										
London Charing Cross 4 ⊖	d														22 04										
London Waterloo (East) 4 ⊖	d																								
London Bridge 4 ⊖	d	*21 28*	21 41									*21b45*			22 11	*22 05*								*22b15*	*22 28*
Norwood Junction 2	d																								
East Croydon 🚊	a	21 52	21 54		21 58		22 03					22 18	22 22		22 24	22 28		22 33						22 48	22 52
	d	21 52	21 54		21 58		22 03					22 18	22 22		22 24	22 28		22 34						22 48	22 52
Purley 4	d				22 03											22 33									
Coulsdon South	d				22 06											22 37				←					
Merstham	d				22 12											22 42				22 42					
Redhill 5	a				22 15				←			22 30				→				22 46				23 00	
	d			22 05	22 16				22 16		22 22	22 31							22 33	22 46		22 52	22 55	23 01	
Reigate	a			22 09	→						22 26								22 38						
Nutfield	d																						22 59		
Godstone	d																						23 05		
Edenbridge	d																						23 10		
Penshurst	d																						23 17		
Leigh (Kent)	d																						23 20		
Tonbridge 4	a																						23 25		
Earlswood (Surrey)	d								22 18											22 49					
Salfords	d								22 22																
Horley 4	d								22 25											22 54					
Gatwick Airport 10 ✈	a		22 10			22 15	22 18		22 28	22 30		22 38		←	22 41		22 45	22 48		22 57	23 00	23 04		23 08	
	d		22 11				22 19		22 29			22 39		22 39	22 41			22 49		22 58				23 09	
Three Bridges 15	a		22 15						22 33			→		22 44	22 45			22 54		23 02				23 15	
	d		22 15						22 36					22 44	22 45			22 54		23 03				23 16	
Crawley	d								22 39											23 06				23 19	
Ifield	d								22 42											23 09					
Faygate	d																								
Littlehaven	d								22 48											23 15					
Horsham 4	a								22 52											23 18				23 27	
Balcombe	d														22 51										
Haywards Heath 3	a	22 15	22 24				22 30						22 45	22 52	22 58			23 02							23 15
	d	22 15	22 26				22 34	22 37					22 45	22 53	22 58			23 03							23 15
Wivelsfield 4	d		22 30				22 38							22 57	23 02										
Lewes 4	a						22 51																		
Burgess Hill 4	d		22 32											22 59	23 04			23 08							
Hassocks 4	d		22 35											23 02	23 08										
Preston Park	d		22 42											23 09	23 15										
Hove 2	a							22 51										23 21							
Brighton 10	a	22 30	22 48										23 00	23 15	23 20										23 30

For general notes see front of timetable
For details of catering facilities see Directory of Train Operators

b London Bridge

Bedford and London → Brighton

Network Diagram - see first page of Table 186

		FC 1	SN 1	SN 1	GX 1	SN 1		SN 1	GX 1	GW 1	SN 1 ◇	SN 1 ◇	SN 1 ◇	FC 1	SN 1	GX 1	SN 1	SN 1	GX 1	SN 1	SN 1 ◇	FC 1	GX 1	SN 1
London Victoria 15 ⊖	d			22 40	22 45	22 47			23 00		23 02	23 06			23 10	23 15	23 17		23 30		23 32		23 45	23 47
Milton Keynes Central 10	d																				22 11			
Watford Junction	d										22 27										22 53			
Shepherd's Bush ⊖	d										22 49										23 21			
Kensington (Olympia) ⊖	d										22 51										23 23			
West Brompton ⊖	d										22 54										23 26			
Clapham Junction 10	d			22 46		22 53					23 08	23 12			23 16		23 23				23 38			23 53
Bedford 7	d																							
Luton 10	d																							
Luton Airport Parkway 7 ✈	d																							
St Albans City	d																							
St Pancras International 15 ⊖	d																							
Farringdon 3 ⊖	d																							
City Thameslink 3	d																							
London Blackfriars 3 ⊖	d																							
London Charing Cross 4 ⊖	d																							
London Waterloo (East) 4 ⊖	d																							
London Bridge 4 ⊖	d	22 41									22 58			23 11							23b15	23 41		23 41
Norwood Junction 2	d																							
East Croydon	a	22 53		22 58		23 03					23 19	23 22		23 24	23 28		23 33				23 51	23 56		00 05
	d	22 53		22 58		23 03					23 20	23 22		23 24	23 28		23 33				23 52	23 57		00 06
Purley 4	d			23 03											23 33									00 12
Coulsdon South	d			23 07											23 37									00 15
Merstham	d			23 12											23 42									00 21
Redhill 5	a			23 16							23 31				23 46						00 03			00 24
	d		23 05	23 16				← 23 16		23 29	23 31				23 46			← 23 46		23 55	00 05			00 25
Reigate	a		23 09	→						23 33					→									
Nutfield	d																							
Godstone	d																							
Edenbridge	d																			00 06				
Penshurst	d																							
Leigh (Kent)	d																							
Tonbridge 4	a																			00 15				
Earlswood (Surrey)	d							23 19										23 49						
Salfords	d							23 22										23 52						
Horley 4	d							23 26										23 56						00 31
Gatwick Airport 10 ✈	a	23 09			23 15	23 18		23 28	23 30		23 38		←	23 41		23 45	23 50	23 58	00 05		00 14	00 17	00 20	00 33
	d	23 10				23 19		23 29			23 39 →		23 39	23 41			23 51	23 59			00 15	00 18		00 34
Three Bridges 15	a	23 14						23 34					23 44	23 47			23 55	00 04			00 19	00 25		00 39
	d	23 14						23 38					23 44	23 47			23 56	00 04			00 20			00 39
Crawley	d							23 41										00 07						00 42
Ifield	d							23 44										00 10						00 45
Faygate	d																							
Littlehaven	d							23 50										00 16						00 51
Horsham 4	a							23 53										00 19						00 54
Balcombe	d													23 53							00 26			
Haywards Heath 3	a	23 23				23 30						23 45	23 52	23 58			00 04				00 31			
	d	23 25				23 34	23 37					23 45	23 53	23 58			00 05				00 31			
Wivelsfield 4	d	23 29				23 38							23 57	00 02							00 35			
Lewes 4	a					23 51																		
Burgess Hill 4	d	23 31											23 59	00 04			00 10				00 37			
Hassocks 4	d	23 34											00 02	00 08							00 41			
Preston Park	d	23 41											00 09	00 15							00 48			
Hove 2	a						23 51										00 21							
Brighton 10	a	23 47										23 59	00 15	00 20							00 52			

For general notes see front of timetable
For details of catering facilities see Directory of Train Operators

b London Bridge

Bedford and London → Brighton

Network Diagram - see first page of Table 186

		SN	FC	SN	SN	SN	SN	GW	SN	FC	SN	GX	SN		FC	SN	GW	FC	GX	SN	FC	FC	SN	FC	SN
		1 ◇	1	1	1	1	1	1	1 ◇	1	1	1	1		1	1	1	1	1	1 ◇	1	1	1	1	1
													A												
London Victoria 15 ⊖	d	23p02		23p10	23p17				23p32		23p47	00 02	00 05			00 14			00 30	01 00			02 00		03 00
Milton Keynes Central 10	d												*22 11*												
Watford Junction	d												*22 53*			*23 29*									
Shepherd's Bush ⊖	d												*23 21*			*23 54*									
Kensington (Olympia) ⊖	d												*23 23*			*23 56*									
West Brompton ⊖	d												*23 26*			*23 59*									
Clapham Junction 10	d	23p08		23p16	23p23				23p38		23p53		00 11			00 20				01 08			02 08		03 08
Bedford 7	d																								
Luton 10	d																								
Luton Airport Parkway 7 ✈	d																								
St Albans City	d																								
St Pancras International 15 ⊖	d																								
Farringdon 3 ⊖	d																								
City Thameslink 3	d																								
London Blackfriars 3 ⊖	d																								
London Charing Cross 4 ⊖	d																								
London Waterloo (East) 4 ⊖	d																								
London Bridge 4 ⊖	d		23p11							23p41	*23 41*		*23 53*		00 11			00 41			01 05	01 35		02 05	
Norwood Junction 2	d																								
East Croydon	a	23p19	23p24	23p28	23p33				23p51	23p56	00 05		00 24		00 26	00 32		00 56		01 21	01 32	02 02	02 21	02 30	03 21
	d	23p20	23p24	23p28	23p33				23p52	23p57	00 06		00 25		00 27	00 33		00 58		01 22	01 32	02 02	02 22	02 32	03 22
Purley 4	d			23p33							00 12					00 38				01 27			02 27		03 27
Coulsdon South	d			23p37							00 15					00 41									
Merstham	d			23p42							00 21					00 47									
Redhill 5	a	23p31		23p46		⟵			00 03		00 24					00 50									
	d	23p31		23p46		23p46	23p55	00 03	00 05		00 25					00 51	00 53								
Reigate	a			⟶																					
Nutfield	d																								
Godstone	d																								
Edenbridge	d						00 06																		
Penshurst	d																								
Leigh (Kent)	d																								
Tonbridge 4	a						00 15																		
Earlswood (Surrey)	d					23p49																			
Salfords	d					23p52																			
Horley 4	d					23p56					00 31					00 57				01 43			02 42		03 42
Gatwick Airport 10 ✈	a	23p38	23p41		23p50	23p58		00 10	00 14	00 17	00 33	00 35	00 43		00 49	00 59	01 02	01 16	01 20	01 45	01 51	02 21	02 44	02 51	03 44
	d	23p39	23p41		23p51	23p59			00 15	00 18	00 34		00 44		00 50			01 17		01 47	01 52	02 22	02 46	02 52	03 46
Three Bridges 15	a	23p44	23p47		23p55	00 04			00 19	00 25	00 39		00 48		00 54			01 24		01 51	01 58	02 28	02 50	02 58	03 50
	d	23p44	23p47		23p56	00 04			00 20		00 39		00 48							01 52					
Crawley	d					00 07					00 42														
Ifield	d					00 10					00 45														
Faygate	d																								
Littlehaven	d					00 16					00 51														
Horsham 4	a					00 19					00 54														
Balcombe	d		23p53						00 26																
Haywards Heath 3	a	23p52	23p58		00 04				00 31				01 00							02 06					
	d	23p53	23p58		00 05				00 31				01 03	01 06						02 06					
Wivelsfield 4	d	23p57	00 02						00 35																
Lewes 4	a													01 20											
Burgess Hill 4	d	23p59	00 04		00 10				00 37																
Hassocks 4	d	00 02	00 08						00 41																
Preston Park	d	00 09	00 15						00 48																
Hove 2	a				00 21								01s25												
Brighton 10	a	00 15	00 20						00 52				01s17							02 23					

For general notes see front of timetable
For details of catering facilities see Directory of Train Operators

A To Eastbourne (Table 189)

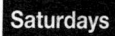

Table 186

Saturdays

Bedford and London → Brighton

Network Diagram - see first page of Table 186

		FC 1	GX 1	FC 1		SN 1 ◇	FC 1	GX 1	FC 1	GX 1	SN 1 ◇	GX 1	FC 1	GW 1	SN 1 A	GW 1	GX 1	SN 1 ◇ B	SN 1 C	GX 1	FC 1	SN 1 ◇ B		GX 1	GW 1
London Victoria 15	⊖ d		03 30			04 00		04 30		05 00	05 02	05 15					05 30	05 32		05 45				06 00	
Milton Keynes Central 10	d																								
Watford Junction	d																								
Shepherd's Bush	⊖ d																								
Kensington (Olympia)	⊖ d																								
West Brompton	⊖ d																								
Clapham Junction 10	d					04 08					05 08							05 38							
Bedford 7	d																								
Luton 10	d																								
Luton Airport Parkway 7	✈ d																								
St Albans City	d																								
St Pancras International 15	⊖ d																								
Farringdon 3	⊖ d																								
City Thameslink 3	d																								
London Blackfriars 3	⊖ d																								
London Charing Cross 4	⊖ d																								
London Waterloo (East) 4	⊖ d																								
London Bridge 4	⊖ d	03 05		03 35			04 05		04 35				05 05								05 51				
Norwood Junction 2	d																								
East Croydon	a	03 30		04 00		04 21	04 30		05 00		05 21		05 32					05 48			06 04				
	d	03 32		04 02		04 22	04 32		05 02		05 22		05 32					05 48			06 05				
Purley 4	d					04 27					05 26							05 53							
Coulsdon South	d										05 30							05 57							
Merstham	d										05 35							06 03				↩			
Redhill 5	a										05 39							06 06							
	d										05 39			05 42		05 49		06 07				06 07			06 14
Reigate	a													05 47				↪							06 18
Nutfield	d																								
Godstone	d																								
Edenbridge	d																								
Penshurst	d																								
Leigh (Kent)	d																								
Tonbridge 4	a																								
Earlswood (Surrey)	d																					06 11			
Salfords	d																					06 15			
Horley 4	d					04 43					05 45											06 18			
Gatwick Airport 10	✈ a	03 51	04 05	04 24		04 45	04 51	05 05	05 21	05 35	05 48	05 52	05 54			05 58	06 00			06 15	06 20	06 21		06 30	
	d	03 52		04 24		04 47	04 51		05 22		05 49		05 54		05 58				06 11		06 20	06 22			
Three Bridges 15	a	03 58		04 30		04 51	04 58		05 27		05 53		06 00		06 02				06 15		06 25	06 26			
	d					04 52			05 28		05 54		06 00		06 03				06 16		06 26	06 30	06 34		
Crawley	d														06 06								06 37		
Ifield	d														06 09								06 40		
Faygate	d																								
Littlehaven	d														06 15								06 46		
Horsham 4	a														06 18								06 49		
Balcombe	d								05 35				06 06								06 32	06 36			
Haywards Heath 3	a					05 00			05 40		06 02		06 12						06 25		06 37	06 41			
	d					05 01			05 42		06 03		06 12						06 25		06 38	06 41			
Wivelsfield 4	d								05 46		06 07		06 16						06 29			06 45			
Lewes 4	a																		06 40						
Burgess Hill 4	d								05 48		06 09		06 18									06 47			
Hassocks 4	d								05 52		06 12		06 22									06 51			
Preston Park	d								05 59		06 19		06 29									06 58			
Hove 2	a																								
Brighton 10	a					05 16			06 07		06 24		06 34								06 51	07 02			

For general notes see front of timetable
For details of catering facilities see Directory of Train Operators

A To Southampton Central (Table 188) and to Bognor Regis (Table 188)
B To Portsmouth Harbour (Table 188)
C To Ore (Table 189)

Table 186

Saturdays

Bedford and London → Brighton

Network Diagram - see first page of Table 186

	SN 1	GW 1	GX 1	GW 1	SN 1 A		FC 1		SN 1 A	GX 1	SN 1 B		GW 1	SN 1	FC 1	GX 1	SN 1	SN 1 B	SN 1	FC 1	GX 1	SN 1	SN 1 ◇	FC 1
London Victoria 15 ⊖ d			06 15		06 02					06 30	06 32					06 45					07 00	06b53	07 06	
Milton Keynes Central 10 d																								
Watford Junction d											*05 51*													
Shepherd's Bush ⊖ d											*06 19*													
Kensington (Olympia) ⊖ d											*06 22*													
West Brompton ⊖ d											*06 25*													
Clapham Junction 10 d					06 08						06 38											06b59	07 12	
Bedford 7 d																								
Luton 10 d																								
Luton Airport Parkway 7 ✈ d																								
St Albans City d																								
St Pancras International 15 ⊖ d																								
Farringdon 3 ⊖ d																								
City Thameslink 3 d																								
London Blackfriars 3 ⊖ d																								
London Charing Cross 4 ⊖ d																								
London Waterloo (East) 4 ⊖ d																								
London Bridge 4 ⊖ d							06 27								06 41					06 56		07 03		07 11
Norwood Junction 2 d																						07 15		
East Croydon a					06 18		06 39				06 48				06 54					07 09		07 18	07 22	07 24
d					06 18		06 39				06 48				06 54					07 09		07 21	07 22	07 24
Purley 4 d					06 23						06 53											07 27		
Coulsdon South d					06 27						06 57											07 30		
Merstham d					06 32						07 02											07 36		
Redhill 5 a					06 36						07 06											→		
d	06 22	06 34		06 41	06 46	06 52			← 06 46		07 10	07 22	07 14	← 07 22				← 07 10						
Reigate a		06 38			→	06 56					→	→	07 18											
Nutfield d	06 26													07 26										
Godstone d	06 32													07 32										
Edenbridge d	06 37													07 37										
Penshurst d	06 44													07 44										
Leigh (Kent) d	06 47													07 47										
Tonbridge 4 a	06 52													07 52										
Earlswood (Surrey) d									06 48									07 12						
Salfords d									06 52									07 16						
Horley 4 d									06 55									07 19						
Gatwick Airport 10 ✈ a			06 45	06 50			06 55		06 58	07 00					07 10	07 15		07 23		07 25	07 30			07 40
d							06 56		06 59						07 11			07 24		07 26				07 41
Three Bridges 15 a							07 00		07 03						07 15			07 29						07 45
d							07 00		07 04						07 15			07 30						07 45
Crawley d									07 07									07 33						
Ifield d									07 10									07 36						
Faygate d																								
Littlehaven d									07 16									07 42						
Horsham 4 a									07 19									07 45						
Balcombe d															07 21									
Haywards Heath 3 a							07 08								07 26					07 36				07 54
d							07 08								07 27		07 33		07 37	07 40				07 55
Wivelsfield 4 d															07 31		07 37							07 59
Lewes 4 a																	07 48							
Burgess Hill 4 d															07 33									08 01
Hassocks 4 d															07 36									08 04
Preston Park d															07 43									08 11
Hove 2 a																			07 51					
Brighton 10 a							07 24								07 49					07 54			07 58	08 17

For general notes see front of timetable
For details of catering facilities see Directory of Train Operators

A To Southampton Central (Table 188)
B To Portsmouth Harbour (Table 188)
b Change at East Croydon

Table 186

Saturdays

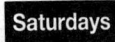

Bedford and London → Brighton

Network Diagram - see first page of Table 186

Station		GX 1	GW 1	GW 1	SN 1 ◇	FC 1	SN 1		SN 1 ◇	GX 1	SN 1	SN 1	SN 1 ◇	SN 1 ◇	FC 1	GX 1	GW 1	SN 1	SN 1		SN 1	FC 1	GX 1	SN 1
London Victoria 15	⊖ d	07 15			07 21					07 30	07 32	07b23	07 36			07 45			07 47				08 00	08 02
Milton Keynes Central 10	d																							
Watford Junction	d										06 55													
Shepherd's Bush	⊖ d										07 19													
Kensington (Olympia)	⊖ d										07 22													
West Brompton	⊖ d										07 25													
Clapham Junction 10	d										07 38	07b29	07 42						07 53					08 08
Bedford 7	d																							
Luton 10	d																							
Luton Airport Parkway 7	✈ d																							
St Albans City	d																							
St Pancras International 15	⊖ d																							
Farringdon 3	⊖ d																							
City Thameslink 3	d																							
London Blackfriars 3	⊖ d																							
London Charing Cross 4	⊖ d																	07 40						
London Waterloo (East) 4	⊖ d																	07 43						
London Bridge 4	⊖ d					07 26						07 33			07 41			07 48				07 56		
Norwood Junction 2	d											07 45												
East Croydon	a				07 37	07 39					07 48	07 48	07 52		07 54			08 02	08 03			08 09		08 18
	d				07 37	07 39					07 48	07 51	07 52		07 54			08 03	08 03			08 09		08 18
Purley 4	d											07 57						08 11						
Coulsdon South	d						←					08 00						08 14						
Merstham	d						07 36					08 06												
Redhill 5	a						07 39				08 00	08 09						08 21			←			08 30
	d		07 34	07 41			07 44	07 52			08 00	08 10					08 14	08 22			08 10			08 30
Reigate	a		07 38					07 56				→					08 18							
Nutfield	d																	08 26						
Godstone	d																	08 32						
Edenbridge	d																	08 37						
Penshurst	d																	08 44						
Leigh (Kent)	d																	08 47						
Tonbridge 4	a																	08 52						
Earlswood (Surrey)	d																				08 12			
Salfords	d																				08 16			
Horley 4	d						07 51														08 19			08 36
Gatwick Airport 10	✈ a	07 45		07 50	07 53	07 55	07 55		←	08 00	08 08				08 10	08 15			08 18		08 23	08 25	08 30	08 39
	d				07 58	07 56	07 56		07 58		08 09				08 11				08 19		08 24	08 26		08 40
Three Bridges 15	a				→		08 01		08 03		08 14				08 15						08 29			08 44
	d						08 01		08 03		08 14				08 15						08 30			08 45
Crawley	d						08 05				08 18										08 33			08 48
Ifield	d						08 07														08 36			
Faygate	d																							
Littlehaven	d						08 14														08 42			
Horsham 4	a						08 17				08 26										08 45			08 56
Balcombe	d														08 21									
Haywards Heath 3	a					08 06			08 12						08 26				08 30			08 36		
	d					08 10			08 17						08 27				08 34	08 37		08 40		
Wivelsfield 4	d								08 21						08 31									
Lewes 4	a																		08 48					
Burgess Hill 4	d								08 23						08 33									
Hassocks 4	d								08 26						08 36									
Preston Park	d								08 33					← 08 33	08 43									
Hove 2	a								→											08 51				
Brighton 10	a					08 24							08 27	08 40	08 49							08 54		

For general notes see front of timetable
For details of catering facilities see Directory of Train Operators

b Change at East Croydon

Bedford and London → Brighton

Saturdays

Network Diagram - see first page of Table 186

	SN 1	SN 1 ◇	FC 1	GX 1	GW 1	GW 1	SN 1	SN 1	SN 1		GW 1	SN 1 ◇	FC 1	SN 1	SN 1 ◇		GX 1	SN 1	SN 1	SN 1 ◇	SN 1 ◇	FC 1	GX 1	GW 1
London Victoria 15 ⊖ d	07b53	08 06		08 15					08 17			08 21					08 30	08 32	08b23	08 36			08 45	
Milton Keynes Central 10 d																								
Watford Junction d																		*07 13*						
Shepherd's Bush ⊖ d																		*07 52*						
Kensington (Olympia) ⊖ d																		*08 19*						
West Brompton ⊖ d																		*08 22*						
Clapham Junction 10 d	07b59	08 12							08 23									*08 25* 08 38	08b29	08 42				
Bedford 7 d																								
Luton 10 d																								
Luton Airport Parkway 7 ✈ d																								
St Albans City d																								
St Pancras International 15 ⊖ d																								
Farringdon 3 ⊖ d																								
City Thameslink 3 d																								
London Blackfriars 3 ⊖ d																								
London Charing Cross 4 ⊖ d								08 10																
London Waterloo (East) 4 ⊖ d								08 13																
London Bridge 4 ⊖ d	08 03		08 11					08 18					08 26						08 33			08 41		
Norwood Junction 2 d	08 15																		08 45					
East Croydon a	08 18	08 22	08 24					08 32	08 33			08 37	08 39					08 48	08 48	08 52		08 54		
d	08 21	08 22	08 24					08 33	08 33			08 37	08 39					08 48	08 51	08 52		08 54		
Purley 4 d	08 27							08 41											08 57					
Coulsdon South d	08 30						←	08 44											09 00					
Merstham d	08 36						08 36												09 06					
Redhill 5 a	→						08 39	08 51										09 00	09 09					
d					08 34	08 41	08 44	08 52			← 08 41							09 00	09 10					09 14
Reigate a					08 38	↪		08 56											↪					09 18
Nutfield d																								
Godstone d																								
Edenbridge d																								
Penshurst d																								
Leigh (Kent) d																								
Tonbridge 4 a																								
Earlswood (Surrey) d																								
Salfords d																								
Horley 4 d							08 51 →							← 08 51										
Gatwick Airport 10 ✈ a			08 40	08 45					08 48		08 50	08 53	08 55	08 55	←		09 00	09 08				09 10	09 15	
d			08 41						08 49			08 58 →	08 56	08 56	08 58			09 09				09 11		
Three Bridges 15 a			08 45											09 01	09 03			09 14				09 15		
d			08 45											09 01	09 03			09 14				09 15		
Crawley d														09 05				09 18						
Ifield d														09 07										
Faygate d																								
Littlehaven d														09 14										
Horsham 4 a														09 17				09 26						
Balcombe d																						09 21		
Haywards Heath 3 a			08 54						09 00				09 06		09 12							09 26		
d			08 55						09 04	09 07			09 10		09 17							09 27		
Wivelsfield 4 d			08 59							09 11					09 21							09 31		
Lewes 4 a										09 22														
Burgess Hill 4 d			09 01						09 09						09 23							09 33		
Hassocks 4 d			09 04												09 26						←	09 36		
Preston Park d			09 11												09 33						09 33	09 43		
Hove 2 a									09 21						→									
Brighton 10 a		08 58	09 17										09 24							09 27	09 40	09 49		

For general notes see front of timetable
For details of catering facilities see Directory of Train Operators

b Change at East Croydon

Bedford and London → Brighton

Network Diagram - see first page of Table 186

		SN 1	SN 1		SN 1	FC 1	GX 1	SN 1	SN 1	SN 1 ◇	FC 1	GX 1	GW 1	GW 1	SN 1	SN 1	SN 1		GW 1	SN 1 ◇	FC 1	SN 1	SN 1 ◇	GX 1
London Victoria 15	⊖ d		08 47				09 00	09 02	08b53	09 06		09 15					09 17			09 21				09 30
Milton Keynes Central 10	d																							
Watford Junction	d																							
Shepherd's Bush	⊖ d																							
Kensington (Olympia)	⊖ d																							
West Brompton	⊖ d																							
Clapham Junction 10	d		08 53					09 08	08b59	09 12							09 23							
Bedford 7	d																							
Luton 10	d																							
Luton Airport Parkway 7	✈ d																							
St Albans City	d																							
St Pancras International 15	⊖ d																							
Farringdon 3	⊖ d																							
City Thameslink 3	d																							
London Blackfriars 3	⊖ d																							
London Charing Cross 4	⊖ d	08 40														09 10								
London Waterloo (East) 4	⊖ d	08 43														09 13								
London Bridge 4	⊖ d	08 48				08 56			09 03		09 11					09 18					09 26			
Norwood Junction 2	d								09 15															
East Croydon	a	09 02	09 03			09 09		09 18	09 18	09 22	09 24					09 32	09 33			09 37	09 39			
	d	09 03	09 03			09 09		09 18	09 21	09 22	09 24					09 33	09 33			09 37	09 39			
Purley 4	d	09 11							09 27							09 41								
Coulsdon South	d	09 14							09 30						←	09 44								
Merstham	d								09 36						09 36									
Redhill 5	a	09 21			←			09 30	→						09 39	09 51			←					
	d	09 22			09 10			09 30					09 34	09 41	09 44	09 52			09 41					
Reigate	a												09 38	→		09 56								
Nutfield	d	09 26																						
Godstone	d	09 32																						
Edenbridge	d	09 37																						
Penshurst	d	09 44																						
Leigh (Kent)	d	09 47																						
Tonbridge 4	a	09 52																						
Earlswood (Surrey)	d				09 12																			
Salfords	d				09 16																	←		
Horley 4	d				09 19			09 36							09 51 →							09 51		
Gatwick Airport 10	✈ a		09 18		09 23	09 25	09 30	09 39			09 40	09 45					09 48		09 50	09 53	09 55	09 55	←	10 00
	d		09 19		09 24	09 26		09 40			09 41						09 49			09 58 →	09 56	09 56	09 58	
Three Bridges 15	a				09 29			09 44			09 45											10 01	10 03	
	d				09 30			09 45			09 45											10 01	10 03	
Crawley	d				09 33			09 48														10 05		
Ifield	d				09 36																	10 07		
Faygate	d																							
Littlehaven	d				09 42																	10 14		
Horsham 4	a				09 45			09 56														10 17		
Balcombe	d																							
Haywards Heath 3	a		09 30			09 36					09 54						10 00				10 06		10 12	
	d		09 34	09 37		09 40					09 55						10 04	10 07			10 10		10 17	
Wivelsfield 4	d										09 59							10 11					10 21	
Lewes 4	a		09 51															10 22						
Burgess Hill 4	d										10 01						10 09						10 23	
Hassocks 4	d										10 04												10 26	
Preston Park	d										10 11												10 33	
Hove 2	a			09 51													10 21						→	
Brighton 10	a					09 54				09 58	10 17										10 24			

For general notes see front of timetable
For details of catering facilities see
Directory of Train Operators

b Change at East Croydon

Table 186

Saturdays

Bedford and London → Brighton

Network Diagram - see first page of Table 186

		SN 1	SN 1	SN 1◇	SN 1◇	FC 1	GX 1	GW 1	SN 1	SN 1		SN 1	FC 1	GX 1	SN 1	SN 1	SN 1◇	FC 1	GX 1	GW 1	GW 1	SN 1	SN 1	SN 1	
London Victoria 15	⊖ d	09 32	09b23	09 36			09 45			09 47				10 00	10 02	09b53	10 06		10 15					10 17	
Milton Keynes Central 10	d	08 13																							
Watford Junction	d	08 51																							
Shepherd's Bush	⊖ d	09 19																							
Kensington (Olympia)	⊖ d	09 22																							
West Brompton	⊖ d	09 25																							
Clapham Junction 10	d	09 38	09b29	09 42						09 53					10 08	09b59	10 12							10 23	
Bedford 7	d																								
Luton 10	d																								
Luton Airport Parkway 7	✈ d																								
St Albans City	d																								
St Pancras International 15	⊖ d																								
Farringdon 3	⊖ d																								
City Thameslink 3	d																								
London Blackfriars 3	⊖ d																								
London Charing Cross 4	⊖ d								09 40														10 10		
London Waterloo (East) 4	⊖ d								09 43														10 13		
London Bridge 4	⊖ d		09 33			09 41			09 48				09 56			10 03		10 11					10 18		
Norwood Junction 2	d		09 45													10 15									
East Croydon	a	09 48	09 48	09 52		09 54			10 02	10 03			10 09		10 18	10 18	10 22	10 24					10 32	10 33	
	d	09 48	09 51	09 52		09 54			10 03	10 03			10 09		10 18	10 21	10 22	10 24					10 33	10 33	
Purley 4	d		09 57						10 11							10 27							10 41		
Coulsdon South	d		10 00						10 14							10 30						←	10 44		
Merstham	d		10 06													10 36						10 36			
Redhill 5	a	10 00	10 09						10 21			←			10 30	→						10 39	10 51		
	d	10 00	10 10					10 14	10 22			10 10			10 30					10 34	10 41	10 44	10 52		
Reigate	a		→					10 18												10 38	→		10 56		
Nutfield	d								10 26																
Godstone	d								10 32																
Edenbridge	d								10 37																
Penshurst	d								10 44																
Leigh (Kent)	d								10 47																
Tonbridge 4	a								10 52																
Earlswood (Surrey)	d											10 12													
Salfords	d											10 16													
Horley 4	d											10 19			10 36										
Gatwick Airport 10	✈ a	10 08				10 10	10 15			10 18		10 23	10 25	10 30	10 39			10 40	10 45			10 51 →		10 48	
	d	10 09				10 11				10 19		10 24	10 26		10 40			10 41						10 49	
Three Bridges 15	a	10 14				10 15						10 29			10 44			10 45							
	d	10 14				10 15						10 30			10 45			10 45							
Crawley	d	10 18										10 33			10 48										
Ifield	d											10 36													
Faygate	d																								
Littlehaven	d											10 42													
Horsham 4	a	10 26										10 45			10 56										
Balcombe	d					10 21																			
Haywards Heath 3	a					10 26				10 30			10 36					10 54						11 00	
	d					10 27				10 34	10 37		10 40					10 55						11 04	11 07
Wivelsfield 4	d					10 31												10 59							11 11
Lewes 4	a									10 51															11 22
Burgess Hill 4	d					10 33												11 01						11 09	
Hassocks 4	d				←	10 36												11 04							
Preston Park	d				10 33	10 43												11 11							
Hove 2	a										10 51													11 21	
Brighton 10	a			10 27	10 40	10 49							10 54				10 58	11 17							

For general notes see front of timetable
For details of catering facilities see
Directory of Train Operators

b Change at East Croydon

Bedford and London → Brighton

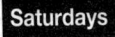

Network Diagram - see first page of Table 186

		GW 1	SN 1 ◊	FC 1	SN 1	SN 1 ◊	GX 1	SN 1	SN 1	SN 1 ◊	SN 1 ◊	FC 1	GX 1	GW 1	SN 1	SN 1	SN 1	FC 1	GX 1	SN 1	SN 1	SN 1 ◊	FC 1
London Victoria 15 ⊖	d		10 21				10 30	10 32	10b23	10 36			10 45			10 47			11 00	11 02	10b53	11 06	
Milton Keynes Central 10	d							09 13															
Watford Junction	d							09 52															
Shepherd's Bush ⊖	d							10 19															
Kensington (Olympia) ⊖	d							10 22															
West Brompton ⊖	d							10 25															
Clapham Junction 10	d							10 38	10b29	10 42						10 53				11 08	10b59	11 12	
Bedford 7	d																						
Luton 10	d																						
Luton Airport Parkway 7 ✈	d																						
St Albans City	d																						
St Pancras International 15 ⊖	d																						
Farringdon 3 ⊖	d																						
City Thameslink 3	d																						
London Blackfriars 3 ⊖	d																						
London Charing Cross 4 ⊖	d														10 40								
London Waterloo (East) 4 ⊖	d														10 43								
London Bridge 4 ⊖	d			10 26					10 33			10 41			10 48			10 56			11 03		11 11
Norwood Junction 2	d								10 45												11 15		
East Croydon	a		10 37	10 39				10 48	10 48	10 52		10 54			11 02	11 03		11 09		11 18	11 18	11 22	11 24
	d		10 37	10 39				10 48	10 51	10 52		10 54			11 03	11 03		11 09		11 18	11 21	11 22	11 24
Purley 4	d								10 57						11 11						11 27		
Coulsdon South	d								11 00						11 14						11 30		
Merstham	d								11 06												11 36		
Redhill 5	a	←						11 00	11 09						11 21		←			11 30	→		
	d	10 41						11 00	11 10					11 14	11 22		11 10			11 30			
Reigate	a								→					11 18									
Nutfield	d														11 26								
Godstone	d														11 32								
Edenbridge	d														11 37								
Penshurst	d														11 44								
Leigh (Kent)	d														11 47								
Tonbridge 4	a														11 52								
Earlswood (Surrey)	d																11 12						
Salfords	d				←												11 16						
Horley 4	d				10 51												11 19			11 36			
Gatwick Airport 10 ✈	a	10 50	10 53	10 55	10 55	←	11 00	11 08				11 10	11 15			11 18	11 23	11 25	11 30	11 39			11 40
	d		10 58	10 56	10 56	10 58		11 09				11 11				11 19	11 24	11 26		11 40			11 41
Three Bridges 15	a		→		11 01	11 03		11 14				11 15					11 29			11 44			11 45
	d				11 01	11 03		11 14				11 15					11 30			11 45			11 45
Crawley	d				11 05			11 18									11 33			11 48			
Ifield	d				11 07												11 36						
Faygate	d																						
Littlehaven	d				11 14												11 42						
Horsham 4	a				11 17			11 26									11 45			11 56			
Balcombe	d											11 21											
Haywards Heath 3	a			11 06		11 12						11 26				11 30		11 36					11 54
	d			11 10		11 17						11 27				11 34	11 37	11 40					11 55
Wivelsfield 4	d					11 21						11 31											11 59
Lewes 4	a															11 51							
Burgess Hill 4	d					11 23						11 33											12 01
Hassocks 4	d					11 26					←	11 36											12 04
Preston Park	d					11 33					11 33	11 43											12 11
Hove 2	a					→											11 51						
Brighton 10	a			11 24						11 27	11 40	11 49						11 54				11 58	12 17

For general notes see front of timetable
For details of catering facilities see Directory of Train Operators

b Change at East Croydon

Table 186

Saturdays

Bedford and London → Brighton

Network Diagram - see first page of Table 186

		GX 1	GW 1	GW 1	SN 1	SN 1	SN 1		GW 1	SN 1 ◇	FC 1	SN 1	SN 1 ◇	GX 1	SN 1	SN 1	SN 1 ◇ 🍴	SN 1 ◇	FC 1	GX 1	GW 1	SN 1	SN 1	
London Victoria 15 ⊖	d	11 15					11 17			11 21				11 30	11 32	11b23	11 36			11 45			11 47	
Milton Keynes Central 10	d														10 13									
Watford Junction	d														10 52									
Shepherd's Bush ⊖	d														11 19									
Kensington (Olympia) ⊖	d														11 22									
West Brompton ⊖	d														11 25									
Clapham Junction 10	d						11 23								11 38	11b29	11 42						11 53	
Bedford 7	d																							
Luton 10	d																							
Luton Airport Parkway 7 ✈	d																							
St Albans City	d																							
St Pancras International 15 ⊖	d																							
Farringdon 3 ⊖	d																							
City Thameslink 3	d																							
London Blackfriars 3 ⊖	d																							
London Charing Cross 4 ⊖	d					11 10																11 40		
London Waterloo (East) 4 ⊖	d					11 13																11 43		
London Bridge 4 ⊖	d					11 18					11 26					11 33			11 41			11 48		
Norwood Junction 2	d															11 45								
East Croydon	a					11 32	11 33			11 37	11 39				11 48	11 48	11 52		11 54			12 02	12 03	
	d					11 33	11 33			11 37	11 39				11 48	11 51	11 52		11 54			12 03	12 03	
Purley 4	d					11 41										11 57						12 11		
Coulsdon South	d				←	11 44										12 00						12 14		
Merstham	d				11 36											12 06								
Redhill 5	a				11 39	11 51									12 00	12 09						12 21		
	d		11 34	11 41	11 44	11 52			← 11 41						12 00	12 10					12 14	12 22		
Reigate	a		11 38	→		11 56										→					12 18			
Nutfield	d																					12 26		
Godstone	d																					12 32		
Edenbridge	d																					12 37		
Penshurst	d																					12 44		
Leigh (Kent)	d																					12 47		
Tonbridge 4	a																					12 52		
Earlswood (Surrey)	d																							
Salfords	d																							
Horley 4	d				11 51							← 11 51												
Gatwick Airport 10 ✈	a	11 45			→		11 48		11 50	11 53	11 55	11 55	←	12 00	12 08				12 10	12 15			12 18	
	d						11 49			11 58	11 56	11 56	11 58		12 09				12 11				12 19	
Three Bridges 15	a									→		12 01	12 03		12 14				12 15					
	d											12 01	12 03		12 14				12 15					
Crawley	d											12 05			12 18									
Ifield	d											12 07												
Faygate	d																							
Littlehaven	d											12 14												
Horsham 4	a											12 17			12 26									
Balcombe	d																		12 21					
Haywards Heath 3	a						12 00				12 06		12 12						12 26				12 30	
	d						12 04	12 07			12 10		12 17						12 27				12 34	12 37
Wivelsfield 4	d							12 11					12 21						12 31					
Lewes 4	a							12 22															12 51	
Burgess Hill 4	d						12 09						12 23						12 33					
Hassocks 4	d												12 26						12 36					
Preston Park	d												12 33					← 12 33	12 43					
Hove 2	a						12 21						→											12 51
Brighton 10	a									12 24							12 27	12 40	12 49					

For general notes see front of timetable
For details of catering facilities see
Directory of Train Operators

b Change at East Croydon

Bedford and London → Brighton

Network Diagram - see first page of Table 186

		SN 1	FC 1	GX 1	SN 1	SN 1	SN 1 ◇	FC 1	GX 1	GW 1	GW 1	SN 1		SN 1	SN 1		GW 1	SN 1 ◇	FC 1	SN 1	SN 1 ◇	GX 1	SN 1	SN 1	SN 1 ◇
London Victoria [15]	⊖ d			12 00	12 02	11b53	12 06		12 15						12 17			12 21				12 30	12 32	12b23	12 36
Milton Keynes Central [10]	d																						11 13		
Watford Junction	d																						11 52		
Shepherd's Bush	⊖ d																						12 19		
Kensington (Olympia)	⊖ d																						12 22		
West Brompton	⊖ d																						12 25		
Clapham Junction [10]	d				12 08	11b59	12 12								12 23								12 38	12b29	12 42
Bedford [7]	d																								
Luton [10]	d																								
Luton Airport Parkway [7]	✈ d																								
St Albans City	d																								
St Pancras International [15]	⊖ d																								
Farringdon [3]	⊖ d																								
City Thameslink [3]	d																								
London Blackfriars [3]	⊖ d																								
London Charing Cross [4]	⊖ d													12 10											
London Waterloo (East) [4]	⊖ d													12 13											
London Bridge [4]	⊖ d		11 56			12 03		12 11						12 18					12 26					12 33	
Norwood Junction [2]	d					12 15																		12 45	
East Croydon	a		12 09		12 18	12 18	12 22	12 24						12 32	12 33			12 37	12 39				12 48	12 48	12 52
	d		12 09		12 18	12 21	12 22	12 24						12 33	12 33			12 37	12 39				12 48	12 51	12 52
Purley [4]	d					12 27								12 41										12 57	
Coulsdon South	d					12 30						←		12 44										13 00	
Merstham	d					12 36						12 36												13 06	
Redhill [5]	a	←			12 30	↪						12 39		12 51			←						13 00	13 09	
	d	12 10			12 30					12 34	12 41	12 44		12 52			12 41						13 00	13 10	
Reigate	a									12 38	↪			12 56										↪	
Nutfield	d																								
Godstone	d																								
Edenbridge	d																								
Penshurst	d																								
Leigh (Kent)	d																								
Tonbridge [4]	a																								
Earlswood (Surrey)	d	12 12																							
Salfords	d	12 16																		←					
Horley [4]	d	12 19			12 36							12 51 ↪								12 51					
Gatwick Airport [10]	✈ a	12 23	12 25	12 30	12 39			12 40	12 45						12 48		12 50	12 53	12 55	12 55	←	13 00	13 08		
	d	12 24	12 26		12 40			12 41							12 49			12 58	12 56	12 56	12 58		13 09		
Three Bridges [15]	a	12 29			12 44			12 45										↪		13 01	13 03		13 14		
	d	12 30			12 45			12 45												13 01	13 03		13 14		
Crawley	d	12 33			12 48															13 05			13 18		
Ifield	d	12 36																		13 07					
Faygate	d																								
Littlehaven	d	12 42																		13 14					
Horsham [4]	a	12 45			12 56															13 17			13 26		
Balcombe	d																								
Haywards Heath [3]	a		12 36					12 54							13 00				13 06		13 12				
	d		12 40					12 55							13 04	13 07			13 10		13 17				
Wivelsfield [4]	d							12 59								13 11					13 21				
Lewes [4]	a															13 22									
Burgess Hill [4]	d							13 01							13 09						13 23				
Hassocks [4]	d							13 04													13 26				
Preston Park	d							13 11													13 33				
Hove [2]	a														13 21						↪				
Brighton [10]	a		12 54				12 58	13 17											13 24						13 27

For general notes see front of timetable
For details of catering facilities see
Directory of Train Operators

b Change at East Croydon

Bedford and London → Brighton

Network Diagram - see first page of Table 186

		SN 1 ◇	FC 1	GX 1	GW 1	SN 1	SN 1		SN 1	FC 1	GX 1	SN 1 (bus)	SN 1	SN 1 ◇ (bus)	FC 1	GX 1		GW 1	GW 1	SN 1	SN 1	SN 1		GW 1	SN 1 ◇
London Victoria 15	⊖ d			12 45			12 47				13 00	13 02	12b53	13 06		13 15						13 17			13 21
Milton Keynes Central 10	d																								
Watford Junction	d																								
Shepherd's Bush	⊖ d																								
Kensington (Olympia)	⊖ d																								
West Brompton	⊖ d																								
Clapham Junction 10	d						12 53					13 08	12b59	13 12								13 23			
Bedford 7	d																								
Luton 10	d																								
Luton Airport Parkway 7	✈ d																								
St Albans City	d																								
St Pancras International 15	⊖ d																								
Farringdon 3	⊖ d																								
City Thameslink 3	d																								
London Blackfriars 3	⊖ d																								
London Charing Cross 4	⊖ d					12 40															13 10				
London Waterloo (East) 4	⊖ d					12 43															13 13				
London Bridge 4	⊖ d		12 41			12 48				12 56			13 03		13 11						13 18				
Norwood Junction 2	d												13 15												
East Croydon	a		12 54			13 02	13 03			13 09		13 18	13 18	13 22	13 24						13 32	13 33			13 37
	d		12 54			13 03	13 03			13 09		13 18	13 21	13 22	13 24						13 33	13 33			13 37
Purley 4	d					13 11							13 27								13 41				
Coulsdon South	d					13 14							13 30								13 44				
Merstham	d												13 36							← 13 36					
Redhill 5	a					13 21						13 30	→							13 39	13 51				
	d				13 14	13 22			← 13 10			13 30						13 34	13 41	13 44	13 52			← 13 41	
Reigate	a				13 18													13 38	→		13 56				
Nutfield	d					13 26																			
Godstone	d					13 32																			
Edenbridge	d					13 37																			
Penshurst	d					13 44																			
Leigh (Kent)	d					13 47																			
Tonbridge 4	a					13 52																			
Earlswood (Surrey)	d								13 12																
Salfords	d								13 16																
Horley 4	d								13 19			13 36													
Gatwick Airport 10	✈ a		13 10	13 15			13 18		13 23	13 25	13 30	13 39			13 40	13 45				13 51 →		13 48		13 50	13 53
	d		13 11				13 19		13 24	13 26		13 40			13 41							13 49			13 58
Three Bridges 15	a		13 15						13 29			13 44			13 45										→
	d		13 15						13 30			13 45			13 45										
Crawley	d								13 33			13 48													
Ifield	d								13 36																
Faygate	d																								
Littlehaven	d								13 42																
Horsham 4	a								13 45			13 56													
Balcombe	d		13 21																						
Haywards Heath 3	a		13 26				13 30			13 36					13 54							14 00			
	d		13 27				13 34	13 37		13 40					13 55							14 04	14 07		
Wivelsfield 4	d		13 31												13 59								14 11		
Lewes 4	a						13 48																14 22		
Burgess Hill 4	d		13 33												14 01							14 09			
Hassocks 4	d	←	13 36												14 04										
Preston Park	d	13 33	13 43												14 11										
Hove 2	a							13 51														14 21			
Brighton 10	a	13 40	13 49							13 54				13 58	14 17										

For general notes see front of timetable
For details of catering facilities see Directory of Train Operators

b Change at East Croydon

Bedford and London → Brighton

Network Diagram - see first page of Table 186

	FC	SN	SN	GX	SN	SN	SN	SN	FC	GX	GW	SN	SN		SN	FC	GX	SN	SN	SN	FC	GX	GW
	1	1	1 ◇	1	1	1	1 ◇ 🚲	1 ◇	1	1	1	1	1		1	1	1	1 🚲	1	1 ◇ 🚲	1	1	1
London Victoria 15 ⊖ d				13 30	13 32	13b23	13 36			13 45			13 47				14 00	14 02	13b53	14 06		14 15	
Milton Keynes Central 10 d					12 13																		
Watford Junction d					12 51																		
Shepherd's Bush ⊖ d					13 19																		
Kensington (Olympia) ⊖ d					13 22																		
West Brompton ⊖ d					13 25																		
Clapham Junction 10 d					13 38	13b29	13 42						13 53					14 08	13b59	14 12			
Bedford 7 d																							
Luton 10 d																							
Luton Airport Parkway 7 ✈ d																							
St Albans City d																							
St Pancras International 15 ⊖ d																							
Farringdon 3 ⊖ d																							
City Thameslink 3 d																							
London Blackfriars 3 ⊖ d																							
London Charing Cross 4 ⊖ d												13 40											
London Waterloo (East) 4 ⊖ d												13 43											
London Bridge 4 ⊖ d	13 26					13 33			13 41			13 48				13 56			14 03		14 11		
Norwood Junction 2 d						13 45													14 15				
East Croydon a	13 39				13 48	13 48	13 52		13 54			14 02	14 03			14 09		14 18	14 18	14 22	14 24		
d	13 39				13 48	13 51	13 52		13 54			14 03	14 03			14 09		14 18	14 21	14 22	14 24		
Purley 4 d						13 57						14 11							14 27				
Coulsdon South d						14 00						14 14							14 30				
Merstham d						14 06													14 36				
Redhill 5 a					14 00	14 09						14 21			←			14 30	→				
d					14 00	14 10					14 14	14 22			14 10			14 30					14 34
Reigate a						→					14 18												14 38
Nutfield d												14 26											
Godstone d												14 32											
Edenbridge d												14 37											
Penshurst d												14 44											
Leigh (Kent) d												14 47											
Tonbridge 4 a												14 52											
Earlswood (Surrey) d															14 12								
Salfords d		←													14 16								
Horley 4 d		13 51													14 19			14 36					
Gatwick Airport 10 ✈ a	13 55	13 55	←	14 00	14 08				14 10	14 15			14 18		14 23	14 25	14 30	14 39			14 40	14 45	
d	13 56	13 56	13 58		14 09				14 11				14 19		14 24	14 26		14 40			14 41		
Three Bridges 15 a		14 01	14 03		14 14				14 15						14 29			14 44			14 45		
d		14 01	14 03		14 14				14 15						14 30			14 45			14 45		
Crawley d		14 05			14 18										14 33			14 48					
Ifield d		14 07													14 36								
Faygate d																							
Littlehaven d		14 14													14 42								
Horsham 4 a		14 17			14 26										14 45			14 56					
Balcombe d									14 21														
Haywards Heath 3 a	14 06		14 12						14 26				14 30			14 36					14 54		
d	14 10		14 17						14 27				14 34	14 37		14 40					14 55		
Wivelsfield 4 d			14 21						14 31												14 59		
Lewes 4 a													14 48										
Burgess Hill 4 d			14 23						14 33												15 01		
Hassocks 4 d			14 26					←	14 36												15 04		
Preston Park d			14 33					14 33	14 43												15 11		
Hove 2 a			→											14 51									
Brighton 10 a	14 24						14 27	14 40	14 49							14 54				14 58	15 17		

For general notes see front of timetable
For details of catering facilities see
Directory of Train Operators

b Change at East Croydon

Saturdays

Bedford and London → Brighton

Network Diagram - see first page of Table 186

	GW 1	SN 1	SN 1	SN 1		GW 1	SN 1 ◇	FC 1	SN 1	SN 1 ◇	GX 1	SN 1	SN 1	SN 1 ◇ ⊼	SN 1 ◇	FC 1	GX 1	GW 1	SN 1	SN 1		SN 1	FC 1	GX 1
London Victoria [15] ⊖ d				14 17			14 21				14 30	14 32	14b23	14 36			14 45			14 47				15 00
Milton Keynes Central [10] d												13 13												
Watford Junction d												13 51												
Shepherd's Bush ⊖ d												14 19												
Kensington (Olympia) ⊖ d												14 22												
West Brompton ⊖ d												14 25												
Clapham Junction [10] d				14 23								14 38	14b29	14 42						14 53				
Bedford [7] d																								
Luton [10] d																								
Luton Airport Parkway [7] ✈ d																								
St Albans City d																								
St Pancras International [15] ⊖ d																								
Farringdon [3] ⊖ d																								
City Thameslink [3] d																								
London Blackfriars [3] ⊖ d																								
London Charing Cross [4] ⊖ d			14 10																14 40					
London Waterloo (East) [4] ⊖ d			14 13																14 43					
London Bridge [4] ⊖ d			14 18					14 26					14 33			14 41			14 48				14 56	
Norwood Junction [2] d													14 45											
East Croydon a			14 32	14 33			14 37	14 39				14 48	14 48	14 52		14 54			15 02	15 03			15 09	
d			14 33	14 33			14 37	14 39				14 48	14 51	14 52		14 54			15 03	15 03			15 09	
Purley [4] d			14 41										14 57						15 11					
Coulsdon South d		←	14 44										15 00						15 14					
Merstham d		14 36											15 06											
Redhill [5] a		14 39	14 51			←						15 00	15 09						15 21			←		
d	14 41	14 44	14 52			14 41						15 00	15 10					15 14	15 22			15 10		
Reigate a	→		14 56										→					15 18						
Nutfield d																			15 26					
Godstone d																			15 32					
Edenbridge d																			15 37					
Penshurst d																			15 44					
Leigh (Kent) d																			15 47					
Tonbridge [4] a																			15 52					
Earlswood (Surrey) d																						15 12		
Salfords d									←													15 16		
Horley [4] d		14 51							14 51													15 19		
Gatwick Airport [10] ✈ a		→		14 48		14 50	14 53	14 55	14 55	←	15 00	15 08				15 10	15 15			15 18		15 23	15 25	15 30
d				14 49			14 58	14 56	14 56	14 58		15 09				15 11				15 19		15 24	15 26	
Three Bridges [15] a							→		15 01	15 03		15 14				15 15						15 29		
d									15 01	15 03		15 14				15 15						15 30		
Crawley d									15 05			15 18										15 33		
Ifield d									15 07													15 36		
Faygate d																								
Littlehaven d									15 14													15 42		
Horsham [4] a									15 17			15 26										15 45		
Balcombe d																15 21								
Haywards Heath [3] a				15 00				15 06		15 12						15 26				15 30			15 36	
d				15 04	15 07			15 10		15 17						15 27				15 34	15 37		15 40	
Wivelsfield [4] d					15 11					15 21						15 31								
Lewes [4] a					15 22															15 48				
Burgess Hill [4] d				15 09						15 23						15 33								
Hassocks [4] d										15 26					←	15 36								
Preston Park d										15 33					15 33	15 43								
Hove [2] a				15 21						→											15 51			
Brighton [10] a								15 24						15 27	15 40	15 49							15 54	

For general notes see front of timetable
For details of catering facilities see Directory of Train Operators

b Change at East Croydon

Bedford and London → Brighton

Network Diagram - see first page of Table 186

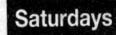

Station		SN 1 (trolley)		SN 1	SN 1 ◇ (trolley)	FC 1	GX 1	GW 1	GW 1	SN 1	SN 1	SN 1		GW 1	SN 1 ◇	FC 1	SN 1	SN 1 ◇	GX 1	SN 1	SN 1	SN 1 ◇ (trolley)	SN 1 ◇	FC 1	GX 1
London Victoria 15 ⊖	d	15 02		14b53	15 06		15 15					15 17			15 21				15 30	15 32	15b23	15 36			15 45
Milton Keynes Central 10	d																			14 13					
Watford Junction	d																			14 51					
Shepherd's Bush ⊖	d																			15 19					
Kensington (Olympia) ⊖	d																			15 22					
West Brompton ⊖	d																			15 25					
Clapham Junction 10	d	15 08		14b59	15 12							15 23								15 38	15b29	15 42			
Bedford 7	d																								
Luton 10	d																								
Luton Airport Parkway 7 ✈	d																								
St Albans City	d																								
St Pancras International 15 ⊖	d																								
Farringdon 3 ⊖	d																								
City Thameslink 3	d																								
London Blackfriars 3 ⊖	d																								
London Charing Cross 4 ⊖	d										15 10														
London Waterloo (East) 4 ⊖	d										15 13														
London Bridge 4 ⊖	d			15 03		15 11					15 18					15 26					15 33			15 41	
Norwood Junction 2	d			15 15																	15 45				
East Croydon (tram)	a	15 18		15 18	15 22	15 24					15 32	15 33			15 37	15 39				15 48	15 48	15 52		15 54	
	d	15 18		15 21	15 22	15 24					15 33	15 33			15 37	15 39				15 48	15 51	15 52		15 54	
Purley 4	d			15 27							15 41										15 57				
Coulsdon South	d			15 30						←	15 44										16 00				
Merstham	d			15 36						15 36											16 06				
Redhill 5	a	15 30		→						15 39	15 51			←						16 00	16 09				
	d	15 30						15 34	15 41	15 44	15 52			15 41						16 00	16 10				
Reigate	a							15 38	→		15 56										→				
Nutfield	d																								
Godstone	d																								
Edenbridge	d																								
Penshurst	d																								
Leigh (Kent)	d																								
Tonbridge 4	a																								
Earlswood (Surrey)	d																								
Salfords	d																←								
Horley 4	d	15 36								15 51							15 51								
Gatwick Airport 10 ✈	a	15 39				15 40	15 45			→		15 48		15 50	15 53	15 55	15 55	←	16 00	16 08				16 10	16 15
	d	15 40				15 41						15 49			15 58	15 56	15 56	15 58		16 09				16 11	
Three Bridges 15	a	15 44				15 45									→		16 01	16 03		16 14				16 15	
	d	15 45				15 45											16 01	16 03		16 14				16 15	
Crawley	d	15 48															16 05			16 18					
Ifield	d																16 07								
Faygate	d																								
Littlehaven	d																16 14								
Horsham 4	a	15 56															16 17			16 26					
Balcombe	d																							16 21	
Haywards Heath 3	a					15 54						16 00				16 06		16 12						16 26	
	d					15 55						16 04	16 07			16 10		16 17						16 27	
Wivelsfield 4	d					15 59							16 11					16 21						16 31	
Lewes 4	a												16 22												
Burgess Hill 4	d					16 01						16 09						16 23						16 33	
Hassocks 4	d					16 04												16 26					←	16 36	
Preston Park	d					16 11												16 33					16 33	16 43	
Hove 2	a											16 21						→							
Brighton 10	a				15 58	16 17										16 24						16 27	16 40	16 49	

For general notes see front of timetable
For details of catering facilities see
Directory of Train Operators

b Change at East Croydon

Saturdays

Bedford and London → Brighton

Network Diagram - see first page of Table 186

		GW 1	SN 1	SN 1		SN 1		FC 1	GX 1	SN 1 🍴	SN 1	SN 1 ◇ 🍴	FC 1	GX 1	GW 1	GW 1	SN 1	SN 1	SN 1		GW 1	SN 1 ◇	FC 1	SN 1	SN 1 ◇
London Victoria 15	⊖ d			15 47					16 00	16 02	15b53	16 06		16 15					16 17			16 21			
Milton Keynes Central 10	d																								
Watford Junction	d																								
Shepherd's Bush	⊖ d																								
Kensington (Olympia)	⊖ d																								
West Brompton	⊖ d																								
Clapham Junction 10	d			15 53						16 08	15b59	16 12							16 23						
Bedford 7	d																								
Luton 10	d																								
Luton Airport Parkway 7	✈ d																								
St Albans City	d																								
St Pancras International 15	⊖ d																								
Farringdon 3	⊖ d																								
City Thameslink 3	d																								
London Blackfriars 3	⊖ d																								
London Charing Cross 4	⊖ d		15 40															16 10							
London Waterloo (East) 4	⊖ d		15 43															16 13							
London Bridge 4	⊖ d		15 48					15 56			16 03		16 11					16 18							
Norwood Junction 2	d										16 15												16 26		
East Croydon	🚋 a		16 02	16 03				16 09		16 18	16 18	16 22	16 24					16 32	16 33			16 37	16 39		
	d		16 03	16 03				16 09		16 18	16 21	16 22	16 24					16 33	16 33			16 37	16 39		
Purley 4	d		16 11								16 27							16 41							
Coulsdon South	d		16 14								16 30						←	16 44							
Merstham	d										16 36						16 36								
Redhill 5	a		16 21			←				16 30	→						16 39	16 51			←				
	d	16 14	16 22			16 10				16 30					16 34	16 41	16 44	16 52			16 41				
Reigate	a	16 18													16 38	→		16 56							
Nutfield	d		16 26																						
Godstone	d		16 32																						
Edenbridge	d		16 37																						
Penshurst	d		16 44																						
Leigh (Kent)	d		16 47																						
Tonbridge 4	a		16 52																						
Earlswood (Surrey)	d					16 12																			
Salfords	d					16 16																		←	
Horley 4	d					16 19				16 36							16 51							16 51	
Gatwick Airport 10	✈ a			16 18		16 23		16 25	16 30	16 39			16 40	16 45			→		16 48		16 50	16 53	16 55	16 55	←
	d			16 19		16 24		16 26		16 40			16 41						16 49			16 58	16 56	16 56	16 58
Three Bridges 15	a					16 29				16 44			16 45									→		17 01	17 03
	d					16 30				16 45			16 45											17 01	17 03
Crawley	d					16 33				16 48														17 05	
Ifield	d					16 36																		17 07	
Faygate	d																								
Littlehaven	d					16 42																		17 14	
Horsham 4	a					16 45				16 56														17 17	
Balcombe	d																								
Haywards Heath 3	a			16 30				16 36					16 54						17 00				17 06		17 12
	d			16 34	16 37			16 40					16 55						17 04	17 07			17 10		17 17
Wivelsfield 4	d												16 59							17 11					17 21
Lewes 4	a			16 51																17 22					
Burgess Hill 4	d												17 01						17 09						17 23
Hassocks 4	d												17 04												17 26
Preston Park	d												17 11												17 33
Hove 2	a				16 51														17 21						→
Brighton 10	a							16 54				16 58	17 17										17 24		

For general notes see front of timetable
For details of catering facilities see Directory of Train Operators

b Change at East Croydon

Table 186

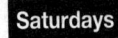

Bedford and London → Brighton

Network Diagram - see first page of Table 186

Station		GX 1	SN 1	SN 1	SN 1 ◇	SN 1 ◇	FC 1	GX 1	GW 1	SN 1	SN 1		SN 1	FC 1	GX 1	SN 1	SN 1	SN 1 ◇	FC 1	GX 1	GW 1	GW 1	SN 1	SN 1
London Victoria 15	⊖ d	16 30	16 32	16b23	16 36			16 45			16 47				17 00	17 02	16b53	17 06		17 15				
Milton Keynes Central 10	d		15 13																					
Watford Junction	d		15 51																					
Shepherd's Bush	⊖ d		16 19																					
Kensington (Olympia)	⊖ d		16 22																					
West Brompton	⊖ d		16 25																					
Clapham Junction 10	d		16 38	16b29	16 42						16 53					17 08	16b59	17 12						
Bedford 7	d																							
Luton 10	d																							
Luton Airport Parkway 7	✈ d																							
St Albans City	d																							
St Pancras International 15	⊖ d																							
Farringdon 3	⊖ d																							
City Thameslink 3	d																							
London Blackfriars 3	⊖ d																							
London Charing Cross 4	⊖ d									16 40														17 10
London Waterloo (East) 4	⊖ d									16 43														17 13
London Bridge 4	⊖ d			16 33			16 41			16 48				16 56			17 03		17 11					17 18
Norwood Junction 2	d			16 45													17 15							
East Croydon	a		16 48	16 48	16 52		16 54			17 02	17 03			17 09		17 18	17 18	17 22	17 24					17 32
	d		16 48	16 51	16 52		16 54			17 03	17 03			17 09		17 18	17 21	17 22	17 24					17 33
Purley 4	d			16 57						17 11							17 27							17 41
Coulsdon South	d			17 00						17 14							17 30						←	17 44
Merstham	d			17 06													17 36						17 36	
Redhill 5	a		17 00	17 09						17 21						17 30	→						17 39	17 51
	d		17 00	17 10					17 14	17 22			← 17 10			17 30					17 34	17 41	17 44	17 52
Reigate	a			→					17 18												17 38	→		17 56
Nutfield	d									17 26														
Godstone	d									17 32														
Edenbridge	d									17 37														
Penshurst	d									17 44														
Leigh (Kent)	d									17 47														
Tonbridge 4	a									17 52														
Earlswood (Surrey)	d												17 12											
Salfords	d												17 16											
Horley 4	d												17 19			17 36							17 51 →	
Gatwick Airport 10	✈ a	17 00	17 08				17 10	17 15			17 18		17 23	17 25	17 30	17 39			17 40	17 45				
	d		17 09				17 11				17 19		17 24	17 26		17 40			17 41					
Three Bridges 15	a		17 14				17 15						17 29			17 44			17 45					
	d		17 14				17 15						17 30			17 45			17 45					
Crawley	d		17 18										17 33			17 48								
Ifield	d												17 36											
Faygate	d																							
Littlehaven	d												17 42											
Horsham 4	a		17 26										17 45			17 56								
Balcombe	d						17 21																	
Haywards Heath 3	a						17 26				17 30			17 36					17 54					
	d						17 27				17 34	17 37		17 40					17 55					
Wivelsfield 4	d						17 31												17 59					
Lewes 4	a										17 51													
Burgess Hill 4	d						17 33												18 01					
Hassocks 4	d					←	17 36												18 04					
Preston Park	d					17 33	17 43												18 11					
Hove 2	a											17 51												
Brighton 10	a				17 27	17 40	17 49							17 54				17 58	18 17					

For general notes see front of timetable
For details of catering facilities see Directory of Train Operators

b Change at East Croydon

Saturdays

Bedford and London → Brighton

Network Diagram - see first page of Table 186

Station		SN 1		GW 1	SN 1 ◇	FC 1	SN 1	SN 1 ◇	GX 1	SN 1	SN 1	SN 1 ◇ ⊥	SN 1 ◇	FC 1		GX 1	GW 1	SN 1	SN 1		SN 1	FC 1	GX 1	SN 1 ⊥	SN 1
London Victoria 15 ⊖	d	17 17			17 21				17 30	17 32	17b23	17 36				17 45			17 47				18 00	18 02	17b53
Milton Keynes Central 10	d									16 13															
Watford Junction	d									16 51															
Shepherd's Bush ⊖	d									17 19															
Kensington (Olympia) ⊖	d									17 22															
West Brompton ⊖	d									17 25															
Clapham Junction 10	d	17 23								17 38	17b29	17 42							17 53					18 08	17b59
Bedford 7	d																								
Luton 10	d																								
Luton Airport Parkway 7 ✈	d																								
St Albans City	d																								
St Pancras International 15 ⊖	d																								
Farringdon 3 ⊖	d																								
City Thameslink 3	d																								
London Blackfriars 3 ⊖	d																								
London Charing Cross 4 ⊖	d																	17 40							
London Waterloo (East) 4 ⊖	d																	17 43							
London Bridge 4 ⊖	d					17 26					17 33			17 41				17 48				17 56			18 03
Norwood Junction 2	d										17 45														18 15
East Croydon	a	17 33			17 37	17 39				17 48	17 48	17 52		17 54				18 02	18 03			18 09		18 18	18 18
	d	17 33			17 37	17 39				17 48	17 51	17 52		17 54				18 03	18 03			18 09		18 18	18 21
Purley 4	d										17 57							18 11							18 27
Coulsdon South	d										18 00							18 14							18 30
Merstham	d										18 06														18 36
Redhill 5	a			←						18 00	18 09							18 21			←			18 30	→
	d			17 41						18 00	18 10						18 14	18 22			18 10			18 30	
Reigate	a										→						18 18								
Nutfield	d																	18 26							
Godstone	d																	18 32							
Edenbridge	d																	18 37							
Penshurst	d																	18 44							
Leigh (Kent)	d																	18 47							
Tonbridge 4	a																	18 52							
Earlswood (Surrey)	d																				18 12				
Salfords	d						←														18 16				
Horley 4	d						17 51														18 19			18 36	
Gatwick Airport 10 ✈	a	17 48		17 50	17 53	17 55	17 55	←	18 00	18 08				18 10		18 15			18 18		18 23	18 25	18 30	18 39	
	d	17 49			17 58	17 56	17 56	17 58		18 09				18 11					18 19		18 24	18 26		18 40	
Three Bridges 15	a				→		18 01	18 03		18 14				18 15							18 29			18 44	
	d						18 01	18 03		18 14				18 15							18 30			18 45	
Crawley	d						18 05			18 18											18 33			18 48	
Ifield	d						18 07														18 36				
Faygate	d																								
Littlehaven	d						18 14														18 42				
Horsham 4	a						18 17			18 26											18 47			18 56	
Balcombe	d													18 21											
Haywards Heath 3	a	18 00				18 06		18 12						18 26					18 30			18 36			
	d	18 04	18 07			18 10		18 17						18 27					18 34	18 37		18 40			
Wivelsfield 4	d		18 11					18 21						18 31											
Lewes 4	a		18 22																18 51						
Burgess Hill 4	d	18 09						18 23						18 33											
Hassocks 4	d							18 26					←	18 36											
Preston Park	d							18 33					18 33	18 43											
Hove 2	a	18 21						→												18 51					
Brighton 10	a					18 24						18 27	18 40	18 49								18 54			

For general notes see front of timetable
For details of catering facilities see Directory of Train Operators

b Change at East Croydon

Table 186

Bedford and London → Brighton

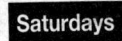

Network Diagram - see first page of Table 186

		SN	FC	GX	GW	GW	SN	SN	SN		GW	SN	FC	SN	SN	GX	SN	SN	SN	SN	FC	GX	GW	SN
		1 ◇	1	1	1	1	1	1	1		1	1 ◇	1	1	1 ◇	1	1	1	1 ◇	1 ◇	1	1	1	1
London Victoria 15	⊖ d	18 06		18 15					18 17			18 21				18 30	18 32	18b23	18 36			18 45		
Milton Keynes Central 10	d																17 13							
Watford Junction	d																17 51							
Shepherd's Bush	⊖ d																18 19							
Kensington (Olympia)	⊖ d																18 22							
West Brompton	⊖ d																18 25							
Clapham Junction 10	d	18 12							18 23								18 38	18b29	18 42					
Bedford 7	d																							
Luton 10	d																							
Luton Airport Parkway 7	✈ d																							
St Albans City	d																							
St Pancras International 15	⊖ d																							
Farringdon 3	⊖ d																							
City Thameslink 3	d																							
London Blackfriars 3	⊖ d																							
London Charing Cross 4	⊖ d							18 10																18 40
London Waterloo (East) 4	⊖ d							18 13																18 43
London Bridge 4	⊖ d		18 11					18 18					18 26					18 33			18 41			18 48
Norwood Junction 2	d																	18 45						
East Croydon	⇌ a	18 22	18 24					18 32	18 33			18 37	18 39				18 48	18 48	18 52		18 54			19 02
	d	18 22	18 24					18 33	18 33			18 37	18 39				18 48	18 51	18 52		18 54			19 03
Purley 4	d							18 41										18 57						19 11
Coulsdon South	d						←	18 44										19 00						19 14
Merstham	d						18 36											19 06						
Redhill 5	a						18 39	18 51			←						19 00	19 09						19 21
	d				18 34	18 41	18 44	18 52			18 41						19 00	19 10					19 14	19 22
Reigate	a				18 38	→		18 56										→					19 18	
Nutfield	d																							19 26
Godstone	d																							19 32
Edenbridge	d																							19 37
Penshurst	d																							19 44
Leigh (Kent)	d																							19 47
Tonbridge 4	a																							19 52
Earlswood (Surrey)	d													←										
Salfords	d																							
Horley 4	d						18 51							18 51										
Gatwick Airport 10	✈ a		18 40	18 45			→		18 48		18 50	18 53	18 55	18 55	←	19 00	19 08				19 10	19 15		
	d		18 41						18 49			18 58	18 56	18 56	18 58		19 09				19 11			
Three Bridges 15	a		18 45									→		19 01	19 03		19 14				19 15			
	d		18 45											19 01	19 03		19 14				19 15			
Crawley	d													19 05			19 18							
Ifield	d													19 07										
Faygate	d																							
Littlehaven	d													19 14										
Horsham 4	a													19 17			19 26							
Balcombe	d																				19 21			
Haywards Heath 3	a		18 54						19 00				19 06		19 12						19 26			
	d		18 55						19 04	19 07			19 10		19 17						19 27			
Wivelsfield 4	d		18 59							19 11					19 21						19 31			
Lewes 4	a									19 22														
Burgess Hill 4	d		19 01						19 09						19 23						19 33			
Hassocks 4	d		19 04												19 26					←	19 36			
Preston Park	d		19 11												19 33					19 33	19 43			
Hove 2	a								19 21						→									
Brighton 10	a	18 58	19 17										19 24						19 27	19 40	19 49			

For general notes see front of timetable
For details of catering facilities see
Directory of Train Operators

b Change at East Croydon

Table 186

Saturdays

Bedford and London → Brighton

Network Diagram - see first page of Table 186

		SN 1		SN 1	FC 1	GX 1	SN 1 ⊼	SN 1	SN 1 ◇ ⊼	FC 1	GX 1	SN 1		GW 1	GW 1	SN 1 ◇	FC 1	SN 1	SN 1	SN 1 ◇	GX 1	SN 1	SN 1	SN 1 ◇
London Victoria 15 ⊖	d	18 47				19 00	19 02	18b53	19 06		19 15	19 17				19 21					19 30	19 32	19b23	19 36
Milton Keynes Central 10	d																					18 13		
Watford Junction	d																					18 51		
Shepherd's Bush ⊖	d																					19 19		
Kensington (Olympia) ⊖	d																					19 22		
West Brompton ⊖	d																					19 25		
Clapham Junction 10	d	18 53					19 08	18b59	19 12			19 23										19 38	19b29	19 42
Bedford 7	d																							
Luton 10	d																							
Luton Airport Parkway 7 ✈	d																							
St Albans City	d																							
St Pancras International 15 ⊖	d																							
Farringdon 3 ⊖	d																							
City Thameslink 3	d																							
London Blackfriars 3 ⊖	d																							
London Charing Cross 4 ⊖	d																							
London Waterloo (East) 4 ⊖	d																							
London Bridge 4 ⊖	d				18 56			19 03		19 11							19 26						19 33	
Norwood Junction 2	d							19 15															19 45	
East Croydon	a	19 03			19 09		19 18	19 18	19 22	19 24		19 33				19 37	19 39					19 48	19 49	19 52
	d	19 03			19 09		19 18	19 21	19 22	19 24		19 33				19 37	19 39					19 48	19 51	19 52
Purley 4	d							19 27															19 57	
Coulsdon South	d							19 30										←					20 00	
Merstham	d							19 36										19 36					20 06	
Redhill 5	a			←			19 30	→										19 39				20 00	20 09	
	d			19 10			19 30							19 34	19 41			19 46	19 51			20 00	20 10	
Reigate	a													19 38									→	
Nutfield	d																		19 55					
Godstone	d																		20 01					
Edenbridge	d																		20 06					
Penshurst	d																		20 13					
Leigh (Kent)	d																		20 16					
Tonbridge 4	a																		20 21					
Earlswood (Surrey)	d			19 12																				
Salfords	d			19 16																				
Horley 4	d			19 19			19 36											19 52						
Gatwick Airport 10 ✈	a	19 18		19 23	19 25	19 30	19 39			19 40	19 45	19 48			19 50	19 53	19 55	19 55		←	20 00	20 08		
	d	19 19		19 24	19 26		19 40			19 41		19 49				19 58	19 56	19 56		19 58		20 09		
Three Bridges 15	a			19 28			19 44			19 45						→		20 01		20 03		20 14		
	d			19 30			19 45			19 45								20 01		20 03		20 14		
Crawley	d			19 33			19 48											20 05				20 18		
Ifield	d			19 36														20 07						
Faygate	d																							
Littlehaven	d			19 42														20 14						
Horsham 4	a			19 45			19 56											20 17				20 26		
Balcombe	d																							
Haywards Heath 3	a	19 30			19 36					19 54		20 00					20 06			20 12				
	d	19 34	19 37		19 40					19 55		20 04	20 07				20 10			20 17				
Wivelsfield 4	d									19 59			20 11							20 21				
Lewes 4	a	19 51											20 22											
Burgess Hill 4	d									20 01		20 09								20 23				
Hassocks 4	d									20 04										20 26				
Preston Park	d									20 11										20 33				
Hove 2	a		19 51									20 21								→				
Brighton 10	a				19 54				19 58	20 17							20 24							20 27

For general notes see front of timetable
For details of catering facilities see Directory of Train Operators

b Change at East Croydon

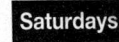

Bedford and London → Brighton

Network Diagram - see first page of Table 186

	SN 1 ◇	FC 1	GX 1	SN 1		SN 1	FC 1	GX 1	GW 1	SN 1	SN 1 ◇	FC 1	SN 1	GX 1	SN 1		GW 1	GW 1	SN 1 ◇	SN 1	GX 1	SN 1	SN 1	SN 1 ◇
London Victoria 15 ⊖ d			19 45	19 47				20 00		20 02	20 06		20 10	20 15	20 17				20 21		20 30		20 32	20 36
Milton Keynes Central 10 d																							19 13	
Watford Junction d													19 31										19 51	
Shepherd's Bush ⊖ d													19 57										20 19	
Kensington (Olympia) ⊖ d													20 00										20 22	
West Brompton ⊖ d													20 03										20 25	
Clapham Junction 10 d				19 53						20 08	20 12		20 16		20 23								20 38	20 42
Bedford 7 d																								
Luton 10 d																								
Luton Airport Parkway 7 ✈ d																								
St Albans City d																								
St Pancras International 15 ⊖ d																								
Farringdon 3 ⊖ d																								
City Thameslink 3 d																								
London Blackfriars 3 ⊖ d																								
London Charing Cross 4 ⊖ d																								
London Waterloo (East) 4 ⊖ d																								
London Bridge 4 ⊖ d		19 41					19 56					20 11	20 08										20 15	
Norwood Junction 2 d																								
East Croydon a		19 54		20 03			20 09			20 19	20 22	20 24	20 28		20 33				20 37				20 48	20 52
d		19 54		20 03			20 09			20 19	20 22	20 24	20 28		20 33				20 37				20 48	20 52
Purley 4 d													20 33							←				
Coulsdon South d													20 37							20 42				
Merstham d													20 42							20 46			21 00	
Redhill 5 a										20 30			→											
d						← 20 10			20 14	20 31							20 34	20 41		20 46		20 51	21 00	
Reigate a									20 18								20 38							
Nutfield d																						20 55		
Godstone d																						21 01		
Edenbridge d																						21 06		
Penshurst d																						21 13		
Leigh (Kent) d																						21 16		
Tonbridge 4 a																						21 21		
Earlswood (Surrey) d						20 12																		
Salfords d						20 16																		
Horley 4 d						20 19														20 52				
Gatwick Airport 10 ✈ a		20 10	20 15	20 18		20 23	20 25	20 30		20 38		20 41		20 45	20 48			20 50	20 52	20 56	21 00		21 08	
d		20 11		20 19		20 24	20 26			20 39		20 41			20 49				20 55	20 57			21 09	
Three Bridges 15 a		20 15				20 29				20 44		20 45							20 59	21 02			21 14	
d		20 15				20 33				20 44		20 45							21 00	21 02			21 14	
Crawley d						20 36				20 48										21 06			21 18	
Ifield d						20 39														21 08				
Faygate d																								
Littlehaven d						20 45														21 15				
Horsham 4 a						20 48				20 56										21 18			21 26	
Balcombe d		20 21										20 51												
Haywards Heath 3 a		20 26		20 30			20 36					20 58			21 00				21 10					
d		20 27		20 34	20 37		20 40					20 58			21 04	21 07			21 17					
Wivelsfield 4 d		20 31		20 38								21 02				21 11			21 21					
Lewes 4 a				20 51												21 22			→					
Burgess Hill 4 d		20 33										21 04			21 09									
Hassocks 4 d	←	20 36										21 08												
Preston Park d	20 33	20 43										21 15												
Hove 2 a					20 51										21 21									
Brighton 10 a	20 40	20 49					20 54				20 58	21 20												21 27

For general notes see front of timetable
For details of catering facilities see
Directory of Train Operators

Bedford and London → Brighton

Saturdays

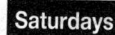

Network Diagram - see first page of Table 186

		SN 1 ◇	FC 1	GW 1		SN 1	GX 1	SN 1		SN 1	GX 1	SN 1 ◇	SN 1 ◇	SN 1 ◇	FC 1	SN 1	GX 1	SN 1		GW 1	SN 1	GW 1	GX 1	SN 1	SN 1
																		A							
London Victoria 15	⊖ d					20 40	20 45	20 47			21 00	21 02	21 06			21 10	21 15	21 17					21 30		21 32
Milton Keynes Central 10	d																								
Watford Junction	d																								*20 43*
Shepherd's Bush	⊖ d																								*21 08*
Kensington (Olympia)	⊖ d																								*21 11*
West Brompton	⊖ d																								*21 14*
Clapham Junction 10	d					20 46		20 53				21 08	21 12			21 16		21 23							21 38
Bedford 7	d																								
Luton 10	d																								
Luton Airport Parkway 7	✈ d																								
St Albans City	d																								
St Pancras International 15	⊖ d																								
Farringdon 3	⊖ d																								
City Thameslink 3	d																								
London Blackfriars 3	⊖ d																								
London Charing Cross 4	⊖ d																								
London Waterloo (East) 4	⊖ d																								
London Bridge 4	⊖ d		20 41									*20 45*			21 11	*21 08*									
Norwood Junction 2	d																								*21 15*
East Croydon	🚋 a		20 54			20 58		21 03				21 18	21 22		21 24	21 28		21 33							21 48
	d		20 54			20 58		21 03				21 18	21 22		21 24	21 28		21 33							21 48
Purley 4	d					21 03										21 33									
Coulsdon South	d					21 06										21 37					←				
Merstham	d					21 12										21 42					21 42				
Redhill 5	a					21 15				←		21 30				→					21 46				21 59
	d			21 14		21 16				21 16		21 31								21 36	21 46	21 49		21 51	22 00
Reigate	a			21 18		→														21 40					
Nutfield	d																							21 55	
Godstone	d																							22 01	
Edenbridge	d																							22 06	
Penshurst	d																							22 13	
Leigh (Kent)	d																							22 16	
Tonbridge 4	a																							22 21	
Earlswood (Surrey)	d									21 18															
Salfords	d									21 22															
Horley 4	d									21 25											21 52				
Gatwick Airport 10	✈ a		21 10				21 15	21 18		21 28	21 30	21 38	←	21 40			21 45	21 48			21 55	21 59	22 00		22 08
	d		21 11					21 19		21 29		21 39	21 39	21 41				21 49			21 56				22 09
Three Bridges 15	a		21 15							21 33		→	21 44	21 45				21 53			22 00				22 14
	d		21 15							21 36			21 44	21 45				21 53			22 01				22 14
Crawley	d									21 39											22 04				22 18
Ifield	d									21 42											22 07				
Faygate	d																								
Littlehaven	d									21 48											22 13				
Horsham 4	a									21 52											22 16				22 26
Balcombe	d													21 51											
Haywards Heath 3	a		21 24					21 30				21 45	21 52	21 58				22 02							
	d	←	21 26					21 34	21 37			21 45	21 53	21 58				22 06	22 08						
Wivelsfield 4	d	21 21	21 30					21 38					21 57	22 02					22 12						
Lewes 4	a							21 51											22 23						
Burgess Hill 4	d	21 23	21 32										21 59	22 04				22 11							
Hassocks 4	d	21 26	21 35										22 02	22 08											
Preston Park	d	21 33	21 42										22 09	22 15											
Hove 2	a								21 51									22 22							
Brighton 10	a	21 40	21 48									22 00	22 15	22 20											

For general notes see front of timetable
For details of catering facilities see Directory of Train Operators

A To Eastbourne (Table 189)

Bedford and London → Brighton

Network Diagram - see first page of Table 186

		SN 1 ◇	FC 1	SN 1	GX 1	SN 1		SN 1		GX 1	SN 1 ◇	SN 1 ◇	SN 1 ◇	FC 1	SN 1	GX 1	SN 1	GW 1	SN 1	GX 1	SN 1	GW 1	SN 1	SN 1 ◇	FC 1
London Victoria 15	⊖ d	21 36		21 40	21 45	21 47				22 00	22 02	22 06			22 10	22 15	22 17			22 30			22 32	22 36	
Milton Keynes Central 10	d																								
Watford Junction	d																						21 43		
Shepherd's Bush	⊖ d																						22 08		
Kensington (Olympia)	⊖ d																						22 11		
West Brompton	⊖ d																						22 14		
Clapham Junction 10	d	21 42		21 46		21 53					22 08	22 12			22 16		22 23						22 38	22 42	
Bedford 7	d																								
Luton 10	d																								
Luton Airport Parkway 7	✈ d																								
St Albans City	d																								
St Pancras International 15	⊖ d																								
Farringdon 3	⊖ d																								
City Thameslink 3	d																								
London Blackfriars 3	⊖ d																								
London Charing Cross 4	⊖ d																								
London Waterloo (East) 4	⊖ d																								
London Bridge 4	⊖ d		21 41								21 45			22 11	22 08								22 15		22 41
Norwood Junction 2	d																								
East Croydon	🚋 a	21 52	21 54	21 58		22 03					22 18	22 22		22 24	22 28		22 33						22 48	22 52	22 54
	d	21 52	21 54	21 58		22 03					22 18	22 22		22 24	22 28		22 33						22 48	22 52	22 54
Purley 4	d			22 03											22 33										
Coulsdon South	d			22 06											22 37										
Merstham	d			22 12											22 42 →				← 22 42						
Redhill 5	a			22 15							22 30								22 46				23 00		
	d			22 16				← 22 16			22 31							22 33	22 46		22 55	22 56	23 01		
Reigate	a			→														22 38							
Nutfield	d																				22 59				
Godstone	d																				23 05				
Edenbridge	d																				23 10				
Penshurst	d																				23 17				
Leigh (Kent)	d																				23 20				
Tonbridge 4	a																				23 25				
Earlswood (Surrey)	d							22 18																	
Salfords	d							22 22																	
Horley 4	d							22 25											22 52						
Gatwick Airport 10	✈ a		22 10		22 15	22 18		22 28		22 30	22 38		←	22 40		22 45	22 48		22 55	23 00		23 03	23 08		23 10
	d		22 11			22 19		22 29			22 39 →		22 39	22 41			22 49		22 56				23 09		23 11
Three Bridges 15	a		22 15					22 33					22 44	22 45			22 54		23 00				23 14		23 15
	d		22 15					22 36					22 44	22 45			22 54		23 01				23 15		23 15
Crawley	d							22 39											23 04				23 18		
Ifield	d							22 42											23 07						
Faygate	d																								
Littlehaven	d							22 48											23 13						
Horsham 4	a							22 52											23 16				23 26		
Balcombe	d													22 51											
Haywards Heath 3	a	22 15	22 24			22 30						22 45	22 52	22 58			23 02							23 15	23 24
	d	22 15	22 26			22 34	22 37					22 45	22 53	22 58			23 03							23 15	23 26
Wivelsfield 4	d		22 30			22 38							22 57	23 02											23 30
Lewes 4	a					22 51																			
Burgess Hill 4	d		22 32										22 59	23 04			23 08								23 32
Hassocks 4	d		22 35										23 02	23 08											23 35
Preston Park	d		22 42										23 09	23 15											23 42
Hove 2	a						22 51										23 21								
Brighton 10	a	22 30	22 48									23 00	23 15	23 20										23 30	23 48

For general notes see front of timetable
For details of catering facilities see
Directory of Train Operators

Table 186

Bedford and London → Brighton

Saturdays

Network Diagram - see first page of Table 186

		SN 1	GX 1	SN 1		SN 1	GX 1	GW 1	SN 1 ◇	SN 1 ◇	SN 1 ◇	FC 1	SN 1	GX 1	SN 1	SN 1	GX 1	SN 1	SN 1	FC 1	GX 1	SN 1
London Victoria 15	⊖ d	22 40	22 45	22 47			23 00		23 02	23 06			23 10	23 15	23 17		23 30		23 32		23 45	23 47
Milton Keynes Central 10	d																					
Watford Junction	d																		*22 48*			
Shepherd's Bush	⊖ d																		*23 13*			
Kensington (Olympia)	⊖ d																		*23 16*			
West Brompton	⊖ d																		*23 19*			
Clapham Junction 10	d	22 46		22 53					23 08	23 12			23 16		23 23				23 38			23 53
Bedford 7	d																					
Luton 10	d																					
Luton Airport Parkway 7	✈ d																					
St Albans City	d																					
St Pancras International 15	⊖ d																					
Farringdon 3	⊖ d																					
City Thameslink 3	d																					
London Blackfriars 3	⊖ d																					
London Charing Cross 4	⊖ d																					
London Waterloo (East) 4	⊖ d																					
London Bridge 4	⊖ d								*22 45*	*22 58*		23 11							*23 15*	23 41		*23 41*
Norwood Junction 2	d																					
East Croydon	a	22 58		23 03					23 18	23 22		23 24	23 28		23 33				23 52	23 56		00 06
	d	22 58		23 03					23 18	23 22		23 24	23 28		23 33				23 52	23 57		00 06
Purley 4	d	23 03											23 33									00 12
Coulsdon South	d	23 07											23 37									00 15
Merstham	d	23 12											23 42									00 21
Redhill 5	a	23 16							23 30				23 46						00 03			00 24
	d	23 16				← 23 16		23 29	23 31				23 46			← 23 46		23 55	00 05			00 25
Reigate	a	↪						23 33					↪									
Nutfield	d																					
Godstone	d																					
Edenbridge	d																	00 06				
Penshurst	d																					
Leigh (Kent)	d																					
Tonbridge 4	a																	00 15				
Earlswood (Surrey)	d					23 19										23 49						
Salfords	d					23 22										23 52						
Horley 4	d					23 26										23 56						00 31
Gatwick Airport 10	✈ a		23 15	23 18		23 28	23 30		23 38		←	23 41		23 45	23 50	23 58	00 05		00 13	00 17	00 20	00 33
	d			23 19		23 29			23 39		23 39	23 41			23 51	23 59			00 14	00 18		00 34
Three Bridges 15	a					23 34			→		23 44	23 47			23 55	00 04			00 19	00 24		00 39
	d					23 38					23 44	23 47			23 56	00 04			00 19			00 39
Crawley	d					23 41										00 07						00 42
Ifield	d					23 44										00 10						00 45
Faygate	d																					
Littlehaven	d					23 50										00 16						00 51
Horsham 4	a					23 53										00 19						00 54
Balcombe	d											23 53							00 27			
Haywards Heath 3	a			23 30						23 45	23 52	23 58			00 04				00 34			
	d			23 34	23 37					23 45	23 53	23 58			00 05				00 34			
Wivelsfield 4	d			23 38							23 57	00 02							00 38			
Lewes 4	a			23 51																		
Burgess Hill 4	d										23 59	00 04			00 10				00 40			
Hassocks 4	d										00 02	00 08							00 44			
Preston Park	d										00 09	00 15							00 51			
Hove 2	a				23 51										00 21							
Brighton 10	a									23 59	00 15	00 20							00 55			

For general notes see front of timetable
For details of catering facilities see Directory of Train Operators

Table 186

Sundays

until 6 September

Bedford and London → Brighton

Network Diagram - see first page of Table 186

		SN 1 ◇	FC 1	SN 1	SN 1	SN 1	SN 1	GW 1	SN 1	FC 1	SN 1	GX 1	SN 1 A		FC 1	SN 1	GW 1	FC 1	GX 1	SN 1	FC 1	SN 1	SN 1	GX 1
London Victoria 15	⊖ d	23p02		23p10	23p17				23p32		23p47	00 02	00 05			00 14			00 30	01 00		02 00	03 00	03 30
Milton Keynes Central 10	d																							
Watford Junction	d												23 25											
Shepherd's Bush	⊖ d												23 49											
Kensington (Olympia)	⊖ d												23 51											
West Brompton	⊖ d												23 54											
Clapham Junction 10	d	23p08		23p16	23p23				23p38		23p53		00 11			00 20				01 08		02 08	03 08	
Bedford 7	d																							
Luton 10	d																							
Luton Airport Parkway 7	✈ d																							
St Albans City	d																							
St Pancras International 15	⊖ d																							
Farringdon 3	⊖ d																							
City Thameslink 3	d																							
London Blackfriars 3	⊖ d																							
London Charing Cross 4	⊖ d																							
London Waterloo (East) 4	⊖ d																							
London Bridge 4	⊖ d		23p11							23p41	*23 41*		*23 53*		00 11			00 41			01 05			
Norwood Junction 2	d																							
East Croydon	a	23p18	23p24	23p28	23p33				23p52	23p56	00 06		00 24		00 27	00 32		00 56		01 21	01 32	02 21	03 21	
	d	23p18	23p24	23p28	23p33				23p52	23p57	00 06		00 25		00 27	00 33		00 57		01 22	01 32	02 22	03 22	
Purley 4	d			23p33							00 12					00 38				01 27		02 27	03 27	
Coulsdon South	d			23p37							00 15					00 41								
Merstham	d			23p42							00 21					00 47								
Redhill 5	a	23p30		23p46		←			00 03		00 24					00 50								
	d	23p31		23p46		23p46	23p55	00 03	00 05		00 25					00 51	00 54							
Reigate	a			↪																				
Nutfield	d																							
Godstone	d																							
Edenbridge	d						00 06																	
Penshurst	d																							
Leigh (Kent)	d																							
Tonbridge 4	a						00 15																	
Earlswood (Surrey)	d					23p49																		
Salfords	d					23p52																		
Horley 4	d					23p56					00 31					00 57				01 43		02 42	03 42	
Gatwick Airport 10	✈ a	23p38	23p41		23p50	23p58		00 10	00 13	00 17	00 33	00 35	00 43		00 49	00 59	01 02	01 16	01 20	01 45	01 51	02 44	03 44	04 05
	d	23p39	23p41		23p51	23p59			00 14	00 18	00 34		00 44		00 50	01 00		01 17		01 47	01 52	02 46	03 46	
Three Bridges 15	a	23p44	23p47		23p55	00 04			00 19	00 24	00 39		00 48		00 54	01 05		01 24		01 51	01 58	03 00	04 00	
	d	23p44	23p47		23p56	00 04			00 19		00 39		00 48							01 52				
Crawley	d					00 07					00 42													
Ifield	d					00 10					00 45													
Faygate	d																							
Littlehaven	d					00 16					00 51													
Horsham 4	a					00 19					00 54													
Balcombe	d		23p53						00 27															
Haywards Heath 3	a	23p52	23p58		00 04				00 34				01 00											
	d	23p53	23p58		00 05				00 34				01 03	01 06										
Wivelsfield 4	d	23p57	00 02						00 38															
Lewes 4	a													01 20										
Burgess Hill 4	d	23p59	00 04		00 10				00 40															
Hassocks 4	d	00 02	00 08						00 44															
Preston Park	d	00 09	00 15						00 51															
Hove 2	a				00 21								01s25											
Brighton 10	a	00 15	00 20						00 55				01s17							02 20				

A To Eastbourne (Table 189)

For general notes see front of timetable
For details of catering facilities see Directory of Train Operators

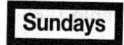

Bedford and London → Brighton

Sundays until 6 September

Network Diagram - see first page of Table 186

		SN 1	GX 1	GX 1	SN 1	GX 1	GX 1	GX 1	SN 1	SN 1 ◇	GX 1	GX 1	GW 1	SN 1	GX 1	GX 1	SN 1 ◇	GW 1	GX 1	GW 1	SN 1	SN 1	FC 1	SN 1
														A							B			B
London Victoria 15	⊖ d	04 00	04 30	05 00	05 02	05 15	05 30	05 45		05 47	06 00	06 15			06 30	06 45	06 32		07 00		07 02			
Milton Keynes Central 10	d																							
Watford Junction	d																							
Shepherd's Bush	⊖ d																							
Kensington (Olympia)	⊖ d																							
West Brompton	⊖ d																							
Clapham Junction 10	d	04 08			05 08					05 53							06 38				07 08			
Bedford 7	d																							
Luton 10	d																							
Luton Airport Parkway 7	✈ d																							
St Albans City	d																							
St Pancras International 15	⊖ d																							
Farringdon 3	⊖ d																							
City Thameslink 3	d																							
London Blackfriars 3	⊖ d																							
London Charing Cross 4	⊖ d																							
London Waterloo (East) 4	⊖ d																							
London Bridge 4	⊖ d																					07 05	07 11	
Norwood Junction 2	d																					07 16		
East Croydon	⇌ a	04 21			05 22					06 05							06 51				07 19	07 20	07 25	
	d	04 22			05 23					06 06							06 52				07 20	07 22	07 25	
Purley 4	d	04 27			05 29												06 56				07 25	07 28		
Coulsdon South	d																07 00					07 31		
Merstham	d																07 05					07 37		
Redhill 5	a									06 18							07 09				07 33	07 40		←
	d									06 19			06 19				07 09	07 15		07 19	07 33	07 41		07 33
Reigate	a												06 23							07 23	→			
Nutfield	d																					07 45		
Godstone	d																					07 51		
Edenbridge	d																					07 56		
Penshurst	d																					08 03		
Leigh (Kent)	d																					08 06		
Tonbridge 4	a																					08 11		
Earlswood (Surrey)	d																							
Salfords	d																							
Horley 4	d	04 43								06 25							07 15							07 39
Gatwick Airport 10	✈ a	04 45	05 05	05 35	05 45	05 50	06 05	06 20		06 31	06 35	06 47			07 05	07 15	07 18	07 27	07 30				07 41	07 42
	d	04 47			05 46				06 29	06 32				06 58			07 19						07 42	07 43
Three Bridges 15	a	04 54			05 50				06 33	06 36				07 02			07 23						07 47	07 47
	d	04 55			05 51				06 40	06 36				07 03			07 24						07 47	07 48
Crawley	d								06 43															07 51
Ifield	d								06 46															07 54
Faygate	d																							
Littlehaven	d								06 52															08 00
Horsham 4	a								06 56															08 03
Balcombe	d																07 30							
Haywards Heath 3	a				05 59					06 46				07 11			07 35						07 56	
	d				06 00					06 47				07 12			07 36						07 56	
Wivelsfield 4	d									06 51							07 40							
Lewes 4	a													07 27										
Burgess Hill 4	d									06 53							07 42						08 01	
Hassocks 4	d									06 56							07 45							
Preston Park	d									07 03							07 52							
Hove 2	a																							
Brighton 10	a	05 21			06 18					07 08							07 58						08 12	

For general notes see front of timetable
For details of catering facilities see Directory of Train Operators

A To Eastbourne (Table 189)
B To Bognor Regis (Table 188)

Sundays

until 6 September

Bedford and London → Brighton

Network Diagram - see first page of Table 186

Station		GX 1	SN 1 ◇	GX 1	SN 1	FC 1	GX 1	SN 1	GW 1	GX 1	GW 1	SN 1 A	SN 1	FC 1	GX 1	SN 1	SN 1 ◇	GX 1	SN 1	FC 1	GX 1	SN 1	SN 1	GX 1
London Victoria 15 ⊖	d	07 15	07 21	07 30	07 32		07 45			08 00		08 02			08 15	08 17	08 21	08 30	08 32		08 45	08 47		09 00
Milton Keynes Central 10	d																							
Watford Junction	d																							
Shepherd's Bush ⊖	d											*07 48*												
Kensington (Olympia) ⊖	d											*07 50*												
West Brompton ⊖	d											*07 52*												
Clapham Junction 10	d		07 27		07 38							08 08				08 23	08 27		08 38			08 53		
Bedford 7	d																							
Luton 10	d																							
Luton Airport Parkway 7 ✈	d																							
St Albans City	d																							
St Pancras International 15 ⊖	d																							
Farringdon 3 ⊖	d																							
City Thameslink 3	d																							
London Blackfriars 3 ⊖	d																							
London Charing Cross 4 ⊖	d																							
London Waterloo (East) 4 ⊖	d																							
London Bridge 4 ⊖	d					07 41						*07 44*	08 05	08 11					*08 14*	08 41				
Norwood Junction 2	d												08 16											
East Croydon	a		07 38		07 49	07 55						08 17	08 20	08 25		08 32	08 38		08 47	08 55		09 02		
	d		07 38		07 50	07 55						08 18	08 21	08 25		08 33	08 38		08 48	08 55		09 03		
Purley 4	d				07 55							08 23	08 27						08 53					
Coulsdon South	d				07 58								08 30						08 57					
Merstham	d				08 04								08 36						09 02					
Redhill 5	a		07 49		08 07			←				08 31	08 39				08 49		09 06				←	
	d		07 50		08 08			08 08	08 18		08 19	08 32	08 40				08 50		09 06				09 06	
Reigate	a				→						08 23								→					
Nutfield	d												08 44											
Godstone	d												08 50											
Edenbridge	d												08 55											
Penshurst	d												09 02											
Leigh (Kent)	d												09 05											
Tonbridge 4	a												09 10											
Earlswood (Surrey)	d							08 10															09 09	
Salfords	d							08 14															09 12	
Horley 4	d							08 17				08 38											09 16	
Gatwick Airport 10 ✈	a	07 45	07 57	08 00		08 11	08 15	08 20	08 25	08 30		08 40		08 41	08 45	08 48	08 57	09 00		09 11	09 15	09 18	09 18	09 30
	d		07 58			08 12		08 21				08 41		08 42		08 49	08 58			09 12		09 19	09 19	
Three Bridges 15	a		08 02			08 17		08 25				08 46		08 47			09 02			09 17			09 24	
	d		08 09			08 17		08 26				08 46		08 47			09 09			09 17			09 24	
Crawley	d							08 30				08 50											09 28	
Ifield	d							08 32															09 31	
Faygate	d																							
Littlehaven	d							08 39															09 37	
Horsham 4	a							08 42				08 58											09 40	
Balcombe	d		08 15														09 15							
Haywards Heath 3	a		08 20			08 26								08 56		09 00	09 20			09 26		09 30		
	d		08 21			08 26								08 56		09 00	09 21			09 26		09 30		
Wivelsfield 4	d		08 25														09 25					09 34		
Lewes 4	a																					09 48		
Burgess Hill 4	d		08 27			08 31								09 01		09 06	09 27			09 31				
Hassocks 4	d		08 30			08 35											09 30			09 35				
Preston Park	d		08 37														09 37							
Hove 2	a															09 18								
Brighton 10	a		08 41			08 44								09 12			09 41			09 44				

For general notes see front of timetable
For details of catering facilities see Directory of Train Operators

A To Bognor Regis (Table 188)

Table 186

Sundays

until 6 September

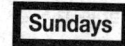

Bedford and London → Brighton

Network Diagram - see first page of Table 186

		GW 1	GW 1	SN 1 A	SN 1	SN 1 ◇	SN 1 A	FC 1	GX 1	SN 1		SN 1 ◇	GX 1	SN 1	SN 1 ◇	SN 1 ◇	FC 1	GX 1	SN 1	SN 1	GX 1	GW 1	GW 1	SN 1 A	SN 1
London Victoria 15	⊖ d			09 02		09 06			09 15	09 17		09 21	09 30	09 32	09 36			09 45	09 47		10 00			10 02	
Milton Keynes Central 10	d																								
Watford Junction	d																							09 17	
Shepherd's Bush	⊖ d			*08 50*																				09 45	
Kensington (Olympia)	⊖ d			*08 53*																				09 48	
West Brompton	⊖ d			*08 56*																				09 50	
Clapham Junction 10	d			09 08		09 12				09 23		09 27		09 38	09 42				09 53					10 08	
Bedford 7	d																								
Luton 10	d																								
Luton Airport Parkway 7	✈ d																								
St Albans City	d																								
St Pancras International 15	⊖ d																								
Farringdon 3	⊖ d																								
City Thameslink 3	d																								
London Blackfriars 3	⊖ d																								
London Charing Cross 4	⊖ d																								
London Waterloo (East) 4	⊖ d																								
London Bridge 4	⊖ d			*08 44*	09 05			09 11						*09 14*										*09 44*	10 05
Norwood Junction 2	d				09 16												09 41								10 16
East Croydon	⇌ a			09 17	09 20	09 22		09 25		09 32		09 38		09 47	09 52		09 55		10 02					10 17	10 20
	d			09 18	09 21	09 22		09 25		09 33		09 38		09 48	09 52		09 55		10 03					10 18	10 21
Purley 4	d			09 23	09 27									09 53										10 23	10 27
Coulsdon South	d				09 30									09 57											10 30
Merstham	d				09 36									10 02											10 36
Redhill 5	a			09 31	09 39		←					09 49		10 06										10 31	10 39
	d	09 19	09 20	09 32	09 40		09 32					09 50		10 06						← 10 06		10 19	10 20	10 32	10 40
Reigate	a	09 23		↪										↪								10 23		↪	
Nutfield	d				09 44																				10 44
Godstone	d				09 50																				10 50
Edenbridge	d				09 55																				10 55
Penshurst	d				10 02																				11 02
Leigh (Kent)	d				10 05																				11 05
Tonbridge 4	a				10 10																				11 10
Earlswood (Surrey)	d																			10 09					
Salfords	d																			10 12					
Horley 4	d						09 38													10 16					
Gatwick Airport 10	✈ a		09 32			09 37	09 40	09 41	09 45	09 48		09 57	10 00				10 11	10 15	10 18	10 18	10 30		10 30		
	d					09 38	09 41	09 42		09 49		09 58					10 12		10 19	10 19					
Three Bridges 15	a						09 46	09 47				10 02					10 17			10 24					
	d						09 46	09 47				10 09					10 17			10 24					
Crawley	d						09 50													10 28					
Ifield	d																			10 31					
Faygate	d																								
Littlehaven	d																			10 37					
Horsham 4	a						09 58													10 40					
Balcombe	d											10 15													
Haywards Heath 3	a							09 56		10 00		10 20					10 26		10 30						
	d							09 56		10 00		10 21 ↪				← 10 21	10 26		10 30						
Wivelsfield 4	d															10 25			10 34						
Lewes 4	a																		10 48						
Burgess Hill 4	d							10 01		10 06						10 27	10 31								
Hassocks 4	d															10 30	10 35								
Preston Park	d															10 37									
Hove 2	a									10 18															
Brighton 10	a					10 00		10 12							10 27	10 41	10 44								

For general notes see front of timetable
For details of catering facilities see Directory of Train Operators

A To Bognor Regis (Table 188)

Table 186

Sundays

until 6 September

Bedford and London → Brighton

Network Diagram - see first page of Table 186

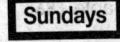

		SN 1 ◇	SN 1 A	FC 1	GX 1	SN 1	SN 1 ◇		GX 1	SN 1	SN 1 ◇	SN 1 ◇	FC 1	GX 1	SN 1 🚌	SN 1	GX 1	GW 1	GW 1	SN 1 A	SN 1	SN 1 ◇	SN 1 A	FC 1	GX 1
London Victoria 15	⊖ d	10 06			10 15	10 17	10 21		10 30	10 32	10 36			10 45	10 47		11 00			11 02		11 06			11 15
Milton Keynes Central 10	d																								
Watford Junction	d																			*10 17*					
Shepherd's Bush	⊖ d																			*10 45*					
Kensington (Olympia)	⊖ d																			*10 48*					
West Brompton	⊖ d																			*10 50*					
Clapham Junction 10	d	10 12				10 23	10 27			10 38	10 42				10 53					11 08		11 12			
Bedford 7	d																								
Luton 10	d																								
Luton Airport Parkway 7	✈ d																								
St Albans City	d																								
St Pancras International 15	⊖ d																								
Farringdon 3	⊖ d																								
City Thameslink 3	d																								
London Blackfriars 3	⊖ d																								
London Charing Cross 4	⊖ d																								
London Waterloo (East) 4	⊖ d																								
London Bridge 4	⊖ d			10 11						*10 14*			10 41							*10 44*	11 05			11 11	
Norwood Junction 2	d																				11 16				
East Croydon	a	10 22		10 25		10 32	10 38			10 47	10 52		10 55		11 02					11 17	11 20	11 22		11 25	
	d	10 22		10 25		10 33	10 38			10 48	10 52		10 55		11 03					11 18	11 21	11 22		11 25	
Purley 4	d									10 53										11 23	11 27				
Coulsdon South	d									10 57											11 30				
Merstham	d									11 02											11 36				
Redhill 5	a		←				10 49			11 06						←				11 31	11 39		←		
	d		10 32				10 50			11 06						11 06		11 19	11 20	11 32	11 40		11 32		
Reigate	a									→								11 23		→					
Nutfield	d																				11 44				
Godstone	d																				11 50				
Edenbridge	d																				11 55				
Penshurst	d																				12 02				
Leigh (Kent)	d																				12 05				
Tonbridge 4	a																				12 10				
Earlswood (Surrey)	d															11 09									
Salfords	d															11 12									
Horley 4	d		10 38													11 16							11 38		
Gatwick Airport 10	✈ a	10 37	10 40	10 41	10 45	10 48	10 57		11 00				11 11	11 15	11 18	11 18	11 30		11 32			11 37	11 40	11 41	11 45
	d	10 38	10 41	10 42		10 49	10 58						11 12		11 19	11 19						11 38	11 41	11 42	
Three Bridges 15	a		10 46	10 47			11 02						11 17			11 24							11 46	11 47	
	d		10 46	10 47			11 09						11 17			11 24							11 46	11 47	
Crawley	d		10 50													11 28							11 50		
Ifield	d															11 31									
Faygate	d																								
Littlehaven	d															11 37									
Horsham 4	a		10 58													11 40							11 58		
Balcombe	d						11 15																		
Haywards Heath 3	a			10 56		11 00	11 20					←	11 26		11 30									11 56	
	d			10 56		11 00	11 21					11 21	11 26		11 30									11 56	
Wivelsfield 4	d						→					11 25			11 34										
Lewes 4	a														11 48										
Burgess Hill 4	d			11 01		11 06						11 27	11 31											12 01	
Hassocks 4	d											11 30	11 35												
Preston Park	d											11 37													
Hove 2	a					11 18																			
Brighton 10	a	11 00		11 12							11 27	11 41	11 44									12 00		12 12	

For general notes see front of timetable
For details of catering facilities see
Directory of Train Operators

A To Bognor Regis (Table 188)

Table 186

Sundays

until 6 September

Bedford and London → Brighton

Network Diagram - see first page of Table 186

		SN	SN	GX		SN	SN	SN	FC	GX	SN	SN	GW	GX	GW	SN	SN	SN	SN	FC	GX	SN	SN		GX
		1	1◇	1		1	1◇	1◇	1	1	1	1	1	1	1	1	1	1◇	1	1	1	1	1◇		1
																A			A						
London Victoria 15	⊖ d	11 17	11 21	11 30		11 32	11 36			11 45	11 47			12 00		12 02		12 06			12 15	12 17	12 21		12 30
Milton Keynes Central 10	d																								
Watford Junction	d															*11 17*									
Shepherd's Bush	⊖ d															*11 45*									
Kensington (Olympia)	⊖ d															*11 48*									
West Brompton	⊖ d															*11 50*									
Clapham Junction 10	d	11 23	11 27			11 38	11 42				11 53					12 08		12 12				12 23	12 27		
Bedford 7	d																								
Luton 10	d																								
Luton Airport Parkway 7	✈ d																								
St Albans City	d																								
St Pancras International 15	⊖ d																								
Farringdon 3	⊖ d																								
City Thameslink 3	d																								
London Blackfriars 3	⊖ d																								
London Charing Cross 4	⊖ d																								
London Waterloo (East) 4	⊖ d																								
London Bridge 4	⊖ d					*11 14*			11 41							*11 44*	12 05			12 11					
Norwood Junction 2	d																12 16								
East Croydon	a	11 32	11 38			11 47	11 52		11 55		12 02					12 17	12 20	12 22		12 24		12 32	12 38		
	d	11 33	11 38			11 48	11 52		11 55		12 03					12 18	12 21	12 22		12 24		12 33	12 38		
Purley 4	d					11 53										12 23	12 27								
Coulsdon South	d					11 57											12 30								
Merstham	d					12 02											12 36								
Redhill 5	a		11 49			12 06										12 31	12 39						12 49		
	d		11 50			12 06						← 12 06	12 18		12 19	12 32	12 40		← 12 32				12 50		
Reigate	a					→									12 23	→									
Nutfield	d																12 44								
Godstone	d																12 50								
Edenbridge	d																12 55								
Penshurst	d																13 02								
Leigh (Kent)	d																13 05								
Tonbridge 4	a																13 10								
Earlswood (Surrey)	d											12 09													
Salfords	d											12 12													
Horley 4	d											12 16							12 38						
Gatwick Airport 10	✈ a	11 48	11 57	12 00					12 11	12 15	12 18	12 18	12 27	12 30				12 37	12 40	12 41	12 45	12 48	12 57		13 00
	d	11 49	11 58						12 12		12 19	12 19						12 38	12 41	12 42		12 49	12 58		
Three Bridges 15	a		12 02						12 17			12 24							12 46	12 47			13 02		
	d		12 09						12 17			12 24							12 46	12 47			13 09		
Crawley	d											12 28							12 50						
Ifield	d											12 31													
Faygate	d																								
Littlehaven	d											12 37													
Horsham 4	a											12 40							12 58						
Balcombe	d		12 15																				13 15		
Haywards Heath 3	a	12 00	12 20					←	12 26		12 30									12 56		13 00	13 20		
	d	12 00	12 21 →					12 21	12 26		12 30									12 56		13 00	13 21 →		
Wivelsfield 4	d							12 25			12 34														
Lewes 4	a										12 48														
Burgess Hill 4	d	12 06						12 27	12 31											13 01		13 06			
Hassocks 4	d							12 30	12 35																
Preston Park	d							12 37																	
Hove 2	a	12 18																				13 18			
Brighton 10	a						12 27	12 41	12 44									13 00		13 12					

For general notes see front of timetable
For details of catering facilities see Directory of Train Operators

A To Bognor Regis (Table 188)

Sundays

until 6 September

Bedford and London → Brighton

Network Diagram - see first page of Table 186

		SN [1]	SN [1] ◇	SN [1] ◇	FC [1]	GX [1]	SN [1]	SN [1]	GX [1]	GW [1]	GW [1]	SN [1]	SN [1]	SN [1] ◇	SN [1]	FC [1]	GX [1]	SN [1]	SN [1] ◇		GX [1]	SN [1]	SN [1] ◇	SN [1] ◇	FC [1]
							🛒					A			A										
London Victoria [15]	⊖ d	12 32	12 36			12 45	12 47		13 00			13 02		13 06			13 15	13 17	13 21		13 30	13 32	13 36		
Milton Keynes Central [10]	d																								
Watford Junction	d											*12 22*													
Shepherd's Bush	⊖ d											*12 45*													
Kensington (Olympia)	⊖ d											*12 48*													
West Brompton	⊖ d											*12 50*													
Clapham Junction [10]	d	12 38	12 42				12 53					13 08		13 12				13 23	13 27			13 38	13 42		
Bedford [7]	d																								
Luton [10]	d																								
Luton Airport Parkway [7]	✈ d																								
St Albans City	d																								
St Pancras International [15]	⊖ d																								
Farringdon [3]	⊖ d																								
City Thameslink [3]	d																								
London Blackfriars [3]	⊖ d																								
London Charing Cross [4]	⊖ d																								
London Waterloo (East) [4]	⊖ d																								
London Bridge [4]	⊖ d	*12 14*			12 41							*12 44*	13 05			13 11						*13 14*			13 41
Norwood Junction [2]	d												13 16												
East Croydon	🚊 a	12 47	12 52		12 55		13 02					13 17	13 20	13 22		13 25		13 32	13 38			13 47	13 52		13 55
	d	12 48	12 52		12 55		13 03					13 18	13 21	13 22		13 25		13 33	13 38			13 48	13 52		13 55
Purley [4]	d	12 53										13 23	13 27									13 53			
Coulsdon South	d	12 57											13 30									13 57			
Merstham	d	13 02											13 36									14 02			
Redhill [5]	a	13 06						⟵				13 31	13 39		⟵				13 49			14 06			
	d	13 06						13 06		13 19	13 20	13 32	13 40		13 32				13 50			14 06			
Reigate	a	⟶								13 23		⟶										⟶			
Nutfield	d												13 44												
Godstone	d												13 50												
Edenbridge	d												13 55												
Penshurst	d												14 02												
Leigh (Kent)	d												14 05												
Tonbridge [4]	a												14 10												
Earlswood (Surrey)	d							13 09																	
Salfords	d							13 12																	
Horley [4]	d							13 16							13 38										
Gatwick Airport [10]	✈ a				13 11	13 15	13 18	13 18	13 30		13 32			13 37	13 40	13 41	13 45	13 48	13 57		14 00				14 11
	d				13 12		13 19	13 19						13 38	13 41	13 42		13 49	13 58						14 12
Three Bridges [15]	a				13 17			13 24							13 46	13 47			14 02						14 17
	d				13 17			13 24							13 46	13 47			14 09						14 17
Crawley	d							13 28							13 50										
Ifield	d							13 31																	
Faygate	d																								
Littlehaven	d							13 37																	
Horsham [4]	a							13 40							13 58										
Balcombe	d																		14 15						
Haywards Heath [3]	a				13 26		13 30									13 56		14 00	14 20					⟵	14 26
	d			13 21	13 26		13 30									13 56		14 00	14 21 ⟶					14 21	14 26
Wivelsfield [4]	d			13 25			13 34																	14 25	
Lewes [4]	a						13 48																		
Burgess Hill [4]	d			13 27	13 31											14 01		14 06						14 27	14 31
Hassocks [4]	d			13 30	13 35																			14 30	14 35
Preston Park	d			13 37																				14 37	
Hove [2]	a																	14 18							
Brighton [10]	a		13 27	13 41	13 44									14 00		14 12							14 27	14 41	14 44

For general notes see front of timetable
For details of catering facilities see Directory of Train Operators

A To Bognor Regis (Table 188)

Table 186

Sundays

until 6 September

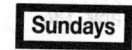

Bedford and London → Brighton

Network Diagram - see first page of Table 186

Station		GX	SN	SN	GW	GX	GW	SN	SN	SN	SN	FC	GX	SN	SN	GX		SN	SN	SN	FC	GX	SN	SN	GX
		1	1	1	1	1	1	1	1	1 ◇	1	1	1	1	1 ◇	1		1	1 ◇	1 ◇	1	1	1	1	1
								A			A														
London Victoria 15 ⊖	d	13 45	13 47			14 00		14 02		14 06			14 15	14 17	14 21	14 30		14 32	14 36			14 45	14 47		15 00
Milton Keynes Central 10	d																								
Watford Junction	d							*13 22*																	
Shepherd's Bush ⊖	d							*13 45*																	
Kensington (Olympia) ⊖	d							*13 48*																	
West Brompton ⊖	d							*13 50*																	
Clapham Junction 10	d		13 53					14 08		14 12				14 23	14 27			14 38	14 42				14 53		
Bedford 7	d																								
Luton 10	d																								
Luton Airport Parkway 7 ✈	d																								
St Albans City	d																								
St Pancras International 15 ⊖	d																								
Farringdon 3 ⊖	d																								
City Thameslink 3	d																								
London Blackfriars 3 ⊖	d																								
London Charing Cross 4 ⊖	d																								
London Waterloo (East) 4 ⊖	d																								
London Bridge 4 ⊖	d							*13 44*	14 05			14 11						*14 14*			14 41				
Norwood Junction 2	d								14 16																
East Croydon	a		14 02					14 17	14 20	14 22		14 25		14 32	14 38			14 47	14 52		14 55		15 02		
	d		14 03					14 18	14 21	14 22		14 25		14 33	14 38			14 48	14 52		14 55		15 03		
Purley 4	d							14 23	14 27									14 53							
Coulsdon South	d								14 30									14 57							
Merstham	d								14 36									15 02							
Redhill 5	a			←				14 31	14 39		←				14 49			15 06						←	
	d			14 06	14 18		14 19	14 32	14 40		14 32				14 50			15 06						15 06	
Reigate	a						14 23	→										→							
Nutfield	d								14 44																
Godstone	d								14 50																
Edenbridge	d								14 55																
Penshurst	d								15 02																
Leigh (Kent)	d								15 05																
Tonbridge 4	a								15 10																
Earlswood (Surrey)	d			14 09																				15 09	
Salfords	d			14 12																				15 12	
Horley 4	d			14 16							14 38													15 16	
Gatwick Airport 10 ✈	a	14 15	14 18	14 18	14 25	14 30				14 37	14 40	14 41	14 45	14 48	14 57	15 00					15 11	15 15	15 18	15 18	15 30
	d		14 19	14 19						14 38	14 41	14 42		14 49	14 58						15 12		15 19	15 19	
Three Bridges 15	a			14 24							14 46	14 47			15 02						15 17			15 24	
	d			14 24							14 46	14 47			15 09						15 17			15 24	
Crawley	d			14 28							14 50													15 28	
Ifield	d			14 31																				15 31	
Faygate	d																								
Littlehaven	d			14 37																				15 37	
Horsham 4	a			14 40							14 58													15 40	
Balcombe	d														15 15										
Haywards Heath 3	a		14 30									14 56		15 00	15 20					←	15 26		15 30		
	d		14 30									14 56		15 00	15 21 →					15 21	15 26		15 30		
Wivelsfield 4	d		14 34																	15 25			15 34		
Lewes 4	a		14 48																				15 48		
Burgess Hill 4	d											15 01		15 06						15 27	15 31				
Hassocks 4	d																			15 30	15 35				
Preston Park	d																			15 37					
Hove 2	a													15 18											
Brighton 10	a									15 00		15 12							15 27	15 41	15 44				

For general notes see front of timetable
For details of catering facilities see Directory of Train Operators

A To Bognor Regis (Table 188)

Bedford and London → Brighton

Network Diagram - see first page of Table 186

		GW	GW	SN	SN	SN	SN	FC	GX	SN	SN	GX	SN		SN	SN	FC	GX	SN	SN	GW	GX	GW	SN	SN
		1	1	1	1	1 ◊	1	1	1	1	1 ◊	1	1		1 ◊	1 ◊	1	1	1	1	1	1	1	1	1
				A			A												[trolley]					A	
London Victoria 15	⊖ d			15 02		15 06			15 15	15 17	15 21	15 30	15 32		15 36			15 45	15 47			16 00		16 02	
Milton Keynes Central 10	d																								
Watford Junction	d			14 22																				15 22	
Shepherd's Bush	⊖ d			14 45																				15 45	
Kensington (Olympia)	⊖ d			14 48																				15 48	
West Brompton	⊖ d			14 50																				15 50	
Clapham Junction 10	d			15 08		15 12				15 23	15 27		15 38		15 42				15 53					16 08	
Bedford 7	d																								
Luton 10	d																								
Luton Airport Parkway 7	✈ d																								
St Albans City	d																								
St Pancras International 15	⊖ d																								
Farringdon 3	⊖ d																								
City Thameslink 3	d																								
London Blackfriars 3	⊖ d																								
London Charing Cross 4	⊖ d																								
London Waterloo (East) 4	⊖ d																								
London Bridge 4	⊖ d			14 44	15 05			15 11					15 14				15 41							15 44	16 05
Norwood Junction 2	d				15 16																				16 16
East Croydon	a			15 17	15 20	15 22		15 25		15 32	15 38		15 47		15 52		15 55		16 02					16 17	16 20
	d			15 18	15 21	15 22		15 25		15 33	15 38		15 48		15 52		15 55		16 03					16 18	16 21
Purley 4	d			15 23	15 27								15 53											16 23	16 27
Coulsdon South	d				15 30								15 57												16 30
Merstham	d				15 36								16 02												16 36
Redhill 5	a			15 31	15 39		←				15 49		16 06							←				16 31	16 39
	d	15 19	15 20	15 32	15 40		15 32				15 50		16 06							16 06	16 18		16 19	16 32	16 40
Reigate	a	15 23		→									→										16 23	→	
Nutfield	d				15 44																				16 44
Godstone	d				15 50																				16 50
Edenbridge	d				15 55																				16 55
Penshurst	d				16 02																				17 02
Leigh (Kent)	d				16 05																				17 05
Tonbridge 4	a				16 10																				17 10
Earlswood (Surrey)	d																			16 09					
Salfords	d																			16 12					
Horley 4	d						15 38													16 16					
Gatwick Airport 10	✈ a		15 32			15 37	15 40	15 41	15 45	15 48	15 57	16 00					16 11	16 15	16 18	16 18	16 25	16 30			
	d					15 38	15 41	15 42		15 49	15 58						16 12		16 19	16 19					
Three Bridges 15	a						15 46	15 47			16 02						16 17			16 24					
	d						15 46	15 47			16 09						16 17			16 24					
Crawley	d						15 50													16 28					
Ifield	d																			16 31					
Faygate	d																								
Littlehaven	d																			16 37					
Horsham 4	a						15 58													16 40					
Balcombe	d										16 15														
Haywards Heath 3	a							15 56		16 00	16 20					←	16 26		16 30						
	d							15 56		16 00	16 21 →					16 21	16 26		16 30						
Wivelsfield 4	d															16 25			16 34						
Lewes 4	a																		16 48						
Burgess Hill 4	d							16 01		16 06						16 27	16 31								
Hassocks 4	d															16 30	16 35								
Preston Park	d															16 37									
Hove 2	a									16 18															
Brighton 10	a					16 00		16 12							16 27	16 41	16 44								

For general notes see front of timetable
For details of catering facilities see
Directory of Train Operators

A To Bognor Regis (Table 188)

Table 186

Sundays

until 6 September

Bedford and London → Brighton

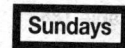

Network Diagram - see first page of Table 186

		SN 1 ◇	SN 1 A	FC 1	GX 1	SN 1	SN 1 ◇	GX 1	SN 1	SN 1 ◇		SN 1 ◇	FC 1	GX 1	SN 1 (bus)	SN 1	GX 1	GW 1	GW 1	SN 1 A	SN 1	SN 1 ◇	SN 1 A	FC 1	GX 1
London Victoria 15	⊖ d	16 06			16 15	16 17	16 21	16 30	16 32	16 36				16 45	16 47		17 00			17 02		17 06			17 15
Milton Keynes Central 10	d																								
Watford Junction	d																			16 22					
Shepherd's Bush	⊖ d																			16 45					
Kensington (Olympia)	⊖ d																			16 48					
West Brompton	⊖ d																			16 50					
Clapham Junction 10	d	16 12				16 23	16 27		16 38	16 42					16 53					17 08		17 12			
Bedford 7	d																								
Luton 10	d																								
Luton Airport Parkway 7	✈ d																								
St Albans City	d																								
St Pancras International 15	⊖ d																								
Farringdon 3	⊖ d																								
City Thameslink 3	d																								
London Blackfriars 3	⊖ d																								
London Charing Cross 4	⊖ d																								
London Waterloo (East) 4	⊖ d																								
London Bridge 4	⊖ d			16 11					16 14				16 41							16 44	17 05			17 11	
Norwood Junction 2	d																				17 16				
East Croydon	🚋 a	16 22		16 25		16 32	16 38		16 47	16 52			16 55		17 02					17 17	17 20	17 22		17 25	
	d	16 22		16 25		16 33	16 38		16 48	16 52			16 55		17 03					17 18	17 21	17 22		17 25	
Purley 4	d								16 53											17 23	17 27				
Coulsdon South	d								16 57												17 30				
Merstham	d								17 02												17 36				
Redhill 5	a		←				16 49		17 06							←				17 31	17 39		←		
	d		16 32				16 50		17 06							17 06		17 19	17 20	17 32	17 40		17 32		
Reigate	a								↪									17 23		↪					
Nutfield	d																				17 44				
Godstone	d																				17 50				
Edenbridge	d																				17 55				
Penshurst	d																				18 02				
Leigh (Kent)	d																				18 05				
Tonbridge 4	a																				18 10				
Earlswood (Surrey)	d															17 09									
Salfords	d															17 12									
Horley 4	d		16 38													17 16							17 38		
Gatwick Airport 10	✈ a	16 37	16 40	16 41	16 45	16 48	16 57	17 00					17 11	17 15	17 18	17 18	17 30		17 32			17 37	17 40	17 41	17 45
	d	16 38	16 41	16 42		16 49	16 58						17 12		17 19	17 19						17 38	17 41	17 42	
Three Bridges 15	a		16 46	16 47			17 02						17 17			17 24							17 46	17 47	
	d		16 46	16 47			17 09						17 17			17 24							17 46	17 47	
Crawley	d		16 50													17 28							17 50		
Ifield	d															17 31									
Faygate	d																								
Littlehaven	d															17 37									
Horsham 4	a		16 58													17 40							17 58		
Balcombe	d						17 15																		
Haywards Heath 3	a			16 56		17 00	17 20					←	17 26		17 30									17 56	
	d			16 56		17 00	17 21					17 21	17 26		17 30									17 56	
Wivelsfield 4	d						↪					17 25			17 34										
Lewes 4	a														17 48										
Burgess Hill 4	d			17 01		17 06						17 27	17 31											18 01	
Hassocks 4	d											17 30	17 35												
Preston Park	d											17 37													
Hove 2	a					17 18																			
Brighton 10	a	17 00		17 12						17 27		17 41	17 44									18 00		18 12	

For general notes see front of timetable
For details of catering facilities see Directory of Train Operators

A To Bognor Regis (Table 188)

Table 186

Sundays

until 6 September

Bedford and London → Brighton

Network Diagram - see first page of Table 186

		SN	SN	GX	SN	SN	SN		FC	GX	SN	SN	GW	GW	GX	SN	SN	SN	SN	FC	GX	SN	SN	GX	SN
		1	1 ◇	1	1	1 ◇	1 ◇		1	1	1	1	1	1	1	1	1	1 ◇	1	1	1	1	1 ◇	1	1
																A			A						
London Victoria 15	⊖ d	17 17	17 21	17 30	17 32	17 36				17 45	17 47				18 00	18 02		18 06			18 15	18 17	18 21	18 30	18 32
Milton Keynes Central 10	d																								
Watford Junction	d															*17 22*									
Shepherd's Bush	⊖ d															*17 45*									
Kensington (Olympia)	⊖ d															*17 48*									
West Brompton	⊖ d															*17 50*									
Clapham Junction 10	d	17 23	17 27		17 38	17 42					17 53					18 08		18 12				18 23	18 27		18 38
Bedford 7	d																								
Luton 10	d																								
Luton Airport Parkway 7	d																								
St Albans City	d																								
St Pancras International 15	⊖ d																								
Farringdon 3	⊖ d																								
City Thameslink 3	d																								
London Blackfriars 3	⊖ d																								
London Charing Cross 4	⊖ d																								
London Waterloo (East) 4	⊖ d																								
London Bridge 4	⊖ d				*17 14*				17 41							*17 44*	18 05			18 11					*18 14*
Norwood Junction 2	d																18 16								
East Croydon	a	17 32	17 38		17 47	17 52			17 55		18 02					18 17	18 20	18 22		18 25		18 32	18 38		18 47
	d	17 33	17 38		17 48	17 52			17 55		18 03					18 18	18 21	18 22		18 25		18 33	18 38		18 48
Purley 4	d				17 53											18 23	18 27								18 53
Coulsdon South	d				17 57												18 30								18 57
Merstham	d				18 02												18 36								19 02
Redhill 5	a		17 49		18 06							←				18 31	18 39		←				18 49		19 06
	d		17 50		18 06							18 06	18 19	18 20		18 32	18 40		18 32				18 50		19 06
Reigate	a				→								18 23			→									→
Nutfield	d																18 44								
Godstone	d																18 50								
Edenbridge	d																18 55								
Penshurst	d																19 02								
Leigh (Kent)	d																19 05								
Tonbridge 4	a																19 10								
Earlswood (Surrey)	d											18 09													
Salfords	d											18 12													
Horley 4	d											18 16							18 38						
Gatwick Airport 10	a	17 48	17 57	18 00					18 11	18 15	18 18	18 18		18 27	18 30			18 37	18 40	18 41	18 45	18 48	18 57	19 00	
	d	17 49	17 58						18 12		18 19	18 19						18 38	18 41	18 42		18 49	18 58		
Three Bridges 15	a		18 02						18 17			18 24							18 46	18 47			19 02		
	d		18 09						18 17			18 24							18 46	18 47			19 09		
Crawley	d											18 28							18 50						
Ifield	d											18 31													
Faygate	d																								
Littlehaven	d											18 37													
Horsham 4	a											18 40							18 58						
Balcombe	d		18 15																				19 15		
Haywards Heath 3	a	18 00	18 20						18 26		18 30									18 56		19 00	19 20		
	d	18 00	18 21 →				← 18 21		18 26		18 30									18 56		19 00	19 21 →		
Wivelsfield 4	d						18 25				18 34														
Lewes 4	a										18 48														
Burgess Hill 4	d	18 06					18 27		18 31											19 01		19 06			
Hassocks 4	d						18 30		18 35																
Preston Park	d						18 37																		
Hove 2	a	18 18																				19 18			
Brighton 10	a					18 27	18 41		18 44									19 00		19 12					

For general notes see front of timetable
For details of catering facilities see
Directory of Train Operators

A To Bognor Regis (Table 188)

Table 186

Bedford and London → Brighton

Sundays

until 6 September

Network Diagram - see first page of Table 186

		SN	SN	FC		GX	SN	SN	GX	GW	GW	SN	SN	SN	SN	FC	GX	SN	SN	GX	SN	SN	SN		FC
		1 ◇	1 ◇	1		1	1	1	1	1	1	1	1	1 ◇	1	1	1	1	1 ◇	1	1	1 ◇	1 ◇		1
							⊼					A			A										
London Victoria 15	⊖ d	18 36				18 45	18 47		19 00			19 02		19 06			19 15	19 17	19 21	19 30	19 32	19 36			
Milton Keynes Central 10	d																								
Watford Junction	d																								
Shepherd's Bush	⊖ d											*18 22*													
Kensington (Olympia)	⊖ d											*18 45*													
West Brompton	⊖ d											*18 48*													
Clapham Junction 10	d	18 42					18 53					*18 50* / 19 08		19 12				19 23	19 27		19 38	19 42			
Bedford 7	d																								
Luton 10	d																								
Luton Airport Parkway 7	✈ d																								
St Albans City	d																								
St Pancras International 15	⊖ d																								
Farringdon 3	⊖ d																								
City Thameslink 3	d																								
London Blackfriars 3	⊖ d																								
London Charing Cross 4	⊖ d																								
London Waterloo (East) 4	⊖ d																								
London Bridge 4	⊖ d			18 41								*18 44*	19 05			19 11					*19 14*				19 41
Norwood Junction 2	d												19 16												
East Croydon	🚋 a	18 52		18 55			19 02					19 17	19 20	19 22		19 25		19 32	19 38		19 47	19 52			19 55
	d	18 52		18 55			19 03					19 18	19 21	19 22		19 25		19 33	19 38		19 48	19 52			19 55
Purley 4	d											19 23	19 27								19 53				
Coulsdon South	d												19 30								19 57				
Merstham	d												19 36								20 02				
Redhill 5	a							←				19 31	19 39		←				19 49		20 06				
	d							19 06		19 19	19 20	19 32	19 40		19 32				19 50		20 06				
Reigate	a									19 23		→									→				
Nutfield	d												19 44												
Godstone	d												19 50												
Edenbridge	d												19 55												
Penshurst	d												20 02												
Leigh (Kent)	d												20 05												
Tonbridge 4	a												20 10												
Earlswood (Surrey)	d							19 09																	
Salfords	d							19 12																	
Horley 4	d							19 16							19 38										
Gatwick Airport 10	✈ a			19 11		19 15	19 18	19 18	19 30		19 32			19 37	19 40	19 41	19 45	19 48	19 57	20 00					20 11
	d			19 12			19 19	19 19						19 38	19 41	19 42		19 49	19 58						20 12
Three Bridges 15	a			19 17				19 24							19 46	19 47			20 02						20 17
	d			19 17				19 24							19 46	19 47			20 09						20 17
Crawley	d							19 28							19 50										
Ifield	d							19 31																	
Faygate	d																								
Littlehaven	d							19 37																	
Horsham 4	a							19 40							19 58										
Balcombe	d																		20 15						
Haywards Heath 3	a		←	19 26			19 30									19 56		20 00	20 20				←		20 26
	d		19 21	19 26			19 30									19 56		20 00	20 21 →				20 21		20 26
Wivelsfield 4	d		19 25				19 34																20 25		
Lewes 4	a						19 48																		
Burgess Hill 4	d		19 27	19 31												20 01		20 06					20 27		20 31
Hassocks 4	d		19 30	19 35																			20 30		20 35
Preston Park	d		19 37																				20 37		
Hove 2	a																	20 18							
Brighton 10	a	19 27	19 41	19 44										20 00		20 12						20 27	20 41		20 44

For general notes see front of timetable
For details of catering facilities see Directory of Train Operators

A To Bognor Regis (Table 188)

Table 186

Sundays

until 6 September

Bedford and London → Brighton

Network Diagram - see first page of Table 186

	GX 1	SN 1	SN 1	GW 1	GW 1	GX 1	SN 1	SN 1	SN 1 ◇	SN 1	FC 1	GX 1	SN 1	SN 1 ◇	GX 1	SN 1	SN 1 ◇	SN 1 ◇		FC 1	GX 1	SN 1	SN 1	GX 1
							A			A														
		catering symbol																						
London Victoria 15 ⊖ d	19 45	19 47				20 00	20 02		20 06			20 15	20 17	20 21	20 30	20 32	20 36				20 45	20 47		21 00
Milton Keynes Central 10 d																								
Watford Junction d							19 22																	
Shepherd's Bush ⊖ d							19 45																	
Kensington (Olympia) ⊖ d							19 48																	
West Brompton ⊖ d							19 50																	
Clapham Junction 10 d		19 53					20 08		20 12				20 23	20 27		20 38	20 42					20 53		
Bedford 7 d																								
Luton 10 d																								
Luton Airport Parkway 7 ✈ d																								
St Albans City d																								
St Pancras International 15 ⊖ d																								
Farringdon 3 ⊖ d																								
City Thameslink 3 d																								
London Blackfriars 3 ⊖ d																								
London Charing Cross 4 ⊖ d																								
London Waterloo (East) 4 ⊖ d																								
London Bridge 4 ⊖ d							19 44	20 05			20 11					20 14				20 41				
Norwood Junction 2 d								20 16																
East Croydon ⇌ a		20 02					20 17	20 20	20 22		20 24		20 32	20 38		20 47	20 52			20 55		21 02		
d		20 03					20 18	20 21	20 22		20 24		20 33	20 38		20 48	20 52			20 55		21 03		
Purley 4 d							20 23	20 27								20 53								
Coulsdon South d								20 30								20 57								
Merstham d			←					20 36		←						21 02							←	
Redhill 5 a							20 31	20 39						20 49		21 06							21 06	
d			20 06	20 19	20 20		20 32	20 40		20 32				20 50		21 06								
Reigate a				20 23			→									→								
Nutfield d								20 44																
Godstone d								20 50																
Edenbridge d								20 55																
Penshurst d								21 02																
Leigh (Kent) d								21 05																
Tonbridge 4 a								21 10																
Earlswood (Surrey) d			20 09																				21 09	
Salfords d			20 12																				21 12	
Horley 4 d			20 16							20 38													21 16	
Gatwick Airport 10 ✈ a	20 15	20 18	20 18		20 27	20 30			20 37	20 40	20 41	20 45	20 48	20 57	21 00					21 11	21 15	21 18	21 18	21 30
d		20 19	20 19						20 38	20 41	20 42		20 49	20 58						21 12		21 19	21 19	
Three Bridges 15 a			20 24							20 46	20 47			21 02						21 17			21 24	
d			20 24							20 46	20 47			21 09						21 17			21 24	
Crawley d			20 28							20 50													21 28	
Ifield d			20 31																				21 31	
Faygate d																							21 37	
Littlehaven d			20 37																				21 40	
Horsham 4 a			20 40							20 58														
Balcombe d														21 15										
Haywards Heath 3 a		20 30									20 56		21 00	21 20						21 26		21 30		
d		20 30									20 56		21 00	21 21 →				← 21 21		21 26		21 30		
Wivelsfield 4 d		20 34																21 25				21 34		
Lewes 4 a		20 48																				21 48		
Burgess Hill 4 d											21 01		21 06					21 27		21 31				
Hassocks 4 d																		21 30		21 35				
Preston Park d																		21 37						
Hove 2 a													21 18											
Brighton 10 a									21 00		21 12						21 27	21 41		21 44				

For general notes see front of timetable
For details of catering facilities see
Directory of Train Operators

A To Bognor Regis (Table 188)

Sundays

until 6 September

Bedford and London → Brighton

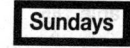

Network Diagram - see first page of Table 186

	GW 1	GW 1	SN 1	SN 1	SN 1 ◇	SN 1	FC 1	GX 1	SN 1	SN 1 ◇	GX 1	SN 1	FC 1	GX 1	SN 1		SN 1	GW 1	GX 1	GW 1	SN 1	SN 1	FC 1	GX 1
			A			A															A			
London Victoria 15 ⊖ d			21 02		21 06			21 15	21 17	21 21	21 30	21 32		21 45	21 47				22 00		22 02			22 15
Milton Keynes Central 10 d																								
Watford Junction d			*20 22*																		*21 17*			
Shepherd's Bush ⊖ d			*20 45*																		*21 45*			
Kensington (Olympia) ⊖ d			*20 48*																		*21 48*			
West Brompton ⊖ d			*20 50*																		*21 50*			
Clapham Junction 10 d			21 08		21 12				21 23	21 27		21 38			21 53						22 08			
Bedford 7 d																								
Luton 10 d																								
Luton Airport Parkway 7 ✈ d																								
St Albans City d																								
St Pancras International 15 ⊖ d																								
Farringdon 3 ⊖ d																								
City Thameslink 3 d																								
London Blackfriars 3 ⊖ d																								
London Charing Cross 4 ⊖ d																								
London Waterloo (East) 4 ⊖ d																								
London Bridge 4 ⊖ d			*20 44*	21 05			21 11					*21 14*	21 41								*21 44*	22 05	22 11	
Norwood Junction 2 d				21 16																		22 16		
East Croydon a			21 17	21 20	21 22		21 25		21 32	21 38		21 47	21 55		22 02						22 17	22 20	22 24	
d			21 18	21 21	21 22		21 25		21 33	21 38		21 48	21 55		22 03						22 18	22 21	22 24	
Purley 4 d			21 23	21 27								21 53									22 23	22 27		
Coulsdon South d				21 30								21 57										22 30		
Merstham d				21 36								22 02										22 36		
Redhill 5 a			21 31	21 39		←				21 49		22 06					←				22 31	22 39		
d	21 20	21 20	21 32	21 40		21 32				21 50		22 06					22 06	22 18		22 20	22 32	22 40		
Reigate a		21 24	→									→								22 24				
Nutfield d				21 44																		22 44		
Godstone d				21 50																		22 50		
Edenbridge d				21 55																		22 55		
Penshurst d				22 02																		23 02		
Leigh (Kent) d				22 05																		23 05		
Tonbridge 4 a				22 10																		23 10		
Earlswood (Surrey) d																	22 09							
Salfords d																	22 12							
Horley 4 d						21 38											22 16				22 38			
Gatwick Airport 10 ✈ a	21 32				21 37	21 40	21 41	21 45	21 48	21 57	22 00		22 11	22 15	22 18		22 18	22 25	22 30		22 40		22 41	22 45
d					21 38	21 41	21 42		21 49	21 58			22 12		22 19		22 19				22 41		22 42	
Three Bridges 15 a						21 46	21 47			22 02			22 17				22 24				22 46		22 47	
d						21 46	21 47			22 03			22 17				22 24				22 46		22 47	
Crawley d						21 50											22 28				22 50			
Ifield d																	22 31							
Faygate d																								
Littlehaven d																	22 37							
Horsham 4 a						21 58											22 40				22 58			
Balcombe d										22 09														
Haywards Heath 3 a							21 56		22 00	22 14			22 26		22 30								22 56	
d							21 56		22 00	22 15			22 26		22 30								22 56	
Wivelsfield 4 d										22 19					22 34									
Lewes 4 a															22 48									
Burgess Hill 4 d							22 01		22 06	22 21			22 31										23 01	
Hassocks 4 d										22 24			22 35											
Preston Park d										22 31														
Hove 2 a									22 18															
Brighton 10 a					22 00		22 12			22 35			22 44										23 12	

For general notes see front of timetable
For details of catering facilities see Directory of Train Operators

A To Bognor Regis (Table 188)

Bedford and London → Brighton

Network Diagram - see first page of Table 186

		SN 1	SN 1 ◇	GX 1	SN 1	FC 1	GX 1	SN 1	SN 1	GX 1	SN 1	GW 1	SN 1		FC 1	GX 1	GW 1	SN 1	SN 1	GX 1	SN 1 ◇	FC 1	GX 1		
London Victoria 15	⊖ d	22 17	22 21	22 30	22 32		22 45	22 47		23 00			23 04			23 15			23 17	23 30	23 32		23 45		
Milton Keynes Central 10	d												22 17												
Watford Junction	d												22 45												
Shepherd's Bush	⊖ d												22 48												
Kensington (Olympia)	⊖ d												22 50												
West Brompton	⊖ d																								
Clapham Junction 10	d	22 23	22 27		22 38			22 53					23 10						23 23		23 38				
Bedford 7	d																								
Luton 10	d																								
Luton Airport Parkway 7	✈ d																								
St Albans City	d																								
St Pancras International 15	⊖ d																								
Farringdon 3	⊖ d																								
City Thameslink 3	d																								
London Blackfriars 3	⊖ d																								
London Charing Cross 4	⊖ d																								
London Waterloo (East) 4	⊖ d																								
London Bridge 4	⊖ d				22 14	22 41							22 44		23 11						23 14	23 41			
Norwood Junction 2	d																								
East Croydon	a	22 32	22 38		22 47	22 55		23 02					23 23		23 25				23 37		23 52	23 56			
	d	22 33	22 38		22 48	22 55		23 03					23 23		23 25				23 38		23 53	23 57			
Purley 4	d				22 53								23 29												
Coulsdon South	d				22 57								23 33					←							
Merstham	d				23 02								23 38					23 38							
Redhill 5	a		22 49		23 06				←				→					23 42			00 05				
	d		22 50		23 06				23 06		23 09	23 20					23 20	23 42			00 05				
Reigate	a				→												23 24								
Nutfield	d										23 13														
Godstone	d										23 19														
Edenbridge	d										23 24														
Penshurst	d										23 31														
Leigh (Kent)	d										23 34														
Tonbridge 4	a										23 39														
Earlswood (Surrey)	d								23 09																
Salfords	d								23 12																
Horley 4	d								23 16									23 50							
Gatwick Airport 10	✈ a	22 48	22 57	23 00		23 11	23 15	23 18	23 18	23 30		23 33			23 41	23 50		23 54	23 59	00 07	00 14	00 17	00 20		
	d	22 49	22 58			23 12		23 19	23 19						23 42			23 55	00 01		00 15	00 18			
Three Bridges 15	a		23 02			23 17			23 24						23 47			00 01	00 05		00 19	00 25			
	d		23 03			23 17			23 24						23 47			00 01	00 06		00 20				
Crawley	d								23 28									00 05							
Ifield	d								23 31									00 07							
Faygate	d																								
Littlehaven	d								23 37									00 14							
Horsham 4	a								23 40									00 17							
Balcombe	d		23 09																		00 26				
Haywards Heath 3	a	23 00	23 14			23 26		23 30							23 56				00 14		00 31				
	d	23 00	23 15			23 26		23 30							23 56				00 15		00 31				
Wivelsfield 4	d		23 19					23 34													00 35				
Lewes 4	a							23 48																	
Burgess Hill 4	d	23 06	23 21			23 31									00 01						00 37				
Hassocks 4	d		23 24			23 35															00 41				
Preston Park	d		23 31																		00 48				
Hove 2	a	23 19																	00 28						
Brighton 10	a		23 35			23 44									00 12						00 52				

For general notes see front of timetable
For details of catering facilities see
Directory of Train Operators

Table 186

Sundays

from 13 September

Bedford and London → Brighton

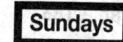

Network Diagram - see first page of Table 186

Station		SN 1 ◇	FC 1	SN 1	SN 1	SN 1	SN 1	GW 1	SN 1	FC 1	SN 1	GX 1	SN 1 A	FC 1	SN 1	GW 1	FC 1	GX 1	SN 1	FC 1	SN 1	SN 1	GX 1	SN 1
London Victoria 15	⊖ d	23p02		23p10	23p17				23p32		23p47	00 02	00 05		00 14			00 30	01 00		02 00	03 00	03 30	04 00
Milton Keynes Central 10	d																							
Watford Junction	d												*23 25*											
Shepherd's Bush	⊖ d												*23 49*											
Kensington (Olympia)	⊖ d												*23 51*											
West Brompton	⊖ d												*23 54*											
Clapham Junction 10	d	23p08		23p16	23p23				23p38		23p53		00 11		00 20				01 08		02 08	03 08		04 08
Bedford 7	d																							
Luton 10	d																							
Luton Airport Parkway 7	✈ d																							
St Albans City	d																							
St Pancras International 15	⊖ d																							
Farringdon 3	⊖ d																							
City Thameslink 3	d																							
London Blackfriars 3	⊖ d																							
London Charing Cross 4	⊖ d																							
London Waterloo (East) 4	⊖ d																							
London Bridge 4	⊖ d		23p11							23p41	*23 41*		*23 53*	00 11			00 41			01 05				
Norwood Junction 2	d																							
East Croydon	🚋 a	23p18	23p24	23p28	23p33				23p52	23p56	00 06		00 24	00 27	00 32		00 56		01 21	01 32	02 21	03 21		04 21
	d	23p18	23p24	23p28	23p33				23p52	23p57	00 06		00 25	00 27	00 33		00 57		01 22	01 32	02 22	03 22		04 22
Purley 4	d			23p33							00 12				00 38				01 27		02 27	03 27		04 27
Coulsdon South	d			23p37							00 15				00 41									
Merstham	d			23p42							00 21				00 47									
Redhill 5	a	23p30		23p46		←			00 03		00 24				00 50									
	d	23p31		23p46		23p46	23p55	00 03	00 05		00 25				00 51	00 54								
Reigate	a			→																				
Nutfield	d																							
Godstone	d																							
Edenbridge	d						00 06																	
Penshurst	d																							
Leigh (Kent)	d																							
Tonbridge 4	a						00 15																	
Earlswood (Surrey)	d					23p49																		
Salfords	d					23p52																		
Horley 4	d					23p56					00 31				00 57				01 43		02 42	03 42		04 43
Gatwick Airport 10	✈ a	23p38	23p41		23p50	23p58		00 10	00 13	00 17	00 33	00 35	00 43	00 49	00 59	01 02	01 16	01 20	01 45	01 51	02 44	03 44	04 05	04 45
	d	23p39	23p41		23p51	23p59			00 14	00 18	00 34		00 44	00 50	01 00		01 17		01 47	01 52	02 46	03 46		04 47
Three Bridges 15	a	23p44	23p47		23p55	00 04			00 19	00 24	00 39		00 48	00 54	01 05		01 24		01 51	01 58	03 00	04 00		04 54
	d	23p44	23p47		23p56	00 04			00 19		00 39		00 48						01 52					04 55
Crawley	d					00 07					00 42													
Ifield	d					00 10					00 45													
Faygate	d																							
Littlehaven	d					00 16					00 51													
Horsham 4	a					00 19					00 54													
Balcombe	d		23p53						00 27															
Haywards Heath 3	a	23p52	23p58		00 04				00 34				01 00											
	d	23p53	23p58		00 05				00 34				01 03 / 01 06											
Wivelsfield 4	d	23p57	00 02						00 38															
Lewes 4	a												01 20											
Burgess Hill 4	d	23p59	00 04		00 10				00 40															
Hassocks 4	d	00 02	00 08						00 44															
Preston Park	d	00 09	00 15						00 51															
Hove 2	a				00 21								01s25											
Brighton 10	a	00 15	00 20						00 55				01s17						02 20					05 21

For general notes see front of timetable
For details of catering facilities see Directory of Train Operators

A To Eastbourne (Table 189)

Table 186

Sundays

from 13 September

Bedford and London → Brighton

Network Diagram - see first page of Table 186

		GX 1	GX 1	SN 1	GX 1	GX 1		GX 1	SN 1	SN 1◇	GX 1	GX 1	GW 1	GX 1	SN 1◇	GX 1	GW 1	GX 1	GW 1	SN 1 A	FC 1	GX 1	GX 1	SN 1◇	SN 1
London Victoria 15	⊖ d	04 30	05 00	05 02	05 15	05 30		05 45		05 47	06 00	06 15		06 30	06 32	06 45		07 00		07 02		07 15	07 30	07 32	07 34
Milton Keynes Central 10	d																								
Watford Junction	d																								
Shepherd's Bush	⊖ d																								
Kensington (Olympia)	⊖ d																								
West Brompton	⊖ d																								
Clapham Junction 10	d			05 08						05 53					06 38					07 08				07 38	07 40
Bedford 7	d																								
Luton 10	d																								
Luton Airport Parkway 7	✈ d																								
St Albans City	d																								
St Pancras International 15	⊖ d																								
Farringdon 3	⊖ d																								
City Thameslink 3	d																								
London Blackfriars 3	⊖ d																								
London Charing Cross 4	⊖ d																								
London Waterloo (East) 4	⊖ d																								
London Bridge 4	⊖ d																				07 11				
Norwood Junction 2	d																								
East Croydon	a			05 22						06 05					06 51					07 23	07 26			07 50	07 53
	d			05 23						06 06					06 52					07 23	07 27			07 51	07 54
Purley 4	d			05 29											06 56					07 28					07 59
Coulsdon South	d														07 00										08 03
Merstham	d														07 05										08 08
Redhill 5	a									06 18					07 09					07 36				08 03	→
	d									06 19			06 19		07 09		07 15		07 19	07 37				08 04	
Reigate	a												06 23						07 23						
Nutfield	d																								
Godstone	d																								
Edenbridge	d																								
Penshurst	d																								
Leigh (Kent)	d																								
Tonbridge 4	a																								
Earlswood (Surrey)	d																								
Salfords	d																								
Horley 4	d									06 25					07 15					07 44					
Gatwick Airport 10	✈ a	05 05	05 35	05 45	05 50	06 05		06 20		06 31	06 35	06 47		07 05	07 18	07 20	07 27	07 35		07 46	07 48	07 50	08 05	08 11	
	d			05 46					06 29	06 32					07 19					07 47	07 50			08 12	
Three Bridges 15	a			05 50					06 33	06 36					07 23					07 52	07 54			08 16	
	d			05 51					06 40	06 36					07 24					07 52	07 54			08 17	
Crawley	d								06 43											07 55					
Ifield	d								06 46											07 58					
Faygate	d																								
Littlehaven	d								06 52											08 04					
Horsham 4	a								06 56											08 07					
Balcombe	d														07 30									08 23	
Haywards Heath 3	a			05 59						06 46					07 35						08 03			08 28	
	d			06 00						06 47					07 36						08 03			08 28	
Wivelsfield 4	d									06 51					07 40									08 32	
Lewes 4	a																								
Burgess Hill 4	d									06 53					07 42						08 08			08 34	
Hassocks 4	d									06 56					07 45									08 38	
Preston Park	d									07 03					07 52									08 45	
Hove 2	a																								
Brighton 10	a			06 18						07 08					07 58						08 22			08 50	

For general notes see front of timetable
For details of catering facilities see
Directory of Train Operators

A To Bognor Regis (Table 188)

Table 186

Sundays

from 13 September

Bedford and London → Brighton

Network Diagram - see first page of Table 186

		FC	GX	SN	SN	GW	GW	GX	SN	FC	GX	SN		GX	SN	SN	FC	GX	SN	SN	SN	GW	GW	GX	SN
		1	1	1	1	1	1	1	1	1	1	1		1	1 ◇	1	1	1	1	1	1	1	1	1	1 ◇
									A																
London Victoria 15	⊖ d		07 45					08 00	08 04		08 15	08 17		08 30	08 32	08 34		08 45			08 47			09 00	09 02
Milton Keynes Central 10	d																								
Watford Junction	d																								
Shepherd's Bush	⊖ d								07 48																08 50
Kensington (Olympia)	⊖ d								07 50																08 53
West Brompton	⊖ d								07 52																08 56
Clapham Junction 10	d								08 10			08 23			08 38	08 40					08 53				09 08
Bedford 7	d																								
Luton 10	d																								
Luton Airport Parkway 7	✈ d																								
St Albans City	d																								
St Pancras International 15	⊖ d																								
Farringdon 3	⊖ d																								
City Thameslink 3	d																								
London Blackfriars 3	⊖ d																								
London Charing Cross 4	⊖ d																								
London Waterloo (East) 4	⊖ d																								
London Bridge 4	⊖ d	07 41							*07 44*	08 11					*08 14*		08 41								*08 44*
Norwood Junction 2	d																								
East Croydon	⇌ a	07 56							08 24	08 27		08 37			08 50	08 53	08 56				09 07				09 21
	d	07 57							08 24	08 27		08 38			08 51	08 54	08 57				09 08				09 22
Purley 4	d								08 30							08 59									
Coulsdon South	d				←											09 03				←					
Merstham	d				08 08											09 08				09 08					
Redhill 5	a				08 12				08 38						09 03	→				09 12					
	d			08 09	08 12	08 19	08 20		08 39						09 04				09 09	09 12		09 19	09 20		
Reigate	a					08 23																09 23			
Nutfield	d			08 13															09 13						
Godstone	d			08 19															09 19						
Edenbridge	d			08 24															09 24						
Penshurst	d			08 31															09 31						
Leigh (Kent)	d			08 34															09 34						
Tonbridge 4	a			08 39															09 39						
Earlswood (Surrey)	d																								
Salfords	d																								
Horley 4	d				08 22				08 45											09 22					
Gatwick Airport 10	✈ a	08 18	08 20		08 24		08 30	08 35	08 47	08 48	08 50	08 54		09 05	09 11		09 18	09 20		09 24	09 27		09 31	09 35	09 39
	d	08 20			08 25				08 48	08 50		08 56			09 12		09 20			09 25	09 29				09 40
Three Bridges 15	a	08 24			08 30				08 53	08 54					09 16		09 24			09 30					
	d	08 24			08 33				08 53	08 54					09 17		09 24			09 33					
Crawley	d				08 36				08 56											09 36					
Ifield	d				08 39															09 39					
Faygate	d																								
Littlehaven	d				08 45															09 45					
Horsham 4	a				08 49				09 04											09 49					
Balcombe	d														09 23										
Haywards Heath 3	a	08 33								09 03		09 06			09 28		09 33				09 40				
	d	08 33								09 03		09 07			09 28		09 33				09 41				
Wivelsfield 4	d														09 32						09 45				
Lewes 4	a																				09 58				
Burgess Hill 4	d	08 38								09 08		09 12			09 34		09 38								
Hassocks 4	d	08 42													09 38		09 42								
Preston Park	d														09 45										
Hove 2	a											09 24													
Brighton 10	a	08 52								09 22					09 50		09 52								10 03

For general notes see front of timetable
For details of catering facilities see Directory of Train Operators

A To Bognor Regis (Table 188)

Table 186

Sundays

from 13 September

Bedford and London → Brighton

Network Diagram - see first page of Table 186

		SN	FC	GX	SN	GX	SN	SN	FC	GX	SN	SN	SN	GW	GW	GX	SN	SN		FC	GX	SN	GX	SN	SN
		1	1	1	1	1	1 ◇	1	1	1	1	1	1	1	1	1	1 ◇	1		1	1	1	1	1 ◇	1
		A					🛒						🛒					A 🛒						🛒	
London Victoria [15] ⊖	d	09 04		09 15	09 17	09 30	09 32	09 34		09 45			09 47			10 00	10 02	10 04			10 15	10 17	10 30	10 32	10 34
Milton Keynes Central [10]	d																								
Watford Junction	d																09 17								
Shepherd's Bush ⊖	d																09 45								
Kensington (Olympia) ⊖	d																09 48								
West Brompton ⊖	d																09 50								
Clapham Junction [10]	d	09 10			09 23		09 38	09 40					09 53				10 08	10 10				10 23		10 38	10 40
Bedford [7]	d																								
Luton [10]	d																								
Luton Airport Parkway [7] ✈	d																								
St Albans City	d																								
St Pancras International [15] ⊖	d																								
Farringdon [3] ⊖	d																								
City Thameslink [3]	d																								
London Blackfriars [3] ⊖	d																								
London Charing Cross [4] ⊖	d																								
London Waterloo (East) [4] ⊖	d																								
London Bridge [4] ⊖	d		09 11				*09 14*		09 41								*09 44*			10 11				*10 14*	
Norwood Junction [2]	d																								
East Croydon 🚊	a	09 24	09 27		09 37		09 50	09 53	09 56				10 07				10 21	10 24		10 27		10 37		10 50	10 53
	d	09 24	09 27		09 38		09 51	09 54	09 57				10 08				10 22	10 24		10 27		10 38		10 51	10 54
Purley [4]	d	09 30						09 59										10 30							10 59
Coulsdon South	d							10 03				←													11 03
Merstham	d							10 08 →				10 08													11 08 →
Redhill [5]	a	09 38					10 03					10 12						10 38						11 03	
	d	09 39					10 04				10 09	10 12		10 19	10 20			10 39						11 04	
Reigate	a													10 23											
Nutfield	d										10 13														
Godstone	d										10 19														
Edenbridge	d										10 24														
Penshurst	d										10 31														
Leigh (Kent)	d										10 34														
Tonbridge [4]	a										10 39														
Earlswood (Surrey)	d																								
Salfords	d																								
Horley [4]	d	09 45										10 22						10 45							
Gatwick Airport [10] ✈	a	09 47	09 48	09 50	09 54	10 05	10 11		10 18	10 20		10 24	10 27		10 31	10 35	10 39	10 47		10 48	10 50	10 54	11 05	11 11	
	d	09 48	09 50		09 56		10 12		10 20			10 25	10 29				10 40	10 48		10 50		10 56		11 12	
Three Bridges [15]	a	09 53	09 54				10 16		10 24			10 30						10 53		10 54				11 16	
	d	09 53	09 54				10 17		10 24			10 33						10 53		10 54				11 17	
Crawley	d	09 56										10 36						10 56							
Ifield	d											10 39													
Faygate	d																								
Littlehaven	d											10 45													
Horsham [4]	a	10 04										10 49						11 04							
Balcombe	d						10 23																	11 23	
Haywards Heath [3]	a		10 03		10 06		10 28		10 33				10 40							11 03		11 06		11 28	
	d		10 03		10 07		10 28		10 33				10 41							11 03		11 07		11 28	
Wivelsfield [4]	d						10 32						10 45											11 32	
Lewes [4]	a												10 58												
Burgess Hill [4]	d		10 08		10 12		10 34		10 38											11 08		11 12		11 34	
Hassocks [4]	d						10 38		10 42															11 38	
Preston Park	d						10 45																	11 45	
Hove [2]	a				10 24																	11 24			
Brighton [10]	a		10 22				10 50		10 52								11 03			11 22				11 50	

For general notes see front of timetable
For details of catering facilities see
Directory of Train Operators

A To Bognor Regis (Table 188)

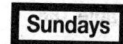

Bedford and London → Brighton

Sundays

from 13 September

Network Diagram - see first page of Table 186

		FC 1	GX 1	SN 1	SN 1	SN 1	GW 1	GW 1	GX 1	SN 1 ◊	SN 1	FC 1	GX 1	SN 1	GX 1	SN 1 ◊	SN 1	FC 1	GX 1	SN 1	SN 1	SN 1	GW 1	GW 1	GX 1
											A														
						🚌										🚌						🚌			
London Victoria 15 ⊖	d		10 45			10 47			11 00	11 02	11 04		11 15	11 17	11 30	11 32	11 34		11 45			11 47			12 00
Milton Keynes Central 10	d																								
Watford Junction	d									*10 17*															
Shepherd's Bush ⊖	d									*10 45*															
Kensington (Olympia) ⊖	d									*10 48*															
West Brompton ⊖	d									*10 50*															
Clapham Junction 10	d					10 53				11 08	11 10			11 23		11 38	11 40					11 53			
Bedford 7	d																								
Luton 10	d																								
Luton Airport Parkway 7 ✈	d																								
St Albans City	d																								
St Pancras International 15 ⊖	d																								
Farringdon 3 ⊖	d																								
City Thameslink 3	d																								
London Blackfriars 3 ⊖	d																								
London Charing Cross 4 ⊖	d																								
London Waterloo (East) 4 ⊖	d																								
London Bridge 4 ⊖	d	10 41								*10 44*		11 11				*11 14*		11 41							
Norwood Junction 2	d																								
East Croydon	a	10 56				11 07				11 21	11 24	11 27		11 37		11 50	11 53	11 56				12 07			
	d	10 57				11 08				11 22	11 24	11 28		11 38		11 51	11 54	11 57				12 08			
Purley 4	d										11 30						11 59								
Coulsdon South	d				←												12 03				←				
Merstham	d				11 08												12 08				12 08				
Redhill 5	a				11 12						11 38					12 03	→				12 12				
	d			11 09	11 12		11 19	11 20			11 39					12 04				12 09	12 12		12 19	12 20	
Reigate	a						11 23																12 23		
Nutfield	d			11 13																12 13					
Godstone	d			11 19																12 19					
Edenbridge	d			11 24																12 24					
Penshurst	d			11 31																12 31					
Leigh (Kent)	d			11 34																12 34					
Tonbridge 4	a			11 39																12 39					
Earlswood (Surrey)	d																								
Salfords	d																								
Horley 4	d				11 22						11 45										12 22				
Gatwick Airport 10 ✈	a	11 18	11 20		11 24	11 27		11 31	11 35	11 39	11 47	11 48	11 50	11 54	12 05	12 11		12 18	12 20		12 24	12 27		12 31	12 35
	d	11 20			11 25	11 29				11 40	11 48	11 50		11 56		12 12		12 20			12 25	12 29			
Three Bridges 15	a	11 24			11 30						11 53	11 54				12 16		12 24			12 30				
	d	11 24			11 33						11 53	11 54				12 17		12 24			12 33				
Crawley	d				11 36						11 56										12 36				
Ifield	d				11 39																12 39				
Faygate	d																								
Littlehaven	d				11 45																12 45				
Horsham 4	a				11 49						12 04										12 49				
Balcombe	d															12 23									
Haywards Heath 3	a	11 33				11 40						12 03		12 06		12 28		12 33				12 40			
	d	11 33				11 41						12 03		12 07		12 28		12 33				12 41			
Wivelsfield 4	d					11 45										12 32						12 45			
Lewes 4	a					11 58																12 58			
Burgess Hill 4	d	11 38										12 08		12 12		12 34		12 38							
Hassocks 4	d	11 42														12 38		12 42							
Preston Park	d															12 45									
Hove 2	a													12 24											
Brighton 10	a	11 52								12 03		12 22				12 49		12 52							

For general notes see front of timetable
For details of catering facilities see Directory of Train Operators

A To Bognor Regis (Table 188)

Sundays
from 13 September

Bedford and London → Brighton

Network Diagram - see first page of Table 186

		SN 1 ◇		SN 1	FC 1	GX 1	SN 1	GX 1	SN 1 ◇	SN 1	FC 1	GX 1	SN 1	SN 1	SN 1	GW 1	GW 1	GX 1	SN 1 ◇	SN 1	FC 1	GX 1	SN 1	GX 1	SN 1 ◇
				A 🍴					🍴						🍴					A 🍴					🍴
London Victoria 15 ⊖	d	12 02		12 04		12 15	12 17	12 30	12 32	12 34		12 45			12 47			13 00	13 02	13 04		13 15	13 17	13 30	13 32
Milton Keynes Central 10	d																								
Watford Junction	d	11 17																	12 22						
Shepherd's Bush ⊖	d	11 45																	12 45						
Kensington (Olympia) ⊖	d	11 48																	12 48						
West Brompton ⊖	d	11 50																	12 50						
Clapham Junction 10	d	12 08		12 10			12 23		12 38	12 40					12 53				13 08	13 10			13 23		13 38
Bedford 7	d																								
Luton 10	d																								
Luton Airport Parkway 7 ✈	d																								
St Albans City	d																								
St Pancras International 15 ⊖	d																								
Farringdon 3 ⊖	d																								
City Thameslink 3	d																								
London Blackfriars 3 ⊖	d																								
London Charing Cross 4 ⊖	d																								
London Waterloo (East) 4 ⊖	d																								
London Bridge 4 ⊖	d	11 44			12 11				12 14		12 41								12 44		13 11				13 14
Norwood Junction 2	d																								
East Croydon	a	12 21		12 24	12 27		12 37		12 50	12 53	12 56				13 07				13 21	13 24	13 27		13 37		13 50
	d	12 22		12 24	12 27		12 38		12 51	12 54	12 57				13 08				13 22	13 24	13 28		13 38		13 51
Purley 4	d			12 30						12 59										13 30					
Coulsdon South	d									13 03				←											
Merstham	d									13 08				13 08											
Redhill 5	a			12 38					13 03	→				13 12						13 38					14 03
	d			12 39					13 04				13 09	13 12		13 19	13 20			13 39					14 04
Reigate	a															13 23									
Nutfield	d												13 13												
Godstone	d												13 19												
Edenbridge	d												13 24												
Penshurst	d												13 31												
Leigh (Kent)	d												13 34												
Tonbridge 4	a												13 39												
Earlswood (Surrey)	d																								
Salfords	d																								
Horley 4	d			12 45										13 22						13 45					
Gatwick Airport 10 ✈	a	12 39		12 47	12 48	12 50	12 54	13 05	13 11		13 18	13 20		13 24	13 27		13 31	13 35	13 39	13 47	13 48	13 50	13 54	14 05	14 11
	d	12 40		12 48	12 50		12 56		13 12		13 20			13 25	13 29				13 40	13 48	13 50		13 56		14 12
Three Bridges 15	a			12 53	12 54				13 16		13 24			13 30						13 53	13 54				14 16
	d			12 53	12 54				13 17		13 24			13 33						13 53	13 54				14 17
Crawley	d			12 56										13 36						13 56					
Ifield	d													13 39											
Faygate	d																								
Littlehaven	d													13 45											
Horsham 4	a			13 04										13 49						14 04					
Balcombe	d								13 23																14 23
Haywards Heath 3	a				13 03		13 06		13 28		13 33				13 40						14 03		14 06		14 28
	d				13 03		13 07		13 28		13 33				13 41						14 03		14 07		14 28
Wivelsfield 4	d								13 32						13 45										14 32
Lewes 4	a														13 58										
Burgess Hill 4	d				13 08		13 12		13 34		13 38										14 08		14 12		14 34
Hassocks 4	d								13 38		13 42														14 38
Preston Park	d								13 45																14 45
Hove 2	a						13 24																14 24		
Brighton 10	a	13 03			13 22				13 50		13 52								14 03		14 22				14 50

For general notes see front of timetable
For details of catering facilities see
Directory of Train Operators

A To Bognor Regis (Table 188)

Sundays

from 13 September

Bedford and London → Brighton

Network Diagram - see first page of Table 186

		SN	FC	GX	SN	SN	SN	GW	GW	GX	SN	SN	FC	GX	SN	GX	SN	SN	FC	GX	SN	SN	SN	GW
		1	1	1	1	1	1	1	1	1	1 ◇	1	1	1	1	1	1 ◇	1	1	1	1	1	1	1
												A												
London Victoria 15	⊖ d	13 34		13 45			13 47			14 00	14 02	14 04		14 15	14 17	14 30	14 32	14 34		14 45			14 47	
Milton Keynes Central 10	d																							
Watford Junction	d										*13 22*													
Shepherd's Bush	⊖ d										*13 45*													
Kensington (Olympia)	⊖ d										*13 48*													
West Brompton	⊖ d										*13 50*													
Clapham Junction 10	d	13 40					13 53				14 08	14 10			14 23		14 38	14 40					14 53	
Bedford 7	d																							
Luton 10	d																							
Luton Airport Parkway 7	✈ d																							
St Albans City	d																							
St Pancras International 15	⊖ d																							
Farringdon 3	⊖ d																							
City Thameslink 3	d																							
London Blackfriars 3	⊖ d																							
London Charing Cross 4	⊖ d																							
London Waterloo (East) 4	⊖ d																							
London Bridge 4	⊖ d		13 41								*13 44*		14 11				*14 14*		14 41					
Norwood Junction 2	d																							
East Croydon	a	13 53	13 56				14 07				14 21	14 24	14 27		14 37		14 50	14 53	14 56				15 07	
	d	13 54	13 57				14 08				14 22	14 24	14 28		14 38		14 51	14 54	14 57				15 08	
Purley 4	d	13 59										14 30						14 59						
Coulsdon South	d	14 03				←												15 03				←		
Merstham	d	14 08				14 08												15 08				15 08		
Redhill 5	a	→				14 12						14 38					15 03	→				15 12		
	d				14 09	14 12		14 19	14 20			14 39					15 04				15 09	15 12		15 19
Reigate	a							14 23																15 23
Nutfield	d				14 13																15 13			
Godstone	d				14 19																15 19			
Edenbridge	d				14 24																15 24			
Penshurst	d				14 31																15 31			
Leigh (Kent)	d				14 34																15 34			
Tonbridge 4	a				14 39																15 39			
Earlswood (Surrey)	d																							
Salfords	d																							
Horley 4	d					14 22						14 45										15 22		
Gatwick Airport 10	✈ a		14 18	14 20		14 24	14 27		14 31	14 35	14 39	14 47	14 48	14 50	14 54	15 05	15 11		15 18	15 20		15 24	15 27	
	d		14 20			14 25	14 29				14 40	14 48	14 50		14 56		15 12		15 20			15 25	15 29	
Three Bridges 15	a		14 24			14 30						14 53	14 54				15 16		15 24			15 30		
	d		14 24			14 33						14 53	14 54				15 17		15 24			15 33		
Crawley	d					14 36						14 56										15 36		
Ifield	d					14 39																15 39		
Faygate	d																							
Littlehaven	d					14 45																15 45		
Horsham 4	a					14 49						15 04										15 49		
Balcombe	d																15 23							
Haywards Heath 3	a		14 33				14 40						15 03		15 06		15 28		15 33				15 40	
	d		14 33				14 41						15 03		15 07		15 28		15 33				15 41	
Wivelsfield 4	d						14 45										15 32						15 45	
Lewes 4	a						14 58																15 58	
Burgess Hill 4	d		14 38										15 08		15 12		15 34		15 38					
Hassocks 4	d		14 42														15 38		15 42					
Preston Park	d																15 45							
Hove 2	a														15 24									
Brighton 10	a		14 52								15 03		15 22				15 50		15 52					

For general notes see front of timetable
For details of catering facilities see Directory of Train Operators

A To Bognor Regis (Table 188)

Sundays

from 13 September

Bedford and London → Brighton

Network Diagram - see first page of Table 186

		GW 1	GX 1	SN 1 ◇	SN 1	FC 1	GX 1	SN 1	GX 1	SN 1 ◇	SN 1	FC 1	GX 1	SN 1		SN 1	SN 1	GW 1	GW 1	GX 1	SN 1 ◇	SN 1	FC 1	GX 1	SN 1
					A 🛒					🛒							B 🛒					A 🛒			
London Victoria 15	⊖ d		15 00	15 02	15 04		15 15	15 17	15 30	15 32	15 34		15 45				15 47			16 00	16 02	16 04		16 15	16 17
Milton Keynes Central 10	d																								
Watford Junction	d			14 22																	15 22				
Shepherd's Bush	⊖ d			14 45																	15 45				
Kensington (Olympia)	⊖ d			14 48																	15 48				
West Brompton	⊖ d			14 50																	15 50				
Clapham Junction 10	d			15 08	15 10			15 23		15 38	15 40						15 53				16 08	16 10			16 23
Bedford 7	d																								
Luton 10	d																								
Luton Airport Parkway 7	✈ d																								
St Albans City	d																								
St Pancras International 15	⊖ d																								
Farringdon 3	⊖ d																								
City Thameslink 3	d																								
London Blackfriars 3	⊖ d																								
London Charing Cross 4	⊖ d																								
London Waterloo (East) 4	⊖ d																				15 44		16 11		
London Bridge 4	⊖ d			14 44		15 11				15 14		15 41													
Norwood Junction 2	d																								
East Croydon	🚊 a			15 21	15 24	15 27		15 37		15 50	15 53	15 56					16 07				16 21	16 24	16 27		16 37
	d			15 22	15 24	15 28		15 38		15 51	15 54	15 57					16 08				16 22	16 24	16 28		16 38
Purley 4	d				15 30						15 59											16 30			
Coulsdon South	d										16 03					←									
Merstham	d										16 08					16 08									
Redhill 5	a				15 38					16 03	→					16 12						16 38			
	d	15 20			15 39					16 04				16 09		16 12		16 19	16 20			16 39			
Reigate	a																	16 23							
Nutfield	d													16 13											
Godstone	d													16 19											
Edenbridge	d													16 24											
Penshurst	d													16 31											
Leigh (Kent)	d													16 34											
Tonbridge 4	a													16 39											
Earlswood (Surrey)	d																								
Salfords	d																								
Horley 4	d				15 45											16 22						16 45			
Gatwick Airport 10	✈ a	15 31	15 35	15 39	15 47	15 48	15 50	15 54	16 05	16 11		16 18	16 20			16 24	16 27		16 31	16 35	16 39	16 47	16 48	16 50	16 54
	d			15 40	15 48	15 50		15 56		16 12		16 20				16 25	16 29				16 40	16 48	16 50		16 56
Three Bridges 15	a				15 53	15 54				16 16		16 24				16 30						16 53	16 54		
	d				15 53	15 54				16 17		16 24				16 33						16 53	16 54		
Crawley	d				15 56											16 36						16 56			
Ifield	d															16 39									
Faygate	d																								
Littlehaven	d															16 45									
Horsham 4	a				16 04											16 49						17 04			
Balcombe	d									16 23															
Haywards Heath 3	a					16 03		16 06		16 28		16 33					16 40						17 03		17 06
	d					16 03		16 07		16 28		16 33					16 41						17 03		17 07
Wivelsfield 4	d									16 32							16 45								
Lewes 4	a																16 58								
Burgess Hill 4	d					16 08		16 12		16 34		16 38											17 08		17 12
Hassocks 4	d									16 38		16 42													
Preston Park	d									16 45															
Hove 2	a							16 24																	17 24
Brighton 10	a			16 03		16 22				16 50		16 52									17 03		17 22		

For general notes see front of timetable
For details of catering facilities see
Directory of Train Operators

A To Bognor Regis (Table 188)
B 🛒 to Lewes

Table 186

Sundays

from 13 September

Bedford and London → Brighton

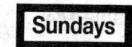

Network Diagram - see first page of Table 186

		GX	SN	SN	FC	GX	SN	SN	SN	GW	GW	GX	SN	SN	FC	GX	SN	GX	SN	SN		FC	GX	SN	SN
		1	1 ◇	1	1	1	1	1	1	1	1	1	1 ◇	1	1	1	1	1	1 ◇	1		1	1	1	1
														A											
London Victoria 15	⊖ d	16 30	16 32	16 34		16 45			16 47			17 00	17 02	17 04		17 15	17 17	17 30	17 32	17 34			17 45		
Milton Keynes Central 10	d																								
Watford Junction	d												16 22												
Shepherd's Bush	⊖ d												16 45												
Kensington (Olympia)	⊖ d												16 48												
West Brompton	⊖ d												16 50												
Clapham Junction 10	d		16 38	16 40					16 53				17 08	17 10			17 23		17 38	17 40					
Bedford 7	d																								
Luton 10	d																								
Luton Airport Parkway 7	✈ d																								
St Albans City	d																								
St Pancras International 15	⊖ d																								
Farringdon 3	⊖ d																								
City Thameslink 3	d																								
London Blackfriars 3	⊖ d																								
London Charing Cross 4	⊖ d																								
London Waterloo (East) 4	⊖ d																								
London Bridge 4	⊖ d		16 14		16 41								16 44		17 11				17 14			17 41			
Norwood Junction 2	d																								
East Croydon	a		16 50	16 53	16 56				17 07				17 21	17 24	17 27		17 37		17 50	17 53		17 56			
	d		16 51	16 54	16 57				17 08				17 22	17 24	17 28		17 38		17 51	17 54		17 57			
Purley 4	d			16 59										17 30						17 59					
Coulsdon South	d			17 03				←												18 03					←
Merstham	d			17 08				17 08												18 08					18 08
Redhill 5	a		17 03	→				17 12						17 38					18 03	→					18 12
	d		17 04				17 09	17 12		17 19	17 20			17 39					18 04					18 09	18 12
Reigate	a									17 23															
Nutfield	d						17 13																	18 13	
Godstone	d						17 19																	18 19	
Edenbridge	d						17 24																	18 24	
Penshurst	d						17 31																	18 31	
Leigh (Kent)	d						17 34																	18 34	
Tonbridge 4	a						17 39																	18 39	
Earlswood (Surrey)	d																								
Salfords	d																								
Horley 4	d							17 22						17 45											18 22
Gatwick Airport 10	✈ a	17 05	17 11		17 18	17 20		17 24	17 27		17 31	17 35	17 39	17 47	17 48	17 50	17 54	18 05	18 11			18 18	18 20		18 24
	d		17 12		17 20			17 25	17 29				17 40	17 48	17 50		17 56		18 12			18 20			18 25
Three Bridges 15	a		17 16		17 24			17 30						17 53	17 54				18 16			18 24			18 30
	d		17 17		17 24			17 33						17 53	17 54				18 17			18 24			18 33
Crawley	d							17 36						17 56											18 36
Ifield	d							17 39																	18 39
Faygate	d																								
Littlehaven	d							17 45																	18 45
Horsham 4	a							17 49						18 04											18 49
Balcombe	d		17 23																18 23						
Haywards Heath 3	a		17 28		17 33				17 40						18 03		18 06		18 28			18 33			
	d		17 28		17 33				17 41						18 03		18 07		18 28			18 33			
Wivelsfield 4	d		17 32						17 45										18 32						
Lewes 4	a								17 58																
Burgess Hill 4	d		17 34		17 38										18 08		18 12		18 34			18 38			
Hassocks 4	d		17 38		17 42														18 38			18 42			
Preston Park	d		17 45																18 45						
Hove 2	a																18 24								
Brighton 10	a		17 50		17 52								18 03		18 22				18 50			18 52			

For general notes see front of timetable
For details of catering facilities see Directory of Train Operators

A To Bognor Regis (Table 188)

Table 186

Sundays

from 13 September

Bedford and London → Brighton

Network Diagram - see first page of Table 186

		SN 1	GW 1	GW 1	GX 1	SN 1 ◇	SN 1	FC 1	GX 1	SN 1	GX 1	SN 1 ◇	SN 1	FC 1	GX 1	SN 1	SN 1	SN 1	GW 1	GW 1	GX 1	SN 1 ◇	SN 1	FC 1	GX 1
							A																A		
		⚲					⚲					⚲						⚲					⚲		
London Victoria 15	⊖ d	17 47			18 00	18 02	18 04		18 15	18 17	18 30	18 32	18 34		18 45			18 47			19 00	19 02	19 04		19 15
Milton Keynes Central 10	d																								
Watford Junction	d					*17 22*																*18 22*			
Shepherd's Bush	⊖ d					*17 45*																*18 45*			
Kensington (Olympia)	⊖ d					*17 48*																*18 48*			
West Brompton	⊖ d					*17 50*																*18 50*			
Clapham Junction 10	d	17 53				18 08	18 10			18 23		18 38	18 40					18 53				19 08	19 10		
Bedford 7	d																								
Luton 10	d																								
Luton Airport Parkway 7	✈ d																								
St Albans City	d																								
St Pancras International 15	⊖ d																								
Farringdon 3	⊖ d																								
City Thameslink 3	d																								
London Blackfriars 3	⊖ d																								
London Charing Cross 4	⊖ d																								
London Waterloo (East) 4	⊖ d																								
London Bridge 4	⊖ d					*17 44*		18 11				*18 14*		18 41								*18 44*		19 11	
Norwood Junction 2	d																								
East Croydon	a	18 07				18 21	18 24	18 27		18 36		18 50	18 53	18 56				19 07				19 21	19 24	19 27	
	d	18 08				18 22	18 24	18 28		18 37		18 51	18 54	18 57				19 08				19 22	19 24	19 28	
Purley 4	d						18 30						18 59										19 30		
Coulsdon South	d												19 03				←								
Merstham	d												19 08				19 08						19 38		
Redhill 5	a						18 38					19 03	→				19 12						19 39		
	d		18 19	18 20			18 39					19 04				19 09	19 12		19 19	19 20					
Reigate	a		18 23																19 23						
Nutfield	d															19 13									
Godstone	d															19 19									
Edenbridge	d															19 24									
Penshurst	d															19 31									
Leigh (Kent)	d															19 34									
Tonbridge 4	a															19 39									
Earlswood (Surrey)	d																								
Salfords	d																								
Horley 4	d						18 45										19 22						19 45		
Gatwick Airport 10	✈ a	18 27		18 31	18 35	18 39	18 47	18 48	18 50	18 54	19 05	19 11		19 18	19 20		19 24	19 27		19 31	19 35	19 39	19 47	19 48	19 50
	d	18 29				18 40	18 48	18 50		18 56		19 12		19 20			19 25	19 29				19 40	19 48	19 50	
Three Bridges 15	a						18 53	18 54				19 16		19 24			19 30						19 53	19 54	
	d						18 53	18 54				19 17		19 24			19 33						19 53	19 54	
Crawley	d						18 56										19 36						19 56		
Ifield	d																19 39								
Faygate	d																								
Littlehaven	d																19 45								
Horsham 4	a						19 04										19 49						20 04		
Balcombe	d											19 23													
Haywards Heath 3	a	18 40						19 03		19 06		19 28		19 33				19 40						20 03	
	d	18 41						19 03		19 07		19 28		19 33				19 41						20 03	
Wivelsfield 4	d	18 45										19 32						19 45							
Lewes 4	a	18 58																19 58							
Burgess Hill 4	d							19 08		19 12		19 34		19 38										20 08	
Hassocks 4	d											19 38		19 42											
Preston Park	d											19 45													
Hove 2	a									19 24															
Brighton 10	a					19 03		19 22				19 50		19 52								20 03		20 22	

For general notes see front of timetable
For details of catering facilities see
Directory of Train Operators

A To Bognor Regis (Table 188)

Table 186

Sundays

from 13 September

Bedford and London → Brighton

Network Diagram - see first page of Table 186

		SN 1	GX 1	SN 1 ◇		SN 1	FC 1	GX 1	SN 1	SN 1	SN 1	GW 1	GW 1	GX 1	SN 1 ◇	SN 1	FC 1	GX 1	SN 1	GX 1	SN 1 ◇	SN 1	FC 1	GX 1	SN 1
																A									
London Victoria 15	⊖ d	19 17	19 30	19 32		19 34		19 45			19 47			20 00	20 02	20 04		20 15	20 17	20 30	20 32	20 34		20 45	
Milton Keynes Central 10	d																								
Watford Junction	d														19 22										
Shepherd's Bush	⊖ d														19 45										
Kensington (Olympia)	⊖ d														19 48										
West Brompton	⊖ d														19 50										
Clapham Junction 10	d	19 23		19 38		19 40					19 53				20 08	20 10			20 23		20 38	20 40			
Bedford 7	d																								
Luton 10	d																								
Luton Airport Parkway 7	✈ d																								
St Albans City	d																								
St Pancras International 15	⊖ d																								
Farringdon 3	⊖ d																								
City Thameslink 3	d																								
London Blackfriars 3	⊖ d																								
London Charing Cross 4	⊖ d																								
London Waterloo (East) 4	⊖ d																								
London Bridge 4	⊖ d			19 14			19 41								19 44		20 11				20 14		20 41		
Norwood Junction 2	d																								
East Croydon	a	19 36		19 50		19 53	19 56				20 07				20 21	20 24	20 27		20 36		20 50	20 53	20 56		
	d	19 37		19 51		19 54	19 57				20 08				20 22	20 24	20 27		20 37		20 51	20 54	20 57		
Purley 4	d					19 59										20 30						20 59			
Coulsdon South	d					20 03																21 03			
Merstham	d					20 08 →				← 20 08												21 08 →			
Redhill 5	a			20 03						20 12						20 38					21 03				
	d			20 04					20 09	20 12		20 19	20 20			20 39					21 04				21 09
Reigate	a											20 23													
Nutfield	d								20 13																21 13
Godstone	d								20 19																21 19
Edenbridge	d								20 24																21 24
Penshurst	d								20 31																21 31
Leigh (Kent)	d								20 34																21 34
Tonbridge 4	a								20 39																21 39
Earlswood (Surrey)	d																								
Salfords	d																								
Horley 4	d									20 22						20 45									
Gatwick Airport 10	✈ a	19 54	20 05	20 11			20 18	20 20		20 24	20 27		20 31	20 35	20 39	20 47	20 48	20 50	20 54	21 05	21 11		21 18	21 20	
	d	19 56		20 12			20 20			20 25	20 29				20 40	20 48	20 50		20 56		21 12		21 20		
Three Bridges 15	a			20 16			20 24			20 30						20 53	20 54				21 16		21 24		
	d			20 17			20 24			20 33						20 53	20 54				21 17		21 24		
Crawley	d									20 36						20 56									
Ifield	d									20 39															
Faygate	d																								
Littlehaven	d									20 45															
Horsham 4	a									20 49						21 04									
Balcombe	d			20 23																	21 23				
Haywards Heath 3	a	20 06		20 28			20 33				20 40						21 03		21 06		21 28		21 33		
	d	20 07		20 28			20 33				20 41						21 03		21 07		21 28		21 33		
Wivelsfield 4	d			20 32							20 45										21 32				
Lewes 4	a										20 58														
Burgess Hill 4	d	20 12		20 34			20 38										21 08		21 12		21 34		21 38		
Hassocks 4	d			20 38			20 42														21 38		21 42		
Preston Park	d			20 45																	21 45				
Hove 2	a	20 24																	21 24						
Brighton 10	a			20 50			20 52								21 03		21 22				21 50		21 52		

For general notes see front of timetable
For details of catering facilities see
Directory of Train Operators

A To Bognor Regis (Table 188)

Sundays

from 13 September

Bedford and London → Brighton

Network Diagram - see first page of Table 186

		SN 1	SN 1	GW 1	GX 1	SN 1 ◇	GW 1	SN 1 A	FC 1	GX 1		SN 1	GX 1	SN 1 ◇	SN 1	FC 1	GX 1	SN 1	SN 1	SN 1	GW 1	GX 1	GW 1	SN 1 A	FC 1
London Victoria 15 ⊖	d		20 47		21 00	21 02		21 04		21 15		21 17	21 30	21 32	21 34		21 45			21 47		22 00		22 04	
Milton Keynes Central 10	d																								
Watford Junction	d					20 22																		21 17	
Shepherd's Bush ⊖	d					20 45																		21 45	
Kensington (Olympia) ⊖	d					20 48																		21 48	
West Brompton ⊖	d					20 50																		21 50	
Clapham Junction 10	d		20 53			21 08		21 10				21 23		21 38	21 40					21 53				22 10	
Bedford 7	d																								
Luton 10	d																								
Luton Airport Parkway 7 ✈	d																								
St Albans City	d																								
St Pancras International 15 ⊖	d																								
Farringdon 3 ⊖	d																								
City Thameslink 3	d																								
London Blackfriars 3 ⊖	d																								
London Charing Cross 4 ⊖	d																								
London Waterloo (East) 4 ⊖	d																								
London Bridge 4 ⊖	d					20 44			21 11					21 14		21 41								21 44	22 11
Norwood Junction 2	d																								
East Croydon	a		21 07			21 21		21 24	21 27			21 36		21 50	21 53	21 56				22 07				22 24	22 27
	d		21 08			21 22		21 24	21 28			21 37		21 51	21 54	21 57				22 08				22 24	22 27
Purley 4	d							21 30							21 59									22 30	
Coulsdon South	d	←													22 03				←						
Merstham	d	21 08													22 08 →				22 08						
Redhill 5	a	21 12						21 38						22 03					22 12					22 38	
	d	21 12		21 20			21 20	21 39						22 04				22 09	22 12		22 20		22 20	22 39	
Reigate	a						21 24																22 24		
Nutfield	d																	22 13							
Godstone	d																	22 19							
Edenbridge	d																	22 24							
Penshurst	d																	22 31							
Leigh (Kent)	d																	22 34							
Tonbridge 4	a																	22 39							
Earlswood (Surrey)	d																								
Salfords	d																								
Horley 4	d	21 22						21 45											22 22					22 45	
Gatwick Airport 10 ✈	a	21 24	21 27	21 31	21 35	21 39		21 47	21 48	21 50		21 54	22 05	22 11		22 18	22 20		22 24	22 27	22 31	22 35		22 47	22 48
	d	21 25	21 29			21 40		21 48	21 50			21 55		22 12		22 20			22 25	22 29				22 48	22 50
Three Bridges 15	a	21 30						21 53	21 54					22 16		22 24			22 30					22 53	22 54
	d	21 33						21 53	21 54					22 17		22 24			22 33					22 53	22 54
Crawley	d	21 36						21 56											22 36					22 56	
Ifield	d	21 39																	22 39						
Faygate	d																								
Littlehaven	d	21 45																	22 45						
Horsham 4	a	21 49						22 04											22 49					23 04	
Balcombe	d													22 23											
Haywards Heath 3	a		21 40						22 03			22 06		22 28		22 33				22 40					23 03
	d		21 41						22 03			22 06		22 28		22 33				22 41					23 03
Wivelsfield 4	d		21 45											22 32						22 45					
Lewes 4	a		21 58																	22 58					
Burgess Hill 4	d								22 08			22 12		22 34		22 38									23 08
Hassocks 4	d													22 38		22 42									
Preston Park	d													22 45											
Hove 2	a											22 24													
Brighton 10	a					22 03			22 22					22 50		22 52									23 22

For general notes see front of timetable
For details of catering facilities see
Directory of Train Operators

A To Bognor Regis (Table 188)

Table 186

Sundays

from 13 September

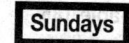

Bedford and London → Brighton

Network Diagram - see first page of Table 186

		GX 1	SN 1	GX 1	SN 1 ◇	SN 1	FC 1	GX 1	SN 1	SN 1	SN 1	GW 1	GX 1	SN 1	FC 1	GX 1	GW 1	SN 1	SN 1	GX 1	SN 1 ◇	FC 1	GX 1
London Victoria 15	⊖ d	22 15	22 17	22 30	22 32	22 34		22 45			22 47		23 00	23 04		23 15			23 17	23 30	23 32		23 45
Milton Keynes Central 10	d																						
Watford Junction	d																						
Shepherd's Bush	⊖ d													22 17									
Kensington (Olympia)	⊖ d													22 45									
West Brompton	⊖ d													22 48									
Clapham Junction 10	d		22 23		22 38	22 40					22 53			22 50 / 23 10					23 23		23 38		
Bedford 7	d																						
Luton 10	d																						
Luton Airport Parkway 7	✈ d																						
St Albans City	d																						
St Pancras International 15	⊖ d																						
Farringdon 3	⊖ d																						
City Thameslink 3	d																						
London Blackfriars 3	⊖ d																						
London Charing Cross 4	⊖ d																						
London Waterloo (East) 4	⊖ d																						
London Bridge 4	⊖ d				22 14		22 41							22 44	23 11						23 14	23 41	
Norwood Junction 2	d																						
East Croydon	🚋 a		22 36		22 50	22 53	22 56				23 07			23 23	23 26				23 37		23 52	23 56	
	d		22 37		22 51	22 54	22 57				23 08			23 23	23 27				23 38		23 53	23 57	
Purley 4	d					22 59								23 29									
Coulsdon South	d					23 03				←				23 33				←					
Merstham	d					23 08				23 08				23 38				23 38					
Redhill 5	a				23 03	→				23 12				→				23 42			00 05		
	d				23 04				23 09	23 12		23 20					23 20	23 42			00 05		
Reigate	a																23 24						
Nutfield	d								23 13														
Godstone	d								23 19														
Edenbridge	d								23 24														
Penshurst	d								23 31														
Leigh (Kent)	d								23 34														
Tonbridge 4	a								23 39														
Earlswood (Surrey)	d																						
Salfords	d																						
Horley 4	d									23 22								23 50					
Gatwick Airport 10	✈ a	22 50	22 54	23 05	23 11		23 18	23 20		23 24	23 27	23 31	23 35		23 48	23 50		23 54	23 59	00 07	00 14	00 17	00 20
	d		22 56		23 12		23 20			23 25	23 29				23 50			23 55	00 01		00 15	00 18	
Three Bridges 15	a				23 16		23 24			23 30					23 54			00 01	00 05		00 19	00 25	
	d				23 17		23 24			23 33					23 54			00 01	00 06		00 20		
Crawley	d									23 36								00 05					
Ifield	d									23 39								00 07					
Faygate	d																						
Littlehaven	d									23 45								00 14					
Horsham 4	a									23 49								00 17					
Balcombe	d				23 23																00 26		
Haywards Heath 3	a		23 06		23 28		23 33				23 40				00 03				00 14		00 31		
	d		23 07		23 28		23 33				23 41				00 03				00 15		00 31		
Wivelsfield 4	d				23 32						23 45										00 35		
Lewes 4	a										23 58												
Burgess Hill 4	d		23 12		23 34		23 38								00 08						00 37		
Hassocks 4	d				23 38		23 42														00 41		
Preston Park	d				23 45																00 48		
Hove 2	a		23 24																00 28				
Brighton 10	a				23 50		23 52								00 22						00 52		

For general notes see front of timetable
For details of catering facilities see Directory of Train Operators

Brighton → London, Bedford

Network Diagram - see first page of Table 186

Miles	Miles	Miles	Station		SN MX 1	SN MO 1	SN MX 1	SN MX 1 ◇	SN MO 1 ◇	FC MX 1	FC MX 1	FC MO 1	FC MX 1	FC MX 1	SN MO 1 ◇	SN MX 1 ◇	GX 1	FC MX 1	FC MO 1	GX 1	GW MO 1	GX 1	GW MX 1	GX 1	SN 1
0	—	—	**Brighton 10**	d				23p02	23p02	23p11	23p11	23p11						23p37	23p44						
—	0	—	Hove 2	d																					
1½	1½	—	Preston Park	d				23p06	23p06									23p41							
7¼	—	—	Hassocks 4	d				23p12	23p12	23p19	23p19	23p19						23p47	23p52						
9¾	—	—	Burgess Hill 4	d				23p16	23p16	23p23	23p23	23p23						23p51	23p56						
—	0	—	Lewes 4	d																					
10	9¼	—	Wivelsfield 4	d				23p19	23p19									23p53							
13	—	—	**Haywards Heath 3**	a				23p23	23p23	23p27	23p27	23p27						23p58	00 01						
—	—	—		d				23p24	23p24	23p28	23p28	23p28						23p59	00 01						
17	—	—	Balcombe	d					23p29									00 04							
—	0	—	**Horsham 4**	d	23p02	23p04																			
—	1	—	Littlehaven	d	23p05	23p07																			
—	3½	—	Faygate	d																					
—	5¾	—	Ifield	d	23p11	23p13																			
—	7	—	Crawley	d	23p14	23p17																			
21½	8½	—	Three Bridges 4	a	23p18	23p20		23p33	23p35	23p37	23p37	23p39			←	←		00 10	00 10						
—	—	—		d	23p18	23p22		23p47 →	23p42 →	23p38	23p38	23p39			23p42	23p47		00 10	00 10						
24¼	—	—	**Gatwick Airport 10** ✈	a	23p22	23p26				23p42	23p42	23p43	←	←	23p46	23p52		00 14	00 14						
—	—	—		d	23p23	23p27				23p43 →	23p43 →	23p44	23p43	23p43	23p47	23p53	00 05	00 15	00 15	00 20		00 35		00 50	01 05
25	—	—	Horley 4	d	23p26	23p30									23p49	23p56									01 07
27½	—	—	Salfords	d	23p29																				
29¼	—	—	Earlswood (Surrey)	d	23p33																				
—	—	0	**Tonbridge 4**	d																					
—	—	2½	Leigh (Kent)	d																					
—	—	4¼	Penshurst	d																					
—	—	9¼	Edenbridge	d																					
—	—	14	Godstone	d																					
—	—	17¾	Nutfield	d																					
—	0	—	**Reigate**	d																	00 26		00 45		
30	1¾	19¾	**Redhill 5**	a	23p36	23p36									23p57	00 02		00 22	00 22		00 30		00 49		
—	—	—		d	23p37	23p37									00 02	00 03		00 22	00 22						
32	—	—	Merstham	d	23p41	23p41																			
35½	—	—	Coulsdon South	d	23p46	23p46	←																		01 22
37½	—	—	Purley 4	d	23p49	23p50	23p49								00 11	00 11									01 27
40½	0	—	**East Croydon**	a	→	23p55	23p55					23p59	00 02	00 02	00 16	00 16		00 35	00 35						
—	—	—		d		23p56	23p58					00 01	00 04	00 04	00 17	00 17		00 36	00 36						01 28
—	1¾	—	Norwood Junction 2	a																					
—	10¼	—	**London Bridge 4** ⊖	a			00 19					00 14	00 19	00 19				00 52	00 52						
—	—	—	**London Waterloo (East) 4** ⊖	a																					
—	—	—	**London Charing Cross 4** ⊖	a																					
—	—	—	**London Blackfriars 3** ⊖	a																					
—	—	—	City Thameslink 3	a																					
—	—	—	Farringdon 3 ⊖	a																					
—	—	—	St Pancras International 15 ⊖	a																					
—	—	—	St Albans City	a																					
—	—	—	Luton Airport Parkway 4 ✈	a																					
—	—	—	Luton 7	a																					
—	—	—	**Bedford 10**	a																					
48¼	0	0	Clapham Junction 10	d		00 11	00 11					00b29			00 30	00 30			01b02						01 41
—	2½	2½	West Brompton ⊖	d																					
—	3¼	3¼	Kensington (Olympia) ⊖	d																					
—	—	4¾	Shepherd's Bush ⊖	d																					
—	18½	—	Watford Junction	a																					
—	50¾	—	Milton Keynes Central 10	a																					
51	—	—	**London Victoria 15** ⊖	a		00 18	00 18					00b37			00 37	00 37	00 40		01b09	00 55		01 10		01 25	01 49

For general notes see front of timetable
For details of catering facilities see
Directory of Train Operators

b Change at East Croydon

Brighton → London, Bedford

Network Diagram - see first page of Table 186

	GX 1	SN 1	FC 1	SN 1	FC 1	SN 1	FC	GX 1	SN 1	SN	FC 1	SN 1	GX 1	SN	SN 1	GW 1	GW 1		SN 1	SN 1	FC 1	GX 1	SN 1	SN 1
Brighton 10 d									03 50												05 09			05 23
Hove 2 d																								
Preston Park d																					05 13			
Hassocks 4 d																					05 19			
Burgess Hill 4 d																					05 23			05 33
Lewes 4 d																								
Wivelsfield 4 d																					05 26			
Haywards Heath 3 a									04 25												05 30			05 38
Haywards Heath d									04 25												05 30			05 38
Balcombe d																								05 44
Horsham 4 d																			05 17					
Littlehaven d																			05 20					
Faygate d																								
Ifield d																			05 26					
Crawley d																			05 29					
Three Bridges 4 a									04 45			←							05 33		05 40			05 49
Three Bridges d		01 59	02 25	02 55	03 25	03 55	04 25		04 54		04 55	04 54							05 33		05 40			05 50
Gatwick Airport 10 ✈ a		02 03	02 29	02 59	03 29	03 59	04 29		→		04 59	05 02							05 37		05 45			05 54
Gatwick Airport d	01 35	02 05	02 30	03 05	03 30	04 00	04 30	04 35			05 00	05 03	05 20				05 31		05 38		05 46	05 50		05 55
Horley 4 d		02 07		03 07		04 03						05 05							05 40					
Salfords d																								
Earlswood (Surrey) d																								
Tonbridge 4 d															05 00					05 20				
Leigh (Kent) d															05 04					05 24				
Penshurst d															05 08					05 28				
Edenbridge d															05 14					05 34				
Godstone d															05 21					05 41				
Nutfield d															05 26					05 46				
Reigate d																05 34								
Redhill 5 a															05 31	05 39	05 41		05 47	05 51				
Redhill d														05 28					05 48				←	
Merstham d																			05 52				05 52	
Coulsdon South d														05 36					→				05 57	
Purley 4 d		02 22		03 22		04 22				05 07		05 23		05 39									06 00	
East Croydon a		02 27	02 47	03 27	03 47	04 27	04 47			05 12	05 17	05 28		05 48							06 01		06 06	06 10
East Croydon d		02 28	02 47	03 28	03 47	04 28	04 47			05 13	05 17	05 29		05 48							06 02		06 07	06 11
Norwood Junction 2 a										05 17														
London Bridge 4 ⊖ a			03 12		04 12					05 41	05 34										06 15		*06 35*	
London Waterloo (East) 4 ⊖ a										05 46														
London Charing Cross 4 ⊖ a										05 49														
London Blackfriars 3 ⊖ a							05 14				05 43										06 24			
City Thameslink 3 a							05 16				05 46										06 26			
Farringdon 3 ⊖ a							05 20				05 50										06 30			
St Pancras International 15 ⊖ a							05 23				05 53										06 33			
St Albans City a							05 57				06 27										06 55			
Luton Airport Parkway 4 ✈ a							06 09				06 39										07 07			
Luton 7 a							06 12				06 42										07 10			
Bedford 10 a							06 38				07 08										07 36			
Clapham Junction 10 d		02 41		03 41		04 47						05 49		06 09									06 18	06 21
West Brompton ⊖ d						*05 40*																		
Kensington (Olympia) ⊖ d						*05 43*																		
Shepherd's Bush ⊖ d						*05 46*																		
Watford Junction a						*06 14*																		
Milton Keynes Central 10 a						*06 55*																		
London Victoria 15 ⊖ a	02 20	02 49		03 49		04 54		05 12				05 58	05 55	06 18								06 20	06 25	06 28

For general notes see front of timetable
For details of catering facilities see
Directory of Train Operators

Brighton → London, Bedford

Network Diagram - see first page of Table 186

		GW 1	SN 1	SN 1	GX 1	FC 1	GX 1	FC 1	SN 1	GW 1	GX 1	FC 1	SN 1	SN 1	SN 1	SN 1	FC 1	GX 1	SN 1	SN 1	SN 1	SN 1	SN 1	GW 1	FC 1
																A						B			
Brighton [10]	d					05 39		05 49							06 01		06 09						06 17		06 23
Hove [2]	d								05 57																
Preston Park	d					05 43		05 53									06 13								06 27
Hassocks [4]	d					05 49		05 59							06 09		06 19						06 25		06 33
Burgess Hill [4]	d					05 53		06 03							06 12		06 23						06 29		06 37
Lewes [4]	d		05 29													06 05									
Wivelsfield [4]	d					05 56		06 05							06 15										06 39
Haywards Heath [3]	a		05 46			06 00		06 09	06 12						06 19	06 22	06 29						06 34		06 44
	d		05 47			06 00		06 09	06 12							06 27	06 30						06 35		06 44
Balcombe	d					06 05											06 35								06 50
Horsham [4]	d			05 38										06 15								06 24			
Littlehaven	d			05 41										06 18								06 27			
Faygate	d																								
Ifield	d			05 47										06 24								06 33			
Crawley	d			05 50										06 28								06 37			
Three Bridges [4]	a			05 54		06 12		06 19	06 21					06 31		06 36	06 40					06 40	06 44		06 55
	d			05 54		06 12		06 20	06 21					06 32		06 37	06 40						06 48		06 55
Gatwick Airport [10] ✈	a		05 58	05 58		06 16		06 24	06 25					06 36		06 41	06 45						06 52		07 00
	d	05 56	05 59	06 00	06 05	06 16	06 20	06 24	06 26		06 35			06 37		06 42	06 46	06 50					06 53	07 00	07 00
Horley [4]	d			06 02										06 40									06 56		
Salfords	d			06 06										06 44											
Earlswood (Surrey)	d			06 10										06 48											
Tonbridge [4]	d												06 14												
Leigh (Kent)	d												06 18												
Penshurst	d												06 22												
Edenbridge	d												06 28												
Godstone	d												06 35												
Nutfield	d												06 40												
Reigate	d									06 34									06 51						
Redhill [5]	a	06 07		06 13				06 32		06 38		⟵	06 45	06 51					06 55		⟵		07 02	07 07	07 10
	d			06 13				06 33 ⟶				06 33	06 46	06 52 ⟶							06 52		07 03		07 11
Merstham	d			06 17																	06 56				
Coulsdon South	d			06 22									06 53							⟵	07 01				
Purley [4]	d			06 26									06 57 ⟶							06 57	07 05				
East Croydon	a		06 14	06 30		06 32			06 41			06 43				06 58	07 01			07 02	07 09		07 15		07 23
	d		06 15	06 31		06 32			06 42			06 44				06 59	07 02			07 02	07 10		07 15		07 24
Norwood Junction [2]	a																								
London Bridge [4]	⊖ a		*06 40*			06 46						06 58				07 14	07 16			07 21			*07 38*		
London Waterloo (East) [4]	⊖ a																								
London Charing Cross [4]	⊖ a																								
London Blackfriars [3]	⊖ a					06 53						07 06					07 23								07 53
City Thameslink [3]	a					06 56						07 08					07 25								07 56
Farringdon [3]	⊖ a					07 00						07 11					07 28								08 00
St Pancras International [15]	⊖ a					07 03						07 15					07 32								08 03
St Albans City	a					07 25						07 39					07 53								08 24
Luton Airport Parkway [4] ✈	a					07 37						07 51					08 05								08 37
Luton [7]	a					07 40						07 54					08 08								08 40
Bedford [10]	a					08 06						08 20					08 34								09 06
Clapham Junction [10]	d		06 25	06 41					06 51			07b07									07 20		07 25		07b39
West Brompton	⊖ d		*06 45*																				*07 46*		
Kensington (Olympia)	⊖ d		*06 48*																				*07 50*		
Shepherd's Bush	⊖ d		*06 51*																				*07 53*		
Watford Junction	a		*07 19*																				*08 20*		
Milton Keynes Central [10]	a		*08 03*																				*09 01*		
London Victoria [15]	⊖ a		06 32	06 48	06 35		06 50		07 00		07 05	07b17						07 20			07 28		07 33		07b48

For general notes see front of timetable
For details of catering facilities see Directory of Train Operators

A From Hastings (Table 189)
B From Havant (Table 188)
b Change at East Croydon

Brighton → London, Bedford

Network Diagram - see first page of Table 186

Station		SN 1	GX 1	SN 1	SN 1	SN 1	SN 1 A	GW 1	SN 1	SN 1	SN 1 B	GX 1	SN 1	SN 1	SN 1	SN 1	SN 1	SN 1 C	GW 1	SN 1	GX 1	FC 1	SN 1 A	SN 1	SN 1
Brighton 10	d		06 30						06 37			06 40				06 51					06 56	07 00			
Hove 2	d						06 31																07 11		
Preston Park	d						06 35					06 44									07 00	07 04			
Hassocks 4	d						06 42					06 52										07 10	07 21		
Burgess Hill 4	d		06 41				06 46					06 56				07 01					07 10	07 14			
Lewes 4	d																	06 50							
Wivelsfield 4	d		06 45				06 49											07 07			07 14	07 18			
Haywards Heath 3	a		06 51				06 54		06 56			07 01				07 06		07 13			07 18	07 23	07 29		
	d		06 52				07 00					07 02				07 06		07 13			07 20	07 23	07 30		
Balcombe	d																	07 19							
Horsham 4	d	06 39									06 54						07 04			07 09					07 19
Littlehaven	d	06 42									06 58									07 12					07 22
Faygate	d	06 46																		07 16					
Ifield	d	06 50									07 04									07 20					07 28
Crawley	d	06 53									07 08						07 13			07 23					07 32
Three Bridges 4	a	06 56									07 11					07 16	07 18	07 24		07 27		07 32			07 35
	d	06 57				07 02					07 12				07 14	07 22		07 25		07 28		07 32			07 36
Gatwick Airport 10 ✈	a	07 02	07 03			07 06	07 11					07 14			07 21			07 29		07 32	07 32	07 37			07 40
	d	07 03	07 05			07 07	07 12					07 20			07 22			07 30		07 33	07 35	07 37			07 41
Horley 4	d	07 05				07 10					07 20				07 25					07 36					07 43
Salfords	d	07 09		←		07 14									07 29					07 40					07 47
Earlswood (Surrey)	d	07 13		07 13		07 17									07 32					→					07 51
Tonbridge 4	d	→			06 47																				→
Leigh (Kent)	d				06 51																				
Penshurst	d				06 55																				
Edenbridge	d				07 01																				
Godstone	d				07 08																				
Nutfield	d				07 13																				
Reigate	d							07 18						07 27					07 34						
Redhill 5	a			07 16	07 18	07 20		07 24			07 27		←	07 31	07 36				07 38						
	d			07 16		07 21					07 27		07 21	07 40										←	
Merstham	d			07 20		→							07 25	07a44										07 44	
Coulsdon South	d			07 25						←			07 30	→										07 50	
Purley 4	d			→						07 25			07 34											07 55	
East Croydon	a						07 27			07 31	07 39		07 39			07 42		07 47				07 53	07 57	08 00	
	d						07 29			07 32	07 39		07 40			07 44		07 47				07 54	07 57	08 00	
Norwood Junction 2	a																								
London Bridge 4 ⊖	a						07 46			07 48								08 04						08 18	
London Waterloo (East) 4 ⊖	a																								
London Charing Cross 4 ⊖	a																								
London Blackfriars 3 ⊖	a																					08 22			
City Thameslink 3	a																					08 24			
Farringdon 3 ⊖	a																					08 28			
St Pancras International 15 ⊖	a																					08 31			
St Albans City	a																					08 51			
Luton Airport Parkway 4 ✈	a																					09 00			
Luton 7	a																					09 04			
Bedford 10	a																					09 26			
Clapham Junction 10	d										07 49		07 52			07 55		08b02					08 07		
West Brompton ⊖	d															08 15									
Kensington (Olympia) ⊖	d															08 18									
Shepherd's Bush ⊖	d															08 21									
Watford Junction	a																								
Milton Keynes Central 10	a																								
London Victoria 15 ⊖	a		07 35								07 57	07 50	08 00			08 03		08b12			08 06		08 16		

For general notes see front of timetable
For details of catering facilities see Directory of Train Operators

A From Littlehampton (Table 188)
B From Bognor Regis (Table 188)
C From Eastbourne (Table 189)

b Change at East Croydon

Brighton → London, Bedford

Network Diagram - see first page of Table 186

Station		SN 1 A ⊼	SN 1	SN 1	SN 1	SN 1	SN 1	SN 1	GX 1 ⊼	SN 1 B	GW 1	SN 1	SN 1 C ⊼	FC 1	GX 1 ⊼	SN 1	SN 1 D	SN 1	SN 1	SN 1	SN 1 ⊼	SN 1 D	FC 1	SN 1	SN 1
Brighton 10	d								07 15					07 24	07 30						07 33				
Hove 2	d									07 20														07 41	
Preston Park	d								07 19					07 28							07 37				
Hassocks 4	d									07 30				07 35	07 39						07 46			07 52	
Burgess Hill 4	d								07 29					07 39											
Lewes 4	d												07 23												07 43
Wivelsfield 4	d									07 35			07 39		07 45						07 49			07 57	08 02
Haywards Heath 3	a								07 34	07 40			07 43	07 45	07 49						07 53			07 59	08 03
	d								07 35	07 40			07 44	07 46	07 51						07 54				
Balcombe	d																				07 59				
Horsham 4	d	07 25														07 40	07 46								
Littlehaven	d	07 29														07 43	07 49								
Faygate	d																								
Ifield	d															07 50	07 56								
Crawley	d	07 37														07 53	08 00								
Three Bridges 4	a	07 40												07 55		07 57	08 05				08 05	←			
	d	07 41												07 55		07 58	08 06				08 05	08 06			
Gatwick Airport 10 ✈	a								07 47					08 00	08 02	08 04	→						←	08 12	
	d							07 45	07 50		07 58			08 01	08 05	08 05							08 01	08 13	
Horley 4	d			←				07 48					07 58	→		08 07									
Salfords	d			07 40	←			07 52								08 11									
Earlswood (Surrey)	d			07 43	07 51			07 55								08 15									
Tonbridge 4	d						07 25									→									
Leigh (Kent)	d						07 29																		
Penshurst	d						07 33																		
Edenbridge	d						07 39																		
Godstone	d						07 46																		
Nutfield	d						07 51																		
Reigate	d		07 40			07 51												08 08							
Redhill 5	a		07 45	07 47	07 54	07 55	07 56	07 58			08 05							08 12					08 12		
	d		07 51		07 54		08 02	08 02															08 14		
Merstham	d				07 59		08 06	08 06				←													
Coulsdon South	d				08 04		08 11	08 11				08 04							←	←					
Purley 4	d				→		08 15	08 15											08 15	08 15					
East Croydon	a	08 00	08 02				→	→		08 08		08 11	08 14						08 20	08 20	08 23	08 26	08 27	08 29	08 31
	d	08 01	08 03							08 09		08 11	08 14						08 21	08 21	08 24	08 27	08 28	08 30	08 33
Norwood Junction 2	a																								
London Bridge 4	⊖ a	*08 24*	08 20							08 26		*08 35*							08 41	08 41	08 43	08 45		*08 57*	08 50
London Waterloo (East) 4	⊖ a																								
London Charing Cross 4	⊖ a																								
London Blackfriars 3	⊖ a																						08 54		
City Thameslink 3	a																						08 56		
Farringdon 3	⊖ a																						09 00		
St Pancras International 15	⊖ a																						09 03		
St Albans City	a																						09 25		
Luton Airport Parkway 4	✈ a																						09 37		
Luton 7	a																						09 40		
Bedford 10	a																						10 08		
Clapham Junction 10	d	08 11										08 21	08 24							08b37				08 41	
West Brompton	⊖ d												*08 46*											*08 55*	
Kensington (Olympia)	⊖ d												*08 50*											*08 58*	
Shepherd's Bush	⊖ d												*08 53*											*09 01*	
Watford Junction	a												*09 20*												
Milton Keynes Central 10	a												*10 01*												
London Victoria 15	⊖ a	08 19							08 20			08 29	08 32		08 35					08b46				08 49	

For general notes see front of timetable
For details of catering facilities see Directory of Train Operators

A From Bognor Regis (Table 188)
B From Littlehampton (Table 188)
C From Seaford (Table 189) and from Hastings (Table 189).
⊼ from Lewes
D From Bognor Regis (Table 188) and from Southampton Central (Table 188)
b Change at East Croydon

Brighton → London, Bedford

Network Diagram - see first page of Table 186

		SN	GX	GX		SN	FC	SN	SN	SN	GW	GX	SN	SN	GW	SN	SN	FC	SN	SN	SN	GX	FC	SN	SN
				🛒				🛒	A 🛒												B				A 🛒
Brighton 10	d			07 44			07 50											08 02					08 16		
Hove 2	d																				08 11				
Preston Park	d			07 48			07 54											08 06			08 15		08 20		
Hassocks 4	d			07 56			08 00											08 12			08 22		08 26		
Burgess Hill 4	d			08 00														08 16			08 26		08 30		
Lewes 4	d								07 54																08 23
Wivelsfield 4	d								08 10									08 18					08 33		08 39
Haywards Heath 3	a			08 05			08 08		08 14									08 23			08 31		08 37		08 44
	d			08 06			08 09		08 15									08 23			08 31		08 38		08 44
Balcombe	d						08 14		08 21																
Horsham 4	d	07 51						08 09									08 12								
Littlehaven	d	07 54															08 15								
Faygate	d	07 58															08 19								
Ifield	d	08 02															08 23								
Crawley	d	08 06						08 18									08 26								
Three Bridges 4	a	08 09						08 22	08 27								08 29	08 33			08 41		08 47		
	d	08 10						08 22	08 28								08 30	08 34			08 42		08 47		
Gatwick Airport 10 ✈	a	08 14		08 17			08 22										08 34	08 38					08 51		08 55
	d	08 15	08 17	08 20			08 22					08 35					08 35	08 38				08 50	08 52		08 56
Horley 4	d	08 17						08 28									08 38								08 59
Salfords	d	08 21				←				←							08 42								
Earlswood (Surrey)	d	08 25				08 15				08 25							08 45								
Tonbridge 4	d	→											07 59			08 16									
Leigh (Kent)	d												08 03			08 20									
Penshurst	d												08 07			08 24									
Edenbridge	d												08 13			08 30									
Godstone	d												08 20			08 37									
Nutfield	d												08 25			08 42									
Reigate	d										08 24			08 27	08 42										
Redhill 5	a					08 18				08 28	08 30		08 30	08 32	08 46	08 47	08 49								
	d					08 18				08 28			08 36	08 36			08 53							←	
Merstham	d					08 22							08 40	08 40			08a57							08 57	
Coulsdon South	d					08 27				08 36			08 46	08 46			→		←	←				09 02	
Purley 4	d					08 31							08 50	08 50					08 50	08 50				09 05	
East Croydon	a					08 36	08 38	08 43	08 46	08 47			→	→				08 54	08 55	08 55	09 01		09 08	09 10	09 14
	d					08 37	08 38	08 44	08 47	08 48								08 54	08 56	08 56	09 01		09 08	09 11	09 14
Norwood Junction 2	a																								
London Bridge 4	⊖ a						09 05			09 08								09 10	09 15	09 15					09 42
London Waterloo (East) 4	⊖ a																								
London Charing Cross 4	⊖ a																								
London Blackfriars 3	⊖ a						09 08											09 20					09 38		
City Thameslink 3	a						09 10											09 22					09 40		
Farringdon 3	⊖ a						09 14											09 28					09 44		
St Pancras International 15	⊖ a						09 17											09 31					09 47		
St Albans City	a						09 40											09 51					10 10		
Luton Airport Parkway 4 ✈	a						09 52											10 00					10 21		
Luton 7	a						09 56											10 04					10 24		
Bedford 10	a						10 22											10 26					10 50		
Clapham Junction 10	d					08 48		08 53	08 57	09b04											09 11			09 21	09 24
West Brompton	⊖ d																				09 31				
Kensington (Olympia)	⊖ d																				09 34				
Shepherd's Bush	⊖ d																				09 37				
Watford Junction	a																								
Milton Keynes Central 10	a																								
London Victoria 15	⊖ a		08 50	08 52		08 57		09 02	09 05	09b14		09 05									09 19	09 20		09 29	09 32

For general notes see front of timetable
For details of catering facilities see Directory of Train Operators

A From Hastings (Table 189). 🛒 from Lewes

B From Littlehampton (Table 188)

b Change at East Croydon

Brighton → London, Bedford

Network Diagram - see first page of Table 186

		SN	GX	SN	FC	SN	SN	GW	SN	SN	SN	FC	SN	GX	SN	SN	SN	FC	GW		GX	SN	SN	GW	SN
		1	1	1	1	1	1	1	1	1	1	1	1	1	1	1	1	1	1		1	1 ◇	1	1	1
																A	B								
				trolley					trolley							trolley						trolley			trolley
Brighton 10	d				08 36				08 45									09 00				09 19			
Hove 2	d																08 52								
Preston Park	d				08 40												08 57								
Hassocks 4	d				08 46												09 04	09 08							
Burgess Hill 4	d				08 50												09 08	09 12							
Lewes 4	d															08 47									
Wivelsfield 4	d															08 59									
Haywards Heath 3	a				08 55				08 57			←				09 04	09 12	09 16							
	d				09 00 →				08 58			09 00				09 06	09 14	09 16							
Balcombe	d											09 06													
Horsham 4	d	08 35		08 49											09 00										09 20
Littlehaven	d	08 38													09 03										
Faygate	d																								
Ifield	d	08 44													09 09										
Crawley	d	08 47		08 58											09 13										09 29
Three Bridges 4	a	08 51		09 01								09 11			09 16	09 17		09 26							09 32
	d	08 51		09 02								09 12			09 18	09 18		09 27							09 33
Gatwick Airport 10 ✈	a	08 55		09 06					09 10			09 16			09 22	09 22	09 26	09 31							09 37
	d	08 56	09 05	09 07				09 07	09 11			09 16		09 20	09 23	09 23	09 27	09 31			09 35				09 38
Horley 4	d	08 59													09 26										09 40
Salfords	d	09 03					←								09 30								←		
Earlswood (Surrey)	d	09 06					09 06								09 33								09 33		
Tonbridge 4	d	→				08 37									→										
Leigh (Kent)	d					08 41																			
Penshurst	d					08 45																			
Edenbridge	d					08 51																			
Godstone	d					08 58																			
Nutfield	d					09 03																			
Reigate	d												09 14						09 24					09 37	
Redhill 5	a					09 08	09 10	09 15					09 18						09 30				09 36	09 42	09 47
	d					09 14	09 14						09 19										09 37		09 47
Merstham	d					09 18	09 18			←	←		09 23										09 41		
Coulsdon South	d					09 23	09 23			09 23	09 23		09 28										09 46		
Purley 4	d					→	→						09 32										09 49		
East Croydon	a			09 22					09 26	09 29	09 29	09 32	09 37			09 39	09 42	09 47				09 54	09 54		09 59
	d			09 22					09 26	09 29	09 29	09 32	09 37			09 39	09 43	09 47				09 55	09 55		10 00
Norwood Junction 2	a												09 41										09 59		
London Bridge 4	⊖ a											09 45	09 56					10 01					10 12		
London Waterloo (East) 4	⊖ a																								
London Charing Cross 4	⊖ a																								
London Blackfriars 3	⊖ a											09 54						10 07							
City Thameslink 3	a											09 56						10 10							
Farringdon 3	⊖ a											10 00						10 14							
St Pancras International 15	⊖ a											10 03						10 17							
St Albans City	a											10 24						10 39							
Luton Airport Parkway 4 ✈	a											10 37						10 51							
Luton 7	a											10 40						10 54							
Bedford 10	a											11 06						11 20							
Clapham Junction 10	d			09 33					09 36	09 39	09 39					09 49	09 53					10 04			10 09
West Brompton	⊖ d			*09 46*																					
Kensington (Olympia)	⊖ d			*09 50*																					
Shepherd's Bush	⊖ d			*09 53*																					
Watford Junction	a			*10 20*																					
Milton Keynes Central 10	a			*11 01*																					
London Victoria 15	⊖ a		09 35	09 41					09 44	09 48	09 48			09 50		09 58	10 00				10 05	10 11			10 16

For general notes see front of timetable
For details of catering facilities see
Directory of Train Operators

A From Seaford (Table 189) and from Hastings (Table 189).
trolley from Lewes

B From Littlehampton (Table 188)

Brighton → London, Bedford

Network Diagram - see first page of Table 186

		FC [1]	SN [1]	GX [1]	SN [1]	SN [1]	SN [1]	FC [1]	GW [1]	GX [1]	SN [1] ◇	SN [1]	SN [1]	FC [1]	SN [1]	GW [1]	GX [1]	SN [1]	SN [1]	SN [1]	SN [1] ◇	FC [1]	GW [1]	GX [1]	SN [1] ◇
						⊤					⊤								A ⊤	⊤					
Brighton [10]	d	09 07						09 34			09 49			09 37							09 55	10 04			
Hove [2]	d						09 22												09 51						
Preston Park	d	09 11												09 41							09 58				
Hassocks [4]	d	09 17												09 47							10 05				
Burgess Hill [4]	d	09 21					09 33							09 51					10 02		10 08				
Lewes [4]	d					09 17														09 49					
Wivelsfield [4]	d	09 23				09 33								09 53							10 11				
Haywards Heath [3]	a	09 28				09 37	09 39	09 47						09 58					10 06	10 09	10 15	10 18			
	d	09 32				09 43		09 48						09 58					10 13		10 16	10 18			
Balcombe	d	09 37																							
Horsham [4]	d				09 30								09 52					10 00							
Littlehaven	d				09 33													10 03							
Faygate	d				09 37																				
Ifield	d				09 41													10 09							
Crawley	d				09 44								10 01					10 13							
Three Bridges [4]	a	09 42			09 48								10 04	10 07				10 16			10 25				←
	d	09 42			09 48								10 05	10 10				10 18			10 31				10 31
Gatwick Airport [10] ✈	a	09 46			09 53	09 54		10 00					10 09	10 15				10 22	10 24		→	10 30			10 35
	d	09 46		09 50	09 54	09 55		10 01	10 03	10 05			10 10	10 16			10 20	10 23	10 25			10 31		10 35	10 38
Horley [4]	d				09 56													10 26							
Salfords	d																	10 30							
Earlswood (Surrey)	d																	10 33							
Tonbridge [4]	d		09 19																						
Leigh (Kent)	d		09 23																						
Penshurst	d		09 27																						
Edenbridge	d		09 33																						
Godstone	d		09 40																						
Nutfield	d		09 45																						
Reigate	d														10 14	10 19							10 34		
Redhill [5]	a		09 50		10 03				10 10				10 17		10 18	10 25		10 36					10 38		
	d		09 51		10 07							←	10 18		10 21			10 37 →							
Merstham	d				10 11 →							10 11													
Coulsdon South	d		09 58									10 16			10 28										
Purley [4]	d		10 02									10 19			10 32										
East Croydon	a	10 02	10 07			10 10		10 16			10 24	10 24	10 29	10 32	10 37				10 40			10 46			10 53
	d	10 02	10 08			10 11		10 17			10 24	10 25	10 29	10 32	10 37				10 41			10 47			10 53
Norwood Junction [2]	a											10 29													
London Bridge [4] ⊖	a	10 16	10 22					10 30				10 42		10 45	10 52							11 00			
London Waterloo (East) [4] ⊖	a		10 27												10 56										
London Charing Cross [4] ⊖	a		10 30												11 00										
London Blackfriars [3] ⊖	a	10 24						10 37						10 54								11 07			
City Thameslink [3]	a	10 26						10 40						10 56								11 10			
Farringdon [3] ⊖	a	10 30						10 44						11 00								11 14			
St Pancras International [15] ⊖	a	10 33						10 47						11 03								11 17			
St Albans City	a	10 54						11 10						11 24								11 39			
Luton Airport Parkway [4] ✈	a	11 06						11 21						11 37								11 51			
Luton [7]	a	11 09						11 24						11 40								11 54			
Bedford [10]	a	11 36						11 50						12 06								12 20			
Clapham Junction [10]	d		10b25			10 20					10 34		10 39		10b55				10 50						11 03
West Brompton ⊖	d										10 47														
Kensington (Olympia) ⊖	d										10 50														
Shepherd's Bush ⊖	d										10 53														
Watford Junction	a										11 19														
Milton Keynes Central [10]	a										12 01														
London Victoria [15] ⊖	a		10b32	10 20		10 27				10 35	10 40		10 45		11b05		10 50		10 57					11 05	11 09

For general notes see front of timetable
For details of catering facilities see Directory of Train Operators

A ⊤ from Haywards Heath
b Change at East Croydon

Brighton → London, Bedford

Network Diagram - see first page of Table 186

	SN 1	SN 1 ◇	SN 1	FC 1	SN 1	GX 1	SN 1	SN 1	SN 1	FC 1	GW 1		GX 1	SN 1 ◇	SN 1	SN 1	FC 1	SN 1	GW 1	GX 1	SN 1	SN 1	SN 1	SN 1 ◇
		✕						A ✕	✕					✕		✕						✕		
Brighton 10 d		10 19		10 07						10 34				10 49			10 37							10 55
Hove 2 d								10 21															10 51	
Preston Park d				10 11													10 41							10 58
Hassocks 4 d				10 17													10 47							11 05
Burgess Hill 4 d				10 21													10 51						11 02	11 08
Lewes 4 d									10 20													10 49		
Wivelsfield 4 d				10 23					10 35								10 53							11 11
Haywards Heath 3 a				10 28				10 35	10 40	10 47							10 58					11 05	11 08	11 15
d				10 32					10 43	10 48							11 02					11 13		11 16
Balcombe d				10 37																				
Horsham 4 d			10 20				10 30									10 50					11 00			
Littlehaven d							10 33														11 03			
Faygate d																								
Ifield d							10 39														11 09			
Crawley d			10 29				10 43									10 59					11 13			
Three Bridges 4 a			10 32	10 42			10 46									11 02	11 11				11 16			11 25
d			10 33	10 42			10 48									11 03	11 12				11 18			11 31 →
Gatwick Airport 10 ✈ a			10 37	10 46			10 52		10 54	11 00						11 07	11 16				11 22	11 24		
d			10 38	10 46		10 50	10 53		10 55	11 01	11 03		11 05			11 08	11 16			11 20	11 23	11 25		
Horley 4 d			10 41				10 56														11 26			
Salfords d																					11 30			
Earlswood (Surrey) d																					11 33			
Tonbridge 4 d					10 19																			
Leigh (Kent) d					10 23																			
Penshurst d					10 27																			
Edenbridge d					10 33																			
Godstone d					10 40																			
Nutfield d					10 45																			
Reigate d																		11 14	11 19					
Redhill 5 a	←		10 47		10 50		11 02				11 10				←	11 15		11 18	11 25		11 36			
d	10 37		10 48		10 51		11 07									11 16		11 21			11 37 →			
Merstham d	10 41						11 11 →								11 11									
Coulsdon South d	10 46				10 58										11 16			11 28						
Purley 4 d	10 49				11 01										11 19			11 31						
East Croydon 🚋 a	10 54	10 56	10 59	11 02	11 06				11 10	11 16				11 23	11 24	11 27	11 32	11 36					11 40	
d	10 55	10 56	11 00	11 02	11 07				11 11	11 17				11 24	11 25	11 28	11 32	11 37					11 41	
Norwood Junction 2 a	10 59														11 29									
London Bridge 4 ⊖ a	11 12			11 15	11 22					11 30					11 42		11 45	11 52						
London Waterloo (East) 4 ⊖ a					11 26													11 56						
London Charing Cross 4 ⊖ a					11 30													12 00						
London Blackfriars 3 ⊖ a				11 23						11 37							11 53							
City Thameslink 3 a				11 26						11 40							11 56							
Farringdon 3 ⊖ a				11 30						11 44							12 00							
St Pancras International 15 ⊖ a				11 33						11 47							12 03							
St Albans City a				11 54						12 09							12 24							
Luton Airport Parkway 4 ✈ a				12 07						12 21							12 37							
Luton 7 a				12 10						12 24							12 40							
Bedford 10 a				12 36						12 50							13 06							
Clapham Junction 10 d		11 06	11 10						11 20					11 33		11 37							11 50	
West Brompton ⊖ d														*11 46*										
Kensington (Olympia) ⊖ d														*11 50*										
Shepherd's Bush ⊖ d														*11 53*										
Watford Junction a														*12 19*										
Milton Keynes Central 10 a														*13 01*										
London Victoria 15 ⊖ a		11 12	11 16			11 20			11 27				11 35	11 40		11 44				11 50			11 57	

For general notes see front of timetable
For details of catering facilities see
Directory of Train Operators

A ✕ from Haywards Heath

Brighton → London, Bedford

Network Diagram - see first page of Table 186

		FC 1	GW 1	GX 1	SN 1 ◇	SN 1	SN 1 ◇	SN 1	FC 1	SN 1	GX 1	SN 1	SN 1	SN 1	FC 1	GW 1	GX 1	SN 1 ◇	SN 1	SN 1	FC 1	SN 1	GW 1	GX 1	SN 1
							🛒						A 🛒	🛒				🛒		🛒					
Brighton 10	d	11 04					11 19		11 07						11 34			11 49			11 37				
Hove 2	d												11 21												
Preston Park	d								11 11												11 41				
Hassocks 4	d								11 17												11 47				
Burgess Hill 4	d								11 21												11 51				
Lewes 4	d													11 20											
Wivelsfield 4	d								11 23					11 34							11 53				
Haywards Heath 3	a	11 18							11 28				11 35	11 40	11 47						11 58				
	d	11 18							11 32				11 43		11 48						12 02				
Balcombe	d								11 37																
Horsham 4	d							11 20				11 30								11 50					12 00
Littlehaven	d											11 33													12 03
Faygate	d																								
Ifield	d											11 39													12 09
Crawley	d							11 29				11 43								11 59					12 13
Three Bridges 4	a							11 32	11 42			11 46								12 02	12 11				12 16
	d				← 11 31			11 33	11 42			11 48								12 03	12 12				12 18
Gatwick Airport 10 ✈	a	11 30			11 35			11 37	11 46			11 52	11 54		12 00					12 07	12 16				12 22
	d	11 31		11 35	11 38			11 38	11 46		11 50	11 53	11 55		12 01	12 03	12 05			12 08	12 16			12 20	12 23
Horley 4	d							11 41				11 56													12 26
Salfords	d																								12 30
Earlswood (Surrey)	d																								12 33
Tonbridge 4	d									11 19															
Leigh (Kent)	d									11 23															
Penshurst	d									11 27															
Edenbridge	d									11 33															
Godstone	d									11 40															
Nutfield	d									11 45															
Reigate	d		11 34																			12 14	12 19		
Redhill 5	a		11 38			←		11 47		11 50		12 02				12 10				12 15		12 18	12 25		12 36
	d					11 37		11 48		11 51		12 07							←	12 16		12 21			12 37 →
Merstham	d					11 41						12 11 →							12 11						
Coulsdon South	d					11 46				11 58									12 16			12 28			
Purley 4	d					11 49				12 02									12 19			12 32			
East Croydon	a	11 46			11 53	11 54	11 56	11 59	12 02	12 07			12 10		12 16			12 23	12 24	12 27	12 32	12 37			
	d	11 47			11 53	11 55	11 56	12 00	12 02	12 07			12 11		12 17			12 24	12 25	12 28	12 32	12 37			
Norwood Junction 2	a					11 59													12 29						
London Bridge 4	⊖ a	12 00				12 12			12 15	12 22					12 30				12 42		12 45	12 52			
London Waterloo (East) 4	⊖ a									12 27												12 57			
London Charing Cross 4	⊖ a									12 30												13 00			
London Blackfriars 3	⊖ a	12 07							12 24						12 37						12 53				
City Thameslink 3	a	12 10							12 26						12 40						12 56				
Farringdon 3	⊖ a	12 14							12 30						12 44						13 00				
St Pancras International 15	⊖ a	12 17							12 33						12 47						13 03				
St Albans City	a	12 39							12 54						13 09						13 24				
Luton Airport Parkway 4 ✈	a	12 51							13 07						13 21						13 37				
Luton 7	a	12 54							13 10						13 24						13 40				
Bedford 10	a	13 20							13 36						13 50						14 06				
Clapham Junction 10	d				12 03		12 06	12 10		12b25			12 20					12 33		12 37		12b55			
West Brompton	⊖ d																	12 46							
Kensington (Olympia)	⊖ d																	12 50							
Shepherd's Bush	⊖ d																	12 53							
Watford Junction	a																	13 19							
Milton Keynes Central 10	a																	14 01							
London Victoria 15	⊖ a			12 05	12 09		12 12	12 18		12b32	12 20		12 28				12 35	12 40		12 44		13b02		12 50	

For general notes see front of timetable
For details of catering facilities see Directory of Train Operators

A 🛒 from Haywards Heath
b Change at East Croydon

Brighton → London, Bedford

Network Diagram - see first page of Table 186

		SN	SN	SN	FC		GW	GX	SN	SN	SN	SN	FC	SN	GX	SN	SN	SN	FC	GW	GX	SN	SN	SN	FC
		[1]	[1]	[1] ◇	[1]		[1]	[1]	[1] ◇	[1]	[1] ◇	[1]	[1]	[1]	[1]	[1]	[1]	[1]	[1]	[1]	[1]	[1] ◇	[1]	[1]	[1]
																	A								
		🛒									🛒	🛒					🛒	🛒				🛒		🛒	
Brighton [10]	d			11 55	12 04						12 19		12 07						12 34			12 49			12 37
Hove [2]	d		11 51														12 21								
Preston Park	d			11 58									12 11												12 41
Hassocks [4]	d			12 05									12 17												12 47
Burgess Hill [4]	d		12 02	12 08									12 21												12 51
Lewes [4]	d	11 50																12 20							
Wivelsfield [4]	d			12 11									12 23					12 34							12 53
Haywards Heath [3]	a	12 05	12 09	12 15	12 18								12 28				12 35	12 40	12 47						12 58
	d		12 13	12 16	12 18								12 32					12 43	12 48						13 02
Balcombe	d												12 37												
Horsham [4]	d											12 20				12 30								12 50	
Littlehaven	d															12 33									
Faygate	d															12 37									
Ifield	d															12 41								12 59	
Crawley	d											12 29				12 44									
Three Bridges [4]	a			12 25								12 32	12 42			12 47								13 02	13 11
	d			12 31 →					← 12 31			12 33	12 42			12 48								13 03	13 12
Gatwick Airport [10] ✈	a		12 24		12 30				12 35			12 37	12 46			12 52		12 54	13 00					13 07	13 16
	d		12 25		12 31			12 35	12 38			12 38	12 46		12 50	12 53		12 55	13 01	13 03	13 05			13 08	13 16
Horley [4]	d											12 41				12 56									
Salfords	d																								
Earlswood (Surrey)	d																								
Tonbridge [4]	d													12 19											
Leigh (Kent)	d													12 23											
Penshurst	d													12 27											
Edenbridge	d													12 33											
Godstone	d													12 40											
Nutfield	d													12 45											
Reigate	d						12 34																		
Redhill [5]	a						12 38					12 47		12 50		13 02				13 10				13 15	
	d									← 12 37		12 48		12 51		13 07								13 16	
Merstham	d									12 41						13 11 →							← 13 11		
Coulsdon South	d									12 46				12 58									13 16		
Purley [4]	d									12 49				13 02									13 19		
East Croydon 🚊	a		12 40		12 46				12 53	12 54	12 56	12 59	13 02	13 07				13 10	13 16			13 23	13 24	13 27	13 32
	d		12 41		12 47				12 53	12 55	12 56	13 00	13 02	13 07				13 11	13 17			13 24	13 25	13 28	13 32
Norwood Junction [2]	a									12 59													13 29		
London Bridge [4]	⊖ a				13 00					13 12			13 15	13 22					13 30				13 42		13 45
London Waterloo (East) [4]	⊖ a													13 27											
London Charing Cross [4]	⊖ a													13 30											
London Blackfriars [3]	⊖ a				13 07								13 24						13 37						13 53
City Thameslink [3]	a				13 10								13 26						13 40						13 56
Farringdon [3]	⊖ a				13 14								13 30						13 44						14 00
St Pancras International [15]	⊖ a				13 17								13 33						13 47						14 03
St Albans City	a				13 39								13 54						14 09						14 24
Luton Airport Parkway [4] ✈	a				13 51								14 07						14 21						14 37
Luton [7]	a				13 54								14 10						14 24						14 40
Bedford [10]	a				14 20								14 36						14 50						15 06
Clapham Junction [10]	d		12 50						13 03		13 06	13 10		13b25				13 20				13 33		13 37	
West Brompton	⊖ d																					*13 46*			
Kensington (Olympia)	⊖ d																					*13 50*			
Shepherd's Bush	⊖ d																					*13 53*			
Watford Junction	a																					*14 19*			
Milton Keynes Central [10]	a																					*15 01*			
London Victoria [15]	⊖ a		12 57					13 05	13 09		13 12	13 16		13b32	13 20			13 28			13 35	13 40		13 44	

For general notes see front of timetable
For details of catering facilities see Directory of Train Operators

A 🛒 from Haywards Heath
b Change at East Croydon

Table 186

Mondays to Fridays

Brighton → London, Bedford

Network Diagram - see first page of Table 186

		SN	GW	GX	SN	SN	SN	SN ◇	FC	GW	GX	SN ◇	SN	SN ◇	SN	FC	SN	GX	SN	SN	SN		FC	GW	GX
		1	1	1	1	1	1	1	1	1	1	1	1	1	1	1	1	1	1	1	1		1	1	1
						T								T	T					A T	T				
Brighton 10	d							12 55	13 04					13 19		13 07							13 34		
Hove 2	d						12 51													13 21					
Preston Park	d							12 58								13 11									
Hassocks 4	d							13 05								13 17									
Burgess Hill 4	d						13 02	13 08								13 21									
Lewes 4	d					12 50															13 20				
Wivelsfield 4	d							13 11								13 23					13 34				
Haywards Heath 3	a					13 05	13 09	13 15	13 18							13 28				13 35	13 40		13 47		
	d					13 13		13 16	13 18							13 32				13 43			13 48		
Balcombe	d															13 37									
Horsham 4	d				13 00										13 20				13 30						
Littlehaven	d				13 03														13 33						
Faygate	d																								
Ifield	d				13 09														13 39						
Crawley	d				13 13										13 29				13 43						
Three Bridges 4	a				13 16			13 25							13 32	13 42			13 46						
	d				13 18			13 31 →				← 13 31			13 33	13 42			13 48						
Gatwick Airport 10 ✈	a				13 22	13 24			13 30			13 35			13 37	13 46			13 52	13 54			14 00		
	d			13 20	13 23	13 25			13 31		13 35	13 38			13 38	13 46		13 50	13 53	13 55			14 01	14 03	14 05
Horley 4	d				13 26										13 41				13 56						
Salfords	d				13 30																				
Earlswood (Surrey)	d				13 33																				
Tonbridge 4	d																13 19								
Leigh (Kent)	d																13 23								
Penshurst	d																13 27								
Edenbridge	d																13 33								
Godstone	d																13 40								
Nutfield	d																13 45								
Reigate	d	13 14	13 19							13 34															
Redhill 5	a	13 18	13 25		13 36					13 38					13 47		13 50		14 02					14 10	
	d	13 21			13 37 →								← 13 37		13 48		13 51		14 07						
Merstham	d												13 41						14 11 →						
Coulsdon South	d	13 28											13 46				13 58								
Purley 4	d	13 32											13 49				14 02								
East Croydon	a	13 37				13 40			13 46			13 53	13 54	13 56	13 59	14 02	14 07			14 10			14 16		
	d	13 37				13 41			13 47			13 53	13 55	13 56	14 00	14 02	14 08			14 11			14 17		
Norwood Junction 2	a												13 59												
London Bridge 4	⊖ a	13 52							14 00				14 12			14 15	14 22						14 30		
London Waterloo (East) 4	⊖ a	13 56															14 27								
London Charing Cross 4	⊖ a	14 00															14 30								
London Blackfriars 3	⊖ a								14 07							14 23							14 37		
City Thameslink 3	a								14 10							14 26							14 40		
Farringdon 3	⊖ a								14 14							14 30							14 44		
St Pancras International 15	⊖ a								14 17							14 33							14 47		
St Albans City	a								14 39							14 54							15 09		
Luton Airport Parkway 4 ✈	a								14 51							15 07							15 21		
Luton 7	a								14 54							15 10							15 24		
Bedford 10	a								15 20							15 36							15 50		
Clapham Junction 10	d	13b55				13 50						14 03		14 06	14 10		14b25			14 20					
West Brompton	⊖ d																								
Kensington (Olympia)	⊖ d																								
Shepherd's Bush	⊖ d																								
Watford Junction	a																								
Milton Keynes Central 10	a																								
London Victoria 15	⊖ a	14b02		13 50		13 57					14 05	14 09		14 12	14 16		14b32	14 20		14 27					14 35

For general notes see front of timetable
For details of catering facilities see Directory of Train Operators

A T from Haywards Heath
b Change at East Croydon

Brighton → London, Bedford

Network Diagram - see first page of Table 186

		SN	SN	SN	FC	SN	GW	GX	SN	SN	SN	SN	FC	GW	GX	SN	SN	SN	SN	FC	SN	GX	SN	SN	SN
		1 ◇	1	1	1	1	1	1	1	1	1	1 ◇	1	1	1	1 ◇	1	1 ◇	1	1	1	1	1	1	1
																								A	
		🛒		🛒						🛒								🛒						🛒	🛒
Brighton 10	d	13 49			13 37							13 55	14 04					14 19		14 07					
Hove 2	d										13 51													14 21	
Preston Park	d				13 41							13 58								14 11					
Hassocks 4	d				13 47							14 05								14 17					
Burgess Hill 4	d				13 51						14 02	14 08								14 21					
Lewes 4	d									13 50															14 20
Wivelsfield 4	d				13 53							14 11								14 23					14 34
Haywards Heath 3	a				13 58					14 05	14 09	14 15	14 18							14 28				14 35	14 40
	d				14 02					14 13		14 16	14 18							14 32					14 43
Balcombe	d																			14 37					
Horsham 4	d			13 50					14 00										14 20				14 30		
Littlehaven	d								14 03														14 33		
Faygate	d																								
Ifield	d								14 09														14 39		
Crawley	d			13 59					14 13										14 29				14 43		
Three Bridges 4	a			14 02	14 11				14 16			14 25							14 32	14 42			14 46		
	d			14 03	14 12				14 18			14 31 →				← 14 31			14 33	14 42			14 48		
Gatwick Airport 10 ✈	a			14 07	14 16				14 22	14 24			14 30			14 35			14 37	14 46			14 52		14 54
	d			14 08	14 16			14 20	14 23	14 25			14 31		14 35	14 38			14 38	14 46		14 50	14 53		14 55
Horley 4	d								14 26										14 41				14 56		
Salfords	d								14 30																
Earlswood (Surrey)	d								14 33																
Tonbridge 4	d																				14 19				
Leigh (Kent)	d																				14 23				
Penshurst	d																				14 27				
Edenbridge	d																				14 33				
Godstone	d																				14 40				
Nutfield	d																				14 45				
Reigate	d					14 14	14 19							14 34											
Redhill 5	a			14 15		14 18	14 25		14 36					14 38					14 47		14 50		15 02		
	d		←	14 16		14 21			14 37 →								← 14 37		14 48		14 51		15 07		
Merstham	d		14 11														14 41						15 11 →		
Coulsdon South	d		14 16			14 28											14 46				14 58				
Purley 4	d		14 19			14 32											14 49				15 02				
East Croydon 🚋	a	14 23	14 24	14 27	14 32	14 37				14 40			14 46			14 53	14 54	14 56	14 59	15 02	15 07				15 10
	d	14 24	14 25	14 28	14 32	14 37				14 41			14 47			14 53	14 55	14 56	15 00	15 02	15 07				15 11
Norwood Junction 2	a		14 29														14 59								
London Bridge 4	⊖ a		14 42		14 45	14 52							15 00				15 12			15 15	15 22				
London Waterloo (East) 4	⊖ a					14 56															15 27				
London Charing Cross 4	⊖ a					15 00															15 30				
London Blackfriars 3	⊖ a				14 53								15 07							15 24					
City Thameslink 3	a				14 56								15 10							15 26					
Farringdon 3	⊖ a				15 00								15 14							15 30					
St Pancras International 15	⊖ a				15 03								15 17							15 33					
St Albans City	a				15 24								15 39							15 54					
Luton Airport Parkway 4 ✈	a				15 37								15 51							16 07					
Luton 7	a				15 40								15 54							16 10					
Bedford 10	a				16 06								16 20							16 36					
Clapham Junction 10	d	14 33		14 37		14b55				14 50						15 03		15 06	15 10		15b25				15 20
West Brompton	⊖ d	14 46																							
Kensington (Olympia)	⊖ d	14 50																							
Shepherd's Bush	⊖ d	14 53																							
Watford Junction	a	15 19																							
Milton Keynes Central 10	a	16 01																							
London Victoria 15	⊖ a	14 40		14 44		15b02		14 50		14 57					15 05	15 09		15 12	15 20		15b32	15 20			15 27

For general notes see front of timetable
For details of catering facilities see
Directory of Train Operators

A 🛒 from Haywards Heath
b Change at East Croydon

Brighton → London, Bedford

Network Diagram - see first page of Table 186

Station		FC 1	GW 1	GX 1	SN 1 ◇	SN 1	SN 1	FC 1	SN 1	GW 1	GX 1	SN 1	SN 1	SN 1		SN 1 ◇	FC 1	GW 1	GX 1	SN 1 ◇	SN 1	SN 1 ◇	SN 1	FC 1	SN 1
Brighton 10	d	14 34			14 49			14 37								14 55	15 04					15 19		15 07	
Hove 2	d													14 51											
Preston Park	d							14 41								14 58								15 11	
Hassocks 4	d							14 47								15 05								15 17	
Burgess Hill 4	d							14 51						15 02		15 08								15 21	
Lewes 4	d												14 50												
Wivelsfield 4	d							14 53								15 11								15 23	
Haywards Heath 3	a	14 47						14 58					15 05	15 09		15 15	15 18							15 28	
	d	14 48						15 02					15 13			15 16	15 18							15 32	
Balcombe	d																							15 37	
Horsham 4	d						14 50					15 00											15 20		
Littlehaven	d											15 03													
Faygate	d																								
Ifield	d											15 09													
Crawley	d						14 59					15 13											15 29		
Three Bridges 4	a						15 02	15 11				15 16				15 25							15 32	15 42	
	d						15 03	15 12				15 18				15 31 →				← 15 31			15 33	15 42	
Gatwick Airport 10 ✈	a	15 00					15 07	15 16				15 22	15 24				15 30			15 35			15 37	15 46	
	d	15 01	15 03	15 05			15 08	15 16			15 20	15 23	15 25				15 31		15 35	15 38			15 38	15 46	
Horley 4	d											15 26											15 41		
Salfords	d											15 30													
Earlswood (Surrey)	d											15 33													
Tonbridge 4	d																								15 19
Leigh (Kent)	d																								15 23
Penshurst	d																								15 27
Edenbridge	d																								15 33
Godstone	d																								15 40
Nutfield	d																								15 45
Reigate	d								15 14	15 19								15 34							
Redhill 5	a		15 10				15 16		15 18	15 25		15 36						15 38					15 47		15 50
	d					←	15 17		15 21			15 37 →									← 15 37		15 48		15 51
Merstham	d					15 11															15 41				
Coulsdon South	d					15 16			15 28												15 46				15 58
Purley 4	d					15 19			15 32												15 49				16 02
East Croydon	a	15 16			15 23	15 24	15 28	15 32	15 37				15 40				15 46			15 53	15 54	15 56	15 59	16 02	16 07
	d	15 17			15 24	15 25	15 28	15 32	15 37				15 41				15 47			15 53	15 55	15 56	16 00	16 02	16 07
Norwood Junction 2	a					15 29															15 59				16 11
London Bridge 4 ⊖	a	15 30				15 42	*15 49*	15 45	15 52								16 00				16 12			16 15	16 25
London Waterloo (East) 4 ⊖	a								15 56																
London Charing Cross 4 ⊖	a								16 00																
London Blackfriars 3 ⊖	a	15 37						15 53									16 07							16 25	
City Thameslink 3	a	15 40						15 56									16 10							16 28	
Farringdon 3 ⊖	a	15 44						16 00									16 13							16 31	
St Pancras International 15 ⊖	a	15 47						16 03									16 17							16 35	
St Albans City	a	16 09						16 24									16 39							16 56	
Luton Airport Parkway 4 ✈	a	16 21						16 37									16 51							17 09	
Luton 7	a	16 24						16 40									16 54							17 12	
Bedford 10	a	16 50						17 06									17 20							17 38	
Clapham Junction 10	d				15 33		15 38		*15b55*				15 50							16 03		16 06	16 10		*16b25*
West Brompton ⊖	d				*15 46*																				
Kensington (Olympia) ⊖	d				*15 50*																				
Shepherd's Bush ⊖	d				*15 53*																				
Watford Junction	a				*16 20*																				
Milton Keynes Central 10	a				*17 00*																				
London Victoria 15 ⊖	a			15 35	15 40		15 44		*16b02*		15 50		15 57						16 05	16 09		16 12	16 20		*16b32*

For general notes see front of timetable
For details of catering facilities see
Directory of Train Operators

b Change at East Croydon

Brighton → London, Bedford

Network Diagram - see first page of Table 186

		GX	SN	SN	SN	FC	GW	GX	SN	SN	SN	FC	SN	SN	GX	GW	SN	SN	SN	SN	FC	GX	SN	SN	SN
		1	1	1	1	1	1	1	1◇	1	1	1	1	1	1	1	1	1	1	1◇	1	1	1◇	1	1
				A																					
				ᴥ	ᴥ				ᴥ		ᴥ		ᴥ					ᴥ							ᴥ
Brighton 10	d					15 34			15 49			15 37								15 55	16 04				16 19
Hove 2	d			15 21															15 51						
Preston Park	d											15 41								15 58					
Hassocks 4	d											15 47								16 05					
Burgess Hill 4	d											15 51							16 02	16 08					
Lewes 4	d				15 19													15 50							
Wivelsfield 4	d				15 35							15 53								16 11					
Haywards Heath 3	a			15 35	15 39	15 48						15 58						16 05	16 09	16 15	16 18				
	d			15 44		15 48						15 58						16 13		16 16	16 19				
Balcombe	d																								
Horsham 4	d		15 30								15 50						16 00								
Littlehaven	d		15 33														16 03								
Faygate	d																								
Ifield	d		15 39														16 09								
Crawley	d		15 43								15 59						16 13								
Three Bridges 4	a		15 46								16 02	16 07					16 16			16 25					
	d		15 48								16 03	16 07					16 18			16 31 →			← 16 31		
Gatwick Airport 10	a		15 52		15 55	16 00					16 07	16 11					16 22	16 24			16 30		16 35		
	d	15 50	15 53		15 56	16 01	16 03	16 05			16 08	16 11			16 20		16 23	16 25			16 31	16 35	16 38		
Horley 4	d		15 56														16 26								
Salfords	d																16 30								
Earlswood (Surrey)	d																16 33								
Tonbridge 4	d																								
Leigh (Kent)	d																								
Penshurst	d																								
Edenbridge	d																								
Godstone	d																								
Nutfield	d																								
Reigate	d													16 14		16 21									
Redhill 5	a		16 02				16 10				16 17			16 18		16 27	16 36								
	d		16 07							←	16 18 →		← 16 18	16 21			16 37 →							← 16 37	
Merstham	d		16 11 →							16 11				16 25										16 41	
Coulsdon South	d									16 16				16 30										16 46	
Purley 4	d									16 19				16 34										16 49	
East Croydon	a				16 11	16 16			16 24	16 24		16 27	16 30	16 39				16 40			16 46		16 53	16 54	16 56
	d				16 11	16 17			16 24	16 25		16 27	16 30	16 40				16 41			16 47		16 53	16 55	16 56
Norwood Junction 2	a									16 29				16 44										16 59	
London Bridge 4	⊖ a					16 39			16 53	16 47		16 42		17 00							17 02			17 12	
London Waterloo (East) 4	⊖ a																								
London Charing Cross 4	⊖ a																								
London Blackfriars 3	⊖ a					16 48						16 53													
City Thameslink 3	a					16 52						16 56													
Farringdon 3	⊖ a					16 57						17 01													
St Pancras International 15	⊖ a					17 01						17 05													
St Albans City	a					17 21						17 26													
Luton Airport Parkway 4	✈ a											17 39													
Luton 7	a					17 34						17 42													
Bedford 10	a					17 58						18 08													
Clapham Junction 10	d				16 21				16 34				16 40	16b55				16 50					17 03		17 06
West Brompton	⊖ d								16 46																
Kensington (Olympia)	⊖ d								16 50																
Shepherd's Bush	⊖ d								16 53																
Watford Junction	a								17 20																
Milton Keynes Central 10	a								17 58																
London Victoria 15	⊖ a	16 22			16 28			16 35	16 42				16 46	17b05	16 52			16 58				17 05	17 09		17 12

For general notes see front of timetable
For details of catering facilities see Directory of Train Operators

A ᴥ from Haywards Heath
b Change at East Croydon

Brighton → London, Bedford

Network Diagram - see first page of Table 186

		GW	SN	FC	SN	GX	SN		SN	FC	SN	SN	SN	SN	GW	GX	SN	SN	FC	SN	GX	SN	SN	GW	SN
		1	1	1	1	1	1		1	1	1	1	1	1	1	1	1	1	1	1	1	1	1	1	
					A ⚲							A ⚲	⚲					⚲		⚲					
Brighton 10	d			16 07						16 22								16 49	16 30						
Hove 2	d				16 21																				
Preston Park	d			16 11															16 34						
Hassocks 4	d			16 17															16 40						
Burgess Hill 4	d			16 21															16 44						
Lewes 4	d												16 19												
Wivelsfield 4	d											←	16 37						16 46						
Haywards Heath 3	a			16 25	16 34 →					16 37		16 34	16 41						16 50						
	d			16 26						16 38		16 45							16 50						
Balcombe	d			16 31															16 57						
Horsham 4	d		16 20								16 30									16 52					17 00
Littlehaven	d										16 33														17 03
Faygate	d										16 37														17 07
Ifield	d										16 41														17 11
Crawley	d		16 29								16 44									17 01					17 14
Three Bridges 4	a		16 32	16 37						16 47	16 47								17 02	17 04					17 17
	d		16 33	16 37						16 47	16 48								17 02	17 05					17 18
Gatwick Airport 10 ✈	a		16 37	16 41						16 52	16 52	16 56							17 06	17 09					17 22
	d		16 38	16 41		16 50				16 53	16 53	16 57			17 03	17 05			17 07	17 10	17 20				17 23
Horley 4	d										16 56														17 26
Salfords	d										17 00														17 30
Earlswood (Surrey)	d										17 03														17 33
Tonbridge 4	d								16 19													16 49	17 03		
Leigh (Kent)	d								16 23													16 53			
Penshurst	d								16 27													16 57			
Edenbridge	d								16 33													17 03	17 13		
Godstone	d								16 40													17 10			
Nutfield	d								16 45													17 15			
Reigate	d	16 40												17 03										17 26	
Redhill 5	a	16 45	16 46						16 50		17 06			17 07	17 10					17 17		17 20	17 25	17 32	17 36
	d		16 47 →				← 16 47		16 51		17 07 →						← 17 07			17 18		17 21	17 28		17 37 →
Merstham	d																17 11					17 25			
Coulsdon South	d								16 58								17 16					17 30			
Purley 4	d								17 02								17 19								
East Croydon	a			16 57			17 01		17 07	17 08		17 12					17 24	17 25	17 27	17 30		17 37	17 40		
	d			16 57			17 01		17 07	17 09		17 12					17 25	17 25	17 28	17 30		17 38	17 41		
Norwood Junction 2	a								17 11								17 29						17 45		
London Bridge 4 ⊖	a								17 26	17 28		*17 38*					17 42			*17 50*			18 00		
London Waterloo (East) 4 ⊖	a																								
London Charing Cross 4 ⊖	a																								
London Blackfriars 3 ⊖	a			17 25						17 36									17 55						
City Thameslink 3	a			17 28						17 38									17 58						
Farringdon 3 ⊖	a			17 31						17 41									18 01						
St Pancras International 15 ⊖	a			17 35						17 45									18 05						
St Albans City	a			17 56						18 06									18 26						
Luton Airport Parkway 4 ✈	a			18 09						18 20									18 39						
Luton 7	a			18 12						18 23									18 42						
Bedford 10	a			18 38						18 48									19 08						
Clapham Junction 10	d						17 11			*17b25*		17 22						17 35		17 41		17 47			
West Brompton ⊖	d						*17 29*					*17 46*													
Kensington (Olympia) ⊖	d						*17 32*					*17 50*													
Shepherd's Bush ⊖	d						*17 35*					*17 53*													
Watford Junction	a											*18 20*													
Milton Keynes Central 10	a											*18 58*													
London Victoria 15 ⊖	a					17 20	17 20			*17b35*		17 28				17 35		17 42		17 50	17 52	17 54			

For general notes see front of timetable
For details of catering facilities see
Directory of Train Operators

A ⚲ from Haywards Heath
b Change at East Croydon

Brighton → London, Bedford

Network Diagram - see first page of Table 186

Station		SN	SN	SN	FC	GW	GX	SN	SN	SN	SN	FC	SN	GX	SN	SN	SN	SN	SN	FC	GW	GX		SN	SN
		1	1	1	1	1	1	1		1	1	1	1	1	1	1	1	1	1	1	1	1		1	1
																		A							
		🛒								🛒	🛒		🛒					🛒	🛒					🛒	
Brighton 10	d			16 55	17 04					17 19		17 09								17 24				17 49	
Hove 2	d		16 51															17 21							
Preston Park	d			16 58								17 13								17 28					
Hassocks 4	d			17 05								17 19								17 34					
Burgess Hill 4	d		17 02	17 08	17 14							17 23								17 38					
Lewes 4	d	16 51																	17 19						
Wivelsfield 4	d			17 11															17 35	17 40					
Haywards Heath 3	a	17 05	17 09	17 15	17 18							17 27						17 35	17 39	17 45					
	d		17 13	17 21 →	17 18			← 17 21				17 32							17 43	17 46					
Balcombe	d							17 27																	
Horsham 4	d										17 22						17 30								
Littlehaven	d																17 33								
Faygate	d																17 37								
Ifield	d																17 41								
Crawley	d										17 31						17 44								
Three Bridges 4	a				17 27			17 32			17 34	17 41					17 47			17 56					
	d				17 27			17 33			17 35	17 41					17 48			17 56					
Gatwick Airport 10 ✈	a		17 24		17 31			17 37			17 39	17 45					17 52		17 54	18 00					
	d		17 25		17 31		17 35	17 38			17 40	17 46		17 50			17 53		17 55	18 01	18 03	18 05			
Horley 4	d																17 56								
Salfords	d																18 00								
Earlswood (Surrey)	d																18 03								
Tonbridge 4	d															17 23									
Leigh (Kent)	d															17 27									
Penshurst	d															17 31									
Edenbridge	d															17 37									
Godstone	d															17 44									
Nutfield	d															17 49									
Reigate	d					17 34									17 44						18 10				
Redhill 5	a					17 38					17 48				17 48	17 54	18 06								
	d								← 17 37		17 49 →		← 17 49		17 52		18 07 →								← 18 07
Merstham	d								17 41						17 56										18 11
Coulsdon South	d								17 46						18 01										18 16
Purley 4	d								17 49																18 19
East Croydon	a		17 40		17 47			17 53	17 54	17 56		18 01	18 01		18 08				18 11	18 16				18 24	18 24
	d		17 41		17 47			17 53	17 55	17 56		18 01	18 02		18 08				18 12	18 17				18 25	18 26
Norwood Junction 2	a								17 59																
London Bridge 4 ⊖	a				18 11				18 15			18 17	*18 28*							*18 42*					
London Waterloo (East) 4 ⊖	a																								
London Charing Cross 4 ⊖	a																								
London Blackfriars 3 ⊖	a				18 21															18 48					
City Thameslink 3	a				18 24															18 52					
Farringdon 3 ⊖	a				18 27															18 57					
St Pancras International 15 ⊖	a				18 31															19 01					
St Albans City	a				18 51															19 21					
Luton Airport Parkway 4 ✈	a																								
Luton 7	a				19 04															19 34					
Bedford 10	a				19 28															19 58					
Clapham Junction 10	d		17 51					18 03		18 06			18 13		18 19				18 22					18 34	18 37
West Brompton ⊖	d																		*18 46*						
Kensington (Olympia) ⊖	d																		*18 50*						
Shepherd's Bush ⊖	d																		*18 53*						
Watford Junction	a																		*19 20*						
Milton Keynes Central 10	a																		*20 06*						
London Victoria 15 ⊖	a		17 58				18 05	18 09		18 12			18 20	18 22	18 26				18 29			18 35		18 41	18 44

For general notes see front of timetable
For details of catering facilities see
Directory of Train Operators

A 🛒 from Haywards Heath

Table 186

Mondays to Fridays

Brighton → London, Bedford

Network Diagram - see first page of Table 186

		SN 1	FC 1	GX 1	SN 1	SN 1	GW 1	SN 1	SN 1	SN 1	SN 1	FC 1	GX 1
Brighton 10	d		17 37								17 55	18 04	
Hove 2	d									17 51			
Preston Park	d		17 41								17 59		
Hassocks 4	d		17 47								18 05		
Burgess Hill 4	d		17 51							18 02	18 09	18 14	
Lewes 4	d								17 50				
Wivelsfield 4	d										18 11		
Haywards Heath 3	a		17 56						18 06	18 09	18 16	18 18	
	d		17 56						18 13		18 22 →	18 18	
Balcombe	d		18 02										
Horsham 4	d	17 52						18 00					
Littlehaven	d							18 03					
Faygate	d							18 07					
Ifield	d							18 11					
Crawley	d	18 01						18 14					
Three Bridges 4	a	18 04	18 10					18 17					
	d	18 05	18 12					18 18					
Gatwick Airport 10 ✈	a	18 09	18 16					18 22	18 26			18 30	
	d	18 10	18 16	18 20				18 23	18 27			18 31	18 35
Horley 4	d							18 26					
Salfords	d							18 30					
Earlswood (Surrey)	d							18 33					
Tonbridge 4	d					17 49							
Leigh (Kent)	d					17 53							
Penshurst	d					17 57							
Edenbridge	d					18 03							
Godstone	d					18 10							
Nutfield	d					18 15							
Reigate	d				18 15		18 26						
Redhill 5	a	18 17			18 19	18 21	18 32	18 36					
	d	18 18			18 24			18 37 →					
Merstham	d				18 28								
Coulsdon South	d				18 33								
Purley 4	d												
East Croydon	a	18 29	18 31		18 39				18 42			18 46	
	d	18 30	18 32		18 40				18 43			18 47	
Norwood Junction 2	a												
London Bridge 4 ⊖	a	*18 54*	18 45									19 00	
London Waterloo (East) 4 ⊖	a												
London Charing Cross 4 ⊖	a												
London Blackfriars 3 ⊖	a		18 53									19 07	
City Thameslink 3	a		18 58									19 14	
Farringdon 3 ⊖	a		19 01									19 17	
St Pancras International 15 ⊖	a		19 05									19 21	
St Albans City	a		19 26									19 46	
Luton Airport Parkway 4 ✈	a		19 39									19 58	
Luton 7	a		19 42									20 02	
Bedford 10	a		20 08									20 28	
Clapham Junction 10	d	18 40			18 49				18 52				
West Brompton ⊖	d												
Kensington (Olympia) ⊖	d												
Shepherd's Bush ⊖	d												
Watford Junction	a												
Milton Keynes Central 10	a												
London Victoria 15 ⊖	a	18 47		18 50	18 56				18 59				19 05

		SN 1	SN 1	SN 1	SN 1	SN 1	GW 1	FC 1	SN 1	GX 1	SN 1	SN 1	SN 1
Brighton 10	d			18 19				18 07					
Hove 2	d												18 21
Preston Park	d							18 11					
Hassocks 4	d							18 17					
Burgess Hill 4	d							18 21					18 33
Lewes 4	d											18 18	
Wivelsfield 4	d							18 23				18 34	
Haywards Heath 3	a							18 28				18 38	18 41
	d	← 18 22						18 32				18 45	
Balcombe	d							18 37					
Horsham 4	d					18 22					18 30		
Littlehaven	d										18 33		
Faygate	d										18 37		
Ifield	d										18 41		
Crawley	d					18 31					18 44		
Three Bridges 4	a	18 31				18 34		18 42			18 47		
	d	18 31				18 35		18 42			18 48		
Gatwick Airport 10 ✈	a	18 36				18 39		18 46			18 52	18 56	
	d	18 38				18 40		18 46		18 50	18 53	18 57	
Horley 4	d										18 56		
Salfords	d										19 00		
Earlswood (Surrey)	d										19 03		
Tonbridge 4	d								18 23				
Leigh (Kent)	d								18 27				
Penshurst	d								18 31				
Edenbridge	d								18 37				
Godstone	d								18 44				
Nutfield	d								18 49				
Reigate	d				18 38		18 42						
Redhill 5	a				18 42	18 47	18 47		18 54		19 06		
	d		← 18 37			18 48			18 57		19 07 →		
Merstham	d		18 41										
Coulsdon South	d		18 46										
Purley 4	d		18 49										
East Croydon	a	18 53	18 54	18 56		18 59		19 02	19 09			19 12	
	d	18 53	18 55	18 57		19 00		19 02	19 09			19 12	
Norwood Junction 2	a												
London Bridge 4 ⊖	a							19 16	19 24				
London Waterloo (East) 4 ⊖	a												
London Charing Cross 4 ⊖	a												
London Blackfriars 3 ⊖	a							19 23					
City Thameslink 3	a							19 26					
Farringdon 3 ⊖	a							19 29					
St Pancras International 15 ⊖	a							19 33					
St Albans City	a							19 55					
Luton Airport Parkway 4 ✈	a							20 07					
Luton 7	a							20 10					
Bedford 10	a							20 36					
Clapham Junction 10	d	19 03	19 06	19 09		19 12			19b25			19 22	
West Brompton ⊖	d												
Kensington (Olympia) ⊖	d												
Shepherd's Bush ⊖	d												
Watford Junction	a												
Milton Keynes Central 10	a												
London Victoria 15 ⊖	a	19 09	19 12	19 15		19 18			19b35	19 20		19 29	

For general notes see front of timetable
For details of catering facilities see Directory of Train Operators

b Change at East Croydon

Brighton → London, Bedford

Network Diagram - see first page of Table 186

Station		FC 1	SN 1	GX 1	SN 1◇	SN 1	SN 1◇	FC 1	SN 1	GW 1	GX 1	SN 1	GW 1	SN 1	SN 1	SN 1		FC 1	GW 1	SN 1	GX 1	SN 1◇	SN 1	SN 1◇	SN 1◇
Brighton 10	d	18 34			18 49			18 37														19 19			18 59
Hove 2	d														18 52										
Preston Park	d							18 41																	19 03
Hassocks 4	d							18 47																	19 09
Burgess Hill 4	d							18 51																	19 13
Lewes 4	d															18 50									
Wivelsfield 4	d							18 53								19 05									19 15
Haywards Heath 3	a	18 47						18 58							19 05	19 10									19 20
	d	18 48						19 02								19 14									19 21
Balcombe	d																								
Horsham 4	d						18 52							19 02										19 17	
Littlehaven	d													19 05											
Faygate	d																								
Ifield	d													19 11											
Crawley	d						19 01							19 14										19 26	
Three Bridges 4	a						19 04	19 12						19 18										19 29	19 31
	d						19 05	19 12						19 18				19 27							19 35
Gatwick Airport 10 ✈	a	19 00					19 09	19 16						19 22		19 25		19 31							19 39
	d	19 01		19 05			19 10	19 16		19 16	19 20			19 23		19 26		19 31			19 35				19 40
Horley 4	d													19 26											
Salfords	d													19 30											
Earlswood (Surrey)	d													19 33											
Tonbridge 4	d								18 50											19 10					
Leigh (Kent)	d								18 54											19 14					
Penshurst	d								18 58											19 18					
Edenbridge	d								19 04											19 24					
Godstone	d								19 11											19 31					
Nutfield	d								19 16											19 36					
Reigate	d		19 02									19 21	19 30						19 34						
Redhill 5	a		19 06				19 17		19 21	19 23		19 25	19 36	19 38					19 38	19 41					19 47
	d					← 19 07	19 18		19 23					19 39 →									← 19 39		19 48
Merstham	d					19 11			19 27														19 43		
Coulsdon South	d					19 16			19 32														19 48		
Purley 4	d					19 19																	19 51		
East Croydon	a	19 16			19 23	19 24	19 28	19 32	19 39							19 42		19 47				19 54	19 56		19 59
	d	19 17			19 24	19 25	19 29	19 32	19 40							19 43		19 47				19 54	19 57		20 00
Norwood Junction 2	a																								
London Bridge 4	⊖ a	19 30					19 51	19 45										20 00							20 21
London Waterloo (East) 4	⊖ a																								
London Charing Cross 4	⊖ a																								
London Blackfriars 3	⊖ a	19 37						19 53										20 07							
City Thameslink 3	a	19 40						19 56										20 10							
Farringdon 3	⊖ a	19 44						20 00										20 13							
St Pancras International 15	⊖ a	19 47						20 03										20 17							
St Albans City	a	20 09						20 25										20 39							
Luton Airport Parkway 4 ✈	a	20 21						20 37										20 51							
Luton 7	a	20 24						20 40										20 54							
Bedford 10	a	20 50						21 06										21 20							
Clapham Junction 10	d				19 33	19 37	19 40		19 49							19 52						20 04	20 08		20 11
West Brompton	⊖ d				19 46																				
Kensington (Olympia)	⊖ d				19 50																				
Shepherd's Bush	⊖ d				19 53																				
Watford Junction	a				20 19																				
Milton Keynes Central 10	a				21 01																				
London Victoria 15	⊖ a			19 35	19 40	19 43	19 47		19 56		19 50					19 59					20 05	20 10	20 14		20 20

For general notes see front of timetable
For details of catering facilities see
Directory of Train Operators

Brighton → London, Bedford

Network Diagram - see first page of Table 186

		FC [1]	GX [1]	SN [1]	SN [1]	SN [1]	SN [1]	FC [1]	GW [1]	GX [1]	SN [1] ◇	SN [1]	SN [1]	SN [1]	FC [1]	GX [1]	SN [1]	SN [1]	SN [1]	SN [1] ◇	FC [1]	GW [1]	SN [1]	GX [1]	SN [1] ◇
Brighton [10]	d	19 07						19 34			19 49				19 37					19 55	20 04				20 19
Hove [2]	d					19 22												19 52							
Preston Park	d	19 11													19 41					19 59					
Hassocks [4]	d	19 17													19 47					20 05					
Burgess Hill [4]	d	19 21				19 32									19 51					20 09					
Lewes [4]	d						19 21												19 50						
Wivelsfield [4]	d	19 23													19 53				20 05	20 11					
Haywards Heath [3]	a	19 28				19 36	19 40	19 47							19 58			20 04	20 10	20 16	20 18				
	d	19 32				19 44		19 48							20 02			20 14		20 22 →	20 18				
Balcombe	d	19 37																							
Horsham [4]	d				19 32								19 52				20 02								
Littlehaven	d				19 35												20 05								
Faygate	d																								
Ifield	d				19 41												20 11								
Crawley	d				19 45								20 01				20 14								
Three Bridges [4]	a	19 42			19 49								20 04		20 11		20 18								
	d	19 42			19 51								20 05		20 12		20 18								
Gatwick Airport [10] ✈	a	19 46			19 55	19 55		20 00					20 10		20 16		20 22	20 25			20 31				
	d	19 46	19 50		19 56	19 56		20 01	20 03	20 05			20 11		20 16	20 20	20 23	20 26			20 31			20 35	
Horley [4]	d				19 59												20 26								
Salfords	d																20 30								
Earlswood (Surrey)	d																20 33								
Tonbridge [4]	d																						20 10		
Leigh (Kent)	d																						20 14		
Penshurst	d																						20 18		
Edenbridge	d																						20 24		
Godstone	d																						20 31		
Nutfield	d																						20 36		
Reigate	d			19 51										20 14								20 34			
Redhill [5]	a			19 55	20 05				20 10				20 18	20 18			20 36					20 38	20 45		
	d				20 08							←	20 18				20 37 →								
Merstham	d				20 12 →							20 12													
Coulsdon South	d											20 17													
Purley [4]	d											20 20													
East Croydon	a	20 02				20 11		20 16			20 23	20 25	20 30		20 32			20 41			20 47				20 54
	d	20 02				20 11		20 17			20 24	20 26	20 30		20 32			20 41			20 47				20 54
Norwood Junction [2]	a																								
London Bridge [4] ⊖	a	20 15						20 30							20 45						21 00				
London Waterloo (East) [4] ⊖	a																								
London Charing Cross [4] ⊖	a																								
London Blackfriars [3] ⊖	a	20 23						20 37							20 53						21 07				
City Thameslink [3]	a	20 26						20 40							20 56						21 10				
Farringdon [3] ⊖	a	20 30						20 43							21 00						21 13				
St Pancras International [15] ⊖	a	20 33						20 47							21 03						21 17				
St Albans City	a	20 55						21 09							21 25						21 39				
Luton Airport Parkway [4] ✈	a	21 07						21 21							21 37						21 51				
Luton [7]	a	21 10						21 24							21 40						21 54				
Bedford [10]	a	21 36						21 50							22 06						22 20				
Clapham Junction [10]	d					20 21					20 33	20 38	20 41					20 51							21 04
West Brompton ⊖	d										*20 46*														
Kensington (Olympia) ⊖	d										*20 50*														
Shepherd's Bush ⊖	d										*20 53*														
Watford Junction	a										*21 19*														
Milton Keynes Central [10]	a										*22 04*														
London Victoria [15] ⊖	a		20 20			20 28				20 35	20 43	20 45	20 48			20 50		20 58						21 05	21 10

For general notes see front of timetable
For details of catering facilities see Directory of Train Operators

Brighton → London, Bedford

Network Diagram - see first page of Table 186

		SN 1	SN 1 ◇	FC 1	GX 1	SN 1	SN 1	SN 1	FC 1		GW 1	GX 1	SN 1 ◇	SN 1	SN 1	SN 1	FC 1	GX 1	GW 1	SN 1	SN 1	SN 1	SN 1	GX 1	SN 1 ◇
Brighton 10	d			20 07					20 34				20 49				20 37								21 19
Hove 2	d					20 22															20 52				
Preston Park	d			20 11													20 41								
Hassocks 4	d			20 17													20 47								
Burgess Hill 4	d			20 21		20 33											20 51								
Lewes 4	d																					20 50			
Wivelsfield 4	d			20 23													20 53					21 05			
Haywards Heath 3	a			20 28		20 37			20 47								20 58				21 05	21 09			
	d		← 20 22	20 32		20 38			20 48								21 02				21 13				
Balcombe	d			20 37																					
Horsham 4	d							20 32								20 52				21 02					
Littlehaven	d							20 35												21 05					
Faygate	d																								
Ifield	d							20 41												21 11					
Crawley	d							20 45								21 01				21 14					
Three Bridges 4	a		20 32	20 42		20 47		20 48								21 05	21 11			21 18					
	d		20 32	20 42		20 47		20 51								21 05	21 12			21 18					
Gatwick Airport 10 ✈	a		20 37	20 46		20 51		20 56	21 00							21 10	21 16			21 22	21 24				
	d		20 38	20 46	20 50	20 53		20 57	21 01		21 03	21 05				21 11	21 16	21 20		21 23	21 25			21 35	
Horley 4	d							20 59												21 26					
Salfords	d																			21 30					
Earlswood (Surrey)	d																			21 33					
Tonbridge 4	d																						21 10		
Leigh (Kent)	d																						21 14		
Penshurst	d																						21 18		
Edenbridge	d																						21 24		
Godstone	d																						21 31		
Nutfield	d																						21 36		
Reigate	d						20 50								21 13				21 24				21 42		
Redhill 5	a		20 47				20 54	21 06			21 10				21 17	21 18			21 30	21 36					
	d	← 20 37	20 48					21 07						←		21 18				21 37 →					
Merstham	d	20 41						21 11 →						21 11											
Coulsdon South	d	20 46												21 16											
Purley 4	d	20 49												21 19											
East Croydon	a	20 57	20 59	21 02		21 09			21 16				21 25	21 25		21 30	21 32				21 40				21 53
	d	20 57	21 00	21 02		21 10			21 17				21 25	21 26		21 30	21 32				21 41				21 53
Norwood Junction 2	a																								
London Bridge 4	⊖ a			21 15					21 30							*22 11*	21 45								
London Waterloo (East) 4	⊖ a																								
London Charing Cross 4	⊖ a																								
London Blackfriars 3	⊖ a			21 23					21 37								21 53								
City Thameslink 3	a			21 26					21 40								21 56								
Farringdon 3	⊖ a			21 30					21 43								22 00								
St Pancras International 15	⊖ a			21 33					21 47								22 03								
St Albans City	a			21 55					22 09								22 25								
Luton Airport Parkway 4 ✈	a			22 07					22 21								22 37								
Luton 7	a			22 10					22 24								22 40								
Bedford 10	a			22 36					22 50								23 06								
Clapham Junction 10	d	21 08	21 11			21 20							21 35	21 38		21 41					21 50				22 03
West Brompton	⊖ d					*21 46*																			
Kensington (Olympia)	⊖ d					*21 50*																			
Shepherd's Bush	⊖ d					*21 53*																			
Watford Junction	a					*22 23*																			
Milton Keynes Central 10	a																								
London Victoria 15	⊖ a	21 14	21 20		21 20	21 27						21 35	21 41	21 45		21 50		21 50			21 57			22 05	22 10

For general notes see front of timetable
For details of catering facilities see Directory of Train Operators

Table 186

Mondays to Fridays

Brighton → London, Bedford

Network Diagram - see first page of Table 186

		SN 1	SN 1◇	GW 1	FC 1	GX 1	SN 1	SN 1	SN 1	SN 1	GX 1	SN 1◇	SN 1	SN 1	SN 1	FC 1	GX 1	GW 1	SN 1	SN 1	SN 1	SN 1	SN 1	GX 1	SN 1◇
Brighton [10]	d		21 02		21 11					21 34		21 49				21 37									22 00
Hove [2]	d						21 22													21 52					
Preston Park	d		21 06													21 41									22 04
Hassocks [4]	d		21 12		21 19											21 47									22 10
Burgess Hill [4]	d		21 16		21 23		21 32									21 51				22 02					22 14
Lewes [4]	d																		21 50						
Wivelsfield [4]	d		21 18													21 53			22 02						22 16
Haywards Heath [3]	a		21 23		21 27		21 37			21 46						21 58			22 06	22 09					22 21
	d		21 23		21 32		21 38			21 46						22 02			22 13						22 22
Balcombe	d				21 37																				
Horsham [4]	d								21 32						21 52							22 02			
Littlehaven	d								21 35													22 05			
Faygate	d																								
Ifield	d								21 41													22 11			
Crawley	d								21 45						22 01							22 14			
Three Bridges [4]	a		21 32		21 42		21 47		21 48	21 55					22 05	22 11						22 18			22 32
	d		21 33		21 42		21 47		21 51	21 56					22 05	22 12						22 21			22 32
Gatwick Airport [10] ✈	a		21 37		21 46		21 51		21 55	22 00					22 10	22 16			22 24			22 25			22 37
	d		21 38		21 46	21 50	21 53		21 56	22 02	22 05				22 11	22 16	22 20	22 22	22 25			22 26		22 35	22 38
Horley [4]	d								21 59													22 29			
Salfords	d																					22 33			
Earlswood (Surrey)	d																					22 36			
Tonbridge [4]	d																						22 10		
Leigh (Kent)	d																						22 14		
Penshurst	d																						22 18		
Edenbridge	d																						22 24		
Godstone	d																						22 31		
Nutfield	d																						22 36		
Reigate	d			21 45				21 52						22 13							22 33				
Redhill [5]	a	←	21 45	21 49				21 57	22 05					22 17	22 18			22 30			22 37	22 39	22 42		22 45
	d	21 37	21 46						22 08				←		22 18							22 40			22 46
Merstham	d	21 41							22 12 →				22 12									22 44			
Coulsdon South	d	21 46											22 17									22 49			
Purley [4]	d	21 49											22 20									22 52			
East Croydon	a	21 54	21 59		22 02		22 09			22 17		22 23	22 25		22 30	22 32			22 40			22 57			22 59
	d	21 57	22 00		22 02		22 10			22 17		22 24	22 26		22 30	22 32			22 40			22 58			23 00
Norwood Junction [2]	a																								
London Bridge [4]	⊖ a				22 17					22 32					*23 11*	22 47									*23 38*
London Waterloo (East) [4]	⊖ a																								
London Charing Cross [4]	⊖ a																								
London Blackfriars [3]	⊖ a																								
City Thameslink [3]	a																								
Farringdon [3]	⊖ a																								
St Pancras International [15]	⊖ a																								
St Albans City	a																								
Luton Airport Parkway [4] ✈	a																								
Luton [7]	a																								
Bedford [10]	a																								
Clapham Junction [10]	d	22 08	22 11				22 20					22 33	22 38		22 41				22 50			23 08			23 11
West Brompton	⊖ d											*22 46*													
Kensington (Olympia)	⊖ d											*22 50*													
Shepherd's Bush	⊖ d											*22 53*													
Watford Junction	a											*23 23*													
Milton Keynes Central [10]	a																								
London Victoria [15]	⊖ a	22 14	22 20			22 20	22 27				22 35	22 40	22 44		22 50		22 50		22 57			23 15		23 05	23 20

For general notes see front of timetable
For details of catering facilities see Directory of Train Operators

Table 186

Mondays to Fridays

Brighton → London, Bedford

Network Diagram - see first page of Table 186

		GW 1		FC 1	GX 1	GX 1	FC 1	SN 1	SN 1	FC 1	GW 1	GX 1	SN 1	SN 1	SN 1 ◇	GX 1	FC 1	FC 1	SN 1	GX 1	GW 1	SN 1 ◇	FC 1		
									A										B						
Brighton 10	d			22 07			22 33								23 02		23 11	23 11					23 37		
Hove 2	d																								
Preston Park	d			22 11			22 37								23 06								23 41		
Hassocks 4	d			22 17			22 43								23 12		23 19	23 19					23 47		
Burgess Hill 4	d			22 21			22 47								23 16		23 23	23 23					23 51		
Lewes 4	d								22 40																
Wivelsfield 4	d			22 23			22 49		22 54						23 19								23 53		
Haywards Heath 3	a			22 28			22 54		22 58						23 23		23 27	23 27					23 58		
	d			22 32			22 54		22 59						23 24		23 28	23 28					23 59		
Balcombe	d			22 37			23 00																00 04		
Horsham 4	d							22 55					23 02						23 25						
Littlehaven	d												23 05						23 28						
Faygate	d																								
Ifield	d												23 11						23 35						
Crawley	d							23 03					23 14						23 38						
Three Bridges 4	a			22 42			23 05	23 07	23 08	←			23 18		23 33		23 37	23 37	23 42			←	00 10		
	d			22 42			23 12 →		23 08	23 12			23 18		23 47 →		23 38	23 38				23 47	00 10		
Gatwick Airport 10 ✈	a			22 46					23 12	23 16			23 22				23 42	23 42				23 52	00 14		
	d			22 46	22 50	23 05			23 13	23 16	23 18	23 20	23 23			23 35	23 43	23 43		23 50		23 53	00 15		
Horley 4	d												23 26									23 56			
Salfords	d												23 29												
Earlswood (Surrey)	d												23 33												
Tonbridge 4	d													23 17											
Leigh (Kent)	d													23 21											
Penshurst	d													23 25											
Edenbridge	d													23 31											
Godstone	d													23 38											
Nutfield	d													23 43											
Reigate	d	22 44																			23 54				
Redhill 5	a	22 48									23 25		23 36	23 49							23 58	00 02	00 22		
	d												23 37									00 03	00 22		
Merstham	d												23 41												
Coulsdon South	d												23 46												
Purley 4	d												23 49									00 11			
East Croydon	a			23 02					23 30	23 32			23 55				00 02	00 02				00 16	00 35		
	d			23 02					23 30	23 32			23 58				00 04	00 04				00 17	00 36		
Norwood Junction 2	a																								
London Bridge 4	⊖ a			23 17						23 47			*00 19*				00 19	00 19				*00 52*	00 52		
London Waterloo (East) 4	⊖ a																								
London Charing Cross 4	⊖ a																								
London Blackfriars 3	⊖ a																								
City Thameslink 3	a																								
Farringdon 3	⊖ a																								
St Pancras International 15	⊖ a																								
St Albans City	a																								
Luton Airport Parkway 4 ✈	a																								
Luton 7	a																								
Bedford 10	a																								
Clapham Junction 10	d			23b25					23 42				00 11					00b29				00 30	01b02		
West Brompton	⊖ d																								
Kensington (Olympia)	⊖ d																								
Shepherd's Bush	⊖ d																								
Watford Junction	a																								
Milton Keynes Central 10	a																								
London Victoria 15	⊖ a			23b35	23 20	23 35			23 52			23 55	00 18			00 10		00b37		00 25		00 37	01b09		

For general notes see front of timetable
For details of catering facilities see
Directory of Train Operators

A From Ore (Table 189)
B From Chichester (Table 188)
b Change at East Croydon

Saturdays

Brighton → London, Bedford

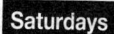

Network Diagram - see first page of Table 186

		SN 1	SN 1 ◇	FC 1	FC 1	SN 1 ◇	GX 1	FC 1	GX 1	GX 1	GW 1	GX 1	SN 1	GX 1	SN 1	FC 1	SN 1	FC 1	SN 1	FC 1	GX 1		FC 1	SN 1	GX 1
Brighton 10	d		23p02	23p11	23p11			23p37																03 50	
Hove 2	d																								
Preston Park	d		23p06					23p41																	
Hassocks 4	d		23p12	23p19	23p19			23p47																	
Burgess Hill 4	d		23p16	23p23	23p23			23p51																	
Lewes 4	d																								
Wivelsfield 4	d		23p19					23p53																	
Haywards Heath 3	a		23p23	23p27	23p27			23p58																	
	d		23p24	23p28	23p28			23p59																04 24	
Balcombe	d							00 04																04 25	
Horsham 4	d	23p02																							
Littlehaven	d	23p05																							
Faygate	d																								
Ifield	d	23p11																							
Crawley	d	23p14																							
Three Bridges 4	a	23p18	23p33	23p37	23p37	←		00 10																04 45	
	d	23p18	23p47 →	23p38	23p38	23p47		00 10							01 59	02 25	02 55	03 25	03 55	04 25			04 55	04 58	
Gatwick Airport 10 ✈	a	23p22		23p42	23p42	23p52		00 14							02 03	02 29	02 59	03 29	03 59	04 29			04 59	05 02	
	d	23p23		23p43	23p43	23p53	00 05	00 15	00 20	00 35		00 50	01 05	01 35	02 05	02 30	03 05	03 30	04 05	04 30	04 35		05 00	05 03	05 20
Horley 4	d	23p26				23p56							01 07		02 07		03 07		04 07					05 05	
Salfords	d	23p29																							
Earlswood (Surrey)	d	23p33																							
Tonbridge 4	d																								
Leigh (Kent)	d																								
Penshurst	d																								
Edenbridge	d																								
Godstone	d																								
Nutfield	d																								
Reigate	d										00 45														
Redhill 5	a	23p36				00 02		00 22			00 49														
	d	23p37				00 03		00 22																	
Merstham	d	23p41																							
Coulsdon South	d	23p46																							
Purley 4	d	23p49				00 11							01 22		02 22		03 22		04 22					05 24	
East Croydon	a	23p55		00 02	00 02	00 16		00 35					01 27		02 27	02 47	03 27	03 47	04 27	04 47			05 17	05 29	
	d	23p58		00 04	00 04	00 17		00 36					01 28		02 28	02 47	03 28	03 47	04 28	04 47			05 17	05 29	
Norwood Junction 2	a																								
London Bridge 4 ⊖	a	*00 19*		00 19	00 19			00 52								03 12		04 12		05 12			05 42		
London Waterloo (East) 4 ⊖	a																								
London Charing Cross 4 ⊖	a																								
London Blackfriars 3 ⊖	a																								
City Thameslink 3	a																								
Farringdon 3 ⊖	a																								
St Pancras International 15 ⊖	a																								
St Albans City	a																								
Luton Airport Parkway 4 ✈	a																								
Luton 7	a																								
Bedford 10	a																								
Clapham Junction 10	d	00 11				00 30		*01b02*					01 41		02 41		03 41		04 41					05 49	
West Brompton ⊖	d																		*05 15*					*06 18*	
Kensington (Olympia) ⊖	d																		*05 18*					*06 21*	
Shepherd's Bush ⊖	d																		*05 21*					*06 24*	
Watford Junction	a																		*05 47*					*06 50*	
Milton Keynes Central 10	a																		*07 00*						
London Victoria 15 ⊖	a	00 18				00 37	00 40	*01b09*	00 55	01 10		01 25	01 49	02 20	02 49		03 49		04 49		05 10			05 58	05 55

For general notes see front of timetable
For details of catering facilities see Directory of Train Operators

b Change at East Croydon

Brighton → London, Bedford

Network Diagram - see first page of Table 186

		FC	GW	GW	SN	SN	GX	SN	SN	SN	FC	SN	GW	GX	SN	GX	SN	SN	SN	SN		FC	GW	GX	SN
		1	1	1	1 ◇	1	1	1 ◇	1	1	1	1	1	1	1	1	1	1 ◇	1	1 ◇		1	1	1	1 ◇
										A		A													
Brighton 10	d							05 21			05 24							05 50		05 56		06 04			
Hove 2	d																		05 54						
Preston Park	d										05 28									06 00					
Hassocks 4	d										05 34									06 06					
Burgess Hill 4	d							05 31			05 38											06 14			
Lewes 4	d									05 25															
Wivelsfield 4	d										05 40									06 11					
Haywards Heath 3	a							05 36		05 40	05 45	⟵						06 02	06 07	06 15		06 18			
	d							05 37		05 49 ⟶	05 45	05 49						06 11		06 16		06 18			
Balcombe	d										05 51														
Horsham 4	d								05 30								06 00								
Littlehaven	d								05 33								06 03								
Faygate	d																								
Ifield	d								05 39								06 09								
Crawley	d								05 43								06 13								
Three Bridges 4	a							05 46	05 46		05 56	05 59					06 16	06 20		06 25					⟵
	d	05 20			05 33			05 46	05 48		05 56	05 59					06 18	06 20		06 31 ⟶					06 31
Gatwick Airport 10 ✈	a	05 24			05 37			05 50	05 52		06 00	06 03					06 22	06 24				06 30			06 35
	d	05 26	05 31		05 38		05 50	05 53	05 53		06 01		06 04	06 05		06 20	06 23	06 25				06 31		06 35	06 38
Horley 4	d				05 40				05 56								06 26								
Salfords	d								06 00								06 30								
Earlswood (Surrey)	d								06 03								06 33								
Tonbridge 4	d					05 24																			
Leigh (Kent)	d					05 28																			
Penshurst	d					05 32																			
Edenbridge	d					05 38																			
Godstone	d					05 45																			
Nutfield	d					05 50																			
Reigate	d			05 34																			06 34		
Redhill 5	a		05 38	05 38	05 47	05 55			06 06				06 12		⟵		06 36						06 38		
	d				05 48				06 07 ⟶						06 07		06 37 ⟶								
Merstham	d														06 11										
Coulsdon South	d														06 16										
Purley 4	d				05 58										06 19										
East Croydon 🚊	a	05 42			06 02			06 10			06 16				06 24			06 40				06 46			06 53
	d	05 42			06 07			06 11			06 17				06 25			06 41				06 47			06 53
Norwood Junction 2	a														06 29										
London Bridge 4	⊖ a	05 57									06 31				06 42							07 02			
London Waterloo (East) 4	⊖ a																								
London Charing Cross 4	⊖ a																								
London Blackfriars 3	⊖ a																								
City Thameslink 3	a																								
Farringdon 3	⊖ a																								
St Pancras International 15	⊖ a																								
St Albans City	a																								
Luton Airport Parkway 4	✈ a																								
Luton 7	a																								
Bedford 10	a																								
Clapham Junction 10	d				06 18			06 22										06 50							07 03
West Brompton	⊖ d							06 46																	
Kensington (Olympia)	⊖ d							06 50																	
Shepherd's Bush	⊖ d							06 53																	
Watford Junction	a							07 19																	
Milton Keynes Central 10	a							08 00																	
London Victoria 15	⊖ a				06 26		06 20	06 30						06 35		06 50		06 57						07 05	07 09

For general notes see front of timetable
For details of catering facilities see Directory of Train Operators

A From Eastbourne (Table 189)

Table 186

Saturdays

Brighton → London, Bedford

Network Diagram - see first page of Table 186

		SN 1	SN 1	GX 1	SN 1	SN 1 ◇	SN 1	FC 1	GW 1	GX 1	SN 1 ◇	SN 1	SN 1	FC 1	SN 1	GW 1	GX 1	SN 1	SN 1	SN 1		SN 1 ◇	FC 1	GW 1	GX 1
Brighton 10	d					06 10		06 24			06 49			06 37								06 55	07 04		
Hove 2	d						06 21													06 51					
Preston Park	d					06 14		06 28						06 41								06 58			
Hassocks 4	d					06 20		06 34						06 47								07 05			
Burgess Hill 4	d					06 24		06 38						06 51						07 02		07 08			
Lewes 4	d																		06 50						
Wivelsfield 4	d					06 26		06 40						06 53								07 11			
Haywards Heath 3	a					06 31	06 35	06 45						06 58					07 05	07 08		07 15	07 18		
	d					06 40		06 45						07 02					07 13			07 16	07 18		
Balcombe	d							06 51																	
Horsham 4	d				06 30								06 52					07 00							
Littlehaven	d				06 33													07 03							
Faygate	d																								
Ifield	d				06 39													07 09							
Crawley	d				06 43								07 01					07 13							
Three Bridges 4	a				06 46	06 49		06 56					07 04	07 11				07 16				07 25			
	d				06 48	06 49		06 56					07 05	07 12				07 18				07 31 →			
Gatwick Airport 10	a				06 52	06 53		07 00					07 09	07 16				07 22	07 24				07 30		
	d			06 50	06 53	06 55		07 01	07 03	07 05			07 10	07 16			07 20	07 23	07 25				07 31		07 35
Horley 4	d				06 56													07 26							
Salfords	d																	07 30							
Earlswood (Surrey)	d																	07 33							
Tonbridge 4	d		06 19																						
Leigh (Kent)	d		06 23																						
Penshurst	d		06 27																						
Edenbridge	d		06 33																						
Godstone	d		06 40																						
Nutfield	d		06 45																						
Reigate	d														07 14	07 18									
Redhill 5	a	←	06 50		07 02				07 10				07 17		07 18	07 25		07 36						07 34	
	d	06 37	06 51		07 07							←	07 18		07 21			07 37 →						07 38	
Merstham	d	06 41			07 11 →							07 11													
Coulsdon South	d	06 46	06 58									07 16			07 28										
Purley 4	d	06 49	07 02									07 19			07 32										
East Croydon	a	06 54	07 07			07 10		07 16			07 23	07 24	07 29	07 32	07 37				07 40				07 46		
	d	06 55	07 07			07 11		07 17			07 24	07 25	07 30	07 32	07 37				07 41				07 47		
Norwood Junction 2	a	06 59										07 29													
London Bridge 4	⊖ a	07 12	07 24					07 31				07 42		07 47	07 52								08 02		
London Waterloo (East) 4	⊖ a		07 28												07 57										
London Charing Cross 4	⊖ a		07 32												08 00										
London Blackfriars 3	⊖ a																								
City Thameslink 3	a																								
Farringdon 3	⊖ a																								
St Pancras International 15	⊖ a																								
St Albans City	a																								
Luton Airport Parkway 4	✈ a																								
Luton 7	a																								
Bedford 10	a																								
Clapham Junction 10	d		07b25			07 20					07 33		07 39		07b55				07 50						
West Brompton	⊖ d										07 46														
Kensington (Olympia)	⊖ d										07 50														
Shepherd's Bush	⊖ d										07 53														
Watford Junction	a										08 19														
Milton Keynes Central 10	a										09 00														
London Victoria 15	⊖ a		07b32	07 20		07 27				07 35	07 40		07 46		08b02		07 50		07 57						08 05

For general notes see front of timetable
For details of catering facilities see Directory of Train Operators

b Change at East Croydon

Table 186

Saturdays

Brighton → London, Bedford

Network Diagram - see first page of Table 186

Station		SN 1 ◊	SN 1	SN 1 ◊	SN 1	FC 1	SN 1	GX 1	SN 1	SN 1 A ⊼	SN 1	FC 1	GW 1	GX 1	SN 1 ◊ ⊼	SN 1	SN 1	FC 1	SN 1		GW 1	GX 1	SN 1	SN 1	SN 1
Brighton 10	d			07 19		07 07						07 34			07 49			07 37							
Hove 2	d									07 22															07 51
Preston Park	d					07 11												07 41							
Hassocks 4	d					07 17												07 47							08 02
Burgess Hill 4	d					07 21												07 51							
Lewes 4	d										07 20													07 50	
Wivelsfield 4	d					07 23					07 34							07 53							
Haywards Heath 3	a					07 28				07 35	07 40	07 48						07 58						08 05	08 09
	d					07 32					07 43	07 48						08 02							08 13
Balcombe	d					07 37																			
Horsham 4	d				07 20				07 30								07 50						08 00		
Littlehaven	d								07 33														08 03		
Faygate	d																								
Ifield	d								07 39														08 09		
Crawley	d				07 29				07 43								07 59						08 13		
Three Bridges 4	a	←			07 32	07 42			07 46								08 02	08 11					08 16		
	d	07 31			07 33	07 42			07 48								08 03	08 12					08 18		
Gatwick Airport 10 ✈	a	07 35			07 37	07 46			07 52		07 54	08 00					08 07	08 16					08 22		08 24
	d	07 38			07 38	07 46		07 50	07 53		07 55	08 01	08 03	08 05			08 08	08 16				08 20	08 23		08 25
Horley 4	d				07 41				07 56														08 26		
Salfords	d																						08 30		
Earlswood (Surrey)	d																						08 33		
Tonbridge 4	d						07 19																		
Leigh (Kent)	d						07 23																		
Penshurst	d						07 27																		
Edenbridge	d						07 33																		
Godstone	d						07 40																		
Nutfield	d						07 45																		
Reigate	d																		08 14		08 19				
Redhill 5	a		←		07 47		07 50		08 02				08 10				08 15		08 18		08 25		08 36		
	d		07 37		07 48		07 51		08 07							←	08 16		08 21				08 37 →		
Merstham	d		07 41						08 11 →							08 11									
Coulsdon South	d		07 46				07 58									08 16			08 28						
Purley 4	d		07 49				08 02									08 19			08 32						
East Croydon	a	07 53	07 54	07 56	07 59	08 02	08 07				08 10	08 16			08 23	08 24	08 27	08 32	08 37						08 40
	d	07 53	07 55	07 56	08 00	08 02	08 07				08 11	08 17			08 24	08 25	08 28	08 32	08 37						08 41
Norwood Junction 2	a		07 59													08 29									
London Bridge 4	⊖ a		08 12			08 17	08 22					08 32				08 42		08 47	08 52						
London Waterloo (East) 4	⊖ a						08 26												08 56						
London Charing Cross 4	⊖ a						08 30												09 00						
London Blackfriars 3	⊖ a																								
City Thameslink 3	a																								
Farringdon 3	⊖ a																								
St Pancras International 15	⊖ a																								
St Albans City	a																								
Luton Airport Parkway 4 ✈	a																								
Luton 7	a																								
Bedford 10	a																								
Clapham Junction 10	d	08 03		08 06	08 10		*08*b25				08 20				08 33		08 37		*08*b55						08 50
West Brompton	⊖ d														*08 46*										
Kensington (Olympia)	⊖ d														*08 50*										
Shepherd's Bush	⊖ d														*08 53*										
Watford Junction	a														*09 19*										
Milton Keynes Central 10	a														*10 00*										
London Victoria 15	⊖ a	08 09		08 12	08 16		*08*b32	08 20			08 27			08 35	08 40		08 44		*09*b02			08 50			08 57

For general notes see front of timetable
For details of catering facilities see
Directory of Train Operators

A ⊼ from Haywards Heath
b Change at East Croydon

Table 186

Saturdays

Brighton → London, Bedford

Network Diagram - see first page of Table 186

	SN 1 ◇	FC 1	GW 1	GX 1	SN 1 ◇	SN 1	SN 1 ◇	SN 1	FC 1	SN 1	GX 1	SN 1	SN 1	SN 1	FC 1	GW 1	GX 1		SN 1 ◇	SN 1	SN 1	FC 1	SN 1	GW 1
							🛒						A 🛒						🛒		🛒			
Brighton 10 d	07 55	08 04					08 19		08 07						08 34				08 49			08 37		
Hove 2 d													08 21											
Preston Park d	07 58								08 11													08 41		
Hassocks 4 d	08 05								08 17													08 47		
Burgess Hill 4 d	08 08								08 21													08 51		
Lewes 4 d														08 20										
Wivelsfield 4 d	08 11								08 23					08 34								08 53		
Haywards Heath 3 a	08 15	08 18							08 28				08 35	08 40	08 48							08 58		
d	08 16	08 18							08 32				08 43		08 48							09 02		
Balcombe d									08 37															
Horsham 4 d								08 20				08 30									08 50			
Littlehaven d												08 33												
Faygate d																								
Ifield d												08 39												
Crawley d								08 29				08 43									08 59			
Three Bridges 4 a	08 25				←			08 32	08 42			08 46									09 02	09 11		
d	08 31				08 31			08 33	08 42			08 48									09 03	09 12		
Gatwick Airport 10 ✈ a	→	08 30			08 35			08 37	08 46			08 52	08 54		09 00						09 07	09 16		
d		08 31		08 35	08 38			08 38	08 46		08 50	08 53	08 55		09 01	09 03	09 05				09 08	09 16		
Horley 4 d								08 41				08 56												
Salfords d																								
Earlswood (Surrey) d																								
Tonbridge 4 d										08 19														
Leigh (Kent) d										08 23														
Penshurst d										08 27														
Edenbridge d										08 33														
Godstone d										08 40														
Nutfield d										08 45														
Reigate d			08 34																				09 14	09 18
Redhill 5 a			08 38			←		08 47		08 50		09 02				09 10					09 15		09 18	09 25
d						08 37		08 48		08 51		09 07								←	09 16		09 21	
Merstham d						08 41						09 11								09 11				
Coulsdon South d						08 46				08 58		→								09 16			09 28	
Purley 4 d						08 49				09 02										09 19			09 32	
East Croydon 🚊 a		08 46			08 53	08 54	08 56	08 59	09 02	09 07			09 10		09 16				09 23	09 24	09 27	09 32	09 37	
d		08 47			08 53	08 55	08 56	09 00	09 02	09 07			09 11		09 17				09 24	09 25	09 28	09 32	09 37	
Norwood Junction 2 a						08 59														09 29				
London Bridge 4 ⊖ a		09 02				09 12			09 17	09 22					09 32					09 42		09 47	09 52	
London Waterloo (East) 4 ⊖ a										09 26													09 56	
London Charing Cross 4 ⊖ a										09 30													10 00	
London Blackfriars 3 ⊖ a																								
City Thameslink 3 a																								
Farringdon 3 ⊖ a																								
St Pancras International 15 ⊖ a																								
St Albans City a																								
Luton Airport Parkway 4 ✈ a																								
Luton 7 a																								
Bedford 10 a																								
Clapham Junction 10 d					09 03		09 06	09 10		*09b25*			09 20						09 33		09 37			
West Brompton ⊖ d																			*09 46*					
Kensington (Olympia) ⊖ d																			*09 50*					
Shepherd's Bush ⊖ d																			*09 53*					
Watford Junction a																			*10 19*					
Milton Keynes Central 10 a																			*11 00*					
London Victoria 15 ⊖ a				09 05	09 09		09 12	09 16		*09b32*	09 20		09 27				09 35		09 40		09 44			

For general notes see front of timetable
For details of catering facilities see
Directory of Train Operators

A 🛒 from Haywards Heath
b Change at East Croydon

Brighton → London, Bedford

Network Diagram - see first page of Table 186

		GX 1	SN 1	SN 1	SN 1	SN 1 ◇	FC 1	GW 1	GX 1	SN 1 ◇	SN 1	SN 1 ◇	SN 1	FC 1	SN 1	GX 1	SN 1	SN 1	SN 1	FC 1	GW 1	GX 1	SN 1 ◇	SN 1
												⊥						A ⊥					⊥	
Brighton [10]	d					08 55	09 04					09 19		09 07						09 34			09 49	
Hove [2]	d				08 51													09 21						
Preston Park	d					08 58								09 11										
Hassocks [4]	d					09 05								09 17										
Burgess Hill [4]	d				09 02	09 08								09 21										
Lewes [4]	d			08 50															09 20					
Wivelsfield [4]	d					09 11								09 23					09 34					
Haywards Heath [3]	a			09 05	09 09	09 15	09 18							09 28				09 35	09 40	09 48				
	d				09 13	09 16	09 18							09 32					09 43	09 48				
Balcombe	d													09 37										
Horsham [4]	d		09 00										09 20				09 30							
Littlehaven	d		09 03														09 33							
Faygate	d																09 39							
Ifield	d		09 09										09 29				09 43							
Crawley	d		09 13																					
Three Bridges [4]	a		09 16			09 25				←			09 32	09 42			09 46							
	d		09 18			09 31 →				09 31			09 33	09 42			09 48							
Gatwick Airport [10] ✈	a		09 22		09 24		09 30			09 35			09 37	09 46			09 52		09 54	10 00				
	d	09 20	09 23		09 25		09 31		09 35	09 38			09 38	09 46		09 50	09 53		09 55	10 01	10 03	10 05		
Horley [4]	d		09 26										09 41				09 56							
Salfords	d		09 30																					
Earlswood (Surrey)	d		09 33																					
Tonbridge [4]	d														09 19									
Leigh (Kent)	d														09 23									
Penshurst	d														09 27									
Edenbridge	d														09 33									
Godstone	d														09 40									
Nutfield	d														09 45									
Reigate	d							09 34			←										10 10			
Redhill [5]	a		09 36					09 38					09 47		09 50		10 02							←
	d		09 37 →								09 37		09 48		09 51		10 07							10 11
Merstham	d										09 41						10 11 →							10 16
Coulsdon South	d										09 46				09 58									10 19
Purley [4]	d										09 49				10 02									10 24
East Croydon	a				09 41		09 46			09 53	09 54	09 56	09 59	10 02	10 07				10 10	10 16			10 23	
	d				09 42		09 47			09 53	09 55	09 56	10 00	10 02	10 07				10 11	10 17			10 24	10 25
Norwood Junction [2]	a										09 59													10 29
London Bridge [4]	⊖ a						10 02				10 12			10 17	10 22					10 32				10 42
London Waterloo (East) [4]	⊖ a														10 26									
London Charing Cross [4]	⊖ a														10 30									
London Blackfriars [3]	⊖ a																							
City Thameslink [3]	a																							
Farringdon [3]	⊖ a																							
St Pancras International [15]	⊖ a																							
St Albans City	a																							
Luton Airport Parkway [4]	✈ a																							
Luton [7]	a																							
Bedford [10]	a																							
Clapham Junction [10]	d				09 51					10 03		10 06	10 10		10b25				10 20				10 33	
West Brompton	⊖ d																						10 47	
Kensington (Olympia)	⊖ d																						10 50	
Shepherd's Bush	⊖ d																						10 53	
Watford Junction	a																						11 20	
Milton Keynes Central [10]	a																						12 00	
London Victoria [15]	⊖ a	09 50			09 58				10 05	10 09		10 12	10 16		10b32	10 20			10 27			10 35	10 40	

For general notes see front of timetable
For details of catering facilities see
Directory of Train Operators

A ⊥ from Haywards Heath
b Change at East Croydon

Table 186

Saturdays

Brighton → London, Bedford

Network Diagram - see first page of Table 186

		SN	FC	SN	GW	GX	SN	SN	SN	SN	FC	GW	GX	SN	SN	SN	SN	FC	SN	GX	SN	SN	SN	FC
		1	1	1	1	1	1	1	1	1 ◇	1	1	1	1 ◇	1	1 ◇	1	1	1	1	1	1	1	1
		🍴														🍴						A 🍴		
Brighton 10	d		09 37							09 55	10 04					10 19		10 07						10 34
Hove 2	d								09 51													10 21		
Preston Park	d		09 41							09 58								10 11						
Hassocks 4	d		09 47							10 05								10 17						
Burgess Hill 4	d		09 51						10 02	10 08								10 21						
Lewes 4	d						09 50																10 20	
Wivelsfield 4	d		09 53							10 11								10 23					10 34	
Haywards Heath 3	a		09 58				10 05		10 08	10 15	10 18							10 28				10 35	10 40	10 48
	d		10 02				10 09		10 12	10 16	10 18							10 32				10 43		10 48
Balcombe	d																	10 37						
Horsham 4	d	09 50						10 00									10 20				10 30			
Littlehaven	d							10 03													10 33			
Faygate	d																							
Ifield	d							10 09													10 39			
Crawley	d	09 59						10 13									10 29				10 43			
Three Bridges 4	a	10 02	10 11					10 16		10 25				←			10 32	10 42			10 46			
	d	10 03	10 12					10 18		10 31 →				10 31			10 33	10 42			10 48			
Gatwick Airport 10 ✈	a	10 07	10 16				10 21	10 22	10 25		10 30			10 35			10 37	10 46			10 52	10 54		11 00
	d	10 08	10 16			10 20	10 22	10 23	10 26		10 31		10 35	10 38			10 38	10 46		10 50	10 53	10 55		11 01
Horley 4	d							10 26									10 41				10 56			
Salfords	d							10 30																
Earlswood (Surrey)	d							10 33																
Tonbridge 4	d																		10 19					
Leigh (Kent)	d																		10 23					
Penshurst	d																		10 27					
Edenbridge	d																		10 33					
Godstone	d																		10 40					
Nutfield	d																		10 45					
Reigate	d			10 14	10 19							10 34												
Redhill 5	a	10 15		10 18	10 25			10 36				10 38			←		10 47		10 50		11 02			
	d	10 16		10 21				10 37 →							10 37		10 48		10 51		11 07			
Merstham	d														10 41						11 11			
Coulsdon South	d			10 28											10 46				10 58		→			
Purley 4	d			10 32											10 49				11 02					
East Croydon	a	10 27	10 32	10 37			10 38		10 42		10 46			10 53	10 54	10 56	10 59	11 02	11 07			11 10		11 16
	d	10 28	10 32	10 37			10 38		10 42		10 47			10 53	10 55	10 56	11 00	11 02	11 07			11 11		11 17
Norwood Junction 2	a														10 59									
London Bridge 4	⊖ a		10 47	10 52							11 02				11 12			11 17	11 22					11 32
London Waterloo (East) 4	⊖ a			10 56															11 26					
London Charing Cross 4	⊖ a			11 00															11 30					
London Blackfriars 3	⊖ a																							
City Thameslink 3	a																							
Farringdon 3	⊖ a																							
St Pancras International 15	⊖ a																							
St Albans City	a																							
Luton Airport Parkway 4	✈ a																							
Luton 7	a																							
Bedford 10	a																							
Clapham Junction 10	d	10 37					10 48		10 52					11 03		11 06	11 10		11b25			11 20		
West Brompton	⊖ d																							
Kensington (Olympia)	⊖ d																							
Shepherd's Bush	⊖ d																							
Watford Junction	a																							
Milton Keynes Central 10	a																							
London Victoria 15	⊖ a	10 44				10 50	10 56		10 59				11 05	11 09		11 12	11 16		11b32	11 20		11 27		

For general notes see front of timetable
For details of catering facilities see Directory of Train Operators

A 🍴 from Haywards Heath
b Change at East Croydon

Brighton → London, Bedford

Network Diagram - see first page of Table 186

		GW 1	GX 1	SN 1 ◇ 🚲	SN 1	SN 1 🚲	FC 1	SN 1	GW 1	GX 1	SN 1	SN 1	SN 1	SN 1 ◇	FC 1	GW 1	GX 1	SN 1 ◇	SN 1	SN 1 ◇ 🚲	SN 1	FC 1	SN 1	GX 1
Brighton 10	d			10 49			10 37							10 55	11 04					11 19		11 07		
Hove 2	d												10 51											
Preston Park	d						10 41							10 58								11 11		
Hassocks 4	d						10 47							11 05								11 17		
Burgess Hill 4	d						10 51						11 02	11 08								11 21		
Lewes 4	d											10 50												
Wivelsfield 4	d						10 53							11 11								11 23		
Haywards Heath 3	a						10 58					11 05	11 09	11 15	11 18							11 28		
	d						11 02						11 13	11 16	11 18							11 32		
Balcombe	d																					11 37		
Horsham 4	d					10 50					11 00										11 20			
Littlehaven	d										11 03													
Faygate	d																							
Ifield	d										11 09													
Crawley	d					10 59					11 13										11 29			
Three Bridges 4	a					11 02	11 11				11 16			11 25				←			11 32	11 42		
	d					11 03	11 12				11 18			11 31 →				11 31			11 33	11 42		
Gatwick Airport 10 ✈	a					11 07	11 16				11 22		11 24		11 30			11 35			11 37	11 46		
	d	11 03	11 05			11 08	11 16			11 20	11 23		11 25		11 31		11 35	11 38			11 38	11 46		11 50
Horley 4	d										11 26										11 41			
Salfords	d										11 30													
Earlswood (Surrey)	d										11 33													
Tonbridge 4	d																						11 19	
Leigh (Kent)	d																						11 23	
Penshurst	d																						11 27	
Edenbridge	d																						11 33	
Godstone	d																						11 40	
Nutfield	d																						11 45	
Reigate	d							11 14	11 18							11 34								
Redhill 5	a	11 10				11 15		11 18	11 25		11 36					11 38			←		11 47		11 50	
	d				←	11 16		11 21			11 37 →								11 37		11 48		11 51	
Merstham	d				11 11														11 41					
Coulsdon South	d				11 16			11 28											11 46				11 58	
Purley 4	d				11 19			11 32											11 49				12 02	
East Croydon 🚋	a			11 23	11 24	11 27	11 32	11 37					11 40		11 46			11 53	11 54	11 56	11 59	12 02	12 07	
	d			11 24	11 25	11 28	11 32	11 37					11 41		11 47			11 53	11 55	11 56	12 00	12 02	12 07	
Norwood Junction 2	a				11 29														11 59					
London Bridge 4	⊖ a				11 42		11 47	11 52							12 02				12 12			12 17	12 22	
London Waterloo (East) 4	⊖ a							11 56															12 26	
London Charing Cross 4	⊖ a							12 00															12 30	
London Blackfriars 3	⊖ a																							
City Thameslink 3	a																							
Farringdon 3	⊖ a																							
St Pancras International 15	⊖ a																							
St Albans City	a																							
Luton Airport Parkway 4	✈ a																							
Luton 7	a																							
Bedford 10	a																							
Clapham Junction 10	d			11 33		11 37		*11b55*					11 50					12 03		12 06	12 10		*12b25*	
West Brompton	⊖ d			*11 46*																				
Kensington (Olympia)	⊖ d			*11 50*																				
Shepherd's Bush	⊖ d			*11 53*																				
Watford Junction	a			*12 19*																				
Milton Keynes Central 10	a			*13 00*																				
London Victoria 15	⊖ a		11 35	11 40		11 44		*12b02*		11 50			11 57				12 05	12 09		12 12	12 16		*12b32*	12 20

For general notes see front of timetable
For details of catering facilities see Directory of Train Operators

b Change at East Croydon

Table 186

Brighton → London, Bedford

Network Diagram - see first page of Table 186

		SN	SN	SN	FC	GW	GX	SN	SN	SN	FC	SN	GW	GX		SN	SN	SN	SN	FC	GW	GX	SN	SN	SN
		1	1	1	1	1	1	1 ◇	1	1	1	1	1	1		1	1	1	1 ◇	1	1	1	1 ◇	1	1 ◇
			A [trolley]					[trolley]		[trolley]															[trolley]
Brighton 10	d				11 34			11 49			11 37								11 55	12 04					12 19
Hove 2	d		11 21															11 51							
Preston Park	d										11 41								11 58						
Hassocks 4	d										11 47								12 05						
Burgess Hill 4	d										11 51							12 02	12 08						
Lewes 4	d			11 20													11 50								
Wivelsfield 4	d			11 34							11 53								12 11						
Haywards Heath 3	a		11 35	11 40	11 48						11 58						12 05	12 09	12 15	12 18					
	d		11 43		11 48						12 02						12 13		12 16	12 18					
Balcombe	d																								
Horsham 4	d	11 30								11 50						12 00									
Littlehaven	d	11 33														12 03									
Faygate	d																								
Ifield	d	11 39														12 09									
Crawley	d	11 43								11 59						12 13									
Three Bridges 4	a	11 46								12 02	12 11					12 16			12 25				←		
	d	11 48								12 03	12 12					12 18			12 31 →				12 31		
Gatwick Airport 10	a	11 52	11 54		12 00					12 07	12 16					12 22	12 24			12 30			12 35		
	d	11 53	11 55		12 01	12 03	12 05			12 08	12 16			12 20		12 23	12 25			12 31		12 35	12 38		
Horley 4	d	11 56														12 26									
Salfords	d															12 30									
Earlswood (Surrey)	d															12 33									
Tonbridge 4	d																								
Leigh (Kent)	d																								
Penshurst	d																								
Edenbridge	d																								
Godstone	d																								
Nutfield	d																								
Reigate	d											12 14	12 19								12 34				
Redhill 5	a	12 02				12 10				12 15		12 18	12 25			12 36					12 38			←	
	d	12 07							←	12 16		12 21				12 37 →								12 37	
Merstham	d	12 11 →							12 11															12 41	
Coulsdon South	d								12 16			12 28												12 46	
Purley 4	d								12 19			12 32												12 49	
East Croydon	a		12 10		12 16			12 23	12 24	12 27	12 32	12 37					12 40			12 46			12 53	12 54	12 56
	d		12 11		12 17			12 24	12 25	12 28	12 32	12 37					12 41			12 47			12 53	12 55	12 56
Norwood Junction 2	a								12 29															12 59	
London Bridge 4	⊖ a				12 32				12 42		12 47	12 52								13 02				13 12	
London Waterloo (East) 4	⊖ a											12 56													
London Charing Cross 4	⊖ a											13 00													
London Blackfriars 3	⊖ a																								
City Thameslink 3	a																								
Farringdon 3	⊖ a																								
St Pancras International 15	⊖ a																								
St Albans City	a																								
Luton Airport Parkway 4	✈ a																								
Luton 7	a																								
Bedford 10	a																								
Clapham Junction 10	d		12 20					12 33		12 37		12b55					12 50						13 03		13 06
West Brompton	⊖ d							12 46																	
Kensington (Olympia)	⊖ d							12 50																	
Shepherd's Bush	⊖ d							12 53																	
Watford Junction	a							13 19																	
Milton Keynes Central 10	a							14 00																	
London Victoria 15	⊖ a		12 27				12 35	12 40		12 44		13b02		12 50			12 57					13 05	13 09		13 12

For general notes see front of timetable
For details of catering facilities see
Directory of Train Operators

A [trolley] from Haywards Heath
b Change at East Croydon

Table 186

Brighton → London, Bedford

Network Diagram - see first page of Table 186

		SN	FC	SN	GX	SN	SN	SN	FC	GW	GX	SN	SN		SN	FC	SN	GW	GX	SN	SN	SN	SN	FC	GW
		1	1	1	1	1	1	1	1	1	1	1 ◇	1		1	1	1	1	1	1	1	1	1 ◇	1	1
							A 🚌					🚌			🚌										
Brighton [10]	d		12 07						12 34			12 49				12 37							12 55	13 04	
Hove [2]	d						12 21															12 51			
Preston Park	d		12 11													12 41							12 58		
Hassocks [4]	d		12 17													12 47							13 05		
Burgess Hill [4]	d		12 21													12 51						13 02	13 08		
Lewes [4]	d							12 20													12 50				
Wivelsfield [4]	d		12 23					12 34								12 53							13 11		
Haywards Heath [3]	a		12 28				12 35	12 40	12 48							12 58					13 05	13 09	13 15	13 18	
	d		12 32					12 43	12 48							13 02						13 13	13 16	13 18	
Balcombe	d		12 37																						
Horsham [4]	d	12 20				12 30									12 50					13 00					
Littlehaven	d					12 33														13 03					
Faygate	d																								
Ifield	d					12 39														13 09					
Crawley	d	12 29				12 43									12 59					13 13					
Three Bridges [4]	a	12 32	12 42			12 46									13 02	13 11				13 16			13 25		
	d	12 33	12 42			12 48									13 03	13 12				13 18			13 31 →		
Gatwick Airport [10] ✈	a	12 37	12 46			12 52		12 54	13 00						13 07	13 16				13 22		13 24		13 30	
	d	12 38	12 46		12 50	12 53		12 55	13 01	13 03	13 05				13 08	13 16			13 20	13 23		13 25		13 31	
Horley [4]	d	12 41				12 56														13 26					
Salfords	d																			13 30					
Earlswood (Surrey)	d																			13 33					
Tonbridge [4]	d			12 19																					
Leigh (Kent)	d			12 23																					
Penshurst	d			12 27																					
Edenbridge	d			12 33																					
Godstone	d			12 40																					
Nutfield	d			12 45																					
Reigate	d																13 14	13 18							13 34
Redhill [5]	a	12 47		12 50		13 02				13 10					13 15		13 18	13 25		13 36					13 38
	d	12 48		12 51		13 07							←		13 16		13 21			13 37 →					
Merstham	d					13 11 →							13 11												
Coulsdon South	d			12 58									13 16				13 28								
Purley [4]	d			13 02									13 19				13 32								
East Croydon	a	12 59	13 02	13 07				13 10	13 16			13 23	13 24		13 27	13 32	13 37					13 40		13 46	
	d	13 00	13 02	13 07				13 11	13 17			13 24	13 25		13 28	13 32	13 37					13 41		13 47	
Norwood Junction [2]	a												13 29												
London Bridge [4]	⊖ a		13 17	13 22					13 32				13 42			13 47	13 52							14 02	
London Waterloo (East) [4]	⊖ a			13 26													13 56								
London Charing Cross [4]	⊖ a			13 30													14 00								
London Blackfriars [3]	⊖ a																								
City Thameslink [3]	a																								
Farringdon [3]	⊖ a																								
St Pancras International [15]	⊖ a																								
St Albans City	a																								
Luton Airport Parkway [4] ✈	a																								
Luton [7]	a																								
Bedford [10]	a																								
Clapham Junction [10]	d	13 10		13b25				13 20				13 33			13 37		13b55					13 50			
West Brompton	⊖ d											13 47													
Kensington (Olympia)	⊖ d											13 50													
Shepherd's Bush	⊖ d											13 53													
Watford Junction	a											14 20													
Milton Keynes Central [10]	a											15 00													
London Victoria [15]	⊖ a	13 16		13b32	13 20			13 27			13 35	13 40			13 44		14b02		13 50			13 57			

For general notes see front of timetable
For details of catering facilities see
Directory of Train Operators

A 🚌 from Haywards Heath
b Change at East Croydon

Table 186

Brighton → London, Bedford

Saturdays

Network Diagram - see first page of Table 186

		GX 1	SN 1 ◇	SN 1	SN 1 ◇ 🛒	SN 1	FC 1	SN 1	GX 1	SN 1	SN 1 A 🛒	SN 1		FC 1	GW 1	GX 1	SN 1 ◇ 🛒	SN 1	SN 1 🛒	FC 1	SN 1	GW 1	GX 1	SN 1	
Brighton 10	d				13 19		13 07							13 34			13 49			13 37					
Hove 2	d										13 21														
Preston Park	d						13 11													13 41					
Hassocks 4	d						13 17													13 47					
Burgess Hill 4	d						13 21													13 51					
Lewes 4	d											13 20													
Wivelsfield 4	d						13 23					13 34								13 53					
Haywards Heath 3	a						13 28				13 35	13 40		13 48						13 58					
	d						13 32				13 43			13 48						14 02					
Balcombe	d						13 37																		
Horsham 4	d					13 20				13 30									13 50					14 00	
Littlehaven	d									13 33														14 03	
Faygate	d																								
Ifield	d									13 39														14 09	
Crawley	d					13 29				13 43									13 59					14 13	
Three Bridges 4	a		←			13 32	13 42			13 46									14 02	14 11				14 16	
	d		13 31			13 33	13 42			13 48									14 03	14 12				14 18	
Gatwick Airport 10 ✈	a		13 35			13 37	13 46			13 52	13 54			14 00					14 07	14 16				14 22	
	d	13 35	13 38			13 38	13 46		13 50	13 53	13 55			14 01	14 03	14 05			14 08	14 16			14 20	14 23	
Horley 4	d					13 41				13 56														14 26	
Salfords	d																							14 30	
Earlswood (Surrey)	d																							14 33	
Tonbridge 4	d							13 19																	
Leigh (Kent)	d							13 23																	
Penshurst	d							13 27																	
Edenbridge	d							13 33																	
Godstone	d							13 40																	
Nutfield	d							13 45																	
Reigate	d																				14 14	14 19			
Redhill 5	a			←		13 47		13 50		14 02					14 10				14 15		14 18	14 25		14 36	
	d			13 37		13 48		13 51		14 07								←	14 16		14 21			14 37 →	
Merstham	d			13 41						14 11 →								14 11							
Coulsdon South	d			13 46				13 58										14 16			14 28				
Purley 4	d			13 49				14 02										14 19			14 32				
East Croydon 🚊	a		13 53	13 54	13 56	13 59	14 02	14 07			14 10			14 16			14 23	14 24	14 27	14 32	14 37				
	d		13 53	13 55	13 56	14 00	14 02	14 07			14 11			14 17			14 24	14 25	14 28	14 32	14 37				
Norwood Junction 2	a			13 59														14 29							
London Bridge 4 ⊖	a			14 12			14 17	14 22						14 32				14 42		14 47	14 52				
London Waterloo (East) 4 ⊖	a							14 26													14 56				
London Charing Cross 4 ⊖	a							14 30													15 00				
London Blackfriars 3 ⊖	a																								
City Thameslink 3	a																								
Farringdon 3 ⊖	a																								
St Pancras International 15 ⊖	a																								
St Albans City	a																								
Luton Airport Parkway 4 ✈	a																								
Luton 7	a																								
Bedford 10	a																								
Clapham Junction 10	d		14 03		14 06	14 10		14b25			14 20						14 33		14 37		14b55				
West Brompton ⊖	d																14 46								
Kensington (Olympia) ⊖	d																14 50								
Shepherd's Bush ⊖	d																14 53								
Watford Junction	a																15 19								
Milton Keynes Central 10	a																16 00								
London Victoria 15 ⊖	a	14 05	14 09		14 12	14 16		14b35	14 20		14 27					14 35	14 40		14 44		15b02		14 50		

For general notes see front of timetable
For details of catering facilities see
Directory of Train Operators

A 🛒 from Haywards Heath
b Change at East Croydon

Table 186

Saturdays

Brighton → London, Bedford

Network Diagram - see first page of Table 186

		SN [1]	SN [1]	SN [1] ◇	FC [1]	GW [1]	GX [1]	SN [1] ◇	SN [1]	SN [1] ◇	SN [1]		FC [1]	SN [1]	GX [1]	SN [1]	SN [1]	SN [1]	FC [1]	GW [1]	GX [1]	SN [1] ◇	SN [1]	SN [1]	FC [1]
										⊤							A ⊤					⊤		⊤	
Brighton [10]	d			13 55	14 04					14 19			14 07						14 34			14 49			14 37
Hove [2]	d		13 51														14 21								
Preston Park	d			13 58									14 11												14 41
Hassocks [4]	d			14 05									14 17												14 47
Burgess Hill [4]	d		14 02	14 08									14 21												14 51
Lewes [4]	d	13 50																14 20							
Wivelsfield [4]	d			14 11									14 23					14 34							14 53
Haywards Heath [3]	a	14 05	14 09	14 15	14 18								14 28				14 35	14 39	14 48						14 58
	d		14 13	14 16	14 18								14 32					14 43	14 48						15 02
Balcombe	d												14 37												
Horsham [4]	d										14 20					14 30								14 50	
Littlehaven	d															14 33									
Faygate	d																								
Ifield	d															14 39									
Crawley	d										14 29					14 43								14 59	
Three Bridges [4]	a			14 25				←			14 32		14 42			14 46								15 02	15 11
	d			14 31				14 31			14 33		14 42			14 48								15 03	15 12
Gatwick Airport [10] ✈	a		14 24	→	14 30			14 35			14 37		14 46			14 52		14 54	15 00					15 07	15 16
	d		14 25		14 31		14 35	14 38			14 38		14 46		14 50	14 53		14 55	15 01	15 03	15 05			15 08	15 16
Horley [4]	d										14 41					14 56									
Salfords	d																								
Earlswood (Surrey)	d																								
Tonbridge [4]	d													14 19											
Leigh (Kent)	d													14 23											
Penshurst	d													14 27											
Edenbridge	d													14 33											
Godstone	d													14 40											
Nutfield	d													14 45											
Reigate	d					14 34																			
Redhill [5]	a					14 38			←		14 47			14 50		15 02				15 10				15 15	
	d								14 37		14 48			14 51		15 07							←	15 16	
Merstham	d								14 41							15 11							15 11		
Coulsdon South	d								14 46					14 58		→							15 16		
Purley [4]	d								14 49					15 02									15 19		
East Croydon	a		14 40		14 46			14 53	14 54	14 56	14 59		15 02	15 07				15 10	15 16			15 23	15 24	15 27	15 32
	d		14 41		14 47			14 53	14 55	14 56	15 00		15 02	15 07				15 11	15 17			15 24	15 25	15 28	15 32
Norwood Junction [2]	a								14 59														15 29		
London Bridge [4] ⊖	a				15 02				15 12				15 17	15 22					15 32				15 42		15 47
London Waterloo (East) [4] ⊖	a													15 26											
London Charing Cross [4] ⊖	a													15 30											
London Blackfriars [3] ⊖	a																								
City Thameslink [3]	a																								
Farringdon [3] ⊖	a																								
St Pancras International [15] ⊖	a																								
St Albans City	a																								
Luton Airport Parkway [4] ✈	a																								
Luton [7]	a																								
Bedford [10]	a																								
Clapham Junction [10]	d		14 50					15 03		15 06	15 10			15b25				15 20				15 33		15 37	
West Brompton ⊖	d																					*15 46*			
Kensington (Olympia) ⊖	d																					*15 50*			
Shepherd's Bush ⊖	d																					*15 53*			
Watford Junction	a																					*16 19*			
Milton Keynes Central [10]	a																					*17 00*			
London Victoria [15] ⊖	a		14 57				15 05	15 09		15 12	15 16			15b32	15 20			15 27			15 35	15 40		15 44	

For general notes see front of timetable
For details of catering facilities see
Directory of Train Operators

A ⊤ from Haywards Heath
b Change at East Croydon

Table 186

Brighton → London, Bedford

Saturdays

Network Diagram - see first page of Table 186

	SN 1	GW 1	GX 1	SN 1	SN 1	SN 1	SN 1 ◇	FC 1	GW 1		GX 1	SN 1 ◇	SN 1	SN 1 ◇	SN 1	FC 1	SN 1	GX 1	SN 1	SN 1	SN 1	FC 1	GW 1	GX 1
														⌶						A ⌶				
Brighton 10 d							14 55	15 04						15 19		15 07						15 34		
Hove 2 d						14 51														15 21				
Preston Park d							14 58									15 11								
Hassocks 4 d							15 05									15 17								
Burgess Hill 4 d						15 02	15 08									15 21								
Lewes 4 d					14 50																15 20			
Wivelsfield 4 d							15 11									15 23					15 34			
Haywards Heath 3 a					15 05	15 09	15 15	15 18								15 28				15 35	15 40	15 48		
d					15 13		15 16	15 18								15 32				15 43		15 48		
Balcombe d																15 37								
Horsham 4 d				15 00											15 20				15 30					
Littlehaven d				15 03															15 33					
Faygate d																								
Ifield d				15 09															15 39					
Crawley d				15 13											15 29				15 43					
Three Bridges 4 a				15 16			15 25					←			15 32	15 42			15 46					
d				15 18			15 31 →					15 31			15 33	15 42			15 48					
Gatwick Airport 10 ✈ a				15 22	15 24			15 30				15 35			15 37	15 46			15 52	15 54		16 00		
d			15 20	15 23	15 25			15 31			15 35	15 38			15 38	15 46		15 50	15 53	15 55		16 01	16 03	16 05
Horley 4 d				15 26											15 41				15 56					
Salfords d				15 30																				
Earlswood (Surrey) d				15 33																				
Tonbridge 4 d																	15 19							
Leigh (Kent) d																	15 23							
Penshurst d																	15 27							
Edenbridge d																	15 33							
Godstone d																	15 40							
Nutfield d																	15 45							
Reigate d	15 14	15 18							15 34															
Redhill 5 a	15 18	15 25		15 36					15 38				←		15 47		15 50		16 02				16 10	
d	15 21			15 37 →									15 37		15 48		15 51		16 07					
Merstham d													15 41						16 11 →					
Coulsdon South d	15 28												15 46				15 58							
Purley 4 d	15 32												15 49				16 02							
East Croydon a	15 37				15 40			15 46				15 53	15 54	15 56	15 59	16 02	16 07			16 10		16 16		
d	15 37				15 41			15 47				15 53	15 55	15 56	16 00	16 02	16 07			16 11		16 17		
Norwood Junction 2 a													15 59											
London Bridge 4 ⊖ a	15 52							16 02					16 12			16 17	16 22					16 32		
London Waterloo (East) 4 ⊖ a	15 56																16 26							
London Charing Cross 4 ⊖ a	16 00																16 30							
London Blackfriars 3 ⊖ a																								
City Thameslink 3 a																								
Farringdon 3 ⊖ a																								
St Pancras International 15 ⊖ a																								
St Albans City a																								
Luton Airport Parkway 4 ✈ a																								
Luton 7 a																								
Bedford 10 a																								
Clapham Junction 10 d	15b55				15 50							16 03		16 06	16 10		16b25			16 20				
West Brompton ⊖ d																								
Kensington (Olympia) ⊖ d																								
Shepherd's Bush ⊖ d																								
Watford Junction a																								
Milton Keynes Central 10 a																								
London Victoria 15 ⊖ a	16b02		15 50		15 57						16 05	16 09		16 12	16 16		16b32	16 20		16 27				16 35

For general notes see front of timetable
For details of catering facilities see Directory of Train Operators

A ⌶ from Haywards Heath
b Change at East Croydon

Table 186

Brighton → London, Bedford

Network Diagram - see first page of Table 186

		SN 1◇ 🚲	SN 1	SN 1 🚲	FC 1	SN 1	GW 1	GX 1	SN 1		SN 1	SN 1	SN 1◇	FC 1	GW 1	GX 1	SN 1◇	SN 1	SN 1◇ 🚲	SN 1	FC 1	SN 1	GX 1	SN 1
Brighton 10	d	15 49			15 37								15 55	16 04					16 19		16 07			
Hove 2	d											15 51												
Preston Park	d				15 41								15 58								16 11			
Hassocks 4	d				15 47								16 05								16 17			
Burgess Hill 4	d				15 51							16 02	16 08								16 21			
Lewes 4	d										15 50													
Wivelsfield 4	d				15 53								16 11								16 23			
Haywards Heath 3	a				15 58						16 05	16 09	16 15	16 18							16 28			
	d				16 02							16 13	16 16	16 18							16 32			
Balcombe	d																				16 37			
Horsham 4	d			15 50					16 00											16 20				16 30
Littlehaven	d								16 03															16 33
Faygate	d																							
Ifield	d								16 09															16 39
Crawley	d			15 59					16 13											16 29				16 43
Three Bridges 4	a			16 02	16 11				16 16				16 25				←			16 32	16 42			16 46
	d			16 03	16 12				16 18				16 31 →				16 31			16 33	16 42			16 48
Gatwick Airport 10 ✈	a			16 07	16 16				16 22			16 24		16 30			16 35			16 37	16 46			16 52
	d			16 08	16 16			16 20	16 23			16 25		16 31		16 35	16 38			16 38	16 46		16 50	16 53
Horley 4	d								16 26											16 41				16 56
Salfords	d								16 30															
Earlswood (Surrey)	d								16 33															
Tonbridge 4	d																					16 19		
Leigh (Kent)	d																					16 23		
Penshurst	d																					16 27		
Edenbridge	d																					16 33		
Godstone	d																					16 40		
Nutfield	d																					16 45		
Reigate	d					16 14	16 19								16 34									
Redhill 5	a			16 15		16 18	16 25		16 36						16 38			←		16 47		16 50		17 02
	d		←	16 16		16 21			16 37 →									16 37		16 48		16 51		17 07
Merstham	d		16 11															16 41						17 11
Coulsdon South	d		16 16			16 28												16 46				16 58		→
Purley 4	d		16 19			16 32												16 49				17 02		
East Croydon	a	16 23	16 24	16 27	16 32	16 37						16 40		16 46			16 53	16 54	16 56	16 59	17 02	17 07		
	d	16 24	16 25	16 28	16 32	16 37						16 41		16 47			16 53	16 55	16 56	17 00	17 02	17 07		
Norwood Junction 2	a		16 29															16 59						
London Bridge 4	⊖ a		16 42		16 47	16 52								17 02				17 12			17 17	17 22		
London Waterloo (East) 4	⊖ a					16 56																17 26		
London Charing Cross 4	⊖ a					17 00																17 30		
London Blackfriars 3	⊖ a																							
City Thameslink 3	a																							
Farringdon 3	⊖ a																							
St Pancras International 15	⊖ a																							
St Albans City	a																							
Luton Airport Parkway 4	✈ a																							
Luton 7	a																							
Bedford 10	a																							
Clapham Junction 10	d	16 33		16 37			16b55					16 50					17 03		17 06	17 10		17b25		
West Brompton	⊖ d	16 46																						
Kensington (Olympia)	⊖ d	16 50																						
Shepherd's Bush	⊖ d	16 53																						
Watford Junction	a	17 19																						
Milton Keynes Central 10	a	18 00																						
London Victoria 15	⊖ a	16 40		16 44			17b02	16 50				16 57				17 05	17 09		17 12	17 16		17b32	17 20	

For general notes see front of timetable
For details of catering facilities see
Directory of Train Operators

b Change at East Croydon

Brighton → London, Bedford

Network Diagram - see first page of Table 186

		SN	SN	FC	GW	GX	SN	SN		SN	FC	SN	GW	GX	SN	SN	SN	SN	FC	GW	GX	SN	SN	SN	SN
		1	1	1	1	1	1 ◇	1		1	1	1	1	1	1	1	1	1 ◇	1	1	1	1 ◇	1	1 ◇	1
		A ⌶					⌶			⌶														⌶	
Brighton 10	d			16 34			16 49				16 37							16 55	17 04					17 19	
Hove 2	d	16 21															16 51								
Preston Park	d										16 41							16 58							
Hassocks 4	d										16 47							17 05							
Burgess Hill 4	d										16 51						17 02	17 08							
Lewes 4	d		16 20													16 50									
Wivelsfield 4	d		16 34								16 53							17 11							
Haywards Heath 3	a	16 35	16 40	16 48							16 58					17 05	17 09	17 15	17 18						
	d	16 43		16 48							17 02					17 13		17 16	17 18						
Balcombe	d																								
Horsham 4	d									16 50					17 00										17 20
Littlehaven	d														17 03										
Faygate	d																								
Ifield	d														17 09										
Crawley	d									16 59					17 13										17 29
Three Bridges 4	a									17 02	17 11				17 16			17 25				←			17 32
	d									17 03	17 12				17 18			17 31 →				17 31			17 33
Gatwick Airport 10 ✈	a	16 54		17 00						17 07	17 16				17 22	17 24			17 30			17 35			17 37
	d	16 55		17 01	17 03	17 05				17 08	17 16			17 20	17 23	17 25			17 31		17 35	17 38			17 38
Horley 4	d														17 26										17 41
Salfords	d														17 30										
Earlswood (Surrey)	d														17 33										
Tonbridge 4	d																								
Leigh (Kent)	d																								
Penshurst	d																								
Edenbridge	d																								
Godstone	d																								
Nutfield	d																								
Reigate	d											17 14	17 18												
Redhill 5	a				17 10					17 15		17 18	17 25		17 36					17 34			←		17 47
	d							←		17 16		17 21			17 37 →					17 38			17 37		17 48
Merstham	d							17 11															17 41		
Coulsdon South	d							17 16				17 28											17 46		
Purley 4	d							17 19				17 32											17 49		
East Croydon	a	17 10		17 16			17 23	17 24		17 27	17 32	17 37				17 40			17 46			17 53	17 54	17 56	17 59
	d	17 11		17 17			17 24	17 25		17 28	17 32	17 37				17 41			17 47			17 53	17 55	17 56	18 00
Norwood Junction 2	a							17 29															17 59		
London Bridge 4 ⊖	a			17 32				17 42			17 47	17 52							18 02				18 12		
London Waterloo (East) 4 ⊖	a											17 56													
London Charing Cross 4 ⊖	a											18 00													
London Blackfriars 3 ⊖	a																								
City Thameslink 3	a																								
Farringdon 3 ⊖	a																								
St Pancras International 15 ⊖	a																								
St Albans City	a																								
Luton Airport Parkway 4 ✈	a																								
Luton 7	a																								
Bedford 10	a																								
Clapham Junction 10	d	17 20					17 33			17 37		17b55				17 50						18 03		18 06	18 10
West Brompton ⊖	d						17 46																		
Kensington (Olympia) ⊖	d						17 50																		
Shepherd's Bush ⊖	d						17 53																		
Watford Junction	a						18 19																		
Milton Keynes Central 10	a						19 00																		
London Victoria 15 ⊖	a	17 27				17 35	17 40			17 44		18b02		17 50		17 57					18 05	18 09		18 12	18 16

For general notes see front of timetable
For details of catering facilities see Directory of Train Operators

A ⌶ from Haywards Heath
b Change at East Croydon

Brighton → London, Bedford

Network Diagram - see first page of Table 186

Station		FC	SN	GX	SN	SN	SN	FC	GW	GX	SN	SN	SN	FC	SN	GW	GX	SN	SN	SN	GW	GX	SN	SN
		1	1	1	1	1	1	1	1	1	1 ◇	1	1	1	1	1	1	1	1	1	1	1	1 ◇	1
						A 🍴					🍴		🍴											
Brighton [10]	d	17 07						17 34			17 49			17 37									17 55	
Hove [2]	d					17 21														17 51				
Preston Park	d	17 11												17 41									17 58	
Hassocks [4]	d	17 17												17 47						18 02			18 05	
Burgess Hill [4]	d	17 21												17 51									18 08	
Lewes [4]	d						17 20												17 50					
Wivelsfield [4]	d	17 23					17 34							17 53									18 11	
Haywards Heath [3]	a	17 28				17 35	17 40	17 48						17 58					18 05	18 09			18 15	
	d	17 32					17 43	17 48						18 02						18 13			18 16	
Balcombe	d	17 37																						
Horsham [4]	d				17 30								17 50					18 00						
Littlehaven	d				17 33													18 03						
Faygate	d																	18 09						
Ifield	d				17 39								17 59					18 13						
Crawley	d				17 43																			
Three Bridges [4]	a	17 42			17 46								18 02	18 11				18 16					18 25	
	d	17 42			17 48								18 03	18 12				18 18					18 31	
Gatwick Airport [10] ✈	a	17 46			17 52		17 54	18 00					18 07	18 16				18 22		18 24			18 35	
	d	17 46		17 50	17 53		17 55	18 01	18 03	18 05			18 08	18 16			18 20	18 23		18 25		18 35	18 38	
Horley [4]	d				17 56													18 26						
Salfords	d																	18 30						
Earlswood (Surrey)	d																	18 33						
Tonbridge [4]	d		17 19																					
Leigh (Kent)	d		17 23																					
Penshurst	d		17 27																					
Edenbridge	d		17 33																					
Godstone	d		17 40																					
Nutfield	d		17 45																					
Reigate	d														18 14	18 19					18 34			
Redhill [5]	a		17 50		18 02				18 10				18 15		18 18	18 25		18 36			18 38			←
	d		17 51		18 07							←	18 16		18 21			18 37 →						18 37
Merstham	d				18 11 →							18 11												18 41
Coulsdon South	d		17 58									18 16			18 28									18 46
Purley [4]	d		18 02									18 19			18 32									18 49
East Croydon	a	18 02	18 07				18 10	18 16			18 23	18 24	18 27	18 32	18 37					18 40			18 53	18 54
	d	18 02	18 07				18 11	18 17			18 24	18 25	18 28	18 32	18 37					18 41			18 53	18 55
Norwood Junction [2]	a											18 29												18 59
London Bridge [4]	⊖ a	18 17	18 22					18 32				18 42		18 47	18 52					19 08				19 12
London Waterloo (East) [4]	⊖ a		18 26												18 56									
London Charing Cross [4]	⊖ a		18 30												19 00									
London Blackfriars [3]	⊖ a																							
City Thameslink [3]	a																							
Farringdon [3]	⊖ a																							
St Pancras International [15]	⊖ a																							
St Albans City	a																							
Luton Airport Parkway [4] ✈	a																							
Luton [7]	a																							
Bedford [10]	a																							
Clapham Junction [10]	d		18b25				18 20				18 33		18 37		18b55					18 50			19 03	
West Brompton	⊖ d										18 47													
Kensington (Olympia)	⊖ d										18 50													
Shepherd's Bush	⊖ d										18 52													
Watford Junction	a										19 21													
Milton Keynes Central [10]	a																							
London Victoria [15]	⊖ a		18b32	18 20			18 27			18 35	18 40		18 44		19b02		18 50			18 57		19 05	19 09	

For general notes see front of timetable
For details of catering facilities see
Directory of Train Operators

A 🍴 from Haywards Heath
b Change at East Croydon

Table 186

Saturdays

Brighton → London, Bedford

Network Diagram - see first page of Table 186

Station		SN 1 ◊	SN 1	FC 1	SN 1	GX 1		SN 1	SN 1 A ✠	SN 1	FC 1	GW 1	GX 1	SN 1 ◊	SN 1	SN 1	SN	FC 1	GW 1	GX 1	SN 1	SN 1	SN 1	SN 1 ◊	FC 1
Brighton 10	d	18 19		18 07							18 34			18 49				18 37						18 55	19 04
Hove 2	d								18 21														18 51		
Preston Park	d			18 11														18 41						18 58	
Hassocks 4	d			18 17														18 47						19 05	
Burgess Hill 4	d			18 21														18 51					19 02	19 08	
Lewes 4	d									18 20												18 50			
Wivelsfield 4	d			18 23						18 34								18 53						19 11	
Haywards Heath 3	a			18 28					18 35	18 40	18 48							18 58				19 05	19 09	19 15	19 18
	d			18 32					18 43		18 48							19 02				19 13		19 16	19 18
Balcombe	d			18 37																					
Horsham 4	d		18 20					18 32								18 50					19 02				
Littlehaven	d							18 35													19 05				
Faygate	d																								
Ifield	d							18 41													19 11				
Crawley	d		18 29					18 45								18 59					19 14				
Three Bridges 4	a		18 32	18 42				18 48								19 02		19 11			19 18			19 25	
	d		18 33	18 42				18 50								19 03		19 12			19 18			19 31	
Gatwick Airport 10 ✈	a		18 37	18 46				18 54	18 54		19 00					19 07		19 16			19 22	19 24		→	19 30
	d		18 38	18 46		18 50		18 55	18 55		19 01	19 03	19 05			19 08		19 16		19 20	19 23	19 25			19 31
Horley 4	d		18 41					18 58								19 11					19 26				
Salfords	d																				19 30				
Earlswood (Surrey)	d																				19 33				
Tonbridge 4	d				18 19																				
Leigh (Kent)	d				18 23																				
Penshurst	d				18 27																				
Edenbridge	d				18 33																				
Godstone	d				18 40																				
Nutfield	d				18 45																				
Reigate	d																19 14		19 18						
Redhill 5	a		18 47		18 50			19 04				19 10				19 17	19 18		19 25		19 36				
	d		18 48		18 51			19 07							←	19 18					19 37				
Merstham	d							19 11							19 11						→				
Coulsdon South	d				18 58			→							19 16										
Purley 4	d														19 20										
East Croydon	a	18 56	18 59	19 02	19 04				19 10		19 16			19 23	19 25	19 28		19 32				19 40			19 46
	d	18 56	19 00	19 02	19 05				19 11		19 17			19 24	19 25	19 29		19 32				19 41			19 47
Norwood Junction 2	a				19 09																				
London Bridge 4 ⊖	a			19 17	19 23						19 32					*19 49*		19 47							20 02
London Waterloo (East) 4 ⊖	a				19 28																				
London Charing Cross 4 ⊖	a				19 31																				
London Blackfriars 3 ⊖	a																								
City Thameslink 3	a																								
Farringdon 3 ⊖	a																								
St Pancras International 15 ⊖	a																								
St Albans City	a																								
Luton Airport Parkway 4 ✈	a																								
Luton 7	a																								
Bedford 10	a																								
Clapham Junction 10	d	19 06	19 10						19 20					19 33	19 37	19 40						19 50			
West Brompton ⊖	d													*19 45*											
Kensington (Olympia) ⊖	d													*19 48*											
Shepherd's Bush ⊖	d													*19 50*											
Watford Junction	a													*20 15*											
Milton Keynes Central 10	a																								
London Victoria 15 ⊖	a	19 12	19 16			19 20			19 27				19 35	19 40	19 44	19 47				19 50		19 57			

For general notes see front of timetable
For details of catering facilities see Directory of Train Operators

A ✠ from Haywards Heath

Table 186

Saturdays

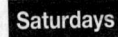

Brighton → London, Bedford

Network Diagram - see first page of Table 186

	GW 1	SN 1	GX 1	SN 1 ◇		SN 1	SN 1 ◇	SN 1	SN 1	FC 1	GX 1	SN 1	SN 1	SN 1	FC 1	GW 1	GX 1	SN 1 ◇	SN 1	SN 1	FC 1	GW 1	GX 1	SN 1
Brighton 10 d							19 19			19 07					19 34			19 49			19 37			
Hove 2 d													19 21											
Preston Park d										19 11											19 41			
Hassocks 4 d										19 17											19 47			
Burgess Hill 4 d										19 21											19 51			
Lewes 4 d														19 20										
Wivelsfield 4 d										19 23				19 34							19 53			
Haywards Heath 3 a										19 28			19 35	19 40	19 48						19 58			
d										19 32				19 43	19 48						20 02			
Balcombe d										19 37														
Horsham 4 d									19 21			19 32								19 52				20 02
Littlehaven d												19 35												20 05
Faygate d																								
Ifield d												19 41												20 11
Crawley d									19 30			19 45								20 01				20 14
Three Bridges 4 a				←					19 33	19 42		19 48								20 05	20 11			20 18
d				19 31					19 34	19 42		19 50								20 05	20 12			20 18
Gatwick Airport 10 ✈ a				19 35					19 38	19 46		19 54		19 54	20 00					20 10	20 16			20 22
d			19 35	19 38					19 39	19 46	19 50	19 55		19 55	20 01	20 03	20 05			20 11	20 16		20 20	20 23
Horley 4 d												19 58												20 26
Salfords d																								20 30
Earlswood (Surrey) d																								20 33
Tonbridge 4 d		19 10																						
Leigh (Kent) d		19 14																						
Penshurst d		19 18																						
Edenbridge d		19 24																						
Godstone d		19 31																						
Nutfield d		19 36																						
Reigate d	19 34																					20 19		
Redhill 5 a	19 38	19 45				←			19 47			20 04				20 10				20 18		20 25		20 37
d						19 37			19 48			20 07							←	20 18				20 39 →
Merstham d						19 41						20 11 →							20 11					
Coulsdon South d						19 46													20 16					
Purley 4 d						19 49													20 19					
East Croydon a				19 53		19 54	19 56	←	19 59	20 02				20 10	20 16			20 23	20 24	20 30	20 32			
d				19 53		19 57 →	19 56	19 57	20 00	20 02				20 11	20 17			20 24	20 25	20 30	20 32			
Norwood Junction 2 a																								
London Bridge 4 ⊖ a										20 17					20 32						20 47			
London Waterloo (East) 4 ⊖ a																								
London Charing Cross 4 ⊖ a																								
London Blackfriars 3 ⊖ a																								
City Thameslink 3 a																								
Farringdon 3 ⊖ a																								
St Pancras International 15 ⊖ a																								
St Albans City a																								
Luton Airport Parkway 4 ✈ a																								
Luton 7 a																								
Bedford 10 a																								
Clapham Junction 10 d				20 03			20 06	20 09	20 12					20 20				20 33	20 38	20 41				
West Brompton ⊖ d														20 32										
Kensington (Olympia) ⊖ d														20 35										
Shepherd's Bush ⊖ d														20 38										
Watford Junction a														21 06										
Milton Keynes Central 10 a																								
London Victoria 15 ⊖ a			20 05	20 09			20 12	20 15	20 20		20 20			20 27			20 35	20 40	20 44	20 50			20 50	

For general notes see front of timetable
For details of catering facilities see Directory of Train Operators

Table 186

Brighton → London, Bedford

Network Diagram - see first page of Table 186

		SN [1]	SN [1]	SN [1] ◇		FC [1]	GW [1]	SN [1]	GX [1]	SN [1] ◇	SN [1]	SN [1] ◇	FC [1]	GX [1]	SN [1]	SN [1]	FC [1]	GW [1]	GX [1]	SN [1] ◇	SN [1]	SN [1]	FC [1]	GW [1]	GX [1]
Brighton [10]	d			19 55		20 04				20 19			20 07				20 34			20 49			20 37		
Hove [2]	d		19 52												20 22										
Preston Park	d			19 59									20 11										20 41		
Hassocks [4]	d			20 05									20 17										20 47		
Burgess Hill [4]	d		20 02	20 09									20 21										20 51		
Lewes [4]	d	19 51																							
Wivelsfield [4]	d	20 03		20 11									20 23										20 53		
Haywards Heath [3]	a	20 07	20 09	20 16		20 18							20 28		20 36		20 48						20 58		
	d	20 13		20 22 →		20 18						← 20 22	20 32		20 38		20 48						21 02		
Balcombe	d												20 37												
Horsham [4]	d															20 32						20 52			
Littlehaven	d															20 35									
Faygate	d																								
Ifield	d															20 41									
Crawley	d															20 45						21 01			
Three Bridges [4]	a											20 32	20 42		20 47	20 48						21 05	21 11		
	d											20 32	20 42		20 48	20 51						21 05	21 12		
Gatwick Airport [10] ✈	a	20 24				20 30						20 37	20 46		20 52	20 56	21 00					21 10	21 16		
	d	20 25				20 31			20 35			20 38	20 46	20 50	20 53	20 57	21 01	21 03	21 05			21 11	21 16		21 20
Horley [4]	d															20 59									
Salfords	d																								
Earlswood (Surrey)	d																								
Tonbridge [4]	d							20 10																	
Leigh (Kent)	d							20 14																	
Penshurst	d							20 18																	
Edenbridge	d							20 24																	
Godstone	d							20 31																	
Nutfield	d							20 36																	
Reigate	d						20 34																	21 18	
Redhill [5]	a						20 38	20 45			←	20 47				21 06		21 10				21 18		21 25	
	d										20 39	20 48				21 07					←	21 18			
Merstham	d										20 43					21 11 →					21 11				
Coulsdon South	d										20 48										21 16				
Purley [4]	d										20 51										21 19				
East Croydon 🚋	a	20 40				20 46				20 53	20 56	20 59	21 02		21 09		21 16			21 23	21 24	21 30	21 32		
	d	20 41				20 47				20 54	20 57	21 00	21 02		21 11		21 17			21 24	21 25	21 30	21 32		
Norwood Junction [2]	a																								
London Bridge [4] ⊖	a					21 02							21 17				21 32					*22 11*	21 47		
London Waterloo (East) [4] ⊖	a																								
London Charing Cross [4] ⊖	a																								
London Blackfriars [3] ⊖	a																								
City Thameslink [3]	a																								
Farringdon [3] ⊖	a																								
St Pancras International [15] ⊖	a																								
St Albans City	a																								
Luton Airport Parkway [4] ✈	a																								
Luton [7]	a																								
Bedford [10]	a																								
Clapham Junction [10]	d	20 50								21 03	21 08	21 11			21 20					21 33	21 38	21 41			
West Brompton ⊖	d																			*21 53*					
Kensington (Olympia) ⊖	d																			*21 56*					
Shepherd's Bush ⊖	d																			*21 59*					
Watford Junction	a																			*22 27*					
Milton Keynes Central [10]	a																								
London Victoria [15] ⊖	a	20 57							21 05	21 10	21 14	21 17		21 20	21 27				21 35	21 40	21 44	21 47			21 50

For general notes see front of timetable
For details of catering facilities see Directory of Train Operators

Table 186

Saturdays

Brighton → London, Bedford

Network Diagram - see first page of Table 186

		SN 1	SN 1	SN 1		SN 1	GX 1	SN 1 ◇	SN 1	GW 1	SN 1 ◇	FC 1	GX 1	SN 1	SN 1 ◇	SN 1	GX 1	SN 1	FC 1	GX 1	GW 1	SN 1	SN 1	SN 1	SN 1
Brighton 10	d							21 19			21 00	21 07			21 49				21 37						
Hove 2	d			20 52										21 22									21 52		
Preston Park	d										21 04	21 11							21 41						
Hassocks 4	d										21 10	21 17							21 47						
Burgess Hill 4	d			21 02							21 14	21 21							21 51				22 02		
Lewes 4	d		20 50																			21 50			
Wivelsfield 4	d		21 02								21 16	21 23							21 53			22 02			
Haywards Heath 3	a		21 06	21 09							21 21	21 28		21 36					21 58			22 06	22 08		
	d			21 13							21 22	21 32		21 38					22 02			22 12			
Balcombe	d											21 37													
Horsham 4	d	21 02														21 32		21 52						22 02	
Littlehaven	d	21 05														21 35								22 05	
Faygate	d																								
Ifield	d	21 11														21 41								22 11	
Crawley	d	21 14														21 45		22 01						22 14	
Three Bridges 4	a	21 18									21 32	21 42		21 47		21 48		22 05	22 11					22 18	
	d	21 18									21 32	21 42		21 48		21 52		22 05	22 12					22 21	
Gatwick Airport 10 ✈	a	21 22		21 24							21 37	21 46		21 52		21 56		22 10	22 16			22 23		22 25	
	d	21 23		21 25			21 35				21 38	21 46	21 50	21 53		21 57	22 05	22 11	22 16	22 20	22 22	22 25		22 26	
Horley 4	d	21 26														22 00								22 29	
Salfords	d	21 30																						22 33	
Earlswood (Surrey)	d	21 33																						22 36	
Tonbridge 4	d					21 10																			22 10
Leigh (Kent)	d					21 14																			22 14
Penshurst	d					21 18																			22 18
Edenbridge	d					21 24																			22 24
Godstone	d					21 31																			22 31
Nutfield	d					21 36																			22 36
Reigate	d									21 40															
Redhill 5	a	21 36				21 41			←	21 44	21 47					22 06		22 18			22 30			22 39	22 42
	d	21 37 →							21 37		21 48					22 07		22 18						22 40	
Merstham	d								21 41							22 11								22 44	
Coulsdon South	d								21 46							22 16								22 49	
Purley 4	d								21 49							22 19								22 52	
East Croydon	a			21 40				21 53	21 54		21 59	22 02		22 09	22 23	22 24		22 30	22 32			22 40		22 57	
	d			21 41				21 54	21 55		22 00	22 02		22 11	22 24	22 25		22 30	22 32			22 40		22 58	
Norwood Junction 2	a																								
London Bridge 4	⊖ a										*22 41*	22 17						*23 11*	22 47						
London Waterloo (East) 4	⊖ a																								
London Charing Cross 4	⊖ a																								
London Blackfriars 3	⊖ a																								
City Thameslink 3	a																								
Farringdon 3	⊖ a																								
St Pancras International 15	⊖ a																								
St Albans City	a																								
Luton Airport Parkway 4 ✈	a																								
Luton 7	a																								
Bedford 10	a																								
Clapham Junction 10	d			21 50				22 03	22 08		22 11			22 20	22 33	22 38		22 41				22 50		23 08	
West Brompton	⊖ d														22 46										
Kensington (Olympia)	⊖ d														22 50										
Shepherd's Bush	⊖ d														22 53										
Watford Junction	a														23 19										
Milton Keynes Central 10	a																								
London Victoria 15	⊖ a			21 57			22 05	22 10	22 14		22 20		22 20	22 27	22 40	22 44	22 35	22 50		22 50		22 57		23 14	

For general notes see front of timetable
For details of catering facilities see
Directory of Train Operators

Table 186

Saturdays

Brighton → London, Bedford

Network Diagram - see first page of Table 186

		GX 1	SN 1 ◇	FC 1	GW 1	GX 1	GX 1	FC 1	SN 1	SN 1 A	FC 1	GW 1	GX 1	SN 1	SN 1	SN 1 ◇	GX 1	FC 1	SN 1 B	GX 1	GW 1	SN 1 ◇	FC 1
Brighton 10	d		22 00	22 07				22 33								23 02		23 11					23 37
Hove 2	d																						
Preston Park	d		22 04	22 11				22 37								23 06							23 41
Hassocks 4	d		22 10	22 17				22 43								23 12		23 19					23 47
Burgess Hill 4	d		22 14	22 21				22 47								23 16		23 23					23 51
Lewes 4	d									22 40													
Wivelsfield 4	d		22 16	22 23				22 49		22 54						23 19							23 53
Haywards Heath 3	a		22 21	22 28				22 54		22 58						23 23		23 27					23 58
	d		22 22	22 32				22 54		22 59						23 24		23 28					23 59
Balcombe	d			22 37				23 00															00 04
Horsham 4	d								22 55					23 02					23 25				
Littlehaven	d													23 05					23 28				
Faygate	d																						
Ifield	d													23 11					23 35				
Crawley	d								23 03					23 14					23 38				
Three Bridges 4	a		22 32	22 42				23 05	23 07	23 08	←			23 18		23 33		23 37	23 42			←	00 10
	d		22 32	22 42				23 12 →		23 08	23 12			23 18		23 47 →		23 38				23 47	00 10
Gatwick Airport 10 ✈	a		22 37	22 46						23 12	23 16			23 22				23 42				23 52	00 14
	d	22 35	22 38	22 46		22 50	23 05			23 13	23 16	23 18	23 20	23 23			23 35	23 43		23 50		23 53	00 15
Horley 4	d													23 26								23 56	
Salfords	d													23 30									
Earlswood (Surrey)	d													23 33									
Tonbridge 4	d														23 17								
Leigh (Kent)	d														23 21								
Penshurst	d														23 25								
Edenbridge	d														23 31								
Godstone	d														23 38								
Nutfield	d														23 43								
Reigate	d				22 48																23 54		
Redhill 5	a		22 46		22 52							23 25		23 36	23 49						23 58	00 02	00 22
	d		22 47											23 37								00 03	00 22
Merstham	d													23 41									
Coulsdon South	d													23 46									
Purley 4	d													23 49								00 11	
East Croydon	a		22 59	23 02						23 30	23 32			23 55				00 02				00 16	00 35
	d		23 00	23 02						23 30	23 32			23 56				00 04				00 17	00 36
Norwood Junction 2	a																						
London Bridge 4 ⊖	a		*23 38*	23 17							23 47			*00 19*				00 19				*00 52*	00 52
London Waterloo (East) 4 ⊖	a																						
London Charing Cross 4 ⊖	a																						
London Blackfriars 3 ⊖	a																						
City Thameslink 3	a																						
Farringdon 3 ⊖	a																						
St Pancras International 15 ⊖	a																						
St Albans City	a																						
Luton Airport Parkway 4 ✈	a																						
Luton 7	a																						
Bedford 10	a																						
Clapham Junction 10	d		23 11	23b25						23 42				00 11				00b28				00 29	01b02
West Brompton ⊖	d																						
Kensington (Olympia) ⊖	d																						
Shepherd's Bush ⊖	d																						
Watford Junction	a																						
Milton Keynes Central 10	a																						
London Victoria 15 ⊖	a	23 05	23 17	23b32		23 20	23 35			23 52			23 55	00 18			00 10	00b36		00 25		00 36	01b09

For general notes see front of timetable
For details of catering facilities see Directory of Train Operators

- **A** From Hastings (Table 189)
- **B** From Chichester (Table 188)
- **b** Change at East Croydon

Sundays

until 6 September

Brighton → London, Bedford

Network Diagram - see first page of Table 186

Station		SN 1	SN 1 ◇	FC 1	SN 1 ◇	GX 1	FC 1	GX 1	GX 1	GW 1	GX 1	SN 1	GX 1	SN 1	SN 1	SN 1	GX 1	SN 1 ◇	FC 1	GX 1		SN 1	GX 1	GX 1	GW 1
Brighton 10	d		23p02	23p11			23p37											03 50							
Hove 2	d																								
Preston Park	d		23p06				23p41																		
Hassocks 4	d		23p12	23p19			23p47																		
Burgess Hill 4	d		23p16	23p23			23p51																		
Lewes 4	d																								
Wivelsfield 4	d		23p19				23p53																		
Haywards Heath 3	a		23p23	23p27			23p58																		
	d		23p24	23p28			23p59																		
Balcombe	d						00 04																		
Horsham 4	d	23p02																							
Littlehaven	d	23p05																							
Faygate	d																								
Ifield	d	23p11																							
Crawley	d	23p14																							
Three Bridges 4	a	23p18	23p33	23p37	←		00 10											04 45							
	d	23p18	23p47	23p38	23p47		00 10					01 10		02 10	03 10	04 10		04 58	05 10			05 30			
Gatwick Airport 10 ✈	a	23p22	→	23p42	23p52		00 14					01 19		02 14	03 14	04 14		05 02	05 14			05 34			
	d	23p23		23p43	23p53	00 05	00 15	00 20	00 35		00 50	01 20	01 35	02 15	03 15	04 15	04 35	05 03	05 15	05 20		05 36	05 50	06 05	06 06
Horley 4	d	23p26			23p56							01 22		02 18	03 18	04 18		05 05				05 38			
Salfords	d	23p30																							
Earlswood (Surrey)	d	23p33																							
Tonbridge 4	d																								
Leigh (Kent)	d																								
Penshurst	d																								
Edenbridge	d																								
Godstone	d																								
Nutfield	d																								
Reigate	d									00 45															
Redhill 5	a	23p36			00 02		00 22			00 49												05 46			06 16
	d	23p37			00 03		00 22															05 46			
Merstham	d	23p41																							
Coulsdon South	d	23p46																							
Purley 4	d	23p49			00 11							01 37		02 33	03 33	04 33		05 22				05 56			
East Croydon	a	23p55		00 02	00 16		00 35					01 42		02 39	03 39	04 39		05 27	05 31			06 01			
	d	23p56		00 04	00 17		00 36					01 43		02 40	03 40	04 40		05 28	05 32			06 02			
Norwood Junction 2	a																								
London Bridge 4	⊖ a	*00 19*		00 19			00 52												05 59						
London Waterloo (East) 4	⊖ a																								
London Charing Cross 4	⊖ a																								
London Blackfriars 3	⊖ a																								
City Thameslink 3	a																								
Farringdon 3	⊖ a																								
St Pancras International 15	⊖ a																								
St Albans City	a																								
Luton Airport Parkway 4 ✈	a																								
Luton 7	a																								
Bedford 10	a																								
Clapham Junction 10	d	00 11			00 29		*01b02*					01 54		02 53	03 53	04 53		05 49				06 14			
West Brompton	⊖ d																								
Kensington (Olympia)	⊖ d																								
Shepherd's Bush	⊖ d																								
Watford Junction	a																								
Milton Keynes Central 10	a																								
London Victoria 15	⊖ a	00 18			00 36	00 40	*01b09*	00 55	01 10		01 25	02 05	02 20	03 05	04 05	05 05	05 10	05 58		05 55		06 22	06 25	06 40	

For general notes see front of timetable
For details of catering facilities see Directory of Train Operators

b Change at East Croydon

Table 186

Sundays

until 6 September

Brighton → London, Bedford

Network Diagram - see first page of Table 186

		FC [1]	GX [1]	SN [1]	GX [1]	FC [1]	GX [1]	SN [1] A	SN [1]	SN [1]	GW [1]	GX [1]	GW [1]	FC [1]	GX [1]	SN [1]	GX [1]	SN [1] ◇		FC [1]	GX [1]	SN [1] ᚎ	SN [1] B	SN [1]	GX [1]
Brighton [10]	d	05 44				06 13		06 16						06 45				07 04		07 17					
Hove [2]	d								06 24																
Preston Park	d							06 19										07 07							
Hassocks [4]	d	05 52						06 26						06 53				07 14							
Burgess Hill [4]	d	05 56				06 26		06 29						06 57				07 17		07 27					
Lewes [4]	d							05 57														07 22			
Wivelsfield [4]	d							06 32										07 20				07 36			
Haywards Heath [3]	a	06 00				06 30		06 36	06 39					07 02				07 24		07 32		07 40			
	d	06 01				06 31		06 37	06 40					07 02				07 25		07 32		07 41			
Balcombe	d																	07 30							
Horsham [4]	d			06 04						06 34						07 00							07 37		
Littlehaven	d			06 07						06 37						07 03									
Faygate	d																								
Ifield	d			06 13						06 43						07 09									
Crawley	d			06 17						06 47						07 13							07 46		
Three Bridges [4]	a	06 10		06 20		06 40		06 46		06 51				07 11		07 16		07 36		07 41			07 50		
	d	06 10		06 21		06 40		06 46		06 53				07 12		07 18		07 36		07 42			07 50		
Gatwick Airport [10] ✈	a	06 14		06 25		06 44		06 51	06 53	06 57				07 16		07 22		07 41		07 46		07 52	07 55		
	d	06 15	06 20		06 35	06 45	06 50		06 54	06 58		07 05	07 08	07 17	07 20	07 23	07 35	07 42		07 47	07 50	07 53	07 56		08 05
Horley [4]	d									07 00						07 26							07 58		
Salfords	d															07 30									
Earlswood (Surrey)	d															07 33									
Tonbridge [4]	d																							07 41	
Leigh (Kent)	d																							07 45	
Penshurst	d																							07 49	
Edenbridge	d																							07 55	
Godstone	d																							08 02	
Nutfield	d																							08 07	
Reigate	d										07 05														
Redhill [5]	a									07 07	07 09		07 17			07 36		07 49					08 05	08 12	
	d									07 07						07 37		07 49					08 05	08 13	
Merstham	d									07 11						07 41								08 17	
Coulsdon South	d									07 16						07 46								08 22	
Purley [4]	d									07 20						07 50							08 14	08 27	
East Croydon	a	06 31				07 01			07 09	07 26				07 33		07 55		08 00		08 03		08 09	08 20	08 32	
	d	06 32				07 02			07 10	07 27				07 33		07 56		08 00		08 03		08 09	08 21	08 34 →	
Norwood Junction [2]	a																								
London Bridge [4] ⊖	a	06 59				07 17								07 47						08 17		08 42			
London Waterloo (East) [4] ⊖	a																								
London Charing Cross [4] ⊖	a																								
London Blackfriars [3] ⊖	a																								
City Thameslink [3]	a																								
Farringdon [3] ⊖	a																								
St Pancras International [15] ⊖	a																								
St Albans City	a																								
Luton Airport Parkway [4] ✈	a																								
Luton [7]	a																								
Bedford [10]	a																								
Clapham Junction [10]	d	07b00							07 19	07 41						08 07		08 11				08 19	08 32		
West Brompton ⊖	d								07 30																
Kensington (Olympia) ⊖	d								07 33									08 22							
Shepherd's Bush ⊖	d								07 36									08 25							
Watford Junction	a																	08 28							
Milton Keynes Central [10]	a																	08 58							
London Victoria [15] ⊖	a	07b08	06 55		07 10		07 20		07 26	07 48		07 35			07 50	08 13	08 05	08 17			08 20	08 25	08 39		08 35

For general notes see front of timetable
For details of catering facilities see Directory of Train Operators

A From Eastbourne (Table 189)
B From Bognor Regis (Table 188)
b Change at East Croydon

Brighton → London, Bedford

Network Diagram - see first page of Table 186

		GW	FC	GW	GX	SN	SN	SN	SN	GX	SN	FC	GX	SN	SN	SN		GX	SN	SN	GW	FC	GW	GX	SN
		1	1	1	1	1	1	1 ◇	1	1	1 ◇	1	1	1	1	1 ◇		1	1	1	1	1	1	1	1
															A				A						
Brighton 10	d		07 45					08 10			08 00	08 17				08 40						08 45			
Hove 2	d						07 54																		
Preston Park	d										08 03														
Hassocks 4	d		07 53								08 10											08 53			
Burgess Hill 4	d		07 57				08 04				08 13	08 27										08 57			
Lewes 4	d													08 22											
Wivelsfield 4	d										08 16			08 36											
Haywards Heath 3	a		08 02				08 09				08 20	08 32		08 40								09 02			
	d		08 02				08 11				08 25	08 32		08 41								09 02			
Balcombe	d										08 30														
Horsham 4	d								08 00						08 37										
Littlehaven	d								08 03																
Faygate	d																								
Ifield	d								08 09																
Crawley	d								08 13						08 46										
Three Bridges 4	a		08 11						08 16		08 36	08 41			08 50							09 11			
	d		08 12						08 18		08 36	08 42			08 50							09 12			
Gatwick Airport 10 ✈	a		08 16				08 22		08 22		08 41	08 46		08 52	08 55	09 01						09 16			
	d	08 08	08 17		08 20		08 23		08 23	08 35	08 42	08 47	08 50	08 53	08 56	09 02		09 05			09 08	09 17		09 20	
Horley 4	d								08 26						08 58										
Salfords	d								08 30																
Earlswood (Surrey)	d								08 33																
Tonbridge 4	d																			08 41					
Leigh (Kent)	d																			08 45					
Penshurst	d																			08 49					
Edenbridge	d																			08 55					
Godstone	d																			09 02					
Nutfield	d																			09 07					
Reigate	d			08 11																			09 13		
Redhill 5	a	08 15		08 15					08 36		08 49				09 05				←	09 12	09 15		09 18		
	d								08 37		08 49				09 05 →				09 05	09 13					
Merstham	d								08 41											09 17					
Coulsdon South	d								08 46											09 22					
Purley 4	d								08 50										09 14	09 27					
East Croydon	a		08 33			←	08 39	08 45	08 55		09 00	09 03		09 09		09 17			09 20	09 32		09 33			←
	d		08 33			08 34	08 39	08 46	08 56		09 00	09 03		09 09		09 17			09 21	09 34 →		09 33			09 34
Norwood Junction 2	a					08 38																			09 38
London Bridge 4	⊖ a		08 47			08 51	*09 12*					09 17		*09 42*								09 47			09 51
London Waterloo (East) 4	⊖ a																								
London Charing Cross 4	⊖ a																								
London Blackfriars 3	⊖ a																								
City Thameslink 3	a																								
Farringdon 3	⊖ a																								
St Pancras International 15	⊖ a																								
St Albans City	a																								
Luton Airport Parkway 4 ✈	a																								
Luton 7	a																								
Bedford 10	a																								
Clapham Junction 10	d						08 49	08 55	09 07		09 11			09 19		09 27			09 32						
West Brompton	⊖ d										*09 22*														
Kensington (Olympia)	⊖ d										*09 25*														
Shepherd's Bush	⊖ d										*09 28*														
Watford Junction	a										*09 58*														
Milton Keynes Central 10	a																								
London Victoria 15	⊖ a				08 50		08 55	09 02	09 13	09 05	09 17		09 20	09 25		09 33		09 35	09 39					09 50	

For general notes see front of timetable
For details of catering facilities see Directory of Train Operators

A From Bognor Regis (Table 188)

Table 186

Sundays

until 6 September

Brighton → London, Bedford

Network Diagram - see first page of Table 186

Station		SN 1	SN 1 ◇	SN 1	GX 1	SN 1 ◇	FC 1	GX 1	SN 1 (bus)	SN 1 A	SN 1 ◇	GX 1	SN 1 A
Brighton 10	d		09 10			09 00	09 17				09 40		
Hove 2	d	08 54											
Preston Park	d					09 03							
Hassocks 4	d					09 10							
Burgess Hill 4	d	09 04				09 13	09 27						
Lewes 4	d								09 22				
Wivelsfield 4	d					09 16			09 36				
Haywards Heath 3	a	09 09				09 20	09 32		09 40				
	d	09 11				09 25	09 32		09 41				
Balcombe	d					09 30							
Horsham 4	d			09 00						09 37			
Littlehaven	d			09 03									
Faygate	d												
Ifield	d			09 09									
Crawley	d			09 13						09 46			
Three Bridges 4	a			09 16		09 36	09 41			09 50			
	d			09 18		09 36	09 42			09 50			
Gatwick Airport 10 ✈	a	09 22		09 22		09 41	09 46		09 52	09 55	10 01		
	d	09 23		09 23	09 35	09 42	09 47	09 50	09 53	09 56	10 02	10 05	
Horley 4	d			09 26						09 58			
Salfords	d			09 30									
Earlswood (Surrey)	d			09 33									
Tonbridge 4	d												
Leigh (Kent)	d												
Penshurst	d												
Edenbridge	d												
Godstone	d												
Nutfield	d												
Reigate	d												
Redhill 5	a			09 36		09 49				10 05			←
	d			09 37		09 49				10 05 →			10 05
Merstham	d			09 41									
Coulsdon South	d			09 46									
Purley 4	d			09 50									10 14
East Croydon	a	09 39	09 45	09 55		10 00	10 03		10 09		10 17		10 20
	d	09 39	09 46	09 56		10 00	10 03		10 09		10 17		10 21
Norwood Junction 2	a												
London Bridge 4	⊖ a	*10 12*					10 17		*10 42*				
London Waterloo (East) 4	⊖ a												
London Charing Cross 4	⊖ a												
London Blackfriars 3	⊖ a												
City Thameslink 3	a												
Farringdon 3	⊖ a												
St Pancras International 15	⊖ a												
St Albans City	a												
Luton Airport Parkway 4 ✈	a												
Luton 7	a												
Bedford 10	a												
Clapham Junction 10	d	09 49	09 55	10 07		10 11			10 19		10 27		10 32
West Brompton	⊖ d					*10 22*							
Kensington (Olympia)	⊖ d					*10 25*							
Shepherd's Bush	⊖ d					*10 28*							
Watford Junction	a					*10 58*							
Milton Keynes Central 10	a												
London Victoria 15	⊖ a	09 55	10 02	10 13	10 05	10 17		10 20	10 25		10 33	10 35	10 39

Station		SN 1		GW 1	FC 1	GW 1	GX 1	SN 1	SN 1	SN 1 ◇	SN 1	GX 1	SN 1 ◇
Brighton 10	d				09 45					10 10			10 00
Hove 2	d								09 54				
Preston Park	d												10 03
Hassocks 4	d				09 53								10 10
Burgess Hill 4	d				09 57				10 04				10 13
Lewes 4	d												
Wivelsfield 4	d												10 16
Haywards Heath 3	a				10 02				10 09				10 20
	d				10 02				10 11				10 25
Balcombe	d												10 30
Horsham 4	d										10 00		
Littlehaven	d										10 03		
Faygate	d												
Ifield	d										10 09		
Crawley	d										10 13		
Three Bridges 4	a				10 11						10 16		10 36
	d				10 12						10 18		10 36
Gatwick Airport 10 ✈	a				10 16				10 22		10 22		10 41
	d			10 08	10 17		10 20		10 23		10 23	10 35	10 42
Horley 4	d										10 26		
Salfords	d										10 30		
Earlswood (Surrey)	d										10 33		
Tonbridge 4	d	09 41											
Leigh (Kent)	d	09 45											
Penshurst	d	09 49											
Edenbridge	d	09 55											
Godstone	d	10 02											
Nutfield	d	10 07											
Reigate	d												
Redhill 5	a	10 12				10 13					10 36		10 49
	d	10 13		10 15		10 17					10 37		10 49
Merstham	d	10 17									10 41		
Coulsdon South	d	10 22									10 46		
Purley 4	d	10 27									10 50		
East Croydon	a	10 32			10 33			←	10 39	10 45	10 55		11 00
	d	10 34 →			10 33			10 34	10 39	10 46	10 56		11 00
Norwood Junction 2	a							10 38					
London Bridge 4	⊖ a				10 47			10 51	*11 12*				
London Waterloo (East) 4	⊖ a												
London Charing Cross 4	⊖ a												
London Blackfriars 3	⊖ a												
City Thameslink 3	a												
Farringdon 3	⊖ a												
St Pancras International 15	⊖ a												
St Albans City	a												
Luton Airport Parkway 4 ✈	a												
Luton 7	a												
Bedford 10	a												
Clapham Junction 10	d								10 49	10 55	11 07		11 11
West Brompton	⊖ d												*11 22*
Kensington (Olympia)	⊖ d												*11 25*
Shepherd's Bush	⊖ d												*11 28*
Watford Junction	a												*11 58*
Milton Keynes Central 10	a												
London Victoria 15	⊖ a						10 50		10 55	11 02	11 13	11 05	11 17

For general notes see front of timetable
For details of catering facilities see Directory of Train Operators

A From Bognor Regis (Table 188)

Sundays

until 6 September

Brighton → London, Bedford

Network Diagram - see first page of Table 186

		FC 1	GX 1	SN 1	SN 1	SN 1 ◇	GX 1	SN 1	SN 1	GW 1	FC 1	GW 1		GX 1	SN 1	SN 1	SN 1 ◇	SN 1	GX 1	SN 1 ◇	FC 1	GX 1	SN 1	SN 1	SN 1 ◇
					A			A																A	
				🍴	🍴			🍴															🍴	🍴	
Brighton 10	d	10 17				10 40					10 45						11 10			11 00	11 17				11 40
Hove 2	d															10 54									
Preston Park	d																			11 03					
Hassocks 4	d										10 53									11 10					
Burgess Hill 4	d	10 27									10 57					11 04				11 13	11 27				
Lewes 4	d			10 22																			11 22		
Wivelsfield 4	d			10 36																11 16			11 36		
Haywards Heath 3	a	10 32		10 40							11 02					11 09				11 20	11 32		11 40		
	d	10 32		10 41							11 02					11 11				11 25	11 32		11 41		
Balcombe	d																			11 30					
Horsham 4	d				10 37													11 00						11 37	
Littlehaven	d																	11 03							
Faygate	d																								
Ifield	d																	11 09							
Crawley	d				10 46													11 13						11 46	
Three Bridges 4	a	10 41			10 50						11 11							11 16		11 36	11 41			11 50	
	d	10 42			10 50						11 12							11 18		11 36	11 42			11 50	
Gatwick Airport 10 ✈	a	10 46		10 52	10 55	11 01					11 16					11 22		11 22		11 41	11 46		11 52	11 55	12 01
	d	10 47	10 50	10 53	10 56	11 02	11 05			11 08	11 17			11 20		11 23		11 23	11 35	11 42	11 47	11 50	11 53	11 56	12 02
Horley 4	d				10 58													11 26						11 58	
Salfords	d																	11 30							
Earlswood (Surrey)	d																	11 33							
Tonbridge 4	d								10 41																
Leigh (Kent)	d								10 45																
Penshurst	d								10 49																
Edenbridge	d								10 55																
Godstone	d								11 02																
Nutfield	d								11 07																
Reigate	d											11 13													
Redhill 5	a				11 05			←	11 12	11 15		11 18						11 36		11 49				12 05	
	d				11 05 →			11 05	11 13									11 37		11 49				12 05 →	
Merstham	d								11 17									11 41							
Coulsdon South	d								11 22									11 46							
Purley 4	d							11 14	11 27									11 50							
East Croydon	a	11 03		11 09		11 17		11 20	11 32		11 33				←	11 39	11 45	11 55		12 00	12 03		12 09		12 17
	d	11 03		11 09		11 17		11 21	11 34 →		11 33				11 34	11 39	11 46	11 56		12 00	12 03		12 09		12 17
Norwood Junction 2	a														11 38										
London Bridge 4 ⊖	a	11 17		*11 42*							11 47				11 51	*12 12*					12 17		*12 42*		
London Waterloo (East) 4 ⊖	a																								
London Charing Cross 4 ⊖	a																								
London Blackfriars 3 ⊖	a																								
City Thameslink 3	a																								
Farringdon 3 ⊖	a																								
St Pancras International 15 ⊖	a																								
St Albans City	a																								
Luton Airport Parkway 4 ✈	a																								
Luton 7	a																								
Bedford 10	a																								
Clapham Junction 10	d			11 19		11 27		11 32								11 49	11 55	12 07		12 11			12 19		12 27
West Brompton ⊖	d																*12 12*								
Kensington (Olympia) ⊖	d																*12 15*								
Shepherd's Bush ⊖	d																*12 18*								
Watford Junction	a																*12 46*								
Milton Keynes Central 10	a																								
London Victoria 15 ⊖	a		11 20	11 25		11 33	11 35	11 39						11 50		11 55	12 02	12 13	12 05	12 17		12 20	12 25		12 33

For general notes see front of timetable
For details of catering facilities see Directory of Train Operators

A From Bognor Regis (Table 188)

Table 186

Brighton → London, Bedford

Sundays

until 6 September

Network Diagram - see first page of Table 186

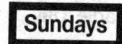

		GX 1	SN 1 A 🍴	SN 1	GW 1	FC 1	GW 1	GX 1	SN 1	SN 1		SN 1 ◇	SN 1	GX 1	SN 1 ◇	FC 1	GX 1	SN 1 🍴	SN 1 A 🍴	SN 1 ◇	GX 1	SN 1 A 🍴	SN 1	GW 1	FC 1
Brighton [10]	d					11 45						12 10			12 00	12 17				12 40					12 45
Hove [2]	d									11 54															
Preston Park	d														12 03										
Hassocks [4]	d					11 53									12 10										12 53
Burgess Hill [4]	d					11 57				12 04					12 13	12 27									12 57
Lewes [4]	d																	12 22							
Wivelsfield [4]	d														12 16			12 36							
Haywards Heath [3]	a					12 02				12 09					12 20	12 32		12 40							13 02
	d					12 02				12 11					12 25	12 32		12 41							13 02
Balcombe	d														12 30										
Horsham [4]	d												12 00						12 37						
Littlehaven	d												12 03												
Faygate	d																								
Ifield	d												12 09												
Crawley	d												12 13						12 46						
Three Bridges [4]	a					12 11							12 16		12 36	12 41			12 50						13 11
	d					12 12							12 18		12 36	12 42			12 50						13 12
Gatwick Airport [10] ✈	a					12 16				12 22			12 22		12 41	12 46		12 52	12 55	13 01					13 16
	d	12 05			12 08	12 17		12 20		12 23			12 23	12 35	12 42	12 47	12 50	12 53	12 56	13 02	13 05			13 08	13 17
Horley [4]	d												12 26						12 58						
Salfords	d												12 30												
Earlswood (Surrey)	d												12 33												
Tonbridge [4]	d			11 41																			12 41		
Leigh (Kent)	d			11 45																			12 45		
Penshurst	d			11 49																			12 49		
Edenbridge	d			11 55																			12 55		
Godstone	d			12 02																			13 02		
Nutfield	d			12 07																			13 07		
Reigate	d						12 11																		
Redhill [5]	a		←	12 12	12 15		12 15						12 36		12 49				13 05			←	13 12	13 15	
	d		12 05	12 13									12 37		12 49				13 05 →			13 05	13 13		
Merstham	d			12 17									12 41										13 17		
Coulsdon South	d			12 22									12 46										13 22		
Purley [4]	d		12 14	12 27									12 50									13 14	13 27		
East Croydon	a		12 20	12 32		12 33			←	12 39		12 45	12 55		13 00	13 03		13 09		13 17		13 20	13 32		13 33
	d		12 21	12 34 →		12 33			12 34	12 39		12 46	12 56		13 00	13 03		13 09		13 17		13 21	13 34 →		13 33
Norwood Junction [2]	a								12 38																
London Bridge [4]	⊖ a					12 47			12 51	*13 12*						13 17		*13 42*							13 47
London Waterloo (East) [4]	⊖ a																								
London Charing Cross [4]	⊖ a																								
London Blackfriars [3]	⊖ a																								
City Thameslink [3]	a																								
Farringdon [3]	⊖ a																								
St Pancras International [15]	⊖ a																								
St Albans City	a																								
Luton Airport Parkway [4] ✈	a																								
Luton [7]	a																								
Bedford [10]	a																								
Clapham Junction [10]	d		12 32							12 49		12 55	13 07		13 11			13 19		13 27		13 32			
West Brompton	⊖ d											*13 12*													
Kensington (Olympia)	⊖ d											*13 15*													
Shepherd's Bush	⊖ d											*13 18*													
Watford Junction	a											*13 46*													
Milton Keynes Central [10]	a																								
London Victoria [15]	⊖ a	12 35	12 39					12 50		12 55		13 02	13 13	13 05	13 17		13 20	13 25		13 33	13 35	13 39			

For general notes see front of timetable
For details of catering facilities see Directory of Train Operators

A From Bognor Regis (Table 188)

Sundays

until 6 September

Brighton → London, Bedford

Network Diagram - see first page of Table 186

Station		GW 1	GX 1	SN 1	SN 1	SN 1 ◇	SN 1	GX 1		SN 1 ◇	FC 1	GX 1	SN 1	SN 1 A	SN 1 ◇	GX 1	SN 1 A	SN 1	GW 1	FC 1	GW 1	GX 1	SN 1	SN 1	SN 1 ◇
Brighton 10	d					13 10				13 00	13 17				13 40					13 45					14 10
Hove 2	d				12 54																			13 54	
Preston Park	d									13 03															
Hassocks 4	d									13 10										13 53					
Burgess Hill 4	d				13 04					13 13	13 27									13 57				14 04	
Lewes 4	d												13 22												
Wivelsfield 4	d									13 16			13 36												
Haywards Heath 3	a				13 09					13 20	13 32		13 40							14 02				14 09	
	d				13 11					13 25	13 32		13 41							14 02				14 11	
Balcombe	d									13 30															
Horsham 4	d						13 00							13 37											
Littlehaven	d						13 03																		
Faygate	d																								
Ifield	d						13 09																		
Crawley	d						13 13							13 46											
Three Bridges 4	a						13 16			13 36	13 41			13 50						14 11					
	d						13 18			13 36	13 42			13 50						14 12					
Gatwick Airport 10 ✈	a				13 22		13 22			13 41	13 46		13 52	13 55	14 01					14 16				14 22	
	d		13 20		13 23		13 23	13 35		13 42	13 47	13 50	13 53	13 56	14 02	14 05			14 08	14 17		14 20		14 23	
Horley 4	d						13 26							13 58											
Salfords	d						13 30																		
Earlswood (Surrey)	d						13 33																		
Tonbridge 4	d																	13 41							
Leigh (Kent)	d																	13 45							
Penshurst	d																	13 49							
Edenbridge	d																	13 55							
Godstone	d																	14 02							
Nutfield	d																	14 07							
Reigate	d	13 13															←	14 12	14 15		14 11				
Redhill 5	a	13 18					13 36			13 49				14 05			14 05	14 13			14 15				
	d						13 37			13 49				14 05 →				14 17							
Merstham	d						13 41											14 22							
Coulsdon South	d						13 46											14 27							
Purley 4	d						13 50										14 14								
East Croydon	a			←	13 39	13 45	13 55			14 00	14 03		14 09		14 17		14 20	14 32		14 33			←	14 39	14 45
	d			13 34	13 39	13 46	13 56			14 00	14 03		14 09		14 17		14 21	14 34 →		14 33			14 34	14 39	14 46
Norwood Junction 2	a			13 38																			14 38		
London Bridge 4 ⊖	a			13 51	*14 12*						14 17		*14 42*							14 47			14 51	*15 12*	
London Waterloo (East) 4 ⊖	a																								
London Charing Cross 4 ⊖	a																								
London Blackfriars 3 ⊖	a																								
City Thameslink 3	a																								
Farringdon 3 ⊖	a																								
St Pancras International 15 ⊖	a																								
St Albans City	a																								
Luton Airport Parkway 4 ✈	a																								
Luton 7	a																								
Bedford 10	a																								
Clapham Junction 10	d				13 49	13 55	14 07			14 11			14 19		14 27		14 32							14 49	14 55
West Brompton ⊖	d					*14 12*																			*15 12*
Kensington (Olympia) ⊖	d					*14 15*																			*15 15*
Shepherd's Bush ⊖	d					*14 18*																			*15 18*
Watford Junction	a					*14 46*																			*15 46*
Milton Keynes Central 10	a																								
London Victoria 15 ⊖	a		13 50		13 55	14 02	14 13	14 05		14 17		14 20	14 25		14 33	14 35	14 39					14 50		14 55	15 02

For general notes see front of timetable
For details of catering facilities see Directory of Train Operators

A From Bognor Regis (Table 188)

Sundays

until 6 September

Brighton → London, Bedford

Network Diagram - see first page of Table 186

Station		SN	GX	SN ◇	FC	GX		SN	SN	SN ◇	GX	SN	SN	GW	FC	GW	GX	SN	SN	SN ◇	SN	GX	SN ◇	FC	GX
									A			A													
Brighton	d			14 00	14 17					14 40					14 45					15 10			15 00	15 17	
Hove	d																		14 54						
Preston Park	d			14 03																			15 03		
Hassocks	d			14 10											14 53								15 10		
Burgess Hill	d			14 13	14 27										14 57				15 04				15 13	15 27	
Lewes	d							14 22																	
Wivelsfield	d			14 16				14 36															15 16		
Haywards Heath	a			14 20	14 32			14 40							15 02				15 09				15 20	15 32	
	d			14 25	14 32			14 41							15 02				15 11				15 25	15 32	
Balcombe	d			14 30																			15 30		
Horsham	d	14 00							14 37												15 00				
Littlehaven	d	14 03																			15 03				
Faygate	d																								
Ifield	d	14 09																			15 09				
Crawley	d	14 13							14 46												15 13				
Three Bridges	a	14 16		14 36	14 41				14 50						15 11						15 16		15 36	15 41	
	d	14 18		14 36	14 42				14 50						15 12						15 18		15 36	15 42	
Gatwick Airport	a	14 22		14 41	14 46			14 52	14 55	15 01					15 16				15 22		15 22		15 41	15 46	
	d	14 23	14 35	14 42	14 47	14 50		14 53	14 56	15 02	15 05			15 08	15 17		15 20		15 23		15 23	15 35	15 42	15 47	15 50
Horley	d	14 26							14 58												15 26				
Salfords	d	14 30																			15 30				
Earlswood (Surrey)	d	14 33																			15 33				
Tonbridge	d												14 41												
Leigh (Kent)	d												14 45												
Penshurst	d												14 49												
Edenbridge	d												14 55												
Godstone	d												15 02												
Nutfield	d												15 07												
Reigate	d															15 13									
Redhill	a	14 36		14 49					15 05			←	15 12	15 15		15 18					15 36		15 49		
	d	14 37		14 49					15 05 →			15 05	15 13								15 37		15 49		
Merstham	d	14 41											15 17								15 41				
Coulsdon South	d	14 46											15 22								15 46				
Purley	d	14 50										15 14	15 27								15 50				
East Croydon	a	14 55		15 00	15 03			15 09		15 17		15 20	15 32		15 33			←	15 39	15 45	15 55		16 00	16 03	
	d	14 56		15 00	15 03			15 09		15 17		15 21	15 34 →		15 33			15 34	15 39	15 46	15 56		16 00	16 03	
Norwood Junction	a																	15 38							
London Bridge	a				15 17			*15 42*							15 47			15 51	*16 12*					16 17	
London Waterloo (East)	a																								
London Charing Cross	a																								
London Blackfriars	a																								
City Thameslink	a																								
Farringdon	a																								
St Pancras International	a																								
St Albans City	a																								
Luton Airport Parkway	a																								
Luton	a																								
Bedford	a																								
Clapham Junction	d	15 07		15 11				15 19		15 27		15 32							15 49	15 55	16 07		16 11		
West Brompton	d																			*16 12*					
Kensington (Olympia)	d																			*16 15*					
Shepherd's Bush	d																			*16 18*					
Watford Junction	a																			*16 46*					
Milton Keynes Central	a																								
London Victoria	a	15 13	15 05	15 17		15 20		15 25		15 33	15 35	15 39					15 50		15 55	16 02	16 13	16 05	16 17		16 20

For general notes see front of timetable
For details of catering facilities see
Directory of Train Operators

A From Bognor Regis (Table 188)

Table 186

Sundays

until 6 September

Brighton → London, Bedford

Network Diagram - see first page of Table 186

		SN	SN	SN		GX	SN	SN	GW	FC	GW	GX	SN	SN	SN	SN	GX	SN	FC	GX	SN	SN	SN	GX	SN
		1	1	1 ◇		1	1	1	1	1	1	1	1	1	1 ◇	1	1	1 ◇	1	1	1	1	1 ◇	1	1
			A				A															A			A
		⚲	⚲				⚲														⚲	⚲			⚲
Brighton 10	d			15 40						15 45					16 10			16 00	16 17				16 40		
Hove 2	d													15 54											
Preston Park	d																	16 03							
Hassocks 4	d									15 53								16 10							
Burgess Hill 4	d									15 57				16 04				16 13	16 27						
Lewes 4	d	15 22																			16 22				
Wivelsfield 4	d	15 36																16 16			16 36				
Haywards Heath 3	a	15 40								16 02				16 09				16 20	16 32		16 40				
	d	15 41								16 02				16 11				16 25	16 32		16 41				
Balcombe	d																	16 30							
Horsham 4	d		15 37													16 00						16 37			
Littlehaven	d															16 03									
Faygate	d																								
Ifield	d															16 09									
Crawley	d		15 46													16 13						16 46			
Three Bridges 4	a		15 50							16 11						16 16		16 36	16 41			16 50			
	d		15 50							16 12						16 18		16 36	16 42			16 50			
Gatwick Airport 10 ✈	a	15 52	15 55	16 01						16 16				16 22		16 22		16 41	16 46		16 52	16 55	17 01		
	d	15 53	15 56	16 02		16 05			16 08	16 17		16 20		16 23		16 23	16 35	16 42	16 47	16 50	16 53	16 56	17 02	17 05	
Horley 4	d		15 58													16 26						16 58			
Salfords	d															16 30									
Earlswood (Surrey)	d															16 33									
Tonbridge 4	d							15 41																	
Leigh (Kent)	d							15 45																	
Penshurst	d							15 49																	
Edenbridge	d							15 55																	
Godstone	d							16 02																	
Nutfield	d							16 07																	
Reigate	d										16 11														
Redhill 5	a		16 05				←	16 12	16 15		16 15					16 36		16 49				17 05			←
	d		16 05 →				16 05	16 13								16 37		16 49				17 05 →			17 05
Merstham	d							16 17								16 41									
Coulsdon South	d							16 22								16 46									
Purley 4	d						16 14	16 27								16 50									17 14
East Croydon	a	16 09		16 17			16 20	16 32		16 33			←	16 39	16 45	16 55		17 00	17 03		17 09		17 17		17 20
	d	16 09		16 17			16 21	16 34 →		16 33			16 34	16 39	16 46	16 56		17 00	17 03		17 09		17 17		17 21
Norwood Junction 2	a												16 38												
London Bridge 4	⊖ a	*16 42*								16 47			16 51	*17 12*					17 17		*17 42*				
London Waterloo (East) 4	⊖ a																								
London Charing Cross 4	⊖ a																								
London Blackfriars 3	⊖ a																								
City Thameslink 3	a																								
Farringdon 3	⊖ a																								
St Pancras International 15	⊖ a																								
St Albans City	a																								
Luton Airport Parkway 4 ✈	a																								
Luton 7	a																								
Bedford 10	a																								
Clapham Junction 10	d	16 19		16 27			16 32							16 49	16 55	17 07		17 11			17 19		17 27		17 32
West Brompton	⊖ d														*17 12*										
Kensington (Olympia)	⊖ d														*17 15*										
Shepherd's Bush	⊖ d														*17 18*										
Watford Junction	a														*17 46*										
Milton Keynes Central 10	a																								
London Victoria 15	⊖ a	16 25		16 33		16 35	16 39					16 50		16 55	17 02	17 13	17 05	17 17		17 20	17 25		17 33	17 35	17 39

For general notes see front of timetable
For details of catering facilities see
Directory of Train Operators

A From Bognor Regis (Table 188)

Table 186

Sundays

until 6 September

Brighton → London, Bedford

Network Diagram - see first page of Table 186

		SN 1		GW 1	FC 1	GW 1	GX 1	SN 1	SN 1	SN 1 ◇	SN 1	GX 1	SN 1 ◇	FC 1	GX 1	SN 1	SN 1	SN 1 ◇	GX 1	SN 1	SN 1	GW 1		FC 1	GW 1
																Bus	A Bus			A Bus					
Brighton 10	d				16 45					17 10			17 00	17 17				17 40						17 45	
Hove 2	d								16 54																
Preston Park	d												17 03												
Hassocks 4	d				16 53								17 10											17 53	
Burgess Hill 4	d				16 57				17 04				17 13	17 27										17 57	
Lewes 4	d															17 22									
Wivelsfield 4	d												17 16			17 36									
Haywards Heath 3	a				17 02				17 09				17 20	17 32		17 40								18 02	
	d				17 02				17 11				17 25	17 32		17 41								18 02	
Balcombe	d												17 30												
Horsham 4	d										17 00						17 37								
Littlehaven	d										17 03														
Faygate	d																								
Ifield	d										17 09														
Crawley	d										17 13						17 46								
Three Bridges 4	a				17 11						17 16		17 36	17 41			17 50							18 11	
	d				17 12						17 18		17 36	17 42			17 50							18 12	
Gatwick Airport 10 ✈	a				17 16				17 22		17 22		17 41	17 46		17 52	17 55	18 01						18 16	
	d			17 08	17 17		17 20		17 23		17 23	17 35	17 42	17 47	17 50	17 53	17 56	18 02	18 05			18 08		18 17	
Horley 4	d										17 26						17 58								
Salfords	d										17 30														
Earlswood (Surrey)	d										17 33														
Tonbridge 4	d	16 41																			17 41				
Leigh (Kent)	d	16 45																			17 45				
Penshurst	d	16 49																			17 49				
Edenbridge	d	16 55																			17 55				
Godstone	d	17 02																			18 02				
Nutfield	d	17 07																			18 07				
Reigate	d					17 13																			
Redhill 5	a	17 12		17 15		17 18					17 36		17 49				18 05			←	18 12	18 15			18 12
	d	17 13									17 37		17 49				18 05 →			18 05	18 13				18 16
Merstham	d	17 17									17 41										18 17				
Coulsdon South	d	17 22									17 46										18 22				
Purley 4	d	17 27									17 50									18 14	18 27				
East Croydon	a	17 32			17 33			←	17 39	17 45	17 55		18 00	18 03		18 09		18 17		18 20	18 32			18 33	
	d	17 34 →			17 33			17 34	17 39	17 46	17 56		18 00	18 03		18 09		18 17		18 21	18 34 →			18 33	
Norwood Junction 2	a							17 38																	
London Bridge 4 ⊖	a				17 47			17 51	*18 12*					18 17		*18 42*								18 47	
London Waterloo (East) 4 ⊖	a																								
London Charing Cross 4 ⊖	a																								
London Blackfriars 3 ⊖	a																								
City Thameslink 3	a																								
Farringdon 3 ⊖	a																								
St Pancras International 15 ⊖	a																								
St Albans City	a																								
Luton Airport Parkway 4 ✈	a																								
Luton 7	a																								
Bedford 10	a																								
Clapham Junction 10	d								17 49	17 55	18 07		18 11			18 19		18 27		18 32					
West Brompton ⊖	d									*18 12*															
Kensington (Olympia) ⊖	d									*18 15*															
Shepherd's Bush ⊖	d									*18 18*															
Watford Junction	a									*18 46*															
Milton Keynes Central 10	a																								
London Victoria 15 ⊖	a						17 50		17 55	18 02	18 13	18 05	18 17		18 20	18 25		18 33	18 35	18 39					

For general notes see front of timetable
For details of catering facilities see Directory of Train Operators

A From Bognor Regis (Table 188)

Sundays

until 6 September

Brighton → London, Bedford

Network Diagram - see first page of Table 186

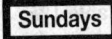

		GX 1	SN 1	SN 1	SN 1 ◇	SN 1	GX 1	SN 1 ◇	FC 1	GX 1	SN 1	SN 1 A	SN 1 ◇	GX 1	SN 1 A	SN 1	GW 1	FC 1	GW 1	GX 1		SN 1	SN 1	SN 1 ◇	SN 1
Brighton 10	d				18 10			18 00	18 17				18 40					18 45						19 10	
Hove 2	d			17 54																			18 54		
Preston Park	d							18 03																	
Hassocks 4	d							18 10										18 53							
Burgess Hill 4	d			18 04				18 13	18 27									18 57					19 04		
Lewes 4	d										18 22														
Wivelsfield 4	d							18 16			18 36														
Haywards Heath 3	a			18 09				18 20	18 32		18 40							19 02					19 09		
	d			18 11				18 25	18 32		18 41							19 02					19 11		
Balcombe	d							18 30																	
Horsham 4	d					18 00						18 37													19 00
Littlehaven	d					18 03																			19 03
Faygate	d																								
Ifield	d					18 09																			19 09
Crawley	d					18 13						18 46													19 13
Three Bridges 4	a					18 16		18 36	18 41			18 50						19 11							19 16
	d					18 18		18 36	18 42			18 50						19 12							19 18
Gatwick Airport 10 ✈	a			18 22		18 22		18 41	18 46		18 52	18 55	19 01					19 16					19 22		19 22
	d	18 20		18 23		18 23	18 35	18 42	18 47	18 50	18 53	18 56	19 02	19 05			19 08	19 17		19 20			19 23		19 23
Horley 4	d					18 26						18 58													19 26
Salfords	d					18 30																			19 30
Earlswood (Surrey)	d					18 33																			19 33
Tonbridge 4	d															18 41									
Leigh (Kent)	d															18 45									
Penshurst	d															18 49									
Edenbridge	d															18 55									
Godstone	d															19 02									
Nutfield	d															19 07									
Reigate	d																		19 13						
Redhill 5	a					18 36		18 49				19 05			←	19 12	19 15		19 18						19 36
	d					18 37		18 49				19 05			19 05	19 13									19 37
Merstham	d					18 41						→				19 17									19 41
Coulsdon South	d					18 46										19 22									19 46
Purley 4	d					18 50									19 14	19 27									19 50
East Croydon	a		←	18 39	18 45	18 55		19 00	19 03		19 09		19 17		19 20	19 32		19 33				←	19 39	19 45	19 55
	d		18 34	18 39	18 46	18 56		19 00	19 03		19 09		19 17		19 21	19 34 →		19 33				19 34	19 39	19 46	19 56
Norwood Junction 2	a		18 38																			19 38			
London Bridge 4	⊖ a		18 51	*19 12*					19 17		*19 42*							19 47				19 51	*20 12*		
London Waterloo (East) 4	⊖ a																								
London Charing Cross 4	⊖ a																								
London Blackfriars 3	⊖ a																								
City Thameslink 3	a																								
Farringdon 3	⊖ a																								
St Pancras International 15	⊖ a																								
St Albans City	a																								
Luton Airport Parkway 4	✈ a																								
Luton 7	a																								
Bedford 10	a																								
Clapham Junction 10	d			18 49	18 55	19 07		19 11			19 19		19 27		19 32								19 49	19 55	20 07
West Brompton	⊖ d				*19 12*																			*20 12*	
Kensington (Olympia)	⊖ d				*19 15*																			*20 15*	
Shepherd's Bush	⊖ d				*19 18*																			*20 18*	
Watford Junction	a				*19 46*																			*20 46*	
Milton Keynes Central 10	a																								
London Victoria 15	⊖ a	18 50		18 55	19 02	19 13	19 05	19 17		19 20	19 25		19 33	19 35	19 39					19 50			19 55	20 02	20 13

For general notes see front of timetable
For details of catering facilities see Directory of Train Operators

A From Bognor Regis (Table 188)

Table 186

Brighton → London, Bedford

Sundays

until 6 September

Network Diagram - see first page of Table 186

		GX 1	SN 1 ◇	FC 1	GX 1	SN 1	SN 1 A	SN 1 ◇	GX 1	SN 1 A	SN 1	GW 1	FC 1	GW 1	GX 1	SN 1	SN 1	SN 1 ◇		SN 1	GX 1	SN 1 ◇	FC 1	GX 1	SN 1
Brighton 10	d		19 00	19 17				19 40					19 45					20 10				20 00	20 17		
Hove 2	d																19 54								
Preston Park	d		19 03																			20 03			
Hassocks 4	d		19 10										19 53									20 10			
Burgess Hill 4	d		19 13	19 27									19 57				20 04					20 13	20 27		
Lewes 4	d					19 22																			20 22
Wivelsfield 4	d		19 16			19 36																20 16			20 36
Haywards Heath 3	a		19 20	19 32		19 40							20 02				20 09					20 20	20 32		20 40
	d		19 25	19 32		19 41							20 02				20 11					20 25	20 32		20 41
Balcombe	d		19 30																			20 30			
Horsham 4	d						19 37													20 00					
Littlehaven	d																			20 03					
Faygate	d																								
Ifield	d																			20 09					
Crawley	d						19 46													20 13					
Three Bridges 4	a		19 36	19 41			19 50						20 11							20 16		20 36	20 41		
	d		19 36	19 42			19 50						20 12							20 18		20 36	20 42		
Gatwick Airport 10 ✈	a		19 41	19 46		19 52	19 55	20 01					20 16				20 22			20 22		20 41	20 46		20 52
	d	19 35	19 42	19 47	19 50	19 53	19 56	20 02	20 05			20 08	20 17		20 20		20 23			20 23	20 35	20 42	20 47	20 50	20 53
Horley 4	d						19 58													20 26					
Salfords	d																			20 30					
Earlswood (Surrey)	d																			20 33					
Tonbridge 4	d										19 41														
Leigh (Kent)	d										19 45														
Penshurst	d										19 49														
Edenbridge	d										19 55														
Godstone	d										20 02														
Nutfield	d										20 07														
Reigate	d													20 11											
Redhill 5	a		19 49				20 05			←	20 12	20 15		20 16						20 36		20 49			
	d		19 49				20 05 →			20 05	20 13									20 37		20 49			
Merstham	d										20 17									20 41					
Coulsdon South	d										20 22									20 46					
Purley 4	d									20 14	20 27									20 50					
East Croydon	a		20 00	20 03		20 09		20 17		20 20	20 32		20 33			←	20 39	20 45		20 55		21 00	21 03		21 09
	d		20 00	20 03		20 09		20 17		20 21	20 34 →		20 33			20 34	20 39	20 46		20 56		21 00	21 03		21 09
Norwood Junction 2	a															20 38									
London Bridge 4	⊖ a			20 17		*20 42*							20 47			20 51	*21 12*						21 17		*21 42*
London Waterloo (East) 4	⊖ a																								
London Charing Cross 4	⊖ a																								
London Blackfriars 3	⊖ a																								
City Thameslink 3	a																								
Farringdon 3	⊖ a																								
St Pancras International 15	⊖ a																								
St Albans City	a																								
Luton Airport Parkway 4 ✈	a																								
Luton 7	a																								
Bedford 10	a																								
Clapham Junction 10	d		20 11			20 19		20 27		20 32							20 49	20 55		21 07		21 11			21 19
West Brompton	⊖ d																					*21 22*			
Kensington (Olympia)	⊖ d																					*21 25*			
Shepherd's Bush	⊖ d																					*21 28*			
Watford Junction	a																					*21b58*			
Milton Keynes Central 10	a																								
London Victoria 15	⊖ a	20 05	20 17		20 20	20 25		20 33	20 35	20 39					20 50		20 55	21 02		21 13	21 05	21 17		21 20	21 25

For general notes see front of timetable
For details of catering facilities see Directory of Train Operators

A From Bognor Regis (Table 188)
b From 19 July arr. 2157

Table 186

Sundays

until 6 September

Brighton → London, Bedford

Network Diagram - see first page of Table 186

		SN 1 A	SN 1 ◇	GX 1	SN 1 A	SN 1	GW 1	GW 1	FC 1	GX 1	SN 1	SN 1	SN 1	GX 1	SN 1 ◇	FC 1		GX 1	SN 1	SN 1 A	SN 1	GX 1	GW 1	GW 1	FC 1
Brighton 10	d		20 40						20 45						21 04	21 17									21 45
Hove 2	d											20 54													
Preston Park	d														21 07										
Hassocks 4	d								20 53						21 14										21 53
Burgess Hill 4	d								20 57			21 04			21 17	21 27									21 57
Lewes 4	d																		21 22						
Wivelsfield 4	d														21 20				21 36						
Haywards Heath 3	a								21 02			21 09			21 24	21 32			21 40						22 02
	d								21 02			21 11			21 25	21 32			21 41						22 02
Balcombe	d														21 30										
Horsham 4	d	20 37											21 00							21 37					
Littlehaven	d												21 03												
Faygate	d																								
Ifield	d												21 09												
Crawley	d	20 46											21 13							21 46					
Three Bridges 4	a	20 50							21 11				21 16		21 36	21 41				21 50					22 11
	d	20 50							21 12				21 18		21 36	21 42				21 50					22 12
Gatwick Airport 10 ✈	a	20 55	21 01						21 16			21 22	21 22		21 41	21 46			21 52	21 55					22 16
	d	20 56	21 02	21 05			21 08		21 17	21 20		21 23	21 23	21 35	21 42	21 47		21 50	21 53	21 56		22 05	22 07		22 17
Horley 4	d	20 58											21 26							21 58					
Salfords	d												21 30												
Earlswood (Surrey)	d												21 33												
Tonbridge 4	d					20 41															21 41				
Leigh (Kent)	d					20 45															21 45				
Penshurst	d					20 49															21 49				
Edenbridge	d					20 55															21 55				
Godstone	d					21 02															22 02				
Nutfield	d					21 07															22 07				
Reigate	d							21 13																22 11	
Redhill 5	a	21 05			←	21 12	21 15	21 18					21 36		21 49					22 05	22 12		22 15	22 15	
	d	21 05 →			21 05	21 13							21 37		21 49					22 05	22 13				
Merstham	d					21 17							21 41								22 17				
Coulsdon South	d					21 22							21 46								22 22				
Purley 4	d				21 14	21 27							21 50							22 14	22 27				
East Croydon	a		21 17		21 20	21 32			21 33		←	21 39	21 55		22 00	22 03			22 09	22 20	22 32				22 33
	d		21 17		21 21	21 34 →			21 33		21 34	21 39	21 56		22 00	22 03			22 09	22 21	22 34 →				22 33
Norwood Junction 2	a										21 38														
London Bridge 4	⊖ a								21 47		21 51	22 12				22 17			22 42						22 47
London Waterloo (East) 4	⊖ a																								
London Charing Cross 4	⊖ a																								
London Blackfriars 3	⊖ a																								
City Thameslink 3	a																								
Farringdon 3	⊖ a																								
St Pancras International 15	⊖ a																								
St Albans City	a																								
Luton Airport Parkway 4	✈ a																								
Luton 7	a																								
Bedford 10	a																								
Clapham Junction 10	d		21 27		21 32							21 49	22 07		22 11				22 19	22 32					
West Brompton	⊖ d														22 22										
Kensington (Olympia)	⊖ d														22 25										
Shepherd's Bush	⊖ d														22 28										
Watford Junction	a														22 58										
Milton Keynes Central 10	a																								
London Victoria 15	⊖ a		21 33	21 35	21 39					21 50		21 55	22 13	22 05	22 17			22 20	22 25	22 39		22 35			

For general notes see front of timetable
For details of catering facilities see Directory of Train Operators

A From Bognor Regis (Table 188)

Brighton → London, Bedford

Sundays

until 6 September

Network Diagram - see first page of Table 186

Station		GX 1	SN 1	SN 1	GX 1	SN 1 ◇	SN 1	FC 1	GX 1	SN 1 A	GX 1	GW 1	GW 1	FC 1		GX 1	SN 1	GX 1	SN 1 ◇	FC 1	SN 1 ◇	GX 1	FC 1		
Brighton 10	d					22 04		22 17						22 45					23 02	23 11			23 44		
Hove 2	d																								
Preston Park	d					22 07													23 06						
Hassocks 4	d					22 14								22 53					23 12	23 19			23 52		
Burgess Hill 4	d					22 17		22 27						22 57					23 16	23 23			23 56		
Lewes 4	d																								
Wivelsfield 4	d					22 20													23 19						
Haywards Heath 3	a					22 24		22 32						23 02					23 23	23 27			00 01		
	d					22 25		22 32						23 02					23 24	23 28			00 01		
Balcombe	d					22 30													23 29						
Horsham 4	d			22 00						22 37							23 04								
Littlehaven	d			22 03													23 07								
Faygate	d																								
Ifield	d			22 09													23 13								
Crawley	d			22 13						22 46							23 17								
Three Bridges 4	a			22 16		22 36		22 41		22 50				23 11			23 20		23 35	23 39	←		00 10		
	d			22 18		22 36		22 42		22 50				23 12			23 22		23 42	23 39	23 42		00 10		
Gatwick Airport 10 ✈	a			22 22		22 41		22 46		22 55				23 16			23 26		→	23 43	23 46		00 14		
	d	22 20		22 23	22 35	22 42		22 47	22 50	22 56	23 05	23 07		23 17		23 20	23 27	23 35		23 44	23 47	23 50	00 15		
Horley 4	d			22 26						22 58							23 30				23 49				
Salfords	d			22 30																					
Earlswood (Surrey)	d			22 33																					
Tonbridge 4	d						22 24																		
Leigh (Kent)	d						22 28																		
Penshurst	d						22 32																		
Edenbridge	d						22 38																		
Godstone	d						22 45																		
Nutfield	d						22 50																		
Reigate	d												23 13												
Redhill 5	a			22 36		22 49	22 55			23 05		23 15	23 18				23 36				23 57		00 22		
	d			22 37		22 49				23 05							23 37				00 02		00 22		
Merstham	d			22 41													23 41								
Coulsdon South	d			22 46													23 46								
Purley 4	d			22 50						23 14							23 50				00 11				
East Croydon	a		←	22 55		23 00		23 03		23 20				23 33			23 55			23 59	00 16		00 35		
	d		22 34	22 56		23 00		23 03		23 21				23 33			23 56			00 01	00 17		00 36		
Norwood Junction 2	a		22 38																						
London Bridge 4	⊖ a		22 51					23 17						23 47			*00 14*			00 14	*00 52*		00 52		
London Waterloo (East) 4	⊖ a																								
London Charing Cross 4	⊖ a																								
London Blackfriars 3	⊖ a																								
City Thameslink 3	a																								
Farringdon 3	⊖ a																								
St Pancras International 15	⊖ a																								
St Albans City	a																								
Luton Airport Parkway 4 ✈	a																								
Luton 7	a																								
Bedford 10	a																								
Clapham Junction 10	d			23 07		23 11				23 32							00 11			00b29	00 30		01b02		
West Brompton	⊖ d																								
Kensington (Olympia)	⊖ d																								
Shepherd's Bush	⊖ d																								
Watford Junction	a																								
Milton Keynes Central 10	a																								
London Victoria 15	⊖ a	22 50		23 14	23 05	23 17			23 20	23 38	23 35					23 55	00 18	00 10		00b37	00 37	00 25	01b09		

For general notes see front of timetable
For details of catering facilities see Directory of Train Operators

A From Bognor Regis (Table 188)
b Change at East Croydon

Table 186

Sundays

from 13 September

Brighton → London and Bedford

Network Diagram - see first page of Table 186

		SN 1	SN 1 ◇	FC 1	SN 1 ◇	GX 1	FC 1	GX 1	GX 1	GW 1	GX 1	SN 1	GX 1	SN 1	SN 1	SN 1	GX 1	SN 1 ◇	FC 1	GX 1	SN 1	GX 1	GX 1	GW 1	FC 1
Brighton 10	d		23p02	23p11			23p37											03 50							05 44
Hove 2	d																								
Preston Park	d		23p06				23p41																		
Hassocks 4	d		23p12	23p19			23p47																		05 52
Burgess Hill 4	d		23p16	23p23			23p51																		05 56
Lewes 4	d																								
Wivelsfield 4	d		23p19				23p53																		
Haywards Heath 3	a		23p23	23p27			23p58																		06 00
	d		23p24	23p28			23p59																		06 01
Balcombe	d						00 04																		
Horsham 4	d	23p02																							
Littlehaven	d	23p05																							
Faygate	d																								
Ifield	d	23p11																							
Crawley	d	23p14																							
Three Bridges 4	a	23p18	23p33	23p37	←		00 10											04 45							06 10
	d	23p18	23p47	23p38	23p47		00 10					01 10		02 10	03 10	04 10		04 58	05 10		05 30				06 10
Gatwick Airport 10 ✈	a	23p22	→	23p42	23p52		00 14					01 19		02 14	03 14	04 14		05 02	05 14		05 34				06 14
	d	23p23		23p43	23p53	00 05	00 15	00 20	00 35		00 50	01 20	01 35	02 15	03 15	04 15	04 35	05 03	05 15	05 20	05 36	05 50	06 05	06 06	06 15
Horley 4	d	23p26			23p56							01 22		02 18	03 18	04 18		05 05			05 38				
Salfords	d	23p30																							
Earlswood (Surrey)	d	23p33																							
Tonbridge 4	d																								
Leigh (Kent)	d																								
Penshurst	d																								
Edenbridge	d																								
Godstone	d																								
Nutfield	d																								
Reigate	d									00 45															
Redhill 5	a	23p36			00 02		00 22			00 49											05 46			06 16	
	d	23p37			00 03		00 22														05 46				
Merstham	d	23p41																							
Coulsdon South	d	23p46																							
Purley 4	d	23p49			00 11							01 37		02 33	03 33	04 33		05 22			05 56				
East Croydon	a	23p55		00 02	00 16		00 35					01 42		02 39	03 39	04 39		05 27	05 31		06 01				06 31
	d	23p56		00 04	00 17		00 36					01 43		02 40	03 40	04 40		05 28	05 32		06 02				06 32
Norwood Junction 2	a																								
London Bridge 4	⊖ a	*00 19*		00 19			00 52												05 59						06 59
London Waterloo (East) 4	⊖ a																								
London Charing Cross 4	⊖ a																								
London Blackfriars 3	⊖ a																								
City Thameslink 3	a																								
Farringdon 3	⊖ a																								
St Pancras International 15	⊖ a																								
St Albans City	a																								
Luton Airport Parkway 4 ✈	a																								
Luton 7	a																								
Bedford 10	a																								
Clapham Junction 10	d	00 11			00 29		*01b02*					01 54		02 53	03 53	04 53		05 48			06 14				*07b00*
West Brompton	⊖ d																								
Kensington (Olympia)	⊖ d																								
Shepherd's Bush	⊖ d																								
Watford Junction	a																								
Milton Keynes Central 10	a																								
London Victoria 15	⊖ a	00 18			00 36	00 40	*01b09*	00 55	01 10		01 25	02 05	02 20	03 05	04 05	05 05	05 10	05 56		05 58	06 22	06 25	06 40		*07b08*

For general notes see front of timetable
For details of catering facilities see
Directory of Train Operators

b Change at East Croydon

Sundays

from 13 September

Brighton → London and Bedford

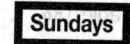

Network Diagram - see first page of Table 186

		GX 1	SN 1	GX 1		FC 1	GX 1	SN 1 ◇	SN 1	GW 1	GX 1	GW 1	FC 1	GX 1	SN 1	GX 1	SN 1 ◇	SN 1	FC 1	GX 1	SN 1 ⚯	SN 1 A	GX 1	GW 1	GW 1
Brighton 10	d					06 13		06 16					06 44				07 00		07 16						
Hove 2	d																								
Preston Park	d							06 19									07 03								
Hassocks 4	d							06 26					06 52				07 10								
Burgess Hill 4	d					06 26		06 29					06 56				07 13		07 26						
Lewes 4	d																				07 20				
Wivelsfield 4	d							06 32									07 16				07 32				
Haywards Heath 3	a					06 30		06 36					07 00				07 20		07 30		07 36				
	d					06 31		06 40					07 01				07 21		07 31		07 39				
Balcombe	d																07 26								
Horsham 4	d		06 04						06 34						07 04							07 42			
Littlehaven	d		06 07						06 37						07 07										
Faygate	d																								
Ifield	d		06 13						06 43						07 13										
Crawley	d		06 17						06 47						07 17							07 51			
Three Bridges 4	a		06 20			06 40		06 49	06 51				07 10		07 20		07 32		07 40			07 54			
	d		06 21			06 40		06 49	06 53				07 10		07 22		07 32		07 40			07 55			
Gatwick Airport 10 ✈	a		06 25			06 44		06 53	06 57				07 14		07 26		07 37		07 44		07 51	07 59			
	d	06 20		06 35		06 45	06 50	06 54	06 58		07 05	07 08	07 15	07 20	07 27	07 35	07 38		07 45	07 50	07 53	08 00	08 05	08 08	
Horley 4	d								07 00						07 30							08 02			
Salfords	d																								
Earlswood (Surrey)	d																								
Tonbridge 4	d																	07 24							
Leigh (Kent)	d																	07 28							
Penshurst	d																	07 32							
Edenbridge	d																	07 38							
Godstone	d																	07 45							
Nutfield	d																	07 50							
Reigate	d									07 05															08 11
Redhill 5	a								07 07	07 09		07 17			07 36		07 45	07 55				08 09		08 15	08 17
	d								07 07						07 37		07 46					08 09			
Merstham	d								07 11						07 41										
Coulsdon South	d								07 16						07 46										
Purley 4	d								07 20						07 49							08 18			
East Croydon	a					07 01		07 10	07 26				07 31		07 54		07 58		08 01		08 09	08 24			
	d					07 02		07 10	07 27				07 32		07 58		08 00		08 02		08 10	08 26			
Norwood Junction 2	a																								
London Bridge 4	⊖ a					07 17							07 47						08 17		*08 42*				
London Waterloo (East) 4	⊖ a																								
London Charing Cross 4	⊖ a																								
London Blackfriars 3	⊖ a																								
City Thameslink 3	a																								
Farringdon 3	⊖ a																								
St Pancras International 15	⊖ a																								
St Albans City	a																								
Luton Airport Parkway 4 ✈	a																								
Luton 7	a																								
Bedford 10	a																								
Clapham Junction 10	d							07 24	07 41						08 09		08 12				08 25	08 38			
West Brompton	⊖ d														*08 22*										
Kensington (Olympia)	⊖ d														*08 25*										
Shepherd's Bush	⊖ d														*08 28*										
Watford Junction	a														*08 58*										
Milton Keynes Central 10	a																								
London Victoria 15	⊖ a	06 55		07 10			07 25	07 31	07 48		07 40			07 55	08 16	08 10	08 18			08 25	08 31	08 46	08 40		

For general notes see front of timetable
For details of catering facilities see Directory of Train Operators

A From Bognor Regis (Table 188)

Sundays

from 13 September

Brighton → London and Bedford

Network Diagram - see first page of Table 186

		FC 1	GX 1	SN 1	SN 1	GX 1	SN 1 ◇ 🛒	SN 1		FC 1	GX 1	SN 1 🛒	SN 1 A 🛒	GX 1	GW 1	GW 1	FC 1	SN 1 ◇	GX 1	SN 1	SN 1	GX 1	SN 1 ◇ 🛒	SN 1	FC 1
Brighton 10	d	07 44					08 00			08 16							08 44	08 51					09 00		09 16
Hove 2	d			07 54																08 54					
Preston Park	d						08 03																09 03		
Hassocks 4	d	07 52					08 10										08 52						09 10		
Burgess Hill 4	d	07 56		08 04			08 13			08 26							08 56			09 04			09 13		09 26
Lewes 4	d											08 16													
Wivelsfield 4	d						08 16					08 31											09 16		
Haywards Heath 3	a	08 00		08 09			08 20			08 30		08 36					09 00			09 09			09 20		09 30
	d	08 01		08 10			08 21			08 31		08 39					09 01			09 10			09 21		09 31
Balcombe	d						08 26																09 26		
Horsham 4	d				08 04								08 42								09 04				
Littlehaven	d				08 07																09 07				
Faygate	d																								
Ifield	d				08 13																09 13				
Crawley	d				08 17								08 51								09 17				
Three Bridges 4	a	08 10			08 20		08 32			08 40			08 54				09 10				09 20		09 32		09 40
	d	08 10			08 22		08 32			08 40			08 55				09 10				09 22		09 32		09 40
Gatwick Airport 10 ✈	a	08 14		08 21	08 26		08 37			08 44		08 51	08 59				09 14	09 17		09 21	09 26		09 37		09 44
	d	08 15	08 20	08 23	08 27	08 35	08 38			08 45	08 50	08 53	09 00	09 05	09 08		09 15	09 18	09 20	09 23	09 27	09 35	09 38		09 45
Horley 4	d				08 30								09 02								09 30				
Salfords	d																								
Earlswood (Surrey)	d																								
Tonbridge 4	d							08 24																09 24	
Leigh (Kent)	d							08 28																09 28	
Penshurst	d							08 32																09 32	
Edenbridge	d							08 38																09 38	
Godstone	d							08 45																09 45	
Nutfield	d							08 50																09 50	
Reigate	d															09 13									
Redhill 5	a				08 36		08 45	08 55					09 09		09 15	09 18					09 36		09 45	09 55	
	d				08 37		08 46						09 09								09 37		09 46		
Merstham	d				08 41																09 41				
Coulsdon South	d				08 46																09 46				
Purley 4	d				08 49								09 18								09 49				
East Croydon 🚋	a	08 31		08 39	08 54		08 58			09 01		09 09	09 24				09 31	09 34		09 39	09 54		09 58		10 01
	d	08 32		08 40	08 58		09 00			09 02		09 10	09 25				09 32	09 35		09 40	09 58		10 00		10 02
Norwood Junction 2	a																								
London Bridge 4 ⊖	a	08 47		*09 12*						09 17		*09 42*					09 47			*10 12*					10 17
London Waterloo (East) 4 ⊖	a																								
London Charing Cross 4 ⊖	a																								
London Blackfriars 3 ⊖	a																								
City Thameslink 3	a																								
Farringdon 3 ⊖	a																								
St Pancras International 15 ⊖	a																								
St Albans City	a																								
Luton Airport Parkway 4 ✈	a																								
Luton 7	a																								
Bedford 10	a																								
Clapham Junction 10	d			08 55	09 09		09 12					09 25	09 38					09 47		09 55	10 09		10 12		
West Brompton ⊖	d				*09 22*																*10 22*				
Kensington (Olympia) ⊖	d				*09 25*																*10 25*				
Shepherd's Bush ⊖	d				*09 28*																*10 28*				
Watford Junction	a				*09 58*																*10 58*				
Milton Keynes Central 10	a																								
London Victoria 15 ⊖	a		08 55	09 01	09 16	09 10	09 18				09 25	09 31	09 46	09 40				09 53	09 55	10 01	10 16	10 10	10 18		

For general notes see front of timetable
For details of catering facilities see Directory of Train Operators

A From Bognor Regis (Table 188)

Table 186

Sundays

from 13 September

Brighton → London and Bedford

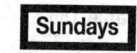

Network Diagram - see first page of Table 186

		GX 1	SN 1 ✕	SN 1 A ✕	GX 1	GW 1	GW 1	FC 1	SN 1 ◇	GX 1	SN 1	SN 1	GX 1	SN 1 ◇ ✕	SN 1	FC 1	GX 1	SN 1 ✕	SN 1 A ✕	GX 1	GW 1	GW 1	FC 1	SN 1 ◇
Brighton 10	d							09 44	09 51					10 00		10 16							10 44	10 51
Hove 2	d										09 54													
Preston Park	d													10 03										
Hassocks 4	d							09 52						10 10									10 52	
Burgess Hill 4	d							09 56			10 04			10 13		10 26							10 56	
Lewes 4	d		09 16															10 16						
Wivelsfield 4	d		09 31											10 16				10 31						
Haywards Heath 3	a		09 35					10 00			10 09			10 20		10 30		10 35					11 00	
	d		09 39					10 01			10 10			10 21		10 31		10 39					11 01	
Balcombe	d													10 26										
Horsham 4	d			09 42								10 04							10 42					
Littlehaven	d											10 07												
Faygate	d																							
Ifield	d											10 13												
Crawley	d			09 51								10 17							10 51					
Three Bridges 4	a			09 54				10 10				10 20		10 32		10 40			10 54				11 10	
	d			09 55				10 10				10 22		10 32		10 40			10 55				11 10	
Gatwick Airport 10 ✈	a		09 51	09 59				10 14	10 17		10 21	10 26		10 37		10 44		10 51	10 59				11 14	11 17
	d	09 50	09 53	10 00	10 05	10 08		10 15	10 18	10 20	10 23	10 27	10 35	10 38		10 45	10 50	10 53	11 00	11 05	11 08		11 15	11 18
Horley 4	d			10 02								10 30							11 02					
Salfords	d																							
Earlswood (Surrey)	d																							
Tonbridge 4	d														10 24									
Leigh (Kent)	d														10 28									
Penshurst	d														10 32									
Edenbridge	d														10 38									
Godstone	d														10 45									
Nutfield	d														10 50									
Reigate	d						10 13															11 13		
Redhill 5	a			10 09		10 15	10 17					10 36		10 45	10 55				11 09		11 15	11 18		
	d			10 09								10 37		10 46					11 09					
Merstham	d											10 41												
Coulsdon South	d											10 46												
Purley 4	d			10 18								10 49							11 18					
East Croydon	a		10 09	10 24				10 31	10 34		10 39	10 54		10 58		11 01		11 09	11 24				11 31	11 34
	d		10 10	10 25				10 32	10 35		10 40	10 58		11 00		11 02		11 10	11 25				11 32	11 35
Norwood Junction 2	a																							
London Bridge 4	⊖ a		*10 42*					10 47			*11 12*					11 17		*11 42*					11 47	
London Waterloo (East) 4	⊖ a																							
London Charing Cross 4	⊖ a																							
London Blackfriars 3	⊖ a																							
City Thameslink 3	a																							
Farringdon 3	⊖ a																							
St Pancras International 15	⊖ a																							
St Albans City	a																							
Luton Airport Parkway 4 ✈	a																							
Luton 7	a																							
Bedford 10	a																							
Clapham Junction 10	d		10 25	10 38					10 47		10 55	11 09		11 12				11 25	11 38					11 47
West Brompton	⊖ d											*11 22*												
Kensington (Olympia)	⊖ d											*11 25*												
Shepherd's Bush	⊖ d											*11 28*												
Watford Junction	a											*11 58*												
Milton Keynes Central 10	a																							
London Victoria 15	⊖ a	10 25	10 31	10 46	10 40				10 53	10 55	11 01	11 16	11 10	11 18			11 25	11 31	11 46	11 40				11 53

For general notes see front of timetable
For details of catering facilities see Directory of Train Operators

A From Bognor Regis (Table 188)

Table 186

Sundays

from 13 September

Brighton → London and Bedford

Network Diagram - see first page of Table 186

		GX 1	SN 1	SN 1	GX 1	SN 1 ◇ 🛒	SN 1	FC 1	GX 1	SN 1 🛒	SN 1 A 🛒	GX 1	GW 1	GW 1	FC 1	SN 1 ◇		GX 1	SN 1	SN 1	GX 1	SN 1 ◇ 🛒	SN 1	FC 1	GX 1
Brighton [10]	d					11 00		11 16							11 44	11 51						12 00		12 16	
Hove [2]	d		10 54																11 54						
Preston Park	d					11 03																12 03			
Hassocks [4]	d					11 10									11 52							12 10			
Burgess Hill [4]	d		11 04			11 13		11 26							11 56				12 04			12 13		12 26	
Lewes [4]	d									11 16															
Wivelsfield [4]	d					11 16				11 31												12 16			
Haywards Heath [3]	a		11 09			11 20		11 30		11 35					12 00				12 09			12 20		12 30	
	d		11 10			11 21		11 31		11 39					12 01				12 10			12 21		12 31	
Balcombe	d					11 26																12 26			
Horsham [4]	d			11 04							11 42									12 04					
Littlehaven	d			11 07																12 07					
Faygate	d																								
Ifield	d			11 13																12 13					
Crawley	d			11 17							11 51									12 17					
Three Bridges [4]	a			11 20		11 32		11 40			11 54				12 10					12 20		12 32		12 40	
	d			11 22		11 32		11 40			11 55				12 10					12 22		12 32		12 40	
Gatwick Airport [10] ✈	a		11 21	11 26		11 37		11 44		11 51	11 59				12 14	12 17			12 22	12 26		12 37		12 44	
	d	11 20	11 23	11 27	11 35	11 38		11 45	11 50	11 53	12 00	12 05	12 08		12 15	12 18		12 20	12 23	12 27	12 35	12 38		12 45	12 50
Horley [4]	d			11 30							12 02									12 30					
Salfords	d																								
Earlswood (Surrey)	d																								
Tonbridge [4]	d						11 24																12 24		
Leigh (Kent)	d						11 28																12 28		
Penshurst	d						11 32																12 32		
Edenbridge	d						11 38																12 38		
Godstone	d						11 45																12 45		
Nutfield	d						11 50																12 50		
Reigate	d													12 13											
Redhill [5]	a			11 36		11 45	11 55				12 09		12 15	12 17						12 36		12 45	12 55		
	d			11 37		11 46					12 09									12 37		12 46			
Merstham	d			11 41																12 41					
Coulsdon South	d			11 46																12 46					
Purley [4]	d			11 49							12 18									12 49					
East Croydon	a		11 39	11 54		11 58		12 01		12 09	12 24				12 31	12 34			12 39	12 54		12 58		13 01	
	d		11 40	11 58		12 00		12 02		12 10	12 25				12 32	12 35			12 40	12 58		13 00		13 02	
Norwood Junction [2]	a																								
London Bridge [4] ⊖	a		*12 12*					12 17		*12 42*					12 47				*13 12*					13 17	
London Waterloo (East) [4] ⊖	a																								
London Charing Cross [4] ⊖	a																								
London Blackfriars [3] ⊖	a																								
City Thameslink [3]	a																								
Farringdon [3] ⊖	a																								
St Pancras International [15] ⊖	a																								
St Albans City	a																								
Luton Airport Parkway [4] ✈	a																								
Luton [7]	a																								
Bedford [10]	a																								
Clapham Junction [10]	d		11 55	12 09		12 12				12 25	12 38					12 47			12 55	13 09		13 12			
West Brompton ⊖	d		*12 12*																*13 12*						
Kensington (Olympia) ⊖	d		*12 15*																*13 15*						
Shepherd's Bush ⊖	d		*12 18*																*13 18*						
Watford Junction	a		*12 46*																*13 46*						
Milton Keynes Central [10]	a																								
London Victoria [15] ⊖	a	11 55	12 01	12 16	12 10	12 18			12 25	12 31	12 46	12 40				12 53		12 55	13 01	13 16	13 10	13 18			13 25

For general notes see front of timetable
For details of catering facilities see
Directory of Train Operators

A From Bognor Regis (Table 188)

Table 186

Brighton → London and Bedford

Sundays

from 13 September

Network Diagram - see first page of Table 186

		SN 1	SN 1	GX 1	GW 1	GW 1	FC 1	SN 1 ◇	GX 1	SN 1	SN 1	GX 1	SN 1 ◇	SN 1	FC 1	GX 1	SN 1	SN 1	GX 1	GW 1		GW 1	FC 1	SN 1 ◇	GX 1
		trolley	A trolley										trolley				trolley	A trolley							
Brighton 10	d						12 44	12 51					13 00		13 16								13 44	13 51	
Hove 2	d									12 54															
Preston Park	d												13 03												
Hassocks 4	d						12 52						13 10										13 52		
Burgess Hill 4	d						12 56			13 04			13 13		13 26								13 56		
Lewes 4	d	12 16															13 16								
Wivelsfield 4	d	12 31											13 16				13 31								
Haywards Heath 3	a	12 35					13 00			13 09			13 20		13 30		13 35						14 00		
	d	12 39					13 01			13 10			13 21		13 31		13 39						14 01		
Balcombe	d												13 26												
Horsham 4	d		12 42								13 04							13 42							
Littlehaven	d										13 07														
Faygate	d																								
Ifield	d										13 13														
Crawley	d		12 51								13 17							13 51							
Three Bridges 4	a		12 54				13 10				13 20		13 32		13 40			13 54					14 10		
	d		12 55				13 10				13 22		13 32		13 40			13 55					14 10		
Gatwick Airport 10 ✈	a	12 52	12 59				13 14	13 17		13 22	13 26		13 37		13 44		13 52	13 59					14 14	14 17	
	d	12 53	13 00	13 05	13 08		13 15	13 18	13 20	13 23	13 27	13 35	13 38		13 45	13 50	13 53	14 00	14 05	14 08			14 15	14 18	14 20
Horley 4	d		13 02								13 30							14 02							
Salfords	d																								
Earlswood (Surrey)	d																								
Tonbridge 4	d													13 24											
Leigh (Kent)	d													13 28											
Penshurst	d													13 32											
Edenbridge	d													13 38											
Godstone	d													13 45											
Nutfield	d													13 50											
Reigate	d					13 13																			
Redhill 5	a		13 09		13 15	13 18					13 36		13 45	13 55				14 09		14 15		14 13			
	d		13 09								13 37		13 46					14 09				14 17			
Merstham	d										13 41														
Coulsdon South	d										13 46														
Purley 4	d		13 18								13 49							14 18							
East Croydon	a	13 09	13 24				13 31	13 34		13 39	13 54		13 58		14 01		14 09	14 24					14 31	14 34	
	d	13 10	13 25				13 32	13 35		13 40	13 58		14 00		14 02		14 10	14 25					14 32	14 35	
Norwood Junction 2	a																								
London Bridge 4 ⊖	a	*13 42*					13 47			*14 12*					14 17		*14 42*						14 47		
London Waterloo (East) 4 ⊖	a																								
London Charing Cross 4 ⊖	a																								
London Blackfriars 3 ⊖	a																								
City Thameslink 3	a																								
Farringdon 3 ⊖	a																								
St Pancras International 15 ⊖	a																								
St Albans City	a																								
Luton Airport Parkway 4 ✈	a																								
Luton 7	a																								
Bedford 10	a																								
Clapham Junction 10	d	13 25	13 38					13 47		13 55	14 09		14 12				14 25	14 38						14 47	
West Brompton ⊖	d									*14 12*															
Kensington (Olympia) ⊖	d									*14 15*															
Shepherd's Bush ⊖	d									*14 18*															
Watford Junction	a									*14 46*															
Milton Keynes Central 10	a																								
London Victoria 15 ⊖	a	13 31	13 46	13 40				13 53	13 55	14 01	14 16	14 10	14 18			14 25	14 31	14 46	14 40					14 53	14 55

For general notes see front of timetable
For details of catering facilities see Directory of Train Operators

A From Bognor Regis (Table 188)

Sundays

from 13 September

Brighton → London and Bedford

Network Diagram - see first page of Table 186

		SN	SN	GX	SN	SN	FC	GX	SN	SN	GX	GW	GW	FC	SN	GX	SN	SN	GX	SN	SN	FC	GX	SN	SN
		1	1	1	1 ◇	1	1	1	1	1	1	1	1	1	1 ◇	1	1	1	1	1 ◇	1	1	1	1	1
										A															A
					✠				✠	✠										✠				✠	✠
Brighton [10]	d				14 00		14 16							14 44	14 51					15 00		15 16			
Hove [2]	d	13 54															14 54								
Preston Park	d				14 03															15 03					
Hassocks [4]	d				14 10									14 52						15 10					
Burgess Hill [4]	d	14 04			14 13		14 26							14 56			15 04			15 13		15 26			
Lewes [4]	d								14 16															15 16	
Wivelsfield [4]	d				14 16				14 31											15 16				15 31	
Haywards Heath [3]	a	14 09			14 20		14 30		14 35					15 00			15 09			15 20		15 30		15 35	
	d	14 10			14 21		14 31		14 39					15 01			15 10			15 21		15 31		15 39	
Balcombe	d				14 26															15 26					
Horsham [4]	d		14 04							14 42								15 04							15 42
Littlehaven	d		14 07															15 07							
Faygate	d																								
Ifield	d		14 13															15 13							
Crawley	d		14 17							14 51								15 17							15 51
Three Bridges [4]	a		14 20		14 32		14 40			14 54				15 10				15 20		15 32		15 40			15 54
	d		14 22		14 32		14 40			14 55				15 10				15 22		15 32		15 40			15 55
Gatwick Airport [10] ✈	a	14 22	14 26		14 37		14 44		14 52	14 59				15 14	15 17		15 22	15 26		15 37		15 44		15 52	15 59
	d	14 23	14 27	14 35	14 38		14 45	14 50	14 53	15 00	15 05	15 08		15 15	15 18	15 20	15 23	15 27	15 35	15 38		15 45	15 50	15 53	16 00
Horley [4]	d		14 30							15 02								15 30							16 02
Salfords	d																								
Earlswood (Surrey)	d																								
Tonbridge [4]	d					14 24															15 24				
Leigh (Kent)	d					14 28															15 28				
Penshurst	d					14 32															15 32				
Edenbridge	d					14 38															15 38				
Godstone	d					14 45															15 45				
Nutfield	d					14 50															15 50				
Reigate	d												15 13												
Redhill [5]	a		14 36		14 45	14 55				15 09		15 15	15 18					15 36		15 45	15 55				16 09
	d		14 37		14 46					15 09								15 37		15 46					16 09
Merstham	d		14 41															15 41							
Coulsdon South	d		14 46															15 46							
Purley [4]	d		14 49							15 18								15 49							16 18
East Croydon 🚋	a	14 39	14 54		14 58		15 01		15 09	15 24				15 31	15 34		15 39	15 54		15 58		16 01		16 09	16 24
	d	14 40	14 58		15 00		15 02		15 10	15 25				15 32	15 35		15 40	15 58		16 00		16 02		16 10	16 25
Norwood Junction [2]	a																								
London Bridge [4] ⊖	a	*15 12*					15 17		*15 42*					15 47			*16 12*					16 17		*16 42*	
London Waterloo (East) [4] ⊖	a																								
London Charing Cross [4] ⊖	a																								
London Blackfriars [3] ⊖	a																								
City Thameslink [3]	a																								
Farringdon [3] ⊖	a																								
St Pancras International [15] ⊖	a																								
St Albans City	a																								
Luton Airport Parkway [4] ✈	a																								
Luton [7]	a																								
Bedford [10]	a																								
Clapham Junction [10]	d	14 55	15 09		15 12				15 25	15 38					15 47		15 55	16 09		16 12				16 25	16 38
West Brompton ⊖	d	*15 12*															*16 12*								
Kensington (Olympia) ⊖	d	*15 15*															*16 15*								
Shepherd's Bush ⊖	d	*15 18*															*16 18*								
Watford Junction	a	*15 46*															*16 46*								
Milton Keynes Central [10]	a																								
London Victoria [15] ⊖	a	15 01	15 16	15 10	15 18			15 25	15 31	15 46	15 40				15 53	15 55	16 01	16 16	16 10	16 18			16 25	16 31	16 46

For general notes see front of timetable
For details of catering facilities see
Directory of Train Operators

A From Bognor Regis (Table 188)

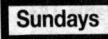

Brighton → London and Bedford

Sundays

from 13 September

Network Diagram - see first page of Table 186

	GX 1		GW 1	GW 1	FC 1	SN 1 ◇	GX 1	SN 1	SN 1	GX 1	SN 1 ◇	SN 1	FC 1	GX 1	SN 1	SN 1	GX 1	GW 1	GW 1	FC 1	SN 1 ◇	GX 1	SN 1	SN 1
															A	B								
											🛒				🛒	🛒								
Brighton 10 d					15 44	15 51					16 00		16 16							16 44	16 51			
Hove 2 d								15 54															16 54	
Preston Park d											16 03													
Hassocks 4 d					15 52						16 10									16 52				
Burgess Hill 4 d					15 56			16 04			16 13		16 26							16 56			17 04	
Lewes 4 d															16 16									
Wivelsfield 4 d											16 16				16 31									
Haywards Heath 3 a					16 00			16 09			16 20		16 30		16 35					17 00			17 09	
d					16 01			16 10			16 21		16 31		16 39					17 01			17 10	
Balcombe d											16 26													
Horsham 4 d									16 04							16 42								17 04
Littlehaven d									16 07															17 07
Faygate d																								
Ifield d									16 13															17 13
Crawley d									16 17							16 51								17 17
Three Bridges 4 a					16 10				16 20		16 32		16 40			16 54				17 10				17 20
d					16 10				16 22		16 32		16 40			16 55				17 10				17 22
Gatwick Airport 10 ✈ a					16 14	16 17		16 22	16 26		16 37		16 44		16 52	16 59				17 14	17 17		17 22	17 26
d	16 05		16 08		16 15	16 18	16 20	16 23	16 27	16 35	16 38		16 45	16 50	16 53	17 00	17 05	17 08		17 15	17 18	17 20	17 23	17 27
Horley 4 d									16 30							17 02								17 30
Salfords d																								
Earlswood (Surrey) d																								
Tonbridge 4 d												16 24												
Leigh (Kent) d												16 28												
Penshurst d												16 32												
Edenbridge d												16 38												
Godstone d												16 45												
Nutfield d												16 50												
Reigate d				16 13															17 13					
Redhill 5 a			16 15	16 17					16 36		16 45	16 55				17 09		17 15	17 19					17 36
d									16 37		16 46					17 09								17 37
Merstham d									16 41															17 41
Coulsdon South d									16 46															17 46
Purley 4 d									16 49							17 18								17 49
East Croydon a					16 31	16 34		16 39	16 54		16 58		17 01		17 09	17 24				17 31	17 34		17 39	17 54
d					16 32	16 35		16 40	16 58		17 00		17 02		17 10	17 25				17 32	17 35		17 40	17 58
Norwood Junction 2 a																								
London Bridge 4 ⊖ a					16 47			*17 12*					17 17		*17 42*					17 47			*18 12*	
London Waterloo (East) 4 ⊖ a																								
London Charing Cross 4 ⊖ a																								
London Blackfriars 3 ⊖ a																								
City Thameslink 3 a																								
Farringdon 3 ⊖ a																								
St Pancras International 15 ⊖ a																								
St Albans City a																								
Luton Airport Parkway 4 ✈ a																								
Luton 7 a																								
Bedford 10 a																								
Clapham Junction 10 d						16 47		16 55	17 09		17 12				17 25	17 38					17 47		17 55	18 09
West Brompton ⊖ d								*17 12*															*18 12*	
Kensington (Olympia) ⊖ d								*17 15*															*18 15*	
Shepherd's Bush ⊖ d								*17 18*															*18 18*	
Watford Junction a								*17 46*															*18 46*	
Milton Keynes Central 10 a																								
London Victoria 15 ⊖ a	16 40					16 53	16 55	17 01	17 16	17 10	17 18			17 25	17 31	17 46	17 40				17 53	17 55	18 01	18 16

For general notes see front of timetable
For details of catering facilities see
Directory of Train Operators

A 🛒 from Lewes
B From Bognor Regis (Table 188)

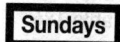

Sundays

from 13 September

Brighton → London and Bedford

Network Diagram - see first page of Table 186

		GX	SN	SN	FC	GX		SN	SN	GX	GW	GW	FC	SN	GX	SN	SN	GX	SN	SN	FC	GX	SN	SN	GX
		1	1 ◊	1	1	1		1	1	1	1	1	1	1 ◊	1	1	1	1	1 ◊	1	1	1	1	1	1
								A	B															B	
			🛒					🛒	🛒														🛒		
Brighton [10]	d		17 00		17 16								17 44	17 51					18 00		18 16				
Hove [2]	d															17 54									
Preston Park	d		17 03																18 03						
Hassocks [4]	d		17 10										17 52						18 10						
Burgess Hill [4]	d		17 13		17 26								17 56			18 04			18 13		18 26				
Lewes [4]	d							17 16															18 16		
Wivelsfield [4]	d		17 16					17 31											18 16				18 31		
Haywards Heath [3]	a		17 20		17 30			17 35					18 00			18 09			18 20		18 30		18 35		
	d		17 21		17 31			17 39					18 01			18 10			18 21		18 31		18 39		
Balcombe	d		17 26																18 26						
Horsham [4]	d								17 42								18 04							18 42	
Littlehaven	d																18 07								
Faygate	d																								
Ifield	d																18 13								
Crawley	d								17 51								18 17							18 51	
Three Bridges [4]	a		17 32		17 40				17 54				18 10				18 20		18 32		18 40			18 54	
	d		17 32		17 40				17 55				18 10				18 22		18 32		18 40			18 55	
Gatwick Airport [10] ✈	a		17 37		17 44			17 52	17 59				18 14	18 17		18 22	18 26		18 37		18 44		18 52	18 59	
	d	17 35	17 38		17 45	17 50		17 53	18 00	18 05	18 08		18 15	18 18	18 20	18 23	18 27	18 35	18 38		18 45	18 50	18 53	19 00	19 05
Horley [4]	d								18 02								18 30							19 02	
Salfords	d																								
Earlswood (Surrey)	d																								
Tonbridge [4]	d			17 24																18 24					
Leigh (Kent)	d			17 28																18 28					
Penshurst	d			17 32																18 32					
Edenbridge	d			17 38																18 38					
Godstone	d			17 45																18 45					
Nutfield	d			17 50																18 50					
Reigate	d											18 13													
Redhill [5]	a		17 45	17 55					18 09		18 15	18 17					18 36		18 45	18 55				19 09	
	d		17 46						18 09								18 37		18 46					19 09	
Merstham	d																18 41								
Coulsdon South	d																18 46								
Purley [4]	d								18 18								18 49							19 18	
East Croydon 🚋	a		17 58		18 01			18 09	18 24				18 31	18 34		18 39	18 54		18 58		19 01		19 09	19 24	
	d		18 00		18 02			18 10	18 25				18 32	18 35		18 40	18 58		19 00		19 02		19 10	19 25	
Norwood Junction [2]	a																								
London Bridge [4]	⊖ a				18 17			*18 42*					18 47			*19 12*					19 17		*19 42*		
London Waterloo (East) [4]	⊖ a																								
London Charing Cross [4]	⊖ a																								
London Blackfriars [3]	⊖ a																								
City Thameslink [3]	a																								
Farringdon [3]	⊖ a																								
St Pancras International [15]	⊖ a																								
St Albans City	a																								
Luton Airport Parkway [4] ✈	a																								
Luton [7]	a																								
Bedford [10]	a																								
Clapham Junction [10]	d		18 12					18 25	18 38					18 47		18 55	19 09		19 12				19 25	19 38	
West Brompton	⊖ d															*19 12*									
Kensington (Olympia)	⊖ d															*19 15*									
Shepherd's Bush	⊖ d															*19 18*									
Watford Junction	a															*19 46*									
Milton Keynes Central [10]	a																								
London Victoria [15]	⊖ a	18 10	18 18			18 25		18 31	18 46	18 40				18 53	18 55	19 01	19 16	19 10	19 18			19 25	19 31	19 46	19 40

For general notes see front of timetable
For details of catering facilities see Directory of Train Operators

A 🛒 from Lewes
B From Bognor Regis (Table 188)

Table 186

Sundays

from 13 September

Brighton → London and Bedford

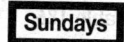

Network Diagram - see first page of Table 186

		GW 1	GW 1	FC 1	SN 1 ◇	GX 1	SN 1	SN 1	GX 1	SN 1 ◇		SN 1	FC 1	GX 1	SN 1	SN 1 A	GX 1	GW 1	GW 1	FC 1	SN 1 ◇	GX 1	SN 1	SN 1	GX 1
Brighton 10	d			18 44	18 51					19 00			19 16							19 44	19 51				
Hove 2	d						18 54																19 54		
Preston Park	d									19 03															
Hassocks 4	d			18 52						19 10										19 52					
Burgess Hill 4	d			18 56			19 04			19 13			19 26							19 56			20 04		
Lewes 4	d														19 16										
Wivelsfield 4	d									19 16					19 31										
Haywards Heath 3	a			19 00			19 09			19 20			19 30		19 35					20 00			20 09		
	d			19 01			19 10			19 21			19 31		19 39					20 01			20 10		
Balcombe	d									19 26															
Horsham 4	d							19 04								19 42								20 04	
Littlehaven	d							19 07																20 07	
Faygate	d																								
Ifield	d							19 13																20 13	
Crawley	d							19 17								19 51								20 17	
Three Bridges 4	a			19 10				19 20		19 32			19 40			19 54				20 10				20 20	
	d			19 10				19 22		19 32			19 40			19 55				20 10				20 22	
Gatwick Airport 10 ✈	a			19 14	19 17		19 22	19 26		19 37			19 44		19 52	19 59				20 14	20 17		20 22	20 26	
	d	19 08		19 15	19 18	19 20	19 23	19 27	19 35	19 38			19 45	19 50	19 53	20 00	20 05	20 08		20 15	20 18	20 20	20 23	20 27	20 35
Horley 4	d							19 30								20 02								20 30	
Salfords	d																								
Earlswood (Surrey)	d																								
Tonbridge 4	d											19 24													
Leigh (Kent)	d											19 28													
Penshurst	d											19 32													
Edenbridge	d											19 38													
Godstone	d											19 45													
Nutfield	d											19 50													
Reigate	d		19 13																20 13						
Redhill 5	a	19 15	19 18					19 36		19 45		19 55				20 09		20 15	20 17					20 36	
	d							19 37		19 46						20 09								20 37	
Merstham	d							19 41																20 41	
Coulsdon South	d							19 46																20 46	
Purley 4	d							19 49								20 18								20 49	
East Croydon	a			19 31	19 34		19 39	19 54		19 58			20 01		20 09	20 24				20 31	20 34		20 39	20 54	
	d			19 32	19 35		19 40	19 58		20 00			20 02		20 10	20 25				20 32	20 35		20 40	20 58	
Norwood Junction 2	a																								
London Bridge 4	⊖ a			19 47			*20 12*						20 17		*20 42*					20 47			*21 12*		
London Waterloo (East) 4	⊖ a																								
London Charing Cross 4	⊖ a																								
London Blackfriars 3	⊖ a																								
City Thameslink 3	a																								
Farringdon 3	⊖ a																								
St Pancras International 15	⊖ a																								
St Albans City	a																								
Luton Airport Parkway 4	✈ a																								
Luton 7	a																								
Bedford 10	a																								
Clapham Junction 10	d				19 47		19 55	20 09		20 12					20 25	20 38					20 47		20 55	21 09	
West Brompton	⊖ d						*20 12*																	*21 22*	
Kensington (Olympia)	⊖ d						*20 15*																	*21 25*	
Shepherd's Bush	⊖ d						*20 18*																	*21 28*	
Watford Junction	a						*20 46*																	*21 57*	
Milton Keynes Central 10	a																								
London Victoria 15	⊖ a				19 53	19 55	20 01	20 16	20 10	20 18				20 25	20 31	20 46	20 40				20 53	20 55	21 01	21 16	21 10

For general notes see front of timetable
For details of catering facilities see Directory of Train Operators

A From Bognor Regis (Table 188)

Sundays

from 13 September

Brighton → London and Bedford

Network Diagram - see first page of Table 186

		SN 1 ◇	SN 1	FC 1	GX 1	SN 1	SN 1	GX 1	GW 1	GW 1	FC 1	SN 1 ◇	GX 1	SN 1		SN 1	GX 1	SN 1 ◇	SN 1	FC 1	GX 1	SN 1	SN 1	GX 1	GW 1
							A																A		
Brighton 10	d	20 00		20 16							20 44	20 51						21 00		21 16					
Hove 2	d													20 54											
Preston Park	d	20 03																21 03							
Hassocks 4	d	20 10									20 52							21 10							
Burgess Hill 4	d	20 13		20 26							20 56			21 04				21 13		21 26					
Lewes 4	d					20 16																21 16			
Wivelsfield 4	d	20 16				20 31												21 16				21 31			
Haywards Heath 3	a	20 20		20 30		20 35					21 00			21 09				21 20		21 30		21 35			
	d	20 21		20 31		20 39					21 01			21 10				21 21		21 31		21 39			
Balcombe	d	20 26																21 26							
Horsham 4	d						20 42									21 04							21 42		
Littlehaven	d															21 07									
Faygate	d																								
Ifield	d															21 13									
Crawley	d						20 51									21 17							21 51		
Three Bridges 4	a	20 32		20 40			20 54				21 10					21 20		21 32		21 40			21 54		
	d	20 32		20 40			20 55				21 10					21 22		21 32		21 40			21 55		
Gatwick Airport 10 ✈	a	20 37		20 44		20 52	20 59				21 14	21 17		21 22		21 26		21 37		21 44		21 52	21 59		
	d	20 38		20 45	20 50	20 53	21 00	21 05	21 08		21 15	21 18	21 20	21 23		21 27	21 35	21 38		21 45	21 50	21 53	22 00	22 05	22 07
Horley 4	d						21 02									21 30							22 02		
Salfords	d																								
Earlswood (Surrey)	d																								
Tonbridge 4	d		20 24																21 24						
Leigh (Kent)	d		20 28																21 28						
Penshurst	d		20 32																21 32						
Edenbridge	d		20 38																21 38						
Godstone	d		20 45																21 45						
Nutfield	d		20 50																21 50						
Reigate	d									21 13															
Redhill 5	a	20 45	20 55				21 09		21 15	21 18						21 36		21 45	21 55				22 09		22 15
	d	20 46					21 09									21 37		21 46					22 09		
Merstham	d															21 41									
Coulsdon South	d															21 46									
Purley 4	d						21 19									21 49							22 18		
East Croydon	a	20 58		21 01		21 09	21 24				21 31	21 34		21 39		21 54		21 58		22 01		22 09	22 24		
	d	21 00		21 02		21 10	21 25				21 32	21 35		21 40		21 58		22 00		22 02		22 10	22 25		
Norwood Junction 2	a																								
London Bridge 4 ⊖	a			21 17		21 42					21 47			22 12						22 17		22 42			
London Waterloo (East) 4 ⊖	a																								
London Charing Cross 4 ⊖	a																								
London Blackfriars 3 ⊖	a																								
City Thameslink 3	a																								
Farringdon 3 ⊖	a																								
St Pancras International 15 ⊖	a																								
St Albans City	a																								
Luton Airport Parkway 4 ✈	a																								
Luton 7	a																								
Bedford 10	a																								
Clapham Junction 10	d	21 12				21 25	21 38					21 47		21 55		22 09		22 12				22 25	22 38		
West Brompton ⊖	d															22 22									
Kensington (Olympia) ⊖	d															22 25									
Shepherd's Bush ⊖	d															22 28									
Watford Junction	a															22 58									
Milton Keynes Central 10	a																								
London Victoria 15 ⊖	a	21 18			21 25	21 31	21 46	21 40				21 53	21 55	22 01		22 16	22 10	22 18			22 25	22 31	22 46	22 40	

For general notes see front of timetable
For details of catering facilities see Directory of Train Operators

A From Bognor Regis (Table 188)

Sundays

from 13 September

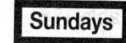

Brighton → London and Bedford

Network Diagram - see first page of Table 186

		GW 1	FC 1	GX 1	SN 1	GX 1	SN 1 ◇	SN 1	FC 1	GX 1	SN 1 A	GX 1	GW 1	GW 1	FC 1	GX 1	SN 1	GX 1	SN 1 ◇	FC 1	SN 1 ◇	GX 1	FC 1
Brighton 10	d		21 44				22 00		22 16						22 44				23 02	23 11			23 44
Hove 2	d																						
Preston Park	d						22 03												23 06				
Hassocks 4	d		21 52				22 10								22 52				23 12	23 19			23 52
Burgess Hill 4	d		21 56				22 13		22 26						22 56				23 16	23 23			23 56
Lewes 4	d																						
Wivelsfield 4	d						22 16												23 19				
Haywards Heath 3	a		22 00				22 20		22 30						23 00				23 23	23 27			00 01
	d		22 01				22 21		22 31						23 01				23 24	23 28			00 01
Balcombe	d						22 26												23 29				
Horsham 4	d				22 04						22 42						23 04						
Littlehaven	d				22 07												23 07						
Faygate	d																						
Ifield	d				22 13												23 13						
Crawley	d				22 17						22 51						23 17						
Three Bridges 4	a		22 10		22 20		22 32		22 40		22 54				23 10		23 20		23 35	23 39	←		00 10
	d		22 10		22 22		22 32		22 40		22 55				23 10		23 22		23 42	23 39	23 42		00 10
Gatwick Airport 10	✈ a		22 14		22 26		22 37		22 44		22 59				23 14		23 26		→	23 43	23 46		00 14
	d		22 15	22 20	22 27	22 35	22 38		22 45	22 50	23 00	23 05	23 07		23 15	23 20	23 27	23 35		23 44	23 47	23 50	00 15
Horley 4	d				22 30						23 02						23 30				23 49		
Salfords	d																						
Earlswood (Surrey)	d																						
Tonbridge 4	d							22 24															
Leigh (Kent)	d							22 28															
Penshurst	d							22 32															
Edenbridge	d							22 38															
Godstone	d							22 45															
Nutfield	d							22 50															
Reigate	d	22 13												23 13									
Redhill 5	a	22 18			22 36		22 45	22 55			23 09		23 15	23 18			23 36				23 57		00 22
	d				22 37		22 46				23 09						23 37				00 02		00 22
Merstham	d				22 41												23 41						
Coulsdon South	d				22 46												23 46						
Purley 4	d				22 49						23 18						23 50				00 11		
East Croydon	🚋 a		22 31		22 54		22 58		23 01		23 24				23 31		23 55			23 59	00 16		00 35
	d		22 32		22 58		23 00		23 02		23 25				23 32		23 56			00 01	00 17		00 36
Norwood Junction 2	a																						
London Bridge 4	⊖ a		22 47						23 17						23 47		*00 14*			00 14	*00 52*		00 52
London Waterloo (East) 4	⊖ a																						
London Charing Cross 4	⊖ a																						
London Blackfriars 3	⊖ a																						
City Thameslink 3	a																						
Farringdon 3	⊖ a																						
St Pancras International 15	⊖ a																						
St Albans City	a																						
Luton Airport Parkway 4	✈ a																						
Luton 7	a																						
Bedford 10	a																						
Clapham Junction 10	d				23 10		23 13				23 38						00 11			00b29	00 30		01b02
West Brompton	⊖ d																						
Kensington (Olympia)	⊖ d																						
Shepherd's Bush	⊖ d																						
Watford Junction	a																						
Milton Keynes Central 10	a																						
London Victoria 15	⊖ a			22 55	23 16	23 10	23 20			23 25	23 46	23 40				23 55	00 18	00 10		00b37	00 37	00 25	01b09

For general notes see front of timetable
For details of catering facilities see Directory of Train Operators

A From Bognor Regis (Table 188)
b Change at East Croydon

London, Gatwick Airport & Brighton → Sussex Coast, Portsmouth and Southampton

Network Diagram - see first page of Table 186

Miles	Miles	Miles			SN MX 1	SN MX 1	SN MX 1	SN MX 1	SN 1	SN MX 1	SN MO 1	SN MX 1	SN 1	SN 1	SN 1	SN 1	SN 1	SN 1	SN 1	SN 1	SN 1	SN 1	SN 1	SN 1	SN 1	SN 1
0	—	0	London Victoria 15 ⊖	d	22p17	22p32		22p47	23 06	23p17	23p17	00 05									04 00					
2¾	—	—	Clapham Junction 10	d	22p23	22p38		22p53	23 12	23p23	23p23	00 11									04 08					
—	0	—	London Bridge 4 ⊖	d					22 58	22 45	23 11	23 53									03b35	04 05				
10½	10¼	—	East Croydon	d	22p34	22p48		23p03	23 22	23p33	23p38	00 25									04 22	04 32				
21	—	—	Redhill 5	d		23p01					23 31	00 25														
26	—	—	Horley	d							23 26	00 31														
26¾	—	—	Gatwick Airport 10 ✈	d	22p49	23p09		23p19	23 19	23p51	00 01	00 43									04 47	04 52				
29½	—	29½	Three Bridges 4	a	22p54	23p15				23p55	00 05	00 48														
—	—	—		d	22p54	23p16			23 14	23p56	00 06	00 48									04 52	04 58				
—	—	31	Crawley	d		23p19																				
—	—	38	Horsham 4	a		23p27																				
—	—	—		d		23p28																				
—	—	40½	Christs Hospital	d		23p31																				
—	—	45¼	Billingshurst	d		23p37																				
—	—	50¼	Pulborough	d		23p44																				
—	—	55	Amberley	d		23p50																				
—	—	58¾	Arundel	d		23p55																				
38	—	—	Haywards Heath 3	d	23p03			23p37	23 45	00 05	00 15	01 03									05 01	05 08				
41¾	—	—	Burgess Hill	d	23p08				23 31	00 10																
—	0	—	Brighton 10	d					00 10									05 14			05 30	05 44	05 53			05 57
51	1½	—	Hove 2	d	23p22			23p52	00a13	00 22	00 29	01s25						05 18			05 34	05a47	05 57			06 01
—	2	—	Aldrington	d														05 20			05 36					06 03
—	3	—	Portslade	d	23p25			23p55		00s25	00s32	01s28						05 22			05 38					06 05
—	3½	—	Fishersgate	d														05 24			05 40					06 07
—	4½	—	Southwick	d	23p28			23p58		00s28	00s35	01s31						05 26			05 42					06 09
—	5½	—	Shoreham-by-Sea	d	23p31			00 01		00s31	00s38	01s34						05 29			05 45		06 03			06 12
—	8¼	—	Lancing	d	23p35			00 05		00s35	00s42	01s38						05 33			05 49					06 16
—	9¾	—	East Worthing	d														05 36			05 52					06 19
—	10½	—	Worthing 4	a	23p39			00 09		00 39	00 46	01 42						05 39			05 55		06 09			06 22
—	—	—		d	23p39													05 39			05 55		06 09			06 22
—	11½	—	West Worthing	d	23p41													05 41			05 57					06 24
—	12¼	—	Durrington-on-Sea	d	23p44													05 44			06 00					06 27
—	13	—	Goring-by-Sea	d	23p46													05 46			06 02					06 29
0	15½	—	Angmering 3	d	23p50													05 50			06 06					06 33
6	—	—	Littlehampton 4	a																						06 42
—	—	—		d													05 35			06 04					06 39	
8	19¾	61	Ford 4	d	23p56	00 01											05 39	05 56		06 08	06 13				06 43	
—	—	—	Bognor Regis 4	d																						
—	22½	—	Barnham	a	00 01	00 05	⟵										05 43	06 01		06 12	06 17		06 24	⟵	06 47	
0	—	—		d	00 09 ⟶	00 06	00 09						04 58	05 02	05 20	05 36	05 44	06 01	06 06	06 27 ⟶	06 18		06 24	06 27	06 48	
3½	—	—	Bognor Regis 4	a			00 15									05 42			06 12					06 33	06 54	
—	28¾	—	Chichester 4	a		00 13							05 05	05 09	05 27		05 51	06 09			06 25		06 32			
—	—	—		d									05 06	05 10	05 28		05 52	06 09			06 26		06 32			
—	30½	—	Fishbourne (Sussex)	d													05 55						06 35			
—	31½	—	Bosham	d													05 58						06 38			
—	33¼	—	Nutbourne	d													06 01						06 42			
—	34¼	—	Southbourne	d													06 04				06 33		06 44			
—	35¾	—	Emsworth	d													06 07				06 36		06 47			
—	37	—	Warblington	d													06 10						06 50			
0	37½	—	Havant	d									05 17	05 21	05 39		06 13	06 20			06 40		06 53			
—	38¼	—	Bedhampton	a											06 04		06 15						06 56			
—	41¼	—	Hilsea	a											06 10		06 20						07 01			
—	44	—	Fratton	a										05 29	05 47		06 24						07 05			
—	44¾	—	Portsmouth & Southsea	a										05 33	05 51		06 28						07 08			
—	45½	—	Portsmouth Harbour	a										05 37	05 55		06 32						07 12			
4	—	—	Cosham	a									05 23					06 27			06 49					
6½	—	—	Portchester	a									05 28								06 54					
9¾	—	—	Fareham	a									05 33					06 36			06 59					
13½	—	—	Swanwick	a									05 40					06 43			07 06					
24¼	—	—	Southampton Central	a									05 59					07 02			07 24					

For general notes see front of timetable
For details of catering facilities see Directory of Train Operators

b Change at East Croydon and Brighton

For complete service between Three Bridges and Horsham see Table 186

London, Gatwick Airport & Brighton → Sussex Coast, Portsmouth and Southampton

Network Diagram - see first page of Table 186

	SN 1	SN 1	SN 1	SN 1	SN 1	SN 1	SN 1	SN 1	SN 1	SN 1	SN 1		SN 1	SN 1	SN 1	SN 1	SN 1	SN 1	SN 1	SN 1	SN 1	SN 1	SN 1	SN 1
London Victoria 15 ⊖ d		05 02				05 02				05b32	06 02			06 02					06b02	06 21	06 32		06b32	
Clapham Junction 10 d		05 08				05 08				05b38	06 08			06 08					06b08	06 27	06 38		06b38	
London Bridge 4 ⊖ d	04 35	04 35						05 31		05 51	05 51			06 21					06 21		06c43		06 43	
East Croydon d	05 02	05 32				05 20		05 52		06 04	06 18			06 36					06 36	06 38	06 49		06 56	
Redhill 5 d		05 44									06 40										07 07			
Horley d		05 44									06 49										07 16			
Gatwick Airport 10 ✈ d	05 22	05 59				05 47		06 08		06 20	06 54								06 52	07 04	07 20		07 12	
Three Bridges 4 a		06 03									06 59										07 24			
d	05 26	06 04				05 52		06 14		06 26	07 00			07 05					06 56	07 09	07 30		07 18	
Crawley d		06 07									07 03			07 08							07 34			
Horsham 4 a		06 19									07 11			07 22							07 46			
d		06 20									07 12										07 46			
Christs Hospital d		06 23									07 15										07 50			
Billingshurst d		06 29									07 21										07 56			
Pulborough d		06 36									07 28										08 03			
Amberley d		06 42									07 34										08 09			
Arundel d		06 47									07 39										08 14			
Haywards Heath 3 d	05 36					06 04		06 25		06 38									07 06	07 21			07 28	
Burgess Hill d	05 42					06 10		06 32		06 44									07 12	07 27			07 34	
Brighton 10 d	06 15		06 27			06 35		06 53		07 06			07 15				07 20	07 30	07 37	07 47		07 50	08 03	
Hove 2 d	06 19		06 31			06 39		06 57		07 10			07 19				07 24	07 34	07 41	07 51		07 54	08 07	
Aldrington d	06 21							06 59									07 26					07 56		
Portslade d	06 23					06 42		07 01					07 22				07 28	07 37	07 44	07 54		07 58		
Fishersgate d	06 25							07 03									07 30					08 00		
Southwick d	06 27					06 45		07 05					07 25				07 32	07 40	07 47	07 57		08 02		
Shoreham-by-Sea d	06 30		06 37			06 48		07 09		07 16			07 28				07 35	07 43	07 50	08 00		08 06	08 13	
Lancing d	06 34					06 52		07 13					07 32				07 39	07 47	07 54	08 04		08 10		
East Worthing d	06 37							07 16									07 42					08 13		
Worthing 4 a	06 40		06 43			06 56		07 18		07 22			07 36				07 45	07 51	07 58	08 08		08 15	08 19	
d	06 40		06 43			06 56		07 19		07 23			07 36				07 45	07 52	07 59	08 08		08 16	08 20	
West Worthing d	06a42		06 45			06 58		07 21		07 25							07 47	07 54	08 01			08 18	08 22	
Durrington-on-Sea d			06 48			07 01		07 23		07 27							07 50	07 56	08 03	08 12		08 20	08 24	
Goring-by-Sea d			06 50			07 03		07 26		07 30							07 52	07 59	08 06			08 23	08 27	
Angmering 3 d			06 54			07 07		07 30		07 34							07 56	08 03	08 10	08 17		08 27	08 31	
Littlehampton 4 a								07 38							←		08 05				08 21	08 35		
d				07 00			07 18	07 48							07 48	07 58					08 26			
Ford 4 d		06 52		07 04		07 13	07 22	→			07 44		07 48		07 52	08 02		08 09	08 17		08 30		08 37	
Bognor Regis 4 d																								
Barnham a		06 56	07 04	07 08		07 18	07 26			07 43	07 49		07 53		07 56	08 06		08 13	08 21	08 27	08 34		08 41	
d		07 13 → / 07 00	07 05	07 09	← 07 13	07 18	07 27		07 39	07 44	07 50		07 53		07 57	08 07		08 14	08 22	08 28	08 35		08 42	08 45
Bognor Regis 4 a					07 20				07 45		07 58					08 13				08 35				08 51
Chichester 4 a		07 07	07 12	07 16		07 26	07 34			07 51			08 01		08 05			08 21	08 29		08 42		08 49	
d		07 08	07 13	07 17		07 28	07 35			07 52			08 01					08 22	08 30				08 50	
Fishbourne (Sussex) d				07 20			07 38						08 04											
Bosham d			07 17				07 41						08 07											
Nutbourne d				07 25			07 44						08 11											
Southbourne d			07 22	07 27			07 47						08 13											
Emsworth d			07 25	07 30			07 50						08 16					08 29	08 37					
Warblington d			07 28				07 53						08 19					08 32	08 40					
Havant d		07 19	07 31	07 35		07 41	07e58			08 03			08 22					08 37	08 44				09 01	
Bedhampton a		07 30		07 37		07 54	08 00						08 25										09 07	
Hilsea a				07 42		08 00	08 05						08 30										09 13	
Fratton a				07 46		07 49	08 09						08 34						08 53				09 11	
Portsmouth & Southsea a				07 50		07 53	08 15						08 37						08 56				09 17	
Portsmouth Harbour a						07 58	08 19						08 41						09 00				09 21	
Cosham a		07 25	07 38							08 09								08 44						
Portchester a		07 30								08 13								08 49						
Fareham a		07 35	07 46							08 18								08 54						
Swanwick a		07 42	07 53							08 26								09 01						
Southampton Central a		08 01	08 13							08 52								09 19						

For general notes see front of timetable
For details of catering facilities see Directory of Train Operators

b Change at East Croydon and Brighton
c Change at Gatwick Airport
e Arr. 0755

For complete service between Three Bridges and Horsham see Table 186

London, Gatwick Airport & Brighton → Sussex Coast, Portsmouth and Southampton

Network Diagram - see first page of Table 186

Station		SN 1	SN 1	SN 1	SN 1	SN 1	SN 1	SN 1	SN 1	SN 1	SN 1	SN 1		GW ◇	SN 1	SN 1	SN 1	SN 1	SN 1	SN 1	SN 1		SN 1		SN 1	SN 1
												A 🛒		B	🛒						A 🛒				🛒	
London Victoria 15 ⊖	d		06b51	07 17			07b07	07b23	07 52			08 02					08 07		08 17		08 32					08 21
Clapham Junction 10	d		06b57	07 23			07b13	07b29	07 58			08 08					08 13		08 23		08 38					08 27
London Bridge 4 ⊖	d		07 01	07c16			07 16	07 33	07 46	07 40		08e00					08b00		08 06	08b06	08 25					08 19
East Croydon	d	07f03	07 16	07 34			07 32	07 49	08 09	07 56		08 18					08 23		08 33	08 26	08 48					08 39
Redhill 5	d			07 46								08 32									09 03					
Horley	d			07 55								08 21									08 50					
Gatwick Airport 10 ✈	d	07 20	07 32	07 59			07 50	08 05	08 25	08 12		08 40					08 29		08 49	08 42	09 11					08 56
Three Bridges 4	a			08 04								08 44									09 16					
	d	07 28	07 38	08 05			07 54	08 10	08 16	08 16		08 45					08 42		08 46	08 46	09 16					08 57
Crawley	d			08 09								08 48									09 19					
Horsham 4	a			08 22								08 56									09 27					
	d			08 23								09 00	09 05 →		← 09 05						09 31	09 36 →			← 09 36	
Christs Hospital	d			08 26											09 08										09 39	
Billingshurst	d			08 32											09 14										09 45	
Pulborough	d			08 39											09 21										09 52	
Amberley	d			08 45											09 27										09 58	
Arundel	d			08 50											09 32										10 03	
Haywards Heath 3	d	07 40	07 48				08 06	08 19	08 37	08 28							08 51		09 04	08 58						09 10
Burgess Hill	d	07 46	07 54				08 12	08 25		08 34							08 49		09 09	09 04						
Brighton 10	d	08 07	08 23				08 39	08 44		08 53				09 00		09 03	09 14			09 23						09 33
Hove 2	d	08 11	08 27				08 43	08a47	08 54	08 57				09 04		09 07	09a18		09 22	09 27						09 37
Aldrington	d		08 29							08 59										09 29						
Portslade	d	08 14	08 31							09 01						09 10			09 25	09 31						09 40
Fishersgate	d		08 33							09 03										09 33						
Southwick	d	08 17	08 35							09 05						09 13				09 35						09 43
Shoreham-by-Sea	d	08 20	08 39				08 49		09 00	09 08				09 13		09 17			09 30	09 39						09 46
Lancing	d	08 24	08 43						09 04	09 12						09 21				09 43						09 50
East Worthing	d		08 46							09 15										09 46						
Worthing 4	a	08 28	08 48				08 55		09 08	09 18				09 21		09 25			09 36	09 48						09 54
	d	08 28	08 49				08 56		09 08	09 18				09 22		09 25			09 37	09 49						09 55
West Worthing	d	08 30	08a51						09 10	09a20									09 39	09a51						09 57
Durrington-on-Sea	d	08 33					08 59		09 13										09 41							09 59
Goring-by-Sea	d	08 35					09 02		09 15										09 44							10 02
Angmering 3	d	08 39					09 06		09 19							09 34			09 48							10 06
Littlehampton 4	a								09 28										09 58							
	d				08 54																		09 54			
Ford 4	d	08 45		08 55	08 59										09 37								09 58		10 08	10 12
Bognor Regis 4	d																									
Barnham	a	08 50		08 59	09 03		09 15					09 26		09 37	09 41	09 44					09 57		10 02		10 12	10 16
	d	08 52		09 00	09 04	09 12	09 16				09 25	09 27		09 38	09 42	09 45		09 52			09 58		10 03		10 13	10 17
Bognor Regis 4	a	08 58				09 18					09 31				09 48			09 58							10 19	
Chichester 4	a			09 07	09 11		09 23					09 34		09 45		09 52					10 05		10 10			10 24
	d			09 08	09 12		09 24					09 35		09 47		09 53					10 06		10 11			10 25
Fishbourne (Sussex)	d				09 15																		10 14			
Bosham	d				09 18																		10 17			
Nutbourne	d				09 21																		10 20			
Southbourne	d			09 15	09 24		09 31									10 00					10 13		10 23			
Emsworth	d			09 18	09 27		09 34									10 03					10 16		10 26			10 33
Warblington	d				09 30																		10 29			
Havant	d			09 23	09 33		09 38					09 46		09 59		10 07					10 20		10 32			10 37
Bedhampton	a			09 32	09 36																10 29		10 34			
Hilsea	a			09 38	09 42																10 36		10 42			
Fratton	a			09 42	09 46							09 54				10 16					10 40		10 46			
Portsmouth & Southsea	a			09 46	09 50							09 58				10 19					10 44		10 50			
Portsmouth Harbour	a											10 02				10 23										
Cosham	a			09 29			09 45							10 05							10 28					10 45
Portchester	a																				10 32					
Fareham	a			09 37			09 53							10 14							10 37					10 53
Swanwick	a			09 44			10 00														10 44					11 00
Southampton Central	a			10 01			10 19							10 41							11 01					11 19

For general notes see front of timetable
For details of catering facilities see Directory of Train Operators

A 🛒 to Horsham
B To Great Malvern (Table 71)
b Change at East Croydon and Brighton
c Change at Gatwick Airport
e Change at East Croydon and Three Bridges
f Change at Three Bridges and Brighton

For complete service between Three Bridges and Horsham see Table 186

London, Gatwick Airport & Brighton → Sussex Coast, Portsmouth and Southampton

Network Diagram - see first page of Table 186

		SN 1	SN 1	SN 1	SN 1	SN 1		SN 1	SN 1	SN 1	SN 1	SN 1	SN 1		SN 1	SN 1	SN 1	SN 1	SN 1	SN 1	SN 1	SN 1		SN 1	SN 1	SN 1
						A [trolley]					B [trolley]		C [trolley]			[trolley]						A [trolley]				
London Victoria 15	⊖ d	08 36		08 47	08 40	09 02		09 06			09 17		09 32				09 36			09 47		10 02		10 06		
Clapham Junction 10	d	08 43		08 53	08 46	09 08		09 12			09 23		09 38				09 42			09 53		10 08		10 12		
London Bridge 4	⊖ d	08b27		08 30	08b30	08 52		08b52			09 09	09 06	09 25				09 25			09 42	09 42	09 58		09 58		
East Croydon	d	08 53		09 03	08 57	09 18		09 22			09 33	09 24	09 48				09 52			10 03	09 54	10 18		10 22		
Redhill 5	d					09 30							10 00									10 30				
Horley	d					09 36							09 50									10 36				
Gatwick Airport 10	✈ d	09 00		09 19	09 14	09 40		09 26			09 49	09 41	10 09				09 57			10 19	10 11	10 40		10 26		
Three Bridges 4	a					09 44							10 14									10 44				
	d	09 05		09 19	09 19	09 45		09 30			09 45	09 45	10 14				10 02			10 15	10 15	10 45				
Crawley	d					09 48							10 18									10 48				
Horsham 4	a					09 56							10 26									10 56				
	d					10 00	10 05						10 30	10 35 →		← 10 35						11 00	11 05			
Christs Hospital	d															10 38										
Billingshurst	d						10 14									10 44							11 14			
Pulborough	d						10 20									10 51							11 20			
Amberley	d															10 57										
Arundel	d						10 29									11 02							11 29			
Haywards Heath 3	d	09 17		09 37	09 28			09 40			10 04	09 57					10 10	10 18		10 37	10 27			10 40		
Burgess Hill	d	09 23			09 36						10 09	10 03						10 24			10 33					
Brighton 10	d	09 44			09 53			10 03	10 14			10 23					10 33	10 44			10 53			11 03	11 14	
Hove 2	d	09a47		09 52	09 57			10 07	10a17		10 22	10 27					10 37	10a47		10 52	10 57			11 07	11a17	
Aldrington	d				09 59							10 29									10 59					
Portslade	d				10 01			10 10			10 25	10 31					10 40				11 01			11 10		
Fishersgate	d				10 03							10 33									11 03					
Southwick	d				10 05			10 13				10 35					10 43				11 05			11 13		
Shoreham-by-Sea	d			09 58	10 09			10 16			10 30	10 39					10 46			10 58	11 09			11 16		
Lancing	d			10 02	10 13			10 20				10 43					10 50			11 02	11 13			11 20		
East Worthing	d				10 16							10 46									11 16					
Worthing 4	a			10 06	10 18			10 24			10 36	10 48					10 54			11 06	11 18			11 24		
	d			10 07	10 19			10 25			10 37	10 49					10 55			11 07	11 19			11 25		
West Worthing	d			10 09	10a21						10 39	10a51					10 57			11 09	11a21					
Durrington-on-Sea	d			10 11							10 41						10 59			11 11						
Goring-by-Sea	d			10 14							10 44						11 02			11 14						
Angmering 3	d			10 18				10 31			10 48						11 06			11 18				11 31		
Littlehampton 4	a			10 27							10 57									11 27						
	d		10 11												10 54				11 11							
Ford 4	d		10 16				10 34								10 58	11 07	11 12		11 16				11 34			
Bognor Regis 4	d																									
Barnham	a		10 20			10 26	10 39	10 42					10 56		11 02	11 11	11 16		11 20			11 26	11 39	11 42		
	d		10 22			10 27	10 39	10 42		10 52			10 57		11 03	11 12	11 17		11 22			11 27	11 39	11 42		11 52
Bognor Regis 4	a		10 28				10 46			10 58						11 18			11 28				11 46			11 58
Chichester 4	a					10 34		10 50					11 04		11 10		11 24					11 34		11 50		
	d					10 35		10 50					11 05		11 11		11 25					11 35		11 50		
Fishbourne (Sussex)	d														11 14											
Bosham	d														11 17											
Nutbourne	d														11 20											
Southbourne	d							10 57					11 12		11 23									11 57		
Emsworth	d							11 00					11 15		11 26		11 33							12 00		
Warblington	d														11 29											
Havant	d					10 46		11 05					11 19		11 32		11 37					11 46		12 05		
Bedhampton	a												11 29		11 34											
Hilsea	a												11 36		11 42											
Fratton	a					10 54		11 13					11 40		11 46							11 54		12 13		
Portsmouth & Southsea	a					10 58		11 17					11 44		11 50							11 58		12 17		
Portsmouth Harbour	a					11 02		11 21														12 02		12 21		
Cosham	a												11 26				11 45									
Portchester	a												11 30													
Fareham	a												11 35				11 53									
Swanwick	a												11 42				12 00									
Southampton Central	a												12 01				12 19									

For general notes see front of timetable
For details of catering facilities see Directory of Train Operators

A [trolley] to Bognor Regis
B [trolley] to Haywards Heath
C [trolley] to Horsham

b Change at East Croydon and Brighton

For complete service between Three Bridges and Horsham see Table 186

London, Gatwick Airport & Brighton → Sussex Coast, Portsmouth and Southampton

Network Diagram - see first page of Table 186

		SN [1] A ⊼	SN [1]	SN [1] B ⊼	SN [1]	SN [1] ⊼	SN [1]	SN [1]	SN [1]	SN [1]	SN [1]	SN [1]	SN [1]	SN [1]	SN [1]	SN [1] A ⊼	SN [1]	SN [1]	SN [1]	SN [1]	SN [1]	SN [1]
London Victoria [15] ⊖	d	10 17		10 32			10 36			10 47		11 02	11 06			11 17		11 32			11 36	
Clapham Junction [10]	d	10 23		10 38			10 42			10 53		11 08	11 12			11 23		11 38			11 42	
London Bridge [4] ⊖	d	10 11	10 11	10 26			10 26			10 41	10 41	10 56	10 56			11 11	11 11	11 26			11 26	
East Croydon	d	10 33	10 24	10 48			10 52			11 03	10 54	11 18	11 22			11 33	11 24	11 48			11 52	
Redhill [5]	d			11 00								11 30						12 00				
Horley	d			10 51								11 36						11 51				
Gatwick Airport [10] ✈	d	10 49	10 41	11 09			10 56	10 58		11 19	11 11	11 40	11 26			11 49	11 41	12 09			11 56	11 58
Three Bridges [4]	a			11 14								11 44						12 14				
	d	10 45	10 45	11 14				11 03		11 15	11 15	11 45				11 45	11 45	12 14				12 03
Crawley	d			11 18								11 48						12 18				
Horsham [4]	a			11 26								11 56						12 26				
	d			11 30 / 11 35 →		← 11 35						12 00 / 12 05						12 30 / 12 35 →		← 12 35		
Christs Hospital	d					11 38														12 38		
Billingshurst	d					11 44						12 14								12 44		
Pulborough	d					11 51						12 20								12 51		
Amberley	d					11 57														12 57		
Arundel	d					12 02						12 29								13 02		
Haywards Heath [3]	d	11 04	10 55				11 08	11 17		11 37	11 27		11 38			12 04	11 55				12 08	12 17
Burgess Hill	d	11 09	11 01					11 23			11 33					12 09	12 01					12 23
Brighton [10]	d		11 23				11 33	11 44			11 53		12 03	12 14			12 23				12 33	12 44
Hove [2]	d	11 22	11 27				11 37	11a47		11 52	11 57		12 07	12a17		12 22	12 27				12 37	12a47
Aldrington	d		11 29								11 59						12 29					
Portslade	d	11 25	11 31				11 40				12 01		12 10			12 25	12 31				12 40	
Fishersgate	d		11 33								12 03						12 33					
Southwick	d		11 35				11 43				12 05		12 13				12 35				12 43	
Shoreham-by-Sea	d	11 30	11 39				11 46			11 58	12 09		12 16			12 30	12 39				12 46	
Lancing	d		11 43				11 50			12 02	12 13		12 20				12 43				12 50	
East Worthing	d		11 46								12 16						12 46					
Worthing [4]	a	11 36	11 48				11 54			12 06	12 18		12 24			12 36	12 48				12 54	
	d	11 37	11 49				11 55			12 07	12 19		12 25			12 37	12 49				12 55	
West Worthing	d	11 39	11a51				11 57			12 09	12a21					12 39	12a51				12 57	
Durrington-on-Sea	d	11 41					11 59			12 11						12 41					12 59	
Goring-by-Sea	d	11 44					12 02			12 14						12 44					13 02	
Angmering [3]	d	11 48					12 06			12 18			12 31			12 48					13 06	
Littlehampton [4]	a	11 57								12 27						12 57						
	d				11 54				12 11										12 54			
Ford [4]	d				11 58	12 07	12 12		12 16			12 34							12 58	13 07	13 12	
Bognor Regis [4]	d																					
Barnham	a			11 56	12 02	12 11	12 16		12 20			12 26 / 12 39	12 42					12 56	13 02	13 11	13 16	
	d			11 57	12 03	12 12	12 17		12 22			12 27 / 12 39	12 42		12 52			12 57	13 03	13 12	13 17	
Bognor Regis [4]	a					12 18			12 28			12 46			12 58					13 18		
Chichester [4]	a			12 04	12 10		12 24					12 34	12 50					13 04	13 10		13 24	
	d			12 05	12 11		12 25					12 35	12 50					13 05	13 11		13 25	
Fishbourne (Sussex)	d				12 14														13 14			
Bosham	d				12 17														13 17			
Nutbourne	d				12 20														13 20			
Southbourne	d			12 12	12 23								12 57					13 12	13 23			
Emsworth	d			12 15	12 26		12 33						13 00					13 15	13 26		13 33	
Warblington	d				12 29														13 29			
Havant	d			12 19	12 32		12 37					12 46	13 05					13 19	13 32		13 37	
Bedhampton	a			12 29	12 34													13 29	13 34			
Hilsea	a			12 36	12 42													13 36	13 42			
Fratton	a			12 40	12 46							12 54	13 13					13 40	13 46			
Portsmouth & Southsea	a			12 44	12 50							12 58	13 17					13 44	13 50			
Portsmouth Harbour	a											13 02	13 21									
Cosham	a			12 26			12 45											13 26			13 45	
Portchester	a			12 30														13 30				
Fareham	a			12 35			12 53											13 35			13 53	
Swanwick	a			12 42			13 00											13 42			14 00	
Southampton Central	a			12 59			13 19											13 59			14 19	

For general notes see front of timetable
For details of catering facilities see Directory of Train Operators

A ⊼ to Haywards Heath
B ⊼ to Horsham

For complete service between Three Bridges and Horsham see Table 186

London, Gatwick Airport & Brighton → Sussex Coast, Portsmouth and Southampton

Network Diagram - see first page of Table 186

Station																										
		SN	SN	SN	SN		SN	SN	SN	SN	SN	SN		SN	SN	SN	SN	SN	SN	SN		SN		SN	SN	SN
		1	1	1	1		1	1	1	1	1	1		1	1	1	1	1	1	1		1		1	1	1
					A					B												C				
					⊼					⊼												⊼				
London Victoria 15 ⊖	d		11 47		12 02		12 06			12 17		12 32				12 36			12 47			13 02		13 06		
Clapham Junction 10	d		11 53		12 08		12 12			12 23		12 38				12 42			12 53			13 08		13 12		
London Bridge 4 ⊖	d		11 41	11 41	11 56		11 56			12 11	12 11	12 26				12 26			12 41	12 41		12 56		12 56		
East Croydon	d		12 03	11 54	12 18		12 22			12 34	12 24	12 48				12 52			13 03	12 54		13 18		13 22		
Redhill 5	d				12 30							13 00										13 30				
Horley	d				12 36							12 51										13 36				
Gatwick Airport 10 ✈	d		12 19	12 11	12 40		12 26			12 50	12 41	13 09				12 56	12 58		13 19	13 11		13 40		13 26		
Three Bridges 4	a				12 44							13 14										13 44				
	d		12 15	12 15	12 45					12 45	12 45	13 14					13 03		13 15	13 15		13 45				
Crawley	d				12 48							13 18										13 48				
Horsham 4	a				12 56							13 26										13 56				
	d				13 00	13 05						13 30	13 35 →		← 13 35							14 00	14 05			
Christs Hospital	d														13 38											
Billingshurst	d					13 14									13 44								14 14			
Pulborough	d					13 20									13 51								14 20			
Amberley	d														13 57											
Arundel	d					13 29									14 02								14 29			
Haywards Heath 3	d		12 37	12 27			12 38			13 04	12 55					13 08	13 17		13 37	13 27				13 38		
Burgess Hill	d			12 33						13 10	13 01						13 23			13 33						
Brighton 10	d			12 53			13 03	13 14			13 23					13 33	13 44			13 53				14 03	14 14	
Hove 2	d		12 52	12 57			13 07	13a19		13 22	13 27					13 37	13a47		13 52	13 57				14 07	14a17	
Aldrington	d			12 59							13 29									13 59						
Portslade	d			13 01			13 10			13 25	13 31					13 40				14 01				14 10		
Fishersgate	d			13 03							13 33									14 03						
Southwick	d			13 05			13 13				13 35					13 43				14 05				14 13		
Shoreham-by-Sea	d		12 58	13 09			13 16			13 30	13 39					13 46			13 58	14 09				14 16		
Lancing	d		13 02	13 13			13 20				13 43					13 50			14 02	14 13				14 20		
East Worthing	d			13 16							13 46									14 16						
Worthing 4	a		13 06	13 18			13 24			13 36	13 48					13 54			14 06	14 18				14 24		
	d		13 07	13 19			13 25			13 37	13 49					13 55			14 07	14 19				14 25		
West Worthing	d		13 09	13a21						13 39	13a51					13 57			14 09	14a21						
Durrington-on-Sea	d		13 11							13 41						13 59			14 11							
Goring-by-Sea	d		13 14							13 44						14 02			14 14							
Angmering 3	d		13 18				13 31			13 48						14 06			14 18					14 31		
Littlehampton 4	a		13 27							13 57									14 27							
	d	13 11												13 54				14 11								
Ford 4	d	13 16				13 34								13 58	14 07	14 12		14 16					14 34			
Bognor Regis 4	d																									
Barnham	a	13 20			13 26	13 39	13 42					13 56		14 02	14 11	14 16		14 20				14 27	14 39	14 42		
	d	13 22			13 27	13 39	13 42		13 52			13 57		14 03	14 12	14 17		14 22				14 28	14 39	14 42		14 52
Bognor Regis 4	a	13 28				13 46			13 58						14 18			14 28					14 46			14 58
Chichester 4	a				13 34		13 50					14 04		14 10		14 24						14 35		14 50		
	d				13 35		13 50					14 05		14 11		14 25						14 36		14 50		
Fishbourne (Sussex)	d													14 14												
Bosham	d													14 17												
Nutbourne	d													14 20												
Southbourne	d						13 57					14 12		14 23										14 57		
Emsworth	d						14 00					14 15		14 26		14 33								15 00		
Warblington	d													14 29												
Havant	d				13 46		14 05					14 19		14 32		14 37						14 47		15 05		
Bedhampton	a											14 29		14 34												
Hilsea	a											14 36		14 42												
Fratton	a				13 54		14 13					14 40		14 46								14 55		15 13		
Portsmouth & Southsea	a				13 58		14 17					14 44		14 50								14 59		15 17		
Portsmouth Harbour	a				14 02		14 21															15 04		15 21		
Cosham	a											14 26				14 45										
Portchester	a											14 30														
Fareham	a											14 35				14 53										
Swanwick	a											14 42				15 00										
Southampton Central	a											14 59				15 19										

For general notes see front of timetable
For details of catering facilities see Directory of Train Operators

A ⊼ to Bognor Regis
B ⊼ to Haywards Heath
C ⊼ to Horsham

For complete service between Three Bridges and Horsham see Table 186

London, Gatwick Airport & Brighton → Sussex Coast, Portsmouth and Southampton

Network Diagram - see first page of Table 186

		SN [1]	SN [1]	SN [1]		SN [1]	SN [1]	SN [1]	SN [1]	SN [1]	SN [1]	SN [1]	SN [1]		SN [1]	SN [1]	SN [1]	SN [1]	SN [1]	SN [1]	SN [1]		SN [1]	SN [1]	SN [1]	SN [1]
		A 🛒		B 🛒			🛒						B 🛒			🛒				A 🛒	B 🛒				🛒	
London Victoria [15]	⊖ d	13 17		13 32				*13 36*			13 47		14 02				*14 06*			14 17	14 32					*14 36*
Clapham Junction [10]	d	13 23		13 38				*13 42*			13 53		14 08				*14 12*			14 23	14 38					*14 42*
London Bridge [4]	⊖ d	*13 11*	*13 11*	*13 26*				*13 26*			*13 41*	*13 41*	*13 56*				*13 56*			*14 11*	*14 26*			*14 11*		*14 26*
East Croydon	d	13 33	*13 24*	13 48				*13 52*			14 03	*13 54*	14 18				*14 22*			14 33	14 48			*14 24*		*14 52*
Redhill [5]	d			14 00									14 30								15 00					
Horley	d			*13 51*									14 36								*14 51*					
Gatwick Airport [10]	✈ d	13 49	*13 41*	14 09				*13 56*	*13 58*		14 19	*14 11*	14 40				*14 26*			14 49	15 09			*14 41*		*14 56*
Three Bridges [4]	a			14 14									14 44								15 14					
	d	*13 45*	*13 45*	14 14					*14 03*		*14 15*	*14 15*	14 45							*14 45*	15 14			*14 45*		
Crawley	d			14 18									14 48								15 18					
Horsham [4]	a			14 26									14 56								15 26					
	d			14 30	14 35 →		← 14 35						15 00	15 05 →		← 15 05					15 30	15 35 →			← 15 35	
Christs Hospital	d						14 38									15 08									15 38	
Billingshurst	d						14 44									15 14									15 44	
Pulborough	d						14 51									15 21									15 51	
Amberley	d						14 57																		15 57	
Arundel	d						15 02									15 30									16 02	
Haywards Heath [3]	d	14 04	*13 55*					*14 08*	*14 17*		14 37	*14 27*					*14 38*			15 04				*14 55*		*15 08*
Burgess Hill	d	14 09	*14 01*						*14 23*			*14 33*								15 09				*15 01*		
Brighton [10]	d		14 23					14 33	14 44			14 53					15 03	15 14						15 23		15 33
Hove [2]	d	14 22	14 27					14 37	14a47		14 52	14 57					15 07	15a17		15 22				15 27		15 37
Aldrington	d		14 29									14 59												15 29		
Portslade	d	14 25	14 31					14 40				15 01					15 10			15 25				15 31		15 40
Fishersgate	d		14 33									15 03												15 33		
Southwick	d		14 35					14 43				15 05					15 13							15 35		15 43
Shoreham-by-Sea	d	14 30	14 39					14 46			14 58	15 09					15 16			15 30				15 39		15 46
Lancing	d		14 43					14 50			15 02	15 13					15 20							15 43		15 50
East Worthing	d		14 46									15 16												15 46		
Worthing [4]	a	14 36	14 48					14 54			15 06	15 18					15 24			15 36				15 48		15 54
	d	14 37	14 49					14 55			15 07	15 19					15 25			15 37				15 49		15 55
West Worthing	d	14 39	14a51					14 57			15 09	15a21					15 27			15 39				15 51		15 57
Durrington-on-Sea	d	14 41						14 59			15 11						15 29			15 41				15 53		15 59
Goring-by-Sea	d	14 44						15 02			15 14						15 32			15 44				15 56		16 02
Angmering [3]	d	14 48						15 06			15 18						15 36			15 48				16 00		16 06
Littlehampton [4]	a	14 57									15 27									15 58				16 11		
	d					14 54				15 11					15 23								15 54			
Ford [4]	d					14 58	15 07	15 12		15 16					15 27	15 35	15 42						15 58		16 07	16 12
Bognor Regis [4]	d																									
Barnham	a			14 56		15 02	15 11	15 16		15 20			15 26		15 31	15 39	15 46				15 56		16 02		16 11	16 16
	d			14 57		15 03	15 12	15 17		15 22			15 27		15 33	15 40	15 47		15 52		15 57		16 03		16 12	16 17
Bognor Regis [4]	a						15 18			15 28						15 46			15 58						16 18	
Chichester [4]	a			15 04		15 10		15 24					15 34		15 40		15 54				16 04		16 10			16 24
	d			15 05		15 11		15 25					15 35		15 41		15 55				16 05		16 11			16 25
Fishbourne (Sussex)	d					15 14									15 44								16 14			
Bosham	d					15 17									15 47								16 17			
Nutbourne	d					15 20									15 50								16 20			
Southbourne	d			15 12		15 23									15 53		16 02				16 12		16 23			
Emsworth	d			15 15		15 26		15 33							15 56		16 05				16 15		16 26			16 33
Warblington	d					15 29									15 59								16 29			
Havant	d			15 19		15 32		15 37					15 46		16 02		16 09				16 19		16 32			16 37
Bedhampton	a			*15 29*		15 34									16 04						*16 29*		16 34			
Hilsea	a			*15 36*		15 42															*16 36*		16 42			
Fratton	a			*15 40*		15 46							15 54		16 12		16 18				*16 40*		16 46			
Portsmouth & Southsea	a			*15 44*		15 50							15 58		16 15		16 21				*16 44*		16 50			
Portsmouth Harbour	a												16 02		16 21		16 25									
Cosham	a			15 26				15 45													16 26					16 45
Portchester	a			15 30																	16 30					
Fareham	a			15 35				15 53													16 35					16 53
Swanwick	a			15 42				16 00													16 42					
Southampton Central	a			15 59				16 19													17 01					17 28

For general notes see front of timetable
For details of catering facilities see
Directory of Train Operators

A 🛒 to Haywards Heath
B 🛒 to Horsham

For complete service between Three Bridges and Horsham see Table 186

London, Gatwick Airport & Brighton → Sussex Coast, Portsmouth and Southampton

Network Diagram - see first page of Table 186

Station																										
		SN 1	SN 1	SN 1	SN 1	SN 1			SN 1	SN 1	SN 1	SN 1	SN 1	SN 1	SN 1	SN 1 ◇		SN 1	SN 1	SN 1	SN 1	SN 1	SN 1	SN 1	SN 1	
						A ⊼				⊼				B ⊼												
London Victoria 15	⊖ d			14 47		15 02					15 06			15 17		15 32				15 36			15 47		16 02	
Clapham Junction 10	d			14 53		15 08					15 12			15 23		15 38				15 42			15 53		16 08	
London Bridge 4	⊖ d			14 41	14 41	14 56					14 56			15 11	15 11	15 26				15 26			15 41	15 41	15 56	
East Croydon	d			15 03	14 54	15 18					15 22			15 33	15 24	15 48				15 52			16 03	15 54	16 18	
Redhill 5	d					15 30										16 00									16 30	
Horley	d					15 36										15 53									16 36	
Gatwick Airport 10	✈ d	14 58		15 19	15 11	15 40					15 26			15 49	15 41	16 09				15 57			16 19	16 11	16 40	
Three Bridges 4	a					15 44										16 14									16 44	
	d	15 03		15 15	15 15	15 45								15 45	15 45	16 14				16 02			16 15	16 15	16 45	
Crawley	d					15 48										16 18									16 48	
Horsham 4	a					15 56										16 26									16 56	
	d					16 00	16 05 →			← 16 05						16 30	16 35 →		← 16 35						17 00	17 05 →
Christs Hospital	d									16 08									16 38							
Billingshurst	d									16 14									16 44							
Pulborough	d									16 21									16 51							
Amberley	d																		16 57							
Arundel	d									16 30									17 02							
Haywards Heath 3	d	15 17		15 37	15 27						15 38			16 04	15 55					16 11	16 17		16 37	16 27		
Burgess Hill	d	15 23			15 33									16 09	16 01						16 23			16 33		
Brighton 10	d	15 44			15 53						16 03	16 14			16 23					16 33	16 44			16 53		
Hove 2	d	15a47		15 52	15 57						16 07	16a17		16 22	16 27					16 37	16a47		16 52	16 57		
Aldrington	d				15 59										16 29									16 59		
Portslade	d				16 01						16 10			16 25	16 31					16 40			16 55	17 01		
Fishersgate	d				16 03										16 33									17 03		
Southwick	d				16 05						16 13				16 35					16 43				17 05		
Shoreham-by-Sea	d			15 58	16 09						16 16			16 30	16 39					16 46			17 00	17 08		
Lancing	d			16 02	16 13						16 20				16 43					16 50			17 04	17 12		
East Worthing	d				16 16										16 46									17 15		
Worthing 4	a			16 06	16 18						16 24			16 36	16 48					16 54			17 08	17 18		
	d			16 07	16 19						16 25			16 37	16 49					16 55			17 08	17 18		
West Worthing	d			16 09	16a21						16 27			16 39	16a51					16 57			17 10	17 20		
Durrington-on-Sea	d			16 11							16 29			16 41						16 59			17 13			
Goring-by-Sea	d			16 14							16 32			16 44						17 02			17 15			
Angmering 3	d			16 18							16 36			16 48						17 06			17 19			
Littlehampton 4	a			16 27										16 57									17 28	17 33		
	d								16 22									16 54				17 11		17 41		
Ford 4	d								16 26	16 35	16 42							16 58	17 07	17 12		17 16		→		
Bognor Regis 4	d																									
Barnham	a					16 26			16 30	16 39	16 46					16 56		17 02	17 11	17 16		17 20			17 26	
	d		16 24			16 27			16 31	16 40	16 47		16 54			16 57		17 03	17 12	17 17		17 24			17 27	
Bognor Regis 4	a		16 30							16 46			17 00						17 18			17 30				
Chichester 4	a					16 34			16 38		16 54					17 04		17 10		17 24					17 34	
	d					16 35			16 39		16 55					17 05		17 11		17 25					17 35	
Fishbourne (Sussex)	d								16 42									17 14							17 38	
Bosham	d								16 45									17 17							17 41	
Nutbourne	d								16 48									17 20								
Southbourne	d								16 51		17 02					17 12		17 23							17 45	
Emsworth	d								16 54		17 05					17 15		17 26		17 33					17 48	
Warblington	d								16 57									17 29								
Havant	d					16 46			17 00		17 09					17 19		17 32		17 37					17 54	
Bedhampton	a								17 02							17 29		17 34							17 56	
Hilsea	a								17 07							17 36		17 42							18 01	
Fratton	a					16 54			17 11		17 18					17 40		17 46		17 59					18 05	
Portsmouth & Southsea	a					16 58			17 16		17 22					17 44		17 50		18 02					18 09	
Portsmouth Harbour	a					17 02			17 20																18 15	
Cosham	a															17 25				17 45						
Portchester	a															17 30										
Fareham	a															17 35				17 53						
Swanwick	a															17 42				18 00						
Southampton Central	a															18 03				18 19						

For general notes see front of timetable
For details of catering facilities see
Directory of Train Operators

A ⊼ to Horsham
B ⊼ to Haywards Heath

For complete service between Three Bridges and Horsham see Table 186

London, Gatwick Airport & Brighton → Sussex Coast, Portsmouth and Southampton

Network Diagram - see first page of Table 186

		GW ◇ A	SN 1	SN 1	SN 1	SN 1	SN 1 B ⌶	SN 1 C ⌶		SN 1	SN 1	SN 1	SN 1	SN 1	SN 1	SN 1	SN 1		SN 1		SN 1	SN 1	SN 1	SN 1	SN 1	
London Victoria 15 ⊖	d	15b47		15b47	16 06		16 17	16 32					16 36	16b17	16 36		16c47		17 02					17 06	17 32	
Clapham Junction 10	d	15b53		15b53	16 12		16 23	16 38					16 42	16b23	16 42		16c53		17 08					17 12	17 38	
London Bridge 4 ⊖	d	15 56		15 56			16 11	16 26			16 11			16 26			16 57							16b59	17 29	
East Croydon	d	16 09		16 09	16 22		16 33	16 48			16 24		16e52	16 40	16 52		17 10		17 18					17 22	17 49	
Redhill 5	d							17 00																		
Horley	d							17 06																		
Gatwick Airport 10 ✈	d	16 26		16 26			16 49	17 09			16 41			16 56			17 20		17 21					17f20	17 50	
Three Bridges 4	a							17 14									17 29		17 36						18 06	
	d	16 30		16 30			16 45	17 18	17 20		16 45		17 20	17 00	17 10		17 29		17 37					17f29	18 07	
Crawley	d							17 22	→				17 26						17 41						18 11	
Horsham 4	a							17 30					17 38						17 49						18 22	
	d		← 17 05					17 30					17 38						17 53	17 58 →		← 17 58			18 26	18 31 →
Christs Hospital	d		17 08										17 42									18 01				
Billingshurst	d		17 15										17 48									18 07				
Pulborough	d		17 21										17 54									18 14				
Amberley	d		17 27																			18 20				
Arundel	d		17 32										18 03									18 25				
Haywards Heath 3	d	16 40		16 40			17 04				16 55			17 10	17 23	17 26	17 39							17 46		
Burgess Hill	d						17 09				17 01					17 32	17 46							17 53		
Brighton 10	d	17 00		17 03	17 14						17 23			17 33	17 45	17 53							18 00	18 14		
Hove 2	d	17 04		17 07	17a17		17 21				17 27			17 37	17 49	17a56	18 01						18 04	18a17		
Aldrington	d										17 29				17 51								18 06			
Portslade	d			17 10			17 24				17 31			17 40	17 53		18 04						18 08			
Fishersgate	d										17 33				17 55								18 10			
Southwick	d			17 13							17 35			17 43	17 57								18 12			
Shoreham-by-Sea	d	17 13		17 16			17 29				17 39			17 46	18 01		18 09						18 16			
Lancing	d			17 20			17 33				17 43			17 50	18 05		18 13						18 20			
East Worthing	d										17 46				18 08								18 23			
Worthing 4	a	17 21		17 24			17 37				17 48			17 54	18 10		18 17						18 25			
	d	17 22		17 25			17 38				17 49			17 55	18 11		18 17						18 27			
West Worthing	d			17 27			17 40				17 51			17 57	18 13		18 19						18 29			
Durrington-on-Sea	d			17 29			17 42				17 53			17 59	18 15		18 22						18 31			
Goring-by-Sea	d			17 32			17 45				17 56			18 02	18 18		18 24						18 34			
Angmering 3	d			17 36			17 49				18 00			18 06	18 22		18 28						18 38			
Littlehampton 4	a					←	18 00				18 08				18 30		18 39									
	d					17 41				17 54											18 18					
Ford 4	d		17 37	17 42		17 46				17 58			18 08	18 12							18 22	18 30	18 44			
Bognor Regis 4	d																									
Barnham	a	17 38	17 42	17 46		17 50		17 57		18 02			18 13	18 16					18 20		18 26	18 34	18 48		18 53	
	d	17 39	17 42	17 47		17 54		17 57		18 04		18 08	18 14	18 17					18 21		18 27	18 35	18 49		18 54	
Bognor Regis 4	a		17 49			18 00						18 14	18 22								18 33	18 43				
Chichester 4	a	17 46		17 54				18 05		18 11				18 24					18 28				18 56		19 01	
	d	17 47		17 55				18 05		18 12				18 25					18 29				18 57		19 02	
Fishbourne (Sussex)	d									18 15									18 32						19 05	
Bosham	d							18 10		18 18									18 35						19 08	
Nutbourne	d									18 21									18 38							
Southbourne	d			18 04				18 14		18 24									18 41						19 12	
Emsworth	d			18 07				18 17		18 27				18 33					18 44						19 15	
Warblington	d			18 10						18 30									18 47							
Havant	d	17 58		18 13				18 22		18 34				18 37					18 54				19 08		19 20	
Bedhampton	a	18 07						18 32		18 36									18 57							
Hilsea	a	18 12						18 39		18 41									19 02				19 17			
Fratton	a	18 16		18 22				18 43		18 45				18 59					19 06				19 21			
Portsmouth & Southsea	a	18 20		18 25				18 46		18 49				19 03					19 09				19 25			
Portsmouth Harbour	a			18 31																						
Cosham	a	18 04						18 28						18 44											19 26	
Portchester	a							18 33																	19 31	
Fareham	a	18 12						18 38						18 52											19 36	
Swanwick	a							18 45						18 59											19 43	
Southampton Central	a	18 41						19 04						19 20											20 03	

For general notes see front of timetable
For details of catering facilities see Directory of Train Operators

A To Worcester Shrub Hill (Table 57)
B ⌶ to Haywards Heath
C ⌶ to Southampton Central
b Change at East Croydon and Brighton
c Change at East Croydon
e Change at Three Bridges
f Change at Haywards Heath and Brighton

For complete service between Three Bridges and Horsham see Table 186

London, Gatwick Airport & Brighton → Sussex Coast, Portsmouth and Southampton

Network Diagram - see first page of Table 186

Station		SN 1	SN 1	SN 1	SN 1	SN 1	SN 1	SN 1	SN 1	SN 1	SN 1	SN 1	SN 1	SN 1	SN 1	SN 1	SN 1	SN 1	SN 1	SN 1	SN 1	SN 1	SN 1	SN 1
London Victoria 15 ⊖	d			17 17			17b36		17c39	18 02		17 47			17e23	18b06	17e49	18 17	18 32					18e17
Clapham Junction 10	d			17 23			17b42		17c45	18 08		17 53			17e30	18b12	17e56	18 23	18 38					18e23
London Bridge 4 ⊖	d			17 11		17 11	17 42		17 47	17 57		17 44			17 32	18 12	17 57		18 26					18 26
East Croydon	d			17 33		17 25	17 55	17f36	18 00	18 18		18 03			17f55	18 25	18 12	18 33	18 48				18f25	18 40
Redhill 5	d			17 27														18 25						
Horley	d			17 36								18 18						18 34						
Gatwick Airport 10 ✈	d			17 48		17 41	18 07	18 00	18 12	18 22		18b14			18 14	18b38	18 35	18 49	18 56				18 46	19 05
Three Bridges 4	a								18 21	18 36		18 23				18 44			19 06					
	d			17 46		17 46	17 56	17f56	18 22	18 37		18 24			18 18	18 45	18 32		19 07				18f45	19 02
Crawley	d								18 26	18 41									19 11					
Horsham 4	a								18 38	18 49									19 22					
	d				← 18 31				18 39	18 53 / 18 58 →			← 18 58						19 26 / 19 31 →		← 19 31			
Christs Hospital	d				18 35				18 42				19 01								19 34			
Billingshurst	d				18 41				18 49				19 07								19 41			
Pulborough	d				18 48				18 56				19 14								19 48			
Amberley	d								19 02												19 54			
Arundel	d				18 57				19 07				19 23								19 59			
Haywards Heath 3	d			18 00		17 57	18 22	18 12				18 33			18 30	18 54	18 47	19 03					18 58	19 17
Burgess Hill	d			18 07		18 03	18 27	18 18				18 41			18 37	19 00	18 53	19 08						19 23
Brighton 10	d					18 28		18 49							19 00		19 15						19 30	19 44
Hove 2	d			18 21		18 32	18 44	18a53				18 58			19 04	19 18	19a19	19 23					19 34	19a48
Aldrington	d					18 34									19 06								19 36	
Portslade	d			18 24		18 36	18 47					19 01			19 08	19 21		19 26					19 38	
Fishersgate	d					18 38									19 10								19 40	
Southwick	d					18 40									19 12								19 42	
Shoreham-by-Sea	d			18 29		18 44	18 52					19 06			19 16	19 26		19 31					19 46	
Lancing	d			18 33		18 48	18 56					19 10			19 20	19 30		19 36					19 50	
East Worthing	d					18 51									19 23								19 53	
Worthing 4	a			18 37		18 53	19 00					19 14			19 25	19 34		19 40					19 55	
	d			18 38		18 54	19 00					19 14			19 26	19 35		19 40					19 56	
West Worthing	d			18 40			19 02					19 16			19 28	19 37		19 42					19 58	
Durrington-on-Sea	d			18 42			19 05					19 19			19 30	19 39		19 45					20 00	
Goring-by-Sea	d			18 45			19 07					19 21			19 33	19 42		19 47					20 03	
Angmering 3	d			18 49		19 00	19 11					19 25			19 37	19 46		19 51					20 07	
Littlehampton 4	a			19 00			19 24					19 36				19 57		20 03						
	d		18 48								19 11			19 35								20 06		
Ford 4	d		18 53		19 02	19 07					19 19		19 28	19 39	19 43							20 10	20 13	
Bognor Regis 4	d																							
Barnham	a		18 57		19 06	19 11			19 15	19 19	19 23		19 32	19 43	19 47				19 52		20 07	20 14	20 18	
	d	18 55	19 00		19 07	19 12			19 16	19 20	19 24		19 33	19 55 →	19 48				19 53	← 19 55	20 08	20 22 →	20 18	
Bognor Regis 4	a	19 01			19 15				19 24		19 30		19 41							20 01	20 16			
Chichester 4	a		19 07			19 19				19 27					19 55				20 00				20 26	
	d		19 11			19 20				19 28					19 56				20 01				20 26	
Fishbourne (Sussex)	d		19 14																20 04					
Bosham	d		19 17																20 07					
Nutbourne	d		19 20																20 10					
Southbourne	d		19 23							19 35									20 13					
Emsworth	d		19 26			19 30				19 38									20 16					
Warblington	d		19 29																20 19					
Havant	d		19 33			19 36				19 46					20 07				20 22				20 37	
Bedhampton	a		19 35			19 44													20 31					
Hilsea	a		19 43			19 49													20 37					
Fratton	a		19 47			19 55				19 56					20 15				20 41				20 57	
Portsmouth & Southsea	a		19 50							20 01					20 20				20 44				21 01	
Portsmouth Harbour	a									20 07														
Cosham	a					19 44													20 28				20 44	
Portchester	a																						20 48	
Fareham	a					19 52													20 36				20 53	
Swanwick	a					19 59													20 43				21 00	
Southampton Central	a					20 18													21 03				21 19	

For general notes see front of timetable
For details of catering facilities see Directory of Train Operators

b Change at Haywards Heath
c Change at East Croydon
e Change at East Croydon and Brighton
f Change at Haywards Heath and Brighton

For complete service between Three Bridges and Horsham see Table 186

London, Gatwick Airport & Brighton → Sussex Coast, Portsmouth and Southampton

Network Diagram - see first page of Table 186

		SN 1	SN 1	SN 1			SN 1	SN 1	SN 1	SN 1	SN 1	SN 1		SN 1	SN 1	SN 1	SN 1	SN 1	SN 1		SN 1	SN 1	SN 1	SN 1	SN 1	
				A 🍴						B 🍴		A 🍴					B 🍴		🍴							
London Victoria 15 ⊖	d	18 47			19 02			18 36	19 06	19 17			19 32			19 36	19 47			20 02	19b53	20 06	20 17			20 32
Clapham Junction 10	d	18 53			19 08			18 42	19 12	19 23			19 38			19 42	19 53			20 08	19b59	20 12	20 23			20 38
London Bridge 4 ⊖	d	18 42			18 59			18 42	18b59	19 12			19 27		19 12	19 27	19 41			20 01	20 01		20 11			20 28
East Croydon	d	19 03			19 18			18 54	19 22	19 33			19 48		19 24	19 52	20 03			20 19	20 14	20 22	20 33			20 48
Redhill 5	d	18 59			19 31								20 00							20 31						21 00
Horley	d	19 08			19 16					19 33			19 56							20 25						20 54
Gatwick Airport 10 ✈	d	19 20			19 40			19 16	19 27	19 49			20 09		19 41	19 56	20 19			20 39	20 31		20 49			21 09
Three Bridges 4	a				19 45								20 14							20 44						21 14
	d	19 02			19 45				19 32	19 45			20 14		19 45	20 02	20 15			20 44	20 15		20 45			21 14
Crawley	d				19 49								20 18							20 48						21 18
Horsham 4	a				19 57								20 26							20 56						21 26
	d			20 01	20 06							20 30	20 35						21 00	21 05					21 30	21 35
Christs Hospital	d				20 09								20 38							21 08						21 38
Billingshurst	d				20 15								20 44							21 14						21 44
Pulborough	d				20 22								20 51							21 21						21 51
Amberley	d				20 28								20 57							21 27						21 57
Arundel	d				20 33								21 02							21 32						22 02
Haywards Heath 3	d	19 37						19 31	19 45	20 04					19 57	20 17	20 34				20 42	20 47	21 04			
Burgess Hill	d	19 42						19 36	19 46	20 09					20 03	20 16	20 39				20 32		21 09			
Brighton 10	d							20 03	20 14						20 30	20 44					21 03	21 14				
Hove 2	d	19 57						20 07	20a17	20 22					20 34	20a48	20 54				21 07	21a17	21 22			
Aldrington	d							20 09							20 36						21 09					
Portslade	d	20 00						20 11		20 25					20 38		20 57				21 11		21 25			
Fishersgate	d							20 13							20 40						21 13					
Southwick	d							20 15							20 42						21 15					
Shoreham-by-Sea	d	20 04						20 19		20 30					20 46		21 01				21 19		21 30			
Lancing	d	20 08						20 23		20 34					20 50		21 05				21 23		21 34			
East Worthing	d							20 26							20 53						21 26					
Worthing 4	a	20 12						20 28		20 38					20 55		21 09				21 28		21 38			
	d	20 13						20 29		20 38					20 56		21 10				21 29		21 38			
West Worthing	d	20 15						20 31		20 40					20 58		21 12				21 31		21 40			
Durrington-on-Sea	d	20 17						20 33		20 43					21 00		21 14				21 33		21 43			
Goring-by-Sea	d	20 20						20 36		20 45					21 03		21 17				21 36		21 45			
Angmering 3	d	20 24						20 40		20 49					21 07		21 21				21 40		21 49			
Littlehampton 4	a	20 35								20 58							21 29						21 58			
	d						20 37							21 06												
Ford 4	d				20 38		20 42	20 46					21 07	21 10	21 13					21 37	21 46					22 07
Bognor Regis 4	d																									
Barnham	a			20 27	20 42		20 46	20 50				20 56	21 11	21 14	21 17				21 26	21 41	21 50				21 56	22 11
	d		← 20 22	20 28	20 43		20 52 →	20 51			← 20 52	20 57	21 12	21 22 →	21 18			← 21 22	21 27	21 42	21 51			21 52	21 57	22 12
Bognor Regis 4	a		20 28		20 49						20 58		21 18					21 28		21 48				21 58		22 18
Chichester 4	a			20 35				20 58				21 04			21 25				21 34		21 58				22 04	
	d			20 36				20 59				21 05			21 26				21 35		21 59				22 05	
Fishbourne (Sussex)	d											21 08													22 08	
Bosham	d											21 11													22 11	
Nutbourne	d											21 14													22 14	
Southbourne	d			20 43								21 17							21 42						22 17	
Emsworth	d			20 46								21 20							21 45						22 20	
Warblington	d											21 23													22 23	
Havant	d			20 52				21 10				21 26			21 37				21 49		22 10				22 26	
Bedhampton	a											21 34													22 34	
Hilsea	a											21 41			21 55				21 58		22 18				22 39	
Fratton	a			21 01				21 18				21 45			21 58				22 01		22 22				22 43	
Portsmouth & Southsea	a			21 06				21 23				21 48							22 05		22 26				22 47	
Portsmouth Harbour	a							21 27																		
Cosham	a											21 34			21 43										22 33	
Portchester	a											21 38														
Fareham	a											21 43			21 51										22 42	
Swanwick	a											21 50			21 58										22 49	
Southampton Central	a											22 08			22 16										23 07	

For general notes see front of timetable
For details of catering facilities see
Directory of Train Operators

A 🍴 to Bognor Regis
B 🍴 to Haywards Heath
b Change at East Croydon and Brighton

For complete service between Three Bridges and Horsham see Table 186

London, Gatwick Airport & Brighton → Sussex Coast, Portsmouth and Southampton

Network Diagram - see first page of Table 186

	SN 1	SN 1	SN 1	SN 1	SN 1	SN 1	SN 1	SN 1	SN 1	SN 1	SN 1	SN 1	SN 1	SN 1	SN 1	SN 1	SN 1	SN 1	SN 1	SN 1	SN 1	SN 1	SN 1		
London Victoria 15 ⊖ d		20b17	20 36	20 47			20b47	21 06		21 17	21 32			21 36	21 47	22 06		22 17	22 36	22 32		22 47	23 17		
Clapham Junction 10 d		20b23	20 42	20 53			20b53	21 12		21 23	21 38			21 42	21 53	22 12		22 23	22 42	22 38		22 53	23 23		
London Bridge 4 ⊖ d		20 28		20 41			20 58			21 11	21 15		21 11	21b28	21 41	21b45		22 11	22b28	22 15		22 41	23 11		
East Croydon d		20 40	20 52	21 04			21 11	21 22		21 33	21 48		21 24	21 52	22 03	22 22		22 34	22 52	22 48		23 03	23 33		
Redhill 5 d										21 31	22 00							22 31		23 01			23 31		
Horley d										21 25	21 54							22 25		22 54			23 26		
Gatwick Airport 10 ✈ d		20 56		21 19			21 27			21 49	22 09		21 41	21c49	22 19	22c19		22 49	22c49	23 09		23 19	23 51		
Three Bridges 4 a										21 53	22 14							22 54		23 15			23 55		
d		21 01		21 15			21 32			21 53	22 14		21 45	21c53	22 15	22 15		22 54	22c54	23 16		23 14	23 56		
Crawley d											22 18									23 19					
Horsham 4 a											22 26									23 27					
d											22 27									23 28					
Christs Hospital d											22 30									23 31					
Billingshurst d											22 36									23 37					
Pulborough d											22 43									23 44					
Amberley d											22 49									23 50					
Arundel d											22 54									23 55					
Haywards Heath 3 d		21 11	21 15	21 34			21 41	21 45		22 06			21 58	22 15	22 37	22 45		23 03	23 15			23 37	00 05		
Burgess Hill d		21 03		21 39			21 32			22 11			22 04			22 32		23 08	23 04				00 10		
Brighton 10 d		21 33	21 44				22 03	22 14					22 33	22 44		23 14			23 44						
Hove 2 d		21 37	21a48	21 54			22 07	22a17		22 23			22 37	22a47	22 52	23a17		23 22	23a47			23 52	00 22		
Aldrington d		21 39					22 09						22 39												
Portslade d		21 41		21 57			22 11			22 26			22 41		22 55			23 25				23 55	00s25		
Fishersgate d		21 43					22 13						22 43												
Southwick d		21 45					22 15						22 45					23 28				23 58	00s28		
Shoreham-by-Sea d		21 49		22 01			22 19			22 31			22 49		23 00			23 31				00 01	00s31		
Lancing d		21 53		22 05			22 23			22 35			22 53		23 04			23 35				00 05	00s35		
East Worthing d		21 56					22 26						22 56												
Worthing 4 a		21 58		22 09			22 28			22 39			22 58		23 08			23 39				00 09	00 39		
d		21 59		22 10			22 29			22 39			22 59		23 08			23 39							
West Worthing d		22 01		22 12			22 31			22 41			23 01		23 10			23 41							
Durrington-on-Sea d		22 03		22 14			22 33			22 44			23 03		23 13			23 44							
Goring-by-Sea d		22 06		22 17			22 36			22 46			23 06		23 15			23 46							
Angmering 3 d		22 10		22 21			22 40			22 50			23 10		23 19			23 50							
Littlehampton 4 a				22 30									23 18		23 28										
d	22 08					22 38							23 23												
Ford 4 d	22 12	22 16				22 42	22 46			22 56	23 00		23 27					23 56		00 01					
Bognor Regis 4 d																									
Barnham a	22 16	22 20				22 46	22 50			23 01	23 04		23 31					00 01		00 05					
d	22 17	22 21			22 22	22 52 →	22 51		← 22 52	23 06 →	23 05	← 23 06	23 32				23 36	00 09 →		00 06	← 00 09				
Bognor Regis 4 a					22 28				22 58			23 12					23 42				00 15				
Chichester 4 a	22 24	22 28					22 58				23 12		23 39							00 13					
d		22 29					22 59				23 13														
Fishbourne (Sussex) d											23 16														
Bosham d											23 19														
Nutbourne d											23 22														
Southbourne d		22 36									23 25														
Emsworth d		22 39									23 28														
Warblington d											23 31														
Havant d		22 43					23 11				23 34														
Bedhampton a		23 01					23 33				00 24														
Hilsea a							23 39				00 30														
Fratton a		22 52					23 20				23 47														
Portsmouth & Southsea a		22 55					23 23				23 51														
Portsmouth Harbour a		22 59					23 27																		
Cosham a																									
Portchester a																									
Fareham a																									
Swanwick a																									
Southampton Central a																									

For general notes see front of timetable
For details of catering facilities see Directory of Train Operators

b Change at East Croydon and Brighton
c Change at Haywards Heath and Brighton

For complete service between Three Bridges and Horsham see Table 186

London, Gatwick Airport & Brighton → Sussex Coast, Portsmouth and Southampton

Network Diagram - see first page of Table 186

		SN 1	SN 1	SN 1	SN 1	SN 1	SN 1	SN 1	SN 1	SN 1	SN 1	SN 1	SN 1		SN 1	SN 1	SN 1	SN 1	SN 1	SN 1	SN 1	SN 1	SN 1	SN 1	SN 1	
London Victoria 15	⊖ d	22p17	22p32		22p47	*23 06*	23p17	00 05									*04 00*									
Clapham Junction 10	d	22p23	22p38		22p53	*23 12*	23p23	00 11									*04 08*									
London Bridge 4	⊖ d					*22b58*	*22 45*	*23 53*									*03b35*						*04 35*			
East Croydon	d	22p34	22p48		23p03	*23 22*	23p33	00 25									*04 22*						*05 02*			
Redhill 5	d		23p01					*00 25*																		
Horley	d							*00 31*																		
Gatwick Airport 10	✈ d	22p49	23p09		23p19	*23c19*	23p51	00 44									*04 47*						*05 22*			
Three Bridges 4	a	22p54	23p15				23p55	00 48																		
	d	22p54	23p16			*23 14*	23p56	00 48									*04 52*						*05 28*			
Crawley	d		23p19																							
Horsham 4	a		23p27																							
	d		23p28																							
Christs Hospital	d		23p31																							
Billingshurst	d		23p37																							
Pulborough	d		23p44																							
Amberley	d		23p50																							
Arundel	d		23p55																							
Haywards Heath 3	d	23p03			23p37	*23 45*	00 05	01 03									*05 01*						*05 42*			
Burgess Hill	d	23p08				*23 31*	00 10																*05 48*			
Brighton 10	d					00 10									05 15		05 27	05 44	05 53			06 01	06 14	06 23		
Hove 2	d	23p22			23p52	00a13	00 22	01s25							05 20		05 31	05a47	05 57			06 05	06a17	06 27		
Aldrington	d																05 33		05 59					06 29		
Portslade	d	23p25			23p55		00s25	01s28							05 23		05 35		06 01			06 08		06 31		
Fishersgate	d																05 37		06 03					06 33		
Southwick	d	23p28			23p58		00s28	01s31									05 39		06 05			06 11		06 35		
Shoreham-by-Sea	d	23p31			00 01		00s31	01s34							05 27		05 43		06 09			06 14		06 39		
Lancing	d	23p35			00 05		00s35	01s38							05 31		05 47		06 13			06 18		06 43		
East Worthing	d																05 50		06 16					06 46		
Worthing 4	a	23p39			00 09		00 39	01 42							05 35		05 52		06 18			06 22		06 48		
	d	23p39													05 36		05 53		06 19			06 23		06 49		
West Worthing	d	23p41													05 38		05 55		06a21			06 25		06a51		
Durrington-on-Sea	d	23p44													05 40		05 57					06 27				
Goring-by-Sea	d	23p46													05 43		06 00					06 30				
Angmering 3	d	23p50													05 47		06 04					06 34				
Littlehampton 4	a																									
	d															05 54					06 19					
Ford 4	d	23p56	00 01												05 53	05 58	06 10					06 40				
Bognor Regis 4	d																									
Barnham	a	00 01	00 05	←											05 57	06 02	06 14				06 26	06 44				
	d	00 09	00 06	00 09					04 57	05 15	05 20	05 30	05 38		05 58	06 03	06 15			06 22	06 27	06 45			06 52	
Bognor Regis 4	a	→		00 15																06 28					06 58	
Chichester 4	a		00 13						05 04	05 22	05 27	05 37	05 45		06 05	06 10	06 22				06 34	06 52				
	d								05 05	05 23	05 28	05 38	05 46		06 06	06 11	06 23				06 35	06 53				
Fishbourne (Sussex)	d															06 14										
Bosham	d														06 10	06 17										
Nutbourne	d															06 20										
Southbourne	d														06 15	06 23	06 30									
Emsworth	d														06 18	06 26	06 33									
Warblington	d														06 21	06 29										
Havant	d								05 16	05 34	05 39	05 49	05 57		06 24	06 32	06 37				06 46	07 04				
Bedhampton	a												*06 03*			06 34						*07 22*				
Hilsea	a												*06 09*			06 42						*07 27*				
Fratton	a									05 42		05 57	06 05			06 46					06 54	07 12				
Portsmouth & Southsea	a									05 46		06 01	06 09			06 50					06 58	07 16				
Portsmouth Harbour	a											06 05	06 16								07 02	07 20				
Cosham	a								05 22		05 49				06 30		06 45									
Portchester	a								05 27						06 34											
Fareham	a								05 32		05 57				06 39		06 53									
Swanwick	a								05 39		06 04				06 46		07 00									
Southampton Central	a								05 59		06 24				07 05		07 18									

For general notes see front of timetable
For details of catering facilities see Directory of Train Operators

b Change at East Croydon and Brighton
c Change at Haywards Heath and Brighton

For complete service between Three Bridges and Horsham see Table 186

Table 188

Saturdays

London, Gatwick Airport & Brighton → Sussex Coast, Portsmouth and Southampton

Network Diagram - see first page of Table 186

		SN 1	SN 1	SN 1	SN 1	SN 1	SN 1	SN 1	SN 1	SN 1	SN 1	SN 1	SN 1	SN 1	SN 1	SN 1	SN 1	SN 1	SN 1	SN 1	SN 1	SN 1	SN 1
London Victoria 15 ⊖	d	05 02			05 02					05 32	05b32				06 02		06b02			06c32	06b32	06 32	07 06
Clapham Junction 10	d	05 08			05 08					05 38	05b38				06 08		06b08			06c38	06b38	06 38	07 12
London Bridge 4 ⊖	d	04 35				05 05				05 05	05 51				06 27		06 27			06 41	06 41	06e41	06 56
East Croydon	d	05 22			05 22	05 32				05 48	06 05				06 18		06 39			06 54	06 54	06 48	07 22
Redhill 5	d	05 39								06 07					06 46							07 10	
Horley	d	05 45								06 18					06 55							07 19	
Gatwick Airport 10 ✈	d	05 58			05 49	05 54				06 22	06 20	06 22			06 59		06 56			07 11	07 11	07 24	07 26
Three Bridges 4	a	06 02								06 26					07 03							07 29	
	d	06 03			05 54	06 00				06 34	06 26	06 30			07 04		07 00			07 15	07 15	07 30	
Crawley	d	06 06								06 37					07 07							07 33	
Horsham 4	a	06 18								06 49					07 19							07 45	
	d	06 19								06 50					07 20							07 50	
Christs Hospital	d	06 22								06 53					07 23							07 53	
Billingshurst	d	06 28								06 59					07 29							07 59	
Pulborough	d	06 35								07 06					07 36							08 06	
Amberley	d	06 41								07 12					07 42							08 12	
Arundel	d	06 46								07 17					07 47							08 17	
Haywards Heath 3	d				06 03	06 12					06 38	06 41					07 08			07 37	07 27		07 40
Burgess Hill	d				06 09	06 18						06 47									07 33		
Brighton 10	d				06 33	06 44		06 48	06 53		07 03	07 14	07 23				07 33	07 44			07 53		08 03
Hove 2	d				06 37	06a47		06 52	06 57		07 07	07a17	07 27				07 37	07a47		07 52	07 57		08 07
Aldrington	d								06 59				07 29								07 59		
Portslade	d				06 40			06 55	07 01		07 10		07 31				07 40				08 01		08 10
Fishersgate	d								07 03				07 33								08 03		
Southwick	d				06 43				07 05		07 13		07 35				07 43				08 05		08 13
Shoreham-by-Sea	d				06 46			06 59	07 09		07 16		07 39				07 46			07 58	08 09		08 16
Lancing	d				06 50			07 03	07 13		07 20		07 43				07 50			08 02	08 13		08 20
East Worthing	d								07 16				07 46								08 16		
Worthing 4	a				06 54			07 07	07 18		07 24		07 48				07 54			08 06	08 18		08 24
	d				06 55			07 08	07 19		07 25		07 49				07 55			08 07	08 19		08 25
West Worthing	d				06 57			07 10	07a21				07a51				07 57			08 09	08a21		
Durrington-on-Sea	d				06 59			07 12									07 59			08 11			
Goring-by-Sea	d				07 02			07 15									08 02			08 14			
Angmering 3	d				07 06			07 19			07 31						08 06			08 18			08 31
Littlehampton 4	a							07 27												08 27			
	d		06 54				07 11									07 54			08 11				
Ford 4	d	06 51	06 58		07 12		07 16			07 22					07 52	07 58	08 12		08 16			08 22	
Bognor Regis 4	d																						
Barnham	a	06 55	07 02		07 16		07 20			07 27	07 41				07 57	08 02	08 16		08 20			08 27	08 41
	d	07 05 → 06 59	07 03	← 07 05	07 17		07 22			07 27	07 41			07 52	07 57	08 03	08 17		08 22			08 27	08 41
Bognor Regis 4	a			07 11			07 28							07 58					08 28				
Chichester 4	a	07 06	07 10		07 24					07 35	07 49				08 05	08 10	08 24					08 35	08 49
	d	07 07	07 11		07 25					07 35	07 49				08 05	08 11	08 25					08 35	08 49
Fishbourne (Sussex)	d		07 14													08 14							
Bosham	d		07 17													08 17							
Nutbourne	d		07 20													08 20							
Southbourne	d	07 14	07 23								07 56				08 12	08 23							08 56
Emsworth	d	07 17	07 26		07 33						07 59				08 15	08 26	08 33						08 59
Warblington	d		07 29													08 29							
Havant	d	07 23	07 32		07 37					07 46	08 04				08 20	08 32	08 37					08 46	09 04
Bedhampton	a		07 34								08 19					08 34							
Hilsea	a		07 42								08 25					08 42							
Fratton	a		07 46							07 55	08 12					08 46						08 55	09 12
Portsmouth & Southsea	a		07 50							07 58	08 16					08 50						08 58	09 16
Portsmouth Harbour	a									08 02	08 20											09 02	09 20
Cosham	a	07 29			07 45										08 28		08 45						
Portchester	a	07 34													08 32								
Fareham	a	07 39			07 53										08 37		08 53						
Swanwick	a	07 45			08 00										08 44		09 00						
Southampton Central	a	08 03			08 17										09 01		09 19						

For general notes see front of timetable
For details of catering facilities see Directory of Train Operators

b Change at East Croydon and Brighton
c Change at East Croydon and Haywards Heath
e Change at Gatwick Airport

For complete service between Three Bridges and Horsham see Table 186

London, Gatwick Airport & Brighton → Sussex Coast, Portsmouth and Southampton

Network Diagram - see first page of Table 186

Station		SN 1	SN 1	SN 1	SN 1		SN 1		SN 1	SN 1	SN 1	SN 1	SN 1
London Victoria 15 ⊖	d				07 32					07 36			07 47
Clapham Junction 10	d				07 38					07 42			07 53
London Bridge 4 ⊖	d		07 11		07 26					07 26			07 41
East Croydon	d		07 24		07 48					07 52			08 03
Redhill 5	d				08 00								
Horley	d				07 51								
Gatwick Airport 10	d		07 41		08 09					07 56	07 58		08 19
Three Bridges 4	a				08 14								
	d		07 45		08 14						08 03		08 15
Crawley	d				08 18								
Horsham 4	a				08 26								
	d				08 30	08 35 →			← 08 35				
Christs Hospital	d								08 38				
Billingshurst	d								08 44				
Pulborough	d								08 51				
Amberley	d								08 57				
Arundel	d								09 02				
Haywards Heath 3	d		07 55							08 10	08 17		08 37
Burgess Hill	d		08 01								08 23		
Brighton 10	d	08 14	08 23							08 33	08 44		
Hove 2	d	08a17	08 27							08 37	08a47		08 52
Aldrington	d		08 29										
Portslade	d		08 31							08 40			
Fishersgate	d		08 33										
Southwick	d		08 35							08 43			
Shoreham-by-Sea	d		08 39							08 46			08 58
Lancing	d		08 43							08 50			09 02
East Worthing	d		08 46										
Worthing 4	a		08 48							08 54			09 06
	d		08 49							08 55			09 07
West Worthing	d		08a51							08 57			09 09
Durrington-on-Sea	d									08 59			09 11
Goring-by-Sea	d									09 02			09 14
Angmering 3	d									09 06			09 18
Littlehampton 4	a												09 27
	d						08 54					09 11	
Ford 4	d						08 58		09 07	09 12		09 16	
Bognor Regis 4	d												
Barnham	a				08 56		09 02		09 11	09 16		09 20	
	d			08 52	08 57		09 03		09 12	09 17		09 22	
Bognor Regis 4	a			08 58					09 18			09 28	
Chichester 4	a				09 04		09 10			09 24			
	d				09 05		09 11			09 25			
Fishbourne (Sussex)	d						09 14						
Bosham	d						09 17						
Nutbourne	d						09 20						
Southbourne	d				09 12		09 23						
Emsworth	d				09 15		09 26			09 33			
Warblington	d						09 29						
Havant	d				09 19		09 32			09 37			
Bedhampton	a				09 29		09 34						
Hilsea	a				09 36		09 42						
Fratton	a				09 40		09 46						
Portsmouth & Southsea	a				09 44		09 50						
Portsmouth Harbour	a												
Cosham	a				09 26					09 45			
Portchester	a				09 30								
Fareham	a				09 35					09 53			
Swanwick	a				09 42					10 00			
Southampton Central	a				09 59					10 17			

Station		SN 1	SN 1		GW ◇ A	SN 1	SN 1	SN 1		SN 1	SN 1	SN 1		SN 1
London Victoria 15 ⊖	d		08 02		07b47	08 06				08 17		08 32		
Clapham Junction 10	d		08 08		07b53	08 12				08 23		08 38		
London Bridge 4 ⊖	d	07 41	07 56		07 56	07 56				08 11	08 11	08 26		
East Croydon	d	07 54	08 18		08 09	08 22				08 33	08 24	08 48		
Redhill 5	d		08 30									09 00		
Horley	d		08 36									08 51		
Gatwick Airport 10	d	08 11	08 40		08 26	08 26				08 49	08 41	09 09		
Three Bridges 4	a		08 44									09 14		
	d	08 15	08 45							08 45	08 45	09 14		
Crawley	d		08 48									09 18		
Horsham 4	a		08 56									09 26		
	d		09 00	09 05								09 30	09 35 →	
Christs Hospital	d													
Billingshurst	d			09 13										
Pulborough	d			09 19										
Amberley	d													
Arundel	d			09 28										
Haywards Heath 3	d	08 27			08 40	08 40				09 04	08 55			
Burgess Hill	d	08 33								09 09	09 01			
Brighton 10	d	08 53			09 00	09 03	09 14				09 23			
Hove 2	d	08 57			09 04	09 07	09a17			09 22	09 27			
Aldrington	d	08 59									09 29			
Portslade	d	09 01				09 10				09 25	09 31			
Fishersgate	d	09 03									09 33			
Southwick	d	09 05				09 13					09 35			
Shoreham-by-Sea	d	09 09			09 13	09 17				09 30	09 39			
Lancing	d	09 13				09 21					09 43			
East Worthing	d	09 16									09 46			
Worthing 4	a	09 18			09 22	09 25				09 36	09 48			
	d	09 19			09 22	09 25				09 37	09 49			
West Worthing	d	09a21								09 39	09a51			
Durrington-on-Sea	d									09 41				
Goring-by-Sea	d									09 44				
Angmering 3	d					09 34				09 48				
Littlehampton 4	a									09 57				
	d													09 54
Ford 4	d			09 33										09 58
Bognor Regis 4	d													
Barnham	a		09 26	09 38	09 40	09 44						09 56		10 02
	d		09 27	09 38	09 41	09 45		09 52				09 57		10 03
Bognor Regis 4	a			09 45				09 58						
Chichester 4	a		09 34		09 48	09 52						10 04		10 10
	d		09 35		09 49	09 53						10 05		10 11
Fishbourne (Sussex)	d													10 14
Bosham	d													10 17
Nutbourne	d													10 20
Southbourne	d					10 00						10 12		10 23
Emsworth	d					10 03						10 15		10 26
Warblington	d													10 29
Havant	d		09 46		10 00	10 07						10 19		10 32
Bedhampton	a											10 29		10 34
Hilsea	a		09 54			10 16						10 36		10 43
Fratton	a		09 58			10 19						10 40		10 47
Portsmouth & Southsea	a		10 02			10 23						10 44		10 50
Portsmouth Harbour	a													
Cosham	a				10 06							10 26		
Portchester	a											10 30		
Fareham	a				10 15							10 35		
Swanwick	a											10 42		
Southampton Central	a				10 40							10 59		

For general notes see front of timetable
For details of catering facilities see
Directory of Train Operators

A To Great Malvern (Table 71)
b Change at East Croydon and Brighton

For complete service between Three Bridges and Horsham see Table 186

Table 188

London, Gatwick Airport & Brighton → Sussex Coast, Portsmouth and Southampton

Saturdays

Network Diagram - see first page of Table 186

Station		SN 1	SN 1	SN 1	SN 1	SN 1	SN 1	SN 1		SN 1		SN 1	SN 1	SN 1	SN 1	SN 1		SN 1	SN 1	SN 1	SN 1	SN 1	SN 1		SN 1	
London Victoria 15 ⊖	d		08 36			08 47		09 02		09 06				09 17		09 32				09 36			09 47			
Clapham Junction 10	d		08 42			08 53		09 08		09 12				09 23		09 38				09 42			09 53			
London Bridge 4 ⊖	d		08 26			08 41	08 41	08 56		08 56				09 11	09 11	09 26				09 26			09 41		09 41	
East Croydon	d		08 52			09 03	08 54	09 18		09 22				09 33	09 24	09 48				09 52			10 03		09 54	
Redhill 5	d							09 30								10 00										
Horley	d							09 36								09 51										
Gatwick Airport 10 ✈	d		08 56	08 58		09 19	09 11	09 40		09 26				09 49	09 41	10 09				09 56	09 58		10 19		10 11	
Three Bridges 4	a							09 44								10 14										
	d			09 03		09 15	09 15	09 45						09 45	09 45	10 14					10 03		10 15		10 15	
Crawley	d							09 48								10 18										
Horsham 4	a							09 56								10 26										
		←																	←							
	d	09 35						10 00	10 05							10 30	10 35 →		10 35							
Christs Hospital	d	09 38																	10 38							
Billingshurst	d	09 44							10 14										10 44							
Pulborough	d	09 51							10 20										10 51							
Amberley	d	09 57																	10 57							
Arundel	d	10 02							10 29										11 02							
Haywards Heath 3	d		09 10	09 17		09 37	09 27			09 40				10 04	09 55					10 10	10 17		10 37		10 27	
Burgess Hill	d			09 23			09 33							10 09	10 01						10 23				10 33	
Brighton 10	d		09 33	09 44			09 53			10 03		10 14			10 23					10 33	10 44				10 53	
Hove 2	d		09 37	09a47		09 52	09 57			10 07		10a17		10 22	10 27					10 37	10a47		10 52		10 57	
Aldrington	d						09 59								10 29										10 59	
Portslade	d		09 40				10 01			10 10				10 25	10 31					10 40					11 01	
Fishersgate	d						10 03								10 33										11 03	
Southwick	d		09 43				10 05			10 13					10 35					10 43					11 05	
Shoreham-by-Sea	d		09 46			09 58	10 09			10 16				10 30	10 39					10 46			10 58		11 09	
Lancing	d		09 50			10 02	10 13			10 20					10 43					10 50			11 02		11 13	
East Worthing	d						10 16								10 46										11 16	
Worthing 4	a		09 54			10 06	10 18			10 24				10 36	10 48					10 54			11 06		11 18	
	d		09 55			10 07	10 19			10 25				10 37	10 49					10 55			11 07		11 19	
West Worthing	d		09 57			10 09	10a21							10 39	10a51					10 57			11 09		11a21	
Durrington-on-Sea	d		09 59			10 11								10 41						10 59			11 11			
Goring-by-Sea	d		10 02			10 14								10 44						11 02			11 14			
Angmering 3	d		10 06			10 18				10 31				10 48						11 06			11 18			
Littlehampton 4	a					10 27								10 57									11 27			
	d				10 11													10 54				11 11				
Ford 4	d	10 07	10 12		10 16				10 34									10 58	11 07	11 12		11 16				
Bognor Regis 4	d																									
Barnham	a	10 11	10 16		10 20			10 26	10 39	10 42						10 56		11 02	11 11	11 16		11 20				
	d	10 12	10 17		10 22			10 27	10 39	10 42			10 52			10 57		11 03	11 12	11 17		11 22				
Bognor Regis 4	a	10 18			10 28				10 46				10 58						11 18			11 28				
Chichester 4	a		10 24					10 34		10 50						11 04		11 10		11 24						
	d		10 25					10 35		10 50						11 05		11 11		11 25						
Fishbourne (Sussex)	d																	11 14								
Bosham	d																	11 17								
Nutbourne	d																	11 20								
Southbourne	d																	11 23								
Emsworth	d		10 33							10 57						11 12		11 26		11 33						
Warblington	d									11 00						11 15		11 29								
Havant	d		10 37					10 46		11 05						11 19		11 32		11 37						
Bedhampton	a																	11 34								
Hilsea	a															*11 29*										
Fratton	a							10 54		11 13						*11 36*		11 42								
Portsmouth & Southsea	a							10 58		11 17						*11 40*		11 46								
Portsmouth Harbour	a							11 02		11 21						*11 44*		11 50								
Cosham	a		10 45													11 26				11 45						
Portchester	a															11 30										
Fareham	a		10 53													11 35				11 53						
Swanwick	a		11 00													11 42				12 00						
Southampton Central	a		11 19													11 59				12 19						

For general notes see front of timetable
For details of catering facilities see Directory of Train Operators

For complete service between Three Bridges and Horsham see Table 186

London, Gatwick Airport & Brighton → Sussex Coast, Portsmouth and Southampton

Network Diagram - see first page of Table 186

		SN 1 A ⌶		SN 1	SN 1	SN 1	SN 1	SN 1	SN 1		SN 1	SN 1	SN 1	
London Victoria [15] ⊖	d	10 02		*10 06*			10 17		10 32				*10 36*	
Clapham Junction [10]	d	10 08		*10 12*			10 23		10 38				*10 42*	
London Bridge [4] ⊖	d	*09 56*		*09 56*			*10 11*	*10 11*	*10 26*				*10 26*	
East Croydon	d	10 18		*10 22*			10 33	*10 24*	10 48				*10 52*	
Redhill [5]	d	10 30							11 00					
Horley	d	10 36							*10 51*					
Gatwick Airport [10] ✈	d	10 40		*10 26*			10 49	*10 41*	11 09				*10 56*	
Three Bridges [4]	a	10 44							11 14					
	d	10 45					*10 45*	*10 45*	11 14					
Crawley	d	10 48							11 18					
Horsham [4]	a	10 56							11 26					
	d	11 00	11 05						11 30	11 35 →		← 11 35		
Christs Hospital	d											11 38		
Billingshurst	d		11 14									11 44		
Pulborough	d		11 20									11 51		
Amberley	d											11 57		
Arundel	d		11 29									12 02		
Haywards Heath [3]	d			*10 40*			11 04	*10 55*					*11 10*	
Burgess Hill	d						11 09	*11 01*						
Brighton [10]	d			11 03	11 14			11 23					11 33	
Hove [2]	d			11 07	11a17		11 22	11 27					11 37	
Aldrington	d							11 29						
Portslade	d			11 10			11 25	11 31					11 40	
Fishersgate	d							11 33						
Southwick	d			11 13				11 35					11 43	
Shoreham-by-Sea	d			11 16			11 30	11 39					11 46	
Lancing	d			11 20				11 43					11 50	
East Worthing	d							11 46						
Worthing [4]	a			11 24			11 36	11 48					11 54	
	d			11 25			11 37	11 49					11 55	
West Worthing	d						11 39	11a51					11 57	
Durrington-on-Sea	d						11 41						11 59	
Goring-by-Sea	d						11 44						12 02	
Angmering [3]	d			11 31			11 48						12 06	
Littlehampton [4]	a						11 57							
	d										11 54			
Ford [4]	d		11 34								11 58	12 07	12 12	
Bognor Regis [4]	d													
Barnham	a	11 26	11 39	11 42					11 56		12 02	12 11	12 16	
	d	11 27	11 39	11 42		11 52			11 57		12 03	12 12	12 17	
Bognor Regis [4]	a		11 46			11 58						12 18		
Chichester [4]	a	11 34		11 50					12 04		12 10		12 24	
	d	11 35		11 50					12 05		12 11		12 25	
Fishbourne (Sussex)	d										12 14			
Bosham	d										12 17			
Nutbourne	d										12 20			
Southbourne	d			11 57					12 12		12 23			
Emsworth	d			12 00					12 15		12 26		12 33	
Warblington	d										12 29			
Havant	d	11 46		12 05					12 19		12 32		12 37	
Bedhampton	a								*12 29*		12 34			
Hilsea	a								*12 36*		12 42			
Fratton	a	11 54		12 13					*12 40*		12 46			
Portsmouth & Southsea	a	11 58		12 17					*12 44*		12 50			
Portsmouth Harbour	a	12 02		12 21										
Cosham	a								12 26				12 45	
Portchester	a								12 30					
Fareham	a								12 35				12 53	
Swanwick	a								12 42				13 00	
Southampton Central	a								12 59				13 19	

		SN 1	SN 1	SN 1	SN 1	SN 1 A ⌶		SN 1	SN 1	SN 1	SN 1	SN 1	
London Victoria [15] ⊖	d			10 47		11 02		*11 06*			11 17		
Clapham Junction [10]	d			10 53		11 08		*11 12*			11 23		
London Bridge [4] ⊖	d			*10 41*	*10 41*	*10 56*		*10 56*			*11 11*	*11 11*	
East Croydon	d			11 03	*10 54*	11 18		*11 22*			11 33	*11 24*	
Redhill [5]	d					11 30							
Horley	d					11 36							
Gatwick Airport [10] ✈	d	*10 58*		11 19	*11 11*	11 40		*11 26*			11 49	*11 41*	
Three Bridges [4]	a					11 44							
	d	*11 03*		*11 15*	*11 15*	11 45					*11 45*	*11 45*	
Crawley	d					11 48							
Horsham [4]	a					11 56							
	d					12 00	12 05						
Christs Hospital	d												
Billingshurst	d						12 14						
Pulborough	d						12 20						
Amberley	d												
Arundel	d						12 29						
Haywards Heath [3]	d	*11 17*		11 37	*11 27*			*11 40*			12 04	*11 55*	
Burgess Hill	d	*11 23*			*11 33*						12 09	*12 01*	
Brighton [10]	d	11 44			11 53			12 03	12 14			12 23	
Hove [2]	d	11a47		11 52	11 57			12 07	12a17		12 22	12 27	
Aldrington	d				11 59							12 29	
Portslade	d				12 01			12 10			12 25	12 31	
Fishersgate	d				12 03							12 33	
Southwick	d				12 05			12 13				12 35	
Shoreham-by-Sea	d			11 58	12 09			12 16			12 30	12 39	
Lancing	d			12 02	12 13			12 20				12 43	
East Worthing	d				12 16							12 46	
Worthing [4]	a			12 06	12 18			12 24			12 36	12 48	
	d			12 07	12 19			12 25			12 37	12 49	
West Worthing	d			12 09	12a21						12 39	12a51	
Durrington-on-Sea	d			12 11							12 41		
Goring-by-Sea	d			12 14							12 44		
Angmering [3]	d			12 18				12 31			12 48		
Littlehampton [4]	a			12 27							12 57		
	d		12 11										
Ford [4]	d		12 16				12 34						
Bognor Regis [4]	d												
Barnham	a		12 20			12 26	12 39	12 42					
	d		12 22			12 27	12 39	12 42		12 52			
Bognor Regis [4]	a		12 28				12 46			12 58			
Chichester [4]	a					12 34		12 50					
	d					12 35		12 50					
Fishbourne (Sussex)	d												
Bosham	d												
Nutbourne	d												
Southbourne	d							12 57					
Emsworth	d							13 00					
Warblington	d												
Havant	d					12 46		13 05					
Bedhampton	a												
Hilsea	a												
Fratton	a					12 54		13 13					
Portsmouth & Southsea	a					12 58		13 17					
Portsmouth Harbour	a					13 02		13 21					
Cosham	a												
Portchester	a												
Fareham	a												
Swanwick	a												
Southampton Central	a												

For general notes see front of timetable
For details of catering facilities see Directory of Train Operators

A ⌶ to Bognor Regis

For complete service between Three Bridges and Horsham see Table 186

Table 188

Saturdays

London, Gatwick Airport & Brighton → Sussex Coast, Portsmouth and Southampton

Network Diagram - see first page of Table 186

		SN 1		SN 1		SN 1	SN 1	SN 1	SN 1	SN 1	SN 1	SN 1 A		SN 1	SN 1	SN 1	SN 1		SN 1	SN 1		SN 1	SN 1	SN 1	SN 1	SN 1
London Victoria 15 ⊖	d	11 32					*11 36*			11 47		12 02		*12 06*			12 17			12 32				*12 36*		
Clapham Junction 10	d	11 38					*11 42*			11 53		12 08		*12 12*			12 23			12 38				*12 42*		
London Bridge 4 ⊖	d	*11 26*					*11 26*			*11 41*	*11 41*	*11 56*		*11 56*			*12 11*		*12 11*	*12 26*				*12 26*		
East Croydon	d	11 48					*11 52*			12 03	*11 54*	12 18		*12 22*			12 33		*12 24*	12 48				*12 52*		
Redhill 5	d	12 00										12 30								13 00						
Horley	d	*11 51*										12 36								*12 51*						
Gatwick Airport 10 ✈	d	12 09					*11 56*	*11 58*		12 19	*12 11*	12 40		*12 26*			12 49		*12 41*	13 09				*12 56*	12 58	
Three Bridges 4	a	12 14										12 44								13 14						
	d	12 14						*12 03*		*12 15*	*12 15*	12 45					*12 45*		*12 45*	13 14					*13 03*	
Crawley	d	12 18										12 48								13 18						
Horsham 4	a	12 26										12 56								13 26						
	d	12 30	12 35 →			← 12 35						13 00	13 05							13 30	13 35 →		← 13 35			
Christs Hospital	d					12 38																	13 38			
Billingshurst	d					12 44																	13 44			
Pulborough	d					12 51							13 14										13 51			
Amberley	d					12 57							13 20										13 57			
Arundel	d					13 02							13 29										14 02			
Haywards Heath 3	d						*12 10*	*12 17*		12 37	*12 27*			*12 40*			13 04		*12 55*					*13 10*	*13 17*	
Burgess Hill	d							*12 23*			*12 33*						13 09		*13 01*						*13 23*	
Brighton 10	d						12 33	12 44			12 53			13 03	13 14				13 23					13 33	13 44	
Hove 2	d						12 37	12a47		12 52	12 57			13 07	13a17		13 22		13 27					13 37	13a47	
Aldrington	d										12 59								13 29							
Portslade	d						12 40				13 01			13 10			13 25		13 31					13 40		
Fishersgate	d										13 03								13 33							
Southwick	d						12 43				13 05			13 13					13 35					13 43		
Shoreham-by-Sea	d						12 46			12 58	13 09			13 16			13 30		13 39					13 46		
Lancing	d						12 50			13 02	13 13			13 20					13 43					13 50		
East Worthing	d										13 16								13 46							
Worthing 4	a						12 54			13 06	13 18			13 24			13 36		13 48					13 54		
	d						12 55			13 07	13 19			13 25			13 37		13 49					13 55		
West Worthing	d						12 57			13 09	13a21						13 39		13a51					13 57		
Durrington-on-Sea	d						12 59			13 11							13 41							13 59		
Goring-by-Sea	d						13 02			13 14							13 44							14 02		
Angmering 3	d						13 06			13 18				13 31			13 48							14 06		
Littlehampton 4	a									13 27							13 57									
	d			12 54					13 11													13 54				14 11
Ford 4	d			12 58		13 07	13 12		13 16				13 34									13 58	14 07	14 12		14 16
Bognor Regis 4	d																									
Barnham	a	12 56		13 02		13 11	13 16		13 20			13 26	13 39	13 42						13 56		14 02	14 11	14 16		14 20
	d	12 57		13 03		13 12	13 17		13 22			13 27	13 39	13 42		13 52				13 57		14 03	14 12	14 17		14 22
Bognor Regis 4	a					13 18			13 28				13 46			13 58							14 18			14 28
Chichester 4	a	13 04		13 10			13 24					13 34		13 50						14 04		14 10		14 24		
	d	13 05		13 11			13 25					13 35		13 50						14 05		14 11		14 25		
Fishbourne (Sussex)	d			13 14																		14 14				
Bosham	d			13 17																		14 17				
Nutbourne	d			13 20																		14 20				
Southbourne	d	13 12		13 23										13 57						14 12		14 23				
Emsworth	d	13 15		13 26			13 33							14 00						14 15		14 26		14 33		
Warblington	d			13 29																		14 29				
Havant	d	13 19		13 32			13 37					13 46		14 05						14 19		14 32		14 37		
Bedhampton	a	*13 29*		13 34																*14 29*		14 34				
Hilsea	a	*13 36*		13 42																*14 36*		14 42				
Fratton	a	*13 40*		13 46								13 54		14 13						*14 40*		14 46				
Portsmouth & Southsea	a	*13 44*		13 50								13 58		14 17						*14 44*		14 50				
Portsmouth Harbour	a											14 02		14 21												
Cosham	a	13 26					13 45													14 26				14 45		
Portchester	a	13 30																		14 30						
Fareham	a	13 35					13 53													14 35				14 53		
Swanwick	a	13 42					14 00													14 42				15 00		
Southampton Central	a	13 59					14 19													14 59				15 19		

For general notes see front of timetable
For details of catering facilities see Directory of Train Operators

A to Bognor Regis

For complete service between Three Bridges and Horsham see Table 186

London, Gatwick Airport & Brighton → Sussex Coast, Portsmouth and Southampton

Network Diagram - see first page of Table 186

		SN 1	SN 1	SN 1		SN 1	SN 1		SN 1	SN 1	SN 1	SN 1		SN 1	SN 1	SN 1	SN 1	SN 1	SN 1	SN 1		SN 1		SN 1	SN 1	SN 1
				A ⊼																		A ⊼				
London Victoria 15 ⊖	d	12 47		13 02		13 06				13 17		13 32				13 36			13 47			14 02		14 06		
Clapham Junction 10	d	12 53		13 08		13 12				13 23		13 38				13 42			13 53			14 08		14 12		
London Bridge 4 ⊖	d	12 41	12 41	12 56		12 56				13 11	13 11	13 26				13 26			13 41	13 41		13 56		13 56		
East Croydon	d	13 03	12 54	13 18		13 22				13 33	13 24	13 48				13 52			14 03	13 54		14 18		14 22		
Redhill 5	d			13 30								14 00										14 30				
Horley	d			13 36								13 51										14 36				
Gatwick Airport 10 ✈	d	13 19	13 11	13 40		13 26				13 49	13 41	14 09				13 56	13 58		14 19	14 11		14 40		14 26		
Three Bridges 4	a			13 44								14 14										14 44				
	d	13 15	13 15	13 45						13 45	13 45	14 14					14 03		14 15	14 15		14 45				
Crawley	d			13 48								14 18										14 48				
Horsham 4	a			13 56								14 26										14 56				
	d			14 00	14 05							14 30	14 35 →		← 14 35							15 00	15 05			
Christs Hospital	d														14 38											
Billingshurst	d				14 14										14 44								15 14			
Pulborough	d				14 20										14 51								15 20			
Amberley	d														14 57											
Arundel	d				14 29										15 02								15 29			
Haywards Heath 3	d	13 37	13 27			13 40				14 04	13 55					14 10	14 17		14 37	14 27				14 40		
Burgess Hill	d		13 33							14 09	14 01						14 23			14 33						
Brighton 10	d		13 53			14 03	14 14				14 23					14 33	14 44			14 53				15 03	15 14	
Hove 2	d	13 52	13 57			14 07	14a17			14 22	14 27					14 37	14a47		14 52	14 57				15 07	15a17	
Aldrington	d		13 59								14 29									14 59						
Portslade	d		14 01			14 10				14 25	14 31					14 40				15 01				15 10		
Fishersgate	d		14 03								14 33									15 03						
Southwick	d		14 05			14 13					14 35					14 43				15 05				15 13		
Shoreham-by-Sea	d	13 58	14 09			14 16				14 30	14 39					14 46			14 58	15 09				15 16		
Lancing	d	14 02	14 13			14 20					14 43					14 50			15 02	15 13				15 20		
East Worthing	d		14 16								14 46									15 16						
Worthing 4	a	14 06	14 18			14 24				14 36	14 48					14 54			15 06	15 18				15 24		
	d	14 07	14 19			14 25				14 37	14 49					14 55			15 07	15 19				15 25		
West Worthing	d	14 09	14a21							14 39	14a51					14 57			15 09	15a21						
Durrington-on-Sea	d	14 11								14 41						14 59			15 11							
Goring-by-Sea	d	14 14								14 44						15 02			15 14							
Angmering 3	d	14 18				14 31				14 48						15 06			15 18					15 31		
Littlehampton 4	a	14 27								14 57									15 27							
	d													14 54				15 11								
Ford 4	d				14 34									14 58	15 07	15 12		15 16					15 34			
Bognor Regis 4	d																									
Barnham	a			14 26	14 39	14 42						14 56		15 02	15 11	15 16		15 20				15 26	15 39	15 42		
	d			14 27	14 39	14 42			14 52			14 57		15 03	15 12	15 17		15 22				15 27	15 39	15 42		15 52
Bognor Regis 4	a				14 46				14 58						15 18			15 28					15 46			15 58
Chichester 4	a			14 34		14 50						15 04		15 10		15 24						15 34		15 50		
	d			14 35		14 50						15 05		15 11		15 25						15 35		15 50		
Fishbourne (Sussex)	d													15 14												
Bosham	d													15 17												
Nutbourne	d													15 20												
Southbourne	d					14 57						15 12		15 23										15 57		
Emsworth	d					15 00						15 15		15 26		15 33								16 00		
Warblington	d													15 29												
Havant	d			14 46		15 05						15 19		15 32		15 37						15 46		16 05		
Bedhampton	a											15 29		15 34												
Hilsea	a											15 36		15 42												
Fratton	a			14 54		15 13						15 40		15 46								15 54		16 13		
Portsmouth & Southsea	a			14 58		15 17						15 44		15 50								15 58		16 17		
Portsmouth Harbour	a			15 02		15 21																16 02		16 21		
Cosham	a											15 26				15 45										
Portchester	a											15 30														
Fareham	a											15 35				15 53										
Swanwick	a											15 42				16 00										
Southampton Central	a											15 59				16 19										

For general notes see front of timetable
For details of catering facilities see
Directory of Train Operators

A ⊼ to Bognor Regis

For complete service between Three Bridges and Horsham see Table 186

Table 188

Saturdays

London, Gatwick Airport & Brighton → Sussex Coast, Portsmouth and Southampton

Network Diagram - see first page of Table 186

		SN 1	SN 1	SN 1		SN 1	SN 1	SN 1	SN 1	SN 1		SN 1	SN 1	SN 1		SN 1	SN 1	SN 1	SN 1	SN 1	SN 1		SN 1		SN 1	SN 1
														A												
London Victoria [15] ⊖	d	14 17		14 32				14 36				14 47		15 02		15 06			15 17		15 32					15 36
Clapham Junction [10]	d	14 23		14 38				14 42				14 53		15 08		15 12			15 23		15 38					15 42
London Bridge [4] ⊖	d	14 11	14 11	14 26				14 26				14 41	14 41	14 56		14 56			15 11	15 11	15 26					15 26
East Croydon	d	14 33	14 24	14 48				14 52				15 03	14 54	15 18		15 22			15 33	15 24	15 48					15 52
Redhill [5]	d			15 00										15 30							16 00					
Horley	d			14 51										15 36							15 51					
Gatwick Airport [10] ✈	d	14 49	14 41	15 09				14 56	14 58			15 19	15 11	15 40		15 26			15 49	15 41	16 09					15 56
Three Bridges [4]	a			15 14										15 44							16 14					
	d	14 45	14 45	15 14					15 03			15 15	15 15	15 45					15 45	15 45	16 14					
Crawley	d			15 18										15 48							16 18					
Horsham [4]	a			15 26										15 56							16 26					
	d			15 30	15 35 →		← 15 35							16 00	16 05						16 30	16 35 →			← 16 35	
Christs Hospital	d						15 38																		16 38	
Billingshurst	d						15 44								16 14										16 44	
Pulborough	d						15 51								16 20										16 51	
Amberley	d						15 57																		16 57	
Arundel	d						16 02								16 29										17 02	
Haywards Heath [3]	d	15 04	14 55					15 10	15 17			15 37	15 27			15 40			16 04	15 55						16 10
Burgess Hill	d	15 09	15 01						15 23				15 33						16 09	16 01						
Brighton [10]	d		15 23					15 33	15 44				15 53			16 03	16 14			16 23						16 33
Hove [2]	d	15 22	15 27					15 37	15a47			15 52	15 57			16 07	16a17		16 22	16 27						16 37
Aldrington	d		15 29										15 59							16 29						
Portslade	d	15 25	15 31					15 40					16 01			16 10			16 25	16 31						16 40
Fishersgate	d		15 33										16 03							16 33						
Southwick	d		15 35					15 43					16 05			16 13				16 35						16 43
Shoreham-by-Sea	d	15 30	15 39					15 46				15 58	16 09			16 16			16 30	16 39						16 46
Lancing	d		15 43					15 50				16 02	16 13			16 20				16 43						16 50
East Worthing	d		15 46										16 16							16 46						
Worthing [4]	a	15 36	15 48					15 54				16 06	16 18			16 24			16 36	16 48						16 54
	d	15 37	15 49					15 55				16 07	16 19			16 25			16 37	16 49						16 55
West Worthing	d	15 39	15a51					15 57				16 09	16a21						16 39	16a51						16 57
Durrington-on-Sea	d	15 41						15 59				16 11							16 41							16 59
Goring-by-Sea	d	15 44						16 02				16 14							16 44							17 02
Angmering [3]	d	15 48						16 06				16 18				16 31			16 48							17 06
Littlehampton [4]	a	15 58										16 27							16 57							
	d					15 54				16 11													16 54			
Ford [4]	d					15 58	16 07	16 12		16 16					16 34								16 58		17 07	17 12
Bognor Regis [4]	d																									
Barnham	a			15 56		16 02	16 11	16 16		16 20				16 26	16 39	16 42					16 56		17 02		17 11	17 16
	d			15 57		16 03	16 12	16 17		16 22				16 27	16 39	16 42		16 52			16 57		17 03		17 12	17 17
Bognor Regis [4]	a						16 18			16 28					16 46			16 58							17 18	
Chichester [4]	a			16 04		16 10		16 24						16 34		16 50					17 04		17 10			17 24
	d			16 05		16 11		16 25						16 35		16 50					17 05		17 11			17 25
Fishbourne (Sussex)	d					16 14																	17 14			
Bosham	d					16 17																	17 17			
Nutbourne	d					16 20																	17 20			
Southbourne	d			16 12		16 23										16 57					17 12		17 23			
Emsworth	d			16 15		16 26		16 33								17 00					17 15		17 26			17 33
Warblington	d					16 29																	17 29			
Havant	d			16 19		16 32		16 37						16 46		17 05					17 19		17 32			17 37
Bedhampton	a			16 29		16 34															17 29		17 34			
Hilsea	a			16 36		16 42															17 36		17 42			
Fratton	a			16 40		16 46								16 54		17 13					17 40		17 46			
Portsmouth & Southsea	a			16 44		16 50								16 58		17 17					17 44		17 50			
Portsmouth Harbour	a													17 02		17 21										
Cosham	a			16 26				16 45													17 26					17 45
Portchester	a			16 30																	17 30					
Fareham	a			16 35				16 53													17 35					17 53
Swanwick	a			16 42				17 00													17 42					18 00
Southampton Central	a			16 59				17 19													17 59					18 19

For general notes see front of timetable
For details of catering facilities see Directory of Train Operators

A to Bognor Regis

For complete service between Three Bridges and Horsham see Table 186

Table 188

Saturdays

London, Gatwick Airport & Brighton → Sussex Coast, Portsmouth and Southampton

Network Diagram - see first page of Table 186

		SN 1	SN 1	SN 1	SN 1	SN 1 A ⚯		GW B	SN 1 ⚯	SN 1	SN 1	SN 1	SN 1		SN 1	SN 1		SN 1	SN 1	SN 1	SN 1	SN 1	SN 1	SN 1	SN 1 C ⚯	
London Victoria 15 ⊖	d			15 47		16 02		15b47		16 06			16 17			16 32				16 36			16 47		17 02	
Clapham Junction 10	d			15 53		16 08		15b53		16 12			16 23			16 38				16 42			16 53		17 08	
London Bridge 4 ⊖	d			15 41	15 41	15 56		15 56		15 56			16 11		16 11	16 26				16 26			16 41	16 41	16 56	
East Croydon	d			16 03	15 54	16 18		16 09		16 22			16 33		16 24	16 48				16 52			17 03	16 54	17 18	
Redhill 5	d					16 30										17 00									17 30	
Horley	d					16 36										16 51									17 36	
Gatwick Airport 10 ✈	d	15 58		16 19	16 11	16 40		16 26		16 26			16 49		16 41	17 09				16 56	16 58		17 19	17 11	17 40	
Three Bridges 4	a					16 44										17 14									17 44	
	d	16 03		16 15	16 15	16 45							16 45		16 45	17 14					17 03		17 15	17 15	17 45	
Crawley	d					16 48										17 18									17 48	
Horsham 4	a					16 56										17 26									17 56	
	d					17 00	17 05 →		← 17 05							17 30	17 35 →		← 17 35						18 00	18 05
Christs Hospital	d																		17 38							
Billingshurst	d								17 14										17 44							18 14
Pulborough	d								17 20										17 51							18 20
Amberley	d																		17 57							
Arundel	d								17 29										18 02							18 29
Haywards Heath 3	d	16 17		16 37	16 27			16 40		16 40			17 04		16 55					17 10	17 17		17 37	17 27		
Burgess Hill	d	16 23			16 33								17 09		17 01						17 23			17 33		
Brighton 10	d	16 44			16 53			17 00		17 03	17 14				17 23					17 33	17 44			17 53		
Hove 2	d	16a47		16 52	16 57			17 04		17 07	17a17		17 22		17 27					17 37	17a47		17 52	17 57		
Aldrington	d				16 59										17 29									17 59		
Portslade	d				17 01					17 10			17 25		17 31					17 40				18 01		
Fishersgate	d				17 03										17 33									18 03		
Southwick	d				17 05					17 13					17 35					17 43				18 05		
Shoreham-by-Sea	d			16 58	17 09			17 13		17 17			17 30		17 39					17 46			17 58	18 09		
Lancing	d			17 02	17 13					17 21					17 43					17 50			18 02	18 13		
East Worthing	d				17 16										17 46									18 16		
Worthing 4	a			17 06	17 18			17 22		17 25			17 36		17 48					17 54			18 06	18 18		
	d			17 07	17 19			17 22		17 25			17 37		17 49					17 55			18 07	18 19		
West Worthing	d			17 09	17a21								17 39		17a51					17 57			18 09	18a21		
Durrington-on-Sea	d			17 11									17 41							17 59			18 11			
Goring-by-Sea	d			17 14									17 44							18 02			18 14			
Angmering 3	d			17 18						17 34			17 48							18 06			18 18			
Littlehampton 4	a			17 27									17 57										18 27			
	d		17 11															17 54				18 11				
Ford 4	d		17 16						17 36									17 58	18 07	18 12		18 16				18 34
Bognor Regis 4	d																									
Barnham	a		17 20			17 26		17 37	17 40	17 43						17 56		18 02	18 11	18 16		18 20			18 26	18 39
	d		17 22			17 27		17 38	17 41	17 44		17 52				17 57		18 03	18 12	18 17		18 22			18 27	18 39
Bognor Regis 4	a		17 28						17 47			17 58							18 18			18 28				18 46
Chichester 4	a					17 34		17 45		17 51						18 04		18 10		18 24					18 34	
	d					17 35		17 46		17 52						18 05		18 11		18 25					18 35	
Fishbourne (Sussex)	d																	18 14								
Bosham	d																	18 17								
Nutbourne	d																	18 20								
Southbourne	d									17 59						18 12		18 23								
Emsworth	d									18 02						18 15		18 26		18 33						
Warblington	d																	18 29								
Havant	d					17 46		18 00		18 06						18 19		18 32		18 37					18 46	
Bedhampton	a															18 29		18 34								
Hilsea	a															18 36		18 42								
Fratton	a					17 54				18 15						18 40		18 46							18 54	
Portsmouth & Southsea	a					17 58				18 18						18 44		18 50							18 58	
Portsmouth Harbour	a					18 02				18 22															19 02	
Cosham	a							18 06								18 26				18 45						
Portchester	a															18 30										
Fareham	a							18 14								18 35				18 53						
Swanwick	a															18 42				19 00						
Southampton Central	a							18 43								18 59				19 19						

For general notes see front of timetable
For details of catering facilities see Directory of Train Operators

A ⚯ to Horsham
B To Cheltenham Spa (Table 57)
C ⚯ to Bognor Regis
b Change at East Croydon and Brighton

For complete service between Three Bridges and Horsham see Table 186

Table 188

Saturdays

London, Gatwick Airport & Brighton → Sussex Coast, Portsmouth and Southampton

Network Diagram - see first page of Table 186

		SN 1	SN 1		SN 1	SN 1	SN 1		SN 1	SN 1	SN 1	SN 1	SN 1	SN 1	SN 1	SN 1 A [trolley]			SN 1	SN 1	SN 1	SN 1	SN 1		SN 1	SN 1
London Victoria 15 ⊖	d	17 06				17 17	17 32					17 36			17 47	18 02			18 06		18 17		18 32		18b17	18 36
Clapham Junction 10	d	17 12				17 23	17 38					17 42			17 53	18 08			18 12		18 23		18 38		18b23	18 42
London Bridge 4 ⊖	d	16 56				17 11	17 26				17 11	17 26			17 41	17 56			17 56		18 11		18 26		18 26	
East Croydon	d	17 22				17 33	17 48				17 24	17 52			18 03	18 18			18 22		18 33		18 48		18 39	18 52
Redhill 5	d						18 00									18 30							19 00			
Horley	d						17 51									18 36							18 51			
Gatwick Airport 10 ✈	d	17 26				17 49	18 09				17 41	17 56	17 58		18 19	18 40			18 26		18 49		19 09		18 56	18 58
Three Bridges 4	a						18 14									18 44							19 14			
	d					17 45	18 14				17 45		18 03		18 15	18 45			18 15		18 45		19 14		18 45	19 03
Crawley	d						18 18									18 48							19 18			
Horsham 4	a						18 26			←						18 56							19 26			
	d						18 30	18 35 →		18 35						19 00	19 05						19 30	19 35		
Christs Hospital	d									18 38														19 38		
Billingshurst	d									18 44							19 14							19 44		
Pulborough	d									18 51							19 20							19 51		
Amberley	d									18 57														19 57		
Arundel	d									19 02							19 29							20 02		
Haywards Heath 3	d	17 40				18 04					17 55	18 10	18 17		18 37				18 40		19 04				19 10	19 17
Burgess Hill	d					18 09					18 01		18 23						18 33		19 09				19 01	19 23
Brighton 10	d	18 03	18 14								18 23	18 33	18 44						19 03	19 14					19 29	19 44
Hove 2	d	18 07	18a17			18 22					18 27	18 37	18a47		18 52				19 07	19a17	19 22				19 33	19a47
Aldrington	d										18 29								19 09						19 35	
Portslade	d	18 10				18 25					18 31	18 40			18 55				19 11		19 25				19 37	
Fishersgate	d										18 33								19 13						19 39	
Southwick	d	18 13									18 35	18 43							19 15						19 41	
Shoreham-by-Sea	d	18 16				18 30					18 39	18 46			19 00				19 19		19 30				19 45	
Lancing	d	18 20									18 43	18 50			19 04				19 23		19 34				19 49	
East Worthing	d										18 46								19 26						19 52	
Worthing 4	a	18 24				18 36					18 48	18 54			19 08				19 28		19 38				19 54	
	d	18 25				18 37					18 49	18 55			19 08				19 29		19 38				19 55	
West Worthing	d					18 39					18 51	18 57			19 10				19 31		19 40				19 57	
Durrington-on-Sea	d					18 41					18 53	18 59			19 13				19 33		19 43				19 59	
Goring-by-Sea	d					18 44					18 56	19 02			19 15				19 36		19 45				20 02	
Angmering 3	d	18 31				18 48					19 00	19 06			19 19				19 40		19 49				20 06	
Littlehampton 4	a					18 57					19 11				19 28						19 58					
	d								18 54					19 11												
Ford 4	d								18 58	19 07		19 12		19 16			19 34		19 46					20 07	20 12	
Bognor Regis 4	d																									
Barnham	a	18 42					18 56		19 02	19 11		19 16		19 20		19 26	19 39		19 50				19 56	20 11	20 16	
	d	18 42			18 52		18 57		19 03	19 12		19 17		19 22		19 27	19 39		19 51			19 52	19 57	20 12	20 17	
Bognor Regis 4	a				18 58					19 18				19 28			19 46					19 58		20 18		
Chichester 4	a	18 50					19 04		19 10			19 24				19 34			19 58				20 04		20 24	
	d	18 50					19 05		19 11			19 25				19 35			19 59				20 05		20 25	
Fishbourne (Sussex)	d								19 14														20 08			
Bosham	d								19 17														20 11			
Nutbourne	d								19 20														20 14			
Southbourne	d	18 57					19 12		19 23														20 17			
Emsworth	d	19 00					19 15		19 26			19 33											20 20		20 33	
Warblington	d								19 29														20 23			
Havant	d	19 05					19 19		19 32			19 37				19 46			20 10				20 26		20 37	
Bedhampton	a						19 29		19 34														20 32			
Hilsea	a						19 36		19 42														20 41			
Fratton	a	19 13					19 40		19 46							19 54			20 18				20 45			
Portsmouth & Southsea	a	19 17					19 44		19 50							19 58			20 22				20 48			
Portsmouth Harbour	a	19 21														20 02			20 26							
Cosham	a						19 26					19 45											20 32		20 45	
Portchester	a						19 30																20 36			
Fareham	a						19 35					19 53											20 41		20 53	
Swanwick	a						19 42					20 00											20 48		21 00	
Southampton Central	a						19 59					20 19											21 05		21 19	

For general notes see front of timetable
For details of catering facilities see Directory of Train Operators

A [trolley] to Bognor Regis
b Change at East Croydon and Brighton

For complete service between Three Bridges and Horsham see Table 186

London, Gatwick Airport & Brighton → Sussex Coast, Portsmouth and Southampton

Network Diagram - see first page of Table 186

Station		SN 1	SN 1	SN 1 A		SN 1	SN 1		SN 1	SN 1	SN 1		SN 1	SN 1	SN 1	SN 1	SN 1	SN 1 A		SN 1		SN 1	SN 1	SN 1	SN 1	
London Victoria 15 ⊖	d		18 47	19 02			19 06		19 17		19 32			19b17	19 36	19 47		20 02		20 06			20 17		20 32	
Clapham Junction 10	d		18 53	19 08			19 12		19 23		19 38			19b23	19 42	19 53		20 08		20 12			20 23		20 38	
London Bridge 4 ⊖	d		18 41	18 56		18 41	18 56		19 11		19 26			19 26		19 41		19 56		19 56			20 11		20 15	
East Croydon	d		19 03	19 18		18 54	19 22		19 33		19 48			19 39	19 52	20 03		20 19		20 22			20 33		20 48	
Redhill 5	d			19 30							20 00							20 31							21 00	
Horley	d			19 36							19 52							20 19							20 52	
Gatwick Airport 10 ✈	d		19 19	19 40		19 11	19 26		19 49		20 09			19 56	19 58	20 19		20 39		20 26			20 49		21 09	
Three Bridges 4	a			19 44							20 14							20 44							21 14	
	d		19 15	19 45		19 15			19 45		20 14			19 45	20 03	20 15		20 44		20 15			20 45		21 14	
Crawley	d			19 48							20 18							20 48							21 18	
Horsham 4	a			19 56							20 26							20 56							21 26	
	d			20 00	20 05						20 30	20 35						21 00	21 05						21 30	21 35
Christs Hospital	d											20 38							21 08							21 38
Billingshurst	d				20 14							20 44							21 14							21 44
Pulborough	d				20 20							20 51							21 21							21 51
Amberley	d											20 57							21 27							21 57
Arundel	d				20 29							21 02							21 32							22 02
Haywards Heath 3	d		19 37			19 27	19 40		20 04					20 10	20 17	20 37				20 40			21 04			
Burgess Hill	d					19 33			20 09					20 01	20 23					20 33			21 09			
Brighton 10	d					19 56	20 14							20 30	20 44					21 03		21 14				
Hove 2	d		19 52			20 00	20a18		20 22					20 34	20a48	20 52				21 07		21a17	21 22			
Aldrington	d					20 02								20 36						21 09						
Portslade	d		19 55			20 04			20 25					20 38		20 55				21 11			21 25			
Fishersgate	d					20 06								20 40						21 13						
Southwick	d					20 08								20 42						21 15						
Shoreham-by-Sea	d		20 00			20 12			20 30					20 46		21 00				21 19			21 30			
Lancing	d		20 04			20 16			20 34					20 50		21 04				21 23			21 34			
East Worthing	d					20 19								20 53						21 26						
Worthing 4	a		20 08			20 21			20 38					20 55		21 08				21 28			21 38			
	d		20 08			20 22			20 38					20 56		21 08				21 29			21 38			
West Worthing	d		20 10			20 24			20 40					20 58		21 10				21 31			21 40			
Durrington-on-Sea	d		20 13			20 26			20 43					21 00		21 13				21 33			21 43			
Goring-by-Sea	d		20 15			20 29			20 45					21 03		21 15				21 36			21 45			
Angmering 3	d		20 19			20 33			20 49					21 07		21 19				21 40			21 49			
Littlehampton 4	a		20 28						20 58							21 28							21 58			
	d	20 11											21 07													
Ford 4	d	20 16			20 34	20 39						21 07	21 11	21 15					21 37	21 46						22 07
Bognor Regis 4	d																									
Barnham	a	20 20		20 26	20 39	20 43					20 56	21 11	21 15	21 19				21 26	21 41	21 50					21 56	22 11
	d	20 22		20 27	20 39	20 44				20 52	20 57	21 12	21 22 →	21 20			← 21 22	21 27	21 42	21 51				21 52	21 57	22 12
Bognor Regis 4	a	20 28			20 46					20 58		21 18					21 28		21 48					21 58		22 18
Chichester 4	a			20 34		20 51					21 04			21 27				21 34		21 58					22 04	
	d			20 35		20 52					21 05			21 28				21 35		21 59					22 05	
Fishbourne (Sussex)	d					20 55																			22 08	
Bosham	d										21 09														22 11	
Nutbourne	d					21 00																			22 14	
Southbourne	d					21 02					21 14							21 42							22 17	
Emsworth	d					21 05					21 17			21 36				21 45							22 20	
Warblington	d										21 20														22 23	
Havant	d			20 46		21 10					21 23			21 40				21 49		22 10					22 26	
Bedhampton	a										21 29														22 33	
Hilsea	a										21 36														22 41	
Fratton	a			20 54		21 18					21 40			21 54				21 59		22 18					22 45	
Portsmouth & Southsea	a			20 58		21 22					21 44			21 58				22 02		22 22					22 49	
Portsmouth Harbour	a			21 02		21 26												22 06		22 26						
Cosham	a										21 29			21 46											22 33	
Portchester	a										21 33															
Fareham	a										21 38			21 54											22 41	
Swanwick	a										21 45			22 01											22 48	
Southampton Central	a										22 02			22 20											23 05	

For general notes see front of timetable
For details of catering facilities see Directory of Train Operators

A to Bognor Regis
b Change at East Croydon and Brighton

For complete service between Three Bridges and Horsham see Table 186

Table 188

Saturdays

London, Gatwick Airport & Brighton → Sussex Coast, Portsmouth and Southampton

Network Diagram - see first page of Table 186

	SN 1	SN 1	SN 1	SN 1	SN 1	SN 1	SN 1	SN 1	SN 1		SN 1	SN 1	SN 1	SN 1	SN 1	SN 1	SN 1	SN 1	SN 1	SN 1	SN 1	SN 1		SN 1	SN 1
London Victoria 15 ⊖ d		20 36		20 47				21 06			21 17	21 32			21 36	21 47	22 06		22 17	22 36	22 32			22 47	23 17
Clapham Junction 10 d		20 42		20 53				21 12			21 23	21 38			21 42	21 53	22 12		22 23	22 42	22 38			22 53	23 23
London Bridge 4 ⊖ d		20b15		20 41			20 41	20b45			21 11	21 15		21 11	21b15	21 41	21b45		22 11	22b15	22 15			22 41	23 11
East Croydon d		20 52		21 03			20 54	21 22			21 33	21 48		21 24	21 52	22 03	22 22		22 33	22 52	22 48			23 03	23 33
Redhill 5 d											21 31	22 00							22 31		23 01				23 31
Horley d											21 25	21 52							22 25		22 52				23 26
Gatwick Airport 10 ✈ d		20 41	20 55	21 19			21 11	21c19			21 49	22 09		21 41	21c49	22 19	22c19		22 49	22c49	23 09			23 19	23 51
Three Bridges 4 a											21 53	22 14							22 54		23 14				23 55
d		20 45	21 00	21 15			21 15				21 53	22 14		21 45	21c53	22 15	22 15		22 54	22c54	23 15			23 15	23 56
Crawley d												22 18									23 18				
Horsham 4 a												22 26									23 26				
d												22 27									23 27				
Christs Hospital d												22 30									23 30				
Billingshurst d												22 36									23 36				
Pulborough d												22 43									23 43				
Amberley d												22 49									23 49				
Arundel d												22 54									23 54				
Haywards Heath 3 d		20 58	21 17	21 37			21 26	21 45			22 06			21 58	22 15	22 37	22 45		23 03	23 15				23 37	00 05
Burgess Hill d		21 04	21 23				21 32				22 11			22 04			22 32		23 08	23 04					00 10
Brighton 10 d		21 33	21 44				22 03	22 14						22 33	22 44		23 14			23 44					
Hove 2 d		21 37	21a48	21 52			22 07	22a17			22 23			22 37	22a47	22 52	23a17		23 22	23a47				23 52	00 22
Aldrington d		21 39					22 09							22 39											
Portslade d		21 41		21 55			22 11				22 26			22 41		22 55			23 25					23 55	00s25
Fishersgate d		21 43					22 13							22 43											
Southwick d		21 45					22 15							22 45					23 28					23 58	00s28
Shoreham-by-Sea d		21 49		22 00			22 19				22 31			22 49		23 00			23 31					00 01	00s31
Lancing d		21 53		22 04			22 23				22 35			22 53		23 04			23 35					00 05	00s35
East Worthing d		21 56					22 26							22 56											
Worthing 4 a		21 58		22 08			22 28				22 39			22 58		23 08			23 39					00 09	00s39
d		21 59		22 08			22 29				22 39			22 59		23 08			23 39						
West Worthing d		22 01		22 10			22 31				22 41			23 01		23 10			23 41						00s41
Durrington-on-Sea d		22 03		22 13			22 33				22 44			23 03		23 13			23 44						00s44
Goring-by-Sea d		22 06		22 15			22 36				22 46			23 06		23 15			23 46						00s46
Angmering 3 d		22 10		22 19			22 40				22 50			23 10		23 19			23 50						00s50
Littlehampton 4 a				22 28										23 18		23 28									
d	22 08					22 38								23 23											
Ford 4 d	22 12	22 16				22 42	22 46				22 56	23 00		23 27					23 56		23 59				00s56
Bognor Regis 4 d																									
Barnham a	22 16	22 20				22 46	22 50				23 01	23 04		23 31					00 01		00 04				01s01
d	22 17	22 21			22 22	22 52 →	22 51		← 22 52		23 06 →	23 05	← 23 06	23 32				23 36	00 09 →		00 05	← 00 09			
Bognor Regis 4 a					22 28				22 58				23 12					23 42				00 15			
Chichester 4 a	22 24	22 28					22 58					23 12		23 39							00 12				01 09
d		22 29					22 59					23 13													
Fishbourne (Sussex) d												23 16													
Bosham d												23 19													
Nutbourne d												23 22													
Southbourne d		22 36										23 25													
Emsworth d		22 39										23 28													
Warblington d												23 31													
Havant d		22 43					23 10					23 36													
Bedhampton a							23 33					00 24													
Hilsea a							23 41					00 30													
Fratton a		22 52					23 18					23 48													
Portsmouth & Southsea a		22 55					23 22					23 51													
Portsmouth Harbour a		22 59					23 26																		
Cosham a																									
Portchester a																									
Fareham a																									
Swanwick a																									
Southampton Central a																									

For general notes see front of timetable
For details of catering facilities see Directory of Train Operators

b Change at East Croydon and Brighton
c Change at Haywards Heath and Brighton

For complete service between Three Bridges and Horsham see Table 186

Table 188

Sundays

until 6 September

London, Gatwick Airport & Brighton → Sussex Coast, Portsmouth and Southampton

Network Diagram - see first page of Table 186

Station		SN 1	SN 1	SN 1	SN 1	SN 1	SN 1	SN 1	SN 1	SN 1	SN 1	SN 1	SN 1	SN 1	SN 1		SN 1	SN 1	SN 1	SN 1	SN 1	SN 1	SN 1	SN 1	SN 1	
London Victoria 15 ⊖	d	22p17	22p32		22p47	23 06	23p17	00 05				05 47						07 02	06 32		07b02		07b32		08 02	
Clapham Junction 10	d	22p23	22p38		22p53	23 12	23p23	00 11				05 53						07 08	06 38		07b08		07b38		08 08	
London Bridge 4 ⊖	d					22b58	23 11	23 53													07 11		07 41		07 44	
East Croydon	d	22p33	22p48		23p03	23 22	23p33	00 25				06 06						07 20	06 52		07 25		07 55		08 18	
Redhill 5	d		23p01					00 25										07 33							08 32	
Horley	d							00 31										07 39							08 38	
Gatwick Airport 10 ✈	d	22p49	23p09		23p19	23c19	23p51	00 44				06 32						07 43	07 19		07 42		08 12		08 41	
Three Bridges 4	a	22p54	23p14				23p55	00 48										07 47							08 46	
	d	22p54	23p15			23 15	23p56	00 48				06 36						07 48	07 24		07 47		08 17		08 46	
Crawley	d		23p18															07 51							08 50	
Horsham 4	a		23p26															08 03							08 58	
	d		23p27															08 04							08 59	
Christs Hospital	d		23p30																						09 02	
Billingshurst	d		23p36															08 12							09 09	
Pulborough	d		23p43															08 19							09 15	
Amberley	d		23p49																						09 21	
Arundel	d		23p54															08 29							09 27	
Haywards Heath 3	d	23p03			23p37	23 45	00 05	01 03				06 47							07 36		07 56		08 26			
Burgess Hill	d	23p08				23 32	00 10					06 53							07 42		08 01		08 31			
Brighton 10	d					00 10						07 12		07 18			07 45		08 12		08 18		08 48	09 12		
Hove 2	d	23p22			23p52	00a13	00 22	01s25				07 16		07 22			07 49		08 16		08 22		08 52	09e22 →		
Aldrington	d													07 24			07 51				08 24		08 54			
Portslade	d	23p25			23p55		00s25	01s28						07 26			07 53				08 26		08 56			
Fishersgate	d													07 28			07 55				08 28		08 58			
Southwick	d	23p28			23p58		00s28	01s31						07 30			07 57				08 30		09 00			
Shoreham-by-Sea	d	23p31			00 01		00s31	01s34				07 22		07 33			08 00		08 22		08 33		09 03			
Lancing	d	23p35			00 05		00s35	01s38						07 37			08 04				08 37		09 07			
East Worthing	d													07 40			08 07				08 40		09 10			
Worthing 4	a	23p39			00 09		00s39	01 42				07 28		07 43			08 10		08 28		08 43		09 13			
	d	23p39										07 28		07 43			08 10		08 28		08 43		09 13			
West Worthing	d	23p41					00s41							07 45			08 12				08 45		09 15			
Durrington-on-Sea	d	23p44					00s44							07 48			08 15				08 48		09 18			
Goring-by-Sea	d	23p46					00s46							07 50			08 17				08 50		09 20			
Angmering 3	d	23p50					00s50					07 35		07 54			08 21		08 35		08 54		09 24			
Littlehampton 4	a																08 30						09 33			
	d									06 42	07 19		07 54							08 54						
Ford 4	d	23p56	23p59				00s56			06 46	07 23	07 41	07 58	08 01				08 34	08 41	08 58	09 01				09 32	
Bognor Regis 4	d																									
Barnham	a	00 01	00 04	←			01s01			06 50	07 27	07 46	08 02	08 05	←			08 38	08 46	09 02	09 05	←			09 37	
	d	00 09 →	00 05	00 09					06 45	06 51	07 28	07 46	08 09 →	08 06	08 09			08 39	08 46	09 09 →	09 06	09 09			09 37	
Bognor Regis 4	a			00 15					06 51		07 34				08 15			08 45				09 15			09 44	
Chichester 4	a		00 12				01 09			06 58		07 54		08 13					08 54		09 13					
	d									06 59		07 54		08 14					08 54		09 14					
Fishbourne (Sussex)	d													08 17							09 17					
Bosham	d													08 20							09 20					
Nutbourne	d													08 23							09 23					
Southbourne	d											08 01		08 26					09 01		09 26					
Emsworth	d											08 04		08 29					09 04		09 29					
Warblington	d													08 32							09 32					
Havant	d									07 10		08 09		08 35					09 09		09 35					
Bedhampton	a													08 37							09 37					
Hilsea	a																									
Fratton	a									07 18		08 17		08 45					09 17		09 45					
Portsmouth & Southsea	a									07 22		08 21		08 48					09 21		09 48					
Portsmouth Harbour	a									07 26		08 25		08 52					09 25		09 52					
Cosham	a																									
Portchester	a																									
Fareham	a																									
Swanwick	a																									
Southampton Central	a																									

For general notes see front of timetable
For details of catering facilities see Directory of Train Operators

b Change at East Croydon and Brighton
c Change at Haywards Heath and Brighton
e Arr. 0915

For complete service between Three Bridges and Horsham see Table 186

Table 188

Sundays

until 6 September

London, Gatwick Airport & Brighton → Sussex Coast, Portsmouth and Southampton

Network Diagram - see first page of Table 186

		SN 1		SN 1	SN 1	SN 1	SN 1		SN 1	SN 1	SN 1		SN 1	SN 1	SN 1	SN 1	SN 1	GW ◇	SN 1	SN 1		SN 1		SN 1	SN 1	SN 1
London Victoria 15 ⊖	d	08 17					08b32		09 06	09 02	09 17					09 36	10 02	10 06	10 06	10 17						10 36
Clapham Junction 10	d	08 23					08b38		09 12	09 08	09 23					09 42	10 08	10 12	10 12	10 23						10 42
London Bridge 4 ⊖	d	08 11					08 41		08b44	08 44	09 11					09 41	09 44	09b44	09b44	10 11						10 41
East Croydon	d	08 33					08 55		09 22	09 18	09 33					09 55	10 18	10 22	10 22	10 33						10 55
Redhill 5	d									09 32							10 32									
Horley	d									09 38							10 38									
Gatwick Airport 10 ✈	d	08 49					09 12		09 38	09 41	09 49					10 12	10 41	10 38	10 38	10 49						11 12
Three Bridges 4	a									09 46							10 46									
	d	08 47					09 17			09 46	09 47					10 17	10 46			10 47						11 17
Crawley	d									09 50							10 50									
Horsham 4	a									09 58							10 58									
	d									09 59							10 59									
Christs Hospital	d									10 02							11 02									
Billingshurst	d									10 09							11 09									
Pulborough	d									10 15							11 15									
Amberley	d									10 21							11 21									
Arundel	d									10 27							11 27									
Haywards Heath 3	d	09 00					09 26				10 00					10 26				11 00						11 26
Burgess Hill	d	09 06					09 31				10 06					10 31				11 06						11 31
Brighton 10	d				←		09 48		10 12					←		10 48		11 08	11 12					←		11 48
Hove 2	d	09 19			09 22		09 52		10c22		10 19			10 22		10 52		11 12	11e22	11 19				11 22		11 52
Aldrington	d				09 24		09 54		→					10 24		10 54			→					11 24		11 54
Portslade	d				09 26		09 56							10 26		10 56								11 26		11 56
Fishersgate	d				09 28		09 58							10 28		10 58								11 28		11 58
Southwick	d				09 30		10 00							10 30		11 00								11 30		12 00
Shoreham-by-Sea	d	09 25			09 33		10 03				10 25			10 33		11 03		11 18		11 25				11 33		12 03
Lancing	d				09 37		10 07							10 37		11 07								11 37		12 07
East Worthing	d				09 40		10 10							10 40		11 10								11 40		12 10
Worthing 4	a	09 31			09 43		10 13				10 31			10 43		11 13		11 24		11 31				11 43		12 13
	d	09 35	09 37		09 43		10 13				10 35	10 37		10 43		11 13		11 27		11 35	11 37			11 43		12 13
West Worthing	d		09 39		09 45		10 15					10 39		10 45		11 15					11 39			11 45		12 15
Durrington-on-Sea	d		09 41		09 48		10 18					10 41		10 48		11 18					11 41			11 48		12 18
Goring-by-Sea	d		09 44		09 50		10 20					10 44		10 50		11 20					11 44			11 50		12 20
Angmering 3	d		09 48		09 54		10 24					10 48		10 54		11 24					11 48			11 54		12 24
Littlehampton 4	a		09 57				10 33					10 57				11 33					11 57					12 33
	d			09 54									10 54									11 54				
Ford 4	d			09 58	10 01					10 32			10 58	11 01			11 32					11 58		12 01		
Bognor Regis 4	d																									
Barnham	a	09 49		10 02	10 05	←				10 37	10 49		11 02	11 05	←		11 37	11 42		11 49		12 02		12 05	←	
	d	09 50		10 09	10 06	10 09				10 37	10 50		11 09	11 06	11 09		11 37	11 43		11 50		12 09		12 06	12 09	
Bognor Regis 4	a			→		10 15				10 44			→		11 15		11 44					→			12 15	
Chichester 4	a	09 57			10 13						10 57			11 13				11 50		11 57				12 13		
	d	09 58			10 14						10 58			11 14				11 55		11 58				12 14		
Fishbourne (Sussex)	d				10 17									11 17										12 17		
Bosham	d				10 20									11 20										12 20		
Nutbourne	d				10 23									11 23										12 23		
Southbourne	d	10 05			10 26						11 05			11 26						12 05				12 26		
Emsworth	d	10 08			10 29						11 08			11 29						12 08				12 29		
Warblington	d				10 32									11 32										12 32		
Havant	d	10 12			10 35						11 12			11 35				12f10		12 12				12 35		
Bedhampton	a				10 37									11 37										12 37		
Hilsea	a																									
Fratton	a	10 21			10 45						11 21			11 45						12 21				12 46		
Portsmouth & Southsea	a	10 24			10 50						11 24			11 48						12 24				12 51		
Portsmouth Harbour	a	10 28			10 54						11 28			11 53						12 28				12 55		
Cosham	a																	12 16								
Portchester	a																									
Fareham	a																	12 31								
Swanwick	a																									
Southampton Central	a																	12 53								

For general notes see front of timetable
For details of catering facilities see Directory of Train Operators

b Change at East Croydon and Brighton
c Arr. 1015
e Arr. 1115
f Arr. 1206

For complete service between Three Bridges and Horsham see Table 186

Table 188

Sundays
until 6 September

London, Gatwick Airport & Brighton → Sussex Coast, Portsmouth and Southampton

Network Diagram - see first page of Table 186

		SN 1	SN 1	SN 1		SN 1	SN 1	SN 1	SN 1	SN 1	SN 1	SN 1		SN 1	SN 1	SN 1	SN 1	SN 1	SN 1	SN 1		SN 1	SN 1	SN 1	SN 1
London Victoria 15 ⊖	d	11 06	11 02	11 17					11 36	12 06	12 02	12 17					12 36	13 06	13 02	13 17					13 36
Clapham Junction 10	d	11 12	11 08	11 23					11 42	12 12	12 08	12 23					12 42	13 12	13 08	13 23					13 42
London Bridge 4 ⊖	d	10b44	10 44	11 11					11 41	11b44	11 44	12 11					12 41	12b44	12 44	13 11					13 41
East Croydon	d	11 22	11 18	11 33					11 55	12 22	12 18	12 33					12 55	13 22	13 18	13 33					13 55
Redhill 5	d		11 32								12 32								13 32						
Horley	d		11 38								12 38								13 38						
Gatwick Airport 10 ✈	d	11 38	11 41	11 49					12 12	12 38	12 41	12 49					13 12	13 38	13 41	13 49					14 12
Three Bridges 4	a		11 46								12 46								13 46						
	d		11 46	11 47					12 17		12 46	12 47					13 17		13 46	13 47					14 17
Crawley	d		11 50								12 50								13 50						
Horsham 4	a		11 58								12 58								13 58						
	d		11 59								12 59								13 59						
Christs Hospital	d		12 02								13 02								14 02						
Billingshurst	d		12 09								13 09								14 09						
Pulborough	d		12 15								13 15								14 15						
Amberley	d		12 21								13 21								14 21						
Arundel	d		12 27								13 27								14 27						
Haywards Heath 3	d			12 00					12 26			13 00					13 26			14 00					14 26
Burgess Hill	d			12 06					12 31			13 06					13 31			14 06					14 31
Brighton 10	d	12 12					←		12 48	13 12					←		13 48	14 12					←		14 48
Hove 2	d	12c22 →		12 19			12 22		12 52	13e22 →		13 19			13 22		13 52	14f22 →		14 19			14 22		14 52
Aldrington	d						12 24		12 54						13 24		13 54						14 24		14 54
Portslade	d						12 26		12 56						13 26		13 56						14 26		14 56
Fishersgate	d						12 28		12 58						13 28		13 58						14 28		14 58
Southwick	d						12 30		13 00						13 30		14 00						14 30		15 00
Shoreham-by-Sea	d			12 25			12 33		13 03			13 25			13 33		14 03			14 25			14 33		15 03
Lancing	d						12 37		13 07						13 37		14 07						14 37		15 07
East Worthing	d						12 40		13 10						13 40		14 10						14 40		15 10
Worthing 4	a			12 31			12 43		13 13			13 31			13 43		14 13			14 31			14 43		15 13
	d			12 35	12 37		12 43		13 13			13 35	13 37		13 43		14 13			14 35	14 37		14 43		15 13
West Worthing	d				12 39		12 45		13 15				13 39		13 45		14 15				14 39		14 45		15 15
Durrington-on-Sea	d				12 41		12 48		13 18				13 41		13 48		14 18				14 41		14 48		15 18
Goring-by-Sea	d				12 44		12 50		13 20				13 44		13 50		14 20				14 44		14 50		15 20
Angmering 3	d				12 48		12 54		13 24				13 48		13 54		14 24				14 48		14 54		15 24
Littlehampton 4	a				12 57				13 33				13 57				14 33				14 57				15 33
	d					12 54								13 54								14 54			
Ford 4	d		12 32			12 58	13 01				13 32			13 58	14 01				14 32			14 58	15 01		
Bognor Regis 4	d																								
Barnham	a		12 37	12 49		13 02	13 05	←			13 37	13 49		14 02	14 05	←			14 37	14 49		15 02	15 05	←	
	d		12 37	12 50		13 09 →	13 06	13 09			13 37	13 50		14 09 →	14 06	14 09			14 37	14 50		15 09 →	15 06	15 09	
Bognor Regis 4	a		12 44					13 15			13 44					14 15			14 44					15 15	
Chichester 4	a			12 57			13 13					13 57			14 13					14 57			15 13		
	d			12 58			13 14					13 58			14 14					14 58			15 14		
Fishbourne (Sussex)	d						13 17								14 17								15 17		
Bosham	d						13 20								14 20								15 20		
Nutbourne	d						13 23								14 23								15 23		
Southbourne	d			13 05			13 26					14 05			14 26					15 05			15 26		
Emsworth	d			13 08			13 29					14 08			14 29					15 08			15 29		
Warblington	d						13 32								14 32								15 32		
Havant	d			13 12			13 35					14 12			14 35					15 12			15 35		
Bedhampton	a						13 37								14 37								15 37		
Hilsea	a																								
Fratton	a			13 21			13 45					14 21			14 45					15 21			15 45		
Portsmouth & Southsea	a			13 24			13 48					14 24			14 48					15 24			15 48		
Portsmouth Harbour	a			13 28			13 52					14 28			14 52					15 28			15 52		
Cosham	a																								
Portchester	a																								
Fareham	a																								
Swanwick	a																								
Southampton Central	a																								

For general notes see front of timetable
For details of catering facilities see Directory of Train Operators

b Change at East Croydon and Brighton
c Arr. 1215
e Arr. 1315
f Arr. 1415

For complete service between Three Bridges and Horsham see Table 186

Table 188

Sundays
until 6 September

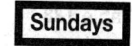

London, Gatwick Airport & Brighton → Sussex Coast, Portsmouth and Southampton

Network Diagram - see first page of Table 186

		SN 1	SN 1	SN 1	SN 1		SN 1	SN 1		SN 1	SN 1	SN 1	GW 1	SN 1	SN 1	SN 1	SN 1	SN 1		SN 1	SN 1	SN 1	SN 1	SN 1	SN 1	
London Victoria 15 ⊖	d			19 36	20 06		20 02	20 17					20 36		21 06	21 02		21 17			22 02	21 21	21b32	22 17	23 17	
Clapham Junction 10	d			19 42	20 12		20 08	20 23					20 42		21 12	21 08		21 23			22 08	21 27	21b38	22 23	23 23	
London Bridge 4 ⊖	d			19 41	19b44		19 44	20 11					20b14	20 41	20b44	20 44		21 11			21 44	21 11	21 41	22 11	23 11	
East Croydon	d			19 55	20 22		20 18	20 33					20 52	20 55	21 22	21 18		21 33			22 18	21 38	21 55	22 33	23 38	
Redhill 5	d						20 32									21 32					22 32				23 42	
Horley	d						20 38									21 38					22 38				23 50	
Gatwick Airport 10 ✈	d			20 12	20 38		20 41	20 49					20 42	21 12	21 38	21 41		21 49			22 41	21 58	22 12	22 49	00 01	
Three Bridges 4	a						20 46									21 46					22 46				00 05	
	d			20 17			20 46	20 47					20 47	21 17		21 46		21 47			22 46	22 03	22 17	22 47	00 06	
Crawley	d						20 50									21 50					22 50					
Horsham 4	a						20 58									21 58					22 58					
	d						20 59									21 59					22 59					
Christs Hospital	d						21 02									22 02					23 02					
Billingshurst	d						21 09									22 09					23 09					
Pulborough	d						21 15									22 15					23 15					
Amberley	d						21 21									22 21					23 21					
Arundel	d						21 27									22 27					23 27					
Haywards Heath 3	d			20 26				21 00					20 56	21 26				22 00				22 15	22 26	23 00	00 15	
Burgess Hill	d			20 31				21 06					21 01	21 31				22 06				22 21	22 31	23 06		
Brighton 10	d	←		20 48	21 12						←		21 43	21 48	22 10							22 40	23 15			
Hove 2	d	20 22		20 52	21c22			21 19			21 22		21 47	21 52	22a13			22 19				22 44	23a18	23e25	00 29	
Aldrington	d	20 24		20 54	→						21 24			21 54								22 46				
Portslade	d	20 26		20 56							21 26			21 56								22 48		23 28	00s32	
Fishersgate	d	20 28		20 58							21 28			21 58								22 50				
Southwick	d	20 30		21 00							21 30			22 00								22 52		23 31	00s35	
Shoreham-by-Sea	d	20 33		21 03				21 25			21 33		21 53	22 03				22 25				22 55		23 34	00s38	
Lancing	d	20 37		21 07							21 37			22 07								22 59		23 38	00s42	
East Worthing	d	20 40		21 10							21 40			22 10								23 02				
Worthing 4	a	20 43		21 13				21 31			21 43		21 59	22 13				22 31				23 05		23 42	00 46	
	d	20 43		21 13				21 35	21 37		21 43		22 00	22 13				22 35	22 37			23 05				
West Worthing	d	20 45		21 15					21 39		21 45			22 15					22 39			23 07				
Durrington-on-Sea	d	20 48		21 18					21 41		21 48			22 18					22 41			23 09				
Goring-by-Sea	d	20 50		21 20					21 44		21 50			22 20					22 44			23 12				
Angmering 3	d	20 54		21 24					21 48		21 54			22 24					22 48			23 16				
Littlehampton 4	a			21 34					21 57					22 34					22 57			23 24				
	d									21 54										23 06		23 29				
Ford 4	d	21 01					21 32			21 58	22 01					22 32				23 10	23 32	23 36				
Bognor Regis 4	d																									
Barnham	a	21 05	←				21 37	21 49		22 02	22 05	←	22 14			22 37		22 49		23 14	23 36	23 40				
	d	21 06	21 09				21 37	21 50		22 09	22 06	22 09	22 15			22 37	22 52	22 56		23 15	23 42	23 45				
Bognor Regis 4	a		21 15				21 44			→		22 15				22 44	22 58			23 21	23 48					
Chichester 4	a	21 13						21 57			22 13		22 22					23 03				23 52				
	d	21 14						21 58			22 14		22 23					23 04								
Fishbourne (Sussex)	d	21 17									22 17															
Bosham	d	21 20									22 20							23 08								
Nutbourne	d	21 23									22 23							23 12								
Southbourne	d	21 26						22 05			22 26							23 14								
Emsworth	d	21 29						22 08			22 29							23 17								
Warblington	d	21 32									22 32															
Havant	d	21 35						22 12			22 35		22 42					23 22								
Bedhampton	a	21 37									22 37							23 41								
Hilsea	a																									
Fratton	a	21 45						22 21			22 45		22 52					23 31								
Portsmouth & Southsea	a	21 48						22 24			22 48		22 57					23 34								
Portsmouth Harbour	a	21 52						22 28			22 52		23 01					23 38								
Cosham	a																									
Portchester	a																									
Fareham	a																									
Swanwick	a																									
Southampton Central	a																									

For general notes see front of timetable
For details of catering facilities see Directory of Train Operators

b Change at East Croydon and Brighton
c Arr. 2115
e Arr. 2319

For complete service between Three Bridges and Horsham see Table 186

Table 188

Sundays

from 13 September

London, Gatwick Airport & Brighton → Sussex Coast, Portsmouth and Southampton

Network Diagram - see first page of Table 186

		SN 1	SN 1	SN 1	SN 1	SN 1	SN 1	SN 1	SN 1	SN 1	SN 1	SN 1	SN 1	SN 1	SN 1	SN 1	SN 1		SN 1	SN 1	SN 1	SN 1	SN 1	SN 1	SN 1	
London Victoria 15 ⊖	d	22p17	22p32		22p47	23 06	23p17	00 05				05 47				07 02	06 32					07 32		08 04	08 17	
Clapham Junction 10	d	22p23	22p38		22p53	23 12	23p23	00 11				05 53				07 08	06 38					07 38		08 10	08 23	
London Bridge 4 ⊖	d					22b58	23 11	23 53													07 11	07 41		07 44	08 11	
East Croydon	d	22p33	22p48		23p03	23c22	23p33	00 25				06 06				07 23	06 52				07 27	07 57		08 24	08 38	
Redhill 5	d		23p01					00 25								07 37								08 39		
Horley	d							00 31								07 44								08 45		
Gatwick Airport 10 ✈	d	22p49	23p09		23p19	23e19	23p51	00 44				06 32				07 47	07 19				07 50	08 20		08 48	08 56	
Three Bridges 4	a	22p54	23p14				23p55	00 48								07 52								08 53		
	d	22p54	23p15			23 15	23p56	00 48				06 36				07 52	07 24				07 54	08 24		08 53	08 54	
Crawley	d		23p18													07 55								08 56		
Horsham 4	a		23p26													08 07								09 04		
	d		23p27													08 08								09 05		
Christs Hospital	d		23p30																					09 08		
Billingshurst	d		23p36													08 16								09 15		
Pulborough	d		23p43													08 23								09 21		
Amberley	d		23p49																					09 27		
Arundel	d		23p54													08 33								09 33		
Haywards Heath 3	d	23p03			23p37	23 45	00 05	01 03				06 47					07 36				08 03	08 33			09 07	
Burgess Hill	d	23p08				23 32	00 10					06 53					07 42				08 08	08 38			09 12	
Brighton 10	d					00 10						07 14		07 22			08 14			08 22	08 50	09 17				
Hove 2	d	23p22			23p52	00a13	00 22	01s25				07 18		07 26			08 18			08 26	08 54	09f26			09 24	
Aldrington	d													07 28						08 28	08 56	⟶				
Portslade	d	23p25			23p55		00s25	01s28						07 30						08 30	08 58					
Fishersgate	d													07 32						08 32	09 00					
Southwick	d	23p28			23p58		00s28	01s31						07 34						08 34	09 02					
Shoreham-by-Sea	d	23p31			00 01		00s31	01s34				07 24		07 37			08 24			08 37	09 05				09 30	
Lancing	d	23p35			00 05		00s35	01s38						07 41						08 41	09 09					
East Worthing	d													07 44						08 44	09 12					
Worthing 4	a	23p39			00 09		00s39	01 42				07 30		07 47			08 30			08 47	09 15				09 36	
	d	23p39										07 30		07 47			08 30			08 47	09 15				09 40	09 42
West Worthing	d	23p41					00s41							07 49						08 49	09 17					09 44
Durrington-on-Sea	d	23p44					00s44							07 51						08 51	09 20					09 46
Goring-by-Sea	d	23p46					00s46							07 54						08 54	09 22					09 49
Angmering 3	d	23p50					00s50					07 37		07 58			08 37			08 58	09 26					09 53
Littlehampton 4	a													08 06						09 06	09 35					10 02
	d									06 42	07 19		07 57	08 11					08 57	09 11						
Ford 4	d	23p56	23p59				00s56			06 46	07 23	07 43	08 01	08 15		08 38	08 43		09 01	09 15				09 39		
Bognor Regis 4	d																									
Barnham	a	00 01	00 04	⟵			01s01			06 50	07 27	07 48	08 08	08 19	⟵	08 42	08 48		09 08	09 19			⟵	09 43	09 54	
	d	00 09	00 05	00 09					06 45	06 51	07 28	07 48	08 26	08 20	08 26	08 43	08 48		09 26	09 20			09 26	09 44	09 55	
Bognor Regis 4	a	⟶		00 15					06 51		07 34		⟶		08 32	08 49			⟶				09 32	09 50		
Chichester 4	a		00 12				01 09			06 58		07 56		08 27			08 56			09 27					10 02	
	d									06 59		07 56		08 28			08 56			09 28					10 03	
Fishbourne (Sussex)	d													08 31						09 31						
Bosham	d													08 34						09 34						
Nutbourne	d													08 37						09 37						
Southbourne	d											08 03		08 40			09 03			09 40					10 10	
Emsworth	d											08 06		08 43			09 06			09 43					10 13	
Warblington	d													08 46						09 46						
Havant	d									07 10		08 11		08 49			09 11			09 49					10 17	
Bedhampton	a											08 41		08 51			09 47			09 51						
Hilsea	a																									
Fratton	a									07 18		08 19		08 59			09 19			09 59					10 26	
Portsmouth & Southsea	a									07 22		08 23		09 03			09 23			10 03					10 29	
Portsmouth Harbour	a									07 26		08 27		09 07			09 27			10 07					10 35	
Cosham	a																									
Portchester	a																									
Fareham	a																									
Swanwick	a																									
Southampton Central	a																									

For general notes see front of timetable
For details of catering facilities see Directory of Train Operators

b Sundays. Change at East Croydon and Brighton
c Sundays
e Change at Haywards Heath and Brighton
f Arr. 0920

For complete service between Three Bridges and Horsham see Table 186

Table 188

Sundays

from 13 September

London, Gatwick Airport & Brighton → Sussex Coast, Portsmouth and Southampton

Network Diagram - see first page of Table 186

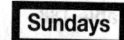

		SN 1	SN 1	SN 1	SN 1	SN 1	SN 1	SN 1		SN 1	SN 1	SN 1	SN 1	SN 1 (trolley)	GW ◇	SN 1	SN 1		SN 1	SN 1	SN 1	SN 1	SN 1	SN 1
London Victoria 15 ⊖	d				07b34	09 02	09 04	09 17						10 04	10 02	10 02	10 17						11 02	11 04
Clapham Junction 10	d				07b40	09 08	09 10	09 23						10 10	10 08	10 08	10 23						11 08	11 10
London Bridge 4 ⊖	d				08 11	08b44	08 44	09 11					09 11	09 44	09b44	09b44	10 11					10 11	10b44	10 44
East Croydon	d				08 27	09 22	09 24	09 38					09 27	10 24	10 22	10 22	10 38					10 27	11 22	11 24
Redhill 5	d						09 39							10 39										11 39
Horley	d						09 45							10 45										11 45
Gatwick Airport 10 ✈	d				08 50	09 40	09 48	09 56					09 50	10 48	10 40	10 40	10 56					10 50	11 40	11 48
Three Bridges 4	a						09 53							10 53										11 53
	d				08 54	09 24	09 53	09 54					09 54	10 53	10 24	10 24	10 54					10 54	11 24	11 53
Crawley	d						09 56							10 56										11 56
Horsham 4	a						10 04							11 04										12 04
	d						10 05							11 05										12 05
Christs Hospital	d						10 08							11 08										12 08
Billingshurst	d						10 15							11 15										12 15
Pulborough	d						10 21							11 21										12 21
Amberley	d						10 27							11 27										12 27
Arundel	d						10 33							11 33										12 33
Haywards Heath 3	d				09 03	09 33		10 07					10 03		10 33	10 33	11 07					11 03	11 33	
Burgess Hill	d				09 08	09 38		10 12					10 08		10 38	10 38	11 12					11 08	11 38	
Brighton 10	d		←		09 50	10 17					←		10 50		11 10	11 17				←		11 50	12 17	
Hove 2	d		09 26		09 54	10c26 →		10 24			10 26		10 54		11 14	11e26 →	11 24			11 26		11 54	12f26 →	
Aldrington	d		09 28		09 56						10 28		10 56							11 28		11 56		
Portslade	d		09 31		09 58						10 31		10 58							11 31		11 58		
Fishersgate	d		09 33		10 00						10 33		11 00							11 33		12 00		
Southwick	d		09 35		10 02						10 35		11 02							11 35		12 02		
Shoreham-by-Sea	d		09 38		10 05			10 30			10 38		11 05		11 20		11 30			11 38		12 05		
Lancing	d		09 42		10 09						10 42		11 09							11 42		12 09		
East Worthing	d		09 45		10 12						10 45		11 12							11 45		12 12		
Worthing 4	a		09 47		10 15			10 36			10 47		11 15		11 26		11 36			11 47		12 15		
	d		09 48		10 15			10 40	10 42		10 48		11 15		11 29		11 40	11 42		11 48		12 15		
West Worthing	d		09 50		10 17				10 44		10 50		11 17					11 44		11 50		12 17		
Durrington-on-Sea	d		09 52		10 20				10 46		10 52		11 20					11 46		11 52		12 20		
Goring-by-Sea	d		09 55		10 22				10 49		10 55		11 22					11 49		11 55		12 22		
Angmering 3	d		09 59		10 26				10 53		10 59		11 26					11 53		11 59		12 26		
Littlehampton 4	a				10 35				11 02				11 35					12 02				12 35		
	d	09 57								10 57									11 57					
Ford 4	d	10 01	10 05				10 38			11 01	11 05			11 38					12 01	12 05				12 38
Bognor Regis 4	d																							
Barnham	a	10 08	10 11	←			10 42	10 54		11 08	11 11	←		11 42	11 45		11 54		12 08	12 11	←			12 42
	d	10 15 →	10 12	10 15			10 43	10 55		11 15 →	11 12	11 15		11 43	11 46		11 55		12 15 →	12 12	12 15			12 43
Bognor Regis 4	a			10 21			10 49					11 21		11 49							12 21			12 49
Chichester 4	a		10 19					11 02			11 19				11 53		12 02			12 19				
	d		10 20					11 03			11 20				11 58		12 03			12 20				
Fishbourne (Sussex)	d		10 23								11 23									12 23				
Bosham	d		10 26								11 26									12 26				
Nutbourne	d		10 29								11 29									12 29				
Southbourne	d		10 32					11 10			11 32						12 10			12 32				
Emsworth	d		10 35					11 13			11 35						12 13			12 35				
Warblington	d		10 38								11 38									12 38				
Havant	d		10 41					11 17			11 44				12 10		12 17			12 44				
Bedhampton	a		10 43					11 41			11 46						12 41			12 46				
Hilsea	a																							
Fratton	a		10 51					11 26			11 54						12 26			12 54				
Portsmouth & Southsea	a		10 54					11 29			11 57						12 29			12 57				
Portsmouth Harbour	a		10 58					11 35			12 01						12 35			13 01				
Cosham	a														12 16									
Portchester	a																							
Fareham	a														12 31									
Swanwick	a																							
Southampton Central	a														12 53									

For general notes see front of timetable
For details of catering facilities see Directory of Train Operators

b Change at East Croydon and Brighton
c Arr. 1020
e Arr. 1120
f Arr. 1220

For complete service between Three Bridges and Horsham see Table 186

Table 188

Sundays

from 13 September

London, Gatwick Airport & Brighton → Sussex Coast, Portsmouth and Southampton

Network Diagram - see first page of Table 186

Station		SN 1		SN 1	SN 1		SN 1	SN 1	SN 1	SN 1	SN 1		SN 1	SN 1	SN 1	SN 1	SN 1	SN 1	SN 1		SN 1	SN 1		SN 1	SN 1	SN 1
										bike									bike							
London Victoria 15 ⊖	d	11 17							12 02	12 04	12 17						13 02	13 04	13 17							14 02
Clapham Junction 10	d	11 23							12 08	12 10	12 23						13 08	13 10	13 23							14 08
London Bridge 4 ⊖	d	11 11						11 11	11b44	11 44	12 11					12 11	12b44	12 44	13 11						13 11	13b44
East Croydon	d	11 38						11 28	12 22	12 24	12 38					12 27	13 22	13 24	13 38						13 28	14 22
Redhill 5	d									12 39								13 39								
Horley	d									12 45								13 45								
Gatwick Airport 10 ✈	d	11 56						11 50	12 40	12 48	12 56					12 50	13 40	13 48	13 56						13 50	14 40
Three Bridges 4	a									12 53								13 53								
	d	11 54						11 54	12 24	12 53	12 54					12 54	13 24	13 53	13 54						13 54	14 24
Crawley	d									12 56								13 56								
Horsham 4	a									13 04								14 04								
	d									13 05								14 05								
Christs Hospital	d									13 08								14 08								
Billingshurst	d									13 15								14 15								
Pulborough	d									13 21								14 21								
Amberley	d									13 27								14 27								
Arundel	d									13 33								14 33								
Haywards Heath 3	d	12 07						12 03	12 33		13 07					13 03	13 33		14 07						14 03	14 33
Burgess Hill	d	12 12						12 08	12 38		13 12					13 08	13 38		14 12						14 08	14 38
Brighton 10	d				←			12 50	13 17					←		13 50	14 17					←			14 50	15 17
Hove 2	d	12 24			12 26			12 54	13c26 →		13 24			13 26		13 54	14e26 →		14 24			14 26			14 54	15f26 →
Aldrington	d				12 28			12 56						13 28		13 56						14 28			14 56	
Portslade	d				12 31			12 58						13 31		13 58						14 31			14 58	
Fishersgate	d				12 33			13 00						13 33		14 00						14 33			15 00	
Southwick	d				12 35			13 02						13 35		14 02						14 35			15 02	
Shoreham-by-Sea	d	12 30			12 38			13 05			13 30			13 38		14 05			14 30			14 38			15 05	
Lancing	d				12 42			13 09						13 42		14 09						14 42			15 09	
East Worthing	d				12 45			13 12						13 45		14 12						14 45			15 12	
Worthing 4	a	12 36			12 47			13 15			13 31			13 47		14 15			14 36			14 47			15 15	
	d	12 40	12 42		12 48			13 15			13 40	13 42		13 48		14 15			14 40	14 42		14 48			15 15	
West Worthing	d		12 44		12 50			13 17				13 44		13 50		14 17				14 44		14 50			15 17	
Durrington-on-Sea	d		12 46		12 52			13 20				13 46		13 52		14 20				14 46		14 52			15 20	
Goring-by-Sea	d		12 49		12 55			13 22				13 49		13 55		14 22				14 49		14 55			15 22	
Angmering 3	d		12 53		12 59			13 26				13 53		13 59		14 26				14 53		14 59			15 26	
Littlehampton 4	a		13 02					13 35				14 02				14 35				15 02					15 35	
	d			12 57									13 57								14 57					
Ford 4	d			13 01	13 05					13 38			14 01	14 05				14 38			15 01	15 05				
Bognor Regis 4	d						←								←									←		
Barnham	a	12 54		13 08	13 11					13 42	13 54		14 08	14 11				14 42	14 54		15 08	15 11				
	d	12 55		13 15 →	13 12		13 15			13 43	13 55		14 15 →	14 12	14 15			14 43	14 55		15 15 →	15 12		15 15		
Bognor Regis 4	a						13 21			13 49					14 21			14 49						15 21		
Chichester 4	a	13 02			13 19						14 02			14 19					15 02			15 19				
	d	13 03			13 20						14 03			14 20					15 03			15 20				
Fishbourne (Sussex)	d				13 23									14 23								15 23				
Bosham	d				13 26									14 26								15 26				
Nutbourne	d				13 29									14 29								15 29				
Southbourne	d	13 10			13 32						14 10			14 32					15 10			15 32				
Emsworth	d	13 13			13 35						14 13			14 35					15 13			15 35				
Warblington	d				13 38									14 38								15 38				
Havant	d	13 17			13 44						14 17			14 44					15 17			15 44				
Bedhampton	a	13 41			13 46						14 41			14 46					15 41			15 46				
Hilsea	a																									
Fratton	a	13 26			13 54						14 26			14 54					15 26			15 54				
Portsmouth & Southsea	a	13 29			13 57						14 29			14 57					15 29			15 57				
Portsmouth Harbour	a	13 35			14 01						14 35			15 01					15 35			16 01				
Cosham	a																									
Portchester	a																									
Fareham	a																									
Swanwick	a																									
Southampton Central	a																									

For general notes see front of timetable
For details of catering facilities see Directory of Train Operators

b Change at East Croydon and Brighton
c Arr. 1320
e Arr. 1420
f Arr. 1520

For complete service between Three Bridges and Horsham see Table 186

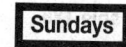

London, Gatwick Airport & Brighton → Sussex Coast, Portsmouth and Southampton

Sundays

from 13 September

Network Diagram - see first page of Table 186

		SN 1 🚲	SN 1		SN 1	SN 1	SN 1	GW ◇	SN 1	SN 1	SN 1 🚲	SN 1		SN 1	SN 1	SN 1		SN 1	SN 1	SN 1 🚲	SN 1		SN 1	SN 1	SN 1	GW ◇
London Victoria [15] ⊖	d	14 04	14 17							15 02	15 04	15 17							16 02	16 04	16 17					
Clapham Junction [10]	d	14 10	14 23							15 08	15 10	15 23							16 08	16 10	16 23					
London Bridge [4] ⊖	d	13 44	14 11					14 11	14 11	14b44	14 44	15 11						15 11	15b44	15 44	16 11					16 11
East Croydon	d	14 24	14 38					14 28	14 28	15 22	15 24	15 38						15 28	16 22	16 24	16 38					16 28
Redhill [5]	d	14 39									15 39									16 39						
Horley	d	14 45									15 45									16 45						
Gatwick Airport [10] ✈	d	14 48	14 56					14 50	14 50	15 40	15 48	15 56						15 50	16 40	16 48	16 56					16 50
Three Bridges [4]	a	14 53									15 53									16 53						
	d	14 53	14 54					14 54	14 54	15 24	15 53	15 54						15 54	16 24	16 53	16 54					16 54
Crawley	d	14 56									15 56									16 56						
Horsham [4]	a	15 04									16 04									17 04						
	d	15 05									16 05									17 05						
Christs Hospital	d	15 08									16 08									17 08						
Billingshurst	d	15 15									16 15									17 15						
Pulborough	d	15 21									16 21									17 21						
Amberley	d	15 27									16 27									17 27						
Arundel	d	15 33									16 33									17 33						
Haywards Heath [3]	d		15 07					15 03	15 03	15 33		16 07						16 03	16 33		17 07					17 03
Burgess Hill	d		15 12					15 08	15 08	15 38		16 12						16 08	16 38		17 12					17 08
Brighton [10]	d					←		15 47	15 50	16 17					←			16 50	17 17					←		17 47
Hove [2]	d		15 24			15 26		15 51	15 54	16c26		16 24			16 26			16 54	17e26		17 24			17 26		17 51
Aldrington	d					15 28			15 56	→					16 28			16 56	→					17 28		
Portslade	d					15 31			15 58						16 31			16 58						17 31		
Fishersgate	d					15 33			16 00						16 33			17 00						17 33		
Southwick	d					15 35			16 02						16 35			17 02						17 35		
Shoreham-by-Sea	d		15 30			15 38		15 57	16 05			16 30			16 38			17 05			17 30			17 38		17 57
Lancing	d					15 42			16 09						16 42			17 09						17 42		
East Worthing	d					15 45			16 12						16 45			17 12						17 45		
Worthing [4]	a		15 36			15 47		16 03	16 15			16 36			16 47			17 15			17 36			17 47		18 03
	d		15 40	15 42		15 48		16 08	16 15			16 40	16 42		16 48			17 15			17 40	17 42		17 48		18 08
West Worthing	d			15 44		15 50			16 17				16 44		16 50			17 17				17 44		17 50		
Durrington-on-Sea	d			15 46		15 52			16 20				16 46		16 52			17 20				17 46		17 52		
Goring-by-Sea	d			15 49		15 55			16 22				16 49		16 55			17 22				17 49		17 55		
Angmering [3]	d			15 53		15 59			16 26				16 53		16 59			17 26				17 53		17 59		
Littlehampton [4]	a			16 02					16 35				17 02					17 35				18 02				
	d				15 57									16 57									17 57			
Ford [4]	d	15 38			16 01	16 05					16 38			17 01	17 05					17 38			18 01	18 05		
Bognor Regis [4]	d																									
Barnham	a	15 42	15 54		16 08	16 11	←	16 25			16 42	16 54		17 08	17 11	←				17 42	17 54		18 08	18 11	←	18 25
	d	15 43	15 55		16 15	16 12	16 15	16 25			16 43	16 55		17 15	17 12	17 15				17 43	17 55		18 15	18 12	18 15	18 25
Bognor Regis [4]	a	15 49			→		16 21				16 49			→		17 21				17 49			→		18 21	
Chichester [4]	a		16 02			16 19		16 33				17 02			17 19						18 02			18 19		18 33
	d		16 03			16 20		16 34				17 03			17 20						18 03			18 20		18 34
Fishbourne (Sussex)	d					16 23									17 23									18 23		
Bosham	d					16 26									17 26									18 26		
Nutbourne	d					16 29									17 29									18 29		
Southbourne	d		16 10			16 32						17 10			17 32						18 10			18 32		
Emsworth	d		16 13			16 35						17 13			17 35						18 13			18 35		
Warblington	d					16 38									17 38									18 38		
Havant	d		16 17			16 44		16 48				17 17			17 44						18 17			18 44		18 48
Bedhampton	a		16 41			16 46						17 41			17 46						18 41			18 46		
Hilsea	a																									
Fratton	a		16 26			16 54						17 26			17 54						18 26			18 54		
Portsmouth & Southsea	a		16 29			16 57						17 29			17 57						18 29			18 57		
Portsmouth Harbour	a		16 35			17 01						17 35			18 01						18 35			19 01		
Cosham	a							16 54																		18 54
Portchester	a																									
Fareham	a							17 02																		19 02
Swanwick	a																									
Southampton Central	a							17 24																		19 24

For general notes see front of timetable
For details of catering facilities see
Directory of Train Operators

b Change at East Croydon and Brighton
c Arr. 1620
e Arr. 1720

For complete service between Three Bridges and Horsham see Table 186

Table 188

Sundays

from 13 September

London, Gatwick Airport & Brighton → Sussex Coast, Portsmouth and Southampton

Network Diagram - see first page of Table 186

		SN 1	SN 1	SN 1	SN 1		SN 1	SN 1	SN 1	SN 1		SN 1	SN 1	SN 1		SN 1	SN 1	SN 1	SN 1	SN 1	SN 1	SN 1		SN 1	SN 1	SN 1
				⚲									⚲								⚲					
London Victoria 15 ⊖	d		*17 02*	17 04	17 17							*18 02*	18 04	18 17						*19 02*	19 04	19 17				
Clapham Junction 10	d		*17 08*	17 10	17 23							*18 08*	18 10	18 23						*19 08*	19 10	19 23				
London Bridge 4 ⊖	d	*16 11*	*16b44*	*16 44*	*17 11*					*17 11*		*17b44*	*17 44*	*18 11*					*18 11*	*18b44*	*18 44*	*19 11*				
East Croydon	d	*16 28*	*17 22*	17 24	17 38					*17 28*		*18 22*	18 24	18 37					*18 28*	*19 22*	19 24	19 37				
Redhill 5	d			17 39									18 39								19 39					
Horley	d			17 45									18 45								19 45					
Gatwick Airport 10 ✈	d	*16 50*	*17 40*	17 48	17 56					*17 50*		*18 40*	18 48	18 56					*18 50*	*19 40*	19 48	19 56				
Three Bridges 4	a			17 53									18 53								19 53					
	d	*16 54*	*17 24*	17 53	*17 54*					*17 54*		*18 24*	18 53	*18 54*					*18 54*	*19 24*	19 53	*19 54*				
Crawley	d			17 56									18 56								19 56					
Horsham 4	a			18 04									19 04								20 04					
	d			18 05									19 05								20 05					
Christs Hospital	d			18 08									19 08								20 08					
Billingshurst	d			18 15									19 15								20 15					
Pulborough	d			18 21									19 21								20 21					
Amberley	d			18 27									19 27								20 27					
Arundel	d			18 33									19 33								20 33					
Haywards Heath 3	d	*17 03*	*17 33*		18 07					*18 03*		*18 33*		19 07					*19 03*	*19 33*		20 07				
Burgess Hill	d	*17 08*	*17 38*		18 12					*18 08*		*18 38*		19 12					*19 08*	*19 38*		20 12				
Brighton 10	d	17 50	18 17					←		18 50		19 17					←		19 50	20 17					←	
Hove 2	d	17 54	18c26 →		18 24			18 26		18 54		19e26 →		19 24			19 26		19 54	20f26 →		20 24			20 26	
Aldrington	d	17 56						18 28		18 56							19 28		19 56						20 28	
Portslade	d	17 58						18 31		18 58							19 31		19 58						20 31	
Fishersgate	d	18 00						18 33		19 00							19 33		20 00						20 33	
Southwick	d	18 02						18 35		19 02							19 35		20 02						20 35	
Shoreham-by-Sea	d	18 05			18 30			18 38		19 05				19 30			19 38		20 05			20 30			20 38	
Lancing	d	18 09						18 42		19 09							19 42		20 09						20 42	
East Worthing	d	18 12						18 45		19 12							19 45		20 12						20 45	
Worthing 4	a	18 15			18 31			18 47		19 15				19 36			19 47		20 15			20 36			20 47	
	d	18 15			18 36	18 42		18 48		19 15				19 40	19 42		19 48		20 15			20 40	20 42		20 48	
West Worthing	d	18 17				18 44		18 50		19 17					19 44		19 50		20 17				20 44		20 50	
Durrington-on-Sea	d	18 20				18 46		18 52		19 20					19 46		19 52		20 20				20 46		20 52	
Goring-by-Sea	d	18 22				18 49		18 55		19 22					19 49		19 55		20 22				20 49		20 55	
Angmering 3	d	18 26				18 55		18 59		19 26					19 53		19 59		20 26				20 53		20 59	
Littlehampton 4	a	18 35				19 02				19 35					20 02				20 35				21 02			
	d						18 57									19 57								20 57		
Ford 4	d			18 38			19 01	19 05					19 38			20 01	20 05				20 38			21 01	21 05	
Bognor Regis 4	d																									
Barnham	a			18 42	18 54		19 08	19 11	←				19 42	19 54		20 08	20 11	←			20 42	20 54		21 08	21 11	←
	d			18 43	18 55		19 15 →	19 12	19 15				19 43	19 55		20 15 →	20 12	20 15			20 43	20 55		21 15 →	21 12	21 15
Bognor Regis 4	a			18 49					19 21				19 49					20 21			20 49					21 21
Chichester 4	a				19 02			19 19						20 02			20 19					21 02			21 19	
	d				19 03			19 20						20 03			20 20					21 03			21 20	
Fishbourne (Sussex)	d							19 23									20 23								21 23	
Bosham	d							19 26									20 26								21 26	
Nutbourne	d							19 29									20 29								21 29	
Southbourne	d				19 10			19 32						20 10			20 32					21 10			21 32	
Emsworth	d				19 13			19 35						20 13			20 35					21 13			21 35	
Warblington	d							19 38									20 38								21 38	
Havant	d				19 17			19 44						20 17			20 44					21 17			21 44	
Bedhampton	a				*19 41*			19 46						*20 41*			20 46					*21 41*			21 46	
Hilsea	a																									
Fratton	a				19 26			19 54						20 26			20 54					21 26			21 54	
Portsmouth & Southsea	a				19 29			19 57						20 29			20 57					21 29			21 57	
Portsmouth Harbour	a				19 35			20 01						20 35			21 01					21 35			22 01	
Cosham	a																									
Portchester	a																									
Fareham	a																									
Swanwick	a																									
Southampton Central	a																									

For general notes see front of timetable
For details of catering facilities see Directory of Train Operators

b Change at East Croydon and Brighton
c Arr. 1820
e Arr. 1920
f Arr. 2020

For complete service between Three Bridges and Horsham see Table 186

Table 188

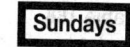

London, Gatwick Airport & Brighton → Sussex Coast, Portsmouth and Southampton

from 13 September

Network Diagram - see first page of Table 186

		SN 1	SN 1	SN 1		SN 1		SN 1	SN 1	SN 1	GW 1	SN 1	SN 1	SN 1	SN 1	SN 1		SN 1	SN 1	SN 1	SN 1	SN 1	SN 1	SN 1	SN 1	
London Victoria 15	⊖ d		20 02	20 04		20 17							21 02	21 04		21 17					21 32	22 04	22 17		23 17	
Clapham Junction 10	d		20 08	20 10		20 23							21 08	21 10		21 23					21 38	22 10	22 23		23 23	
London Bridge 4	⊖ d	19 11	19b44	19 44		20 11					20 11		20b44	20 44		21 11				21 11	21 41	21 44	22 11		23 11	
East Croydon	d	19 28	20 22	20 24		20 37					20 27		21 22	21 24		21 37				21 28	21 57	22 24	22 37		23 38	
Redhill 5	d			20 39										21 39								22 39			23 42	
Horley	d			20 45										21 45								22 45			23 50	
Gatwick Airport 10	✈ d	19 50	20 40	20 48		20 56					20 50		21 40	21 48		21 55				21 50	22 20	22 48	22 56		00 01	
Three Bridges 4	a			20 53										21 53								22 53			00 05	
	d	19 54	20 24	20 53		20 54					20 54		21 24	21 53		21 54				21 54	22 24	22 53	22 54		00 06	
Crawley	d			20 56										21 56								22 56				
Horsham 4	a			21 04										22 04								23 04				
	d			21 05										22 05								23 05				
Christs Hospital	d			21 08										22 08								23 08				
Billingshurst	d			21 15										22 15								23 15				
Pulborough	d			21 21										22 21								23 21				
Amberley	d			21 27										22 27								23 27				
Arundel	d			21 33										22 33								23 33				
Haywards Heath 3	d	20 03	20 33			21 07					21 03		21 33			22 06				22 03	22 33		23 07		00 15	
Burgess Hill	d	20 08	20 38			21 12					21 08		21 38			22 12				22 08	22 38		23 12			
Brighton 10	d	20 50	21 17						←		21 46	21 50	22 10							22 40	23 15					
Hove 2	d	20 54	21c26			21 24			21 26		21 50	21 54	22a13			22 25				22 44	23a18		23 25		00 29	
Aldrington	d	20 56	→						21 28			21 56								22 46						
Portslade	d	20 58							21 31			21 58								22 48			23 28		00s32	
Fishersgate	d	21 00							21 33			22 00								22 50						
Southwick	d	21 02							21 35			22 02								22 52			23 31		00s35	
Shoreham-by-Sea	d	21 05				21 30			21 38		21 56	22 05				22 30				22 55			23 34		00s38	
Lancing	d	21 09							21 42			22 09								22 59			23 38		00s42	
East Worthing	d	21 12							21 45			22 12								23 02						
Worthing 4	a	21 15				21 36			21 47		22 02	22 15				22 36				23 05			23 42		00 46	
	d	21 15				21 40	21 42		21 48		22 03	22 15				22 41	22 42			23 05						
West Worthing	d	21 17					21 44		21 50			22 17					22 44			23 07						
Durrington-on-Sea	d	21 20					21 46		21 52			22 20					22 46			23 09						
Goring-by-Sea	d	21 22					21 49		21 55			22 22					22 49			23 12						
Angmering 3	d	21 26					21 53		21 59			22 26					22 53			23 16						
Littlehampton 4	a	21 35					22 02					22 35					23 02			23 24						
	d							21 57											23 06	23 29						
Ford 4	d			21 38				22 01	22 05					22 38					23 10	23 33		23 38				
Bognor Regis 4	d																									
Barnham	a			21 42		21 54		22 08	22 11	←	22 17			22 42		22 55			23 14	23 37		23 42		←		
	d			21 43		21 55		22 15	22 12	22 15	22 18			22 43	22 56	22 56		22 57	23 15	23 45		23 43		23 45		
Bognor Regis 4	a			21 49				→		22 21				22 49	23 02			23 03	23 21	→		23 49				
Chichester 4	a					22 02			22 19		22 25					23 03								23 52		
	d					22 03			22 20		22 26					23 04										
Fishbourne (Sussex)	d								22 23																	
Bosham	d								22 26							23 08										
Nutbourne	d								22 29							23 12										
Southbourne	d					22 10			22 32							23 14										
Emsworth	d					22 13			22 35							23 17										
Warblington	d								22 38																	
Havant	d					22 17			22 44		22 47					23 22										
Bedhampton	a					22 41			22 46							23 41										
Hilsea	a																									
Fratton	a					22 26			22 54		22 57					23 31										
Portsmouth & Southsea	a					22 29			22 57		23 00					23 34										
Portsmouth Harbour	a					22 35			23 01		23 04					23 38										
Cosham	a																									
Portchester	a																									
Fareham	a																									
Swanwick	a																									
Southampton Central	a																									

For general notes see front of timetable
For details of catering facilities see Directory of Train Operators

b Change at East Croydon and Brighton
c Arr. 2120

For complete service between Three Bridges and Horsham see Table 186

Southampton, Portsmouth and Sussex Coast → Brighton, Gatwick Airport & London

Network Diagram - see first page of Table 186

Miles	Miles	Miles			SN MX 1	SN MX 1	SN MX 1	SN 1	SN 1	SN 1	SN 1	SN 1	SN 1	SN 1	SN 1	SN 1	SN 1	SN 1		SN 1	SN 1	SN 1	SN 1	SN 1	SN 1	SN 1
0	—	—	**Southampton Central**	d																						
10¾	—	—	Swanwick	d																						
14½	—	—	Fareham	d																						
17¾	—	—	Portchester	d																						
20¼	—	—	Cosham	d																						
—	0	—	**Portsmouth Harbour**	d	22p44		23p15															05 33		05 47		
—	¾	—	Portsmouth & Southsea	d	22p48		23p19			*04b35*												05 37		05 51		
—	1½	—	Fratton	d	22p52		23p23			*04c39*												05 41		05 55		
—	4¼	—	Hilsea	d	22p56		23p27			*04e43*												05 45		05 59		
—	7¼	—	Bedhampton	d	23p01		23p33			*04f48*												05 50		06 04		
24¼	8	—	**Havant**	d	23p05		23p36			05 01				05 30								05 53		06 07		
—	8½	—	Warblington	d			23p38															05 56				
—	9¾	—	Emsworth	d			23p41															05 58		06 11		
—	11¼	—	Southbourne	d			23p44															06 01		06 14		
—	12¼	—	Nutbourne	d			23p47															06 03				
—	14	—	Bosham	d			23p50															06 07		06 18		
—	15¼	—	Fishbourne (Sussex)	d			23p53															06 10		06 21		
—	16¾	—	**Chichester 4**	a	23p16		23p57			05 15				05 40								06 13		06 25		
—	—	—		d	23p17	23p52	23p57			05 16				05 41								06 14		06 29		
0	—	—	**Bognor Regis 4**	d					05 13				05 35		05 49			05 55		06 04	06 11		06 22			
3½	23	—	Barnham	a	23p24	23p59	00 05		05 19	05 23	⟵		05 41	05 48	05 55			06 01		06 10	06 17	06 21	06 28	06 36		
—	—	—		d	23p25	00 01	00 06	04 48	05 27 ⟶	05 24	05 27		05 42	05 49				06 02		06 11	06 18	06 22	06 29	06 37		
—	—	—	Bognor Regis 4	a																						
0	25¾	0	Ford 4	d	23p29	00 05	00 10	04g52			05 31		05 46					06 06		06 15		06 26	06 33			
—	—	2	**Littlehampton 4**	a	23p34	00 10	00 15	04 57			05 36									06 20			06 38			
2	—	—		d	23p39	*23h23*		05 02					*05h35*			05 54				*06h04*					06 32	
8	30	—	Angmering 3	d	23p47			05 10		05 33			05 53			06 02		06 13				06 32			06 40	
—	32½	—	Goring-by-Sea	d	23p51			05 14					05 57			06 06		06 17				06 36			06 44	
—	33¼	—	Durrington-on-Sea	d	23p53			05 17					05 59			06 09		06 19				06 39			06 47	
—	34	—	West Worthing	d	23p55			05 19					06 01			06 11		06 21				06 41			06 49	
—	35	—	**Worthing 4**	a	23p58			05 21		05 40			06 04			06 13		06 24				06 44			06 52	
—	—	—		d	23p59			05 22		05 41			06 04			06 14		06 24				06 44			06 52	
—	35¾	—	East Worthing	d	00 01			05 24					06 07					06 27				06 46				
—	37¼	—	Lancing	d	00 04			05 27		05 45			06 10			06 18		06 30				06 49			06 57	
—	40	—	Shoreham-by-Sea	d	00 08			05 32		05 49			06 14			06 22		06 34				06 53			07 01	
—	41	—	Southwick	d	00 11			05 35					06 17					06 37				06 56				
—	42	—	Fishersgate	d	00 13			05 37					06 19					06 39				06 58				
—	42½	—	Portslade	d	00 15			05 39		05 53			06 21			06 27		06 41				07 00			07 06	
—	43½	—	Aldrington	d	00 18			05 41					06 23					06 43				07 03				
0	44	—	Hove 2	d	00 20			05 44		05 57		05 59	06 26			06 31	06 36	06 46				07 05			07 11	07 17
—	45½	—	**Brighton 10**	a	00 25			05 48				06 03	06 30				06 40	06 50				07 09				07 21
9¼	—	—	Burgess Hill	a												06 46										
13	—	—	Haywards Heath 3	a				*06 19*		06 12		*06 29*	*07 01*			06 54	*07 06*	*07 18*				*07 34*			07 29	*07 49*
—	—	2¼	Arundel	d										05 57							06 25					
—	—	6	Amberley	d																	06 30					
—	—	10¾	Pulborough	d										06 06							06 37					
—	—	15¾	Billingshurst	d										06 13							06 43					
—	—	20½	Christs Hospital	d										06 19							06 50					
—	—	23	**Horsham 4**	a										06 23							06 54			07 03		
—	—	—		d										06 24							06 54			07 04		
—	—	30	Crawley	d										06 37							07 08			07 13		
21½	—	31½	**Three Bridges 4**	a				*06 36*		06 21		*06 40*		06 40		*07 16*	*07 16*	*07 32*			07 11	*07 55*		07 18		*08 05*
—	—	—		d						06 21				06 48							07 12			07 22		
24¼	—	—	**Gatwick Airport 10** ✈	a				*06 41*		06 25		*06 45*	*07 14*	06 52		07 11	*07j29*	*07 32*				*07 47*		*07 29*	*07 47*	*08 02*
25	—	—	Horley	a						*06 39*				06 56		*07 24*					07 19					
30	—	—	Redhill 5	a						*06 51*				07 02		*07 36*					07 27					
40½	0	—	**East Croydon**	a				*06 58*		06 41		*07 01*		07 15		07 27	*07 42*	*07 53*			07 39	*08k08*		07 42	07 57	*08 23*
—	10¼	—	London Bridge 4 ⊖	a				*07 14*		*07 14*		*07 16*		*07 38*		07 46	*08m04*	*08m18*				*08k26*		*08 04*	*08 20*	*08 43*
48¼	—	—	Clapham Junction 10	a						06 51		*07m19*		07 24			*07 54*	*08m10*			07 48			07 54	08 06	*08m40*
51	—	61	**London Victoria 15** ⊖	a						07 00		*07n20*	*07 50*	07 33		*07q50*	*08 03*	*08 06*			07 57	*08 20*		08 03	08 16	*08 35*

For general notes see front of timetable
For details of catering facilities see Directory of Train Operators

b From 28 September dep. 0430

c From 28 September dep. 0434

e From 28 September dep. 0438

f From 28 September dep. 0443

g Also, connection applies. Ford. Change at Littlehampton. Arr. 0539

h Change at Ford

j Change at Brighton and Three Bridges

k Change at Brighton and Haywards Heath

m Change at Brighton and East Croydon

n Change at Brighton and Gatwick Airport

q Change at Gatwick Airport

For complete service between Horsham and Three Bridges see Table 186

Southampton, Portsmouth and Sussex Coast → Brighton, Gatwick Airport & London

Network Diagram - see first page of Table 186

		SN 1	SN 1	SN 1 🚲	SN 1	SN 1	SN 1	SN 1	SN 1	SN 1		SN 1	SN 1	SN 1	SN 1 🚲	SN 1	SN 1 🚲	SN 1	SN 1	GW	SN 1	SN 1	SN 1	SN 1	SN 1 🚲	SN 1
Southampton Central	d								05 48				06 10													07 06
Swanwick	d								06 06				06 27													07 24
Fareham	d								06 13				06 34													07 31
Portchester	d								06 18				06 40													07 36
Cosham	d								06 23				06 44													07 40
Portsmouth Harbour	d		06 04															06 46		07 01			07 20			
Portsmouth & Southsea	d		06 08										*06 20*					06 50		07 05			07 24			
Fratton	d		06 12										*06 24*					06 54		07 10			07 28			
Hilsea	d		*06 03*															06 58		*07 08*			*07 08*			
Bedhampton	d		*06 08*						06 34									07 03		*07 13*			*07 13*			
Havant	d		06 20						06 37				06 53					07 06		07 20			07 36			07 47
Warblington	d								06 39									07 08								07 49
Emsworth	d		06 24						06 42				06 57					07 11								07 52
Southbourne	d		06 27						06 45				07 00					07 14								07 55
Nutbourne	d								06 48									07 16								07 58
Bosham	d								06 51									07 20								08 01
Fishbourne (Sussex)	d								06 54									07 23								08 04
Chichester 4	a		06 34						06 58				07 07					07 26		07 31			07 47			08 08
	d		06 35						06 59				07 08					07 28		07 32			07 47			08 08
Bognor Regis 4	d			06 41			06 50	06 57							07 16	07 27						07 38			07 55	
Barnham	a		06 42	06 47			06 56	07 03	07 07				07 15		07 22	07 33		07 35		07 39		07 44	07 55		08 01	08 16
	d		06 43	06 48			06 57	07 11					07 16		07 23			07 36		07 40		07 45	07 55		08 02	08 16
Bognor Regis 4	a																									
Ford 4	d		06 47	06 52			07 01						07 20									07 50	08 00		08 06	
Littlehampton 4	a						07 06															07 54				
	d	06 42	*06b39*							07 03			*07b00*	07 22					07 32		07 45	*07b18*	*07b48*	08 01	*07b58*	
Angmering 3	d	06 50	06 56							07 11			07 26	07c33					07 41		07 53		08 06	08 10		
Goring-by-Sea	d	06 54	07 00							07 15			07 30	07 37					07 45		07 57			08 14		
Durrington-on-Sea	d	06 57	07 03							07 17			07 33	07 39					07 47		08 00		08 12	08 17		
West Worthing	d	06 59	07 05		07 12					07 20			07 35	07 42					07 50		08 02			08 19		
Worthing 4	a	06 57	07 07		07 14					07 22			07 37	07 44					07 52	07 56	08 04		08 16	08 21		
	d	07 02	07 08		07 15					07 23			07 38	07 45					07 53	08 00	08 05		08 16	08 22		
East Worthing	d				07 17									07 47							08 07			08 24		
Lancing	d	07 07	07 12		07 20					07 27			07 42	07 50					07 57		08 10		08 20	08 27		
Shoreham-by-Sea	d	07 11	07 16		07 25					07 31			07 46	07 55					08 01	08 06	08 15		08 24	08 32		
Southwick	d		07 19		07 28								07 49	07 58							08 18		08 27	08 35		
Fishersgate	d				07 30									08 00							08 20			08 37		
Portslade	d	07 16	07 22		07 32					07 36			07 52	08 02					08 06		08 22		08 31	08 39		
Aldrington	d				07 34									08 04							08 24			08 41		
Hove 2	d	07 20	07 26		07 37					07 41		07 49	07 56	08 07					08 11	08 14	08 27		08 34	08 44		
Brighton 10	a		07 30		07 41							07 54	08 00	08 11						08 20	08 31		08 38	08 48		
Burgess Hill	a					←				07 51									08 26							
Haywards Heath 3	a	07 40	*08 05*		*08 08*	07 40				07 57		*08 23*		*08 37*					08 31		*08 55*		*08 57*	*09 16*		
Arundel	d			06 58				07 18							07 30										08 11	
Amberley	d														07 35										08 16	
Pulborough	d			07 07				07 28							07 41										08 22	
Billingshurst	d			07 14				07 35							07 48		←								08 29	
Christs Hospital	d			07 20				07 41							07 55		07 55								08 35	
Horsham 4	a			07 24				07 45							→		07 59	08 05							08 39	08 45
	d			07 25				07 46									08 09								08 49	
Crawley	d			07 37				08 00									08 18								08 58	
Three Bridges 4	a	*07 55*		07 40	*08e27*			08 03		*08 27*		*08 33*		*08 47*			08 22		08 41				*09e11*	*09 26*	09 01	
	d			07 41				08 04									08 22		08 42						09 02	
Gatwick Airport 10 ✈	a	*08 00*	*08 17*	*08 00*	*08 22*			*08 14*		08 12		*08 38*		*08 51*			*08 34*		*08 51*				*09 10*	*09 31*	09 06	
Horley	a	→								*08 38*							08 28								*09 26*	
Redhill 5	a									*08 49*															*09 36*	
East Croydon	a			08 00	*08 38*	08 08		08 26		08 29		*08 54*		*09 08*			08 43		09 01				*09 26*	*09 47*	09 22	
London Bridge 4 ⊖	a			*08 24*	*09f05*	08 26		08 45		08g50		*09 10*		*09f42*			*09 08*		*09 42*				*09f45*	*10 01*	*09 45*	
Clapham Junction 10	a			08 10	*08f53*	08h23		08h47		08 39		*09f10*		*09f23*			08 53		09 10				*09 35*		09 32	
London Victoria 15 ⊖	a		*08 52*	08 19	*09f02*	08h32		08j52		08 48		*09f19*		*09f32*			09 02		09 19				*09 44*		09 41	

For general notes see front of timetable
For details of catering facilities see Directory of Train Operators

b Change at Ford
c Arr. 0730
e Change at Brighton and Haywards Heath
f Change at Brighton and East Croydon
g Change at Haywards Heath
h Change at East Croydon
j Change at Three Bridges and Gatwick Airport

For complete service between Horsham and Three Bridges see Table 186

Table 188 — **Mondays to Fridays**

Southampton, Portsmouth and Sussex Coast → Brighton, Gatwick Airport & London

Network Diagram - see first page of Table 186

		SN	SN		SN	SN	SN	SN	SN	SN	SN	SN	SN	SN	SN	SN	SN	SN		SN	SN	SN	SN	SN	SN	SN
		1	1		1	1	1	1	1	1	1	1	1	1	1	1	1	1		1	1	1	1	1	1	1
							⊼				⊼													A ⊼		
Southampton Central	d							07 33															08 10			
Swanwick	d							07 51															08 28			
Fareham	d							07 58															08 35			
Portchester	d																						08 40			
Cosham	d							08 07															08 44			
Portsmouth Harbour	d											08 10						08 29								
Portsmouth & Southsea	d							07 50		08 03		08 14						08 33								
Fratton	d							07 54		08 07		08 18						08 37								
Hilsea	d							07 41		08 11								08 32								
Bedhampton	d							07 48		08 16								08 37								
Havant	d							08 13		08 19		08 27						08 46					08 51			
Warblington	d									08 21													08 53			
Emsworth	d									08 24		08 31						08 50					08 56			
Southbourne	d									08 27								08 53					08 59			
Nutbourne	d									08 29													09 01			
Bosham	d							08 21															09 05			
Fishbourne (Sussex)	d							08 24															09 08			
Chichester 4	a							08 27		08 35		08 40						09 00					09 11			
	d					08 21		08 28		08 36		08 41						09 00		09 07			09 13			
Bognor Regis 4	d				08 13		08 26		08 32					08 48	08 56						09 09					
Barnham	a				08 19	08 28	08 32	08 35	08 38	08 43		08 48		08 55	09 02			09 08		09 14	09 15		09 20			
	d				08 20	08 29	08 33	08 36		08 44		08 49			09 03			09 08		09 15			09 21			
Bognor Regis 4	a																									
Ford 4	d				08 24	08 33	08 37	08 40		08 48					09 07					09 19						
Littlehampton 4	a					08 38				08 53										09 24						
	d	08 15					08b26						08 45		08b54									09 15		
Angmering 3	d	08 23			08 30			08 46					08 53					09 17						09 23		
Goring-by-Sea	d	08 27			08 34								08 57											09 27		
Durrington-on-Sea	d	08 30			08 37			08 52					09 00											09 30		
West Worthing	d	08 32			08 39								09 02				09 09							09 32		09 39
Worthing 4	a	08 34			08 41			08 56					09 04				09 11	09 24						09 34		09 41
	d	08 35			08 42			08 56					09 05				09 12	09 26						09 36		09 42
East Worthing	d				08 44												09 14									09 44
Lancing	d	08 39			08 47			09 00					09 09				09 17	09 30								09 47
Shoreham-by-Sea	d	08 43			08 52			09 04					09 13				09 22	09 34						09 42		09 52
Southwick	d				08 55			09 07									09 25	09 37								09 55
Fishersgate	d				08 57												09 27									09 57
Portslade	d	08 48			08 59			09 11					09 18				09 29	09 40						09 47		09 59
Aldrington	d				09 01												09 31									10 01
Hove 2	d	08 52	08 54		09 04			09 14					09 22			09 24	09 34	09 44						09 51	09 54	10 04
Brighton 10	a		08 58		09 08			09 18								09 28	09 38	09 48							09 58	10 08
Burgess Hill	a	09 07											09 33											10 01		
Haywards Heath 3	a	09 12	09 28										09 39			09 47		10 15						10 06	10 18	
Arundel	d						08 42								09 12											
Amberley	d						08 47								09 17											
Pulborough	d						08 53								09 23											
Billingshurst	d						09 00								09 29											
Christs Hospital	d						09 06 →				← 09 06				09 36 →							← 09 36				
Horsham 4	a										09 10	09 16										09 40	09 48			
	d										09 20											09 52				
Crawley	d										09 29											10 01				
Three Bridges 4	a	09 26	09 42								09 32		10 07			10 07		10 25				10 04		10 25	10 42	
	d										09 33											10 05				
Gatwick Airport 10 ✈	a	09 26	09 46								09 37		09 54			10 00						10 09		10 24	10 30	
Horley	a										09 40											10 26				
Redhill 5	a										09 47		10 10									10 17				
East Croydon	a	09 42			09 54						09 59		10 10			10 16	10 24					10 29		10 40	10 46	10 56
London Bridge 4 ⊖	a	10 01			10c16						10e16		10 30			10 30	10c45					10e45		11 00	11 00	11c15
Clapham Junction 10	a	09 52			10 04						10 09		10 20				10 33					10 38		10 50	11c02	11 05
London Victoria 15 ⊖	a	10 00			10 11						10 16		10 27			10f35	10 40					10 45		10 57	11f05	11 12

For general notes see front of timetable
For details of catering facilities see Directory of Train Operators

A ⊼ from Haywards Heath
b Change at Ford
c Change at Brighton and East Croydon
e Change at Gatwick Airport
f Change at Brighton and Gatwick Airport

For complete service between Horsham and Three Bridges see Table 186

Southampton, Portsmouth and Sussex Coast → Brighton, Gatwick Airport & London

Network Diagram - see first page of Table 186

		SN 1	SN 1	SN 1	SN 1	SN 1	SN 1	SN 1	SN 1	SN 1		SN 1	SN 1	SN 1	SN 1	SN 1	SN 1	SN 1	SN 1	SN 1	SN 1	SN 1	SN 1	SN 1	SN 1	SN 1
								A 🚌	🚌						🚌											A 🚌
Southampton Central	d	08 33														09 10				09 33						
Swanwick	d	08 50														09 28				09 50						
Fareham	d	08 57														09 37				09 56						
Portchester	d															09 42										
Cosham	d	09 05														09 46				10 05						
Portsmouth Harbour	d			08 52			09 12						09 29												10 12	
Portsmouth & Southsea	d	08 50		08 56			09 16						09 33							09 50		09 56			10 16	
Fratton	d	08 54		09 00			09 20						09 37							09 54		10 01			10 20	
Hilsea	d			09 04									09 32									10 05				
Bedhampton	d			09 13									09 37									10 13				
Havant	d	09 12		09 16			09 30						09 46			09 54				10 11		10 16			10 30	
Warblington	d			09 18																		10 18				
Emsworth	d	09 16		09 21									09 50			10 00				10 15		10 21				
Southbourne	d			09 24									09 53			10 03						10 24				
Nutbourne	d			09 26																		10 26				
Bosham	d			09 30																		10 30				
Fishbourne (Sussex)	d			09 33																		10 33				
Chichester 4	a	09 24		09 36			09 40						10 00			10 10				10 23		10 36			10 40	
	d	09 25		09 37			09 41						10 00			10 11				10 25		10 37			10 41	
Bognor Regis 4	d		09 30		09 39				09 56					10 07							10 30		10 39			
Barnham	a	09 32	09 36	09 44	09 45		09 48		10 02				10 08	10 13		10 18				10 32	10 36	10 44	10 45		10 48	
	d	09 33	09 37	09 45			09 49		10 03				10 08	10 15		10 19				10 33	10 37	10 45			10 49	
Bognor Regis 4	a																									
Ford 4	d	09 37	09 41	09 49					10 07					10 19						10 37	10 41	10 49				
Littlehampton 4	a			09 54										10 24								10 54				
	d							09 45	09b54								10 15			10b11						10 45
Angmering 3	d	09 43						09 54					10 17				10 23			10 43						10 53
Goring-by-Sea	d	09 47						09 58									10 27			10 47						10 57
Durrington-on-Sea	d	09 50						10 00									10 30			10 50						11 00
West Worthing	d	09 52						10 02				10 09					10 32		10 39	10 52						11 02
Worthing 4	a	09 54						10 05				10 11	10 24				10 34		10 41	10 54						11 04
	d	09 56						10 06				10 12	10 26				10 36		10 42	10 56						11 06
East Worthing	d											10 14							10 44							
Lancing	d	10 00						10 10				10 17	10 30						10 47	11 00						11 10
Shoreham-by-Sea	d	10 04						10 14				10 22	10 34				10 42		10 52	11 04						11 14
Southwick	d	10 07										10 25	10 37						10 55	11 07						
Fishersgate	d											10 27							10 57							
Portslade	d	10 10										10 29	10 40				10 47		10 59	11 10						
Aldrington	d											10 31							11 01							
Hove 2	d	10 14						10 21		10 24		10 34	10 44				10 51	10 54	11 04	11 14						11 21
Brighton 10	a	10 18								10 28		10 38	10 48					10 58	11 08	11 18						
Burgess Hill	a																11 01									
Haywards Heath 3	a							10 35		10 47			11 15				11 08	11 18								11 35
Arundel	d		09 46						10 12												10 46					
Amberley	d								10 17																	
Pulborough	d		09 55						10 23												10 55					
Billingshurst	d		10 01 →			← 10 01			10 29												11 01 →			← 11 01		
Christs Hospital	d								10 36 →						← 10 36											
Horsham 4	a					10 10	10 16								10 40	10 46								11 10	11 16	
	d					10 20									10 50									11 20		
Crawley	d					10 29									10 59									11 29		
Three Bridges 4	a					10 32		11 11		11 11			11 25		11 02		11 25	11 42						11 32		12 11
	d					10 33									11 03									11 33		
Gatwick Airport 10 ✈	a					10 37		10 54		11 00					11 07		11 24	11 30						11 37		11 54
Horley	a					10 41									11 26									11 41		
Redhill 5	a					10 47		11 10							11 15									11 47		12 10
East Croydon	a					10 59		11 10		11 16		11 23			11 27		11 40	11 46	11 56					11 59		12 10
London Bridge 4 ⊖	a					11c15		11 30		11 30		11e45			11 45		12 00	12 00	12e15					12c15		12 30
Clapham Junction 10	a					11 09		11 20				11 33			11 37		11 50	12e02	12 05					12 09		12 19
London Victoria 15 ⊖	a					11 16		11 27		11f35		11 40			11 44		11 57	12f05	12 12					12 18		12 28

For general notes see front of timetable
For details of catering facilities see Directory of Train Operators

A 🚌 from Haywards Heath
b Change at Ford
c Change at Gatwick Airport
e Change at Brighton and East Croydon
f Change at Brighton and Gatwick Airport

For complete service between Horsham and Three Bridges see Table 186

Southampton, Portsmouth and Sussex Coast → Brighton, Gatwick Airport & London

Network Diagram - see first page of Table 186

		SN	SN	SN	SN	SN	SN	SN	SN	SN	SN	SN	SN	SN	SN	SN	SN	SN	SN	SN	SN	SN	SN
		1	1	1	1	1	1	1	1	1	1	1	1	1	1	1	1	1	1	1	1	1	1
																		A					
		🛒					🛒						🛒			🛒		🛒	🛒				
Southampton Central	d							10 10				10 33											
Swanwick	d							10 28				10 50											
Fareham	d							10 37				10 56											
Portchester	d							10 42															
Cosham	d							10 46				11 05											
Portsmouth Harbour	d				10 29												11 12					11 29	
Portsmouth & Southsea	d				10 33							10 50		10 56			11 16					11 33	
Fratton	d				10 37							10 54		11 01			11 20					11 37	
Hilsea	d				10 32									11 05								11 32	
Bedhampton	d				10 37									11 13								11 37	
Havant	d				10 46			10 54				11 12		11 16			11 30					11 46	
Warblington	d													11 18									
Emsworth	d				10 50			11 00				11 16		11 21								11 50	
Southbourne	d				10 53			11 03						11 24								11 53	
Nutbourne	d													11 26									
Bosham	d													11 30									
Fishbourne (Sussex)	d													11 33									
Chichester 4	a				11 00			11 10				11 24		11 36			11 40					12 00	
	d				11 00			11 11				11 25		11 37			11 41					12 00	
Bognor Regis 4	d	10 56				11 07							11 30		11 39				11 56				12 07
Barnham	a	11 02			11 08	11 13		11 18				11 32	11 36	11 44	11 45		11 48		12 02			12 08	12 13
	d	11 03			11 08	11 15		11 19				11 33	11 37	11 45			11 49		12 03			12 08	12 15
Bognor Regis 4	a																						
Ford 4	d	11 07				11 19						11 37	11 41	11 49					12 07				12 19
Littlehampton 4	a					11 24								11 54									12 24
	d	10b54							11 15			11b11						11 45	11b54				
Angmering 3	d				11 17				11 23			11 43						11 53				12 17	
Goring-by-Sea	d								11 27			11 47						11 57					
Durrington-on-Sea	d								11 30			11 50						12 00					
West Worthing	d			11 09					11 32		11 39	11 52						12 02			12 09		
Worthing 4	a			11 11	11 24				11 34		11 41	11 54						12 04			12 11	12 24	
	d			11 12	11 26				11 36		11 42	11 56						12 06			12 12	12 26	
East Worthing	d			11 14							11 44										12 14		
Lancing	d			11 17	11 30						11 47	12 00						12 10			12 17	12 30	
Shoreham-by-Sea	d			11 22	11 34				11 42		11 52	12 04						12 14			12 22	12 34	
Southwick	d			11 25	11 37						11 55	12 07									12 25	12 37	
Fishersgate	d			11 27							11 57										12 27		
Portslade	d			11 29	11 40				11 47		11 59	12 10									12 29	12 40	
Aldrington	d			11 31							12 01										12 31		
Hove 2	d		11 24	11 34	11 44				11 51	11 54	12 04	12 14						12 21		12 24	12 34	12 44	
Brighton 10	a		11 28	11 38	11 48					11 58	12 08	12 18								12 28	12 38	12 48	
Burgess Hill	a								12 01														
Haywards Heath 3	a		11 47		12 15				12 09	12 18								12 35		12 47		13 15	
Arundel	d	11 12											11 46						12 12				
Amberley	d	11 17																	12 17				
Pulborough	d	11 23											11 55						12 23				
Billingshurst	d	11 29											12 01 →			← 12 01			12 29				
Christs Hospital	d	11 36 →					← 11 36												12 36 →				
Horsham 4	a						11 40	11 46								12 10	12 16						
	d							11 50									12 20						
Crawley	d							11 59									12 29						
Three Bridges 4	a		12 11		12 25			12 02	12 25	12 42							12 32	13 11		13 11		13 25	
	d							12 03									12 33						
Gatwick Airport 10	a		12 00					12 07	12 24	12 30							12 37	12 54		13 00			
Horley	a							12 26									12 41						
Redhill 5	a							12 15									12 47	13 10					
East Croydon	a		12 16	12 23				12 27	12 40	12 46	12 56						12 59	13 10		13 16	13 23		
London Bridge 4	a		12 30	12c45				12 45	13 00	13 00	13c15						13e15	13 30		13 30	13c45		
Clapham Junction 10	a			12 33				12 37	12 50	13c02	13 05						13 09	13 20			13 33		
London Victoria 15	a		12f35	12 40				12 44	12 57	13f05	13 12						13 16	13 28		13f35	13 40		

For general notes see front of timetable
For details of catering facilities see Directory of Train Operators

A 🛒 from Haywards Heath
b Change at Ford
c Change at Brighton and East Croydon
e Change at Gatwick Airport
f Change at Brighton and Gatwick Airport

For complete service between Horsham and Three Bridges see Table 186

Southampton, Portsmouth and Sussex Coast → Brighton, Gatwick Airport & London

Network Diagram - see first page of Table 186

		SN 1	SN 1	SN 1	SN 1	SN 1	SN 1	SN 1	SN 1	SN 1		SN 1	SN 1	SN 1	SN 1	SN 1	SN 1	SN 1	SN 1	SN 1	SN 1	SN 1	SN 1	SN 1	SN 1	SN 1
		🛒						🛒				🛒		A 🛒	🛒					🛒						
Southampton Central	d		11 13				11 33														12 13				12 33	
Swanwick	d		11 33				11 50														12 33				12 50	
Fareham	d		11 40				11 57														12 40				12 56	
Portchester	d		11 45																		12 45					
Cosham	d		11 49				12 05														12 49				13 05	
Portsmouth Harbour	d												12 12					12 29								
Portsmouth & Southsea	d						11 50		11 56				12 16					12 33							12 50	
Fratton	d						11 54		12 01				12 20					12 37							12 54	
Hilsea	d								12 05									12 32								
Bedhampton	d								12 13									12 37								
Havant	d		11 56				12 12		12 16				12 30					12 46			12 56				13 11	
Warblington	d								12 18																	
Emsworth	d		12 00				12 16		12 21									12 50			13 00				13 15	
Southbourne	d		12 03						12 24									12 53			13 03					
Nutbourne	d								12 26																	
Bosham	d								12 30																	
Fishbourne (Sussex)	d								12 33																	
Chichester 4	a		12 10				12 24		12 36				12 40					13 00			13 10				13 23	
	d		12 11				12 25		12 37				12 41					13 00			13 11				13 25	
Bognor Regis 4	d							12 30		12 39					12 56				13 07							13 30
Barnham	a		12 18				12 32	12 36	12 44	12 45			12 48		13 02			13 08	13 13		13 18				13 32	13 36
	d		12 19				12 33	12 37	12 45				12 49		13 03			13 08	13 15		13 19				13 33	13 37
Bognor Regis 4	a																									
Ford 4	d						12 37	12 41	12 49						13 07				13 19						13 37	13 41
Littlehampton 4	a								12 54										13 24							
	d			12 15			12b11							12 45	12b54							13 15			13b11	
Angmering 3	d			12 23			12 43							12 53				13 17				13 23			13 43	
Goring-by-Sea	d			12 27			12 47							12 57								13 27			13 47	
Durrington-on-Sea	d			12 30			12 50							13 00								13 30			13 50	
West Worthing	d			12 32		12 39	12 52							13 02			13 09					13 32		13 39	13 52	
Worthing 4	a			12 34		12 41	12 54							13 04			13 11	13 24				13 34		13 41	13 54	
	d			12 36		12 42	12 56							13 06			13 12	13 26				13 36		13 42	13 56	
East Worthing	d					12 44											13 14							13 44		
Lancing	d					12 47	13 00							13 10			13 17	13 30						13 47	14 00	
Shoreham-by-Sea	d			12 42		12 52	13 04							13 14			13 22	13 34				13 42		13 52	14 04	
Southwick	d					12 55	13 07										13 25	13 37						13 55	14 07	
Fishersgate	d					12 57											13 27							13 57		
Portslade	d			12 47		12 59	13 10										13 29	13 40				13 47		13 59	14 10	
Aldrington	d					13 01											13 31							14 01		
Hove 2	d			12 51	12 54	13 04	13 14							13 21		13 24	13 34	13 44				13 51	13 54	14 04	14 14	
Brighton 10	a				12 58	13 08	13 18									13 28	13 38	13 48					13 58	14 08	14 18	
Burgess Hill	a			13 01																		14 01				
Haywards Heath 3	a			13 09	13 18									13 35		13 47		14 15				14 09	14 18			
Arundel	d							12 46							13 12											13 46
Amberley	d														13 17											
Pulborough	d							12 55							13 23											13 55
Billingshurst	d	←						13 01 →				← 13 01			13 29					←						14 01 →
Christs Hospital	d	12 36													13 36 →					13 36						
Horsham 4	a	12 40	12 46									13 10	13 16							13 40	13 46					
	d	12 50										13 20								13 50						
Crawley	d	12 59										13 29								13 59						
Three Bridges 4	a	13 02		13 25	13 42							13 32		14 11		14 11		14 25		14 02		14 25	14 42			
	d	13 03										13 33								14 03						
Gatwick Airport 10 ✈	a	13 07		13 24	13 30							13 37		13 54		14 00				14 07		14 24	14 30			
Horley	a	13 26										13 41								14 26						
Redhill 5	a	13 15										13 47		14 10						14 15						
East Croydon	a	13 27		13 40	13 46	13 56						13 59		14 10		14 16	14 23			14 27		14 40	14 46	14 56		
London Bridge 4 ⊖	a	13 45		14 00	14 00	14c15						14e15		14 30		14 30	14c45			14 45		15 00	15 00	15c15		
Clapham Junction 10	a	13 37		13 50	14c02	14 05						14 09		14 20			14 33			14 37		14 50	15c02	15 05		
London Victoria 15 ⊖	a	13 44		13 57	14f05	14 12						14 16		14 27		14f35	14 40			14 44		14 57	15f05	15 12		

For general notes see front of timetable
For details of catering facilities see Directory of Train Operators

A 🛒 from Haywards Heath
b Change at Ford
c Change at Brighton and East Croydon
e Change at Gatwick Airport
f Change at Brighton and Gatwick Airport

For complete service between Horsham and Three Bridges see Table 186

Southampton, Portsmouth and Sussex Coast → Brighton, Gatwick Airport & London

Network Diagram - see first page of Table 186

		SN 1		SN 1	SN 1	SN 1	SN 1	SN 1	SN 1	SN 1	SN 1	SN 1	SN 1	SN 1	SN 1	SN 1	SN 1		SN 1	SN 1	SN 1	SN 1	SN 1	SN 1	SN 1	SN 1
							A 🚲	🚲					🚲							🚲			🚲		A 🚲	🚲
Southampton Central	d													13 13					13 33							
Swanwick	d													13 33					13 50							
Fareham	d													13 40					13 56							
Portchester	d													13 45												
Cosham	d													13 49					14 05							
Portsmouth Harbour	d					13 12					13 29													14 12		
Portsmouth & Southsea	d	12 56				13 16					13 33								13 50		13 56			14 16		
Fratton	d	13 01				13 20					13 37								13 54		14 01			14 20		
Hilsea	d	13 05									13 32										14 05					
Bedhampton	d	13 13									13 37										14 13					
Havant	d	13 16				13 30					13 46			13 56					14 11		14 16			14 30		
Warblington	d	13 18																			14 18					
Emsworth	d	13 21									13 50			14 00					14 15		14 21					
Southbourne	d	13 24									13 53			14 03							14 24					
Nutbourne	d	13 26																			14 26					
Bosham	d	13 30																			14 30					
Fishbourne (Sussex)	d	13 33																			14 33					
Chichester 4	a	13 36				13 40					14 00			14 10					14 23		14 36			14 40		
	d	13 37				13 41					14 00			14 11					14 25		14 37			14 41		
Bognor Regis 4	d			13 39				13 56				14 07								14 30		14 40				14 56
Barnham	a	13 44		13 45		13 48		14 02			14 08	14 13		14 18					14 32	14 36	14 44	14 46		14 48		15 02
	d	13 45				13 49		14 03			14 08	14 15		14 19					14 33	14 37	14 45			14 49		15 03
Bognor Regis 4	a																									
Ford 4	d	13 49						14 07				14 19							14 37	14 41	14 49					15 07
Littlehampton 4	a	13 54										14 24									14 54					
	d						13 45	13b54							14 15				14b11						14 45	14b54
Angmering 3	d						13 53				14 17				14 23				14 43						14 53	
Goring-by-Sea	d						13 57								14 27				14 47						14 57	
Durrington-on-Sea	d						14 00								14 30				14 50						15 00	
West Worthing	d						14 02			14 09					14 32		14 39		14 52						15 02	
Worthing 4	a						14 04			14 11	14 24				14 34		14 41		14 54						15 04	
	d						14 06			14 12	14 26				14 36		14 42		14 56						15 06	
East Worthing	d									14 14							14 44									
Lancing	d						14 10			14 17	14 30						14 47		15 00						15 10	
Shoreham-by-Sea	d						14 14			14 22	14 34				14 42		14 52		15 04						15 14	
Southwick	d									14 25	14 37						14 55		15 07							
Fishersgate	d									14 27							14 57									
Portslade	d									14 29	14 40				14 47		14 59		15 10							
Aldrington	d									14 31							15 01									
Hove 2	d						14 21		14 24	14 34	14 44				14 51	14 54	15 04		15 14						15 21	
Brighton 10	a								14 28	14 38	14 48					14 58	15 08		15 18							
Burgess Hill	a														15 01											
Haywards Heath 3	a						14 35		14 47		15 15				15 09	15 18									15 35	
Arundel	d							14 12												14 46						15 12
Amberley	d							14 17																		15 17
Pulborough	d							14 23												14 55						15 23
Billingshurst	d				← 14 01			14 29												15 01 →			← 15 01			15 29
Christs Hospital	d							14 36 →					← 14 36													15 36 →
Horsham 4	a				14 10	14 16							14 40	14 46									15 10	15 16		
	d					14 20								14 50										15 20		
Crawley	d					14 29								14 59										15 29		
Three Bridges 4	a					14 32	15 11		15 11		15 25			15 02	15 25	15 42								15 32	16 07	
	d					14 33								15 03										15 33		
Gatwick Airport 10 ✈	a					14 37	14 54		15 00					15 07	15 24	15 30								15 37	15 55	
Horley	a					14 41								15 26										15 41		
Redhill 5	a					14 47	15 10							15 16										15 47	16 10	
East Croydon	a					14 59	15 10		15 16	15 23				15 28	15 40	15 46	15 56							15 59	16 11	
London Bridge 4 ⊖	a					15c15	15 30		15 30	15e45				15c45	16 00	16 00	16e15							16c15	16 39	
Clapham Junction 10	a					15 09	15 20			15 33				15 37	15 50	16e02	16 05							16 09	16 20	
London Victoria 15 ⊖	a					15 20	15 27		15f35	15 40				15 44	15 57	16f05	16 12							16 20	16 28	

For general notes see front of timetable
For details of catering facilities see Directory of Train Operators

A 🚲 from Haywards Heath
b Change at Ford
c Change at Gatwick Airport
e Change at Brighton and East Croydon
f Change at Brighton and Gatwick Airport

For complete service between Horsham and Three Bridges see Table 186

Southampton, Portsmouth and Sussex Coast → Brighton, Gatwick Airport & London

Network Diagram - see first page of Table 186

		SN	SN	SN	SN	SN	SN	SN	SN	SN	GW	SN	SN	SN	SN	SN	SN	SN	SN	SN	SN	SN	SN
		1	1	1	1	1	1	1	1	1	◇	1	1	1	1	1	1	1	1	1	1	1	1
						🚲					A							B 🚲	🚲				
Southampton Central	d						14 13				14 34	14 27											
Swanwick	d						14 33																
Fareham	d						14 40				14 56	15 00											
Portchester	d						14 45																
Cosham	d						14 49				15 04												
Portsmouth Harbour	d			14 29													15 12					15 29	
Portsmouth & Southsea	d			14 33							14 50	14 50			14 56		15 16					15 33	
Fratton	d			14 37							14 54	14 54			15 01		15 20					15 37	
Hilsea	d			14 32											15 05							15 32	
Bedhampton	d			14 37											15 14							15 37	
Havant	d			14 46			14 56				15 11	15 14			15 17		15 30					15 46	
Warblington	d														15 19								
Emsworth	d			14 50			15 00								15 22							15 50	
Southbourne	d			14 53			15 03								15 25							15 53	
Nutbourne	d														15 28								
Bosham	d														15 31								
Fishbourne (Sussex)	d														15 34								
Chichester 4	a			15 00			15 10				15 21	15 25			15 37		15 41					16 00	
	d			15 00			15 11				15 22	15 25			15 38		15 42					16 00	
Bognor Regis 4	d				15 07								15 30	15 39					15 56				16 09
Barnham	a			15 08	15 13		15 18				15 29	15 33	15 36	15 45	15 45		15 49		16 02			16 08	16 15
	d			15 08	15 15		15 19				15 30	15 33	15 37		15 46		15 50		16 03			16 08	
Bognor Regis 4	a																						
Ford 4	d				15 19							15 38	15 41		15 50				16 07				
Littlehampton 4	a				15 24										15 55								
	d							15 15				15b23						15 45	15b54		15 50		
Angmering 3	d			15 17				15 23				15 44						15 53			16 00	16 17	
Goring-by-Sea	d							15 27				15 48						15 57			16 04		
Durrington-on-Sea	d							15 30				15 50						16 00			16 07		
West Worthing	d		15 09					15 32		15 39		15 52						16 02			16 09		
Worthing 4	a		15 11	15 24				15 34		15 41	15 45	15 55						16 04			16 11	16 24	
	d		15 12	15 26				15 36		15 42	15 50	15 56						16 06			16 12	16 26	
East Worthing	d		15 14							15 44											16 14		
Lancing	d		15 17	15 30						15 47		16 00						16 10			16 17	16 30	
Shoreham-by-Sea	d		15 22	15 34				15 42		15 52	15 57	16 04						16 14			16 22	16 34	
Southwick	d		15 25	15 37						15 55		16 07									16 25	16 37	
Fishersgate	d		15 27							15 57											16 27		
Portslade	d		15 29	15 40				15 47		15 59		16 10									16 29	16 40	
Aldrington	d		15 31							16 01											16 31		
Hove 2	d	15 24	15 34	15 44				15 51	15 54	16 04	16 08	16 14						16 21		16 24	16 34	16 44	
Brighton 10	a	15 28	15 38	15 48					15 58	16 08	16 14	16 18								16 28	16 38	16 48	
Burgess Hill	a							16 01															
Haywards Heath 3	a	15 48		16 15				16 09	16 18			16 37						16 34				17 15	
Arundel	d												15 46						16 12				
Amberley	d																		16 17				
Pulborough	d												15 55						16 23				
Billingshurst	d												16 01 →			← 16 01			16 29				
Christs Hospital	d					← 15 36													16 36 →				
Horsham 4	a					15 40	15 46									16 10	16 16						
	d					15 50										16 20							
Crawley	d					15 59										16 29							
Three Bridges 4	a	16 07		16 25		16 02		16 25	16 37			16 47				16 32		16 47					
	d					16 03										16 33							
Gatwick Airport 10 ✈	a	16 00				16 07		16 24	16 30			16 52				16 37		16 56					
Horley	a					16 26										16 56							
Redhill 5	a					16 17										16 46		17 10					
East Croydon	a	16 16	16 24			16 30		16 40	16 46	16 56	16 56	17 08				17 01		17 12			17 25		
London Bridge 4 ⊖	a	16c39	16c53			16e42		17 02	17 02	17c26	17c26	17 28				17 26		17f28			17c50		
Clapham Junction 10	a		16 33			16 39		16 50	17c02	17 05	17 05	17c25				17 10		17 21			17 34		
London Victoria 15 ⊖	a	16g35	16 42			16 46		16 58	17g05	17 12	17 12	17g28				17 20		17 28			17 42		

For general notes see front of timetable
For details of catering facilities see Directory of Train Operators

A From Great Malvern (Table 71)
B 🚲 from Haywards Heath
b Change at Ford
c Change at Brighton and East Croydon
e Change at Three Bridges
f Change at Haywards Heath
g Change at Brighton and Gatwick Airport

For complete service between Horsham and Three Bridges see Table 186

Southampton, Portsmouth and Sussex Coast → Brighton, Gatwick Airport & London

Network Diagram - see first page of Table 186

		SN 1	SN 1	SN 1	SN 1	SN 1	SN 1	SN 1	SN 1	SN 1	SN 1	SN 1	SN 1	SN 1	SN 1		SN 1	SN 1	SN 1	SN 1	SN 1	SN 1	SN 1	SN 1	SN 1	SN 1
													A													
		╤						╤			╤		╤	╤					╤							
Southampton Central	d		15 13				15 33													16 12					16 33	
Swanwick	d		15 33				15 50													16 29					16 50	
Fareham	d		15 40				15 57													16 36					16 56	
Portchester	d		15 45																	16 41						
Cosham	d		15 49				16 05													16 45					17 05	
Portsmouth Harbour	d											16 12						16 29						16 40		
Portsmouth & Southsea	d						*15 50*		15 56			16 16						16 33						16 46	*16 50*	
Fratton	d						*15 54*		16 01			16 20						16 37						16 50	*16 54*	
Hilsea	d								16 05									*16 32*						16 54		
Bedhampton	d								16 13									*16 37*								
Havant	d		15 58				16 12		16 16			16 30						16 46		16 52				17 00	17 11	
Warblington	d								16 18															17 02		
Emsworth	d		16 02				16 16		16 21									16 50		16 56				17 05	17 15	
Southbourne	d		16 05						16 24									16 53		16 59				17 08		
Nutbourne	d								16 26															17 10		
Bosham	d								16 30															17 14		
Fishbourne (Sussex)	d								16 33															17 17		
Chichester 4	a		16 12				16 24		16 36			16 40						17 00		17 06				17 20	17 24	
	d		16 13				16 25		16 37			16 43						17 00		17 13				17 21	17 25	
Bognor Regis 4	d							16 30		16 39				16 56								17 18				17 30
Barnham	a		16 20				16 32	16 36	16 44	16 45		16 50		17 02				17 08		17 20		17 24		17 28	17 32	17 36
	d		16 21				16 33	16 37	16 45			16 51		17 03				17 08		17 21		17 25		17 29	17 33	17 37
Bognor Regis 4	a																					17 29			17 37	17 41
Ford 4	d						16 37	16 41	16 49					17 07												
Littlehampton 4	a								16 54													17 36				
	d			16 15			*16b22*						16 45	*16b54*							17 15	*17b11*				
Angmering 3	d			16 23			16 43						16 53					17 17			17 23				17 43	
Goring-by-Sea	d			16 27			16 47						16 57								17 27				17 47	
Durrington-on-Sea	d			16 30			16 50						17 00								17 30				17 50	
West Worthing	d			16 32		16 39	16 52						17 02				17 09				17 32				17 52	
Worthing 4	a			16 34		16 41	16 54						17 04				17 11	17 24			17 34			17 43	17 54	
	d			16 36		16 42	16 56						17 06				17 12	17 26			17 36			17 43	17 56	
East Worthing	d					16 44											17 14							17 46		
Lancing	d					16 47	17 00						17 10				17 17	17 30						17 49	18 00	
Shoreham-by-Sea	d			16 42		16 52	17 04						17 14				17 22	17 34			17 42			17 53	18 04	
Southwick	d					16 55	17 07										17 25	17 37						17 56	18 07	
Fishersgate	d					16 57											17 27							17 58		
Portslade	d			16 47		16 59	17 10										17 29	17 40			17 47			18 00	18 10	
Aldrington	d					17 01											17 31							18 02		
Hove 2	d			16 51	16 54	17 04	17 14						17 21		17 24		17 34	17 44			17 51		18 00	18 05	18 14	
Brighton 10	a				16 58	17 08	17 18								17 28		17 38	17 48					18 04	18 09	18 18	
Burgess Hill	a			17 01																	18 01					
Haywards Heath 3	a			17 09	*17 18*		*17 45*						17 35		*17 56*			*18 16*			18 09					
Arundel	d							16 46						17 12												17 46
Amberley	d													17 17												
Pulborough	d							16 55						17 23												17 55
Billingshurst	d	←						17 01			←			17 29					←							18 01
Christs Hospital	d	16 36						17 08			17 08			17 36					17 36							18 08
Horsham 4	a	16 40	16 48					→			17 12	17 18		→					17 40	17 48						→
	d		16 52									17 22								17 52						
Crawley	d		17 01									17 31								18 01						
Three Bridges 4	a		17 04	*17 27*	*17 27*		*17 56*					17 34	*17 56*		*18 10*			*18 31*		18 04	*18 31*					
	d		17 05									17 35								18 05						
Gatwick Airport 10 ✈	a		17 09	17 24	*17 31*		*18 00*					17 39	17 54		*18 16*			*18 30*		18 09	18 26					
Horley	a		*17 26*									*17 56*								*18 26*						
Redhill 5	a		17 17									17 48	*18 10*							18 17						
East Croydon	a		17 30	17 40	*17 47*	*17 56*	*18 16*					18 01	18 11				*18 24*	*18 46*		18 29	18 42			*18 56*		
London Bridge 4 ⊖	a		*17 50*	*18 11*	*18 11*	18c17	18c42					*18e17*	*18 42*				18c45	*19 00*		*18e45*	*19 00*			*19c16*		
Clapham Junction 10	a		17 40	17 50	*18c02*	*18 05*						18 13	18 21				*18 34*	*19 02*		18 40	18 52			*19 08*		
London Victoria 15 ⊖	a		17 50	17 58	*18c09*	*18 12*	18f35					18 20	18 29				*18 41*	19f05		18 47	18 59			*19 15*		

For general notes see front of timetable
For details of catering facilities see Directory of Train Operators

- **A** ╤ from Haywards Heath
- **b** Change at Ford
- **c** Change at Brighton and East Croydon
- **e** Change at Gatwick Airport
- **f** Change at Brighton and Gatwick Airport

For complete service between Horsham and Three Bridges see Table 186

Southampton, Portsmouth and Sussex Coast → Brighton, Gatwick Airport & London

Network Diagram - see first page of Table 186

Station		SN 1	SN 1	SN 1	SN 1	SN 1	SN 1 ◇ 🚲		SN 1	SN 1	SN 1 ◇ 🚲	SN 1	SN 1	SN 1	SN 1	SN 1	SN 1	SN 1	SN 1	SN 1	SN 1	SN 1		SN 1	SN 1	SN 1
Southampton Central	d											17 13					17 33									
Swanwick	d											17 33					17 50									
Fareham	d											17 40					17 56									
Portchester	d											17 45														
Cosham	d											17 49					18 05									
Portsmouth Harbour	d			17 12						17 29															18 28	
Portsmouth & Southsea	d	16 56		17 16						17 33					17 46		*17 50*		17 56						18 32	
Fratton	d	17 01		17 20						17 37					17 50		*17 54*		18 01						18 36	
Hilsea	d	17 05								*17 32*					17 54				18 05						*18 32*	
Bedhampton	d	17 13								*17 37*									18 13						*18 37*	
Havant	d	17 16		17 30						17 46		17 56			18 00		18 11		18 16						18 44	
Warblington	d	17 18													18 02				18 18							
Emsworth	d	17 21								17 50		18 00			18 05		18 15		18 21						18 48	
Southbourne	d	17 24								17 53		18 03			18 08				18 24						18 51	
Nutbourne	d	17 26													18 10				18 26							
Bosham	d	17 30													18 14				18 30							
Fishbourne (Sussex)	d	17 33													18 17				18 33							
Chichester 4	a	17 36		17 40						18 00		18 10			18 20		18 24		18 36						18 58	
	d	17 37		17 43						18 00		18 13			18 21		18 25		18 37						18 59	
Bognor Regis 4	d					17 51	17 57							18 19				18 33						18 46		19 03
Barnham	a	17 44		17 50		17 57	18 03			18 08		18 20		18 25	18 28		18 32	18 39	18 44					18 52	19 06	19 09
	d	17 45		17 51			18 04			18 08		18 21			18 29		18 33	18 40	18 45					18 53	19 07	19 10
Bognor Regis 4	a																									
Ford 4	d	17 49					18 08								18 33			18 44						18 57		19 14
Littlehampton 4	a	17 54													18 39									19 02		19 19
	d				17 45		*17b54*						18 15		*18b18*							18 52		*18b48*		
Angmering 3	d				17 53					18 18			18 23				18 42	18 53				19 00			19 16	
Goring-by-Sea	d				17 57								18 27					18 57				19 04				
Durrington-on-Sea	d				18 00								18 30				18 48	19 00				19 07				
West Worthing	d				18 02								18 32					19 02				19 09				
Worthing 4	a				18 04					18 25			18 34				18 52	19 04				19 11			19 23	
	d				18 06					18 25			18 35				18 52	19 05 →		← 19 05		19 12			19 24	
East Worthing	d									18 28							18 55					19 14			19 26	
Lancing	d				18 10					18 31			18 39				18 58			19 09		19 17			19 29	
Shoreham-by-Sea	d				18 14					18 35			18 43				19 02			19 13		19 22			19 33	
Southwick	d									18 38							19 05					19 25			19 36	
Fishersgate	d									18 40							19 07					19 27			19 38	
Portslade	d									18 42			18 48				19 09			19 18		19 29			19 40	
Aldrington	d									18 44							19 11					19 31			19 43	
Hove 2	d				18 21				18 24	18 47			18 52			19 00	19 14			19 22	19 24	19 34			19 45	
Brighton 10	a								18 28	18 52						19 04	19 18				19 28	19 38			19 49	
Burgess Hill	a				18 32															19 32						
Haywards Heath 3	a				18 41				*18 47*	*19 20*			19 05							19 36	*19 47*				*20 16*	
Arundel	d						18 13												18 52							
Amberley	d						18 18																			
Pulborough	d						18 24												19 01							
Billingshurst	d						18 30												19 08							
Christs Hospital	d		← 18 08				18 37 →				← 18 37															
Horsham 4	a		18 12	18 18							18 41	18 48							19 16							
	d		18 22								18 52								19 17							
Crawley	d		18 31								19 01								19 26							
Three Bridges 4	a		18 34		*19 12*				*19 12*	*19 31*	19 04		*19 31*						19 29	*20 11*	*20 11*					
	d		18 35								19 05								19 35							
Gatwick Airport 10 ✈	a		18 39		18 56				*19 00*	*19 39*	19 09		19 25						19 39	19 55	*20 00*					
Horley	a		*18 56*								*19 26*								*19 59*							
Redhill 5	a		18 47								19 17								19 47	*20 10*						
East Croydon	a		18 59		19 12				*19 16*		19 28		19 42			*19 54*			19 59	20 11	*20 16*	20 23				
London Bridge 4 ⊖	a		*19c16*		*19 30*				*19 30*		*19c45*		*20 00*			*20e15*			*20c15*	20 30	20 30	*20e45*				
Clapham Junction 10	a		19 11		19 21				*19 33*		19 40		19 52			*20 03*			20 10	20 20		20 33				
London Victoria 15 ⊖	a		19 18		19 29				*19f35*		19 47		19 59			*20 10*			20 20	20 28	*20f35*	20 43				

For general notes see front of timetable
For details of catering facilities see Directory of Train Operators

b Change at Ford
c Change at Gatwick Airport
e Change at Brighton and East Croydon
f Change at Brighton and Gatwick Airport

For complete service between Horsham and Three Bridges see Table 186

Southampton, Portsmouth and Sussex Coast → Brighton, Gatwick Airport & London

Network Diagram - see first page of Table 186

		SN [1]	SN [1]	SN [1]	SN [1]	SN [1]	SN [1]	SN [1]	SN [1]	SN [1]	SN [1]	SN [1]	SN [1]	SN [1]
Southampton Central	d	18 11				18 33							19 12	
Swanwick	d	18 28				18 50							19 29	
Fareham	d	18 35				18 56							19 36	
Portchester	d	18 40											19 41	
Cosham	d	18 44				19 05							19 46	
Portsmouth Harbour	d			18 37										
Portsmouth & Southsea	d			18 42		*18 50*				18 56	19 32			
Fratton	d			18 46		*18 54*				19 01	19 36			
Hilsea	d			18 50						19 05	*19 32*			
Bedhampton	d									19 13	*19 37*			
Havant	d	18 51		18 56		19 11				19 16	19 44		19 52	
Warblington	d			18 58						19 18				
Emsworth	d	18 55		19 01						19 21	19 48		19 56	
Southbourne	d	18 58		19 04						19 24	19 51		19 59	
Nutbourne	d			19 07						19 26				
Bosham	d			19 10						19 30				
Fishbourne (Sussex)	d			19 13						19 33				
Chichester [4]	a	19 05		19 17		19 22				19 36	19 58		20 06	
	d	19 06		19 17		19 22				19 40	19 59		20 07	
Bognor Regis [4]	d						19 36					20 04		
Barnham	a	19 13		19 25		19 30	19 42			19 47	20 06	20 10	20 14	
	d	19 14		19 25		19 30	19 43			19 48	20 07	20 11	20 15	
Bognor Regis [4]	a													
Ford [4]	d	19 18		19 30			19 47			19 52		20 15	20 19	
Littlehampton [4]	a			19 38						19 58		20 20		
	d		19 15	*19b11*			*19b35*		19 52			*20b06*		20 15
Angmering [3]	d		19 23			19 40	19 53		20 00		20 16			20 23
Goring-by-Sea	d		19 27			19 44	19 57		20 04					20 27
Durrington-on-Sea	d		19 30			19 46	20 00		20 07					20 30
West Worthing	d		19 32			19 48	20 02		20 09					20 32
Worthing [4]	a		19 34			19 51	20 04		20 11		20 23			20 34
	d		19 35			19 52	20 05		20 12		20 23			20 35
East Worthing	d					19 55			20 14		20 26			
Lancing	d		19 39			19 58	20 09		20 17		20 29			20 39
Shoreham-by-Sea	d		19 43			20 02	20 13		20 22		20 33			20 43
Southwick	d					20 05			20 25		20 36			
Fishersgate	d					20 07			20 27		20 38			
Portslade	d		19 48			20 09	20 18		20 29		20 40			20 48
Aldrington	d					20 11			20 31		20 42			
Hove [2]	d		19 52		19 54	20 14	20 22	20 24	20 34		20 45			20 52
Brighton [10]	a				19 58	20 18		20 28	20 38		20 49			
Burgess Hill	a						20 32							
Haywards Heath [3]	a		20 04		*20 18*		20 37	*20 47*						21 05
Arundel	d	19 23											20 24	
Amberley	d	19 28											20 29	
Pulborough	d	19 34											20 35	
Billingshurst	d	19 41											20 41	
Christs Hospital	d	19 47											20 48	
Horsham [4]	a	19 51											20 52	
	d	19 52											20 52	
Crawley	d	20 01											21 01	
Three Bridges [4]	a	20 04	*20 32*		*20c32*		20 47	*21 11*					21 05	*21 32*
	d	20 05					20 47						21 05	
Gatwick Airport [10] ✈	a	20 10	20 25		*20 31*		20 51	*21 00*					21 10	21 24
Horley	a	*20 26*					*20 59*						*21 26*	
Redhill [5]	a	20 18	*20 47*				*21 06*						21 18	*21 45*
East Croydon 🚊	a	20 30	20 41		*20 47*		21 09	*21 16*	*21 25*				21 30	21 40
London Bridge [4] ⊖	a	*20e45*	*21 00*		*21 00*		*21 30*	*21 30*	*21f45*				*21e45*	*22 17*
Clapham Junction [10]	a	20 40	20 50		*21 03*		21 19		*21 34*				21 40	21 50
London Victoria [15] ⊖	a	20 48	20 58		*21 10*		21 27	*21g35*	*21 41*				21 50	21 57

			SN [1]	SN [1]	SN [1]	SN [1]	SN [1]	SN [1]	SN [1]	SN [1]	SN [1]	SN [1]	SN [1]
Southampton Central	d				19 33							20 11	
Swanwick	d				19 51							20 28	
Fareham	d				19 57							20 35	
Portchester	d											20 40	
Cosham	d				20 06							20 44	
Portsmouth Harbour	d		19 40										
Portsmouth & Southsea	d		19 44		*19 50*				19 56	20 32			
Fratton	d		19 48		*19 54*				20 01	20 36			
Hilsea	d								20 05	*20 32*			
Bedhampton	d								20 14	*20 37*			
Havant	d		19 57		20 12				20 17	20 44		20 51	
Warblington	d		19 59						20 19				
Emsworth	d		20 02		20 16				20 22	20 48		20 55	
Southbourne	d		20 05						20 25	20 51		20 58	
Nutbourne	d		20 07						20 27				
Bosham	d		20 11						20 31				
Fishbourne (Sussex)	d		20 14						20 34				
Chichester [4]	a		20 17		20 24				20 37	20 58		21 05	
	d		20 18		20 25				20 38	20 59		21 07	
Bognor Regis [4]	d					20 33					21 04		
Barnham	a		20 25		20 32	20 39			20 45	21 06	21 10	21 14	
	d		20 27		20 33	20 40			20 46	21 07	21 11	21 15	
Bognor Regis [4]	a												
Ford [4]	d		20 31			20 44			20 50		21 15	21 19	
Littlehampton [4]	a		20 36						20 55		21 20		
	d							20 52	*20b37*		*21b06*		21 15
Angmering [3]	d				20 42	20 53		21 00		21 16			21 23
Goring-by-Sea	d					20 57		21 04					21 27
Durrington-on-Sea	d				20 48	21 00		21 07					21 30
West Worthing	d					21 02		21 09					21 32
Worthing [4]	a				20 52	21 04		21 11		21 23			21 34
	d				20 52	21 05		21 12		21 23			21 35
East Worthing	d				20 55			21 14		21 26			
Lancing	d				20 58	21 09		21 17		21 29			21 39
Shoreham-by-Sea	d				21 02	21 13		21 22		21 33			21 43
Southwick	d				21 05			21 25		21 36			
Fishersgate	d				21 07			21 27		21 38			
Portslade	d				21 09	21 18		21 29		21 40			21 48
Aldrington	d				21 11			21 31		21 42			
Hove [2]	d			20 54	21 14	21 22	21 24	21 34		21 45			21 52
Brighton [10]	a			20 58	21 18		21 28	21 38		21 49			
Burgess Hill	a					21 32							22 02
Haywards Heath [3]	a			*21 23*		21 37	*21 46*			*22 21*			22 09
Arundel	d											21 24	
Amberley	d											21 29	
Pulborough	d											21 35	
Billingshurst	d											21 41	
Christs Hospital	d											21 48	
Horsham [4]	a											21 52	
	d											21 52	
Crawley	d											22 01	
Three Bridges [4]	a			*21 32*		21 47	*21 55*			*22 32*		22 05	*22 32*
	d					21 47						22 05	
Gatwick Airport [10] ✈	a			*21 37*		21 51	*22 00*			*22 37*		22 10	22 24
Horley	a					*21 59*						*22 29*	*23 26*
Redhill [5]	a					*22 05*						22 18	*22 45*
East Croydon 🚊	a			*21 53*		22 09	*22 17*	*22 23*		*22 59*		22 30	22 40
London Bridge [4] ⊖	a			*22 17*		*22 32*	*22 32*	*23f11*				*22e47*	*23 17*
Clapham Junction [10]	a			*22 02*		22 19		*22 33*		*23 10*		22 40	22 49
London Victoria [15] ⊖	a			*22 10*		22 27		*22 40*		*23 20*		22 50	22 57

For general notes see front of timetable
For details of catering facilities see Directory of Train Operators

b Change at Ford
c Change at Brighton and Haywards Heath
e Change at Gatwick Airport
f Change at Brighton and East Croydon
g Change at Brighton and Gatwick Airport

For complete service between Horsham and Three Bridges see Table 186

Southampton, Portsmouth and Sussex Coast → Brighton, Gatwick Airport & London

Network Diagram - see first page of Table 186

		SN 1	SN 1	SN 1	SN 1	SN 1		SN 1	SN 1	SN 1	SN 1	SN 1	SN 1	SN 1	SN 1	SN 1	SN 1	SN 1	SN 1	SN 1	SN 1		SN 1	SN 1	SN 1	SN 1
Southampton Central	d			20 33								21 13			21 32				22 13					22 22		
Swanwick	d			20 50								21 33			21 51				22 30							
Fareham	d			20 57								21 40			21 58				22 37					23 00		
Portchester	d											21 45			22 03				22 42							
Cosham	d			21 06								21 49			22 07				22 47					23 08		
Portsmouth Harbour	d	20 40											21 40					22 15					22 44			23 15
Portsmouth & Southsea	d	20 44		20 50					21 15			21 33	21 44					22 19	22 24				22 48			23 19
Fratton	d	20 48		20 54					21 19			21 37	21 48					22 23	22 28				22 52			23 23
Hilsea	d								21 23			21 41	21 52					22 27	22 32				22 56			23 27
Bedhampton	d								21 28			21 47	21 57					22 32	22 37				23 01			23 33
Havant	d	20 57		21 12					21 31			21 56	22 00		22 14			22 35	22 57				23 05	23 15		23 36
Warblington	d	20 59							21 33						22 16											23 38
Emsworth	d	21 02		21 16					21 36						22 19			22 39	23 01							23 41
Southbourne	d	21 05							21 39						22 22			22 42	23 04							23 44
Nutbourne	d	21 07							21 41						22 24											23 47
Bosham	d	21 11							21 45						22 28											23 50
Fishbourne (Sussex)	d	21 14							21 48						22 31											23 53
Chichester 4	a	21 17		21 24					21 51			22 06	22 10		22 34			22 49	23 11				23 16	23 25		23 57
	d	21 18		21 25					21 52			22 07	22 11		22 34	22 40		22 52	23 11				23 17	23 26	23 52	23 57
Bognor Regis 4	d				21 39					22 00				22 30						23 15						
Barnham	a	21 25		21 32	21 45				21 59	22 06		22 14	22 18	22 36	22 42	22 47		22 59	23 19	23 21			23 24	23 33	23 59	00 05
	d	21 26		21 33					22 00			22 15	22 19	22 37		22 48		23 00	23 19				23 25	23 34	00 01	00 06
Bognor Regis 4	a																									
Ford 4	d	21 30		21 37					22 04			22 19	22 23	22 41		22 52		23 04					23 29		00 05	00 10
Littlehampton 4	a	21 35										22 24		22 46					23 31				23 34	23 42	00 10	00 15
	d							21 52				22 33				22b38							23 39		23b23	
Angmering 3	d			21 43				22 00	22 11			22 41						23 11					23 47			
Goring-by-Sea	d			21 47				22 04	22 15			22 45						23 15					23 51			
Durrington-on-Sea	d			21 50				22 07	22 18			22 47						23 17					23 53			
West Worthing	d			21 52				22 09	22 20			22 49						23 19					23 55			
Worthing 4	a			21 54				22 11	22 22			22 52						23 22					23 58			
	d			21 55				22 12	22 23			22 52						23 22					23 59			
East Worthing	d			21 57				22 14	22 25			22 55						23 25					00 01			
Lancing	d			22 00				22 17	22 28			22 58						23 28					00 04			
Shoreham-by-Sea	d			22 04				22 22	22 32			23 02						23 32					00 08			
Southwick	d			22 07				22 25	22 35			23 05						23 35					00 11			
Fishersgate	d			22 09				22 27	22 37			23 07						23 37					00 13			
Portslade	d			22 11				22 29	22 39			23 09						23 39					00 15			
Aldrington	d			22 14				22 31	22 42			23 11						23 41					00 18			
Hove 2	d		21 54	22 16		22 24		22 34	22 44		22 54	23 14					23 24	23 44			23 54		00 20			
Brighton 10	a		21 58	22 21		22 28		22 38	22 48		22 58	23 18					23 28	23 48			23 58		00 25			
Burgess Hill	a																									
Haywards Heath 3	a		22 28			22 54					23 23						23 58									
Arundel	d												22 28			22 57										
Amberley	d															23 02										
Pulborough	d												22 37			23 08										
Billingshurst	d												22 43			23 14										
Christs Hospital	d												22 50			23 21										
Horsham 4	a												22 54			23 25										
	d												22 55			23 25										
Crawley	d												23 03			23 38										
Three Bridges 4	a		22 42			23 05					23 33		23 07			23 42	00 10									
	d																									
Gatwick Airport 10 ✈	a		22 46			23c12					23 42		23 16			23 52	00 14									
Horley	a																									
Redhill 5	a																									
East Croydon	a		23 02			23 32					00 02		23 32			00 16	00 35									
London Bridge 4 ⊖	a		23 17			23 47					00 19		23 47			00 52	00 52									
Clapham Junction 10	a		23e25			00e11					00 29		00 11			00 29	01e02									
London Victoria 15 ⊖	a		23f52			00f18					00g25		00 18			00 37	00g55									

For general notes see front of timetable
For details of catering facilities see Directory of Train Operators

- b Change at Ford
- c Change at Brighton and Haywards Heath
- e Change at Brighton and East Croydon
- f Change at Brighton and Three Bridges
- g Change at Brighton and Gatwick Airport

For complete service between Horsham and Three Bridges see Table 186

Southampton, Portsmouth and Sussex Coast → Brighton, Gatwick Airport & London

Network Diagram - see first page of Table 186

		SN 1	SN 1	SN 1	SN 1	SN 1	SN 1	SN 1	SN 1	SN 1	SN 1	SN 1	SN 1	SN 1	SN 1	SN 1	SN 1		SN 1	SN 1	SN 1	SN 1	SN 1	SN 1	SN 1	SN 1 A
Southampton Central	d																									
Swanwick	d																									
Fareham	d																									
Portchester	d																									
Cosham	d																									
Portsmouth Harbour	d	22p44		23p15																					06 12	
Portsmouth & Southsea	d	22p48		23p19			04 56							05b24								05 56			06 16	
Fratton	d	22p52		23p23			05 00							05c28								06 01			06 20	
Hilsea	d	22p56		23p27			04e56							05f32								06 05				
Bedhampton	d	23p01		23p33			05g01							05h37								06 13				
Havant	d	23p05		23p36			05 08							05 52								06 16			06 30	
Warblington	d			23p38																		06 18				
Emsworth	d			23p41										05 56								06 21				
Southbourne	d			23p44										05 59								06 24				
Nutbourne	d			23p47																		06 26				
Bosham	d			23p50																		06 30				
Fishbourne (Sussex)	d			23p53																		06 33				
Chichester 4	a	23p16		23p57			05 19							06 06								06 36			06 40	
	d	23p17	23p52	23p57			05 19							06 06						06 25		06 37			06 41	
Bognor Regis 4	d					05 13						05 43	06 04			06 13					06 30		06 39			
Barnham	a	23p24	23p59	00 05		05 19	05 27	←				05 49	06 10	06 14		06 19				06 32	06 36	06 44	06 45		06 48	
	d	23p25	00 01	00 06	04 48	05 31 →	05 27	05 31				05 50		06 14		06 20				06 33	06 37	06 45			06 49	
Bognor Regis 4	a																									
Ford 4	d	23p29	00 05	00 10	04 52			05 35				05 54		06 19		06 24				06 37	06 41	06 49				
Littlehampton 4	a	23p34	00 10	00 15	04 57			05 40								06 29						06 54				
	d	23p39	23j23		05 02					05 45				05j54	06 15											06 45
Angmering 3	d	23p47			05 10					05 53		06 00			06 23					06 43						06 55
Goring-by-Sea	d	23p51			05 14					05 57		06 04			06 27					06 47						06 59
Durrington-on-Sea	d	23p53			05 17					06 00		06 07			06 30					06 50						07 02
West Worthing	d	23p55			05 19					06 02		06 09			06 32				06 39	06 52						07 04
Worthing 4	a	23p58			05 21		05 41			06 04		06 11			06 34				06 41	06 54						07 06
	d	23p59			05 22		05 42			06 05		06 12			06 35				06 42	06 56						07 07
East Worthing	d	00 01			05 24							06 14							06 44							
Lancing	d	00 04			05 27					06 09		06 17			06 39				06 47	07 00						07 11
Shoreham-by-Sea	d	00 08			05 32		05 48			06 13		06 22			06 43				06 52	07 04						07 15
Southwick	d	00 11			05 35							06 25							06 55	07 07						
Fishersgate	d	00 13			05 37							06 27							06 57							
Portslade	d	00 15			05 39					06 17		06 29			06 47				06 59	07 10						
Aldrington	d	00 18			05 41							06 31							07 01							
Hove 2	d	00 20			05 44		05 54		05 56	06 21	06 24	06 34			06 51		06 54		07 04	07 14						07 22
Brighton 10	a	00 25			05 48				06 00		06 28	06 38					06 58		07 08	07 18						
Burgess Hill	a														07 01											
Haywards Heath 3	a				*06 15*		06 07		*06 18*	06 35	*06 58*	*07 15*			07 08		*07 18*									07 35
Arundel	d													06 23							06 46					
Amberley	d													06 28												
Pulborough	d													06 34							06 55					
Billingshurst	d													06 41							07 01 →			← 07 01		
Christs Hospital	d													06 47												
Horsham 4	a													06 51										07 10	07 16	
	d													06 52											07 20	
Crawley	d													07 01											07 29	
Three Bridges 4	a				*06 25*		06 20		*06 49*	06 49	*07 11*	*07 25*		07 04	*07 25*		*07 42*								07 32	*08 11*
	d						06 20			06 49				07 05											07 33	
Gatwick Airport 10 ✈	a						06 24		*06 30*	06 53	*07 16*			07 09	07 24		*07 30*								07 37	07 54
Horley	a						*06 56*							*07 26*											07 41	
Redhill 5	a						*07 02*			*07 10*				07 17											07 47	*08 10*
East Croydon	a						06 40		*06 46*	07 10		*07 23*		07 29	07 40		*07 46*		*07 56*						07 59	08 10
London Bridge 4 ⊖	a						*07 02*		*07 02*	*07 31*		*07k47*		*07m47*	*08 02*		*08 02*		*08k17*						*08m17*	*08 32*
Clapham Junction 10	a						06 50		*07k02*	07 20		*07 33*		07 39	07 50		*08k02*		*08 05*						08 09	08 20
London Victoria 15 ⊖	a						06 57		*07n05*	07 27		*07 40*		07 46	07 57		*08n05*		*08 12*						08 16	08 27

For general notes see front of timetable
For details of catering facilities see Directory of Train Operators

A from Haywards Heath

b From 3 October dep. 0519
c From 3 October dep. 0523
e From 3 October dep. 0451
f From 3 October dep. 0527
g From 3 October dep. 0456
h From 3 October dep. 0532
j Change at Ford
k Change at Brighton and East Croydon
m Change at Gatwick Airport
n Change at Brighton and Gatwick Airport

For complete service between Horsham and Three Bridges see Table 186

Table 188

Saturdays

Southampton, Portsmouth and Sussex Coast → Brighton, Gatwick Airport & London

Network Diagram - see first page of Table 186

Station		SN 1	SN 1	SN 1	SN 1	SN 1	SN 1	SN 1	SN 1	SN 1	SN 1		GW	SN 1	SN 1	SN 1	SN 1	SN 1	SN 1	SN 1	SN 1	SN 1	SN 1	SN 1	SN 1	
																				A 🛒	🛒					
Southampton Central	d							06 13						06 33												
Swanwick	d							06 33						06 50												
Fareham	d							06 40						06 56												
Portchester	d							06 45																		
Cosham	d							06 49						07 05												
Portsmouth Harbour	d				06 29								06 48						07 12					07 29		
Portsmouth & Southsea	d				06 33								06 54	06 50		06 56			07 16					07 33		
Fratton	d				06 37								06 58	06 54		07 01			07 20					07 37		
Hilsea	d				06 32											07 05								07 32		
Bedhampton	d				06 37											07 13								07 37		
Havant	d				06 46			06 56					07 08	07 11		07 16			07 30					07 46		
Warblington	d															07 18										
Emsworth	d				06 50			07 00						07 15		07 21								07 50		
Southbourne	d				06 53			07 03								07 24								07 53		
Nutbourne	d															07 26										
Bosham	d															07 30										
Fishbourne (Sussex)	d															07 33										
Chichester 4	a				07 00			07 10					07 19	07 23		07 36			07 40					08 00		
	d				07 00			07 11					07 20	07 25		07 37			07 41					08 00		
Bognor Regis 4	d	06 56				07 07									07 30		07 39				07 56				08 07	
Barnham	a	07 02			07 08	07 13		07 18					07 27	07 32	07 36	07 44	07 45		07 48		08 02			08 08	08 13	
	d	07 03			07 08	07 15		07 19					07 28	07 33	07 37	07 45			07 49		08 03			08 08	08 15	
Bognor Regis 4	a																									
Ford 4	d	07 07				07 19								07 37	07 41	07 49					08 07				08 19	
Littlehampton 4	a					07 24										07 54									08 24	
	d	06b54							07 15					07b11						07 45	07b54					
Angmering 3	d				07 17				07 23					07 43						07 53				08 17		
Goring-by-Sea	d								07 27					07 47						07 57						
Durrington-on-Sea	d								07 30					07 50						08 00						
West Worthing	d			07 09					07 32		07 39			07 52						08 02			08 09			
Worthing 4	a			07 11	07 24				07 34		07 41		07 45	07 54						08 04			08 11	08 24		
	d			07 12	07 26				07 36		07 42		07 50	07 56						08 06			08 12	08 26		
East Worthing	d			07 14							07 44												08 14			
Lancing	d			07 17	07 30						07 47			08 00						08 10			08 17	08 30		
Shoreham-by-Sea	d			07 22	07 34				07 42		07 52		07 57	08 04						08 14			08 22	08 34		
Southwick	d			07 25	07 37						07 55			08 07									08 25	08 37		
Fishersgate	d			07 27							07 57												08 27			
Portslade	d			07 29	07 40				07 47		07 59			08 10									08 29	08 40		
Aldrington	d			07 31							08 01												08 31			
Hove 2	d		07 24	07 34	07 44				07 51	07 54	08 04		08 08	08 14						08 21		08 24	08 34	08 44		
Brighton 10	a		07 28	07 38	07 48					07 58	08 08		08 15	08 18								08 28	08 38	08 48		
Burgess Hill	a								08 01																	
Haywards Heath 3	a		07 48		08 15				08 09	08 18										08 35		08 48		09 15		
Arundel	d	07 12													07 46						08 12					
Amberley	d	07 17																			08 17					
Pulborough	d	07 23													07 55						08 23					
Billingshurst	d	07 29													08 01 →			← 08 01			08 29					
Christs Hospital	d	07 36 →					← 07 36														08 36 →					
Horsham 4	a						07 40	07 46										08 10	08 16							
	d						07 50											08 20								
Crawley	d						07 59											08 29								
Three Bridges 4	a		08 11		08 25		08 02		08 25	08 42								08 32		09 11		09 11		09 25		
	d						08 03											08 33								
Gatwick Airport 10 ✈	a		08 00				08 07		08 24	08 30								08 37		08 54		09 00				
Horley	a						08 26											08 41								
Redhill 5	a						08 15											08 47		09 10						
East Croydon	a		08 16	08 23			08 27		08 40	08 46	08 56		08 56					08 59		09 10		09 16	09 23			
London Bridge 4 ⊖	a		08 32	08c47			08 47		09 02	09 02	09c17		09c17					09e17		09 32		09 32	09c47			
Clapham Junction 10	a			08 33			08 37		08 50	09c02	09 05		09 05					09 09		09 20			09 33			
London Victoria 15 ⊖	a		08f35	08 40			08 44		08 57	09f05	09 12		09 12					09 16		09 27		09f35	09 40			

For general notes see front of timetable
For details of catering facilities see Directory of Train Operators

A 🛒 from Haywards Heath
b Change at Ford
c Change at Brighton and East Croydon
e Change at Gatwick Airport
f Change at Brighton and Gatwick Airport

For complete service between Horsham and Three Bridges see Table 186

Southampton, Portsmouth and Sussex Coast → Brighton, Gatwick Airport & London

Network Diagram - see first page of Table 186

		SN 1	SN 1	SN 1	SN 1		SN 1	SN 1	SN 1	SN 1	SN 1	SN 1	SN 1	SN 1	SN 1	SN 1	SN 1	SN 1	SN 1	SN 1	SN 1	SN 1		SN 1	SN 1	SN 1
		🛒												A 🛒	🛒					🛒						
Southampton Central	d		07 13					07 33													08 13					08 33
Swanwick	d		07 33					07 50													08 33					08 50
Fareham	d		07 40					07 56													08 40					08 56
Portchester	d		07 45																		08 45					
Cosham	d		07 49					08 05													08 49					09 05
Portsmouth Harbour	d												08 12					08 29								
Portsmouth & Southsea	d							*07 50*		07 56			08 16					08 33								*08 50*
Fratton	d							*07 54*		08 01			08 20					08 37								*08 54*
Hilsea	d									08 05								*08 32*								
Bedhampton	d									08 13								*08 37*								
Havant	d		07 56					08 11		08 16			08 30					08 46			08 56					09 11
Warblington	d									08 18																
Emsworth	d		08 00					08 15		08 21								08 50			09 00					09 15
Southbourne	d		08 03							08 24								08 53			09 03					
Nutbourne	d									08 26																
Bosham	d									08 30																
Fishbourne (Sussex)	d									08 33																
Chichester 4	a		08 10					08 23		08 36			08 40					09 00			09 10					09 23
	d		08 11					08 25		08 37			08 41					09 00			09 11					09 25
Bognor Regis 4	d								08 30		08 39				08 56				09 07							
Barnham	a		08 18					08 32	08 36	08 44	08 45		08 48		09 02			09 08	09 13		09 18					09 32
	d		08 19					08 33	08 37	08 45			08 49		09 03			09 08	09 15		09 19					09 33
Bognor Regis 4	a							08 37	08 41	08 49					09 07				09 19							09 37
Ford 4	d																									
Littlehampton 4	a									08 54									09 24							
	d			08 15				*08b11*						08 45	*08b54*							09 15				*09b11*
Angmering 3	d			08 23				08 43						08 53				09 17				09 23				09 43
Goring-by-Sea	d			08 27				08 47						08 57								09 27				09 47
Durrington-on-Sea	d			08 30				08 50						09 00								09 30				09 50
West Worthing	d			08 32			08 39	08 52						09 02			09 09					09 32			09 39	09 52
Worthing 4	a			08 34			08 41	08 54						09 04			09 11	09 24				09 34			09 41	09 54
	d			08 36			08 42	08 56						09 06			09 12	09 26				09 36			09 42	09 56
East Worthing	d						08 44										09 14								09 44	
Lancing	d						08 47	09 00						09 10			09 17	09 30							09 47	10 00
Shoreham-by-Sea	d			08 42			08 52	09 04						09 14			09 22	09 34				09 42			09 52	10 04
Southwick	d						08 55	09 07									09 25	09 37							09 55	10 07
Fishersgate	d						08 57										09 27								09 57	
Portslade	d			08 47			08 59	09 10									09 29	09 40				09 47			09 59	10 10
Aldrington	d						09 01										09 31								10 01	
Hove 2	d			08 51	08 54		09 04	09 14						09 21		09 24	09 34	09 44				09 51		09 54	10 04	10 14
Brighton 10	a				08 58		09 08	09 18								09 28	09 38	09 48						09 58	10 08	10 18
Burgess Hill	a			09 01																		10 01				
Haywards Heath 3	a			09 09	*09 18*									09 35		*09 48*		*10 15*				10 08		*10 18*		
Arundel	d								08 46						09 12											
Amberley	d														09 17											
Pulborough	d								08 55			←			09 23											
Billingshurst	d	←							09 01 →			09 01			09 29					←						
Christs Hospital	d	08 36													09 36 →					09 36						
Horsham 4	a	08 40	08 46									09 10	09 16							09 40	09 46					
	d		08 50										09 20								09 50					
Crawley	d		08 59										09 29								09 59					
Three Bridges 4	a		09 02	*09 25*	*09 42*								09 32	*10 11*		*10 11*		*10 25*			10 02	*10 25*		*10 42*		
	d		09 03										09 33								10 03					
Gatwick Airport 10 ✈	a		09 07	09 24	*09 30*								09 37	09 54		*10 00*					10 07	10 25		*10 30*		
Horley	a		*09 26*										09 41								*10 26*					
Redhill 5	a		09 15										09 47	*10 10*							10 15					
East Croydon	a		09 27	09 41	09 46		09 56						09 59	10 10		10 16	10 23				10 27	10 42		10 46	10 56	
London Bridge 4 ⊖	a		*09 47*	*10 02*	*10 02*		*10c17*						*10e17*	*10 32*		*10 32*	*10c47*				*10 47*	*11 02*		*11 02*	*11c17*	
Clapham Junction 10	a		09 37	09 51	*10c02*		*10 05*						10 09	10 20			*10 33*				10 37	10 51		*11c02*	11 05	
London Victoria 15 ⊖	a		09 44	09 58	*10f05*		*10 12*						10 16	10 27		*10f35*	10 40				10 44	10 59		*11f05*	11 12	

For general notes see front of timetable
For details of catering facilities see Directory of Train Operators

A 🛒 from Haywards Heath
b Change at Ford
c Change at Brighton and East Croydon
e Change at Gatwick Airport
f Change at Brighton and Gatwick Airport

For complete service between Horsham and Three Bridges see Table 186

Table 188

Saturdays

Southampton, Portsmouth and Sussex Coast → Brighton, Gatwick Airport & London

Network Diagram - see first page of Table 186

		SN 1	SN 1	SN 1	SN 1	SN 1	SN 1	SN 1	SN 1	SN 1	SN 1	SN 1	SN 1	SN 1	SN 1	SN 1		SN 1	SN 1	SN 1	SN 1	SN 1	SN 1	SN 1	SN 1	SN 1
							A ᴛ	ᴛ					ᴛ												A ᴛ	ᴛ
Southampton Central	d													09 13					09 33							
Swanwick	d													09 33					09 50							
Fareham	d													09 40					09 56							
Portchester	d													09 45												
Cosham	d													09 49					10 05							
Portsmouth Harbour	d					09 12					09 29													10 12		
Portsmouth & Southsea	d		08 56			09 16					09 33								*09 50*		09 56			10 16		
Fratton	d		09 01			09 20					09 37								*09 54*		10 01			10 20		
Hilsea	d		09 05								*09 32*										10 05					
Bedhampton	d		09 13								*09 37*										10 13					
Havant	d		09 16			09 30					09 46			09 56					10 11		10 16			10 30		
Warblington	d		09 18																		10 18					
Emsworth	d		09 21								09 50			10 00					10 15		10 21					
Southbourne	d		09 24								09 53			10 03							10 24					
Nutbourne	d		09 26																		10 26					
Bosham	d		09 30																		10 30					
Fishbourne (Sussex)	d		09 33																		10 33					
Chichester 4	a		09 36			09 40					10 00			10 10					10 23		10 36			10 40		
	d		09 37			09 41					10 00			10 11					10 25		10 37			10 41		
Bognor Regis 4	d	09 30		09 39				09 56				10 07								10 30		10 39				10 56
Barnham	a	09 36	09 44	09 45		09 48		10 02			10 08	10 13		10 18					10 32	10 36	10 44	10 45		10 48		11 02
	d	09 37	09 45			09 49		10 03			10 08	10 15		10 19					10 33	10 37	10 45			10 49		11 03
Bognor Regis 4	a																									
Ford 4	d	09 41	09 49					10 07				10 19							10 37	10 41	10 49					11 07
Littlehampton 4	a		09 54									10 24									10 54					
	d						09 45	*09b54*							10 15				*10b11*						10 45	*10b54*
Angmering 3	d						09 53				10 17				10 23				10 43						10 53	
Goring-by-Sea	d						09 57								10 27				10 47						10 57	
Durrington-on-Sea	d						10 00								10 30				10 50						11 00	
West Worthing	d						10 02			10 09					10 32			10 39	10 52						11 02	
Worthing 4	a						10 04			10 11	10 24				10 34			10 41	10 54						11 04	
	d						10 06			10 12	10 26				10 36			10 42	10 56						11 06	
East Worthing	d									10 14								10 44								
Lancing	d						10 10			10 17	10 30							10 47	11 00						11 10	
Shoreham-by-Sea	d						10 14			10 22	10 34				10 42			10 52	11 04						11 14	
Southwick	d									10 25	10 37							10 55	11 07							
Fishersgate	d									10 27								10 57								
Portslade	d									10 29	10 40				10 47			10 59	11 10							
Aldrington	d									10 31								11 01								
Hove 2	d						10 21		10 24	10 34	10 44				10 51	10 54		11 04	11 14						11 21	
Brighton 10	a								10 28	10 38	10 48					10 58		11 08	11 18							
Burgess Hill	a														11 01											
Haywards Heath 3	a						10 35		*10 48*		*11 15*				11 09	*11 18*									11 35	
Arundel	d	09 46						10 12												10 46						11 12
Amberley	d							10 17																		11 17
Pulborough	d	09 55						10 23												10 55						11 23
Billingshurst	d	10 01 →			← 10 01			10 29												11 01 →			← 11 01			11 29
Christs Hospital	d							10 36 →					← 10 36													11 36 →
Horsham 4	a				10 10	10 16							10 40	10 46									11 10	11 16		
	d				10 20								10 50										11 20			
Crawley	d				10 29								10 59										11 29			
Three Bridges 4	a				10 32		*11 11*		*11 11*		*11 25*		11 02		*11 25*	*11 42*							11 32		*12 11*	
	d				10 33								11 03										11 33			
Gatwick Airport 10 ✈	a				10 37		10 54		*11 00*				11 07		11 24	*11 30*							11 37		11 54	
Horley	a				10 41								*11 26*										11 41			
Redhill 5	a				10 47		*11 10*						11 15										11 47		*12 10*	
East Croydon	a				10 59		11 10		*11 16*	*11 23*			11 27		11 40	*11 46*		*11 56*					11 59		12 10	
London Bridge 4 ⊖	a				*11c17*		*11 32*		*11 32*	*11e47*			*11 47*		*12 02*	*12 02*		*12e17*					*12c17*		*12 32*	
Clapham Junction 10	a				11 09		11 20			*11 33*			11 37		11 50	*12e02*		*12 05*					12 09		12 20	
London Victoria 15 ⊖	a				11 16		11 27		*11f35*	*11 40*			11 44		11 57	*12f05*		*12 12*					12 16		12 27	

For general notes see front of timetable
For details of catering facilities see Directory of Train Operators

A ᴛ from Haywards Heath
b Change at Ford
c Change at Gatwick Airport
e Change at Brighton and East Croydon
f Change at Brighton and Gatwick Airport

For complete service between Horsham and Three Bridges see Table 186

Southampton, Portsmouth and Sussex Coast → Brighton, Gatwick Airport & London

Network Diagram - see first page of Table 186

		SN 1	SN 1	SN 1	SN 1	SN 1	SN 1	SN 1	SN 1	SN 1	SN 1	SN 1	SN 1	SN 1	SN 1	SN 1	SN 1	SN 1	SN 1	SN 1	SN 1	SN 1	SN 1	SN 1	SN 1
						🚌											A 🚌	🚌					🚌		
Southampton Central	d						10 13				10 33													11 13	
Swanwick	d						10 33				10 50													11 33	
Fareham	d						10 40				10 56													11 40	
Portchester	d						10 45																	11 45	
Cosham	d						10 49				11 05													11 49	
Portsmouth Harbour	d			10 29												11 12					11 29				
Portsmouth & Southsea	d			10 33							*10 50*		10 56			11 16					11 33				
Fratton	d			10 37							*10 54*		11 01			11 20					11 37				
Hilsea	d			*10 32*									11 05								*11 32*				
Bedhampton	d			*10 37*									11 13								*11 37*				
Havant	d			10 46			10 56				11 11		11 16			11 30					11 46			11 56	
Warblington	d												11 18												
Emsworth	d			10 50			11 00				11 15		11 21								11 50			12 00	
Southbourne	d			10 53			11 03						11 24								11 53			12 03	
Nutbourne	d												11 26												
Bosham	d												11 30												
Fishbourne (Sussex)	d												11 33												
Chichester 4	a			11 00			11 10				11 23		11 36			11 40					12 00			12 10	
	d			11 00			11 11				11 25		11 37			11 41					12 00			12 11	
Bognor Regis 4	d				11 07							11 30		11 39				11 56				12 07			
Barnham	a			11 08	11 13		11 18				11 32	11 36	11 44	11 45		11 48		12 02			12 08	12 13		12 18	
	d			11 08	11 15		11 19				11 33	11 37	11 45			11 49		12 03			12 08	12 15		12 19	
Bognor Regis 4	a																								
Ford 4	d				11 19						11 37	11 41	11 49					12 07				12 19			
Littlehampton 4	a				11 24								11 54									12 24			
	d							11 15			*11b11*						11 45	*11b54*							12 15
Angmering 3	d			11 17				11 23			11 43						11 53				12 17				12 23
Goring-by-Sea	d							11 27			11 47						11 57								12 27
Durrington-on-Sea	d							11 30			11 50						12 00								12 30
West Worthing	d		11 09					11 32		11 39	11 52						12 02			12 09					12 32
Worthing 4	a		11 11	11 24				11 34		11 41	11 54						12 04			12 11	12 24				12 34
	d		11 12	11 26				11 36		11 42	11 56						12 06			12 12	12 26				12 36
East Worthing	d		11 14							11 44										12 14					
Lancing	d		11 17	11 30						11 47	12 00						12 10			12 17	12 30				
Shoreham-by-Sea	d		11 22	11 34				11 42		11 52	12 04						12 14			12 22	12 34				12 42
Southwick	d		11 25	11 37						11 55	12 07									12 25	12 37				
Fishersgate	d		11 27							11 57										12 27					
Portslade	d		11 29	11 40				11 47		11 59	12 10									12 29	12 40				12 47
Aldrington	d		11 31							12 01										12 31					
Hove 2	d	11 24	11 34	11 44				11 51	11 54	12 04	12 14						12 21		12 24	12 34	12 44				12 51
Brighton 10	a	11 28	11 38	11 48					11 58	12 08	12 18								12 28	12 38	12 48				
Burgess Hill	a							12 01																	13 01
Haywards Heath 3	a	*11 48*		*12 15*				12 09	*12 18*								12 35		*12 48*		*13 15*				13 09
Arundel	d											11 46						12 12							
Amberley	d																	12 17							
Pulborough	d											11 55						12 23							
Billingshurst	d											12 01 →			← 12 01			12 29							
Christs Hospital	d					← 11 36												12 36 →					← 12 36		
Horsham 4	a					11 40	11 46								12 10	12 16							12 40	12 46	
	d						11 50									12 20								12 50	
Crawley	d						11 59									12 29								12 59	
Three Bridges 4	a	*12 11*		*12 25*			12 02	*12 25*	*12 42*							12 32	*13 11*		*13 11*		*13 25*			13 02	*13 25*
	d						12 03									12 33								13 03	
Gatwick Airport 10 ✈	a	*12 00*					12 07	12 24	*12 30*							12 37	12 54		*13 00*					13 07	13 24
Horley	a						*12 26*									12 41								*13 26*	
Redhill 5	a						12 15									12 47	*13 10*							13 15	
East Croydon	a	*12 16*	*12 23*				12 27	12 40	*12 46*	12 56						12 59	13 10		*13 16*	*13 23*				13 27	13 40
London Bridge 4 ⊖	a	*12 32*	12c47				*12 47*	*13 02*	*13 02*	13c17						13e17	*13 32*		*13 32*	13c47				*13 47*	*14 02*
Clapham Junction 10	a		*12 33*				12 37	12 50	13c02	*13 05*						13 09	13 20			*13 33*				13 37	13 50
London Victoria 15 ⊖	a	12f35	*12 40*				12 44	12 57	13f05	*13 12*						13 16	13 27		13f35	*13 40*				13 44	13 57

For general notes see front of timetable
For details of catering facilities see
Directory of Train Operators

A 🚌 from Haywards Heath
b Change at Ford
c Change at Brighton and East Croydon
e Change at Gatwick Airport
f Change at Brighton and Gatwick Airport

For complete service between Horsham and Three Bridges see Table 186

Saturdays

Southampton, Portsmouth and Sussex Coast → Brighton, Gatwick Airport & London

Network Diagram - see first page of Table 186

		SN 1	SN 1	SN 1		SN 1	SN 1	SN 1	SN 1	SN 1	SN 1	SN 1	SN 1	SN 1	SN 1	SN 1	SN 1	SN 1	SN 1	SN 1	SN 1		SN 1	SN 1	SN 1	SN 1
											A 🚲	🚲					🚲									
Southampton Central	d			11 33														12 13					12 33			
Swanwick	d			11 50														12 33					12 50			
Fareham	d			11 56														12 40					12 56			
Portchester	d																	12 45								
Cosham	d			12 05														12 49					13 05			
Portsmouth Harbour	d									12 12					12 29											
Portsmouth & Southsea	d			*11 50*			11 56			12 16					12 33								*12 50*		12 56	
Fratton	d			*11 54*			12 01			12 20					12 37								*12 54*		13 01	
Hilsea	d						12 05								*12 32*										13 05	
Bedhampton	d						12 13								*12 37*										13 13	
Havant	d			12 11			12 16			12 30					12 46			12 56					13 11		13 16	
Warblington	d						12 18																		13 18	
Emsworth	d			12 15			12 21								12 50			13 00					13 15		13 21	
Southbourne	d						12 24								12 53			13 03							13 24	
Nutbourne	d						12 26																		13 26	
Bosham	d						12 30																		13 30	
Fishbourne (Sussex)	d						12 33																		13 33	
Chichester 4	a			12 23			12 36			12 40					13 00			13 10					13 23		13 36	
	d			12 25			12 37			12 41					13 00			13 11					13 25		13 37	
Bognor Regis 4	d					12 30		12 39				12 56				13 07								13 30		13 39
Barnham	a			12 32		12 36	12 44	12 45		12 48		13 02			13 08	13 13		13 18					13 32	13 36	13 44	13 45
	d			12 33		12 37	12 45			12 49		13 03			13 08	13 15		13 19					13 33	13 37	13 45	
Bognor Regis 4	a																									
Ford 4	d			12 37		12 41	12 49					13 07				13 19							13 37	13 41	13 49	
Littlehampton 4	a						12 54									13 24									13 54	
	d			*12b11*							12 45	*12b54*						13 15					*13b11*			
Angmering 3	d			12 43							12 53				13 17			13 23					13 43			
Goring-by-Sea	d			12 47							12 57							13 27					13 47			
Durrington-on-Sea	d			12 50							13 00							13 30					13 50			
West Worthing	d		12 39	12 52							13 02			13 09				13 32		13 39			13 52			
Worthing 4	a		12 41	12 54							13 04			13 11	13 24			13 34		13 41			13 54			
	d		12 42	12 56							13 06			13 12	13 26			13 36		13 42			13 56			
East Worthing	d		12 44											13 14						13 44						
Lancing	d		12 47	13 00							13 10			13 17	13 30					13 47			14 00			
Shoreham-by-Sea	d		12 52	13 04							13 14			13 22	13 34			13 42		13 52			14 04			
Southwick	d		12 55	13 07										13 25	13 37					13 55			14 07			
Fishersgate	d		12 57											13 27						13 57						
Portslade	d		12 59	13 10										13 29	13 40			13 47		13 59			14 10			
Aldrington	d		13 01											13 31						14 01						
Hove 2	d	12 54	13 04	13 14							13 21		13 24	13 34	13 44			13 51	13 54	14 04			14 14			
Brighton 10	a	12 58	13 08	13 18									13 28	13 38	13 48				13 58	14 08			14 18			
Burgess Hill	a																	14 01								
Haywards Heath 3	a	*13 18*									13 35		*13 48*		*14 15*			14 09	*14 18*							
Arundel	d					12 46						13 12												13 46		
Amberley	d											13 17														
Pulborough	d					12 55			←			13 23												13 55		
Billingshurst	d					13 01			13 01			13 29					←							14 01		
Christs Hospital	d					→						13 36					13 36							→		
Horsham 4	a								13 10	13 16		→					13 40	13 46								
	d								13 20								13 50									
Crawley	d								13 29								13 59									
Three Bridges 4	a	*13 42*							13 32		*14 11*		*14 11*		*14 25*		14 02	*14 25*	*14 42*							
	d								13 33								14 03									
Gatwick Airport 10 ✈	a	*13 30*							13 37		13 54		*14 00*				14 07	14 24	*14 30*							
Horley	a								13 41								*14 26*									
Redhill 5	a								13 47		*14 10*						14 15									
East Croydon	a	*13 46*	*13 56*						13 59		14 10		*14 16*	14 23			14 27	14 40	*14 46*	*14 56*						
London Bridge 4 ⊖	a	*14 02*	*14c17*						*14e17*		*14 32*		*14 32*	*14c47*			*14 47*	*15 02*	*15 02*	*15c17*						
Clapham Junction 10	a	*14c02*	*14 05*						14 09		14 20			*14 33*			14 37	14 50	*15c02*	*15 05*						
London Victoria 15 ⊖	a	*14f05*	*14 12*						14 16		14 27		*14f35*	14 40			14 44	14 57	*15f05*	*15 12*						

For general notes see front of timetable
For details of catering facilities see Directory of Train Operators

A 🚲 from Haywards Heath
b Change at Ford
c Change at Brighton and East Croydon
e Change at Gatwick Airport
f Change at Brighton and Gatwick Airport

For complete service between Horsham and Three Bridges see Table 186

Table 188

Saturdays

Southampton, Portsmouth and Sussex Coast → Brighton, Gatwick Airport & London

Network Diagram - see first page of Table 186

		SN 1	SN 1	SN 1	SN 1	SN 1	SN 1	SN 1	SN 1	SN 1	SN 1	SN 1	SN 1	SN 1	SN 1		SN 1	SN 1	SN 1	SN 1	SN 1	SN 1	SN 1	SN 1	SN 1	SN 1
				A 🛒	🛒					🛒												A 🛒	🛒			
Southampton Central	d										13 13				13 33											
Swanwick	d										13 33				13 50											
Fareham	d										13 40				13 56											
Portchester	d										13 45															
Cosham	d										13 49				14 05											
Portsmouth Harbour	d		13 12					13 29													14 12					14 29
Portsmouth & Southsea	d		13 16					13 33							13 50			13 56			14 16					14 33
Fratton	d		13 20					13 37							13 54			14 01			14 20					14 37
Hilsea	d							13 32										14 05								14 32
Bedhampton	d							13 37										14 13								14 37
Havant	d		13 30					13 46			13 56				14 11			14 16			14 30					14 46
Warblington	d																	14 18								
Emsworth	d							13 50			14 00				14 15			14 21								14 50
Southbourne	d							13 53			14 03							14 24								14 53
Nutbourne	d																	14 26								
Bosham	d																	14 30								
Fishbourne (Sussex)	d																	14 33								
Chichester 4	a		13 40					14 00			14 10				14 23			14 36			14 40					15 00
	d		13 41					14 00			14 11				14 25			14 37			14 41					15 00
Bognor Regis 4	d				13 56				14 07								14 30		14 39				14 56			
Barnham	a		13 48		14 02			14 08	14 13		14 18				14 32		14 36	14 44	14 45		14 48		15 02			15 08
	d		13 49		14 03			14 08	14 15		14 19				14 33		14 37	14 45			14 49		15 03			15 08
Bognor Regis 4	a																									
Ford 4	d				14 07				14 19						14 37		14 41	14 49					15 07			
Littlehampton 4	a								14 24									14 54								
	d			13 45	13b54							14 15			14b11							14 45	14b54			
Angmering 3	d			13 53				14 17				14 23			14 43							14 53				15 17
Goring-by-Sea	d			13 57								14 27			14 47							14 57				
Durrington-on-Sea	d			14 00								14 30			14 50							15 00				
West Worthing	d			14 02			14 09					14 32		14 39	14 52							15 02			15 09	
Worthing 4	a			14 04			14 11	14 24				14 34		14 41	14 54							15 04			15 11	15 24
	d			14 06			14 12	14 26				14 36		14 42	14 56							15 06			15 12	15 26
East Worthing	d						14 14							14 44											15 14	
Lancing	d			14 10			14 17	14 30						14 47	15 00							15 10			15 17	15 30
Shoreham-by-Sea	d			14 14			14 22	14 34				14 42		14 52	15 04							15 14			15 22	15 34
Southwick	d						14 25	14 37						14 55	15 07										15 25	15 37
Fishersgate	d						14 27							14 57											15 27	
Portslade	d						14 29	14 40				14 47		14 59	15 10										15 29	15 40
Aldrington	d						14 31							15 01											15 31	
Hove 2	d			14 21		14 24	14 34	14 44				14 51	14 54	15 04	15 14							15 21		15 24	15 34	15 44
Brighton 10	a					14 28	14 38	14 48					14 58	15 08	15 18									15 28	15 38	15 48
Burgess Hill	a											15 01														
Haywards Heath 3	a			14 35		14 48		15 15				15 09	15 18									15 35		15 48		16 15
Arundel	d				14 12												14 46						15 12			
Amberley	d				14 17																		15 17			
Pulborough	d				14 23												14 55						15 23			
Billingshurst	d	← 14 01			14 29												15 01 →			← 15 01			15 29			
Christs Hospital	d				14 36 →					← 14 36													15 36 →			
Horsham 4	a	14 10	14 16							14 40	14 46									15 10	15 16					
	d		14 20								14 50										15 20					
Crawley	d		14 29								14 59										15 29					
Three Bridges 4	a		14 32	15 11		15 11		15 25			15 02	15 25	15 42								15 32	16 11		16 11		16 25
	d		14 33								15 03										15 33					
Gatwick Airport 10 ✈	a		14 37	14 54		15 00					15 07	15 24	15 30								15 37	15 54		16 00		
Horley	a		14 41								15 26										15 41					
Redhill 5	a		14 47	15 10							15 15										15 47	16 10				
East Croydon	a		14 59	15 10		15 16	15 23				15 27	15 40	15 46	15 56							15 59	16 10		16 16	16 23	
London Bridge 4 ⊖	a		15c17	15 32		15 32	15e47				15 47	16 02	16 02	16e17							16c17	16 32		16 32	16e47	
Clapham Junction 10	a		15 09	15 20			15 33				15 37	15 50	16e02	16 05							16 09	16 20			16 33	
London Victoria 15 ⊖	a		15 16	15 27		15f35	15 40				15 44	15 57	16f05	16 12							16 16	16 27		16f35	16 40	

For general notes see front of timetable
For details of catering facilities see Directory of Train Operators

- A 🛒 from Haywards Heath
- b Change at Ford
- c Change at Gatwick Airport
- e Change at Brighton and East Croydon
- f Change at Brighton and Gatwick Airport

For complete service between Horsham and Three Bridges see Table 186

Table 188

Saturdays

Southampton, Portsmouth and Sussex Coast → Brighton, Gatwick Airport & London

Network Diagram - see first page of Table 186

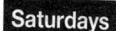

		SN	SN	SN	SN	SN	SN	GW	SN		SN	SN	SN	SN	SN	SN	SN	SN	SN	SN	SN	SN	SN	SN	SN	SN
		1	1	1	1	1	1	◇	1		1	1	1	1	1	1	1	1	1	1	1	1	1	1	1	1
								A								B										
			🛒													🛒	🛒					🛒				
Southampton Central	d			14 13				14 34	14 27														15 13			
Swanwick	d			14 33																			15 33			
Fareham	d			14 40				14 55	15 00														15 40			
Portchester	d			14 45																			15 45			
Cosham	d			14 49				15 03															15 49			
Portsmouth Harbour	d														15 12					15 29						
Portsmouth & Southsea	d							14 50	14 50				14 56		15 16					15 33						
Fratton	d							14 54	14 54				15 01		15 20					15 37						
Hilsea	d												15 05							15 32						
Bedhampton	d												15 14							15 37						
Havant	d			14 56				15 10	15 14				15 17		15 30					15 46			15 56			
Warblington	d												15 19													
Emsworth	d			15 00									15 22							15 50			16 00			
Southbourne	d			15 03									15 25							15 53			16 03			
Nutbourne	d												15 28													
Bosham	d												15 31													
Fishbourne (Sussex)	d												15 34													
Chichester 4	a			15 10				15 21	15 25				15 37		15 41					16 00			16 10			
	d			15 11				15 21	15 25				15 38		15 42					16 00			16 11			
Bognor Regis 4	d	15 07									15 30	15 39					15 56				16 07					
Barnham	a	15 13		15 18				15 29	15 33		15 36	15 45	15 45		15 49		16 02			16 08	16 13		16 18			
	d	15 15		15 19				15 29	15 33		15 37		15 46		15 50		16 03			16 08	16 15		16 19			
Bognor Regis 4	a																									
Ford 4	d	15 19							15 38		15 41		15 50				16 07				16 19					
Littlehampton 4	a	15 24											15 55								16 24					
	d				15 15				15b11							15 45	15b54							16 15		
Angmering 3	d				15 23				15 44							15 53				16 17				16 23		
Goring-by-Sea	d				15 27				15 48							15 57								16 27		
Durrington-on-Sea	d				15 30				15 50							16 00								16 30		
West Worthing	d				15 32		15 39		15 52							16 02			16 09					16 32		16 39
Worthing 4	a				15 34		15 41	15 44	15 55							16 04			16 11	16 24				16 34		16 41
	d				15 36		15 42	15 48	15 56							16 06			16 12	16 26				16 36		16 42
East Worthing	d						15 44												16 14							16 44
Lancing	d						15 47		16 00							16 10			16 17	16 30						16 47
Shoreham-by-Sea	d				15 42		15 52	15 56	16 04							16 14			16 22	16 34				16 42		16 52
Southwick	d						15 55		16 07										16 25	16 37						16 55
Fishersgate	d						15 57												16 27							16 57
Portslade	d				15 47		15 59		16 10										16 29	16 40				16 47		16 59
Aldrington	d						16 01												16 31							17 01
Hove 2	d				15 51	15 54	16 04	16 08	16 14							16 21		16 24	16 34	16 44				16 51	16 54	17 04
Brighton 10	a					15 58	16 08	16 14	16 18									16 28	16 38	16 48					16 58	17 08
Burgess Hill	a				16 01																			17 01		
Haywards Heath 3	a				16 09	16 18										16 35		16 48		17 15				17 09	17 18	
Arundel	d										15 46						16 12									
Amberley	d																16 17									
Pulborough	d										15 55						16 23									
Billingshurst	d										16 01 →			← 16 01			16 29									
Christs Hospital	d		← 15 36														16 36 →					← 16 36				
Horsham 4	a		15 40	15 46										16 10	16 16							16 40	16 46			
	d		15 50											16 20								16 50				
Crawley	d		15 59											16 29								16 59				
Three Bridges 4	a		16 02		16 25	16 42								16 32		17 11		17 11		17 25		17 02		17 25	17 42	
	d		16 03											16 33								17 03				
Gatwick Airport 10 ✈	a		16 07		16 24	16 30								16 37		16 54		17 00				17 07		17 24	17 30	
Horley	a		16 26											16 41								17 26				
Redhill 5	a		16 15											16 47		17 10						17 15				
East Croydon	a		16 27		16 40	16 46	16 56	16 56						16 59		17 10		17 16	17 23			17 27		17 40	17 46	17 56
London Bridge 4 ⊖	a		16 47		17 02	17 02	17c17	17c17						17e17		17 32		17 32	17c47			17 47		18 02	18 02	18c17
Clapham Junction 10	a		16 37		16 50	17c02	17 05	17 05						17 09		17 20			17 33			17 37		17 50	18c02	18 05
London Victoria 15 ⊖	a		16 44		16 57	17f05	17 12	17 12						17 16		17 27		17f35	17 40			17 44		17 57	18f05	18 12

For general notes see front of timetable
For details of catering facilities see Directory of Train Operators

A From Great Malvern (Table 71)
B 🛒 from Haywards Heath
b Change at Ford
c Change at Brighton and East Croydon
e Change at Gatwick Airport
f Change at Brighton and Gatwick Airport

For complete service between Horsham and Three Bridges see Table 186

Table 188

Saturdays

Southampton, Portsmouth and Sussex Coast → Brighton, Gatwick Airport & London

Network Diagram - see first page of Table 186

		SN 1	SN 1	SN 1	SN 1	SN 1	SN 1	SN 1 A ⌶	SN 1 ⌶	SN 1	SN 1	SN 1	SN 1	SN 1 ⌶	SN 1	SN 1	SN 1	SN 1	SN 1	SN 1	SN 1	SN 1	SN 1	SN 1
Southampton Central	d	15 33													16 13				16 33					
Swanwick	d	15 50													16 33				16 50					
Fareham	d	15 56													16 40				16 56					
Portchester	d														16 45									
Cosham	d	16 05													16 49				17 05					
Portsmouth Harbour	d						16 12					16 29												17 12
Portsmouth & Southsea	d	15 50		15 56			16 16					16 33							16 50		16 56			17 16
Fratton	d	15 54		16 01			16 20					16 37							16 54		17 01			17 20
Hilsea	d			16 05								16 32									17 05			17 18
Bedhampton	d			16 13								16 37									17 13			
Havant	d	16 11		16 16			16 30					16 46			16 56				17 11		17 16			17 30
Warblington	d			16 18																	17 18			
Emsworth	d	16 15		16 21								16 50			17 00				17 15		17 21			
Southbourne	d			16 24								16 53			17 03						17 24			
Nutbourne	d			16 26																	17 26			
Bosham	d			16 30																	17 30			
Fishbourne (Sussex)	d			16 33																	17 33			
Chichester 4	a	16 23		16 36			16 40					17 00			17 10				17 23		17 36			17 40
	d	16 25		16 37			16 41					17 00			17 11				17 25		17 37			17 41
Bognor Regis 4	d		16 30		16 39				16 56				17 07							17 30		17 39		
Barnham	a	16 32	16 36	16 44	16 45		16 48		17 02			17 08	17 13		17 18				17 32	17 36	17 44	17 45		17 48
	d	16 33	16 37	16 45			16 49		17 03			17 08	17 15		17 19				17 33	17 37	17 45			17 49
Bognor Regis 4	a																							
Ford 4	d	16 37	16 41	16 49					17 07				17 19						17 37	17 41	17 49			
Littlehampton 4	a			16 54									17 24								17 54			
	d	16b11						16 45	16b54							17 15			17b11					
Angmering 3	d	16 43						16 53				17 17				17 23			17 43					
Goring-by-Sea	d	16 47						16 57								17 27			17 47					
Durrington-on-Sea	d	16 50						17 00								17 30			17 50					
West Worthing	d	16 52						17 02			17 09					17 32		17 39	17 52					
Worthing 4	a	16 54						17 04			17 11	17 24				17 34		17 41	17 54					
	d	16 56						17 06			17 12	17 26				17 36		17 42	17 56					
East Worthing	d										17 14							17 44						
Lancing	d	17 00						17 10			17 17	17 30						17 47	18 00					
Shoreham-by-Sea	d	17 04						17 14			17 22	17 34				17 42		17 52	18 04					
Southwick	d	17 07									17 25	17 37						17 55	18 07					
Fishersgate	d										17 27							17 57						
Portslade	d	17 10									17 29	17 40				17 47		17 59	18 10					
Aldrington	d										17 31							18 01						
Hove 2	d	17 14						17 21		17 24	17 34	17 44				17 51	17 54	18 04	18 14					
Brighton 10	a	17 18								17 28	17 38	17 48					17 58	18 08	18 18					
Burgess Hill	a															18 01								
Haywards Heath 3	a							17 35		17 48		18 15				18 09	18 28							
Arundel	d		16 46						17 12											17 46				
Amberley	d								17 17															
Pulborough	d		16 55						17 23											17 55				
Billingshurst	d		17 01 →			← 17 01			17 29											18 01 →			← 18 01	
Christs Hospital	d								17 36 →					← 17 36										
Horsham 4	a					17 10	17 16							17 40	17 46								18 10	18 16
	d						17 20								17 50									18 20
Crawley	d						17 29								17 59									18 29
Three Bridges 4	a						17 32	18 11		18 11		18 25			18 02	18 25	18 42							18 32
	d						17 33								18 03									18 33
Gatwick Airport 10 ✈	a						17 37	17 54		18 00		18 35			18 07	18 24	18 46							18 37
Horley	a						17 41								18 26									18 41
Redhill 5	a						17 47	18 10							18 15									18 47
East Croydon	a						17 59	18 10		18 16	18 23	18 53			18 27	18 40		18 56						18 59
London Bridge 4 ⊖	a						18c17	18 32		18 32	18e47				18 47	19 08		19e17						19c17
Clapham Junction 10	a						18 09	18 20			18 33	19 02			18 37	18 50		19 05						19 09
London Victoria 15 ⊖	a						18 16	18 27		18f35	18 40	19 09			18 44	18 57		19 12						19 16

For general notes see front of timetable
For details of catering facilities see Directory of Train Operators

A ⌶ from Haywards Heath
b Change at Ford
c Change at Gatwick Airport
e Change at Brighton and East Croydon
f Change at Brighton and Gatwick Airport

For complete service between Horsham and Three Bridges see Table 186

Table 188

Saturdays

Southampton, Portsmouth and Sussex Coast → Brighton, Gatwick Airport & London

Network Diagram - see first page of Table 186

Station		SN 1 A 🍴	SN 1	SN 1	SN 1	SN 1	SN 1	SN 1	SN 1	SN 1	SN 1	SN 1	SN 1	SN 1	SN 1	SN 1	SN 1	SN 1	SN 1	SN 1	SN 1	SN 1	SN 1	SN 1	SN 1
Southampton Central	d								17 13				17 33										18 11		
Swanwick	d								17 33				17 50										18 28		
Fareham	d								17 40				17 56										18 35		
Portchester	d								17 45														18 40		
Cosham	d								17 49				18 05										18 44		
Portsmouth Harbour	d					17 29														18 12	18 29				
Portsmouth & Southsea	d					17 33							*17 50*		17 56					18 16	18 33				
Fratton	d					17 37							*17 54*		18 01					18 20	18 37				
Hilsea	d					*17 32*									18 05						*18 32*				
Bedhampton	d					*17 37*									18 13						*18 37*				
Havant	d					17 46			17 56				18 11		18 16					18 30	18 46		18 51		
Warblington	d														18 18										
Emsworth	d					17 50			18 00				18 15		18 21					18 34	18 50		18 55		
Southbourne	d					17 53			18 03						18 24					18 37	18 53		18 58		
Nutbourne	d														18 26										
Bosham	d														18 30										
Fishbourne (Sussex)	d														18 33										
Chichester 4	a					18 00			18 10				18 23		18 36					18 44	19 00		19 05		
	d					18 00			18 11				18 25		18 37					18 45	19 00		19 07		
Bognor Regis 4	d		17 56				18 07							18 33		18 39						19 03			
Barnham	a		18 02			18 08	18 13		18 18				18 32	18 40	18 44	18 46				18 52	19 08	19 09	19 14		←
	d		18 03			18 08	18 15		18 19				18 33	18 41	18 45					18 53	19 08	19 22 →	19 15		19 22
Bognor Regis 4	a																								
Ford 4	d		18 07				18 19						18 37	18 45	18 49					18 57			19 19		19 26
Littlehampton 4	a						18 24													19 02					19 32
	d	17 45	*17b54*							18 15			*18b11*						18 51				*18b54*	19 15	*19b11*
Angmering 3	d	17 53				18 17				18 23			18 43	18 53					19 00		19 17			19 23	
Goring-by-Sea	d	17 57								18 27			18 47	18 57					19 04					19 27	
Durrington-on-Sea	d	18 00								18 30			18 50	19 00			←		19 07					19 30	
West Worthing	d	18 02			18 09					18 32		18 39	18 52	19 02			19 02		19 09					19 32	
Worthing 4	a	18 04			18 11	18 24				18 34		18 41	18 54	→			19 04		19 11		19 24			19 34	
	d	18 06			18 12	18 26				18 36		18 42	18 56				19 06		19 12		19 26			19 35	
East Worthing	d				18 14							18 44							19 14						
Lancing	d	18 10			18 17	18 30						18 47	19 00				19 10		19 17		19 30			19 39	
Shoreham-by-Sea	d	18 14			18 22	18 34				18 42		18 52	19 04				19 14		19 22		19 34			19 43	
Southwick	d				18 25	18 37						18 55	19 07						19 25		19 37				
Fishersgate	d				18 27							18 57							19 27						
Portslade	d				18 29	18 40				18 47		18 59	19 10						19 29		19 40			19 48	
Aldrington	d				18 31							19 01							19 31						
Hove 2	d	18 21		18 24	18 34	18 44				18 51	18 54	19 04	19 14				19 21	19 24	19 34		19 44			19 52	
Brighton 10	a			18 28	18 38	18 48					18 58	19 08	19 18					19 28	19 38		19 48				
Burgess Hill	a									19 01														20 02	
Haywards Heath 3	a	18 35		*18 48*		*19 15*				19 09	*19 18*						19 35	*19 48*			*20 16*			20 09	
Arundel	d		18 12												18 54								19 24		
Amberley	d		18 17												18 59								19 29		
Pulborough	d		18 23												19 05								19 35		
Billingshurst	d		18 29					←							19 11								19 41		
Christs Hospital	d		18 36					18 36															19 48		
Horsham 4	a		→					18 40	18 46						19 20								19 52		
	d							18 50							19 21								19 52		
Crawley	d							18 59							19 30								20 01		
Three Bridges 4	a			*19 11*		*19 25*		19 02		*19 25*	*19 42*				19 33		*20 11*	*20 11*					20 05	*20 32*	
	d							19 03							19 34								20 05		
Gatwick Airport 10 ✈	a	18 54		*19 00*				19 07		19 24	*19 30*				19 38		19 54	*20 00*					20 10	20 24	
Horley	a							19 11							*19 58*								*20 26*		
Redhill 5	a							19 17							19 47		*20 10*						20 18	*20 47*	
East Croydon 🚊	a	19 10		*19 16*	*19 23*			19 28		19 40	*19 46*	*19 56*			19 59		20 10	*20 16*	*20 23*				20 30	20 40	
London Bridge 4 ⊖	a			*19 32*	*19c47*			*19e47*		*20 02*	*20 02*	*20c17*			*20e17*		*20 32*	*20 32*	*20c47*				*20e47*	*21 02*	
Clapham Junction 10	a	19 20			*19 33*			19 40		19 50	*20c02*	*20 05*			20 11		20 20		*20 33*				20 40	20 50	
London Victoria 15 ⊖	a	19 27		*19f35*	*19 40*			19 47		19 57	*20f05*	*20 12*			20 20		20 27	*20f35*	*20 40*				20 50	20 57	

For general notes see front of timetable
For details of catering facilities see Directory of Train Operators

A 🍴 from Haywards Heath
b Change at Ford
c Change at Brighton and East Croydon
e Change at Gatwick Airport
f Change at Brighton and Gatwick Airport

For complete service between Horsham and Three Bridges see Table 186

Table 188

Southampton, Portsmouth and Sussex Coast → Brighton, Gatwick Airport & London

Network Diagram - see first page of Table 186

Station		SN 1	SN 1	SN 1	SN 1	SN 1	SN 1	SN 1		SN 1	SN 1	SN 1	SN 1	SN 1	SN 1	SN 1	SN 1	SN 1	SN 1	SN 1	SN 1	SN 1	SN 1	SN 1	SN 1	SN 1
Southampton Central	d		18 33										19 11			19 33								20 11		
Swanwick	d		18 50										19 28			19 50								20 28		
Fareham	d		18 56										19 35			19 56								20 35		
Portchester	d												19 40											20 40		
Cosham	d		19 05										19 44			20 05								20 44		
Portsmouth Harbour	d									19 12	19 29											20 28				20 40
Portsmouth & Southsea	d		18 50				18 56			19 16	19 33					19 50				19 56		20 32				20 44
Fratton	d		18 54				19 01			19 20	19 37					19 54				20 01		20 36				20 48
Hilsea	d						19 05				19 32									20 05		20 32				
Bedhampton	d						19 13				19 37									20 13		20 37				
Havant	d		19 11				19 16			19 30	19 46		19 52			20 11				20 16		20 44		20 51		20 57
Warblington	d						19 18													20 18						20 59
Emsworth	d		19 15				19 21			19 34			19 56			20 15				20 21		20 48		20 55		21 02
Southbourne	d						19 24			19 37			19 59							20 24		20 51		20 58		21 05
Nutbourne	d						19 26													20 26						21 07
Bosham	d						19 30													20 30						21 11
Fishbourne (Sussex)	d						19 33													20 33						21 14
Chichester 4	a		19 23				19 36			19 44	19 57		20 06			20 23				20 36		20 58		21 05		21 17
	d		19 25				19 37			19 45	19 59		20 07			20 25				20 37		20 59		21 07		21 18
Bognor Regis 4	d			19 33				19 39				20 04					20 33				20 39		21 04			
Barnham	a		19 32	19 40			19 44	19 46		19 52	20 06	20 10	20 14			20 32	20 39			20 44	20 45	21 06	21 10	21 14		21 25
	d		19 33	19 41			19 45			19 53	20 07	20 11	20 15			20 33	20 40			20 45		21 07	21 11	21 15		21 26
Bognor Regis 4	a																									
Ford 4	d		19 37	19 45			19 49			19 57		20 15	20 19				20 44			20 49			21 15	21 19		21 30
Littlehampton 4	a						19 54			20 02		20 20								20 54			21 20			21 35
	d					19 52								20 15			20b11		20 52				21b07		21 15	
Angmering 3	d		19 43	19 53		20 00					20 16			20 23		20 42	20 53		21 00			21 16			21 23	
Goring-by-Sea	d			19 57		20 04								20 27			20 57		21 04						21 27	
Durrington-on-Sea	d		19 49	20 00		20 07								20 30		20 48	21 00		21 07						21 30	
West Worthing	d			20 02		20 09								20 32			21 02		21 09						21 32	
Worthing 4	a		19 53	20 04		20 11					20 23			20 34		20 52	21 04		21 11			21 23			21 34	
	d		19 53	20 05		20 12					20 23			20 35		20 52	21 05		21 12			21 23			21 35	
East Worthing	d		19 56			20 14					20 26					20 55			21 14			21 26				
Lancing	d		19 59	20 09		20 17					20 29			20 39		20 58	21 09		21 17			21 29			21 39	
Shoreham-by-Sea	d		20 03	20 13		20 22					20 33			20 43		21 02	21 13		21 22			21 33			21 43	
Southwick	d		20 06			20 25					20 36					21 05			21 25			21 36				
Fishersgate	d		20 08			20 27					20 38					21 07			21 27			21 38				
Portslade	d		20 10	20 17		20 29					20 40			20 48		21 09	21 18		21 29			21 40			21 48	
Aldrington	d		20 12			20 31					20 42					21 11			21 31			21 42				
Hove 2	d	19 54	20 15	20 22	20 24	20 34					20 45			20 52	20 54	21 14	21 22	21 24	21 34			21 45			21 52	
Brighton 10	a	19 58	20 19		20 28	20 38					20 49				20 58	21 18		21 28	21 38			21 49				
Burgess Hill	a													21 02											22 02	
Haywards Heath 3	a	20 18		20 36	20 48						21 21			21 09	21 28		21 36	21 58				22 21			22 08	
Arundel	d												20 24											21 24		
Amberley	d												20 29											21 29		
Pulborough	d												20 35											21 35		
Billingshurst	d												20 41											21 41		
Christs Hospital	d												20 48											21 48		
Horsham 4	a												20 52											21 52		
	d												20 52											21 52		
Crawley	d												21 01											22 01		
Three Bridges 4	a	20c32		20 47	21 11						21 32		21 05	21 32	21 42		21 47	22 11				22 32		22 05	22 32	
	d			20 48									21 05				21 48							22 05		
Gatwick Airport 10 ✈	a	20 30		20 52	21 00						21 37		21 10	21 24	21 46		21 52	22 16				22 37		22 10	22 23	
Horley	a			20 59									21 26				22 00							22 29	23 26	
Redhill 5	a			21 06									21 18	21 47			22 06							22 18	22 46	
East Croydon	a	20 46		21 09	21 16	21 23							21 30	21 40	21 53		22 09		22 23			22 59		22 30	22 40	
London Bridge 4 ⊖	a	21 02		21 32	21 32	21e47							21f47	22 17	22 17		22 47	22 47	23e11					22f47	23 17	
Clapham Junction 10	a	21 03		21 20		21 33							21 40	21 50	22 03		22 20		22 33			23 10		22 40	22 49	
London Victoria 15 ⊖	a	21g05		21 27	21g35	21 40							21 47	21 57	22 10		22 27		22 40			23 17		22 50	22 57	

For general notes see front of timetable
For details of catering facilities see
Directory of Train Operators

b Change at Ford
c Change at Brighton and Haywards Heath
e Change at Brighton and East Croydon
f Change at Gatwick Airport
g Change at Brighton and Gatwick Airport

For complete service between Horsham and Three Bridges see Table 186

Southampton, Portsmouth and Sussex Coast → Brighton, Gatwick Airport & London

Saturdays

Network Diagram - see first page of Table 186

		SN 1		SN 1	SN 1	SN 1	SN 1	SN 1	SN 1	SN 1	SN 1	SN 1	SN 1	SN 1	SN 1	SN 1	SN 1	SN 1	SN 1		SN 1	SN 1	SN 1	SN 1	SN 1	
Southampton Central	d			20 33							21 13			21 23				22 13					22 33			
Swanwick	d			20 50							21 33			21 45				22 31					22 50			
Fareham	d			20 56							21 40			21 56				22 39					23 00			
Portchester	d										21 45			22 01				22 44								
Cosham	d			21 05							21 49			22 06				22 48					23 08			
Portsmouth Harbour	d							21 11				21 40					22 15					22 44			23 15	
Portsmouth & Southsea	d			20 50				21 15			21 24	21 44					22 19	22 24				22 48			23 19	
Fratton	d			20 54				21 19			21 28	21 48					22 23	22 28				22 52			23 23	
Hilsea	d							21 23			21 32	21 52					22 27	22 32				22 56			23 27	
Bedhampton	d							21 28			21 37	21 57					22 32	22 37				23 01			23 33	
Havant	d			21 11				21 31			21 56	22 00		22 12			22 35	22 55				23 05	23 15		23 36	
Warblington	d							21 33						22 14											23 38	
Emsworth	d			21 15				21 36						22 17			22 39	22 59							23 41	
Southbourne	d							21 39						22 20			22 42	23 02							23 44	
Nutbourne	d							21 41						22 23											23 47	
Bosham	d							21 45						22 26											23 50	
Fishbourne (Sussex)	d							21 48						22 29											23 53	
Chichester 4	a			21 23				21 51			22 06	22 10		22 33			22 49	23 09				23 16	23 25		23 57	
	d			21 25				21 52			22 07	22 11		22 33	22 40		22 52	23 09				23 18	23 26	23 52	23 57	
Bognor Regis 4	d				21 39				22 00				22 30						23 15							
Barnham	a			21 32	21 45			21 59	22 06		22 14	22 18	22 36	22 41	22 47		22 59	23 17	23 21			23 26	23 33	23 59	00 05	
	d			21 33				22 00			22 15	22 19	22 37		22 48		23 00	23 17				23 26	23 34	00 01	00 06	
Bognor Regis 4	a																									
Ford 4	d			21 37				22 04			22 19	22 23	22 41		22 52		23 04					23 31		00 05	00 10	
Littlehampton 4	a										22 24		22 46					23 25				23 35	23 42	00 10	00 15	
	d						21 52				22 33				22b38							23 40		23b23		
Angmering 3	d			21 43			22 00	22 11			22 41						23 11					23 48				
Goring-by-Sea	d			21 47			22 04	22 15			22 45						23 15					23 52				
Durrington-on-Sea	d			21 50			22 07	22 18			22 47						23 17					23 54				
West Worthing	d			21 52			22 09	22 20			22 49						23 19					23 56				
Worthing 4	a			21 54			22 11	22 22			22 52						23 22					23 59				
	d			21 55			22 12	22 23			22 52						23 22					23 59				
East Worthing	d			21 57			22 14	22 25			22 55						23 25					00 02				
Lancing	d			22 00			22 17	22 28			22 58						23 28					00 05				
Shoreham-by-Sea	d			22 04			22 22	22 32			23 02						23 32					00 09				
Southwick	d			22 07			22 25	22 35			23 05						23 35					00 12				
Fishersgate	d			22 09			22 27	22 37			23 07						23 37					00 14				
Portslade	d			22 11			22 29	22 39			23 09						23 39					00 16				
Aldrington	d			22 14			22 31	22 42			23 11						23 41					00 18				
Hove 2	d	21 54		22 16		22 24	22 34	22 44		22 54	23 14					23 24	23 44				23 54	00 21				
Brighton 10	a	21 58		22 21		22 28	22 38	22 48		22 58	23 18					23 28	23 48				23 58	00 25				
Burgess Hill	a																									
Haywards Heath 3	a	22 28				22 54				23 23						23 58										
Arundel	d											22 28			22 57											
Amberley	d														23 02											
Pulborough	d											22 37			23 08											
Billingshurst	d											22 43			23 14											
Christs Hospital	d											22 50			23 21											
Horsham 4	a											22 54			23 25											
	d											22 55			23 25											
Crawley	d											23 03			23 38											
Three Bridges 4	a	22 42				23 05				23 33		23 07			23 42	00 10										
	d																									
Gatwick Airport 10 ✈	a	22 46				23c12				23 42		23 16			23 52	00 14										
Horley	a																									
Redhill 5	a																									
East Croydon	a	23 02				23 32				00 02		23 32			00 16	00 35										
London Bridge 4 ⊖	a	23 17				23 47				00 19		23 47			00 52	00 52										
Clapham Junction 10	a	23e25				00e11				00e29		00f11			01f02	01e02										
London Victoria 15 ⊖	a	23g52				00g18				00h25		00 18			00 36	00h55										

For general notes see front of timetable
For details of catering facilities see Directory of Train Operators

- **b** Change at Ford
- **c** Change at Brighton and Haywards Heath
- **e** Change at Brighton and East Croydon
- **f** Change at Three Bridges and East Croydon
- **g** Change at Brighton and Three Bridges
- **h** Change at Brighton and Gatwick Airport

For complete service between Horsham and Three Bridges see Table 186

Table 188

Sundays

until 6 September

Southampton, Portsmouth and Sussex Coast → Brighton, Gatwick Airport & London

Network Diagram - see first page of Table 186

		SN 1	SN 1	SN 1	SN 1	SN 1	SN 1	SN 1		SN 1	SN 1	SN 1	SN 1	SN 1
Southampton Central	d													
Swanwick	d													
Fareham	d													
Portchester	d													
Cosham	d													
Portsmouth Harbour	d	22p44		23p15									07 05	
Portsmouth & Southsea	d	22p48		23p19									07 09	
Fratton	d	22p52		23p23									07 13	
Hilsea	d	22p56		23p27										
Bedhampton	d	23p01		23p33									07 20	
Havant	d	23p05		23p36									07b27	
Warblington	d			23p38									07 29	
Emsworth	d			23p41									07 32	
Southbourne	d			23p44									07 35	
Nutbourne	d			23p47									07 38	
Bosham	d			23p50									07 41	
Fishbourne (Sussex)	d			23p53									07 44	
Chichester 4	a	23p16		23p57									07 47	
	d	23p18	23p52	23p57	05 41								07 48	
Bognor Regis 4	d						06 52					07 36		07 52
Barnham	a	23p26	23p59	00 05	05 48		06 58					07 42	07 55	07 58
	d	23p26	00 01	00 06	05 49	06 06	06 59					07 43	08 02 →	07 59
Bognor Regis 4	a													
Ford 4	d	23p31	00 05	00 10		06e46	07 03					07 47		08 03
Littlehampton 4	a	23p35	00 10	00 15		06 13						07 52		
	d	23p40	23f23			06 20	06f42	07 14			07 38	07f19		07f54
Angmering 3	d	23p48						07 22			07 46			
Goring-by-Sea	d	23p52						07 26			07 50			
Durrington-on-Sea	d	23p54						07 29			07 52			
West Worthing	d	23p56						07 31			07 54			
Worthing 4	a	23p59			06 03	06 33		07 33			07 57			
	d	23p59			06 05	06 33		07 35			07 57			
East Worthing	d	00 02									08 00			
Lancing	d	00 05			06 09	06 37		07 39			08 03			
Shoreham-by-Sea	d	00 09			06 13	06 41		07 43			08 07			
Southwick	d	00 12			06 16	06 44		07 46			08 10			
Fishersgate	d	00 14									08 12			
Portslade	d	00 16			06 20	06 48		07 49			08 14			
Aldrington	d	00 18									08 16			
Hove 2	d	00 21			06 24	06 51		07 54		07 56	08 19			
Brighton 10	a	00 25				06 55				08 00	08 23			
Burgess Hill	a							08 04						
Haywards Heath 3	a				06 39	07 24		08 09		08 32	09 02			
Arundel	d						07 08							08 08
Amberley	d						07 13							08 13
Pulborough	d						07 19							08 19
Billingshurst	d						07 26							08 26
Christs Hospital	d						07 32							08 32
Horsham 4	a						07 37							08 37
	d						07 37							08 37
Crawley	d						07 46							08 46
Three Bridges 4	a				07 11	07 36	07 50	08 36		08 41	09 11			08 50
	d						07 50							08 50
Gatwick Airport 10 ✈	a				06 53	07 41	07 55	08 22		08 46	09 01			08 55
Horley	a				07 00		07 58							08 58
Redhill 5	a				07 07		08 05	08 49						09 05
East Croydon	a				07 09	08 00	08 20	08 39		08 45	09 17			09 20
London Bridge 4 ⊖	a				07 47	08 17	08 47	09 12		09 17	09 47			09 47
Clapham Junction 10	a				07 19	08 10	08 31	08 48		08 55	09 26			09 31
London Victoria 15 ⊖	a				07 26	08 17	08 39	08 55		09 02	09 33			09 39

		SN 1	SN 1	SN 1		SN 1	SN 1	SN 1	SN 1	SN 1	SN 1	SN 1	SN 1
Southampton Central	d												
Swanwick	d												
Fareham	d												
Portchester	d												
Cosham	d												
Portsmouth Harbour	d			07 43					08 05				08 43
Portsmouth & Southsea	d			07 47					08 09				08 47
Fratton	d			07 51					08 13				08 51
Hilsea	d												
Bedhampton	d								08 20				
Havant	d			08 00					08c27				09 00
Warblington	d								08 29				
Emsworth	d			08 04					08 32				09 04
Southbourne	d			08 07					08 35				09 07
Nutbourne	d								08 38				
Bosham	d								08 41				
Fishbourne (Sussex)	d								08 44				
Chichester 4	a			08 14					08 47				09 14
	d			08 14					08 48				09 14
Bognor Regis 4	d							08 36		08 52			
Barnham	a	←		08 22				08 42	08 55	08 58	←		09 22
	d	08 02		08 22				08 43	09 02 →	08 59	09 02		09 22
Bognor Regis 4	a												
Ford 4	d	08 06						08 47		09 03	09 06		
Littlehampton 4	a							08 52					
	d		08 14				08 38			08f54		09 14	
Angmering 3	d	08 12	08 22				08 46				09 12	09 22	
Goring-by-Sea	d	08 16	08 26				08 50				09 16	09 26	
Durrington-on-Sea	d	08 19	08 29				08 52				09 19	09 29	
West Worthing	d	08 21	08 31				08 54				09 21	09 31	
Worthing 4	a	08 23	08 33	08 37			08 57				09 23	09 33	09 37
	d	08 24	08 41				08 57				09 24	09 41	
East Worthing	d	08 26					09 00				09 26		
Lancing	d	08 29					09 03				09 29		
Shoreham-by-Sea	d	08 33	08 47				09 07				09 33	09 47	
Southwick	d	08 36					09 10				09 36		
Fishersgate	d	08 38					09 12				09 38		
Portslade	d	08 40					09 14				09 40		
Aldrington	d	08 43					09 16				09 43		
Hove 2	d	08 45	08 54			09 01	09 19				09 45	09 54	
Brighton 10	a	08 49				09 05	09 23				09 49		
Burgess Hill	a		09 04									10 04	
Haywards Heath 3	a	09 20	09 09			09 32	10 02				10 20	10 09	
Arundel	d									09 08			
Amberley	d									09 13			
Pulborough	d									09 19			
Billingshurst	d									09 26			
Christs Hospital	d									09 32			
Horsham 4	a									09 37			
	d									09 37			
Crawley	d									09 46			
Three Bridges 4	a	09 36	09 36			09 41	10 11			09 50	10 36	10 36	
	d									09 50			
Gatwick Airport 10 ✈	a	09 41	09 22			09 46	10 01			09 55	10 41	10 22	
Horley	a									09 58			
Redhill 5	a		09 49							10 05		10 49	
East Croydon	a		09 39			09 45	10 17			10 20		10 39	
London Bridge 4 ⊖	a		10 12			10 17	10 47			10 47		11g12	
Clapham Junction 10	a		09 48			09 55	10 26			10 31		10 48	
London Victoria 15 ⊖	a		09 55			10 02	10 33			10 39		10 55	

For general notes see front of timetable
For details of catering facilities see Directory of Train Operators

b Arr. 0723
c Arr. 0823
e Change at Littlehampton
f Change at Ford
g London Bridge

For complete service between Horsham and Three Bridges see Table 186

Table 188

Southampton, Portsmouth and Sussex Coast → Brighton, Gatwick Airport & London

Sundays

until 6 September

Network Diagram - see first page of Table 186

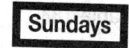

		GW 1 A 🚲	SN 1		SN 1	SN 1	SN 1	SN 1 🚲	SN 1	SN 1	SN 1		SN 1	SN 1	SN 1	SN 1	SN 1 🚲	SN 1	SN 1	SN 1		SN 1	SN 1	SN 1	SN 1	SN 1 🚲
Southampton Central	d	08 31																								
Swanwick	d																									
Fareham	d	08 52																								
Portchester	d																									
Cosham	d	09 00																								
Portsmouth Harbour	d						09 05				09 43					10 05				10 43					11 05	
Portsmouth & Southsea	d						09 09				09 47					10 09				10 47					11 09	
Fratton	d						09 13				09 51					10 13				10 51					11 13	
Hilsea	d																									
Bedhampton	d						09 20									10 20									11 20	
Havant	d	09 11					09b27				10 00					10c27				11 00					11e27	
Warblington	d						09 29									10 29									11 29	
Emsworth	d						09 32				10 04					10 32				11 04					11 32	
Southbourne	d						09 35				10 07					10 35				11 07					11 35	
Nutbourne	d						09 38									10 38									11 38	
Bosham	d						09 41									10 41									11 41	
Fishbourne (Sussex)	d						09 44									10 44									11 44	
Chichester 4	a	09 22					09 47				10 14					10 47				11 14					11 47	
	d	09 22					09 48				10 14					10 48				11 14					11 48	
Bognor Regis 4	d					09 30		09 52							10 30		10 52							11 30		11 52
Barnham	a	09 30				09 36	09 55	09 58	←		10 22				10 36	10 55	10 58	←		11 22				11 36	11 55	11 58
	d	09 30				09 37	10 02 →	09 59	10 02		10 22				10 37	11 02 →	10 59	11 02		11 22				11 37	12 02 →	11 59
Bognor Regis 4	a																									
Ford 4	d					09 41		10 03	10 06						10 41		11 03	11 06						11 41		12 03
Littlehampton 4	a					09 46									10 46									11 46		
	d				09 38			09f54		10 14				10 38			10f54		11 14				11 38			11f54
Angmering 3	d				09 46				10 12	10 22				10 46				11 12	11 22				11 46			
Goring-by-Sea	d				09 50				10 16	10 26				10 50				11 16	11 26				11 50			
Durrington-on-Sea	d				09 52				10 19	10 29				10 52				11 19	11 29				11 52			
West Worthing	d				09 54				10 21	10 31				10 54				11 21	11 31				11 54			
Worthing 4	a	09 45			09 57				10 23	10 33	10 37			10 57				11 23	11 33	11 37			11 57			
	d	09 45			09 57				10 24	10 41				10 57				11 24	11 41				11 57			
East Worthing	d				10 00				10 26					11 00				11 26					12 00			
Lancing	d				10 03				10 29					11 03				11 29					12 03			
Shoreham-by-Sea	d	09 52			10 07				10 33	10 47				11 07				11 33	11 47				12 07			
Southwick	d				10 10				10 36					11 10				11 36					12 10			
Fishersgate	d				10 12				10 38					11 12				11 38					12 12			
Portslade	d				10 14				10 40					11 14				11 40					12 14			
Aldrington	d				10 16				10 43					11 16				11 43					12 16			
Hove 2	d	09 59	10 02		10 19				10 45	10 54			11 01	11 19				11 45	11 54			12 01	12 19			
Brighton 10	a	10 05	10 06		10 23				10 49				11 05	11 23				11 49				12 05	12 23			
Burgess Hill	a									11 04									12 04							
Haywards Heath 3	a		10 32		11 02				11 20	11 09			11 32	12 02				12 20	12 09			12 32	13 02			
Arundel	d							10 08									11 08									12 08
Amberley	d							10 13									11 13									12 13
Pulborough	d							10 19									11 19									12 19
Billingshurst	d							10 26									11 26									12 26
Christs Hospital	d							10 32									11 32									12 32
Horsham 4	a							10 37									11 37									12 37
	d							10 37									11 37									12 37
Crawley	d							10 46									11 46									12 46
Three Bridges 4	a		10 41		11 11			10 50	11 36	11 36			11 41	12 11			11 50	12 36	12 36			12 41	13 11			12 50
	d							10 50									11 50									12 50
Gatwick Airport 10 ✈	a		10 46		11 01			10 55	11 41	11 22			11 46	12 01			11 55	12 41	12 22			12 46	13 01			12 55
Horley	a							10 58									11 58									12 58
Redhill 5	a							11 05		11 49							12 05		12 49							13 05
East Croydon	a		10 45		11 17			11 20		11 39			11 45	12 17			12 20		12 39			12 45	13 17			13 20
London Bridge 4 ⊖	a		11 17		11 47			11 47		12 12			12 17	12 47			12 47		13 12			13 17	13 47			13 47
Clapham Junction 10	a		10 55		11 26			11 31		11 48			11 55	12 26			12 31		12 48			12 55	13 26			13 31
London Victoria 15 ⊖	a		11 02		11 33			11 39		11 55			12 02	12 33			12 39		12 55			13 02	13 33			13 39

For general notes see front of timetable
For details of catering facilities see Directory of Train Operators

A From Romsey (Table 158)
b Arr. 0923
c Arr. 1023
e Arr. 1123
f Change at Ford

For complete service between Horsham and Three Bridges see Table 186

Southampton, Portsmouth and Sussex Coast → Brighton, Gatwick Airport & London

Network Diagram - see first page of Table 186

		SN 1	SN 1	SN 1	SN 1	SN 1	SN 1	SN 1	SN 1 🚲	SN 1	SN 1	SN 1	SN 1	SN 1	SN 1	SN 1	SN 1 🚲	SN 1	SN 1	SN 1	GW ◇ 🚲	SN 1	SN 1
Southampton Central	d																				13 08		
Swanwick	d																						
Fareham	d																				13 34		
Portchester	d																						
Cosham	d																				13 42		
Portsmouth Harbour	d			11 43				12 05				12 43				13 05				13 43			
Portsmouth & Southsea	d			11 47				12 09				12 47				13 09				13 47			
Fratton	d			11 51				12 13				12 51				13 13				13 51			
Hilsea	d																						
Bedhampton	d							12 20								13 20							
Havant	d			12 00				12b27				13 00				13c27				14 00	14 04		
Warblington	d							12 29								13 29							
Emsworth	d			12 04				12 32				13 04				13 32				14 04			
Southbourne	d			12 07				12 35				13 07				13 35				14 07			
Nutbourne	d							12 38								13 38							
Bosham	d							12 41								13 41							
Fishbourne (Sussex)	d							12 44								13 44							
Chichester 4	a			12 14				12 47				13 14				13 47				14 14	14 19		
	d			12 14				12 48				13 14				13 48				14 14	14 19		
Bognor Regis 4	d						12 30		12 52						13 30		13 52						
Barnham	a	←		12 22			12 36	12 55	12 58	←		13 22			13 36	13 55	13 58	←		14 22	14 27		
	d	12 02		12 22			12 37	13 02 →	12 59	13 02		13 22			13 37	14 02 →	13 59	14 02		14 22	14 27		
Bognor Regis 4	a																						
Ford 4	d	12 06					12 41		13 03	13 06					13 41		14 03	14 06					
Littlehampton 4	a						12 46								13 46								
	d		12 14			12 38			12e54		13 14			13 38			13e54		14 14				14 38
Angmering 3	d	12 12	12 22			12 46				13 12	13 22			13 46				14 12	14 22				14 46
Goring-by-Sea	d	12 16	12 26			12 50				13 16	13 26			13 50				14 16	14 26				14 50
Durrington-on-Sea	d	12 19	12 29			12 52				13 19	13 29			13 52				14 19	14 29				14 52
West Worthing	d	12 21	12 31			12 54				13 21	13 31			13 54				14 21	14 31				14 54
Worthing 4	a	12 23	12 33	12 37		12 57				13 23	13 33	13 37		13 57				14 23	14 33	14 37	14 44		14 57
	d	12 24		12 41		12 57				13 24		13 41		13 57				14 24		14 41	14 45		14 57
East Worthing	d	12 26				13 00				13 26				14 00				14 26					15 00
Lancing	d	12 29				13 03				13 29				14 03				14 29					15 03
Shoreham-by-Sea	d	12 33		12 47		13 07				13 33		13 47		14 07				14 33		14 47	14 51		15 07
Southwick	d	12 36				13 10				13 36				14 10				14 36					15 10
Fishersgate	d	12 38				13 12				13 38				14 12				14 38					15 12
Portslade	d	12 40				13 14				13 40				14 14				14 40					15 14
Aldrington	d	12 43				13 16				13 43				14 16				14 43					15 16
Hove 2	d	12 45		12 54	13 01	13 19				13 45		13 54	14 01	14 19				14 45		14 54	14 58	15 01	15 19
Brighton 10	a	12 49			13 05	13 23				13 49			14 05	14 23				14 49			15 04	15 05	15 23
Burgess Hill	a			13 04								14 04								15 04			
Haywards Heath 3	a	13 20		13 09	13 32	14 02				14 20		14 09	14 32	15 02				15 20		15 09		15 32	16 02
Arundel	d								13 08								14 08						
Amberley	d								13 13								14 13						
Pulborough	d								13 19								14 19						
Billingshurst	d								13 26								14 26						
Christs Hospital	d								13 32								14 32						
Horsham 4	a								13 37								14 37						
	d								13 37								14 37						
Crawley	d								13 46								14 46						
Three Bridges 4	a	13 36		13 36	13 41	14 11			13 50	14 36		14 36	14 41	15 11			14 50	15 36		15 36		15 41	16 11
	d								13 50								14 50						
Gatwick Airport 10 ✈	a	13 41		13 22	13 46	14 01			13 55	14 41		14 22	14 46	15 01			14 55	15 41		15 22		15 46	16 01
Horley	a								13 58								14 58						
Redhill 5	a			13 49					14 05			14 49					15 05			15 49			
East Croydon	a			13 39	13 45	14 17			14 20			14 39	14 45	15 17			15 20			15 39		15 45	16 17
London Bridge 4 ⊖	a			14 12	14 17	14 47			14 47			15 12	15 17	15 47			15 47			16 12		16 17	16 47
Clapham Junction 10	a			13 48	13 55	14 26			14 31			14 48	14 55	15 26			15 31			15 48		15 55	16 26
London Victoria 15 ⊖	a			13 55	14 02	14 33			14 39			14 55	15 02	15 33			15 39			15 55		16 02	16 33

For general notes see front of timetable
For details of catering facilities see Directory of Train Operators

b Arr. 1223
c Arr. 1323
e Change at Ford

For complete service between Horsham and Three Bridges see Table 186

Table 188

Sundays

until 6 September

Southampton, Portsmouth and Sussex Coast → Brighton, Gatwick Airport & London

Network Diagram - see first page of Table 186

Station		SN 1	SN 1	SN 1 🚲	SN 1	SN 1	SN 1		SN 1	SN 1	SN 1	SN 1	SN 1 🚲	SN 1	SN 1	SN 1		GW ◇ 🚲	SN 1	SN 1	SN 1	SN 1	SN 1 🚲	SN 1		
Southampton Central	d																	15 22								
Swanwick	d																									
Fareham	d																	15 51								
Portchester	d																									
Cosham	d																	16 01								
Portsmouth Harbour	d		14 05				14 43					15 05				15 43						16 05				
Portsmouth & Southsea	d		14 09				14 47					15 09				15 47						16 09				
Fratton	d		14 13				14 51					15 13				15 51						16 13				
Hilsea	d																									
Bedhampton	d		14 20									15 20										16 20				
Havant	d		14b27				15 00					15c27				16 00		16 11				16e27				
Warblington	d		14 29									15 29										16 29				
Emsworth	d		14 32				15 04					15 32				16 04						16 32				
Southbourne	d		14 35				15 07					15 35				16 07						16 35				
Nutbourne	d		14 38									15 38										16 38				
Bosham	d		14 41									15 41										16 41				
Fishbourne (Sussex)	d		14 44									15 44										16 44				
Chichester 4	a		14 47				15 14					15 47				16 14		16 22				16 47				
	d		14 48				15 14					15 48				16 14		16 22				16 48				
Bognor Regis 4	d	14 30		14 52							15 30		15 52								16 30		16 52			
Barnham	a	14 36	14 55	14 58	←		15 22				15 36	15 55	15 58	←		16 22		16 30			16 36	16 55	16 58	←		
	d	14 37	15 02	14 59	15 02		15 22				15 37	16 02	15 59	16 02		16 22		16 30			16 37	17 02	16 59	17 02		
Bognor Regis 4	a		→									→										→				
Ford 4	d	14 41		15 03	15 06						15 41		16 03	16 06							16 41		17 03	17 06		
Littlehampton 4	a	14 46									15 46										16 46					
	d			*14f54*		15 14				15 38			*15f54*		16 14					16 38			*16f54*			
Angmering 3	d				15 12	15 22				15 46				16 12	16 22					16 46				17 12		
Goring-by-Sea	d				15 16	15 26				15 50				16 16	16 26					16 50				17 16		
Durrington-on-Sea	d				15 19	15 29				15 52				16 19	16 29					16 52				17 19		
West Worthing	d				15 21	15 31				15 54				16 21	16 31					16 54				17 21		
Worthing 4	a				15 23	15 33	15 37			15 57				16 23	16 33	16 37		16 45		16 57				17 23		
	d				15 24	15 41				15 57				16 24	16 41			16 45		16 57				17 24		
East Worthing	d				15 26					16 00				16 26						17 00				17 26		
Lancing	d				15 29					16 03				16 29						17 03				17 29		
Shoreham-by-Sea	d				15 33	15 47				16 07				16 33	16 47			16 52		17 07				17 33		
Southwick	d				15 36					16 10				16 36						17 10				17 36		
Fishersgate	d				15 38					16 12				16 38						17 12				17 38		
Portslade	d				15 40					16 14				16 40						17 14				17 40		
Aldrington	d				15 43					16 16				16 43						17 16				17 43		
Hove 2	d				15 45	15 54			16 01	16 19				16 45	16 54			16 59	17 02	17 19				17 45		
Brighton 10	a				15 49				16 05	16 23				16 49				17 05	17 06	17 23				17 49		
Burgess Hill	a					16 04									17 04											
Haywards Heath 3	a				*16 20*	16 09			*16 32*	*17 02*				*17 20*	17 09				*17 32*	*18 02*				*18 20*		
Arundel	d			15 08									16 08										17 08			
Amberley	d			15 13									16 13										17 13			
Pulborough	d			15 19									16 19										17 19			
Billingshurst	d			15 26									16 26										17 26			
Christs Hospital	d			15 32									16 32										17 32			
Horsham 4	a			15 37									16 37										17 37			
	d			15 37									16 37										17 37			
Crawley	d			15 46									16 46										17 46			
Three Bridges 4	a			15 50	*16 36*	16 36			*16 41*	*17 11*			16 50	*17 36*	*17 36*				*17 41*	*18 11*			17 50	*18 36*		
	d			15 50									16 50										17 50			
Gatwick Airport 10 ✈	a			15 55	*16 41*	16 22			*16 46*	*17 01*			16 55	*17 41*	17 22				*17 46*	*18 01*			17 55	*18 41*		
Horley	a			15 58									16 58										17 58			
Redhill 5	a			16 05		*16 49*							17 05		*17 49*								18 05			
East Croydon	a			16 20		16 39			*16 45*	*17 17*			17 20		17 39				*17 45*	*18 17*			18 20			
London Bridge 4 ⊖	a			*16 47*		*17 12*			*17 17*	*17 47*			*17 47*		*18 12*				*18 17*	*18 47*			*18 47*			
Clapham Junction 10	a			16 31		16 48			*16 55*	*17 26*			17 31		17 48				*17 55*	*18 26*			18 31			
London Victoria 15 ⊖	a			16 39		16 55			*17 02*	*17 33*			17 39		17 55				*18 02*	*18 33*			18 39			

For general notes see front of timetable
For details of catering facilities see Directory of Train Operators

b Arr. 1423
c Arr. 1523
e Arr. 1623
f Change at Ford

For complete service between Horsham and Three Bridges see Table 186

Sundays

until 6 September

Southampton, Portsmouth and Sussex Coast → Brighton, Gatwick Airport & London

Network Diagram - see first page of Table 186

		SN	SN	SN	SN	SN	SN	SN		SN	SN	SN	SN	SN	SN	SN		SN	SN	SN	SN	SN	SN	SN		SN
		1	1	1	1	1	1	1		1	1	1	1	1	1	1		1	1	1	1	1	1	1		1
Southampton Central	d																									
Swanwick	d																									
Fareham	d																									
Portchester	d																									
Cosham	d																									
Portsmouth Harbour	d		16 43				17 05					17 43				18 05					18 43					19 05
Portsmouth & Southsea	d		16 47				17 09					17 47				18 09					18 47					19 09
Fratton	d		16 51				17 13					17 51				18 13					18 51					19 13
Hilsea	d																									
Bedhampton	d						17 20									18 20										19 20
Havant	d		17 00				17b27					18 00				18c27					19 00					19e27
Warblington	d						17 29									18 29										19 29
Emsworth	d		17 04				17 32					18 04				18 32					19 04					19 32
Southbourne	d		17 07				17 35					18 07				18 35					19 07					19 35
Nutbourne	d						17 38									18 38										19 38
Bosham	d						17 41									18 41										19 41
Fishbourne (Sussex)	d						17 44									18 44										19 44
Chichester 4	a		17 14				17 47					18 14				18 47					19 14					19 47
	d		17 14				17 48					18 14				18 48					19 14					19 48
Bognor Regis 4	d					17 30		17 52							18 30			18 52						19 30		
Barnham	a		17 22			17 36	17 55	17 58		←		18 22			18 36	18 55		18 58	←		19 22			19 36		19 55
	d		17 22			17 37	18 02 →	17 59		18 02		18 22			18 37	19 02 →		18 59	19 02		19 22			19 37		20 02 →
Bognor Regis 4	a																									
Ford 4	d					17 41		18 03		18 06					18 41			19 03	19 06					19 41		
Littlehampton 4	a					17 46									18 46									19 46		
	d	17 14			17 38			17f54			18 14			18 38				18f54		19 14			19 38			
Angmering 3	d	17 22			17 46					18 12	18 22			18 46					19 12	19 22			19 46			
Goring-by-Sea	d	17 26			17 50					18 16	18 26			18 50					19 16	19 26			19 50			
Durrington-on-Sea	d	17 29			17 52					18 19	18 29			18 53					19 19	19 29			19 52			
West Worthing	d	17 31			17 54					18 21	18 31			18 55					19 21	19 31			19 54			
Worthing 4	a	17 33	17 37		17 57					18 23	18 33	18 37		18 57					19 23	19 33	19 37		19 57			
	d		17 41		17 57					18 24		18 41		18 58					19 24		19 41		19 57			
East Worthing	d				18 00					18 26				19 00					19 26				20 00			
Lancing	d				18 03					18 29				19 03					19 29				20 03			
Shoreham-by-Sea	d		17 47		18 07					18 33		18 47		19 07					19 33		19 47		20 07			
Southwick	d				18 10					18 36				19 10					19 36				20 10			
Fishersgate	d				18 12					18 38				19 12					19 38				20 12			
Portslade	d				18 14					18 40				19 14					19 40				20 14			
Aldrington	d				18 16					18 43				19 17					19 43				20 16			
Hove 2	d		17 54	18 01	18 19					18 45		18 54	19 01	19 19					19 45		19 54	20 01	20 19			
Brighton 10	a			18 05	18 23					18 49			19 05	19 23					19 49			20 05	20 23			
Burgess Hill	a		18 04									19 04									20 04					
Haywards Heath 3	a		18 09	18 32	19 02					19 20		19 09	19 32	20 02					20 20		20 09	20 32	21 02			
Arundel	d							18 08										19 08								
Amberley	d							18 13										19 13								
Pulborough	d							18 19										19 19								
Billingshurst	d							18 26										19 26								
Christs Hospital	d							18 32										19 32								
Horsham 4	a							18 37										19 37								
	d							18 37										19 37								
Crawley	d							18 46										19 46								
Three Bridges 4	a		18 36	18 41	19 11			18 50		19 36		19 36	19 41	20 11				19 50	20 36		20 36	20 41	21 11			
	d							18 50										19 50								
Gatwick Airport 10 ✈	a		18 22	18 46	19 01			18 55		19 41		19 22	19 46	20 01				19 55	20 41		20 22	20 46	21 01			
Horley	a							18 58										19 58								
Redhill 5	a		18 49					19 05				19 49						20 05			20 49					
East Croydon	a		18 39	18 45	19 17			19 20				19 39	19 45	20 17				20 20			20 39	20 45	21 17			
London Bridge 4 ⊖	a		19 12	19 17	19 47			19 47				20 12	20 17	20 47				20 47			21 12	21 17	21 47			
Clapham Junction 10	a		18 48	18 55	19 26			19 31				19 48	19 55	20 26				20 31			20 48	20 55	21 26			
London Victoria 15 ⊖	a		18 55	19 02	19 33			19 39				19 55	20 02	20 33				20 39			20 55	21 02	21 33			

For general notes see front of timetable
For details of catering facilities see Directory of Train Operators

b Arr. 1723
c Arr. 1823
e Arr. 1923
f Change at Ford

For complete service between Horsham and Three Bridges see Table 186

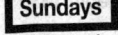

Southampton, Portsmouth and Sussex Coast → Brighton, Gatwick Airport & London

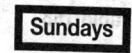

Sundays
until 6 September

Network Diagram - see first page of Table 186

Station		SN 1	SN 1	SN 1	SN 1	SN 1	GW ◇	SN 1		SN 1	SN 1	SN 1	SN 1	SN 1	SN 1	SN 1		SN 1	SN 1	SN 1	SN 1	SN 1	SN 1	SN 1		
Southampton Central	d						19 27																			
Swanwick	d																									
Fareham	d						19 49																			
Portchester	d																									
Cosham	d						19 59																			
Portsmouth Harbour	d				19 43						20 05			20 43		21 05					21 43	22 14	22 43			
Portsmouth & Southsea	d				19 47						20 09			20 47		21 09					21 47	22 18	22 47			
Fratton	d				19 51						20 13			20 51		21 13					21 51	22 22	22 51			
Hilsea	d																									
Bedhampton	d										20 20					21 20						22 30				
Havant	d				20 00		20 11				20b27			21 00		21c27					22 00	22 33	23 00			
Warblington	d										20 29					21 29						22 35				
Emsworth	d				20 04						20 32			21 04		21 32					22 04	22 38	23 04			
Southbourne	d				20 07						20 35			21 07		21 35					22 07	22 41	23 07			
Nutbourne	d										20 38					21 38						22 43				
Bosham	d										20 41					21 41						22 47				
Fishbourne (Sussex)	d										20 44					21 44						22 50				
Chichester 4	a				20 14		20 21				20 47			21 14		21 47					22 14	22 53	23 14			
	d				20 14		20 22				20 48			21 14		21 48					22 14	22 53	23 14			
Bognor Regis 4	d	19 52								20 30		20 52			21 30			21 52		22 11						
Barnham	a	19 58	←		20 22		20 29			20 36	20 55	20 58	←	21 22	21 36	21 55		21 58	←	22 18	22 22	23 01	23 22			
	d	19 59	20 02		20 22		20 30			20 37	21 02 →	20 59	21 02	21 22	21 37	22 02 →		21 59	22 02		22 22	23 01	23 22	23 37		
Bognor Regis 4	a																									
Ford 4	d	20 03	20 06							20 41		21 03	21 06	21 27	21 41			22 03	22 06		22 27	23 06	23 27	23 42		
Littlehampton 4	a									20 46				21 31	21 46						22 31	23 10	23 32	23 46		
	d	19e54		20 14				20 41				20e54		21 42				21e54			22 42		23e06	23e29		
Angmering 3	d		20 12	20 22				20 49					21 12	21 50					22 12		22 50					
Goring-by-Sea	d		20 16	20 26				20 53					21 16	21 54					22 16		22 54					
Durrington-on-Sea	d		20 19	20 29				20 55					21 19	21 57					22 19		22 57					
West Worthing	d		20 21	20 31				20 57					21 21	21 59					22 21		22 59					
Worthing 4	a		20 23	20 33	20 37		20 51	21 00					21 23	22 01					22 23		23 01					
	d		20 24	20 41			20 51	21 00					21 24	22 02					22 24		23 02					
East Worthing	d		20 26					21 02					21 26	22 04					22 26		23 04					
Lancing	d		20 29					21 05					21 29	22 07					22 29		23 07					
Shoreham-by-Sea	d		20 33	20 47			20 58	21 09					21 33	22 11					22 33		23 11					
Southwick	d		20 36					21 12					21 36	22 14					22 36		23 14					
Fishersgate	d		20 38					21 14					21 38	22 16					22 38		23 16					
Portslade	d		20 40					21 16					21 40	22 18					22 40		23 18					
Aldrington	d		20 43					21 19					21 43	22 21					22 43		23 21					
Hove 2	d		20 45	20 54		21 01	21 05	21 21					21 45	22 23					22 45		23 25					
Brighton 10	a		20 49			21 05	21 10	21 25					21 49	22 27					22 49		23 29					
Burgess Hill	a			21 04																						
Haywards Heath 3	a		21 24	21 09		21 32	21 32	22 02					22 24	23 02					23 23		00 01					
Arundel	d	20 08										21 08						22 08								
Amberley	d	20 13										21 13						22 13								
Pulborough	d	20 19										21 19						22 19								
Billingshurst	d	20 26										21 26						22 26								
Christs Hospital	d	20 32										21 32						22 32								
Horsham 4	a	20 37										21 37						22 37								
	d	20 37										21 37						22 37								
Crawley	d	20 46										21 46						22 46								
Three Bridges 4	a	20 50	21 36	21 36		21 41	21 41	22 11				21 50	22 36	23 11				22 50	23 35		00 10					
	d	20 50										21 50						22 50								
Gatwick Airport 10 ✈	a	20 55	21 41	21 22		21 46	21 46	22 16				21 55	22 41	23 16				22 55	23 43		00 14					
Horley	a	20 58										21 58						22 58								
Redhill 5	a	21 05		21 49								22 05						23 05								
East Croydon	a	21 20	22 00	21 39		22 03	22 03	22 33				22 20	23 00	23 33				23 20	00 16		00 35					
London Bridge 4 ⊖	a	21 47		22 12		22 17	22 17	22 47				22 47	23 17	23 47				23 47	00 14		00 52					
Clapham Junction 10	a	21 31	22 10	21 48		22f18	22f18	23f07				22 31	23 10	00f10				23 31			01f02					
London Victoria 15 ⊖	a	21 39	22 17	21 55		22g39	22g39	23g14				22 39	23 17					23 38	00 37		00h55					

At Worthing the 20 33 and 20 37 arrivals are bracketed together to form the 20 41 departure.

For general notes see front of timetable
For details of catering facilities see Directory of Train Operators

- **b** Arr. 2023
- **c** Arr. 2123
- **e** Change at Ford
- **f** Change at Brighton and East Croydon
- **g** Change at Brighton and Three Bridges
- **h** Change at Brighton and Gatwick Airport

For complete service between Horsham and Three Bridges see Table 186

Table 188

Sundays

from 13 September

Southampton, Portsmouth and Sussex Coast → Brighton, Gatwick Airport & London

Network Diagram - see first page of Table 186

		SN 1	SN 1	SN 1	SN 1	SN 1	SN 1	SN 1		SN 1	SN 1	SN 1	SN 1 🚲	SN 1	SN 1	SN 1		SN 1	SN 1	SN 1	SN 1	SN 1 🚲	SN 1	SN 1	SN 1	SN 1
Southampton Central	d																									
Swanwick	d																									
Fareham	d																									
Portchester	d																									
Cosham	d																									
Portsmouth Harbour	d	22p44		23p15								07 14				07 43					08 14				08 43	
Portsmouth & Southsea	d	22p48		23p19								07 18				07 47					08 18				08 47	
Fratton	d	22p52		23p23								07 22				07 51					08 22				08 51	
Hilsea	d	22p56		23p27																						
Bedhampton	d	23p01		23p33								07 30									08 30					
Havant	d	23p05		23p36								07 33				08 00					08 33				09 00	
Warblington	d			23p38								07 35									08 35					
Emsworth	d			23p41								07 38				08 04					08 38				09 04	
Southbourne	d			23p44								07 41				08 07					08 41				09 07	
Nutbourne	d			23p47								07 43									08 43					
Bosham	d			23p50								07 47									08 47					
Fishbourne (Sussex)	d			23p53								07 50									08 50					
Chichester 4	a	23p16		23p57								07 53				08 14					08 53				09 14	
	d	23p18	23p52	23p57								07 53				08 14					08 53				09 14	
Bognor Regis 4	d					06 57					07 36		07 57							08 36		08 57				
Barnham	a	23p26	23p59	00 05		07 03					07 42	08 01	08 03	←		08 22				08 42	09 01	09 03	←		09 22	
	d	23p26	00 01	00 06	06 06	07 05					07 43	08 08 →	08 05	08 08		08 22				08 43	09 08 →	09 05	09 08		09 22	
Bognor Regis 4	a																									
Ford 4	d	23p31	00 05	00 10	06b46	07 09					07 47		08 09	08 12						08 47		09 09	09 12			
Littlehampton 4	a	23p35	00 10	00 15	06 13						07 52									08 52						
	d	23p40	23c23		06 20	06c42	07 14			07 40	07c19		07c57		08 14				08 40	08c11		08c57		09 14		
Angmering 3	d	23p48					07 22			07 48				08 18	08 22				08 48				09 18	09 22		
Goring-by-Sea	d	23p52					07 26			07 52				08 22	08 26				08 52				09 22	09 26		
Durrington-on-Sea	d	23p54					07 29			07 55				08 25	08 29				08 55				09 25	09 29		
West Worthing	d	23p56					07 31			07 57				08 27	08 31				08 57				09 27	09 31		
Worthing 4	a	23p59			06 33		07 33			07 59				08 29	08 33	08 37			08 59				09 29	09 33	09 37	
	d	23p59			06 33		07 35			08 00				08 30		08 41			09 00				09 30		09 41	
East Worthing	d	00 02								08 02				08 32					09 02				09 32			
Lancing	d	00 05			06 37		07 39			08 05				08 35					09 05				09 35			
Shoreham-by-Sea	d	00 09			06 41		07 43			08 09				08 39		08 47			09 09				09 39		09 47	
Southwick	d	00 12			06 44		07 46			08 12				08 42					09 12				09 42			
Fishersgate	d	00 14								08 14				08 44					09 14				09 44			
Portslade	d	00 16			06 48		07 49			08 16				08 46					09 16				09 46			
Aldrington	d	00 18								08 19				08 49				←	09 19				09 49			←
Hove 2	d	00 21			06 51		07 54	07 56		08 21				08e56 →		08 54		08 56	09 21				09f56 →		09 54	09 56
Brighton 10	a	00 25			06 55			08 00		08 26								09 00	09 25							10 00
Burgess Hill	a						08 04									09 04									10 04	
Haywards Heath 3	a				07 20		08 09	08 30		09 00						09 09		09 30	10 00						10 09	
Arundel	d					07 14							08 14									09 14				
Amberley	d					07 19							08 19									09 19				
Pulborough	d					07 25							08 25									09 25				
Billingshurst	d					07 31							08 31									09 31				
Christs Hospital	d					07 38							08 38									09 38				
Horsham 4	a					07 42							08 42									09 42				
	d					07 42							08 42									09 42				
Crawley	d					07 51							08 51									09 51				
Three Bridges 4	a				07 32	07 54	08 32	08 40		09 10			08 54			09 32		09 40	10 10			09 54			10 32	
	d					07 55							08 55									09 55				
Gatwick Airport 10 ✈	a				07 37	07 59	08 21	08 44		09 14			08 59			09 21		09 44	10 14			09 59			10 21	
Horley	a					08 02	08 30						09 02			09 30						10 02			10 30	
Redhill 5	a					08 09	08 36						09 09			09 36						10 09			10 36	
East Croydon	a				07 58	08 24	08 39	09 01		09 31			09 24			09 39		10 01	10 31			10 24			10 39	
London Bridge 4 ⊖	a				08 17	08 47	09 12	09 17		09 47			09 47			10 12		10 17	10 47			10 47			11 12	
Clapham Junction 10	a				08 11	08 37	08 54	09g24		09 47			09 37			09 54		10g24	10 47			10 37			10 54	
London Victoria 15 ⊖	a				08 18	08 46	09 01	09h25		09 53			09 46			10 01		10h25	10 53			10 46			11 01	

For general notes see front of timetable
For details of catering facilities see Directory of Train Operators

b Change at Littlehampton
c Change at Ford
e Arr. 0851
f Arr. 0951
g Change at Brighton and East Croydon
h Change at Brighton and Gatwick Airport

For complete service between Horsham and Three Bridges see Table 186

Table 188

Sundays

Southampton, Portsmouth and Sussex Coast → Brighton, Gatwick Airport & London

from 13 September

Network Diagram - see first page of Table 186

		GW		SN	SN	SN	SN	SN	SN	SN		SN	SN	SN	SN	SN	SN	SN	SN		SN	SN	SN	SN	SN	SN
		1		1	1	1	1	1	1	1		1	1	1	1	1	1	1	1		1	1	1	1	1	1
		A 🛒					🛒									🛒									🛒	
Southampton Central	d	08 31																								
Swanwick	d																									
Fareham	d	08 52																								
Portchester	d																									
Cosham	d	09 00																								
Portsmouth Harbour	d					09 14				09 43					10 14				10 43					11 14		
Portsmouth & Southsea	d					09 18				09 47					10 18				10 47					11 18		
Fratton	d					09 22				09 51					10 22				10 51					11 22		
Hilsea	d																									
Bedhampton	d					09 30									10 30									11 30		
Havant	d	09 11				09 33				10 00					10 33				11 00					11 33		
Warblington	d					09 35									10 35									11 35		
Emsworth	d					09 38				10 04					10 38				11 04					11 38		
Southbourne	d					09 41				10 07					10 41				11 07					11 41		
Nutbourne	d					09 43									10 43									11 43		
Bosham	d					09 47									10 47									11 47		
Fishbourne (Sussex)	d					09 50									10 50									11 50		
Chichester 4	a	09 22				09 53				10 14					10 53				11 14					11 53		
	d	09 22				09 53				10 14					10 53				11 14					11 53		
Bognor Regis 4	d				09 36		09 57							10 36		10 57							11 36		11 57	
Barnham	a	09 30			09 42	10 01	10 03	←		10 22				10 42	11 01	11 03	←		11 22				11 42	12 01	12 03	←
	d	09 30			09 43	10 08 →	10 05	10 08		10 22				10 43	11 08 →	11 05	11 08		11 22				11 43	12 08 →	12 05	12 08
Bognor Regis 4	a																									
Ford 4	d				09 47		10 09	10 12						10 47		11 09	11 12						11 47		12 09	12 12
Littlehampton 4	a				09 52									10 52									11 52			
	d			09 40	09b11		09b57		10 14				10 40			10b57		11 14				11 40			11b57	
Angmering 3	d			09 48				10 18	10 22				10 48				11 18	11 22				11 48				12 18
Goring-by-Sea	d			09 52				10 22	10 26				10 52				11 22	11 26				11 52				12 22
Durrington-on-Sea	d			09 55				10 25	10 29				10 55				11 25	11 29				11 55				12 25
West Worthing	d			09 57				10 27	10 31				10 57				11 27	11 31				11 57				12 27
Worthing 4	a	09 45		09 59				10 29	10 33	10 37			10 59				11 29	11 33	11 37			11 59				12 29
	d	09 45		10 00				10 30	10 41				11 00				11 30	11 41				12 00				12 30
East Worthing	d			10 02				10 32					11 02				11 32					12 02				12 32
Lancing	d			10 05				10 35					11 05				11 35					12 05				12 35
Shoreham-by-Sea	d	09 52		10 09				10 39	10 47				11 09				11 39	11 47				12 09				12 39
Southwick	d			10 12				10 42					11 12				11 42					12 12				12 42
Fishersgate	d			10 14				10 44					11 14				11 44					12 14				12 44
Portslade	d			10 16				10 46					11 16				11 46					12 16				12 46
Aldrington	d			10 19				10 49				←	11 19				11 49				←	12 19				12 49
Hove 2	d	09 59		10 21				10c56	10 54			10 56	11 21				11e56	11 54			11 56	12 21				12f56
Brighton 10	a	10 05		10 25				→				11 00	11 25				→				12 00	12 25				→
Burgess Hill	a								11 04									12 04								
Haywards Heath 3	a	*10 30*		*11 00*					11 09			*11 30*	*12 00*					12 09			*12 30*	*13 00*				
Arundel	d						10 14									11 14									12 14	
Amberley	d						10 19									11 19									12 19	
Pulborough	d						10 25									11 25									12 25	
Billingshurst	d						10 31									11 31									12 31	
Christs Hospital	d						10 38									11 38									12 38	
Horsham 4	a						10 42									11 42									12 42	
	d						10 42									11 42									12 42	
Crawley	d						10 51									11 51									12 51	
Three Bridges 4	a	*10 40*		*11 10*			10 54		*11 32*			*11 40*	*12 10*			11 54		*12 32*			*12 40*	*13 10*			12 54	
	d						10 55									11 55									12 55	
Gatwick Airport 10 ✈	a	*10 44*		*11 14*			10 59		11 21			*11 44*	*12 14*			11 59		12 22			*12 44*	*13 14*			12 59	
Horley	a						11 02		*11 30*							12 02		*12 30*							13 02	
Redhill 5	a						11 09		*11 36*							12 09		*12 36*							13 09	
East Croydon	a	*11 01*		*11 31*			11 24		11 39			*12 01*	*12 31*			12 24		12 39			*13 01*	*13 31*			13 24	
London Bridge 4 ⊖	a	*11 17*		*11 47*			*11 47*		*12 12*			*12 17*	*12 47*			*12 47*		*13 12*			*13 17*	*13 47*			*13 47*	
Clapham Junction 10	a	*11g24*		*11 47*			11 37		11 54			*12g24*	*12 47*			12 37		12 54			*13g24*	*13 47*			13 37	
London Victoria 15 ⊖	a	*11h25*		*11 53*			11 46		12 01			*12h25*	*12 53*			12 46		13 01			*13h25*	*13 53*			13 46	

For general notes see front of timetable
For details of catering facilities see Directory of Train Operators

A From Romsey (Table 158)
b Change at Ford
c Arr. 1051
e Arr. 1151
f Arr. 1251
g Change at Brighton and East Croydon
h Change at Brighton and Gatwick Airport

For complete service between Horsham and Three Bridges see Table 186

Table 188

Sundays

from 13 September

Southampton, Portsmouth and Sussex Coast → Brighton, Gatwick Airport & London

Network Diagram - see first page of Table 186

Station		SN 1	SN 1	SN 1		SN 1	SN 1	SN 1	SN 1	SN 1	SN 1	SN 1		SN 1	SN 1	SN 1	SN 1	SN 1	SN 1	SN 1	SN 1		SN 1	GW ◇	SN 1	SN 1
Southampton Central	d																							13 08		
Swanwick	d																									
Fareham	d																							13 34		
Portchester	d																									
Cosham	d																							13 42		
Portsmouth Harbour	d		11 43					12 14				12 43					13 14				13 43					
Portsmouth & Southsea	d		11 47					12 18				12 47					13 18				13 47					
Fratton	d		11 51					12 22				12 51					13 22				13 51					
Hilsea	d																									
Bedhampton	d							12 30									13 30									
Havant	d		12 00					12 33				13 00					13 33				14 00			14 04		
Warblington	d							12 35									13 35									
Emsworth	d		12 04					12 38				13 04					13 38				14 04					
Southbourne	d		12 07					12 41				13 07					13 41				14 07					
Nutbourne	d							12 43									13 43									
Bosham	d							12 47									13 47									
Fishbourne (Sussex)	d							12 50									13 50									
Chichester 4	a		12 14					12 53				13 14					13 53				14 14			14 19		
	d		12 14					12 53				13 14					13 53				14 14			14 19		
Bognor Regis 4	d						12 36		12 57							13 36		13 57								14 36
Barnham	a		12 22				12 42	13 01	13 03	←		13 22				13 42	14 01	14 03	←		14 22			14 27		14 42
	d		12 22				12 43	13 08	13 05	13 08		13 22				13 43	14 08	14 05	14 08		14 22			14 27		14 43
Bognor Regis 4	a							→									→									
Ford 4	d						12 47		13 09	13 12						13 47		14 09	14 12							14 47
Littlehampton 4	a						12 52									13 52										14 52
	d	12 14				12 40			12b57		13 14				13 40			13b57		14 14					14 40	
Angmering 3	d	12 22				12 48				13 18	13 22				13 48				14 18	14 22					14 48	
Goring-by-Sea	d	12 26				12 52				13 22	13 26				13 52				14 22	14 26					14 52	
Durrington-on-Sea	d	12 29				12 55				13 25	13 29				13 55				14 25	14 29					14 55	
West Worthing	d	12 31				12 57				13 27	13 31				13 57				14 27	14 31					14 57	
Worthing 4	a	12 33	12 37			12 59				13 29	13 33	13 37			13 59				14 29	14 33	14 37			14 44	14 59	
	d		12 41			13 00				13 30		13 41			14 00				14 30		14 41			14 45	15 00	
East Worthing	d					13 02				13 32					14 02				14 32						15 02	
Lancing	d					13 05				13 35					14 05				14 35						15 05	
Shoreham-by-Sea	d		12 47			13 09				13 39		13 47			14 09				14 39		14 47			14 51	15 09	
Southwick	d					13 12				13 42					14 12				14 42						15 12	
Fishersgate	d					13 14				13 44					14 14				14 44						15 14	
Portslade	d					13 16				13 46					14 16				14 46						15 16	
Aldrington	d			←		13 19				13 49				←	14 19				14 49				←		15 19	
Hove 2	d		12 54	12 56		13 21				13c56		13 54		13 56	14 21				14e55		14 54		14 55	15 00	15 21	
Brighton 10	a			13 00		13 25				→				14 00	14 25				→				14 59	15 06	15 25	
Burgess Hill	a		13 04									14 04									15 04					
Haywards Heath 3	a		13 09	13 30		14 00						14 09		14 30	15 00						15 09		15 30	15 30	16 00	
Arundel	d								13 14									14 14								
Amberley	d								13 19									14 19								
Pulborough	d								13 25									14 25								
Billingshurst	d								13 31									14 31								
Christs Hospital	d								13 38									14 38								
Horsham 4	a								13 42									14 42								
	d								13 42									14 42								
Crawley	d								13 51									14 51								
Three Bridges 4	a		13 32	13 40		14 10			13 54			14 32		14 40	15 10			14 54			15 32		15 40	15 40	16 10	
	d								13 55									14 55								
Gatwick Airport 10 ✈	a		13 22	13 44		14 14			13 59			14 22		14 44	15 14			14 59			15 22		15 44	15 44	16 14	
Horley	a		13 30						14 02			14 30						15 02			15 30					
Redhill 5	a		13 36						14 09			14 36						15 09			15 36					
East Croydon	a		13 39	14 01		14 31			14 24			14 39		15 01	15 31			15 24			15 39		16 01	16 01	16 31	
London Bridge 4 ⊖	a		14 12	14 17		14 47			14 47			15 12		15 17	15 47			15 47			16 12		16 17	16 17	16 47	
Clapham Junction 10	a		13 54	14f24		14 47			14 37			14 54		15f24	15 47			15 37			15 54		16f24	16f24	16 47	
London Victoria 15 ⊖	a		14 01	14g25		14 53			14 46			15 01		15g25	15 53			15 46			16 01		16g25	16g25	16 53	

For general notes see front of timetable
For details of catering facilities see
Directory of Train Operators

b Change at Ford
c Arr. 1351
e Arr. 1451
f Change at Brighton and East Croydon
g Change at Brighton and Gatwick Airport

For complete service between Horsham and Three Bridges see Table 186

Table 188

Sundays

from 13 September

Southampton, Portsmouth and Sussex Coast → Brighton, Gatwick Airport & London

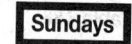

Network Diagram - see first page of Table 186

		SN 1	SN 1 🛒	SN 1	SN 1	SN 1		SN 1	SN 1	SN 1	SN 1	SN 1 🛒	SN 1	SN 1
Southampton Central	d													
Swanwick	d													
Fareham	d													
Portchester	d													
Cosham	d													
Portsmouth Harbour	d	14 14				14 43					15 14			
Portsmouth & Southsea	d	14 18				14 47					15 18			
Fratton	d	14 22				14 51					15 22			
Hilsea	d													
Bedhampton	d	14 30									15 30			
Havant	d	14 33				15 00					15 33			
Warblington	d	14 35									15 35			
Emsworth	d	14 38				15 04					15 38			
Southbourne	d	14 41				15 07					15 41			
Nutbourne	d	14 43									15 43			
Bosham	d	14 47									15 47			
Fishbourne (Sussex)	d	14 50									15 50			
Chichester 4	a	14 53				15 14					15 53			
	d	14 53				15 14					15 53			
Bognor Regis 4	d		14 57							15 36		15 57		
Barnham	a	15 01	15 03	←		15 22				15 42	16 01	16 03	←	
	d	15 08	15 05	15 08		15 22				15 43	16 08	16 05	16 08	
Bognor Regis 4	a	→									→			
Ford 4	d		15 09	15 12						15 47		16 09	16 12	
Littlehampton 4	a									15 52				
	d		14b57		15 14				15 40			15b57		16 14
Angmering 3	d			15 18	15 22				15 48				16 18	16 22
Goring-by-Sea	d			15 22	15 26				15 52				16 22	16 26
Durrington-on-Sea	d			15 25	15 29				15 55				16 25	16 29
West Worthing	d			15 27	15 31				15 57				16 27	16 31
Worthing 4	a			15 29	15 33	15 37			15 59				16 29	16 33
	d			15 30	15 41				16 00				16 30	16 41
East Worthing	d			15 32					16 02				16 32	
Lancing	d			15 35					16 05				16 35	
Shoreham-by-Sea	d			15 39	15 47				16 09				16 39	16 47
Southwick	d			15 42					16 12				16 42	
Fishersgate	d			15 44					16 14				16 44	
Portslade	d			15 46					16 16				16 46	
Aldrington	d			15 49				←	16 19				16 49	
Hove 2	d			15c56	15 54			15 56	16 21				16e56	16 54
Brighton 10	a			→				16 00	16 25				→	
Burgess Hill	a				16 04									17 04
Haywards Heath 3	a				16 09			16 30	17 00					17 09
Arundel	d		15 14									16 14		
Amberley	d		15 19									16 19		
Pulborough	d		15 25									16 25		
Billingshurst	d		15 31									16 31		
Christs Hospital	d		15 38									16 38		
Horsham 4	a		15 42									16 42		
	d		15 42									16 42		
Crawley	d		15 51									16 51		
Three Bridges 4	a		15 54		16 32			16 40	17 10			16 54		17 32
	d		15 55									16 55		
Gatwick Airport 10 ✈	a		15 59		16 22			16 44	17 14			16 59		17 22
Horley	a		16 02		16 30							17 02		17 30
Redhill 5	a		16 09		16 36							17 09		17 36
East Croydon	a		16 24		16 39			17 01	17 31			17 24		17 39
London Bridge 4 ⊖	a		16 47		17 12			17 17	17 47			17 47		18 12
Clapham Junction 10	a		16 37		16 54			17g24	17 47			17 37		17 54
London Victoria 15 ⊖	a		16 46		17 01			17h25	17 53			17 46		18 01

		SN 1		SN 1	GW ◇ 🛒	SN 1	SN 1	SN 1	SN 1 🛒	SN 1		SN 1	SN 1
Southampton Central	d				15 22								
Swanwick	d												
Fareham	d				15 51								
Portchester	d												
Cosham	d				16 01								
Portsmouth Harbour	d	15 43						16 14					16 43
Portsmouth & Southsea	d	15 47						16 18					16 47
Fratton	d	15 51						16 22					16 51
Hilsea	d												
Bedhampton	d							16 30					
Havant	d	16 00			16 11			16 33					17 00
Warblington	d							16 35					
Emsworth	d	16 04						16 38					17 04
Southbourne	d	16 07						16 41					17 07
Nutbourne	d							16 43					
Bosham	d							16 47					
Fishbourne (Sussex)	d							16 50					
Chichester 4	a	16 14			16 22			16 53					17 14
	d	16 14			16 22			16 53					17 14
Bognor Regis 4	d						16 36		16 57				
Barnham	a	16 22			16 30		16 42	17 01	17 03	←			17 22
	d	16 22			16 30		16 43	17 08	17 05	17 08			17 22
Bognor Regis 4	a							→					
Ford 4	d						16 47		17 09	17 12			
Littlehampton 4	a						16 52						
	d					16 40			16b57			17 14	
Angmering 3	d					16 48				17 18		17 22	
Goring-by-Sea	d					16 52				17 22		17 26	
Durrington-on-Sea	d					16 55				17 25		17 29	
West Worthing	d					16 57				17 27		17 31	
Worthing 4	a	16 37			16 45	16 59				17 29		17 33	17 37
	d				16 45	17 00				17 30		17 41	
East Worthing	d					17 02				17 32			
Lancing	d					17 05				17 35			
Shoreham-by-Sea	d				16 52	17 09				17 39		17 47	
Southwick	d					17 12				17 42			
Fishersgate	d					17 14				17 44			
Portslade	d					17 16				17 46			
Aldrington	d			←		17 19				17 49			
Hove 2	d			16 56	16 59	17 21				17f56		17 54	
Brighton 10	a			17 00	17 05	17 25				→			
Burgess Hill	a											18 04	
Haywards Heath 3	a			17 30	17 30	18 00						18 09	
Arundel	d								17 14				
Amberley	d								17 19				
Pulborough	d								17 25				
Billingshurst	d								17 31				
Christs Hospital	d								17 38				
Horsham 4	a								17 42				
	d								17 42				
Crawley	d								17 51				
Three Bridges 4	a			17 40	17 40	18 10			17 54			18 32	
	d								17 55				
Gatwick Airport 10 ✈	a			17 44	17 44	18 14			17 59			18 22	
Horley	a								18 02			18 30	
Redhill 5	a								18 09			18 36	
East Croydon	a			18 01	18 01	18 31			18 24			18 39	
London Bridge 4 ⊖	a			18 17	18 17	18 47			18 47			19 12	
Clapham Junction 10	a			18g24	18g24	18 47			18 37			18 54	
London Victoria 15 ⊖	a			18h25	18h25	18 53			18 46			19 01	

For general notes see front of timetable
For details of catering facilities see Directory of Train Operators

b Change at Ford
c Arr. 1551
e Arr. 1651
f Arr. 1751
g Change at Brighton and East Croydon
h Change at Brighton and Gatwick Airport

For complete service between Horsham and Three Bridges see Table 186

Sundays

from 13 September

Southampton, Portsmouth and Sussex Coast → Brighton, Gatwick Airport & London

Network Diagram - see first page of Table 186

		SN 1	SN 1	SN 1	SN 1	SN 1	SN 1	SN 1	SN 1	SN 1	SN 1	SN 1	SN 1	SN 1	SN 1	SN 1	SN 1	SN 1	SN 1	SN 1	SN 1	SN 1	SN 1
Southampton Central	d																						
Swanwick	d																						
Fareham	d																						
Portchester	d																						
Cosham	d																						
Portsmouth Harbour	d				17 14				17 43				18 14				18 43					19 14	
Portsmouth & Southsea	d				17 18				17 47				18 18				18 47					19 18	
Fratton	d				17 22				17 51				18 22				18 51					19 22	
Hilsea	d																						
Bedhampton	d				17 30								18 30									19 30	
Havant	d				17 33				18 00				18 33				19 00					19 33	
Warblington	d				17 35								18 35									19 35	
Emsworth	d				17 38				18 04				18 38				19 04					19 38	
Southbourne	d				17 41				18 07				18 41				19 07					19 41	
Nutbourne	d				17 43								18 43									19 43	
Bosham	d				17 47								18 47									19 47	
Fishbourne (Sussex)	d				17 50								18 50									19 50	
Chichester 4	a				17 53				18 14				18 53				19 14					19 53	
	d				17 53				18 14				18 53				19 14					19 53	
Bognor Regis 4	d			17 36		17 57						18 36		18 57						19 36		19 57	
Barnham	a			17 42	18 01	18 03	←		18 22			18 42	19 01	19 03	←		19 22			19 42	20 01	20 03	←
	d			17 43	18 08 →	18 05	18 08		18 22			18 43	19 08 →	19 05	19 08		19 22			19 43	20 08 →	20 05	20 08
Bognor Regis 4	a																						
Ford 4	d			17 47		18 09	18 12					18 47		19 09	19 12					19 47		20 09	20 12
Littlehampton 4	a			17 52								18 52								19 52			
	d		17 40			17b57		18 14			18 40			18b57		19 14			19 40			19b57	
Angmering 3	d		17 48				18 18	18 22			18 48				19 18	19 22			19 48				20 18
Goring-by-Sea	d		17 52				18 22	18 26			18 52				19 22	19 26			19 52				20 22
Durrington-on-Sea	d		17 55				18 25	18 29			18 55				19 25	19 29			19 55				20 25
West Worthing	d		17 57				18 27	18 31			18 57				19 27	19 31			19 57				20 27
Worthing 4	a		17 59				18 29	18 33	18 37		18 59				19 29	19 33	19 37		19 59				20 29
	d		18 00				18 30		18 41		19 00				19 30		19 41		20 00				20 30
East Worthing	d		18 02				18 32				19 02				19 32				20 02				20 32
Lancing	d		18 05				18 35				19 05				19 35				20 05				20 35
Shoreham-by-Sea	d		18 09				18 39		18 47		19 09				19 39		19 47		20 09				20 39
Southwick	d		18 12				18 42				19 12				19 42				20 12				20 42
Fishersgate	d		18 14				18 44				19 14				19 44				20 14				20 44
Portslade	d		18 16				18 46				19 16				19 46				20 16				20 46
Aldrington	d	←	18 19				18 49			←	19 19				19 49			←	20 19				20 49
Hove 2	d	17 56	18 21				18c56 →		18 54	18 56	19 21				19e56 →		19 54	19 56	20 21				20f56 →
Brighton 10	a	18 00	18 25							19 00	19 25							20 00	20 25				
Burgess Hill	a								19 04								20 04						
Haywards Heath 3	a	18 30	19 00						19 09	19 30	20 00						20 09	20 30	21 00				
Arundel	d					18 14								19 14								20 14	
Amberley	d					18 19								19 19								20 19	
Pulborough	d					18 25								19 25								20 25	
Billingshurst	d					18 31								19 31								20 31	
Christs Hospital	d					18 38								19 38								20 38	
Horsham 4	a					18 42								19 42								20 42	
	d					18 42								19 42								20 42	
Crawley	d					18 51								19 51								20 51	
Three Bridges 4	a	18 40	19 10			18 54			19 32	19 40	20 10			19 54			20 32	20 40	21 10			20 54	
	d					18 55								19 55								20 55	
Gatwick Airport 10 ✈	a	18 44	19 14			18 59			19 22	19 44	20 14			19 59			20 22	20 44	21 14			20 59	
Horley	a					19 02			19 30					20 02			20 30					21 02	
Redhill 5	a					19 09			19 36					20 09			20 36					21 09	
East Croydon	a	19 01	19 31			19 24			19 39	20 01	20 31			20 24			20 39	21 01	21 31			21 24	
London Bridge 4 ⊖	a	19 17	19 47			19 47			20g12	20 17	20 47			20 47			21 12	21 17	21 47			21 47	
Clapham Junction 10	a	19h24	19 47			19 37			19 54	20h24	20 47			20 37			20 54	21h24	21 47			21 37	
London Victoria 15 ⊖	a	19j25	19 53			19 46			20 01	20j25	20 53			20 46			21 01	21j25	21 53			21 46	

For general notes see front of timetable
For details of catering facilities see Directory of Train Operators

b Change at Ford
c Arr. 1851
e Arr. 1951
f Arr. 2051
g London Bridge
h Change at Brighton and East Croydon
j Change at Brighton and Gatwick Airport

For complete service between Horsham and Three Bridges see Table 186

Sundays

from 13 September

Southampton, Portsmouth and Sussex Coast → Brighton, Gatwick Airport & London

Network Diagram - see first page of Table 186

		SN 1	SN 1	SN 1		GW ◇	SN 1	SN 1	SN 1	SN 1	SN 1	SN 1		SN 1	SN 1	SN 1	SN 1	SN 1	SN 1	SN 1		SN 1	SN 1
Southampton Central	d					19 27																	
Swanwick	d																						
Fareham	d					19 49																	
Portchester	d																						
Cosham	d					19 59																	
Portsmouth Harbour	d		19 43						20 14			20 43			21 14				21 43	22 14		22 43	
Portsmouth & Southsea	d		19 47						20 18			20 47			21 18				21 47	22 18		22 47	
Fratton	d		19 51						20 22			20 51			21 22				21 51	22 22		22 51	
Hilsea	d																						
Bedhampton	d								20 30						21 30					22 30			
Havant	d		20 00			20 11			20 33			21 00			21 33				22 00	22 33		23 00	
Warblington	d								20 35						21 35					22 35			
Emsworth	d		20 04						20 38			21 04			21 38				22 04	22 38		23 04	
Southbourne	d		20 07						20 41			21 07			21 41				22 07	22 41		23 07	
Nutbourne	d								20 43						21 43					22 43			
Bosham	d								20 47						21 47					22 47			
Fishbourne (Sussex)	d								20 50						21 50					22 50			
Chichester 4	a		20 14			20 21			20 53			21 14			21 53				22 14	22 53		23 14	
	d		20 14			20 22			20 53			21 14			21 53				22 14	22 53		23 14	
Bognor Regis 4	d							20 36		20 57				21 36		21 57		22 11					
Barnham	a		20 22			20 29		20 42	21 01	21 03	←	21 22		21 42	22 01	22 03	←	22 18	22 22	23 01		23 22	
	d		20 22			20 30		20 43	21 08 →	21 05	21 08	21 22		21 43	22 08 →	22 05	22 08		22 22	23 01		23 22	23 37
Bognor Regis 4	a																						
Ford 4	d							20 47		21 09	21 12	21 27		21 47		22 09	22 12		22 27	23 06		23 27	23 42
Littlehampton 4	a							20 52				21 31		21 52					22 31	23 10		23 32	23 46
	d	20 14					20 40			20b57		21 42				21b57			22 42			23b06	23b29
Angmering 3	d	20 22					20 48				21 18	21 50					22 18		22 50				
Goring-by-Sea	d	20 26					20 52				21 22	21 54					22 22		22 54				
Durrington-on-Sea	d	20 29					20 55				21 25	21 57					22 25		22 57				
West Worthing	d	20 31					20 57				21 27	21 59					22 27		22 59				
Worthing 4	a	20 33	20 37			20 51	20 59				21 29	22 01					22 29		23 01				
	d	20 41				20 51	21 00				21 30	22 02					22 30		23 02				
East Worthing	d						21 02				21 32	22 04					22 32		23 04				
Lancing	d						21 05				21 35	22 07					22 35		23 07				
Shoreham-by-Sea	d	20 47				20 58	21 09				21 39	22 11					22 39		23 11				
Southwick	d						21 12				21 42	22 14					22 42		23 14				
Fishersgate	d						21 14				21 44	22 16					22 44		23 16				
Portslade	d						21 16				21 46	22 18					22 46		23 18				
Aldrington	d			←			21 19				21 49	22 21					22 49		23 21				
Hove 2	d	20 54		20 56		21 05	21 21				21 51	22 23					22 51		23 25				
Brighton 10	a			21 00		21 10	21 25				21 55	22 27					22 56		23 29				
Burgess Hill	a	21 04																					
Haywards Heath 3	a	21 09		21 30		21 30	22 00				22 20	23 00					23 23		00 01				
Arundel	d									21 14						22 14							
Amberley	d									21 19						22 19							
Pulborough	d									21 25						22 25							
Billingshurst	d									21 31						22 31							
Christs Hospital	d									21 38						22 38							
Horsham 4	a									21 42						22 42							
	d									21 42						22 42							
Crawley	d									21 51						22 51							
Three Bridges 4	a	21 32		21 40		21 40	22 10			21 54	22 32	23 10				22 54	23 35		00 10				
	d									21 55						22 55							
Gatwick Airport 10 ✈	a	21 22		21 44		21 44	22 14			21 59	22 37	23 14				22 59	23 43		00 14				
Horley	a	21 30								22 02						23 02							
Redhill 5	a	21 36								22 09						23 09							
East Croydon	a	21 39		22 01		22 01	22 31			22 24	22 58	23 31				23 24	23 59		00 35				
London Bridge 4 ⊖	a	22 12		22 17		22 17	22 47			22 47	23 17	23 47				23 47	00 14		00 52				
Clapham Junction 10	a	21 54		22c24		22c24	23c10			22 37	23 12	00c10				23 37	00c29		01c02				
London Victoria 15 ⊖	a	22 01		22e25		22e25	22e55			22 46	23 20	23e55				23 46	00e25		00e55				

For general notes see front of timetable
For details of catering facilities see Directory of Train Operators

b Change at Ford
c Change at Brighton and East Croydon
e Change at Brighton and Gatwick Airport

For complete service between Horsham and Three Bridges see Table 186

London, Haywards Heath and Brighton → Lewes, Seaford, Eastbourne, Hastings and Ashford

Network Diagram - see first page of Table 184

Miles	Miles			SN	SN	SN	SN	SN	SN	SN	SN	SN	SN	SN	SN	SN	SN	SN	SN	SN	SN		SN	SE	SN
				MO	MX	MX	MX	MO	MO	MX															
				1	1	1	1	1	1	1	1	1	1	1	1	1	1	1	1	1	1		1	1	1
				A				A	B															C	
—	—	**London Victoria 15** ⊖	d	22p47		22p47			22p47	00 05					04 00						05 02				
—	—	Clapham Junction 10	d	22p53		22p53			22p53	00 11					04 08						05 08				
—	—	**London Bridge 4** ⊖	d							23 53					03b35				04 05		04 35				
—	—	East Croydon	d	23p03		23p03			23p08	00 25					04 22				04 32		05 32				
—	—	**Gatwick Airport 10**	d	23p19		23p19			23p29	00 43					04 47				04 52		05 54				
—	0	**Haywards Heath 3**	d	23p30		23p34			23p41	01 06					05 01				05 08		06 13				
—	3	Wivelsfield 4	d	23p34		23p38			23p45												06 17				
—	6¾	Plumpton	d	23p40		23p44			23p51																
—	9½	Cooksbridge	d																						
0	—	**Brighton 10**	d		23p34										05 30				05 45	06 00					
¾	—	London Road (Brighton)	d		23p37														05 48	06 03					
1¾	—	Moulsecoomb	d		23p39														05 50	06 05					
3½	—	Falmer	d		23p43														05 54	06 09					
8	12¼	**Lewes 4**	a	23p48	23p49	23p51	←	←	23p58	01 20					05 41				06 00	06 15	06 28				
—	—		d	23p59	23p56	23p53	23p56	23p59	23p59	01 20					05 41				06 05		06 29				
—	15¾	Southease	d	→	→																				
—	18½	Newhaven Town	d				00 04												06 14		06 37				
—	18¾	Newhaven Harbour	d				00 06												06 15		06 39				
—	20¼	Bishopstone	d				00 09												06 18		06 42				
—	21¼	**Seaford**	a				00 12												06 22		06 45				
11	—	Glynde	d																						
15½	—	Berwick	d			00 02																			
19¾	—	Polegate	d			00 07		00 11	00 11	01s32					05 53										
21¾	—	Hampden Park 4 §	d			00 11		00 15	00 15	01s36															
23¾	—	**Eastbourne 4**	a			00 16		00 20	00 20	01 41					06 00										
—	—		d			00 22					04 54		05 24			06 04	06 15						06 34		06 51
25¾	—	Hampden Park 4 §	d														06 19								06 55
28¾	—	Pevensey & Westham	d			00 29							05 31				06 24						06 41		07 00
29½	—	Pevensey Bay	d																						
31½	—	Normans Bay	d																				06 46		
33¼	—	Cooden Beach	d			00 35											06 30								07 06
34¾	—	Collington	d			00 38											06 33								07 09
35½	—	**Bexhill 4**	d			00 40					05 08		05 40			06 19	06 35						06 52		07 11
39¼	—	**St Leonards Warrior Sq 4**	d			00 47					05 15		05 46			06 26	06 41						06 58	07 07	07 17
40	0	**Hastings 4**	a			00 50					05 19		05 50			06 29	06 45						07 02	07 11	07 22
—	—		d									05 30		05 55		06 30								07 15	
—	1	Ore	d									05 32		05 57										07a18	
—	3¾	Three Oaks	d											06 03											
—	5	Doleham	d											06 06											
—	9¼	Winchelsea	d											06 12											
—	11¼	**Rye**	a									05 53		06 16		06 47									
—	—		d									05 53		06 16		06 49		07 19							
—	18	Appledore (Kent)	d									06 02		06 25		06 58		07 28							
—	21	Ham Street	d									06 07		06 30		07 03		07 33							
—	26½	**Ashford International**	a									06 15		06 39		07 11		07 41							
—	—	London Bridge 4 ⊖	a									07c54		08c14		08c34		09c22							
—	—	London Cannon Street 4 ⊖	a									08c00		08c20		08c41		09c28							
—	—	London Waterloo (East) 4 ⊖	a											08c04		08c41		09c01							
—	—	London Charing Cross 4 ⊖	a									08e07		08c09		08c47		09c07							

For general notes see front of timetable
For details of catering facilities see Directory of Train Operators

§ For additional trains between Hampden Park and Eastbourne see Hastings to London pages

A Until 7 September
B From 14 September
C From Tonbridge (Table 206)
b Change at East Croydon and Brighton
c Until 9 October only
e Until 9 October only. Change at Ashford International and London Bridge

London, Haywards Heath and Brighton → Lewes, Seaford, Eastbourne, Hastings and Ashford

Network Diagram - see first page of Table 184

Station		SN 1	SN 1	SN 1	SN 1	SN 1	SN 1	SN 1	SN 1	SN 1	SN 1	SN 1	SN 1	SN 1	SN 1	SN 1	SN 1	SN 1		SN 1	SN 1	SN 1	SN 1	SN 1	SN 1
London Victoria 15 ⊖	d		05 02	05 32				05b32		06c02					06 47	06b02	06 21	06b32		06b51		07b07	07 47		07b23
Clapham Junction 10	d		05 08	05 38				05b38		06c08					06 53	06b08	06 27	06b38		06b57		07b13	07 53		07b29
London Bridge 4 ⊖	d	04 35		05e31		05 31		05 51		06 21						06 21		06 43		07 01		07 16	07f40		07 33
East Croydon	d	05 02	05 20	05 49	05 32	05 52		06 04		06 36					07 03	06 36	06 38	06 56		07 16		07 32	08 03		07 49
Gatwick Airport 10 ✈	d	05 22	05 47	06 20	05 54	06 08		06 20		06 52					07 19	06 52	07 04	07 12		07 32		07 50	08 19		08 05
Haywards Heath 3	d	05 36	06 04	06 34	06 10	06 25		06 38		07 10					07 33	07 06	07 21	07 28		07 48		08 06	08 32		08 19
Wivelsfield 4	d	05 40	06 08	06 38	06 14	06 29		06 42		07 14					07 37	07 10	07 25	07 32		07 44		08 10	08 36		
Plumpton	d									07 20					07 43								08 42		
Cooksbridge	d									07 24					07 47								08 47		
Brighton 10	d	06 15	06 32		06 39	06 52	07 00	07 10				07 22		07 32		07 40	07 52	08 03		08 13	08 22	08 32		08 38	08 45
London Road (Brighton)	d	06 18			06 42	06 55	07 03	07 13				07 25				07 43	07 55	08 06		08 16	08 25			08 41	08 48
Moulsecoomb	d	06 20			06 44	06 57	07 05	07 15				07 27				07 45	07 57	08 08		08 18	08 27			08 43	08 50
Falmer	d	06 24			06 48	07 01	07 09	07 19				07 31				07 49	08 01	08 12		08 22	08 31			08 47	08 54
Lewes 4	a	06 30	06 43	06 49	06 54	07 08	07 17	07 26		07 29	←	07 37		07 43	07 52	07 56	08 08	08 19		08 29	08 37	08 43	08 51	08 53	09 00
	d	06 32	06 44	06 51	06 55	07 10		07 34		07 31	07 34			07 44	07 53	07 58	08 09	08 23		08 30		08 44	08 52		09 02
Southease	d							→																	
Newhaven Town ⛴	d				07 03	07 18					07 42					08 06				08 38					09 10
Newhaven Harbour	d				07 05	07g23					07 44					08 08				08 40					09 12
Bishopstone	d				07 08	07 26					07 47					08 11				08 43					09 15
Seaford	a				07 11	07 29					07 50					08 14				08 46					09 18
Glynde	d	06 37		06 56						07 36							08 14	08 28							
Berwick	d	06 43		07 02						07 42							08 20	08 34							
Polegate	d	06 48	06 57	07 07						07 47				07 57	08 05		08 25	08 39				08 57	09 04		
Hampden Park 4 §	d	06 52		07 11						07 53					08 09		08 29	08 43					09 08		
Eastbourne 4	a	07 00	07 04	07 16						07 58				08 04	08 14		08 34	08 48				09 04	09 13		
	d		07 08	07 21									07 38	08 08	08 21		08 40					09 08	09 20		
Hampden Park 4 §	d			07 25									07 42		08 25		08 44						09 24		
Pevensey & Westham	d			07 30									07 47	08 16	08 30		08 49						09 29		
Pevensey Bay	d												07 49		08 32										
Normans Bay	d												07 53		08 36		08 53								
Cooden Beach	d			07 36									07 56		08 39		08 57						09 35		
Collington	d			07 39									07 59		08 42		09 00						09 38		
Bexhill 4	d		07 23	07 41									08 01	08 25	08 45		09 02					09 23	09 41		
St Leonards Warrior Sq 4	d		07 30	07 49									08 08	08 32	08 52		09 08					09 30	09 48		
Hastings 4	a		07 33	07 52									08 13	08 35	08 56		09 12					09 33	09 51		
	d		07 34	07 53									08 14	08 36	08 57		09 13					09 34	09 53		
Ore	d			07a56									08a17		09a00		09a16						09a56		
Three Oaks	d																								
Doleham	d																								
Winchelsea	d																								
Rye	a		07 51											08 53								09 51			
	d		07 54						08 23					08 54								09 54			
Appledore (Kent)	d		08 03						08 32					09 03								10 03			
Ham Street	d		08 08						08 37					09 08								10 08			
Ashford International	a		08 16						08 45					09 16								10 16			
London Bridge 4 ⊖	a		09h39											11h13								11h43			
London Cannon Street 4 ⊖	a		09j57											11j20								11j50			
London Waterloo (East) 4 ⊖	a		09h45											10h32								11h32			
London Charing Cross 4 ⊖	a		09h50											10h36								11h36			

For general notes see front of timetable
For details of catering facilities see Directory of Train Operators

§ For additional trains between Hampden Park and Eastbourne see Hastings to London pages

b Change at East Croydon and Brighton
c Change at East Croydon and Haywards Heath
e Change at Gatwick Airport
f London Bridge
g Arr. 0720
h Until 9 October only
j Until 9 October only. Change at Ashford International and London Bridge

London, Haywards Heath and Brighton → Lewes, Seaford, Eastbourne, Hastings and Ashford

Network Diagram - see first page of Table 184

Station		SN 1	SN 1	SN 1	SN 1	SN 1	SN 1	SN 1	SN 1	SN 1	SN 1	SN 1	SN 1	SN 1	SN 1		SN 1	SN 1	SN 1	SN 1	SN 1	SN 1	SN 1	SN 1	SN 1
								A ⚲			A ⚲				A ⚲				A ⚲				A ⚲		
London Victoria 15	⊖ d		07b36	08 17		08 07	08 21	08 47	08 36		09 17	09 06		09 36	09 47				10 17	10 06		10 36	10 47		
Clapham Junction 10	d		07b42	08 23		08 13	08 27	08 53	08 43		09 23	09 12		09 42	09 53				10 23	10 12		10 42	10 53		
London Bridge 4	⊖ d		07 53	08c19		08b00	08 19		08b27			08b52		09 25						09 58	10 11	10 26			
East Croydon	d		08e09	08 33		08 23	08 39	09 03	08 53		09 33	09 22		09 52	10 03				10 33	10 22	10 24	10 52	11 03		
Gatwick Airport 10	✈ d		08 29	08 49			08 56	09 19		09 00	09 49	09 26		09 57	10 19				10 49	10 26	10 41	10 56	11 19		10 58
Haywards Heath 3	d		08 43	09 13		08 51	09 10	09 34		09 17	10 07	09 40		10 10	10 34			10 18	11 07	10 40	10 55	11 08	11 34		11 17
Wivelsfield 4	d		08 47	09 17			09 02			09 21	10 11	09 34		10 01				10 22	11 11	10 31	10 59				11 21
Plumpton	d							09 43							10 43										
Cooksbridge	d							09 48																	
Brighton 10	d	08 52	09 10			09 22	09 32		09 40	09 52		10 10	10 22	10 32			10 40	10 52		11 10	11 22	11 32		11 40	11 52
London Road (Brighton)	d	08 55	09 13			09 25			09 43	09 55		10 13	10 25				10 43	10 55		11 13	11 25			11 43	11 55
Moulsecoomb	d	08 57	09 15			09 27			09 45	09 57		10 15	10 27				10 45	10 57		11 15	11 27			11 45	11 57
Falmer	d	09 01	09 19			09 31			09 49	10 01		10 19	10 31				10 49	11 01		11 19	11 31			11 49	12 01
Lewes 4	a	09 07	09 25	09 28	←	09 37	09 43	09 52	09 56	10 07	10 22	10 25	10 37	10 43	10 51		10 55	11 07	11 22	11 25	11 37	11 43	11 48	11 55	12 07
	d	09 08	09 32	09 29	09 32		09 44	09 53	09 58	10 09	10 23	10 28		10 44	10 53		10 58	11 09	11 23	11 28		11 44	11 53	11 58	12 09
Southease	d		→		09 38							10 34								11 34					
Newhaven Town	⛴ d				09 42				10 06			10 38					11 06			11 38				12 06	
Newhaven Harbour	d				09 44				10 08			10 40					11 08			11 40				12 08	
Bishopstone	d				09 47				10 11			10 43					11 11			11 43				12 11	
Seaford	a				09 50				10 14			10 46					11 14			11 46				12 14	
Glynde	d	09 13								10 14								11 14							12 14
Berwick	d	09 19								10 20								11 20							12 20
Polegate	d	09 24		09 41			09 57	10 05		10 25	10 35			10 57	11 05			11 25	11 35			11 57	12 05		12 25
Hampden Park 4 §	d	09 28		09 45						10 29	10 39							11 29	11 39						12 29
Eastbourne 4	a	09 33		09 50			10 04	10 13		10 34	10 44			11 04	11 13			11 34	11 44			12 04	12 13		12 34
	d	09 37					10 08	10 19		10 40				11 08	11 19			11 40				12 08	12 19		12 40
Hampden Park 4 §	d	09 41						10 23		10 44					11 23			11 44					12 23		12 44
Pevensey & Westham	d	09 46						10 28		10 49					11 28			11 49					12 28		12 49
Pevensey Bay	d																								
Normans Bay	d	09 51								10 53								11 53							12 53
Cooden Beach	d	09 54						10 34		10 57					11 34			11 57					12 34		12 57
Collington	d	09 57						10 37		11 00					11 37			12 00					12 37		13 00
Bexhill 4	d	10 00					10 23	10 39		11 02				11 23	11 39			12 02				12 23	12 39		13 02
St Leonards Warrior Sq 4	d	10 06					10 30	10 45		11 08				11 30	11 45			12 08				12 30	12 45		13 08
Hastings 4	a	10 10					10 33	10 50		11 12				11 33	11 50			12 12				12 33	12 50		13 12
	d	10 12					10 34	10 51		11 13				11 34	11 51			12 13				12 34	12 51		13 13
Ore	d	10a15						10a54		11a16					11a54			12a16					12a54		13a16
Three Oaks	d																								
Doleham	d																								
Winchelsea	d																								
Rye	a						10 51							11 51								12 51			
	d						10 54							11 54								12 54			
Appledore (Kent)	d						11 03							12 03								13 03			
Ham Street	d						11 08							12 08								13 08			
Ashford International	a						11 16							12 16								13 16			
London Bridge 4	⊖ a						12f43							13f43								14f43			
London Cannon Street 4	⊖ a						12g50							13g50								14g50			
London Waterloo (East) 4	⊖ a						12f32							13f32								14f32			
London Charing Cross 4	⊖ a						12f36							13f36								14f36			

For general notes see front of timetable
For details of catering facilities see Directory of Train Operators

§ For additional trains between Hampden Park and Eastbourne see Hastings to London pages

A ⚲ to Lewes
b Change at East Croydon and Brighton
c Change at Haywards Heath
e Change at Gatwick Airport and Brighton
f Until 9 October only
g Until 9 October only. Change at Ashford International and London Bridge

London, Haywards Heath and Brighton → Lewes, Seaford, Eastbourne, Hastings and Ashford

Network Diagram - see first page of Table 184

		SN 1 A	SN 1	SN 1	SN 1	SN 1 A	SN 1	SN 1	SN 1 A	SN 1	SN 1	SN 1		SN 1 A	SN 1	SN 1	SN 1 A	SN 1	SN 1	SN 1	SN 1 A	SN 1	SN 1	SN 1 A	SN 1
London Victoria 15 ⊖	d	11 17	11 06		11 36	11 47			12 17	12 06		12 36		12 47			13 17	13 06		13 36	13 47			14 17	14 06
Clapham Junction 10	d	11 23	11 12		11 42	11 53			12 23	12 12		12 42		12 53			13 23	13 12		13 42	13 53			14 23	14 12
London Bridge 4 ⊖	d		10 56	11 11	11 26					11 56	12 11	12 26						12 56	13 11	13 26					13 56
East Croydon	d	11 33	11 22	11 24	11 52	12 03			12 34	12 22	12 24	12 52		13 03			13 33	13 22	13 24	13 52	14 03			14 33	14 22
Gatwick Airport 10	d	11 49	11 26	11 41	11 56	12 19		11 58	12 50	12 26	12 41	12 56		13 19		12 58	13 49	13 26	13 41	13 56	14 19		13 58	14 49	14 26
Haywards Heath 3	d	12 07	11 38	11 55	12 08	12 34		12 17	13 07	12 38	12 55	13 08		13 34		13 17	14 07	13 38	13 55	14 08	14 34		14 17	15 07	14 38
Wivelsfield 4	d	12 11	11 31	11 59				12 21	13 11	12 31	12 59					13 21	14 11	13 31	13 59				14 21	15 11	14 31
Plumpton	d					12 43																			
Cooksbridge	d																								
Brighton 10	d		12 10	12 22	12 32		12 40	12 52		13 10	13 22	13 32			13 40	13 52		14 10	14 22	14 32		14 40	14 52		15 10
London Road (Brighton)	d		12 13	12 25			12 43	12 55		13 13	13 25				13 43	13 55		14 13	14 25			14 43	14 55		15 13
Moulsecoomb	d		12 15	12 27			12 45	12 57		13 15	13 27				13 45	13 57		14 15	14 27			14 45	14 57		15 15
Falmer	d		12 19	12 31			12 49	13 01		13 19	13 31				13 49	14 01		14 19	14 31			14 49	15 01		15 19
Lewes 4	a	12 22	12 25	12 37	12 43	12 51	12 55	13 07	13 22	13 25	13 37	13 43		13 48	13 55	14 07	14 22	14 25	14 37	14 43	14 48	14 55	15 07	15 22	15 25
	d	12 23	12 28		12 44	12 53	12 58	13 09	13 23	13 28		13 44		13 53	13 58	14 09	14 23	14 28		14 44	14 53	14 58	15 09	15 23	15 28
Southease	d		12 34							13 34								14 34							15 34
Newhaven Town ⛴	d		12 38				13 06			13 38					14 06			14 38				15 06			15 38
Newhaven Harbour	d		12 40				13 08			13 40					14 08			14 40				15 08			15 40
Bishopstone	d		12 43				13 11			13 43					14 11			14 43				15 11			15 43
Seaford	a		12 46				13 14			13 46					14 14			14 46				15 14			15 46
Glynde	d							13 14								14 14							15 14		
Berwick	d							13 20								14 20							15 20		
Polegate	d	12 35			12 57	13 05		13 25	13 35			13 57		14 05		14 25	14 35			14 57	15 05		15 25	15 35	
Hampden Park 4 §	d	12 39						13 29	13 39							14 29	14 39						15 29	15 39	
Eastbourne 4	a	12 44			13 04	13 13		13 34	13 44			14 04		14 13		14 34	14 44			15 04	15 13		15 34	15 44	
	d				13 08	13 19		13 40				14 08		14 19		14 40				15 08	15 19		15 40		
Hampden Park 4 §	d					13 23		13 44						14 23		14 44					15 23		15 44		
Pevensey & Westham	d					13 28		13 49						14 28		14 49					15 28		15 49		
Pevensey Bay	d																				15 30				
Normans Bay	d							13 53								14 53					15 34		15 53		
Cooden Beach	d					13 34		13 57						14 34		14 57					15 37		15 57		
Collington	d					13 37		14 00						14 37		15 00					15 40		16 00		
Bexhill 4	d				13 23	13 39		14 02				14 23		14 39		15 02				15 23	15 42		16 02		
St Leonards Warrior Sq 4	d				13 30	13 45		14 08				14 30		14 45		15 08				15 30	15 49		16 08		
Hastings 4	a				13 33	13 50		14 12				14 33		14 50		15 12				15 33	15 52		16 12		
	d				13 34	13 51		14 13				14 34		14 51		15 13				15 34	15 54		16 13		
Ore	d					13a54		14a16						14a54		15a16					15a57		16a16		
Three Oaks	d																								
Doleham	d																								
Winchelsea	d																								
Rye	a				13 51							14 51								15 51					
	d				13 54							14 54								15 54					
Appledore (Kent)	d				14 03							15 03								16 03					
Ham Street	d				14 08							15 08								16 08					
Ashford International	a				14 16							15 16								16 16					
London Bridge 4 ⊖	a				15b43							16b29								17b31					
London Cannon Street 4 ⊖	a				15c50							16c36								17c39					
London Waterloo (East) 4 ⊖	a				15b32							16b34								17b36					
London Charing Cross 4 ⊖	a				15b36							16b38								17b41					

For general notes see front of timetable
For details of catering facilities see Directory of Train Operators

§ For additional trains between Hampden Park and Eastbourne see Hastings to London pages

A ⚲ to Lewes

b Until 9 October only

c Until 9 October only. Change at Ashford International and London Bridge

London, Haywards Heath and Brighton → Lewes, Seaford, Eastbourne, Hastings and Ashford

Network Diagram - see first page of Table 184

		SN 1	SN 1	SN 1	SN 1	SN 1	SN 1	SN 1	SN 1		SN 1	SN 1	SN 1	SN 1	SN 1	SN 1	SN 1	SN 1	SN 1	SN 1	SE 1	SN 1	SN 1	SN 1	SN 1
				A 🛒				A 🛒					A 🛒				A 🛒				B			A 🛒	
London Victoria [15]	⊖ d		14 36	14 47				15 17	15 06			15 36	15 47				16 17	16 06		16b17				16 47	
Clapham Junction [10]	d		14 42	14 53				15 23	15 12			15 42	15 53				16 23	16 12		16b23				16 53	
London Bridge [4]	⊖ d	14 11	14 26						14 56		15 11	15 26					16c11	15 56		16 26				16e46	
East Croydon	⛴ d	14 24	14 52	15 03				15 33	15 22		15 24	15 52	16 03				16 33	16 22		16 40				17 03	
Gatwick Airport [10]	✈ d	14 41	14 56	15 19			14 58	15 49	15 26		15 41	15 57	16 19				16 49	16 26		16 56				17 20	
Haywards Heath [3]	d	14 55	15 08	15 34			15 17	16 07	15 38		15 55	16 11	16 33			16 17	17 06	16 40		17 10				17 36	
Wivelsfield [4]	d	14 59		15 38			15 21	16 11	15 31		15 59		16 37			16 21	17 10	16 31		16 59				17 41	
Plumpton	d			15 44									16 43											17 47	
Cooksbridge	d												16 48											17 52	
Brighton [10]	d	15 22	15 32			15 40	15 52		16 10		16 22	16 32			16 40	16 52		17 10	17 20	17 32			17 40		
London Road (Brighton)	d	15 25				15 43	15 55		16 13		16 25				16 43	16 55		17 13	17 23				17 43		
Moulsecoomb	d	15 27				15 45	15 57		16 15		16 27				16 45	16 57		17 15	17 25				17 45		
Falmer	d	15 31				15 49	16 01		16 19		16 31				16 49	17 01		17 19	17 29				17 49		
Lewes [4]	a	15 37	15 43	15 51		15 55	16 07	16 22	16 25		16 37	16 43	16 52		16 55	17 07	17 21	17 25	17 35	17 43			17 55	17 56	←
	d		15 44	15 53		15 58	16 09	16 23	16 28			16 44	16 53		16 58	17 09	17 22	17 28	17 36	17 44			18 01	17 57	18 01
Southease	d					16 04			16 34									17 34					→		18 08
Newhaven Town	⛴ d					16 08			16 38						17 06			17 38							18 12
Newhaven Harbour	d					16 10			16 40						17 08			17 40							18 13
Bishopstone	d					16 13			16 43						17 11			17 43							18 16
Seaford	a					16 16			16 46						17 14			17 46							18 20
Glynde	d						16 14									17 14									
Berwick	d						16 20						17 02			17 20	17 31		17 45						
Polegate	d		15 57	16 05			16 25	16 35				16 57	17 07			17 25	17 36		17 50	17 57				18 09	
Hampden Park [4] §	d						16 29	16 39								17 29	17 40		17 55					18 13	
Eastbourne [4]	a		16 04	16 13			16 34	16 44				17 04	17 14			17 34	17 48		18 00	18 04				18 18	
	d		16 08	16 19			16 40					17 08	17 21			17 40				18 08				18 25	
Hampden Park [4] §	d			16 23			16 44						17 25			17 44								18 29	
Pevensey & Westham	d			16 28			16 49						17 30			17 49								18 34	
Pevensey Bay	d												17 32			17 51									
Normans Bay	d						16 53						17 36			17 55									
Cooden Beach	d			16 34			16 57						17 39			17 58								18 40	
Collington	d			16 37			17 00						17 42			18 01								18 43	
Bexhill [4]	d		16 23	16 39			17 02					17 23	17 44			18 03				18 24				18 45	
St Leonards Warrior Sq [4]	d		16 30	16 45			17 08					17 30	17 51			18 10				18 31	18 47			18 52	
Hastings [4]	a		16 33	16 50			17 12					17 33	17 54			18 13				18 34	18 51			18 56	
	d		16 34	16 51	17 08		17 13					17 34	17 56			18 14				18 35	18 52			18 56	
Ore	d			16a54	17 10		17a16						17a59			18a17					18a57			19a01	
Three Oaks	d				17 16																				
Doleham	d				17 19																				
Winchelsea	d				17 25																				
Rye	a		16 51		17 29							17 51								18 52					
	d		16 54		17 30							17 54		18 31						18 54		19 31			
Appledore (Kent)	d		17 03		17 39							18 03		18 40						19 03		19 40			
Ham Street	d		17 08		17 44							18 08		18 45						19 08		19 45			
Ashford International	a		17 16		17 52							18 16		18 53						19 16		19 53			
London Bridge [4]	⊖ a		18f28		19f25							20f08								20f38					
London Cannon Street [4]	⊖ a		18g37		19g37							20g27													
London Waterloo (East) [4]	⊖ a		18f33		19f31							19f46								20f43					
London Charing Cross [4]	⊖ a		18f37		19f35							19f50								20f48					

For general notes see front of timetable
For details of catering facilities see Directory of Train Operators

§ For additional trains between Hampden Park and Eastbourne see Hastings to London pages

A 🛒 to Lewes
B From London Charing Cross (Table 206)
b Change at East Croydon and Brighton
c London Bridge
e Change at Gatwick Airport
f Until 9 October only
g Until 9 October only. Change at Ashford International and London Bridge

London, Haywards Heath and Brighton → Lewes, Seaford, Eastbourne, Hastings and Ashford

Network Diagram - see first page of Table 184

		SN 1	SN 1	SN 1	SN 1	SN 1	SN 1	SN 1	SE 1	SN 1	SN 1	SN 1	SN 1		SN 1	SN 1	SN 1	SN 1	SN 1	SN 1	SN 1	SN 1	SN 1	SN 1
						A			B	A			A							A			A	
London Victoria 15 ⊖	d	16 36	17b17	16c39	17 06	17 36							18 06		17c47	18b17		17c49		18 47	18c17	18 36	19 17	19 06
Clapham Junction 10	d	16 42	17b23	16c45	17 12	17 42							18 12		17c53	18b23		17c56		18 53	18c23	18 42	19 23	19 12
London Bridge 4 ⊖	d		17 23	16 46	16c59	17 32		17 11					17 59		17 52	18 22		17 57			18 26	18c29		18c59
East Croydon	d	16 52	17 36	17 00	17 22	17 52		17 25			17e36		18 22		18 09	18 37		18 12	18e25	19 03	18 40	18f54	19 33	19 22
Gatwick Airport 10 ✈	d		17 48	17 16	17e20	18 07		17 41			18 00		18 38		18 25	18 49		18 35	18 46	19 20	18 56	19 16	19 49	19 27
Haywards Heath 3	d	17 23	18 05	17 33	17 46	18 18		17 57			18 12		18 50		18 36	19 06		18 47	18 58	19 34	19 12	19 28	20 07	19 45
Wivelsfield 4	d		18 09	17 37	17 50	18 23							18 54		18 40	19 11				19 38		19 24	20 11	
Plumpton	d					18 29							19 00			19 17				19 44				
Cooksbridge	d					18 33							19 05			19 22				19 49				
Brighton 10	d	17 52		18 08	18 17			18 32			18 38	18 52			19 08			19 22	19 32		19 40	19 52		20 10
London Road (Brighton)	d	17 55		18 11	18 20						18 41	18 55			19 11			19 25			19 43	19 55		20 13
Moulsecoomb	d	17 57		18 13	18 22						18 43	18 57			19 13			19 27			19 45	19 57		20 15
Falmer	d	18 01		18 17	18 26						18 47	19 01			19 17			19 31			19 49	20 01		20 19
Lewes 4	a	18 07	18 20	18 23	18 32	18 38	←	18 44			18 53	19 08	19 09		19 23	19 27	←	19 37	19 43	19 53	19 55	20 07	20 22	20 25
	d	18 08	18 21	18 24	18 42	18 38	18 42	18 45			18 54		19 13	19 16	19 31	19 27	19 31		19 44	19 54	19 58	20 09	20 23	20 28
Southease	d				→						19 00				→		19 37				20 04			
Newhaven Town ⛴	d			18 33			18 50				19 04		19 21				19 41				20 08			20 36
Newhaven Harbour	d										19g09						19 44				20 10			20 38
Bishopstone	d			18 37			18 54				19 12		19 29				19 47				20 13			20 41
Seaford	a			18 40			18 58				19 15		19 34				19 50				20 16			20 45
Glynde	d	18 13	18 26											19 21		19 33						20 14	20 28	
Berwick	d	18 19	18 32											19 27		19 39						20 20	20 34	
Polegate	d	18 24	18 37			18 51		18 58						19 32		19 45		19 57	20 06			20 25	20 39	
Hampden Park 4 §	d	18 28	18 41			18 56								19 36		19 49						20 29	20 43	
Eastbourne 4	a	18 34	18 48			19 01		19 05		←				19 41		19 56		20 04	20 14			20 34	20 48	
	d	18 41				19 19		19 09		19 19				19 49				20 08	20 20					
Hampden Park 4 §	d	18 45				→				19 23				19 53					20 24					
Pevensey & Westham	d	18 50						19 17		19 28				19 58					20 29					
Pevensey Bay	d																							
Normans Bay	d	18 54																						
Cooden Beach	d	18 58								19 34				20 04					20 35					
Collington	d	19 01								19 37				20 07					20 38					
Bexhill 4	d	19 03						19 25		19 39				20 09				20 23	20 40					
St Leonards Warrior Sq 4	d	19 09						19 32	19 35	19 46				20 16				20 30	20 46					
Hastings 4	a	19 13						19 35	19 39	19 49				20 19				20 34	20 50					
	d	19 14						19 36	19 40	19 50				20 20				20 35	20 51					
Ore	d	19a17							19a45	19a55				20a25					20a56					
Three Oaks	d																							
Doleham	d																							
Winchelsea	d																							
Rye	a							19 53										20 52						
	d							19 54										20 54						
Appledore (Kent)	d							20 03										21 03						
Ham Street	d							20 08										21 08						
Ashford International	a							20 16										21 16						
London Bridge 4 ⊖	a							21h38										22h38						
London Cannon Street 4 ⊖	a																							
London Waterloo (East) 4 ⊖	a							21h43										22h43						
London Charing Cross 4 ⊖	a							21h48										22h48						

For general notes see front of timetable
For details of catering facilities see Directory of Train Operators

§ For additional trains between Hampden Park and Eastbourne see Hastings to London pages

A to Lewes
B From London Charing Cross (Table 206)
b Change at Haywards Heath
c Change at East Croydon and Brighton
e Change at Haywards Heath and Brighton
f Change at Gatwick Airport and Brighton
g Arr. 1906
h Until 9 October only

London, Haywards Heath and Brighton → Lewes, Seaford, Eastbourne, Hastings and Ashford

Network Diagram - see first page of Table 184

	SN	SN	SN	SN	SN	SN	SN	SN	SN	SN	SN	SN	SN	SN	SN	SN	SN	SN	SN	SN	SN
		A ⌶																			
London Victoria 15 ⊖ d		19 47	19 36	19b53	20 17		20b17	20 47	20 36	21 06	21 17			21 36	21 47		22 06		22 36	22 47	
Clapham Junction 10 d		19 53	19 42	19b59	20 23		20b23	20 53	20 42	21 12	21 23			21 42	21 53		22 12		22 42	22 53	
London Bridge 4 ⊖ d	19 12		19 27	20 01			20 28			20 58			21 11	21b28	21 41		21b45	22 11	22b28	22 41	
East Croydon d	19 24	20 03	19 52	20 14	20 33		20 40	21 04	20 52	21 22	21 33		21 24	21 52	22 03		22 22	22 24	22 52	23 03	
Gatwick Airport 10 ✈ d	19 41	20 19	19 56	20 31	20 49		20 56	21 19		21 27	21 49		21 41	21c49	22 19		22c19	22 41	22c49	23 19	
Haywards Heath 3 d	19 57	20 36	20 17	20 42	21 07		21 11	21 37	21 15	21 45	22 08		21 58	22 15	22 34		22 45	22 58	23 15	23 34	
Wivelsfield 4 d	20 01	20 40		20 30	21 11		21 01	21 41		21 30	22 12		22 02		22 38		22 30	23 02		23 38	
Plumpton d		20 46						21 47							22 44					23 44	
Cooksbridge d		20 50																			
Brighton 10 d	20 30		20 40	21 04			21 30		21 40	22 04			22 28	22 34			23 04	23 28	23 34		
London Road (Brighton) d			20 43	21 07					21 43	22 07				22 37			23 07		23 37		
Moulsecoomb d			20 45	21 09					21 45	22 09				22 39			23 09		23 39		
Falmer d			20 49	21 13					21 49	22 13				22 43			23 13		23 43		
Lewes 4 a	20 43	20 55	20 55	21 19	21 22	←	21 43	21 54	21 55	22 19	22 23	←	22 39	22 49	22 51	←	23 19	23 39	23 49	23 51	←
d	20 44	20 55	21 00	21 28	21 23	21 28	21 44	21 55	21 58	22 28	22 23	22 28	22 39	22 58	22 53	22 58	23 20	23 39	23 56	23 53	23 56
Southease d				→					22 04	→				→		23 04			→		
Newhaven Town ⛴ d			21 08			21 36			22 08			22 36				23 08					00 04
Newhaven Harbour d			21 10			21 38			22 10			22 38				23 10					00 06
Bishopstone d			21 13			21 41			22 13			22 41				23 13					00 09
Seaford a			21 16			21 44			22 16			22 44				23 16					00 12
Glynde d					21 28						22 29						23 25				
Berwick d					21 34						22 34						23 31			00 02	
Polegate d	20 57	21 08			21 39		21 57	22 07			22 39		22 52		23 05		23 36	23 52		00 07	
Hampden Park 4 § d					21 43						22 43				23 09		23 41			00 11	
Eastbourne 4 a	21 04	21 15			21 48		22 04	22 15			22 48		23 03		23 14		23 46	23 59		00 16	
d	21 08	21 21					22 08	22 21							23 20					00 22	
Hampden Park 4 § d		21 25						22 25							23 24						
Pevensey & Westham d		21 30						22 30							23 29					00 29	
Pevensey Bay d																					
Normans Bay d																					
Cooden Beach d		21 36						22 36							23 35					00 35	
Collington d		21 39						22 39							23 38					00 38	
Bexhill 4 d	21 23	21 41					22 23	22 41							23 40					00 40	
St Leonards Warrior Sq 4 d	21 30	21 47					22 30	22 47							23 46					00 47	
Hastings 4 a	21 33	21 51					22 33	22 51							23 50					00 50	
d	21 34	21 53																			
Ore d	21 36	21a56																			
Three Oaks d	21 42																				
Doleham d	21 45																				
Winchelsea d	21 51																				
Rye a	21 55																				
d	21 57																				
Appledore (Kent) d	22 06																				
Ham Street d	22 11																				
Ashford International a	22 19																				
London Bridge 4 ⊖ a	23e51																				
London Cannon Street 4 ⊖ a																					
London Waterloo (East) 4 ⊖ a	23e56																				
London Charing Cross 4 ⊖ a	00 01																				

For general notes see front of timetable
For details of catering facilities see Directory of Train Operators

§ For additional trains between Hampden Park and Eastbourne see Hastings to London pages

A ⌶ to Lewes
b Change at East Croydon and Brighton
c Change at Haywards Heath and Brighton
e Until 9 October only

London, Haywards Heath and Brighton → Lewes, Seaford, Eastbourne, Hastings and Ashford

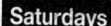

Network Diagram - see first page of Table 184

		SN 1	SN 1	SN 1	SN 1	SN 1	SN 1	SN 1	SN 1	SN 1
London Victoria 15	⊖ d		22p47		00 05			04 00		
Clapham Junction 10	d		22p53		00 11			04 08		
London Bridge 4	⊖ d				23 53			03b35		
East Croydon	d		23p03		00 25			04 22		
Gatwick Airport 10	d		23p19		00 44			04 47		
Haywards Heath 3	d		23p34		01 06			05 01		
Wivelsfield 4	d		23p38							
Plumpton	d		23p44							
Cooksbridge	d									
Brighton 10	d	23p34						05 30		
London Road (Brighton)	d	23p37								
Moulsecoomb	d	23p39								
Falmer	d	23p43								
Lewes 4	a	23p49	23p51	←	01 20			05 41		
	d	23p56	23p53	23p56	01 20			05 41		
Southease	d	↪								
Newhaven Town	d			00 04						
Newhaven Harbour	d			00 06						
Bishopstone	d			00 09						
Seaford	a			00 12						
Glynde	d									
Berwick	d		00 02							
Polegate	d		00 07		01s32			05 53		
Hampden Park 4 §	d		00 11		01s36					
Eastbourne 4	a		00 16		01 41			06 00		
	d		00 22				05 45		06 05	06 18
Hampden Park 4 §	d									06 22
Pevensey & Westham	d		00 29							06 27
Pevensey Bay	d									
Normans Bay	d									06 31
Cooden Beach	d		00 35							06 35
Collington	d		00 38							06 38
Bexhill 4	d		00 40				06 00		06 19	06 40
St Leonards Warrior Sq 4	d		00 47				06 06		06 26	06 49
Hastings 4	a		00 50				06 10		06 30	06 53
	d					05 34	06 11		06 30	06 54
Ore	d					05 37	06a14			06a57
Three Oaks	d					05 43				
Doleham	d					05 46				
Winchelsea	d					05 52				
Rye	a					05 55			06 47	
	d					05 56			06 50	
Appledore (Kent)	d					06 05			06 59	
Ham Street	d					06 10			07 04	
Ashford International	a					06 18			07 13	
London Bridge 4	⊖ a					08 10			08 40	
London Cannon Street 4	⊖ a					08e20			08e47	
London Waterloo (East) 4	⊖ a					08 14			08 45	
London Charing Cross 4	⊖ a					08 18			08 48	

		SN 1	SN 1	SN 1	SN 1	SN 1	SN 1	SN 1	SN 1	SN 1	SN 1	SN 1	SN 1	SN 1
London Victoria 15	⊖ d			05 02		05 02				05 32		06b02	06c32	
Clapham Junction 10	d			05 08		05 08				05 38		06b08	06c38	
London Bridge 4	⊖ d			05 05		04 35		05 05		05 51		06 27	06 41	
East Croydon	d			05 32		05 22		05 32		06 05		06 39	06 54	
Gatwick Airport 10	d			06 11		05 49		05 54		06 22		06 56	07 11	
Haywards Heath 3	d			06 25		06 03		06 12		06 41		07 08	07 33	
Wivelsfield 4	d			06 29		06 07		06 16		06 45			07 37	
Plumpton	d													
Cooksbridge	d													
Brighton 10	d	05 52	06 10			06 32		06 40	06 52	07 10	07 22	07 32		07 40
London Road (Brighton)	d	05 55	06 13					06 43	06 55	07 13	07 25			07 43
Moulsecoomb	d	05 57	06 15					06 45	06 57	07 15	07 27			07 45
Falmer	d	06 01	06 19					06 49	07 01	07 19	07 31			07 49
Lewes 4	a	06 07	06 25	06 40		06 43	←	06 55	07 07	07 25	07 37	07 43	07 48	07 55
	d	06 08	06 28	06 53		06 44	06 53	06 58	07 09	07 28		07 44	07 53	07 58
Southease	d			↪										
Newhaven Town	d	06 16	06 36					07 06		07 36				08 06
Newhaven Harbour	d	06 18	06 38					07 08		07 38				08 08
Bishopstone	d		06 41					07 11		07 41				08 11
Seaford	a	06 23	06 44					07 14		07 44				08 14
Glynde	d								07 14					
Berwick	d						07 02		07 20					
Polegate	d					06 57	07 07		07 25			07 57	08 05	
Hampden Park 4 §	d						07 11		07 29					
Eastbourne 4	a					07 04	07 16		07 34			08 04	08 13	
	d				06 45	07 08	07 21		07 40			08 08	08 19	
Hampden Park 4 §	d						07 25		07 44				08 23	
Pevensey & Westham	d						07 30		07 49				08 28	
Pevensey Bay	d													
Normans Bay	d								07 53					
Cooden Beach	d						07 36		07 57				08 34	
Collington	d						07 39		08 00				08 37	
Bexhill 4	d				07 00	07 23	07 41		08 02			08 23	08 39	
St Leonards Warrior Sq 4	d				07 06	07 30	07 47		08 08			08 30	08 45	
Hastings 4	a				07 10	07 33	07 51		08 12			08 33	08 50	
	d				07 11	07 34	07 52		08 13			08 34	08 51	
Ore	d				07a14		07a55		08a16				08a54	
Three Oaks	d													
Doleham	d													
Winchelsea	d													
Rye	a					07 51						08 51		
	d					07 54						08 54		
Appledore (Kent)	d					08 03						09 03		
Ham Street	d					08 08						09 08		
Ashford International	a					08 16						09 16		
London Bridge 4	⊖ a					09 43						10 43		
London Cannon Street 4	⊖ a					09e50						10e50		
London Waterloo (East) 4	⊖ a					09 32						10 32		
London Charing Cross 4	⊖ a					09 36						10 36		

For general notes see front of timetable
For details of catering facilities see Directory of Train Operators

§ For additional trains between Hampden Park and Eastbourne see Hastings to London pages

b Change at East Croydon and Brighton
c Change at East Croydon and Haywards Heath
e Change at Ashford International and London Bridge

Table 189

Saturdays

London, Haywards Heath and Brighton → Lewes, Seaford, Eastbourne, Hastings and Ashford

Network Diagram - see first page of Table 184

		SN 1	SN 1	SN 1	SN 1	SN 1	SN 1	SN 1		SN 1	SN 1	SN 1	SN 1
London Victoria 15	⊖ d		07 06		07 36	07 47				08 17	08 06		08 36
Clapham Junction 10	d		07 12		07 42	07 53				08 23	08 12		08 42
London Bridge 4	⊖ d		06 56	07 11	07 26	07 41				08 11	07 56	08 11	08 26
East Croydon	d		07 22	07 24	07 52	08 03				08 33	08 22	08 24	08 52
Gatwick Airport 10	d		07 26	07 41	07 56	08 19		07 58		08 49	08 26	08 41	08 56
Haywards Heath 3	d		07 40	07 55	08 10	08 34		08 17		09 07	08 40	08 55	09 10
Wivelsfield 4	d		07 31	07 59				08 21		09 11	08 31	08 59	
Plumpton	d												
Cooksbridge	d												
Brighton 10	d	07 52	08 10	08 22	08 32		08 40	08 52			09 10	09 22	09 32
London Road (Brighton)	d	07 55	08 13	08 25			08 43	08 55			09 13	09 25	
Moulsecoomb	d	07 57	08 15	08 27			08 45	08 57			09 15	09 27	
Falmer	d	08 01	08 19	08 31			08 49	09 01			09 19	09 31	
Lewes 4	a	08 07	08 25	08 37	08 43	08 48	08 55	09 07		09 22	09 25	09 37	09 43
	d	08 09	08 28		08 44	08 53	08 58	09 09		09 23	09 28		09 44
Southease	d										09 34		
Newhaven Town	d		08 36				09 06				09 38		
Newhaven Harbour	d		08 38				09 08				09 40		
Bishopstone	d		08 41				09 11				09 43		
Seaford	a		08 44				09 14				09 46		
Glynde	d	08 14						09 14					
Berwick	d	08 20						09 20					
Polegate	d	08 25			08 57	09 05		09 25		09 35			09 57
Hampden Park 4 §	d	08 29						09 29		09 39			
Eastbourne 4	a	08 34			09 04	09 13		09 34		09 44			10 04
	d	08 40			09 08	09 19		09 40					10 08
Hampden Park 4 §	d	08 44				09 23		09 44					
Pevensey & Westham	d	08 49				09 28		09 49					
Pevensey Bay	d												
Normans Bay	d	08 53						09 53					
Cooden Beach	d	08 57				09 34		09 57					
Collington	d	09 00				09 37		10 00					
Bexhill 4	d	09 02			09 23	09 39		10 02					10 23
St Leonards Warrior Sq 4	d	09 08			09 30	09 45		10 08					10 30
Hastings 4	a	09 12			09 33	09 50		10 12					10 33
	d	09 13			09 34	09 51		10 13					10 34
Ore	d	09a16				09a54		10a16					
Three Oaks	d												
Doleham	d												
Winchelsea	d												
Rye	a				09 51								10 51
	d				09 54								10 54
Appledore (Kent)	d				10 03								11 03
Ham Street	d				10 08								11 08
Ashford International	a				10 16								11 16
London Bridge 4	⊖ a				11 43								12 43
London Cannon Street 4	⊖ a				11b50								12b50
London Waterloo (East) 4	⊖ a				11 32								12 32
London Charing Cross 4	⊖ a				11 36								12 36

		SN 1	SN 1	SN 1	SN 1	SN 1		SN 1	SN 1	SN 1	SN 1	SN 1	SN 1
London Victoria 15	⊖ d	08 47			09 17	09 06			09 36	09 47			10 17
Clapham Junction 10	d	08 53			09 23	09 12			09 42	09 53			10 23
London Bridge 4	⊖ d	08 41			09 11	08 56		09 11	09 26	09 41			10 11
East Croydon	d	09 03			09 33	09 22		09 24	09 52	10 03			10 33
Gatwick Airport 10	d	09 19		08 58	09 49	09 26		09 41	09 56	10 19		09 58	10 49
Haywards Heath 3	d	09 34		09 17	10 07	09 40		09 55	10 10	10 34		10 17	11 07
Wivelsfield 4	d			09 21	10 11	09 31		09 59				10 21	11 11
Plumpton	d	09 43								10 43			
Cooksbridge	d												
Brighton 10	d		09 40	09 52		10 10		10 22	10 32		10 40	10 52	
London Road (Brighton)	d		09 43	09 55		10 13		10 25			10 43	10 55	
Moulsecoomb	d		09 45	09 57		10 15		10 27			10 45	10 57	
Falmer	d		09 49	10 01		10 19		10 31			10 49	11 01	
Lewes 4	a	09 51	09 55	10 07	10 22	10 25		10 37	10 43	10 51	10 55	11 07	11 22
	d	09 53	09 58	10 09	10 23	10 28			10 44	10 53	10 58	11 09	11 23
Southease	d					10 34							
Newhaven Town	d		10 06			10 38					11 06		
Newhaven Harbour	d		10 08			10 40					11 08		
Bishopstone	d		10 11			10 43					11 11		
Seaford	a		10 14			10 46					11 14		
Glynde	d			10 14								11 14	
Berwick	d			10 20								11 20	
Polegate	d	10 05		10 25	10 35				10 57	11 05		11 25	11 35
Hampden Park 4 §	d			10 29	10 39							11 29	11 39
Eastbourne 4	a	10 13		10 34	10 44				11 04	11 13		11 34	11 44
	d	10 19		10 40					11 08	11 19		11 40	
Hampden Park 4 §	d	10 23		10 44						11 23		11 44	
Pevensey & Westham	d	10 28		10 49						11 28		11 49	
Pevensey Bay	d												
Normans Bay	d			10 53								11 53	
Cooden Beach	d	10 34		10 57						11 34		11 57	
Collington	d	10 37		11 00						11 37		12 00	
Bexhill 4	d	10 39		11 02					11 23	11 39		12 02	
St Leonards Warrior Sq 4	d	10 45		11 08					11 30	11 45		12 08	
Hastings 4	a	10 50		11 12					11 33	11 50		12 12	
	d	10 51		11 13					11 34	11 51		12 13	
Ore	d	10a54		11a16						11a54		12a16	
Three Oaks	d												
Doleham	d												
Winchelsea	d												
Rye	a								11 51				
	d								11 54				
Appledore (Kent)	d								12 03				
Ham Street	d								12 08				
Ashford International	a								12 16				
London Bridge 4	⊖ a								13 43				
London Cannon Street 4	⊖ a								13b50				
London Waterloo (East) 4	⊖ a								13 32				
London Charing Cross 4	⊖ a								13 36				

For general notes see front of timetable
For details of catering facilities see Directory of Train Operators

§ For additional trains between Hampden Park and Eastbourne see Hastings to London pages

b Change at Ashford International and London Bridge

Table 189

Saturdays

London, Haywards Heath and Brighton → Lewes, Seaford, Eastbourne, Hastings and Ashford

Network Diagram - see first page of Table 184

		SN 1	SN 1	SN 1	SN 1	SN 1		SN 1	SN 1	SN 1	SN 1	SN 1	SN 1	SN 1	SN 1	SN 1		SN 1	SN 1	SN 1	SN 1	SN 1	SN 1	SN 1	SN 1
London Victoria 15 ⊖	d	10 06		10 36	10 47				11 17	11 06		11 36	11 47			12 17		12 06		12 36	12 47			13 17	13 06
Clapham Junction 10	d	10 12		10 42	10 53				11 23	11 12		11 42	11 53			12 23		12 12		12 42	12 53			13 23	13 12
London Bridge 4 ⊖	d	09 56	10 11	10 26	10 41				11 11	10 56	11 11	11 26	11 41			12 11		11 56	12 11	12 26	12 41			13 11	12 56
East Croydon	d	10 22	10 24	10 52	11 03				11 33	11 22	11 24	11 52	12 03			12 33		12 22	12 24	12 52	13 03			13 33	13 22
Gatwick Airport 10 ✈	d	10 26	10 41	10 56	11 19			10 58	11 49	11 26	11 41	11 56	12 19		11 58	12 49		12 26	12 41	12 56	13 19		12 58	13 49	13 26
Haywards Heath 3	d	10 40	10 55	11 10	11 34			11 17	12 07	11 40	11 55	12 10	12 34		12 17	13 07		12 40	12 55	13 10	13 34		13 17	14 07	13 40
Wivelsfield 4	d	10 31	10 59					11 21	12 11	11 31	11 59				12 21	13 11		12 31	12 59				13 21	14 11	13 31
Plumpton	d				11 43								12 43												
Cooksbridge	d																								
Brighton 10	d	11 10	11 22	11 32		11 40		11 52		12 10	12 22	12 32		12 40	12 52			13 10	13 22	13 32		13 40	13 52		14 10
London Road (Brighton)	d	11 13	11 25			11 43		11 55		12 13	12 25			12 43	12 55			13 13	13 25			13 43	13 55		14 13
Moulsecoomb	d	11 15	11 27			11 45		11 57		12 15	12 27			12 45	12 57			13 15	13 27			13 45	13 57		14 15
Falmer	d	11 19	11 31			11 49		12 01		12 19	12 31			12 49	13 01			13 19	13 31			13 49	14 01		14 19
Lewes 4	a	11 25	11 37	11 43	11 51	11 55		12 07	12 22	12 25	12 37	12 43	12 51	12 55	13 07	13 22		13 25	13 37	13 43	13 48	13 55	14 07	14 22	14 25
	d	11 28		11 44	11 53	11 58		12 09	12 23	12 28		12 44	12 53	12 58	13 09	13 23		13 28		13 44	13 53	13 58	14 09	14 23	14 28
Southease	d	11 34								12 34								13 34							14 34
Newhaven Town ⛴	d	11 38				12 06				12 38				13 06				13 38				14 06			14 38
Newhaven Harbour	d	11 40				12 08				12 40				13 08				13 40				14 08			14 40
Bishopstone	d	11 43				12 11				12 43				13 11				13 43				14 11			14 43
Seaford	a	11 46				12 14				12 46				13 14				13 46				14 14			14 46
Glynde	d							12 14							13 14								14 14		
Berwick	d							12 20							13 20								14 20		
Polegate	d			11 57	12 05			12 25	12 35			12 57	13 05		13 25	13 35				13 57	14 05		14 25	14 35	
Hampden Park 4 §	d							12 29	12 39						13 29	13 39							14 29	14 39	
Eastbourne 4	a			12 04	12 13			12 34	12 44			13 04	13 13		13 34	13 44				14 04	14 13		14 34	14 44	
	d			12 08	12 19			12 40				13 08	13 19		13 40					14 08	14 19		14 40		
Hampden Park 4 §	d				12 23			12 44					13 23		13 44						14 23		14 44		
Pevensey & Westham	d				12 28			12 49					13 28		13 49						14 28		14 49		
Pevensey Bay	d																								
Normans Bay	d							12 53							13 53								14 53		
Cooden Beach	d				12 34			12 57					13 34		13 57						14 34		14 57		
Collington	d				12 37			13 00					13 37		14 00						14 37		15 00		
Bexhill 4	d			12 23	12 39			13 02				13 23	13 39		14 02					14 23	14 39		15 02		
St Leonards Warrior Sq 4	d			12 30	12 45			13 08				13 30	13 45		14 08					14 30	14 45		15 08		
Hastings 4	a			12 33	12 50			13 12				13 33	13 50		14 12					14 33	14 50		15 12		
	d			12 34	12 51			13 13				13 34	13 51		14 13					14 34	14 51		15 13		
Ore	d				12a54			13a16					13a54		14a16						14a54		15a16		
Three Oaks	d																								
Doleham	d																								
Winchelsea	d																								
Rye	a			12 51								13 51								14 51					
	d			12 54								13 54								14 54					
Appledore (Kent)	d			13 03								14 03								15 03					
Ham Street	d			13 08								14 08								15 08					
Ashford International	a			13 16								14 16								15 16					
London Bridge 4 ⊖	a			14 43								15 43								16 43					
London Cannon Street 4 ⊖	a			14b50								15b50								16b50					
London Waterloo (East) 4 ⊖	a			14 32								15 32								16 32					
London Charing Cross 4 ⊖	a			14 36								15 36								16 36					

For general notes see front of timetable
For details of catering facilities see Directory of Train Operators

§ For additional trains between Hampden Park and Eastbourne see Hastings to London pages

b Change at Ashford International and London Bridge

London, Haywards Heath and Brighton → Lewes, Seaford, Eastbourne, Hastings and Ashford

Network Diagram - see first page of Table 184

Station		SN 1	SN 1	SN 1		SN 1	SN 1	SN 1	SN 1	SN 1	SN 1	SN 1	SN 1	SN 1		SN 1	SN 1	SN 1	SN 1	SN 1	SN 1	SN 1	SN 1	SN 1	SN 1
London Victoria 15 ⊖	d		13 36	13 47				14 17	14 06		14 36	14 47				15 17	15 06		15 36	15 47			16 17	16 06	
Clapham Junction 10	d		13 42	13 53				14 23	14 12		14 42	14 53				15 23	15 12		15 42	15 53			16 23	16 12	
London Bridge 4 ⊖	d	13 11	13 26	13 41				14 11	13 56	14 11	14 26	14 41				15 11	14 56	15 11	15 26	15 41			16 11	15 56	16 11
East Croydon	d	13 24	13 52	14 03				14 33	14 22	14 24	14 52	15 03				15 33	15 22	15 24	15 52	16 03			16 33	16 22	16 24
Gatwick Airport 10 ✈	d	13 41	13 56	14 19			13 58	14 49	14 26	14 41	14 56	15 19		14 58		15 49	15 26	15 41	15 56	16 19		15 58	16 49	16 26	16 41
Haywards Heath 3	d	13 55	14 10	14 34			14 17	15 07	14 40	14 55	15 10	15 34		15 17		16 07	15 40	15 55	16 10	16 34		16 17	17 07	16 40	16 55
Wivelsfield 4	d	13 59					14 21	15 11	14 31	14 59				15 21		16 11	15 31	15 59				16 21	17 11	16 31	16 59
Plumpton	d																			16 43					
Cooksbridge	d																								
Brighton 10	d	14 22	14 32			14 40	14 52		15 10	15 22	15 32		15 40	15 52			16 10	16 22	16 32		16 40	16 52		17 10	17 22
London Road (Brighton)	d	14 25				14 43	14 55		15 13	15 25			15 43	15 55			16 13	16 25			16 43	16 55		17 13	17 25
Moulsecoomb	d	14 27				14 45	14 57		15 15	15 27			15 45	15 57			16 15	16 27			16 45	16 57		17 15	17 27
Falmer	d	14 31				14 49	15 01		15 19	15 31			15 49	16 01			16 19	16 31			16 49	17 01		17 19	17 31
Lewes 4	a	14 37	14 43	14 48		14 55	15 07	15 22	15 25	15 37	15 43	15 48	15 55	16 07		16 22	16 25	16 37	16 43	16 51	16 55	17 07	17 22	17 25	17 37
	d		14 44	14 53		14 58	15 09	15 23	15 28		15 44	15 53	15 58	16 09		16 23	16 29		16 44	16 53	16 58	17 09	17 23	17 28	
Southease	d								15 34								16 35							17 34	
Newhaven Town ⛴	d					15 06			15 38				16 06				16 39				17 06			17 38	
Newhaven Harbour	d					15 08			15 40				16 08				16 41				17 08			17 40	
Bishopstone	d					15 11			15 43				16 11				16 44				17 11			17 43	
Seaford	a					15 14			15 50				16 14				16 47				17 14			17 46	
Glynde	d						15 14							16 14								17 14			
Berwick	d						15 20							16 20								17 20			
Polegate	d		14 57	15 05			15 25	15 35			15 57	16 05		16 25		16 35			16 57	17 05		17 25	17 35		
Hampden Park 4 §	d						15 29	15 39						16 29		16 39						17 29	17 39		
Eastbourne 4	a		15 04	15 13			15 34	15 44			16 04	16 13		16 34		16 44			17 04	17 13		17 34	17 44		
	d		15 08	15 19			15 40				16 08	16 19		16 40					17 08	17 19		17 40			
Hampden Park 4 §	d			15 23			15 44					16 23		16 44						17 23		17 44			
Pevensey & Westham	d			15 28			15 49					16 28		16 49						17 28		17 49			
Pevensey Bay	d																								
Normans Bay	d						15 53							16 53								17 53			
Cooden Beach	d			15 34			15 57					16 34		16 57						17 34		17 57			
Collington	d			15 37			16 00					16 37		17 00						17 37		18 00			
Bexhill 4	d		15 23	15 39			16 02				16 23	16 39		17 02					17 23	17 39		18 02			
St Leonards Warrior Sq 4	d		15 30	15 45			16 08				16 30	16 45		17 08					17 30	17 46		18 08			
Hastings 4	a		15 33	15 50			16 12				16 33	16 50		17 12					17 33	17 50		18 12			
	d		15 34	15 51			16 13				16 34	16 51		17 13					17 34	17 52		18 13			
Ore	d			15a54			16a16					16a54		17a16						17a55		18a16			
Three Oaks	d																								
Doleham	d																								
Winchelsea	d																								
Rye	a		15 51								16 51								17 51						
	d		15 54								16 54								17 54						
Appledore (Kent)	d		16 03								17 03								18 03						
Ham Street	d		16 08								17 08								18 08						
Ashford International	a		16 16								17 16								18 16						
London Bridge 4 ⊖	a		17 43								19 08								19 38						
London Cannon Street 4 ⊖	a		17b50																						
London Waterloo (East) 4 ⊖	a		17 32								19 14								19 44						
London Charing Cross 4 ⊖	a		17 36								19 19								19 49						

For general notes see front of timetable
For details of catering facilities see
Directory of Train Operators

§ For additional trains between Hampden Park and Eastbourne see Hastings to London pages

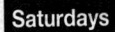

b Change at Ashford International and London Bridge

Table 189

Saturdays

London, Haywards Heath and Brighton → Lewes, Seaford, Eastbourne, Hastings and Ashford

Network Diagram - see first page of Table 184

		SN 1		SN 1	SN 1	SN 1	SN 1	SN 1	SN 1	SN 1	SN 1	SN 1		SN 1	SN 1	SN 1	SN 1	SN 1	SN 1	SN 1	SN 1	SN 1		SN 1	SN 1
London Victoria 15	⊖ d	16 36		16 47			17 17	17 06		17 36	17 47				18 17	18 06		18 36	18 47			19 17		19 06	19 36
Clapham Junction 10	d	16 42		16 53			17 23	17 12		17 42	17 53				18 23	18 12		18 42	18 53			19 23		19 12	19 42
London Bridge 4	⊖ d	16 26		16 41			17 11	16 56	17 11	17 26	17 41				18 11	17 56	18 11	18 26	18 41		18 41	19 11		18 56	19 26
East Croydon	d	16 52		17 03			17 33	17 22	17 24	17 52	18 03				18 33	18 22	18 24	18 52	19 03		18 54	19 33		19 22	19 52
Gatwick Airport 10	✈ d	16 56		17 19		16 58	17 49	17 26	17 41	17 56	18 19			17 58	18 49	18 26	18 41	18 56	19 19		19 11	19 49		19 26	19 56
Haywards Heath 3	d	17 10		17 34		17 17	18 07	17 40	17 55	18 10	18 34			18 17	19 07	18 40	18 55	19 10	19 34		19 27	20 07		19 40	20 10
Wivelsfield 4	d					17 21	18 11	17 31	17 59					18 21	19 11	18 31	18 59				19 31	20 11			19 59
Plumpton	d			17 43							18 43								19 43						
Cooksbridge	d																								
Brighton 10	d	17 32			17 40	17 52		18 10	18 22	18 32		18 40		18 52		19 10	19 22	19 32		19 40	19 53			20 10	20 32
London Road (Brighton)	d				17 43	17 55		18 13	18 25			18 43		18 55		19 13	19 25			19 43	19 56			20 13	
Moulsecoomb	d				17 45	17 57		18 15	18 27			18 45		18 57		19 15	19 27			19 45	19 58			20 15	
Falmer	d				17 49	18 01		18 19	18 31			18 49		19 01		19 19	19 31			19 49	20 02			20 19	
Lewes 4	a	17 43		17 51	17 55	18 07	18 22	18 25	18 37	18 43	18 51	18 55		19 07	19 22	19 25	19 37	19 43	19 51	19 55	20 08	20 22		20 25	20 43
	d	17 44		17 53	17 58	18 09	18 23	18 28		18 44	18 53	18 58		19 09	19 23	19 28		19 44	19 53	19 58	20 09	20 23		20 28	20 44
Southease	d							18 34								19 34									
Newhaven Town	⛴ d				18 06			18 38				19 06				19 38				20 06				20 36	
Newhaven Harbour	d				18 08			18 40				19 08				19 40				20 08				20 38	
Bishopstone	d				18 11			18 43				19 11				19 43				20 11				20 41	
Seaford	a				18 14			18 46				19 14				19 46				20 14				20 44	
Glynde	d					18 14								19 14							20 14	20 28			
Berwick	d					18 20								19 20							20 20	20 34			
Polegate	d	17 57		18 05		18 25	18 35			18 57	19 05			19 25	19 35			19 57	20 05		20 25	20 39			20 57
Hampden Park 4 §	d					18 29	18 39							19 29	19 39						20 29	20 43			
Eastbourne 4	a	18 04		18 13		18 34	18 44			19 04	19 13			19 34	19 44			20 04	20 13		20 34	20 48			21 04
	d	18 08		18 19		18 40				19 08	19 19			19 40				20 08	20 19			20 54			21 08
Hampden Park 4 §	d			18 23		18 44					19 23			19 44					20 23						
Pevensey & Westham	d			18 28		18 49					19 28			19 49					20 28			21 01			
Pevensey Bay	d																								
Normans Bay	d					18 53								19 53											
Cooden Beach	d			18 34		18 57					19 34			19 57					20 34			21 07			
Collington	d			18 37		19 00					19 37			20 00					20 37						
Bexhill 4	d	18 23		18 39		19 02					19 39			20 02				20 23	20 39			21 11			21 24
St Leonards Warrior Sq 4	d	18 30		18 46		19 08				19 23	19 46			20 08				20 30	20 46			21 18			21 30
Hastings 4	a	18 33		18 50		19 12				19 30	19 50			20 12				20 33	20 50			21 21			21 34
	d	18 34		18 52		19 13				19 34	19 52			20 13				20 34	20 52						21 34
Ore	d			18a55		19a16					19a55			20a16					20a55						21 37
Three Oaks	d																								21 43
Doleham	d																								21 46
Winchelsea	d																								21 52
Rye	a	18 51								19 51								20 51							21 55
	d	18 54								19 54								20 54							21 57
Appledore (Kent)	d	19 03								20 03								21 03							22 06
Ham Street	d	19 08								20 08								21 08							22 11
Ashford International	a	19 16								20 16								21 16							22 19
London Bridge 4	⊖ a	20 38								21 38								22 38							23 53
London Cannon Street 4	⊖ a																								
London Waterloo (East) 4	⊖ a	20 44								21 44								22 44							23 57
London Charing Cross 4	⊖ a	20 49								21 49								22 49							00 01

For general notes see front of timetable
For details of catering facilities see Directory of Train Operators

§ For additional trains between Hampden Park and Eastbourne see Hastings to London pages

Table 189

Saturdays

London, Haywards Heath and Brighton → Lewes, Seaford, Eastbourne, Hastings and Ashford

Network Diagram - see first page of Table 184

		SN 1	SN 1	SN 1	SN 1	SN 1	SN 1	SN 1	SN 1	SN 1		SN 1	SN 1	SN 1	SN 1	SN 1	SN 1	SN 1	SN 1	SN 1		SN 1	SN 1		
London Victoria 15 ⊖	d	19 47		20 06	20 17		20 36	20 47		21 06		21 17			21 36	21 47		22 06		22 36		22 47			
Clapham Junction 10	d	19 53		20 12	20 23		20 42	20 53		21 12		21 23			21 42	21 53		22 12		22 42		22 53			
London Bridge 4 ⊖	d	19 41		19 56	20 11		20b15	20 41		20b45		21 11		21 11	21b15	21 41		21b45	22 11	22b15		22 41			
East Croydon	d	20 03		20 22	20 33		20 52	21 03		21 22		21 33		21 24	21 52	22 03		22 22	22 24	22 52		23 03			
Gatwick Airport 10 ✈	d	20 19		20 26	20 49		20 41	21 19		21c19		21 49		21 41	21c49	22 19		22c19	22 41	22c49		23 19			
Haywards Heath 3	d	20 34		20 40	21 07		20 58	21 34		21 45		22 08		21 58	22 15	22 34		22 45	22 58	23 15		23 34			
Wivelsfield 4	d	20 38		20 31	21 11		21 02	21 38		21 30		22 12		22 02		22 38		22 30	23 02			23 38			
Plumpton	d	20 44						21 44								22 44						23 44			
Cooksbridge	d																								
Brighton 10	d		20 40	21 04			21 32		21 40	22 04				22 28	22 34			23 04	23 28	23 34					
London Road (Brighton)	d		20 43	21 07					21 43	22 07					22 37			23 07		23 37					
Moulsecoomb	d		20 45	21 09					21 45	22 09					22 39			23 09		23 39					
Falmer	d		20 49	21 13					21 49	22 13					22 43			23 13		23 43					
Lewes 4	a	20 51	20 55	21 19	21 22	←	21 43	21 51	21 55	22 19		22 23	←	22 39	22 49	22 51	←	23 19	23 39	23 49		23 51	←		
	d	20 53	20 58	21 28	21 23	21 28	21 44	21 53	21 58	22 28		22 23	22 28	22 39	22 58	22 53	22 58	23 20	23 39	23 56		23 53	23 56		
				→						→					→					→					
Southease	d																								
Newhaven Town ⛴	d		21 06			21 36			22 06				22 36				23 06						00 04		
Newhaven Harbour	d		21 08			21 38			22 08				22 38				23 08						00 06		
Bishopstone	d		21 11			21 41			22 11				22 41				23 11						00 09		
Seaford	a		21 14			21 44			22 14				22 44				23 14						00 12		
Glynde	d				21 28							22 29						23 25							
Berwick	d				21 34							22 34						23 31				00 02			
Polegate	d	21 05			21 39		21 57	22 05				22 39		22 52		23 05		23 36	23 52			00 07			
Hampden Park 4 §	d				21 43							22 43				23 09		23 41				00 11			
Eastbourne 4	a	21 13			21 48		22 04	22 15				22 48		23 03		23 14		23 46	23 59			00 16			
	d	21 19					22 08	22 21						23 10		23 20						00 22			
Hampden Park 4 §	d	21 23						22 25								23 24									
Pevensey & Westham	d	21 28						22 30								23 29						00 29			
Pevensey Bay	d																								
Normans Bay	d																								
Cooden Beach	d	21 34						22 36								23 35						00 35			
Collington	d	21 37						22 39								23 38						00 38			
Bexhill 4	d	21 39					22 23	22 41						23 24		23 40						00 40			
St Leonards Warrior Sq 4	d	21 45					22 30	22 47						23 31		23 46						00 47			
Hastings 4	a	21 49					22 33	22 51						23 34		23 50						00 50			
	d	21 51																							
Ore	d	21a54																							
Three Oaks	d																								
Doleham	d																								
Winchelsea	d																								
Rye	a																								
	d																								
Appledore (Kent)	d																								
Ham Street	d																								
Ashford International	a																								
London Bridge 4 ⊖	a																								
London Cannon Street 4 ⊖	a																								
London Waterloo (East) 4 ⊖	a																								
London Charing Cross 4 ⊖	a																								

For general notes see front of timetable
For details of catering facilities see Directory of Train Operators

§ For additional trains between Hampden Park and Eastbourne see Hastings to London pages

b Change at East Croydon and Brighton
c Change at Haywards Heath and Brighton

Table 189

Sundays

until 6 September

London, Haywards Heath and Brighton → Lewes, Seaford, Eastbourne, Hastings and Ashford

Network Diagram - see first page of Table 184

		SN	SN	SN	SN	SN	SN	SN	SN	SN	SN	SN	SN	SN	SN	SN	SN	SN	SN		SN	SN	SN	SN	SN
		1	1	1	1	1	1	1	1	1	1	1	1	1	1	1	1	1	1		1	1	1	1	1
																								A	
London Victoria 15 ⊖	d		22p47		00 05	04 00			05 02	05 47	05 47					06 32	07b02		07b32			08b02		08 47	
Clapham Junction 10	d		22p53		00 11	04 08			05 08	05 53	05 53					06 38	07b08		07b38			08b08		08 53	
London Bridge 4 ⊖	d				23 53												07 11		07 41			08 11		08 41	
East Croydon	d		23p03		00 25	04 22			05 23	06 06	06 06					06 52	07 25		07 55			08 25		09 03	
Gatwick Airport 10	d		23p19		00 44	04 47			05 46	06 58	06 32					07 19	07 42		08 12			08 42		09 19	
Haywards Heath 3	d		23p34		01 06				06 00	07 12	06 47					07 36	07 56		08 26			08 56		09 30	
Wivelsfield 4	d		23p38								06 51					07 40			08 25					09 34	
Plumpton	d		23p44																					09 40	
Cooksbridge	d																								
Brighton 10	d	23p34				06 20			07 09		07 15			07 43	07 49	08 09	08 20	08 43	08 49		09 09	09 20	09 29		
London Road (Brighton)	d	23p37							07 12		07 18			07 46	07 52	08 12		08 46	08 52		09 12		09 32		
Moulsecoomb	d	23p39							07 14		07 20			07 48	07 54	08 14		08 48	08 54		09 14		09 34		
Falmer	d	23p43							07 18		07 24			07 52	07 58	08 18		08 52	08 58		09 18		09 38		
Lewes 4	a	23p49	23p51	←	01 20	06 31			07 24	07 27	07 31		←	07 58	08 04	08 24	08 31	08 58	09 04		09 24	09 31	09 44	09 48	←
	d	23p56	23p53	23p56	01 20	06 31			07 25	07 37	07 32		07 37	07 59	08 05	08 25	08 32	08 59	09 05		09 25	09 32	09 52	09 48	09 52
Southease	d	→								→					08 11				09 11				→		09 58
Newhaven Town ⛴	d			00 04		06 40					07 40				08 15	08 33			09 15		09 33				10 02
Newhaven Harbour	d			00 06		06 41					07 42				08 17	08 35			09 17		09 35				10 04
Bishopstone	d			00 09							07 45				08 20	08 38			09 20		09 38				10 07
Seaford	a			00 12		06 46					07 48				08 23	08 41			09 23		09 41				10 10
Glynde	d								07 30								08 37					09 37			
Berwick	d		00 02						07 36								08 43					09 43			
Polegate	d		00 07		01s32				07 41				07 49	08 11			08 49	09 11				09 49		10 01	
Hampden Park 4 §	d		00 11		01s36				07 45				07 53				08 53					09 53			
Eastbourne 4	a		00 16		01 41				07 50				08 01	08 19			08 58	09 19				09 58		10 08	
	d		00 22					07 26				07 58		08 26			09 02	09 26				10 02		10 15	
Hampden Park 4 §	d							07 30						08 30				09 30						10 19	
Pevensey & Westham	d		00 29					07 35						08 35				09 35						10 24	
Pevensey Bay	d																								
Normans Bay	d																								
Cooden Beach	d		00 35					07 41						08 41				09 41						10 30	
Collington	d		00 38					07 44						08 44				09 44						10 33	
Bexhill 4	d		00 40					07 46				08 11		08 46			09 16	09 46				10 16		10 35	
St Leonards Warrior Sq 4	d		00 47					07 53				08 18		08 53			09 23	09 53				10 23		10 42	
Hastings 4	a		00 50					07 56				08 22		08 56			09 26	09 56				10 26		10 45	
	d						07 22	07 57				08 22		08 57			09 27	09 57				10 27		10 46	
Ore	d						07 24	08a00						09a00				10a00						10a49	
Three Oaks	d						07 30																		
Doleham	d						07 33																		
Winchelsea	d						07 39																		
Rye	a						07 43					08 39					09 44					10 44			
	d						07 43					08 41					09 46					10 46			
Appledore (Kent)	d						07 52					08 50					09 55					10 55			
Ham Street	d						07 57					08 55					10 00					11 00			
Ashford International	a						08 06					09 03					10 08					11 08			
London Bridge 4 ⊖	a						09 39					10 39					11 39					12 39			
London Cannon Street 4 ⊖	a																								
London Waterloo (East) 4 ⊖	a						09 44					10 44					11 44					12 44			
London Charing Cross 4 ⊖	a						09 48					10 48					11 48					12 48			

For general notes see front of timetable
For details of catering facilities see Directory of Train Operators

§ For additional trains between Hampden Park and Eastbourne see Hastings to London pages

A ⌶ to Lewes

b Change at East Croydon and Brighton

Table 189

Sundays
until 6 September

London, Haywards Heath and Brighton → Lewes, Seaford, Eastbourne, Hastings and Ashford

Network Diagram - see first page of Table 184

	SN 1	SN 1	SN 1	SN 1	SN 1	SN 1	SN 1	SN 1	SN 1	SN 1	SN 1	SN 1	SN 1	SN 1	SN 1		SN 1	SN 1	SN 1	SN 1	SN 1	SN 1	SN 1	SN 1
				A					A					A						A				
London Victoria 15 ⊖ d	09 06			09 47		10 06			10 47		11 06			11 47			12 06			12 47		13 06		
Clapham Junction 10 d	09 12			09 53		10 12			10 53		11 12			11 53			12 12			12 53		13 12		
London Bridge 4 ⊖ d	08b44	09 11		09 41		09b44	10 11		10 41		10b44	11 11		11 41			11b44	12 11		12 41		12b44	13 11	
East Croydon d	09 22	09 25		10 03		10 22	10 25		11 03		11 22	11 25		12 03			12 22	12 24		13 03		13 22	13 25	
Gatwick Airport 10 ✈ d	09 38	09 42		10 19		10 38	10 42		11 19		11 38	11 42		12 19			12 38	12 42		13 19		13 38	13 42	
Haywards Heath 3 d	09 26	09 56		10 30		10 26	10 56		11 30		11 26	11 56		12 30			12 26	12 56		13 30		13 26	13 56	
Wivelsfield 4 d	09 25			10 34		10 25			11 34		11 25			12 34			12 25			13 34		13 25		
Plumpton d				10 40					11 40					12 40										
Cooksbridge d																								
Brighton 10 d	10 09	10 20	10 29			11 09	11 20	11 29			12 09	12 20	12 29				13 09	13 20	13 29			14 09	14 20	14 29
London Road (Brighton) d	10 12		10 32			11 12		11 32			12 12		12 32				13 12		13 32			14 12		14 32
Moulsecoomb d	10 14		10 34			11 14		11 34			12 14		12 34				13 14		13 34			14 14		14 34
Falmer d	10 18		10 38			11 18		11 38			12 18		12 38				13 18		13 38			14 18		14 38
Lewes 4 a	10 24	10 31	10 44	10 48	←	11 24	11 31	11 44	11 48	←	12 24	12 31	12 44	12 48	←		13 24	13 31	13 44	13 48	←	14 24	14 31	14 44
d	10 25	10 32	10 52	10 48	10 52	11 25	11 32	11 52	11 48	11 52	12 25	12 32	12 52	12 48	12 52		13 25	13 32	13 52	13 48	13 52	14 25	14 32	14 52
Southease d			→		10 58			→		11 58			→		12 58				→		13 58			→
Newhaven Town ⛴ d	10 33				11 02	11 33				12 02	12 33				13 02		13 33				14 02	14 33		
Newhaven Harbour d	10 35				11 04	11 35				12 04	12 35				13 04		13 35				14 04	14 35		
Bishopstone d	10 38				11 07	11 38				12 07	12 38				13 07		13 38				14 07	14 38		
Seaford a	10 41				11 10	11 41				12 10	12 41				13 10		13 41				14 10	14 41		
Glynde d		10 37					11 37					12 37						13 37					14 37	
Berwick d		10 43					11 43					12 43						13 43					14 43	
Polegate d		10 49		11 01			11 49		12 01			12 49		13 01				13 49		14 01			14 49	
Hampden Park 4 § d		10 53					11 53					12 53						13 53					14 53	
Eastbourne 4 a		10 58		11 08			11 58		12 08			12 58		13 08				13 58		14 08			14 58	
d		11 02		11 15			12 02		12 15			13 02		13 15				14 02		14 15			15 02	
Hampden Park 4 § d				11 19					12 19					13 19						14 19				
Pevensey & Westham d				11 24					12 24					13 24						14 24				
Pevensey Bay d																								
Normans Bay d																								
Cooden Beach d				11 30					12 30					13 30						14 30				
Collington d				11 33					12 33					13 33						14 33				
Bexhill 4 d		11 16		11 35			12 16		12 35			13 16		13 35				14 16		14 35			15 16	
St Leonards Warrior Sq 4 d		11 23		11 42			12 23		12 42			13 23		13 42				14 23		14 42			15 23	
Hastings 4 a		11 26		11 45			12 26		12 45			13 26		13 45				14 26		14 45			15 26	
d		11 27		11 46			12 27		12 46			13 27		13 46				14 27		14 46			15 27	
Ore d				11a49					12a49					13a49						14a49				
Three Oaks d																								
Doleham d																								
Winchelsea d																								
Rye a		11 44					12 44					13 44						14 44					15 44	
d		11 46					12 46					13 46						14 46					15 46	
Appledore (Kent) d		11 55					12 55					13 55						14 55					15 55	
Ham Street d		12 00					13 00					14 00						15 00					16 00	
Ashford International a		12 08					13 08					14 08						15 08					16 08	
London Bridge 4 ⊖ a		13 39					14 39					15 39						16 39					17 39	
London Cannon Street 4 ⊖ a																								
London Waterloo (East) 4 ⊖ a		13 44					14 44					15 44						16 44					17 44	
London Charing Cross 4 ⊖ a		13 48					14 48					15 48						16 48					17 48	

For general notes see front of timetable
For details of catering facilities see Directory of Train Operators

§ For additional trains between Hampden Park and Eastbourne see Hastings to London pages

A Trolley service to Lewes
b Change at East Croydon and Brighton

Table 189

Sundays

until 6 September

London, Haywards Heath and Brighton → Lewes, Seaford, Eastbourne, Hastings and Ashford

Network Diagram - see first page of Table 184

		SN 1 A ⊼	SN 1	SN 1	SN 1	SN 1	SN 1 A ⊼	SN 1	SN 1	SN 1	SN 1	SN 1 A ⊼	SN 1		SN 1	SN 1	SN 1	SN 1 A ⊼	SN 1	SN 1	SN 1	SN 1	SN 1 A ⊼	SN 1	SN 1
London Victoria [15]	⊖ d	13 47		14 06			14 47		15 06			15 47			16 06			16 47		17 06			17 47		18 06
Clapham Junction [10]	d	13 53		14 12			14 53		15 12			15 53			16 12			16 53		17 12			17 53		18 12
London Bridge [4]	⊖ d	13 41		13b44	14 11		14 41		14b44	15 11		15 41			15b44	16 11		16 41		16b44	17 11		17 41		17b44
East Croydon	🚊 d	14 03		14 22	14 25		15 03		15 22	15 25		16 03			16 22	16 25		17 03		17 22	17 25		18 03		18 22
Gatwick Airport [10]	✈ d	14 19		14 38	14 42		15 19		15 38	15 42		16 19			16 38	16 42		17 19		17 38	17 42		18 19		18 38
Haywards Heath [3]	d	14 30		14 26	14 56		15 30		15 26	15 56		16 30			16 26	16 56		17 30		17 26	17 56		18 30		18 26
Wivelsfield [4]	d	14 34		14 25			15 34		15 25			16 34			16 25			17 34		17 25			18 34		18 25
Plumpton	d											16 40						17 40					18 40		
Cooksbridge	d																								
Brighton [10]	d			15 09	15 20	15 29			16 09	16 20	16 29				17 09	17 20	17 29			18 09	18 20	18 29			19 09
London Road (Brighton)	d			15 12		15 32			16 12		16 32				17 12		17 32			18 12		18 32			19 12
Moulsecoomb	d			15 14		15 34			16 14		16 34				17 14		17 34			18 14		18 34			19 14
Falmer	d			15 18		15 38			16 18		16 38				17 18		17 38			18 18		18 38			19 18
Lewes [4]	a	14 48	←	15 24	15 31	15 44	15 48	←	16 24	16 31	16 44	16 48	←		17 24	17 31	17 44	17 48	←	18 24	18 31	18 44	18 48	←	19 24
	d	14 48	14 52	15 25	15 32	15 52	15 48	15 52	16 25	16 32	16 52	16 48	16 52		17 25	17 32	17 52	17 48	17 52	18 25	18 32	18 52	18 48	18 52	19 25
Southease	d		14 58			↪		15 58			↪		16 58				↪		17 58			↪		18 58	
Newhaven Town	⛴ d		15 02	15 33				16 02	16 33				17 02		17 33				18 02	18 33				19 02	19 33
Newhaven Harbour	d		15 04	15 35				16 04	16 35				17 04		17 35				18 04	18 35				19 04	19 35
Bishopstone	d		15 07	15 38				16 07	16 38				17 07		17 38				18 07	18 38				19 07	19 38
Seaford	a		15 10	15 41				16 10	16 41				17 10		17 41				18 10	18 41				19 10	19 41
Glynde	d				15 37					16 37						17 37					18 37				
Berwick	d				15 43					16 43						17 43					18 43				
Polegate	d	15 01			15 49		16 01			16 49		17 01				17 49		18 01			18 49		19 01		
Hampden Park [4] §	d				15 53					16 53						17 53					18 53				
Eastbourne [4]	a	15 08			15 58		16 08			16 58		17 08				17 58		18 08			18 58		19 08		
	d	15 15			16 02		16 15			17 02		17 15				18 02		18 15			19 02		19 15		
Hampden Park [4] §	d	15 19					16 19					17 19						18 19					19 19		
Pevensey & Westham	d	15 24					16 24					17 24						18 24					19 24		
Pevensey Bay	d																								
Normans Bay	d																								
Cooden Beach	d	15 30					16 30					17 30						18 30					19 30		
Collington	d	15 33					16 33					17 33						18 33					19 33		
Bexhill [4]	d	15 35			16 16		16 35			17 16		17 35				18 16		18 35			19 16		19 35		
St Leonards Warrior Sq [4]	d	15 42			16 23		16 42			17 23		17 42				18 23		18 42			19 23		19 42		
Hastings [4]	a	15 45			16 26		16 45			17 26		17 45				18 26		18 45			19 26		19 45		
	d	15 46			16 27		16 46			17 27		17 46				18 27		18 46			19 27		19 46		
Ore	d	15a49					16a49					17a49						18a49					19a49		
Three Oaks	d																								
Doleham	d																								
Winchelsea	d																								
Rye	a				16 44					17 44						18 44					19 44				
	d				16 46					17 46						18 46					19 46				
Appledore (Kent)	d				16 55					17 55						18 55					19 55				
Ham Street	d				17 00					18 00						19 00					20 00				
Ashford International	a				17 08					18 08						19 08					20 08				
London Bridge [4]	⊖ a				18 39					19 39						20 39					21 40				
London Cannon Street [4]	⊖ a																								
London Waterloo (East) [4]	⊖ a				18 44					19 44						20 44					21 44				
London Charing Cross [4]	⊖ a				18 48					19 48						20 48					21 48				

For general notes see front of timetable
For details of catering facilities see Directory of Train Operators

§ For additional trains between Hampden Park and Eastbourne see Hastings to London pages

A ⊼ to Lewes

b Change at East Croydon and Brighton

Sundays

until 6 September

London, Haywards Heath and Brighton → Lewes, Seaford, Eastbourne, Hastings and Ashford

Network Diagram - see first page of Table 184

		SN	SN	SN	SN	SN	SN	SN	SN	SN	SN	SN	SN	SN	SN	SN	SN	SN	SN	SN	SN	SN	SN		
		1	1	1	1	1	1	1	1	1	1	1	1	1	1	1	1	1	1	1	1	1	1		
				A 🚌					A 🚌																
London Victoria 15 ⊖	d			18 47		19 06			19 47		20 06			20 47		21 06		21 47	21 21	21b32	22b02	22 47	22 21		
Clapham Junction 10	d			18 53		19 12			19 53		20 12			20 53		21 12		21 53	21 27	21b38	22b08	22 53	22 27		
London Bridge 4 ⊖	d	18 11		18 41		18b44	19 11		19 41		19b44	20 11		20 41		20b44	21 11	21 41		21 41	22 11	22 41			
East Croydon	d	18 25		19 03		19 22	19 25		20 03		20 22	20 24		21 03		21 22	21 25	22 03	21 38	21 55	22 24	23 03	22 38		
Gatwick Airport 10 ✈	d	18 42		19 19		19 38	19 42		20 19		20 38	20 42		21 19		21 38	21 42	22 19	21 58	22 12	22 42	23 19	22 58		
Haywards Heath 3	d	18 56		19 30		19 26	19 56		20 30		20 26	20 56		21 30		21 26	21 56	22 30	22 15	22 26	22 56	23 30	23 15		
Wivelsfield 4	d			19 34		19 25			20 34		20 25			21 34		21 25		22 34	22 19			23 34	23 19		
Plumpton	d			19 40					20 40					21 40				22 40				23 40			
Cooksbridge	d																								
Brighton 10	d	19 20	19 29			20 09	20 20	20 29			21 09	21 20	21 29			22 09	22 20		22 39	23 09	23 20		23 39		
London Road (Brighton)	d		19 32			20 12		20 32			21 12		21 32			22 12			22 42	23 12			23 42		
Moulsecoomb	d		19 34			20 14		20 34			21 14		21 34			22 14			22 44	23 14			23 44		
Falmer	d		19 38			20 18		20 38			21 18		21 38			22 18			22 48	23 18			23 48		
Lewes 4	a	19 31	19 44	19 48	←	20 24	20 31	20 44	20 48	←	21 24	21 31	21 44	21 48	←	22 24	22 31	22 48	22 54	23 24	23 31	23 48	23 54		
	d	19 32	19 52	19 48	19 52	20 25	20 32	20 52	20 48	20 52	21 25	21 32	21 52	21 48	21 52	22 25	22 32	22 59	23 03		23 32	23 59			
			→					→					→												
Southease	d				19 58																				
Newhaven Town ⛴	d				20 02	20 33				21 00	21 33				22 00	22 33			23 11						
Newhaven Harbour	d				20 04	20 35				21 04	21 35				22 02	22 35			23 13						
Bishopstone	d				20 07	20 38				21 07	21 38				22 05	22 38			23 16						
Seaford	a				20 10	20 41				21 10	21 41				22 08	22 41			23 19						
Glynde	d	19 37					20 37					21 37					22 37				23 37				
Berwick	d	19 43					20 43					21 43					22 43				23 43				
Polegate	d	19 49		20 01			20 49		21 01			21 49		22 01			22 49	23 11			23 49	00 11			
Hampden Park 4 §	d	19 53					20 53					21 53					22 53				23 53	00 15			
Eastbourne 4	a	19 58		20 08			20 58		21 08			21 58		22 08			22 58	23 19			23 58	00 20			
	d	20 02		20 15			21 02		21 15			22 02		22 15				23 26							
Hampden Park 4 §	d			20 19					21 19					22 19				23 30							
Pevensey & Westham	d			20 24					21 24					22 24				23 35							
Pevensey Bay	d																								
Normans Bay	d																								
Cooden Beach	d			20 30					21 30					22 30				23 41							
Collington	d			20 33					21 33					22 33				23 44							
Bexhill 4	d	20 16		20 35			21 16		21 35			22 16		22 35				23 46							
St Leonards Warrior Sq 4	d	20 23		20 42			21 23		21 42			22 23		22 42				23 53							
Hastings 4	a	20 26		20 45			21 26		21 45			22 26		22 45				23 56							
	d	20 27		20 46			21 27		21 46																
Ore	d			20a49					21a49																
Three Oaks	d																								
Doleham	d																								
Winchelsea	d																								
Rye	a	20 44					21 44																		
	d	20 46					21 46																		
Appledore (Kent)	d	20 55					21 55																		
Ham Street	d	21 00					22 00																		
Ashford International	a	21 08					22 08																		
London Bridge 4 ⊖	a	22 40																							
London Cannon Street 4 ⊖	a																								
London Waterloo (East) 4 ⊖	a	22 44																							
London Charing Cross 4 ⊖	a	22 48																							

For general notes see front of timetable
For details of catering facilities see Directory of Train Operators

§ For additional trains between Hampden Park and Eastbourne see Hastings to London pages

A 🚌 to Lewes
b Change at East Croydon and Brighton

Table 189

London, Haywards Heath and Brighton → Lewes, Seaford, Eastbourne, Hastings and Ashford

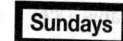

Sundays

from 13 September

Network Diagram - see first page of Table 184

		SN 1	SN 1	SN 1	SN 1	SN 1	SN 1	SN 1	SN 1	SN 1	SN 1	SN 1	SN 1	SN 1		SN 1	SN 1	SN 1	SN 1	SN 1	SN 1 A 🚌	SN 1	SN 1	SN 1	SN 1
London Victoria 15	⊖ d		22p47		00 05			05 02	05 47				06 32					07 32		07b34	08 47		09 02		
Clapham Junction 10	d		22p53		00 11			05 08	05 53				06 38					07 38		07b40	08 53		09 08		
London Bridge 4	⊖ d				23 53											07 11		07 41		08 11	08 41		08b44		09 11
East Croydon	d		23p03		00 25			05 23	06 06				06 52			07 27		07 57		08 27	09 08		09 22		09 27
Gatwick Airport 10	✈ d		23p19		00 44			05 46	06 32				07 19			07 50		08 20		08 50	09 29		09 40		09 50
Haywards Heath 3	d		23p34		01 06			06 00	06 47				07 36			08 03		08 33		09 03	09 41		09 33		10 03
Wivelsfield 4	d		23p38						06 51				07 40					08 32			09 45		09 32		
Plumpton	d		23p44																		09 51				
Cooksbridge	d																								
Brighton 10	d	23p34						07 09	07 15		07 43	07 49	08 09	08 20		08 43	08 49	09 09	09 20	09 39			10 09	10 20	10 39
London Road (Brighton)	d	23p37						07 12	07 18		07 46	07 52	08 12			08 46	08 52	09 12		09 42			10 12		10 42
Moulsecoomb	d	23p39						07 14	07 20		07 48	07 54	08 14			08 48	08 54	09 14		09 44			10 14		10 44
Falmer	d	23p43						07 18	07 24		07 52	07 58	08 18			08 52	08 58	09 18		09 48			10 18		10 48
Lewes 4	a	23p49	23p51	⟵	01 20			07 24	07 31		07 58	08 04	08 24	08 31		08 58	09 04	09 24	09 31	09 54	09 58	⟵	10 24	10 31	10 54
	d	23p56	23p53	23p56	01 20			07 25	07 32		07 59	08 05	08 25	08 32		08 59	09 05	09 25	09 32	10 03	09 59	10 03	10 25	10 32	11 03
Southease	d	⟶										08 11					09 11			⟶		10 09			⟶
Newhaven Town	⛴ d			00 04					07 40			08 15	08 33				09 15	09 33				10 13	10 33		
Newhaven Harbour	d			00 06					07 42			08 17	08 35				09 17	09 35				10 15	10 35		
Bishopstone	d			00 09					07 45			08 20	08 38				09 20	09 38				10 18	10 38		
Seaford	a			00 12					07 48			08 23	08 41				09 23	09 41				10 21	10 41		
Glynde	d							07 30						08 37					09 37					10 37	
Berwick	d		00 02					07 36						08 43					09 43					10 43	
Polegate	d		00 07		01s32			07 41			08 11			08 49		09 11			09 49		10 11			10 49	
Hampden Park 4 §	d		00 11		01s36			07 45						08 53					09 53					10 53	
Eastbourne 4	a		00 16		01 41			07 50			08 19			08 58		09 19			09 58		10 19			10 58	
	d		00 22				07 26			07 58	08 26			09 02		09 26			10 02		10 26			11 02	
Hampden Park 4 §	d						07 30				08 30					09 30					10 30				
Pevensey & Westham	d		00 29				07 35				08 35					09 35					10 35				
Pevensey Bay	d																								
Normans Bay	d																								
Cooden Beach	d		00 35				07 41				08 41					09 41					10 41				
Collington	d		00 38				07 44				08 44					09 44					10 44				
Bexhill 4	d		00 40				07 46			08 11	08 46			09 16		09 46			10 16		10 46			11 16	
St Leonards Warrior Sq 4	d		00 47				07 53			08 18	08 53			09 23		09 53			10 23		10 53			11 23	
Hastings 4	a		00 50				07 56			08 22	08 56			09 26		09 56			10 26		10 56			11 26	
	d					07 22	07 57			08 22	08 57			09 27		09 57			10 27		10 57			11 27	
Ore	d					07 24	08a00				09a00					10a00					11a00				
Three Oaks	d					07 30																			
Doleham	d					07 33																			
Winchelsea	d					07 39																			
Rye	a					07 43				08 39				09 44					10 44					11 44	
	d					07 43				08 41				09 46					10 46					11 46	
Appledore (Kent)	d					07 52				08 50				09 55					10 55					11 55	
Ham Street	d					07 57				08 55				10 00					11 00					12 00	
Ashford International	a					08 06				09 03				10 08					11 08					12 08	
London Bridge 4	⊖ a					09 39				10 39				11 39					12 39					13 39	
London Cannon Street 4	⊖ a																								
London Waterloo (East) 4	⊖ a					09 44				10 44				11 44					12 44					13 44	
London Charing Cross 4	⊖ a					09 48				10 48				11 48					12 48					13 48	

For general notes see front of timetable
For details of catering facilities see Directory of Train Operators

§ For additional trains between Hampden Park and Eastbourne see Hastings to London pages

A 🚌 to Lewes
b Change at East Croydon and Brighton

Table 189

Sundays

from 13 September

London, Haywards Heath and Brighton → Lewes, Seaford, Eastbourne, Hastings and Ashford

Network Diagram - see first page of Table 184

		SN 1 A ⊼	SN 1	SN 1	SN 1	SN 1	SN 1 A ⊼	SN 1	SN 1	SN 1	SN 1	SN 1 A ⊼	SN 1	SN 1	SN 1	SN 1	SN 1 A ⊼	SN 1	SN 1	SN 1	SN 1	SN 1 A ⊼	SN 1
London Victoria 15 ⊖	d	09 47		10 02			10 47		11 02			11 47		12 02			12 47		13 02			13 47	
Clapham Junction 10	d	09 53		10 08			10 53		11 08			11 53		12 08			12 53		13 08			13 53	
London Bridge 4 ⊖	d	09 41		09b44		10 11	10 41		10b44		11 11	11 41		11b44		12 11	12 41		12b44		13 11	13 41	
East Croydon	d	10 08		10 22		10 27	11 08		11 22		11 28	12 08		12 22		12 27	13 08		13 22		13 28	14 08	
Gatwick Airport 10	d	10 29		10 40		10 50	11 29		11 40		11 50	12 29		12 40		12 50	13 29		13 40		13 50	14 29	
Haywards Heath 3	d	10 41		10 33		11 03	11 41		11 33		12 03	12 41		12 33		13 03	13 41		13 33		14 03	14 41	
Wivelsfield 4	d	10 45		10 32			11 45		11 32			12 45		12 32			13 45		13 32			14 45	
Plumpton	d	10 51					11 51					12 51											
Cooksbridge	d																						
Brighton 10	d			11 09	11 20	11 39			12 09	12 20	12 39			13 09	13 20	13 39			14 09	14 20	14 39		
London Road (Brighton)	d			11 12		11 42			12 12		12 42			13 12		13 42			14 12		14 42		
Moulsecoomb	d			11 14		11 44			12 14		12 44			13 14		13 44			14 14		14 44		
Falmer	d			11 18		11 48			12 18		12 48			13 18		13 48			14 18		14 48		
Lewes 4	a	10 58	←	11 24	11 31	11 54	11 58	←	12 24	12 31	12 54	12 58	←	13 24	13 31	13 54	13 58	←	14 24	14 31	14 54	14 58	←
	d	10 59	11 03	11 25	11 32	12 03	11 59	12 03	12 25	12 32	13 03	12 59	13 03	13 25	13 32	14 03	13 59	14 03	14 25	14 32	15 03	14 59	15 03
Southease	d		11 09			→		12 09			→		13 09			→		14 09			→		15 09
Newhaven Town	d		11 13	11 33				12 13	12 33				13 13	13 33				14 13	14 33				15 13
Newhaven Harbour	d		11 15	11 35				12 15	12 35				13 15	13 35				14 15	14 35				15 15
Bishopstone	d		11 18	11 38				12 18	12 38				13 18	13 38				14 18	14 38				15 18
Seaford	a		11 21	11 41				12 21	12 41				13 21	13 41				14 21	14 41				15 21
Glynde	d				11 37					12 37					13 37					14 37			
Berwick	d				11 43					12 43					13 43					14 43			
Polegate	d	11 11			11 49		12 11			12 49		13 11			13 49		14 11			14 49		15 11	
Hampden Park 4 §	d				11 53					12 53					13 53					14 53			
Eastbourne 4	a	11 19			11 58		12 19			12 58		13 19			13 58		14 19			14 58		15 19	
	d	11 26			12 02		12 26			13 02		13 26			14 02		14 26			15 02		15 26	
Hampden Park 4 §	d	11 30					12 30					13 30					14 30					15 30	
Pevensey & Westham	d	11 35					12 35					13 35					14 35					15 35	
Pevensey Bay	d																						
Normans Bay	d																						
Cooden Beach	d	11 41					12 41					13 41					14 41					15 41	
Collington	d	11 44					12 44					13 44					14 44					15 44	
Bexhill 4	d	11 46			12 16		12 46			13 16		13 46			14 16		14 46			15 16		15 46	
St Leonards Warrior Sq 4	d	11 53			12 23		12 53			13 23		13 53			14 23		14 53			15 23		15 53	
Hastings 4	a	11 56			12 26		12 56			13 26		13 56			14 26		14 56			15 26		15 56	
	d	11 57			12 27		12 57			13 27		13 57			14 27		14 57			15 27		15 57	
Ore	d	12a00					13a00					14a00					15a00					16a00	
Three Oaks	d																						
Doleham	d																						
Winchelsea	d																						
Rye	a				12 44					13 44					14 44					15 44			
	d				12 46					13 46					14 46					15 46			
Appledore (Kent)	d				12 55					13 55					14 55					15 55			
Ham Street	d				13 00					14 00					15 00					16 00			
Ashford International	a				13 08					14 08					15 08					16 08			
London Bridge 4 ⊖	a				14 39					15 39					16 39					17 39			
London Cannon Street 4 ⊖	a																						
London Waterloo (East) 4 ⊖	a				14 44					15 44					16 44					17 44			
London Charing Cross 4 ⊖	a				14 48					15 48					16 48					17 48			

For general notes see front of timetable
For details of catering facilities see Directory of Train Operators

§ For additional trains between Hampden Park and Eastbourne see Hastings to London pages

A ⊼ to Lewes
b Change at East Croydon and Brighton

Table 189

Sundays

from 13 September

London, Haywards Heath and Brighton → Lewes, Seaford, Eastbourne, Hastings and Ashford

Network Diagram - see first page of Table 184

		SN 1	SN 1	SN 1	SN 1	SN 1	SN 1	SN 1	SN 1	SN 1	SN 1	SN 1		SN 1	SN 1	SN 1	SN 1	SN 1	SN 1	SN 1	SN 1	SN 1	SN 1	SN 1	SN 1
					A ⌶					A ⌶						A ⌶					A ⌶				
London Victoria 15	⊖ d	14 02			14 47		15 02			15 47		16 02				16 47		17 02			17 47		18 02		
Clapham Junction 10	d	14 08			14 53		15 08			15 53		16 08				16 53		17 08			17 53		18 08		
London Bridge 4	⊖ d	13b44		14 11	14 41		14b44		15 11	15 41		15b44			16 11	16 41		16b44		17 11	17 41		17b44		18 11
East Croydon	d	14 22		14 28	15 08		15 22		15 28	16 08		16 22			16 28	17 08		17 22		17 28	18 08		18 22		18 28
Gatwick Airport 10	d	14 40		14 50	15 29		15 40		15 50	16 29		16 40			16 50	17 29		17 40		17 50	18 29		18 40		18 50
Haywards Heath 3	d	14 33		15 03	15 41		15 33		16 03	16 41		16 33			17 03	17 41		17 33		18 03	18 41		18 33		19 03
Wivelsfield 4	d	14 32			15 45		15 32			16 45		16 32				17 45		17 32			18 45		18 32		
Plumpton	d									16 51						17 51					18 51				
Cooksbridge	d																								
Brighton 10	d	15 09	15 20	15 39			16 09	16 20	16 39			17 09		17 20	17 39			18 09	18 20	18 39			19 09	19 20	19 39
London Road (Brighton)	d	15 12		15 42			16 12		16 42			17 12			17 42			18 12		18 42			19 12		19 42
Moulsecoomb	d	15 14		15 44			16 14		16 44			17 14			17 44			18 14		18 44			19 14		19 44
Falmer	d	15 18		15 48			16 18		16 48			17 18			17 48			18 18		18 48			19 18		19 48
Lewes 4	a	15 24	15 31	15 54	15 58	←	16 24	16 31	16 54	16 58	←	17 24		17 31	17 54	17 58	←	18 24	18 31	18 54	18 58	←	19 24	19 31	19 54
	d	15 25	15 32	16 03	15 59	16 03	16 25	16 32	17 03	16 59	17 03	17 25		17 32	18 03	17 59	18 03	18 25	18 32	19 03	18 59	19 03	19 25	19 32	20 03
Southease	d			→		16 09			→		17 09				→		18 09			→		19 09			→
Newhaven Town	d	15 33				16 13	16 33				17 13	17 33					18 13	18 33				19 13	19 33		
Newhaven Harbour	d	15 35				16 15	16 35				17 15	17 35					18 15	18 35				19 15	19 35		
Bishopstone	d	15 38				16 18	16 38				17 18	17 38					18 18	18 38				19 18	19 38		
Seaford	a	15 41				16 21	16 41				17 21	17 41					18 21	18 41				19 21	19 41		
Glynde	d		15 37					16 37						17 37					18 37					19 37	
Berwick	d		15 43					16 43						17 43					18 43					19 43	
Polegate	d		15 49		16 11			16 49		17 11				17 49		18 11			18 49		19 11			19 49	
Hampden Park 4 §	d		15 53					16 53						17 53					18 53					19 53	
Eastbourne 4	a		15 58		16 19			16 58		17 19				17 58		18 19			18 58		19 19			19 58	
	d		16 02		16 26			17 02		17 26				18 02		18 26			19 02		19 26			20 02	
Hampden Park 4 §	d				16 30					17 30						18 30					19 30				
Pevensey & Westham	d				16 35					17 35						18 35					19 35				
Pevensey Bay	d																								
Normans Bay	d																								
Cooden Beach	d				16 41					17 41						18 41					19 41				
Collington	d				16 44					17 44						18 44					19 44				
Bexhill 4	d		16 16		16 46			17 16		17 46				18 16		18 46			19 16		19 46			20 16	
St Leonards Warrior Sq 4	d		16 23		16 53			17 23		17 53				18 23		18 53			19 23		19 53			20 23	
Hastings 4	a		16 26		16 56			17 26		17 56				18 26		18 56			19 26		19 56			20 26	
	d		16 27		16 57			17 27		17 57				18 27		18 57			19 27		19 57			20 27	
Ore	d				17a00					18a00						19a00					20a00				
Three Oaks	d																								
Doleham	d																								
Winchelsea	d																								
Rye	a		16 44					17 44						18 44					19 44					20 44	
	d		16 46					17 46						18 46					19 46					20 46	
Appledore (Kent)	d		16 55					17 55						18 55					19 55					20 55	
Ham Street	d		17 00					18 00						19 00					20 00					21 00	
Ashford International	a		17 08					18 08						19 08					20 08					21 08	
London Bridge 4	⊖ a		18 39					19 39						20 39					21 40					22 40	
London Cannon Street 4	⊖ a																								
London Waterloo (East) 4	⊖ a		18 44					19 44						20 44					21 44					22 44	
London Charing Cross 4	⊖ a		18 48					19 48						20 48					21 48					22 48	

For general notes see front of timetable
For details of catering facilities see Directory of Train Operators

§ For additional trains between Hampden Park and Eastbourne see Hastings to London pages

A ⌶ to Lewes

b Change at East Croydon and Brighton

Sundays

from 13 September

London, Haywards Heath and Brighton → Lewes, Seaford, Eastbourne, Hastings and Ashford

Network Diagram - see first page of Table 184

	SN 1	SN 1	SN 1		SN 1	SN 1	SN 1	SN 1	SN 1	SN 1	SN 1	SN 1	SN 1	SN 1	SN 1	SN 1	SN 1	SN 1	SN 1	SN 1	SN 1	SN 1		
	A						A																	
London Victoria 15 ⊖ d	18 47		19 02				19 47		20 02			20 47		21 02			21 47		21 32		21b47	22 47		
Clapham Junction 10 d	18 53		19 08				19 53		20 08			20 53		21 08			21 53		21 38		21b53	22 53		
London Bridge 4 ⊖ d	18 41		18b44			19 11	19 41		19b44		20 11	20 41		20b44		21 11	21 41		21 41		22 11	22 41		
East Croydon d	19 08		19 22			19 28	20 08		20 22		20 27	21 08		21 22		21 28	22 08		21 57		22 27	23 08		
Gatwick Airport 10 d	19 29		19 40			19 50	20 29		20 40		20 50	21 29		21 40		21 50	22 29		22 20		22 50	23 29		
Haywards Heath 3 d	19 41		19 33			20 03	20 41		20 33		21 03	21 41		21 33		22 03	22 41		22 33		23 03	23 41		
Wivelsfield 4 d	19 45		19 32				20 45		20 32			21 45		21 32			22 45		22 32			23 45		
Plumpton d	19 51						20 51					21 51					22 51					23 51		
Cooksbridge d																								
Brighton 10 d			20 09		20 20	20 39			21 09	21 20	21 39			22 09	22 20	22 39			23 09	23 20	23 39			
London Road (Brighton) d			20 12			20 42			21 12		21 42			22 12		22 42			23 12		23 42			
Moulsecoomb d			20 14			20 44			21 14		21 44			22 14		22 44			23 14		23 44			
Falmer d			20 18			20 48			21 18		21 48			22 18		22 48			23 18		23 48			
Lewes 4 a	19 58	←	20 24		20 31	20 54	20 58	←	21 24	21 31	21 54	21 58	←	22 24	22 31	22 54	22 58	←	23 24	23 31	23 54	23 58		
Lewes 4 d	19 59	20 03	20 25		20 32	21 03	20 59	21 03	21 25	21 32	22 03	21 59	22 03	22 25	22 32	23 03	22 59	23 03		23 32		23 59		
						→					→					→								
Southease d		20 09																						
Newhaven Town d		20 13	20 33					21 11	21 33				22 11	22 33				23 11						
Newhaven Harbour d		20 15	20 35					21 13	21 35				22 13	22 35				23 13						
Bishopstone d		20 18	20 38					21 16	21 38				22 16	22 38				23 16						
Seaford a		20 21	20 41					21 19	21 41				22 19	22 41				23 19						
Glynde d					20 37					21 37					22 37					23 37				
Berwick d					20 43					21 43					22 43					23 43				
Polegate d	20 11				20 49		21 11			21 49		22 11			22 49		23 11			23 49		00 11		
Hampden Park 4 § d					20 53					21 53					22 53					23 53		00 15		
Eastbourne 4 a	20 19				20 58		21 19			21 58		22 19			22 58		23 19			23 58		00 20		
Eastbourne 4 d	20 26				21 02		21 26			22 02		22 26					23 26							
Hampden Park 4 § d	20 30						21 30					22 30					23 30							
Pevensey & Westham d	20 35						21 35					22 35					23 35							
Pevensey Bay d																								
Normans Bay d																								
Cooden Beach d	20 41						21 41					22 41					23 41							
Collington d	20 44						21 44					22 44					23 44							
Bexhill 4 d	20 46				21 16		21 46			22 16		22 46					23 46							
St Leonards Warrior Sq 4 d	20 53				21 23		21 53			22 23		22 57					23 53							
Hastings 4 a	20 56				21 26		21 56			22 26		23 00					23 56							
d	20 57				21 27		21 57																	
Ore d	21a00						22a00																	
Three Oaks d																								
Doleham d																								
Winchelsea d																								
Rye a					21 44																			
Rye d					21 46																			
Appledore (Kent) d					21 55																			
Ham Street d					22 00																			
Ashford International a					22 08																			
London Bridge 4 ⊖ a																								
London Cannon Street 4 ⊖ a																								
London Waterloo (East) 4 ⊖ a																								
London Charing Cross 4 ⊖ a																								

For general notes see front of timetable
For details of catering facilities see
Directory of Train Operators

§ For additional trains between Hampden Park and Eastbourne see Hastings to London pages

A to Lewes
b Change at East Croydon and Brighton

Table 189

Mondays to Fridays

Ashford, Hastings, Eastbourne, Seaford and Lewes → Brighton, Haywards Heath and London

Network Diagram - see first page of Table 184

Miles	Miles	Station		SN MX 1	SN 1	SN 1	SN 1	SN 1	SN 1	SN 1	SN 1	SN 1	SN 1	SN 1	SN 1	SN 1	SE 1 A	SE 1 B	SN 1	SN 1	SN 1 C	SN 1	SE 1 D
—	—	London Charing Cross 4	⊖ d																				
—	—	London Waterloo (East) 4	⊖ d																				
—	—	London Cannon Street 4	⊖ d																				
—	—	London Bridge 4	⊖ d																				
—	0	**Ashford International**	d																				
—	5½	Ham Street	d																				
—	8½	Appledore (Kent)	d																				
—	15¼	Rye	a																				
—	—		d																				
—	17¼	Winchelsea	d																				
—	21½	Doleham	d																				
—	22¾	Three Oaks	d																				
—	25½	Ore	d														06 07	06 10					06 35
—	26½	**Hastings 4**	a														06 10	06 13					06 38
0	—		d	23p13						05 07	05 36					06 03	06 11	06 14				06 19	06 39
¾	—	**St Leonards Warrior Sq 4**	d	23p16						05 10	05 39					06 06	06a14	06a17				06 22	06a42
4½	—	**Bexhill 4**	d	23p22						05 16	05 46					06 12						06 28	
5¼	—	Collington	d	23p24						05 18	05 48											06 30	
6¾	—	Cooden Beach	d	23p27						05 21	05 51											06 33	
8½	—	Normans Bay	d																				
10½	—	Pevensey Bay	d																				
11¼	—	Pevensey & Westham	d	23p33						05 27	05 57											06 39	
14¼	—	Hampden Park 4 §	d	23p38						05 32	06 02					06 24						06 44	
16¼	—	**Eastbourne 4**	a	23p43						05 37	06 07					06 30						06 49	
—	—		d	23p48		05 08		05 32		05 42					06 24	06 38			06 47			06 56	
18¼	—	Hampden Park 4 §	d	23p52		05 12		05 36		05 46					06 28				06 51			07 00	
20¼	—	Polegate	d	23p56		05 16		05 41		05 50					06 32	06 45			06 55			07 04	
24½	—	Berwick	d							05 55					06 37				07 00				
29	—	Glynde	d												06 43				07 06				
—	0	**Seaford**	d		05 09				05 45					06 30							06 56		
—	1	Bishopstone	d		05 11				05 47					06 32							06 58		
—	2½	Newhaven Harbour	d		05 14				05 50					06 35							07 01		
—	2¾	Newhaven Town ⛴	d		05 16				05 52					06 37							07 03		
—	5½	Southease	d																		07 07		
32	9	**Lewes 4**	a	00 08	05 25	05 28	←	05 53	06 01	06 04		←		06 46	06 49	06 58			07 11		07 15	07 18	
—	—		d	00 08	05 32	05 29	05 32	05 54	06 09	06 05		06 09	06 26	06 47	06 50	07 00			07 12	07 23	07 22		
36½	—	Falmer	d	00 15	→		05 39	06 01	→			06 16	06 33	06 54		07 07			07 19	07 30			
38¼	—	Moulsecoomb	d	00 18			05 42	06 05				06 19	06 36	06 57		07 11			07 22	07 33			
39¼	—	London Road (Brighton)	d	00 21			05 43	06 07				06 21	06 38	06 59		07 13			07 24	07 35			
40	—	**Brighton 10**	a	00 24			05 48	06 11				06 25	06 42	07 03		07 17			07 28	07 39			
—	11¾	Cooksbridge	d												06 55						07 27		
—	14½	Plumpton	d			05 37				06 13					07 00						07 32		
—	18¼	Wivelsfield 4	a				06 15	06 39				06 45	07 13		07 07	07 44			07 48		07 39		
—	21¼	**Haywards Heath 3**	a			05 46	06 19	06 34		06 22		06 51	07 06	07 34	07 13	07 45			07 53	08 05	07 43		
—	—	**Gatwick Airport 10** ✈	a			05 58	06 41	06 52		06 41		07 03	07b29	07 47	07 29	08 00			08b12	08 17	08 00		
—	—	East Croydon	a			06 14	06 58	07 15		06 58		07c27	07 42	08b08	07 47				08 23	08 38	08 14		
—	—	**London Bridge 4**	⊖ a			06 40	07 14	07e38		07 14			08e04		08 04				08 43	09e05	08 41		
—	—	Clapham Junction 10	a			06 25	07e19	07 24		07f19			07 54		08f02				08e40	08e53	08 23		
—	—	**London Victoria 15**	⊖ a			06 32	07e28	07 33		07f28			08 03		08f12				08e49	09e02	08 32		

For general notes see front of timetable
For details of catering facilities see Directory of Train Operators

§ For additional trains between Hampden Park and Eastbourne see London to Hastings pages

A From 12 October. To London Charing Cross
B Until 9 October. To London Charing Cross (Table 206)
C from Lewes
D From 12 October. To London Cannon Street
b Change at Brighton and Haywards Heath
c Change at Brighton and Gatwick Airport
e Change at Brighton and East Croydon
f Change at East Croydon

Ashford, Hastings, Eastbourne, Seaford and Lewes → Brighton, Haywards Heath and London

Network Diagram - see first page of Table 184

		SE 1 A		SN 1	SN 1	SN 1	SN 1 B	SN 1	SN 1		SN 1	SN 1	SN 1 B	SN 1	SN 1	SN 1 B	SN 1		SE 1 C	SE 1 D	SN 1	SN 1	SN 1	SN 1	SN 1 B
London Charing Cross 4	⊖ d																					05b30			
London Waterloo (East) 4	⊖ d																					05b33			
London Cannon Street 4	⊖ d																								
London Bridge 4	⊖ d																					05b38			
Ashford International	d								06 24		06 46											07 30	07 50		
Ham Street	d								06 33		06 55											07 39	07 59		
Appledore (Kent)	d								06 38		07 00											07 44	08 04		
Rye	a								06 47		07 09											07 53	08 13		
	d								06 48													07 54			
Winchelsea	d								06 51																
Doleham	d								06 58																
Three Oaks	d								07 01																
Ore	d	06 38							07 07										07 43	07 46					
Hastings 4	a	06 41							07 10										07 46	07 49		08 11			
	d	06 42					06 50		07 12				07 19				07 38		07 47	07 50		08 15			
St Leonards Warrior Sq 4	d	06a45					06 53		07 15				07 22				07 41		07a50	07a53		08 18			
Bexhill 4	d						07 00		07 22				07 31				07 47					08 25			
Collington	d						07 02						07 33				07 49								
Cooden Beach	d						07 05						07 36				07 52								
Normans Bay	d																07 55								
Pevensey Bay	d																07 59								
Pevensey & Westham	d						07 11						07 42				08 01								
Hampden Park 4 §	d						07 16						07 46				08 06								
Eastbourne 4	a						07 24		07 37				07 51				08 11					08 40			
	d				07 14		07 32		07 45				07 57	08 04			08 18					08 45			08 56
Hampden Park 4 §	d				07 18								08 01	08 08											09 00
Polegate	d				07 23		07 39		07 52				08 05	08 12			08 25					08 52			09 04
Berwick	d				07 29		07 44						08 11	08 18			08 30								
Glynde	d				07 33								08 16	08 23			08 36								
Seaford	d			07 16		07 33						07 58				08 21								08 57	
Bishopstone	d			07 18		07 35						08 00				08 23								08 59	
Newhaven Harbour	d			07 21		07 38						08 03				08 26								09 02	
Newhaven Town	⛴ d			07 23		07 40						08 05				08 28								09 04	
Southease	d			07 27		07 44						08 09				08 32									
Lewes 4	a			07 33	07 41	07 50	07 53		08 07			08 16	08 22	08 29		08 39	08 42					09 07		09 13	09 16
	d			07 34	07 42	07 51	07 54	07 58	08 07			08 17	08 23	08 30	08 46		08 47				08 58	09 07		09 14	09 17
Falmer	d			07 41		07 58		08 05				08 25		08 37	08 53						09 05			09 21	
Moulsecoomb	d			07 44		08 01		08 08				08 28		08 40	08 56						09 08			09 24	
London Road (Brighton)	d			07 46		08 03		08 10				08 30		08 42	08 58						09 10			09 27	
Brighton 10	a			07 50		08 07		08 14	08 20			08 35		08 46	09 02						09 14	09 20		09 30	
Cooksbridge	d				07 48		07 59						08 28												09 22
Plumpton	d				07 53		08 04						08 33												09 27
Wivelsfield 4	a			08 18		08 33	08 10						08 39		09 23		08 59							09 53	09 33
Haywards Heath 3	a			08 23	08 02	08 37	08 14		08 55			08 57	08 44	09 16	09 28		09 04							09 47	09 37
Gatwick Airport 10	✈ a			08 38	08 17	08 51	08 38					09 10	08 55	09 31	09 46		09 22							10 00	09 54
East Croydon	a			08 54	08 31	09 08	08 46					09 26	09 14	09 47			09 39				09 54			10 16	10 10
London Bridge 4	⊖ a			09c10	08 50	09e42	09 10					09e45	09 42	10 01							10e16			10 30	
Clapham Junction 10	a			09e10	08f47	09e23	08 56					09 35	09 23				09 48				10 04				10 20
London Victoria 15	⊖ a			09e19	08f57	09e32	09 05					09 44	09 32				09 58				10 11				10 27

For general notes see front of timetable
For details of catering facilities see Directory of Train Operators

§ For additional trains between Hampden Park and Eastbourne see London to Hastings pages

A Until 9 October. To London Cannon Street (Table 206)

B 🛒 from Lewes

C From 12 October. To London Charing Cross (Table 204)

D Until 9 October. To London Charing Cross (Table 206)

b Until 9 October only

c London Bridge

e Change at Brighton and East Croydon

f Change at East Croydon

Ashford, Hastings, Eastbourne, Seaford and Lewes → Brighton, Haywards Heath and London

Network Diagram - see first page of Table 184

	SN [1]		SN [1]	SN [1] A 🛒	SN [1]	SN [1]	SN [1]	SN [1] A 🛒		SN [1]	SN [1]	SN [1]	SN [1] A 🛒	SN [1]	SN [1]		SN [1]	SN [1] A 🛒	SN [1]	SN [1]	SN [1] A 🛒	SN [1]		SN [1]
London Charing Cross [4] ⊖ d						06b25					07b00				07b52									08b58
London Waterloo (East) [4] ⊖ d						06b28					07b03				07b55									09b01
London Cannon Street [4] ⊖ d						06c22					06c52				07c54									08c54
London Bridge [4] ⊖ d						06b33					07b08				08b02									09b08
Ashford International d						08 30					08 50				09 30									10 30
Ham Street d						08 39					08 59				09 39									10 39
Appledore (Kent) d						08 44					09 04				09 44									10 44
Rye a						08 53					09 13				09 53									10 53
d						08 55					09 14				09 54									10 54
Winchelsea d											09 17													
Doleham d											09 24													
Three Oaks d											09 27													
Ore d	08 21			08 45						09 21	09 33		09 47						10 21		10 50			
Hastings [4] a	08 24			08 48		09 12				09 24	09 36		09 50		10 11				10 24		10 53			11 11
d	08 25			08 52		09 13				09 25			09 52		10 12				10 25		10 55			11 12
St Leonards Warrior Sq [4] d	08 28			08 55		09 16				09 28			09 55		10 15				10 28		10 58			11 15
Bexhill [4] d	08 35			09 02		09 23				09 35			10 02		10 22				10 35		11 05			11 22
Collington d	08 37			09 04						09 37			10 04						10 37		11 07			
Cooden Beach d	08 40			09 07						09 40			10 07						10 40		11 10			
Normans Bay d	08 43									09 43									10 43					
Pevensey Bay d																								
Pevensey & Westham d	08 48			09 13						09 48			10 13						10 48		11 16			
Hampden Park [4] § d	08 52			09 17						09 52			10 17						10 52		11 20			
Eastbourne [4] a	08 57			09 23		09 38				09 57			10 22		10 37				10 57		11 25			11 37
d	09 03			09 29		09 45		09 56		10 03			10 28		10 45			10 58	11 03		11 31			11 45
Hampden Park [4] § d	09 07							10 00		10 07								11 02	11 07					
Polegate d	09 11			09 36		09 52		10 04		10 11			10 34		10 52			11 06	11 11		11 37			11 52
Berwick d	09 17							10 09		10 17									11 17					
Glynde d	09 22									10 22									11 22					
Seaford d			09 25				09 58					10 25					10 58			11 25				
Bishopstone d			09 27				10 00					10 27					11 00			11 27				
Newhaven Harbour d			09 30				10 03					10 30					11 03			11 30				
Newhaven Town ⛴ d			09 32				10 05					10 32					11 05			11 32				
Southease d			09 36									10 36								11 36				
Lewes [4] a	09 28		09 44	09 48		10 07	10 14	10 19		10 28		10 44	10 48		11 07		11 14	11 18	11 28	11 44	11 49			12 07
d	09 28		09 44	09 49	09 58	10 07	10 14	10 20		10 28		10 44	10 49	10 58	11 07		11 14	11 20	11 28	11 44	11 50	11 58		12 07
Falmer d	09 35		09 51		10 05		10 21			10 35		10 51		11 05			11 21		11 35	11 51		12 05		
Moulsecoomb d	09 38		09 54		10 08		10 24			10 38		10 54		11 08			11 24		11 38	11 54		12 08		
London Road (Brighton) d	09 40		09 57		10 10		10 27			10 40		10 57		11 10			11 27		11 40	11 57		12 10		
Brighton [10] a	09 44		10 00		10 14	10 20	10 30			10 44		11 00		11 14	11 20		11 30		11 44	12 00		12 14		12 20
Cooksbridge d				09 54									10 54											
Plumpton d				09 59				10 28										11 28						
Wivelsfield [4] a	*10 11*		*10 23*				*10 53*	10 35		*11 11*		*11 23*					*11 53*	11 34	*12 11*	*12 23*				
Haywards Heath [3] a	*10 15*		*10 18*	10 09			*10 47*	10 40		*11 15*		*11 18*	11 05				*11 47*	11 40	*12 15*	*12 18*	12 05			
Gatwick Airport [10] ✈ a			*10 30*	10 24			*11 00*	10 54				*11 30*	11 24				*12 00*	11 54		*12 30*	12 24			
East Croydon 🚊 a	*10 24*		*10 46*	10 40	*10 56*		*11 16*	11 10		*11 23*		*11 46*	11 40	*11 56*			*12 16*	12 10	*12 23*	*12 46*	12 40	*12 56*		
London Bridge [4] ⊖ a	*10e45*		*11 00*	*11 00*	*11e15*		*11 30*	*11 30*		*11e45*		*12 00*	*12 00*	*12e15*			*12 30*	*12 30*	*12e45*	*13 00*	*13 00*	*13e15*		
Clapham Junction [10] a	*10 33*		*11e02*	10 50	*11 05*			11 20		*11 33*		*12e02*	11 50	*12 05*				12 19	*12 33*	*13e02*	12 50	*13 05*		
London Victoria [15] ⊖ a	*10 40*		*11e09*	10 57	*11 12*			11 27		*11 40*		*12e09*	11 57	*12 12*				12 28	*12 40*	*13e09*	12 57	*13 12*		

For general notes see front of timetable
For details of catering facilities see Directory of Train Operators

§ For additional trains between Hampden Park and Eastbourne see London to Hastings pages

A 🛒 from Lewes

b Until 9 October only

c Until 9 October only. Change at London Bridge and Ashford International

e Change at Brighton and East Croydon

Ashford, Hastings, Eastbourne, Seaford and Lewes → Brighton, Haywards Heath and London

Network Diagram - see first page of Table 184

		SN 1	SN 1 A	SN 1	SN 1	SN 1 A	SN 1		SN 1	SN 1	SN 1 A	SN 1	SN 1	SN 1 A		SN 1	SN 1	SN 1	SN 1 A	SN 1	SN 1		SN 1 A	SN 1	SN 1
London Charing Cross 4	⊖ d								09b53								10b53								11b53
London Waterloo (East) 4	⊖ d								09b56								10b56								11b56
London Cannon Street 4	⊖ d								09c30								10c30								11c30
London Bridge 4	⊖ d								09b38								10b38								11b38
Ashford International	d								11 30								12 30								13 30
Ham Street	d								11 39								12 39								13 39
Appledore (Kent)	d								11 44								12 44								13 44
Rye	a								11 53								12 53								13 53
	d								11 54								12 54								13 54
Winchelsea	d																								
Doleham	d																								
Three Oaks	d																								
Ore	d			11 21		11 50						12 21		12 50						13 21			13 50		
Hastings 4	a			11 24		11 53			12 11			12 24		12 53			13 11			13 24			13 53		14 11
	d			11 25		11 55			12 12			12 25		12 55			13 12			13 25			13 55		14 12
St Leonards Warrior Sq 4	d			11 28		11 58			12 15			12 28		12 58			13 15			13 28			13 58		14 15
Bexhill 4	d			11 35		12 05			12 22			12 35		13 05			13 22			13 35			14 05		14 22
Collington	d			11 37		12 07						12 37		13 07						13 37			14 07		
Cooden Beach	d			11 40		12 10						12 40		13 10						13 40			14 10		
Normans Bay	d			11 43								12 43								13 43					
Pevensey Bay	d																								
Pevensey & Westham	d			11 48		12 16						12 48		13 16						13 48			14 16		
Hampden Park 4 §	d			11 52		12 20						12 52		13 20						13 52			14 20		
Eastbourne 4	a			11 57		12 25			12 37			12 57		13 25			13 37			13 57			14 25		14 37
	d		11 58	12 03		12 31			12 45		12 58	13 03		13 31			13 45		13 58	14 03			14 31		14 45
Hampden Park 4 §	d		12 02	12 07		12 37			12 52		13 02	13 07		13 37			13 52		14 02	14 07			14 37		14 52
Polegate	d		12 06	12 11							13 06	13 11							14 06	14 11					
Berwick	d			12 17								13 17								14 17					
Glynde	d			12 22								13 22								14 22					
Seaford	d	11 58			12 25					12 58			13 25					13 58			14 25				
Bishopstone	d	12 00			12 27					13 00			13 27					14 00			14 27				
Newhaven Harbour	d	12 03			12 30					13 03			13 30					14 03			14 30				
Newhaven Town ⛴	d	12 05			12 32					13 05			13 32					14 05			14 32				
Southease	d				12 36								13 36								14 36				
Lewes 4	a	12 14	12 18	12 28	12 44	12 49			13 07	13 14	13 18	13 28	13 44	13 49			14 07	14 14	14 18	14 28	14 44		14 49		15 07
	d	12 14	12 20	12 28	12 44	12 50	12 58		13 07	13 14	13 20	13 28	13 44	13 50		13 58	14 07	14 14	14 20	14 28	14 44		14 50	14 58	15 07
Falmer	d	12 21		12 35	12 51		13 05			13 21		13 35	13 51			14 05		14 21		14 35	14 51			15 05	
Moulsecoomb	d	12 24		12 38	12 54		13 08			13 24		13 38	13 54			14 08		14 24		14 38	14 54			15 08	
London Road (Brighton)	d	12 27		12 40	12 57		13 10			13 27		13 40	13 57			14 10		14 27		14 40	14 57			15 10	
Brighton 10	a	12 30		12 44	13 00		13 14		13 20	13 30		13 44	14 00			14 14	14 20	14 30		14 44	15 00			15 14	15 20
Cooksbridge	d																								
Plumpton	d		12 28																						
Wivelsfield 4	a	12 53	12 34	13 11	13 23					13 53	13 34	14 11	14 23					14 53	14 34	15 11	15 23				
Haywards Heath 3	a	12 47	12 40	13 15	13 18	13 05				13 47	13 40	14 15	14 18	14 05				14 47	14 40	15 15	15 18		15 05		
Gatwick Airport 10 ✈	a	13 00	12 54		13 30	13 24				14 00	13 54		14 30	14 24				15 00	14 54		15 30		15 24		
East Croydon	a	13 16	13 10	13 23	13 46	13 40	13 56			14 16	14 10	14 23	14 46	14 40		14 56		15 16	15 10	15 23	15 46		15 40	15 56	
London Bridge 4	⊖ a	13 30	13 30	13e45	14 00	14 00	14e15			14 30	14 30	14e45	15 00	15 00		15e15		15 30	15 30	15e45	16 00		16 00	16e15	
Clapham Junction 10	a		13 20	13 33	14e02	13 50	14 05				14 20	14 33	15e02	14 50		15 05			15 20	15 33	16e02		15 50	16 05	
London Victoria 15	⊖ a		13 28	13 40	14e09	13 57	14 12				14 27	14 40	15e09	14 57		15 12			15 27	15 40	16e09		15 57	16 12	

For general notes see front of timetable
For details of catering facilities see Directory of Train Operators

§ For additional trains between Hampden Park and Eastbourne see London to Hastings pages

A 🛒 from Lewes
b Until 9 October only
c Until 9 October only. Change at London Bridge and Ashford International
e Change at Brighton and East Croydon

Table 189

Mondays to Fridays

Ashford, Hastings, Eastbourne, Seaford and Lewes → Brighton, Haywards Heath and London

Network Diagram - see first page of Table 184

Station		SN 1	SN 1 A 🛒	SN 1	SN 1	SN 1 A 🛒		SN 1	SN 1	SN 1	SN 1 A 🛒	SN 1	SN 1		SN 1 A 🛒	SN 1	SN 1	SN 1	SN 1 A 🛒	SN 1		SN 1	SN 1 A 🛒	SN 1	SN 1
London Charing Cross 4 ⊖	d								12b53								13b53							14b53	
London Waterloo (East) 4 ⊖	d								12b56								13b56							14b56	
London Cannon Street 4 ⊖	d								12c30								13c30							14c30	
London Bridge 4 ⊖	d								12b38								13b38							14b38	
Ashford International	d								14 30								15 30							16 30	
Ham Street	d								14 39								15 39							16 39	
Appledore (Kent)	d								14 44								15 44							16 44	
Rye	a								14 53								15 53							16 53	
	d								14 54								15 54							16 54	
Winchelsea	d																								
Doleham	d																								
Three Oaks	d																								
Ore	d			14 21		14 50						15 20			15 48					16 21			16 50		
Hastings 4	a			14 24		14 53			15 11			15 23			15 51		16 11			16 24			16 53	17 14	
	d			14 25		14 55			15 12			15 24			15 53		16 12			16 25			16 55	17 16	
St Leonards Warrior Sq 4	d			14 28		14 58			15 15			15 27			15 56		16 15			16 28			16 58	17 19	
Bexhill 4	d			14 35		15 05			15 22			15 33			16 03		16 23			16 35			17 05	17 26	
Collington	d			14 37		15 07						15 35			16 05					16 37			17 07		
Cooden Beach	d			14 40		15 10						15 38			16 08					16 40			17 10		
Normans Bay	d			14 43								15 41			16 11					16 43					
Pevensey Bay	d											15 45			16 14										
Pevensey & Westham	d			14 48		15 16						15 47			16 17					16 48			17 16		
Hampden Park 4 §	d			14 52		15 20						15 52			16 21					16 52			17 20		
Eastbourne 4	a			14 57		15 25			15 37			15 57			16 26		16 38			16 57			17 25	17 41	
	d		14 58	15 03		15 31			15 45		15 58	16 03			16 32		16 45		16 58	17 03			17 31	17 45	
Hampden Park 4 §	d		15 02	15 07							16 02	16 07					16 49		17 02	17 07					
Polegate	d		15 06	15 11		15 37			15 52		16 06	16 11			16 38		16 54		17 06	17 11			17 37	17 52	
Berwick	d			15 17								16 17								17 17					
Glynde	d			15 22								16 22								17 22					
Seaford	d	14 58			15 25					15 58			16 26					16 58				17 25			17 58
Bishopstone	d	15 00			15 27					16 00			16 28					17 00				17 27			18 00
Newhaven Harbour	d	15 03			15 30					16 03			16 31					17 03				17 30			18 03
Newhaven Town ⛴	d	15 05			15 32					16 05			16 33					17 05				17 32			18 05
Southease	d				15 36								16 37									17 36			
Lewes 4	a	15 14	15 18	15 28	15 44	15 49			16 07	16 14	16 18	16 28	16 44		16 50		17 07	17 14	17 18	17 28		17 44	17 49	18 05	18 14
	d	15 14	15 19	15 28	15 44	15 50		15 58	16 07	16 14	16 19	16 28	16 44		16 51	16 58	17 07	17 14	17 19	17 28		17 44	17 50	18 06	18 14
Falmer	d	15 21		15 35	15 51			16 05		16 21		16 35	16 51			17 05		17 21		17 35		17 51		18 13	18 21
Moulsecoomb	d	15 24		15 38	15 54			16 08		16 24		16 38	16 54			17 08		17 24		17 38		17 54		18 17	18 24
London Road (Brighton)	d	15 27		15 40	15 57			16 10		16 27		16 40	16 57			17 10		17 27		17 40		17 57		18 19	18 27
Brighton 10	a	15 30		15 44	16 00			16 14	16 20	16 30		16 44	17 00			17 14	17 20	17 30		17 44		18 00		18 23	18 30
Cooksbridge	d		15 24								16 24								17 24						
Plumpton	d		15 29								16 29								17 29						
Wivelsfield 4	a	*15 53*	15 35	*16 11*					*16 46*		16 37	*17 11*					*17 40*		17 35	*18 11*		*18 23*			*18 53*
Haywards Heath 3	a	*15 48*	15 39	*16 15*	*16 18*	16 05		*16 37*	*16 50*		16 41	*17 15*	*17 18*		17 05		*17 45*	*17 56*	17 39	*18 16*		*18 18*	18 06		*18 47*
Gatwick Airport 10 ✈	a	*16 00*	15 55		*16 30*	16 24		*16 52*	*17 06*		16 56		*17 31*		17 24		*18 00*	*18 16*	17 54			*18 30*	18 26		*19 00*
East Croydon 🚊	a	*16 16*	16 11	*16 24*	*16 46*	16 40		*16 56*			17 12	*17 25*	*17 47*		17 40	*17 56*	*18 16*		18 11	*18 24*		*18 46*	18 42		*19 16*
London Bridge 4 ⊖	a	*16e39*	16 39	*16e53*	*17 02*			*17e26*			*17 38*	*17e50*	*18 11*			*18e17*	*18e42*		*18 42*	*18e45*		*19 00*	*19 00*		*19 30*
Clapham Junction 10	a		16 20	*16 33*	*17e02*	16 50		*17 05*			17 21	*17 34*	*18e02*		17 50	*18 05*			18 21	*18 34*		*19e02*	18 52		
London Victoria 15 ⊖	a		16 28	*16 42*	*17e09*	16 58		*17 12*			17 28	*17 42*	*18e09*		17 58	*18 12*			18 29	*18 41*		*19e09*	18 59		

For general notes see front of timetable
For details of catering facilities see Directory of Train Operators

§ For additional trains between Hampden Park and Eastbourne see London to Hastings pages

A 🛒 from Lewes
b Until 9 October only
c Until 9 October only. Change at London Bridge and Ashford International
e Change at Brighton and East Croydon

Ashford, Hastings, Eastbourne, Seaford and Lewes → Brighton, Haywards Heath and London

Network Diagram - see first page of Table 184

		SN	SN	SN	SN	SN	SN	SN	SN	SN	SN	SN	SN	SN	SN	SN	SN	SN	SN	SN	SN	SN
		1	1	1	1	1	1	1	1	1	1	1	1	1	1	1	1	1	1	1	1	1
		A ⌶																				
London Charing Cross 4	⊖ d					16b00	16b30									16b46	17b34					
London Waterloo (East) 4	⊖ d					16b03	16b33									16b49	17b37					
London Cannon Street 4	⊖ d					16c00	16c28									16c46	17b44					
London Bridge 4	⊖ d					16b08	16b39									16b54						
Ashford International	d					17 30	17 58									18 30	18 58					
Ham Street	d					17 39	18 07									18 39	19 07					
Appledore (Kent)	d					17 44	18 12									18 44	19 12					
Rye	a					17 53	18 21									18 53	19 21					
	d					17 54										18 54						
Winchelsea	d																					
Doleham	d																					
Three Oaks	d																					
Ore	d		17 21		17 50							18 21		18 50					19 24		19 50	
Hastings 4	a		17 24		17 53	18 11						18 24		18 53		19 11			19 27		19 53	
	d		17 25		17 55	18 12						18 25		18 55		19 12			19 27		19 55	
St Leonards Warrior Sq 4	d		17 28		17 58	18 15						18 28		18 58		19 15			19 30		19 58	
Bexhill 4	d		17 35		18 05	18 23						18 35		19 05		19 22			19 37		20 05	
Collington	d		17 37		18 07							18 37		19 07					19 39		20 07	
Cooden Beach	d		17 40		18 10							18 40		19 10					19 42		20 10	
Normans Bay	d		17 43									18 43										
Pevensey Bay	d																					
Pevensey & Westham	d		17 48		18 16							18 48		19 16					19 48		20 16	
Hampden Park 4 §	d		17 52		18 20							18 52		19 20					19 52		20 20	
Eastbourne 4	a		17 57		18 25	18 38						18 57		19 25		19 37			19 57		20 25	
	d	17 57	18 01		18 31	18 45					18 58	19 04		19 31		19 45			20 02		20 31	
Hampden Park 4 §	d	18 01	18 05								19 02	19 08							20 06			
Polegate	d	18 05	18 11		18 37	18 52					19 06	19 12		19 37		19 52			20 11		20 37	
Berwick	d		18 17									19 17							20 17			
Glynde	d		18 22									19 23							20 22			
Seaford	d			18 26			18 44			19 02			19 19		19 37			19 58		20 28		
Bishopstone	d			18 28			18 46			19 04			19 21		19 39			20 00		20 30		
Newhaven Harbour	d			18 31									19 24		19 42			20 03		20 33		
Newhaven Town ⛴	d			18 33			18 50			19 08			19 26		19 44			20 05		20 35		
Southease	d			18 37											19 48					20 39		
Lewes 4	a	18 17	18 28	18 44	18 49	18 59	19 05			19 17	19 20	19 28	19 35	19 49	19 55	20 07		20 14	20 28	20 46	20 49	←
	d	18 18	18 28	18 44	18 50	18 59	19 06		19 12	19 20	19 21	19 29	19 38	19 50	19 58	20 07		20 14	20 28	20 53 →	20 50	20 53
Falmer	d		18 35	18 51		19 06			19 19	19 27		19 36	19 45		20 05			20 21	20 35			21 00
Moulsecoomb	d		18 38	18 54		19 09			19 22	19 30		19 39	19 48		20 08			20 24	20 38			21 03
London Road (Brighton)	d		18 41	18 57		19 12			19 24	19 32		19 41	19 50		20 10			20 27	20 40			21 05
Brighton 10	a		18 44	19 00		19 15	19 21		19 28	19 36		19 45	19 55		20 14	20 20		20 33	20 44			21 09
Cooksbridge	d	18 23									19 26										20 58	
Plumpton	d	18 28			18 58						19 31										21 05	
Wivelsfield 4	a	18 34	19 15	19 23	19 05				19 53			20 11	20 23	20 05				20 53			21 09	
Haywards Heath 3	a	18 38	19 20	19 28	19 10				19 47		19 40	20 16	20 18	20 10		20 47		20 58				
Gatwick Airport 10	✈ a	18 56	19 39	19 46	19 25				20 00		19 55		20 31	20 25		21 00		21 16			21 24	
East Croydon	⇌ a	19 12	19 23		19 42	19 54			20 16		20 11	20 23	20 47	20 41	20 54	21 16			21 25		21 40	21 53
London Bridge 4	⊖ a	19 30	19e45		20 00	20e15			20 30		20 30	20e45	21 00	21 00	21e15	21 30			21e45		22 17	22e17
Clapham Junction 10	a	19 21	19 33		19 52	20 03					20 20	20 33		20 50	21 03				21 34		21 50	22 02
London Victoria 15	⊖ a	19 29	19 40		19 59	20 10					20 28	20 43		20 58	21 10				21 41		21 57	22 10

For general notes see front of timetable
For details of catering facilities see Directory of Train Operators

§ For additional trains between Hampden Park and Eastbourne see London to Hastings pages

A ⌶ from Lewes
b Until 9 October only
c Until 9 October only. Change at London Bridge and Ashford International
e Change at Brighton and East Croydon

Ashford, Hastings, Eastbourne, Seaford and Lewes → Brighton, Haywards Heath and London

Network Diagram - see first page of Table 184

		SN 1	SN 1	SN 1		SN 1	SN 1	SN 1	SN 1	SN 1	SN 1		SN 1	SN 1	SN 1	SN 1	SN 1	SN 1		SN 1	SN 1	SN 1	SN 1		
London Charing Cross 4	⊖ d	17b58				18b23				19c00							20c00				21c00				
London Waterloo (East) 4	⊖ d	17c59				18c19				19c03							20c03				21c03				
London Cannon Street 4	⊖ d	18c05				18c30				18b50							20b00				21b00				
London Bridge 4	⊖ d	18c09				18c34				19c08							20c08				21c08				
Ashford International	d	19 30				19 58				20 30							21 30				22 24				
Ham Street	d	19 39				20 07				20 39							21 39				22 33				
Appledore (Kent)	d	19 44				20 12				20 44							21 44				22 38				
Rye	a	19 53				20 21				20 53							21 53				22 47				
	d	19 54				20 22				20 54							21 57				22 47				
Winchelsea	d																				22 50				
Doleham	d																				22 57				
Three Oaks	d																				23 00				
Ore	d			20 20				20 50							21 22					22 22	23 06				
Hastings 4	a	20 11		20 23		20 39		20 53		21 11					21 25		22 14			22 25	23 09				
	d	20 12		20 24				20 55		21 12					21 30		22 16			22 26			23 13		
St Leonards Warrior Sq 4	d	20 15		20 27				20 58		21 15					21 33		22 19			22 29			23 16		
Bexhill 4	d	20 22		20 35				21 05		21 22					21 39		22 26			22 38			23 22		
Collington	d			20 37				21 07							21 41					22 40			23 24		
Cooden Beach	d			20 40				21 10							21 44					22 43			23 27		
Normans Bay	d																			22 46					
Pevensey Bay	d																								
Pevensey & Westham	d			20 46				21 16							21 50					22 51			23 33		
Hampden Park 4 §	d			20 52				21 20							21 55					22 55			23 38		
Eastbourne 4	a	20 37		20 57				21 25		21 37					22 00		22 41			23 00			23 43		
	d	20 45		21 03				21 31		21 45			22 03		22 15		22 45			23 05			23 48		
Hampden Park 4 §	d			21 07									22 07		22 19					23 09			23 52		
Polegate	d	20 52		21 11				21 37		21 52			22 11		22 23		22 52			23 13			23 56		
Berwick	d			21 17									22 17		22 29					23 18					
Glynde	d			21 22									22 22							23 24					
Seaford	d		20 58				21 28				21 58			22 20				22 58				23 25			
Bishopstone	d		21 00				21 30				22 00			22 22				23 00				23 27			
Newhaven Harbour	d		21 03				21 33				22 03			22 25				23 03				23 30			
Newhaven Town	d		21 05				21 35				22 05			22 27				23 05				23 32			
Southease	d																								
Lewes 4	a	21 07	21 14	21 28			21 44	21 49	←	22 07	22 14		22 28	22 35	22 38	←	23 07	23 14		23 29		23 40	00 08		
	d	21 07	21 14	21 28			21 53 →	21 50	21 53	22 07	22 14		22 28	22 42 →	22 40	22 42	23 07	23 14		23 29		23 40	00 08		
Falmer	d		21 21	21 35					22 00		22 21		22 37			22 49		23 21		23 37		23 47	00 15		
Moulsecoomb	d		21 24	21 38					22 03		22 24		22 40			22 52		23 24		23 40		23 50	00 18		
London Road (Brighton)	d		21 27	21 40					22 05		22 27		22 42			22 54		23 27		23 42		23 53	00 21		
Brighton 10	a	21 20	21 33	21 44					22 09	22 20	22 31		22 46			22 58	23 20	23 31		23 46		23 56	00 24		
Cooksbridge	d																								
Plumpton	d														22 48										
Wivelsfield 4	a		21 53					22 02		22 49					22 54	23 19		23 53							
Haywards Heath 3	a	21 46	21 58					22 06		22 54					22 58	23 23		23 58							
Gatwick Airport 10	a	22 00	22 16					22 24		23e12					23 12	23 42		00 14							
East Croydon	a	22 17		22 23				22 40		23 32					23 30	00 02		00 35							
London Bridge 4	⊖ a	22 32		22f47				23 17		23 47					00 19	00 19		00 52							
Clapham Junction 10	a			22 33				22 49		00f11					23 42	00 29		01f02							
London Victoria 15	⊖ a			22 40				22 57		00f18					23 52	00 37		01f09							

For general notes see front of timetable
For details of catering facilities see Directory of Train Operators

§ For additional trains between Hampden Park and Eastbourne see London to Hastings pages

b Until 9 October only. Change at London Bridge and Ashford International

c Until 9 October only

e Change at Brighton and Haywards Heath

f Change at Brighton and East Croydon

Ashford, Hastings, Eastbourne, Seaford and Lewes → Brighton, Haywards Heath and London

Network Diagram - see first page of Table 184

Station		SN 1	SN 1	SN 1	SN 1	SN 1	SN 1		SN 1	SN 1	SN 1	SN 1	SN 1	SN 1		SN 1	SN 1	SN 1	SN 1	SN 1	SN 1		SN 1	SN 1	SN 1
London Charing Cross 4	⊖ d																								
London Waterloo (East) 4	⊖ d																								
London Cannon Street 4	⊖ d																								
London Bridge 4	⊖ d																								
Ashford International	d																	06 23							
Ham Street	d																	06 32							
Appledore (Kent)	d																	06 37							
Rye	a																	06 46							
	d																	06 48							
Winchelsea	d																	06 51							
Doleham	d																	06 58							
Three Oaks	d																	07 01							
Ore	d												06 21			06 50		07 07			07 21			07 50	
Hastings 4	a												06 24			06 53		07 10			07 24			07 53	
	d	23p13											06 25			06 55		07 11			07 25			07 55	
St Leonards Warrior Sq 4	d	23p16											06 28			06 58		07 14			07 28			07 58	
Bexhill 4	d	23p22											06 35			07 05		07 22			07 35			08 05	
Collington	d	23p24											06 37			07 07					07 37			08 07	
Cooden Beach	d	23p27											06 40			07 10					07 40			08 10	
Normans Bay	d												06 43								07 43				
Pevensey Bay	d																								
Pevensey & Westham	d	23p33											06 48			07 16					07 48			08 16	
Hampden Park 4 §	d	23p38											06 52			07 20					07 52			08 20	
Eastbourne 4	a	23p43											06 57			07 25		07 37			07 57			08 25	
	d	23p48		05 03		05 50			06 24	06 37		06 58	07 03			07 31		07 45		07 58	08 03			08 31	
Hampden Park 4 §	d	23p52		05 07					06 28			07 02	07 07							08 02	08 07				
Polegate	d	23p56		05 12		05 57			06 32	06 44		07 06	07 11			07 37		07 52		08 06	08 11			08 37	
Berwick	d								06 38				07 17								08 17				
Glynde	d								06 43				07 22								08 22				
Seaford	d		05 05				06 28				06 58			07 28					07 58				08 25		
Bishopstone	d		05 07				06 30				07 00			07 30					08 00				08 27		
Newhaven Harbour	d		05 10				06 33				07 03			07 33					08 03				08 30		
Newhaven Town	⛴ d		05 12				06 35				07 05			07 35					08 05				08 32		
Southease	d																						08 36		
Lewes 4	a	00 08	05 21	05 24	←	06 10	06 44		06 49	06 57	07 14	07 18	07 28	07 44		07 49		08 07	08 14	08 18	08 28		08 44	08 49	
	d	00 08	05 28	05 25	05 28	06 10	06 44		06 50	06 58	07 14	07 20	07 28	07 44		07 50	07 58	08 07	08 14	08 20	08 28		08 44	08 50	08 58
Falmer	d	00 15	→		05 35	06 18	06 51			07 05	07 21		07 35	07 51			08 05		08 21		08 35		08 51		09 05
Moulsecoomb	d	00 18			05 38	06 21	06 54			07 09	07 24		07 38	07 54			08 08		08 24		08 38		08 54		09 08
London Road (Brighton)	d	00 21			05 40	06 24	06 57			07 11	07 27		07 40	07 57			08 10		08 27		08 40		08 57		09 10
Brighton 10	a	00 24			05 44	06 27	07 00			07 15	07 30		07 44	08 00			08 14	08 20	08 30		08 44		09 00		09 14
Cooksbridge	d																								
Plumpton	d											07 28								08 28					
Wivelsfield 4	a				06 11	06 53	07 23				07 53	07 34	08 11	08 23					08 53	08 34	09 11		09 23		
Haywards Heath 3	a			05 40	06 02	06 58	07 18		07 05		07 48	07 40	08 15	08 18		08 05			08 48	08 40	09 15		09 18	09 05	
Gatwick Airport 10	✈ a			06 03	06 24	07 16	07 30		07 24		08 00	07 54		08 30		08 24			09 00	08 54			09 30	09 24	
East Croydon	a			06b16	06 40	07 23	07 46		07 40	07 56	08 16	08 10	08 23	08 46		08 40	08 56		09 16	09 10	09 23		09 46	09 41	09 56
London Bridge 4	⊖ a			06b31	07 02	07 47	08 02		08 02	08c17	08 32	08 32	08c47	09 02		09 02	09c17		09 32	09 32	09c47		10 02	10 02	10c17
Clapham Junction 10	a			06 50	06 50	07 33	08c02		07 50	08 05		08 20	08 33	09c02		08 50	09 05			09 20	09 33		10c02	09 51	10 05
London Victoria 15	⊖ a			06 57	06 57	07 40	08c09		07 57	08 12		08 27	08 40	09c09		08 57	09 12			09 27	09 40		10c09	09 58	10 12

For general notes see front of timetable
For details of catering facilities see Directory of Train Operators

§ For additional trains between Hampden Park and Eastbourne see London to Hastings pages

b Change at Haywards Heath

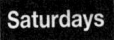

c Change at Brighton and East Croydon

Table 189

Saturdays

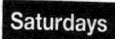

Ashford, Hastings, Eastbourne, Seaford and Lewes → Brighton, Haywards Heath and London

Network Diagram - see first page of Table 184

Station		SN ■1	SN ■1	SN ■1	SN ■1	SN ■1	SN ■1	SN ■1	SN ■1	SN ■1	SN ■1	SN ■1	SN ■1	SN ■1	SN ■1	SN ■1	SN ■1	SN ■1	SN ■1	SN ■1	SN ■1	SN ■1
London Charing Cross ■4	⊖ d								*07 00*							*07 30*						
London Waterloo (East) ■4	⊖ d								*07 03*							*07 33*						
London Cannon Street ■4	⊖ d																					
London Bridge ■4	⊖ d								*07 08*							*07 38*						
Ashford International	d	07 30							08 30							09 30						
Ham Street	d	07 39							08 39							09 39						
Appledore (Kent)	d	07 44							08 44							09 44						
Rye	a	07 53							08 53							09 53						
	d	07 54							08 54							09 54						
Winchelsea	d																					
Doleham	d																					
Three Oaks	d																					
Ore	d				08 21		08 50					09 21		09 50					10 21		10 50	
Hastings ■4	a	08 11			08 24		08 53		09 11			09 24		09 53		10 11			10 24		10 53	
	d	08 12			08 25		08 55		09 12			09 25		09 55		10 12			10 25		10 55	
St Leonards Warrior Sq ■4	d	08 15			08 28		08 58		09 15			09 28		09 58		10 15			10 28		10 58	
Bexhill ■4	d	08 22			08 35		09 05		09 22			09 35		10 05		10 22			10 35		11 05	
Collington	d				08 37		09 07					09 37		10 07					10 37		11 07	
Cooden Beach	d				08 40		09 10					09 40		10 10					10 40		11 10	
Normans Bay	d				08 43							09 43							10 43			
Pevensey Bay	d																					
Pevensey & Westham	d				08 48		09 16					09 48		10 16					10 48		11 16	
Hampden Park ■4 §	d				08 52		09 20					09 52		10 20					10 52		11 20	
Eastbourne ■4	a	08 37			08 57		09 25		09 37			09 57		10 25		10 37			10 57		11 25	
	d	08 45		08 58	09 03		09 31		09 45		09 58	10 03		10 31		10 45		10 58	11 03		11 31	
Hampden Park ■4 §	d			09 02	09 07						10 02	10 07						11 02	11 07			
Polegate	d	08 52		09 06	09 11		09 37		09 52		10 06	10 11		10 37		10 52		11 06	11 11		11 37	
Berwick	d				09 17							10 17							11 17			
Glynde	d				09 22							10 22							11 22			
Seaford	d		08 58			09 25				09 58			10 25				10 58			11 25		
Bishopstone	d		09 00			09 27				10 00			10 27				11 00			11 27		
Newhaven Harbour	d		09 03			09 30				10 03			10 30				11 03			11 30		
Newhaven Town ⛴	d		09 05			09 32				10 05			10 32				11 05			11 32		
Southease	d					09 36							10 36							11 36		
Lewes ■4	a	09 07	09 14	09 18	09 28	09 44	09 49		10 07	10 14	10 18	10 28	10 44	10 49		11 07	11 14	11 18	11 28	11 44	11 49	
	d	09 07	09 14	09 20	09 28	09 44	09 50	09 58	10 07	10 14	10 20	10 28	10 44	10 50	10 58	11 07	11 14	11 20	11 28	11 44	11 50	11 58
Falmer	d		09 21		09 35	09 51		10 05		10 21		10 35	10 51		11 05		11 21		11 35	11 51		12 05
Moulsecoomb	d		09 24		09 38	09 54		10 08		10 24		10 38	10 54		11 08		11 24		11 38	11 54		12 08
London Road (Brighton)	d		09 27		09 40	09 57		10 10		10 27		10 40	10 57		11 10		11 27		11 40	11 57		12 10
Brighton ■10	a	09 20	09 30		09 44	10 00		10 14	10 20	10 30		10 44	11 00		11 14	11 20	11 30		11 44	12 00		12 14
Cooksbridge	d																					
Plumpton	d			09 28							10 28											
Wivelsfield ■4	a		*09 53*	09 34	*10 11*	*10 23*				*10 53*	10 34	*11 11*	*11 23*				*11 53*	11 34	*12 11*	*12 23*		
Haywards Heath ■3	a		*09 48*	09 40	*10 15*	*10 18*	10 05			*10 48*	10 40	*11 15*	*11 18*	11 05			*11 48*	11 40	*12 15*	*12 18*	12 05	
Gatwick Airport ■10 ✈	a		*10 00*	09 54		*10 30*	10 21			*11 00*	10 54		*11 30*	11 24			*12 00*	11 54		*12 30*	12 24	
East Croydon ⛴	a		*10 16*	10 10	*10 23*	*10 46*	10 38	*10 56*		*11 16*	11 10	*11 23*	*11 46*	11 40	*11 56*		*12 16*	12 10	*12 23*	*12 46*	12 40	*12 56*
London Bridge ■4	⊖ a		*10 32*	*10 32*	*10b47*	*11 02*	*11 02*	*11b17*		*11 32*	*11 32*	*11b47*	*12 02*	*12 02*	*12b17*		*12 32*	*12 32*	*12b47*	*13 02*	*13 02*	*13b17*
Clapham Junction ■10	a			10 20	*10 33*	*11b02*	10 47	*11 05*			11 20	*11 33*	*12b02*	11 50	*12 05*			12 20	*12 33*	*13b02*	12 50	*13 05*
London Victoria ■15	⊖ a			10 27	*10 40*	*11b09*	10 56	*11 12*			11 27	*11 40*	*12b09*	11 57	*12 12*			12 27	*12 40*	*13b09*	12 57	*13 12*

For general notes see front of timetable
For details of catering facilities see
Directory of Train Operators

§ For additional trains between Hampden Park and Eastbourne see London to Hastings pages

b Change at Brighton and East Croydon

Table 189

Saturdays

Ashford, Hastings, Eastbourne, Seaford and Lewes → Brighton, Haywards Heath and London

Network Diagram - see first page of Table 184

Station		SN 1	SN 1	SN 1	SN 1		SN 1	SN 1	SN 1	SN 1	SN 1	SN 1		SN 1	SN 1	SN 1	SN 1	SN 1	SN 1		SN 1	SN 1	SN 1	SN 1	SN 1
London Charing Cross 4	⊖ d	08 30								09 53								10 53							
London Waterloo (East) 4	⊖ d	08 33								09 56								10 56							
London Cannon Street 4	⊖ d	08b30								09b30								10b30							
London Bridge 4	⊖ d	08 38								09 38								10 38							
Ashford International	d	10 30								11 30								12 30							
Ham Street	d	10 39								11 39								12 39							
Appledore (Kent)	d	10 44								11 44								12 44							
Rye	a	10 53								11 53								12 53							
	d	10 54								11 54								12 54							
Winchelsea	d																								
Doleham	d																								
Three Oaks	d																								
Ore	d				11 21			11 50						12 21		12 50						13 21		13 50	
Hastings 4	a	11 11			11 24			11 53		12 11				12 24		12 53		13 11				13 24		13 53	
	d	11 12			11 25			11 55		12 12				12 25		12 55		13 12				13 25		13 55	
St Leonards Warrior Sq 4	d	11 15			11 28			11 58		12 15				12 28		12 58		13 15				13 28		13 58	
Bexhill 4	d	11 22			11 35			12 05		12 22				12 35		13 05		13 22				13 35		14 05	
Collington	d				11 37			12 07						12 37		13 07						13 37		14 07	
Cooden Beach	d				11 40			12 10						12 40		13 10						13 40		14 10	
Normans Bay	d				11 43									12 43								13 43			
Pevensey Bay	d																								
Pevensey & Westham	d				11 48			12 16						12 48		13 16						13 48		14 16	
Hampden Park 4 §	d				11 52			12 20						12 52		13 20						13 52		14 20	
Eastbourne 4	a	11 37			11 57			12 25		12 37				12 57		13 25		13 37				13 57		14 25	
	d	11 45		11 58	12 03			12 31		12 45		12 58		13 03		13 31		13 45			13 58	14 03		14 31	
Hampden Park 4 §	d			12 02	12 07							13 02		13 07							14 02	14 07			
Polegate	d	11 52		12 06	12 11			12 37		12 52		13 06		13 11		13 37		13 52			14 06	14 11		14 37	
Berwick	d				12 17									13 17								14 17			
Glynde	d				12 22									13 22								14 22			
Seaford	d		11 58				12 25				12 58				13 25				13 58				14 25		
Bishopstone	d		12 00				12 27				13 00				13 27				14 00				14 27		
Newhaven Harbour	d		12 03				12 30				13 03				13 30				14 03				14 30		
Newhaven Town	⛴ d		12 05				12 32				13 05				13 32				14 05				14 32		
Southease	d						12 36								13 36								14 36		
Lewes 4	a	12 07	12 14	12 18	12 28		12 44	12 49		13 07	13 14	13 18		13 28	13 44	13 49		14 07	14 14		14 18	14 28	14 44	14 49	
	d	12 07	12 14	12 20	12 28		12 44	12 50	12 58	13 07	13 14	13 20		13 28	13 44	13 50	13 58	14 07	14 14		14 20	14 28	14 44	14 50	14 58
Falmer	d		12 21		12 35		12 51		13 05		13 21			13 35	13 51		14 05		14 21			14 35	14 51		15 05
Moulsecoomb	d		12 24		12 38		12 54		13 08		13 24			13 38	13 54		14 08		14 24			14 38	14 54		15 08
London Road (Brighton)	d		12 27		12 40		12 57		13 10		13 27			13 40	13 57		14 10		14 27			14 40	14 57		15 10
Brighton 10	a	12 20	12 30		12 44		13 00		13 14	13 20	13 30			13 44	14 00		14 14	14 20	14 30			14 44	15 00		15 14
Cooksbridge	d																								
Plumpton	d			12 28																					
Wivelsfield 4	a		12 53	12 34	13 11		13 23				13 53	13 34		14 11	14 23				14 53		14 34	15 11	15 23		
Haywards Heath 3	a		12 48	12 40	13 15		13 18	13 05			13 48	13 40		14 15	14 18	14 05			14 48		14 39	15 15	15 18	15 05	
Gatwick Airport 10	✈ a		13 00	12 54			13 30	13 24			14 00	13 54			14 30	14 24			15 00		14 54		15 30	15 24	
East Croydon	a		13 16	13 10	13 23		13 46	13 40	13 56		14 16	14 10		14 23	14 46	14 40	14 56		15 16		15 10	15 23	15 46	15 40	15 56
London Bridge 4	⊖ a		13 32	13 32	13c47		14 02	14 02	14c17		14 32	14 32		14c47	15 02	15 02	15c17		15 32		15 32	15c47	16 02	16 02	16c17
Clapham Junction 10	a			13 20	13 33		14c02	13 50	14 05			14 20		14 33	15c02	14 50	15 05				15 20	15 33	16c02	15 50	16 05
London Victoria 15	⊖ a			13 27	13 40		14c09	13 57	14 12			14 27		14 40	15c09	14 57	15 12				15 27	15 40	16c09	15 57	16 12

For general notes see front of timetable
For details of catering facilities see Directory of Train Operators

§ For additional trains between Hampden Park and Eastbourne see London to Hastings pages

b Change at London Bridge and Ashford International
c Change at Brighton and East Croydon

Table 189

Saturdays

Ashford, Hastings, Eastbourne, Seaford and Lewes → Brighton, Haywards Heath and London

Network Diagram - see first page of Table 184

Station		SN 1	SN 1	SN 1		SN 1	SN 1	SN 1	SN 1	SN 1	SN 1		SN 1	SN 1	SN 1	SN 1	SN 1	SN 1		SN 1	SN 1	SN 1	SN 1	SN 1	SN 1
London Charing Cross 4	⊖ d	11 53								12 53								13 53							
London Waterloo (East) 4	⊖ d	11 56								12 56								13 56							
London Cannon Street 4	⊖ d	11b30								12b30								13b30							
London Bridge 4	⊖ d	11 38								12 38								13 38							
Ashford International	d	13 30								14 30								15 30							
Ham Street	d	13 39								14 39								15 39							
Appledore (Kent)	d	13 44								14 44								15 44							
Rye	a	13 53								14 53								15 53							
	d	13 54								14 54								15 54							
Winchelsea	d																								
Doleham	d																								
Three Oaks	d																								
Ore	d					14 21		14 50						15 21		15 50						16 21		16 50	
Hastings 4	a	14 11				14 24		14 53		15 11				15 24		15 53		16 11				16 24		16 53	
	d	14 12				14 25		14 55		15 12				15 25		15 55		16 12				16 25		16 55	
St Leonards Warrior Sq 4	d	14 15				14 28		14 58		15 15				15 28		15 58		16 15				16 28		16 58	
Bexhill 4	d	14 22				14 35		15 05		15 22				15 35		16 05		16 22				16 35		17 05	
Collington	d					14 37		15 07						15 37		16 07						16 37		17 07	
Cooden Beach	d					14 40		15 10						15 40		16 10						16 40		17 10	
Normans Bay	d					14 43								15 43								16 43			
Pevensey Bay	d																								
Pevensey & Westham	d					14 48		15 16						15 48		16 16						16 48		17 16	
Hampden Park 4 §	d					14 52		15 20						15 52		16 20						16 52		17 20	
Eastbourne 4	a	14 37				14 57		15 25		15 37				15 57		16 25		16 37				16 57		17 25	
	d	14 45		14 58		15 03		15 31		15 45			15 58	16 03		16 31		16 45			16 58	17 03		17 31	
Hampden Park 4 §	d			15 02		15 07							16 02	16 07							17 02	17 07			
Polegate	d	14 52		15 06		15 11		15 37		15 52			16 06	16 11		16 37		16 52			17 06	17 11		17 37	
Berwick	d					15 17								16 17								17 17			
Glynde	d					15 22								16 22								17 22			
Seaford	d		14 58				15 25				15 58				16 25					16 58			17 25		
Bishopstone	d		15 00				15 27				16 00				16 27					17 00			17 27		
Newhaven Harbour	d		15 03				15 30				16 03				16 30					17 03			17 30		
Newhaven Town ⛴	d		15 05				15 32				16 05				16 32					17 05			17 32		
Southease	d						15 36								16 36								17 36		
Lewes 4	a	15 07	15 14	15 18		15 28	15 44	15 49		16 07	16 14		16 18	16 28	16 44	16 49		17 07		17 14	17 18	17 28	17 44	17 49	
	d	15 07	15 14	15 20		15 28	15 44	15 50	15 58	16 07	16 14		16 20	16 28	16 44	16 50	16 58	17 07		17 14	17 20	17 28	17 44	17 50	17 58
Falmer	d		15 21			15 35	15 51		16 05		16 21			16 35	16 51		17 05			17 21		17 35	17 51		18 05
Moulsecoomb	d		15 24			15 38	15 54		16 08		16 24			16 38	16 54		17 08			17 24		17 38	17 54		18 08
London Road (Brighton)	d		15 27			15 40	15 57		16 10		16 27			16 40	16 57		17 10			17 27		17 40	17 57		18 10
Brighton 10	a	15 20	15 30			15 44	16 00		16 14	16 20	16 30			16 44	17 00		17 14	17 20		17 30		17 44	18 00		18 14
Cooksbridge	d																								
Plumpton	d												16 28								17 28				
Wivelsfield 4	a		15 53	15 34		16 11	16 23				16 53		16 34	17 11	17 23					17 53	17 34	18 11	18 23		
Haywards Heath 3	a		15 48	15 40		16 15	16 18	16 05			16 48		16 40	17 15	17 18	17 05				17 48	17 40	18 15	18 28	18 05	
Gatwick Airport 10 ✈	a		16 00	15 54			16 30	16 24			17 00		16 54		17 30	17 24				18 00	17 54	18 35	18 46	18 24	
East Croydon 🚋	a		16 16	16 10		16 23	16 46	16 40	16 56		17 16		17 10	17 23	17 46	17 40	17 56			18 16	18 10	18 23		18 40	18 56
London Bridge 4	⊖ a		16 32	16 32		16c47	17 02	17 02	17c17		17 32		17 32	17c47	18 02	18 02	18c17			18 32	18 32	18c47		19 08	19c17
Clapham Junction 10	a			16 20		16 33	17c02	16 50	17 05				17 20	17 33	18c02	17 50	18 05				18 20	18 33		18 50	19 05
London Victoria 15	⊖ a			16 27		16 40	17c09	16 57	17 12				17 27	17 40	18c09	17 57	18 12				18 27	18 40		18 57	19 12

For general notes see front of timetable
For details of catering facilities see Directory of Train Operators

§ For additional trains between Hampden Park and Eastbourne see London to Hastings pages

b Change at London Bridge and Ashford International
c Change at Brighton and East Croydon

Table 189

Ashford, Hastings, Eastbourne, Seaford and Lewes → Brighton, Haywards Heath and London

Network Diagram - see first page of Table 184

		SN 1	SN 1		SN 1	SN 1	SN 1	SN 1	SN 1	SN 1		SN 1	SN 1	SN 1	SN 1	SN 1	SN 1		SN 1	SN 1	SN 1	SN 1	SN 1	SN 1	SN 1
London Charing Cross 4	⊖ d	14 53								15 53									16 53						18 23
London Waterloo (East) 4	⊖ d	14 56								15 56									16 56						18 26
London Cannon Street 4	⊖ d	14b30								15b30									16b30						17b30
London Bridge 4	⊖ d	14 38								15 38									16 38						17 38
Ashford International	d	16 30								17 30									18 30						19 30
Ham Street	d	16 39								17 39									18 39						19 39
Appledore (Kent)	d	16 44								17 44									18 44						19 44
Rye	a	16 53								17 53									18 53						19 53
	d	16 54								17 54									18 54						19 54
Winchelsea	d																								
Doleham	d																								
Three Oaks	d																								
Ore	d					17 21		17 50						18 21		18 50					19 21		19 50		
Hastings 4	a	17 11				17 24		17 53		18 11				18 24		18 53			19 11		19 24		19 53		20 11
	d	17 12				17 25		17 55		18 12				18 25		18 55			19 12		19 25		19 55		20 12
St Leonards Warrior Sq 4	d	17 15				17 28		17 58		18 15				18 28		18 58			19 15		19 28		19 58		20 15
Bexhill 4	d	17 22				17 35		18 05		18 22				18 35		19 05			19 22		19 35		20 05		20 22
Collington	d					17 37		18 07						18 37		19 07					19 37		20 07		
Cooden Beach	d					17 40		18 10						18 40		19 10					19 40		20 10		
Normans Bay	d					17 43								18 43							19 43				
Pevensey Bay	d																								
Pevensey & Westham	d					17 48		18 16						18 48		19 16					19 48		20 16		
Hampden Park 4 §	d					17 52		18 20						18 52		19 21					19 52		20 20		
Eastbourne 4	a	17 37				17 57		18 25		18 37				18 57		19 26			19 37		19 57		20 25		20 37
	d	17 45			17 58	18 03		18 31		18 45			18 58	19 03		19 32			19 45		20 03		20 31		20 45
Hampden Park 4 §	d				18 02	18 07							19 02	19 07							20 07				
Polegate	d	17 52			18 06	18 11		18 37		18 52			19 06	19 11		19 38			19 52		20 11		20 37		20 52
Berwick	d					18 17								19 17							20 17				
Glynde	d					18 22								19 22							20 22				
Seaford	d		17 58				18 25					18 58			19 25					19 58		20 28			
Bishopstone	d		18 00				18 27					19 00			19 27					20 00		20 30			
Newhaven Harbour	d		18 03				18 30					19 03			19 30					20 03		20 33			
Newhaven Town	⛴ d		18 05				18 32					19 05			19 32					20 05		20 35			
Southease	d						18 36								19 36										
Lewes 4	a	18 07	18 14		18 18	18 28	18 44	18 49		19 07		19 14	19 18	19 28	19 44	19 50			20 07	20 14	20 28	20 44	20 49	←	21 07
	d	18 07	18 14		18 20	18 28	18 44	18 50	18 58	19 07		19 14	19 20	19 28	19 44	19 51	19 58		20 07	20 14	20 30	20 53	20 50	20 53	21 07
Falmer	d		18 21			18 35	18 51		19 05			19 21		19 35	19 51		20 05			20 21	20 37	→		21 00	
Moulsecoomb	d		18 24			18 38	18 54		19 08			19 24		19 38	19 54		20 08			20 24	20 40			21 03	
London Road (Brighton)	d		18 27			18 40	18 57		19 10			19 27		19 40	19 57		20 10			20 27	20 42			21 05	
Brighton 10	a	18 20	18 30			18 44	19 00		19 14	19 20		19 30		19 44	20 00		20 14		20 20	20 30	20 46			21 09	21 20
Cooksbridge	d																								
Plumpton	d				18 28								19 28												
Wivelsfield 4	a		*18 53*		18 34	*19 11*	*19 23*					*19 53*	19 34	*20 11*	*20 23*	20 03				*20 53*	*21 16*		21 02		
Haywards Heath 3	a		*18 48*		18 40	*19 15*	*19 18*	19 05				*19 48*	19 40	*20 16*	*20 18*	20 07				*20 48*	*21 21*		21 06		
Gatwick Airport 10	✈ a		*19 00*		18 54		*19 30*	19 24				*20 00*	19 54		*20 30*	20 24				*21 00*	*21 37*		21 24		
East Croydon	a		*19 16*		19 10	*19 23*	*19 46*	19 40	*19 56*			*20 16*	20 10	*20 23*	*20 46*	20 40	*20 53*			*21 16*			21 40	*21 53*	
London Bridge 4	⊖ a		*19 32*		*19 32*	*19c47*	*20 02*	*20 02*	*20c17*			*20 32*	*20 32*	*20c47*	*21 02*	*21 02*	*21c17*			*21 32*			*22 17*	*22c17*	
Clapham Junction 10	a				19 20	*19 33*	*20c02*	19 50	*20 05*				20 20	*20 33*		20 50	*21 03*			*21 33*			21 50	*22 03*	
London Victoria 15	⊖ a				19 27	*19 40*	*20c09*	19 57	*20 12*				20 27	*20 40*		20 57	*21 10*			*21 40*			21 57	*22 10*	

For general notes see front of timetable
For details of catering facilities see Directory of Train Operators

§ For additional trains between Hampden Park and Eastbourne see London to Hastings pages

b Change at London Bridge and Ashford International
c Change at Brighton and East Croydon

Table 189

Saturdays

Ashford, Hastings, Eastbourne, Seaford and Lewes → Brighton, Haywards Heath and London

Network Diagram - see first page of Table 184

		SN 1		SN 1	SN 1	SN 1	SN 1	SN 1	SN 1		SN 1	SN 1	SN 1	SN 1	SN 1	SN 1		SN 1	SN 1	SN 1	SN 1				
London Charing Cross 4	⊖ d							19 00							20 00				20 30						
London Waterloo (East) 4	⊖ d							19 03							20 03				20 33						
London Cannon Street 4	⊖ d							19b00							19b14										
London Bridge 4	⊖ d							19 08							20 08				20 38						
Ashford International	d							20 30							21 30				22 24						
Ham Street	d							20 39							21 39				22 33						
Appledore (Kent)	d							20 44							21 44				22 38						
Rye	a							20 53							21 53				22 47						
	d							20 54							21 57				22 47						
Winchelsea	d																		22 51						
Doleham	d																		22 57						
Three Oaks	d																		23 01						
Ore	d			20 21		20 50					21 21							22 22	23 06						
Hastings 4	a			20 24		20 53		21 11			21 24				22 14			22 25	23 09						
	d			20 25		20 55		21 12			21 25		21 42		22 16			22 26			23 13				
St Leonards Warrior Sq 4	d			20 28		20 58		21 15			21 28		21 45		22 19			22 29			23 16				
Bexhill 4	d			20 35		21 05		21 22			21 35		21 51		22 25			22 38			23 22				
Collington	d			20 37		21 07					21 37		21 53					22 40			23 24				
Cooden Beach	d			20 40		21 10					21 40		21 56					22 43			23 27				
Normans Bay	d			20 43														22 46							
Pevensey Bay	d																								
Pevensey & Westham	d			20 48		21 16					21 46		22 02					22 51			23 33				
Hampden Park 4 §	d			20 52		21 20					21 51		22 07					22 55			23 38				
Eastbourne 4	a			20 57		21 25		21 37			21 56		22 12		22 40			23 00			23 43				
	d			21 03		21 31		21 45			22 03		22 18		22 45			23 05			23 48				
Hampden Park 4 §	d			21 07							22 07							23 09			23 52				
Polegate	d			21 11		21 37		21 52			22 11		22 25		22 52			23 13			23 56				
Berwick	d			21 17							22 17							23 18							
Glynde	d			21 22							22 22							23 24							
Seaford	d	20 58			21 28				21 58			22 20				22 58				23 25					
Bishopstone	d	21 00			21 30				22 00			22 22				23 00				23 27					
Newhaven Harbour	d	21 03			21 33				22 03			22 25				23 03				23 30					
Newhaven Town	d	21 05			21 35				22 05			22 27				23 05				23 32					
Southease	d																								
Lewes 4	a	21 14		21 28	21 44	21 49	←	22 07	22 14		22 28	22 35	22 38	←	23 07	23 14		23 29		23 40	00 08				
	d	21 14		21 28	21 53	21 50	21 53	22 07	22 14		22 28	22 42	22 40	22 42	23 07	23 14		23 29		23 40	00 08				
Falmer	d	21 21		21 36	→		22 00		22 21		22 35	→		22 49		23 21		23 37		23 47	00 15				
Moulsecoomb	d	21 24		21 39			22 03		22 24		22 38			22 52		23 24		23 40		23 50	00 18				
London Road (Brighton)	d	21 27		21 41			22 05		22 27		22 40			22 54		23 27		23 42		23 53	00 21				
Brighton 10	a	21 30		21 45			22 09	22 20	22 31		22 44			22 58	23 20	23 31		23 46		23 56	00 24				
Cooksbridge	d																								
Plumpton	d												22 48												
Wivelsfield 4	a	21 53		22 16		22 02		22 49					22 54	23 19		23 53									
Haywards Heath 3	a	21 58		22 21		22 06		22 54					22 58	23 23		23 58									
Gatwick Airport 10	a	22 16		22 37		22 23		23c12					23 12	23 42		00 14									
East Croydon	a			22 23		22 40	23e30	23 32					23 30	00 02		00 35									
London Bridge 4	⊖ a			22f47		23 17		23 47					00 19	00f52											
Clapham Junction 10	a			22 33		22 49		00f11					23 42	00f28		01f02									
London Victoria 15	⊖ a			22 40		22 58		00f18					23 52	00f36		01f09									

For general notes see front of timetable
For details of catering facilities see Directory of Train Operators

§ For additional trains between Hampden Park and Eastbourne see London to Hastings pages

b Change at London Bridge and Ashford International
c Change at Brighton and Haywards Heath
e Change at Brighton and Wivelsfield
f Change at Brighton and East Croydon

Sundays
until 6 September

Ashford, Hastings, Eastbourne, Seaford and Lewes → Brighton, Haywards Heath and London

Network Diagram - see first page of Table 184

Station		SN 1	SN 1	SN 1	SN 1	SN 1	SN 1	SN 1	SN 1	SN 1	SN 1	SN 1	SN 1
					A 🛒			A 🛒				A 🛒	
London Charing Cross [4]	⊖ d												
London Waterloo (East) [4]	⊖ d												
London Cannon Street [4]	⊖ d												
London Bridge [4]	⊖ d												
Ashford International	d												
Ham Street	d												
Appledore (Kent)	d												
Rye	a												
	d												
Winchelsea	d												
Doleham	d												
Three Oaks	d												
Ore	d											08 14	
Hastings [4]	a											08 17	
	d	23p13						07 13				08 18	
St Leonards Warrior Sq [4]	d	23p16						07 16				08 21	
Bexhill [4]	d	23p22						07 23				08 28	
Collington	d	23p24						07 25				08 30	
Cooden Beach	d	23p27						07 28				08 33	
Normans Bay	d												
Pevensey Bay	d												
Pevensey & Westham	d	23p33						07 34				08 39	
Hampden Park [4] §	d	23p38						07 38				08 43	
Eastbourne [4]	a	23p43						07 44				08 49	
	d	23p48	05 37		06 58	07 30		07 55		08 34		08 59	
Hampden Park [4] §	d	23p52			07 02	07 34				08 38			
Polegate	d	23p56	05 44		07 06	07 38		08 02		08 42		09 06	
Berwick	d					07 44				08 48			
Glynde	d					07 49				08 53			
Seaford	d			06 57			07 57		08 27		08 57		09 27
Bishopstone	d			06 59			07 59		08 29		08 59		09 29
Newhaven Harbour	d			07 02			08 02		08 32		09 02		09 32
Newhaven Town ⛴	d			07 04			08 04		08 34		09 04		09 34
Southease	d			07 08			08 08				09 08		
Lewes [4]	a	00 08	05 56	07 15	07 18	07 55	08 15	08 18	08 43	08 59	09 15	09 18	09 43
	d	00 08	05 57	07 22	07 22	07 56	08 22	08 22	08 44	09 00	09 22	09 22	09 44
Falmer	d	00 15		07 29		08 03	08 29		08 51		09 29		09 51
Moulsecoomb	d	00 18		07 32		08 07	08 32		08 54		09 32		09 54
London Road (Brighton)	d	00 21		07 34		08 09	08 34		08 56		09 34		09 56
Brighton [10]	a	00 24	06 09	07 38		08 13	08 38		09 00	09 12	09 38		10 00
Cooksbridge	d												
Plumpton	d							08 30				09 30	
Wivelsfield [4]	a		06 32	08 16	07 36		09 16	08 36			10 16	09 36	
Haywards Heath [3]	a		06 36	08 02	07 40	08 32	09 02	08 40		09 32	10 02	09 40	
Gatwick Airport [10] ✈	a		06 51	08 16	07 52	08 46	09 16	08 52		09 46	10 16	09 52	
East Croydon	a		07b01	08 33	08 09	09 03	09 33	09 09	09 45	10 03	10 33	10 09	10 45
London Bridge [4]	⊖ a		07b17	08 47	08c42	09 17	09 47	09c42		10 17	10 47	10c42	
Clapham Junction [10]	a		07e19	08f48	08 18	09f18	09f48	09 18	09 55	10f18	10f48	10 18	10 55
London Victoria [15]	⊖ a		07e26	08f55	08 25	09f25	09f55	09 25	10 02	10f25	10f55	10 25	11 02

Station		SN 1	SN 1	SN 1	SN 1	SN 1	SN 1	SN 1	SN 1	SN 1	SN 1	SN 1	SN 1
				A 🛒				A 🛒				A 🛒	
London Charing Cross [4]	⊖ d									09 00			
London Waterloo (East) [4]	⊖ d									09 03			
London Cannon Street [4]	⊖ d												
London Bridge [4]	⊖ d									09 08			
Ashford International	d	08 16				09 21				10 21			
Ham Street	d	08 25				09 30				10 30			
Appledore (Kent)	d	08 30				09 35				10 35			
Rye	a	08 39				09 44				10 44			
	d	08 41				09 46				10 46			
Winchelsea	d	08 44											
Doleham	d	08 51											
Three Oaks	d	08 54											
Ore	d	09 00		09 14				10 14				11 14	
Hastings [4]	a	09 03		09 17		10 03		10 17		11 03		11 17	
	d	09 04		09 18		10 04		10 18		11 04		11 18	
St Leonards Warrior Sq [4]	d	09 07		09 21		10 07		10 21		11 07		11 21	
Bexhill [4]	d	09 14		09 28		10 14		10 28		11 14		11 28	
Collington	d			09 30				10 30				11 30	
Cooden Beach	d			09 33				10 33				11 33	
Normans Bay	d												
Pevensey Bay	d												
Pevensey & Westham	d			09 39				10 39				11 39	
Hampden Park [4] §	d			09 43				10 43				11 43	
Eastbourne [4]	a	09 29		09 49		10 29		10 49		11 29		11 49	
	d	09 34		09 59		10 34		10 59		11 34		11 59	
Hampden Park [4] §	d	09 38				10 38				11 38			
Polegate	d	09 42		10 06		10 42		11 06		11 42		12 06	
Berwick	d	09 48				10 48				11 48			
Glynde	d	09 53				10 53				11 53			
Seaford	d		09 57		10 27		10 57		11 27		11 57		12 27
Bishopstone	d		09 59		10 29		10 59		11 29		11 59		12 29
Newhaven Harbour	d		10 02		10 32		11 02		11 32		12 02		12 32
Newhaven Town ⛴	d		10 04		10 34		11 04		11 34		12 04		12 34
Southease	d		10 08				11 08				12 08		
Lewes [4]	a	09 59	10 15	10 18	10 43	10 59	11 15	11 18	11 43	11 59	12 15	12 18	12 43
	d	10 00	10 22	10 22	10 44	11 00	11 22	11 22	11 44	12 00	12 22	12 22	12 44
Falmer	d		10 29		10 51		11 29		11 51		12 29		12 51
Moulsecoomb	d		10 32		10 54		11 32		11 54		12 32		12 54
London Road (Brighton)	d		10 34		10 56		11 34		11 56		12 34		12 56
Brighton [10]	a	10 12	10 38		11 00	11 12	11 38		12 00	12 12	12 38		13 00
Cooksbridge	d												
Plumpton	d			10 30				11 30				12 30	
Wivelsfield [4]	a		11 16	10 36			12 16	11 36			13 16	12 36	
Haywards Heath [3]	a	10 32	11 02	10 40		11 32	12 02	11 40		12 32	13 02	12 40	
Gatwick Airport [10] ✈	a	10 46	11 16	10 52		11 46	12 16	11 52		12 46	13 16	12 52	
East Croydon	a	11 03	11 33	11 09	11 45	12 03	12 33	12 09	12 45	13 03	13 33	13 09	13 45
London Bridge [4]	⊖ a	11 17	11 47	11c42		12 17	12 47	12c42		13 17	13 47	13c42	
Clapham Junction [10]	a	11f18	11f48	11 18	11 55	12f18	12f48	12 18	12 55	13f18	13f48	13 18	13 55
London Victoria [15]	⊖ a	11f25	11f55	11 25	12 02	12f25	12f55	12 25	13 02	13f25	13f55	13 25	14 02

For general notes see front of timetable
For details of catering facilities see Directory of Train Operators

§ For additional trains between Hampden Park and Eastbourne see London to Hastings pages

A 🛒 from Lewes
b Change at Brighton
c London Bridge
e Change at Haywards Heath
f Change at Brighton and East Croydon

Table 189

Ashford, Hastings, Eastbourne, Seaford and Lewes → Brighton, Haywards Heath and London

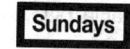

Sundays
until 6 September

Network Diagram - see first page of Table 184

Station		SN 1		SN 1	SN 1 A 🛒	SN 1	SN 1	SN 1	SN 1 A 🛒	SN 1	SN 1	SN 1	SN 1 A 🛒	SN 1	SN 1	SN 1	SN 1 A 🛒	SN 1	SN 1	SN 1	SN 1 A 🛒	SN 1	SN 1	SN 1	SN 1 A 🛒
London Charing Cross 4 ⊖	d	10 00					11 00				12 00				13 00				14 00				15 00		
London Waterloo (East) 4 ⊖	d	10 03					11 03				12 03				13 03				14 03				15 03		
London Cannon Street 4 ⊖	d																								
London Bridge 4 ⊖	d	10 08					11 08				12 08				13 08				14 08				15 08		
Ashford International	d	11 21					12 21				13 21				14 21				15 21				16 21		
Ham Street	d	11 30					12 30				13 30				14 30				15 30				16 30		
Appledore (Kent)	d	11 35					12 35				13 35				14 35				15 35				16 35		
Rye	a	11 44					12 44				13 44				14 44				15 44				16 44		
	d	11 46					12 46				13 46				14 46				15 46				16 46		
Winchelsea	d																								
Doleham	d																								
Three Oaks	d																								
Ore	d				12 14				13 14				14 14				15 14				16 14				17 14
Hastings 4	a	12 03			12 17		13 03		13 17		14 03		14 17		15 03		15 17		16 03		16 17		17 03		17 17
St Leonards Warrior Sq 4	d	12 04			12 18		13 04		13 18		14 04		14 18		15 04		15 18		16 04		16 18		17 04		17 18
Bexhill 4	d	12 07			12 21		13 07		13 21		14 07		14 21		15 07		15 21		16 07		16 21		17 07		17 21
Collington	d	12 14			12 28		13 14		13 28		14 14		14 28		15 14		15 28		16 14		16 28		17 14		17 28
Cooden Beach	d				12 30				13 30				14 30				15 30				16 30				17 30
Normans Bay	d				12 33				13 33				14 33				15 33				16 33				17 33
Pevensey Bay	d																								
Pevensey & Westham	d				12 39				13 39				14 39				15 39				16 39				17 39
Hampden Park 4 §	d				12 43				13 43				14 43				15 43				16 43				17 43
Eastbourne 4	a	12 29			12 49		13 29		13 49		14 29		14 49		15 29		15 49		16 29		16 49		17 29		17 49
	d	12 34			12 59		13 34		13 59		14 34		14 59		15 34		15 59		16 34		16 59		17 34		17 59
Hampden Park 4 §	d	12 38					13 38				14 38				15 38				16 38				17 38		
Polegate	d	12 42			13 06		13 42		14 06		14 42		15 06		15 42		16 06		16 42		17 06		17 42		18 06
Berwick	d	12 48					13 48				14 48				15 48				16 48				17 48		
Glynde	d	12 53					13 53				14 53				15 53				16 53				17 53		
Seaford	d			12 57		13 27		13 57		14 27		14 57		15 27		15 57		16 27		16 57		17 27		17 57	
Bishopstone	d			12 59		13 29		13 59		14 29		14 59		15 29		15 59		16 29		16 59		17 29		17 59	
Newhaven Harbour	d			13 02		13 32		14 02		14 32		15 02		15 32		16 02		16 32		17 02		17 32		18 02	
Newhaven Town ⛴	d			13 04		13 34		14 04		14 34		15 04		15 34		16 04		16 34		17 04		17 34		18 04	
Southease	d			13 08				14 08				15 08				16 08				17 08				18 08	
Lewes 4	a	12 59		13 15	13 18	13 43	13 59	14 15	14 18	14 43	14 59	15 15	15 18	15 43	15 59	16 15	16 18	16 43	16 59	17 15	17 18	17 43	17 59	18 15	18 18
	d	13 00		13 22	13 22	13 44	14 00	14 22	14 22	14 44	15 00	15 22	15 22	15 44	16 00	16 22	16 22	16 44	17 00	17 22	17 22	17 44	18 00	18 22	18 22
Falmer	d			13 29		13 51		14 29		14 51		15 29		15 51		16 29		16 51		17 29		17 51		18 29	
Moulsecoomb	d			13 32		13 54		14 32		14 54		15 32		15 54		16 32		16 54		17 32		17 54		18 32	
London Road (Brighton)	d			13 34		13 56		14 34		14 56		15 34		15 56		16 34		16 56		17 34		17 56		18 34	
Brighton 10	a	13 12		13 38		14 00	14 12	14 38		15 00	15 12	15 38		16 00	16 12	16 38		17 00	17 12	17 38		18 00	18 12	18 38	
Cooksbridge	d																								
Plumpton	d																16 30				17 30				18 30
Wivelsfield 4	a			14 16	13 36			15 16	14 36			16 16	15 36			17 16	16 36			18 16	17 36			19 16	18 36
Haywards Heath 3	a	13 32		14 02	13 40		14 32	15 02	14 40		15 32	16 02	15 40		16 32	17 02	16 40		17 32	18 02	17 40		18 32	19 02	18 40
Gatwick Airport 10 ✈	a	13 46		14 16	13 52		14 46	15 16	14 52		15 46	16 16	15 52		16 46	17 16	16 52		17 46	18 16	17 52		18 46	19 16	18 52
East Croydon 🚌	a	14 03		14 33	14 09	14 45	15 03	15 33	15 09	15 45	16 03	16 33	16 09	16 45	17 03	17 33	17 09	17 45	18 03	18 33	18 09	18 45	19 03	19 33	19 09
London Bridge 4 ⊖	a	14 17		14 47	14b42		15 17	15 47	15b42		16 17	16 47	16b42		17 17	17 47	17b42		18 17	18 47	18b42		19 17	19 47	19b42
Clapham Junction 10	a	14c18		14c48	14 18	14 55	15c18	15c48	15 18	15 55	16c18	16c48	16 18	16 55	17c18	17c48	17 18	17 55	18c18	18c48	18 18	18 55	19c18	19c48	19 18
London Victoria 15 ⊖	a	14c25		14c55	14 25	15 02	15c25	15c55	15 25	16 02	16c25	16c55	16 25	17 02	17c25	17c55	17 25	18 02	18c25	18c55	18 25	19 02	19c25	19c55	19 25

For general notes see front of timetable
For details of catering facilities see Directory of Train Operators

§ For additional trains between Hampden Park and Eastbourne see London to Hastings pages

A 🛒 from Lewes
b London Bridge
c Change at Brighton and East Croydon

Table 189

Sundays

until 6 September

Ashford, Hastings, Eastbourne, Seaford and Lewes → Brighton, Haywards Heath and London

Network Diagram - see first page of Table 184

		SN 1	SN 1	SN 1	SN 1	SN 1	SN 1	SN 1	SN 1	SN 1	SN 1	SN 1	SN 1	SN 1	SN 1	SN 1	SN 1	SN 1	SN 1	SN 1	SN 1	SN 1	SN 1
London Charing Cross 4	⊖ d		16 00				17 00				18 00				19 00				20 00			21 00	
London Waterloo (East) 4	⊖ d		16 03				17 03				18 03				19 03				20 03			21 03	
London Cannon Street 4	⊖ d																						
London Bridge 4	⊖ d		16 08				17 08				18 08				19 08				20 08			21 08	
Ashford International	d		17 21				18 21				19 21				20 21				21 21			22 20	
Ham Street	d		17 30				18 30				19 30				20 30				21 30			22 29	
Appledore (Kent)	d		17 35				18 35				19 35				20 35				21 35			22 34	
Rye	a		17 44				18 44				19 44				20 44				21 44			22 43	
	d		17 46				18 46				19 46				20 46				21 46			22 43	
Winchelsea	d																					22 47	
Doleham	d																					22 53	
Three Oaks	d																					22 57	
Ore	d				18 14				19 14				20 14				21 14				22 14	23 02	
Hastings 4	a		18 03		18 17		19 03		19 17		20 03		20 17		21 03		21 17		22 03		22 17	23 05	
	d		18 04		18 18		19 04		19 18		20 04		20 18		21 04		21 18		22 04		22 18		23 18
St Leonards Warrior Sq 4	d		18 07		18 21		19 07		19 21		20 07		20 21		21 07		21 21		22 07		22 21		23 21
Bexhill 4	d		18 14		18 28		19 14		19 28		20 14		20 28		21 14		21 28		22 14		22 28		23 28
Collington	d				18 30				19 30				20 30				21 30				22 30		23 30
Cooden Beach	d				18 33				19 33				20 33				21 33				22 33		23 33
Normans Bay	d																						
Pevensey Bay	d																						
Pevensey & Westham	d				18 39				19 39				20 39				21 39				22 39		23 39
Hampden Park 4 §	d				18 43				19 43				20 43				21 43				22 43		23 43
Eastbourne 4	a		18 29		18 49		19 29		19 49		20 29		20 49		21 29		21 49		22 29		22 49		23 48
	d		18 34		18 59		19 34		19 59		20 34		20 59		21 34		21 59		22 34		22 59		
Hampden Park 4 §	d		18 38				19 38				20 38				21 38				22 38				
Polegate	d		18 42		19 06		19 42		20 06		20 42		21 06		21 42		22 06		22 42		23 06		
Berwick	d		18 48				19 48				20 48				21 48				22 48				
Glynde	d		18 53				19 53				20 53				21 53				22 53				
Seaford	d	18 27		18 57		19 27		19 57		20 27		20 57		21 27		21 53		22 27		22 53			
Bishopstone	d	18 29		18 59		19 29		19 59		20 29		20 59		21 29		21 55		22 29		22 55			
Newhaven Harbour	d	18 32		19 02		19 32		20 02		20 32		21 02		21 32		21 58		22 32		22 58			
Newhaven Town	⛴ d	18 34		19 04		19 34		20 04		20 34		21 04		21 34		22 00		22 34		23 00			
Southease	d			19 08				20 08															
Lewes 4	a	18 43	18 59	19 15	19 18	19 43	19 59	20 15	20 18	20 43	20 59	21 13	21 18	21 43	21 59	22 09	22 18	22 43	22 59	23 09	23 18		
	d	18 44	19 00	19 22	19 22	19 44	20 00	20 22	20 22	20 44	21 00	21 22	21 22	21 44	22 00	22 10	22 19	22 44	23 00	23 10	23 19		
Falmer	d	18 51		19 29		19 51		20 29		20 51		21 29		21 51		22 17	22 26	22 51		23 17	23 26		
Moulsecoomb	d	18 54		19 32		19 54		20 32		20 54		21 32		21 54		22 20	22 29	22 54		23 20	23 29		
London Road (Brighton)	d	18 56		19 34		19 56		20 34		20 56		21 34		21 56		22 22	22 31	22 56		23 22	23 31		
Brighton 10	a	19 00	19 12	19 38		20 00	20 12	20 38		21 00	21 12	21 38		22 00	22 12	22 26	22 35	23 00	23 12	23 26	23 35		
Cooksbridge	d																						
Plumpton	d				19 30				20 30				21 30										
Wivelsfield 4	a			20 16	19 36				20 36	21 20			21 36	22 20			23 19				00 01		
Haywards Heath 3	a		19 32	20 02	19 40		20 32	21 02	20 40	21 24	21 32	22 02	21 40	22 24	22 32		23 02	23 27					
Gatwick Airport 10	✈ a		19 46	20 16	19 52		20 46	21 16	20 52	21 41	21 46	22 16	21 52	22 41	22 46		23 16	23 43			00 14		
East Croydon	🚋 a	19 45	20 03	20 33	20 09	20 45	21 03	21 33	21 09	22 00	22 03	22 33	22 09	23 00	23 03		23 33	23 59			00 35		
London Bridge 4	⊖ a		20 17	20 47	20b42		21 17	21 47	21b42		22 17	22 47	22b42		23 17		23 47	00 14					
Clapham Junction 10	a	19 55	20c18	20c48	20 18	20 55	21c18	21c48	21 18	22 10	22c18	23c07	22 18	23 10	23c31		00c10	00c29			01c02		
London Victoria 15	⊖ a	20 02	20c25	20c55	20 25	21 02	21c25	21c55	21 25	22 17	22c25	23c14	22 25	23 17	23c38		00c18	00c37			01c09		

For general notes see front of timetable
For details of catering facilities see
Directory of Train Operators

§ For additional trains between Hampden Park and Eastbourne see London to Hastings pages

b London Bridge
c Change at Brighton and East Croydon

Table 189

Sundays
from 13 September

Ashford, Hastings, Eastbourne, Seaford and Lewes → Brighton, Haywards Heath and London

Network Diagram - see first page of Table 184

		SN 1	SN 1	SN 1	SN 1	SN 1	SN 1		SN 1	SN 1	SN 1	SN 1	SN 1	SN 1		SN 1	SN 1	SN 1	SN 1	SN 1	SN 1		SN 1	SN 1	SN 1
				A			A						A						A						A
London Charing Cross 4	⊖ d																								
London Waterloo (East) 4	⊖ d																								
London Cannon Street 4	⊖ d																								
London Bridge 4	⊖ d																								
Ashford International	d																08 16						09 21		
Ham Street	d																08 25						09 30		
Appledore (Kent)	d																08 30						09 35		
Rye	a																08 39						09 44		
	d																08 41						09 46		
Winchelsea	d																08 44								
Doleham	d																08 51								
Three Oaks	d																08 54								
Ore	d												08 14				09 00		09 14						10 14
Hastings 4	a												08 17				09 03		09 17				10 03		10 17
	d	23p13											08 18				09 04		09 18				10 04		10 18
St Leonards Warrior Sq 4	d	23p16											08 21				09 07		09 21				10 07		10 21
Bexhill 4	d	23p22											08 28				09 14		09 28				10 14		10 28
Collington	d	23p24											08 30						09 30						10 30
Cooden Beach	d	23p27											08 33						09 33						10 33
Normans Bay	d																								
Pevensey Bay	d																								
Pevensey & Westham	d	23p33											08 39						09 39						10 39
Hampden Park 4 §	d	23p38											08 43						09 43						10 43
Eastbourne 4	a	23p43											08 49				09 29		09 49				10 29		10 49
	d	23p48		06 54	07 30		07 55				08 34		08 55				09 34		09 55				10 34		10 55
Hampden Park 4 §	d	23p52		06 58	07 34						08 38						09 38						10 38		
Polegate	d	23p56		07 02	07 38		08 02				08 42		09 02				09 42		10 02				10 42		11 02
Berwick	d				07 44						08 48						09 48						10 48		
Glynde	d				07 49						08 53						09 53						10 53		
Seaford	d					07 53				08 27		08 53				09 27		09 53			10 27			10 53	
Bishopstone	d					07 55				08 29		08 55				09 29		09 55			10 29			10 55	
Newhaven Harbour	d					07 58				08 32		08 58				09 32		09 58			10 32			10 58	
Newhaven Town	⛴ d					08 00				08 34		09 00				09 34		10 00			10 34			11 00	
Southease	d					08 04						09 04						10 04						11 04	
Lewes 4	a	00 08		07 14	07 55	08 11	08 14		←	08 43	08 59	09 11	09 14	←		09 43	09 59	10 11	10 14	←	10 43		10 59	11 11	11 14
	d	00 08	07 18	07 20	07 56	08 18	08 16		08 18	08 44	09 00	09 18	09 16	09 18		09 44	10 00	10 18	10 16	10 18	10 44		11 00	11 18	11 16
Falmer	d	00 15	07 25		08 03	→			08 25	08 51		→		09 25		09 51		→		10 25	10 51			→	
Moulsecoomb	d	00 18	07 28		08 07				08 28	08 54				09 28		09 54				10 28	10 54				
London Road (Brighton)	d	00 21	07 30		08 09				08 30	08 56				09 30		09 56				10 30	10 56				
Brighton 10	a	00 24	07 34		08 13				08 34	09 00	09 12			09 34		10 00	10 12			10 34	11 00		11 12		
Cooksbridge	d																								
Plumpton	d						08 24						09 24						10 24						11 24
Wivelsfield 4	a		08 16	07 32			08 31		09 16				09 31	10 16					10 31	11 16					11 31
Haywards Heath 3	a		08 00	07 36			08 36		09 00		09 30		09 35	10 00			10 30		10 35	11 00			11 30		11 35
Gatwick Airport 10	✈ a		08 14	07 51			08 51		09 14		09 44		09 51	10 14			10 44		10 51	11 14			11 44		11 51
East Croydon	a		08 31	08 09			09 09		09 31		10 01		10 09	10 31			11 01		11 09	11 31			12 01		12 09
London Bridge 4	⊖ a		08 47	08 42			09 42		09 47		10 17		10b42	10 47			11 17		11 42	11 47			12 17		12 42
Clapham Junction 10	a		08c54	08 24			09 24		09 47		10c24		10 24	10 47			11c24		11 24	11 47			12c24		12 24
London Victoria 15	⊖ a		09c01	08 31			09 31		09 53		10c31		10 31	10 53			11c31		11 31	11 53			12c31		12 31

For general notes see front of timetable
For details of catering facilities see Directory of Train Operators

§ For additional trains between Hampden Park and Eastbourne see London to Hastings pages

A ✠ from Lewes
b London Bridge
c Change at Brighton and East Croydon

Table 189

Sundays

from 13 September

Ashford, Hastings, Eastbourne, Seaford and Lewes → Brighton, Haywards Heath and London

Network Diagram - see first page of Table 184

		SN	SN	SN	SN	SN	SN	SN	SN	SN	SN	SN
		1	1	1	1	1	1	1	1	1	1	1
						A ⌶					A ⌶	
London Charing Cross 4 ⊖	d			09 00					10 00			
London Waterloo (East) 4 ⊖	d			09 03					10 03			
London Cannon Street 4 ⊖	d											
London Bridge 4 ⊖	d			09 08					10 08			
Ashford International	d			10 21					11 21			
Ham Street	d			10 30					11 30			
Appledore (Kent)	d			10 35					11 35			
Rye	a			10 44					11 44			
	d			10 46					11 46			
Winchelsea	d											
Doleham	d											
Three Oaks	d											
Ore	d					11 14					12 14	
Hastings 4	a			11 03		11 17			12 03		12 17	
	d			11 04		11 18			12 04		12 18	
St Leonards Warrior Sq 4	d			11 07		11 21			12 07		12 21	
Bexhill 4	d			11 14		11 28			12 14		12 28	
Collington	d					11 30					12 30	
Cooden Beach	d					11 33					12 33	
Normans Bay	d											
Pevensey Bay	d											
Pevensey & Westham	d					11 39					12 39	
Hampden Park 4 §	d					11 43					12 43	
Eastbourne 4	a			11 29		11 49			12 29		12 49	
	d			11 34		11 55			12 34		12 55	
Hampden Park 4 §	d			11 38					12 38			
Polegate	d			11 42		12 02			12 42		13 02	
Berwick	d			11 48					12 48			
Glynde	d			11 53					12 53			
Seaford	d		11 27		11 53			12 27		12 53		
Bishopstone	d		11 29		11 55			12 29		12 55		
Newhaven Harbour	d		11 32		11 58			12 32		12 58		
Newhaven Town ⛴	d		11 34		12 00			12 34		13 00		
Southease	d				12 04					13 04		
Lewes 4	a	⟵	11 43	11 59	12 11	12 14	⟵	12 43	12 59	13 11	13 14	⟵
	d	11 18	11 44	12 00	12 18 ⟶	12 16	12 18	12 44	13 00	13 18 ⟶	13 16	13 18
Falmer	d	11 25	11 51				12 25	12 51				13 25
Moulsecoomb	d	11 28	11 54				12 28	12 54				13 28
London Road (Brighton)	d	11 30	11 56				12 30	12 56				13 30
Brighton 10	a	11 34	12 00	12 12			12 34	13 00	13 12			13 34
Cooksbridge	d											
Plumpton	d					12 24						
Wivelsfield 4	a	12 16				12 31	13 16				13 31	14 16
Haywards Heath 3	a	12 00		12 30		12 35	13 00		13 30		13 35	14 00
Gatwick Airport 10 ✈	a	12 14		12 44		12 52	13 14		13 44		13 52	14 14
East Croydon 🚋	a	12 31		13 01		13 09	13 31		14 01		14 09	14 31
London Bridge 4 ⊖	a	12 47		13 17		13 42	13 47		14 17		14 42	14 47
Clapham Junction 10	a	12 47		13b24		13 24	13 47		14b24		14 24	14 47
London Victoria 15 ⊖	a	12 53		13b31		13 31	13 53		14b31		14 31	14 53

		SN	SN	SN	SN	SN	SN	SN	SN	SN	SN
		1	1	1	1	1	1	1	1	1	1
					A ⌶					A ⌶	
London Charing Cross 4 ⊖	d		11 00					12 00			
London Waterloo (East) 4 ⊖	d		11 03					12 03			
London Cannon Street 4 ⊖	d										
London Bridge 4 ⊖	d		11 08					12 08			
Ashford International	d		12 21					13 21			
Ham Street	d		12 30					13 30			
Appledore (Kent)	d		12 35					13 35			
Rye	a		12 44					13 44			
	d		12 46					13 46			
Winchelsea	d										
Doleham	d										
Three Oaks	d										
Ore	d				13 14					14 14	
Hastings 4	a		13 03		13 17			14 03		14 17	
	d		13 04		13 18			14 04		14 18	
St Leonards Warrior Sq 4	d		13 07		13 21			14 07		14 21	
Bexhill 4	d		13 14		13 28			14 14		14 27	
Collington	d				13 30					14 29	
Cooden Beach	d				13 33					14 32	
Normans Bay	d										
Pevensey Bay	d										
Pevensey & Westham	d				13 39					14 38	
Hampden Park 4 §	d				13 43					14 43	
Eastbourne 4	a		13 29		13 49			14 29		14 48	
	d		13 34		13 55			14 34		14 55	
Hampden Park 4 §	d		13 38					14 38			
Polegate	d		13 42		14 02			14 42		15 02	
Berwick	d		13 48					14 48			
Glynde	d		13 53					14 53			
Seaford	d	13 27		13 53			14 27		14 53		
Bishopstone	d	13 29		13 55			14 29		14 55		
Newhaven Harbour	d	13 32		13 58			14 32		14 58		
Newhaven Town ⛴	d	13 34		14 00			14 34		15 00		
Southease	d			14 04					15 04		
Lewes 4	a	13 43	13 59	14 11	14 14	⟵	14 43	14 59	15 11	15 14	⟵
	d	13 44	14 00	14 18 ⟶	14 16	14 18	14 44	15 00	15 18 ⟶	15 16	15 18
Falmer	d	13 51				14 25	14 51				15 25
Moulsecoomb	d	13 54				14 28	14 54				15 28
London Road (Brighton)	d	13 56				14 30	14 56				15 30
Brighton 10	a	14 00	14 12			14 34	15 00	15 12			15 34
Cooksbridge	d										
Plumpton	d										
Wivelsfield 4	a				14 31	15 16				15 31	16 16
Haywards Heath 3	a		14 30		14 35	15 00		15 30		15 35	16 00
Gatwick Airport 10 ✈	a		14 44		14 52	15 14		15 44		15 52	16 14
East Croydon 🚋	a		15 01		15 09	15 31		16 01		16 09	16 31
London Bridge 4 ⊖	a		15 17		15 42	15 47		16 17		16 42	16 47
Clapham Junction 10	a		15b24		15 24	15 47		16b24		16 24	16 47
London Victoria 15 ⊖	a		15b31		15 31	15 53		16b31		16 31	16 53

For general notes see front of timetable
For details of catering facilities see Directory of Train Operators

§ For additional trains between Hampden Park and Eastbourne see London to Hastings pages

A ⌶ from Lewes

b Change at Brighton and East Croydon

Table 189

Sundays

from 13 September

Ashford, Hastings, Eastbourne, Seaford and Lewes → Brighton, Haywards Heath and London

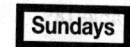

Network Diagram - see first page of Table 184

		SN 1	SN 1	SN 1	SN 1		SN 1	SN 1	SN 1	SN 1	SN 1	SN 1		SN 1	SN 1	SN 1	SN 1	SN 1	SN 1		SN 1	SN 1	SN 1	SN 1	SN 1
					A 🚌						A 🚌						A 🚌								
London Charing Cross 4 ⊖	d		13 00						14 00						15 00						16 00				
London Waterloo (East) 4 ⊖	d		13 03						14 03						15 03						16 03				
London Cannon Street 4 ⊖	d																								
London Bridge 4 ⊖	d		13 08						14 08						15 08						16 08				
Ashford International	d		14 21						15 21						16 21						17 21				
Ham Street	d		14 30						15 30						16 30						17 30				
Appledore (Kent)	d		14 35						15 35						16 35						17 35				
Rye	a		14 44						15 44						16 44						17 44				
	d		14 46						15 46						16 46						17 46				
Winchelsea	d																								
Doleham	d																								
Three Oaks	d																								
Ore	d				15 14						16 14						17 14						18 14		
Hastings 4	a		15 03		15 17				16 03		16 17				17 03		17 17				18 03		18 17		
	d		15 04		15 18				16 04		16 18				17 04		17 18				18 04		18 18		
St Leonards Warrior Sq 4	d		15 07		15 21				16 07		16 21				17 07		17 21				18 07		18 21		
Bexhill 4	d		15 14		15 27				16 14		16 27				17 14		17 28				18 14		18 28		
Collington	d				15 29						16 29						17 30						18 30		
Cooden Beach	d				15 32						16 32						17 33						18 33		
Normans Bay	d																								
Pevensey Bay	d																								
Pevensey & Westham	d				15 38						16 38						17 39						18 39		
Hampden Park 4 §	d				15 43						16 43						17 43						18 43		
Eastbourne 4	a		15 29		15 48				16 29		16 48				17 29		17 49				18 29		18 49		
	d		15 34		15 55				16 34		16 55				17 34		17 55				18 34		18 55		
Hampden Park 4 §	d		15 38						16 38						17 38						18 38				
Polegate	d		15 42		16 02				16 42		17 02				17 42		18 02				18 42		19 02		
Berwick	d		15 48						16 48						17 48						18 48				
Glynde	d		15 53						16 53						17 53						18 53				
Seaford	d	15 27		15 53				16 27		16 53				17 27		17 53			18 27			18 53			19 27
Bishopstone	d	15 29		15 55				16 29		16 55				17 29		17 55			18 29			18 55			19 29
Newhaven Harbour	d	15 32		15 58				16 32		16 58				17 32		17 58			18 32			18 58			19 32
Newhaven Town ⛴	d	15 34		16 00				16 34		17 00				17 34		18 00			18 34			19 00			19 34
Southease	d			16 04						17 04						18 04						19 04			
Lewes 4	a	15 43	15 59	16 11	16 14		←	16 43	16 59	17 11	17 14	←		17 43	17 59	18 11	18 14	←	18 43		18 59	19 11	19 14	←	19 43
	d	15 44	16 00	16 18 →	16 16		16 18	16 44	17 00	17 18 →	17 16	17 18		17 44	18 00	18 18 →	18 16	18 18	18 44		19 00	19 18 →	19 16	19 18	19 44
Falmer	d	15 51					16 25	16 51				17 25		17 51				18 25	18 51					19 25	19 51
Moulsecoomb	d	15 54					16 28	16 54				17 28		17 54				18 28	18 54					19 28	19 54
London Road (Brighton)	d	15 56					16 30	16 56				17 30		17 56				18 30	18 56					19 30	19 56
Brighton 10	a	16 00	16 12				16 34	17 00	17 12			17 34		18 00	18 12			18 34	19 00		19 12			19 34	20 00
Cooksbridge	d																								
Plumpton	d				16 24						17 24						18 24						19 24		
Wivelsfield 4	a				16 31		17 16				17 31	18 16					18 31	19 16					19 31	20 16	
Haywards Heath 3	a		16 30		16 35		17 00		17 30		17 35	18 00			18 30		18 35	19 00			19 30		19 35	20 00	
Gatwick Airport 10 ✈	a		16 44		16 52		17 14		17 44		17 52	18 14			18 44		18 52	19 14			19 44		19 52	20 14	
East Croydon 🚊	a		17 01		17 09		17 31		18 01		18 09	18 31			19 01		19 09	19 31			20 01		20 09	20 31	
London Bridge 4 ⊖	a		17 17		17 42		17 47		18 17		18 42	18 47			19 17		19 42	19 47			20 17		20 42	20 47	
Clapham Junction 10	a		17b24		17 24		17 47		18b24		18 24	18 47			19b24		19 24	19 47			20b24		20 24	20 47	
London Victoria 15 ⊖	a		17b31		17 31		17 53		18b31		18 31	18 53			19b31		19 31	19 53			20b31		20 31	20 53	

For general notes see front of timetable
For details of catering facilities see Directory of Train Operators

§ For additional trains between Hampden Park and Eastbourne see London to Hastings pages

A 🚌 from Lewes

b Change at Brighton and East Croydon

Table 189

Sundays

from 13 September

Ashford, Hastings, Eastbourne, Seaford and Lewes → Brighton, Haywards Heath and London

Network Diagram - see first page of Table 184

		SN 1	SN 1	SN 1		SN 1	SN 1	SN 1	SN 1	SN 1	SN 1		SN 1	SN 1	SN 1	SN 1	SN 1	SN 1		SN 1	SN 1	SN 1	SN 1		
London Charing Cross 4	⊖ d	17 00						18 00						19 00				20 00				21 00			
London Waterloo (East) 4	⊖ d	17 03						18 03						19 03				20 03				21 03			
London Cannon Street 4	⊖ d																								
London Bridge 4	⊖ d	17 08						18 08						19 08				20 08				21 08			
Ashford International	d	18 21						19 21						20 21				21 21				22 20			
Ham Street	d	18 30						19 30						20 30				21 30				22 29			
Appledore (Kent)	d	18 35						19 35						20 35				21 35				22 34			
Rye	a	18 44						19 44						20 44				21 44				22 43			
	d	18 46						19 46						20 46				21 46				22 43			
Winchelsea	d																					22 47			
Doleham	d																					22 53			
Three Oaks	d																					22 57			
Ore	d			19 14						20 14						21 14					22 14	23 02			
Hastings 4	a	19 03		19 17				20 03		20 17				21 03		21 17		22 03			22 17	23 05			
	d	19 04		19 18				20 04		20 18				21 04		21 18		22 04			22 18		23 18		
St Leonards Warrior Sq 4	d	19 07		19 21				20 07		20 21				21 07		21 21		22 07			22 21		23 21		
Bexhill 4	d	19 14		19 28				20 14		20 28				21 14		21 28		22 14			22 28		23 28		
Collington	d			19 30						20 30						21 30					22 30		23 30		
Cooden Beach	d			19 33						20 33						21 33					22 33		23 33		
Normans Bay	d																								
Pevensey Bay	d																								
Pevensey & Westham	d			19 39						20 39						21 39					22 39		23 39		
Hampden Park 4 §	d			19 43						20 43						21 43					22 43		23 43		
Eastbourne 4	a	19 29		19 49				20 29		20 49				21 29		21 49		22 29			22 49		23 48		
	d	19 34		19 55				20 34		20 55				21 34		21 59		22 34			22 59				
Hampden Park 4 §	d	19 38						20 38						21 38				22 38							
Polegate	d	19 42		20 02				20 42		21 02				21 42		22 06		22 42			23 06				
Berwick	d	19 48						20 48						21 48				22 48							
Glynde	d	19 53						20 53						21 53				22 53							
Seaford	d		19 53				20 27		20 53				21 27		21 53		22 27			22 53					
Bishopstone	d		19 55				20 29		20 55				21 29		21 55		22 29			22 55					
Newhaven Harbour	d		19 58				20 32		20 58				21 32		21 58		22 32			22 58					
Newhaven Town	⛴ d		20 00				20 34		21 00				21 34		22 00		22 34			23 00					
Southease	d		20 04																						
Lewes 4	a	19 59	20 11	20 14		←	20 43	20 59	21 09	21 14	←		21 43	21 59	22 09	22 18	22 43	22 59		23 09	23 18				
	d	20 00	20 18 →	20 16		20 18	20 44	21 00	21 18 →	21 16	21 18		21 44	22 00	22 10	22 19	22 44	23 00		23 10	23 19				
Falmer	d					20 25	20 51				21 25		21 51		22 17	22 26	22 51			23 17	23 26				
Moulsecoomb	d					20 28	20 54				21 28		21 54		22 20	22 29	22 54			23 20	23 29				
London Road (Brighton)	d					20 30	20 56				21 30		21 56		22 22	22 31	22 56			23 22	23 31				
Brighton 10	a	20 12				20 34	21 00	21 12			21 34		22 00	22 12	22 26	22 35	23 00	23 12		23 26	23 35				
Cooksbridge	d																								
Plumpton	d			20 24						21 24															
Wivelsfield 4	a			20 31		21 16				21 31	22 16					23 19									
Haywards Heath 3	a	20 30		20 35		21 00		21 30		21 35	22 00			22 30		23 00	23 27				00 01				
Gatwick Airport 10	✈ a	20 44		20 52		21 14		21 44		21 52	22 14			22 44		23 14	23 43				00 14				
East Croydon	a	21 01		21 09		21 31		22 01		22 09	22 31			23 01		23 31	23 59				00 35				
London Bridge 4	⊖ a	21 17		21 42		21 47		22 17		22 42	22 47			23 17		23 47	00 14								
Clapham Junction 10	a	21b24		21 24		21 47		22b24		22 24	23b10			23b37		00b10	00b29				01b02				
London Victoria 15	⊖ a	21b31		21 31		21 53		22b31		22 31	23b16			23b46		00b18	00b37				01b09				

For general notes see front of timetable
For details of catering facilities see Directory of Train Operators

§ For additional trains between Hampden Park and Eastbourne see London to Hastings pages

b Change at Brighton and East Croydon

Southeastern

These notes apply to Southeastern services on Tables 195 to 212. Southeastern services can be identified by the operator code SE at the head of the train column.

Spring Holiday

Monday 25 May — A normal Sunday service will operate

Late Summer Holiday

Monday 31 August — A normal Sunday service will operate

Network Diagram for Tables 195, 196 | also 199★

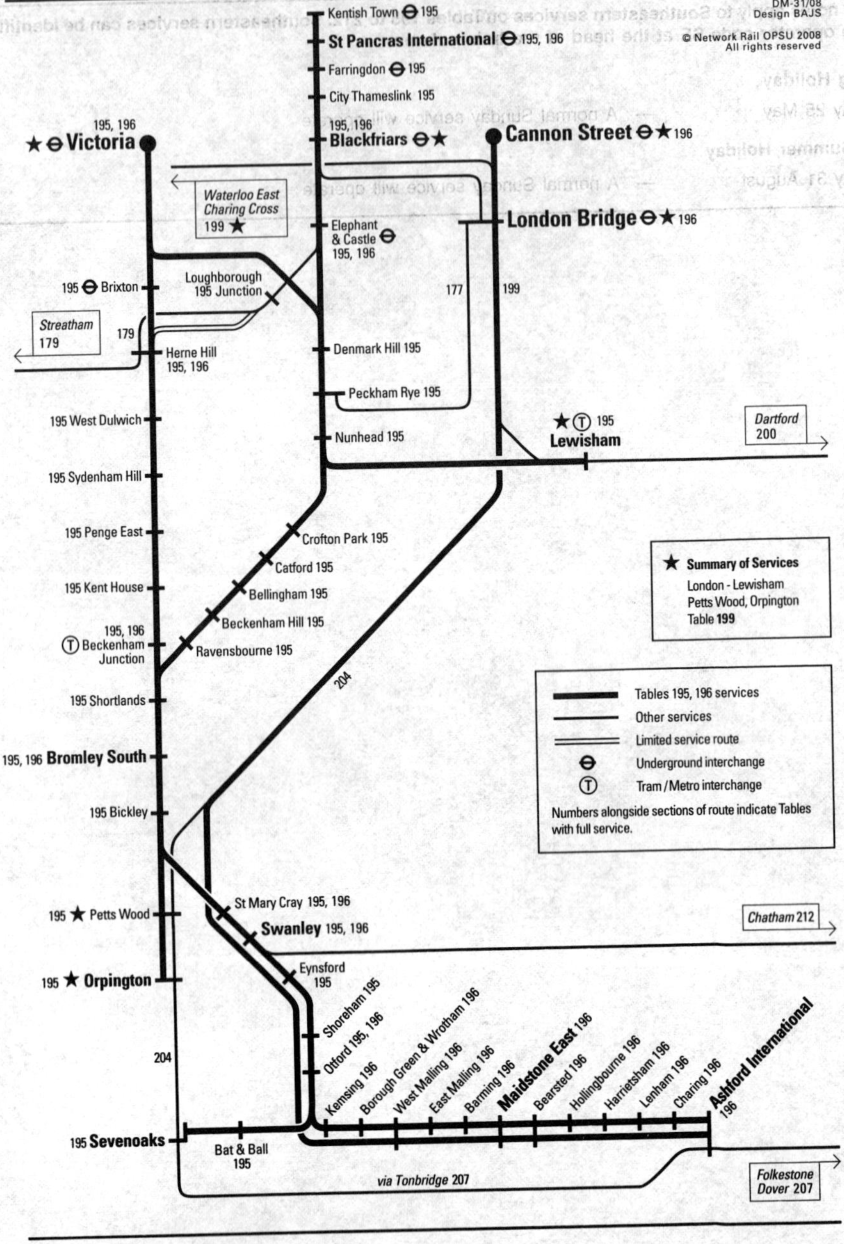

DM-31/08
Design BAJS
© Network Rail OPSU 2008
All rights reserved
Kentish Town ⊖ 195
St Pancras International ⊖ 195, 196
Farringdon ⊖ 195
City Thameslink 195
195, 196
Blackfriars ⊖★
195, 196
★ ⊖ Victoria
Cannon Street ⊖★ 196
Waterloo East
Charing Cross
199 ★
London Bridge ⊖★ 196
Elephant & Castle ⊖
195, 196
195 ⊖ Brixton
Loughborough
195 Junction
177
199
Streatham
179
179
Herne Hill
195, 196
Denmark Hill 195
Peckham Rye 195
195 West Dulwich
★ Ⓣ 195
Lewisham
Dartford
200
Nunhead 195
195 Sydenham Hill
195 Penge East
Crofton Park 195
Catford 195
Bellingham 195
195 Kent House
Beckenham Hill 195
195, 196
Ⓣ Beckenham Junction
Ravensbourne 195
★ Summary of Services
London - Lewisham
Petts Wood, Orpington
Table 199
204
195 Shortlands
Tables 195, 196 services
Other services
Limited service route
Underground interchange
Tram / Metro interchange
Numbers alongside sections of route indicate Tables with full service.
195, 196 Bromley South
195 Bickley
St Mary Cray 195, 196
195 ★ Petts Wood
Swanley 195, 196
Chatham 212
195 ★ Orpington
Eynsford
195
Shoreham 195
Otford 195, 196
Kemsing 196
Borough Green & Wrotham 196
West Malling 196
East Malling 196
Barming 196
Maidstone East 196
Bearsted 196
Hollingbourne 196
Harrietsham 196
Lenham 196
Charing 196
Ashford International
196
204
195 Sevenoaks
Bat & Ball
195
via Tonbridge 207
Folkestone
Dover 207

For details of Bank Holiday service alterations please see first page of this table

London → Catford, Beckenham Junction, Bromley South, Orpington, Otford and Sevenoaks

Network Diagram - see first page of Table 195

Miles	Miles	Miles			SE MX 1	SE MO 1	SE MX 1 A	SE MX	SE MX	SE	SE 1	SE	SE	SE	SE 1 B	SE	FC	SE 1	SE		SE 1	SE	SE 1 C	SE	FC
0	—	0	**London Victoria 15**	⊖ d	23p39	23p42	23p51	23p42	23p53	00 35	05 32		05 36		06 10	06 04		06 16			06 39	06 36	06 47		
3¼	—	—	Brixton	⊖ d					23p59				05 43			06 12						06 43			
—	—	—	Kentish Town	⊖ d																					06 29
—	—	—	St Pancras International 15	⊖ d													05 56								06 34
—	—	—	Farringdon	⊖ d													06 01								06 39
—	—	—	City Thameslink 3	d								05 26					06 03		06 07					06 38	06 43
—	0	—	**London Blackfriars 3**	⊖ d								05 28					06 06		06 10					06 40	06 46
—	1¼	—	Elephant & Castle	⊖ d								05 32					06 09		06 13					06 44	06 49
—	—	—	Loughborough Jn	d													06 13								06 53
4	—	—	Herne Hill 4	d					00 02	00 43			05 45			06 14	06a17					06 45			06a57
5	—	—	West Dulwich	d					00 04				05 47			06 16						06 47			
5¾	—	—	Sydenham Hill	d					00 06				05 49			06 18						06 49			
7¼	—	—	Penge East	d					00 09	00 48			05 52			06 21						06 52			
7¾	—	—	Kent House 4	d					00 11				05 54			06 23						06 54			
8¾	—	—	**Beckenham Junction 4**	d					00 13	00 51			05 56			06 25						06 56			
—	3¾	4¼	Denmark Hill 4	d				23p52				05 37							06 20					06 50	
—	4½	5	Peckham Rye 4	d				23p55				05 39							06 23					06 52	
—	5¼	5¾	Nunhead 4	d				23p57				05 41							06 25					06 54	
—	—	7½	Lewisham 4	a																					
—	6½	—	Crofton Park	d				23p59				05 44							06 28					06 57	
—	7½	—	Catford	d				00 01				05 46							06 30					06 59	
—	8¼	—	Bellingham	d				00 04				05 48							06 32					07 01	
—	9	—	Beckenham Hill	d				00 06				05 50							06 34					07 03	
—	9¾	—	Ravensbourne	d				00 08				05 52							06 36					07 05	
10	10½	—	Shortlands 4	d				00 10	00 16			05 54	05 59			06 28			06 39			06 59		07 07	
11	11½	—	**Bromley South 4**	d	23p58	00 01	00 07	00 13	00 18	00 55	05 48	05 58	06 02		06 30	06 31		06 34	06 42		06 59	07 03	07 04	07 10	
12	12½	—	Bickley 4	d				00 16	00 21			06 00	06 05			06 34			06 44			07 05		07 13	
13¾	—	—	Petts Wood 4	d				00 20	00 25				06 10			06 39						07 10			
15	—	—	**Orpington 4**	d				00a24	00a28				06a13			06a42						07a13			
—	14¾	—	St Mary Cray	d	00 04	00 08	00 14			01 02	05 55	06 06						06 41	06 50		07 05			07 18	
—	17½	—	**Swanley 4**	d	00a09	00a12	00 18			01a06	06a00	06 11		06 35	06 39			06a45	06 55		07a10		07 13	07 23	
—	20½	—	Eynsford	d			00 23					06 15		06 39					06 59					07 28	
—	22¾	—	Shoreham (Kent)	d			00 27					06 19		06 43					07 03					07 31	
—	24	—	Otford 4	d			00a30					06 22		06 46	06a49				07 06				07a22	07 34	
—	25¾	—	Bat & Ball	d								06 25		06 49					07 09					07 37	
—	27	—	**Sevenoaks 4**	a								06 28		06 52					07 13					07 43	

		SE 1	SE	SE 1 D	FC 1 E G	FC	FC 1	SE 1	FC 1 G H	FC H	SE 1	SE	FC		SE 1	FC E G	SE 1	FC E G	FC G H	FC 1	SE 1	SE	FC	FC 1 E	FC H
London Victoria 15	⊖ d	07 07	07 06	07 19				07 33			07 39	07 37			07 49		08 03				08 09	08 06			
Brixton	⊖ d		07 13									07 44										08 13			
Kentish Town	⊖ d					06 59				07 19									07 39				07 51		08 03
St Pancras International 15	⊖ d				06 48	07 04	07 08		07 12	07 24			07 28			07 32		07 40	07 44	07 48			07 56	08 04	08 08
Farringdon	⊖ d				06 53	07 09	07 13		07 17	07 29			07 33			07 37		07 45	07 49	07 53			08 01	08 09	08 13
City Thameslink 3	d				06 57	07 13	07 17		07 21	07 33			07 37			07 41		07 49	07 53	07 57			08 05	08 13	08 17
London Blackfriars 3	⊖ d				07b06	07 16	07 20		07 24	07 35			07 40			07 44		07 52	07 56	08 00			08 08	08 16	08 20
Elephant & Castle	⊖ d				07 09	07 19	07 23		07 27				07 43			07 47		07 55	07 59				08 11		
Loughborough Jn	d					07 23	07 27						07 47										08 15		
Herne Hill 4	d		07 15			07a27	07a32			07 45		07 47	07a51							08a09		08 15	08a19		08 29
West Dulwich	d		07 17									07 50										08 18			
Sydenham Hill	d		07 19									07 52										08 20			
Penge East	d		07 22									07 55										08 23			
Kent House 4	d		07 24									07 56										08 24			
Beckenham Junction 4	d		07 26							07a52		07 59										08 27			08a35
Denmark Hill 4	d				07 15				07 34							07 53		08 01	08 06						
Peckham Rye 4	d				07 20				07 37							07 56		08 04	08 09						
Nunhead 4	d				07 22				07 39							07 58		08 06	08 11						
Lewisham 4	a																								
Crofton Park	d				07 24				07 41									08 08	08 13						
Catford	d				07 26				07 44							08 02		08 10	08 16						
Bellingham	d				07 29				07 47							08 04		08 13	08 19						
Beckenham Hill	d				07 31				07 49									08 15	08 21						
Ravensbourne	d				07 33				07 51									08 17	08 23						
Shortlands 4	d		07 29		07 35				07 53			08 02				08 09		08 19	08 25			08 30			
Bromley South 4	d	07 27	07 33	07 36	07 38			07a51	07 56		08 01	08 05			08 07	08a11	08a19	08 22	08 28		08 31	08 33		08a35	
Bickley 4	d		07 35		07 40				07 58			08 07						08 24	08 30			08 35			
Petts Wood 4	d		07 40									08 12						08 29				08 41			
Orpington 4	d		07a43									08a15						08a33				08a44			
St Mary Cray	d	07 34			07 46				08 04		08 07								08 36		08 37				
Swanley 4	d	07a38		07 45	07 50				08 08		08a11				08 17				08 40		08a42				
Eynsford	d				07 55				08 13										08 45						
Shoreham (Kent)	d				07 58				08 16										08 48						
Otford 4	d			07a54	08 02				08 20						08a26				08 52						
Bat & Ball	d				08 05				08 23										08 55						
Sevenoaks 4	a				08 08				08 26										08 58						

For general notes see front of timetable
For details of catering facilities see Directory of Train Operators

- **A** To Ashford International (Table 196)
- **B** To Margate (Table 207)
- **C** To Ramsgate (Table 207)
- **D** To Canterbury West (Table 207)
- **E** From Bedford (Table 52)
- **G** TOC SE from London Blackfriars
- **H** From Luton (Table 52)
- **b** Arr. 0700

For details of Bank Holiday service alterations please see first page of this table

London → Catford, Beckenham Junction, Bromley South, Orpington, Otford and Sevenoaks

Network Diagram - see first page of Table 195

Station		SE 1	SE	SE 1	FC	FC 1	FC 1		SE 1	SE	FC	FC 1	SE	FC	FC	FC	SE	SE 1	FC	FC	SE 1	SE	FC		SE 1
					A B									C A					A D						
London Victoria 15	⊖ d	08 18	08 21	08 33					08 39	08 36			08 49				09 01	09 03			09 09	09 06			09 19
Brixton	⊖ d									08 43												09 13			
Kentish Town	⊖ d										08 19					08 35							08 51		
St Pancras International 15	⊖ d				08 12	08 16	08 20				08 24	08 28		08 32	08 36	08 40			08 44	08 52			08 56		
Farringdon	⊖ d				08 17	08 21	08 25				08 29	08 33		08 37	08 41	08 45			08 49	08 57			09 01		
City Thameslink 3	d				08 21	08 25	08 29				08 33	08 37		08 41	08 45	08 49			08 53	09 01			09 05		
London Blackfriars 3	⊖ d				08 24	08 28	08 32				08 36	08 40		08 44	08 48	08 52			08 56	09 04			09 08		
Elephant & Castle	⊖ d				08 28	08 31					08 39	08a44		08 47	08a52	08 55			09 01	09 07			09 11		
Loughborough Jn	d					08 35					08 43					08 59				09 11			09 15		
Herne Hill 4	d					08a39	08a43			08 46	08a47					09a03				09a15		09 15	09a21		
West Dulwich	d									08 48												09 18			
Sydenham Hill	d									08 50												09 20			
Penge East	d									08 53												09 23			
Kent House 4	d									08 55												09 24			
Beckenham Junction 4	d									08 57												09 26			
Denmark Hill 4	d		08 31		08 35									08 52			09 12		09 07						
Peckham Rye 4	d		08 35		08 38									08 55			09 14		09 10						
Nunhead 4	d		08 37		08 40									08 57			09 16		09 12						
Lewisham 4	a		08 43														09 25								
Crofton Park	d				08 42									08 59					09 15						
Catford	d				08 44									09 01					09 17						
Bellingham	d				08 47									09 04					09 19						
Beckenham Hill	d				08 49									09 06					09 21						
Ravensbourne	d				08 51									09 08					09 23						
Shortlands 4	d				08 53					09 00				09 10					09 25			09 29			
Bromley South 4	d	08 40		08a50	08 56				09 00	09 04			09 08	09 13				09a18	09a28		09 29	09 32			09 37
Bickley 4	d				08 58					09 06				09 16								09 35			
Petts Wood 4	d									09 12												09 39			
Orpington 4	d									09a15												09a42			
St Mary Cray	d				09 04				09 07					09 21							09 35				
Swanley 4	d				09 08				09a11				09 16	09 26							09a40				
Eynsford	d				09 13									09 30											
Shoreham (Kent)	d				09 16									09 34											
Otford 4	d	08a57			09 20								09a25	09 37											09a53
Bat & Ball	d				09 23									09 40											
Sevenoaks 4	a				09 26									09 43											

Station		FC	SE	FC	SE	SE 1	SE 1	SE	SE	FC	FC	SE	FC	SE	SE 1	SE 1		SE	SE 1	FC	FC	FC 1	SE	FC	SE
		A D								A B										A					
London Victoria 15	⊖ d		09 21		09 31	09 33	09 39	09 36	09 48			09 51		10 01	10 03	10 09		10 06	10 18				10 21		10 31
Brixton	⊖ d		09 28					09 43				09 58						10 13					10 28		
Kentish Town	⊖ d			09 11						09 26			09 42							09 56	10 00			10 13	
St Pancras International 15	⊖ d	09 00		09 16						09 30	09 34		09 48							10 00	10 04	10 14		10 18	
Farringdon	⊖ d	09 05		09 21						09 35	09 39		09 53							10 05	10 09	10 19		10 23	
City Thameslink 3	d	09 09		09 25						09 39	09 43		09 57							10 09	10 13	10 22		10 27	
London Blackfriars 3	⊖ d	09 12		09 28						09 42	09 46		10 00							10 12	10 16	10 26		10 30	
Elephant & Castle	⊖ d	09 16		09 31						09 45	09 49		10 03							10 15	10 19	10a30		10 33	
Loughborough Jn	d			09 35							09 53		10 07								10 23			10 37	
Herne Hill 4	d		09 30	09a39				09 45			09a57	10 00	10a11					10 15			10a27		10 30	10a41	
West Dulwich	d		09 32					09 48				10 03						10 18					10 33		
Sydenham Hill	d		09 34					09 50				10 05						10 20					10 35		
Penge East	d		09 37					09 53				10 08						10 23					10 38		
Kent House 4	d		09 39					09 54				10 09						10 24					10 39		
Beckenham Junction 4	d		09 41					09 56				10 11						10 26					10 41		
Denmark Hill 4	d	09 22			09 42					09 52				10 12						10 22					10 42
Peckham Rye 4	d	09 25			09 44					09 55				10 14						10 25					10 44
Nunhead 4	d	09 27			09 46					09 57				10 16						10 27					10 46
Lewisham 4	a				09 52									10 22											10 52
Crofton Park	d	09 29								09 59										10 29					
Catford	d	09 31								10 01										10 31					
Bellingham	d	09 34								10 04										10 34					
Beckenham Hill	d	09 36								10 06										10 36					
Ravensbourne	d	09 38								10 08										10 38					
Shortlands 4	d	09 40	09 44					09 59		10 10		10 14						10 29		10 40			10 44		
Bromley South 4	d	09 43	09 47			09a50	09 59	10 03	10 04	10 13		10 17			10a18	10 29		10 32	10 34	10 43			10 47		
Bickley 4	d	09 45	09 50					10 05		10 15		10 20						10 35		10 45			10 50		
Petts Wood 4	d		09 54					10 09				10 26						10 39					10 54		
Orpington 4	d		09a57					10a13				10a29						10a42					10a57		
St Mary Cray	d	09 51					10 05			10 21						10 35				10 51					
Swanley 4	d	09 55					10a10		10 13	10 25						10a40				10 55					
Eynsford	d	10 00								10 30										11 00					
Shoreham (Kent)	d	10 03								10 33										11 03					
Otford 4	d	10 06							10a23	10 36									10a51	11 06					
Bat & Ball	d	10 09								10 39										11 09					
Sevenoaks 4	a	10 12								10 42										11 12					

For general notes see front of timetable
For details of catering facilities see Directory of Train Operators

A TOC SE from London Blackfriars
B From St Albans City (Table 52)
C From Bedford (Table 52)
D From Luton (Table 52)

For details of Bank Holiday service alterations please see first page of this table

London → Catford, Beckenham Junction, Bromley South, Orpington, Otford and Sevenoaks

Network Diagram - see first page of Table 195

		SE 1 🚲	SE 1	SE	SE	FC A	FC	FC 1	SE	FC		SE	SE 1 🚲	SE 1	SE	SE 1	FC A	FC	FC	SE	FC	SE	SE 1 🚲	SE 1	SE
London Victoria 15	⊖ d	10 33	10 39	10 36	10 48				10 51			11 01	11 03	11 09	11 06	11 18				11 21		11 31	11 33	11 39	11 36
Brixton	⊖ d			10 43					10 58						11 13					11 28					11 43
Kentish Town	⊖ d					10 26	10 30			10 42							10 56	11 00			11 12				
St Pancras International 15	⊖ d					10 30	10 34	10 44		10 48							11 00	11 04	11 14		11 18				
Farringdon	⊖ d					10 35	10 39	10 49		10 53							11 05	11 09	11 19		11 23				
City Thameslink 3	d					10 39	10 43	10 52		10 57							11 09	11 13	11 22		11 27				
London Blackfriars 3	⊖ d					10 42	10 46	10 56		11 00							11 12	11 16	11 26		11 30				
Elephant & Castle	⊖ d					10 45	10 49	11a00		11 03							11 15	11 19	11a30		11 33				
Loughborough Jn	d						10 53			11 07								11 23			11 37				
Herne Hill 4	d			10 45			10a57		11 00	11a11					11 15			11a27		11 30	11a41				11 45
West Dulwich	d			10 48					11 03						11 18					11 33					11 48
Sydenham Hill	d			10 50					11 05						11 20					11 35					11 50
Penge East	d			10 53					11 08						11 23					11 38					11 53
Kent House 4	d			10 54					11 09						11 24					11 39					11 54
Beckenham Junction 4	🚊 d			10 56					11 11						11 26					11 41					11 56
Denmark Hill 4	d					10 52						11 12					11 22					11 43			
Peckham Rye 4	d					10 55						11 14					11 25					11 45			
Nunhead 4	d					10 57						11 16					11 27					11 47			
Lewisham 4	🚊 a											11 22										11 52			
Crofton Park	d					10 59											11 29								
Catford	d					11 01											11 31								
Bellingham	d					11 04											11 34								
Beckenham Hill	d					11 06											11 36								
Ravensbourne	d					11 08											11 38								
Shortlands 4	d			10 59		11 10			11 14						11 29		11 40			11 44					11 59
Bromley South 4	d	10a48	10 59	11 02	11 04	11 13			11 17				11a18	11 29	11 32	11 34	11 43			11 47			11a48	11 59	12 02
Bickley 4	d			11 05		11 15			11 20						11 35		11 45			11 50					12 05
Petts Wood 4	d			11 09					11 24						11 39					11 54					12 09
Orpington 4	d			11a12					11a27						11a42					11a57					12a12
St Mary Cray	d		11 05			11 21								11 35			11 51							12 05	
Swanley 4	d		11a10		11 13	11 25								11a40			11 55							12a10	
Eynsford	d					11 30											12 00								
Shoreham (Kent)	d					11 33											12 03								
Otford 4	d				11a23	11 36										11a51	12 06								
Bat & Ball	d					11 39											12 09								
Sevenoaks 4	a					11 42											12 12								

		SE	FC A	FC		SE	FC	SE	SE 1 🚲	SE 1	SE	SE 1	FC A	FC	SE	FC	SE	SE 1 🚲	SE 1	SE		SE	FC A	FC	SE
London Victoria 15	⊖ d	11 48				11 51		12 01	12 03	12 09	12 06	12 18			12 21		12 31	12 33	12 39	12 36		12 48			12 51
Brixton	⊖ d					11 58					12 13				12 28					12 43					12 58
Kentish Town	⊖ d		11 26	11 30			11 42						11 56	12 00		12 12							12 26	12 30	
St Pancras International 15	⊖ d		11 30	11 34			11 48						12 00	12 04		12 18							12 30	12 34	
Farringdon	⊖ d		11 35	11 39			11 53						12 05	12 09		12 23							12 35	12 39	
City Thameslink 3	d		11 39	11 43			11 57						12 09	12 13		12 27							12 39	12 43	
London Blackfriars 3	⊖ d		11 42	11 46			12 00						12 12	12 16		12 30							12 42	12 46	
Elephant & Castle	⊖ d		11 45	11 49			12 03						12 15	12 19		12 33							12 45	12 49	
Loughborough Jn	d			11 53			12 07							12 23		12 37								12 53	
Herne Hill 4	d			11a57		12 00	12a11				12 15			12a27	12 30	12a41				12 45				12a57	13 00
West Dulwich	d					12 03					12 18				12 33					12 48					13 03
Sydenham Hill	d					12 05					12 20				12 35					12 50					13 05
Penge East	d					12 08					12 23				12 38					12 53					13 08
Kent House 4	d					12 09					12 24				12 39					12 54					13 09
Beckenham Junction 4	🚊 d					12 11					12 26				12 41					12 56					13 11
Denmark Hill 4	d		11 52					12 12					12 22				12 42						12 52		
Peckham Rye 4	d		11 55					12 14					12 25				12 44						12 55		
Nunhead 4	d		11 57					12 16					12 27				12 46						12 57		
Lewisham 4	🚊 a							12 22									12 52								
Crofton Park	d		11 59										12 29										12 59		
Catford	d		12 01										12 31										13 01		
Bellingham	d		12 04										12 34										13 04		
Beckenham Hill	d		12 06										12 36										13 06		
Ravensbourne	d		12 08										12 38										13 08		
Shortlands 4	d		12 10			12 14					12 29		12 40		12 44					12 59			13 10		13 14
Bromley South 4	d	12 04	12 13			12 17			12a18	12 29	12 32	12 34	12 43		12 47			12a48	12 59	13 02		13 04	13 13		13 17
Bickley 4	d		12 15			12 20					12 35		12 45		12 50					13 05			13 15		13 20
Petts Wood 4	d					12 24					12 39				12 54					13 09					13 24
Orpington 4	d					12a27					12a42				12a57					13a12					13a27
St Mary Cray	d		12 21							12 35			12 51						13 05				13 21		
Swanley 4	d	12 13	12 25							12a40			12 55						13a10			13 13	13 25		
Eynsford	d		12 30										13 00										13 30		
Shoreham (Kent)	d		12 33										13 03										13 33		
Otford 4	d	12a23	12 36									12a51	13 06									13a23	13 36		
Bat & Ball	d		12 39										13 09										13 39		
Sevenoaks 4	a		12 42										13 12										13 42		

For general notes see front of timetable
For details of catering facilities see Directory of Train Operators

A TOC SE from London Blackfriars

For details of Bank Holiday service alterations please see first page of this table

London → Catford, Beckenham Junction, Bromley South, Orpington, Otford and Sevenoaks

Network Diagram - see first page of Table 195

		FC	SE	SE [1]	SE [1]	SE	SE [1]	FC	FC	SE	FC	SE	SE [1]	SE [1]		SE	SE	FC	FC	SE	FC	SE	SE [1]	SE [1]	SE
								A										A							
				🚲																			🚲		
London Victoria [15]	⊖ d		13 01	13 03	13 09	13 06	13 18			13 21		13 31	13 33	13 39		13 36	13 48			13 51		14 01	14 03	14 09	14 06
Brixton	⊖ d					13 13				13 28						13 43				13 58					14 13
Kentish Town	⊖ d	12 42						12 56	13 00		13 12							13 26	13 30		13 42				
St Pancras International [15]	⊖ d	12 48						13 00	13 04		13 18							13 30	13 34		13 48				
Farringdon	⊖ d	12 53						13 05	13 09		13 23							13 35	13 39		13 53				
City Thameslink [3]	d	12 57						13 09	13 13		13 27							13 39	13 43		13 57				
London Blackfriars [3]	⊖ d	13 00						13 12	13 16		13 30							13 42	13 46		14 00				
Elephant & Castle	⊖ d	13 03						13 15	13 19		13 33							13 45	13 49		14 03				
Loughborough Jn	d	13 07							13 23		13 37								13 53		14 07				
Herne Hill [4]	d	13a11				13 15			13a27	13 30	13a41					13 45			13a57	14 00	14a11				14 15
West Dulwich	d					13 18				13 33						13 48				14 03					14 18
Sydenham Hill	d					13 20				13 35						13 50				14 05					14 20
Penge East	d					13 23				13 38						13 53				14 08					14 23
Kent House [4]	d					13 24				13 39						13 54				14 09					14 24
Beckenham Junction [4]	🚋 d					13 26				13 41						13 56				14 11					14 26
Denmark Hill [4]	d		13 12					13 22				13 42						13 52				14 12			
Peckham Rye [4]	d		13 14					13 25				13 44						13 55				14 14			
Nunhead [4]	d		13 16					13 27				13 46						13 57				14 16			
Lewisham [4]	🚋 a		13 22									13 52										14 22			
Crofton Park	d							13 29										13 59							
Catford	d							13 31										14 01							
Bellingham	d							13 34										14 04							
Beckenham Hill	d							13 36										14 06							
Ravensbourne	d							13 38										14 08							
Shortlands [4]	d					13 29		13 40		13 44						13 59		14 10		14 14					14 29
Bromley South [4]	d			13a18	13 29	13 32	13 34	13 43		13 47			13a48	13 59		14 02	14 04	14 13		14 17			14a18	14 29	14 32
Bickley [4]	d					13 35		13 45		13 50						14 05		14 15		14 20					14 35
Petts Wood [4]	d					13 39				13 54						14 09				14 24					14 39
Orpington [4]	d					13a42				13a57						14a12				14a27					14a42
St Mary Cray	d				13 35			13 51						14 05				14 21						14 35	
Swanley [4]	d				13a40			13 55						14a10			14 13	14 25						14a40	
Eynsford	d							14 00										14 30							
Shoreham (Kent)	d							14 03										14 33							
Otford [4]	d						13a51	14 06									14a23	14 36							
Bat & Ball	d							14 09										14 39							
Sevenoaks [4]	a							14 12										14 42							

		SE [1]	FC	FC	SE	FC	SE	SE [1]		SE [1]	SE	SE [1]	FC	FC	SE	FC	SE	SE [1]	SE [1]	SE	SE [1]	FC	FC	SE	FC
			A										A									A			
								🚲										🚲							
London Victoria [15]	⊖ d	14 18			14 21		14 31	14 33		14 39	14 36	14 48			14 51		15 01	15 03	15 09	15 06	15 18			15 21	
Brixton	⊖ d				14 28						14 43				14 58					15 13				15 28	
Kentish Town	⊖ d		13 56	14 00		14 12							14 26	14 30		14 42						14 56	15 00		15 12
St Pancras International [15]	⊖ d		14 00	14 04		14 18							14 30	14 34		14 48						15 00	15 04		15 18
Farringdon	⊖ d		14 05	14 09		14 23							14 35	14 39		14 53						15 05	15 09		15 23
City Thameslink [3]	d		14 09	14 13		14 27							14 39	14 43		14 57						15 09	15 13		15 27
London Blackfriars [3]	⊖ d		14 12	14 16		14 30							14 42	14 46		15 00						15 12	15 16		15 30
Elephant & Castle	⊖ d		14 15	14 19		14 33							14 45	14 49		15 03						15 15	15 19		15 33
Loughborough Jn	d			14 23		14 37								14 53		15 07							15 23		15 37
Herne Hill [4]	d			14a27	14 30	14a41					14 45			14a57	15 00	15a11				15 15			15a27	15 30	15a41
West Dulwich	d				14 33						14 48				15 03					15 18				15 33	
Sydenham Hill	d				14 35						14 50				15 05					15 20				15 35	
Penge East	d				14 38						14 53				15 08					15 23				15 38	
Kent House [4]	d				14 39						14 54				15 09					15 24				15 39	
Beckenham Junction [4]	🚋 d				14 41						14 56				15 11					15 26				15 41	
Denmark Hill [4]	d		14 22				14 42						14 52				15 12					15 22			
Peckham Rye [4]	d		14 25				14 44						14 55				15 14					15 25			
Nunhead [4]	d		14 27				14 46						14 57				15 16					15 27			
Lewisham [4]	🚋 a						14 52										15 22								
Crofton Park	d		14 29										14 59									15 29			
Catford	d		14 31										15 01									15 31			
Bellingham	d		14 34										15 04									15 34			
Beckenham Hill	d		14 36										15 06									15 36			
Ravensbourne	d		14 38										15 08									15 38			
Shortlands [4]	d		14 40		14 44						14 59		15 10		15 14					15 29		15 40		15 44	
Bromley South [4]	d	14 34	14 43		14 47			14a48		14 59	15 02	15 04	15 13		15 17			15a18	15 29	15 32	15 34	15 43		15 47	
Bickley [4]	d		14 45		14 50						15 05		15 15		15 20					15 35		15 45		15 50	
Petts Wood [4]	d				14 54						15 09				15 24					15 39				15 54	
Orpington [4]	d				14a57						15a12				15a27					15a42				15a57	
St Mary Cray	d		14 51							15 05			15 21						15 35			15 51			
Swanley [4]	d		14 55							15a10		15 13	15 25						15a40		15 43	15 55			
Eynsford	d		15 00										15 30									16 00			
Shoreham (Kent)	d		15 03										15 33									16 03			
Otford [4]	d	14a51	15 06									15a23	15 36								15a52	16 06			
Bat & Ball	d		15 09										15 39									16 09			
Sevenoaks [4]	a		15 12										15 42									16 12			

For general notes see front of timetable
For details of catering facilities see
Directory of Train Operators

A TOC SE from London Blackfriars

For details of Bank Holiday service alterations please see first page of this table

London → Catford, Beckenham Junction, Bromley South, Orpington, Otford and Sevenoaks

Network Diagram - see first page of Table 195

		SE		SE 1	SE 1	SE	SE 1	FC	FC	SE	FC	SE 1	SE	SE	SE	SE	SE 1	FC		FC	SE 1	SE 1	SE	SE	SE 1
				⊼				A				B ⊼		C	D		E	A			G		C	D	
London Victoria 15 ⊖	d	15 31		15 33	15 39	15 36	15 48			15 51		16 03	16 00	16 06	16 06	16 14	16 23				16 22	16 27	16 26	16 26	16 42
Brixton ⊖	d					15 43				15 58				16 13	16 13								16 33	16 33	
Kentish Town ⊖	d							15 26	15 30		15 42							15 56		16 00					
St Pancras International 15 ⊖	d							15 30	15 34		15 48							16 00		16 04					
Farringdon ⊖	d							15 35	15 39		15 53							16 05		16 09					
City Thameslink 3	d							15 39	15 43		15 57							16 09		16 13					
London Blackfriars 3 ⊖	d							15 42	15 46		16 00							16 12		16 16					
Elephant & Castle ⊖	d							15 45	15 49		16 03							16 15		16 19					
Loughborough Jn	d								15 53		16 07									16 23					
Herne Hill 4	d					15 45			15a57	16 00	16a11			16 15	16 15					16a27			16 35	16 35	
West Dulwich	d					15 48				16 03				16 18	16 18								16 37	16 37	
Sydenham Hill	d					15 50				16 05				16 20	16 20								16 39	16 39	
Penge East	d					15 53				16 08				16 23	16 23								16 42	16 42	
Kent House 4	d					15 54				16 09				16 24	16 24								16 44	16 44	
Beckenham Junction 4	d					15 56				16 11				16 26	16 26								16 47	16 47	
Denmark Hill 4	d	15 42						15 52								16 27		16 22							
Peckham Rye 4	d	15 44						15 55								16 29		16 25							
Nunhead 4	d	15 46						15 57								16 31		16 27							
Lewisham 4	a	15 52														16 40									
Crofton Park	d							15 59										16 29							
Catford	d							16 01										16 31							
Bellingham	d							16 04										16 34							
Beckenham Hill	d							16 06										16 36							
Ravensbourne	d							16 08										16 38							
Shortlands 4	d					15 59		16 10		16 14				16 29	16 29			16 40					16 50	16 50	
Bromley South 4	d			15a48	16 00	16 02	16 04	16 13		16 17		16a18	16 23	16 32	16 32		16a39	16 43			16 44	16 48	16 53	16 53	16a58
Bickley 4	d					16 05		16 15		16 20				16 35	16 35			16 45					16 56	16 56	
Petts Wood 4	d					16 09				16 24				16 39	16 39								17 01	17 01	
Orpington 4	d					16a12				16a27				16a42	16a44								17a04	17a06	
St Mary Cray	d				16 06			16 21					16 30					16 51			16 50				
Swanley 4	d				16a11		16 13	16 25					16a34					16 55			16a55	16 59			
Eynsford	d							16 30										17 00							
Shoreham (Kent)	d							16 33										17 03							
Otford 4	d						16a23	16 36										17 06				17a10			
Bat & Ball	d							16 39										17 09							
Sevenoaks 4	a							16 42										17 12							

		FC	FC	SE	FC	FC	SE 1	SE	SE	FC 1	FC	SE		SE 1	SE	SE 1	FC 1	FC	SE	SE 1	FC	FC	SE	SE	FC
		A			A			C	D	H				J			H A			K ⊼	L				A N
London Victoria 15 ⊖	d			16 45			16 56	16 51	16 51			17 00		17 05	17 12	17 22			17 19	17 27			17 32	17 35	
Brixton ⊖	d							16 58	16 58						17 19									17 42	
Kentish Town ⊖	d	16 09	16 13		16 24	16 30					16 42							16 58				17 12			
St Pancras International 15 ⊖	d	16 14	16 18		16 28	16 34				16 40	16 46						16 56	17 02			17 14	17 18			17 25
Farringdon ⊖	d	16 19	16 23		16 33	16 39				16 45	16 51						17 01	17 07			17 19	17 23			17 30
City Thameslink 3	d	16 23	16 27		16 37	16 43				16 49	16 55						17 05	17 11			17 23	17 27			17 33
London Blackfriars 3 ⊖	d	16 26	16 30		16b42	16 46				16 52	16 58						17 10	17 14			17 26	17 30			17 36
Elephant & Castle ⊖	d	16 30	16 33		16 45	16 50				16 56	17 02						17 14	17 18			17 30	17 34			17 39
Loughborough Jn	d		16 37			16 54				16 59	17 06							17 22				17 38			
Herne Hill 4	d		16a41			16a57		17 00	17 00	17 04	17a10			17 13	17 21			17a25			17 37	17a41		17 45	
West Dulwich	d							17 02	17 02	17 06					17 23									17 47	
Sydenham Hill	d							17 04	17 04	17 08					17 25									17 49	
Penge East	d							17 07	17 07	17 11					17 28									17 52	
Kent House 4	d							17 09	17 09	17 13					17 30									17 54	
Beckenham Junction 4	d							17 12	17 12	17a16					17 33								17 47	17 57	
Denmark Hill 4	d	16 36			16 52							17 09					17 20		17 28						17 45
Peckham Rye 4	d	16 40			16 55							17 12					17 24		17 31						17 48
Nunhead 4	d	16 42			16 57							17 14					17 26		17 33						17 50
Lewisham 4	a											17 23							17 43						
Crofton Park	d	16 45			16 59												17 29								17 52
Catford	d	16 47			17 02												17 32								17 54
Bellingham	d	16 50			17 05												17 35								17 57
Beckenham Hill	d	16 52			17 07												17 37								17 59
Ravensbourne	d	16 54			17 09												17 39								18 01
Shortlands 4	d	16 56			17 11			17 15	17 15						17 36		17 41							18 00	18 03
Bromley South 4	d	17 00		17 03	17 15		17 15	17 18	17 18					17 24	17 39	17 40	17 46			17a44	17 48		17 51	18 03	18 06
Bickley 4	d	17 02			17 17			17 21	17 21						17 42		17 49							18 05	18 09
Petts Wood 4	d	17 07						17 25	17 25						17 49									18 10	
Orpington 4	d	17a12						17a29	17a30						17a53									18a15	
St Mary Cray	d			17 10	17 25									17 30		17 47	17 56				17 57		18 00		18 15
Swanley 4	d			17a14	17 30									17a35		17 52	18 01				18a01		18 05		18 20
Eynsford	d				17 34												18 06								18 24
Shoreham (Kent)	d				17 38												18 09								18 28
Otford 4	d				17 41		17a33									18a01	18 13						18a17		18 32
Bat & Ball	d				17 44												18 16								18 36
Sevenoaks 4	a				17 47												18 19								18 40

For general notes see front of timetable
For details of catering facilities see Directory of Train Operators

A TOC SE from London Blackfriars

B From 12 October to Ramsgate and to Dover Priory. ⊼ from Rochester, from 12 October

C Until 9 October

D From 12 October

E From 12 October to Ramsgate and to Dover Priory

G From 12 October to Rochester

H From Bedford (Table 52)

J Until 9 October to Canterbury East (Table 212). From 12 October to Canterbury East

K From 12 October to Ramsgate

L From Bedford (Table 52) to Gillingham (Kent) (Table 212)

N From Luton (Table 52)

b Arr. 1639

For details of Bank Holiday service alterations please see first page of this table

London → Catford, Beckenham Junction, Bromley South, Orpington, Otford and Sevenoaks

Network Diagram - see first page of Table 195

	FC	SE	SE 1 A	SE B	SE	FC	FC 1	SE 1	FC 1 C	SE 1 A	SE D	SE E	FC	SE	FC G	FC H J	FC	SE 1	FC G	SE	SE 1 K	FC H
London Victoria 15 ⊖ d		17 41	17 48	17 45	17 52			17 58		18 04	18 02	18 02		18 08				18 18		18 21	18 33	
Brixton ⊖ d					17 59						18 09	18 09								18 28		
Kentish Town ⊖ d	17 26					17 34	17 38						17 46				18 00					18 08
St Pancras International 15 ⊖ d	17 30					17 38	17 42		17 46				17 50		17 54	17 58	18 04					18 12
Farringdon ⊖ d	17 35					17 43	17 47		17 51				17 55		17 59	18 03	18 09					18 17
City Thameslink 3 d	17 39					17 47	17 51		17 55				17 59		18 03	18 07	18 13					18 21
London Blackfriars 3 ⊖ d	17 42					17 50	17 54		17 58				18 02		18 06	18 10	18 16					18 24
Elephant & Castle ⊖ d	17 46					17 54			18 03				18 06		18 10	18 14	18 20					18 28
Loughborough Jn d	17 50					17 58							18 10				18 24					
Herne Hill 4 d	17a53			17 57	18 02	18b04	18a06				18 11	18 11	18a13			18 22	18a27			18 30		
West Dulwich d					18 05	18 08					18 14	18 14								18 33		
Sydenham Hill d					18 07	18 10					18 16	18 16								18 35		
Penge East d					18 10	18 13					18 19	18 19								18 38		
Kent House 4 d					18 11	18 14					18 20	18 20								18 40		
Beckenham Junction 4 d				18 05	18 14	18a17					18 23	18 23								18 42		
Denmark Hill 4 d		17 51												18 17	18c20							18 34
Peckham Rye 4 d		17 54												18 20	18 23							18 37
Nunhead 4 d		17 56												18 22	18 25							18 39
Lewisham 4 a		18 05												18 28								
Crofton Park d															18 28				←			18 42
Catford d															18 30 →				18 30			18 44
Bellingham d																			18 33			18 47
Beckenham Hill d																			18 35			18 49
Ravensbourne d																			18 37			18 51
Shortlands 4 d					18 17						18 26	18 26							18 39	18 45		18 53
Bromley South 4 d			18a07	18 10	18 20			18 18	18 21	18a24	18 29	18 29				18 32		18 36	18 42	18 48	18a49	18 56
Bickley 4 d					18 23						18 31	18 31							18 45	18 51		18 59
Petts Wood 4 d					18 29						18 36	18 36								18 56		
Orpington 4 d					18a33						18a40	18a41								19a01		
St Mary Cray d				18 19					18 28							18 39		18 43	18 51			19 04
Swanley 4 d				18a23					18 33							18a43		18 48	18 55			19 09
Eynsford d																			19 00			19 13
Shoreham (Kent) d																			19 03			19 17
Otford 4 d								18a36	18a42									18a58	19 07			19 20
Bat & Ball d																			19 10			19 23
Sevenoaks 4 a																			19 14			19 26

	FC	SE 1 L	SE D	SE E	SE	SE 1	FC 1 N H	FC	SE	FC	SE 1	SE 1	SE	SE	SE 1	FC H G	FC	SE	FC	SE 1	SE 1	SE	SE
London Victoria 15 ⊖ d		18 41	18 38	18 38	18 46	18 48			18 51		19 03	19 09	19 06	19 16	19 18			19 22		19 33	19 39	19 37	19 46
Brixton ⊖ d			18 45	18 45					18 58				19 14					19 29				19 44	
Kentish Town ⊖ d	18 12							18 28		18 43						18 56							
St Pancras International 15 ⊖ d	18 16						18 24	18 34		18 48						19 00	19 04		19 18				
Farringdon ⊖ d	18 21						18 29	18 39		18 53						19 05	19 09		19 23				
City Thameslink 3 d	18 25						18 33	18 43		18 57						19 09	19 13		19 27				
London Blackfriars 3 ⊖ d	18e30						18f42	18 46		19 00						19 12	19 16		19 30				
Elephant & Castle ⊖ d	18 34						18 45	18 49		19 04						19 15	19 19		19 33				
Loughborough Jn d	18 38							18 53		19 08							19 23		19 37				
Herne Hill 4 d	18a41		18 47	18 47				18a57	19 00	19a11			19 16				19a27	19 31	19a41			19 46	
West Dulwich d			18 49	18 49					19 03				19 19					19 33				19 48	
Sydenham Hill d			18 51	18 51					19 05				19 21					19 35				19 50	
Penge East d			18 54	18 54					19 08				19 24					19 38				19 53	
Kent House 4 d			18 56	18 56					19 09				19 25					19 40				19 55	
Beckenham Junction 4 d			18 58	18 58					19 11				19 28					19 42				19 57	
Denmark Hill 4 d					18 57		18 52							19 27		19 22							19 57
Peckham Rye 4 d					19 00		18 55							19 31		19 25							20 01
Nunhead 4 d					19 02		18 57							19 33		19 27							20 03
Lewisham 4 a					19 08									19 44									20 14
Crofton Park d							18 59									19 29							
Catford d							19 01									19 31							
Bellingham d							19 04									19 34							
Beckenham Hill d							19 06									19 36							
Ravensbourne d							19 08									19 38							
Shortlands 4 d			19 02	19 02			19 10		19 15				19 31			19 40		19 45				20 01	
Bromley South 4 d		19 01	19 05	19 05		19 06	19 13		19 18		19a18	19 29	19 34		19 35	19 43		19 48		19a49	19 59	20 04	
Bickley 4 d			19 07	19 07			19 15		19 21				19 37			19 45		19 51				20 07	
Petts Wood 4 d			19 12	19 12					19 26				19 41					19 55				20 11	
Orpington 4 d			19a15	19a17					19a31				19a44					19a58				20a14	
St Mary Cray d		19 10				19 12	19 21					19 35				19 51					20 05		
Swanley 4 d		19a15				19 16	19 25					19a40			19 44	19 55					20a10		
Eynsford d							19 30									20 00							
Shoreham (Kent) d							19 33									20 03							
Otford 4 d						19a26	19 36								19a53	20 06							
Bat & Ball d							19 39									20 09							
Sevenoaks 4 a							19 42									20 12							

For general notes see front of timetable
For details of catering facilities see Directory of Train Operators

- **A** From 12 October to Broadstairs and to Dover Priory
- **B** To Rochester (Table 212)
- **C** From Bedford (Table 52) to Ashford International (Table 196)
- **D** Until 9 October
- **E** From 12 October
- **G** From St Albans City (Table 52)
- **H** TOC SE from London Blackfriars
- **J** From Bedford (Table 52) to Gillingham (Kent) (Table 212)
- **K** From 12 October to Ramsgate and to Dover Priory
- **L** From 12 October to Faversham
- **N** From Bedford (Table 52)
- **b** Arr. 1801
- **c** Arr. 1816
- **e** Arr. 1827
- **f** Arr. 1836

For details of Bank Holiday service alterations please see first page of this table

London → Catford, Beckenham Junction, Bromley South, Orpington, Otford and Sevenoaks

Network Diagram - see first page of Table 195

Station		SE 1	FC	FC	SE	FC	SE 1	SE 1	SE 1	FC		FC	SE	FC	SE 1	SE 1	SE 1	FC	FC	SE	SE 1	SE 1	FC	FC	SE
			A B							A								A							
London Victoria 15	⊖ d	19 48			19 52		20 03	20 09	20 18				20 22		20 33	20 39	20 48			20 52	21 03	21 09			21 22
Brixton	⊖ d				19 59								20 29							20 59					21 29
Kentish Town	⊖ d		19 26			19 44				19 56		20 00		20 14				20 26	20 30				20 56	21 00	
St Pancras International 15	⊖ d		19 30	19 34		19 48				20 00		20 04		20 18				20 30	20 34				21 00	21 04	
Farringdon	⊖ d		19 35	19 39		19 53				20 05		20 09		20 23				20 35	20 39				21 05	21 09	
City Thameslink 3	d		19 39	19 43		19 57				20 09		20 13		20 27				20 39	20 43				21 09	21 13	
London Blackfriars 3	⊖ d		19 42	19 46		20 00				20 12		20 16		20 30				20 42	20 46				21 12	21 16	
Elephant & Castle	⊖ d		19 45	19 49		20 03				20 15		20 19		20 33				20 45	20 49				21 15	21 19	
Loughborough Jn	d			19 53		20 07						20 23		20 37					20 53					21 23	
Herne Hill 4	d			19a57	20 01	20a11						20a27	20 31	20a41					20a57	21 01				21a27	21 31
West Dulwich	d				20 03								20 33							21 03					21 33
Sydenham Hill	d				20 05								20 35							21 05					21 35
Penge East	d				20 08								20 38							21 08					21 38
Kent House 4	d				20 10								20 40							21 10					21 40
Beckenham Junction 4	d				20 12				20 32				20 42				21 02			21 12					21 42
Denmark Hill 4	d		19 52							20 22								20 52					21 22		
Peckham Rye 4	d		19 55							20 25								20 55					21 25		
Nunhead 4	d		19 57							20 27								20 57					21 27		
Lewisham 4	a																								
Crofton Park	d		19 59							20 29								20 59					21 29		
Catford	d		20 01							20 31								21 01					21 31		
Bellingham	d		20 04							20 34								21 04					21 34		
Beckenham Hill	d		20 06							20 36								21 06					21 36		
Ravensbourne	d		20 08							20 38								21 08					21 38		
Shortlands 4	d		20 10		20 15					20 40			20 45					21 10		21 15			21 40		21 45
Bromley South 4	d	20 07	20 13		20 19		20a18	20 29	20 37	20 43			20 48		20a48	20 59	21 07	21 13		21 17	21a18	21 29	21 43		21 48
Bickley 4	d		20 15		20 22					20 45			20 51					21 15		21 20			21 45		21 51
Petts Wood 4	d				20 26								20 55							21 24					21 55
Orpington 4	d				20a29								20a58							21a27					21a58
St Mary Cray	d		20 21					20 35		20 51						21 06		21 21				21 35	21 51		
Swanley 4	d		20 25					20a40	20 45	20 55						21a10		21 25				21 40	21 55		
Eynsford	d		20 30							21 00								21 30					22 00		
Shoreham (Kent)	d		20 33							21 03								21 33					22 03		
Otford 4	d	20a23	20 36						20a54	21 06							21a23	21 36				21a49	22 06		
Bat & Ball	d		20 39							21 09								21 39					22 09		
Sevenoaks 4	a		20 42							21 12								21 42					22 12		

Station		FC	SE 1	SE		SE	FC	SE 1	SE 1	SE	SE	SE 1	SE	SE	SE 1	SE 1	SE	SE	SE 1	SE 1		SE	SE		
																C				D					
London Victoria 15	⊖ d		21 39	21 42		21 52		22 03	22 09	22 12	22 22	22 39	22 42	22 52	23 03	23 09	23 12	23 22	23 39	23 51		23 42	23 53		
Brixton	⊖ d					21 59					22 29			22 59				23 29					23 59		
Kentish Town	⊖ d	21 30					22 00																		
St Pancras International 15	⊖ d	21 34					22 04																		
Farringdon	⊖ d	21 39					22 09																		
City Thameslink 3	d	21 43					22 13																		
London Blackfriars 3	⊖ d	21 46					22 16																		
Elephant & Castle	⊖ d	21 49					22 19																		
Loughborough Jn	d	21 53					22 23																		
Herne Hill 4	d	21a57				22 01	22a27				22 31			23 01				23 31					00 02		
West Dulwich	d					22 03					22 33			23 03				23 33					00 04		
Sydenham Hill	d					22 05					22 35			23 05				23 35					00 06		
Penge East	d					22 08					22 38			23 08				23 38					00 09		
Kent House 4	d					22 10					22 40			23 10				23 40					00 11		
Beckenham Junction 4	d					22 12					22 42			23 12				23 42					00 13		
Denmark Hill 4	d			21 52						22 22			22 52				23 22					23 52			
Peckham Rye 4	d			21 55						22 25			22 55				23 25					23 55			
Nunhead 4	d			21 57						22 27			22 57				23 27					23 57			
Lewisham 4	a																								
Crofton Park	d			21 59						22 29			22 59				23 29					23 59			
Catford	d			22 01						22 31			23 01				23 31					00 01			
Bellingham	d			22 04						22 34			23 04				23 34					00 04			
Beckenham Hill	d			22 06						22 36			23 06				23 36					00 06			
Ravensbourne	d			22 08						22 38			23 08				23 38					00 08			
Shortlands 4	d			22 10		22 15				22 40	22 45		23 10	23 15			23 40	23 45				00 10	00 16		
Bromley South 4	d		21 59	22 13		22 18		22a18	22 29	22 43	22 48	22 59	23 13	23 18	23a18	23 29	23 43	23 48	23 58	00 07		00 13	00 18		
Bickley 4	d			22 15		22 21				22 45	22 51		23 16	23 21			23 46	23 51				00 16	00 21		
Petts Wood 4	d					22 25					22 55		23 20	23 26			23 50	23 55				00 20	00 25		
Orpington 4	d					22a28					22a58		23a24	23a30			23a54	23a58				00a24	00a28		
St Mary Cray	d		22 05	22 21					22 35	22 51		23 05				23 35			00 04	00 14					
Swanley 4	d		22a10	22 25					22 40	22 55		23a10				23 40			00a09	00 18					
Eynsford	d			22 29						23 00										00 23					
Shoreham (Kent)	d			22 33						23 03										00 27					
Otford 4	d			22 36					22a49	23 06						23a49				00a30					
Bat & Ball	d			22 39						23 09															
Sevenoaks 4	a			22 42						23 12															

For general notes see front of timetable
For details of catering facilities see Directory of Train Operators

A TOC SE from London Blackfriars
B From Luton (Table 52)
C To Canterbury West (Table 207)
D To Ashford International (Table 196)

Saturdays

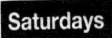

For details of Bank Holiday service alterations please see first page of this table

London → Catford, Beckenham Junction, Bromley South, Orpington, Otford and Sevenoaks

Network Diagram - see first page of Table 195

		SE 1	SE 1 A	SE	SE	SE	SE 1	SE 1	SE		SE 1 B	SE	SE 1	SE	SE	SE	SE 1 B	SE		SE	SE 1	SE 1	SE 1	SE	SE
London Victoria 15	⊖ d	23p39	23p51	23p42	23p53	00 35		05 39	05 51		06 18	06 13	06 39	06 42	06 51	07 09	07 18	07 12		07 21	07 33	07 39	07 48	07 42	07 51
Brixton	⊖ d				23p59				05 58						06 58					07 28					07 58
Kentish Town	⊖ d																								
St Pancras International 15	⊖ d																								
Farringdon	⊖ d																								
City Thameslink 3	d																								
London Blackfriars 3	⊖ d																								
Elephant & Castle	⊖ d																								
Loughborough Jn	d																								
Herne Hill 4	d				00 02	00 43			06 00						07 00					07 30					08 00
West Dulwich	d				00 04				06 03						07 03					07 33					08 03
Sydenham Hill	d				00 06				06 05						07 05					07 35					08 05
Penge East	d				00 09	00 48			06 08						07 08					07 38					08 08
Kent House 4	d				00 11				06 09						07 09					07 39					08 09
Beckenham Junction 4	d				00 13	00 51			06 11						07 11					07 41					08 11
Denmark Hill 4	d			23p52								06 22		06 52				07 22						07 52	
Peckham Rye 4	d			23p55								06 25		06 55				07 25						07 55	
Nunhead 4	d			23p57								06 27		06 57				07 27						07 57	
Lewisham 4	a																								
Crofton Park	d			23p59								06 30		07 00				07 30						08 00	
Catford	d			00 01								06 32		07 02				07 32						08 02	
Bellingham	d			00 04								06 34		07 04				07 34						08 04	
Beckenham Hill	d			00 06								06 36		07 06				07 36						08 06	
Ravensbourne	d			00 08								06 38		07 08				07 38						08 08	
Shortlands 4	d			00 10	00 16				06 14			06 40		07 10	07 14			07 40		07 44				08 10	08 14
Bromley South 4	d	23p58	00 07	00 13	00 18	00 55		05 59	06 17		06 34	06 43	06 59	07 13	07 17	07 29	07 34	07 43		07 47	07a48	07 59	08 04	08 13	08 17
Bickley 4	d			00 16	00 21				06 20			06 46		07 16	07 20			07 46		07 50				08 16	08 20
Petts Wood 4	d			00 20	00 25				06 24						07 24					07 54					08 24
Orpington 4	d			00a24	00a28		05 58		06a27						07a27					07a57					08a27
St Mary Cray	d	00 04	00 14			01 02		06 05			06 41	06 52	07 05	07 22		07 35	07 41	07 52				08 05		08 22	
Swanley 4	d	00a09	00 18			01a06		06a10			06 45	06 56	07a10	07 26		07a40	07 45	07 56				08a10	08 13	08 26	
Eynsford	d		00 23									07 01		07 31				08 01						08 31	
Shoreham (Kent)	d		00 27									07 04		07 34				08 04						08 34	
Otford 4	d		00a30								06a54	07 07		07 37			07a54	08 07					08a23	08 37	
Bat & Ball	d											07 10		07 40				08 10						08 40	
Sevenoaks 4	a						06 07					07 13		07 43				08 13						08 43	

		SE	SE 1	SE 1	SE		SE 1	SE	SE	SE	SE 1	SE 1	SE	SE		SE	SE	SE	SE 1	SE 1	SE	SE 1	SE		SE
London Victoria 15	⊖ d	08 01	08 03	08 09	08 06		08 18	08 12	08 21	08 31	08 33	08 39	08 36	08 48		08 42	08 51	09 01	09 03	09 09	09 06	09 18	09 12		09 21
Brixton	⊖ d				08 13				08 28				08 43				08 58				09 13				09 28
Kentish Town	⊖ d																								
St Pancras International 15	⊖ d																								
Farringdon	⊖ d																								
City Thameslink 3	d																								
London Blackfriars 3	⊖ d																								
Elephant & Castle	⊖ d																								
Loughborough Jn	d																								
Herne Hill 4	d				08 15				08 30				08 45				09 00				09 15				09 30
West Dulwich	d				08 18				08 33				08 48				09 03				09 18				09 33
Sydenham Hill	d				08 20				08 35				08 50				09 05				09 20				09 35
Penge East	d				08 23				08 38				08 53				09 08				09 23				09 38
Kent House 4	d				08 24				08 39				08 54				09 09				09 24				09 39
Beckenham Junction 4	d				08 26				08 41				08 56				09 11				09 26				09 41
Denmark Hill 4	d	08 12						08 22		08 42						08 52		09 12					09 22		
Peckham Rye 4	d	08 14						08 25		08 44						08 55		09 14					09 25		
Nunhead 4	d	08 16						08 27		08 46						08 57		09 16					09 27		
Lewisham 4	a	08 22								08 52								09 22							
Crofton Park	d							08 30								09 00							09 30		
Catford	d							08 32								09 02							09 32		
Bellingham	d							08 34								09 04							09 34		
Beckenham Hill	d							08 36								09 06							09 36		
Ravensbourne	d							08 38								09 08							09 38		
Shortlands 4	d				08 29			08 40	08 44				08 59			09 10	09 14				09 29		09 40		09 44
Bromley South 4	d		08a18	08 29	08 32		08 34	08 43	08 47		08a48	08 59	09 02	09 04		09 13	09 17		09a18	09 29	09 32	09 34	09 43		09 47
Bickley 4	d				08 35			08 46	08 50				09 05			09 16	09 20				09 35		09 46		09 50
Petts Wood 4	d				08 39				08 54				09 09				09 24				09 39				09 54
Orpington 4	d				08a42				08a57				09a12				09a27				09a42				09a57
St Mary Cray	d			08 35				08 52				09 05		09 13		09 22				09 35			09 52		
Swanley 4	d			08a40				08 56				09a10				09 26				09a40			09 56		
Eynsford	d							09 01								09 31							10 01		
Shoreham (Kent)	d							09 04								09 34							10 04		
Otford 4	d						08a51	09 07						09a23		09 37						09a51	10 07		
Bat & Ball	d							09 10								09 40							10 10		
Sevenoaks 4	a							09 13								09 43							10 13		

For general notes see front of timetable
For details of catering facilities see Directory of Train Operators

A To Ashford International (Table 196)
B To Ramsgate (Table 207)

Saturdays

For details of Bank Holiday service alterations please see first page of this table

London → Catford, Beckenham Junction, Bromley South, Orpington, Otford and Sevenoaks

Network Diagram - see first page of Table 195

	SE		SE 1	SE 1	SE	SE	SE	SE	SE	SE 1 ⚲	SE 1	SE	SE 1	SE	SE	SE		SE 1	SE 1	SE	SE 1	SE
London Victoria 15 ⊖ d	09 31		09 33	09 39	09 36	09 48	09 42	09 51	10 01	10 03	10 09	10 06	10 18	10 12	10 21	10 31		18 33	18 39	18 36	18 48	18 42
Brixton ⊖ d					09 43			09 58				10 13			10 28					18 43		
Kentish Town ⊖ d																						
St Pancras International 15 ⊖ d																						
Farringdon ⊖ d																						
City Thameslink 3 d																						
London Blackfriars 3 ⊖ d																						
Elephant & Castle ⊖ d																						
Loughborough Jn d																						
Herne Hill 4 d					09 45			10 00				10 15			10 30					18 45		
West Dulwich d					09 48			10 03				10 18			10 33					18 48		
Sydenham Hill d					09 50			10 05				10 20			10 35					18 50		
Penge East d					09 53			10 08				10 23			10 38					18 53		
Kent House 4 d					09 54			10 09				10 24			10 39					18 54		
Beckenham Junction 4 🚊 d					09 56			10 11				10 26			10 41					18 56		
Denmark Hill 4 d	09 42						09 52		10 12					10 22		10 42						18 52
Peckham Rye 4 d	09 44						09 55		10 14					10 25		10 44						18 55
Nunhead 4 d	09 46						09 57		10 16					10 27		10 46						18 57
Lewisham 4 🚈 a	09 52								10 22							10 52						
Crofton Park d							10 00							10 30								19 00
Catford d							10 02							10 32								19 02
Bellingham d							10 04							10 34								19 04
Beckenham Hill d							10 06							10 36								19 06
Ravensbourne d							10 08							10 38								19 08
Shortlands 4 d					09 59		10 10	10 14				10 29		10 40	10 44					18 59		19 10
Bromley South 4 d			09a48	09 59	10 02	10 04	10 13	10 17		10a18	10 29	10 32	10 34	10 43	10 47			18a48	18 59	19 02	19 04	19 13
Bickley 4 d					10 05		10 16	10 20				10 35		10 46	10 50					19 05		19 16
Petts Wood 4 d					10 09			10 24				10 39			10 54					19 09		
Orpington 4 d					10a12			10a27				10a42			10a57					19a12		
St Mary Cray d				10 05			10 22				10 35			10 52					19 05			19 22
Swanley 4 d				10a10		10 13	10 26				10a40			10 56					19a10		19 13	19 26
Eynsford d							10 31							11 01								19 31
Shoreham (Kent) d							10 34							11 04								19 34
Otford 4 d						10a23	10 37						10a51	11 07							19a23	19 37
Bat & Ball d							10 40							11 10								19 40
Sevenoaks 4 a							10 43							11 13								19 43

	SE	SE	SE 1 ⚲	SE	SE 1		SE	SE	SE	SE 1	SE	SE	SE	SE 1		SE 1	SE	SE	SE 1	SE	SE	SE 1	SE 1	SE
London Victoria 15 ⊖ d	18 51	19 01	19 03	19 06	19 18		19 12	19 21	19 31	19 39	19 36	19 42	19 51	20 03		20 18	20 12	20 21	20 39	20 42	20 51	21 03	21 18	21 12
Brixton ⊖ d	18 58			19 13				19 28			19 43		19 58					20 28			20 58			
Kentish Town ⊖ d																								
St Pancras International 15 ⊖ d																								
Farringdon ⊖ d																								
City Thameslink 3 d																								
London Blackfriars 3 ⊖ d																								
Elephant & Castle ⊖ d																								
Loughborough Jn d																								
Herne Hill 4 d	19 00			19 15				19 30			19 45		20 00					20 30			21 00			
West Dulwich d	19 03			19 18				19 33			19 48		20 03					20 33			21 03			
Sydenham Hill d	19 05			19 20				19 35			19 50		20 05					20 35			21 05			
Penge East d	19 08			19 23				19 38			19 53		20 08					20 38			21 08			
Kent House 4 d	19 09			19 24				19 39			19 54		20 09					20 39			21 09			
Beckenham Junction 4 🚊 d	19 11			19 26				19 41			19 56		20 11					20 41			21 11			
Denmark Hill 4 d		19 12					19 22		19 42			19 52					20 22			20 52				21 22
Peckham Rye 4 d		19 14					19 25		19 44			19 55					20 25			20 55				21 25
Nunhead 4 d		19 16					19 27		19 46			19 57					20 27			20 57				21 27
Lewisham 4 🚈 a		19 23							19 53															
Crofton Park d							19 30					20 00					20 30			21 00				21 30
Catford d							19 32					20 02					20 32			21 02				21 32
Bellingham d							19 34					20 04					20 34			21 04				21 34
Beckenham Hill d							19 36					20 06					20 36			21 06				21 36
Ravensbourne d							19 38					20 08					20 38			21 08				21 38
Shortlands 4 d	19 14			19 29			19 40	19 44			19 59	20 10	20 14				20 40	20 44		21 10	21 14			21 40
Bromley South 4 d	19 17		19a18	19 32	19 34		19 43	19 47		19 59	20 02	20 13	20 17	20a18		20 34	20 43	20 47	20 59	21 13	21 17	21a18	21 34	21 43
Bickley 4 d	19 20			19 35			19 46	19 50			20 05	20 16	20 20				20 46	20 50		21 16	21 20			21 46
Petts Wood 4 d	19 24			19 39				19 54			20 09		20 24					20 54			21 24			
Orpington 4 d	19a27			19a42				19a57			20a12		20a27					20a57			21a27			
St Mary Cray d					19 41		19 52			20 05		20 22				20 41	20 52		21 05	21 22			21 41	21 52
Swanley 4 d					19 45		19 56			20a10		20 26				20 45	20 56		21a10	21 26			21 45	21 56
Eynsford d							20 01					20 31					21 01			21 31				22 01
Shoreham (Kent) d							20 04					20 34					21 04			21 34				22 04
Otford 4 d					19a54		20 07					20 37				20a54	21 07			21 37			21a54	22 07
Bat & Ball d							20 10					20 40					21 10			21 40				22 10
Sevenoaks 4 a							20 13					20 43					21 13			21 43				22 13

For general notes see front of timetable
For details of catering facilities see Directory of Train Operators

Saturdays

For details of Bank Holiday service alterations please see first page of this table

London → Catford, Beckenham Junction, Bromley South, Orpington, Otford and Sevenoaks

Network Diagram - see first page of Table 195

		SE		SE 1	SE	SE	SE 1	SE 1	SE	SE	SE 1		SE	SE	SE 1	SE 1 A	SE	SE	SE 1	SE 1 B		SE	SE		
London Victoria 15	⊖ d	21 21		21 39	21 42	21 51	22 03	22 18	22 12	22 21	22 39		22 42	22 51	23 03	23 18	23 12	23 21	23 39	23 51		23 42	23 53		
Brixton	⊖ d	21 28				21 58				22 28				22 58				23 28					23 59		
Kentish Town	⊖ d																								
St Pancras International 15	⊖ d																								
Farringdon	⊖ d																								
City Thameslink 3	d																								
London Blackfriars 3	⊖ d																								
Elephant & Castle	⊖ d																								
Loughborough Jn	d																								
Herne Hill 4	d	21 30				22 00				22 30				23 00				23 30					00 02		
West Dulwich	d	21 33				22 03				22 33				23 03				23 33					00 04		
Sydenham Hill	d	21 35				22 05				22 35				23 05				23 35					00 06		
Penge East	d	21 38				22 08				22 38				23 08				23 38					00 09		
Kent House 4	d	21 39				22 09				22 39				23 09				23 39					00 11		
Beckenham Junction 4	🚊 d	21 41				22 11				22 41				23 11				23 41					00 13		
Denmark Hill 4	d				21 52				22 22				22 52				23 22					23 52			
Peckham Rye 4	d				21 55				22 25				22 55				23 25					23 55			
Nunhead 4	d				21 57				22 27				22 57				23 27					23 57			
Lewisham 4	🚊 a																								
Crofton Park	d				22 00				22 30				23 00				23 30					23 59			
Catford	d				22 02				22 32				23 02				23 32					00 01			
Bellingham	d				22 04				22 34				23 04				23 34					00 04			
Beckenham Hill	d				22 06				22 36				23 06				23 36					00 06			
Ravensbourne	d				22 08				22 38				23 08				23 38					00 08			
Shortlands 4	d	21 44			22 10	22 14			22 40	22 44			23 10	23 14			23 40	23 44				00 10	00 16		
Bromley South 4	d	21 47		21 59	22 13	22 17	22a18	22 34	22 43	22 47	22 59		23 13	23 17	23a18	23 34	23 43	23 47	23 59	00 07		00 13	00 19		
Bickley 4	d	21 50			22 16	22 20			22 46	22 50			23 16	23 20			23 46	23 50				00 15	00 21		
Petts Wood 4	d	21 54				22 24				22 54			23 20	23 24			23 50	23 54				00 20	00 26		
Orpington 4	d	21a57				22a27				22a57			23a23	23a27			23a53	23a57				00a23	00a29		
St Mary Cray	d			22 05	22 22			22 41	22 52		23 05					23 41			00 05	00 14					
Swanley 4	d			22a10	22 26			22 45	22 56		23a10					23 45			00a10	00 18					
Eynsford	d				22 31				23 01											00 23					
Shoreham (Kent)	d				22 34				23 04											00 27					
Otford 4	d				22 37			22a54	23 07							23a54				00a30					
Bat & Ball	d				22 40				23 10																
Sevenoaks 4	a				22 43				23 13																

Sundays

		SE 1	SE 1 B	SE		SE	SE	SE 1		SE 1 A	SE	SE		SE 1	SE	SE 1		SE	SE 1 A	SE		SE	SE 1	SE	SE 1
London Victoria 15	⊖ d	23p39	23p51	23p42		23p53	00 35	07 35		07 42	07 38	07 51		08 03	08 08	08 24		08 21	08 42	08 38		08 51	09 03	09 08	09 24
Brixton	⊖ d					23p59						07 58						08 28				08 58			
Kentish Town	⊖ d																								
St Pancras International 15	⊖ d																								
Farringdon	⊖ d																								
City Thameslink 3	d																								
London Blackfriars 3	⊖ d																								
Elephant & Castle	⊖ d																								
Loughborough Jn	d																								
Herne Hill 4	d					00 02	00 43					08 00						08 30				09 00			
West Dulwich	d					00 04						08 03						08 33				09 03			
Sydenham Hill	d					00 06						08 05						08 35				09 05			
Penge East	d					00 09	00 48					08 08						08 38				09 08			
Kent House 4	d					00 11						08 09						08 39				09 09			
Beckenham Junction 4	🚊 d					00 13	00 51					08 11						08 41				09 11			
Denmark Hill 4	d			23p52							07 47				08 17					08 47				09 17	
Peckham Rye 4	d			23p55							07 49				08 19					08 49				09 19	
Nunhead 4	d			23p57							07 51				08 21					08 51				09 21	
Lewisham 4	🚊 a																								
Crofton Park	d			23p59							07 54				08 24					08 54				09 24	
Catford	d			00 01							07 56				08 26					08 56				09 26	
Bellingham	d			00 04							07 58				08 28					08 58				09 28	
Beckenham Hill	d			00 06							08 00				08 30					09 00				09 30	
Ravensbourne	d			00 08							08 02				08 32					09 02				09 32	
Shortlands 4	d			00 10		00 16					08 04	08 14			08 34			08 44		09 04		09 14		09 34	
Bromley South 4	d	23p59	00 07	00 13		00 19	00 55	07 52		07 59	08 07	08 17		08a18	08 37	08 43		08 47	08 59	09 07		09 17	09a18	09 37	09 43
Bickley 4	d			00 15		00 21					08 10	08 20			08 40			08 50		09 10		09 20		09 40	
Petts Wood 4	d			00 20		00 26						08 24						08 54				09 24			
Orpington 4	d			00a23		00a29						08a27						08a57				09a27			
St Mary Cray	d	00 05	00 14				01 01	07 58		08 05	08 15				08 45	08 50			09 05	09 15				09 45	09 50
Swanley 4	d	00a10	00 18				01a05	08a03		08 10	08 20				08 50	08a54			09 10	09 20				09 50	09a54
Eynsford	d		00 23								08 24				08 54					09 24				09 54	
Shoreham (Kent)	d		00 27								08 28				08 58					09 28				09 58	
Otford 4	d		00a30							08a19	08 31				09 01				09a19	09 31				10 01	
Bat & Ball	d										08 34				09 04					09 34				10 04	
Sevenoaks 4	a										08 37				09 07					09 37				10 07	

For general notes see front of timetable
For details of catering facilities see Directory of Train Operators

A To Canterbury West (Table 207)
B To Ashford International (Table 196)

Table 195

Sundays

London → Catford, Beckenham Junction, Bromley South, Orpington, Otford and Sevenoaks

Network Diagram - see first page of Table 195

Station		SE	SE 1 A	SE	SE	SE 1 🛒
London Victoria 15	⊖ d	09 21	09 42	09 38	09 51	10 03
Brixton	⊖ d	09 28			09 58	
Kentish Town	⊖ d					
St Pancras International 15	⊖ d					
Farringdon	⊖ d					
City Thameslink 3	d					
London Blackfriars 3	⊖ d					
Elephant & Castle	⊖ d					
Loughborough Jn	d					
Herne Hill 4	d	09 30			10 00	
West Dulwich	d	09 33			10 03	
Sydenham Hill	d	09 35			10 05	
Penge East	d	09 38			10 08	
Kent House 4	d	09 39			10 09	
Beckenham Junction 4	🚊 d	09 41			10 11	
Denmark Hill 4	d			09 47		
Peckham Rye 4	d			09 49		
Nunhead 4	d			09 51		
Lewisham 4	🚊 a					
Crofton Park	d			09 54		
Catford	d			09 56		
Bellingham	d			09 58		
Beckenham Hill	d			10 00		
Ravensbourne	d			10 02		
Shortlands 4	d	09 44		10 04	10 14	
Bromley South 4	d	09 47	09 59	10 07	10 17	10a18
Bickley 4	d	09 50		10 10	10 20	
Petts Wood 4	d	09 54			10 24	
Orpington 4	d	09a57			10a27	
St Mary Cray	d		10 05	10 15		
Swanley 4	d		10 10	10 20		
Eynsford	d			10 24		
Shoreham (Kent)	d			10 28		
Otford 4	d		10a19	10 31		
Bat & Ball	d			10 34		
Sevenoaks 4	a			10 37		

Station		SE	SE 1	SE	SE 1 A	SE	SE	SE 1 🛒
London Victoria 15	⊖ d	10 08	10 24	10 21	10 42	10 38	10 51	11 03
Brixton	⊖ d			10 28			10 58	
Kentish Town	⊖ d							
St Pancras International 15	⊖ d							
Farringdon	⊖ d							
City Thameslink 3	d							
London Blackfriars 3	⊖ d							
Elephant & Castle	⊖ d							
Loughborough Jn	d							
Herne Hill 4	d			10 30			11 00	
West Dulwich	d			10 33			11 03	
Sydenham Hill	d			10 35			11 05	
Penge East	d			10 38			11 08	
Kent House 4	d			10 39			11 09	
Beckenham Junction 4	🚊 d			10 41			11 11	
Denmark Hill 4	d	10 17				10 47		
Peckham Rye 4	d	10 19				10 49		
Nunhead 4	d	10 21				10 51		
Lewisham 4	🚊 a							
Crofton Park	d	10 24				10 54		
Catford	d	10 26				10 56		
Bellingham	d	10 28				10 58		
Beckenham Hill	d	10 30				11 00		
Ravensbourne	d	10 32				11 02		
Shortlands 4	d	10 34		10 44		11 04	11 14	
Bromley South 4	d	10 37	10 43	10 47	10 59	11 07	11 17	11a18
Bickley 4	d	10 40		10 50		11 10	11 20	
Petts Wood 4	d			10 54			11 24	
Orpington 4	d			10a57			11a27	
St Mary Cray	d	10 45	10 50		11 05	11 15		
Swanley 4	d	10 50	10a54		11 10	11 20		
Eynsford	d	10 54				11 24		
Shoreham (Kent)	d	10 58				11 28		
Otford 4	d	11 01			11a19	11 31		
Bat & Ball	d	11 04				11 34		
Sevenoaks 4	a	11 07				11 37		

Station		SE	SE 1	SE	SE 1	SE
London Victoria 15	⊖ d	18 08	18 24	18 21	18 42	18 38
Brixton	⊖ d			18 28		
Kentish Town	⊖ d					
St Pancras International 15	⊖ d					
Farringdon	⊖ d					
City Thameslink 3	d					
London Blackfriars 3	⊖ d					
Elephant & Castle	⊖ d					
Loughborough Jn	d					
Herne Hill 4	d			18 30		
West Dulwich	d			18 33		
Sydenham Hill	d			18 35		
Penge East	d			18 38		
Kent House 4	d			18 39		
Beckenham Junction 4	🚊 d			18 41		
Denmark Hill 4	d	18 17				18 47
Peckham Rye 4	d	18 19				18 49
Nunhead 4	d	18 21				18 51
Lewisham 4	🚊 a					
Crofton Park	d	18 24				18 54
Catford	d	18 26				18 56
Bellingham	d	18 28				18 58
Beckenham Hill	d	18 30				19 00
Ravensbourne	d	18 32				19 02
Shortlands 4	d	18 34		18 44		19 04
Bromley South 4	d	18 37	18 43	18 47	18 59	19 07
Bickley 4	d	18 40		18 50		19 10
Petts Wood 4	d			18 54		
Orpington 4	d			18a57		
St Mary Cray	d	18 45	18 50		19 05	19 15
Swanley 4	d	18 50	18a54		19 10	19 20
Eynsford	d	18 54				19 24
Shoreham (Kent)	d	18 58				19 28
Otford 4	d	19 01			19a19	19 31
Bat & Ball	d	19 04				19 34
Sevenoaks 4	a	19 07				19 37

Station		SE	SE 1 🛒	SE	SE 1	SE	SE 1	SE	SE	SE 1
London Victoria 15	⊖ d	18 51	19 03	19 08	19 24	19 21	19 42	19 38	19 51	20 03
Brixton	⊖ d	18 58				19 28			19 58	
Kentish Town	⊖ d									
St Pancras International 15	⊖ d									
Farringdon	⊖ d									
City Thameslink 3	d									
London Blackfriars 3	⊖ d									
Elephant & Castle	⊖ d									
Loughborough Jn	d									
Herne Hill 4	d	19 00				19 30			20 00	
West Dulwich	d	19 03				19 33			20 03	
Sydenham Hill	d	19 05				19 35			20 05	
Penge East	d	19 08				19 38			20 08	
Kent House 4	d	19 09				19 39			20 09	
Beckenham Junction 4	🚊 d	19 11				19 41			20 11	
Denmark Hill 4	d			19 17				19 47		
Peckham Rye 4	d			19 19				19 49		
Nunhead 4	d			19 21				19 51		
Lewisham 4	🚊 a									
Crofton Park	d			19 24				19 54		
Catford	d			19 26				19 56		
Bellingham	d			19 28				19 58		
Beckenham Hill	d			19 30				20 00		
Ravensbourne	d			19 32				20 02		
Shortlands 4	d	19 14		19 34		19 44		20 04	20 14	
Bromley South 4	d	19 17	19a18	19 37	19 43	19 47	19 59	20 07	20 17	20a18
Bickley 4	d	19 20		19 40		19 50		20 10	20 20	
Petts Wood 4	d	19 24				19 54			20 24	
Orpington 4	d	19a27				19a57			20a27	
St Mary Cray	d			19 45	19 50		20 05	20 15		
Swanley 4	d			19 50	19a54		20 10	20 20		
Eynsford	d			19 54				20 24		
Shoreham (Kent)	d			19 58				20 28		
Otford 4	d			20 01			20a19	20 31		
Bat & Ball	d			20 04				20 34		
Sevenoaks 4	a			20 07				20 37		

Station		SE	SE 1	SE	SE 1	SE	SE	SE 1	SE	SE 1	SE
London Victoria 15	⊖ d	20 08	20 24	20 21	20 42	20 38	20 51	21 03	21 08	21 24	21 21
Brixton	⊖ d			20 28			20 58				21 28
Kentish Town	⊖ d										
St Pancras International 15	⊖ d										
Farringdon	⊖ d										
City Thameslink 3	d										
London Blackfriars 3	⊖ d										
Elephant & Castle	⊖ d										
Loughborough Jn	d										
Herne Hill 4	d			20 30			21 00				21 30
West Dulwich	d			20 33			21 03				21 33
Sydenham Hill	d			20 35			21 05				21 35
Penge East	d			20 38			21 08				21 38
Kent House 4	d			20 39			21 09				21 39
Beckenham Junction 4	🚊 d			20 41			21 11				21 41
Denmark Hill 4	d	20 17				20 47			21 17		
Peckham Rye 4	d	20 19				20 49			21 19		
Nunhead 4	d	20 21				20 51			21 21		
Lewisham 4	🚊 a										
Crofton Park	d	20 24				20 54			21 24		
Catford	d	20 26				20 56			21 26		
Bellingham	d	20 28				20 58			21 28		
Beckenham Hill	d	20 30				21 00			21 30		
Ravensbourne	d	20 32				21 02			21 32		
Shortlands 4	d	20 34		20 44		21 04	21 14		21 34		21 44
Bromley South 4	d	20 37	20 43	20 47	20 59	21 07	21 17	21a18	21 37	21 43	21 47
Bickley 4	d	20 40		20 50		21 10	21 20		21 40		21 50
Petts Wood 4	d			20 54			21 24				21 54
Orpington 4	d			20a57			21a27				21a57
St Mary Cray	d	20 45	20 50		21 05	21 15			21 45	21 50	
Swanley 4	d	20 50	20a54		21 10	21 20			21 50	21a54	
Eynsford	d	20 54				21 24			21 54		
Shoreham (Kent)	d	20 58				21 28			21 58		
Otford 4	d	21 01			21a19	21 31			22 01		
Bat & Ball	d	21 04				21 34			22 04		
Sevenoaks 4	a	21 07				21 37			22 07		

For general notes see front of timetable
For details of catering facilities see Directory of Train Operators

A To Canterbury West (Table 207)

Table 195

Sundays

London → Catford, Beckenham Junction, Bromley South, Orpington, Otford and Sevenoaks

Network Diagram - see first page of Table 195

		SE 1		SE	SE	SE 1		SE	SE	SE 1		SE 1	SE	SE		SE 1	SE	SE		SE 1					
London Victoria 15	⊖ d	21 42		21 38	21 51	22 03		22 08	22 21	22 35		22 42	22 38	22 51		23 03	23 08	23 21		23 42					
Brixton	⊖ d				21 58				22 28					22 58				23 28							
Kentish Town	⊖ d																								
St Pancras International 15	⊖ d																								
Farringdon	⊖ d																								
City Thameslink 3	d																								
London Blackfriars 3	⊖ d																								
Elephant & Castle	⊖ d																								
Loughborough Jn	d																								
Herne Hill 4	d				22 00				22 30					23 00				23 30							
West Dulwich	d				22 03				22 33					23 03				23 33							
Sydenham Hill	d				22 05				22 35					23 05				23 35							
Penge East	d				22 08				22 38					23 08				23 38							
Kent House 4	d				22 09				22 39					23 09				23 39							
Beckenham Junction 4	🚌 d				22 11				22 41					23 11				23 41							
Denmark Hill 4	d			21 47				22 17					22 47				23 17								
Peckham Rye 4	d			21 49				22 19					22 49				23 19								
Nunhead 4	d			21 51				22 21					22 51				23 21								
Lewisham 4	🚌 a																								
Crofton Park	d			21 54				22 24					22 54				23 24								
Catford	d			21 56				22 26					22 56				23 26								
Bellingham	d			21 58				22 28					22 58				23 28								
Beckenham Hill	d			22 00				22 30					23 00				23 30								
Ravensbourne	d			22 02				22 32					23 02				23 32								
Shortlands 4	d			22 04	22 14			22 34	22 44				23 04	23 14			23 34	23 44							
Bromley South 4	d	21 59		22 07	22 17	22a18		22 37	22 47	22 55		22 59	23 07	23 17		23a18	23 37	23 47		00 01					
Bickley 4	d			22 10	22 20			22 40	22 50				23 10	23 20			23 40	23 50							
Petts Wood 4	d				22 24				22 54				23 14	23 24			23 44	23 54							
Orpington 4	d				22a27				22a57				23a17	23a27			23a47	23a57							
St Mary Cray	d	22 05		22 15				22 45		23 01		23 05								00 08					
Swanley 4	d	22 10		22 20				22 50		23a06		23 10								00a12					
Eynsford	d			22 24				22 54																	
Shoreham (Kent)	d			22 28				22 58																	
Otford 4	d	22a19		22 31				23 01				23a19													
Bat & Ball	d			22 34				23 04																	
Sevenoaks 4	a			22 37				23 07																	

For general notes see front of timetable
For details of catering facilities see Directory of Train Operators

For details of Bank Holiday service alterations please see first page of this table

Sevenoaks, Otford, Orpington, Bromley South, Beckenham Junction and Catford → London

Network Diagram - see first page of Table 195

Miles	Miles	Miles			SE	SE [1] A	SE [1] B	SE	SE A	SE B	FC C	SE	FC C	SE	SE [1]		SE D	FC	SE	SE [1]	FC	SE D	SE [1]	SE [1] E	SE
—	0	—	**Sevenoaks** [4]	d													05 40					06 13			
—	1¼	—	Bat & Ball	d													05 43					06 16			
—	3	—	Otford [4]	d													05 46					06 19	06 28		
—	4¼	—	Shoreham (Kent)	d													05 49					06 22			
—	6½	—	Eynsford	d													05 52					06 25			
—	9½	—	**Swanley** [4]	d		04 33	04 33										05 57			06 30		06 31		06 41	
—	12¼	—	St Mary Cray	d		04 37	04 37										06 01			06 35		06 35		06 46	
0	—	—	**Orpington** [4]	d	04 36			04 58	05 25	05 25		05 36		05 50					06 20						06 44
1¼	—	—	Petts Wood [4]	d	04 39			05 01	05 28	05 28		05 39		05 53					06 23						06 47
3	14½	—	Bickley [4]	d	04 43	04 43	04 43	05 05	05 32	05 32		05 43		05 57			06 06		06 27			06 41			06 51
4	15½	—	**Bromley South** [4]	d	04 46	04b51	04b51	05 08	05 36	05 36		05 46		06 01	06 14		06c15		06 31	06 42		06 44	06 48	06 52	06 54
5	16½	—	Shortlands [4]	d	04 48	04 53	04 53	05 10	05 38	05 38		05 48		06 03			06 17		06 33			06 46			06 56
—	17¼	—	Ravensbourne	d	04 51							05 51					06 20					06 49			
—	18	—	Beckenham Hill	d	04 53							05 53					06 22					06 51			
—	18¾	—	Bellingham	d	04 55							05 55					06 24					06 53			
—	19½	—	Catford	d	04 57							05 57					06 26					06 55			
—	20½	—	Crofton Park	d	04 59							06 00					06 28					06 58			
—	—	0	Lewisham [4]	d																					
—	21¾	1¾	Nunhead [4]	d	05 02							06 02					06 31					07 00			
—	22½	2½	Peckham Rye [4]	d	05 04							06 04					06 33					07 02			
—	23¼	3¼	Denmark Hill [4]	d	05 06							06 07					06 35					07 05			
6¼	—	—	**Beckenham Junction** [4]	d		04 56	04 56	05 13	05 40	05 40				06 06					06 36						06 58
7¼	—	—	Kent House [4]	d		04 58	04 58	05 15	05 42	05 42				06 08					06 38						07 00
7¾	—	—	Penge East	d		05 00	05 00	05 17	05 44	05 44				06 10					06 40						07 02
9¼	—	—	Sydenham Hill	d		05 03	05 03	05 20	05 47	05 47				06 13					06 43						07 05
10	—	—	West Dulwich	d		05 05	05 05	05 22	05 49	05 49				06 15					06 45						07 07
11	—	—	Herne Hill [4]	d		05 07	05 07	05 25	05 52	05 52	05 54		06 14	06 18				06 42	06 48		07 00		06 58		07 10
—	—	—	Loughborough Jn	d									06 17					06 45			07 03				
—	25¾	—	Elephant & Castle	⊖ d	05 13			05 31			06 00	06 13	06 22				06 40	06 50			07 08	07 12			
—	27	—	**London Blackfriars** [3]	⊖ d	05 17			05 35			06 04	06 17	06 30				06 44	06 58			07 12	07 16			
—	—	—	City Thameslink [3]	a	05 19			05 38			06 06	06 19	06 32				06 46	07 00			07 14	07 18			
—	—	—	Farringdon	⊖ a							06 10		06 36				06 50	07 04			07 17	07 21			
—	—	—	St Pancras International [15]	⊖ a							06 13		06 39				06 53	07 07			07 21	07 25			
—	—	—	Kentish Town	⊖ a							06 20		06 46				06 58					07 30			
11¾	—	—	Brixton	⊖ d		05 09	05 09		05 54	05 54				06 20					06 50						07 12
15	—	7½	**London Victoria** [15]	⊖ a		05 16	05 18		06 01	06 03				06e29	06e32				06e59	07e01			07 08	07 12	07e21

			SE [1] G	SE [1] H	SE [1] E	FC		SE D J	SE D	SE	SE [1]	SE	SE [1] K	SE D L	SE	SE	SE [1] N	FC		SE	SE D	SE [1] E	SE	SE D Q	SE [1] N	SE
Sevenoaks [4]	d								06 43							07 10										
Bat & Ball	d								06 46							07 13										
Otford [4]	d		06 36	06 38					06 49		07 12					07 16	07 21								07 32	
Shoreham (Kent)	d								06 52							07 19										
Eynsford	d								06 55							07 22										
Swanley [4]	d		06 49	06 49					07 01			07 18				07 28	07 31				←		07 40		07 44	
St Mary Cray	d								07 06			07 23				07 32					07 32		07 45			
Orpington [4]	d							07 02		07 06				07 23	07 27	→										
Petts Wood [4]	d							07 05		07 09				07 26	07 30											
Bickley [4]	d							07 09	07 11	07 13				07 30	07 34						07 37					
Bromley South [4]	d		06 58	06 58	07 01			07 12	07 16	07 16	07 29	07 29	07 32	07 34	07 37		07 40				07 41	07 51	07 52		07 54	
Shortlands [4]	d							07 14	07 18	07 18				07 36	07 39						07 43					
Ravensbourne	d								07 21												07 46					
Beckenham Hill	d								07 23												07 48					
Bellingham	d								07 25												07 50					
Catford	d								07 27												07 52					
Crofton Park	d								07 29												07 55					
Lewisham [4]	d																			07 44						
Nunhead [4]	d								07 32											07 52	07 57					
Peckham Rye [4]	d								07 34											07 55	08 00					
Denmark Hill [4]	d								07 37											07 59	08 02				08 06	
Beckenham Junction [4]	d							07 17		07 21				07 39	07 42									08 00		
Kent House [4]	d							07 19		07 23				07 41	07 44									08 02		08 05
Penge East	d							07 22		07 25				07 43	07 46									08 04		08 07
Sydenham Hill	d							07 25		07 28				07 46	07 49									08 07		08 10
West Dulwich	d							07 27		07 30				07 47	07 52									08 08		08 12
Herne Hill [4]	d					07 24		07 32		07 34			07 43	07 50	07 57			08 01						08 13		08 15
Loughborough Jn	d					07 27		07 35						07 53				08 04						08 16		
Elephant & Castle	⊖ d		07 16	07 16		07 32		07 40	07 43					07 58			08 02	08 09			08 13			08 21		
London Blackfriars [3]	⊖ d		07 20	07 20		07 36		07 44	07 48					08 02			08 06	08 14			08 18			08 26		
City Thameslink [3]	a		07 22	07 22		07 38		07 46	07 50					08 04			08 08	08 16			08 20			08 28		
Farringdon	⊖ a		07 26	07 26		07 42		07 50	07 54					08 08			08 12	08 20			08 24			08 31		
St Pancras International [15]	⊖ a		07 31	07 31		07 47		07 53	07 57					08 11			08 15	08 23			08 27			08 35		
Kentish Town	⊖ a								08 02					08 16							08 32					
Brixton	⊖ d									07 37					07 59											08 17
London Victoria [15]	⊖ a				07 24					07e46	07 49	07 54	07 52		08e08					08e12		08 11	08 14		08 17	08 25

For general notes see front of timetable
For details of catering facilities see Directory of Train Operators

- **A** Until 9 October
- **B** From 12 October
- **C** From Selhurst (Table 177)
- **D** TOC FC from London Blackfriars
- **E** From 12 October from Ramsgate
- **G** From 12 October. From Bearsted (Table 196)
- **H** Until 9 October. From Bearsted (Table 196)
- **J** To Luton (Table 52)
- **K** From Dover Priory (Table 212)
- **L** To St Albans City (Table 52)
- **N** From Ashford International (Table 196)
- **Q** To Bedford (Table 52)
- **b** Arr. 0446
- **c** Arr. 0608
- **e** Until 9 October arr 2 minutes earlier

For details of Bank Holiday service alterations please see first page of this table

Sevenoaks, Otford, Orpington, Bromley South, Beckenham Junction and Catford → London

Network Diagram - see first page of Table 195

Station	SE	SE	SE	SE	FC	SE		SE	SE 1	SE 1	FC	SE	SE	SE	SE	FC 1	SE	SE 1		SE 1	SE 1	SE	FC 1	SE
	A B			A C		A		D						A			A	E		G		A B		
Sevenoaks 4 d						07 40											07 52							
Bat & Ball d						07 43											07 55							
Otford 4 d						07 46			07 50								07 58	08 08						
Shoreham (Kent) d						07 49											08 01							
Eynsford d						07 52											08 04							
Swanley 4 d				07 55		07 58		07 59	08 00								08 10				08 21			
St Mary Cray d				08 00		08 02		08 04									08 14				08 26			
Orpington 4 d	07 44	07 50													08 10									08 30
Petts Wood 4 d	07 47	07 53													08 13									08 33
Bickley 4 d	07 53	07 57													08 17		08 20							08 37
Bromley South 4 d	07 56	08 01		08 06		08 09		08 11		08 15				08 18	08 21		08 23	08 24		08 31	08 32			08 41
Shortlands 4 d	07 58	08 03												08 20	08 23		08 26							08 43
Ravensbourne d						08 12								08 23										
Beckenham Hill d						08 14								08 25										
Bellingham d	08 04					08 16								08 27			08 32							
Catford d	08 08					08 18								08 29			08 37							
Crofton Park d	08 10																08 40							
Lewisham 4 d			08 04										08 24											
Nunhead 4 d	08 13		08 09										08 29				08 43							
Peckham Rye 4 d	08 15		08 11										08 32	08 35			08 45							
Denmark Hill 4 d	08 18		08 14			08 26		08 29					08 35	08 37			08 48	08 40						
Beckenham Junction 4 d		08 06							08 15			08 22			08 27									08 46
Kent House 4 d		08 08										08 24			08 29							08 43		08 48
Penge East d		08 10										08 26										08 45		08 50
Sydenham Hill d		08 13										08 29										08 48		08 53
West Dulwich d		08 15										08 31			08 35							08 49		08 55
Herne Hill 4 d		08 18			08 22						08 31	08 35			08 39	08 43						08 52	08 58	09 00
Loughborough Jn d					08 25						08 34											08 55		
Elephant & Castle ⊖ d	08 25			08 29	08 32	08 36					08 41			08 45			08 54					09 00		
London Blackfriars 3 ⊖ d	08 30			08 34	08 38	08 42					08 47			08 50		08 54	09 00					09 04	09 08	
City Thameslink 3 a	08 32			08 36	08 40	08 44					08 49			08 52		08 56	09 02					09 06	09 10	
Farringdon ⊖ a	08 35			08 40	08 44	08 47					08 53			08 56		09 00	09 06					09 10	09 14	
St Pancras International 15 ⊖ a	08 39			08 43	08 47	08 51					08 56			08 59		09 03	09 09					09 13	09 17	
Kentish Town ⊖ a	08 44					08 58					09 01											09 18		
Brixton ⊖ d												08 37												09 03
London Victoria 15 ⊖ a		08b29	08b29					08 41	08 31	08 33		08 45	08b47		08b50			08 52		08 53	08 57			09b12

Station	SE	FC	SE	SE	SE 1	SE 1	SE	SE 1		SE	SE	FC	SE	SE 1	SE	SE 1	SE 1	FC	SE	SE		FC	SE	SE 1
			A	A			A						A							H			A	
Sevenoaks 4 d				08 22									08 40										09 12	
Bat & Ball d				08 25									08 43										09 15	
Otford 4 d				08 28				08 40					08 46			09 07							09 18	09 27
Shoreham (Kent) d				08 31									08 49										09 21	
Eynsford d				08 34									08 52										09 24	
Swanley 4 d				08 40	08 43			08 50					08 58	09 07									09 30	09 36
St Mary Cray d				08 44	08 48								09 02	09 12									09 35	
Orpington 4 d							08 47			08 53					09 08				09 23					
Petts Wood 4 d							08 50			08 56					09 11				09 26					
Bickley 4 d				08 49			08 55			09 00			09 06		09 15				09 30				09 39	
Bromley South 4 d			08 45	08 52	08 54	08 56	08 58	09 00		09 03			09 09	09 19	09 20	09 27	09 30		09 33				09 43	09 45
Shortlands 4 d			08 47	08 54			09 00			09 05			09 11		09 22				09 35				09 45	
Ravensbourne d			08 49				09 03						09 14										09 47	
Beckenham Hill d			08 51				09 05						09 16										09 49	
Bellingham d			08 54	09 00			09 07						09 18										09 51	
Catford d			08 56	09 02			09 09						09 21										09 53	
Crofton Park d			08 59				09 11						09 23										09 56	
Lewisham 4 d	08 44										09 10									09 40			09 59	
Nunhead 4 d	08 52		09 01				09 14				09 16		09 26										10 01	
Peckham Rye 4 d	08 55		09 04	09 08			09 16				09 18		09 28										10 04	
Denmark Hill 4 d	08 59		09 07	09 11			09 19				09 20		09 31											
Beckenham Junction 4 d										09 08					09 25				09 38	09a52				
Kent House 4 d										09 10					09 27				09 40					
Penge East d										09 12					09 29				09 42					
Sydenham Hill d										09 15					09 32				09 45					
West Dulwich d										09 17					09 34				09 47					
Herne Hill 4 d		09 02								09 20		09 23			09 36			09 42	09 50			10 01		
Loughborough Jn d		09 05										09 26						09 45				10 04		
Elephant & Castle ⊖ d		09 10	09 14	09 18			09 26					09 30	09 40					09 50				10 09	10 12	
London Blackfriars 3 ⊖ d		09 14	09 18	09 26			09 30					09 34	09 44					09 58				10 14	10 18	
City Thameslink 3 a		09 16	09 20	09 28			09 32					09 36	09 46					10 00				10 16	10 20	
Farringdon ⊖ a		09 20	09 24	09 32			09 36					09 40	09 50					10 04				10 20	10 23	
St Pancras International 15 ⊖ a		09 23	09 27	09 35			09 39					09 43	09 53					10 07				10 23	10 27	
Kentish Town ⊖ a			09 32				09 46					09 48	09 58					10 12				10 28	10 34	
Brixton ⊖ d										09 22					09 38				09 52					
London Victoria 15 ⊖ a	09b12				09 15	09 27		09 19		09b31	09b33			09 37	09b47	09 49	09 50		10b01					10b04

For general notes see front of timetable
For details of catering facilities see Directory of Train Operators

- A TOC FC from London Blackfriars
- B To Luton (Table 52)
- C From Rochester (Table 212)
- D From Gillingham (Kent) (Table 212)
- E From Ashford International (Table 196)
- G From 12 October from Ramsgate
- H From London Cannon Street (Table 199)
- b Until 9 October arr 2 minutes earlier

For details of Bank Holiday service alterations please see first page of this table

Sevenoaks, Otford, Orpington, Bromley South, Beckenham Junction and Catford → London

Network Diagram - see first page of Table 195

		SE [1]	SE	SE	SE [1]	FC	SE	SE A	SE [1] B	SE	FC	SE	SE [1]	FC	SE	SE A	SE	SE	FC	SE	SE [1]	SE [1]	FC
Sevenoaks [4]	d							09 34								10 04							
Bat & Ball	d							09 37								10 07							
Otford [4]	d							09 40	09 56							10 10	10 27						
Shoreham (Kent)	d							09 43								10 13							
Eynsford	d							09 47								10 17							
Swanley [4]	d	09 36						09 52	10 06							10 22	10 36				10 42		
St Mary Cray	d	09 41						09 56								10 26					10 47		
Orpington [4]	d		09 38				09 53					10 08			10 23					10 38			
Petts Wood [4]	d		09 41				09 56					10 11			10 26					10 41			
Bickley [4]	d		09 45				10 00	10 01				10 15			10 30	10 31				10 45			
Bromley South [4]	d	09 48	09 48		09 59		10 03	10 05	10 15			10 18	10 30		10 33	10 35	10 45			10 48	10 54	11 00	
Shortlands [4]	d		09 50				10 05	10 07				10 20			10 35	10 37				10 50			
Ravensbourne	d							10 09								10 39							
Beckenham Hill	d							10 11								10 41							
Bellingham	d							10 13								10 43							
Catford	d							10 15								10 45							
Crofton Park	d							10 18								10 48							
Lewisham [4]	d			09 51						10 21								10 51					
Nunhead [4]	d			09 56				10 20		10 26						10 50		10 56					
Peckham Rye [4]	d			09 58				10 22		10 28						10 52		10 58					
Denmark Hill [4]	d			10 01				10 25		10 31						10 55		11 01					
Beckenham Junction [4]	d		09 53				10 08					10 23			10 38					10 53			
Kent House [4]	d		09 55				10 10					10 25			10 40					10 55			
Penge East	d		09 57				10 12					10 27			10 42					10 57			
Sydenham Hill	d		10 00				10 15					10 30			10 45					11 00			
West Dulwich	d		10 02				10 17					10 32			10 47					11 02			
Herne Hill [4]	d		10 05			10 16	10 20				10 31	10 35		10 46	10 50				11 01	11 05			11 16
Loughborough Jn	d					10 19					10 34			10 49					11 04				11 19
Elephant & Castle	⊖ d					10 24		10 30			10 39			10 54		11 00			11 09				11 24
London Blackfriars [3]	⊖ d					10 28		10 34			10 44			10 58		11 04			11 14				11 28
City Thameslink [3]	a					10 30		10 36			10 46			11 00		11 06			11 16				11 30
Farringdon	⊖ a					10 34		10 40			10 50			11 04		11 10			11 20				11 34
St Pancras International [15]	⊖ a					10 37		10 43			10 53			11 07		11 13			11 23				11 37
Kentish Town	⊖ a					10 42		10 50			10 58			11 12		11 20			11 28				11 42
Brixton	⊖ d		10b07				10 22					10 37			10 52					11 07			
London Victoria [15]	⊖ a	10 07	10 14	10b14	10 17		10 29		10 32	10 42		10 44	10 47		10 59		11 02	11 12		11 14	11 17	11 17	

		SE	SE A	SE [1]	SE	FC	SE	SE [1]	SE [1]	FC	SE	and at the same minutes past each hour until	SE A	SE	SE	FC	SE	SE [1]	SE [1]	FC [1]	FC	SE	SE [1] A
Sevenoaks [4]	d		10 34										15 04										15 34
Bat & Ball	d		10 37										15 07										15 37
Otford [4]	d		10 40	10 57									15 10	15 27									15 40
Shoreham (Kent)	d		10 43										15 13										15 43
Eynsford	d		10 47										15 17										15 47
Swanley [4]	d		10 52					11 12					15 22	15 36				15 42					15 52
St Mary Cray	d		10 56					11 17					15 26					15 47					15 56
Orpington [4]	d	10 53					11 08				11 23						15 38					15 53	
Petts Wood [4]	d	10 56					11 11				11 26						15 41					15 56	
Bickley [4]	d	11 00	11 01				11 15				11 30		15 31				15 45					16 00	16 01
Bromley South [4]	d	11 03	11 05	11 15			11 18	11 24	11 30		11 33		15 35	15 45			15 48	15 53	16 00			16 03	16 05
Shortlands [4]	d	11 05	11 07				11 20				11 35		15 37				15 50					16 05	16 07
Ravensbourne	d		11 09										15 39										16 09
Beckenham Hill	d		11 11										15 41										16 11
Bellingham	d		11 13										15 43										16 13
Catford	d		11 15										15 45										16 15
Crofton Park	d		11 18										15 48										16 18
Lewisham [4]	d				11 21										15 51								
Nunhead [4]	d		11 20		11 26								15 50		15 56								16 20
Peckham Rye [4]	d		11 22		11 28								15 52		15 58								16 22
Denmark Hill [4]	d		11 25		11 31								15 55		16 01								16 25
Beckenham Junction [4]	d	11 08					11 23				11 38						15 53					16 08	
Kent House [4]	d	11 10					11 25				11 40						15 55					16 10	
Penge East	d	11 12					11 27				11 42						15 57					16 12	
Sydenham Hill	d	11 15					11 30				11 45						16 00					16 15	
West Dulwich	d	11 17					11 32				11 47						16 02					16 17	
Herne Hill [4]	d	11 20				11 31	11 35			11 46	11 50					16 01	16 05				16 16	16 20	
Loughborough Jn	d					11 34				11 49						16 04					16 19		
Elephant & Castle	⊖ d		11 30			11 39				11 54			16 00			16 09				16 18	16 24		16 30
London Blackfriars [3]	⊖ d		11 34			11 44				11 58			16 04			16 14				16 22	16 30		16 36
City Thameslink [3]	a		11 36			11 46				12 00			16 06			16 16				16 24	16 32		16 38
Farringdon	⊖ a		11 40			11 50				12 04			16 10			16 19				16 27	16 35		16 41
St Pancras International [15]	⊖ a		11 43			11 53				12 07			16 13			16 23				16 31	16 39		16 45
Kentish Town	⊖ a		11 50			11 58				12 12			16 20			16 28					16 44		
Brixton	⊖ d	11 22					11 37				11 52						16 07					16 22	
London Victoria [15]	⊖ a	11 29		11 32	11 42		11 44	11 46	11 47		11 59			16 02	16 12		16 14	16 17	16 17			16 30	

For general notes see front of timetable
For details of catering facilities see Directory of Train Operators

A TOC FC from London Blackfriars
B From Margate (Table 207)
b Until 9 October arr 2 minutes earlier

For details of Bank Holiday service alterations please see first page of this table

Sevenoaks, Otford, Orpington, Bromley South, Beckenham Junction and Catford → London

Network Diagram - see first page of Table 195

		SE 1	FC		SE	SE 1	SE 1	FC 1	FC	SE	FC	SE 1	FC	SE	SE		SE 1	SE	SE 1	SE	FC 1	FC	SE	SE	SE 1
							🛒	A				B					🛒	B					B		C
Sevenoaks 4	d											16 05						16 26					16 35		
Bat & Ball	d											16 08						16 29					16 38		
Otford 4	d	15 55										16 11			16 27			16 32					16 41		16 54
Shoreham (Kent)	d											16 14						16 35					16 44		
Eynsford	d											16 18						16 39					16 48		
Swanley 4	d					16 12						16 23			16 38		16 42	16 46					16 54		17 05
St Mary Cray	d					16 17						16 27					16 47						16 58		
Orpington 4	d				16 08									16 36										17 04	
Petts Wood 4	d				16 11									16 39										17 07	
Bickley 4	d				16 15							16 32		16 44									17 03	17 11	
Bromley South 4	d	16 14			16 19	16 23	16 30					16 35		16 47	16 47		16 53	16 55	17 00				17 06	17b17 →	17 14
Shortlands 4	d				16 21							16 37		16 49									17 08		
Ravensbourne	d											16 40											17 11		
Beckenham Hill	d											16 42											17 13		
Bellingham	d											16 44											17 15		
Catford	d											16 46											17 17		
Crofton Park	d											16 48											17 19		
Lewisham 4	d									16 35										17 05					
Nunhead 4	d									16 40		16 51								17 13			17 22		
Peckham Rye 4	d									16 42		16 53								17 15			17 24		
Denmark Hill 4	d									16 46		16 56								17 18			17 26		
Beckenham Junction 4	d				16 25									16 52											
Kent House 4	d				16 27									16 54											
Penge East	d				16 29									16 56											
Sydenham Hill	d				16 32									16 59											
West Dulwich	d				16 33									17 00											
Herne Hill 4	d		16 31		16 36			16 38	16 46				17 01	17 03				17 06				17 18			
Loughborough Jn	d		16 34						16 49													17 21			
Elephant & Castle	⊖ d		16 39					16 45	16 54		17 00	17 04	17 08					17 12			17 16	17 26	17 34		
London Blackfriars 3	⊖ d		16 44					16 50	17 00		17 04	17 08	17 12					17 16			17 20	17c32	17e42		
City Thameslink 3	a		16 46					16 52	17 02		17 06	17 10	17 14					17 18			17 22	17 34	17 44		
Farringdon	⊖ a		16 49					16 57	17 05		17 09	17 13	17 17					17 23			17 27	17 37	17 47		
St Pancras International 15	⊖ a		16 53					17 01	17 09		17 13	17 17	17 21					17 27			17 31	17 41	17 51		
Kentish Town	⊖ a		16 58								17 18							17 32				17 46			
Brixton	⊖ d				16 38									17 05											
London Victoria 15	⊖ a	16 33			16 45	16 48	16 51			17 03				17 12	17 10		17 17		17 17	17 28					17 33

		SE	SE 1	SE 1	FC		FC 1	FC 1	FC	FC	SE	SE	SE 1	SE	SE 1	SE 1	FC		FC 1	FC	SE 1	SE 1	FC	SE	SE 1
				🛒							B					🛒					B				
Sevenoaks 4	d										17 05										17 35				
Bat & Ball	d										17 08										17 38				
Otford 4	d										17 12		17 30								17 41	17 53			
Shoreham (Kent)	d										17 15										17 44				
Eynsford	d										17 19										17 47				
Swanley 4	d		17 13								17 24				17 43						17 53	18 04			18 12
St Mary Cray	d		17 18								17 28				17 47						17 57				18 16
Orpington 4	d											17 36												18 06	
Petts Wood 4	d											17 39												18 09	
Bickley 4	d	←									17 33	17 44									18 02			18 14	
Bromley South 4	d	17 17	17 25	17 33							17 36	17 47	17 47		17 54	17 59					18 05	18 14		18 17	18 25
Shortlands 4	d	17 19									17 38	17 49									18 08			18 19	
Ravensbourne	d										17 41										18 10				
Beckenham Hill	d										17 43										18 12				
Bellingham	d										17 45										18 14				
Catford	d										17 47										18 16				
Crofton Park	d										17 49										18 19				
Lewisham 4	d													17 54											
Nunhead 4	d										17 52			18 01							18 21				
Peckham Rye 4	d										17 54			18 03							18 23				
Denmark Hill 4	d										17 57			18 06							18 25				
Beckenham Junction 4	d	17 22										17 52												18 22	
Kent House 4	d	17 24										17 54												18 24	
Penge East	d	17 26										17 56												18 26	
Sydenham Hill	d	17 29										17 59												18 29	
West Dulwich	d	17 30										18 00												18 30	
Herne Hill 4	d	17 33			17 36			17 46		17 54		18 03					18 06			18 18			18 31	18 33	
Loughborough Jn	d				17 39					17 57							18 09			18 21				18 34	
Elephant & Castle	⊖ d				17 44		17 48		17 58	18 02	18 06						18 14		18 22	18 26	18 32			18 39	
London Blackfriars 3	⊖ d				17 48		17 52	17 56	18 02	18 06	18f14						18 18		18 26	18 32	18 36			18 46	
City Thameslink 3	a				17 50		17 54	17 58	18 04	18 08	18 16						18 20		18 28	18 34	18 38			18 48	
Farringdon	⊖ a				17 53		17 57	18 01	18 07	18 11	18 19						18 23		18 31	18 37	18 41			18 51	
St Pancras International 15	⊖ a				17 57		18 01	18 05	18 11	18 15	18 23						18 27		18 35	18 41	18 45			18 55	
Kentish Town	⊖ a				18 02				18 16								18 32			18 46				19 00	
Brixton	⊖ d	17 35										18 05												18 35	
London Victoria 15	⊖ a	17 42	17 48	17 57								18 12	18 09	18 16	18 19	18 17						18 32		18 42	18 49

For general notes see front of timetable
For details of catering facilities see Directory of Train Operators

A From Brighton (Table 52)
B TOC FC from London Blackfriars
C From Canterbury West (Table 207)
b Arr. 1713
c Arr. 1729
e Arr. 1739
f Arr. 1809

For details of Bank Holiday service alterations please see first page of this table

Sevenoaks, Otford, Orpington, Bromley South, Beckenham Junction and Catford → London

Network Diagram - see first page of Table 195

	SE 1	FC 1	SE	FC	SE 1	SE		SE 1	FC	SE	SE 1	SE 1	SE	FC	SE	SE 1	FC	SE		SE 1	SE	SE 1	FC	SE
		A			B										B									
Sevenoaks 4 d					17 59	18 16									18 37						18 55			
Bat & Ball d					18b06	18 19									18 40						18 58			
Otford 4 d					18 10	18 22		18 29							18 43	18 56					19 02			
Shoreham (Kent) d					18 13	18 25									18 46						19 05			
Eynsford d					18 17	18 29									18 49						19 08			
Swanley 4 d					18 22	18a34					18 42				18c58	19 05				19 12	19a13			
St Mary Cray d					18 26						18 47				19 02					19 17				
Orpington 4 d										18 36								19 08						19 23
Petts Wood 4 d										18 39								19 11						19 26
Bickley 4 d					18 32					18 44					19 06			19 16						19 30
Bromley South 4 d	18 31				18 35			18 45		18 47	18 53	19 01			19 10	19 14		19 19		19 23		19 30		19 33
Shortlands 4 d					18 37					18 49					19 12			19 21						19 35
Ravensbourne d					18 39										19 14									
Beckenham Hill d					18 41										19 16									
Bellingham d					18 43										19 18									
Catford d					18 45										19 20									
Crofton Park d					18 48										19 23									
Lewisham 4 d			18 41										19 06											
Nunhead 4 d			18 45		18 50								19 10		19 25									
Peckham Rye 4 d			18 47		18 52								19 12		19 28									
Denmark Hill 4 d			18 50		18 55								19 15		19 31									
Beckenham Junction 4 d										18 53								19 24						19 38
Kent House 4 d										18 55								19 26						19 40
Penge East d										18 57								19 28						19 42
Sydenham Hill d										19 00								19 31						19 45
West Dulwich d										19 01								19 33						19 47
Herne Hill 4 d		18 38		18 48					19 01	19 04				19 18			19 32	19 36					19 48	19 50
Loughborough Jn d				18 51					19 04					19 21			19 35						19 51	
Elephant & Castle ⊖ d		18 45		18 56	19 02				19 09					19 26	19 38		19 40						19 56	
London Blackfriars 3 ⊖ d		18 50		19 00	19 06				19 16					19 32	19 42		19 46						20 00	
City Thameslink 3 a		18 52		19 02	19 08				19 18					19 34	19 44		19 48						20 02	
Farringdon ⊖ a		18 57		19 05	19 11				19 21					19 38	19 47		19 51						20 05	
St Pancras International 15 ⊖ a		19 01		19 09	19 15				19 25					19 41	19 51		19 55						20 09	
Kentish Town ⊖ a				19 14					19 30					19 46	19 58		20 00						20 14	
Brixton ⊖ d										19 06								19 38						19 52
London Victoria 15 ⊖ a	18 48		19 01					19 03		19 13	19 16	19 17	19 25			19 31		19 45		19 47		19 49		19 59

	SE	SE	SE	FC 1	SE	SE 1	SE 1	FC		SE	SE	SE 1	FC 1	SE	SE 1	FC	SE	FC 1	SE	SE 1		SE	SE 1	FC
	B										B						B						C	
Sevenoaks 4 d	19 06		19 21								19 34						20 04					20 34		
Bat & Ball d	19 09		19 24								19 37						20 07					20 37		
Otford 4 d	19 12	19 27	19 29								19 40	19 55					20 10					20 40	20 53	
Shoreham (Kent) d	19 15		19 32								19 43						20 13					20 43		
Eynsford d	19 18		19 36								19 46						20 16					20 46		
Swanley 4 d	19 24	19 36	19a41			19 42					19 52	20 04					20 22			20 42		20 52	21 02	
St Mary Cray d	19 28					19 47					19 56	20 08					20 26			20 47		20 56	21 07	
Orpington 4 d					19 38					19 53				20 08					20 38					
Petts Wood 4 d					19 41					19 56				20 11					20 41					
Bickley 4 d	19 32				19 46					20 00	20 01			20 16			20 31		20 46			21 01		
Bromley South 4 d	19 35	19 45			19 49	19 53	19 58			20 03	20 05	20 15		20 19	20 29		20 35		20 49	20 53		21 04	21 13	
Shortlands 4 d	19 37				19 51					20 05	20 07			20 21			20 37		20 51			21 06		
Ravensbourne d	19 40										20 09						20 39					21 09		
Beckenham Hill d	19 42										20 11						20 41					21 11		
Bellingham d	19 44										20 13						20 43					21 13		
Catford d	19 46										20 15						20 45					21 15		
Crofton Park d	19 48										20 18						20 48					21 17		
Lewisham 4 d																								
Nunhead 4 d	19 51										20 20						20 50					21 20		
Peckham Rye 4 d	19 53										20 22						20 52					21 22		
Denmark Hill 4 d	19 55										20 25						20 55					21 24		
Beckenham Junction 4 d					19 54					20 08				20 24					20 54					
Kent House 4 d					19 56					20 10				20 26					20 56					
Penge East d					19 58					20 12				20 28					20 58					
Sydenham Hill d					20 01					20 15				20 31					21 01					
West Dulwich d					20 02					20 17				20 32					21 02					
Herne Hill 4 d				20 03	20 05			20 16		20 20			20 33	20 35		20 46		21 03	21 05					21 16
Loughborough Jn d				20 07				20 19					20 37			20 49		21 07						21 19
Elephant & Castle ⊖ d	20 00			20 11				20 24			20 30		20 41			20 54	21 00	21 11						21 24
London Blackfriars 3 ⊖ d	20 04			20 16				20e30			20 34		20 46			21f00	21 04	21 16						21g30
City Thameslink 3 a	20 06			20 18				20 32			20 36		20 48			21 02	21 06	21 18						21 32
Farringdon ⊖ a	20 09			20 21				20 35			20 39		20 51			21 05	21 09	21 21						21 35
St Pancras International 15 ⊖ a	20 13			20 25				20 39			20 43		20 55			21 09	21 13	21 25						21 39
Kentish Town ⊖ a	20 20			20 30				20 44			20 50		21 00			21 14	21 20	21 30						21 44
Brixton ⊖ d					20 07					20 22				20 37					21 07					
London Victoria 15 ⊖ a		20 02			20 14	20 15	20 19			20 30		20 31		20 44	20 49				21 14	21 16		21 33	21 29	

For general notes see front of timetable
For details of catering facilities see Directory of Train Operators

A From Brighton (Table 52)
B TOC FC from London Blackfriars
C From Canterbury West (Table 207)
b Arr. 1802
c Arr. 1854
e Arr. 2027
f Arr. 2057
g Arr. 2127

For details of Bank Holiday service alterations please see first page of this table

Sevenoaks, Otford, Orpington, Bromley South, Beckenham Junction and Catford → London

Network Diagram - see first page of Table 195

		FC 1	SE	SE 1	SE	FC	SE	SE 1	SE	SE 1	SE		SE 1	SE	SE	SE 1	SE	SE	SE 1	SE 1	SE 1				
Sevenoaks 4	d				21 04				21 34					22 04			22 34								
Bat & Ball	d				21 07				21 37					22 07			22 37								
Otford 4	d				21 10				21 40	21 54				22 10			22 40		23 04						
Shoreham (Kent)	d				21 13				21 43					22 13			22 43								
Eynsford	d				21 16				21 46					22 16			22 46								
Swanley 4	d				21 22			21 42	21 52	22 03				22 22		22 42	22 52		23 13		23 45				
St Mary Cray	d				21 26			21 47	21 56	22 07				22 26		22 47	22 56		23 17		23 49				
Orpington 4	d		21 08				21 38				22 08				22 38			23 08							
Petts Wood 4	d		21 11				21 41				22 11				22 41			23 11							
Bickley 4	d		21 16		21 31		21 46		22 01		22 16			22 31	22 46		23 01	23 16							
Bromley South 4	d		21 19	21 30	21 34		21 49	21 53	22 04	22 14	22 19		22 30	22 34	22 49	22 53	23 04	23 19	23 24	23 30	23 56				
Shortlands 4	d		21 21		21 36		21 51		22 06		22 21			22 36	22 51		23 06	23 21							
Ravensbourne	d				21 39				22 09					22 39			23 09								
Beckenham Hill	d				21 41				22 11					22 41			23 11								
Bellingham	d				21 43				22 13					22 43			23 13								
Catford	d				21 45				22 15					22 45			23 15								
Crofton Park	d				21 47				22 17					22 47			23 17								
Lewisham 4	d																								
Nunhead 4	d				21 50				22 20					22 50			23 20								
Peckham Rye 4	d				21 52				22 22					22 52			23 22								
Denmark Hill 4	d				21 54				22 24					22 54			23 24								
Beckenham Junction 4	d		21 24				21 54				22 24				22 54			23 24							
Kent House 4	d		21 26				21 56				22 26				22 56			23 26							
Penge East	d		21 28				21 58				22 28				22 58			23 28							
Sydenham Hill	d		21 31				22 01				22 31				23 01			23 31							
West Dulwich	d		21 32				22 02				22 32				23 02			23 32							
Herne Hill 4	d	21 33	21 35			21 54	22 05				22 35				23 05			23 35							
Loughborough Jn	d	21 37				21 57																			
Elephant & Castle	⊖ d	21 41				22 02																			
London Blackfriars 3	⊖ d	21 46				22 06																			
City Thameslink 3	a	21 48				22 08																			
Farringdon	⊖ a	21 51				22 11																			
St Pancras International 15	⊖ a	21 55				22 15																			
Kentish Town	⊖ a	22 00				22 20																			
Brixton	⊖ d		21 37				22 07				22 37				23 07			23 37							
London Victoria 15	⊖ a		21 44	21 47	22 03		22 15	22 16	22 37	22 32	22 44		22 48	23 03	23 15	23 14	23 33	23 44	23 44	23 47	00 18				

Saturdays

For details of Bank Holiday service alterations please see first page of this table

		SE	SE 1	SE	SE	SE	SE 1	SE 1	SE	SE 1		SE	SE	SE 1	SE 1	SE	SE	SE	SE 1	SE 1		SE	SE 1	SE	SE
Sevenoaks 4	d				06 04				06 34							07 04						07 34			
Bat & Ball	d				06 07				06 37							07 07						07 37			
Otford 4	d				06 10				06 40	06 55						07 10						07 40	07 55		
Shoreham (Kent)	d				06 13				06 43							07 13						07 43			
Eynsford	d				06 17				06 47							07 17						07 47			
Swanley 4	d		06 05		06 22		06 42		06 52	07 04				07 12		07 22			07 42			07 52	08 04		
St Mary Cray	d		06 10		06 26		06 47		06 56	07 08				07 17		07 26			07 47			07 56	08 08		
Orpington 4	d	05 54		06 08		06 38							07 08					07 38							08 08
Petts Wood 4	d	05 57		06 11		06 41							07 11					07 41							08 11
Bickley 4	d	06 01		06 15	06 31	06 45			07 01				07 15			07 31		07 45				08 01			08 15
Bromley South 4	d	06 05	06 16	06 18	06 35	06 48	06 54	07 00	07 05	07 15			07 18	07 24	07 30	07 35		07 48	07 54	08 00		08 05	08 15		08 18
Shortlands 4	d	06 07		06 20	06 37	06 50			07 07				07 20			07 37		07 50				08 07			08 20
Ravensbourne	d	06 09			06 39				07 09							07 39						08 09			
Beckenham Hill	d	06 11			06 41				07 11							07 41						08 11			
Bellingham	d	06 13			06 43				07 13							07 43						08 13			
Catford	d	06 15			06 45				07 15							07 45						08 15			
Crofton Park	d	06 18			06 48				07 18							07 48						08 18			
Lewisham 4	d											07 20					07 50							08 20	
Nunhead 4	d	06 20			06 50				07 20			07 25				07 50	07 55					08 20		08 25	
Peckham Rye 4	d	06 22			06 52				07 22			07 28				07 52	07 58					08 22		08 28	
Denmark Hill 4	d	06 25			06 55				07 25			07 31				07 55	08 01					08 25		08 31	
Beckenham Junction 4	d			06 23		06 53							07 23					07 53							08 23
Kent House 4	d			06 25		06 55							07 25					07 55							08 25
Penge East	d			06 27		06 57							07 27					07 57							08 27
Sydenham Hill	d			06 30		07 00							07 30					08 00							08 30
West Dulwich	d			06 32		07 02							07 32					08 02							08 32
Herne Hill 4	d			06 35		07 05							07 35					08 05							08 34
Loughborough Jn	d																								
Elephant & Castle	⊖ d																								
London Blackfriars 3	⊖ d																								
City Thameslink 3	a																								
Farringdon	⊖ a																								
St Pancras International 15	⊖ a																								
Kentish Town	⊖ a																								
Brixton	⊖ d			06 37		07 07							07 37					08 07							08 36
London Victoria 15	⊖ a	06 35	06 32	06 44	07 06	07 15	07 17	07 17	07 36	07 32		07 41	07 45	07 46	07 47	08 06	08 12	08 15	08 16	08 17		08 36	08 32	08 42	08 43

For general notes see front of timetable
For details of catering facilities see
Directory of Train Operators

Table 195

Saturdays

For details of Bank Holiday service alterations please see first page of this table

Sevenoaks, Otford, Orpington, Bromley South, Beckenham Junction and Catford → London

Network Diagram - see first page of Table 195

		SE 1	SE 1	SE	SE	SE	SE	SE	SE 1	SE 1	SE	SE	SE 1	SE	SE	SE 1	SE 1 🚲	SE	SE	SE	SE	SE	SE 1
Sevenoaks 4	d				08 04							08 34							09 04				
Bat & Ball	d				08 07							08 37							09 07				
Otford 4	d				08 10	08 26						08 40	08 57						09 10	09 26			
Shoreham (Kent)	d				08 13							08 43							09 13				
Eynsford	d				08 17							08 47							09 17				
Swanley 4	d	08 12			08 22	08 35			08 42			08 52				09 12			09 22	09 35			09 42
St Mary Cray	d	08 17			08 26				08 47			08 56				09 17			09 26				09 47
Orpington 4	d			08 23				08 38			08 53				09 08			09 23				09 38	
Petts Wood 4	d			08 26				08 41			08 56				09 11			09 26				09 41	
Bickley 4	d			08 30	08 31			08 45			09 00	09 01			09 15			09 30	09 31			09 45	
Bromley South 4	d	08 24	08 30	08 33	08 35	08 45		08 48	08 54	09 00	09 03	09 05	09 15		09 18	09 24	09 30	09 33	09 35	09 45		09 48	09 54
Shortlands 4	d			08 35	08 37			08 50			09 05	09 07			09 20			09 35	09 37			09 50	
Ravensbourne	d				08 39							09 09							09 39				
Beckenham Hill	d				08 41							09 11							09 41				
Bellingham	d				08 43							09 13							09 43				
Catford	d				08 45							09 15							09 45				
Crofton Park	d				08 48							09 18							09 48				
Lewisham 4 🚊	d						08 50							09 20							09 50		
Nunhead 4	d				08 50		08 55					09 20		09 25					09 50		09 55		
Peckham Rye 4	d				08 52		08 58					09 22		09 28					09 52		09 58		
Denmark Hill 4	d				08 55		09 01					09 25		09 31					09 55		10 01		
Beckenham Junction 4 🚊	d			08 38				08 53			09 08				09 23			09 38				09 53	
Kent House 4	d			08 40				08 55			09 10				09 25			09 40				09 55	
Penge East	d			08 42				08 57			09 12				09 27			09 42				09 57	
Sydenham Hill	d			08 45				09 00			09 15				09 30			09 45				10 00	
West Dulwich	d			08 47				09 02			09 17				09 32			09 47				10 02	
Herne Hill 4	d			08 50				09 05			09 20				09 35			09 50				10 05	
Loughborough Jn	d																						
Elephant & Castle	⊖ d																						
London Blackfriars 3	⊖ d																						
City Thameslink 3	a																						
Farringdon	⊖ a																						
St Pancras International 15	⊖ a																						
Kentish Town	⊖ a																						
Brixton	⊖ d			08 52				09 07			09 22				09 37			09 52				10 07	
London Victoria 15	⊖ a	08 46	08 47	08 59	09 06	09 02	09 12	09 15	09 16	09 17	09 29	09 36	09 32	09 42	09 45	09 46	09 47	09 59	10 06	10 02	10 12	10 15	10 16

		SE 1 🚲	SE	SE	SE 1	SE	SE	SE 1	SE 1 🚲	SE	SE	SE	SE	SE	SE 1	SE 1 🚲	SE	SE	SE 1	SE
Sevenoaks 4	d			09 34							10 04							10 34		
Bat & Ball	d			09 37							10 07							10 37		
Otford 4	d			09 40	09 57						10 10	10 26						10 40	10 57	
Shoreham (Kent)	d			09 43							10 13							10 43		
Eynsford	d			09 47							10 17							10 47		
Swanley 4	d			09 52				10 12			10 22	10 35			10 42			10 52		
St Mary Cray	d			09 56				10 17			10 26				10 47			10 56		
Orpington 4	d		09 53				10 08			10 23				10 38			10 53			
Petts Wood 4	d		09 56				10 11			10 26				10 41			10 56			
Bickley 4	d		10 00	10 01			10 15			10 30	10 31			10 45			11 00	11 01		
Bromley South 4	d	10 00	10 03	10 05	10 15		10 18	10 24	10 30	10 33	10 35	10 45		10 48	10 54	11 00	11 03	11 05	11 15	
Shortlands 4	d		10 05	10 07			10 20			10 35	10 37			10 50			11 05	11 07		
Ravensbourne	d			10 09							10 39							11 09		
Beckenham Hill	d			10 11							10 41							11 11		
Bellingham	d			10 13							10 43							11 13		
Catford	d			10 15							10 45							11 15		
Crofton Park	d			10 18							10 48							11 18		
Lewisham 4 🚊	d					10 20							10 50							11 20
Nunhead 4	d			10 20		10 25					10 50		10 55					11 20		11 25
Peckham Rye 4	d			10 22		10 28					10 52		10 58					11 22		11 28
Denmark Hill 4	d			10 25		10 31					10 55		11 01					11 25		11 31
Beckenham Junction 4 🚊	d		10 08				10 23			10 38				10 53			11 08			
Kent House 4	d		10 10				10 25			10 40				10 55			11 10			
Penge East	d		10 12				10 27			10 42				10 57			11 12			
Sydenham Hill	d		10 15				10 30			10 45				11 00			11 15			
West Dulwich	d		10 17				10 32			10 47				11 02			11 17			
Herne Hill 4	d		10 20				10 35			10 50				11 05			11 20			
Loughborough Jn	d																			
Elephant & Castle	⊖ d																			
London Blackfriars 3	⊖ d																			
City Thameslink 3	a																			
Farringdon	⊖ a																			
St Pancras International 15	⊖ a																			
Kentish Town	⊖ a																			
Brixton	⊖ d		10 22				10 37			10 52				11 07			11 22			
London Victoria 15	⊖ a	10 17	10 29	10 36	10 32	10 42	10 45	10 46	10 47	10 59	11 06	11 02	11 12	11 15	11 16	11 17	11 29	11 36	11 32	11 42

For general notes see front of timetable
For details of catering facilities see Directory of Train Operators

Table 195

Saturdays

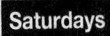

For details of Bank Holiday service alterations please see first page of this table

Sevenoaks, Otford, Orpington, Bromley South, Beckenham Junction and Catford → London

Network Diagram - see first page of Table 195

Station		SE	and at the same minutes past each hour until	SE 1	SE 1 ⚲	SE	SE	SE	SE	SE	SE 1	SE 1 ⚲	SE	SE	SE 1	SE	SE	SE 1	SE 1	SE	SE	SE
Sevenoaks 4	d						17 04							17 34							18 04	
Bat & Ball	d						17 07							17 37							18 07	
Otford 4	d						17 10	17 26						17 40	17 57						18 10	18 26
Shoreham (Kent)	d						17 13							17 43							18 13	
Eynsford	d						17 17							17 47							18 17	
Swanley 4	d			17 12			17 22	17 35			17 42			17 52				18 12			18 22	18 35
St Mary Cray	d			17 17			17 26				17 47			17 56				18 17			18 26	
Orpington 4	d	11 08				17 23				17 38			17 53				18 08			18 23		
Petts Wood 4	d	11 11				17 26				17 41			17 56				18 11			18 26		
Bickley 4	d	11 15				17 30	17 31			17 45			18 00	18 01			18 15			18 30	18 31	
Bromley South 4	d	11 18		17 24	17 30	17 33	17 35	17 45		17 48	17 54	18 00	18 03	18 05	18 15		18 18	18 24	18 30	18 33	18 35	18 45
Shortlands 4	d	11 20				17 35	17 37			17 50			18 05	18 07			18 20			18 35	18 37	
Ravensbourne	d						17 39							18 09							18 39	
Beckenham Hill	d						17 41							18 11							18 41	
Bellingham	d						17 43							18 13							18 43	
Catford	d						17 45							18 15							18 45	
Crofton Park	d						17 48							18 18							18 48	
Lewisham 4	d								17 50							18 20						
Nunhead 4	d						17 50		17 55					18 20		18 25					18 50	
Peckham Rye 4	d						17 52		17 58					18 22		18 28					18 52	
Denmark Hill 4	d						17 55		18 01					18 25		18 31					18 55	
Beckenham Junction 4	d	11 23				17 38				17 53			18 08				18 23			18 38		
Kent House 4	d	11 25				17 40				17 55			18 10				18 25			18 40		
Penge East	d	11 27				17 42				17 57			18 12				18 27			18 42		
Sydenham Hill	d	11 30				17 45				18 00			18 15				18 30			18 45		
West Dulwich	d	11 32				17 47				18 02			18 17				18 32			18 47		
Herne Hill 4	d	11 35				17 50				18 05			18 20				18 35			18 50		
Loughborough Jn	d																					
Elephant & Castle	⊖ d																					
London Blackfriars 3	⊖ d																					
City Thameslink 3	a																					
Farringdon	⊖ a																					
St Pancras International 15	⊖ a																					
Kentish Town	⊖ a																					
Brixton	⊖ d	11 37				17 52				18 07			18 22				18 37			18 52		
London Victoria 15	⊖ a	11 45		17 46	17 47	17 59	18 06	18 02	18 12	18 15	18 16	18 17	18 29	18 36	18 32	18 42	18 45	18 46	18 47	18 59	19 06	19 02

Station		SE	SE	SE 1	SE 1	SE	SE	SE 1 A	SE	SE 1	SE 1	SE	SE	SE	SE 1	SE 1	SE	SE	SE 1	SE	SE 1	SE 1
Sevenoaks 4	d						18 34						19 04					19 34				
Bat & Ball	d						18 37						19 07					19 37				
Otford 4	d						18 40	18 55					19 10					19 40	19 55			
Shoreham (Kent)	d						18 43						19 13					19 43				
Eynsford	d						18 47						19 17					19 47				
Swanley 4	d			18 42			18 52	19 04		19 12			19 22		19 42			19 52	20 04		20 12	
St Mary Cray	d			18 47			18 56	19 08		19 17			19 26		19 47			19 56	20 08		20 17	
Orpington 4	d		18 38			18 53			19 08			19 23		19 38			19 53			20 08		
Petts Wood 4	d		18 41			18 56			19 11			19 26		19 41			19 56			20 11		
Bickley 4	d		18 45			19 00	19 01		19 15			19 30	19 31	19 45			20 00	20 01		20 15		
Bromley South 4	d		18 48	18 54	19 00	19 03	19 05	19 15	19 18	19 24	19 30	19 33	19 35	19 48	19 54	20 00	20 03	20 05	20 15	20 18	20 24	20 30
Shortlands 4	d		18 50			19 05	19 07		19 20			19 35	19 37	19 50			20 05	20 07		20 20		
Ravensbourne	d						19 09						19 39					20 09				
Beckenham Hill	d						19 11						19 41					20 11				
Bellingham	d						19 13						19 43					20 13				
Catford	d						19 15						19 45					20 15				
Crofton Park	d						19 18						19 48					20 18				
Lewisham 4	d	18 50																				
Nunhead 4	d	18 55					19 20						19 50					20 20				
Peckham Rye 4	d	18 58					19 22						19 52					20 22				
Denmark Hill 4	d	19 01					19 25						19 55					20 25				
Beckenham Junction 4	d		18 53			19 08			19 23			19 38		19 53			20 08			20 23		
Kent House 4	d		18 55			19 10			19 25			19 40		19 55			20 10			20 25		
Penge East	d		18 57			19 12			19 27			19 42		19 57			20 12			20 27		
Sydenham Hill	d		19 00			19 15			19 30			19 45		20 00			20 15			20 30		
West Dulwich	d		19 02			19 17			19 32			19 47		20 02			20 17			20 32		
Herne Hill 4	d		19 05			19 20			19 35			19 50		20 05			20 20			20 35		
Loughborough Jn	d																					
Elephant & Castle	⊖ d																					
London Blackfriars 3	⊖ d																					
City Thameslink 3	a																					
Farringdon	⊖ a																					
St Pancras International 15	⊖ a																					
Kentish Town	⊖ a																					
Brixton	⊖ d		19 07			19 22			19 37			19 52		20 07			20 22			20 37		
London Victoria 15	⊖ a	19 12	19 15	19 16	19 17	19 29	19 36	19 32	19 44	19 46	19 47	19 59	20 06	20 14	20 17	20 17	20 29	20 36	20 32	20 44	20 47	20 47

For general notes see front of timetable
For details of catering facilities see Directory of Train Operators

A From Canterbury West (Table 207)

Table 195

Saturdays

For details of Bank Holiday service alterations please see first page of this table

Sevenoaks, Otford, Orpington, Bromley South, Beckenham Junction and Catford → London

Network Diagram - see first page of Table 195

	SE	SE	SE 1	SE	SE 1	SE	SE 1	SE	SE		SE 1	SE
Sevenoaks 4 d	20 04			20 34				21 04				21 34
Bat & Ball d	20 07			20 37				21 07				21 37
Otford 4 d	20 10			20 40	20 55			21 10				21 40
Shoreham (Kent) d	20 13			20 43				21 13				21 43
Eynsford d	20 17			20 47				21 17				21 47
Swanley 4 d	20 22		20 42	20 52	21 04			21 22			21 42	21 52
St Mary Cray d	20 26		20 47	20 56	21 08			21 26			21 47	21 56
Orpington 4 d		20 38				21 08			21 38			
Petts Wood 4 d		20 41				21 11			21 41			
Bickley 4 d	20 31	20 45		21 01		21 15		21 31	21 45			22 01
Bromley South 4 d	20 35	20 48	20 54	21 05	21 15	21 18	21 30	21 35	21 48		21 54	22 05
Shortlands 4 d	20 37	20 50		21 07		21 20		21 37	21 50			22 07
Ravensbourne d	20 39			21 09				21 39				22 09
Beckenham Hill d	20 41			21 11				21 41				22 11
Bellingham d	20 43			21 13				21 43				22 13
Catford d	20 45			21 15				21 45				22 15
Crofton Park d	20 48			21 18				21 48				22 18
Lewisham 4 d												
Nunhead 4 d	20 50			21 20				21 50				22 20
Peckham Rye 4 d	20 52			21 22				21 52				22 22
Denmark Hill 4 d	20 55			21 25				21 55				22 25
Beckenham Junction 4 d		20 53				21 23			21 53			
Kent House 4 d		20 55				21 25			21 55			
Penge East d		20 57				21 27			21 57			
Sydenham Hill d		21 00				21 30			22 00			
West Dulwich d		21 02				21 32			22 02			
Herne Hill 4 d		21 05				21 35			22 05			
Loughborough Jn d												
Elephant & Castle ⊖ d												
London Blackfriars 3 ⊖ d												
City Thameslink 3 a												
Farringdon ⊖ a												
St Pancras International 15 ⊖ a												
Kentish Town ⊖ a												
Brixton ⊖ d		21 07				21 37			22 07			
London Victoria 15 ⊖ a	21 06	21 14	21 16	21 36	21 32	21 45	21 47	22 06	22 15	.	22 16	22 36

	SE 1	SE	SE 1	SE	SE	SE 1	SE		SE 1	SE	SE 1	SE 1
Sevenoaks 4 d				22 04			22 34					
Bat & Ball d				22 07			22 37					
Otford 4 d	21 55			22 10			22 40		22 55			
Shoreham (Kent) d				22 13			22 43					
Eynsford d				22 17			22 47					
Swanley 4 d	22 04			22 22		22 42	22 52		23 04			23 42
St Mary Cray d	22 08			22 26		22 47	22 56		23 08			23 47
Orpington 4 d		22 08			22 38					23 08		
Petts Wood 4 d		22 11			22 41					23 11		
Bickley 4 d		22 15		22 31	22 45		23 01			23 15		
Bromley South 4 d	22 15	22 18	22 30	22 35	22 48	22 54	23 05		23 15	23 18	23 30	23 54
Shortlands 4 d		22 20		22 37	22 50		23 07			23 20		
Ravensbourne d				22 39			23 09					
Beckenham Hill d				22 41			23 11					
Bellingham d				22 43			23 13					
Catford d				22 45			23 15					
Crofton Park d				22 48			23 18					
Lewisham 4 d												
Nunhead 4 d				22 50			23 20					
Peckham Rye 4 d				22 52			23 22					
Denmark Hill 4 d				22 55			23 25					
Beckenham Junction 4 d		22 23			22 53					23 23		
Kent House 4 d		22 25			22 55					23 25		
Penge East d		22 27			22 57					23 27		
Sydenham Hill d		22 30			23 00					23 30		
West Dulwich d		22 32			23 02					23 32		
Herne Hill 4 d		22 35			23 05					23 35		
Loughborough Jn d												
Elephant & Castle ⊖ d												
London Blackfriars 3 ⊖ d												
City Thameslink 3 a												
Farringdon ⊖ a												
St Pancras International 15 ⊖ a												
Kentish Town ⊖ a												
Brixton ⊖ d		22 37			23 07					23 37		
London Victoria 15 ⊖ a	22 32	22 45	22 47	23 06	23 15	23 16	23 36	.	23 32	23 45	23 47	00 10

Sundays

	SE	SE		SE	SE 1		SE	SE		SE 1	SE 1	
Sevenoaks 4 d												
Bat & Ball d												
Otford 4 d											07 56	
Shoreham (Kent) d												
Eynsford d												
Swanley 4 d					07 29						08 05	
St Mary Cray d					07 34						08 10	
Orpington 4 d	06 44	07 08		07 14			07 38	07 44				
Petts Wood 4 d	06 47	07 11		07 17			07 41	07 47				
Bickley 4 d	06 51	07 15		07 21			07 45	07 51				
Bromley South 4 d	06 54	07 18		07 24	07 40		07 48	07 54		08 00	08 16	
Shortlands 4 d	06 56	07 20		07 26			07 50	07 56				
Ravensbourne d	06 59			07 29				07 59				
Beckenham Hill d	07 01			07 31				08 01				
Bellingham d	07 03			07 33				08 03				
Catford d	07 05			07 35				08 05				
Crofton Park d	07 07			07 37				08 07				
Lewisham 4 d												
Nunhead 4 d	07 10			07 40				08 10				
Peckham Rye 4 d	07 12			07 42				08 12				
Denmark Hill 4 d	07 14			07 44				08 14				
Beckenham Junction 4 d		07 23					07 53					
Kent House 4 d		07 25					07 55					
Penge East d		07 27					07 57					
Sydenham Hill d		07 30					08 00					
West Dulwich d		07 31					08 01					
Herne Hill 4 d		07 34					08 04					
Loughborough Jn d												
Elephant & Castle ⊖ d												
London Blackfriars 3 ⊖ d												
City Thameslink 3 a												
Farringdon ⊖ a												
St Pancras International 15 ⊖ a												
Kentish Town ⊖ a												
Brixton ⊖ d		07 36					08 06					
London Victoria 15 ⊖ a	07 23	07 43	.	07 54	08 01	.	08 13	08 24	.	08 16	08 32	.

	SE	SE		SE 1	SE		SE	SE 1		SE 1	SE	SE
Sevenoaks 4 d		07 55					08 25					08 55
Bat & Ball d		07 58					08 28					08 58
Otford 4 d		08 01					08 31			08 56		09 01
Shoreham (Kent) d		08 04					08 34					09 04
Eynsford d		08 07					08 37					09 07
Swanley 4 d		08 12		08 29			08 42			09 05		09 12
St Mary Cray d		08 16		08 34			08 46			09 10		09 16
Orpington 4 d	08 08				08 38						09 08	
Petts Wood 4 d	08 11				08 41						09 11	
Bickley 4 d	08 15	08 21			08 45		08 51				09 15	09 21
Bromley South 4 d	08 18	08 24		08 40	08 48		08 54	09 00		09 16	09 18	09 24
Shortlands 4 d	08 20	08 26			08 50		08 56				09 20	09 26
Ravensbourne d		08 29					08 59					09 29
Beckenham Hill d		08 31					09 01					09 31
Bellingham d		08 33					09 03					09 33
Catford d		08 35					09 05					09 35
Crofton Park d		08 37					09 07					09 37
Lewisham 4 d												
Nunhead 4 d		08 40					09 10					09 40
Peckham Rye 4 d		08 42					09 12					09 42
Denmark Hill 4 d		08 44					09 14					09 44
Beckenham Junction 4 d	08 23				08 53						09 23	
Kent House 4 d	08 25				08 55						09 25	
Penge East d	08 27				08 57						09 27	
Sydenham Hill d	08 30				09 00						09 30	
West Dulwich d	08 31				09 01						09 31	
Herne Hill 4 d	08 34				09 04						09 34	
Loughborough Jn d												
Elephant & Castle ⊖ d												
London Blackfriars 3 ⊖ d												
City Thameslink 3 a												
Farringdon ⊖ a												
St Pancras International 15 ⊖ a												
Kentish Town ⊖ a												
Brixton ⊖ d	08 36				09 06						09 36	
London Victoria 15 ⊖ a	08 43	08 54	.	09 01	09 13	.	09 24	09 16	.	09 32	09 43	09 54

For general notes see front of timetable
For details of catering facilities see Directory of Train Operators

Table 195

Sundays

Sevenoaks, Otford, Orpington, Bromley South, Beckenham Junction and Catford → London

Network Diagram - see first page of Table 195

		SE		SE	SE		SE	SE		SE		SE	SE	SE	SE	SE	SE	SE			SE	SE		SE
		1					1	1					1			1	1					1		
							H									H	A							
Sevenoaks 4	d				09 25							09 55			10 25						20 55			
Bat & Ball	d				09 28							09 58			10 28						20 58			
Otford 4	d				09 31			09 56				10 01			10 31		10 56				21 01			
Shoreham (Kent)	d				09 34							10 04			10 34						21 04			
Eynsford	d				09 37							10 07			10 37						21 07			
Swanley 4	d	09 29			09 42			10 05				10 12	10 29		10 42		11 05				21 12	21 29		
St Mary Cray	d	09 34			09 46			10 10				10 16	10 34		10 46		11 10				21 16	21 34		
Orpington 4	d			09 38						10 08				10 38				11 08						21 38
Petts Wood 4	d			09 41						10 11				10 41				11 11						21 41
Bickley 4	d			09 45	09 51					10 15		10 21		10 45	10 51			11 15			21 21			21 45
Bromley South 4	d	09 40		09 48	09 54		10 00	10 16		10 18		10 24	10 40	10 48	10 54	11 00	11 16	11 18	and at		21 24	21 40		21 48
Shortlands 4	d			09 50	09 56					10 20		10 26		10 50	10 56			11 20			21 26			21 50
Ravensbourne	d				09 59							10 29			10 59				the same		21 29			
Beckenham Hill	d				10 01							10 31			11 01						21 31			
Bellingham	d				10 03							10 33			11 03				minutes		21 33			
Catford	d				10 05							10 35			11 05						21 35			
Crofton Park	d				10 07							10 37			11 07				past		21 37			
Lewisham 4	🚊 d																		each					
Nunhead 4	d				10 10							10 40			11 10						21 40			
Peckham Rye 4	d				10 12							10 42			11 12				hour until		21 42			
Denmark Hill 4	d				10 14							10 44			11 14						21 44			
Beckenham Junction 4	🚊 d			09 53						10 23				10 53				11 23						21 53
Kent House 4	d			09 55						10 25				10 55				11 25						21 55
Penge East	d			09 57						10 27				10 57				11 27						21 57
Sydenham Hill	d			10 00						10 30				11 00				11 30						22 00
West Dulwich	d			10 01						10 31				11 01				11 31						22 01
Herne Hill 4	d			10 04						10 34				11 04				11 34						22 04
Loughborough Jn	d																							
Elephant & Castle	⊖ d																							
London Blackfriars 3	⊖ d																							
City Thameslink 3	a																							
Farringdon	⊖ a																							
St Pancras International 15	⊖ a																							
Kentish Town	⊖ a																							
Brixton	⊖ d			10 06						10 36				11 06				11 36						22 06
London Victoria 15	⊖ a	10 01		10 13	10 24		10 16	10 32		10 43		10 54	11 01	11 13	11 24	11 16	11 32	11 43			21 54	22 01		22 13

		SE	SE		SE	SE		SE	SE		SE	SE		SE	SE		SE	SE
			1		1				1					1	1			1
Sevenoaks 4	d	21 25						21 55				22 25						
Bat & Ball	d	21 28						21 58				22 28						
Otford 4	d	21 31			21 56			22 01				22 31			22 56			
Shoreham (Kent)	d	21 34						22 04				22 34						
Eynsford	d	21 37						22 07				22 37						
Swanley 4	d	21 42			22 05			22 12	22 29			22 42			23 05			23 32
St Mary Cray	d	21 46			22 10			22 16	22 34			22 46			23 10			23 36
Orpington 4	d					22 08					22 38						23 14	
Petts Wood 4	d					22 11					22 41						23 17	
Bickley 4	d	21 51				22 15		22 21			22 45	22 51					23 21	
Bromley South 4	d	21 54	22 00		22 16	22 18		22 24	22 40		22 48	22 54		23 00	23 16		23 24	23 42
Shortlands 4	d	21 56				22 20		22 26			22 50	22 56					23 26	
Ravensbourne	d	21 59						22 29				22 59					23 29	
Beckenham Hill	d	22 01						22 31				23 01					23 31	
Bellingham	d	22 03						22 33				23 03					23 33	
Catford	d	22 05						22 35				23 05					23 35	
Crofton Park	d	22 07						22 37				23 07					23 37	
Lewisham 4	🚊 d																	
Nunhead 4	d	22 10						22 40				23 10					23 40	
Peckham Rye 4	d	22 12						22 42				23 12					23 42	
Denmark Hill 4	d	22 14						22 44				23 14					23 44	
Beckenham Junction 4	🚊 d					22 23					22 53							
Kent House 4	d					22 25					22 55							
Penge East	d					22 27					22 57							
Sydenham Hill	d					22 30					23 00							
West Dulwich	d					22 31					23 01							
Herne Hill 4	d					22 34					23 04							
Loughborough Jn	d																	
Elephant & Castle	⊖ d																	
London Blackfriars 3	⊖ d																	
City Thameslink 3	a																	
Farringdon	⊖ a																	
St Pancras International 15	⊖ a																	
Kentish Town	⊖ a																	
Brixton	⊖ d					22 36					23 06							
London Victoria 15	⊖ a	22 24	22 16		22 32	22 43		22 54	23 01		23 13	23 24		23 16	23 32		23 53	23 59

For general notes see front of timetable
For details of catering facilities see
Directory of Train Operators

A From Canterbury West (Table 207)

For details of Bank Holiday service alterations please see first page of Table 195

London → Maidstone East and Ashford International

Network Diagram - see first page of Table 195

Miles	Miles	Miles		SE MO 1	SE MX 1 A	SE MX 1	SE 1 B	SE 1 C	SE 1 C	SE 1 B	SE 1 A	SE 1	SE 1 A	SE	SE 1	SE 1 A	SE	SE 1	SE 1 A
0	—	—	**London Victoria 15** ⊖ 195 d	22p42	23p09	23p51			06 10	06 47	07 19	07 49	08 18	08 49		09 19	09 48		10 18
—	—	—	**St Pancras International** ⊖ 195 d																
—	0	—	**London Blackfriars 3** ⊖ 195 d																
—	1¼	—	Elephant & Castle ⊖ 195 d																
4	—	—	Herne Hill 4 195 d																
8¾	—	—	Beckenham Junction 4 195 ⛴ d																
11	11½	—	Bromley South 4 195 d	22p59	23p29	00 07			06 30	07 04	07 36	08 07	08 40	09 08		09 37	10 04		10 34
—	—	—	London Charing Cross 4 ⊖ d																
—	—	—	London Waterloo (East) 4 ⊖ d																
—	—	0	**London Cannon Street 4** ⊖ d												09 13			10 14	
—	—	¾	London Bridge 4 ⊖ d												09 17			10 18	
14¾	—	—	St Mary Cray 195 d	23p05	23p35	00 14													
17½	—	—	Swanley 4 195 d	23p10	23p40	00 18			06 39	07 13	07 45	08 17		09 16			10 13		
24	—	—	Otford 4 195 d	23p19	23p49	00 30			06 49	07 22	07 54	08 26	08 57	09 25		09 53	10 23		10 51
27	—	—	Kemsing d						06 55	07 27	07 58	08 30		09 30			10 27		
29½	—	—	Borough Green & Wrotham d	23p26	23p56	00 37			06 59	07 31	08 03	08 35	09 04	09 34		10 00	10 32		10 58
34¾	—	—	West Malling d	23p32	00 02	00 43			07 05	07 37	08 09	08 41	09 10	09 40	09 57	10 06	10 38	10 57	11 04
35¾	—	—	East Malling d	23p35	00 04	00 46			07 08	07 40	08 11	08 43		09 43			10 41		
37½	—	—	Barming d	23p38	00 08	00 49			07 11	07 43	08 15	08 47		09 46			10 44		
40	—	37¾	**Maidstone East 4** a	23p43	00 12	00 54			07 16	07 48	08 19	08 51	09 17	09 51	10 05	10 13	10 49	11 05	11 11
—	—	—	d	23p43	00 13	00 54	05 56	06 33	07 23	07 49	08 21		09 17		10 05	10 14		11 05	11 13
42¾	—	—	Bearsted d	23p48	00 18	00 59	06 01	06 38	07 28	07 54	08 26		09 22		10 11	10 19		11 11	11 18
45	—	—	Hollingbourne d	23p52	00 22	01 03	06 05	06 42	07 32	07 58	08 30		09 26			10 23			11 22
47½	—	—	Harrietsham d	23p56	00 26	01 07	06 09	06 46	07 36	08 02	08 34		09 30			10 27			11 26
49¼	—	—	Lenham d	00 01	00 30	01 11	06 12	06 49	07 39	08 06	08 37		09 34			10 30			11 30
53¼	—	—	Charing d	00 05	00 35	01 16	06 17	06 54	07 44	08 11	08 42		09 39			10 35			11 35
59¼	—	57	**Ashford International** a	00 12	00 42	01 23	06 25	07 02	07 52	08 21	08 53		09 46		10 28	10 43		11 28	11 43

	SE	SE 1	SE 1 A	SE	SE 1	SE 1 A	SE	SE 1	SE 1 A	SE	SE 1	SE 1	SE 1	SE 1	SE 1	SE 1	SE 1	SE 1	SE 1
London Victoria 15 ⊖ 195 d	10 48		11 18	11 48		12 18	12 48		13 18	13 48		14 18	14 48		15 18	15 48		16 27	16 56
St Pancras International ⊖ 195 d																			
London Blackfriars 3 ⊖ 195 d																			
Elephant & Castle ⊖ 195 d																			
Herne Hill 4 195 d																			
Beckenham Junction 4 195 ⛴ d																			
Bromley South 4 195 d	11 04		11 34	12 04		12 34	13 04		13 34	14 04		14 34	15 04		15 34	16 04		16 48	17 15
London Charing Cross 4 ⊖ d																			
London Waterloo (East) 4 ⊖ d																			
London Cannon Street 4 ⊖ d		11 14			12 14			13 14			14 14			15 14			16 14		
London Bridge 4 ⊖ d		11 18			12 18			13 18			14 18			15 18			16 18		
St Mary Cray 195 d																			
Swanley 4 195 d	11 13			12 13			13 13			14 13			15 13		15 43	16 13		16 59	
Otford 4 195 d	11 23		11 51	12 23		12 51	13 23		13 51	14 23		14 51	15 23		15 52	16 23	16 48	17 10	17 33
Kemsing d	11 27			12 27			13 27			14 27			15 27		15 57			17 15	
Borough Green & Wrotham d	11 32		11 58	12 32		12 58	13 32		13 58	14 32		14 58	15 32		16 02	16 30		17 20	17 40
West Malling d	11 38	11 57	12 04	12 38	12 57	13 04	13 38	13 57	14 04	14 38	14 57	15 04	15 38	15 57	16 08	16 36	17 00	17 26	17 46
East Malling d	11 41			12 41			13 41			14 41			15 41		16 11			17 28	
Barming d	11 44			12 44			13 44			14 44			15 44		16 14			17 32	
Maidstone East 4 a	11 49	12 05	12 11	12 49	13 05	13 11	13 49	14 05	14 11	14 49	15 05	15 11	15 49	16 05	16 19	16 44	17 07	17 36	17 53
d		12 05	12 13		13 05	13 13		14 05	14 13		15 05	15 21	15 50	16 05	16 19	16 44	17 07	17 38	17 54
Bearsted d		12 11	12 18		13 11	13 18		14 11	14 18		15 11	15 26	15 55	16 11	16 24	16 49	17 13	17 43	17 59
Hollingbourne d			12 22			13 22			14 22			15 30			16 28	16 53	17 17	17 47	18 03
Harrietsham d			12 26			13 26			14 26			15 34			16 32	16 57	17 21	17 51	18 07
Lenham d			12 30			13 30			14 30			15 40	16 03		16 36	17 01	17 24	17 54	18 10
Charing d			12 35			13 35			14 35			15 45			16 41	17 06	17 29	17 59	18 15
Ashford International a		12 29	12 43		13 28	13 43		14 28	14 43		15 27	15 54	16 14	16 28	16 48	17 13	17b40	18 07	18b25

	SE 1	SE	SE 1	FC 1 D E	SE 1	SE 1	SE 1	SE 1	SE 1	SE 1	SE 1	SE 1	SE 1	SE 1 A	SE 1
London Victoria 15 ⊖ 195 d	17 22	17 32	17 58		18 18	18 48		19 18	19 48	20 18	20 48	21 09	22 09	23 09	23 51
St Pancras International ⊖ 195 d				17 46											
London Blackfriars 3 ⊖ 195 d				17 58											
Elephant & Castle ⊖ 195 d				18 03											
Herne Hill 4 195 d															
Beckenham Junction 4 195 ⛴ d		17 47								20 32	21 02				
Bromley South 4 195 d	17 40	17 51	18 18	18 21	18 36	19 06		19 35	20 07	20 37	21 07	21 29	22 29	23 29	00 07
London Charing Cross 4 ⊖ d															
London Waterloo (East) 4 ⊖ d															
London Cannon Street 4 ⊖ d							19 14								
London Bridge 4 ⊖ d							19 18								
St Mary Cray 195 d	17 47	18 00		18 28	18 43	19 12						21 35	22 35	23 35	00 14
Swanley 4 195 d	17 52	18 05		18 33	18 48	19 16		19 44		20 45		21 40	22 40	23 40	00 18
Otford 4 195 d	18 01	18 18	18 36	18 42	18 58	19 26	19 48	19 53	20 23	20 54	21 23	21 49	22 49	23 49	00 30
Kemsing d	18 06	18 22		18 46	19 02			19 58		20 59					
Borough Green & Wrotham d	18 11	18 27	18 43	18 51	19 07	19 33		20 02	20 30	21 03	21 30	21 56	22 56	23 56	00 37
West Malling d	18 17	18 33	18 49	18 57	19 13	19 39	20 00	20 08	20 36	21 09	21 36	22 02	23 02	00 02	00 43
East Malling d	18 19	18 35		18 59	19 15	19 41		20 11		21 12		22 04	23 04	00 04	00 46
Barming d	18 23	18 39		19 03	19 19	19 45		20 14		21 15		22 08	23 08	00 08	00 49
Maidstone East 4 a	18 27	18 44	18 56	19 07	19 23	19 49	20 07	20 19	20 43	21 20	21 43	22 12	23 12	00 12	00 54
d	18 29		18 56	19 08	19 25	19 50	20 08	20 20	20 44	21 21	21 44	22 13	23 13	00 13	00 54
Bearsted d	18 34		19 01	19 13	19 30	19 55	20 13	20 25	20 49	21 26	21 49	22 18	23 18	00 18	00 59
Hollingbourne d	18 38		19 05	19 17	19 34	19 59		20 29	20 53	21 30	21 53	22 22	23 22	00 22	01 03
Harrietsham d	18 42		19 09	19 21	19 38	20 03		20 33	20 57	21 34	21 57	22 26	23 26	00 26	01 07
Lenham d	18 45		19 13	19 24	19 41	20 07		20 36	21 01	21 37	22 01	22 30	23 30	00 30	01 11
Charing d	18 50		19 18	19 29	19 46	20 12		20 41	21 06	21 42	22 06	22 35	23 35	00 35	01 16
Ashford International a	18 59		19b28	19 37	19 55	20b21	20 32	20 49	21 14	21 50	22 15	22 42	23 42	00 42	01 23

For general notes see front of timetable
For details of catering facilities see Directory of Train Operators

A To Canterbury West (Table 207)
B To Ramsgate (Table 207)
C To Margate (Table 207)
D From Bedford (Table 52)
E TOC SE from London Blackfriars
b Until 9 October arr 2 minutes earlier

Table 196

Saturdays

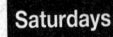

London → Maidstone East and Ashford International

Network Diagram - see first page of Table 195

		SE 1	SE 1	SE 1	SE 1	SE 1	SE 1	SE 1	SE	SE 1	SE 1	SE	SE 1	SE 1	SE	SE 1		SE 1	SE	SE 1	SE 1	SE	SE 1	SE 1	SE
		A		B	C	C		A			A			A				A			A			A	
London Victoria 15	⊖ 195 d	23p09	23p51		06 18	07 18	07 48	08 18	08 48		09 18	09 48		10 18	10 48			11 18	11 48		12 18	12 48		13 18	13 48
St Pancras International	⊖ 195 d																								
London Blackfriars 3	⊖ 195 d																								
Elephant & Castle	⊖ 195 d																								
Herne Hill 4	195 d																								
Beckenham Junction 4	195 d																								
Bromley South 4	195 d	23p29	00 07		06 34	07 34	08 04	08 34	09 04		09 34	10 04		10 34	11 04			11 34	12 04		12 34	13 04		13 34	14 04
London Charing Cross 4	⊖ d																								
London Waterloo (East) 4	⊖ d																								
London Cannon Street 4	⊖ d									09 14			10 14			11 14				12 14			13 14		
London Bridge 4	⊖ d									09 18			10 18			11 18				12 18			13 18		
St Mary Cray	195 d	23p35	00 14		06 41	07 41																			
Swanley 4	195 d	23p40	00 18		06 45	07 45	08 13		09 13			10 13			11 13				12 13			13 13			14 13
Otford 4	195 d	23p49	00 30		06 54	07 54	08 23	08 51	09 23		09 51	10 23		10 51	11 23			11 51	12 23		12 51	13 23		13 51	14 23
Kemsing	d						08 27		09 27			10 27			11 27				12 27			13 27			14 27
Borough Green & Wrotham	d	23p56	00 37		07 02	08 02	08 32	08 58	09 32		09 58	10 32		10 58	11 32			11 58	12 32		12 58	13 32		13 58	14 32
West Malling	d	00 02	00 43		07 08	08 08	08 38	09 04	09 38	09 57	10 04	10 38	10 57	11 04	11 38	11 57		12 04	12 38	12 57	13 04	13 38	13 57	14 04	14 38
East Malling	d	00 04	00 46		07 10	08 10	08 41		09 41			10 41			11 41				12 41			13 41			14 41
Barming	d	00 08	00 49		07 14	08 14	08 44		09 44			10 44			11 44				12 44			13 44			14 44
Maidstone East 4	a	00 12	00 54		07 18	08 18	08 49	09 11	09 49	10 05	10 11	10 49	11 05	11 11	11 49	12 05		12 11	12 49	13 05	13 11	13 49	14 05	14 11	14 49
	d	00 13	00 54	06 19	07 19	08 19	08 50	09 13		10 05	10 13		11 05	11 13		12 05		12 13		13 05	13 13		14 05	14 13	
Bearsted	d	00 18	00 59	06 24	07 24	08 24	08 55	09 18		10 11	10 18		11 11	11 18		12 11		12 18		13 11	13 18		14 11	14 18	
Hollingbourne	d	00 22	01 03	06 28	07 28	08 28		09 22			10 22			11 22				12 22			13 22			14 22	
Harrietsham	d	00 26	01 07	06 32	07 32	08 32		09 26			10 26			11 26				12 26			13 26			14 26	
Lenham	d	00 30	01 11	06 35	07 35	08 35		09 30			10 30			11 30				12 30			13 30			14 30	
Charing	d	00 35	01 16	06 40	07 40	08 40		09 35			10 35			11 35				12 35			13 35			14 35	
Ashford International	a	00 42	01 23	06 48	07 48	08 48	09 12	09 43		10 27	10 43		11 27	11 43		12 27		12 43		13 27	13 43		14 27	14 43	

		SE 1	SE 1	SE	SE 1	SE 1	SE	SE 1	SE 1	SE	SE 1	SE 1	SE	SE 1	SE 1	SE 1	SE 1	SE 1	SE 1	SE 1	SE 1	SE 1	SE 1		
			A			A																A			
London Victoria 15	⊖ 195 d		14 18	14 48		15 18	15 48		16 18	16 48		17 18	17 48		18 18	18 48		19 18	20 18	21 18	22 18	23 18	23 51		
St Pancras International	⊖ 195 d																								
London Blackfriars 3	⊖ 195 d																								
Elephant & Castle	⊖ 195 d																								
Herne Hill 4	195 d																								
Beckenham Junction 4	195 d																								
Bromley South 4	195 d		14 34	15 04		15 34	16 04		16 34	17 04		17 34	18 04		18 34	19 04		19 34	20 34	21 34	22 34	23 34	00 07		
London Charing Cross 4	⊖ d																								
London Waterloo (East) 4	⊖ d																								
London Cannon Street 4	⊖ d	14 14			15 14			16 14			17 14			18 14			19 14								
London Bridge 4	⊖ d	14 18			15 18			16 18			17 18			18 18			19 18								
St Mary Cray	195 d																	19 41	20 41	21 41	22 41	23 41	00 14		
Swanley 4	195 d			15 13			16 13			17 13			18 13			19 13		19 45	20 45	21 45	22 45	23 45	00 18		
Otford 4	195 d		14 51	15 23		15 51	16 23		16 51	17 23		17 51	18 23		18 51	19 23		19 54	20 54	21 54	22 54	23 54	00 30		
Kemsing	d			15 27			16 27			17 27			18 27			19 27									
Borough Green & Wrotham	d		14 58	15 32		15 58	16 32		16 58	17 32		17 58	18 32		18 58	19 32		20 02	21 02	22 02	23 02	00 02	00 37		
West Malling	d	14 57	15 04	15 38	15 57	16 04	16 38	16 57	17 04	17 38	17 57	18 04	18 38	18 57	19 04	19 38	19 57	20 08	21 08	22 08	23 08	00 08	00 43		
East Malling	d			15 41			16 41			17 41			18 41			19 41		20 10	21 10	22 10	23 10	00 10	00 46		
Barming	d			15 44			16 44			17 44			18 44			19 44		20 14	21 14	22 14	23 14	00 14	00 49		
Maidstone East 4	a	15 05	15 11	15 49	16 05	16 11	16 49	17 05	17 11	17 49	18 05	18 11	18 49	19 05	19 11	19 49	20 05	20 18	21 18	22 18	23 18	00 18	00 54		
	d	15 05	15 13		16 05	16 13		17 05	17 13		18 05	18 13		19 05	19 13		20 05	20 19	21 19	22 19	23 19	00 19	00 54		
Bearsted	d	15 11	15 18		16 11	16 18		17 11	17 18		18 11	18 18		19 11	19 18		20 11	20 24	21 24	22 24	23 24	00 24	00 59		
Hollingbourne	d		15 22			16 22			17 22			18 22			19 22			20 28	21 28	22 28	23 28	00 28	01 03		
Harrietsham	d		15 26			16 26			17 26			18 26			19 26			20 32	21 32	22 32	23 32	00 32	01 07		
Lenham	d		15 30			16 30			17 29			18 29			19 29			20 35	21 35	22 35	23 35	00 35	01 11		
Charing	d		15 35			16 35			17 34			18 34			19 34			20 40	21 40	22 40	23 40	00 40	01 16		
Ashford International	a	15 27	15 43		16 27	16 43		17 27	17 43		18 27	18 42		19 27	19 42		20 27	20 48	21 48	22 48	23 48	00 48	01 23		

For general notes see front of timetable
For details of catering facilities see
Directory of Train Operators

A To Canterbury West (Table 207)
B To Margate (Table 207)
C To Ramsgate (Table 207)

Table 196

Sundays

London → Maidstone East and Ashford International

Network Diagram - see first page of Table 195

		SE	SE	SE	SE	SE	SE	SE	SE	SE	SE	SE	SE	SE	SE	SE	SE	SE	SE
		1	1	1	1	1	1	1	1	1	1	1	1	1	1	1	1	1	1
		A		A	A	A	A	A	A	A	A	A	A	A					
London Victoria 15	⊖ 195 d	23p18	23p51	07 42	08 42	09 42	10 42	11 42	12 42	13 42	14 42	15 42	16 42	17 42	18 42	19 42	20 42	21 42	22 42
St Pancras International	⊖ 195 d																		
London Blackfriars 3	⊖ 195 d																		
Elephant & Castle	⊖ 195 d																		
Herne Hill 4	195 d																		
Beckenham Junction 4	195 🚋 d																		
Bromley South 4	195 d	23p34	00 07	07 59	08 59	09 59	10 59	11 59	12 59	13 59	14 59	15 59	16 59	17 59	18 59	19 59	20 59	21 59	22 59
London Charing Cross 4	⊖ d																		
London Waterloo (East) 4	⊖ d																		
London Cannon Street 4	⊖ d																		
London Bridge 4	⊖ d																		
St Mary Cray	195 d	23p41	00 14	08 05	09 05	10 05	11 05	12 05	13 05	14 05	15 05	16 05	17 05	18 05	19 05	20 05	21 05	22 05	23 05
Swanley 4	195 d	23p45	00 18	08 10	09 10	10 10	11 10	12 10	13 10	14 10	15 10	16 10	17 10	18 10	19 10	20 10	21 10	22 10	23 10
Otford 4	195 d	23p54	00 30	08 19	09 19	10 19	11 19	12 19	13 19	14 19	15 19	16 19	17 19	18 19	19 19	20 19	21 19	22 19	23 19
Kemsing	d																		
Borough Green & Wrotham	d	00 02	00 37	08 26	09 26	10 26	11 26	12 26	13 26	14 26	15 26	16 26	17 26	18 26	19 26	20 26	21 26	22 26	23 26
West Malling	d	00 08	00 43	08 32	09 32	10 32	11 32	12 32	13 32	14 32	15 32	16 32	17 32	18 32	19 32	20 32	21 32	22 32	23 32
East Malling	d	00 10	00 46	08 35	09 35	10 35	11 35	12 35	13 35	14 35	15 35	16 35	17 35	18 35	19 35	20 35	21 35	22 35	23 35
Barming	d	00 14	00 49	08 38	09 38	10 38	11 38	12 38	13 38	14 38	15 38	16 38	17 38	18 38	19 38	20 38	21 38	22 38	23 38
Maidstone East 4	a	00 18	00 54	08 43	09 43	10 43	11 43	12 43	13 43	14 43	15 43	16 43	17 43	18 43	19 43	20 43	21 43	22 43	23 43
	d	00 19	00 54	08 43	09 43	10 43	11 43	12 43	13 43	14 43	15 43	16 43	17 43	18 43	19 43	20 43	21 43	22 43	23 43
Bearsted	d	00 24	00 59	08 48	09 48	10 48	11 48	12 48	13 48	14 48	15 48	16 48	17 48	18 48	19 48	20 48	21 48	22 48	23 48
Hollingbourne	d	00 28	01 03	08 52	09 52	10 52	11 52	12 52	13 52	14 52	15 52	16 52	17 52	18 52	19 52	20 52	21 52	22 52	23 52
Harrietsham	d	00 32	01 07	08 56	09 56	10 56	11 56	12 56	13 56	14 56	15 56	16 56	17 56	18 56	19 56	20 56	21 56	22 56	23 56
Lenham	d	00 35	01 11	09 00	10 00	11 00	12 00	13 00	14 00	15 00	16 00	17 00	18 00	19 00	20 00	21 00	22 00	23 00	00 01
Charing	d	00 40	01 16	09 05	10 05	11 05	12 05	13 05	14 05	15 05	16 05	17 05	18 05	19 05	20 05	21 05	22 05	23 05	00 05
Ashford International	a	00 48	01 23	09 12	10 12	11 12	12 12	13 12	14 12	15 12	16 12	17 12	18 12	19 12	20 12	21 12	22 12	23 12	00 12

For general notes see front of timetable
For details of catering facilities see
Directory of Train Operators

A To Canterbury West (Table 207)

For details of Bank Holiday service alterations please see first page of Table 195

Ashford International and Maidstone East to London

Network Diagram - see first page of Table 195

Miles	Miles	Miles	Station		SE [1] A	SE [1] B	SE [1] C D	SE [1] D E	SE [1]	SE [1] D G	SE [1]	SE [1]	SE [1]	SE [1]	SE [1] H	SE [1]	SE [1]	SE [1] J	SE [1]
0	—	0	**Ashford International**	d	05 30	05 33			06 15	06 23	06 36	06 54	07 13	07 43	08 14	08 32		09 04	09 34
6	—	—	Charing	d	05 38	05 41			06 23	06 31	06 44	07 02	07 21	07 51	08 22			09 12	
10	—	—	Lenham	d	05 43	05 46			06 28	06 36	06 49	07 07	07 26	07 56	08 27			09 17	
11¾	—	—	Harrietsham	d	05 46	05 49			06 31	06 39	06 52	07 10	07 29	07 59	08 30			09 20	
14¼	—	—	Hollingbourne	d	05 50	05 53			06 35	06 43	06 56	07 14	07 33	08 03	08 34			09 24	
16½	—	—	Bearsted	d	05 54	05 57	06 07	06 09	06 39	06 47	07 00	07 18	07 37	08 07	08 38	08 48		09 28	09 51
19¼	—	19¼	**Maidstone East [4]**	a	05 59	06 02	06 12	06 14	06 44	06 52	07 05	07 23	07 42	08 12	08 43	08 53		09 33	09 56
—	—	—		d	06 00	06 03	06 13	06 15	06 44	06 52	07 05	07 23	07 42	08 13	08 45	08 53	09 00	09 33	09 57
21¾	—	—	Barming	d	06 04	06 07			06 49	06 57	07 10	07 28	07 47	08 18			09 04		
23½	—	—	East Malling	d	06 08	06 11			06 52	07 01	07 13	07 31		08 21			09 08		
24½	—	—	West Malling	d	06 10	06 13	06 21	06 23	06 55	07 03	07 16	07 34	07 51	08 24	08 52	09 01	09 10	09 41	10 05
29¾	—	—	Borough Green & Wrotham	d	06 17	06 20	06 28	06 30	07 02	07 10	07 23	07 41	07 59	08 31	08 59		09 17	09 48	
32¼	—	—	Kemsing	d					07 07	07 15	07 27	07 45		08 35			09 22		
35¼	—	—	Otford [4]	195 a	06 28	06 28	06 36	06 38	07 12	07 21	07 32	07 50	08 08	08 40	09 07		09 27	09 56	
41¾	—	—	Swanley [4]	195 a			06 48	06 48		07 30	07 43	08 00		08 49			09 36	10 05	
44½	—	—	St Mary Cray	195 a															
—	—	56¼	London Bridge [4]	⊖ a												09 39			10 50
—	—	57	**London Cannon Street [4]**	⊖ a															10 54
—	—	—	London Waterloo (East) [4]	⊖ a												09 45			
—	—	—	London Charing Cross [4]	⊖ a												09b51			
48¼	0	—	Bromley South [4]	195 a	06 47	06 47	06 57	06 57	07 29	07 40	07 54		08 24	09 00	09 27		09 44	10 14	
50½	—	—	Beckenham Junction [4]	195 a								08 15							
55¼	—	—	Herne Hill [4]	195 a	06 57	06 57													
—	10¼	—	Elephant & Castle	⊖ 195 a			07 15	07 15		08 01									
—	11½	—	**London Blackfriars [3]**	⊖ 195 a			07 20	07 20		08 06									
—	—	—	**St Pancras International**	⊖ 195 a			07 31	07 31		08 15									
59¼	—	—	**London Victoria [15]**	⊖ 195 a	07 08	07 08			07 49		08 17	08 31	08 52	09 19	09 49			10c04	10 32

Station		SE	SE [1] H	SE [1]	SE	SE [1] H	SE [1]	SE	SE [1] H	SE [1]	SE	SE [1] H	SE [1]	SE	SE [1] H	SE [1]	SE
Ashford International	d		10 05	10 36		11 05	11 36		12 05	12 36		13 05	13 36		14 05	14 36	
Charing	d		10 13			11 13			12 13			13 13			14 13		
Lenham	d		10 19			11 18			12 18			13 18			14 18		
Harrietsham	d		10 22			11 21			12 21			13 21			14 21		
Hollingbourne	d		10 26			11 25			12 25			13 25			14 25		
Bearsted	d		10 29	10 52		11 29	11 52		12 29	12 52		13 29	13 52		14 29	14 52	
Maidstone East [4]	a		10 34	10 57		11 34	11 57		12 34	12 57		13 34	13 57		14 34	14 57	
	d	10 00	10 35	10 57	11 00	11 34	11 57	12 00	12 34	12 57	13 00	13 34	13 57	14 00	14 34	14 57	15 00
Barming	d	10 04			11 04			12 04			13 04			14 04			15 04
East Malling	d	10 08			11 08			12 08			13 08			14 08			15 08
West Malling	d	10 10	10 42	11 05	11 10	11 42	12 05	12 10	12 42	13 05	13 10	13 42	14 05	14 10	14 42	15 05	15 10
Borough Green & Wrotham	d	10 17	10 50		11 17	11 49		12 17	12 49		13 17	13 49		14 17	14 49		15 17
Kemsing	d	10 22			11 22			12 22			13 22			14 22			15 22
Otford [4]	195 a	10 27	10 57		11 27	11 57		12 27	12 57		13 27	13 57		14 27	14 57		15 27
Swanley [4]	195 a	10 36			11 36			12 36			13 36			14 36			15 36
St Mary Cray	195 a																
London Bridge [4]	⊖ a			11 50			12 50			13 50			14 50			15 50	
London Cannon Street [4]	⊖ a			11 54			12 54			13 54			14 54			15 54	
London Waterloo (East) [4]	⊖ a																
London Charing Cross [4]	⊖ a																
Bromley South [4]	195 a	10 44	11 14		11 44	12 14		12 44	13 14		13 44	14 14		14 44	15 14		15 44
Beckenham Junction [4]	195 a																
Herne Hill [4]	195 a																
Elephant & Castle	⊖ 195 a																
London Blackfriars [3]	⊖ 195 a																
St Pancras International	⊖ 195 a																
London Victoria [15]	⊖ 195 a	11 02	11 32		12 02	12 32		13 02	13 32		14 02	14 32		15 02	15 32		16 02

Station		SE [1] H	SE [1]	SE	SE [1] H	SE [1]	SE [1]	SE [1]	SE [1]	SE [1]	SE [1]	SE	SE [1]	SE [1] H	SE [1]	SE [1]
Ashford International	d	15 03	15 21	15 27	15 59	16 24	16 34	16 58	17 26	17 31	18 00		19 00	19 58	20 58	22 08
Charing	d	15 11		15 35	16 07		16 42	17 06		17 39	18 08		19 08	20 06	21 06	22 16
Lenham	d	15 16		15 40	16 12		16 47	17 11		17 44	18 13		19 13	20 11	21 11	22 21
Harrietsham	d	15 19		15 43	16 15		16 50	17 14		17 47	18 16		19 16	20 14	21 14	22 24
Hollingbourne	d	15 23		15 47	16 19		16 54	17 18		17 51	18 20		19 20	20 18	21 18	22 28
Bearsted	d	15 27	15 37	15 51	16 23	16 40	16 58	17 22	17 42	17 55	18 24		19 24	20 22	21 22	22 32
Maidstone East [4]	a	15 32	15 42	15 56	16 28	16 45	17 03	17 27	17 47	18 00	18 29		19 29	20 27	21 27	22 37
	d	15 32	15 43	16 00	16 28	16 46	17 03	17 28	17 48	18 02	18 30	19 00	19 29	20 28	21 28	22 38
Barming	d			16 05	16 33		17 08	17 32		18 07	18 35	19 04	19 34	20 32	21 33	22 42
East Malling	d			16 08	16 36		17 11	17 36		18 10	18 38	19 08	19 37	20 36	21 36	22 46
West Malling	d	15 40	15 50	16 11	16 39	16 54	17 14	17 38	17 55	18 13	18 41	19 10	19 40	20 38	21 39	22 48
Borough Green & Wrotham	d	15 47		16 18	16 46		17 21	17 45		18 20	18 48	19 17	19 47	20 45	21 46	22 55
Kemsing	d			16 22			17 25			18 24		19 22				
Otford [4]	195 a	15 55		16 27	16 54		17 30	17 53		18 29	18 56	19 27	19 55	20 53	21 54	23 04
Swanley [4]	195 a			16 38	17 05			18 04			19 05	19 36	20 04	21 02	22 03	23 13
St Mary Cray	195 a												20 08	21 07	22 07	23 17
London Bridge [4]	⊖ a		16 34			17 38			18 40							
London Cannon Street [4]	⊖ a															
London Waterloo (East) [4]	⊖ a		16 39			17 44			18 45							
London Charing Cross [4]	⊖ a		16 45			17 48			18 48							
Bromley South [4]	195 a	16 14		16 47	17 14		17 47	18 13		18 45	19 14	19 44	20 14	21 13	22 13	23 23
Beckenham Junction [4]	195 a															
Herne Hill [4]	195 a															
Elephant & Castle	⊖ 195 a															
London Blackfriars [3]	⊖ 195 a															
St Pancras International	⊖ 195 a															
London Victoria [15]	⊖ 195 a	16 33		17 10	17 33		18 09	18 32		19 03	19 31	20 02	20 31	21 29	22 32	23 44

For general notes see front of timetable
For details of catering facilities see Directory of Train Operators

A From 12 October
B Until 9 October
C From 12 October. To Bedford (Table 52)
D TOC FC from London Blackfriars
E Until 9 October. To Bedford (Table 52)
G To Bedford (Table 52)
H From Canterbury West (Table 207)
J From Margate (Table 207)
b Until 9 October arr 1 minute earlier
c Until 9 October arr 2 minutes earlier

Table 196

Saturdays

Ashford International and Maidstone East to London

Network Diagram - see first page of Table 195

	SE 1	SE 1	SE 1	SE		SE 1	SE 1	SE	SE 1		SE 1	SE	SE 1 A	SE 1		SE	SE 1 A	SE 1	SE		SE 1 A	SE 1	SE	SE 1 A
Ashford International d	06 00	07 00	07 36			08 05	08 36		09 05		09 36		10 05	10 36			11 05	11 36			12 05	12 36		13 05
Charing d	06 08	07 08				08 13			09 13				10 13				11 13				12 13			13 13
Lenham d	06 13	07 13				08 18			09 18				10 18				11 18				12 18			13 18
Harrietsham d	06 16	07 16				08 21			09 21				10 21				11 21				12 21			13 21
Hollingbourne d	06 20	07 20				08 25			09 25				10 25				11 25				12 25			13 25
Bearsted d	06 24	07 24	07 52			08 29	08 52		09 29		09 52		10 29	10 52			11 29	11 52			12 29	12 52		13 29
Maidstone East 4 a	06 29	07 29	07 57			08 34	08 57		09 34		09 57		10 34	10 57			11 34	11 57			12 34	12 57		13 34
d	06 30	07 30	07 57	08 00		08 34	08 57	09 00	09 34		09 57	10 00	10 34	10 57		11 00	11 34	11 57	12 00		12 34	12 57	13 00	13 34
Barming d	06 34	07 34		08 04				09 04				10 04				11 04			12 04				13 04	
East Malling d	06 38	07 38		08 08				09 08				10 08				11 08			12 08				13 08	
West Malling d	06 40	07 40	08 05	08 10		08 42	09 05	09 10	09 42		10 05	10 10	10 42	11 05		11 10	11 42	12 05	12 10		12 42	13 05	13 10	13 42
Borough Green & Wrotham d	06 47	07 47		08 17		08 49		09 17	09 49			10 17	10 49			11 17	11 49		12 17		12 49		13 17	13 49
Kemsing d				08 22				09 22				10 22				11 22			12 22				13 22	
Otford 4 195 a	06 55	07 55		08 26		08 57		09 26	09 57			10 26	10 57			11 26	11 57		12 26		12 57		13 26	13 57
Swanley 4 195 a	07 04	08 04		08 35				09 35				10 35				11 35			12 35				13 35	
St Mary Cray 195 a	07 08	08 08																						
London Bridge 4 ⊖ a			08 50				09 50				10 50			11 50				12 50				13 50		
London Cannon Street 4 ⊖ a			08 54				09 54				10 54			11 54				12 54				13 54		
London Waterloo (East) 4 ⊖ a																								
London Charing Cross 4 ⊖ a																								
Bromley South 4 195 a	07 14	08 14		08 44		09 14		09 44	10 14			10 44	11 14			11 44	12 14		12 44		13 14		13 44	14 14
Beckenham Junction 4 195 a																								
Herne Hill 4 195 a																								
Elephant & Castle ⊖ 195 a																								
London Blackfriars 3 ⊖ 195 a																								
St Pancras International ⊖ 195 a																								
London Victoria 15 ⊖ 195 a	07 32	08 32		09 02		09 32		10 02	10 32			11 02	11 32			12 02	12 32		13 02		13 32		14 02	14 32

	SE 1	SE		SE 1 A	SE 1	SE	SE 1 A		SE 1	SE	SE 1 A	SE 1		SE	SE 1 A	SE 1	SE	SE 1 A	SE 1	SE 1	SE 1	SE 1		
Ashford International d	13 36			14 05	14 36		15 05		15 36		16 05	16 36			17 05	17 36		18 00	19 00	20 00	21 00	22 00		
Charing d				14 13			15 13				16 13				17 13			18 08	19 08	20 08	21 08	22 08		
Lenham d				14 18			15 18				16 18				17 18			18 13	19 13	20 13	21 13	22 13		
Harrietsham d				14 21			15 21				16 21				17 21			18 16	19 16	20 16	21 16	22 16		
Hollingbourne d				14 25			15 25				16 25				17 25			18 20	19 20	20 20	21 20	22 20		
Bearsted d	13 52			14 29	14 52		15 29		15 52		16 29	16 52			17 29	17 52		18 24	19 24	20 24	21 24	22 24		
Maidstone East 4 a	13 57			14 34	14 57		15 34		15 57		16 34	16 57			17 34	17 57		18 29	19 29	20 29	21 29	22 29		
d	13 57	14 00		14 34	14 57	15 00	15 34		15 57	16 00	16 34	16 57		17 00	17 34	17 57	18 00	18 30	19 30	20 30	21 30	22 30		
Barming d		14 04				15 04				16 04				17 04			18 04	18 34	19 34	20 34	21 34	22 34		
East Malling d		14 08				15 08				16 08				17 08			18 08	18 38	19 38	20 38	21 38	22 38		
West Malling d	14 05	14 10		14 42	15 05	15 10	15 42		16 05	16 10	16 42	17 05		17 10	17 42	18 05	18 10	18 40	19 40	20 40	21 40	22 40		
Borough Green & Wrotham d		14 17		14 49		15 17	15 49			16 17	16 49			17 17	17 49		18 17	18 47	19 47	20 47	21 47	22 47		
Kemsing d		14 22				15 22				16 22				17 22			18 22							
Otford 4 195 a		14 26		14 57		15 26	15 57			16 26	16 57			17 26	17 57		18 26	18 55	19 55	20 55	21 55	22 55		
Swanley 4 195 a		14 35				15 35				16 35				17 35			18 35	19 04	20 04	21 04	22 04	23 04		
St Mary Cray 195 a																		19 08	20 08	21 08	22 08	23 08		
London Bridge 4 ⊖ a	14 50				15 50				16 50			17 50				18 50								
London Cannon Street 4 ⊖ a	14 54				15 54				16 54			17 54				18 54								
London Waterloo (East) 4 ⊖ a																								
London Charing Cross 4 ⊖ a																								
Bromley South 4 195 a		14 44		15 14		15 44	16 14			16 44	17 14			17 44	18 14		18 44	19 14	20 14	21 14	22 14	23 14		
Beckenham Junction 4 195 a																								
Herne Hill 4 195 a																								
Elephant & Castle ⊖ 195 a																								
London Blackfriars 3 ⊖ 195 a																								
St Pancras International ⊖ 195 a																								
London Victoria 15 ⊖ 195 a		15 02		15 32		16 02	16 32			17 02	17 32			18 02	18 32		19 02	19 32	20 32	21 32	22 32	23 32		

For general notes see front of timetable
For details of catering facilities see
Directory of Train Operators

A From Canterbury West (Table 207)

Table 196

Sundays

Ashford International and Maidstone East to London

Network Diagram - see first page of Table 195

		SE 1	SE 1		SE 1	SE 1		SE 1	SE 1		SE 1	SE 1		SE 1	SE 1		SE 1	SE 1		SE 1	SE 1	SE 1	SE 1		
						A		A	A		A	A		A	A		A	A		A	A				
Ashford International	d	07 01	08 01		09 01	10 01		11 01	12 01		13 01	14 01		15 01	16 01		17 01	18 01		19 01	20 01	21 01	22 01		
Charing	d	07 09	08 09		09 09	10 09		11 09	12 09		13 09	14 09		15 09	16 09		17 09	18 09		19 09	20 09	21 09	22 09		
Lenham	d	07 14	08 14		09 14	10 14		11 14	12 14		13 14	14 14		15 14	16 14		17 14	18 14		19 14	20 14	21 14	22 14		
Harrietsham	d	07 17	08 17		09 17	10 17		11 17	12 17		13 17	14 17		15 17	16 17		17 17	18 17		19 17	20 17	21 17	22 17		
Hollingbourne	d	07 21	08 21		09 21	10 21		11 21	12 21		13 21	14 21		15 21	16 21		17 21	18 21		19 21	20 21	21 21	22 21		
Bearsted	d	07 25	08 25		09 25	10 25		11 25	12 25		13 25	14 25		15 25	16 25		17 25	18 25		19 25	20 25	21 25	22 25		
Maidstone East 4	a	07 30	08 30		09 30	10 30		11 30	12 30		13 30	14 30		15 30	16 30		17 30	18 30		19 30	20 30	21 30	22 30		
	d	07 30	08 30		09 30	10 30		11 30	12 30		13 30	14 30		15 30	16 30		17 30	18 30		19 30	20 30	21 30	22 30		
Barming	d	07 35	08 35		09 35	10 35		11 35	12 35		13 35	14 35		15 35	16 35		17 35	18 35		19 35	20 35	21 35	22 35		
East Malling	d	07 38	08 38		09 38	10 38		11 38	12 38		13 38	14 38		15 38	16 38		17 38	18 38		19 38	20 38	21 38	22 38		
West Malling	d	07 41	08 41		09 41	10 41		11 41	12 41		13 41	14 41		15 41	16 41		17 41	18 41		19 41	20 41	21 41	22 41		
Borough Green & Wrotham	d	07 48	08 48		09 48	10 48		11 48	12 48		13 48	14 48		15 48	16 48		17 48	18 48		19 48	20 48	21 48	22 48		
Kemsing	d																								
Otford 4	195 a	07 56	08 56		09 56	10 56		11 56	12 56		13 56	14 56		15 56	16 56		17 56	18 56		19 56	20 56	21 56	22 56		
Swanley 4	195 a	08 05	09 05		10 05	11 05		12 05	13 05		14 05	15 05		16 05	17 05		18 05	19 05		20 05	21 05	22 05	23 05		
St Mary Cray	195 a	08 10	09 10		10 10	11 10		12 10	13 10		14 10	15 10		16 10	17 10		18 10	19 10		20 10	21 10	22 10	23 10		
London Bridge 4	⊖ a																								
London Cannon Street 4	⊖ a																								
London Waterloo (East) 4	⊖ a																								
London Charing Cross 4	⊖ a																								
Bromley South 4	195 a	08 16	09 16		10 16	11 16		12 16	13 16		14 16	15 16		16 16	17 16		18 16	19 16		20 16	21 16	22 16	23 16		
Beckenham Junction 4	195 🚋 a																								
Herne Hill 4	195 a																								
Elephant & Castle	⊖ 195 a																								
London Blackfriars 3	⊖ 195 a																								
St Pancras International	⊖ 195 a																								
London Victoria 15	⊖ 195 a	08 32	09 32		10 32	11 32		12 32	13 32		14 32	15 32		16 32	17 32		18 32	19 32		20 32	21 32	22 32	23 32		

For general notes see front of timetable
For details of catering facilities see Directory of Train Operators

A From Canterbury West (Table 207)

London → Lewisham, Hither Green, Petts Wood and Orpington (Summary of Services)

For details of Bank Holiday service alterations please see first page of Table 195

		SE MX	SE MO	SE MX	SE MX	SE MO	SE MX	SE MO	SE MO	SE MX 50	SE MX 02	SN MX	SE	SE 14	SE	SE	SE	SE	FC 1	SE	SE	SE 1	SE	SE	SE
London Charing Cross 4	⊖ d	23p26	23p26			23p47	23p52	23p53	23p56	00 04	00 10	00 12	00 14	00 48	04 50	04 56	05 04	05 18			05 26	05 30		05 34	05 40
London Waterloo (East) 4	⊖ d	23p29	23p29			23p50	23p55	23p56	23p59	00 07	00 13	00 15	00 17	00 51	04 53	04 59	05 07	05 21			05 29	05 33		05 37	05 43
London Cannon Street 4	⊖ d																								
London Blackfriars 3	⊖ d																		05 24						
London Bridge 4	⊖ d	23p34	23p35			23p55	23p58	00 02	00 05	00 13	00 18	00a19	00 23	00 56	04 58	05 04	05a11	05b28	05a30		05 34	05 38		05 42	05 48
London Victoria 15	⊖ d			23p42	23p53																		05 36		
New Cross 4	⊖ d					23p59	00 04	00 07		00 18			00 28	01 01	05 03	05 09		05 33		05 37	05 39				05 53
St Johns	d						00 06	00 09																	
Lewisham 4	a	23p42	23p44			00 03	00 08	00 11	00 14	00 22			00 32	01 05	05 07	05 13		05 37		05 41	05 43			05 51	05 57
Hither Green 4	a	23p47	23p49			00 08			00 19	00 27				01 09	05 11			05 41							06 01
Petts Wood 4	a	00 01	00 01	00 20	00 25				00 31		00 39			01 23									06 10		06 13
Orpington 4	a	00 03	00 04	00 24	00 28				00 34		00 42			01 26								05 54	06 13		06 16

		FC 1	SE	SE	SE	SE	SE	SE	SE	SN	SE	FC 1	SE 1	SE	SE	SE 1	SE	SE	SE 1	SE	SE	FC 1	SE	SE	SE
London Charing Cross 4	⊖ d		05 46		05 49	05 54		06 02		06 05			06 16		06 20	06 25		06 27			06 32		06 40		06 47
London Waterloo (East) 4	⊖ d		05 49		05 52	05 57		06 05		06 08			06 19		06 23	06 28		06 30			06 35		06 43		06 50
London Cannon Street 4	⊖ d			05 50					06 06		06 12			06 22			06 30							06 48	
London Blackfriars 3	⊖ d	05 44										06 14										06 34			
London Bridge 4	⊖ d	05a50	05 54	05a53	05 57	06a01		06 10	06a09	06a12	06 16	06a20	06 24	06a25	06 28	06 33	06a33	06 35			06 40	06a42	06 48	06 52	06 56
London Victoria 15	⊖ d						06 04													06 36					
New Cross 4	⊖ d		05 59					06 15							06 33			06 41			06 47				
St Johns	d		06 01					06 17										06 43							
Lewisham 4	a		06 03		06 05			06 19			06 23				06 37			06 45	←		06 51		06 55	06 59	
Hither Green 4	a		06 07										06 33 →		06 41				06 33					07 03	07 06
Petts Wood 4	a						06 39												06 46	07 10					07 22
Orpington 4	a						06 42									06 49			06 50	07 13					07 25

		SE	FC 1	SE	SE	SE	SE 1	SE	SE	SE	FC 1	SE	SE 1	SE	SE	SE	SE	SE	SE	SE 1	SE	FC 1	SE	SE	SE 1
London Charing Cross 4	⊖ d			06 51	06 54		07 00	07 03	07 06			07 10	07 16			07 20	07 22			07 28	07 30			07 37	
London Waterloo (East) 4	⊖ d			06 54	06 57		07 03	07 06	07 09			07 13	07 19			07 23	07 25			07 31	07 33			07 40	
London Cannon Street 4	⊖ d	06 52				07 04				07 10					07 22			07 32					07 39		07 45
London Blackfriars 3	⊖ d		06 50								07 10											07 32			
London Bridge 4	⊖ d	06a55	06a56	06 59	07a02	07 08	07 08	07 11	07a13	07 14	07a16	07 19	07 24		07 26	07 28	07a29	07a35		07 36	07 38	07a39	07 43	07 45	07 49
London Victoria 15	⊖ d													07 06											
New Cross 4	⊖ d			07 05		07 13				07 20						07 33					07 43		07 49		
St Johns	d			07 07		07 15				07 22											07 45				
Lewisham 4	a			07 09		07 17		07 21		07 24					07 33	07 37			←		07 47		07 53		
Hither Green 4	a											07 29 →				07 41			07 29				07 57	07 53 →	
Petts Wood 4	a													07 40					07 42						
Orpington 4	a						07 25						07 40	07 43					07 45	07 54					08 08

		SE	SE	SE	SE	SE	SE	SE 1	SE	SE	FC	SE	SE	SE	SE	SE 1	SE	FC 1		SE	SE 1	SE	SE	SE	SE 1
London Charing Cross 4	⊖ d	07 42		07 45				07 52		07 56				08 00	08 03	08 08					08 14			08 20	08 22
London Waterloo (East) 4	⊖ d	07 45		07 48				07 55		07 59				08 03	08 06	08 11					08 17			08 23	08 25
London Cannon Street 4	⊖ d		07 48				07 54		07 58			08 03					08 14			08 17		08 20			
London Blackfriars 3	⊖ d										07 52							08 12							
London Bridge 4	⊖ d	07 50	07a51	07 53			07 58	08 02	08 02	08 04		08 07		08 09	08a10	08 16	08 18	08a18		08 21	08a22	08 24		08 28	08 30
London Victoria 15	⊖ d					07 37							08 06										08 21		
New Cross 4	⊖ d			07 59			08 03		08 07			08 12					08 23			08 26		08 29			
St Johns	d			08 01			08 05										08 25					08 31			
Lewisham 4	a			08 04	←		08 07		08 11			08 16					08 27			08 31		08 33	08 43		
Hither Green 4	a	08 01			07 53							08 20		08 18		08 27								08 37 →	
Petts Wood 4	a				08 09	08 12					08 29	08 33	08 41												
Orpington 4	a				08 12	08 15		08 19		08 24	08 33	08 36	08 44												08 47

		SE	SE	SE	SE	SE	SE	SE	SE	SE	SE	SE 1	SE	SE	SE	SE	SE	SE 1	SE	SE	SE	FC 1	SE	SE 1	SE
London Charing Cross 4	⊖ d		08 24	08 26	08 28	08 29		08 36			08 38		08 41	08 44			08 52	08 54	08 56					08 58	
London Waterloo (East) 4	⊖ d		08 27	08 29	08 31	08 32		08 39			08 41		08 44	08 47			08 55	08 57	08 59					09 01	
London Cannon Street 4	⊖ d	08 26					08 34			08 40		08 45			08 50	08 54							09 02		
London Blackfriars 3	⊖ d																					08 59			←
London Bridge 4	⊖ d	08 30	08a31	08a33	08 36	08 38	08 38	08a43		08 44	08 46	08 49	08a49	08 52	08 54	08 58	08a59	09a01	09 04 →			09a05	09 06	09 08	09 04
London Victoria 15	⊖ d																				08 36				
New Cross 4	⊖ d				08 42		08 45			08 49						09 05							09 11		
St Johns	d						08 47			08 51						09 07									
Lewisham 4	a				08 46		08 49		←	08 53					09 02	09 09				←			09 15		
Hither Green 4	a	08 41					08 53		08 37		08 55 →			09 02						08 55					09 15
Petts Wood 4	a								08 50											09 09	09 12			09 23	09 30
Orpington 4	a					08 55			08 56			09 07								09 12	09 15			09 26	09 33

For general notes see front of timetable
For details of catering facilities see Directory of Train Operators

b Arr. 0525

London → Lewisham, Hither Green, Petts Wood and Orpington (Summary of Services)

For details of Bank Holiday service alterations please see first page of Table 195

		SE	SE	SE	SE 1	SE 1	SE	SE	FC 1	SE	SE	SE	SE	SE	SE	SE 1	SE	SE	SE	SE	SE	SE	FC 1	SE	SE
London Charing Cross 4	⊖ d	09 02						09 14			09 15		09 20	09 26		09 30				09 32				09 36	
London Waterloo (East) 4	⊖ d	09 06						09 17			09 20		09 23	09 29		09 33				09 35				09 39	
London Cannon Street 4	⊖ d			09 10	09 13	09 17				09 20		09 24			09 30			09 34							09 42
London Blackfriars 3	⊖ d								09 16														09 34		
London Bridge 4	⊖ d	09 12		09a13	09a16	09 21		09a21	09a23	09 24	09 26	09 28	09a29	09 34	09 34	09 38		09 38		09 40			09a41	09a44	09a45
London Victoria 15	⊖ d		09 01				09 06										09 21				09 31	09 36			
New Cross 4	⊖ d									09 29		09 35						09 44							
St Johns	d									09 31		09 37							←						
Lewisham 4	a	09 19	09 25							09 33	09 35	09 39		09 42 →				09 47	09 42	09 49	09 52				
Hither Green 4	a	09 23								09 37									09 47	09 53					
Petts Wood 4	a						09 39										09 54		10 00			10 09			
Orpington 4	a					09 39	09 42									09 54	09 57		10 03			10 13			

		SE	SE 1	SE	FC 1	SE	SE	SE	SE	SE	SE	SE	SE	SE	SE	FC 1	SE	SE	SE 1	SE	SE 1	SE	SE	FC 1	SE
London Charing Cross 4	⊖ d		09 45	09 48			09 52	09 56		10 00				10 02				10 06			10 15		10 17		
London Waterloo (East) 4	⊖ d		09 48	09 51			09 55	09 59		10 03				10 05				10 09			10 18		10 20		
London Cannon Street 4	⊖ d	09 48				09 54			10 00			10 04					10 10		10 14	10 18					10 24
London Blackfriars 3	⊖ d				09 50											10 05								10 20	
London Bridge 4	⊖ d	09 52	09a52	09 57	09a57	09 58	09a59	10 04	10 04	10 08		10 08		10 10		10a11	10a13	10a14	10a17	10 22	10 23		10 25	10a26	10 28
London Victoria 15	⊖ d										09 51				10 01							10 06			
New Cross 4	⊖ d	09 57				10 05						10 14								10 27					10 33
St Johns	d	09 59				10 07							←							10 29					10 35
Lewisham 4	a			10 05		10 09		10 12 →				10 17	10 12	10 19	10 22								10 34		10 37
Hither Green 4	a	10 05											10 17	10 23						10 35					
Petts Wood 4	a									10 22	10 26		10 30									10 39			
Orpington 4	a									10 25	10 29		10 33								10 39	10 42			

		SE	SE	SE	SE 1	SE	SE	SE	SE	SE	SE	FC 1	SE	SE		SN 1		SE	SE 1	SE	FC 1	SE	SE	SE	SE
London Charing Cross 4	⊖ d	10 20	10 26		10 30				10 32					10 36		10 40			10 45	10 47			10 50	10 56	
London Waterloo (East) 4	⊖ d	10 23	10 29		10 33				10 35					10 39		10 43			10 48	10 50			10 53	10 59	
London Cannon Street 4	⊖ d			10 30			10 34						10 40					10 48				10 54			11 00
London Blackfriars 3	⊖ d											10 35									10 50				
London Bridge 4	⊖ d	10a28	10 34	10 34	10 38		10 38		10 40			10a41	10a43	10a44		10a47		10 52	10a52	10 55	10a56	10 58	10a58	11 04	11 04
London Victoria 15	⊖ d					10 21				10 31	10 36														
New Cross 4	⊖ d						10 44											10 57				11 03			
St Johns	d							←										10 59				11 05			
Lewisham 4	a		10 42 →				10 47	10 42	10 49	10 52										11 04		11 07		11 12 →	
Hither Green 4	a							10 47	10 53									11 05							
Petts Wood 4	a					10 54		11 00			11 09														
Orpington 4	a				10 53	10 57		11 03			11 12														

		SE 1	SE	SE	SE	SE	SE	FC 1	SE	SE	SN 1	SE 1	SE	SE 1	SE	SE	FC 1	SE	SE	SE	SE	SE 1	SE	SE	SE
London Charing Cross 4	⊖ d	11 00				11 02				11 06	11 10			11 15		11 17			11 20	11 26		11 30			
London Waterloo (East) 4	⊖ d	11 03				11 05				11 09	11 13			11 18		11 20			11 23	11 29		11 33			
London Cannon Street 4	⊖ d			11 04					11 10			11 14	11 18					11 24			11 30			11 34	
London Blackfriars 3	⊖ d							11 05									11 20								
London Bridge 4	⊖ d	11 08		11 08		11 10		11a11	11a13	11a14	11a17	11a17	11 22	11 23		11 25	11a26	11 28	11a28	11 34	11 34	11 38		11 38	
London Victoria 15	⊖ d		10 51				11 01								11 06								11 21		
New Cross 4	⊖ d			11 14									11 27					11 33						11 44	
St Johns	d				←								11 29					11 35							←
Lewisham 4	a			11 17	11 12	11 19	11 22									11 34		11 37		11 42 →				11 47	11 42
Hither Green 4	a				11 17	11 23							11 35												11 47
Petts Wood 4	a	11 22	11 24		11 30										11 39								11 54		12 00
Orpington 4	a	11 25	11 27		11 33									11 39	11 42							11 53	11 57		12 03

		SE	SE	SE	FC 1	SE	SE	SN 1	and at	SE	SE 1	SE	FC 1	SE	SE	SE	SE	SE	SE	SE 1	SE	FC 1	SE	SE
London Charing Cross 4	⊖ d	11 32					11 36	11 40	the same		15 45	15 47			15 50		15 56			16 00	16 02		16 06	
London Waterloo (East) 4	⊖ d	11 35					11 39	11 43			15 48	15 50			15 53		15 59			16 03	16 05		16 09	
London Cannon Street 4	⊖ d					11 40			minutes	15 48				15 54				16 00						16 10
London Blackfriars 3	⊖ d				11 35								15 50									16 05		
London Bridge 4	⊖ d	11 40			11a41	11a43	11a44	11a47	past	15 52	15a52	15 55	15a56	15 58	15 59		16 04	16a03		16a07	16 10	16a11	16 14	16 14
London Victoria 15	⊖ d		11 31	11 36												15 51			16 06					
New Cross 4	⊖ d								each	15 57				16 03							16 16			16 20
St Johns	d									15 59				16 05										16 22
Lewisham 4	a	11 49	11 52						hour until			16 04		16 07	16 09		16 12				16 19		16 22	16 26
Hither Green 4	a	11 53								16 04							16 17				16 23			16 31
Petts Wood 4	a			12 09												16 24	16 29		16 39					
Orpington 4	a			12 12												16 27	16 32		16b44					

For general notes see front of timetable
For details of catering facilities see
Directory of Train Operators

b Until 9 October arr 2 minutes earlier

London → Lewisham, Hither Green, Petts Wood and Orpington (Summary of Services)

For details of Bank Holiday service alterations please see first page of Table 195

Station		SN 1	SE 1	SE	SE	SE 1	SE	SE	FC 1	SE	SE	SE	FC	SE 1	SE	SE	SE	SE 1	SE	SE	FC 1	SE	SE	SE 1	SE
London Charing Cross 4	⊖ d	16 08		16 11		16 15	16 16			16 21				16 23		16 25	16 26	16 30	16 33				16 37		16 42
London Waterloo (East) 4	⊖ d	16 11		16 14		16 18	16 19			16 24				16 26		16 28	16 29	16 33	16 36				16 40		16 45
London Cannon Street 4	⊖ d		16 14		16 18			16 22							16 28					16 38		16 42		16 44	
London Blackfriars 3	⊖ d								16 20				16 26								16 36				
London Bridge 4	⊖ d	16a15	16a17	16 19	16a21	16a22	16 25	16 26	16a26	16 29				16a30	16a31	16 33	16 34	16a38	16 41	16 42	16a43	16 46	16b48	16a47	16 50
London Victoria 15	⊖ d										16 14	16 26													
New Cross 4	⊖ d			16 25																					
St Johns	d															16 39				16 49					
Lewisham 4	a			16 28												16 41				16 51					
Hither Green 4	a							16 34		16 37	16 40						16 44		16 50	16 53		16 55	16 58		
Petts Wood 4	a							16 39								16 46				16 57					
Orpington 4	a						16 43 16c49	16 51 16 55				17 00 17e06	17 06 17 12												17 02 17 15 17 21

Station		SE	SE	SE 1	SE	SE	SE 1	SE	SE	SE	SE	SE 1	SE		SE	SE	SE	SE	SE	SE	SE	SE	SE	SE	SE
London Charing Cross 4	⊖ d		16 44	16 46	16 48		16 50	16 52			16 55		16 58			17 00				17 04	17 06				
London Waterloo (East) 4	⊖ d		16 47	16 49	16 51		16 53	16 55			16 58		17 01			17 03				17 07	17 09				
London Cannon Street 4	⊖ d	16 46				16 52			16 56			17 00			17 02		17 04		17 06			17 10	17 14		17 16
London Blackfriars 3	⊖ d																								
London Bridge 4	⊖ d	16 50	16a51	16a53	16a55	16 56	16a57	16a59	17 00		17 03	17a03	17 06		17a05	17 08	17 08		17a09	17 12	17a13	17 14	17 18		17 20
London Victoria 15	⊖ d									16 51								17 00						17 12	
New Cross 4	⊖ d	16 56				17 02																			
St Johns	d	16 58															17 16					17 20			17 26
Lewisham 4	a	17 01				17 05											17 18					17 22			
Hither Green 4	a										17 14					17 17	17 20	17 23				17 25			17 29
Petts Wood 4	a												17 16							17 22		17 30			
Orpington 4	a								17 21 17 24	17 25 17c30										17 35 17c42			17 43 17 46	17 49 17 53	

Station		SE	SE	SE	SE 1	SE	SE	SE	SE	FC 1	SE	SE	SE	SE	SE	SE	SE	SE	SE 1	SE	SE	SE	SE	FC 1	SE 1
London Charing Cross 4	⊖ d	17 14	17 18		17 20		17 21				17 28		17 29				17 37		17 41			17 43			
London Waterloo (East) 4	⊖ d	17 17	17 21		17 23		17 24				17 31		17 32				17 40		17 44			17 46			
London Cannon Street 4	⊖ d			17 22		17 24		17 26				17 32		17 36	17 40			17 42		17 46			17 48		17 50
London Blackfriars 3	⊖ d									17 22														17 46	
London Bridge 4	⊖ d	17a21	17 26	17 26	17a27	17a27	17 30	17 30		17a31		17 36	17a38	17 40	17 44		17 45	17 46	17a48	17 50		17 51	17a51	17a52	17a53
London Victoria 15	⊖ d								17 19							17 35					17 41				
New Cross 4	⊖ d			17 32																					
St Johns	d											17 42		17 47				17 52							
Lewisham 4	a		17 35									17 44													
Hither Green 4	a						17 40	17 38	17 43			17 46		17 50			17 53	17 56		17 59	18 05				
Petts Wood 4	a										17 46			17 55								18 00			
Orpington 4	a			17 51 17 57							17 58 18c05				18 05 18 08	18 09 18 15									

Station		SE	SE	SE	SE	SE	SE	SE	SE	SE	SE 1	SE	SE 1	SE	SE	SE 1	SE	SE	SE	SE	SE	SE	SE	SE	SE
London Charing Cross 4	⊖ d		17 49		17 54				17 58			18 01	18 04		18 05		18 08			18 12			18 14		
London Waterloo (East) 4	⊖ d		17 52		17 57				18 01			18 04	18 07		18 08		18 11			18 15			18 17		
London Cannon Street 4	⊖ d	17 52		17 56		18 00				18 02	18 05			18 08		18 10		18 12			18 16			18 19	18 22
London Blackfriars 3	⊖ d																								
London Bridge 4	⊖ d	17 56	17 57	18 00	18a01	18 04			18a05	18 06	18a08	18 10	18a11	18a11	18 14	18a13	18 16	18 16			18 20		18a21	18 23	18 26
London Victoria 15	⊖ d						17 52	18 02											18 08			18 21			
New Cross 4	⊖ d	18 02		18 06																					
St Johns	d	18 04		18 08														18 22			18 26				18 32
Lewisham 4	a	18 07		18 11														18 24							
Hither Green 4	a		18 07	18 16						18 14		18 19			18 23			18 26	18 28		18 30			18 32	18 35
Petts Wood 4	a																18 26			18 29					18 40
Orpington 4	a		18 19 18c26			18 25 18 29	18 29 18 33	18 35 18c41												18 43 18e49	18 46 18 51	18 56 19 01			

Station		FC 1	SE 1	SE	SE	SE 1	SE 1	SE	SE	SE	SE	SE 1	SE	SE 1	SE	SE	SE	SE	SE	FC 1	SE	SE	SE	SE	SE 1
London Charing Cross 4	⊖ d			18 23	18 25		18 28	18 30	18 32		18 34	18 40	18 42				18 46				18 52	18 54	18 56		19 00
London Waterloo (East) 4	⊖ d			18 26	18 28		18 31	18 33	18 35		18 37	18 43	18 45				18 49				18 55	18 57	18 59		19 03
London Cannon Street 4	⊖ d		18 26			18 30				18 36				18 46					18 50					19 02	
London Blackfriars 3	⊖ d	18 20																		18 50					
London Bridge 4	⊖ d	18a26	18a29	18 31	18 34	18a33	18a35	18 38	18 40	18 40	18a41	18 48	18 50	18a49			18 54		18 54	18a56	19 00	19 02	19a03	19 06	19a07
London Victoria 15	⊖ d															18 38		18 46							
New Cross 4	⊖ d																								
St Johns	d									18 46							19 00							19 12	
Lewisham 4	a									18 48														19 14	
Hither Green 4	a			18 40	18 43			18 46		18 51			18 59		←		19 04	19 08				19 11		19 16	
Petts Wood 4	a								18 50 →	18 56					18 50						19 10				
Orpington 4	a											19 04			19 04 19 10	19 12 19e17			19 17 19e23		19 23 19 27				

For general notes see front of timetable
For details of catering facilities see Directory of Train Operators

b Arr. 1645
c Until 9 October arr 1 minute earlier
e Until 9 October arr 2 minutes earlier

London → Lewisham, Hither Green, Petts Wood and Orpington (Summary of Services)

For details of Bank Holiday service alterations please see first page of Table 195

		SE 1	SE	SE	SE	FC 1	SE	SE	SE 1		SE	SE	SE 1	SE	SE	FC 1	SE	SE	SE 1	SE	SE	SE	SE 1	SE	SE
London Charing Cross 4	⊖ d				19 02		19 06				19 11		19 15	19 17			19 21		19 24		19 26			19 30	
London Waterloo (East) 4	⊖ d				19 05		19 09				19 14		19 18	19 20			19 24		19 27		19 29			19 33	
London Cannon Street 4	⊖ d	19 06						19 10	19 14			19 18			19 22			19 26		19 28			19 32		
London Blackfriars 3	⊖ d					19 04										19 20									
London Bridge 4	⊖ d	19 10			19 10	19a11	19 14	19a13	19a17		19a18	19 22	19a22	19 25	19 26	19a26	19 29	19 30	19a31	19a31	19 34		19a35	19 38	
London Victoria 15	⊖ d		18 51	19 06																		19 16			19 22
New Cross 4	⊖ d						19 20								19 31			19 35							
St Johns	d						19 22								19 33			19 37							
Lewisham 4	a				19 21		19 24					19 30		19 34			19 37	19 39			19 42 →	19 44			
Hither Green 4	a				19 25							19 35			19 37										
Petts Wood 4	a		19 26	19 41								19 48													19 55
Orpington 4	a	19 27	19 31	19 44								19 52												19 54	19 58

		SE	FC 1	SE	SE	SE	SE	SN	SE	SE	SE	SE 1	SE	SE	SE	SE	SE 1	FC 1	SE 81	SE	SE	SE	SE 1	FC 1	SE
London Charing Cross 4	⊖ d					19 34		19 37	19 38	19 41		19 45	19 47		19 50		19 52				19 56		20 00		20 04
London Waterloo (East) 4	⊖ d					19 37		19 40	19 41	19 44		19 48	19 50		19 53		19 55				19 59		20 03		20 07
London Cannon Street 4	⊖ d	19 36					19 40				19 48			19 52		19 56			20 00						
London Blackfriars 3	⊖ d		19 34															19 54						20 04	
London Bridge 4	⊖ d	19 40	19a40			19 43	19a43	19a44	19 46	19a48	19 52	19a52	19 55	19 56	19 59	20 00	20a00	20a01	20a03		20 04		20a07	20a10	20 13
London Victoria 15	⊖ d				19 37															19 52		19 46			
New Cross 4	⊖ d	19 45				19 48			19 52					20 01		20 05									20 18
St Johns	d	19 47		←					19 54					20 04		20 07									
Lewisham 4	a	19 49		19 42		19 52			19 56		20 00		20 03		20 07	20 09					20 12	20 14			20 22
Hither Green 4	a			19 47		19 57					20 05			20 09							20 17				20 27
Petts Wood 4	a			19 59	20 11						20 17									20 26	20 29				
Orpington 4	a			20 02	20 14						20 20									20 29	20 32				

		SN	SE	SE	SE 1	SE	SE	SE	SE	SE	SE 1	SE	SE	SE	FC 1	SE	SN	SE	SE 1	SE	SE	SE	SE	SE	SE 1
London Charing Cross 4	⊖ d	20 07	20 10		20 15	20 17	20 20	20 22	20 26		20 30					20 34	20 37	20 40	20 45	20 47	20 50	20 52	20 56		21 00
London Waterloo (East) 4	⊖ d	20 10	20 13		20 18	20 20	20 23	20 25	20 29		20 33					20 37	20 40	20 43	20 48	20 50	20 53	20 55	20 59		21 03
London Cannon Street 4	⊖ d			20 15						20 30				20 35										21 00	
London Blackfriars 3	⊖ d														20 34										
London Bridge 4	⊖ d	20a14	20a17	20a18	20 23	20 25	20 29	20 30	20 34	20a33	20 38			20 39	20a40	20 43	20a44	20a47	20 53	20 55	20 59	21 00	21 04	21a03	21 08
London Victoria 15	⊖ d											20 22													
New Cross 4	⊖ d					20 30		20 35						20 44		20 48				21 00		21 05			
St Johns	d							20 37					←	20 46								21 07			
Lewisham 4	a					20 34	20 37	20 39	20 42 →				20 42	20 48		20 52				21 04	21 07	21 09	21 12 →		
Hither Green 4	a												20 47	20 53		20 57									
Petts Wood 4	a											20 55	21 00	21 05											
Orpington 4	a				20 40						20 54	20 58	21 03	21 10					21 10						21 24

		SE	FC 1	SE	SE	SN	SE	SE 1	SE	SE	SE	SE	SE 1	SE	FC 1	SE	SE	SN	SE	SE 1	SE	SE	SE	SE	SE 1
London Charing Cross 4	⊖ d				21 04	21 07	21 10	21 15	21 17	21 20	21 22	21 26	21 30				21 34	21 37	21 40	21 45	21 47	21 50	21 52	21 56	22 00
London Waterloo (East) 4	⊖ d				21 07	21 10	21 13	21 18	21 20	21 23	21 25	21 29	21 33				21 37	21 40	21 43	21 48	21 50	21 53	21 55	21 59	22 03
London Cannon Street 4	⊖ d																								
London Blackfriars 3	⊖ d		21 04												21 34										
London Bridge 4	⊖ d		21a10		21 13	21a14	21a17	21 23	21 25	21 29	21 30	21 34	21 38		21a40		21 43	21a44	21a47	21 53	21 55	21 59	22 00	22 04	22 08
London Victoria 15	⊖ d	20 52												21 22											
New Cross 4	⊖ d				21 18				21 30		21 35						21 48				22 00		22 05		
St Johns	d			←							21 37					←							22 07		
Lewisham 4	a			21 12	21 22				21 34	21 37	21 39	21 42 →				21 42	21 52				22 04	22 07	22 09	22 12 →	
Hither Green 4	a			21 17	21 27											21 47	21 57								
Petts Wood 4	a	21 24		21 29										21 55		22 00									
Orpington 4	a	21 27		21 32				21 40					21 54	21 58		22 03				22 10					22 24

		SE	FC 1	SE	SE	SN	SE	SE 1	SE	SE	SE	SE	SE 1	SE	SE	SE	SN	SE	SE 1	SE	SE	SE	SE	SE	SE 2 1
London Charing Cross 4	⊖ d				22 04	22 07	22 10	22 15	22 17	22 20	22 22	22 26	22 30			22 34	22 37	22 40	22 45		22 47	22 50	22 52	22 56	23 00
London Waterloo (East) 4	⊖ d				22 07	22 10	22 13	22 18	22 20	22 23	22 25	22 29	22 33			22 37	22 40	22 43	22 48		22 50	22 53	22 55	22 59	23 03
London Cannon Street 4	⊖ d																								
London Blackfriars 3	⊖ d		22 04																						
London Bridge 4	⊖ d		22a10		22 13	22a14	22a17	22 23	22 25	22 29	22 30	22 34	22 38			22 43	22a44	22a47	22 53		22 55	22 59	23 00	23 04	23 08
London Victoria 15	⊖ d	21 52												22 22						22 42					
New Cross 4	⊖ d				22 18				22 30		22 35					22 48					23 00		23 05		
St Johns	d			←							22 37				←								23 07		
Lewisham 4	a			22 12	22 22				22 34	22 37	22 39	22 42 →			22 42	22 52					23 04	23 07	23 09	23 12 →	
Hither Green 4	a			22 17	22 27										22 47	22 57									
Petts Wood 4	a	22 25		22 30										22 55	23 00					23 20					
Orpington 4	a	22 28		22 33				22 40					22 54	22 58	23 03				23 10	23 24					23 24

For general notes see front of timetable
For details of catering facilities see Directory of Train Operators

London → Lewisham, Hither Green, Petts Wood and Orpington (Summary of Services)

For details of Bank Holiday service alterations please see first page of Table 195

		SE	SE	SE	SN	SE	SE	SE	SE	SE	SE	SE	SE	SE	SE	SE	SE	SE	SE	SN	SE	SE	SE
							1						2 1					1					
London Charing Cross 4	⊖ d			23 04	23 07	23 10	23 15		23 17	23 20	23 22	23 26	23 30				23 34	23 37	23 40	23 45		23 47	23 52
London Waterloo (East) 4	⊖ d			23 07	23 10	23 13	23 18		23 20	23 23	23 25	23 29	23 33				23 37	23 40	23 43	23 48		23 50	23 55
London Cannon Street 4	⊖ d																						
London Blackfriars 3	⊖ d																						
London Bridge 4	⊖ d			23 13	23a14	23a17	23 23		23 25	23 29	23 30	23 34	23 38				23 43	23a44	23a47	23a52		23 55	23 58
London Victoria 15	⊖ d	22 52						23 12						23 22		23 42					23 53		
New Cross 4	⊖ d			23 18					23 30		23 35						23 48					23 58	00 04
St Johns	d		←								23 37				←								00 06
Lewisham 4	a		23 12	23 22					23 34	23 37	23 39	23 42 →			23 42		23 52					00 04	00 08
Hither Green 4	a		23 17	23 27											23 47		23 57						
Petts Wood 4	a	23 26	23 30					23 50						23 55	00 01	00 20					00 25		
Orpington 4	a	23 30	23 33				23 40	23 54					23 56	23 58	00 03	00 24					00 28		

Saturdays

		SE	SE	SE	SE	SE	SE	SN	SE	SE	SE	SE	SE	SE	SE	SE	SE	SE	SE	SE	SE	SE	SE	SE	SE
							1											1							
London Charing Cross 4	⊖ d	23p26			23p52	00 04	00 10	00 12	00 14	00 48	05 04	05 34	05 40	05 47	05 50	05 52	05 56	06 00			06 04	06 10	06 17	06 20	06 22
London Waterloo (East) 4	⊖ d	23p29			23p55	00 07	00 13	00 15	00 17	00 51	05 07	05 37	05 43	05 50	05 53	05 55	05 59	06 03			06 07	06 13	06 20	06 23	06 25
London Cannon Street 4	⊖ d																								
London Blackfriars 3	⊖ d																								
London Bridge 4	⊖ d	23p34			23p58	00 13	00 18	00a19	00 23	00 56	05 13	05 43	05a47	05 55	05 59	06 01	06 04	06 08			06 13	06a17	06 25	06 29	06 31
London Victoria 15	⊖ d		23p42	23p53															05 51						
New Cross 4	⊖ d				00 04	00 18			00 28	01 01	05 18	05 48				06 06					06 18				06 36
St Johns	d				00 06											06 08				←					06 38
Lewisham 4	a	23p42			00 08	00 22			00 32	01 05	05 22	05 52		06 04	06 06	06 10	06 12 →			06 12	06 22		06 34	06 36	06 40
Hither Green 4	a	23p47				00 27				01 09	05 27	05 57								06 17	06 27				
Petts Wood 4	a	00 01	00 20	00 25			00 39			01 23									06 24	06 30					
Orpington 4	a	00 03	00 24	00 28			00 42			01 26								06 26	06 27	06 33					

		SE	SE	SE		SE	SE	SE	SE	SE	SE	SE	SE	SE	SE	SE	SE	SE	SE	SE	SE	SE	SN	SE	SE
										1									1				1		1
London Charing Cross 4	⊖ d	06 26	06 34	06 40		06 47	06 50	06 52	06 56	07 00			07 04	07 10	07 17	07 20	07 22	07 26	07 30			07 34	07 40	07 42	07 45
London Waterloo (East) 4	⊖ d	06 29	06 37	06 43		06 50	06 53	06 55	06 59	07 03			07 07	07 13	07 20	07 23	07 25	07 29	07 33			07 37	07 43	07 45	07 48
London Cannon Street 4	⊖ d																								
London Blackfriars 3	⊖ d																								
London Bridge 4	⊖ d	06 34	06 43	06a47		06 55	06 59	07 01	07 04	07 08			07 13	07a17	07 25	07 29	07 31	07 34	07 38			07 43	07a47	07a49	07 53
London Victoria 15	⊖ d										06 51									07 21					
New Cross 4	⊖ d		06 48					07 06					07 18				07 36					07 48			
St Johns	d							07 08				←					07 38				←				
Lewisham 4	a	06 42	06 52			07 04	07 06	07 10	07 12 →			07 12	07 22		07 34	07 36	07 40	07 42 →			07 42	07 52			
Hither Green 4	a	06 47	06 57									07 17	07 27								07 47	07 57			
Petts Wood 4	a	07 00									07 24	07 30								07 54	08 00				
Orpington 4	a	07 03								07 26	07 27	07 33							07 55	07 57	08 03				08 09

		SE	SE	SE	SE	SE	SE	SE		SE	SE	SE	SN	SE	SE	SE	SE	SE	SE	SE	SE	SE	SE	SE	SE
						1							1	1							1				
London Charing Cross 4	⊖ d	07 47	07 50	07 52	07 56	08 00				08 02			08 10	08 15		08 17	08 20	08 22	08 26		08 30			08 32	
London Waterloo (East) 4	⊖ d	07 50	07 53	07 55	07 59	08 03				08 05			08 13	08 18		08 20	08 23	08 25	08 29		08 33			08 35	
London Cannon Street 4	⊖ d											08 10								08 30					
London Blackfriars 3	⊖ d																								
London Bridge 4	⊖ d	07 55	07 59	08 01	08 04	08 08				08 10		08a13	08a17	08 23		08 25	08 29	08 31	08 34	08 34	08 38			08 40	
London Victoria 15	⊖ d						07 51				08 01				08 06							08 21			08 31
New Cross 4	⊖ d			08 06						08 15								08 36						08 45	
St Johns	d			08 08				←										08 38					←		
Lewisham 4	a	08 04	08 06	08 10	08 12 →			08 12		08 19	08 22					08 33	08 36	08 40	08 42 →				08 42	08 49	08 52
Hither Green 4	a							08 17		08 23													08 47	08 53	
Petts Wood 4	a						08 24	08 30							08 39							08 54	09 00		
Orpington 4	a					08 25	08 27	08 33						08 39	08 42						08 55	08 57	09 03		

		SE	SE	SN	SE	SE	SE	SE	SE	SE	SE	SE		SE	SE	SE	SE	SE	SE	SE	SN	SE	SE	SE	SE
				1		1						1									1	1		1	
London Charing Cross 4	⊖ d			08 40		08 45	08 47		08 50	08 56		09 00					09 02			09 06	09 10			09 15	
London Waterloo (East) 4	⊖ d			08 43		08 48	08 50		08 53	08 59		09 03					09 05			09 09	09 13			09 18	
London Cannon Street 4	⊖ d		08 40		08 48			08 54			09 00				09 04				09 10			09 14	09 18		
London Blackfriars 3	⊖ d																								
London Bridge 4	⊖ d		08a43	08a47	08 52	08a52	08 55	08 58	08a58	09 04	09 04	09 08			09 08		09 10		09a13	09a14	09a17	09a17	09 22	09 23	
London Victoria 15	⊖ d	08 36												08 51				09 01							09 06
New Cross 4	⊖ d				08 57			09 03							09 14								09 27		
St Johns	d				08 59			09 05								←							09 29		
Lewisham 4	a						09 04	09 07		09 12 →					09 17	09 12	09 19	09 22							
Hither Green 4	a				09 04											09 17	09 23						09 34		
Petts Wood 4	a	09 09												09 24		09 30									09 39
Orpington 4	a	09 12										09 26		09 27		09 33								09 39	09 42

For general notes see front of timetable
For details of catering facilities see Directory of Train Operators

Table 199

Saturdays

London → Lewisham, Hither Green, Petts Wood and Orpington (Summary of Services)

		SE	SE	SE	SE	SE	SE 1	SE	SE	SE	SE	SE	SE	SE	SE	SN 1			SE	SE 1	SE	SE	SE	SE	SE
London Charing Cross 4	⊖ d	09 17		09 20	09 26		09 30				09 32				09 36	09 40				09 45	09 47		09 50	09 56	
London Waterloo (East) 4	⊖ d	09 20		09 23	09 29		09 33				09 35				09 39	09 43				09 48	09 50		09 53	09 59	
London Cannon Street 4	⊖ d		09 24			09 30			09 34					09 40					09 48			09 54			10 00
London Blackfriars 3	⊖ d																								
London Bridge 4	⊖ d	09 25	09 28	09a28	09 34	09 34	09 38		09 38		09 40			09a43	09a44	09a47			09 52	09a52	09 55	09 58	09a58	10 04	10 04
London Victoria 15	⊖ d							09 21				09 31	09 36												
New Cross 4	⊖ d		09 33						09 44	←									09 57			10 03			
St Johns	d		09 35																09 59			10 05			
Lewisham 4	a	09 34	09 37		09 42 →				09 47	09 42	09 49	09 52									10 04	10 07	10 12 →		
Hither Green 4	a									09 47	09 53								10 04						
Petts Wood 4	a							09 54		10 00			10 09												
Orpington 4	a						09 53	09 57		10 03			10 12												

		SE 1	SE	SE	SE	SE	SE	SE	SE	SN 1	SE 1	SE	SE 1	SE	SE	SE	SE	SE	SE	SE 1	SE	SE	SE	SE	SE
London Charing Cross 4	⊖ d	10 00				10 02			10 06	10 10			10 15		10 17		10 20	10 26		10 30				10 32	
London Waterloo (East) 4	⊖ d	10 03				10 05			10 09	10 13			10 18		10 20		10 23	10 29		10 33				10 35	
London Cannon Street 4	⊖ d			10 04				10 10			10 14	10 18				10 24			10 30			10 34			
London Blackfriars 3	⊖ d																								
London Bridge 4	⊖ d	10 08		10 08		10 10		10a13	10a14	10a17	10a17	10 22	10 23		10 25	10 28	10a28	10 34	10 34	10 38		10 38		10 40	
London Victoria 15	⊖ d		09 51				10 01							10 06							10 21				10 31
New Cross 4	⊖ d			10 14	←							10 27				10 33						10 44	←		
St Johns	d											10 29				10 35									
Lewisham 4	a			10 17	10 12	10 19	10 22								10 34	10 37		10 42 →				10 47	10 42	10 49	10 52
Hither Green 4	a				10 17	10 23						10 34											10 47	10 53	
Petts Wood 4	a	10 22	10 24		10 30									10 39							10 54		11 00		
Orpington 4	a	10 26	10 27		10 33								10 39	10 42						10 53	10 57		11 03		

		SE	SE	SE	SN 1	and at		SE	SE 1	SE	SE	SE	SE	SE	SE 1	SE	SE	SE	SE	SE	SE	SE	SN 1	SE 1
London Charing Cross 4	⊖ d			10 36	10 40	the same			17 45	17 47		17 50	17 56		18 00				18 02			18 06	18 10	
London Waterloo (East) 4	⊖ d			10 39	10 43				17 48	17 50		17 53	17 59		18 03				18 05			18 09	18 13	
London Cannon Street 4	⊖ d		10 40			minutes		17 48			17 54			18 00			18 04				18 10			18 14
London Blackfriars 3	⊖ d																							
London Bridge 4	⊖ d		10a43	10a44	10a47	past		17 52	17a52	17 55	17 58	17a58	18 04	18a03	18 08		18 08		18 10		18a13	18a14	18a17	18a17
London Victoria 15	⊖ d	10 36														17 51				18 01				
New Cross 4	⊖ d					each		17 57			18 03						18 14	←						
St Johns	d							17 59			18 05													
Lewisham 4	a					hour until				18 04	18 07		18 12 →				18 17	18 12	18 19	18 22				
Hither Green 4	a							18 04										18 17	18 23					
Petts Wood 4	a	11 09													18 22	18 24		18 30						
Orpington 4	a	11 12													18 26	18 27		18 33						

		SE	SE 1	SE	SE	SE	SE	SE	SE	SE	SE 1		SE	SE	SE	SE	SE	SE	SE	SN 1	SE	SE 1	SE	SE	SE
London Charing Cross 4	⊖ d		18 15		18 17		18 20			18 26	18 30				18 32				18 36	18 40		18 45	18 47	18 50	18 52
London Waterloo (East) 4	⊖ d		18 18		18 20		18 23			18 29	18 33				18 35				18 39	18 43		18 48	18 50	18 53	18 55
London Cannon Street 4	⊖ d	18 18				18 24		18 30										18 40			18 48				
London Blackfriars 3	⊖ d																								
London Bridge 4	⊖ d	18 22	18 23		18 25	18 28	18 29	18a33		18 34	18 38				18 40			18a43	18a44	18a47	18 52	18a52	18 55	18 59	19 01
London Victoria 15	⊖ d			18 06					←				18 21			18 31	18 36								
New Cross 4	⊖ d	18 27				18 35 →			18 35					←							18 57				19 06
St Johns	d	18 29							18 37												18 59				19 08
Lewisham 4	a				18 33		18 36		18 39	18 44 →				18 44	18 49	18 51							19 04	19 07	19 10
Hither Green 4	a	18 34												18 48	18 53						19 04				
Petts Wood 4	a			18 39									18 54	19 00			19 09								
Orpington 4	a		18 40	18 42							18 54		18 57	19 03			19 12								

		SE	SE	SE 1	SE	SE	SE	SE	SN	SE	SE 1	SE 1	SE	SE	SE		SE	SE	SE 1	SE	SE	SE	SE	SN	SE
London Charing Cross 4	⊖ d	18 56		19 00			19 04		19 07	19 10		19 15		19 17	19 20		19 22	19 26	19 30			19 34		19 37	19 40
London Waterloo (East) 4	⊖ d	18 59		19 03			19 07		19 10	19 13		19 18		19 20	19 23		19 25	19 29	19 33			19 37		19 40	19 43
London Cannon Street 4	⊖ d		19 00								19 14														
London Blackfriars 3	⊖ d																								
London Bridge 4	⊖ d	19 04	19a03	19 08			19 13		19a14	19a17	19a17	19 23		19 25	19 29		19 31	19 34	19 38			19 43		19a44	19a47
London Victoria 15	⊖ d				18 51			19 01					19 06							19 21			19 31		
New Cross 4	⊖ d					←											19 36				←	19 48			
St Johns	d																19 38								
Lewisham 4	a	19 14 →				19 14	19 20	19 23						19 34	19 36		19 40	19 42 →			19 42	19 52	19 53		
Hither Green 4	a					19 18	19 24														19 47	19 57			
Petts Wood 4	a				19 24	19 30							19 39							19 54	20 00				
Orpington 4	a			19 24	19 27	19 33						19 40	19 42						19 54	19 57	20 03				

		SE 1	SE	SE	SE	SE	SE	SE 1	SE	SE	SE	SN	SE	SE	SE	SE	SE	SE 1	SE		SE	SE	SN	SE	SE 1
London Charing Cross 4	⊖ d	19 45		19 47	19 50	19 52	19 56	20 00			20 04	20 07	20 10	20 17	20 20	20 22	20 26	20 30				20 34	20 37	20 40	20 45
London Waterloo (East) 4	⊖ d	19 48		19 50	19 53	19 55	19 59	20 03			20 07	20 10	20 13	20 20	20 23	20 25	20 29	20 33				20 37	20 40	20 43	20 48
London Cannon Street 4	⊖ d																								
London Blackfriars 3	⊖ d																								
London Bridge 4	⊖ d	19 53		19 55	19 59	20 01	20 04	20 08			20 13	20a14	20a17	20 25	20 29	20 31	20 34	20 38				20 43	20a44	20a47	20 53
London Victoria 15	⊖ d		19 36						19 51										20 21						
New Cross 4	⊖ d			20 00		20 06				←	20 18			20 30		20 36					←	20 48			
St Johns	d					20 08										20 38									
Lewisham 4	a			20 04	20 06	20 10	20 12 →			20 12	20 22			20 34	20 36	20 40	20 42 →				20 42	20 52			
Hither Green 4	a									20 17	20 27										20 47	20 57			
Petts Wood 4	a		20 09						20 24	20 30									20 54		21 00				
Orpington 4	a	20 10	20 12					20 24	20 27	20 33								20 54	20 57		21 03				21 10

For general notes see front of timetable
For details of catering facilities see
Directory of Train Operators

Table 199

Saturdays

London → Lewisham, Hither Green, Petts Wood and Orpington (Summary of Services)

		SE	SE	SE	SE	SE 1	SE	SE	SE	SN	SE	SE	SE	SE	SE	SE 1	SE	SE	SE	SN	SE	SE 1	SE		SE
London Charing Cross 4	⊖ d	20 47	20 50	20 52	20 56	21 00			21 04	21 07	21 10	21 17	21 20	21 22	21 26	21 30			21 34	21 37	21 40	21 45	21 47		21 50
London Waterloo (East) 4	⊖ d	20 50	20 53	20 55	20 59	21 03			21 07	21 10	21 13	21 20	21 23	21 25	21 29	21 33			21 37	21 40	21 43	21 48	21 50		21 53
London Cannon Street 4	⊖ d																								
London Blackfriars 3	⊖ d																								
London Bridge 4	⊖ d	20 55	20 59	21 01	21 04	21 08			21 13	21a14	21a17	21 25	21 29	21 31	21 34	21 38			21 43	21a44	21a47	21 53	21 55		21 59
London Victoria 15	⊖ d						20 51										21 21								
New Cross 4	⊖ d	21 00		21 06					21 18			21 30		21 36					21 48				22 00		
St Johns	d			21 08				←						21 38				←							
Lewisham 4	a	21 04	21 06	21 10	21 12			21 12	21 22			21 34	21 36	21 40	21 42			21 42	21 52				22 04		22 06
Hither Green 4	a				→			21 17	21 27						→			21 47	21 57						
Petts Wood 4	a						21 24	21 30									21 54	22 00							
Orpington 4	a					21 24	21 27	21 33								21 54	21 57	22 03				22 10			

		SE	SE	SE 1	SE	SE	SE	SN	SE	SE	SE	SE	SE	SE 1	SE	SE	SE	SN	SE	SE 1	SE	SE	SE	SE	SE
London Charing Cross 4	⊖ d	21 52	21 56	22 00			22 04	22 07	22 10	22 17	22 20	22 22	22 26	22 30			22 34	22 37	22 40	22 45		22 47	22 50	22 52	22 56
London Waterloo (East) 4	⊖ d	21 55	21 59	22 03			22 07	22 10	22 13	22 20	22 23	22 25	22 29	22 33			22 37	22 40	22 43	22 48		22 50	22 53	22 55	22 59
London Cannon Street 4	⊖ d																								
London Blackfriars 3	⊖ d																								
London Bridge 4	⊖ d	22 01	22 04	22 08			22 13	22a14	22a17	22 25	22 29	22 31	22 34	22 38			22 43	22a44	22a47	22 53		22 55	22 59	23 01	23 04
London Victoria 15	⊖ d				21 51										22 21						22 42				
New Cross 4	⊖ d	22 06					22 18			22 30		22 36					22 48					23 00		23 06	
St Johns	d	22 08				←						22 38				←								23 08	
Lewisham 4	a	22 10	22 12			22 12	22 22			22 34	22 36	22 40	22 42			22 42	22 52					23 04	23 06	23 10	23 12
Hither Green 4	a		→			22 17	22 27						→			22 47	22 57								→
Petts Wood 4	a				22 24	22 30									22 54	23 00					23 20				
Orpington 4	a			22 24	22 27	22 33								22 54	22 57	23 03				23 10	23 23				

		SE 1	SE	SE		SE	SE	SN	SE	SE	SE	SE	SE	SE 1	SE	SE	SE	SE	SN	SE	SE	SE	SE		
London Charing Cross 4	⊖ d	23 00					23 04	23 07	23 10	23 17	23 20	23 22	23 26	23 30				23 34	23 45		23 47	23 49	23 52		
London Waterloo (East) 4	⊖ d	23 03					23 07	23 10	23 13	23 20	23 23	23 25	23 29	23 33				23 37	23 48		23 50	23 52	23 55		
London Cannon Street 4	⊖ d																								
London Blackfriars 3	⊖ d																								
London Bridge 4	⊖ d	23 08					23 13	23a14	23a17	23 25	23 29	23 31	23 34	23 38				23 43	23a52		23 55	23a56	23 58		
London Victoria 15	⊖ d		22 51			23 12									23 21		23 42			23 53					
New Cross 4	⊖ d						23 18			23 30		23 36						23 48			00 01		00 04		
St Johns	d			←								23 38				←							00 06		
Lewisham 4	a			23 12			23 22			23 34	23 36	23 40	23 42			23 42		23 52			00 04		00 08		
Hither Green 4	a			23 17			23 27						→			23 47		23 57							
Petts Wood 4	a		23 24	23 30		23 50									23 54	00 01	00 20			00 26					
Orpington 4	a	23 24	23 27	23 33		23 53								23 54	23 57	00 03	00 23			00 29					

Sundays

		SE	SE	SE	SE	SE	SE	SE 1	SN	SE	SE	SE	SN	SE	SE	SE	SE	SE	SE	SN	SE	SE	SE 1	SE	SE
London Charing Cross 4	⊖ d	23p26			23p47	23p52	00 04	00 10	00 12	00 14	00 48		07 34	07 37	07 40		07 47	07 53	07 56	08 04	08 07	08 10	08 14	08 17	08 20
London Waterloo (East) 4	⊖ d	23p29			23p50	23p55	00 07	00 13	00 15	00 17	00 51		07 37	07 40	07 43		07 50	07 56	07 59	08 07	08 10	08 13	08 17	08 20	08 23
London Cannon Street 4	⊖ d																								
London Blackfriars 3	⊖ d																								
London Bridge 4	⊖ d	23p34			23p55	23p58	00 13	00 18	00a19	00 22	00 56		07a42	07 45	07a47		07 55	08 02	08 05	08a12	08 15	08a17	08 22	08 25	08 29
London Victoria 15	⊖ d		23p42	23p53								07 35				07 51									
New Cross 4	⊖ d				00 01	00 04	00 18			00 27	01 01			07 50			08 00	08 07			08 20			08 30	
St Johns	d					00 06												08 09							
Lewisham 4	a	23p42			00 04	00 08	00 22			00 31	01 05	07 44		07 54			08 04	08 11	08 14		08 24			08 34	08 37
Hither Green 4	a	23p47					00 27				01 09	07 49					08 09		08 19					08 39	
Petts Wood 4	a	00 01	00 20	00 26				00 39			01 23	08 01				08 24			08 31						
Orpington 4	a	00 03	00 23	00 29				00 42			01 26	08 04				08 27			08 34				08 38		

		SE	SE	SE 1	SE	SN	SE	SE		SE	SE	SE	SE	SE	SE 1	SE	SN	SE	SE	SE	SE 1	SE	SE	SE	SE
London Charing Cross 4	⊖ d	08 23	08 26	08 30		08 34	08 37	08 40			08 47	08 50	08 53	08 56	09 00		09 04	09 07	09 10		09 14	09 17	09 20	09 23	09 26
London Waterloo (East) 4	⊖ d	08 26	08 29	08 33		08 37	08 40	08 43			08 50	08 53	08 56	08 59	09 03		09 07	09 10	09 13		09 17	09 20	09 23	09 26	09 29
London Cannon Street 4	⊖ d																								
London Blackfriars 3	⊖ d																								
London Bridge 4	⊖ d	08 32	08 35	08 38		08a42	08 45	08a47			08 55	08 59	09 02	09 05	09 08		09a12	09 15	09a17		09 22	09 25	09 29	09 32	09 35
London Victoria 15	⊖ d				08 21											08 51									
New Cross 4	⊖ d	08 37					08 50				09 00		09 07					09 20				09 30		09 37	
St Johns	d	08 39								←			09 09							←				09 39	
Lewisham 4	a	08 41	08 44				08 54			08 44	09 04	09 07	09 11	09 14				09 24		09 14		09 34	09 37	09 41	09 44
Hither Green 4	a		→							08 49	09 09			→						09 19		09 39			→
Petts Wood 4	a				08 54					09 01						09 24				09 31					
Orpington 4	a			08 54	08 57					09 04					09 24	09 27				09 34	09 38				

For general notes see front of timetable
For details of catering facilities see
Directory of Train Operators

Table 199

Sundays

London → Lewisham, Hither Green, Petts Wood and Orpington (Summary of Services)

		SE [1]	SE	SN	SE	SE	SE	SE [1]	SE	SE	SE	SE	SE [1]	SE	SN	SE		SE	SE	SE [1]	SE	SE		SE	SE
London Charing Cross [4]	⊖ d	09 30		09 34	09 37	09 40		09 44	09 47	09 50	09 53	09 56	10 00		10 04	10 07		10 10		10 14	10 17	10 20		10 23	10 26
London Waterloo (East) [4]	⊖ d	09 33		09 37	09 40	09 43		09 47	09 50	09 53	09 56	09 59	10 03		10 07	10 10		10 13		10 17	10 20	10 23		10 26	10 29
London Cannon Street [4]	⊖ d																								
London Blackfriars [3]	⊖ d																								
London Bridge [4]	⊖ d	09 38		09a42	09 45	09a47		09 52	09 55	09 59	10 02	10 05	10 08		10a12	10 15		10a17		10 22	10 25	10 29		10 32	10 35
London Victoria [15]	⊖ d		09 21											09 51											
New Cross [4]	⊖ d				09 50		←		10 00		10 07					10 20			←		10 30			10 37	
St Johns	d										10 09													10 39	
Lewisham [4]	a				09 54		09 44		10 04	10 07	10 11	10 15 →				10 24			10 15		10 34	10 37		10 41	10 44 →
Hither Green [4]	a						09 49		10 09										10 19		10 39				
Petts Wood [4]	a		09 54				10 01							10 24					10 31						
Orpington [4]	a	09 54	09 57				10 04	10 08					10 24	10 27					10 35	10 38					

		SE [1]	SE	SN	SE	SE	SE	SE [1]	SE	SE	SE	SE	SE [1]	SE	SN	SE	SE	SE	SE [1]	SE	SE		SE	SE
London Charing Cross [4]	⊖ d	10 30		10 34	10 37	10 40		10 44	10 47	10 50	10 53	10 56	11 00		11 04	11 07	11 10		11 14	11 17	11 20	and at the same minutes past each hour until	17 23	17 26
London Waterloo (East) [4]	⊖ d	10 33		10 37	10 40	10 43		10 47	10 50	10 53	10 56	10 59	11 03		11 07	11 10	11 13		11 17	11 20	11 23		17 26	17 29
London Cannon Street [4]	⊖ d																							
London Blackfriars [3]	⊖ d																							
London Bridge [4]	⊖ d	10 38		10a42	10 45	10a47		10 52	10 55	10 59	11 02	11 05	11 08		11a12	11 15	11a17		11 22	11 25	11 29		17 32	17 35
London Victoria [15]	⊖ d		10 21											10 51										
New Cross [4]	⊖ d				10 50		←		11 00		11 07					11 20		←		11 30			17 37	
St Johns	d										11 09												17 39	
Lewisham [4]	a				10 54		10 44		11 04	11 07	11 11	11 14 →				11 24		11 14		11 34	11 37		17 41	17 44 →
Hither Green [4]	a						10 49		11 09									11 19		11 39				
Petts Wood [4]	a		10 54				11 01							11 24				11 31						
Orpington [4]	a	10 54	10 57				11 04	11 08					11 24	11 27				11 34	11 38					

		SE [1]	SE	SN	SE		SE	SE	SE [1]	SE	SE	SE	SE	SE [1]	SE	SN	SE	SE	SE	SE [1]	SE	SE	SE	SE	SE [1]
London Charing Cross [4]	⊖ d	17 30		17 34	17 37		17 40		17 44	17 47	17 50	17 53	17 56	18 00		18 04	18 07	18 10		18 14	18 17	18 20	18 23	18 26	18 30
London Waterloo (East) [4]	⊖ d	17 33		17 37	17 40		17 43		17 47	17 50	17 53	17 56	17 59	18 03		18 07	18 10	18 13		18 17	18 20	18 23	18 26	18 29	18 33
London Cannon Street [4]	⊖ d																								
London Blackfriars [3]	⊖ d																								
London Bridge [4]	⊖ d	17 38		17a42	17 45		17a47		17 52	17 55	17 59	18 02	18 05	18 08		18a12	18 15	18a17		18 22	18 25	18 29	18 32	18 35	18 38
London Victoria [15]	⊖ d		17 21												17 51										
New Cross [4]	⊖ d				17 50			←		18 00		18 07					18 20		←		18 30		18 37		
St Johns	d											18 09											18 39		
Lewisham [4]	a				17 54			17 44		18 04	18 07	18 11	18 14 →				18 24		18 14		18 34	18 37	18 41	18 44 →	
Hither Green [4]	a							17 49		18 09									18 19		18 39				
Petts Wood [4]	a		17 54					18 01							18 24				18 31						
Orpington [4]	a	17 54	17 57					18 04	18 08					18 24	18 27				18 34	18 38					18 54

		SE	SN	SE	SE	SE	SE [1]	SE	SE	SE	SE	SE [1]	SE		SN	SE	SE	SE	SE [1]	SE	SE	SE	SE	SE [1]	SE
London Charing Cross [4]	⊖ d		18 34	18 37	18 40		18 44	18 47	18 50	18 53	18 56	19 00			19 04	19 07	19 10		19 14	19 17	19 20	19 23	19 26	19 30	
London Waterloo (East) [4]	⊖ d		18 37	18 40	18 43		18 47	18 50	18 53	18 56	18 59	19 03			19 07	19 10	19 13		19 17	19 20	19 23	19 26	19 29	19 33	
London Cannon Street [4]	⊖ d																								
London Blackfriars [3]	⊖ d																								
London Bridge [4]	⊖ d		18a42	18 45	18a47		18 52	18 55	18 59	19 02	19 05	19 08			19a12	19 15	19a17		19 22	19 25	19 29	19 32	19 35	19 38	
London Victoria [15]	⊖ d	18 21											18 51												19 21
New Cross [4]	⊖ d			18 50		←		19 00		19 07						19 20		←		19 30		19 37			
St Johns	d									19 09												19 39			
Lewisham [4]	a			18 54		18 44		19 04	19 07	19 11	19 14 →					19 24		19 14		19 34	19 37	19 41	19 44 →		
Hither Green [4]	a					18 49		19 09										19 19		19 39					
Petts Wood [4]	a	18 54				19 01							19 24					19 31							19 54
Orpington [4]	a	18 57				19 04	19 08					19 24	19 27					19 34	19 38					19 54	19 57

		SN	SE	SE	SE	SE [1]	SE	SE	SE	SE	SE [1]	SE	SN	SE	SE	SE	SE [1]	SE	SE	SE	SE		SE [1]	SE	SN
London Charing Cross [4]	⊖ d	19 34	19 37	19 40		19 44	19 47	19 50	19 53	19 56	20 00		20 04	20 07	20 10		20 14	20 17	20 20	20 23	20 26		20 30		20 34
London Waterloo (East) [4]	⊖ d	19 37	19 40	19 43		19 47	19 50	19 53	19 56	19 59	20 03		20 07	20 10	20 13		20 17	20 20	20 23	20 26	20 29		20 33		20 37
London Cannon Street [4]	⊖ d																								
London Blackfriars [3]	⊖ d																								
London Bridge [4]	⊖ d	19a42	19 45	19a47		19 52	19 55	19 59	20 02	20 05	20 08		20a12	20 15	20a17		20 22	20 25	20 29	20 32	20 35		20 38		20a42
London Victoria [15]	⊖ d											19 51												20 21	
New Cross [4]	⊖ d		19 50		←		20 00		20 07					20 20		←		20 30		20 37					
St Johns	d								20 09											20 39					
Lewisham [4]	a		19 54		19 44		20 04	20 07	20 11	20 14 →				20 24		20 14		20 34	20 37	20 41	20 44 →				
Hither Green [4]	a				19 49		20 09									20 19		20 39							
Petts Wood [4]	a				20 01							20 24				20 31								20 54	
Orpington [4]	a				20 04	20 08					20 24	20 27				20 34	20 38						20 54	20 57	

		SE	SE	SE	SE	SE	SE	SE	SE [1]	SE	SN	SE	SE	SE	SE [1]	SE	SE	SE	SE	SE [1]	SE	SN	SE	SE	SE
London Charing Cross [4]	⊖ d	20 37	20 40		20 47	20 50	20 53	20 56	21 00		21 04	21 07	21 10		21 14	21 17	21 20	21 23	21 26	21 30		21 34	21 37	21 40	
London Waterloo (East) [4]	⊖ d	20 40	20 43		20 50	20 53	20 56	20 59	21 03		21 07	21 10	21 13		21 17	21 20	21 23	21 26	21 29	21 33		21 37	21 40	21 43	
London Cannon Street [4]	⊖ d																								
London Blackfriars [3]	⊖ d																								
London Bridge [4]	⊖ d	20 45	20a47		20 55	20 59	21 02	21 05	21 08		21a12	21 15	21a17		21 22	21 25	21 29	21 32	21 35	21 38		21a42	21 45	21a47	
London Victoria [15]	⊖ d									20 51											21 21				
New Cross [4]	⊖ d	20 50		←	21 00		21 07					21 20		←		21 30		21 37					21 50		←
St Johns	d						21 09											21 39							
Lewisham [4]	a	20 54		20 44	21 04	21 07	21 11	21 14 →				21 24		21 14		21 34	21 37	21 41	21 44 →				21 54		21 44
Hither Green [4]	a			20 49	21 09									21 19		21 39									21 49
Petts Wood [4]	a			21 01						21 24				21 31							21 54				22 01
Orpington [4]	a			21 04					21 24	21 27				21 34	21 38					21 54	21 57				22 04

For general notes see front of timetable
For details of catering facilities see
Directory of Train Operators

Table 199

Sundays

London → Lewisham, Hither Green, Petts Wood and Orpington (Summary of Services)

		SE	SE	SE	SE	SE 1	SE		SN	SE	SE	SE	SE 1	SE	SE	SE	SE	SE 1	SE	SN	SE	SE	SE	SE	SE
London Charing Cross 4	⊖ d	21 47	21 50	21 53	21 56	22 00			22 04	22 07	22 10		22 14	22 17	22 20	22 23	22 26	22 30		22 34			22 37	22 40	
London Waterloo (East) 4	⊖ d	21 50	21 53	21 56	21 59	22 03			22 07	22 10	22 13		22 17	22 20	22 23	22 26	22 29	22 33		22 37			22 40	22 43	
London Cannon Street 4	⊖ d																								
London Blackfriars 3	⊖ d																								
London Bridge 4	⊖ d	21 55	21 59	22 02	22 05	22 08			22a12	22 15	22a17		22 22	22 25	22 29	22 32	22 35	22 38		22a42			22 45	22a47	
London Victoria 15	⊖ d						21 51												22 21			22 38			22 51
New Cross 4	⊖ d	22 00		22 07						22 20				22 30		22 37							22 50		
St Johns	d			22 09												22 39									
Lewisham 4	a	22 04	22 07	22 11	22 14 →					22 24		← 22 14		22 34	22 37	22 41	22 44 →				← 22 44		22 54		
Hither Green 4	a	22 09										22 19		22 39							22 49				
Petts Wood 4	a						22 24					22 31							22 54		23 01	23 14			23 24
Orpington 4	a					22 24	22 27					22 34	22 38					22 54	22 57		23 04	23 17			23 27

		SE	SE	SE	SE	SN	SE	SE	SE 1	SE	SE	SE	SE	SE	SE 1	SE	SN	SE	SE	SE	SE	SE	SE		
London Charing Cross 4	⊖ d	22 47	22 50	22 53	22 56	23 04	23 07	23 10	23 14		23 17	23 20	23 23	23 26	23 30		23 34	23 37	23 40		23 47	23 53	23 56		
London Waterloo (East) 4	⊖ d	22 50	22 53	22 56	22 59	23 07	23 10	23 13	23 17		23 20	23 23	23 26	23 29	23 33		23 37	23 40	23 43		23 50	23 56	23 59		
London Cannon Street 4	⊖ d																								
London Blackfriars 3	⊖ d																								
London Bridge 4	⊖ d	22 55	22 59	23 02	23 05	23a12	23 15	23a17	23 22		23 25	23 29	23 32	23 35	23 38		23a42	23 45	23a47		23 55	00 02	00 05		
London Victoria 15	⊖ d									23 08						23 21									
New Cross 4	⊖ d	23 00		23 07			23 20				23 30		23 37					23 50			23 59	00 07			
St Johns	d			23 09									23 39									00 09			
Lewisham 4	a	23 04	23 07	23 11	23 14		23 24				23 34	23 37	23 41	23 44 →				23 54		← 23 44	00 03	00 11	00 14		
Hither Green 4	a	23 09			23 19						23 39									23 49	00 08		00 19		
Petts Wood 4	a				23 31					23 44						23 54				00 01			00 31		
Orpington 4	a				23 35				23 38	23 47					23 54	23 57				00 04			00 34		

For general notes see front of timetable
For details of catering facilities see
Directory of Train Operators

Orpington, Petts Wood, Hither Green and Lewisham → London (Summary of Services)

For details of Bank Holiday service alterations please see first page of Table 195

	SE	SE	SE	FC 1	SE	SN	SE	SE	SE	SE	SE	SE	SE	SE	SE 1	SE	SE	SE	FC 1	SE	SE	SE	SE	SE
Orpington 4 d	04 36		04 58					05 20					05 25	05 36	05 50							05 50	06 00	
Petts Wood 4 d	04 39		05 01					05 23					05 28	05 39								05 53	06 03	
Hither Green 4 d		05 08			05 23			05 35								05 55							06 15	
Lewisham 4 d		05 13			05 28				05 40		05 48					06 00				06 10	06 16		06 20	
St Johns d									05 42											06 12				
New Cross 4 ⊖ d		05 16			05 32			05 40	05 44		05 52					06 04				06 14	06 20		06 24	
London Victoria 15 ⊖ a													06b03									06b29		
London Bridge 4 ⊖ d		05 22		05 34	05 38	05 41	05 42	05 46	05 50	05 53	05 58	05 58			06 06	06 10	06 13	06 14	06 15	06 20	06 26		06 30	06 30
London Blackfriars 3 ⊖ a	05 17		05 35	05 43										06 16					06 24					
London Cannon Street 4 ⊖ a							05 45					06 01						06 17						06 33
London Waterloo (East) 4 ⊖ d		05 28			05 44	05 46		05 51	05 55	05 58	06 03				06 11	06 15	06 18			06 25	06 31		06 35	
London Charing Cross 4 ⊖ a		05 31			05 47	05 49		05b56	06b00	06 02	06 06				06 14	06 18	06 21			06b30	06 34		06 38	

	SE	SE	SE 1	SE 1	SE	SE	SE	FC 1	SE	SE	SE	SE	SE	SE	SE 1	FC 1	SE	SE	SE		SE 1	SE	SE 1	SE
Orpington 4 d			06 17						06 20	06 24	06 31													
Petts Wood 4 d									06 23	06 27			←											
Hither Green 4 d					06 25					06 39 →			06 39											06 52
Lewisham 4 d	06 24				06 30		06 34					06 40	06 44	06 47			06 50	06 52	←			06 56		06 56
St Johns d					06 32							06 42					06 52 →		06 52					06 58
New Cross 4 ⊖ d					06 34		06 38					06 44							06 54					
London Victoria 15 ⊖ a									06b59															
London Bridge 4 ⊖ d	06 33	06 34	06 37	06 37	06 40	06 43	06 44	06 46			06 50	06 50	06 53	06 56	06 56	06 59		07 01	07 02		07 04	07 06	07 08	07 09
London Blackfriars 3 ⊖ a								06 53								07 06								
London Cannon Street 4 ⊖ a		06b40	06b43				06 47				06b55			07 00					07 06				07c14	
London Waterloo (East) 4 ⊖ d	06 38			06 42	06 45	06 48						06 55	06 58		07 01			07 06			07 09	07 11		07 13
London Charing Cross 4 ⊖ a	06 41			06 48	06 48	06 51						07b00	07b03		07b06			07b11			07c15	07c16		07c18

	SE	SE	SE	SE	FC 1	SE	SE	SE	SE	SE 1	SE	SE	SE	SE	SE 1	SE	SE	SE	SE	SE 1	SE	SE	SE	SE
Orpington 4 d				06 44		06 49	06 57	06 59									07 02	07 06	07 10	07 13				
Petts Wood 4 d				06 47		06 52	07 00						←				07 05	07 09	07 13 →					
Hither Green 4 d						07 06	07 14 →		07 02			07 10	07 14										07 22	
Lewisham 4 d	07 00		07 04						07 08			07 15		07 18		07 20					07 22	←		07 25
St Johns d									07 10							07 25 →						07 25		07 27
New Cross 4 ⊖ d	07 04		07 07						07 12				07 19									07 27		07 29
London Victoria 15 ⊖ a				07c21														07c46						
London Bridge 4 ⊖ d	07 11	07 14	07 15		07 16			07 17	07 19	07 22	07 23	07 25	07 26	07 28	07 28					07 31	07 31	07 34	07 34	07 36
London Blackfriars 3 ⊖ a					07 23												07 44							
London Cannon Street 4 ⊖ a			07 19					07c22	07c25		07c29		07c32		07c34					07c37		07 38		07c42
London Waterloo (East) 4 ⊖ d	07 16	07 19				07 24				07 27		07 30		07 33							07 36		07 39	
London Charing Cross 4 ⊖ a	07c21	07c25				07c29				07c33		07c35		07c38							07c41		07c44	

	SE	SE	SE	SE	SE	SE	SE 1	SE 1	SE	SE	SE 1	SE	SE	SE	SE	SE	SE		SE	SE	SE	SE	SE	SE 1
Orpington 4 d	←											07 23		07 27	07 30				07 36					
Petts Wood 4 d	07 13											07 26		07 30	07 33				07 39					
Hither Green 4 d	07 26		07 26							07 42					07 46						07 49			
Lewisham 4 d			07 32	07 35	07 38				07 41							07 44	07 50				07 54	07 56		
St Johns d									07 44								07 52							
New Cross 4 ⊖ d			07 36						07 46								07 54				07 59			
London Victoria 15 ⊖ a														08c08		08c12								
London Bridge 4 ⊖ d	07 37	07 41	07 42	07 44		07 45	07 50	07 50	07 53	07 54	07 55		07 58		07 59		08 01		08 02	08 04	08 06	08 07	08 08	08 10
London Blackfriars 3 ⊖ a												08 02												
London Cannon Street 4 ⊖ a			07 48			07c52		07c56	07c58		08c01				08 04		08c07			08c10	08c12		08b15	08c16
London Waterloo (East) 4 ⊖ d	07 42	07 46		07 48	07 51		07 55			07 58			08 03						08 08			08 12		
London Charing Cross 4 ⊖ a	07c47	07c52		07 53	07c57		07 59			08 03			08c08						08c13			08c18		

	SE 1	SE	SE	SE 1	SE	SE	SE	SE	SE	SE	SE	SE	SE 1	SE	SE	SE	SE	SE 1	SE 1	SE	SE	SE 1	SE	SE
Orpington 4 d					07 44		07 50	07 53		07 56						08 00								08 10
Petts Wood 4 d					07 47		07 53	07 56		07 59						08 03								08 13
Hither Green 4 d			08 02												08 09	08 16					08 22			
Lewisham 4 d		08 01				08 04					08 10	08 12			08 14		08 18			08 21			08 24	
St Johns d		08 04									08 12									08 24				
New Cross 4 ⊖ d		08 06									08 14				08 18					08 26				
London Victoria 15 ⊖ a						08c29	08c29																08c47	08c50
London Bridge 4 ⊖ d	08 11	08 13	08 15	08 15				08 18	08 19		08 21	08 23	08 23	08 25	08 27	08 27	08 29	08 31	08 31	08 34	08 35	08 36		
London Blackfriars 3 ⊖ a					08 30																			
London Cannon Street 4 ⊖ a		08c19		08c21				08c24			08c27		08c29	08c31	08c33		08c35		08c37	08 39		08c42		
London Waterloo (East) 4 ⊖ d	08 16		08 20						08 24	08 26		08 28				08 32		08 36			08 40			
London Charing Cross 4 ⊖ a	08 21		08c25						08c29	08c31		08c33				08c37		08 41			08c45			

	SE	SE	SE	SE	SE	SE	SE	SE	SE	SE 1	SE 1	SE	SE	SE 1	SE		SE	SE	SE	SE	SE	SE	SE 1	SE
Orpington 4 d	08 13						08 20										08 30	08 33		08 38				
Petts Wood 4 d	08 16						08 23										08 33	08 36		08 41				
Hither Green 4 d						08 29	08 36						08 42									08 49		
Lewisham 4 d			08 30			08 34		08 36				08 41			08 44						08 50	08 54		08 56
St Johns d			08 32									08 44									08 52			
New Cross 4 ⊖ d			08 34			08 38						08 46						08 52			08 54	09 00 →		
London Victoria 15 ⊖ a															09c12		09c12							
London Bridge 4 ⊖ d	08 38	08 39	08 41	08 43	08 43	08 46		08 47	08 49	08 51	08 51	08 54	08 55	08 56				08 58	08 59		09 01		09 03	09 05
London Blackfriars 3 ⊖ a																								
London Cannon Street 4 ⊖ a	08b45		08c47		08b50	08c52			08c55		08c57	09c00		09c02				09c04			09c07		09 08	
London Waterloo (East) 4 ⊖ d		08 44		08 48			08 50	08 52		08 56			09 00						09 04	09 06				09 10
London Charing Cross 4 ⊖ a		08c49		08c53			08c55	08c57		09 01			09c05						09c09	09b13				09c15

For general notes see front of timetable
For details of catering facilities see
Directory of Train Operators

b Until 9 October Arr 2 minutes earlier
c Until 9 October Arr 1 minute earlier

Orpington, Petts Wood, Hither Green and Lewisham → London (Summary of Services)

For details of Bank Holiday service alterations please see first page of Table 195

	SE	SE	SE	FC 1	SE 1	SE	SE	SE	SE 1	SE	SE 1	SE	SE	SE	SE	SE	SE	SE 1	SE	SE	SE	SE 1	SE	SE
Orpington 4 d												08 47	08 53		09 00									09 08
Petts Wood 4 d												08 50	08 56		09 03									09 11
Hither Green 4 d		08 56													09 16		09 20			09 23				
Lewisham 4 d								09 04						09 10		09 20			09 24	09 28	←			
St Johns d	←							09 06									09 24		09 28		09 28			
New Cross 4 ⊖ d	09 00							09 08									09 26		→		09 30			
London Victoria 15 ⊖ a													09b31	09b33										09b47
London Bridge 4 ⊖ d	09 06	09 08	09 09	09 11	09 11	09 13	09 14	09 16	09 19	09 22	09 23				09 26	09 30	09 33	09 34		09 37	09 38	09 40	09 40	
London Blackfriars 3 ⊖ a				09 20								09 30												
London Cannon Street 4 ⊖ a	09b12		09b15		09b17	09b19		09c23			09 28						09b39				09b44		09c47	
London Waterloo (East) 4 ⊖ d		09 14					09 20		09 24	09 27					09 31	09 35		09 39		09 42		09 45		
London Charing Cross 4 ⊖ a		09c20					09b25		09 29	09b32					09b36	09b40		09 44		09b48		09b51		

	SE	SE	FC 1	SE	SE	SE	SE	SE 1	SE	SE	SE 1	FC 1	SE		SE	SE	SE	SE	SE	SE	SE	SE	SE 1	FC 1
Orpington 4 d	09 12					09 23	09 33	09 36									09 38	09 53					09 55	
Petts Wood 4 d	09 15					09 26	09 36									←	09 41	09 56					09 59	
Hither Green 4 d	09 28						09 48			09 44						09 48			09 54					
Lewisham 4 d	09 33			09 36			→		09 46				09 48		09 51	09 54			09 59			10 02		
St Johns d				09 38						09 48			09 52											
New Cross 4 ⊖ d				09 40						09 50			09 54											
London Victoria 15 ⊖ a						10b01									10c14		10b14	10 29						
London Bridge 4 ⊖ d	09 42	09 44	09 45	09 49	09 52			09 52	09 55	09 57	09 58	10 01	10 03			10 04				10 08	10 10	10 11	10 13	10 16
London Blackfriars 3 ⊖ a			09 54									10 07												10 24
London Cannon Street 4 ⊖ a	09c49				09b58					10 01			10 06								10 13			
London Waterloo (East) 4 ⊖ d		09 49		09 55				09 58	10 00		10 03					10 09			10 11	10 14		10 16	10 19	
London Charing Cross 4 ⊖ a		09c54		10 00				10 01	10 05		10c09					10 12			10 14	10 17		10 20	10 22	

	SE	SE	SE	SN 1	SE 1	SE	SE	FC 1	SE	SE	SE	SE	SE	SE	SE		SE 1	SE	FC 1	SE	SE	SE 1	SN 1	SE
Orpington 4 d											10 05			10 08	10 23		10 25							
Petts Wood 4 d											10 08			10 11	10 26		10 29							
Hither Green 4 d			10 10								10 20	10 24												10 40
Lewisham 4 d	10 06					10 16				10 21	10 25	10 29	10 32							10 36				
St Johns d	10 08		10 14																	10 38				10 45
New Cross 4 ⊖ d	10 10		10 16			10 20														10 40				10 47
London Victoria 15 ⊖ a										10 42				10 44	10 59									
London Bridge 4 ⊖ d	10 17	10 19	10 22	10 23	10 25	10 27	10 29	10 30	10 30		10 35	10 38	10 41				10 43	10 44	10 45	10 47	10 49	10 51	10 52	10 54
London Blackfriars 3 ⊖ a								10 37											10 54					
London Cannon Street 4 ⊖ a	10 20		10 27			10 30			10 33									10 47		10 50		10 54		10 57
London Waterloo (East) 4 ⊖ d		10 24		10 27	10 30		10 35				10 40	10 43	10 46				10 48				10 54		10 57	
London Charing Cross 4 ⊖ a		10 28		10 30	10 33		10 39				10 44	10 47	10 50				10 51				10 58		11 00	

	SE 1	SE	SE	FC 1	SE	SE	SE	SE	SE	SE	SE	SE 1	SE	FC 1	SE	SE	SN 1	SE	SE 1	SE	SE	FC 1	SE	SE
Orpington 4 d							10 35			10 38	10 53	10 57							11 05					
Petts Wood 4 d							10 38			10 41	10 56													
Hither Green 4 d							10 50	10 54										11 10						
Lewisham 4 d		10 46				10 51	10 55	10 59	11 02						11 06					11 16				11 21
St Johns d															11 08			11 15						
New Cross 4 ⊖ d		10 50													11 10			11 17		11 20				
London Victoria 15 ⊖ a						11 12				11 14	11 29													11 42
London Bridge 4 ⊖ d	10 55	10 57	10 59	11 00	11 00		11 05	11 08	11 11			11 13	11 14	11 15	11 17	11 19	11 22	11 24	11 25	11 27	11 29	11 30	11 30	
London Blackfriars 3 ⊖ a				11 07										11 23								11 37		
London Cannon Street 4 ⊖ a		11 00			11 03								11 17		11 20			11 27		11 30			11 33	
London Waterloo (East) 4 ⊖ d	11 00		11 05				11 10	11 13	11 16			11 18				11 24	11 27		11 30		11 35			
London Charing Cross 4 ⊖ a	11 03		11 09				11 14	11 17	11 20			11 21				11 28	11 30		11 33		11 39			

	SE	SE	SE	SE	SE			SE 1	SE	FC 1	SE	SE	SE 1	SN 1	SE	SE 1	SE	SE	FC 1	SE	SE	SE	SE
Orpington 4 d	11 05			11 08	11 23	and at		15 25														15 35	
Petts Wood 4 d	11 08			11 11	11 26	the same		15 29														15 38	
Hither Green 4 d	11 20	11 24				minutes									15 40							15 50	15 54
Lewisham 4 d	11 25	11 29	11 32			past					15 36						15 46				15 51	15 55	15 59
St Johns d						each					15 38				15 45								
New Cross 4 ⊖ d						hour until					15 40				15 47		15 50						
London Victoria 15 ⊖ a				11 44	11 59																16 12		
London Bridge 4 ⊖ d	11 35	11 38	11 41					15 43	15 44	15 45	15 47	15 49	15 51	15 52	15 54	15 55	15 57	15 59	16 00	16 00		16 04	16 08
London Blackfriars 3 ⊖ a										15 53									16 07				
London Cannon Street 4 ⊖ a									15 47		15 50		15 54		15 57		16 00			16 03			
London Waterloo (East) 4 ⊖ d	11 40	11 43	11 46					15 48				15 54		15 57		16 00		16 04				16 10	16 14
London Charing Cross 4 ⊖ a	11 44	11 47	11 50					15 51				15 58		16 00		16 03		16 07				16 13	16 17

	SE	SE	SE	SE 1	SE	FC 1	SE	SE	SE	SE	SE 1	SE	SE 1	SE	SE	SE	SE 1	SE	FC 1	SE	SE	SE	SE	SE
Orpington 4 d		15 38	15 53	15 57						16 05	16 07										16 08	16 20		16 33
Petts Wood 4 d		15 41	15 56							16 08								←			16 11	16 23		16 36
Hither Green 4 d									16 11	16 20								16 20		16 28		16 36		
Lewisham 4 d	16 02						16 08			→		16 16			16 21	16 24		16 28		16 33				→
St Johns d							16 10		16 15											16 35				
New Cross 4 ⊖ d							16 12		16 17											16 37				
London Victoria 15 ⊖ a		16 14	16 30																		16 45			
London Bridge 4 ⊖ d	16 11			16 13	16 14	16 15	16 19	16 20	16 24		16 24	16 27	16 29	16 30	16 32	16 33	16 34	16 38	16 42	16 43		16 46	16 48	
London Blackfriars 3 ⊖ a						16 25													16 53					
London Cannon Street 4 ⊖ a					16 17		16 22		16 27					16 33		16 36				16 46			16 52	
London Waterloo (East) 4 ⊖ d	16 18			16 18				16 25			16 29	16 33	16 35		16 37		16 39	16 43				16 52		
London Charing Cross 4 ⊖ a	16 23			16 21				16 28			16 33	16 36	16 38		16 40		16 45	16 47				16 55		

For general notes see front of timetable
For details of catering facilities see Directory of Train Operators

b Until 9 October Arr 1 minute earlier
c Until 9 October Arr 2 minutes earlier

For details of Bank Holiday service alterations please see first page of Table 195

Orpington, Petts Wood, Hither Green and Lewisham → London (Summary of Services)

	SE	SE	SE	SE 1	SE		SE	SE 1	SE	SE	SE	SE	SE	SE	SE 1	SE	SE	SE	SE	SE	SE	SE	SE	SE
Orpington [4] d				16 34						←				16 36	16 50	16 52		16 56				←		
Petts Wood [4] d										16 36				16 39		16 55 →						16 55		
Hither Green [4] d							16 42			16 52	16 50	16 56							17 02			17 09	17 05	17 13
Lewisham [4] d	16 35	16 38			16 46				16 50		16 56								17 04					
St Johns d		16 40					16 47												17 06					
New Cross [4] ⊖ d		16 42					16 49		16 54															
London Victoria [15] ⊖ a	17 03													17 12									17 28	
London Bridge [4] ⊖ d		16 50	16 52	16 53	16 55		16 57	17 00	17 01	17 03	17 05	17 07	17 09		17 09		17 12	17 13	17 15	17 16	17 19	17 19		17 24
London Blackfriars [3] ⊖ a																								
London Cannon Street [4] ⊖ a			16 55				17 00		17 05		17 08		17 13				17 15		17 18		17 23			
London Waterloo (East) [4] ⊖ d		16 56		16 58	17 00			17 05		17 08		17 12			17 15			17 19		17 21		17 24		17 29
London Charing Cross [4] ⊖ a		16 59		17 01	17 03			17 10		17 13		17 15			17 19			17 24		17 25		17 28		17 32

	SE	SE 1	SE	FC 1	SE	SE	SE	SE 1	SE	SE	SE	SE 1	SE	SE	SE	SE 1	SE	SE	SE	SE	SE	SE	SE	SE
Orpington [4] d		17 02				17 04	17 07	17 13		←				17 25		17 26			←	17 34				17 36
Petts Wood [4] d						17 07	17 10 →			17 10				17 28 →					17 28	17 37				17 39
Hither Green [4] d	17 06				17 16					17 23			17 24		17 31				17 40					
Lewisham [4] d	17 12		17 18						17 21				17 31				17 36					17 44	17 47	
St Johns d	17 14								17 23				17 33											
New Cross [4] ⊖ d	17 16								17 25				17 35				17 39							
London Victoria [15] ⊖ a						17 42																		18 12
London Bridge [4] ⊖ d	17 24	17 27	17 27	17 29	17 30			17 32	17 33	17 35	17 36	17 39	17 42		17 42	17 44	17 46	17 48	17 49	17 52	17 54	17 55	17 58	
London Blackfriars [3] ⊖ a				17 36																				
London Cannon Street [4] ⊖ a	17 29	17 31			17 33				17 36		17 39		17 45				17 51	17 53			17 57		18 01	
London Waterloo (East) [4] ⊖ d			17 32					17 37		17 40		17 44			17 47	17 50			17 54	17 58		18 00		
London Charing Cross [4] ⊖ a			17 35					17 41		17 46		17 48			17 50	17 55			17 57	18 01		18 03		

	SE 1	SE	SE		SE	SE	SE	SE	FC 1	SE	SE	SE	SE	SE 1	SE	SE	SE	SE	SE	SE	SE 1	SE	SE	SE
Orpington [4] d	17 40							17 51						18 00				18 06	18 08	18 11	18 12			←
Petts Wood [4] d								17 54										18 09		18 14 →				18 14
Hither Green [4] d			17 44		17 50	17 55		18 06				18 04											18 18	18 26
Lewisham [4] d			17 51							17 54			18 10				18 14					18 20	18 24	
St Johns d			17 55														18 17						18 26	
New Cross [4] ⊖ d			17 57														18 19						18 28	
London Victoria [15] ⊖ a										18 16								18 42						
London Bridge [4] ⊖ d		18 01	18 04		18 05	18 07	18 10		18 11		18 12	18 16		18 20	18 21	18 23	18 26		18 26		18 29	18 31	18 34	18 35
London Blackfriars [3] ⊖ a									18 21															
London Cannon Street [4] ⊖ a			18 08								18 15				18 24		18 29						18 37	
London Waterloo (East) [4] ⊖ d	18 04	18 06			18 10	18 12	18 16	18 20				18 22	18 24	18 27		18 28			18 32		18 34	18 37		18 40
London Charing Cross [4] ⊖ a	18 07	18 09			18 13	18 15	18 19	18 23				18 25	18 27	18 30		18 33			18 37		18 37	18 40		18 45

	SE	SE 1	SE	SE	FC 1	SE	SE 1	SE 1	SE	SE	SE	SE	SE 1	FC 1	SE	SE	SE	SE	SE	SE	SE 1	FC 1	SE	SE
Orpington [4] d							18 33	18 36			18 36	18 39	18 40					←			18 56			
Petts Wood [4] d											18 39	18 42 →						18 42						
Hither Green [4] d				18 32												18 44		18 54						
Lewisham [4] d	18 29					18 36			18 41	18 45						18 49	18 56		19 01				19 06	19 09
St Johns d						18 38										18 51	18 58							19 11
New Cross [4] ⊖ d						18 40										18 53	19 00							19 13
London Victoria [15] ⊖ a									19 01		19 13												19 25	
London Bridge [4] ⊖ d	18 38	18 40	18 42	18 43	18 45	18 49	18 50	18 52		18 55			18 58	19 00	19 02	19 03	19 06	19 06	19 10	19 12	19 13	19 17		19 19
London Blackfriars [3] ⊖ a					18 53									19 07								19 23		
London Cannon Street [4] ⊖ a			18 45				18 53								19 05		19 10			19 15				
London Waterloo (East) [4] ⊖ d	18 44	18 45		18 49		18 54		18 57		19 00			19 03			19 08		19 11	19 16		19 18			19 25
London Charing Cross [4] ⊖ a	18 49	18 48		18 53		18 57		19 00		19 05			19 07			19 11		19 14	19 20		19 21			19 29

	SE		SE	SE	SE 1	SE	FC 1	SE	SE	SE	SE 1	SE	SE	SN	SE	FC 1	SE	SE	SE	SE	SE	SE 1	SE	FC 1
Orpington [4] d				19 05	19 08					19 08	19 14								19 23	19 35		19 38		
Petts Wood [4] d				19 08						19 11		←							19 26	19 38				
Hither Green [4] d	19 07			19 20 →								19 20			19 26					19 50 →				
Lewisham [4] d	19 12		19 15			19 17		19 26				19 28			19 31			19 45					19 47	
St Johns d						19 19							←										19 49	
New Cross [4] ⊖ d						19 21		19 30 →					19 30		19 34								19 51	
London Victoria [15] ⊖ a										19 45									19 59					
London Bridge [4] ⊖ d	19 22		19 23		19 26	19 29	19 30		19 34		19 34	19 36	19 38	19 39	19 44	19 45	19 49	19 53			19 54	19 56	19 59	20 00
London Blackfriars [3] ⊖ a							19 37									19 53								20 07
London Cannon Street [4] ⊖ a	19 25								19 37				19 41								19 57			
London Waterloo (East) [4] ⊖ d			19 29		19 32	19 34					19 39	19 42		19 46	19 50		19 55	19 58				20 01	20 04	
London Charing Cross [4] ⊖ a			19 32		19 35	19 37					19 42	19 45		19 49	19 53		19 59	20 01				20 04	20 07	

	SE	SE	SE	SE	SE 1	SN	SE	FC 1	SE	SE	SE	SE	SE	SE 1	SE	FC 1	SE	SE	SE	SE	SE 1		SN	SE
Orpington [4] d				19 38	19 50							19 53	20 05	20 08						20 08	20 20			
Petts Wood [4] d		←		19 41								19 56	20 08					←		20 11				
Hither Green [4] d		19 50					19 56						20 20 →					20 20						20 26
Lewisham [4] d	19 52	19 57					20 02			20 15					20 17		20 22	20 27						20 31
St Johns d															20 19									
New Cross [4] ⊖ d	19 56						20 05								20 21		20 26							20 34
London Victoria [15] ⊖ a				20 14								20 30								20 44				
London Bridge [4] ⊖ d	20 04	20 06	20 08		20 09	20 11	20 14	20 15	20 19	20 23	20 24			20 26	20 29	20 30	20 34	20 36	20 38		20 39		20 41	20 44
London Blackfriars [3] ⊖ a								20 23								20 37								
London Cannon Street [4] ⊖ a			20 11								20 27								20 41					
London Waterloo (East) [4] ⊖ d	20 09	20 11			20 14	20 17	20 19		20 25	20 28				20 31	20 34		20 39	20 41			20 44		20 47	20 49
London Charing Cross [4] ⊖ a	20 13	20 15			20 18	20 20	20 22		20 29	20 31				20 34	20 37		20 43	20 45			20 48		20 50	20 52

For general notes see front of timetable
For details of catering facilities see
Directory of Train Operators

Orpington, Petts Wood, Hither Green and Lewisham → London (Summary of Services)

For details of Bank Holiday service alterations please see first page of Table 195

		FC 1	SE	SE	SE	SE 1	SE	FC 1	SE	SE	SE	SE 1	SN	SE	FC 1	SE	SE	SE	SE 1	SE	FC 1	SE	SE	SE	SE 1
Orpington 4	d				20 35	20 38					20 38	20 50						21 05	21 08					21 08	21 20
Petts Wood 4	d				20 38					←	20 41							21 08					←	21 11	
Hither Green 4	d				20 50					20 50				20 56				21 20					21 20		
Lewisham 4	d			20 44	→		20 47		20 52	20 57				21 01			21 14	→		21 17		21 22	21 27		
St Johns	d						20 49													21 19					
New Cross 4	⊖ d						20 51		20 56					21 04						21 21		21 26			
London Victoria 15	⊖ a										21 14													21 44	
London Bridge 4	⊖ d	20 45	20 49	20 53		20 56	20 59	21 00	21 04	21 06		21 09	21 11	21 14	21 15	21 19	21 23		21 26	21 29	21 30	21 34	21 36		21 39
London Blackfriars 3	⊖ a	20 53						21 07							21 23						21 37				
London Cannon Street 4	⊖ a																								
London Waterloo (East) 4	⊖ d		20 55	20 58		21 01	21 04		21 09	21 11		21 14	21 17	21 19		21 25	21 28		21 31	21 34		21 39	21 41		21 44
London Charing Cross 4	⊖ a		20 59	21 01		21 04	21 07		21 13	21 15		21 18	21 20	21 22		21 29	21 31		21 34	21 37		21 43	21 45		21 48

		SN	SE	FC 1	SE	SE	SE	SE 1	SE	SE	SE	SE	SE 1	SN	SE	SE	SE	SE	SE 1	SE		SE	SE	SE	SE 1
Orpington 4	d						21 35	21 38				21 38	21 50					22 05	22 08					22 08	22 20
Petts Wood 4	d						21 38				←	21 41						22 08					←	22 11	
Hither Green 4	d		21 26				21 50				21 50				21 56			22 20					22 20		
Lewisham 4	d		21 31			21 44	→		21 47	21 52	21 57				22 01		22 14	→		22 17		22 22	22 27		
St Johns	d								21 49											22 19					
New Cross 4	⊖ d		21 34						21 51	21 56					22 04					22 21		22 26			
London Victoria 15	⊖ a											22 15												22 44	
London Bridge 4	⊖ d	21 41	21 44	21 45	21 49	21 53		21 56	21 59	22 04	22 06		22 09	22 11	22 14	22 19	22 23		22 26	22 29		22 34	22 36		22 39
London Blackfriars 3	⊖ a			21 53																					
London Cannon Street 4	⊖ a																								
London Waterloo (East) 4	⊖ d	21 47	21 49		21 55	21 58		22 01	22 04	22 09	22 11		22 14	22 17	22 19	22 25	22 28		22 31	22 34		22 39	22 41		22 44
London Charing Cross 4	⊖ a	21 50	21 52		21 59	22 01		22 04	22 07	22 13	22 15		22 18	22 20	22 22	22 29	22 31		22 34	22 37		22 43	22 45		22 48

		SN	SE	SE	SE	SE	SE 1	SE	SE	SE	SE	SE 1	SN	SE	SE 1	SE	SE	SE	SN	SE	SE	SE	SE 1		
Orpington 4	d					22 35	22 38				22 38	22 50			23 02			23 05			23 08		23 34		
Petts Wood 4	d					22 38				←	22 41							23 08			23 11				
Hither Green 4	d		22 26			22 50				22 50						23 06		23 20							
Lewisham 4	d		22 31		22 44	→		22 47	22 52	22 57						23 13	23 17	23 27				23 32			
St Johns	d							22 49									23 19								
New Cross 4	⊖ d		22 34					22 51	22 56							23 16	23 21					23 36			
London Victoria 15	⊖ a										23 15										23 44				
London Bridge 4	⊖ d	22 41	22 44	22 49	22 53		22 56	22 59	23 04	23 06		23 09	23 11	23 14	23 20	23 24	23 29	23 36	23 39	23 41		23 44	23 52		
London Blackfriars 3	⊖ a																								
London Cannon Street 4	⊖ a																								
London Waterloo (East) 4	⊖ d	22 47	22 49	22 55	22 58		23 01	23 04	23 09	23 11		23 14	23 17	23 19	23 25	23 29	23 34	23 41	23 44	23 47		23 50	23 57		
London Charing Cross 4	⊖ a	22 50	22 52	22 59	23 01		23 04	23 07	23 13	23 15		23 18	23 20	23 22	23 28	23 32	23 37	23 44	23 48	23 50		23 53	00 01		

Saturdays

		SE	SE	SE	SE	SE	SE	SE	SE	SE	SE	SE	SE 1		SE	SE	SE	SE	SE	SE	SE	SE	SE	SE	SN 1
Orpington 4	d			05 35					05 54	06 05		06 08	06 21						06 35			06 38			
Petts Wood 4	d			05 38					05 57	06 08		06 11							06 38			06 41			
Hither Green 4	d			05 50		05 56				06 20					06 26				06 50		06 56				
Lewisham 4	d		05 47	05 57	05 59	06 02		06 17		06 27	06 29				06 31		06 41	06 47	06 57	06 59	07 02			07 11	
St Johns	d		05 49					06 19										06 49							
New Cross 4	⊖ d		05 51			06 05		06 21							06 34			06 51			07 05				
London Victoria 15	⊖ a								06 35			06 44										07 15			
London Bridge 4	⊖ d	05 49	05 59	06 05	06 08	06 14	06 19	06 29		06 35	06 38		06 40		06 44	06 48	06 51	06 59	07 05	07 08	07 14		07 19	07 22	07 24
London Blackfriars 3	⊖ a																								
London Cannon Street 4	⊖ a																								
London Waterloo (East) 4	⊖ d	05 55	06 04	06 10	06 12	06 19	06 25	06 34		06 40	06 42		06 45		06 49	06 55	06 55	07 04	07 10	07 12	07 19		07 25	07 26	07 29
London Charing Cross 4	⊖ a	05 59	06 07	06 13	06 15	06 23	06 29	06 37		06 43	06 45		06 48		06 52	06 59	06 58	07 07	07 13	07 15	07 22		07 29	07 29	07 32

		SE	SE 1	SE		SE	SE	SE	SE	SE 1	SE	SE	SE	SN 1	SE 1	SE	SE		SE	SE	SE	SE	SE 1	SE	SE
Orpington 4	d	07 05	07 08						07 08	07 20					07 35					07 35		07 38	07 53		
Petts Wood 4	d	07 08					←		07 11											07 38		07 41			
Hither Green 4	d	07 20					07 20				07 26									07 49				07 56	
Lewisham 4	d	→		07 17		07 20	07 27	07 29			07 32		07 41			07 47			07 50	07 55	07 59			08 02	08 06
St Johns	d			07 19												07 49									08 08
New Cross 4	⊖ d			07 21							07 35					07 51								08 05	08 10
London Victoria 15	⊖ a					07 41			07 45										08 12			08 15			
London Bridge 4	⊖ d		07 27	07 29			07 35	07 38		07 40	07 44	07 46	07 50	07 53	07 55	07 59	08 00			08 05	08 08		08 10	08 14	08 17
London Blackfriars 3	⊖ a																								
London Cannon Street 4	⊖ a											07 50					08 03								08 20
London Waterloo (East) 4	⊖ d		07 31	07 34			07 40	07 42		07 45	07 49		07 54	07 57	08 00	08 04				08 10	08 12		08 15	08 19	
London Charing Cross 4	⊖ a		07 34	07 37			07 43	07 45		07 48	07 52		07 58	08 00	08 05	08 07				08 14	08 15		08 18	08 22	

For general notes see front of timetable
For details of catering facilities see Directory of Train Operators

Orpington, Petts Wood, Hither Green and Lewisham → London (Summary of Services)

	SE	SN 1	SE	SE 1	SE	SE	SE		SE	SE	SE	SE 1	SE	SE	SE	SE	SE 1	SN 1	SE	SE		SE 1	SE	SE
Orpington [4] d				08 05					08 05		08 08	08 20								08 23		08 35		
Petts Wood [4] d									08 08		08 11									08 26				
Hither Green [4] d			08 10						08 19	08 24									08 40					
Lewisham [4] d	08 11						08 20		08 25	08 29			08 32		08 36	08 41								
St Johns d			08 15												08 38				08 45					
New Cross [4] ⊖ d			08 17							08 32					08 40				08 47					
London Victoria [15] ⊖ a							08 42				08 43									08 59				
London Bridge [4] ⊖ d	08 19	08 22	08 23	08 25	08 29	08 30			08 35	08 38		08 41	08 43	08 44	08 47	08 49	08 51	08 52	08 53			08 55	08 59	09 00
London Blackfriars [3] ⊖ a																								
London Cannon Street [4] ⊖ a			08 27			08 33								08 47	08 50		08 54		08 57					09 03
London Waterloo (East) [4] ⊖ d	08 24	08 27		08 30	08 35				08 40	08 43		08 45	08 48			08 54		08 57				09 00	09 05	
London Charing Cross [4] ⊖ a	08 28	08 30		08 33	08 39				08 44	08 47		08 48	08 51			08 58		09 00				09 03	09 09	

	SE	SE	SE	SE	SE 1	SE	SE	SE	SE	SN 1	SE		SE	SE 1	SE	SE	SE	SE	SE	SE	SE	SE	SE	SE
Orpington [4] d		08 35		08 38	08 53								08 53	09 05					09 05				09 08	09 23
Petts Wood [4] d		08 38		08 41									08 56						09 08				09 11	09 26
Hither Green [4] d		08 49	08 54								09 10								09 19	09 24				
Lewisham [4] d	08 50	08 55	08 59			09 02		09 06							09 16			09 20	09 25	09 29	09 32			
St Johns d								09 08			09 14													
New Cross [4] ⊖ d			09 02					09 10			09 17				09 20					09 32				
London Victoria [15] ⊖ a	09 12			09 15									09 29					09 42					09 45	09 59
London Bridge [4] ⊖ d		09 05	09 08		09 11	09 13	09 14	09 17	09 19	09 22	09 23			09 25	09 27	09 29	09 30		09 35	09 38	09 41	09 44		
London Blackfriars [3] ⊖ a																								
London Cannon Street [4] ⊖ a							09 17	09 20			09 27				09 30		09 33					09 47		
London Waterloo (East) [4] ⊖ d		09 10	09 13		09 15	09 18			09 24	09 27				09 30		09 35			09 40	09 43	09 46			
London Charing Cross [4] ⊖ a		09 14	09 17		09 18	09 21			09 28	09 30				09 33		09 39			09 44	09 47	09 50			

	SE 1	SE		SE	SE 1	SN 1	SE	SE 1		SE	SE	SE	SE	SE	SE	SE	SE	SE	SE 1	SE	SE	SE	SN 1	SE
Orpington [4] d	09 26							09 36						09 35			09 38	09 53	09 57					
Petts Wood [4] d	09 29													09 38			09 41	09 56						
Hither Green [4] d							09 40							09 50	09 54									10 10
Lewisham [4] d		09 36								09 46			09 50	09 55	09 59	10 02					10 06			
St Johns d		09 38					09 44														10 08			10 14
New Cross [4] ⊖ d		09 40					09 47			09 50											10 10			10 17
London Victoria [15] ⊖ a													10 12				10 15	10 29						
London Bridge [4] ⊖ d	09 44	09 47		09 49	09 51	09 52	09 54	09 55		09 57	09 59	10 00		10 05	10 08	10 11			10 13	10 14	10 17	10 19	10 22	10 24
London Blackfriars [3] ⊖ a																								
London Cannon Street [4] ⊖ a		09 50			09 54		09 57			10 00		10 03								10 17	10 20			10 27
London Waterloo (East) [4] ⊖ d	09 48			09 54		09 57		10 00			10 05			10 10	10 13	10 16			10 18			10 24	10 27	
London Charing Cross [4] ⊖ a	09 51			09 58		10 00		10 03			10 09			10 14	10 17	10 20			10 21			10 28	10 30	

	SE 1	SE	SE	SE	SE	SE	SE	SE	SE	SE	SE	SE 1	SE	SE	SE 1	SN 1	SE	SE 1	and at the same minutes past each hour until		SE	SE	SE
Orpington [4] d	10 05					10 05				10 08	10 23	10 26											
Petts Wood [4] d						10 08				10 11	10 26	10 29											
Hither Green [4] d						10 19	10 24										10 40						
Lewisham [4] d		10 16			10 20	10 25	10 29	10 32					10 36								17 46		
St Johns d													10 38				10 44						
New Cross [4] ⊖ d		10 20											10 40				10 47				17 50		
London Victoria [15] ⊖ a					10 42					10 45	10 59												
London Bridge [4] ⊖ d	10 25	10 27	10 29	10 30		10 35	10 38	10 41	10 44			10 44	10 47	10 49	10 51	10 52	10 54	10 55			17 57	17 59	18 00
London Blackfriars [3] ⊖ a																							
London Cannon Street [4] ⊖ a		10 30		10 34					10 47				10 50		10 54		10 57				18 00		18 03
London Waterloo (East) [4] ⊖ d	10 30		10 35			10 40	10 43	10 46				10 48		10 54		10 57		11 00				18 05	
London Charing Cross [4] ⊖ a	10 33		10 39			10 44	10 47	10 50				10 51		10 58		11 00		11 03				18 09	

	SE	SE	SE	SE	SE	SE	SE 1	SE	SE	SE	SN 1		SE	SE	SE 1	SE	SE	SE	SE 1	SE	SE	SE	SE	SE
Orpington [4] d		17 35			17 38	17 53	17 57							18 05	18 05			18 08	18 11			←		
Petts Wood [4] d		17 38			17 41	17 56								18 08				18 11						
Hither Green [4] d		17 50	17 54										18 10	18 19								18 19	18 24	
Lewisham [4] d	17 50	17 55	17 59	18 02					18 06					→		18 16	18 20				18 23	18 26	18 29	18 32
St Johns d									18 08				18 14										18 31	
New Cross [4] ⊖ d									18 10				18 17			18 20							18 32	
London Victoria [15] ⊖ a	18 12				18 15	18 29											18 42	18 45						
London Bridge [4] ⊖ d		18 05	18 08	18 11			18 13	18 14	18 17	18 19	18 22		18 24		18 25	18 27			18 28	18 30	18 34	18 36	18 38	18 41
London Blackfriars [3] ⊖ a																								
London Cannon Street [4] ⊖ a								18 17	18 20				18 27			18 30				18 33				
London Waterloo (East) [4] ⊖ d		18 10	18 13	18 16			18 18			18 24	18 27				18 30				18 33		18 38	18 42	18 44	18 46
London Charing Cross [4] ⊖ a		18 14	18 17	18 20			18 21			18 28	18 30				18 33				18 36		18 41	18 45	18 48	18 50

	SE	SE 1		SE	SE	SN 1	SE 1	SE	SE	SE	SE	SE	SE 1	SE	SE		SE	SE	SE	SE	SE	SN 1	SE 1	SE
Orpington [4] d				18 23	18 35		18 36				←	18 38	18 51							18 53	19 05		19 08	
Petts Wood [4] d				18 26	18 38							18 41								18 56	19 08			
Hither Green [4] d					18 49						18 49			18 56							19 20			
Lewisham [4] d	18 41				→			18 47		18 50	18 55			19 01	19 02				19 11		→			19 17
St Johns d								18 49									←							19 19
New Cross [4] ⊖ d								18 51						19 04			19 04							19 21
London Victoria [15] ⊖ a				18 59						19 12		19 15		→						19 29				
London Bridge [4] ⊖ d	18 50	18 51				18 52	18 55	18 59	19 04		19 06		19 09		19 11		19 14	19 19	19 21			19 24	19 26	19 29
London Blackfriars [3] ⊖ a																								
London Cannon Street [4] ⊖ a		18 54																						
London Waterloo (East) [4] ⊖ d	18 54					18 57	19 01	19 04	19 10		19 12		19 15		19 16		19 19	19 23	19 26			19 28	19 31	19 34
London Charing Cross [4] ⊖ a	18 58					19 00	19 06	19 07	19 13		19 15		19 19		19 20		19 22	19 26	19 29			19 31	19 34	19 37

For general notes see front of timetable
For details of catering facilities see
Directory of Train Operators

Table 199

Saturdays

Orpington, Petts Wood, Hither Green and Lewisham → London (Summary of Services)

Station		SE	SE	SE	SE 1	SN	SE		SE	SE	SE	SE	SE	SE	SE	SE 1	SN	SE	SE	SE		SE	SE	SE 1	SE
Orpington 4	d			19 08	19 20						19 23			19 35	19 38	19 51						19 53	20 05	20 08	
Petts Wood 4	d		←	19 11							19 26			19 38	19 41							19 56	20 08		
Hither Green 4	d		19 20				19 26							19 50				19 56					20 20		
Lewisham 4	d	19 22	19 27				19 31			19 44		19 47	19 52	19 57				20 01		20 14			→		20 17
St Johns	d											19 49													20 19
New Cross 4	⊖ d	19 26					19 34					19 51	19 56					20 04							20 21
London Victoria 15	⊖ a			19 44							19 59				20 14							20 29			
London Bridge 4	⊖ d	19 34	19 36		19 39	19 41	19 44		19 49	19 53		19 59	20 04	20 06		20 09	20 11	20 14	20 19	20 23				20 26	20 29
London Blackfriars 3	⊖ a																								
London Cannon Street 4	⊖ a																								
London Waterloo (East) 4	⊖ d	19 39	19 41		19 45	19 48	19 49		19 55	19 58		20 04	20 09	20 11		20 15	20 18	20 19	20 25	20 28				20 31	20 34
London Charing Cross 4	⊖ a	19 43	19 45		19 49	19 51	19 52		19 59	20 01		20 07	20 13	20 15		20 19	20 21	20 22	20 29	20 31				20 34	20 37

Station		SE	SE	SE	SE 1	SN	SE	SE	SE	SE	SE		SE	SE	SE 1	SN	SE	SE	SE	SE	SE 1	SE	SE	SE	SE
Orpington 4	d			20 08	20 20								20 35	20 38	20 51					21 05	21 08				21 08
Petts Wood 4	d		←	20 11									20 38	20 41						21 08				←	21 11
Hither Green 4	d		20 20				20 26						20 50				20 56			21 20				21 20	
Lewisham 4	d	20 22	20 27				20 31		20 44	20 47	20 52		20 57				21 01		21 14	→		21 17	21 22	21 27	
St Johns	d									20 49												21 19			
New Cross 4	⊖ d	20 26					20 34			20 51	20 56						21 04					21 21	21 26		
London Victoria 15	⊖ a			20 44										21 14											21 45
London Bridge 4	⊖ d	20 34	20 36		20 39	20 41	20 44	20 49	20 53	20 59	21 04		21 06		21 09	21 11	21 14	21 19	21 23		21 26	21 29	21 34	21 36	
London Blackfriars 3	⊖ a																								
London Cannon Street 4	⊖ a																								
London Waterloo (East) 4	⊖ d	20 39	20 41		20 45	20 48	20 49	20 55	20 58	21 04	21 09		21 11		21 15	21 18	21 19	21 25	21 28		21 31	21 34	21 39	21 41	
London Charing Cross 4	⊖ a	20 43	20 45		20 49	20 51	20 52	20 59	21 01	21 07	21 13		21 15		21 19	21 21	21 22	21 29	21 31		21 34	21 37	21 43	21 45	

Station		SE 1		SN	SE	SE	SE	SE	SE	SE	SE	SE 1	SN	SE	SE		SE	SE	SE 1	SE	SE	SE	SE	SE 1	SN
Orpington 4	d	21 20								21 35	21 38	21 51						22 05	22 08				22 08	22 20	
Petts Wood 4	d									21 38	21 41							22 08				←	22 11		
Hither Green 4	d				21 26					21 50				21 56				22 20				22 20			
Lewisham 4	d				21 31		21 44	21 47	21 52	21 57				22 01			22 14	→		22 17	22 22	22 27			
St Johns	d							21 49												22 19					
New Cross 4	⊖ d				21 34			21 51	21 56					22 04						22 21	22 26				
London Victoria 15	⊖ a										22 15												22 45		
London Bridge 4	⊖ d	21 39		21 41	21 44	21 49	21 53	21 59	22 04	22 06		22 09	22 11	22 14	22 19		22 23		22 26	22 29	22 34	22 36		22 39	22 41
London Blackfriars 3	⊖ a																								
London Cannon Street 4	⊖ a																								
London Waterloo (East) 4	⊖ d	21 45		21 48	21 49	21 55	21 58	22 04	22 09	22 11		22 15	22 18	22 19	22 25		22 28		22 31	22 34	22 39	22 41		22 45	22 48
London Charing Cross 4	⊖ a	21 49		21 51	21 52	21 59	22 01	22 07	22 13	22 15		22 19	22 21	22 22	22 29		22 31		22 34	22 37	22 43	22 45		22 49	22 51

Station		SE	SE	SE	SE	SE		SE	SE	SE 1	SN	SE	SE	SE	SE	SN	SE	SE	SE		SE 1				
Orpington 4	d							22 35	22 38	22 51					23 05				23 08		23 37				
Petts Wood 4	d							22 38	22 41						23 08				23 11						
Hither Green 4	d	22 26						22 50					23 06		23 20										
Lewisham 4	d	22 31		22 44	22 47	22 52		22 57					23 11	23 17	23 27			23 32							
St Johns	d				22 49									23 19											
New Cross 4	⊖ d	22 34			22 51	22 56							23 14	23 21				23 36							
London Victoria 15	⊖ a								23 15										23 45						
London Bridge 4	⊖ d	22 44	22 49	22 53	22 59	23 04		23 06		23 09	23 11	23 14	23 24	23 29	23 35	23 39	23 41	23 44			23 53				
London Blackfriars 3	⊖ a																								
London Cannon Street 4	⊖ a																								
London Waterloo (East) 4	⊖ d	22 49	22 55	22 58	23 04	23 09		23 11		23 14	23 17	23 19	23 29	23 34	23 40	23 44	23 47	23 50			23 58				
London Charing Cross 4	⊖ a	22 52	22 59	23 03	23 07	23 13		23 15		23 18	23 20	23 22	23 32	23 37	23 43	23 48	23 50	23 53			00 01				

Sundays

Station		SN	SE	SE	SE	SE	SE	SE	SE	SE 1	SN		SE	SE	SE	SE	SE 1	SE	SE	SE	SN	SE		SE	SE
Orpington 4	d		06 44		07 01			07 08	07 14	07 24					07 31	07 38	07 41								07 44
Petts Wood 4	d		06 47		07 04			07 11	07 17						07 34	07 41		←							07 47
Hither Green 4	d				07 15		07 21								07 45			07 45		07 51					
Lewisham 4	d			07 16	07 20		07 26						07 36	07 45	→			07 50		07 56		08 06		08 11	
St Johns	d																							08 13	
New Cross 4	⊖ d			07 20			07 30						07 40							08 00		08 10		08 15	
London Victoria 15	⊖ a		07 23					07 43	07 54							08 13									08 24
London Bridge 4	⊖ d	07 12		07 27	07 30	07 34	07 37			07 40	07 42		07 48	07 54			07 57	07 59	08 04	08 07	08 12	08 18		08 21	
London Blackfriars 3	⊖ a																								
London Cannon Street 4	⊖ a																								
London Waterloo (East) 4	⊖ d	07 17		07 31	07 34	07 39	07 42			07 45	07 47		07 53	07 59			08 02	08 04	08 09	08 12	08 17	08 23		08 26	
London Charing Cross 4	⊖ a	07 20		07 36	07 38	07 42	07 45			07 48	07 50		07 56	08 02			08 05	08 09	08 12	08 15	08 20	08 26		08 29	

For general notes see front of timetable
For details of catering facilities see
Directory of Train Operators

Table 199

Sundays

Orpington, Petts Wood, Hither Green and Lewisham → London (Summary of Services)

		SE	SE	SE	SE	SE	SE [1]	SN	SE	SE	SE		SE	SE	SE [1]	SE	SE	SE	SE [1]	SN	SE	SE		SE	SE
Orpington [4]	d		08 01			08 08	08 24						08 31	08 38	08 39				08 54						09 01
Petts Wood [4]	d		08 04			08 11							08 34	08 41		←									09 04
Hither Green [4]	d		08 15		08 21								08 45 →			08 45		08 51							09 15 →
Lewisham [4]	d	08 15	08 20		08 26				08 36	08 41	08 45					08 50		08 56			09 06	09 11		09 15	
St Johns	d									08 43												09 13			
New Cross [4]	⊖ d				08 30				08 40	08 45								09 00			09 10	09 15			
London Victoria [15]	⊖ a					08 43								09 13											
London Bridge [4]	⊖ d	08 24	08 29	08 34	08 37		08 40	08 42	08 48	08 51	08 54				08 56	08 59	09 04	09 07	09 10	09 12	09 18	09 21		09 24	
London Blackfriars [3]	⊖ a																								
London Cannon Street [4]	⊖ a																								
London Waterloo (East) [4]	⊖ d	08 29	08 34	08 39	08 42		08 45	08 47	08 53	08 56	08 59				09 02	09 04	09 09	09 12	09 15	09 17	09 23	09 26		09 29	
London Charing Cross [4]	⊖ a	08 32	08 37	08 42	08 45		08 48	08 50	08 56	08 59	09 02				09 05	09 07	09 12	09 15	09 18	09 20	09 26	09 29		09 32	

		SE	SE [1]	SE	SE	SE	SE [1]	SN	SE	SE	SE		SE	SE	SE [1]	SE	SE	SE	SE [1]	SN	SE	SE		SE	SE
Orpington [4]	d	09 08	09 09				09 24						09 31	09 38	09 39				09 54						10 01
Petts Wood [4]	d	09 11		←									09 34	09 41		←									10 04
Hither Green [4]	d			09 15		09 21							09 45 →			09 45		09 51							10 15 →
Lewisham [4]	d			09 20		09 26			09 36	09 41	09 45					09 50		09 56			10 06	10 11		10 15	
St Johns	d									09 43												10 13			
New Cross [4]	⊖ d					09 30			09 40	09 45								10 00			10 10	10 15			
London Victoria [15]	⊖ a	09 43												10 13											
London Bridge [4]	⊖ d		09 26	09 29	09 34	09 37	09 40	09 42	09 48	09 51	09 54				09 56	09 59	10 04	10 07	10 10	10 12	10 18	10 21		10 24	
London Blackfriars [3]	⊖ a																								
London Cannon Street [4]	⊖ a																								
London Waterloo (East) [4]	⊖ d		09 32	09 34	09 39	09 42	09 45	09 47	09 53	09 56	09 59				10 02	10 04	10 09	10 12	10 15	10 17	10 23	10 26		10 29	
London Charing Cross [4]	⊖ a		09 35	09 37	09 42	09 45	09 48	09 50	09 56	09 59	10 02				10 05	10 07	10 12	10 15	10 18	10 20	10 26	10 29		10 32	

		SE	SE [1]	SE	SE	SE		SE [1]	SN	SE	SE	SE	SE	SE	SE [1]	SE	SE	SE	SE [1]	SN	SE	SE	SE	SE	SE
Orpington [4]	d	10 08	10 09					10 24					10 31	10 38	10 39				10 54					11 01	11 08
Petts Wood [4]	d	10 11		←									10 34	10 41		←								11 04	11 11
Hither Green [4]	d			10 15		10 21							10 45 →			10 45		10 51						11 15 →	
Lewisham [4]	d			10 20		10 26				10 36	10 41	10 45				10 50		10 56			11 06	11 11	11 15		
St Johns	d										10 43											11 13			
New Cross [4]	⊖ d					10 30				10 40	10 45							11 00			11 10	11 15			
London Victoria [15]	⊖ a	10 43												11 13											11 43
London Bridge [4]	⊖ d		10 26	10 29	10 34	10 37		10 40	10 42	10 48	10 51	10 54			10 56	10 59	11 04	11 07	11 10	11 12	11 18	11 21	11 24		
London Blackfriars [3]	⊖ a																								
London Cannon Street [4]	⊖ a																								
London Waterloo (East) [4]	⊖ d		10 32	10 34	10 39	10 42		10 45	10 47	10 53	10 56	10 59			11 02	11 04	11 09	11 12	11 15	11 17	11 23	11 26	11 29		
London Charing Cross [4]	⊖ a		10 35	10 37	10 42	10 45		10 48	10 50	10 56	10 59	11 02			11 06	11 07	11 12	11 15	11 18	11 20	11 26	11 29	11 32		

		SE [1]	SE	SE	SE			SE [1]	SN	SE	SE	SE	SE	SE	SE [1]	SE	SE		SE	SE [1]	SN	SE	SE	SE
Orpington [4]	d	11 09				and at		18 24					18 31	18 38	18 39					18 54				
Petts Wood [4]	d		←			the same							18 34	18 41		←								
Hither Green [4]	d		11 15		11 21	minutes							18 45 →			18 45			18 51					
Lewisham [4]	d		11 20		11 26					18 36	18 41	18 45				18 50			18 56			19 06	19 11	19 15
St Johns	d										18 43												19 13	
New Cross [4]	⊖ d				11 30	past				18 40	18 45								19 00			19 10	19 15	
London Victoria [15]	⊖ a													19 14										
London Bridge [4]	⊖ d	11 26	11 29	11 34	11 37	each		18 40	18 42	18 48	18 51	18 54			18 56	18 59	19 04		19 07	19 10	19 12	19 18	19 21	19 24
London Blackfriars [3]	⊖ a					hour until																		
London Cannon Street [4]	⊖ a																							
London Waterloo (East) [4]	⊖ d	11 32	11 34	11 39	11 42			18 45	18 47	18 53	18 56	18 59			19 02	19 04	19 09		19 12	19 15	19 17	19 23	19 26	19 29
London Charing Cross [4]	⊖ a	11 35	11 37	11 42	11 45			18 48	18 50	18 56	18 59	19 02			19 06	19 07	19 12		19 15	19 18	19 20	19 26	19 29	19 32

		SE	SE	SE [1]	SE	SE	SE		SE [1]	SN	SE	SE	SE	SE	SE	SE [1]	SE	SE		SE	SE [1]	SN	SE	SE	SE
Orpington [4]	d	19 01	19 08	19 09					19 24					19 31	19 38	19 40					19 54				
Petts Wood [4]	d	19 04	19 11		←									19 34	19 41		←								
Hither Green [4]	d	19 15 →			19 15		19 21							19 45 →			19 45			19 51					
Lewisham [4]	d				19 20		19 26				19 36	19 41	19 45				19 50			19 56			20 06	20 11	20 15
St Johns	d											19 43												20 13	
New Cross [4]	⊖ d						19 30				19 40	19 45								20 00			20 10	20 15	
London Victoria [15]	⊖ a		19 43												20 14										
London Bridge [4]	⊖ d			19 26	19 29	19 34	19 37		19 40	19 42	19 48	19 51	19 54			19 56	19 59	20 04		20 07	20 10	20 12	20 18	20 21	20 24
London Blackfriars [3]	⊖ a																								
London Cannon Street [4]	⊖ a																								
London Waterloo (East) [4]	⊖ d			19 32	19 34	19 39	19 42		19 45	19 47	19 53	19 56	19 59			20 02	20 04	20 09		20 12	20 15	20 17	20 23	20 26	20 29
London Charing Cross [4]	⊖ a			19 35	19 37	19 42	19 45		19 48	19 50	19 56	19 59	20 02			20 05	20 07	20 12		20 15	20 18	20 20	20 26	20 29	20 32

		SE	SE	SE	SE	SE [1]	SN		SE	SE	SE	SE	SE	SE [1]	SE	SE	SE	SE [1]		SN	SE	SE	SE	SE	SE
Orpington [4]	d	20 01			20 08	20 24						20 31	20 38	20 40				20 54						21 01	
Petts Wood [4]	d	20 04			20 11							20 34	20 41		←									21 04	
Hither Green [4]	d	20 15		20 21								20 45 →			20 45		20 51							21 15	
Lewisham [4]	d	20 20		20 26					20 36	20 41	20 45				20 50		20 56				21 06	21 11	21 15	21 20	
St Johns	d									20 43												21 13			
New Cross [4]	⊖ d			20 30					20 40	20 45							21 00				21 10	21 15			
London Victoria [15]	⊖ a				20 43								21 13												
London Bridge [4]	⊖ d	20 29	20 34	20 37		20 40	20 42		20 48	20 51	20 54			20 56	20 59	21 04	21 07	21 10		21 12	21 18	21 21	21 24	21 29	21 34
London Blackfriars [3]	⊖ a																								
London Cannon Street [4]	⊖ a																								
London Waterloo (East) [4]	⊖ d	20 34	20 39	20 42		20 45	20 47		20 53	20 56	20 59			21 02	21 04	21 09	21 12	21 15		21 17	21 23	21 26	21 29	21 34	21 39
London Charing Cross [4]	⊖ a	20 37	20 42	20 45		20 48	20 50		20 56	20 59	21 02			21 05	21 07	21 12	21 15	21 18		21 20	21 26	21 29	21 32	21 37	21 42

For general notes see front of timetable
For details of catering facilities see
Directory of Train Operators

Table 199

Sundays

Orpington, Petts Wood, Hither Green and Lewisham → London (Summary of Services)

		SE	SE	SE [1]	SN	SE	SE		SE	SE	SE	SE [1]	SE	SE	SE	SE [1]	SN	SE		SE	SE	SE	SE	SE	SE
Orpington [4]	d		21 08	21 24						21 31	21 38	21 40	←			21 54						22 01			22 08
Petts Wood [4]	d		21 11							21 34	21 41		←									22 04			22 11
Hither Green [4]	d	21 21								21 45 →			21 45		21 51							22 15		22 21	
Lewisham [4]	d	21 26				21 36	21 41		21 45	→			21 50		21 56			22 06		22 11	22 15	22 20		22 26	
St Johns	d						21 43													22 13					
New Cross [4]	⊖ d	21 30				21 40	21 45								22 00			22 10		22 15				22 30	
London Victoria [15]	⊖ a		21 43								22 13														22 43
London Bridge [4]	⊖ d	21 37		21 40	21 42	21 48	21 51		21 54			21 56	21 59	22 04	22 07	22 10	22 12	22 18		22 21	22 24	22 29	22 34	22 37	
London Blackfriars [3]	⊖ a																								
London Cannon Street [4]	⊖ a																								
London Waterloo (East) [4]	⊖ d	21 42		21 45	21 47	21 53	21 56		21 59			22 02	22 04	22 09	22 12	22 15	22 17	22 23		22 26	22 29	22 34	22 39	22 42	
London Charing Cross [4]	⊖ a	21 45		21 48	21 50	21 56	21 59		22 02			22 05	22 07	22 12	22 15	22 18	22 20	22 26		22 29	22 32	22 37	22 42	22 45	

		SE [1]	SN	SE	SE	SE	SE		SE	SE [1]	SE	SE	SE	SE [1]	SN	SE	SE	SE		SE	SE	SE			
Orpington [4]	d	22 24					22 31		22 38	22 40	←			22 54				23 01				23 14			
Petts Wood [4]	d						22 34		22 41		←							23 04				23 17			
Hither Green [4]	d						22 45 →				22 45		22 51					23 15		23 21					
Lewisham [4]	d			22 36	22 41	22 45	→				22 50		22 56			23 06	23 11	23 20		23 26	23 41				
St Johns	d				22 43												23 13				23 43				
New Cross [4]	⊖ d			22 40	22 45								23 00			23 10	23 15			23 30	23 45				
London Victoria [15]	⊖ a								23 13													23 53			
London Bridge [4]	⊖ d	22 40	22 42	22 48	22 51	22 54				22 56	22 59	23 04	23 07	23 10	23 12	23 18	23 21	23 29		23 37	23 51				
London Blackfriars [3]	⊖ a																								
London Cannon Street [4]	⊖ a																								
London Waterloo (East) [4]	⊖ d	22 45	22 47	22 53	22 56	22 59				23 02	23 04	23 09	23 12	23 15	23 17	23 23	23 26	23 34		23 42	23 56				
London Charing Cross [4]	⊖ a	22 48	22 50	22 56	22 59	23 02				23 05	23 07	23 12	23 15	23 19	23 20	23 26	23 30	23 37		23 45	23 59				

For general notes see front of timetable
For details of catering facilities see Directory of Train Operators

Network Diagram for Tables 200, 203, 204

also 199★

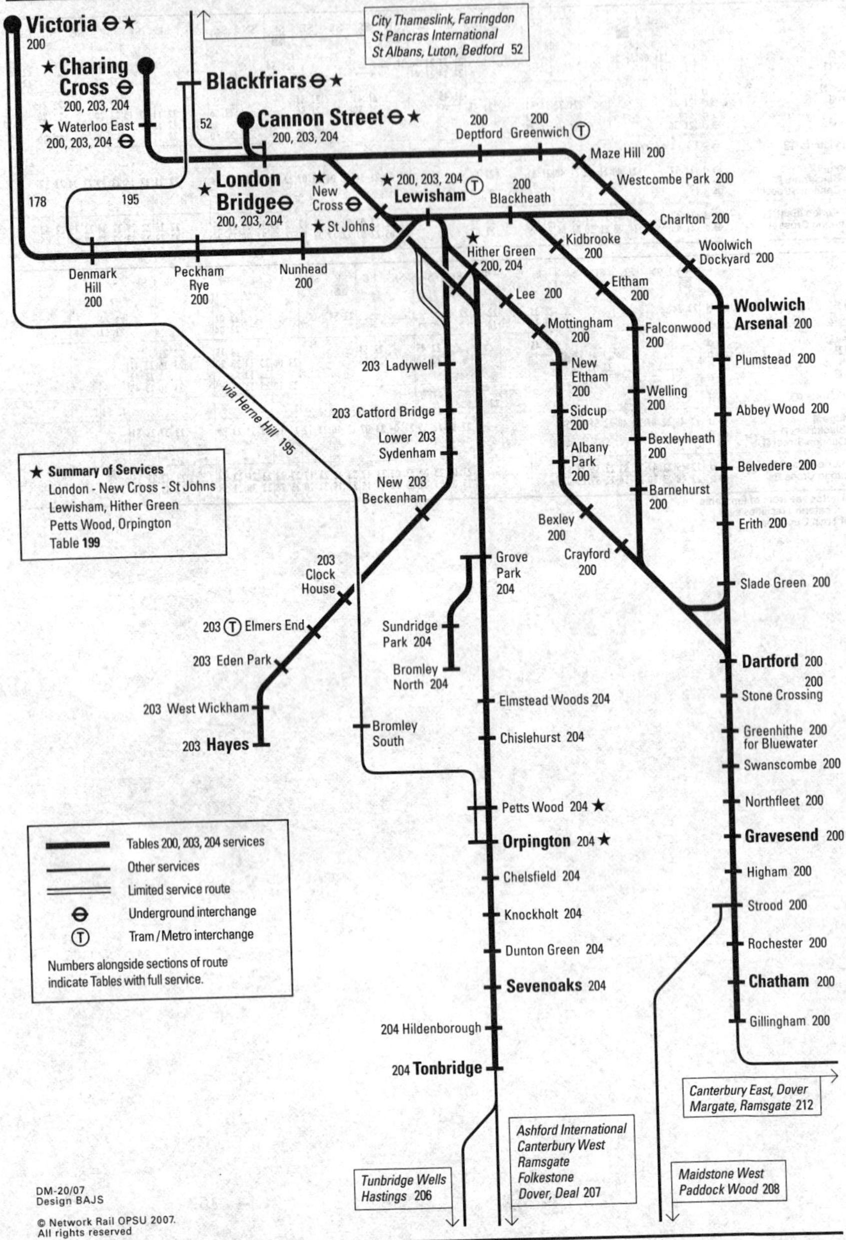

DM-20/07
Design BAJS

Mondays to Fridays

For details of Bank Holiday service alterations please see first page of Table 195

London → Dartford and Gillingham

Network Diagram - see first page of Table 200

Miles	Miles	Miles	Miles	Miles			SE MO	SE MX	SE MO	SE MX	SE MX	SE MO	SE MO	SE MX	SE MO	SE MX	SE MX 50	SE	SE 1 A	SE	SE	SE	SE	SE	SE
0	—	0	0	—	**London Charing Cross 4**	⊖ d	22p50	22p50	23p20	23p20	23p34	23p37	23p40	23p40	23p47	23p47	00 04	00 14		04 50	04 56	05 04	05 18	05 26	05 34
¾	—	¾	¾	—	**London Waterloo (East) 4**	⊖ d	22p53	22p53	23p23	23p23	23p37	23p40	23p43	23p43	23p50	23p50	00 07	00 17		04 53	04 59	05 07	05 21	05 29	05 37
—	0	—	—	—	**London Cannon Street 4**	⊖ d																			
1¾	¾	1¾	1¾	—	**London Bridge 4**	⊖ d	22p59	22p59	23p29	23p29	23p43	23p45	23p48	23p48	23p55	23p55	00 13	00 23		04 58	05 04	05 12	05 28	05 34	05 42
—	3¾	—	—	—	Deptford	d							23p53	23p54								05 17			
—	4¼	—	—	—	Greenwich 4	d							23p55	23p56								05 19			
—	5¼	—	—	—	Maze Hill	d							23p59	00 01								05 23			
—	5¾	—	—	—	Westcombe Park	d							00 01	00 02								05 25			
—	—	—	—	0	**London Victoria 15**	⊖ d																			
—	—	—	—	4¼	Denmark Hill 4	d																			
—	—	—	—	5	Peckham Rye 4	d																			
—	—	—	—	5¾	Nunhead 4	d																			
—	—	4¾	4¾	—	New Cross 4	⊖ d					23p48	23p50			23p59	23p58	00 18	00 28		05 03	05 09		05 33	05 39	
—	—	5½	5½	—	St Johns	d																			
6	—	6	6	7½	Lewisham 4	d	23p08	23p08	23p38	23p38	23p53	23p55			00 04	00 05	00 23	00 33		05 08	05 14		05 38	05 44	05 52
7	—	7	—	8½	Blackheath 4	d	23p11	23p11	23p41	23p41		23p58				00 07		00 36			05 16			05 46	05 54
—	—	8	—	9½	Kidbrooke	d						00 01				00 10					05 19			05 49	
—	—	9	—	10½	Eltham	d						00 04				00 14					05 23			05 53	
—	—	10¼	—	11¾	Falconwood	d						00 07				00 16					05 25			05 55	
—	—	11¼	—	12¾	Welling	d						00 09				00 19					05 28			05 58	
—	—	12¾	—	14¼	Bexleyheath	d						00 12				00 21					05 30			06 00	
—	—	14	—	15½	Barnehurst 4	d						00 15				00 24					05 33			06 03	
—	—	—	7¼	—	Hither Green 4	d					23p57				00 08		00 27			05 11			05 41		
—	—	—	8	—	Lee	d					23p59				00 10		00 29			05 13			05 43		
—	—	—	9½	—	Mottingham	d					00 02				00 13		00 32			05 16			05 46		
—	—	—	10½	—	New Eltham	d					00 05				00 16		00 35			05 19			05 49		
—	—	—	12	—	Sidcup 4	d					00 08				00 19		00 38			05 22			05 52		
—	—	—	13	—	Albany Park	d					00 10				00 21		00 40			05 24			05 54		
—	—	—	14	—	Bexley	d					00 12				00 23		00 42			05 26			05 56		
—	—	—	15½	—	Crayford	d					00 15				00 26		00 45			05 29			05 59		
9	6½	—	—	—	Charlton 4	d	23p15	23p15	23p45	23p45			00 03	00 04				00 40				05 28			05 58
10	7½	—	—	—	Woolwich Dockyard	d							00 06	00 07											
10¾	8¼	—	—	—	**Woolwich Arsenal 4**	d	23p20	23p20	23p50	23p50			00 09	00 10				00 45				05 33			06 03
11¼	8¾	—	—	—	Plumstead	d							00 11	00 12				00 47				05 35			
12¾	10½	—	—	—	Abbey Wood	d	23p25	23p25	23p55	23p55			00 14	00 15				00 50				05 39			06 08
14¼	11¾	—	—	—	Belvedere	d							00 17	00 18				00 53				05 41			
15½	13	—	—	—	Erith	d							00 20	00 21				00 56				05 44			
16¾	14¼	—	—	—	Slade Green 4	d							00 23	00 24				00 58				05 48			06 13
18¾	16¼	17	17¼	18½	**Dartford 4**	a	23p33	23p33	00 03	00 04	00 20	00 21	00 27	00 29	00 30	00 31	00 50	01 03		05 33	05 41	05 53	06 03	06 11	06 19
—	—	—	—	—		d	23p34	23p34	00 04	00 04								01 04	05 06		05 42	05 54		06 12	06 20
20¾	—	—	19¼	—	Stone Crossing	d	23p37	23p37		00 08											05 45	05 57		06 15	06 23
21½	—	—	20	—	Greenhithe for Bluewater	d	23p40	23p40	00 09	00 10								01 09	05 11		05 48	06 00		06 18	06 26
22¾	—	—	21¼	—	Swanscombe	d	23p42	23p42		00 12											05 50	06 02		06 20	06 28
23½	—	—	22	—	Northfleet	d	23p44	23p44		00 14											05 52	06 04		06 22	06 30
25½	—	—	24	—	**Gravesend 4**	d	23p48	23p50	00 16	00 20								01 16	05 18		05 56	06a08		06 26	06 34
30	—	—	28½	—	Higham	d	23p54	23p56	00 22	00 26								01 22	05 24		06 02			06 32	06 40
32¾	—	—	31¼	—	Strood 4	d	23p58	00 02	00 27	00 32								01 28	05 29		06 08			06 38	06a45
—	—	—	—	—	Maidstone West 4	a													*06 03*		*06 41*				
33¾	—	—	32¼	—	Rochester 4	d	00 03	00 07	00 31	00 39								01 31	05 33		06 11			06 41	
34¼	—	—	32¾	—	**Chatham 4**	d	00 06	00 09	00 34	00 42								01 34	05 36		06 14			06 44	
36	—	—	34½	—	**Gillingham (Kent) 4**	a	00 09	00 13	00 37	00 45								01 37	05 39		06 17			06 47	

For general notes see front of timetable
For details of catering facilities see Directory of Train Operators

A To Dover Priory (Table 212)

For details of Bank Holiday service alterations please see first page of Table 195

London → Dartford and Gillingham

Network Diagram - see first page of Table 200

Station		SE	SE	SE	SE	SE	SE	SE	SE	SE	SE	SE	SE	SE	SE	SE	SE	SE	SE	SE	SE	SE	SE	SE	SE
London Charing Cross 4	⊖ d	05 46	05 54	06 02		06 20		06 32	06 40		06 54		07 03		07 20		07 30			07 42					08 00
London Waterloo (East) 4	⊖ d	05 49	05 57	06 05		06 23		06 35	06 43		06 57		07 06		07 23		07 33			07 45					08 03
London Cannon Street 4	⊖ d				06 12		06 30			06 48		07 04		07 22		07 32		07 39			07 48	07 54	07 58		
London Bridge 4	⊖ d	05 54	06 02	06 10	06 16	06 28	06 34	06 40	06 48	06 52	07 04	07 08	07 11	07 26	07 28	07 36	07 38	07 43		07 50	07 52	07 58	08 02		08 09
Deptford	d		06 07				06 39				07 09					07 41									
Greenwich 4	⛴ d		06 09				06 41				07 11					07 43					07 59				
Maze Hill	d		06 13				06 45				07 15					07 47									
Westcombe Park	d		06 15				06 47				07 17					07 49									
London Victoria 15	⊖ d																								
Denmark Hill 4	d																								
Peckham Rye 4	d																								
Nunhead 4	d																								
New Cross 4	⊖ d	05 59		06 15		06 33		06 47				07 13			07 33		07 43	07 49				08 03	08 07		
St Johns	d	06 01		06 17								07 15					07 45					08 05			
Lewisham 4	⛴ d	06 04		06 20	06 24	06 38		06 52	06 56	07 00		07 18	07 22	07 34	07 38		07 48	07 53				08 08	08 12		
Blackheath 4	d			06 22	06 26			06 54	06 58			07 20	07 24	07 36			07 50					08 10	08 14		
Kidbrooke	d			06 25				06 57				07 23		07 39			07 53					08 13			
Eltham	d			06 29				07 01				07 27		07 43			07 57					08 17			
Falconwood	d			06 31				07 03				07 29		07 45			07 59					08 19			
Welling	d			06 34				07 06				07 32		07 48			08 02					08 22			
Bexleyheath	d			06 36				07 08				07 34		07 50			08 04					08 24			
Barnehurst 4	d			06 39				07 11				07 37		07a53			08 07					08 27		07 56	
Hither Green 4	d	06 07				06 41				07 03					07 41			07 57		08 01					08 18
Lee	d	06 09				06 43				07 05					07 43					08 03					
Mottingham	d	06 12				06 46				07 08					07 46					08 06					
New Eltham	d	06 15				06 49				07 11					07 49			08a05		08 09					08 26
Sidcup 4	d	06 18				06 52				07 14					07 52					08 12					08 28
Albany Park	d	06 20				06 54				07 16					07 54					08 14					08 30
Bexley	d	06 22				06 56				07 18					07 56					08 16					08a33
Crayford	d	06 25				06 59				07 21	07a46				07 59					08 19					
Charlton 4	d		06 18		06 30		06 50		07 02		07 20		07 28			07 52			←		08 06		08 18	08a19	
Woolwich Dockyard	d		06 20				06 52				07 22					07 54 →			07 54						
Woolwich Arsenal 4	d		06 23		06 35		06 55		07 07		07 25		07 33						07 57		08 11		08 23		
Plumstead	d		06 25				06 57				07 27								07 59						
Abbey Wood	d		06 29		06 40		07 01		07 12		07 31		07 38						08 03		08 16		08 28		
Belvedere	d		06 31				07 03				07 33								08 05						
Erith	d		06 34				07 06				07 36								08 08						
Slade Green 4	d		06 38		06 45		07 09				07a39		07 43						08 11					08a00	
Dartford 4	a	06 30	06 43	06 45	06 51	07 04	07 15	07 16	07 22	07 25		07 46	07 49		08 04		08 13		08 16	08 24	08 26	08 33	08 36		
	d	06 30		06 46	06 52	07 05		07 16	07 28	07 30					08 05						08 28	08 34			
Stone Crossing	d				06 55	07 08				07 33					08 08						08 31				
Greenhithe for Bluewater	d				06 58	07 11		07 21	07 33	07 36					08 11						08 34	08 39			
Swanscombe	d				07 00	07 13				07 38					08 13						08 36				
Northfleet	d				07 02	07 15				07 40					08 15						08 38				
Gravesend 4	d	06a40		06 56	07 06	07 19		07 28	07 40	07a45					08 19						08a42	08 46			
Higham	d			07 02	07 12	07 25		07 34	07 46						08 25							08 52			
Strood 4	d			07 08	07a18	07 32		07a40	07b54						08 32							08 58			
Maidstone West 4	a			*07 35*		*07 57*			*08 19*						*08 57*							*09 24*			
Rochester 4	d			07c18		07a36			07 57						08a36							09 01			
Chatham 4	d			07 21					08 00													09 04			
Gillingham (Kent) 4	a			07 24					08 03													09 07			

For general notes see front of timetable
For details of catering facilities see Directory of Train Operators

b Arr. 0751
c Arr. 0712

For details of Bank Holiday service alterations please see first page of Table 195

London → Dartford and Gillingham

Network Diagram - see first page of Table 200

Station		SE	SE	SE	SE	SE	SE	SE	SE	SE	SE	SE	SE	SE	SE	SE	SE	SE	SE	SE	SE	SE	SE	SE	SE
			1																		A			A	
London Charing Cross 4	⊖ d	08 03	08 08						08 24	08 28			08 41	08 44				09 02				09 15	09 20		
London Waterloo (East) 4	⊖ d	08 06	08 11						08 27	08 31			08 44	08 47				09 06				09 20	09 23		
London Cannon Street 4	⊖ d				08 14	08 17	08 26				08 34					08 50	09 02			09 10	09 20			09 30	09 34
London Bridge 4	⊖ d	08 12	08 16		08 18	08 21	08 30		08 32	08 36	08 38		08 50	08 52		08 54	09 06	09 12		09 14	09 24	09 26	09 29	09 34	09 38
Deptford	d	08 18							08 38				08 56							09 20				09 40	
Greenwich 4	⛴ d	08 20							08 40				08 58							09 22			09 37	09 42	
Maze Hill	d	08 24							08 44				09 02							09 26				09 46	
Westcombe Park	d	08 26							08 46				09 04							09 28				09 48	
London Victoria 15	⊖ d							08 21											09 01						
Denmark Hill 4	d							08 31											09 12						
Peckham Rye 4	d							08 35											09 14						
Nunhead 4	d							08 37											09 16						
New Cross 4	⊖ d				08 23	08 26				08 42	08 45						09 11				09 29				09 44
St Johns	d				08 25						08 47										09 31				
Lewisham 4	⛴ d				08 28	08 32		08 44		08 48	08 50					09 04	09 16	09 20	09 26		09 34	09 36			09 48
Blackheath 4	d				08 30	08 34		08 46		08 50						09 06	09 18		09 28			09 38			09 50
Kidbrooke	d				08 33			08 49		08 53							09 21		09 31			09 41			
Eltham	d				08 37			08 53		08 57		←					09 25		09 35			09 45			
Falconwood	d				08 39			08 55		08 59		08 59					09 27		09 37			09 47			
Welling	d				08 42			08 58		→		09 02					09 30		09 40			09 50			
Bexleyheath	d				08 44			09 00				09 04					09 32		09 42			09 52			
Barnehurst 4	d				08 47			09 03				09 08					09 35		09 45			09 55			
Hither Green 4	d		08 27				08 41				08 53			09 03				09 23			09 37				
Lee	d		08 29				08 43				08 55			09 05				09 25			09 39				
Mottingham	d		08 32				08 46				08 58			09 08				09 28			09 42				
New Eltham	d		08 35				08 49				09 01			09 11				09 31			09 45				
Sidcup 4	d		08 38				08 52				09 04			09 14				09 34			09 48				
Albany Park	d		08 40				08 54				09 06			09 16				09 36			09 50				
Bexley	d		08 42				08 56				09 08			09 18				09 38			09 52				
Crayford	d		08 45				08 59				09 11			09 21				09 41			09 58				
Charlton 4	d	08 28		←		08 40			08 48				09 06		←	09 12				09 30			09 44	09 50	09 57
Woolwich Dockyard	d	08 30		08 30					08 50				09 08		09 08					09 32				09 52	
Woolwich Arsenal 4	d	→		08 33		08 45			08 53				→		09 11	09 17				09 35			09 49	09 55	10 02
Plumstead	d			08 35					08 55						09 13					09 37				09 57	10a04
Abbey Wood	d			08 39		08 50			08 59						09 17	09 22				09 41			09 53	10 01	
Belvedere	d			08 41					09 01						09 19					09 43				10 03	
Erith	d			08 44					09 04						09 22					09 46				10 06	
Slade Green 4	d			08 47					09 07						09 25					09 49	10a04			10a09	
Dartford 4	a		08 50	08 51	08 54	09 00	09 04	09 09	09 13		09 15	09 18		09 26	09 30	09 33	09 41	09 45	09 51	09 55		10 03	10 03		
	d			08 52		09 02					09 16					09 34		09 46					10 04		
Stone Crossing	d			08 55							09 19							09 49							
Greenhithe for Bluewater	d			08 58		09 07					09 22					09 39		09 52					10 09		
Swanscombe	d			09 00							09 24							09 54							
Northfleet	d			09 02							09 26							09 56							
Gravesend 4	d			09a06		09 14					09a30					09 46		10a00					10 16		
Higham	d					09 20										09 52							10 22		
Strood 4	d					09 26										09 58							10 28		
Maidstone West 4	a					*09 54*										*10 24*							*10 54*		
Rochester 4	d					09 29										10 01							10 31		
Chatham 4	d					09 32										10 04							10 34		
Gillingham (Kent) 4	a					09 35										10 07							10 37		

For general notes see front of timetable
For details of catering facilities see Directory of Train Operators

A To London Cannon Street (Table 199)

For details of Bank Holiday service alterations please see first page of Table 195

London → Dartford and Gillingham

Network Diagram - see first page of Table 200

		SE	SE	SE	SE	SE	SE	SE	SE		SE	SE	SE	SE	SE	SE	SE	SE	SE	SE	SE	SE	SE	SE	SE
					A			A						A			A					A			A
London Charing Cross 4	⊖ d	09 32				09 48	09 52				10 02				10 17	10 20			10 32				10 47	10 50	
London Waterloo (East) 4	⊖ d	09 35				09 51	09 55				10 05				10 20	10 23			10 35				10 50	10 53	
London Cannon Street 4	⊖ d			09 42	09 48			10 00	10 04				10 10	10 18			10 30	10 34			10 40	10 48			11 00
London Bridge 4	⊖ d	09 40		09 46	09 52	09 57	10 00	10 04	10 08		10 10		10 14	10 22	10 25	10 29	10 34	10 38	10 40		10 44	10 52	10 55	10 59	11 04
Deptford	d			09 52				10 10					10 20				10 40				10 50				11 10
Greenwich 4	d			09 54			10 07	10 12					10 22			10 37	10 42				10 52			11 07	11 12
Maze Hill	d			09 58				10 16					10 26				10 46				10 56				11 16
Westcombe Park	d			10 00				10 18					10 28				10 48				10 58				11 18
London Victoria 15	⊖ d		09 31									10 01								10 31					
Denmark Hill 4	d		09 42									10 12								10 42					
Peckham Rye 4	d		09 44									10 14								10 44					
Nunhead 4	d		09 46									10 16								10 46					
New Cross 4	⊖ d				09 57			11a17	10 14					10 27				10 44				10 57			
St Johns	d				09 59									10 29								10 59			
Lewisham 4	d	09 50	09 53			10 06			10 18		10 20	10 23			10 35			10 48	10 50	10 53			11 05		
Blackheath 4	d		09 55			10 08			10 20			10 25			10 37			10 50		10 55			11 07		
Kidbrooke	d		09 58			10 11						10 28			10 40					10 58			11 10		
Eltham	d		10 02			10 15						10 32			10 44					11 02			11 14		
Falconwood	d		10 04			10 17						10 34			10 46					11 04			11 16		
Welling	d		10 07			10 20						10 37			10 49					11 07			11 19		
Bexleyheath	d		10 09			10 22						10 39			10 51					11 09			11 21		
Barnehurst 4	d		10 12			10 25						10 42			10 54					11 12			11 24		
Hither Green 4	d	09 53			10 05						10 23			10 35					10 53			11 05			
Lee	d	09 55			10 07						10 25			10 37					10 55			11 07			
Mottingham	d	09 58			10 10						10 28			10 40					10 58			11 10			
New Eltham	d	10 01			10 13						10 31			10 43					11 01			11 13			
Sidcup 4	d	10 04			10 16						10 34			10 46					11 04			11 16			
Albany Park	d	10 06			10 18						10 36			10 48					11 06			11 18			
Bexley	d	10 08			10 20						10 38			10 50					11 08			11 20			
Crayford	d	10 11			10b28						10 41			10c58					11 11			11e28			
Charlton 4	d			10 02			10 14	10 20	10 25				10 30			10 44	10 50	10 55			11 00			11 14	11 20
Woolwich Dockyard	d			10 04				10 22					10 32				10 52				11 02				11 22
Woolwich Arsenal 4	d			10 07			10 19	10 25	10 30				10 35			10 49	10 55	11 00			11 05			11 19	11 25
Plumstead	d			10 09				10 27	10a32				10 37				10 57	11a02			11 07				11 27
Abbey Wood	d			10 13			10 23	10 31					10 41			10 53	11 01				11 11			11 23	11 31
Belvedere	d			10 15				10 33					10 43				11 03				11 13				11 33
Erith	d			10 18				10 36					10 46				11 06				11 16				11 36
Slade Green 4	d			10 21	10a36			10a39					10 49	11a06			11a09				11 19	11a36			11a39
Dartford 4	a	10 15	10 17	10 27		10 31	10 33				10 45	10 47	10 53		11 01	11 03			11 15	11 17	11 23		11 31	11 33	
	d	10 16					10 34				10 46					11 04			11 16					11 34	
Stone Crossing	d	10 19									10 49								11 19						
Greenhithe for Bluewater	d	10 22					10 39				10 52					11 09			11 22					11 39	
Swanscombe	d	10 24									10 54								11 24						
Northfleet	d	10 26									10 56								11 26						
Gravesend 4	d	10a30					10 46				11a00					11 16			11a30					11 46	
Higham	d						10 52									11 22								11 52	
Strood 4	d						10 58									11 28								11 58	
Maidstone West 4	a						*11 24*									*11 54*								*12 24*	
Rochester 4	d						11 01									11 31								12 01	
Chatham 4	d						11 04									11 34								12 04	
Gillingham (Kent) 4	a						11 07									11 37								12 07	

For general notes see front of timetable
For details of catering facilities see Directory of Train Operators

A To London Cannon Street (Table 199)
b Arr. 1024
c Arr. 1054
e Arr. 1124

Table 200

Mondays to Fridays

For details of Bank Holiday service alterations please see first page of Table 195

London → Dartford and Gillingham

Network Diagram - see first page of Table 200

		SE		SE	SE	SE	SE	SE	SE	SE	SE	SE	SE	SE	SE	SE	SE	SE	SE	SE	SE	SE	SE	SE
							A			A											A			
London Charing Cross 4	⊖ d			15 02				15 17	15 20			15 32				15 47	15 50		16 02			16 11		
London Waterloo (East) 4	⊖ d			15 05				15 20	15 23			15 35				15 50	15 53		16 05			16 14		
London Cannon Street 4	⊖ d	11 04				15 10	15 18			15 30	15 34			15 40	15 48			16 00			16 10		16 18	
London Bridge 4	⊖ d	11 08		15 10		15 14	15 22	15 25	15 29	15 34	15 38	15 40		15 44	15 52	15 55	15 59	16 04	16 10		16 14	16 19	16 22	
Deptford	d					15 20				15 40				15 50				16 10						
Greenwich 4	⛴ d					15 22			15 37	15 42				15 52				16 12					16 29	
Maze Hill	d					15 26				15 46				15 56				16 16						
Westcombe Park	d					15 28				15 48				15 58				16 18						
London Victoria 15	⊖ d				15 01								15 31											
Denmark Hill 4	d				15 12								15 42											
Peckham Rye 4	d				15 14								15 44											
Nunhead 4	d				15 16								15 46											
New Cross 4	⊖ d	11 14					15 27				15 44				15 57				16 16		16 20	16 25		
St Johns	d						15 29								15 59						16 22			
Lewisham 4	⛴ d	11 18		15 20	15 23			15 35			15 48	15 50	15 53			16 05	16 10		16 20		16 27	16 29		
Blackheath 4	d	11 20			15 25			15 37			15 50		15 55			16 07	16 13					16 32		
Kidbrooke	d		and at the same minutes past each hour until		15 28			15 40					15 58			16 10						16 35		←
Eltham	d				15 32			15 44					16 02			16 14						16 39 →		16 39
Falconwood	d				15 34			15 46					16 04			16 16								16 41
Welling	d				15 37			15 49					16 07			16 19								16 44
Bexleyheath	d				15 39			15 51					16 09			16 21								16 47
Barnehurst 4	d				15 42			15 54					16 12			16 24								16 50
Hither Green 4	d			15 23			15 35					15 53			16 05					16 23		16 31		
Lee	d			15 25			15 37					15 55			16 07					16 25		16 33		
Mottingham	d			15 28			15 40					15 58			16 10					16 28		16 36		
New Eltham	d			15 31			15 43					16 01			16 13					16 31		16 39		
Sidcup 4	d			15 34			15 46					16 04			16a17					16 34		16 42		
Albany Park	d			15 36			15 48					16 06								16 36		16 44		
Bexley	d			15 38			15 50					16 08								16 38		16 46		
Crayford	d			15 41			15b58					16 11								16 41		16c58		
Charlton 4	d	11 25				15 30			15 44	15 50	15 55			16 00			16 17	16 22		←			16 35	
Woolwich Dockyard	d					15 32				15 52				16 02				16 25 →		16 25				
Woolwich Arsenal 4	d	11 30				15 35			15 49	15 55	16 00			16 05			16 23			16 28			16 41	
Plumstead	d	11a32				15 37				15 57	16a02			16 07						16 30				
Abbey Wood	d					15 41			15 53	16 01				16 11			16 28			16 34			16 46	
Belvedere	d					15 43				16 03				16 13						16 37				
Erith	d					15 46				16 06				16 16						16 40				
Slade Green 4	d					15 49	16a04			16a09				16 19						16 43	17a08		16 52	
Dartford 4	a			15 45	15 47	15 53		16 01	16 03			16 15	16 17	16 24		16 34	16 36		16 45	16e50			16e59	17 00
	d			15 46					16 04			16 16					16 36		16 46					
Stone Crossing	d			15 49								16 19							16 49					
Greenhithe for Bluewater	d			15 52					16 09			16 22					16 41		16 52					
Swanscombe	d			15 54								16 24							16 54					
Northfleet	d			15 56								16 26							16 56					
Gravesend 4	d			16a00					16 16			16a30					16 48		17a02					
Higham	d								16 22								16 54							
Strood 4	d								16 28								17f04							
Maidstone West 4	a																*17 28*							
Rochester 4	d								16 31								17 07							
Chatham 4	d								16 34								17 10							
Gillingham (Kent) 4	a								16 37								17 18							

For general notes see front of timetable
For details of catering facilities see Directory of Train Operators

A To London Cannon Street (Table 199)
b Arr. 1554
c Arr. 1650
e Until 9 October arr 2 minutes earlier
f Arr. 1701

For details of Bank Holiday service alterations please see first page of Table 195

London → Dartford and Gillingham

Network Diagram - see first page of Table 200

		SE	SE	SE	SE	SE	SE	SE	SE	SE	SE	SE	SE	SE	SE	SE	SE	SE	SE	SE	SE	SE	SE	SE	SE
London Charing Cross 4 ⊖	d	16 21			16 25		16 33			16 37	16 44	16 48				16 55	16 58		17 00		17 10			17 06	
London Waterloo (East) 4 ⊖	d	16 24			16 28		16 36			16 40	16 47	16 51				16 58	17 01		17 03		17 13			17 09	
London Cannon Street 4 ⊖	d			16 28				16 38	16 42						16 52			17 02		17 06			17 10		17 16
London Bridge 4 ⊖	d	16 29		16 32	16 33		16 41	16 42	16 46	16 48	16 52	16 56			16 56	17 03	17 06	17 06	17 08	17 10			17 14	17 15	17 20
Deptford	d			16 38							16 58									17 16				17 22	
Greenwich 4	d			16 40							17 00							17 13		17 18				17 24	
Maze Hill	d			16 44							17 04									17 22				17 28	
Westcombe Park	d			16 46							17 06									17 24				17 30	
London Victoria 15 ⊖	d		16 14																			17 00			
Denmark Hill 4	d		16 27																			17 09			
Peckham Rye 4	d		16 29																			17 12			
Nunhead 4	d		16 31																			17 14			
New Cross 4 ⊖	d				16 39			16 49							17 02								17 20		17 26
St Johns	d				16 41			16 51															17 22		
Lewisham 4	d	16 38	16 41				16 52	16 53	16 56	16 59					17 06	17 15			17 18			17 24	17 27		17 30
Blackheath 4	d	16 41	16 44				16 55		16 59	17 02					17 09	17 18			17 21			17 27			17 33
Kidbrooke	d		16 47				16 58			17 05			←		17 12	17 21						17 30			17 36
Eltham	d		16 51				17 02			17 09			17 09		17 16	17 25						17 34			17 40
Falconwood	d		16 53				17 04			→			17 12		17 18	17 27						17 36			17 42
Welling	d		16 56				17 07						17 14		17 21	17 30						17 39			17 45
Bexleyheath	d		16 59				17 10						17 17		17 24	17 33						17 42			17 48
Barnehurst 4	d		17 02				17 13						17 20		17b30	17 36						17 45			17b54
Hither Green 4	d				16 46			16 57									17 16						17 30		
Lee	d				16 48			16 59									17 18						17 32		
Mottingham	d				16 52			17 02									17 22						17 36		
New Eltham	d				16 55			17 05				17 11					17 25				17 31		17 39		
Sidcup 4	d				16 58			17b11				17 14					17b31				17 34		17 42		
Albany Park	d				17 00							17 16									17 36		17 44		
Bexley	d				17 02							17 18									17 38		17 46		
Crayford	d				17 05		17b30					17 21									17 41		17 49		
Charlton 4	d	16 45		16 48		←			17 03		17 08			←					17 25	17 28				17 34	
Woolwich Dockyard	d			16 51		16 51					17 11			17 11						17 31				17 37	
Woolwich Arsenal 4	d	16 51		→		16 54			17 09		→			17 14				17 24	17 31	17 34				17 40	
Plumstead	d					16 56								17 16						17 36				17 42	
Abbey Wood	d	16 56				17 00			17 14					17 20				17 29	17 36	17 40				17 46	
Belvedere	d					17 03								17 23						17 43				17 49	
Erith	d					17 06								17 26						17 46				17 52	
Slade Green 4	d					17 09								17 29		17c42		17 35		17c51				17 55	
Dartford 4	a	17 05	17 09		17 09	17c15			17 22			17 25	17 29	17c35				17 39	17 45		17 48	17 52	17 54	18 00	
	d	17 06			17 10				17 22			17 26	17 30					17 40	17 46		17 50				
Stone Crossing	d				17 13								17 33								17 53				
Greenhithe for Bluewater	d	17 11			17 16				17 27			17 31	17 36					17 45	17 51		17 56				
Swanscombe	d				17 18								17 39								17 59				
Northfleet	d				17 20								17 41								18 01				
Gravesend 4	d	17 18			17a26				17 34			17e40	17a46					17 52	17 58		18c07				
Higham	d	17 24							17 40			17f49						17 58	18 04						
Strood 4	d	17 30							17b47			17 55						18c06	18g17						
Maidstone West 4	a	17 59																18 31							
Rochester 4	d	17 35										18 00							18 22						
Chatham 4	d	17 38										18 03							18 25						
Gillingham (Kent) 4	a	17c43										18 08							18 29						

For general notes see front of timetable
For details of catering facilities see Directory of Train Operators

b Until 9 October arr 2 minutes earlier
c Until 9 October arr 1 minute earlier
e Arr. 1737
f Arr. 1746
g Arr. 1814

For details of Bank Holiday service alterations please see first page of Table 195

London → Dartford and Gillingham

Network Diagram - see first page of Table 200

		SE	SE	SE	SE A	SE	SE	SE	SE	SE	SE	SE	SE	SE	SE	SE	SE	SE	SE	SE	SE	SE	SE	SE	SE
London Charing Cross 4	⊖ d	17 18				17 21	17 32	17 25		17 29			17 37			17 43		17 52	17 46			17 54		18 01	
London Waterloo (East) 4	⊖ d	17 21				17 24	17 35	17 28		17 32			17 40			17 46		17 55	17 49			17 57		18 04	
London Cannon Street 4	⊖ d		17 24	17 26							17 36			17 42	17 46		17 48				17 56		18 02		18 08
London Bridge 4	⊖ d	17 26	17 28	17 30		17 30				17 38	17 40		17 45	17 46	17 50	17 51	17 52				18 00	18 02	18 06	18 10	18 12
Deptford	d		17 34							17 44							17 58					18 08			
Greenwich 4	⛴ d		17 36							17 46							18 00					18 10			18 20
Maze Hill	d		17 40							17 50							18 04					18 14			
Westcombe Park	d		17 42							17 52							18 06					18 16			
London Victoria 15	⊖ d								17 19											17 41					
Denmark Hill 4	d								17 28											17 51					
Peckham Rye 4	d								17 31											17 54					
Nunhead 4	d								17 33											17 56					
New Cross 4	⊖ d										17 47			17 52							18 06				
St Johns	d																				18 08				
Lewisham 4	⛴ d	17 35		17 38					17b46		17 52		17 54	17 57	18 00					18 06	18 12		18 15	18 20	
Blackheath 4	d	17 38		17 41					17 49				17 57	18 00	18 02					18 09			18 18	18 23	
Kidbrooke	d	17 41						17 48	17 52				18 00	18 04					18 08	18 12			18 21	18 26	
Eltham	d	17 45						17 52	17 56				18 04	18 08					18 12	18 16			18 25	18 30	
Falconwood	d	17 47						17 55	17 58				18 06	18 10					18 14	18 18			18 27	18 32	
Welling	d	17 50						17 58	18 01				18 09	18 13					18 17	18 21			18 30	→	
Bexleyheath	d	17 53						18 01	18 04				18 12	18 16					18 20	18 24			18 33		
Barnehurst 4	d	17 58			17 31			18 04	18 07				18 16	18 20		18a30			18 23	18 27			18 37		
Hither Green 4	d					17 40					17 55					18 00					18 16				
Lee	d					17 42					17 57					18 02					18 18				
Mottingham	d					17 46					18 01					18 06					18 22				
New Eltham	d					17 49	17 53				18 04					18 09		18 14			18 25				
Sidcup 4	d					17c55	17 57				18 07					18 12		18 17			18 28				
Albany Park	d						17 59				18 09					18 14		18 19			18 30				
Bexley	d						18 01				18 11					18 16		18 21			18 32				
Crayford	d						18 04				18 14					18a20		18 24			18 35				
Charlton 4	d		17 48	17 45						17 54		←			18 06		18 10					18 18			
Woolwich Dockyard	d		17 51							17 57		17 57					18 13					18 21			
Woolwich Arsenal 4	d		17 54	17 51						→		18 00			18 12		18 16					18 24			18 31
Plumstead	d		17 56									18 02					18 18					18 26			
Abbey Wood	d		18 00	17 56								18 06			18 17		18 22					18 30			18 36
Belvedere	d		18 03									18 09					18 25					18 32			
Erith	d		18 06									18 12					18 28					18 36			
Slade Green 4	d	18c10	18e11		17a35							18 15	18a23	18e27			18a32					18 39	18e43		18 42
Dartford 4	a			18 05			18 08	18 12	18 14		18e20	18c22			18 25			18 29	18 32	18 34	18 40	18c46			18 46
	d			18 06			18 10	18 14							18 26			18 30	18 34						18 48
Stone Crossing	d							18 17											18 37						
Greenhithe for Bluewater	d			18 11			18 15	18 20							18 31			18 35	18 40						18 53
Swanscombe	d							18 23											18 43						
Northfleet	d							18 25											18 45						
Gravesend 4	d			18 18			18f25	18e31							18 38			18 42	18e51						19 00
Higham	d			18 24			18 33								18 44			18g52							19 06
Strood 4	d			18e31			18 39								18e51			18 59							19h14
Maidstone West 4	a						19 05																		19 39
Rochester 4	d						18 43											19 02							19 19
Chatham 4	d						18 46											19 05							19 22
Gillingham (Kent) 4	a						18 50											19 10							19e27

For general notes see front of timetable
For details of catering facilities see Directory of Train Operators

- **A** To London Cannon Street
- **b** Arr. 1743
- **c** Until 9 October arr 2 minutes earlier
- **e** Until 9 October arr 1 minute earlier
- **f** Arr. 1821
- **g** Arr. 1848
- **h** Arr. 1911

For details of Bank Holiday service alterations please see first page of Table 195

London → Dartford and Gillingham

Network Diagram - see first page of Table 200

		SE	SE	SE	SE	SE	SE	SE	SE	SE	SE	SE	SE	SE	SE	SE	SE	SE	SE	SE	SE	SE	SE	SE	SE
London Charing Cross 4	⊖ d	18 05	18 08			18 20	18 14			18 25	18 30	18 37		18 34	18 46		18 54	18 56		19 02			19 11	19 17	
London Waterloo (East) 4	⊖ d	18 08	18 11			18 23	18 17			18 28	18 33	18 40		18 37	18 49		18 57	18 59		19 05			19 14	19 20	
London Cannon Street 4	⊖ d							18 19	18 22				18 36						19 02			19 10			19 22
London Bridge 4	⊖ d	18 14	18 16				18 22	18 23	18 26	18 34	18 38		18 40	18 42	18 54		19 02	19 04	19 06	19 10		19 14	19 20	19 25	19 26
Deptford	d						18 28							18 48				19 10				19 20	19 26		
Greenwich 4	d						18 30							18 50				19 12				19 22	19 28		
Maze Hill	d						18 34							18 54				19 16				19 26	19 32		
Westcombe Park	d						18 36							18 56				19 18				19 28	19 34		
London Victoria 15	⊖ d				18 08											18 46									
Denmark Hill 4	d				18 17											18 57									
Peckham Rye 4	d				18 20											19 00									
Nunhead 4	d				18 22											19 02									
New Cross 4	⊖ d								18 32				18 46		19 00				19 12						19 31
St Johns	d												18 48						19 14						19 33
Lewisham 4	d	18 24			18 29			18 33	18 36	18 44	18 48		18 52		19 04	19 08	19 12		19 17	19 22				19 35	
Blackheath 4	d	18 27			18 34			18 37		18 47	18 51				19 07	19 12	19 15		19 19					19 37	
Kidbrooke	d				18 37			18 40		18 50					19 10	19 15			19 22					19 40	
Eltham	d			←	18 41			18 44		18 54					19 14	19 19			19 26					19 44	
Falconwood	d			18 32	18 43			18 46		18 56					19 16	19 21			19 28					19 46	
Welling	d			18 35	18 46			18 49		18 59					19 19	19 24			19 31					19 49	
Bexleyheath	d			18 38	18 49			18 52		19 02					19 22	19 27			19 33					19 51	
Barnehurst 4	d			18 41	18 52			18b58		19 05					19 25	19 30			19a37					19 54	
Hither Green 4	d		18 26						18 40				18 56							19 25					19 37
Lee	d		18 28			18 38			18 42			18 55	18 58							19 27					19 39
Mottingham	d		18 32			18 42			18 46			18 58	19 02							19 30					19 42
New Eltham	d		18 35			18 45			18 49			19 01	19 05							19 33					19 45
Sidcup 4	d		18b41			18 48			18 52			19 05	19 08							19 36					19 49
Albany Park	d					18 50			18 54			19 07	19 10							19 38					19 51
Bexley	d					18 52			18 56			19 09	19 12							19 40					19 53
Crayford	d					18 55			18 59			19 12	19 15							19 43					19 56
Charlton 4	d	18 31					18 38				18 55			18 58			19 19	19 22			←	19 30	19 36		
Woolwich Dockyard	d						18 41							19 01				19 25 →			19 25	19 33	19 39		
Woolwich Arsenal 4	d	18 37					18 44				19 01			19 04			19 25				19 28	19 36	19 42		
Plumstead	d						18 46							19 06							19 30	19 38	19 44		
Abbey Wood	d	18 42					18 50				19 06			19 10			19 30				19 34	19 41	19 47		
Belvedere	d						18 53							19 13							19 37	19 44	19 50		
Erith	d						18 56							19 16							19 40	19 47	19 53		
Slade Green 4	d						18 59							19 19							19 43	19a50	19 56		20a04
Dartford 4	a	18 51		18b52	18 58	18 59	19b06		19b06	19b14	19 15	19 18	19 22	19b26	19b34	19 36	19 39			19 47	19 48		20 01	20 03	
	d	18 52				19 00					19 16	19 20					19 40			19 48					
Stone Crossing	d	18 55										19 23								19 51					
Greenhithe for Bluewater	d	18 58				19 05					19 21	19 26					19 45			19 54					
Swanscombe	d	19 01										19 29								19 56					
Northfleet	d	19 03										19 31								19 58					
Gravesend 4	d	19c09				19 12					19 28	19c37					19 52			20a02					
Higham	d					19 18					19 34						19 58								
Strood 4	d					19e28					19f44						20 04								
Maidstone West 4	a					19 59											20 34								
Rochester 4	d					19 32					19 48						20 08								
Chatham 4	d					19 35					19 51						20 11								
Gillingham (Kent) 4	a					19c40					19 55						20 16								

For general notes see front of timetable
For details of catering facilities see Directory of Train Operators

b Until 9 October arr 2 minutes earlier
c Until 9 October arr 1 minute earlier
e Arr. 1923
f Arr. 1939

For details of Bank Holiday service alterations please see first page of Table 195

London → Dartford and Gillingham

Network Diagram - see first page of Table 200

Station		SE	SE	SE	SE	SE	SE	SE	SE	SE	SE	SE 81	SE	SE	SE	SE	SE	SE	SE	SE	SE	SE	SE	SE	SE
London Charing Cross 4	⊖ d	19 21				19 34	19 41	19 47		19 50			20 04	20 10	20 17	20 20		20 34	20 40	20 47	20 50		21 04	21 10	21 17
London Waterloo (East) 4	⊖ d	19 24				19 37	19 44	19 50		19 53			20 07	20 13	20 20	20 23		20 37	20 43	20 50	20 53		21 07	21 13	21 20
London Cannon Street 4	⊖ d			19 28	19 36				19 52			20 00					20 30					21 00			
London Bridge 4	⊖ d	19 29		19 32	19 40	19 43	19 49	19 55	19 56	19 59		20 04	20 13	20 18	20 25	20 29	20 34	20 43	20 48	20 55	20 59	21 04	21 13	21 18	21 25
Deptford	d			19 38			19 54					20 10		20 24			20 40		20 54			21 10		21 24	
Greenwich 4	⛴ d			19 40			19 56					20 12		20 26			20 42		20 56			21 12		21 26	
Maze Hill	d			19 44			20 00					20 16		20 30			20 46		21 00			21 16		21 30	
Westcombe Park	d			19 46			20 02					20 18		20 32			20 48		21 02			21 18		21 32	
London Victoria 15	⊖ d		19 16								19 46														
Denmark Hill 4	d		19 27								19 57														
Peckham Rye 4	d		19 31								20 01														
Nunhead 4	d		19 33								20 03														
New Cross 4	⊖ d				19 45	19 48			20 01				20 18		20 30			20 48		21 00			21 18		21 30
St Johns	d				19 47				20 04																
Lewisham 4	⛴ d	19 38	19 45		19 50	19 53		20 05		20 08	20 15		20 23		20 35	20 38		20 53		21 05	21 08		21 23		21 35
Blackheath 4	d	19 41	19 47		19 52			20 07		20 11	20 17				20 37	20 41				21 07	21 11				21 37
Kidbrooke	d		19 50		19 55			20 10			20 20				20 40					21 10					21 40
Eltham	d		19 54		19 59			20 14			20 24				20 44					21 14					21 44
Falconwood	d		19 56		20 01			20 16			20 26				20 46					21 16					21 46
Welling	d		19 59		20 04			20 19			20 29				20 49					21 19					21 49
Bexleyheath	d		20 01		20 06			20 21			20 31				20 51					21 21					21 51
Barnehurst 4	d		20 04		20a10			20 24			20 34				20 54					21 24					21 54
Hither Green 4	d					19 57			20 09				20 27					20 57					21 27		
Lee	d					19 59			20 11				20 29					20 59					21 29		
Mottingham	d					20 02			20 14				20 32					21 02					21 32		
New Eltham	d					20 05			20 17				20 35					21 05					21 35		
Sidcup 4	d					20 08			20 20				20 38					21 08					21 38		
Albany Park	d					20 10			20 22				20 40					21 10					21 40		
Bexley	d					20 12			20 24				20 42					21 12					21 42		
Crayford	d					20 15			20 27				20 45					21 15					21 45		
Charlton 4	d	19 45		19 50			20 04			20 15		20 20		20 34		20 45	20 50		21 04		21 15	21 20		21 34	
Woolwich Dockyard	d			19 53			20 07					20 23		20 37			20 53		21 07			21 23		21 37	
Woolwich Arsenal 4	d	19 50		19 56			20 10			20 20		20 26		20 40		20 50	20 56		21 10		21 20	21 26		21 40	
Plumstead	d			19 58			20 12					20 28		20 42			20 58		21 12			21 28		21 42	
Abbey Wood	d	19 55		20 01			20 15			20 25		20 31		20 45		20 55	21 01		21 15		21 25	21 31		21 45	
Belvedere	d			20 04			20 18					20 34		20 48			21 04		21 18			21 34		21 48	
Erith	d			20 07			20 21					20 37		20 51			21 07		21 21			21 37		21 51	
Slade Green 4	d			20 10			20 24		20a34			20 40		20 54			21 10		21 24			21 40		21 54	
Dartford 4	a	20 05	20 11	20 15		20 19	20 29	20 31		20 33	20 41	20 45	20 50	20 59	21 01	21 03	21 15	21 22	21 29	21 31	21 33	21 45	21 52	21 59	22 01
	d	20 06				20 20				20 34						21 04					21 34				
Stone Crossing	d					20 23				20 37											21 37				
Greenhithe for Bluewater	d	20 11				20 26				20 40						21 09					21 40				
Swanscombe	d					20 28				20 42											21 42				
Northfleet	d					20 30				20 44											21 44				
Gravesend 4	d	20 18				20a34				20 50						21 16					21 50				
Higham	d	20 24								20 56						21 22					21 56				
Strood 4	d	20 30								21b04						21 28					22 02				
Maidstone West 4	a	*20 56*								*21 30*						*21 56*									
Rochester 4	d	20 33								21 09						21 31					22 07				
Chatham 4	d	20 36								21 12						21 34					22 09				
Gillingham (Kent) 4	a	20 39								21 17						21 37					22 13				

For general notes see front of timetable
For details of catering facilities see Directory of Train Operators

b Arr. 2101

For details of Bank Holiday service alterations please see first page of Table 195

London → Dartford and Gillingham

Network Diagram - see first page of Table 200

		SE	SE	SE	SE	SE	SE	SE	SE	SE	SE	SE	SE	SE	SE	SE	SE	SE	SE	SE	SE	SE	SE	SE	
London Charing Cross [4]	⊖ d	21 20			21 34	21 40	21 47	21 50		22 04	22 10	22 17	22 20	22 34	22 40	22 47	22 50	23 04	23 10	23 17	23 20	23 34	23 40	23 47	
London Waterloo (East) [4]	⊖ d	21 23			21 37	21 43	21 50	21 53		22 07	22 13	22 20	22 23	22 37	22 43	22 50	22 53	23 07	23 13	23 20	23 23	23 37	23 43	23 50	
London Cannon Street [4]	⊖ d																								
London Bridge [4]	⊖ d	21 29		21 34	21 43	21 48	21 55	21 59	22 04	22 13	22 18	22 25	22 29	22 43	22 48	22 55	22 59	23 13	23 18	23 25	23 29	23 43	23 48	23 55	
Deptford	d			21 40		21 54			22 10		22 24				22 54				23 24				23 54		
Greenwich [4]	d			21 42		21 56			22 12		22 26				22 56				23 26				23 56		
Maze Hill	d			21 46		22 00			22 16		22 30				23 00				23 30				00 01		
Westcombe Park	d			21 48		22 02			22 18		22 32				23 02				23 32				00 02		
London Victoria [15]	⊖ d																								
Denmark Hill [4]	d																								
Peckham Rye [4]	d																								
Nunhead [4]	d																								
New Cross [4]	⊖ d				21 48		22 00			22 18		22 30		22 48		23 00		23 18		23 30		23 48		23 58	
St Johns	d																								
Lewisham [4]	d	21 38			21 53		22 05	22 08		22 23		22 35	22 38	22 53		23 05	23 08	23 23		23 35	23 38	23 53		00 05	
Blackheath [4]	d	21 41					22 07	22 11				22 37	22 41			23 07	23 11			23 37	23 41			00 07	
Kidbrooke	d						22 10					22 40				23 10				23 40				00 10	
Eltham	d						22 14					22 44				23 14				23 44				00 14	
Falconwood	d						22 16					22 46				23 16				23 46				00 16	
Welling	d						22 19					22 49				23 19				23 49				00 19	
Bexleyheath	d						22 21					22 51				23 21				23 51				00 21	
Barnehurst [4]	d						22 24					22 54				23 24				23 54				00 24	
Hither Green [4]	d				21 57					22 27				22 57				23 27				23 57			
Lee	d				21 59					22 29				22 59				23 29				23 59			
Mottingham	d				22 02					22 32				23 02				23 32				00 02			
New Eltham	d				22 05					22 35				23 05				23 35				00 05			
Sidcup [4]	d				22 08					22 38				23 08				23 38				00 08			
Albany Park	d				22 10					22 40				23 10				23 40				00 10			
Bexley	d				22 12					22 42				23 12				23 42				00 12			
Crayford	d				22 15					22 45				23 15				23 45				00 15			
Charlton [4]	d	21 45		21 50		22 04		22 15	22 20		22 34		22 45		23 04		23 15		23 34		23 45		00 04		
Woolwich Dockyard	d			21 53		22 07			22 23		22 37				23 07				23 37				00 07		
Woolwich Arsenal [4]	d	21 50		21 56		22 10		22 20	22 26		22 40		22 50		23 10		23 20		23 40		23 50		00 10		
Plumstead	d			21 58		22 12			22 28		22 42				23 12				23 42				00 12		
Abbey Wood	d	21 55		22 01		22 15		22 25	22 31		22 45		22 55		23 15		23 25		23 45		23 55		00 15		
Belvedere	d			22 04		22 18			22 34		22 48				23 18				23 48				00 18		
Erith	d			22 07		22 21			22 37		22 51				23 21				23 51				00 21		
Slade Green [4]	d			22 10		22 24			22 40		22 54				23 24				23 54				00 24		
Dartford [4]	a	22 03		22 15	22 22	22 29	22 31	22 33	22 45	22 50	22 59	23 01	23 03	23 20	23 29	23 31	23 33	23 50	23 59	00 01	00 04	00 20	00 29	00 31	
	d	22 04						22 34					23 04				23 34				00 04				
Stone Crossing	d							22 37									23 37				00 08				
Greenhithe for Bluewater	d	22 09						22 40					23 09				23 40				00 10				
Swanscombe	d							22 42									23 42				00 12				
Northfleet	d							22 44									23 44				00 14				
Gravesend [4]	d	22 16						22 50					23 16				23 50				00 20				
Higham	d	22 22						22 56					23 22				23 56				00 26				
Strood [4]	d	22 28	22 46					23 02					23 28				00 02				00 32				
Maidstone West [4]	a	22 56																							
Rochester [4]	d	22 31	22 49					23 07					23 31				00 07				00 39				
Chatham [4]	d	22 34	22 52					23 09					23 34				00 09				00 42				
Gillingham (Kent) [4]	a	22 37	22 55					23 13					23 37				00 13				00 45				

For general notes see front of timetable
For details of catering facilities see Directory of Train Operators

Table 200

Saturdays

For details of Bank Holiday service alterations please see first page of Table 195

London → Dartford and Gillingham

Network Diagram - see first page of Table 200

		SE	SE	SE	SE	SE	SE	SE	SE 1 A	SE	SE	SE	SE	SE	SE	SE	SE	SE	SE	SE	SE	SE	SE
London Charing Cross	⊖ d	22p50	23p20	23p34	23p40	23p47	00 04	00 14		05 04	05 34	05 40	05 47		05 50	06 04	06 10	06 17	06 20	06 34	06 40	06 47	06 50
London Waterloo (East)	⊖ d	22p53	23p23	23p37	23p43	23p50	00 07	00 17		05 07	05 37	05 43	05 50		05 53	06 07	06 13	06 20	06 23	06 37	06 43	06 50	06 53
London Cannon Street	⊖ d																						
London Bridge	⊖ d	22p59	23p29	23p43	23p48	23p55	00 13	00 23		05 13	05 43	05 48	05 55		05 59	06 13	06 18	06 25	06 29	06 43	06 48	06 55	06 59
Deptford	d				23p54							05 54					06 24				06 54		
Greenwich	d				23p56							05 56					06 26				06 56		
Maze Hill	d				00 01							06 00					06 30				07 00		
Westcombe Park	d				00 02							06 02					06 32				07 02		
London Victoria	⊖ d																						
Denmark Hill	d																						
Peckham Rye	d																						
Nunhead	d																						
New Cross	⊖ d			23p48		23p58	00 18	00 28		05 18	05 48					06 18				06 48			
St Johns	d																						
Lewisham	d	23p08	23p38	23p53		00 05	00 23	00 33		05 23	05 53		06 05		06 07	06 23		06 35	06 37	06 53		07 05	07 07
Blackheath	d	23p11	23p41			00 07		00 36					06 07		06 09			06 38	06 40			07 08	07 10
Kidbrooke	d					00 10							06 10					06 41				07 11	
Eltham	d					00 14							06 14					06 44				07 14	
Falconwood	d					00 16							06 16					06 47				07 17	
Welling	d					00 19							06 19					06 49				07 19	
Bexleyheath	d					00 21							06 21					06 52				07 22	
Barnehurst	d					00 24							06 24					06 54				07 24	
Hither Green	d			23p57			00 27			05 27	05 57					06 27				06 57			
Lee	d			23p59			00 29			05 29	05 59					06 29				06 59			
Mottingham	d			00 02			00 32			05 32	06 02					06 32				07 02			
New Eltham	d			00 05			00 35			05 35	06 05					06 35				07 05			
Sidcup	d			00 08			00 38			05 38	06 08					06 38				07 08			
Albany Park	d			00 10			00 40			05 40	06 10					06 40				07 10			
Bexley	d			00 12			00 42			05 42	06 12					06 42				07 12			
Crayford	d			00 15			00 45			05 45	06 16					06 46				07 16			
Charlton	d	23p15	23p45		00 04			00 40				06 04		←	06 14		06 34		06 44		07 04		07 14
Woolwich Dockyard	d				00 07							06 07		06 07			06 37				07 07		
Woolwich Arsenal	d	23p20	23p50		00 10			00 45				→		06 10	06 19		06 40		06 49		07 10		07 19
Plumstead	d				00 12			00 47						06 12			06 42				07 12		
Abbey Wood	d	23p25	23p55		00 15			00 50						06 15	06 23		06 45		06 53		07 15		07 23
Belvedere	d				00 18			00 53						06 18			06 48				07 18		
Erith	d				00 21			00 56						06 21			06 51				07 21		
Slade Green	d				00 24			00 58						06 26			06 54				07 24		
Dartford	a	23p33	00 04	00 20	00 29	00 31	00 50	01 03		05 49	06 20		06 29	06 31	06 34	06 50	06 59	07 01	07 03	07 20	07 28	07 31	07 33
	d	23p34	00 04					01 04	05 17	05 49	06 21				06 34	06 51			07 04	07 21			07 34
Stone Crossing	d	23p37	00 08								06 24					06 54				07 24			
Greenhithe for Bluewater	d	23p40	00 10					01 09	05 22	05 54	06 27				06 39	06 57			07 09	07 27			07 39
Swanscombe	d	23p42	00 12								06 29					06 59				07 29			
Northfleet	d	23p44	00 14								06 31					07 01				07 31			
Gravesend	d	23p50	00 20					01 16	05 29	06 01	06a35				06 46	07a05			07 16	07a35			07 46
Higham	d	23p56	00 26					01 22	05 35	06 07					06 52				07 22				07 52
Strood	d	00 02	00 32					01 28	05 40	06 12					06 58				07 28				07 58
Maidstone West	a								*06 25*	*06 53*					*07 24*				*07 54*				*08 24*
Rochester	d	00 07	00 39					01 31	05 44	06 16					07 01				07 31				08 01
Chatham	d	00 09	00 42					01 34	05 46	06 19					07 04				07 34				08 04
Gillingham (Kent)	a	00 13	00 45					01 37	05 50	06 22					07 07				07 37				08 07

For general notes see front of timetable
For details of catering facilities see Directory of Train Operators

A To Dover Priory (Table 212)

Saturdays

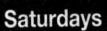

For details of Bank Holiday service alterations please see first page of Table 195

London → Dartford and Gillingham

Network Diagram - see first page of Table 200

Station		SE	SE	SE	SE	SE	SE	SE		SE	SE	SE	SE	SE	SE	SE A	SE	SE		SE	SE A	SE	SE	SE A	SE
London Charing Cross 4	⊖ d	07 04	07 10	07 17	07 20	07 34	07 42	07 47		07 50	08 02			08 17	08 20		08 32					08 47	08 50		
London Waterloo (East) 4	⊖ d	07 07	07 13	07 20	07 23	07 37	07 45	07 50		07 53	08 05			08 20	08 23		08 35					08 50	08 53		
London Cannon Street 4	⊖ d												08 10			08 30				08 40	08 48			09 00	09 04
London Bridge 4	⊖ d	07 13	07 18	07 25	07 29	07 43	07 50	07 55		07 59	08 10		08 14	08 25	08 29	08 34	08 40			08 44	08 52	08 55	08 59	09 04	09 08
Deptford	d		07 24				07 55						08 20			08 40				08 50				09 10	
Greenwich 4	d		07 26				07 57						08 22			08 42				08 52			09 07	09 12	
Maze Hill	d		07 30				08 01						08 26			08 46				08 56				09 16	
Westcombe Park	d		07 32				08 03						08 28			08 48				08 58				09 18	
London Victoria 15	⊖ d											08 01						08 31							
Denmark Hill 4	d											08 12						08 42							
Peckham Rye 4	d											08 14						08 44							
Nunhead 4	d											08 16						08 46							
New Cross 4	⊖ d	07 18				07 48					08 15						08 45				08 57				09 14
St Johns	d																				08 59				
Lewisham 4	d	07 23		07 35	07 37	07 53		08 05		08 07	08 20	08 23		08 33	08 37		08 50	08 53				09 06			09 18
Blackheath 4	d			07 38	07 40			08 08		08 10		08 25		08 38	08 40			08 55				09 08			09 20
Kidbrooke	d			07 41				08 11				08 28		08 41				08 58				09 11			
Eltham	d			07 44				08 14				08 32		08 45				09 02				09 15			
Falconwood	d			07 47				08 17				08 34		08 47				09 04				09 17			
Welling	d			07 49				08 19				08 37		08 50				09 07				09 20			
Bexleyheath	d			07 52				08 22				08 39		08 52				09 09				09 22			
Barnehurst 4	d			07 54				08 24				08 42		08 55				09 12				09 25			
Hither Green 4	d	07 27				07 57					08 23						08 53				09 05				
Lee	d	07 29				07 59					08 25						08 55				09 07				
Mottingham	d	07 32				08 02					08 28						08 58				09 10				
New Eltham	d	07 35				08 05					08 31						09 01				09 13				
Sidcup 4	d	07 38				08 08					08 34						09 04				09 16				
Albany Park	d	07 40				08 10					08 36						09 06				09 18				
Bexley	d	07 42				08 12					08 38						09 08				09 20				
Crayford	d	07 46				08 16					08 41						09 11				09b28				
Charlton 4	d		07 34		07 44		08 05			08 14			08 30		08 44	08 50				09 00			09 14	09 20	09 25
Woolwich Dockyard	d		07 37				08 08						08 32			08 52				09 02				09 22	
Woolwich Arsenal 4	d		07 40		07 49		08 11			08 19			08 35		08 49	08 55				09 05			09 19	09 25	09 30
Plumstead	d		07 42				08 13						08 37			08 57				09 07				09 27	09a32
Abbey Wood	d		07 45		07 53		08 16			08 23			08 41		08 53	09 01				09 11			09 23	09 31	
Belvedere	d		07 48				08 19						08 43			09 03				09 13				09 33	
Erith	d		07 51				08 22						08 46			09 06				09 16				09 36	
Slade Green 4	d		07 54				08 24						08 49			09a09				09 19	09a34			09a39	
Dartford 4	a	07 50	07 59	08 00	08 03	08 20	08 28	08 30		08 33	08 45	08 47	08 53	09 00	09 03		09 15	09 17		09 23		09 30	09 33		
	d	07 51			08 04	08 21				08 34	08 46				09 04		09 16						09 34		
Stone Crossing	d	07 54				08 24					08 49						09 19								
Greenhithe for Bluewater	d	07 57			08 09	08 27				08 39	08 52				09 09		09 22						09 39		
Swanscombe	d	07 59				08 29					08 54						09 24								
Northfleet	d	08 01				08 31					08 56						09 26								
Gravesend 4	d	08a05			08 16	08a35				08 46	09a00				09 16		09a30						09 46		
Higham	d				08 22					08 52					09 22								09 52		
Strood 4	d				08 28					08 58					09 28								09 58		
Maidstone West 4	a				*08 54*					*09 24*					*09 54*								*10 24*		
Rochester 4	d				08 31					09 01					09 31								10 01		
Chatham 4	d				08 34					09 04					09 34								10 04		
Gillingham (Kent) 4	a				08 37					09 07					09 37								10 07		

For general notes see front of timetable
For details of catering facilities see Directory of Train Operators

A To London Cannon Street (Table 199)
b Arr. 0924

Table 200

Saturdays

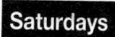

For details of Bank Holiday service alterations please see first page of Table 195

London → Dartford and Gillingham

Network Diagram - see first page of Table 200

		SE	SE	SE	SE A		SE	SE	SE A	SE	SE	SE	SE	SE A	SE	SE	SE A	SE	SE	SE	SE	SE A		SE
London Charing Cross 4	⊖ d	09 02					09 17	09 20			09 32				09 47	09 50			10 02					16 17
London Waterloo (East) 4	⊖ d	09 05					09 20	09 23			09 35				09 50	09 53			10 05					16 20
London Cannon Street 4	⊖ d			09 10	09 18				09 30	09 34			09 40	09 48			10 00	10 04			10 10	10 18		
London Bridge 4	⊖ d	09 10		09 14	09 22		09 25	09 29	09 34	09 38	09 40		09 44	09 52	09 55	09 59	10 04	10 08	10 10		10 14	10 22		16 25
Deptford	d			09 20	10a36				09 40				09 50				10 10				10 20			
Greenwich 4	⛴ d			09 22				09 37	09 42				09 52			10 07	10 12				10 22			
Maze Hill	d			09 26					09 46				09 56				10 16				10 26			
Westcombe Park	d			09 28					09 48				09 58				10 18				10 28			
London Victoria 15	⊖ d		09 01									09 31								10 01				
Denmark Hill 4	d		09 12									09 42								10 12				
Peckham Rye 4	d		09 14									09 44								10 14				
Nunhead 4	d		09 16									09 46								10 16				
New Cross 4	⊖ d				09 27					09 44				09 57				10 14				10 27		
St Johns	d				09 29									09 59								10 29		
Lewisham 4	⛴ d	09 20	09 23				09 36			09 48	09 50	09 53			10 06			10 18	10 20	10 23				16 36
Blackheath 4	d		09 25				09 38			09 50		09 55			10 08			10 20		10 25				16 38
Kidbrooke	d		09 28				09 41					09 58			10 11					10 28				16 41
Eltham	d		09 32				09 45					10 02			10 15					10 32				16 45
Falconwood	d		09 34				09 47					10 04			10 17					10 34			and at	16 47
Welling	d		09 37				09 50					10 07			10 20					10 37			the same	16 50
Bexleyheath	d		09 39				09 52					10 09			10 22					10 39			minutes	16 52
Barnehurst 4	d		09 42				09 55					10 12			10 25					10 42			past	16 55
Hither Green 4	d	09 23			09 35						09 53			10 05					10 23			10 35	each	
Lee	d	09 25			09 37						09 55			10 07					10 25			10 37	hour until	
Mottingham	d	09 28			09 40						09 58			10 10					10 28			10 40		
New Eltham	d	09 31			09 43						10 01			10 13					10 31			10 43		
Sidcup 4	d	09 34			09 46						10 04			10 16					10 34			10 46		
Albany Park	d	09 36			09 48						10 06			10 18					10 36			10 48		
Bexley	d	09 38			09 50						10 08			10 20					10 38			10 50		
Crayford	d	09 41			09b58						10 11			10c28					10 41			10e58		
Charlton 4	d			09 30				09 44	09 50	09 55			10 00			10 14	10 20	10 25			10 30			
Woolwich Dockyard	d			09 32					09 52				10 02				10 22				10 32			
Woolwich Arsenal 4	d			09 35				09 49	09 55	10 00			10 05			10 19	10 25	10 30			10 35			
Plumstead	d			09 37					09 57	10a02			10 07				10 27	10a32			10 37			
Abbey Wood	d			09 41				09 53	10 01				10 11			10 23	10 31				10 41			
Belvedere	d			09 43					10 03				10 13				10 33				10 43			
Erith	d			09 46					10 06				10 16				10 36				10 46			
Slade Green 4	d			09 49	10a04				10a09				10 19	10a34			10a39				10 49	11a04		
Dartford 4	a	09 45	09 47	09 53			10 00	10 03			10 15	10 17	10 23		10 30	10 33			10 45	10 47	10 53			17 00
	d	09 46						10 04			10 16					10 34			10 46					
Stone Crossing	d	09 49									10 19								10 49					
Greenhithe for Bluewater	d	09 52						10 09			10 22					10 39			10 52					
Swanscombe	d	09 54									10 24								10 54					
Northfleet	d	09 56									10 26								10 56					
Gravesend 4	d	10a00						10 16			10a30					10 46			11a00					
Higham	d							10 22								10 52								
Strood 4	d							10 28								10 58								
Maidstone West 4	a							*10 54*								*11 24*								
Rochester 4	d							10 31								11 01								
Chatham 4	d							10 34								11 04								
Gillingham (Kent) 4	a							10 37								11 07								

For general notes see front of timetable
For details of catering facilities see Directory of Train Operators

A To London Cannon Street (Table 199)
b Arr. 0954
c Arr. 1024
e Arr. 1054

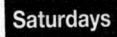

For details of Bank Holiday service alterations please see first page of Table 195

London → Dartford and Gillingham

Network Diagram - see first page of Table 200

		SE		SE A	SE	SE	SE	SE	SE A	SE	SE	SE A		SE	SE	SE	SE	SE	SE	SE	SE	SE		SE	SE
London Charing Cross 4	⊖ d	16 20				16 32				16 47	16 50				17 02				17 17	17 20				17 32	
London Waterloo (East) 4	⊖ d	16 23				16 35				16 50	16 53				17 05				17 20	17 23				17 35	
London Cannon Street 4	⊖ d			16 30	16 34			16 40	16 48			17 00		17 04			17 10	17 18			17 30	17 34			
London Bridge 4	⊖ d	16 29		16 34	16 38	16 40		16 44	16 52	16 55	16 59	17 04		17 08	17 10		17 14	17 22	17 25	17 29	17 34	17 38		17 40	
Deptford	d			16 40				16 50				17 10					17 20				17 40				
Greenwich 4	⛴ d	16 37		16 42				16 52			17 07	17 12					17 22			17 37	17 42				
Maze Hill	d			16 46				16 56				17 16					17 26				17 46				
Westcombe Park	d			16 48				16 58				17 18					17 28				17 48				
London Victoria 15	⊖ d						16 31									17 01									17 31
Denmark Hill 4	d						16 42									17 12									17 42
Peckham Rye 4	d						16 44									17 14									17 44
Nunhead 4	d						16 46									17 16									17 46
New Cross 4	⊖ d				16 44				16 57			18a17		17 14				17 27				17 44			
St Johns	d								16 59									17 29							
Lewisham 4	⛴ d				16 48	16 50	16 53			17 06				17 18	17 20	17 23			17 36			17 48		17 50	17 53
Blackheath 4	d				16 50		16 55			17 08				17 20		17 25			17 38			17 50			17 55
Kidbrooke	d						16 58			17 11						17 28			17 41						17 58
Eltham	d						17 02			17 15						17 32			17 45						18 02
Falconwood	d						17 04			17 17						17 34			17 47						18 04
Welling	d						17 07			17 20						17 37			17 50						18 07
Bexleyheath	d						17 09			17 22						17 39			17 52						18 09
Barnehurst 4	d						17 12			17 25						17 42			17 55						18 12
Hither Green 4	d					16 53			17 05						17 23			17 35						17 53	
Lee	d					16 55			17 07						17 25			17 37						17 55	
Mottingham	d					16 58			17 10						17 28			17 40						17 58	
New Eltham	d					17 01			17 13						17 31			17 43						18 01	
Sidcup 4	d					17 04			17 16						17 34			17 46						18 04	
Albany Park	d					17 06			17 18						17 36			17 48						18 06	
Bexley	d					17 08			17 20						17 38			17 50						18 08	
Crayford	d					17 11			17b28						17 41			17a54						18 11	
Charlton 4	d	16 44		16 50	16 55			17 00			17 14	17 20		17 25			17 30			17 44	17 50	17 55			
Woolwich Dockyard	d			16 52				17 02				17 22					17 32				17 52				
Woolwich Arsenal 4	d	16 49		16 55	17 00			17 05			17 19	17 25		17 30			17 35			17 49	17 55	18 00			
Plumstead	d			16 57	17a02			17 07				17 27		17a32			17 37				17 57	18a02			
Abbey Wood	d	16 53		17 01				17 11			17 23	17 31					17 41			17 53	18 01				
Belvedere	d			17 03				17 13				17 33					17 43				18 03				
Erith	d			17 06				17 16				17 36					17 46				18 06				
Slade Green 4	d			17a09				17 19	17a34			17a39					17 49				18a09				
Dartford 4	a	17 03				17 15	17 17	17 23		17 30	17 33				17 45	17 47	17 53		18 00	18 03				18 15	18 17
	d	17 04				17 16					17 34				17 46					18 04				18 16	
Stone Crossing	d					17 19									17 49									18 19	
Greenhithe for Bluewater	d	17 09				17 22					17 39				17 52					18 09				18 22	
Swanscombe	d					17 24									17 54									18 24	
Northfleet	d					17 26									17 56									18 26	
Gravesend 4	d	17 16				17a30					17 46				18a00					18 16				18a30	
Higham	d	17 22									17 52									18 22					
Strood 4	d	17 28									17 58									18 28					
Maidstone West 4	a	17 54									18 24									18 54					
Rochester 4	d	17 31									18 01									18 31					
Chatham 4	d	17 34									18 04									18 34					
Gillingham (Kent) 4	a	17 37									18 07									18 37					

For general notes see front of timetable
For details of catering facilities see Directory of Train Operators

A To London Cannon Street (Table 199)
b Arr. 1724

Saturdays

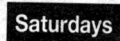

For details of Bank Holiday service alterations please see first page of Table 195

London → Dartford and Gillingham

Network Diagram - see first page of Table 200

		SE	SE	SE	SE	SE	SE	SE	SE	SE		SE	SE	SE	SE	SE	SE	SE	SE	SE		SE	SE	SE	SE
London Charing Cross 4	⊖ d			17 47	17 50			18 02					18 17	18 20		18 32				18 47		18 50		19 04	
London Waterloo (East) 4	⊖ d			17 50	17 53			18 05					18 20	18 23		18 35				18 50		18 53		19 07	
London Cannon Street 4	⊖ d	17 40	17 48			18 00	18 04			18 10		18 18			18 30			18 40	18 48				19 00		
London Bridge 4	⊖ d	17 44	17 52	17 55	17 59	18 04	18 08	18 10		18 14		18 22	18 25	18 29	18 34	18 40		18 44	18 52	18 55		18 59	19 04	19 13	
Deptford	d	17 50				18 10				18 20					18 40			18 50					19 10		
Greenwich 4	d	17 52			18 07	18 12				18 22					18 42			18 52					19 12		
Maze Hill	d	17 56				18 16				18 26					18 46			18 56					19 16		
Westcombe Park	d	17 58				18 18				18 28					18 48			18 58					19 18		
London Victoria 15	⊖ d								18 01								18 31								19 01
Denmark Hill 4	d								18 12								18 42								19 12
Peckham Rye 4	d								18 14								18 44								19 14
Nunhead 4	d								18 16								18 46								19 16
New Cross 4	⊖ d		17 57				18 14					18 27							18 57						
St Johns	d		17 59									18 29							18 59						
Lewisham 4	d			18 06			18 18	18 20	18 23				18 33	18 37		18 50	18 53			19 05		19 08		19 21	19 23
Blackheath 4	d			18 08			18 20		18 25				18 36	18 39			18 55			19 09		19 10			19 25
Kidbrooke	d			18 11					18 28				18 41				18 58			19 12					19 28
Eltham	d			18 15					18 32				18 45				19 02			19 15					19 32
Falconwood	d			18 17					18 34				18 47				19 04			19 18					19 34
Welling	d			18 20					18 37				18 50				19 07			19 20					19 37
Bexleyheath	d			18 22					18 39				18 52				19 09			19 23					19 39
Barnehurst 4	d			18 25					18 42				18 55				19 12			19 25					19 42
Hither Green 4	d		18 05					18 23				18 35				18 53			19 05					19 24	
Lee	d		18 07					18 25				18 37				18 55			19 07					19 26	
Mottingham	d		18 10					18 28				18 40				18 58			19 10					19 29	
New Eltham	d		18 13					18 31				18 43				19 01			19 13					19 32	
Sidcup 4	d		18 16					18 34				18 46				19 04			19 16					19 35	
Albany Park	d		18 18					18 36				18 48				19 06			19 18					19 37	
Bexley	d		18 20					18 38				18 50				19 08			19 20					19 39	
Crayford	d		18a24					18 41				18a54				19 11			19a24					19 42	
Charlton 4	d	18 00			18 14	18 20	18 25			18 30				18 44	18 50			19 00				19 14	19 20		
Woolwich Dockyard	d	18 02				18 22				18 32					18 52			19 02					19 22		
Woolwich Arsenal 4	d	18 05			18 19	18 25	18 30			18 35				18 49	18 55			19 05				19 19	19 25		
Plumstead	d	18 07				18 27	18a32			18 37					18 57			19 07					19 27		
Abbey Wood	d	18 11			18 23	18 31				18 41				18 53	19 01			19 11				19 23	19 31		
Belvedere	d	18 13				18 33				18 43					19 03			19 13					19 33		
Erith	d	18 16				18 36				18 46					19 06			19 16					19 36		
Slade Green 4	d	18 19				18a39				18 49					19a09			19 19					19a39		
Dartford 4	a	18 23		18 30	18 33			18 45	18 48	18 55			19 00	19 03		19 15	19 17	19 25		19 31		19 33		19 46	19 48
	d				18 34			18 46						19 04		19 16						19 34		19 47	
Stone Crossing	d							18 49								19 19								19 50	
Greenhithe for Bluewater	d				18 39			18 52						19 09		19 22						19 39		19 53	
Swanscombe	d							18 54								19 24								19 55	
Northfleet	d							18 56								19 26								19 57	
Gravesend 4	d				18 46			19a00						19 16		19a30						19 46		20a01	
Higham	d				18 52									19 22								19 52			
Strood 4	d				18 58									19 28								19 58			
Maidstone West 4	a				19 24									19 54								20 24			
Rochester 4	d				19 01									19 31								20 01			
Chatham 4	d				19 04									19 34								20 04			
Gillingham (Kent) 4	a				19 07									19 37								20 07			

For general notes see front of timetable
For details of catering facilities see Directory of Train Operators

Table 200

Saturdays

For details of Bank Holiday service alterations please see first page of Table 195

London → Dartford and Gillingham

Network Diagram - see first page of Table 200

Station		SE	SE	SE	SE	SE	SE	SE		SE	SE	SE	SE	SE	SE	SE	SE	SE		SE	SE	SE	SE	SE	SE
London Charing Cross 4	⊖ d	19 10	19 17	19 20	19 34			19 40		19 47	19 50	20 04	20 10	20 17	20 20	20 34	20 40	20 47		20 50	21 04	21 10	21 17	21 20	21 34
London Waterloo (East) 4	⊖ d	19 13	19 20	19 23	19 37			19 43		19 50	19 53	20 07	20 13	20 20	20 23	20 37	20 43	20 50		20 53	21 07	21 13	21 20	21 23	21 37
London Cannon Street 4	⊖ d																								
London Bridge 4	⊖ d	19 18	19 25	19 29	19 43			19 48		19 55	19 59	20 13	20 18	20 25	20 29	20 43	20 48	20 55		20 59	21 13	21 18	21 25	21 29	21 43
Deptford	d	19 24						19 54					20 24				20 54					21 24			
Greenwich 4	d	19 26						19 56					20 26				20 56					21 26			
Maze Hill	d	19 30						20 00					20 30				21 00					21 30			
Westcombe Park	d	19 32						20 02					20 32				21 02					21 32			
London Victoria 15	⊖ d					19 31																			
Denmark Hill 4	d					19 42																			
Peckham Rye 4	d					19 44																			
Nunhead 4	d					19 46																			
New Cross 4	⊖ d				19 48					20 00		20 18		20 30		20 48		21 00			21 18		21 30		21 48
St Johns	d																								
Lewisham 4	d		19 35	19 37	19 53	19 54				20 05	20 07	20 23		20 35	20 37	20 53		21 05		21 07	21 23		21 35	21 37	21 53
Blackheath 4	d		19 37	19 39		19 56				20 07	20 09			20 37	20 39			21 07		21 09			21 37	21 39	
Kidbrooke	d		19 40			19 59				20 10				20 40				21 10					21 40		
Eltham	d		19 44			20 03				20 14				20 44				21 14					21 44		
Falconwood	d		19 46			20 05				20 16				20 46				21 16					21 46		
Welling	d		19 49			20 08				20 19				20 49				21 19					21 49		
Bexleyheath	d		19 51			20 10				20 21				20 51				21 21					21 51		
Barnehurst 4	d		19 54			20 13				20 24				20 54				21 24					21 54		
Hither Green 4	d				19 57							20 27				20 57					21 27				21 57
Lee	d				19 59							20 29				20 59					21 29				21 59
Mottingham	d				20 02		←					20 32				21 02					21 32				22 02
New Eltham	d				20 05 →		20 05					20 35				21 05					21 35				22 05
Sidcup 4	d						20 08					20 38				21 08					21 38				22 08
Albany Park	d						20 10					20 40				21 10					21 40				22 10
Bexley	d						20 12					20 42				21 12					21 42				22 12
Crayford	d						20 15					20 45				21 15					21 45				22 15
Charlton 4	d	19 34		19 44				20 04			20 14		20 34		20 44		21 04			21 14		21 34		21 44	
Woolwich Dockyard	d	19 37						20 07					20 37				21 07					21 37			
Woolwich Arsenal 4	d	19 40		19 49				20 10			20 19		20 40		20 49		21 10			21 19		21 40		21 49	
Plumstead	d	19 42						20 12					20 42				21 12					21 42			
Abbey Wood	d	19 45		19 53				20 15			20 23		20 45		20 53		21 15			21 23		21 45		21 53	
Belvedere	d	19 48						20 18					20 48				21 18					21 48			
Erith	d	19 51						20 21					20 51				21 21					21 51			
Slade Green 4	d	19 54						20 24					20 54				21 24					21 54			
Dartford 4	a	19 59	20 01	20 03		20 18	20 20	20 29		20 31	20 33	20 50	20 59	21 01	21 03	21 20	21 29	21 31		21 33	21 50	21 59	22 01	22 03	22 20
	d			20 04							20 34				21 04					21 34				22 04	
Stone Crossing	d										20 37									21 37					
Greenhithe for Bluewater	d			20 09							20 40				21 09					21 40				22 09	
Swanscombe	d										20 42									21 42					
Northfleet	d										20 44									21 44					
Gravesend 4	d			20 16							20 48				21 16					21 50				22 16	
Higham	d			20 22							20 54				21 22					21 56				22 22	
Strood 4	d			20 28							21 01				21 28					22 02				22 28	
Maidstone West 4	a			20 54							21 24				21 54										
Rochester 4	d			20 31							21 05				21 31					22 06				22 31	
Chatham 4	d			20 34							21 08				21 34					22 09				22 34	
Gillingham (Kent) 4	a			20 37							21 13				21 37					22 13				22 37	

For general notes see front of timetable
For details of catering facilities see Directory of Train Operators

Saturdays

For details of Bank Holiday service alterations please see first page of Table 195

London → Dartford and Gillingham

Network Diagram - see first page of Table 200

		SE	SE	SE	SE	SE		SE	SE	SE	SE	SE	SE	SE	SE	SE		SE	SE	SE	SE				
London Charing Cross 4	⊖ d	21 40	21 47	21 50	22 04	22 10		22 17	22 20	22 34	22 40	22 47	22 50	23 04	23 10	23 17		23 20	23 34	23 47	23 49				
London Waterloo (East) 4	⊖ d	21 43	21 50	21 53	22 07	22 13		22 20	22 23	22 37	22 43	22 50	22 53	23 07	23 13	23 20		23 23	23 37	23 50	23 52				
London Cannon Street 4	⊖ d																								
London Bridge 4	⊖ d	21 48	21 55	21 59	22 13	22 18		22 25	22 29	22 43	22 48	22 55	22 59	23 13	23 18	23 25		23 29	23 43	23 55	23 57				
Deptford	d	21 54				22 24					22 54				23 24						00 03				
Greenwich 4	⛴ d	21 56				22 26					22 56				23 26						00 05				
Maze Hill	d	22 00				22 30					23 00				23 30						00 09				
Westcombe Park	d	22 02				22 32					23 02				23 32						00 11				
London Victoria 15	⊖ d																								
Denmark Hill 4	d																								
Peckham Rye 4	d																								
Nunhead 4	d																								
New Cross 4	⊖ d		22 00		22 18			22 30		22 48		23 00		23 18		23 30			23 48	00 01					
St Johns	d																								
Lewisham 4	⛴ d		22 05	22 07	22 23			22 35	22 37	22 53		23 05	23 07	23 23		23 35		23 37	23 53	00 05					
Blackheath 4	d		22 07	22 09				22 37	22 39			23 07	23 09			23 37		23 39		00 07					
Kidbrooke	d		22 10					22 40				23 10				23 40				00 10					
Eltham	d		22 14					22 44				23 14				23 44				00 14					
Falconwood	d		22 16					22 46				23 16				23 46				00 17					
Welling	d		22 19					22 49				23 19				23 49				00 20					
Bexleyheath	d		22 21					22 51				23 21				23 51				00 23					
Barnehurst 4	d		22 24					22 54				23 24				23 54				00 25					
Hither Green 4	d				22 27					22 57				23 27					23 57						
Lee	d				22 29					22 59				23 29					23 59						
Mottingham	d				22 32					23 02				23 32					00 02						
New Eltham	d				22 35					23 05				23 35					00 05						
Sidcup 4	d				22 38					23 08				23 38					00 08						
Albany Park	d				22 40					23 10				23 40					00 10						
Bexley	d				22 42					23 12				23 42					00 12						
Crayford	d				22 45					23 15				23 45					00 15						
Charlton 4	d	22 04		22 14		22 34			22 44		23 04		23 14		23 34			23 44			00 13				
Woolwich Dockyard	d	22 07				22 37					23 07				23 37						00 16				
Woolwich Arsenal 4	d	22 10		22 19		22 40			22 49		23 10		23 19		23 40			23 49			00 19				
Plumstead	d	22 12				22 42					23 12				23 42						00 21				
Abbey Wood	d	22 15		22 23		22 45			22 53		23 15		23 23		23 45			23 53			00 24				
Belvedere	d	22 18				22 48					23 18				23 48						00 27				
Erith	d	22 21				22 51					23 21				23 51						00 30				
Slade Green 4	d	22 24				22 54					23 24				23 54						00 33				
Dartford 4	a	22 28	22 30	22 33	22 50	22 59		23 01	23 03	23 20	23 29	23 31	23 33	23 50	23 59	00 01		00 03	00 20	00 31	00 38				
	d			22 34					23 04				23 34					00 04							
Stone Crossing	d			22 37									23 37					00 07							
Greenhithe for Bluewater	d			22 40					23 09				23 40					00 09							
Swanscombe	d			22 42									23 42					00 12							
Northfleet	d			22 44									23 44					00 14							
Gravesend 4	d			22 50					23 16				23 50					00 17							
Higham	d			22 56					23 22				23 56					00 23							
Strood 4	d			23 02					23 28				00 02					00 28							
Maidstone West 4	a																								
Rochester 4	d			23 06					23 31				00 06					00 32							
Chatham 4	d			23 09					23 34				00 09					00 35							
Gillingham (Kent) 4	a			23 13					23 37				00 13					00 38							

For general notes see front of timetable
For details of catering facilities see Directory of Train Operators

Sundays

London → Dartford and Gillingham

Network Diagram - see first page of Table 200

		SE	SE	SE	SE	SE	SE	SE	SE	SE	SE	SE	SE	SE	SE	SE	SE	SE	SE	SE	SE	SE	SE	SE	SE
London Charing Cross 4	⊖ d	22p50	23p20	23p34	23p47	23p49	00 04	00 14		07 37	07 40	07 47	08 07	08 10	08 17	08 20	08 37	08 40	08 47	08 50	09 07	09 10	09 17	09 20	
London Waterloo (East) 4	⊖ d	22p53	23p23	23p37	23p50	23p52	00 07	00 17		07 40	07 43	07 50	08 10	08 13	08 20	08 23	08 40	08 43	08 50	08 53	09 10	09 13	09 20	09 23	
London Cannon Street 4	⊖ d																								
London Bridge 4	⊖ d	22p59	23p29	23p43	23p55	23p57	00 13	00 22		07 45	07 48	07 55	08 15	08 18	08 25	08 29	08 45	08 48	08 55	08 59	09 15	09 18	09 25	09 29	09 36
Deptford	d					00 03					07 53			08 23				08 53				09 23			09 41
Greenwich 4	d					00 05					07 55			08 25				08 55				09 25			09 43
Maze Hill	d					00 09					07 59			08 29				08 59				09 29			09 47
Westcombe Park	d					00 11					08 01			08 31				09 01				09 31			09 49
London Victoria 15	⊖ d																								
Denmark Hill 4	d																								
Peckham Rye 4	d																								
Nunhead 4	d																								
New Cross 4	⊖ d			23p48	00 01		00 18	00 27		07 50		08 00	08 20		08 30		08 50		09 00		09 20		09 30		
St Johns	d																								
Lewisham 4	d	23p07	23p37	23p53	00 05		00 23	00 31		07 55		08 05	08 25		08 35	08 38	08 55		09 05	09 08	09 25		09 35	09 38	
Blackheath 4	d	23p09	23p39		00 07			00 34		07 58			08 28			08 41	08 58			09 11	09 28			09 41	
Kidbrooke	d				00 10					08 01			08 31				09 01				09 31				
Eltham	d				00 14					08 04			08 34				09 04				09 34				
Falconwood	d				00 17					08 07			08 37				09 07				09 37				
Welling	d				00 20					08 09			08 39				09 09				09 39				
Bexleyheath	d				00 23					08 12			08 42				09 12				09 42				
Barnehurst 4	d				00 25					08 15			08 45				09 15				09 45				
Hither Green 4	d			23p57			00 27					08 09			08 39				09 09				09 39		
Lee	d			23p59			00 29					08 11			08 41				09 11				09 41		
Mottingham	d			00 02			00 32					08 14			08 44				09 14				09 44		
New Eltham	d			00 05			00 35					08 16			08 46				09 16				09 46		
Sidcup 4	d			00 08			00 38					08 20			08 50				09 20				09 50		
Albany Park	d			00 10			00 40					08 22			08 52				09 22				09 52		
Bexley	d			00 12			00 42					08 24			08 54				09 24				09 54		
Crayford	d			00 15			00 45					08 27			08 57				09 27				09 57		
Charlton 4	d	23p14	23p44			00 13		00 38			08 03			08 33		08 45		09 03		09 15		09 33		09 45	09 51
Woolwich Dockyard	d					00 16					08 06			08 36				09 06				09 36			09 54
Woolwich Arsenal 4	d	23p19	23p49			00 19		00 42			08 09			08 39		08 50		09 09		09 20		09 39		09 50	09 57
Plumstead	d					00 21		00 44			08 11			08 41				09 11				09 41			09a59
Abbey Wood	d	23p23	23p53			00 24		00 47			08 14			08 44		08 55		09 14		09 25		09 44		09 55	
Belvedere	d					00 27		00 50			08 17			08 47				09 17				09 47			
Erith	d					00 30		00 53			08 20			08 50				09 20				09 50			
Slade Green 4	d					00 33		00 55	07 57		08 23			08 53				09 23				09 53			
Dartford 4	a	23p33	00 03	00 20	00 31	00 38	00 50	00 59	08 01	08 21	08 27	08 31	08 51	08 57	09 01	09 03	09 21	09 27	09 31	09 33	09 51	09 57	10 01	10 03	
	d	23p34	00 04					01 00	08 02	08 22	08 28		08 52			09 04	09 22			09 34	09 52			10 04	
Stone Crossing	d	23p37	00 07						08 05	08 25	08 31		08 55				09 25				09 55				
Greenhithe for Bluewater	d	23p40	00 09					01 05	08 08	08 28	08 34		08 58			09 09	09 28			09 39	09 58			10 09	
Swanscombe	d	23p42	00 12						08 10	08 30	08 36		09 00				09 30				10 00				
Northfleet	d	23p44	00 14						08 12	08 32	08 38		09 02				09 32				10 02				
Gravesend 4	d	23p50	00 17					01 12	08 16	08a36	08 42		09a06			09 16	09a36			09 46	10a06			10 16	
Higham	d	23p56	00 23					01 18	08 22		08 48					09 22				09 52				10 22	
Strood 4	d	00 02	00 28					01 23	08 28		08 54					09 27				09 57				10 27	
Maidstone West 4	a										09 25									10 25					
Rochester 4	d	00 06	00 32					01 27	08 32		08 58					09 31				10 01				10 31	
Chatham 4	d	00 09	00 35					01 30	08 35		09 01					09 34				10 04				10 34	
Gillingham (Kent) 4	a	00 13	00 38					01 33	08 38		09 04					09 37				10 07				10 37	

For general notes see front of timetable
For details of catering facilities see
Directory of Train Operators

Table 200

Sundays

London → Dartford and Gillingham

Network Diagram - see first page of Table 200

		SE		SE	SE	SE	SE		SE	SE	SE	SE	SE	SE	SE	SE	SE	SE		SE	SE	SE	SE	SE
London Charing Cross 4	⊖ d	09 37		09 40	09 47	09 50			10 07	10 10	10 17	10 20		10 37	10 40	10 47	10 50			18 07	18 10	18 17	18 20	
London Waterloo (East) 4	⊖ d	09 40		09 43	09 50	09 53			10 10	10 13	10 20	10 23		10 40	10 43	10 50	10 53			18 10	18 13	18 20	18 23	
London Cannon Street 4	⊖ d																							
London Bridge 4	⊖ d	09 45		09 48	09 55	09 59	10 06		10 15	10 18	10 25	10 29	10 36	10 45	10 48	10 55	10 59	11 06		18 15	18 18	18 25	18 29	18 36
Deptford	d			09 53			10 11			10 23			10 41		10 53			11 11			18 23			18 41
Greenwich 4	d			09 55			10 13			10 25			10 43		10 55			11 13			18 25			18 43
Maze Hill	d			09 59			10 17			10 29			10 47		10 59			11 17			18 29			18 47
Westcombe Park	d			10 01			10 19			10 31			10 49		11 01			11 19			18 31			18 49
London Victoria 15	⊖ d																							
Denmark Hill 4	d																							
Peckham Rye 4	d																							
Nunhead 4	d																							
New Cross 4	⊖ d	09 50			10 00				10 20		10 30			10 50		11 00				18 20		18 30		
St Johns	d																							
Lewisham 4	d	09 55			10 05	10 08			10 25		10 35	10 38		10 55		11 05	11 08			18 25		18 35	18 38	
Blackheath 4	d	09 58				10 11			10 28			10 41		10 58			11 11			18 28			18 41	
Kidbrooke	d	10 01							10 31					11 01						18 31				
Eltham	d	10 04							10 34					11 04						18 34				
Falconwood	d	10 07							10 37					11 07					and at	18 37				
Welling	d	10 09							10 39					11 09					the same	18 39				
Bexleyheath	d	10 12							10 42					11 12					minutes	18 42				
Barnehurst 4	d	10 15							10 45					11 15					past	18 45				
Hither Green 4	d				10 09						10 39					11 09			each			18 39		
Lee	d				10 11						10 41					11 11			hour until			18 41		
Mottingham	d				10 14						10 44					11 14						18 44		
New Eltham	d				10 16						10 46					11 16						18 46		
Sidcup 4	d				10 20						10 50					11 20						18 50		
Albany Park	d				10 22						10 52					11 22						18 52		
Bexley	d				10 24						10 54					11 24						18 54		
Crayford	d				10 27						10 57					11 27						18 57		
Charlton 4	d			10 03		10 15	10 21			10 33		10 45	10 51		11 03		11 15	11 21			18 33		18 45	18 51
Woolwich Dockyard	d			10 06			10 24			10 36			10 54		11 06			11 24			18 36			18 54
Woolwich Arsenal 4	d			10 09		10 20	10 27			10 39		10 50	10 57		11 09		11 20	11 27			18 39		18 50	18 57
Plumstead	d			10 11			10a29			10 41			10a59		11 11			11a29			18 41			18a59
Abbey Wood	d			10 14		10 25				10 44		10 55			11 14		11 25				18 44		18 55	
Belvedere	d			10 17						10 47					11 17						18 47			
Erith	d			10 20						10 50					11 20						18 50			
Slade Green 4	d			10 23						10 53					11 23						18 53			
Dartford 4	a	10 21		10 27	10 31	10 33			10 51	10 57	11 01	11 03		11 21	11 27	11 31	11 33			18 51	18 57	19 01	19 03	
	d	10 22				10 34			10 52			11 04		11 22			11 34			18 52			19 04	
Stone Crossing	d	10 25							10 55					11 25						18 55				
Greenhithe for Bluewater	d	10 28				10 39			10 58			11 09		11 28			11 39			18 58			19 09	
Swanscombe	d	10 30							11 00					11 30						19 00				
Northfleet	d	10 32							11 02					11 32						19 02				
Gravesend 4	d	10a36				10 46			11a06			11 16		11a36			11 46			19a06			19 16	
Higham	d					10 52						11 22					11 52						19 22	
Strood 4	d					10 57						11 27					11 57						19 27	
Maidstone West 4	a					*11 25*											*12 25*							
Rochester 4	d					11 01						11 31					12 01						19 31	
Chatham 4	d					11 04						11 34					12 04						19 34	
Gillingham (Kent) 4	a					11 07						11 37					12 07						19 37	

For general notes see front of timetable
For details of catering facilities see Directory of Train Operators

London → Dartford and Gillingham

Network Diagram - see first page of Table 200

Station		SE	SE	SE	SE	SE	SE	SE	SE	SE	SE	SE	SE	SE	SE	SE	SE	SE	SE	SE	SE	SE	SE	SE
London Charing Cross 4	⊖ d	18 37	18 40	18 47	18 50		19 07	19 10	19 17	19 20	19 37	19 40	19 47	19 50	20 07	20 10	20 17	20 20	20 37	20 40	20 47	20 50	21 07	21 10
London Waterloo (East) 4	⊖ d	18 40	18 43	18 50	18 53		19 10	19 13	19 20	19 23	19 40	19 43	19 50	19 53	20 10	20 13	20 20	20 23	20 40	20 43	20 50	20 53	21 10	21 13
London Cannon Street 4	⊖ d																							
London Bridge 4	⊖ d	18 45	18 48	18 55	18 59	19 06	19 15	19 18	19 25	19 29	19 45	19 48	19 55	19 59	20 15	20 18	20 25	20 29	20 45	20 48	20 55	20 59	21 15	21 18
Deptford	d		18 53			19 11		19 23				19 53				20 23				20 53				21 23
Greenwich 4	d		18 55			19 13		19 25				19 55				20 25				20 55				21 25
Maze Hill	d		18 59			19 17		19 29				19 59				20 29				20 59				21 29
Westcombe Park	d		19 01			19 19		19 31				20 01				20 31				21 01				21 31
London Victoria 15	⊖ d																							
Denmark Hill 4	d																							
Peckham Rye 4	d																							
Nunhead 4	d																							
New Cross 4	⊖ d	18 50		19 00			19 20		19 30		19 50		20 00		20 20		20 30		20 50		21 00		21 20	
St Johns	d																							
Lewisham 4	d	18 55		19 05	19 08		19 25		19 35	19 38	19 55		20 05	20 08	20 25		20 35	20 38	20 55		21 05	21 08	21 25	
Blackheath 4	d	18 58			19 11		19 28			19 41	19 58			20 11	20 28			20 41	20 58			21 11	21 28	
Kidbrooke	d	19 01					19 31				20 01				20 31				21 01				21 31	
Eltham	d	19 04					19 34				20 04				20 34				21 04				21 34	
Falconwood	d	19 07					19 37				20 07				20 37				21 07				21 37	
Welling	d	19 09					19 39				20 09				20 39				21 09				21 39	
Bexleyheath	d	19 12					19 42				20 12				20 42				21 12				21 42	
Barnehurst 4	d	19 15					19 45				20 15				20 45				21 15				21 45	
Hither Green 4	d			19 09					19 39				20 09				20 39				21 09			
Lee	d			19 11					19 41				20 11				20 41				21 11			
Mottingham	d			19 14					19 44				20 14				20 44				21 14			
New Eltham	d			19 16					19 46				20 16				20 46				21 16			
Sidcup 4	d			19 20					19 50				20 20				20 50				21 20			
Albany Park	d			19 22					19 52				20 22				20 52				21 22			
Bexley	d			19 24					19 54				20 24				20 54				21 24			
Crayford	d			19 27					19 57				20 27				20 57				21 27			
Charlton 4	d		19 03		19 15	19 21		19 33		19 45		20 03		20 15		20 33		20 45		21 03		21 15		21 33
Woolwich Dockyard	d		19 06			19 24		19 36				20 06				20 36				21 06				21 36
Woolwich Arsenal 4	d		19 09		19 20	19 27		19 39		19 50		20 09		20 20		20 39		20 50		21 09		21 20		21 39
Plumstead	d		19 11			19a29		19 41				20 11				20 41				21 11				21 41
Abbey Wood	d		19 14		19 25			19 44		19 55		20 14		20 25		20 44		20 55		21 14		21 25		21 44
Belvedere	d		19 17					19 47				20 17				20 47				21 17				21 47
Erith	d		19 20					19 50				20 20				20 50				21 20				21 50
Slade Green 4	d		19 23					19 53				20 23				20 53				21 23				21 53
Dartford 4	a	19 21	19 28	19 31	19 33		19 51	19 57	20 01	20 03	20 21	20 27	20 31	20 33	20 51	20 57	21 01	21 03	21 21	21 27	21 31	21 33	21 51	21 57
	d				19 34					20 04				20 34				21 04				21 34		
Stone Crossing	d				19 37									20 37								21 37		
Greenhithe for Bluewater	d				19 40					20 09				20 40				21 09				21 40		
Swanscombe	d				19 42									20 42								21 42		
Northfleet	d				19 44									20 44								21 44		
Gravesend 4	d				19 48					20 16				20 48				21 16				21 48		
Higham	d				19 54					20 22				20 54				21 22				21 54		
Strood 4	d				20 00					20 27				21 00				21 27				22 00		
Maidstone West 4	a				20 26									21 26								22 26		
Rochester 4	d				20 04					20 31				21 04				21 31				22 04		
Chatham 4	d				20 07					20 34				21 07				21 34				22 07		
Gillingham (Kent) 4	a				20 10					20 37				21 10				21 37				22 10		

For general notes see front of timetable
For details of catering facilities see Directory of Train Operators

Sundays

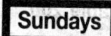

London → Dartford and Gillingham

Network Diagram - see first page of Table 200

		SE	SE	SE	SE	SE	SE	SE	SE	SE	SE	SE	SE	SE	SE	SE	SE	SE	SE	SE	SE	SE	SE
London Charing Cross 4	⊖ d	21 17	21 20		21 37	21 40	21 47	21 50	22 07	22 10	22 17	22 20	22 37	22 40	22 47	22 50	23 07	23 10	23 17	23 20	23 37	23 40	23 47
London Waterloo (East) 4	⊖ d	21 20	21 23		21 40	21 43	21 50	21 53	22 10	22 13	22 20	22 23	22 40	22 43	22 50	22 53	23 10	23 13	23 20	23 23	23 40	23 43	23 50
London Cannon Street 4	⊖ d																						
London Bridge 4	⊖ d	21 25	21 29		21 45	21 48	21 55	21 59	22 15	22 18	22 25	22 29	22 45	22 48	22 55	22 59	23 15	23 18	23 25	23 29	23 45	23 48	23 55
Deptford	d					21 53				22 23				22 53				23 23				23 53	
Greenwich 4	⛴ d					21 55				22 25				22 55				23 25				23 55	
Maze Hill	d					21 59				22 29				22 59				23 29				23 59	
Westcombe Park	d					22 01				22 31				23 01				23 31				00 01	
London Victoria 15	⊖ d																						
Denmark Hill 4	d																						
Peckham Rye 4	d																						
Nunhead 4	d																						
New Cross 4	⊖ d	21 30			21 50		22 00		22 20		22 30		22 50		23 00		23 20		23 30		23 50		23 59
St Johns	d																						
Lewisham 4	⛴ d	21 35	21 38		21 55		22 05	22 08	22 25		22 35	22 38	22 55		23 05	23 08	23 25		23 35	23 38	23 55		00 04
Blackheath 4	d		21 41		21 58			22 11	22 28			22 41	22 58			23 11	23 28			23 41	23 58		
Kidbrooke	d				22 01				22 31				23 01				23 31				00 01		
Eltham	d				22 04				22 34				23 04				23 34				00 04		
Falconwood	d				22 07				22 37				23 07				23 37				00 07		
Welling	d				22 09				22 39				23 09				23 39				00 09		
Bexleyheath	d				22 12				22 42				23 12				23 42				00 12		
Barnehurst 4	d				22 15				22 45				23 15				23 45				00 15		
Hither Green 4	d	21 39					22 09				22 39				23 09				23 39				00 08
Lee	d	21 41					22 11				22 41				23 11				23 41				00 10
Mottingham	d	21 44					22 14				22 44				23 14				23 44				00 13
New Eltham	d	21 46					22 16				22 46				23 16				23 46				00 16
Sidcup 4	d	21 50					22 20				22 50				23 20				23 50				00 19
Albany Park	d	21 52					22 22				22 52				23 22				23 52				00 21
Bexley	d	21 54					22 24				22 54				23 24				23 54				00 23
Crayford	d	21 57					22 27				22 57				23 27				23 57				00 26
Charlton 4	d		21 45			22 03		22 15		22 33		22 45		23 03		23 15		23 33		23 45		00 03	
Woolwich Dockyard	d					22 06				22 36				23 06				23 36				00 06	
Woolwich Arsenal 4	d		21 50			22 09		22 20		22 39		22 50		23 09		23 20		23 39		23 50		00 09	
Plumstead	d					22 11				22 41				23 11				23 41				00 11	
Abbey Wood	d		21 55			22 14		22 25		22 44		22 55		23 14		23 25		23 44		23 55		00 14	
Belvedere	d					22 17				22 47				23 17				23 47				00 17	
Erith	d					22 20				22 50				23 20				23 50				00 20	
Slade Green 4	d					22 23				22 53				23 23				23 53				00 23	
Dartford 4	a	22 01	22 03		22 21	22 27	22 31	22 33	22 51	22 57	23 01	23 03	23 21	23 27	23 31	23 33	23 51	23 57	00 01	00 03	00 21	00 27	00 30
	d		22 04					22 34				23 04				23 34				00 04			
Stone Crossing	d							22 37								23 37							
Greenhithe for Bluewater	d		22 09					22 40				23 09				23 40				00 09			
Swanscombe	d							22 42								23 42							
Northfleet	d							22 44								23 44							
Gravesend 4	d		22 16					22 48				23 16				23 48				00 16			
Higham	d		22 22					22 54				23 22				23 54				00 22			
Strood 4	d		22 27	22 42				23 00				23 27				23 58				00 27			
Maidstone West 4	a																						
Rochester 4	d		22 31	22 47				23 04				23 31				00 03				00 31			
Chatham 4	d		22 34	22 50				23 07				23 34				00 06				00 34			
Gillingham (Kent) 4	a		22 37	22 53				23 10				23 37				00 09				00 37			

For general notes see front of timetable
For details of catering facilities see Directory of Train Operators

For details of Bank Holiday service alterations please see first page of Table 195

Gillingham and Dartford → London

Network Diagram - see first page of Table 200

Miles	Miles	Miles	Miles	Miles			SE MX A	SE	SE	SE	SE	SE	SE	SE	SE	SE	SE	SE	SE	SE		SE	SE	SE	SE
0	—	—	0	—	**Gillingham (Kent)** [4]	d	00 07	04 12				04 51	04 56				05 22							05 52	06 03
1¾	—	—	1¾	—	**Chatham** [4]	d	00 11	04 16				04 55	05 00				05 26							05 56	06 07
2¼	—	—	2¼	—	Rochester [4]	d	00 13	04 18				04 57	05 02				05 28							05 58	06 09
—	—	—	—	—	Maidstone West [4]	d																			
3¼	—	—	3¼	—	Strood [4]	d	00 17	04 23				05 03	05a06				05 33							06 03	06a14
6	—	—	6	—	Higham	d	00 22	04 28				05 08					05 38							06 08	
10½	—	—	10½	—	**Gravesend** [4]	d	00 28	04 35				05 15					05 45		05 48					06 15	
12½	—	—	12½	—	Northfleet	d						05 19							05 51						
13¼	—	—	13¼	—	Swanscombe	d						05 21							05 53						
14½	—	—	14½	—	Greenhithe for Bluewater	d	00 34					05 24					05 50		05 56					06 20	
15¼	—	—	15¼	—	Stone Crossing	d						05 27							05 58						
17¼	0	0	17¼	0	**Dartford** [4]	a	00 41	04 44				05 30					05 56		06 02					06 25	
—	—	—	—	—		d	00 42	04 46	05 02	05 12	05 18	05 32		05 34		05 48	05 58	06 00	06 02				06 22	06 26	
19¼	2	—	—	—	Slade Green [4]	d				05 16		05 36							06 06						
20½	3¼	—	—	—	Erith	d				05 18		05 38							06 08						
21¾	4½	—	—	—	Belvedere	d				05 21		05 41							06 11						
23¼	6	—	—	—	Abbey Wood	d				05 24		05 44					06 07		06 14					06 35	
24¾	7½	—	—	—	Plumstead	d				05 27		05 47			←				06 17						
25¼	8	—	—	—	**Woolwich Arsenal** [4]	d				05 30		05 50 →			05 50		06 12		06 20					06 40	
26	8¾	—	—	—	Woolwich Dockyard	d													06 22						
27	9¾	—	—	—	Charlton [4]	d				05 35					05 55				06 25						
—	—	—	19	—	Crayford	d		04 49	05 05					05 37				06 03							
—	—	—	20½	—	Bexley	d		04 52	05 08					05 40				06 06							
—	—	—	21½	—	Albany Park	d		04 54	05 10					05 42				06 08							
—	—	—	22½	—	Sidcup [4]	d		04 57	05 13					05 45				06 11							
—	—	—	24	—	New Eltham	d		05 00	05 16					05 48				06 14							
—	—	—	25	—	Mottingham	d		05 02	05 18					05 50				06 16							
—	—	—	26½	—	Lee	d		05 05	05 21					05 53				06 19							
—	—	—	27¼	—	Hither Green [4]	d		05 08	05 23					05 55				06b25							
—	—	3	—	3	Barnehurst [4]	d					05 24					05 54				06 12		06 25	06c32		
—	—	4¼	—	4¼	Bexleyheath	d					05 27					05 57				06 15		06 28	06 35		
—	—	5¾	—	5¾	Welling	d					05 30					06 00				06 18		06 31	06 38 →		
—	—	6¾	—	6¾	Falconwood	d					05 33					06 03				06 21		06 34			
—	—	8	—	8	Eltham	d					05 36					06 06				06 24		06 37			
—	—	9	—	9	Kidbrooke	d					05 39					06 09				06 27		06 40			
29	—	10	—	10	Blackheath [4]	d					05 42					06 12	06 20			06 30		06 43		06 48	
30	—	11	28½	11	Lewisham [4]	d		05 13	05 28		05e48			06 00		06 16	06 24	06 30		06 34		06 47		06 52	
—	—	11½	29	—	St Johns	d												06 32							
—	—	12¼	29¾	—	New Cross [4]	⊖ d		05 16	05 32		05 52			06 04		06 20		06 34		06 38					
—	—	—	—	12¾	Nunhead [4]	d																			
—	—	—	—	13½	Peckham Rye [4]	d																			
—	—	—	—	14¼	Denmark Hill [4]	d																			
—	—	—	—	18½	**London Victoria** [15]	⊖ a	01 13																		
—	10½	—	—	—	Westcombe Park	d				05 37					05 57				06 27						
—	11	—	—	—	Maze Hill	d				05 39					05 59				06 29						
—	12	—	—	—	Greenwich [4]	d				05 43					06 03				06 33						
—	12½	—	—	—	Deptford	d				05 45					06 05				06 35						
34¼	15½	15¼	32¾	—	**London Bridge** [4]	⊖ a		05 22	05 38	05 53	05 58			06 10	06 13	06 26	06 33	06 40	06 43	06 43		06 54		07 01	
—	16¼	—	—	—	**London Cannon Street** [4]	⊖ a														06 47		07 00			
35¼	—	16¼	33¾	—	**London Waterloo (East)** [4]	⊖ a		05 27	05 43	05 58	06 03			06 15	06 18	06 31	06 38	06 45	06 48					07 06	
36	—	17	34½	—	**London Charing Cross** [4]	⊖ a		05 31	05 47	06 02	06 06			06 18	06 21	06 34	06 41	06 48	06 51					07f11	

For general notes see front of timetable
For details of catering facilities see Directory of Train Operators

- **A** From Faversham (Table 212)
- **b** Arr. 0622
- **c** Arr. 0628
- **e** Arr. 0545
- **f** Until 9 October arr 1 minute earlier

For details of Bank Holiday service alterations please see first page of Table 195

Gillingham and Dartford → London

Network Diagram - see first page of Table 200

Station		SE	SE	SE	SE	SE	SE	SE	SE	SE	SE	SE	SE	SE	SE	SE	SE	SE	SE	SE	SE	SE	SE	SE
Gillingham (Kent) [4]	d									06 20							06 36							
Chatham [4]	d									06 24							06 40							
Rochester [4]	d									06 26							06 42							
Maidstone West [4]	d																*06 19*							
Strood [4]	d									06 32							06 48							
Higham	d									06 37							06 53							
Gravesend [4]	d					06 20				06 44					06 48		07 00							07 10
Northfleet	d					06 24									06 52									07 14
Swanscombe	d					06 26									06 54									07 16
Greenhithe for Bluewater	d					06 29				06 50					06 57		07 06							07 19
Stone Crossing	d					06 31									06 59									07 22
Dartford [4]	a					06 36				06 55					07 03		07 11							07 26
	d		06 28	06 32		06 37		06 45	06 48	06 56			07 00	07 02	07 04		07 12				07 16		07 24	07 26
Slade Green [4]	d			06 36			06 46						07 04			07 08					07 20	07 26		
Erith	d			06 38			06 48						07 06			07 10					07 22	07 28		
Belvedere	d			06 41			06 51						07 09			07 13					07 25	07 31		
Abbey Wood	d			06 44			06 54			07 05			07 12			07 16	07 21				07 28	07 34		
Plumstead	d			06 47			06 57						07 15			07 19					07 31	07 37		
Woolwich Arsenal [4]	d			06 50			07 00			07 10			07 18			07 22	07 26				07 34	07 40		
Woolwich Dockyard	d			06 52			07 02						07 20			07 24					07 36	07 42		
Charlton [4]	d			06 55			07 05						07 23			07 27					07 39	07 45		
Crayford	d		06 31			06 41		06 49			07 02			07 06						07 22			07 28	
Bexley	d		06 34			06 44		06 52			07 05			07 09						07 25			07 31	
Albany Park	d		06 36			06 47		06 55			07 08			07 12						07 28			07 34	
Sidcup [4]	d		06 39			06 50		06 58			07 11			07 15						07 31			07 37	
New Eltham	d		06 42			06 53		07 01			07 14			07 18						07 34			07 40	
Mottingham	d		06 44			06 55		07 03			07 16			07 20						07 36			07 42	
Lee	d		06 47			06 58		07 06			07 19			07 23						07 39			07 45	
Hither Green [4]	d		06 52			07 02		07 10			07 22			07 26						07 42			07 49	
Barnehurst [4]	d				06 42				06 54			07 03			07 10			07 19	07 23					07 33
Bexleyheath	d	←			06 45				06 57			07 06			07 13			07 22	07 26					07 36
Welling	d	06 38			06 48				07 00			07 09			07 16			07 25	07 29					07 39
Falconwood	d	06 41			06 51				07 03			07 11			07 19			07 27	07 31					07 41
Eltham	d	06 44			06 54				07 06			07 14			07 22			07 30	07 34					07 44
Kidbrooke	d	06 47			06 57				07 09			07 17			07 25			07 33	07 37					07 47
Blackheath [4]	d	06 52			07 00				07 12	07 18		07 21				07 32		07 38	07 41					07 51
Lewisham [4]	⛴ d	06 56			07 04	07 08		07 15	07 18	07 22		07 25		07 32		07 38		07 41	07 44				07 54	07 56
St Johns	d		06 56			07 10						07 27						07 44						
New Cross [4]	⊖ d		06 58		07 07	07 12						07 29		07 36				07 46					07 59	
Nunhead [4]	d																		07 52					
Peckham Rye [4]	d																		07 55					
Denmark Hill [4]	d																		07 59					
London Victoria [15]	⊖ a																		08b12					
Westcombe Park	d			06 57			07 07						07 25								07 41	07 47		
Maze Hill	d			06 59			07 09						07 27								07 43	07 49		
Greenwich [4]	⛴ d			07 03			07 13						07 31								07 47	07 53		
Deptford	d			07 05			07 15						07 33								07 49	07 55		
London Bridge [4]	⊖ a	07 06	07 08	07 13	07 14	07 17	07 21	07 25	07 27	07 30	07 33	07 35	07 40	07 41			07 44	07 52		07 53	07 57	08 02	08 04	08 06
London Cannon Street [4]	⊖ a				07 19	07b25	07b29					07b42		07 48			07b52	07b58				08b10	08b12	
London Waterloo (East) [4]	⊖ a	07 11	07 13	07 19				07 30	07 33	07 36	07 39		07 46		07 44	07 51				07 58	08 02			08 11
London Charing Cross [4]	⊖ a	07b16	07b18	07b25				07b35	07b38	07b41	07b44		07b52		07b50	07b57				08 03	08b08			08b18

For general notes see front of timetable
For details of catering facilities see Directory of Train Operators

b Until 9 October arr 1 minute earlier

For details of Bank Holiday service alterations please see first page of Table 195

Gillingham and Dartford → London

Network Diagram - see first page of Table 200

		SE	SE	SE	SE A	SE		SE	SE	SE	SE	SE	SE	SE	SE	SE	SE	SE	SE	SE	SE		SE	SE	SE
Gillingham (Kent) 4	d	06 53															07 12	07 28							
Chatham 4	d	06 57															07 16	07 32							
Rochester 4	d	06 59															07 18	07 34							
Maidstone West 4	d																06 54								
Strood 4	d	07 06		07 10													07b28			07 36					
Higham	d	07 10		07 14													07 32			07 40					
Gravesend 4	d	07 18		07 22											07 34		07 40			07 48					07 52
Northfleet	d														07 38										07 56
Swanscombe	d														07 40										07 58
Greenhithe for Bluewater	d	07 24		07 28											07 43		07 46			07 54					08 00
Stone Crossing	d														07 45										08 02
Dartford 4	a	07 29		07 33											07 49		07 51			07 59					08 06
	d	07 30		07 34		07 36					07 42	07 44			07 50		07 52		07 56	08 00				08 02	08 06
Slade Green 4	d				07 39					07 40	07 46				07 54								08 00	08 06	
Erith	d									07 42	07 48												08 02	08 08	
Belvedere	d									07 45	07 51												08 05	08 11	
Abbey Wood	d	07 39								07 48	07 54				08 01								08 08	08 14	
Plumstead	d									07 51	07 57		⟵										08 11	08 17	
Woolwich Arsenal 4	d	07 44								07 54	08 00		08 00		08 06								08 14	08 20	
Woolwich Dockyard	d									07 56	⟶		08 02										08 16	08 22	
Charlton 4	d									07 59			08 05										08 19	08 25	
Crayford	d			07 38	07a46									07 48			07 56								
Bexley	d			07 41										07 51			07 59								
Albany Park	d			07 44										07 54			08 02								
Sidcup 4	d			07 47					07 51					07 57			08 05				08 11				
New Eltham	d			07 50					07 54					08 00			08 08				08 14				
Mottingham	d								07 56					08 02							08 16				
Lee	d								07 59					08 05							08 19				
Hither Green 4	d								08 02					08 09							08 22				
Barnehurst 4	d		07 39			07 43		07 47				07 50				07 59			08 03	08 07			07 56		08 13
Bexleyheath	d		07 42			07 46		07 50				07 53				08 02			08 06	08 10					08 16
Welling	d		07 45			07 49		07 53				07 56				08 05			08 09	08 13					08 19
Falconwood	d		07 47			07 51		07 55				07 59				08 07			08 11	08 15					08 21 ⟶
Eltham	d		07 50			07 54		07 58				08 02				08 10			08 14	08 18					
Kidbrooke	d		07 53			07 57		08 01				08 05				08 13			08 17	08 21					
Blackheath 4	d	07 54	07 58			08 01		08 05				08 08			08 14	08 18			08 21						
Lewisham 4	d		08 01			08 04						08 12		08 14	08 18	08 21			08 24						
St Johns	d		08 04													08 24									
New Cross 4	⊖ d		08 06											08 18		08 26									
Nunhead 4	d					08 09													08 29						
Peckham Rye 4	d					08 11													08 32						
Denmark Hill 4	d					08 14												08 29	08 35						
London Victoria 15	⊖ a					08c29												08 41	08c47						
Westcombe Park	d									08 01			08 07										08 21	08 27	
Maze Hill	d									08 03			08 09										08 23	08 29	
Greenwich 4	d									08 07			08 13										08 27	08 33	
Deptford	d									08 09			08 15										08 29	08 35	
London Bridge 4	⊖ a	08 06	08 12						08 13	08 18		08 21	08 23	08 25	08 27	08 33					08 33		08 38	08 41	
London Cannon Street 4	⊖ a	08e15	08c19										08c31	08c33	08c35	08 39								08e50	
London Waterloo (East) 4	⊖ a			08 08				08 17	08 19	08 23		08 27					08 29			08 37	08 39		08 43		
London Charing Cross 4	⊖ a			08c14				08c24	08c25	08c29		08c33					08c35			08c43	08c45		08c49		

For general notes see front of timetable
For details of catering facilities see Directory of Train Operators

A From London Charing Cross
b Arr. 0724
c Until 9 October arr 1 minute earlier
e Until 9 October arr 2 minutes earlier

For details of Bank Holiday service alterations please see first page of Table 195

Gillingham and Dartford → London

Network Diagram - see first page of Table 200

		SE	SE	SE	SE	SE	SE	SE	SE	SE	SE	SE	SE	SE		SE	SE	SE	SE	SE	SE	SE	SE	SE	SE
Gillingham (Kent) 4	d	07 33																				08 15			
Chatham 4	d	07 37																				08 19			
Rochester 4	d	07 39																07 58				08 21			
Maidstone West 4	d										*07 26*											*08 01*			
Strood 4	d	07 46									07 56							08b08				08 28			
Higham	d	07 50									08 00							08 12				08 32			
Gravesend 4	d	07 58									08 08							08 20				08 40			
Northfleet	d																	08 23							
Swanscombe	d																	08 25							
Greenhithe for Bluewater	d	08 04									08 14							08 28				08 46			
Stone Crossing	d																	08 30							
Dartford 4	a	08 09									08 19							08 34				08 52			
	d	08 10	08 12								08 20	08 24	08 26				08 32	08 35			08 43	08 53		08 57	09 01
Slade Green 4	d							08 17		08 18	08 24					08 30		08 39		08 43				09 03	
Erith	d									08 20						08 32				08 45				09 05	
Belvedere	d									08 23						08 35				08 48				09 08	
Abbey Wood	d	08 19								08 26	08 31					08 38		08 45		08 51				09 11	
Plumstead	d					←				08 29						08 41				08 54				09 14	
Woolwich Arsenal 4	d	08 24				08 24				08 32	08 36					08 44		08 50		08 57				09 17	
Woolwich Dockyard	d	→								08 34						08 46				08 59				→	
Charlton 4	d									08 37						08 49				09 02					
Crayford	d		08 16	08 08								08 28					08 36		08 35				09 00		09 04
Bexley	d		08 19	08 11								08 31					08 39						09 02		09 07
Albany Park	d		08 22	08 14								08 34					08 42						09 05		09 09
Sidcup 4	d		08 25	08 17					08 31			08 37					08 45						09 08		09 12
New Eltham	d		08 28	08 20					08 34			08 40					08 48						09 12		09 15
Mottingham	d			08 22					08 36			08 42					08 50						09 14		09 17
Lee	d			08 25					08 39			08 45					08 53						09 17		09 20
Hither Green 4	d			08 29					08 42			08 49					08 56						09 20		09 23
Barnehurst 4	d						08 19	08 23					08 33						08 43		08 49	08 59			
Bexleyheath	d						08 22	08 26					08 36						08 46		08 52	09 02			
Welling	d				←		08 25	08 29					08 39						08 49		08 55	09 05			
Falconwood	d				08 21		08 27	08 31					08 41						08 51		08 57	09 07			
Eltham	d				08 24		08 31	08 34					08 44						08 54		09 00	09 10			
Kidbrooke	d				08 27		08 34	08 37					08 47						08 57		09 03	09 13			
Blackheath 4	d				08 31	08 34	08 38	08 41			08 44		08 51					08 58	09 01		09 07	09 17			
Lewisham 4	⛴ d			08 34	08 36		08 41	08 44				08 54	08 56						09 04		09 10	09 20			09 28
St Johns	d						08 44							←					09 06				09 24		
New Cross 4	⊖ d			08 38			08 46					09 00		09 00					09 08				09 26		
Nunhead 4	d							08 52				→									09 16				
Peckham Rye 4	d							08 55													09 18				
Denmark Hill 4	d							08 59													09 20				
London Victoria 15	⊖ a							09 12													09c33				
Westcombe Park	d									08 39						08 51				09 04					
Maze Hill	d									08 41						08 53				09 06					
Greenwich 4	⛴ d									08 45						08 57				09 10					
Deptford	d									08 47						08 59				09 12					
London Bridge 4	⊖ a		08 42	08 44	08 46	08 47	08 52		08 53	08 57			09 04	09 06		09 07	09 07	09 11	09 14	09 21		09 29	09 31		09 36
London Cannon Street 4	⊖ a			08c52		08c55	09c00							09c12		09c15		09c19	09e23				09c39		
London Waterloo (East) 4	⊖ a		08 47		08 51				08 59	09 03	08 57		09 09				09 13			09 26		09 34			09 42
London Charing Cross 4	⊖ a		08c53		08c57				09c05	09c09	09c04		09c15				09e20			09c32		09c40			09c48

For general notes see front of timetable
For details of catering facilities see Directory of Train Operators

- **b** Arr. 0802
- **c** Until 9 October arr 1 minute earlier
- **e** Until 9 October arr 2 minutes earlier

For details of Bank Holiday service alterations please see first page of Table 195

Gillingham and Dartford → London

Network Diagram - see first page of Table 200

Station		SE	SE	SE	SE	SE	SE		SE	SE	SE	SE	SE	SE	SE	SE	SE	SE	SE	SE	SE	SE		SE	SE
																				A		A			
Gillingham (Kent) [4]	d												09 14								09 44				
Chatham [4]	d												09 18								09 48				
Rochester [4]	d				08 52								09 20								09 50				
Maidstone West [4]	d				*08 29*																*09 28*				
Strood [4]	d				08 57								09 25								09 55				
Higham	d				09 01								09 29								09 59				
Gravesend [4]	d		08 50		09 08					09 14			09 36					09 42			10 06				
Northfleet	d		08 54							09 18								09 46							
Swanscombe	d		08 56							09 20								09 48							
Greenhithe for Bluewater	d		08 59		09 13					09 23			09 41					09 51			10 11				
Stone Crossing	d		09 01							09 25								09 53							
Dartford [4]	a		09 06		09 19					09 30			09 46					09 57			10 16				
	d		09 07		09 21		09 24		09 27	09 31	09 35	09 43	09 47			09 49	09 54	10 01	10 05		10 17				10 19
Slade Green [4]	d			09 15					09 33							09 53				10 07		10 10			10 23
Erith	d			09 17					09 35							09 55				10 09					10 25
Belvedere	d			09 20					09 38							09 58				10 12					10 28
Abbey Wood	d			09 23	09 29				09 41				09 55			10 01				10 15	10 25				10 31
Plumstead	d	←		09 26					09 44						10 01	10 04				10 18				10 31	10 34
Woolwich Arsenal [4]	d	09 17		09 29	09 33				09 47				09 59		10 03	10 07				10 21	10 29			10 33	10 37
Woolwich Dockyard	d	09 19		09 31					09 49							10 09				10 23					10 39
Charlton [4]	d	09 22		09 34	09 38				09 52				10 04		10 08	10 12				10 26	10 34			10 38	10 42
Crayford	d					09 24				09 35		09b50						10 05				10 20			
Bexley	d					09 27				09 38		09 52						10 08				10 22			
Albany Park	d					09 29				09 40		09 55						10 10				10 25			
Sidcup [4]	d					09 32				09 43		09 58		←				10 13				10 28			
New Eltham	d					09 35				09 46		10 01		10 01				10 16				10 31			
Mottingham	d					09 37				09 48		→		10 03				10 18				10 33			
Lee	d					09 40				09 51				10 06				10 21				10 36			
Hither Green [4]	d					09 44				09 54				10 10				10 24				10 40			
Barnehurst [4]	d		09 13				09 29				09 41						10 00		10 11						
Bexleyheath	d		09 16				09 32				09 44						10 02		10 14						
Welling	d		09 19				09 35				09 47						10 05		10 17						
Falconwood	d		09 21				09 37				09 49						10 08		10 19						
Eltham	d		09 24				09 40				09 52						10 11		10 22						
Kidbrooke	d		09 27				09 43				09 55						10 14		10 25						
Blackheath [4]	d		09 31		09 43		09 47				09 59				10 13		10 17		10 29					10 43	
Lewisham [4]	d		09 36		09 46		09 51			09 59	10 02				10 16		10 21	10 29	10 32					10 46	
St Johns	d		09 38			09 48								10 14								10 45			
New Cross [4]	⊖ d		09 40			09 50								10 16	10 20							10 47		10 50	
Nunhead [4]	d						09 56										10 26								
Peckham Rye [4]	d						09 58										10 28								
Denmark Hill [4]	d						10 01										10 31								
London Victoria [15]	⊖ a						10c14										10 42								
Westcombe Park	d	09 24		09 36					09 54							10 14				10 28					10 44
Maze Hill	d	09 26		09 38					09 56							10 16				10 30					10 46
Greenwich [4]	d	09 30		09 42					10 00				10 10			10 20				10 34	10 40				10 50
Deptford	d	09 32		09 44					10 02							10 22				10 36					10 52
London Bridge [4]	⊖ a	09 39	09 49	09 50	09 54	09 56			10 09		10 10		10 19	10 21	10 26	10 29		10 37	10 40	10 43	10 49	10 53		10 56	10 59
London Cannon Street [4]	⊖ a	09c47		09e58		10 01			10 13					10 27	10 30	10 33					10 47	10 57		11 00	11 03
London Waterloo (East) [4]	⊖ a		09 54		09 59					10 11	10 16		10 24					10 42	10 45		10 54				
London Charing Cross [4]	⊖ a		10 00		10 05					10 14	10 20		10 28					10 47	10 50		10 58				

For general notes see front of timetable
For details of catering facilities see Directory of Train Operators

A From London Cannon Street (Table 199)
b Arr. 0947
c Until 9 October arr 2 minutes earlier
e Until 9 October arr 1 minute earlier

Table 200

Mondays to Fridays

For details of Bank Holiday service alterations please see first page of Table 195

Gillingham and Dartford → London

Network Diagram - see first page of Table 200

		SE	SE	SE	SE A	SE	SE A	SE	SE	SE	SE	SE	SE A	SE	SE A	SE	SE	SE	SE	SE	SE A	SE	SE A	SE
Gillingham (Kent) 4	d					10 14								10 44								11 14		
Chatham 4	d					10 18								10 48								11 18		
Rochester 4	d					10 20								10 50								11 20		
Maidstone West 4	d					*09 58*								*10 27*								*10 58*		
Strood 4	d					10 25								10 55								11 25		
Higham	d					10 29								10 59								11 29		
Gravesend 4	d		10 12			10 36					10 42			11 06					11 12			11 36		
Northfleet	d		10 16								10 46								11 16					
Swanscombe	d		10 18								10 48								11 18					
Greenhithe for Bluewater	d		10 21			10 41					10 51			11 11					11 21			11 41		
Stone Crossing	d		10 23								10 53								11 23					
Dartford 4	a		10 29			10 46					10 57			11 16					11 27			11 46		
	d	10 24	10 31	10 35		10 47			10 49	10 54	11 01	11 05		11 17			11 19	11 24	11 31	11 35		11 47		
Slade Green 4	d				10 37		10 40		10 53				11 07		11 10		11 23				11 37		11 40	
Erith	d				10 39				10 55				11 09				11 25				11 39			
Belvedere	d				10 42				10 58				11 12				11 28				11 42			
Abbey Wood	d				10 45	10 55			11 01				11 15	11 25			11 31				11 45	11 55		
Plumstead	d				10 48			11 01	11 04				11 18			11 31	11 34				11 48			12 01
Woolwich Arsenal 4	d				10 51	10 59		11 03	11 07				11 21	11 29		11 33	11 37				11 51	11 59		12 03
Woolwich Dockyard	d				10 53				11 09				11 23				11 39				11 53			
Charlton 4	d				10 56	11 04		11 08	11 12				11 26	11 34		11 38	11 42				11 56	12 04		12 08
Crayford	d		10 35				10 50				11 05				11 20				11 35				11 50	
Bexley	d		10 38				10 52				11 08				11 22				11 38				11 52	
Albany Park	d		10 40				10 55				11 10				11 25				11 40				11 55	
Sidcup 4	d		10 43				10 58				11 13				11 28				11 43				11 58	
New Eltham	d		10 46				11 01				11 16				11 31				11 46				12 01	
Mottingham	d		10 48				11 03				11 18				11 33				11 48				12 03	
Lee	d		10 51				11 06				11 21				11 36				11 51				12 06	
Hither Green 4	d		10 54				11 10				11 24				11 40				11 54				12 10	
Barnehurst 4	d	10 30		10 41						11 00		11 11						11 30		11 41				
Bexleyheath	d	10 32		10 44						11 02		11 14						11 32		11 44				
Welling	d	10 35		10 47						11 05		11 17						11 35		11 47				
Falconwood	d	10 38		10 49						11 08		11 19						11 38		11 49				
Eltham	d	10 41		10 52						11 11		11 22						11 41		11 52				
Kidbrooke	d	10 44		10 55						11 14		11 25						11 44		11 55				
Blackheath 4	d	10 47		10 59				11 13		11 17		11 29				11 43		11 47		11 59				12 13
Lewisham 4	d	10 51	10 59	11 02				11 16		11 21	11 29	11 32				11 46		11 51	11 59	12 02				12 16
St Johns	d						11 15								11 45								12 15	
New Cross 4	⊖ d						11 17	11 20							11 47	11 50							12 17	12 20
Nunhead 4	d	10 56								11 26								11 56						
Peckham Rye 4	d	10 58								11 28								11 58						
Denmark Hill 4	d	11 01								11 31								12 01						
London Victoria 15	⊖ a	11 12								11 42								12 12						
Westcombe Park	d				10 58				11 14				11 28				11 44				11 58			
Maze Hill	d				11 00				11 16				11 30				11 46				12 00			
Greenwich 4	d				11 04	11 10			11 20				11 34	11 40			11 50				12 04	12 10		
Deptford	d				11 06				11 22				11 36				11 52				12 06			
London Bridge 4	⊖ a		11 07	11 10	11 13	11 19	11 23	11 26	11 29		11 37	11 40	11 43	11 49	11 53	11 56	11 59		12 07	12 10	12 13	12 19	12 23	12 26
London Cannon Street 4	⊖ a				11 17		11 27	11 30	11 33				11 47		11 57	12 00	12 03				12 17		12 27	12 30
London Waterloo (East) 4	⊖ a		11 12	11 15		11 24					11 42	11 45		11 54					12 12	12 15		12 24		
London Charing Cross 4	⊖ a		11 17	11 20		11 28					11 47	11 50		11 58					12 17	12 20		12 28		

For general notes see front of timetable
For details of catering facilities see Directory of Train Operators

A From London Cannon Street (Table 199)

For details of Bank Holiday service alterations please see first page of Table 195

Gillingham and Dartford → London

Network Diagram - see first page of Table 200

Station		SE	SE	SE	SE	SE A
Gillingham (Kent) [4]	d					
Chatham [4]	d					
Rochester [4]	d					
Maidstone West [4]	d					
Strood [4]	d					
Higham	d					
Gravesend [4]	d			11 42		
Northfleet	d			11 46		
Swanscombe	d			11 48		
Greenhithe for Bluewater	d			11 51		
Stone Crossing	d			11 53		
Dartford [4]	a			11 57		
	d	11 49	11 54	12 01	12 05	
Slade Green [4]	d	11 53				12 07
Erith	d	11 55				12 09
Belvedere	d	11 58				12 12
Abbey Wood	d	12 01				12 15
Plumstead	d	12 04				12 18
Woolwich Arsenal [4]	d	12 07				12 21
Woolwich Dockyard	d	12 09				12 23
Charlton [4]	d	12 12				12 26
Crayford	d			12 05		
Bexley	d			12 08		
Albany Park	d			12 10		
Sidcup [4]	d			12 13		
New Eltham	d			12 16		
Mottingham	d			12 18		
Lee	d			12 21		
Hither Green [4]	d			12 24		
Barnehurst [4]	d		12 00		12 11	
Bexleyheath	d		12 02		12 14	
Welling	d		12 05		12 17	
Falconwood	d		12 08		12 19	
Eltham	d		12 11		12 22	
Kidbrooke	d		12 14		12 25	
Blackheath [4]	d		12 17		12 29	
Lewisham [4]	d		12 21	12 29	12 32	
St Johns	d					
New Cross [4]	⊖ d					
Nunhead [4]	d		12 26			
Peckham Rye [4]	d		12 28			
Denmark Hill [4]	d		12 31			
London Victoria [15]	⊖ a		12 42			
Westcombe Park	d	12 14				12 28
Maze Hill	d	12 16				12 30
Greenwich [4]	d	12 20				12 34
Deptford	d	12 22				12 36
London Bridge [4]	⊖ a	12 29		12 37	12 40	12 43
London Cannon Street [4]	⊖ a	12 33				12 47
London Waterloo (East) [4]	⊖ a			12 42	12 45	
London Charing Cross [4]	⊖ a			12 47	12 50	

and at the same minutes past each hour until

Station		SE	SE A	SE	SE	SE	SE	SE	SE A	SE	SE A	SE	SE	SE	SE		SE
Gillingham (Kent) [4]	d	14 44								15 14							
Chatham [4]	d	14 48								15 18							
Rochester [4]	d	14 50								15 20							
Maidstone West [4]	d	*14 27*								*14 58*							
Strood [4]	d	14 55								15 25							
Higham	d	14 59								15 29							
Gravesend [4]	d	15 06					15 12			15 36				15 40			
Northfleet	d						15 16							15 44			
Swanscombe	d						15 18							15 46			
Greenhithe for Bluewater	d	15 11					15 21			15 41				15 49			
Stone Crossing	d						15 23							15 51			
Dartford [4]	a	15 16					15 27			15 46				15 55			
	d	15 17			15 19	15 24	15 31	15 35		15 47			15 49	15 56	16 01		16 05
Slade Green [4]	d		15 10		15 23				15 37		15 40		15 53				
Erith	d				15 25				15 39				15 55				
Belvedere	d				15 28				15 42				15 58				
Abbey Wood	d	15 25			15 31				15 45	15 55			16 01				
Plumstead	d			15 31	15 34				15 48			16 01	16 04				
Woolwich Arsenal [4]	d	15 29		15 33	15 37				15 51	15 59		16 03	16 07				
Woolwich Dockyard	d				15 39				15 53				16 09				
Charlton [4]	d	15 34		15 38	15 42				15 56	16 04		16 08	16 12				
Crayford	d		15 20				15 35				15 50				16 05		
Bexley	d		15 22				15 38				15 52				16 08		
Albany Park	d		15 25				15 40				15 55				16 10		
Sidcup [4]	d		15 28				15 43				15 58				16 13		
New Eltham	d		15 31				15 46				16 01				16 16		
Mottingham	d		15 33				15 48				16 03				16 18		
Lee	d		15 36				15 51				16 06				16 21		
Hither Green [4]	d		15 40				15 54				16 11				16b28		
Barnehurst [4]	d					15 30		15 41						16 02			16 11
Bexleyheath	d					15 32		15 44						16 05			16 14
Welling	d					15 35		15 47						16 08			16 17
Falconwood	d					15 38		15 49						16 10			16 19
Eltham	d					15 41		15 52						16 13			16 22
Kidbrooke	d					15 44		15 55						16 16			16 25
Blackheath [4]	d			15 43		15 47		15 59				16 13		16 20			16 29
Lewisham [4]	d			15 46		15 51	15 59	16 02				16 16		16 24	16 33		16 35
St Johns	d		15 45								16 15				16 35		
New Cross [4]	⊖ d		15 47	15 50							16 17				16 37		
Nunhead [4]	d					15 56											16 40
Peckham Rye [4]	d					15 58											16 42
Denmark Hill [4]	d					16 01											16 46
London Victoria [15]	⊖ a					16 12											17 03
Westcombe Park	d				15 44				15 58				16 14				
Maze Hill	d				15 46				16 00				16 16				
Greenwich [4]	d	15 40			15 50				16 04	16 10			16 20				
Deptford	d				15 52				16 06				16 22				
London Bridge [4]	⊖ a	15 49	15 53	15 56	15 59		16 07	16 11	16 13	16 19	16 23	16 26	16 29	16 32	16 42		
London Cannon Street [4]	⊖ a		15 57	16 00	16 03				16 17		16 27		16 33	16 36	16 46		
London Waterloo (East) [4]	⊖ a	15 54					16 13	16 18		16 24		16 32					
London Charing Cross [4]	⊖ a	15 58					16 17	16 23		16 28		16 36					

For general notes see front of timetable
For details of catering facilities see Directory of Train Operators

A From London Cannon Street (Table 199)
b Arr. 1624

For details of Bank Holiday service alterations please see first page of Table 195

Gillingham and Dartford → London

Network Diagram - see first page of Table 200

		SE A	SE	SE	SE A	SE	SE	SE	SE	SE	SE	SE	SE	SE	SE		SE	SE	SE	SE	SE	SE A	SE	SE	SE
Gillingham (Kent) [4]	d			15 44											16 14									16 44	
Chatham [4]	d			15 48											16 18									16 48	
Rochester [4]	d			15 50											16 20									16 50	
Maidstone West [4]	d														15 44									16 27	
Strood [4]	d			15 55											16 25									16 55	
Higham	d			15 59											16 29									16 59	
Gravesend [4]	d			16 08					16 12						16 36				16 42					17 06	
Northfleet	d								16 16										16 46						
Swanscombe	d								16 18										16 48						
Greenhithe for Bluewater	d			16 14					16 21						16 41				16 51					17 11	
Stone Crossing	d								16 23										16 53						
Dartford [4]	a			16 20					16 29						16 46				16 57					17 17	
	d		16 15	16 21		16 23		16 29	16 31		16 37			16 43	16 49			16 51	17 01		17 05		17 11	17 19	17 21
Slade Green [4]	d	16 09			16 10			16 35		16 29			16 42					16 55				17 09	17 15		
Erith	d	16 11						16 37		16 31								16 57				17 11	17 17		
Belvedere	d	16 14						16 40		16 34								17 00				17 14	17 20		
Abbey Wood	d	16 17	16 25	16 29				16 43		16 37			16 49		16 57			17 03				17 17	17 23	17 29	
Plumstead	d	16 20						16 46		16 40		←						17 06				17 20	17 26		
Woolwich Arsenal [4]	d	16 23	16 29	16 33				16 49		16 43		16 49	16 53		17 02			17 09				17 23	17 29	17 34	
Woolwich Dockyard	d	16 25						→		16 45		16 51						17 11				17 25	17 31		
Charlton [4]	d	16 28	16 34	16 38						16 48		16 54	16 58		17 07			17 14				17 28	17 34	17 39	
Crayford	d				16 20				16 35					16 47			16 57		17 05						17 25
Bexley	d				16 22				16 37					16 50			16 59		17 07						17 27
Albany Park	d				16 25				16 40					16 52			17 02		17 10						17 30
Sidcup [4]	d				16 28		16 38		16 43					16 55			17 05		17 13	17 25					17 33
New Eltham	d				16 31		16 41		16 46					16 58			17 08		17 16						17 36
Mottingham	d				16 33		16 43		16 48					17 00			17 10		17 18						17 38
Lee	d				16 36		16 46		16 51					17 03			17 13		17 21						→
Hither Green [4]	d				16b42		16 50		16c56					17 06			17 16		17 24	17 31					
Barnehurst [4]	d					16 29					16 43										17 13				
Bexleyheath	d					16 32					16 46										17 16				
Welling	d					16 35					16 49										17 19				
Falconwood	d					16 37					16 51										17 21				
Eltham	d					16 40					16 54										17 24				
Kidbrooke	d					16 43					16 57										17 27				
Blackheath [4]	d			16 42		16 47					17 01				17 12						17 31			17 43	
Lewisham [4]	d			16 46		16 50	16 56				17 05			17 12	17e18				17 31		17 36			17 47	
St Johns	d				16 47									17 14					17 33						
New Cross [4]	⊖ d				16 49	16 54								17 16					17 35		17 39				
Nunhead [4]	d										17 13														
Peckham Rye [4]	d										17 15														
Denmark Hill [4]	d										17 18														
London Victoria [15]	⊖ a										17 28														
Westcombe Park	d	16 30								16 50		16 56						17 16				17 30	17 36		
Maze Hill	d	16 32								16 52		16 58						17 18				17 32	17 38		
Greenwich [4]	d	16 36	16 40							16 56		17 02	17 06					17 22				17 36	17 42		
Deptford	d	16 38								16 58		17 04						17 24				17 38	17 44		
London Bridge [4]	⊖ a	16 46	16 50	16 55	16 56	16 59	17 04		17 06	17 07		17 11	17 17	17 23	17 26		17 29	17 35	17 41	17 41	17 45	17 48	17 53	17 56	
London Cannon Street [4]	⊖ a	16 52	16 55		17 00	17 05	17 08			17 13		17 15	17 23	17 29			17 33	17 39	17 45		17 51	17 53	17 57	18 01	
London Waterloo (East) [4]	⊖ a			17 00					17 11						17 31					17 46					
London Charing Cross [4]	⊖ a			17 03					17 15						17 35					17 50					

For general notes see front of timetable
For details of catering facilities see Directory of Train Operators

A From London Cannon Street (Table 199)
b Arr. 1639
c Arr. 1653
e Arr. 1715

For details of Bank Holiday service alterations please see first page of Table 195

Gillingham and Dartford → London

Network Diagram - see first page of Table 200

		SE	SE	SE	SE	SE	SE	SE		SE	SE	SE	SE	SE	SE	SE	SE A	SE B	SE	SE	SE	SE	SE		SE
Gillingham (Kent) 4	d										17 14									17 48					
Chatham 4	d										17 18									17 52					
Rochester 4	d										17 20									17 54					
Maidstone West 4	d										*16 55*									*17 25*					
Strood 4	d										17 25									17 59					
Higham	d										17 29									18 03					
Gravesend 4	d	17 08								17 32	17 38			17 52						18 10		18 14			
Northfleet	d	17 12								17 36				17 56								18 18			
Swanscombe	d	17 14								17 38				17 58								18 20			
Greenhithe for Bluewater	d	17 17								17 41	17 45			18 01						18 15		18 23			
Stone Crossing	d	17 19								17 43				18 03								18 25			
Dartford 4	a	17 23								17 47	17 50			18 07						18 20		18 30			
	d	17 25				17 27	17 41			17 47	17 53		18 01	18 09		18 11				18 21	18 31	18 33	18 39		
Slade Green 4	d	17 31			17 35			17 43				17 52	18 05		18 12				18 23		18 35				
Erith	d				17 37			17 45					18 07						18 25		18 37				
Belvedere	d				17 40			17 48					18 10						18 28		18 40				
Abbey Wood	d	17 37			17 43			17 51			18 01		18 13		18 19				18 31		18 43				
Plumstead	d				17 46			17 54					18 16						18 34		18 46				←
Woolwich Arsenal 4	d	17 41			17 49			17 57			18 06		18 19		18 23				18 37		18 49 →				18 49
Woolwich Dockyard	d				17 51			17 59					18 21						18 39						18 51
Charlton 4	d	17 46			17 54			18 02			18 11		18 24		18 28				18 42						18 54
Crayford	d			17 35			17 45					18 01		18 13			18 20	18 20		18 25					
Bexley	d			17 37			17 47					18 03		18 15						18 27					
Albany Park	d			17 40			17 50					18 06		18 18						18 30					
Sidcup 4	d			17 43			17 53					18 09		18 21						18 33					
New Eltham	d		←				17 56					18 12		18 24						18 36					
Mottingham	d		17 38				17 58							18 26						18 38					
Lee	d		17 41				18 01							18 29						18 41					
Hither Green 4	d		17 44	17 50			18 04					18 18		18 32			18 00	18 00		18 44					
Barnehurst 4	d				17 31	17 33				17 53						18 17	18a28	18a30				18 39	18 45		
Bexleyheath	d					17 36				17 56						18 20						18 42	18 48		
Welling	d					17 39				17 59						18 23						18 45	18 51		
Falconwood	d					17 41				18 01						18 25						18 47	18 53		
Eltham	d					17 44				18 04						18 28						18 50	18 56		
Kidbrooke	d					17 47				18 07						18 31						18 53	18 59		
Blackheath 4	d					17 51				18 11	18 15				18 32	18 36						18 57	19 02		
Lewisham 4	d		17 51			17 54				18 14	18 20	18 24			18 36	18 41				18 49		19 01	19 06		
St Johns	d		17 55							18 17		18 26			18 38					18 51					
New Cross 4	⊖ d		17 57							18 19		18 28			18 40					18 53					
Nunhead 4	d					18 01										18 45							19 10		
Peckham Rye 4	d					18 03										18 47							19 12		
Denmark Hill 4	d					18 06										18 50							19 15		
London Victoria 15	⊖ a					18 16										19 01							19 25		
Westcombe Park	d				17 56			18 04					18 26						18 44						18 56
Maze Hill	d				17 58			18 06					18 28						18 46						18 58
Greenwich 4	d	17 52			18 02			18 10					18 32						18 50						19 02
Deptford	d				18 04			18 12					18 34						18 52						19 04
London Bridge 4	⊖ a	18 00	18 03	18 03	18 11		18 15	18 20		18 25	18 31	18 33	18 41	18 42	18 48				19 01	19 02		19 09			19 11
London Cannon Street 4	⊖ a		18 08		18 15			18 24		18 29		18 37	18 45						19 05						19 15
London Waterloo (East) 4	⊖ a	18 05		18 09			18 21				18 36			18 48	18 53					19 07		19 15			
London Charing Cross 4	⊖ a	18 09		18 13			18 25				18 40			18 53	18 57					19 11		19 20			

For general notes see front of timetable
For details of catering facilities see Directory of Train Operators

A Until 9 October. From London Charing Cross (Table 199)

B From 12 October. From London Charing Cross (Table 199)

For details of Bank Holiday service alterations please see first page of Table 195

Gillingham and Dartford → London

Network Diagram - see first page of Table 200

		SE	SE	SE	SE	SE	SE	SE	SE	SE	SE	SE	SE	SE	SE	SE	SE	SE	SE	SE	SE	SE	SE	SE
Gillingham (Kent) [4]	d		18 14					18 44					19 14					19 44					20 16	
Chatham [4]	d		18 18					18 48					19 18					19 48					20 20	
Rochester [4]	d		18 20					18 50					19 20					19 50					20 22	
Maidstone West [4]	d							*18 12*					*18 47*					*19 27*					*20 00*	
Strood [4]	d		18 25					18 55					19 25					19 55					20 27	
Higham	d		18 29					18 59					19 29					19 59					20 31	
Gravesend [4]	d		18 36			18 44		19 06			19 16		19 36			19 46		20 06			20 12		20 38	
Northfleet	d					18 48					19 20					19 50					20 16			
Swanscombe	d					18 50					19 22					19 52					20 18			
Greenhithe for Bluewater	d		18 41			18 53		19 11			19 25		19 41			19 55		20 11			20 21		20 43	
Stone Crossing	d					18 55					19 27					19 57					20 23			
Dartford [4]	a		18 46			18 59		19 17			19 31		19 46			20 00		20 16			20 27		20 48	
	d	18 43	18 49	18 53	18 59	19 03	19 07	19 19	19 23	19 27	19 33	19 37	19 49	19 53	19 57	20 03	20 07	20 19	20 23	20 27	20 33	20 37	20 49	20 53
Slade Green [4]	d			18 58			19 11			19 31		19 41			20 01		20 11			20 31		20 42		
Erith	d			19 00			19 13			19 33		19 43			20 03		20 13			20 33		20 44		
Belvedere	d			19 03			19 16			19 36		19 46			20 06		20 16			20 36		20 47		
Abbey Wood	d		18 57	19 06			19 19	19 27		19 39		19 49	19 57		20 09		20 19	20 27		20 39		20 50	20 57	
Plumstead	d			19 09			19 22			19 42		19 52			20 12		20 22			20 42		20 53		
Woolwich Arsenal [4]	d		19 01	19 12			19 25	19 31		19 45		19 55	20 01		20 15		20 25	20 31		20 45		20 56	21 01	
Woolwich Dockyard	d			19 14			19 27			19 47		19 57			20 17		20 27			20 47		20 58		
Charlton [4]	d		19 06	19 17			19 30	19 36		19 50		20 00	20 06		20 20		20 30	20 36		20 50		21 01	21 06	
Crayford	d	18 47				19 07					19 37					20 07					20 37			
Bexley	d	18 50				19 10					19 39					20 10					20 40			
Albany Park	d	18 52				19 12					19 42					20 12					20 42			
Sidcup [4]	d	18 55				19 15					19 45					20 15					20 45			
New Eltham	d	18 58				19 18					19 48					20 18					20 48			
Mottingham	d	19 00				19 20					19 50					20 20					20 50			
Lee	d	19 03				19 23					19 53					20 23					20 53			
Hither Green [4]	d	19 07				19 26					19 56					20 26					20 56			
Barnehurst [4]	d				19 05				19 31					20 01					20 31					21 01
Bexleyheath	d				19 08				19 34					20 04					20 34					21 04
Welling	d				19 11				19 37					20 07					20 37					21 07
Falconwood	d				19 13				19 39					20 09					20 39					21 09
Eltham	d				19 16				19 42					20 12					20 42					21 12
Kidbrooke	d				19 19				19 45					20 15					20 45					21 15
Blackheath [4]	d		19 10		19 23			19 40	19 49				20 10	20 19				20 40	20 49				21 10	21 19
Lewisham [4]	d	19 12	19 15		19 26	19 31		19 45	19 52		20 02		20 15	20 22		20 31		20 44	20 52		21 01		21 14	21 22
St Johns	d																							
New Cross [4]	⊖ d				19 30	19 34			19 56		20 05			20 26		20 34			20 56		21 04			21 26
Nunhead [4]	d																							
Peckham Rye [4]	d																							
Denmark Hill [4]	d																							
London Victoria [15]	⊖ a																							
Westcombe Park	d			19 19			19 32			19 52		20 02			20 22		20 32			20 52		21 03		
Maze Hill	d			19 21			19 34			19 54		20 04			20 24		20 34			20 54		21 05		
Greenwich [4]	d			19 25			19 38			19 58		20 08			20 28		20 38			20 58		21 09		
Deptford	d			19 27			19 40			20 00		20 10			20 30		20 40			21 00		21 11		
London Bridge [4]	⊖ a	19 21	19 23	19 33	19 36	19 43	19 49	19 53	20 03	20 07	20 13	20 19	20 23	20 33	20 37	20 43	20 49	20 53	21 03	21 07	21 13	21 19	21 23	21 33
London Cannon Street [4]	⊖ a	19 25		19 37	19 41					20 11					20 41									
London Waterloo (East) [4]	⊖ a		19 28			19 49	19 54	19 58	20 08		20 18	20 24	20 28	20 38		20 48	20 54	20 58	21 08		21 18	21 24	21 28	21 38
London Charing Cross [4]	⊖ a		19 32			19 53	19 59	20 01	20 13		20 22	20 29	20 31	20 43		20 52	20 59	21 01	21 13		21 22	21 29	21 31	21 43

For general notes see front of timetable
For details of catering facilities see Directory of Train Operators

For details of Bank Holiday service alterations please see first page of Table 195

Gillingham and Dartford → London

Network Diagram - see first page of Table 200

		SE	SE	SE	SE	SE	SE	SE		SE	SE	SE	SE	SE	SE	SE	SE	SE	SE	SE	SE
Gillingham (Kent)	d				20 42						21 14					21 42				22 22	
Chatham	d				20 46						21 18					21 46				22 26	
Rochester	d				20 48						21 20					21 48				22 28	
Maidstone West	d				20 24						21 00					21 27				22 02	
Strood	d				20 53						21b27					21 53				22 33	
Higham	d				20 57						21 31					21 57				22 37	
Gravesend	d		20 44		21 04						21 38					22 04				22 44	
Northfleet	d		20 48		21 07											22 07				22 47	
Swanscombe	d		20 50		21 09											22 09				22 49	
Greenhithe for Bluewater	d		20 53		21 12						21 43					22 12				22 52	
Stone Crossing	d		20 55		21 14											22 14				22 54	
Dartford	a		20 59		21 18						21 48					22 18				22 58	
	d	20 57	21 03	21 07	21 19	21 23	21 27	21 33		21 37	21 49	21 53	21 57	22 03	22 07	22 19	22 23	22 31	22 43	23 01	23 03
Slade Green	d	21 01		21 11			21 31			21 41			22 01		22 11			22 35		23 05	
Erith	d	21 03		21 13			21 33			21 43			22 03		22 13			22 37		23 07	
Belvedere	d	21 06		21 16			21 36			21 46			22 06		22 16			22 40		23 10	
Abbey Wood	d	21 09		21 19	21 27		21 39			21 49	21 57		22 09		22 19	22 27		22 43		23 13	
Plumstead	d	21 12		21 22			21 42			21 52			22 12		22 22			22 46		23 16	
Woolwich Arsenal	d	21 15		21 25	21 31		21 45			21 55	22 01		22 15		22 25	22 31		22 49		23 19	
Woolwich Dockyard	d	21 17		21 27			21 47			21 57			22 17		22 27			22 51		23 21	
Charlton	d	21 20		21 30	21 36		21 50			22 00	22 06		22 20		22 30	22 36		22 54		23 24	
Crayford	d		21 07					21 37						22 07					22 47		
Bexley	d		21 10					21 40						22 10					22 49		
Albany Park	d		21 12					21 42						22 12					22 52		
Sidcup	d		21 15					21 45						22 15					22 55		
New Eltham	d		21 18					21 48						22 18					22 58		
Mottingham	d		21 20					21 50						22 20					23 00		
Lee	d		21 23					21 53						22 23					23 03		
Hither Green	d		21 26					21 56						22 26					23 06		
Barnehurst	d					21 31						22 01					22 31				23 11
Bexleyheath	d					21 34						22 04					22 34				23 14
Welling	d					21 37						22 07					22 37				23 17
Falconwood	d					21 39						22 09					22 39				23 19
Eltham	d					21 42						22 12					22 42				23 22
Kidbrooke	d					21 45						22 15					22 45				23 25
Blackheath	d				21 40	21 49					22 10	22 19				22 40	22 49				23 29
Lewisham	d		21 31		21 44	21 52		22 01			22 14	22 22		22 31		22 44	22 52		23c13		23 32
St Johns	d																				
New Cross	⊖ d		21 34			21 56		22 04				22 26		22 34			22 56		23 16		23 36
Nunhead	d																				
Peckham Rye	d																				
Denmark Hill	d																				
London Victoria	⊖ a																				
Westcombe Park	d	21 22		21 32			21 52			22 02			22 22		22 32			22 56		23 26	
Maze Hill	d	21 24		21 34			21 54			22 04			22 24		22 34			22 58		23 28	
Greenwich	d	21 28		21 38			21 58			22 08			22 28		22 38			23 02		23 32	
Deptford	d	21 30		21 40			22 00			22 10			22 30		22 40			23 04		23 34	
London Bridge	⊖ a	21 37	21 43	21 49	21 53	22 03	22 07	22 13		22 19	22 23	22 33	22 37	22 43	22 49	22 53	23 03	23 13	23 22	23 41	23 43
London Cannon Street	⊖ a																				
London Waterloo (East)	⊖ a		21 48	21 54	21 58	22 08		22 18		22 24	22 28	22 38		22 48	22 54	22 58	23 08	23 18	23 28	23 46	23 49
London Charing Cross	⊖ a		21 52	21 59	22 01	22 13		22 22		22 29	22 31	22 43		22 52	22 59	23 01	23 13	23 22	23 32	23 50	23 53

For general notes see front of timetable
For details of catering facilities see Directory of Train Operators

b Arr. 2124
c Arr. 2310

Saturdays

For details of Bank Holiday service alterations please see first page of Table 195

Gillingham and Dartford → London

Network Diagram - see first page of Table 200

		SE A	SE	SE	SE	SE	SE		SE	SE	SE	SE	SE	SE		SE	SE	SE	SE	SE	SE		SE	SE	SE
Gillingham (Kent) 4	d	00 07			04 53				05 23		05 44	05 48						06 13	06 16						
Chatham 4	d	00 11			04 57				05 27		05 48	05 52						06 17	06 20						
Rochester 4	d	00 13			04 59				05 29		05 50	05 54						06 19	06 22						
Maidstone West 4	d																								
Strood 4	d	00 17			05 04				05 34		05 54	05a59						06 24	06a27						
Higham	d	00 22			05 09				05 39		05 59							06 29							
Gravesend 4	d	00 28			05 16				05 46		06 05		06 12					06 35			06 42				
Northfleet	d				05 19				05 49				06 16								06 46				
Swanscombe	d				05 21				05 51				06 18								06 48				
Greenhithe for Bluewater	d	00 34			05 24				05 54		06 10		06 21					06 40			06 51				
Stone Crossing	d				05 26				05 56				06 23								06 53				
Dartford 4	a	00 41			05 30				06 00		06 15		06 27					06 45			06 57				
	d	00 42	05 07	05 32	05 33	05 37	06 02		06 03	06 07	06 16		06 29	06 32			06 37	06 46		06 54	06 59		07 02		07 07
Slade Green 4	d		05 11			05 41				06 11							06 41								07 11
Erith	d		05 13			05 43				06 13							06 43								07 13
Belvedere	d		05 16			05 46				06 16							06 46								07 16
Abbey Wood	d		05 19			05 49				06 19	06 24						06 49	06 54							07 19
Plumstead	d		05 22			05 52				06 22							06 52								07 22
Woolwich Arsenal 4	d		05 25			05 55				06 25	06 28						06 55	06 58							07 25
Woolwich Dockyard	d		05 27			05 57				06 27							06 57								07 27
Charlton 4	d		05 30			06 00				06 30	06 33						07 00	07 03							07 30
Crayford	d				05 37				06 07				06 36								07 06				
Bexley	d				05 40				06 10				06 40								07 10				
Albany Park	d				05 42				06 12				06 42								07 12				
Sidcup 4	d				05 45				06 15				06 45 →			← 06 45					07 15 →			← 07 15	
New Eltham	d				05 48				06 18							06 48								07 18	
Mottingham	d				05 50				06 20							06 50								07 20	
Lee	d				05 53				06 23							06 53								07 23	
Hither Green 4	d				05 56				06 26							06 56								07 26	
Barnehurst 4	d			05 38			06 08							06 38						06 59			07 08		
Bexleyheath	d			05 41			06 11							06 41						07 02			07 11		
Welling	d			05 44			06 14							06 44						07 05			07 14		
Falconwood	d			05 46			06 16							06 46						07 07			07 16		
Eltham	d			05 49			06 19							06 49						07 10			07 19		
Kidbrooke	d			05 52			06 22							06 52						07 13			07 22		
Blackheath 4	d			05 56			06 26				06 38			06 56				07 08		07 17			07 26		
Lewisham 4	d			05 59	06 02		06 29		06 31		06 41			06 59		07 02		07 11		07 20			07 29	07 32	
St Johns	d																								
New Cross 4	⊖ d				06 05				06 34							07 05								07 35	
Nunhead 4	d																			07 25					
Peckham Rye 4	d																			07 28					
Denmark Hill 4	d																			07 31					
London Victoria 15	⊖ a	01 13																		07 41					
Westcombe Park	d		05 32			06 02				06 32							07 02								07 32
Maze Hill	d		05 34			06 04				06 34							07 04								07 34
Greenwich 4	d		05 38			06 08				06 38							07 08								07 38
Deptford	d		05 40			06 10				06 40							07 10								07 40
London Bridge 4	⊖ a		05 49	06 07	06 13	06 19	06 37		06 43	06 48	06 50			07 07		07 13	07 19	07 21					07 37	07 43	07 46
London Cannon Street 4	⊖ a																								07 50
London Waterloo (East) 4	⊖ a		05 54	06 12	06 18	06 24	06 42		06 48	06 54	06 55			07 12		07 18	07 24	07 26					07 42	07 48	
London Charing Cross 4	⊖ a		05 59	06 15	06 23	06 29	06 45		06 52	06 59	06 58			07 15		07 22	07 29	07 29					07 45	07 52	

For general notes see front of timetable
For details of catering facilities see Directory of Train Operators

A From Faversham (Table 212)

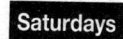

Saturdays

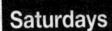

For details of Bank Holiday service alterations please see first page of Table 195

Gillingham and Dartford → London

Network Diagram - see first page of Table 200

		SE	SE	SE	SE	SE		SE	SE	SE	SE	SE	SE		SE	SE	SE	SE	SE	SE		SE	SE	SE	SE
Gillingham (Kent) [4]	d	06 44							07 14								07 44								08 14
Chatham [4]	d	06 48							07 18								07 48								08 18
Rochester [4]	d	06 50							07 20								07 50								08 20
Maidstone West [4]	d	06 27							06 57								07 27								07 58
Strood [4]	d	06 54							07 24								07 54								08 25
Higham	d	06 59							07 29								07 59								08 29
Gravesend [4]	d	07 05			07 12				07 35				07 42				08 05					08 12			08 36
Northfleet	d				07 16								07 46									08 16			
Swanscombe	d				07 18								07 48									08 18			
Greenhithe for Bluewater	d	07 10			07 21				07 40				07 51				08 10					08 21			08 41
Stone Crossing	d				07 23								07 53									08 23			
Dartford [4]	a	07 15			07 27				07 45				07 57				08 15					08 27			08 46
	d	07 16	07 19	07 24	07 30	07 32			07 46		07 49	07 54	08 01		08 05		08 16		08 19	08 24		08 31	08 35		08 47
Slade Green [4]	d		07 23								07 53					08 07			08 23					08 37	
Erith	d		07 26								07 56					08 09			08 26					08 39	
Belvedere	d		07 29								07 59					08 12			08 29					08 42	
Abbey Wood	d	07 24	07 31						07 54		08 01					08 15	08 24		08 31					08 45	08 55
Plumstead	d		07 34								08 04					08 18			08 34					08 48	
Woolwich Arsenal [4]	d	07 28	07 37						07 58		08 07					08 21	08 28		08 37					08 51	08 59
Woolwich Dockyard	d		07 39								08 09					08 23			08 39					08 53	
Charlton [4]	d	07 33	07 42						08 03		08 12					08 26	08 33		08 42					08 56	09 04
Crayford	d				07 36					07 51			08 05					08 21				08 35			
Bexley	d				07 40					07 53			08 08					08 23				08 38			
Albany Park	d				07 42			←		07 56			08 10					08 26				08 40			
Sidcup [4]	d				07 45			07 45		07 59			08 13					08 29				08 43			
New Eltham	d				→			07 48		08 02			08 16					08 32				08 46			
Mottingham	d							07 50		08 04			08 18					08 34				08 48			
Lee	d							07 53		08 07			08 21					08 37				08 51			
Hither Green [4]	d							07 56		08 10			08 24					08 40				08 54			
Barnehurst [4]	d			07 29		07 38						07 59			08 11					08 29			08 41		
Bexleyheath	d			07 32		07 41						08 02			08 14					08 32			08 44		
Welling	d			07 35		07 44						08 05			08 17					08 35			08 47		
Falconwood	d			07 37		07 46						08 07			08 19					08 37			08 49		
Eltham	d			07 40		07 49						08 10			08 22					08 40			08 52		
Kidbrooke	d			07 43		07 52						08 13			08 25					08 43			08 55		
Blackheath [4]	d	07 38		07 47		07 56			08 08			08 17			08 29		08 37			08 47			08 59		
Lewisham [4]	d	07 41		07 50		07 59		08 02	08 11			08 20	08 29		08 32		08 41			08 50		08 59	09 02		
St Johns	d									08 15								08 45							
New Cross [4]	⊖ d							08 05		08 17			08 32					08 47				09 02			
Nunhead [4]	d			07 55								08 25								08 55					
Peckham Rye [4]	d			07 58								08 28								08 58					
Denmark Hill [4]	d			08 01								08 31								09 01					
London Victoria [15]	⊖ a			08 12								08 42								09 12					
Westcombe Park	d		07 44								08 14					08 28			08 44					08 58	
Maze Hill	d		07 46								08 16					08 30			08 46					09 00	
Greenwich [4]	d		07 50								08 20					08 34			08 50					09 04	09 10
Deptford	d		07 52								08 22					08 36			08 52					09 06	
London Bridge [4]	⊖ a	07 49	07 59			08 07		08 13	08 19	08 23	08 29		08 38		08 43	08 43	08 49	08 53	08 59			09 08	09 13	09 13	09 19
London Cannon Street [4]	⊖ a		08 03							08 27	08 33					08 47		08 57	09 03					09 17	
London Waterloo (East) [4]	⊖ a	07 54				08 12		08 18	08 24				08 42		08 47		08 54					09 12	09 17		09 24
London Charing Cross [4]	⊖ a	07 58				08 15		08 22	08 28				08 47		08 51		08 58					09 17	09 21		09 28

For general notes see front of timetable
For details of catering facilities see Directory of Train Operators

Saturdays

For details of Bank Holiday service alterations please see first page of Table 195

Gillingham and Dartford → London

Network Diagram - see first page of Table 200

Station		SE	SE	SE	SE		SE	SE	SE	SE	SE A	SE		
Gillingham (Kent)	d									08 44				
Chatham	d									08 48				
Rochester	d									08 50				
Maidstone West	d									*08 27*				
Strood	d									08 55				
Higham	d									08 59				
Gravesend	d						08 42			09 06				
Northfleet	d						08 45							
Swanscombe	d						08 47							
Greenhithe for Bluewater	d						08 50			09 11				
Stone Crossing	d						08 52							
Dartford	a						08 56			09 16				
	d			08 49	08 54		09 01	09 05		09 17				
Slade Green	d			08 53					09 07		09 10			
Erith	d			08 55					09 09					
Belvedere	d			08 58					09 12					
Abbey Wood	d			09 01					09 15	09 25				
Plumstead	d		09 01	09 04					09 18			09 31		
Woolwich Arsenal	d		09 03	09 07					09 21	09 29		09 33		
Woolwich Dockyard	d			09 09					09 23					
Charlton	d		09 08	09 12					09 26	09 34		09 38		
Crayford	d	08 51					09 05				09 20			
Bexley	d	08 53					09 08				09 22			
Albany Park	d	08 56					09 10				09 25			
Sidcup	d	08 59					09 13				09 28			
New Eltham	d	09 02					09 16				09 31			
Mottingham	d	09 04					09 18				09 33			
Lee	d	09 07					09 21				09 36			
Hither Green	d	09 10					09 24				09 40			
Barnehurst	d				08 59			09 11						
Bexleyheath	d				09 02			09 14						
Welling	d				09 05			09 17						
Falconwood	d				09 07			09 19						
Eltham	d				09 10			09 22						
Kidbrooke	d				09 13			09 25						
Blackheath	d		09 13		09 17			09 29				09 43		
Lewisham	d		09 16		09 20		09 29	09 32				09 46		
St Johns	d	09 14									09 44			
New Cross	⊖ d	09 17	09 20				09 32				09 47	09 50		
Nunhead	d				09 25									
Peckham Rye	d				09 28									
Denmark Hill	d				09 31									
London Victoria	⊖ a				09 42									
Westcombe Park	d			09 14					09 28					
Maze Hill	d			09 16					09 30					
Greenwich	d			09 20					09 34	09 40				
Deptford	d			09 22					09 36					
London Bridge	⊖ a	09 23	09 26	09 29			09 38	09 40	09 43	09 49	09 53	09 56		
London Cannon Street	⊖ a	09 27	09 30	09 33					09 47		09 57	10 00		
London Waterloo (East)	⊖ a						09 42	09 45		09 54				
London Charing Cross	⊖ a						09 47	09 50		09 58				

Station		SE	SE	SE	SE	SE A	SE	SE A	SE	SE	SE	SE
Gillingham (Kent)	d						09 14					
Chatham	d						09 18					
Rochester	d						09 20					
Maidstone West	d						*08 58*					
Strood	d						09 25					
Higham	d						09 29					
Gravesend	d			09 12			09 36					09 42
Northfleet	d			09 16								09 46
Swanscombe	d			09 18								09 48
Greenhithe for Bluewater	d			09 21			09 41					09 51
Stone Crossing	d			09 23								09 53
Dartford	a			09 27			09 46					09 57
	d	09 19	09 24	09 31	09 35		09 47			09 49	09 54	10 01
Slade Green	d	09 23				09 37		09 40		09 53		
Erith	d	09 25				09 39				09 55		
Belvedere	d	09 28				09 42				09 58		
Abbey Wood	d	09 31				09 45	09 55			10 01		
Plumstead	d	09 34				09 48			10 01	10 04		
Woolwich Arsenal	d	09 37				09 51	09 59		10 03	10 07		
Woolwich Dockyard	d	09 39				09 53				10 09		
Charlton	d	09 42				09 56	10 04		10 08	10 12		
Crayford	d			09 35				09 50				10 05
Bexley	d			09 38				09 52				10 08
Albany Park	d			09 40				09 55				10 10
Sidcup	d			09 43				09 58				10 13
New Eltham	d			09 46				10 01				10 16
Mottingham	d			09 48				10 03				10 18
Lee	d			09 51				10 06				10 21
Hither Green	d			09 54				10 10				10 24
Barnehurst	d		09 29		09 41						09 59	
Bexleyheath	d		09 32		09 44						10 02	
Welling	d		09 35		09 47						10 05	
Falconwood	d		09 37		09 49						10 07	
Eltham	d		09 40		09 52						10 10	
Kidbrooke	d		09 43		09 55						10 13	
Blackheath	d		09 47		09 59				10 13		10 17	
Lewisham	d		09 50	09 59	10 02				10 16		10 20	10 29
St Johns	d							10 14				
New Cross	⊖ d							10 17	10 20			
Nunhead	d		09 55								10 25	
Peckham Rye	d		09 58								10 28	
Denmark Hill	d		10 01								10 31	
London Victoria	⊖ a		10 12								10 42	
Westcombe Park	d	09 44				09 58				10 14		
Maze Hill	d	09 46				10 00				10 16		
Greenwich	d	09 50				10 04	10 10			10 20		
Deptford	d	09 52				10 06				10 22		
London Bridge	⊖ a	09 59		10 07	10 10	10 13	10 19	10 23	10 26	10 29		10 37
London Cannon Street	⊖ a	10 03				10 17		10 27	10 30	10 34		
London Waterloo (East)	⊖ a			10 12	10 15		10 24					10 42
London Charing Cross	⊖ a			10 17	10 20		10 28					10 47

For general notes see front of timetable
For details of catering facilities see Directory of Train Operators

A From London Cannon Street (Table 199)

Saturdays

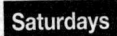

For details of Bank Holiday service alterations please see first page of Table 195

Gillingham and Dartford → London

Network Diagram - see first page of Table 200

		SE	SE A	SE	SE A	SE		SE	SE	SE	SE	SE A	SE		SE A	SE	SE	SE	SE	SE		SE	SE
Gillingham (Kent) [4]	d			09 44									17 14									17 44	
Chatham [4]	d			09 48									17 18									17 48	
Rochester [4]	d			09 50									17 20									17 50	
Maidstone West [4]	d			*09 27*									*16 58*									*17 27*	
Strood [4]	d			09 55									17 25									17 55	
Higham	d			09 59									17 29									17 59	
Gravesend [4]	d			10 06						17 12			17 36						17 42			18 06	
Northfleet	d									17 16									17 46				
Swanscombe	d									17 18									17 48				
Greenhithe for Bluewater	d			10 11						17 21			17 41						17 51			18 11	
Stone Crossing	d									17 23									17 53				
Dartford [4]	a			10 16						17 27			17 46						17 57			18 16	
	d	10 05		10 17				17 19	17 24	17 31	17 35		17 47				17 49	17 54	18 01	18 05		18 17	18 19
Slade Green [4]	d		10 07		10 10			17 23				17 37			17 40		17 53						18 23
Erith	d		10 09					17 25				17 39					17 55						18 25
Belvedere	d		10 12					17 28				17 42					17 58						18 28
Abbey Wood	d		10 15	10 25				17 31				17 45	17 55				18 01					18 25	18 31
Plumstead	d		10 18			10 31		17 34				17 48				18 01	18 04						18 34
Woolwich Arsenal [4]	d		10 21	10 29		10 33		17 37				17 51	17 59			18 03	18 07					18 29	18 37
Woolwich Dockyard	d		10 23					17 39				17 53					18 09						18 39
Charlton [4]	d		10 26	10 34		10 38	and at	17 42				17 56	18 04			18 08	18 12					18 34	18 42
Crayford	d				10 20		the same			17 35					17 50				18 05				
Bexley	d				10 22					17 38					17 52				18 08				
Albany Park	d				10 25		minutes			17 40					17 55				18 10				
Sidcup [4]	d				10 28					17 43					17 58				18 13				
New Eltham	d				10 31		past			17 46					18 01				18 16				
Mottingham	d				10 33					17 48					18 03				18 18				
Lee	d				10 36		each			17 51					18 06				18 21				
Hither Green [4]	d				10 40					17 54					18 10				18 24				
Barnehurst [4]	d	10 11					hour until		17 29		17 41							17 59		18 11			
Bexleyheath	d	10 14							17 32		17 44							18 02		18 14			
Welling	d	10 17							17 35		17 47							18 05		18 17			
Falconwood	d	10 19							17 37		17 49							18 07		18 19			
Eltham	d	10 22							17 40		17 52							18 10		18 22			
Kidbrooke	d	10 25							17 43		17 55							18 13		18 25			
Blackheath [4]	d	10 29				10 43			17 47		17 59					18 13		18 17		18 29		18 38	
Lewisham [4]	d	10 32				10 46			17 50	17 59	18 02					18 16		18 20	18 29	18 32		18 41	
St Johns	d				10 44										18 14				18 31				
New Cross [4]	⊖ d				10 47	10 50									18 17	18 20			18 32				
Nunhead [4]	d								17 55									18 25					
Peckham Rye [4]	d								17 58									18 28					
Denmark Hill [4]	d								18 01									18 31					
London Victoria [15]	⊖ a								18 12									18 42					
Westcombe Park	d		10 28					17 44				17 58					18 14						18 44
Maze Hill	d		10 30					17 46				18 00					18 16						18 46
Greenwich [4]	d		10 34	10 40				17 50				18 04	18 10				18 20						18 50
Deptford	d		10 36					17 52				18 06					18 22						18 53
London Bridge [4]	⊖ a	10 40	10 43	10 49	10 53	10 56		17 59		18 07	18 10	18 13	18 19		18 23	18 26	18 29		18 38	18 40		18 49	19 03
London Cannon Street [4]	⊖ a		10 47		10 57	11 00		18 03				18 17			18 27	18 30	18 33						
London Waterloo (East) [4]	⊖ a	10 45		10 54						18 12	18 15		18 24						18 43	18 45		18 54	19 09
London Charing Cross [4]	⊖ a	10 50		10 58						18 17	18 20		18 28						18 48	18 50		18 58	19 13

For general notes see front of timetable
For details of catering facilities see Directory of Train Operators

A From London Cannon Street (Table 199)

Table 200

Saturdays

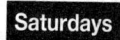

For details of Bank Holiday service alterations please see first page of Table 195

Gillingham and Dartford → London

Network Diagram - see first page of Table 200

		SE	SE	SE	SE	SE	SE	SE	SE	SE	SE	SE	SE	SE	SE	SE	SE	SE	SE	SE	SE	SE
Gillingham (Kent) [4]	d						18 14				18 44				19 14				19 44			
Chatham [4]	d						18 18				18 48				19 18				19 48			
Rochester [4]	d						18 20				18 50				19 20				19 50			
Maidstone West [4]	d						*17 58*				*18 27*				*18 58*				*19 27*			
Strood [4]	d						18 25				18 55				19 25				19 55			
Higham	d						18 29				18 59				19 29				19 59			
Gravesend [4]	d		18 12				18 36		18 42		19 06		19 12		19 36		19 42		20 06		20 12	
Northfleet	d		18 16						18 46				19 16				19 46				20 16	
Swanscombe	d		18 18						18 48				19 18				19 48				20 18	
Greenhithe for Bluewater	d		18 21				18 41		18 51		19 11		19 21		19 41		19 51		20 11		20 21	
Stone Crossing	d		18 23						18 53				19 23				19 53				20 23	
Dartford [4]	a		18 27				18 46		18 57		19 16		19 27		19 46		19 57		20 16		20 27	
	d	18 24	18 31	18 35		18 37	18 47	18 53	19 03	19 07	19 19	19 23	19 33	19 37	19 49	19 53	20 03	20 07	20 19	20 23	20 33	20 37
Slade Green [4]	d					18 41				19 11				19 41				20 11				20 41
Erith	d					18 43				19 13				19 43				20 13				20 43
Belvedere	d					18 46				19 16				19 46				20 16				20 46
Abbey Wood	d					18 49	18 55			19 19	19 27			19 49	19 57			20 19	20 27			20 49
Plumstead	d					18 52				19 22				19 52				20 22				20 52
Woolwich Arsenal [4]	d					18 55	18 59			19 25	19 31			19 55	20 01			20 25	20 31			20 55
Woolwich Dockyard	d					18 57				19 27				19 57				20 27				20 57
Charlton [4]	d					19 00	19 04			19 30	19 36			20 00	20 06			20 30	20 36			21 00
Crayford	d		18 37						19 07				19 37				20 07				20 37	
Bexley	d		18 40						19 10				19 40				20 10				20 40	
Albany Park	d		18 42						19 12				19 42				20 12				20 42	
Sidcup [4]	d		18 45						19 15				19 45				20 15				20 45	
New Eltham	d		18 48						19 18				19 48				20 18				20 48	
Mottingham	d		18 50						19 20				19 50				20 20				20 50	
Lee	d		18 53						19 23				19 53				20 23				20 53	
Hither Green [4]	d		18 56						19 26				19 56				20 26				20 56	
Barnehurst [4]	d	18 29		18 41				19 01				19 31				20 01				20 31		
Bexleyheath	d	18 32		18 44				19 04				19 34				20 04				20 34		
Welling	d	18 35		18 47				19 07				19 37				20 07				20 37		
Falconwood	d	18 37		18 49				19 09				19 39				20 09				20 39		
Eltham	d	18 40		18 52				19 12				19 42				20 12				20 42		
Kidbrooke	d	18 43		18 55				19 15				19 45				20 15				20 45		
Blackheath [4]	d	18 47		18 59			19 08	19 19			19 40	19 49			20 10	20 19			20 40	20 49		
Lewisham [4] ⛴	d	18 50	19 01	19 02			19 11	19 22	19 31		19 44	19 52	20 01		20 14	20 22	20 31		20 44	20 52	21 01	
St Johns	d				⟵																	
New Cross [4] ⊖	d		19 04		19 04			19 26	19 34			19 56	20 04			20 26	20 34			20 56	21 04	
Nunhead [4]	d	18 55	⟶																			
Peckham Rye [4]	d	18 58																				
Denmark Hill [4]	d	19 01																				
London Victoria [15] ⊖	a	19 12																				
Westcombe Park	d					19 02				19 32				20 02				20 32				21 02
Maze Hill	d					19 04				19 34				20 04				20 34				21 04
Greenwich [4] ⛴	d					19 08				19 38				20 08				20 38				21 08
Deptford	d					19 10				19 40				20 10				20 40				21 10
London Bridge [4] ⊖	a			19 11	19 13	19 18	19 21	19 33	19 43	19 49	19 53	20 03	20 13	20 19	20 23	20 33	20 43	20 49	20 53	21 03	21 13	21 19
London Cannon Street [4] ⊖	a																					
London Waterloo (East) [4] ⊖	a			19 16	19 18	19 23	19 25	19 38	19 48	19 54	19 58	20 08	20 18	20 24	20 28	20 38	20 48	20 54	20 58	21 08	21 18	21 24
London Charing Cross [4] ⊖	a			19 20	19 22	19 26	19 29	19 43	19 52	19 59	20 01	20 13	20 22	20 29	20 31	20 43	20 52	20 59	21 01	21 13	21 22	21 29

For general notes see front of timetable
For details of catering facilities see Directory of Train Operators

Table 200

Saturdays

For details of Bank Holiday service alterations please see first page of Table 195

Gillingham and Dartford → London

Network Diagram - see first page of Table 200

		SE	SE	SE	SE	SE		SE	SE	SE	SE	SE	SE		SE	SE	SE	SE	SE	SE		SE			
Gillingham (Kent) [4]	d	20 14				20 42					21 14					21 42				22 22					
Chatham [4]	d	20 18				20 46					21 18					21 46				22 26					
Rochester [4]	d	20 20				20 48					21 20					21 48				22 28					
Maidstone West [4]	d	*19 58*				*20 27*					*20 58*					*21 28*									
Strood [4]	d	20 25				20 53					21 25					21 53				22 33					
Higham	d	20 29				20 57					21 29					21 57				22 37					
Gravesend [4]	d	20 36				21 04					21 36					22 04				22 44					
Northfleet	d					21 07										22 07				22 47					
Swanscombe	d					21 09										22 09				22 49					
Greenhithe for Bluewater	d	20 41				21 12					21 41					22 12				22 52					
Stone Crossing	d					21 14										22 14				22 54					
Dartford [4]	a	20 46				21 18					21 46					22 18				22 58					
	d	20 49	20 53	21 03	21 07	21 19		21 23	21 33	21 37	21 49	21 53	22 03		22 07	22 19	22 23	22 31	22 43	23 00		23 03			
Slade Green [4]	d				21 11					21 41					22 11			22 35		23 05					
Erith	d				21 13					21 43					22 13			22 37		23 07					
Belvedere	d				21 16					21 46					22 16			22 40		23 10					
Abbey Wood	d	20 57			21 19	21 27				21 49	21 57				22 19	22 27		22 43		23 13					
Plumstead	d				21 22					21 52					22 22			22 46		23 16					
Woolwich Arsenal [4]	d	21 01			21 25	21 31				21 55	22 01				22 25	22 31		22 49		23 19					
Woolwich Dockyard	d				21 27					21 57					22 27			22 51		23 21					
Charlton [4]	d	21 06			21 30	21 36				22 00	22 06				22 30	22 36		22 54		23 24					
Crayford	d			21 07					21 37				22 07						22 47						
Bexley	d			21 10					21 40				22 10						22 49						
Albany Park	d			21 12					21 42				22 12						22 52						
Sidcup [4]	d			21 15					21 45				22 15						22 55						
New Eltham	d			21 18					21 48				22 18						22 58						
Mottingham	d			21 20					21 50				22 20						23 00						
Lee	d			21 23					21 53				22 23						23 03						
Hither Green [4]	d			21 26					21 56				22 26						23 06						
Barnehurst [4]	d		21 01					21 31				22 01					22 31					23 11			
Bexleyheath	d		21 04					21 34				22 04					22 34					23 14			
Welling	d		21 07					21 37				22 07					22 37					23 17			
Falconwood	d		21 09					21 39				22 09					22 39					23 19			
Eltham	d		21 12					21 42				22 12					22 42					23 22			
Kidbrooke	d		21 15					21 45				22 15					22 45					23 25			
Blackheath [4]	d	21 10	21 19			21 40		21 49			22 10	22 19				22 40	22 49					23 29			
Lewisham [4]	d	21 14	21 22	21 31		21 44		21 52	22 01		22 14	22 22	22 31			22 44	22 52		23 11			23 32			
St Johns	d																								
New Cross [4]	⊖ d		21 26	21 34				21 56	22 04			22 26	22 34				22 56		23 14			23 36			
Nunhead [4]	d																								
Peckham Rye [4]	d																								
Denmark Hill [4]	d																								
London Victoria [15]	⊖ a																								
Westcombe Park	d				21 32					22 02					22 32			22 56		23 26					
Maze Hill	d				21 34					22 04					22 34			22 58		23 28					
Greenwich [4]	d				21 38					22 08					22 38			23 02		23 32					
Deptford	d				21 40					22 10					22 40			23 04		23 34					
London Bridge [4]	⊖ a	21 23	21 33	21 43	21 49	21 53		22 03	22 13	22 19	22 23	22 33	22 43		22 49	22 53	23 03	23 13	23 22	23 41		23 43			
London Cannon Street [4]	⊖ a																								
London Waterloo (East) [4]	⊖ a	21 28	21 38	21 48	21 54	21 58		22 08	22 18	22 24	22 28	22 38	22 48		22 54	22 58	23 08	23 18	23 28	23 46		23 49			
London Charing Cross [4]	⊖ a	21 31	21 43	21 52	21 59	22 01		22 13	22 22	22 29	22 31	22 43	22 52		22 59	23 03	23 13	23 22	23 32	23 50		23 53			

For general notes see front of timetable
For details of catering facilities see Directory of Train Operators

Table 200

Sundays

Gillingham and Dartford → London

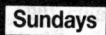

Network Diagram - see first page of Table 200

		SE A	SE	SE	SE	SE	SE	SE	SE	SE	SE	SE	SE	SE	SE	SE	SE	SE	SE	SE	SE	SE	SE
Gillingham (Kent) [4]	d	00 05					06 36	06 40				07 15				07 40					08 15		
Chatham [4]	d	00 09					06 40	06 44				07 19				07 44					08 19		
Rochester [4]	d	00 11					06 43	06 47				07 22				07 47					08 22		
Maidstone West [4]	d											*07 00*											
Strood [4]	d	00 15					06a47	06 52				07 27				07 52					08 27		
Higham	d	00 20						06 56				07 32				07 56					08 32		
Gravesend [4]	d	00 26						07 03				07 38				08 03					08 38		
Northfleet	d							07 07								08 07							
Swanscombe	d							07 09								08 09							
Greenhithe for Bluewater	d	00 32						07 12				07 44				08 12					08 44		
Stone Crossing	d							07 15								08 15							
Dartford [4]	a	00 39						07 18				07 49				08 18					08 49		
	d	00 40	06 48	06 53	06 57	07 08		07 19	07 23	07 27	07 38	07 49	07 53	07 57	08 08	08 19	08 23	08 27		08 38	08 49	08 53	08 57
Slade Green [4]	d			06 57					07 27				07 57				08 27					08 57	
Erith	d			07 00					07 30				08 00				08 30					09 00	
Belvedere	d			07 03					07 33				08 03				08 33					09 03	
Abbey Wood	d			07 06				07 28	07 36			07 58	08 06			08 28	08 36				08 58	09 06	
Plumstead	d			07 09					07 39				08 09				08 39		08 49			09 09	
Woolwich Arsenal [4]	d			07 11				07 32	07 41			08 02	08 11			08 32	08 41		08 51		09 02	09 11	
Woolwich Dockyard	d			07 13					07 43				08 13				08 43		08 53			09 13	
Charlton [4]	d			07 17				07 37	07 47			08 07	08 17			08 37	08 47		08 57		09 07	09 17	
Crayford	d				07 01					07 31				08 01				08 31					09 01
Bexley	d				07 04					07 34				08 04				08 34					09 04
Albany Park	d				07 06					07 36				08 06				08 36					09 06
Sidcup [4]	d				07 09					07 39				08 09				08 39					09 09
New Eltham	d				07 12					07 42				08 12				08 42					09 12
Mottingham	d				07 14					07 44				08 14				08 44					09 14
Lee	d				07 17					07 47				08 17				08 47					09 17
Hither Green [4]	d				07 21					07 51				08 21				08 51					09 21
Barnehurst [4]	d		06 54			07 14					07 44				08 14					08 44			
Bexleyheath	d		06 56			07 16					07 46				08 16					08 46			
Welling	d		06 59			07 19					07 49				08 19					08 49			
Falconwood	d		07 02			07 22					07 52				08 22					08 52			
Eltham	d		07 05			07 25					07 55				08 25					08 55			
Kidbrooke	d		07 08			07 28					07 58				08 28					08 58			
Blackheath [4]	d		07 11			07 31		07 41			08 01	08 11			08 31	08 41				09 01	09 11		
Lewisham [4]	d		07 16		07 26	07 36		07 45		07 56	08 06	08 15		08 26	08 36	08 45		08 56		09 06	09 15		09 26
St Johns	d																						
New Cross [4]	⊖ d		07 20		07 30	07 40				08 00	08 10			08 30	08 40			09 00		09 10			09 30
Nunhead [4]	d																						
Peckham Rye [4]	d																						
Denmark Hill [4]	d																						
London Victoria [15]	⊖ a	01 11																					
Westcombe Park	d			07 19					07 49				08 19				08 49		08 59			09 19	
Maze Hill	d			07 21					07 51				08 21				08 51		09 01			09 21	
Greenwich [4]	d			07 25					07 55				08 25				08 55		09 05			09 25	
Deptford	d			07 27					07 57				08 27				08 57		09 07			09 27	
London Bridge [4]	⊖ a		07 26	07 34	07 36	07 48		07 53	08 04	08 06	08 18	08 23	08 34	08 36	08 48	08 53	09 04	09 06	09 14	09 18	09 23	09 34	09 36
London Cannon Street [4]	⊖ a																						
London Waterloo (East) [4]	⊖ a		07 31	07 39	07 41	07 53		07 58	08 09	08 11	08 23	08 28	08 39	08 41	08 53	08 58	09 09	09 11		09 23	09 28	09 39	09 41
London Charing Cross [4]	⊖ a		07 36	07 42	07 45	07 56		08 02	08 12	08 15	08 26	08 32	08 42	08 45	08 56	09 02	09 12	09 15		09 26	09 32	09 42	09 45

For general notes see front of timetable
For details of catering facilities see Directory of Train Operators

A From Faversham (Table 212)

Table 200

Sundays

Gillingham and Dartford → London

Network Diagram - see first page of Table 200

Station		SE		SE	SE	SE	SE	SE	SE	SE		SE	SE	SE	SE		SE	SE	SE	SE	SE	SE	SE	SE	SE
Gillingham (Kent) 4	d				08 45					09 15							09 45					10 15			
Chatham 4	d				08 49					09 19							09 49					10 19			
Rochester 4	d				08 52					09 22							09 52					10 22			
Maidstone West 4	d				*08 15*												*09 20*								
Strood 4	d				08 57					09 27							09 57					10 27			
Higham	d				09 02					09 32							10 02					10 32			
Gravesend 4	d			08 52	09 08				09 22	09 38					09 52		10 08				10 22	10 38			
Northfleet	d			08 56					09 26						09 56						10 26				
Swanscombe	d			08 58					09 28						09 58						10 28				
Greenhithe for Bluewater	d			09 01	09 14				09 31	09 44					10 01		10 14				10 31	10 44			
Stone Crossing	d			09 03					09 33						10 03						10 33				
Dartford 4	a			09 07	09 19				09 37	09 49					10 07		10 19				10 37	10 49			
	d			09 08	09 19	09 23	09 27		09 38	09 49		09 53	09 57		10 08		10 19	10 23	10 27		10 38	10 49	10 53	10 57	
Slade Green 4	d					09 27						09 57						10 27					10 57		
Erith	d					09 30						10 00						10 30					11 00		
Belvedere	d					09 33						10 03						10 33					11 03		
Abbey Wood	d				09 28	09 36				09 58		10 06					10 28	10 36				10 58	11 06		
Plumstead	d	09 19				09 39		09 49				10 09		10 19				10 39		10 49			11 09		11 19
Woolwich Arsenal 4	d	09 21			09 32	09 41		09 51		10 02		10 11		10 21			10 32	10 41		10 51		11 02	11 11		11 21
Woolwich Dockyard	d	09 23				09 43		09 53				10 13		10 23				10 43		10 53			11 13		11 23
Charlton 4	d	09 27			09 37	09 47		09 57		10 07		10 17		10 27			10 37	10 47		10 57		11 07	11 17		11 27
Crayford	d						09 31						10 01						10 31					11 01	
Bexley	d						09 34						10 04						10 34					11 04	
Albany Park	d						09 36						10 06						10 36					11 06	
Sidcup 4	d						09 39						10 09						10 39					11 09	
New Eltham	d						09 42						10 12						10 42					11 12	
Mottingham	d						09 44						10 14						10 44					11 14	
Lee	d						09 47						10 17						10 47					11 17	
Hither Green 4	d						09 51						10 21						10 51					11 21	
Barnehurst 4	d			09 14					09 44						10 14						10 44				
Bexleyheath	d			09 16					09 46						10 16						10 46				
Welling	d			09 19					09 49						10 19						10 49				
Falconwood	d			09 22					09 52						10 22						10 52				
Eltham	d			09 25					09 55						10 25						10 55				
Kidbrooke	d			09 28					09 58						10 28						10 58				
Blackheath 4	d			09 31	09 41				10 01	10 11					10 31		10 41				11 01	11 11			
Lewisham 4	d			09 36	09 45		09 56		10 06	10 15			10 26		10 36		10 45		10 56		11 06	11 15		11 26	
St Johns	d																								
New Cross 4	⊖ d			09 40			10 00		10 10				10 30		10 40				11 00		11 10			11 30	
Nunhead 4	d																								
Peckham Rye 4	d																								
Denmark Hill 4	d																								
London Victoria 15	⊖ a																								
Westcombe Park	d	09 29				09 49		09 59				10 19		10 29				10 49		10 59			11 19		11 29
Maze Hill	d	09 31				09 51		10 01				10 21		10 31				10 51		11 01			11 21		11 31
Greenwich 4	d	09 35				09 55		10 05				10 25		10 35				10 55		11 05			11 25		11 35
Deptford	d	09 37				09 57		10 07				10 27		10 37				10 57		11 07			11 27		11 37
London Bridge 4	⊖ a	09 44		09 48	09 53	10 04	10 06	10 14	10 18	10 23		10 34	10 36	10 44	10 48		10 53	11 04	11 06	11 14	11 18	11 23	11 34	11 36	11 44
London Cannon Street 4	⊖ a																								
London Waterloo (East) 4	⊖ a			09 53	09 58	10 09	10 11		10 23	10 28		10 39	10 41		10 53		10 58	11 09	11 11		11 23	11 28	11 39	11 41	
London Charing Cross 4	⊖ a			09 56	10 02	10 12	10 15		10 26	10 32		10 42	10 45		10 56		11 02	11 12	11 15		11 26	11 32	11 42	11 45	

For general notes see front of timetable
For details of catering facilities see
Directory of Train Operators

Table 200

Sundays

Gillingham and Dartford → London

Network Diagram - see first page of Table 200

Station		SE		SE	SE	SE	SE	SE	SE	SE	SE	SE	SE	SE	SE	SE	SE	SE	SE	SE	SE
Gillingham (Kent)	d		and at the same minutes past each hour until	17 45				18 15				18 45				19 15				19 43	
Chatham	d			17 49				18 19				18 49				19 19				19 47	
Rochester	d			17 52				18 22				18 52				19 22				19 49	
Maidstone West	d			*17 20*								*18 20*								*19 20*	
Strood	d			17 57				18 27				18 57				19 27				19 54	
Higham	d			18 02				18 32				19 02				19 32				19 59	
Gravesend	d	10 52		18 08			18 22	18 38			18 52	19 08			19 22	19 38				20 05	
Northfleet	d	10 56					18 26				18 56				19 26					20 09	
Swanscombe	d	10 58					18 28				18 58				19 28					20 11	
Greenhithe for Bluewater	d	11 01		18 14			18 31	18 44			19 01	19 14			19 31	19 44				20 14	
Stone Crossing	d	11 03					18 33				19 03				19 33					20 16	
Dartford	a	11 07		18 19			18 37	18 49			19 07	19 19			19 37	19 49				20 19	
	d	11 08		18 19	18 23	18 27	18 38	18 49	18 53	18 57	19 08	19 19	19 23	19 27	19 38	19 49	19 53	19 57	20 08	20 19	20 23
Slade Green	d				18 27				18 57				19 27				19 57				20 27
Erith	d				18 30				19 00				19 30				20 00				20 30
Belvedere	d				18 33				19 03				19 33				20 03				20 33
Abbey Wood	d			18 28	18 36			18 58	19 06			19 28	19 36			19 58	20 06			20 28	20 36
Plumstead	d				18 39				19 09				19 39				20 09				20 39
Woolwich Arsenal	d			18 32	18 41			19 02	19 11			19 32	19 41			20 02	20 11			20 32	20 41
Woolwich Dockyard	d				18 43				19 13				19 43				20 13				20 43
Charlton	d			18 37	18 47			19 07	19 17			19 37	19 47			20 07	20 17			20 37	20 47
Crayford	d					18 31				19 01				19 31				20 01			
Bexley	d					18 34				19 04				19 34				20 04			
Albany Park	d					18 36				19 06				19 36				20 06			
Sidcup	d					18 39				19 09				19 39				20 09			
New Eltham	d					18 42				19 12				19 42				20 12			
Mottingham	d					18 44				19 14				19 44				20 14			
Lee	d					18 47				19 17				19 47				20 17			
Hither Green	d					18 51				19 21				19 51				20 21			
Barnehurst	d	11 14					18 44				19 14				19 44				20 14		
Bexleyheath	d	11 16					18 46				19 16				19 46				20 16		
Welling	d	11 19					18 49				19 19				19 49				20 19		
Falconwood	d	11 22					18 52				19 22				19 52				20 22		
Eltham	d	11 25					18 55				19 25				19 55				20 25		
Kidbrooke	d	11 28					18 58				19 28				19 58				20 28		
Blackheath	d	11 31		18 41			19 01	19 11			19 31	19 41			20 01	20 11			20 31	20 41	
Lewisham	d	11 36		18 45		18 56	19 06	19 15		19 26	19 36	19 45		19 56	20 06	20 15		20 26	20 36	20 45	
St Johns	d																				
New Cross	⊖ d	11 40				19 00	19 10			19 30	19 40			20 00	20 10			20 30	20 40		
Nunhead	d																				
Peckham Rye	d																				
Denmark Hill	d																				
London Victoria	⊖ a																				
Westcombe Park	d				18 49				19 19				19 49				20 19				20 49
Maze Hill	d				18 51				19 21				19 51				20 21				20 51
Greenwich	d				18 55				19 25				19 55				20 25				20 55
Deptford	d				18 57				19 27				19 57				20 27				20 57
London Bridge	⊖ a	11 48		18 53	19 04	19 06	19 18	19 23	19 34	19 36	19 48	19 53	20 04	20 06	20 18	20 23	20 34	20 36	20 48	20 53	21 04
London Cannon Street	⊖ a																				
London Waterloo (East)	⊖ a	11 53		18 58	19 09	19 11	19 23	19 28	19 39	19 41	19 53	19 58	20 09	20 11	20 23	20 28	20 39	20 41	20 53	20 58	21 09
London Charing Cross	⊖ a	11 56		19 02	19 12	19 15	19 26	19 32	19 42	19 45	19 56	20 02	20 12	20 15	20 26	20 32	20 42	20 45	20 56	21 02	21 12

For general notes see front of timetable
For details of catering facilities see Directory of Train Operators

Table 200

Sundays

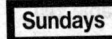

Gillingham and Dartford → London

Network Diagram - see first page of Table 200

		SE	SE	SE	SE	SE		SE	SE	SE	SE	SE	SE	SE		SE	SE	SE	SE	SE	SE	SE			
Gillingham (Kent) 4	d			20 15					20 40				21 15					21 40				22 15			
Chatham 4	d			20 19					20 44				21 19					21 44				22 19			
Rochester 4	d			20 22					20 47				21 22					21 47				22 22			
Maidstone West 4	d								*20 20*									*21 20*							
Strood 4	d			20 27					20 52				21 27					21 52				22 27			
Higham	d			20 32					20 56				21 32					21 56				22 32			
Gravesend 4	d			20 38					21 03				21 38					22 03				22 39			
Northfleet	d								21 07									22 07				22 43			
Swanscombe	d								21 09									22 09				22 45			
Greenhithe for Bluewater	d			20 44					21 12				21 44					22 12				22 48			
Stone Crossing	d								21 15									22 15				22 50			
Dartford 4	a			20 49					21 18				21 49					22 18				22 53			
	d	20 27	20 38	20 49	20 53	20 57		21 08	21 19	21 23	21 27	21 38	21 49	21 53		21 57	22 08	22 19	22 23	22 27	22 38	22 57			
Slade Green 4	d				20 57					21 27				21 57					22 27						
Erith	d				21 00					21 30				22 00					22 30						
Belvedere	d				21 03					21 33				22 03					22 33						
Abbey Wood	d			20 58	21 06				21 28	21 36			21 58	22 06				22 28	22 36						
Plumstead	d				21 09					21 39				22 09					22 39						
Woolwich Arsenal 4	d			21 02	21 11				21 32	21 41			22 02	22 11				22 32	22 41						
Woolwich Dockyard	d				21 13					21 43				22 13					22 43						
Charlton 4	d			21 07	21 17				21 37	21 47			22 07	22 17				22 37	22 47						
Crayford	d	20 31				21 01					21 31					22 01				22 31		23 01			
Bexley	d	20 34				21 04					21 34					22 04				22 34		23 04			
Albany Park	d	20 36				21 06					21 36					22 06				22 36		23 06			
Sidcup 4	d	20 39				21 09					21 39					22 09				22 39		23 09			
New Eltham	d	20 42				21 12					21 42					22 12				22 42		23 12			
Mottingham	d	20 44				21 14					21 44					22 14				22 44		23 14			
Lee	d	20 47				21 17					21 47					22 17				22 47		23 17			
Hither Green 4	d	20 51				21 21					21 51					22 21				22 51		23 21			
Barnehurst 4	d		20 44					21 14				21 44					22 14				22 44				
Bexleyheath	d		20 46					21 16				21 46					22 16				22 46				
Welling	d		20 49					21 19				21 49					22 19				22 49				
Falconwood	d		20 52					21 22				21 52					22 22				22 52				
Eltham	d		20 55					21 25				21 55					22 25				22 55				
Kidbrooke	d		20 58					21 28				21 58					22 28				22 58				
Blackheath 4	d		21 01	21 11				21 31	21 41			22 01	22 11				22 31	22 41			23 01				
Lewisham 4	d	20 56	21 06	21 15		21 26		21 36	21 45		21 56	22 06	22 15			22 26	22 36	22 45		22 56	23 06	23 26			
St Johns	d																								
New Cross 4	⊖ d	21 00	21 10			21 30		21 40			22 00	22 10				22 30	22 40			23 00	23 10	23 30			
Nunhead 4	d																								
Peckham Rye 4	d																								
Denmark Hill 4	d																								
London Victoria 15	⊖ a																								
Westcombe Park	d				21 19					21 49				22 19					22 49						
Maze Hill	d				21 21					21 51				22 21					22 51						
Greenwich 4	d				21 25					21 55				22 25					22 55						
Deptford	d				21 27					21 57				22 27					22 57						
London Bridge 4	⊖ a	21 06	21 18	21 23	21 34	21 36		21 48	21 53	22 04	22 06	22 18	22 23	22 34		22 36	22 48	22 53	23 04	23 06	23 18	23 36			
London Cannon Street 4	⊖ a																								
London Waterloo (East) 4	⊖ a	21 11	21 23	21 28	21 39	21 41		21 53	21 58	22 09	22 11	22 23	22 28	22 39		22 41	22 53	22 58	23 09	23 11	23 23	23 41			
London Charing Cross 4	⊖ a	21 15	21 26	21 32	21 42	21 45		21 56	22 02	22 12	22 15	22 26	22 32	22 42		22 45	22 56	23 02	23 12	23 15	23 26	23 45			

For general notes see front of timetable
For details of catering facilities see
Directory of Train Operators

Mondays to Fridays

For details of Bank Holiday service alterations please see first page of Table 195

London → Hayes (Kent) via Catford Bridge

Network Diagram - see first page of Table 200

Miles	Miles			SE MO	SE MX	SE MO	SE	SE	SE	SE	SE	SE	SE	SE	SE	SE	SE	SE	SE	SE	SE	SE
0	—	London Charing Cross 4	⊖ d	23p23	23p52	23p53		05 49	06 27	06 51	07 06		07 22	07 45		08 26	08 36			08 52		09 14
¾	—	London Waterloo (East) 4	⊖ d	23p26	23p55	23p56		05 52	06 30	06 54	07 09		07 25	07 48		08 29	08 39			08 55		09 17
—	0	London Cannon Street 4	⊖ d									07 10			08 20			08 40	08 54			
1¾	¾	London Bridge 4	⊖ d	23p32	23p58	00 02		05 57	06 35	06 59	07 13	07 14	07 30	07 53	08 24	08 34	08 44	08 44	08 58	09 00		09 22
4¾	—	New Cross 4	⊖ d	23p37	00 04	00 07	05 37		06 41	07 05		07 20		07 59	08 29			08 49	09 05		←	
5½	—	St Johns	d	23p39	00 06	00 09			06 43	07 07		07 22		08 01	08 31			08 51	09 07		09 07	
6	—	Lewisham 4	d	23p42	00 09	00 12	05 42	06 06	06 46	07 10		07b27		08 04	08 34			08 54	→		09c12	
6¾	—	Ladywell	d	23p44	00 11	00 14	05 44	06 08	06 48	07 12		07 29	07 39	08 07	08 37	08 43	08 53	08 57		09 09	09 14	09 32
7½	—	Catford Bridge	d	23p46	00 13	00 16	05 46	06 10	06 50	07 14		07 31	07 41	08 09	08 39	08 45	08 55	08 59		09 11	09 16	09 34
9	—	Lower Sydenham	d	23p49	00 16	00 19	05 49	06 13	06 53	07 17		07 34	07 44	08 12	08 42	08 48	08 58	09 02			09 19	09 37
9½	—	New Beckenham 4	d	23p51	00 18	00 21	05 51	06 15	06 55	07 19	07 28	07 36	07 46	08 14	08 44	08 50	09a00	09 06		09 16	09 22	09 39
10¼	—	Clock House	d	23p53	00 20	00 23	05 53	06 17	06 57	07 21	07 30	07 38	07 48	08 16	08 46	08 52		09 08		09 18	09 24	09 41
11	—	Elmers End 4	d	23p56	00 23	00 26	05 56	06 20	07 00	07 24	07 33	07 41	07 51	08 19	08 49	08 55		09 11		09 21	09 27	09 44
12½	—	Eden Park	d	00 01	00 27	00 30	06 00	06 24	07 04	07 28		07 45	07 55	08 23	08 53	08 59		09 15			09 31	09 48
13¼	—	West Wickham	d	00 02	00 29	00 32	06 02	06 26	07 06	07 30		07 47	07 57	08 25	08 55	09 01		09 17			09 33	09 50
14½	—	Hayes (Kent)	a	00 05	00 32	00 35	06 05	06 29	07 09	07 33	07 40	07 50	08 00	08 28	08 58	09 04		09 20		09 28	09 38	09 53

		SE A	SE	SE	SE	SE	SE	SE		SE	SE	SE	SE	SE	SE	SE	SE	SE	SE	SE
London Charing Cross 4	⊖ d		09 36		10 06		10 36		and at	15 06		15 36		16 06	16 26		16 52		17 14	
London Waterloo (East) 4	⊖ d		09 39		10 09		10 39		the same	15 09		15 39		16 09	16 29		16 55		17 17	
London Cannon Street 4	⊖ d	09 24		09 54		10 24		10 54	minutes		15 24		15 54			16 46		17 04		17 32
London Bridge 4	⊖ d	09 28	09 45	09 58	10 15	10 28	10 45	10 58	past	15 15	15 28	15 45	15 58	16 14	16 34	16 50	17 00	17 08	17 22	17 36
New Cross 4	⊖ d	09 35		10 05		10 33		11 03	each		15 33		16 03			16 56		17 16		17 42
St Johns	d	09 37		10 07		10 35		11 05	hour until		15 35		16 05			16 58		17 18		17 44
Lewisham 4	d	09 40		10 10		10 38		11 08			15 38		16 08	16 24	16 44	17 02		17 22		17 46
Ladywell	d	09 42	09 55	10 12	10 25	10 40	10 55	11 10		15 25	15 40	15 55	16 10	16 27	16 47	17 05	17 11	17 25	17 35	17 49
Catford Bridge	d	09 44	09 57	10 14	10 27	10 42	10 57	11 12		15 27	15 42	15 57	16 12	16 29	16 49	17 07	17 13	17 27	17 37	17 51
Lower Sydenham	d	09 47	10 00	10 17	10 30	10 45	11 00	11 15		15 30	15 45	16 00	16 15	16 32	16 52	17 10	17 16	17 30	17 40	17 54
New Beckenham 4	d	09a49	10 02	10 19	10 32	10 47	11 02	11 17		15 32	15 47	16 02	16 17	16 34	16 54	17 12	17 18	17 32	17 42	17 56
Clock House	d		10 04	10 21	10 34	10 49	11 04	11 19		15 34	15 49	16 04	16 19	16 37	16 57	17 15	17 21	17 35	17 45	17 59
Elmers End 4	d		10 07	10 24	10 37	10 52	11 07	11 22		15 37	15 52	16 07	16 22	16 40	17 00	17 18	17 24	17 38	17 48	18 02
Eden Park	d		10 11	10 28	10 41	10 56	11 11	11 26		15 41	15 56	16 11	16 26	16 43	17 03	17 21	17 27	17 41	17 51	18 05
West Wickham	d		10 13	10 30	10 43	10 58	11 13	11 28		15 43	15 58	16 13	16 28	16 45	17 05	17 23	17 29	17 43	17 53	18 07
Hayes (Kent)	a		10 16	10 33	10 46	11 01	11 16	11 31		15 46	16 01	16 16	16 31	16e51	17e11	17 28	17e35	17 48	17 58	18 12

		SE	SE	SE	SE	SE	SE	SE	SE	SE	SE	SE	SE	SE	SE	SE	SE	SE	SE
London Charing Cross 4	⊖ d	17 38		17 58		18 23	18 42	19 06		19 38		20 22	20 52	21 22	21 52	22 22	22 52	23 22	23 52
London Waterloo (East) 4	⊖ d	17 41		18 01		18 26	18 45	19 09		19 41		20 25	20 55	21 25	21 55	22 25	22 55	23 25	23 55
London Cannon Street 4	⊖ d		17 52		18 12				19 26		19 56								
London Bridge 4	⊖ d		17 56	18 06	18 16	18 31	18 50	19 14	19 30	19 46	20 00	20 30	21 00	21 30	22 00	22 30	23 00	23 30	23 58
New Cross 4	⊖ d		18 02		18 22			19 20	19 35	19 52	20 05	20 35	21 05	21 35	22 05	22 35	23 05	23 35	00 04
St Johns	d		18 04		18 24			19 22	19 37	19 54	20 07	20 37	21 07	21 37	22 07	22 37	23 07	23 37	00 06
Lewisham 4	d		18 08		18 26	18 40	19 00	19 24	19 40	19 57	20 10	20 40	21 10	21 40	22 10	22 40	23 10	23 40	00 09
Ladywell	d	17 57	18 11	18 19	18 29	18 43	19 03	19 27	19 42	19 59	20 12	20 42	21 12	21 42	22 12	22 42	23 12	23 42	00 11
Catford Bridge	d	17 59	18 13	18 21	18 31	18 45	19 05	19 29	19 45	20 01	20 14	20 44	21 14	21 44	22 14	22 44	23 14	23 44	00 13
Lower Sydenham	d	18 02	18 16	18 24	18 34	18 48	19 08	19 32	19 47	20 04	20 17	20 47	21 17	21 47	22 17	22 47	23 17	23 47	00 16
New Beckenham 4	d	18 04	18 18	18 26	18 36	18 50	19 10	19 34	19 50	20 06	20 19	20 49	21 19	21 49	22 19	22 49	23 19	23 49	00 18
Clock House	d	18 07	18 21	18 29	18 39	18 53	19 13	19 37	19 52	20 08	20 21	20 51	21 21	21 51	22 21	22 51	23 21	23 51	00 20
Elmers End 4	d	18 10	18 24	18 32	18 42	18 56	19 16	19 40	19 55	20 11	20 24	20 54	21 24	21 54	22 24	22 54	23 24	23 54	00 23
Eden Park	d	18 13	18 27	18 35	18 45	18 59	19 19	19 43	19 58	20 15	20 28	20 58	21 28	21 58	22 28	22 58	23 28	23 58	00 27
West Wickham	d	18 15	18 29	18 37	18 47	19 01	19 21	19 45	20 00	20 17	20 30	21 00	21 30	22 00	22 30	23 00	23 30	23 59	00 29
Hayes (Kent)	a	18e21	18 34	18e43	18e53	19e07	19e27	19 50	20 05	20 20	20 33	21 03	21 33	22 03	22 33	23 03	23 33	00 03	00 32

Saturdays

		SE	SE	SE	SE	SE	SE	SE	SE	SE	SE	SE	SE	SE	SE	SE
London Charing Cross 4	⊖ d	23p52	05 52	06 22	06 52	07 22	07 52	08 22		09 06		09 36		10 06		10 36
London Waterloo (East) 4	⊖ d	23p55	05 55	06 25	06 55	07 25	07 55	08 25		09 09		09 39		10 09		10 39
London Cannon Street 4	⊖ d								08 54		09 24		09 54		10 24	
London Bridge 4	⊖ d	23p58	06 01	06 31	07 01	07 31	08 01	08 31	08 58	09 15	09 28	09 45	09 58	10 15	10 28	10 45
New Cross 4	⊖ d	00 04	06 06	06 36	07 06	07 36	08 06	08 36	09 03		09 33		10 03		10 33	
St Johns	d	00 06	06 08	06 38	07 08	07 38	08 08	08 38	09 05		09 35		10 05		10 35	
Lewisham 4	d	00 09	06 10	06 40	07 10	07 40	08 10	08 40	09 08		09 38		10 08		10 38	
Ladywell	d	00 11	06 13	06 43	07 13	07 43	08 13	08 43	09 10	09 25	09 40	09 55	10 10	10 25	10 40	10 55
Catford Bridge	d	00 13	06 15	06 45	07 15	07 45	08 15	08 45	09 12	09 27	09 42	09 57	10 12	10 27	10 42	10 57
Lower Sydenham	d	00 16	06 18	06 48	07 18	07 48	08 18	08 48	09 15	09 30	09 45	10 00	10 15	10 30	10 45	11 00
New Beckenham 4	d	00 18	06 20	06 50	07 20	07 50	08 20	08 50	09 17	09 32	09 47	10 02	10 17	10 32	10 47	11 02
Clock House	d	00 20	06 22	06 52	07 22	07 52	08 22	08 52	09 19	09 34	09 49	10 04	10 19	10 34	10 49	11 04
Elmers End 4	d	00 23	06 25	06 55	07 25	07 55	08 25	08 55	09 22	09 35	09 52	10 05	10 22	10 37	10 52	11 07
Eden Park	d	00 27	06 29	06 59	07 29	07 59	08 29	08 59	09 26	09 39	09 56	10 09	10 26	10 41	10 56	11 11
West Wickham	d	00 29	06 31	07 01	07 31	08 01	08 31	09 01	09 28	09 41	09 58	10 11	10 28	10 43	10 58	11 13
Hayes (Kent)	a	00 32	06 34	07 04	07 34	08 04	08 34	09 04	09 31	09 46	10 01	10 16	10 31	10 46	11 01	11 16

For general notes see front of timetable
For details of catering facilities see Directory of Train Operators

A To Beckenham Junction (Table 195)
b Arr. 0724
c Arr. 0909
e Until 9 October arr 1 minute earlier

Table 203

Saturdays

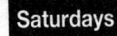

London → Hayes (Kent) via Catford Bridge

Network Diagram - see first page of Table 200

		SE		SE	SE	SE	SE	SE	SE	SE	SE	SE	SE	SE	SE	SE	SE
London Charing Cross 4	⊖ d	.		18 06	.	18 36	18 52	19 22	19 52	20 22	20 52	21 22	21 52	22 22	22 52	23 22	23 52
London Waterloo (East) 4	⊖ d	.		18 09	.	18 39	18 55	19 25	19 55	20 25	20 55	21 25	21 55	22 25	22 55	23 25	23 55
London Cannon Street 4	⊖ d	10 54	and at	.	18 24	.	.	.	.	.	.	.	.	.	.	.	.
London Bridge 4	⊖ d	10 58	the same	18 15	18 28	18 45	19 01	19 31	20 01	20 31	21 01	21 31	22 01	22 31	23 01	23 31	23 58
New Cross 4	⊖ d	11 03	minutes	.	18 35	.	19 06	19 36	20 06	20 36	21 06	21 36	22 06	22 36	23 06	23 36	00 04
St Johns	d	11 05		.	18 37	.	19 08	19 38	20 08	20 38	21 08	21 38	22 08	22 38	23 08	23 38	00 06
Lewisham 4	d	11 08	past	.	18 40	.	19 10	19 40	20 10	20 40	21 10	21 40	22 10	22 40	23 10	23 40	00 09
Ladywell	d	11 10		18 25	18 42	18 55	19 13	19 43	20 13	20 43	21 13	21 43	22 13	22 43	23 13	23 43	00 11
Catford Bridge	d	11 12	each	18 27	18 44	18 57	19 15	19 45	20 15	20 45	21 15	21 45	22 15	22 45	23 15	23 45	00 13
Lower Sydenham	d	11 15		18 30	18 47	19 00	19 18	19 48	20 18	20 48	21 18	21 48	22 18	22 48	23 18	23 48	00 16
New Beckenham 4	d	11 17	hour until	18 32	18 49	19 02	19 20	19 50	20 20	20 50	21 20	21 50	22 20	22 50	23 20	23 50	00 18
Clock House	d	11 19		18 34	18 51	19 04	19 22	19 52	20 22	20 52	21 22	21 52	22 22	22 52	23 22	23 52	00 20
Elmers End 4	d	11 22		18 35	18 53	19 07	19 25	19 55	20 25	20 55	21 25	21 55	22 25	22 55	23 25	23 55	00 23
Eden Park	d	11 26		18 39	18 57	19 11	19 29	19 59	20 29	20 59	21 29	21 59	22 29	22 59	23 29	23 59	00 27
West Wickham	d	11 28		18 41	18 59	19 13	19 31	20 01	20 31	21 01	21 31	22 01	22 31	23 01	23 31	00 01	00 29
Hayes (Kent)	a	11 31		18 46	19 02	19 16	19 34	20 04	20 34	21 04	21 34	22 04	22 34	23 04	23 34	00 04	00 32

Sundays

		SE	SE	SE	SE	SE	SE		SE	SE	SE
London Charing Cross 4	⊖ d	23p22	23p52	07 53	08 23	08 53	09 23		22 53	23 23	23 53
London Waterloo (East) 4	⊖ d	23p25	23p55	07 56	08 26	08 56	09 26		22 56	23 26	23 56
London Cannon Street 4	⊖ d	.	.	.	.	.	.	and	.	.	.
London Bridge 4	⊖ d	23p31	23p58	08 02	08 32	09 02	09 32		23 02	23 32	00 02
New Cross 4	⊖ d	23p36	00 04	08 07	08 37	09 07	09 37	every 30	23 07	23 37	00 07
St Johns	d	23p38	00 06	08 09	08 39	09 09	09 39		23 09	23 39	00 09
Lewisham 4	d	23p40	00 09	08 12	08 42	09 12	09 42	minutes	23 12	23 42	00 12
Ladywell	d	23p43	00 11	08 14	08 44	09 14	09 44		23 14	23 44	00 14
Catford Bridge	d	23p45	00 13	08 16	08 46	09 16	09 46	until	23 16	23 46	00 16
Lower Sydenham	d	23p48	00 16	08 19	08 49	09 19	09 49		23 19	23 49	00 19
New Beckenham 4	d	23p50	00 18	08 21	08 51	09 21	09 51		23 21	23 51	00 21
Clock House	d	23p52	00 20	08 23	08 53	09 23	09 53		23 23	23 53	00 23
Elmers End 4	d	23p55	00 23	08 26	08 56	09 26	09 56		23 26	23 56	00 26
Eden Park	d	23p59	00 27	08 30	09 00	09 30	10 00		23 30	00 01	00 30
West Wickham	d	00 01	00 29	08 32	09 02	09 32	10 02		23 32	00 02	00 32
Hayes (Kent)	a	00 04	00 32	08 35	09 05	09 35	10 05		23 35	00 05	00 35

For general notes see front of timetable
For details of catering facilities see Directory of Train Operators

For details of Bank Holiday service alterations please see first page of Table 195

Hayes (Kent) → London via Catford Bridge

Network Diagram - see first page of Table 200

Miles	Miles			SE A	SE B	SE A	SE B		SE A	SE B	SE	SE		SE	SE	SE	SE		SE	SE	SE	SE		SE	SE
0	—	**Hayes (Kent)**	d	05 13	05 16	05 43	05 46		06 13	06 16	06 26	06 36		06 55	07 10	07 25	07 37		07 45	07 57	08 05	08 17		08 25	08 40
1¼	—	West Wickham	d	05 16	05 19	05 46	05 49		06 16	06 19	06 29	06 39		06 58	07 13	07 28	07 40		07 48	08 00	08 08	08 20		08 28	08 43
2	—	Eden Park	d	05 18	05 21	05 48	05 51		06 18	06 21	06 31	06 41		07 00	07 15	07 30	07 42		07 50	08 02	08 10	08 22		08 30	08 45
3½	—	Elmers End 4	d	05 22	05 25	05 52	05 55		06 22	06 25	06 35	06 45		07 04	07 19	07 34	07 46		07 54	08 06	08 14	08 26		08 34	08 49
4¼	—	Clock House	d	05 24	05 27	05 54	05 57		06 24	06 27	06 37	06 47		07 07	07 21	07 36	07 48		07 56	08 08	08 16	08 28		08 36	08 51
5	—	New Beckenham 4	d	05 26	05 29	05 56	05 59		06 26	06 29	06 39	06 49		07 09	07 24	07 39	07 51		07 59	08 11	08 19	08 31		08 39	08 54
5½	—	Lower Sydenham	d	05 28	05 31	05 58	06 01		06 28	06 31	06 41	06 51		07 11	07 25	07 40	07 52		08 00	08 12	08 20	08 32		08 40	08 55
7	—	**Catford Bridge**	d	05 31	05 34	06 01	06 04		06 31	06 34	06 44	06 54		07 14	07 29	07 44	07 56		08 04	08 16	08 24	08 36		08 44	08 59
7¾	—	Ladywell	d	05 36	05 36	06 06	06 06		06 36	06 36	06 46	06 56		07 16	07 31	07 46	07 58		08 06	08 18	08 26	08 38		08 46	09 01
8½	—	**Lewisham 4**	d	05 40	05 40	06 10	06 10		06 40	06 40	06 50	07 00		07 20	07 35	07 50			08 10		08 30			08 50	
9	—	St Johns	a	05 42	05 42	06 12	06 12		06 42	06 42	06 52			07 25		07 52			08 12		08 32			08 52	
9¾	—	New Cross 4	⊖ a	05 44	05 44	06 14	06 14		06 44	06 44	06 54	07 04		07 27		07 54			08 14		08 34			08 54	
12¾	0	**London Bridge 4**	⊖ a	05 50	05 50	06 20	06 20		06 50	06 50	07 01	07 11		07 33	07 43	08 00			08 20		08 40			09 00	09 13
—	¾	**London Cannon Street 4**	⊖ a								07 06			07 38		08b07			08b27		08b47			09b07	
13¾	—	**London Waterloo (East) 4**	⊖ a	05 55	05 55	06 25	06 25		06 55	06 55		07 16			07 48		08 13			08 33		08 53			09 19
14½	—	**London Charing Cross 4**	⊖ a	06 00	05 58	06 30	06 28		07 00	06 58		07b21			07 53		08b19			08b39		09c00			09b25

		SE	SE	SE	SE		SE	SE	SE		SE	SE	SE	SE			SE	SE C	SE	SE		SE	SE	SE
Hayes (Kent)	d	09 00	09 15	09 25	09 35		09 42	09 57	10 12		10 27	10 42	10 57	11 12			15 27		15 42	15 57		16 12	16 37	16 47
West Wickham	d	09 03	09 18	09 28	09 38		09 45	10 00	10 15		10 30	10 45	11 00	11 15			15 30		15 45	16 00		16 15	16 40	
Eden Park	d	09 05	09 20	09 30	09 40		09 47	10 02	10 17		10 32	10 47	11 02	11 17	and at		15 32		15 47	16 02		16 17	16 42	
Elmers End 4	d	09 09	09 24	09 34	09 44		09 51	10 06	10 21		10 36	10 51	11 06	11 21			15 36		15 51	16 06		16 21	16 46	16 54
Clock House	d	09 11	09 26	09 36	09 46		09 53	10 08	10 23		10 38	10 53	11 08	11 23	the same		15 38		15 53	16 08		16 23	16 48	16 56
New Beckenham 4	d	09 14	09 28	09 38	09 48		09 55	10 10	10 25		10 40	10 55	11 10	11 25			15 40	15 48	15 55	16 10		16 25	16 50	16 58
Lower Sydenham	d	09 15	09 30	09 40	09 50		09 57	10 12	10 27		10 42	10 57	11 12	11 27	minutes		15 42	15 49	15 57	16 12		16 27	16 52	
Catford Bridge	d	09 19	09 33	09 43	09 53		10 00	10 15	10 30		10 45	11 00	11 15	11 30			15 45	15 53	16 00	16 15		16 30	16 55	17 02
Ladywell	d	09 21	09 35	09 45	09 55		10 02	10 17	10 32		10 47	11 02	11 17	11 32	past		15 47	15 55	16 02	16 17		16 32	16 57	17 04
Lewisham 4	d	09 24		09 48			10 06		10 36			11 06		11 36					16 08	16 21		16e38	17 02	
St Johns	a	09 28		09 52			10 08		10 38			11 08		11 38	each				16 10			16 40	17 04	
New Cross 4	⊖ a	09 30		09 54			10 10		10 40			11 10		11 40					16 12			16 42	17 06	
London Bridge 4	⊖ a	09 37	09 43	10 01	10 07		10 16	10 27	10 46		10 57	11 16	11 27	11 46	hour until		15 57		16 18	16 31		16 49	17 14	17 15
London Cannon Street 4	⊖ a	09b44		10 06			10 20		10 50			11 20		11 50					16 22				17 18	
London Waterloo (East) 4	⊖ a		09 48		10 14			10 34			11 04		11 34				16 03	16 11		16 36		16 55		17 20
London Charing Cross 4	⊖ a		09c54		10 17			10 39			11 09		11 39				16 07	16 15		16 40		16 59		17 25

		SE	SE	SE		SE	SE	SE	SE		SE	SE	SE	SE		SE	SE	SE	SE		SE	SE	SE		
Hayes (Kent)	d	16 57	17 17	17 37		17 43	17 55	18 05	18 21		18 31	18 43	18 53	19 23		19 53	20 23	20 53	21 23		21 53	22 23	22 53		
West Wickham	d	17 00	17 20	17 40		17 46		18 08	18 24		18 34	18 46	18 56	19 26		19 56	20 26	20 56	21 26		21 56	22 26	22 56		
Eden Park	d	17 02	17 22	17 42		17 48		18 10	18 26		18 36	18 48	18 58	19 28		19 58	20 28	20 58	21 28		21 58	22 28	22 58		
Elmers End 4	d	17 06	17 26	17 46		17 54	18 01	18 14	18 30		18 40	18 52	19 02	19 32		20 02	20 32	21 02	21 32		22 02	22 32	23 02		
Clock House	d	17 08	17 28	17 48		17 56	18 03	18 16	18 32		18 42	18 54	19 04	19 34		20 04	20 34	21 04	21 34		22 04	22 34	23 04		
New Beckenham 4	d	17 10	17 30	17 50		17 58	18 06	18 18	18 34		18 44	18 56	19 06	19 36		20 06	20 36	21 06	21 36		22 06	22 36	23 06		
Lower Sydenham	d	17 12	17 32	17 52		18 00		18 20	18 36		18 46	18 58	19 08	19 38		20 08	20 38	21 08	21 38		22 08	22 38	23 08		
Catford Bridge	d	17 15	17 35	17 55		18 03	18 10	18 23	18 39		18 49	19 01	19 11	19 41		20 11	20 41	21 11	21 41		22 11	22 41	23 11		
Ladywell	d	17 17	17 37	17 57		18 05	18 12	18 25	18 41		18 51	19 03	19 13	19 43		20 13	20 43	21 13	21 43		22 13	22 43	23 13		
Lewisham 4	d	17 21	17f44			18 10		18 29	18 45		18 56	19g09	19 17	19 47		20 17	20 47	21 17	21 47		22 17	22 47	23 17		
St Johns	a	17 23									18 58	19 11	19 19	19 49		20 19	20 49	21 19	21 49		22 19	22 49	23 19		
New Cross 4	⊖ a	17 25									19 00	19 13	19 21	19 51		20 21	20 51	21 21	21 51		22 21	22 51	23 21		
London Bridge 4	⊖ a	17 32	17 54	18 09			18 22	18 37	18 54		19 05	19 19	19 28	19 58		20 28	20 58	21 28	21 58		22 28	22 58	23 28		
London Cannon Street 4	⊖ a	17 36									19 10														
London Waterloo (East) 4	⊖ a		17 59	18 15		18 23	18 27	18 42	18 59			19 24	19 33	20 03		20 33	21 03	21 33	22 03		22 33	23 03	23 33		
London Charing Cross 4	⊖ a		18 03	18 19		18 27	18 33	18 49	19 05			19 29	19 37	20 07		20 37	21 07	21 37	22 07		22 37	23 07	23 37		

Saturdays

		SE	SE		SE	SE		SE	SE		SE	SE		SE	SE		SE		SE	SE	SE	SE		SE
Hayes (Kent)	d	05 23	05 53		06 23	06 53		07 23	07 42		07 57	08 12		08 27	08 42		08 57		09 12	09 27	09 42	09 57		17 12
West Wickham	d	05 26	05 56		06 26	06 56		07 26	07 45		08 00	08 15		08 30	08 45		09 00		09 15	09 30	09 45	10 00		17 15
Eden Park	d	05 28	05 58		06 28	06 58		07 28	07 47		08 02	08 17		08 32	08 47		09 02		09 17	09 32	09 47	10 02	and at	17 17
Elmers End 4	d	05 32	06 02		06 32	07 02		07 32	07 51		08 06	08 21		08 36	08 51		09 06		09 21	09 36	09 51	10 06		17 21
Clock House	d	05 34	06 04		06 34	07 04		07 34	07 53		08 08	08 23		08 38	08 53		09 08		09 23	09 38	09 53	10 08	the same	17 23
New Beckenham 4	d	05 36	06 06		06 36	07 06		07 36	07 55		08 10	08 25		08 40	08 55		09 10		09 25	09 40	09 55	10 10		17 25
Lower Sydenham	d	05 38	06 08		06 38	07 08		07 38	07 57		08 12	08 27		08 42	08 57		09 12		09 27	09 42	09 57	10 12	minutes	17 27
Catford Bridge	d	05 41	06 11		06 41	07 11		07 41	08 00		08 15	08 30		08 45	09 00		09 15		09 30	09 45	10 00	10 15		17 30
Ladywell	d	05 43	06 13		06 43	07 13		07 43	08 02		08 17	08 32		08 47	09 02		09 17		09 32	09 47	10 02	10 17	past	17 32
Lewisham 4	d	05 47	06 17		06 47	07 17		07 47	08 06			08 36			09 06				09 36		10 06			17 36
St Johns	a	05 49	06 19		06 49	07 19		07 49	08 08			08 38			09 08				09 38		10 08		each	17 38
New Cross 4	⊖ a	05 51	06 21		06 51	07 21		07 51	08 10			08 40			09 10				09 40		10 10			17 40
London Bridge 4	⊖ a	05 58	06 29		06 58	07 29		07 58	08 16		08 27	08 46		08 57	09 16		09 27		09 46	09 57	10 16	10 27	hour until	17 46
London Cannon Street 4	⊖ a								08 20			08 50			09 20				09 50		10 20			17 50
London Waterloo (East) 4	⊖ a	06 03	06 34		07 03	07 33		08 03			08 34			09 04			09 34			10 04		10 34		
London Charing Cross 4	⊖ a	06 07	06 37		07 07	07 37		08 07			08 39			09 09			09 39			10 09		10 39		

For general notes see front of timetable
For details of catering facilities see Directory of Train Operators

- A From 12 October
- B Until 9 October
- C From Beckenham Junction
- b Until 9 October Arr. 1 minute earlier
- c Until 9 October Arr. 2 minutes earlier
- e Arr. 1635
- f Arr. 1740
- g Arr. 1906

Table 203

Hayes (Kent) → London via Catford Bridge

Saturdays

Network Diagram - see first page of Table 200

		SE	SE	SE	SE	SE	SE	SE	SE	SE	SE	SE	SE	SE
Hayes (Kent)	d	17 27	17 42	17 57	18 23	18 53	19 23	19 53	20 23	20 53	21 23	21 53	22 23	22 53
West Wickham	d	17 30	17 45	18 00	18 26	18 56	19 26	19 56	20 26	20 56	21 26	21 56	22 26	22 56
Eden Park	d	17 32	17 47	18 02	18 28	18 58	19 28	19 58	20 28	20 58	21 28	21 58	22 28	22 58
Elmers End [4]	d	17 36	17 51	18 06	18 32	19 02	19 32	20 02	20 32	21 02	21 32	22 02	22 32	23 02
Clock House	d	17 38	17 53	18 08	18 34	19 04	19 34	20 04	20 34	21 04	21 34	22 04	22 34	23 04
New Beckenham [4]	d	17 40	17 55	18 10	18 36	19 06	19 36	20 06	20 36	21 06	21 36	22 06	22 36	23 06
Lower Sydenham	d	17 42	17 57	18 12	18 38	19 08	19 38	20 08	20 38	21 08	21 38	22 08	22 38	23 08
Catford Bridge	d	17 45	18 00	18 15	18 41	19 11	19 41	20 11	20 41	21 11	21 41	22 11	22 41	23 11
Ladywell	d	17 47	18 02	18 17	18 43	19 13	19 43	20 13	20 43	21 13	21 43	22 13	22 43	23 13
Lewisham [4]	d	.	18 06	18 23	18 47	19 17	19 47	20 17	20 47	21 17	21 47	22 17	22 47	23 17
St Johns	a	.	18 08	.	18 49	19 19	19 49	20 19	20 49	21 19	21 49	22 19	22 49	23 19
New Cross [4]	⊖ a	.	18 10	.	18 51	19 21	19 51	20 21	20 51	21 21	21 51	22 21	22 51	23 21
London Bridge [4]	⊖ a	17 57	18 16	18 33	18 58	19 28	19 58	20 28	20 58	21 28	21 58	22 28	22 58	23 28
London Cannon Street [4]	⊖ a	.	18 20	.	.	.	.	.	.	.	.	.	.	.
London Waterloo (East) [4]	⊖ a	18 04	.	18 38	19 03	19 33	20 03	20 33	21 03	21 33	22 03	22 33	23 03	23 33
London Charing Cross [4]	⊖ a	18 09	.	18 41	19 07	19 37	20 07	20 37	21 07	21 37	22 07	22 37	23 07	23 37

Sundays

		SE	SE	SE		SE	SE	SE
Hayes (Kent)	d	07 47	08 17	08 47		22 17	22 47	23 17
West Wickham	d	07 50	08 20	08 50		22 20	22 50	23 20
Eden Park	d	07 52	08 22	08 52		22 22	22 52	23 22
Elmers End [4]	d	07 56	08 26	08 56		22 26	22 56	23 26
Clock House	d	07 58	08 28	08 58	and	22 28	22 58	23 28
New Beckenham [4]	d	08 00	08 30	09 00		22 30	23 00	23 30
Lower Sydenham	d	08 02	08 32	09 02	every 30	22 32	23 02	23 32
Catford Bridge	d	08 05	08 35	09 05		22 35	23 05	23 35
Ladywell	d	08 07	08 37	09 07	minutes	22 37	23 07	23 37
Lewisham [4]	d	08 11	08 41	09 11		22 41	23 11	23 41
St Johns	a	08 13	08 43	09 13	until	22 43	23 13	23 43
New Cross [4]	⊖ a	08 15	08 45	09 15		22 45	23 15	23 45
London Bridge [4]	⊖ a	08 21	08 51	09 21		22 51	23 21	23 51
London Cannon Street [4]	⊖ a	.	.	.		.	.	.
London Waterloo (East) [4]	⊖ a	08 26	08 56	09 26		22 56	23 26	23 56
London Charing Cross [4]	⊖ a	08 29	08 59	09 29		22 59	23 30	23 59

For general notes see front of timetable
For details of catering facilities see Directory of Train Operators

For details of Bank Holiday service alterations please see first page of Table 195

London → Grove Park, Bromley North, Orpington, Sevenoaks and Tonbridge

Network Diagram - see first page of Table 200

Miles	Miles		SE MX	SE MO	SE MO 1	SE MX 2 1 A	SE MX	SE MO	SE MX 1	SE MX	SE MX	SE MO	SE MX 02	SE MX 01	SE 14	SE 1 B	SE	SE	SE	SE	SE 1 C	SE 1 B	SE 1 C
0	—	London Charing Cross 4 ⊖ d	23p26	23p26	23p30	23p30			23p37			23p56	00 10		00 48	05 30		05 40			06 16	06 25	
¾	—	London Waterloo (East) 4 ⊖ d	23p29	23p29	23p33	23p33			23p40			23p59	00 13		00 51	05 33		05 43			06 19	06 28	
—	—	London Cannon Street 4 ⊖ d																					
1¾	—	London Bridge 4 ⊖ d	23p34	23p35	23p38	23p38			23p45			00 05	00 18		00 56	05 38		05 48			06 24	06 33	
4¾	—	New Cross 4 ⊖ d													01 01			05 53					
5½	—	St Johns d																					
6	—	Lewisham 4 d	23p43	23p45								00 15			01 05			05 57					
7¼	—	Hither Green 4 d	23p47	23p49			←	←				00 19			01 09			06 01			06 33		
9	0	Grove Park 4 d	23p51	23p53			23p51	23p53				00 23	00 29	00 33	01 13			06 04	06 17		06 36		
—	1¼	Sundridge Park d	→	→										00 36					06 20				
—	1¾	Bromley North a												00 38					06 22				←
10¼	—	Elmstead Woods d					23p53	23p55				00 25	00 32		01 16			06 07			06 39		06 39
11½	—	Chislehurst d					23p56	23p58				00 28	00 35		01 19			06 09			→		06 41
12¾	—	Petts Wood 4 d					00 01	00 01		00 20	00 25	00 31	00 39		01 23		06 10	06 13		06 39			06 46
13¾	—	Orpington 4 a			23p54	23p56	00 03	00 04		00 24	00 28	00 34	00 42		01 26	05 54	06 13	06 16		06 42		06 49	06 50
—	—	d			23p54	23p56							00 42			05 54		06 22				06 50	06 54
15¼	—	Chelsfield 3 d											00 46			05 58		06 25					06 57
16½	—	Knockholt d														06 01		06 27					06 59
20½	—	Dunton Green d														06 07		06 32					07 04
22	—	Sevenoaks 4 a			00 04	00 06			00 10				00 54			06 10		06 36				06 59	07 08
—	—	d			00 04	00 06			00 10				00 54			06 11						07 00	07 08
27	—	Hildenborough d				00 12							01 00			06 17						07 06	07 14
29½	—	Tonbridge 4 a			00 13	00 17			00 20				01 05			06 21						07 10	07 19

	SE	SE	SE	SE	SE 1	SE	SE	SE	SE 1 C	SE	SE	SE 1 D	SE	SE	SE 1 E	SE	SE	SE	SE 1 G	SE	SE	SE
London Charing Cross 4 ⊖ d			06 47		07 00			07 10	07 16			07 28		07 37					07 52	07 56		
London Waterloo (East) 4 ⊖ d			06 50		07 03			07 13	07 19			07 31		07 40					07 55	07 59		
London Cannon Street 4 ⊖ d															07 45							08 03
London Bridge 4 ⊖ d			06 56		07 08			07 19	07 24			07 36		07 45	07 49				08 02	08 04		08 07
New Cross 4 ⊖ d																						08 12
St Johns d																						
Lewisham 4 d																						08 16
Hither Green 4 d			07 06					07 29						07 53								08 20
Grove Park 4 d	06 42	07 03	07 13				07 24	07 33					07 44	07 57			08 05			08 17		08 24
Sundridge Park d	06 45	07 06					07 27						07 47				08 08					
Bromley North a	06 47	07 08				←	07 29				←		07 49			←	08 10					
Elmstead Woods d			07 16			07 16		07 35			07 35			08 02		08 02						08 27
Chislehurst d			→			07 19		→			07 39			→		08 05						08 30
Petts Wood 4 d				07 10		07 22				07 40	07 42					08 09		08 12			08 29	08 33
Orpington 4 a				07 13	07 25	07 25			07 40	07 43	07 45	07 54			08 08	08 12		08 15	08 19	08 24	08 33	08 36
d					07 26	07 28			07 41		07 46	07 55			08 09				08 20	08 24		
Chelsfield 3 d						07 31					07 49				08 12					08 27		
Knockholt d						07 33					07 51				08 15					08 30		
Dunton Green d						07 38					07 56				08 20					08 35		
Sevenoaks 4 a					07 35	07 42			07 50		08 01	08 04			08 24				08 29	08 38		
d					07 36				07 51			08 05			08 24				08 30			
Hildenborough d									07 57			08 11							08 36			
Tonbridge 4 a					07 44				08 01			08 15			08 32				08 40			

	SE 1 🍴	SE	SE	SE	SE 1	SE	SE	SE	SE	SE 1 H 🍴	SE 1	SE	SE	SE	SE	SE 1 J	SE	SE 1 🍴	SE	SE	SE	SE 1 A	SE 1 🍴
London Charing Cross 4 ⊖ d	08 14		08 20		08 22	08 29			08 38		08 54				08 56	08 58					09 26	09 30	09 45
London Waterloo (East) 4 ⊖ d	08 17		08 23		08 25	08 32			08 41		08 57				08 59	09 01					09 29	09 33	09 48
London Cannon Street 4 ⊖ d										08 45								09 17					
London Bridge 4 ⊖ d	08 23		08 28		08 30	08 38			08 46	08 49	09 02				09 04	09 08		09 21			09 34	09 38	09 53
New Cross 4 ⊖ d																							
St Johns d																							
Lewisham 4 d																					09 43		
Hither Green 4 d			08 37						08 56						09 17		←				09 47		
Grove Park 4 d		08 25	08 41					08 45	09 00				09 05		09 21		09 21		09 26		09 51		
Sundridge Park d		08 28						08 48					09 08		→				09 29		→		
Bromley North a		08 30					←	08 50				←	09 10						09 31				
Elmstead Woods d			08 44				08 44		09 03			09 03					09 23						
Chislehurst d			→				08 47		→			09 06					09 26						
Petts Wood 4 d				08 41			08 50					09 09		09 12		09 23	09 30			09 39			
Orpington 4 a				08 44	08 47	08 55	08 56			09 07		09 12		09 15		09 26	09 33	09 39		09 42		09 54	
d					08 48	08 56				09 08						09 26	09 33	09 40				09 54	
Chelsfield 3 d						08 59											09 36						
Knockholt d						09 01											09 39						
Dunton Green d						09 06											09 44						
Sevenoaks 4 a	08 46				08 57	09 10				09 17						09 36	09 47	09 50				10 04	10 16
d	08 47				08 58					09 18						09 36		09 50				10 04	10 16
Hildenborough d										09 24						09 42						10 10	
Tonbridge 4 a	08 55				09 06					09 28	09 35					09 47		09 59				10 15	10 24

For general notes see front of timetable
For details of catering facilities see Directory of Train Operators

A To Dover Priory (Table 207)
B To Ramsgate (Table 207)
C To Tunbridge Wells (Table 206)
D To Hastings (Table 206) and to Dover Priory (Table 207)
E To Hastings (Table 206)
G To Ramsgate (Table 207) and to Margate (Table 207)
H To Hastings (Table 206) and to Hastings (Table 206)
J To Margate (Table 207)

For details of Bank Holiday service alterations please see first page of Table 195

London → Grove Park, Bromley North, Orpington, Sevenoaks and Tonbridge

Network Diagram - see first page of Table 200

		SE	SE	SE	SE 1	SE	SE	SE	SE	SE	SE 1	SE	SE 1	SE	SE	SE 1	SN 1	SE 1	SE	SE	SE	SE 1	SE
								A								A							
					⊥						⊥		⊥					⊥				⊥	
London Charing Cross 4	⊖ d				09 53		09 56	10 00			10 15		10 23		10 26	10 30	10 40	10 45				10 53	
London Waterloo (East) 4	⊖ d				09 56		09 59	10 03			10 18		10 26		10 29	10 33	10 43	10 48				10 56	
London Cannon Street 4	⊖ d																						
London Bridge 4	⊖ d						10 04	10 08			10 23				10 34	10 38	10 48	10 53					
New Cross 4	⊖ d																						
St Johns	d																						
Lewisham 4	d						10 13								10 43								
Hither Green 4	d		←				10 17			←					10 47					←			
Grove Park 4	d		09 51	09 56			10 21 →			10 21		10 26			10 51 →					10 51	10 56		
Sundridge Park	d			09 59								10 29									10 59		
Bromley North	a			10 01								10 31									11 01		
Elmstead Woods	d		09 53							10 23										10 53			
Chislehurst	d		09 56							10 26										10 56			
Petts Wood 4	d	09 54	10 00			10 09		10 22	10 26	10 30				10 39					10 54	11 00			11 09
Orpington 4	a	09 57	10 03			10 13		10 25	10 29	10 33	10 39			10 42		10 53			10 57	11 03			11 12
	d							10 26		10 33	10 40					10 54							
Chelsfield 3	d									10 36													
Knockholt	d									10 39													
Dunton Green	d									10 44													
Sevenoaks 4	a							10 36		10 47	10 50					11 04		11 15					
	d							10 36			10 50					11 04		11 16					
Hildenborough	d							10 42								11 10							
Tonbridge 4	a				10 30			10 47			10 59		11 02			11 15	11 52	11 24				11 30	

		SE	SE 1	SE	SE		SE 1	SE	SE 1	SE	SE	SE 1	SN 1	SE	SE	SE 1	SE	SE 1	SE	SE	SE 1	SE
			A									A									A	
							⊥									⊥		⊥				
London Charing Cross 4	⊖ d	10 56	11 00				15 15		15 23		15 26	15 30	15 40			15 45		15 53		15 56	16 00	
London Waterloo (East) 4	⊖ d	10 59	11 03				15 18		15 26		15 29	15 33	15 43			15 48		15 56		15 59	16 03	
London Cannon Street 4	⊖ d																					
London Bridge 4	⊖ d	11 04	11 08			and at	15 23				15 34	15 38	15 48			15 53				16 04	16 08	
New Cross 4	⊖ d																					
St Johns	d					the same																
Lewisham 4	d	11 13									15 43									16 13		
Hither Green 4	d	11 17			←	minutes					15 47				←					16 17		
Grove Park 4	d	11 21 →			11 21			15 26			15 51 →				15 51		15 56			16 21		
Sundridge Park	d					past		15 29									15 59					
Bromley North	a							15 31									16 01					
Elmstead Woods	d				11 23	each									15 53					16 23		
Chislehurst	d				11 26										15 56					16 26 →		
Petts Wood 4	d		11 22	11 24	11 30	hour until				15 39				15 54	15 59				16 09			16 24
Orpington 4	a		11 25	11 27	11 33		15 39			15 42		15 53		15 57	16 02				16 12			16 27
	d		11 26		11 33		15 40					15 54			16 02							
Chelsfield 3	d				11 36										16 05							
Knockholt	d				11 39										16 08							
Dunton Green	d				11 44										16 13							
Sevenoaks 4	a		11 36		11 47		15 50					16 04			16 16	16 19					16 32	
	d		11 36				15 50					16 04				16 20					16 32	
Hildenborough	d		11 42									16 10									16 38	
Tonbridge 4	a		11 47				15 59		16 02			16 15	16 52			16 28		16 32			16 43	

		SE	SE 1	SE	SE	SE	SE	SE 1	SE 1	SE	SE	SE	SE	SE	SE 1	SE 1	SE	SE 1	SE	SE	SE	SE	SE	SE 1
			B						A							C		D						
			⊥					⊥							⊥									
London Charing Cross 4	⊖ d		16 15			16 16		16 23	16 30					16 42	16 46	16 50						17 04		17 12
London Waterloo (East) 4	⊖ d		16 18			16 19		16 26	16 33					16 45	16 49	16 53						17 07		17 15
London Cannon Street 4	⊖ d						16 22										16 56	17 00					17 14	
London Bridge 4	⊖ d		16 23			16 25	16 26	16 31	16 39					16 50	16 54	16 58	17 00	17 04				17 12	17 18	
New Cross 4	⊖ d																							
St Johns	d																							
Lewisham 4	d						16 35																	
Hither Green 4	d						16 39							17 03								17 23		
Grove Park 4	d			16 26		16 38	16 43				16 47			17 07			17 12			17 16		17 27	17 33	
Sundridge Park	d			16 29							16 50									17 19				
Bromley North	a			16 31							16 52									17 21				
Elmstead Woods	d	←					16 45			←				17 09			17 15					17 29	17 35	
Chislehurst	d	16 26					16 48 →			16 48				17 12			17 18		←			17 32	17 38 →	
Petts Wood 4	d	16 29			16 39	16 43				16 51		17 01	17 07	17 15			17 21 →		17 21		17 25	17 35		
Orpington 4	a	16 32			16b44	16c49				16 55		17b06	17 12	17 21					17 24		17c30	17c42		
	d	16 33								16 56									17 24					
Chelsfield 3	d	16 36								17 00									17 27					
Knockholt	d	16 39								17 03									17 30					
Dunton Green	d	16 44								17 08									17 36					
Sevenoaks 4	a	16 47	16 49					16 55	17 02	17 13						17 21		17 27	17c42					
	d		16 50					16 56	17 02							17 22		17 28						
Hildenborough	d								17 08							17 28		17 34						
Tonbridge 4	a		16 58					17 04	17 13						17 24	17 32		17 38						17 50

For general notes see front of timetable
For details of catering facilities see
Directory of Train Operators

A To Ashford International (Table 207)
B From 12 October to Hastings
C To Tunbridge Wells (Table 206)
D To Hastings (Table 206)

b Until 9 October Arr. 2 minutes earlier
c Until 9 October Arr. 1 minute earlier

For details of Bank Holiday service alterations please see first page of Table 195

London → Grove Park, Bromley North, Orpington, Sevenoaks and Tonbridge

Network Diagram - see first page of Table 200

		SE 1 A	SE	SE 1 🛒	SE 1 🛒		SE	SE	SE	SE 1 B	SE	SE	SE	SE 1 C	SE 1 B	SE	SE	SE	SE		SE	SE 1 A	SE 1 B	SE	SE
London Charing Cross 4	⊖ d			17 34	17 56					17 20	17 28				17 41				17 49				18 04		
London Waterloo (East) 4	⊖ d			17 37	17 59					17 23	17 31				17 44				17 52				18 07		
London Cannon Street 4	⊖ d	17 20							17 22				17 40	17 44							18 00	18 05			
London Bridge 4	⊖ d								17 26	17 28			17 44		17 49				17 57		18 04	18 09	18 12		
New Cross 4	⊖ d								17 32																
St Johns	d																								
Lewisham 4	d																								
Hither Green 4	d										17 46								18 07						
Grove Park 4	d		17 36						17 41		17 50		17 57				18 02		18 11		18 17				18 21
Sundridge Park	d		17 39														18 05								18 24
Bromley North	a		17 41														18 07								18 26
Elmstead Woods	d						←		17 43		17 53		17 59			←			18 13		18 19			←	
Chislehurst	d						17 38		17 46		17 56		18 02			18 02			18 16		18 22			18 22	
Petts Wood 4	d						17 43	17 49	17 51		17 58		→			18 05		18 10	18 19		→			18 25	
Orpington 4	a						17 46	17 53	17 57		18b05					18 08		18 15	18b26					18 29	
	d						17 46									18 08								18 30	
Chelsfield 3	d						17 49			17 47					18 07	18 11							18 31	18 33	
Knockholt	d						17 52					←				18 14								18 36	
Dunton Green	d						17 58					17 58				18 20								18 41	
Sevenoaks 4	a	17 51					→			17 55		18 03		18 11	18 16	18b26						18 33	18 39	18b47	
	d	17 52								17 56				18 12	18 16							18 34	18 40		
Hildenborough	d	17 58								18 02					18 22							18 40	18 46		
Tonbridge 4	a	18 02		18 15	18 34					18 06				18 20	18 27							18 44	18 51		

		SE	SE	SE	SE 1 🛒	SE	SE 1	SE 1 B	SE	SE	SE		SE	SE 1	SE 1 🛒	SE	SE	SE	SE	SE	SE 1 A 🛒	SE 1 D	SE	SE	SE
London Charing Cross 4	⊖ d			18 12	18 16			18 28			18 32			18 40	18 50					18 52	19 00				
London Waterloo (East) 4	⊖ d			18 15	18 19			18 31			18 35			18 43	18 53					18 55	19 03				
London Cannon Street 4	⊖ d					18 16	18 30												18 50			19 06			
London Bridge 4	⊖ d					18 20	18 34	18 36			18 40			18 48					18 54	19 00	19 08	19 10			
New Cross 4	⊖ d					18 26																			
St Johns	d																								
Lewisham 4	d					18 30																			
Hither Green 4	d			18 29							18 51									19 10					
Grove Park 4	d			18 33		18 37				18 42	18 55						19 02		19 06	19 14				19 22	
Sundridge Park	d									18 45							19 05							19 25	
Bromley North	a								←	18 47						←	19 07						←	19 27	
Elmstead Woods	d			18 35		18 39			18 39		18 57					18 57			19 08	19 16			19 16		
Chislehurst	d			18 38		→			18 42		→					19 00			19 11	→			19 19		
Petts Wood 4	d	18 29	18 36	18 43					18 46				18 56			19 04		19 12	19 17				19 23		19 26
Orpington 4	a	18 33	18b41	18c49					18 51				19 01	19 04		19 10		19c17	19b23			19 27	19 27		19 31
	d								18 56					19 05		19 16						19 28	19 30		
Chelsfield 3	d							18 56	18 59							19 19					19 26		19 33		
Knockholt	d								19 02							19 22							19 36		
Dunton Green	d								19 07							19 27							19 41		
Sevenoaks 4	a				18 48		18 58	19 04	19 12					19 14	19 20	19 32					19 34	19 37	19 46		
	d				18 48		18 58	19 05						19 15	19 20						19 34	19 38			
Hildenborough	d							19 11													19 40	19 44			
Tonbridge 4	a				18 57		19 07	19 15						19 23	19 29						19 45	19 48			

		SE	SE		SE 1	SE 1	SE	SE B	SE	SE	SE	SE	SE	SE 1 🛒	SE 1	SE	SE 1 E 🛒		SE	SE	SE 1	SE	SE	SE 1 E 🛒	SE
London Charing Cross 4	⊖ d				19 15	19 24	19 26	19 30						19 45	19 52	19 56	20 00				20 15		20 26	20 30	
London Waterloo (East) 4	⊖ d				19 18	19 27	19 29	19 33						19 48	19 55	19 59	20 03				20 18		20 29	20 33	
London Cannon Street 4	⊖ d		19 18										19 48												
London Bridge 4	⊖ d		19 22		19 23	19 32	19 34	19 38					19 52	19 53	20 01	20 04	20 08				20 23		20 34	20 38	
New Cross 4	⊖ d																								
St Johns	d																								
Lewisham 4	d		19 31				19 43						20 01			20 13							20 43		
Hither Green 4	d		19 35				19 47			←			20 05			20 17							20 47		
Grove Park 4	d		19 39				19 51			19 51	19 55		20 09			20 21						20 25	20 51		
Sundridge Park	d						→				19 58											20 28	→		
Bromley North	a										20 00											20 30			
Elmstead Woods	d		19 41							19 53			20 11			20 23				←					
Chislehurst	d		19 44							19 56			20 14			20 26				20 26					
Petts Wood 4	d	19 41	19 48						19 55	19 59		20 11	20 17			→			20 26	20 29					20 55
Orpington 4	a	19 44	19 52					19 54	19 58	20 02		20 14	20 20						20 29	20 32	20 40			20 54	20 58
	d							19 54		20 02										20 32	20 40			20 54	
Chelsfield 3	d							19 58		20 05										20 35					
Knockholt	d									20 08										20 38					
Dunton Green	d									20 13										20 43					
Sevenoaks 4	a				19 50			20 06		20 16				20 19			20 31			20 46	20 50			21 04	
	d				19 50			20 06						20 20			20 32				20 50			21 04	
Hildenborough	d							20 12									20 38							21 10	
Tonbridge 4	a				19 59	20 02		20 17						20 28	20 32		20 42				20 58			21 15	

For general notes see front of timetable
For details of catering facilities see Directory of Train Operators

A To Ashford International (Table 207)
B To Tunbridge Wells (Table 206)
C From 12 October to Canterbury West and to Folkestone Central
D To Hastings (Table 206)
E To Ramsgate (Table 207)
b Until 9 October Arr. 1 minute earlier
c Until 9 October Arr. 2 minutes earlier

For details of Bank Holiday service alterations please see first page of Table 195

London → Grove Park, Bromley North, Orpington, Sevenoaks and Tonbridge

Network Diagram - see first page of Table 200

Station		SE	SE	SE	SE 1	SE	SE 1 A	SE	SE		SE 1	SE	SE
London Charing Cross [4]	⊖ d				20 45	20 56	21 00				21 15		21 26
London Waterloo (East) [4]	⊖ d				20 48	20 59	21 03				21 18		21 29
London Cannon Street [4]	⊖ d			20 35									
London Bridge [4]	⊖ d			20 39	20 53	21 04	21 08				21 23		21 34
New Cross [4]	⊖ d			20 44									
St Johns	d			20 46									
Lewisham [4]	d			20 49		21 13							21 43
Hither Green [4]	d	←		20 53		21 17			←				21 47
Grove Park [4]	d	20 51	20 55	20 57		21 21			21 21			21 25	21 51
Sundridge Park	d		20 58			→						21 28	→
Bromley North	a		21 00									21 30	
Elmstead Woods	d	20 53		20 59					21 23				
Chislehurst	d	20 56		21 02					21 26				
Petts Wood [4]	d	21 00		21 05				21 24	21 29				
Orpington [4]	a	21 03		21 10	21 10		21 24	21 27	21 32		21 40		
	d				21 10		21 24		21 32		21 40		
Chelsfield [3]	d								21 35				
Knockholt	d								21 38				
Dunton Green	d								21 43				
Sevenoaks [4]	a				21 20		21 34		21 46		21 50		
	d				21 20		21 34				21 50		
Hildenborough	d						21 40						
Tonbridge [4]	a				21 28		21 45				21 58		

Station		SE 1 B	SE	SE	SE 1	SE	SE	SE 1 A	SE	SE	SE 1 C		SE
London Charing Cross [4]	⊖ d	21 30			21 45		21 56	22 00			22 15		
London Waterloo (East) [4]	⊖ d	21 33			21 48		21 59	22 03			22 18		
London Cannon Street [4]	⊖ d												
London Bridge [4]	⊖ d	21 38			21 53		22 04	22 08			22 23		
New Cross [4]	⊖ d												
St Johns	d												
Lewisham [4]	d						22 13						
Hither Green [4]	d			←			22 17			←			
Grove Park [4]	d			21 51		21 55	22 21			22 21			22 25
Sundridge Park	d					21 58	→						22 28
Bromley North	a					22 00							22 30
Elmstead Woods	d			21 53						22 23			
Chislehurst	d			21 56						22 26			
Petts Wood [4]	d		21 55	22 00					22 25	22 30			
Orpington [4]	a	21 54	21 58	22 03	22 10			22 24	22 28	22 33	22 40		
	d	21 54			22 10			22 24			22 40		
Chelsfield [3]	d										22 44		
Knockholt	d												
Dunton Green	d												
Sevenoaks [4]	a	22 04			22 20			22 34			22 52		
	d	22 04			22 20			22 34			22 52		
Hildenborough	d	22 10						22 40					
Tonbridge [4]	a	22 15			22 28			22 45			23 00		

Station		SE	SE 1 D	SE	SE	SE 1	SE	SE	SE 2 1 E	SE	SE	SE	SE 1 C
London Charing Cross [4]	⊖ d	22 26	22 30			22 45		22 56	23 00				23 15
London Waterloo (East) [4]	⊖ d	22 29	22 33			22 48		22 59	23 03				23 18
London Cannon Street [4]	⊖ d												
London Bridge [4]	⊖ d	22 34	22 38			22 53		23 04	23 08				23 23
New Cross [4]	⊖ d												
St Johns	d												
Lewisham [4]	d	22 43						23 13					
Hither Green [4]	d	22 47			←			23 17				←	
Grove Park [4]	d	22 51			22 51		22 55	23 21				23 21	
Sundridge Park	d	→					22 58	→					
Bromley North	a						23 00						
Elmstead Woods	d				22 53							23 23	
Chislehurst	d				22 56							23 26	
Petts Wood [4]	d			22 55	23 00					23 20	23 26	23 30	
Orpington [4]	a		22 54	22 58	23 03	23 10			23 24	23 24	23 30	23 33	23 40
	d		22 54			23 10			23 24				23 40
Chelsfield [3]	d												23 44
Knockholt	d												
Dunton Green	d												
Sevenoaks [4]	a		23 04			23 20			23 34				23 52
	d		23 04			23 20			23 34				23 52
Hildenborough	d		23 10						23 40				
Tonbridge [4]	a		23 14			23 28			23 45				00 01

Station		SE		SE	SE	SE 2 1 E	SE 1	SE	SE	SE			
London Charing Cross [4]	⊖ d			23 26		23 30	23 37						
London Waterloo (East) [4]	⊖ d			23 29		23 33	23 40						
London Cannon Street [4]	⊖ d												
London Bridge [4]	⊖ d			23 34		23 38	23 45						
New Cross [4]	⊖ d												
St Johns	d												
Lewisham [4]	d			23 43									
Hither Green [4]	d			23 47					←				
Grove Park [4]	d	23 25		23 51					23 51	23 56			
Sundridge Park	d	23 28		→						23 59			
Bromley North	a	23 30								00 01			
Elmstead Woods	d								23 53				
Chislehurst	d								23 56				
Petts Wood [4]	d				23 50			23 55	00 01				
Orpington [4]	a				23 54	23 56		23 58	00 03				
	d					23 56							
Chelsfield [3]	d												
Knockholt	d												
Dunton Green	d												
Sevenoaks [4]	a					00 06	00 10						
	d					00 06	00 10						
Hildenborough	d					00 12							
Tonbridge [4]	a					00 17	00 20						

For general notes see front of timetable
For details of catering facilities see Directory of Train Operators

A To Ramsgate (Table 207)
B To Margate (Table 207)
C To Tunbridge Wells (Table 206)
D To Canterbury West (Table 207)
E To Dover Priory (Table 207)

Table 204

Saturdays

London → Grove Park, Bromley North, Orpington, Sevenoaks and Tonbridge

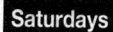

Network Diagram - see first page of Table 200

		SE	SE 2 [1] A	SE	SE [1]	SE	SE	SE [1]	SE	SE	SE [1] B	SE	SE [1] C		SE	SE	SE	SE	SE	SE	SE [1] C	SE	SE	SE	SE
London Charing Cross 4	⊖ d	23p26	23p30		23p37			00 10		00 48		05 56	06 00					06 26		06 56	07 00				07 26
London Waterloo (East) 4	⊖ d	23p29	23p33		23p40			00 13		00 51		05 59	06 03					06 29		06 59	07 03				07 29
London Cannon Street 4	⊖ d																								
London Bridge 4	⊖ d	23p34	23p38		23p45			00 18		00 56		06 04	06 08					06 34		07 04	07 08				07 34
New Cross 4	⊖ d									01 01															
St Johns	d																								
Lewisham 4	d	23p43								01 05		06 13						06 43		07 13					07 43
Hither Green 4	d	23p47		←						01 09		06 17				←		06 47		07 17			←		07 47
Grove Park 4	d	23p51 →		23p51				00 29	00 33	01 13		06 21 →				06 21	06 26	06 51	06 56	07 21 →			07 21	07 26	07 51 →
Sundridge Park	d								00 36								06 29		06 59					07 29	
Bromley North	a								00 38								06 31		07 01					07 31	
Elmstead Woods	d			23p53				00 32		01 16						06 23		06 53					07 23		
Chislehurst	d			23p56				00 35		01 19						06 26		06 56					07 26		
Petts Wood 4	d			00 01		00 20	00 25	00 39		01 23					06 24	06 30		07 00				07 24	07 30		
Orpington 4	a		23p56	00 03		00 24	00 28	00 42		01 26			06 26		06 27	06 33		07 03			07 26	07 27	07 33		
	d		23p56					00 42			05 58		06 26			06 33					07 26		07 33		
Chelsfield 3	d							00 46								06 36							07 36		
Knockholt	d															06 39							07 39		
Dunton Green	d															06 44							07 44		
Sevenoaks 4	a		00 06		00 10			00 54			06 07		06 36			06 47					07 36		07 47		
	d		00 06		00 10			00 54			06 08		06 36								07 36				
Hildenborough	d		00 12					01 00			06 14		06 42								07 42				
Tonbridge 4	a		00 17		00 20			01 05			06 18		06 47								07 47				

		SE [1]	SN [1]	SE		SE	SE [1]	SE	SE	SE [1] D	SE	SE	SE [1]	SE	SE	SE	SE [1]		SN [1]	SE [1]	SE	SE	SE	SE	SE
London Charing Cross 4	⊖ d	07 30	07 40				07 45		07 56	08 00			08 15			08 26	08 30		08 40	08 45					08 56
London Waterloo (East) 4	⊖ d	07 33	07 43				07 48		07 59	08 03			08 18			08 29	08 33		08 43	08 48					08 59
London Cannon Street 4	⊖ d																								
London Bridge 4	⊖ d	07 38	07 48				07 53		08 04	08 08			08 23			08 34	08 38		08 48	08 53					09 04
New Cross 4	⊖ d																								
St Johns	d																								
Lewisham 4	d								08 13							08 43									09 13
Hither Green 4	d					←			08 17			←				08 47							←		09 17
Grove Park 4	d					07 51		07 56	08 21 →			08 21		08 26		08 51 →						08 56	08 51		09 21 →
Sundridge Park	d							07 59						08 29								08 59			
Bromley North	a							08 01						08 31								09 01			
Elmstead Woods	d					07 53						08 23											08 53		
Chislehurst	d					07 56						08 26											08 56		
Petts Wood 4	d			07 54		08 00					08 24	08 30			08 39						08 54		09 00	09 09	
Orpington 4	a	07 55		07 57		08 03	08 09			08 25	08 27	08 33	08 39		08 42		08 55				08 57		09 03	09 12	
	d	07 56					08 10			08 26		08 33	08 40				08 56								
Chelsfield 3	d											08 36													
Knockholt	d											08 39													
Dunton Green	d											08 44													
Sevenoaks 4	a	08 05					08 20			08 35		08 47	08 50				09 05			09 15					
	d	08 06					08 20			08 36			08 51				09 06			09 16					
Hildenborough	d									08 42															
Tonbridge 4	a	08 14	08 52				08 28			08 46			08 59				09 14		09 52	09 24					

		SE [1] D	SE	SE	SE [1]	SE	SE	SE		SE [1] E	SN [1]	SE [1]	SE	SE	SE [1]	SE	SE		SE	SE [1] E	SE	SE	SE [1] 🚲	SE	SE [1] 🚲
London Charing Cross 4	⊖ d	09 00			09 15			09 26		09 30	09 40	09 45			09 53				09 56	10 00			10 15		10 23
London Waterloo (East) 4	⊖ d	09 03			09 18			09 29		09 33	09 43	09 48			09 56				09 59	10 03			10 18		10 26
London Cannon Street 4	⊖ d																								
London Bridge 4	⊖ d	09 08			09 23			09 34		09 38	09 48	09 53							10 04	10 08			10 23		
New Cross 4	⊖ d																								
St Johns	d																								
Lewisham 4	d							09 43											10 13						
Hither Green 4	d			←				09 47								←			10 17			←			
Grove Park 4	d			09 21		09 26		09 51 →						09 56		09 51			10 21 →			10 21		10 26	
Sundridge Park	d					09 29								09 59										10 29	
Bromley North	a					09 31								10 01										10 31	
Elmstead Woods	d			09 23												09 53						10 23			
Chislehurst	d			09 26												09 56						10 26			
Petts Wood 4	d		09 24	09 30			09 39						09 54			10 00	10 09			10 22	10 24	10 30			
Orpington 4	a	09 26	09 27	09 33	09 39		09 42			09 53			09 57			10 03	10 12			10 26	10 27	10 33	10 39		
	d	09 26		09 33	09 40					09 54										10 26		10 33	10 40		
Chelsfield 3	d			09 36																		10 36			
Knockholt	d			09 39																		10 39			
Dunton Green	d			09 44																		10 44			
Sevenoaks 4	a	09 36		09 47	09 50					10 04		10 15								10 36		10 47	10 50		
	d	09 36			09 51					10 04		10 16								10 36			10 51		
Hildenborough	d	09 42								10 11										10 43					
Tonbridge 4	a	09 47			09 59					10 15	10 52	10 24			10 30					10 47			10 59		11 02

For general notes see front of timetable
For details of catering facilities see Directory of Train Operators

A To Dover Priory (Table 207)
B To Ramsgate (Table 207)
C To Margate (Table 207)
D To Ramsgate (Table 207) and to Margate (Table 207)
E To Ashford International (Table 207)

Table 204

Saturdays

London → Grove Park, Bromley North, Orpington, Sevenoaks and Tonbridge

Network Diagram - see first page of Table 200

		SE	SE	SE 1 A	SN 1	SE 1 🛒	SE	SE	SE 1 🛒	SE	SE			SE	SE 1 A	SE	SE	SE 1 🛒	SE	SE 1 🛒	SE	SE	SE 1	SN 1
London Charing Cross [4]	⊖ d		10 26	10 30	10 40	10 45			10 53					17 56	18 00			18 15		18 23		18 26	18 30	18 40
London Waterloo (East) [4]	⊖ d		10 29	10 33	10 43	10 48			10 56					17 59	18 03			18 18		18 26		18 29	18 33	18 43
London Cannon Street [4]	⊖ d																							
London Bridge [4]	⊖ d		10 34	10 38	10 48	10 53						and at		18 04	18 08			18 23				18 34	18 38	18 48
New Cross [4]	⊖ d											the same												
St Johns	d											minutes												
Lewisham [4]	d		10 43									past		18 13								18 44		
Hither Green [4]	d		10 47							←		each		18 17			←					18 48		
Grove Park [4]	d		10 51					10 56		10 51		hour until		18 21			18 21		18 26			18 52		
Sundridge Park	d		→					10 59						→					18 29			→		
Bromley North	a							11 01											18 31					
Elmstead Woods	d									10 53							18 23							
Chislehurst	d									10 56							18 26							
Petts Wood [4]	d	10 39					10 54			11 00	11 09				18 22	18 24	18 30				18 39			
Orpington [4]	a	10 42		10 53			10 57			11 03	11 12				18 26	18 27	18 33	18 40			18 42		18 54	
	d			10 54											18 26		18 33	18 40					18 54	
Chelsfield [3]	d																18 36							
Knockholt	d																18 39							
Dunton Green	d																18 44							
Sevenoaks [4]	a			11 04		11 15									18 36		18 47	18 50					19 04	
	d			11 04		11 16									18 36			18 51					19 04	
Hildenborough	d			11 11											18 43									
Tonbridge [4]	a			11 15	11 52	11 24			11 30						18 47			18 59		19 02			19 13	19 52

		SE 1 🛒	SE	SE		SE	SE	SE	SE 1 B 🛒	SE	SE	SE 1	SE	SE	SE	SE 1 🛒	SE		SE	SE 1	SE	SE	SE	SE 1 B 🛒	SE
London Charing Cross [4]	⊖ d	18 45						18 56	19 00			19 15			19 26	19 30				19 45			19 56	20 00	
London Waterloo (East) [4]	⊖ d	18 48						18 59	19 03			19 18			19 29	19 33				19 48			19 59	20 03	
London Cannon Street [4]	⊖ d																								
London Bridge [4]	⊖ d	18 53						19 04	19 08			19 23			19 34	19 38				19 53			20 04	20 08	
New Cross [4]	⊖ d																								
St Johns	d																								
Lewisham [4]	d							19 14							19 43								20 13		
Hither Green [4]	d					←		19 18			←				19 47				←				20 17		
Grove Park [4]	d			18 56		18 52		19 22			19 22		19 26		19 51				19 51		19 56		20 21		
Sundridge Park	d			18 59				→					19 29		→						19 59		→		
Bromley North	a			19 01									19 31								20 01				
Elmstead Woods	d					18 55					19 24								19 53						
Chislehurst	d					18 57					19 27								19 56						
Petts Wood [4]	d		18 54			19 00	19 09			19 24	19 30			19 39			19 54		20 00			20 09			20 24
Orpington [4]	a		18 57			19 03	19 12		19 24	19 27	19 33	19 40		19 42		19 54	19 57		20 03	20 10		20 12		20 24	20 27
	d								19 24		19 33	19 40				19 54				20 10				20 24	
Chelsfield [3]	d										19 36														
Knockholt	d										19 39														
Dunton Green	d										19 44														
Sevenoaks [4]	a	19 16							19 34		19 47	19 51				20 04				20 20				20 34	
	d	19 17							19 34			19 51				20 04				20 20				20 34	
Hildenborough	d								19 40															20 40	
Tonbridge [4]	a	19 25							19 45			19 59				20 13				20 28				20 45	

		SE	SE	SE	SE 1	SE	SE	SE 1		SE	SE	SE 1 B	SE	SE	SE	SE	SE 1	SE	SE	SE 1	SE		SE	SE 1 B	SE
London Charing Cross [4]	⊖ d			20 26	20 30			20 45			20 56	21 00				21 26	21 30			21 45			21 56	22 00	
London Waterloo (East) [4]	⊖ d			20 29	20 33			20 48			20 59	21 03				21 29	21 33			21 48			21 59	22 03	
London Cannon Street [4]	⊖ d																								
London Bridge [4]	⊖ d			20 34	20 38			20 53			21 04	21 08				21 34	21 38			21 53			22 04	22 08	
New Cross [4]	⊖ d																								
St Johns	d																								
Lewisham [4]	d			20 43							21 13					21 43							22 13		
Hither Green [4]	d	←		20 47			←				21 17			←		21 47			←				22 17		
Grove Park [4]	d	20 21	20 26	20 51			20 51			20 56	21 21			21 21	21 26	21 51			21 51		21 56		22 21		
Sundridge Park	d		20 29	→						20 59	→				21 29	→					21 59		→		
Bromley North	a		20 31							21 01					21 31						22 01				
Elmstead Woods	d	20 23					20 53							21 23					21 53						
Chislehurst	d	20 26					20 56							21 26					21 56						
Petts Wood [4]	d	20 30				20 54	21 00						21 24	21 30				21 54	22 00						22 24
Orpington [4]	a	20 33			20 54	20 57	21 03	21 10				21 24	21 27	21 33			21 54	21 57	22 03	22 10				22 24	22 27
	d	20 33			20 54			21 10				21 24		21 33			21 54			22 10				22 24	
Chelsfield [3]	d	20 36												21 36										22 28	
Knockholt	d	20 39												21 39											
Dunton Green	d	20 44												21 44											
Sevenoaks [4]	a	20 47			21 04			21 20				21 34		21 47			22 04			22 20				22 36	
	d				21 04			21 20				21 34					22 04			22 20				22 36	
Hildenborough	d											21 40												22 42	
Tonbridge [4]	a				21 13			21 28				21 45					22 13			22 28				22 47	

For general notes see front of timetable
For details of catering facilities see
Directory of Train Operators

A To Ashford International (Table 207)
B To Ramsgate (Table 207)

Table 204

London → Grove Park, Bromley North, Orpington, Sevenoaks and Tonbridge

Saturdays

Network Diagram - see first page of Table 200

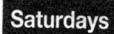

		SE	SE	SE	SE 1	SE	SE	SE 1	SE	SE	SE	SE 1 A		SE	SE	SE	SE	SE	SE 1 A	SE	SE	SE
London Charing Cross 4	⊖ d			22 26	22 30			22 45			22 56	23 00						23 26	23 30			
London Waterloo (East) 4	⊖ d			22 29	22 33			22 48			22 59	23 03						23 29	23 33			
London Cannon Street 4	⊖ d																					
London Bridge 4	⊖ d			22 34	22 38			22 53			23 04	23 08						23 34	23 38			
New Cross 4	⊖ d																					
St Johns	d																					
Lewisham 4	d			22 43							23 13							23 43				
Hither Green 4	d		←	22 47			←				23 17				←			23 47			←	
Grove Park 4	d	22 26	22 21	22 51			22 51		22 56		23 21				23 21	23 26		23 51			23 51	23 56
Sundridge Park	d	22 29		→					22 59		→					23 29		→				23 59
Bromley North	a	22 31							23 01							23 31						00 01
Elmstead Woods	d		22 23				22 53								23 23						23 53	
Chislehurst	d		22 26				22 56								23 26						23 56	
Petts Wood 4	d		22 30			22 54	23 00			23 20				23 24	23 30		23 50			23 54	00 01	
Orpington 4	a		22 33		22 54	22 57	23 03	23 10		23 23		23 24		23 27	23 33		23 53		23 54	23 57	00 03	
	d				22 54			23 10				23 24							23 54			
Chelsfield 3	d											23 28										
Knockholt	d																					
Dunton Green	d																					
Sevenoaks 4	a				23 04			23 20				23 36							00 04			
	d				23 04			23 20				23 36							00 04			
Hildenborough	d											23 42							00 10			
Tonbridge 4	a				23 13			23 28				23 46							00 15			

Sundays

		SE	SE 1 A	SE	SE	SE		SE 1	SE	SE	SE	SE		SE	SE 1	SE	SE	SE 1 B		SE	SE	SE	SE 1	SE	SE
London Charing Cross 4	⊖ d	23p26	23p30					00 10		00 48				07 56	08 14		08 26	08 30				08 56	09 00		
London Waterloo (East) 4	⊖ d	23p29	23p33					00 13		00 51				07 59	08 17		08 29	08 33				08 59	09 03		
London Cannon Street 4	⊖ d																								
London Bridge 4	⊖ d	23p34	23p38					00 18		00 56	07 35			08 05	08 22		08 35	08 38				09 05	09 08		
New Cross 4	⊖ d									01 01															
St Johns	d																								
Lewisham 4	d	23p43								01 05	07 45			08 15			08 45					09 15			
Hither Green 4	d	23p47		←						01 09	07 49			08 19			08 49				←	09 19			←
Grove Park 4	d	23p51		23p51				00 29	00 34	01 13	07 53			08 23			08 53				08 53	09 23			09 23
Sundridge Park	d	→							00 37								→					→			
Bromley North	a								00 39																
Elmstead Woods	d			23p53				00 32		01 16	07 55			08 25							08 55				09 25
Chislehurst	d			23p56				00 35		01 19	07 58			08 28							08 58				09 28
Petts Wood 4	d			00 01	00 20	00 26		00 39		01 23	08 01	08 24		08 31						08 54	09 01			09 24	09 31
Orpington 4	a		23p54	00 03	00 23	00 29		00 42		01 26	08 04	08 27		08 34	08 38	←		08 54		08 57	09 04		09 24	09 27	09 34
	d		23p54					00 42						08 42 →	08 38	08 42		08 54					09 24		09 42 →
Chelsfield 3	d							00 46								08 45									
Knockholt	d															08 48									
Dunton Green	d															08 53									
Sevenoaks 4	a		00 04					00 54							08 48	08 56		09 04					09 34		
	d		00 04					00 54							08 48			09 04					09 34		
Hildenborough	d		00 10					01 00										09 10							
Tonbridge 4	a		00 15					01 05							08 56			09 15					09 43		

		SE 1		SE		SE	SE 1 C	SE	SE	SE 1	SE	SE 1	SE	SE	SE 1	SE			SE	SE 1 D	SE	SE	SE 1	SE
London Charing Cross 4	⊖ d	09 14				09 26	09 30			09 44	09 56	10 00			10 14		and at the same minutes past each hour until		19 26	19 30			19 44	19 56
London Waterloo (East) 4	⊖ d	09 17				09 29	09 33			09 47	09 59	10 03			10 17				19 29	19 33			19 47	19 59
London Cannon Street 4	⊖ d																							
London Bridge 4	⊖ d	09 22				09 35	09 38			09 52	10 05	10 08			10 22				19 35	19 38			19 52	20 05
New Cross 4	⊖ d																							
St Johns	d																							
Lewisham 4	d					09 45					10 15								19 45					20 15
Hither Green 4	d					09 49			←		10 19			←					19 49			←		20 19
Grove Park 4	d					09 53			09 53		10 23			10 23					19 53			19 53		20 23
Sundridge Park	d					→					→								→					→
Bromley North	a																							
Elmstead Woods	d								09 55					10 26								19 55		
Chislehurst	d								09 58					10 28								19 58		
Petts Wood 4	d							09 54	10 01				10 24	10 31							19 54	20 01		
Orpington 4	a	09 38		←			09 54	09 57	10 04	10 08		10 24	10 27	10 35	10 38	←				19 54	19 57	20 04	20 08	
	d	09 38		09 42			09 54			10 08		10 24		10 42 →	10 38	10 42				19 54			20 08	
Chelsfield 3	d			09 45												10 45								
Knockholt	d			09 48												10 48								
Dunton Green	d			09 53												10 53								
Sevenoaks 4	a	09 48		09 56			10 04			10 18		10 34			10 48	10 56				20 04			20 18	
	d	09 48					10 04			10 18		10 34			10 48					20 04			20 18	
Hildenborough	d						10 10													20 10				
Tonbridge 4	a	09 56					10 15			10 26		10 43			10 56					20 15			20 26	

For general notes see front of timetable
For details of catering facilities see Directory of Train Operators

A To Dover Priory (Table 207)
B To Margate (Table 207) and to Ramsgate (Table 207)
C To Margate (Table 207)
D To Ramsgate (Table 207)

Table 204

Sundays

London → Grove Park, Bromley North, Orpington, Sevenoaks and Tonbridge

Network Diagram - see first page of Table 200

		SE 1		SE	SE	SE 1 A	SE	SE 1 B		SE	SE	SE	SE 1	SE		SE	SE 1 A	SE	SE 1 B	SE		SE	SE	SE 1	SE
London Charing Cross 4	⊖ d	20 00				20 14	20 26	20 30				20 56	21 00				21 14	21 26	21 30				21 56	22 00	
London Waterloo (East) 4	⊖ d	20 03				20 17	20 29	20 33				20 59	21 03				21 17	21 29	21 33				21 59	22 03	
London Cannon Street 4	⊖ d																								
London Bridge 4	⊖ d	20 08				20 22	20 35	20 38				21 05	21 08				21 22	21 35	21 38				22 05	22 08	
New Cross 4	⊖ d																								
St Johns	d																								
Lewisham 4	d						20 45					21 15						21 45					22 15		
Hither Green 4	d				←		20 49				←	21 19				←		21 49				←	22 19		
Grove Park 4	d				20 23		20 53				20 53	21 23				21 23		21 53				21 53	22 23		
Sundridge Park	d						→					→						→					→		
Bromley North	a																								
Elmstead Woods	d				20 25						20 55					21 25						21 55			
Chislehurst	d				20 28						20 58					21 28						21 58			
Petts Wood 4	d			20 24	20 31					20 54	21 01			21 24		21 31				21 54		22 01			22 24
Orpington 4	a	20 24		20 27	20 34	20 38		20 54		20 57	21 04		21 24	21 27		21 34	21 38		21 54	21 57		22 04		22 24	22 27
	d	20 24				20 38		20 54					21 24				21 38		21 54					22 24	
Chelsfield 3	d					20 42											21 42								
Knockholt	d																								
Dunton Green	d																								
Sevenoaks 4	a	20 34				20 50		21 04					21 34				21 50		22 04					22 34	
	d	20 34				20 50		21 04					21 34				21 50		22 04					22 34	
Hildenborough	d							21 10											22 10						
Tonbridge 4	a	20 43				20 58		21 15					21 43				21 58		22 15					22 43	

		SE	SE 1 A	SE		SE 1 C	SE	SE	SE	SE		SE	SE 1 A	SE	SE	SE 1		SE	SE	SE					
London Charing Cross 4	⊖ d		22 14	22 26		22 30						22 56	23 14		23 26	23 30				23 56					
London Waterloo (East) 4	⊖ d		22 17	22 29		22 33						22 59	23 17		23 29	23 33				23 59					
London Cannon Street 4	⊖ d																								
London Bridge 4	⊖ d		22 22	22 35		22 38						23 05	23 22		23 35	23 38				00 05					
New Cross 4	⊖ d																								
St Johns	d																								
Lewisham 4	d			22 45								23 15			23 45					00 15					
Hither Green 4	d	←		22 49				←				23 19			23 49				←	00 19					
Grove Park 4	d	22 23		22 53				22 53				23 23			23 53				23 53	00 23					
Sundridge Park	d			→											→										
Bromley North	a																								
Elmstead Woods	d	22 25						22 55				23 25							23 55	00 25					
Chislehurst	d	22 28						22 58				23 28							23 58	00 28					
Petts Wood 4	d	22 31					22 54	23 01	23 14	23 24		23 31		23 44				23 54	00 01	00 31					
Orpington 4	a	22 34	22 38			22 54	22 57	23 04	23 17	23 27		23 35	23 38	23 47		23 54		23 57	00 04	00 34					
	d		22 38			22 54							23 38			23 54									
Chelsfield 3	d		22 42										23 42												
Knockholt	d																								
Dunton Green	d																								
Sevenoaks 4	a		22 50			23 04							23 50			00 04									
	d		22 50			23 04							23 50			00 04									
Hildenborough	d					23 10																			
Tonbridge 4	a		22 58			23 15							23 58			00 13									

For general notes see front of timetable
For details of catering facilities see Directory of Train Operators

A To Hastings (Table 206)
B To Ramsgate (Table 207)
C To Dover Priory (Table 207)

For details of Bank Holiday service alterations please see first page of Table 195

Tonbridge, Sevenoaks, Orpington Bromley North, Grove Park → London

Network Diagram - see first page of Table 200

Miles	Miles			SE MX 01	SE	SE	SE [1] A	SE	SE	SE [1]	SE [1]	SE	SE	SE	SE	SE	SE [1]	SE [1]	SE	SE	SE	SE	SE	SE [1]	SE
0	—	**Tonbridge** [4]	d		04 56		05 26			05 55	06 02				06 05		06 18	06 30						06 45	
2½	—	Hildenborough	d		05 00		05 31			06 00							06 22							06 49	
7½	—	**Sevenoaks** [4]	a		05 08		05 38			06 07	06 12				06 15		06 30	06 39						06 57	
—	—		d		05 09		05 39			06 07	06 13				06 16		06 30	06 40					06 44	06 58	
1½	—	Dunton Green	d												06 18								06 46		
5½	—	Knockholt	d												06 24								06 52		
6¾	—	Chelsfield [3]	d		05 17		05 47								06 27								06 55		
8¼	—	**Orpington** [4]	a		05 20		05 50			06 16					06 30								06 58		
—	—		d		05 20	05 25	05 50	05 50	06 00	06 17		06 20		06 24	06 31				06 44		06 49	06 57	06 59		
9¼	—	Petts Wood [4]	d		05 23	05a28		05a53	06 03			06a23		06 27					06a47		06 52	07 00			
10¾	—	Chislehurst	d		05 26				06 06					06 30		←					06 57	07 04			←
11¾	—	Elmstead Woods	d		05 28				06 08					06 32		06 32					06 59	07 06			07 06
—	0	**Bromley North**	d	00 06									06 26	→						06 52		→			
—	½	Sundridge Park	d	00 08									06 28							06 54					
13	1¾	**Grove Park** [4]	d	00a11	05 31				06 11				06a31			06 35				06a57	07 02				07 09
14¾	—	Hither Green [4]	d		05 35				06 15							06 39					07 06				07 14
16	—	**Lewisham** [4]	d						06 20							06 44									
16½	—	St Johns	a																						
17¼	—	New Cross [4]	⊖ a		05 40				06 24																07 19
20¼	—	**London Bridge** [4]	⊖ a		05 46		06 06		06 30	06 35	06 36				06 48	06 53	06 55	07 03					07 15	07 21	07 25
—	—	**London Cannon Street** [4]	⊖ a							06b43					06b55								07c22		07c32
21¼	—	**London Waterloo (East)** [4]	⊖ a		05 51		06 11		06 35		06 41					06 58	07 00	07 08			07 24			07 27	
22	—	**London Charing Cross** [4]	⊖ a		05b56		06 14		06 38		06b48					07b03	07c06	07c15			07c29			07c33	

		SE	SE	SE	SE	SE [1]	SE	SE	SE	SE	SE	SE [1] A	SE [1]	SE [1]	SE	SE	SE	SE	SE	SE [1] A	SE [1]	SE	SE [1]	SE	SE
Tonbridge [4]	d					06 53						07 06	07 16	07 25						07 31	07 36		07 42		
Hildenborough	d											07 10	07 20							07 36	07 40				
Sevenoaks [4]	a					07 03						07 18	07 28	07 35						07 43	07 48		07 52		
	d					07 03					07 13	07 19	07 29	07 35				07 38		07 44	07 49		07 53		
Dunton Green	d										07 16							07 40							
Knockholt	d										07 22							07 46							
Chelsfield [3]	d										07 25	07 28						07 49		07 53					
Orpington [4]	a					07 12					07 28							07 52							
	d	07 02	07 06		07 10	07 13		07 23	07 27		07 30					07 36	07 50	07 53						07 56	08 00
Petts Wood [4]	d	07a05	07a09		07 13			07a26	07a30		07 33				←	07 39	07a53	07 56				←		07 59	08 03
Chislehurst	d				07 17		←				07 37				07 37	07 43		07 59				07 59		08 03	08 07
Elmstead Woods	d				07 19		07 19				→				07 39	07 45		→				08 01		08 05	08 09
Bromley North	d			07 13	→					07 33									07 54						
Sundridge Park	d			07 15						07 35									07 56						
Grove Park [4]	d			07a18			07 22			07a38					07 42	07 48			07a59			08 04		08 08	08 12
Hither Green [4]	d						07 26								07 46										08 16
Lewisham [4]	d																								
St Johns	a																								
New Cross [4]	⊖ a																								
London Bridge [4]	⊖ a					07 29	07 36					07 50	07 54		07 58	08 01				08 10	08 14	08 16			08 26
London Cannon Street [4]	⊖ a					07c37							08c01		08 04						08c21	08c24			
London Waterloo (East) [4]	⊖ a						07 42					07 55		08 04		08 07				08 15			08 21	08 25	08 31
London Charing Cross [4]	⊖ a						07c47					07 59		08 09		08c13				08 21			08c27	08c31	08c37

		SE	SE	SE [1] A	SE [1]	SE [1]	SE	SE	SE	SE	SE	SE	SE [1] A	SE [1]	SE [1]	SE	SE	SE	SE	SE [1] A	SE [1]	SE	SE	SE	SE [1] B
Tonbridge [4]	d			07 51	07 58	08 02							08 11	08 17	08 25					08 36	08 46				09 00
Hildenborough	d			07 56									08 16	08 21						08 41					
Sevenoaks [4]	a			08 03	08 08	08 12							08 23	08 29						08 48	08 56				09 09
	d		07 58	08 04	08 09	08 13					08 18		08 24	08 30						08 49	08 57			09 00	09 10
Dunton Green	d		08 00								08 20									08 52					
Knockholt	d		08 06								08 26									08 58					
Chelsfield [3]	d		08 09	08 13							08 29		08 33							09 01				09 08	
Orpington [4]	a		08 12								08 32													09 11	
	d	08 10	08 13						08 20	08 30	08 33						08 38		08 53			09 00	09 08	09 12	
Petts Wood [4]	d	08a13	08 16					←	08 23	08a33	08 36					←	08 41		08a56			09 03	09a11	09 15	
Chislehurst	d		08 19					08 19	08 27		08 39					08 39	08 44					09 07		09 19	
Elmstead Woods	d		→					08 21	08 29		→					08 41	08 46					09 09		→	
Bromley North	d						08 15					08 35						08 55							
Sundridge Park	d						08 17					08 37						08 57							
Grove Park [4]	d						08a20	08 24	08 32			08a40				08 44	08 50	09a00				09 12			
Hither Green [4]	d								08 36													09 16			
Lewisham [4]	d																								
St Johns	a																								
New Cross [4]	⊖ a															08 52									
London Bridge [4]	⊖ a			08 30	08 34			08 36					08 50	08 54		08 58				09 18	09 22	09 25			09 33
London Cannon Street [4]	⊖ a				08c42			08b45						09c02		09c04					09 28				
London Waterloo (East) [4]	⊖ a			08 35		08 41			08 49				08 55		09 01		09 06			09 23		09 31			09 38
London Charing Cross [4]	⊖ a			08 41		08 47			08c55				09 01		09 07		09b13			09 29		09c36			09 44

For general notes see front of timetable
For details of catering facilities see Directory of Train Operators

A From Tunbridge Wells (Table 206)
B From 12 October from Ore (Table 189) and from Ashford International
b Until 9 October Arr. 2 minutes earlier
c Until 9 October Arr. 1 minute earlier

For details of Bank Holiday service alterations please see first page of Table 195

Tonbridge, Sevenoaks, Orpington Bromley North, Grove Park → London

Network Diagram - see first page of Table 200

	SE	SE	SE	SE	SE [1] A 🛒	SE [1]	SE	SE	SE	SE	SE [1]	SN [1]	SE [1] 🛒	SE [1] 🛒	SE	SE	SE	SE	SE [1] B	SE	SE [1]	SE [1] 🛒	SE	SE
Tonbridge [4] d					09 14	09 24					09 28	09 19	09 46	09 58					10 04		10 18	10 28		
Hildenborough d					09 18						09 32								10 08					
Sevenoaks [4] a					09 26	09 34					09 39		09 55						10 15		10 27			
d				09 18	09 26	09 34					09 40		09 56						10 16	10 18	10 28			
Dunton Green d				09 20							09 43									10 20				
Knockholt d				09 26							09 49									10 26				
Chelsfield [3] d				09 29							09 52									10 29				
Orpington [4] a				09 32	09 35						09 55								10 25	10 32				
d			09 23	09 33	09 36			09 38		09 53	09 55					10 05	10 08	10 23	10 25	10 35				←
Petts Wood [4] d		←	09a26	09 36				09a41		09a56	09 59					10 08	10a11	10a26	10 29	10 38 →				10 38
Chislehurst d		09 19		09 39					←							10 11								10 41
Elmstead Woods d		09 21		09 41 →					09 41							10 13								10 43
Bromley North d	09 15						09 35								10 05								10 35	
Sundridge Park d	09 17						09 37								10 07								10 37	
Grove Park [4] d	09a20	09 24					09a40		09 44						10a10	10 16							10a40	10 46
Hither Green [4] d		09 28							09 48							10 20								10 50
Lewisham [4] d		09 33							09 54							10 25								10 55
St Johns a																								
New Cross [4] ⊖ a																								
London Bridge [4] ⊖ a		09 41			09 51	09 57			10 04		10 13	10 22	10 24			10 34			10 43		10 54			11 04
London Cannon Street [4] ⊖ a		09b49																						
London Waterloo (East) [4] ⊖ a					09 58	10 03			10 09		10 18	10 27	10 29	10 32		10 39			10 48		10 59	11 02		11 09
London Charing Cross [4] ⊖ a					10 01	10b09			10 12		10 22	10 30	10 33	10 36		10 44			10 51		11 03	11 06		11 14

	SE	SE	SE		SE [1] C	SN [1]	SE [1] 🛒	SE [1] 🛒	SE	SE	SE	SE [1] C	SE	SE [1]	SE [1] 🛒	SE	SE	SE	SE	SE		SE [1] C	SN [1]
Tonbridge [4] d					10 36	10 19	10 46	10 58				11 04		11 18	11 28							14 36	14 19
Hildenborough d					10 39							11 08										14 40	
Sevenoaks [4] a					10 48		10 55					11 15		11 27							and at	14 47	
d					10 48		10 56					11 16	11 18	11 28								14 48	
Dunton Green d													11 20								the same		
Knockholt d													11 26										
Chelsfield [3] d													11 29								minutes		
Orpington [4] a					10 57		11 05					11 25	11 32									14 57	
d	10 38	10 53			10 57		11 05		11 05	11 08	11 23	11 25	11 35				←	11 38	11 53		past	14 57	
Petts Wood [4] d	10a41	10a56							11 08	11a11	11a26	11 29	11 38 →				11 38	11a41	11a56				
Chislehurst d									11 11								11 41				each		
Elmstead Woods d									11 13								11 43						
Bromley North d			11 05													11 35				12 05	hour until		
Sundridge Park d			11 07													11 37				12 07			
Grove Park [4] d			11a10						11 16							11a40	11 46			12a10			
Hither Green [4] d									11 20								11 50						
Lewisham [4] d									11 25								11 55						
St Johns a																							
New Cross [4] ⊖ a																							
London Bridge [4] ⊖ a					11 13	11 22	11 24		11 34			11 43		11 54			12 04					15 13	15 22
London Cannon Street [4] ⊖ a																							
London Waterloo (East) [4] ⊖ a					11 18	11 26	11 29	11 32	11 39			11 48		11 59	12 02		12 09					15 18	15 27
London Charing Cross [4] ⊖ a					11 21	11 30	11 33	11 36	11 44			11 51		12 03	12 06		12 14					15 21	15 30

	SE [1] 🛒	SE [1] 🛒	SE	SE	SE	SE [1] C	SE	SE [1]	SE [1] 🛒	SE	SE	SE	SE	SE	SE [1] C	SE	SE [1] A	SE [1] 🛒	SE	SE	SE	SE	SE	SE [1] A
Tonbridge [4] d	14 46	14 58				15 04		15 18	15 28						15 36		15 46	15 54						16 06
Hildenborough d						15 08									15 40									16 10
Sevenoaks [4] a	14 55					15 15		15 27							15 48		15 55	16 03						16 18
d	14 56					15 16	15 18	15 28							15 48		15 56	16 04						16 18
Dunton Green d							15 20																	16 20
Knockholt d							15 26																	16 26
Chelsfield [3] d							15 29										16 04							16 29
Orpington [4] a	15 05					15 25	15 32								15 57		16 07							16 34
d	15 05		15 05	15 08	15 23	15 25	15 35				←	15 38	15 53		15 57	16 05	16 07		16 08		16 20	16 33		16 34
Petts Wood [4] d			15 08	15a11	15a26	15 29	15 38 →				15 38	15a41	15a56			16 08			16a11		16 23	16 36		
Chislehurst d			15 11								15 41					16 11				←	16 26	16 39		
Elmstead Woods d			15 13								15 43					16 13 →				16 13	16 28	16 41 →		
Bromley North d										15 35				16 05									16 35	
Sundridge Park d										15 37				16 07									16 37	
Grove Park [4] d			15 16							15a40	15 46			16a10						16 16	16 31		16a40	
Hither Green [4] d			15 20								15 50									16 20	16 36			
Lewisham [4] d			15 25								15 55									16c28				
St Johns a																								
New Cross [4] ⊖ a																								
London Bridge [4] ⊖ a	15 24		15 34			15 43		15 54			16 04				16 13		16 24	16 29		16 37	16 45			16 52
London Cannon Street [4] ⊖ a																								
London Waterloo (East) [4] ⊖ a	15 29	15 32	15 40			15 48		15 59	16 02		16 09				16 18		16 29	16 34		16 43	16 51			16 57
London Charing Cross [4] ⊖ a	15 33	15 36	15 44			15 51		16 03	16 06		16 13				16 21		16 33	16 38		16 47	16 55			17 01

For general notes see front of timetable
For details of catering facilities see Directory of Train Operators

A From Hastings (Table 206)
B From Tunbridge Wells (Table 206)
C From Ashford International (Table 207)
b Until 9 October Arr. 2 minutes earlier
c Arr. 1624

For details of Bank Holiday service alterations please see first page of Table 195

Tonbridge, Sevenoaks, Orpington Bromley North, Grove Park → London

Network Diagram - see first page of Table 200

Station		SE	SE ■1	SE	SE	SE ■1 A	SE	SE	SE	SE ■1 B	SE	SE	SE ■1 C 🛒	SE	SE	SE	SE ■1	SE	SE	SE	SE ■1 D 🛒	SE	SE	SE ■1 🛒	SE
Tonbridge 4	d		16 23			16 28				16 40			16 51				17 06				17 18			17 40	
Hildenborough	d									16 44			16 55								17 22				
Sevenoaks 4	a		16 32			16 37				16 52			17 03				17 15				17 30			17 50	
	d		16 33			16 38		16 42		16 52			17 03				17 16		17 20		17 30			17 50	
Dunton Green	d							16 44											17 22						
Knockholt	d							16 50											17 28						
Chelsfield 3	d					16 46		16 52											17 30						
Orpington 4	a					16 49		16 55		17 02			17 12				17 26		17 33		17 39			17 59	
	d	16 36				16 50	16 52	16 56		17 02	17 04	17 07	17 13			17 25	17 26		17 34	17 36	17 40		17 51	18 00	18 06
Petts Wood 4	d	16a39					16 55				17a07	17 10				17 28			17 37	17a39			17 54		18a09
Chislehurst	d			←			16 58		←			17 13		←		17 31		←					17 57		
Elmstead Woods	d			16 41			17 00		17 00			17 15		17 15		17 33		17 33					17 59		
Bromley North	d				16 56		→					→			17 25	→						17 45			
Sundridge Park	d				16 58										17 27							17 47			
Grove Park 4	d			16 44	17a01				17 03					17 18	17a30			17 36				17a50	18 02		
Hither Green 4	d			16 52					17 09					17 23				17 40					18 06		
Lewisham 4	d																								
St Johns	a																								
New Cross 4 ⊖	a																								
London Bridge 4 ⊖	a		17 00	17 02		17 09		17 13	17 18	17 26			17 31	17 35			17 44	17 49	17 51					18 19	
London Cannon Street 4 ⊖	a									17 31															
London Waterloo (East) 4 ⊖	a		17 05	17 07		17 14		17 17	17 23				17 36	17 40			17 50	17 54	17 57		18 03		18 19	18 26	
London Charing Cross 4 ⊖	a		17 10	17 13		17 19		17 24	17 28				17 41	17 46			17 55	17 57	18 01		18 07		18 23	18 30	

Station		SE	SE	SE	SE ■1 E	SE	SE	SE ■1 G	SE ■1 🛒	SE	SE	SE ■1	SE	SE	SE ■1	SE	SE	SE ■1 H	SE ■1	SE	SE ■1 🛒	SE	SE	SE	SE
Tonbridge 4	d				17 50			18 06	18 16			18 20			18 36			18 46	18 54		19 11				
Hildenborough	d				17 54			18 10										18 50							
Sevenoaks 4	a				18 02			18 18	18 25			18 29			18 46			18 58	19 04						
	d	17 54			18 02			18 18	18 26			18 30			18 46	18 50		18 58	19 05						19 22
Dunton Green	d	17 56						18 21								18 52									
Knockholt	d	18 02						18 26								18 58									
Chelsfield 3	d	18 05						18 29								19 01									19 30
Orpington 4	a	18 08			18 11			18 32	18 35			18 39			18 55	19 04		19 07	19 14						19 33
	d	18 08		18 11	18 12			18 33	18 36	18 36	18 39	18 40			18 56	19 05	19 08	19 08	19 14				19 23		19 35
Petts Wood 4	d			18 14						18a39	18 42					19 08	19a11						19a26		19 38
Chislehurst	d			18 17		←					18 45		←			19 11				←					19 41
Elmstead Woods	d			18 19		18 19					18 47		18 47			19 13				19 13					19 43
Bromley North	d		18 11	→			18 30				→			18 52		→						19 12		19 32	→
Sundridge Park	d		18 13				18 32							18 54								19 14		19 34	
Grove Park 4	d		18a16			18 22	18a35						18 50	18a57						19 16		19a17		19a37	
Hither Green 4	d					18 26							18 54							19 20					
Lewisham 4	d																			19b28					
St Johns	a																								
New Cross 4 ⊖	a																								
London Bridge 4 ⊖	a	18 25			18 28	18 35		18 49	18 51			18 57	19 05		19 12			19 25	19 33	19 36					
London Cannon Street 4 ⊖	a							18 53																	
London Waterloo (East) 4 ⊖	a	18 30			18 33	18 40			18 56			19 02	19 10		19 17			19 31	19 38	19 41	19 46				
London Charing Cross 4 ⊖	a	18 37			18 37	18 45			19 00			19 07	19 14		19 21			19 35	19 42	19 45	19 50				

Station		SE ■1 A	SE	SE	SE	SE ■1 🛒	SE	SE	SE ■1	SE	SE	SE	SE ■1 🛒	SE	SE ■1 G	SE	SE	SE	SE ■1	SE	SE ■1	SE	SE	SE	SE ■1
Tonbridge 4	d	19 16				19 30			19 48				20 00		20 16				20 31		20 48				21 00
Hildenborough	d	19 20													20 20										
Sevenoaks 4	a	19 28				19 39			19 57				20 09		20 28				20 40		20 57				21 09
	d	19 28				19 40		19 50	19 58				20 10	20 22	20 28				20 40		20 58				21 10
Dunton Green	d							19 52																	
Knockholt	d							19 58																	
Chelsfield 3	d							20 01						20 30											
Orpington 4	a	19 37				19 49		20 04	20 07				20 19	20 33	20 37				20 49		21 07				21 19
	d	19 38	19 38			19 50	19 53	20 05	20 08	20 08			20 20	20 35	20 38	20 38			20 50	21 05	21 08	21 08			21 20
Petts Wood 4	d		19a41				19a56	20 08		20a11				20 38		20a41				21 08		21a11			
Chislehurst	d			←				20 11			←			20 41			←			21 11			←		
Elmstead Woods	d			19 43				20 13			20 13			20 43			20 43			21 13			21 13		
Bromley North	d				20 05			→				20 35		→				21 05		→				21 35	
Sundridge Park	d				20 07							20 37						21 07						21 37	
Grove Park 4	d			19 46	20a10						20 16	20a40					20 46	21a10					21 16	21a40	
Hither Green 4	d			19 50							20 20						20 50						21 20		
Lewisham 4	d			19c57							20e27						20f57						21g27		
St Johns	a																								
New Cross 4 ⊖	a																								
London Bridge 4 ⊖	a	19 55		20 06		20 08			20 25		20 36		20 38		20 55		21 06		21 08		21 25		21 36		21 38
London Cannon Street 4 ⊖	a																								
London Waterloo (East) 4 ⊖	a	20 00		20 11		20 13			20 30		20 41		20 43		21 00		21 11		21 13		21 30		21 41		21 43
London Charing Cross 4 ⊖	a	20 04		20 15		20 18			20 34		20 45		20 48		21 04		21 15		21 18		21 34		21 45		21 48

For general notes see front of timetable
For details of catering facilities see Directory of Train Operators

- A From Hastings (Table 206)
- B From Ashford International (Table 207)
- C From Dover Priory (Table 207) and from Ramsgate (Table 207)
- D From Ramsgate (Table 207) and from Margate (Table 207)
- E From Ramsgate (Table 207) and from Ramsgate (Table 207)
- G From Tunbridge Wells (Table 206)
- H From Ramsgate (Table 207)
- b Arr. 1924
- c Arr. 1954
- e Arr. 2024
- f Arr. 2054
- g Arr. 2124

For details of Bank Holiday service alterations please see first page of Table 195

Tonbridge, Sevenoaks, Orpington Bromley North, Grove Park → London

Network Diagram - see first page of Table 200

Mondays to Fridays

Station		SE	SE 1 A	SE	SE	SE	SE 1	SE	SE 1	SE	SE	SE	SE 1	SE	SE 1 A	SE	SE	SE	SE 1	SE 1	SE	SE	SE 1 B	SE
Tonbridge 4	d		21 16				21 30		21 48				22 00		22 16				22 30	22 42			23 10	
Hildenborough	d		21 20												22 20								23 14	
Sevenoaks 4	a		21 28				21 39		21 57				22 09		22 28				22 39	22 51			23 22	
	d	21 22	21 28				21 40		21 58				22 10	22 22	22 28				22 40	22 52			23 22	
Dunton Green	d																							
Knockholt	d																							
Chelsfield 3	d	21 30												22 30									23 30	
Orpington 4	a	21 33	21 37				21 49		22 07				22 19	22 33	22 37				22 49	23 01			23 33	
	d	21 35	21 38	21 38			21 50	22 05	22 08	22 08			22 20	22 35	22 38	22 38			22 50	23 02	23 05	23 08	23 34	
Petts Wood 4	d	21 38		21a41				22 08		22a11				22 38		22a41					23 08	23a11		
Chislehurst	d	21 41			←			22 11			←			22 41			←				23 11			
Elmstead Woods	d	21 43 →			21 43			22 13 →			22 13			22 43 →			22 43				23 13			
Bromley North	d					22 05						22 35						23 05						23 35
Sundridge Park	d					22 07						22 37						23 07						23 37
Grove Park 4	d				21 46	22a10					22 16	22a40					22 46	23a10			23 16			23a40
Hither Green 4	d				21 50						22 20						22 50				23 20			
Lewisham 4	d				21b57						22c27						22e57				23f27			
St Johns	a																							
New Cross 4	a																							
London Bridge 4	a		21 55		22 06		22 08		22 25		22 36		22 38		22 55		23 06		23 08	23 19	23 35		23 51	
London Cannon Street 4	a																							
London Waterloo (East) 4	a		22 00		22 11		22 13		22 30		22 41		22 43		23 00		23 11		23 13	23 24	23 40		23 56	
London Charing Cross 4	a		22 04		22 15		22 18		22 34		22 45		22 48		23 04		23 15		23 18	23 28	23 44		00 01	

Saturdays

Station		SE	SE	SE	SE	SE	SE 1 C	SE	SE		SN 1	SE	SE	SE	SE 1	SE	SE	SE 1 C		SE	SE 1	SE	SE	SE	SE
Tonbridge 4	d						06 00				06 19				06 46			06 59			07 16				
Hildenborough	d						06 04											07 03							
Sevenoaks 4	a						06 12								06 56			07 11			07 26				
	d		05 22				06 12		06 22						06 57			07 11		07 18	07 26				
Dunton Green	d																			07 20					
Knockholt	d																			07 26					
Chelsfield 3	d		05 29						06 29											07 29					
Orpington 4	a		05 32				06 21		06 32						07 07			07 20		07 32	07 35				
	d		05 35	05 54	06 05	06 08	06 21		06 35			06 38		07 05	07 08	07 08		07 20		07 35	07 35		07 38		
Petts Wood 4	d		05 38	05a57	06 08	06a11			06 38			06a41		07 08		07a11				07 38			07a41		
Chislehurst	d		05 41		06 11				06 41					07 11			←			07 41				←	
Elmstead Woods	d		05 43		06 13				06 43					07 13 →			07 13			07 43 →				07 43	
Bromley North	d	00 06						06 35					07 05									07 35			08 05
Sundridge Park	d	00 08						06 37					07 07									07 37			08 07
Grove Park 4	d	00a11	05 46		06 16			06a40	06 46				07a10				07 16					07a40		07 46	08a10
Hither Green 4	d		05 50		06 20				06 50								07 20							07 49	
Lewisham 4	d		05g57		06h27				06j57								07k27							07 55	
St Johns	a																								
New Cross 4	a																								
London Bridge 4	a		06 05		06 35		06 40		07 05		07 24				07 26		07 35	07 40			07 54			08 05	
London Cannon Street 4	a																								
London Waterloo (East) 4	a		06 10		06 40		06 44		07 10		07 28				07 31		07 40	07 44			07 59			08 09	
London Charing Cross 4	a		06 13		06 43		06 48		07 13		07 32				07 34		07 43	07 48			08 05			08 14	

Station		SE 1 D	SN 1	SE 1	SE		SE	SE 1	SE	SE	SE 1	SE	SE	SE		SE	SE	SE 1 D	SN 1	SE 1	SE 1	SE	SE		SE
Tonbridge 4	d	07 31	07 19	07 46				08 00			08 16							08 31	08 19	08 46	08 58				
Hildenborough	d	07 36																08 36							
Sevenoaks 4	a	07 43		07 55				08 09			08 26							08 43		08 55					
	d	07 44		07 56				08 10		08 18	08 26							08 44		08 56					
Dunton Green	d									08 20															
Knockholt	d									08 26															
Chelsfield 3	d									08 29															
Orpington 4	a	07 53		08 05				08 19		08 32	08 35							08 53		09 05					
	d	07 53		08 05	08 05		08 08	08 20	08 23	08 35	08 35		08 38			08 53		08 53		09 05		09 05	09 08		09 23
Petts Wood 4	d				08 08		08a11		08a26	08 38			08a41			08a56						09 08	09a11		09a26
Chislehurst	d				08 11					08 41				←								09 11			
Elmstead Woods	d				08 13					08 43 →				08 43								09 13			
Bromley North	d											08 35					09 05								
Sundridge Park	d											08 37					09 07								
Grove Park 4	d				08 16							08a40		08 46			09a10					09 16			
Hither Green 4	d				08 19									08 49								09 19			
Lewisham 4	d				08 25									08 55								09 25			
St Johns	a																								
New Cross 4	a																								
London Bridge 4	a	08 10	08 22	08 24	08 35			08 40			08 54			09 05				09 10	09 22	09 24		09 34			
London Cannon Street 4	a																								
London Waterloo (East) 4	a	08 14	08 26	08 29	08 39			08 45			08 59			09 09				09 15	09 26	09 29	09 32	09 39			
London Charing Cross 4	a	08 18	08 30	08 33	08 44			08 48			09 03			09 14				09 18	09 30	09 33	09 36	09 44			

For general notes see front of timetable
For details of catering facilities see Directory of Train Operators

A From Tunbridge Wells (Table 206)
B From Ramsgate (Table 207)
C From Dover Priory (Table 207)
D From Ramsgate (Table 207) and from Ramsgate (Table 207)
b Arr. 2154
c Arr. 2224
e Arr. 2254
f Arr. 2324
g Arr. 0554
h Arr. 0624
j Arr. 0654
k Arr. 0724

Table 204

Saturdays

Tonbridge, Sevenoaks, Orpington Bromley North, Grove Park → London

Network Diagram - see first page of Table 200

		SE 1 A	SE	SE 1 🛒	SE 1 🛒	SE	SE	SE	SE		SE	SE 1 A	SN 1		SE 1 🛒	SE 1 🛒	SE	SE	SE	SE 1 A	SE	SE 1 🛒	SE 1 🛒	SE	SE
Tonbridge [4]	d	09 04		09 17	09 28							09 37	09 19		09 46	09 58				10 04		10 18	10 28		
Hildenborough	d	09 08										09 41								10 08					
Sevenoaks [4]	a	09 15		09 27								09 48			09 55					10 15		10 28			
	d	09 16	09 18	09 27								09 48			09 56					10 16	10 18	10 28			
Dunton Green	d		09 20																		10 20				
Knockholt	d		09 26																		10 26				
Chelsfield [3]	d		09 29																		10 29				
Orpington [4]	a	09 25	09 32	09 36								09 57			10 05					10 25	10 32				
	d	09 26	09 35	09 36			09 38		09 53			09 57			10 05		10 05	10 08	10 23	10 26	10 35				←
Petts Wood [4]	d	09 29	09 38				09a41		09a56								10 08	10a11	10a26	10 29	10 38				10 38
Chislehurst	d		09 41					←									10 11				→				10 41
Elmstead Woods	d		09 43					09 43									10 13								10 43
Bromley North	d		→			09 35					10 05													10 35	
Sundridge Park	d					09 37					10 07													10 37	
Grove Park [4]	d					09a40		09 46			10a10						10 16							10a40	10 46
Hither Green [4]	d							09 50									10 19								10 50
Lewisham [4]	d							09 55									10 25								10 55
St Johns	a																								
New Cross [4]	⊖ a																								
London Bridge [4]	⊖ a	09 43		09 54				10 04				10 13	10 22		10 24		10 34			10 43		10 54			11 04
London Cannon Street [4]	⊖ a																								
London Waterloo (East) [4]	⊖ a	09 48		09 59	10 02			10 09				10 18	10 26		10 29	10 32	10 39			10 48		10 59	11 02		11 09
London Charing Cross [4]	⊖ a	09 51		10 03	10 06			10 14				10 21	10 30		10 33	10 36	10 44			10 51		11 03	11 06		11 14

		SE	SE	SE	SE 1 A	SN 1			SE 1 🛒	SE 1 🛒	SE	SE	SE	SE 1 A	SE	SE 1 🛒		SE 1 🛒	SE	SE	SE	SE	SE	SE 1 A
Tonbridge [4]	d				10 36	10 19			16 46	16 58				17 04		17 18		17 28						17 36
Hildenborough	d				10 40									17 08										17 40
Sevenoaks [4]	a				10 47				16 55					17 15		17 27								17 47
	d				10 48				16 56					17 16	17 18	17 28								17 48
Dunton Green	d														17 20									
Knockholt	d						and at the same minutes past each hour until								17 26									
Chelsfield [3]	d														17 29									
Orpington [4]	a				10 57				17 05					17 25	17 32									17 57
	d	10 38	10 53		10 57				17 05		17 05	17 08	17 23	17 26	17 35					←	17 38	17 53		17 57
Petts Wood [4]	d	10a41	10a56								17 08	17a11	17a26	17 29	17 38					17 38	17a41	17a56		
Chislehurst	d										17 11				→					17 41				
Elmstead Woods	d										17 13									17 43				
Bromley North	d			11 05															17 35				18 05	
Sundridge Park	d			11 07															17 37				18 07	
Grove Park [4]	d			11a10							17 16								17a40	17 46			18a10	
Hither Green [4]	d										17 19									17 50				
Lewisham [4]	d										17 25									17 55				
St Johns	a																							
New Cross [4]	⊖ a																							
London Bridge [4]	⊖ a				11 13	11 22			17 24		17 34			17 43		17 54				18 04				18 13
London Cannon Street [4]	⊖ a																							
London Waterloo (East) [4]	⊖ a				11 18	11 26			17 29	17 32	17 39			17 48		17 59		18 02		18 09				18 18
London Charing Cross [4]	⊖ a				11 21	11 30			17 33	17 36	17 44			17 51		18 03		18 06		18 14				18 21

		SN 1	SE	SE 1 🛒		SE	SE 1 B 🛒	SE	SE	SE	SE	SE 1	SE		SE	SE	SE 1 C 🛒	SN 1	SE	SE	SE 1	SE		SE	SE
Tonbridge [4]	d	17 19		17 46			17 48					18 17					18 30	18 19			18 46				
Hildenborough	d						17 53										18 34								
Sevenoaks [4]	a			17 55			18 00					18 26					18 42				18 56				
	d			17 56			18 01				18 18	18 27					18 42				18 57				
Dunton Green	d										18 20														
Knockholt	d										18 26														
Chelsfield [3]	d										18 29														
Orpington [4]	a			18 05			18 10				18 32	18 36					18 51				19 07				
	d		18 05	18 05		18 08	18 11		18 23		18 35	18 36	18 38				18 51		18 53	19 05	19 08	19 08			
Petts Wood [4]	d		18 08			18a11			18a26		18 38		18a41						18a56	19 08		19a11			
Chislehurst	d		18 11					←			18 41				←					19 11				←	
Elmstead Woods	d		18 13					18 13			18 43				18 43					19 13				19 13	
Bromley North	d		→							18 35	→					19 05				→					19 35
Sundridge Park	d									18 37						19 07									19 37
Grove Park [4]	d							18 16		18a40					18 46	19a10								19 16	19a40
Hither Green [4]	d							18 19							18 49									19 20	
Lewisham [4]	d							18 26							18 55									19b27	
St Johns	a																								
New Cross [4]	⊖ a																								
London Bridge [4]	⊖ a	18 22		18 24			18 28	18 35				18 54			19 06		19 08	19 23			19 26			19 36	
London Cannon Street [4]	⊖ a																								
London Waterloo (East) [4]	⊖ a	18 26		18 29			18 32	18 41				19 00			19 11		19 14	19 28			19 30			19 41	
London Charing Cross [4]	⊖ a	18 30		18 33			18 36	18 45				19 06			19 15		19 19	19 31			19 34			19 45	

For general notes see front of timetable
For details of catering facilities see Directory of Train Operators

A From Ashford International (Table 207)
B From Ramsgate (Table 207) and from Ramsgate (Table 207)
C From Ramsgate (Table 207)
b Arr. 1924

Table 204

Tonbridge, Sevenoaks, Orpington
Bromley North, Grove Park → London

Network Diagram - see first page of Table 200

Station		SE 1	SE	SE	SE	SE	SE 1 A	SE	SE		SE 1	SE	SE	SE	SE 1	SE	SE	SE		SE 1 A	SE	SE 1	SE	SE	SE
Tonbridge 4	d	19 00					19 30				19 46				20 00					20 30		20 46			
Hildenborough	d						19 34													20 34					
Sevenoaks 4	a	19 09					19 42				19 56				20 09					20 42		20 56			
	d	19 10		19 18			19 42				19 57				20 10	20 18				20 42		20 57			
Dunton Green	d			19 20												20 20									
Knockholt	d			19 26												20 26									
Chelsfield 3	d			19 29												20 29									
Orpington 4	a	19 19		19 32			19 51				20 07				20 19	20 32				20 51		21 07			
	d	19 20	19 23	19 35	19 38		19 51	19 53	20 05		20 08	20 08			20 20	20 35	20 38			20 51	21 05	21 08	21 08		
Petts Wood 4	d		19a26	19 38	19a41			19a56	20 08			20a11				20 38	20a41				21 08		21a11		
Chislehurst	d			19 41					20 11							20 41					21 11				
Elmstead Woods	d			19 43					20 13 →				← 20 13			20 43					21 13 →			← 21 13	
Bromley North	d					20 05								20 35				21 05							21 35
Sundridge Park	d					20 07								20 37				21 07							21 37
Grove Park 4	d			19 46		20a10							20 16	20a40		20 46		21a10						21 16	21a40
Hither Green 4	d			19 50									20 20			20 50								21 20	
Lewisham 4	d			19b57									20c27			20e57								21f27	
St Johns	a																								
New Cross 4	⊖ a																								
London Bridge 4	⊖ a	19 38		20 06			20 08				20 26		20 36		20 38	21 06				21 08		21 25		21 36	
London Cannon Street 4	⊖ a																								
London Waterloo (East) 4	⊖ a	19 44		20 11			20 14				20 30		20 41		20 44	21 11				21 14		21 30		21 41	
London Charing Cross 4	⊖ a	19 49		20 15			20 19				20 34		20 45		20 49	21 15				21 19		21 34		21 45	

Station		SE 1	SE	SE	SE		SE 1 A	SE	SE 1	SE	SE	SE	SE 1	SE		SE	SE	SE 1 B	SE	SE	SE	SE 1 A		
Tonbridge 4	d	21 00					21 30		21 46				22 00					22 30				23 13		
Hildenborough	d						21 34											22 34				23 18		
Sevenoaks 4	a	21 09					21 42		21 56				22 09					22 42				23 25		
	d	21 10	21 22				21 42		21 57				22 10	22 22				22 42				23 26		
Dunton Green	d																							
Knockholt	d																					23 34		
Chelsfield 3	d		21 29											22 29								23 37		
Orpington 4	a	21 19	21 32				21 51		22 07				22 19	22 32				22 51				23 37		
	d	21 20	21 35	21 38			21 51	22 05	22 08	22 08			22 20	22 35		22 38		22 51	23 05	23 08				
Petts Wood 4	d		21 38	21a41				22 08		22a11				22 38		22a41			23 08	23a11				
Chislehurst	d		21 41					22 11						22 41					23 11					
Elmstead Woods	d		21 43					22 13 →			← 22 13			22 43					23 13					
Bromley North	d				22 05							22 35					23 05				23 35			
Sundridge Park	d				22 07							22 37					23 07				23 37			
Grove Park 4	d		21 46		22a10						22 16	22a40		22 46			23a10		23 16		23a40			
Hither Green 4	d		21 50								22 20			22 50					23 20					
Lewisham 4	d		21g57								22h27			22j57					23k27					
St Johns	a																							
New Cross 4	⊖ a																							
London Bridge 4	⊖ a	21 38	22 06				22 08		22 25		22 36		22 38	23 06				23 08	23 35			23 53		
London Cannon Street 4	⊖ a																							
London Waterloo (East) 4	⊖ a	21 44	22 11				22 14		22 30		22 41		22 44	23 11				23 13	23 40			23 57		
London Charing Cross 4	⊖ a	21 49	22 15				22 19		22 34		22 45		22 49	23 15				23 18	23 43			00 01		

Sundays

Station		SE	SE	SE	SE	SE	SE 1	SE	SE	SE 1 C	SE	SE		SE	SE	SE 1 C	SE	SE	SE 1	SE	SE 1	SE	SE	SE 1	SE
Tonbridge 4	d						07 01			07 17						08 00			08 19		08 33			08 49	
Hildenborough	d						07 05			07 21						08 04									
Sevenoaks 4	a						07 13			07 29						08 12			08 28		08 43			08 58	
	d						07 14			07 29						08 12	08 17		08 29		08 44			08 59	
Dunton Green	d																08 19								
Knockholt	d																08 25								
Chelsfield 3	d									07 37						08 20	08 27								
Orpington 4	a						07 23			07 40						08 23	08 30		08 38		08 53			09 08	
	d		06 44	07 01	07 08	07 14	07 24	07 31	07 38	07 41		07 44		08 01	08 08	08 24	08 31	08 38	08 39		08 54	09 01	09 08	09 09	
Petts Wood 4	d		06a47	07 04	07a11	07a17		07 34	07a41			07a47		08 04	08a11		08 34	08a41				09 04	09a11		
Chislehurst	d			07 07				07 37						08 07			08 37					09 07			
Elmstead Woods	d			07 09				07 39 →			← 07 39			08 09			08 39 →			← 08 39		09 09 →			← 09 09
Bromley North	d	00 05																							
Sundridge Park	d	00 07																							
Grove Park 4	d	00a10		07 12							07 42			08 12						08 42					09 12
Hither Green 4	d			07 15							07 45			08 15						08 45					09 15
Lewisham 4	d			07 20							07 50			08 20						08 50					09 20
St Johns	a																								
New Cross 4	⊖ a																								
London Bridge 4	⊖ a			07 29			07 39			07 56	07 59			08 28		08 39			08 56	08 58	09 09			09 26	09 28
London Cannon Street 4	⊖ a																								
London Waterloo (East) 4	⊖ a			07 34			07 44			08 01	08 03			08 33		08 44			09 01	09 03	09 14			09 31	09 33
London Charing Cross 4	⊖ a			07 38			07 48			08 05	08 09			08 37		08 48			09 05	09 07	09 18			09 35	09 37

For general notes see front of timetable
For details of catering facilities see Directory of Train Operators

A From Ramsgate (Table 207)

B From Ramsgate (Table 207) and from Ramsgate (Table 207)

C From Ashford International (Table 207)

b Arr. 1954

c Arr. 2024

e Arr. 2054

f Arr. 2124

g Arr. 2154

h Arr. 2224

j Arr. 2254

k Arr. 2324

Table 204

Sundays

Tonbridge, Sevenoaks, Orpington Bromley North, Grove Park → London

Network Diagram - see first page of Table 200

		SE 1 A		SE	SE	SE 1	SE	SE 1	SE	SE	SE 1	SE	SE 1 B	SE		SE	SE 1	SE	SE 1	SE	SE	SE 1	SE		
Tonbridge 4	d	09 01				09 19		09 33			09 49		10 01				10 20		10 33			10 49			
Hildenborough	d	09 05											10 05												
Sevenoaks 4	a	09 13				09 28		09 43			09 58		10 13				10 29		10 43			10 58			
	d	09 14		09 17		09 29		09 44			09 59		10 14	10 17			10 30		10 44			10 59			
Dunton Green	d			09 19										10 19											
Knockholt	d			09 25										10 25											
Chelsfield 3	d			09 27										10 27											
Orpington 4	a	09 23		09 30		09 38		09 53			10 08		10 23	10 30			10 39		10 53			11 08			
	d	09 24		09 31	09 38	09 39		09 54	10 01	10 08	10 09		10 24	10 31		10 38	10 39		10 54	11 01	11 08	11 09			
Petts Wood 4	d			09 34	09a41				10 04	10a11				10 34		10a41				11 04	11a11				
Chislehurst	d			09 37			←		10 07			←		10 37				←		11 07			←		
Elmstead Woods	d			09 39			09 39		10 09			10 09		10 39				10 39		11 09			11 09		
Bromley North	d			↪					↪					↪						↪					
Sundridge Park	d																								
Grove Park 4	d						09 42					10 12						10 42					11 12		
Hither Green 4	d						09 45					10 15						10 45					11 15		
Lewisham 4	d						09 50					10 20						10 50					11 20		
St Johns	a																								
New Cross 4	⊖ a																								
London Bridge 4	⊖ a	09 39				09 56	09 58	10 09			10 26	10 28	10 39				10 56	10 58	11 09			11 26	11 28		
London Cannon Street 4	⊖ a																								
London Waterloo (East) 4	⊖ a	09 44				10 01	10 03	10 14			10 31	10 33	10 44				11 01	11 03	11 14			11 31	11 33		
London Charing Cross 4	⊖ a	09 48				10 05	10 07	10 18			10 35	10 37	10 48				11 06	11 07	11 18			11 35	11 37		

			SE 1 B	SE	SE	SE 1	SE	SE 1	SE	SE	SE 1	SE			SE 1 B	SE	SE	SE 1 C	SE	SE 1	SE	SE	SE 1 B	SE
Tonbridge 4	d		11 01			11 20		11 33			11 49				19 01			19 19		19 33			20 01	
Hildenborough	d		11 05												19 05								20 05	
Sevenoaks 4	a		11 13			11 29		11 43			11 58				19 13			19 28		19 43			20 13	
	d		11 14	11 17		11 30		11 44			11 59				19 14	19 17		19 29		19 44			20 14	20 17
Dunton Green	d			11 19												19 19								20 19
Knockholt	d			11 25												19 25								20 25
Chelsfield 3	d			11 27												19 27		19 37						20 27
Orpington 4	a		11 23	11 30		11 39		11 53			12 08		and at the same minutes past each hour until		19 23	19 30		19 40		19 53			20 23	20 30
	d		11 24	11 31	11 38	11 39		11 54	12 01	12 08	12 09				19 24	19 31	19 38	19 40		19 54	20 01	20 08	20 24	20 31
Petts Wood 4	d			11 34	11a41				12 04	12a11						19 34	19a41				20 04	20a11		20 34
Chislehurst	d			11 37			←		12 07			←				19 37			←		20 07			20 37
Elmstead Woods	d			11 39			11 39		12 09			12 09				19 39			19 39		20 09			20 39
Bromley North	d			↪					↪							↪								↪
Sundridge Park	d																							
Grove Park 4	d						11 42					12 12							19 42		20 12			
Hither Green 4	d						11 45					12 15							19 45		20 15			
Lewisham 4	d						11 50					12 20							19 50		20 20			
St Johns	a																							
New Cross 4	⊖ a																							
London Bridge 4	⊖ a		11 39			11 56	11 58	12 09			12 26	12 28			19 39			19 56	19 58	20 09	20 28		20 39	
London Cannon Street 4	⊖ a																							
London Waterloo (East) 4	⊖ a		11 44			12 01	12 03	12 14			12 31	12 33			19 44			20 01	20 03	20 14	20 33		20 44	
London Charing Cross 4	⊖ a		11 48			12 06	12 07	12 18			12 35	12 37			19 48			20 05	20 07	20 18	20 37		20 48	

		SE	SE 1 C	SE		SE 1	SE	SE	SE 1 B	SE	SE	SE 1 C	SE	SE 1	SE	SE		SE 1 B	SE	SE	SE 1 C	SE	SE 1 D	SE	SE
Tonbridge 4	d		20 19			20 33			21 02			21 19		21 33				22 02			22 19		22 31		
Hildenborough	d								21 07									22 07					22 35		
Sevenoaks 4	a		20 28			20 43			21 14			21 28		21 43				22 14			22 28		22 43		
	d		20 29			20 44			21 15			21 29		21 44				22 15			22 29		22 44		
Dunton Green	d																								
Knockholt	d																								
Chelsfield 3	d		20 37									21 37									22 37				
Orpington 4	a		20 40			20 53			21 24			21 40		21 53				22 24			22 40		22 53		
	d	20 38	20 40			20 54	21 01	21 08	21 24	21 31	21 38	21 40		21 54	22 01	22 08		22 24	22 31	22 38	22 40		22 54	23 01	23 14
Petts Wood 4	d	20a41					21 04	21a11		21 34	21a41				22 04	22a11			22 34	22a41				23 04	23a17
Chislehurst	d			←			21 07			21 37			←		22 07				22 37			←		23 07	
Elmstead Woods	d			20 39			21 09			21 39			21 39		22 09				22 39			22 39		23 09	
Bromley North	d									↪									↪						
Sundridge Park	d																								
Grove Park 4	d			20 42			21 12						21 42		22 12							22 42		23 12	
Hither Green 4	d			20 45			21 15						21 45		22 15							22 45		23 15	
Lewisham 4	d			20 50			21 20						21 50		22 20							22 50		23 20	
St Johns	a																								
New Cross 4	⊖ a																								
London Bridge 4	⊖ a		20 56	20 58		21 09	21 28		21 40			21 56	21 58	22 09	22 28			22 40			22 56	22 58	23 09	23 28	
London Cannon Street 4	⊖ a																								
London Waterloo (East) 4	⊖ a		21 01	21 03		21 14	21 33		21 44			22 01	22 03	22 14	22 33			22 44			23 01	23 03	23 14	23 33	
London Charing Cross 4	⊖ a		21 05	21 07		21 18	21 37		21 48			22 05	22 07	22 18	22 37			22 48			23 05	23 07	23 19	23 37	

For general notes see front of timetable
For details of catering facilities see Directory of Train Operators

A From Ramsgate (Table 207)
B From Margate (Table 207)
C From Hastings (Table 206)
D From Ramsgate (Table 207) and from Ramsgate (Table 207)

Network Diagram for Tables 206, 207, 208

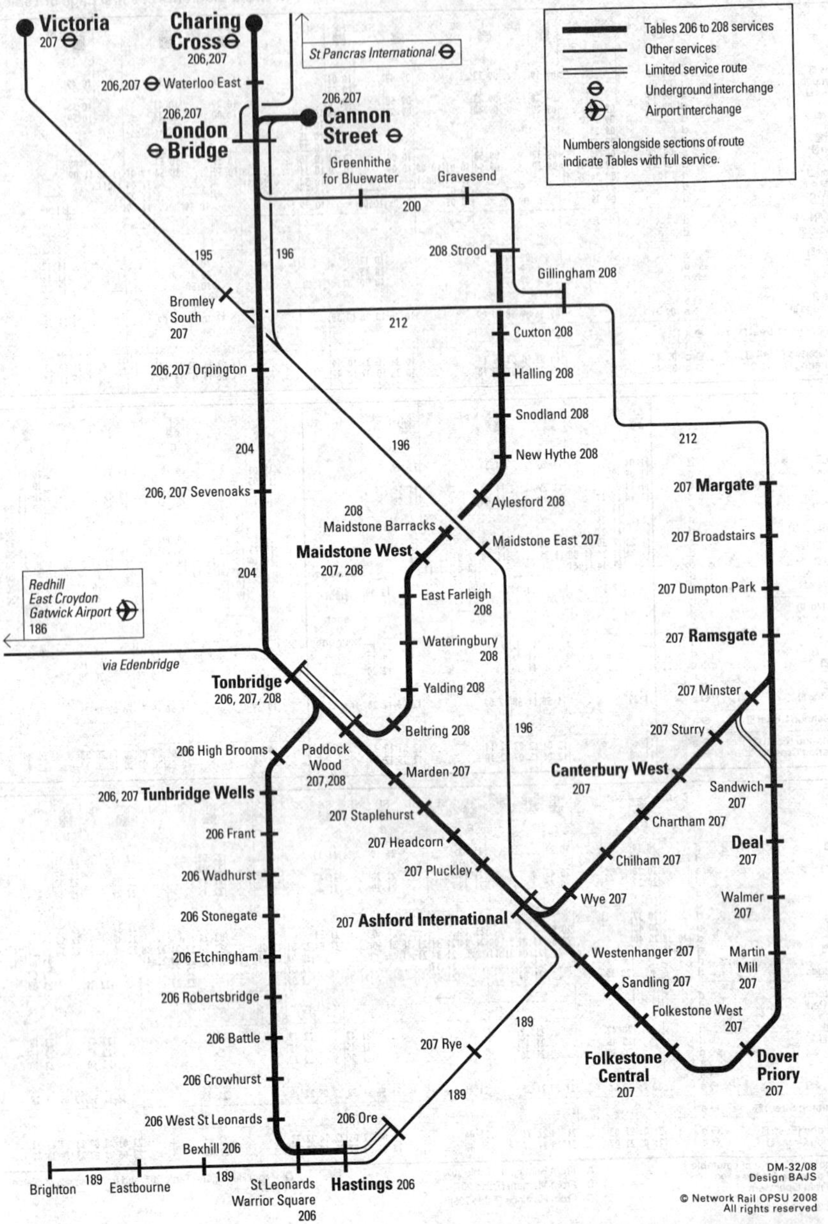

Victoria 207
Charing Cross 206,207
St Pancras International
206,207 Waterloo East
206,207 Cannon Street
206,207 London Bridge
Greenhithe for Bluewater
Gravesend
200
195
196
208 Strood
Gillingham 208
Bromley South 207
212
Cuxton 208
206,207 Orpington
Halling 208
Snodland 208
204
196
New Hythe 208
212
206, 207 Sevenoaks
Aylesford 208
207 Margate
208 Maidstone Barracks
Maidstone East 207
Maidstone West 207, 208
207 Broadstairs
204
East Farleigh 208
207 Dumpton Park
Redhill
East Croydon
Gatwick Airport
186
Wateringbury 208
207 Ramsgate
via Edenbridge
Tonbridge 206, 207, 208
Yalding 208
207 Minster
Beltring 208
196
207 Sturry
206 High Brooms
Paddock Wood 207,208
Marden 207
Canterbury West 207
206, 207 Tunbridge Wells
Sandwich 207
207 Staplehurst
Chartham 207
206 Frant
207 Headcorn
Deal 207
206 Wadhurst
207 Pluckley
Chilham 207
Wye 207
Walmer 207
206 Stonegate
207 Ashford International
206 Etchingham
Westenhanger 207
Martin Mill 207
Sandling 207
206 Robertsbridge
Folkestone West 207
189
206 Battle
207 Rye
Folkestone Central 207
Dover Priory 207
206 Crowhurst
189
206 West St Leonards
206 Ore
Bexhill 206
Brighton
189
Eastbourne
189
St Leonards Warrior Square 206
Hastings 206
Tables 206 to 208 services
Other services
Limited service route
Underground interchange
Airport interchange
Numbers alongside sections of route indicate Tables with full service.
DM-32/08
Design BAJS

For details of Bank Holiday service alterations please see first page of Table 195

London and Tonbridge → Tunbridge Wells and Hastings

Network Diagram - see first page of Table 206

Miles	Station		SE MX [1]	SE MO [1]	SE MX [1]		SE MX [1]	SE [1]	SE [1]		SE [1]	SE [1]	SE [1]		SE [1]	SE [1]	SE [1]		SE [1]	SE [1]	SE [1]		SE [1] 🛒		SE [1] 🛒
0	London Charing Cross [4]	⊖ d	22p45	23p14	23p15		23p37								06 16		07 00		07 16	07 28			08 14		
3/4	London Waterloo (East) [4]	⊖ d	22p48	23p17	23p18		23p40								06 19		07 03		07 19	07 31			08 17		
—	London Cannon Street [4]	⊖ d																			07 45				08 45
1 3/4	London Bridge [4]	⊖ d	22p53	23p22	23p23		23p45								06 24		07 08		07 24	07 36	07 49		08 23		08 49
13 3/4	Orpington [4]	d	23p10	23p38	23p40										06 54		07 26		07 41	07 55	08 09				09 08
22	Sevenoaks [4]	d	23p20	23p50	23p52		00 10								07 08		07 36		07 51	08 05	08 24		08 47		09 18
29 1/2	Tonbridge [4]	a	23p28	23p58	00 01		00 20								07 19		07 44		08 01	08 15	08 32		08 55		09 28
—		d	23p29	23p59	00 01		00 21	05 00	05 28		06 10	06 24	06 44		07 21	07 32	07 54		08 10	08 19	08 33		08 57		09 29
33	High Brooms	d	23p35	00 05	00 07		00 27	05 06	05 34		06 16	06 30	06 50		07 27	07 37	08 00		08 15	08 25	08 41		09 03		09 35
34 1/2	Tunbridge Wells [4]	a	23p39	00 09	00 11		00 31	05 09	05 37		06 20	06 33	06 54		07 30	07 41	08 06		08 19	08 29	08 45		09 09		09 39
—		d	23p40	00 09			00 32				06 24		06 54			07 42				08 30	08 50		09 15	09 45	09 50
36 3/4	Frant	d	23p44	00 14			00 36				06 28		06 59			07 46					08 54				09 54
39 1/4	Wadhurst	d	23p49	00 18			00 41				06 33		07 03			07 51				08 37	08 59		09 22	09 52	10 00
43 1/4	Stonegate	d	23p55	00 24			00 47				06 39		07 09			07 57					09 05				10 06
47 1/2	Etchingham	d	23p59	00 29			00 52				06 44		07 14			08 02					09 10				10 11
49 1/4	Robertsbridge	d	00 04	00 33			00 56				06 48		07b22			08 06					09 14				10 15
55 1/2	Battle	d	00 11	00 41			01 03				06 55		07 29			08 13				08 53	09 21		09 39	10 09	10 22
57 1/2	Crowhurst	d	00 15	00 45			01 07				06 59		07 33			08 17					09 25				10 26
60 3/4	West St Leonards	d	00 20	00 50			01 12				07 04		07 38			08 22					09 30				10 32
61 3/4	St Leonards Warrior Sq [4]	d	00 23	00 53			01 15				07 07		07 41			08 25				09 03	09 33		09 53	10 19	10 35
—	Bexhill [4]	a									07 21		08 24			09 01				09 22	10 01		10 21	10 35	
62 1/2	Hastings [4]	a	00 27	00 56			01 19				07 11		07 45			08 29				09 07	09 37		09 57	10 23	10 38
63 1/2	Ore	a									07 18														

Station		SE [1] 🛒	SE [1]		SE [1] 🛒	SE [1]	SE [1] 🛒		SE [1]	SE [1] 🛒	SE [1]		SE [1] 🛒	SE [1]	SE [1] 🛒		SE [1]	SE [1] 🛒	SE [1]		SE [1] 🛒	SE [1]	SE [1] 🛒		SE [1]
London Charing Cross [4]	⊖ d				09 45		10 15			10 45			11 15		11 45			12 15			12 45		13 15		
London Waterloo (East) [4]	⊖ d				09 48		10 18			10 48			11 18		11 48			12 18			12 48		13 18		
London Cannon Street [4]	⊖ d	09 17																							
London Bridge [4]	⊖ d	09 21			09 53		10 23			10 53			11 23		11 53			12 23			12 53		13 23		
Orpington [4]	d	09 40					10 40						11 40					12 40					13 40		
Sevenoaks [4]	d	09 50			10 16		10 50			11 16			11 50		12 16			12 50			13 16		13 50		
Tonbridge [4]	a	09 59			10 24		10 59			11 24			11 59		12 24			12 59			13 24		13 59		
	d	10 02	10 09		10 25	10 38	10 59		11 09	11 25	11 38		11 59	12 09	12 25		12 38	12 59	13 09		13 25	13 38	13 59		14 09
High Brooms	d	10 08	10 15		10 31	10 44	11 07		11 15	11 31	11 44		12 07	12 15	12 31		12 44	13 07	13 15		13 31	13 44	14 07		14 15
Tunbridge Wells [4]	a	10 12	10 19		10 36	10 48	11 11		11 19	11 35	11 48		12 11	12 19	12 35		12 48	13 11	13 19		13 35	13 48	14 11		14 19
	d	10 15			10 40		11 16			11 40			12 12		12 40			13 12			13 40		14 12		
Frant	d	10 19					11 20						12 16					13 16					14 16		
Wadhurst	d	10 26			10 47		11 26			11 47			12 21		12 47			13 21			13 47		14 21		
Stonegate	d	10 32					11 32						12 27					13 27					14 27		
Etchingham	d	10 37					11 37						12 32					13 32					14 32		
Robertsbridge	d	10 41					11 41						12 36					13 36					14 36		
Battle	d	10 48			11 03		11 48			12 03			12 43		13 03			13 43			14 03		14 43		
Crowhurst	d	10 52					11 52						12 47					13 47					14 47		
West St Leonards	d	10 57					11 57						12 52					13 52					14 52		
St Leonards Warrior Sq [4]	d	11 00			11 13		12 00			12 13			12 55		13 13			13 55			14 13		14 55		
Bexhill [4]	a	11 21			11 35		12 21			12 35			13 21		13 35			14 21			14 35		15 21		
Hastings [4]	a	11 04			11 17		12 04			12 17			12 59		13 17			13 59			14 17		14 59		
Ore	a																								

Station		SE [1] 🛒	SE [1]	SE [1] 🛒		SE [1]	SE [1] 🛒	SE		SE [1] 🛒	SE [1]	SE [1] 🛒		SE [1] 🛒	SE	SE [1]		SE [1]	SE [1]	SE [1]			SE [1] 🛒	SE [1]	SE [1]
London Charing Cross [4]	⊖ d	13 45		14 15			14 45			15 15		15 45		16 15		16 50			17 16	17 20				17 41	18 00
London Waterloo (East) [4]	⊖ d	13 48		14 18			14 48			15 18		15 48		16 18		16 53			17 19	17 23				17 44	18 03
London Cannon Street [4]	⊖ d																	17 00					17 38		
London Bridge [4]	⊖ d	13 53		14 23			14 53			15 23		15 53		16 23		16 58		17 04		17 28				17 49	
Orpington [4]	d			14 40						15 40															
Sevenoaks [4]	d	14 16		14 50			15 16			15 50		16 20		16 50		17 22		17 28		17 56				18 16	
Tonbridge [4]	a	14 24		14 59			15 24			15 59		16 28		16 58		17 32		17 38		18 06				18 27	
	d	14 25	14 38	14 59		15 09	15 25	15 46		15 59	16 13	16 29		16 59	17 09	17 33		17 39		18 07				18 28	
High Brooms	d	14 31	14 44	15 07		15 15	15 31	15 52		16 05	16 19	16 35		17 05	17 15	17 39		17 45	17 59	18 13			18 19	18 34	18 43
Tunbridge Wells [4]	a	14 35	14 48	15 11		15 19	15 35	15 56		16 09	16 23	16 39		17 09	17 19	17 44		17 49	18 03	18 18			18 23	18 40	18 47
	d	14 40		15 12			15 40			16 12		16 40		17 10				17 50	18 04			18 28	18 32		18 52
Frant	d			15 16						16 16		16 44		17 14				17 54	18 08				18 36		18 56
Wadhurst	d	14 47		15 21			15 47			16 21		16 49		17 19				17 59	18 13			18 35	18 41		19 01
Stonegate	d			15 27						16 27		16 55		17 25				18 05	18 19				18 47		19 07
Etchingham	d			15 32						16 32		17 00		17 30				18 10	18 24			18 44	18 52		19 12
Robertsbridge	d			15 36			15 57			16 36		17 04		17 34				18 14	18 28				18 56		19 16
Battle	d	15 03		15 43			16 05			16 43		17 11		17 41				18 21	18 35			18 54	19 03		19 23
Crowhurst	d			15 47						16 47		17 15		17 45				18 25	18 39				19 07		19 27
West St Leonards	d			15 52						16 52		17 20		17 52				18 32	18 44				19 12		19 32
St Leonards Warrior Sq [4]	d	15 13		15 55			16 15			16 55		17 23		17 56				18 35	18 47			19 03	19 15		19 35
Bexhill [4]	a	15 33		16 22			16 35			17 25		17 35		18 22					19 04			19 21			20 04
Hastings [4]	a	15 17		15 59			16 19			16 59		17 27		18 01				18 41	18 51			19 09	19 21		19 39
Ore	a																		18 57						19 45

For general notes see front of timetable
For details of catering facilities see Directory of Train Operators

b Arr. 0718

From 12 October due to seasonal difficulties a large number of trains on this table will have minor retimings that could mean slightly earlier departure or later arrival times at certain stations. For further details see local publicity or contact National Rail Enquiries 08457 48 49 50.

For details of Bank Holiday service alterations please see first page of Table 195

London and Tonbridge → Tunbridge Wells and Hastings

Network Diagram - see first page of Table 206

	SE 1	SE 1 ⌶	SE 1	SE 1 ⌶	SE 1	SE 1	SE	SE 1 ⌶	SE 1	SE 1	SE 1	SE 1	SE 1	SE 1	SE 1	SE 1
London Charing Cross 4 ⊖ d	18 04		18 28	18 50		19 15	19 30	19 45	20 15	20 45	21 15	21 45	22 15	22 45	23 15	23 37
London Waterloo (East) 4 ⊖ d	18 07		18 31	18 53		19 18	19 33	19 48	20 18	20 48	21 18	21 48	22 18	22 48	23 18	23 40
London Cannon Street 4 ⊖ d		18 26			19 06											
London Bridge 4 ⊖ d	18 12	18 30	18 36		19 10	19 23	19 38	19 53	20 23	20 53	21 23	21 53	22 23	22 53	23 23	23 45
Orpington 4 d					19 28		19 54		20 40	21 10	21 40	22 10	22 40	23 10	23 40	
Sevenoaks 4 d	18 40		19 05	19 20	19 38	19 50	20 06	20 20	20 50	21 20	21 50	22 20	22 52	23 20	23 52	00 10
Tonbridge 4 a	18 51		19 15	19 29	19 48	19 59	20 17	20 28	20 58	21 28	21 58	22 28	23 00	23 28	00 01	00 20
d	18 52		19 16	19 31	19 49	19 59	20 17	20 29	20 59	21 29	21 59	22 29	23 05	23 29	00 01	00 21
High Brooms d	18 58	19 06	19 22	19 37	19 55	20 06	20 23	20 35	21 05	21 35	22 05	22 35	23 11	23 35	00 07	00 27
Tunbridge Wells 4 a	19 04	19 12	19 28	19 41	19 59	20 10	20 28	20 42	21 09	21 39	22 10	22 39	23 15	23 39	00 11	00 31
d		19 17		19 42	20 00	20 10		20 42	21 10	21 40		22 40		23 40		00 32
Frant d		19 21		19 46	20 04	20 15			21 14	21 44		22 44		23 44		00 36
Wadhurst d		19 26		19 51	20 09	20 19		20 50	21 19	21 49		22 49		23 49		00 41
Stonegate d		19 32		19 57	20 15	20 25			21 25	21 55		22 55		23 55		00 47
Etchingham d		19 37		20 02	20 20	20 30		20 59	21 30	22 00		23 00		23 59		00 52
Robertsbridge d		19 41		20 06	20 24	20 34			21 34	22 04		23 04		00 04		00 56
Battle d		19 48		20 14	20 31	20 42		21 08	21 41	22 11		23 11		00 11		01 03
Crowhurst d		19 52		20 18		20 46			21 45	22 15		23 15		00 15		01 07
West St Leonards d		19 59		20 23		20 51			21 50	22 20		23 20		00 20		01 12
St Leonards Warrior Sq 4 d		20 02		20 26	20 41	20 54		21 18	21 53	22 23		23 23		00 23		01 15
Bexhill 4 a		*20 21*			*21 04*	*21 21*		*21 39*	*22 25*	*22 38*						
Hastings 4 a		20 08		20 30	20 45	20 57		21 21	21 57	22 27		23 27		00 27		01 19
Ore a																

Saturdays

For details of Bank Holiday service alterations please see first page of Table 195

	SE 1	SE 1	SE 1	SE 1	SE 1	SE 1	SE 1	SE 1	SE 1	SE 1	SE 1	SE 1	SE 1	SE 1	SE 1	SE 1	SE 1 ⌶	SE 1	SE 1 ⌶	SE 1	SE 1 ⌶
London Charing Cross 4 ⊖ d	22p45	23p15	23p37				07 45		08 15		08 45		09 15		09 45		10 15		10 45		11 15
London Waterloo (East) 4 ⊖ d	22p48	23p18	23p40				07 48		08 18		08 48		09 18		09 48		10 18		10 48		11 18
London Cannon Street 4 ⊖ d																					
London Bridge 4 ⊖ d	22p53	23p23	23p45				07 53		08 23		08 53		09 23		09 53		10 23		10 53		11 23
Orpington 4 d	23p10	23p40					08 10		08 40				09 40				10 40				11 40
Sevenoaks 4 d	23p20	23p52	00 10				08 20		08 51		09 16		09 51		10 16		10 51		11 16		11 51
Tonbridge 4 a	23p28	00 01	00 20				08 28		08 59		09 24		09 59		10 24		10 59		11 24		11 59
d	23p29	00 01	00 21	07 00	08 00	08 09	08 31	08 38	09 00	09 09	09 26	09 38	10 00	10 09	10 26	10 38	11 00	11 09	11 26	11 38	12 00
High Brooms d	23p35	00 07	00 27	07 06	08 06	08 15	08 38	08 44	09 07	09 15	09 33	09 44	10 07	10 15	10 33	10 44	11 07	11 15	11 33	11 44	12 07
Tunbridge Wells 4 a	23p39	00 11	00 31	07 10	08 10	08 19	08 42	08 48	09 11	09 19	09 37	09 48	10 11	10 19	10 37	10 48	11 11	11 19	11 37	11 48	12 11
d	23p40		00 32	07 10	08 10		08 43		09 12		09 40		10 12		10 40		11 12		11 40		12 12
Frant d	23p44		00 36	07 15	08 15		08 47		09 16				10 16				11 16				12 16
Wadhurst d	23p49		00 41	07 19	08 19		08 52		09 21		09 47		10 21		10 47		11 21		11 47		12 21
Stonegate d	23p55		00 47	07 25	08 25		08 58		09 27				10 27				11 27				12 27
Etchingham d	23p59		00 52	07 30	08 30		09 03		09 32				10 32				11 32				12 32
Robertsbridge d	00 04		00 56	07 34	08 34		09 07		09 36				10 36				11 36				12 36
Battle d	00 11		01 03	07 42	08 42		09 15		09 43		10 03		10 43		11 03		11 43		12 03		12 43
Crowhurst d	00 15		01 07	07 46	08 46		09 19		09 47				10 47				11 47				12 47
West St Leonards d	00 20		01 12	07 51	08 51		09b31		09 52				10 52				11 52				12 52
St Leonards Warrior Sq 4 d	00 23		01 15	07 54	08 54		09 34		09 55		10 13		10 55		11 13		11 55		12 13		12 55
Bexhill 4 a				*08 21*	*09 21*		*10 04*		*10 21*		*10 35*		*11 21*		*11 35*		*12 21*		*12 35*		*13 21*
Hastings 4 a	00 27		01 19	07 58	08 58		09 37		09 59		10 17		10 59		11 17		11 59		12 17		12 59
Ore a																					

	SE 1		SE 1 ⌶	SE 1	SE 1 ⌶	SE 1	SE 1 ⌶	SE 1	SE 1 ⌶	SE 1 ⌶	SE 1	SE 1	SE 1	SE 1	SE 1	SE 1	SE 1	SE 1	SE 1	SE 1
London Charing Cross 4 ⊖ d		and at	16 45		17 15		17 45		18 15	18 45	19 15	19 45		20 45		21 45		22 45		23 30
London Waterloo (East) 4 ⊖ d		the same	16 48		17 18		17 48		18 18	18 48	19 18	19 48		20 48		21 48		22 48		23 33
London Cannon Street 4 ⊖ d		minutes																		
London Bridge 4 ⊖ d		past	16 53		17 23		17 53		18 23	18 53	19 23	19 53		20 53		21 53		22 53		23 38
Orpington 4 d		each			17 40				18 40		19 40	20 10		21 10		22 10		23 10		23 54
Sevenoaks 4 d		hour until	17 16		17 51		18 16		18 51	19 17	19 51	20 20		21 20		22 20		23 20		00 04
Tonbridge 4 a			17 24		17 59		18 24		18 59	19 25	19 59	20 28		21 28		22 28		23 28		00 15
d	12 09		17 26	17 38	18 00	18 09	18 26	18 38	19 00	19 26	20 00	20 30	20 50	21 30	21 50	22 30	22 56	23 30	23 50	00 21
High Brooms d	12 15		17 33	17 44	18 07	18 15	18 33	18 44	19 07	19 33	20 06	20 36	20 55	21 36	21 56	22 36	23 02	23 36	23 55	00 27
Tunbridge Wells 4 a	12 19		17 37	17 48	18 11	18 19	18 37	18 48	19 11	19 37	20 10	20 40	20 59	21 40	21 59	22 40	23 06	23 40	23 59	00 31
d			17 40		18 12		18 40		19 12	19 40	20 10	20 40		21 40		22 40		23 40		00 31
Frant d					18 16				19 16		20 15	20 45		21 45		22 45		23 45		00 36
Wadhurst d			17 47		18 21		18 47		19 21	19 47	20 19	20 49		21 49		22 49		23 49		00 40
Stonegate d					18 27				19 27		20 25	20 55		21 55		22 55		23 55		00 46
Etchingham d					18 32				19 32		20 30	21 00		22 00		23 00		00 01		00 51
Robertsbridge d					18 36				19 36		20 34	21 04		22 04		23 04		00 04		00 55
Battle d			18 03		18 43		19 03		19 43	20 03	20 42	21 14		22 12		23 12		00 12		01 03
Crowhurst d					18 47				19 47		20 46	21 18		22 16		23 16		00 16		01 07
West St Leonards d					18 52				19 52		20 51	21 23		22 21		23 21		00 21		01 12
St Leonards Warrior Sq 4 d			18 13		18 55		19 13		19 55	20 13	20 54	21 26		22 24		23 24		00 24		01 15
Bexhill 4 a			*18 35*		*19 21*		*19 35*		*20 21*	*20 35*	*21 21*	*21 51*		*22 38*						
Hastings 4 a			18 17		18 59		19 17		19 59	20 17	20 57	21 29		22 27		23 27		00 27		01 18
Ore a																				

For general notes see front of timetable
For details of catering facilities see Directory of Train Operators

b Arr. 0924

From 12 October due to seasonal difficulties a large number of trains on this table will have minor retimings that could mean slightly earlier departure or later arrival times at certain stations. For further details see local publicity or contact National Rail Enquiries 08457 48 49 50.

Table 206

Sundays

London and Tonbridge → Tunbridge Wells and Hastings

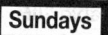

Network Diagram - see first page of Table 206

		SE 1	SE 1		SE 1	SE 1		SE 1		SE 1	SE 1	
London Charing Cross 4	⊖ d	22p45	23p30			08 14				09 14	09 44	and at
London Waterloo (East) 4	⊖ d	22p48	23p33			08 17				09 17	09 47	the same
London Cannon Street 4	⊖ d											minutes
London Bridge 4	⊖ d	22p53	23p37			08 22				09 22	09 52	past
Orpington 4	d	23p10	23p53			08 38				09 38	10 08	each
Sevenoaks 4	d	23p20	00 04			08 48				09 48	10 18	hour until
Tonbridge 4	a	23p28	00 15			08 56				09 56	10 26	
	d	23p30	00 21		08 19	08 57		09 27		09 57	10 27	
High Brooms	d	23p36	00 27		08 25	09 03		09 33		10 03	10 33	
Tunbridge Wells 4	a	23p40	00 31		08 29	09 07		09 37		10 07	10 37	
	d	23p40	00 31			09 08		09 39		10 08	10 38	
Frant	d	23p45	00 36			09 13				10 13		
Wadhurst	d	23p49	00 40			09 17		09 46		10 17	10 46	
Stonegate	d	23p55	00 46			09 23				10 23		
Etchingham	d	00 01	00 51			09 29				10 28		
Robertsbridge	d	00 04	00 55			09 33		09 56			10 56	
Battle	d	00 12	01 03			09 41		10 04		10 38	11 03	
Crowhurst	d	00 16	01 07			09 45		10 08			11 07	
West St Leonards	d	00 21	01 12			09b54		10 13			11 12	
St Leonards Warrior Sq 4	d	00 24	01 15			09 58		10 16		10 47	11 15	
Bexhill 4	a					*10 13*		*10 27*		*11 13*	*11 27*	
Hastings 4	a	00 27	01 18			10 01		10 19		10 51	11 19	
Ore	a											

			SE 1	SE 1		SE 1	SE 1		SE 1	SE 1			
London Charing Cross 4	⊖ d		19 14	19 44		20 14	21 14		22 14	23 14			
London Waterloo (East) 4	⊖ d		19 17	19 47		20 17	21 17		22 17	23 17			
London Cannon Street 4	⊖ d												
London Bridge 4	⊖ d		19 22	19 52		20 22	21 22		22 22	23 22			
Orpington 4	d		19 38	20 08		20 38	21 38		22 38	23 38			
Sevenoaks 4	d		19 48	20 18		20 50	21 50		22 50	23 50			
Tonbridge 4	a		19 56	20 26		20 58	21 58		22 58	23 58			
	d		19 57	20 27		20 59	21 59		22 59	23 59			
High Brooms	d		20 03	20 33		21 05	22 05		23 05	00 05			
Tunbridge Wells 4	a		20 07	20 37		21 09	22 09		23 09	00 09			
	d		20 08			21 11	22 09		23 11	00 09			
Frant	d		20 13			21 16	22 14		23 16	00 14			
Wadhurst	d		20 17			21 20	22 18		23 20	00 18			
Stonegate	d		20 23			21 26	22 24		23 26	00 24			
Etchingham	d		20 28			21 32	22 29		23 32	00 29			
Robertsbridge	d					21 36	22 33		23 36	00 33			
Battle	d		20 38			21 44	22 41		23 44	00 41			
Crowhurst	d					21 48	22 45		23 48	00 45			
West St Leonards	d		20 45			21 54	22 50		23 54	00 50			
St Leonards Warrior Sq 4	d		20 48			21 58	22 53		23 57	00 53			
Bexhill 4	a		*21 13*			*22 13*	*23 27*						
Hastings 4	a		20 52			22 01	22 56		00 01	00 56			
Ore	a												

For general notes see front of timetable
For details of catering facilities see Directory of Train Operators

b Arr. 0950

For details of Bank Holiday service alterations please see first page of Table 195

Hastings and Tunbridge Wells → Tonbridge and London

Network Diagram - see first page of Table 206

Miles																									
			SE 1	SE 1	SE 1	SE 1	SE 1	SE 1		SE 1	SE 1	SE 1	SE 1	SE 1	SE 1		SE 1	SE 1	SE 1	SE 1	SE 1	SE 1		SE 1	SE 1
										🚲			🚲		🚲			🚲			🚲	🚲			
0	Ore	d								06 10			06 38							07 46					
1	**Hastings** 3	d			05 16	05 44	05 56			06 14	06 26		06 42		07 02			07 25		07 50	08 10	08 42			09 30
—	Bexhill 3	d			*05 08*		*05 40*								*06 52*			*07 11*		*07 23*	*08 01*	*08 25*			*09 02*
1¾	St Leonards Warrior Sq 3	d			05 19	05 47	05 59			06 17	06 29		06 45		07 05			07 28		07 53	08 13	08 45			09 33
2¾	West St Leonards	d			05 22	05 50				06 20			06 48		07 08			07 31		07 56	08 16	08 48			
6	Crowhurst	d			05 27	05 55				06 25			06 53		07 13			07 37		08 01	08 21	08 53			
8	Battle	d			05 31	05 59	06 09			06 29	06 39		06 57		07 17			07 41		08 05	08 25	08 57			09 44
14¼	Robertsbridge	d			05 39	06 07				06 37			07 05		07 25			07 48		08 15	08 33	09 05			
16	Etchingham	d			05 43	06 11	06 20			06 41	06 50		07 09		07 29			07 52		08 19	08 37	09 09			
19¾	Stonegate	d			05 48	06 16				06 46			07 14		07 34			07 58		08 25	08 43	09 14			
24¼	Wadhurst	d			05 55	06 23	06 30			06 53	07 00		07 21		07 41			08 04		08 31	08 49	09 21			10 00
26¾	Frant	d			05 59	06 27				06 57			07 25		07 45			08 09		08 36	08 54	09 25			
29	**Tunbridge Wells** 3	a			06 05	06 33	06 38			07 03	07 08		07 31		07 51			08 14		08 40	08 58	09 30			10 07
—		d	05 16	05 44	06 06	06 42		06 56		07 12		07 20	07 35	07 41	07 56		08 00	08 19	08 26	08 42	09 02	09 36		09 54	10 08
30½	High Brooms	d	05 20	05 47	06 10	06 46		07 00		07 16		07 24	07 40	07 45	08 00		08 04	08 23	08 30	08 46	09 06	09 39		09 57	10 11
34	**Tonbridge** 3	a	05 26	05 52	06 17	06 53		07 05				07 29		07 50			08 10		08 36	08 52	09 13	09 45		10 03	10 17
—		d	05 26		06 18	06 53		07 06				07 31		07 51			08 11		08 36	09 00	09 14	09 46		10 04	10 18
41½	Sevenoaks 3	a	05 38		06 30	07 03		07 18				07 43		08 03			08 23		08 48	09 09	09 26	09 55		10 15	10 27
49¾	Orpington 3	a	05 50			07 12															09 35			10 25	
61¾	**London Bridge** 3	⊖ a	06 06		06 55	07 29		07 50				08 10	08 21	08 30			08 50	09 03	09 18	09 33	09 51	10 24		10 43	10 54
—	**London Cannon Street** 3	⊖ a				07 36							08 28					09 08							
62¾	**London Waterloo (East)** 3	⊖ a	06 11		07 00			07 55		08 00		08 15		08 35	08 45		08 55		09 23	09 38	09 58	10 29		10 48	10 59
63½	**London Charing Cross** 3	⊖ a	06 14		07 05			07 59		08 05		08 21		08 41	08 51		09 01		09 29	09 44	10 01	10 33		10 51	11 03

		SE 1	SE 1	SE 1	SE 1	SE 1	SE 1		SE 1	SE 1	SE 1	SE 1	SE 1	SE 1		SE 1	SE 1	SE 1	SE 1	SE 1	SE 1		SE 1	SE 1	SE 1
			🚲				🚲					🚲					🚲				🚲				
Ore	d																								
Hastings 4	d		09 47		10 30		10 47			11 30		11 47		12 30			12 47		13 30		13 47			14 30	
Bexhill 4	d		*09 23*		*10 00*		*10 39*			*11 02*		*11 39*		*12 02*			*12 39*		*13 02*		*13 39*			*14 02*	
St Leonards Warrior Sq 4	d		09 50		10 33		10 50			11 33		11 50		12 33			12 50		13 33		13 50			14 33	
West St Leonards	d		09 53				10 53					11 53					12 53				13 53				
Crowhurst	d		09 58				10 58					11 58					12 58				13 58				
Battle	d		10 02		10 44		11 02			11 44		12 02		12 44			13 02		13 44		14 02			14 44	
Robertsbridge	d		10 10				11 10					12 10					13 10				14 10				
Etchingham	d		10 14				11 14					12 14					13 14				14 14				
Stonegate	d		10 19				11 19					12 19					13 19				14 19				
Wadhurst	d		10 26		11 00		11 26			12 00		12 26		13 00			13 26		14 00		14 26			15 00	
Frant	d		10 30				11 30					12 30					13 30				14 30				
Tunbridge Wells 4	a		10 35		11 07		11 35			12 07		12 35		13 07			13 35		14 07		14 35			15 07	
	d	10 24	10 36	10 53	11 08	11 24	11 36		11 53	12 08	12 24	12 36	12 53	13 08		13 24	13 36	13 53	14 08	14 24	14 36		14 53	15 08	15 24
High Brooms	d	10 27	10 39	10 56	11 11	11 27	11 39		11 56	12 11	12 27	12 39	12 56	13 11		13 27	13 39	13 56	14 11	14 27	14 39		14 56	15 11	15 27
Tonbridge 4	a	10 33	10 45	11 02	11 17	11 33	11 45		12 02	12 17	12 33	12 45	13 02	13 17		13 33	13 45	14 02	14 17	14 33	14 45		15 02	15 17	15 33
	d		10 46		11 18		11 46			12 18		12 46		13 18			13 46		14 18		14 46			15 18	
Sevenoaks 4	a		10 55		11 27		11 55			12 27		12 55		13 27			13 55		14 27		14 55			15 27	
Orpington 4	a		11 05				12 05					13 05					14 05				15 05				
London Bridge 4	⊖ a		11 24		11 54		12 24			12 54		13 24		13 54			14 24		14 54		15 24			15 54	
London Cannon Street 4	⊖ a																								
London Waterloo (East) 4	⊖ a		11 29		11 59		12 29			12 59		13 29		13 59			14 29		14 59		15 29			15 59	
London Charing Cross 4	⊖ a		11 33		12 03		12 33			13 03		13 33		14 03			14 33		15 03		15 33			16 03	

		SE 1	SE 1	SE 1	SE 1	SE 1		SE 1	SE 1	SE 1	SE 1	SE 1	SE 1		SE 1	SE 1	SE 1	SE 1	SE 1	SE 1	SE 1	SE 1	SE		
								🚲		🚲															
Ore	d																								
Hastings 4	d	14 47	15 07	15 35		16 07		16 35		17 11		17 47	18 17		18 47		19 47		20 47		21 35	22 05			
Bexhill 4	d	*14 39*		*15 23*		*15 42*		*16 23*		*17 02*		*17 23*	*18 03*		*18 24*		*19 25*		*20 23*		*21 23*	*21 41*			
St Leonards Warrior Sq 4	d	14 50	15 10	15 38		16 10		16 38		17 14		17 50	18 20		18 50		19 50		20 50		21 38	22 08			
West St Leonards	d	14 53	15 13			16 13		16 41		17 17		17 53	18 23		18 53		19 53		20 53		21 41	22 11			
Crowhurst	d	14 58	15 18			16 18		16 46		17 22		17 58	18 28		18 59		19 58		20 58		21 46	22 16			
Battle	d	15 02	15 22	15 48		16 22		16 50		17 26		18 02	18 32		19 03		20 02		21 02		21 50	22 20			
Robertsbridge	d	15 10	15 30			16 30		16 58		17 34		18 10	18 40		19 10		20 10		21 10		21 58	22 28			
Etchingham	d	15 14	15 34			16 34		17 02		17 38		18 14	18 44		19 14		20 14		21 14		22 02	22 32			
Stonegate	d	15 19	15 39			16 39		17 07		17 43		18 19	18 49		19 20		20 19		21 19		22 07	22 37			
Wadhurst	d	15 26	15 46	16 04		16 46		17 14		17 50		18 26	18 56		19 26		20 26		21 26		22 14	22 44			
Frant	d	15 30	15 50			16 50		17 18		17 54		18 30	19 00		19 31		20 30		21 30		22 18	22 48			
Tunbridge Wells 4	a	15 35	15 55	16 11		16 55		17 24		17 59		18 39	19 05		19 35		20 35		21 35		22 23	22 53			
	d	15 36	15 56	16 16	16 36	16 56		17 30	17 54	18 04	18 26	18 40	19 06		19 38	20 06	20 36	21 06	21 36	22 06	22 26	22 56	23 30		
High Brooms	d	15 39	15 59	16 19	16 39	16 59		17 33	17 57	18 07	18 29	18 43	19 09		19 41	20 09	20 39	21 09	21 39	22 09	22 29	22 59	23 33		
Tonbridge 4	a	15 45	16 06	16 26	16 46	17 06		17 40	18 03	18 15	18 36	18 50	19 15		19 47	20 15	20 46	21 15	21 46	22 15	22 36	23 05	23 39		
	d	15 46	16 06	16 28		17 06		17 40	18 06	18 16	18 36	18 54	19 16		19 48	20 16	20 48	21 16	21 48	22 16	22 42				
Sevenoaks 4	a	15 55	16 18	16 37		17 15		17 50	18 18	18 25	18 46	19 04	19 28		19 57	20 28	20 57	21 28	21 57	22 28	22 51				
Orpington 4	a	16 07	16 34	16 49		17 26		17 59	18 32	18 35	18 55	19 14	19 37		20 07	20 37	21 07	21 37	22 07	22 37	23 01				
London Bridge 4	⊖ a	16 24	16 52	17 09		17 44		18 19	18 49	18 51	19 12	19 33	19 55		20 25	20 55	21 25	21 55	22 25	22 55	23 19				
London Cannon Street 4	⊖ a								18 53																
London Waterloo (East) 4	⊖ a	16 29	16 57	17 14		17 50		18 26		18 56	19 17	19 38	20 00		20 30	21 00	21 30	22 00	22 30	23 00	23 24				
London Charing Cross 4	⊖ a	16 33	17 01	17 19		17 55		18 30		19 00	19 21	19 42	20 04		20 34	21 04	21 34	22 04	22 34	23 04	23 28				

For general notes see front of timetable
For details of catering facilities see Directory of Train Operators

From 12 October due to seasonal difficulties a large number of trains on this table will have minor retimings that could mean slightly earlier departure or later arrival times at certain stations. For further details see local publicity or contact National Rail Enquiries 08457 48 49 50.

Saturdays

For details of Bank Holiday service alterations please see first page of Table 195

Hastings and Tunbridge Wells → Tonbridge and London

Network Diagram - see first page of Table 206

		SE 1	SE 1	SE 1	SE 1	SE 1	SE 1	SE 1	SE 1	SE 1 ⚮	SE 1	SE 1 ⚮	SE 1	SE 1 ⚮	SE 1	and at the same minutes past each hour until	SE 1 ⚮
Ore	d																
Hastings 4	d		05 47	06 16	06 47	07 18		07 47		08 18		08 47		09 30			16 47
Bexhill 4	d			*06 00*	*06 19*	*07 00*		*07 23*		*08 02*		*08 39*		*09 02*			*16 39*
St Leonards Warrior Sq 4	d		05 50	06 19	06 50	07 21		07 50		08 21		08 50		09 33			16 50
West St Leonards	d		05 53	06 22	06 53			07 53				08 53					16 53
Crowhurst	d		05 58	06 27	06 58			07 58				08 58					16 58
Battle	d		06 02	06 32	07 02	07 32		08 02		08 32		09 02		09 44			17 02
Robertsbridge	d		06 10	06 40	07 10	07 44		08 10		08 44		09 10					17 10
Etchingham	d		06 14	06 44	07 14	07 48		08 14		08 48		09 14					17 14
Stonegate	d		06 20	06 50	07 20			08 20				09 20					17 20
Wadhurst	d		06 26	06 56	07 26	07 58		08 26		08 58		09 26		10 00			17 26
Frant	d		06 31	07 01	07 31			08 31				09 31					17 31
Tunbridge Wells 4	a		06 35	07 05	07 35	08 05		08 35		09 05		09 35		10 07			17 35
	d	05 37	06 36	07 06	07 36	08 06	08 24	08 36	08 53	09 05	09 24	09 36	09 53	10 08	10 24		17 36
High Brooms	d	05 40	06 39	07 09	07 39	08 09	08 27	08 39	08 56	09 08	09 27	09 39	09 56	10 11	10 27		17 39
Tonbridge 4	a	05 46	06 45	07 16	07 45	08 16	08 33	08 45	09 02	09 16	09 33	09 45	10 02	10 18	10 33		17 45
	d		06 46	07 16	07 46	08 16		08 46		09 17		09 46		10 18			17 46
Sevenoaks 4	a		06 56	07 26	07 55	08 26		08 55		09 27		09 55		10 28			17 55
Orpington 4	a		07 07	07 35	08 05	08 35		09 05		09 36		10 05					18 05
London Bridge 4	⊖ a		07 26	07 54	08 24	08 54		09 24		09 54		10 24		10 54			18 24
London Cannon Street 4	⊖ a																
London Waterloo (East) 4	⊖ a		07 31	07 59	08 29	08 59		09 29		09 59		10 29		10 59			18 29
London Charing Cross 4	⊖ a		07 34	08 05	08 33	09 03		09 33		10 03		10 33		11 03			18 33

		SE 1	SE 1	SE 1	SE 1	SE 1	SE 1	SE 1	SE 1	SE 1	SE 1	SE 1	SE 1	SE 1
Ore	d													
Hastings 4	d		17 19		17 47		18 47		19 47		20 47		22 07	
Bexhill 4	d		*17 02*		*17 23*		*18 23*		*19 23*		*20 23*		*21 39*	
St Leonards Warrior Sq 4	d		17 22		17 50		18 50		19 50		20 50		22 10	
West St Leonards	d				17 53		18 53		19 53		20 53		22 13	
Crowhurst	d				17 58		18 58		19 58		20 58		22 18	
Battle	d		17 32		18 02		19 02		20 02		21 02		22 22	
Robertsbridge	d		17 44		18 10		19 10		20 10		21 10		22 30	
Etchingham	d		17 48		18 14		19 14		20 14		21 14		22 34	
Stonegate	d				18 20		19 20		20 20		21 20		22 39	
Wadhurst	d		17 58		18 26		19 26		20 26		21 26		22 46	
Frant	d				18 31		19 31		20 31		21 31		22 50	
Tunbridge Wells 4	a		18 05		18 35		19 35		20 35		21 35		22 55	
	d	17 53	18 05	18 24	18 36	19 10	19 36	20 10	20 36	21 10	21 36	22 10	22 55	23 30
High Brooms	d	17 56	18 08	18 27	18 39	19 13	19 39	20 13	20 39	21 13	21 39	22 13	22 59	23 33
Tonbridge 4	a	18 02	18 16	18 33	18 45	19 19	19 45	20 19	20 45	21 19	21 45	22 19	23 05	23 39
	d		18 17		18 46		19 46		20 46		21 46			
Sevenoaks 4	a		18 26		18 56		19 56		20 56		21 56			
Orpington 4	a		18 36		19 07		20 07		21 07		22 07			
London Bridge 4	⊖ a		18 54		19 26		20 26		21 25		22 25			
London Cannon Street 4	⊖ a													
London Waterloo (East) 4	⊖ a		19 00		19 30		20 30		21 30		22 30			
London Charing Cross 4	⊖ a		19 06		19 34		20 34		21 34		22 34			

Sundays

		SE 1	SE 1	SE 1	SE 1	SE 1	SE 1	and at the same minutes past each hour until	SE 1	SE 1	SE 1	SE 1	SE 1	SE 1	SE 1	SE 1
Ore	d															
Hastings 4	d	07 18		08 13	08 54	09 28	09 54		17 28	17 54	18 12	19 12		20 12	21 12	22 12
Bexhill 4	d			*07 46*	*08 11*	*09 16*			*17 16*	*17b35*	*17c35*	*18e35*		*19f35*	*20g35*	*21h35*
St Leonards Warrior Sq 4	d	07 21		08 16	08 57	09 31	09 57		17 31	17 57	18 15	19 15		20 15	21 15	22 15
West St Leonards	d	07 24		08 20		09 34			17 34		18 19	19 19		20 19	21 18	22 18
Crowhurst	d	07 29		08 25		09 39			17 39		18 24	19 24		20 24	21 24	22 23
Battle	d	07 34		08 30	09 07	09 43	10 07		17 43	18 07	18 29	19 29		20 29	21 28	22 27
Robertsbridge	d	07 41		08 38		09 51			17 51		18 40	19 40		20 40	21 36	22 35
Etchingham	d	07 45		08 42	09 17		10 17			18 17	18 45	19 45		20 45	21 41	22 39
Stonegate	d	07 51		08 48	09 22		10 22			18 22	18 50	19 50		20 50	21 46	22 44
Wadhurst	d	07 57		08 54	09 29	10 01	10 29		18 01	18 29	18 57	19 57		20 57	21 53	22 51
Frant	d	08 02		08 59	09 33		10 33			18 33	19 01	20 01		21 01	21 57	22 55
Tunbridge Wells 4	a	08 07		09 04	09 38	10 08	10 38		18 08	18 38	19 06	20 06		21 06	22 02	23 00
	d	08 08	08 38	09 08	09 39	10 10	10 39		18 10	18 39	19 08	20 08	20 48	21 08	22 08	23 00
High Brooms	d	08 12	08 42	09 12	09 42	10 13	10 42		18 13	18 42	19 12	20 12	20 51	21 12	22 12	23 04
Tonbridge 4	a	08 18	08 48	09 18	09 48	10 19	10 48		18 19	18 48	19 18	20 18	20 57	21 18	22 18	23 10
	d	08 19	08 49	09 19	09 49	10 20	10 49		18 20	18 49	19 19	20 19		21 19	22 19	
Sevenoaks 4	a	08 28	08 58	09 28	09 58	10 29	10 58		18 29	18 58	19 28	20 28		21 28	22 28	
Orpington 4	a	08 38	09 08	09 38	10 08	10 39	11 08		18 39	19 08	19 40	20 40		21 40	22 40	
London Bridge 4	⊖ a	08 56	09 26	09 56	10 26	10 56	11 26		18 56	19 26	19 56	20 56		21 56	22 56	
London Cannon Street 4	⊖ a															
London Waterloo (East) 4	⊖ a	09 01	09 31	10 01	10 31	11 01	11 31		19 01	19 31	20 01	21 01		22 01	23 01	
London Charing Cross 4	⊖ a	09 05	09 35	10 05	10 35	11 06	11 35		19 06	19 35	20 05	21 05		22 05	23 05	

For general notes see front of timetable
For details of catering facilities see Directory of Train Operators

b From 13 September dep. 1716
c From 13 September dep. 1746
e From 13 September dep. 1846
f From 13 September dep. 1946
g From 13 September dep. 2046
h From 13 September dep. 2146

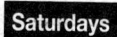

Table 207

Mondays to Fridays

For details of Bank Holiday service alterations please see first page of Table 195

London and Tonbridge → Ashford International, Folkestone, Dover, Canterbury West, Ramsgate and Margate

Network Diagram - see first page of Table 206

Miles	Miles	Miles		SE MO 1	SE MX 1	SE MX 1	SE MO 1	SE MX 2 1	SE MX 1	SE MO 1	SE MX 2 1	SE 1	SE 1 A		SE 1	SE	SE 1	SE 1	SE 1	SE	SE 1	SE	SE 1	SE 1
0	—	—	London Charing Cross 4 ⊖ d	22p00	22p00	22p30	22p30	23p00		23p30	23p30							05 30					06 25	
¾	—	—	London Waterloo (East) 4 ⊖ d	22p03	22p03	22p33	22p33	23p03		23p33	23p33							05 33					06 28	
—	—	—	London Cannon Street 4 ⊖ d																				06 22	
1¾	—	—	London Bridge 4 ⊖ d	22p08	22p08	22p38	22p38	23p08		23p38	23p38							05 38					06 33	
13¾	—	—	Orpington 4 d	22p24	22p24	22p54	22p54	23p24		23p54	23p56							05 54					06 50	
22	—	—	Sevenoaks 4 d	22p34	22p34	23p04	23p04	23p34		00 04	00 06							06 11					07 00	
29½	—	—	Tonbridge 4 a	22p43	22p45	23p14	23p15	23p45		00 13	00 17							06 21					07 10	
—	—	—	d	22p43	22p45	23p15	23p15	23p45		00 13	00 17	04 53						06 22					07 11	
34¾	—	—	Paddock Wood 4 d	22p50	22p52	23p22	23p22	23p52		00 20	00 24	05 00				05 55		06 29		06 33		07 06	07 18	
—	—	—	Maidstone West 4 a									06 15				06 15		06 53		06 53		07 26		
39½	—	—	Marden d			23p28	23p28			00 26	00 30	05 06						06 35					07 24	
41¾	—	—	Staplehurst d	22p59	23p01	23p32	23p33	00 01		00 31	00 35	05 10						06 39					07 28	
45¼	—	—	Headcorn 4 d		23p06	23p37	23p38	00 06		00 36	00 40	05 15						06 44					07 33	
50½	—	—	Pluckley d			23p44	23p45			00 43	00 47	05 21						06 51					07 40	
—	0	—	London Victoria 15 ⊖ d					22 09	23p09		23 09													06 10
—	11	—	Bromley South 4 d					22 29	23p29		23 29													06 30
—	40	—	Maidstone East 4 d					23 13	00 13		00 13				05 56				06 33					07 23
56	59¼	—	Ashford International a	23p12	23p17	23p52	23p52	00 17	00 42	00 50	00 54	05 29			06 25			06 59	07 02				07 52	07 52
—	—	—	d	23p18	23p20	23p53	23p53	00 20	00 57		00 58	05 34	06 12		06 28		06 35	07 03	07 07				07 55	07 56
—	—	—	Rye a									06 47			07 09				07 53					
—	63½	—	Wye d			23p58			01 03						06 34				07 13					08 02
—	68¼	—	Chilham d			00 05			01 09						06 41				07 19					08 09
—	70¼	—	Chartham d			00 09			01 13						06 44				07 23					08 12
—	73½	—	Canterbury West 4 d			00a15			01a18						06 50				07 30					08b20
—	75¾	—	Sturry d												06 55				07 34					08 24
64¼	—	—	Westenhanger d	23p27	23p30		00 02	00 30			01 07	05 43	06 21				06 44	07 12					08 05	
65½	—	—	Sandling d	23p30	23p33		00 05	00 33			01 10	05 46	06 24				06 47	07 15					08 08	
69¼	—	—	Folkestone West d	23p35	23p38		00 10	00 38			01 15	05 51	06 29				06 52	07 20					08 13	
70	—	—	Folkestone Central d	23p38	23p41		00 13	00 41			01 18	05 54	06 33				06 55	07 23					08 15	
77¼	—	—	Dover Priory 4 a	23p50	23p52		00 25	00 52			01 30	06 05	06 44				07 06	07 35			←		08 27	
—	—	—	d	23p50	23p54							06 06					07 12	07 53			07 53		08 28	
82¼	—	—	Martin Mill d	23p59	00 03							06 15					07 21	→			08 02		08 37	
85	—	—	Walmer d	00 04	00 07							06 19					07 25				08 06		08 41	
86½	—	—	Deal d	00 07	00 11							06 22					07 29				08 11		08 45	
90¾	—	0	Sandwich d	00 14	00 17							06 29					07 35				08 19		08 51	
—	84¾	4¾	Minster 4 d												07 06				07 45		08c31			08 36
99	88¾	—	Ramsgate 4 a	00 25	00 30							06 44			07 12		07 48		07 52		08 38		09 04	08 42
100	89¾	—	Dumpton Park a									06 52			07 24		07 54		07 58					08 45
101¼	91	—	Broadstairs a									06 55			07 27		07 57		08 01		08 48			08 48
104½	94¼	—	Margate 4 a									06 59			07 31		08 01		08 06		08 53			08 53

	SE 1	SE 1		SE 1	SE 1	SE	SE 1	SE 1	SE 1		SE	SE 1	SE 1		SE 1	SE 1	SE 1	SE	SE 1	SE 1		SE	SE	
London Charing Cross 4 ⊖ d		07 00					07 28		07 52			08 22			08 54	08 58			09 30	09 53		10 00		
London Waterloo (East) 4 ⊖ d		07 03					07 31		07 55			08 25			08 57	09 01			09 33	09 56		10 03		
London Cannon Street 4 ⊖ d		06 52					07 22		07 54						08 54				09 30					
London Bridge 4 ⊖ d		07 08					07 36		08 02			08 30			09 02	09 08			09 38			10 08		
Orpington 4 d		07 26					07 55		08 20			08 48				09 26			09 54			10 26		
Sevenoaks 4 d		07 36					08 05		08 30			08 58				09 36			10 04			10 36		
Tonbridge 4 a		07 44					08 15		08 40			09 06			09 35	09 47			10 15	10 30		10 47		
d		07 49					08 23		08 41		09 00	09 08			09 35	09 47			10 15	10 31		10 47		
Paddock Wood 4 d		07 56				08 09	08 30		08 48		09 08	09 15			09 42	09 54		10 03	10 22			10 54	11 01	
Maidstone West 4 a		08 29				08 29			09 28		09 28					10 23		10 23	11 21				11 21	
Marden d		08 02							08 54			09 21				10 00			10 28			11 00		
Staplehurst d		08 06					08 38		08 59			09 25			09 51	10 05			10 33			11 05		
Headcorn 4 d		08 11					08 43		09 04			09 30				10 10			10 38			11 10		
Pluckley d		08 18							09 11			09 37				10 17						11 17		
London Victoria 15 ⊖ d	06 47	06 47			07 19		07 19						08 18		08 18		09 19		09 19					
Bromley South 4 d	07 04	07 04			07 36		07 36						08 40		08 40		09 37		09 37					
Maidstone East 4 d	07 49	07 49			08 21		08 21						09 17				10 14							
Ashford International a	08 21	08 27		←	08 53		08 55	←	09 18			09 45	09 46		10 05	10 25	10 43		10 49	10 53		11 26		
d	08 32	08 28		08 32	09 03		09 02	09 03	09 22	09 26		09 50	09 51		10 09	10 27	10 50		10 50	10 58	11 01			
Rye a	08 53	09 13			→					09 53						10 53					11 53			
Wye d	→			08 39				09 09					09 57								11 08			
Chilham d				08 45				09 15					10 03								11 14			
Chartham d				08 49				09 19					10 07								11 18			
Canterbury West 4 d				08 55				09a24		09 44			10a12			10 46	11a06				11 24			
Sturry d				08 59						09 48						10 50					11 29			
Westenhanger d		08 37					09 11					09 59			10 18					11 07				
Sandling d		08 40					09 14					10 02			10 21					11 10				
Folkestone West d		08 45					09 19					10 07			10 26					11 15				
Folkestone Central d		08 48					09 22		09 37			10 10			10 29				11 05	11 18				
Dover Priory 4 a		08 59					09 34		09 48			10 24			10 40				11 17	11 30				
d		09 00							09 49			10 28								11 31				
Martin Mill d		09 09							09 58			10 37								11 40				
Walmer d		09 13							10 02			10 41								11 44				
Deal d		09 17							10 06			10 45								11 48				
Sandwich d		09 23							10 12			10 51								11 54				
Minster 4 d				09 10						09 59						11 01					11 40			
Ramsgate 4 a		09 35		09 17					10 24	10 06		11 05				11 09				12 06	11 46			
Dumpton Park a		09 40		09 24						10 09						11 13								
Broadstairs a		09 43		09 28					11 03	10 12		11 16				11 16								
Margate 4 a		09 48		09 32					11 08	10 17		11 22				11 22								

For general notes see front of timetable
For details of catering facilities see Directory of Train Operators

A To Faversham (Table 212)
b Arr. 0817
c Arr. 0826

From 12 October due to seasonal difficulties a large number of trains on this table will have minor retimings that could mean slightly earlier departure or later arrival times at certain stations. For further details see local publicity or contact National Rail Enquiries 08457 48 49 50.

London and Tonbridge → Ashford International, Folkestone, Dover, Canterbury West, Ramsgate and Margate

For details of Bank Holiday service alterations please see first page of Table 195

Network Diagram - see first page of Table 206

	SE 1		SE 1		SE 1	SE 1 🛒		SE 1	SE	SE 1 🛒		SE 1	SE 1	SE 1 🛒			SE 1	SE	SE 1 🛒		SE 1	SE 1	SE 1 🛒	
London Charing Cross [4] ⊖ d	10 23				10 30	10 53		11 00		11 23			11 30	11 53			12 00		12 23			12 30	12 53	
London Waterloo (East) [4] ⊖ d	10 26				10 33	10 56		11 03		11 26			11 33	11 56			12 03		12 26			12 33	12 56	
London Cannon Street [4] ⊖ d					10 30								11 30									12 30		
London Bridge [4] ⊖ d					10 38			11 08					11 38				12 08					12 38		
Orpington [4] d					10 54			11 26					11 54				12 26					12 54		
Sevenoaks [4] d					11 04			11 36					12 04				12 36					13 04		
Tonbridge [4] a	11 02				11 15	11 30		11 47		12 02			12 15	12 30			12 47		13 02			13 15	13 30	
d	11 03				11 15	11 31		11 47		12 03			12 15	12 31			12 47		13 03			13 15	13 31	
Paddock Wood [4] d	11 10				11 22			11 54	12 06	12 10			12 22				12 54	13 06	13 10			13 22		
Maidstone West [4] a									12 26									13 26						
Marden d								12 00									13 00							
Staplehurst d	11 18				11 31			12 05		12 18			12 31				13 05		13 18			13 31		
Headcorn [4] d					11 36			12 10					12 36				13 10					13 36		
Pluckley d								12 17									13 17							
London Victoria [15] ⊖ d	09b48		10 18			10 18				10b48		11 18		11 18					11b48		12 18		12 18	
Bromley South [4] d	10b04		10 34			10 34				11b04		11 34		11 34					12b04		12 34		12 34	
Maidstone East [4] d	11 05		11 13							12 05		12 13							13 05		13 13			
Ashford International a	11 32		11 43		11 50	11 53		12 26		12 32		12 43	12 50	12 53			13 26		13 32		13 43	13 50	13 53	
d	11 36	11 38	11 46			11 58	12 01			12 36	12 38	12 46		12 58	13 01				13 36	13 38	13 46		13 58	14 01
Rye a							12 53								13 53									14 53
Wye d			11 52									12 52									13 52			
Chilham d			11 58									12 58									13 58			
Chartham d			12 02									13 02									14 02			
Canterbury West [4] d	11 54		12a07				12 20			12 54		13a07			13 20				13 54		14a07			14 20
Sturry d	11 59									12 59									13 59					
Westenhanger d		11 47									12 47									13 47				
Sandling d		11 50									12 50									13 50				
Folkestone West d		11 55									12 55									13 55				
Folkestone Central d		11 58				12 12					12 58			13 12						13 58			14 12	
Dover Priory [4] ⛴ a		12 10				12 24					13 10			13 24						14 10			14 24	
d						12 25								13 25									14 25	
Martin Mill d						12 35								13 35									14 35	
Walmer d						12 39								13 39									14 39	
Deal d						12 43								13 43									14 43	
Sandwich d						12 49								13 49									14 49	
Minster [4] d	12 10									13 10									14 10					
Ramsgate [4] ✈ a	12 17					13 02	12 38			13 17				14 02	13 38				14 16				15 02	14 41
Dumpton Park a	12 24						12 43			13 24					13 43				14 20					
Broadstairs a	12 28						12 46			13 28				14 23	13 46				14 23				15 23	
Margate [4] a	12 32						12 51			13 32				14 28	13 51				14 28				15 28	

	SE 1	SE	SE 1 🛒			SE 1	SE	SE 1 🛒		SE 1	SE	SE 1	SE 1 🛒		SE 1		SE 1 🛒		SE 1	SE 1	SE	SE 1		SE 1
London Charing Cross [4] ⊖ d	13 00		13 23				13 30	13 53		14 00			14 23		14 30		14 53			15 00		15 23		15 30
London Waterloo (East) [4] ⊖ d	13 03		13 26				13 33	13 56		14 03			14 26		14 33		14 56			15 03		15 26		15 33
London Cannon Street [4] ⊖ d							13 30								14 30									15 30
London Bridge [4] ⊖ d	13 08						13 38			14 08					14 38					15 08				15 38
Orpington [4] d	13 26						13 54			14 26					14 54					15 26				15 54
Sevenoaks [4] d	13 36						14 04			14 36					15 04					15 36				16 04
Tonbridge [4] a	13 47		14 02				14 15	14 30		14 47			15 02		15 15		15 30			15 47		16 02		16 15
d	13 47		14 03				14 15	14 31		14 47			15 03		15 15		15 31			15 47		16 03		16 15
Paddock Wood [4] d	13 54	14 06	14 10				14 22			14 54	15 06		15 10		15 22					15 54	16 06	16 10		16 22
Maidstone West [4] a		14 26									15 26									16 26	16 26			16 48
Marden d	14 00									15 00										16 00				16 28
Staplehurst d	14 05		14 18				14 31			15 05			15 18		15 31					16 05		16 18		16 33
Headcorn [4] d	14 10						14 36			15 10					15 36					16 10				16 38
Pluckley d	14 17									15 17										16 17				16 45
London Victoria [15] ⊖ d			12b48			13 18		13 18					13b48				14 18					14 48		
Bromley South [4] d			13b04			13 34		13 34					14b04				14 34					15 04		
Maidstone East [4] d			14 05			14 13							15 05				15 21					16 05		
Ashford International a	14 26		14 32			14 43	14 50	14 53		15 26			15 32		15 50		15 53			16 26		16 32		16 54
d			14 36	14 38		14 46		14 58	15 01				15 36	15 39			15 58	16 01				16 36	16 40	
Rye a									15 53									16 53						
Wye d						14 52							15 43				16 05					16 43		
Chilham d						14 58							15 49				16 11					16 49		
Chartham d						15 02							15 53				16 15					16 53		
Canterbury West [4] d			14 54			15a07			15 20				15 59				16 21					16 59		
Sturry d			14 59						15 24				16 04				16 26					17 04		
Westenhanger d				14 47										15 48				16 10					16 49	
Sandling d				14 50										15 51				16 13					16 52	
Folkestone West d				14 55										15 56				16 18					16 57	
Folkestone Central d				14 58				15 12						15 59				16 21					17 00	
Dover Priory [4] ⛴ a				15 10				15 24						16 11				16 34	←				17 12	
d								15 27				←		16 12 →				16 35	16 12				17 12 →	
Martin Mill d								15 36 →				15 36						16 44	16 21					
Walmer d												15 41						16 48	16 25					
Deal d												15 44						16 52	16 29					
Sandwich d												15c54						16 58	16 35					
Minster [4] d			15 10						15 35			16e06	16 15				16 37		16f47			17 15		
Ramsgate [4] ✈ a			15 16						15 43			16 12	16 23				16 44	17 10	16 54			17 22		
Dumpton Park a			15 20									16 16					16 50					17 52		
Broadstairs a			15 23									16 19					16 53		17 28			17 55		
Margate [4] a			15 28									16 24					16 58					18 00		

For general notes see front of timetable
For details of catering facilities see Directory of Train Operators

b Change at Maidstone East and Ashford International
c Arr. 1551
e Arr. 1601
f Arr. 1643

From 12 October due to seasonal difficulties a large number of trains on this table will have minor retimings that could mean slightly earlier departure or later arrival times at certain stations. For further details see local publicity or contact National Rail Enquiries 08457 48 49 50.

London and Tonbridge → Ashford International, Folkestone, Dover, Canterbury West, Ramsgate and Margate

For details of Bank Holiday service alterations please see first page of Table 195

Network Diagram - see first page of Table 206

Station		SE	SE 1		SE 1	SE 1	SE	SE 1		SE 1	SE 1		SE	SE 1	SE 1	SE 1	SE	SE 1		SE 1		SE 1	SE
London Charing Cross 4 ⊖	d		15 53			16 00		16 23		16 30	16 46			17 12	16b50	17 34		17b20		17 56			
London Waterloo (East) 4 ⊖	d		15 56			16 03		16 26		16 33	16 49			17 15	16b53	17 37		17b23		17 59		17b44	
London Cannon Street 4 ⊖	d					16 00		16 22							17 20			17 44				18 05	
London Bridge 4 ⊖	d					16 08		16 31		16 39	16 54				17 04			17 28				18 09	
Orpington 4	d					16 02		16 33							17 24			17 46				18 08	
Sevenoaks 4	d					16 32		16 56		17 02					17 52			18 12				18 34	
Tonbridge 4	a		16 32			16 43		17 04		17 13	17 24			17 50	18 02	18 15		18 20		18 34		18 44	
	d		16 33			16 43		17 05		17 13	17 25			17 51	18 03	18 15		18 21		18 35		18 45	
Paddock Wood 4	d	16 28				16 50	17 02	17 12		17 20	17 32		17 52	17 58	18 11	18 23	18 27	18 28		18 43		18 52	18 57
Maidstone West 4	a	16 48				17 22	17 22				18 12		18 12			18 47	18 47					19 17	19 17
Marden	d					16 56				17 26				18 04	18 17					18 49		18 58	
Staplehurst	d					17 01		17 20		17 31	17 40			18 09	18 22	18 31				18 53		19 03	
Headcorn 4	d					17 06				17 36	17 45			18 14	18 27	18 36				18 58		19 08	
Pluckley	d					17 13				17 43				18 21		18 43				19 05		19 15	
London Victoria 15 ⊖	d		15 18					15 48															
Bromley South 4	d		15 34					16 04						17 15									
Maidstone East 4	d		16 19					16 44			17 07			17 54									
Ashford International	a		16 57			17 24		17 35		17 52	17 57			18 29	18 41	18 51		18 53		19 14		19 24	
	d		17 01	17 03				17 39	17 42		18 02	18 05		18 32		18 56		18 58	18 59	19 18	19 20		
Rye	a					17 53				18 21		18 53							19 21			19 53	
Wye	d		17 08						17 49			18 12		18 39				19 04			19 27		
Chilham	d		17 14						17 55			18 18		18 45				19 11			19 33		
Chartham	d		17 18						17 59			18 22		18 49				19 14			19 37		
Canterbury West 4	d		17 24						18 05			18 29		18 55				19a19			19c45		
Sturry	d		17 29						18 10			18 33		19 00							19 49		
Westenhanger	d			17 12				17 48			18 11					19 05			19 09	19 27			
Sandling	d			17 15				17 51			18 14					19 08			19 12	19 30			
Folkestone West	d			17 20				17 56			18 19					19 13			19 18	19 35			
Folkestone Central	d			17 23				17 59			18 22					19 16			19a20	19 38			
Dover Priory 4	a			17 35	←			18 11			18 34					19 29				19 50			
	d			17 36	17 12			18 12			18 36					19 29				19 55			
Martin Mill	d			17 45	17 21			18 21			18 45					19 38				20 04			
Walmer	d			17 49	17 26			18 25			18 49					19 43				20 08			
Deal	d			17 53	17 29			18 29			18 53					19 46				20 12			
Sandwich	d			17 59	17 36			18 35			18 59					19 53				20 18			
Minster 4	d		17 40		17e49				18 21			18 44		19 11							20 02		
Ramsgate 4	a		17 47	18 10	17 56			18 50	18 28		19 11	18 51		19 20		20 06				20 32	20 11		
Dumpton Park	a			18 15	18 15				18 50		19 15	18 55		19 52							20 14		
Broadstairs	a			18 18	18 18			19 18			19 18	18 58		19 55		20 17				20 44	20 17		
Margate 4	a			18 23	18 23			19 26			19 26	19 05		19 59		20 22					20 22		

Station		SE 1	SE 1		SE 1	SE	SE 1	SE	SE 1		SE 1	SE 1	SE	SE 1	SE 1	SE	SE 1	SE 1	SE 1	SE 2 1	SE 1	SE 2 1
London Charing Cross 4 ⊖	d	18 16			18 40		19 00		19 24		19 52	20 00		20 30	21 00		21 30	22 00	22 30	23 00		23 30
London Waterloo (East) 4 ⊖	d	18 19			18 43		19 03		19 27		19 55	20 03		20 33	21 03		21 33	22 03	22 33	23 03		23 33
London Cannon Street 4 ⊖	d	18 05	18 30						19 22		19 52	20 00		20 30	21 00				21f00			
London Bridge 4 ⊖	d	18 12	18 34		18 48		19 08		19 32		20 01	20 08		20 38	21 08		21 38	22 08	22 38	23 08		23 38
Orpington 4	d		18 30		19 05							20 02		20 54	21 24		21 54	22 24	22 54	23 24		23 56
Sevenoaks 4	d	18 48	18 58		19 15		19 34					20 32		21 04	21 34		22 04	22 34	23 04	23 34		00 06
Tonbridge 4	a	18 57	19 07		19 23		19 45		20 02		20 32	20 42		21 15	21 45		22 15	22 45	23 14	23 45		00 17
	d	18 57	19 07		19 24	19 28	19 45		20 03		20 33	20 43		21 15	21 45		22 15	22 45	23 15	23 45		00 17
Paddock Wood 4	d	19 05	19 14		19 31	19g38	19 52	20 03	20 10		20 40	20 50	21 01	21 22	21 52	21 57	22 22	22 52	23 22	23 52		00 24
Maidstone West 4	a					19 58	20 23	20 23				21 21	21 21		22 17	22 17						
Marden	d		19 20		19 37		19 58		20 16			20 56		21 28			22 28		23 28			00 30
Staplehurst	d	19 13	19 25		19 41		20 03		20 21		20 49	21 01		21 33	22 01		22 33	23 01	23 32	00 01		00 35
Headcorn 4	d	19 18	19 30		19 46		20 08		20 26		20 54	21 06		21 38	22 06		22 38	23 06	23 37	00 06		00 40
Pluckley	d		19 37		19 53		20 15					21 13		21 45			22 45		23 44			00 47
London Victoria 15 ⊖	d	17 58							18 48		19 18	19 48			20 48		21 09		22 09	22 09	23 09	23 09
Bromley South 4	d	17h51	18 21						19 06		19 35	20 07			21 07		21 29		22 29	22 29	23 29	23 29
Maidstone East 4	d	18 56	19 08						20 08		20 20	20 44			21 44		22 13		23 13	23 13	00 13	
Ashford International	a	19 30	19 45		20 02		20 24		20 38		21 06	21 21		21 52	22 17		22 52	23 17	23 52	00 17	00 42	00 54
	d	19 33	19 51	19 53	20 06				20 42	20 44	21 07	21 24		21 53	22 20		22 53	23 20	23 53	00 20	00 57	00 58
Rye	a			20 21			20 53					21 53			22 47							
Wye	d			19 59	20 13					20 51	21 14			22 00			23 00		23 58		01 03	
Chilham	d			20 05	20 19					20 57	21 20			22 06			23 06		00 05		01 09	
Chartham	d			20 09	20 23					21 01	21 24			22 10			23 10		00 09		01 13	
Canterbury West 4	d			20 15	20 30					21 07	21 30			22 16			23 16		00a15		01a18	
Sturry	d			20 20	20 34					21 11	21 35			22 21			23 21					
Westenhanger	d	19 42	20 00						20 51			21 33			22 30			23 30		00 30		01 07
Sandling	d	19 45	20 03						20 54			21 36			22 33			23 33		00 33		01 10
Folkestone West	d	19 50	20 09						20 59			21 41			22 38			23 38		00 38		01 15
Folkestone Central	d	19 53	20 12						21 02			21 44			22 41			23 41		00 41		01 18
Dover Priory 4	a	20 05	20 26						21 14			21 56			22 52			23 52		00 52		01 30
	d	20 05							21 15			22 00			22 54			23 54				
Martin Mill	d	20 14							21 24			22 09			23 03			00 03				
Walmer	d	20 19							21 28			22 13			23 07			00 07				
Deal	d	20 22							21 32			22 17			23 11			00 11				
Sandwich	d	20 29							21 38			22 23			23 17			00 17				
Minster 4	d			20 31	20 45					21 22	21 46			22 32			23 32					
Ramsgate 4	a	20 43		20 37	20 52				21 49	21 29	21 53	22 36		22 40	23 30		23 39	00 30				
Dumpton Park	a	20 52		20 41					21 57	21 32				22 55			23 43					
Broadstairs	a	20 55		20 44	21 35				22 00	21 35	22 15			22 58	23 46		23 46					
Margate 4	a	20 59		20 51					22 04	21 40	22 19			23 03	23 51		23 51					

For general notes see front of timetable
For details of catering facilities see Directory of Train Operators

b Change at Sevenoaks
c Arr. 1942
e Arr. 1743
f Change at London Bridge and Orpington
g Arr. 1935
h Change at Maidstone East and Ashford International

From 12 October due to seasonal difficulties a large number of trains on this table will have minor retimings that could mean slightly earlier departure or later arrival times at certain stations. For further details see local publicity or contact National Rail Enquiries 08457 48 49 50.

Table 207

Saturdays

London and Tonbridge → Ashford International, Folkestone, Dover, Canterbury West, Ramsgate and Margate

For details of Bank Holiday service alterations please see first page of Table 195

Network Diagram - see first page of Table 206

		SE	SE	SE 2	SE	SE 2	SE	SE	SE		SE	SE	SE	SE	SE	SE	SE			SE	SE	SE	SE		SE
		1	1	1	1	1	1	1	1		1		1	1		1	1			1		1	1		1
London Charing Cross 4	⊖ d	22p00	22p30	23p00		23p30			06 00				07 00			07 30	08 00					08 30	09 00		
London Waterloo (East) 4	⊖ d	22p03	22p33	23p03		23p33			06 03				07 03			07 33	08 03					08 33	09 03		
London Cannon Street 4	⊖ d																					08 30	09 00		
London Bridge 4	⊖ d	22p08	22p38	23p08		23p38			06 08				07 08			07 38	08 08					08 38	09 08		
Orpington 4	d	22p24	22p54	23p24		23p56		05 58	06 26				07 26			07 56	08 26					08 56	09 26		
Sevenoaks 4	d	22p34	23p04	23p34		00 06		06 08	06 36				07 36			08 06	08 36					09 06	09 36		
Tonbridge 4	a	22p45	23p14	23p45		00 17		06 18	06 47				07 47			08 14	08 46					09 14	09 47		
	d	22p45	23p15	23p45		00 17		06 19	06 47				07 47			08 15	08 47					09 15	09 47		
Paddock Wood 4	d	22p52	23p22	23p52		00 24		06 26	06 54			07 01	07 54		08 01	08 23	08 54				09 01	09 23	09 55		
Maidstone West 4	a								07 21			07 21	08 21		08 21		09 21				09 21		10 21		
Marden	d		23p28			00 30			07 00				08 00				09 01						10 01		
Staplehurst	d	23p01	23p32	00 01		00 35		06 34	07 05				08 05			08 32	09 05					09 32	10 06		
Headcorn 4	d	23p06	23p37	00 06		00 40		06 39	07 10				08 10			08 37	09 11					09 37	10 11		
Pluckley	d		23p44			00 47			07 17				08 17				09 18						10 18		
London Victoria 15	⊖ d			22 09	23p09	23 18					06 18		06 18	07 18		07 18	07 48			08 18		08 18	08b48		09 18
Bromley South 4	d			22 29	23p29	23 34					06 34		06 34	07 34		07 34	08 04			08 34		08 34	09b04		09 34
Maidstone East 4	d			23 13	00 13	00 19	06 19				07 19			08 19			08 50			09 13			10 05		10 13
Ashford International	a	23p17	23p52	00 17	00 42	00 54	06 48	06 50	07 26		07 48		08 24	08 48		08 48	09 26			09 43		09 49	10 26		10 43
	d	23p20	23p53	00 20	00 57	00 58	06 53	06 57	07 28		07 51		08 25	08 51		08 54	09 31	09 36		09 46		09 57	10 32	10 36	10 46
Rye	a							07 53					08 53			09 53						10 53			
Wye	d		23p58		01 03		06 59				07 57			08 57						09 52					10 52
Chilham	d		00 05		01 09		07 05				08 03			09 03						09 58					10 58
Chartham	d		00 09		01 13		07 09				08 07			09 07						10 02					11 02
Canterbury West 4	d		00a15		01a18		07 14				08 13			09 13				09 54		10a07				10 54	11a07
Sturry	d						07 19				08 18			09 18				09 58						10 58	
Westenhanger	d	23p30		00 30		01 07		07 06	07 37				08 34			09 07						10 06			
Sandling	d	23p33		00 33		01 10		07 09	07 40				08 37			09 10						10 09			
Folkestone West	d	23p38		00 38		01 15		07 14	07 45				08 42			09 15						10 14			
Folkestone Central	d	23p41		00 41		01 18		07 17	07 48				08 45			09 18	09 46					10 17	10 47		
Dover Priory 4	⛴ a	23p52		00 52		01 30		07 28	07 59				08 56			09 29	09 58					10 28	10 58		
	d	23p54						07 29	08 00				08 59			09 30	09 58					10 29	10 59		
Martin Mill	d	00 03						07 38	08 09				09 08			09 39	10 07					10 38	11 08		
Walmer	d	00 07						07 42	08 13				09 12			09 43	10 12					10 42	11 12		
Deal	d	00 11						07 46	08 17				09 16			09 47	10 15					10 46	11 16		
Sandwich	d	00 17						07 52	08 23				09 22			09 53	10 22					10 52	11 22		
Minster 4	d						07 31				08 31			09 31				10 09						11 09	
Ramsgate 4	✈ a	00 30					07 37	08 03	08 34		08 38		09 33	09 38		10 04	10 33	10 16				11 03	11 33	11 16	
Dumpton Park	a						07 40	08 24	08 38		09 24		09 37					10 19						11 19	
Broadstairs	a						07 43	08 28	08 41		09 03		09 40	10 03		10 22	11 03	10 22				11 22	11 47	11 22	
Margate 4	a						07 48	08 32	08 46		09 08		09 45	10 08		10 27	11 08	10 27				11 27	11 52	11 27	

For general notes see front of timetable
For details of catering facilities see Directory of Train Operators

b Change at Maidstone East and Ashford International

For details of Bank Holiday service alterations please see first page of Table 195

London and Tonbridge → Ashford International, Folkestone, Dover, Canterbury West, Ramsgate and Margate

Network Diagram - see first page of Table 206

		SE	SE 1	SE 1			SE 1	SE	SE 1 🛒		SE 1	SE 1	SE 1 🛒			SE 1	SE	SE 1 🛒		SE 1	SE 1	SE 1 🛒			SE 1
London Charing Cross 4	⊖ d		09 30	09 53			10 00		10 23			10 30	10 53			11 00		11 23			11 30	11 53			12 00
London Waterloo (East) 4	⊖ d		09 33	09 56			10 03		10 26			10 33	10 56			11 03		11 26			11 33	11 56			12 03
London Cannon Street 4	⊖ d		09 30									10 30									11 30				
London Bridge 4	⊖ d		09 38				10 08					10 38				11 08					11 38				12 08
Orpington 4	d		09 54				10 26					10 54				11 26					11 54				12 26
Sevenoaks 4	d		10 04				10 36					11 04				11 36					12 04				12 36
Tonbridge 4	a		10 15	10 30			10 47		11 02			11 15	11 30			11 47		12 02			12 15	12 30			12 47
	d		10 15	10 31			10 47		11 03			11 15	11 31			11 47		12 03			12 15	12 31			12 47
Paddock Wood 4	d	10 01	10 23				10 55	11 01	11 10			11 23				11 55	12 01	12 10			12 23				12 55
Maidstone West 4	a	10 21						11 21									12 21								
Marden	d						11 01									12 01									13 01
Staplehurst	d		10 32				11 06		11 18			11 32				12 06		12 18			12 32				13 06
Headcorn 4	d		10 37				11 11					11 37				12 11					12 37				13 11
Pluckley	d						11 18									12 18									13 18
London Victoria 15	⊖ d			09 18					09b48		10 18		10 18					10b48		11 18		11 18			
Bromley South 4	d			09 34					10b04		10 34		10 34					11b04		11 34		11 34			
Maidstone East 4	d								11 05		11 13							12 05		12 13					
Ashford International	a		10 50	10 52			11 26		11 32		11 43	11 50	11 52			12 26		12 32		12 43	12 50	12 52			13 26
	d			11 01	11 04				11 36	11 38	11 46		11 57	12 01				12 36	12 38	12 46		12 57	13 00		
Rye	a				11 53									12 53									13 53		
Wye	d										11 52									12 52					
Chilham	d										11 58									12 58					
Chartham	d										12 02									13 02					
Canterbury West 4	d				11 22				11 54		12a07			12 20				12 54		13a07			13c20		
Sturry	d								11 59									12 59							
Westenhanger	d			11 10						11 47									12 47						
Sandling	d			11 13						11 50									12 50						
Folkestone West	d			11 18						11 55									12 55						
Folkestone Central	d			11 21						11 58			12 11						12 58			13 11			
Dover Priory 4	a			11 32						12 09			12 23						13 09			13 23			
	d			11 33						12 10			12 25						13 10			13 25			
Martin Mill	d			11 42						12 19			12 35						13 19			13 35			
Walmer	d			11 46						12 23			12 39						13 23			13 39			
Deal	d			11 50						12 27			12 43						13 27			13 43			
Sandwich	d			11 56						12 33			12 49						13 33			13 49			
Minster 4	d								12 10									13 10							
Ramsgate 4	a			12 07	11 40				12 17	12 44			13 02	12 38				13 17	13 44			14 02	13 38		
Dumpton Park	a				11 44				12 24					12 43				13 24					13 43		
Broadstairs	a				11 47				12 28					12 46				13 28					13 46		
Margate 4	a				11 52				12 32					12 51				13 32					13 51		

		SE	SE 1 🛒		SE 1	SE 1	SE 1 🛒		SE 1		SE	SE 1 🛒		SE 1	SE 1	SE 1 🛒		SE 1		SE	SE 1 🛒		SE 1	SE 1	
London Charing Cross 4	⊖ d		12 23			12 30	12 53		13 00			13 23			13 30	13 53		14 00			14 23			14 30	
London Waterloo (East) 4	⊖ d		12 26			12 33	12 56		13 03			13 26			13 33	13 56		14 03			14 26			14 33	
London Cannon Street 4	⊖ d					12 30									13 30									14 30	
London Bridge 4	⊖ d					12 38			13 08						13 38			14 08						14 38	
Orpington 4	d					12 54			13 26						13 54			14 26						14 54	
Sevenoaks 4	d					13 04			13 36						14 04			14 36						15 04	
Tonbridge 4	a		13 02			13 15	13 30		13 47			14 02			14 15	14 30		14 47			15 02			15 15	
	d		13 03			13 15	13 31		13 47			14 03			14 15	14 31		14 47			15 03			15 15	
Paddock Wood 4	d	13 01	13 10			13 23			13 55		14 01	14 10			14 23			14 55		15 01	15 10			15 23	
Maidstone West 4	a	13 21									14 21									15 21					
Marden	d								14 01									15 01							
Staplehurst	d		13 18			13 32			14 06			14 18			14 32			15 06			15 18			15 32	
Headcorn 4	d					13 37			14 11						14 37			15 11						15 37	
Pluckley	d								14 18									15 18							
London Victoria 15	⊖ d		11b48		12 18		12 18					12b48		13 18		13 18					13b48		14 18		
Bromley South 4	d		12b04		12 34		12 34					13b04		13 34		13 34					14b04		14 34		
Maidstone East 4	d		13 05		13 13							14 05		14 13							15 05		15 13		
Ashford International	a		13 32		13 43	13 50	13 52		14 26			14 32		14 43	14 50	14 52		15 26			15 32		15 43	15 50	
	d		13 36	13 38	13 46		13 57	14 00				14 36	14 38	14 46		14 57	15 00				15 36	15 39	15 46		
Rye	a							14 53									15 53								
Wye	d				13 52									14 52									15 52		
Chilham	d				13 58									14 58									15 58		
Chartham	d				14 02									15 02									16 02		
Canterbury West 4	d		13 54		14a07			14e20				14 54		15a07			15f20				15 54		16a07		
Sturry	d		13 59									14 59									15 59				
Westenhanger	d			13 47									14 47									15 48			
Sandling	d			13 50									14 50									15 51			
Folkestone West	d			13 55									14 55									15 56			
Folkestone Central	d			13 58			14 11						14 58			15 11						15 59			
Dover Priory 4	a			14 09			14 23						15 09			15 23						16 10			
	d			14 10			14 25						15 10			15 25						16 11			
Martin Mill	d			14 19			14 35						15 19			15 35						16 20			
Walmer	d			14 23			14 39						15 23			15 39						16 24			
Deal	d			14 27			14 43						15 27			15 43						16 28			
Sandwich	d			14 33			14 49						15 33			15 49						16 34			
Minster 4	d		14 10									15 10									16 10				
Ramsgate 4	a		14 17	14 44			15 02	14 38				15 17	15 44			16 02	15 38				16 17	16 45			
Dumpton Park	a		14 24					14 43				15 24					15 43				16 24				
Broadstairs	a		14 28					14 46				15 28					15 46				16 28				
Margate 4	a		14 32					14 51				15 32					15 51				16 32				

For general notes see front of timetable
For details of catering facilities see Directory of Train Operators

b Change at Maidstone East and Ashford International
c Arr. 1317
e Arr. 1417
f Arr. 1517

Table 207

Saturdays

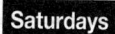

London and Tonbridge → Ashford International, Folkestone, Dover, Canterbury West, Ramsgate and Margate

For details of Bank Holiday service alterations please see first page of Table 195

Network Diagram - see first page of Table 206

	SE 1 ⌶		SE 1	SE		SE 1 ⌶		SE 1	SE 1	SE 1 ⌶		SE 1	SE		SE 1 ⌶		SE 1	SE 1 ⌶		SE 1	SE	SE 1 ⌶		SE 1
London Charing Cross 4 ⊖ d	14 53		15 00			15 23			15 30	15 53		16 00			16 23		16 30	16 53		17 00		17 23		17 30
London Waterloo (East) 4 ⊖ d	14 56		15 03			15 26			15 33	15 56		16 03			16 26		16 33	16 56		17 03		17 26		17 33
London Cannon Street 4 ⊖ d									*15 30*															
London Bridge 4 ⊖ d			15 08						15 38			16 08					16 38			17 08				17 38
Orpington 4 d			15 26						15 54			16 26					16 54			17 26				17 54
Sevenoaks 4 d			15 36						16 04			16 36					17 04			17 36				18 04
Tonbridge 4 a	15 30		15 47			16 02			16 15	16 30		16 47			17 02		17 15	17 30		17 47		18 02		18 15
d	15 31		15 47			16 03			16 15	16 31		16 47			17 03		17 15	17 31		17 47		18 03		18 15
Paddock Wood 4 d			15 55	16 01		16 10			16 23			16 55	17 01		17 10		17 23			17 55	18 01	18 10		18 23
Maidstone West 4 a				16 21									17 21								18 21			
Marden d			16 01									17 01								18 01				
Staplehurst d			16 06			16 18			16 32			17 06			17 18		17 32			18 06		18 18		18 32
Headcorn 4 d			16 11						16 37			17 11					17 37			18 11				18 37
Pluckley d			16 18									17 18								18 18				
London Victoria 15 ⊖ d	*14 18*					*14b48*		15 18		*15 18*					*15b48*			*16 18*				*16b48*		
Bromley South 4 d	*14 34*					*15b04*		15 34		*15 34*					*16b04*			*16 34*				*17b04*		
Maidstone East 4 d						*16 05*		16 13							*17 05*			*17 13*				*18 05*		
Ashford International a	15 52		16 26			16 32		16 43	16 50	16 56		17 26			17 32		17 50	17 52		18 26		18 32		18 50
d	15 57	16 01				16 36	16 39	16 46		16 57	17 00				17 36	17 38		17 57	18 00			18 36	18 38	
Rye a		*16 53*									*17 53*								*18 53*					
Wye d								16 52							17 43							18 43		
Chilham d								16 58							17 49							18 49		
Chartham d								17 02							17 53							18 53		
Canterbury West 4 d		16 20				16 54		17a07			17c20				17 59				18e20			18 59		
Sturry d						16 59									18 04							19 04		
Westenhanger d							16 48									17 47							18 47	
Sandling d							16 51									17 50							18 50	
Folkestone West d							16 56									17 55							18 55	
Folkestone Central d	16 11						16 59			17 11						17 58		18 11					18 58	
Dover Priory 4 ⛴ a	16 23						17 10			17 23						18 09		18 23					19 09	
d	16 25						17 11			17 27						18 10		18 25					19 10	
Martin Mill d	16 35						17 20			17 37						18 19		18 35					19 19	
Walmer d	16 39						17 24			17 41						18 23		18 39					19 23	
Deal d	16 43						17 28			17 45						18 27		18 43					19 27	
Sandwich d	16 49						17 34			17 51						18 33		18 49					19 33	
Minster 4 d						17 10									18 15							19 15		
Ramsgate 4 a	17 02	16 38				17 17	17 45			18 06	17 38				18 23	18 44		19 02	18 38			19 22	19 44	
Dumpton Park a		16 43				*17 24*				*18 24*	17 43					*18 54*			18 43			19 27	*19 54*	
Broadstairs a		16 46				*17 28*				*18 28*	17 46				*18 46*			*19 30*	18 46			19 30		
Margate 4 a		16 51				*17 32*				*18 32*	17 51				*18 51*			*19 35*	18 51			19 35		

	SE 1 ⌶		SE 1		SE 1 ⌶	SE 1	SE	SE 1	SE 1 ⌶	SE	SE 1 ⌶	SE 1 ⌶		SE	SE 1	SE 1	SE 1	SE 1	SE 1	SE 1	SE 1	SE 1	SE 1	
London Charing Cross 4 ⊖ d	17 53		18 00		18 23			18 30	19 00		19 30	20 00			20 30	21 00	21 30	22 00	22 30	23 00		23 30		
London Waterloo (East) 4 ⊖ d	17 56		18 03		18 26			18 33	19 03		19 33	20 03			20 33	21 03	21 33	22 03	22 33	23 03		23 33		
London Cannon Street 4 ⊖ d								*18 30*	*19 00*		*19 14*				*19f14*									
London Bridge 4 ⊖ d			18 08					18 38	19 08		19 38	20 08			20 38	21 08	21 38	22 08	22 38	23 08		23 38		
Orpington 4 d			18 26					18 54	19 24		19 54	20 24			20 54	21 24	21 54	22 24	22 54	23 24		23 54		
Sevenoaks 4 d			18 36					19 04	19 34		20 04	20 34			21 04	21 34	22 04	22 36	23 04	23 36		00 04		
Tonbridge 4 a	18 30		18 47		19 02			19 13	19 45		20 13	20 45			21 13	21 45	22 13	22 47	23 13	23 46		00 15		
d	18 31		18 47		19 03			19 15	19 45		20 15	20 45			21 15	21 45	22 15	22 47	23 15	23 47		00 18		
Paddock Wood 4 d			18 55				19 01	19 22	19 52	20 01	20 22	20 52		21 01	21 22	21 52	22 22	22 55	23 22	23 54		00 25		
Maidstone West 4 a							19 21		*20 21*	20 21		*21 21*		21 21										
Marden d			19 01			←			19 58			20 58				21 58		23 01		23 59		00 31		
Staplehurst d			19 06 →			19 06		19 31	20 03		20 31	21 03			21 31	22 03	22 31	23 06	23 31	00 04		00 36		
Headcorn 4 d						19g18		19 36	20 08		20 36	21 08			21 36	22 08	22 36	23 11	23 36	00 09		00 41		
Pluckley d						19 25			20 15			21 15				22 15		23 18		00 16		00 48		
London Victoria 15 ⊖ d	*17 18*							*18 18*			*18b48*	*19 18*				*20 18*		*21 18*		*22 18*	23 18	*23 18*		
Bromley South 4 d	*17 34*							*18 34*			*19b04*	*19 34*				*20 34*		*21 34*		*22 34*	23 34	*23 34*		
Maidstone East 4 d	*18 13*							*19 13*			*20 05*	*20 19*				*21 19*		*22 19*		*23 19*	00 19	*00 19*		
Ashford International a	18 52				19 24	19 32		19 48	20 23		20 48	21 23			21 48	22 23	22 48	23 26	23 48	00 24	00 48	00 55	←	
d	18 57	19 00			19 27			19 49	20 23		20 49	21 23			21 49	22 24	22 49	23 27	23 51	00 27	00 58 →	00 56	00 58	
Rye a					*19 53*				*20 53*			*21 53*			*22 47*									
Wye d		19 07						19 56			20 56				21 56		22 56		23 58				01 04	
Chilham d		19 13						20 02			21 02				22 02		23 02		00 04				01 10	
Chartham d		19 17						20 06			21 06				22 06		23 06		00 08				01 14	
Canterbury West 4 d		19 24						20 12			21 12				22 12		23 12		00a13				01a19	
Sturry d		19 28						20 17			21 17				22 17		23 17							
Westenhanger d					19 36				20 33			21 33				22 33		23 36		00 37		01 05		
Sandling d					19 39				20 36			21 36				22 36		23 40		00 40		01 08		
Folkestone West d					19 44				20 41			21 41				22 41		23 45		00 45		01 13		
Folkestone Central d	19 11				19 47				20 43			21 43				22 44		23 48		00 47		01 16		
Dover Priory 4 ⛴ a	19 23				19 58				20 55			21 55				22 55		23 59		00 59		01 27		
d	19 25				19 59				20 55			21 58				22 56		23 59						
Martin Mill d	19 35				20 08				21 04			22 07				23 05		00 08						
Walmer d	19 39				20 12				21 09			22 12				23 09		00 13						
Deal d	19 43				20 16				21 12			22 15				23 13		00 16						
Sandwich d	19 49				20 22				21 19			22 22				23 19		00 23						
Minster 4 d		19h42						20 28			21 28				22 28		23 28							
Ramsgate 4 a	20 02	19 49			20 33			20 37	21 30		21 35	22 33			22 37	23 30	23 35	00 35						
Dumpton Park a	20 15	*20 15*						*20 54*			21 41				22 41		23 41							
Broadstairs a	20 18							*20 58*	*21 44*		21 44	22 44			22 44	*23 44*	23 44							
Margate 4 a	20 23							*21 02*	*21 49*		21 49	22 49			22 49	*23 49*	23 49							

For general notes see front of timetable
For details of catering facilities see Directory of Train Operators

b Change at Maidstone East and Ashford International
c Arr. 1717
e Arr. 1817
f Change at London Bridge and Orpington
g Arr. 1911
h Arr. 1939

Table 207

Sundays

London and Tonbridge → Ashford International, Folkestone, Dover, Canterbury West, Ramsgate and Margate

Network Diagram - see first page of Table 206

		SE 1	SE 1	SE 1	SE 1	SE 1	SE 1	SE	SE 1	SE 1		SE 1	SE	SE 1		SE 1	SE 1	SE	SE 1	SE 1		SE 1	SE	SE 1	SE 1
London Charing Cross 4	⊖ d	22p00	22p30	23p00		23p30								08 30			09 00		09 30			10 00		10 30	
London Waterloo (East) 4	⊖ d	22p03	22p33	23p03		23p33								08 33			09 03		09 33			10 03		10 33	
London Cannon Street 4	⊖ d																								
London Bridge 4	⊖ d	22p08	22p38	23p08		23p38								08 38			09 08		09 38			10 08		10 38	
Orpington 4	d	22p24	22p54	23p24		23p54								08 54			09 24		09 54			10 24		10 54	
Sevenoaks 4	d	22p36	23p04	23p36		00 04								09 04			09 34		10 04			10 34		11 04	
Tonbridge 4	a	22p47	23p13	23p46		00 15								09 15			09 43		10 15			10 43		11 15	
	d	22p47	23p15	23p47		00 18			08 15					09 15			09 43		10 16			10 43		11 15	
Paddock Wood 4	d	22p55	23p22	23p54		00 25		07 55	08 22				09 00	09 22			09 50	10 00	10 24			10 50	11 00	11 22	
Maidstone West 4	a							08 15	*09 20*				09 20					10 20				*11 20*	11 20		
Marden	d	23p01		23p59		00 31			08 28					09 28					10 30					11 28	
Staplehurst	d	23p06	23p31	00 04		00 36			08 33					09 33			09 59		10 35			10 59		11 33	
Headcorn 4	d	23p11	23p36	00 09		00 41			08 38					09 38					10 40					11 38	
Pluckley	d	23p18		00 16		00 48			08 45					09 45					10 47					11 45	
London Victoria 15	⊖ d			*22 09*	23p18	*22 42*						07 42		*07 42*		08 42	*08 42*			09 42		*09 42*			10 42
Bromley South 4	d			*22 29*	23p34	*22 59*						07 59		*07 59*		08 59	*08 59*			09 59		*09 59*			10 59
Maidstone East 4	d			*23 13*	00 19	*23 43*						08 43				09 43				10 43					11 43
Ashford International	a	23p26	23p48	00 24	00 48	00 55	←		08 53			09 12		09 52		10 12	10 12		10 56	11 12		11 12		11 52	12 12
	d	23p27	23p51	00 27	00 58 →	00 56	00 58		08 56	08 58		09 16		09 56	09 58	10 17	10 17		10 57	11 16		11 17		11 53	12 16
Rye	a											*09 44*					*10 44*					*11 44*			
Wye	d		23p58				01 04		09 03					10 03					11 04					12 00	
Chilham	d		00 04				01 10		09 09					10 09					11 10					12 06	
Chartham	d		00 08				01 14		09 13					10 13					11 14					12 10	
Canterbury West 4	d		00a13				01a19		09 19			09a32		10 19		10a33			11 20	11a32				12 16	12a32
Sturry	d								09 23					10 23					11 24					12 20	
Westenhanger	d	23p36		00 37		01 05				09 07					10 07		10 26					11 26			
Sandling	d	23p40		00 40		01 08				09 10					10 10		10 29					11 29			
Folkestone West	d	23p45		00 45		01 13				09 15					10 15		10 34					11 34			
Folkestone Central	d	23p48		00 47		01 16				09 18					10 18		10 37					11 37			
Dover Priory 4	⛴ a	23p59		00 59		01 27				09 30					10 30		10 49					11 49			
	d	23p59								09 30					10 30		10 49					11 49			
Martin Mill	d	00 08								09 39					10 39		10 58					11 58			
Walmer	d	00 13								09 44					10 44		11 03					12 03			
Deal	d	00 16								09 47					10 47		11 06					12 06			
Sandwich	d	00 23								09 54					10 54		11 13					12 13			
Minster 4	d								09 34					10 34					11 35					12 31	
Ramsgate 4	a	00 35							09 41	10 05				10 41	11 05		11 24		11 42			12 24		12 38	
Dumpton Park	a								09 46	*10 24*				10 46	*11 24*				11 45					12 43	
Broadstairs	a								09 49	*10 28*				10 49			*11 48*		11 48			*12 46*		12 46	
Margate 4	a								09 54	*10 32*				10 54			*11 53*		11 53			*12 51*		12 51	

		SE 1	SE	SE 1	SE 1	SE 1	SE	SE 1		SE 1	SE 1	SE	SE 1	SE 1	SE 1	SE	SE 1	SE 1		SE 1	SE	SE 1	SE 1	SE 1	SE
London Charing Cross 4	⊖ d	11 00		11 30		12 00		12 30			13 00		13 30		14 00		14 30			15 00		15 30		16 00	
London Waterloo (East) 4	⊖ d	11 03		11 33		12 03		12 33			13 03		13 33		14 03		14 33			15 03		15 33		16 03	
London Cannon Street 4	⊖ d																								
London Bridge 4	⊖ d	11 08		11 38		12 08		12 38			13 08		13 38		14 08		14 38			15 08		15 38		16 08	
Orpington 4	d	11 24		11 54		12 24		12 54			13 24		13 54		14 24		14 54			15 24		15 54		16 24	
Sevenoaks 4	d	11 34		12 04		12 34		13 04			13 34		14 04		14 34		15 04			15 34		16 04		16 34	
Tonbridge 4	a	11 43		12 15		12 43		13 15			13 43		14 15		14 43		15 15			15 43		16 15		16 43	
	d	11 43		12 15		12 43		13 15			13 43		14 15		14 43		15 15			15 43		16 15		16 43	
Paddock Wood 4	d	11 50	12 00	12 22		12 50	13 00	13 22			13 50	14 00	14 22		14 50	15 00	15 22			15 50	16 00	16 22		16 50	17 00
Maidstone West 4	a	*12 20*	12 20			*13 20*	13 20				*14 20*	14 20			*15 20*	15 20				*16 20*	16 20			*17 20*	17 20
Marden	d			12 28				13 28					14 28				15 28					16 28			
Staplehurst	d	11 59		12 33		12 59		13 33			13 59		14 33		14 59		15 33			15 59		16 33		16 59	
Headcorn 4	d			12 38				13 38					14 38				15 38					16 38			
Pluckley	d			12 45				13 45					14 45				15 45					16 45			
London Victoria 15	⊖ d	*10 42*			11 42	*11 42*				12 42	*12 42*			13 42	*13 42*			14 42		*14 42*			15 42	*15 42*	
Bromley South 4	d	*10 59*			11 59	*11 59*				12 59	*12 59*			13 59	*13 59*			14 59		*14 59*			15 59	*15 59*	
Maidstone East 4	d				12 43					13 43				14 43				15 43					16 43		
Ashford International	a	12 12		12 52	13 12	13 12		13 52		14 12	14 12		14 52	15 12	15 12		15 52	16 12		16 12		16 52	17 12	17 12	
	d	12 17		12 53	13 16	13 17		13 53		14 16	14 17		14 53	15 16	15 17		15 53	16 16		16 17		16 58	17 16	17 17	
Rye	a	*12 44*				*13 44*					*14 44*				*15 44*					*16 44*				*17 44*	
Wye	d			13 00				14 00					15 00				16 00					17 05			
Chilham	d			13 06				14 06					15 06				16 06					17 11			
Chartham	d			13 10				14 10					15 10				16 10					17 15			
Canterbury West 4	d			13 16	13a32			14 16		14a32			15 16	15a32			16 16	16a32				17 21	17a32		
Sturry	d			13 20				14 20					15 20				16 20					17 25			
Westenhanger	d	12 26				13 26					14 26				15 26					16 26				17 26	
Sandling	d	12 29				13 29					14 29				15 29					16 29				17 29	
Folkestone West	d	12 34				13 34					14 34				15 34					16 34				17 34	
Folkestone Central	d	12 37				13 37					14 37				15 37					16 37				17 37	
Dover Priory 4	⛴ a	12 49				13 49					14 49				15 49					16 49				17 49	
	d	12 49				13 49					14 49				15 49					16 49				17 49	
Martin Mill	d	12 58				13 58					14 58				15 58					16 58				17 58	
Walmer	d	13 03				14 03					15 03				16 03					17 03				18 03	
Deal	d	13 06				14 06					15 06				16 06					17 06				18 06	
Sandwich	d	13 13				14 13					15 13				16 13					17 13				18 13	
Minster 4	d			13 31				14 31					15 31				16 31					17 36			
Ramsgate 4	a	13 24		13 38		14 24		14 38			15 24		15 38		16 24		16 38			17 24		17 43		18 24	
Dumpton Park	a			13 43				14 43					15 43				16 43					17 48			
Broadstairs	a	*13 46*		13 46		*14 46*		14 46			*15 46*		15 46		*16 46*		16 46			*17 51*		17 51		*18 46*	
Margate 4	a	*13 51*		13 51		*14 51*		14 51			*15 51*		15 51		*16 51*		16 51			*17 56*		17 56		*18 51*	

For general notes see front of timetable
For details of catering facilities see
Directory of Train Operators

Table 207

Sundays

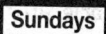

London and Tonbridge → Ashford International, Folkestone, Dover, Canterbury West, Ramsgate and Margate

Network Diagram - see first page of Table 206

		SE 1	SE 1	SE 1	SE	SE 1		SE 1	SE 1	SE	SE 1	SE 1	SE	SE 1	SE 1	SE	SE 1	SE 1	SE	SE 1	SE 1	SE 1	SE 1		
London Charing Cross 4	⊖ d	16 30		17 00		17 30			18 00		18 30	19 00		19 30	20 00		20 30	21 00		21 30	22 00	22 30	23 30		
London Waterloo (East) 4	⊖ d	16 33		17 03		17 33			18 03		18 33	19 03		19 33	20 03		20 33	21 03		21 33	22 03	22 33	23 33		
London Cannon Street 4	⊖ d																								
London Bridge 4	⊖ d	16 38		17 08		17 38			18 08		18 38	19 08		19 38	20 08		20 38	21 08		21 38	22 08	22 38	23 38		
Orpington 4	d	16 54		17 24		17 54			18 24		18 54	19 24		19 54	20 24		20 54	21 24		21 54	22 24	22 54	23 54		
Sevenoaks 4	d	17 04		17 34		18 04			18 34		19 04	19 34		20 04	20 34		21 04	21 34		22 04	22 34	23 04	00 04		
Tonbridge 4	a	17 15		17 43		18 15			18 43		19 15	19 43		20 15	20 43		21 15	21 43		22 15	22 43	23 15	00 13		
	d	17 15		17 43		18 15			18 43		19 15	19 43		20 15	20 43		21 15	21 43		22 15	22 43	23 15	00 13		
Paddock Wood 4	d	17 22		17 50	18 00	18 22			18 50	19 00	19 22	19 50	20 00	20 22	20 50	21 00	21 22	21 50	21 56	22 22	22 50	23 22	00 20		
Maidstone West 4	a			*18 20*	18 20				*19 20*	19 20		*20 20*	20 20		*21 20*	21 20		*22 16*	22 16						
Marden	d	17 28				18 28					19 28			20 28			21 28			22 28		23 28	00 26		
Staplehurst	d	17 33		17 59		18 33			18 59		19 33	19 59		20 33	20 59		21 33	21 59		22 33	22 59	23 33	00 31		
Headcorn 4	d	17 38				18 38					19 38			20 38			21 38			22 38		23 38	00 36		
Pluckley	d	17 45				18 45					19 45			20 45			21 45			22 45		23 45	00 43		
London Victoria 15	⊖ d		16 42	*16 42*				17 42	*17 42*			*18 42*			*19 42*			*20 42*			*21 42*				
Bromley South 4	d		16 59	*16 59*				17 59	*17 59*			*18 59*			*19 59*			*20 59*			*21 59*				
Maidstone East 4	d		17 43					18 43				*19 43*			*20 43*			*21 43*			*22 43*				
Ashford International	a	17 52	18 12	18 12		18 52		19 12	19 12		19 52	20 12		20 52	21 12		21 52	22 12		22 52	23 12	23 52	00 50		
	d	17 53	18 16	18 17		18 53		19 16	19 17		19 53	20 17		20 53	21 17		21 53	22 17		22 53	23 18	23 53			
Rye	a			*18 44*					*19 44*			*20 44*			*21 44*			*22 43*							
Wye	d	18 00				19 00					20 00			21 00			22 00			23 00					
Chilham	d	18 06				19 06					20 06			21 06			22 06			23 06					
Chartham	d	18 10				19 10					20 10			21 10			22 10			23 10					
Canterbury West 4	d	18 16	18a32			19 16		19a32			20 16			21 16			22 16			23 16					
Sturry	d	18 20				19 20					20 20			21 20			22 20			23 20					
Westenhanger	d			18 26					19 26			20 26			21 26			22 26			23 27	00 02			
Sandling	d			18 29					19 29			20 29			21 29			22 29			23 30	00 05			
Folkestone West	d			18 34					19 34			20 34			21 34			22 34			23 35	00 10			
Folkestone Central	d			18 37					19 37			20 37			21 37			22 37			23 38	00 13			
Dover Priory 4	⛴ a			18 49					19 49			20 49			21 49			22 49			23 50	00 25			
	d			18 49					19 49			20 49			21 49			22 49			23 50				
Martin Mill	d			18 58					19 58			20 58			21 58			22 58			23 59				
Walmer	d			19 03					20 03			21 03			22 03			23 03			00 04				
Deal	d			19 06					20 06			21 06			22 06			23 06			00 07				
Sandwich	d			19 13					20 13			21 13			22 13			23 13			00 14				
Minster 4	d	18 31				19 31					20 31			21 31			22 31			23 31					
Ramsgate 4	✈ a	18 38		19 24		19 38			20 24		20 38	21 24		21 38	22 24		22 38	23 24		23 38	00 25				
Dumpton Park	a	18 43				19 43					20 43			*21 54*											
Broadstairs	a	18 46		*19 46*		19 46			*20 46*		20 46			*21 57*											
Margate 4	a	18 51		*19 51*		19 51			*20 51*		20 51			*22 02*											

For general notes see front of timetable
For details of catering facilities see Directory of Train Operators

For details of Bank Holiday service alterations please see first page of Table 195

Margate, Ramsgate, Canterbury West, Dover, Folkestone, Ashford International, → Tonbridge and London

Network Diagram - see first page of Table 206

Miles	Miles	Miles	Station		SE 1	SE	SE 1	SE 1	SE	SE 1	SE	SE 1	SE 1	SE 1	SE 1		SE 1	SE 1	SE	SE 1	SE 1	SE 1	SE 1	SE	SE 1
0	0	—	Margate 4	d													06 07	06 07			06 41		06 41		
3¼	3¼	—	Broadstairs	d													06 12	06 12			06 46		06 46		
4½	4½	—	Dumpton Park	d													06 15	06 15			06 49				
5½	5½	—	Ramsgate 4	d				04 48		05 18			05 38		06 12		06 32	06 19			06 53		06 59		
—	9½	0	Minster 4	d						05 24					06 18		06 38				06 59				
13¾	—	4¾	Sandwich	d				05 01					05 51					06 31					07 11		
18	—	—	Deal	d				05 07					05 57					06 38					07 17		
19½	—	—	Walmer	d				05 10					06 00					06 41					07 20		
22¼	—	—	Martin Mill	d				05 16					06 06					06 47					07 26		
27¼	—	—	Dover Priory 4	a				05 24					06 14					06 55					07 34		
—	—	—		d			04 51	05 25					06 15	06 25				06 56		07 05			07 35		
34½	—	—	Folkestone Central	d			05 03	05 37					06 27	06 37				07 09		07 17			07 47		
35¼	—	—	Folkestone West	d			05 05	05 39					06 29	06 39				07 11		07 19			07 49		
39	—	—	Sandling	d			05 11	05 45					06 35	06 45				07 17		07 25			07 55		
40¼	—	—	Westenhanger	d			05 14	05 48					06 38	06 48				07 20		07 28			07 58		
—	18½	—	Sturry	d						05 36					06 30		06 50				07 10				
—	20¾	—	Canterbury West 4	d						05 42					06 36		06 56				07 16	07 47			
—	24	—	Chartham	d						05 47					06 41		07 01				07 22				
—	26	—	Chilham	d						05 51					06 45		07 05				07 26				
—	30¾	—	Wye	d						05 58					06 52		07 12				07 32	07 59			
—	—	—	Rye	d								05 53	06 16				06 49						07 19		
48½	35	—	Ashford International	a			05 23	05 57		06 06			06 47	06 57	07 00		07 20	07 29		07 37	07 40	08 05	08 07		
—	—	—		d	05 19		05 24	05 58		06 07		06 38	06 50	06 58	07 02		07 22	07 30		07 38	07 45	08 14 →	08 10		08 14
—	54¼	—	Maidstone East 4	a			06 02			06 44			07 23		07 42					08 12			08 43		
—	83¼	—	Bromley South 4	a			06 47			07 29					08 24					09 00			09 27		
—	94¼	—	London Victoria 15	a			07 08			07 49			08 31		08 52					09 19			09 49		
54	—	—	Pluckley	d			05 31			06 14			06 57	07 05	07 09		07 29			07 45	07 52				08 21
59¼	—	—	Headcorn 4	d	05 30		05 37	06 08		06 20		06 51	07 03	07 11	07 15		07 35	07 40		07 51	07 58		08 20		08 27
62¾	—	—	Staplehurst	d	05 36		05 42	06 13		06 25		06 56	07 08	07 16	07 20		07 40	07 45		07 56	08 03		08 26		08 32
65	—	—	Marden	d	05 40		05 47			06 30		07 01		07 21	07 25					08 01	08 08				08 37
—	—	—	Maidstone West 4	d		05 30	05 30		06 05	06 05	06 43	06 43							07 39	07 39				08 19	08 19
69¾	—	—	Paddock Wood 4	d	05 46	05a49	05 53	06 21	06a25	06 36	07a02	07 07	07 16	07 27	07 31		07 48	07 53	07a59	08 07	08 14		08 34	08 40	08 43
75	—	—	Tonbridge 4	a	05 54		06 01	06 29		06 44		07 16	07 25	07 35	07 38		07 58	08 02		08 16	08 25		08 44	08 49	08 55
—	—	—		d	05 55		06 02	06 30		06 45		07 16	07 25	07 36	07 42		07 58	08 02		08 17	08 25		08 46		09 00
82¼	—	—	Sevenoaks 4	a	06 07		06 12	06 39		06 57		07 28	07 35	07 48	07 52		08 08	08 12		08 29			08 56		09 09
90¾	—	—	Orpington 4	a	06 16		06 30	06 58		07 12		07 52			08 12			08 32					09 11		09 32
102¾	—	—	London Bridge 4	a	06 35		06 36	07 03		07 21		07 54	08 10	08 14	08 30		08 34	08 50		08 54			09 22		09 33
—	—	—	London Cannon Street 4	a	06 41		06 47	07 13		07 31		08 00	08 20	08 20	08b39		08 41	08b59		09 01			09 28		09 43
103¾	—	—	London Waterloo (East) 4	a			06 41	07 08		07 27			08 04		08 21			08 41		09c23	09 01				09 38
104½	—	—	London Charing Cross 4	a			06 46	07 14		07 32			08 09		08 26			08 47		09c29	09 07				09 44

Station		SE 1	SE 1	SE 1	SE 1		SE 1	SE 1	SE	SE 1	SE 1	SE 1	SE 1	SE 1	SE 1	SE 1	SE		SE 1	SE 1	SE 1	SE 1	SE 1	SE 1	SE
Margate 4	d		07 07	07 07	07 28					07 43	07 43	08 13		09 04	08 18							09 20			
Broadstairs	d		07 12	07 12	07 33					07 48	07 48	08 18		09 09											
Dumpton Park	d		07 15		07 36					07 50		08 21		09 12											
Ramsgate 4	d		07 19	07 27	07 42					07 55	08 05	08 29		09 17	08 50							09 43			
Minster 4	d			07e38	07 48					08 01	08f16	08 35										09 49			
Sandwich	d		07 31	07 45							08 24				09 02										
Deal	d		07 37	07 51							08 30				09 08										
Walmer	d		07 40	07 55							08 33				09 11										
Martin Mill	d		07 46	08 00							08 39				09 17										
Dover Priory 4	a		07 54	08 09				←			08 47				09 25										
	d		07 55	08 10 →				08 10			08 48				09 26						09 50				
Folkestone Central	d		08 07					08 21			09 00				09 38						10 01				
Folkestone West	d		08 09					08 24							09 40						10 04				
Sandling	d		08 15					08 29							09 46						10 09				
Westenhanger	d		08 18					08 32							09 49						10 12				
Sturry	d				07 59					08 12		08 47										10 00			
Canterbury West 4	d				08 06					08g20		08 53		09 37					09 43			10 06		10 24	
Chartham	d				08 11					08 25		08 58							09 48					10 29	
Chilham	d				08 15					08 28		09 02							09 52					10 33	
Wye	d				08 22					08 34		09 09							09 58					10 39	
Rye	d				07 54		←			08 23	08 54										09 54				
Ashford International	a	←	08 27		08 31		08 27	08 41		08 42	09 13	09 16		09 54	09 58				10 05		10 21	10 24		10 48	
	d	08 14			08 32		08 46			09 04	09 21		09 56	10 01					10 05	10 20	10 28			11 05 →	10 57
Maidstone East 4	a	08 43			08 53					09 33	09 56								10 34		10 57				
Bromley South 4	a	09 27	09h44		09 44		10 14			10 14	10h44			11 14					11 14						
London Victoria 15	a	09 49	10h02 →		10 02		10 32			10 32	11h02			11 32					11 32				←		
Pluckley	d						08 53				09 28		10 03							10 27 →			10 27		
Headcorn 4	d						08 59				09 34		10j13			←							10k40		11m14
Staplehurst	d						09 04				09 39		10 18 →			10 18					10 41		10 45		11 19 →
Marden	d						09 09				09 44					10 22							10 50		
Maidstone West 4	d								09 25		09 25						10 24				10 24				
Paddock Wood 4	d						09 15		09a45		09 50					10 28	10a44				10 49		10 56		
Tonbridge 4	a						09 23				09 57			10 25		10 35					10 57		11 03		
	d						09 24				09 58			10 28		10 36					10 58		11 04		
Sevenoaks 4	a						09 34									10 48							11 15		
Orpington 4	a						09 55									10 57							11 25		
London Bridge 4	a				09 39		09 57									11 13							11 43		
London Cannon Street 4	a				09 57		10 06																		
London Waterloo (East) 4	a				09 45		10 03				10 32			11 02		11 18					11 32		11 48		
London Charing Cross 4	a				09 50		10 07				10 36			11 06		11 21					11 36		11 51		

For general notes see front of timetable
For details of catering facilities see Directory of Train Operators

b Change at Sevenoaks and London Bridge
c Change at Sevenoaks
e Arr. 0733
f Arr. 0811
g Arr. 0817
h Change at Ashford International and Maidstone East
j Arr. 1009
k Arr. 1034
m Arr. 1108

From 12 October due to seasonal difficulties a large number of trains on this table will have minor retimings that could mean slightly earlier departure or later arrival times at certain stations. For further details see local publicity or contact National Rail Enquiries 08457 48 49 50.

Margate, Ramsgate, Canterbury West, Dover, Folkestone, Ashford International, → Tonbridge and London

For details of Bank Holiday service alterations please see first page of Table 195

Network Diagram - see first page of Table 206

		SE 1	SE 1	SE	SE	SE 1	SE 1		SE 1	SE 1	SE 1	SE 1	SE	SE 1	SE 1	SE	SE	SE 1	SE 1		SE 1	SE 1	SE 1	SE 1	SE 1
Margate 4	d	10 04	09 43							10 19				11 04	10 41							11 15			
Broadstairs	d	10 09												11 09											
Dumpton Park	d	10 12												11 12											
Ramsgate 4	d	10 19	09 57							10 43				11 19	10 57							11 43			
Minster 4	d									10 49												11 49			
Sandwich	d		10 09												11 09										
Deal	d		10 15												11 15										
Walmer	d		10 18												11 18										
Martin Mill	d		10 24												11 24										
Dover Priory 4	a		10 32												11 32										
	d		10 33						10 50						11 33						11 50				
Folkestone Central	d		10 45						11 01						11 45						12 01				
Folkestone West	d								11 04												12 04				
Sandling	d								11 09												12 09				
Westenhanger	d								11 12												12 12				
Sturry	d									11 00												12 00			
Canterbury West 4	d	10 39								11 06		11 24		11 39								12 06		12 24	
Chartham	d											11 29												12 29	
Chilham	d											11 33												12 33	
Wye	d											11 39												12 39	
Rye	d								10 54												11 54				
Ashford International	a	10 56	10 59						11 21	11 24		11 46		11 56	11 59						12 21	12 24		12 46	
	d	11 03				← 11 05	11 20		11 28			12 05 →	11 57	12 03				← 12 05	12 20		12 28			13 05 →	12 57
Maidstone East 4	a	11 34				11 34			11 57					12 34				12 34			12 57				
Bromley South 4	a	12 14				12 14								13 14				13 14							
London Victoria 15	⊖ a	12 32				12 32								13 32				13 32							
Pluckley	d						11 27 →				← 11 27								12 27 →				← 12 27		
Headcorn 4	d										11b40		12c14										12e40		13f14
Staplehurst	d			← 11 19					11 41		11 45		12 19 →			← 12 19					12 41		12 45		13 19 →
Marden	d										11 50												12 50		
Maidstone West 4	d				11 24				11 24								12 24				12 24				
Paddock Wood 4	d			11 28	11a44				11 49		11 56					12 28	12a44				12 49		12 56		
Tonbridge 4	a	11 25		11 35					11 57		12 03			12 25		12 35					12 57		13 03		
	d	11 28		11 36					11 58		12 04			12 28		12 36					12 58		13 04		
Sevenoaks 4	a			11 47							12 15					12 47							13 15		
Orpington 4	a			11 57							12 25					12 57							13 25		
London Bridge 4	⊖ a			12 13							12 43					13 13							13 43		
London Cannon Street 4	⊖ a																								
London Waterloo (East) 4	⊖ a	12 02		12 18					12 32		12 48			13 02		13 18					13 32		13 48		
London Charing Cross 4	⊖ a	12 06		12 21					12 36		12 51			13 06		13 21					13 36		13 51		

		SE 1	SE 1	SE 1	SE	SE 1	SE 1	SE 1	SE 1		SE 1	SE 1	SE 1	SE 1	SE 1	SE 1	SE	SE 1	SE 1	SE 1	SE 1		SE 1	SE 1	SE 1
Margate 4	d	12 04	11 41						12 15					13 04	12 41						13 15				
Broadstairs	d	12 09												13 09											
Dumpton Park	d	12 12												13 12											
Ramsgate 4	d	12 19	11 57						12 43					13 19	12 57						13 43				
Minster 4	d								12 49												13 49				
Sandwich	d		12 09												13 09										
Deal	d		12 15												13 15										
Walmer	d		12 18												13 18										
Martin Mill	d		12 24												13 24										
Dover Priory 4	a		12 32												13 32										
	d		12 33					12 50							13 33					13 50					
Folkestone Central	d		12 45					13 01							13 45					14 02					
Folkestone West	d							13 04												14 04					
Sandling	d							13 09												14 10					
Westenhanger	d							13 12												14 13					
Sturry	d								13 00												14 00				
Canterbury West 4	d	12 39							13 06			13 24		13 39							14 06			14 24	
Chartham	d											13 29												14 29	
Chilham	d											13 33												14 33	
Wye	d											13 39												14 39	
Rye	d							12 54												13 54					
Ashford International	a	12 56	12 59					13 21	13 24			13 46		13 56	13 59					14 21	14 24			14 46	
	d	13 03				← 13 05	13 20	13 28				14 05 →	13 57	14 03				← 14 05	14 20	14 28				15 03 →	14 52
Maidstone East 4	a	13 34				13 34		13 57						14 34				14 34		14 57					
Bromley South 4	a	14 14				14 14								15 14				15 14							
London Victoria 15	⊖ a	14 32				14 32								15 32				15 32							
Pluckley	d						13 27 →				← 13 27								14 27 →				← 14 27		14 59
Headcorn 4	d										13g40		14h14										14j40		15k13
Staplehurst	d			← 13 19				13 41			13 45		14 19 →			← 14 19				14 41			14 45		15 18 →
Marden	d										13 50												14 50		
Maidstone West 4	d				13 24			13 24									14 24			14 24					
Paddock Wood 4	d			13 28	13a44			13 49			13 56					14 28	14a44			14 49			14 56		
Tonbridge 4	a	13 25		13 35				13 57			14 03			14 25		14 35				14 57			15 03		
	d	13 28		13 36				13 58			14 04			14 28		14 36				14 58			15 04		
Sevenoaks 4	a			13 47							14 15					14 47							15 15		
Orpington 4	a			13 57							14 25					14 57							15 25		
London Bridge 4	⊖ a			14 13							14 43					15 13							15 43		
London Cannon Street 4	⊖ a																								
London Waterloo (East) 4	⊖ a	14 02		14 18				14 32			14 48			15 02		15 18				15 32			15 48		
London Charing Cross 4	⊖ a	14 06		14 21				14 36			14 51			15 06		15 21				15 36			15 51		

For general notes see front of timetable
For details of catering facilities see Directory of Train Operators

b Arr. 1134
c Arr. 1208
e Arr. 1234
f Arr. 1308
g Arr. 1334
h Arr. 1408
j Arr. 1434
k Arr. 1507

From 12 October due to seasonal difficulties a large number of trains on this table will have minor retimings that could mean slightly earlier departure or later arrival times at certain stations. For further details see local publicity or contact National Rail Enquiries 08457 48 49 50.

For details of Bank Holiday service alterations please see first page of Table 195

Margate, Ramsgate, Canterbury West, Dover, Folkestone, Ashford International, → Tonbridge and London

Network Diagram - see first page of Table 206

		SE 1 ⚒	SE 1	SE 1	SE	SE 1	SE 1 ⚒	SE 1	SE 1	SE 1	SE		SE 1	SE 1	SE 1 ⚒	SE 1	SE	SE 1 ⚒	SE 1	SE 1 ⚒	SE 1	SE	SE 1	SE 1	SE 1 ⚒
Margate 4	d	14 04	13 41					14 15		14 50						14 50			15 36	15 41			16 36	16 15	
Broadstairs	d	14 09							14 20	14 55								15 20	15 41	15 46			16 41		16 52
Dumpton Park	d	14 12								14 58								15 23	15 44				16 44		
Ramsgate 4 ✈	d	14 19	13 57					14 38	14 34	15 02						15 27		15 31	15 48	16 04	16 27		16 48	16 32	17 10
Minster 4	d							14 44								15 33			15 54		16 33		16 54		17b20
Sandwich	d		14 09						14 47									15 44		16 16				16 44	17 28
Deal	d		14 15						14 53									15 50		16 22				16 50	17 34
Walmer	d		14 18						14 56									15 53		16 25				16 53	17 37
Martin Mill	d		14 24						15 02									15 59		16 31				16 59	17 43
Dover Priory 4 ⛴	a		14 32						15 11									16 07		16 39				17 07	17 51
	d		14 33				14 46		15 12						15 40			16 08		16 40				17 08	17 52 →
Folkestone Central	d		14 45				14 58		15 24						15 52			16 20		16 52				17 20	
Folkestone West	d						15 00								15 54					16 54					
Sandling	d						15 06								16 00					17 00					
Westenhanger	d						15 09								16 03					17 03					
Sturry	d							14 56								15 45			16 05		16 45		17 05		
Canterbury West 4	d	14 39						15 02		15 22			15 32			15 51			16 11		16 51		17 11		
Chartham	d												15 37			15 56			16 17		16 56		17 17		
Chilham	d												15 41			16 00			16 21		17 00		17 21		
Wye	d												15 47			16 07			16 27		17 07		17 27		
Rye	d						14 54											15 54					16 54		
Ashford International	a	14 56	14 59			←	15 17	15 20	15 37	15 42			15 54		16 12	16 14		16 34	16 36	17 12	17 14		17 34	17 36	
	d		15 02			15 03		15 24		15 46			15 59	16 06		16 19			16 41		17 19			17 41	
Maidstone East 4	a		15 32			15 32		15 56					16 28			16 45			17 27		17 47			18 29	
Bromley South 4	a		16 14			16 14		16 47					17 14			17 47			18 13		18 45			19 14	
London Victoria 15 ⊖	a		16 33			16 33		17 10		17 33			17 33			18 09			18 32		19 03			19 31	
Pluckley	d									15 53									16 48					17 48	
Headcorn 4	d			←						15 59						16 29			16 54					17 54	
Staplehurst	d			15 18				15 37		16 04				16 20		16 34			16 59		17 32			17 59	
Marden	d			15 22						16 09									17 04					18 04	
Maidstone West 4	d				15 24						15 55			15 55			16 38		16 38			17 28		17 28	
Paddock Wood 4	d			15 28	15a44			15 45		16 15	16a15			16 28		16 42	16a58		17 10		17 40	17a48		18 10	
Tonbridge 4	a		15 25	15 36				15 53		16 22				16 36		16 50			17 17		17 49			18 18	
	d		15 28	15 36				15 54		16 23				16 40		16 51			17 18		17 50			18 20	
Sevenoaks 4	a			15 48				16 03		16 32				16 52		17 03			17 30		18 02			18 29	
Orpington 4	a			15 57				16 34		16 49				17 02		17 12			17 39		18 11			18 39	
London Bridge 4 ⊖	a			16 13				16 29		17 00				17 26		17 31			18 19		18 28			18 57	
London Cannon Street 4 ⊖	a							16 36		17 08				17 31		17 39			18c29		18 37			19 05	
London Waterloo (East) 4 ⊖	a		16 02	16 18				16 34		17 05						17 36			18 03		18 33			19 02	
London Charing Cross 4 ⊖	a		16 06	16 21				16 38		17 10						17 41			18 07		18 37			19 07	

		SE		SE 1	SE	SE 1 ⚒	SE 1 ⚒	SE 1	SE 1 ⚒	SE 1	SE	SE 1	SE 1	SE 1		SE	SE 1	SE 1	SE	SE 1	SE 1	SE 1	SE 1		
Margate 4	d						17 45		18 13			18 52		18 52			19 41			20 47		21 43	22 16		
Broadstairs	d						17 51		18 19			18 57		18 57			19 47			20 52		21 48	22 21		
Dumpton Park	d						17 53		18 21			19 00					19 49			20 55		21 27	22 24		
Ramsgate 4 ✈	d			17 27			18 04	18 09	18 36			19 04		19 14			20 04	20 20		21 04	21 20	22 22	22 32		
Minster 4	d			17 33			18 10	18e20	18 42			19 10					20 10			21 10		22 27			
Sandwich	d							18 27						19 26				20 32			21 32		22 44		
Deal	d							18 33						19 32				20 38			21 38		22 50		
Walmer	d							18 37						19 35				20 41			21 41		22 53		
Martin Mill	d							18 42						19 41				20 47			21 47		22 59		
Dover Priory 4 ⛴	a					←		18 51		←				19 49				20 55			21 55		23 08		
	d					17 52		18 52 →		18 52				19 50				20 56			22 00		23 20		
Folkestone Central	d					18 04				19 04				20 02				21 08			22 12		23 32		
Folkestone West	d					18 06				19 06				20 04				21 11			22 14		23 34		
Sandling	d					18 12				19 12				20 10				21 16			22 20		23 40		
Westenhanger	d					18 15				19 15				20 13				21 19			22 23		23 43		
Sturry	d			17 45			18 21		18 53			19 21					20 21			21 21		22 38			
Canterbury West 4	d			17 51			18 27		18 59			19 27	19 34				20 27			21 27		22 45			
Chartham	d			17 56			18 33		19 05			19 33	19 39				20 33			21 33		22 50			
Chilham	d			18 00			18 37		19 09			19 37	19 43				20 37			21 37		22 53			
Wye	d			18 07			18 43		19 15			19 43	19 49				20 43			21 43		22 59			
Rye	d					17 54			18 54				19 31	19 54				20 54			21 57				
Ashford International	a			18 14		18 23	18 50		19 22	19 24		19 50	19 57	20 22			20 50	21 28		21 50	22 32	23 06	23 51		
	d			18 16		18 25	18 51			19 29		19 51	19 58	20 29			20 51	21 29		21 51	22 33				
Maidstone East 4	a						19 29						20 27				21 27			22 37					
Bromley South 4	a						20 14					21 13	21 13				22 13			23 23					
London Victoria 15 ⊖	a						20 31					21 29	21 29				22 32			23 44					
Pluckley	d					18 32	18 58					19 58					20 58			21 58	22 40				
Headcorn 4	d					18 38	19 04					20 04					21 04			22 04	22 46				
Staplehurst	d			18 29		18 43	19 09			19 42		20 09		20 42			21 09	21 42		22 09	22 51				
Marden	d					18 48	19 14					20 14					21 14			22 14	22 56				
Maidstone West 4	d	17 59		17 59	18 31		18 31				19 39	19 39				20 35	20 35		21 32	21 32					
Paddock Wood 4	d	18a19		18 37	18a51	18 54	19 20			19 50	19a59	20 20		20 50		20a55	21 20	21 50	21a52	22 20	23 02				
Tonbridge 4	a			18 45		19 03	19 27			19 58		20 27		20 58			21 28	21 58		22 28	23 09				
	d			18 46		19 11	19 30			20 00		20 31		21 00			21 30	22 00		22 30	23 10				
Sevenoaks 4	a			18 58			19 39			20 09		20 40		21 09			21 39	22 09		22 39	23 22				
Orpington 4	a			19 07			19 49			20 19		20 49		21 19			21 49	22 19		22 49	23 33				
London Bridge 4 ⊖	a			19 25			20 08			20 38		21 08		21 38			22 08	22 38		23 08	23 51				
London Cannon Street 4 ⊖	a			19 37			20 27																		
London Waterloo (East) 4 ⊖	a			19 31		19 46	20 13			20 43		21 13		21 43			22 13	22 43		23 13	23 56				
London Charing Cross 4 ⊖	a			19 35		19 50	20 18			20 48		21 18		21 48			22 18	22 48		23 18	00 01				

For general notes see front of timetable
For details of catering facilities see Directory of Train Operators

b Arr. 1716
c Change at Orpington and London Bridge
e Arr. 1815

From 12 October due to seasonal difficulties a large number of trains on this table will have minor retimings that could mean slightly earlier departure or later arrival times at certain stations. For further details see local publicity or contact National Rail Enquiries 08457 48 49 50.

Table 207

Saturdays

Margate, Ramsgate, Canterbury West, Dover, Folkestone, Ashford International, → Tonbridge and London

For details of Bank Holiday service alterations please see first page of Table 195

Network Diagram - see first page of Table 206

		SE 1	SE	SE 1	SE 1	SE 1	SE	SE 1	SE 1	SE 1		SE	SE 1	SE 1	SE 1	SE 1	SE 1	SE 1 ✠	SE 1		SE 1	SE 1	SE	SE 1 ✠	SE 1
Margate 4	d													06 49	07 26			08 04	07 26					07 46	
Broadstairs	d													06 54	07 31			08 09						07 51	
Dumpton Park	d													06 56	07 34			08 12						07 53	
Ramsgate 4	d				06 01	05 42		06 18	07 01	06 47				07 14	07 38			08 16	07 57					08 12	08 43
Minster 4	d				06 07				07 07						07 44										08 49
Sandwich	d					05 54		06 30		06 59				07 26					08 09					08 26	
Deal	d					06 00		06 36		07 05				07 32					08 15					08 32	
Walmer	d					06 03		06 39		07 08				07 36					08 18					08 36	
Martin Mill	d					06 09		06 45		07 14				07 41					08 24					08 41	
Dover Priory 4	a					06 17		06 53		07 22				07 50					08 32					08 50	
	d	04 44		05 43		06 18		06 54		07 23				07 50					08 33					08 50	
Folkestone Central	d	04 56		05 55		06 29		07 06		07 35				08 02					08 45					09 02	
Folkestone West	d	04 58		05 57		06 32		07 08						08 04										09 04	
Sandling	d	05 04		06 03		06 37		07 14						08 10										09 10	
Westenhanger	d	05 07		06 06		06 40		07 17						08 13										09 13	
Sturry	d				06 18				07 18						07 55										09 00
Canterbury West 4	d				06 24				07 24						08 01			08 35							09 06
Chartham	d				06 29				07 29						08 07			08 40							
Chilham	d				06 33				07 33						08 11			08 44							
Wye	d				06 40				07 40						08 17			08 51							
Rye	d				*05 56*			*06 50*						*07 54*										*08 54*	
Ashford International	a	05 15		06 14	06 47	06 49		07 26	07 47	07 49				08 21	08 24			08 58	09 00					09 21	09 24
	d	05 21		06 20	06 52			07 26	07 52				08 20	08 28			08 58	09 04			09 20			09 28	
Maidstone East 4	a	*06 29*			*07 29*			*07 57*	*08 34*					*08 57*				*09 34*						*09 57*	
Bromley South 4	a	*07 14*			*08 14*				*09 14*									*10 14*							
London Victoria 15	⊖ a	*07 32*			*08 32*				*09 32*							←		*10 32*							
Pluckley	d	05 28		06 27	06 59				07 59				08 27 →			08 27					09 27 →				
Headcorn 4	d	05 34		06 33	07 06			07 37	08 06							08b40	09c15								
Staplehurst	d	05 39		06 38	07 11			07 42	08 11							08 45	09 20 →					←			
Marden	d	05 44		06 43	07 15				08 15					08 41		08 50						09 20		09 41	
Maidstone West 4	d		06 26	*06 26*			07 24	*07 24*				08 24		*08 24*									09 24	*09 24*	
Paddock Wood 4	d	05 50	06a45	06 49	07 21		07a44	07 50	08 21			08a44		08 49		08 56						09 29	09a44	09 49	
Tonbridge 4	a	05 58		06 57	07 31			07 58	08 29					08 57		09 03		09 25				09 36		09 57	
	d	06 00		06 59	07 31			08 00	08 31					08 58		09 04		09 28				09 37		09 58	
Sevenoaks 4	a	06 12		07 11	07 43			08 09	08 43							09 15						09 48			
Orpington 4	a	06 21		07 20	07 53			08 19	08 53							09 25						09 57			
London Bridge 4	⊖ a	06 40		07 40	08 10			08 40	09 10							09 43						10 13			
London Cannon Street 4	⊖ a			*07 50*	*08 20*			*08 47*	*09 17*							*09 50*									
London Waterloo (East) 4	⊖ a	06 44		07 44	08 14			08 45	09 15					09 32		09 48		10 02				10 18		10 32	
London Charing Cross 4	⊖ a	06 48		07 48	08 18			08 48	09 18					09 36		09 51		10 06				10 21		10 36	

For general notes see front of timetable
For details of catering facilities see Directory of Train Operators

b Arr. 0834
c Arr. 0909

Saturdays

For details of Bank Holiday service alterations please see first page of Table 195

Margate, Ramsgate, Canterbury West, Dover, Folkestone, Ashford International, → Tonbridge and London

Network Diagram - see first page of Table 206

		SE 1	SE 1	SE 1	SE 1	SE 1		SE 1	SE	SE 1	SE 1	SE 1	SE 1	SE 1	SE 1		SE 1	SE 1	SE 1	SE 1	SE	SE 1	SE 1	SE 1	SE 1
					🚌							🚌						🚌						🚌	
Margate 4	d				09 04							*08 48*						10 04	*09 41*						*10 15*
Broadstairs	d				09 09							*08 53*						10 09							
Dumpton Park	d				09 12							*08 56*						10 12							
Ramsgate 4 ✈	d				09 20	08 57						09 14	09 43					10 19	09 57					10 14	10 43
Minster 4	d												09 49												10 49
Sandwich	d					09 09						09 26							10 09					10 26	
Deal	d					09 15						09 32							10 15					10 32	
Walmer	d					09 18						09 36							10 18					10 36	
Martin Mill	d					09 24						09 41							10 24					10 41	
Dover Priory 4 ⛴	a					09 32						09 50							10 32					10 50	
	d					09 33						09 50							10 33					10 50	
Folkestone Central	d					09 45						10 02							10 45					11 02	
Folkestone West	d											10 04												11 04	
Sandling	d											10 10												11 10	
Westenhanger	d											10 13												11 13	
Sturry	d												10 00												11 00
Canterbury West 4	d		09 24		09 39								10 06		10 24			10 38							11 06
Chartham	d		09 29												10 29										
Chilham	d		09 33												10 33										
Wye	d		09 39												10 39										
Rye	d											*09 54*												*10 54*	
Ashford International	a		09 46		09 56	09 59				←		10 21	10 24		10 46			10 55	10 59			←		11 21	11 24
	d		10 05 →	09 57	10 03					10 05	10 20	10 28			11 05 →		10 57	11 03				11 05	11 20	11 28	
Maidstone East 4	a				*10 34*					10 34		*10 57*						*11 34*				11 34		*11 57*	
Bromley South 4	a				*11 14*					11 14								*12 14*				12 14			
London Victoria 15 ⊖	a	←			*11 32*					11 32				←				*12 32*				12 32			
Pluckley	d	09 27									10 27 →			10 27									11 27 →		
Headcorn 4	d	09b40		10c14				←						10e40			11f14			←					
Staplehurst	d	09 45		10 19 →				10 19				10 41		10 45			11 19 →			11 19				11 41	
Marden	d	09 50												10 50											
Maidstone West 4	d								10 24			*10 24*									11 24			*11 24*	
Paddock Wood 4	d	09 56						10 28	10a44			10 49		10 56						11 28	11a44			11 49	
Tonbridge 4	a	10 03			10 25			10 35				10 57		11 03				11 25		11 35				11 57	
	d	10 04			10 28			10 36				10 58		11 04				11 28		11 36				11 58	
Sevenoaks 4	a	10 15						10 47						11 15						11 47					
Orpington 4	a	10 25						10 57						11 25						11 57					
London Bridge 4 ⊖	a	10 43						11 13						11 43						12 13					
London Cannon Street 4 ⊖	a	*10 50*						*11 20*						*11 50*											
London Waterloo (East) 4 ⊖	a	10 48			11 02			11 18				11 32		11 48				12 02		12 18				12 32	
London Charing Cross 4 ⊖	a	10 51			11 06			11 21				11 36		11 51				12 06		12 21				12 36	

		SE 1	SE 1		SE 1	SE 1	SE 1	SE 1	SE	SE 1	SE 1	SE 1	SE 1		SE 1	SE 1	SE 1	SE 1	SE 1	SE 1	SE	SE 1		SE 1	
						🚌						🚌						🚌							
Margate 4	d					11 04	*10 41*						*11 15*					12 04	*11 41*						
Broadstairs	d					11 09												12 09							
Dumpton Park	d					11 12												12 12							
Ramsgate 4 ✈	d					11 20	10 57					11 14	11 43					12 20	11 57						
Minster 4	d												11 49												
Sandwich	d						11 09					11 26							12 09						
Deal	d						11 15					11 32							12 15						
Walmer	d						11 18					11 36							12 18						
Martin Mill	d						11 24					11 41							12 24						
Dover Priory 4 ⛴	a						11 32					11 50							12 32						
	d						11 33					11 50							12 33						
Folkestone Central	d						11 45					12 02							12 45						
Folkestone West	d											12 04													
Sandling	d											12 10													
Westenhanger	d											12 13													
Sturry	d												12 00												
Canterbury West 4	d		11 24			11 39							12 06			12 24		12 39							
Chartham	d		11 29													12 29									
Chilham	d		11 33													12 33									
Wye	d		11 39													12 39									
Rye	d											*11 54*													
Ashford International	a		11 46			11 56	11 59			←		12 21	12 24			12 46		12 56	12 59			←			
	d		12 05 →		11 57	12 03				12 05	12 20	12 28				13 05 →	12 57	13 03				13 05		13 20	
Maidstone East 4	a					*12 34*				12 34		*12 57*						*13 34*				13 34			
Bromley South 4	a					*13 14*				13 14								*14 14*				14 14			
London Victoria 15 ⊖	a	←				*13 32*				13 32					←			*14 32*				14 32			
Pluckley	d	11 27									12 27 →				12 27									13 27 →	
Headcorn 4	d	11g40			12h14			←							12j40		13k14			←					
Staplehurst	d	11 45			12 19 →			12 19				12 41			12 45		13 19 →			13 19					
Marden	d	11 50													12 50										
Maidstone West 4	d								12 24			*12 24*									13 24				
Paddock Wood 4	d	11 56						12 28	12a44			12 49			12 56					13 28	13a44				
Tonbridge 4	a	12 03				12 25		12 35				12 57			13 03			13 25		13 35					
	d	12 04				12 28		12 36				12 58			13 04			13 28		13 36					
Sevenoaks 4	a	12 15						12 47							13 15					13 47					
Orpington 4	a	12 25						12 57							13 25					13 57					
London Bridge 4 ⊖	a	12 43						13 13							13 43					14 13					
London Cannon Street 4 ⊖	a																								
London Waterloo (East) 4 ⊖	a	12 48				13 02		13 18				13 32			13 48			14 02		14 18					
London Charing Cross 4 ⊖	a	12 51				13 06		13 21				13 36			13 51			14 06		14 21					

For general notes see front of timetable
For details of catering facilities see Directory of Train Operators

- b Arr. 0934
- c Arr. 1008
- e Arr. 1034
- f Arr. 1108
- g Arr. 1134
- h Arr. 1208
- j Arr. 1234
- k Arr. 1308

Table 207

Saturdays

Margate, Ramsgate, Canterbury West, Dover, Folkestone, Ashford International, → Tonbridge and London

For details of Bank Holiday service alterations please see first page of Table 195

Network Diagram - see first page of Table 206

		SE 1 🛒	SE 1	SE 1	SE 1	SE 1	SE 1 🛒	SE 1	SE 1		SE	SE 1	SE 1	SE 1 🛒	SE 1	SE 1	SE 1	SE 1		SE 1 🛒	SE 1	SE 1	SE	SE 1	SE 1
Margate ■4	d		12 15				13 04	12 41							13 15					14 04	13 41				
Broadstairs	d						13 09													14 09					
Dumpton Park	d						13 12													14 12					
Ramsgate ■4	d	12 14	12 43				13 20	12 57						13 14	13 43					14 20	13 57				
Minster ■4	d		12 49												13 49										
Sandwich	d	12 26						13 09						13 26							14 09				
Deal	d	12 32						13 15						13 32							14 15				
Walmer	d	12 36						13 18						13 36							14 18				
Martin Mill	d	12 41						13 24						13 41							14 24				
Dover Priory ■4	a	12 50						13 32						13 50							14 32				
	d	12 50						13 33						13 50							14 33				
Folkestone Central	d	13 02						13 45						14 02							14 45				
Folkestone West	d	13 04												14 04											
Sandling	d	13 10												14 10											
Westenhanger	d	13 13												14 13											
Sturry	d		13 00												14 00										
Canterbury West ■4	d		13 06		13 24		13 39								14 06		14 24			14 39					
Chartham	d				13 29												14 29								
Chilham	d				13 33												14 33								
Wye	d				13 39												14 39								
Rye	d	12 54												13 54											
Ashford International	a	13 21	13 24		13 46		13 56	13 59						14 21	14 24		14 46			14 56	14 59				
	d	13 28			14 05 →	13 57	14 03					← 14 05	14 20	14 28			15 05 →	14 57		15 03				← 15 05	15 20
Maidstone East ■4	a	13 57					14 34					14 34		14 57						15 34				15 34	
Bromley South ■4	a						15 14					15 14								16 14				16 14	
London Victoria ■15	⊖ a			←			15 32					15 32				←				16 32				16 32	
Pluckley	d			13 27									14 27 →			14 27									15 27 →
Headcorn ■4	d			13b40		14c14			←							14e40		15f14				←			
Staplehurst	d	13 41		13 45		14 19 →			14 19					14 41		14 45		15 19 →				15 19			
Marden	d			13 50												14 50									
Maidstone West ■4	d	13 24									14 24			14 24									15 24		
Paddock Wood ■4	d	13 49		13 56					14 28		14a44			14 49		14 56						15 28	15a44		
Tonbridge ■4	a	13 57		14 03			14 25		14 35					14 57		15 03				15 25		15 35			
	d	13 58		14 04			14 28		14 36					14 58		15 04				15 28		15 36			
Sevenoaks ■4	a			14 15					14 47							15 15						15 47			
Orpington ■4	a			14 25					14 57							15 25						15 57			
London Bridge ■4	⊖ a			14 43					15 13							15 43						16 13			
London Cannon Street ■4	⊖ a																								
London Waterloo (East) ■4	⊖ a	14 32		14 48			15 02		15 18					15 32		15 48				16 02		16 18			
London Charing Cross ■4	⊖ a	14 36		14 51			15 06		15 21					15 36		15 51				16 06		16 21			

		SE 1 🛒	SE 1	SE 1	SE 1		SE 1	SE 1 🛒	SE 1	SE 1	SE	SE 1	SE 1	SE 1 🛒	SE 1		SE 1	SE 1	SE 1	SE 1 🛒	SE 1	SE 1	SE 1	SE 1 🛒	SE 1
Margate ■4	d		14 15					15 04	14 41						15 15					16 04				15 41	
Broadstairs	d							15 09												16 09				15 46	
Dumpton Park	d							15 12												16 12					
Ramsgate ■4	d	14 14	14 43					15 20	14 57					15 14	15 43					16 16	15 49			16 01	16 25
Minster ■4	d		14 49												15 49										16 31
Sandwich	d	14 26							15 09					15 26							16 01			16 13	
Deal	d	14 32							15 15					15 32							16 07			16 19	
Walmer	d	14 36							15 18					15 36							16 10			16 22	
Martin Mill	d	14 41							15 24					15 41							16 16			16 28	
Dover Priory ■4	a	14 50							15 32					15 50							16 25			16 36	
	d	14 50							15 33					15 50							16 28			16 37	
Folkestone Central	d	15 02							15 45					16 02							16 39			16 49	
Folkestone West	d	15 04												16 04							16 42				
Sandling	d	15 10												16 10							16 48				
Westenhanger	d	15 13												16 13							16 51				
Sturry	d		15 00												16 00										16 42
Canterbury West ■4	d		15 06		15 24			15 39							16 06			16 24		16g39					16 48
Chartham	d				15 29													16 29							
Chilham	d				15 33													16 33							
Wye	d				15 39													16 39							
Rye	d	14 54												15 54											
Ashford International	a	15 21	15 24		15 46			15 56	15 59					16 21	16 24			16 46		16 56	16 59			17 02	17 05
	d	15 28			16 05 →		15 57	16 03				← 16 05	16 20	16 28				17 05 →	16 57	17 03			← 17 05	17 09	
Maidstone East ■4	a	15 57						16 34				16 34		16 57						17 34			17 34	17 57	
Bromley South ■4	a							17 14				17 14								18 14			18 14		
London Victoria ■15	⊖ a			←				17 32				17 32					←			18 32			18 32		
Pluckley	d			15 27									16 27 →				16 27							17 16	
Headcorn ■4	d			15h40			16j14			←							16g40		17k14			←		17 23	
Staplehurst	d	15 41		15 45			16 19 →			16 19				16 41			16 45		17 19 →			17 19		17 28	
Marden	d			15 50													16 50							17 32	
Maidstone West ■4	d	15 24									16 24			16 24											
Paddock Wood ■4	d	15 49		15 56						16 28	16a44			16 49			16 56					17 28		17 38	
Tonbridge ■4	a	15 57		16 03				16 25		16 35				16 57			17 03			17 25		17 35		17 48	
	d	15 58		16 04				16 28		16 36				16 58			17 04			17 28		17 36		17 48	
Sevenoaks ■4	a			16 15						16 47							17 15					17 47		18 00	
Orpington ■4	a			16 25						16 57							17 25					17 57		18 10	
London Bridge ■4	⊖ a			16 43						17 13							17 43					18 13		18 28	
London Cannon Street ■4	⊖ a																					18 20		18 54	
London Waterloo (East) ■4	⊖ a	16 32		16 48				17 02		17 18				17 32			17 48			18 02		18 18		18 32	
London Charing Cross ■4	⊖ a	16 36		16 51				17 06		17 21				17 36			17 51			18 06		18 21		18 36	

For general notes see front of timetable
For details of catering facilities see Directory of Train Operators

b Arr. 1334
c Arr. 1408
e Arr. 1434
f Arr. 1508
g Arr. 1634
h Arr. 1534
j Arr. 1608
k Arr. 1708

Table 207

Saturdays

For details of Bank Holiday service alterations please see first page of Table 195

Margate, Ramsgate, Canterbury West, Dover, Folkestone, Ashford International, → Tonbridge and London

Network Diagram - see first page of Table 206

		SE	SE 1		SE 1	SE	SE 1	SE 1	SE 1	SE	SE 1	SE 1		SE	SE 1	SE 1	SE 1	SE 1	SE 1	SE 1	SE 1		SE 1	SE 1
Margate 4	d				16 15			17 15			18 15				19 15		20 15		20 15	21 24			21 47	22 17
Broadstairs	d				16 20			17 20			18 20				19 20		20 20			21 29	20 52		21 52	22 22
Dumpton Park	d				16 23			17 23			18 23				19 23		20 23			21 32	20 54		21 54	22 25
Ramsgate 4 ✈	d				16 43			17 39	17 43		18 39	18 43			19 39	19 43	20 39	21 00	20 35	21 36	21 29		22 20	22 32
Minster 4	d							17 45			18 45				19 45		20 45	21 06		21 42			22 26	
Sandwich	d				16 55				17 55			18 55				19 55			20 47		21 41			22 44
Deal	d				17 01				18 01			19 01				20 01			20 53		21 47			22 50
Walmer	d				17 04				18 04			19 04				20 04			20 56		21 50			22 53
Martin Mill	d				17 10				18 10			19 10				20 10			21 02		21 56			22 59
Dover Priory 4 ⛴	a				17 18				18 18			19 18				20 18			21 12		22 04			23 07
	d				17 19				18 19			19 19				20 19			21 15		22 05			23 08
Folkestone Central	d				17 31				18 31			19 31				20 31			21 27		22 16			23 19
Folkestone West	d				17 33				18 33			19 33				20 33			21 29		22 19			23 22
Sandling	d				17 39				18 39			19 39				20 39			21 35		22 24			23 27
Westenhanger	d				17 42				18 42			19 42				20 42			21 38		22 27			23 30
Sturry	d							17 56			18 56				19 56		20 56	21 17		21 53			22 37	
Canterbury West 4	d		17 24					18b04			19c04				20e04		21f04	21 23		21 59			22 43	
Chartham	d		17 29					18 10			19 10				20 10		21 10	21 28		22 05			22 49	
Chilham	d		17 33					18 14			19 14				20 14		21 14	21 32		22 09			22 53	
Wye	d		17 39					18 20			19 20				20 20		21 20	21 39		22 15			22 59	
Rye	d				16 54			17 54			18 54				19 54		20 54				21 57			
Ashford International	a		17 46		17 50			18 28	18 50		19 28	19 50			20 28	20 50	21 28	21 46	21 48	22 22	22 36		23 06	23 39
	d		18 00		17 51		← 18 00	18 28	18 51		19 28	19 51			20 28	20 51	21 28	21 52			22 36			
Maidstone East 4	a		→		18 29		18 29		19 29			20 29				21 29		22 29						
Bromley South 4	a				19 14		19 14		20 14			21 14				22 14		23 14						
London Victoria 15 ⊖	a				19 32		19 32		20 32			21 32				22 32		23 32						
Pluckley	d				17 58				18 58			19 58				20 58		21 59			22 43			
Headcorn 4	d				18 04			18 39	19 04		19 39	20 04			20 39	21 04	21 39	22 05			22 50			
Staplehurst	d				18 09			18 44	19 09		19 44	20 09			20 44	21 09	21 44	22 10			22 55			
Marden	d				18 14				19 14			20 14				21 14		22 15			22 59			
Maidstone West 4	d	17 24			17 24	18 24		18 24		19 24	19 24			20 24	20 24									
Paddock Wood 4	d	17a44			18 20	18a44		18 52	19 20	19a44	19 52	20 20		20a44	20 52	21 20	21 52	22 21			23 05			
Tonbridge 4	a				18 28			18 59	19 28		19 59	20 28			20 59	21 28	21 59	22 28			23 13			
	d				18 30			19 00	19 30		20 00	20 30			21 00	21 30	22 00	22 30			23 13			
Sevenoaks 4	a				18 42			19 09	19 42		20 09	20 42			21 09	21 42	22 09	22 42			23 25			
Orpington 4	a				18 51			19 19	19 51		20 19	20 51			21 19	21 51	22 19	22 51			23 37			
London Bridge 4 ⊖	a				19 08			19 38	20 08		20 38	21 08			21 38	22 08	22 38	23 08			23 53			
London Cannon Street 4 ⊖	a																							
London Waterloo (East) 4 ⊖	a				19 14			19 44	20 14		20 44	21 14			21 44	22 14	22 44	23 13			23 57			
London Charing Cross 4 ⊖	a				19 19			19 49	20 19		20 49	21 19			21 49	22 19	22 49	23 18			00 01			

For general notes see front of timetable
For details of catering facilities see Directory of Train Operators

b Arr. 1801
c Arr. 1901
e Arr. 2001
f Arr. 2101

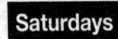

Table 207

Sundays

Margate, Ramsgate, Canterbury West, Dover, Folkestone, Ashford International, → Tonbridge and London

Network Diagram - see first page of Table 206

		SE 1	SE	SE 1	SE 1	SE		SE 1	SE 1	SE	SE 1	SE 1		SE 1	SE	SE 1	SE 1	SE 1		SE	SE 1	SE 1	SE 1	SE	SE 1
Margate 4	d										08 24			*08 24*		09 24		*09 24*			10 24		*10 24*		11 24
Broadstairs	d										08 29			*08 29*		09 29		*09 29*			10 29		*10 29*		11 29
Dumpton Park	d										08 32					09 32					10 32				11 32
Ramsgate 4	d				06 56			07 36	07 56		08 36			08 56		09 36		09 56			10 36		10 56		11 36
Minster 4	d							07 42			08 42					09 42					10 42				11 42
Sandwich	d				07 08				08 08					09 08				10 08					11 08		
Deal	d				07 14				08 14					09 14				10 14					11 14		
Walmer	d				07 17				08 17					09 17				10 17					11 17		
Martin Mill	d				07 23				08 23					09 23				10 23					11 23		
Dover Priory 4	a				07 31				08 31					09 31				10 31					11 31		
	d				07 32				08 32					09 32				10 32					11 32		
Folkestone Central	d				07 44				08 44					09 44				10 44					11 44		
Folkestone West	d				07 46				08 46					09 46				10 46					11 46		
Sandling	d				07 52				08 52					09 52				10 52					11 52		
Westenhanger	d				07 55				08 55					09 55				10 55					11 55		
Sturry	d							07 54			08 54					09 54					10 54				11 54
Canterbury West 4	d							08 00			09 00	09 44				10 00	10 44				11 00	11 44			12 00
Chartham	d							08 05			09 05					10 05					11 05				12 05
Chilham	d							08 09			09 09					10 09					11 09				12 09
Wye	d							08 16			09 16					10 16					11 16				12 16
Rye	d							*07 43*			*08 41*					*09 46*					*10 46*				*11 46*
Ashford International	a				08 03			08 23	09 03		09 23	10 00		10 03		10 23	11 00	11 03			11 23	12 00	12 03		12 23
	d	06 40		07 23	08 04			08 24	09 04		09 24	10 01		10 04		10 24	11 01	11 04			11 24	12 01	12 04		12 24
Maidstone East 4	a							*09 30*				10 30					11 30					12 30			
Bromley South 4	a							*10 16*			*11 16*	11 16				*12 16*	12 16				*13 16*	13 16			*14 16*
London Victoria 15	⊖ a							*10 32*			*11 32*	11 32				*12 32*	12 32				*13 32*	13 32			*14 32*
Pluckley	d	06 47		07 30				08 31			09 31					10 31					11 31				12 31
Headcorn 4	d	06 53		07 36				08 37			09 37					10 37					11 37				12 37
Staplehurst	d	06 58		07 41	08 17			08 42	09 17		09 42			10 17		10 42		11 17			11 42		12 17		12 42
Marden	d	07 03		07 46				08 47			09 47					10 47					11 47				12 47
Maidstone West 4	d		07 23	*07 23*		08 23		*08 23*		09 25	*09 25*				10 25	*10 25*				11 25	*11 25*			12 25	*12 25*
Paddock Wood 4	d	07 09	07a43	07 52	08 25	08a43		08 53	09 25	09a45	09 53			10 25	10a45	10 53		11 25		11a45	11 53		12 25	12a45	12 53
Tonbridge 4	a	07 16		07 59	08 32			09 00	09 32		10 00			10 32		11 00		11 32			12 00		12 32		13 00
	d	07 17		08 00	08 33			09 01	09 33		10 01			10 33		11 01		11 33			12 01		12 33		13 01
Sevenoaks 4	a	07 29		08 12	08 43			09 13	09 43		10 13			10 43		11 13		11 43			12 13		12 43		13 13
Orpington 4	a	07 40		08 23	08 53			09 23	09 53		10 23			10 53		11 23		11 53			12 23		12 53		13 23
London Bridge 4	⊖ a	07 56		08 39	09 09			09 39	10 09		10 39			11 09		11 39		12 09			12 39		13 09		13 39
London Cannon Street 4	⊖ a																								
London Waterloo (East) 4	⊖ a	08 01		08 44	09 14			09 44	10 14		10 44			11 14		11 44		12 14			12 44		13 14		13 44
London Charing Cross 4	⊖ a	08 05		08 48	09 18			09 48	10 18		10 48			11 18		11 48		12 18			12 48		13 18		13 48

		SE 1		SE 1	SE	SE 1	SE 1	SE 1		SE	SE 1	SE 1	SE 1	SE		SE 1	SE 1	SE 1	SE	SE 1		SE 1	SE 1	SE	SE 1
Margate 4	d			*11 24*		12 24		*12 24*			13 24		*13 24*			14 24		*14 24*		15 24			*15 24*		16 24
Broadstairs	d			*11 29*		12 29		*12 29*			13 29		*13 29*			14 29		*14 29*		15 29			*15 29*		16 29
Dumpton Park	d					12 32					13 32					14 32				15 32					16 32
Ramsgate 4	d			11 56		12 36		12 56			13 36		13 56			14 36		14 56		15 36			15 56		16 36
Minster 4	d					12 42					13 42					14 42				15 42					16 42
Sandwich	d			12 08				13 08					14 08					15 08					16 08		
Deal	d			12 14				13 14					14 14					15 14					16 14		
Walmer	d			12 17				13 17					14 17					15 17					16 17		
Martin Mill	d			12 23				13 23					14 23					15 23					16 23		
Dover Priory 4	a			12 31				13 31					14 31					15 31					16 31		
	d			12 32				13 32					14 32					15 32					16 32		
Folkestone Central	d			12 44				13 44					14 44					15 44					16 44		
Folkestone West	d			12 46				13 46					14 46					15 46					16 46		
Sandling	d			12 52				13 52					14 52					15 52					16 52		
Westenhanger	d			12 55				13 55					14 55					15 55					16 55		
Sturry	d					12 54					13 54					14 54				15 54					16 54
Canterbury West 4	d	12 44				13 00	13 44				14 00	14 44				15 00	15 44			16 00		16 44			17 00
Chartham	d					13 05					14 05					15 05				16 05					17 05
Chilham	d					13 09					14 09					15 09				16 09					17 09
Wye	d					13 16					14 16					15 16				16 16					17 16
Rye	d					*12 46*					*13 46*					*14 46*				*15 46*					*16 46*
Ashford International	a	13 00		13 03		13 23	14 00	14 03			14 23	15 00	15 03			15 23	16 00	16 03		16 23		17 00	17 03		17 23
	d	13 01		13 04		13 24	14 01	14 04			14 24	15 01	15 04			15 24	16 01	16 04		16 24		17 01	17 04		17 24
Maidstone East 4	a	13 30					14 30					15 30					16 30					17 30			
Bromley South 4	a	14 16				*15 16*	15 16				*16 16*	16 16				*17 16*	17 16			*18 16*		18 16			*19 16*
London Victoria 15	⊖ a	14 32				*15 32*	15 32				*16 32*	16 32				*17 32*	17 32			*18 32*		18 32			*19 32*
Pluckley	d					13 31					14 31					15 31				16 31					17 31
Headcorn 4	d					13 37					14 37					15 37				16 37					17 37
Staplehurst	d			13 17		13 42		14 17			14 42		15 17			15 42		16 17		16 42			17 17		17 42
Marden	d					13 47					14 47					15 47				16 47					17 47
Maidstone West 4	d				13 25	*13 25*				14 25	*14 25*			15 25		*15 25*			16 25	*16 25*				17 25	*17 25*
Paddock Wood 4	d			13 25	13a45	13 53		14 25		14a45	14 53		15 25	15a45		15 53		16 25	16a45	16 53			17 25	17a45	17 53
Tonbridge 4	a			13 32		14 00		14 32			15 00		15 32			16 00		16 32		17 00			17 32		18 00
	d			13 33		14 01		14 33			15 01		15 33			16 01		16 33		17 01			17 33		18 01
Sevenoaks 4	a			13 43		14 13		14 43			15 13		15 43			16 13		16 43		17 13			17 43		18 13
Orpington 4	a			13 53		14 23		14 53			15 23		15 53			16 23		16 53		17 23			17 53		18 23
London Bridge 4	⊖ a			14 09		14 39		15 09			15 39		16 09			16 39		17 09		17 39			18 09		18 39
London Cannon Street 4	⊖ a																								
London Waterloo (East) 4	⊖ a			14 14		14 44		15 14			15 44		16 14			16 44		17 14		17 44			18 14		18 44
London Charing Cross 4	⊖ a			14 18		14 48		15 18			15 48		16 18			16 48		17 18		17 48			18 18		18 48

For general notes see front of timetable
For details of catering facilities see Directory of Train Operators

Table 207

Sundays

Margate, Ramsgate, Canterbury West, Dover, Folkestone, Ashford International, → Tonbridge and London

Network Diagram - see first page of Table 206

		SE 1	SE 1	SE		SE 1	SE 1	SE 1	SE	SE 1		SE 1	SE 1	SE	SE 1	SE 1		SE	SE 1	SE 1	SE 1	SE 1			
Margate [4]	d		16 24			17 24		17 24		18 24			18 24		19 24	19 24			20 24	20 45		21 24			
Broadstairs	d		16 29			17 29		17 29		18 29			18 29		19 29	19 29			20 29	20 50		21 29			
Dumpton Park	d					17 32				18 32					19 32				20 32	20 53		21 32			
Ramsgate [4]	d		16 56			17 36		17 56		18 36			18 56		19 36	19 56			20 36	21 00	20 43	21 36			
Minster [4]	d					17 42				18 42					19 42				20 42	21 06					
Sandwich	d		17 08					18 08					19 08			20 08					20 55	21 48			
Deal	d		17 14					18 14					19 14			20 14					21 01	21 54			
Walmer	d		17 17					18 17					19 17			20 17					21 04	21 57			
Martin Mill	d		17 23					18 23					19 23			20 23					21 10	22 03			
Dover Priory [4]	a		17 31					18 31					19 31			20 31					21 18	22 11			
	d		17 32					18 32					19 32			20 32					21 19	22 12			
Folkestone Central	d		17 44					18 44					19 44			20 44					21 31	22 24			
Folkestone West	d		17 46					18 46					19 46			20 46					21 33	22 26			
Sandling	d		17 52					18 52					19 52			20 52					21 39	22 32			
Westenhanger	d		17 55					18 55					19 55			20 55					21 42	22 35			
Sturry	d					17 54				18 54					19 54				20 54	21 18					
Canterbury West [4]	d	17 44				18 00	18 44			19 00		19 44			20 00				21 00	21 24					
Chartham	d					18 05				19 05					20 05				21 05	21 29					
Chilham	d					18 09				19 09					20 09				21 09	21 33					
Wye	d					18 16				19 16					20 16				21 16	21 40					
Rye	d					17 46				18 46					19 46				20 46						
Ashford International	a	18 00	18 03			18 23	19 00	19 03		19 23		20 00	20 03		20 23	21 03			21 23	21 47	21 50	22 43			
	d	18 01	18 04			18 24	19 01	19 04		19 24		20 01	20 04		20 24	21 04			21 24	21 54					
Maidstone East [4]	a	18 30					19 30					20 30			21 30					22 30					
Bromley South [4]	a	19 16				20 16	20 16			21 16		21 16			22 16					23 16					
London Victoria [15]	⊖ a	19 32				20 32	20 32			21 32		21 32			22 32					23 32					
Pluckley	d					18 31				19 31					20 31				21 31	22 01					
Headcorn [4]	d					18 37				19 37					20 37				21 37	22 07					
Staplehurst	d		18 17			18 42		19 17		19 42			20 17		20 42	21 17			21 42	22 12					
Marden	d					18 47				19 47					20 47				21 47	22 17					
Maidstone West [4]	d			18 25		18 25			19 25	19 25				20 26	20 26			21 26	21 26						
Paddock Wood [4]	d		18 25	18a45		18 53		19 25	19a45	19 53			20 25	20a46	20 53	21 25		21a46	21 53	22 23					
Tonbridge [4]	a		18 32			19 00		19 32		20 00			20 32		21 02	21 32			22 02	22 30					
	d		18 33			19 01		19 33		20 01			20 33		21 02	21 33			22 02	22 31					
Sevenoaks [4]	a		18 43			19 13		19 43		20 13			20 43		21 14	21 43			22 14	22 43					
Orpington [4]	a		18 53			19 23		19 53		20 23			20 53		21 24	21 53			22 24	22 53					
London Bridge [4]	⊖ a		19 09			19 39		20 09		20 39			21 09		21 40	22 09			22 40	23 09					
London Cannon Street [4]	⊖ a																								
London Waterloo (East) [4]	⊖ a		19 14			19 44		20 14		20 44			21 14		21 44	22 14			22 44	23 14					
London Charing Cross [4]	⊖ a		19 18			19 48		20 18		20 48			21 18		21 48	22 18			22 48	23 19					

For general notes see front of timetable
For details of catering facilities see Directory of Train Operators

For details of Bank Holiday service alterations please see first page of Table 195

Strood → Maidstone West and Paddock Wood

Network Diagram - see first page of Table 206

Miles			SE	SE	SE A	SE	SE	SE	SE	SE	SE	SE	SE	SE	SE	SE	SE	SE
—	**London Charing Cross** ⊖	d			04b56	06 02	06 20	06 40	07 20				09 20	09 52	10 20	10 50	11 20	11 50
—	**London Waterloo (East)** ⊖	d			04b59	06 05	06 23	06 43	07 23				09 23	09 55	10 23	10 53	11 23	11 53
—	**London Cannon Street** ⊖	d				05c50	06 12	06c30	07c10	07 54	08 17	08 50	09c20	09c48	10c18	10c48	11c18	11c48
—	**London Bridge** ⊖	d																
—	Greenhithe for Bluewater	d		05 11	05b48	06 26	07 11	07 33	08 11	08 39	09 07	09 39	10 09	10 39	11 09	11 39	12 09	12 39
—	Gravesend	d		05 18	05b56	06 56	07 19	07 40	08 19	08 46	09 14	09 46	10 16	10 46	11 16	11 46	12 16	12 46
—	Gillingham (Kent)	d	04 56	05 22	06 03	06 53	07 12	07 33	08 15		09 14	09 44	10 14	10 44	11 14	11 44	12 14	12 44
0	**Strood**	d	05 10	05 40	06 18	07 12	07 34	07 55	08 34	09 01	09 31	10 01	10 31	11 01	11 31	12 01	12 31	13 01
2¼	Cuxton	d		05 44	06 23	07 16	07 38	07 59	08 38	09 05	09 35	10 05	10 35	11 05	11 35	12 05	12 35	13 05
4	Halling	d		05 48	06 26	07 20	07 42	08 03	08 42	09 09	09 39	10 09	10 39	11 09	11 39	12 09	12 39	13 09
5½	Snodland	d	05 17	05 51	06 29	07 23	07 45	08 06	08 45	09 12	09 42	10 12	10 42	11 12	11 42	12 12	12 42	13 12
7	New Hythe	d	05 20	05 53	06 32	07 25	07 47	08 09	08 47	09 14	09 44	10 14	10 44	11 14	11 44	12 14	12 44	13 14
7¾	Aylesford	d	05 22	05 56	06 34	07 28	07 50	08 12	08 50	09 17	09 47	10 17	10 47	11 17	11 47	12 17	12 47	13 17
11	Maidstone Barracks	d	05 27	06 01	06 39	07 33	07 55	08 17	08 55	09 22	09 52	10 22	10 52	11 22	11 52	12 22	12 52	13 22
11¼	**Maidstone West**	a	05 29	06 03	06 41	07 35	07 57	08 19	08 57	09 24	09 54	10 24	10 54	11 24	11 54	12 24	12 54	13 24
—		d	05 30	06 05	06 43	07 39		08 19		09 25		10 24		11 24		12 24		13 24
13	East Farleigh	d	05 33	06 09	06 46	07 43		08 23		09 29		10 28		11 28		12 28		13 28
16	Wateringbury	d	05 38	06 14	06 51	07 48		08 28		09 34		10 33		11 33		12 33		13 33
17¾	Yalding	d	05 42	06 17	06 55	07 51		08 31		09 37		10 36		11 36		12 36		13 36
19½	Beltring	d	05 45	06 21	06 58	07 55		08 35		09 41		10 40		11 40		12 40		13 40
21¼	**Paddock Wood**	a	05 49	06 25	07 02	07 59		08 39		09 45		10 44		11 44		12 44		13 44
26½	Tonbridge	a	06e29	06e44	07e16	08e16		08 49		09e57		10e57		11e57		12e57		13e57
—	**London Bridge** ⊖	a	07e03	07e21	07e54	08e54		09 33		11e13		11e43		12e43		13e43		14e43
—	**London Cannon Street** ⊖	a	07f13	07f31	08e00	09e01		09g43		11f27		11f54		12f54		13f54		14f54
—	**London Waterloo (East)** ⊖	a	07e08	07e27	08e04	09e01		09 38		10e32		11e32		12e32		13e32		14e32
—	**London Charing Cross** ⊖	a	07e14	07e32	08e09	09e07		09 44		10e36		11e36		12e36		13e36		14e36

		SE	SE	SE	SE	SE	SE	SE	SE	SE	SE	SE	SE	SE	SE	SE	SE	SE
London Charing Cross ⊖	d	12 20	12 50	13 20	13 50	14 20	14 50	15 50	16 21	16 48	17 32	17 52	18 20	18 54	19 21	19 50	20 20	21 20
London Waterloo (East) ⊖	d	12 23	12 53	13 23	13 53	14 23	14 53	15 53	16 24	16 51	17 35	17 55	18 23	18 57	19 24	19 53	20 23	21 23
London Cannon Street ⊖	d	12c18	12c48	13c18	13c48	14c18	14c48	15c48	16c18	17 02	17 26	18 08		18c50	19c18	19c48	20c15	21c00
London Bridge ⊖	d																	
Greenhithe for Bluewater	d	13 09	13 39	14 09	14 39	15 09	15 39	16 41	17 11	17 45	18 15	18 53	19 05	19 45	20 11	20 40	21 09	22 09
Gravesend	d	13 16	13 46	14 16	14 46	15 16	15 46	16 48	17 18	17 52	18 25	19 00	19 12	19 52	20 18	20 50	21 16	22 16
Gillingham (Kent)	d	13 14	13 44	14 14	14 44	15 14	15 44	16 44	17 14	17 48	18 14	18 44	19 14	19 44	20 16	20 42	21 14	21 42
Strood	d	13 31	14 01	14 31	15 01	15 31	16 12	17 05	17 36	18 08	18 42	19 16	19 36	20 11	20 33	21 07	21 33	22 33
Cuxton	d	13 35	14 05	14 35	15 05	15 35	16 16	17 09	17 40	18 12	18 46	19 20	19 40	20 15	20 37	21 11	21 37	22 37
Halling	d	13 39	14 09	14 39	15 09	15 39	16 20	17 13	17 44	18 16	18 50	19 24	19 44	20 19	20 41	21 15	21 41	22 41
Snodland	d	13 42	14 12	14 42	15 12	15 42	16 23	17 16	17 47	18 19	18 53	19 27	19 47	20 22	20 44	21 18	21 44	22 44
New Hythe	d	13 44	14 14	14 44	15 14	15 44	16 25	17 18	17 49	18 21	18 55	19 29	19 49	20 24	20 46	21 20	21 46	22 46
Aylesford	d	13 47	14 17	14 47	15 17	15 47	16 28	17 21	17 52	18 24	18 58	19 32	19 52	20 27	20 49	21 23	21 49	22 49
Maidstone Barracks	d	13 52	14 22	14 52	15 22	15 52	16 33	17 26	17 57	18 29	19 03	19 37	19 57	20 32	20 54	21 28	21 54	22 54
Maidstone West	a	13 54	14 24	14 54	15 24	15 54	16 35	17 28	17 59	18 31	19 05	19 39	19 59	20 34	20 56	21 30	21 56	22 56
	d		14 24		15 24	15 55	16 38	17 28	17 59	18 31		19 39		20 35		21 32		
East Farleigh	d		14 28		15 28	15 59	16 42	17 32	18 03	18 35		19 43		20 39		21 36		
Wateringbury	d		14 33		15 33	16 04	16 47	17 37	18 08	18 40		19 48		20 44		21 41		
Yalding	d		14 36		15 36	16 07	16 50	17 40	18 11	18 43		19 51		20 47		21 44		
Beltring	d		14 40		15 40	16 11	16 54	17 44	18 15	18 47		19 55		20 51		21 48		
Paddock Wood	a		14 44		15 44	16 15	16 58	17 48	18 19	18 51		19 59		20 55		21 52		
Tonbridge	a		14e57		16e22	16e36	17e17	18e18	18e45	19e27		20e27		21e28		22e28		
London Bridge ⊖	a		15e43		17e00	17e26	18e28	18e57	19e25	20e08		21e08		22e08		23e08		
London Cannon Street ⊖	a		15f54		17f08	17e31	18f37	19f05	19f37	20f27								
London Waterloo (East) ⊖	a		15e32		17e05	17e36	18e03	19e02	19e31	20e13		21e13		22e13		23e13		
London Charing Cross ⊖	a		15e36		17e10	17e41	18e07	19e07	19e35	20e18		21e18		22e18		23e18		

Saturdays

		SE	SE	SE	SE	SE	SE	SE	SE	SE	SE	SE	SE	SE	SE	SE	SE	SE
London Charing Cross ⊖	d		05b04	05 50	06 20	06 50	07 20	07 50	08 20	08 50	09 20	09 50	10 20	10 50	11 20	11 50	12 20	12 50
London Waterloo (East) ⊖	d		05b07	05 53	06 23	06 53	07 23	07 53	08 23	08 53	09 23	09 53	10 23	10 53	11 23	11 53	12 23	12 53
London Cannon Street ⊖	d								08c10	08c48	09c18	09c48	10c18	10c48	11c18	11c48	12c18	12c48
London Bridge ⊖	d																	
Greenhithe for Bluewater	d	05b22	05b54	06 39	07 09	07 39	08 09	08 39	09 09	09 39	10 09	10 39	11 09	11 39	12 09	12 39	13 09	13 39
Gravesend	d	05b29	06b01	06 46	07 16	07 46	08 16	08 46	09 16	09 46	10 16	10 46	11 16	11 46	12 16	12 46	13 16	13 46
Gillingham (Kent)	d	05 48	06 16	06 44	07 14	07 44	08 14	08 44	09 14	09 44	10 14	10 44	11 14	11 44	12 14	12 44	13 14	13 44
Strood	d	06 02	06 30	07 01	07 31	08 01	08 31	09 01	09 31	10 01	10 31	11 01	11 31	12 01	12 31	13 01	13 31	14 01
Cuxton	d	06 07	06 35	07 05	07 35	08 05	08 35	09 05	09 35	10 05	10 35	11 05	11 35	12 05	12 35	13 05	13 35	14 05
Halling	d	06 10	06 38	07 09	07 39	08 09	08 39	09 09	09 39	10 09	10 39	11 09	11 39	12 09	12 39	13 09	13 39	14 09
Snodland	d	06 13	06 41	07 12	07 42	08 12	08 42	09 12	09 42	10 12	10 42	11 12	11 42	12 12	12 42	13 12	13 42	14 12
New Hythe	d	06 16	06 44	07 14	07 44	08 14	08 44	09 14	09 44	10 14	10 44	11 14	11 44	12 14	12 44	13 14	13 44	14 14
Aylesford	d	06 18	06 46	07 17	07 47	08 17	08 47	09 17	09 47	10 17	10 47	11 17	11 47	12 17	12 47	13 17	13 47	14 17
Maidstone Barracks	d	06 23	06 51	07 22	07 52	08 22	08 52	09 22	09 52	10 22	10 52	11 22	11 52	12 22	12 52	13 22	13 52	14 22
Maidstone West	a	06 25	06 53	07 24	07 54	08 24	08 54	09 24	09 54	10 24	10 54	11 24	11 54	12 24	12 54	13 24	13 54	14 24
	d	06 26		07 24		08 24		09 24		10 24		11 24		12 24		13 24		14 24
East Farleigh	d	06 29		07 28		08 28		09 28		10 28		11 28		12 28		13 28		14 28
Wateringbury	d	06 34		07 33		08 33		09 33		10 33		11 33		12 33		13 33		14 33
Yalding	d	06 38		07 36		08 36		09 36		10 36		11 36		12 36		13 36		14 36
Beltring	d	06 41		07 40		08 40		09 40		10 40		11 40		12 40		13 40		14 40
Paddock Wood	a	06 45		07 44		08 44		09 44		10 44		11 44		12 44		13 44		14 44
Tonbridge	a	07 31		07 58		08 57		09 57		10 57		11 57		12 57		13 57		14 57
London Bridge ⊖	a	08 10		08 40		09 43		10 43		11 43		12 43		13 43		14 43		15 43
London Cannon Street ⊖	a	08h20		08h50		09h54		10h54		11h54		12h54		13h54		14h54		15h54
London Waterloo (East) ⊖	a	08 14		08 45		09 32		10 32		11 32		12 32		13 32		14 32		15 32
London Charing Cross ⊖	a	08 18		08 48		09 36		10 36		11 36		12 36		13 36		14 36		15 36

For general notes see front of timetable
For details of catering facilities see Directory of Train Operators

- **A** Also stops at Chatham 0607 and Rochester 0609
- **b** Change at Strood
- **c** Change at London Bridge and Strood
- **e** Until 9 October only
- **f** Until 9 October only. Change at Paddock Wood and London Bridge
- **g** Change at Tonbridge and London Bridge
- **h** Change at Paddock Wood and London Bridge

Table 208

Saturdays

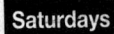

Strood → Maidstone West and Paddock Wood

Network Diagram - see first page of Table 206

		SE		SE	SE		SE	SE		SE	SE		SE	SE		SE	SE		SE	SE		SE	SE		
London Charing Cross 4	⊖ d	13 20		13 50	14 20		14 50	15 20		15 50	16 20		16 50	17 20		17 50	18 20		18 50	19 20		19 50	20 20		
London Waterloo (East) 4	⊖ d	13 23		13 53	14 23		14 53	15 23		15 53	16 23		16 53	17 23		17 53	18 23		18 53	19 23		19 53	20 23		
London Cannon Street 4	⊖ d	13b18		13b48	14b18		14b48	15b18		15b48	16b18		16b48	17b18		17b48	18b18		18b48	19b14					
London Bridge 4	⊖ d																								
Greenhithe for Bluewater	d	14 09		14 39	15 09		15 39	16 09		16 39	17 09		17 39	18 09		18 39	19 09		19 39	20 09		20 40	21 09		
Gravesend 4	d	14 16		14 46	15 16		15 46	16 16		16 46	17 16		17 46	18 16		18 46	19 16		19 46	20 16		20 48	21 16		
Gillingham (Kent) 4	d	14 14		14 44	15 14		15 44	16 14		16 44	17 14		17 44	18 14		18 44	19 14		19 44	20 14		20 42	21 14		
Strood 4	d	14 31		15 01	15 31		16 01	16 31		17 01	17 31		18 01	18 31		19 01	19 31		20 01	20 31		21 01	21 31		
Cuxton	d	14 35		15 05	15 35		16 05	16 35		17 05	17 35		18 05	18 35		19 05	19 35		20 05	20 35		21 05	21 35		
Halling	d	14 39		15 09	15 39		16 09	16 39		17 09	17 39		18 09	18 39		19 09	19 39		20 09	20 39		21 09	21 39		
Snodland	d	14 42		15 12	15 42		16 12	16 42		17 12	17 42		18 12	18 42		19 12	19 42		20 12	20 42		21 12	21 42		
New Hythe	d	14 44		15 14	15 44		16 14	16 44		17 14	17 44		18 14	18 44		19 14	19 44		20 14	20 44		21 14	21 44		
Aylesford	d	14 47		15 17	15 47		16 17	16 47		17 17	17 47		18 17	18 47		19 17	19 47		20 17	20 47		21 17	21 47		
Maidstone Barracks	d	14 52		15 22	15 52		16 22	16 52		17 22	17 52		18 22	18 52		19 22	19 52		20 22	20 52		21 22	21 52		
Maidstone West 4	a	14 54		15 24	15 54		16 24	16 54		17 24	17 54		18 24	18 54		19 24	19 54		20 24	20 54		21 24	21 54		
	d			15 24			16 24			17 24			18 24			19 24			20 24						
East Farleigh	d			15 28			16 28			17 28			18 28			19 28			20 28						
Wateringbury	d			15 33			16 33			17 33			18 33			19 33			20 33						
Yalding	d			15 36			16 36			17 36			18 36			19 36			20 36						
Beltring	d			15 40			16 40			17 40			18 40			19 40			20 40						
Paddock Wood 4	a			15 44			16 44			17 44			18 44			19 44			20 44						
Tonbridge 4	a			15 57			16 57			18 28			18 59			19 59			20 59						
London Bridge 4	⊖ a			16 43			17 43			19 08			19 38			20 38			21 38						
London Cannon Street 4	⊖ a			16c54			17c54																		
London Waterloo (East) 4	⊖ a			16 32			17 32			19 14			19 44			20 44			21 44						
London Charing Cross 4	⊖ a			16 36			17 36			19 19			19 49			20 49			21 49						

Sundays

		SE	SE		SE	SE		SE	SE		SE	SE		SE	SE		SE	SE		SE	SE	SE	SE		
London Charing Cross 4	⊖ d				07 40	08 50		09 50	10 50		11 50	12 50		13 50	14 50		15 50	16 50		17 50	18 50	19 50	20 50		
London Waterloo (East) 4	⊖ d				07 43	08 53		09 53	10 53		11 53	12 53		13 53	14 53		15 53	16 53		17 53	18 53	19 53	20 53		
London Cannon Street 4	⊖ d																								
London Bridge 4	⊖ d																								
Greenhithe for Bluewater	d				08 34	09 39		10 39	11 39		12 39	13 39		14 39	15 39		16 39	17 39		18 39	19 40	20 40	21 40		
Gravesend 4	d				08 42	09 46		10 46	11 46		12 46	13 46		14 46	15 46		16 46	17 46		18 46	19 48	20 48	21 48		
Gillingham (Kent) 4	d	06 44	07 40		08 45	09 45		10 45	11 45		12 45	13 45		14 45	15 45		16 45	17 45		18 45	19 43	20 40	21 40		
Strood 4	d	07 00	08 00		09 02	10 02		11 02	12 02		13 02	14 02		15 02	16 02		17 02	18 02		19 02	20 03	21 03	22 03		
Cuxton	d	07 04	08 04		09 06	10 06		11 06	12 06		13 06	14 06		15 06	16 06		17 06	18 06		19 06	20 07	21 07	22 07		
Halling	d	07 08	08 08		09 10	10 10		11 10	12 10		13 10	14 10		15 10	16 10		17 10	18 10		19 10	20 11	21 11	22 11		
Snodland	d	07 11	08 11		09 13	10 13		11 13	12 13		13 13	14 13		15 13	16 13		17 13	18 13		19 13	20 14	21 14	22 14		
New Hythe	d	07 13	08 13		09 15	10 15		11 15	12 15		13 15	14 15		15 15	16 15		17 15	18 15		19 15	20 16	21 16	22 16		
Aylesford	d	07 16	08 16		09 18	10 18		11 18	12 18		13 18	14 18		15 18	16 18		17 18	18 18		19 18	20 19	21 19	22 19		
Maidstone Barracks	d	07 21	08 21		09 23	10 23		11 23	12 23		13 23	14 23		15 23	16 23		17 23	18 23		19 23	20 24	21 24	22 24		
Maidstone West 4	a	07 23	08 23		09 25	10 25		11 25	12 25		13 25	14 25		15 25	16 25		17 25	18 25		19 25	20 26	21 26	22 26		
	d	07 23	08 23		09 25	10 25		11 25	12 25		13 25	14 25		15 25	16 25		17 25	18 25		19 25	20 26	21 26			
East Farleigh	d	07 27	08 27		09 29	10 29		11 29	12 29		13 29	14 29		15 29	16 29		17 29	18 29		19 29	20 30	21 30			
Wateringbury	d	07 32	08 32		09 34	10 34		11 34	12 34		13 34	14 34		15 34	16 34		17 34	18 34		19 34	20 35	21 35			
Yalding	d	07 35	08 35		09 37	10 37		11 37	12 37		13 37	14 37		15 37	16 37		17 37	18 37		19 37	20 38	21 38			
Beltring	d	07 39	08 39		09 41	10 41		11 41	12 41		13 41	14 41		15 41	16 41		17 41	18 41		19 41	20 42	21 42			
Paddock Wood 4	a	07 43	08 43		09 45	10 45		11 45	12 45		13 45	14 45		15 45	16 45		17 45	18 45		19 45	20 46	21 46			
Tonbridge 4	a	07 59	09 00		10 00	11 00		12 00	13 00		14 00	15 00		16 00	17 00		18 00	19 00		20 00	21 02	22 02			
London Bridge 4	⊖ a	08 39	09 39		10 39	11 39		12 39	13 39		14 39	15 39		16 39	17 39		18 39	19 39		20 39	21 40	22 40			
London Cannon Street 4	⊖ a																								
London Waterloo (East) 4	⊖ a	08 44	09 44		10 44	11 44		12 44	13 44		14 44	15 44		16 44	17 44		18 44	19 44		20 44	21 44	22 44			
London Charing Cross 4	⊖ a	08 48	09 48		10 48	11 48		12 48	13 48		14 48	15 48		16 48	17 48		18 48	19 48		20 48	21 48	22 48			

For general notes see front of timetable
For details of catering facilities see
Directory of Train Operators

b Change at London Bridge and Strood
c Change at Paddock Wood and London Bridge

Mondays to Fridays

For details of Bank Holiday service alterations please see first page of Table 195

Paddock Wood and Maidstone West → Strood

Network Diagram - see first page of Table 206

Miles			SE	SE	SE	SE	SE	SE	SE	SE	SE	SE	SE	SE	SE	SE	SE	SE
—	**London Charing Cross**	⊖ d			05b30		07b00		08 14		08b58		10b00		11b00		12b00	
—	**London Waterloo (East)**	⊖ d			05b33		07b03		08 17		09b01		10b03		11b03		12b03	
—	**London Cannon Street**	⊖ d					06c52		08e14		08c54		10c00		11c00		12c00	
—	**London Bridge**	⊖ d																
0	Tonbridge	d							09 00									
5¼	**Paddock Wood**	d	05 55	06 33	07 06		08 09		09 08		10 03		11 01		12 06		13 06	
7	Beltring	d	05 59	06 37	07 10		08 13		09 12		10 07		11 05		12 10		13 10	
8¾	Yalding	d	06 03	06 41	07 14		08 17		09 16		10 11		11 09		12 14		13 14	
10½	Wateringbury	d	06 06	06 44	07 17		08 20		09 19		10 14		11 12		12 17		13 17	
13½	East Farleigh	d	06 11	06 49	07 22		08 25		09 24		10 19		11 17		12 22		13 22	
15¼	**Maidstone West**	a	06 15	06 53	07 26		08 29		09 28		10 23		11 21		12 26		13 26	
—		d	06 19	06 54	07 26	08 01	08 29	09 01	09 28	09 58	10 27	10 58	11 27	11 58	12 27	12 58	13 27	13 58
15½	Maidstone Barracks	d	06 21	06 56	07 28	08 03	08 31	09 03	09 30	10 00	10 29	11 00	11 29	12 00	12 29	13 00	13 29	14 00
18¾	Aylesford	d	06 26	07 01	07 33	08 08	08 36	09 08	09 35	10 05	10 34	11 05	11 34	12 05	12 34	13 05	13 34	14 05
19½	New Hythe	d	06 29	07 04	07 36	08 10	08 39	09 10	09 38	10 07	10 37	11 07	11 37	12 07	12 37	13 07	13 37	14 07
21	Snodland	d	06 31	07 06	07 38	08 13	08 41	09 13	09 40	10 10	10 39	11 10	11 39	12 10	12 39	13 10	13 39	14 10
22½	Halling	d	06 34	07 09	07 41	08 16	08 44	09 16	09 43	10 13	10 42	11 13	11 42	12 13	12 42	13 13	13 42	14 13
24¼	Cuxton	d	06 38	07 13	07 45	08 19	08 48	09 19	09 47	10 16	10 46	11 16	11 46	12 16	12 46	13 16	13 46	14 16
26½	**Strood**	a	06 42	07 17	07 49	08 24	08 52	09 24	09 51	10 21	10 50	11 21	11 50	12 21	12 50	13 21	13 50	14 21
—	Gillingham (Kent)	a	07 24		08 03		09 07	09 35	10 07	10 37	11 07	11 37	12 07	12 37	13 07	13 37	14 07	14 37
—	Gravesend	a	06 59	07 39	08 07	08 39	09 08		10 06	10 36	11 06	11 36	12 06	12 36	13 06	13 36	14 06	14 36
—	Greenhithe for Bluewater	a	07 06	07 46	08 14	08 46	09 13		10 11	10 41	11 11	11 41	12 11	12 41	13 11	13 41	14 11	14 41
—	**London Bridge**	⊖ a	07 44	08 47	09 11	09 29	09 54		10 49	11 19	11 49	12 19	12 49	13 19	13 49	14 19	14 49	15 19
—	London Cannon Street	⊖ a	07f51	08g54	09h18	09j43	10k06		10k57	11k27	12k00	12k27	12k57	13k27	13k57	14k27	14k57	15k27
—	London Waterloo (East)	⊖ a	08 08	08 29	08 57	09 34	09 59		10 54	11 24	11 54	12 24	12 54	13 24	13 54	14 24	14 54	15 24
—	London Charing Cross	⊖ a	08m13	08n34	09q03	09r39	10 05		10 58	11 28	11 58	12 28	12 58	13 28	13 58	14 28	14 58	15 28

		SE	SE	SE	SE	SE	SE	SE	SE	SE	SE	SE	SE	SE	SE	SE	SE
London Charing Cross	⊖ d	13b00		14b00	15b00	15b30	16b00	16b46	17b12		17b56	18 40	19b00		20b00		21b00
London Waterloo (East)	⊖ d	13b03		14b03	15b03	15b33	16b03	16b49	17b15		17b59	18 43	19b03		20b03		21b03
London Cannon Street	⊖ d	13c00		14c00	15c00	15c30	16c00	16c46	17b20		18b05	18e36	18c50		20c00		21c00
London Bridge	⊖ d																
Tonbridge	d											19 28					
Paddock Wood	d	14 06		15 06	16 06	16 28	17 02	17 52	18 27		18 57	19 38	20 03		21 01		21 57
Beltring	d	14 10		15 10	16 10	16 32	17 06	17 56	18 31		19 01	19 42	20 07		21 05		22 01
Yalding	d	14 14		15 14	16 14	16 36	17 10	18 00	18 35		19 05	19 45	20 11		21 09		22 05
Wateringbury	d	14 17		15 17	16 17	16 39	17 13	18 03	18 38		19 08	19 49	20 14		21 12		22 08
East Farleigh	d	14 22		15 22	16 22	16 44	17 18	18 08	18 43		19 13	19 54	20 19		21 17		22 13
Maidstone West	a	14 26		15 26	16 26	16 48	17 22	18 12	18 47		19 17	19 58	20 23		21 21		22 17
	d	14 27	14 58	15 44	16 27	16 55	17 25	18 12	18 47	19 09	19 27	20 00	20 24	21 00	21 27	22 02	22 19
Maidstone Barracks	d	14 29	15 00	15 46	16 29	16 57	17 27	18 14	18 49	19 11	19 29	20 01	20 26	21 02	21 29	22 04	22 21
Aylesford	d	14 34	15 05	15 51	16 34	17 02	17 32	18 19	18 54	19 16	19 34	20 06	20 31	21 07	21 34	22 09	22 26
New Hythe	d	14 37	15 07	15 54	16 37	17 05	17 35	18 22	18 57	19 18	19 37	20 09	20 34	21 09	21 37	22 11	22 29
Snodland	d	14 39	15 10	15 56	16 39	17 07	17 37	18 24	18 59	19 21	19 39	20 11	20 36	21 12	21 39	22 14	22 31
Halling	d	14 42	15 13	15 59	16 42	17 10	17 40	18 27	19 02	19 24	19 42	20 14	20 39	21 15	21 42	22 17	22 34
Cuxton	d	14 46	15 16	16 03	16 46	17 14	17 44	18 31	19 06	19 27	19 46	20 17	20 43	21 18	21 46	22 20	22 38
Strood	a	14 50	15 21	16 07	16 50	17 18	17 48	18 35	19 10	19 32	19 50	20 22	20 47	21 23	21 50	22 25	22 42
Gillingham (Kent)	a	15 07	15 37	16 37	17 18	17 42	18 07	18 50	19 26	19 55	20 16	20 39	21 17	21 37	22 13	22 37	22 55
Gravesend	a	15 06	15 36	16 36	17 06	17 36	18 10	19 06	19 36		20 06	20 38	21 04	21 38	22 04	22 44	00t28
Greenhithe for Bluewater	a	15 11	15 41	16 41	17 11	17 45	18 15	19 11	19 41		20 11	20 43	21 12	21 43	22 12	22 52	00t34
London Bridge	⊖ a	15 49	16 19	17 26	17 56	18 31	19 02	19 53	20 23		20 53	21 23	21 53	22 23	22 53	23 41	
London Cannon Street	⊖ a	15k57	16k27	17k36	18 01	18k45	19k15	20k11	20k41								
London Waterloo (East)	⊖ a	15 54	16 24	17 31		18 36	19 07	19 58	20 28		20 58	21 28	21 58	22 28	22 58	23 46	
London Charing Cross	⊖ a	15 58	16 28	17 35		18 40	19 11	20 01	20 31		21 01	21 31	22 01	22 31	23 01	23 50	

Saturdays

		SE	SE	SE	SE	SE	SE	SE	SE	SE	SE	SE	SE	SE	SE	SE	SE	SE
London Charing Cross	⊖ d			06 00		07 00		08 00		09 00		10 00		11 00		12 00		13 00
London Waterloo (East)	⊖ d			06 03		07 03		08 03		09 03		10 03		11 03		12 03		13 03
London Cannon Street	⊖ d									09v00		10v00		11v00		12v00		13v00
London Bridge	⊖ d																	
Tonbridge	d																	
Paddock Wood	d			07 01		08 01		09 01		10 01		11 01		12 01		13 01		14 01
Beltring	d			07 05		08 05		09 05		10 05		11 05		12 05		13 05		14 05
Yalding	d			07 09		08 09		09 09		10 09		11 09		12 09		13 09		14 09
Wateringbury	d			07 12		08 12		09 12		10 12		11 12		12 12		13 12		14 12
East Farleigh	d			07 17		08 17		09 17		10 17		11 17		12 17		13 17		14 17
Maidstone West	a			07 21		08 21		09 21		10 21		11 21		12 21		13 21		14 21
	d	06 27	06 57	07 27	07 58	08 27	08 58	09 27	09 58	10 27	10 58	11 27	11 58	12 27	12 58	13 27	13 58	14 27
Maidstone Barracks	d	06 29	06 59	07 29	08 00	08 29	09 00	09 29	10 00	10 29	11 00	11 29	12 00	12 29	13 00	13 29	14 00	14 29
Aylesford	d	06 34	07 04	07 34	08 05	08 34	09 05	09 34	10 05	10 34	11 05	11 34	12 05	12 34	13 05	13 34	14 05	14 34
New Hythe	d	06 36	07 06	07 37	08 07	08 37	09 07	09 37	10 07	10 37	11 07	11 37	12 07	12 37	13 07	13 37	14 07	14 37
Snodland	d	06 39	07 09	07 39	08 10	08 39	09 10	09 39	10 10	10 39	11 10	11 39	12 10	12 39	13 10	13 39	14 10	14 39
Halling	d	06 42	07 12	07 42	08 13	08 42	09 13	09 42	10 13	10 42	11 13	11 42	12 13	12 42	13 13	13 42	14 13	14 42
Cuxton	d	06 45	07 15	07 46	08 16	08 46	09 16	09 46	10 16	10 46	11 16	11 46	12 16	12 46	13 16	13 46	14 16	14 46
Strood	a	06 50	07 20	07 50	08 21	08 50	09 21	09 50	10 21	10 50	11 21	11 50	12 21	12 50	13 21	13 50	14 21	14 50
Gillingham (Kent)	a	07 07	07 37	08 07	08 37	09 07	09 37	10 07	10 37	11 07	11 37	12 07	12 37	13 07	13 37	14 07	14 37	15 07
Gravesend	a	07 05	07 35	08 05	08 36	09 06	09 36	10 06	10 36	11 06	11 36	12 06	12 36	13 06	13 36	14 06	14 36	15 06
Greenhithe for Bluewater	a	07 10	07 40	08 10	08 41	09 11	09 41	10 11	10 41	11 11	11 41	12 11	12 41	13 11	13 41	14 11	14 41	15 11
London Bridge	⊖ a	07 49	08 19	08 49	09 19	09 49	10 19	10 49	11 19	11 49	12 19	12 49	13 19	13 49	14 19	14 49	15 19	15 49
London Cannon Street	⊖ a	08k03	08k33	09k03	09k30	09k57	10k27	10k57	11k27	11k57	12k27	12k57	13k27	13k57	14k27	14k57	15k27	15k57
London Waterloo (East)	⊖ a	07 54	08 24	08 54	09 24	09 54	10 24	10 54	11 24	11 54	12 24	12 54	13 24	13 54	14 24	14 54	15 24	15 54
London Charing Cross	⊖ a	07 58	08 28	08 58	09 28	09 58	10 28	10 58	11 28	11 58	12 28	12 58	13 28	13 58	14 28	14 58	15 28	15 58

For general notes see front of timetable
For details of catering facilities see Directory of Train Operators

- **b** Until 9 October only
- **c** Until 9 October only. Change at London Bridge and Paddock Wood
- **e** Change at London Bridge and Tonbridge
- **f** From 12 October arr. 0752
- **g** From 12 October arr. 0855
- **h** From 12 October arr. 0919
- **j** Change at Strood and London Bridge. From 12 October arr. 0944
- **k** Change at Strood and London Bridge
- **m** From 12 October arr. 0814
- **n** From 12 October arr. 0835
- **q** From 12 October arr. 0904
- **r** From 12 October arr. 0940
- **t** Change at Strood
- **v** Change at London Bridge and Paddock Wood

Table 208

Saturdays

Paddock Wood and Maidstone West → Strood

Network Diagram - see first page of Table 206

		SE	SE	SE	SE	SE	SE	SE	SE	SE	SE	SE	SE	SE	SE
London Charing Cross 4	⊖ d		14 00		15 00		16 00		17 00		18 00		19 00		20 00
London Waterloo (East) 4	⊖ d		14 03		15 03		16 03		17 03		18 03		19 03		20 03
London Cannon Street 4	⊖ d		14b00		15b00		16b00		17b00		18b00		19b00		19b14
London Bridge 4	⊖ d														
Tonbridge 4	d														
Paddock Wood 4	d		15 01		16 01		17 01		18 01		19 01		20 01		21 01
Beltring	d		15 05		16 05		17 05		18 05		19 05		20 05		21 05
Yalding	d		15 09		16 09		17 09		18 09		19 09		20 09		21 09
Wateringbury	d		15 12		16 12		17 12		18 12		19 12		20 12		21 12
East Farleigh	d		15 17		16 17		17 17		18 17		19 17		20 17		21 17
Maidstone West 4	a		15 21		16 21		17 21		18 21		19 21		20 21		21 28
	d	14 58	15 27	15 58	16 27	16 58	17 27	17 58	18 27	18 58	19 27	19 58	20 27	20 58	21 30
Maidstone Barracks	d	15 00	15 29	16 00	16 29	17 00	17 29	18 00	18 29	19 00	19 29	20 00	20 29	21 00	21 35
Aylesford	d	15 05	15 34	16 05	16 34	17 05	17 34	18 05	18 34	19 05	19 34	20 05	20 34	21 05	21 37
New Hythe	d	15 07	15 37	16 07	16 37	17 07	17 37	18 07	18 37	19 07	19 37	20 07	20 37	21 07	21 40
Snodland	d	15 10	15 39	16 10	16 39	17 10	17 39	18 10	18 39	19 10	19 39	20 10	20 39	21 10	21 43
Halling	d	15 13	15 42	16 13	16 42	17 13	17 42	18 13	18 42	19 13	19 42	20 13	20 42	21 13	21 46
Cuxton	d	15 16	15 46	16 16	16 46	17 16	17 46	18 16	18 46	19 16	19 46	20 16	20 46	21 16	21 51
Strood 4	a	15 21	15 50	16 21	16 50	17 21	17 50	18 21	18 50	19 21	19 50	20 21	20 50	21 21	
Gillingham (Kent) 4	a	15 37	16 07	16 37	17 07	17 37	18 07	18 37	19 07	19 37	20 07	20 37	21 13	21 37	22 13
Gravesend 4	a	15 36	16 06	16 36	17 06	17 36	18 06	18 36	19 06	19 36	20 06	20 36	21 04	21 36	22 04
Greenhithe for Bluewater	a	15 41	16 11	16 41	17 11	17 41	18 11	18 41	19 11	19 41	20 11	20 41	21 12	21 41	22 12
London Bridge 4	⊖ a	16 19	16 49	17 19	17 49	18 19	18 49	19 21	19 53	20 23	20 53	21 23	21 53	22 23	22 53
London Cannon Street 4	⊖ a	16c27	16c57	17c27	17c57	18c27									
London Waterloo (East) 4	⊖ a	16 24	16 54	17 24	17 54	18 24	18 54	19 25	19 58	20 28	20 58	21 28	21 58	22 28	22 58
London Charing Cross 4	⊖ a	16 28	16 58	17 28	17 58	18 28	18 58	19 29	20 01	20 31	21 01	21 31	22 01	22 31	23 01

Sundays

		SE	SE	SE	SE	SE	SE	SE	SE	SE	SE	SE	SE	SE	SE	SE	SE
London Charing Cross 4	⊖ d				09 00	10 00	11 00	12 00	13 00	14 00	15 00	16 00	17 00	18 00	19 00	20 00	21 00
London Waterloo (East) 4	⊖ d				09 03	10 03	11 03	12 03	13 03	14 03	15 03	16 03	17 03	18 03	19 03	20 03	21 03
London Cannon Street 4	⊖ d																
London Bridge 4	⊖ d																
Tonbridge 4	d																
Paddock Wood 4	d		07 55	09 00	10 00	11 00	12 00	13 00	14 00	15 00	16 00	17 00	18 00	19 00	20 00	21 00	21 56
Beltring	d		07 59	09 04	10 04	11 04	12 04	13 04	14 04	15 04	16 04	17 04	18 04	19 04	20 04	21 04	22 00
Yalding	d		08 03	09 08	10 08	11 08	12 08	13 08	14 08	15 08	16 08	17 08	18 08	19 08	20 08	21 08	22 04
Wateringbury	d		08 06	09 11	10 11	11 11	12 11	13 11	14 11	15 11	16 11	17 11	18 11	19 11	20 11	21 11	22 07
East Farleigh	d		08 11	09 16	10 16	11 16	12 16	13 16	14 16	15 16	16 16	17 16	18 16	19 16	20 16	21 16	22 12
Maidstone West 4	a		08 15	09 20	10 20	11 20	12 20	13 20	14 20	15 20	16 20	17 20	18 20	19 20	20 20	21 20	22 16
	d	07 00	08 15	09 20	10 20	11 20	12 20	13 20	14 20	15 20	16 20	17 20	18 20	19 20	20 20	21 20	22 16
Maidstone Barracks	d	07 02	08 17	09 22	10 22	11 22	12 22	13 22	14 22	15 22	16 22	17 22	18 22	19 22	20 22	21 22	22 18
Aylesford	d	07 07	08 22	09 27	10 27	11 27	12 27	13 27	14 27	15 27	16 27	17 27	18 27	19 27	20 27	21 27	22 23
New Hythe	d	07 09	08 25	09 30	10 30	11 30	12 30	13 30	14 30	15 30	16 30	17 30	18 30	19 30	20 30	21 30	22 25
Snodland	d	07 12	08 27	09 32	10 32	11 32	12 32	13 32	14 32	15 32	16 32	17 32	18 32	19 32	20 32	21 32	22 28
Halling	d	07 15	08 30	09 35	10 35	11 35	12 35	13 35	14 35	15 35	16 35	17 35	18 35	19 35	20 35	21 35	22 31
Cuxton	d	07 18	08 34	09 39	10 39	11 39	12 39	13 39	14 39	15 39	16 39	17 39	18 39	19 39	20 39	21 39	22 34
Strood 4	a	07 23	08 38	09 43	10 43	11 43	12 43	13 43	14 43	15 43	16 43	17 43	18 43	19 43	20 43	21 43	22 39
Gillingham (Kent) 4	a	08 38	09 04	10 07	11 07	12 07	13 07	14 07	15 07	16 07	17 07	18 07	19 07	20 10	21 10	22 10	22 53
Gravesend 4	a	07 38	09 08	10 08	11 08	12 08	13 08	14 08	15 08	16 08	17 08	18 08	19 08	20 05	21 03	22 03	
Greenhithe for Bluewater	a	07 44	09 14	10 14	11 14	12 14	13 14	14 14	15 14	16 14	17 14	18 14	19 14	20 14	21 12	22 12	
London Bridge 4	⊖ a	08 23	09 53	10 53	11 53	12 53	13 53	14 53	15 53	16 53	17 53	18 53	19 53	20 53	21 53	22 53	
London Cannon Street 4	⊖ a																
London Waterloo (East) 4	⊖ a	08 28	09 58	10 58	11 58	12 58	13 58	14 58	15 58	16 58	17 58	18 58	19 58	20 58	21 58	22 58	
London Charing Cross 4	⊖ a	08 32	10 02	11 02	12 02	13 02	14 02	15 02	16 02	17 02	18 02	19 02	20 02	21 02	22 02	23 02	

For general notes see front of timetable
For details of catering facilities see Directory of Train Operators

b Change at London Bridge and Paddock Wood
c Change at Strood and London Bridge

Network Diagram for Table 212

DM-33/08
Design BAJS

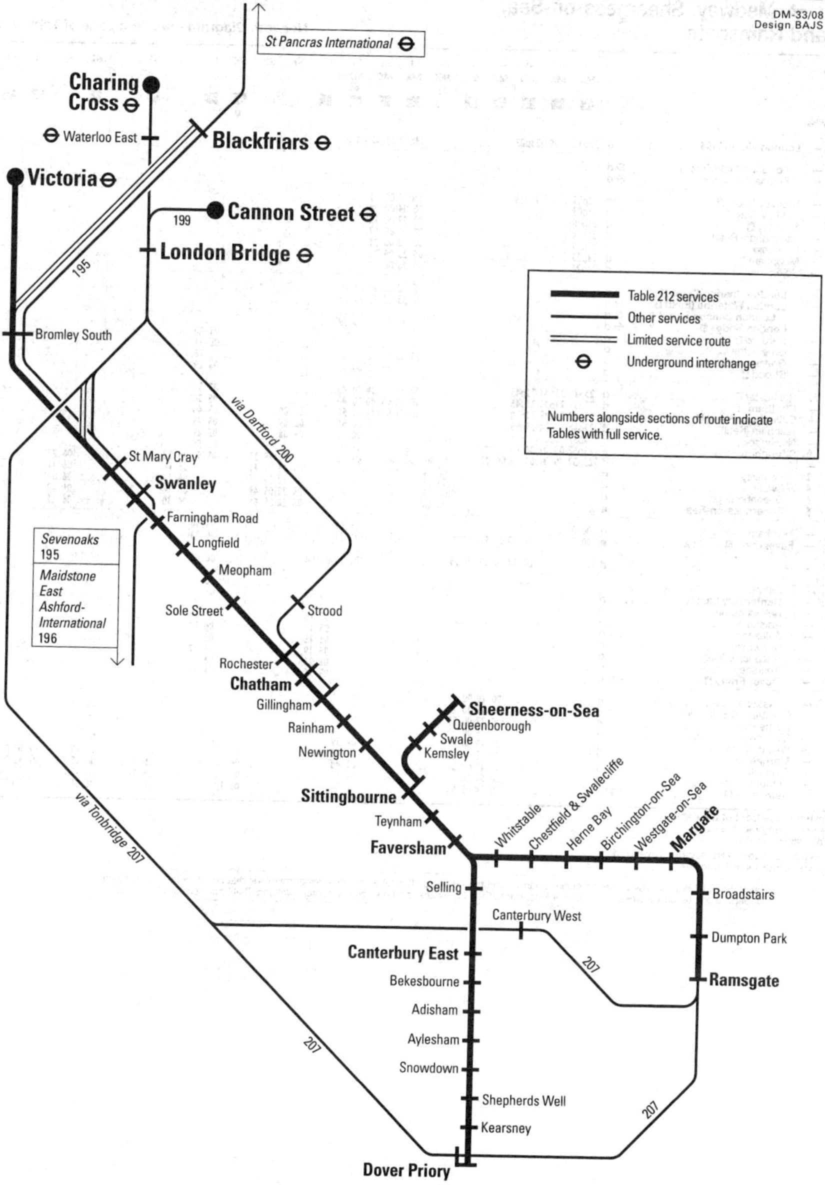

St Pancras International
Charing Cross
Waterloo East
Blackfriars
Victoria
Cannon Street
199
London Bridge
195
Bromley South
via Dartford 200
Table 212 services
Other services
Limited service route
Underground interchange
Numbers alongside sections of route indicate Tables with full service.
St Mary Cray
Swanley
Farningham Road
Longfield
Meopham
Sole Street
Sevenoaks 195
Maidstone East Ashford-International 196
Strood
Rochester
Chatham
Gillingham
Rainham
Newington
Sheerness-on-Sea
Queenborough
Swale
Kemsley
Sittingbourne
Teynham
Faversham
Whitstable
Chestfield & Swalecliffe
Herne Bay
Birchington-on-Sea
Westgate-on-Sea
Margate
Broadstairs
Dumpton Park
Ramsgate
via Tonbridge 207
Selling
Canterbury West
207
Canterbury East
Bekesbourne
Adisham
Aylesham
Snowdown
Shepherds Well
Kearsney
207
207
Dover Priory

For details of Bank Holiday service alterations please see first page of Table 195

London → Medway, Sheerness-on-Sea, Dover and Ramsgate

Network Diagram - see first page of Table 212

Miles	Miles	Miles			SE MX 1	SE MX 1	SE MO 1	SE MX 1	SE MO 1	SE MX 01	SE MX 1	SE MO 1	SE MX 50 1	SE 1	SE	SE	SE 1	SE 1	SE	SE 1		SE 1	SE	SE 1	SE 1
0	0	—	**London Victoria 15**	⊖ d	22p39	23p03	23p03				23p39	23p42	00 03												
—	—	—	**London Blackfriars 3**	⊖ d																					
—	—	—	Elephant & Castle	⊖ d																					
11	11	—	Bromley South 4	d	22p59	23p19	23p19				23p58	00 01													
14¾	14¾	—	St Mary Cray	d	23p05						00 04	00 08													
17½	17½	—	Swanley 4	d	23p10						00 09	00 12													
20½	20½	—	Farningham Road	d	23p14						00 13	00 17													
23½	23½	—	Longfield	d	23p19						00 18	00 21													
26	26	—	Meopham	d	23p23						00 23	00 26													
27	27	—	Sole Street	d	23p26						00 26	00 28													
—	—	—	**London Charing Cross 4**	⊖ d							22 50	23 20	23 20												
—	—	—	**London Waterloo (East) 4**	⊖ d							22 53	23 23	23 23												
—	—	0	**London Cannon Street 4**	⊖ d																					
—	—	—	**London Bridge 4**	⊖ d							22 59	23 29	23 29												
—	—	—	Dartford 4	d							23 34	23 34						05 06							
—	—	—	Greenhithe for Bluewater	d							23 40	23 40						05 11							
—	—	—	Gravesend 4	d							23 50	23 48						05 18							
—	—	—	Strood 4	d							00 02	23 58	00 32					05 29							
33¾	33¾	32	Rochester 4	d	23p36	23p43	23p43				00 35	00 38	00 43					05 33							
34¼	34¼	—	**Chatham 4**	d	23p39	23p46	23p46				00 38	00 40	00 46					05 36							
36	36	—	**Gillingham (Kent) 4**	d	23p43	23p49	23p50				00a41	00a44	00 50		05 00			05 40							
39	39	—	Rainham (Kent)	d	23p48	23p54	23p55						00 55		05 04			05 45							
41½	41½	—	Newington	d	23p52								00 58		05 08			05 49							
44¾	44¾	0	**Sittingbourne 4**	a	23p57	00 01	00 02	←					01 03					05 54							
—	—	—		d	23p57	00 01 →	00 02	00 01		00 08			01 03			05 37		05 54	06 12				06 27		
—	—	2	Kemsley	d						00 12					05 14	05 41			06 16				06 31		
—	—	4	Swale	d						00 15					05 17	05 45			06 19				06 34		
—	—	6	Queenborough	d						00 20					05 22	05 49			06 24				06 40		
—	—	8	**Sheerness-on-Sea**	a						00 26					05 28	05 55			06 30				06 46		
47½	47½	—	Teynham	d	00 01								01 07					05 58							
52	52	—	**Faversham 2**	a	00 07		00 10	00 11	←				01 12					06 04							
—	—	—		d			00 14 →	00 12	00 14				01 13	04 50				06 05				06 13			
—	55½	—	Selling	d														06 10							
—	61¾	—	**Canterbury East 4**	d										05 02				06 19							
—	64¾	—	Bekesbourne	d														06 23							
—	67¾	—	Adisham	d										05 10				06 28							
—	68¾	—	Aylesham	d										05 12				06 30							
—	69¾	—	Snowdown	d										05 15				06 33							
—	71¾	—	Shepherds Well	d										05 19				06 37							
—	75	—	Kearsney	d										05 23				06 41							
—	77¼	—	**Dover Priory 4**	a										05 28				06 48							
59	—	—	Whitstable	d				00 20	00 22				01 21									06 21			
60½	—	—	Chestfield & Swalecliffe	d				00 23	00 25				01 24									06 24			
62¾	—	—	**Herne Bay**	d				00 27	00 29				01 27									06 28			
70¾	—	—	Birchington-on-Sea	d				00 36	00 38				01 36									06 37			
72½	—	—	Westgate-on-Sea	d				00 39	00 41				01 39									06 41			
73¾	—	—	**Margate 4**	d				00 43	00 45				01 43				06 07			06 41		06 45		07 07	07 28
77	—	—	Broadstairs	d				00 48	00 50				01 48				06 12			06 46		06 50		07 12	07 33
78¼	—	—	Dumpton Park	d				00 51	00 53				01 51				06 15			06 49		06 52		07 15	07 36
79¼	—	—	**Ramsgate 4**	a				00 54	00 56				01 54				06 18			06 52		06 56		07 18	07 39

For general notes see front of timetable
For details of catering facilities see Directory of Train Operators

For services from London to Ramsgate, Dover and Canterbury via Ashford see Table 207

From 12 October due to seasonal difficulties a large number of trains on this table will have minor retimings that could mean slightly earlier departure or later arrival times at certain stations. For further details see local publicity or contact National Rail Enquiries 08457 48 49 50.

Mondays to Fridays

For details of Bank Holiday service alterations please see first page of Table 195

London → Medway, Sheerness-on-Sea, Dover and Ramsgate

Network Diagram - see first page of Table 212

	SE 1	SE	SE 1	SE	SE 1	SE 1	SE 1	SE 1	SE 1	SE	SE 1	SE 1	SE	SE 1		SE	SE 1	SE 1	SE 1	SE 1	SE 1		SE	SE 1
					A												🛒							
London Victoria 15 ⊖ d	05 32							06 16			06 39			07 07				07 33		07 39	08 03			08 09
London Blackfriars 3 ⊖ d								05 28			06 10			06 40				07 06		07 24	07 44			07 56
Elephant & Castle ⊖ d								05 32			06 13			06 44				07 09		07 27	07 47			07 59
Bromley South 4 d	05 48							06 34			06 59			07 27				07 52		08 01	08 20			08 31
St Mary Cray d	05 55							06 41			07 05			07 34						08 07				08 37
Swanley 4 d	06 00							06 46			07 10			07 39						08 12				08 42
Farningham Road d	06 05							06 51			07 14			07 44						08 16				08 47
Longfield d	06 10							06 56			07 19			07 48						08 21				08 51
Meopham d	06 15							07 01			07 23			07 53						08 25				08 56
Sole Street d	06 17							07 03			07 26			07 56						08 28				08 58
London Charing Cross 4 ⊖ d	04 56							05 26			06 02			06 40				06 40			07 20			07b45
London Waterloo (East) 4 ⊖ d	04 59							05 29			06 05			06 43				06 43			07 23			07b48
London Cannon Street 4 ⊖ d											05b50			06b30				06c30			07b10			07 54
London Bridge 4 ⊖ d	05 04							05 34			06 10			06 48				06 48			07 28			07 58
Dartford 4 d	05 42							06 12			06 46			07 28				07 28			08 05			08 34
Greenhithe for Bluewater d	05 48							06 18			06e26			07 33				07 33			08 11			08 39
Gravesend 4 d	05 56							06 26			06 56			07 40				07 40			08 19			08 46
Strood 4 d	06 08							06 38			07 08			07 54				07 54			08 32			08 58
Rochester 4 d	06 26							07 15			07 39			08 06						08 38	08 45			09 09
Chatham 4 d	06 29							07 17			07 42			08 08				08 19		08 41	08 48			09 11
Gillingham (Kent) 4 d	06 33							07 21			07 45			08 12				08 23		08 45	08 51			09 15
Rainham (Kent) d	06 38							07 26			07 50			08 17				08 28		08 50	08 56			09 20
Newington d	06 42							07 30			07 54			08 21						08 54				09 24
Sittingbourne 4 a	06 47							07 35			07 59			08 26				08 36		08 59	09 03			09 29
d	06 48	06 58		07 19				07 35		07 46	08 04		08 15	08 27		08 28		08 37		08 59	09 04		09 05	09 29
Kemsley d		07 04		07f26						07 50			08 19			08 32							09 09	
Swale d		07 08		07 32						07 55			08 22			08 36							09 12	
Queenborough d		07 12		07 36						07 59			08 27			08 41							09 17	
Sheerness-on-Sea a		07 18		07 41						08 04			08 32			08 47							09 23	
Teynham d	06 52							07 39			08 09			08 31						09 03				09 33
Faversham 2 a	07 00							07 45			08 15			08 37				08 45	←	09 09	09 12			09 39
d	07 01		07 04			07 20		07 46	07 51		08 17	08 19		08 49				08 47	08 49		09 16	09 18		
Selling d			07 09						07 56		08 22			→					08 54					
Canterbury East 4 d			07 18						08g08		08 32								09 04			09 32		
Bekesbourne d			07 22						08 12		08 36								09 08					
Adisham d			07 27						08 17		08 41								09 13					
Aylesham d			07 29						08 19		08 43								09 15					
Snowdown d			07 32						08 22		08 46								09 18					
Shepherds Well d			07 36						08 26		08 50								09 22					
Kearsney d			07 40						08 30		08 54								09 26					
Dover Priory 4 ⛴ a			07 45						08 36		09 00								09 32			09 52		
Whitstable d	07 09					07 28		07 54				08 28						08 56			09 24			
Chestfield & Swalecliffe d	07 12					07 31		07 57				08 31						08 59						
Herne Bay d	07 16					07 35		08 01				08 35						09 03			09 29			
Birchington-on-Sea d	07 25					07 44		08 10				08 44						09 12			09 37			
Westgate-on-Sea d	07 29					07 48		08 14				08 47						09 16						
Margate 4 d	07 33				07 43	07 52	08 13	08 18				08 52					09 04	09 20			09 43			
Broadstairs d	07 38				07 48	07 57	08 18	08 23				08 57					09 09	09 25			09 48			
Dumpton Park d	07 40				07 50	07 59	08 21	08 26				09 00					09 12	09 27						
Ramsgate 4 ✈ a	07 43				07 53	08 03	08 24	08 29				09 03					09 15	09 30			09 52			

For general notes see front of timetable
For details of catering facilities see Directory of Train Operators

For services from London to Ramsgate, Dover and Canterbury via Ashford see Table 207

A To London Victoria (Table 196)
b Change at London Bridge and Rochester
c Change at London Bridge and Chatham
e Change at Gravesend and Rochester
f Arr. 0723
g Arr. 0805

From 12 October due to seasonal difficulties a large number of trains on this table will have minor retimings that could mean slightly earlier departure or later arrival times at certain stations. For further details see local publicity or contact National Rail Enquiries 08457 48 49 50.

For details of Bank Holiday service alterations please see first page of Table 195

London → Medway, Sheerness-on-Sea, Dover and Ramsgate

Network Diagram - see first page of Table 212

Station		SE 1 🚲	SE 1		SE	SE 1	SE 1		SE	SE 1	
London Victoria 15	⊖ d		08 33			08 39	09 03			09 09	
London Blackfriars 3	⊖ d		08 16			08 24	08 44				
Elephant & Castle	⊖ d					08 28	08 47				
Bromley South 4	d		08 51			09 00	09 19			09 29	
St Mary Cray	d					09 07				09 35	
Swanley 4	d					09 11				09 40	
Farningham Road	d					09 16				09 44	
Longfield	d					09 20				09 49	
Meopham	d					09 25				09 53	
Sole Street	d					09 27				09 56	
London Charing Cross 4	⊖ d					08b08				08b41	
London Waterloo (East) 4	⊖ d					08b11				08b44	
London Cannon Street 4	⊖ d					08 17				08 50	
London Bridge 4	⊖ d					08 21				08 54	
Dartford 4	d					09 02				09 34	
Greenhithe for Bluewater	d					09 07				09 39	
Gravesend 4	d					09 14				09 46	
Strood 4	d					09 26				09 58	
Rochester 4	d		09 16			09 36	09 43			10 05	
Chatham 4	d		09 18			09 39	09 47			10 08	
Gillingham (Kent) 4	d		09 22			09 43	09 50			10 12	
Rainham (Kent)	d		09 26			09 48	09 55			10 17	
Newington	d					09 52				10 21	
Sittingbourne 4	a		09 34			09 57	10 02			10 26	
	d		09 34		09 36	09 57	10 02		10 05	10 26	
Kemsley	d				09 40				10 09		
Swale	d				09 43				10 12		
Queenborough	d				09 47				10 17		
Sheerness-on-Sea	a				09 53				10 23		
Teynham	d					10 01				10 30	
Faversham 2	a		09 42			10 07	10 10			10 36	
	d		09 46	09 48			10 14	10 16			
Selling	d			09 53							
Canterbury East 4	d			10c08				10 28			
Bekesbourne	d			10 13							
Adisham	d			10 17							
Aylesham	d			10 20							
Snowdown	d			10 22							
Shepherds Well	d			10 26							
Kearsney	d			10 31							
Dover Priory 4	⛴ a			10 35				10 45			
Whitstable	d		09 55				10 22				
Chestfield & Swalecliffe	d		09 58								
Herne Bay	d		10 02				10 27				
Birchington-on-Sea	d		10 11				10 35				
Westgate-on-Sea	d		10 15								
Margate 4	d	10 04	10 19				10 41				
Broadstairs	d	10 09	10 24				10 46				
Dumpton Park	d	10 12	10 27								
Ramsgate 4	✈ a	10 15	10 30				10 51				

Station		SE 1 🚲	SE 1		SE	SE 1	SE 1 🚲		SE	SE 1	SE 1 🚲	SE 1 🚲		SE	SE 1
London Victoria 15	⊖ d		09 33			09 39	10 03			10 09		10 33			10 39
London Blackfriars 3	⊖ d		09 12				09 42					10 12			
Elephant & Castle	⊖ d		09 16				09 45					10 15			
Bromley South 4	d		09 50			09 59	10 19			10 29		10 49			10 59
St Mary Cray	d					10 05				10 35					11 05
Swanley 4	d					10 10				10 40					11 10
Farningham Road	d					10 14				10 44					11 14
Longfield	d					10 19				10 49					11 19
Meopham	d					10 23				10 53					11 23
Sole Street	d					10 26				10 56					11 26
London Charing Cross 4	⊖ d					09 20				09 52					10 20
London Waterloo (East) 4	⊖ d					09 23				09 55					10 23
London Cannon Street 4	⊖ d					09b20				09b48					10b18
London Bridge 4	⊖ d					09 29				10 00					10 29
Dartford 4	d					10 04				10 34					11 04
Greenhithe for Bluewater	d					10 09				10 39					11 09
Gravesend 4	d					10 16				10 46					11 16
Strood 4	d					10 28				10 58					11 28
Rochester 4	d		10 15			10 35	10 44			11 05		11 13			11 35
Chatham 4	d		10 17			10 38	10 47			11 08		11 17			11 38
Gillingham (Kent) 4	d		10 21			10 41	10 50			11 11		11 20			11 41
Rainham (Kent)	d		10 26			10 46	10 55			11 16		11 25			11 46
Newington	d					10 50				11 20					11 50
Sittingbourne 4	a		10 33			10 55	11 02			11 25		11 32			11 55
	d		10 33		10 35	10 55	11 02		11 05	11 25		11 32		11 35	11 55
Kemsley	d				10 39				11 09					11 39	
Swale	d				10 42				11 12					11 42	
Queenborough	d				10 47				11 17					11 47	
Sheerness-on-Sea	a				10 53				11 23					11 53	
Teynham	d					10 59				11 29					11 59
Faversham 2	a		10 41			11 05	11 10			11 35		11 40			12 05
	d		10 44	10 47			11 14	11 16				11 44	11 46		
Selling	d			10 52									11 51		
Canterbury East 4	d			11 01				11 28					12 00		
Bekesbourne	d			11 05									12 05		
Adisham	d			11 10									12 09		
Aylesham	d			11 12									12 12		
Snowdown	d			11 15									12 14		
Shepherds Well	d			11 19									12 18		
Kearsney	d			11 23									12 23		
Dover Priory 4	⛴ a			11 27				11 44					12 28		
Whitstable	d		10 53				11 22					11 52			
Chestfield & Swalecliffe	d		10 56									11 55			
Herne Bay	d		11 00				11 27					11 59			
Birchington-on-Sea	d		11 08				11 35					12 08			
Westgate-on-Sea	d		11 11									12 11			
Margate 4	d	11 04	11 15				11 41				12 04	12 15			
Broadstairs	d	11 09	11 21				11 46				12 09	12 20			
Dumpton Park	d	11 12	11 23								12 12	12 23			
Ramsgate 4	✈ a	11 15	11 27				11 51				12 15	12 26			

For general notes see front of timetable
For details of catering facilities see Directory of Train Operators

For services from London to Ramsgate, Dover and Canterbury via Ashford see Table 207

b Change at London Bridge and Rochester
c Arr. 1002

From 12 October due to seasonal difficulties a large number of trains on this table will have minor retimings that could mean slightly earlier departure or later arrival times at certain stations. For further details see local publicity or contact National Rail Enquiries 08457 48 49 50.

For details of Bank Holiday service alterations please see first page of Table 195

London → Medway, Sheerness-on-Sea, Dover and Ramsgate

Network Diagram - see first page of Table 212

Station		SE 1 ⚲	SE	SE 1		SE 1 ⚲	SE 1 ⚲	SE	SE 1	SE 1 ⚲	SE	SE 1	SE 1 ⚲	SE 1 ⚲	SE	SE 1	SE 1 ⚲		SE	SE 1
London Victoria 15 ⊖	d	11 03		11 09			11 33		11 39	12 03		12 09		12 33		12 39	13 03			13 09
London Blackfriars 3 ⊖	d	*10 42*					*11 12*			*11 42*				*12 12*			*12 42*			
Elephant & Castle ⊖	d	*10 45*					*11 15*			*11 45*				*12 15*			*12 45*			
Bromley South 4	d	11 19		11 29			11 49		11 59	12 19		12 29		12 49		12 59	13 19			13 29
St Mary Cray	d			11 35					12 05			12 35				13 05				13 35
Swanley 4	d			11 40					12 10			12 40				13 10				13 40
Farningham Road	d			11 44					12 14			12 44				13 14				13 44
Longfield	d			11 49					12 19			12 49				13 19				13 49
Meopham	d			11 53					12 23			12 53				13 23				13 53
Sole Street	d			11 56					12 26			12 56				13 26				13 56
London Charing Cross 4 ⊖	d			*10 50*					*11 20*			*11 50*				*12 20*				*12 50*
London Waterloo (East) 4 ⊖	d			*10 53*					*11 23*			*11 53*				*12 23*				*12 53*
London Cannon Street 4 ⊖	d			*10*b*48*					*11*b*18*			*11*b*48*				*12*b*18*				*12*b*48*
London Bridge 4 ⊖	d			*10 59*					*11 29*			*11 59*				*12 29*				*12 59*
Dartford 4	d			*11 34*					*12 04*			*12 34*				*13 04*				*13 34*
Greenhithe for Bluewater	d			*11 39*					*12 09*			*12 39*				*13 09*				*13 39*
Gravesend 4	d			*11 46*					*12 16*			*12 46*				*13 16*				*13 46*
Strood 4	d			*11 58*					*12 28*			*12 58*				*13 28*				*13 58*
Rochester 4	d	11 43		12 05			12 13		12 35	12 43		13 05		13 13		13 35	13 43			14 05
Chatham 4	d	11 47		12 08			12 17		12 38	12 47		13 08		13 17		13 38	13 47			14 08
Gillingham (Kent) 4	d	11 50		12 11			12 20		12 41	12 50		13 11		13 20		13 41	13 50			14 11
Rainham (Kent)	d	11 55		12 16			12 25		12 46	12 55		13 16		13 25		13 46	13 55			14 16
Newington	d			12 20					12 50			13 20				13 50				14 20
Sittingbourne 4	a	12 02		12 25			12 32		12 55	13 02		13 25		13 32		13 55	14 02			14 25
	d	12 02	12 05	12 25			12 32	12 35	12 55	13 02	13 05	13 25		13 32	13 35	13 55	14 02		14 05	14 25
Kemsley	d		12 09					12 39			13 09				13 39				14 09	
Swale	d		12 12					12 42			13 12				13 42				14 12	
Queenborough	d		12 17					12 47			13 17				13 47				14 17	
Sheerness-on-Sea	a		12 23					12 53			13 23				13 53				14 23	
Teynham	d			12 29					12 59			13 29				13 59				14 29
Faversham 2	a	12 10		12 35			12 40		13 05	13 10		13 35		13 40		14 05	14 10			14 35

Station		SE 1 ⚲	SE 1 ⚲	SE	SE 1		SE 1 ⚲	SE 1 ⚲	SE 1 ⚲	SE	SE 1	SE 1 ⚲	SE 1 ⚲	SE	SE 1	SE 1 ⚲	SE 1 ⚲	SE 1 ⚲	SE	SE 1	SE 1 ⚲	SE 1 ⚲		SE	SE 1
Faversham 2	d	12 14	12 16					12 44	12 46			13 14	13 16				13 44	13 46			14 14	14 16			
Selling	d								12 51									13 51							
Canterbury East 4	d		12 28						13 00				13 28					14 00				14 28			
Bekesbourne	d								13 05									14 05							
Adisham	d								13 09									14 09							
Aylesham	d								13 12									14 12							
Snowdown	d								13 14									14 14							
Shepherds Well	d								13 18									14 18							
Kearsney	d								13 23									14 23							
Dover Priory 4 ⛴	a		12 44						13 28				13 44					14 28				14 44			
Whitstable	d	12 22						12 52				13 22					13 52				14 22				
Chestfield & Swalecliffe	d							12 55									13 55								
Herne Bay	d	12 27						12 59				13 27					13 59				14 27				
Birchington-on-Sea	d	12 35						13 08				13 35					14 08				14 35				
Westgate-on-Sea	d							13 11									14 11								
Margate 4	d	12 41					13 04	13 15				13 41				14 04	14 15				14 41				
Broadstairs	d	12 46					13 09	13 20				13 46				14 09	14 20				14 46				
Dumpton Park	d						13 12	13 23								14 12	14 23								
Ramsgate 4 ✈	a	12 51					13 15	13 26				13 51				14 15	14 26				14 51				

For general notes see front of timetable
For details of catering facilities see Directory of Train Operators

For services from London to Ramsgate, Dover and Canterbury via Ashford see Table 207

b Change at London Bridge and Rochester

From 12 October due to seasonal difficulties a large number of trains on this table will have minor retimings that could mean slightly earlier departure or later arrival times at certain stations. For further details see local publicity or contact National Rail Enquiries 08457 48 49 50.

For details of Bank Holiday service alterations please see first page of Table 195

London → Medway, Sheerness-on-Sea, Dover and Ramsgate

Network Diagram - see first page of Table 212

		SE 1	SE 1 🛒		SE	SE 1	SE 1	SE 1 🛒		SE	SE 1	SE 1 🛒		SE	SE 1	SE 1	SE 1 🛒		SE	SE 1	SE 1 🛒		SE	SE 1
London Victoria 15 ⊖	d		13 33			13 39		14 03			14 09	14 33			14 39		15 03			15 09	15 33			15 39
London Blackfriars 3 ⊖	d		13 12					13 42				14 12					14 42				15 12			
Elephant & Castle ⊖	d		13 15					13 45				14 15					14 45				15 15			
Bromley South 4	d		13 49			13 59		14 19			14 29	14 49			14 59		15 19			15 29	15 49			16 00
St Mary Cray	d					14 05					14 35				15 05					15 35				16 06
Swanley 4	d					14 10					14 40				15 10					15 40				16 11
Farningham Road	d					14 14					14 44				15 14					15 44				16 15
Longfield	d					14 19					14 49				15 19					15 49				16 20
Meopham	d					14 23					14 53				15 23					15 53				16 24
Sole Street	d					14 26					14 56				15 26					15 56				16 27
London Charing Cross 4 ⊖	d					13 20					13 50				14 20					14 50				15 20
London Waterloo (East) 4 ⊖	d					13 23					13 53				14 23					14 53				15 23
London Cannon Street 4 ⊖	d					13b18					13b48				14b18					14b48				15b18
London Bridge 4 ⊖	d					13 29					13 59				14 29					14 59				15 29
Dartford 4	d					14 04					14 34				15 04					15 34				16 04
Greenhithe for Bluewater	d					14 09					14 39				15 09					15 39				16 09
Gravesend 4	d					14 16					14 46				15 16					15 46				16 16
Strood 4	d					14 28					14 58				15 28					15 58				16 28
Rochester 4	d		14 13			14 35		14 43			15 05	15 13			15 35		15 43			16 05	16 13			16 36
Chatham 4	d		14 17			14 38		14 47			15 08	15 17			15 38		15 47			16 08	16 16			16 39
Gillingham (Kent) 4	d		14 21			14 41		14 50			15 11	15 20			15 41		15 51			16 12	16 20			16 43
Rainham (Kent)	d		14 26			14 46		14 55			15 16	15 25			15 46		15 56			16 17	16 25			16 48
Newington	d					14 50					15 20				15 50					16 21				16 52
Sittingbourne 4	a		14 33			14 55		15 02			15 25	15 32			15 55		16 03			16 26	16 32			16 57
	d		14 33		14 35	14 55		15 02		15 05	15 25	15 32		15 35	15 55		16 03		16 05	16 26	16 32		16 35	16 57
Kemsley	d				14 39					15 09				15 39					16 09				16 39	
Swale	d				14 43					15 13				15 43					16 13				16 43	
Queenborough	d				14 47					15 17				15 47					16 17				16 47	
Sheerness-on-Sea	a				14 53					15 23				15 53					16 23				16 53	
Teynham	d					14 59					15 29				15 59					16 30				17 01
Faversham 2	a		14 41			15 05		15 10			15 35	15 40			16 05		16 11			16 36	16 40			17 07
	d		14 44	14 47				15 14	15 16			15 44	15 46				16 15	16 17			16 44	16 47		
Selling	d			14 52									15 51					16 22				16 52		
Canterbury East 4	d			15 02					15 28				16 00					16 32				17 01		
Bekesbourne	d			15 06									16 05					16 36				17 06		
Adisham	d			15 11									16 09					16 41				17 10		
Aylesham	d			15 13									16 12					16 43				17 13		
Snowdown	d			15 16									16 14					16 46				17 15		
Shepherds Well	d			15 20									16 18					16 50				17 19		
Kearsney	d			15 24									16 23					16 54				17 24		
Dover Priory 4 ⛴	a			15 30					15 44				16 27					16 59				17 28		
Whitstable	d		14 52					15 22				15 52					16 23				16 52			
Chestfield & Swalecliffe	d		14 55									15 55					16 26				16 55			
Herne Bay	d		14 59					15 27				15 59					16 30				16 59			
Birchington-on-Sea	d		15 08					15 35				16 08					16 39				17 08			
Westgate-on-Sea	d		15 11									16 11					16 42				17 11			
Margate 4	d	14 50	15 15				15 36	15 41				16 15				16 36	16 47				17 16			
Broadstairs	d	14 55	15 20				15 41	15 46				16 20				16 41	16 52				17 21			
Dumpton Park	d	14 58	15 23				15 44					16 23				16 44	16 55				17 24			
Ramsgate 4 ✈	a	15 01	15 26				15 47	15 51				16 26				16 47	16 58				17 27			

For general notes see front of timetable
For details of catering facilities see Directory of Train Operators

For services from London to Ramsgate, Dover and Canterbury via Ashford see Table 207

b Change at London Bridge and Rochester

From 12 October due to seasonal difficulties a large number of trains on this table will have minor retimings that could mean slightly earlier departure or later arrival times at certain stations. For further details see local publicity or contact National Rail Enquiries 08457 48 49 50.

For details of Bank Holiday service alterations please see first page of Table 195

London → Medway, Sheerness-on-Sea, Dover and Ramsgate

Network Diagram - see first page of Table 212

		SE 1	SE	SE	SE 1	SE	SE 1	SE 1	SE 1	SE	SE 1	
		🛒										
London Victoria [15]	⊖ d	16 03	16 00		16 23		16 22	16 42		16 45		
London Blackfriars [3]	⊖ d	15 42						16 12		16 26		
Elephant & Castle	⊖ d	15 45						16 15		16 30		
Bromley South [4]	d	16 19	16 23		16 40		16 44	16 58		17 03		
St Mary Cray	d		16 30				16 50			17 10		
Swanley [4]	d		16 35				16 55			17 15		
Farningham Road	d		16 39				17 00			17 19		
Longfield	d		16 44				17 04			17 24		
Meopham	d		16 48				17 09			17 28		
Sole Street	d		16 51				17 11			17 31		
London Charing Cross [4]	⊖ d				15 20			15 50	16b33			
London Waterloo (East) [4]	⊖ d				15 23			15 53	16b36			
London Cannon Street [4]	⊖ d				15e18			15e48	16 44			
London Bridge [4]	⊖ d				15 29			15 59	16 48			
Dartford [4]	d				16 04			16 36				
Greenhithe for Bluewater	d				16 09			16 41				
Gravesend [4]	d				16 16			16 48				
Strood [4]	d				16 28			17 04				
Rochester [4]	d	16 43	17a03				17a23	17 07		17a43		
Chatham [4]	d	16 47			17 08			17 28	17 32			
Gillingham (Kent) [4]	d	16 50			17 12			17 32	17 36			
Rainham (Kent)	d	16 55			17 17			17 37	17 41			
Newington	d				17 21							
Sittingbourne [4]	a	17 02			17 26			17 45	17 50			
	d	17 03		17 07	17 27	17 29		17 45	17 50			
Kemsley	d			17 11		17 33						
Swale	d			17 14		17 36						
Queenborough	d			17 19		17 41						
Sheerness-on-Sea	a			17 25		17 47						
Teynham	d				17 31							
Faversham [2]	a	17 11			17 37			17 54	17 59		←	
	d	17 15 / 17 18			17 41 / 17 45			18 03	18 00		18 03	
Selling	d	17 23			17 50			→			18 08	
Canterbury East [4]	d	17 33			18 00						18 18	
Bekesbourne	d	17 37			18 04						18 22	
Adisham	d	17 42			18 09						18 27	
Aylesham	d	17 44			18 11						18 29	
Snowdown	d	17 47			18 14						18 32	
Shepherds Well	d	17 51			18 18						18 36	
Kearsney	d	17 55			18 22						18 40	
Dover Priory [4]	⛴ a	18 03			18 30						18 48	
Whitstable	d	17 23			17 49				18 08			
Chestfield & Swalecliffe	d	17 26			17 52				18 11			
Herne Bay	d	17 30			17 57				18 16			
Birchington-on-Sea	d	17 38			18 06				18 25			
Westgate-on-Sea	d	17 41			18 09				18 28			
Margate [4]	d	17 45			18 13				18 32			
Broadstairs	d	17 51			18 19				18 37			
Dumpton Park	d	17 53			18 21				18 40			
Ramsgate [4]	✈ a	17 56			18 26				18 46			

		SE	SE 1	SE 1	SE 1	SE 1	SE 1	SE 1	SE 1	SE	SE
						🛒	🛒			A	
London Victoria [15]	⊖ d			17 05		17 09	17 27				
London Blackfriars [3]	⊖ d			16 42						17 26	
Elephant & Castle	⊖ d			16 45						17 30	
Bromley South [4]	d			17 24			17 44			17 48	
St Mary Cray	d			17 30						17 57	
Swanley [4]	d			17 37						18 01	
Farningham Road	d			17 41					←	18 06	
Longfield	d			17 46					17 46	18 11	
Meopham	d			→					17 51	18 16	
Sole Street	d								17 54	18 19	
London Charing Cross [4]	⊖ d		16c21			16 21	16 48		16 48	17 00	
London Waterloo (East) [4]	⊖ d		16c24			16 24	16 51		16 51	17 03	
London Cannon Street [4]	⊖ d		17 08			16f22	16e46	17 30	16f46	17f00	
London Bridge [4]	⊖ d		16 29			16 29	16 56		16 56	17 08	
Dartford [4]	d		17 06			17 06	17 26		17 26	17 46	
Greenhithe for Bluewater	d		17 11			17 11	17 31		17 31	17 51	
Gravesend [4]	d		17 18			17 18	17 40		17 40	17 58	
Strood [4]	d		17 30			17 30	17 55		17 55	18 17	
Rochester [4]	d		17 35			17 53	18 00		18g18	18 28	
Chatham [4]	d		17 49			17 56	18 10	18 14	18 21	18 31	
Gillingham (Kent) [4]	d		17 54			18 00	18 15	18 19	18 25	18a36	
Rainham (Kent)	d		17 59			18 05	18 20	18 24	18 30		
Newington	d		18 03			18 09			18 34		
Sittingbourne [4]	a		18 08			18 14	18 27	18 31	18 39		
	d	17 58	18 08			18 15	18 27	18 31	18 39		18 41
Kemsley	d	18 02									18 45
Swale	d	18 06									18 48
Queenborough	d	18 10									18 53
Sheerness-on-Sea	a	18 16									18 59
Teynham	d		18 13			18 19			18 44		
Faversham [2]	a		18 19			18 25	18 35	18 40	18 50		
	d		18 19			18 29 / 18 34	18 40	18 44	18 50		
Selling	d					18 39			18 55		
Canterbury East [4]	d					18 49			19a04		
Bekesbourne	d					18 53					
Adisham	d					18 58					
Aylesham	d					19 00					
Snowdown	d					19 03					
Shepherds Well	d					19 07					
Kearsney	d					19 11					
Dover Priory [4]	⛴ a					19 17					
Whitstable	d		18 27			18 38	18 48	18 52			
Chestfield & Swalecliffe	d					18 41	18 51	18 55			
Herne Bay	d		18 33			18 45	18 56	19 00			
Birchington-on-Sea	d		18 42			18 55	19 05	19 09			
Westgate-on-Sea	d					18 58	19 08	19 12			
Margate [4]	d		18 48		18 52	19 03	19 12	19 16			
Broadstairs	d		18 54		18 57	19 08	19 18	19 22			
Dumpton Park	d				19 00	19 11	19 21				
Ramsgate [4]	✈ a		18 59		19 03	19 17	19 25	19 29			

For general notes see front of timetable
For details of catering facilities see Directory of Train Operators

For services from London to Ramsgate, Dover and Canterbury via Ashford see Table 207

A From Bedford (Table 52)
b Change at London Bridge
c Change at Chatham
e Change at London Bridge and Chatham
f Change at London Bridge and Rochester
g Arr. 1803

From 12 October due to seasonal difficulties a large number of trains on this table will have minor retimings that could mean slightly earlier departure or later arrival times at certain stations. For further details see local publicity or contact National Rail Enquiries 08457 48 49 50.

For details of Bank Holiday service alterations please see first page of Table 195

London → Medway, Sheerness-on-Sea, Dover and Ramsgate

Network Diagram - see first page of Table 212

		SE 1		SE 1	SE	SE 1	SE	SE 1			SE 1	SE	SE 1	SE	SE 1		SE	SE 1	SE 1	SE 1		SE	SE 1	SE 1	
								⌶				A			⌶					⌶					
London Victoria 15	⊖ d	17 48			17 45			18 04							18 33				18 41	19 03			19 09		
London Blackfriars 3	⊖ d	17 26			17 36			17 58				18 10			18 10				18 24	18 42					
Elephant & Castle	⊖ d	17 30			17 39			18 03				18 14			18 14				18 28	18 45					
Bromley South 4	d	18 07			18 10			18 24				18 32			18 49				19 01	19 19			19 29		
St Mary Cray	d				18 19							18 39							19 10				19 35		
Swanley 4	d				18 24							18 44							19 15				19 40		
Farningham Road	d				18 28							18 48							19 19				19 44		
Longfield	d				18 33							18 53							19 24				19 49		
Meopham	d				18 37							18 57							19 28				19 53		
Sole Street	d				18 40							19 00							19 31				19 56		
London Charing Cross 4	⊖ d	17 00		17b43							18b01							18b34	17c58	17e58			18 30	19b24	
London Waterloo (East) 4	⊖ d	17 03		17b46							18b04							18b37	18c01	18e01			18 33	19b27	
London Cannon Street 4	⊖ d	17e00		17 50							18 10							18 46	18 08	18 08			18c30	19 32	
London Bridge 4	⊖ d	17 08		17 54				17f30			18 14	17g50			17f50			18 50	18g14	18f14			18 38	19 36	
Dartford 4	d	17 46						18 10				18 30			18 30			18 48	19 00	19 00			19 16	19 40	
Greenhithe for Bluewater	d	17 51						18 15				18 35			18 35			18 53	19 05	19 05			19 21	19 45	
Gravesend 4	d	17 58						18 25				18 42			18 42			19 00	19 12	19 12			19 28	19 52	
Strood 4	d	18 17						18 39				18 59			18 59			19 14	19 28	19 28			19 44	20 04	
Rochester 4	d	18 22			18a51			18 43				19 10			19 02			19 19	19 40				20 05	20 12	
Chatham 4	d	18 35		18 39				18 55			18 59	19 12			19 17			19 28	19 43	19 47			20 07	20 15	
Gillingham (Kent) 4	d	18 39		18 43				18 59			19 03	19a18			19 21			19 32	19 47	19 52			20 11	20 20	
Rainham (Kent)	d	18 45		18 49				19 04			19 08				19 27			19 37	19 52	19 57			20 16	20 25	
Newington	d										19 12							19 41	19 56				20 20	20 35	
Sittingbourne 4	a	18 52		18 56				19 12			19 17				19 34			19 46	20 01	20 04			20 27	→	
	d	18 53		18 57			18 58	19 12			19 18			19 27	19 35		19 42	19 47	20 01	20 05		20 13	20 27		
Kemsley	d						19 02							19 31			19 46					20 17			
Swale	d						19 05							19 35			19 50					20 21			
Queenborough	d						19 10							19 39			19 55					20 25			
Sheerness-on-Sea	a						19 16							19 45			20 01					20 30			
Teynham	d										19 22							19 51	20 05				20 31		
Faversham 2	a	19 01		19 05		←		19 21			19 28		←		19 43			19 57	20 12	20 15			20 37		
	d	19 11	19 05	19 09		19 11		19 32	19 24		19 29		19 32		19 47	19 49		19 58		20 19	20 21				
Selling	d	→				19 16		→					19 37			19 54					20 26				
Canterbury East 4	d					19 26							19 47			20h06					20 36				
Bekesbourne	d					19 30							19 51			20 10					20 40				
Adisham	d					19 35							19 56			20 15					20 45				
Aylesham	d					19 37							19 58			20 17					20 47				
Snowdown	d					19 40							20 01			20 20					20 50				
Shepherds Well	d					19 44							20 05			20 24					20 54				
Kearsney	d					19 48							20 09			20 28					20 58				
Dover Priory 4	⛴ a					19 55							20 15			20 33					21 03				
Whitstable	d		19 13	19 17					19 33		19 38				19 56			20 06		20 27					
Chestfield & Swalecliffe	d			19 20					19 36		19 41				19 59			20 09							
Herne Bay	d		19 20	19 25					19 40		19 45				20 03			20 13		20 32					
Birchington-on-Sea	d		19 29	19 34					19 49		19 54				20 12			20 22		20 41					
Westgate-on-Sea	d			19 37					19 53		19 58				20 16			20 26							
Margate 4	d		19 34	19 41					19 57		20 03				20 20			20 30		20 47					
Broadstairs	d		19a40	19 47					20a02		20 09				20 26			20a36		20 52					
Dumpton Park	d			19 49							20 12				20 28					20 55					
Ramsgate 4	✈ a			19 54							20 18				20 32					20 59					

For general notes see front of timetable
For details of catering facilities see Directory of Train Operators
For services from London to Ramsgate, Dover and Canterbury via Ashford see Table 207

A From Bedford (Table 52)
b Change at London Bridge
c Change at London Bridge and Rochester
e Change at London Bridge and Chatham
f Change at Dartford and Chatham
g Change at Dartford and Rochester
h Arr. 2002

From 12 October due to seasonal difficulties a large number of trains on this table will have minor retimings that could mean slightly earlier departure or later arrival times at certain stations. For further details see local publicity or contact National Rail Enquiries 08457 48 49 50.

Table 212

Mondays to Fridays

For details of Bank Holiday service alterations please see first page of Table 195

London → Medway, Sheerness-on-Sea, Dover and Ramsgate

Network Diagram - see first page of Table 212

Station		SE 1		SE		SE 1	SE 1	SE 1		SE	SE 1	SE 1		SE 1	SE 1		SE	SE 1	SE 1	SE 1	SE	SE 1	SE 1	SE 1	
London Victoria 15 ⊖	d	19 33					19 39	20 03			20 09	20 33		20 39	21 03			21 39	22 03			22 39	23 03	23 39	
London Blackfriars 3 ⊖	d	*19 12*						*19 42*				*20 12*			*20 42*			*21 12*							
Elephant & Castle ⊖	d	*19 15*						*19 45*				*20 15*			*20 45*			*21 15*							
Bromley South 4	d	19 50					19 59	20 19			20 29	20 49		20 59	21 19			21 59	22 19			22 59	23 19	23 58	
St Mary Cray	d						20 05				20 35			21 06				22 05				23 05		00 04	
Swanley 4	d						20 10				20 40			21 10				22 10				23 10		00 09	
Farningham Road	d						20 14				20 44			21 15				22 14				23 14		00 13	
Longfield	d						20 19				20 49			21 19	21 33			22 19				23 19		00 18	
Meopham	d						20 23				20 53			21 24				22 23				23 23		00 23	
Sole Street	d						20 26				20 56			21 26				22 26				23 26		00 26	
London Charing Cross 4 ⊖	d	*18 54*					*19 21*					*19 50*		*20 20*				*21 20*				*22 20*		*22 50*	
London Waterloo (East) 4 ⊖	d	*18 57*					*19 24*					*19 53*		*20 23*				*21 23*				*22 23*		*22 53*	
London Cannon Street 4 ⊖	d	*18b50*					*19b22*					*19b52*		*20b15*				*21b00*							
London Bridge 4 ⊖	d						*19 29*					*19 59*		*20 29*				*21 29*				*22 29*		*22 59*	
Dartford 4	d						*20 06*					*20 34*		*21 04*				*22 04*				*23 04*		*23 34*	
Greenhithe for Bluewater	d						*20 11*					*20 40*		*21 09*				*22 09*				*23 09*		*23 40*	
Gravesend 4	d						*20 18*					*20 50*		*21 16*				*22 16*				*23 16*		*23 50*	
Strood 4	d						*20 30*					*21 04*		*21 28*				*22 28*				*23 28*		*00 02*	
Rochester 4	d	20 16					20 37	20 43			21 05	21 13		21 35	21 47			22 35	22 43			23 36	23 43	00 35	
Chatham 4	d	20 19					20 40	20 47			21 07	21 16		21 38	21 50			22 38	22 46			23 39	23 46	00 38	
Gillingham (Kent) 4	d	20 24					20 43	20 50			21 11	21 21		21 41	21 53			22 41	22 49			23 43	23 49	00a41	
Rainham (Kent)	d	20 29				←	20 48	20 55			21 16	21 26		21 46	21 58			22 46	22 54			23 48	23 54		
Newington	d					20 35	20 52				21 20			21 50				22 50				23 52			
Sittingbourne 4	a	20 36				20 42	20 57	21 02			21 25	21 33		21 55	22 05			22 55	23 01			23 57	00 01		
	d	20 36		20 39		20 43	20 57	21 02		21 05	21 25	21 33		21 55	22 05		22 09	22 55	23 01		23 07	23 57	00 01		
Kemsley	d			20 43						21 09							22 13				23 11				
Swale	d			20 47						21 13							22 17				23 14				
Queenborough	d			20 51						21 17							22 21				23 19				
Sheerness-on-Sea	a			20 57						21 23							22 26				23 25				
Teynham	d					20 47	21 02				21 29			22 00				23 00				00 01			
Faversham 2	a	20 44				20 54	21 08	21 12			21 35	21 41		22 06	22 13			23 06	23 10	←		00 07	00 11		
	d	20 48	20 52					21 16	21 18			21 45	21 47		22 17	22 20		23 13	23 11	23 13			00 12		
Selling	d		20 57						21 23				21 52			22 25		→		23 18					
Canterbury East 4	d		21 06						21 32				22a00			22 34				23 27					
Bekesbourne	d		21 11						21 36							22 38									
Adisham	d		21 15						21 41							22 43									
Aylesham	d		21 17						21 43							22 45									
Snowdown	d		21 19						21 46							22 48				23 36					
Shepherds Well	d		21 23						21 50							22 52									
Kearsney	d		21 27						21 54							22 56									
Dover Priory 4 ⛴	a		21 33						21 59							23 01				23 47					
Whitstable	d	20 56						21 24				21 53			22 25				23 19				00 20		
Chestfield & Swalecliffe	d	20 59										21 56			22 28				23 22				00 23		
Herne Bay	d	21 03						21 29				22 00			22 32				23 26				00 27		
Birchington-on-Sea	d	21 11						21 37				22 09			22 41				23 35				00 36		
Westgate-on-Sea	d	21 14										22 12			22 44				23 38				00 39		
Margate 4	d	21 19						21 43				22 16			22 48				23 42				00 43		
Broadstairs	d	21 24						21 48				22 21			22 53				23 47				00 48		
Dumpton Park	d	21 27										22 24			22 56				23 50				00 51		
Ramsgate 4 ✈	a	21 30						21 53				22 27			22 59				23 53				00 54		

For general notes see front of timetable
For details of catering facilities see Directory of Train Operators

For services from London to Ramsgate, Dover and Canterbury via Ashford see Table 207

b Change at London Bridge and Rochester

From 12 October due to seasonal difficulties a large number of trains on this table will have minor retimings that could mean slightly earlier departure or later arrival times at certain stations. For further details see local publicity or contact National Rail Enquiries 08457 48 49 50.

For details of Bank Holiday service alterations please see first page of Table 195

London → Medway, Sheerness-on-Sea, Dover and Ramsgate

Network Diagram - see first page of Table 212

		SE 1	SE 1	SE	SE 1	SE 1	SE 1	SE 1	SE	SE 1	SE 1	SE 1	SE	SE 1	SE 1			SE	SE	SE 1	SE 1		SE	SE 1
London Victoria 15	⊖ d	22p39	23p03		23p39	00 03					05 39				06 39				07 09		07 33			07 39
London Blackfriars 3	⊖ d																							
Elephant & Castle	⊖ d																							
Bromley South 4	d	22p59	23p19		23p58						05 59				06 59				07 29		07 49			07 59
St Mary Cray	d	23p05			00 04						06 05				07 05				07 35					08 05
Swanley 4	d	23p10			00 09						06 10				07 10				07 40					08 10
Farningham Road	d	23p14			00 13						06 14				07 14				07 44					08 14
Longfield	d	23p19			00 18						06 19				07 19				07 49					08 19
Meopham	d	23p23			00 23						06 23				07 23				07 53					08 23
Sole Street	d	23p26			00 26						06 26				07 26				07 56					08 26
London Charing Cross 4	⊖ d				22 50	23 20					05 04				06 20				06 50		06 50			07 20
London Waterloo (East) 4	⊖ d				22 53	23 23					05 07				06 23				06 53		06 53			07 23
London Cannon Street 4	⊖ d																							
London Bridge 4	⊖ d				22 59	23 29					05 13				06 29				06 59		06 59			07 29
Dartford 4	d				23 34		05 17				05 49				07 04				07 34		07 34			08 04
Greenhithe for Bluewater	d				23 40		05 22				05 54				07 09				07 39		07 39			08 09
Gravesend 4	d				23 50		05 29				06 01				07 16				07 46		07 46			08 16
Strood 4	d				00 02	00 32	05 40				06 12				07 28				07 58		07 58			08 28
Rochester 4	d	23p36	23p43		00 35	00 43	05 44				06 36				07 36				08 06		08 13			08 36
Chatham 4	d	23p39	23p46		00 38	00 46	05 46				06 38				07 38				08 08		08 17			08 38
Gillingham (Kent) 4	d	23p43	23p49		00a41	00 50	05 50				06 41				07 41				08 11		08 20			08 41
Rainham (Kent)	d	23p48	23p54			00 55	05 54				06 46				07 46				08 16		08 25			08 46
Newington	d	23p52				00 58	05 58				06 50				07 50				08 20					08 50
Sittingbourne 4	a	23p57	00 01			01 03	06 03				06 55				07 55				08 25		08 32			08 55
	d	23p57	00 01	00 08		01 03	06 03		06 05		06 55		07 05		07 55			08 05	08 25		08 32		08 35	08 55
Kemsley	d			00 12					06 09				07 09					08 09					08 39	
Swale	d			00 15					06 12				07 12					08 12					08 42	
Queenborough	d			00 20					06 17				07 17					08 17					08 47	
Sheerness-on-Sea	a			00 26					06 22				07 22					08 22					08 52	
Teynham	d	00 01				01 07	06 08				06 59				07 59				08 29					08 59
Faversham 2	a	00 07	00 11			01 12	06 14				07 05				08 05				08 35		08 40			09 05
	d		00 12			01 13	06 15	06 17			07 14	07 16			08 14	08 16					08 44	08 46		
Selling	d						06 20					07 21			08 19							08 51		
Canterbury East 4	d						06 29					07 30			08b30							09 00		
Bekesbourne	d						06 33					07 35			08 35							09 05		
Adisham	d						06 38					07 39			08 39							09 09		
Aylesham	d						06 40					07 42			08 42							09 12		
Snowdown	d						06 43					07 44			08 44							09 14		
Shepherds Well	d						06 47					07 48			08 48							09 18		
Kearsney	d						06 51					07 53			08 53							09 23		
Dover Priory 4	a						06 56					07 57			08 57							09 28		
Whitstable	d		00 20			01 21		06 25			07 22					08 25					08 52			
Chestfield & Swalecliffe	d		00 23			01 24		06 28			07 25					08 28					08 55			
Herne Bay	d		00 27			01 27		06 32			07 29					08 32					08 59			
Birchington-on-Sea	d		00 36			01 36		06 41			07 38					08 41					09 08			
Westgate-on-Sea	d		00 39			01 39		06 45			07 42					08 44					09 11			
Margate 4	d		00 43			01 43		06 49		07 26	07 46			08 04		08 48				09 04	09 15			
Broadstairs	d		00 48			01 48		06 54		07 31	07 51			08 09		08 53				09 09	09 20			
Dumpton Park	d		00 51			01 51		06 56		07 34	07 53			08 12		08 56				09 12	09 23			
Ramsgate 4	a		00 54			01 54		06 59		07 37	07 58			08 15		08 59				09 15	09 26			

b Arr. 0827

For general notes see front of timetable
For details of catering facilities see
Directory of Train Operators

For services from London to Ramsgate, Dover and Canterbury via Ashford see Table 207

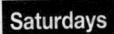

Saturdays

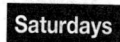

For details of Bank Holiday service alterations please see first page of Table 195

London → Medway, Sheerness-on-Sea, Dover and Ramsgate

Network Diagram - see first page of Table 212

	SE 1		SE	SE 1	SE 1 ☕	SE 1		SE	SE 1		SE 1		SE	SE 1	SE 1 ☕	SE 1		SE	SE 1	SE 1 ☕		SE	SE 1	SE 1 ☕
London Victoria 15 ⊖ d	08 03			08 09		08 33			08 39		09 03			09 09		09 33			09 39	10 03			10 09	
London Blackfriars 3 ⊖ d																								
Elephant & Castle ⊖ d																								
Bromley South 4 d	08 19			08 29		08 49			08 59		09 19			09 29		09 49			09 59	10 19			10 29	
St Mary Cray d				08 35					09 05					09 35					10 05				10 35	
Swanley 4 d				08 40					09 10					09 40					10 10				10 40	
Farningham Road d				08 44					09 14					09 44					10 14				10 44	
Longfield d				08 49					09 19					09 49					10 19				10 49	
Meopham d				08 53					09 23					09 53					10 23				10 53	
Sole Street d				08 56					09 26					09 56					10 26				10 56	
London Charing Cross 4 ⊖ d				07 50					08 20					08 50					09 20				09 50	
London Waterloo (East) 4 ⊖ d				07 53					08 23					08 53					09 23				09 53	
London Cannon Street 4 ⊖ d									08b10					08b48					09b18				09b48	
London Bridge 4 ⊖ d				07 59					08 29					08 59					09 29				09 59	
Dartford 4 d				08 34					09 04					09 34					10 04				10 34	
Greenhithe for Bluewater d				08 39					09 09					09 39					10 09				10 39	
Gravesend 4 d				08 46					09 16					09 46					10 16				10 46	
Strood 4 d				08 58					09 28					09 58					10 28				10 58	
Rochester 4 d	08 43			09 06		09 13			09 36		09 43			10 06		10 13			10 36	10 43			11 06	
Chatham 4 d	08 47			09 08		09 17			09 38		09 47			10 08		10 17			10 38	10 47			11 08	
Gillingham (Kent) 4 d	08 50			09 11		09 20			09 41		09 50			10 11		10 20			10 41	10 50			11 11	
Rainham (Kent) d	08 55			09 16		09 25			09 46		09 55			10 16		10 25			10 46	10 55			11 16	
Newington d				09 20					09 50					10 20					10 50				11 20	
Sittingbourne 4 a	09 02			09 25		09 32			09 55		10 02			10 25		10 32			10 55	11 02			11 25	
Sittingbourne 4 d	09 02		09 05	09 25		09 32		09 35	09 55		10 02		10 05	10 25		10 32		10 35	10 55	11 02		11 05	11 25	
Kemsley d			09 09					09 39					10 09					10 39				11 09		
Swale d			09 12					09 42					10 12					10 42				11 12		
Queenborough d			09 17					09 47					10 17					10 47				11 17		
Sheerness-on-Sea a			09 22					09 52					10 22					10 52				11 22		
Teynham d				09 29					09 59					10 29					10 59				11 29	
Faversham 2 a	09 10			09 35		09 40			10 05		10 10			10 35		10 40			11 05	11 10			11 35	
Faversham 2 d	09 14	09 16				09 44	09 46				10 14	10 16				10 44	10 46			11 14	11 16			
Selling d							09 51										10 51							
Canterbury East 4 d		09c31					10 00					10e31					11 00				11f31			
Bekesbourne d							10 05										11 05							
Adisham d							10 09										11 09							
Aylesham d							10 12										11 12							
Snowdown d							10 14										11 14							
Shepherds Well d							10 18										11 18							
Kearsney d							10 23										11 23							
Dover Priory 4 ⛴ a		09 46					10 28					10 46					11 28				11 46			
Whitstable d	09 22					09 52					10 22					10 52				11 22				
Chestfield & Swalecliffe d						09 55										10 55								
Herne Bay d	09 27					09 59					10 27					10 59				11 27				
Birchington-on-Sea d	09 35					10 08					10 35					11 08				11 35				
Westgate-on-Sea d						10 11										11 11								
Margate 4 d	09 41				10 04	10 15					10 41				11 04	11 15				11 41				12 04
Broadstairs d	09 46				10 09	10 20					10 46				11 09	11 20				11 46				12 09
Dumpton Park d					10 12	10 23									11 12	11 23								12 12
Ramsgate 4 ✈ a	09 51				10 15	10 26					10 51				11 15	11 26				11 51				12 15

For general notes see front of timetable
For details of catering facilities see Directory of Train Operators

For services from London to Ramsgate, Dover and Canterbury via Ashford see Table 207

b Change at London Bridge and Rochester
c Arr. 0928
e Arr. 1028
f Arr. 1128

Table 212

Saturdays

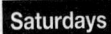

For details of Bank Holiday service alterations please see first page of Table 195

London → Medway, Sheerness-on-Sea, Dover and Ramsgate

Network Diagram - see first page of Table 212

		SE 1		SE		SE 1	SE 1		SE	SE 1	SE 1	SE 1		SE	SE 1	SE 1		SE	SE 1	SE 1		SE 1		SE	SE 1
London Victoria 15 ⊖	d	10 33				10 39	11 03			11 09		11 33			11 39	12 03			12 09			12 33			12 39
London Blackfriars 3 ⊖	d																								
Elephant & Castle ⊖	d																								
Bromley South 4	d	10 49				10 59	11 19			11 29		11 49			11 59	12 19			12 29			12 49			12 59
St Mary Cray	d					11 05				11 35					12 05				12 35						13 05
Swanley 4	d					11 10				11 40					12 10				12 40						13 10
Farningham Road	d					11 14				11 44					12 14				12 44						13 14
Longfield	d					11 19				11 49					12 19				12 49						13 19
Meopham	d					11 23				11 53					12 23				12 53						13 23
Sole Street	d					11 26				11 56					12 26				12 56						13 26
London Charing Cross 4 ⊖	d					10 20				10 50					11 20				11 50						12 20
London Waterloo (East) 4 ⊖	d					10 23				10 53					11 23				11 53						12 23
London Cannon Street 4 ⊖	d					10b18				10b48					11b18				11b48						12b18
London Bridge 4 ⊖	d					10 29				10 59					11 29				11 59						12 29
Dartford 4	d					11 04				11 34					12 04				12 34						13 04
Greenhithe for Bluewater	d					11 09				11 39					12 09				12 39						13 09
Gravesend 4	d					11 16				11 46					12 16				12 46						13 16
Strood 4	d					11 28				11 58					12 28				12 58						13 28
Rochester 4	d	11 13				11 36	11 43			12 06		12 13			12 36	12 43			13 06			13 13			13 36
Chatham 4	d	11 17				11 38	11 47			12 08		12 17			12 38	12 47			13 08			13 17			13 38
Gillingham (Kent) 4	d	11 20				11 41	11 50			12 11		12 20			12 41	12 50			13 11			13 20			13 41
Rainham (Kent)	d	11 25				11 46	11 55			12 16		12 25			12 46	12 55			13 16			13 25			13 46
Newington	d					11 50				12 20					12 50				13 20						13 50
Sittingbourne 4	a	11 32				11 55	12 02			12 25		12 32			12 55	13 02			13 25			13 32			13 55
	d	11 32		11 35		11 55	12 02		12 05	12 25		12 32		12 35	12 55	13 02		13 05	13 25			13 32		13 35	13 55
Kemsley	d			11 39					12 09					12 39				13 09						13 39	
Swale	d			11 42					12 12					12 42				13 12						13 42	
Queenborough	d			11 47					12 17					12 47				13 17						13 47	
Sheerness-on-Sea	a			11 52					12 22					12 52				13 22						13 52	
Teynham	d					11 59				12 29					12 59				13 29						13 59
Faversham 2	a	11 40				12 05	12 10			12 35		12 40			13 05	13 10			13 35			13 40			14 05
	d	11 44	11 46				12 14	12 16				12 44	12 46			13 14	13 16					13 44	13 46		
Selling	d		11 51										12 51										13 51		
Canterbury East 4	d		12 00					12c31					13 00				13e31						14 00		
Bekesbourne	d		12 05										13 05										14 05		
Adisham	d		12 09										13 09										14 09		
Aylesham	d		12 12										13 12										14 12		
Snowdown	d		12 14										13 14										14 14		
Shepherds Well	d		12 18										13 18										14 18		
Kearsney	d		12 23										13 23										14 23		
Dover Priory 4 ⛴	a		12 28					12 46					13 28				13 46						14 28		
Whitstable	d	11 52					12 22					12 52				13 22						13 52			
Chestfield & Swalecliffe	d	11 55										12 55										13 55			
Herne Bay	d	11 59					12 27					12 59				13 27						13 59			
Birchington-on-Sea	d	12 08					12 35					13 08				13 35						14 08			
Westgate-on-Sea	d	12 11										13 11										14 11			
Margate 4	d	12 15					12 41				13 04	13 15				13 41				14 04		14 15			
Broadstairs	d	12 20					12 46				13 09	13 20				13 46				14 09		14 20			
Dumpton Park	d	12 23									13 12	13 23								14 12		14 23			
Ramsgate 4 ✈	a	12 26					12 51				13 15	13 26				13 51				14 15		14 26			

For general notes see front of timetable
For details of catering facilities see Directory of Train Operators
For services from London to Ramsgate, Dover and Canterbury via Ashford see Table 207

b Change at London Bridge and Rochester
c Arr. 1228
e Arr. 1328

Table 212

Saturdays

For details of Bank Holiday service alterations please see first page of Table 195

London → Medway, Sheerness-on-Sea, Dover and Ramsgate

Network Diagram - see first page of Table 212

	SE 1 ⚲		SE	SE 1	SE 1 ⚲	SE 1		SE	SE 1	SE 1 ⚲		SE	SE 1	SE 1 ⚲	SE 1		SE	SE 1	SE 1 ⚲		SE	SE 1
London Victoria 15 ⊖ d	13 03			13 09		13 33			13 39	14 03			14 09		14 33			14 39	15 03			15 09
London Blackfriars 3 ⊖ d																						
Elephant & Castle ⊖ d																						
Bromley South 4 d	13 19			13 29		13 49			13 59	14 19			14 29		14 49			14 59	15 19			15 29
St Mary Cray d				13 35					14 05				14 35					15 05				15 35
Swanley 4 d				13 40					14 10				14 40					15 10				15 40
Farningham Road d				13 44					14 14				14 44					15 14				15 44
Longfield d				13 49					14 19				14 49					15 19				15 49
Meopham d				13 53					14 23				14 53					15 23				15 53
Sole Street d				13 56					14 26				14 56					15 26				15 56
London Charing Cross 4 ⊖ d				12 50					13 20				13 50					14 20				14 50
London Waterloo (East) 4 ⊖ d				12 53					13 23				13 53					14 23				14 53
London Cannon Street 4 ⊖ d				12b48					13b18				13b48					14b18				14b48
London Bridge 4 ⊖ d				12 59					13 29				13 59					14 29				14 59
Dartford 4 d				13 34					14 04				14 34					15 04				15 34
Greenhithe for Bluewater d				13 39					14 09				14 39					15 09				15 39
Gravesend 4 d				13 46					14 16				14 46					15 16				15 46
Strood 4 d				13 58					14 28				14 58					15 28				15 58
Rochester 4 d	13 43			14 06		14 13			14 36	14 43			15 06		15 13			15 36	15 43			16 06
Chatham 4 d	13 47			14 08		14 17			14 38	14 47			15 08		15 17			15 38	15 47			16 08
Gillingham (Kent) 4 d	13 50			14 11		14 20			14 41	14 50			15 11		15 20			15 41	15 50			16 11
Rainham (Kent) d	13 55			14 16		14 25			14 46	14 55			15 16		15 25			15 46	15 55			16 16
Newington d				14 20					14 50				15 20					15 50				16 20
Sittingbourne 4 a	14 02			14 25		14 32			14 55	15 02			15 25		15 32			15 55	16 02			16 25
d	14 02		14 05	14 25		14 32		14 35	14 55	15 02		15 05	15 25		15 32		15 35	15 55	16 02		16 05	16 25
Kemsley d			14 09					14 39				15 09					15 39				16 09	
Swale d			14 12					14 42				15 12					15 43				16 12	
Queenborough d			14 17					14 47				15 17					15 47				16 17	
Sheerness-on-Sea a			14 22					14 52				15 22					15 52				16 22	
Teynham d				14 29					14 59				15 29					15 59				16 29
Faversham 2 a	14 10			14 35		14 40			15 05	15 10			15 35		15 40			16 05	16 10			16 35
d	14 14	14 16				14 44	14 46			15 14	15 16				15 44	15 46			16 14	16 16		
Selling d							14 51									15 51						
Canterbury East 4 d		14c31					15 00				15e31					16 00				16f31		
Bekesbourne d							15 05									16 05						
Adisham d							15 09									16 09						
Aylesham d							15 12									16 12						
Snowdown d							15 14									16 14						
Shepherds Well d							15 18									16 18						
Kearsney d							15 23									16 23						
Dover Priory 4 ⛴ a		14 46					15 28				15 46					16 28				16 46		
Whitstable d	14 22					14 52				15 22					15 52				16 22			
Chestfield & Swalecliffe d						14 55									15 55							
Herne Bay d	14 27					14 59				15 27					15 59				16 27			
Birchington-on-Sea d	14 35					15 08				15 35					16 08				16 35			
Westgate-on-Sea d						15 11									16 11							
Margate 4 d	14 41				15 04	15 15				15 41				16 04	16 15				16 41			
Broadstairs d	14 46				15 09	15 20				15 46				16 09	16 20				16 46			
Dumpton Park d					15 12	15 23								16 12	16 23							
Ramsgate 4 ⛴ a	14 51				15 15	15 26				15 51				16 15	16 26				16 51			

For general notes see front of timetable
For details of catering facilities see Directory of Train Operators

For services from London to Ramsgate, Dover and Canterbury via Ashford see Table 207

b Change at London Bridge and Rochester
c Arr. 1428
e Arr. 1528
f Arr. 1628

Saturdays

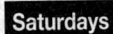

For details of Bank Holiday service alterations please see first page of Table 195

London → Medway, Sheerness-on-Sea, Dover and Ramsgate

Network Diagram - see first page of Table 212

	SE 1	SE	SE 1	SE 1 🚲	SE		SE 1	SE 1	SE	SE 1	SE 1 🚲	SE	SE 1	SE 1	SE 1	SE 1 🚲	SE	SE 1
London Victoria 15 ⊖ d	15 33		15 39	16 03			16 09	16 33		16 39	17 03		17 09	17 33	17 39	18 03		18 09
London Blackfriars 3 ⊖ d																		
Elephant & Castle ⊖ d																		
Bromley South 4 d	15 49		15 59	16 19			16 29	16 49		16 59	17 19		17 29	17 49	17 59	18 19		18 29
St Mary Cray d			16 05				16 35			17 05			17 35		18 05			18 35
Swanley 4 d			16 10				16 40			17 10			17 40		18 10			18 40
Farningham Road d			16 14				16 44			17 14			17 44		18 14			18 44
Longfield d			16 19				16 49			17 19			17 49		18 19			18 49
Meopham d			16 23				16 53			17 23			17 53		18 23			18 53
Sole Street d			16 26				16 56			17 26			17 56		18 26			18 56
London Charing Cross 4 ⊖ d			15 20				15 50			16 20			16 50		17 20			17 50
London Waterloo (East) 4 ⊖ d			15 23				15 53			16 23			16 53		17 23			17 53
London Cannon Street 4 ⊖ d			15b18				15b48			16b18			16b48		17b18			17b48
London Bridge 4 ⊖ d			15 29				15 59			16 29			16 59		17 29			17 59
Dartford 4 d			16 04				16 34			17 04			17 34		18 04			18 34
Greenhithe for Bluewater d			16 09				16 39			17 09			17 39		18 09			18 39
Gravesend 4 d			16 16				16 46			17 16			17 46		18 16			18 46
Strood 4 d			16 28				16 58			17 28			17 58		18 28			18 58
Rochester 4 d	16 13		16 36	16 43			17 06	17 13		17 36	17 43		18 06	18 13	18 36	18 43		19 06
Chatham 4 d	16 17		16 38	16 47			17 08	17 17		17 38	17 47		18 08	18 17	18 38	18 47		19 08
Gillingham (Kent) 4 d	16 20		16 41	16 50			17 11	17 20		17 41	17 50		18 11	18 20	18 41	18 50		19 11
Rainham (Kent) d	16 25		16 46	16 55			17 16	17 25		17 46	17 55		18 16	18 25	18 46	18 55		19 16
Newington d			16 50				17 20			17 50			18 20		18 50			19 20
Sittingbourne 4 a	16 32		16 55	17 02			17 25	17 32		17 55	18 02		18 25	18 32	18 55	19 02		19 25
d	16 32	16 35	16 55	17 02	17 05		17 25	17 32	17 35	17 55	18 02	18 05	18 25	18 32	18 55	19 02	19 05	19 25
Kemsley d		16 39			17 09				17 39			18 09					19 09	
Swale d		16 42			17 12				17 42			18 12					19 12	
Queenborough d		16 47			17 17				17 47			18 17					19 17	
Sheerness-on-Sea a		16 52			17 22				17 52			18 22					19 22	
Teynham d			16 59				17 29			17 59			18 29		18 59			19 29
Faversham 2 a	16 40		17 05	17 10			17 35	17 40		18 05	18 10		18 35	18 40	19 05	19 10		19 35
d	16 44 / 16 46			17 14 / 17 16				17 44 / 17 46			18 14 / 18 16			18 44 / 18 46		19 14 / 19 16		
Selling d	16 51							17 51						18 51				
Canterbury East 4 d	17 00			17c31				18 00			18e31			19 00		19f31		
Bekesbourne d	17 05							18 05						19 05				
Adisham d	17 09							18 09						19 09				
Aylesham d	17 12							18 12						19 12				
Snowdown d	17 14							18 14						19 14				
Shepherds Well d	17 18							18 18						19 18				
Kearsney d	17 23							18 23						19 23				
Dover Priory 4 a	17 28			17 46				18 28			18 46			19 28		19 46		
Whitstable d	16 52			17 22				17 52			18 22			18 52		19 22		
Chestfield & Swalecliffe d	16 55							17 55						18 55				
Herne Bay d	16 59			17 27				17 59			18 27			18 59		19 27		
Birchington-on-Sea d	17 08			17 35				18 08			18 35			19 08		19 35		
Westgate-on-Sea d	17 11							18 11						19 11				
Margate 4 d	17 15			17 41				18 15			18 41			19 15		19 41		
Broadstairs d	17 20			17 46				18 20			18 46			19 20		19 46		
Dumpton Park d	17 23							18 23						19 23				
Ramsgate 4 a	17 26			17 51				18 26			18 51			19 26		19 51		

For general notes see front of timetable
For details of catering facilities see Directory of Train Operators

For services from London to Ramsgate, Dover and Canterbury via Ashford see Table 207

b Change at London Bridge and Rochester
c Arr. 1728
e Arr. 1828
f Arr. 1928

Saturdays

For details of Bank Holiday service alterations please see first page of Table 195

London → Medway, Sheerness-on-Sea, Dover and Ramsgate

Network Diagram - see first page of Table 212

		SE 1		SE 1		SE 1 (bicycle)		SE	SE 1	SE 1	SE 1		SE	SE 1	SE 1	SE 1		SE	SE 1	SE 1		SE	SE 1	SE 1	SE 1
London Victoria 15	⊖ d	18 33		18 39		19 03			19 39		20 03			20 39		21 03			21 39	22 03			22 39	23 03	23 39
London Blackfriars 3	⊖ d																								
Elephant & Castle	⊖ d																								
Bromley South 4	d	18 49		18 59		19 19			19 59		20 19			20 59		21 19			21 59	22 19			22 59	23 19	23 59
St Mary Cray	d			19 05					20 05					21 05					22 05				23 05		00 05
Swanley 4	d			19 10					20 10					21 10					22 10				23 10		00 10
Farningham Road	d			19 14					20 14					21 14					22 14				23 14		00 14
Longfield	d			19 19		19 33			20 19		20 33			21 19		21 33			22 19				23 19		00 19
Meopham	d			19 23					20 23					21 23					22 23				23 23		00 23
Sole Street	d			19 26					20 26					21 26					22 26				23 26		00 26
London Charing Cross 4	⊖ d			18 20					19 20					20 20					21 20				22 20		23 20
London Waterloo (East) 4	⊖ d			18 23					19 23					20 23					21 23				22 23		23 23
London Cannon Street 4	⊖ d			18b18					19b14																
London Bridge 4	⊖ d			18 29					19 29					20 29					21 29				22 29		23 29
Dartford 4	d			19 04					20 04					21 04					22 04				23 04		23 34
Greenhithe for Bluewater	d			19 09					20 09					21 09					22 09				23 09		23 40
Gravesend 4	d			19 16					20 16					21 16					22 16				23 16		23 50
Strood 4	d			19 28					20 28					21 28					22 28				23 28		00 28
Rochester 4	d	19 13		19 36		19 47			20 36		20 47			21 36		21 47			22 36	22 47			23 36	23 47	00 36
Chatham 4	d	19 17		19 38		19 49			20 38		20 49			21 38		21 49			22 38	22 49			23 38	23 49	00 39
Gillingham (Kent) 4	d	19 20		19 41		19 53			20 41		20 53			21 41		21 53			22 41	22 53			23 41	23 53	00a42
Rainham (Kent)	d	19 25		19 46		19 58			20 46		20 58			21 46		21 58			22 46	22 58			23 46	23 58	
Newington	d			19 50					20 50					21 50					22 50				23 50		
Sittingbourne 4	a	19 32		19 55		20 05			20 55		21 05			21 55		22 05			22 55	23 05			23 55	00 05	
	d	19 32		19 55		20 05		20 07	20 55		21 05		21 07	21 55		22 05		22 07	22 55	23 05		23 07	23 55	00 05	
Kemsley	d							20 11					21 11					22 11				23 11			
Swale	d							20 14					21 14					22 14				23 14			
Queenborough	d							20 19					21 19					22 19				23 19			
Sheerness-on-Sea	a							20 24					21 24					22 24				23 24			
Teynham	d			19 59					20 59					21 59					22 59				23 59		
Faversham 2	a	19 40		20 05		20 13			21 05		21 13			22 05		22 13			23 05	23 13			00 05	00 13	
	d	19 44	19 46			20 16	20 18				21 16	21 18				22 16	22 18			23 16	23 18			00 16	
Selling	d		19 51				20 23					21 23					22 23								
Canterbury East 4	d		20 00				20 33					21 33					22 33				23 32				
Bekesbourne	d		20 05				20 37					21 37					22 38								
Adisham	d		20 09				20 42					21 42					22 43								
Aylesham	d		20 12				20 44					21 44					22 46								
Snowdown	d		20 14				20 47					21 47					22 49								
Shepherds Well	d		20 18				20 51					21 51					22 54								
Kearsney	d		20 23				20 55					21 55					22 59								
Dover Priory 4	⛴ a		20 28				21 01					22 01					23 03				23 47				
Whitstable	d	19 52				20 24					21 24					22 24				23 24				00 24	
Chestfield & Swalecliffe	d	19 55				20 27					21 27					22 27				23 27				00 27	
Herne Bay	d	19 59				20 31					21 31					22 31				23 31				00 31	
Birchington-on-Sea	d	20 08				20 40					21 40					22 40				23 40				00 40	
Westgate-on-Sea	d	20 11				20 43					21 43					22 43				23 43				00 43	
Margate 4	d	20 15				20 47				21 24	21 47				22 17	22 47				23 47				00 47	
Broadstairs	d	20 20				20 52				21 29	21 52				22 22	22 52				23 52				00 52	
Dumpton Park	d	20 23				20 54				21 32	21 54				22 25	22 54				23 54				00 55	
Ramsgate 4	✈ a	20 26				20 57				21 35	21 57				22 28	22 57				23 57				00 58	

For general notes see front of timetable
For details of catering facilities see Directory of Train Operators

For services from London to Ramsgate, Dover and Canterbury via Ashford see Table 207

b Change at London Bridge and Rochester

Sundays

London → Medway, Sheerness-on-Sea, Dover and Ramsgate

Network Diagram - see first page of Table 212

		SE 1	SE	SE 1	SE 1	SE	SE 1		SE 1	SE	SE 1	SE 1		SE 1		SE	SE 1	SE 1		SE 1	SE		SE 1	SE 1	
London Victoria 15	⊖ d	23p03		23p39	00 03				07 35			08 03		08 24				09 03		09 24				10 03	
London Blackfriars 3	⊖ d																								
Elephant & Castle	⊖ d																								
Bromley South 4	d	23p19		23p59					07 52			08 19		08 43				09 19		09 43				10 19	
St Mary Cray	d			00 05					07 58					08 50						09 50					
Swanley 4	d			00 10					08 03					08 54						09 54					
Farningham Road	d			00 14					08 07					08 59						09 59					
Longfield	d			00 19					08 12					09 03						10 03					
Meopham	d			00 23					08 16					09 08						10 08					
Sole Street	d			00 26					08 19					09 10						10 10					
London Charing Cross 4	⊖ d			23 20										07 40				08 20		08 50				09 20	
London Waterloo (East) 4	⊖ d			23 23										07 43				08 23		08 53				09 23	
London Cannon Street 4	⊖ d																								
London Bridge 4	⊖ d			23 29										07 48				08 29		08 59				09 29	
Dartford 4	d			23 34								08 02		08 28				09 04		09 34				10 04	
Greenhithe for Bluewater	d			23 40								08 08		08 34				09 09		09 39				10 09	
Gravesend 4	d			23 50								08 16		08 42				09 16		09 46				10 16	
Strood 4	d			00 28								08 28		08 54				09 27		09 57				10 27	
Rochester 4	d	23p47		00 36	00 47				08 28			08 43		09 20				09 43		10 20				10 43	
Chatham 4	d	23p49		00 39	00 49				08 31			08 46		09 22				09 46		10 22				10 46	
Gillingham (Kent) 4	d	23p53		00a42	00 53				08 35			08 50		09 26				09 50		10 26				10 50	
Rainham (Kent)	d	23p58			00 58				08 40			08 55		09 31				09 55		10 31				10 55	
Newington	d				01 01				08 44					09 35						10 35					
Sittingbourne 4	a	00 05			01 06				08 49			09 02		09 40				10 02		10 40				11 02	
	d	00 05	00 07		01 06	07 48			08 49	08 52		09 02		09 41		09 48		10 02		10 41	10 48			11 02	
Kemsley	d		00 11			07 52				08 56						09 52					10 52				
Swale	d		00 14			07 55				08 59						09 55					10 55				
Queenborough	d		00 19			08 00				09 04						10 00					11 00				
Sheerness-on-Sea	a		00 24			08 05				09 09						10 05					11 05				
Teynham	d				01 10				08 54					09 45						10 45					
Faversham 2	a	00 13			01 15				09 00			09 10		09 52				10 10		10 52				11 10	
	d	00 16			01 16							09 14	09 16	09 52				10 14	10 16	10 52				11 14	11 16
Selling	d												09 21						10 21						11 21
Canterbury East 4	d												09 30	10a04					10 30	11a04					11 30
Bekesbourne	d												09 35						10 35						11 35
Adisham	d												09 39						10 39						11 39
Aylesham	d												09 42						10 42						11 42
Snowdown	d												09 44						10 44						11 44
Shepherds Well	d												09 48						10 48						11 48
Kearsney	d												09 53						10 53						11 53
Dover Priory 4	⛴ a												09 58						10 58						11 58
Whitstable	d	00 24			01 24							09 22						10 22						11 22	
Chestfield & Swalecliffe	d	00 27			01 27							09 25						10 25						11 25	
Herne Bay	d	00 31			01 31							09 29						10 29						11 29	
Birchington-on-Sea	d	00 40			01 40							09 38						10 38						11 38	
Westgate-on-Sea	d	00 43			01 43							09 41						10 41						11 41	
Margate 4	d	00 47			01 47		08 24				09 24	09 45					10 24	10 45					11 24	11 45	
Broadstairs	d	00 52			01 52		08 29				09 29	09 50					10 29	10 50					11 29	11 50	
Dumpton Park	d	00 55			01 55		08 32				09 32	09 53					10 32	10 53					11 32	11 53	
Ramsgate 4	✈ a	00 58			01 58		08 35				09 35	09 56					10 35	10 56					11 35	11 56	

For general notes see front of timetable
For details of catering facilities see Directory of Train Operators

For services from London to Ramsgate, Dover and Canterbury via Ashford see Table 207

Table 212

Sundays

London → Medway, Sheerness-on-Sea, Dover and Ramsgate

Network Diagram - see first page of Table 212

		SE 1	SE	SE 1	SE 1 ⚒			SE 1	SE	SE 1	SE 1 ⚒		SE 1		SE	SE 1	SE 1 ⚒		SE 1	SE		SE 1	SE 1 ⚒		SE 1
London Victoria 15	⊖ d	10 24			11 03			11 24			12 03		12 24				13 03		13 24				14 03		14 24
London Blackfriars 3	⊖ d																								
Elephant & Castle	⊖ d																								
Bromley South 4	d	10 43			11 19			11 43			12 19		12 43				13 19		13 43				14 19		14 43
St Mary Cray	d	10 50						11 50					12 50						13 50						14 50
Swanley 4	d	10 54						11 54					12 54						13 54						14 54
Farningham Road	d	10 59						11 59					12 59						13 59						14 59
Longfield	d	11 03						12 03					13 03						14 03						15 03
Meopham	d	11 08						12 08					13 08						14 08						15 08
Sole Street	d	11 10						12 10					13 10						14 10						15 10
London Charing Cross 4	⊖ d	09 50			10 20			10 50			11 20		11 50				12 20		12 50				13 20		13 50
London Waterloo (East) 4	⊖ d	09 53			10 23			10 53			11 23		11 53				12 23		12 53				13 23		13 53
London Cannon Street 4	⊖ d																								
London Bridge 4	⊖ d	09 59			10 29			10 59			11 29		11 59				12 29		12 59				13 29		13 59
Dartford 4	d	10 34			11 04			11 34			12 04		12 34				13 04		13 34				14 04		14 34
Greenhithe for Bluewater	d	10 39			11 09			11 39			12 09		12 39				13 09		13 39				14 09		14 39
Gravesend 4	d	10 46			11 16			11 46			12 16		12 46				13 16		13 46				14 16		14 46
Strood 4	d	10 57			11 27			11 57			12 27		12 57				13 27		13 57				14 27		14 57
Rochester 4	d	11 20			11 43			12 20			12 43		13 20				13 43		14 20				14 43		15 20
Chatham 4	d	11 22			11 46			12 22			12 46		13 22				13 46		14 22				14 46		15 22
Gillingham (Kent) 4	d	11 26			11 50			12 26			12 50		13 26				13 50		14 26				14 50		15 26
Rainham (Kent)	d	11 31			11 55			12 31			12 55		13 31				13 55		14 31				14 55		15 31
Newington	d	11 35						12 35					13 35						14 35						15 35
Sittingbourne 4	a	11 40			12 02			12 40			13 02		13 40				14 02		14 40				15 02		15 40
	d	11 41	11 48		12 02			12 41	12 48		13 02		13 41		13 48		14 02		14 41	14 48			15 02		15 41
Kemsley	d		11 52						12 52						13 52					14 52					
Swale	d		11 55						12 55						13 55					14 55					
Queenborough	d		12 00						13 00						14 00					15 00					
Sheerness-on-Sea	a		12 05						13 05						14 05					15 05					
Teynham	d	11 45						12 45					13 45						14 45						15 45
Faversham 2	a	11 52			12 10			12 52			13 10		13 52				14 10		14 52				15 10		15 52
	d	11 52			12 14	12 16		12 52			13 14	13 16	13 52				14 14	14 16	14 52				15 14	15 16	15 52
Selling	d					12 21						13 21						14 21						15 21	
Canterbury East 4	d	12a04				12 30		13a04				13 30	14a04					14 30	15a04					15 30	16a04
Bekesbourne	d					12 35						13 35						14 35						15 35	
Adisham	d					12 39						13 39						14 39						15 39	
Aylesham	d					12 42						13 42						14 42						15 42	
Snowdown	d					12 44						13 44						14 44						15 44	
Shepherds Well	d					12 48						13 48						14 48						15 48	
Kearsney	d					12 53						13 53						14 53						15 53	
Dover Priory 4	⛴ a					12 58						13 58						14 58						15 58	
Whitstable	d				12 22						13 22						14 22						15 22		
Chestfield & Swalecliffe	d				12 25						13 25						14 25						15 25		
Herne Bay	d				12 29						13 29						14 29						15 29		
Birchington-on-Sea	d				12 38						13 38						14 38						15 38		
Westgate-on-Sea	d				12 41						13 41						14 41						15 41		
Margate 4	d			12 24	12 45					13 24	13 45					14 24	14 45					15 24	15 45		
Broadstairs	d			12 29	12 50					13 29	13 50					14 29	14 50					15 29	15 50		
Dumpton Park	d			12 32	12 53					13 32	13 53					14 32	14 53					15 32	15 53		
Ramsgate 4	✈ a			12 35	12 56					13 35	13 56					14 35	14 56					15 35	15 56		

For general notes see front of timetable
For details of catering facilities see Directory of Train Operators

For services from London to Ramsgate, Dover and Canterbury via Ashford see Table 207

Table 212

Sundays

London → Medway, Sheerness-on-Sea, Dover and Ramsgate

Network Diagram - see first page of Table 212

		SE	SE 1	SE 1			SE 1	SE	SE 1	SE 1		SE 1		SE	SE 1	SE 1		SE 1	SE		SE 1	SE 1		SE 1	SE
London Victoria 15	⊖ d			15 03			15 24			16 03		16 24				17 03		17 24				18 03		18 24	
London Blackfriars 3	⊖ d																								
Elephant & Castle	⊖ d																								
Bromley South 4	d			15 19			15 43			16 19		16 43				17 19		17 43				18 19		18 43	
St Mary Cray	d						15 50					16 50						17 50						18 50	
Swanley 4	d						15 54					16 54						17 54						18 54	
Farningham Road	d						15 59					16 59						17 59						18 59	
Longfield	d						16 03					17 03						18 03						19 03	
Meopham	d						16 08					17 08						18 08						19 08	
Sole Street	d						16 10					17 10						18 10						19 10	
London Charing Cross 4	⊖ d			14 20			14 50			15 20		15 50				16 20		16 50				17 20		17 50	
London Waterloo (East) 4	⊖ d			14 23			14 53			15 23		15 53				16 23		16 53				17 23		17 53	
London Cannon Street 4	⊖ d																								
London Bridge 4	⊖ d			14 29			14 59			15 29		15 59				16 29		16 59				17 29		17 59	
Dartford 4	d			15 04			15 34			16 04		16 34				17 04		17 34				18 04		18 34	
Greenhithe for Bluewater	d			15 09			15 39			16 09		16 39				17 09		17 39				18 09		18 39	
Gravesend 4	d			15 16			15 46			16 16		16 46				17 16		17 46				18 16		18 46	
Strood 4	d			15 27			15 57			16 27		16 57				17 27		17 57				18 27		18 57	
Rochester 4	d			15 43			16 20			16 43		17 20				17 43		18 20				18 43		19 20	
Chatham 4	d			15 46			16 22			16 46		17 22				17 46		18 22				18 46		19 22	
Gillingham (Kent) 4	d			15 50			16 26			16 50		17 26				17 50		18 26				18 50		19 26	
Rainham (Kent)	d			15 55			16 31			16 55		17 31				17 55		18 31				18 55		19 31	
Newington	d						16 35					17 35						18 35						19 35	
Sittingbourne 4	a			16 02			16 40			17 02		17 40				18 02		18 40				19 02		19 40	
	d	15 48		16 02			16 41	16 48		17 02		17 41		17 48		18 02		18 41	18 48			19 02		19 41	19 48
Kemsley	d	15 52						16 52						17 52					18 52						19 52
Swale	d	15 55						16 55						17 55					18 55						19 55
Queenborough	d	16 00						17 00						18 00					19 00						20 00
Sheerness-on-Sea	a	16 05						17 05						18 05					19 05						20 05
Teynham	d						16 45					17 45						18 45						19 45	
Faversham 2	a			16 10			16 52			17 10		17 52				18 10		18 52				19 10		19 51	
	d			16 14	16 16		16 52			17 14	17 16	17 52				18 14	18 16	18 52				19 14	19 16		
Selling	d				16 21						17 21						18 21						19 21		
Canterbury East 4	d				16 30		17a04				17 30	18a04					18 30	19a04					19 30		
Bekesbourne	d				16 35						17 35						18 35						19 35		
Adisham	d				16 39						17 39						18 39						19 39		
Aylesham	d				16 42						17 42						18 42						19 42		
Snowdown	d				16 44						17 44						18 44						19 44		
Shepherds Well	d				16 48						17 48						18 48						19 48		
Kearsney	d				16 53						17 53						18 53						19 53		
Dover Priory 4	a				16 58						17 58						18 58						19 58		
Whitstable	d			16 22						17 22						18 22						19 22			
Chestfield & Swalecliffe	d			16 25						17 25						18 25						19 25			
Herne Bay	d			16 29						17 29						18 29						19 29			
Birchington-on-Sea	d			16 38						17 38						18 38						19 38			
Westgate-on-Sea	d			16 41						17 41						18 41						19 41			
Margate 4	d		16 24	16 45					17 24	17 45					18 24	18 45					19 24	19 45			
Broadstairs	d		16 29	16 50					17 29	17 50					18 29	18 50					19 29	19 50			
Dumpton Park	d		16 32	16 53					17 32	17 53					18 32	18 53					19 32	19 53			
Ramsgate 4	a		16 35	16 56					17 35	17 56					18 35	18 56					19 35	19 56			

For general notes see front of timetable
For details of catering facilities see Directory of Train Operators

For services from London to Ramsgate, Dover and Canterbury via Ashford see Table 207

Table 212

Sundays

London → Medway, Sheerness-on-Sea, Dover and Ramsgate

Network Diagram - see first page of Table 212

		SE 1	SE 1			SE 1	SE	SE 1	SE 1		SE 1		SE	SE 1		SE 1	SE	SE 1			SE 1	SE 1	SE 1		
London Victoria 15	⊖ d		19 03			19 24			20 03		20 24			21 03		21 24		22 03			22 35	23 03	23 42		
London Blackfriars 3	⊖ d																								
Elephant & Castle	⊖ d																								
Bromley South 4	d		19 19			19 43			20 19		20 43			21 19		21 43		22 19			22 55	23 19	00 01		
St Mary Cray	d					19 50					20 50					21 50					23 01		00 08		
Swanley 4	d					19 54					20 54					21 54					23 06		00 12		
Farningham Road	d					19 59					20 59					21 59					23 11		00 17		
Longfield	d					20 03					21 03					22 03					23 16		00 21		
Meopham	d					20 08					21 08					22 08					23 21		00 26		
Sole Street	d					20 10					21 10					22 10					23 24		00 28		
London Charing Cross 4	⊖ d		*18 20*			*18 50*			*19 20*		*19 50*			*20 20*		*20 50*		*21 20*			*22 20*		*23 20*		
London Waterloo (East) 4	⊖ d		*18 23*			*18 53*			*19 23*		*19 53*			*20 23*		*20 53*		*21 23*			*22 23*		*23 23*		
London Cannon Street 4	⊖ d																								
London Bridge 4	⊖ d		*18 29*			*18 59*			*19 29*		*19 59*			*20 29*		*20 59*		*21 29*			*22 29*		*23 29*		
Dartford 4	d		*19 04*			*19 34*			*20 04*		*20 34*			*21 04*		*21 34*		*22 04*			*23 04*		*00 04*		
Greenhithe for Bluewater	d		*19 09*			*19 40*			*20 09*		*20 40*			*21 09*		*21 40*		*22 09*			*23 09*		*00 09*		
Gravesend 4	d		*19 16*			*19 48*			*20 16*		*20 48*			*21 16*		*21 48*		*22 16*			*23 16*		*00 16*		
Strood 4	d		*19 27*			*20 00*			*20 27*		*21 00*			*21 27*		*22 00*		*22 27*			*23 27*		*00 27*		
Rochester 4	d		19 43			20 20			20 43		21 20			21 43		22 20		22 43			23 35	23 43	00 38		
Chatham 4	d		19 46			20 22			20 46		21 22			21 46		22 22		22 46			23 38	23 46	00 40		
Gillingham (Kent) 4	d		19 50			20 26			20 50		21 26			21 50		22 26		22 50			23 41	23 50	00a44		
Rainham (Kent)	d		19 55			20 31			20 55		21 31			21 55		22 31		22 55			23 46	23 55			
Newington	d					20 35					21 35					22 35					23 50				
Sittingbourne 4	a		20 02			20 40			21 02		21 40			22 02		22 40		23 02			23 55	00 02			
	d		20 02			20 41	20 48		21 02		21 41		21 48	22 02		22 41	22 48	23 02			23 55	00 02			
Kemsley	d						20 52						21 52				22 52								
Swale	d						20 55						21 55				22 55								
Queenborough	d						21 00						22 00				23 00								
Sheerness-on-Sea	a						21 05						22 05				23 05								
Teynham	d					20 45					21 45					22 45					23 59				
Faversham 2	a		20 10			20 51			21 10		21 51			22 10		22 51		23 10			00 06	00 10			
	d		20 14	20 16					21 14	21 16				22 14	22 16			23 14	23 16			00 14			
Selling	d			20 21						21 21					22 21										
Canterbury East 4	d			20 30						21 30					22 30				23 30						
Bekesbourne	d			20 35						21 35					22 35										
Adisham	d			20 39						21 39					22 39										
Aylesham	d			20 42						21 42					22 42										
Snowdown	d			20 44						21 44					22 44										
Shepherds Well	d			20 48						21 48					22 48										
Kearsney	d			20 53						21 53					22 53										
Dover Priory 4	a			20 58						21 58					22 58				23 46						
Whitstable	d		20 22						21 22					22 22				23 22				00 22			
Chestfield & Swalecliffe	d		20 25						21 25					22 25				23 25				00 25			
Herne Bay	d		20 29						21 29					22 29				23 29				00 29			
Birchington-on-Sea	d		20 38						21 38					22 38				23 38				00 38			
Westgate-on-Sea	d		20 41						21 41					22 41				23 41				00 41			
Margate 4	d	20 24	20 45					21 24	21 45					22 45				23 45				00 45			
Broadstairs	d	20 29	20 50					21 29	21 50					22 50				23 50				00 50			
Dumpton Park	d	20 32	20 53					21 32	21 53					22 53				23 53				00 53			
Ramsgate 4	a	20 35	20 56					21 35	21 56					22 56				23 56				00 56			

For general notes see front of timetable
For details of catering facilities see Directory of Train Operators

For services from London to Ramsgate, Dover and Canterbury via Ashford see Table 207

For details of Bank Holiday service alterations please see first page of Table 195

Ramsgate, Dover, Sheerness-on-Sea and Medway → London

Network Diagram - see first page of Table 212

Miles	Miles	Miles			SE MX	SE 1	SE	SE 1	SE	SE 1	SE 1	SE	SE 1	SE 1	SE 1	SE	SE 1	SE 1	SE	SE	SE 1	SE 1	SE	SE 1	SE
0	—	—	**Ramsgate 4**	d		04 38				05 04			05 28		05 45						06 11				
1	—	—	Dumpton Park	d		04 40							05 30		05 48						06 14				
2¼	—	—	Broadstairs	d		04 43				05 09			05 33		05 51						06 17	06 24			
5½	—	—	**Margate 4**	d		04 48				05 14			05 38		05 56						06 22	06 29			
6¾	—	—	Westgate-on-Sea	d		04 51							05 41		06 00						06 25				
8½	—	—	Birchington-on-Sea	d		04 54				05 19			05 44		06 03						06 29	06 34			
16½	—	—	**Herne Bay**	d		05 03				05 28			05 53		06 12						06 37	06 43			
18½	—	—	Chestfield & Swalecliffe	d		05 07							05 56		06 16						06 40				
20½	—	—	Whitstable	d		05 10				05 33			06 00		06 19						06 44	06 49			
—	0	—	**Dover Priory 4**	d				04 50			05 12						05 49							06 24	
—	2¼	—	Kearsney	d				04 54			05 16						05 53							06 28	
—	5½	—	Shepherds Well	d				04 59			05 22						05 58							06 33	
—	7½	—	Snowdown	d				05 02			05 26						06 01							06 36	
—	8½	—	Aylesham	d				05 05			05 28						06 04							06 39	
—	9½	—	Adisham	d				05 07			05 31						06 06							06 41	
—	12½	—	Bekesbourne	d				05 12			05 35						06 11							06 46	
—	15½	—	**Canterbury East 4**	d				05 17			05 41						06 16							06 51	
—	22	—	Selling	d				05 26			05 51						06 25							07 00	
27¼	25¼	—	**Faversham 2**	a		05 18		05 30		05 41	05 55		06 09		06 28		06 29	←			06 52	06 57		07 06	
—	—	—		d	23p42	05 19	05 22	05 31		05 43	05 58		06 10	06 13	06 36		06 31	06 36			06 53	06 58			
31¾	29¾	—	Teynham	d	23p47		05 27	05 36		05 48				06 18	→		06 36	06 41							
—	—	0	**Sheerness-on-Sea**	d					05 31			05 58							06 36				06 57		
—	—	2	Queenborough	d					05 36			06 03							06 41				07 02		
—	—	4	Swale	d					05 40			06 08							06 46				07 05		
—	—	6	Kemsley	d					05 43			06 11							06 49				07 09		
34½	32½	8	**Sittingbourne 4**	a	23p52	05 27	05 32	05 41	05 48	05 53	06 06	06 16	06 18	06 23			06 41	06 46	06 54		07 01	07 06	07 15		
—	—	—		d	23p52	05 28	05 32	05 41		05 54	06 06		06 18	06 24			06 41	06 46			07 02	07 06			
37¾	35¾	—	Newington	d	23p57		05 37	05 46		05 59				06 29			06 47	06 52							
40¼	38¼	—	Rainham (Kent)	d	00 01	05 36	05 42	05 50		06 04	06 15		06 26	06 34			06 51	06 56			07 10	07 14			
43¼	41¼	—	**Gillingham (Kent) 4**	d	00 07	05 42	05 48	05 56		06 09	06 23		06 32	06 39		06 44	06 57	07 02		07 06	07 16	07 20			
45	43	—	**Chatham 4**	d	00 11	05 46	05 52	06 01		06 13	06 28		06 36	06 44		06 48	07 02	07 06		07 10	07 20	07 24			
45½	43½	0	Rochester 4	d	00 13	05 58	05 54	06 03		06 15			06 42	06 46		06 50		07 18		07 13		07 34			
—	—	—	Strood 4	a	00 17	06 03	06 03			06 31			06 48	07 04		07 04		07 24		07 24		07 44			
—	—	—	Gravesend 4	a	00 28	06 14	06 14			06 44			06 59	07 17		07 17		07 39		07 39		07 57			
—	—	—	Greenhithe for Bluewater	a	00 34	06 20	06 20			06 50			07 06	07 24		07 24		07 46		07 46		08 04			
—	—	—	Dartford 4	a	00 41	06 25	06 25			06 55			07 11	07 29		07 29		07 51		07 51		08 09			
—	—	—	**London Bridge 4**	⊖ a		07 01	06 33			07 30	07 07		07 44	07 26		08 06		07 49		08b41		08 08			
—	—	30	**London Cannon Street 4**	⊖ a		07c13	06 38			07e38	07 13		07 51	07 33		08 13		07 55			08 54	08 15			
—	—	—	**London Waterloo (East) 4**	⊖ a		07 06	06f41			07 36	07f16		07c55	07f36		08e15		07f58			08c55	08f19			
—	—	—	**London Charing Cross 4**	⊖ a		07 10	06f46			07 40	07f20		07c59	07f40		08e21		08f03			09c01	08f24			
52¼	50¼	—	Sole Street	d				06 14		06 24						07 01				07 24					←
53¼	51¼	—	Meopham	d				06 16		06 26						07 03				07 26 →					07 26
55¾	53¾	—	Longfield	d				06 20		06 30						07 08									07 30
58¾	56¾	—	Farningham Road	d				06 24		06 34						07 12									07 34
61¾	59¾	—	Swanley 4	a				06 29		06 40						07 17									07 39
64½	62½	—	St Mary Cray	a				06 35		06 45						07 22									07 44
68¼	66¼	—	Bromley South 4	a		06 13		06 42		06 51			07 01			07 29	07 32				07 50				07 51
—	—	—	Elephant & Castle	⊖ a		07 11				07 15			07 39			07 57	08 01				08 24				08 24
—	—	—	**London Blackfriars 3**	⊖ a		07 16				07 20			07 44			08 02	08 06				08 30				08 30
79¼	77¼	—	**London Victoria 15**	⊖ a	01 13	06 30		06 59		07 12			07 24			07 54	07 52				08 11				08 14

For general notes see front of timetable
For details of catering facilities see Directory of Train Operators

For services from Ramsgate, Dover and Canterbury to London via Ashford see Table 207

b Change at Rochester and Dartford
c Change at Chatham and London Bridge
e Change at Rochester and London Bridge
f Change at London Bridge

From 12 October due to seasonal difficulties a large number of trains on this table will have minor retimings that could mean slightly earlier departure or later arrival times at certain stations. For further details see local publicity or contact National Rail Enquiries 08457 48 49 50.

Table 212

Mondays to Fridays

For details of Bank Holiday service alterations please see first page of Table 195

Ramsgate, Dover, Sheerness-on-Sea and Medway → London

Network Diagram - see first page of Table 212

		SE	SE	SE 1	SE 1	SE	SE 1	SE 1	SE 1	SE 1	SE	SE 1	SE 1	SE 1	SE 1	SE 1	SE 1	SE 1	SE	SE 1	SE 1	SE 1	SE	SE
		A					B																	
Ramsgate 4 ✈	d			06 30					06 50					07 11		07 22				07 52	07 56			
Dumpton Park	d			06 32					06 52					07 14		07 24				07 54	07 58			
Broadstairs	d			06 35	06 47				06 55	07 06				07 17		07 27				07 57	08 01			
Margate 4	d			06 40	06 52				07 00	07 11				07 22		07 32				08 02	08a06			
Westgate-on-Sea	d			06 43					07 03	07 15				07 26		07 35				08 05				
Birchington-on-Sea	d			06 47	06 57				07 06	07 18				07 29		07 38				08 08				
Herne Bay	d			06 57	07 06				07 16	07 27				07 38		07 48				08 17				
Chestfield & Swalecliffe	d			07 00					07 19	07 31				07 42		07 51				08 21				
Whitstable	d			07 04	07 12				07 23	07 35				07 45		07 55				08 24				
Dover Priory 4 ⛴	d						06 45					07 09						07 50						
Kearsney	d						06 49					07 13						07 54						
Shepherds Well	d						06 54					07 18						07 59						
Snowdown	d						06 57					07 21						08 02						
Aylesham	d						07 00					07 24						08 05						
Adisham	d						07 02					07 26						08 07						
Bekesbourne	d						07 07					07 31						08 12						
Canterbury East 4	d						07 13					07 37						08 18						
Selling	d						07 22					07 46						08 27						
Faversham 2	a			07 12	07 20		07 28		07 31	07 43		07 50		07 54		08 03	←	08 31		08 32		←		
	d			07 13	07 21				07 32	07 44		08 07		07 55		08 04	08 07	08 38		08 34		08 38		
Teynham	d			07 18					07 37			→		08 00			08 12	→				08 43		
Sheerness-on-Sea	d					07 21					07 44								08 07				08 36	08 50
Queenborough	d					07 25					07 48								08 12				08 42	08 55
Swale	d					07 29					07 52								08 16				08 47	08 59
Kemsley	d					07 33					07 56								08 19				08 50	09 03
Sittingbourne 4	a			07 23	07 29	07 38			07 42	07 52	08 02			08 05		08 12	08 17		08 23	08 42		08 48	08 55	09 08
	d			07 24	07 29				07 43	07 52				08 05		08 12	08 18			08 43		08 49		
Newington	d			07 29					07 48					08 11			08 23					08 54		
Rainham (Kent)	d			07 34	07 37				07 53	08 00				08 15		08 20	08 28			08 51		08 58		
Gillingham (Kent) 4	d		07 28	07 39	07 43			07 47	07 58	08 06				08 21		08 25	08 33			08 56		09 03		
Chatham 4	d		07 32	07 43	07 47			07 51	08 02	08 10				08 25		08 29	08 37			09 00		09 07		
Rochester 4	d	07 29	07 34					07 53		*08 21*					08 16	08 31	08 39					09 09		
Strood 4	a		*07 44*					*08 02*		*08 26*							*08 56*			*09 24*		*09 24*		
Gravesend 4	a		*07 57*					*08 19*		*08 39*							*09 08*			*09 36*		*09 36*		
Greenhithe for Bluewater	a		*08 04*					*08 28*		*08 46*							*09 13*			*09 41*		*09 41*		
Dartford 4	a		*08 09*					*08 34*		*08 52*							*09 19*			*09 46*		*09 46*		
London Bridge 4	⊖ a		*08 47*		08 29			*09 11*		08 49				09 09			*09 54*			*10 19*		*10 19*		
London Cannon Street 4	⊖ a		*08 54*		08 36			*09 18*	09b38	08 56				09 16			10c06			10b30		10c30		
London Waterloo (East) 4	⊖ a		08c55		08e39			09c23	*09 34*	08e59				09e19			*09 59*			*10 24*		*10 24*		
London Charing Cross 4	⊖ a		09c01		08e44			09c29	*09 39*	09e04				09e24			*10 05*			*10 28*		*10 28*		
Sole Street	d	07 40						08 04					←		08 27		08 50					09 20		
Meopham	d	07 42	07 46					08 07					08 07		08 29		08 53					09 23		
Longfield	d	07 46	07 51					→					08 11		08 33		08 58					09 27		
Farningham Road	d	07 50											08 15		08 37		09 02					09 31		
Swanley 4	a	07 55	07 58										08 20		08 42		09 07					09 36		
St Mary Cray	a	08 00	08 03										08 25		08 47		09 12					09 41		
Bromley South 4	a	08 06	08 11	08 15					08 30				08 32		08 54	08 56	09 18			09 29		09 47		
Elephant & Castle	⊖ a	08 28	*08 44*	08 52									*09 13*		*09 25*	*09 39*				*10 11*				
London Blackfriars 3	⊖ a	08 34	*08 50*	*08 58*									*09 18*		*09 30*	*09 44*				*10 17*				
London Victoria 15	⊖ a		08 41	08 33					08 53				08 57		09 15	09 27	09 37			09 50		10 07		

For general notes see front of timetable
For details of catering facilities see Directory of Train Operators

For services from Ramsgate, Dover and Canterbury to London via Ashford see Table 207

- **A** To Bedford (Table 52)
- **B** From Ashford International (Table 207)
- **b** Change at Chatham and London Bridge
- **c** Change at Rochester and London Bridge
- **e** Change at London Bridge

From 12 October due to seasonal difficulties a large number of trains on this table will have minor retimings that could mean slightly earlier departure or later arrival times at certain stations. For further details see local publicity or contact National Rail Enquiries 08457 48 49 50.

Table 212

Mondays to Fridays

For details of Bank Holiday service alterations please see first page of Table 195

Ramsgate, Dover, Sheerness-on-Sea and Medway → London

Network Diagram - see first page of Table 212

		SE 1	SE 1	SE 1	SE	SE 1	SE 1	SE 1	SE	SE 1	SE 1	SE 1	SE 1	SE	SE 1	SE 1	SE 1	SE 1	SE	SE 1	SE 1	SE 1	SE	SE 1	SE 1
				A																					
		🚲				🚲				🚲					🚲					🚲				🚲	
Ramsgate 4	d		08 17	08 43			08 50				09 22	09 37				09 59	10 06				10 22				10 59
Dumpton Park	d		08 19	08 45			08 52				09 24	09 40					10 09				10 24				
Broadstairs	d		08 22	08 48			08 56				09 28	09 43				10 03	10 12				10 28				11 03
Margate 4	d		08 28	08a53			09 02				09 34	09a48				10 08	10a17				10 34				11 08
Westgate-on-Sea	d		08 31				09 05				09 37										10 37				
Birchington-on-Sea	d		08 34				09 09				09 40					10 13					10 40				11 13
Herne Bay	d		08 44				09 18				09 49					10 21					10 49				11 21
Chestfield & Swalecliffe	d		08 47				09 22				09 52										10 52				
Whitstable	d		08 50				09 26				09 56					10 26					10 56				11 26
Dover Priory 4	d	08 17				09 04				09 22					10 04					10 22				11 04	
Kearsney	d	08 21								09 26										10 26					
Shepherds Well	d	08 26								09 31										10 31					
Snowdown	d	08 29								09 35										10 35					
Aylesham	d	08 32								09 37										10 37					
Adisham	d	08 34								09 39										10 39					
Bekesbourne	d	08 39								09 43										10 43					
Canterbury East 4	d	08 44				09 21				09 49					10 21					10 49				11 21	
Selling	d	08 53								09 58										10 58					
Faversham 2	a	08 57	08 59			09 32	09 35			10 02	10 05				10 32	10 35				11 02	11 05			11 32	11 35
	d	09 03				09 38		09 45		10 08			10 15		10 38			10 45		11 08		11 15		11 38	
Teynham	d	09 08						09 50					10 20					10 50				11 20			
Sheerness-on-Sea	d				09 26				09 56					10 26					10 56				11 26		
Queenborough	d				09 31				10 01					10 31					11 01				11 31		
Swale	d				09 36				10 06					10 36					11 06				11 36		
Kemsley	d				09 39				10 09					10 39					11 09				11 39		
Sittingbourne 4	a	09 13			09 44	09 46		09 55	10 14	10 16			10 25	10 44	10 46			10 55	11 14	11 16		11 25	11 44	11 46	
	d	09 13				09 47		09 55		10 17			10 25		10 47			10 55		11 17		11 25		11 47	
Newington	d							10 00					10 30					11 00				11 30			
Rainham (Kent)	d	09 21				09 54		10 05		10 24			10 35		10 54			11 05		11 24		11 35		11 54	
Gillingham (Kent) 4	d	09 26				09 59		10 10		10 29			10 40		10 59			11 10		11 29		11 40		11 59	
Chatham 4	d	09 30				10 03		10 14		10 33			10 44		11 03			11 14		11 33		11 44		12 03	
Rochester 4	d	09 32				10 06		10 16		10 36			10 46		11 06			11 16		11 36		11 46		12 06	
Strood 4	a	09 54						10 24					10 54					11 24				11 54			
Gravesend 4	a	10 06						10 36					11 06					11 36				12 06			
Greenhithe for Bluewater	a	10 11						10 41					11 11					11 41				12 11			
Dartford 4	a	10 16						10 46					11 16					11 46				12 16			
London Bridge 4	⊖ a	10 49						11 19					11 49					12 19				12 49			
London Cannon Street 4	⊖ a	10b57						11b27					11b57					12b27				12b57			
London Waterloo (East) 4	⊖ a	10 54						11 24					11 54					12 24				12 54			
London Charing Cross 4	⊖ a	10 58						11 28					11 58					12 28				12 58			
Sole Street	d							10 27					10 57					11 27				11 57			
Meopham	d	09 42						10 29					10 59					11 29				11 59			
Longfield	d	09 46						10 33					11 03					11 33				12 03			
Farningham Road	d							10 37					11 07					11 37				12 07			
Swanley 4	a							10 42					11 12					11 42				12 12			
St Mary Cray	a							10 47					11 17					11 47				12 17			
Bromley South 4	a	09 59				10 29		10 54		10 59			11 24		11 29			11 54		11 59		12 24		12 29	
Elephant & Castle	⊖ a	10 30				11 00				11 30					12 00					12 30				13 00	
London Blackfriars 3	⊖ a	10 34				11 04				11 34					12 04					12 34				13 04	
London Victoria 15	⊖ a	10 17				10 47		11 17		11 17			11 46		11 47			12 16		12 19		12 46		12 47	

For general notes see front of timetable
For details of catering facilities see Directory of Train Operators

For services from Ramsgate, Dover and Canterbury to London via Ashford see Table 207

A From London Victoria (Table 196)
b Change at Rochester and London Bridge

From 12 October due to seasonal difficulties a large number of trains on this table will have minor retimings that could mean slightly earlier departure or later arrival times at certain stations. For further details see local publicity or contact National Rail Enquiries 08457 48 49 50.

For details of Bank Holiday service alterations please see first page of Table 195

Ramsgate, Dover, Sheerness-on-Sea and Medway → London

Network Diagram - see first page of Table 212

	SE 1	SE 1	SE	SE 1	SE 1	SE 1	SE	SE 1	SE 1	SE 1	SE	SE 1	SE 1	SE 1	SE 1	SE	SE 1	SE 1	SE 1	SE	SE 1	SE 1	SE 1	SE 1
Ramsgate 4 d	11 10				11 22				11 59				12 22	12 40				12 59				13 22	13 40	
Dumpton Park d	11 13				11 24								12 24	12 43								13 24	13 43	
Broadstairs d	11 16				11 28				12 03				12 28	12 46				13 03				13 28	13 46	
Margate 4 d	11a22				11 34				12 08				12 34	12a51				13 08				13 34	13a51	
Westgate-on-Sea d					11 37								12 37									13 37		
Birchington-on-Sea d					11 40				12 13				12 40					13 13				13 40		
Herne Bay d					11 49				12 21				12 49					13 21				13 49		
Chestfield & Swalecliffe d					11 52								12 52									13 52		
Whitstable d					11 56				12 26				12 56					13 26				13 56		
Dover Priory 4 d				11 22				12 04				12 22					13 04				13 22			
Kearsney d				11 26								12 26									13 26			
Shepherds Well d				11 31								12 31									13 31			
Snowdown d				11 35								12 35									13 35			
Aylesham d				11 37								12 37									13 37			
Adisham d				11 39								12 39									13 39			
Bekesbourne d				11 43								12 43									13 43			
Canterbury East 4 d				11 49				12 21				12 49					13 21				13 49			
Selling d				11 58								12 58									13 58			
Faversham 2 a				12 02	12 05			12 32	12 35			13 02	13 05				13 32	13 35			14 02	14 05		
d		11 45		12 08		12 15		12 38		12 45		13 08			13 15		13 38		13 45		14 08			14 15
Teynham d		11 50				12 20				12 50					13 20				13 50					14 20
Sheerness-on-Sea d			11 56				12 26				12 56					13 26				13 56				
Queenborough d			12 01				12 31				13 01					13 31				14 01				
Swale d			12 06				12 36				13 06					13 36				14 06				
Kemsley d			12 09				12 39				13 09					13 39				14 09				
Sittingbourne 4 a		11 55	12 14	12 16		12 25	12 44	12 46		12 55	13 14	13 16			13 25	13 44	13 46		13 55	14 14	14 16			14 25
d		11 55		12 17		12 25		12 47		12 55		13 17			13 25		13 47		13 55		14 17			14 25
Newington d		12 00				12 30				13 00					13 30				14 00					14 30
Rainham (Kent) d		12 05		12 24		12 35		12 54		13 05		13 24			13 35		13 54		14 05		14 24			14 35
Gillingham (Kent) 4 d		12 10		12 29		12 40		12 59		13 10		13 29			13 40		13 59		14 10		14 29			14 40
Chatham 4 d		12 14		12 33		12 44		13 03		13 14		13 33			13 44		14 03		14 14		14 33			14 44
Rochester 4 d		12 16		12 36		12 46		13 06		13 16		13 36			13 46		14 06		14 16		14 36			14 46
Strood 4 a		12 24				12 54				13 24					13 54				14 24					14 54
Gravesend 4 a		12 36				13 06				13 36					14 06				14 36					15 06
Greenhithe for Bluewater a		12 41				13 11				13 41					14 11				14 41					15 11
Dartford 4 a		12 46				13 16				13 46					14 16				14 46					15 16
London Bridge 4 ⊖ a		13 19				13 49				14 19					14 49				15 19					15 49
London Cannon Street 4 ⊖ a		13b27				13b57				14b27					14b57				15b27					15b57
London Waterloo (East) 4 ⊖ a		13 24				13 54				14 24					14 54				15 24					15 54
London Charing Cross 4 ⊖ a		13 28				13 58				14 28					14 58				15 28					15 58
Sole Street d		12 27				12 57				13 27					13 57				14 27					14 57
Meopham d		12 29				12 59				13 29					13 59				14 29					14 59
Longfield d		12 33				13 03				13 33					14 03				14 33					15 03
Farningham Road d		12 37				13 07				13 37					14 07				14 37					15 07
Swanley 4 a		12 42				13 12				13 42					14 12				14 42					15 12
St Mary Cray a		12 47				13 17				13 47					14 17				14 47					15 17
Bromley South 4 a		12 54		12 59		13 24		13 29		13 54		13 59			14 24		14 29		14 54		14 59			15 24
Elephant & Castle ⊖ a				13 30				14 00				14 30					15 00				15 30			
London Blackfriars 3 ⊖ a				13 34				14 04				14 34					15 04				15 34			
London Victoria 15 ⊖ a		13 16		13 17		13 46		13 47		14 16		14 17			14 46		14 47		15 16		15 17			15 46

For general notes see front of timetable
For details of catering facilities see Directory of Train Operators

For services from Ramsgate, Dover and Canterbury to London via Ashford see Table 207

b Change at Rochester and London Bridge

From 12 October due to seasonal difficulties a large number of trains on this table will have minor retimings that could mean slightly earlier departure or later arrival times at certain stations. For further details see local publicity or contact National Rail Enquiries 08457 48 49 50.

For details of Bank Holiday service alterations please see first page of Table 195

Ramsgate, Dover, Sheerness-on-Sea and Medway → London

Network Diagram - see first page of Table 212

		SE 1 🚲	SE 1	SE 1	SE	SE 1	SE 1 🚲	SE 1	SE	SE 1	SE 1 🚲	SE 1	SE 1	SE	SE 1	SE 1 🚲	SE 1	SE	SE 1	SE 1 🚲	SE 1	SE 1	SE	SE 1
Ramsgate 4 ✈	d		13 59	14 17				14 21				14 57	15 17				15 21				15 52	16 13		
Dumpton Park	d			14 20				14 23					15 20				15 23				15 54	16 16		
Broadstairs	d		14 03	14 23				14 27				15 01	15 23				15 27				15 58	16 19		
Margate 4	d		14 08	14a28				14 33				15 06	15a28				15 33				16 04	16a24		
Westgate-on-Sea	d							14 36									15 36				16 07			
Birchington-on-Sea	d		14 13					14 39				15 11					15 39				16 10			
Herne Bay	d		14 21					14 48				15 19					15 48				16 19			
Chestfield & Swalecliffe	d							14 51									15 51				16 22			
Whitstable	d		14 26					14 55				15 24					15 55				16 26			
Dover Priory 4 ⛴	d	14 04					14 20				15 02					15 20				15 52				
Kearsney	d						14 24									15 24				15 56				
Shepherds Well	d						14 29									15 29				16 01				
Snowdown	d						14 33									15 33				16 05				
Aylesham	d						14 35									15 35				16 07				
Adisham	d						14 37									15 37				16 09				
Bekesbourne	d						14 41									15 41				16 13				
Canterbury East 4	d	14 21					14 47				15 19					15 47				16 19				
Selling	d						14 56									15 56				16 28				
Faversham 2	a	14 32	14 35				15 00	15 03			15 30	15 33				16 00	16 03			16 32	16 35			
	d		14 38			14 45		15 06		15 15		15 36			15 44		16 06		16 14		16 38			16 44
Teynham	d					14 50				15 20					15 49				16 19					16 49
Sheerness-on-Sea	d				14 30				15 00					15 30				16 00					16 30	
Queenborough	d				14 35				15 05					15 35				16 05					16 35	
Swale	d				14 39				15 09					15 39				16 09					16 39	
Kemsley	d				14 43				15 13					15 43				16 13					16 43	
Sittingbourne 4	a		14 46		14 48	14 55		15 14	15 18	15 25		15 44		15 49	15 54		16 14	16 18	16 24		16 46		16 48	16 54
	d		14 47			14 55		15 15		15 25		15 45			15 54		16 15		16 24		16 47			16 54
Newington	d					15 00				15 30					15 59				16 29					16 59
Rainham (Kent)	d		14 54			15 05		15 22		15 35		15 52			16 04		16 22		16 34		16 54			17 04
Gillingham (Kent) 4	d		14 59			15 10		15 27		15 40		15 57			16 09		16 27		16 39		16 59			17 09
Chatham 4	d		15 03			15 14		15 31		15 44		16 01			16 13		16 31		16 43		17 03			17 13
Rochester 4	d		15 06			15 16		15 34		15 46		16 03			16 15		16 33		16 45		17 06			17 15
Strood 4	a					15 24				15 54					16 24				16 54					17 24
Gravesend 4	a					15 36				16 08					16 36				17 06					17 36
Greenhithe for Bluewater	a					15 41				16 14					16 41				17 11					17 45
Dartford 4	a					15 46				16 20					16 46				17 17					17 50
London Bridge 4 ⊖	a					16 19				16 55					17 26				17 56					18 31
London Cannon Street 4 ⊖	a					16b27				17b05					17b33				18 01					18b45
London Waterloo (East) 4 ⊖	a					16 24				17 00					17 31				18b05					18 36
London Charing Cross 4 ⊖	a					16 28				17 03					17 35				18b09					18 40
Sole Street	d					15 27				15 57					16 26				16 56					17 26
Meopham	d					15 29				15 59					16 29				16 59					17 29
Longfield	d					15 33				16 03					16 33				17 03					17 33
Farningham Road	d					15 37				16 07					16 37				17 08					17 37
Swanley 4	a					15 42				16 12					16 42				17 13					17 43
St Mary Cray	a					15 47				16 17					16 47				17 18					17 47
Bromley South 4	a		15 29			15 53		15 59		16 23		16 30			16 53		16 59		17 25		17 33			17 53
Elephant & Castle ⊖	a		16 00					16 30				17 03					17 33		18 05					
London Blackfriars 3 ⊖	a		16 04					16 34				17 07					17 39		18 09					
London Victoria 15 ⊖	a		15 47			16 17		16 17		16 48		16 51			17 17		17 17		17 48		17 57			18 19

For general notes see front of timetable
For details of catering facilities see Directory of Train Operators

For services from Ramsgate, Dover and Canterbury to London via Ashford see Table 207

b Change at Rochester and London Bridge

From 12 October due to seasonal difficulties a large number of trains on this table will have minor retimings that could mean slightly earlier departure or later arrival times at certain stations. For further details see local publicity or contact National Rail Enquiries 08457 48 49 50.

Mondays to Fridays

For details of Bank Holiday service alterations please see first page of Table 195

Ramsgate, Dover, Sheerness-on-Sea and Medway → London

Network Diagram - see first page of Table 212

		SE 1	SE 1	SE	SE 1	SE 1	SE 1	SE	SE 1	SE	SE 1	SE 1	SE 1	SE 1	SE 1	SE 1	SE	SE 1	SE 1	SE 1	SE	SE	SE 1	SE 1	SE 1
Ramsgate 4	d		16 20				16 48					17 22			17 50	18 12				18 21			18 48		18 52
Dumpton Park	d		16 22				16 50					17 24			17 52	18 15				18 23			18 50		18 55
Broadstairs	d		16 26				16 53					17 28			17 55	18 18				18 26			18 53		18 58
Margate 4	d		16 32				16 59					17 34			18 01	18a23				18 32			18 59		19a05
Westgate-on-Sea	d		16 35				17 02					17 37			18 04					18 35			19 02		
Birchington-on-Sea	d		16 38				17 06					17 40			18 08					18 39			19 06		
Herne Bay	d		16 47				17 15					17 49			18 17					18 48			19 15		
Chestfield & Swalecliffe	d		16 50				17 19					17 52			18 21					18 52			19 19		
Whitstable	d		16 54				17 22					17 56			18 24					18 55			19 22		
Dover Priory 4	d	16 20				16 48					17 22			17 50					18 21					18 54	
Kearsney	d	16 24				16 52					17 26			17 54					18 25					18 58	
Shepherds Well	d	16 29				16 57					17 31			17 59					18 30					19 03	
Snowdown	d	16 33				17 00					17 35			18 02					18 33					19 06	
Aylesham	d	16 35				17 03					17 37			18 05					18 36					19 09	
Adisham	d	16 37				17 05					17 39			18 07					18 38					19 11	
Bekesbourne	d	16 41				17 10					17 43			18 12					18 43					19 16	
Canterbury East 4	d	16 47				17 16					17 49			18 18					18 49					19 22	
Selling	d	16 56				17 25					17 58			18 27					18 58					19 31	
Faversham 2	a	17 00	17 03			17 29	17 31				18 02	18 06		18 31	18 33				19 02	19 04			19 31	19 35	
	d	17 06			17 14	17 35			17 44		18 09		18 14	18 37				18 44	19 08				19 39		
Teynham	d				17 19				17 49				18 19					18 49							
Sheerness-on-Sea	d			17 00				17 36		17 53							18 28				19 02	19 20			
Queenborough	d			17 05				17 41		17 58							18 33				19b11	19 25			
Swale	d			17 10				17 45		18 02							18 38				19 15	19 29			
Kemsley	d			17 13				17 49		18 06							18 41				19 19	19 33			
Sittingbourne 4	a	17 14		17 18	17 24	17 43		17 53	17 54	18 11	18 17		18 24	18 45			18 46	18 54	19 16		19 23	19 38	19 47		
	d	17 15			17 24	17 43			17 54		18 17		18 24	18 45				18 54	19 17				19 47		
Newington	d				17 29				17 59				18 29					18 59							
Rainham (Kent)	d	17 22			17 34	17 51			18 04		18 25		18 34	18 53				19 04	19 24				19 55		
Gillingham (Kent) 4	d	17 27			17 39	17 56			18 09		18 31		18 40	18 58				19 10	19 29				20 00		
Chatham 4	d	17 31			17 43	18 00			18 13		18 35		18 44	19 02				19 14	19 33				20 04		
Rochester 4	d	17 33			17 45	18 02			18 15		18 37		18 46	19 04				19 16	19 35				20 06		
Strood 4	a				17 58				18 24				18 54					19 24	19 54						
Gravesend 4	a				18 10				18 36				19 06					19 36	20 06						
Greenhithe for Bluewater	a				18 15				18 41				19 11					19 41	20 11						
Dartford 4	a				18 20				18 46				19 17					19 46	20 16						
London Bridge 4	⊖ a				19 02				19 23				19 53					20 23	20 53						
London Cannon Street 4	⊖ a				19c10				19c37				20c11					20c41							
London Waterloo (East) 4	⊖ a				19 07				19 28				19 58					20 28	20 58						
London Charing Cross 4	⊖ a				19 11				19 32				20 01					20 31	21 01						
Sole Street	d				17 56				18 26				18 57					19 27							
Meopham	d				17 59				18 29				19 00					19 30							
Longfield	d				18 03				18 33				19 04					19 34							
Farningham Road	d				18 07				18 37				19 08					19 38							
Swanley 4	a				18 12				18 42				19 12					19 42							
St Mary Cray	a				18 16				18 47				19 17					19 47							
Bromley South 4	a	17 59			18 23	18 31			18 53		19 00		19 23	19 30				19 53	19 58				20 29		
Elephant & Castle	⊖ a	18 31				19 01					19 37			20 00					20 30				21 00		
London Blackfriars 3	⊖ a	18 35				19 05					19 41			20 03					20 33				21 03		
London Victoria 15	⊖ a	18 17			18 49	18 48			19 16		19 17		19 47	19 49				20 15	20 19				20 49		

For general notes see front of timetable
For details of catering facilities see Directory of Train Operators

For services from Ramsgate, Dover and Canterbury to London via Ashford see Table 207

b Arr. 1907

c Change at Rochester and London Bridge

From 12 October due to seasonal difficulties a large number of trains on this table will have minor retimings that could mean slightly earlier departure or later arrival times at certain stations. For further details see local publicity or contact National Rail Enquiries 08457 48 49 50.

For details of Bank Holiday service alterations please see first page of Table 195

Ramsgate, Dover, Sheerness-on-Sea and Medway → London

Network Diagram - see first page of Table 212

		SE 1	SE 1	SE	SE	SE 1	SE 1	SE 1	SE	SE 1	SE 1	SE	SE	SE 1	SE 1	SE 1	SE 1	SE	SE 1	SE 1	SE 1	SE	SE 1	SE 1	SE
Ramsgate 4 ✈	d	19 12				19 50		20 11			20 39			20 50		21 29				21 55	22 10			22 53	
Dumpton Park	d	19 15				19 52		20 14			20 41			20 52		21 32				21 57				22 55	
Broadstairs	d	19 18				19 55		20 17			20 44			20 55		21 35				22 00	22 15			22 58	
Margate 4	d	19a26				20 00		20a22			20a51			21 01		21a40				22 06	22 20			23 04	
Westgate-on-Sea	d					20 03								21 04						22 09				23 07	
Birchington-on-Sea	d					20 06								21 07						22 12	22 25			23 11	
Herne Bay	d					20 16								21 17						22 22	22 34			23 20	
Chestfield & Swalecliffe	d					20 19								21 20						22 25				23 24	
Whitstable	d					20 23								21 24						22 29	22 39			23 27	
Dover Priory 4 ⛴	d						19 52								20 52				21 55				23 01		
Kearsney	d						19 56								20 56				21 59						
Shepherds Well	d						20 01								21 01				22 04						
Snowdown	d						20 04								21 04				22 07						
Aylesham	d						20 07								21 07				22 10						
Adisham	d						20 09								21 09				22 12						
Bekesbourne	d						20 14								21 14				22 17						
Canterbury East 4	d						20 19								21 20				22 22				23 18		
Selling	d						20 28								21 29				22 31						
Faversham 2	a					20 31	20 33							21 32	21 34				22 35	22 37	22 47		23 30	23 36	
	d		19 45				20 37			20 45					21 38		21 45			22 38	22 48				23 42
Teynham	d		19 50							20 50							21 50				22 53				23 47
Sheerness-on-Sea	d			19 50	20 05				20 34			21 01	21 26					22 30				23 28			
Queenborough	d			19 56	20 10				20 39			21 06	21 31					22 35				23 33			
Swale	d			20 01	20 15				20 43			21 10	21 36					22 39				23 38			
Kemsley	d			20 04	20 18				20 47			21 14	21 39					22 42				23 41			
Sittingbourne 4	a		19 55	20 09	20 23		20 45		20 52	20 55			21 44		21 46		21 55	22 46		22 47	22 58	23 46			23 52
	d		19 55				20 45			20 55					21 47		21 55			22 47	22 58				23 52
Newington	d		20 00							21 00		21 21					22 00				23 03				23 57
Rainham (Kent)	d		20 05				20 53			21 05		21 25			21 54		22 05			22 54	23 08				00 01
Gillingham (Kent) 4	d		20 10				20 58			21 10		21a30			21 59		22 10			22 59	23 13				00 07
Chatham 4	d		20 14				21 02			21 14					22 03		22 14			23 03	23 17				00 11
Rochester 4	d		20 16				21 04			21 16							22 16				23 19				00 13
Strood 4	a		20 26							21 24					22 32		22 32				00 17				00 17
Gravesend 4	a		20 38							21 38					22 44		22 44				00 28				00 28
Greenhithe for Bluewater	a		20 43							21 43					22 52		22 52				00 34				00 34
Dartford 4	a		20 48							21 48					22 58		22 58				00 41				00 41
London Bridge 4	⊖ a		21 23							22 23					23 41		23 41								
London Cannon Street 4	⊖ a																								
London Waterloo (East) 4	⊖ a		21 28							22 28					23 46		23 46								
London Charing Cross 4	⊖ a		21 31							22 31					23 50		23 50								
Sole Street	d		20 27							21 27							22 27				23 30				
Meopham	d		20 30							21 30							22 30				23 32				
Longfield	d		20 34							21 34							22 34				23 36				
Farningham Road	d		20 38							21 38							22 38				23 40				
Swanley 4	a		20 42							21 42							22 42				23 45				
St Mary Cray	a		20 47							21 47							22 47				23 49				
Bromley South 4	a		20 53				21 29			21 53					22 30		22 53			23 30	23 55				
Elephant & Castle	⊖ a																								
London Blackfriars 3	⊖ a																								
London Victoria 15	⊖ a		21 16				21 47			22 16					22 48		23 14			23 47	00 18				01 13

For general notes see front of timetable
For details of catering facilities see Directory of Train Operators

For services from Ramsgate, Dover and Canterbury to London via Ashford see Table 207

From 12 October due to seasonal difficulties a large number of trains on this table will have minor retimings that could mean slightly earlier departure or later arrival times at certain stations. For further details see local publicity or contact National Rail Enquiries 08457 48 49 50.

For details of Bank Holiday service alterations please see first page of Table 195

Ramsgate, Dover, Sheerness-on-Sea and Medway → London

Network Diagram - see first page of Table 212

Station		SE [1]
Ramsgate [4]	d	23 40
Dumpton Park	d	23 43
Broadstairs	d	23 46
Margate [4]	d	23a51
Westgate-on-Sea	d	
Birchington-on-Sea	d	
Herne Bay	d	
Chestfield & Swalecliffe	d	
Whitstable	d	
Dover Priory [4]	d	
Kearsney	d	
Shepherds Well	d	
Snowdown	d	
Aylesham	d	
Adisham	d	
Bekesbourne	d	
Canterbury East [4]	d	
Selling	d	
Faversham [2]	a	
	d	
Teynham	d	
Sheerness-on-Sea	d	
Queenborough	d	
Swale	d	
Kemsley	d	
Sittingbourne [4]	a	
	d	
Newington	d	
Rainham (Kent)	d	
Gillingham (Kent) [4]	d	
Chatham [4]	d	
Rochester [4]	d	
Strood [4]	a	
Gravesend [4]	a	
Greenhithe for Bluewater	a	
Dartford [4]	a	
London Bridge [4]	⊖ a	
London Cannon Street [4]	⊖ a	
London Waterloo (East) [4]	⊖ a	
London Charing Cross [4]	⊖ a	
Sole Street	d	
Meopham	d	
Longfield	d	
Farningham Road	d	
Swanley [3]	a	
St Mary Cray	a	
Bromley South [4]	a	
Elephant & Castle	⊖ a	
London Blackfriars [3]	⊖ a	
London Victoria [15]	⊖ a	

For general notes see front of timetable
For details of catering facilities see Directory of Train Operators

For services from Ramsgate, Dover and Canterbury to London via Ashford see Table 207

From 12 October due to seasonal difficulties a large number of trains on this table will have minor retimings that could mean slightly earlier departure or later arrival times at certain stations. For further details see local publicity or contact National Rail Enquiries 08457 48 49 50.

Ramsgate, Dover, Sheerness-on-Sea and Medway → London

Network Diagram - see first page of Table 212

Station		SE	SE 1	SE 1	SE 1	SE 1	SE 1		SE	SE 1	SE 1	SE 1	SE 1	SE 1		SE 1	SE	SE 1	SE 1	SE 1	SE 1	SE 1		SE 1	SE 1
Ramsgate 4	d		04 38			05 22					05 59			06 22					06 59			07 22		07 38	
Dumpton Park	d					05 24								06 24								07 24		07 40	
Broadstairs	d					05 28					06 03			06 28					07 03			07 28		07 43	
Margate 4	d		04 46			05 34					06 08			06 34					07 08			07 34		07a48	
Westgate-on-Sea	d					05 37								06 37								07 37			
Birchington-on-Sea	d					05 40					06 13			06 40					07 13			07 40			
Herne Bay	d		04 58			05 49					06 21			06 49					07 21			07 49			
Chestfield & Swalecliffe	d					05 52								06 52								07 52			
Whitstable	d		05 03			05 56					06 26			06 56					07 26			07 56			
Dover Priory 4	d				05 22					06 04			06 22					07 04			07 22				
Kearsney	d				05 26								06 26								07 26				
Shepherds Well	d				05 31								06 31								07 31				
Snowdown	d				05 35								06 35								07 35				
Aylesham	d				05 37								06 37								07 37				
Adisham	d				05 39								06 39								07 39				
Bekesbourne	d				05 43								06 43								07 43				
Canterbury East 4	d				05 49					06 21			06 49					07 21			07 49				
Selling	d				05 58								06 58								07 58				
Faversham 2	a		05 11		06 02	06 05				06 32	06 35		07 02	07 05				07 32	07 35		08 02	08 05			
	d	23p42	05 12	05 45	06 08		06 15			06 38		06 45	07 08			07 15		07 38		07 45	08 08				08 15
Teynham	d	23p47		05 50			06 20					06 50				07 20				07 50					08 20
Sheerness-on-Sea	d								06 26								07 26								
Queenborough	d								06 31								07 31								
Swale	d								06 36								07 36								
Kemsley	d								06 39								07 39								
Sittingbourne 4	a	23p52	05 20	05 55	06 16		06 25		06 44	06 46		06 55	07 16			07 25	07 44	07 46		07 55	08 16				08 25
	d	23p52	05 20	05 55	06 17		06 25			06 47		06 55	07 17			07 25		07 47		07 55	08 17				08 25
Newington	d	23p57		06 00			06 30					07 00				07 30				08 00					08 30
Rainham (Kent)	d	00 01	05 28	06 05	06 24		06 35			06 54		07 05	07 24			07 35		07 54		08 05	08 24				08 35
Gillingham (Kent) 4	d	00 07	05 33	06 10	06 29		06 40			06 59		07 10	07 29			07 40		07 59		08 10	08 29				08 40
Chatham 4	d	00 11	05 37	06 13	06 33		06 44			07 03		07 14	07 33			07 44		08 03		08 14	08 33				08 44
Rochester 4	d	00 13	05 39	06 15	06 36		06 46			07 06		07 16	07 36			07 46		08 06		08 16	08 36				08 46
Strood 4	a	00 17	05 54	06 23			06 54					07 24				07 54				08 24					08 54
Gravesend 4	a	00 28	06 05	06 35			07 05					07 35				08 05				08 36					09 06
Greenhithe for Bluewater	a	00 34	06 10	06 40			07 10					07 40				08 10				08 41					09 11
Dartford 4	a	00 41	06 15	06 45			07 15					07 45				08 15				08 46					09 16
London Bridge 4	⊖ a		06 50	07 21			07 49					08 19				08 49				09 19					09 49
London Cannon Street 4	⊖ a		07b50	07c50			08c03					08c27				08c57				09c27					09c57
London Waterloo (East) 4	⊖ a		06 55	07 26			07 54					08 24				08 54				09 24					09 54
London Charing Cross 4	⊖ a		06 58	07 29			07 58					08 28				08 58				09 28					09 58
Sole Street	d		05 50	06 27			06 57					07 27				07 57				08 27					08 57
Meopham	d		05 52	06 29			06 59					07 29				07 59				08 29					08 59
Longfield	d		05 56	06 33			07 03					07 33				08 03				08 33					09 03
Farningham Road	d		06 00	06 37			07 07					07 37				08 07				08 37					09 07
Swanley 4	a		06 05	06 42			07 12					07 42				08 12				08 42					09 12
St Mary Cray	a		06 10	06 47			07 17					07 47				08 17				08 47					09 17
Bromley South 4	a		06 16	06 54	06 59		07 24			07 29		07 54	07 59			08 24		08 29		08 54	08 59				09 24
Elephant & Castle	⊖ a																								
London Blackfriars 3	⊖ a																								
London Victoria 15	⊖ a	01 13	06 32	07 17	07 17		07 46			07 47		08 16	08 17			08 46		08 47		09 16	09 17				09 46

For general notes see front of timetable
For details of catering facilities see Directory of Train Operators

For services from Ramsgate, Dover and Canterbury to London via Ashford see Table 207

b Change at Chatham and London Bridge
c Change at Rochester and London Bridge

Table 212

Ramsgate, Dover, Sheerness-on-Sea and Medway → London

Network Diagram - see first page of Table 212

		SE	SE 1	SE 1	SE 1	SE	SE 1	SE 1		SE 1	SE 1	SE	SE 1	SE 1	SE 1		SE	SE 1	SE 1	SE 1	SE 1	SE		SE 1	SE 1
Ramsgate 4	d			07 59				08 22		08 35				08 59					09 22	09 34					09 59
Dumpton Park	d							08 24		08 38									09 24	09 37					
Broadstairs	d			08 03				08 28		08 41				09 03					09 28	09 40					10 03
Margate 4	d			08 08				08 34		08a46				09 08					09 34	09a45					10 08
Westgate-on-Sea	d							08 37											09 37						
Birchington-on-Sea	d			08 13				08 40						09 13					09 40						10 13
Herne Bay	d			08 21				08 49						09 21					09 49						10 21
Chestfield & Swalecliffe	d							08 52											09 52						
Whitstable	d			08 26				08 56						09 26					09 56						10 26
Dover Priory 4	d		08 04				08 22						09 04					09 22						10 04	
Kearsney	d						08 26											09 26							
Shepherds Well	d						08 31											09 31							
Snowdown	d						08 35											09 35							
Aylesham	d						08 37											09 37							
Adisham	d						08 39											09 39							
Bekesbourne	d						08 43											09 43							
Canterbury East 4	d		08 21				08 49						09 21					09 49						10 21	
Selling	d						08 58											09 58							
Faversham 2	a		08 32	08 35			09 02	09 05					09 32	09 35				10 02	10 05					10 32	10 35
	d		08 38		08 45		09 08				09 15		09 38		09 45			10 08			10 15			10 38	
Teynham	d				08 50						09 20				09 50						10 20				
Sheerness-on-Sea	d	08 26				08 56						09 26					09 56					10 26			
Queenborough	d	08 31				09 01						09 31					10 01					10 31			
Swale	d	08 36				09 06						09 36					10 06					10 36			
Kemsley	d	08 39				09 09						09 39					10 09					10 39			
Sittingbourne 4	a	08 44	08 46		08 55	09 14	09 16				09 25	09 44	09 46		09 55		10 14	10 16			10 25	10 44		10 46	
	d		08 47		08 55		09 17				09 25		09 47		09 55			10 17			10 25			10 47	
Newington	d				09 00						09 30				10 00						10 30				
Rainham (Kent)	d		08 54		09 05		09 24				09 35		09 54		10 05			10 24			10 35			10 54	
Gillingham (Kent) 4	d		08 59		09 10		09 29				09 40		09 59		10 10			10 29			10 40			10 59	
Chatham 4	d		09 03		09 14		09 33				09 44		10 03		10 14			10 33			10 44			11 03	
Rochester 4	d		09 06		09 16		09 36				09 46		10 06		10 16			10 36			10 46			11 06	
Strood 4	a				*09 24*						*09 54*				*10 24*						*10 54*				
Gravesend 4	a				*09 36*						*10 06*				*10 36*						*11 06*				
Greenhithe for Bluewater	a				*09 41*						*10 11*				*10 41*						*11 11*				
Dartford 4	a				*09 46*						*10 16*				*10 46*						*11 16*				
London Bridge 4	⊖ a				*10 19*						*10 49*				*11 19*						*11 49*				
London Cannon Street 4	⊖ a				*10b27*						*10b57*				*11b27*						*11b57*				
London Waterloo (East) 4	⊖ a				*10 24*						*10 54*				*11 24*						*11 54*				
London Charing Cross 4	⊖ a				*10 28*						*10 58*				*11 28*						*11 58*				
Sole Street	d				09 27						09 57				10 27						10 57				
Meopham	d				09 29						09 59				10 29						10 59				
Longfield	d				09 33						10 03				10 33						11 03				
Farningham Road	d				09 37						10 07				10 37						11 07				
Swanley 4	a				09 42						10 12				10 42						11 12				
St Mary Cray	a				09 47						10 17				10 47						11 17				
Bromley South 4	a		09 29		09 54		10 00				10 24		10 29		10 54			10 59			11 24			11 29	
Elephant & Castle	⊖ a																								
London Blackfriars 3	⊖ a																								
London Victoria 15	⊖ a		09 47		10 16		10 17				10 46		10 47		11 16			11 17			11 46			11 47	

For general notes see front of timetable
For details of catering facilities see Directory of Train Operators

For services from Ramsgate, Dover and Canterbury to London via Ashford see Table 207

b Change at Rochester and London Bridge

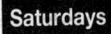

Ramsgate, Dover, Sheerness-on-Sea and Medway → London

Network Diagram - see first page of Table 212

		SE 1	SE 1	SE	SE 1	SE 1	SE 1		SE	SE 1	SE 1	SE 1	SE 1	SE		SE 1	SE 1	SE 1	SE 1	SE	SE 1	SE 1		SE 1	SE
					⛴					⛴						⛴		⛴			⛴				
Ramsgate [4] ⛴	d	10 16				10 22					10 59	11 16					11 22	11 41				11 59			
Dumpton Park	d	10 19				10 24						11 19					11 24	11 44							
Broadstairs	d	10 22				10 28					11 03	11 22					11 28	11 47				12 03			
Margate [4]	d	10a27				10 34					11 08	11a27					11 34	11a52				12 08			
Westgate-on-Sea	d					10 37											11 37								
Birchington-on-Sea	d					10 40					11 13						11 40					12 13			
Herne Bay	d					10 49					11 21						11 49					12 21			
Chestfield & Swalecliffe	d					10 52											11 52								
Whitstable	d					10 56					11 26						11 56					12 26			
Dover Priory [4] ⛴	d				10 22					11 04						11 22					12 04				
Kearsney	d				10 26											11 26									
Shepherds Well	d				10 31											11 31									
Snowdown	d				10 35											11 35									
Aylesham	d				10 37											11 37									
Adisham	d				10 39											11 39									
Bekesbourne	d				10 43											11 43									
Canterbury East [4]	d				10 49					11 21						11 49					12 21				
Selling	d				10 58											11 58									
Faversham [2]	a				11 02	11 05				11 32	11 35					12 02	12 05				12 32	12 35			
	d		10 45			11 08	11 15				11 38		11 45				12 08		12 15			12 38		12 45	
Teynham	d		10 50				11 20						11 50						12 20					12 50	
Sheerness-on-Sea	d			10 56					11 26					11 56						12 26					12 56
Queenborough	d			11 01					11 31					12 01						12 31					13 01
Swale	d			11 06					11 36					12 06						12 36					13 06
Kemsley	d			11 09					11 39					12 09						12 39					13 09
Sittingbourne [4]	a		10 55	11 14		11 16	11 25		11 44		11 46		11 55	12 14			12 16		12 25	12 44		12 46		12 55	13 14
	d		10 55			11 17	11 25				11 47		11 55				12 17		12 25			12 47		12 55	
Newington	d		11 00				11 30						12 00						12 30					13 00	
Rainham (Kent)	d		11 05			11 24	11 35				11 54		12 05				12 24		12 35			12 54		13 05	
Gillingham (Kent) [4]	d		11 10			11 29	11 40				11 59		12 10				12 29		12 40			12 59		13 10	
Chatham [4]	d		11 14			11 33	11 44				12 03		12 14				12 33		12 44			13 03		13 14	
Rochester [4]	d		11 16			11 36	11 46				12 06		12 16				12 36		12 46			13 06		13 16	
Strood [4]	a		11 24				11 54						12 24						12 54					13 24	
Gravesend [4]	a		11 36				12 06						12 36						13 06					13 36	
Greenhithe for Bluewater	a		11 41				12 11						12 41						13 11					13 41	
Dartford [4]	a		11 46				12 16						12 46						13 16					13 46	
London Bridge [4]	⊖ a		12 19				12 49						13 19						13 49					14 19	
London Cannon Street [4]	⊖ a		12b27				12b57						13b27						13b57					14b27	
London Waterloo (East) [4]	⊖ a		12 24				12 54						13 24						13 54					14 24	
London Charing Cross [4]	⊖ a		12 28				12 58						13 28						13 58					14 28	
Sole Street	d		11 27				11 57						12 27						12 57					13 27	
Meopham	d		11 29				11 59						12 29						12 59					13 29	
Longfield	d		11 33				12 03						12 33						13 03					13 33	
Farningham Road	d		11 37				12 07						12 37						13 07					13 37	
Swanley [4]	a		11 42				12 12						12 42						13 12					13 42	
St Mary Cray	a		11 47				12 17						12 47						13 17					13 47	
Bromley South [4]	a		11 54			11 59	12 24				12 29		12 54				12 59		13 24			13 29		13 54	
Elephant & Castle	⊖ a																								
London Blackfriars [3]	⊖ a																								
London Victoria [15]	⊖ a		12 16			12 17	12 46				12 47		13 16				13 17		13 46			13 47		14 16	

For general notes see front of timetable
For details of catering facilities see Directory of Train Operators

For services from Ramsgate, Dover and Canterbury to London via Ashford see Table 207

b Change at Rochester and London Bridge

Table 212

Saturdays

Ramsgate, Dover, Sheerness-on-Sea and Medway → London

Network Diagram - see first page of Table 212

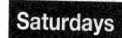

		SE 1 🛒	SE 1	SE 1 🛒	SE 1	SE	SE 1 🛒	SE 1		SE 1	SE	SE 1 🛒	SE 1	SE 1 🛒	SE 1		SE	SE 1 🛒	SE 1	SE 1	SE	SE 1 🛒	SE 1		SE 1 🛒
Ramsgate 4 ✈	d		12 22	12 40				12 59					13 22	13 40					13 59				14 22		14 40
Dumpton Park	d		12 24	12 43									13 24	13 43									14 24		14 43
Broadstairs	d		12 28	12 46				13 03					13 28	13 46					14 03				14 28		14 46
Margate 4	d		12 34	12a51				13 08					13 34	13a51					14 08				14 34		14a51
Westgate-on-Sea	d		12 37										13 37										14 37		
Birchington-on-Sea	d		12 40					13 13					13 40						14 13				14 40		
Herne Bay	d		12 49					13 21					13 49						14 21				14 49		
Chestfield & Swalecliffe	d		12 52										13 52										14 52		
Whitstable	d		12 56					13 26					13 56						14 26				14 56		
Dover Priory 4 ⛴	d	12 22					13 04					13 22						14 04				14 22			
Kearsney	d	12 26										13 26										14 26			
Shepherds Well	d	12 31										13 31										14 31			
Snowdown	d	12 35										13 35										14 35			
Aylesham	d	12 37										13 37										14 37			
Adisham	d	12 39										13 39										14 39			
Bekesbourne	d	12 43										13 43										14 43			
Canterbury East 4	d	12 49					13 21					13 49						14 21				14 49			
Selling	d	12 58										13 58										14 58			
Faversham 2	a	13 02	13 05				13 32	13 35				14 02	14 05					14 32	14 35			15 02	15 05		
	d	13 08			13 15		13 38			13 45		14 08			14 15			14 38		14 45		15 08			
Teynham	d				13 20					13 50					14 20					14 50					
Sheerness-on-Sea	d					13 26					13 56						14 26				14 56				
Queenborough	d					13 31					14 01						14 31				15 01				
Swale	d					13 36					14 06						14 36				15 06				
Kemsley	d					13 39					14 09						14 39				15 09				
Sittingbourne 4	a	13 16			13 25	13 44	13 46			13 55	14 14	14 16			14 25		14 44	14 46		14 55	15 14	15 16			
	d	13 17			13 25		13 47			13 55		14 17			14 25			14 47		14 55		15 17			
Newington	d				13 30					14 00					14 30					15 00					
Rainham (Kent)	d	13 24			13 35		13 54			14 05		14 24			14 35			14 54		15 05		15 24			
Gillingham (Kent) 4	d	13 29			13 40		13 59			14 10		14 29			14 40			14 59		15 10		15 29			
Chatham 4	d	13 33			13 44		14 03			14 14		14 33			14 44			15 03		15 14		15 33			
Rochester 4	d	13 36			13 46		14 06			14 16		14 36			14 46			15 06		15 16		15 36			
Strood 4	a				13 54					14 24					14 54					15 24					
Gravesend 4	a				14 06					14 36					15 06					15 36					
Greenhithe for Bluewater	a				14 11					14 41					15 11					15 41					
Dartford 4	a				14 16					14 46					15 16					15 46					
London Bridge 4 ⊖	a				14 49					15 19					15 49					16 19					
London Cannon Street 4 ⊖	a				14b57					15b27					15b57					16b27					
London Waterloo (East) 4 ⊖	a				14 54					15 24					15 54					16 24					
London Charing Cross 4 ⊖	a				14 58					15 28					15 58					16 28					
Sole Street	d				13 57					14 27					14 57					15 27					
Meopham	d				13 59					14 29					14 59					15 29					
Longfield	d				14 03					14 33					15 03					15 33					
Farningham Road	d				14 07					14 37					15 07					15 37					
Swanley 4	a				14 12					14 42					15 12					15 42					
St Mary Cray	a				14 17					14 47					15 17					15 47					
Bromley South 4	a	13 59			14 24		14 29			14 54		14 59			15 24			15 29		15 54		15 59			
Elephant & Castle ⊖	a																								
London Blackfriars 3 ⊖	a																								
London Victoria 15 ⊖	a	14 17			14 46		14 47			15 16		15 17			15 46			15 47		16 16		16 17			

For general notes see front of timetable
For details of catering facilities see Directory of Train Operators

For services from Ramsgate, Dover and Canterbury to London via Ashford see Table 207

b Change at Rochester and London Bridge

Ramsgate, Dover, Sheerness-on-Sea and Medway → London

Network Diagram - see first page of Table 212

		SE 1	SE	SE 1 🚲	SE 1	SE 1	SE		SE 1 🚲	SE 1	SE 1 🚲	SE 1	SE	SE 1 🚲	SE 1		SE 1	SE	SE 1 🚲	SE 1	SE 1 🚲	SE 1		SE	
Ramsgate 4 ✈	d				14 59					15 22	15 40				15 59					16 22	16 40				
Dumpton Park	d									15 24	15 43									16 24	16 43				
Broadstairs	d				15 03					15 28	15 46				16 03					16 28	16 46				
Margate 4	d				15 08					15 34	15a51				16 08					16 34	16a51				
Westgate-on-Sea	d									15 37										16 37					
Birchington-on-Sea	d				15 13					15 40					16 13					16 40					
Herne Bay	d				15 21					15 49					16 21					16 49					
Chestfield & Swalecliffe	d									15 52										16 52					
Whitstable	d				15 26					15 56					16 26					16 56					
Dover Priory 4 ⛴	d			15 04					15 22					16 04					16 22						
Kearsney	d								15 26										16 26						
Shepherds Well	d								15 31										16 31						
Snowdown	d								15 35										16 35						
Aylesham	d								15 37										16 37						
Adisham	d								15 39										16 39						
Bekesbourne	d								15 43										16 43						
Canterbury East 4	d			15 21					15 49					16 21					16 49						
Selling	d								15 58										16 58						
Faversham 2	a			15 32	15 35				16 02	16 05				16 32	16 35				17 02	17 05					
	d	15 15			15 38	15 45				16 08		16 15			16 38		16 45			17 08		17 15			
Teynham	d	15 20				15 50						16 20					16 50					17 20			
Sheerness-on-Sea	d		15 26				15 56						16 26					16 56						17 26	
Queenborough	d		15 31				16 01						16 31					17 01						17 31	
Swale	d		15 36				16 06						16 36					17 06						17 36	
Kemsley	d		15 39				16 09						16 39					17 09						17 39	
Sittingbourne 4	a	15 25	15 44		15 46	15 55	16 14			16 16		16 25	16 44		16 46		16 55	17 14		17 16		17 25		17 44	
	d	15 25			15 47	15 55				16 17		16 25			16 47		16 55			17 17		17 25			
Newington	d	15 30				16 00						16 30					17 00					17 30			
Rainham (Kent)	d	15 35			15 54	16 05				16 24		16 35			16 54		17 05			17 24		17 35			
Gillingham (Kent) 4	d	15 40			15 59	16 10				16 29		16 40			16 59		17 10			17 29		17 40			
Chatham 4	d	15 44			16 03	16 14				16 33		16 44			17 03		17 14			17 33		17 44			
Rochester 4	d	15 46			16 06	16 16				16 36		16 46			17 06		17 16			17 36		17 46			
Strood 4	a	15 54				16 24						16 54					17 24					17 54			
Gravesend 4	a	16 06				16 36						17 06					17 36					18 06			
Greenhithe for Bluewater	a	16 11				16 41						17 11					17 41					18 11			
Dartford 4	a	16 16				16 46						17 16					17 46					18 16			
London Bridge 4 ⊖	a	16 49				17 19						17 49					18 19					18 49			
London Cannon Street 4 ⊖	a	16b57				17b27						17b57					18b27								
London Waterloo (East) 4 ⊖	a	16 54				17 24						17 54					18 24					18 54			
London Charing Cross 4 ⊖	a	16 58				17 28						17 58					18 28					18 58			
Sole Street	d	15 57				16 27						16 57					17 27					17 57			
Meopham	d	15 59				16 29						16 59					17 29					17 59			
Longfield	d	16 03				16 33						17 03					17 33					18 03			
Farningham Road	d	16 07				16 37						17 07					17 37					18 07			
Swanley 4	a	16 12				16 42						17 12					17 42					18 12			
St Mary Cray	a	16 17				16 47						17 17					17 47					18 17			
Bromley South 4	a	16 24			16 29	16 54				16 59		17 24			17 29		17 54			17 59		18 24			
Elephant & Castle ⊖	a																								
London Blackfriars 3 ⊖	a																								
London Victoria 15 ⊖	a	16 46			16 47	17 16				17 17		17 46			17 47		18 16			18 17		18 46			

For general notes see front of timetable
For details of catering facilities see Directory of Train Operators

For services from Ramsgate, Dover and Canterbury to London via Ashford see Table 207

b Change at Rochester and London Bridge

Table 212

Saturdays

Ramsgate, Dover, Sheerness-on-Sea and Medway → London

Network Diagram - see first page of Table 212

Station		SE 1	SE 1	SE 1	SE	SE 1	SE 1		SE 1 ⊼	SE 1	SE	SE 1	SE 1	SE 1		SE 1	SE 1	SE 1 ⊼	SE 1	SE	SE 1	SE 1		SE 1 ⊼	SE 1
Ramsgate 4 ✈	d		16 59				17 22		17 40				17 59				18 22	18 40				18 52		19 24	
Dumpton Park	d						17 24		17 43								18 24	18 43				18 54		19 27	
Broadstairs	d		17 03				17 28		17 46				18 03				18 28	18 46				18 58		19 30	
Margate 4	d		17 08				17 34		17a51				18 08				18 34	18a51				19 04		19a35	
Westgate-on-Sea	d						17 37										18 37					19 07			
Birchington-on-Sea	d		17 13				17 40						18 13				18 40					19 10			
Herne Bay	d		17 21				17 49						18 21				18 49					19 19			
Chestfield & Swalecliffe	d						17 52										18 52					19 22			
Whitstable	d		17 26				17 56						18 26				18 56					19 26			
Dover Priory 4 ⛴	d	17 04				17 22						18 04				18 22					18 52				
Kearsney	d					17 26										18 26					18 56				
Shepherds Well	d					17 31										18 31					19 01				
Snowdown	d					17 35										18 35					19 05				
Aylesham	d					17 37										18 37					19 07				
Adisham	d					17 39										18 39					19 09				
Bekesbourne	d					17 43										18 43					19 13				
Canterbury East 4	d	17 21				17 49						18 21				18 49					19 19				
Selling	d					17 58										18 58					19 28				
Faversham 2	a	17 32	17 35			18 02	18 05					18 32	18 35			19 02	19 05				19 32	19 35			
	d	17 38		17 45		18 08				18 15		18 38		18 45		19 08			19 15		19 38				19 45
Teynham	d			17 50						18 20				18 50					19 20						19 50
Sheerness-on-Sea	d				17 56						18 26									19 26					
Queenborough	d				18 01						18 31									19 31					
Swale	d				18 06						18 36									19 36					
Kemsley	d				18 09						18 39									19 39					
Sittingbourne 4	a	17 46		17 55	18 14	18 16				18 25	18 44	18 46		18 55		19 16			19 25	19 44	19 46				19 55
	d	17 47		17 55		18 17				18 25		18 47		18 55		19 17			19 25		19 47				19 55
Newington	d			18 00						18 30				19 00					19 30						20 00
Rainham (Kent)	d	17 54		18 05		18 24				18 35		18 54		19 05		19 24			19 35		19 54				20 05
Gillingham (Kent) 4	d	17 59		18 10		18 29				18 40		18 59		19 10		19 29			19 40		19 59				20 10
Chatham 4	d	18 03		18 14		18 33				18 44		19 03		19 14		19 33			19 44		20 03				20 14
Rochester 4	d	18 06		18 16		18 36				18 46		19 06		19 16		19 36			19 46		20 06				20 16
Strood 4	a			18 24						18 54				19 24					19 54						20 24
Gravesend 4	a			18 36						19 06				19 36					20 06						20 36
Greenhithe for Bluewater	a			18 41						19 11				19 41					20 11						20 41
Dartford 4	a			18 46						19 16				19 46					20 16						20 46
London Bridge 4	⊖ a			19 21						19 53				20 23					20 53						21 23
London Cannon Street 4	⊖ a																								
London Waterloo (East) 4	⊖ a			19 25						19 58				20 28					20 58						21 28
London Charing Cross 4	⊖ a			19 29						20 01				20 31					21 01						21 31
Sole Street	d			18 27						18 57				19 27					19 57						20 27
Meopham	d			18 29						18 59				19 29					19 59						20 29
Longfield	d			18 33						19 03				19 33					20 03						20 33
Farningham Road	d			18 37						19 07				19 37					20 07						20 37
Swanley 4	a			18 42						19 12				19 42					20 12						20 42
St Mary Cray	a			18 47						19 17				19 47					20 17						20 47
Bromley South 4	a	18 29		18 54		18 59				19 24		19 29		19 54		19 59			20 24		20 29				20 54
Elephant & Castle	⊖ a																								
London Blackfriars 3	⊖ a																								
London Victoria 15	⊖ a	18 47		19 16		19 17				19 46		19 47		20 17		20 17			20 47		20 47				21 16

For general notes see front of timetable
For details of catering facilities see Directory of Train Operators

For services from Ramsgate, Dover and Canterbury to London via Ashford see Table 207

Table 212

Saturdays

Ramsgate, Dover, Sheerness-on-Sea and Medway → London

Network Diagram - see first page of Table 212

Station		SE 1	SE 1	SE 1	SE	SE 1	SE 1	SE 1		SE	SE 1	SE 1	SE 1	SE 1	SE		SE 1	SE 1	SE	SE 1	SE 1	SE		SE 1	
Ramsgate 4	d		19 52	20 12				20 52				21 38		21 52				22 38			22 55			23 38	
Dumpton Park	d		19 54	20 15				20 54				21 41		21 54				22 41			22 57			23 41	
Broadstairs	d		19 58	20 18				20 58				21 44		21 58				22 44			23 00			23 44	
Margate 4	d		20 04	20a23				21 04				21a49		22 04				22a49			23 06			23a49	
Westgate-on-Sea	d		20 07					21 07						22 07							23 09				
Birchington-on-Sea	d		20 10					21 10						22 10							23 13				
Herne Bay	d		20 19					21 19						22 19							23 22				
Chestfield & Swalecliffe	d		20 22					21 22						22 22							23 26				
Whitstable	d		20 26					21 26						22 26							23 29				
Dover Priory 4	d	19 52					20 52						21 52							23 04					
Kearsney	d	19 56					20 56						21 56												
Shepherds Well	d	20 01					21 01						22 01												
Snowdown	d	20 05					21 05						22 05												
Aylesham	d	20 07					21 07						22 07												
Adisham	d	20 09					21 09						22 09												
Bekesbourne	d	20 13					21 13						22 13												
Canterbury East 4	d	20 19					21 19						22 19							23 22					
Selling	d	20 28					21 28						22 28												
Faversham 2	a	20 32	20 35				21 32	21 35					22 32	22 35						23 34	23 38				
	d	20 38				20 45	21 38				21 45		22 38				22 45					23 42			
Teynham	d					20 50					21 50						22 50					23 47			
Sheerness-on-Sea	d				20 30					21 30					22 30				23 30						
Queenborough	d				20 35					21 35					22 35				23 35						
Swale	d				20 40					21 40					22 40				23 40						
Kemsley	d				20 43					21 43					22 43				23 43						
Sittingbourne 4	a	20 46			20 48	20 55	21 46			21 48	21 55		22 46		22 48		22 55		23 48			23 52			
	d	20 47				20 55	21 47				21 55		22 47				22 55					23 52			
Newington	d					21 00					22 00						23 00								
Rainham (Kent)	d	20 54				21 05	21 54				22 05		22 54				23 05					23 59			
Gillingham (Kent) 4	d	20 59				21 10	21 59				22 10		22 59				23 10					00 05			
Chatham 4	d	21 03				21 14	22 03				22 14		23 03				23 14					00 09			
Rochester 4	d	21 06				21 16	22 06				22 16		23 06				23 16					00 11			
Strood 4	a					*21 24*					*22 32*						*00 15*					00 15			
Gravesend 4	a					*21 36*					*22 44*						*00 26*					00 26			
Greenhithe for Bluewater	a					*21 41*					*22 52*						*00 32*					00 32			
Dartford 4	a					*21 46*					*22 58*						*00 39*					00 39			
London Bridge 4	⊖ a					*22 23*					*23 41*														
London Cannon Street 4	⊖ a																								
London Waterloo (East) 4	⊖ a					*22 28*					*23 46*														
London Charing Cross 4	⊖ a					*22 31*					*23 50*														
Sole Street	d					21 27					22 27						23 27								
Meopham	d					21 29					22 29						23 29								
Longfield	d					21 33					22 33						23 33								
Farningham Road	d					21 37					22 37						23 37								
Swanley 4	a					21 42					22 42						23 42								
St Mary Cray	a					21 47					22 47						23 47								
Bromley South 4	a	21 29				21 54	22 29				22 54		23 29				23 54								
Elephant & Castle	⊖ a																								
London Blackfriars 3	⊖ a																								
London Victoria 15	⊖ a	21 47				22 16	22 47				23 16		23 47				00 10					01 11			

For general notes see front of timetable
For details of catering facilities see Directory of Train Operators

For services from Ramsgate, Dover and Canterbury to London via Ashford see Table 207

Sundays

Ramsgate, Dover, Sheerness-on-Sea and Medway → London

Network Diagram - see first page of Table 212

	SE	SE 1	SE 1	SE 1		SE 1 ⊼	SE 1	SE	SE 1		SE 1 ⊼	SE 1	SE	SE 1		SE 1 ⊼	SE 1	SE 1	SE		SE 1	SE 1 ⊼	SE 1	SE 1
Ramsgate 4 ⇌ d			06 22				07 22					08 22					09 22	09 43					10 22	10 43
Dumpton Park d			06 24				07 24					08 24					09 24	09 46					10 24	10 46
Broadstairs d			06 28				07 28					08 28					09 28	09 49					10 28	10 49
Margate 4 d			06 34				07 34					08 34					09 34	09a54					10 34	10a54
Westgate-on-Sea d			06 37				07 37					08 37					09 37						10 37	
Birchington-on-Sea d			06 40				07 40					08 40					09 40						10 40	
Herne Bay d			06 49				07 49					08 49					09 49						10 49	
Chestfield & Swalecliffe d			06 52				07 52					08 52					09 52						10 52	
Whitstable d			06 56				07 56					08 56					09 56						10 56	
Dover Priory 4 ⛴ d						07 22					08 22					09 22						10 22		
Kearsney d						07 26					08 26					09 26						10 26		
Shepherds Well d						07 31					08 31					09 31						10 31		
Snowdown d						07 35					08 35					09 35						10 35		
Aylesham d						07 37					08 37					09 37						10 37		
Adisham d						07 39					08 39					09 39						10 39		
Bekesbourne d						07 43					08 43					09 43						10 43		
Canterbury East 4 d						07 49					08 49					09 49					10 19	10 49		
Selling d						07 57					08 57					09 57						10 57		
Faversham 2 a			07 05			08 02	08 05				09 02	09 05				10 02	10 05				10 31	11 02	11 05	
d	23p42	06 32	07 08	07 32		08 08			08 32		09 08			09 32		10 08					10 32	11 08		
Teynham d	23p47	06 37		07 37					08 37					09 37							10 37			
Sheerness-on-Sea d								08 18					09 18						10 18					
Queenborough d								08 23					09 23						10 23					
Swale d								08 27					09 27						10 27					
Kemsley d								08 31					09 31						10 31					
Sittingbourne 4 a	23p52	06 42	07 16	07 42		08 16		08 35	08 42		09 16		09 35	09 42		10 16			10 35		10 42	11 16		
d	23p52	06 42	07 17	07 42		08 17			08 42		09 17			09 42		10 17					10 42	11 17		
Newington d		06 47		07 47					08 47					09 47							10 47			
Rainham (Kent) d	23p59	06 52	07 24	07 52		08 24			08 52		09 24			09 52		10 24					10 52	11 24		
Gillingham (Kent) 4 d	00 05	06 57	07 30	07 57		08 29			08 57		09 29			09 57		10 29					10 57	11 29		
Chatham 4 d	00 09	07 01	07 33	08 01		08 33			09 01		09 33			10 01		10 33					11 01	11 33		
Rochester 4 d	00 11	07 03	07 35	08 03		08 36			09 03		09 36			10 03		10 36					11 03	11 36		
Strood 4 a	00 15	07 26	07 51	08 26		08 56			09 26		09 56			10 26		10 56					11 26	11 56		
Gravesend 4 a	00 26	07 38	08 03	08 38		09 08			09 38		10 08			10 38		11 08					11 38	12 08		
Greenhithe for Bluewater a	00 32	07 44	08 12	08 44		09 14			09 44		10 14			10 44		11 14					11 44	12 14		
Dartford 4 a	00 39	07 49	08 18	08 49		09 19			09 49		10 19			10 49		11 19					11 49	12 19		
London Bridge 4 ⊖ a		08 23	08 53	09 23		09 53			10 23		10 53			11 23		11 53					12 23	12 53		
London Cannon Street 4 ⊖ a																								
London Waterloo (East) 4 ⊖ a		08 28	08 58	09 28		09 58			10 28		10 58			11 28		11 58					12 28	12 58		
London Charing Cross 4 ⊖ a		08 32	09 02	09 32		10 02			10 32		11 02			11 32		12 02					12 32	13 02		
Sole Street d		07 14		08 14					09 14					10 14							11 14			
Meopham d		07 16		08 16					09 16					10 16							11 16			
Longfield d		07 20		08 20					09 20					10 20							11 20			
Farningham Road d		07 24		08 24					09 24					10 24							11 24			
Swanley 4 a		07 29		08 29					09 29					10 29							11 29			
St Mary Cray a		07 34		08 34					09 34					10 34							11 34			
Bromley South 4 a		07 40	08 00	08 40		09 00			09 40		10 00			10 40		11 00					11 40	12 00		
Elephant & Castle ⊖ a																								
London Blackfriars 3 ⊖ a																								
London Victoria 15 ⊖ a	01 11	08 01	08 16	09 01		09 16			10 01		10 16			11 01		11 16					12 01	12 16		

For general notes see front of timetable
For details of catering facilities see Directory of Train Operators

For services from Ramsgate, Dover and Canterbury to London via Ashford see Table 207

Ramsgate, Dover, Sheerness-on-Sea and Medway → London

Network Diagram - see first page of Table 212

Station		SE	SE 1	SE 1 (trolley)	SE 1	SE 1	SE	SE 1	SE 1 (trolley)	SE 1	SE 1	SE	SE 1	SE 1 (trolley)	SE 1	SE 1	SE	SE 1	SE 1 (trolley)	SE 1	SE 1
Ramsgate 4 ✈	d				11 22	11 42				12 22	12 40				13 22	13 40				14 22	14 40
Dumpton Park	d				11 24	11 45				12 24	12 43				13 24	13 43				14 24	14 43
Broadstairs	d				11 28	11 48				12 28	12 46				13 28	13 46				14 28	14 46
Margate 4	d				11 34	11a53				12 34	12a51				13 34	13a51				14 34	14a51
Westgate-on-Sea	d				11 37					12 37					13 37					14 37	
Birchington-on-Sea	d				11 40					12 40					13 40					14 40	
Herne Bay	d				11 49					12 49					13 49					14 49	
Chestfield & Swalecliffe	d				11 52					12 52					13 52					14 52	
Whitstable	d				11 56					12 56					13 56					14 56	
Dover Priory 4 ⛴	d			11 22					12 22					13 22					14 22		
Kearsney	d			11 26					12 26					13 26					14 26		
Shepherds Well	d			11 31					12 31					13 31					14 31		
Snowdown	d			11 35					12 35					13 35					14 35		
Aylesham	d			11 37					12 37					13 37					14 37		
Adisham	d			11 39					12 39					13 39					14 39		
Bekesbourne	d			11 43					12 43					13 43					14 43		
Canterbury East 4	d		11 19	11 49				12 19	12 49				13 19	13 49				14 19	14 49		
Selling	d			11 57					12 57					13 57					14 57		
Faversham 2	a		11 31	12 02	12 05			12 31	13 02	13 05			13 31	14 02	14 05			14 31	15 02	15 05	
	d		11 32	12 08				12 32	13 08				13 32	14 08				14 32	15 08		
Teynham	d		11 37					12 37					13 37					14 37			
Sheerness-on-Sea	d	11 18					12 18					13 18					14 18				
Queenborough	d	11 23					12 23					13 23					14 23				
Swale	d	11 27					12 27					13 27					14 27				
Kemsley	d	11 31					12 31					13 31					14 31				
Sittingbourne 4	a	11 35	11 42	12 16			12 35	12 42	13 16			13 35	13 42	14 16			14 35	14 42	15 16		
	d		11 42	12 17				12 42	13 17				13 42	14 17				14 42	15 17		
Newington	d		11 47					12 47					13 47					14 47			
Rainham (Kent)	d		11 52	12 24				12 52	13 24				13 52	14 24				14 52	15 24		
Gillingham (Kent) 4	d		11 57	12 29				12 57	13 29				13 57	14 29				14 57	15 29		
Chatham 4	d		12 01	12 33				13 01	13 33				14 01	14 33				15 01	15 33		
Rochester 4	d		12 03	12 36				13 03	13 36				14 03	14 36				15 03	15 36		
Strood 4	a		12 26	12 56				13 26	13 56				14 26	14 56				15 26	15 56		
Gravesend 4	a		12 38	13 08				13 38	14 08				14 38	15 08				15 38	16 08		
Greenhithe for Bluewater	a		12 44	13 14				13 44	14 14				14 44	15 14				15 44	16 14		
Dartford 4	a		12 49	13 19				13 49	14 19				14 49	15 19				15 49	16 19		
London Bridge 4 ⊖	a		13 23	13 53				14 23	14 53				15 23	15 53				16 23	16 53		
London Cannon Street 4 ⊖	a																				
London Waterloo (East) 4 ⊖	a		13 28	13 58				14 28	14 58				15 28	15 58				16 28	16 58		
London Charing Cross 4 ⊖	a		13 32	14 02				14 32	15 02				15 32	16 02				16 32	17 02		
Sole Street	d		12 14					13 14					14 14					15 14			
Meopham	d		12 16					13 16					14 16					15 16			
Longfield	d		12 20					13 20					14 20					15 20			
Farningham Road	d		12 24					13 24					14 24					15 24			
Swanley 4	a		12 29					13 29					14 29					15 29			
St Mary Cray	a		12 34					13 34					14 34					15 34			
Bromley South 4	a		12 40	13 00				13 40	14 00				14 40	15 00				15 40	16 00		
Elephant & Castle ⊖	a																				
London Blackfriars 3 ⊖	a																				
London Victoria 15 ⊖	a		13 01	13 16				14 01	14 16				15 01	15 16				16 01	16 16		

For general notes see front of timetable
For details of catering facilities see Directory of Train Operators

For services from Ramsgate, Dover and Canterbury to London via Ashford see Table 207

Table 212

Sundays

Ramsgate, Dover, Sheerness-on-Sea and Medway → London

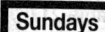

Network Diagram - see first page of Table 212

Station		SE		SE 1	SE 1 ⊼	SE 1	SE 1		SE	SE 1	SE 1 ⊼	SE 1		SE 1	SE	SE 1	SE 1	SE 1		SE 1	SE	SE 1	SE 1	SE 1	SE 1
Ramsgate 4 ✈	d					15 22	15 40					16 22		16 40				17 22		17 45				18 22	18 40
Dumpton Park	d					15 24	15 43					16 24		16 43				17 24		17 48				18 24	18 43
Broadstairs	d					15 28	15 46					16 28		16 46				17 28		17 51				18 28	18 46
Margate 4	d					15 34	15a51					16 34		16a51				17 34		17a56				18 34	18a51
Westgate-on-Sea	d					15 37						16 37						17 37						18 37	
Birchington-on-Sea	d					15 40						16 40						17 40						18 40	
Herne Bay	d					15 49						16 49						17 49						18 49	
Chestfield & Swalecliffe	d					15 52						16 52						17 52						18 52	
Whitstable	d					15 56						16 56						17 56						18 56	
Dover Priory 4 ⛴	d				15 22						16 22						17 22						18 22		
Kearsney	d				15 26						16 26						17 26						18 26		
Shepherds Well	d				15 31						16 31						17 31						18 31		
Snowdown	d				15 35						16 35						17 35						18 35		
Aylesham	d				15 37						16 37						17 37						18 37		
Adisham	d				15 39						16 39						17 39						18 39		
Bekesbourne	d				15 43						16 43						17 43						18 43		
Canterbury East 4	d			15 19	15 49					16 19	16 49					17 19	17 49					18 19	18 49		
Selling	d				15 57						16 57						17 57						18 57		
Faversham 2	a			15 31	16 02	16 05				16 31	17 02	17 05				17 31	18 02	18 05				18 31	19 02	19 05	
	d			15 32	16 08					16 32	17 08					17 32	18 08					18 32	19 08		
Teynham	d			15 37						16 37						17 37						18 37			
Sheerness-on-Sea	d	15 18							16 18						17 18						18 18				
Queenborough	d	15 23							16 23						17 23						18 23				
Swale	d	15 27							16 27						17 27						18 27				
Kemsley	d	15 31							16 31						17 31						18 31				
Sittingbourne 4	a	15 35		15 42	16 16				16 35	16 42	17 16				17 35	17 42	18 16				18 35	18 42	19 16		
	d			15 42	16 17					16 42	17 17					17 42	18 17					18 42	19 17		
Newington	d			15 47						16 47						17 47						18 47			
Rainham (Kent)	d			15 52	16 24					16 52	17 24					17 52	18 24					18 52	19 24		
Gillingham (Kent) 4	d			15 57	16 29					16 57	17 29					17 57	18 29					18 57	19 29		
Chatham 4	d			16 01	16 33					17 01	17 33					18 01	18 33					19 01	19 33		
Rochester 4	d			16 03	16 36					17 03	17 36					18 03	18 36					19 03	19 36		
Strood 4	a			16 26	16 56					17 26	17 56					18 26	18 56					19 26	19 54		
Gravesend 4	a			16 38	17 08					17 38	18 08					18 38	19 08					19 38	20 05		
Greenhithe for Bluewater	a			16 44	17 14					17 44	18 14					18 44	19 14					19 44	20 14		
Dartford 4	a			16 49	17 19					17 49	18 19					18 49	19 19					19 49	20 19		
London Bridge 4 ⊖	a			17 23	17 53					18 23	18 53					19 23	19 53					20 23	20 53		
London Cannon Street 4 ⊖	a																								
London Waterloo (East) 4 ⊖	a			17 28	17 58					18 28	18 58					19 28	19 58					20 28	20 58		
London Charing Cross 4 ⊖	a			17 32	18 02					18 32	19 02					19 32	20 02					20 32	21 02		
Sole Street	d			16 14						17 14						18 14						19 14			
Meopham	d			16 16						17 16						18 16						19 16			
Longfield	d			16 20						17 20						18 20						19 20			
Farningham Road	d			16 24						17 24						18 24						19 24			
Swanley 4	a			16 29						17 29						18 29						19 29			
St Mary Cray	a			16 34						17 34						18 34						19 34			
Bromley South 4	a			16 40	17 00					17 40	18 00					18 40	19 00					19 40	20 00		
Elephant & Castle ⊖	a																								
London Blackfriars 3 ⊖	a																								
London Victoria 15 ⊖	a			17 01	17 16					18 01	18 16					19 01	19 17					20 01	20 17		

For general notes see front of timetable
For details of catering facilities see Directory of Train Operators

For services from Ramsgate, Dover and Canterbury to London via Ashford see Table 207

Table 212

Sundays

Ramsgate, Dover, Sheerness-on-Sea and Medway → London

Network Diagram - see first page of Table 212

		SE		SE 1	SE 1	SE 1	SE 1		SE	SE 1	SE 1	SE 1		SE 1	SE	SE 1	SE 1	SE 1		SE	SE 1	SE 1			
Ramsgate 4 ✈	d					19 22	19 40					20 22		20 40				21 22				21 52			
Dumpton Park	d					19 24	19 43					20 24		20 43				21 24				21 54			
Broadstairs	d					19 28	19 46					20 28		20 46				21 28				21 57			
Margate 4	d					19 34	19a51					20 34		20a51				21 34				22 04			
Westgate-on-Sea	d					19 37						20 37						21 37				22 07			
Birchington-on-Sea	d					19 40						20 40						21 40				22 10			
Herne Bay	d					19 49						20 49						21 49				22 18			
Chestfield & Swalecliffe	d					19 52						20 52						21 52				22 22			
Whitstable	d					19 56						20 56						21 56				22 25			
Dover Priory 4 ⛴	d				19 22						20 22						21 22				21 52				
Kearsney	d				19 26						20 26						21 26				21 57				
Shepherds Well	d				19 31						20 31						21 31				22 02				
Snowdown	d				19 35						20 35						21 35				22 05				
Aylesham	d				19 37						20 37						21 37				22 07				
Adisham	d				19 39						20 39						21 39				22 10				
Bekesbourne	d				19 43						20 43						21 43				22 14				
Canterbury East 4	d			19 19	19 49						20 49						21 49				22 19				
Selling	d				19 57						20 57						21 57				22 28				
Faversham 2	a			19 31	20 02	20 05					21 02	21 05					22 02	22 05			22 32	22 34			
	d			19 32	20 08					20 32	21 08					21 32	22 08					22 35			
Teynham	d			19 37						20 37						21 37						22 40			
Sheerness-on-Sea	d	19 18							20 18						21 18					22 18					
Queenborough	d	19 23							20 23						21 23					22 23					
Swale	d	19 27							20 27						21 27					22 27					
Kemsley	d	19 31							20 31						21 31					22 31					
Sittingbourne 4	a	19 35		19 42	20 16				20 35	20 42	21 16				21 35	21 42	22 16			22 35		22 44			
	d			19 42	20 17					20 42	21 17					21 42	22 17					22 45			
Newington	d			19 47						20 47						21 47						22 50			
Rainham (Kent)	d			19 52	20 24					20 52	21 24					21 52	22 24					22 54			
Gillingham (Kent) 4	d			19 57	20 29					20 57	21 29					21 57	22 29					22 59			
Chatham 4	d			20 01	20 33					21 01	21 33					22 01	22 33					23 03			
Rochester 4	d			20 03	20 36					21 03	21 36					22 03	22 36					23 05			
Strood 4	a			20 26	20 51					21 26	21 51					22 26									
Gravesend 4	a			20 38	21 03					21 38	22 03					22 39									
Greenhithe for Bluewater	a			20 44	21 12					21 44	22 12					22 48									
Dartford 4	a			20 49	21 18					21 49	22 18					22 53									
London Bridge 4	⊖ a			21 23	21 53					22 23	22 53					23 36									
London Cannon Street 4	⊖ a																								
London Waterloo (East) 4	⊖ a			21 28	21 58					22 28	22 58					23 41									
London Charing Cross 4	⊖ a			21 32	22 02					22 32	23 02					23 45									
Sole Street	d			20 14						21 14						22 14						23 15			
Meopham	d			20 16						21 16						22 16						23 17			
Longfield	d			20 20						21 20						22 20						23 21			
Farningham Road	d			20 24						21 24						22 24						23 26			
Swanley 4	a			20 29						21 29						22 29						23 32			
St Mary Cray	a			20 34						21 34						22 34						23 36			
Bromley South 4	a			20 40	21 00					21 40	22 00					22 40	23 00					23 42			
Elephant & Castle	⊖ a																								
London Blackfriars 3	⊖ a																								
London Victoria 15	⊖ a			21 01	21 16					22 01	22 16					23 01	23 16					23 59			

For general notes see front of timetable
For details of catering facilities see Directory of Train Operators

For services from Ramsgate, Dover and Canterbury to London via Ashford see Table 207

Network Diagram for Tables 216, 217, 218, 219, 221, 222

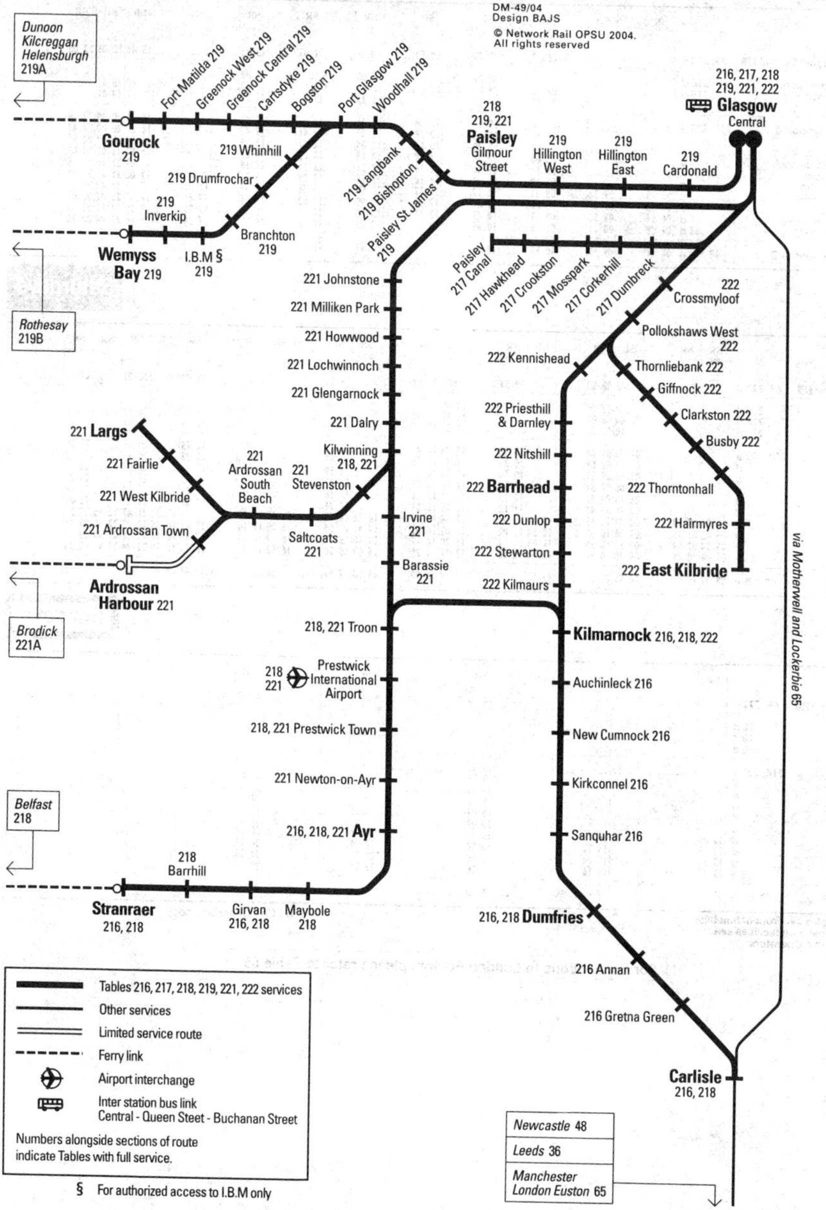

Table 216

Mondays to Fridays

Glasgow Central, Stranraer and Kilmarnock → Dumfries and Carlisle

Network Diagram - see first page of Table 216

Miles	Miles			SR	SR	SR	SR	SR	SR ◇	SR	SR	SR	SR	SR	SR
0	—	**Glasgow Central** 15	65, 222 d			06b42	08 28	09 53	11b03	12 03	13 03		15 48	20 03	22 03
—	0	**Stranraer**	218 d				07 09		10 00		11 48				
—	38¼	Girvan	218 d			06 40	08 01		10 52	11 40	12 40		14 40	18 42	
—	59¼	Ayr	218 d			07 10	08 36		11 22	12 09	13 09		15 17	19 09	
24¼	74½	**Kilmarnock** 3	218, 222 a			07 40	09 06	10 38	11 46	12 41	13 42		16 25	20 39	22 39
—	—		d			07 41	09 13	10 39	11 47	12 41	13 42		16 27	20 40	22 43
38	89¼	Auchinleck	d			07 57	09 29	10 56	12 04	12 57	13 59		16 44	20 57	22 59
45½	96¾	New Cumnock	d			08 06	09 38	11 04	12 13	13 06	14 07		16 52	21 07	23 08
52¾	104½	Kirkconnel	d			08 14	09 46	11 13	12 21	13 14	14 16		17 01	21 16	23 16
56	107¾	Sanquhar	d			08 19	09 51	11 18	12 26	13 19	14 21		17 06	21 21	23 21
82¼	135	**Dumfries**	d	06 28	07 34	08 49	10 17	11 47	12 54	13 48	14 47	17 01	17 32	21 47	23 49
97¾	150½	Annan	d	06 43	07 49	09 06	10 32	12 02	13 09	14 03	15 04	17 16	17 47	22 02	00 06
105½	158	Gretna Green	d	06 54	07 58	09 15	10 43	12 11	13 20	14 12	15 17	17 25	17 56	22 11	00 15
115½	168	**Carlisle** 3	65 a	07 08	08 11	09 28	10 56	12 26	13 32	14 26	15 33	17 38	18 16	22 24	00 26
—	—	Newcastle 3	48 a	08 57	09 59	10 55	12 57		14 57	16 00	18 08		19 47		

Saturdays

		SR	SR	SR	SR	SR	SR	SR ◇	SR	SR	SR	SR	SR	SR	SR	SR	SR	SR
Glasgow Central 15	65, 222 d			06b42	08 28		09 53	11b03	12 03		13 03			15 48		20 03		22 03
Stranraer	218 d				07 09			10 00			11 48							
Girvan	218 d			06 40	08 01			10 52	11 40		12 40			14 40		18 42		
Ayr	218 d			07 10	08 36			11 22	12 09		13 09			15 17		19 09		
Kilmarnock 3	218, 222 a			07 40	09 06		10 38	11 46	12 41		13 42			16 25		20 39		22 39
	d			07 41	09 09		10 39	11 47	12 41		13 42			16 27		20 40		22 43
Auchinleck	d			07 57	09 25		10 56	12 04	12 57		13 59			16 44		20 57		22 59
New Cumnock	d			08 06	09 34		11 04	12 13	13 06		14 07			16 52		21 07		23 08
Kirkconnel	d			08 14	09 42		11 13	12 21	13 14		14 16			17 01		21 16		23 16
Sanquhar	d			08 19	09 47		11 18	12 26	13 19		14 21			17 06		21 21		23 21
Dumfries	d	06 28	07 34	08 49	10 15	10 39	11 47	12 54	13 48	14 26	14 47	16 15	17 01	17 31	18 20	21 47	22 10	23 53
Annan	d	06 43	07 49	09 06	10 30	10 54	12 02	13 09	14 03	14 41	15 04	16 30	17 16	17 47	18 35	22 02	22 25	00 08
Gretna Green	d	06 54	07 58	09 15	10 39	11 03	12 11	13 20	14 12	14 50	15 11	16 39	17 25	17 55	18 41	22 11	22 34	00 17
Carlisle 8	65 a	07 08	08 11	09 28	10 54	11 14	12 26	13 32	14 26	15 03	15 26	16 52	17 38	18 16	18 59	22 24	22 47	00 34
Newcastle 8	48 a	08 57	10 01	10 55		12 57		14 59	16 00	16 50	17 59	18 56		19 47	21 14			

Sundays

		SR	SR	SR	SR	SR
Glasgow Central 15	65, 222 d			14 48		22 28
Stranraer	218 d					
Girvan	218 d					
Ayr	218 d					
Kilmarnock 3	218, 222 a			15 27		23 04
	d			15 28		23 05
Auchinleck	d			15 45		23 22
New Cumnock	d			15 53		23 30
Kirkconnel	d			16 02		23 39
Sanquhar	d			16 07		23 44
Dumfries	d	13 00	14 37	16 35	22 14	00 12
Annan	d	13 15	14 52	16 50	22 29	00 27
Gretna Green	d	13 24	15 04	16 59	22 38	00 36
Carlisle 8	65 a	13 37	15 16	17 18	22 51	00 49
Newcastle 8	48 a	15 40	17 40	19 40		

For general notes see front of timetable
For details of catering facilities see Directory of Train Operators

b Change at Kilmarnock

For connections to London Euston, please refer to Table 65

Table 216

Mondays to Fridays

Carlisle and Dumfries → Kilmarnock, Stranraer and Glasgow Central

Network Diagram - see first page of Table 216

Miles	Miles			SR	SR	SR A	SR B	SR	SR	SR ◇	SR	SR	SR	SR ◇	SR	SR
—	—	Newcastle [8]	48 ⛴ d			06 49	06 54	*09 24*	*11 24*	12 39		*14 24*	*15 25*	17 13	*19 10*	*21b22*
0	0	**Carlisle** [8]	65 d	05 40	06 09	08 19	08 19	11 07	13 09	14 22	15 00	16 14	17 58	18 52	21 08	23 07
9¾	9¾	Gretna Green	d	05 51	06 20	08 30	08 30	11 18	13 21	14 33	15 10	16 25	18 09	19 05	21 19	23 18
17½	17½	Annan	d	06 00	06 31	08 38	08 38	11 26	13 30	14 42	15 20	16 34	18 17	19 13	21 28	23 27
33	33	**Dumfries**	d	06a18	06 50	08 55	08 55	11 43	13 47	14 58	15 39	16a49	18 34	19 30	21 44	23a44
59¼	59¼	Sanquhar	d		07 16	09 21	09 21	12 09	14 12	15 24	16 05		19 00	19 56	22 10	
62½	62½	Kirkconnel	d		07 21	09 26	09 26	12 14	14 17	15 29	16 10		19 05	20 01	22 15	
69¾	69¾	New Cumnock	d		07 30	09 35	09 36	12 23	14 26	15 43	16 19		19 14	20 10	22 24	
77¼	77¼	Auchinleck	d		07 38	09 43	09 44	12 31	14 35	15 51	16 28		19 22	20 18	22 32	
91	91	**Kilmarnock** [3]	218, 222 a		07 57	10 02	10 00	12 48	14 53	16 07	16 44		19 41	20 37	22 49	
—	—		d		07 58	10 04	10 04	12 50	14 55	16 09	16 46		19 50	20 38	22 50	
—	106¼	Ayr	218 a		*09 39*			*13 36*		16 32	*18 39*			20 59		
—	127¼	Girvan	218 a		*10 08*			*14 05*		16 59				21 26		
—	168	**Stranraer**	218 a		*11 11*					17 55				22 24		
115¼	—	**Glasgow Central** [15]	65, 222 a		08 37	10 41	10 41	13 27	15 33		17 31		20 27	*21c27*	23 28	

Saturdays

		SR	SR	SR	SR	SR	SR	SR	SR	SR	SR	SR	SR	SR	SR	SR	SR	SR
Newcastle [8]	48 ⛴ d			06 35		*09 24*	*10 24*	*11 22*	12 39	*13 24*		*14 24*	*15 24*		17 13	*18 24*	*19 10*	
Carlisle [8]	65 d	05 40	06 12	08 19	09 52	11 07	12 18	13 09	14 22	15 02	15 22	16 16	17 24	17 58	18 52	20 08	21 08	22 56
Gretna Green	d	05 51	06 23	08 30	10 03	11 18	12 29	13 21	14 33	15 16	15 34	16 27	17 35	18 09	19 05	20 19	21 19	23 07
Annan	d	06 00	06 32	08 38	10 12	11 26	12 38	13 29	14 42	15 25	15 43	16 36	17 44	18 17	19 13	20 28	21 28	23 16
Dumfries	d	06a18	06 50	08 55	10a29	11 43	12a55	13 47	14 59	15 41	16a00	16a53	18a01	18 34	19 30	20 44	21a45	23a33
Sanquhar	d		07 16	09 21		12 09		14 13	15 25	16 07				19 00	19 56	21 10		
Kirkconnel	d		07 21	09 26		12 14		14 18	15 30	16 12				19 05	20 01	21 15		
New Cumnock	d		07 30	09 36		12 23		14 27	15 39	16 21				19 14	20 10	21 24		
Auchinleck	d		07 38	09 44		12 31		14 35	15 48	16 29				19 22	20 18	21 32		
Kilmarnock [3]	218, 222 a		07 57	10 00		12 48		14 53	16 07	16 46				19 38	20 37	21 49		
	d		07 58	10 04		12 50		14 55	16 09	16 47				19 50	20 38	21 50		
Ayr	218 a		*09 38*			*13 36*			16 32	*18 38*					20 59	*23 10*		
Girvan	218 a		*10 08*			*14 05*			16 59						21 26	*23 36*		
Stranraer	218 a		*11 11*						17 55						22 24	*00 37*		
Glasgow Central [15]	65, 222 a		08 37	10 41		13 29		15 32		17 31				20 27	*21c27*	22 27		

Sundays

		SR ◇	SR	SR	SR
Newcastle [8]	48 ⛴ d	*11 10*		*17 10*	*18 10*
Carlisle [8]	65 d	12 53	13 47	19 35	21 12
Gretna Green	d	13 04	13 58	19 46	21 23
Annan	d	13 12	14 07	19 54	21 32
Dumfries	d	13 28	14a24	20 11	21a49
Sanquhar	d	13 54		20 37	
Kirkconnel	d	13 59		20 42	
New Cumnock	d	14 08		20 51	
Auchinleck	d	14 16		20 59	
Kilmarnock [3]	218, 222 a	14 34		21 16	
	d	14 35		21 18	
Ayr	218 a			*23 10*	
Girvan	218 a			*23 36*	
Stranraer	218 a			*00 37*	
Glasgow Central [15]	65, 222 a	15 14		21 55	

For general notes see front of timetable
For details of catering facilities see Directory of Train Operators

A From 7 September
B Until 4 September
b Until 4 September only
c Change at Kilmarnock

For connections from London Euston, please refer to Table 65

Glasgow Central — Paisley Canal

Network Diagram - see first page of Table 216

Miles			SR SO	SR	SR		SR	SR
0	**Glasgow Central** 15	d	00 07	06 07	06 37	and every 30 minutes until	22 37	23 07
1¾	Dumbreck	d	00 13	06 13	06 43		22 43	23 13
3¼	Corkerhill	d	00 15	06 15	06 45		22 45	23 15
3¾	Mosspark	d	00 17	06 17	06 47		22 47	23 17
4½	Crookston	d	00 19	06 19	06 49		22 49	23 19
6½	Hawkhead	d	00 22	06 22	06 52		22 52	23 22
7	**Paisley Canal**	a	00 25	06 25	06 55		22 55	23 25

Sundays
from 29 November

		SR	SR		SR
Glasgow Central 15	d	09 37	10 37	and every hour until	17 37
Dumbreck	d	09 43	10 43		17 43
Corkerhill	d	09 45	10 45		17 45
Mosspark	d	09 47	10 47		17 47
Crookston	d	09 49	10 49		17 49
Hawkhead	d	09 52	10 52		17 52
Paisley Canal	a	09 55	10 55		17 55

Mondays to Saturdays

Miles			SR	SR	SR	SR	SR	SR	SR		SR	SR	SR	SR
0	**Paisley Canal**	d	06 30	07 00	07 30	08 00	08 30	09 00	09 30	and every 30 minutes until	21 30	22 00	22 30	23 00
½	Hawkhead	d	06 33	07 03	07 33	08 03	08 33	09 03	09 33		21 33	22 03	22 33	23 03
2½	Crookston	d	06 36	07 06	07 36	08 06	08 36	09 06	09 36		21 36	22 06	22 36	23 06
3¼	Mosspark	d	06 38	07 08	07 38	08 08	08 38	09 08	09 38		21 38	22 08	22 38	23 08
3¾	Corkerhill	d	06 40	07 10	07 40	08 10	08 40	09 10	09 40		21 40	22 10	22 40	23 10
5¼	Dumbreck	d	06 43	07 13	07 43	08 13	08 43	09 13	09 43		21 43	22 13	22 43	23 13
7	**Glasgow Central** 15	a	06 49	07 19	07 52	08 21	08 52	09 19	09 49		21 49	22 19	22 50	23 20

Sundays
from 29 November

		SR	SR		SR
Paisley Canal	d	09 00	10 00	and every hour until	17 00
Hawkhead	d	09 03	10 03		17 03
Crookston	d	09 06	10 06		17 06
Mosspark	d	09 08	10 08		17 08
Corkerhill	d	09 10	10 10		17 10
Dumbreck	d	09 13	10 13		17 13
Glasgow Central 15	a	09 19	10 19		17 19

For general notes see front of timetable
For details of catering facilities see Directory of Train Operators

Mondays to Saturdays

Glasgow Central and Kilmarnock → Girvan, Stranraer and Belfast

Network Diagram - see first page of Table 216

Miles	Miles		SR	SR	SR	SR SO	SR SX	SR SX	SR SO	SR	SR	SR	SR	SR	SR	SR SO	SR SX	SR	SR	SR	SR
				◇	R A					◇		R A	◇					R A		◇	
0	—	**Glasgow Central** 15 219, 221, 222 d		07 13		08b30	08b30	09 03	09 03	11 42	12b30		15b30	16b00	17c13				18 30	20b00	22b00
7¼	—	Paisley Gilmour Street 219, 221 ✈ d		07 24		08b41	08b41	09b11	09b11	11 53	12b41		15b41	16b11	17c24				18 41	20b11	22b11
26¾	—	Kilwinning 221 d		07 41		09b05	09b03	09b32	09b29	12 10	12b59		15b59	16b29	17c42				19 01	20b29	22b29
—	—	Newcastle 8 48 d									09e24		12 39	12 39		13e24				17 13	18f24
—	—	Carlisle 8 216 d				06 12	06 09				11 07		14 22			15 02	15 00			18 52	20g08
—	—	Dumfries 216 d				06 50	06 50				11 43		14h58	14h58		15 41	15 41			19 30	20g44
—	0	**Kilmarnock** 3 222 a						09 47	09 48				16 07							20 37	
—	—	d				09 10	09 10	09 54	09 55		13 10		16 09	16 31		18 11	18 15			20 38	22 44
35	10¾	Troon 221 d				09 24	09 24	10 06	10 07		13 22		16 21	16 44		18 24	18 27			20 51	22 56
37¾	11¾	Prestwick Int. Airport 221 ✈ d		07j45		09 29	09 29	10 11	10 12	12 15	13 27		16 15	16 49	17k56	18 29	18 32		19 17	20 43	23 01
38¼	12½	Prestwick Town 221 d		07j47		09 31	09 31	10 13	10 14	12 17	13 29		16 17	16 51	17k58	18 31	18 34		19 19	20 45	23 03
41½	15½	**Ayr** 221 a		07 59		09 38	09 39	10 20	10 21	12 29	13 36		16 32	16 58		18 38	18 39			20 59	23 10
—	—	d	06 00	08 00		09 43	09 43	10 22	10 22	12 30	13 38		16 34	17 00	18 10				19 31	21 01	23 11
50½	24½	Maybole d	06 11	08 11		09 54	09 54	10 34	10 34	12 41	13 49		16 45	17 11	18 21				19 42	21 12	23 22
62¾	36½	**Girvan** d	06a27	08 26		10 09	10 09	10a51	10a51	13 01	14a05		17 00	17a27	18a37				19 57	21 27	23 37
75	51¼	Barrhill d		08 45		10m35	10m35			13 20			17 19						20 16	21 46	00 01
101	77¼	**Stranraer** a		09 21		11 11	11 11			13 56			17 55						20 52	22 24	00 37
—	—	Stranraer Harbour § ⛴ d			09 50							14 40						19 50			
—	—	Belfast Port § ⛴ a			11 50							16 40						22 10			

Sundays

	SR	SR	SR	SR	SR	SR	SR
	R A	◇ B	◇ C	R A	◇	R A	
Glasgow Central 15 219, 221, 222 d		11 37	11 43		16 25		22b00
Paisley Gilmour Street 219, 221 ✈ d		11 48	11 54		16 39		22b11
Kilwinning 221 d		12 05	12 11		16 56		22b29
Newcastle 8 48 d							17e10
Carlisle 8 216 d							19 35
Dumfries 216 d							20 11
Kilmarnock 3 222 a							
d							22 44
Troon 221 d							22 56
Prestwick Int. Airport 221 ✈ d		12n13	12 13		16 45		23 01
Prestwick Town 221 d		12n15	12 15		16 47		23 03
Ayr 221 a		12 29	12 29		17 17		23 10
d		12 30	12 30		17 19		23 11
Maybole d		12 41	12 41		17 30		23 22
Girvan d		12 56	12 56		17 47		23 37
Barrhill d		13 14	13 14		18 06		00 01
Stranraer a		13 51	13 51		18 42		00 37
Stranraer Harbour § ⛴ d	09 50			14 40		19 50	
Belfast Port § ⛴ a	11 50			16 40		22 10	

For general notes see front of timetable
For details of catering facilities see Directory of Train Operators

§ Stena HSS and shipping services operated by Stena Line
A Ship service
B Until 22 November
C 29 November and 6 December

b Change at Ayr
c Saturdays dep. Glasgow Central 1700, Paisley Gilmour Street 1711, Kilwinning 1735
e Change at Carlisle and Kilmarnock
f Saturdays only. Change at Carlisle and Kilmarnock
g Saturdays only
h Saturdays dep. 1459

j Saturdays dep. Prestwick Int. Airport 0743, Prestwick Town 0745
k Saturdays dep. Prestwick Int. Airport 1751, Prestwick Town 1753
m Arr. 1030
n 4 October to 22 November dep. Prestwick Int. Airport 1145, Prestwick Town 1147

Belfast, Stranraer and Girvan → Kilmarnock and Glasgow Central

Network Diagram - see first page of Table 216

Miles	Miles	Station		SR	SR	SR	SR	SR	SR	SR	SR	SR	SR	SR	SR	SR	SR	SR
					◇	[R] A	◇		◇	[R] A		◇			[R] A	◇	◇	SX ◇
—	—	Belfast Port §	⛴ d			07 25				12 15					17 05			
—	—	Stranraer Harbour §	⛴ a			09 25				14 15					19 25			
0	—	**Stranraer**	d		07 09		10 00		11 48			14 37				19 40	21 10	23 25
26	—	Barrhill	d		07 43		10 34		12 22			15 11				20b19	21 50	23 59
38¼	—	**Girvan**	d	06 40	08 01		10 52	11 40	12 40		14 40	15 29	17 32	18 42		20 37	22 08	00 19
50½	—	Maybole	d	06 56	08 25		11 08	11 56	12 56		14 56	15 45	17 48	18 58		20 53	22 24	00 35
59¼	—	**Ayr**	a	07 08	08 35		11 20	12 08	13 08		15 08	15 56	18c00	19 08		21 05	22 37	00 47
—	—		d	07 10	08 36		11 22	12 09	13 09		15 17	15 56		19 09		21 06	22 38	
62½	—	Prestwick Town	221 a	07 19	08 41		11 48	12 14	13 14		15 22	16 19	18 19	19 14		21 19	23 06	
63	—	Prestwick Int. Airport	221 ✈ a	07 21	08 43		11 50	12 16	13 16		15 24	16 21	18 21	19 16		21 21	23 08	
63¾	0	Troon	221 a	07 18	08 48		11 30	12 21	13 21		15 29			19 21				
—	10¾	**Kilmarnock** [3]	a	07 40	09 03		11 46	12 37	13 37		15 42			19 42				
—	—		d	07 41	09 12		11 47		13 50		15 48							
—	—	Dumfries	216 a	08 49	10e17		12 53	13 47	14f47		17 31			21 46				
—	—	Carlisle [3]	216 a	09 28	10e56		13 32	14 26	15f33		18 16			22 24				
—	—	Newcastle [3]	48 a	10 55	12g57		14h57	16j00	18k08		19 47							
74¼	—	Kilwinning	221 a	07m36	09m04		12m04	12m36	13m36		15m36	16 13	18 36	19m37		21 21	22 54	
93¾	—	Paisley Gilmour Street	219, 221 ✈ a	07n57	09m24		12m22	12m55	13m55		15m57	16 33	18 57	19m55		21 44	23 14	
101	—	**Glasgow Central** [15]	219, 221, 222 a	08n09	09q50		12r27	13m07	14t27		16v32	16 45	19 09	20m08		21 55	23 26	

Sundays

Station		SR	SR	SR	SR	SR	SR
		[R] A	◇	[R] A	◇	[R] A	◇
Belfast Port §	⛴ d	07 25		12 15		17 05	
Stranraer Harbour §	⛴ a	09 25		14 15		19 25	
Stranraer	d		10 40		14 40		19 40
Barrhill	d		11 14		15 14		20 15
Girvan	d		11 32		15 32		20 33
Maybole	d		11 48		15 48		20 49
Ayr	a		12 00		15 59		20 59
	d		12 00		15 59		21 00
Prestwick Town	221 a		12w18		16y18		21 48
Prestwick Int. Airport	221 ✈ a		12w20		16y20		21 50
Troon	221 a						
Kilmarnock [3]	a						
	d						
Dumfries	216 a						
Carlisle [8]	216 a						
Newcastle [8]	48 a						
Kilwinning	221 a		12 15		16 14		21 15
Paisley Gilmour Street	219, 221 ✈ a		12 36		16 37		21 36
Glasgow Central [15]	219, 221, 222 a		12 51		16 49		21 48

For general notes see front of timetable
For details of catering facilities see Directory of Train Operators

- § Stena HSS and shipping services operated by Stena Line
- A Ship service
- b Arr. 2014
- c Saturdays arr. 1803
- e Saturdays arr. Dumfries 1014, Carlisle 1054
- f Saturdays arr. Dumfries 1446, Carlisle 1526
- g Change at Kilmarnock and Carlisle. Mondays to Fridays from 7 September arr. 1258
- h Saturdays arr. 1459
- j Change at Kilmarnock and Carlisle. Mondays to Fridays from 7 September arr. 1558
- k Change at Kilmarnock and Carlisle. Mondays to Fridays from 7 September arr. 1809. Saturdays until 5 September arr. 1759, from 12 September arr. 1801
- m Change at Ayr
- n Change at Ayr. Saturdays arr. Paisley Gilmour Street 0804, Glasgow Central 0816
- q By changing at Ayr, passengers may arrive at 0936
- r Change at Kilmarnock
- t By changing at Ayr, passengers may arrive at 1407
- v By changing at Ayr, passengers may arrive at 1609
- w 4 October to 22 November arr. Prestwick Town 1248, Prestwick Int. Airport 1250
- y 4 October to 22 November arr. Prestwick Town 1648, Prestwick Int. Airport 1650

Table 219

Mondays to Saturdays

Glasgow Central → Wemyss Bay and Gourock

Network Diagram - see first page of Table 216

Miles	Miles			SR	SR	SR	SR	SR	SR	SR	SR	SR	SR	SR	SR	SR	SR	SR	SR	SR
0	0	**Glasgow Central** 15 221	d	05 55	06 05	06 25	06 32	06 55	07 05	07 25	07 35	07 50	08 05	08 25	08b36	08 50	09 05	09 25	09 35	09 50
3¾	3¾	Cardonald	d				06 39		07 12	07 32	07 42		08 12		08 42		09 12		09 42	
4½	4½	Hillington East	d		06 13		06 41		07 14	07 34	07 44		08 14		08 44		09 14		09 44	
5	5	Hillington West	d	06 03	06 15		06 43	07 03	07 16	07 36	07 46	07 58	08 16		08 46		09 16		09 46	
7¼	7¼	Paisley Gilmour Street 221 ✈	d	06 07	06 19	06 36	06 47	07 07	07 20	07 40	07 50	08 02	08 20	08 36	08 50	09 01	09 20	09 36	09 50	10 01
8	8	Paisley St James	d			06 38			07 22		07 52		08 22		08 52		09 22		09 52	
12¼	12¼	Bishopton	d	06 13	06 25	06 44	06 53	07 13	07 28	07 46	07 58	08 08	08 28	08 42	08 58	09 07	09 28	09 42	09 58	10 07
16¼	16¼	Langbank	d			06 49			07 34		08 04		08 34		09 04		09 34		10 04	
19	19	Woodhall	d		06 33	06 53	07 01		07 38	07 54	08 08		08 38		09 08		09 38		10 08	
20¼	20¼	Port Glasgow	d	06 23	06 36	06 56	07 04	07 23	07 41	07 57	08 11	08 18	08 41	08 51	09 11	09 16	09 41	09 51	10 11	10 16
—	22½	Whinhill	d		06 40		07 08					08 22				09 21				10 21
—	23	Drumfrochar	d		06 43		07 11					08 25				09 23				10 23
—	24¾	Branchton	d		06 46		07 14					08 28				09 26				10 26
—	25½	I.B.M. §	d		06 48		07 16					08 30				09 29				10 29
—	28¾	Inverkip	d		06 53		07 25					08 35				09 34				10 34
—	31	**Wemyss Bay**	a		06 58		07 30					08 40				09 40				10 40
21¼	—	Bogston	d			06 58		07 25	07 43	07 59	08 13		08 43		09 13		09 43		10 13	
22	—	Cartsdyke	d	06 26		07 01		07 27	07 45	08 01	08 15		08 45		09 15		09 45		10 15	
23	—	Greenock Central	d	06 28		07 03		07 29	07 47	08 03	08 17		08 47	08 56	09 17		09 47	09 56	10 17	
23¾	—	Greenock West	d	06 31		07 05		07 32	07 50	08 06	08 20		08 50	08 59	09 20		09 50	09 59	10 20	
25	—	Fort Matilda	d			07 08		07 35	07 53	08 09	08 23		08 53	09 02	09 23		09 53	10 02	10 23	
26¼	—	**Gourock**	a	06 36		07 13		07 39	07 57	08 13	08 27		08 57	09 07	09 27		09 58	10 06	10 27	

		SR		SR	SR	SR	SR	SR	SR	SR	SR	SR	SR	SR	SR	SR	SR	SR	SR
Glasgow Central 15 221	d	10 05		15 05	15 25	15 35	15 50	16 05	16 23	16 33	16 55	17 05	17 15	17 25	17 40	17 50	18 05	18 25	18 35
Cardonald	d	10 12		15 12		15 42		16 12	16 30	16 40		17 12	17 22		17 47		18 12		18 42
Hillington East	d	10 14		15 14		15 44		16 14	16 32	16 42		17 14	17 24		17 49		18 14		18 44
Hillington West	d	10 16		15 16		15 46	15 58	16 16	16 34	16 44	17 03	17 16			17 51		18 16		18 46
Paisley Gilmour Street 221 ✈	d	10 20		15 20	15 36	15 50	16 02	16 20	16 38	16 48	17 07	17 20	17 29	17 36	17 55	18 01	18 20	18 36	18 50
Paisley St James	d	10 22	and at	15 22		15 52		16 22	16 40			17 22			17 57		18 22		18 52
Bishopton	d	10 28		15 28	15 42	15 58	16 08	16 28	16 46	16 54	17 13	17 28	17 35		18 03	18 07	18 28	18 42	18 58
Langbank	d	10 34	the same	15 34		16 04		16 34	16 52			17 34			18 09		18 34		19 04
Woodhall	d	10 38		15 38		16 08		16 38	16 56			17 38			18 12		18 38		19 08
Port Glasgow	d	10 41	minutes	15 41	15 51	16 11	16 18	16 41	16 59	17 04	17 23	17 41	17 45	17 50	18 14	18 18	18 41	18 51	19 11
Whinhill	d		past				16 22			17 08			17 49			18 22			
Drumfrochar	d						16 25			17 11			17 52			18 25			
Branchton	d		each				16 28			17 14			17 55			18 28			
I.B.M. §	d						16 30						17 57			18 30			
Inverkip	d		hour until				16 35			17 19			18 02			18 35			
Wemyss Bay	a						16 40			17 25			18 08			18 41			
Bogston	d	10 43		15 43		16 13		16 43	17 01		17 25	17 43			18 18		18 43		19 13
Cartsdyke	d	10 45		15 45		16 15		16 45	17 03		17 27	17 45			18 20		18 45		19 15
Greenock Central	d	10 47		15 47	15 56	16 17		16 47	17 05		17 29	17 47		17 55	18 22		18 47	18 56	19 17
Greenock West	d	10 50		15 50	15 59	16 20		16 50	17 08		17 32	17 50		17 57	18 25		18 50	18 59	19 20
Fort Matilda	d	10 53		15 53	16 02	16 23		16 53	17 11		17 35	17 53		18 00	18 28		18 53	19 02	19 23
Gourock	a	10 57		15 57	16 06	16 27		16 57	17 15		17 39	17 57		18 05	18 32		18 57	19 06	19 27

		SR	SR	SR	SR	SR	SR	SR	SR	SR	SR	SR	SR	SR	SR	SR	SR
Glasgow Central 15 221	d	18 50	19 05	19 25	19 38	19 50	20 05	20 35	20 50	21 05	21 35	21 50	22 05	22 35	22 50	23 20	23 50
Cardonald	d		19 12		19 45		20 12	20 42		21 12	21 42		22 12	22 42		23 27	23 57
Hillington East	d		19 14		19 47		20 14	20 44		21 14	21 44		22 14	22 44		23 29	23 59
Hillington West	d		19 16		19 49		20 16	20 46		21 16	21 46		22 16	22 46		23 31	00 01
Paisley Gilmour Street 221 ✈	d	19 01	19 20	19 36	19 53	20 01	20 20	20 50	21 01	21 20	21 50	22 01	22 20	22 50	23 01	23 35	00 05
Paisley St James	d		19 22		19 55		20 22	20 52		21 22	21 52		22 22	22 52		23 37	00 07
Bishopton	d	19 07	19 28	19 42	20 01	20 07	20 28	20 58	21 07	21 28	21 58	22 07	22 28	22 58	23 07	23 43	00 13
Langbank	d		19 34		20 07		20 34	21 04		21 34	22 04		22 34	23 04		23 49	00 19
Woodhall	d		19 38		20 11		20 38	21 08		21 38	22 08		22 38	23 08		23 53	00 23
Port Glasgow	d	19 16	19 41	19 51	20 14	20 16	20 41	21 11	21 16	21 41	22 11	22 16	22 41	23 11	23 16	23 56	00 26
Whinhill	d	19 21			20 18			21 15			22 15			23 15			
Drumfrochar	d	19 23			20 21			21 18			22 18			23 18			
Branchton	d	19 26			20 24			21 21			22 21			23 21			
I.B.M. §	d	19 29			20 26			21 23			22 23			23 23			
Inverkip	d	19 34			20 31			21 28			22 28			23 28			
Wemyss Bay	a	19 40			20 37			21 34			22 34			23 34			
Bogston	d		19 43				20 43			21 43			22 43			23 58	00 28
Cartsdyke	d		19 45			20 20	20 45		21 20	21 45		22 20	22 45		23 20	23 59	00 30
Greenock Central	d		19 47	19 56		20 22	20 47		21 22	21 47		22 22	22 47		23 22	00 02	00 32
Greenock West	d		19 50	19 59		20 24	20 50		21 24	21 50		22 24	22 50		23 24	00 05	00 35
Fort Matilda	d		19 53	20 02		20 27	20 53		21 27	21 53		22 29	22 53		23 29	00 08	00 38
Gourock	a		19 57	20 06		20 33	20 57		21 32	21 57		22 33	22 57		23 33	00 12	00 42

For general notes see front of timetable
For details of catering facilities see Directory of Train Operators

b Saturdays dep. 1 minute earlier

§ For authorised access to and from I.B.M. only

Table 219

Glasgow Central → Wemyss Bay and Gourock

Sundays

until 22 November

Network Diagram - see first page of Table 216

		SR	SR	SR	SR	SR	SR	SR	SR A	SR	
Glasgow Central 15 221	d	07 20	07 50	08 20	08 50	09 20	09 50	10 20	10 50	11 20	
Cardonald	d	07 27		08 27		09 27		10 27		11 27	
Hillington East	d	07 29	07 58	08 29	08 58	09 29	09 58	10 29	10 58	11 29	
Hillington West	d	07 31		08 31		09 31		10 31		11 31	
Paisley Gilmour Street 221 ⇌	d	07 35	08 03	08 35	09 03	09 35	10 03	10 35	11 03	11 35	and at
Paisley St James	d			08 37		09 37		10 37		11 37	
Bishopton	d	07 41	08 09	08 43	09 09	09 43	10 09	10 43	11 09	11 43	the same
Langbank	d			08 49		09 49		10 49		11 49	
Woodhall	d	07 49		08 53		09 53		10 53		11 53	minutes
Port Glasgow	d	07 52	08 19	08 56	09 19	09 56	10 19	10 56	11 19	11 56	past
Whinhill	d		08 23		09 23		10 23		11 23		
Drumfrochar	d		08 26		09 26		10 26		11 26		each
Branchton	d		08 29		09 29		10 29		11 29		
I.B.M. §	d		08 31		09 31		10 31		11 31		hour until
Inverkip	d		08 36		09 36		10 36		11 36		
Wemyss Bay	a		08 42		09 42		10 42		11 42		
Bogston	d	07 54		08 58		09 58		10 58		11 58	
Cartsdyke	d	07 56		09 00		10 00		11 00		12 00	
Greenock Central	d	07 58		09 02		10 02		11 02		12 02	
Greenock West	d	08 01		09 05		10 05		11 05		12 05	
Fort Matilda	d			09 08		10 08		11 08		12 08	
Gourock	a	08 06		09 12		10 12		11 12		12 12	

		SR	SR	SR	SR	SR	SR
Glasgow Central 15 221	d	19 20	19 50	20 20	21 20	22 20	23 20
Cardonald	d	19 27		20 27	21 27	22 27	23 27
Hillington East	d	19 29	19 58	20 29	21 29	22 29	23 29
Hillington West	d	19 31		20 31	21 31	22 31	23 31
Paisley Gilmour Street 221 ⇌	d	19 35	20 03	20 35	21 35	22 35	23 35
Paisley St James	d	19 37		20 37	21 37	22 37	23 37
Bishopton	d	19 43	20 09	20 43	21 43	22 43	23 43
Langbank	d	19 49		20 49	21 49	22 49	23 49
Woodhall	d	19 53		20 53	21 53	22 53	23 53
Port Glasgow	d	19 56	20 19	20 56	21 56	22 56	23 56
Whinhill	d		20 23				
Drumfrochar	d		20 26				
Branchton	d		20 29				
I.B.M. §	d		20 31				
Inverkip	d		20 36				
Wemyss Bay	a		20 42				
Bogston	d	19 58		20 58	21 58	22 58	23 58
Cartsdyke	d	20 00		21 00	22 00	23 00	23 59
Greenock Central	d	20 02		21 02	22 02	23 02	00 02
Greenock West	d	20 05		21 05	22 05	23 05	00 05
Fort Matilda	d	20 08		21 08	22 08	23 08	00 08
Gourock	a	20 12		21 12	22 12	23 12	00 12

Sundays

from 29 November

		SR	SR	SR	SR	SR	SR	SR	SR	SR	SR A	SR	SR	
Glasgow Central 15 221	d	07 20	07 50	08 20	08 50	09 20	09 35	09 50	10 20	10 35	10 50	11 20	11 35	
Cardonald	d	07 27		08 27		09 27	09 42		10 27	10 42		11 27	11 42	
Hillington East	d	07 29	07 58	08 29	08 58	09 29	09 44	09 58	10 29	10 44	10 58	11 29	11 44	
Hillington West	d	07 31		08 31		09 31	09 46		10 31	10 46		11 31	11 46	
Paisley Gilmour Street 221 ⇌	d	07 35	08 03	08 35	09 03	09 35	09 50	10 03	10 35	10 50	11 03	11 35	11 50	and at
Paisley St James	d			08 37		09 37	09 52		10 37	10 52		11 37	11 52	
Bishopton	d	07 41	08 09	08 43	09 09	09 43	09 58	10 09	10 43	10 58	11 09	11 43	11 58	the same
Langbank	d			08 49		09 49	10 04		10 49	11 04		11 49	12 04	
Woodhall	d	07 49		08 53		09 53	10 08		10 53	11 08		11 53	12 08	minutes
Port Glasgow	d	07 52	08 19	08 56	09 19	09 56	10 11	10 19	10 56	11 11	11 19	11 56	12 11	past
Whinhill	d		08 23		09 23			10 23			11 23			
Drumfrochar	d		08 26		09 26			10 26			11 26			each
Branchton	d		08 29		09 29			10 29			11 29			
I.B.M. §	d		08 31		09 31			10 31			11 31			hour until
Inverkip	d		08 36		09 36			10 36			11 36			
Wemyss Bay	a		08 42		09 42			10 42			11 42			
Bogston	d	07 54		08 58		09 58	10 13		10 58	11 13		11 58	12 13	
Cartsdyke	d	07 56		09 00		10 00	10 15		11 00	11 15		12 00	12 15	
Greenock Central	d	07 58		09 02		10 02	10 17		11 02	11 17		12 02	12 17	
Greenock West	d	08 01		09 05		10 05	10 20		11 05	11 20		12 05	12 20	
Fort Matilda	d			09 08		10 08	10 23		11 08	11 23		12 08	12 23	
Gourock	a	08 06		09 12		10 12	10 27		11 12	11 27		12 12	12 27	

		SR	SR	SR	SR	SR	SR	SR	SR	SR	SR
Glasgow Central 15 221	d	17 35	17 50	18 20	18 50	19 20	19 50	20 20	21 20	22 20	23 20
Cardonald	d	17 42		18 27		19 27		20 27	21 27	22 27	23 27
Hillington East	d	17 44	17 58	18 29	18 58	19 29	19 58	20 29	21 29	22 29	23 29
Hillington West	d	17 46		18 31		19 31		20 31	21 31	22 31	23 31
Paisley Gilmour Street 221 ⇌	d	17 50	18 03	18 35	19 03	19 35	20 03	20 35	21 35	22 35	23 35
Paisley St James	d	17 52		18 37		19 37		20 37	21 37	22 37	23 37
Bishopton	d	17 58	18 09	18 43	19 09	19 43	20 09	20 43	21 43	22 43	23 43
Langbank	d	18 04		18 49		19 49		20 49	21 49	22 49	23 49
Woodhall	d	18 08		18 53		19 53		20 53	21 53	22 53	23 53
Port Glasgow	d	18 11	18 19	18 56	19 19	19 56	20 19	20 56	21 56	22 56	23 56
Whinhill	d		18 23		19 23		20 23				
Drumfrochar	d		18 26		19 26		20 26				
Branchton	d		18 29		19 29		20 29				
I.B.M. §	d		18 31		19 31		20 31				
Inverkip	d		18 36		19 36		20 36				
Wemyss Bay	a		18 42		19 42		20 42				
Bogston	d	18 13		18 58		19 58		20 58	21 58	22 58	23 58
Cartsdyke	d	18 15		19 00		20 00		21 00	22 00	23 00	23 59
Greenock Central	d	18 17		19 02		20 02		21 02	22 02	23 02	00 02
Greenock West	d	18 20		19 05		20 05		21 05	22 05	23 05	00 05
Fort Matilda	d	18 23		19 08		20 08		21 08	22 08	23 08	00 08
Gourock	a	18 27		19 12		20 12		21 12	22 12	23 12	00 12

For general notes see front of timetable
For details of catering facilities see
Directory of Train Operators

§ For authorised access to and from I.B.M. only

A 1250 from Glasgow Central stops additionally at Hillington West dep. 1300

Gourock and Wemyss Bay → Glasgow Central

Network Diagram - see first page of Table 216

Miles	Miles		SR	SR SX	SR SO	SR SX	SR A	SR SX	SR SO	SR	SR SX	SR SO	SR SX	SR	SR	SR SX	SR	SR	SR	SR
0	—	**Gourock** d	06 05	06 22	06 36	06 44		07 06	07 06		07 22	07 36	07 47	07 52		08 08	08 24	08 36		09 06
1¼	—	Fort Matilda d	06 08	06 25	06 39	06 47		07 09	07 09		07 25	07 39		07 55		08 11	08 27	08 39		09 09
2½	—	Greenock West d	06 11	06 28	06 42	06 50		07 12	07 12		07 28	07 42	07 52	07 58		08 14	08 30	08 42		09 12
3¼	—	Greenock Central d	06 14	06 31	06 45	06 53		07 15	07 15		07 31	07 45	07 55	08 01		08 17	08 33	08 45		09 15
4¼	—	Cartsdyke d	06 16	06 33	06 47	06 55		07 17	07 17		07 33	07 47		08 03			08 35	08 47		09 17
5	—	Bogston d		06 35	06 49	06 57		07 19	07 19		07 35	07 49		08 05			08 37	08 49		09 19
—	0	**Wemyss Bay** d								07 13					07 50				08 50	
—	2¼	Inverkip d								07 18					07 54				08 54	
—	4¾	I.B.M. § d								07 23					07 59				08 59	
—	6¼	Branchton d								07 25					08 02				09 02	
—	8	Drumfrochar d								07 28					08 04				09 04	
—	8½	Whinhill d								07 30					08 07				09 07	
6	10¾	Port Glasgow d	06 19	06 38	06 52	07 00		07 22	07 22	07 35	07 38	07 52	07 59	08 08	08 11	08 21	08 40	08 52	09 11	09 22
7¼	12	Woodhall d		06 40	06 54	07 02			07 24	07 37	07 40	07 54		08 10	08 14		08 42	08 54		09 24
10	14¾	Langbank d		06 45	06 59	07 07			07 29		07 45	07 59			08 18		08 47	08 59		09 29
14	18	Bishopton d	06 28	06 50	07 04	07 12		07 31	07 34	07 45	07 50	08 04	08 08	08 18	08 24	08 30	08 52	09 04	09 20	09 34
18¼	22¼	Paisley St James d	06 34	06 56	07 10	07 18			07 40		07 56	08 10			08 29		08 58	09 10		09 40
19	23	Paisley Gilmour Street 221 ⇌ d	06 37	06 59	07 13	07 21	07 34	07 38	07 43	07 52	07 59	08 13	08 15	08 25	08 32	08 37	09 01	09 13	09 27	09 43
21¼	25¼	Hillington West d	06 40	07 02	07 16	07 24	07 38	07 41	07 46	07 55	08 02	08 16	08 18	08 28			09 04	09 16		09 46
21¾	25¾	Hillington East d	06 42	07 04	07 18	07 26		07 43	07 48	07 57	08 04	08 18	08 20	08 30			09 06	09 18		09 48
22½	26½	Cardonald d	06 44	07 06	07 20	07 28		07 45	07 50	07 59	08 06	08 20	08 22	08 32			09 08	09 20		09 50
26½	31	**Glasgow Central** 15 221 a	06 52	07 14	07 28	07 36	07 47	07 54	07 58	08 07	08 14	08 28	08 30	08 40	08 44	08 48	09 16	09 28	09 38	09 58

	SR		SR	SR	SR	SR	SR	SR	SR	SR	SR	SR	SR	SR	SR	SR	SR	SR	SR
Gourock d	09 23		14 23	14 36		15 06	15 23	15 36		16 06	16 23	16 36		17 06	17 23	17 45		18 06	18 23
Fort Matilda d	09 26		14 26	14 39		15 09	15 26	15 39		16 09	16 26	16 39		17 09	17 26	17 48		18 09	18 26
Greenock West d	09 29		14 29	14 42		15 12	15 29	15 42		16 12	16 29	16 42		17 12	17 29	17 51		18 12	18 29
Greenock Central d	09 32		14 32	14 45		15 15	15 32	15 45		16 15	16 32	16 45		17 15	17 32	17 54		18 15	18 32
Cartsdyke d				14 47		15 17		15 47		16 17		16 47		17 17		17 56		18 17	
Bogston d		and at		14 49		15 19		15 49		16 19		16 49		17 19		17 58		18 19	
Wemyss Bay d		the same			14 50				15 55				16 45				17 49		
Inverkip d		minutes			14 54				15 59				16 49				17 53		
I.B.M. § d		past			14 59				16 04				16 54				18 02		
Branchton d		each			15 02				16 07				16 57				18 04		
Drumfrochar d		hour until			15 04				16 09				16 59				18 07		
Whinhill d					15 07				16 12				17 02				18 09		
Port Glasgow d	09 36		14 36	14 52	15 11	15 22	15 36	15 52	16 16	16 22	16 36	16 52	17 06	17 22	17 36	18 01	18 14	18 22	18 36
Woodhall d				14 54		15 24		15 54		16 24		16 54		17 24		18 03		18 24	
Langbank d				14 59		15 29		15 59		16 29		16 59		17 29		18 08		18 29	
Bishopton d	09 45		14 45	15 04	15 20	15 34	15 45	16 04	16 25	16 34	16 45	17 04	17 15	17 34	17 45	18 13	18 23	18 34	18 45
Paisley St James d				15 10		15 40		16 10		16 40		17 10		17 40		18 19		18 40	
Paisley Gilmour Street 221 ⇌ d	09 52		14 52	15 13	15 27	15 43	15 52	16 13	16 32	16 43	16 52	17 13	17 22	17 43	17 52	18 22	18 31	18 43	18 52
Hillington West d				15 16		15 46	15 55	16 16		16 46	16 55	17 16		17 46		18 25		18 46	
Hillington East d				15 18		15 48		16 18		16 48		17 18		17 48		18 27		18 48	
Cardonald d				15 20		15 50		16 20		16 50		17 20		17 50		18 29		18 50	
Glasgow Central 15 221 a	10 03		15 03	15 27	15 38	15 58	16 05	16 28	16 43	16 58	17 05	17 28	17 33	17 58	18 03	18 39	18 43	18 58	19 03

	SR	SR	SR	SR	SR	SR	SR	SR	SR	SR	SR	SR	SR SX	SR SO	SR	SR	SR	SR	SR SO
Gourock d		18 40		19 06	19 20	19 45		20 20	20 47		21 20	21 45			22 20	22 45		23 20	
Fort Matilda d		18 43		19 09	19 23	19 48		20 23	20 50		21 23	21 48			22 23	22 48		23 23	
Greenock West d		18 46		19 12	19 26	19 51		20 26	20 53		21 26	21 51			22 26	22 51		23 26	
Greenock Central d		18 49		19 15	19 29	19 54		20 29	20 56		21 29	21 54			22 29	22 54		23 29	
Cartsdyke d		18 51		19 17	19 31	19 56		20 31	20 58		21 31	21 56			22 31	22 56		23 31	
Bogston d		18 53		19 19	19 33			20 33			21 33				22 33			23 33	
Wemyss Bay d	18 23		18 55				19 45			20 44			21 44	21 50			22 44		23 40
Inverkip d	18 27		18 59				19 48			20 48			21 48	21 54			22 48		23 44
I.B.M. § d	18 36		19 04				19 53			20 53			21 53	21 59			22 53		23 49
Branchton d	18 38		19 07				19 56			20 56			21 56	22 02			22 56		23 52
Drumfrochar d	18 41		19 09				19 58			20 58			21 58	22 04			22 58		23 54
Whinhill d	18 43		19 12				20 01			21 01			22 01	22 07			23 01		23 57
Port Glasgow d	18 48	18 56	19 16	19 22	19 36	19 59	20 06	20 36	21 01	21 06	21 36	21 59	22 06	22 11	22 36	22 59	23 06	23 36	00 01
Woodhall d		18 58		19 24	19 38		20 08	20 38		21 08	21 38		22 08	22 14	22 38		23 08	23 38	
Langbank d		19 03		19 29	19 43		20 13	20 43		21 13	21 43		22 13	22 18	22 43		23 13	23 43	
Bishopton d	18 57	19 08	19 25	19 34	19 48	20 08	20 18	20 48	21 10	21 18	21 48	22 08	22 18	22 24	22 48	23 08	23 18	23 48	00 10
Paisley St James d		19 14		19 40	19 54		20 24	20 54		21 24	21 54		22 24	22 29	22 54		23 24	23 54	
Paisley Gilmour Street 221 ⇌ d	19 03	19 17	19 32	19 43	19 57	20 15	20 27	20 57	21 18	21 27	21 57	22 15	22 27	22 32	22 57	23 17	23 27	23 57	00 17
Hillington West d		19 20		19 46	20 00		20 30	21 00		21 30	22 00		22 30	22 35	23 00		23 30	00 01	
Hillington East d		19 22		19 48	20 02		20 32	21 02		21 32	22 02		22 32	22 37	23 02		23 32	00 02	
Cardonald d		19 24		19 50	20 04		20 34	21 04		21 34	22 04		22 34	22 39	23 04		23 34	00 04	
Glasgow Central 15 221 a	19 15	19 32	19 43	19 58	20 12	20 26	20 43	21 12	21 29	21 42	22 14	22 26	22 42	22 46	23 14	23 28	23 42	00 12	00 28

For general notes see front of timetable
For details of catering facilities see
Directory of Train Operators

A From Largs (Table 221)

§ For authorised access to and from I.B.M. only

Table 219

Sundays until 22 November

Gourock and Wemyss Bay → Glasgow Central

Network Diagram - see first page of Table 216

		SR	SR	SR	SR	SR	SR	SR	SR	SR	SR	SR	SR	SR
Gourock	d	08 23		09 23		10 23		11 23		12 23		13 23		14 23
Fort Matilda	d	08 26		09 26		10 26		11 26		12 26		13 26		14 26
Greenock West	d	08 29		09 29		10 29		11 29		12 29		13 29		14 29
Greenock Central	d	08 32		09 32		10 32		11 32		12 32		13 32		14 32
Cartsdyke	d	08 34		09 34		10 34		11 34		12 34		13 34		14 34
Bogston	d	08 36		09 36		10 36		11 36		12 36		13 36		14 36
Wemyss Bay	d		08 50		09 50		10 55		11 50		12 50		13 50	
Inverkip	d		08 54		09 54		10 59		11 54		12 54		13 54	
I.B.M. §	d		08 59		09 59		11 04		11 59		12 59		13 59	
Branchton	d		09 02		10 02		11 07		12 02		13 02		14 02	
Drumfrochar	d		09 04		10 04		11 09		12 04		13 04		14 04	
Whinhill	d		09 07		10 07		11 12		12 07		13 07		14 07	
Port Glasgow	d	08 39	09 11	09 39	10 11	10 39	11 16	11 39	12 11	12 39	13 11	13 39	14 11	14 39
Woodhall	d	08 41		09 41		10 41		11 41		12 41		13 41		14 41
Langbank	d	08 46		09 46		10 46		11 46		12 46		13 46		14 46
Bishopton	d	08 51	09 20	09 51	10 20	10 51	11 25	11 51	12 20	12 51	13 20	13 51	14 20	14 51
Paisley St James	d	08 57		09 57		10 57		11 57		12 57		13 57		14 57
Paisley Gilmour Street 221 ✈	d	09 00	09 28	10 00	10 28	11 00	11 32	12 00	12 28	13 00	13 27	14 00	14 27	15 00
Hillington West	d	09 03		10 03		11 03		12 03		13 03		14 03		15 03
Hillington East	d	09 05	09 32	10 05	10 32	11 05	11 36	12 05	12 32	13 05	13 31	14 05	14 31	15 05
Cardonald	d	09 07		10 07		11 07		12 07		13 07		14 07		15 07
Glasgow Central 15	221 a	09 15	09 40	10 15	10 40	11 15	11 46	12 15	12 40	13 15	13 40	14 15	14 40	15 15

		SR	SR	SR	SR	SR	SR	SR	SR	SR	SR	SR	SR	SR	SR	SR
Gourock	d		15 23		16 23		17 23		18 23		19 23		20 23		21 23	22 23
Fort Matilda	d		15 26		16 26		17 26		18 26		19 26		20 26		21 26	22 26
Greenock West	d		15 29		16 29		17 29		18 29		19 29		20 29		21 29	22 29
Greenock Central	d		15 32		16 32		17 32		18 32		19 32		20 32		21 32	22 32
Cartsdyke	d		15 34		16 34		17 34		18 34		19 34		20 34		21 34	22 34
Bogston	d		15 36		16 36		17 36		18 36		19 36		20 36		21 36	22 36
Wemyss Bay	d	14 50		15 55		16 50		17 50		18 55		19 50		20 50		
Inverkip	d	14 54		15 59		16 54		17 54		18 59		19 54		20 54		
I.B.M. §	d	14 59		16 04		16 59		17 59		19 04		19 59		20 59		
Branchton	d	15 02		16 07		17 02		18 02		19 07		20 02		21 02		
Drumfrochar	d	15 04		16 09		17 04		18 04		19 09		20 04		21 04		
Whinhill	d	15 07		16 12		17 07		18 07		19 12		20 07		21 07		
Port Glasgow	d	15 11	15 39	16 16	16 39	17 11	17 39	18 11	18 39	19 16	19 39	20 11	20 39	21 11	21 39	22 39
Woodhall	d		15 41		16 41		17 41		18 41		19 41		20 41		21 41	22 41
Langbank	d		15 46		16 46		17 46		18 46		19 46		20 46		21 46	22 46
Bishopton	d	15 20	15 51	16 25	16 51	17 20	17 51	18 20	18 51	19 25	19 51	20 20	20 51	21 20	21 51	22 51
Paisley St James	d		15 57		16 57		17 57		18 57		19 57		20 57		21 57	22 57
Paisley Gilmour Street 221 ✈	d	15 27	16 00	16 32	17 00	17 27	18 00	18 27	19 00	19 32	20 00	20 27	21 00	21 27	22 00	23 00
Hillington West	d		16 03		17 03		18 03		19 03		20 03		21 03		22 03	23 03
Hillington East	d	15 31	16 05	16 36	17 05	17 31	18 05	18 31	19 05	19 36	20 05	20 31	21 05	21 31	22 05	23 05
Cardonald	d		16 07		17 07		18 07		19 07		20 07		21 07		22 07	23 07
Glasgow Central 15	221 a	15 40	16 15	16 45	17 15	17 40	18 15	18 40	19 15	19 44	20 15	20 40	21 15	21 40	22 15	23 15

Sundays from 29 November

		SR	SR	SR	SR	SR	SR	SR	SR	SR	SR	SR	SR	SR	SR	SR	SR	SR	SR	SR
Gourock	d	08 23		09 23	09 36		10 23	10 36		11 23	11 36		12 23	12 36		13 23	13 36		14 23	14 36
Fort Matilda	d	08 26		09 26	09 39		10 26	10 39		11 26	11 39		12 26	12 39		13 26	13 39		14 26	14 39
Greenock West	d	08 29		09 29	09 42		10 29	10 42		11 29	11 42		12 29	12 42		13 29	13 42		14 29	14 42
Greenock Central	d	08 32		09 32	09 45		10 32	10 45		11 32	11 45		12 32	12 45		13 32	13 45		14 32	14 45
Cartsdyke	d	08 34		09 34	09 47		10 34	10 47		11 34	11 47		12 34	12 47		13 34	13 47		14 34	14 47
Bogston	d	08 36		09 36	09 49		10 36	10 49		11 36	11 49		12 36	12 49		13 36	13 49		14 36	14 49
Wemyss Bay	d		08 50			09 50			10 55			11 50			12 50			13 50		
Inverkip	d		08 54			09 54			10 59			11 54			12 54			13 54		
I.B.M. §	d		08 59			09 59			11 04			11 59			12 59			13 59		
Branchton	d		09 02			10 02			11 07			12 02			13 02			14 02		
Drumfrochar	d		09 04			10 04			11 09			12 04			13 04			14 04		
Whinhill	d		09 07			10 07			11 12			12 07			13 07			14 07		
Port Glasgow	d	08 39	09 11	09 39	09 52	10 11	10 39	10 52	11 16	11 39	11 52	12 11	12 39	12 52	13 11	13 39	13 52	14 11	14 39	14 52
Woodhall	d	08 41		09 41	09 54		10 41	10 54		11 41	11 54		12 41	12 54		13 41	13 54		14 41	14 54
Langbank	d	08 46		09 46	09 59		10 46	10 59		11 46	11 59		12 46	12 59		13 46	13 59		14 46	14 59
Bishopton	d	08 51	09 20	09 51	10 04	10 20	10 51	11 04	11 25	11 51	12 04	12 20	12 51	13 04	13 20	13 51	14 04	14 20	14 51	15 04
Paisley St James	d	08 57		09 57	10 10		10 57	11 10		11 57	12 10		12 57	13 10		13 57	14 10		14 57	15 10
Paisley Gilmour Street 221 ✈	d	09 00	09 28	10 00	10 13	10 28	11 00	11 13	11 32	12 00	12 13	12 28	13 00	13 13	13 27	14 00	14 13	14 27	15 00	15 13
Hillington West	d	09 03		10 03	10 16		11 03	11 16		12 03	12 16		13 03	13 18		14 03	14 16		15 03	15 16
Hillington East	d	09 05	09 32	10 05	10 19	10 32	11 05	11 18	11 36	12 05	12 18	12 32	13 05	13 20	13 31	14 05	14 18	14 31	15 05	15 18
Cardonald	d	09 07		10 07	10 20		11 07	11 20		12 07	12 20		13 07	13 22		14 07	14 20		15 07	15 20
Glasgow Central 15	221 a	09 15	09 40	10 15	10 28	10 40	11 15	11 28	11 46	12 15	12 28	12 40	13 15	13 30	13 40	14 15	14 28	14 40	15 15	15 28

For general notes see front of timetable
For details of catering facilities see
Directory of Train Operators

§ For authorised access to and from I.B.M. only

Sundays

from 29 November

Gourock and Wemyss Bay → Glasgow Central

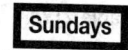

Network Diagram - see first page of Table 216

		SR	SR	SR	SR	SR	SR	SR	SR	SR	SR	SR	SR	SR	SR	SR	SR	SR	SR
Gourock	d	-	15 23	15 36	-	16 23	16 36	-	17 23	17 36	-	18 23	-	19 23	-	20 23	-	21 23	22 23
Fort Matilda	d	-	15 26	15 39	-	16 26	16 39	-	17 26	17 39	-	18 26	-	19 26	-	20 26	-	21 26	22 26
Greenock West	d	-	15 29	15 42	-	16 29	16 42	-	17 29	17 42	-	18 29	-	19 29	-	20 29	-	21 29	22 29
Greenock Central	d	-	15 32	15 45	-	16 32	16 45	-	17 32	17 45	-	18 32	-	19 32	-	20 32	-	21 32	22 32
Cartsdyke	d	-	15 34	15 47	-	16 34	16 47	-	17 34	17 47	-	18 34	-	19 34	-	20 34	-	21 34	22 34
Bogston	d	-	15 36	15 49	-	16 36	16 49	-	17 36	17 49	-	18 36	-	19 36	-	20 36	-	21 36	22 36
Wemyss Bay	d	14 50	-	-	15 55	-	-	16 50	-	-	17 50	-	18 55	-	19 50	-	20 50	-	-
Inverkip	d	14 54	-	-	15 59	-	-	16 54	-	-	17 54	-	18 59	-	19 54	-	20 54	-	-
I.B.M. §	d	14 59	-	-	16 04	-	-	16 59	-	-	17 59	-	19 04	-	19 59	-	20 59	-	-
Branchton	d	15 02	-	-	16 07	-	-	17 02	-	-	18 02	-	19 07	-	20 02	-	21 02	-	-
Drumfrochar	d	15 04	-	-	16 09	-	-	17 04	-	-	18 04	-	19 09	-	20 04	-	21 04	-	-
Whinhill	d	15 07	-	-	16 12	-	-	17 07	-	-	18 07	-	19 12	-	20 07	-	21 07	-	-
Port Glasgow	d	15 11	15 39	15 52	16 16	16 39	16 52	17 11	17 39	17 52	18 11	18 39	19 16	19 39	20 11	20 39	21 11	21 39	22 39
Woodhall	d	-	15 41	15 54	-	16 41	16 54	-	17 41	17 54	-	18 41	-	19 41	-	20 41	-	21 41	22 41
Langbank	d	-	15 46	15 59	-	16 46	16 59	-	17 46	17 59	-	18 46	-	19 46	-	20 46	-	21 46	22 46
Bishopton	d	15 20	15 51	16 04	16 25	16 51	17 04	17 20	17 51	18 04	18 20	18 51	19 25	19 51	20 20	20 51	21 20	21 51	22 51
Paisley St James	d	-	15 57	16 10	-	16 57	17 10	-	17 57	18 10	-	18 57	-	19 57	-	20 57	-	21 57	22 57
Paisley Gilmour Street 221 ✈	d	15 27	16 00	16 13	16 32	17 00	17 13	17 27	18 00	18 13	18 27	19 00	19 32	20 00	20 27	21 00	21 27	22 00	23 00
Hillington West	d	-	16 03	16 16	-	17 03	17 16	-	18 03	18 16	-	19 03	-	20 03	-	21 03	-	22 03	23 03
Hillington East	d	15 31	16 05	16 18	16 36	17 05	17 18	17 31	18 05	18 18	18 31	19 05	19 36	20 05	20 31	21 05	21 31	22 05	23 05
Cardonald	d	-	16 07	16 20	-	17 07	17 20	-	18 07	18 20	-	19 07	-	20 07	-	21 07	-	22 07	23 07
Glasgow Central 15 221	a	15 40	16 15	16 28	16 45	17 15	17 28	17 40	18 15	18 28	18 40	19 15	19 44	20 15	20 40	21 15	21 40	22 15	23 15

For general notes see front of timetable
For details of catering facilities see Directory of Train Operators

§ For authorised access to and from I.B.M. only

Glasgow and Gourock → Dunoon, Kilcreggan and Helensburgh Pier

Cowal Ferries Ltd in association with First ScotRail Limited

All Kilcreggan and Helensburgh Pier sailings operated by Clyde Marine Motoring Ltd. Tel 01475 721281

Mondays to Saturdays until 24 October

			SX		SX	SX		SX																		
Glasgow Central 15	219 d	05 55	05 55		06 25	06 25		06 55	07 05		07 25	07 35		08 25	09 05		09 25	10 25		10 35	11 25		11 25	12 25		13 25
Paisley Gilmour Street	219 d	06 07	06 07		06 36	06 36		07 07	07 20		07 40	07 50		08 36	09 20		09 36	10 36		10 50	11 36		11 36	12 36		13 36
Gourock	219 a	06 36	06 36		07 13	07 13		07 39	07 57		08 13	08 27		09 07	09 58		10 06	11 06		11 27	12 06		12 06	13 06		14 06
Gourock	⛴ d	06 50	07 00		07 20	07 30		07 50	08 05		08 20	08 35		09 20	10 05		10 20	11 20		11 35	12 20		12 25	13 20		14 15
Dunoon	⛴ a	07 13			07 43			08 13			08 43			09 43			10 43	11 43			12 43			13 43		
Kilcreggan	⛴ a		07 12			07 42			08 17						10 20					11 47			12 37			14 30
Helensburgh Pier	⛴ a											09 05			10 45											14 55

														SX												
Glasgow Central 15	219 d	13 25	14 25		14 35	15 25		15 25	15 35		16 05	16 23		16 23	17 25		17 25	18 25		19 25						
Paisley Gilmour Street	219 d	13 36	14 36		14 50	15 36		15 36	15 50		16 20	16 38		16 38	17 36		17 36	18 36		19 36						
Gourock	219 a	14 06	15 06		15 27	16 06		16 06	16 27		16 57	17 15		17 15	18 05		18 05	19 06		20 06						
Gourock	⛴ d	14 20	15 20		15 45	16 15		16 20	16 50		17 20	17 25		17 45	18 10		18 20	19 20		20 18						
Dunoon	⛴ a	14 43	15 43					16 43			17 43			18 08			18 43	19 43		20 41						
Kilcreggan	⛴ a				15 57	16 27			17 03			17 37			18 25											
Helensburgh Pier	⛴ a														18 50											

Sundays until 18 October

Glasgow Central 15	219 d	07 20	08 20	09 20		09 20	10 20	10 20		11 20	11 20	12 20		13 20	13 20	14 20		14 20	15 20	16 20		17 20	18 20	19 20		
Paisley Gilmour Street	219 d	07 35	08 35	09 35		09 35	10 35	10 35		11 35	11 35	12 35		13 35	13 35	14 35		14 35	15 35	16 35		17 35	18 35	19 35		
Gourock	219 a	08 06	09 12	10 12		10 12	11 12	11 12		12 12	12 12	13 12		14 12	14 12	15 12		15 12	16 12	17 12		18 12	19 12	20 12		
Gourock	⛴ d	08 20	09 20	10 20		11 15	11 20	11 45		12 20	13 15	13 20		14 20	14 25	15 20		16 15	16 20	17 20		18 20	19 20	20 18		
Dunoon	⛴ a	08 43	09 43	10 43			11 43			12 43		13 43		14 43		15 43			16 43	17 43		18 43	19 43	20 41		
Kilcreggan	⛴ a					11 27									14 40			16 27								
Helensburgh Pier	⛴ a							12 15			13 45				15 10											

For general notes see front of timetable
For details of catering facilities see Directory of Train Operators

For details of sailings from 25 October 2009 telephone Cowal Ferries on 08000 66 5000

Table 219A

SHIPPING SERVICES

Mondays to Saturdays

until 24 October

Helensburgh Pier, Kilcreggan and Dunoon → Gourock and Glasgow

Cowal Ferries Ltd in association with First ScotRail Limited

All Helenburgh Pier and Kilcreggan sailings operated by Clyde Marine Motoring Ltd. Tel 01475 721281

		SX	SX			SX		SX			SX															
Helensburgh Pier	⛴ d													09 10				10 50								
Kilcreggan	⛴ d		07 15			07 50			08 20					09 40				11 15		11 50			12 45			
Dunoon	⛴ d	06 50			07 20			07 50			08 20	08 50			09 50		10 50				11 50			12 50		13 50
Gourock	⛴ a	07 13	07 27		07 43	08 02		08 13	08 32		08 43	09 13		09 52	10 13		11 13	11 27		12 02	12 13		12 57	13 13		14 13
Gourock	219 d	07 22	07 47		07 52	08 08		08 24	09 06		09 06	09 23		10 06	10 23		11 23	11 36		12 23	12 23		13 06	13 23		14 23
Paisley Gilmour Street	219 d	07 58	08 14		08 24	08 36		09 00	09 42		09 42	09 51		10 42	10 51		11 51	12 12		12 51	12 51		13 42	13 51		14 51
Glasgow Central 15	219 a	08 14	08 30		08 40	08 48		09 16	09 58		09 58	10 03		10 58	11 03		12 03	12 28		13 03	13 03		13 58	14 03		15 03

															SX											
Helensburgh Pier	⛴ d		15 00															18 55								
Kilcreggan	⛴ d		15 30			16 00		16 30			17 05	17 40						19 20								
Dunoon	⛴ d	14 50			15 50				16 50					17 50	18 15		18 50			19 50	20 45					
Gourock	⛴ a	15 13	15 42		16 13	16 12		16 42	17 13		17 17	17 52		18 13	18 38		19 13	19 32		20 13	21 08					
Gourock	219 d	15 23	16 06		16 23	16 23		17 06	17 23		17 23	18 06		18 23	19 06		19 20	19 45		20 20	21 20					
Paisley Gilmour Street	219 d	15 51	16 42		16 51	16 51		17 42	17 51		17 51	18 42		18 51	19 42		19 56	20 14		20 56	21 56					
Glasgow Central 15	219 a	16 05	16 58		17 05	17 05		17 58	18 03		18 03	18 58		19 03	19 58		20 12	20 26		21 12	22 14					

Sundays

until 18 October

Helensburgh Pier	⛴ d							12 20				13 50			15 15											
Kilcreggan	⛴ d					11 30									15 45			16 30								
Dunoon	⛴ d	08 50	09 50	10 50			11 50			12 50	13 50			14 50		15 50			16 50	17 50		18 50	19 50	20 45		
Gourock	⛴ a	09 13	10 13	11 13		11 42	12 13	12 50		13 13	14 13	14 20		15 13	15 57	16 13		16 42	17 13	18 13		19 13	20 13	21 08		
Gourock	219 d	09 23	10 23	11 23		12 23	12 23	13 23		13 23	14 23	15 23		15 23	16 23	17 23		17 23	17 23	18 23		19 23	20 23	21 23		
Paisley Gilmour Street	219 d	09 59	10 59	11 59		12 59	12 59	13 59		13 59	14 59	15 59		15 59	16 59	17 59		17 59	17 59	18 59		19 59	20 59	21 59		
Glasgow Central 15	219 a	10 15	11 15	12 15		13 15	13 15	14 15		14 15	15 15	16 15		16 15	17 15	18 15		18 15	18 15	19 15		20 15	21 15	22 15		

For general notes see front of timetable
For details of catering facilities see Directory of Train Operators

For details of sailings from 25 October 2009 telephone Cowal Ferries on 08000 66 5000

Glasgow and Wemyss Bay — Rothesay (Bute)

Caledonian MacBrayne Ltd in association with First ScotRail Limited

Mondays to Saturdays
until 24 October

		SX															SX	SX		SX	SX	SX	FSO	SO A		
Glasgow Central 15	219 d	06 05	06 32		07 50	08 50		09 50	10 50		11 50	12 50		13 50	14 50		15 50	16 33		17 15	17 50	18 50	19 38	20 35		
Paisley Gilmour Street	219 d	06 19	06 47		08 02	09 01		10 01	11 01		12 01	13 01		14 01	15 01		16 02	16 48		17 29	18 01	19 01	19 53	20 50		
Wemyss Bay	219 a	06 58	07 30		08 40	09 40		10 40	11 40		12 40	13 40		14 40	15 40		16 40	17 25		18 08	18 41	19 40	20 37	21 34		
Wemyss Bay	⛴ d	07 15	08 00		08 45	10 15		11 00	12 15		13 00	13 45		15 15	16 00		16 45	17 30		18 15	19 00	19 45	20 45	22 00		
Rothesay	⛴ a	07 50	08 35		09 20	10 50		11 35	12 50		13 35	14 20		15 50	16 35		17 20	18 05		18 50	19 35	20 20	21 20	22 35		

Sundays
until 8 October

Glasgow Central 15	219 d	07 50		08 50		09 50		10 50		11 50		12 50		14 50		15 50		16 50		17 50		18 50				
Paisley Gilmour Street	219 d	08 03		09 03		10 03		11 03		12 03		13 03		15 03		16 03		17 03		18 03		19 03				
Wemyss Bay	219 a	08 42		09 42		10 42		11 42		12 43		13 42		15 42		16 42		17 42		18 42		19 42				
Wemyss Bay	⛴ d	08 45		10 15		11 00		12 15		13 00		14 30		16 00		17 30		18 15		19 00		19 45				
Rothesay	⛴ a	09 20		10 50		11 35		12 50		13 35		15 05		16 35		18 05		18 50		19 35		20 20				

Mondays to Saturdays
until 24 October

		SX																					FSO	SO A		
Rothesay	⛴ d	06 30	07 00		08 00	08 45		10 10	11 00		11 50	13 00		13 45	15 15		16 00	16 45		17 30	18 15	19 00	19 45	21 10		
Wemyss Bay	⛴ a	07 05	07 35		08 35	09 20		10 45	11 35		12 25	13 35		14 20	15 50		16 35	17 20		18 05	18 50	19 35	20 20	21 45		
Wemyss Bay	219 d	07 13	07 50		08 50	09 50		10 55	11 50		12 50	13 50		14 50	15 55		16 45	17 49		18 23	18 55	19 45	20 44	21 50		
Paisley Gilmour Street	219 d	07 51	08 31		09 26	10 26		11 31	12 26		13 26	14 25		15 26	16 31		17 21	18 30		19 02	19 31	20 26	21 26	22 31		
Glasgow Central 15	219 a	08 07	08 44		09 38	10 38		11 43	12 38		13 38	14 38		15 38	16 43		17 33	18 43		19 15	19 43	20 43	21 42	22 46		

Sundays
until 18 October

Rothesay	⛴ d	08 00		10 10		11 00		11 50		13 00		13 45		15 15		16 00		16 45		18 15		19 00		19 45		
Wemyss Bay	⛴ a	08 35		10 45		11 35		12 25		13 35		14 20		15 50		16 35		17 20		18 50		19 35		20 20		
Wemyss Bay	219 d	08 50		10 55		11 50		12 50		13 50		14 50		15 55		16 50		17 50		18 55		19 50		20 50		
Paisley Gilmour Street	219 d	09 27		11 31		12 27		13 26		14 26		15 26		16 31		17 26		18 26		19 31		20 26		21 26		
Glasgow Central 15	219 a	09 40		11 46		12 40		13 40		14 40		15 40		16 45		17 40		18 40		19 44		20 40		21 40		

A 6 June to 22 August

For general notes see front of timetable
For details of catering facilities see
Directory of Train Operators

For details of sailings from 25 October 2009 telephone Caledonian MacBrayne on 08000 66 5000

Network Diagram for Tables 220, 223, 224, 226, 232

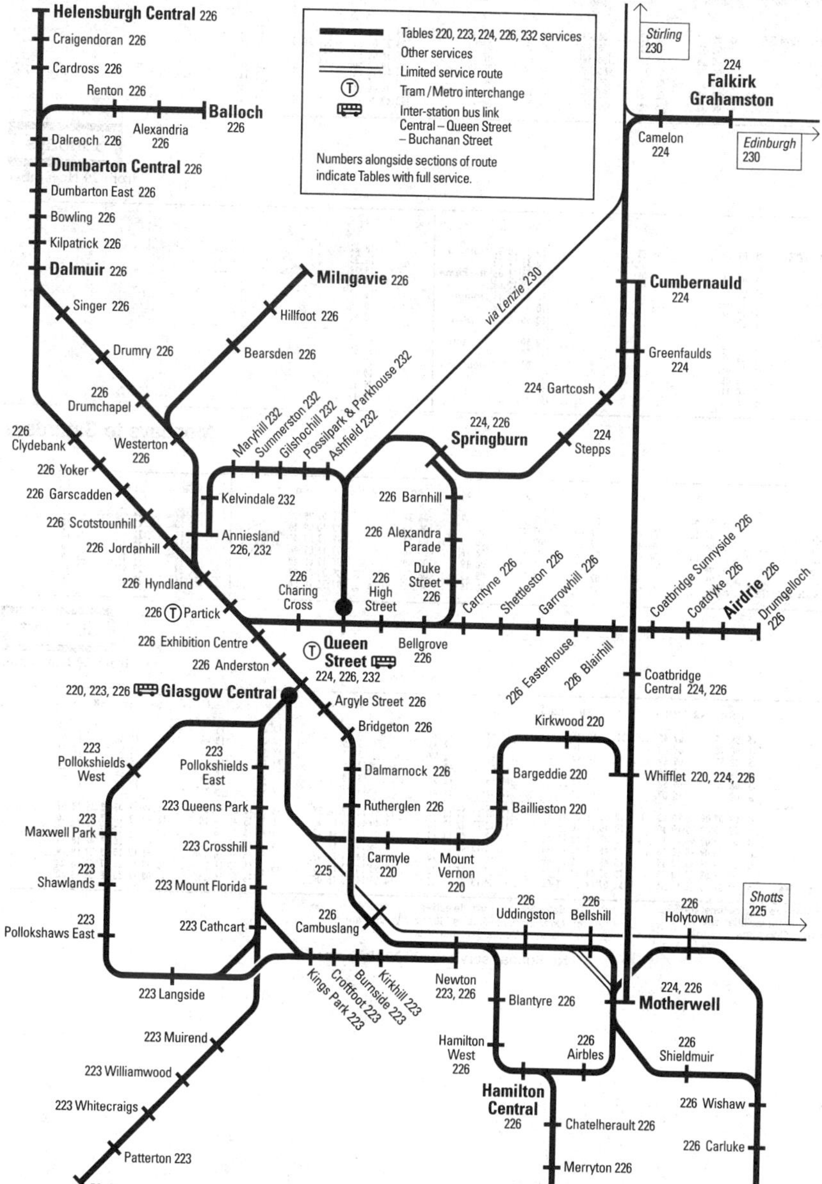

Tables 220, 223, 224, 226, 232 services
Other services
Limited service route
Tram / Metro interchange
Inter-station bus link Central – Queen Street – Buchanan Street
Numbers alongside sections of route indicate Tables with full service.
Helensburgh Central 226
Craigendoran 226
Cardross 226
Renton 226
Balloch 226
Alexandria 226
Dalreoch 226
Dumbarton Central 226
Dumbarton East 226
Bowling 226
Kilpatrick 226
Dalmuir 226
Singer 226
Drumry 226
226 Drumchapel
226 Clydebank
Westerton 226
226 Yoker
226 Garscadden
226 Scotstounhill
226 Jordanhill
226 Hyndland
226 Partick
226 Exhibition Centre
226 Anderston
220, 223, 226 Glasgow Central
Milngavie 226
Hillfoot 226
Bearsden 226
Maryhill 232
Summerston 232
Gilshochill 232
Possilpark & Parkhouse 232
Ashfield 232
Kelvindale 232
Anniesland 226, 232
226 Charing Cross
Queen Street 224, 226, 232
226 High Street
Duke Street 226
226 Alexandra Parade
226 Barnhill
224, 226 Springburn
Bellgrove 226
Carntyne 226
Shettleston 226
Garrowhill 226
226 Easterhouse
226 Blairhill
Coatbridge Sunnyside 226
Coatdyke 226
Airdrie 226
Drumgelloch 226
via Lenzie 230
Stirling 230
224 Falkirk Grahamston
Camelon 224
Edinburgh 230
Cumbernauld 224
Greenfaulds 224
224 Gartcosh
224 Stepps
Coatbridge Central 224, 226
Kirkwood 220
Bargeddie 220
Baillieston 220
Whifflet 220, 224, 226
Argyle Street 226
Bridgeton 226
Dalmarnock 226
Rutherglen 226
Carmyle 220
Mount Vernon 220
225
226 Cambuslang
226 Uddingston
226 Bellshill
226 Holytown
Shotts 225
Newton 223, 226
Kirkhill 223
Burnside 223
Croftfoot 223
Kings Park 223
Blantyre 226
224, 226 Motherwell
Hamilton West 226
226 Airbles
226 Shieldmuir
Hamilton Central 226
Chatelherault 226
Merryton 226
226 Larkhall
226 Wishaw
226 Carluke
226 Lanark
223 Pollokshields West
223 Pollokshields East
223 Queens Park
223 Crosshill
223 Mount Florida
223 Cathcart
223 Maxwell Park
223 Shawlands
223 Pollokshaws East
223 Langside
223 Muirend
223 Williamwood
223 Whitecraigs
Patterton 223
Neilston 223

DM-36/05(2)
Design BAJS

Table 220

Mondays to Saturdays

Glasgow Central — Whifflet

Network Diagram - see first page of Table 220

Miles			SR SO	SR	SR	SR	SR	SR	SR		SR
0	**Glasgow Central** 15	d	00 13	06 13	06 43	07 13	07 43	08 13	08 43	and every 30 minutes until	23 13
5½	Carmyle	d	00 23	06 23	06 53	07 23	07 53	08 23	08 53		23 23
6¾	Mount Vernon	d	00 26	06 26	06 56	07 26	07 56	08 26	08 56		23 26
8	Baillieston	d	00 29	06 29	06 59	07 29	07 59	08 29	08 59		23 29
9¼	Bargeddie	d	00 32	06 32	07 02	07 32	08 02	08 32	09 02		23 32
10	Kirkwood	d	00 35	06 35	07 05	07 35	08 05	08 35	09 05		23 35
12½	**Whifflet**	a	00 42	06 44	07 12	07 45	08 12	08 42	09 12		23 42

Sundays

from 29 November

		SR	SR	SR	SR		SR
Glasgow Central 15	d	09 22	09 52	10 22	10 52	and at	18 22
Carmyle	d	09 33	10 02	10 33	11 02		18 33
Mount Vernon	d	09 36	10 05	10 36	11 05	the same	18 36
Baillieston	d	09 39	10 08	10 39	11 08		18 39
Bargeddie	d	09 42	10 11	10 42	11 11	minutes	18 42
Kirkwood	d	09 45	10 14	10 45	11 14		18 45
Whifflet	a	09 50	10 21	10 50	11 21	past	18 50
	d	09 50		10 50		each	18 50
Holytown	d	09 59		10 59		hour until	18 59
Carfin	d	10 01		11 01			19 01
Cleland	d	10 05		11 05			19 05
Hartwood	d	10 11		11 11			19 11
Shotts	a	10 17		11 17			19 17

Mondays to Saturdays

Miles			SR	SR	SR	SR	SR	SR	SR	SR		SR	SR	SR
0	**Whifflet**	d	06 07	06 37	07 07	07 37	08 07	08 37	09 07	09 37	and every 30 minutes until	22 07	22 37	23 07
2½	Kirkwood	d	06 10	06 40	07 10	07 40	08 10	08 40	09 10	09 40		22 10	22 40	23 10
3¼	Bargeddie	d	06 13	06 43	07 13	07 43	08 13	08 43	09 13	09 43		22 13	22 43	23 13
4½	Baillieston	d	06 16	06 46	07 16	07 46	08 16	08 46	09 16	09 46		22 16	22 46	23 16
5¾	Mount Vernon	d	06 19	06 49	07 19	07 49	08 19	08 49	09 19	09 49		22 19	22 49	23 19
7	Carmyle	d	06 23	06 53	07 23	07 53	08 23	08 53	09 23	09 53		22 23	22 53	23 23
12½	**Glasgow Central** 15	a	06 36	07 06	07 36	08 06	08 36	09b05	09c36	10 06		22 36	23 06	23 36

Sundays

from 29 November

		SR	SR	SR	SR	SR	SR	SR	SR	SR	SR	SR	SR	SR	SR	SR	SR	SR	SR	SR
Shotts	d	08 45		09 45		10 45		11 45		12 45		13 45		14 45		15 45		16 45		17 45
Hartwood	d	08 48		09 48		10 48		11 48		12 48		13 48		14 48		15 48		16 48		17 48
Cleland	d	08 52		09 52		10 52		11 52		12 52		13 52		14 52		15 52		16 52		17 52
Carfin	d	08 56		09 56		10 56		11 56		12 56		13 56		14 56		15 56		16 56		17 56
Holytown	d	08 58		09 58		10 58		11 58		12 58		13 58		14 58		15 58		16 58		17 58
Whifflet	a	09 07		10 07		11 07		12 07		13 07		14 07		15 07		16 07		17 07		18 07
	d	09 07	09 36	10 07	10 37	11 07	11 37	12 07	12 39	13 07	13 37	14 07	14 37	15 07	15 37	16 07	16 39	17 07	17 39	18 07
Kirkwood	d	09 10	09 39	10 10	10 40	11 10	11 40	12 10	12 42	13 10	13 40	14 10	14 40	15 10	15 40	16 10	16 42	17 10	17 42	18 10
Bargeddie	d	09 13	09 42	10 13	10 43	11 13	11 43	12 13	12 45	13 13	13 43	14 13	14 43	15 13	15 43	16 13	16 45	17 13	17 45	18 13
Baillieston	d	09 16	09 45	10 16	10 46	11 16	11 46	12 16	12 48	13 16	13 46	14 16	14 46	15 16	15 46	16 16	16 48	17 16	17 48	18 16
Mount Vernon	d	09 19	09 48	10 19	10 49	11 19	11 49	12 19	12 51	13 19	13 49	14 19	14 49	15 19	15 49	16 19	16 51	17 19	17 51	18 19
Carmyle	d	09 23	09 52	10 23	10 53	11 23	11 53	12 23	12 55	13 23	13 53	14 23	14 53	15 23	15 53	16 23	16 55	17 23	17 55	18 23
Glasgow Central 15	a	09 38	10 06	10 36	11 07	11 35	12 06	12 34	13 08	13 38	14 06	14 38	15 08	15 40	16 06	16 36	17 08	17 36	18 08	18 40

For general notes see front of timetable
For details of catering facilities see
Directory of Train Operators

b Saturdays arr. 1 minute earlier
c On Mondays to Fridays 1507 from Whifflet arrives Glasgow Central 1 minute earlier

No Sunday service until 29 November

Glasgow Central → Ardrossan, Largs and Ayr

Network Diagram - see first page of Table 216

Miles	Miles	Miles			SR MX	SR	SR	SR	SR SX	SR SO	SR SO	SR SX	SR ◇ A	SR SX	SR SO	SR	SR	SR SX	SR SX	SR SO	SR B	SR	SR	SR SO	SR SX	SR SX C
0	0	—	**Glasgow Central** 15 219	d	00 15	06 00	06 15	06 30	06 45	06 45	07 00	07 00	07 13	07 15	07 15	07 30	08 00	08 15	08 30	08 30		08 33	08 45	09 00	09 00	09 03
7¼	7¼	—	Paisley Gilmour Street 219 ✈	d	00 26	06 11	06 26	06 41	06 56	06 56	07 11	07 11	07 24	07 26	07 26	07 41	08 11	08 26	08 41	08 41		08 44	08 56	09 11	09 11	
10¾	10¾	—	Johnstone	d	00 30	06 15	06 30	06 45	07 00	07 00	07 15	07 15		07 30	07 30	07 45	08 15	08 30	08 45	08 45		08 48	09 00	09 15	09 15	
11½	11½	—	Milliken Park	d			06 33		07 03	07 03				07 33	07 33			08 33				08 51	09 03			
13	13	—	Howwood	d			06 36			07 06		07 19			07 36			08 36		08 49						
16½	16½	—	Lochwinnoch	d			06 40							07 38	07 40			08 40				08 56				
20½	20½	—	Glengarnock	d			06 45		07 11	07 13				07 43	07 45		08 24	08 45	08 54	08 56		09 01	09 11			
23¼	23¼	—	Dalry	d			06 49		07 15	07 17				07 47	07 49		08 28	08 49	08 58	09 00		09 05				
26¾	26¾	—	Kilwinning	d	00 42	06 29	06 54	06 59	07 20	07 22	07 29	07 31	07 41	07 52	07 54	07 59	08 33	08 54	09 03	09 05		09 10	09 18	09 29	09 32	
—	29	—	Stevenston	d			06 57		07 23	07 25				07 55	07 57			08 57				09 13	09 21			
—	30¼	—	Saltcoats	d			07 00		07 26	07 28				08 00	08 02			09 00				09 16	09 24			
—	31¼	—	Ardrossan South Beach	d			07 02		07 28	07 30				08 02	08 04			09a02				09 18	09 26			
—	—	31¾	Ardrossan Town	d					07 35	07 35												09 22				
—	—	32¼	**Ardrossan Harbour**	a					07 38	07 38												09 25				
—	35¾	—	West Kilbride	d			07 08							08 08	08 10								09 32			
—	39¾	—	Fairlie	d			07 13							08 14	08 16								09 37			
—	42¾	—	**Largs**	a			07 20							08 20	08 22								09 44			
30	—	—	Irvine	d	00 46	06 33		07 03			07 33	07 35				08 03	08 37		09 07	09 09				09 33	09 36	
33¾	—	—	Barassie	d	00 51			07 08								08 08	08 42		09 12	09 14						
35	—	—	Troon	d	00 54	06 39		07 11			07 39	07 41				08 11	08 45		09 15	09 17	09 24			09 39	09 42	10 06
37¾	—	—	Prestwick Int. Airport ✈	d	00 58	06 43		07 15			07 43	07 45				08 15	08 49		09 19	09 21	09 29			09 43	09 46	10 11
38¼	—	—	Prestwick Town	d	01 00	06 45		07 17			07 45	07 47				08 17	08 51		09 21	09 23	09 31			09 45	09 48	10 13
40¼	—	—	Newton-on-Ayr	d	01 03			07 20								08 20	08 54		09 24	09 26						
41½	—	—	**Ayr**	a	01 10	06 52		07 24			07 52	07 54	07 59			08 25	08 58		09 31	09 30	09b39			09 52	09 53	10 20

		SR SO C	SR	SR	SR	SR	SR	SR	SR	SR SO	SR SX	SR	SR	SR ◇ A	SR	SR	SR	SR	SR D	SR	SR	SR	SR	SR	SR	SR
Glasgow Central 15 219	d	09 03	09 15	09 30	09 45	10 00	10 15	10 30	10 45	11 00	11 00	11 15	11 30	11 42	11 45	12 00	12 15	12 30		12 45	13 00	13 15	13 30	13 45	14 00	14 15
Paisley Gilmour Street 219 ✈	d		09 26	09 41	09 56	10 11	10 26	10 41	10 56	11 11	11 11	11 26	11 41	11 53	11 56	12 11	12 26	12 41		12 56	13 11	13 26	13 41	13 56	14 11	14 26
Johnstone	d		09 30	09 45	10 00	10 15	10 30	10 45	11 00	11 15	11 15	11 30	11 45		12 00	12 15	12 30	12 45		13 00	13 15	13 30	13 45	14 00	14 15	14 30
Milliken Park	d		09 33		10 03		10 33		11 03			11 33			12 03		12 33			13 03		13 33		14 03		14 33
Howwood	d		09 36				10 36					11 36					12 36					13 36				14 36
Lochwinnoch	d		09 40				10 40					11 40					12 40					13 40				14 40
Glengarnock	d		09 45	09 54	10 11		10 45	10 54	11 11			11 45			12 11		12 45			13 11		13 45		14 11		14 45
Dalry	d		09 49		10 15	10 26	10 49					11 49					12 49			13 15		13 49			14 26	14 49
Kilwinning	d		09 54	10 01	10 20	10 31	10 54	11 01	11 18	11 29	11 29	11 54	11 59	12 10	12 18	12 29	12 54	12 59		13 20	13 29	13 54	13 59	14 18	14 31	14 54
Stevenston	d		09 57		10 23		10 57		11 21			11 57			12 21		12 57			13 23		13 57		14 21		14 57
Saltcoats	d		10 00		10 26		11 00		11 24			12 00			12 24		13 00			13 26		14 00		14 24		15 00
Ardrossan South Beach	d		10 02		10 28		11 02		11 26			12 02			12 26		13 02			13 28		14 02		14 26		15 01
Ardrossan Town	d		10 06				11 06					12 06					13 06					14 06				15 06
Ardrossan Harbour	a		10 08				11 08					12 09					13 09					14 09				15 09
West Kilbride	d				10 34				11 32						12 32					13 34				14 32		
Fairlie	d				10 39				11 37						12 37					13 39				14 37		
Largs	a				10 47				11 44						12 44					13 46				14 44		
Irvine	d			10 05		10 35		11 05		11 33	11 33		12 03			12 33		13 03			13 33		14 03		14 35	
Barassie	d			10 10				11 10					12 08					13 08					14 08			
Troon	d	10 07		10 13		10 41		11 13		11 39	11 43		12 11			12 39		13 11	13 22		13 39		14 11		14 41	
Prestwick Int. Airport ✈	d	10 12		10 17		10 45		11 17		11 43	11 47		12 15			12 43		13 15	13 27		13 43		14 15		14 45	
Prestwick Town	d	10 14		10 19		10 47		11 19		11 45	11 49		12 17			12 45		13 17	13 29		13 45		14 17		14 47	
Newton-on-Ayr	d			10 22				11 22					12 20					13 20					14 20			
Ayr	a	10 21		10 26		10 54		11 26		11 52	11 54		12 24	12 29		12 52		13 24	13 36		13 52		14 24		14 54	

		SR	SR	SR	SR	SR	SR ◇ E	SR	SR	SR D	SR	SR	SR	SR	SR SX	SR	SR SX	SR SO	SR SO G	SR	SR SX G	SR	SR	SR	SR	SR
Glasgow Central 15 219	d	14 30	14 45	15 00	15 15	15 30		15 45	16 00		16 18	16 30	16 50	17 00	17 13	17 20	17 30	17 30		17 35		17 45	18 00	18 15	18 30	18 45
Paisley Gilmour Street 219 ✈	d	14 41	14 56	15 11	15 26	15 41		15 56	16 11		16 29	16 41	17 01	17 11	17u24	17 32	17u41	17 41		17 46		17 56	18 11	18 26	18 41	18 56
Johnstone	d	14 45	15 00	15 15	15 30	15 45		16 00	16 15		16 33	16 45	17 05	17 15		17 36		17 45		17 50		18 00	18 15	18 30	18 45	19 00
Milliken Park	d		15 03		15 33			16 03			16 36		17 08			17 39				17 53		18 03		18 33		19 03
Howwood	d				15 36						16 39		17 11							17 56				18 36		
Lochwinnoch	d				15 40						16 43			17 21						18 00				18 40		
Glengarnock	d		15 11		15 45			16 11			16 48		17 18	17 26	17 35					18 05		18 11		18 45		19 11
Dalry	d				15 49						16 52		17 22	17 30		17 49				18 09		18 15	18 26	18 49	18 56	
Kilwinning	d	14 59	15 18	15 29	15 54	15 59		16 18	16 29		16 57	16 59	17 27	17 35	17 42	17 54		17 59		18 14		18 20	18 31	18 54	19 01	19 18
Stevenston	d		15 21		15 57			16 21			17 01		17 30			17 57				18 17		18 23		18 57		19 21
Saltcoats	d		15 24		16 00			16 24			17c09		17 33			18 01				18 20		18 26		19 00		19 24
Ardrossan South Beach	d		15 26		16 02			16 26			17 11		17 37			18 03				18 22		18 28		19 02		19 26
Ardrossan Town	d				16 06								17 40							18a26				19 06		
Ardrossan Harbour	a				16 09								17 44											19 09		
West Kilbride	d		15 32					16 32			17 17					18 09						18 34				19 32
Fairlie	d		15 37					16 37			17 22					18 14						18 39				19 37
Largs	a		15 44					16 44			17 28					18 20						18 48				19 44
Irvine	d	15 03		15 33		16 03			16 33			17 03		17 39	17 46		17 59	18 03					18 35		19 05	
Barassie	d	15 08				16 08						17 08		17 44			18 04	18 08					18 40		19 10	
Troon	d	15 11		15 39		16 11	16 21		16 39	16 44		17 11		17 47	17 52		18 07	18 11	18 24		18 27		18 43		19 13	
Prestwick Int. Airport ✈	d	15 15		15 43		16 15			16 43	16 49		17 15		17 51	17 56		18 11	18 15	18 29		18 32		18 47		19 17	
Prestwick Town	d	15 17		15 45		16 17			16 45	16 51		17 17		17 53	17 58		18 13	18 17	18 31		18 34		18 49		19 19	
Newton-on-Ayr	d	15 20				16 20						17 20		17 56			18 16	18 20					18 52		19 22	
Ayr	a	15 24		15 52		16 24	16 32		16 52	16 58		17 25		18 00	18 05		18 20	18 24	18 38		18 39		18 56		19 26	

For general notes see front of timetable
For details of catering facilities see Directory of Train Operators

A To Stranraer (Table 218)
B From Kilmarnock to Stranraer (Table 218)
C To Girvan (Table 218)
D From Kilmarnock to Girvan (Table 218)
E From Newcastle (Table 48) to Stranraer (Table 218)
G From Kilmarnock (Table 218)
b Saturdays arr. 1 minute earlier
c Arr. 1704

Glasgow Central → Ardrossan, Largs and Ayr

Network Diagram - see first page of Table 216

Mondays to Saturdays

Station		SR	SR	SR	SR	SR	SR ◇ A	SR	SR	SR	SR	SR	SR	SR	SR	SR B	SR	SR	SR	SR	SR FX	SR FO	SR	SR FSX	SR FO
Glasgow Central 15	219 d	19 00	19 15	19 30	19 45	20 00		20 15	20 30	20 45	21 00	21 15	21 30	21 45	22 00		22 15	22 30	22 45	23 00	23 15	23 15	23 30	23 45	23 45
Paisley Gilmour Street	219 ✈ d	19 11	19 26	19 41	19 56	20 11		20 26	20 41	20 56	21 11	21 26	21 41	21 56	22 11		22 26	22 41	22 56	23 11	23 26	23 26	23 41	23 56	23 56
Johnstone	d	19 15	19 30	19 45	20 00	20 15		20 30	20 45	21 00	21 15	21 30	21 45	22 00	22 15		22 30	22 45	23 00	23 15	23 30	23 30	23 45	23 59	23 59
Milliken Park	d		19 33		20 03			20 33		21 03		21 33		22 03			22 33		23 03		23 33	23 33		00 03	00 03
Howwood	d		19 36					20 36				21 36					22 36				23 36	23 36		00 06	00 06
Lochwinnoch	d		19 40					20 40				21 40					22 40				23 40	23 40		00 10	00 10
Glengarnock	d		19 45		20 11			20 45		21 11		21 45		22 11			22 45		23 11		23 45	23 45		00 15	00 15
Dalry	d		19 49					20 49				21 49					22 49				23 49	23 49		00 19	00 19
Kilwinning	d	19 29	19 54	19 59	20 18	20 29		20 54	20 59	21 18	21 29	21b53	21 59	22 18	22 29		22 54	22 59	23 18	23 29	23 54	23 54	23 59	00 24	00 24
Stevenston	d		19 57		20 21			20 57		21 21		21 57		22 21			22 57		23 21		23 57	23 57		00 27	00 27
Saltcoats	d		20 00		20 24			21 00		21 24		22 00		22 24			23 00		23 24		23 59	23 59		00 30	00 30
Ardrossan South Beach	d		20 02		20 26			21 02		21 26		22 02		22 26			23 02		23 26		00 02	00 02		00a32	00 32
Ardrossan Town	d		20 06					21 06				22 06					23a06					00a06			
Ardrossan Harbour	a		20 09					21 09				22 09													
West Kilbride	d				20 32					21 32				22 32					23 32		00 08				00 38
Fairlie	d				20 37					21 37				22 37					23 37		00 14				00 43
Largs	a				20 44					21 44				22 44					23 44		00 19				00 49
Irvine	d	19 33		20 03		20 33			21 03		21 33		22 03		22 33			23 03		23 33			00 03		
Barassie	d			20 08					21 08				22 08					23 08					00 08		
Troon	d	19 39		20 11		20 39	20 51		21 11		21 39		22 11		22 39	22 56		23 11		23 39			00 11		
Prestwick Int. Airport ✈	d	19 43		20 15		20 43			21 15		21 43		22 15		22 43	23 01		23 15		23 43			00 15		
Prestwick Town	d	19 45		20 17		20 45			21 17		21 45		22 17		22 45	23 03		23 17		23 45			00 17		
Newton-on-Ayr	d			20 20					21 20				22 20					23 20					00 20		
Ayr	a	19 52		20 24		20 52	20 59		21 24		21 52		22c24		22 52	23 10		23 24		23 52			00 25		

Sundays

until 27 September

Station		SR	SR	SR	SR	SR	SR	SR	SR	SR	SR	SR ◇ C	SR		SR	SR	SR	SR	SR	SR	SR	SR	SR	SR	SR	SR
Glasgow Central 15	219 d	08 40	09 00	09 30	09 40	10 00	10 30	10 40	11 00	11 15	11 30	11 37	11 40		12 00	12 30	12 40	13 00	13 30	13 40	14 00	14 05	14 30	14 40	15 00	15 30
Paisley Gilmour Street	219 ✈ d	08 51	09 11	09 41	09 51	10 11	10 41	10 51	11 11	11 26	11 41	11 48	11 50		12 11	12 41	12 51	13 11	13 41	13 51	14 11	14 16	14 41	14 51	15 11	15 41
Johnstone	d	08 55	09 15	09 45	09 55	10 15	10 45	10 55	11 15	11 30	11 45		11 54		12 15	12 45	12 55	13 15	13 45	13 55	14 15	14 20	14 45	14 55	15 15	15 45
Milliken Park	d	08 58			09 58			10 58		11 33			11 57				12 58			13 58		14 23		14 58		
Howwood	d				10 01			11 01					12 00				13 01			14 01				15 01		
Lochwinnoch	d				10 05			11 05					12 04				13 05			14 05				15 05		
Glengarnock	d	09 06			10 10			11 10					12 09				13 10			14 10				15 10		
Dalry	d	09 10			10 14			11 14					12 13				13 14			14 14				15 14		
Kilwinning	d	09 15	09 29	09 59	10 19	10 29	10 59	11 19	11 29	11 46	11 59	12 05	12 18		12 29	12 59	13 19	13 29	13 59	14 19	14 29	14 39	14 59	15 19	15 29	15 59
Stevenston	d	09 18			10 22			11 22		11 49			12 21				13 22			14 22		14 42		15 22		
Saltcoats	d	09 21			10 25			11 25		11 52			12 24				13 25			14 25		14 45		15 25		
Ardrossan South Beach	d	09 23			10 27			11 27		11 54			12 26				13 27			14 27		14 47		15 27		
Ardrossan Town	d																					14 59				
Ardrossan Harbour	a	09 30								12 02																
West Kilbride	d				10 33			11 33					12 32				13 33			14 33				15 33		
Fairlie	d				10 39			11 39					12 38				13 39			14 39				15 39		
Largs	a				10 45			11 45					12 45				13 45			14 45				15 45		
Irvine	d		09 33	10 03		10 33	11 03		11 33		12 03				12 33	13 03		13 33	14 03		14 33		15 03		15 33	16 03
Barassie	d		09 38			10 38			11 38						12 38			13 38			14 38				15 38	
Troon	d		09 41	10 09		10 41	11 09		11 41		12 09				12 41	13 09		13 41	14 09		14 41		15 09		15 41	16 09
Prestwick Int. Airport ✈	d		09 45	10 13		10 45	11 13		11 45		12 13				12 45	13 13		13 45	14 13		14 45		15 13		15 45	16 13
Prestwick Town	d		09 47	10 15		10 47	11 15		11 47		12 15				12 47	13 15		13 47	14 15		14 47		15 15		15 47	16 15
Newton-on-Ayr	d																									
Ayr	a		09 54	10 22		10 54	11 22		11 54		12 22	12 29			12 54	13 22		14 01	14 22		14 54		15 22		15 54	16 22

Station		SR	SR		SR ◇ C	SR	SR	SR	SR	SR	SR	SR	SR	SR	SR	SR	SR	SR	SR	SR	SR	SR B	SR	SR		
Glasgow Central 15	219 d	15 40	16 00		16 25	16 30	16 40	16 55	17 00	17 30	17 40	18 00	18 30	18 40	19 00	19 40	20 00	20 40	21 00	21 40	22 00		22 40	23 00		
Paisley Gilmour Street	219 ✈ d	15 51	16 11		16 39	16 43	16 51	17 07	17 11	17 41	17 51	18 11	18 41	18 51	19 11	19 51	20 11	20 51	21 11	21 51	22 11		22 51	23 11		
Johnstone	d	15 55	16 15			16 47	16 55	17 11	17 15	17 45	17 55	18 15	18 45	18 55	19 15	19 55	20 15	20 55	21 15	21 55	22 15		22 55	23 15		
Milliken Park	d	15 58					16 58	17 14			17 58			18 58		19 58		20 58		21 58			22 58			
Howwood	d	16 01					17 01				18 01			19 01		20 01		21 01		22 01			23 01			
Lochwinnoch	d	16 05					17 05				18 05			19 05		20 05		21 05		22 05			23 05			
Glengarnock	d	16 10					17 10				18 10			19 10		20 10		21 10		22 10			23 10			
Dalry	d	16 14					17 14				18 14			19 14		20 14		21 14		22 14			23 14			
Kilwinning	d	16 19	16 29		16 56	17 01	17 19	17 27	17 29	17 59	18 19	18 29	18 59	19 19	19 29	20 19	20 29	21 19	21 29	22 19	22 29		23 18	23 29		
Stevenston	d	16 22					17 22	17 30			18 22			19 22		20 22		21 22		22 22			23 22			
Saltcoats	d	16 25					17 25	17 33			18 25			19 25		20 25		21 25		22 25			23 24			
Ardrossan South Beach	d	16 27					17 27	17 35			18 27			19 27		20 27		21 27		22 27			23 26			
Ardrossan Town	d																									
Ardrossan Harbour	a							17 43																		
West Kilbride	d	16 33					17 33				18 33			19 33		20 33		21 33		22 33			23 32			
Fairlie	d	16 39					17 39				18 39			19 39		20 39		21 39		22 39			23 38			
Largs	a	16 45					17 45				18 45			19 45		20 45		21 46		22 45			23 44			
Irvine	d		16 33			17 05			17 33	18 03		18 33	19 03		19 33		20 33		21 33		22 33			23 33		
Barassie	d		16 38						17 38			18 38			19 38		20 38		21 38		22 38			23 38		
Troon	d		16 41			17 11			17 41	18 09		18 41	19 09		19 41		20 41		21 41		22 41	22 56		23 41		
Prestwick Int. Airport ✈	d		16 45			17 15			17 45	18 13		18 45	19 13		19 45		20 45		21 45		22 45	23 01		23 45		
Prestwick Town	d		16 47			17 17			17 47	18 15		18 47	19 15		19 47		20 47		21 47		22 47	23 03		23 47		
Newton-on-Ayr	d																									
Ayr	a		16 54		17 17	17 24			17 54	18 22		18 54	19 22		19 54		20 54		21 54		22 54	23 10		23 54		

For general notes see front of timetable
For details of catering facilities see Directory of Train Operators

- **A** From Newcastle (Table 48) to Stranraer (Table 218)
- **B** From Kilmarnock to Stranraer (Table 218)
- **C** To Stranraer (Table 218)
- **b** Saturdays dep. 1 minute later
- **c** Saturdays arr. 2 minutes later

Table 221

Sundays

4 October to 22 November

Glasgow Central → Ardrossan, Largs and Ayr

Network Diagram - see first page of Table 216

	SR	SR	SR	SR	SR	SR	SR	SR	SR ◇ A	SR	SR	SR	SR	SR	SR	SR	SR	SR	SR
Glasgow Central 15 219 d	08 40	08 40	09 00	09 40	10 00	10 40	11 00	11 15	11 37	11 40	12 00	12 40	13 00	13 40	14 00	14 05	14 40	15 00	15 40
Paisley Gilmour Street 219 ✈ d	08 51	08 51	09 11	09 51	10 11	10 51	11 11	11 26	11 48	11 51	12 11	12 51	13 11	13 51	14 11	14 16	14 51	15 11	15 51
Johnstone d	08 55	08 55	09 15	09 55	10 15	10 55	11 15	11 30		11 55	12 15	12 55	13 15	13 55	14 15	14 20	14 55	15 15	15 55
Milliken Park d	08 58	08 58		09 58		10 58		11 33		11 58		12 58		13 58		14 23	14 58		15 58
Howwood d				10 01		11 01				12 01		13 01		14 01			15 01		16 01
Lochwinnoch d				10 05		11 05				12 05		13 05		14 05			15 05		16 05
Glengarnock d	09 06	09 06		10 10		11 10				12 10		13 10		14 10			15 10		16 10
Dalry d	09 10	09 10		10 14		11 14				12 14		13 14		14 14			15 14		16 14
Kilwinning d	09 15	09 15	09 29	10 19	10 29	11 19	11 29	11 46	12 05	12 19	12 29	13 19	13 29	14 19	14 29	14 39	15 19	15 29	16 19
Stevenston d	09 18	09 18		10 22		11 22		11 49		12 22		13 22		14 22		14 42	15 22		16 22
Saltcoats d	09 21	09 21		10 25		11 25		11 52		12 25		13 25		14 25		14 45	15 25		16 25
Ardrossan South Beach d	09 23	09 23		10 27		11 27		11 54		12 27		13 27		14 27		14 47	15 27		16 27
Ardrossan Town d																			
Ardrossan Harbour a	09 30	09 37						12 02											
West Kilbride d				10 33		11 33				12 33		13 33		14 33		14 59	15 33		16 33
Fairlie d				10 39		11 39				12 39		13 39		14 39			15 39		16 39
Largs a				10 52		11 52				12 52		13 52		14 52			15 52		16 52
Irvine d			09 33		10 33		11 33				12 33		13 33		14 33			15 33	
Barassie d			09 38		10 38		11 38				12 38		13 38		14 38			15 38	
Troon d			09 41		10 41		11 41				12 41		13 41		14 41			15 41	
Prestwick Int. Airport ✈ d			09 45		10 45		11 45				12 45		13 45		14 45			15 45	
Prestwick Town d			09 47		10 47		11 47				12 47		13 47		14 47			15 47	
Newton-on-Ayr d																			
Ayr a			10 01		11 01		12 01		12 29		13 01		14 01		15 01			16 01	

	SR	SR ◇ A	SR	SR	SR	SR	SR	SR	SR	SR	SR	SR	SR	SR	SR B	SR	SR
Glasgow Central 15 219 d	16 00	16 25	16 40	16 55	17 40	18 00	18 40	19 00	19 40	20 00	20 40	21 00	21 40	22 00		22 40	23 00
Paisley Gilmour Street 219 ✈ d	16 11	16 39	16 51	17 07	17 51	18 11	18 51	19 11	19 51	20 11	20 51	21 11	21 51	22 11		22 51	23 11
Johnstone d	16 15		16 55	17 11	17 55	18 15	18 55	19 15	19 55	20 15	20 55	21 15	21 55	22 15		22 55	23 15
Milliken Park d			16 58	17 14	17 58		18 58		19 58		20 58		21 58			22 58	
Howwood d			17 01		18 01		19 01		20 01		21 01		22 01			23 01	
Lochwinnoch d			17 05		18 05		19 05		20 05		21 05		22 05			23 05	
Glengarnock d			17 10		18 10		19 10		20 10		21 10		22 10			23 10	
Dalry d			17 14		18 14		19 14		20 14		21 14		22 14			23 14	
Kilwinning d	16 29	16 56	17 19	17 27	18 19	18 29	19 19	19 29	20 19	20 29	21 19	21 29	22 19	22 29		23 19	23 29
Stevenston d			17 22	17 30	18 22		19 22		20 22		21 22		22 22			23 22	
Saltcoats d			17 25	17 33	18 25		19 25		20 25		21 25		22 25			23 25	
Ardrossan South Beach d			17 27	17 35	18 27		19 27		20 27		21 27		22 27			23 27	
Ardrossan Town d																	
Ardrossan Harbour a				17 43													
West Kilbride d			17 33		18 33		19 33		20 33		21 33		22 33			23 33	
Fairlie d			17 39		18 39		19 39		20 39		21 39		22 39			23 39	
Largs a			17 45		18 45		19 45		20 45		21 44		22 44			23 45	
Irvine d	16 33					18 33		19 33		20 33		21 33		22 33			23 33
Barassie d	16 38					18 38		19 38		20 38		21 38		22 38			23 38
Troon d	16 41					18 41		19 41		20 41		21 41		22 41	22 56		23 41
Prestwick Int. Airport ✈ d	16 45					18 45		19 45		20 45		21 45		22 45	23 01		23 45
Prestwick Town d	16 47					18 47		19 47		20 47		21 47		22 47	23 03		23 47
Newton-on-Ayr d																	
Ayr a	16 54	17 17				18 54		19 54		20 54		21 54		22 54	23 10		23 54

Sundays

from 29 November

	SR	SR	SR	SR	SR	SR	SR	SR	SR	SR	SR ◇ A	SR
Glasgow Central 15 219 d	08 40	09 00	09 30	09 45	10 00	10 30	10 45	11 00	11 15	11 30	11 43	11 45
Paisley Gilmour Street 219 ✈ d	08 51	09 11	09 41	09 58	10 11	10 41	10 59	11 11	11 26	11 41	11 54	11 58
Johnstone d	08 55	09 15	09 45	10 01	10 15	10 45	11 03	11 15	11 30	11 45		12 02
Milliken Park d	08 58			10 05			11 06		11 33			12 05
Howwood d				10 08			11 09					12 08
Lochwinnoch d				10 12			11 13					12 12
Glengarnock d	09 06			10 17			11 18					12 17
Dalry d	09 10			10 21			11 22					12 21
Kilwinning d	09 15	09 29	09 59	10 26	10 29	10 59	11 27	11 29	11 46	11 59	12 11	12 26
Stevenston d	09 18			10 28			11 30		11 49			12 29
Saltcoats d	09 21			10 32			11 33		11 52			12 32
Ardrossan South Beach d	09 23			10 33			11 35		11 54			12 34
Ardrossan Town d												
Ardrossan Harbour a	09 30								12 02			
West Kilbride d				10 39			11 41					12 40
Fairlie d				10 46			11 47					12 47
Largs a				10 51			11 52					12 52
Irvine d		09 33	10 03		10 33	11 03		11 33		12 03		
Barassie d		09 38			10 38			11 38				
Troon d		09 41	10 09		10 41	11 09		11 41		12 09		
Prestwick Int. Airport ✈ d		09 45	10 13		10 45	11 13		11 45		12 13		
Prestwick Town d		09 47	10 15		10 47	11 15		11 47		12 15		
Newton-on-Ayr d												
Ayr a		09 54	10 22		10 54	11 22		11 54		12 22	12 29	

	SR	SR	SR	SR	SR	SR	SR	SR	SR	SR	SR	SR
Glasgow Central 15 219 d	12 00	12 30	12 45	13 00	13 30	13 45	14 00	14 05	14 30	14 45	15 00	15 30
Paisley Gilmour Street 219 ✈ d	12 11	12 41	12 59	13 11	13 41	13 59	14 11	14 16	14 41	14 59	15 11	15 41
Johnstone d	12 15	12 45	13 03	13 15	13 45	14 03	14 15	14 20	14 45	15 03	15 15	15 45
Milliken Park d			13 06			14 06		14 23		15 06		
Howwood d			13 09			14 09				15 09		
Lochwinnoch d			13 13			14 13				15 13		
Glengarnock d			13 18			14 18				15 18		
Dalry d			13 22			14 22				15 22		
Kilwinning d	12 29	12 59	13 27	13 29	13 59	14 27	14 29	14 39	14 59	15 27	15 29	15 59
Stevenston d			13 30			14 30		14 42		15 30		
Saltcoats d			13 33			14 33		14 45		15 33		
Ardrossan South Beach d			13 35			14 35		14 47		15 35		
Ardrossan Town d												
Ardrossan Harbour a												
West Kilbride d			13 41			14 41		14 59		15 41		
Fairlie d			13 47			14 47				15 47		
Largs a			13 52			14 52				15 52		
Irvine d	12 33	13 03		13 33	14 03		14 33		15 03		15 33	16 04
Barassie d	12 38			13 38			14 38				15 38	
Troon d	12 41	13 09		13 41	14 09		14 41		15 09		15 41	16 09
Prestwick Int. Airport ✈ d	12 45	13 13		13 45	14 13		14 45		15 13		15 45	16 13
Prestwick Town d	12 47	13 15		13 47	14 15		14 47		15 15		15 47	16 15
Newton-on-Ayr d												
Ayr a	12 54	13 22		13 54	14 22		14 54		15 22		15 54	16 22

For general notes see front of timetable
For details of catering facilities see Directory of Train Operators

A To Stranraer (Table 218)
B From Kilmarnock to Stranraer (Table 218)

Sundays

from 29 November

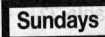

Glasgow Central → Ardrossan, Largs and Ayr

Network Diagram - see first page of Table 216

		SR	SR		SR ◇ A	SR	SR	SR	SR	SR	SR	SR	SR	SR	SR	SR	SR	SR	SR	SR	SR	SR B	SR	SR		
Glasgow Central 15 219	d	15 45	16 00		16 25	16 30	16 45	16 55	17 00	17 30	17 45	18 00	18 30	18 40	19 00	19 40	20 00	20 40	21 00	21 40	22 00		22 40	23 00		
Paisley Gilmour Street 219 ⇄	d	15 59	16 11		16 39	16 41	16 56	17 07	17 12	17 41	17 56	18 11	18 41	18 51	19 11	19 51	20 11	20 51	21 11	21 51	22 11		22 51	23 11		
Johnstone	d	16 03	16 15			16 45	17 00	17 11	17 16	17 45	18 00	18 15	18 45	18 55	19 15	19 55	20 15	20 55	21 15	21 55	22 15		22 55	23 15		
Milliken Park	d	16 06					17 03	17 14			18 03			18 58		19 58		20 58		21 58			22 58			
Howwood	d	16 09					17 06				18 06			19 01		20 01		21 01		22 01			23 01			
Lochwinnoch	d	16 13					17 10				18 10			19 05		20 05		21 05		22 05			23 05			
Glengarnock	d	16 18					17 15				18 15			19 10		20 10		21 10		22 10			23 10			
Dalry	d	16 22					17 19				18 19			19 14		20 14		21 14		22 14			23 14			
Kilwinning	d	16 25	16 29		16 56	16 59	17 24	17 27	17 29	17 59	18 24	18 29	18 59	19 19	19 29	20 19	20 29	21 19	21 29	22 19	22 29		23 18	23 29		
Stevenston	d	16 28					17 27	17 30			18 27			19 22		20 22		21 22		22 22			23 22			
Saltcoats	d	16 31					17 30	17 33			18 30			19 25		20 25		21 25		22 25			23 24			
Ardrossan South Beach	d	16 33					17 32	17 35			18 32			19 27		20 27		21 27		22 27			23 26			
Ardrossan Town	d																									
Ardrossan Harbour	a							17 43																		
West Kilbride	d	16 39					17 38				18 38			19 33		20 33		21 33		22 33			23 32			
Fairlie	d	16 45					17 44				18 44			19 39		20 39		21 39		22 39			23 38			
Largs	a	16 52					17 50				18 50			19 45		20 45		21 45		22 44			23 44			
Irvine	d		16 33			17 03			17 33	18 03		18 33	19 03		19 33		20 33		21 33		22 33			23 33		
Barassie	d		16 38						17 38			18 38			19 38		20 38		21 38		22 38			23 38		
Troon	d		16 41			17 09			17 41	18 09		18 41	19 09		19 41		20 41		21 41		22 41	22 56		23 41		
Prestwick Int. Airport ✈	d		16 45			17 13			17 45	18 13		18 45	19 13		19 45		20 45		21 45		22 45	23 01		23 45		
Prestwick Town	d		16 47			17 15			17 47	18 15		18 47	19 15		19 47		20 47		21 47		22 47	23 03		23 47		
Newton-on-Ayr	d																									
Ayr	a		16 54		17 17	17 24			17 55	18 22		18 54	19 22		19 54		20 54		21 54		22 54	23 10		23 54		

For general notes see front of timetable
For details of catering facilities see
Directory of Train Operators

A To Stranraer (Table 218)
B From Kilmarnock to Stranraer (Table 218)

Ayr, Largs and Ardrossan → Glasgow Central

Network Diagram - see first page of Table 216

Miles	Miles	Miles			SR	SR	SR	SR	SR	SR SX	SR A	SR SX		SR SO	SR SX	SR SX	SR	SR	SR SX	SR SX	SR		SR SX	SR	SR ◇ B	SR SX
0	—	—	**Ayr**	d	05 40	06 13		06 43		06 57	07 10	07 13		07 13	07 25		07 43		07 58		08 13			08 43	08 36	
1¼	—	—	Newton-on-Ayr	d	05 43	06 16		06 46				07 16		07 16					08 01		08 16					
3¼	—	—	Prestwick Town	d	05 46	06 19		06 49		07 02		07 19		07 19	07 30		07 48		08 03		08 19			08 48	08 41	
3¾	—	—	Prestwick Int. Airport ✈	d	05 48	06 21		06 51		07 04		07 21		07 21	07 32		07 50		08 06		08 21			08 50	08 43	
6½	—	—	Troon	d	05 52	06 25		06 55		07 08	07a18	07 25		07 25	07 36		07 54		08 10		08 25			08 54	08 48	
7¾	—	—	Barassie	d	05 54	06 27		06 57		07 10		07 27		07 27	07 38				08 12		08 27					
11½	—	—	Irvine	d	05 59	06 32		07 02		07 15		07 32		07 32	07 43		07 59		08 17		08 32			08 59		
—	0	—	**Largs**	d					06 41							07 23		07 42					08 28			
—	3	—	Fairlie	d					06 46							07 28		07 47					08 33			
—	7	—	West Kilbride	d					06 51							07 33		07 52					08 38			
—	—	0	**Ardrossan Harbour**	d																08 11						
—	—	½	Ardrossan Town	d			06 31													08 14						
—	11½	1	Ardrossan South Beach	d			06 34		06 57							07 39		07 58		08 17			08 44			09 07
—	12½	2	Saltcoats	d			06 36		07 02							07 41		08 00		08 19			08 46			09 09
—	13¾	3¼	Stevenston	d			06 39		07 05							07 44		08 03		08 22			08 49			09 12
14¾	16	5½	Kilwinning	d	06 04	06 37	06 43	07 07	07 10	07 20		07 37		07 37		07 49	08 04	08 08	08 22	08 25	08b37		08 53	09 04		09 16
18½	19¾	9¼	Dalry	d	06 08		06 47		07 14	07 24		07 41		07 41		07 53		08 12		08 30			08 58			
21	22¼	11¾	Glengarnock	d	06 12		06 51		07 18	07 28				07 45	07 52			08 16		08 34			09 02			09 22
25	26¼	15¾	Lochwinnoch	d	06 17		06 56			07 33				07 50		08 00		08 21		08 39						09 27
28½	29¾	19¼	Howwood	d	06 21		07 00			07 37				07 54	07 59					08 43						09 31
30	31¼	20¾	Milliken Park	d	06 24		07 03		07 26	07 40				07 57		08 05		08 26		08 46			09 10			09 32
30¾	32	21½	Johnstone	d	06 27	06 50	07 06	07 20	07 29	07 43		07 52		08 00	08 03	08 08	08 18	08 29	08 35	08 48	08 50		09 12	09 18		09 35
34¼	35½	25	Paisley Gilmour Street 219 ✈	d	06 32	06 55	07 11	07 26	07 34	07 48		07 57		08 05	08 08	08 13	08 23	08 34	08 41	08 53	08 56		09 17	09 24		09 40
41½	42¾	32¼	**Glasgow Central** 15	219 a	06 43	07 07	07 22	07 38	07 47	07 59		08 09		08 16	08 18	08 24	08 34	08 46	08 54	09 04	09 07		09 30	09 36	09 50	09 53

		SR SO	SR	SR	SR	SR	SR		SR	SR	SR	SR	SR	SR ◇ C	SR	SR		SR D	SR	SR	SR	SR	SR	SR	SR ◇ B	SR
Ayr	d		09 13		09 43		10 13			10 43		11 13		11 22	11 43			12 09	12 13		12 43		13 13		13 09	13 43
Newton-on-Ayr	d		09 16				10 16					11 16							12 16				13 16			
Prestwick Town	d		09 19		09 48		10 19			10 48		11 19			11 48			12 14	12 19		12 48		13 19		13 14	13 48
Prestwick Int. Airport ✈	d		09 21		09 50		10 21			10 50		11 21			11 50			12 16	12 21		12 50		13 22		13 16	13 50
Troon	d		09 25		09 54		10 25			10 54		11 25		11a30	11 54			12a21	12 25		12 54		13 25		13 21	13 54
Barassie	d		09 27				10 27					11 27							12 27				13 27			
Irvine	d		09 32		09 59		10 32			10 59		11 32			11 59				12 32		12 59		13 32			13 59
Largs	d	08 51				09 53					10 53					11 53						12 53				
Fairlie	d	08 56				09 58					10 58					11 58						12 58				
West Kilbride	d	09 01				10 03					11 03					12 03						13 03				
Ardrossan Harbour	d			09 30					10 28				11 28							12 28				13 28		
Ardrossan Town	d			09 33					10 31				11 31							12 31				13 31		
Ardrossan South Beach	d	09 07		09 36		10 09			10 34		11 09		11 34			12 09				12 34		13 09		13 34		
Saltcoats	d	09 09		09 38		10 11			10 36		11 11		11 36			12 11				12 36		13 11		13 36		
Stevenston	d	09 12		09 41		10 14			10 39		11 14		11 39			12 14				12 39		13 14		13 39		
Kilwinning	d	09 16	09 37	09 45	10 04	10 18	10 37		10 43	11 04	11 18	11 37	11 43		12 04	12 18			12 37	12 43	13 04	13 18	13 37	13 43		14 04
Dalry	d		09 41	09 49					10 47				11 47							12 47				13 47		
Glengarnock	d	09 22		09 53		10 25			10 51		11 25		11 51			12 25				12 51		13 25		13 51		
Lochwinnoch	d	09 27		09 58					10 56				11 56							12 56				13 56		
Howwood	d	09 31			10 16				11 00				12 00							13 00				14 00		
Milliken Park	d	09 32		10 03		10 33			11 03		11 33		12 03			12 33				13 03		13 33		14 03		
Johnstone	d	09 35	09 52	10 06	10 20	10 35	10 50		11 06	11 18	11 35	11 50	12 06		12 18	12 35			12 50	13 06	13 18	13 35	13 50	14 06		14 18
Paisley Gilmour Street 219 ✈	d	09 40	09 57	10 11	10 25	10 40	10 55		11 11	11 23	11 40	11 55	12 11		12 23	12 40			12 55	13 11	13 23	13 40	13 55	14 11		14 23
Glasgow Central 15	219 a	09 53	10 09	10 22	10 36	10 52	11 07		11 22	11 36	11 52	12 07	12 22		12c36	12 52			13 07	13 22	13c36	13 52	14 07	14c24	14 27	14 34

		SR		SR	SR	SR	SR	SR	SR	SR E	SR		SR ◇ B	SR	SR	SR	SR	SR	SR	SR		SR	SR	SR	SR	SR
Ayr	d			14 13		14 43		15 13		15 17	15 43		15 56		16 13		16 43		17 13				17 43		18 13	
Newton-on-Ayr	d			14 16				15 16							16 16		16 46		17 16						18 16	
Prestwick Town	d			14 19		14 48		15 19		15 22	15 48				16 19		16 49		17 19				17 48		18 19	
Prestwick Int. Airport ✈	d			14 21		14 50		15 21		15 24	15 50				16 21		16 51		17 21				17 50		18 21	
Troon	d			14 25		14 54		15 25		15 29	15 54				16 25		16 55		17 25				17 54		18 25	
Barassie	d			14 27				15 27							16 27				17 27						18 27	
Irvine	d			14 32		14 59		15 32			15 59				16 32		17 00		17 32				17 59		18 32	
Largs	d	13 53					14 53							15 53				16 50				17 35				
Fairlie	d	13 58					14 58							15 58				16 55				17 40				
West Kilbride	d	14 03					15 03							16 03				17 00				17 45				
Ardrossan Harbour	d				14 28				15 28							16 28								18 00		
Ardrossan Town	d				14 31				15 31							16 31								18 03		18 31
Ardrossan South Beach	d	14 09			14 33		15 09		15 34					16 09		16 34		17 06		17 40		17 51		18 06		18 34
Saltcoats	d	14 11			14 35		15 11		15 36					16 11		16 36		17 08		17 42		17 53		18 09		18 36
Stevenston	d	14 14			14 38		15 14		15 39					16 14		16 39		17 11		17 45		17 56		18 12		18 39
Kilwinning	d	14 18		14 37	14 42	15 04	15 18	15 37	15 43		16 04		16 13	16 18	16 37	16 43	17 05	17 15	17 36	17 48		18 00	18 04	18 16	18 37	18 43
Dalry	d				14 47				15 47							16 47		17 20	17 41	17 53		18 05	18 09		18 41	18 47
Glengarnock	d	14 25			14 51		15 25	15 43	15 51					16 25	16 43	16 51		17 24		17 57			18 13	18 23		18 51
Lochwinnoch	d				14 56				15 56							16 56		17 29					18 18			18 56
Howwood	d				15 00				16 00							17 00						18 14		18 30		19 00
Milliken Park	d	14 33			15 03		15 33		16 03					16 33		17 03		17 34		18 05				18 33		19 03
Johnstone	d	14 35		14 50	15 05	15 18	15 35	15 52	16 06		16 18			16 35	16 52	17 06	17 19	17 36	17 52	18 07		18 18	18 24	18 35	18 52	19 06
Paisley Gilmour Street 219 ✈	d	14 40		14 55	15 10	15 25	15 40	15 57	16 11		16 23		16 34	16 40	16 57	17 11	17 24	17 41	17 57	18 12		18 23	18 29	18b41	18 57	19 11
Glasgow Central 15	219 a	14 52		15 07	15 22	15 36	15 52	16 09	16 24	16 32	16 34		16 45	16 52	17 09	17 22	17 35	17 55	18 09	18 23		18c36	18 41	18 52	19 09	19 22

For general notes see front of timetable
For details of catering facilities see Directory of Train Operators

A From Girvan (Table 218) to Newcastle (Table 216)
B From Stranraer (Table 218)
C From Stranraer (Table 218) to Newcastle (Table 48)
D From Girvan to Kilmarnock (Table 218)
E From Girvan (Table 218)
b Saturdays dep. 1 minute earlier
c Saturdays arr. 2 minutes earlier

Ayr, Largs and Ardrossan → Glasgow Central

Network Diagram - see first page of Table 216

Mondays to Saturdays

		SR	SR	SR	SR	SR		SR	SR	SR	SR	SR	SR	SR	SR		SR	SR	SR	SR	SR	SR	SR	SR
				A										◇ B								◇ B		
Ayr	d	18 43		19 09	19 13			19 43		20 13		20 43		21 06	21 13			21 43		22 13		22 38		23 00
Newton-on-Ayr	d				19 16					20 16					21 16					22 16				23 03
Prestwick Town	d	18 48		19 14	19 19			19 48		20 19		20 48			21 19			21 48		22 19				23 06
Prestwick Int. Airport ✈	d	18 50		19 16	19 21			19 50		20 21		20 50			21 21			21 50		22 21				23 08
Troon	d	18 54		19a21	19 25			19 54		20 25		20 54			21 25			21 54		22 25				23 12
Barassie	d				19 27					20 27					21 27					22 27				23 14
Irvine	d	18 59			19 32			19 59		20 32		20 59			21 32			21 59		22 32				23 19
Largs	d		18 53						19 53				20 53						21 53				22 53	
Fairlie	d		18 58						19 58				20 58						21 58				22 58	
West Kilbride	d		19 03						20 03				21 03						22 03				23 03	
Ardrossan Harbour	d					19 28					20 33						21 28				22 28			
Ardrossan Town	d					19 31					20 36						21 31				22 31			
Ardrossan South Beach	d		19 09			19 34			20 09		20 39		21 09				21 34		22 09		22 34		23 09	
Saltcoats	d		19 11			19 36			20 11		20 41		21 11				21 36		22 11		22 36		23 11	
Stevenston	d		19 14			19 39			20 14		20 44		21 14				21 39		22 14		22 39		23 14	
Kilwinning	d	19 04	19 18		19 37	19 43		20 04	20 18	20 37	20 48	21 04	21 18	21 21	21 37		21 43	22 04	22 18	22 37	22 43	22 54	23 18	23 24
Dalry	d					19 47					20 52				21 41		21 47	22 09	22 23	22 41	22 47			23 28
Glengarnock	d		19 25			19 51			20 25		20 56		21 25				21 51		22 27		22 51		23 25	23 32
Lochwinnoch	d					19 56					21 01						21 56				22 56			
Howwood	d					20 00					21 05						22 00				23 00		23 32	
Milliken Park	d		19 33			20 03			20 33		21 08		21 33				22 03		22 35		23 03		23 35	
Johnstone	d	19 18	19 35		19 50	20 06		20 18	20 35	20 50	21 11	21 18	21 35		21 52		22 06	22 20	22 37	22 52	23 06		23 37	23 41
Paisley Gilmour Street 219 ✈	d	19 23	19 40		19 55	20 11		20 23	20 40	20 55	21 16	21 23	21 40	21 44	21 57		22 11	22 25	22 42	22 57	23 11	23 15	23 42	23 46
Glasgow Central 15 219	a	19 34	19 52		20 08	20b22		20 34	20 52	21 07	21 27	21 34	21 52	21 55	22 09		22 22	22 36	22 54	23 09	23 22	23 26	23 54	23 58

Sundays

until 27 September

		SR	SR	SR	SR	SR	SR	SR	SR	SR	SR	SR	SR	SR	SR	SR	SR		SR	SR	SR	SR	SR	SR	SR	SR
											◇ B															
Ayr	d		09 13	09 43		10 13	10 43		11 13	11 43	12 00		12 13		12 43		13 13		13 43		14 13	14 43			15 13	15 43
Newton-on-Ayr	d																									
Prestwick Town	d		09 18	09 48		10 18	10 48		11 18	11 48			12 18		12 48		13 18		13 48		14 18	14 48			15 18	15 48
Prestwick Int. Airport ✈	d		09 20	09 50		10 20	10 50		11 20	11 50			12 20		12 50		13 20		13 50		14 20	14 50			15 20	15 50
Troon	d		09 24	09 54		10 24	10 54		11 24	11 54			12 24		12 54		13 24		13 54		14 24	14 54			15 24	15 54
Barassie	d			09 56			10 56			11 56					12 56				13 56			14 56				15 56
Irvine	d		09 29	10 01		10 29	11 01		11 29	12 01			12 29		13 01		13 29		14 01		14 29	15 01			15 29	16 01
Largs	d	08 53			09 58			10 53				11 53				12 53				13 53				14 53		
Fairlie	d	08 58			10 03			10 58				11 58				12 58				13 58				14 58		
West Kilbride	d	09 03			10 08			11 03				12 03				13 03				14 03				15 03		
Ardrossan Harbour	d													12 35									15 04			
Ardrossan Town	d																									
Ardrossan South Beach	d	09 09			10 14			11 09				12 09		12 40		13 09				14 09			15 09	15 14		
Saltcoats	d	09 11			10 16			11 11				12 11		12 42		13 11				14 11			15 11	15 16		
Stevenston	d	09 14			10 19			11 14				12 14		12 45		13 14				14 14			15 14	15 19		
Kilwinning	d	09 18	09 34	10 06	10 23	10 34	11 06	11 18	11 34	12 06	12 15	12 18	12 34	12 49	13 06	13 18	13 34		14 06	14 18	14 34	15 06	15 18	15 23	15 34	16 06
Dalry	d	09 23			10 28			11 23				12 23				13 23				14 23				15 27		
Glengarnock	d	09 27			10 32			11 27				12 27				13 27				14 27				15 31		
Lochwinnoch	d	09 32			10 37			11 32				12 32				13 32				14 32				15 36		
Howwood	d	09 36			10 41			11 36				12 36				13 36				14 36				15 40		
Milliken Park	d	09 39			10 44			11 39				12 39		13 02		13 39				14 39			15 31	15 43		
Johnstone	d	09 41	09 48	10 19	10 46	10 48	11 19	11 41	11 48	12 19		12 41	12 48	13 04	13 19	13 41	13 48		14 19	14 41	14 48	15 19	15 33	15 46	15 51	16 19
Paisley Gilmour Street 219 ✈	d	09 47	09 53	10 20	10 52	10 53	11 24	11 47	11 53	12 20	12 37	12 47	12 53	13 10	13 20	13 47	13 53		14 20	14 47	14 53	15 20	15 38	15 51	15 56	16 24
Glasgow Central 15 219	a	09 58	10 04	10 36	11 03	11 07	11 36	11 58	12 04	12 36	12 51	12 58	13 04	13 28	13 36	13 58	14 04		14 36	14 58	15 04	15 36	15 50	16 01	16 06	16 36

		SR	SR	SR	SR	SR	SR	SR	SR	SR	SR	SR	SR	SR	SR	SR	SR	SR	SR	SR	SR	SR	SR	SR
		◇ B																	◇ B					
Ayr	d	15 59		16 13	16 43		17 13	17 43			18 13	18 43		19 13	19 43			20 43	21 00		21 43		23 00	
Newton-on-Ayr	d																							
Prestwick Town	d			16 18	16 48		17 18	17 48			18 18	18 48		19 18	19 48			20 48			21 48		23 05	
Prestwick Int. Airport ✈	d			16 20	16 50		17 20	17 50			18 20	18 50		19 20	19 50			20 50			21 50		23 07	
Troon	d			16 24	16 54		17 24	17 54			18 24	18 54		19 24	19 54			20 54			21 54		23 11	
Barassie	d				16 56			17 56				18 56			19 56			20 56			21 56		23 13	
Irvine	d			16 29	17 01		17 29	18 01			18 29	19 01		19 29	20 01			21 01			22 01		23 18	
Largs	d		15 53			16 53				17 53			18 53			19 53				20 53		21 53		22 58
Fairlie	d		15 58			16 58				17 58			18 58			19 58				20 58		21 58		23 03
West Kilbride	d		16 03			17 03				18 03			19 03			20 03				21 03		22 03		23 08
Ardrossan Harbour	d								18 00								20 31							
Ardrossan Town	d																							
Ardrossan South Beach	d		16 09			17 09			18 05	18 09			19 09			20 09	20 36			21 09		22 09		23 14
Saltcoats	d		16 11			17 11			18 07	18 11			19 11			20 11	20 38			21 11		22 11		23 16
Stevenston	d		16 14			17 14			18 10	18 14			19 14			20 14	20 41			21 14		22 14		23 19
Kilwinning	d	16 15	16 20	16 34	17 06	17 18	17 34	18 06	18 14	18 18	18 34	19 06	19 18	19 34	20 06	20 18	20 45	21 06	21 15	21 18	22 06	22 18	23 23	23 27
Dalry	d		16 25			17 23				18 23			19 23			20 23				21 23		22 23		23 31
Glengarnock	d		16 29			17 27				18 27			19 27			20 27				21 27		22 27		23 35
Lochwinnoch	d		16 34			17 32				18 32			19 32			20 32				21 32		22 32		23 40
Howwood	d		16 38			17 36				18 36			19 36			20 36				21 36		22 36		23 44
Milliken Park	d		16 41			17 39			18 27	18 39			19 39			20 39	20 58			21 39		22 39		23 47
Johnstone	d		16 43	16 48	17 19	17 41	17 48	18 19	18 29	18 41	18 48	19 19	19 41	19 48	20 19	20 41	21 00	21 19		21 41	22 19	22 41	23 36	23 50
Paisley Gilmour Street 219 ✈	d	16 38	16 49	16 53	17 24	17 47	17 53	18 24	18 39	18 47	18 53	19 24	19 47	19 53	20 24	20 47	21 06	21 24	21 36	21 46	22 24	22 47	23 41	23 55
Glasgow Central 15 219	a	16 49	16 59	17 04	17 36	17 58	18 04	18 36	18 49	18 58	19 04	19 36	19 58	20 04	20 36	20 58	21 17	21 36	21 48	21 58	22 36	22 58	23 53	00 05

For general notes see front of timetable
For details of catering facilities see
Directory of Train Operators

A From Girvan to Kilmarnock (Table 218)
B From Stranraer (Table 218)
b Saturdays arr. 2 minutes earlier

Sundays

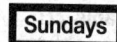

4 October to 22 November

Ayr, Largs and Ardrossan → Glasgow Central

Network Diagram - see first page of Table 216

		SR	SR	SR	SR	SR	SR ◇ A	SR	SR	SR	SR	SR	SR	SR	SR	SR	SR	SR ◇ A
Ayr	d	09 43		10 43		11 43	12 00			12 43		13 43		14 43			15 43	15 59
Newton-on-Ayr	d																	
Prestwick Town	d	09 48		10 48		11 48				12 48		13 48		14 48			15 48	
Prestwick Int. Airport	d	09 50		10 50		11 50				12 50		13 50		14 50			15 50	
Troon	d	09 54		10 54		11 54				12 54		13 54		14 54			15 54	
Barassie	d	09 56		10 56		11 56				12 56		13 56		14 56			15 56	
Irvine	d	10 01		11 01		12 01				13 01		14 01		15 01			16 01	
Largs	d		09 58		10 58			11 58			12 58		13 58			14 58		
Fairlie	d		10 03		11 03			12 03			13 03		14 03			15 03		
West Kilbride	d		10 08		11 08			12 08			13 08		14 08			15 08		
Ardrossan Harbour	d								12 35						15 04			
Ardrossan Town	d																	
Ardrossan South Beach	d		10 14		11 14			12 14	12 40		13 14		14 14		15 09	15 14		
Saltcoats	d		10 16		11 16			12 16	12 42		13 16		14 16		15 11	15 16		
Stevenston	d		10 19		11 19			12 19	12 45		13 19		14 19		15 14	15 19		
Kilwinning	d	10 06	10 23	11 06	11 23	12 06	12 15	12 23	12 49	13 06	13 23	14 06	14 23	15 06	15 18	15 23	16 06	16 15
Dalry	d		10 28		11 28			12 28			13 28		14 28			15 28		
Glengarnock	d		10 32		11 32			12 32			13 32		14 32			15 32		
Lochwinnoch	d		10 37		11 37			12 37			13 37		14 37			15 37		
Howwood	d		10 41		11 41			12 41			13 41		14 41			15 41		
Milliken Park	d		10 44		11 44			12 44	13 02		13 44		14 44		15 31	15 44		
Johnstone	d	10 19	10 46	11 19	11 46	12 19		12 46	13 04	13 19	13 46	14 19	14 46	15 19	15 33	15 46	16 19	
Paisley Gilmour Street 219	d	10 27	10 52	11 27	11 52	12 27	12 37	12 52	13 10	13 27	13 52	14 27	14 52	15 27	15 39	15 52	16 20	16 38
Glasgow Central 15 219	a	10 43	11 10	11 43	12 10	12 43	12 51	13 10	13 28	13 43	14 10	14 43	15 10	15 43	15 50	16 10	16 43	16 49

		SR	SR	SR	SR	SR	SR	SR	SR	SR	SR	SR	SR	SR ◇ A	SR	SR	SR	SR	SR
Ayr	d		16 43		17 43			18 43		19 43			20 43	21 00		21 43		23 00	
Newton-on-Ayr	d																		
Prestwick Town	d		16 48		17 48			18 48		19 48			20 48			21 48		23 05	
Prestwick Int. Airport	d		16 50		17 50			18 50		19 50			20 50			21 50		23 07	
Troon	d		16 54		17 54			18 54		19 54			20 54			21 54		23 11	
Barassie	d		16 56		17 56			18 56		19 56			20 56			21 56		23 13	
Irvine	d		17 01		18 01			19 01		20 01			21 01			22 01		23 18	
Largs	d	15 58		16 58			17 58		18 58		19 58				20 58		21 58		22 58
Fairlie	d	16 03		17 03			18 03		19 03		20 03				21 03		22 03		23 03
West Kilbride	d	16 08		17 08			18 08		19 08		20 08				21 08		22 08		23 08
Ardrossan Harbour	d					18 00						20 31							
Ardrossan Town	d																		
Ardrossan South Beach	d	16 14		17 14		18 05	18 14		19 14		20 14	20 36			21 14		22 14		23 14
Saltcoats	d	16 16		17 16		18 07	18 16		19 16		20 16	20 38			21 16		22 16		23 16
Stevenston	d	16 19		17 19		18 10	18 19		19 19		20 19	20 41			21 19		22 19		23 19
Kilwinning	d	16 23	17 06	17 23	18 06	18 14	18 23	19 06	19 23	20 06	20 23	20 45	21 06	21 15	21 23	22 06	22 23	23 23	23 27
Dalry	d	16 28		17 28			18 28		19 28		20 28				21 28		22 28		23 31
Glengarnock	d	16 32		17 32			18 32		19 32		20 32				21 32		22 32		23 35
Lochwinnoch	d	16 37		17 37			18 37		19 37		20 37				21 37		22 37		23 40
Howwood	d	16 41		17 41			18 41		19 41		20 41				21 41		22 41		23 44
Milliken Park	d	16 44		17 44		18 27	18 44		19 44		20 44	20 58			21 44		22 44		23 47
Johnstone	d	16 46	17 19	17 46	18 19	18 29	18 46	19 19	19 46	20 19	20 46	21 00	21 19		21 46	22 19	22 46	23 36	23 50
Paisley Gilmour Street 219	d	16 52	17 24	17 52	18 24	18 39	18 52	19 24	19 52	20 24	20 52	21 06	21 24	21 36	21 52	22 24	22 52	23 41	23 55
Glasgow Central 15 219	a	17 10	17 36	18 03	18 36	18 49	19 03	19 36	20 03	20 36	21 03	21 17	21 36	21 48	22 03	22 36	23 03	23 53	00 05

Sundays

from 29 November

		SR	SR	SR	SR	SR	SR	SR	SR	SR	SR ◇ A	SR	SR	SR	SR	SR	SR	SR	SR	SR	SR	SR	SR	SR	SR
Ayr	d	08 43	09 13	09 43		10 13	10 43		11 13	11 43	12 00		12 13		12 43		13 13	13 43		14 13	14 43			15 13	15 43
Newton-on-Ayr	d																								
Prestwick Town	d	08 48	09 18	09 48		10 18	10 48		11 18	11 48			12 18		12 48		13 18	13 48		14 18	14 48			15 18	15 48
Prestwick Int. Airport	d	08 50	09 20	09 50		10 20	10 50		11 20	11 50			12 20		12 50		13 20	13 50		14 20	14 50			15 20	15 50
Troon	d	08 54	09 24	09 54		10 24	10 54		11 24	11 54			12 24		12 54		13 24	13 54		14 24	14 54			15 24	15 54
Barassie	d	08 56		09 56			10 56			11 56					12 56			13 56			14 56				15 56
Irvine	d	09 01	09 29	10 01		10 29	11 01		11 29	12 01			12 29		13 01		13 29	14 01		14 29	15 01			15 29	16 01
Largs	d				09 58			10 58				11 58				12 58			13 58				14 58		
Fairlie	d				10 03			11 03				12 03				13 03			14 03				15 03		
West Kilbride	d				10 08			11 08				12 08				13 08			14 08				15 08		
Ardrossan Harbour	d													12 35								15 04			
Ardrossan Town	d																								
Ardrossan South Beach	d				10 14			11 14				12 14		12 40		13 14			14 14			15 09	15 14		
Saltcoats	d				10 16			11 16				12 16		12 42		13 16			14 16			15 11	15 16		
Stevenston	d				10 19			11 19				12 19		12 45		13 19			14 19			15 14	15 19		
Kilwinning	d	09 06	09 34	10 06	10 23	10 34	11 06	11 23	11 34	12 06	12 15	12 23	12 34	12 49	13 06	13 23	13 34	14 06	14 23	14 34	15 06	15 18	15 23	15 34	16 06
Dalry	d				10 28			11 28				12 28				13 28			14 28				15 27		
Glengarnock	d				10 32			11 32				12 32				13 32			14 32				15 31		
Lochwinnoch	d				10 37			11 37				12 37				13 37			14 37				15 36		
Howwood	d				10 41			11 41				12 41				13 41			14 41				15 40		
Milliken Park	d				10 44			11 44				12 44		13 02		13 44			14 44			15 31	15 43		
Johnstone	d	09 19	09 48	10 19	10 46	10 48	11 19	11 46	11 51	12 19		12 46	12 51	13 04	13 19	13 46	13 51	14 19	14 46	14 48	15 19	15 33	15 46	15 48	16 19
Paisley Gilmour Street 219	d	09 24	09 53	10 24	10 52	10 53	11 24	11 51	11 56	12 23	12 37	12 52	12 56	13 10	13 24	13 51	13 56	14 24	14 52	14 53	15 24	15 39	15 51	15 53	16 24
Glasgow Central 15 219	a	09 36	10 04	10 36	11 03	11 07	11 36	12 03	12 06	12 36	12 51	13 03	13 06	13 28	13 36	14 03	14 07	14 36	15 03	15 07	15 36	15 50	16 00	16 06	16 36

For general notes see front of timetable
For details of catering facilities see Directory of Train Operators

A From Stranraer (Table 218)

Sundays

from 29 November

Ayr, Largs and Ardrossan → Glasgow Central

Network Diagram - see first page of Table 216

		SR ◇ A	SR		SR	SR	SR	SR	SR	SR	SR	SR	SR	SR	SR	SR	SR	SR	SR ◇ A	SR	SR	SR	SR	SR		
Ayr	d	15 59			16 13	16 43	16 43		17 13	17 43			18 43		19 43			20 43	21 00		21 43		23 00			
Newton-on-Ayr	d																									
Prestwick Town	d				16 18	16 48	16 48		17 18	17 48			18 48		19 48			20 48			21 48		23 05			
Prestwick Int. Airport ✈	d				16 20	16 50	16 50		17 20	17 50			18 50		19 50			20 50			21 50		23 07			
Troon	d				16 24	16 54	16 54		17 24	17 54			18 54		19 54			20 54			21 54		23 11			
Barassie	d					16 56	16 56			17 56			18 56		19 56			20 56			21 56		23 13			
Irvine	d				16 29	17 01	17 01		17 29	18 01			19 01		20 01			21 01			22 01		23 18			
Largs	d		15 58					16 58				17 58		18 58		19 58				20 58		21 58		22 58		
Fairlie	d		16 03					17 03				18 02		19 03		20 03				21 02		22 03		23 03		
West Kilbride	d		16 08					17 08				18 06		19 08		20 08				21 07		22 08		23 08		
Ardrossan Harbour	d										18 00						20 31									
Ardrossan Town	d																									
Ardrossan South Beach	d		16 14					17 14			18 05	18 12		19 14		20 14	20 36			21 13		22 14		23 14		
Saltcoats	d		16 16					17 16			18 07	18 14		19 16		20 16	20 38			21 15		22 16		23 16		
Stevenston	d		16 19					17 19			18 10	18 17		19 19		20 19	20 41			21 18		22 19		23 19		
Kilwinning	d	16 15	16 23		16 34	17 06	17 06	17 23	17 34	18 06	18 14	18 21	19 06	19 23	20 06	20 23	20 45	21 06	21 15	21 21	22 06	22 23	23 23	23 27		
Dalry	d		16 28					17 28				18 27		19 28		20 28				21 26		22 28		23 31		
Glengarnock	d		16 32					17 32				18 31		19 32		20 32				21 30		22 32		23 35		
Lochwinnoch	d		16 37					17 37				18 36		19 37		20 37				21 35		22 37		23 40		
Howwood	d		16 41					17 41				18 40		19 41		20 41				21 39		22 41		23 44		
Milliken Park	d		16 44					17 44			18 27	18 43		19 44		20 44	20 58			21 42		22 44		23 47		
Johnstone	d		16 46		16 50	17 19	17 19	17 46	17 51	18 19	18 29	18 44	19 19	19 46	20 19	20 46	21 00	21 19		21 45	22 19	22 46	23 36	23 50		
Paisley Gilmour Street 219 ✈	d	16 38	16 51		16 55	17 24	17 24	17 52	17 56	18 24	18 39	18 50	19 24	19 51	20 24	20 52	21 06	21 24	21 36	21 50	22 24	22 52	23 41	23 55		
Glasgow Central 15 219	a	16 49	17 04		17 06	17 36	17 36	18 03	18 07	18 36	18 49	19 03	19 36	20 03	20 36	21 03	21 17	21 36	21 48	22 03	22 36	23 03	23 53	00 05		

For general notes see front of timetable
For details of catering facilities see Directory of Train Operators

A From Stranraer (Table 218)

Table 221A **SHIPPING SERVICES** **Mondays to Saturdays**

until 24 October

Glasgow and Ardrossan — Brodick (Arran)

Caledonian MacBrayne Ltd in association with First ScotRail Limited

						FO
Glasgow Central [15]	221 d	08 33	11 15	14 15	16 50	19 15
Paisley Gilmour Street	221 d	08 44	11 26	14 26	17 01	19 26
Ardrossan Harbour	221 a	09 25	12 09	15 09	17 44	20 09
Ardrossan Harbour	⛴ d	**09 45**	**12 30**	**15 15**	**18 00**	**20 30**
Brodick	⛴ a	**10 40**	**13 25**	**16 10**	**18 55**	**21 25**

Sundays

until 18 October

Glasgow Central [15]	221 d	08 40	11 15	14 05	16 55
Paisley Gilmour Street	221 d	08 51	11 26	14 16	17 07
Ardrossan Harbour	221 a	09b30	12 02	14 59	17 43
Ardrossan Harbour	⛴ d	**09 45**	**12 30**	**15 15**	**18 00**
Brodick	⛴ a	**10 40**	**13 25**	**16 10**	**18 55**

Mondays to Saturdays

until 24 October

Brodick	⛴ d	**08 20**	**11 05**	**13 50**	**16 40**	**19 20**
Ardrossan Harbour	⛴ a	**09 15**	**12 00**	**14 45**	**17 35**	**20 15**
Ardrossan Harbour	221 d	09 30	12 28	15 28	18 00	20 33
Paisley Gilmour Street	221 d	10 10	13 10	16 10	18 40	21 15
Glasgow Central [15]	221 a	10 22	13 22	16 24	18 52	21 27

Sundays

until 18 October

Brodick	⛴ d	**11 05**	**13 50**	**16 40**	**19 20**
Ardrossan Harbour	⛴ a	**12 00**	**14 45**	**17 35**	**20 15**
Ardrossan Harbour	221 d	12 35	15 04	18 00	20 31
Paisley Gilmour Street	221 d	13 09	15 38	18 38	21 05
Glasgow Central [15]	221 a	13 28	15 50	18 49	21 17

For general notes see front of timetable
For details of catering facilities see Directory of Train Operators

b 0937 from 4 October

For details of sailings from 25 October 2009 telephone Caledonian MacBrayne on 08000 66 5000

Glasgow Central → East Kilbride, Barrhead and Kilmarnock

Network Diagram - see first page of Table 216

Miles	Miles			SR SO	SR SO	SR	SR	SR	SR	SR SX	SR SX	SR SO		SR SX	SR	SR SO	SR SX	SR A	SR SX	SR	SR B	SR		SR	SR	SR	SR A
0	0	**Glasgow Central** 15	d	00 03	00 12	06 12	06 42	06 53	07 07	07 33	07 37	07 42		07 52	08 07	08 12	08 17	08 28	08 33	08 42	09 03	09 07		09 12	09 37	09 42	09 53
2¼	2¼	Crossmyloof	d	00 09	00 18	06 18		06 59	07 13	07 39	07 43	07 48		07 58	08 13	08 18	08 23		08 39	08 48		09 13		09 18	09 43	09 48	
3¼	3¼	Pollokshaws West	d	00 12	00 21	06 21		07 02	07 16	07 42	07 46	07 51		08 01	08 16	08 21	08 26		08 42	08 51		09 16		09 21	09 46	09 51	
—	4¼	Thornliebank	d		00 24	06 24		07 05		07 45		07 54		08 04		08 24	08 29			08 54				09 24		09 54	
—	5¼	Giffnock	d		00 27	06 27		07 08		07 48		07 57		08 07		08 27	08 32			08 57				09 27		09 57	
—	6½	Clarkston	d		00 30	06 30		07 11		07 51		08 00		08 10		08 30	08 35			09 00				09 30		10 00	
—	7¼	Busby	d		00 33	06 33		07 15		07 56		08 03		08 15		08 33	08 40			09 03				09 33		10 03	
—	8½	Thorntonhall	d			06 36						08 06					08 42			09 06						10 06	
—	10	Hairmyres	d		00 39	06 40		07 21		08 02		08 10		08 21		08 39	08 46			09 10				09 39		10 10	
—	11½	**East Kilbride**	a		00 42	06 43		07 24		08 09		08 13		08 24		08 42	08 50			09 15				09 43		10 13	
4½	—	Kennishead	d	00 15			06 50		07 19		07 49				08 19				08 45			09 19			09 49		
5	—	Priesthill & Darnley	d	00 17			06 52		07 21		07 51				08 21				08 47			09 21			09 51		
5¾	—	Nitshill	d	00 20			06 55		07 24		07 54				08 24				08 50			09 24			09 54		
7½	—	**Barrhead**	d	00 23			06 59		07a27		07a59				08a27			08 40	08a55		09 15	09a29			09a57		10 05
16½	—	Dunlop	d	00 35			07 11											08 51			09 34						10 26
18¾	—	Stewarton	d	00 39			07 15											08 55			09 38						10 30
22	—	Kilmaurs	d	00 44			07 20											09 00			09 43						10 35
24¼	—	**Kilmarnock** 3	a	00 49			07 25											09 06			09b47						10 38

		SR	SR	SR	SR	SR	SR	SR		SR	SR	SR A	SR	SR	SR	SR	SR A	SR		SR	SR	SR	SR	SR	SR	SR	SR
Glasgow Central 15	d	10 07	10 12	10 37	10 42	11 03	11 07	11 12		11 37	11 42	12 03	12 07	12 12	12 37	12 42	13 03	13 07		13 12	13 37	13 42	14 03	14 07	14 12	14 37	14 42
Crossmyloof	d	10 13	10 18	10 43	10 48		11 13	11 18		11 43	11 48		12 13	12 18	12 43	12 48		13 13		13 18	13 43	13 48		14 13	14 18	14 43	14 48
Pollokshaws West	d	10 16	10 21	10 46	10 51		11 16	11 21		11 46	11 51		12 16	12 21	12 46	12 51		13 16		13 21	13 46	13 51		14 16	14 21	14 46	14 51
Thornliebank	d		10 24		10 54			11 24			11 54			12 24		12 54				13 24		13 54			14 24		14 54
Giffnock	d		10 27		10 57			11 27			11 57			12 27		12 57				13 27		13 57			14 27		14 57
Clarkston	d		10 30		11 00			11 30			12 00			12 30		13 00				13 30		14 00			14 30		15 00
Busby	d		10 33		11 03			11 33			12 03			12 33		13 03				13 33		14 03			14 33		15 03
Thorntonhall	d				11 06						12 06					13 06						14 06					15 06
Hairmyres	d		10 39		11 10			11 39			12 10			12 39		13 10				13 39		14 10			14 39		15 10
East Kilbride	a		10 42		11 13			11 42			12 13			12 42		13 13				13 42		14 13			14 42		15 13
Kennishead	d	10 19		10 49			11 19			11 49			12 19		12 49			13 19			13 49			14 19		14 49	
Priesthill & Darnley	d	10 21		10 51			11 21			11 51			12 21		12 51			13 21			13 51			14 21		14 51	
Nitshill	d	10 24		10 54			11 24			11 54			12 24		12 54			13 24			13 54			14 24		14 54	
Barrhead	d	10c27		10a57		11 15	11a27			11a57		12 15	12a27		12a57		13 15	13a27			13a57		14 15	14a27		14a57	
Dunlop	d					11 27						12 27					13 27						14 27				
Stewarton	d					11 31						12 31					13 31						14 31				
Kilmaurs	d					11 36						12 36					13 36						14 36				
Kilmarnock 3	a					11 41						12 41					13 42						14 41				

		SR	SR	SR		SR	SR SX	SR SO	SR C	SR	SR	SR	SR	SR		SR SX	SR SO	SR SX	SR SO	SR SX	SR SX	SR	SR	SR SX		SR	SR
Glasgow Central 15	d	15 03	15 07	15 12		15 37	15 41	15 42	15 48	16 07	16 12	16 33	16 42	16 48		16 52	17 07	17 10	17 12	17 14	17 23	17 37	17 42	17 57		18 03	18 07
Crossmyloof	d		15 13	15 18		15 43	15 48	15 48		16 13	16 18	16 39	16 48			16 58	17 13	17 16	17 18		17 29	17 43	17 48	18 03			18 13
Pollokshaws West	d		15 16	15 21		15 46	15 51	15 51		16 16	16 21	16 42	16 51			17 01	17 16	17 19	17 21		17 32	17 45	17 51	18 06			18 16
Thornliebank	d			15 24			15 54	15 54			16 24		16 54			17 04			17 24		17 35		17 54	18 09			
Giffnock	d			15 27			15 57	15 57			16 27		16 57			17 07			17 27		17 38		17 57	18 12			
Clarkston	d			15 30			16 01	16 00			16 30		17 00			17 10			17 30	17 29	17 41		18 00	18 15			
Busby	d			15 33			16 04	16 03			16 33		17 03			17a14			17 33		17 44		18 03	18 18			
Thorntonhall	d						16 07	16 06			16 36		17 06						17 36		17 47		18 06				
Hairmyres	d			15 39			16 11	16 10			16 40		17 10						17 40	17 36	17 51		18 10	18 24			
East Kilbride	a			15 42			16 14	16 13			16 43		17 13						17 43	17 40	17 54		18 13	18 27			
Kennishead	d		15 19			15 49				16 19		16 45					17 19	17 22				17 48					18 19
Priesthill & Darnley	d		15 21			15 51				16 21		16 47					17 21	17 24				17 50					18 21
Nitshill	d		15 24			15 54				16 24		16 50					17 24	17 27				17 53					18 24
Barrhead	d	15 16	15a27			15a57			16 00	16a27		16a53		17 00			17a27	17a30				17a59				18 15	18a28
Dunlop	d	15 28							16 12					17 12												18 27	
Stewarton	d	15 32							16 16					17 16												18 31	
Kilmaurs	d	15 37							16 20					17 20												18 36	
Kilmarnock 3	a	15 46							16 25					17 25												18 43	

		SR SO	SR SX	SR	SR	SR	SR	SR SX	SR SO	SR		SR A	SR	SR	SR	SR	SR	SR	SR	SR A	SR	SR	SR	SR	SR		
Glasgow Central 15	d	18 12	18 23	18 37	18 42	19 03	19 12	19 22	19 24	19 42		20 03	20 12	20 22	20 42	21 03	21 12	21 22	21 42	22 03	22 12	22 22	22 42	23 03	23 12		
Crossmyloof	d	18 18	18 29	18e42	18 48		19 18	19 28	19 28	19 48			20 18	20 28	20 48		21 18	21 28	21 48		22 18	22 28	22 48	23 09	23 18		
Pollokshaws West	d	18 21	18 32	18 46	18 51		19 21	19 31	19 31	19 51			20 21	20 31	20 51		21 21	21 31	21 51		22 21	22 31	22 51	23 12	23 21		
Thornliebank	d	18 24	18 35		18 54		19 24			19 54			20 24		20 54		21 24		21 54		22 24		22 54		23 24		
Giffnock	d	18 27	18 38		18 57		19 27			19 57			20 27		20 57		21 27		21 57		22 27		22 57		23 27		
Clarkston	d	18 30	18 41		19 00		19 30			20 00			20 30		21 00		21 30		22 00		22 30		23 00		23 30		
Busby	d	18 33	18 44		19 03		19 33			20 03			20 33		21 03		21 33		22 03		22 33		23 03		23 33		
Thorntonhall	d				19 06					20 06					21 06				22 06				23 06		23 36		
Hairmyres	d	18 39	18 50		19 10		19 39			20 10			20 39		21 10		21 39		22 10		22 39		23 10		23 40		
East Kilbride	a	18 42	18 53		19 13		19 42			20 13			20 42		21 13		21 42		22 13		22 42		23 13		23 43		
Kennishead	d			18 49				19 34	19 34					20 34				21 34				22 34		23 15			
Priesthill & Darnley	d			18 51				19 36	19 36					20 36				21 36				22 36		23 17			
Nitshill	d			18 54				19 39	19 39					20 39				21 39				22 39		23 20			
Barrhead	d			18a57		19 15		19a42	19a44			20 15		20a42		21 15		21a42		22 15		22a42		23 23			
Dunlop	d					19 27						20 27				21 27				22 27				23 35			
Stewarton	d					19 31						20 31				21 31				22 31				23 39			
Kilmaurs	d					19 36						20 36				21 36				22 36				23 44			
Kilmarnock 3	a					19 41						20 39				21 41				22 39				23 49			

For general notes see front of timetable
For details of catering facilities see Directory of Train Operators

A To Carlisle (Table 216)
B To Girvan (Table 218)
C To Newcastle (Table 48)
b Saturdays arr. 1 minute later
c Arrival time. Saturdays arr. 1029
e Saturdays dep. 1 minute later

Table 222

Sundays

Glasgow Central → East Kilbride, Barrhead and Kilmarnock

Network Diagram - see first page of Table 216

		SR	SR	SR	SR	SR	SR	SR	SR	SR	SR	SR	SR	SR	SR	SR	SR	SR	SR	SR	SR A	SR
Glasgow Central 15	d	08 42	08 48	09 12	09 42	09 48	10 12	10 42	10 48	11 12	11 42	11 48	12 12	12 42	12 48	13 12	13 42	13 48	14 12	14 42	14 48	15 12
Crossmyloof	d	08 48		09 18	09 48		10 18	10 48		11 18	11 48		12 18	12 48		13 18	13 48		14 18	14 48		15 18
Pollokshaws West	d	08 51	08 56	09 21	09 51	09 56	10 21	10 51	10 56	11 21	11 51	11 56	12 21	12 51	12 56	13 21	13 51	13 56	14 21	14 51	14 56	15 21
Thornliebank	d	08 54		09 24	09 54		10 24	10 54		11 24	11 54		12 24	12 54		13 24	13 54		14 24	14 54		15 24
Giffnock	d	08 57		09 27	09 57		10 27	10 57		11 27	11 57		12 27	12 57		13 27	13 57		14 27	14 57		15 27
Clarkston	d	09 00		09 30	10 00		10 30	11 00		11 30	12 00		12 30	13 00		13 30	14 00		14 30	15 00		15 30
Busby	d	09 03		09 33	10 03		10 33	11 03		11 33	12 03		12 33	13 03		13 33	14 03		14 33	15 03		15 33
Thorntonhall	d	09 06			10 06			11 06			12 06			13 06			14 06			15 06		
Hairmyres	d	09 10		09 39	10 10		10 39	11 10		11 39	12 10		12 39	13 10		13 39	14 10		14 39	15 10		15 39
East Kilbride	a	09 13		09 42	10 13		10 42	11 13		11 42	12 13		12 42	13 13		13 42	14 13		14 42	15 13		15 42
Kennishead	d																					
Priesthill & Darnley	d																					
Nitshill	d																					
Barrhead	d		09 02			10 02			11 02			12 02			13 02			14 02			15 02	
Dunlop	d		09 15			10 15			11 15			12 15			13 15			14 15			15 15	
Stewarton	d		09 19			10 19			11 19			12 19			13 19			14 19			15 19	
Kilmaurs	d		09 24			10 24			11 24			12 24			13 24			14 24			15 24	
Kilmarnock 3	a		09 29			10 29			11 29			12 29			13 29			14 29			15 27	

		SR	SR	SR	SR	SR	SR	SR	SR	SR	SR	SR	SR	SR	SR	SR	SR	SR	SR	SR A	SR	SR
Glasgow Central 15	d	15 42	15 48	16 12	16 42	16 48	17 12	17 42	17 48	18 12	18 42	18 48	19 12	19 42	20 12	20 42	21 12	21 42	22 12	22 28	22 42	23 12
Crossmyloof	d	15 48		16 18	16 48		17 18	17 48		18 18	18 48		19 18	19 48	20 18	20 48	21 18	21 48	22 18		22 48	23 18
Pollokshaws West	d	15 51	15 56	16 21	16 51	16 56	17 21	17 51	17 56	18 21	18 51	18 56	19 21	19 51	20 21	20 51	21 21	21 51	22 21		22 51	23 21
Thornliebank	d	15 54		16 24	16 54		17 24	17 54		18 24	18 54		19 24	19 54	20 24	20 54	21 24	21 54	22 24		22 54	23 24
Giffnock	d	15 57		16 27	16 57		17 27	17 57		18 27	18 57		19 27	19 57	20 27	20 57	21 27	21 57	22 27		22 57	23 27
Clarkston	d	16 00		16 30	17 00		17 30	18 00		18 30	19 00		19 30	20 00	20 30	21 00	21 30	22 00	22 30		23 00	23 30
Busby	d	16 03		16 33	17 03		17 33	18 03		18 33	19 03		19 33	20 03	20 33	21 03	21 33	22 03	22 33		23 03	23 33
Thorntonhall	d	16 06			17 06			18 06			19 06			20 06		21 06		22 06			23 06	23 36
Hairmyres	d	16 10		16 39	17 10		17 39	18 10		18 39	19 10		19 39	20 10	20 39	21 10	21 39	22 10	22 39		23 10	23 40
East Kilbride	a	16 13		16 42	17 13		17 42	18 13		18 42	19 13		19 42	20 13	20 42	21 13	21 42	22 13	22 42		23 13	23 43
Kennishead	d																					
Priesthill & Darnley	d																					
Nitshill	d																					
Barrhead	d		16 02			17 02			18 02			19 02								22 40		
Dunlop	d		16 15			17 15			18 15			19 15								22 52		
Stewarton	d		16 19			17 19			18 19			19 19								22 56		
Kilmaurs	d		16 24			17 24			18 24			19 24								23 01		
Kilmarnock 3	a		16 29			17 29			18 29			19 29								23 04		

For general notes see front of timetable
For details of catering facilities see Directory of Train Operators

A To Carlisle (Table 216)

Kilmarnock, Barrhead and East Kilbride → Glasgow Central

Network Diagram - see first page of Table 216

Miles	Miles			SR SX	SR	SR	SR	SR SX	SR SX	SR SX	SR SO	SR SO	SR SX	SR SX	SR A	SR SX	SR SO	SR SX	SR	SR SX	SR SO	SR SX	SR SX	SR	SR ◇ B
0	—	**Kilmarnock** 3	d		06 32				07 32			07 32			07 58										09 12
2¼	—	Kilmaurs	d		06 36				07 36			07 36			08 02										09 16
5½	—	Stewarton	d		06 41				07 41			07 41			08 08										09 21
7¾	—	Dunlop	d		06 46				07 46			07 46			08 13										09 26
16¾	—	**Barrhead**	d		06 56		07 35		07 56			07 56	08 05		08 24				08 35				09 10		09 37
18½	—	Nitshill	d		06 59		07 38					07 59	08 08						08 38				09 13		
19½	—	Priesthill & Darnley	d		07 01		07 40					08 01	08 10						08 40				09 15		
20	—	Kennishead	d		07 03		07 42					08 03	08 12						08 42				09 17		
—	0	**East Kilbride**	d	06 18		07 05		07 29		07 47	07 46			08 03			08 18	08 17		08 30	08 48	08 55		09 20	
—	1½	Hairmyres	d	06 21		07 08		07 32		07 51	07 49			08 07			08 21	08 24		08 33	08 51	08 58		09 23	
—	3	Thorntonhall	d	06 25		07 12		07 36			07 53			08 10			08 25	08 27		08 37	08 55	09 02			
—	4¼	Busby	d	06 28		07 15		07 39			07 56			08 14		08 23	08 28	08 30		08 40	08 58	09 05		09 28	
—	5	Clarkston	d	06 30		07 18		07 42		07 59	07 58			08 17		08 26	08 30	08 33		08 42	09 00	09 07		09 31	
—	6¼	Giffnock	d	06 33		07 21		07 46			08 01			08 20		08 29	08 32	08 36		08 45	09 03	09 10		09 33	
—	7¼	Thornliebank	d	06 36		07 23		07 49			08 04			08 23		08 31	08 35	08 38		08 48	09 06	09 13		09 36	
21¼	8¼	Pollokshaws West	d	06 39	07 07	07 26	07 45	07 52			08 06	08 11	08 15	08 26		08 34	08 38	08 42	08 45		09 09	09 16	09 20	09 39	
22¼	9¼	Crossmyloof	d	06 42	07 10	07 29	07 48	07 54			08 09	08 13	08 18	08 29		08 37	08 42	08 45	08 48		09 12	09 19	09 23	09 42	
24¼	11½	**Glasgow Central** 15	a	06 48	07 18	07 35	07 55	08 01	08 09	08 13	08 15	08 21	08 25	08 35	08 37	08 43	08 48	08 51	08 55	08 57	09 18	09 25	09 30	09 48	09 50

		SR	SR	SR	NT C	SR	SR	SR	SR	SR	SR	SR	SR	SR	SR	SR	SR	SR	SR A	SR	SR	SR	SR
Kilmarnock 3	d				10 04					10 50					11 50				12 50				
Kilmaurs	d				10 08					10 54					11 54				12 54				
Stewarton	d				10 13					10 59					11 59				12 59				
Dunlop	d				10 18					11 04					12 04				13 04				
Barrhead	d	09 40		10 05	10 28		10 35		11 05	11 14		11 35		12 05	12 14		12 35		13 05	13 14		13 35		14 05
Nitshill	d	09 43		10 08			10 38		11 08			11 38		12 08			12 38		13 08			13 38		14 08
Priesthill & Darnley	d	09 45		10 10			10 40		11 10			11 40		12 10			12 40		13 10			13 40		14 10
Kennishead	d	09 47		10 12			10 42		11 12			11 42		12 12			12 42		13 12			13 42		14 12
East Kilbride	d		09 48			10 20		10 48			11 20		11 48			12 20		12 48			13 20		13 48	
Hairmyres	d		09 51			10 23		10 51			11 23		11 51			12 23		12 51			13 23		13 51	
Thorntonhall	d		09 55					10 55					11 55					12 55					13 55	
Busby	d		09 58			10 28		10 58			11 28		11 58			12 28		12 58			13 28		13 58	
Clarkston	d		10 00			10 31		11 00			11 31		12 00			12 31		13 00			13 31		14 00	
Giffnock	d		10 03			10 33		11 03			11 33		12 03			12 33		13 03			13 33		14 03	
Thornliebank	d		10 06			10 36		11 06			11 36		12 06			12 36		13 06			13 36		14 06	
Pollokshaws West	d	09 50	10 09	10 15		10 39	10 45	11 09	11 15		11 39	11 45	12 09	12 15		12 39	12 45	13 09	13 15		13 39	13 45	14 09	14 15
Crossmyloof	d	09 53	10 12	10 18		10 42	10 48	11 12	11 18		11 42	11 48	12 12	12 18		12 42	12 48	13 12	13 18		13 42	13 48	14 12	14 18
Glasgow Central 15	a	10b00	10 18	10 25	10 41	10 48	10 55	11 18	11 25	11 27	11 48	11 55	12 18	12 25	12 27	12 48	12 55	13 18	13 25	13c27	13 48	13 55	14 18	14 25

		SR ◇ B	SR	SR	SR	SR	SR A	SR	SR	SR	SR	SR D	SR	SR	SR	SR	SR A	SR	SR	SR	SR	SR	SR	SR
Kilmarnock 3	d	13 50					14 55					15 48					16 46			17 28				
Kilmaurs	d	13 54					14 59					15 52					16 50			17 32				
Stewarton	d	13 59					15 04					15 57					16 55			17 37				
Dunlop	d	14 04					15 09					16 02					17 00			17 42				
Barrhead	d	14 14		14 35		15 05	15 19		15 35		16 05	16 17		16 35		17 05	17 18		17 35	17 59		18 05		18 35
Nitshill	d			14 38		15 08			15 38		16 08			16 38		17 08			17 38			18 08		18 38
Priesthill & Darnley	d			14 40		15 10			15 40		16 10			16 40		17 10			17 40			18 10		18 40
Kennishead	d			14 42		15 12			15 42		16 12			16 42		17 12			17 42			18 12		18 42
East Kilbride	d		14 20		14 48			15 20		15 48			16 20		16 48			17 20			17e47		18 20	
Hairmyres	d		14 23		14 51			15 23		15 51			16 23		16 51			17 23			17 51		18 23	
Thorntonhall	d				14 55					15 55					16 55						17 55			
Busby	d		14 28		14 58			15 28		15 58			16 28		16 58			17 28			17 58		18 28	
Clarkston	d		14 31		15 00			15 31		16 00			16 31		17 00			17 31			18 00		18 31	
Giffnock	d		14 33		15 03			15 33		16 03			16 33		17 03			17 33			18 03		18 33	
Thornliebank	d		14 36		15 06			15 36		16 06			16 36		17 06			17 36			18 06		18 36	
Pollokshaws West	d		14 39	14 45	15 09	15 15		15 39	15 45	16 09	16 15		16 39	16 45	17 09	17 15		17 39	17 45		18 09	18 15	18 39	18 45
Crossmyloof	d		14 42	14 48	15 12	15 18		15 42	15 48	16 12	16 18		16 42	16 48	17 12	17 18		17 42	17 48		18 12	18 18	18 42	18 48
Glasgow Central 15	a	14 27	14 48	14 55	15 18	15 25	15f33	15 48	15 55	16 18	16 25	16 32	16 48	16 55	17 18	17 27	17 31	17 51	17 55	18 12	18 20	18 25	18 51	18 55

		SR	SR	SR	SR	SR	SR	SR A	SR	SR	SR	SR	SR	SR	SR	SR	SR	SR	SR	SR A	SR	SR
Kilmarnock 3	d			18 50				19 50				20 50				21 50				22 50		
Kilmaurs	d			18 54				19 54				20 54				21 54				22 54		
Stewarton	d			18 59				19 59				20 59				21 59				22 59		
Dunlop	d			19 04				20 04				21 04				22 04				23 04		
Barrhead	d		19 05	19 14		19 50		20 14		20 50		21 14		21 50		22 14		22 50		23 14		
Nitshill	d		19 08			19 53				20 53				21 53				22 53				
Priesthill & Darnley	d		19 10			19 55				20 55				21 55				22 55				
Kennishead	d		19 12			19 57				20 57				21 57				22 57				
East Kilbride	d	18g46			19 20		19 48		20 20		20 48		21 20		21 48		22 20		22 48		23 20	23 48
Hairmyres	d	18 51			19 23		19 51		20 23		20 51		21 23		21 51		22 23		22 51		23 23	23 51
Thorntonhall	d	18 55					19 55				20 55				21 55				22 55			23 55
Busby	d	18 58			19 28		19 58		20 28		20 58		21 28		21 58		22 28		22 58		23 28	23 58
Clarkston	d	19 00			19 31		20 00		20 31		21 00		21 31		22 00		22 31		23 00		23 31	00 01
Giffnock	d	19 03			19 33		20 03		20 33		21 03		21 33		22 03		22 33		23 03		23 33	00 03
Thornliebank	d	19 06			19 36		20 06		20 36		21 06		21 36		22 06		22 36		23 06		23 36	00 06
Pollokshaws West	d	19 09	19 15		19 39	20 00	20 09		20 39	21 00	21 09		21 39	22 00	22 09		22 39	23 00	23 09		23 39	00 09
Crossmyloof	d	19 12	19 18		19 42	20 03	20 12		20 42	21 03	21 12		21 42	22 03	22 12		22 42	23 03	23 12		23 42	00 12
Glasgow Central 15	a	19 19	19 25	19 27	19 48	20 10	20 18	20 27	20 48	21 10	21 18	21 27	21 48	22 10	22 18	22h29	22 48	23h12	23 18	23f28	23 48	00 18

For general notes see front of timetable
For details of catering facilities see
Directory of Train Operators

A From Carlisle (Table 216)
B From Stranraer (Table 218)
C From Newcastle (Table 216)
D From Girvan (Table 218)
b Saturdays arr. 1 minute later
c Saturdays arr. 2 minutes later
e Saturdays dep. 1 minute later
f Saturdays arr. 1 minute earlier
g Saturdays dep. 2 minutes later
h Saturdays arr. 2 minutes earlier

Sundays

Kilmarnock, Barrhead and East Kilbride → Glasgow Central

Network Diagram - see first page of Table 216

		SR	SR	SR	SR	SR	SR	SR	SR	SR	SR	SR
Kilmarnock 3	d			09 35			10 35			11 35		
Kilmaurs	d			09 39			10 39			11 39		
Stewarton	d			09 44			10 44			11 44		
Dunlop	d			09 49			10 49			11 49		
Barrhead	d			09 59			10 59			11 59		
Nitshill	d											
Priesthill & Darnley	d											
Kennishead	d											
East Kilbride	d	08 48	09 20		09 48	10 20		10 48	11 20		11 48	12 20
Hairmyres	d	08 51	09 23		09 51	10 23		10 51	11 23		11 51	12 23
Thorntonhall	d	08 55			09 55			10 55			11 55	
Busby	d	08 58	09 28		09 58	10 28		10 58	11 28		11 58	12 28
Clarkston	d	09 00	09 31		10 00	10 31		11 00	11 31		12 00	12 31
Giffnock	d	09 03	09 34		10 03	10 34		11 03	11 34		12 03	12 34
Thornliebank	d	09 06	09 36		10 06	10 36		11 06	11 36		12 06	12 36
Pollokshaws West	d	09 09	09 39	10 05	10 09	10 39	11 05	11 09	11 39	12 05	12 09	12 39
Crossmyloof	d	09 12	09 42		10 12	10 42		11 12	11 42		12 12	12 42
Glasgow Central 15	a	09 18	09 48	10 14	10 18	10 48	11 14	11 18	11 48	12 14	12 18	12 48

		SR	SR	SR	SR	SR	SR	SR ◇ A	SR	SR	SR	SR
Kilmarnock 3	d	12 35			13 35			14 35			15 35	
Kilmaurs	d	12 39			13 39			14 39			15 39	
Stewarton	d	12 44			13 44			14 44			15 44	
Dunlop	d	12 49			13 49			14 49			15 49	
Barrhead	d	12 59			13 59			14 59			15 59	
Nitshill	d											
Priesthill & Darnley	d											
Kennishead	d											
East Kilbride	d		12 48	13 20		13 48	14 20		14 48	15 20		15 48
Hairmyres	d		12 51	13 23		13 51	14 23		14 51	15 23		15 51
Thorntonhall	d		12 55			13 55			14 55			15 55
Busby	d		12 58	13 28		13 58	14 28		14 58	15 28		15 58
Clarkston	d		13 00	13 31		14 00	14 31		15 00	15 31		16 00
Giffnock	d		13 03	13 34		14 03	14 34		15 03	15 34		16 03
Thornliebank	d		13 06	13 36		14 06	14 36		15 06	15 36		16 06
Pollokshaws West	d	13 05	13 09	13 39	14 05	14 09	14 39	15 05	15 09	15 39	16 05	16 09
Crossmyloof	d		13 12	13 42		14 12	14 42		15 12	15 42		16 12
Glasgow Central 15	a	13 14	13 18	13 48	14 14	14 18	14 48	15 14	15 18	15 48	16 14	16 18

		SR	SR	SR	SR	SR	SR	SR	SR	SR	SR	SR
Kilmarnock 3	d		16 35			17 35			18 35			19 35
Kilmaurs	d		16 39			17 39			18 39			19 39
Stewarton	d		16 44			17 44			18 44			19 44
Dunlop	d		16 49			17 49			18 49			19 49
Barrhead	d		16 59			17 59			18 59			19 59
Nitshill	d											
Priesthill & Darnley	d											
Kennishead	d											
East Kilbride	d	16 20		16 48	17 20		17 48	18 20		18 48	19 20	
Hairmyres	d	16 23		16 51	17 23		17 51	18 23		18 51	19 23	
Thorntonhall	d			16 55			17 55			18 55		
Busby	d	16 28		16 58	17 28		17 58	18 28		18 58	19 28	
Clarkston	d	16 31		17 00	17 31		18 00	18 31		19 00	19 31	
Giffnock	d	16 34		17 03	17 34		18 03	18 34		19 03	19 33	
Thornliebank	d	16 36		17 06	17 36		18 06	18 36		19 06	19 36	
Pollokshaws West	d	16 39	17 05	17 09	17 39	18 05	18 09	18 39	19 05	19 09	19 39	20 05
Crossmyloof	d	16 42		17 12	17 42		18 12	18 42		19 12	19 42	
Glasgow Central 15	a	16 48	17 14	17 18	17 48	18 14	18 18	18 48	19 14	19 18	19 48	20 14

		SR	SR	SR	SR	SR A	SR	SR	SR	SR	SR
Kilmarnock 3	d					21 18					
Kilmaurs	d					21 22					
Stewarton	d					21 27					
Dunlop	d					21 32					
Barrhead	d					21 42					
Nitshill	d										
Priesthill & Darnley	d										
Kennishead	d										
East Kilbride	d	19 48	20 20	20 48	21 20		21 48	22 20	22 48	23 20	23 48
Hairmyres	d	19 51	20 23	20 51	21 23		21 51	22 23	22 51	23 23	23 51
Thorntonhall	d	19 55		20 55			21 55		22 55		23 55
Busby	d	19 58	20 28	20 58	21 28		21 58	22 28	22 58	23 28	23 58
Clarkston	d	20 00	20 31	21 00	21 31		22 00	22 31	23 00	23 31	00 01
Giffnock	d	20 03	20 33	21 03	21 33		22 03	22 33	23 03	23 33	00 03
Thornliebank	d	20 06	20 36	21 06	21 36		22 06	22 36	23 06	23 36	00 06
Pollokshaws West	d	20 09	20 39	21 09	21 39		22 09	22 39	23 09	23 39	00 09
Crossmyloof	d	20 12	20 42	21 12	21 42		22 12	22 42	23 12	23 42	00 12
Glasgow Central 15	a	20 18	20 48	21 18	21 48	21 55	22 18	22 48	23 18	23 48	00 18

For general notes see front of timetable
For details of catering facilities see Directory of Train Operators

A From Carlisle (Table 216)

Glasgow Central, Cathcart Circle, Neilston and Newton

Network Diagram - see first page of Table 220

Miles	Miles	Miles		SR SO A	SR SO	SR	SR	SR A	SR	SR SX B	SR	SR SX	SR SX	SR SX A	SR SO	SR SX	SR SO	SR SX	SR	SR SX	SR SX B	SR	SR SX	SR SX
0	0	0	**Glasgow Central** 15 226 d	00 05	00 10	06 10	06 20	06 27	06 35	06 40	06 50	06 58	07 03	07 05	07 10	07 20	07 20	07 25	07 35	07 39	07 44	07 50	07 55	07 59
2¼	—	—	Pollokshields West d	00 10				06 32	06 40					07 10					07 40				08 00	
2¾	—	—	Maxwell Park d	00 12				06 34	06 42					07 12					07 42				08 02	
3¼	—	—	Shawlands d	00 14				06 36	06 44					07 14					07 44				08 04	
3¾	—	—	Pollokshaws East d	00 15				06 37	06 45					07 15					07 45				08 05	
4¼	—	—	Langside d	00 17				06 39	06 47					07 17					07 47				08 07	
—	1¾	1¾	Pollokshields East d		00 14	06 14	06 24			06 44	06 54	07 02	07 07		07 14	07 24	07 24	07 29			07 48	07 54		08 03
—	2¼	2¼	Queens Park d		00 16	06 16	06 26			06 46	06 56	07 04	07 09		07 16	07 26	07 26	07 31			07 50	07 56		08 05
—	2½	2½	Crosshill d		00 17	06 17	06 27			06 47	06 57	07 05	07 10		07 17	07 27	07 27	07 32			07 51	07 57		08 06
—	3¼	3¼	Mount Florida d		00 19	06 19	06 29			06 49	06 59	07 07	07 12		07 19	07 29	07 29	07 34			07 53	07 59		08 08
5¼	—	4	Cathcart d	00a21			06 31	06a41		06a51	07 01		07 14	07a19			07 31	07 36			07a55	08 01	08a09	
—	—	4¾	Muirend d				06 33				07 03		07 16				07 33	07 38		07 48		08 03		
—	—	6	Williamwood d				06 36				07 06		07 19				07 36	07 41		07 51		08 06		
—	—	6¾	Whitecraigs d				06 38				07 08		07 21				07 38	07 43		07 53		08 08		
—	—	7¾	Patterton d				06 41				07 11		07 24				07 41	07 46		07 55		08 11		
—	—	11¾	**Neilston** a				06 47				07 17		07 30				07 47	07 52		08 01		08 17		
5¾	4½	—	Kings Park d		00 21	06 21			06 51			07 09			07 21	07 31			07 50					08 10
6	4¾	—	Croftfoot d		00 23	06 23			06 53			07 11			07 23	07 33			07 52					08 12
7	5¾	—	Burnside d		00 26	06 26			06 55			07 14			07 26	07 36			07 56					08 15
8½	7¼	—	Kirkhill a		00 29	06 29			06 58			07 17			07 29	07 39			07 59					08 18
10	8¾	—	**Newton** 226 a		00 32	06 32			07 01			07 20			07 32	07 43			08 02					08 21

	SR SX	SR SX B	SR SO	SR SX A	SR SO	SR SX	SR SX B	SR SX	SR SX A	SR	SR SO	SR SX	SR SX B	SR SX A	SR	SR	SR	SR B	SR
Glasgow Central 15 226 d	08 05	08 10	08 10	08 19	08 20	08 21	08 23	08 26	08 30	08 35	08 50	08 52	08 57	09 05	09 10	09 20	09 35	09 40	09 50
Pollokshields West d				08 24					08 36	08 40				09 10			09 40		
Maxwell Park d				08 26					08 38	08 42				09 12			09 42		
Shawlands d				08 28					08 40	08 44				09 14			09 44		
Pollokshaws East d				08 29					08 41	08 45				09 15			09 45		
Langside d				08 31					08 43	08 47				09 17			09 47		
Pollokshields East d	08 09	08 14	08 14		08 24	08 25	08 27	08 30			08 54	08 56	09 01		09 14	09 24		09 44	09 54
Queens Park d	08 11	08 16	08 16		08 26	08 27	08 29	08 32			08 56	08 58	09 03		09 16	09 26		09 46	09 56
Crosshill d	08 12	08 17	08 17		08 27	08 28	08 30	08 33			08 57	08 59	09 04		09 17	09 27		09 47	09 57
Mount Florida d	08 14	08 19	08 19		08 29	08 30	08 32	08 35			08 59	09 01	09 06		09 19	09 29		09 49	09 59
Cathcart d	08 16	08a21		08a33	08 31	08 32	08a34		08a46		09 01	09 03	09a08	09a20		09 31		09a51	10 01
Muirend d	08 18				08 33	08 34					09 03	09 05				09 33			10 03
Williamwood d	08 21				08 36	08 37					09 06	09 08				09 36			10 06
Whitecraigs d	08 23				08 38	08 39					09 08	09 10				09 38			10 08
Patterton d	08 26				08 41	08 43					09 11	09 13				09 41			10 11
Neilston a	08 32				08 47	08 48					09 17	09 18				09 47			10 17
Kings Park d			08 21					08 37		08 51					09 21		09 51		
Croftfoot d			08 23					08 39		08 53					09 23		09 53		
Burnside d			08 26					08 42		08 55					09 26		09 55		
Kirkhill a			08 29					08 45		08 58					09 29		09 58		
Newton 226 a			08 32					08 48		09 03					09 32		10 01		

	SR A	and at the same minutes past each hour until	SR A	SR	SR SO	SR SX	SR	SR SX B	SR SO B	SR SO	SR SX	SR SX B	SR A	SR	SR	SR	SR B	SR	SR SX	SR A	SR SX	SR SO
Glasgow Central 15 226 d	10 05		15 05	15 10	15 20	15 20	15 35	15 39	15 40	15 50	15 56	16 00	16 05	16 10	16 20	16 35	16 40	16 50	17 03	17 05	17 08	17 10
Pollokshields West d	10 10		15 10				15 40						16 10			16 40				17 10		
Maxwell Park d	10 12		15 12				15 42						16 12			16 42				17 12		
Shawlands d	10 14		15 14				15 44						16 14			16 44				17 14		
Pollokshaws East d	10 15		15 15				15 45						16 15			16 45				17 15		
Langside d	10 17		15 17				15 47						16 17			16 47				17 17		
Pollokshields East d				15 14	15 24	15 24		15 43	15 44	15 54	16 00	16 04		16 14	16 24		16 44	16 54	17 07			17 14
Queens Park d				15 16	15 26	15 26		15 45	15 46	15 56	16 02	16 06		16 16	16 26		16 46	16 56	17 09			17 16
Crosshill d				15 17	15 27	15 27		15b53	15 47	15 57	16 03	16 07		16 17	16 27		16 47	16 57	17 10			17 17
Mount Florida d				15 19	15 29	15 29		15 55	15 49	15 59	16 05	16 09		16 19	16 29		16 49	16 59	17 12			17 19
Cathcart d	10a20		15a20		15 31	15 31		15a57	15a51	16 01	16 07	16a11	16a19		16 31		16a51	17 01		17a20		
Muirend d					15 33	15 33				16 03	16 09				16 33			17 03			17 17	
Williamwood d					15 36	15 36				16 06	16 12				16 36			17 06			17 20	
Whitecraigs d					15 38	15 38				16 08	16 14				16 38			17 08			17 22	
Patterton d					15 41	15 45				16 11	16 17				16 41			17 11			17 24	
Neilston a					15 47	15 50				16 17	16 23				16 47			17 17			17 30	
Kings Park d				15 21			15 51							16 21		16 51			17 14			17 21
Croftfoot d				15 23			15 53							16 23		16 53			17 16			17 23
Burnside d				15 26			15 55							16 26		16 55			17 19			17 26
Kirkhill a				15 29			15 58							16 29		16 58			17 22			17 29
Newton 226 a				15 32			16 01							16 32		17 01			17 25			17 32

	SR SX	SR SX A	SR SX	SR SO	SR SX	SR	SR SO B	SR SX B	SR	SR A	SR SO	SR SX	SR	SR	SR B	SR	SR A	SR	and at the same minutes past each hour until	SR	SR
Glasgow Central 15 226 d	17 12	17 16	17 20	17 20	17 28	17 35	17 40	17 44	17 50	18 05	18 10	18 11	18 20	18 35	18 40	18 50	19 05	19 10		23 10	23 20
Pollokshields West d		17 21				17 40				18 10				18 40			19 10				
Maxwell Park d		17 23				17 42				18 12				18 42			19 12				
Shawlands d		17 25				17 44				18 14				18 44			19 14				
Pollokshaws East d		17 26				17 45				18 15				18 45			19 15				
Langside d		17 28				17 47				18 17				18 47			19 17				
Pollokshields East d	17 16		17 24	17 24	17 32		17 44	17 48	17 54		18 14	18 16	18 24		18 44	18 54		19 14		23 14	23 24
Queens Park d	17 18		17 26	17 26	17 34		17 46	17 50	17 56		18 16	18 17	18 26		18 46	18 56		19 16		23 16	23 26
Crosshill d	17 19		17 27	17 27	17 35		17 47	17 51	17 57		18 17	18 19	18 27		18 47	18 57		19 17		23 17	23 27
Mount Florida d	17 21		17 29	17 29	17 37		17 49	17 53	17 59		18 19	18 20	18 29		18 49	18 59		19 19		23 19	23 29
Cathcart d	17 24	17a30		17 31	17 39		17a51	17a55	18 01	18a19			18 31		18a51	19 01	19a20				23 31
Muirend d	17 27			17 33	17 41				18 03				18 33			19 03					23 33
Williamwood d	17 30			17 36	17 44				18 06				18 36			19 06					23 36
Whitecraigs d	17 32			17 38	17 46				18 08				18 38			19 08					23 38
Patterton d	17 34			17 41	17 49				18 11				18 41			19 11					23 41
Neilston a	17 41			17 47	17 55				18 17				18 47			19 17					23 47
Kings Park d			17 31			17 51					18 21	18 23		18 51				19 21		23 21	
Croftfoot d			17 33			17 53					18 23	18 25		18 53				19 23		23 23	
Burnside d			17 36			17 55					18 26	18 27		18 55				19 26		23 26	
Kirkhill a			17 39			17 58					18 29	18 30		18 58				19 29		23 29	
Newton 226 a			17 45			18 02					18 32	18 34		19 00				19 32		23 32	

For general notes see front of timetable
For details of catering facilities see Directory of Train Operators

A To Glasgow Central via Queens Park
B To Glasgow Central via Maxwell Park
b Arr. 1546

Glasgow Central, Cathcart Circle, Neilston and Newton

Network Diagram - see first page of Table 220

Mondays to Saturdays

		SR FO
Glasgow Central 15	226 d	23 50
Pollokshields West	d	
Maxwell Park	d	
Shawlands	d	
Pollokshaws East	d	
Langside	d	
Pollokshields East	d	23 54
Queens Park	d	23 56
Crosshill	d	23 57
Mount Florida	d	23 59
Cathcart	d	00 01
Muirend	d	00 03
Williamwood	d	00 06
Whitecraigs	d	00 08
Patterton	d	00 11
Neilston	a	00 17
Kings Park	d	
Croftfoot	d	
Burnside	d	
Kirkhill	a	
Newton	226 a	

Sundays

		SR	SR	SR	SR		SR	SR	SR	SR
Glasgow Central 15	226 d	08 20	08 35	08 50	09 10		22 20	22 35	22 50	23 10
Pollokshields West	d		08 40					22 40		
Maxwell Park	d		08 42					22 42		
Shawlands	d		08 44					22 44		
Pollokshaws East	d		08 45					22 45		
Langside	d		08 47			and at		22 47		
Pollokshields East	d	08 24		08 54	09 14	the same	22 24		22 54	23 14
Queens Park	d	08 26		08 56	09 16	minutes	22 26		22 56	23 16
Crosshill	d	08 27		08 57	09 17		22 27		22 57	23 17
Mount Florida	d	08 29		08 59	09 19	past	22 29		22 59	23 19
Cathcart	d	08 31		09 01			22 31		23 01	
Muirend	d	08 33		09 03		each	22 33		23 03	
Williamwood	d	08 36		09 06			22 36		23 06	
Whitecraigs	d	08 38		09 08		hour until	22 38		23 08	
Patterton	d	08 41		09 11			22 41		23 11	
Neilston	a	08 47		09 17			22 47		23 17	
Kings Park	d		08 51		09 21			22 51		23 21
Croftfoot	d		08 53		09 23			22 53		23 23
Burnside	d		08 55		09 26			22 55		23 26
Kirkhill	a		08 58		09 29			22 58		23 29
Newton	226 a		09 01		09 32			23 03		23 32

For general notes see front of timetable
For details of catering facilities see Directory of Train Operators

Table 223

Mondays to Saturdays

Newton, Neilston, Cathcart Circle and Glasgow Central

Network Diagram - see first page of Table 220

Miles	Miles	Miles			SR SO A	SR	SR A	SR	SR SX B	SR		SR SX A	SR	SR	SR SX	SR SO	SR SX		SR SX B	SR SX	SR SX A	SR SO	SR SX	SR SX		SR SX B
0	0	—	**Newton** 226	d		06 11		06 41					07 11		07 34	07 44				07 48						
1½	1½	—	Kirkhill	d		06 14		06 44					07 14		07 38	07 46				07 51						
2¾	2¾	—	Burnside	d		06 17		06 47					07 17		07 41	07 48				07 54						
3¾	3¾	—	Croftfoot	d		06 19		06 49					07 19		07 43	07 50				07 56						
4¼	4¼	—	Kings Park	d		06 21		06 51					07 21		07 45	07 52				07 58						
—	—	0	**Neilston**	d						06 56				07 26			07 39					07 56	08 03	08 10		
—	—	3¾	Patterton	d						07 01				07 31			07 44					08 01	08 08	08 15		
—	—	4¾	Whitecraigs	d						07 03				07 33			07 46					08 03	08 10	08 17		
—	—	5½	Williamwood	d						07 06				07 36			07 49					08 06	08 13	08 20		
—	—	7	Muirend	d						07 09				07 39			07 51					08 09	08 15	08 22		
4¾	—	7¾	Cathcart	d	00 21		06 41		06 52	07 11		07 21		07 41			07 53		07 55		08 09	08 11	08 17			08 21
—	5½	8½	Mount Florida	d	00 23		06 43	06 53		07 13		07 23		07 43	07 47	07 54	07 55				08 11	08 13	08 19			
—	6	9	Crosshill	d	00 25		06 45	06 55		07 15		07 25		07 45	07 49	07 56	07 57				08 13	08 15	08 21			
—	6½	9½	Queens Park	d	00 27		06 47	06 57		07 17		07 27		07 47	07 51	07 58	07 59				08 15	08 17	08 23			
—	6¾	9¾	Pollokshields East	d	00 28		06 48	06 58		07 18		07 28		07 48	07 52	07 59	08 00				08 16	08 18	08 24			
5¾	—	—	Langside	d		06 24			06 54				07 24						07 57	08 01						08 24
6¼	—	—	Pollokshaws East	d		06 26			06 56				07 26						07 59	08 03						08 26
6¾	—	—	Shawlands	d		06 28			06 58				07 28						08 01	08 05						08 28
7½	—	—	Maxwell Park	d		06 29			06 59				07 29						08 02	08 06						08 29
8	—	—	Pollokshields West	d		06 31			07 01				07 31						08 04	08 08						08 31
10	8¾	11¾	**Glasgow Central** 15 226	a	00 33	06 37	06 53	07 03	07 07	07 23		07 33	07 38	07 53	07 57	08 05	08 05		08 11	08 15	08 21	08 23	08 30	08 32		08 39

		SR SO	SR SX	SR SX A	SR SX B	SR	SR SX A		SR SX	SR SO	SR SX	SR SX	SR SX B	SR SO		SR SX	SR SX A	SR	SR	SR SO	SR SX			SR B	SR	SR A
Newton 226	d	08 11	08 17						08 34	08 41		08 58						09 11		09 41	09 42					
Kirkhill	d	08 14	08 20						08 38	08 44		09 01						09 14		09 44	09 45					
Burnside	d	08 17	08 23						08 41	08 47		09 04						09 17		09 47	09 48					
Croftfoot	d	08 19	08 25						08 43	08 49		09 06						09 19		09 49	09 50					
Kings Park	d	08 21	08 27						08 45	08 51		09 08						09 21		09 51	09 52					
Neilston	d					08 26					08 41			08 56		09 02			09 26						09 56	
Patterton	d					08 31					08 46			09 01		09 07			09 31						10 01	
Whitecraigs	d					08 33					08 48			09 03		09 09			09 33						10 03	
Williamwood	d					08 36					08 51			09 06		09 12			09 36						10 06	
Muirend	d					08 39					08 53			09 09		09 14			09 39						10 09	
Cathcart	d			08 34	08 34	08 41	08 46				08 55		09 08	09 11		09 16	09 21		09 41					09 52	10 11	10 21
Mount Florida	d		08 29	08 36		08 43	08 48			08 53	08 57	09 10		09 13		09 18	09 23		09 43	09 53	09 54				10 13	10 23
Crosshill	d		08 31	08 38		08 45	08 50			08 55	08 59	09 12		09 15		09 20	09 25		09 45	09 55	09 56				10 15	10 25
Queens Park	d		08 35	08 40		08 47	08 52			08 57	09 01	09 14		09 17		09 22	09 27		09 47	09 57	09 58				10 17	10 27
Pollokshields East	d		08 36	08 41		08 48	08 53			08 58	09 02	09 15		09 18		09 23	09 28		09 48	09 58	09 59				10 18	10 28
Langside	d	08 24			08 36				08 48				09 10					09 24						09 54		
Pollokshaws East	d	08 26			08 38				08 50				09 12					09 26						09 56		
Shawlands	d	08 28			08 40				08 52				09 14					09 28						09 58		
Maxwell Park	d	08 29			08 41				08 53				09 15					09 29						09 59		
Pollokshields West	d	08 31			08 43				08 55				09 17					09 31						10 01		
Glasgow Central 15 226	a	08 39	08 41	08 47	08 49	08 53	08 59		09 01	09 03	09 07	09 20	09 23	09 23		09 28	09 33	09 38	09 53	10 04	10 04			10 07	10 23	10 33

		SR	SR	SR		SR	SR SO B		SR SX B	SR	SR SX B	SR A	SR	SR SO		SR SX	SR	SR B	SR SO	SR SX	SR A		SR	SR SX A	SR
Newton 226	d	10 11		10 41		15 41							16 11				16 41						17 11		
Kirkhill	d	10 14		10 44		15 44							16 14				16 44						17 14		
Burnside	d	10 17		10 47		15 47							16 17				16 47						17 17		
Croftfoot	d	10 19		10 49		15 49							16 19				16 49						17 19		
Kings Park	d	10 21		10 51	and at	15 51							16 21				16 51						17 21		
Neilston	d		10 26		the same					15 56				16 26		16 33			16 56	17 02					17 26
Patterton	d		10 31		minutes					16 01				16 31		16 38			17 01	17 07					17 31
Whitecraigs	d		10 33		past					16 03				16 33		16 40			17 03	17 09					17 33
Williamwood	d		10 36		each					16 06				16 36		16 43			17 06	17 12					17 36
Muirend	d		10 39		hour until					16 09				16 39		16 45			17 09	17 14					17 39
Cathcart	d		10 41				15 52		15 58	16 11	16 13	16 21		16 41		16 47		16 52	17 11	17 16	17 21			17 32	17 41
Mount Florida	d		10 43	10 53		15 53				16 13		16 23		16 43		16 49	16 53		17 13	17 18	17 23			17 34	17 43
Crosshill	d		10 45	10 55		15 55				16 15		16 25		16 45		16 51	16 55		17 15	17 20	17 25			17 36	17 45
Queens Park	d		10 47	10 57		15 57				16 17		16 27		16 47		16 53	16 57		17 17	17 22	17 27			17 37	17 47
Pollokshields East	d		10 48	10 58		15 58				16 18		16 28		16 48		16 54	16 58		17 18	17 23	17 28			17 39	17 48
Langside	d	10 24					15 54		16 00		16 15		16 24					16 54					17 24		
Pollokshaws East	d	10 26					15 56		16 02		16 17		16 26					16 56					17 26		
Shawlands	d	10 28					15 58		16 04		16 19		16 28					16 58					17 28		
Maxwell Park	d	10 29					15 59		16 05		16 20		16 29					16 59					17 29		
Pollokshields West	d	10 31					16 01		16 07		16 22		16 31					17 01					17 31		
Glasgow Central 15 226	a	10 38	10 53	11 03		16 03	16 07		16 13	16 23	16 28	16 33	16 38	16 53		16 59	17 03	17 07	17 23	17 29	17 33		17 38	17 44	17 53

For general notes see front of timetable
For details of catering facilities see
Directory of Train Operators

A From Glasgow Central via Maxwell Park
B From Glasgow Central via Queens Park

Newton, Neilston, Cathcart Circle and Glasgow Central

Network Diagram - see first page of Table 220

		SR SX	SR SO	SR SO A	SR SX	SR SX A		SR	SR B	SR	SR SX	SR	SR		SR A	SR	SR B	SR	SR	SR		SR A	SR	SR B	SR	SR
Newton	226 d	17 41	17 41							18 11			18 41					19 11		19 41					20 11	
Kirkhill	d	17 44	17 44							18 14			18 44					19 14		19 44					20 14	
Burnside	d	17 47	17 47							18 17			18 47					19 17		19 47					20 17	
Croftfoot	d	17 49	17 49							18 19			18 49					19 19		19 49					20 19	
Kings Park	d	17 51	17 51							18 21			18 51					19 21		19 51					20 21	
Neilston	d				17 42			17 56			18 13	18 26				18 56			19 26				19 56			20 26
Patterton	d							18 01			18 18	18 31				19 01			19 31				20 01			20 31
Whitecraigs	d							18 03			18 20	18 33				19 03			19 33				20 03			20 33
Williamwood	d							18 06			18 23	18 36				19 06			19 36				20 06			20 36
Muirend	d							18 09			18 26	18 39				19 09			19 39				20 09			20 39
Cathcart	d			17 52	17 54	17 55		18 11	18 21		18 28	18 41			18 52	19 11	19 21		19 41			19 52	20 11	20 21		20 41
Mount Florida	d	17 53	17 53		17 56			18 13	18 23		18 30	18 43	18 53			19 13	19 23		19 43	19 53			20 13	20 23		20 43
Crosshill	d		17 55		17 58			18 15	18 25		18 32	18 45	18 55			19 15	19 25		19 45	19 55			20 15	20 25		20 45
Queens Park	d		17 57		18 00			18 17	18 27		18 34	18 47	18 57			19 17	19 27		19 47	19 57			20 17	20 27		20 47
Pollokshields East	d		17 58		18 01			18 18	18 28		18 35	18 48	18 58			19 18	19 28		19 48	19 58			20 18	20 28		20 48
Langside	d			17 54		17 57				18 24					18 54			19 24				19 54			20 24	
Pollokshaws East	d			17 56		17 59				18 26					18 56			19 26				19 56			20 26	
Shawlands	d			17 58		18 01				18 28					18 58			19 28				19 58			20 28	
Maxwell Park	d			17 59		18 02				18 29					18 59			19 29				19 59			20 29	
Pollokshields West	d			18 01		18 04				18 31					19 01			19 31				20 01			20 31	
Glasgow Central 15	226 a	18 03	18 03	18 07	18 07	18 10		18 23	18 33	18 38	18 40	18 53	19 05		19 07	19 23	19b33	19 38	19c54	20 03		20 07	20 23	20 33	20 38	20 53

		SR	SR A	SR		SR B	SR	SR	SR	SR A	SR		SR B	SR	SR	SR	SR A	SR SO		SR SX	SR B	SR	SR			
Newton	226 d	20 41					21 11		21 41					22 11		22 41						23 11				
Kirkhill	d	20 44					21 14		21 44					22 14		22 44						23 14				
Burnside	d	20 47					21 17		21 47					22 17		22 47						23 17				
Croftfoot	d	20 49					21 19		21 49					22 19		22 49						23 19				
Kings Park	d	20 51					21 21		21 51					22 21		22 51						23 21				
Neilston	d			20 56				21 26			21 56				22 26			22 56		22 56			23 26			
Patterton	d			21 01				21 31			22 01				22 31			23 01		23 01			23 31			
Whitecraigs	d			21 03				21 33			22 03				22 33			23 03		23 03			23 33			
Williamwood	d			21 06				21 36			22 06				22 36			23 06		23 06			23 36			
Muirend	d			21 09				21 39			22 09				22 39			23 09		23 09			23 39			
Cathcart	d		20 52	21 11		21 21		21 41		21 52	22 11		22 21		22 41		22 52	23 11		23 11	23 21		23 41			
Mount Florida	d	20 53		21 13		21 23		21 43	21 53		22 13		22 23		22 43	22 53		23 13		23 13	23 23		23 43			
Crosshill	d	20 55		21 15		21 25		21 45	21 55		22 15		22 25		22 45	22 55		23 15		23 15	23 25		23 45			
Queens Park	d	20 57		21 17		21 27		21 47	21 57		22 17		22 27		22 47	22 57		23 17		23 17	23 27		23 47			
Pollokshields East	d	20 58		21 18		21 28		21 48	21 58		22 18		22 28		22 48	22 58		23 18		23 18	23 28		23 48			
Langside	d		20 54				21 24			21 54				22 24			22 54					23 24				
Pollokshaws East	d		20 56				21 26			21 56				22 26			22 56					23 26				
Shawlands	d		20 58				21 28			21 58				22 28			22 58					23 28				
Maxwell Park	d		20 59				21 29			21 59				22 29			22 59					23 29				
Pollokshields West	d		21 01				21 31			22 01				22 31			23 01					23 31				
Glasgow Central 15	226 a	21 03	21 07	21 23		21 33	21 38	21 53	22 03	22c08	22 23		22 33	22 38	22 53	23 03	23c08	23 23		23 24	23 33	23 38	23 53			

Sundays

			SR	SR	SR	SR			SR		SR		SR		SR										
Newton	226 d			09 11		09 41			22 41				23 11												
Kirkhill	d			09 14		09 44			22 44				23 14												
Burnside	d			09 17		09 47			22 47				23 17												
Croftfoot	d			09 19		09 49			22 49				23 19												
Kings Park	d			09 21		09 51			22 51				23 21												
Neilston	d		08 56		09 26		and at the same minutes past each hour until				22 56				23 26										
Patterton	d		09 01		09 31						23 01				23 31										
Whitecraigs	d		09 03		09 33						23 03				23 33										
Williamwood	d		09 06		09 36						23 06				23 36										
Muirend	d		09 09		09 39						23 09				23 39										
Cathcart	d		09 11		09 41						23 11				23 41										
Mount Florida	d		09 13		09 43	09 53			22 53		23 13				23 43										
Crosshill	d		09 15		09 45	09 55			22 55		23 15				23 45										
Queens Park	d		09 17		09 47	09 57			22 57		23 17				23 47										
Pollokshields East	d		09 18		09 48	09 58			22 58		23 18				23 48										
Langside	d			09 24									23 24												
Pollokshaws East	d			09 26									23 26												
Shawlands	d			09 28									23 28												
Maxwell Park	d			09 29									23 29												
Pollokshields West	d			09 31									23 31												
Glasgow Central 15	226 a		09 23	09 38	09 53	10 03			23 03		23 23		23 38		23 53										

For general notes see front of timetable
For details of catering facilities see Directory of Train Operators

A From Glasgow Central via Queens Park
B From Glasgow Central via Maxwell Park
b Saturdays arr. 1 minute later
c Saturdays arr. 1 minute earlier

Motherwell and Glasgow Queen Street → Cumbernauld and Falkirk Grahamston

Network Diagram - see first page of Table 220

Miles	Miles			SR	SR	SR	SR	SR		SR	SR SX A	SR	SR	SR		SR	SR	SR	SR	SR		SR	SR	SR	SR	SR
—	0	**Motherwell** 226	d			06 11					07 12	07 34				08 37			09 37				10 37			11 37
—	4½	Whifflet	d			06 20					07 19	07 42				08 45			09 45				10 45			11 45
—	5¼	**Coatbridge Central**	d			06a23	06 45				07a23	07 45				08 48			09 48				10 48			11 48
0	—	**Glasgow Queen Street** 10	d	05 51	06 21			06 51		07 20			07 52	08 24			08 53	09 21		09 51		10 21		10 51	11 23	
1½	—	Springburn	d	05 55	06 25			06 55		07 25			07 55	08 25			08 55	09 25		09 55		10 25		10 55	11 25	
5¼	—	Stepps	d	06 02	06 32			07 02		07 32			08 02	08 32			09 02	09 32		10 02		10 32		11 02	11 32	
7¾	—	Gartcosh	d	06 06	06 36			07 06		07 36			08 06	08 36			09 06	09 36		10 06		10 36		11 06	11 36	
13¼	11	Greenfaulds	d	06 14	06 44		06 54	07 14		07 44		07 53	08 14	08 44		08 56	09 14	09 44	09 57	10 14		10 44	10 57	11 14	11 44	11 57
14	11¾	**Cumbernauld**	d	06a18	06 46		06a57	07a18		07 46		07a57	08a19	08 46		09a01	09a20	09 46	10a00	10a18		10 46	11a00	11a18	11 46	12a00
22½	—	Camelon	d		06 57					08 04				09 04				10 04				11 04			12 04	
24	—	**Falkirk Grahamston**	a		07 03					08 11				09 10				10 10				11 10			12 13	
—	—	Edinburgh 10	a		08 14					09 02				10b02				11 02				12 01			13 02	
—	—	Stirling	a		07 53					08 53				09 52				10 54				11 53			12 53	

		SR	SR		SR	SR	SR	SR	SR		SR	SR	SR	SR	SR		SR	SR SX	SR SO	SR	SR		SR SX B	SR	SR SX B	SR
Motherwell 226	d				12 37			13 37				14 37			15 37					16 37			16 42		17 12	17 37
Whifflet	d				12 45			13 45				14 45			15 45					16 45			16 48		17 18	17 45
Coatbridge Central	d				12 48			13 48				14 48			15 48					16 48			16a53		17a22	17 48
Glasgow Queen Street 10	d	11 51	12 24			12 51	13 21		13 51		14 21		14 51	15 23			15 54	16 22	16 22		16 52			17 22		
Springburn	d	11 55	12 26			12 55	13 25		13 55		14 25		14 55	15 26			15 56	16 26	16 26		16 56			17 26		
Stepps	d	12 02	12 33			13 02	13 32		14 02		14 32		15 02	15 33			16 03	16 33	16 33		17 03			17 33		
Gartcosh	d	12 06	12 37			13 06	13 36		14 06		14 36		15 06	15 37			16 07	16 37	16 37		17 07			17 37		
Greenfaulds	d	12 14	12 45		12 57	13 14	13 44	13 57	14 14		14 44	14 57	15 14	15 45	15 57		16 15	16 45	16 45	16 57	17 15			17 45		17 57
Cumbernauld	d	12a18	12 47		13a00	13a18	13 46	14a00	14a18		14 46	15a00	15a18	15 47	16a00		16a21	16 47	16 47	17a00	17a19			17 47		18a00
Camelon	d		13 04				14 04				15 04			16 04				17 01	17 07					18 05		
Falkirk Grahamston	a		13 10				14 10				15 10			16 10				17 04	17 10					18 11		
Edinburgh 10	a		14 01				15 02				16 01			17c02				18 02	18 02					19e01		
Stirling	a		13 53				14 53				15 53			16 53				17 27	17 53					18 53		

		SR	SR SX C	SR		SR	SR	SR	SR	SR		SR	SR	SR	SR	SR		SR	SR	SR	SR B	SR		SR		
Motherwell 226	d		17 57			18 37			19 37				20 37			21 37					22 42					
Whifflet	d		18 03			18 45			19 45				20 45			21 45					22 48					
Coatbridge Central	d		18a06			18 48			19 48				20 48			21 48					22a52					
Glasgow Queen Street 10	d	17 51		18 24			18 51	19 21		19 51		20 21		20 51	21 23			21 51	22 21	22 51		23 21		23 51		
Springburn	d	17 55		18 26			18 55	19 25		19 55		20 25		20 55	21 26			21 55	22 25	22 55		23 25		23 55		
Stepps	d	18 02		18 33			19 02	19 32		20 02		20 32		21 02	21 33			22 02	22 32	23 02		23 32		00 02		
Gartcosh	d	18 06		18 37			19 06	19 36		20 06		20 36		21 06	21 36			22 06	22 36	23 06		23 36		00 06		
Greenfaulds	d	18 14		18 45		18 57	19 14	19 44	19 57	20 14		20 44	20 59	21 14	21 44	21 59		22 14	22 44	23 14		23 44		00 14		
Cumbernauld	d	18a18		18 47		19a00	19a18	19a48	20a00	20 16		20a48	21a02	21 16	21a51	22a03		22 16	22a48	23 16		23a48		00a18		
Camelon	d			19 04						20 35				21 27				22 28		23 29						
Falkirk Grahamston	a			19 10						20 40				21 33				22 34		23 35						
Edinburgh 10	a			20 02						21 31				23 01				00 09								
Stirling	a			19 53						21 23				22 23				23 24		00 23						

Sundays

until 22 November

		SR	SR		SR	SR		SR	SR		SR	SR		SR	SR		SR	SR		SR	SR		SR		
Glasgow Queen Street	d	08 19	09 22		10 21	11 21		12 23	13 21		14 21	15 21		16 21	17 21		18 23	19 22		20 21	21 26		22 23		
Springburn	d	08 24	09 27		10 26	11 26		12 26	13 25		14 25	15 25		16 25	17 25		18 27	19 26		20 25	21 30		22 27		
Stepps	d	08 30	09 33		10 32	11 32		12 32	13 32		14 32	15 32		16 32	17 32		18 34	19 33		20 32	21 37		22 34		
Gartcosh	d	08 34	09 37		10 36	11 36		12 36	13 36		14 36	15 36		16 36	17 36		18 38	19 37		20 36	21 41		22 38		
Greenfaulds	d	08 42	09 45		10 44	11 44		12 44	13 44		14 44	15 44		16 44	17 44		18 46	19 45		20 44	21 49		22 46		
Cumbernauld	a	08 46	09 49		10 48	11 48		12 50	13 48		14 48	15 48		16 48	17 48		18 50	19 49		20 48	21 53		22 50		

Sundays

from 29 November

		SR	SR	SR	SR	SR	SR	SR	SR	SR	SR	SR	SR	SR	SR	SR	SR	SR	SR	SR	SR	SR	SR	SR	SR	SR
Glasgow Queen Street	d	08 19	08 42	09 22	09 51	10 21	10 51	11 21	11 51	12 23	12 52	13 21	13 51	14 21	14 51	15 21	15 54	16 21	16 52	17 21	17 51	18 23	19 22	20 21	21 26	22 23
Springburn	d	08 24	08 47	09 27	09 56	10 26	10 56	11 26	11 56	12 26	12 57	13 25	13 55	14 25	14 55	15 25	16 00	16 25	16 56	17 25	17 55	18 27	19 26	20 25	21 30	22 27
Stepps	d	08 30	08 54	09 33	10 02	10 32	11 02	11 32	12 02	12 32	13 04	13 32	14 02	14 32	15 02	15 32	16 07	16 32	17 03	17 32	18 02	18 34	19 33	20 32	21 37	22 34
Gartcosh	d	08 34	08 58	09 37	10 06	10 36	11 06	11 36	12 06	12 36	13 07	13 36	14 06	14 36	15 06	15 36	16 11	16 36	17 07	17 36	18 06	18 38	19 37	20 36	21 41	22 38
Greenfaulds	d	08 42	09 06	09 45	10 14	10 44	11 14	11 44	12 14	12 44	13 15	13 44	14 14	14 44	15 14	15 44	16 19	16 44	17 15	17 44	18 14	18 46	19 45	20 44	21 49	22 46
Cumbernauld	a	08 46	09 09	09 49	10 18	10 48	11 18	11 48	12 20	12 50	13 20	13 48	14 18	14 48	15 18	15 48	16 22	16 48	17 19	17 48	18 18	18 50	19 49	20 48	21 53	22 50

For general notes see front of timetable
For details of catering facilities see Directory of Train Operators

- A From Garscadden (Table 226)
- B From Milngavie (Table 226)
- C From Dalmuir (Table 226)
- b Saturdays arr. 1004
- c Saturdays arr. 1704
- e Saturdays arr. 1902

Table 224

Mondays to Saturdays

Falkirk Grahamston and Cumbernauld → Glasgow Queen Street and Motherwell

Network Diagram - see first page of Table 220

Miles	Miles			SR	SR A	SR	SR	SR	SR SX A	SR	SR	SR	SR	SR	SR	SR	SR	SR	SR	SR	SR	SR
—	—	Stirling	d				05 30				07 16			08 05			09 06			10 06		
—	—	Edinburgh 10	d				05 18				07 04			08 03			09 04			10 04		
0	—	**Falkirk Grahamston**	d	05 41			06 42				07 41			08 41			09 41			10 41		
1½	—	Camelon	d	05 44			06 44				07 43			08 44			09 44			10 44		
10	0	**Cumbernauld**	d	05 58		06 28	06 58	07 08		07 29	07 57	08 10	08 28	08 58	09 10	09 28	09 58	10 10	10 28	10 58	11 10	11 28
10¾	¾	Greenfaulds	d	05 59		06 29	06 59	07 10		07 30	07 59	08 12	08 29	08 59	09 12	09 29	09 59	10 12	10 29	10 59	11 12	11 29
16¼	—	Gartcosh	d	06 06		06 36	07 06			07 37	08 06		08 36	09 06		09 36	10 06		10 36	11 06		11 36
18¾	—	Stepps	d	06 10		06 40	07 10			07 41	08 10		08 40	09 10		09 40	10 10		10 40	11 10		11 40
22¾	—	Springburn	d	06 16		06 46	07 16			07 47	08 16		08 46	09 16		09 46	10 16		10 46	11 16		11 46
24	—	**Glasgow Queen Street 10**	a	06 25		06 55	07 28			07 56	08 29		08 57	09 25		09 55	10 25		10 55	11 25		11 55
—	6¼	**Coatbridge Central**	d		06 39			07 18	07 39			08 20			09 20			10 20			11 20	
—	7¼	Whifflet	d		06 41			07 20	07 41			08 22			09 22			10 22			11 22	
—	11¾	**Motherwell**	226 a		06 49			07 30	07 49			08 32			09 32			10 32			11 32	

		SR	SR	SR	SR	SR	SR	SR	SR	SR	SR	SR SO	SR SX	SR	SR	SR	SR	SR	SR	SR SX B	SR
Stirling	d	11 06			12 06			13 06			14 06				15 06			16 06			
Edinburgh 10	d	11 04			12 04			13b04			14 04				15 04			16 04			
Falkirk Grahamston	d	11 41			12 41			13 41			14 41				15 42			16 41			
Camelon	d	11 44			12 44			13 44			14 44				15 45			16 44			
Cumbernauld	d	11 58	12 10	12 28	12 57	13 10	13 28	13 58	14 10	14 28	14 58	15 11	15 11	15 28	15 59	16 10	16 29	16 58	17 10		17 28
Greenfaulds	d	11 59	12 12	12 29	12 59	13 12	13 29	13 59	14 12	14 30	14 59	15 13	15 13	15 29	16 00	16 12	16 30	16 59	17 12		17 29
Gartcosh	d	12 06		12 36	13 06		13 36	14 06		14 36	15 06			15 36	16 07		16 37	17 06			17 36
Stepps	d	12 10		12 40	13 10		13 40	14 10		14 40	15 10			15 40	16 11		16 41	17 10			17 40
Springburn	d	12 16		12 46	13 16		13 46	14 16		14 46	15 16			15 46	16 17		16 47	17 16			17 46
Glasgow Queen Street 10	a	12 25		12 55	13 25		13 55	14 25		14 55	15 25			15 55	16 26		16 56	17 25			17 55
Coatbridge Central	d		12 20			13 20			14 20			15 20	15 21			16 20			17 20	17 30	
Whifflet	d		12 22			13 22			14 22			15 22	15 23			16 22			17 22	17 32	
Motherwell	226 a		12 32			13 32			14 32			15 32	15 33			16 32			17 32	17 39	

		SR SX B	SR	SR	SR SX A	SR	SR	SR	SR	SR	SR	SR	SR	SR	SR	SR	SR	SR	SR	SR
Stirling	d		17 06				18 06			19 06					20 36			21 06		22 06
Edinburgh 10	d		17 04				18 04			19 04					20 34			21 33		22c33
Falkirk Grahamston	d		17 41				18 41			19 41					21 11			22 11		23 11
Camelon	d		17 44				18 44			19 44					21 14			22 14		23 14
Cumbernauld	d		17 58	18 10		18 28	18 58	19 10	19 28	19 58	20 10	20 28	20 58	21 10	21 28	21 58	22 10	22 28	22 58	23 31
Greenfaulds	d		17 59	18 12		18 29	18 59	19 12	19 29	19 59	20 12	20 29	20 59	21 12	21 29	21 59	22 12	22 29	22 59	23 32
Gartcosh	d		18 06			18 36	19 06		19 36	20 06		20 36	21 06		21 36	22 06		22 36	23 06	23 39
Stepps	d		18 10			18 40	19 10		19 40	20 10		20 40	21 10		21 40	22 10		22 40	23 10	23 43
Springburn	d		18 16			18 46	19 16		19 46	20 16		20 46	21 16		21 46	22 16		22 46	23 16	23 49
Glasgow Queen Street 10	a		18 25			18 55	19 25		19 55	20 25		20 55	21 25		21 55	22 25		22 55	23 25	23 58
Coatbridge Central	d	17 56		18 20	18 39			19 20			20 20			21 20			22 20			
Whifflet	d	17 58		18 22	18 41			19 22			20 22			21 22			22 22			
Motherwell	226 a	18 07		18 32	18 49			19 32			20 32			21 32			22 32			

Sundays
until 22 November

		SR	SR	SR	SR	SR	SR	SR	SR	SR	SR	SR	SR	SR	SR	SR	SR	SR
Cumbernauld	d	08 55	09 58	10 58	11 58	12 58	13 58	14 58	15 58	16 58	17 59	18 59	19 58	21 03	22 00	22 58		
Greenfaulds	d	08 56	09 59	10 59	11 59	12 59	13 59	14 59	16 00	16 59	18 00	19 00	19 59	21 05	22 01	22 59		
Gartcosh	d	09 03	10 06	11 06	12 06	13 06	14 06	15 06	16 07	17 06	18 07	19 07	20 06	21 10	22 08	23 06		
Stepps	d	09 07	10 10	11 10	12 10	13 10	14 10	15 10	16 11	17 10	18 11	19 11	20 10	21 14	22 12	23 10		
Springburn	d	09 13	10 16	11 16	12 16	13 16	14 16	15 16	16 17	17 16	18 17	19 17	20 16	21 18	22 18	23 16		
Glasgow Queen Street	a	09 22	10 25	11 25	12 25	13 26	14 26	15 25	16 25	17 25	18 26	19 26	20 26	21 28	22 27	23 25		

Sundays
from 29 November

		SR	SR	SR	SR	SR	SR	SR	SR	SR	SR	SR	SR	SR	SR	SR	SR	SR	SR	SR	SR	SR	SR	SR	SR	SR
Cumbernauld	d	08 55	09 28	09 58	10 28	10 58	11 26	11 58	12 29	12 58	13 28	13 58	14 28	14 58	15 32	15 58	16 29	16 58	17 28	17 59	18 28	18 59	19 58	21 03	22 00	22 58
Greenfaulds	d	08 56	09 29	09 59	10 29	10 59	11 28	11 59	12 31	12 59	13 29	13 59	14 29	14 59	15 34	16 00	16 30	16 59	17 29	18 00	18 29	19 00	19 59	21 05	22 01	22 59
Gartcosh	d	09 03	09 36	10 06	10 36	11 06	11 35	12 06	12 38	13 06	13 36	14 06	14 36	15 06	15 41	16 07	16 37	17 06	17 36	18 07	18 36	19 07	20 06	21 10	22 08	23 06
Stepps	d	09 07	09 40	10 10	10 40	11 10	11 39	12 10	12 42	13 10	13 40	14 10	14 40	15 10	15 45	16 11	16 41	17 10	17 40	18 11	18 40	19 11	20 10	21 14	22 12	23 10
Springburn	d	09 13	09 46	10 16	10 46	11 16	11 45	12 16	12 48	13 16	13 46	14 16	14 46	15 16	15 51	16 17	16 47	17 16	17 46	18 17	18 46	19 17	20 16	21 18	22 18	23 16
Glasgow Queen Street	a	09 22	09 55	10 25	10 55	11 25	11 54	12 25	12 58	13 26	13 57	14 26	14 57	15 25	15 59	16 25	16 58	17 25	17 57	18 26	18 57	19 26	20 26	21 28	22 27	23 25

For general notes see front of timetable
For details of catering facilities see Directory of Train Operators

A To Milngavie (Table 226)
B To Dalmuir (Table 226)
b Saturdays dep. 1303
c Saturdays dep. 2234

Network Diagram for Tables 225, 228, 229, 230, 238, 240, 242

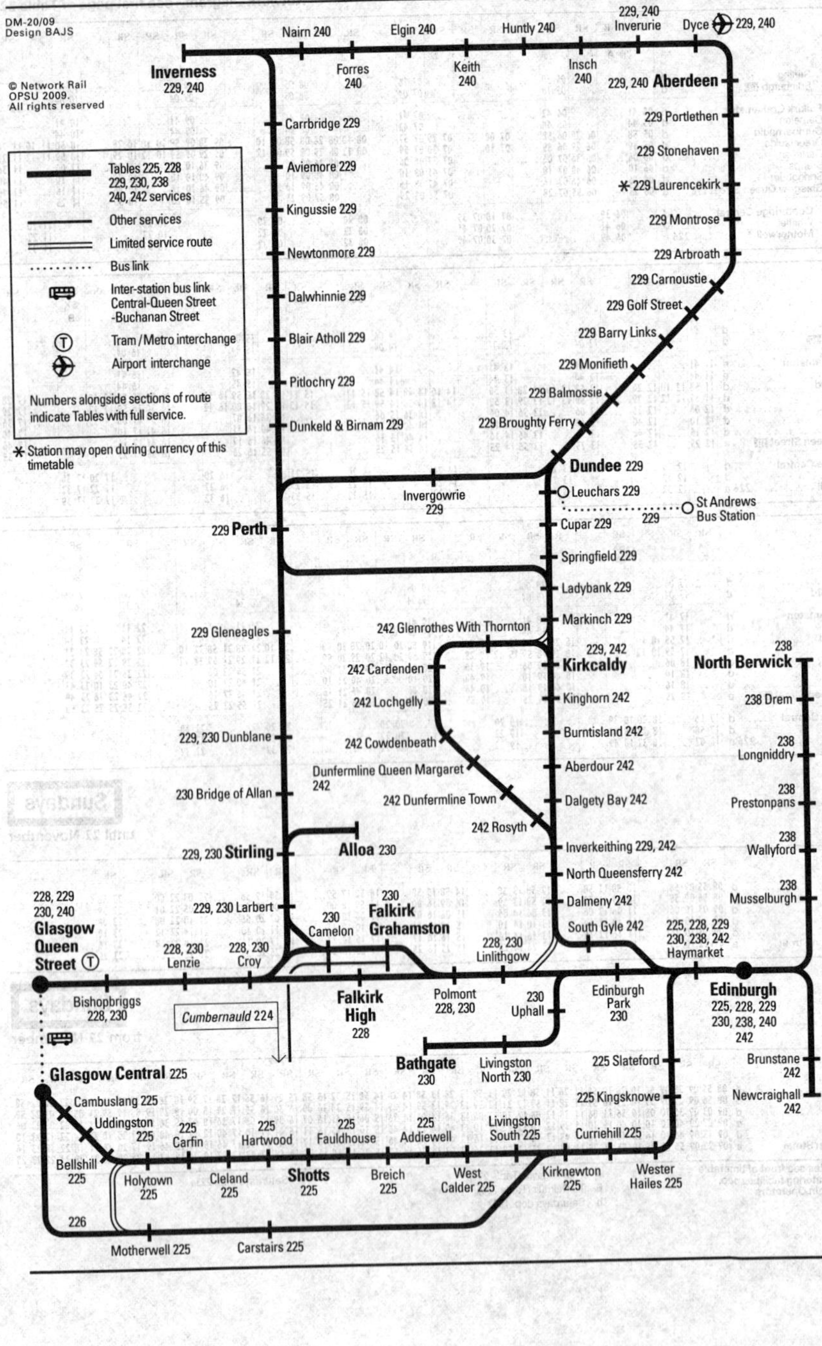

DM-20/09
Design BAJS
© Network Rail
OPSU 2009.
All rights reserved
Tables 225, 228 229, 230, 238 240, 242 services
Other services
Limited service route
Bus link
Inter-station bus link Central-Queen Street -Buchanan Street
Tram / Metro interchange
Airport interchange
Numbers alongside sections of route indicate Tables with full service.
* Station may open during currency of this timetable
Inverness 229, 240
Nairn 240
Forres 240
Elgin 240
Keith 240
Huntly 240
Insch 240
229, 240 Inverurie
Dyce 229, 240
229, 240 Aberdeen
229 Portlethen
229 Stonehaven
* 229 Laurencekirk
229 Montrose
229 Arbroath
229 Carnoustie
229 Golf Street
229 Barry Links
229 Monifieth
229 Balmossie
229 Broughty Ferry
Dundee 229
Carrbridge 229
Aviemore 229
Kingussie 229
Newtonmore 229
Dalwhinnie 229
Blair Atholl 229
Pitlochry 229
Dunkeld & Birnam 229
Invergowrie 229
229 Perth
Leuchars 229
St Andrews Bus Station
229
Cupar 229
Springfield 229
Ladybank 229
Markinch 229
242 Glenrothes With Thornton
229 Gleneagles
229, 242 Kirkcaldy
242 Cardenden
242 Lochgelly
242 Cowdenbeath
Kinghorn 242
Burntisland 242
Aberdour 242
Dalgety Bay 242
Dunfermline Queen Margaret 242
242 Dunfermline Town
242 Rosyth
229, 230 Dunblane
230 Bridge of Allan
229, 230 Stirling
Alloa 230
Inverkeithing 229, 242
North Queensferry 242
Dalmeny 242
South Gyle 242
238 North Berwick
238 Drem
238 Longniddry
238 Prestonpans
238 Wallyford
238 Musselburgh
229, 230 Larbert
230 Camelon
230 Falkirk Grahamston
228, 229 230, 240 Glasgow Queen Street
228, 230 Lenzie
228, 230 Croy
228, 230 Linlithgow
225, 228, 229 230, 238, 242 Haymarket
Edinburgh 225, 228, 229 230, 238, 240 242
Bishopbriggs 228, 230
Cumbernauld 224
Falkirk High 228
Polmont 228, 230
230 Uphall
Edinburgh Park 230
Bathgate 230
Livingston North 230
225 Slateford
225 Kingsknowe
Brunstane 242
Newcraighall 242
Glasgow Central 225
Cambuslang 225
Uddingston 225
225 Carfin
225 Hartwood
225 Fauldhouse
225 Addiewell
Livingston South 225
Curriehill 225
Bellshill 225
Holytown 225
Cleland 225
Shotts 225
Breich 225
West Calder 225
Kirknewton 225
Wester Hailes 225
226
Motherwell 225
Carstairs 225

Edinburgh → Shotts, Carstairs, Motherwell and Glasgow Central

Network Diagram - see first page of Table 225

Miles	Miles			SR	SR	XC 1 ◇ A	SR	SR B	GR R 1 C	SR	SR D	SR	GR R 1 E	SR	SR	SR	GR R 1 G	SR	SR	SR	GR R 1 G	SR
0	0	**Edinburgh** 10	230, 238, 242 d	05 51	06 56	07 26			08 08	08 23	08 38		09 22	09 26	10 25	11 25	11 38		12 25	13 25	13 41	
1¼	1¼	Haymarket	230, 238, 242 d	05 55	06 59	07 30			08 13	08 27	08 41		09 27	09 28	10 28	11 28	11 43		12 28	13 28		
3	3	Slateford	d	05 59	07 02					08 30				09 31	10 31	11 31			12 31	13 31		
3¾	3¾	Kingsknowe	d	06 02	07 05					08 33				09 34	10 34	11 34			12 34	13 34		
4¾	4¾	Wester Hailes	d	06 05	07 08					08 36				09 37	10 37	11 37			12 37	13 37		
7½	7½	Curriehill	d	06 09	07 12					08 40				09 41	10 41	11 41			12 41	13 41		
11	11	Kirknewton	d	06 16	07 19					08 47	08 52			09 48	10 48	11 48			12 48	13 48		
14	—	Livingston South	d	06 22	07 27					08 54				09 55	10 55	11 55			12 55	13 55		
16¾	—	West Calder	a	06 27	07 32					08 59				10 01	11 00	12 00			13 00	14 00		
—	—		d	06 27	07 32		←			08 59				10 01	11 00	12 00			13 00	14 00		←
18½	—	Addiewell	d	06 31	07 36		07 36			09 03				10 04	11 04	12 04			13 04	14 04		14 04
21	—	Breich	d		→													←		→		
23¼	—	Fauldhouse	d	06 38			07 43			09 10				10 11	11 11	12 11		12 11	13 11			14 11
26¾	—	**Shotts**	d	06 49			07 49			09 19		←		10 19	11 19	→		12 19	13 19			14 19
28¼	—	Hartwood	d	06 52			07 52			09 22		09 22		10 21	11 21			12 21	13 21			14 21
31½	—	Cleland	d	06 56			07 56			→		09 26		10 26	11 26			12 26	13 26			14 26
33¼	—	Carfin	d	07 00			08 00					09 30		10 29	11 29			12 29	13 29			14 29
34¼	—	Holytown	d	07 02			08 02					09 32		10 32	11 32			12 32	13 32			14 32
—	28½	Carstairs	d					08 05			09 17											
—	44½	**Motherwell**	a			08 09		08 26	08 59		09 34		10 05				12 25				14 26	
—	—		d			08 10		08 27	08 59		09 34		10 05				12 25				14 26	
36	—	Bellshill	226 d	07 06			08 06					09 36		10 36	11 36			12 36	13 36			14 36
38¾	—	Uddingston	226 d	07 12				08a32				09 42		10 42	11 42			12 41	13 42			14 42
42	—	Cambuslang	226 d	07 17								09 47		10 47	11 48			12 47	13 47			14 47
47¼	57¼	**Glasgow Central** 15	226 a	07 30		08 29	08 30		09 22		09 56	10 00	10 29	11 00	12 01		12 47	13 02	14 02		14 47	15 02

		SR	GR R 1 G	SR	SR	SR	GR R 1 G	SR	SR	SR	SR D	XC 1 ◇ H	GR R 1 G	SR	XC 1 ◇ H	SR	XC 1 ◇ J	SR	GR R 1 G	SR
Edinburgh 10	230, 238, 242 d	14 25	15 22	15 25	16 25	17 21	17 39			17 52	18 26	19 07	19 18	19 25		20 25	21 14	22 10	22 26	
Haymarket	230, 238, 242 d	14 28		15 28	16 28	17 25	17 44			17 55	18 29	19 12	19 22	19 28		20 28	21 19	22 14	22 30	
Slateford	d	14 31		15 31	16 31	17 29				17 59	18 31			19 31		20 31		22 18		
Kingsknowe	d	14 34		15 34	16 34	17 32				18 02	18 34			19 34		20 34		22 21		
Wester Hailes	d	14 37		15 37	16 37	17 35				18 05	18 36			19 37		20 37		22 24		
Curriehill	d	14 41		15 41	16 41	17 39				18 09	18 40			19 41		20 41		22 28		
Kirknewton	d	14 48		15 48	16 48	17 46				18 16	18 46			19 48		20 48		22 35		
Livingston South	d	14 55		15 55	16 55	17 52				18 23				19 55		20 55		22 41		
West Calder	a	15 00		16 01	17 00	17 58		←		18 29				20 04		21 00		22 46		
	d	15 00		16 01	17 00	17 58		17 58		18 29						21 00		22 46		
Addiewell	d	15 04		16 04	17 04	→		18 02		18 33						21 04		22 50		
Breich	d									18 36						21x09				←
Fauldhouse	d	15 11		16 11	17 11			18 09		18 40						21 11		22 57		22 57
Shotts	d	15 19		16 19	17 19			18 16		18 50						21 19		→		23 03
Hartwood	d	15 21		16 21	17 21			18 19		18 52						21 21				23 06
Cleland	d	15 26		16 26	17 26			18 22		18 56						21 26				23 10
Carfin	d	15 29		16 29	17 29			18 27		19 00						21 29				23 14
Holytown	d	15 32		16 33	17 32			18 29		19 02						21 32				23 16
Carstairs	d								18 36		19 10									
Motherwell	a		16 06				18 23	18 35	18 56		19 31	19 55	19 59		←		22 04		23 13	
	d		16 06				18 23				19 32	19 56	19 59		19 56		22 06		23 13	
Bellshill	226 d	15 36		16 37	17 36					19 06		→				21 36				23 20
Uddingston	226 d	15 42		16 43	17 41					19 12						21 42				23 26
Cambuslang	226 d	15 47		16 48	17 47					19 17						21 47				23 31
Glasgow Central 15	226 a	16 04	16 27	17 00	18 01		18 41			19 30	19 52		20 18		20 25	22 01	22 35		23 32	23 43

For general notes see front of timetable
For details of catering facilities see Directory of Train Operators

A From Dunbar (Table 26)
B To Garscadden (Table 226)
C From Newcastle (Table 26)
D From North Berwick (Table 238)
E From Doncaster (Table 26)
G From London Kings Cross (Table 26)
H From Penzance (Table 135)
J From Plymouth (Table 51)

Table 225

Saturdays

Edinburgh → Shotts, Carstairs, Motherwell and Glasgow Central

Network Diagram - see first page of Table 225

		SR	SR	XC 1 ◇	SR	GR R 1 A	SR	SR B	SR	GR R 1 C	SR	SR	SR	GR R 1 D Ø	SR	SR	SR	GR R 1 D Ø
Edinburgh 10	230, 238, 242 d	05 51	06 56	07 25	07 53	08 12	08 25	08 57	09 26	09 38		10 25	11 25	11 39		12 25	13 25	13 40
Haymarket	230, 238, 242 d	05 55	06 59	07 29	07 57		08 29	08 59	09 29	09 42		10 28	11 28	11 43		12 28	13 28	13 44
Slateford	d	06 02	07 03		08 01		08 31	09 02	09 32			10 31	11 31			12 31	13 31	
Kingsknowe	d	06 05	07 06		08 04		08 34	09 05	09 35			10 34	11 34			12 34	13 34	
Wester Hailes	d	06 08	07 09		08 07		08 37	09 08	09 38			10 37	11 37			12 37	13 37	
Curriehill	d	06 12	07 13		08 11		08 41	09 12	09 42			10 41	11 41			12 41	13 41	
Kirknewton	d	06 19	07 20		08 18		08 48	09 19	09 49			10 48	11 48			12 48	13 48	
Livingston South	d	06 26	07 26		08 24		08 55		09 56			10 55	11 55			12 55	13 55	
West Calder	a	06 30	07 31		08 31		09 01		10 02			11 00	12 00			13 00	14 00	
	d	06 32	07 32				09 01		10 02			11 00	12 00			13 00	14 00	
Addiewell	d	06 36	07 36				09 05		10 05			11 04	12 04			13 04	14 04	
Breich	d										←				←			
Fauldhouse	d	06 43	07 43				09 12		10 12 →		10 12	11 11	12 11 →		12 11	13 11	14 11 →	
Shotts	d	06 49	07 49				09 19				10 18	11 19			12 19	13 19		
Hartwood	d	06 52	07 52				09 22				10 21	11 21			12 21	13 21		
Cleland	d	06 56	07 56				09 26				10 26	11 26			12 26	13 26		
Carfin	d	07 00	08 00				09 30				10 29	11 29			12 29	13 29		
Holytown	d	07 02	08 02				09 32				10 31	11 32			12 32	13 32		
Carstairs	d							09 40										
Motherwell	a			08 15		08 57		09 56		10 27				12 28				14 27
	d			08 16		08 57		09 57		10 27				12 28				14 27
Bellshill	226 d	07 06	08 06				09 36				10 36	11 36			12 36	13 36		
Uddingston	226 d	07 12	08 12				09 40				10 42	11 40			12 42	13 41		
Cambuslang	226 d	07 17	08 17				09 47				10 47	11 45			12 47	13 47		
Glasgow Central 15	226 a	07 30	08 30	08 35		09 15	09 59	10 14		10 48	11 00	12 01		12 50	13 01	14 01		14 47

		SR	SR	SR	GR R 1 D	SR	SR B	SR	SR	GR R 1 D Ø	SR	SR	XC 1 ◇ E	GR R 1 D	SR	XC 1 ◇ G	SR	GR R 1 D	SR
Edinburgh 10	230, 238, 242 d		14 25	15 25	15 36		15 53	16 25	17 25	17 40		18 25	19 10	19 39	20 25	21 10	21 23	21 39	22 40
Haymarket	230, 238, 242 d		14 28	15 28	15 41		15 57	16 28	17 28	17 45		18 28	19 14	19 43	20 29	21 14	21 27	21 43	22 44
Slateford	d		14 31	15 31			16 01	16 31	17 31			18 31			20 32		21 31		22 48
Kingsknowe	d		14 34	15 34			16 03	16 34	17 34			18 34			20 35		21 34		22 51
Wester Hailes	d		14 37	15 37			16 06	16 37	17 37			18 37			20 38		21 37		22 54
Curriehill	d		14 41	15 41			16 09	16 41	17 41			18 41			20 42		21 41		22 58
Kirknewton	d		14 48	15 48			16 15	16 48	17 48			18 48			20 49		21 48		23 05
Livingston South	d		14 55	15 55				16 55	17 55			18 55			20 55		21 53		23 11
West Calder	a		15 00	16 01				17 00	18 00		←	19 00			21 00		22 01		23 16
	d		15 00	16 01				17 00	18 00 →		18 00	19 00			21 00				23 16
Addiewell	d		15 04	16 04				17 04			18 04	19 04			21 04				23 20
Breich	d	←				←						19 07			21x09				
Fauldhouse	d	14 11	15 11	16 11 →		16 11		17 11			18 11	19 11			21 11				23 27
Shotts	d	14 19	15 19			16 19		17 19			18 19	19 19			21 19				23 35
Hartwood	d	14 21	15 21			16 21		17 21			18 21	19 21			21 21				23 37
Cleland	d	14 26	15 26			16 26		17 26			18 26	19 26			21 26				23 41
Carfin	d	14 29	15 29			16 29		17 29			18 29	19 29			21 29				23 45
Holytown	d	14 32	15 32			16 32		17 32			18 32	19 32			21 32				23 48
Carstairs	d						16 35												
Motherwell	a				16 27		16 54			18 28	18 39		20 00	20 22		21 55		22 26	
	d				16 27		16 55			18 28			20 01	20 22		21 56		22 26	
Bellshill	226 d	14 34	15 36			16 36		17 36				19 36			21 36				23 52
Uddingston	226 d	14 42	15 41			16 42		17 42				19 42			21 42				23 58
Cambuslang	226 d	14 47	15 46			16 47		17 47				19 47			21 47				00 03
Glasgow Central 15	226 a	15 01	16 04		16 50	17 01	17 20	18 01		18 50		20 01	20 29	20 44	22 01	22 23		22 46	00 15

Sundays

		GR R 1 H	XC 1 ◇ J	SR	GR R 1 J	SR	GR R 1 D	SR	GR R 1 D Ø	SR	GR R 1 D	XC 1 ◇ K	SR	XC 1 ◇ K	GR R 1 D Ø
Edinburgh 10	230, 242 d	12 03	12 12	12 24	12 42	14 23	15 13	16 23	17 41	18 24	19 37	20 12	20 23	21 12	21 41
Haymarket	230, 242 d	12 07	12 16	12 28	12 47	14 27	15 18	16 27	17 45	18 27	19 42	20 16	20 27	21 16	21 45
Slateford	d			12 32		14 31		16 31		18 31			20 31		
Kingsknowe	d			12 35		14 34		16 34		18 34			20 34		
Wester Hailes	d			12 38		14 37		16 37		18 37			20 37		
Curriehill	d			12 42		14 41		16 41		18 41			20 41		
Kirknewton	d			12 49		14 48		16 48		18 48			20 48		
Livingston South	d			12 55		14 54		16 54		18 54			20 54		
West Calder	a			13 02		15 01		17 01		19 01			21 01		
Motherwell	a	12 47	12 53		13 32		15 56		18 24		20 19	20 53		21 53	22 23
	d	12 47	12 54		13 32		15 56		18 24		20 19	20 54		21 54	22 23
Glasgow Central	a	13 05	13 19		13 54		16 14		18 44		20 37	21 17		22 19	22 45

For general notes see front of timetable
For details of catering facilities see Directory of Train Operators

A From Newcastle (Table 26)
B From North Berwick (Table 238)
C From Doncaster (Table 26)
D From London Kings Cross (Table 26)
E From Penzance (Table 135)
G From Plymouth (Table 51)
H From York (Table 26)
J From Leeds (Table 26)
K From Penzance (Table 135) (from 8 November from Birmingham New Street) (Table 51)

Glasgow Central, Motherwell, Carstairs and Shotts → Edinburgh

Network Diagram - see first page of Table 225

Miles	Miles		XC	SR	SR	GR	SR	SR	SR	GR	XC	SR	SR	GR	SR	SR	GR	SR	SR	GR
			[1] ◊ A			[R] [1] B Ø		C		[R] [1] B Ø	[1] ◊ D			[R] [1] B Ø			[R] [1] B E Ø			[R] [1] B Ø
0	0	**Glasgow Central** [15] 226 d	06 00	06 16		06 50		07 05	07 13	07 50	09 00		09 15	09 50	10 15	11 15	11 50	12 15	13 15	13 50
5¼	—	Cambuslang 226 d		06 23					07 23				09 23		10 23	11 23		12 23	13 23	
8½	—	Uddingston 226 d		06 28					07 28				09 28		10 28	11 28		12 28	13 28	
11¼	—	Bellshill 226 d		06 34					07 34				09 34		10 34	11 34		12 34	13 34	
—	12¼	**Motherwell** a				07 04		07 27		08 04	09 14			10 04			12 06			14 05
—	—	d			06 59	07 04		07 28		08 04	09 15			10 04			12 06			14 05
—	28½	Carstairs d			07a25			07 42												
13¼	—	Holytown d		06 38					07 38				09 38		10 38	11 38		12 38	13 38	
14	—	Carfin d		06 40					07 40				09 40		10 40	11 40		12 40	13 40	
15¾	—	Cleland d		06 44					07 44				09 44		10 44	11 44		12 44	13 44	
19	—	Hartwood d		06 50					07 50				09 50		10 50	11 50		12 50	13 50	
20½	—	**Shotts** d		06 56					07 54				09 58		10b59	11 57		12 59	13 56	
24	—	Fauldhouse d		07 01					08 00				10 04		11 04	12 03		13 04	14 01	
26½	—	Breich d							08 03											
28¾	—	Addiewell d		07 08					08 07				10 10		11 11	12 10		13 11	14 08	
30½	—	West Calder d		07 11			07 39		08 11			09 39	10 14		11 15	12 14		13 15	14 11	
33¼	—	Livingston South d		07 16			07 44		08 15			09 43	10 18		11 19	12 18		13 19	14 16	
36¼	46¼	Kirknewton d		07 23			07 49	08 04	08 21			09 48	10 24		11 24	12 23		13 24	14 21	
40¾	49¾	Curriehill d		07 28			07 54	08 09	08 26			09 54	10 30		11 30	12 29		13 30	14 27	
42½	52½	Wester Hailes d		07 32				08 12	08 30			09 57	10 33		11 33	12 32		13 33	14 30	
43½	53½	Kingsknowe d		07 34				08 15	08 32			10 00	10 36		11 36	12 35		13 36	14 33	
44¼	54¼	Slateford d		07 36				08 17	08 35			10 02	10 38		11 38	12 37		13 38	14 35	
46	56	Haymarket 230, 238, 242 d	06 55	07 43		07 46	08 04	08 22	08 38	08 49	09 54	10 08	10 42	10 48	11 43	12 42	12 49	13 44	14 42	14 49
47¼	57¼	**Edinburgh** [10] 230, 238, 242 a	06 59	07 49		07 52	08 11	08 35	08 47	08 56	09 59	10 14	10 51	10 56	11 52	12 52	12 56	13 52	14 50	14 56

	SR	SR	SR	SR	GR	SR	SR	SR	SR	GR	SR	SR	GR	SR	XC	SR
			C		[R] [1] B			G	G	[R] [1] B			[R] [1] H		[1] ◊	
Glasgow Central [15] 226 d	14 15	15 15	15 19		15 50	16 15	17 19			17 50	18 15		19 50	20 15	20 48	23 06
Cambuslang 226 d	14 23	15 23				16 23		17 41	17 41		18 23			20 23		23 15
Uddingston 226 d	14 28	15 28				16 28		17 45	17 45		18 28			20 28		23 20
Bellshill 226 d	14 34	15 34				16 34	17 34	17 50	17 50		18 34			20 34		23 26
Motherwell a			15 35		16 04			18 00	18 00	18 05			20 04		21 07	
d			15 38		16 04			18 01	18 01	18 05			20 04		21 08	
Carstairs d			15 56					18a27	18a27							
Holytown d	14 38	15 38				16 38	17 38				18 38			20 38		23 30
Carfin d	14 40	15 40				16 40	17 40				18 40			20 40		23 32
Cleland d	14 44	15 44				16 44	17 44				18 44			20 44		23 36
Hartwood d	14 50	15 50				16 50	17 50				18 50			20 50		23 42
Shotts d	14c59	16e00		←		16 55	17 56				18f59			20 56		23 46
Fauldhouse d	15 04	16 04		16 04		17 01	18 01				19 04			21 01		23 52
Breich d		→														
Addiewell d	15 11			16 11		17 07	18 08				19 11			21 08		23 58
West Calder d	15 13			16 15		17 10	18 11				19 15	20 12		21 11		00 02
Livingston South d	15 19			16 19		17 15	18 16				19 19	20 16		21 16		00 06
Kirknewton d	15 24			16 24		17 21	18 21				19 24	20 21		21 21		00 11
Curriehill d	15 30			16 30		17 26	18 26				19 30	20 27		21 26		00 17
Wester Hailes d	15 33			16 33		17 30	18 30				19 33	20 30		21 30		00 21
Kingsknowe d	15 36			16 36		17 32	18 32				19 36	20 33		21 32		00 23
Slateford d	15 38			16 38		17 35	18 35				19 38	20 35		21 35		00 26
Haymarket 230, 238, 242 d	15 43		16 34	16 43	16 50	17 39	18 43			18 49	19 43	20 42	20 49	21 42	21 52	00 31
Edinburgh [10] 230, 238, 242 a	15 53		16 39	16 52	16 56	17 47	18 53			18 56	19 51	20 47	20 55	21 51	22 02	00 38

For general notes see front of timetable
For details of catering facilities see Directory of Train Operators

A To Plymouth (Table 51)
B To London Kings Cross (Table 26)
C To North Berwick (Table 238)
D To Penzance (Table 135)
E **The Flying Scotsman**
G From Dalmuir (Table 226)
H To York (Table 26)
b Arr. 1054
c Arr. 1454
e Arr. 1554
f Arr. 1854

Saturdays

Glasgow Central, Motherwell, Carstairs and Shotts → Edinburgh

Network Diagram - see first page of Table 225

		SR	SR	GR	XC	SR	GR	SR	SR	GR	XC	SR	GR	SR	SR	GR	SR	SR
				R 1 A	1 ◊ B	C	R 1 A			R 1 A	1 ◊ D		R 1 A			R 1 A E		
Glasgow Central 15	226 d	00 06	06 16	06 50	07 00	07 05	07 50		08 15	08 50	09 00	09 15	09 50	10 15	11 15	11 50	12 15	13 15
Cambuslang	226 d	00 15	06 23						08 22			09 23		10 23	11 23		12 23	13 23
Uddingston	226 d	00 20	06 28						08 27			09 28		10 28	11 28		12 28	13 28
Bellshill	226 d	00 26	06 34						08 33			09 34		10 34	11 34		12 34	13 34
Motherwell	a			07 05		07 20	08 04			09 04			10 04			12 04		
	d			07 05		07 20	08 04			09 04			10 04			12 04		
Carstairs	d					07 42												
Holytown	d	00 30	06 38						08 37			09 38		10 38	11 38		12 38	13 38
Carfin	d	00 32	06 40						08 40			09 40		10 40	11 40		12 40	13 40
Cleland	d	00 36	06 44						08 44			09 44		10 44	11 44		12 44	13 44
Hartwood	d	00 42	06 50						08 50			09 50		10 50	11 50		12 50	13 50
Shotts	d	00 46	06 56						08 54			09 54		10 55	11 55		12 55	13 55
Fauldhouse	d	00 52	07 01						09 00			10 01		11 01	12 00		13 00	14 00
Breich	d								09 03									
Addiewell	d	00 58	07 08						09 07			10 07		11 07	12 07		13 07	14 07
West Calder	d	01 02	07 11					08 39	09 11			10 10		11 10	12 10		13 10	14 10
Livingston South	d	01a08	07 16					08 43	09 15			10 15		11 16	12 15		13 15	14 15
Kirknewton	d		07 23			08 04		08 48	09 21			10 20		11 21	12 20		13 21	14 20
Curriehill	d		07 28			08 09		08 54	09 26			10 25		11 26	12 25		13 26	14 25
Wester Hailes	d		07 32			08 12		08 57	09 30			10 29		11 30	12 29		13 30	14 29
Kingsknowe	d		07 34			08 15		09 00	09 32			10 31		11 32	12 31		13 32	14 31
Slateford	d		07 36			08 17		09 02	09 35			10 34		11 35	12 34		13 35	14 34
Haymarket	230, 238, 242 d		07 43	07 49	07 54	08 25	08 49	09 08	09 38	09 46	09 55	10 39	10 49	11 40	12 39	12 49	13 40	14 39
Edinburgh 10	230, 238, 242 a		07 49	07 56	07 59	08 33	08 56	09 14	09 47	09 53	09 59	10 47	10 56	11 47	12 47	12 56	13 47	14 47

		GR	SR	SR	SR	SR	GR	SR	SR	GR	SR	SR	XC	SR	SR
		R 1 A			C		R 1 A			R 1 G			1 ◊		
Glasgow Central 15	226 d	13 50	14 15	15 15	15 19		15 50	16 15	17 15	17 50	18 15	20 15	21 00		23 06
Cambuslang	226 d		14 23	15 23				16 23	17 23		18 23	20 23			23 15
Uddingston	226 d		14 28	15 28				16 28	17 28		18 28	20 28			23 20
Bellshill	226 d		14 34	15 34				16 34	17 34		18 34	20 34			23 26
Motherwell	a	14 04			15 38		16 04			18 04					
	d	14 04			15 38		16 04			18 04					
Carstairs	d				15 56										
Holytown	d		14 38	15 38				16 38	17 38		18 38	20 38			23 30
Carfin	d		14 40	15 40				16 40	17 40		18 40	20 40			23 32
Cleland	d		14 44	15 44				16 44	17 44		18 44	20 44			23 36
Hartwood	d		14 50	15 50				16 50	17 50		18 50	20 50			23 42
Shotts	d		14 55	15 54				16 54	17 54		18 59	20 58			23 46
Fauldhouse	d		15 00	16 00 →		← 16 00		17 00	18 00		19 04	21 03			23 52
Breich	d														
Addiewell	d		15 07			16 07		17 07	18 07		19 11	21 10			23 58
West Calder	d		15 10			16 10		17 10	18 10		19 15	21 13		22 40	00 02
Livingston South	d		15 15			16 15		17 15	18 15		19 19	21 18		22 45	00 06
Kirknewton	d		15 20			16 20		17 22	18 20		19 24	21 23		22 50	00 11
Curriehill	d		15 26			16 25		17 27	18 25		19 30	21 28		22 55	00 17
Wester Hailes	d		15 29			16 29		17 31	18 29		19 33	21 32		22 59	00 21
Kingsknowe	d		15 32			16 31		17 33	18 31		19 36	21 34		23 01	00 23
Slateford	d		15 34			16 34		17 36	18 34		19 38	21 37		23 04	00 26
Haymarket	230, 238, 242 d	14 49	15 40		16 27	16 42	16 49	17 41	18 39	18 48	19 43	21 41	22 01	23 11	00 31
Edinburgh 10	230, 238, 242 a	14 56	15 47		16 35	16 51	16 56	17 48	18 47	18 56	19 51	21 49	22 10	23 16	00 38

Sundays

		GR	XC	XC	SR	GR	XC	SR	GR	GR	SR	GR	SR	GR	SR
		R 1 A	1 ◊ H	1 ◊ J		R 1 A	1 ◊ K		R 1 A	R 1 A		R 1 A		R 1 L	
Glasgow Central	d	10 50	11 37	11 37		12 50	13 45		14 50	15 50		17 50		19 50	
Motherwell	a	11 05	11 55	11 56		13 05	14 00		15 05	16 05		18 05		20 04	
	d	11 05	11 56	11 57		13 05	14 01		15 05	16 05		18 05		20 04	
West Calder	d				13 13			15 13			17 14		19 14		21 14
Livingston South	d				13 17			15 15			17 16		19 18		21 17
Kirknewton	d				13 22			15 20			17 22		19 23		21 23
Curriehill	d				13 27			15 26			17 27		19 29		21 27
Wester Hailes	d				13 31			15 29			17 31		19 32		21 32
Kingsknowe	d				13 33			15 32			17 33		19 35		21 33
Slateford	d				13 36			15 34			17 36		19 37		21 37
Haymarket	230, 242 d	11 48	12 38	12 38	13 42	13 50	14 43	15 42	15 50	16 44	17 43	18 46	19 44	20 45	21 44
Edinburgh 10	230, 242 a	11 54	12 43	12 43	13 47	13 55	14 47	15 47	15 55	16 51	17 48	18 52	19 48	20 50	21 48

For general notes see front of timetable
For details of catering facilities see Directory of Train Operators

- **A** To London Kings Cross (Table 26)
- **B** To Newquay (Table 135) (from 12 September to Plymouth) (Table 51)
- **C** To North Berwick (Table 238)
- **D** To Penzance (Table 135)
- **E** **The Flying Scotsman**
- **G** To Leeds (Table 26)
- **H** Until 6 September. To Plymouth (Table 51)
- **J** From 13 September. To Plymouth (from 8 November to Birmingham New Street) (Table 51)
- **K** To Plymouth (from 8 November to Birmingham New Street) (Table 51)
- **L** To Newcastle (Table 26)

Lanark, Coatbridge, Motherwell, Larkhall, Hamilton, Drumgelloch, Airdrie and Springburn → Glasgow → Milngavie, Dalmuir, Balloch and Helensburgh

Network Diagram - see first page of Table 220

Miles	Miles	Miles	Miles	Miles			SR	SR R A	SR	SR	SR	SR	SR	SR	SR	SR	SR	SR	SR		SR	SR	SR	SR	SR
0	—	—	—	—	**Lanark**	d																	06 23		
8½	—	—	—	—	Carluke	d																	06 33		
13	—	—	—	—	Wishaw	d																	06 38		
16½	—	—	—	—	Holytown	d																			
15	—	—	—	—	Shieldmuir	d																	06 42		
—	—	—	—	0	**Coatbridge Central**	d																			06 39
—	—	—	—	1	Whifflet	d																			06 41
16¼	0	0	—	5½	**Motherwell**	a																	06 45		06 49
—	—	—	—	—		d									06 16		06 20						06 46		06 50
—	3	—	—	—	Bellshill	d									06 22								06 52		
20½	5½	—	—	—	Uddingston	d									06 26								06 56		
—	—	¾	—	—	Airbles	d											06 22								06 52
—	—	—	—	0	**Larkhall**	d						06 07							06 37						
—	—	—	—	1½	Merryton	d						06 09							06 39						
—	—	—	—	2¾	Chatelherault	d						06 12							06 42						
—	—	3	—	5¼	**Hamilton Central**	d						06 15					06 27		06 45						06 57
—	—	3¾	—	0	Hamilton West	d						06 18					06 30		06 48						07 00
—	—	5¾	—	—	Blantyre	d						06 21					06 33		06 51						07 03
22½	—	8¼	—	—	Newton	d											06 37								07 07
24	9	—	—	—	Cambuslang	d									06 31		06 41						07 01		07 11
25¾	10¾	—	—	—	Rutherglen	d						06 29			06 34		06 45		06 59				07 04		07 15
26½	11½	—	—	—	Dalmarnock	d									06 36		06 47						07 06		07 17
27	12	—	—	—	Bridgeton	d									06 38		06 49						07 08		07 19
—	—	—	0	—	**Drumgelloch**	d			05 27				06 08								06 38				
—	—	—	1½	—	**Airdrie**	a			05 30				06 11								06 41				
—	—	—	—	—		d			05 31		05 57		06 12			06 27					06 42			06 57	
—	—	—	2½	—	Coatdyke	d			05 33		05 59		06 14			06 29					06 44			06 59	
—	—	—	3½	—	Coatbridge Sunnyside	d			05 35		06 01		06 16			06 31					06 46			07 01	
—	—	—	4	—	Blairhill	d			05 38		06 04		06 19			06 34					06 49			07 04	
—	—	—	6¾	—	Easterhouse	d			05 42		06 08		06 23			06 38					06 53			07 08	
—	—	—	7¾	—	Garrowhill	d			05 44		06 10		06 25			06 40					06 55			07 10	
—	—	—	9	—	Shettleston	d			05 47		06 13		06 28			06 43					06 58			07 13	
—	—	—	9¾	—	Carntyne	d			05 49		06 15		06 30			06 45					07 00			07 15	
—	—	—	—	0	**Springburn**	d												06 49							
—	—	—	—	½	Barnhill	d												06 50							
—	—	—	—	1½	Alexandra Parade	d												06 53							
—	—	—	—	1¾	Duke Street	d												06 54							
—	—	—	11½	2¼	Bellgrove	d			05 52		06 18		06 33			06 48		06 56			07 03			07 18	
—	—	—	12	2¾	High Street	d			05 54		06 20		06 35			06 50		06 58			07 05			07 20	
—	—	—	12½	3¼	**Glasgow Queen Street** 10 §	a			05 56		06 22		06 37			06 52		07 01			07 07			07 22	
—	—	—	—	—		d	05b30		05 57		06 23		06 38			06 53		07 02			07 10			07 23	
—	—	—	13¼	4	Charing Cross	d			06 00		06 25		06 42			06 55		07 04			07 12			07 25	
28¼	13¼	—	—	—	Argyle Street	d						06 34			06 42		06 53		07 04				07 12		07 23
28¾	13¾	—	—	—	**Glasgow Central** 15 §	a						06 37			06 46		06 56		07 07				07 16		07 26
—	—	—	—	—		d						06 37			06 46		06 58		07 07				07 16		07 28
29¼	14¼	—	—	—	Anderston	d						06 39			06 48		06 59		07 09				07 18		07 29
29¾	14¾	—	—	—	Exhibition Centre	d						06 41			06 50		07 01		07 11				07 20		07 31
31	16	—	15¼	6	Partick	d			06 04		06 30	06 45	06 47		06 54	07 00	07 05	07 09	07 15		07 17		07 24	07 30	07 35
31½	16½	0	15¾	6½	Hyndland	d			06 06		06 32	06 47	06 50		06 56	07 02	07 08	07 11	07 17		07 20		07 26	07 32	07 38
—	—	½	—	—	Jordanhill	d			06 08						06 58			07 13					07 28		
—	—	1½	—	—	Scotstounhill	d			06 11						07 00			07 15					07 30		
—	—	2	—	—	Garscadden	d			06 13				06 54		07 02			07 17					07 32		
—	—	3	—	—	Yoker	d			06 15						07 05			07 20					07 35		
—	—	4	—	—	Clydebank	d			06 17						07 07			07 22					07 37		
32½	17½	—	16¾	7½	Anniesland	d					06 35	06 50				07 05	07 11		07 20					07 35	07 41
33¾	18¾	—	18	8¾	Westerton	d	05a43	05 56			06 38	06 53				07 08	07 14		07 23					07 38	07 44
35	—	—	—	—	Bearsden	d											07 16								07 46
35¾	—	—	—	—	Hillfoot	d											07 18								07 48
37¼	—	—	—	—	**Milngavie**	a								←			07 22					←			07 52
—	20	—	19¼	10	Drumchapel	d					06 40	06 55		06 55		07 10			07 25			07 25		07 40	
—	20¾	—	20	10¾	Drumry	d					06 42	→		06 57		07 12			→			07 27		07 42	
—	21¾	—	21	11¾	Singer	d					06 45			07 00		07 15						07 30		07 45	
—	22½	5¼	21¾	12½	**Dalmuir**	a		06 03	06 21		06 47		06 59	07 02	07 11	07 17		07 26			07 28	07 32	07 41	07 47	
—	—	—	—	—		d		06 04	06 21	06 32	06 48		06 59			07 18					07 29			07 48	
—	—	—	23	13¾	Kilpatrick	d				06 34	06 51					07 21								07 51	
—	—	—	24¾	15½	Bowling	d				06 37	06 54					07 24								07 54	
—	—	—	27½	18¼	Dumbarton East	d			06 29	06 42	06 58		07 06			07 28					07 36			07 58	
—	—	—	28¼	19	Dumbarton Central	d			06 30	06 44	07 00		07 08			07 30					07 38			08 00	
—	—	—	28½	19¼	Dalreoch	d			06 32	06 46	07 02		07 10			07 32					07 40			08 02	
—	—	—	—	20¾	Renton	d			06 35		07 05					07 35								08 05	
—	—	—	—	22	Alexandria	d			06 37		07 07					07 37								08 07	
—	—	—	—	23	**Balloch**	a			06 40		07 10					07 40								08 10	
—	—	—	31¾	—	Cardross	d				06 51			07 15								07 45				
—	—	—	35½	—	Craigendoran	d				06 56			07 20								07 50				
—	—	—	36½	—	**Helensburgh Central**	a		06c26		06 59			07 23								07 53				

For general notes see front of timetable
For details of catering facilities see Directory of Train Operators

§ Low Level

A From Edinburgh (Table 225) to Fort William (Table 227)
b Glasgow Queen Street High Level
c Helensburgh Upper

Lanark, Coatbridge, Motherwell, Larkhall, Hamilton, Drumgelloch, Airdrie and Springburn → Glasgow → Milngavie, Dalmuir, Balloch and Helensburgh

Network Diagram - see first page of Table 220

Station		SR	SR	SR	SR	SR	SR	SR	SR	SR	SR		SR	SR	SR	SR	SR	SR	SR	SR	SR	SR	SR	SR	SR
		A															◇ B					A			
Lanark	d							06 53					07 23											07 45	
Carluke	d							07 03					07 33											07 55	
Wishaw	d							07 08					07 38											08 03	
Holytown	d	07 02																				08 02			
Shieldmuir	d							07 12					07 42											08 08	
Coatbridge Central	d																				07 39				
Whifflet	d																				07 41				
Motherwell	a							07 16					07 45								07 49			08 12	
	d							07 16		07 20			07 46							07 50	07 50			08 13	
Bellshill	d	07 06						07 22												07 55		08 06			
Uddingston	d	07 12						07 26												08 00				08 19	
Airbles	d									07 22											07 52				
Larkhall	d			07 07														07 37							08 07
Merryton	d			07 09														07 39							08 09
Chatelherault	d			07 12														07 42							08 12
Hamilton Central	d			07 15						07 27								07 45			07 57				08 15
Hamilton West	d			07 18						07 30								07 48			08 00				08 18
Blantyre	d			07 21						07 33								07 51			08 03				08 21
Newton	d									07 37								07 55			08 07				
Cambuslang	d	07 17						07 31		07 41								08 00		08 05	08 11				08 27
Rutherglen	d			07 29				07 34		07 45			07 56					08 04		08 10	08 15			08 26	
Dalmarnock	d							07 36		07 47								08 06		08 12	08 17				
Bridgeton	d							07 38		07 49								08 08		08 14	08 19				
Drumgelloch	d				07 08									07 38											
Airdrie	a				07 11									07 41											
	d				07 12		07 22		07 27					07 42	07 52				07 57						
Coatdyke	d				07 14		07 24		07 29					07 44	07 54				07 59						
Coatbridge Sunnyside	d				07 16		07 26		07 31					07 46	07 56				08 01						
Blairhill	d				07 19		07 29		07 34					07 49	07 59				08 04						
Easterhouse	d				07 23				07 38					07 53					08 08						
Garrowhill	d				07 25				07 40					07 55					08 10						
Shettleston	d				07 28				07 43					07 58					08 13						
Carntyne	d				07 30				07 45					08 00					08 15						
Springburn	d		07 19								07 49												08 19		
Barnhill	d		07 20								07 50												08 20		
Alexandra Parade	d		07 23								07 53												08 23		
Duke Street	d		07 24								07 54												08 24		
Bellgrove	d		07 26		07 33				07 48		07 56			08 03					08 18				08 26		
High Street	d		07 28		07 35		07 40		07 50		07 58			08 05	08 10				08 20				08 28		
Glasgow Queen Street 10 §	a		07 31		07 37		07 42		07 52		08 01			08 07	08 12				08 22				08 31		
	d		07 32		07 40		07 43		07 53		08 02			08 10	08 13		08b21		08 23				08 32		
Charing Cross	d		07 34		07 42		07 45		07 55		08 04			08 12	08 15				08 25				08 34		
Argyle Street	d			07 34				07 42		07 53			08 02					08 12		08 18	08 23			08 31	08 34
Glasgow Central 15 §	a	07c30		07 37				07 46		07 56			08 06					08 16		08 19	08 26	08c30		08 32	08 37
	d			07 37				07 46		07 58			08 07					08 16		08 19	08 28			08 33	08 37
Anderston	d			07 39				07 48		07 59			08 09					08 18		08a23	08 29			08 35	08 39
Exhibition Centre	d			07 41				07 50		08 01			08 11					08 20			08 31			08 38	08 41
Partick	d		07 39	07 45	07 46		07 50	07 54	08 00	08 05	08 09		08 15	08 17	08 20			08 24	08 30		08 35		08 39	08 42	08 45
Hyndland	d		07 41	07 47	07 49		07 53	07 56	08 02	08 08	08 11		08 17	08 20	08 23			08 26	08 32		08 38		08 41	08 44	08 47
Jordanhill	d		07 43					07 58			08 13							08 28					08 43	08 46	
Scotstounhill	d		07 45					08 00			08 15							08 30					08 45	08 48	
Garscadden	d		07 47					08 02			08 17							08 32					08 47	08a51	
Yoker	d		07 50					08 05			08 20							08 36					08 50		
Clydebank	d		07 52					08 07			08 22							08 38					08 52		
Anniesland	d			07 50			07 56		08 05	08 11			08 20		08 26				08 35		08 41				08 50
Westerton	d			07 53			07 59		08 08	08 14			08 23		08 29				08 38		08 44				08 53
Bearsden	d						08 01			08 16					08 31						08 46				
Hillfoot	d						08 03			08 18					08 33						08 48				
Milngavie	a					←	08 07			08 27					08 37	←					08 52				
Drumchapel	d			07 55 →		07 55			08 10				08 25 →			08 25			08 40						08 55 →
Drumry	d					07 57			08 12							08 27			08 42						
Singer	d					08 00			08 15							08 30			08 45						
Dalmuir	a		07 56		07 59	08 02		08 11	08 17		08 28			08 29		08 32	08 38	08 42	08 47				08 56		
	d				07 59				08 18					08 29			08 39		08 48						
Kilpatrick	d								08 21										08 51						
Bowling	d								08 24										08 54						
Dumbarton East	d				08 06				08 28					08 36					08 58						
Dumbarton Central	d				08 08				08 30					08 38			08 48		09 00						
Dalreoch	d				08 10				08 32					08 40					09 02						
Renton	d								08 35										09 05						
Alexandria	d								08 37										09 07						
Balloch	a								08 40										09 10						
Cardross	d				08 20									08 45											
Craigendoran	d				08 25									08 50											
Helensburgh Central	a				08 28									08 55			09e03								

For general notes see front of timetable
For details of catering facilities see Directory of Train Operators

§ Low Level

A From Edinburgh (Table 225)
B To Oban (from 28 September also conveys portion to Mallaig) (Table 227)
b Glasgow Queen Street High Level
c Glasgow Central High Level
e Helensburgh Upper

Lanark, Coatbridge, Motherwell, Larkhall, Hamilton, Drumgelloch, Airdrie and Springburn → Glasgow → Milngavie, Dalmuir, Balloch and Helensburgh

Network Diagram - see first page of Table 220

		SR	SR		SR	SR ◇ A 🍴	SR	SR	SR B	SR	SR	SR	SR	SR	SR	SR	SR		SR	SR	SR	SR	SR	SR	SR
Lanark	d												08 23												
Carluke	d								08 13				08 33												
Wishaw	d								08 18				08 38												
Holytown	d																								
Shieldmuir	d								08 23				08 42												
Coatbridge Central	d																								
Whifflet	d																								
Motherwell	a								08 26				08 45												
	d						08 16	08 20	08 27				08 46						08 49		08 50				
Bellshill	d						08 22												08 54						
Uddingston	d						08 26		08 32										08 58						
Airbles	d							08 22													08 52				
Larkhall	d													08 37									09 07		
Merryton	d													08 39									09 09		
Chatelherault	d													08 42									09 12		
Hamilton Central	d							08 27						08 45							08 57		09 15		
Hamilton West	d							08 30						08 48							09 00		09 18		
Blantyre	d							08 33			←			08 51							09 03		09 21		
Newton	d							08 37			08 37										09 07				
Cambuslang	d						08 31	↪			08 41								09 03		09 11				
Rutherglen	d						08 34				08 45		08 56	08 59					09 07		09 15		09 29		
Dalmarnock	d						08 36				08 47								09 09		09 17				
Bridgeton	d						08 38				08 49								09 11		09 19				
Drumgelloch	d	08 08													08 38									09 08	
Airdrie	a	08 11													08 41									09 11	
	d	08 12	08 22							08 27					08 42					08 57				09 12	
Coatdyke	d	08 14	08 24							08 29					08 44					08 59				09 14	
Coatbridge Sunnyside	d	08 16	08 26							08 31					08 46					09 01				09 16	
Blairhill	d	08 19	08 29							08 34					08 49					09 04				09 19	
Easterhouse	d	08 23								08 38					08 53					09 08				09 23	
Garrowhill	d	08 25								08 40					08 55					09 10				09 25	
Shettleston	d	08 28								08 43					08 58					09 13				09 28	
Carntyne	d	08 30								08 45					09 00					09 15				09 30	
Springburn	d											08 49										09 19			
Barnhill	d											08 50										09 20			
Alexandra Parade	d											08 53										09 23			
Duke Street	d											08 54										09 24			
Bellgrove	d	08 33								08 48		08 56			09 03		09 08			09 18		09 26		09 33	09 38
High Street	d	08 35	08 40							08 50		08 58			09 05		09 10			09 20		09 28		09 35	09 40
Glasgow Queen Street 10 § 🚢	a	08 37	08 42							08 52		09 01			09 07		09 12			09 22		09 31		09 37	09 42
	d	08 40	08 43			09b07				08 53		09 02			09 10		09 13			09 23		09 32		09 40	09 43
Charing Cross	d	08 42	08 45							08 55		09 04			09 12		09 15			09 25		09 34		09 42	09 45
Argyle Street	d						08 42		08 47		08 53		09 01	09 04					09 14		09 23		09 34		
Glasgow Central 15 §	a						08 46		08 48		08 56		09 03	09 06					09 19		09 26		09 37		
	d						08 46		08 49		08 58		09 03	09 07					09 19		09 28		09 37		
Anderston	d						08 48		08 50		08 59		09 05	09 09					09 20		09 29		09 39		
Exhibition Centre	d						08 50		08 53		09 01		09 08	09 11					09 22		09 31		09 41		
Partick 🚢	d	08 47	08 50				08 54		08 57	09 00	09 05	09 09	09 12	09 15	09 17		09 20		09 26	09 30	09 35	09 39	09 45	09 47	09 50
Hyndland	d	08 50	08 53				08 56		08 59	09 02	09 08	09 11	09 14	09 17	09 20		09 23		09 28	09 32	09 38	09 41	09 47	09 50	09 53
Jordanhill	d						08 58		09 01			09 13	09 16						09 30			09 43			
Scotstounhill	d						09 00		09 03			09 15	09 19						09 33			09 45			
Garscadden	d						09 02		09a06			09 17	09a21						09 36			09 47			
Yoker	d						09 05					09 20							09 38			09 50			
Clydebank	d						09 07					09 22							09 40			09 52			
Anniesland	d		08 56							09 05	09 11			09 20			09 26			09 35	09 41		09 50		09 56
Westerton	d		08 59							09 08	09 14			09 23			09 29			09 38	09 44		09 53		09 59
Bearsden	d		09 01								09 16						09 31				09 46				10 01
Hillfoot	d		09 03								09 18						09 33				09 48				10 03
Milngavie	a		09 07		←						09 22					←	09 37				09 52				10 07
Drumchapel	d				08 55					09 10				09 25 ↪		09 25				09 40			09 55 ↪		
Drumry	d				08 57					09 12						09 27				09 42					
Singer	d				09 00					09 15						09 30				09 45					
Dalmuir	a	08 59			09 02	09 26	09 11			09 17		09 26			09 29	09 32			09 43	09 47		09 56		09 59	
	d	08 59				09 26				09 18					09 29					09 48				09 59	
Kilpatrick	d									09 21										09 51					
Bowling	d									09 24										09 54					
Dumbarton East	d	09 06								09 28					09 36					09 58				10 06	
Dumbarton Central	d	09 08				09 34				09 30					09 38					10 00				10 08	
Dalreoch	d	09 10								09 32					09 40					10 02				10 10	
Renton	d									09 35										10 05					
Alexandria	d									09 37										10 07					
Balloch	a									09 40										10 10					
Cardross	d	09 15													09 45									10 15	
Craigendoran	d	09 20													09 50									10 20	
Helensburgh Central	a	09 25				09c50									09 55									10 23	

For general notes see front of timetable
For details of catering facilities see Directory of Train Operators

§ Low Level

A Until 25 September. To Mallaig (Table 227)

B From Carstairs (Table 225)

b Glasgow Queen Street High Level

c Helensburgh Upper

Lanark, Coatbridge, Motherwell, Larkhall, Hamilton, Drumgelloch, Airdrie and Springburn → Glasgow → Milngavie, Dalmuir, Balloch and Helensburgh

Network Diagram - see first page of Table 220

		SR	SR	SR	SR	SR A	SR	SR	SR		SR B	SR	SR	SR	SR	SR	SR	SR	SR	SR	SR	SR	SR		SR
Lanark	d													09 23											09 53
Carluke	d					09 27								09 33											10 02
Wishaw	d													09 38											10 08
Holytown	d										09 32														10 13
Shieldmuir	d													09 42											
Coatbridge Central	d																								
Whifflet	d																								
Motherwell	a					09 34								09 46											10 20
	d		09 16		09 20	09 34								09 46		09 50						10 16			10 20
Bellshill	d		09 22								09 36			09 52								10 22			
Uddingston	d		09 26								09 42			09 56								10 26			
Airbles	d				09 22											09 52									10 22
Larkhall	d							09 37										10 07							
Merryton	d							09 39										10 09							
Chatelherault	d							09 42										10 12							
Hamilton Central	d				09 27			09 45								09 57		10 15							10 27
Hamilton West	d				09 30			09 48								10 00		10 18							10 30
Blantyre	d				09 33			09 51								10 03		10 21							10 33
Newton	d				09 37											10 07									10 37
Cambuslang	d		09 31		09 41						09 47			10 01		10 11						10 31			10 41
Rutherglen	d		09 34		09 46			09 59						10 04		10 15		10 29				10 34			10 45
Dalmarnock	d		09 36		09 48									10 06		10 17						10 36			10 47
Bridgeton	d		09 38		09 50									10 08		10 19						10 38			10 49
Drumgelloch	d								09 38										10 08						
Airdrie	a								09 41										10 11						
	d			09 27					09 42						09 57				10 12				10 27		
Coatdyke	d			09 29					09 44						09 59				10 14				10 29		
Coatbridge Sunnyside	d			09 31					09 46						10 01				10 16				10 31		
Blairhill	d			09 34					09 49						10 04				10 19				10 34		
Easterhouse	d			09 38					09 53						10 08				10 23				10 38		
Garrowhill	d			09 40					09 55						10 10				10 25				10 40		
Shettleston	d			09 43					09 58						10 13				10 28				10 43		
Carntyne	d			09 45					10 00						10 15				10 30				10 45		
Springburn	d						09 49										10 19								
Barnhill	d						09 50										10 20								
Alexandra Parade	d						09 53										10 23								
Duke Street	d						09 54										10 24								
Bellgrove	d			09 48			09 56		10 03				10 08		10 18		10 26		10 33		10 38		10 48		
High Street	d			09 50			09 58		10 05				10 10		10 20		10 28		10 35		10 40		10 50		
Glasgow Queen Street 10 §	a			09 52			10 01		10 07				10 12		10 22		10 31		10 37		10 42		10 52		
	d			09 53			10 02		10 10				10 13		10 23		10 32		10 40		10 43		10 53		
Charing Cross	d			09 55			10 04		10 12				10 15		10 25		10 34		10 42		10 45		10 55		
Argyle Street	d		09 42		09 53			10 04						10 12		10 23		10 34				10 42			10 53
Glasgow Central 15 §	a		09 46		09 57	09 56		10 07			10b00			10 16		10 26		10 37				10 46			10 56
	d		09 46		09 58			10 07						10 16		10 28		10 37				10 48			10 58
Anderston	d		09 48		09 59			10 09						10 18		10 29		10 39				10 51			10 59
Exhibition Centre	d		09 50		10 01			10 11						10 20		10 31		10 41				10 52			11 01
Partick	d		09 54	10 00	10 05		10 09	10 15	10 17				10 20	10 24	10 30	10 35	10 39	10 45	10 47		10 50	10 55	11 00		11 05
Hyndland	d		09 56	10 02	10 08		10 11	10 17	10 20				10 23	10 26	10 32	10 38	10 41	10 47	10 50		10 53	10 57	11 02		11 08
Jordanhill	d		09 58				10 13							10 28			10 43					10 59			
Scotstounhill	d		10 00				10 15							10 30			10 45					11 01			
Garscadden	d		10 02				10 17							10 32			10 47					11 04			
Yoker	d		10 05				10 20							10 35			10 50					11 07			
Clydebank	d		10 07				10 22							10 37			10 52					11 09			
Anniesland	d			10 05	10 11			10 20					10 26		10 35	10 41		10 50			10 56		11 05		11 11
Westerton	d			10 08	10 14			10 23					10 29		10 38	10 44		10 53			10 59		11 08		11 14
Bearsden	d				10 16								10 31			10 46					11 01				11 16
Hillfoot	d				10 18								10 33			10 48					11 03				11 18
Milngavie	a	←			10 22							←	10 37			10 52				←	11 07				11 24
Drumchapel	d	09 55		10 10				10 25 →				10 25			10 40			10 55 →		10 55			11 10		
Drumry	d	09 57		10 12								10 27			10 42					10 57			11 12		
Singer	d	10 00		10 15								10 30			10 45					11 00			11 15		
Dalmuir	a	10 02	10 11	10 17			10 26		10 29			10 32		10 41	10 47		10 56		10 59	11 02		11 13	11 17		
	d			10 18					10 29						10 48				10 59				11 18		
Kilpatrick	d			10 21											10 51								11 21		
Bowling	d			10 24											10 54								11 24		
Dumbarton East	d			10 28					10 36						10 58				11 06				11 28		
Dumbarton Central	d			10 30					10 38						11 00				11 08				11 30		
Dalreoch	d			10 32					10 40						11 02				11 10				11 32		
Renton	d			10 35											11 05								11 35		
Alexandria	d			10 37											11 07								11 37		
Balloch	a			10 40											11 10								11 40		
Cardross	d								10 45										11 15						
Craigendoran	d								10 50										11 20						
Helensburgh Central	a								10 56										11 25						

For general notes see front of timetable
For details of catering facilities see Directory of Train Operators

§ Low Level

A From North Berwick (Table 238)
B From Edinburgh (Table 225)
b Glasgow Central High Level

Table 226

Mondays to Fridays

Lanark, Coatbridge, Motherwell, Larkhall, Hamilton, Drumgelloch, Airdrie and Springburn → Glasgow → Milngavie, Dalmuir, Balloch and Helensburgh

Network Diagram - see first page of Table 220

Station		SR A	SR	SR	SR	SR	SR	SR	SR	SR	SR	SR	SR	SR	SR	SR	SR	SR	SR A	SR	SR	SR	SR	SR
Lanark	d							10 23										10 53						
Carluke	d							10 33										11 03						
Wishaw	d							10 38										11 08						
Holytown	d	10 32																11 13	11 32					
Shieldmuir	d							10 42																
Coatbridge Central	d																							
Whifflet	d																							
Motherwell	a							10 46										11 19						
	d							10 46		10 50						11 16		11 20						
Bellshill	d	10 36						10 52								11 22			11 36					
Uddingston	d	10 42						10 56								11 26			11 42					
Airbles	d									10 52								11 22						
Larkhall	d			10 37								11 07									11 37			
Merryton	d			10 39								11 09									11 39			
Chatelherault	d			10 42								11 12									11 42			
Hamilton Central	d			10 45						10 57		11 15						11 27			11 45			
Hamilton West	d			10 48						11 00		11 18						11 30			11 48			
Blantyre	d			10 51						11 03		11 21						11 33			11 51			
Newton	d									11 07								11 37						
Cambuslang	d	10 47						11 01		11 11						11 31		11 41	11 48					
Rutherglen	d			10 59				11 04		11 15		11 29				11 34		11 45			11 59			
Dalmarnock	d							11 06		11 17						11 36		11 47						
Bridgeton	d							11 08		11 19						11 38		11 49						
Drumgelloch	d				10 38								11 08									11 38		
Airdrie	a				10 41								11 11									11 41		
	d				10 42				10 57				11 12				11 27					11 42		
Coatdyke	d				10 44				10 59				11 14				11 29					11 44		
Coatbridge Sunnyside	d				10 46				11 01				11 16				11 31					11 46		
Blairhill	d				10 49				11 04				11 19				11 34					11 49		
Easterhouse	d				10 53				11 08				11 23				11 38					11 53		
Garrowhill	d				10 55				11 10				11 25				11 40					11 55		
Shettleston	d				10 58				11 13				11 28				11 43					11 58		
Carntyne	d				11 00				11 15				11 30				11 45					12 00		
Springburn	d		10 49								11 19									11 49				
Barnhill	d		10 50								11 20									11 50				
Alexandra Parade	d		10 53								11 23									11 53				
Duke Street	d		10 54								11 24									11 54				
Bellgrove	d		10 56		11 03		11 08		11 18		11 26		11 33		11 38		11 48			11 56		12 03		12 08
High Street	d		10 58		11 05		11 10		11 20		11 28		11 35		11 40		11 50			11 58		12 05		12 10
Glasgow Queen Street 10 §	a		11 01		11 07		11 12		11 22		11 31		11 37		11 42		11 52			12 01		12 07		12 12
	d		11 02		11 10		11 13		11 23		11 32		11 40		11 43		11 53			12 02		12 10		12 13
Charing Cross	d		11 04		11 12		11 15		11 25		11 34		11 42		11 45		11 55			12 04		12 12		12 15
Argyle Street	d			11 04				11 12		11 23		11 34				11 42		11 53			12 04			
Glasgow Central 15 §	a	11b00		11 07				11 16		11 26		11 37				11 46		11 56	12b01		12 07			
	d			11 07				11 16		11 28		11 37				11 46		11 58			12 07			
Anderston	d			11 09				11 18		11 29		11 39				11 48		11 59			12 09			
Exhibition Centre	d			11 11				11 20		11 31		11 41				11 50		12 01			12 11			
Partick	d		11 09	11 15	11 17		11 20	11 24	11 30	11 35	11 39	11 45	11 47		11 50	11 54	12 00	12 05		12 09	12 15	12 17		12 20
Hyndland	d		11 11	11 17	11 20		11 23	11 26	11 32	11 38	11 41	11 47	11 50		11 53	11 56	12 02	12 08		12 11	12 17	12 20		12 23
Jordanhill	d		11 13					11 28			11 43					11 58				12 13				
Scotstounhill	d		11 15					11 30			11 45					12 00				12 15				
Garscadden	d		11 17					11 32			11 47					12 02				12 17				
Yoker	d		11 20					11 35			11 50					12 05				12 20				
Clydebank	d		11 22					11 36			11 52					12 07				12 22				
Anniesland	d			11 20			11 26		11 35	11 41		11 50			11 56		12 05	12 11			12 20			12 26
Westerton	d			11 23			11 29		11 38	11 44		11 53			11 59		12 08	12 14			12 23			12 29
Bearsden	d						11 31			11 46					12 01			12 16						12 31
Hillfoot	d						11 33			11 48					12 03			12 18						12 33
Milngavie	a					←	11 37			11 52				←	12 07			12 22					←	12 37
Drumchapel	d			11 25 →		11 25			11 40			11 55 →		11 55			12 10				12 25 →		12 25	
Drumry	d					11 27			11 42					11 57			12 12						12 27	
Singer	d					11 30			11 45					12 00			12 15						12 30	
Dalmuir	a		11 26		11 29	11 32		11 41	11 47		11 56		11 59	12 02		12 11	12 17			12 26		12 29	12 32	
	d				11 29				11 48				11 59				12 18					12 29		
Kilpatrick	d								11 51								12 21							
Bowling	d								11 54								12 24							
Dumbarton East	d				11 36				11 58				12 06				12 28					12 36		
Dumbarton Central	d				11 38				12 00				12 08				12 30					12 38		
Dalreoch	d				11 40				12 02				12 10				12 32					12 40		
Renton	d								12 05								12 35							
Alexandria	d								12 07								12 37							
Balloch	a								12 10								12 40							
Cardross	d				11 45								12 15									12 45		
Craigendoran	d				11 50								12 20									12 50		
Helensburgh Central	a				11 53								12 23									12 53		

For general notes see front of timetable
For details of catering facilities see Directory of Train Operators

§ Low Level

A From Edinburgh (Table 225)
b Glasgow Central High Level

Lanark, Coatbridge, Motherwell, Larkhall, Hamilton, Drumgelloch, Airdrie and Springburn → Glasgow → Milngavie, Dalmuir, Balloch and Helensburgh

Network Diagram - see first page of Table 220

		SR	SR	SR	SR	SR		SR	SR	SR	SR	SR	SR	SR	SR	SR	SR	SR	SR	SR		SR	SR	SR	SR
		◇ A													B										
Lanark	d		11 23											11 53								12 23			
Carluke	d		11 33											12 03								12 33			
Wishaw	d		11 39											12 08								12 38			
Holytown	d													12 13	12 32										
Shieldmuir	d		11 43																			12 42			
Coatbridge Central	d																								
Whifflet	d																								
Motherwell	a		11 47											12 20								12 46			
	d		11 47		11 50							12 16		12 20								12 46		12 50	
Bellshill	d		11 54									12 22			12 36							12 52			
Uddingston	d		11 58									12 26			12 41							12 56			
Airbles	d				11 52									12 22										12 52	
Larkhall	d							12 07									12 37								
Merryton	d							12 09									12 39								
Chatelherault	d							12 12									12 42								
Hamilton Central	d				11 57			12 15						12 27			12 45							12 57	
Hamilton West	d				12 00			12 18						12 30			12 48							13 00	
Blantyre	d				12 03			12 21						12 33			12 51							13 03	
Newton	d				12 07									12 37										13 07	
Cambuslang	d		12 03		12 11			12 29				12 31		12 41	12 47		12 59					13 01		13 11	
Rutherglen	d		12 06		12 15							12 34		12 45								13 05		13 15	
Dalmarnock	d		12 08		12 17							12 36		12 47								13 07		13 17	
Bridgeton	d		12 10		12 19							12 38		12 49								13 09		13 19	
Drumgelloch	d								12 08									12 38							
Airdrie	a								12 11									12 41							
	d			11 57					12 12				12 27					12 42					12 57		
Coatdyke	d			11 59					12 14				12 29					12 44					12 59		
Coatbridge Sunnyside	d			12 01					12 16				12 31					12 46					13 01		
Blairhill	d			12 04					12 19				12 34					12 49					13 04		
Easterhouse	d			12 08					12 23				12 38					12 53					13 08		
Garrowhill	d			12 10					12 25				12 40					12 55					13 10		
Shettleston	d			12 13					12 28				12 43					12 58					13 13		
Carntyne	d			12 15					12 30				12 45					13 00					13 15		
Springburn	d					12 19										12 49									13 19
Barnhill	d					12 20										12 50									13 20
Alexandra Parade	d					12 23										12 53									13 23
Duke Street	d					12 24										12 54									13 24
Bellgrove	d			12 18		12 26			12 33		12 38		12 48			12 56		13 03		13 08			13 18		13 26
High Street	d			12 20		12 28			12 35		12 40		12 50			12 58		13 05		13 10			13 20		13 28
Glasgow Queen Street 10 §	a			12 22		12 31			12 37		12 42		12 52			13 01		13 07		13 12			13 22		13 31
	d	12b21		12 23		12 32			12 40		12 43		12 53			13 02		13 10		13 13			13 23		13 32
Charing Cross	d			12 25		12 34			12 42		12 45		12 55			13 04		13 12		13 15			13 25		13 34
Argyle Street	d		12 14		12 23			12 34				12 42		12 53			13 04					13 13		13 23	
Glasgow Central 15 §	a		12 19		12 26			12 37				12 46		12 56	13c02		13 07					13 16		13 26	
	d		12 19		12 28			12 37				12 46		12 58			13 07					13 17		13 28	
Anderston	d		12 21		12 29			12 39				12 48		12 59			13 09					13 19		13 29	
Exhibition Centre	d		12 23		12 31			12 41				12 50		13 01			13 11					13 20		13 31	
Partick	d		12 27	12 30	12 35	12 39		12 45	12 48		12 50	12 54	13 00	13 05		13 09	13 15	13 17		13 20		13 25	13 30	13 35	13 39
Hyndland	d		12 29	12 32	12 38	12 41		12 47	12 51		12 53	12 56	13 02	13 08		13 11	13 17	13 20		13 23		13 26	13 32	13 38	13 41
Jordanhill	d		12 31			12 43						12 58				13 13						13 28			13 43
Scotstounhill	d		12 33			12 45						13 00				13 15						13 30			13 45
Garscadden	d		12 36			12 47						13 02				13 17						13 32			13 47
Yoker	d		12 39			12 50						13 05				13 20						13 35			13 50
Clydebank	d		12 41			12 52						13 07				13 22						13 37			13 52
Anniesland	d			12 35	12 41			12 50			12 56		13 05	13 11			13 20			13 26			13 35	13 41	
Westerton	d			12 38	12 44			12 53			12 59		13 08	13 14			13 23			13 29			13 38	13 44	
Bearsden	d				12 46						13 01			13 16						13 31				13 46	
Hillfoot	d				12 48						13 03			13 18						13 33				13 48	
Milngavie	a				12 52					←	13 07			13 22					←	13 37				13 52	
Drumchapel	d			12 40				12 55 →		12 55			13 10				13 25 →		13 25				13 40		
Drumry	d			12 42						12 57			13 12						13 27				13 42		
Singer	d			12 45						13 00			13 15						13 30				13 45		
Dalmuir	a	12 38	12 44	12 47		12 56			12 59	13 02		13 11	13 17			13 26		13 29	13 32			13 42	13 47		13 56
	d	12 42		12 48					12 59				13 18					13 29					13 48		
Kilpatrick	d			12 51									13 21										13 51		
Bowling	d			12 54									13 24										13 54		
Dumbarton East	d			12 58					13 06				13 28					13 36					13 58		
Dumbarton Central	d	12 48		13 00					13 08				13 30					13 38					14 00		
Dalreoch	d			13 02					13 10				13 32					13 40					14 02		
Renton	d			13 05									13 35										14 05		
Alexandria	d			13 07									13 37										14 07		
Balloch	a			13 10									13 40										14 10		
Cardross	d								13 15									13 45							
Craigendoran	d								13 20									13 50							
Helensburgh Central	a	13e03							13 26									13 53							

For general notes see front of timetable
For details of catering facilities see Directory of Train Operators

§ Low Level

A To Oban and Mallaig (Table 227)
B From Edinburgh (Table 225)
b Glasgow Queen Street High Level
c Glasgow Central High Level
e Helensburgh Upper

Table 226

Mondays to Fridays

Lanark, Coatbridge, Motherwell, Larkhall, Hamilton, Drumgelloch, Airdrie and Springburn → Glasgow → Milngavie, Dalmuir, Balloch and Helensburgh

Network Diagram - see first page of Table 220

		SR	SR	SR	SR	SR	SR	SR	SR	SR	SR	SR		SR	SR	SR	SR	SR	SR	SR	SR	SR	SR	SR	SR
									A																
Lanark	d							12 53								13 23									
Carluke	d							13 03								13 33									
Wishaw	d							13 08								13 38									
Holytown	d							13 13	13 32																
Shieldmuir	d															13 42									
Coatbridge Central	d																								
Whifflet	d																								
Motherwell	a							13 19								13 46									
	d					13 16		13 20								13 46		13 50						14 16	
Bellshill	d					13 22			13 36							13 52								14 22	
Uddingston	d					13 26			13 42							13 56								14 26	
Airbles	d							13 22										13 52							
Larkhall	d	13 07									13 37									14 07					
Merryton	d	13 09									13 39									14 09					
Chatelherault	d	13 12									13 42									14 12					
Hamilton Central	d	13 15						13 27			13 45							13 57		14 15					
Hamilton West	d	13 18						13 30			13 48							14 00		14 18					
Blantyre	d	13 21						13 33			13 51							14 03		14 21					
Newton	d							13 37										14 07							
Cambuslang	d					13 31		13 41	13 47							14 01		14 11						14 31	
Rutherglen	d	13 29				13 34		13 45			13 59					14 06		14 15		14 29				14 34	
Dalmarnock	d					13 36		13 47								14 08		14 17						14 36	
Bridgeton	d					13 38		13 49								14 10		14 19						14 38	
Drumgelloch	d		13 08									13 38									14 08				
Airdrie	a		13 11									13 41									14 11				
	d		13 12				13 27					13 42					13 57				14 12				14 27
Coatdyke	d		13 14				13 29					13 44					13 59				14 14				14 29
Coatbridge Sunnyside	d		13 16				13 31					13 46					14 01				14 16				14 31
Blairhill	d		13 19				13 34					13 49					14 04				14 19				14 34
Easterhouse	d		13 23				13 38					13 53					14 08				14 23				14 38
Garrowhill	d		13 25				13 40					13 55					14 10				14 25				14 40
Shettleston	d		13 28				13 43					13 58					14 13				14 28				14 43
Carntyne	d		13 30				13 45					14 00					14 15				14 30				14 45
Springburn	d									13 49									14 19						
Barnhill	d									13 50									14 20						
Alexandra Parade	d									13 53									14 23						
Duke Street	d									13 54									14 24						
Bellgrove	d		13 33		13 38		13 48			13 56		14 03			14 08		14 18		14 26		14 33		14 38		14 48
High Street	d		13 35		13 40		13 50			13 58		14 05			14 10		14 20		14 28		14 35		14 40		14 50
Glasgow Queen Street 10 §	⛴ a		13 37		13 42		13 52			14 01		14 07			14 12		14 22		14 31		14 37		14 42		14 52
	d		13 40		13 43		13 53			14 02		14 10			14 13		14 23		14 32		14 40		14 43		14 53
Charing Cross	d		13 42		13 45		13 55			14 04		14 12			14 15		14 25		14 34		14 42		14 45		14 55
Argyle Street	d	13 34				13 42		13 53			14 04					14 14		14 23		14 34				14 42	
Glasgow Central 15 §	a	13 37				13 46		13 56	14b02		14 07					14 17		14 26		14 37				14 46	
	d	13 37				13 46		13 58			14 07					14 18		14 28		14 37				14 46	
Anderston	d	13 39				13 48		13 59			14 09					14 20		14 29		14 39				14 48	
Exhibition Centre	d	13 41				13 50		14 01			14 11					14 22		14 31		14 41				14 50	
Partick	⛴ d	13 45	13 47		13 50	13 54	14 00	14 05		14 09	14 15	14 17			14 20	14 26	14 30	14 35	14 39	14 45	14 47		14 50	14 54	15 00
Hyndland	d	13 47	13 50		13 53	13 56	14 02	14 08		14 11	14 17	14 20			14 23	14 28	14 32	14 38	14 41	14 47	14 50		14 53	14 56	15 02
Jordanhill	d					13 58				14 13						14 30			14 43					14 58	
Scotstounhill	d					14 00				14 15						14 33			14 45					15 00	
Garscadden	d					14 02				14 17						14 36			14 47					15 02	
Yoker	d					14 05				14 20						14 38			14 50					15 05	
Clydebank	d					14 07				14 22						14 40			14 52					15 07	
Anniesland	d	13 50			13 56		14 05	14 11			14 20				14 26		14 35	14 41		14 50			14 56		15 05
Westerton	d	13 53			13 59		14 08	14 14			14 23				14 29		14 38	14 44		14 53			14 59		15 08
Bearsden	d				14 01			14 16							14 32			14 46					15 01		
Hillfoot	d				14 03			14 18							14 33			14 48					15 03		
Milngavie	a			←	14 07			14 22						←	14 37			14 52				←	15 07		
Drumchapel	d	13 55 →		13 55			14 10				14 25 →			14 25			14 40			14 55 →		14 55			15 10
Drumry	d			13 57			14 12							14 27			14 42					14 57			15 12
Singer	d			14 00			14 15							14 30			14 45					15 00			15 15
Dalmuir	a		13 59	14 02		14 11	14 17			14 26		14 29		14 32		14 43	14 47		14 56		14 59	15 02		15 13	15 17
	d		13 59				14 18					14 29					14 48				14 59				15 18
Kilpatrick	d						14 21										14 51								15 21
Bowling	d						14 24										14 54								15 24
Dumbarton East	d		14 06				14 28					14 36					14 58				15 06				15 28
Dumbarton Central	d		14 08				14 30					14 38					15 00				15 08				15 30
Dalreoch	d		14 10				14 32					14 40					15 02				15 10				15 32
Renton	d						14 35										15 05								15 35
Alexandria	d						14 37										15 07								15 37
Balloch	a						14 40										15 10								15 40
Cardross	d		14 15									14 45									15 15				
Craigendoran	d		14 20									14 50									15 20				
Helensburgh Central	a		14 23									14 54									15 26				

For general notes see front of timetable
For details of catering facilities see Directory of Train Operators

§ Low Level

A From Edinburgh (Table 225)
b Glasgow Central High Level

Lanark, Coatbridge, Motherwell, Larkhall, Hamilton, Drumgelloch, Airdrie and Springburn → Glasgow → Milngavie, Dalmuir, Balloch and Helensburgh

Network Diagram - see first page of Table 220

		SR	SR A	SR		SR	SR	SR	SR	SR	SR	SR	SR	SR	SR	SR	SR		SR	SR	SR	SR	SR A	SR
Lanark	d	13 53								14 23													14 53		
Carluke	d	14 03								14 33													15 03		
Wishaw	d	14 08								14 38													15 08		
Holytown	d	14 13	14 32																				15 13	15 32	
Shieldmuir	d									14 42															
Coatbridge Central	d																								
Whifflet	d																								
Motherwell	a	14 20								14 46													15 19		
	d	14 20								14 46		14 50								15 16			15 20		
Bellshill	d		14 36							14 52										15 22				15 36	
Uddingston	d		14 42							14 56										15 26				15 42	
Airbles	d	14 22										14 52											15 22		
Larkhall	d					14 37									15 07										
Merryton	d					14 39									15 09										
Chatelherault	d					14 42									15 12										
Hamilton Central	d	14 27				14 45						14 57			15 15								15 27		
Hamilton West	d	14 30				14 48						15 00			15 18								15 30		
Blantyre	d	14 33				14 51						15 03			15 21								15 33		
Newton	d	14 37										15 07											15 37		
Cambuslang	d	14 41	14 47							15 01		15 11								15 31			15 41	15 47	
Rutherglen	d	14 45				14 59				15 04		15 15			15 29					15 34			15 45		
Dalmarnock	d	14 47								15 06		15 17								15 36			15 47		
Bridgeton	d	14 49								15 08		15 19								15 38			15 49		
Drumgelloch	d						14 38									15 08									
Airdrie	a						14 41									15 11									
	d						14 42				14 57					15 12					15 27				
Coatdyke	d						14 44				14 59					15 14					15 29				
Coatbridge Sunnyside	d						14 46				15 01					15 16					15 31				
Blairhill	d						14 49				15 04					15 19					15 34	15 41			
Easterhouse	d						14 53				15 08					15 23					15 38				
Garrowhill	d						14 55				15 10					15 25					15 40	15a48			
Shettleston	d						14 58				15 13					15 28					15 43				
Carntyne	d						15 00				15 15					15 30					15 45				
Springburn	d			14 49										15 19											15 49
Barnhill	d			14 50										15 20											15 50
Alexandra Parade	d			14 53										15 23											15 53
Duke Street	d			14 54										15 24											15 54
Bellgrove	d			14 56			15 03		15 08		15 18			15 26		15 33	15 38				15 48				15 56
High Street	d			14 58			15 05		15 10		15 20			15 28		15 35	15 40				15 50				15 58
Glasgow Queen Street 10 §	a			15 01			15 07		15 12		15 22			15 31		15 37	15 42				15 52				16 01
	d			15 02			15 10		15 13		15 23			15 32		15 40	15 43				15 53				16 02
Charing Cross	d			15 04			15 12		15 15		15 25			15 34		15 42	15 45				15 55				16 04
Argyle Street	d	14 53				15 04				15 12		15 23			15 34					15 42			15 53		
Glasgow Central 15 §	a	14 56	15b02			15 07				15 16		15 26			15 37					15 46			15 56	16b04	
	d	14 58				15 07				15 16		15 28			15 37					15 46			15 58		
Anderston	d	14 59				15 09				15 18		15 29			15 39					15 48			15 59		
Exhibition Centre	d	15 01				15 11				15 20		15 31			15 41					15 50			16 01		
Partick	d	15 05		15 09		15 15	15 17		15 20	15 24	15 30	15 35		15 39	15 45	15 47	15 50			15 54	16 00		16 05		16 09
Hyndland	d	15 08		15 11		15 17	15 20		15 23	15 26	15 32	15 38		15 41	15 47	15 50	15 53			15 56	16 02		16 08		16 11
Jordanhill	d			15 13						15 28				15 43						15 58					16 13
Scotstounhill	d			15 15						15 30				15 45						16 00					16 15
Garscadden	d			15 17						15 32				15 47						16 02					16 17
Yoker	d			15 20						15 35				15 50						16 05					16 20
Clydebank	d			15 22						15 37			15 44	15 52						16 07					16 22
Anniesland	d	15 11				15 20			15 26		15 35	15 41			15 50		15 56				16 05		16 11		
Westerton	d	15 14				15 23			15 29		15 38	15 44			15 53		15 59				16 08		16 14		
Bearsden	d	15 16							15 31			15 46					16 01						16 16		
Hillfoot	d	15 18							15 33			15 48					16 03						16 18		
Milngavie	a	15 24						←	15 37			15 53					16 07	←					16 22		
Drumchapel	d					15 25 →		15 25			15 40				15 55 →			15 55			16 10				
Drumry	d							15 27			15 42							15 57			16 12				
Singer	d							15 30			15 45							16 00			16 15				
Dalmuir	a			15 26			15 29	15 32		15 41	15 47			15 56		15 59		16 02		16 11	16 17				16 25
	d						15 29				15 48					15 59					16 18				
Kilpatrick	d										15 51		15a54								16 21				
Bowling	d										15 54										16 24				
Dumbarton East	d						15 36				15 58					16 06					16 28				
Dumbarton Central	d						15 38				16 00					16 08					16 30				
Dalreoch	d						15c45				16 02					16 10					16 32				
Renton	d										16 05										16 35				
Alexandria	d										16 07										16 37				
Balloch	a										16 10										16 40				
Cardross	d						15 50									16 15									
Craigendoran	d						15 55									16 20									
Helensburgh Central	a						15 58									16 23									

For general notes see front of timetable
For details of catering facilities see Directory of Train Operators

§ Low Level

A From Edinburgh (Table 225)
b Glasgow Central High Level
c Arr. 1540

Lanark, Coatbridge, Motherwell, Larkhall, Hamilton, Drumgelloch, Airdrie and Springburn → Glasgow → Milngavie, Dalmuir, Balloch and Helensburgh

Network Diagram - see first page of Table 220

Station		SR	SR	SR	SR	SR	SR	SR	SR	SR		SR	SR	SR	SR	SR	SR	SR A	SR	SR	SR	SR	SR	SR	SR
Lanark	d					15 23											15 53								16 23
Carluke	d					15 33											16 03								16 33
Wishaw	d					15 38											16 08								16 38
Holytown	d																16 13	16 33							
Shieldmuir	d					15 42																			16 42
Coatbridge Central	d																								
Whifflet	d																								
Motherwell	a					15 46											16 20								16 46
	d					15 46		15 50							16 16		16 20								16 46
Bellshill	d					15 52									16 22			16 37							16 52
Uddingston	d					15 56									16 26			16 43							16 56
Airbles	d							15 52									16 22								
Larkhall	d	15 37								16 07										16 37					
Merryton	d	15 39								16 09										16 39					
Chatelherault	d	15 42								16 12										16 42					
Hamilton Central	d	15 45						15 57		16 15							16 27			16 45					
Hamilton West	d	15 48						16 00		16 18							16 30			16 48					
Blantyre	d	15 51						16 03		16 21							16 33			16 51					
Newton	d							16 07									16 37								
Cambuslang	d					16 01		16 11							16 31		16 41	16 48							17 01
Rutherglen	d	15 59				16 05		16 15		16 29					16 34		16 45			16 59					17 04
Dalmarnock	d					16 07		16 17							16 36		16 47								17 06
Bridgeton	d					16 09		16 19							16 38		16 49								17 08
Drumgelloch	d		15 38									16 08									16 38				
Airdrie	a		15 41									16 11									16 41				
	d		15 42				15 57					16 12				16 27					16 42				
Coatdyke	d		15 44				15 59					16 14				16 29					16 44				
Coatbridge Sunnyside	d		15 46				16 01					16 16				16 31					16 46				
Blairhill	d		15 49				16 04					16 19				16 34					16 49				
Easterhouse	d		15 53				16 08					16 23				16 38					16 53				
Garrowhill	d		15 55				16 10					16 25				16 40					16 55				
Shettleston	d		15 58				16 13					16 28				16 43					16 58				
Carntyne	d		16 00				16 15					16 30				16 45					17 00				
Springburn	d								16 22										16 52						
Barnhill	d								16 23										16 53						
Alexandra Parade	d								16 26										16 56						
Duke Street	d								16 27										16 57						
Bellgrove	d		16 03		16 08		16 18		16 29			16 33		16 38		16 48			16 59		17 03			17 08	
High Street	d		16 05		16 10		16 20		16 31			16 35		16 40		16 50			17 01		17 05			17 10	
Glasgow Queen Street 10 §	a		16 07		16 12		16 22		16 34			16 37		16 42		16 52			17 04		17 07			17 12	
	d		16 10		16 13		16 23		16 35			16 40		16 43		16 53			17 05		17 10			17 13	
Charing Cross	d		16 12		16 15		16 25		16 37			16 42		16 45		16 55			17 07		17 12			17 15	
Argyle Street	d	16 04				16 13		16 23		16 34					16 42		16 53			17 04					17 12
Glasgow Central 15 §	a	16 07				16 17		16 26		16 37					16 46		16 56	17b00		17 07					17 16
	d	16 07				16 17		16 28		16 37					16 46		16 58			17 07					17 16
Anderston	d	16 09				16 19		16 29		16 39					16 48		16 59			17 09					17 18
Exhibition Centre	d	16 11				16 20		16 31		16 41					16 50		17 01			17 11					17 20
Partick	d	16 15	16 17		16 20	16 24	16 30	16 35	16 42	16 45		16 47		16 50	16 54	17 00	17 05		17 12	17 15	17 17			17 20	17 24
Hyndland	d	16 17	16 20		16 23	16 26	16 32	16 38	16 44	16 47		16 50		16 53	16 56	17 02	17 08		17 14	17 17	17 20			17 23	17 26
Jordanhill	d					16 28			16 46						16 58				17 16						17 28
Scotstounhill	d					16 30			16 48						17 00				17 18			←			17 30
Garscadden	d					16 32			16 50						17 02				17 20			17 20			17 32
Yoker	d					16 35			16 53						17 05				→			17 23			17 35
Clydebank	d					16 37			16 55						17 07							17 25			17 37
Anniesland	d	16 20			16 26		16 35	16 41		16 50				16 56		17 05	17 11			17 20				17 26	
Westerton	d	16 23			16 29		16 38	16 44		16 53				16 59		17 08	17 14			17 23				17 29	
Bearsden	d				16 31			16 46						17 01			17 16							17 31	
Hillfoot	d				16 33			16 48						17 03			17 18							17 33	
Milngavie	a			←	16 37			16 52					←	17 07			17 22						←	17 37	
Drumchapel	d	16 25		16 25			16 40			16 55			16 55			17 10				17 25			17 25		
Drumry	d	→		16 27			16 42			→			16 57			17 12				→			17 27		
Singer	d			16 30			16 45						17 00			17 15							17 30		
Dalmuir	a		16 29	16 32		16 42	16 47		16 59			16 59	17 02		17 11	17 17					17 28	17 29	17 32		17 41
	d		16 29				16 48					16 59				17 18					17 29				
Kilpatrick	d						16 51									17 21									
Bowling	d						16 54									17 24									
Dumbarton East	d		16 36				16 58					17 06				17 28					17 36				
Dumbarton Central	d		16 38				17 00					17 08				17 30					17 38				
Dalreoch	d		16 40				17 02					17 10				17 32					17 40				
Renton	d						17 05									17 35									
Alexandria	d						17 07									17 37									
Balloch	a						17 10									17 41									
Cardross	d		16 45									17 15									17 45				
Craigendoran	d		16 50									17 20									17 50				
Helensburgh Central	a		16 53									17 26									17 56				

For general notes see front of timetable
For details of catering facilities see Directory of Train Operators

§ Low Level

A From Edinburgh (Table 225)
b Glasgow Central High Level

Lanark, Coatbridge, Motherwell, Larkhall, Hamilton, Drumgelloch, Airdrie and Springburn → Glasgow → Milngavie, Dalmuir, Balloch and Helensburgh

Network Diagram - see first page of Table 220

		SR		SR	SR	SR	SR	SR	SR	SR	SR	SR	SR	SR	SR	SR		SR	SR	SR	SR	SR	SR	SR	SR
																A							◇ B		
Lanark	d												16 53											17 23	
Carluke	d												17 03											17 33	
Wishaw	d												17 08											17 38	
Holytown	d															17 32									
Shieldmuir	d												17 12											17 42	
Coatbridge Central	d																		17 30						
Whifflet	d																		17 32						
Motherwell	a												17 16						17 39					17 45	
	d				16 50								17 16		17 20				17 39					17 46	
Bellshill	d												17 22			17 36								17 52	
Uddingston	d												17 26			17 41								17 56	
Airbles	d				16 52										17 22				17 42						
Larkhall	d								17 07																
Merryton	d								17 09																
Chatelherault	d								17 12																
Hamilton Central	d				16 57				17 15						17 27				17 47						
Hamilton West	d				17 00				17 18						17 30				17 49						
Blantyre	d				17 03				17 21						17 33				17 53						
Newton	d				17 07										17 37										
Cambuslang	d				17 11								17 31		17 41	17 47								18 01	
Rutherglen	d				17 15				17 29				17 35		17 46				18 00					18 04	
Dalmarnock	d				17 17								17 37		17 48									18 06	
Bridgeton	d				17 19								17 39		17 50									18 08	
Drumgelloch	d									17 08										17 38					
Airdrie	a									17 11										17 41					
	d			16 57						17 12				17 27						17 42					17 57
Coatdyke	d			16 59						17 14				17 29						17 44					17 59
Coatbridge Sunnyside	d			17 01						17 16				17 31						17 46					18 01
Blairhill	d			17 04						17 19				17 34						17 49					18 04
Easterhouse	d			17 08						17 23				17 38						17 53					18 08
Garrowhill	d			17 10						17 25				17 40						17 55					18 10
Shettleston	d			17 13						17 28				17 43						17 58					18 13
Carntyne	d			17 15						17 30				17 45						18 00					18 15
Springburn	d							17 22										17 49							
Barnhill	d							17 23										17 50							
Alexandra Parade	d							17 26										17 53							
Duke Street	d							17 27										17 54							
Bellgrove	d	17 15		17 18		17 27		17 29		17 33		17 38		17 48				17 56		18 03		18 08			18 18
High Street	d	17 17		17 20		17 29		17 31		17 35		17 40		17 50				17 58		18 05		18 10			18 20
Glasgow Queen Street 10 §	a	17 19		17 22		17 31		17 34		17 37		17 42		17 52				18 01		18 07		18 12			18 22
	d	17 20		17 23		17 31		17 35		17 40		17 43		17 53				18 02		18 10		18 13	18b21		18 23
Charing Cross	d	17 22		17 25		17 34		17 37		17 42		17 45		17 55				18 04		18 12		18 15			18 25
Argyle Street	d				17 23				17 34				17 43		17 54				18 05					18 12	
Glasgow Central 15 §	a				17 26				17 37				17 47		17 58	18c01			18 07					18 16	
	d				17 28				17 37				17 47		17 58				18 07					18 16	
Anderston	d				17 29				17 39				17 49		18 00				18 09					18 18	
Exhibition Centre	d				17 31				17 41				17 50		18 01				18 11					18 20	
Partick	d	17 27		17 30	17 35	17 39		17 42	17 45	17 47		17 50	17 54	18 00	18 05			18 09	18 15	18 17		18 20		18 24	18 30
Hyndland	d			17 32	17 38			17 44	17 47	17 50		17 53	17 56	18 02	18 08			18 11	18 17	18 20		18 23		18 26	18 32
Jordanhill	d							17 46					17 58					18 13						18 28	
Scotstounhill	d							17 48					18 00					18 15						18 30	
Garscadden	d							17 50					18 02					18 17						18 32	
Yoker	d							17 53					18 05					18 20						18 35	
Clydebank	d							17 55					18 07					18 22						18 37	
Anniesland	d			17 35	17 41				17 50			17 56		18 05	18 11				18 20			18 26			18 35
Westerton	d			17 38	17 44				17 53			17 59		18 08	18 14				18 23			18 29			18 38
Bearsden	d				17 46							18 01			18 16							18 31			
Hillfoot	d				17 48							18 03			18 18							18 33			
Milngavie	a				17 52						←	18 08			18 22						←	18 37			
Drumchapel	d			17 40			←		17 55		17 55			18 10					18 25		18 25				18 40
Drumry	d			17 42			17 42		→		17 57			18 12					→		18 27				18 42
Singer	d			→			17 45				18 00			18 15							18 30				18 45
Dalmuir	a						17 47	17 59		17 59	18 04		18 11	18 17				18 26		18 29	18 32		18 35	18 41	18 47
	d						17 50			17 59				18 18						18 29			18 37		18 48
Kilpatrick	d						17 52							18 21											18 51
Bowling	d						17 55							18 24											18 54
Dumbarton East	d						18 00			18 06				18 28						18 36					18 58
Dumbarton Central	d	17 46				17 59	18 03			18 08				18 30						18 38			18 46		19 00
Dalreoch	d	17 48				18 00	18 04			18 10				18 32						18 40					19 02
Renton	d					18 03								18 35											19 05
Alexandria	d					18 06								18 37											19 07
Balloch	a					18 08								18 40											19 10
Cardross	d	17 53					18 08			18 15										18 45					
Craigendoran	d	17 58					18 17			18 20										18 50					
Helensburgh Central	a	18 01					18 20			18 26										18 53			19e02		

For general notes see front of timetable
For details of catering facilities see
Directory of Train Operators

§ Low Level

A From Edinburgh (Table 225)
B To Oban and Mallaig (Table 227)
b Glasgow Queen Street High Level
c Glasgow Central High Level
e Helensburgh Upper

Table 226

Mondays to Fridays

Lanark, Coatbridge, Motherwell, Larkhall, Hamilton, Drumgelloch, Airdrie and Springburn → Glasgow → Milngavie, Dalmuir, Balloch and Helensburgh

Network Diagram - see first page of Table 220

		SR	SR	SR	SR	SR	SR	SR		SR A	SR	SR	SR	SR	SR	SR	SR B	SR A	SR	SR	SR	SR		SR	SR C
Lanark	d													18 23										18 53	
Carluke	d													18 33			18 44							19 03	19 19
Wishaw	d													18 38			18 50							19 08	19 24
Holytown	d									18 29								19 02						19 13	
Shieldmuir	d													18 42			18 53								
Coatbridge Central	d			17 56												18 39									
Whifflet	d			17 58												18 41									
Motherwell	a			18 07						18 35				18 45		18 49	18 56							19 19	19 31
	d			18 10				18 20						18 46		18 50					19 16			19 20	19 32
Bellshill	d			18 16										18 52				19 06			19 22				
Uddingston	d			18 20										18 56				19 12			19 26				
Airbles	d							18 22								18 52								19 22	
Larkhall	d	17 49				18 06						18 37							19 07						
Merryton	d	17 51				18 08						18 39							19 09						
Chatelherault	d	17 54				18 15						18 42							19 12						
Hamilton Central	d	17 57				18 19		18 27				18 45				18 57			19 15					19 27	
Hamilton West	d	18 00				18 21		18 30				18 48				19 00			19 18					19 30	
Blantyre	d	18 03				18 25		18 33				18 51				19 03			19 21					19 33	
Newton	d	18 07						18 37								19 07								19 37	
Cambuslang	d	18 11				18 31		18 41						19 01		19 11		19 17			19 31			19 41	
Rutherglen	d	18 15		18 29		18 34		18 45				18 59		19 04		19 15			19 29		19 34			19 45	
Dalmarnock	d	18 17				18 36		18 47						19 06		19 17					19 36			19 47	
Bridgeton	d	18 19				18 38		18 49						19 08		19 19					19 38			19 49	
Drumgelloch	d				18 08								18 38							19 08					
Airdrie	a				18 11								18 41							19 11					
	d				18 12		18 27						18 42							19 12					
Coatdyke	d				18 14		18 29						18 44							19 14					
Coatbridge Sunnyside	d				18 16		18 31						18 46							19 16					
Blairhill	d				18 19		18 34						18 49							19 19					
Easterhouse	d				18 23		18 38						18 53							19 23					
Garrowhill	d				18 25		18 40						18 55							19 25					
Shettleston	d				18 28		18 43						18 58							19 28					
Carntyne	d				18 30		18 45						19 00							19 30					
Springburn	d		18 19								18 49				19 09							19 39			
Barnhill	d		18 20								18 50				19 10							19 40			
Alexandra Parade	d		18 23								18 53				19 13							19 43			
Duke Street	d		18 24								18 54				19 14							19 44			
Bellgrove	d		18 26		18 33		18 48				18 56		19 03		19 16					19 33		19 46			
High Street	d		18 28		18 35		18 50				18 58		19 05		19 18					19 35		19 48			
Glasgow Queen Street 10 §	a		18 31		18 37		18 52				19 01		19 07		19 21					19 37		19 51			
	d		18 32		18 40		18 53				19 02		19 10		19 23					19 40		19 53			
Charing Cross	d		18 34		18 42		18 55				19 04		19 12		19 25					19 42		19 55			
Argyle Street	d	18 23		18 34		18 42		18 53				19 04		19 12		19 23			19 34		19 42			19 53	
Glasgow Central 15 §	a	18 26		18 37		18 46		18 56				19 07		19 16		19 26		19b30	19 37		19 46			19 56	19 52
	d	18 28		18 37		18 46		18 58				19 07		19 16		19 28			19 37		19 46			19 58	
Anderston	d	18 29		18 39		18 48		18 59				19 09		19 18		19 29			19 39		19 48			19 59	
Exhibition Centre	d	18 31		18 41		18 50		19 01				19 11		19 20		19 31			19 41		19 50			20 01	
Partick	d	18 35	18 39	18 45	18 47	18a53	19 00	19 05			19 09	19 15	19 17	19a23	19 30	19 35			19 44	19 47	19a53	20 00		20 05	
Hyndland	d	18 38	18 41	18 47	18 50		19 02	19 08			19 11	19 17	19 20		19 32	19 38			19 47	19 50		20 02		20 08	
Jordanhill	d		18 43		18 52						19 13		19 22							19 52					
Scotstounhill	d		18 45		18 54						19 15		19 24							19 54					
Garscadden	d		18a47		18 56						19a17		19 26							19 56					
Yoker	d				18 59								19 29							19 59					
Clydebank	d				19 01								19 31							20 01					
Anniesland	d	18 41		18 50			19 05	19 11				19 20			19 35	19 41			19 50			20 05		20 11	
Westerton	d	18 44		18 53			19 08	19 14				19 23			19 38	19 44			19 53			20 08		20 14	
Bearsden	d	18 46						19 16								19 46								20 16	
Hillfoot	d	18 48						19 18								19 48								20 18	
Milngavie	a	18 52						19 22								19 52								20 22	
Drumchapel	d			18 55			19 10					19 25			19 40				19 55			20 10			
Drumry	d			18 57			19 12					19 27			19 42				19 57			20 12			
Singer	d			19 00			19 15					19 30			19 45				20 00			20 15			
Dalmuir	a			19 02	19 04		19 17					19 32	19 34		19 47				20 02	20 04		20 17			
	d				19 05		19 18						19 35		19 48					20 05		20 18			
Kilpatrick	d						19 21								19 51							20 21			
Bowling	d						19 24								19 54							20 24			
Dumbarton East	d				19 12		19 28						19 42		19 58					20 12		20 28			
Dumbarton Central	d				19 14		19 30						19 44		20 00					20 14		20 30			
Dalreoch	d				19 16		19 32						19 46		20 02					20 16		20 32			
Renton	d						19 35								20 05							20 35			
Alexandria	d						19 37								20 07							20 37			
Balloch	a						19 40								20 10							20 40			
Cardross	d				19 21								19 51							20 21					
Craigendoran	d				19 26								19 56							20 26					
Helensburgh Central	a				19 29								19 59							20 29					

For general notes see front of timetable
For details of catering facilities see Directory of Train Operators

§ Low Level

A From Edinburgh (Table 225)
B From Carstairs (Table 225)
C From North Berwick (Table 238)

b Glasgow Central High Level

Lanark, Coatbridge, Motherwell, Larkhall, Hamilton, Drumgelloch, Airdrie and Springburn → Glasgow → Milngavie, Dalmuir, Balloch and Helensburgh

Network Diagram - see first page of Table 220

		SR	SR	SR	SR	SR	SR	SR	SR	SR	SR	SR	SR	SR		SR	SR	SR	SR	SR	SR	SR	SR A	SR	SR
Lanark	d			19 23							19 53			20 23								20 53			
Carluke	d			19 33							20 03			20 33								21 03			
Wishaw	d			19 38							20 08			20 38								21 08			
Holytown	d										20 13											21 13	21 32		
Shieldmuir	d			19 42										20 42											
Coatbridge Central	d																								
Whifflet	d																								
Motherwell	a			19 46							20 20			20 46								21 19			
	d			19 46		19 50			20 16		20 20			20 46			20 50			21 16		21 20			
Bellshill	d			19 52					20 22					20 52						21 22			21 36		
Uddingston	d			19 56					20 26					20 56						21 26			21 42		
Airbles	d					19 52					20 22						20 52					21 22			
Larkhall	d	19 37					20 07					20 37						21 07						21 37	
Merryton	d	19 39					20 09					20 39						21 09						21 39	
Chatelherault	d	19 42					20 12					20 42						21 12						21 42	
Hamilton Central	d	19 45				19 57	20 15				20 27	20 45					20 57	21 15				21 27		21 45	
Hamilton West	d	19 48				20 00	20 18				20 30	20 48					21 00	21 18				21 30		21 48	
Blantyre	d	19 51				20 03	20 21				20 33	20 51					21 03	21 21				21 33		21 51	
Newton	d					20 07					20 37						21 07					21 37			
Cambuslang	d			20 01		20 11			20 33		20 41			21 01			21 11			21 31		21 41	21 47		
Rutherglen	d	19 59		20 05		20 15	20 29		20 37		20 45	20 59		21 04			21 15	21 29		21 34		21 45		21 59	
Dalmarnock	d			20 07		20 17			20 39		20 47			21 06			21 17			21 36		21 47			
Bridgeton	d			20 09		20 19			20 41		20 49			21 08			21 19			21 38		21 49			
Drumgelloch	d		19 38					20 08					20 38						21 08						21 38
Airdrie	a		19 41					20 11					20 41						21 11						21 41
	d		19 42					20 12					20 42						21 12						21 42
Coatdyke	d		19 44					20 14					20 44						21 14						21 44
Coatbridge Sunnyside	d		19 46					20 16					20 46						21 16						21 46
Blairhill	d		19 49					20 19					20 49						21 19						21 49
Easterhouse	d		19 53					20 23					20 53						21 23						21 53
Garrowhill	d		19 55					20 25					20 55						21 25						21 55
Shettleston	d		19 58					20 28					20 58						21 28						21 58
Carntyne	d		20 00					20 30					21 00						21 30						22 00
Springburn	d				20 09					20 39						21 09					21 39				
Barnhill	d				20 10					20 40						21 10					21 40				
Alexandra Parade	d				20 13					20 43						21 13					21 43				
Duke Street	d				20 14					20 44						21 14					21 44				
Bellgrove	d		20 03		20 16			20 33		20 46			21 03			21 16			21 33		21 46				22 03
High Street	d		20 05		20 18			20 35		20 48			21 05			21 18			21 35		21 48				22 05
Glasgow Queen Street 10 §	a		20 07		20 21			20 37		20 51			21 07			21 21			21 37		21 51				22 07
	d		20 10		20 23			20 40		20 53			21 10			21 23			21 40		21 53				22 10
Charing Cross	d		20 12		20 25			20 42		20 55			21 12			21 25			21 42		21 55				22 12
Argyle Street	d	20 04		20 13		20 23	20 34		20 44		20 53	21 04		21 12			21 23	21 34		21 42		21 53		22 04	
Glasgow Central 15 §	a	20 07		20 15		20 26	20 37		20 49		20 56	21 07		21 16			21 26	21 37		21 46		21 56	22b01	22 07	
	d	20 07		20 15		20 28	20 37		20 49		20 58	21 07		21 16			21 28	21 37		21 46		21 58		22 07	
Anderston	d	20 09		20 17		20 29	20 39		20 51		20 59	21 09		21 18			21 29	21 39		21 48		21 59		22 09	
Exhibition Centre	d	20 11		20 19		20 31	20 41		20 53		21 01	21 11		21 20			21 31	21 41		21 50		22 01		22 11	
Partick	d	20 15	20 17	20a23	20 30	20 35	20 45	20 47	20a56	21 00	21 05	21 15	21 17	21a23		21 30	21 35	21 45	21 47	21a53	22 00	22 05		22 15	22 17
Hyndland	d	20 17	20 20		20 32	20 38	20 47	20 50		21 02	21 08	21 17	21 20			21 32	21 38	21 47	21 50		22 02	22 08		22 17	22 20
Jordanhill	d		20 22					20 52					21 22						21 52						22 22
Scotstounhill	d		20 24					20 54					21 24						21 54						22 24
Garscadden	d		20 26					20 56					21 26						21 56						22 26
Yoker	d		20 29					20 59					21 29						21 59						22 29
Clydebank	d		20 31					21 01					21 31						22 01						22 31
Anniesland	d	20 20			20 35	20 41	20 50			21 05	21 11	21 20				21 35	21 41	21 50			22 05	22 11		22 20	
Westerton	d	20 23			20 38	20 44	20 53			21 08	21 14	21 23				21 38	21 44	21 53			22 08	22 14		22 23	
Bearsden	d					20 46					21 16						21 46					22 16			
Hillfoot	d					20 48					21 18						21 48					22 18			
Milngavie	a					20 52					21 24						21 52					22 22			
Drumchapel	d	20 25			20 40		20 55			21 10		21 25				21 40		21 55			22 10			22 25	
Drumry	d	20 27			20 42		20 57			21 12		21 27				21 42		21 57			22 12			22 27	
Singer	d	20 30			20 45		21 00			21 15		21 30				21 45		22 00			22 15			22 30	
Dalmuir	a	20 32	20 34		20 47		21 02	21 04		21 17		21 32	21 34			21 47		22 02	22 04		22 17			22 32	22 34
	d		20 35		20 48			21 05		21 18			21 35			21 48			22 05		22 18				22 35
Kilpatrick	d				20 51					21 21						21 51					22 21				
Bowling	d				20 54					21 24						21 54					22 24				
Dumbarton East	d		20 42		20 58			21 12		21 28			21 42			21 58			22 12		22 28				22 42
Dumbarton Central	d		20 44		21 00			21 14		21 30			21 44			22 00			22 14		22 30				22 44
Dalreoch	d		20 46		21 02			21 16		21 32			21 46			22 02			22 16		22 32				22 46
Renton	d				21 05					21 35						22 05					22 35				
Alexandria	d				21 07					21 37						22 07					22 37				
Balloch	a				21 10					21 40						22 10					22 40				
Cardross	d		20 51					21 21					21 51						22 21						22 51
Craigendoran	d		20 56					21 26					21 56						22 26						22 56
Helensburgh Central	a		20 59					21 29					21 59						22 29						22 59

For general notes see front of timetable
For details of catering facilities see Directory of Train Operators

§ Low Level

A From Edinburgh (Table 225)

b Glasgow Central High Level

Table 226

Mondays to Fridays

Lanark, Coatbridge, Motherwell, Larkhall, Hamilton, Drumgelloch, Airdrie and Springburn → Glasgow → Milngavie, Dalmuir, Balloch and Helensburgh

Network Diagram - see first page of Table 220

		SR	SR	SR	SR	SR		SR	SR	SR	SR	SR	SR	SR	SR	SR	SR	SR	SR	SR		SR	SR
																			FO	FX		FO	FO
																		A					
Lanark	d	21 23								21 53			22 23										
Carluke	d	21 33								22 03			22 33										
Wishaw	d	21 38								22 08			22 39										
Holytown	d									22 13								23 16					
Shieldmuir	d	21 42											22 42										
Coatbridge Central	d																						
Whifflet	d																						
Motherwell	a	21 46								22 19			22 46										
	d	21 46		21 50				22 16		22 20			22 47		22 53							23 20	
Bellshill	d	21 52						22 23					22 53					23 20					
Uddingston	d	21 56						22 27					22 57					23 26					
Airbles	d			21 52						22 22					22 55							23 22	
Larkhall	d				22 07						22 37					23 07							23 37
Merryton	d				22 09						22 39					23 09							23 39
Chatelherault	d				22 12						22 42					23 12							23 42
Hamilton Central	d			21 57	22 15					22 27	22 45				23 00	23 15						23 27	23 45
Hamilton West	d			22 00	22 18					22 30	22 48				23 03	23 18						23 30	23 48
Blantyre	d			22 03	22 21					22 33	22 51				23 06	23 21						23 33	23 51
Newton	d			22 07						22 37					23 13							23 37	
Cambuslang	d	22 01		22 11				22 32		22 41			23 02		23 16			23 31				23 41	
Rutherglen	d	22 04		22 15	22 29			22 35		22 45	22 59		23 05		23 20	23 29						23 45	23 59
Dalmarnock	d	22 06		22 17				22 37		22 47			23 08		23 22							23 47	
Bridgeton	d	22 08		22 19				22 39		22 49			23 10		23 24							23 49	
Drumgelloch	d					22 08						22 38					23 08						
Airdrie	a					22 11						22 41					23 11						
	d					22 12						22 42					23 12						
Coatdyke	d					22 14						22 44					23 14						
Coatbridge Sunnyside	d					22 16						22 46					23 16						
Blairhill	d					22 19						22 49					23 19						
Easterhouse	d					22 23						22 53					23 23						
Garrowhill	d					22 25						22 55					23 25						
Shettleston	d					22 28						22 58					23 28						
Carntyne	d					22 30						23 00					23 30						
Springburn	d		22 09						22 39					23 09					23 39	23 39			
Barnhill	d		22 10						22 40					23 10					23 40	23 40			
Alexandra Parade	d		22 13						22 43					23 13					23 43	23 43			
Duke Street	d		22 14						22 44					23 14					23 44	23 44			
Bellgrove	d		22 16			22 33			22 46			23 03		23 16			23 33		23 46	23 46			
High Street	d		22 18			22 35			22 48			23 05		23 18			23 35		23 48	23 48			
Glasgow Queen Street 10 § ⛴	a		22 21			22 37			22 51			23 07		23 21			23 37		23 51	23 51			
	d		22 23			22 40			22 53			23 10		23 23			23 45		23 53	23 53			
Charing Cross	d		22 25			22 42			22 55			23 12		23 25			23 47		23 55	23 55			
Argyle Street	d	22 12		22 23	22 34			22 43		22 53	23 04		23 13		23 27	23 34						23 53	00 04
Glasgow Central 15 §	a	22 15		22 26	22 37			22 48		22 56	23 07		23 18		23 29	23 37		23b43				23 56	00 07
	d	22 16		22 28	22 37			22 48		22 58	23 07		23 18		23 29	23 37						23 58	00 07
Anderston	d	22 18		22 29	22 39			22 50		22 59	23 09		23 19		23 30	23 39						23 59	00 09
Exhibition Centre	d	22 20		22 31	22 41			22 52		23 01	23 11		23 20		23 32	23 41						00 01	00 11
Partick ⛴	d	22a23	22 30	22 35	22 45	22 47		22a55	23 00	23 05	23 15	23 17	23 24	23 30	23 36	23 45	23 52		23 59	23 59		00 05	00 15
Hyndland	d		22 32	22 38	22 47	22 50			23 02	23 08	23 17	23 20	23 26	23 32	23 38	23 47	23 55		00 02	00 01		00 08	00 17
Jordanhill	d					22 52						23 22	23 28			23 49	23 57			00 03			
Scotstounhill	d					22 54						23 24	23 30			23 51	23 59			00 05			
Garscadden	d					22 56						23 26	23a33			23a53	00 01			00a07			
Yoker	d					22 59						23 29					00 04						
Clydebank	d					23 01						23 31					00 06						
Anniesland	d		22 35	22 41	22 50				23 05	23 11	23 20			23 35	23 41				00 05			00 11	00 20
Westerton	d		22 38	22 44	22 53				23 08	23 14	23 23			23 38	23 44				00 08			00 14	00 23
Bearsden	d			22 46						23 16					23 46							00 16	
Hillfoot	d			22 48						23 18					23 49							00 18	
Milngavie	a			22 52						23 22					23 52							00 22	
Drumchapel	d		22 40		22 55				23 10		23 25			23 40					00 10				00 25
Drumry	d		22 42		22 57				23 12		23 27			23 42					00 12				00 27
Singer	d		22 45		23 00				23 15		23 30			23 45					00 15				00 30
Dalmuir	a		22 47		23 02	23 04			23 17		23 33	23 34		23 47			00 09		00 17				00 32
	d		22 48			23 05			23 18			23 35		23 48			00 10		00 18				
Kilpatrick	d		22 51						23 21					23 51					00 21				
Bowling	d		22 54						23 24					23 54					00 24				
Dumbarton East	d		22 58			23 12			23 28			23 42		23 58			00 17		00 28				
Dumbarton Central	d		23 00			23 14			23 30			23 44		23 59			00 19		00 30				
Dalreoch	d		23 02			23 16			23 32			23 46		00 02			00 21		00 32				
Renton	d		23 05						23 35					00 05					00 35				
Alexandria	d		23 07						23 37					00 07					00 37				
Balloch	a		23 10						23 40					00 10					00 40				
Cardross	d					23 21						23 51					00 26						
Craigendoran	d					23 26						23 56					00 31						
Helensburgh Central	a					23 29						23 59					00 34						

For general notes see front of timetable
For details of catering facilities see Directory of Train Operators

§ Low Level

A From Edinburgh (Table 225)
b Glasgow Central High Level

Table 226

Lanark, Coatbridge, Motherwell, Larkhall, Hamilton, Drumgelloch, Airdrie and Springburn → Glasgow → Milngavie, Dalmuir, Balloch and Helensburgh

Network Diagram - see first page of Table 220

		SR	SR	SR	SR	SR	SR	SR	SR	SR	SR	SR	SR	SR	SR	SR	SR	SR	SR	SR	SR	SR	SR	SR	SR
		R A																B							
Lanark	d														06 23										
Carluke	d														06 33										
Wishaw	d														06 38										
Holytown	d																	07 02							
Shieldmuir	d														06 42										
Coatbridge Central	d																06 39								
Whifflet	d																06 41								
Motherwell	a														06 45		06 49								
	d								06 16		06 20				06 46		06 50					07 16		07 20	
Bellshill	d								06 22						06 52			07 06				07 22			
Uddingston	d								06 26						06 56			07 12				07 26			
Airbles	d										06 22						06 52							07 22	
Larkhall	d					06 07						06 37							07 07						07 37
Merryton	d					06 09						06 39							07 09						07 39
Chatelherault	d					06 12						06 42							07 12						07 42
Hamilton Central	d					06 15					06 27	06 45					06 57		07 15					07 27	07 45
Hamilton West	d					06 18					06 30	06 48					07 00		07 18					07 30	07 48
Blantyre	d					06 21					06 33	06 51					07 03		07 21					07 33	07 51
Newton	d										06 37						07 07							07 37	
Cambuslang	d								06 31		06 41				07 01		07 11	07 17				07 31		07 41	
Rutherglen	d					06 29			06 34		06 45	06 59			07 04		07 15		07 29			07 34		07 45	07 59
Dalmarnock	d								06 36		06 47				07 06		07 17					07 36		07 47	
Bridgeton	d								06 38		06 49				07 08		07 19					07 38		07 49	
Drumgelloch	d		05 27				06 08						06 38							07 08					
Airdrie	a		05 30				06 11						06 41							07 11					
	d		05 31		05 57		06 12						06 42							07 12					
Coatdyke	d		05 33		05 59		06 14						06 44							07 14					
Coatbridge Sunnyside	d		05 35		06 01		06 16						06 46							07 16					
Blairhill	d		05 38		06 04		06 19						06 49							07 19					
Easterhouse	d		05 42		06 08		06 23						06 53							07 23					
Garrowhill	d		05 44		06 10		06 25						06 55							07 25					
Shettleston	d		05 47		06 13		06 28						06 58							07 28					
Carntyne	d		05 49		06 15		06 30						07 00							07 30					
Springburn	d									06 39						07 09							07 39		
Barnhill	d									06 40						07 10							07 40		
Alexandra Parade	d									06 43						07 13							07 43		
Duke Street	d									06 44						07 14							07 44		
Bellgrove	d		05 52		06 18		06 33			06 46			07 03			07 16				07 33			07 46		
High Street	d		05 54		06 20		06 35			06 48			07 05			07 18				07 35			07 48		
Glasgow Queen Street 10 §	a		05 56		06 22		06 37			06 51			07 07			07 21				07 37			07 51		
	d		05 57		06 23		06 40			06 53			07 10			07 23				07 40			07 53		
Charing Cross	d		06 00		06 25		06 42			06 55			07 12			07 25				07 42			07 55		
Argyle Street	d					06 34			06 42		06 53	07 04			07 12		07 23		07 34			07 42		07 53	08 04
Glasgow Central 15 §	a					06 37			06 46		06 56	07 07			07 16		07 26	07b30	07 37			07 46		07 56	08 07
	d					06 37			06 46		06 58	07 07			07 16		07 28		07 37			07 46		07 58	08 07
Anderston	d					06 39			06 48		06 59	07 09			07 18		07 29		07 39			07 48		07 59	08 09
Exhibition Centre	d					06 41			06 50		07 01	07 11			07 20		07 31		07 41			07 50		08 01	08 11
Partick	d		06 04		06 30	06 45	06 47		06 54	07 00	07 05	07 15	07 17		07 24	07 30	07 35		07 45	07 47		07 54	08 00	08 05	08 15
Hyndland	d		06 06		06 32	06 47	06 50		06 56	07 02	07 08	07 17	07 20		07 26	07 32	07 38		07 47	07 50		07 56	08 02	08 08	08 17
Jordanhill	d		06 08						06 58						07 28							07 58			
Scotstounhill	d		06 11						07 00						07 30							08 00			
Garscadden	d		06 13				06 54		07 02						07 32							08 02			
Yoker	d		06 15						07 05						07 35							08 05			
Clydebank	d		06 17						07 07						07 37							08 07			
Anniesland	d				06 35	06 50				07 05	07 11	07 20				07 35	07 41		07 50				08 05	08 11	08 20
Westerton	d	05 56			06 38	06 53				07 08	07 14	07 23				07 38	07 44		07 53				08 08	08 14	08 23
Bearsden	d										07 16						07 46							08 16	
Hillfoot	d										07 18						07 48							08 18	
Milngavie	a							←			07 22			←			07 52				←			08 22	
Drumchapel	d				06 40	06 55 →		06 55		07 10		07 25 →		07 25		07 40			07 55 →		07 55		08 10		08 25 →
Drumry	d				06 42			06 57		07 12				07 27		07 42					07 57		08 12		
Singer	d				06 45			07 00		07 15				07 30		07 45					08 00		08 15		
Dalmuir	a	06 03	06 21		06 47		06 58	07 02	07 11	07 17			07 28	07 32	07 41	07 47				07 59	08 02	08 11	08 17		
	d	06 04	06 21	06 32	06 48		06 59			07 18			07 29			07 48				07 59			08 18		
Kilpatrick	d			06 34	06 51					07 21						07 51							08 21		
Bowling	d			06 37	06 54					07 24						07 54							08 24		
Dumbarton East	d		06 29	06 42	06 58		07 06			07 28			07 36			07 58				08 06			08 28		
Dumbarton Central	d		06 30	06 44	07 00		07 08			07 30			07 38			08 00				08 08			08 30		
Dalreoch	d		06 32	06 46	07 02		07 10			07 32			07 40			08 02				08 10			08 32		
Renton	d		06 35		07 05					07 35						08 05							08 35		
Alexandria	d		06 37		07 07					07 37						08 07							08 37		
Balloch	a		06 40		07 10					07 40						08 10							08 40		
Cardross	d			06 51			07 15						07 45							08 15					
Craigendoran	d			06 56			07 20						07 50							08 20					
Helensburgh Central	a	06c26		06 59			07 23						07 53							08 23					

For general notes see front of timetable
For details of catering facilities see Directory of Train Operators

§ Low Level

A From Edinburgh (Table 225) to Fort William (Table 227)
B From Edinburgh (Table 225)
b Glasgow Central High Level
c Helensburgh Upper

Table 226

Saturdays

Lanark, Coatbridge, Motherwell, Larkhall, Hamilton, Drumgelloch, Airdrie and Springburn → Glasgow → Milngavie, Dalmuir, Balloch and Helensburgh

Network Diagram - see first page of Table 220

		SR	SR	SR ◇ A	SR	SR	SR	SR B	SR	SR	SR	SR	SR	SR	SR	SR	SR	SR	SR	SR	SR	SR	SR	SR	SR
Lanark	d				07 23									07 53				08 23							
Carluke	d				07 33									08 03				08 33							
Wishaw	d				07 38									08 08				08 38							
Holytown	d							08 02						08 13											
Shieldmuir	d				07 42													08 42							
Coatbridge Central	d																								
Whifflet	d																								
Motherwell	a				07 45									08 20				08 46							
	d				07 46		07 50					08 16		08 20				08 46		08 50					
Bellshill	d				07 52			08 06				08 22						08 52							
Uddingston	d				07 56			08 12				08 26						08 56							
Airbles	d						07 52							08 22						08 52					
Larkhall	d								08 07						08 37							09 07			
Merryton	d								08 09						08 39							09 09			
Chatelherault	d								08 12						08 42							09 12			
Hamilton Central	d						07 57		08 15					08 27	08 45					08 57		09 15			
Hamilton West	d						08 00		08 18					08 30	08 48					09 00		09 18			
Blantyre	d						08 03		08 21					08 33	08 51					09 03		09 21			
Newton	d						08 07							08 37						09 07					
Cambuslang	d				08 01		08 11	08 17				08 31		08 41				09 01		09 11					
Rutherglen	d				08 04		08 15		08 29			08 34		08 46	08 59			09 04		09 15		09 29			
Dalmarnock	d				08 06		08 17					08 36		08 48				09 06		09 17					
Bridgeton	d				08 08		08 19					08 38		08 50				09 08		09 19					
Drumgelloch	d	07 38								08 08						08 38							09 08		
Airdrie	a	07 41								08 11						08 41							09 11		
	d	07 42								08 12						08 42							09 12		
Coatdyke	d	07 44								08 14						08 44							09 14		
Coatbridge Sunnyside	d	07 46								08 16						08 46							09 16		
Blairhill	d	07 49								08 19						08 49							09 19		
Easterhouse	d	07 53								08 23						08 53							09 23		
Garrowhill	d	07 55								08 25						08 55							09 25		
Shettleston	d	07 58								08 28						08 58							09 28		
Carntyne	d	08 00								08 30						09 00							09 30		
Springburn	d					08 09							08 39						09 09		09 19				
Barnhill	d					08 10							08 40						09 10		09 20				
Alexandra Parade	d					08 13							08 43						09 13		09 23				
Duke Street	d					08 14							08 44						09 14		09 24				
Bellgrove	d	08 03				08 16				08 33			08 46			09 03			09 16		09 26		09 33		09 38
High Street	d	08 05				08 18				08 35			08 48			09 05			09 18		09 28		09 35		09 40
Glasgow Queen Street [10] §	a	08 07				08 21				08 37			08 51			09 07			09 21		09 31		09 37		09 42
	d	08 10		08b21		08 23				08 40			08 53			09 10			09 23		09 32		09 40		09 43
Charing Cross	d	08 12				08 25				08 42			08 55			09 12			09 25		09 34		09 42		09 45
Argyle Street	d				08 12		08 23		08 34			08 42		08 55	09 04			09 12		09 23		09 34			
Glasgow Central [15] §	a				08 16		08 26	08c30	08 37			08 46		08 57	09 07			09 16		09 26		09 37			
	d				08 16		08 28		08 37			08 46		08 58	09 07			09 16		09 28		09 37			
Anderston	d				08 18		08 29		08 39			08 48		09 00	09 09			09 18		09 29		09 39			
Exhibition Centre	d				08 20		08 31		08 41			08 50		09 02	09 11			09 20		09 31		09 41			
Partick	d	08 17			08 24	08 30	08 35		08 45	08 47		08 54	09 00	09 05	09 15	09 17		09 24	09 30	09 35	09 39	09 45	09 47		09 50
Hyndland	d	08 20			08 26	08 32	08 38		08 47	08 50		08 56	09 02	09 08	09 17	09 20		09 26	09 32	09 38	09 41	09 47	09 50		09 53
Jordanhill	d				08 28							08 58						09 28			09 43				
Scotstounhill	d				08 30							09 00						09 30			09 45				
Garscadden	d				08 32							09 02						09 32			09 47				
Yoker	d				08 35							09 05						09 35			09 50				
Clydebank	d				08 37							09 07						09 37			09 52				
Anniesland	d					08 35	08 41		08 50				09 05	09 11	09 20				09 35	09 41		09 50			09 56
Westerton	d					08 38	08 44		08 53				09 08	09 14	09 23				09 38	09 44		09 53			09 59
Bearsden	d						08 46							09 16						09 46					10 01
Hillfoot	d						08 48							09 18						09 48					10 03
Milngavie	a		←				08 52				←			09 22			←			09 52				←	10 07
Drumchapel	d		08 25			08 40			08 55		08 55		09 10		09 25		09 25		09 40			09 55		09 55	
Drumry	d		08 27			08 42			→		08 57		09 12		→		09 27		09 42			→		09 57	
Singer	d		08 30			08 45					09 00		09 15				09 30		09 45					10 00	
Dalmuir	a	08 29	08 32	08 38	08 41	08 47				08 59	09 02	09 11	09 17			09 29	09 32	09 41	09 47		09 56		09 59	10 02	
	d	08 29		08 39		08 48				08 59			09 18			09 29			09 48				09 59		
Kilpatrick	d					08 51							09 21						09 51						
Bowling	d					08 54							09 24						09 54						
Dumbarton East	d	08 36				08 58				09 06			09 28			09 36			09 58				10 06		
Dumbarton Central	d	08 38		08 48		09 00				09 08			09 30			09 38			10 00				10 08		
Dalreoch	d	08 40				09 02				09 10			09 32			09 40			10 02				10 10		
Renton	d					09 05							09 35						10 05						
Alexandria	d					09 07							09 37						10 07						
Balloch	a					09 10							09 40						10 10						
Cardross	d	08 45								09 15						09 45							10 15		
Craigendoran	d	08 50								09 20						09 50							10 20		
Helensburgh Central	a	08 55		09e03						09 25						09 55							10 23		

For general notes see front of timetable
For details of catering facilities see Directory of Train Operators

§ Low Level

A To Oban (Table 227) and Mallaig (Table 227)
B From Edinburgh (Table 225)
b Glasgow Queen Street High Level
c Glasgow Central High Level
e Helensburgh Upper

Table 226

Saturdays

Lanark, Coatbridge, Motherwell, Larkhall, Hamilton, Drumgelloch, Airdrie and Springburn → Glasgow → Milngavie, Dalmuir, Balloch and Helensburgh

Network Diagram - see first page of Table 220

		SR	SR	SR	SR	SR	SR	SR	SR	SR	SR	SR	SR	SR	SR	SR	SR	SR	SR	SR	SR	SR		SR	SR
					A									B	◇ C										A
Lanark	d			08 53							09 23													09 53	
Carluke	d			09 03							09 33			09 49										10 02	
Wishaw	d			09 08							09 38													10 08	
Holytown	d			09 13	09 32																			10 13	10 31
Shieldmuir	d										09 42														
Coatbridge Central	d																								
Whifflet	d																								
Motherwell	a			09 20							09 46			09 56										10 20	
	d	09 16		09 20							09 46		09 50	09 57							10 16			10 20	
Bellshill	d	09 22			09 36						09 52										10 22				10 36
Uddingston	d	09 26			09 40						09 56										10 26				10 42
Airbles	d			09 22									09 52											10 22	
Larkhall	d						09 37										10 07								
Merryton	d						09 39										10 09								
Chatelherault	d						09 42										10 12								
Hamilton Central	d			09 27			09 45						09 57				10 15							10 27	
Hamilton West	d			09 30			09 48						10 00				10 18							10 30	
Blantyre	d			09 33			09 51						10 03				10 21							10 33	
Newton	d			09 37									10 07											10 37	
Cambuslang	d	09 31		09 43	09 47						10 01		10 11								10 31			10 41	10 47
Rutherglen	d	09 34		09 45			09 59				10 04		10 15				10 29				10 34			10 45	
Dalmarnock	d	09 36		09 47							10 06		10 17								10 36			10 47	
Bridgeton	d	09 38		09 49							10 08		10 19								10 38			10 49	
Drumgelloch	d							09 38										10 08							
Airdrie	a							09 41										10 11							
	d		09 27					09 42				09 57						10 12				10 27			
Coatdyke	d		09 29					09 44				09 59						10 14				10 29			
Coatbridge Sunnyside	d		09 31					09 46				10 01						10 16				10 31			
Blairhill	d		09 34					09 49				10 04						10 19				10 34			
Easterhouse	d		09 38					09 53				10 08						10 23				10 38			
Garrowhill	d		09 40					09 55				10 10						10 25				10 40			
Shettleston	d		09 43					09 58				10 13						10 28				10 43			
Carntyne	d		09 45					10 00				10 15						10 30				10 45			
Springburn	d					09 49										10 19									
Barnhill	d					09 50										10 20									
Alexandra Parade	d					09 53										10 23									
Duke Street	d					09 54										10 24									
Bellgrove	d		09 48			09 56		10 03		10 08		10 18				10 26		10 33		10 38		10 48			
High Street	d		09 50			09 58		10 05		10 10		10 20				10 28		10 35		10 40		10 50			
Glasgow Queen Street 10 §	a		09 52			10 01		10 07		10 12		10 22				10 31		10 37		10 42		10 52			
	d		09 53			10 02		10 10		10 13		10 23			10b37	10 32		10 40		10 43		10 53			
Charing Cross	d		09 55			10 04		10 12		10 15		10 25				10 34		10 42		10 45		10 55			
Argyle Street	d	09 42		09 53			10 04				10 12		10 23				10 34				10 42			10 53	
Glasgow Central 15 §	a	09 46		09 55	09c59		10 07				10 16		10 26	10 14			10 37				10 46			10 56	11c00
	d	09 46		09 58			10 07				10 16		10 28				10 37				10 46			10 58	
Anderston	d	09 48		09 59			10 09				10 18		10 29				10 39				10 48			10 59	
Exhibition Centre	d	09 50		10 01			10 11				10 20		10 31				10 41				10 50			11 01	
Partick	d	09 54	10 00	10 05		10 09	10 15	10 17		10 20	10 24	10 30	10 35			10 39	10 45	10 47		10 50	10 54	11 00		11 05	
Hyndland	d	09 56	10 02	10 08		10 11	10 17	10 20		10 23	10 26	10 32	10 38			10 41	10 47	10 50		10 53	10 56	11 02		11 08	
Jordanhill	d	09 58				10 13					10 28					10 43					10 58				
Scotstounhill	d	10 00				10 15					10 30					10 45					11 00				
Garscadden	d	10 02				10 17					10 32					10 47					11 02				
Yoker	d	10 05				10 20					10 35					10 50					11 05				
Clydebank	d	10 07				10 22					10 37					10 52					11 07				
Anniesland	d		10 05	10 11			10 20			10 26		10 35	10 41				10 50			10 56		11 05		11 11	
Westerton	d		10 08	10 14			10 23			10 29		10 38	10 44				10 53			10 59		11 08		11 14	
Bearsden	d			10 16						10 31			10 46							11 01				11 16	
Hillfoot	d			10 18					←	10 33			10 48						←	11 03				11 18	
Milngavie	a			10 22						10 37			10 52							11 07				11 24	
Drumchapel	d		10 10				10 25 →		10 25			10 40					10 55 →		10 55			11 10			
Drumry	d		10 12						10 27			10 42							10 57			11 12			
Singer	d		10 15						10 30			10 45							11 00			11 15			
Dalmuir	a	10 11	10 17			10 26		10 29	10 32		10 41	10 47			10 50	10 56		10 59	11 02		11 11	11 17			
	d		10 18					10 29				10 48			10 50			10 59				11 18			
Kilpatrick	d		10 21									10 51										11 21			
Bowling	d		10 24									10 54										11 24			
Dumbarton East	d		10 28					10 36				10 58						11 06				11 28			
Dumbarton Central	d		10 30					10 38				11 00			11 04			11 08				11 30			
Dalreoch	d		10 32					10 40				11 02						11 10				11 32			
Renton	d		10 35									11 05										11 35			
Alexandria	d		10 37									11 07										11 37			
Balloch	a		10 40									11 10										11 40			
Cardross	d							10 45										11 15							
Craigendoran	d							10 50										11 20							
Helensburgh Central	a							10 56							11e20			11 25							

For general notes see front of timetable
For details of catering facilities see Directory of Train Operators

§ Low Level

A From Edinburgh (Table 225)
B From North Berwick (Table 238)
C Until 24 October. To Oban (Table 227)

b Glasgow Queen Street High Level
c Glasgow Central High Level
e Helensburgh Upper

Table 226

Lanark, Coatbridge, Motherwell, Larkhall, Hamilton, Drumgelloch, Airdrie and Springburn → Glasgow → Milngavie, Dalmuir, Balloch and Helensburgh

Network Diagram - see first page of Table 220

Station		SR	SR	SR	SR	SR	SR	SR	SR	SR	SR	SR	SR
Lanark	d						10 23						
Carluke	d						10 33						
Wishaw	d						10 39						
Holytown	d												
Shieldmuir	d						10 42						
Coatbridge Central	d												
Whifflet	d												
Motherwell	a						10 46						
	d						10 47		10 50				
Bellshill	d						10 53						
Uddingston	d						10 57						
Airbles	d								10 52				
Larkhall	d		10 37								11 07		
Merryton	d		10 39								11 09		
Chatelherault	d		10 42								11 12		
Hamilton Central	d		10 45						10 57		11 15		
Hamilton West	d		10 48						11 00		11 18		
Blantyre	d		10 51						11 03		11 21		
Newton	d								11 07				
Cambuslang	d						11 02		11 11				
Rutherglen	d		10 59				11 05		11 15		11 29		
Dalmarnock	d						11 07		11 17				
Bridgeton	d						11 09		11 19				
Drumgelloch	d			10 38								11 08	
Airdrie	a			10 41								11 11	
	d			10 42				10 57				11 12	
Coatdyke	d			10 44				10 59				11 14	
Coatbridge Sunnyside	d			10 46				11 01				11 16	
Blairhill	d			10 49				11 04				11 19	
Easterhouse	d			10 53				11 08				11 23	
Garrowhill	d			10 55				11 10				11 25	
Shettleston	d			10 58				11 13				11 28	
Carntyne	d			11 00				11 15				11 30	
Springburn	d	10 49								11 19			
Barnhill	d	10 50								11 20			
Alexandra Parade	d	10 53								11 23			
Duke Street	d	10 54								11 24			
Bellgrove	d	10 56		11 03		11 08		11 18		11 26		11 33	
High Street	d	10 58		11 05		11 10		11 20		11 28		11 35	
Glasgow Queen Street [10] §	a	11 01		11 07		11 12		11 22		11 31		11 37	
	d	11 02		11 10		11 13		11 23		11 32		11 40	
Charing Cross	d	11 04		11 12		11 15		11 25		11 34		11 42	
Argyle Street	d		11 04				11 13		11 23		11 34		
Glasgow Central [15] §	a		11 07				11 18		11 26		11 37		
	d		11 07				11 18		11 28		11 37		
Anderston	d		11 09				11 20		11 29		11 39		
Exhibition Centre	d		11 11				11 22		11 31		11 41		
Partick	d	11 09	11 15	11 17		11 20	11 25	11 30	11 35	11 39	11 45	11 47	
Hyndland	d	11 11	11 17	11 20		11 23	11 27	11 32	11 38	11 41	11 47	11 50	
Jordanhill	d	11 13					11 29			11 43			
Scotstounhill	d	11 15					11 32			11 45			
Garscadden	d	11 17					11 35			11 47			
Yoker	d	11 20					11 37			11 50			
Clydebank	d	11 22					11 39			11 52			
Anniesland	d		11 20			11 26		11 35	11 41		11 50		
Westerton	d		11 23			11 29		11 38	11 44		11 53		
Bearsden	d					11 31			11 46				
Hillfoot	d					11 33			11 48				
Milngavie	a				←	11 37			11 52				←
Drumchapel	d		11 25 →		11 25			11 40			11 55 →		11 55
Drumry	d				11 27			11 42					11 57
Singer	d				11 30			11 45					12 00
Dalmuir	a	11 26		11 29	11 32		11 42	11 47		11 56		11 59	12 02
	d			11 29				11 48				11 59	
Kilpatrick	d							11 51					
Bowling	d							11 54					
Dumbarton East	d			11 36				11 58				12 06	
Dumbarton Central	d			11 38				12 00				12 08	
Dalreoch	d			11 40				12 02				12 10	
Renton	d							12 05					
Alexandria	d							12 07					
Balloch	a							12 10					
Cardross	d			11 45								12 15	
Craigendoran	d			11 50								12 20	
Helensburgh Central	a			11 53								12 23	

Station		SR	SR	SR	SR	SR	SR	SR	SR	SR	SR	SR	SR
						A						◇ B	
Lanark	d				10 53								11 23
Carluke	d				11 03								11 33
Wishaw	d				11 08								11 39
Holytown	d				11 13	11 32							
Shieldmuir	d												11 42
Coatbridge Central	d												
Whifflet	d												
Motherwell	a				11 19								11 46
	d		11 16		11 20								11 47
Bellshill	d		11 22			11 36							11 53
Uddingston	d		11 26			11 40							11 57
Airbles	d				11 22								
Larkhall	d							11 37					
Merryton	d							11 39					
Chatelherault	d							11 42					
Hamilton Central	d				11 27			11 45					
Hamilton West	d				11 30			11 48					
Blantyre	d				11 33			11 51					
Newton	d				11 37								
Cambuslang	d		11 31		11 41	11 45							12 02
Rutherglen	d		11 34		11 45			11 59					12 06
Dalmarnock	d		11 36		11 47								12 08
Bridgeton	d		11 38		11 49								12 10
Drumgelloch	d								11 38				
Airdrie	a								11 41				
	d			11 27					11 42				
Coatdyke	d			11 29					11 44				
Coatbridge Sunnyside	d			11 31					11 46				
Blairhill	d			11 34					11 49				
Easterhouse	d			11 38					11 53				
Garrowhill	d			11 40					11 55				
Shettleston	d			11 43					11 58				
Carntyne	d			11 45					12 00				
Springburn	d						11 49						
Barnhill	d						11 50						
Alexandra Parade	d						11 53						
Duke Street	d						11 54						
Bellgrove	d	11 38		11 48			11 56		12 03		12 08		
High Street	d	11 40		11 50			11 58		12 05		12 10		
Glasgow Queen Street [10] §	a	11 42		11 52			12 01		12 07		12 12		
	d	11 43		11 53			12 02		12 10		12 13	12b21	
Charing Cross	d	11 45		11 55			12 04		12 12		12 15		
Argyle Street	d		11 42		11 53			12 04					12 13
Glasgow Central [15] §	a		11 46		11 56	12c01		12 07					12 18
	d		11 46		11 58			12 07					12 18
Anderston	d		11 48		11 59			12 09					12 20
Exhibition Centre	d		11 50		12 01			12 11					12 22
Partick	d	11 50	11 54	12 00	12 05		12 09	12 15	12 17		12 20		12 25
Hyndland	d	11 53	11 56	12 02	12 08		12 11	12 17	12 20		12 23		12 27
Jordanhill	d		11 58				12 13						12 29
Scotstounhill	d		12 00				12 15						12 32
Garscadden	d		12 02				12 17						12 35
Yoker	d		12 05				12 20						12 37
Clydebank	d		12 07				12 22						12 39
Anniesland	d	11 56		12 05	12 11			12 20			12 26		
Westerton	d	11 59		12 08	12 14			12 23			12 29		
Bearsden	d	12 01			12 16						12 31		
Hillfoot	d	12 03			12 18						12 33		
Milngavie	a	12 07			12 22					←	12 37		
Drumchapel	d			12 10				12 25 →		12 25			
Drumry	d			12 12						12 27			
Singer	d			12 15						12 30			
Dalmuir	a		12 11	12 17			12 26		12 29	12 32		12 38	12 42
	d			12 18					12 29			12 42	
Kilpatrick	d			12 21									
Bowling	d			12 24									
Dumbarton East	d			12 28					12 36				
Dumbarton Central	d			12 30					12 38				
Dalreoch	d			12 32					12 40			12 48	
Renton	d			12 35									
Alexandria	d			12 37									
Balloch	a			12 40									
Cardross	d								12 45				
Craigendoran	d								12 50				
Helensburgh Central	a								12 53			13e03	

For general notes see front of timetable
For details of catering facilities see Directory of Train Operators

§ Low Level

A From Edinburgh (Table 225)
B To Oban (Table 227) and Mallaig (Table 227)
b Glasgow Queen Street High Level
c Glasgow Central High Level
e Helensburgh Upper

Lanark, Coatbridge, Motherwell, Larkhall, Hamilton, Drumgelloch, Airdrie and Springburn → Glasgow → Milngavie, Dalmuir, Balloch and Helensburgh

Network Diagram - see first page of Table 220

		SR	SR	SR	SR	SR	SR	SR	SR	SR	SR	SR	SR	SR	SR	SR	SR	SR	SR	SR	SR	SR	SR	SR	SR
												A													
Lanark	d										11 53							12 23							
Carluke	d										12 03							12 33							
Wishaw	d										12 08							12 39							
Holytown	d										12 13	12 32													
Shieldmuir	d																	12 42							
Coatbridge Central	d																								
Whifflet	d																								
Motherwell	a										12 20							12 46							
	d		11 50						12 16		12 20							12 47		12 50					
Bellshill	d								12 22			12 36						12 53							
Uddingston	d								12 26			12 42						12 57							
Airbles	d		11 52								12 22									12 52					
Larkhall	d				12 07									12 37								13 07			
Merryton	d				12 09									12 39								13 09			
Chatelherault	d				12 12									12 42								13 12			
Hamilton Central	d		11 57		12 15						12 27			12 45						12 57		13 15			
Hamilton West	d		12 00		12 18						12 30			12 48						13 00		13 18			
Blantyre	d		12 03		12 21						12 33			12 51						13 03		13 21			
Newton	d		12 07								12 37									13 07					
Cambuslang	d		12 11						12 31		12 41	12 47						13 02		13 11		13 29			
Rutherglen	d		12 15		12 29				12 34		12 45			12 59				13 06		13 15					
Dalmarnock	d		12 17						12 36		12 47							13 08		13 17					
Bridgeton	d		12 19						12 38		12 49							13 10		13 19					
Drumgelloch	d					12 08									12 38								13 08		
Airdrie	a					12 11									12 41								13 11		
	d	11 57				12 12				12 27					12 42				12 57				13 12		
Coatdyke	d	11 59				12 14				12 29					12 44				12 59				13 14		
Coatbridge Sunnyside	d	12 01				12 16				12 31					12 46				13 01				13 16		
Blairhill	d	12 04				12 19				12 34					12 49				13 04				13 19		
Easterhouse	d	12 08				12 23				12 38					12 53				13 08				13 23		
Garrowhill	d	12 10				12 25				12 40					12 55				13 10				13 25		
Shettleston	d	12 13				12 28				12 43					12 58				13 13				13 28		
Carntyne	d	12 15				12 30				12 45					13 00				13 15				13 30		
Springburn	d			12 19									12 49								13 19				
Barnhill	d			12 20									12 50								13 20				
Alexandra Parade	d			12 23									12 53								13 23				
Duke Street	d			12 24									12 54								13 24				
Bellgrove	d	12 18		12 26		12 33		12 38		12 48			12 56		13 03		13 08		13 18		13 26		13 33		13 38
High Street	d	12 20		12 28		12 35		12 40		12 50			12 58		13 05		13 10		13 20		13 28		13 35		13 40
Glasgow Queen Street 10 §	a	12 22		12 31		12 37		12 42		12 52			13 01		13 07		13 12		13 22		13 31		13 37		13 42
	d	12 23		12 32		12 40		12 43		12 53			13 02		13 10		13 13		13 23		13 32		13 40		13 43
Charing Cross	d	12 25		12 34		12 42		12 45		12 55			13 04		13 12		13 15		13 25		13 34		13 42		13 45
Argyle Street	d		12 23		12 34				12 42		12 53			13 04				13 14		13 23		13 34			
Glasgow Central 15 §	a		12 26		12 37				12 46		12 56	13b01		13 07				13 19		13 26		13 37			
	d		12 28		12 37				12 46		12 58			13 07				13 19		13 28		13 37			
Anderston	d		12 29		12 39				12 48		12 59			13 09				13 21		13 29		13 39			
Exhibition Centre	d		12 31		12 41				12 50		13 01			13 11				13 23		13 31		13 41			
Partick	d	12 30	12 35	12 39	12 45	12 47		12 50	12 54	13 00	13 05		13 09	13 15	13 17		13 20	13 26	13 30	13 35	13 39	13 45	13 47		13 50
Hyndland	d	12 32	12 38	12 41	12 47	12 50		12 53	12 56	13 02	13 08		13 11	13 17	13 20		13 23	13 28	13 32	13 38	13 41	13 47	13 50		13 53
Jordanhill	d			12 43					12 58				13 13					13 30			13 43				
Scotstounhill	d			12 45					13 00				13 15					13 33			13 45				
Garscadden	d			12 47					13 02				13 17					13 36			13 47				
Yoker	d			12 50					13 05				13 20					13 38			13 50				
Clydebank	d			12 52					13 07				13 22					13 40			13 52				
Anniesland	d	12 35	12 41		12 50			12 56		13 05	13 11			13 20			13 26		13 35	13 41		13 50			13 56
Westerton	d	12 38	12 44		12 53			12 59		13 08	13 14			13 23			13 29		13 38	13 44		13 53			13 59
Bearsden	d		12 46					13 01			13 16						13 31			13 46					14 01
Hillfoot	d		12 48					13 03			13 18						13 33			13 48					14 03
Milngavie	a		12 52				←	13 07			13 22					←	13 37			13 52				←	14 07
Drumchapel	d	12 40			12 55 →		12 55			13 10				13 25 →		13 25			13 40			13 55 →		13 55	
Drumry	d	12 42					12 57			13 12						13 27			13 42					13 57	
Singer	d	12 45					13 00			13 15						13 30			13 45					14 00	
Dalmuir	a	12 47		12 56		12 59	13 02		13 11	13 17			13 26		13 29	13 32		13 43	13 47		13 56		13 59	14 02	
	d	12 48				12 59				13 18					13 29				13 48				13 59		
Kilpatrick	d	12 51								13 21									13 51						
Bowling	d	12 54								13 24									13 54						
Dumbarton East	d	12 58				13 06				13 28					13 36				13 58				14 06		
Dumbarton Central	d	13 00				13 08				13 30					13 38				14 00				14 08		
Dalreoch	d	13 02				13 10				13 32					13 40				14 02				14 10		
Renton	d	13 05								13 35									14 05						
Alexandria	d	13 07								13 37									14 07						
Balloch	a	13 10								13 40									14 10						
Cardross	d					13 15									13 45								14 15		
Craigendoran	d					13 20									13 50								14 20		
Helensburgh Central	a					13 26									13 53								14 23		

For general notes see front of timetable
For details of catering facilities see Directory of Train Operators

§ Low Level

A From Edinburgh (Table 225)
b Glasgow Central High Level

Table 226

Saturdays

Lanark, Coatbridge, Motherwell, Larkhall, Hamilton, Drumgelloch, Airdrie and Springburn → Glasgow → Milngavie, Dalmuir, Balloch and Helensburgh

Network Diagram - see first page of Table 220

		SR	SR	SR	SR A	SR	SR	SR	SR	SR	SR	SR	SR	SR	SR	SR	SR	SR	SR	SR	SR	SR A		SR	SR
Lanark	d			12 53							13 23										13 53				
Carluke	d			13 03							13 33										14 03				
Wishaw	d			13 08							13 39										14 08				
Holytown	d			13 13	13 32																14 13	14 32			
Shieldmuir	d										13 42														
Coatbridge Central	d																								
Whifflet	d																								
Motherwell	a			13 19							13 46										14 20				
	d	13 16		13 20							13 47		13 50						14 16		14 20				
Bellshill	d	13 22			13 36						13 53								14 22			14 34			
Uddingston	d	13 26			13 41						13 57								14 26			14 42			
Airbles	d			13 22									13 52								14 22				
Larkhall	d						13 37								14 07										14 37
Merryton	d						13 39								14 09										14 39
Chatelherault	d						13 42								14 12										14 42
Hamilton Central	d			13 27			13 45						13 57		14 15						14 27				14 45
Hamilton West	d			13 30			13 48						14 00		14 18						14 30				14 48
Blantyre	d			13 33			13 51						14 03		14 21						14 33				14 51
Newton	d			13 37									14 07								14 37				
Cambuslang	d	13 31		13 41	13 47						14 02		14 11						14 31		14 41	14 47			
Rutherglen	d	13 34		13 45			13 59				14 06		14 15		14 29				14 34		14 45				14 59
Dalmarnock	d	13 36		13 47							14 08		14 17						14 36		14 47				
Bridgeton	d	13 38		13 49							14 10		14 19						14 38		14 49				
Drumgelloch	d							13 38								14 08									
Airdrie	a							13 41								14 11									
	d		13 27					13 42				13 57				14 12				14 27					
Coatdyke	d		13 29					13 44				13 59				14 14				14 29					
Coatbridge Sunnyside	d		13 31					13 46				14 01				14 16				14 31					
Blairhill	d		13 34					13 49				14 04				14 19				14 34					
Easterhouse	d		13 38					13 53				14 08				14 23				14 38					
Garrowhill	d		13 40					13 55				14 10				14 25				14 40					
Shettleston	d		13 43					13 58				14 13				14 28				14 43					
Carntyne	d		13 45					14 00				14 15				14 30				14 45					
Springburn	d					13 49								14 19										14 49	
Barnhill	d					13 50								14 20										14 50	
Alexandra Parade	d					13 53								14 23										14 53	
Duke Street	d					13 54								14 24										14 54	
Bellgrove	d		13 48			13 56		14 03		14 08		14 18		14 26		14 33		14 38		14 48				14 56	
High Street	d		13 50			13 58		14 05		14 10		14 20		14 28		14 35		14 40		14 50				14 58	
Glasgow Queen Street 10 §	a		13 52			14 01		14 07		14 12		14 22		14 31		14 37		14 42		14 52				15 01	
	d		13 53			14 02		14 10		14 13		14 23		14 32		14 40		14 43		14 53				15 02	
Charing Cross	d		13 55			14 04		14 12		14 15		14 25		14 34		14 42		14 45		14 55				15 04	
Argyle Street	d	13 42		13 53			14 04				14 14		14 23		14 34				14 42		14 53				15 04
Glasgow Central 15 §	a	13 46		13 56	14b01		14 07				14 18		14 26		14 37				14 46		14 56	15b01			15 07
	d	13 46		13 58			14 07				14 19		14 28		14 37				14 46		14 58				15 07
Anderston	d	13 48		13 59			14 09				14 20		14 29		14 39				14 48		14 59				15 09
Exhibition Centre	d	13 50		14 01			14 11				14 22		14 31		14 41				14 50		15 01				15 11
Partick	d	13 54	14 00	14 05		14 09	14 15	14 17		14 20	14 26	14 30	14 35	14 39	14 45	14 47		14 50	14 54	15 00	15 05			15 09	15 15
Hyndland	d	13 56	14 02	14 08		14 11	14 17	14 20		14 23	14 28	14 32	14 38	14 41	14 47	14 50		14 53	14 56	15 02	15 08			15 11	15 17
Jordanhill	d	13 58				14 13					14 30			14 43					14 58					15 13	
Scotstounhill	d	14 00				14 15					14 33			14 45					15 00					15 15	
Garscadden	d	14 02				14 17					14 36			14 47					15 02					15 17	
Yoker	d	14 05				14 20					14 38			14 50					15 05					15 20	
Clydebank	d	14 07				14 22					14 40			14 52					15 07					15 22	
Anniesland	d		14 05	14 11			14 20			14 26		14 35	14 41		14 50			14 56		15 05	15 11				15 20
Westerton	d		14 08	14 14			14 23			14 29		14 38	14 44		14 53			14 59		15 08	15 14				15 23
Bearsden	d			14 16						14 31			14 46					15 01			15 16				
Hillfoot	d			14 18						14 33			14 48					15 03			15 18				
Milngavie	a			14 22					←	14 37			14 52				←	15 07			15 24				
Drumchapel	d		14 10				14 25 →		14 25			14 40			14 55 →		14 55			15 10					15 25 →
Drumry	d		14 12						14 27			14 42					14 57			15 12					
Singer	d		14 15						14 30			14 45					15 00			15 15					
Dalmuir	a	14 11	14 17			14 26		14 29	14 32		14 43	14 47		14 56		14 59	15 02		15 13	15 17				15 26	
	d		14 18					14 29				14 48				14 59				15 18					
Kilpatrick	d		14 21									14 51								15 21					
Bowling	d		14 24									14 54								15 24					
Dumbarton East	d		14 28					14 36				14 58				15 06				15 28					
Dumbarton Central	d		14 30					14 38				15 00				15 08				15 30					
Dalreoch	d		14 32					14 40				15 02				15 10				15 32					
Renton	d		14 35									15 05								15 35					
Alexandria	d		14 37									15 07								15 37					
Balloch	a		14 40									15 10								15 40					
Cardross	d							14 45								15 15									
Craigendoran	d							14 50								15 20									
Helensburgh Central	a							14 54								15 26									

For general notes see front of timetable
For details of catering facilities see
Directory of Train Operators

§ Low Level

A From Edinburgh (Table 225)
b Glasgow Central High Level

Table 226

Saturdays

Lanark, Coatbridge, Motherwell, Larkhall, Hamilton, Drumgelloch, Airdrie and Springburn → Glasgow → Milngavie, Dalmuir, Balloch and Helensburgh

Network Diagram - see first page of Table 220

		SR	SR	SR	SR	SR	SR	SR	SR	SR	SR	SR	SR	SR	SR	SR A	SR	SR	SR	SR	SR	SR	SR	SR	SR
Lanark	d				14 23										14 53							15 23			
Carluke	d				14 33										15 03							15 33			
Wishaw	d				14 39										15 08							15 39			
Holytown	d														15 13	15 32									
Shieldmuir	d				14 42																	15 42			
Coatbridge Central	d																								
Whifflet	d																								
Motherwell	a				14 46										15 19							15 46			
	d				14 47		14 50						15 16		15 20							15 47		15 50	
Bellshill	d				14 53								15 22			15 36						15 53			
Uddingston	d				14 57								15 26			15 41						15 57			
Airbles	d						14 52								15 22									15 52	
Larkhall	d								15 07									15 37							
Merryton	d								15 09									15 39							
Chatelherault	d								15 12									15 42							
Hamilton Central	d						14 57		15 15						15 27			15 45						15 57	
Hamilton West	d						15 00		15 18						15 30			15 48						16 00	
Blantyre	d						15 03		15 21						15 33			15 51						16 03	
Newton	d						15 07								15 37									16 07	
Cambuslang	d				15 02		15 11						15 31		15 41	15 46						16 02		16 11	
Rutherglen	d				15 05		15 15		15 29				15 34		15 45			15 59				16 06		16 15	
Dalmarnock	d				15 07		15 17						15 36		15 47							16 08		16 17	
Bridgeton	d				15 09		15 19						15 38		15 49							16 10		16 19	
Drumgelloch	d	14 38								15 08									15 38						
Airdrie	a	14 41								15 11									15 41						
	d	14 42				14 57				15 12				15 27					15 42				15 57		
Coatdyke	d	14 44				14 59				15 14				15 29					15 44				15 59		
Coatbridge Sunnyside	d	14 46				15 01				15 16				15 31					15 46				16 01		
Blairhill	d	14 49				15 04				15 19				15 34					15 49				16 04		
Easterhouse	d	14 53				15 08				15 23				15 38					15 53				16 08		
Garrowhill	d	14 55				15 10				15 25				15 40					15 55				16 10		
Shettleston	d	14 58				15 13				15 28				15 43					15 58				16 13		
Carntyne	d	15 00				15 15				15 30				15 45					16 00				16 15		
Springburn	d							15 19									15 49								16 19
Barnhill	d							15 20									15 50								16 20
Alexandra Parade	d							15 23									15 53								16 23
Duke Street	d							15 24									15 54								16 24
Bellgrove	d	15 03		15 08		15 18		15 26		15 33		15 38		15 48			15 56		16 03		16 08		16 18		16 26
High Street	d	15 05		15 10		15 20		15 28		15 35		15 40		15 50			15 58		16 05		16 10		16 20		16 28
Glasgow Queen Street 10 §	a	15 07		15 12		15 22		15 31		15 37		15 42		15 52			16 01		16 07		16 12		16 22		16 31
	d	15 10		15 13		15 23		15 32		15 40		15 43		15 53			16 02		16 10		16 13		16 23		16 32
Charing Cross	d	15 12		15 15		15 25		15 34		15 42		15 45		15 55			16 04		16 12		16 15		16 25		16 34
Argyle Street	d				15 13		15 23		15 34				15 42		15 53			16 04				16 14		16 23	
Glasgow Central 15 §	a				15 18		15 26		15 37				15 46		15 56	16b04		16 07				16 18		16 26	
	d				15 18		15 28		15 37				15 46		15 58			16 07				16 19		16 28	
Anderston	d				15 20		15 29		15 39				15 48		15 59			16 09				16 20		16 29	
Exhibition Centre	d				15 22		15 31		15 41				15 50		16 01			16 11				16 22		16 31	
Partick	d	15 17		15 20	15 25	15 30	15 35	15 39	15 45	15 47		15 50	15 54	16 00	16 05		16 09	16 15	16 17		16 20	16 26	16 30	16 35	16 39
Hyndland	d	15 20		15 23	15 27	15 32	15 38	15 41	15 47	15 50		15 53	15 56	16 02	16 08		16 11	16 17	16 20		16 23	16 28	16 32	16 38	16 41
Jordanhill	d				15 29			15 43					15 58				16 13					16 30			16 43
Scotstounhill	d				15 32			15 45					16 00				16 15					16 33			16 45
Garscadden	d				15 35			15 47					16 02				16 17					16 36			16 47
Yoker	d				15 37			15 50					16 05				16 20					16 38			16 50
Clydebank	d				15 39			15 52					16 07				16 22					16 40			16 52
Anniesland	d			15 26		15 35	15 41		15 50			15 56		16 05	16 11			16 20			16 26		16 35	16 41	
Westerton	d			15 29		15 38	15 44		15 53			15 59		16 08	16 14			16 23			16 29		16 38	16 44	
Bearsden	d			15 31			15 46					16 01			16 16						16 31			16 46	
Hillfoot	d			15 33			15 48					16 03			16 18						16 33			16 48	
Milngavie	a		←	15 37			15 54				←	16 07			16 22					←	16 37			16 52	
Drumchapel	d		15 25			15 40			15 55 →		15 55			16 10				16 25 →		16 25			16 40		
Drumry	d		15 27			15 42					15 57			16 12						16 27			16 42		
Singer	d		15 30			15 45					16 00			16 15						16 30			16 45		
Dalmuir	a	15 28	15 32		15 42	15 47		15 56		15 59	16 02		16 13	16 17			16 25		16 29	16 32		16 43	16 47		16 56
	d	15 29				15 48				15 59				16 18					16 29				16 48		
Kilpatrick	d					15 51								16 21									16 51		
Bowling	d					15 54								16 24									16 54		
Dumbarton East	d	15 36				15 58				16 06				16 28					16 36				16 58		
Dumbarton Central	d	15 38				16 00				16 08				16 30					16 38				17 00		
Dalreoch	d	15 40				16 02				16 10				16 32					16 40				17 02		
Renton	d					16 05								16 35									17 05		
Alexandria	d					16 07								16 37									17 07		
Balloch	a					16 10								16 40									17 10		
Cardross	d	15 45								16 15									16 45						
Craigendoran	d	15 50								16 20									16 50						
Helensburgh Central	a	15 53								16 23									16 53						

For general notes see front of timetable
For details of catering facilities see Directory of Train Operators

§ Low Level

A From Edinburgh (Table 225)
b Glasgow Central High Level

Table 226

Saturdays

Lanark, Coatbridge, Motherwell, Larkhall, Hamilton, Drumgelloch, Airdrie and Springburn → Glasgow → Milngavie, Dalmuir, Balloch and Helensburgh

Network Diagram - see first page of Table 220

Station		SR	SR	SR	SR	SR	SR	SR	SR	SR	SR	SR	SR	SR	SR	SR	SR	SR	SR	SR	SR	SR	SR	SR	SR
									A									B							
Lanark	d							15 53							16 23										
Carluke	d							16 03							16 33			16 45							
Wishaw	d							16 08							16 39			16 51							
Holytown	d							16 13	16 32																
Shieldmuir	d														16 42										
Coatbridge Central	d																								
Whifflet	d																								
Motherwell	a							16 20							16 46			16 54							
	d					16 16		16 20							16 47		16 50	16 55						17 16	
Bellshill	d					16 22			16 36						16 53									17 22	
Uddingston	d					16 26			16 42						16 57									17 26	
Airbles	d							16 22									16 52								
Larkhall	d	16 07									16 37									17 07					
Merryton	d	16 09									16 39									17 09					
Chatelherault	d	16 12									16 42									17 12					
Hamilton Central	d	16 15						16 27			16 45						16 57			17 15					
Hamilton West	d	16 18						16 30			16 48						17 00			17 18					
Blantyre	d	16 21						16 33			16 51						17 03			17 21					
Newton	d							16 37									17 07								
Cambuslang	d					16 31		16 41	16 47						17 02		17 11							17 31	
Rutherglen	d	16 29				16 34		16 45			16 59				17 05		17 15			17 29				17 34	
Dalmarnock	d					16 36		16 47							17 07		17 17							17 36	
Bridgeton	d					16 38		16 49							17 09		17 19							17 38	
Drumgelloch	d		16 08									16 38									17 08				
Airdrie	a		16 11									16 41									17 11				
	d		16 12				16 27					16 42				16 57					17 12				17 27
Coatdyke	d		16 14				16 29					16 44				16 59					17 14				17 29
Coatbridge Sunnyside	d		16 16				16 31					16 46				17 01					17 16				17 31
Blairhill	d		16 19				16 34					16 49				17 04					17 19				17 34
Easterhouse	d		16 23				16 38					16 53				17 08					17 23				17 38
Garrowhill	d		16 25				16 40					16 55				17 10					17 25				17 40
Shettleston	d		16 28				16 43					16 58				17 13					17 28				17 43
Carntyne	d		16 30				16 45					17 00				17 15					17 30				17 45
Springburn	d									16 49									17 19						
Barnhill	d									16 50									17 20						
Alexandra Parade	d									16 53									17 23						
Duke Street	d									16 54									17 24						
Bellgrove	d		16 33		16 38		16 48			16 56		17 03		17 08		17 18			17 26		17 33		17 38		17 48
High Street	d		16 35		16 40		16 50			16 58		17 05		17 10		17 20			17 28		17 35		17 40		17 50
Glasgow Queen Street 10 §	a		16 37		16 42		16 52			17 01		17 07		17 12		17 22			17 31		17 37		17 42		17 52
	d		16 40		16 43		16 53			17 02		17 10		17 13		17 23			17 32		17 40		17 43		17 53
Charing Cross	d		16 42		16 45		16 55			17 04		17 12		17 15		17 25			17 34		17 42		17 45		17 55
Argyle Street	d	16 34				16 42		16 53			17 04				17 13		17 23			17 34				17 42	
Glasgow Central 15 §	a	16 37				16 46		16 56	17b01		17 07				17 18		17 26	17 20		17 37				17 46	
	d	16 37				16 46		16 58			17 07				17 18		17 28			17 37				17 46	
Anderston	d	16 39				16 48		16 59			17 09				17 20		17 29			17 39				17 48	
Exhibition Centre	d	16 41				16 50		17 01			17 11				17 22		17 31			17 41				17 50	
Partick	d	16 45	16 47		16 50	16 54	17 00	17 05		17 09	17 15	17 17		17 20	17 26	17 30	17 35		17 39	17 45	17 47		17 50	17 54	18 00
Hyndland	d	16 47	16 50		16 53	16 56	17 02	17 08		17 11	17 17	17 20		17 23	17 28	17 32	17 38		17 41	17 47	17 50		17 53	17 56	18 02
Jordanhill	d					16 58				17 13					17 30				17 43					17 58	
Scotstounhill	d					17 00				17 15					17 32				17 45					18 00	
Garscadden	d					17 02				17 17					17 35				17 47					18 02	
Yoker	d					17 05				17 20					17 38				17 50					18 05	
Clydebank	d					17 07				17 22					17 40				17 52					18 07	
Anniesland	d	16 50			16 56		17 05	17 11			17 20			17 26		17 35	17 41			17 50			17 56		18 05
Westerton	d	16 53			16 59		17 08	17 14			17 23			17 29		17 38	17 44			17 53			17 59		18 08
Bearsden	d				17 01			17 16						17 31			17 46						18 01		
Hillfoot	d				17 03			17 18						17 33			17 48						18 03		
Milngavie	a			←	17 07			17 22					←	17 37			17 52					←	18 08		
Drumchapel	d	16 55 →		16 55			17 10				17 25 →		17 25			17 40				17 55 →		17 55			18 10
Drumry	d			16 57			17 12						17 27			17 42						17 57			18 12
Singer	d			17 00			17 15						17 30			17 45						18 00			18 15
Dalmuir	a		16 59	17 02		17 11	17 17			17 26		17 28	17 32		17 43	17 47			17 56		17 59	18 04		18 13	18 17
	d		16 59				17 18					17 29				17 48					17 59				18 18
Kilpatrick	d						17 21									17 51									18 21
Bowling	d						17 24									17 54									18 24
Dumbarton East	d		17 06				17 28					17 36				17 58					18 06				18 28
Dumbarton Central	d		17 08				17 30					17 38				18 00					18 08				18 30
Dalreoch	d		17 10				17 32					17 40				18 02					18 10				18 32
Renton	d						17 35									18 05									18 35
Alexandria	d						17 37									18 07									18 37
Balloch	a						17 41									18 10									18 40
Cardross	d		17 15									17 45									18 15				
Craigendoran	d		17 20									17 50									18 20				
Helensburgh Central	a		17 26									17 56									18 26				

For general notes see front of timetable
For details of catering facilities see Directory of Train Operators

§ Low Level

A From Edinburgh (Table 225)
B From North Berwick (Table 238)
b Glasgow Central High Level

Table 226

Saturdays

Lanark, Coatbridge, Motherwell, Larkhall, Hamilton, Drumgelloch, Airdrie and Springburn → Glasgow → Milngavie, Dalmuir, Balloch and Helensburgh

Network Diagram - see first page of Table 220

		SR	SR	SR	SR	SR	SR	SR	SR	SR	SR	SR	SR	SR	SR	SR	SR	SR	SR	SR	SR	SR	SR	SR	SR
			A						◇ B													A			
Lanark	d	16 53								17 23								17 53					18 23		
Carluke	d	17 03								17 33								18 03					18 33		
Wishaw	d	17 08								17 39								18 08					18 39		
Holytown	d	17 13	17 32															18 13				18 32			
Shieldmuir	d									17 42													18 42		
Coatbridge Central	d																								
Whifflet	d																								
Motherwell	a	17 19								17 46								18 20				18 39	18 46		
	d	17 20								17 47		17 50				18 16		18 20					18 47		18 50
Bellshill	d		17 36							17 53						18 22							18 53		
Uddingston	d		17 42							17 57						18 26							18 57		
Airbles	d	17 22										17 52						18 22							18 52
Larkhall	d				17 37									18 07						18 37					
Merryton	d				17 39									18 09						18 39					
Chatelherault	d				17 42									18 12						18 42					
Hamilton Central	d	17 27			17 45							17 57		18 15				18 27		18 45					18 57
Hamilton West	d	17 30			17 48							18 00		18 18				18 30		18 48					19 00
Blantyre	d	17 33			17 51							18 03		18 21				18 33		18 51					19 03
Newton	d	17 37										18 07						18 37							19 07
Cambuslang	d	17 41	17 47							18 02		18 11				18 31		18 41					19 02		19 11
Rutherglen	d	17 45			17 59					18 06		18 15		18 29		18 34		18 45		18 59			19 05		19 15
Dalmarnock	d	17 47								18 08		18 17				18 36		18 47					19 07		19 17
Bridgeton	d	17 49								18 10		18 19				18 38		18 49					19 09		19 19
Drumgelloch	d					17 38									18 08						18 38				
Airdrie	a					17 41									18 11						18 41				
	d					17 42					17 57				18 12		18 27				18 42				
Coatdyke	d					17 44					17 59				18 14		18 29				18 44				
Coatbridge Sunnyside	d					17 46					18 01				18 16		18 31				18 46				
Blairhill	d					17 49					18 04				18 19		18 34				18 49				
Easterhouse	d					17 53					18 08				18 23		18 38				18 53				
Garrowhill	d					17 55					18 10				18 25		18 40				18 55				
Shettleston	d					17 58					18 13				18 28		18 43				18 58				
Carntyne	d					18 00					18 15				18 30		18 45				19 00				
Springburn	d			17 49									18 19						18 49					19 09	
Barnhill	d			17 50									18 20						18 50					19 10	
Alexandra Parade	d			17 53									18 23						18 53					19 13	
Duke Street	d			17 54									18 24						18 54					19 14	
Bellgrove	d			17 56		18 03		18 08			18 18		18 26		18 33		18 48		18 56		19 03			19 16	
High Street	d			17 58		18 05		18 10			18 20		18 28		18 35		18 50		18 58		19 05			19 18	
Glasgow Queen Street 10 §	a			18 01		18 07		18 12			18 22		18 31		18 37		18 52		19 01		19 07			19 21	
	d			18 02		18 10		18 13	18b21		18 23		18 32		18 40		18 53		19 02		19 10			19 23	
Charing Cross	d			18 04		18 12		18 15			18 25		18 34		18 42		18 55		19 04		19 12			19 25	
Argyle Street	d	17 53			18 04					18 14		18 23		18 34		18 42		18 53		19 04			19 13		19 23
Glasgow Central 15 §	a	17 56	18c01		18 07					18 18		18 26		18 37		18 46		18 56		19 07			19 18		19 26
	d	17 58			18 07					18 19		18 28		18 37		18 46		18 58		19 07			19 18		19 28
Anderston	d	17 59			18 09					18 20		18 29		18 39		18 48		18 59		19 09			19 20		19 29
Exhibition Centre	d	18 01			18 11					18 22		18 31		18 41		18 50		19 01		19 11			19 22		19 31
Partick	d	18 05		18 09	18 15	18 17		18 20		18 26	18 30	18 35	18 39	18 45	18 47	18a53	19 00	19 05	19 09	19 15	19 17		19a25	19 30	19 35
Hyndland	d	18 08		18 11	18 17	18 20		18 23		18 28	18 32	18 38	18 41	18 47	18 50		19 02	19 08	19 11	19 17	19 20			19 32	19 38
Jordanhill	d			18 13						18 30			18 43		18 52				19 13		19 22				
Scotstounhill	d			18 15						18 33			18 45		18 54				19 15		19 24				
Garscadden	d			18 17						18 36			18a47		18 56				19a17		19 26				
Yoker	d			18 20						18 38					18 59						19 29				
Clydebank	d			18 22						18 40					19 01						19 31				
Anniesland	d	18 11			18 20			18 26			18 35	18 41		18 50			19 05	19 11		19 20				19 35	19 41
Westerton	d	18 14			18 23			18 29			18 38	18 44		18 53			19 08	19 14		19 23				19 38	19 44
Bearsden	d	18 16						18 31				18 46						19 16							19 46
Hillfoot	d	18 18						18 33				18 48						19 18							19 48
Milngavie	a	18 22					←	18 37				18 52						19 22							19 52
Drumchapel	d				18 25 →		18 25				18 40			18 55			19 10			19 25				19 40	
Drumry	d						18 27				18 42			18 57			19 12			19 27				19 42	
Singer	d						18 30				18 45			19 00			19 15			19 30				19 45	
Dalmuir	a			18 26		18 29	18 32		18 35	18 43	18 47			19 02	19 04		19 17			19 32	19 34			19 47	
	d					18 29			18 37		18 48				19 05		19 18				19 35			19 48	
Kilpatrick	d										18 51						19 21							19 51	
Bowling	d										18 54						19 24							19 54	
Dumbarton East	d					18 36					18 58				19 12		19 28				19 42			19 58	
Dumbarton Central	d					18 38			18 46		19 00				19 14		19 30				19 44			20 00	
Dalreoch	d					18 40					19 02				19 16		19 32				19 46			20 02	
Renton	d										19 05						19 35							20 05	
Alexandria	d										19 07						19 37							20 07	
Balloch	a										19 10						19 40							20 10	
Cardross	d					18 45									19 21						19 51				
Craigendoran	d					18 50									19 26						19 56				
Helensburgh Central	a					18 53			19e02						19 29						19 59				

For general notes see front of timetable
For details of catering facilities see Directory of Train Operators

§ Low Level

A From Edinburgh (Table 225)
B To Oban (Table 227) and Mallaig (Table 227)
b Glasgow Queen Street High Level
c Glasgow Central High Level
e Helensburgh Upper

Table 226

Saturdays

Lanark, Coatbridge, Motherwell, Larkhall, Hamilton, Drumgelloch, Airdrie and Springburn → Glasgow → Milngavie, Dalmuir, Balloch and Helensburgh

Network Diagram - see first page of Table 220

		SR	SR	SR	SR	SR	SR	SR	SR	SR	SR	SR	SR	SR	SR	SR	SR	SR	SR	SR	SR	SR	SR	SR	SR
							A																		
Lanark	d					18 53				19 23							19 53			20 23					
Carluke	d					19 03				19 33							20 03			20 33					
Wishaw	d					19 08				19 39							20 08			20 39					
Holytown	d					19 13	19 32										20 13								
Shieldmuir	d									19 42										20 42					
Coatbridge Central	d																								
Whifflet	d																								
Motherwell	a					19 19				19 46							20 20			20 46					
	d			19 16		19 20				19 47		19 50			20 16		20 20			20 47		20 50			21 16
Bellshill	d			19 22			19 36			19 53					20 22					20 53					21 22
Uddingston	d			19 26			19 42			19 57					20 26					20 57					21 26
Airbles	d					19 22						19 52					20 22					20 52			
Larkhall	d	19 07						19 37					20 07					20 37					21 07		
Merryton	d	19 09						19 39					20 09					20 39					21 09		
Chatelherault	d	19 12						19 42					20 12					20 42					21 12		
Hamilton Central	d	19 15				19 27		19 45				19 57	20 15				20 27	20 45				20 57	21 15		
Hamilton West	d	19 18				19 30		19 48				20 00	20 18				20 30	20 48				21 00	21 18		
Blantyre	d	19 21				19 33		19 51				20 03	20 21				20 33	20 51				21 03	21 21		
Newton	d					19 37						20 07					20 37					21 07			
Cambuslang	d			19 31		19 41	19 47			20 02		20 11			20 31		20 41			21 02		21 11			21 31
Rutherglen	d	19 29		19 34		19 45		19 59		20 05		20 15	20 29		20 34		20 45	20 59		21 05		21 15	21 29		21 34
Dalmarnock	d			19 36		19 47				20 07		20 17			20 36		20 47			21 07		21 17			21 36
Bridgeton	d			19 38		19 49				20 09		20 19			20 38		20 49			21 09		21 19			21 38
Drumgelloch	d		19 08						19 38					20 08					20 38					21 08	
Airdrie	a		19 11						19 41					20 11					20 41					21 11	
	d		19 12						19 42					20 12					20 42					21 12	
Coatdyke	d		19 14						19 44					20 14					20 44					21 14	
Coatbridge Sunnyside	d		19 16						19 46					20 16					20 46					21 16	
Blairhill	d		19 19						19 49					20 19					20 49					21 19	
Easterhouse	d		19 23						19 53					20 23					20 53					21 23	
Garrowhill	d		19 25						19 55					20 25					20 55					21 25	
Shettleston	d		19 28						19 58					20 28					20 58					21 28	
Carntyne	d		19 30						20 00					20 30					21 00					21 30	
Springburn	d				19 39						20 09					20 39					21 09				
Barnhill	d				19 40						20 10					20 40					21 10				
Alexandra Parade	d				19 43						20 13					20 43					21 13				
Duke Street	d				19 44						20 14					20 44					21 14				
Bellgrove	d		19 33		19 46				20 03		20 16			20 33		20 46			21 03		21 16			21 33	
High Street	d		19 35		19 48				20 05		20 18			20 35		20 48			21 05		21 18			21 35	
Glasgow Queen Street 10 §	a		19 37		19 51				20 07		20 21			20 37		20 51			21 07		21 21			21 37	
	d		19 40		19 53				20 10		20 23			20 40		20 53			21 10		21 23			21 40	
Charing Cross	d		19 42		19 55				20 12		20 25			20 42		20 55			21 12		21 25			21 42	
Argyle Street	d	19 34		19 42		19 53		20 04		20 13		20 23	20 34		20 42		20 53	21 04		21 13		21 23	21 34		21 42
Glasgow Central 15 §	a	19 37		19 46		19 56	20b01	20 07		20 18		20 26	20 37		20 46		20 56	21 07		21 18		21 26	21 37		21 46
	d	19 37		19 46		19 58		20 07		20 18		20 28	20 37		20 46		20 58	21 07		21 18		21 28	21 37		21 46
Anderston	d	19 39		19 48		19 59		20 09		20 20		20 29	20 39		20 48		20 59	21 09		21 20		21 29	21 39		21 48
Exhibition Centre	d	19 41		19 50		20 01		20 11		20 22		20 31	20 41		20 50		21 01	21 11		21 22		21 31	21 41		21 50
Partick	d	19 45	19 47	19a53	20 00	20 05		20 15	20 17	20a25	20 30	20 35	20 45	20 47	20a53	21 00	21 05	21 15	21 17	21a25	21 30	21 35	21 45	21 47	21a53
Hyndland	d	19 47	19 50		20 02	20 08		20 17	20 20		20 32	20 38	20 47	20 50		21 02	21 08	21 17	21 20		21 32	21 38	21 47	21 50	
Jordanhill	d		19 52						20 22					20 52					21 22					21 52	
Scotstounhill	d		19 54						20 24					20 54					21 24					21 54	
Garscadden	d		19 56						20 26					20 56					21 26					21 56	
Yoker	d		19 59						20 29					20 59					21 29					21 59	
Clydebank	d		20 01						20 31					21 01					21 31					22 01	
Anniesland	d	19 50			20 05	20 11		20 20			20 35	20 41	20 50			21 05	21 11	21 20			21 35	21 41	21 50		
Westerton	d	19 53			20 08	20 14		20 23			20 38	20 44	20 53			21 08	21 14	21 23			21 38	21 44	21 53		
Bearsden	d					20 16						20 46					21 18					21 46			
Hillfoot	d					20 18						20 48					21 19					21 48			
Milngavie	a					20 22						20 52					21 24					21 52			
Drumchapel	d	19 55			20 10			20 25			20 40		20 55			21 10		21 25			21 40		21 55		
Drumry	d	19 57			20 12			20 27			20 42		20 57			21 12		21 27			21 42		21 57		
Singer	d	20 00			20 15			20 30			20 45		21 00			21 15		21 30			21 45		22 00		
Dalmuir	a	20 02	20 04		20 17			20 32	20 34		20 47		21 02	21 04		21 17		21 32	21 34		21 47		22 02	22 04	
	d		20 05		20 18				20 35		20 48			21 05		21 18			21 35		21 48			22 05	
Kilpatrick	d				20 21						20 51					21 21					21 51				
Bowling	d				20 24						20 54					21 24					21 54				
Dumbarton East	d		20 12		20 28				20 42		20 58			21 12		21 28			21 42		21 58			22 12	
Dumbarton Central	d		20 14		20 30				20 44		21 00			21 14		21 30			21 44		22 00			22 14	
Dalreoch	d		20 16		20 32				20 46		21 02			21 16		21 32			21 46		22 02			22 16	
Renton	d				20 35						21 05					21 35					22 05				
Alexandria	d				20 37						21 07					21 37					22 07				
Balloch	a				20 40						21 10					21 40					22 10				
Cardross	d		20 21						20 51					21 21					21 51					22 21	
Craigendoran	d		20 26						20 56					21 26					21 56					22 26	
Helensburgh Central	a		20 29						20 59					21 29					21 59					22 29	

For general notes see front of timetable
For details of catering facilities see Directory of Train Operators

§ Low Level

A From Edinburgh (Table 225)
b Glasgow Central High Level

Table 226

Saturdays

Lanark, Coatbridge, Motherwell, Larkhall, Hamilton, Drumgelloch, Airdrie and Springburn → Glasgow → Milngavie, Dalmuir, Balloch and Helensburgh

Network Diagram - see first page of Table 220

		SR	SR	SR A	SR	SR	SR	SR	SR	SR	SR	SR	SR	SR	SR	SR	SR	SR	SR	SR	SR	SR	SR A
Lanark	d		20 53				21 23							21 53			22 23						
Carluke	d		21 03				21 33							22 03			22 33						
Wishaw	d		21 08				21 39							22 08			22 39						
Holytown	d		21 13	21 32										22 13									23 48
Shieldmuir	d						21 42										22 42						
Coatbridge Central	d																						
Whifflet	d																						
Motherwell	a		21 19				21 46							22 19			22 46						
	d		21 20				21 47		21 50			22 16		22 20			22 47		22 53				
Bellshill	d			21 36			21 53					22 22					22 53						23 52
Uddingston	d			21 42			21 57					22 26					22 57						23 58
Airbles	d		21 22						21 52					22 22					22 55				
Larkhall	d				21 37					22 07					22 37					23 07			
Merryton	d				21 39					22 09					22 39					23 09			
Chatelherault	d				21 42					22 12					22 42					23 12			
Hamilton Central	d		21 27		21 45				21 57	22 15				22 27	22 45				23 00	23 15			
Hamilton West	d		21 30		21 48				22 00	22 18				22 30	22 48				23 03	23 18			
Blantyre	d		21 33		21 51				22 03	22 21				22 33	22 51				23 06	23 21			
Newton	d		21 37						22 07					22 37					23 13				
Cambuslang	d		21 41	21 47			22 02		22 11			22 31		22 41			23 02		23 16				00 03
Rutherglen	d		21 45		21 59		22 05		22 15	22 29		22 34		22 45	22 59		23 05		23 20	23 29			
Dalmarnock	d		21 47				22 07		22 17			22 36		22 47			23 07		23 22				
Bridgeton	d		21 49				22 09		22 19			22 38		22 49			23 09		23 24				
Drumgelloch	d					21 38					22 08					22 38					23 08		
Airdrie	a					21 41					22 11					22 41					23 11		
	d					21 42					22 12					22 42					23 12		
Coatdyke	d					21 44					22 14					22 44					23 14		
Coatbridge Sunnyside	d					21 46					22 16					22 46					23 16		
Blairhill	d					21 49					22 19					22 49					23 19		
Easterhouse	d					21 53					22 23					22 53					23 23		
Garrowhill	d					21 55					22 25					22 55					23 25		
Shettleston	d					21 58					22 28					22 58					23 28		
Carntyne	d					22 00					22 30					23 00					23 30		
Springburn	d	21 39						22 09					22 39					23 09				23 39	
Barnhill	d	21 40						22 10					22 40					23 10				23 40	
Alexandra Parade	d	21 43						22 13					22 43					23 13				23 43	
Duke Street	d	21 44						22 14					22 44					23 14				23 44	
Bellgrove	d	21 46				22 03		22 16			22 33		22 46			23 03		23 16			23 33	23 46	
High Street	d	21 48				22 05		22 18			22 35		22 48			23 05		23 18			23 35	23 48	
Glasgow Queen Street 10 §	a	21 51				22 07		22 21			22 37		22 51			23 07		23 21			23 37	23 51	
	d	21 53				22 10		22 23			22 40		22 53			23 10		23 23			23 45	23 53	
Charing Cross	d	21 55				22 12		22 25			22 42		22 55			23 12		23 25			23 47	23 55	
Argyle Street	d		21 53		22 04		22 13		22 23	22 34		22 42		22 53	23 04		23 13		23 27	23 34			00b15
Glasgow Central 15 §	a		21 56	22b01	22 07		22 18		22 26	22 37		22 46		22 56	23 07		23 18		23 29	23 37			
	d		21 58		22 07		22 18		22 28	22 37		22 46		22 58	23 07		23 18		23 29	23 37			
Anderston	d		21 59		22 09		22 20		22 29	22 39		22 48		22 59	23 09		23 20		23 30	23 39			
Exhibition Centre	d		22 01		22 11		22 22		22 31	22 41		22 50		23 01	23 11		23 22		23 32	23 41			
Partick	d	22 00	22 05		22 15	22 17	22a25	22 30	22 35	22 45	22 47	22a53	23 00	23 05	23 15	23 17	23 26	23 30	23 36	23 45	23 52	23 59	
Hyndland	d	22 02	22 08		22 17	22 20		22 32	22 38	22 47	22 50		23 02	23 08	23 17	23 20	23 28	23 32	23 38	23 47	23 55	00 01	
Jordanhill	d					22 22					22 52					23 22	23 30			23 49	23 57	00 03	
Scotstounhill	d					22 24					22 54					23 24	23 32			23 51	23 59	00 05	
Garscadden	d					22 26					22 56					23 26	23a34			23a53	00 01	00a07	
Yoker	d					22 29					22 59					23 29					00 04		
Clydebank	d					22 31					23 01					23 31					00 06		
Anniesland	d	22 05	22 11		22 20			22 35	22 41	22 50			23 05	23 11	23 20			23 35	23 41				
Westerton	d	22 08	22 14		22 23			22 38	22 44	22 53			23 08	23 14	23 23			23 38	23 44				
Bearsden	d		22 16						22 46					23 16					23 46				
Hillfoot	d		22 18						22 48					23 18					23 49				
Milngavie	a		22 22						22 52					23 22					23 52				
Drumchapel	d	22 10			22 25			22 40		22 55			23 10		23 25			23 40					
Drumry	d	22 12			22 27			22 42		22 57			23 12		23 27			23 42					
Singer	d	22 15			22 30			22 45		23 00			23 15		23 30			23 45					
Dalmuir	a	22 17			22 32	22 34		22 47		23 02	23 04		23 17		23 33	23 34		23 47			00 09		
	d	22 18				22 35		22 48			23 05		23 18			23 35		23 48			00 10		
Kilpatrick	d	22 21						22 51					23 21					23 51					
Bowling	d	22 24						22 54					23 24					23 54					
Dumbarton East	d	22 28				22 42		22 58			23 12		23 28			23 42		23 58			00 17		
Dumbarton Central	d	22 30				22 44		23 00			23 14		23 30			23 44		23 59			00 19		
Dalreoch	d	22 32				22 46		23 02			23 16		23 32			23 46		00 02			00 21		
Renton	d	22 35						23 05					23 35					00 05					
Alexandria	d	22 37						23 07					23 37					00 07					
Balloch	a	22 40						23 10					23 40					00 10					
Cardross	d					22 51					23 21					23 51					00 26		
Craigendoran	d					22 56					23 26					23 56					00 31		
Helensburgh Central	a					22 59					23 29					23 59					00 34		

For general notes see front of timetable
For details of catering facilities see Directory of Train Operators

§ Low Level

A From Edinburgh (Table 225)
b Glasgow Central High Level

Table 226

Sundays
until 22 November

Lanark, Coatbridge, Motherwell, Larkhall, Hamilton, Drumgelloch, Airdrie and Springburn → Glasgow → Milngavie, Dalmuir, Balloch and Helensburgh

Network Diagram - see first page of Table 220

		SR	SR	SR	SR	SR	SR	SR	SR	SR ◇ A	SR	SR		SR	SR	SR	SR	SR	SR	SR	SR	SR	SR	SR	SR
Lanark	d																				10 12				
Carluke	d																				10 22				
Wishaw	d																				10 27				
Holytown	d																								
Shieldmuir	d																				10 31				
Coatbridge Central	d																								
Whifflet	d																								
Motherwell	a																				10 35				
	d					08 36	08 40		09 10					09 36	09 40		10 06	10 10			10 36	10 40		11 08	11 10
Bellshill	d					08 42								09 42			10 12				10 42			11 14	
Uddingston	d					08 46								09 46			10 16				10 46			11 18	
Airbles	d						08 42		09 12						09 42			10 12				10 42			11 12
Larkhall	d											09 25								10 25					
Merryton	d											09 27								10 27					
Chatelherault	d											09 30								10 30					
Hamilton Central	d						08 47		09 17			09 33			09 47			10 17		10 33		10 47			11 17
Hamilton West	d						08 50		09 20			09 36			09 50			10 20		10 36		10 50			11 20
Blantyre	d						08 53		09 23			09 39			09 53			10 23		10 39		10 53			11 23
Newton	d						08 57		09 27						09 57			10 27				10 57			11 27
Cambuslang	d					08 51	09 01		09 31					09 51	10 01		10 21	10 31			10 51	11 01		11 23	11 31
Rutherglen	d					08 54	09 04		09 34			09 49		09 54	10 04		10 24	10 34		10 49	10 54	11 04		11 26	11 34
Dalmarnock	d																								
Bridgeton	d					08 57	09 07		09 37					09 57	10 07		10 27	10 37			10 57	11 07		11 29	11 37
Drumgelloch	d		07 54		08 24			08 54			09 24					09 54			10 24				10 54		
Airdrie	a		07 57		08 27			08 57			09 27					09 57			10 27				10 57		
	d		07 58		08 28			08 58			09 28					09 58			10 28				10 58		
Coatdyke	d		08 00		08 30			09 00			09 30					10 00			10 30				11 00		
Coatbridge Sunnyside	d		08 02		08 32			09 02			09 32					10 02			10 32				11 02		
Blairhill	d		08 05		08 35			09 05			09 35					10 05			10 35				11 05		
Easterhouse	d		08 09		08 39			09 09			09 39					10 09			10 39				11 09		
Garrowhill	d		08 11		08 41			09 11			09 41					10 11			10 41				11 11		
Shettleston	d		08 14		08 44			09 14			09 44					10 14			10 44				11 14		
Carntyne	d		08 16		08 46			09 16			09 46					10 16			10 46				11 16		
Springburn	d																								
Barnhill	d																								
Alexandra Parade	d																								
Duke Street	d																								
Bellgrove	d		08 19		08 49			09 19			09 49					10 19			10 49				11 19		
High Street	d		08 21		08 51			09 21			09 51					10 21			10 51				11 21		
Glasgow Queen Street 10 §	a		08 23		08 53			09 23			09 53					10 23			10 53				11 23		
	d		08 24		08 54			09 24		09b55	09 54					10 24			10 54				11 24		
Charing Cross	d		08 27		08 57			09 27			09 57					10 27			10 57				11 27		
Argyle Street	d													10 01	10 13		10 31	10 41		10 54	11 01	11 11		11 33	11 41
Glasgow Central 15 §	a					09 04	09 14		09 44			09 57		10 04	10 14		10 34	10 44		10 57	11 04	11 14		11 36	11 44
	d					09 04	09 14		09 44			09 57		10 04	10 14		10 34	10 44		10 57	11 04	11 14		11 36	11 44
Anderston	d																								
Exhibition Centre	d					09 08	09 18		09 48			10 01		10 08	10 18		10 38	10 48		11 01	11 08	11 18		11 40	11 48
Partick	d		08 32		09 02	09 12	09 22	09 32	09 52		10 02	10a04		10 12	10 22	10 32	10 42	10 52	11 02	11a04	11 12	11 22	11 32	11 44	11 52
Hyndland	d		08 34		09 04	09 16	09 24	09 34	09 54		10 04			10 16	10 24	10 34	10 46	10 54	11 04		11 16	11 24	11 34	11 48	11 54
Jordanhill	d						09 26		09 56						10 26			10 56				11 26			11 56
Scotstounhill	d						09 28		09 58						10 28			10 58				11 28			11 58
Garscadden	d						09 30		10 00						10 30			11 00				11 30			12 00
Yoker	d	08 33		09 03			09 33		10 03						10 33			11 03				11 33			12 03
Clydebank	d	08 35		09 05			09 35		10 05						10 35			11 05				11 35			12 05
Anniesland	d		08 37		09 07	09 19		09 37			10 07			10 19		10 37	10 49		11 07		11 19		11 37	11 51	
Westerton	d		08 40		09 10	09 22		09 40			10 10			10 22		10 40	10 52		11 10		11 22		11 40	11 54	
Bearsden	d					09 25								10 25			10 55				11 25			11 57	
Hillfoot	d					09 27								10 27			10 57				11 27			11 59	
Milngavie	a					09 30								10 30			11 00				11 30			12 02	
Drumchapel	d		08 42		09 12			09 42			10 12					10 42			11 12				11 42		
Drumry	d		08 44		09 14			09 44			10 14					10 44			11 14				11 44		
Singer	d		08 47		09 17			09 47			10 17					10 47			11 17				11 47		
Dalmuir	a	08 38	08 49	09 08	09 19		09 39	09 49	10 09	10 12	10 19				10 39	10 49		11 09	11 19			11 39	11 49		12 09
	d	08 39	08 50	09 09	09 20		09 39	09 50	10 09	10 13	10 20				10 39	10 50		11 09	11 20			11 39	11 50		12 09
Kilpatrick	d	08 41		09 11			09 41		10 11						10 41			11 11				11 41			12 11
Bowling	d	08 44		09 14			09 44		10 14						10 44			11 14				11 44			12 14
Dumbarton East	d	08 49	08 58	09 19	09 28		09 49	09 58	10 19		10 28				10 49	10 58		11 19	11 28			11 49	11 58		12 19
Dumbarton Central	d	08 51	09 00	09 21	09 30		09 51	10 00	10 21	10 22	10 30				10 51	11 00		11 21	11 30			11 51	12 00		12 21
Dalreoch	d	08 52	09 01	09 22	09 31		09 52	10 01	10 22		10 31				10 52	11 01		11 22	11 31			11 52	12 01		12 22
Renton	d	08 55		09 25			09 55		10 25						10 55			11 25				11 55			12 25
Alexandria	d	08 58		09 28			09 58		10 28						10 58			11 28				11 58			12 28
Balloch	a	09 00		09 30			10 00		10 30						11 00			11 30				12 00			12 30
Cardross	d		09 06		09 36			10 06			10 36					11 06			11 36				12 06		
Craigendoran	d		09 11		09 41			10 11			10 41					11 11			11 41				12 11		
Helensburgh Central	a		09 14		09 44			10 14		10c37	10 44					11 14			11 44				12 14		

For general notes see front of timetable
For details of catering facilities see Directory of Train Operators

§ Low Level

A Until 27 September. To Oban (Table 227)

b Glasgow Queen Street High Level

c Helensburgh Upper

Sundays

until 22 November

Lanark, Coatbridge, Motherwell, Larkhall, Hamilton, Drumgelloch, Airdrie and Springburn → Glasgow → Milngavie, Dalmuir, Balloch and Helensburgh

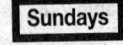

Network Diagram - see first page of Table 220

		SR		SR	SR	SR ◇ A	SR	SR	SR	SR	SR	SR	SR	SR		SR	SR	SR	SR	SR	SR	SR	SR	SR	SR
Lanark	d				11 12								12 12								13 12				
Carluke	d				11 22								12 22								13 22				
Wishaw	d				11 27								12 27								13 28				
Holytown	d																								
Shieldmuir	d				11 31								12 31								13 31				
Coatbridge Central	d																								
Whifflet	d																								
Motherwell	a				11 35								12 35								13 35				
	d				11 36		11 40		12 06	12 10			12 36	12 40			13 08	13 10			13 36	13 40		14 06	14 10
Bellshill	d				11 42				12 12				12 42				13 12				13 42			14 12	
Uddingston	d				11 46				12 16				12 46				13 18				13 46			14 16	
Airbles	d						11 42			12 12				12 42				13 12				13 42			14 12
Larkhall	d			11 25								12 25								13 25					
Merryton	d			11 27								12 27								13 27					
Chatelherault	d			11 30								12 30								13 30					
Hamilton Central	d			11 33			11 47			12 17		12 33		12 47				13 17		13 33		13 47			14 17
Hamilton West	d			11 36			11 50			12 20		12 36		12 50				13 20		13 36		13 50			14 20
Blantyre	d			11 39			11 53			12 23		12 39		12 53				13 23		13 39		13 53			14 23
Newton	d						11 57			12 27				12 57				13 27				13 57			14 27
Cambuslang	d				11 51		12 01		12 21	12 31			12 51	13 01			13 23	13 31			13 51	14 01		14 21	14 31
Rutherglen	d			11 49	11 54		12 04		12 24	12 34		12 49	12 54	13 04			13 26	13 34		13 49	13 54	14 04		14 24	14 34
Dalmarnock	d																								
Bridgeton	d				11 57		12 07		12 27	12 37			12 57	13 07			13 29	13 37			13 57	14 07		14 27	14 37
Drumgelloch	d	11 24						11 54			12 24					12 54			13 24				13 54		
Airdrie	a	11 27						11 57			12 27					12 57			13 27				13 57		
	d	11 28						11 58			12 28					12 58			13 28				13 58		
Coatdyke	d	11 30						12 00			12 30					13 00			13 30				14 00		
Coatbridge Sunnyside	d	11 32						12 02			12 32					13 02			13 32				14 02		
Blairhill	d	11 35						12 05			12 35					13 05			13 35				14 05		
Easterhouse	d	11 39						12 09			12 39					13 09			13 39				14 09		
Garrowhill	d	11 41						12 11			12 41					13 11			13 41				14 11		
Shettleston	d	11 44						12 14			12 44					13 14			13 44				14 14		
Carntyne	d	11 46						12 16			12 46					13 16			13 46				14 16		
Springburn	d																								
Barnhill	d																								
Alexandra Parade	d																								
Duke Street	d																								
Bellgrove	d	11 49						12 19			12 49					13 19			13 49				14 19		
High Street	d	11 51						12 21			12 51					13 21			13 51				14 21		
Glasgow Queen Street 10 §	a	11 53						12 23			12 53					13 23			13 53				14 23		
	d	11 54				12b20		12 24			12 54					13 24			13 54				14 24		
Charing Cross	d	11 57						12 27			12 57					13 27			13 57				14 27		
Argyle Street	d			11 54	12 01		12 11		12 31	12 41		12 54	13 01	13 11			13 33	13 41		13 54	14 01	14 11		14 31	14 41
Glasgow Central 15 §	a			11 57	12 04		12 14		12 34	12 44		12 57	13 04	13 14			13 36	13 44		13 57	14 04	14 14		14 34	14 44
	d			11 57	12 04		12 14		12 34	12 44		12 57	13 04	13 14			13 36	13 44		13 57	14 04	14 14		14 34	14 44
Anderston	d																								
Exhibition Centre	d			12 01	12 08		12 18		12 38	12 48		13 01	13 08	13 18			13 40	13 48		14 01	14 08	14 18		14 38	14 48
Partick	d	12 02		12a04	12 13		12 22	12 32	12 42	12 52	13 02	13a04	13 12	13 22		13 32	13 44	13 52	14 02	14a04	14 12	14 22	14 32	14 42	14 52
Hyndland	d	12 04			12 16		12 24	12 34	12 46	12 54	13 04		13 16	13 24		13 34	13 48	13 54	14 04		14 16	14 24	14 34	14 46	14 54
Jordanhill	d						12 26			12 56				13 26				13 56				14 26			14 56
Scotstounhill	d						12 28			12 58				13 28				13 58				14 28			14 58
Garscadden	d						12 30			13 00				13 30				14 00				14 30			15 00
Yoker	d						12 33			13 03				13 33				14 03				14 33			15 03
Clydebank	d						12 35			13 05				13 35				14 05				14 35			15 05
Anniesland	d	12 07			12 19			12 37	12 49		13 07		13 19			13 37	13 51		14 07		14 19		14 37	14 49	
Westerton	d	12 10			12 22			12 40	12 52		13 10		13 22			13 40	13 54		14 10		14 22		14 40	14 52	
Bearsden	d				12 25				12 55				13 25				13 57				14 25			14 55	
Hillfoot	d				12 27				12 57				13 27				13 59				14 27			14 57	
Milngavie	a				12 30				13 01				13 30				14 02				14 30			15 00	
Drumchapel	d	12 12						12 42			13 12					13 42			14 12				14 42		
Drumry	d	12 14						12 44			13 14					13 44			14 14				14 44		
Singer	d	12 17						12 47			13 17					13 47			14 17				14 47		
Dalmuir	a	12 19				12 35	12 39	12 49		13 09	13 19			13 39		13 49		14 09	14 19			14 39	14 49		15 09
	d	12 20				12 35	12 39	12 50		13 09	13 20			13 39		13 50		14 09	14 20			14 39	14 50		15 09
Kilpatrick	d						12 41			13 11				13 41				14 11				14 41			15 11
Bowling	d						12 44			13 14				13 44				14 14				14 44			15 14
Dumbarton East	d	12 28					12 49	12 58		13 19	13 28			13 49		13 58		14 19	14 28			14 49	14 58		15 19
Dumbarton Central	d	12 30				12 43	12 51	13 00		13 21	13 30			13 51		14 00		14 21	14 30			14 51	15 00		15 21
Dalreoch	d	12 31					12 52	13 01		13 22	13 31			13 52		14 01		14 22	14 31			14 52	15 01		15 22
Renton	d						12 55			13 25				13 55				14 25				14 55			15 25
Alexandria	d						12 58			13 28				13 58				14 28				14 58			15 28
Balloch	a						13 00			13 30				14 00				14 30				15 00			15 30
Cardross	d	12 36						13 06			13 36					14 06			14 36				15 06		
Craigendoran	d	12 41						13 11			13 41					14 11			14 41				15 11		
Helensburgh Central	a	12 44				12c58		13 14			13 44					14 14			14 44				15 14		

For general notes see front of timetable
For details of catering facilities see Directory of Train Operators

§ Low Level

A Until 25 October. To Oban (until 27 September also conveys portion to Mallaig) (Table 227)

b Glasgow Queen Street High Level

c Helensburgh Upper

Table 226

Sundays

until 22 November

Lanark, Coatbridge, Motherwell, Larkhall, Hamilton, Drumgelloch, Airdrie and Springburn → Glasgow → Milngavie, Dalmuir, Balloch and Helensburgh

Network Diagram - see first page of Table 220

		SR	SR	SR		SR	SR	SR	SR	SR	SR	SR	SR	SR	SR	SR		SR	SR	SR	SR	SR	SR	SR	SR
Lanark	d			14 12								15 12								16 12					
Carluke	d			14 22								15 22								16 22					
Wishaw	d			14 27								15 27								16 27					
Holytown	d																								
Shieldmuir	d			14 31								15 31								16 31					
Coatbridge Central	d																								
Whifflet	d																								
Motherwell	a			14 35								15 35								16 35					
	d			14 36		14 40		15 06	15 10			15 36	15 40		16 06	16 10				16 36	16 40		17 06	17 10	
Bellshill	d			14 42				15 12				15 42			16 12					16 42			17 12		
Uddingston	d			14 46				15 16				15 46			16 16					16 46			17 16		
Airbles	d					14 42			15 12				15 42			16 12					16 42			17 12	
Larkhall	d		14 25								15 25								16 25						
Merryton	d		14 27								15 27								16 27						
Chatelherault	d		14 30								15 30								16 30						
Hamilton Central	d		14 33			14 47			15 17		15 33		15 47			16 17			16 33		16 47			17 17	
Hamilton West	d		14 36			14 50			15 20		15 36		15 50			16 20			16 36		16 50			17 20	
Blantyre	d		14 39			14 53			15 23		15 39		15 53			16 23			16 39		16 53			17 23	
Newton	d					14 57			15 27				15 57			16 27					16 57			17 27	
Cambuslang	d			14 51		15 01		15 21	15 31			15 51	16 01		16 21	16 31				16 51	17 01		17 21	17 31	
Rutherglen	d		14 49	14 54		15 04		15 24	15 34		15 49	15 54	16 04		16 24	16 34			16 49	16 54	17 04		17 24	17 34	
Dalmarnock	d																								
Bridgeton	d			14 57		15 07		15 27	15 37			15 57	16 07		16 27	16 37				16 57	17 07		17 27	17 37	
Drumgelloch	d	14 24					14 54			15 24				15 54				16 24				16 54			17 24
Airdrie	a	14 27					14 57			15 27				15 57				16 27				16 57			17 27
	d	14 28					14 58			15 28				15 58				16 28				16 58			17 28
Coatdyke	d	14 30					15 00			15 30				16 00				16 30				17 00			17 30
Coatbridge Sunnyside	d	14 32					15 02			15 32				16 02				16 32				17 02			17 32
Blairhill	d	14 35					15 05			15 35				16 05				16 35				17 05			17 35
Easterhouse	d	14 39					15 09			15 39				16 09				16 39				17 09			17 39
Garrowhill	d	14 41					15 11			15 41				16 11				16 41				17 11			17 41
Shettleston	d	14 44					15 14			15 44				16 14				16 44				17 14			17 44
Carntyne	d	14 46					15 16			15 46				16 16				16 46				17 16			17 46
Springburn	d																								
Barnhill	d																								
Alexandra Parade	d																								
Duke Street	d																								
Bellgrove	d	14 49					15 19			15 49				16 19				16 49				17 19			17 49
High Street	d	14 51					15 21			15 51				16 21				16 51				17 21			17 51
Glasgow Queen Street 10 §	a	14 53					15 23			15 53				16 23				16 53				17 23			17 53
	d	14 54					15 24			15 54				16 24				16 54				17 24			17 54
Charing Cross	d	14 57					15 27			15 57				16 27				16 57				17 27			17 57
Argyle Street	d		14 54	15 01		15 11		15 31	15 41		15 54	16 01	16 11		16 31	16 41			16 54	17 01	17 11		17 31	17 41	
Glasgow Central 15 §	a		14 57	15 04		15 14		15 34	15 44		15 57	16 04	16 14		16 34	16 44			16 57	17 04	17 14		17 34	17 44	
	d		14 57	15 04		15 14		15 34	15 44		15 57	16 04	16 14		16 34	16 44			16 57	17 04	17 14		17 34	17 44	
Anderston	d																								
Exhibition Centre	d		15 01	15 08		15 18		15 38	15 48		16 01	16 08	16 18		16 38	16 48			17 01	17 08	17 18		17 38	17 48	
Partick	d	15 02	15a04	15 12		15 22	15 32	15 42	15 52	16 02	16a04	16 12	16 22	16 32	16 42	16 52		17 02	17a04	17 12	17 22	17 32	17 42	17 52	18 02
Hyndland	d	15 04		15 16		15 24	15 34	15 46	15 54	16 04		16 16	16 24	16 34	16 46	16 54		17 04		17 16	17 24	17 34	17 46	17 54	18 04
Jordanhill	d					15 26			15 56				16 26			16 56					17 26			17 56	
Scotstounhill	d					15 28			15 58				16 28			16 58					17 28			17 58	
Garscadden	d					15 30			16 00				16 30			17 00					17 30			18 00	
Yoker	d					15 33			16 03				16 33			17 03					17 33			18 03	
Clydebank	d					15 35			16 05				16 35			17 05					17 35			18 05	
Anniesland	d	15 07		15 19			15 37	15 49		16 07		16 19		16 37	16 49			17 07		17 19		17 37	17 49		18 07
Westerton	d	15 10		15 22			15 40	15 52		16 10		16 22		16 40	16 52			17 10		17 22		17 40	17 52		18 10
Bearsden	d			15 25				15 55				16 25			16 55					17 25			17 55		
Hillfoot	d			15 27				15 57				16 27			16 57					17 27			17 57		
Milngavie	a			15 30				16 00				16 30			17 00					17 30			18 00		
Drumchapel	d	15 12					15 42			16 12				16 42				17 12				17 42			18 12
Drumry	d	15 14					15 44			16 14				16 44				17 14				17 44			18 14
Singer	d	15 17					15 47			16 17				16 47				17 17				17 47			18 17
Dalmuir	a	15 19				15 39	15 49		16 09	16 19			16 39	16 49		17 09		17 19			17 39	17 49		18 09	18 19
	d	15 20				15 39	15 50		16 09	16 20			16 39	16 50		17 09		17 20			17 39	17 50		18 09	18 20
Kilpatrick	d					15 41			16 11				16 41			17 11					17 41			18 11	
Bowling	d					15 44			16 14				16 44			17 14					17 44			18 14	
Dumbarton East	d	15 28				15 49	15 58		16 19	16 28			16 49	16 58		17 19		17 28			17 49	17 58		18 19	18 28
Dumbarton Central	d	15 30				15 51	16 00		16 21	16 30			16 51	17 00		17 21		17 30			17 51	18 00		18 21	18 30
Dalreoch	d	15 31				15 52	16 01		16 22	16 31			16 52	17 01		17 22		17 31			17 52	18 01		18 22	18 31
Renton	d					15 55			16 25				16 55			17 25					17 55			18 25	
Alexandria	d					15 58			16 28				16 58			17 28					17 58			18 28	
Balloch	a					16 00			16 30				17 00			17 30					18 00			18 30	
Cardross	d	15 36					16 06			16 36				17 06				17 36				18 06			18 36
Craigendoran	d	15 41					16 11			16 41				17 11				17 41				18 11			18 41
Helensburgh Central	a	15 44					16 14			16 44				17 14				17 44				18 14			18 44

For general notes see front of timetable
For details of catering facilities see Directory of Train Operators

§ Low Level

Sundays

until 22 November

Lanark, Coatbridge, Motherwell, Larkhall, Hamilton, Drumgelloch, Airdrie and Springburn → Glasgow → Milngavie, Dalmuir, Balloch and Helensburgh

Network Diagram - see first page of Table 220

		SR	SR	SR ◇ A	SR	SR		SR	SR	SR	SR	SR	SR	SR	SR	SR	SR	SR		SR	SR	SR	SR	SR	SR
Lanark	d		17 13									18 12								19 12					
Carluke	d		17 23									18 22								19 22					
Wishaw	d		17 28									18 27								19 27					
Holytown	d																								
Shieldmuir	d		17 32									18 31								19 31					
Coatbridge Central	d																								
Whifflet	d																								
Motherwell	a		17 36									18 35								19 35					
	d		17 37		17 40			18 06	18 10			18 36	18 40		19 06	19 10				19 36	19 40		20 06	20 10	
Bellshill	d		17 43					18 12				18 42			19 12					19 42			20 12		
Uddingston	d		17 47					18 16				18 46			19 16					19 46			20 16		
Airbles	d				17 42				18 12				18 42			19 12					19 42			20 12	
Larkhall	d	17 25									18 25							19 25							
Merryton	d	17 27									18 27							19 27							
Chatelherault	d	17 30									18 30							19 30							
Hamilton Central	d	17 33			17 47				18 17		18 33		18 47			19 17		19 33			19 47			20 17	
Hamilton West	d	17 36			17 50				18 20		18 36		18 50			19 20		19 36			19 50			20 20	
Blantyre	d	17 39			17 53				18 23		18 39		18 53			19 23		19 39			19 53			20 23	
Newton	d				17 57				18 27				18 57			19 27					19 57			20 27	
Cambuslang	d		17 52		18 01			18 21	18 31			18 51	19 01		19 21	19 31				19 51	20 01		20 21	20 31	
Rutherglen	d	17 49	17 55		18 04			18 24	18 34		18 49	18 54	19 04		19 24	19 34		19 49		19 54	20 04		20 24	20 34	
Dalmarnock	d																								
Bridgeton	d		17 58		18 07			18 27	18 37			18 57	19 07		19 27	19 37				19 57	20 07		20 27	20 37	
Drumgelloch	d					17 54				18 24				18 54			19 24					19 54			20 24
Airdrie	a					17 57				18 27				18 57			19 27					19 57			20 27
	d					17 58				18 28				18 58			19 28					19 58			20 28
Coatdyke	d					18 00				18 30				19 00			19 30					20 00			20 30
Coatbridge Sunnyside	d					18 02				18 32				19 02			19 32					20 02			20 32
Blairhill	d					18 05				18 35				19 05			19 35					20 05			20 35
Easterhouse	d					18 09				18 39				19 09			19 39					20 09			20 39
Garrowhill	d					18 11				18 41				19 11			19 41					20 11			20 41
Shettleston	d					18 14				18 44				19 14			19 44					20 14			20 44
Carntyne	d					18 16				18 46				19 16			19 46					20 16			20 46
Springburn	d																								
Barnhill	d																								
Alexandra Parade	d																								
Duke Street	d																								
Bellgrove	d					18 19				18 49				19 19			19 49					20 19			20 49
High Street	d					18 21				18 51				19 21			19 51					20 21			20 51
Glasgow Queen Street 10 § ⛴	a					18 23				18 53				19 23			19 53					20 23			20 53
	d			18b20		18 24				18 54				19 24			19 54					20 24			20 54
Charing Cross	d					18 27				18 57				19 27			19 57					20 27			20 57
Argyle Street	d	17 54	18 02		18 11			18 34	18 44		18 57	19 04	19 14		19 34	19 44		19 57		20 04	20 14		20 34	20 44	
Glasgow Central 15 §	a	17 57	18 05		18 14			18 34	18 44		18 57	19 04	19 14		19 34	19 44		19 57		20 04	20 14		20 34	20 44	
	d	17 57	18 05		18 14																				
Anderston	d																								
Exhibition Centre	d	18 01	18 09		18 18			18 38	18 48		19 01	19 08	19 18		19 38	19 48		20 01		20 08	20 18		20 38	20 48	
Partick ⛴	d	18a04	18 13		18 22	18 32		18 42	18 52	19 02	19a04	19 12	19 22	19 32	19 42	19 52	20 02	20a04		20 12	20 22	20 32	20 42	20 52	21 02
Hyndland	d		18 16		18 24	18 34		18 46	18 54	19 04		19 16	19 24	19 34	19 46	19 54	20 04			20 16	20 24	20 34	20 46	20 54	21 04
Jordanhill	d				18 26				18 56				19 26			19 56					20 26			20 56	
Scotstounhill	d				18 28				18 58				19 28			19 58					20 28			20 58	
Garscadden	d				18 30				19 00				19 30			20 00					20 30			21 00	
Yoker	d				18 33				19 03				19 33			20 03					20 33			21 03	
Clydebank	d				18 35				19 05				19 35			20 05					20 35			21 05	
Anniesland	d		18 19			18 37		18 49		19 07		19 19		19 37	19 49		20 07			20 19		20 37	20 49		21 07
Westerton	d		18 22			18 40		18 52		19 10		19 22		19 40	19 52		20 10			20 22		20 40	20 52		21 10
Bearsden	d		18 25					18 55				19 25			19 55					20 25			20 55		
Hillfoot	d		18 27					18 57				19 27			19 57					20 27			20 57		
Milngavie	a		18 30					19 00				19 30			20 00					20 30			21 00		
Drumchapel	d					18 42				19 12				19 42			20 12					20 42			21 12
Drumry	d					18 44				19 14				19 44			20 14					20 44			21 14
Singer	d					18 47				19 17				19 47			20 17					20 47			21 17
Dalmuir	a			18 35	18 39	18 49			19 09	19 19			19 39	19 49		20 09	20 19				20 39	20 49		21 09	21 19
	d			18 35	18 39	18 50			19 09	19 20			19 39	19 50		20 09	20 20				20 39	20 50		21 09	21 20
Kilpatrick	d				18 41				19 11				19 41			20 11					20 41			21 11	
Bowling	d				18 44				19 14				19 44			20 14					20 44			21 14	
Dumbarton East	d				18 49	18 58			19 19	19 28			19 49	19 58		20 19	20 28				20 49	20 58		21 19	21 28
Dumbarton Central	d			18 44	18 51	19 00			19 21	19 30			19 51	20 00		20 21	20 30				20 51	21 00		21 21	21 30
Dalreoch	d				18 52	19 01			19 22	19 31			19 52	20 01		20 22	20 31				20 52	21 01		21 22	21 31
Renton	d				18 55				19 25				19 55			20 25					20 55			21 25	
Alexandria	d				18 58				19 28				19 58			20 28					20 58			21 28	
Balloch	a				19 00				19 30				20 00			20 30					21 00			21 30	
Cardross	d					19 06				19 36				20 06			20 36					21 06			21 36
Craigendoran	d					19 11				19 41				20 11			20 41					21 11			21 41
Helensburgh Central	a			19c00		19 14				19 44				20 14			20 44					21 14			21 44

For general notes see front of timetable
For details of catering facilities see Directory of Train Operators

§ Low Level

A To Oban and Mallaig (Table 227)
b Glasgow Queen Street High Level
c Helensburgh Upper

Table 226

Sundays

until 22 November

Lanark, Coatbridge, Motherwell, Larkhall, Hamilton, Drumgelloch, Airdrie and Springburn → Glasgow → Milngavie, Dalmuir, Balloch and Helensburgh

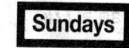

Network Diagram - see first page of Table 220

		SR	SR	SR	SR	SR	SR	SR		SR	SR	SR	SR	SR	SR	SR	SR	SR	SR	SR	SR	SR	SR		
Lanark	d		20 12								21 12							22 12							
Carluke	d		20 22								21 22							22 22							
Wishaw	d		20 27								21 27							22 27							
Holytown	d																								
Shieldmuir	d		20 31								21 31							22 31							
Coatbridge Central	d																								
Whifflet	d																								
Motherwell	a		20 35								21 35							22 35							
	d		20 36	20 40		21 06	21 10				21 36	21 40		22 06	22 10			22 36	22 40		23 08	23 10			
Bellshill	d		20 42			21 12					21 42			22 12				22 42			23 14				
Uddingston	d		20 46			21 16					21 46			22 16				22 46			23 18				
Airbles	d			20 42			21 12					21 42			22 12				22 42			23 12			
Larkhall	d	20 25								21 25							22 25								
Merryton	d	20 27								21 27							22 27								
Chatelherault	d	20 30								21 30							22 30								
Hamilton Central	d	20 33		20 47			21 17			21 33		21 47			22 17		22 33		22 47			23 17			
Hamilton West	d	20 36		20 50			21 20			21 36		21 50			22 20		22 36		22 50			23 20			
Blantyre	d	20 39		20 53			21 23			21 39		21 53			22 23		22 39		22 53			23 23			
Newton	d			20 57			21 27					21 57			22 27				22 57			23 27			
Cambuslang	d		20 51	21 01		21 21	21 31				21 51	22 01		22 21	22 31			22 51	23 01		23 23	23 31			
Rutherglen	d	20 49	20 54	21 04		21 24	21 34			21 49	21 54	22 04		22 24	22 34		22 49	22 54	23 04		23 26	23 34			
Dalmarnock	d																								
Bridgeton	d		20 57	21 07		21 27	21 37				21 57	22 07		22 27	22 37			22 57	23 07		23 29	23 37			
Drumgelloch	d				20 54			21 24					21 54			22 24				22 54			23 24		
Airdrie	a				20 57			21 27					21 57			22 27				22 57			23 27		
	d				20 58			21 28					21 58			22 28				22 58			23 28		
Coatdyke	d				21 00			21 30					22 00			22 30				23 00			23 30		
Coatbridge Sunnyside	d				21 02			21 32					22 02			22 32				23 02			23 32		
Blairhill	d				21 05			21 35					22 05			22 35				23 05			23 35		
Easterhouse	d				21 09			21 39					22 09			22 39				23 09			23 39		
Garrowhill	d				21 11			21 41					22 11			22 41				23 11			23 41		
Shettleston	d				21 14			21 44					22 14			22 44				23 14			23 44		
Carntyne	d				21 16			21 46					22 16			22 46				23 16			23 46		
Springburn	d																								
Barnhill	d																								
Alexandra Parade	d																								
Duke Street	d																								
Bellgrove	d				21 19			21 49					22 19			22 49				23 19			23 49		
High Street	d				21 21			21 51					22 21			22 51				23 21			23 51		
Glasgow Queen Street 10 § ⛴	a				21 23			21 53					22 23			22 53				23 23			23 53		
	d				21 24			21 54					22 24			22 54				23 24			23 54		
Charing Cross	d				21 27			21 57					22 27			22 57				23 27			23 57		
Argyle Street	d																								
Glasgow Central 15 §	a	20 57	21 04	21 14		21 34	21 44			21 57	22 04	22 14		22 34	22 44		22 57	23 04	23 14		23 34	23 44			
	d	20 57	21 04	21 14		21 34	21 44			21 57	22 04	22 14		22 34	22 44		22 57	23 04	23 14		23 34	23 44			
Anderston	d																								
Exhibition Centre	d	21 01	21 08	21 18		21 38	21 48			22 01	22 08	22 18		22 38	22 48		23 01	23 08	23 18		23 38	23 48			
Partick ⛴	d	21a04	21 12	21 22	21 32	21 42	21 52	22 02		22a04	22 12	22 22	22 32	22 42	22 52	23 02	23a04	23 12	23 22	23 32	23 42	23 52	00 02		
Hyndland	d		21 16	21 24	21 34	21 46	21 54	22 04			22 16	22 24	22 34	22 46	22 54	23 04		23 16	23 24	23 34	23 44	23 54	00 04		
Jordanhill	d			21 26			21 56					22 26			22 56				23 26		23 46	23 56	00 06		
Scotstounhill	d			21 28			21 58					22 28			22 58				23 28		23 48	23 58	00 08		
Garscadden	d			21 30			22 00					22 30			23 00				23 30		23a50	00a01	00a10		
Yoker	d			21 33			22 03					22 33			23 03				23 33						
Clydebank	d			21 35			22 05					22 35			23 05				23 35						
Anniesland	d		21 19		21 37	21 49		22 07			22 19		22 37	22 49		23 07		23 19		23 37					
Westerton	d		21 22		21 40	21 52		22 10			22 22		22 40	22 52		23 10		23 22		23 40					
Bearsden	d		21 25			21 55					22 25			22 55				23 25							
Hillfoot	d		21 27			21 57					22 27			22 57				23 27							
Milngavie	a		21 30			22 00					22 30			23 00				23 30							
Drumchapel	d				21 42			22 12					22 42			23 12				23 42					
Drumry	d				21 44			22 14					22 44			23 14				23 44					
Singer	d				21 47			22 17					22 47			23 17				23 47					
Dalmuir	a			21 39	21 49		22 09	22 19				22 39	22 49		23 09	23 19			23 39	23 49					
	d			21 39	21 50		22 09	22 20				22 39	22 50		23 09	23 20			23 39	23 50					
Kilpatrick	d			21 41			22 11					22 41			23 11				23 41						
Bowling	d			21 44			22 14					22 44			23 14				23 44						
Dumbarton East	d			21 49	21 58		22 19	22 28				22 49	22 58		23 19	23 28			23 49	23 58					
Dumbarton Central	d			21 51	22 00		22 21	22 30				22 51	23 00		23 21	23 30			23 51	23 59					
Dalreoch	d			21 52	22 01		22 22	22 31				22 52	23 01		23 22	23 31			23 52	00 01					
Renton	d			21 55			22 25					22 55			23 25				23 55						
Alexandria	d			21 58			22 28					22 58			23 28				23 58						
Balloch	a			22 00			22 30					23 00			23 30				00 01						
Cardross	d				22 06			22 36					23 06			23 36				00 06					
Craigendoran	d				22 11			22 41					23 11			23 41				00 11					
Helensburgh Central	a				22 14			22 44					23 14			23 44				00 14					

For general notes see front of timetable
For details of catering facilities see Directory of Train Operators

§ Low Level

Table 226

Sundays

from 29 November

Lanark, Coatbridge, Motherwell, Larkhall, Hamilton, Drumgelloch, Airdrie and Springburn → Glasgow → Milngavie, Dalmuir, Balloch and Helensburgh

Network Diagram - see first page of Table 220

		SR	SR	SR	SR	SR	SR	SR		SR	SR	SR	SR	SR	SR	SR		SR	SR	SR	SR	SR	SR	SR	SR
Lanark	d																								
Carluke	d																								
Wishaw	d																								
Holytown	d																								
Shieldmuir	d																								
Coatbridge Central	d																								
Whifflet	d																								
Motherwell	a																								
	d					08 36	08 40					09 10				09 36			09 40			10 06		10 10	
Bellshill	d					08 42										09 42						10 12			
Uddingston	d					08 46										09 46						10 16			
Airbles	d						08 42					09 12							09 42					10 12	
Larkhall	d													09 25											
Merryton	d													09 27											
Chatelherault	d													09 30											
Hamilton Central	d						08 47					09 17		09 33					09 47					10 17	
Hamilton West	d						08 50					09 20		09 36					09 50					10 20	
Blantyre	d						08 53					09 23		09 39					09 53					10 23	
Newton	d						08 57					09 27							09 57					10 27	
Cambuslang	d					08 51	09 01					09 31				09 51			10 01			10 21		10 31	
Rutherglen	d					08 54	09 04					09 34		09 49		09 54			10 04			10 24		10 34	
Dalmarnock	d																								
Bridgeton	d					08 57	09 07					09 37				09 57			10 07			10 27		10 37	
Drumgelloch	d		07 54		08 24			08 54					09 24							09 54					10 24
Airdrie	a		07 57		08 27			08 57					09 27							09 57					10 27
	d		07 58		08 28			08 58			09 13		09 28					09 43		09 58			10 13		10 28
Coatdyke	d		08 00		08 30			09 00			09 15		09 30					09 45		10 00			10 15		10 30
Coatbridge Sunnyside	d		08 02		08 32			09 02			09 17		09 32					09 47		10 02			10 17		10 32
Blairhill	d		08 05		08 35			09 05			09 20		09 35					09 50		10 05			10 20		10 35
Easterhouse	d		08 09		08 39			09 09			09 24		09 39					09 54		10 09			10 24		10 39
Garrowhill	d		08 11		08 41			09 11			09 26		09 41					09 56		10 11			10 26		10 41
Shettleston	d		08 14		08 44			09 14			09 29		09 44					09 59		10 14			10 29		10 44
Carntyne	d		08 16		08 46			09 16			09 31		09 46					10 01		10 16			10 31		10 46
Springburn	d									09 19					09 49						10 19				
Barnhill	d									09 20					09 50						10 20				
Alexandra Parade	d									09 23					09 53						10 23				
Duke Street	d									09 25					09 55						10 25				
Bellgrove	d		08 19		08 49			09 19		09 27	09 34		09 49		09 57			10 04		10 19	10 27		10 34		10 49
High Street	d		08 21		08 51			09 21		09 29	09 36		09 51		09 59			10 06		10 21	10 29		10 36		10 51
Glasgow Queen Street 10 §	a		08 23		08 53			09 23		09 31	09 39		09 53		10 01			10 09		10 23	10 31		10 39		10 53
	d		08 24		08 54			09 24		09 31	09 39		09 54		10 01			10 09		10 24	10 31		10 39		10 54
Charing Cross	d		08 27		08 57			09 27		09 33	09 42		09 57		10 03			10 12		10 27	10 33		10 42		10 57
Argyle Street	d															10 01			10 13			10 31		10 41	
Glasgow Central 15 §	a					09 04	09 14					09 44		09 57		10 04			10 14			10 34		10 44	
	d					09 04	09 14					09 44		09 57		10 04			10 14			10 34		10 44	
Anderston	d																								
Exhibition Centre	d					09 08	09 18					09 48		10 01		10 08			10 18			10 38		10 48	
Partick	d		08 32		09 02	09 12	09 22	09 32		09 37	09 47	09 52	10 02	10a04	10 09	10 12		10 17	10 22	10 32	10 37	10 42	10 47	10 52	11 02
Hyndland	d		08 34		09 04	09 16	09 24	09 34		09 39	09 49	09 54	10 04		10 11	10 16		10 19	10 24	10 34	10 39	10 46	10 49	10 54	11 04
Jordanhill	d						09 26			09 41		09 56			10 13				10 26		10 41			10 56	
Scotstounhill	d						09 28			09 43		09 58			10 15				10 28		10 43			10 58	
Garscadden	d						09 30			09 46		10 00			10 18				10 30		10 46			11 00	
Yoker	d	08 33		09 03			09 33			09 48		10 03			10 20				10 33		10 48			11 03	
Clydebank	d	08 35		09 05			09 35			09 50		10 05			10 22				10 35		10 50			11 05	
Anniesland	d		08 37		09 07	09 19		09 37			09 52		10 07			10 19		10 22		10 37		10 49	10 52		11 07
Westerton	d		08 40		09 10	09 22		09 40			09 55		10 10			10 22		10 25		10 40		10 52	10 55		11 10
Bearsden	d					09 25										10 25						10 55			
Hillfoot	d					09 27										10 27						10 57			
Milngavie	a					09 30										10 30						11 00			
Drumchapel	d		08 42		09 12			09 42			09 57		10 12					10 27		10 42			10 57		11 12
Drumry	d		08 44		09 14			09 44			09 59		10 14					10 29		10 44			10 59		11 14
Singer	d		08 47		09 17			09 47			10 02		10 17					10 32		10 47			11 02		11 17
Dalmuir	a	08 38	08 49	09 08	09 19		09 39	09 49		09 53	10 04	10 09	10 19		10 25			10 34	10 39	10 49	10 53		11 04	11 09	11 19
	d	08 39	08 50	09 09	09 20		09 39	09 50				10 09	10 20						10 39	10 50				11 09	11 20
Kilpatrick	d	08 41		09 11			09 41					10 11							10 41					11 11	
Bowling	d	08 44		09 14			09 44					10 14							10 44					11 14	
Dumbarton East	d	08 49	08 58	09 19	09 28		09 49	09 58				10 19	10 28						10 49	10 58				11 19	11 28
Dumbarton Central	d	08 51	09 00	09 21	09 30		09 51	10 00				10 21	10 30						10 51	11 00				11 21	11 30
Dalreoch	d	08 52	09 01	09 22	09 31		09 52	10 01				10 22	10 31						10 52	11 01				11 22	11 31
Renton	d	08 55		09 25			09 55					10 25							10 55					11 25	
Alexandria	d	08 58		09 28			09 58					10 28							10 58					11 28	
Balloch	a	09 00		09 30			10 00					10 30							11 00					11 30	
Cardross	d		09 06		09 36			10 06					10 36							11 06					11 36
Craigendoran	d		09 11		09 41			10 11					10 41							11 11					11 41
Helensburgh Central	a		09 14		09 44			10 14					10 44							11 14					11 44

For general notes see front of timetable
For details of catering facilities see Directory of Train Operators

§ Low Level

Table 226

Sundays

from 29 November

Lanark, Coatbridge, Motherwell, Larkhall, Hamilton, Drumgelloch, Airdrie and Springburn → Glasgow → Milngavie, Dalmuir, Balloch and Helensburgh

Network Diagram - see first page of Table 220

		SR		SR	SR	SR	SR	SR	SR	SR		SR	SR	SR	SR	SR	SR	SR		SR	SR	SR	SR	SR	SR
Lanark	d				10 12												11 12								
Carluke	d				10 22												11 22								
Wishaw	d				10 27												11 27								
Holytown	d																								
Shieldmuir	d				10 31												11 31								
Coatbridge Central	d																								
Whifflet	d																								
Motherwell	a				10 35												11 35								
	d				10 36		10 40			11 08			11 10				11 36			11 40			12 06		12 10
Bellshill	d				10 42					11 14							11 42						12 12		
Uddingston	d				10 46					11 18							11 46						12 16		
Airbles	d						10 42						11 12							11 42					12 12
Larkhall	d	10 25													11 25										
Merryton	d	10 27													11 27										
Chatelherault	d	10 30													11 30										
Hamilton Central	d	10 33					10 47						11 17		11 33					11 47					12 17
Hamilton West	d	10 36					10 50						11 20		11 36					11 50					12 20
Blantyre	d	10 39					10 53						11 23		11 39					11 53					12 23
Newton	d						10 57						11 27							11 57					12 27
Cambuslang	d				10 51		11 01			11 23			11 31				11 51			12 01			12 21		12 31
Rutherglen	d	10 49			10 54		11 04			11 26			11 34		11 49		11 54			12 04			12 24		12 34
Dalmarnock	d																								
Bridgeton	d				10 57		11 07			11 29			11 37				11 57			12 07			12 27		12 37
Drumgelloch	d							10 54						11 24							11 54				
Airdrie	a							10 57						11 27							11 57				
	d					10 43		10 58				11 13		11 28				11 43			11 58			12 13	
Coatdyke	d					10 45		11 00				11 15		11 30				11 45			12 00			12 15	
Coatbridge Sunnyside	d					10 47		11 02				11 17		11 32				11 47			12 02			12 17	
Blairhill	d					10 50		11 05				11 20		11 35				11 50			12 05			12 20	
Easterhouse	d					10 54		11 09				11 24		11 39				11 54			12 09			12 24	
Garrowhill	d					10 56		11 11				11 26		11 41				11 56			12 11			12 26	
Shettleston	d					10 59		11 14				11 29		11 44				11 59			12 14			12 29	
Carntyne	d					11 01		11 16				11 31		11 46				12 01			12 16			12 31	
Springburn	d			10 49					11 19							11 49						12 19			
Barnhill	d			10 50					11 20							11 50						12 20			
Alexandra Parade	d			10 53					11 23							11 53						12 23			
Duke Street	d			10 55					11 25							11 55						12 25			
Bellgrove	d			10 57		11 04		11 19	11 27			11 34		11 49		11 57		12 04			12 19	12 27		12 34	
High Street	d			10 59		11 06		11 21	11 29			11 36		11 51		11 59		12 06			12 21	12 29		12 36	
Glasgow Queen Street 10 §	a			11 01		11 09		11 23	11 31			11 39		11 53		12 01		12 09			12 23	12 31		12 39	
	d			11 01		11 09		11 24	11 31			11 39		11 54		12 01		12 09			12 24	12 31		12 39	
Charing Cross	d			11 03		11 12		11 27	11 33			11 42		11 57		12 03		12 12			12 27	12 33		12 42	
Argyle Street	d	10 54			11 01		11 11			11 33			11 41		11 54		12 01			12 11			12 31		12 41
Glasgow Central 15 §	a	10 57			11 04		11 14			11 36			11 44		11 57		12 04			12 14			12 34		12 44
	d	10 57			11 04		11 14			11 36			11 44		11 57		12 04			12 14			12 34		12 44
Anderston	d																								
Exhibition Centre	d	11 01			11 08		11 18			11 40			11 48		12 01		12 08			12 18			12 38		12 48
Partick	d	11a04		11 07	11 12	11 16	11 22	11 32	11 37	11 44		11 49	11 52	12 02	12a04	12 09	12 13	12 17		12 22	12 32	12 37	12 42	12 47	12 52
Hyndland	d			11 09	11 16	11 18	11 24	11 34	11 39	11 48		11 51	11 54	12 04		12 11	12 16	12 19		12 24	12 34	12 39	12 46	12 49	12 54
Jordanhill	d			11 11			11 26		11 41				11 56			12 13				12 26		12 41			12 56
Scotstounhill	d			11 13			11 28		11 43				11 58			12 15				12 28		12 43			12 58
Garscadden	d			11 16			11 30		11 46				12 00			12 18				12 30		12 46			13 00
Yoker	d			11 18			11 33		11 48				12 03			12 20				12 33		12 48			13 03
Clydebank	d			11 20			11 35		11 50				12 05			12 22				12 35		12 50			13 05
Anniesland	d				11 19	11 22		11 37		11 51		11 54		12 07			12 19	12 22			12 37		12 49	12 52	
Westerton	d				11 22	11 24		11 40		11 54		11 57		12 10			12 22	12 25			12 40		12 52	12 55	
Bearsden	d				11 25					11 57							12 25						12 55		
Hillfoot	d				11 27					11 59							12 27						12 57		
Milngavie	a				11 30					12 02							12 30						13 01		
Drumchapel	d					11 26		11 42				11 59		12 12				12 27			12 42			12 57	
Drumry	d					11 28		11 44				12 01		12 14				12 29			12 44			12 59	
Singer	d					11 32		11 47				12 04		12 17				12 32			12 47			13 02	
Dalmuir	a			11 23		11 33	11 39	11 49	11 53			12 06	12 09	12 19		12 25		12 34		12 39	12 49	12 53		13 04	13 09
	d						11 39	11 50					12 09	12 20						12 39	12 50				13 09
Kilpatrick	d						11 41						12 11							12 41					13 11
Bowling	d						11 44						12 14							12 44					13 14
Dumbarton East	d						11 49	11 58					12 19	12 28						12 49	12 58				13 19
Dumbarton Central	d						11 51	12 00					12 21	12 30						12 51	13 00				13 21
Dalreoch	d						11 52	12 01					12 22	12 31						12 52	13 01				13 22
Renton	d						11 55						12 25							12 55					13 25
Alexandria	d						11 58						12 28							12 58					13 28
Balloch	a						12 00						12 30							13 00					13 30
Cardross	d							12 06						12 36							13 06				
Craigendoran	d							12 11						12 41							13 11				
Helensburgh Central	a							12 14						12 44							13 14				

For general notes see front of timetable
For details of catering facilities see Directory of Train Operators

§ Low Level

Table 226

Sundays

from 29 November

Lanark, Coatbridge, Motherwell, Larkhall, Hamilton, Drumgelloch, Airdrie and Springburn → Glasgow → Milngavie, Dalmuir, Balloch and Helensburgh

Network Diagram - see first page of Table 220

		SR	SR	SR		SR	SR	SR	SR	SR	SR	SR		SR	SR	SR	SR	SR	SR	SR		SR	SR	SR	SR
Lanark	d						12 12												13 12						
Carluke	d						12 22												13 22						
Wishaw	d						12 27												13 28						
Holytown	d																								
Shieldmuir	d						12 31												13 31						
Coatbridge Central	d																								
Whifflet	d																								
Motherwell	a						12 35												13 35						
	d						12 36		12 40			13 08			13 10				13 36			13 40			14 06
Bellshill	d						12 42					13 12							13 42						14 12
Uddingston	d						12 46					13 18							13 46						14 16
Airbles	d								12 42						13 12							13 42			
Larkhall	d		12 25														13 25								
Merryton	d		12 27														13 27								
Chatelherault	d		12 30														13 30								
Hamilton Central	d		12 33						12 47						13 17		13 33					13 47			
Hamilton West	d		12 36						12 50						13 20		13 36					13 50			
Blantyre	d		12 39						12 53						13 23		13 39					13 53			
Newton	d								12 57						13 27							13 57			
Cambuslang	d						12 51		13 01			13 23			13 31				13 51			14 01			14 21
Rutherglen	d		12 49				12 54		13 04			13 26			13 34		13 49		13 54			14 04			14 24
Dalmarnock	d																								
Bridgeton	d						12 57		13 07			13 29			13 37				13 57			14 07			14 27
Drumgelloch	d	12 24								12 54						13 24							13 54		
Airdrie	a	12 27								12 57						13 27							13 57		
	d	12 28						12 43		12 58				13 13		13 28				13 43			13 58		
Coatdyke	d	12 30						12 45		13 00				13 15		13 30				13 45			14 00		
Coatbridge Sunnyside	d	12 32						12 47		13 02				13 17		13 32				13 47			14 02		
Blairhill	d	12 35						12 50		13 05				13 20		13 35				13 50			14 05		
Easterhouse	d	12 39						12 54		13 09				13 24		13 39				13 54			14 09		
Garrowhill	d	12 41						12 56		13 11				13 26		13 41				13 56			14 11		
Shettleston	d	12 44						12 59		13 14				13 29		13 44				13 59			14 14		
Carntyne	d	12 46						13 01		13 16				13 31		13 46				14 01			14 16		
Springburn	d					12 49					13 19							13 49						14 18	
Barnhill	d					12 50					13 20							13 50						14 19	
Alexandra Parade	d					12 53					13 23							13 53						14 22	
Duke Street	d					12 55					13 25							13 55						14 24	
Bellgrove	d	12 49				12 57		13 04		13 19	13 27			13 34		13 49		13 57		14 04			14 19	14 26	
High Street	d	12 51				12 59		13 06		13 21	13 29			13 36		13 51		13 59		14 06			14 21	14 28	
Glasgow Queen Street 10 §	a	12 53				13 01		13 09		13 23	13 31			13 39		13 53		14 01		14 09			14 23	14 30	
	d	12 54		12 55		13 01		13 09		13 24	13 31			13 39		13 54		14 01		14 09			14 24	14 30	
Charing Cross	d	12 57				13 03		13 12		13 27	13 33			13 42		13 57		14 03		14 12			14 27	14 32	
Argyle Street	d		12 54				13 01		13 11			13 33			13 41		13 54		14 01			14 11			14 31
Glasgow Central 15 §	a		12 57				13 04		13 14			13 36			13 44		13 57		14 04			14 14			14 34
	d		12 57				13 04		13 14			13 36			13 44		13 57		14 04			14 14			14 34
Anderston	d																								
Exhibition Centre	d		13 01				13 08		13 18			13 40			13 48		14 01		14 08			14 18			14 38
Partick	d	13 02	13a04			13 07	13 12	13 17	13 22	13 32	13 37	13 44		13 49	13 52	14 02	14a04	14 09	14 12	14 17		14 22	14 32	14 36	14 42
Hyndland	d	13 04				13 09	13 16	13 19	13 24	13 34	13 39	13 48		13 51	13 54	14 04		14 11	14 16	14 19		14 24	14 34	14 38	14 46
Jordanhill	d					13 11			13 26		13 41				13 56			14 13				14 26		14 40	
Scotstounhill	d					13 13			13 28		13 43				13 58			14 14				14 28		14 42	
Garscadden	d					13 16			13 30		13 46				14 00			14 17				14 30		14 45	
Yoker	d					13 18			13 33		13 48				14 03			14 20				14 33		14 47	
Clydebank	d					13 20			13 35		13 50				14 05			14 22				14 35		14 49	
Anniesland	d	13 07		13a15			13 19	13 22		13 37		13 51		13 54		14 07			14 19	14 22			14 37		14 49
Westerton	d	13 10					13 22	13 25		13 40		13 54		13 57		14 10			14 22	14 25			14 40		14 52
Bearsden	d						13 25					13 57							14 25						14 55
Hillfoot	d						13 27					13 59							14 27						14 57
Milngavie	a						13 30					14 02							14 30						15 00
Drumchapel	d	13 12						13 27		13 42				13 59		14 12				14 27			14 42		
Drumry	d	13 14						13 29		13 44				14 01		14 14				14 29			14 44		
Singer	d	13 17						13 32		13 47				14 04		14 17				14 32			14 47		
Dalmuir	a	13 19				13 23		13 34	13 39	13 49	13 53			14 06	14 09	14 19		14 25		14 34		14 39	14 49	14 52	
	d	13 20							13 39	13 50					14 09	14 20						14 39	14 50		
Kilpatrick	d								13 41						14 11							14 41			
Bowling	d								13 44						14 14							14 44			
Dumbarton East	d	13 28							13 49	13 58					14 19	14 28						14 49	14 58		
Dumbarton Central	d	13 30							13 51	14 00					14 21	14 30						14 51	15 00		
Dalreoch	d	13 31							13 52	14 01					14 22	14 31						14 52	15 01		
Renton	d								13 55						14 25							14 55			
Alexandria	d								13 58						14 28							14 58			
Balloch	a								14 00						14 30							15 00			
Cardross	d	13 36								14 06						14 36							15 06		
Craigendoran	d	13 41								14 11						14 41							15 11		
Helensburgh Central	a	13 44								14 14						14 44							15 14		

For general notes see front of timetable
For details of catering facilities see
Directory of Train Operators

§ Low Level

Table 226

Sundays

from 29 November

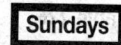

Lanark, Coatbridge, Motherwell, Larkhall, Hamilton, Drumgelloch, Airdrie and Springburn → Glasgow → Milngavie, Dalmuir, Balloch and Helensburgh

Network Diagram - see first page of Table 220

		SR	SR	SR	SR	SR		SR	SR	SR	SR	SR	SR	SR		SR	SR	SR	SR	SR	SR	SR		SR	SR
Lanark	d							14 12												15 12					
Carluke	d							14 22												15 22					
Wishaw	d							14 27												15 27					
Holytown	d																								
Shieldmuir	d							14 31												15 31					
Coatbridge Central	d																								
Whifflet	d																								
Motherwell	a							14 35												15 35					
	d		14 10					14 36		14 40			15 06			15 10				15 36		15 40			
Bellshill	d							14 42					15 12							15 42					
Uddingston	d							14 46					15 16							15 46					
Airbles	d		14 12							14 42						15 12						15 42			
Larkhall	d				14 25													15 25							
Merryton	d				14 27													15 27							
Chatelherault	d				14 30													15 30							
Hamilton Central	d		14 17		14 33					14 47						15 17		15 33				15 47			
Hamilton West	d		14 20		14 36					14 50						15 20		15 36				15 50			
Blantyre	d		14 23		14 39					14 53						15 23		15 39				15 53			
Newton	d		14 27							14 57						15 27						15 57			
Cambuslang	d		14 31					14 51		15 01			15 21			15 31				15 51		16 01			
Rutherglen	d		14 34		14 49			14 54		15 04			15 24			15 34		15 49		15 54		16 04			
Dalmarnock	d																								
Bridgeton	d		14 37					14 57		15 07			15 27			15 37				15 57		16 07			
Drumgelloch	d			14 24							14 54						15 24							15 54	
Airdrie	a			14 27							14 57						15 27							15 57	
	d	14 13		14 28					14 43		14 58			15 13			15 28				15 43			15 58	
Coatdyke	d	14 15		14 30					14 45		15 00			15 15			15 30				15 45			16 00	
Coatbridge Sunnyside	d	14 17		14 32					14 47		15 02			15 17			15 32				15 47			16 02	
Blairhill	d	14 20		14 35					14 50		15 05			15 20			15 35				15 50			16 05	
Easterhouse	d	14 24		14 39					14 54		15 09			15 24			15 39				15 54			16 09	
Garrowhill	d	14 26		14 41					14 56		15 11			15 26			15 41				15 56			16 11	
Shettleston	d	14 29		14 44					14 59		15 14			15 29			15 44				15 59			16 14	
Carntyne	d	14 31		14 46					15 01		15 16			15 31			15 46				16 01			16 16	
Springburn	d					14 49						15 19							15 48						16 19
Barnhill	d					14 50						15 20							15 49						16 20
Alexandra Parade	d					14 53						15 23							15 52						16 23
Duke Street	d					14 55						15 25							15 54						16 25
Bellgrove	d	14 34		14 49		14 57			15 04		15 19	15 27		15 34			15 49		15 56		16 04			16 19	16 27
High Street	d	14 36		14 51		14 59			15 06		15 21	15 29		15 36			15 51		15 58		16 06			16 21	16 29
Glasgow Queen Street [10] §	a	14 39		14 53		15 01			15 09		15 23	15 31		15 39			15 53		16 00		16 09			16 23	16 31
	d	14 39		14 54		15 01			15 09		15 24	15 31		15 39			15 54		16 00		16 09			16 24	16 31
Charing Cross	d	14 42		14 57		15 05			15 12		15 27	15 33		15 42			15 57		16 02		16 12			16 27	16 33
Argyle Street	d		14 41		14 54			15 01		15 11			15 31			15 41		15 54		16 01		16 11			
Glasgow Central [15] §	a		14 44		14 57			15 04		15 14			15 34			15 44		15 57		16 04		16 14			
	d		14 44		14 57			15 04		15 14			15 34			15 44		15 57		16 04		16 14			
Anderston	d																								
Exhibition Centre	d		14 48		15 01			15 08		15 18			15 38			15 48		16 01		16 08		16 18			
Partick	d	14 47	14 52	15 02	15a04	15 09		15 12	15 17	15 22	15 32	15 37	15 42	15 47		15 52	16 02	16a04	16 08	16 12	16 17	16 22		16 32	16 37
Hyndland	d	14 49	14 54	15 04		15 11		15 16	15 19	15 24	15 34	15 39	15 46	15 49		15 54	16 04		16 10	16 16	16 19	16 24		16 34	16 39
Jordanhill	d		14 56			15 13				15 26		15 41				15 56			16 12			16 26			16 41
Scotstounhill	d		14 58			15 14				15 28		15 43				15 58			16 14			16 28			16 43
Garscadden	d		15 00			15 17				15 30		15 46				16 00			16 17			16 30			16 46
Yoker	d		15 03			15 20				15 33		15 48				16 03			16 19			16 33			16 48
Clydebank	d		15 05			15 22				15 35		15 50				16 05			16 21			16 35			16 50
Anniesland	d	14 52		15 07				15 19	15 22		15 37		15 49	15 52			16 07			16 19	16 22			16 37	
Westerton	d	14 55		15 10				15 22	15 25		15 40		15 52	15 55			16 10			16 22	16 25			16 40	
Bearsden	d							15 25					15 55							16 25					
Hillfoot	d							15 27					15 57							16 27					
Milngavie	a							15 30					16 00							16 30					
Drumchapel	d	14 57		15 12					15 27		15 42			15 57			16 12				16 27			16 42	
Drumry	d	14 59		15 14					15 29		15 44			15 59			16 14				16 29			16 44	
Singer	d	15 02		15 17					15 32		15 47			16 02			16 17				16 32			16 47	
Dalmuir	a	15 05	15 09	15 19		15 25			15 34	15 39	15 49	15 53		16 04		16 09	16 19		16 25		16 34	16 39		16 49	16 53
	d		15 09	15 20						15 39	15 50					16 09	16 20					16 39		16 50	
Kilpatrick	d		15 11							15 41						16 11						16 41			
Bowling	d		15 14							15 44						16 14						16 44			
Dumbarton East	d		15 19	15 28						15 49	15 58					16 19	16 28					16 49		16 58	
Dumbarton Central	d		15 21	15 30						15 51	16 00					16 21	16 30					16 51		17 00	
Dalreoch	d		15 22	15 31						15 52	16 01					16 22	16 31					16 52		17 01	
Renton	d		15 25							15 55						16 25						16 55			
Alexandria	d		15 28							15 58						16 28						16 58			
Balloch	a		15 30							16 00						16 30						17 00			
Cardross	d			15 36							16 06						16 36							17 06	
Craigendoran	d			15 41							16 11						16 41							17 11	
Helensburgh Central	a			15 44							16 14						16 44							17 14	

For general notes see front of timetable
For details of catering facilities see Directory of Train Operators

§ Low Level

Table 226

Sundays

from 29 November

Lanark, Coatbridge, Motherwell, Larkhall, Hamilton, Drumgelloch, Airdrie and Springburn → Glasgow → Milngavie, Dalmuir, Balloch and Helensburgh

Network Diagram - see first page of Table 220

		SR	SR	SR	SR	SR	SR	SR		SR	SR	SR	SR	SR	SR	SR		SR	SR	SR	SR	SR	SR ◇ A	SR	SR
Lanark	d							16 12													17 13				
Carluke	d							16 22													17 23				
Wishaw	d							16 27													17 28				
Holytown	d																								
Shieldmuir	d							16 31													17 32				
Coatbridge Central	d																								
Whifflet	d																								
Motherwell	a							16 35													17 36				
	d	16 06		16 10				16 36			16 40			17 06		17 10					17 37			17 40	
Bellshill	d	16 12						16 42						17 12							17 43				
Uddingston	d	16 16						16 46						17 16							17 47				
Airbles	d			16 12							16 42					17 12								17 42	
Larkhall	d					16 25													17 25						
Merryton	d					16 27													17 27						
Chatelherault	d					16 30													17 30						
Hamilton Central	d			16 17		16 33					16 47					17 17			17 33					17 47	
Hamilton West	d			16 20		16 36					16 50					17 20			17 36					17 50	
Blantyre	d			16 23		16 39					16 53					17 23			17 39					17 53	
Newton	d			16 27							16 57					17 27								17 57	
Cambuslang	d	16 21		16 31				16 51			17 01			17 21		17 31					17 52			18 01	
Rutherglen	d	16 24		16 34		16 49		16 54			17 04			17 24		17 34			17 49		17 55			18 04	
Dalmarnock	d																								
Bridgeton	d	16 27		16 37				16 57			17 07			17 27		17 37					17 58			18 07	
Drumgelloch	d				16 24							16 54						17 24							
Airdrie	a				16 27							16 57						17 27							
	d		16 13		16 28					16 43		16 58			17 13			17 28				17 43			
Coatdyke	d		16 15		16 30					16 45		17 00			17 15			17 30				17 45			
Coatbridge Sunnyside	d		16 17		16 32					16 47		17 02			17 17			17 32				17 47			
Blairhill	d		16 20		16 35					16 50		17 05			17 20			17 35				17 50			
Easterhouse	d		16 24		16 39					16 54		17 09			17 24			17 39				17 54			
Garrowhill	d		16 26		16 41					16 56		17 11			17 26			17 41				17 56			
Shettleston	d		16 29		16 44					16 59		17 14			17 29			17 44				17 59			
Carntyne	d		16 31		16 46					17 01		17 16			17 31			17 46				18 01			
Springburn	d						16 49						17 19							17 49					
Barnhill	d						16 50						17 20							17 50					
Alexandra Parade	d						16 53						17 23							17 53					
Duke Street	d						16 55						17 25							17 55					
Bellgrove	d		16 34		16 49		16 57			17 04		17 19	17 27		17 34			17 49		17 57		18 04			
High Street	d		16 36		16 51		16 59			17 06		17 21	17 29		17 36			17 51		17 59		18 06			
Glasgow Queen Street 10 §	a		16 39		16 53		17 01			17 09		17 23	17 31		17 39			17 53		18 01		18 09			
	d		16 39		16 54		17 01			17 09		17 24	17 31		17 39			17 54		18 01		18 09	18b20		
Charing Cross	d		16 42		16 57		17 03			17 12		17 27	17 33		17 42			17 57		18 03		18 12			
Argyle Street	d	16 31		16 41		16 54		17 01			17 11			17 31		17 41			17 54		18 02			18 11	
Glasgow Central 15 §	a	16 34		16 44		16 57		17 04			17 14			17 34		17 44			17 57		18 05			18 14	
	d	16 34		16 44		16 57		17 04			17 14			17 34		17 44			17 57		18 05			18 14	
Anderston	d																								
Exhibition Centre	d	16 38		16 48		17 01		17 08			17 18			17 38		17 48			18 01		18 09			18 18	
Partick	d	16 42	16 47	16 52	17 02	17a04	17 09	17 12		17 17	17 22	17 32	17 37	17 42	17 47	17 52		18 02	18a04	18 10	18 13	18 17		18 22	
Hyndland	d	16 46	16 49	16 54	17 04		17 11	17 16		17 19	17 24	17 34	17 39	17 46	17 49	17 54		18 04		18 12	18 16	18 19		18 24	
Jordanhill	d			16 56			17 13				17 26		17 41			17 56				18 14				18 26	
Scotstounhill	d			16 58			17 15				17 28		17 43			17 58				18 16				18 28	
Garscadden	d			17 00			17 18				17 30		17 46			18 00				18 19				18 30	
Yoker	d			17 03			17 20				17 33		17 48			18 03				18 21				18 33	
Clydebank	d			17 05			17 22				17 35		17 50			18 05				18 23				18 35	
Anniesland	d	16 49	16 52		17 07			17 19		17 22		17 37		17 49	17 52			18 07			18 19	18 26			
Westerton	d	16 52	16 55		17 10			17 22		17 25		17 40		17 52	17 55			18 10			18 22	18 33			
Bearsden	d	16 55						17 25						17 55							18 25				
Hillfoot	d	16 57						17 27						17 57							18 27				←
Milngavie	a	17 00						17 30						18 00							18 30				
Drumchapel	d		16 57		17 12					17 27		17 42			17 57			18 12				18 35 →			18 35
Drumry	d		16 59		17 14					17 29		17 44			17 59			18 14							18 37
Singer	d		17 02		17 17					17 32		17 47			18 02			18 17							18 40
Dalmuir	a		17 04	17 09	17 19		17 25			17 34	17 39	17 49	17 53		18 04	18 09		18 19		18 26			18 35	18 39	18 42
	d			17 09	17 20						17 39	17 50				18 09		18 20					18 35	18 39	
Kilpatrick	d			17 11							17 41					18 11								18 41	
Bowling	d			17 14							17 44					18 14								18 44	
Dumbarton East	d			17 19	17 28						17 49	17 58				18 19		18 28						18 49	
Dumbarton Central	d			17 21	17 30						17 51	18 00				18 21		18 30					18 44	18 51	
Dalreoch	d			17 22	17 31						17 52	18 01				18 22		18 31						18 52	
Renton	d			17 25							17 55					18 25								18 55	
Alexandria	d			17 28							17 58					18 28								18 58	
Balloch	a			17 30							18 00					18 30								19 00	
Cardross	d				17 36							18 06						18 36							
Craigendoran	d				17 41							18 11						18 41							
Helensburgh Central	a				17 44							18 14						18 44					19c00		

For general notes see front of timetable
For details of catering facilities see Directory of Train Operators

§ Low Level

A To Oban and Mallaig (Table 227)
b Glasgow Queen Street High Level
c Helensburgh Upper

Table 226

Sundays

from 29 November

Lanark, Coatbridge, Motherwell, Larkhall, Hamilton, Drumgelloch, Airdrie and Springburn → Glasgow → Milngavie, Dalmuir, Balloch and Helensburgh

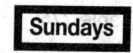

Network Diagram - see first page of Table 220

		SR		SR	SR	SR	SR	SR	SR	SR		SR	SR	SR	SR	SR	SR	SR		SR	SR	SR	SR	SR	SR
Lanark	d							18 12								19 12								20 12	
Carluke	d							18 22								19 22								20 22	
Wishaw	d							18 27								19 27								20 27	
Holytown	d																								
Shieldmuir	d							18 31								19 31								20 31	
Coatbridge Central	d																								
Whifflet	d																								
Motherwell	a							18 35								19 35								20 35	
	d			18 06	18 10			18 36	18 40			19 06	19 10			19 36	19 40			20 06	20 10			20 36	20 40
Bellshill	d			18 12				18 42				19 12				19 42				20 12				20 42	
Uddingston	d			18 16				18 46				19 16				19 46				20 16				20 46	
Airbles	d				18 12				18 42				19 12				19 42				20 12				20 42
Larkhall	d						18 25								19 25								20 25		
Merryton	d						18 27								19 27								20 27		
Chatelherault	d						18 30								19 30								20 30		
Hamilton Central	d				18 17		18 33		18 47				19 17		19 33		19 47				20 17		20 33		20 47
Hamilton West	d				18 20		18 36		18 50				19 20		19 36		19 50				20 20		20 36		20 50
Blantyre	d				18 23		18 39		18 53				19 23		19 39		19 53				20 23		20 39		20 53
Newton	d				18 27				18 57				19 27				19 57				20 27				20 57
Cambuslang	d			18 21	18 31			18 51	19 01			19 21	19 31			19 51	20 01			20 21	20 31			20 51	21 01
Rutherglen	d			18 24	18 34		18 49	18 54	19 04			19 24	19 34		19 49	19 54	20 04			20 24	20 34		20 49	20 54	21 04
Dalmarnock	d																								
Bridgeton	d			18 27	18 37			18 57	19 07			19 27	19 37			19 57	20 07			20 27	20 37			20 57	21 07
Drumgelloch	d	17 54				18 24				18 54				19 24				19 54				20 24			
Airdrie	a	17 57				18 27				18 57				19 27				19 57				20 27			
	d	17 58				18 28				18 58				19 28				19 58				20 28			
Coatdyke	d	18 00				18 30				19 00				19 30				20 00				20 30			
Coatbridge Sunnyside	d	18 02				18 32				19 02				19 32				20 02				20 32			
Blairhill	d	18 05				18 35				19 05				19 35				20 05				20 35			
Easterhouse	d	18 09				18 39				19 09				19 39				20 09				20 39			
Garrowhill	d	18 11				18 41				19 11				19 41				20 11				20 41			
Shettleston	d	18 14				18 44				19 14				19 44				20 14				20 44			
Carntyne	d	18 16				18 46				19 16				19 46				20 16				20 46			
Springburn	d																								
Barnhill	d																								
Alexandra Parade	d																								
Duke Street	d																								
Bellgrove	d	18 19				18 49				19 19				19 49				20 19				20 49			
High Street	d	18 21				18 51				19 21				19 51				20 21				20 51			
Glasgow Queen Street 10 §	a	18 23				18 53				19 23				19 53				20 23				20 53			
	d	18 24				18 54				19 24				19 54				20 24				20 54			
Charing Cross	d	18 27				18 57				19 27				19 57				20 27				20 57			
Argyle Street	d																								
Glasgow Central 15 §	a			18 34	18 44		18 57	19 04	19 14			19 34	19 44		19 57	20 04	20 14			20 34	20 44		20 57	21 04	21 14
	d			18 34	18 44		18 57	19 04	19 14			19 34	19 44		19 57	20 04	20 14			20 34	20 44		20 57	21 04	21 14
Anderston	d																								
Exhibition Centre	d			18 38	18 48		19 01	19 08	19 18			19 38	19 48		20 01	20 08	20 18			20 38	20 48		21 01	21 08	21 18
Partick	d	18 32		18 42	18 52	19 02	19a04	19 12	19 22	19 32		19 42	19 52	20 02	20a04	20 12	20 22	20 32		20 42	20 52	21 02	21a04	21 12	21 22
Hyndland	d	18 34		18 46	18 54	19 04		19 16	19 24	19 34		19 46	19 54	20 04		20 16	20 24	20 34		20 46	20 54	21 04		21 16	21 24
Jordanhill	d				18 56				19 26				19 56				20 26				20 56				21 26
Scotstounhill	d				18 58				19 28				19 58				20 28				20 58				21 28
Garscadden	d				19 00				19 30				20 00				20 30				21 00				21 30
Yoker	d				19 03				19 33				20 03				20 33				21 03				21 33
Clydebank	d				19 05				19 35				20 05				20 35				21 05				21 35
Anniesland	d	18 37		18 49		19 07		19 19		19 37		19 49		20 07		20 19		20 37		20 49		21 07		21 19	
Westerton	d	18 40		18 52		19 10		19 22		19 40		19 52		20 10		20 22		20 40		20 52		21 10		21 22	
Bearsden	d			18 55				19 25				19 55				20 25				20 55				21 25	
Hillfoot	d			18 57				19 27				19 57				20 27				20 57				21 27	
Milngavie	a			19 00				19 30				20 00				20 30				21 00				21 30	
Drumchapel	d	18 42				19 12				19 42				20 12				20 42				21 12			
Drumry	d	18 44				19 14				19 44				20 14				20 44				21 14			
Singer	d	18 47				19 17				19 47				20 17				20 47				21 17			
Dalmuir	a	18 49			19 09	19 19			19 39	19 49			20 09	20 19			20 39	20 49			21 09	21 19			21 39
	d	18 50			19 09	19 20			19 39	19 50			20 09	20 20			20 39	20 50			21 09	21 20			21 39
Kilpatrick	d				19 11				19 41				20 11				20 41				21 11				21 41
Bowling	d				19 14				19 44				20 14				20 44				21 14				21 44
Dumbarton East	d	18 58			19 19	19 28			19 49	19 58			20 19	20 28			20 49	20 58			21 19	21 28			21 49
Dumbarton Central	d	19 00			19 21	19 30			19 51	20 00			20 21	20 30			20 51	21 00			21 21	21 30			21 51
Dalreoch	d	19 01			19 22	19 31			19 52	20 01			20 22	20 31			20 52	21 01			21 22	21 31			21 52
Renton	d				19 25				19 55				20 25				20 55				21 25				21 55
Alexandria	d				19 28				19 58				20 28				20 58				21 28				21 58
Balloch	a				19 30				20 00				20 30				21 00				21 30				22 00
Cardross	d	19 06				19 36				20 06				20 36				21 06				21 36			
Craigendoran	d	19 11				19 41				20 11				20 41				21 11				21 41			
Helensburgh Central	a	19 14				19 44				20 14				20 44				21 14				21 44			

For general notes see front of timetable
For details of catering facilities see Directory of Train Operators

§ Low Level

Sundays

from 29 November

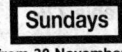

Lanark, Coatbridge, Motherwell, Larkhall, Hamilton, Drumgelloch, Airdrie and Springburn → Glasgow → Milngavie, Dalmuir, Balloch and Helensburgh

Network Diagram - see first page of Table 220

		SR	SR	SR	SR	SR	SR	SR	SR	SR	SR	SR	SR	SR	SR	SR	SR	SR	SR
Lanark	d						21 12							22 12					
Carluke	d						21 22							22 22					
Wishaw	d						21 27							22 27					
Holytown	d																		
Shieldmuir	d						21 31							22 31					
Coatbridge Central	d																		
Whifflet	d																		
Motherwell	a						21 35							22 35					
	d		21 06	21 10			21 36	21 40		22 06	22 10			22 36	22 40		23 08	23 10	
Bellshill	d		21 12				21 42			22 12				22 42			23 14		
Uddingston	d		21 16				21 46			22 16				22 46			23 18		
Airbles	d			21 12				21 42			22 12				22 42			23 12	
Larkhall	d					21 25							22 25						
Merryton	d					21 27							22 27						
Chatelherault	d					21 30							22 30						
Hamilton Central	d			21 17		21 33		21 47			22 17		22 33		22 47			23 17	
Hamilton West	d			21 20		21 36		21 50			22 20		22 36		22 50			23 20	
Blantyre	d			21 23		21 39		21 53			22 23		22 39		22 53			23 23	
Newton	d			21 27				21 57			22 27				22 57			23 27	
Cambuslang	d		21 21	21 31			21 51	22 01		22 21	22 31			22 51	23 01		23 23	23 31	
Rutherglen	d		21 24	21 34		21 49	21 54	22 04		22 24	22 34		22 49	22 54	23 04		23 26	23 34	
Dalmarnock	d																		
Bridgeton	d		21 27	21 37			21 57	22 07		22 27	22 37			22 57	23 07		23 29	23 37	
Drumgelloch	d	20 54			21 24				21 54			22 24				22 54			23 24
Airdrie	a	20 57			21 27				21 57			22 27				22 57			23 27
	d	20 58			21 28				21 58			22 28				22 58			23 28
Coatdyke	d	21 00			21 30				22 00			22 30				23 00			23 30
Coatbridge Sunnyside	d	21 02			21 32				22 02			22 32				23 02			23 32
Blairhill	d	21 05			21 35				22 05			22 35				23 05			23 35
Easterhouse	d	21 09			21 39				22 09			22 39				23 09			23 39
Garrowhill	d	21 11			21 41				22 11			22 41				23 11			23 41
Shettleston	d	21 14			21 44				22 14			22 44				23 14			23 44
Carntyne	d	21 16			21 46				22 16			22 46				23 16			23 46
Springburn	d																		
Barnhill	d																		
Alexandra Parade	d																		
Duke Street	d																		
Bellgrove	d	21 19			21 49				22 19			22 49				23 19			23 49
High Street	d	21 21			21 51				22 21			22 51				23 21			23 51
Glasgow Queen Street 10 §	a	21 23			21 53				22 23			22 53				23 23			23 53
	d	21 24			21 54				22 24			22 54				23 24			23 54
Charing Cross	d	21 27			21 57				22 27			22 57				23 27			23 57
Argyle Street	d																		
Glasgow Central 15 §	a		21 34	21 44		21 57	22 04	22 14		22 34	22 44		22 57	23 04	23 14		23 34	23 44	
	d		21 34	21 44		21 57	22 04	22 14		22 34	22 44		22 57	23 04	23 14		23 34	23 44	
Anderston	d																		
Exhibition Centre	d		21 38	21 48		22 01	22 08	22 18		22 38	22 48		23 01	23 08	23 18		23 38	23 48	
Partick	d	21 32	21 42	21 52	22 02	22a04	22 12	22 22	22 32	22 42	22 52	23 02	23a04	23 12	23 22	23 32	23 42	23 52	00 02
Hyndland	d	21 34	21 46	21 54	22 04		22 16	22 24	22 34	22 46	22 54	23 04		23 16	23 24	23 34	23 44	23 54	00 04
Jordanhill	d			21 56				22 26			22 56				23 26		23 46	23 56	00 06
Scotstounhill	d			21 58				22 28			22 58				23 28		23 48	23 58	00 08
Garscadden	d			22 00				22 30			23 00				23 30		23a50	00a01	00a10
Yoker	d			22 03				22 33			23 03				23 33				
Clydebank	d			22 05				22 35			23 05				23 35				
Anniesland	d	21 37	21 49		22 07		22 19		22 37	22 49		23 07		23 19		23 37			
Westerton	d	21 40	21 52		22 10		22 22		22 40	22 52		23 10		23 22		23 40			
Bearsden	d		21 55				22 25			22 55				23 25					
Hillfoot	d		21 57				22 27			22 57				23 27					
Milngavie	a		22 00				22 30			23 00				23 30					
Drumchapel	d	21 42			22 12				22 42			23 12				23 42			
Drumry	d	21 44			22 14				22 44			23 14				23 44			
Singer	d	21 47			22 17				22 47			23 17				23 47			
Dalmuir	a	21 49		22 09	22 19			22 39	22 49		23 09	23 19			23 39	23 49			
	d	21 50		22 09	22 20			22 39	22 50		23 09	23 20			23 39	23 50			
Kilpatrick	d			22 11				22 41			23 11				23 41				
Bowling	d			22 14				22 44			23 14				23 44				
Dumbarton East	d	21 58		22 19	22 28			22 49	22 58		23 19	23 28			23 49	23 58			
Dumbarton Central	d	22 00		22 21	22 30			22 51	23 00		23 21	23 30			23 51	23 59			
Dalreoch	d	22 01		22 22	22 31			22 52	23 01		23 22	23 31			23 52	00 01			
Renton	d			22 25				22 55			23 25				23 55				
Alexandria	d			22 28				22 58			23 28				23 58				
Balloch	a			22 30				23 00			23 30				00 01				
Cardross	d	22 06			22 36				23 06			23 36				00 06			
Craigendoran	d	22 11			22 41				23 11			23 41				00 11			
Helensburgh Central	a	22 14			22 44				23 14			23 44				00 14			

For general notes see front of timetable
For details of catering facilities see Directory of Train Operators

§ Low Level

Helensburgh, Balloch, Dalmuir and Milngavie → Glasgow → Springburn, Airdrie, Drumgelloch, Hamilton, Larkhall, Motherwell, Coatbridge and Lanark

Network Diagram - see first page of Table 220

Miles	Miles	Miles	Miles	Miles			SR MX	SR	SR	SR	SR	SR	SR	SR	SR	SR	SR	SR	SR	SR	SR		SR	SR	SR
											A						B								
0	—	—	—	—	**Helensburgh Central**	d																	06 10		
1¼	—	—	—	—	Craigendoran	d																	06 13		
4¼	—	—	—	—	Cardross	d																	06 18		
—	0	—	—	—	**Balloch**	d																			
—	1	—	—	—	Alexandria	d																			
—	2¼	—	—	—	Renton	d																			
8	3¾	—	—	—	Dalreoch	d																	06 23		
8¼	4	—	—	—	Dumbarton Central	d																	06 25		
9	4¾	—	—	—	Dumbarton East	d																	06 27		
11¾	7½	—	—	—	Bowling	d																			
13½	9¼	—	—	—	Kilpatrick	d																			
14¾	10½	0	0	—	**Dalmuir**	a																	06 35		
—	—	—	—	—		d				05 48					06 01				06 16	06 23	06 31		06 36		
15½	11¼	—	¾	—	Singer	d									06 03				06 18		06 33				
16½	12¼	—	1¾	—	Drumry	d									06 05				06 20		06 35			←	
17¼	13	—	2½	—	Drumchapel	d									06 08				06 23		06 38			06 38	
—	—	—	—	0	**Milngavie**	d															→				
—	—	—	—	1½	Hillfoot	d																			
—	—	—	—	2¼	Bearsden	d																			
18½	14¼	—	3¾	3½	Westerton	d	00 05								06 10				06 25					06 40	
19¾	15½	—	5	4¾	Anniesland	d									06 14				06 28					06 44	
—	—	1¼	—	—	Clydebank	d				05 50										06 25					
—	—	2¼	—	—	Yoker	d				05 52										06 27					
—	—	3¼	—	—	Garscadden	d				05 55			06 00	06 08		06 16		06 20		06 31					06 46
—	—	3¾	—	—	Scotstounhill	d				05 57			06 02	06 10		06 18		06 22		06 33					06 48
—	—	4¾	—	—	Jordanhill	d				05 59			06 05	06 12		06 20		06 24		06 35					06 50
20¾	16½	5¼	6	5¾	Hyndland	d				06 01			06 07	06 14	06 17	06 22		06 26	06 31	06 37			06 44	06 47	06 52
21¼	17	—	6½	6¼	Partick	d				06 04			06 10	06 17	06 20	06 25		06 29	06 34	06 40			06 47	06 50	06 55
—	—	—	8¼	7½	Exhibition Centre	d							06 13		06 23			06 32		06 43				06 53	
—	—	—	8½	8	Anderston	d							06 15		06 25			06 34		06 45				06 55	
—	—	—	8¾	8½	**Glasgow Central** 15 §	a							06 17		06 26			06 35		06 47				06 56	
—	—	—	—	—		d					06b16		06 17		06 27			06 37		06 47				06 57	
—	—	—	9¼	9	Argyle Street	d							06 19		06 29			06 39		06 49				06 59	
23¼	19	—	—	—	Charing Cross	d				06 08				06 22		06 29			06 38				06 52		06 59
24	19¾	—	—	—	**Glasgow Queen Street** 10 §	a	00 20			06 10				06 24		06 31			06 40				06 54		07 01
—	—	—	—	—		d				06 12				06 27		06 32			06 42				06 57		07 02
24½	20¼	—	—	—	High Street	d				06 14				06 29		06 34			06 44				06 59		07 04
25	20¾	—	—	—	Bellgrove	d				06 16				06 31		06 36			06 46				07 01		07 06
—	21¼	—	—	—	Duke Street	d										06 38									07 08
—	21½	—	—	—	Alexandra Parade	d										06 39									07 09
—	22¾	—	—	—	Barnhill	d										06 42									07 12
—	23	—	—	—	**Springburn**	a										06 44									07 14
26¾	—	—	—	—	Carntyne	d				06 19				06 34					06 49				07 04		
27½	—	—	—	—	Shettleston	d				06 22				06 37					06 52				07 07		
28¾	—	—	—	—	Garrowhill	d				06 24				06 39					06 54				07 09		
29¾	—	—	—	—	Easterhouse	d				06 27				06 42					06 57				07 12		
32½	—	—	—	—	Blairhill	d				06 31				06 46					07 01				07 16		
33	—	—	—	—	Coatbridge Sunnyside	d				06 33				06 48					07 03				07 18		
34	—	—	—	—	Coatdyke	d				06 36				06 51					07 06				07 21		
35	—	—	—	—	**Airdrie**	a				06 39				06 53					07 09				07 24		
—	—	—	—	—		d								06 54									07 24		
36½	—	—	—	—	**Drumgelloch**	a								06 58									07 28		
—	—	—	10½	10¼	Bridgeton	d							06 22					06 42		06 52					
—	—	—	11	10¾	Dalmarnock	d							06 24					06 44		06 54					
—	—	—	11¾	11½	Rutherglen	d							06 26					06 46		06 56					
—	—	—	13½	13¼	Cambuslang	d					06 23		06 31		06 34			06 50		07 01				07 04	
—	—	0	—	14¾	Newton	d												06 54							
—	—	2½	—	—	Blantyre	d									06 44			06 58						07 14	
—	—	4½	—	—	Hamilton West	d									06 47			07 01						07 17	
0	—	5¼	—	—	**Hamilton Central**	d									06 50			07 03						07 20	
2¼	—	—	—	—	Chatelherault	d									06 54									07 24	
3¾	—	—	—	—	Merryton	d									06 58									07 28	
5¼	—	—	—	—	**Larkhall**	a									07 00									07 31	
0	—	7½	—	—	Airbles	d												07 08							
—	—	—	17	16¾	Uddingston	d					06 28		06 35							07 05					
—	—	—	19½	—	Bellshill	d					06 34		06 40							07 10					
—	—	8¼	22½	21	**Motherwell**	a							06 45					07 11		07 17					
—	0	—	—	—		d		05 48	06 24			06 37	06 46				06 59	07 12							
—	4½	—	—	—	Whifflet	a												07 19							
—	5¼	—	—	—	**Coatbridge Central**	a												07 23							
—	—	—	—	22½	Shieldmuir	d		05 51	06 28				06 50				07 02								
—	—	—	—	21¼	Holytown	d					06a38	06 43													
—	—	—	—	24¼	Wishaw	d		05 55	06 31			06 48	06 53				07 06								
—	—	—	—	28¾	Carluke	d		06 02	06 36			06 55	07 00				07a14								
—	—	—	—	37¼	**Lanark**	a		06 12	06 48			07 07	07 13												

For general notes see front of timetable
For details of catering facilities see Directory of Train Operators

§ Low Level

A To Edinburgh (Table 225)
B To Carstairs (Table 225)
b Glasgow Central High Level

Helensburgh, Balloch, Dalmuir and Milngavie → Glasgow → Springburn, Airdrie, Drumgelloch, Hamilton, Larkhall, Motherwell, Coatbridge and Lanark

Network Diagram - see first page of Table 220

		SR A	SR	SR	SR B	SR	SR	SR	SR	SR	SR	SR	SR	SR	SR	SR	SR	SR	SR	SR	SR	SR	SR	SR
Helensburgh Central	d							06 40								07 10								07 35
Craigendoran	d							06 43								07 13								07 38
Cardross	d							06 48								07 18								07 43
Balloch	d			06 23								06 53								07 23				
Alexandria	d			06 25								06 55								07 25				
Renton	d			06 28								06 58								07 28				
Dalreoch	d			06 31				06 53				07 01				07 23				07 31				07 48
Dumbarton Central	d			06 32				06 55				07 02				07 25				07 32				07 50
Dumbarton East	d			06 34				06 57				07 04				07 27				07 34				07 52
Bowling	d			06 39								07 09								07 39				07 57
Kilpatrick	d			06 42								07 12								07 42				08 00
Dalmuir	a			06 45				07 05				07 15				07 35				07 45				08 03
	d			06 46		06 53	07 01	07 06				07 16	07 23		07 31	07 36		07 38		07 46	07 53		08 01	08 04
Singer	d			06 48			07 03					07 18			07 33					07 48			08 03	
Drumry	d			06 50			07 05		←			07 20			07 35		←			07 50			08 05	
Drumchapel	d			06 53			07 08		07 08			07 23			07 38		07 38			07 53			08 08	
Milngavie	d		06 42				→				07 12			07 27	→				07 42			07 57	→	
Hillfoot	d		06 45								07 15			07 30					07 45			08 00		
Bearsden	d		06 47								07 17			07 32					07 47			08 02		
Westerton	d		06 50	06 55					07 10		07 20	07 25		07 35			07 40		07 50	07 55		08 05		
Anniesland	d		06 53	06 58					07 14		07 23	07 28		07 38			07 44		07 53	07 58		08 08		
Clydebank	d					06 55							07 25					07 40			07 55			08 06
Yoker	d					06 57							07 27					07 42			07 57			
Garscadden	d					07 01				07 16			07 31					07 46			08 01			
Scotstounhill	d					07 03				07 18			07 33					07 48			08 03			
Jordanhill	d					07 05				07 20			07 35					07 50			08 05			
Hyndland	d		06 56	07 01		07 07		07 14	07 17	07 22	07 26	07 31	07 37	07 41		07 44	07 47	07 52	07 56	08 01	08 07	08 11		08 14
Partick	d		06 59	07 04		07 10		07 17	07 20	07 25	07 29	07 34	07 40	07 44		07 47	07 50	07 55	07 59	08 04	08 10	08 14		08 17
Exhibition Centre	d		07 02			07 13			07 23		07 32		07 43				07 53		08 02		08 13	08 17		
Anderston	d		07 04			07 15			07 25		07 34		07 45				07 55		08 04		08 15	08 19		
Glasgow Central 15 §	a		07 05			07 17			07 26		07 35		07 46				07 56		08 05		08 17	08 20		
	d	07 05	07 07		07b13	07 17			07 27		07 37		07 46				07 57		08 07		08 17	08 21		
Argyle Street	d		07 09			07 19			07 29		07 39		07 49				07 59		08 09		08 19	08 23		
Charing Cross	d			07 08				07 22		07 29		07 38		07 49		07 52		07 59		08 08				08 22
Glasgow Queen Street 10 §	a			07 10				07 24		07 31		07 40		07 51		07 54		08 01		08 10				08 24
	d			07 12				07 27		07 32		07 42		07 51		07 57		08 02		08 12				08 27
High Street	d			07 14				07 29		07 34		07 44		07a53		07 59		08 04		08 14				08 29
Bellgrove	d			07 16				07 31		07 36		07 46				08 01		08 06		08 16				08 31
Duke Street	d									07 38								08 08						
Alexandra Parade	d									07 39								08 09						
Barnhill	d									07 42								08 12						
Springburn	a									07 44								08 14						
Carntyne	d			07 19				07 34				07 49				08 04				08 19				08 34
Shettleston	d			07 22				07 37				07 52				08 07				08 22				08 37
Garrowhill	d			07 24				07 39				07 54				08 09				08 24				08 39
Easterhouse	d			07 27				07 42				07 57				08 12				08 27				08 42
Blairhill	d			07 31				07 46				08 01				08 16				08 31				08 46
Coatbridge Sunnyside	d			07 33				07 48				08 03				08 18				08 33				08 48
Coatdyke	d			07 36				07 51				08 06				08 21				08 36				08 51
Airdrie	a			07 39				07 54				08 09				08 24				08 39				08 53
	d							07 54								08 24								08 54
Drumgelloch	a							07 58								08 28								08 58
Bridgeton	d		07 12			07 22					07 42		07 52						08 12		08 22	08 26		
Dalmarnock	d		07 14			07 24					07 44		07 54						08 14		08 24	08 28		
Rutherglen	d		07 16			07 26			07 34		07 46		07 56				08 04		08 16		08 26	08 30		
Cambuslang	d		07 20		07 23	07 31					07 50		08 01						08 20		08 31			
Newton	d		07 24								07 54								08 24					
Blantyre	d		07 28						07 44		07 58						08 14		08 28					
Hamilton West	d		07 31						07 47		08 01						08 17		08 31					
Hamilton Central	d		07 33						07 50		08 03						08 20		08 33					
Chatelherault	d								07 54								08 24							
Merryton	d								07 58								08 28							
Larkhall	a								08 00								08 30							
Airbles	d		07 38								08 08								08 38					
Uddingston	d				07 28	07 35							08 05								08 35 →			
Bellshill	d				07 34	07 40							08 10											
Motherwell	a	07 27	07 41			07 46					08 11		08 17						08 41			08 44		
	d	07 28				07 46																		
Whifflet	a																							
Coatbridge Central	a																							
Shieldmuir	d					07 50																		
Holytown	d				07a38																			
Wishaw	d	07 33				07 53																		
Carluke	d	07a37				08 00																		
Lanark	a					08 15																		

For general notes see front of timetable
For details of catering facilities see Directory of Train Operators

§ Low Level

A To North Berwick (Table 238)
B To Edinburgh (Table 225)
b Glasgow Central High Level

Helensburgh, Balloch, Dalmuir and Milngavie → Glasgow → Springburn, Airdrie, Drumgelloch, Hamilton, Larkhall, Motherwell, Coatbridge and Lanark

Network Diagram - see first page of Table 220

		SR A	SR	SR	SR	SR	SR	SR	SR 1		SR	SR	SR	SR	SR	SR	SR	SR	SR	SR	SR	SR	SR	SR B	SR	SR
Helensburgh Central	d	07b42					07 54				08 01							08 08								
Craigendoran	d						07 57				08 04							08 11								
Cardross	d	07 51					08 02				08 09							08 16								
Balloch	d			07 53																		08 23				
Alexandria	d			07 55																		08 25				
Renton	d			07 58																		08 28				
Dalreoch	d			08 01			08 07											08 21				08 31				
Dumbarton Central	d	07 57		08 03			08 09				08 15							08 23				08 32				
Dumbarton East	d						08 11											08 25				08 34				
Bowling	d																	08 30				08 39				
Kilpatrick	d																	08 33				08 42				
Dalmuir	a						08 19											08 35				08 45				
	d				08 08		08 19								08 23		08 31	08 36		08 38		08 46		08 53		
Singer	d	08 06					08 21						←				08 33					08 48				
Drumry	d		←				08 24						08 24				08 35		←			08 50				
Drumchapel	d		08 08				→						08 26				08 38		08 38			08 53				
Milngavie	d					08 10			08 18							08 27	→				08 42				08 57
Hillfoot	d					08 13			08 21							08 30					08 45				09 00
Bearsden	d					08 16			08 24							08 32					08 47				09 02
Westerton	d		08 10			08 19							08 29			08 35			08 40		08 50	08 55			09 05
Anniesland	d		08 14			08 23							08 32			08 38			08 44		08 53	08 58			09 08
Clydebank	d				08 10										08 25					08 40				08 55	
Yoker	d				08 12										08 27					08 42				08 57	
Garscadden	d				08 16										08 31					08 46				09 01	
Scotstounhill	d				08 18						08 28				08 33					08 48				09 03	
Jordanhill	d				08 21										08 35					08 50				09 05	
Hyndland	d		08 17		08 23	08 26					08 33		08 35		08 37	08 41		08 44	08 47	08 52	08 56	09 01		09 07	09 11
Partick	d		08 20	08 22	08 26	08 29					08 35		08 38		08 40	08 44		08 47	08 50	08 55	08 59	09 04		09 10	09 14
Exhibition Centre	d		08 23			08 32									08 43				08 53		09 02			09 13	
Anderston	d		08 25			08 34						08 38			08 45				08 55		09 04			09 15	
Glasgow Central 15 §	a		08 26			08 35						08 39			08 47				08 56		09 05			09 17	
	d		08 27			08 37						08 40			08 47				08 57		09 07		09c15	09 17	
Argyle Street	d		08 29			08 39						08 42			08 49				08 59		09 09			09 19	
Charing Cross	d			08 27	08 31				08 36		08 40		08 42			08 49		08 52		08 59		09 08			09 19
Glasgow Queen Street 10 §	a	08e37		08 29	08 33				08 37		08 42		08 44			08 51		08 54		09 01		09 10			09 21
	d			08 30	08 33				08 38		08 42		08 45			08 51		08 57		09 02		09 12			09 21
High Street	d			08 32	08a35				08 40		08 44		08a47			08a53		08 59		09 04		09 14			09a23
Bellgrove	d			08 34					08 42		08 46							09 01		09 06		09 16			
Duke Street	d			08 36					08 44											09 08					
Alexandra Parade	d			08 37					08 45											09 09					
Barnhill	d			08 40					08 48											09 12					
Springburn	a			08 42					08 53											09 14					
Carntyne	d										08 49							09 04				09 19			
Shettleston	d										08 52							09 07				09 22			
Garrowhill	d										08 54							09 09				09 24			
Easterhouse	d										08 57							09 12				09 27			
Blairhill	d										09 01							09 16				09 31			
Coatbridge Sunnyside	d										09 04							09 18				09 33			
Coatdyke	d										09 06							09 21				09 36			
Airdrie	a										09 09							09 23				09 39			
	d																	09 24							
Drumgelloch	a																	09 28							
Bridgeton	d					08 42						08 45			08 52						09 12			09 22	
Dalmarnock	d					08 44						08 47			08 54						09 14			09 24	
Rutherglen	d		08 34			08 46						08 49			08 56				09 04		09 16			09 26	
Cambuslang	d					08 50						08 54			09 01						09 20		09 23	09 31	
Newton	d					08 54															09 24				
Blantyre	d		08 44			08 58								←					09 14		09 28				
Hamilton West	d		08 47			09 01								09 01					09 17		09 31				
Hamilton Central	d		08 50			→								09 03					09 20		09 33				
Chatelherault	d		08 54																09 24						
Merryton	d		08 58																09 28						
Larkhall	a		09 00																09 30						
Airbles	d							←						09 08							09 38				
Uddingston	d							08 35				09 01			09 05								09 28	09 35	
Bellshill	d							08 40							09 10								09 34	09 40	
Motherwell	a							08 46				09 07		09 11	09 16						09 41			09 46	
	d							08 46							09 16						09 42				
Whifflet	a																								
Coatbridge Central	a																								
Shieldmuir	d							08 50							09 20										
Holytown	d																				09 47		09a38		
Wishaw	d							08 53							09 23						09 53				
Carluke	d							09 00							09 30						10 00				
Lanark	a							09 12							09 44						10 15				

For general notes see front of timetable
For details of catering facilities see Directory of Train Operators

§ Low Level

A From Arrochar & Tarbet (Table 227)
B To Edinburgh (Table 225)
b Helensburgh Upper
c Glasgow Central High Level
e Glasgow Queen Street High Level

Table 226

Mondays to Fridays

Helensburgh, Balloch, Dalmuir and Milngavie → Glasgow → Springburn, Airdrie, Drumgelloch, Hamilton, Larkhall, Motherwell, Coatbridge and Lanark

Network Diagram - see first page of Table 220

		SR	SR	SR	SR	SR	SR	SR	SR	SR	SR	SR	SR	SR	SR	SR A	SR	SR	SR	SR	SR	SR	SR
Helensburgh Central	d		08 40								09 10									09 40			
Craigendoran	d		08 43								09 13									09 43			
Cardross	d		08 48								09 18									09 48			
Balloch	d						08 53								09 23								
Alexandria	d						08 55								09 25								
Renton	d						08 58								09 28								
Dalreoch	d		08 53				09 01				09 23				09 31					09 53			
Dumbarton Central	d		08 55				09 02				09 25				09 32					09 55			
Dumbarton East	d		08 57				09 04				09 27				09 34					09 57			
Bowling	d						09 09								09 39								
Kilpatrick	d						09 12								09 42								
Dalmuir	a		09 05				09 15				09 35				09 45					10 05			
	d	09 01	09 06		09 08		09 16	09 23		09 31	09 36		09 38		09 46		09 53		10 01	10 06		10 08	
Singer	d	09 03					09 18			09 33					09 48				10 03				
Drumry	d	09 05		←			09 20			09 35		←			09 50				10 05		←		
Drumchapel	d	09 08		09 08			09 23			09 38		09 38			09 53				10 08		10 08		
Milngavie	d	→				09 12			09 27	→				09 42				09 57	→				10 12
Hillfoot	d					09 15			09 30					09 45				10 00					10 15
Bearsden	d					09 17			09 32					09 47				10 02					10 17
Westerton	d			09 10		09 20	09 25		09 35			09 40		09 50	09 55			10 05			10 10		10 20
Anniesland	d			09 14		09 23	09 28		09 38			09 44		09 53	09 58			10 08			10 14		10 23
Clydebank	d				09 10			09 25					09 40				09 55					10 10	
Yoker	d				09 12			09 27					09 42				09 57					10 12	
Garscadden	d				09 16			09 31					09 46				10 01					10 16	
Scotstounhill	d				09 18			09 33					09 48				10 03					10 18	
Jordanhill	d				09 20			09 35					09 50				10 05					10 20	
Hyndland	d		09 14	09 17	09 22	09 26	09 31	09 37	09 41		09 44	09 47	09 52	09 56	10 01		10 07	10 11		10 14	10 18	10 22	10 26
Partick	d		09 17	09 20	09 25	09 29	09 34	09 40	09 44		09 47	09 50	09 55	09 59	10 04		10 10	10 14		10 17	10 20	10 25	10 29
Exhibition Centre	d			09 23		09 32		09 43				09 53		10 02			10 13				10 23		10 32
Anderston	d			09 25		09 34		09 45				09 55		10 04			10 15				10 25		10 34
Glasgow Central 15 §	a			09 26		09 35		09 47				09 56		10 05		10b15	10 17				10 27		10 35
	d			09 27		09 37		09 47				09 57		10 07			10 17				10 27		10 37
Argyle Street	d			09 29		09 39		09 49				09 59		10 09			10 19				10 29		10 39
Charing Cross	d		09 22		09 29		09 38		09 49		09 52		09 59		10 08			10 19		10 22		10 29	
Glasgow Queen Street 10 §	a		09 24		09 31		09 40		09 51		09 54		10 01		10 10			10 21		10 24		10 31	
	d		09 27		09 32		09 42		09 51		09 57		10 02		10 12			10 21		10 27		10 32	
High Street	d		09 29		09 34		09 44		09a53		09 59		10 04		10 14			10a23		10 29		10 34	
Bellgrove	d		09 31		09 36		09 46				10 01		10 06		10 16					10 31		10 36	
Duke Street	d				09 38								10 08									10 38	
Alexandra Parade	d				09 39								10 09									10 39	
Barnhill	d				09 42								10 12									10 42	
Springburn	a				09 44								10 14									10 44	
Carntyne	d		09 34				09 49				10 04				10 19					10 34			
Shettleston	d		09 37				09 52				10 07				10 22					10 37			
Garrowhill	d		09 39				09 54				10 09				10 24					10 39			
Easterhouse	d		09 42				09 57				10 12				10 27					10 42			
Blairhill	d		09 46				10 01				10 16				10 31					10 46			
Coatbridge Sunnyside	d		09 48				10 03				10 18				10 33					10 48			
Coatdyke	d		09 51				10 06				10 21				10 36					10 51			
Airdrie	a		09 53				10 09				10 23				10 39					10 53			
	d		09 54								10 24									10 54			
Drumgelloch	a		09 58								10 28									10 58			
Bridgeton	d					09 42		09 52						10 12			10 22						10 42
Dalmarnock	d					09 44		09 54						10 14			10 24						10 44
Rutherglen	d			09 34		09 46		09 56				10 04		10 16			10 26				10 34		10 50
Cambuslang	d					09 50		10 01						10 20		10 23	10 31						10 51
Newton	d					09 54								10 24									10 54
Blantyre	d			09 44		09 58						10 14		10 28							10 44		10 58
Hamilton West	d			09 47		10 01						10 17		10 31							10 47		11 01
Hamilton Central	d			09 50		10 03						10 20		10 33							10 50		11 04
Chatelherault	d			09 54								10 24									10 54		
Merryton	d			09 58								10 28									10 58		
Larkhall	a			10 00								10 30									11 00		
Airbles	d					10 08								10 38									11 09
Uddingston	d							10 05								10 28	10 35						
Bellshill	d							10 10								10 34	10 40						
Motherwell	a					10 11		10 16						10 41			10 46						11 14
	d							10 16						10 42									
Whifflet	a																						
Coatbridge Central	a																						
Shieldmuir	d							10 20															
Holytown	d													10 47		10a38							
Wishaw	d							10 23						10 53									
Carluke	d							10 30						11 00									
Lanark	a							10 43						11 12									

For general notes see front of timetable
For details of catering facilities see Directory of Train Operators

§ Low Level

A To Edinburgh (Table 225)
b Glasgow Central High Level

Helensburgh, Balloch, Dalmuir and Milngavie → Glasgow → Springburn, Airdrie, Drumgelloch, Hamilton, Larkhall, Motherwell, Coatbridge and Lanark

Network Diagram - see first page of Table 220

		SR	SR	SR	SR	SR	SR	SR	SR	SR	SR	SR	SR	SR	SR	SR	SR	SR	SR	SR	SR	SR	SR	SR
											A					◇ B								
Helensburgh Central	d					10 10									10 40	10b41								11 10
Craigendoran	d					10 13									10 43									11 13
Cardross	d					10 18									10 48									11 18
Balloch	d	09 53								10 23										10 53				
Alexandria	d	09 55								10 25										10 55				
Renton	d	09 58								10 28										10 58				
Dalreoch	d	10 01				10 23				10 31					10 53					11 01				11 23
Dumbarton Central	d	10 02				10 25				10 32					10 55	10 58				11 02				11 25
Dumbarton East	d	10 04				10 27				10 34					10 57					11 04				11 27
Bowling	d	10 09								10 39										11 09				
Kilpatrick	d	10 12								10 42										11 12				
Dalmuir	a	10 15				10 35				10 45					11 05	11 08				11 15				11 35
	d	10 16	10 23		10 31	10 36		10 38		10 46		10 53		11 01	11 06	11 08		11 08		11 16	11 23		11 31	11 36
Singer	d	10 18			10 33					10 48				11 03						11 18			11 33	
Drumry	d	10 20			10 35		←			10 50				11 05			←			11 20			11 35	
Drumchapel	d	10 23			10 38		10 38			10 53				11 08			11 08			11 23			11 38	
Milngavie	d			10 27	↪				10 42				10 57	↪					11 12			11 27	↪	
Hillfoot	d			10 30					10 45				11 00						11 15			11 30		
Bearsden	d			10 32					10 47				11 02						11 17			11 32		
Westerton	d	10 25		10 35			10 40		10 50	10 55			11 05				11 10		11 20	11 25		11 35		
Anniesland	d	10 28		10 38			10 44		10 53	10 58			11 08				11 14		11 23	11 28		11 38		
Clydebank	d		10 25					10 40				10 55						11 10			11 25			
Yoker	d		10 27					10 42				10 57						11 12			11 27			
Garscadden	d		10 31					10 46				11 01						11 16			11 31			
Scotstounhill	d		10 33					10 48				11 03						11 18			11 33			
Jordanhill	d		10 35					10 50				11 05						11 20			11 35			
Hyndland	d	10 31	10 37	10 41		10 44	10 47	10 52	10 56	11 01		11 07	11 11		11 14		11 17	11 22	11 26	11 31	11 37	11 41		11 44
Partick	d	10 34	10 40	10 44		10 47	10 50	10 55	10 59	11 04		11 10	11 14		11 17		11 20	11 25	11 29	11 34	11 40	11 44		11 47
Exhibition Centre	d		10 43				10 53		11 02			11 13					11 23		11 32		11 43			
Anderston	d		10 45				10 55		11 04			11 15					11 25		11 34		11 45			
Glasgow Central 15 §	a		10 47				10 56		11 05			11 17					11 26		11 37		11 47			
	d		10 47				10 57		11 07		11c15	11 17					11 27		11 37		11 47			
Argyle Street	d		10 49				10 59		11 09			11 19					11 29		11 39		11 49			
Charing Cross	d	10 38		10 49		10 52		10 59		11 08			11 19		11 22			11 29		11 38		11 49		11 52
Glasgow Queen Street 10 §	a	10 40		10 51		10 54		11 01		11 10			11 21		11 24	11e30		11 31		11 40		11 51		11 54
	d	10 42		10 51		10 57		11 02		11 12			11 21		11 27			11 32		11 42		11 51		11 57
High Street	d	10 44		10a53		10 59		11 04		11 14			11a23		11 29			11 34		11 44		11a53		11 59
Bellgrove	d	10 46				11 01		11 06		11 16					11 31			11 36		11 46				12 01
Duke Street	d							11 08										11 38						
Alexandra Parade	d							11 09										11 39						
Barnhill	d							11 12										11 42						
Springburn	a							11 14										11 44						
Carntyne	d	10 49				11 05				11 19					11 34					11 49				12 04
Shettleston	d	10 52				11 07				11 22					11 37					11 52				12 07
Garrowhill	d	10 54				11 09				11 24					11 39					11 54				12 09
Easterhouse	d	10 57				11 12				11 27					11 42					11 57				12 12
Blairhill	d	11 01				11 16				11 31					11 46					12 01				12 16
Coatbridge Sunnyside	d	11 03				11 18				11 33					11 48					12 03				12 18
Coatdyke	d	11 06				11 21				11 36					11 51					12 06				12 21
Airdrie	a	11 09				11 23				11 39					11 53					12 09				12 23
	d					11 24									11 54									12 24
Drumgelloch	a					11 28									11 58									12 28
Bridgeton	d		10 52						11 12			11 22							11 42		11 52			
Dalmarnock	d		10 54						11 14			11 24							11 44		11 54			
Rutherglen	d		10 56				11 04		11 16			11 26					11 34		11 46		11 56			
Cambuslang	d		11 01						11 20		11 23	11 31							11 50		12 01			
Newton	d								11 24										11 54					
Blantyre	d						11 14		11 28								11 44		11 58					
Hamilton West	d						11 17		11 31								11 47		12 01					
Hamilton Central	d						11 20		11 33								11 50		12 03					
Chatelherault	d						11 24										11 54							
Merryton	d						11 28										11 58							
Larkhall	a						11 30										12 00							
Airbles	d								11 38										12 08					
Uddingston	d		11 05								11 28	11 35									12 05			
Bellshill	d		11 10								11 34	11 40									12 10			
Motherwell	a		11 16						11 41			11 48							12 11		12 16			
	d		11 16						11 42												12 16			
Whifflet	a																							
Coatbridge Central	a																							
Shieldmuir	d		11 20																		12 20			
Holytown	d								11 47		11a38													
Wishaw	d		11 23						11 53												12 23			
Carluke	d		11 30						12 00												12 30			
Lanark	a		11 42						12 12												12 42			

For general notes see front of timetable
For details of catering facilities see Directory of Train Operators

§ Low Level

A To Edinburgh (Table 225)
B From Mallaig and Oban (Table 227)
b Helensburgh Upper. Until 25 September dep. 1044
c Glasgow Central High Level
e Glasgow Queen Street High Level

Helensburgh, Balloch, Dalmuir and Milngavie → Glasgow → Springburn, Airdrie, Drumgelloch, Hamilton, Larkhall, Motherwell, Coatbridge and Lanark

Network Diagram - see first page of Table 220

		SR	SR	SR	SR	SR A	SR		SR	SR	SR	SR	SR	SR	SR	SR	SR	SR	SR	SR	SR	SR	SR		SR A
Helensburgh Central	d										11 40								12 10						
Craigendoran	d										11 43								12 13						
Cardross	d										11 48								12 18						
Balloch	d				11 23										11 53								12 23		
Alexandria	d				11 25										11 55								12 25		
Renton	d				11 28										11 58								12 28		
Dalreoch	d				11 31						11 53				12 01				12 23				12 31		
Dumbarton Central	d				11 32						11 55				12 02				12 25				12 32		
Dumbarton East	d				11 34						11 57				12 04				12 27				12 34		
Bowling	d				11 39										12 09								12 39		
Kilpatrick	d				11 42										12 12								12 42		
Dalmuir	a				11 45						12 05				12 15				12 35				12 46		
	d		11 38		11 46		11 53			12 01	12 06		12 08		12 16	12 23		12 31	12 36		12 38		12 46		
Singer	d				11 48					12 03					12 18			12 33					12 48		
Drumry	d	←			11 50					12 05		←			12 20			12 35		←			12 50		
Drumchapel	d	11 38			11 53					12 08		12 08			12 23			12 38		12 38			12 53		
Milngavie	d			11 42					11 57	→				12 12			12 27	→				12 42			
Hillfoot	d			11 45					12 00					12 15			12 30					12 45			
Bearsden	d			11 47					12 02					12 17			12 32					12 47			
Westerton	d	11 40		11 50	11 55				12 05			12 10		12 20	12 25		12 35			12 40		12 50	12 55		
Anniesland	d	11 44		11 53	11 58				12 08			12 14		12 23	12 28		12 38			12 44		12 53	12 58		
Clydebank	d		11 40				11 55						12 10			12 25					12 40				
Yoker	d		11 42				11 57						12 12			12 27					12 42				
Garscadden	d		11 46				12 01						12 16			12 31					12 46				
Scotstounhill	d		11 48				12 03						12 18			12 33					12 48				
Jordanhill	d		11 50				12 05						12 20			12 35					12 50				
Hyndland	d	11 48	11 52	11 56	12 01		12 07		12 11		12 14	12 17	12 22	12 26	12 31	12 37	12 41		12 44	12 48	12 52	12 56	13 01		
Partick	d	11 50	11 55	11 59	12 04		12 10		12 14		12 17	12 20	12 25	12 29	12 34	12 40	12 44		12 47	12 50	12 55	12 59	13 04		
Exhibition Centre	d	11 53		12 02			12 13					12 23		12 32		12 43				12 53		13 02			
Anderston	d	11 55		12 04			12 15					12 25		12 34		12 45				12 55		13 04			
Glasgow Central 15 §	a	11 56		12 05			12 17					12 26		12 35		12 47				12 56		13 05			13b15
	d	11 57		12 07		12b15	12 17					12 27		12 37		12 47				12 57		13 07			
Argyle Street	d	11 59		12 09			12 19					12 29		12 39		12 49				12 59		13 09			
Charing Cross	d		11 59		12 08				12 19		12 22		12 29		12 38		12 49		12 52		12 59		13 08		
Glasgow Queen Street 10 §	a		12 01		12 10				12 21		12 24		12 31		12 40		12 51		12 54		13 01		13 10		
	d		12 02		12 12				12 21		12 27		12 32		12 42		12 51		12 57		13 02		13 12		
High Street	d		12 04		12 14				12a23		12 29		12 34		12 44		12a53		12 59		13 04		13 14		
Bellgrove	d		12 06		12 16						12 31		12 36		12 46				13 01		13 06		13 16		
Duke Street	d		12 08										12 38								13 08				
Alexandra Parade	d		12 09										12 39								13 09				
Barnhill	d		12 12										12 42								13 12				
Springburn	a		12 14										12 44								13 14				
Carntyne	d				12 19						12 34				12 49				13 04				13 19		
Shettleston	d				12 22						12 37				12 52				13 07				13 22		
Garrowhill	d				12 24						12 39				12 54				13 09				13 24		
Easterhouse	d				12 27						12 42				12 57				13 12				13 27		
Blairhill	d				12 31						12 46				13 01				13 16				13 31		
Coatbridge Sunnyside	d				12 33						12 48				13 03				13 18				13 33		
Coatdyke	d				12 36						12 51				13 06				13 21				13 36		
Airdrie	a				12 39						12 53				13 09				13 23				13 39		
	d										12 54								13 24						
Drumgelloch	a										12 58								13 28						
Bridgeton	d			12 12			12 22							12 42		12 52						13 12			
Dalmarnock	d			12 14			12 24							12 44		12 54						13 14			
Rutherglen	d	12 04		12 16			12 26					12 34		12 46		12 56				13 04		13 16			13 23
Cambuslang	d			12 20		12 23	12 31							12 50		13 01						13 20			
Newton	d			12 24										12 54								13 24			
Blantyre	d	12 14		12 28								12 44		12 58						13 14		13 28			
Hamilton West	d	12 17		12 31								12 47		13 01						13 17		13 31			
Hamilton Central	d	12 20		12 33								12 50		13 04						13 20		13 33			
Chatelherault	d	12 24										12 54								13 24					
Merryton	d	12 28										12 58								13 28					
Larkhall	a	12 30										13 00								13 30					
Airbles	d			12 38										13 08								13 38			
Uddingston	d					12 28	12 35									13 05									13 28
Bellshill	d					12 34	12 40									13 10									13 34
Motherwell	a			12 41			12 48							13 11		13 16						13 41			
	d			12 42												13 16						13 42			
Whifflet	a																								
Coatbridge Central	a																								
Shieldmuir	d															13 20									
Holytown	d			12 47		12a38																13 50			13a38
Wishaw	d			12 53												13 23						13 55			
Carluke	d			13 00												13 30						14 01			
Lanark	a			13 12												13 42						14 13			

For general notes see front of timetable
For details of catering facilities see Directory of Train Operators

§ Low Level

A To Edinburgh (Table 225)
b Glasgow Central High Level

Helensburgh, Balloch, Dalmuir and Milngavie → Glasgow → Springburn, Airdrie, Drumgelloch, Hamilton, Larkhall, Motherwell, Coatbridge and Lanark

Network Diagram - see first page of Table 220

		SR	SR	SR	SR	SR	SR	SR	SR	SR	SR	SR	SR	SR	SR	SR	SR	SR A	SR	SR	SR	SR	SR	SR
Helensburgh Central	d				12 40								13 10									13 40		
Craigendoran	d				12 43								13 13									13 43		
Cardross	d				12 48								13 18									13 48		
Balloch	d								12 53								13 23							
Alexandria	d								12 55								13 25							
Renton	d								12 58								13 28							
Dalreoch	d				12 53				13 01				13 23				13 31					13 53		
Dumbarton Central	d				12 55				13 02				13 25				13 32					13 55		
Dumbarton East	d				12 57				13 04				13 27				13 34					13 57		
Bowling	d								13 09								13 39							
Kilpatrick	d								13 12								13 42							
Dalmuir	a				13 05				13 15				13 35				13 45					14 05		
	d	12 53		13 01	13 06		13 08		13 16	13 23		13 31	13 36		13 38		13 46		13 53		14 01	14 06		14 08
Singer	d			13 03					13 18			13 33					13 48				14 03			
Drumry	d			13 05		←			13 20			13 35		←			13 50				14 05		←	
Drumchapel	d			13 08		13 08			13 23			13 38		13 38			13 53				14 08		14 08	
Milngavie	d		12 57	→				13 12			13 27	→				13 42				13 57	→			
Hillfoot	d		13 00					13 15			13 30					13 45				14 00				
Bearsden	d		13 02					13 17			13 32					13 47				14 02				
Westerton	d		13 05			13 10		13 20	13 25		13 35			13 40		13 50	13 55			14 05			14 10	
Anniesland	d		13 08			13 14		13 23	13 28		13 38			13 44		13 53	13 58			14 08			14 14	
Clydebank	d	12 55					13 10			13 25					13 40				13 55					14 10
Yoker	d	12 57					13 12			13 27					13 42				13 57					14 12
Garscadden	d	13 01					13 16			13 31					13 46				14 01					14 16
Scotstounhill	d	13 03					13 18			13 33					13 48				14 03					14 18
Jordanhill	d	13 05					13 20			13 35					13 50				14 05					14 20
Hyndland	d	13 07	13 11		13 14	13 17	13 22	13 26	13 31	13 37	13 41		13 44	13 47	13 52	13 56	14 01		14 07	14 11		14 14	14 17	14 22
Partick	d	13 10	13 14		13 17	13 20	13 25	13 29	13 34	13 40	13 44		13 47	13 50	13 55	13 59	14 04		14 10	14 14		14 17	14 20	14 25
Exhibition Centre	d	13 13				13 23		13 32		13 43				13 53		14 02			14 13				14 23	
Anderston	d	13 15				13 25		13 34		13 45				13 55		14 04			14 15				14 25	
Glasgow Central 15 §	a	13 17				13 27		13 35		13 47				13 56		14 05			14 17				14 26	
	d	13 17				13 27		13 37		13 47				13 57		14 07		14b15	14 17				14 27	
Argyle Street	d	13 19				13 29		13 39		13 49				13 59		14 09			14 19				14 29	
Charing Cross	d		13 19		13 22		13 29		13 38		13 49		13 52		13 59		14 08			14 19		14 22		14 29
Glasgow Queen Street 10 §	a		13 21		13 24		13 31		13 40		13 51		13 54		14 01		14 10			14 21		14 24		14 31
	d		13 21		13 27		13 32		13 42		13 51		13 57		14 02		14 12			14 21		14 27		14 32
High Street	d		13a23		13 29		13 34		13 44		13a53		13 59		14 04		14 14			14a23		14 29		14 34
Bellgrove	d				13 31		13 36		13 46				14 01		14 06		14 16					14 31		14 36
Duke Street	d						13 38								14 08									14 38
Alexandra Parade	d						13 39								14 09									14 39
Barnhill	d						13 42								14 12									14 42
Springburn	a						13 44								14 14									14 44
Carntyne	d				13 34				13 49				14 04				14 19					14 34		
Shettleston	d				13 37				13 52				14 07				14 22					14 37		
Garrowhill	d				13 39				13 54				14 09				14 24					14 39		
Easterhouse	d				13 42				13 57				14 12				14 27					14 42		
Blairhill	d				13 46				14 01				14 16				14 31					14 46		
Coatbridge Sunnyside	d				13 48				14 03				14 18				14 33					14 48		
Coatdyke	d				13 51				14 06				14 21				14 36					14 51		
Airdrie	a				13 53				14 09				14 23				14 39					14 53		
	d				13 54								14 24									14 54		
Drumgelloch	a				13 58								14 28									14 58		
Bridgeton	d	13 22						13 42		13 52						14 12			14 22					
Dalmarnock	d	13 24						13 44		13 54						14 14			14 24					
Rutherglen	d	13 26				13 34		13 46		13 56				14 04		14 16			14 26				14 34	
Cambuslang	d	13 31						13 50		14 01						14 20		14 23	14 31					
Newton	d							13 54								14 24								
Blantyre	d					13 44		13 58						14 14		14 28							14 44	
Hamilton West	d					13 47		14 01						14 17		14 31							14 47	
Hamilton Central	d					13 50		14 03						14 20		14 33							14 50	
Chatelherault	d					13 54								14 24									14 54	
Merryton	d					13 58								14 28									14 58	
Larkhall	a					14 00								14 30									15 00	
Airbles	d							14 08								14 38								
Uddingston	d	13 35								14 05								14 28	14 35					
Bellshill	d	13 40								14 10								14 34	14 40					
Motherwell	a	13 46						14 11		14 16						14 41			14 48					
	d									14 16						14 42								
Whifflet	a																							
Coatbridge Central	a																							
Shieldmuir	d									14 19														
Holytown	d															14 47		14a38						
Wishaw	d									14 23						14 53								
Carluke	d									14 29						15 00								
Lanark	a									14 43						15 12								

For general notes see front of timetable
For details of catering facilities see Directory of Train Operators

§ Low Level

A To Edinburgh (Table 225)
b Glasgow Central High Level

Table 226

Mondays to Fridays

Helensburgh, Balloch, Dalmuir and Milngavie → Glasgow → Springburn, Airdrie, Drumgelloch, Hamilton, Larkhall, Motherwell, Coatbridge and Lanark

Network Diagram - see first page of Table 220

		SR	SR	SR	SR	SR	SR	SR	SR	SR		SR	SR	SR	SR	SR	SR	SR	SR	SR	SR	SR	SR	SR	SR
										A		B						◇ C ✠							
Helensburgh Central	d						14 10											14b39	14 40						
Craigendoran	d						14 13												14 43						
Cardross	d						14 18												14 48						
Balloch	d		13 53											14 23									14 53		
Alexandria	d		13 55											14 25									14 55		
Renton	d		13 58											14 28									14 58		
Dalreoch	d		14 01				14 23							14 31					14 53				15 01		
Dumbarton Central	d		14 02				14 25							14 32				14 52	14 55				15 02		
Dumbarton East	d		14 04				14 27							14 34					14 57				15 04		
Bowling	d		14 09											14 39									15 09		
Kilpatrick	d		14 12											14 42									15 12		
Dalmuir	a		14 15				14 35							14 45				15 04	15 06				15 15		
	d		14 16	14 23		14 31	14 36		14 38					14 46	14 53		15 01	15 04	15 06		15 08		15 16	15 23	
Singer	d		14 18			14 33								14 48			15 03						15 18		
Drumry	d		14 20			14 35		←						14 50			15 05			←			15 20		
Drumchapel	d		14 23			14 38		14 38						14 53			15 08			15 08			15 23		
Milngavie	d	14 12			14 27	→							14 42			14 57	→					15 12			15 27
Hillfoot	d	14 15			14 30								14 45			15 00						15 15			15 30
Bearsden	d	14 17			14 32								14 47			15 02						15 17			15 32
Westerton	d	14 20	14 25		14 35			14 40					14 50	14 55		15 05				15 10		15 20	15 25		15 35
Anniesland	d	14 23	14 28		14 38			14 44					14 53	14 58		15 08				15 14		15 23	15 28		15 38
Clydebank	d			14 25					14 40						14 55						15 10			15 25	
Yoker	d			14 27					14 42						14 57						15 12			15 27	
Garscadden	d			14 31					14 46						15 01						15 16			15 31	
Scotstounhill	d			14 33					14 48						15 03						15 18			15 33	
Jordanhill	d			14 35					14 50						15 05						15 20			15 35	
Hyndland	d	14 26	14 31	14 37	14 41		14 44	14 47	14 52				14 56	15 01	15 07	15 11			15 14	15 17	15 22	15 27	15 31	15 37	15 41
Partick	d	14 29	14 34	14 40	14 44		14 47	14 50	14 55				14 59	15 04	15 10	15 14			15 17	15 20	15 25	15 29	15 34	15 40	15 44
Exhibition Centre	d	14 32		14 43				14 53					15 02		15 13					15 23		15 32		15 43	
Anderston	d	14 34		14 45				14 55					15 04		15 15					15 25		15 34		15 45	
Glasgow Central 15 §	a	14 35		14 47				14 56					15 05		15 17					15 26		15 35		15 47	
	d	14 37		14 47				14 57		15c15		15 19	15 07		15 17					15 27		15 37		15 47	
Argyle Street	d	14 39		14 49				14 59					15 09		15 19					15 29		15 39		15 49	
Charing Cross	d		14 38		14 49		14 52		14 59					15 08		15 19			15 22		15 29		15 38		15 49
Glasgow Queen Street 10 §	a		14 40		14 51		14 54		15 01					15 10		15 21		15e30	15 24		15 31		15 41		15 51
	d		14 42		14 51		14 57		15 02					15 12		15 21			15 27		15 32		15 42		15 51
High Street	d		14 44		14a53		14 59		15 04					15 14		15a23			15 29		15 34		15 44		15a53
Bellgrove	d		14 46				15 01		15 06					15 16					15 31		15 36		15 46		
Duke Street	d								15 08												15 38				
Alexandra Parade	d								15 09												15 39				
Barnhill	d								15 12												15 42				
Springburn	a								15 14												15 44				
Carntyne	d		14 49				15 04							15 19					15 34				15 49		
Shettleston	d		14 52				15 07							15 22					15 37				15 52		
Garrowhill	d		14 54				15 09							15 24					15 39				15 54		
Easterhouse	d		14 57				15 12							15 27					15 42				15 57		
Blairhill	d		15 01				15 16							15 31					15 46				16 01		
Coatbridge Sunnyside	d		15 03				15 18							15 33					15 48				16 03		
Coatdyke	d		15 06				15 21							15 36					15 51				16 06		
Airdrie	a		15 09				15 23							15 39					15 53				16 09		
	d						15 24												15 54						
Drumgelloch	a						15 28												15 58						
Bridgeton	d	14 42		14 52									15 12		15 22							15 42		15 52	
Dalmarnock	d	14 44		14 54									15 14		15 24							15 44		15 54	
Rutherglen	d	14 46		14 56				15 04					15 16		15 26					15 34		15 46		15 56	
Cambuslang	d	14 50		15 01						15 23			15 20		15 31							15 50		16 01	
Newton	d	14 54											15 24									15 54			
Blantyre	d	14 58						15 14					15 28							15 44		15 58			
Hamilton West	d	15 01						15 17					15 31							15 47		16 01			
Hamilton Central	d	15 03						15 20					15 33							15 50		16 03			
Chatelherault	d							15 24												15 54					
Merryton	d							15 28												15 58					
Larkhall	a							15 30												16 00					
Airbles	d	15 08											15 38									16 08			
Uddingston	d			15 05						15 28					15 36									16 05	
Bellshill	d			15 10						15 34					15 40									16 10	
Motherwell	a	15 11		15 16								15 35	15 41		15 46							16 11		16 16	
	d			15 16								15 38	15 42											16 16	
Whifflet	a																								
Coatbridge Central	a																								
Shieldmuir	d			15 20																				16 20	
Holytown	d									15a38			15 48												
Wishaw	d			15 23									15 53											16 23	
Carluke	d			15 30								15a47	16 00											16 30	
Lanark	a			15 42									16 13											16 42	

For general notes see front of timetable
For details of catering facilities see Directory of Train Operators

§ Low Level

A To Edinburgh (Table 225)
B To North Berwick (Table 238)
C From Oban (from 28 September also conveys portion from Mallaig) (Table 227)

b Helensburgh Upper
c Glasgow Central High Level
e Glasgow Queen Street High Level

Table 226

Mondays to Fridays

Helensburgh, Balloch, Dalmuir and Milngavie → Glasgow → Springburn, Airdrie, Drumgelloch, Hamilton, Larkhall, Motherwell, Coatbridge and Lanark

Network Diagram - see first page of Table 220

		SR	SR	SR ◇ A		SR	SR	SR	SR	SR B	SR	SR	SR	SR	SR	SR	SR	SR	SR	SR		SR	SR	SR	SR
Helensburgh Central	d		15 10	15b15										15 40											16 10
Craigendoran	d		15 13											15 45											16 13
Cardross	d		15 18											15 48											16 18
Balloch	d								15 23											15 53					
Alexandria	d								15 25											15 55					
Renton	d								15 28											15 58					
Dalreoch	d		15 23						15 31					15 53						16 01					
Dumbarton Central	d		15 25	15 28					15 32					15 55						16 02					16 23
Dumbarton East	d		15 27						15 34					15 57						16 04					16 25
Bowling	d								15 39											16 09					16 27
Kilpatrick	d								15 42											16 12					
Dalmuir	a		15 35	15 37					15 45					16 04						16 15					16 35
	d	15 31	15 36	15 37			15 38		15 46		15 53		16 01	16 06			16 08			16 16		16 23		16 31	16 36
Singer	d	15 33							15 48				16 03							16 18				16 33	
Drumry	d	15 35				←			15 50				16 05			←				16 20				16 35	
Drumchapel	d	15 38				15 38			15 53				16 08			16 08				16 23				16 38	
Milngavie	d	→						15 42				15 57	→						16 12				16 27	→	
Hillfoot	d							15 45				16 00							16 15				16 30		
Bearsden	d							15 47				16 02							16 17				16 32		
Westerton	d					15 40		15 50	15 55			16 05				16 10			16 20	16 25			16 35		
Anniesland	d					15 44		15 53	15 58			16 08				16 14			16 23	16 28			16 38		
Clydebank	d						15 40				15 55						16 10					16 25			
Yoker	d						15 42				15 57						16 12					16 27			
Garscadden	d						15 46				16 01						16 15					16 31			
Scotstounhill	d						15 48				16 03						16 18					16 33			
Jordanhill	d						15 50				16 05						16 20					16 35			
Hyndland	d		15 44			15 47	15 52	15 56	16 01		16 07	16 11		16 14		16 17	16 22		16 26	16 31		16 37	16 41		16 44
Partick	d		15 47			15 50	15 55	15 59	16 04		16 10	16 14		16 17		16 20	16 25		16 29	16 34		16 40	16 44		16 47
Exhibition Centre	d					15 53		16 02			16 13					16 23			16 32			16 43			
Anderston	d					15 55		16 04			16 15				16 23	16 25			16 34			16 45			
Glasgow Central 15 §	a					15 56		16 05			16 17				16 24	16 26			16 35			16 47			
	d					15 57		16 07		16c15	16 17				16 25	16 27			16 37			16 47			
Argyle Street	d					15 59		16 09			16 19				16 27	16 29			16 39			16 49			
Charing Cross	d		15 52				15 59		16 08			16 19		16 23			16 29			16 38			16 49		16 52
Glasgow Queen Street 10 §	a		15 54	15e58			16 01		16 11			16 21		16 24			16 31			16 40			16 51		16 54
	d		15 57				16 02		16 12			16 22		16 27			16 32			16 42			16 51		16 57
High Street	d		15 59				16 04		16 14			16 24		16 29			16 34			16 44			16 54		16 59
Bellgrove	d		16 01				16 06		16 16					16 31			16 36			16 46					17 01
Duke Street	d						16 08										16 38								
Alexandra Parade	d						16 09										16 39								
Barnhill	d						16 12										16 42								
Springburn	a						16 14										16 44								
Carntyne	d		16 04						16 19					16 34						16 49					17 04
Shettleston	d		16 07						16 22					16 37						16 52					17 07
Garrowhill	d		16 09						16 24					16 39						16 54					17 09
Easterhouse	d		16 12						16 27					16 42						16 57					17 12
Blairhill	d		16 16						16 31			16 35		16 46						17 01			17 05		17 16
Coatbridge Sunnyside	d		16 18						16 33			16 38		16 48						17 03			17 08		17 18
Coatdyke	d		16 21						16 36			16 40		16 51						17 06			17 10		17 21
Airdrie	a		16 23						16 39			16 45		16 53						17 09			17 15		17 23
	d		16 24											16 54											17 24
Drumgelloch	a		16 28											16 58											17 28
Bridgeton	d							16 12			16 22								16 42			16 52			
Dalmarnock	d							16 14			16 24								16 44			16 54			
Rutherglen	d					16 04		16 16			16 26				16 32	16 34			16 46			16 56			
Cambuslang	d							16 20		16 23	16 31								16 50			17 01			
Newton	d							16 24											16 54						
Blantyre	d					16 14		16 28								16 45			16 58						
Hamilton West	d					16 17		16 31								16 48			17 01						
Hamilton Central	d					16 20		16 33								16 50			17 03						
Chatelherault	d					16 24										16 55									
Merryton	d					16 28										16 58									
Larkhall	a					16 30										17 02									
Airbles	d							16 38										←	17 08						
Uddingston	d									16 28	16 35							16 35				17 05			
Bellshill	d									16 34	→							16 40				17 10			
Motherwell	a							16 41							16 44			16 47	17 11			17 16			
	d							16 42							16 47				17 12						
Whifflet	a							16 48											17 18						
Coatbridge Central	a							16 53											17 22						
Shieldmuir	d														16 50										
Holytown	d									16a38															
Wishaw	d														16 53										
Carluke	d														17 03										
Lanark	a														17 15										

For general notes see front of timetable
For details of catering facilities see Directory of Train Operators

§ Low Level

A Until 25 September. From Oban (Table 227)
B To Edinburgh (Table 225)
b Helensburgh Upper
c Glasgow Central High Level
e Glasgow Queen Street High Level

Helensburgh, Balloch, Dalmuir and Milngavie → Glasgow → Springburn, Airdrie, Drumgelloch, Hamilton, Larkhall, Motherwell, Coatbridge and Lanark

Network Diagram - see first page of Table 220

		SR	SR	SR	SR	SR	SR	SR	SR	SR	SR	SR	SR	SR		SR	SR	SR	SR	SR	SR	SR	SR	SR	SR
									A	B		A						A							
Helensburgh Central	d										16 40												17 10		
Craigendoran	d										16 43												17 13		
Cardross	d										16 48												17 18		
Balloch	d					16 23													16 53						
Alexandria	d					16 25													16 55						
Renton	d					16 28													16 58						
Dalreoch	d					16 31					16 53								17 01				17 23		
Dumbarton Central	d					16 32					16 55								17 02				17 25		
Dumbarton East	d					16 34					16 57								17 04				17 27		
Bowling	d					16 39													17 09						
Kilpatrick	d					16 42													17 12						
Dalmuir	a					16 45					17 05								17 15				17 35		
	d		16 38			16 46	16 53		17 01		17 06		17 08						17 16	17 23		17 31	17 36		17 38
Singer	d					16 48			17 03			←							17 18			17 33		←	
Drumry	d	←				16 50			17 05										17 20			17 35			
Drumchapel	d	16 38				16 53			17 08			17 08							17 23			17 38		17 38	
Milngavie	d				16 42			16 57	→								17 12				17 27	→			
Hillfoot	d				16 45			17 00									17 15				17 30				
Bearsden	d				16 47			17 02									17 17				17 32				
Westerton	d	16 40			16 50	16 55		17 05				17 10					17 20		17 25		17 35			17 40	
Anniesland	d	16 44			16 53	16 58		17 08				17 14					17 23		17 28		17 38			17 44	
Clydebank	d		16 40				16 55						17 10							17 25					17 40
Yoker	d		16 42				16 57						17 12							17 27					17 42
Garscadden	d		16 46				17 01						17 16							17 31					17 46
Scotstounhill	d		16 48				17 03						17 18							17 33					17 48
Jordanhill	d		16 50				17 05						17 20							17 35					17 50
Hyndland	d	16 47	16 52		16 56	17 01	17 07	17 11			17 14	17 17	17 22				17 26		17 31	17 37	17 41		17 44	17 47	17 52
Partick	d	16 49	16 55		16 59	17 04	17 10	17 14			17 17	17 20	17 25				17 29		17 34	17 40	17 44		17 47	17 50	17 55
Exhibition Centre	d	16 53			17 04		17 13					17 23					17 34			17 43				17 53	
Anderston	d	16 55		17 04	17 06		17 15					17 25		17 34		17 34	17 36			17 45				17 55	
Glasgow Central 15 §	a	16 56		17 05	17 08		17 17					17 26		17 35		17 35	17 38			17 47				17 56	
	d	16 57		17 07	17 09		17 21			17b19		17 27		17 37		17 37	17 39			17 47				17 57	
Argyle Street	d	16 59		17 09	17 11		17 23					17 29		17 39		17 39	17 41			17 49				17 59	
Charing Cross	d		16 59			17 08		17 19			17 22		17 29						17 38		17 49		17 52		17 59
Glasgow Queen Street 10 §	a		17 01			17 10		17 21			17 24		17 31						17 40		17 51		17 54		18 01
	d		17 02			17 12		17 22			17 27		17 32						17 42		17 51		17 57		18 02
High Street	d		17 04			17 14		17 24			17 29		17 34						17 44		17a53		17 59		18 04
Bellgrove	d		17 06			17 16					17 31		17 36						17 46				18 01		18 06
Duke Street	d		17 08										17 38												18 08
Alexandra Parade	d		17 09										17 39												18 09
Barnhill	d		17 12										17 42												18 12
Springburn	a		17 14										17 44												18 15
Carntyne	d					17 19					17 34								17 49				18 04		
Shettleston	d					17 22					17 37								17 52				18 07		
Garrowhill	d					17 24					17 39								17 54				18 09		
Easterhouse	d					17 27					17 42								17 57				18 12		
Blairhill	d					17 31		17 35			17 46								18 01				18 16		
Coatbridge Sunnyside	d					17 33		17 38			17 48								18 03				18 18		
Coatdyke	d					17 36		17 40			17 51								18 06				18 21		
Airdrie	a					17 39		17 45			17 53								18 09				18 23		
	d										17 54												18 24		
Drumgelloch	a										17 58												18 28		
Bridgeton	d			17 12	17 15		17 26					17 32					17 45			17 52					
Dalmarnock	d				17 17		17 28					17 34					17 47			17 54					
Rutherglen	d	17 04			17 19		17 31					17 37		17 44		17 44	17 49			17 56				18 04	
Cambuslang	d	17 08			17 23		17 35					17 41					17 53			18 01					
Newton	d				17 27		17 38										17 57							18 14	
Blantyre	d	17 14			17 33		17 42										18 01							18 17	
Hamilton West	d	17 17			17 36		17 45										18 04							18 20	
Hamilton Central	d	17 20			17 38		17 48										18 06								
Chatelherault	d	17 24			17 43												18 11							18 24	
Merryton	d	17 28			17 46												18 14							18 28	
Larkhall	a	17 30			17 48												18 16							18 30	
Airbles	d						17 53											←							
Uddingston	d			17 20								17 45 →						17 45		18 05					
Bellshill	d									17 34								17 50		18 10					
Motherwell	a			17 28			17 56							17 57		17 57		18 00		18 17					
	d			17 29			17 57							17 57		17 57		18 01							
Whifflet	a						18 03																		
Coatbridge Central	a						18 06																		
Shieldmuir	d			17 32										17 58		18 01		18 05							
Holytown	d									17a38															
Wishaw	d			17 36										18 01		18 04		18 08							
Carluke	d			17 43										18 07		18 11		18a19							
Lanark	a			17 54										18 21		18 22									

For general notes see front of timetable
For details of catering facilities see
Directory of Train Operators

§ Low Level

A To Carstairs (Table 225)
B To Edinburgh (Table 225)
b Glasgow Central High Level

Helensburgh, Balloch, Dalmuir and Milngavie → Glasgow → Springburn, Airdrie, Drumgelloch, Hamilton, Larkhall, Motherwell, Coatbridge and Lanark

Network Diagram - see first page of Table 220

		SR	SR	SR A	SR	SR	SR	SR		SR	SR	SR	SR	SR	SR	SR	SR	SR	SR	SR	SR	SR	SR	SR	SR
Helensburgh Central	d						17 40						18 10					18 40					19 10		
Craigendoran	d						17 43						18 13					18 43					19 13		
Cardross	d						17 48						18 18					18 48					19 18		
Balloch	d		17 23							17 53					18 23					18 53					19 23
Alexandria	d		17 25							17 55					18 25					18 55					19 25
Renton	d		17 28							17 58					18 28					18 58					19 28
Dalreoch	d		17 31				17 53			18 01			18 23		18 31			18 53		19 01			19 23		19 31
Dumbarton Central	d		17 32				17 55			18 02			18 25		18 32			18 55		19 02			19 25		19 32
Dumbarton East	d		17 34				17 57			18 04			18 27		18 34			18 57		19 04			19 27		19 34
Bowling	d		17 39							18 09					18 39					19 09					19 39
Kilpatrick	d		17 42							18 12					18 42					19 12					19 42
Dalmuir	a		17 45				18 05			18 15			18 35		18 45			19 05		19 15			19 35		19 45
	d		17 46		17 53	18 01	18 05			18 16	18 23	18 31	18 35		18 46		19 01	19 05		19 16		19 31	19 35		19 46
Singer	d		17 48			18 03				18 18		18 33			18 48		19 03			19 18		19 33			19 48
Drumry	d		17 50			18 05				18 20		18 35			18 50		19 05			19 20		19 35			19 50
Drumchapel	d		17 53			18 08				18 23		18 38			18 53		19 08			19 23		19 38			19 53
Milngavie	d	17 42						18 12						18 42					19 12					19 42	
Hillfoot	d	17 45						18 15						18 45					19 15					19 45	
Bearsden	d	17 47						18 17						18 47					19 17					19 47	
Westerton	d	17 50	17 55			18 10		18 20		18 25		18 40		18 50	18 55		19 10		19 20	19 25		19 40		19 50	19 55
Anniesland	d	17 53	17 58			18 14		18 23		18 28		18 44		18 53	18 58		19 14		19 23	19 28		19 44		19 53	19 58
Clydebank	d				17 55		18 07				18 25		18 37					19 07					19 37		
Yoker	d				17 57		18 09				18 27		18 39					19 09					19 39		
Garscadden	d				18 01		18 13				18 31		18 43					19 13					19 43		
Scotstounhill	d				18 03		18 15				18 33		18 45					19 15					19 45		
Jordanhill	d				18 05		18 17				18 35		18 47					19 17					19 47		
Hyndland	d	17 56	18 01		18 07	18 17	18 21	18 26		18 31	18 37	18 47	18 51	18 55	19 01		19 17	19 21	19 26	19 31		19 47	19 51	19 56	20 01
Partick	d	17 59	18 04		18 10	18 20	18 24	18 29		18 34	18 40	18 50	18 54	18 59	19 04	19 10	19 20	19 24	19 29	19 34	19 40	19 50	19 54	19 59	20 04
Exhibition Centre	d	18 02			18 13	18 23		18 32			18 43	18 53		19 02		19 13	19 23		19 32		19 43	19 53		20 02	
Anderston	d	18 04			18 15	18 25		18 34			18 45	18 55		19 04		19 15	19 25		19 34		19 45	19 55		20 04	
Glasgow Central 15 §	a	18 05			18 17	18 26		18 35			18 47	18 56		19 05		19 16	19 26		19 35		19 46	19 56		20 05	
	d	18 07		18b15	18 17	18 27		18 37			18 47	18 57		19 07		19 17	19 27		19 37		19 47	19 57		20 07	
Argyle Street	d	18 09			18 19	18 29		18 39			18 49	18 59		19 09		19 19	19 29		19 39		19 49	19 59		20 09	
Charing Cross	d		18 08				18 29			18 38			18 59		19 08			19 29		19 38			19 59		20 08
Glasgow Queen Street 10 §	a		18 10				18 31			18 40			19 01		19 10			19 31		19 40			20 01		20 10
	d		18 12				18 32			18 44			19 02		19 14			19 32		19 44			20 02		20 14
High Street	d		18 14				18 34			18 46			19 04		19 16			19 34		19 46			20 04		20 16
Bellgrove	d		18 16				18 36			18 48			19 06		19 18			19 36		19 48			20 06		20 18
Duke Street	d									18 50					19 20					19 50					20 20
Alexandra Parade	d									18 51					19 21					19 51					20 21
Barnhill	d									18 54					19 24					19 54					20 24
Springburn	a									18 56					19 26					19 56					20 26
Carntyne	d		18 19				18 39						19 09					19 39					20 09		
Shettleston	d		18 22				18 42						19 12					19 42					20 12		
Garrowhill	d		18 24				18 44						19 14					19 44					20 14		
Easterhouse	d		18 27				18 47						19 17					19 47					20 17		
Blairhill	d		18 31				18 51						19 21					19 51					20 21		
Coatbridge Sunnyside	d		18 33				18 53						19 23					19 53					20 23		
Coatdyke	d		18 36				18 56						19 26					19 56					20 26		
Airdrie	a		18 39				18 58						19 28					19 58					20 28		
	d						18 59						19 29					19 59					20 29		
Drumgelloch	a						19 03						19 33					20 03					20 33		
Bridgeton	d	18 12			18 22			18 42			18 52			19 12		19 22			19 42		19 52			20 12	
Dalmarnock	d	18 14			18 24			18 44			18 54			19 14		19 24			19 44		19 54			20 14	
Rutherglen	d	18 16			18 26	18 34		18 46			18 56	19 04		19 16		19 26	19 34		19 46		19 56	20 04		20 16	
Cambuslang	d	18 20		18 23	18 31			18 50			19 01			19 20		19 31			19 50		20 01			20 20	
Newton	d	18 24						18 54						19 24					19 54					20 24	
Blantyre	d	18 28				18 44		18 58				19 14		19 28			19 44		19 58			20 14		20 28	
Hamilton West	d	18 31				18 47		19 01				19 17		19 31			19 47		20 01			20 17		20 31	
Hamilton Central	d	18 33				18 50		19 03				19 20		19 33			19 50		20 03			20 20		20 33	
Chatelherault	d					18 54						19 24					19 54					20 24			
Merryton	d					18 58						19 28					19 58					20 28			
Larkhall	a					19 00						19 30					20 00					20 30			
Airbles	d	18 38						19 08						19 38					20 08					20 38	
Uddingston	d			18 28	18 35						19 05					19 35					20 05				
Bellshill	d			18 34	18 40						19 10					19 40					20 10				
Motherwell	a	18 41			18 46			19 11			19 16			19 41		19 46			20 11		20 16			20 41	
	d	18 42									19 16			19 42							20 16			20 42	
Whifflet	a																								
Coatbridge Central	a																								
Shieldmuir	d										19 20										20 20				
Holytown	d	18 47		18a38										19 48										20 47	
Wishaw	d	18 53									19 23			19 53							20 23			20 53	
Carluke	d	19 00									19 30			20 00							20 30			21 00	
Lanark	a	19 13									19 43			20 13							20 42			21 12	

For general notes see front of timetable
For details of catering facilities see Directory of Train Operators

§ Low Level

A To Edinburgh (Table 225)
b Glasgow Central High Level

Table 226 — Mondays to Fridays

Helensburgh, Balloch, Dalmuir and Milngavie → Glasgow → Springburn, Airdrie, Drumgelloch, Hamilton, Larkhall, Motherwell, Coatbridge and Lanark

Network Diagram - see first page of Table 220

		SR A		SR	SR	SR	SR	SR	SR	SR	SR	SR	SR	SR ◇ B	SR	SR	SR		SR	SR	SR	SR	SR	SR
Helensburgh Central	d					19 40				20 10					20b40	20 40						21 10			
Craigendoran	d					19 43				20 13						20 43						21 13			
Cardross	d					19 48				20 18						20 48						21 18			
Balloch	d							19 53				20 23						20 53						21 23	
Alexandria	d							19 55				20 25						20 55						21 25	
Renton	d							19 58				20 28						20 58						21 28	
Dalreoch	d					19 53		20 01		20 23		20 31				20 53		21 01				21 23		21 31	
Dumbarton Central	d					19 55		20 02		20 25		20 32			20 53	20 55		21 02				21 25		21 32	
Dumbarton East	d					19 57		20 04		20 27		20 34				20 57		21 04				21 27		21 34	
Bowling	d							20 09				20 39						21 09						21 39	
Kilpatrick	d							20 12				20 42						21 12						21 42	
Dalmuir	a					20 05		20 15		20 35		20 45			21 04	21 05		21 15				21 35		21 45	
	d				20 01	20 05		20 16	20 31	20 35		20 46		21 01	21 04	21 05		21 16			21 31	21 35		21 46	
Singer	d				20 03			20 18	20 33			20 48		21 03				21 18			21 33			21 48	
Drumry	d				20 05			20 20	20 35			20 50		21 05				21 20			21 35			21 50	
Drumchapel	d				20 08			20 23	20 38			20 53		21 08				21 23			21 38			21 53	
Milngavie	d						20 12				20 42						21 12						21 42		
Hillfoot	d						20 15				20 45						21 15						21 45		
Bearsden	d						20 17				20 47						21 17						21 47		
Westerton	d				20 10		20 20	20 25	20 40		20 50	20 55		21 10			21 20	21 25			21 40		21 50	21 55	
Anniesland	d				20 14		20 23	20 28	20 44		20 53	20 58		21 14			21 23	21 28			21 44		21 53	21 58	
Clydebank	d					20 07				20 37						21 07						21 37			
Yoker	d					20 09				20 39						21 09						21 39			
Garscadden	d					20 13				20 43						21 13						21 43			
Scotstounhill	d					20 15				20 45						21 15						21 45			
Jordanhill	d					20 17				20 47						21 17						21 47			
Hyndland	d				20 17	20 21	20 26	20 31	20 47	20 51	20 56	21 01		21 17		21 21	21 26	21 31			21 47	21 51	21 56	22 01	
Partick	d			20 10	20 20	20 24	20 29	20 34	20 50	20 54	20 59	21 04	21 10	21 20		21 24	21 29	21 34		21 40	21 50	21 54	21 59	22 04	22 10
Exhibition Centre	d			20 13	20 23		20 32		20 53		21 02		21 13	21 23			21 32			21 43	21 53		22 02		22 13
Anderston	d			20 15	20 25		20 34		20 55		21 04		21 15	21 25			21 34			21 45	21 55		22 04		22 15
Glasgow Central 15 §	a			20 16	20 26		20 35		20 56		21 05		21 16	21 26			21 35			21 46	21 56		22 05		22 16
	d	20c15		20 17	20 27		20 37		20 57		21 07		21 17	21 27			21 37			21 47	21 57		22 07		22 17
Argyle Street	d			20 19	20 29		20 39		20 59		21 09		21 19	21 29			21 39			21 49	21 59		22 09		22 19
Charing Cross	d					20 29		20 38		20 59		21 08				21 29		21 38				21 59		22 08	
Glasgow Queen Street 10 §	a					20 31		20 40		21 01		21 10			21e29	21 31		21 40				22 01		22 10	
	d					20 32		20 44		21 02		21 14				21 32		21 44				22 02		22 14	
High Street	d					20 34		20 46		21 04		21 16				21 34		21 46				22 04		22 16	
Bellgrove	d					20 36		20 48		21 06		21 18				21 36		21 48				22 06		22 18	
Duke Street	d							20 50				21 20						21 50						22 20	
Alexandra Parade	d							20 51				21 21						21 51						22 21	
Barnhill	d							20 54				21 24						21 54						22 24	
Springburn	a							20 56				21 26						21 56						22 26	
Carntyne	d					20 39				21 09						21 39						22 09			
Shettleston	d					20 42				21 12						21 42						22 12			
Garrowhill	d					20 44				21 14						21 44						22 14			
Easterhouse	d					20 47				21 17						21 47						22 17			
Blairhill	d					20 51				21 21						21 51						22 21			
Coatbridge Sunnyside	d					20 53				21 23						21 53						22 23			
Coatdyke	d					20 56				21 26						21 56						22 26			
Airdrie	a					20 58				21 28						21 58						22 28			
	d					20 59				21 29						21 59						22 29			
Drumgelloch	a					21 03				21 33						22 03						22 33			
Bridgeton	d			20 22			20 42				21 12		21 22				21 42			21 52			22 12		22 22
Dalmarnock	d			20 24			20 44				21 14		21 24				21 44			21 54			22 14		22 24
Rutherglen	d			20 26	20 34		20 46		21 04		21 16		21 26	21 34			21 46			21 56	22 04		22 16		22 26
Cambuslang	d	20 23		20 31			20 50				21 20		21 31				21 50			22 01			22 20		22 31
Newton	d						20 54				21 24						21 54						22 24		
Blantyre	d				20 44		20 58		21 14		21 28			21 44			21 58				22 14		22 28		
Hamilton West	d				20 47		21 01		21 17		21 31			21 47			22 01				22 17		22 31		
Hamilton Central	d				20 50		21 03		21 20		21 33			21 50			22 03				22 20		22 33		
Chatelherault	d				20 54				21 24					21 54							22 24				
Merryton	d				20 58				21 28					21 58							22 28				
Larkhall	a				21 00				21 30					22 00							22 30				
Airbles	d						21 08				21 38						22 08						22 38		
Uddingston	d	20 28		20 35									21 35							22 05					22 35
Bellshill	d	20 34		20 40									21 40							22 10					22 40
Motherwell	a			20 46			21 11				21 41		21 46				22 11			22 16			22 41		22 48
	d										21 42									22 16			22 42		
Whifflet	a																						22 48		
Coatbridge Central	a																						22 52		
Shieldmuir	d																			22 20					
Holytown	d	20a38									21 47														
Wishaw	d										21 53									22 23					
Carluke	d										22 00									22 30					
Lanark	a										22 13									22 42					

For general notes see front of timetable
For details of catering facilities see Directory of Train Operators

§ Low Level

A To Edinburgh (Table 225)
B From Mallaig and Oban (Table 227)
b Helensburgh Upper
c Glasgow Central High Level
e Glasgow Queen Street High Level

Table 226

Mondays to Fridays

Helensburgh, Balloch, Dalmuir and Milngavie → Glasgow → Springburn, Airdrie, Drumgelloch, Hamilton, Larkhall, Motherwell, Coatbridge and Lanark

Network Diagram - see first page of Table 220

		SR	SR	SR	SR	SR	SR	SR	SR A	SR	SR	SR	SR	SR FO	SR FX	SR FX	SR FO	SR FO	SR	SR FO	SR	SR R B
Helensburgh Central	d		21 40					22 10						22 40	22 40				23 10			23b24
Craigendoran	d		21 43					22 13						22 43	22 43				23 13			
Cardross	d		21 48					22 18						22 48	22 48				23 18			
Balloch	d				21 53						22 23					22 53	22 53				23 23	
Alexandria	d				21 55						22 25					22 55	22 55				23 25	
Renton	d				21 58						22 28					22 58	22 58				23 28	
Dalreoch	d		21 53		22 01			22 23			22 31			22 53	22 53	23 01	23 01		23 23		23 31	
Dumbarton Central	d		21 55		22 02			22 25			22 32			22 55	22 55	23 02	23 02		23 25		23 32	
Dumbarton East	d		21 57		22 04			22 27			22 34			22 57	22 57	23 04	23 04		23 27		23 34	
Bowling	d				22 09						22 39					23 09	23 09				23 39	
Kilpatrick	d				22 12						22 42					23 12	23 12				23 42	
Dalmuir	a		22 05		22 15			22 35			22 45			23 05	23 05	23 15	23 15		23 35		23 45	23 49
	d	22 01	22 05		22 16		22 31	22 35			22 46		23 01	23 05	23 05	23 16	23 16	23 31	23 35			23 51
Singer	d	22 03			22 18		22 33				22 48		23 03			23 18	23 18	23 33				
Drumry	d	22 05			22 20		22 35				22 50		23 05			23 20	23 20	23 35				
Drumchapel	d	22 08			22 23		22 38				22 53		23 08			23 23	23 23	23 38				
Milngavie	d			22 12						22 42										23 42		
Hillfoot	d			22 15						22 45										23 45		
Bearsden	d			22 17						22 47										23 47		
Westerton	d	22 10		22 20	22 25		22 40			22 50	22 55		23 10			23 25	23 25	23 40		23 50		23a56
Anniesland	d	22 14		22 23	22 28		22 44			22 53	22 58		23 14			23 28	23 28	23 44		23 53		
Clydebank	d		22 07					22 37						23 07	23 07				23 37			
Yoker	d		22 09					22 39						23 09	23 09				23 39			
Garscadden	d		22 13					22 43						23 13	23 13				23 43			
Scotstounhill	d		22 15					22 45						23 15	23 15				23 45			
Jordanhill	d		22 17					22 47						23 17	23 18				23 47			
Hyndland	d	22 17	22 21	22 26	22 31		22 47	22 51		22 56	23 01		23 17	23 21	23 22	23 31	23 31	23 47	23 51	23 56		
Partick	d	22 20	22 24	22 29	22 34	22 40	22 50	22 54		22 59	23 04	23 10	23 20	23 24	23 24	23 34	23 34	23 50	23 54	23 59		
Exhibition Centre	d	22 23		22 32		22 43	22 53			23 02		23 13	23 23					23 53		00 02		
Anderston	d	22 25		22 34		22 45	22 55			23 04		23 15	23 25					23 55		00 04		
Glasgow Central 15 §	a	22 26		22 35		22 46	22 56			23 05		23 16	23 26					23 56		00 05		
	d	22 27		22 37		22 47	22 57		23c06	23 07		23 17	23 27					23 57		00 07		
Argyle Street	d	22 29		22 39		22 49	22 59			23 09		23 19	23 29					23 59		00 09		
Charing Cross	d		22 29		22 38			22 59			23 08			23 29	23 29	23 38	23 38		23 59			
Glasgow Queen Street 10 §	a		22 31		22 40			23 01			23 10			23 31	23 31	23 40	23 40		00 01			
	d		22 32		22 44			23 02			23 14			23 32	23 32	23 44	23 44		00 02			
High Street	d		22 34		22 46			23 04			23 16			23 34	23 34	23 46	23 46		00 04			
Bellgrove	d		22 36		22 48			23 06			23 18			23 36	23 36	23 48	23 48		00 06			
Duke Street	d				22 50						23 20						23 50					
Alexandra Parade	d				22 51						23 21						23 51					
Barnhill	d				22 54						23 24						23 54					
Springburn	a				22 56						23 26						23 56					
Carntyne	d		22 39					23 09						23 39	23 39	23 51			00 09			
Shettleston	d		22 42					23 12						23 42	23 42	23 54			00 12			
Garrowhill	d		22 44					23 14						23 44	23 44	23 56			00 14			
Easterhouse	d		22 47					23 17						23 47	23 47	23 59			00 17			
Blairhill	d		22 51					23 21						23 51	23 51	00 03			00 21			
Coatbridge Sunnyside	d		22 53					23 23						23 53	23 53	00 05			00 23			
Coatdyke	d		22 56					23 26						23 56	23 56	00 08			00 26			
Airdrie	a		22 58					23 28						23 59	23 59	00 10			00 28			
	d		22 59					23 29						23 59		00 10			00 29			
Drumgelloch	a		23 03					23 33						00 03		00 14			00 33			
Bridgeton	d			22 42		22 52				23 12		23 22								00 12		
Dalmarnock	d			22 44		22 54				23 14		23 24								00 14		
Rutherglen	d	22 34		22 46		22 56	23 04			23 16		23 26	23 34					00 04		00 16		
Cambuslang	d			22 50		23 01			23 15	23 20		23 31								00 20		
Newton	d			22 54						23 24										00 24		
Blantyre	d	22 44		22 58			23 14			23 28			23 44					00 14		00 28		
Hamilton West	d	22 47		23 01			23 17			23 31			23 47					00 17		00 31		
Hamilton Central	d	22 50		23 03			23 20			23 33			23 50					00 20		00 33		
Chatelherault	d	22 54					23 24						23 54					00 24				
Merryton	d	22 58					23 28						23 58					00 28				
Larkhall	a	23 00					23 30						00 01					00 30				
Airbles	d			23 08						23 38										00 38		
Uddingston	d					23 05			23 20			23 35										
Bellshill	d					23 10			23 26			23 40										
Motherwell	a			23 11		23 16				23 41		23 46								00 41		
	d					23 16																
Whifflet	a																					
Coatbridge Central	a																					
Shieldmuir	d					23 20																
Holytown	d								23a30													
Wishaw	d					23 23																
Carluke	d					23 30																
Lanark	a					23 42																

For general notes see front of timetable
For details of catering facilities see Directory of Train Operators

§ Low Level

A To Edinburgh (Table 225)
B From Fort William (Table 227) to Edinburgh (Table 225)
b Helensburgh Upper
c Glasgow Central High Level

Table 226

Saturdays

Helensburgh, Balloch, Dalmuir and Milngavie → Glasgow → Springburn, Airdrie, Drumgelloch, Hamilton, Larkhall, Motherwell, Coatbridge and Lanark

Network Diagram - see first page of Table 220

		SR	SR	SR	SR	SR	SR	SR	SR	SR	SR	SR	SR	SR	SR	SR	SR	SR	SR	SR	SR	SR	SR	SR	SR
				A											B										
Helensburgh Central	d												06 10							06 40					
Craigendoran	d												06 13							06 43					
Cardross	d												06 18							06 48					
Balloch	d																06 23						06 53		
Alexandria	d																06 25						06 55		
Renton	d																06 28						06 58		
Dalreoch	d												06 23				06 31			06 53			07 01		
Dumbarton Central	d												06 25				06 32			06 55			07 02		
Dumbarton East	d												06 27				06 34			06 57			07 04		
Bowling	d																06 39						07 09		
Kilpatrick	d																06 42						07 12		
Dalmuir	a												06 35				06 45			07 05			07 15		
	d		05 48				06 01			06 16	06 23	06 31	06 36				06 46	06 53	07 01	07 06			07 16	07 23	07 31
Singer	d						06 03			06 18		06 33					06 48		07 03				07 18		07 33
Drumry	d						06 05			06 20		06 35		←			06 50		07 05		←		07 20		07 35
Drumchapel	d						06 08			06 23		06 38		06 38			06 53		07 08		07 08		07 23		07 38
Milngavie	d											→				06 42			→			07 12			→
Hillfoot	d															06 45						07 15			
Bearsden	d															06 47						07 17			
Westerton	d						06 10			06 25				06 40		06 50	06 55				07 10	07 20	07 25		
Anniesland	d						06 14			06 28				06 44		06 53	06 58				07 14	07 23	07 28		
Clydebank	d		05 50								06 25							06 55						07 25	
Yoker	d		05 52								06 27							06 57						07 27	
Garscadden	d		05 55		06 00	06 08			06 20		06 31							07 01						07 31	
Scotstounhill	d		05 57		06 02	06 10			06 22		06 33							07 03						07 33	
Jordanhill	d		05 59		06 05	06 12			06 24		06 35							07 05						07 35	
Hyndland	d		06 01		06 07	06 14	06 17		06 26	06 31	06 37		06 44	06 47		06 56	07 01	07 07		07 14	07 17	07 26	07 31	07 37	
Partick	d		06 04		06 10	06 17	06 20		06 29	06 34	06 40		06 47	06 50		06 59	07 04	07 10		07 17	07 20	07 29	07 34	07 40	
Exhibition Centre	d				06 13		06 23		06 32		06 43			06 53		07 02		07 13			07 23	07 32		07 43	
Anderston	d				06 15		06 25		06 34		06 45			06 55		07 04		07 15			07 25	07 34		07 45	
Glasgow Central 15 §	a				06 17		06 26		06 35		06 47			06 56		07 05		07 17			07 26	07 35		07 47	
	d			06b16	06 17		06 27		06 37		06 47			06 57	07 05	07 07		07 17			07 27	07 37		07 47	
Argyle Street	d				06 19		06 29		06 39		06 49			06 59		07 09		07 19			07 29	07 39		07 49	
Charing Cross	d		06 08			06 22				06 38			06 52				07 08			07 22			07 38		
Glasgow Queen Street 10 §	a		06 10			06 24				06 40			06 54				07 10			07 24			07 40		
	d		06 14			06 27				06 44			06 57				07 14			07 27			07 44		
High Street	d		06 16			06 29				06 46			06 59				07 16			07 29			07 46		
Bellgrove	d		06 18			06 31				06 48			07 01				07 18			07 31			07 48		
Duke Street	d		06 20							06 50							07 20						07 50		
Alexandra Parade	d		06 21							06 51							07 21						07 51		
Barnhill	d		06 24							06 54							07 24						07 54		
Springburn	a		06 26							06 56							07 26						07 56		
Carntyne	d					06 34							07 04							07 34					
Shettleston	d					06 37							07 07							07 37					
Garrowhill	d					06 39							07 09							07 39					
Easterhouse	d					06 42							07 12							07 42					
Blairhill	d					06 46							07 16							07 46					
Coatbridge Sunnyside	d					06 48							07 18							07 48					
Coatdyke	d					06 51							07 21							07 51					
Airdrie	a					06 53							07 24							07 54					
	d					06 54							07 24							07 54					
Drumgelloch	a					06 58							07 28							07 58					
Bridgeton	d				06 22				06 42		06 52					07 12		07 22				07 42		07 52	
Dalmarnock	d				06 24				06 44		06 54					07 14		07 24				07 44		07 54	
Rutherglen	d				06 26		06 34		06 46		06 56			07 03		07 16		07 26			07 34	07 46		07 56	
Cambuslang	d			06 23	06 31				06 50		07 01					07 20		07 31				07 50		08 01	
Newton	d								06 54							07 24						07 54			
Blantyre	d						06 44		06 58					07 14		07 28					07 44	07 58			
Hamilton West	d						06 47		07 01					07 17		07 31					07 47	08 01			
Hamilton Central	d						06 50		07 03					07 20		07 33					07 50	08 03			
Chatelherault	d						06 54							07 24							07 54				
Merryton	d						06 58							07 28							07 58				
Larkhall	a						07 00							07 31							08 00				
Airbles	d								07 08							07 38						08 08			
Uddingston	d			06 28	06 35						07 05							07 35						08 05	
Bellshill	d			06 34	06 40						07 10							07 40						08 10	
Motherwell	a				06 46				07 11		07 17				07 20	07 41		07 46				08 11		08 16	
	d	05 48			06 46			07 10							07 20	07 42								08 16	
Whifflet	a																								
Coatbridge Central	a																								
Shieldmuir	d	05 51			06 50			07 13																08 20	
Holytown	d			06a38												07 47									
Wishaw	d	05 55			06 53			07 17							07 26	07 53								08 23	
Carluke	d	06 03			07 00			07 26							07a33	07 59								08 30	
Lanark	a	06 13			07 13			07 37								08 13								08 41	

For general notes see front of timetable
For details of catering facilities see Directory of Train Operators

§ Low Level

A To Edinburgh (Table 225)
B To North Berwick (Table 238)
b Glasgow Central High Level

Table 226

Saturdays

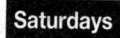

Helensburgh, Balloch, Dalmuir and Milngavie → Glasgow → Springburn, Airdrie, Drumgelloch, Hamilton, Larkhall, Motherwell, Coatbridge and Lanark

Network Diagram - see first page of Table 220

		SR	SR	SR	SR	SR A	SR	SR	SR	SR	SR	SR	SR	SR	SR	SR		SR	SR	SR	SR A	SR	SR	SR	SR
Helensburgh Central	d	07 10							07 40						08 10									08 40	
Craigendoran	d	07 13							07 43						08 13									08 43	
Cardross	d	07 18							07 48						08 18									08 48	
Balloch	d				07 23							07 53								08 23					
Alexandria	d				07 25							07 55								08 25					
Renton	d				07 28							07 58								08 28					
Dalreoch	d	07 23			07 31				07 53			08 01			08 23					08 31				08 53	
Dumbarton Central	d	07 25			07 32				07 55			08 02			08 25					08 32				08 55	
Dumbarton East	d	07 27			07 34				07 57			08 04			08 27					08 34				08 57	
Bowling	d				07 39							08 09								08 39					
Kilpatrick	d				07 42							08 12								08 42					
Dalmuir	a	07 35			07 45				08 05			08 15			08 35					08 45				09 05	
	d	07 36			07 46		07 53	08 01	08 06			08 16	08 23	08 31	08 36					08 46		08 53	09 01	09 06	
Singer	d				07 48			08 03				08 18		08 33						08 48			09 03		
Drumry	d		←		07 50			08 05		←		08 20		08 35		←				08 50			09 05		←
Drumchapel	d		07 38		07 53			08 08		08 08		08 23		08 38		08 38				08 53			09 08		09 08
Milngavie	d			07 42				→			08 12			→					08 42				→		
Hillfoot	d			07 45							08 15								08 45						
Bearsden	d			07 47							08 17								08 47						
Westerton	d		07 40	07 50	07 55					08 10	08 20	08 25				08 40			08 50	08 55					09 10
Anniesland	d		07 44	07 53	07 58					08 14	08 23	08 28				08 44			08 53	08 58					09 14
Clydebank	d						07 55						08 25									08 55			
Yoker	d						07 57						08 27									08 57			
Garscadden	d						08 01						08 31					08 46				09 01			
Scotstounhill	d						08 03						08 33					08 48				09 03			
Jordanhill	d						08 05						08 35					08 50				09 05			
Hyndland	d	07 44	07 47	07 56	08 01		08 07		08 14	08 17	08 26	08 31	08 37		08 44	08 47		08 52	08 56	09 01		09 07		09 14	09 17
Partick	d	07 47	07 50	07 59	08 04		08 10		08 17	08 20	08 29	08 34	08 40		08 47	08 50		08 55	08 59	09 04		09 10		09 17	09 20
Exhibition Centre	d		07 53	08 02			08 13			08 23	08 32		08 43			08 53			09 02			09 13			09 23
Anderston	d		07 55	08 04			08 15			08 25	08 34		08 45			08 55			09 04			09 15			09 25
Glasgow Central 15 §	a		07 56	08 05			08 17			08 26	08 35		08 47			08 56			09 05			09 17			09 26
	d		07 57	08 07		08b15	08 17			08 27	08 37		08 47			08 57			09 07		09b15	09 17			09 27
Argyle Street	d		07 59	08 09			08 19			08 29	08 39		08 49			08 59			09 09			09 19			09 29
Charing Cross	d	07 52			08 08				08 22			08 38			08 52			08 59		09 09				09 22	
Glasgow Queen Street 10 §	a	07 54			08 10				08 24			08 40			08 54			09 01		09 10				09 24	
	d	07 57			08 14				08 27			08 44			08 57			09 02		09 12				09 27	
High Street	d	07 59			08 16				08 29			08 46			08 59			09 04		09 16				09 29	
Bellgrove	d	08 01			08 18				08 31			08 48			09 01			09 06		09 18				09 31	
Duke Street	d				08 20							08 50						09 08							
Alexandra Parade	d				08 21							08 51						09 09							
Barnhill	d				08 24							08 54						09 12							
Springburn	a				08 26							08 56						09 14							
Carntyne	d	08 04							08 34						09 04					09 19				09 34	
Shettleston	d	08 07							08 37						09 07					09 22				09 37	
Garrowhill	d	08 09							08 39						09 09					09 24				09 39	
Easterhouse	d	08 12							08 42						09 12					09 27				09 42	
Blairhill	d	08 16							08 46						09 16					09 31				09 46	
Coatbridge Sunnyside	d	08 18							08 48						09 18					09 33				09 48	
Coatdyke	d	08 21							08 51						09 21					09 36				09 51	
Airdrie	a	08 24							08 53						09 23					09 41				09 53	
	d	08 24							08 54						09 24									09 54	
Drumgelloch	a	08 28							08 58						09 28									09 58	
Bridgeton	d			08 12			08 22				08 42		08 52						09 12			09 22			
Dalmarnock	d			08 14			08 24				08 44		08 54						09 14			09 24			
Rutherglen	d		08 04	08 16			08 26			08 34	08 46		08 56			09 04			09 16			09 26			09 34
Cambuslang	d			08 20		08 22	08 31				08 50		09 01						09 20		09 23	09 31			
Newton	d			08 24							08 54								09 24						
Blantyre	d		08 14	08 28						08 44	08 58					09 14			09 28						09 44
Hamilton West	d		08 17	08 31						08 47	09 01					09 17			09 31						09 47
Hamilton Central	d		08 20	08 33						08 50	09 03					09 20			09 33						09 50
Chatelherault	d		08 24							08 54						09 24									09 54
Merryton	d		08 28							08 58						09 28									09 58
Larkhall	a		08 30							09 00						09 30									10 00
Airbles	d			08 38							09 08								09 38						
Uddingston	d					08 27	08 35						09 05								09 28	09 35			
Bellshill	d					08 33	08 40						09 10								09 34	09 40			
Motherwell	a			08 41			08 46				09 11		09 16						09 41			09 46			
	d			08 42									09 16						09 42						
Whifflet	a																								
Coatbridge Central	a																								
Shieldmuir	d												09 20												
Holytown	d			08 47		08a37													09 47		09a38				
Wishaw	d			08 53									09 23						09 53						
Carluke	d			08 59									09 30						10 00						
Lanark	a			09 12									09 42						10 12						

For general notes see front of timetable
For details of catering facilities see Directory of Train Operators

§ Low Level

A To Edinburgh (Table 225)
b Glasgow Central High Level

Table 226

Saturdays

Helensburgh, Balloch, Dalmuir and Milngavie → Glasgow → Springburn, Airdrie, Drumgelloch, Hamilton, Larkhall, Motherwell, Coatbridge and Lanark

Network Diagram - see first page of Table 220

		SR	SR	SR	SR	SR	SR	SR	SR	SR	SR	SR	SR	SR	SR	SR	SR	SR	SR	SR	SR	SR	SR	SR	SR
													A												
Helensburgh Central	d							09 10									09 40								10 10
Craigendoran	d							09 13									09 43								10 13
Cardross	d							09 18									09 48								10 18
Balloch	d			08 53								09 23									09 53				
Alexandria	d			08 55								09 25									09 55				
Renton	d			08 58								09 28									09 58				
Dalreoch	d			09 01				09 23				09 31					09 53				10 01				10 23
Dumbarton Central	d			09 02				09 25				09 32					09 55				10 02				10 25
Dumbarton East	d			09 04				09 27				09 34					09 57				10 04				10 27
Bowling	d			09 09								09 39									10 09				
Kilpatrick	d			09 12								09 42									10 12				
Dalmuir	a			09 15				09 35				09 45					10 05				10 15				10 35
	d	09 08		09 16	09 23		09 31	09 36		09 38		09 46		09 53		10 01	10 06		10 08		10 16	10 23		10 31	10 36
Singer	d			09 18			09 33					09 48				10 03					10 18			10 33	
Drumry	d			09 20			09 35		←			09 50				10 05		←			10 20			10 35	
Drumchapel	d			09 23			09 38		09 38			09 53				10 08		10 08			10 23			10 38	
Milngavie	d		09 12			09 27	→				09 42				09 57	→				10 12			10 27	→	
Hillfoot	d		09 15			09 30					09 45				10 00					10 15			10 30		
Bearsden	d		09 17			09 32					09 47				10 02					10 17			10 32		
Westerton	d		09 20	09 25		09 35			09 40		09 50	09 55			10 05			10 10		10 20	10 25		10 35		
Anniesland	d		09 23	09 28		09 38			09 44		09 53	09 58			10 08			10 14		10 23	10 28		10 38		
Clydebank	d	09 10			09 25					09 40				09 55					10 10			10 25			
Yoker	d	09 12			09 27					09 42				09 57					10 12			10 27			
Garscadden	d	09 16			09 31					09 46				10 01					10 16			10 31			
Scotstounhill	d	09 18			09 33					09 48				10 03					10 18			10 33			
Jordanhill	d	09 20			09 35					09 50				10 05					10 20			10 35			
Hyndland	d	09 22	09 26	09 31	09 37	09 41		09 44	09 47	09 52	09 56	10 01		10 07	10 11		10 14	10 17	10 22	10 26	10 31	10 37	10 41		10 44
Partick	d	09 25	09 29	09 34	09 40	09 44		09 47	09 50	09 55	09 59	10 04		10 10	10 14		10 17	10 20	10 25	10 29	10 34	10 40	10 44		10 47
Exhibition Centre	d		09 32		09 43				09 53		10 02			10 13				10 23		10 32		10 43			
Anderston	d		09 34		09 45				09 55		10 04			10 15				10 25		10 34		10 45			
Glasgow Central 15 §	a		09 35		09 47				09 56		10 05			10 17				10 26		10 35		10 47			
	d		09 37		09 47				09 57		10 07		10b15	10 17				10 27		10 37		10 47			
Argyle Street	d		09 39		09 49				09 59		10 09			10 19				10 29		10 39		10 49			
Charing Cross	d	09 29		09 38		09 49		09 52		09 59		10 08			10 19		10 22		10 29		10 38		10 49		10 52
Glasgow Queen Street 10 §	a	09 31		09 40		09 51		09 54		10 01		10 10			10 21		10 24		10 31		10 40		10 51		10 54
	d	09 32		09 42		09 51		09 57		10 02		10 12			10 21		10 27		10 32		10 42		10 51		10 57
High Street	d	09 34		09 44		09a53		09 59		10 04		10 14			10a23		10 29		10 34		10 44		10a53		10 59
Bellgrove	d	09 36		09 46				10 01		10 06		10 16					10 31		10 36		10 46				11 01
Duke Street	d	09 38								10 08									10 38						
Alexandra Parade	d	09 39								10 09									10 39						
Barnhill	d	09 42								10 12									10 42						
Springburn	a	09 44								10 14									10 44						
Carntyne	d			09 49				10 04				10 19					10 34				10 49				11 04
Shettleston	d			09 52				10 07				10 22					10 37				10 52				11 07
Garrowhill	d			09 54				10 09				10 24					10 39				10 54				11 09
Easterhouse	d			09 57				10 12				10 27					10 42				10 57				11 12
Blairhill	d			10 01				10 16				10 31					10 46				11 01				11 16
Coatbridge Sunnyside	d			10 03				10 18				10 33					10 48				11 03				11 18
Coatdyke	d			10 06				10 21				10 36					10 51				11 06				11 21
Airdrie	a			10 09				10 23				10 39					10 53				11 09				11 23
	d							10 24									10 54								11 24
Drumgelloch	a							10 28									10 58								11 28
Bridgeton	d		09 42		09 52						10 12			10 22						10 42		10 52			
Dalmarnock	d		09 44		09 54						10 14			10 24						10 44		10 54			
Rutherglen	d		09 46		09 56				10 04		10 16			10 26				10 34		10 46		10 56			
Cambuslang	d		09 50		10 01						10 20		10 23	10 31						10 50		11 01			
Newton	d		09 54								10 24									10 54					
Blantyre	d		09 58						10 14		10 28							10 44		10 58					
Hamilton West	d		10 01						10 17		10 31							10 47		11 01					
Hamilton Central	d		10 03						10 20		10 33							10 50		11 03					
Chatelherault	d								10 24									10 54							
Merryton	d								10 28									10 58							
Larkhall	a								10 30									11 00							
Airbles	d		10 08								10 38									11 08					
Uddingston	d				10 05								10 28	10 35								11 05			
Bellshill	d				10 10								10 34	10 40								11 10			
Motherwell	a		10 11		10 16						10 41			10 48						11 11		11 16			
	d				10 16						10 42											11 16			
Whifflet	a																								
Coatbridge Central	a																								
Shieldmuir	d				10 20																	11 20			
Holytown	d										10 47		10a38												
Wishaw	d				10 23						10 53											11 23			
Carluke	d				10 30						11 00											11 30			
Lanark	a				10 42						11 12											11 42			

For general notes see front of timetable
For details of catering facilities see Directory of Train Operators

§ Low Level

A To Edinburgh (Table 225)
b Glasgow Central High Level

Table 226

Saturdays

Helensburgh, Balloch, Dalmuir and Milngavie → Glasgow → Springburn, Airdrie, Drumgelloch, Hamilton, Larkhall, Motherwell, Coatbridge and Lanark

Network Diagram - see first page of Table 220

		SR	SR	SR	SR	SR	SR	SR	SR	SR		SR	SR	SR	SR	SR	SR	SR	SR	SR	SR	SR	SR	SR	SR
						A						◇ B 🍴													A
Helensburgh Central	d									10 40		10b41								11 10					
Craigendoran	d									10 43										11 13					
Cardross	d									10 48										11 18					
Balloch	d				10 23											10 53								11 23	
Alexandria	d				10 25											10 55								11 25	
Renton	d				10 28											10 58								11 28	
Dalreoch	d				10 31					10 53						11 01				11 23				11 31	
Dumbarton Central	d				10 32					10 55		10 58				11 02				11 25				11 32	
Dumbarton East	d				10 34					10 57						11 04				11 27				11 34	
Bowling	d				10 39											11 09								11 39	
Kilpatrick	d				10 42											11 12								11 42	
Dalmuir	a				10 45					11 05		11 08				11 15				11 35				11 45	
	d		10 38		10 46		10 53		11 01	11 06		11 08		11 08		11 16	11 23		11 31	11 36		11 38		11 46	
Singer	d				10 48				11 03							11 18			11 33					11 48	
Drumry	d	←			10 50				11 05				←			11 20			11 35		←			11 50	
Drumchapel	d	10 38			10 53				11 08				11 08			11 23			11 38		11 38			11 53	
Milngavie	d			10 42				10 57	→						11 12			11 27	→				11 42		
Hillfoot	d			10 45				11 00							11 15			11 30					11 45		
Bearsden	d			10 47				11 02							11 17			11 32					11 47		
Westerton	d	10 40		10 50	10 55			11 05					11 10		11 20	11 25		11 35			11 40		11 50	11 55	
Anniesland	d	10 44		10 53	10 58			11 08					11 14		11 23	11 28		11 38			11 44		11 53	11 58	
Clydebank	d		10 40				10 55							11 10			11 25					11 40			
Yoker	d		10 42				10 57							11 12			11 27					11 42			
Garscadden	d		10 46				11 01							11 16			11 31					11 46			
Scotstounhill	d		10 48				11 03							11 18			11 33					11 48			
Jordanhill	d		10 50				11 05							11 20			11 35					11 50			
Hyndland	d	10 47	10 52	10 56	11 01		11 07	11 11		11 14			11 17	11 22	11 26	11 31	11 37	11 41		11 44	11 47	11 52	11 56	12 01	
Partick	d	10 50	10 55	10 59	11 04		11 10	11 14		11 17			11 20	11 25	11 29	11 34	11 40	11 44		11 47	11 50	11 55	11 59	12 04	
Exhibition Centre	d	10 53		11 02			11 13						11 23		11 32		11 43				11 53		12 02		
Anderston	d	10 55		11 04			11 15						11 25		11 34		11 45				11 55		12 04		
Glasgow Central 15 §	a	10 56		11 05			11 17						11 26		11 37		11 47				11 56		12 05		
	d	10 57		11 07		11c15	11 17						11 27		11 37		11 47				11 57		12 07		12c15
Argyle Street	d	10 59		11 09			11 19						11 29		11 39		11 49				11 59		12 09		
Charing Cross	d		10 59		11 08			11 19		11 22				11 29		11 38		11 49		11 52		11 59		12 08	
Glasgow Queen Street 10 §	a		11 01		11 10			11 21		11 24		11e30		11 31		11 40		11 51		11 54		12 01		12 10	
	d		11 02		11 12			11 21		11 27				11 32		11 42		11 51		11 57		12 02		12 12	
High Street	d		11 04		11 14			11a23		11 29				11 34		11 44		11a53		11 59		12 04		12 14	
Bellgrove	d		11 06		11 16					11 31				11 36		11 46				12 01		12 06		12 16	
Duke Street	d		11 08											11 38								12 08			
Alexandra Parade	d		11 09											11 39								12 09			
Barnhill	d		11 12											11 42								12 12			
Springburn	a		11 14											11 44								12 14			
Carntyne	d				11 19					11 34						11 49				12 04				12 19	
Shettleston	d				11 22					11 37						11 52				12 07				12 22	
Garrowhill	d				11 24					11 39						11 54				12 09				12 24	
Easterhouse	d				11 27					11 42						11 57				12 12				12 27	
Blairhill	d				11 31					11 46						12 01				12 16				12 31	
Coatbridge Sunnyside	d				11 33					11 48						12 03				12 18				12 33	
Coatdyke	d				11 36					11 51						12 06				12 21				12 36	
Airdrie	a				11 39					11 53						12 09				12 23				12 39	
	d									11 54										12 24					
Drumgelloch	a									11 58										12 28					
Bridgeton	d			11 12			11 22								11 42		11 52						12 12		
Dalmarnock	d			11 14			11 24								11 44		11 54						12 14		
Rutherglen	d	11 04		11 16			11 26						11 34		11 46		11 56				12 04		12 16		
Cambuslang	d			11 20		11 23	11 31								11 50		12 01						12 20		12 23
Newton	d			11 24											11 54								12 24		
Blantyre	d	11 14		11 28									11 44		11 58						12 14		12 28		
Hamilton West	d	11 17		11 31									11 47		12 01						12 17		12 31		
Hamilton Central	d	11 20		11 33									11 50		12 03						12 20		12 33		
Chatelherault	d	11 24											11 54								12 24				
Merryton	d	11 28											11 58								12 28				
Larkhall	a	11 30											12 00								12 30				
Airbles	d			11 38											12 08								12 38		
Uddingston	d					11 28	11 35										12 05								12 28
Bellshill	d					11 34	11 40										12 10								12 34
Motherwell	a			11 41			11 48								12 11		12 16						12 41		
	d			11 42													12 16						12 42		
Whifflet	a																								
Coatbridge Central	a																								
Shieldmuir	d																12 20								
Holytown	d			11 47		11a38																	12 47		12a38
Wishaw	d			11 53													12 23						12 53		
Carluke	d			12 00													12 30						13 00		
Lanark	a			12 12													12 43						13 12		

For general notes see front of timetable
For details of catering facilities see Directory of Train Operators

§ Low Level

A To Edinburgh (Table 225)
B From Mallaig and Oban (Table 227)
b Helensburgh Upper
c Glasgow Central High Level
e Glasgow Queen Street High Level

Helensburgh, Balloch, Dalmuir and Milngavie → Glasgow → Springburn, Airdrie, Drumgelloch, Hamilton, Larkhall, Motherwell, Coatbridge and Lanark

Network Diagram - see first page of Table 220

		SR	SR	SR	SR	SR	SR	SR	SR	SR	SR	SR	SR	SR	SR	SR	SR	SR	SR	SR	SR	SR	SR	SR	SR
																		A							
Helensburgh Central	d				11 40								12 10									12 40			
Craigendoran	d				11 43								12 13									12 43			
Cardross	d				11 48								12 18									12 48			
Balloch	d								11 53								12 23								
Alexandria	d								11 55								12 25								
Renton	d								11 58								12 28								
Dalreoch	d				11 53				12 01				12 23				12 31					12 53			
Dumbarton Central	d				11 55				12 02				12 25				12 32					12 55			
Dumbarton East	d				11 57				12 04				12 27				12 34					12 57			
Bowling	d								12 09								12 39								
Kilpatrick	d								12 12								12 42								
Dalmuir	a				12 05				12 15				12 35				12 46					13 05			
	d	11 53		12 01	12 06		12 08		12 16	12 23		12 31	12 36		12 38		12 46		12 53		13 01	13 06		13 08	
Singer	d			12 03					12 18			12 33					12 48				13 03				
Drumry	d			12 05		←			12 20			12 35			←		12 50				13 05		←		
Drumchapel	d			12 08		12 08			12 23			12 38			12 38		12 53				13 08		13 08		
Milngavie	d		11 57	→				12 12			12 27	→				12 42				12 57	→				13 12
Hillfoot	d		12 00					12 15			12 30					12 45				13 00					13 15
Bearsden	d		12 02					12 17			12 32					12 47				13 02					13 17
Westerton	d		12 05			12 10		12 20	12 25		12 35			12 40		12 50	12 55			13 05			13 10		13 20
Anniesland	d		12 08			12 14		12 23	12 28		12 38			12 44		12 53	12 58			13 08			13 14		13 23
Clydebank	d	11 55					12 10			12 25					12 40				12 55					13 10	
Yoker	d	11 57					12 12			12 27					12 42				12 57					13 12	
Garscadden	d	12 01					12 16			12 31					12 46				13 01					13 16	
Scotstounhill	d	12 03					12 18			12 33					12 48				13 03					13 18	
Jordanhill	d	12 05					12 20			12 35					12 50				13 05					13 20	
Hyndland	d	12 07	12 11		12 14	12 17	12 22	12 26	12 31	12 37	12 41		12 44	12 47	12 52	12 56	13 01		13 07	13 11		13 14	13 17	13 22	13 26
Partick	d	12 10	12 14		12 17	12 20	12 25	12 29	12 34	12 40	12 44		12 47	12 50	12 55	12 59	13 04		13 10	13 14		13 17	13 20	13 25	13 29
Exhibition Centre	d	12 13				12 23		12 32		12 43				12 53		13 02			13 13				13 23		13 32
Anderston	d	12 15				12 25		12 34		12 45				12 55		13 04			13 15				13 25		13 34
Glasgow Central 15 §	a	12 17				12 26		12 35		12 47				12 56		13 05			13 17				13 26		13 35
	d	12 17				12 27		12 37		12 47				12 57		13 07		13b15	13 17				13 27		13 37
Argyle Street	d	12 19				12 29		12 39		12 49				12 59		13 09			13 19				13 29		13 39
Charing Cross	d		12 19		12 22		12 29		12 38		12 49		12 52		12 59		13 08			13 19		13 22		13 29	
Glasgow Queen Street 10 §	a		12 21		12 24		12 31		12 40		12 51		12 54		13 01		13 10			13 21		13 24		13 31	
	d		12 21		12 27		12 32		12 42		12 51		12 57		13 02		13 12			13 21		13 27		13 32	
High Street	d		12a23		12 29		12 34		12 44		12a53		12 59		13 04		13 14			13a23		13 29		13 34	
Bellgrove	d				12 31		12 36		12 46				13 01		13 06		13 16					13 31		13 36	
Duke Street	d						12 38								13 08									13 38	
Alexandra Parade	d						12 39								13 09									13 39	
Barnhill	d						12 42								13 12									13 42	
Springburn	a						12 44								13 14									13 44	
Carntyne	d				12 34				12 49				13 04				13 19					13 34			
Shettleston	d				12 37				12 52				13 07				13 22					13 37			
Garrowhill	d				12 39				12 54				13 09				13 24					13 39			
Easterhouse	d				12 42				12 57				13 12				13 27					13 42			
Blairhill	d				12 46				13 01				13 16				13 31					13 46			
Coatbridge Sunnyside	d				12 48				13 03				13 18				13 33					13 48			
Coatdyke	d				12 51				13 06				13 21				13 36					13 51			
Airdrie	a				12 53				13 09				13 23				13 39					13 53			
	d				12 54								13 24									13 54			
Drumgelloch	a				12 58								13 28									13 58			
Bridgeton	d	12 22						12 42		12 52						13 12			13 22						13 42
Dalmarnock	d	12 24						12 44		12 54						13 14			13 24						13 44
Rutherglen	d	12 26				12 34		12 46		12 56				13 04		13 16			13 26				13 34		13 46
Cambuslang	d	12 31						12 50		13 01						13 20		13 23	13 31						13 50
Newton	d							12 54								13 24									13 54
Blantyre	d					12 44		12 58						13 14		13 28							13 44		13 58
Hamilton West	d					12 47		13 01						13 17		13 31							13 47		14 01
Hamilton Central	d					12 50		13 03						13 20		13 33							13 50		14 03
Chatelherault	d					12 54								13 24									13 54		
Merryton	d					12 58								13 28									13 58		
Larkhall	a					13 00								13 30									14 00		
Airbles	d							13 08								13 38									14 08
Uddingston	d	12 35								13 05								13 28	13 35						
Bellshill	d	12 40								13 10								13 34	13 40						
Motherwell	a	12 48						13 11		13 16						13 41			13 48						14 11
	d									13 16						13 42									
Whifflet	a																								
Coatbridge Central	a																								
Shieldmuir	d									13 20															
Holytown	d															13 47		13a38							
Wishaw	d									13 23						13 53									
Carluke	d									13 30						14 00									
Lanark	a									13 42						14 12									

For general notes see front of timetable
For details of catering facilities see Directory of Train Operators

§ Low Level

A To Edinburgh (Table 225)
b Glasgow Central High Level

Table 226

Saturdays

Helensburgh, Balloch, Dalmuir and Milngavie → Glasgow → Springburn, Airdrie, Drumgelloch, Hamilton, Larkhall, Motherwell, Coatbridge and Lanark

Network Diagram - see first page of Table 220

		SR	SR	SR		SR	SR	SR	SR	SR	SR A	SR	SR	SR	SR	SR	SR	SR	SR	SR	SR	SR	SR	SR	SR
Helensburgh Central	d						13 10								13 40								14 10		
Craigendoran	d						13 13								13 43								14 13		
Cardross	d						13 18								13 48								14 18		
Balloch	d	12 53								13 23									13 53						
Alexandria	d	12 55								13 25									13 55						
Renton	d	12 58								13 28									13 58						
Dalreoch	d	13 01					13 23			13 31					13 53				14 01				14 23		
Dumbarton Central	d	13 02					13 25			13 32					13 55				14 02				14 25		
Dumbarton East	d	13 04					13 27			13 34					13 57				14 04				14 27		
Bowling	d	13 09								13 39									14 09						
Kilpatrick	d	13 12								13 42									14 12						
Dalmuir	a	13 15					13 35			13 45					14 05				14 15				14 35		
	d	13 16	13 23			13 31	13 36	13 38		13 46		13 53		14 01	14 06		14 08		14 16	14 23		14 31	14 36		14 38
Singer	d	13 18				13 33				13 48				14 03					14 18			14 33			
Drumry	d	13 20				13 35				13 50				14 05					14 20			14 35			
Drumchapel	d	13 23				13 38				13 53				14 08		← 14 08			14 23			14 38		← 14 38	
Milngavie	d			13 27		→			13 42				13 57	→				14 12			14 27	→			
Hillfoot	d			13 30					13 45				14 00					14 15			14 30				
Bearsden	d			13 32					13 47				14 02					14 17			14 32				
Westerton	d	13 25		13 35					13 50	13 55			14 05			14 10		14 20	14 25		14 35			14 40	
Anniesland	d	13 28		13 38					13 53	13 58			14 08			14 14		14 23	14 28		14 38			14 44	
Clydebank	d		13 25					13 40				13 55					14 10			14 25					14 40
Yoker	d		13 27					13 42				13 57					14 12			14 27					14 42
Garscadden	d		13 31					13 46				14 01					14 16			14 31					14 46
Scotstounhill	d		13 33					13 48				14 03					14 18			14 33					14 48
Jordanhill	d		13 35					13 50				14 05					14 20			14 35					14 50
Hyndland	d	13 31	13 37	13 41			13 44	13 52	13 56	14 01		14 07	14 11		14 14	14 17	14 22	14 26	14 31	14 37	14 41		14 44	14 47	14 52
Partick	d	13 34	13 40	13 44			13 47	13 55	13 59	14 04		14 10	14 14		14 17	14 20	14 25	14 29	14 34	14 40	14 44		14 47	14 50	14 55
Exhibition Centre	d		13 43						14 02			14 13				14 23		14 32		14 43				14 53	
Anderston	d		13 45						14 04			14 15				14 25		14 34		14 45				14 55	
Glasgow Central 15 §	a		13 47						14 05			14 17				14 26		14 35		14 47				14 56	
	d		13 47						14 07		14b15	14 17				14 27		14 37		14 47				14 57	
Argyle Street	d		13 49						14 09			14 19				14 29		14 39		14 49				14 59	
Charing Cross	d	13 38		13 49			13 52	13 59		14 08			14 19		14 22		14 29		14 38		14 49		14 52		14 59
Glasgow Queen Street 10 §	a	13 40		13 51			13 54	14 01		14 10			14 21		14 24		14 31		14 40		14 51		14 54		15 01
	d	13 42		13 51			13 57	14 02		14 12			14 21		14 27		14 32		14 42		14 51		14 57		15 02
High Street	d	13 44		13a53			13 59	14 04		14 14			14a23		14 29		14 34		14 44		14a53		14 59		15 04
Bellgrove	d	13 46					14 01	14 06		14 16					14 31		14 36		14 46				15 01		15 06
Duke Street	d							14 08									14 38								15 08
Alexandra Parade	d							14 09									14 39								15 09
Barnhill	d							14 12									14 42								15 12
Springburn	a							14 14									14 44								15 14
Carntyne	d	13 49					14 04			14 19					14 34				14 49				15 04		
Shettleston	d	13 52					14 07			14 22					14 37				14 52				15 07		
Garrowhill	d	13 54					14 09			14 24					14 39				14 54				15 09		
Easterhouse	d	13 57					14 12			14 27					14 42				14 57				15 12		
Blairhill	d	14 01					14 16			14 31					14 46				15 01				15 16		
Coatbridge Sunnyside	d	14 03					14 18			14 33					14 48				15 03				15 18		
Coatdyke	d	14 06					14 21			14 36					14 51				15 06				15 21		
Airdrie	a	14 09					14 23			14 39					14 53				15 09				15 23		
	d						14 24								14 54								15 24		
Drumgelloch	a						14 28								14 58								15 28		
Bridgeton	d		13 52						14 12			14 22						14 42		14 52					
Dalmarnock	d		13 54						14 14			14 24						14 44		14 54					
Rutherglen	d		13 56						14 16			14 26				14 34		14 46		14 56				15 04	
Cambuslang	d		14 01						14 20		14 23	14 31						14 50		15 01					
Newton	d								14 24									14 54							
Blantyre	d								14 28							14 44		14 58						15 14	
Hamilton West	d								14 31							14 47		15 01						15 17	
Hamilton Central	d								14 33							14 50		15 03						15 20	
Chatelherault	d															14 54								15 24	
Merryton	d															14 58								15 28	
Larkhall	a															15 00								15 30	
Airbles	d								14 38									15 08							
Uddingston	d		14 05								14 28	14 35								15 05					
Bellshill	d		14 10								14 34	14 40								15 10					
Motherwell	a		14 16						14 41			14 48						15 11		15 16					
	d		14 16						14 42											15 16					
Whifflet	a																								
Coatbridge Central	a																								
Shieldmuir	d		14 20																	15 20					
Holytown	d								14 47		14a38														
Wishaw	d		14 23						14 53											15 23					
Carluke	d		14 30						15 00											15 30					
Lanark	a		14 42						15 12											15 42					

For general notes see front of timetable
For details of catering facilities see Directory of Train Operators

§ Low Level

A To Edinburgh (Table 225)
b Glasgow Central High Level

Table 226

Saturdays

Helensburgh, Balloch, Dalmuir and Milngavie → Glasgow → Springburn, Airdrie, Drumgelloch, Hamilton, Larkhall, Motherwell, Coatbridge and Lanark

Network Diagram - see first page of Table 220

		SR	SR	SR	SR	SR	SR	SR	SR	SR	SR	SR	SR	SR	SR	SR	SR	SR	SR	SR	SR	SR	SR	SR
		A	B						◇ C ⇌														A	
Helensburgh Central	d								14b39	14 40								15 10						
Craigendoran	d									14 43								15 13						
Cardross	d									14 48								15 18						
Balloch	d				14 23									14 53								15 23		
Alexandria	d				14 25									14 55								15 25		
Renton	d				14 28									14 58								15 28		
Dalreoch	d				14 31					14 53				15 01				15 23				15 31		
Dumbarton Central	d				14 32				14 52	14 55				15 02				15 25				15 32		
Dumbarton East	d				14 34					14 57				15 04				15 27				15 34		
Bowling	d				14 39									15 09								15 39		
Kilpatrick	d				14 42									15 12								15 42		
Dalmuir	a				14 45				15 04	15 06				15 15				15 35				15 45		
	d				14 46	14 53		15 01	15 04	15 06		15 08		15 16	15 23		15 31	15 36		15 38		15 46		15 53
Singer	d				14 48			15 03						15 18			15 33					15 48		
Drumry	d				14 50			15 05			←			15 20			15 35		←			15 50		
Drumchapel	d				14 53			15 08			15 08			15 23			15 38		15 38			15 53		
Milngavie	d			14 42			14 57	→					15 12			15 27	→				15 42			
Hillfoot	d			14 45			15 00						15 15			15 30					15 45			
Bearsden	d			14 47			15 02						15 17			15 32					15 47			
Westerton	d			14 50	14 55		15 05				15 10		15 20	15 25		15 35			15 40		15 50	15 55		
Anniesland	d			14 53	14 58		15 08				15 14		15 23	15 28		15 38			15 44		15 53	15 58		
Clydebank	d					14 55						15 10			15 25					15 40				15 55
Yoker	d					14 57						15 12			15 27					15 42				15 57
Garscadden	d					15 01						15 16			15 31					15 46				16 01
Scotstounhill	d					15 03						15 18			15 33					15 48				16 03
Jordanhill	d					15 05						15 20			15 35					15 50				16 05
Hyndland	d			14 56	15 01	15 07	15 11			15 14	15 17	15 22	15 27	15 31	15 37	15 41		15 44	15 47	15 52	15 56	16 01		16 07
Partick	d			14 59	15 04	15 10	15 14			15 17	15 20	15 25	15 29	15 34	15 40	15 44		15 47	15 50	15 55	15 59	16 04		16 10
Exhibition Centre	d			15 02		15 13					15 23		15 32		15 43				15 53		16 02			16 13
Anderston	d			15 04		15 15					15 25		15 34		15 45				15 55		16 04			16 15
Glasgow Central 15 §	a			15 05		15 17					15 26		15 35		15 47				15 56		16 05			16 17
	d	15c15	15 19	15 07		15 17					15 27		15 37		15 47				15 57		16 07		16c15	16 17
Argyle Street	d			15 09		15 19					15 29		15 39		15 49				15 59		16 09			16 19
Charing Cross	d				15 08		15 19			15 22		15 29		15 38		15 49		15 52		15 59		16 08		
Glasgow Queen Street 10 §	a				15 10		15 21		15e30	15 24		15 31		15 41		15 51		15 54		16 01		16 11		
	d				15 12		15 21			15 27		15 32		15 42		15 51		15 57		16 02		16 12		
High Street	d				15 14		15a23			15 29		15 34		15 44		15a53		15 59		16 04		16 14		
Bellgrove	d				15 16					15 31		15 36		15 46				16 01		16 06		16 16		
Duke Street	d											15 38								16 08				
Alexandra Parade	d											15 39								16 09				
Barnhill	d											15 42								16 12				
Springburn	a											15 44								16 14				
Carntyne	d				15 19					15 34				15 49				16 04				16 19		
Shettleston	d				15 22					15 37				15 52				16 07				16 22		
Garrowhill	d				15 24					15 39				15 54				16 09				16 24		
Easterhouse	d				15 27					15 42				15 57				16 12				16 27		
Blairhill	d				15 31					15 46				16 01				16 16				16 31		
Coatbridge Sunnyside	d				15 33					15 48				16 03				16 18				16 33		
Coatdyke	d				15 36					15 51				16 06				16 21				16 36		
Airdrie	a				15 39					15 53				16 09				16 23				16 39		
	d									15 54								16 24						
Drumgelloch	a									15 58								16 28						
Bridgeton	d			15 12		15 22							15 42		15 52						16 12			16 22
Dalmarnock	d			15 14		15 24							15 44		15 54						16 14			16 24
Rutherglen	d			15 16		15 26					15 34		15 46		15 56				16 04		16 16			16 26
Cambuslang	d	15 23		15 20		15 31							15 50		16 01						16 20		16 23	16 31
Newton	d			15 24									15 54								16 24			
Blantyre	d			15 28							15 44		15 58						16 14		16 28			
Hamilton West	d			15 31							15 47		16 01						16 17		16 31			
Hamilton Central	d			15 33							15 50		16 03						16 20		16 33			
Chatelherault	d										15 54								16 24					
Merryton	d										15 58								16 28					
Larkhall	a										16 00								16 30					
Airbles	d			15 38									16 08								16 38			
Uddingston	d	15 28				15 35									16 05								16 28	16 35
Bellshill	d	15 34				15 40									16 10								16 34	16 40
Motherwell	a		15 38	15 41		15 48							16 11		16 16						16 41			16 48
	d		15 38	15 42											16 16						16 42			
Whifflet	a																							
Coatbridge Central	a																							
Shieldmuir	d														16 20									
Holytown	d	15a38		15 47																	16 47		16a38	
Wishaw	d			15 53											16 23						16 53			
Carluke	d		15a48	16 00											16 30						17 00			
Lanark	a			16 12											16 42						17 15			

For general notes see front of timetable
For details of catering facilities see Directory of Train Operators

§ Low Level

A To Edinburgh (Table 225)
B To North Berwick (Table 238)
C From Mallaig and Oban (Table 227)
b Helensburgh Upper
c Glasgow Central High Level
e Glasgow Queen Street High Level

Table 226

Saturdays

Helensburgh, Balloch, Dalmuir and Milngavie → Glasgow → Springburn, Airdrie, Drumgelloch, Hamilton, Larkhall, Motherwell, Coatbridge and Lanark

Network Diagram - see first page of Table 220

		SR	SR	SR	SR	SR	SR	SR	SR	SR	SR	SR	SR	SR	SR	SR	SR	SR	SR	SR	SR	SR	SR	SR	SR
																	A								
Helensburgh Central	d			15 40								16 10									16 40				
Craigendoran	d			15 43								16 13									16 43				
Cardross	d			15 48								16 18									16 48				
Balloch	d							15 53								16 23									16 53
Alexandria	d							15 55								16 25									16 55
Renton	d							15 58								16 28									16 58
Dalreoch	d			15 53				16 01				16 23				16 31					16 53				17 01
Dumbarton Central	d			15 55				16 02				16 25				16 32					16 55				17 02
Dumbarton East	d			15 57				16 04				16 27				16 34					16 57				17 04
Bowling	d							16 09								16 39									17 09
Kilpatrick	d							16 12								16 42									17 12
Dalmuir	a			16 05				16 15				16 35				16 45					17 05				17 15
	d		16 01	16 06		16 08		16 16	16 23		16 31	16 36		16 38		16 46		16 53		17 01	17 06		17 08		17 16
Singer	d		16 03					16 18			16 33					16 48				17 03					17 18
Drumry	d		16 05		←			16 20			16 35		←			16 50				17 05		←			17 20
Drumchapel	d		16 08		16 08			16 23			16 38		16 38			16 53				17 08		17 08			17 23
Milngavie	d	15 57	→				16 12			16 27	→				16 42				16 57	→				17 12	
Hillfoot	d	16 00					16 15			16 30					16 45				17 00					17 15	
Bearsden	d	16 02					16 17			16 32					16 47				17 02					17 17	
Westerton	d	16 05			16 10		16 20	16 25		16 35			16 40		16 50	16 55			17 05			17 10		17 20	17 25
Anniesland	d	16 08			16 14		16 23	16 28		16 38			16 44		16 53	16 58			17 08			17 14		17 23	17 28
Clydebank	d					16 10			16 25					16 40				16 55					17 10		
Yoker	d					16 12			16 27					16 42				16 57					17 12		
Garscadden	d					16 15			16 31					16 46				17 01					17 16		
Scotstounhill	d					16 18			16 33					16 48				17 03					17 18		
Jordanhill	d					16 20			16 35					16 50				17 05					17 20		
Hyndland	d	16 11		16 14	16 17	16 22	16 26	16 31	16 37	16 41		16 44	16 47	16 52	16 56	17 01		17 07	17 11		17 14	17 17	17 22	17 26	17 31
Partick	d	16 14		16 17	16 20	16 25	16 29	16 34	16 40	16 44		16 47	16 50	16 55	16 59	17 04		17 10	17 14		17 17	17 20	17 25	17 29	17 34
Exhibition Centre	d				16 23		16 32		16 43				16 53		17 02			17 13				17 23		17 32	
Anderston	d				16 25		16 34		16 45				16 55		17 04			17 15				17 25		17 34	
Glasgow Central 15 §	a				16 26		16 35		16 47				16 56		17 05			17 17				17 26		17 35	
	d				16 27		16 37		16 47				16 57		17 07		17b15	17 17				17 27		17 37	
Argyle Street	d				16 29		16 39		16 49				16 59		17 09			17 19				17 29		17 39	
Charing Cross	d	16 19		16 22		16 29		16 38		16 49		16 52		16 59		17 08			17 19		17 22		17 29		17 38
Glasgow Queen Street 10 §	a	16 21		16 24		16 31		16 40		16 51		16 54		17 01		17 10			17 21		17 24		17 31		17 40
	d	16 21		16 27		16 32		16 42		16 51		16 57		17 02		17 12			17 21		17 27		17 32		17 42
High Street	d	16a23		16 29		16 34		16 44		16a53		16 59		17 04		17 14			17a23		17 29		17 34		17 44
Bellgrove	d			16 31		16 36		16 46				17 01		17 06		17 16					17 31		17 36		17 46
Duke Street	d					16 38								17 08									17 38		
Alexandra Parade	d					16 39								17 09									17 39		
Barnhill	d					16 42								17 12									17 42		
Springburn	a					16 44								17 14									17 44		
Carntyne	d			16 34				16 49				17 04				17 19					17 34				17 49
Shettleston	d			16 37				16 52				17 07				17 22					17 37				17 52
Garrowhill	d			16 39				16 54				17 09				17 24					17 39				17 54
Easterhouse	d			16 42				16 57				17 12				17 27					17 42				17 57
Blairhill	d			16 46				17 01				17 16				17 31					17 46				18 01
Coatbridge Sunnyside	d			16 48				17 03				17 18				17 33					17 48				18 03
Coatdyke	d			16 51				17 06				17 21				17 36					17 51				18 06
Airdrie	a			16 53				17 09				17 23				17 39					17 53				18 09
	d			16 54								17 24									17 54				
Drumgelloch	a			16 58								17 28									17 58				
Bridgeton	d						16 42		16 52						17 12			17 22						17 42	
Dalmarnock	d						16 44		16 54						17 14			17 24						17 44	
Rutherglen	d				16 34		16 46		16 56				17 04		17 16			17 26				17 34		17 46	
Cambuslang	d						16 50		17 01				17 08		17 20		17 23	17 31						17 50	
Newton	d						16 54								17 24									17 54	
Blantyre	d				16 44		16 58						17 14		17 28							17 44		17 58	
Hamilton West	d				16 47		17 01						17 17		17 31							17 47		18 01	
Hamilton Central	d				16 50		17 03						17 20		17 33							17 50		18 03	
Chatelherault	d				16 54								17 24									17 54			
Merryton	d				16 58								17 28									17 58			
Larkhall	a				17 00								17 30									18 00			
Airbles	d						17 08								17 38									18 08	
Uddingston	d								17 05								17 28	17 35							
Bellshill	d								17 10								17 34	17 40							
Motherwell	a						17 11		17 16						17 41			17 48						18 11	
	d								17 16						17 42										
Whifflet	a																								
Coatbridge Central	a																								
Shieldmuir	d								17 20																
Holytown	d														17 47		17a38								
Wishaw	d								17 23						17 53										
Carluke	d								17 30						18 00										
Lanark	a								17 42						18 12										

For general notes see front of timetable
For details of catering facilities see Directory of Train Operators

§ Low Level

A To Edinburgh (Table 225)
b Glasgow Central High Level

Helensburgh, Balloch, Dalmuir and Milngavie → Glasgow → Springburn, Airdrie, Drumgelloch, Hamilton, Larkhall, Motherwell, Coatbridge and Lanark

Network Diagram - see first page of Table 220

Station		SR	SR	SR	SR	SR	SR	SR	SR	SR A	SR	SR	SR	SR		SR	SR	SR	SR	SR	SR	SR ◇ B	SR	SR	SR
Helensburgh Central	d				17 10								17 40						18 10			18b34			18 40
Craigendoran	d				17 13								17 43						18 13						18 43
Cardross	d				17 18								17 48						18 18						18 48
Balloch	d								17 23							17 53					18 23				
Alexandria	d								17 25							17 55					18 25				
Renton	d								17 28							17 58					18 28				
Dalreoch	d				17 23				17 31				17 53			18 01			18 23		18 31	18 47			18 53
Dumbarton Central	d				17 25				17 32				17 55			18 02			18 25		18 32				18 55
Dumbarton East	d				17 27				17 34				17 57			18 04			18 27		18 34				18 57
Bowling	d								17 39							18 09					18 39				
Kilpatrick	d								17 42							18 12					18 42				
Dalmuir	a				17 35				17 45				18 05			18 15			18 35		18 45	18 56			19 05
	d	17 23		17 31	17 36		17 38		17 46		17 53	18 01	18 05			18 16	18 23	18 31	18 35		18 46	18 56		19 01	19 05
Singer	d			17 33					17 48			18 03				18 18		18 33			18 48			19 03	
Drumry	d			17 35		←			17 50			18 05				18 20		18 35			18 50			19 05	
Drumchapel	d			17 38		17 38			17 53			18 08				18 23		18 38			18 53			19 08	
Milngavie	d		17 27	→				17 42						18 12						18 42					
Hillfoot	d		17 30					17 45						18 15						18 45					
Bearsden	d		17 32					17 47						18 17						18 47					
Westerton	d		17 35			17 40		17 50	17 55			18 10		18 20		18 25		18 40		18 50	18 55			19 10	
Anniesland	d		17 38			17 44		17 53	17 58			18 14		18 23		18 28		18 44		18 53	18 58			19 14	
Clydebank	d	17 25					17 40				17 55		18 07				18 25		18 37						19 07
Yoker	d	17 27					17 42				17 57		18 09				18 27		18 39						19 09
Garscadden	d	17 31					17 46				18 01		18 13				18 31		18 43						19 13
Scotstounhill	d	17 33					17 48				18 03		18 15				18 33		18 45						19 15
Jordanhill	d	17 35					17 50				18 05		18 17				18 35		18 47						19 17
Hyndland	d	17 37	17 41		17 44	17 47	17 52	17 56	18 01		18 07	18 17	18 21	18 26		18 31	18 37	18 47	18 51	18 55	19 01			19 17	19 21
Partick	d	17 40	17 44		17 47	17 50	17 55	17 59	18 04		18 10	18 20	18 24	18 29		18 34	18 40	18 50	18 54	18 59	19 04		19 10	19 20	19 24
Exhibition Centre	d	17 43				17 53		18 02			18 13	18 23		18 32			18 43	18 53		19 02			19 13	19 23	
Anderston	d	17 45				17 55		18 04			18 15	18 25		18 34			18 45	18 55		19 04			19 15	19 25	
Glasgow Central 15 §	a	17 47				17 56		18 05			18 17	18 26		18 35			18 47	18 56		19 05			19 16	19 26	
	d	17 47				17 57		18 07		18c15	18 17	18 27		18 37			18 47	18 57		19 07			19 17	19 27	
Argyle Street	d	17 49				17 59		18 09			18 19	18 29		18 39			18 49	18 59		19 09			19 19	19 29	
Charing Cross	d		17 49		17 52		17 59		18 08				18 29			18 38			18 59		19 08				19 29
Glasgow Queen Street 10 §	a		17 51		17 54		18 01		18 10				18 31			18 40			19 01		19 10	19e18			19 31
	d		17 51		17 57		18 02		18 12				18 32			18 44			19 02		19 14				19 32
High Street	d		17a53		17 59		18 04		18 14				18 34			18 46			19 04		19 16				19 34
Bellgrove	d				18 01		18 06		18 16				18 36			18 48			19 06		19 18				19 36
Duke Street	d						18 08									18 50					19 20				
Alexandra Parade	d						18 09									18 51					19 21				
Barnhill	d						18 12									18 54					19 24				
Springburn	a						18 15									18 56					19 26				
Carntyne	d				18 04				18 19				18 39						19 09						19 39
Shettleston	d				18 07				18 22				18 42						19 12						19 42
Garrowhill	d				18 09				18 24				18 44						19 14						19 44
Easterhouse	d				18 12				18 27				18 47						19 17						19 47
Blairhill	d				18 16				18 31				18 51						19 21						19 51
Coatbridge Sunnyside	d				18 18				18 33				18 53						19 23						19 53
Coatdyke	d				18 21				18 36				18 56						19 26						19 56
Airdrie	a				18 23				18 39				18 58						19 28						19 58
	d				18 24								18 59						19 29						19 59
Drumgelloch	a				18 28								19 03						19 33						20 03
Bridgeton	d	17 52						18 12			18 22			18 42			18 52			19 12			19 22		
Dalmarnock	d	17 54						18 14			18 24			18 44			18 54			19 14			19 24		
Rutherglen	d	17 56				18 04		18 16			18 26	18 34		18 46			18 56	19 04		19 16			19 26	19 34	
Cambuslang	d	18 01						18 20		18 23	18 31			18 50			19 01			19 20			19 31		
Newton	d							18 24						18 54						19 24					
Blantyre	d					18 14		18 28				18 44		18 58				19 14		19 28				19 44	
Hamilton West	d					18 17		18 31				18 47		19 01				19 17		19 31				19 47	
Hamilton Central	d					18 20		18 33				18 50		19 03				19 20		19 33				19 50	
Chatelherault	d					18 24						18 54						19 24						19 54	
Merryton	d					18 28						18 58						19 28						19 58	
Larkhall	a					18 30						19 00						19 30						20 00	
Airbles	d							18 38						19 08						19 38					
Uddingston	d	18 05								18 28	18 35						19 05						19 35		
Bellshill	d	18 10								18 34	18 40						19 10						19 40		
Motherwell	a	18 16						18 41			18 48			19 11			19 16			19 41			19 48		
	d	18 16						18 42									19 16			19 42					
Whifflet	a																								
Coatbridge Central	a																								
Shieldmuir	d	18 20															19 20								
Holytown	d							18 47		18a38										19 47					
Wishaw	d	18 23						18 53									19 23			19 53					
Carluke	d	18 30						19 00									19 30			20 00					
Lanark	a	18 42						19 12									19 42			20 12					

For general notes see front of timetable
For details of catering facilities see Directory of Train Operators

§ Low Level

A To Edinburgh (Table 225)
B Until 24 October. From Oban (Table 227)
b Helensburgh Upper
c Glasgow Central High Level
e Glasgow Queen Street High Level

Table 226

Saturdays

Helensburgh, Balloch, Dalmuir and Milngavie → Glasgow → Springburn, Airdrie, Drumgelloch, Hamilton, Larkhall, Motherwell, Coatbridge and Lanark

Network Diagram - see first page of Table 220

Station		SR	SR	SR	SR	SR	SR	SR	SR	SR	SR	SR	SR	SR	SR	SR	SR	SR	SR	SR	SR	SR	SR	SR	SR
									A													◇ B			
Helensburgh Central	d					19 10						19 40					20 10					20b40	20 40		
Craigendoran	d					19 13						19 43					20 13						20 43		
Cardross	d					19 18						19 48					20 18						20 48		
Balloch	d		18 53					19 23						19 53					20 23						20 53
Alexandria	d		18 55					19 25						19 55					20 25						20 55
Renton	d		18 58					19 28						19 58					20 28						20 58
Dalreoch	d		19 01			19 23		19 31				19 53		20 01			20 23		20 31				20 53		21 01
Dumbarton Central	d		19 02			19 25		19 32				19 55		20 02			20 25		20 32				20 55		21 02
Dumbarton East	d		19 04			19 27		19 34				19 57		20 04			20 27		20 34			20 53	20 57		21 04
Bowling	d		19 09					19 39						20 09					20 39						21 09
Kilpatrick	d		19 12					19 42						20 12					20 42						21 12
Dalmuir	a		19 15			19 35		19 45				20 05		20 15			20 35		20 45			21 04	21 05		21 15
	d		19 16		19 31	19 35		19 46			20 01	20 05		20 16		20 31	20 35		20 46		21 01	21 04	21 05		21 16
Singer	d		19 18		19 33			19 48			20 03			20 18		20 33			20 48		21 03				21 18
Drumry	d		19 20		19 35			19 50			20 05			20 20		20 35			20 50		21 05				21 20
Drumchapel	d		19 23		19 38			19 53			20 08			20 23		20 38			20 53		21 08				21 23
Milngavie	d	19 12					19 42						20 12					20 42						21 12	
Hillfoot	d	19 15					19 45						20 15					20 45						21 15	
Bearsden	d	19 17					19 47						20 17					20 47						21 17	
Westerton	d	19 20	19 25		19 40		19 50	19 55			20 10		20 20	20 25		20 40		20 50	20 55		21 10			21 20	21 25
Anniesland	d	19 23	19 28		19 44		19 53	19 58			20 14		20 23	20 28		20 44		20 53	20 58		21 14			21 23	21 28
Clydebank	d					19 37						20 07					20 37						21 07		
Yoker	d					19 39						20 09					20 39						21 09		
Garscadden	d					19 43						20 13					20 43						21 13		
Scotstounhill	d					19 45						20 15					20 45						21 15		
Jordanhill	d					19 47						20 17					20 47						21 17		
Hyndland	d	19 26	19 31		19 47	19 51	19 56	20 01			20 17	20 21	20 26	20 31		20 47	20 51	20 56	21 01		21 17		21 21	21 26	21 31
Partick	d	19 29	19 34	19 40	19 50	19 54	19 59	20 04		20 10	20 20	20 24	20 29	20 34	20 40	20 50	20 54	20 59	21 04	21 10	21 20		21 24	21 29	21 34
Exhibition Centre	d	19 32		19 43	19 53		20 02			20 13	20 23		20 32		20 43	20 53		21 02		21 13	21 23			21 32	
Anderston	d	19 34		19 45	19 55		20 04			20 15	20 25		20 34		20 45	20 55		21 04		21 15	21 25			21 34	
Glasgow Central 15 §	a	19 35		19 46	19 56		20 05			20 16	20 26		20 35		20 46	20 56		21 05		21 16	21 26			21 35	
	d	19 37		19 47	19 57		20 07		20c15	20 17	20 27		20 37		20 47	20 57		21 07		21 17	21 27			21 37	
Argyle Street	d	19 39		19 49	19 59		20 09			20 19	20 29		20 39		20 49	20 59		21 09		21 19	21 29			21 39	
Charing Cross	d		19 38			19 59		20 08				20 29		20 38			20 59		21 08				21 29		21 38
Glasgow Queen Street 10 §	a		19 40			20 01		20 10				20 31		20 40			21 01		21 10			21e29	21 31		21 40
	d		19 44			20 02		20 14				20 32		20 44			21 02		21 14				21 32		21 44
High Street	d		19 46			20 04		20 16				20 34		20 46			21 04		21 16				21 34		21 46
Bellgrove	d		19 48			20 06		20 18				20 36		20 48			21 06		21 18				21 36		21 48
Duke Street	d		19 50					20 20						20 50					21 20						21 50
Alexandra Parade	d		19 51					20 21						20 51					21 21						21 51
Barnhill	d		19 54					20 24						20 54					21 24						21 54
Springburn	a		19 56					20 26						20 56					21 26						21 56
Carntyne	d					20 09						20 39					21 09						21 39		
Shettleston	d					20 12						20 42					21 12						21 42		
Garrowhill	d					20 14						20 44					21 14						21 44		
Easterhouse	d					20 17						20 47					21 17						21 47		
Blairhill	d					20 21						20 51					21 21						21 51		
Coatbridge Sunnyside	d					20 23						20 53					21 23						21 53		
Coatdyke	d					20 26						20 56					21 26						21 56		
Airdrie	a					20 28						20 58					21 28						21 58		
	d					20 29						20 59					21 29						21 59		
Drumgelloch	a					20 33						21 03					21 33						22 03		
Bridgeton	d	19 42		19 52			20 12			20 22			20 42		20 52			21 12		21 22				21 42	
Dalmarnock	d	19 44		19 54			20 14			20 24			20 44		20 54			21 14		21 24				21 44	
Rutherglen	d	19 46		19 56	20 04		20 16			20 26	20 34		20 46		20 56	21 04		21 16		21 26	21 34			21 46	
Cambuslang	d	19 50		20 01			20 20		20 23	20 31			20 50		21 01			21 20		21 31				21 50	
Newton	d	19 54					20 24						20 54					21 24						21 54	
Blantyre	d	19 58			20 14		20 28				20 44		20 58			21 14		21 28			21 44			21 58	
Hamilton West	d	20 01			20 17		20 31				20 47		21 01			21 17		21 31			21 47			22 01	
Hamilton Central	d	20 03			20 20		20 33				20 50		21 03			21 20		21 33			21 50			22 03	
Chatelherault	d				20 24						20 54					21 24					21 54				
Merryton	d				20 28						20 58					21 28					21 58				
Larkhall	a				20 30						21 00					21 30					22 00				
Airbles	d	20 08					20 38						21 08					21 38						22 08	
Uddingston	d			20 05					20 28	20 35					21 05					21 35					
Bellshill	d			20 10					20 34	20 40					21 10					21 40					
Motherwell	a	20 11		20 16			20 41			20 48			21 11		21 16			21 41		21 48				22 11	
	d			20 16			20 42								21 16			21 42							
Whifflet	a																								
Coatbridge Central	a																								
Shieldmuir	d			20 20											21 20										
Holytown	d						20 47		20a38									21 47							
Wishaw	d			20 23			20 53								21 23			21 53							
Carluke	d			20 30			21 00								21 30			22 00							
Lanark	a			20 42			21 12								21 42			22 12							

For general notes see front of timetable
For details of catering facilities see Directory of Train Operators

§ Low Level

A To Edinburgh (Table 225)
B From Mallaig and Oban (Table 227)
b Helensburgh Upper
c Glasgow Central High Level
e Glasgow Queen Street High Level

Table 226

Saturdays

Helensburgh, Balloch, Dalmuir and Milngavie → Glasgow → Springburn, Airdrie, Drumgelloch, Hamilton, Larkhall, Motherwell, Coatbridge and Lanark

Network Diagram - see first page of Table 220

		SR	SR	SR	SR	SR	SR	SR	SR	SR	SR	SR	SR	SR	SR A	SR	SR	SR	SR	SR	SR	SR	SR
Helensburgh Central	d			21 10					21 40					22 10						22 40		23 10	
Craigendoran	d			21 13					21 43					22 13						22 43		23 13	
Cardross	d			21 18					21 48					22 18						22 48		23 18	
Balloch	d					21 23					21 53						22 23				22 53		23 23
Alexandria	d					21 25					21 55						22 25				22 55		23 25
Renton	d					21 28					21 58						22 28				22 58		23 28
Dalreoch	d			21 23		21 31			21 53		22 01			22 23			22 31			22 53	23 01	23 23	23 31
Dumbarton Central	d			21 25		21 32			21 55		22 02			22 25			22 32			22 55	23 02	23 25	23 32
Dumbarton East	d			21 27		21 34			21 57		22 04			22 27			22 34			22 57	23 04	23 27	23 34
Bowling	d					21 39					22 09						22 39				23 09		23 39
Kilpatrick	d					21 42					22 12						22 42				23 12		23 42
Dalmuir	a			21 35		21 45			22 05		22 15			22 35			22 45			23 05	23 15	23 35	23 45
	d		21 31	21 35		21 46		22 01	22 05		22 16		22 31	22 35			22 46		23 01	23 05	23 16	23 35	
Singer	d		21 33			21 48		22 03			22 18		22 33				22 48		23 03		23 18		
Drumry	d		21 35			21 50		22 05			22 20		22 35				22 50		23 05		23 20		
Drumchapel	d		21 38			21 53		22 08			22 23		22 38				22 53		23 08		23 23		
Milngavie	d				21 42					22 12						22 42							
Hillfoot	d				21 45					22 15						22 45							
Bearsden	d				21 47					22 17						22 47							
Westerton	d		21 40		21 50	21 55		22 10		22 20	22 25		22 40			22 50	22 55		23 10		23 25		
Anniesland	d		21 44		21 53	21 58		22 14		22 23	22 28		22 44			22 53	22 58		23 14		23 28		
Clydebank	d			21 37					22 07					22 37						23 07		23 37	
Yoker	d			21 39					22 09					22 39						23 09		23 39	
Garscadden	d			21 43					22 13					22 43						23 13		23 43	
Scotstounhill	d			21 45					22 15					22 45						23 15		23 45	
Jordanhill	d			21 47					22 17					22 47						23 17		23 47	
Hyndland	d		21 47	21 51	21 56	22 01		22 17	22 21	22 26	22 31		22 47	22 51		22 56	23 01		23 17	23 21	23 31	23 51	
Partick	d	21 40	21 50	21 54	21 59	22 04	22 10	22 20	22 24	22 29	22 34	22 40	22 50	22 54		22 59	23 04	23 10	23 20	23 24	23 34	23 54	
Exhibition Centre	d	21 43	21 53		22 02		22 13	22 23		22 32		22 43	22 53			23 02		23 13	23 23				
Anderston	d	21 45	21 55		22 04		22 15	22 25		22 34		22 45	22 55			23 04		23 15	23 25				
Glasgow Central 15 §	a	21 46	21 56		22 05		22 16	22 26		22 35		22 46	22 56			23 05		23 16	23 26				
	d	21 47	21 57		22 07		22 17	22 27		22 37		22 47	22 57		23b06	23 07		23 17	23 27				
Argyle Street	d	21 49	21 59		22 09		22 19	22 29		22 39		22 49	22 59			23 09		23 19	23 29				
Charing Cross	d			21 59		22 08			22 29		22 38			22 59			23 08			23 29	23 38	23 59	
Glasgow Queen Street 10 §	a			22 01		22 10			22 31		22 40			23 01			23 10			23 31	23 40	00 01	
	d			22 02		22 14			22 32		22 44			23 02			23 14			23 32	23 44	00 02	
High Street	d			22 04		22 16			22 34		22 46			23 04			23 16			23 34	23 46	00 04	
Bellgrove	d			22 06		22 18			22 36		22 48			23 06			23 18			23 36	23 48	00 06	
Duke Street	d					22 20					22 50						23 20						
Alexandra Parade	d					22 21					22 51						23 21						
Barnhill	d					22 24					22 54						23 24						
Springburn	a					22 26					22 56						23 26						
Carntyne	d			22 09					22 39					23 09						23 39	23 51	00 09	
Shettleston	d			22 12					22 42					23 12						23 42	23 54	00 12	
Garrowhill	d			22 14					22 44					23 14						23 44	23 56	00 14	
Easterhouse	d			22 17					22 47					23 17						23 47	23 59	00 17	
Blairhill	d			22 21					22 51					23 21						23 51	00 03	00 21	
Coatbridge Sunnyside	d			22 23					22 53					23 23						23 53	00 05	00 23	
Coatdyke	d			22 26					22 56					23 26						23 56	00 08	00 26	
Airdrie	a			22 28					22 58					23 28						23 59	00 10	00 28	
	d			22 29					22 59					23 29							00 10	00 29	
Drumgelloch	a			22 33					23 03					23 33							00 14	00 33	
Bridgeton	d	21 52			22 12		22 22			22 42		22 52				23 12		23 22					
Dalmarnock	d	21 54			22 14		22 24			22 44		22 54				23 14		23 24					
Rutherglen	d	21 56	22 04		22 16		22 26	22 34		22 46		22 56	23 04			23 16		23 26	23 34				
Cambuslang	d	22 01			22 20		22 31			22 50		23 01			23 15	23 20		23 31					
Newton	d				22 24					22 54						23 24							
Blantyre	d		22 14		22 28			22 44		22 58			23 14			23 28			23 44				
Hamilton West	d		22 17		22 31			22 47		23 01			23 17			23 31			23 47				
Hamilton Central	d		22 20		22 33			22 50		23 03			23 20			23 33			23 50				
Chatelherault	d		22 24					22 54					23 24						23 54				
Merryton	d		22 28					22 58					23 28						23 58				
Larkhall	a		22 30					23 00					23 30						00 01				
Airbles	d				22 38					23 08						23 38							
Uddingston	d	22 05					22 35					23 05			23 20			23 35					
Bellshill	d	22 10					22 40					23 10			23 26			23 40					
Motherwell	a	22 16			22 41		22 49			23 11		23 16				23 41		23 46					
	d	22 16			22 42							23 16											
Whifflet	a				22 48																		
Coatbridge Central	a				22 52																		
Shieldmuir	d	22 20										23 20											
Holytown	d														23a30								
Wishaw	d	22 23										23 23											
Carluke	d	22 30										23 30											
Lanark	a	22 42										23 42											

For general notes see front of timetable
For details of catering facilities see Directory of Train Operators

§ Low Level

A To Edinburgh (Table 225)
b Glasgow Central High Level

Table 226

Sundays

until 22 November

Helensburgh, Balloch, Dalmuir and Milngavie → Glasgow → Springburn, Airdrie, Drumgelloch, Hamilton, Larkhall, Motherwell, Coatbridge and Lanark

Network Diagram - see first page of Table 220

		SR	SR	SR	SR	SR	SR	SR	SR	SR	SR	SR		SR	SR	SR	SR	SR	SR	SR	SR	SR	SR	SR	SR
Helensburgh Central	d			07 55			08 25				08 55				09 25				09 55			10 25			
Craigendoran	d			07 58			08 28				08 58				09 28				09 58			10 28			
Cardross	d			08 03			08 33				09 03				09 33				10 03			10 33			
Balloch	d				08 09			08 39				09 09				09 39				10 09			10 39		
Alexandria	d				08 11			08 41				09 11				09 41				10 11			10 41		
Renton	d				08 14			08 44				09 14				09 44				10 14			10 44		
Dalreoch	d			08 08	08 17		08 38	08 47			09 08	09 17			09 38	09 47			10 08	10 17		10 38	10 47		
Dumbarton Central	d			08 10	08 18		08 40	08 48			09 10	09 18			09 40	09 48			10 10	10 18		10 40	10 48		
Dumbarton East	d			08 12	08 20		08 42	08 50			09 12	09 20			09 42	09 50			10 12	10 20		10 42	10 50		
Bowling	d				08 24			08 54				09 24				09 54				10 24			10 54		
Kilpatrick	d				08 28			08 58				09 28				09 58				10 28			10 58		
Dalmuir	a			08 19	08 30		08 49	09 00			09 19	09 30			09 49	10 00			10 19	10 30		10 49	11 00		
	d	07 50	08 01	08 20	08 31		08 50	09 01			09 20	09 31			09 50	10 01			10 20	10 31		10 50	11 01		
Singer	d	07 52		08 22			08 52				09 22				09 52				10 22			10 52			
Drumry	d	07 55		08 25			08 55				09 25				09 55				10 25			10 55			
Drumchapel	d	07 57		08 27			08 57				09 27				09 57				10 27			10 57			
Milngavie	d								09 11					09 41			10 11				10 41			11 11	
Hillfoot	d								09 14					09 44			10 14				10 44			11 14	
Bearsden	d								09 16					09 46			10 16				10 46			11 16	
Westerton	d	08 00		08 30			09 00		09 19		09 30			09 49	10 00		10 19		10 30		10 49	11 00		11 19	
Anniesland	d	08 03		08 33			09 03		09 22		09 33			09 52	10 03		10 22		10 33		10 52	11 03		11 22	
Clydebank	d		08 03		08 33			09 03				09 33				10 03				10 33			11 03		
Yoker	d		08 05		08 35			09 05				09 35				10 05				10 35			11 05		
Garscadden	d		08 09		08 39			09 09				09 39				10 09				10 39			11 09		
Scotstounhill	d		08 11		08 41			09 11				09 41				10 11				10 41			11 11		
Jordanhill	d		08 13		08 43			09 13				09 43				10 13				10 43			11 13		
Hyndland	d	08 05	08 15	08 35	08 45	08 55	09 05	09 15	09 25		09 35	09 45		09 54	10 05	10 15	10 25		10 35	10 45	10 55	11 05	11 15	11 25	
Partick	d	08 08	08 18	08 38	08 48	08 58	09 08	09 18	09 28	09 34	09 38	09 48		09 57	10 08	10 18	10 28	10 34	10 38	10 48	10 58	11 08	11 18	11 28	11 34
Exhibition Centre	d		08 21		08 51	09 01		09 21	09 31	09 37		09 51		10 00		10 21	10 31	10 37		10 51	11 01		11 21	11 31	11 37
Anderston	d																								
Glasgow Central 15 §	a		08 23		08 53	09 03		09 23	09 33	09 39		09 53		10 02		10 23	10 33	10 39		10 53	11 03		11 23	11 33	11 39
	d		08 24		08 54	09 04		09 24	09 34	09 40		09 54		10 03		10 24	10 34	10 40		10 54	11 04		11 24	11 34	11 40
Argyle Street	d											09 56		10 06		10 26	10 36	10 42		10 56	11 06		11 26	11 36	11 42
Charing Cross	d	08 13		08 43			09 13				09 43				10 13				10 43			11 13			
Glasgow Queen Street 10 §	a	08 15		08 45			09 15				09 45				10 15				10 45			11 15			
	d	08 17		08 47			09 17				09 47				10 17				10 47			11 17			
High Street	d	08 19		08 49			09 19				09 49				10 19				10 49			11 19			
Bellgrove	d	08 21		08 51			09 21				09 51				10 21				10 51			11 21			
Duke Street	d																								
Alexandra Parade	d																								
Barnhill	d																								
Springburn	a																								
Carntyne	d	08 24		08 54			09 24				09 54				10 24				10 54			11 24			
Shettleston	d	08 27		08 57			09 27				09 57				10 27				10 57			11 27			
Garrowhill	d	08 29		08 59			09 29				09 59				10 29				10 59			11 29			
Easterhouse	d	08 32		09 02			09 32				10 02				10 32				11 02			11 32			
Blairhill	d	08 36		09 06			09 36				10 06				10 36				11 06			11 36			
Coatbridge Sunnyside	d	08 38		09 08			09 38				10 08				10 38				11 08			11 38			
Coatdyke	d	08 41		09 11			09 41				10 11				10 41				11 11			11 41			
Airdrie	a	08 44		09 14			09 44				10 14				10 44				11 14			11 44			
	d	08 45		09 15			09 45				10 15				10 45				11 15			11 45			
Drumgelloch	a	08 48		09 18			09 48				10 18				10 48				11 18			11 48			
Bridgeton	d		08 29		08 59	09 09		09 29	09 39			09 59		10 09		10 29	10 39			10 59	11 07		11 29	11 39	
Dalmarnock	d																								
Rutherglen	d		08 32		09 02	09 12		09 32	09 42	09 47		10 02		10 12		10 32	10 42	10 47		11 02	11 12		11 32	11 42	11 47
Cambuslang	d		08 36		09 06	09 16		09 36	09 46			10 06		10 16		10 36	10 46			11 06	11 16		11 36	11 46	
Newton	d				09 09			09 39				10 09				10 39				11 09			11 39		
Blantyre	d				09 13			09 43		09 55		10 13				10 43		10 55		11 13			11 43		11 55
Hamilton West	d				09 16			09 46		09 58		10 16				10 46		10 58		11 16			11 46		11 58
Hamilton Central	d				09 20			09 50		10 01		10 20				10 50		11 01		11 20			11 50		12 01
Chatelherault	d									10 06								11 06							12 06
Merryton	d									10 09								11 09							12 09
Larkhall	a									10 11								11 15							12 12
Airbles	d				09 25			09 55				10 25				10 55				11 25			11 55		
Uddingston	d		08 40			09 20			09 52					10 20			10 50				11 20			11 50	
Bellshill	d		08 45			09 25			09 57					10 25			10 55				11 25			11 55	
Motherwell	a		08 53		09 27	09 33		09 57	10 03			10 27		10 33		10 57	11 03			11 27	11 33		11 57	12 03	
	d					09 33								10 33							11 33				
Whifflet	a																								
Coatbridge Central	a																								
Shieldmuir	d					09 37								10 37							11 37				
Holytown	d																								
Wishaw	d					09 40								10 40							11 40				
Carluke	d					09 47								10 47							11 47				
Lanark	a					09 59								10 59							11 59				

For general notes see front of timetable
For details of catering facilities see Directory of Train Operators

§ Low Level

Table 226

Sundays

until 22 November

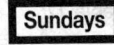

Helensburgh, Balloch, Dalmuir and Milngavie → Glasgow → Springburn, Airdrie, Drumgelloch, Hamilton, Larkhall, Motherwell, Coatbridge and Lanark

Network Diagram - see first page of Table 220

		SR		SR	SR	SR	SR	SR	SR	SR	SR	SR	SR	SR		SR	SR	SR	SR	SR	SR	SR	SR	SR	SR
Helensburgh Central	d	10 55				11 25				11 55		12 25					12 55			13 25				13 55	
Craigendoran	d	10 58				11 28				11 58		12 28					12 58			13 28				13 58	
Cardross	d	11 03				11 33				12 03		12 33					13 03			13 33				14 03	
Balloch	d			11 09			11 39				12 09		12 39					13 09			13 39				14 09
Alexandria	d			11 11			11 41				12 11		12 41					13 11			13 41				14 11
Renton	d			11 14			11 44				12 14		12 44					13 14			13 44				14 14
Dalreoch	d	11 08		11 17		11 38	11 47			12 08	12 17	12 38	12 47				13 08	13 17		13 38	13 47			14 08	14 17
Dumbarton Central	d	11 10		11 18		11 40	11 48			12 10	12 18	12 40	12 48				13 10	13 18		13 40	13 48			14 10	14 18
Dumbarton East	d	11 12		11 20		11 42	11 50			12 12	12 20	12 42	12 50				13 12	13 20		13 42	13 50			14 12	14 20
Bowling	d			11 24			11 54				12 24		12 54					13 24			13 54				14 24
Kilpatrick	d			11 28			11 58				12 28		12 58					13 28			13 58				14 28
Dalmuir	a	11 19		11 30		11 49	12 00			12 19	12 30	12 49	13 00				13 19	13 30		13 49	14 00			14 19	14 30
	d	11 20		11 31		11 50	12 01			12 20	12 31	12 50	13 01				13 20	13 31		13 50	14 01			14 20	14 31
Singer	d	11 22				11 52				12 22		12 52					13 22			13 52				14 22	
Drumry	d	11 25				11 55				12 25		12 55					13 25			13 55				14 25	
Drumchapel	d	11 27				11 57				12 27		12 57					13 27			13 57				14 27	
Milngavie	d				11 41			12 11						13 11					13 41			14 11			
Hillfoot	d				11 44			12 14						13 14					13 44			14 14			
Bearsden	d				11 46			12 16						13 16					13 46			14 16			
Westerton	d	11 30			11 49	12 00		12 19		12 30		13 00		13 19			13 30		13 49	14 00		14 19		14 30	
Anniesland	d	11 33			11 52	12 03		12 22		12 33		13 03		13 22			13 33		13 52	14 03		14 22		14 33	
Clydebank	d			11 33			12 03				12 33		13 03					13 33			14 03				14 33
Yoker	d			11 35			12 05				12 35		13 05					13 35			14 05				14 35
Garscadden	d			11 39			12 09				12 39		13 09					13 39			14 09				14 39
Scotstounhill	d			11 41			12 11				12 41		13 11					13 41			14 11				14 41
Jordanhill	d			11 43			12 13				12 43		13 13					13 43			14 13				14 43
Hyndland	d	11 35		11 45	11 55	12 05	12 15	12 24		12 35	12 45	13 05	13 15	13 25			13 35	13 45	13 55	14 05	14 15	14 25		14 35	14 45
Partick	d	11 38		11 48	11 58	12 08	12 18	12 27	12 34	12 38	12 48	13 08	13 18	13 28		13 34	13 38	13 48	13 58	14 08	14 18	14 28	14 34	14 38	14 48
Exhibition Centre	d			11 51	12 01		12 21	12 30	12 37		12 51		13 21	13 31		13 37		13 51	14 01		14 21	14 31	14 37		14 51
Anderston	d																								
Glasgow Central 15 §	a			11 53	12 03		12 23	12 33	12 39		12 53		13 23	13 33		13 39		13 53	14 03		14 23	14 33	14 39		14 53
	d			11 54	12 04		12 24	12 33	12 40		12 54		13 24	13 34		13 40		13 54	14 04		14 24	14 34	14 40		14 54
Argyle Street	d			11 56	12 06		12 26	12 35	12 42		12 56		13 26	13 36		13 42		13 56	14 06		14 26	14 36	14 42		14 56
Charing Cross	d	11 43				12 13				12 43		13 13					13 43			14 13				14 43	
Glasgow Queen Street 10 §	a	11 45				12 15				12 45		13 15					13 45			14 15				14 45	
	d	11 47				12 17				12 47		13 17					13 47			14 17				14 47	
High Street	d	11 49				12 19				12 49		13 19					13 49			14 19				14 49	
Bellgrove	d	11 51				12 21				12 51		13 21					13 51			14 21				14 51	
Duke Street	d																								
Alexandra Parade	d																								
Barnhill	d																								
Springburn	a																								
Carntyne	d	11 54				12 24				12 54		13 24					13 54			14 24				14 54	
Shettleston	d	11 57				12 27				12 57		13 27					13 57			14 27				14 57	
Garrowhill	d	11 59				12 29				12 59		13 29					13 59			14 29				14 59	
Easterhouse	d	12 02				12 32				13 02		13 32					14 02			14 32				15 02	
Blairhill	d	12 06				12 36				13 06		13 36					14 06			14 36				15 06	
Coatbridge Sunnyside	d	12 08				12 38				13 08		13 38					14 08			14 38				15 08	
Coatdyke	d	12 11				12 41				13 11		13 41					14 11			14 41				15 11	
Airdrie	a	12 14				12 44				13 14		13 44					14 14			14 44				15 14	
	d	12 15				12 45				13 15		13 45					14 15			14 45				15 15	
Drumgelloch	a	12 18				12 48				13 18		13 48					14 18			14 48				15 18	
Bridgeton	d			11 59	12 09		12 29	12 38			12 59		13 29	13 39				13 59	14 09		14 29	14 39			14 59
Dalmarnock	d																								
Rutherglen	d			12 02	12 12		12 32	12 42	12 47		13 02		13 31	13 42		13 47		14 02	14 12		14 32	14 42	14 47		15 02
Cambuslang	d			12 06	12 16		12 36	12 46			13 06		13 36	13 46				14 06	14 16		14 36	14 46			15 06
Newton	d			12 09			12 39				13 09		13 39					14 09			14 39				15 09
Blantyre	d			12 13			12 43		12 55		13 13		13 43			13 55		14 13			14 43		14 54		15 13
Hamilton West	d			12 16			12 46		12 58		13 16		13 46			13 58		14 16			14 46		14 57		15 16
Hamilton Central	d			12 20			12 50		13 01		13 20		13 50			14 01		14 20			14 50		15 01		15 20
Chatelherault	d								13 06							14 06							15 06		
Merryton	d								13 09							14 09							15 09		
Larkhall	a								13 15							14 13							15 11		
Airbles	d			12 25			12 55				13 25		13 55					14 25			14 55				15 25
Uddingston	d				12 20			12 50						13 50					14 20			14 50			
Bellshill	d				12 25			12 55						13 55					14 25			14 55			
Motherwell	a			12 27	12 33		12 57	13 03			13 27		13 57	14 03				14 27	14 33		14 57	15 03			15 27
	d				12 33														14 33						
Whifflet	a																								
Coatbridge Central	a																								
Shieldmuir	d				12 37														14 37						
Holytown	d																								
Wishaw	d				12 40														14 40						
Carluke	d				12 47														14 47						
Lanark	a				12 59														14 59						

For general notes see front of timetable
For details of catering facilities see
Directory of Train Operators

§ Low Level

Table 226

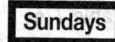

Sundays
until 22 November

Helensburgh, Balloch, Dalmuir and Milngavie → Glasgow → Springburn, Airdrie, Drumgelloch, Hamilton, Larkhall, Motherwell, Coatbridge and Lanark

Network Diagram - see first page of Table 220

		SR	SR	SR	SR	SR	SR	SR	SR	SR	SR	SR	SR	SR	SR	SR	SR	SR	SR	SR	SR	SR	SR
					◇ A	◇ B																	
Helensburgh Central	d		14 25		14b39	14b43			14 55			15 25				15 55			16 25				16 55
Craigendoran	d		14 28						14 58			15 28				15 58			16 28				16 58
Cardross	d		14 33						15 03			15 33				16 03			16 33				17 03
Balloch	d			14 39						15 09			15 39				16 09			16 39			
Alexandria	d			14 41						15 11			15 41				16 11			16 41			
Renton	d			14 44						15 14			15 44				16 14			16 44			
Dalreoch	d		14 38	14 47					15 08	15 17		15 38	15 47			16 08	16 17		16 38	16 47			17 08
Dumbarton Central	d		14 40	14 48	14 56	14 56			15 10	15 18		15 40	15 48			16 10	16 18		16 40	16 48			17 10
Dumbarton East	d		14 42	14 50					15 12	15 20		15 42	15 50			16 12	16 20		16 42	16 50			17 12
Bowling	d			14 54						15 24			15 54				16 24			16 54			
Kilpatrick	d			14 58						15 28			15 58				16 28			16 58			
Dalmuir	a		14 49	15 00	15 05	15 05			15 19	15 30		15 49	16 00			16 19	16 30		16 49	17 00			17 19
	d		14 50	15 01	15 05	15 05			15 20	15 31		15 50	16 01			16 20	16 31		16 50	17 01			17 20
Singer	d		14 52						15 22			15 52				16 22			16 52				17 22
Drumry	d		14 55						15 25			15 55				16 25			16 55				17 25
Drumchapel	d		14 57						15 27			15 57				16 27			16 57				17 27
Milngavie	d	14 41					15 11				15 41			16 10				16 41			17 11		
Hillfoot	d	14 44					15 14				15 44			16 13				16 44			17 14		
Bearsden	d	14 46					15 16				15 46			16 15				16 46			17 16		
Westerton	d	14 49	15 00				15 19		15 30		15 49	16 00		16 18		16 30		16 49	17 00		17 19		17 30
Anniesland	d	14 52	15 03				15 22		15 33		15 52	16 03		16 21		16 33		16 52	17 03		17 22		17 33
Clydebank	d			15 03						15 33			16 03				16 33			17 03			
Yoker	d			15 05						15 35			16 05				16 35			17 05			
Garscadden	d			15 09						15 39			16 09				16 39			17 09			
Scotstounhill	d			15 11						15 41			16 11				16 41			17 11			
Jordanhill	d			15 13						15 43			16 13				16 43			17 13			
Hyndland	d	14 55	15 05	15 15			15 25		15 35	15 45	15 55	16 05	16 15	16 24		16 35	16 45	16 55	17 05	17 15	17 25		17 35
Partick	d	14 58	15 08	15 18			15 28	15 34	15 38	15 48	15 58	16 08	16 18	16 27	16 34	16 38	16 48	16 58	17 08	17 18	17 28	17 34	17 38
Exhibition Centre	d	15 01		15 21			15 31	15 37		15 51	16 01		16 21	16 30	16 37		16 51	17 01		17 21	17 31	17 37	
Anderston	d																						
Glasgow Central 15 §	a	15 03		15 23			15 33	15 39		15 53	16 03		16 23	16 33	16 39		16 53	17 03		17 23	17 33	17 39	
	d	15 04		15 24			15 34	15 40		15 54	16 04		16 24	16 34	16 40		16 54	17 04		17 24	17 34	17 40	
Argyle Street	d	15 06		15 26			15 36	15 42		15 56	16 06		16 26	16 36	16 42		16 56	17 06		17 26	17 36	17 42	
Charing Cross	d		15 13						15 43			16 13				16 43			17 13				17 43
Glasgow Queen Street 10 §	a		15 15		15c31	15c31			15 45			16 15				16 45			17 15				17 45
	d		15 17						15 47			16 17				16 47			17 17				17 47
High Street	d		15 19						15 49			16 19				16 49			17 19				17 49
Bellgrove	d		15 21						15 51			16 21				16 51			17 21				17 51
Duke Street	d																						
Alexandra Parade	d																						
Barnhill	d																						
Springburn	a																						
Carntyne	d		15 24						15 54			16 24				16 54			17 24				17 54
Shettleston	d		15 27						15 57			16 27				16 57			17 27				17 57
Garrowhill	d		15 29						15 59			16 29				16 59			17 29				17 59
Easterhouse	d		15 32						16 02			16 32				17 02			17 32				18 02
Blairhill	d		15 36						16 06			16 36				17 06			17 36				18 06
Coatbridge Sunnyside	d		15 38						16 08			16 38				17 08			17 38				18 08
Coatdyke	d		15 41						16 11			16 41				17 11			17 41				18 11
Airdrie	a		15 44						16 14			16 44				17 14			17 44				18 14
	d		15 45						16 15			16 45				17 15			17 45				18 15
Drumgelloch	a		15 48						16 18			16 48				17 18			17 48				18 18
Bridgeton	d	15 09		15 29			15 39			15 59	16 09		16 29	16 39			16 59	17 09		17 29	17 39		
Dalmarnock	d																						
Rutherglen	d	15 12		15 32			15 42	15 47		16 02	16 12		16 32	16 42	16 47		17 02	17 12		17 32	17 42	17 47	
Cambuslang	d	15 16		15 36			15 46			16 06	16 16		16 36	16 46			17 06	17 16		17 36	17 46		
Newton	d			15 39						16 09			16 39				17 09			17 39			
Blantyre	d			15 43				15 55		16 13			16 43		16 55		17 13			17 43		17 55	
Hamilton West	d			15 46				15 58		16 16			16 46		16 58		17 16			17 46		17 58	
Hamilton Central	d			15 50				16 01		16 20			16 50		17 01		17 20			17 50		18 01	
Chatelherault	d							16 06							17 06							18 06	
Merryton	d							16 09							17 09							18 09	
Larkhall	a							16 15							17 11							18 11	
Airbles	d			15 55						16 25			16 55				17 25			17 55			
Uddingston	d	15 20					15 50				16 20			16 50				17 20			17 50		
Bellshill	d	15 25					15 55				16 25			16 55				17 25			17 55		
Motherwell	a	15 33		15 57			16 02			16 27	16 33		16 57	17 03			17 27	17 33		17 57	18 02		
	d	15 33									16 33							17 33					
Whifflet	a																						
Coatbridge Central	a																						
Shieldmuir	d	15 37									16 37							17 37					
Holytown	d																						
Wishaw	d	15 40									16 40							17 40					
Carluke	d	15 47									16 47							17 47					
Lanark	a	15 59									16 59							17 59					

For general notes see front of timetable
For details of catering facilities see Directory of Train Operators

§ Low Level

A 4 to 25 October. From Oban (Table 227)

B Until 27 September. From Oban and Mallaig (Table 227)

b Helensburgh Upper

c Glasgow Queen Street High Level

Table 226

Sundays

until 22 November

Helensburgh, Balloch, Dalmuir and Milngavie → Glasgow → Springburn, Airdrie, Drumgelloch, Hamilton, Larkhall, Motherwell, Coatbridge and Lanark

Network Diagram - see first page of Table 220

		SR	SR	SR	SR	SR		SR	SR	SR	SR	SR ◇ A ✕	SR
Helensburgh Central	d			17 25					17 55		18 25	18b34	
Craigendoran	d			17 28					17 58		18 28		
Cardross	d			17 33					18 03		18 33		
Balloch	d	17 09			17 39					18 09			18 39
Alexandria	d	17 11			17 41					18 11			18 41
Renton	d	17 14			17 44					18 14			18 44
Dalreoch	d	17 17		17 38	17 47				18 08	18 17	18 38		18 47
Dumbarton Central	d	17 18		17 40	17 48				18 10	18 18	18 40	18 47	18 48
Dumbarton East	d	17 20		17 42	17 50				18 12	18 20	18 42		18 50
Bowling	d	17 24			17 54					18 24			18 54
Kilpatrick	d	17 28			17 58					18 28			18 58
Dalmuir	a	17 30		17 49	18 00				18 19	18 30	18 49	18 56	19 00
	d	17 31		17 50	18 01				18 20	18 31	18 50	18 56	19 01
Singer	d			17 52					18 22		18 52		
Drumry	d			17 55					18 25		18 55		
Drumchapel	d			17 57					18 27		18 57		
Milngavie	d		17 41			18 11							
Hillfoot	d		17 44			18 14							
Bearsden	d		17 46			18 16							
Westerton	d		17 49	18 00		18 19			18 30		19 00		
Anniesland	d		17 52	18 03		18 22			18 33		19 03		
Clydebank	d	17 33			18 03					18 33			19 03
Yoker	d	17 35			18 05					18 35			19 05
Garscadden	d	17 39			18 09					18 39			19 09
Scotstounhill	d	17 41			18 11					18 41			19 11
Jordanhill	d	17 43			18 13					18 43			19 13
Hyndland	d	17 45	17 55	18 05	18 15	18 25			18 35	18 45	19 05		19 15
Partick	d	17 48	17 58	18 08	18 18	18 28		18 34	18 38	18 48	19 08		19 18
Exhibition Centre	d	17 51	18 01		18 21	18 31		18 37		18 51			19 21
Anderston	d												
Glasgow Central 15 §	a	17 53	18 03		18 23	18 33		18 39		18 53			19 23
	d	17 54	18 04		18 24	18 34		18 40		18 54			19 24
Argyle Street	d	17 56	18 06										
Charing Cross	d			18 13					18 43		19 13		
Glasgow Queen Street 10 §	a			18 15					18 45		19 15	19c15	
	d			18 17					18 47		19 17		
High Street	d			18 19					18 49		19 19		
Bellgrove	d			18 21					18 51		19 21		
Duke Street	d												
Alexandra Parade	d												
Barnhill	d												
Springburn	a												
Carntyne	d			18 24					18 54		19 24		
Shettleston	d			18 27					18 57		19 27		
Garrowhill	d			18 29					18 59		19 29		
Easterhouse	d			18 32					19 02		19 32		
Blairhill	d			18 36					19 06		19 36		
Coatbridge Sunnyside	d			18 38					19 08		19 38		
Coatdyke	d			18 41					19 11		19 41		
Airdrie	a			18 44					19 14		19 44		
	d			18 45					19 15		19 45		
Drumgelloch	a			18 48					19 18		19 48		
Bridgeton	d	17 59	18 09		18 29	18 39				18 59			19 29
Dalmarnock	d												
Rutherglen	d	18 02	18 12		18 32	18 42		18 47		19 02			19 32
Cambuslang	d	18 06	18 16		18 36	18 46				19 06			19 36
Newton	d	18 09			18 39					19 09			19 39
Blantyre	d	18 13			18 43			18 55		19 13			19 43
Hamilton West	d	18 16			18 46			18 58		19 16			19 46
Hamilton Central	d	18 20			18 50			19 01		19 20			19 50
Chatelherault	d							19 06					
Merryton	d							19 09					
Larkhall	a							19 12					
Airbles	d	18 25			18 55					19 25			19 55
Uddingston	d		18 20			18 50							
Bellshill	d		18 25			18 55							
Motherwell	a	18 27	18 33		18 57	19 03				19 27			19 57
	d		18 33										
Whifflet	a												
Coatbridge Central	a												
Shieldmuir	d		18 37										
Holytown	d												
Wishaw	d		18 40										
Carluke	d		18 47										
Lanark	a		18 59										

		SR	SR	SR	SR	SR		SR	SR	SR	SR	SR	SR
Helensburgh Central	d			18 55				19 25				19 55	
Craigendoran	d			18 58				19 28				19 58	
Cardross	d			19 03				19 33				20 03	
Balloch	d				19 09				19 39				20 09
Alexandria	d				19 11				19 41				20 11
Renton	d				19 14				19 44				20 14
Dalreoch	d			19 08	19 17			19 38	19 47			20 08	20 17
Dumbarton Central	d			19 10	19 18			19 40	19 48			20 10	20 18
Dumbarton East	d			19 12	19 20			19 42	19 50			20 12	20 20
Bowling	d				19 24				19 54				20 24
Kilpatrick	d				19 28				19 58				20 28
Dalmuir	a			19 19	19 30			19 49	20 00			20 19	20 30
	d			19 20	19 31			19 50	20 01			20 20	20 31
Singer	d			19 22				19 52				20 22	
Drumry	d			19 25				19 55				20 25	
Drumchapel	d			19 27				19 57				20 27	
Milngavie	d	19 11				19 41				20 11			
Hillfoot	d	19 14				19 44				20 14			
Bearsden	d	19 16				19 46				20 16			
Westerton	d	19 19		19 30		19 49		20 00		20 19		20 30	
Anniesland	d	19 22		19 33		19 52		20 03		20 22		20 33	
Clydebank	d				19 33				20 03				20 33
Yoker	d				19 35				20 05				20 35
Garscadden	d				19 39				20 09				20 39
Scotstounhill	d				19 41				20 11				20 41
Jordanhill	d				19 43				20 13				20 43
Hyndland	d	19 25		19 35	19 45	19 55		20 05	20 15	20 25		20 35	20 45
Partick	d	19 28	19 34	19 38	19 48	19 58		20 08	20 18	20 28	20 34	20 38	20 48
Exhibition Centre	d	19 31	19 37		19 51	20 01			20 21	20 31	20 37		20 51
Anderston	d												
Glasgow Central 15 §	a	19 33	19 39		19 53	20 03			20 23	20 33	20 39		20 53
	d	19 34	19 40		19 54	20 04			20 24	20 34	20 40		20 54
Argyle Street	d												
Charing Cross	d			19 43				20 13				20 43	
Glasgow Queen Street 10 §	a			19 45				20 15				20 45	
	d			19 47				20 17				20 47	
High Street	d			19 49				20 19				20 49	
Bellgrove	d			19 51				20 21				20 51	
Duke Street	d												
Alexandra Parade	d												
Barnhill	d												
Springburn	a												
Carntyne	d			19 54				20 24				20 54	
Shettleston	d			19 57				20 27				20 57	
Garrowhill	d			19 59				20 29				20 59	
Easterhouse	d			20 02				20 32				21 02	
Blairhill	d			20 06				20 36				21 06	
Coatbridge Sunnyside	d			20 08				20 38				21 08	
Coatdyke	d			20 11				20 41				21 11	
Airdrie	a			20 14				20 44				21 14	
	d			20 15				20 45				21 15	
Drumgelloch	a			20 18				20 48				21 18	
Bridgeton	d	19 39			19 59	20 09			20 29	20 39			20 59
Dalmarnock	d												
Rutherglen	d	19 42	19 47		20 02	20 12			20 32	20 42	20 47		21 02
Cambuslang	d	19 46			20 06	20 16			20 36	20 46			21 06
Newton	d				20 09				20 39				21 09
Blantyre	d		19 55		20 13				20 43		20 55		21 13
Hamilton West	d		19 58		20 16				20 46		20 58		21 16
Hamilton Central	d		20 01		20 20				20 50		21 01		21 20
Chatelherault	d		20 06								21 06		
Merryton	d		20 09								21 09		
Larkhall	a		20 11								21 11		
Airbles	d				20 25				20 55				21 25
Uddingston	d	19 50				20 20				20 50			
Bellshill	d	19 55				20 25				20 55			
Motherwell	a	20 03			20 27	20 33			20 57	21 04			21 27
	d					20 33							
Whifflet	a												
Coatbridge Central	a												
Shieldmuir	d					20 37							
Holytown	d												
Wishaw	d					20 40							
Carluke	d					20 47							
Lanark	a					20 59							

For general notes see front of timetable
For details of catering facilities see Directory of Train Operators

§ Low Level

A Until 27 September. From Oban (Table 227)

b Helensburgh Upper

c Glasgow Queen Street High Level

Table 226

Sundays

until 22 November

Helensburgh, Balloch, Dalmuir and Milngavie → Glasgow → Springburn, Airdrie, Drumgelloch, Hamilton, Larkhall, Motherwell, Coatbridge and Lanark

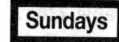

Network Diagram - see first page of Table 220

		SR	SR	SR	SR	SR	SR	SR		SR	SR	SR	SR	SR	SR	SR	SR	SR	SR	SR	SR	SR	SR		
					◇ A ⚲																[R] B ⚲				
Helensburgh Central	d		20 25		20b40			20 55				21 25				21 55			22 25		22b37	22 55			
Craigendoran	d		20 28					20 58				21 28				21 58			22 28			22 58			
Cardross	d		20 33					21 03				21 33				22 03			22 33			23 03			
Balloch	d			20 39						21 09			21 39				22 09			22 39			23 09		
Alexandria	d			20 41						21 11			21 41				22 11			22 41			23 11		
Renton	d			20 44						21 14			21 44				22 14			22 44			23 14		
Dalreoch	d		20 38	20 47				21 08		21 17		21 38	21 47			22 08	22 17		22 38	22 47		23 08	23 17		
Dumbarton Central	d		20 40	20 48	20 53			21 10		21 18		21 40	21 48			22 10	22 18		22 40	22 48		23 10	23 18		
Dumbarton East	d		20 42	20 50				21 12		21 20		21 42	21 50			22 12	22 20		22 42	22 50		23 12	23 20		
Bowling	d			20 54						21 24			21 54				22 24			22 55			23 25		
Kilpatrick	d			20 58						21 28			21 58				22 28			22 58			23 28		
Dalmuir	a		20 49	21 00	21 05			21 19		21 30		21 49	22 00			22 19	22 30		22 49	23 01	23 02	23 19	23 31		
	d		20 50	21 01	21 05			21 20		21 31		21 50	22 01			22 20	22 31		22 50	23 01	23 04		23 31		
Singer	d		20 52					21 22				21 52				22 22			22 52						
Drumry	d		20 55					21 25				21 55				22 25			22 55						
Drumchapel	d		20 57					21 27				21 57				22 27			22 57						
Milngavie	d	20 41				21 11					21 41			22 11				22 41							
Hillfoot	d	20 44				21 14					21 44			22 14				22 44							
Bearsden	d	20 46				21 16					21 46			22 16				22 46							
Westerton	d	20 49	21 00			21 19		21 30			21 49	22 00		22 19		22 30		22 49	23 00		23a11				
Anniesland	d	20 52	21 03			21 22		21 33			21 52	22 03		22 22		22 33		22 52	23 03						
Clydebank	d			21 03						21 33			22 03				22 33			23 03			23 33		
Yoker	d			21 05						21 35			22 05				22 35			23a05			23a35		
Garscadden	d			21 09						21 39			22 09				22 39								
Scotstounhill	d			21 11						21 41			22 11				22 41								
Jordanhill	d			21 13						21 43			22 13				22 43								
Hyndland	d	20 55	21 05	21 15		21 25		21 35		21 45	21 55	22 05	22 15	22 25		22 35	22 45	22 55	23 05						
Partick	d	20 58	21 08	21 18		21 28	21 34	21 38		21 48	21 58	22 08	22 18	22 28	22 34	22 38	22 48	22 58	23 08						
Exhibition Centre	d	21 01		21 21		21 31	21 37			21 51	22 01		22 21	22 31	22 37		22 51	23 01							
Anderston	d																								
Glasgow Central 15 §	a	21 03		21 23		21 33	21 39			21 53	22 03		22 23	22 33	22 39		22 53	23 03							
	d	21 04		21 24		21 34	21 40			21 54	22 04		22 24	22 34	22 40		22 54	23 04							
Argyle Street	d																								
Charing Cross	d		21 13					21 43				22 13				22 43			23 13						
Glasgow Queen Street 10 §	a		21 15		21c26			21 45				22 15				22 45			23 15						
	d		21 17					21 47				22 17				22 47			23 17						
High Street	d		21 19					21 49				22 19				22 49			23 19						
Bellgrove	d		21 21					21 51				22 21				22 51			23 21						
Duke Street	d																								
Alexandra Parade	d																								
Barnhill	d																								
Springburn	a																								
Carntyne	d		21 24					21 54				22 24				22 54			23 24						
Shettleston	d		21 27					21 57				22 27				22 57			23 27						
Garrowhill	d		21 29					21 59				22 29				22 59			23 29						
Easterhouse	d		21 32					22 02				22 32				23 02			23 32						
Blairhill	d		21 36					22 06				22 36				23 06			23 36						
Coatbridge Sunnyside	d		21 38					22 08				22 38				23 08			23 38						
Coatdyke	d		21 41					22 11				22 41				23 11			23 41						
Airdrie	a		21 44					22 14				22 44				23 14			23 44						
	d		21 45					22 15				22 45				23 15			23 45						
Drumgelloch	a		21 48					22 18				22 48				23 18			23 48						
Bridgeton	d	21 09		21 29		21 39				21 59	22 09		22 29	22 39			22 59	23 09							
Dalmarnock	d																								
Rutherglen	d	21 12		21 32		21 42	21 47			22 02	22 12		22 32	22 42	22 47		23 02	23 12							
Cambuslang	d	21 16		21 36		21 46				22 06	22 16		22 36	22 46			23 06	23 16							
Newton	d			21 39						22 09			22 39				23 09								
Blantyre	d			21 43			21 55			22 13			22 43		22 55		23 13								
Hamilton West	d			21 46			21 58			22 16			22 46		22 58		23 16								
Hamilton Central	d			21 50			22 01			22 20			22 50		23 01		23 20								
Chatelherault	d						22 06								23 06										
Merryton	d						22 09								23 09										
Larkhall	a						22 13								23 11										
Airbles	d			21 55						22 25			22 55				23 25								
Uddingston	d	21 20				21 50					22 20			22 50				23 20							
Bellshill	d	21 25				21 55					22 25			22 55				23 25							
Motherwell	a	21 33		21 57		22 02				22 27	22 33		22 57	23 06			23 27	23 33							
	d	21 33									22 33														
Whifflet	a																								
Coatbridge Central	a																								
Shieldmuir	d	21 37									22 37														
Holytown	d																								
Wishaw	d	21 40									22 40														
Carluke	d	21 47									22 47														
Lanark	a	21 59									22 59														

For general notes see front of timetable
For details of catering facilities see Directory of Train Operators

§ Low Level

A From Oban and Mallaig (Table 227)
B From Fort William (Table 227) to Edinburgh (Table 225)
b Helensburgh Upper
c Glasgow Queen Street High Level

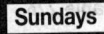

Sundays
from 29 November

Helensburgh, Balloch, Dalmuir and Milngavie → Glasgow → Springburn, Airdrie, Drumgelloch, Hamilton, Larkhall, Motherwell, Coatbridge and Lanark

Network Diagram - see first page of Table 220

		SR	SR	SR	SR	SR	SR	SR	SR	SR	SR	SR	SR
Helensburgh Central	d			07 55			08 25						08 55
Craigendoran	d			07 58			08 28						08 58
Cardross	d			08 03			08 33						09 03
Balloch	d				08 09			08 39					
Alexandria	d				08 11			08 41					
Renton	d				08 14			08 44					
Dalreoch	d			08 08	08 17		08 38	08 47					09 08
Dumbarton Central	d			08 10	08 18		08 40	08 48					09 10
Dumbarton East	d			08 12	08 20		08 42	08 50					09 12
Bowling	d				08 24			08 54					
Kilpatrick	d				08 28			08 58					
Dalmuir	a			08 19	08 30		08 49	09 00					09 19
	d	07 50	08 01	08 20	08 31		08 50	09 01	09 05		09 15		09 20
Singer	d	07 52		08 22			08 52		09 07				09 22
Drumry	d	07 55		08 25			08 55		09 09				09 25
Drumchapel	d	07 57		08 27			08 57		09 12				09 27
Milngavie	d									09 11			
Hillfoot	d									09 14			
Bearsden	d									09 16			
Westerton	d	08 00		08 30			09 00		09 14	09 19			09 30
Anniesland	d	08 03		08 33			09 03		09 17	09 22			09 33
Clydebank	d		08 03		08 33			09 03			09 17		
Yoker	d		08 05		08 35			09 05			09 19		
Garscadden	d		08 09		08 39			09 09			09 22		
Scotstounhill	d		08 11		08 41			09 11			09 24		
Jordanhill	d		08 13		08 43			09 13			09 26		
Hyndland	d	08 05	08 15	08 35	08 45	08 55	09 05	09 15	09 20	09 25	09 28		09 35
Partick	d	08 08	08 18	08 38	08 48	08 58	09 08	09 18	09 22	09 28	09 30	09 34	09 38
Exhibition Centre	d		08 21		08 51	09 01		09 21		09 31		09 37	
Anderston	d												
Glasgow Central 15 §	a		08 23		08 53	09 03		09 23		09 33		09 39	
	d		08 24		08 54	09 04		09 24		09 34		09 40	
Argyle Street	d												
Charing Cross	d	08 13		08 43			09 13		09 26		09 34		09 43
Glasgow Queen Street 10 §	a	08 15		08 45			09 15		09 28		09 36		09 45
	d	08 17		08 47			09 17		09 29		09 37		09 47
High Street	d	08 19		08 49			09 19		09 31		09 39		09 49
Bellgrove	d	08 21		08 51			09 21		09 33		09 41		09 51
Duke Street	d								09 35				
Alexandra Parade	d								09 36				
Barnhill	d								09 39				
Springburn	a								09 41				
Carntyne	d	08 24		08 54			09 24				09 44		09 54
Shettleston	d	08 27		08 57			09 27				09 47		09 57
Garrowhill	d	08 29		08 59			09 29				09 49		09 59
Easterhouse	d	08 32		09 02			09 32				09 52		10 02
Blairhill	d	08 36		09 06			09 36				09 56		10 06
Coatbridge Sunnyside	d	08 38		09 08			09 38				09 58		10 08
Coatdyke	d	08 41		09 11			09 41				10 01		10 11
Airdrie	a	08 44		09 14			09 44				10 04		10 14
	d	08 45		09 15			09 45						10 15
Drumgelloch	a	08 48		09 18			09 48						10 18
Bridgeton	d		08 29		08 59	09 09		09 29		09 39			
Dalmarnock	d												
Rutherglen	d		08 32		09 02	09 12		09 32		09 42		09 47	
Cambuslang	d		08 36		09 06	09 16		09 36		09 46			
Newton	d				09 09			09 39					
Blantyre	d				09 13			09 43				09 55	
Hamilton West	d				09 16			09 46				09 58	
Hamilton Central	d				09 20			09 50				10 01	
Chatelherault	d											10 06	
Merryton	d											10 09	
Larkhall	a											10 11	
Airbles	d				09 25			09 55					
Uddingston	d		08 40			09 20				09 52			
Bellshill	d		08 45			09 25				09 57			
Motherwell	a		08 53		09 27	09 33		09 57		10 03			
	d					09 33							
Whifflet	a												
Coatbridge Central	a												
Shieldmuir	d					09 37							
Holytown	d												
Wishaw	d					09 40							
Carluke	d					09 47							
Lanark	a					09 59							

		SR	SR	SR	SR	SR	SR	SR	SR	SR	SR	SR	SR
Helensburgh Central	d					09 25						09 55	
Craigendoran	d					09 28						09 58	
Cardross	d					09 33						10 03	
Balloch	d	09 09					09 39						10 09
Alexandria	d	09 11					09 41						10 11
Renton	d	09 14					09 44						10 14
Dalreoch	d	09 17				09 38	09 47					10 08	10 17
Dumbarton Central	d	09 18				09 40	09 48					10 10	10 18
Dumbarton East	d	09 20				09 42	09 50					10 12	10 20
Bowling	d	09 24					09 54						10 24
Kilpatrick	d	09 28					09 58						10 28
Dalmuir	a	09 30				09 49	10 00					10 19	10 30
	d	09 31	09 35		09 45	09 50	10 01	10 05		10 15		10 20	10 31
Singer	d		09 37			09 52		10 07				10 22	
Drumry	d		09 39			09 55		10 09				10 25	
Drumchapel	d		09 42			09 57		10 12				10 27	
Milngavie	d			09 41					10 11				
Hillfoot	d			09 44					10 14				
Bearsden	d			09 46					10 16				
Westerton	d		09 44	09 49		10 00		10 14	10 19			10 30	
Anniesland	d		09 47	09 52		10 03		10 17	10 22			10 33	
Clydebank	d	09 33			09 47		10 03			10 17			10 33
Yoker	d	09 35			09 49		10 05			10 19			10 35
Garscadden	d	09 39			09 52		10 09			10 22			10 39
Scotstounhill	d	09 41			09 54		10 11			10 24			10 41
Jordanhill	d	09 43			09 56		10 13			10 26			10 43
Hyndland	d	09 45	09 50	09 54	09 59	10 05	10 15	10 20	10 25	10 28		10 35	10 45
Partick	d	09 48	09 52	09 57	10 01	10 08	10 18	10 22	10 28	10 30	10 34	10 38	10 48
Exhibition Centre	d	09 51		10 00			10 21		10 31		10 37		10 51
Anderston	d												
Glasgow Central 15 §	a	09 53		10 02			10 23		10 33		10 39		10 53
	d	09 54		10 03			10 24		10 34		10 40		10 54
Argyle Street	d	09 56		10 06			10 26		10 36		10 42		10 56
Charing Cross	d		09 56		10 05	10 13		10 26		10 35		10 43	
Glasgow Queen Street 10 §	a		09 58		10 07	10 15		10 28		10 37		10 45	
	d		09 59		10 07	10 17		10 29		10 37		10 47	
High Street	d		10 01		10 09	10 19		10 31		10 39		10 49	
Bellgrove	d		10 03		10 11	10 21		10 33		10 41		10 51	
Duke Street	d		10 05					10 35					
Alexandra Parade	d		10 06					10 36					
Barnhill	d		10 09					10 39					
Springburn	a		10 11					10 41					
Carntyne	d				10 15	10 24				10 45		10 54	
Shettleston	d				10 17	10 27				10 47		10 57	
Garrowhill	d				10 20	10 29				10 50		10 59	
Easterhouse	d				10 22	10 32				10 52		11 02	
Blairhill	d				10 26	10 36				10 56		11 06	
Coatbridge Sunnyside	d				10 29	10 38				10 59		11 08	
Coatdyke	d				10 31	10 41				11 01		11 11	
Airdrie	a				10 34	10 44				11 04		11 14	
	d					10 45						11 15	
Drumgelloch	a					10 48						11 18	
Bridgeton	d	09 59		10 09			10 29		10 39				10 59
Dalmarnock	d												
Rutherglen	d	10 02		10 12			10 32		10 42		10 47		11 02
Cambuslang	d	10 06		10 16			10 36		10 46				11 06
Newton	d	10 09					10 39						11 09
Blantyre	d	10 13					10 43				10 55		11 13
Hamilton West	d	10 16					10 46				10 58		11 16
Hamilton Central	d	10 20					10 50				11 01		11 20
Chatelherault	d										11 06		
Merryton	d										11 09		
Larkhall	a										11 15		
Airbles	d	10 25					10 55						11 25
Uddingston	d			10 20					10 50				
Bellshill	d			10 25					10 55				
Motherwell	a	10 27		10 33			10 57		11 03				11 27
	d			10 33									
Whifflet	a												
Coatbridge Central	a												
Shieldmuir	d			10 37									
Holytown	d												
Wishaw	d			10 40									
Carluke	d			10 47									
Lanark	a			10 59									

For general notes see front of timetable
For details of catering facilities see Directory of Train Operators

§ Low Level

Table 226

Sundays

from 29 November

Helensburgh, Balloch, Dalmuir and Milngavie → Glasgow → Springburn, Airdrie, Drumgelloch, Hamilton, Larkhall, Motherwell, Coatbridge and Lanark

Network Diagram - see first page of Table 220

Station		SR	SR	SR	SR	SR	SR	SR	SR	SR	SR	SR	SR
Helensburgh Central	d				10 25						10 55		
Craigendoran	d				10 28						10 58		
Cardross	d				10 33						11 03		
Balloch	d					10 39						11 09	
Alexandria	d					10 41						11 11	
Renton	d					10 44						11 14	
Dalreoch	d				10 38	10 47					11 08	11 17	
Dumbarton Central	d				10 40	10 48					11 10	11 18	
Dumbarton East	d				10 42	10 50					11 12	11 20	
Bowling	d					10 54						11 24	
Kilpatrick	d					10 58						11 28	
Dalmuir	a				10 49	11 00					11 19	11 30	
	d	10 35		10 45	10 50	11 01	11 05		11 15		11 20	11 31	11 35
Singer	d	10 37			10 52		11 07				11 22		11 37
Drumry	d	10 39			10 55		11 09				11 25		11 39
Drumchapel	d	10 42			10 57		11 12				11 27		11 42
Milngavie	d		10 41					11 11					
Hillfoot	d		10 44					11 14					
Bearsden	d		10 46					11 16					
Westerton	d	10 44	10 49		11 00		11 14	11 19			11 30		11 44
Anniesland	d	10 47	10 52		11 03		11 17	11 22			11 33		11 47
Clydebank	d			10 47		11 03			11 17			11 33	
Yoker	d			10 49		11 05			11 19			11 35	
Garscadden	d			10 52		11 09			11 22			11 39	
Scotstounhill	d			10 54		11 11			11 24			11 41	
Jordanhill	d			10 56		11 13			11 26			11 43	
Hyndland	d	10 50	10 55	10 59	11 05	11 15	11 20	11 25	11 28		11 35	11 45	11 50
Partick	d	10 52	10 58	11 01	11 08	11 18	11 22	11 28	11 30	11 34	11 38	11 48	11 52
Exhibition Centre	d		11 01			11 21		11 31		11 37		11 51	
Anderston	d												
Glasgow Central 15 §	a		11 03			11 23		11 33		11 39		11 53	
	d		11 04			11 24		11 34		11 40		11 54	
Argyle Street	d		11 06			11 26		11 36		11 42		11 56	
Charing Cross	d	10 56		11 05	11 13		11 26		11 34		11 43		
Glasgow Queen Street 10 §	a	10 58		11 07	11 15		11 28		11 36		11 45		
	d	10 59		11 07	11 17		11 29		11 37		11 47		
High Street	d	11 01		11 09	11 19		11 31		11 39		11 49		
Bellgrove	d	11 03		11 11	11 21		11 33		11 41		11 51		
Duke Street	d	11 05					11 35						
Alexandra Parade	d	11 06					11 36						
Barnhill	d	11 09					11 39						
Springburn	a	11 11					11 41						
Carntyne	d			11 15	11 24				11 44		11 54		
Shettleston	d			11 17	11 27				11 47		11 57		
Garrowhill	d			11 20	11 29				11 49		11 59		
Easterhouse	d			11 22	11 32				11 52		12 02		
Blairhill	d			11 26	11 36				11 56		12 06		
Coatbridge Sunnyside	d			11 29	11 38				11 58		12 08		
Coatdyke	d			11 31	11 41				12 01		12 11		
Airdrie	a			11 34	11 44				12 04		12 14		
	d				11 45						12 15		
Drumgelloch	a				11 48						12 18		
Bridgeton	d		11 07			11 29		11 39				11 59	
Dalmarnock	d												
Rutherglen	d		11 12			11 32		11 42		11 47		12 02	
Cambuslang	d		11 16			11 36		11 46				12 06	
Newton	d					11 39						12 09	
Blantyre	d					11 43				11 55		12 13	
Hamilton West	d					11 46				11 58		12 16	
Hamilton Central	d					11 50				12 01		12 20	
Chatelherault	d									12 06			
Merryton	d									12 09			
Larkhall	a									12 12			
Airbles	d					11 55						12 25	
Uddingston	d		11 20					11 50					
Bellshill	d		11 25					11 55					
Motherwell	a		11 33			11 57		12 03				12 27	
	d		11 33										
Whifflet	a												
Coatbridge Central	a												
Shieldmuir	d		11 37										
Holytown	d												
Wishaw	d		11 40										
Carluke	d		11 47										
Lanark	a		11 59										

Station		SR	SR	SR	SR	SR	SR	SR	SR	SR	SR	SR	SR
Helensburgh Central	d			11 25						11 55			
Craigendoran	d			11 28						11 58			
Cardross	d			11 33						12 03			
Balloch	d				11 39						12 09		
Alexandria	d				11 41						12 11		
Renton	d				11 44						12 14		
Dalreoch	d			11 38	11 47					12 08	12 17		
Dumbarton Central	d			11 40	11 48					12 10	12 18		
Dumbarton East	d			11 42	11 50					12 12	12 20		
Bowling	d				11 54						12 24		
Kilpatrick	d				11 58						12 28		
Dalmuir	a			11 49	12 00					12 19	12 30		
	d		11 45	11 50	12 01	12 05		12 15		12 20	12 31	12 35	12 45
Singer	d			11 52		12 07				12 22		12 37	
Drumry	d			11 55		12 09				12 25		12 39	
Drumchapel	d			11 57		12 12				12 27		12 42	
Milngavie	d	11 41					12 11						
Hillfoot	d	11 44					12 14						
Bearsden	d	11 46					12 16						
Westerton	d	11 49		12 00		12 14	12 19			12 30		12 44	
Anniesland	d	11 52		12 03		12 17	12 22			12 33		12 47	
Clydebank	d		11 47		12 03			12 17			12 33		12 47
Yoker	d		11 49		12 05			12 19			12 35		12 49
Garscadden	d		11 52		12 09			12 22			12 39		12 52
Scotstounhill	d		11 54		12 11			12 24			12 41		12 54
Jordanhill	d		11 56		12 13			12 26			12 43		12 56
Hyndland	d	11 55	11 59	12 05	12 15	12 20	12 24	12 28		12 35	12 45	12 50	12 58
Partick	d	11 58	12 01	12 08	12 18	12 22	12 27	12 30	12 34	12 38	12 48	12 52	13 00
Exhibition Centre	d	12 01			12 21		12 30		12 37		12 51		
Anderston	d												
Glasgow Central 15 §	a	12 03			12 23		12 33		12 39		12 53		
	d	12 04			12 24		12 33		12 40		12 54		
Argyle Street	d	12 06			12 26		12 35		12 42		12 56		
Charing Cross	d		12 05	12 13		12 26		12 34		12 43		12 56	13 04
Glasgow Queen Street 10 §	a		12 07	12 15		12 28		12 36		12 45		12 58	13 06
	d		12 07	12 17		12 29		12 37		12 47		12 59	13 07
High Street	d		12 09	12 19		12 31		12 39		12 49		13 01	13 09
Bellgrove	d		12 11	12 21		12 33		12 41		12 51		13 03	13 11
Duke Street	d					12 35						13 05	
Alexandra Parade	d					12 36						13 06	
Barnhill	d					12 39						13 09	
Springburn	a					12 41						13 11	
Carntyne	d		12 15	12 24				12 44		12 54			13 14
Shettleston	d		12 17	12 27				12 47		12 57			13 17
Garrowhill	d		12 20	12 29				12 49		12 59			13 19
Easterhouse	d		12 22	12 32				12 52		13 02			13 22
Blairhill	d		12 26	12 36				12 56		13 06			13 26
Coatbridge Sunnyside	d		12 29	12 38				12 58		13 08			13 28
Coatdyke	d		12 31	12 41				13 01		13 11			13 31
Airdrie	a		12 34	12 44				13 04		13 14			13 34
	d			12 45						13 15			
Drumgelloch	a			12 48						13 18			
Bridgeton	d	12 09			12 29		12 38				12 59		
Dalmarnock	d												
Rutherglen	d	12 12			12 32		12 42		12 47		13 02		
Cambuslang	d	12 16			12 36		12 46				13 06		
Newton	d				12 39						13 09		
Blantyre	d				12 43				12 55		13 13		
Hamilton West	d				12 46				12 58		13 16		
Hamilton Central	d				12 50				13 01		13 20		
Chatelherault	d								13 06				
Merryton	d								13 09				
Larkhall	a								13 15				
Airbles	d				12 55						13 25		
Uddingston	d	12 20					12 50						
Bellshill	d	12 25					12 55						
Motherwell	a	12 33			12 57		13 03				13 27		
	d	12 33											
Whifflet	a												
Coatbridge Central	a												
Shieldmuir	d	12 37											
Holytown	d												
Wishaw	d	12 40											
Carluke	d	12 47											
Lanark	a	12 59											

For general notes see front of timetable
For details of catering facilities see Directory of Train Operators

§ Low Level

Table 226

Sundays

from 29 November

Helensburgh, Balloch, Dalmuir and Milngavie → Glasgow → Springburn, Airdrie, Drumgelloch, Hamilton, Larkhall, Motherwell, Coatbridge and Lanark

Network Diagram - see first page of Table 220

		SR	SR	SR	SR	SR	SR	SR	SR	SR	SR	SR	SR	SR	SR	SR	SR	SR	SR	SR	SR	SR	SR	SR	SR
Helensburgh Central	d	12 25						12 55					13 25						13 55					14 25	
Craigendoran	d	12 28						12 58					13 28						13 58					14 28	
Cardross	d	12 33						13 03					13 33						14 03					14 33	
Balloch	d		12 39						13 09					13 39						14 09					14 39
Alexandria	d		12 41						13 11					13 41						14 11					14 41
Renton	d		12 44						13 14					13 44						14 14					14 44
Dalreoch	d	12 38	12 47					13 08	13 17				13 38	13 47					14 08	14 17				14 38	14 47
Dumbarton Central	d	12 40	12 48					13 10	13 18				13 40	13 48					14 10	14 18				14 40	14 48
Dumbarton East	d	12 42	12 50					13 12	13 20				13 42	13 50					14 12	14 20				14 42	14 50
Bowling	d		12 54						13 24					13 54						14 24					14 54
Kilpatrick	d		12 58						13 28					13 58						14 28					14 58
Dalmuir	a	12 49	13 00					13 19	13 30				13 49	14 00					14 19	14 30				14 49	15 00
	d	12 50	13 01	13 05		13 15		13 20	13 31	13 35		13 45	13 50	14 01	14 05		14 15		14 20	14 31	14 35		14 45	14 50	15 01
Singer	d	12 52		13 07				13 22		13 37			13 52		14 07				14 22		14 37			14 52	
Drumry	d	12 55		13 09				13 25		13 39			13 55		14 09				14 25		14 39			14 55	
Drumchapel	d	12 57		13 12				13 27		13 42			13 57		14 12				14 27		14 42			14 57	
Milngavie	d				13 11						13 41					14 11						14 41			
Hillfoot	d				13 14						13 44					14 14						14 44			
Bearsden	d				13 16						13 46					14 16						14 46			
Westerton	d	13 00		13 14	13 19			13 30		13 44	13 49		14 00		14 14	14 19			14 30		14 44	14 49		15 00	
Anniesland	d	13 03		13 17	13 22			13 33		13 47	13 52		14 03		14 17	14 22			14 33		14 47	14 52		15 03	
Clydebank	d		13 03			13 17			13 33			13 47		14 03			14 17			14 33			14 47		15 03
Yoker	d		13 05			13 19			13 35			13 49		14 05			14 19			14 35			14 49		15 05
Garscadden	d		13 09			13 22			13 39			13 52		14 09			14 22			14 39			14 52		15 09
Scotstounhill	d		13 11			13 24			13 41			13 54		14 11			14 24			14 41			14 54		15 11
Jordanhill	d		13 13			13 26			13 43			13 56		14 13			14 26			14 43			14 56		15 13
Hyndland	d	13 05	13 15	13 20	13 25	13 28		13 35	13 45	13 50	13 55	13 58	14 05	14 15	14 20	14 25	14 28		14 35	14 45	14 50	14 55	14 58	15 05	15 15
Partick	d	13 08	13 18	13 22	13 28	13 30	13 34	13 38	13 48	13 52	13 58	14 00	14 08	14 18	14 22	14 28	14 30	14 34	14 38	14 48	14 52	14 58	15 00	15 08	15 18
Exhibition Centre	d		13 21		13 31		13 37		13 51		14 01			14 21		14 31		14 37		14 51		15 01			15 21
Anderston	d																								
Glasgow Central 15 §	a		13 23		13 33		13 39		13 53		14 03			14 23		14 33		14 39		14 53		15 03			15 23
	d		13 24		13 34		13 40		13 54		14 04			14 24		14 34		14 40		14 54		15 04			15 24
Argyle Street	d		13 26		13 36		13 42		13 56		14 06			14 26		14 36		14 42		14 56		15 06			15 26
Charing Cross	d	13 13		13 26		13 34		13 43		13 56		14 04	14 13		14 26		14 34		14 43		14 56		15 04	15 13	
Glasgow Queen Street 10 §	a	13 15		13 28		13 36		13 45		13 58		14 06	14 15		14 28		14 36		14 45		14 58		15 06	15 15	
	d	13 17		13 29		13 37		13 47		13 59		14 07	14 17		14 29		14 37		14 47		14 59		15 07	15 17	
High Street	d	13 19		13 31		13 39		13 49		14 01		14 09	14 19		14 31		14 39		14 49		15 01		15 09	15 19	
Bellgrove	d	13 21		13 33		13 41		13 51		14 03		14 11	14 21		14 33		14 41		14 51		15 03		15 11	15 21	
Duke Street	d			13 35						14 05					14 35						15 05				
Alexandra Parade	d			13 36						14 06					14 36						15 06				
Barnhill	d			13 39						14 09					14 39						15 09				
Springburn	a			13 41						14 11					14 41						15 11				
Carntyne	d	13 24				13 44		13 54				14 14	14 24				14 44		14 54				15 14	15 24	
Shettleston	d	13 27				13 47		13 57				14 17	14 27				14 47		14 57				15 17	15 27	
Garrowhill	d	13 29				13 49		13 59				14 19	14 29				14 49		14 59				15 19	15 29	
Easterhouse	d	13 32				13 52		14 02				14 22	14 32				14 52		15 02				15 22	15 32	
Blairhill	d	13 36				13 56		14 06				14 26	14 36				14 56		15 06				15 26	15 36	
Coatbridge Sunnyside	d	13 38				13 58		14 08				14 28	14 38				14 58		15 08				15 28	15 38	
Coatdyke	d	13 41				14 01		14 11				14 31	14 41				15 01		15 11				15 31	15 41	
Airdrie	a	13 44				14 04		14 14				14 34	14 44				15 04		15 14				15 34	15 44	
	d	13 45						14 15					14 45						15 15					15 45	
Drumgelloch	a	13 48						14 18					14 48						15 18					15 48	
Bridgeton	d		13 29		13 39				13 59		14 09			14 29		14 39				14 59		15 09			15 29
Dalmarnock	d																								
Rutherglen	d		13 31		13 42		13 47		14 02		14 12			14 32		14 42		14 47		15 02		15 12			15 32
Cambuslang	d		13 36		13 46				14 06		14 16			14 36		14 46				15 06		15 16			15 36
Newton	d		13 39						14 09					14 39						15 09					15 39
Blantyre	d		13 43				13 55		14 13					14 43				14 54		15 13					15 43
Hamilton West	d		13 46				13 58		14 16					14 46				14 57		15 16					15 46
Hamilton Central	d		13 50				14 01		14 20					14 50				15 01		15 20					15 50
Chatelherault	d						14 06											15 06							
Merryton	d						14 09											15 09							
Larkhall	a						14 13											15 11							
Airbles	d		13 55						14 25					14 55						15 25					15 55
Uddingston	d				13 50						14 20					14 50						15 20			
Bellshill	d				13 55						14 25					14 55						15 25			
Motherwell	a		13 57		14 03				14 27		14 33			14 57		15 03				15 27		15 33			15 57
	d										14 33											15 33			
Whifflet	a																								
Coatbridge Central	a																								
Shieldmuir	d										14 37											15 37			
Holytown	d																								
Wishaw	d										14 40											15 40			
Carluke	d										14 47											15 47			
Lanark	a										14 59											15 59			

For general notes see front of timetable
For details of catering facilities see Directory of Train Operators

§ Low Level

Table 226

Sundays

from 29 November

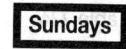

Helensburgh, Balloch, Dalmuir and Milngavie → Glasgow → Springburn, Airdrie, Drumgelloch, Hamilton, Larkhall, Motherwell, Coatbridge and Lanark

Network Diagram - see first page of Table 220

		SR	SR	SR	SR	SR	SR	SR	SR	SR	SR	SR	SR	SR	SR	SR	SR	SR	SR	SR	SR	SR	SR	SR	SR
Helensburgh Central	d					14 55					15 25						15 55					16 25			
Craigendoran	d					14 58					15 28						15 58					16 28			
Cardross	d					15 03					15 33						16 03					16 33			
Balloch	d						15 09					15 39						16 09					16 39		
Alexandria	d						15 11					15 41						16 11					16 41		
Renton	d						15 14					15 44						16 14					16 44		
Dalreoch	d					15 08	15 17				15 38	15 47					16 08	16 17				16 38	16 47		
Dumbarton Central	d					15 10	15 18				15 40	15 48					16 10	16 18				16 40	16 48		
Dumbarton East	d					15 12	15 20				15 42	15 50					16 12	16 20				16 42	16 50		
Bowling	d						15 24					15 54						16 24					16 54		
Kilpatrick	d						15 28					15 58						16 28					16 58		
Dalmuir	a					15 19	15 30				15 49	16 00					16 19	16 30				16 49	17 00		
	d	15 05		15 15		15 20	15 31	15 35		15 45	15 50	16 01	16 05		16 15		16 20	16 31	16 35		16 45	16 50	17 01	17 05	
Singer	d	15 07				15 22		15 37			15 52		16 07				16 22		16 37			16 52		17 07	
Drumry	d	15 09				15 25		15 39			15 55		16 09				16 25		16 39			16 55		17 09	
Drumchapel	d	15 12				15 27		15 42			15 57		16 12				16 27		16 42			16 57		17 12	
Milngavie	d		15 11						15 41					16 10						16 41					17 11
Hillfoot	d		15 14						15 44					16 13						16 44					17 14
Bearsden	d		15 16						15 46					16 15						16 46					17 16
Westerton	d	15 14	15 19			15 30		15 44	15 49		16 00		16 14	16 18			16 30		16 44	16 49		17 00		17 14	17 19
Anniesland	d	15 17	15 22			15 33		15 47	15 52		16 03		16 17	16 21			16 33		16 47	16 52		17 03		17 17	17 22
Clydebank	d			15 17			15 33			15 47		16 03			16 17			16 33			16 47		17 03		
Yoker	d			15 19			15 35			15 49		16 05			16 19			16 35			16 49		17 05		
Garscadden	d			15 22			15 39			15 52		16 09			16 22			16 39			16 52		17 09		
Scotstounhill	d			15 24			15 41			15 54		16 11			16 24			16 41			16 54		17 11		
Jordanhill	d			15 26			15 43			15 56		16 13			16 26			16 43			16 56		17 13		
Hyndland	d	15 20	15 25	15 28		15 35	15 45	15 50	15 55	15 58	16 05	16 15	16 20	16 24	16 28		16 35	16 45	16 50	16 55	16 59	17 05	17 15	17 20	17 25
Partick	d	15 22	15 28	15 30	15 34	15 38	15 48	15 52	15 58	16 00	16 08	16 18	16 22	16 27	16 30	16 34	16 38	16 48	16 52	16 58	17 01	17 08	17 18	17 22	17 28
Exhibition Centre	d		15 31		15 37		15 51		16 01			16 21		16 30		16 37		16 51		17 01			17 21		17 31
Anderston	d																								
Glasgow Central 15 §	a		15 33		15 39		15 53		16 03			16 23		16 33		16 39		16 53		17 03			17 23		17 33
	d		15 34		15 40		15 54		16 04			16 24		16 34		16 40		16 54		17 04			17 24		17 34
Argyle Street	d		15 36		15 42		15 56		16 06			16 26		16 36		16 42		16 56		17 06			17 26		17 36
Charing Cross	d	15 26		15 34		15 43		15 56		16 04	16 13		16 26		16 34		16 43		16 56		17 05	17 13		17 26	
Glasgow Queen Street 10 §	a	15 28		15 36		15 45		15 58		16 06	16 15		16 28		16 36		16 45		16 58		17 07	17 15		17 28	
	d	15 29		15 37		15 47		15 59		16 07	16 17		16 29		16 37		16 47		16 59		17 07	17 17		17 29	
High Street	d	15 31		15 39		15 49		16 01		16 09	16 19		16 31		16 39		16 49		17 01		17 09	17 19		17 31	
Bellgrove	d	15 33		15 41		15 51		16 03		16 11	16 21		16 33		16 41		16 51		17 03		17 11	17 21		17 33	
Duke Street	d	15 35						16 05					16 35						17 05					17 35	
Alexandra Parade	d	15 36						16 06					16 36						17 06					17 36	
Barnhill	d	15 39						16 09					16 39						17 09					17 39	
Springburn	a	15 41						16 11					16 41						17 11					17 41	
Carntyne	d			15 44		15 54				16 14	16 24				16 44		16 54				17 15	17 24			
Shettleston	d			15 47		15 57				16 17	16 27				16 47		16 57				17 17	17 27			
Garrowhill	d			15 49		15 59				16 19	16 29				16 49		16 59				17 20	17 29			
Easterhouse	d			15 52		16 02				16 22	16 32				16 52		17 02				17 22	17 32			
Blairhill	d			15 56		16 06				16 26	16 36				16 56		17 06				17 26	17 36			
Coatbridge Sunnyside	d			15 58		16 08				16 28	16 38				16 58		17 08				17 29	17 38			
Coatdyke	d			16 01		16 11				16 31	16 41				17 01		17 11				17 31	17 41			
Airdrie	a			16 04		16 14				16 34	16 44				17 04		17 14				17 34	17 44			
	d					16 15					16 45						17 15					17 45			
Drumgelloch	a					16 18					16 48						17 18					17 48			
Bridgeton	d		15 39				15 59		16 09			16 29		16 39				16 59		17 09			17 29		17 39
Dalmarnock	d																								
Rutherglen	d		15 42		15 47		16 02		16 12			16 32		16 42		16 47		17 02		17 12			17 32		17 42
Cambuslang	d		15 46				16 06		16 16			16 36		16 46				17 06		17 16			17 36		17 46
Newton	d						16 09					16 39						17 09					17 39		
Blantyre	d				15 55		16 13					16 43				16 55		17 13					17 43		
Hamilton West	d				15 58		16 16					16 46				16 58		17 16					17 46		
Hamilton Central	d				16 01		16 20					16 50				17 01		17 20					17 50		
Chatelherault	d				16 06											17 06									
Merryton	d				16 09											17 09									
Larkhall	a				16 15											17 11									
Airbles	d						16 25					16 55						17 25					17 55		
Uddingston	d		15 50						16 20					16 50						17 20					17 50
Bellshill	d		15 55						16 25					16 55						17 25					17 55
Motherwell	a		16 02				16 27		16 33			16 57		17 03				17 27		17 33			17 57		18 02
	d								16 33											17 33					
Whifflet	a																								
Coatbridge Central	a																								
Shieldmuir	d								16 37											17 37					
Holytown	d																								
Wishaw	d								16 40											17 40					
Carluke	d								16 47											17 47					
Lanark	a								16 59											17 59					

For general notes see front of timetable
For details of catering facilities see Directory of Train Operators

§ Low Level

Table 226

Sundays

from 29 November

Helensburgh, Balloch, Dalmuir and Milngavie → Glasgow → Springburn, Airdrie, Drumgelloch, Hamilton, Larkhall, Motherwell, Coatbridge and Lanark

Network Diagram - see first page of Table 220

		SR	SR	SR	SR	SR	SR	SR	SR	SR	SR	SR	SR	SR	SR	SR	SR	SR	SR	SR	SR	SR	SR	SR	SR
Helensburgh Central	d			16 55					17 25				17 55		18 25				18 55		19 25				
Craigendoran	d			16 58					17 28				17 58		18 28				18 58		19 28				
Cardross	d			17 03					17 33				18 03		18 33				19 03		19 33				
Balloch	d				17 09					17 39				18 09		18 39				19 09		19 39			
Alexandria	d				17 11					17 41				18 11		18 41				19 11		19 41			
Renton	d				17 14					17 44				18 14		18 44				19 14		19 44			
Dalreoch	d			17 08	17 17				17 38	17 47			18 08	18 17	18 38	18 47			19 08	19 17	19 38	19 47			
Dumbarton Central	d			17 10	17 18				17 40	17 48			18 10	18 18	18 40	18 48			19 10	19 18	19 40	19 48			
Dumbarton East	d			17 12	17 20				17 42	17 50			18 12	18 20	18 42	18 50			19 12	19 20	19 42	19 50			
Bowling	d				17 24					17 54				18 24		18 54				19 24		19 54			
Kilpatrick	d				17 28					17 58				18 28		18 58				19 28		19 58			
Dalmuir	a			17 19	17 30				17 49	18 00			18 19	18 30	18 49	19 00			19 19	19 30	19 49	20 00			
	d	17 15		17 20	17 31	17 35		17 45	17 50	18 01			18 20	18 31	18 50	19 01			19 20	19 31	19 50	20 01			
Singer	d			17 22		17 37			17 52				18 22		18 52				19 22		19 52				
Drumry	d			17 25		17 39			17 55				18 25		18 55				19 25		19 55				
Drumchapel	d			17 27		17 42			17 57				18 27		18 57				19 27		19 57				
Milngavie	d						17 41				18 11						19 11				19 41			20 11	
Hillfoot	d						17 44				18 14						19 14				19 44			20 14	
Bearsden	d						17 46				18 16						19 16				19 46			20 16	
Westerton	d			17 30		17 44	17 49		18 00		18 19		18 30		19 00		19 19		19 30		19 49	20 00		20 19	
Anniesland	d			17 33		17 47	17 52		18 03		18 22		18 33		19 03		19 22		19 33		19 52	20 03		20 22	
Clydebank	d	17 17			17 33			17 47		18 03				18 33		19 03				19 33			20 03		
Yoker	d	17 19			17 35			17 49		18 05				18 35		19 05				19 35			20 05		
Garscadden	d	17 22			17 39			17 52		18 09				18 39		19 09				19 39			20 09		
Scotstounhill	d	17 24			17 41			17 54		18 11				18 41		19 11				19 41			20 11		
Jordanhill	d	17 26			17 43			17 56		18 13				18 43		19 13				19 43			20 13		
Hyndland	d	17 28		17 35	17 45	17 50	17 55	17 58	18 05	18 15	18 25		18 35	18 45	19 05	19 15	19 25		19 35	19 45	19 55	20 05	20 15	20 25	
Partick	d	17 30	17 34	17 38	17 48	17 52	17 58	18 00	18 08	18 18	18 28	18 34	18 38	18 48	19 08	19 18	19 28	19 34	19 38	19 48	19 58	20 08	20 18	20 28	20 34
Exhibition Centre	d		17 37		17 51		18 01			18 21	18 31	18 37		18 51		19 21	19 31	19 37		19 51	20 01		20 21	20 31	20 37
Anderston	d																								
Glasgow Central 15 §	a		17 39		17 53		18 03			18 23	18 33	18 39		18 53		19 23	19 33	19 39		19 53	20 03		20 23	20 33	20 39
	d		17 40		17 54		18 04			18 24	18 34	18 40		18 54		19 24	19 34	19 40		19 54	20 04		20 24	20 34	20 40
Argyle Street	d		17 42		17 56		18 06																		
Charing Cross	d	17 34		17 43		17 56		18 04	18 13				18 43		19 13				19 43			20 13			
Glasgow Queen Street 10 §	a	17 36		17 45		17 58		18 06	18 15				18 45		19 15				19 45			20 15			
	d	17 37		17 47		17 59		18 07	18 17				18 47		19 17				19 47			20 17			
High Street	d	17 39		17 49		18 01		18 09	18 19				18 49		19 19				19 49			20 19			
Bellgrove	d	17 41		17 51		18 03		18 11	18 21				18 51		19 21				19 51			20 21			
Duke Street	d					18 05																			
Alexandra Parade	d					18 06																			
Barnhill	d					18 09																			
Springburn	a					18 11																			
Carntyne	d	17 44		17 54				18 14	18 24				18 54		19 24				19 54			20 24			
Shettleston	d	17 47		17 57				18 17	18 27				18 57		19 27				19 57			20 27			
Garrowhill	d	17 49		17 59				18 19	18 29				18 59		19 29				19 59			20 29			
Easterhouse	d	17 52		18 02				18 22	18 32				19 02		19 32				20 02			20 32			
Blairhill	d	17 56		18 06				18 26	18 36				19 06		19 36				20 06			20 36			
Coatbridge Sunnyside	d	17 58		18 08				18 28	18 38				19 08		19 38				20 08			20 38			
Coatdyke	d	18 01		18 11				18 31	18 41				19 11		19 41				20 11			20 41			
Airdrie	a	18 04		18 14				18 34	18 44				19 14		19 44				20 14			20 44			
	d			18 15					18 45				19 15		19 45				20 15			20 45			
Drumgelloch	a			18 18					18 48				19 18		19 48				20 18			20 48			
Bridgeton	d				17 59		18 09			18 29	18 39			18 59		19 29	19 39			19 59	20 09		20 29	20 39	
Dalmarnock	d																								
Rutherglen	d		17 47		18 02		18 12			18 32	18 42	18 47		19 02		19 32	19 42	19 47		20 02	20 12		20 32	20 42	20 47
Cambuslang	d				18 06		18 16			18 36	18 46			19 06		19 36	19 46			20 06	20 16		20 36	20 46	
Newton	d				18 09					18 39				19 09		19 39				20 09			20 39		
Blantyre	d		17 55		18 13					18 43		18 55		19 13		19 43		19 55		20 13			20 43		20 55
Hamilton West	d		17 58		18 16					18 46		18 58		19 16		19 46		19 58		20 16			20 46		20 58
Hamilton Central	d		18 01		18 20					18 50		19 01		19 20		19 50		20 01		20 20			20 50		21 01
Chatelherault	d		18 06									19 06						20 06							21 06
Merryton	d		18 09									19 09						20 09							21 09
Larkhall	a		18 11									19 12						20 11							21 11
Airbles	d				18 25					18 55				19 25		19 55				20 25			20 55		
Uddingston	d						18 20				18 50						19 50				20 20			20 50	
Bellshill	d						18 25				18 55						19 55				20 25			20 55	
Motherwell	a				18 27		18 33			18 57	19 03			19 27		19 57	20 03			20 27	20 33		20 57	21 04	
	d						18 33														20 33				
Whifflet	a																								
Coatbridge Central	a																								
Shieldmuir	d						18 37														20 37				
Holytown	d																								
Wishaw	d						18 40														20 40				
Carluke	d						18 47														20 47				
Lanark	a						18 59														20 59				

For general notes see front of timetable
For details of catering facilities see
Directory of Train Operators

§ Low Level

Table 226

Sundays from 29 November

Helensburgh, Balloch, Dalmuir and Milngavie → Glasgow → Springburn, Airdrie, Drumgelloch, Hamilton, Larkhall, Motherwell, Coatbridge and Lanark

Network Diagram - see first page of Table 220

		SR	SR	SR	SR	SR	SR	SR	SR	SR	SR	SR	SR	SR	SR	SR	SR	SR	SR	SR	SR	SR	SR	SR
							◇ A															R B		
Helensburgh Central	d	19 55			20 25		20b40			20 55			21 25				21 55			22 25		22b37	22 55	
Craigendoran	d	19 58			20 28					20 58			21 28				21 58			22 28			22 58	
Cardross	d	20 03			20 33					21 03			21 33				22 03			22 33			23 03	
Balloch	d		20 09			20 39					21 09			21 39				22 09			22 39			23 09
Alexandria	d		20 11			20 41					21 11			21 41				22 11			22 41			23 11
Renton	d		20 14			20 44					21 14			21 44				22 14			22 44			23 14
Dalreoch	d	20 08	20 17		20 38	20 47				21 08	21 17		21 38	21 47			22 08	22 17		22 38	22 47		23 08	23 17
Dumbarton Central	d	20 10	20 18		20 40	20 48	20 53			21 10	21 18		21 40	21 48			22 10	22 18		22 40	22 48		23 10	23 18
Dumbarton East	d	20 12	20 20		20 42	20 50				21 12	21 20		21 42	21 50			22 12	22 20		22 42	22 50		23 12	23 20
Bowling	d		20 24			20 54					21 24			21 54				22 24			22 55			23 25
Kilpatrick	d		20 28			20 58					21 28			21 58				22 28			22 58			23 28
Dalmuir	a	20 19	20 30		20 49	21 00	21 05			21 19	21 30		21 49	22 00			22 19	22 30		22 49	23 01	23 02	23 19	23 31
	d	20 20	20 31		20 50	21 01	21 05			21 20	21 31		21 50	22 01			22 20	22 31		22 50	23 01	23 04		23 31
Singer	d	20 22			20 52					21 22			21 52				22 22			22 52				
Drumry	d	20 25			20 55					21 25			21 55				22 25			22 55				
Drumchapel	d	20 27			20 57					21 27			21 57				22 27			22 57				
Milngavie	d			20 41				21 11				21 41			22 11				22 41					
Hillfoot	d			20 44				21 14				21 44			22 14				22 44					
Bearsden	d			20 46				21 16				21 46			22 16				22 46					
Westerton	d	20 30		20 49	21 00			21 19		21 30		21 49	22 00		22 19		22 30		22 49	23 00				
Anniesland	d	20 33		20 52	21 03			21 22		21 33		21 52	22 03		22 22		22 33		22 52	23 03		23a11		
Clydebank	d		20 33			21 03					21 33			22 03				22 33			23 03			23 33
Yoker	d		20 35			21 05					21 35			22 05				22 35			23a05			23a35
Garscadden	d		20 39			21 09					21 39			22 09				22 39						
Scotstounhill	d		20 41			21 11					21 41			22 11				22 41						
Jordanhill	d		20 43			21 13					21 43			22 13				22 43						
Hyndland	d	20 35	20 45	20 55	21 05	21 15		21 25		21 35	21 45	21 55	22 05	22 15	22 25		22 35	22 45	22 55	23 05				
Partick	d	20 38	20 48	20 58	21 08	21 18		21 28	21 34	21 38	21 48	21 58	22 08	22 18	22 28	22 34	22 38	22 48	22 58	23 08				
Exhibition Centre	d		20 51	21 01		21 21		21 31	21 37		21 51	22 01		22 21	22 31	22 37		22 51	23 01					
Anderston	d																							
Glasgow Central 15 §	a		20 53	21 03		21 23		21 33	21 39		21 53	22 03		22 23	22 33	22 39		22 53	23 03					
	d		20 54	21 04		21 24		21 34	21 40		21 54	22 04		22 24	22 34	22 40		22 54	23 04					
Argyle Street	d																							
Charing Cross	d	20 43			21 13					21 43			22 13				22 43			23 13				
Glasgow Queen Street 10 §	a	20 45			21 15		21c26			21 45			22 15				22 45			23 15				
	d	20 47			21 17					21 47			22 17				22 47			23 17				
High Street	d	20 49			21 19					21 49			22 19				22 49			23 19				
Bellgrove	d	20 51			21 21					21 51			22 21				22 51			23 21				
Duke Street	d																							
Alexandra Parade	d																							
Barnhill	d																							
Springburn	a																							
Carntyne	d	20 54			21 24					21 54			22 24				22 54			23 24				
Shettleston	d	20 57			21 27					21 57			22 27				22 57			23 27				
Garrowhill	d	20 59			21 29					21 59			22 29				22 59			23 29				
Easterhouse	d	21 02			21 32					22 02			22 32				23 02			23 32				
Blairhill	d	21 06			21 36					22 06			22 36				23 06			23 36				
Coatbridge Sunnyside	d	21 08			21 38					22 08			22 38				23 08			23 38				
Coatdyke	d	21 11			21 41					22 11			22 41				23 11			23 41				
Airdrie	a	21 14			21 44					22 14			22 44				23 14			23 44				
	d	21 15			21 45					22 15			22 45				23 15			23 45				
Drumgelloch	a	21 18			21 48					22 18			22 48				23 18			23 48				
Bridgeton	d		20 59	21 09		21 29		21 39			21 59	22 09		22 29	22 39			22 59	23 09					
Dalmarnock	d																							
Rutherglen	d		21 02	21 12		21 32		21 42	21 47		22 02	22 12		22 32	22 42	22 47		23 02	23 12					
Cambuslang	d		21 06	21 16		21 36		21 46			22 06	22 16		22 36	22 46			23 06	23 16					
Newton	d		21 09			21 39					22 09			22 39				23 09						
Blantyre	d		21 13			21 43			21 55		22 13			22 43		22 55		23 13						
Hamilton West	d		21 16			21 46			21 58		22 16			22 46		22 58		23 16						
Hamilton Central	d		21 20			21 50			22 01		22 20			22 50		23 01		23 20						
Chatelherault	d								22 06							23 06								
Merryton	d								22 09							23 09								
Larkhall	a								22 13							23 11								
Airbles	d		21 25			21 55					22 25			22 55				23 25						
Uddingston	d			21 20				21 50				22 20			22 50				23 20					
Bellshill	d			21 25				21 55				22 25			22 55				23 25					
Motherwell	a		21 27	21 33		21 57		22 02			22 27	22 33		22 57	23 06			23 27	23 33					
	d			21 33								22 33												
Whifflet	a																							
Coatbridge Central	a																							
Shieldmuir	d			21 37								22 37												
Holytown	d																							
Wishaw	d			21 40								22 40												
Carluke	d			21 47								22 47												
Lanark	a			21 59								22 59												

For general notes see front of timetable
For details of catering facilities see Directory of Train Operators

§ Low Level

A From Oban and Mallaig (Table 227)
B From Fort William (Table 227) to Edinburgh (Table 225)
b Helensburgh Upper
c Glasgow Queen Street High Level

Network Diagram for Tables 227, 239

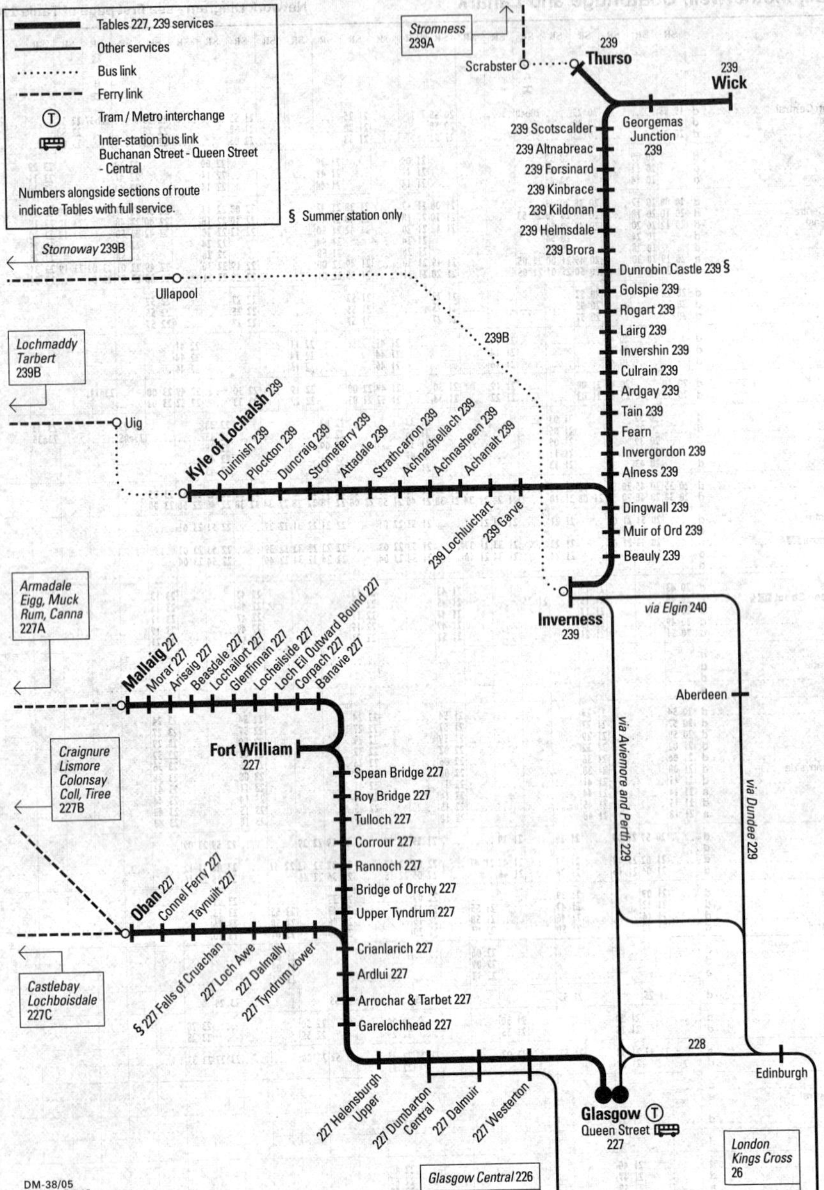

Tables 227, 239 services
Other services
Bus link
Ferry link
Tram / Metro interchange
Inter-station bus link
Buchanan Street - Queen Street
- Central
Numbers alongside sections of route
indicate Tables with full service.
§ Summer station only
Stromness
239A
Scrabster
239
Thurso
239
Wick
Georgemas
Junction
239
239 Scotscalder
239 Altnabreac
239 Forsinard
239 Kinbrace
239 Kildonan
239 Helmsdale
239 Brora
Dunrobin Castle 239 §
Golspie 239
Rogart 239
Lairg 239
Invershin 239
Culrain 239
Ardgay 239
Tain 239
Fearn
Invergordon 239
Alness 239
Dingwall 239
Muir of Ord 239
Beauly 239
Inverness
239
via Elgin 240
Stornoway 239B
Ullapool
239B
Lochmaddy
Tarbert
239B
Uig
Kyle of Lochalsh 239
Duirinish 239
Plockton 239
Duncraig 239
Stromeferry 239
Attadale 239
Strathcarron 239
Achnashellach 239
Achnasheen 239
Achanalt 239
239 Lochluichart
239 Garve
Armadale
Eigg, Muck
Rum, Canna
227A
Mallaig 227
Morar 227
Arisaig 227
Beasdale 227
Lochailort 227
Glenfinnan 227
Locheilside 227
Loch Eil Outward Bound 227
Corpach 227
Banavie 227
Fort William
227
Spean Bridge 227
Roy Bridge 227
Tulloch 227
Corrour 227
Rannoch 227
Bridge of Orchy 227
Upper Tyndrum 227
Crianlarich 227
Ardlui 227
Arrochar & Tarbet 227
Garelochhead 227
Craignure
Lismore
Colonsay
Coll, Tiree
227B
Oban 227
Connel Ferry 227
Taynuilt 227
§ 227 Falls of Cruachan
227 Loch Awe
227 Dalmally
227 Tyndrum Lower
Castlebay
Lochboisdale
227C
Aberdeen
via Aviemore and Perth 229
via Dundee 229
228
Edinburgh
227 Helensburgh Upper
227 Dumbarton Central
227 Dalmuir
227 Westerton
Glasgow
Queen Street
227
London
Kings Cross
26
Glasgow Central 226

DM-38/05
Design BAJS

Glasgow Queen Street → Oban, Fort William and Mallaig

Network Diagram - see first page of Table 227

Miles	Miles		SR ◇	SR R A	WR R 1 B	SR SX ◇ C	SR SX ◇ D	SR SX ◇ D	SR SO ◇	SR SO ◇	SR SX ◇ C	SR SO ◇ E	SR ◇	SR ◇	SR ◇	SR ◇
—	—	Edinburgh 228 d		04 50												
0	0	**Glasgow Queen Street** 10 226 d				08 21	08 21		08 21		09 07	10 37	12 21		18 21	
5½	5½	Westerton 226 d		05 56												
10	10	Dalmuir 226 d		06 04		08 39	08 39		08 39		09 26	10 50	12 42		18 37	
16½	16½	Dumbarton Central 226 d				08 48	08 48		08 48		09 34	11 04	12 48		18 46	
25½	25½	Helensburgh Upper a		06 26		09 03	09 03		09 03		09 50	11 20	13 03		19 02	
—	—	d		06 28		09 06	09 06		09 06		09 52	11 23	13 06		19 04	
32¼	32¼	Garelochhead d		06 41		09 17	09 17		09 17		10 04	11 34	13 17		19 16	
43	43	Arrochar & Tarbet d		07 07		09 37	09 37		09 37		10 27	11 54	13 37		19 36	
51	51	Ardlui d		07x21		09 53	09 53		09 53		10 39	12 08	13 53		19 51	
59¾	59¾	**Crianlarich** a		07 42		10 09	10 09		10 09		10 55	12 24	14 09		20 08	
—	—	d		07 43		10 15	10 15	10 21	10 15	10 21	10 58	12 27	14 15	14 21	20 14	20 17
64¾	—	Tyndrum Lower d				10 24	10 24		10 24			12 36	14 24		20 23	
76¾	—	Dalmally d				10 42	10 42		10 42			12 57	14 42		20 41	
79½	—	Loch Awe d				10 47	10 47		10 47			13 02	14 47		20 46	
83½	—	Falls of Cruachan § d				10 52			10b52			13b07	14b52		20b51	
88½	—	Taynuilt d				11 03	11 03		11 03			13 18	15 03		21 02	
95¼	—	Connel Ferry d				11 14	11 14		11 14			13 29	15 14		21 13	
101½	—	**Oban** a				11 27	11 27		11 27			13 42	15 27		21 26	
—	64½	Upper Tyndrum d		07 56				10 32		10 32	11 09			14 32		20 28
—	72¼	Bridge of Orchy d		08 13				10 46		10 46	11 23			14 46		20 42
—	87¾	Rannoch d		08c45				11 08		11 08	11 45			15 08		21 07
—	95	Corrour d		08x58				11 20		11 20	11 57			15 20		21 19
—	105	Tulloch d		09 18				11 36		11 36	12 13			15 36		21 35
—	110¾	Roy Bridge d		09x29				11 46		11 46	12 23			15 46		21 45
—	114	Spean Bridge d		09 37				11 54		11 54	12 30			15 53		21 52
—	122¾	**Fort William** a		09 54				12 07		12 07	12 43			16 06		22 05
—	—	d	08 30		10 20			12 12		12 12	12 48			16 19		22 10
—	125	Banavie d	08 36					12 18		12 18	12 54			16 25		22 16
—	126	Corpach d	08 41					12 23		12 23	12 59			16 30		22 21
—	129	Loch Eil Outward Bound d	08 47					12 29		12 29	13 05			16 36		22 27
—	132¾	Locheilside d	08x52					12x34		12x34	13x10			16x41		22x32
—	139¼	Glenfinnan d	09 03					12 46		12 46	13 21			16 54		22 43
—	148½	Lochailort d	09x19					13x01		13x01	13x37			17x10		22x59
—	153¼	Beasdale d	09x28					13x10		13x10	13x46			17x19		23x08
—	156¾	Arisaig d	09 36					13 18		13 18	13 54			17 27		23 16
—	161¼	Morar d	09 44					13 26		13 26	14 01			17 35		23 24
—	164¼	**Mallaig** a	09 52		12 25			13 34		13 34	14 08			17 43		23 31

For general notes see front of timetable
For details of catering facilities see Directory of Train Operators

§ Summer Station Only

A Limited seating accommodation. Overnight Sleeping Car accommodation from London Euston (Tables 65 and 404)

B Mondays to Fridays until 16 October, and Saturdays until 10 October

C Until 25 September

D From 28 September

E Until 24 October

b Until 26 September

c Arr. 0840

Glasgow Queen Street → Oban, Fort William and Mallaig

Network Diagram - see first page of Table 227

		WR	SR	SR	SR	SR	SR	SR	SR
		R 1	◇	◇	◇	◇		◇	
		A	B	B	C	B			
Edinburgh	228 d								
Glasgow Queen Street 10	226 d			09 55	12 20	12 20		18 20	
Westerton	226 d								
Dalmuir	226 d			10 13	12 35	12 35		18 35	
Dumbarton Central	226 d			10 22	12 43	12 43		18 44	
Helensburgh Upper	a			10 37	12 58	12 58		19 00	
	d			10 40	13 03	13 03		19 03	
Garelochhead	d			10 51	13 14	13 14		19 14	
Arrochar & Tarbet	d			11 11	13 34	13 34		19 34	
Ardlui	d			11 27	13 51	13b53		19 52	
Crianlarich	a			11 43	14 09	14 11		20 08	
	d			11 49	14 15	14 17	14 23	20 14	20 20
Tyndrum Lower	d			11 58	14 24	14 26		20 23	
Dalmally	d			12 16	14 42	14 44		20 41	
Loch Awe	d			12 21	14 47	14 49		20 46	
Falls of Cruachan §	d			12 26		14 54		20c51	
Taynuilt	d			12 37	15 03	15 05		21 02	
Connel Ferry	d			12 48	15 14	15 16		21 13	
Oban	a			13 01	15 27	15 29		21 26	
Upper Tyndrum	d						14 34		20 31
Bridge of Orchy	d						14 48		20 42
Rannoch	d						15 10		21 07
Corrour	d						15 22		21 19
Tulloch	d						15 38		21 35
Roy Bridge	d						15 48		21 45
Spean Bridge	d						15 55		21 52
Fort William	a						16 08		22 05
	d	10 20	12 12				16 19		22 10
Banavie	d		12 18				16 25		22 16
Corpach	d		12 23				16 30		22 21
Loch Eil Outward Bound	d		12 29				16 36		22 27
Locheilside	d		12x34				16x41		22x32
Glenfinnan	d		12 45				16 54		22 43
Lochailort	d		13x01				17x10		22x59
Beasdale	d		13x10				17x19		23x08
Arisaig	d		13 18				17 27		23 16
Morar	d		13 26				17 35		23 24
Mallaig	a	12 25	13 34				17 43		23 31

For general notes see front of timetable
For details of catering facilities see Directory of Train Operators

§ Summer Station Only

A Until 11 October
B Until 27 September
C 4 to 25 October

b Arr. 1347

Table 227

Mondays to Saturdays

Mallaig, Fort William and Oban → Glasgow Queen Street

Network Diagram - see first page Table 227

Miles	Miles			SR SX	SR ◇ A ⌶	SR ◇ B ⌶	SR ◇ C ⌶	SR ◇ C ⌶	SR SO ◇ D	SR SO ◇ D ⌶	SR ◇ E ⌶	SR ◇ A ⌶	SR SX ◇ C ⌶	SR SX ◇ C	WR R 1 G 🍴	SR SO ◇ H ⌶	SR ◇ J ⌶	SR ◇ K	SR ◇ ⌶	SR SX R L 🍴
—	0	**Mallaig**	d			06 03		06 03		10 10		10 10	10 10		14 10		16 05		18 15	
—	3	Morar	d			06 09		06 09		10 16		10 16	10 16				16 11		18 21	
—	7½	Arisaig	d			06 19		06 19		10 26		10 26	10 26				16 21		18 31	
—	11	Beasdale	d			06x25		06x25		10x32		10x32	10x32				16x27		18x37	
—	15¾	Lochailort	d			06x34		06x34		10x41		10x41	10x41				16x36		18x46	
—	25	Glenfinnan	d			06 51		06 51		10 58		10 58	10 57				16 51		19 03	
—	31½	Locheilside	d			07x01		07x01		11x07		11x08	11x07				17x01		19x11	
—	35¼	Loch Eil Outward Bound	d			07 07		07 07		11 14		11 14	11 13				17 07		19 17	
—	38¼	Corpach	d			07 13		07 13		11 20		11 20	11 19				17 13		19 23	
—	39¼	Banavie	d			07 17		07 17		11 24		11 24	11 23				17 17		19 27	
—	41½	**Fort William**	a			07 25		07 25		11 32		11 32	11 32		16 02		17 27		19 37	
—	—		d			07 42		07 42		11 39		11 40	11 40				17 37			19 50
—	50¼	Spean Bridge	d			07 55		07 55		11b56		11 53	11 53				17 50			20 10
—	53½	Roy Bridge	d			08 02		08 02		12 02		12 00	12 00				17 57			20x17
—	59¼	Tulloch	d			08 13		08 13		12 14		12 11	12 14				18 08			20 30
—	69¼	Corrour	d			08 30		08 30		12 30		12 28	12 30				18 25			20x51
—	76½	Rannoch	d			08 43		08 43		12 44		12 43	12 42				18 36			21 06
—	92	Bridge of Orchy	d			09 03		09 03		13 03		13 02	13 03				18 56			21 34
—	99¾	Upper Tyndrum	d			09 19		09 19		13 19		13 18	13 19				19 12			21 52
0	—	**Oban**	d		08 11		08 11		12 11		12 11			12 56		16 11		18 11		
6¼	—	Connel Ferry	d		08 23		08 23		12 23		12 23			13 08		16 27		18 23		
13	—	Taynuilt	d		08 35		08 35		12 35		12 35			13 20		16 39		18 35		
18½	—	Falls of Cruachan §	d		08 43		08 43		12 43		12 43			13 28		16c47		18c43		
22	—	Loch Awe	d		08 50		08 50		12 50		12 50			13 35		16 53		18 50		
24¾	—	Dalmally	d		08 56		08 56		12 56		12 56			13 41		17 00		18 56		
36¾	—	Tyndrum Lower	d		09 15		09 15		13 15		13 15			14 00		17 19		19 15		
42	104½	**Crianlarich**	a		09 29	09 30	09 29	09 30	13 24	13 30	13 29	13 30	13 32	14 10		17 28	19 26	19 27		22 04
—	—		d		09 36		09 36		13 36		13 36		13 36	14 12		17 31	19 33			22 05
50¾	113¼	Ardlui	d		09 52		09 52		13 52		13 52		13 52	14 28		17 47	19e53			22x26
58¾	121¼	Arrochar & Tarbet	d	07 08	10 07		10 07		14 07		14 07		14 07	14 43		18 02	20 08			22 44
69½	132	Garelochhead	d	07 30	10 29		10 32		14 27		14 27		14 27	15 03		18 22	20 28			23 10
76¼	138¾	Helensburgh Upper	a	07 41	10 39		10 42		14 38		14 38		14 38	15 14		18 33	20 39			23 23
—	—		d	07 42	10 41		10 44		14 39		14 39		14 39	15 15		18 34	20 40			23 24
85¼	147¾	Dumbarton Central	226 a	07 57	10 58		10 58		14 52		14 52		14 52	15 28		18 47	20 53			
92½	154¼	Dalmuir	226 a		11 08		11 08		15 04		15 04		15 04	15 37		18 56	21 04			23 49
96	157¾	Westerton	226 a																	23 56
101½	164¼	**Glasgow Queen Street** 10	226 ⛴ a	08 37	11 30		11 30		15 30		15 30		15 30	15 58		19 18	21 29			
—	—	Edinburgh	228 a																	00 50

For general notes see front of timetable
For details of catering facilities see Directory of Train Operators

§ Summer Station Only
A From 28 September
B From 28 September. ⌶ from Fort William
C Until 25 September
D Until 26 September
E From 28 September. ⌶ Mondays to Fridays
G Mondays to Fridays until 16 October, and Saturdays until 10 October
H Until 24 October
J ⌶ from Fort William
K ⌶ Mondays to Fridays
L Limited seating accommodation. Also conveys Sleeping Car accommodation to London Euston (Tables 65 and 404)
b Arr. 1151
e Arr. 1948

Sundays

Mallaig, Fort William and Oban → Glasgow Queen Street

Network Diagram - see first page Table 227

		SR	SR	SR	WR	SR	SR		SR	SR
		◇ A	◇ B	◇ B	R 1 C	◇ D	◇	◇	R E	◇ D
Mallaig	d		10 10		14 10		16 05			18 15
Morar	d		10 16				16 11			18 21
Arisaig	d		10 26				16 21			18 31
Beasdale	d		10x32				16x27			18x37
Lochailort	d		10x41				16x36			18x46
Glenfinnan	d		10 58				16 53			19 03
Locheilside	d		11x07				17x03			19x11
Loch Eil Outward Bound	d		11 14				17 09			19 17
Corpach	d		11 20				17 15			19 23
Banavie	d		11 24				17 19			19 27
Fort William	a		11 32		16 02		17 27			19 37
	d		11 44				17 37		19 00	
Spean Bridge	d		11 56				17 50		19 20	
Roy Bridge	d		12 02				17 57		19x27	
Tulloch	d		12 14				18 08		19 40	
Corrour	d		12 30				18 25		20x01	
Rannoch	d		12 44				18 36		20 15	
Bridge of Orchy	d		13 03				18 56		20b47	
Upper Tyndrum	d		13 19				19 12		21 05	
Oban	d	12 11		12 11		16 11		18 11		
Connel Ferry	d	12 23		12 23		16 27		18 27		
Taynuilt	d	12 35		12 38		16 39		18 39		
Falls of Cruachan §	d			12 47		16x47		18x47		
Loch Awe	d	12 50		12 53		16 53		18 53		
Dalmally	d	12 56		13 00		17 00		19 00		
Tyndrum Lower	d	13 15		13 19		17 19		19 19		
Crianlarich	a	13 29	13 33	13 33		17 28	19 26	19 28	21 16	
	d	13 36		13 39		17 31	19 33		21 18	
Ardlui	d	13 52		13 56		17 47	19c53		21x39	
Arrochar & Tarbet	d	14 07		14 10		18 02	20 08		21 57	
Garelochhead	d	14 27		14 31		18 22	20 28		22 23	
Helensburgh Upper	a	14 38		14 41		18 33	20 39		22 35	
	d	14 39		14 43		18 34	20 40		22 37	
Dumbarton Central 226	a	14 56		14 56		18 47	20 53		23 02	
Dalmuir 226	a	15 05		15 05		18 56	21 05		23 11	
Westerton 226	a									
Glasgow Queen Street 10 226	a	15 31		15 31		19 15	21 26			
Edinburgh 228	a								00 15	

For general notes see front of timetable
For details of catering facilities see Directory of Train Operators

§ Summer Station Only

A 4 to 25 October
B Until 25 October
C Until 11 October
D Until 27 September
E Limited seating accommodation. Overnight Sleeping Car accommodation to London Euston (Tables 65 and 404)
b Arr. 2041
c Arr. 1948

Mallaig — Armadale (Skye) and Small Isles

Operated By Caledonian MacBrayne Ltd.

Mondays to Saturdays
until 24 October

		ThO	WO A	MO	TO		FO	B	SO C	SX D	
Glasgow Queen Street 10	227 ⛴ d							08 21	08 21	08 51	12 21
Fort William	227 d	08 30	08 30	08 30	08 30	08 30	08 30	12 12	12 12	12 47	16 19
Mallaig	227 a	09 52	09 52	09 52	09 52	09 52	09 52	13 34	13 34	14 08	17 43
Mallaig	⛴ d	10 15	10 15	10 15	10 15	10 55	12 40	13 45	14 25	15 05	18 00
Armadale	⛴ a					11 25		14 15		15 35	18 30
Eigg	⛴ d	11 30		11 30	12 45				15 40		
Muck	⛴ d	12 20			11 55				16 25		
Rum	⛴ d		11 35	12 45			14 00		19 25		
Canna	⛴ a		12 45	13 55			15 10		18 15		

Sundays
until 18 October

		E	
Glasgow Queen Street 10	227 ⛴ d		12 20
Fort William	227 d	12 12	16 19
Mallaig	227 a	13 34	17 43
Mallaig	⛴ d	14 40	18 00
Armadale	⛴ a	15 10	18 30
Eigg	⛴ d		
Muck	⛴ d		
Rum	⛴ d		
Canna	⛴ a		

Mondays to Saturdays
until 24 October

			FO	SO G	ThO		TO H	WO		MO	FO
Canna	⛴ d			10 15				14 35		14 10	15 25
Rum	⛴ d			09 05				15 45		15 20	16 35
Muck	⛴ d		10 20	12 00	12 35		13 50				
Eigg	⛴ d		11 10	12 50	13 20		13 00			16 35	
Armadale	⛴ d	08 50				14 25			17 05		
Mallaig	⛴ a	09 20	12 25	14 05	14 35	14 55	15 30	17 05	17 35	17 50	17 55
Mallaig	227 d	10 10	16 05	16 05	16 05	16 05	16 05	18 15	18 15	18 15	18 15
Fort William	227 a	11 32	17 27	17 27	17 27	17 27	17 27	19 37	19 37	19 37	19 37
Glasgow Queen Street 10	227 ⛴ a	15 30	21 29	21 29	21 29	21 29	21 29	00b19	00c20	00b19	00b19

Sundays
until 18 October

			E	
Canna	⛴ d			
Rum	⛴ d			
Muck	⛴ d			
Eigg	⛴ d			
Armadale	⛴ d	09 30	15 20	16 50
Mallaig	⛴ a	10 00	15 50	17 20
Mallaig	227 d	10 10	16 05	18 15
Fort William	227 a	11 32	17 27	19 37
Glasgow Queen Street 10	227 ⛴ a	15 30	21 26	

For general notes see front of timetable
For details of catering facilities see Directory of Train Operators

A Sails via Muck
B All Saturdays, also Mondays to Fridays from 28 September
C Sails via Canna
D Until 25 September
E 7 June to 30 August
G Sails from Rum
H Sails from Eigg
b Following day. Change at Fort William and Westerton. Reservations compulsory from Fort William
c Tuesday to Saturday mornings only. Change at Fort William and Westerton. Reservations compulsory from Fort William

For details of sailings from 25 October 2009 telephone Caledonian MacBrayne on 08000 66 5000

Oban — Craignure (Mull), Lismore, Colonsay, Coll and Tiree
Operated by Caledonian MacBrayne Ltd.

Mondays to Saturdays
until 24 October

		WFO A	SO	MO	ThO B	SO	SX	SO	SX	TO	WO			MFO	FO
Glasgow Queen Street 10	227 d	18b21	18b21	18b20	18b21	08 21	08 21	10 37	08 21	08 21	08 21	12 21	12 21	12 21	18 21
Oban	227 a	21b26	21b26	21b26	21b26	11 27	11 27	13 42	11 27	11 27	11 27	15 27	15 27	15 27	21 26
Oban	d	06 00	07 00	08 00	08 30	11 45	11 55	14 00	14 00	15 00	15 30	16 00	17 00	17 00	22 30
Craignure	a					12 31	12 41	14 46				16 46			23 16
Lismore	a								14 50				17 50		
Colonsay	a										17 45			19 20	
Coll	a	10 30	09 40	10 55	11 10					17 40					
Tiree	a	09 20	10 45	12 05	12 15					18 40					

Sundays
until 18 October

			C	C		
Glasgow Queen Street 10	227 d	18b21	09 55	09 55	12 20	12 20
Oban	227 a	21b26	13 01	13 01	15 29	15 29
Oban	d	09 00	14 00	15 00	16 00	17 30
Craignure	a		14 46		16 46	
Lismore	a			15 50		
Colonsay	a					19 50
Coll	a	11 55				
Tiree	a	13 00				

Mondays to Saturdays
until 24 October

		ThO	SO	SO	TO D	TO E	SX G	SX H	SO	SX G	SX H	SO	WFO	WO	ThO	SO	SO	SX	MO	
Tiree	d												09 35			11 15			12 25	
Coll	d												10 35			12 20			13 35	
Colonsay	d				07 50	07 50								11 45	11 55					
Lismore	d			09 00			11 00	11 00				12 00						15 00		
Craignure	d	06 45	07 00						10 30	10 55	10 55						15 00			17 00
Oban	a	07 31	07 46	09 50	10 10	10 10	11 50	11 50	11 16	11 41	11 41	12 50	13 15	14 10	14 15	15 00	15 46	15 50	16 30	17 46
Oban	227 d	08 11	08 11	12 11	12 11	12 56	12 11	12 56	12 11	12 11	12 56	16 11	18 11	18 11	18 11	16 11	16 11	18 11	18 11	18 11
Glasgow Queen Street 10	227 a	11 30	11 30	15 30	15 30	15 58	15 30	15 58	15 30	15 30	15 58	19 18	21 29	21 29	21 29	19 18	19 18	21 29	21 29	21 29

Sundays
until 18 October

			C	C			
Tiree	d					13 15	
Coll	d					14 20	
Colonsay	d						
Lismore	d		12 00		16 00		
Craignure	d	10 55		15 00			17 00
Oban	a	11 41	12 50	15 46	16 50	17 15	17 46
Oban	227 d	12 11	16 11	16 11	18 11	18 11	18 11
Glasgow Queen Street 10	227 a	15 31	19 15	19 15	21 26	21 26	21 26

For general notes see front of timetable
For details of catering facilities see Directory of Train Operators

A Sails via Tree
B Sails to Barra arr. 1515
C Until 27 September
D From 29 September
E Until 22 September
G From 28 September
H Until 25 September
b Previous night

For details of sailings from 25 October telephone Caledonian MacBrayne on 08000 66 5000

Table 227C | **SHIPPING SERVICES** | **Mondays to Saturdays** until 24 October

Oban — Castlebay (Barra) and Lochboisdale (South Uist)

Operated by Caledonian MacBrayne Ltd

		WFO	MSO	TThO A
Glasgow Queen Street 10	227 🚢 d	08 21	12 21	12 21
Oban	227 a	11 27	15 27	15 27
Oban	⛴ d	13 40	15 40	15 40
Castlebay	⛴ a	18 30	20 30	23 00
Lochboisdale	⛴ a	.	.	21 00

Sundays until 18 October

Glasgow Queen Street 10	227 🚢 d	12 20
Oban	227 a	15 29
Oban	⛴ d	15 40
Castlebay	⛴ a	20 30
Lochboisdale	⛴ a	22 20

Mondays to Saturdays until 24 October

		MO	TO	WFO B
Lochboisdale	⛴ d	07 30	.	09 00
Castlebay	⛴ d	09 20	09 20	07 00
Oban	⛴ a	14 10	14 10	14 20
Oban	227 d	18 11	18 11	18 11
Glasgow Queen Street 10	227 🚢 a	21 29	21 29	21 29

Sundays until 18 October

		C	D
Lochboisdale	⛴ d		
Castlebay	⛴ d	09 20	09 20
Oban	⛴ a	14 10	14 10
Oban	227 d	16 11	18 11
Glasgow Queen Street 10	227 🚢 a	19 15	21 26

For general notes see front of timetable
For details of catering facilities see Directory of Train Operators

A Sails via Lochboisdale
B Sails from Castlebay
C Until 27 September
D 4, 11 and 18 October

For details of sailings from 25 October 2009 telephone Caledonian MacBrayne on 08000 66 5000

Edinburgh → Falkirk High → Glasgow Queen Street

Network Diagram - see first page of Table 225

Mondays to Fridays

Miles	Station		SR 1	SR 1 ⊥	SR 1 ⊥	SR 1 ⊥	SR 1 ⊥	SR 1 ⊥	SR A	SR 1 ⊥	SR A	SR 1 ⊥	SR 1 ⊥	SR 1 ⊥	SR 1 ⊥	SR 1 ⊥	SR 1 ⊥	SR 1 ⊥	SR 1 ⊥	SR 1 ⊥	SR 1 ⊥	SR 1 ⊥	SR 1 ⊥
0	**Edinburgh** 10	225, 230, 242 d	05 55	06 30	06 45	07 00	07 15	07 30		07 45		08 00	08 15	08 30	08 45	09 00	09 15	09 30	09 45	10 00	10 15	10 30	10 45
1¼	Haymarket	225, 230, 242 d	05 59	06 33	06 49	07 03	07 18	07 33		07 48		08 03	08 18	08 33	08 48	09 03	09 18	09 33	09 48	10 03	10 18	10 33	10 48
17½	Linlithgow	230 d	06 13	06 48	07 03		07 33	07 48	07 59	08 03			08 33		09 03		09 33		10 03		10 33		11 03
22¼	Polmont 3	230 d	06 19	06 55		07 19		07 54			←	08 19	08 39		09 09		09 39		10 09		10 39		11 09
25½	**Falkirk High**	d	06 24	07 00	07 13	07 24	07 42	07 59	08b10	08 12	08b10	08 25	08 44	08 54	09 14	09 23	09 44	09 53	10 14	10 23	10 44	10 53	11 14
35¾	Croy 3	230 a	06 34	07 09	07 23		07 52	08 09	→			08 36		09 03		09 33		10 02		10 33		11 03	
41	Lenzie 3	230 a	06 47	07 21	07 48		08 05	08 35		08 24	08 30	08 47		09 19		09 47		10 17		10 47		11 17	
44	Bishopbriggs	230 a	06 51	07 25	07 52		08 10	08 39		08 35	08 35	08 51		09 23		09 51		10 21		10 51		11 21	
47¼	**Glasgow Queen Street** 10	230 ⛴ a	06 49	07 25	07 39	07 51	08 07	08 25		08 40	08 46	08 54	09 06	09 21	09 36	09 50	10 06	10 19	10 36	10 49	11 06	11 19	11 37

Station		SR 1 ⊥	SR 1 ⊥	SR 1 ⊥	SR 1 ⊥	SR 1 ⊥	SR 1 ⊥	SR 1 ⊥	SR 1 ⊥	SR 1 ⊥	SR 1 ⊥	SR 1 ⊥	SR 1 ⊥	SR 1 ⊥	SR 1 ⊥	SR 1 ⊥	SR 1 ⊥	SR 1 ⊥	SR 1 ⊥	SR 1 ⊥	SR 1 ⊥	SR 1 ⊥	SR 1 ⊥
Edinburgh 10	225, 230, 242 d	11 00	11 15	11 30	11 45	12 00	12 15	12 30	12 45	13 00	13 15	13 30	13 45	14 00	14 15	14 30	14 45	15 00	15 15	15 30	15 46	16 00	16 15
Haymarket	225, 230, 242 d	11 03	11 18	11 33	11 48	12 03	12 18	12 33	12 48	13 03	13 18	13 33	13 48	14 03	14 18	14 33	14 48	15 03	15 18	15 33	15 49	16 03	16 18
Linlithgow	230 d		11 33		12 03		12 33		13 03		13 33		14 03		14 33		15 03		15 33		16 04		16 33
Polmont 3	230 d		11 39		12 09		12 39		13 09		13 39		14 09		14 39		15 08		15 39		16 09		16 39
Falkirk High	d	11 23	11 44	11 53	12 14	12 23	12 44	12 53	13 14	13 23	13 44	13 53	14 14	14 23	14 44	14 53	15 14	15 23	15 44	15 53	16 14	16 23	16 44
Croy 3	230 a	11 33		12 03		12 32		13 03		13 33		14 03		14 33		15 03		15 33		16 03		16 32	
Lenzie 3	230 a	11 47		12 17		12 47		13 17		13 47		14 17		14 47		15 17		15 47		16 17		16 47	
Bishopbriggs	230 a	11 51		12 21		12 51		13 21		13 51		14 21		14 51		15 21		15 51		16 21		16 51	
Glasgow Queen Street 10	230 ⛴ a	11 49	12 05	12 19	12 38	12 49	13 05	13 19	13 35	13 49	14 05	14 19	14 35	14 49	15 05	15 20	15 37	15 50	16 07	16 19	16 37	16 51	17 06

Station		SR 1 ⊥	SR 1 ⊥	SR 1 ⊥	SR 1 ⊥	SR 1 ⊥	SR 1 ⊥	SR 1 ⊥	SR 1 ⊥	SR 1 ⊥	SR 1 ⊥	SR 1 ⊥	SR 1 ⊥	SR 1 ⊥	SR 1 ⊥	SR 1 ⊥	SR 1	SR 1	SR 1	SR 1	SR 1	SR 1
Edinburgh 10	225, 230, 242 d	16 30	16 45	17 00	17 15	17 30	17 45	18 00	18 15	18 30	18 45	19 00	19 15	19 30	20 00	20 30	21 00	21 30	22 00	22 30	23 00	23 30
Haymarket	225, 230, 242 d	16 33	16 48	17 03	17 18	17 33	17 47	18 03	18 18	18 33	18 48	19 03	19 18	19 33	20 03	20 33	21 03	21 33	22 03	22 33	23 03	23 33
Linlithgow	230 d		17 03		17 33		18 03		18 33		19 03		19 33	19 48	20 18	20 48	21 18	21 48	22 18	22 48	23 18	23 48
Polmont 3	230 d		17 09		17 39		18 09		18 39		19 09		19 39		20 24		21 24		22 24		23 24	23 54
Falkirk High	d	16 53	17 14	17 23	17 44	17 53	18 14	18 23	18 44	18 53	19 14	19 23	19 44	19 57	20 29	20 57	21 29	21 57	22 29	22 57	23 28	23 59
Croy 3	230 a	17 02		17 33		18 03		18 33		19 02		19 33		20 07		21 07		22 07		23 07	23 38	00 08
Lenzie 3	230 a	17 17		17 47		18 08		18 46		19 17		19 48		20 19		21 17		22 17		23 12	23 43	00 14
Bishopbriggs	230 a	17 21		17 51		18 21		18 50		19 21		19 52		20 23		21 21		22 21		23 21	23 49	
Glasgow Queen Street 10	230 ⛴ a	17 21	17 36	17 51	18 06	18 22	18 38	18 51	19 06	19 21	19 36	19 49	20 05	20 22	20 50	21 22	21 50	22 22	22 50	23 30	00 03	00 27

Saturdays

Station		SR 1	SR 1	SR 1 ⊥	SR 1 ⊥	SR 1 ⊥	SR 1 ⊥	SR 1 ⊥	SR 1 ⊥	SR 1 ⊥	SR 1 ⊥	SR 1 ⊥	SR 1 ⊥	SR 1 ⊥	SR 1 ⊥	SR 1 ⊥	SR 1 ⊥	SR 1 ⊥	SR 1 ⊥	SR 1 ⊥	SR 1 ⊥	SR 1 ⊥
Edinburgh 10	225, 230, 242 d	05 55	06 30	07 00	07 15	07 30	07 45	08 00	08 15	08 30	08 45	09 00	09 15	09 30	09 45	10 00	10 15	10 30	10 45	11 00	11 15	11 30
Haymarket	225, 230, 242 d	05 59	06 33	07 03	07 18	07 33	07 48	08 03	08 18	08 33	08 48	09 03	09 18	09 33	09 48	10 03	10 18	10 33	10 48	11 03	11 18	11 33
Linlithgow	230 d	06 13	06 48		07 33	07 47	08 03		08 33		09 03		09 33		10 03		10 33		11 03		11 33	
Polmont 3	230 d	06 19	06 55	07 19		07 54		08 19	08 39		09 09		09 39		10 09		10 39		11 09		11 39	
Falkirk High	d	06 24	07 00	07 24	07 42	07 59	08 12	08 25	08 44	08 53	09 14	09 23	09 44	09 53	10 14	10 23	10 44	10 53	11 14	11 23	11 44	11 53
Croy 3	230 a	06 34	07 09		07 52	08 09		08 36		09 03		09 33		10 02		10 33		11 03		11 33		12 03
Lenzie 3	230 a	06 47	07 21		08 06	08 35	08 24	08 47		09 19		09 47		10 17		10 47		11 17		11 47		12 17
Bishopbriggs	230 a	06 51	07 25		08 11	08 39	08 30	08 51		09 23		09 51		10 21		10 51		11 21		11 51		12 21
Glasgow Queen Street 10	230 ⛴ a	06 49	07 25	07 48	08 07	08 25	08 40	08 54	09 07	09 21	09 36	09 51	10 06	10 19	10 36	10 49	11 06	11 19	11 37	11 51	12 05	12 19

Station		SR 1 ⊥	SR 1 ⊥	SR 1 ⊥	SR 1 ⊥	SR 1 ⊥	SR 1 ⊥	SR 1 ⊥	SR 1 ⊥	SR 1 ⊥	SR 1 ⊥	SR 1 ⊥	SR 1 ⊥	SR 1 ⊥	SR 1 ⊥	SR 1 ⊥	SR 1 ⊥	SR 1 ⊥	SR 1 ⊥	SR 1 ⊥	SR 1 ⊥	SR 1 ⊥
Edinburgh 10	225, 230, 242 d	11 45	12 00	12 15	12 30	12 45	13 00	13 15	13 30	13 45	14 00	14 15	14 30	14 45	15 00	15 15	15 30	15 45	16 00	16 15	16 30	16 45
Haymarket	225, 230, 242 d	11 48	12 03	12 18	12 33	12 48	13 03	13 18	13 33	13 48	14 03	14 18	14 33	14 48	15 03	15 18	15 33	15 48	16 03	16 18	16 33	16 48
Linlithgow	230 d	12 03		12 33		13 03		13 33		14 03		14 33		15 03		15 33		16 03		16 33		17 03
Polmont 3	230 d	12 09		12 39		13 09		13 39		14 09		14 39		15 08		15 39		16 09		16 39		17 09
Falkirk High	d	12 14	12 23	12 44	12 53	13 14	13 23	13 44	13 53	14 14	14 23	14 44	14 53	15 14	15 23	15 44	15 53	16 14	16 23	16 44	16 53	17 14
Croy 3	230 a		12 32		13 03		13 33		14 03		14 33		15 03		15 33		16 03		16 32		17 02	
Lenzie 3	230 a		12 47		13 17		13 47		14 17		14 47		15 17		15 47		16 17		16 47		17 17	
Bishopbriggs	230 a		12 51		13 21		13 51		14 21		14 51		15 21		15 51		16 21		16 51		17 21	
Glasgow Queen Street 10	230 ⛴ a	12 38	12 49	13 06	13 19	13 36	13 49	14 06	14 19	14 36	14 49	15 06	15 20	15 37	15 50	16 07	16 19	16 37	16 51	17 06	17 21	17 36

Station		SR 1 ⊥	SR 1 ⊥	SR 1 ⊥	SR 1 ⊥	SR 1 ⊥	SR 1 ⊥	SR 1 ⊥	SR 1 ⊥	SR 1 ⊥	SR 1 ⊥	SR 1 ⊥	SR 1 ⊥	SR 1 ⊥	SR 1	SR 1	SR 1	SR 1	SR 1	SR 1
Edinburgh 10	225, 230, 242 d	17 00	17 15	17 30	17 45	18 00	18 15	18 30	18 45	19 00	19 15	19 30	20 00	20 30	21 00	21 30	22 00	22 30	23 00	23 30
Haymarket	225, 230, 242 d	17 03	17 18	17 33	17 47	18 02	18 18	18 33	18 48	19 03	19 18	19 33	20 03	20 33	21 03	21 33	22 03	22 33	23 03	23 33
Linlithgow	230 d		17 33		18 03		18 33		19 03		19 33	19 48	20 18	20 48	21 18	21 48	22 18	22 48	23 18	23 48
Polmont 3	230 d		17 39		18 09		18 39		19 09		19 39		20 24		21 24		22 24		23 24	23 54
Falkirk High	d	17 23	17 44	17 53	18 14	18 23	18 44	18 53	19 14	19 23	19 44	19 57	20 29	20 57	21 29	21 57	22 29	22 57	23 29	23 59
Croy 3	230 a	17 33		18 03		18 33		19 02		19 33		20 07		21 07		22 07		23 07	23 38	00 08
Lenzie 3	230 a	17 47		18 08		18 46		19 17		19 48		20 19		21 17		22 17		23 12	23 43	00 14
Bishopbriggs	230 a	17 51		18 21		18 50		19 21		19 52		20 23		21 21		22 21		23 21	23 49	
Glasgow Queen Street 10	230 ⛴ a	17 51	18 06	18 22	18 38	18 50	19 06	19 21	19 36	19 49	20 05	20 22	20 50	21 22	21 50	22 22	22 50	23 30	00 03	00 28

For general notes see front of timetable
For details of catering facilities see
Directory of Train Operators

A From Kirkcaldy (Table 242). Also stops at Camelon 0814

b Falkirk Grahamston

Table 228

Sundays

Edinburgh → Falkirk High → Glasgow Queen Street

Network Diagram - see first page of Table 225

		SR 1	SR 1	SR 1	SR 1	SR 1	SR 1	SR 1	SR 1	SR 1	SR 1	SR 1	SR 1	SR 1
		🛒		🛒	🛒	🛒	🛒	🛒	🛒	🛒		🛒	🛒	🛒
Edinburgh 10	225, 230, 242 d	08 00	09 00	10 00	11 00	12 00	12 30	13 00	13 30	14 00	14 30	15 00	15 30	16 00
Haymarket	225, 230, 242 d	08 03	09 03	10 03	11 03	12 03	12 33	13 03	13 33	14 03	14 33	15 03	15 33	16 03
Linlithgow	230 d	08 18	09 18	10 18	11 18	12 18	12 48	13 18	13 48	14 18	14 48	15 18	15 46	16 18
Polmont 3	230 d	08 24	09 24	10 24	11 24	12 24		13 24		14 24		15 24		16 24
Falkirk High	d	08 29	09 29	10 29	11 29	12 29	12 57	13 29	13 57	14 29	14 57	15 29	15 55	16 29
Croy 3	230 a	08 39	09 39	10 39	11 39	12 38	13 07		14 07		15 07		16 05	
Lenzie 3	230 a	*09b55*	*09 55*	*10 52*	*11 52*	*12 52*	*13c52*		*14e52*		*15f52*		*16g52*	
Bishopbriggs	230 a	*09b59*	*09 59*	*10 56*	*11 56*	*12 56*	*13c56*		*14e56*		*15f56*		*16g56*	
Glasgow Queen Street 10	230 a	08 59	10 00	11 00	11 56	12 54	13 23	13 51	14 23	14 51	15 22	15 51	16 22	16 51

		SR 1	SR 1	SR 1	SR 1	SR 1	SR 1	SR 1	SR 1	SR 1	SR 1	SR 1	SR 1	SR 1
		🛒	🛒		🛒	🛒	🛒	🛒	🛒	🛒	🛒			
Edinburgh 10	225, 230, 242 d	16 30	17 00	17 30	18 00	18 30	19 00	19 30	20 00	20 30	21 00	22 00	23 00	23 30
Haymarket	225, 230, 242 d	16 33	17 03	17 33	18 03	18 33	19 03	19 33	20 03	20 33	21 03	22 02	23 02	23 33
Linlithgow	230 d	16 48	17 18	17 48	18 18	18 48	19 18	19 48	20 18	20 48	21 18	22 18	23 18	23 48
Polmont 3	230 d		17 24		18 24		19 24		20 24		21 23	22 24	23 24	23 54
Falkirk High	d	16 57	17 29	17 57	18 29	18 57	19 29	19 57	20 29	20 57	21 29	22 29	23 29	23 59
Croy 3	230 a	17 07		18 07		19 07		20 07		21 07	21 38	22 39	23 39	00 09
Lenzie 3	230 a	*17h52*		*18j52*		*19k51*		*20 52*			*21 52*			
Bishopbriggs	230 a	*17h56*		*18j56*		*19k55*		*20 56*			*21 56*			
Glasgow Queen Street 10	230 a	17 22	17 52	18 22	18 51	19 22	19 51	20 22	20 51	21 22	21 55	22 55	23 55	00 25

For general notes see front of timetable
For details of catering facilities see Directory of Train Operators

b 29 November and 6 December arr. Lenzie 0856, Bishopbriggs 0900

c 29 November and 6 December arr. Lenzie 1321, Bishopbriggs 1326

e 29 November and 6 December arr. Lenzie 1421, Bishopbriggs 1426

f 29 November and 6 December arr. Lenzie 1521, Bishopbriggs 1526

g 29 November and 6 December arr. Lenzie 1621, Bishopbriggs 1626

h 29 November and 6 December arr. Lenzie 1721, Bishopbriggs 1726

j 29 November and 6 December arr. Lenzie 1821, Bishopbriggs 1826

k 29 November and 6 December arr. Lenzie 1919, Bishopbriggs 1924

Glasgow Queen Street → Falkirk High → Edinburgh

Network Diagram - see first page of Table 225

Mondays to Fridays

Miles	Station		SR	SR	SR	SR	SR	SR	SR	SR	SR		SR	SR	SR	SR	SR	SR	SR	SR	SR		SR	SR	SR
			1	1	1	1	1	1	1	1	1		1	1	1	1	1	1	1	1	1		1	1	1
				🚲	🚲	🚲	🚲	🚲		🚲	🚲		🚲	🚲	🚲	🚲	🚲	🚲	🚲	🚲	🚲		🚲	🚲	🚲
0	Glasgow Queen Street 10	230 d	06 00	06 30	06 45	07 00	07 15	07 30	07 45	08 00	08 15	.	08 30	08 45	09 00	09 15	09 30	09 45	10 00	10 15	10 30	.	10 45	11 00	11 15
3¼	Bishopbriggs	230 d	.	06 20	06 20	06 53	.	07 23	.	07 53	.	.	08 23	.	08 53	.	09 23	.	09 53	.	10 23	.	.	10 53	.
6¼	Lenzie 3	230 d	.	06 38	06 24	07 09	.	07 29	.	07 59	.	.	08 29	.	08 59	.	09 29	.	09 59	.	10 29	.	.	10 59	.
11½	Croy 3	230 d	.	.	06 56	.	.	07 41	.	08 11	.	.	08 41	.	09 11	.	09 41	.	10 11	.	10 41	.	.	11 11	.
21¾	Falkirk High	d	06 17	06 51	07 06	07 22	07 32	07 51	08 02	08 21	08 32	.	08 51	09 02	09 21	09 32	09 51	10 02	10 21	10 32	10 51	.	11 02	11 21	11 32
25	Polmont 3	230 a	06 21	06 56	.	07 26	07 37	.	08 07	08 26	.	.	.	09 07	.	09 37	.	10 07	.	10 37	.	.	11 07	.	11 37
29¾	Linlithgow	230 a	06 29	07 02	07 13	07 33	07 43	07 58	08 13	.	08 41	.	.	09 13	.	09 43	.	10 13	.	10 43	.	.	11 13	.	11 43
46	Haymarket	225, 230, 242 a	06s45	07s18	07s31	07s49	08s01	08s16	08s32	08s45	09s00	.	09s13	09s31	09s43	10s01	10s12	10s30	10s41	11s00	11s13	.	11s30	11s42	12s00
47¼	Edinburgh 10	225, 230, 242 a	06 50	07 24	07 37	07 55	08 07	08 22	08 37	08 50	09 05	.	09 19	09 36	09 48	10 06	10 17	10 35	10 47	11 05	11 19	.	11 35	11 49	12 05

Station		SR	SR	SR	SR	SR	SR	SR	SR		SR	SR	SR	SR	SR	SR	SR	SR	SR		SR	SR	SR	SR	SR
		1	1	1	1	1	1	1	1		1	1	1	1	1	1	1	1	1		1	1	1	1	1
		🚲	🚲	🚲	🚲	🚲	🚲	🚲	🚲		🚲	🚲	🚲	🚲	🚲	🚲	🚲	🚲	🚲		🚲	🚲	🚲	🚲	🚲
Glasgow Queen Street 10	230 d	11 30	11 45	12 00	12 15	12 30	12 45	13 00	13 15	.	13 30	13 45	14 00	14 15	14 30	14 45	15 00	15 15	15 30	.	15 45	16 00	16 15	16 30	16 45
Bishopbriggs	230 d	11 23	.	11 53	.	12 23	.	12 53	.	.	13 23	.	13 53	.	14 23	.	14 53	.	15 23	.	.	15 53	.	16 24	.
Lenzie 3	230 d	11 29	.	11 59	.	12 29	.	12 59	.	.	13 29	.	13 59	.	14 29	.	14 59	.	15 29	.	.	15 59	.	16 30	.
Croy 3	230 d	11 41	.	12 11	.	12 41	.	13 11	.	.	13 41	.	14 11	.	14 41	.	15 11	.	15 41	.	.	16 11	.	16 41	.
Falkirk High	d	11 51	12 02	12 21	12 32	12 51	13 02	13 21	13 32	.	13 51	14 02	14 21	14 32	14 51	15 02	15 21	15 32	15 51	.	16 02	16 21	16 32	16 51	17 02
Polmont 3	230 a	.	12 07	.	12 37	.	13 07	.	13 37	.	.	14 07	.	14 37	.	15 07	.	15 37	.	.	16 07	.	16 37	.	17 07
Linlithgow	230 a	.	12 13	.	12 44	.	13 13	.	13 43	.	.	14 13	.	14 43	.	15 13	.	15 43	.	.	16 13	.	16 43	.	17 13
Haymarket	225, 230, 242 a	12s12	12s29	12s41	13s01	13s12	13s30	13s43	14s00	.	14s12	14s30	14s41	15s00	15s12	15s30	15s42	16s00	16s11	.	16s30	16s42	17s00	17s10	17s33
Edinburgh 10	225, 230, 242 a	12 19	12 35	12 49	13 05	13 19	13 35	13 49	14 05	.	14 19	14 35	14 47	15 05	15 17	15 35	15 48	16 05	16 17	.	16 36	16 49	17 06	17 19	17 39

Station		SR	SR	SR	SR	SR	SR		SR	SR	SR	SR	SR	SR	SR	SR	SR	SR	SR	SR	SR	SR	SR		
		1	1	1		1			1	1	1	1	1	1	1	1	1	1	1	1	1	1	1		
					A		A																		
		🚲	🚲	🚲		🚲			🚲	🚲	🚲	🚲	🚲	🚲	🚲	🚲	🚲								
Glasgow Queen Street 10	230 d	17 00	17 15	17 30	17 33	17 45	.	.	18 00	18 15	18 30	18 45	19 00	19 15	19 30	20 00	20 30	21 00	21 30	22 00	22 30	23 00	23 30	.	.
Bishopbriggs	230 d	16 53	.	17 23	17 38	.	.	.	17 53	.	18 23	.	18 53	.	.	19 53	.	20 53	.	21 53	.	22 53	23 23	.	.
Lenzie 3	230 d	16 59	.	17 29	17 43	.	.	.	17 59	.	18 29	.	18 59	.	.	19 59	.	20 59	.	21 59	.	22 59	23 29	.	.
Croy 3	230 d	17 11	.	17 41	.	.	←	.	18 11	.	18 41	.	19 11	.	.	20 11	.	21 11	.	22 11	.	23 11	23 41	.	.
Falkirk High	d	17 21	17 32	17 51	18b04 →	18 02	18b04	.	18 21	18 32	18 51	19 02	19 21	19 32	19 47	20 21	20 47	21 21	21 47	22 21	22 47	23 21	23 51	.	.
Polmont 3	230 a	17 27	.	17 56	.	18 07	18 13	.	.	18 37	.	19 07	.	19 37	19 52	.	20 52	.	21 52	.	22 52	23 26	23 57	.	.
Linlithgow	230 a	.	17 40	18 03	.	18 13	18 19	.	.	18 43	.	19 13	.	19 43	19 58	20 28	20 58	21 28	21 58	22 28	22 58	23 33	00 03	.	.
Haymarket	225, 230, 242 a	17s45	18s00	18s21	.	18s31	.	.	18s42	19s00	19s12	19s30	19s42	20s01	20s15	20s46	21s13	21s46	22s18	22s45	23s15	23s49	00s19	.	.
Edinburgh 10	225, 230, 242 a	17 50	18 06	18 26	.	18 37	.	.	18 49	19 05	19 18	19 36	19 47	20 06	20 21	20 51	21 20	21 53	22 24	22 50	23 20	23 54	00 25	.	.

Saturdays

Station		SR	SR	SR	SR	SR	SR		SR	SR	SR	SR	SR	SR		SR	SR	SR	SR	SR	SR		SR	SR	SR
		1	1	1	1	1	1		1	1	1	1	1	1		1	1	1	1	1	1		1	1	1
				🚲	🚲	🚲			🚲	🚲	🚲	🚲	🚲	🚲		🚲		🚲	🚲	🚲	🚲		🚲	🚲	🚲
Glasgow Queen Street 10	230 d	06 00	06 30	07 00	07 15	07 30	07 45	.	08 00	08 15	08 30	08 45	09 00	09 15	.	09 30	09 45	10 00	10 15	10 30	10 45	.	11 00	11 15	11 30
Bishopbriggs	230 d	.	06 20	06 53	.	07 23	.	.	07 53	.	08 23	.	08 53	.	.	09 23	.	09 53	.	10 23	.	.	10 53	.	11 23
Lenzie 3	230 d	.	06 38	07 09	.	07 29	.	.	07 59	.	08 29	.	08 59	.	.	09 29	.	09 59	.	10 29	.	.	10 59	.	11 29
Croy 3	230 d	.	06 44	.	.	07 41	.	.	08 11	.	08 41	.	09 11	.	.	09 41	.	10 11	.	10 41	.	.	11 11	.	11 41
Falkirk High	d	06 17	06 54	07 22	07 32	07 51	08 02	.	08 21	08 32	08 51	09 02	09 21	09 32	.	09 51	10 02	10 21	10 32	10 51	11 02	.	11 21	11 32	11 51
Polmont 3	230 a	06 21	06 58	07 26	07 37	.	08 07	.	08 26	.	.	09 07	.	09 37	.	.	10 07	.	10 37	.	11 07	.	.	11 37	.
Linlithgow	230 a	06 29	07 05	07 33	07 43	07 58	08 13	.	.	08 41	.	09 13	.	09 43	.	.	10 13	.	10 43	.	11 13	.	.	11 43	.
Haymarket	225, 230, 242 a	06s45	07s21	07s48	08s01	08s16	08s32	.	08s44	09s00	09s13	09s31	09s45	10s01	.	10s12	10s30	10s45	11s00	11s13	11s29	.	11s46	12s00	12s12
Edinburgh 10	225, 230, 242 a	06 50	07 26	07 54	08 06	08 22	08 37	.	08 50	09 08	09 19	09 37	09 50	10 07	.	10 17	10 35	10 52	11 06	11 22	11 35	.	11 52	12 05	12 19

Station		SR	SR	SR	SR	SR		SR	SR	SR	SR	SR	SR		SR	SR	SR	SR	SR	SR		SR	SR	SR	SR
		1	1	1	1	1		1	1	1	1	1	1		1	1	1	1	1	1		1	1	1	1
		🚲	🚲	🚲	🚲	🚲		🚲	🚲	🚲	🚲	🚲	🚲		🚲	🚲	🚲	🚲	🚲	🚲		🚲	🚲	🚲	
Glasgow Queen Street 10	230 d	11 45	12 00	12 15	12 30	12 45	.	13 00	13 15	13 30	13 45	14 00	14 15	.	14 30	14 45	15 00	15 15	15 30	15 45	.	16 00	16 15	16 30	16 45
Bishopbriggs	230 d	.	11 53	.	12 23	.	.	12 53	.	13 23	.	13 53	.	.	14 23	.	14 53	.	15 23	.	.	15 53	.	16 24	.
Lenzie 3	230 d	.	11 59	.	12 29	.	.	12 59	.	13 29	.	13 59	.	.	14 29	.	14 59	.	15 29	.	.	15 59	.	16 30	.
Croy 3	230 d	.	12 11	.	12 41	.	.	13 11	.	13 41	.	14 11	.	.	14 41	.	15 11	.	15 41	.	.	16 11	.	16 41	.
Falkirk High	d	12 02	12 21	12 32	12 51	13 02	.	13 21	13 32	13 51	14 02	14 21	14 32	.	14 51	15 02	15 21	15 32	15 51	16 02	.	16 21	16 32	16 51	17 02
Polmont 3	230 a	12 07	.	12 37	.	13 07	.	.	13 37	.	14 07	.	14 37	.	.	15 07	.	15 37	.	16 07	.	.	16 37	.	17 07
Linlithgow	230 a	12 13	.	12 43	.	13 13	.	.	13 43	.	14 13	.	14 43	.	.	15 13	.	15 43	.	16 13	.	.	16 43	.	17 13
Haymarket	225, 230, 242 a	12s29	12s45	13s00	13s12	13s29	.	13s45	13s59	14s12	14s30	14s45	15s00	.	15s12	15s30	15s45	16s00	16s11	16s33	.	16s42	17s00	17s13	17s34
Edinburgh 10	225, 230, 242 a	12 35	12 52	13 05	13 22	13 35	.	13 52	14 05	14 19	14 37	14 52	15 06	.	15 17	15 37	15 50	16 05	16 16	16 39	.	16 48	17 07	17 22	17 39

Station		SR	SR	SR	SR		SR	SR	SR	SR	SR	SR		SR	SR	SR	SR	SR	SR		SR	SR	SR		
		1	1	1	1		1	1	1	1	1	1		1	1	1	1	1	1		1	1	1		
		🚲	🚲	🚲	🚲		🚲	🚲	🚲	🚲	🚲	🚲		🚲	🚲	🚲									
Glasgow Queen Street 10	230 d	17 00	17 15	17 30	17 45	.	18 00	18 15	18 30	18 45	19 00	19 15	.	19 30	20 00	20 30	21 00	21 30	22 00	.	22 30	23 00	23 30	.	.
Bishopbriggs	230 d	16 53	.	17 23	.	.	17 53	.	18 23	.	18 53	.	.	.	19 53	.	20 53	.	21 53	.	.	22 53	23 23	.	.
Lenzie 3	230 d	16 59	.	17 29	.	.	17 59	.	18 29	.	18 59	.	.	.	19 59	.	20 59	.	21 59	.	.	22 59	23 29	.	.
Croy 3	230 d	17 11	.	17 41	.	.	18 11	.	18 41	.	19 11	.	.	.	20 11	.	21 11	.	22 11	.	.	23 11	23 42	.	.
Falkirk High	d	17 21	17 32	17 51	18 02	.	18 21	18 32	18 51	19 02	19 21	19 32	.	19 47	20 21	20 47	21 21	21 47	22 21	.	22 47	23 21	23 52	.	.
Polmont 3	230 a	17 27	.	17 56	18 07	.	.	18 37	.	19 07	.	19 37	.	19 52	.	20 52	.	21 52	.	.	22 52	23 26	23 57	.	.
Linlithgow	230 a	.	17 40	18 02	18 13	.	.	18 43	.	19 13	.	19 43	.	19 58	20 28	20 58	21 28	21 58	22 28	.	22 58	23 33	00 03	.	.
Haymarket	225, 230, 242 a	17s47	18s01	18s21	18s32	.	18s45	19s00	19s11	19s32	19s42	20s01	.	20s15	20s45	21s13	21s46	22s18	22s44	.	23s15	23s49	00s20	.	.
Edinburgh 10	225, 230, 242 a	17 52	18 06	18 26	18 40	.	18 50	19 05	19 19	19 39	19 47	20 09	.	20 20	20 50	21 20	21 53	22 23	22 50	.	23 22	23 54	00 25	.	.

For general notes see front of timetable
For details of catering facilities see
Directory of Train Operators

A To Kirkcaldy (Table 242)
b Falkirk Grahamston

Sundays

Glasgow Queen Street → Falkirk High → Edinburgh

Network Diagram - see first page of Table 225

		SR	SR	SR	SR	SR	SR	SR	SR	SR	SR	SR	SR	SR
		1	1	1	1	1	1	1	1	1	1	1	1	1
			🛒	🛒	🛒	🛒	🛒	🛒		🛒	🛒			🛒
Glasgow Queen Street 10	230 ⛴ d	07 50	08 30	09 30	10 30	11 30	12 30	13 00	13 30	14 00	14 30	15 00	15 30	16 00
Bishopbriggs	230 d	.	*08b21*	*09b18*	*10 21*	*11 21*	*12 21*	*12b53*	.	*13c21*	.	*14e21*	.	*15f21*
Lenzie 3	230 d		*08b27*	*09b24*	*10 27*	*11 27*	*12 27*	*12b59*		*13c27*		*14e27*		*15f27*
Croy 3	230 d	08 01	08 41	09 41	10 41	11 41	12 41	13 11	.	14 11	.	15 11	.	16 11
Falkirk High	d	08 11	08 51	09 51	10 51	11 51	12 51	13 21	13 47	14 21	14 47	15 21	15 47	16 21
Polmont 3	230 a	08 16	08 56	09 56	10 56	11 56	12 56	.	13 52	.	14 52	.	15 52	.
Linlithgow	230 a	08 22	09 02	10 02	11 02	12 02	13 02	13 28	13 58	14 28	14 58	15 28	15 58	16 28
Haymarket	225, 230, 242 a	08s44	09s23	10s23	11s19	12s19	13s21	13s46	14s17	14s47	15s16	15 46	16s17	16s48
Edinburgh 10	225, 230, 242 a	08 49	09 28	10 28	11 24	12 24	13 26	13 51	14 22	14 52	15 21	15 51	16 22	16 53

		SR	SR	SR	SR	SR	SR	SR	SR	SR	SR	SR	SR	SR
		1	1	1	1	1	1	1	1	1	1	1	1	1
		🛒	🛒	🛒	🛒	🛒	🛒	🛒	🛒	🛒				
Glasgow Queen Street 10	230 ⛴ d	16 30	17 00	17 30	18 00	18 30	19 00	19 30	20 00	20 30	21 00	21 30	22 30	23 30
Bishopbriggs	230 d	.	*16g21*	.	*17h21*	.	*18 21*	.	*19 21*	.	*20 21*	*21 21*	*22 21*	.
Lenzie 3	230 d		*16g27*		*17h27*		*18 27*		*19 27*		*20 27*	*21 27*	*22 27*	
Croy 3	230 d	.	17 11	.	18 11	.	19 11	.	20 11	.	21 11	21 41	22 41	23 41
Falkirk High	d	16 47	17 21	17 47	18 21	18 47	19 21	19 47	20 21	20 47	21 21	21 51	22 51	23 51
Polmont 3	230 a	16 53	.	17 53	.	18 53	.	19 53	.	20 53	.	21 56	22 56	23 56
Linlithgow	230 a	16 58	17 28	17 58	18 28	18 58	19 28	19 58	20 28	20 58	21 28	22 02	23 02	00 02
Haymarket	225, 230, 242 a	17s16	17s47	18s17	18s50	19s16	19s47	20s16	20s46	21s17	21s45	22s19	23s19	00s19
Edinburgh 10	225, 230, 242 a	17 21	17 52	18 22	18 55	19 21	19 52	20 21	20 51	21 22	21 53	22 24	23 24	00 24

For general notes see front of timetable
For details of catering facilities see Directory of Train Operators

b 29 November and 6 December only

c 29 November and 6 December dep. Bishopbriggs 1354, Lenzie 1400

e 29 November and 6 December dep. Bishopbriggs 1453, Lenzie 1459

f 29 November and 6 December dep. Bishopbriggs 1554, Lenzie 1600

g 29 November and 6 December dep. Bishopbriggs 1653, Lenzie 1659

h 29 November and 6 December dep. Bishopbriggs 1754, Lenzie 1800

Edinburgh and Glasgow Queen Street → Perth, Inverness, Dundee, Aberdeen, Dyce and Inverurie

Network Diagram - see first page of Table 225

Miles	Miles	Miles	Miles	Miles		SR	SR	SR	XC	SR	XC	SR	SR	SR	SR	SR	SR	SR	SR	SR	SR
						1	1 ◇	1	1 ◇	1 ◇	1 ◇	1 ◇	1	1 ◇	1 ◇	1 ◇	1	1 ◇	1 ◇	1 ◇	1
																		A			
											[restaurant]	[trolley]			[trolley]	[trolley]		[trolley]	[trolley]	[trolley]	
—	0	—	0	0	**Edinburgh** [10] 242 d					05 30	05 33	05b18	06 29	06b33	07 30	07b04	08 00	08 29	08b03	08 33	08 59
—	1¼	—	1¼	1¼	Haymarket 242 d					05 33		05b22	06 33	06b36	07 33	07b07	08 03	08 33	08b06	08 37	09 03
—	13¾	—	13¾	—	Inverkeithing 242 d					05 46	06 06		06 47				08 17				09 17
—	26	—	26	—	Kirkcaldy 242 d					06 02			07 03		08 02		08 33			09 06	09 33
—	33¼	—	33¼	—	Markinch d					06 11	06 39		07 12		08 11		08 42			09 15	09 42
—	39¼	—	39¼	—	Ladybank d					06 19			07 19		08 19		08 50				09 50
—	42¼	—	—	—	Springfield d												08 55				
—	44½	—	—	—	Cupar d					06 25	06 51				08 25		08 59				09 56
—	51	—	—	—	Leuchars [3] d					06 32	06 58				08 32		09 06	09 23			10 03
—	—	—	—	—	St Andrews Bus Station a						07c15				09c00		09e28	09c45			10c27
0	—	0	—	—	**Glasgow Queen Street** [10] 230 d							05 55		07 06		07 41			08 41		
21	—	21	—	28¼	Larbert 230 d							06 15									
29	—	29	—	36½	Stirling 230 d							06 24		07 33		08 07			09 07		
34½	—	34½	—	42	Dunblane 230 d							06 31		07 39		08 14					
46¾	—	46¾	—	54¼	Gleneagles d							06 43									
62½	—	62½	57	70¾	**Perth** a							06 59	07 47	08 04		08 40			09 36	09 48	
—	—	—	—	—	d			06 01				07 00	07 47	08 04		08 41			09 36	09 50	
79¾	—	—	—	—	Invergowrie d								08 05								
83¼	59¼	—	—	—	**Dundee** a			06 22		06 45	07 18	07 21	08 13		08 44	09 03	09 21	09 36	09 59		10 18
—	—	—	—	—	d			06 23	06 40	06 51		07 23			08 45	09 04		09 37	10 00		
87¼	63¼	—	—	—	Broughty Ferry d																
94	70	—	—	—	Carnoustie d					07 03						09 16					
100¼	76¼	—	—	—	Arbroath d			06 40	06 56	07 10		07 39			09 02	09 23		09 53	10 17		
114	90	—	—	—	Montrose d		06 25	06 56	07 11	07 23		07 54			09 16	09 38			10 31		
124	100	—	—	—	Laurencekirk § d		06 35			07 35		08 05						10 16			
138¼	114¼	—	—	—	Stonehaven d		06 49	07 22	07 32	07 48		08 18			09 38			10 29	10 53		
146½	122½	—	—	—	Portlethen d		06 58			07 59		08 27							11 02		
154½	130½	—	—	—	**Aberdeen** a		07 13	07 44	07 55	08 13		08 39			09 57	10 16		10 53	11 17		
—	—	—	—	—	240 d		07 14	07 50				08 50			10 00			11 04			
160¾	136¾	—	—	—	**Dyce** 240 a		07 24	08 00		08 33		09 01			10 08			11 13			
171½	147½	—	—	—	**Inverurie** 240 a		07 44	08 17							10 22			11 30			
—	—	78	72½	86¼	Dunkeld & Birnam d									08f29							
—	—	91	85½	99¼	Pitlochry d									08 42						10 19	
—	—	97¾	92¼	106	Blair Atholl d									08 52							
—	—	121	116½	130¼	Dalwhinnie d									09 16							
—	—	131¼	126¾	140½	Newtonmore d									09 27							
—	—	134	129½	143¼	Kingussie d									09 32						11 01	
—	—	145¾	141¼	155	Aviemore d	07 57								09 44						11 14	
—	—	152¾	148¼	162	Carrbridge d	08 05								09g57							
—	—	180	175	188¾	**Inverness** a	08 43	09h40							10 29						11 54	

	SR SX	SR SO	SR SO	SR SX	SR	SR	SR	GR	SR	SR	SR	SR	SR	SR	SR	SR	SR	SR	SR
	1 ◇	1 ◇	1 ◇	1 ◇	1	1 ◇	1	R 1	1 ◇	1	1	1 ◇	1 ◇	1 ◇	1	1 ◇	1 ◇	1	1 ◇
								B											
	[trolley]	[trolley]	[trolley]	[trolley]		[trolley]		[restaurant] [trolley]	[trolley]			[trolley]	[trolley]	[trolley]		[trolley]	[trolley]		[trolley]
Edinburgh [10] 242 d	09 30	09 30	09b04	09b04	09 35	09j37	10 00	10 27	10b04	10 34	11 00	11 30	11b04	11 35	12 00	12 30	12b04	13 00	13 30
Haymarket 242 d	09 34	09 34	09b07	09b07	09 39	09j40	10 03	10 32	10b07	10 38	11 04	11 33	11b07	11u39	12 03	12k34	12b07	13 03	13 33
Inverkeithing 242 d					09 53		10 18	10 47		10 53	11 17				12 17			13 17	
Kirkcaldy 242 d					10 09		10 34	11 04		11 10	11 33			12u08	12 35			13 33	
Markinch d					10 18		10 43			11 20	11 42			12 17	12 42			13 42	
Ladybank d					10 25		10 50			11 27	11 50				12 49			13 50	
Springfield d																			
Cupar d							10 57				11 56				12 56			13 56	
Leuchars [3] d		10 23					11 04	11 29			12 03	12 23			13 03	13 23		14 03	14 23
St Andrews Bus Station a		10c45					11c27	11c45			12c30	12c45			13c30	13c45		14c30	14c45
Glasgow Queen Street [10] 230 d			09 41	09 41		10 11			10 41				11 41				12 41		
Larbert 230 d																			
Stirling 230 d			10 07	10 07		10 42			11 07				12 07				13 07		
Dunblane 230 d						10 49													
Gleneagles d						11 01													
Perth a			10 34	10 34	10 52	11 19			11 34	11 54			12 36	12 52			13 36		
d			10 36	10 36		11 19			11 36				12 37	12 53			13 36		
Invergowrie d																			
Dundee a	10 32	10 35	10 57	10 57			11 20	11 43	11 59		12 18	12 36	12 59		13 18	13 35	14 00	14 18	14 35
d	10 33	10 36	11 00	11 00				11 44	12 00			12 37	13 00			13 36	14 00		14 36
Broughty Ferry d																			
Carnoustie d			11 11	11 11									13 12						
Arbroath d	10 50	10 53	11 18	11 18				12 01	12 17			12 53	13 19			13 53	14 18		14 53
Montrose d	11 04	11 07	11 32	11 34				12 17	12 32				13 33			14 07	14 32		
Laurencekirk § d									12 43										
Stonehaven d	11 26	11 29		12 04				12 42				13 27				14 29	14 54		15 27
Portlethen d																			
Aberdeen a	11 45	11 48	12 14	12 33				13 07	13 14			13 46	14 12			14 53	15 13		15 46
240 d																14 56			15 55
Dyce 240 a	12 08	12 08	13 00	13 00					13 50							15 04	15 35		16 03
Inverurie 240 a																15 19			16 18
Dunkeld & Birnam d						11 38								13 11					
Pitlochry d						11 51								13 24					
Blair Atholl d						12 01								13 33					
Dalwhinnie d						12 25													
Newtonmore d														14 11					
Kingussie d						12 38								14 16					
Aviemore d						12 50								14 28					
Carrbridge d						12 59													
Inverness a						13 37								15 06					

For general notes see front of timetable
For details of catering facilities see Directory of Train Operators

§ Will open during the currency of the timetable
A [trolley] to Aberdeen
B From Leeds (Table 26)
b Change at Stirling
c By bus
e By bus. Saturdays arr. 0930
f Arr. 0824
g Arr. 0952
h Via Elgin (Table 240)
j Change at Stirling. Saturdays dep. Edinburgh 0933, Haymarket 0938
k Saturdays dep. 1 minute earlier

Table 229

Mondays to Saturdays

Edinburgh and Glasgow Queen Street → Perth, Inverness, Dundee, Aberdeen, Dyce and Inverurie

Network Diagram - see first page of Table 225

		SR	SR	SR	SR	SR	SR	GR	SR	SR	SR	SR	SR	SR	SR	SR	SR	SR	SR	GR	SR
									SO	SX							SO	SX			SX
		1◇ ⫪	R 1 ⫪	1	1◇ ⫪	1◇ ⫪	1	R 1 A B ⊘ ☕	1	1	1◇ ⫪	1◇ ⫪	1	1◇ ⫪	1	1◇ ⫪	1◇ ⫪	1◇ ⫪	1	R 1 C D ⊘ ⫪	
Edinburgh 10	242 d	13b04	13 35	14 00	14 30	14c04	14 35	15 00	15 03	15 03	15 30	15c04	15 35	15c34	16 00	16 29	16c04		16 32	16 33	16c37
Haymarket	242 d	13b07	13u39	14 04	14 33	14c07	14 38	15 04	15 08	15 09	15 34	15c07	15 39	15c37	16 04	16u33	16c07		16 37	16 38	16c41
Inverkeithing	242 d			14 17			14 53	15 19	15 25	15 25			15 53		16 17				16 51		
Kirkcaldy	242 d		14u07	14 33			15 09	15 36	15 42	15 42			16 09		16 33				17 07		
Markinch	d		14 17	14 42			15 18		15 51	15 51			16 18		16 42				17 17		
Ladybank	d			14 50			15 25		15 59	15 59			16 25		16 50				17 24		
Springfield	d																				
Cupar	d			14 56					16 05	16 05					16 56	17 17					
Leuchars 3	d			15 03	15 23			16 00	16 12	16 12	16 23				17 03	17 24					
St Andrews Bus Station	🚌 a			15e23	15f45				16f30	16f30	16f45				17g34	17h49					
Glasgow Queen Street 10	230 ⛴ d	13 41				14 41						15 41		16 11			16 41	16 41			17 12
Larbert	230 d																				17 33
Stirling	230 d	14 07				15 07						16 07		16 37			17 07			17 20	17 45
Dunblane	230 d													16 48							17 54
Gleneagles	d													17 00						17 40	18 06
Perth	a	14 36	14 52			15 36	15 53					16 36	16 53	17 18			17 36	17 36	17 52	18 00	18 23
	d	14 36	14 54			15 36						16 36		17 18			17 36	17 37		18 00	
Invergowrie	d																				
Dundee	a	14 59		15 18	15 37	15 59		16 18	16 28	16 28	16 35	16 59			17 20	17 38	17 59	18 00			
	d	15 00			15 37	16 00		16 18			16 36	17 00				17 39	18 00	18 00			
Broughty Ferry	d															17 47					
Carnoustie	d	15 12										17 13				17 55	18 13	18 13			
Arbroath	d	15 19			15 54	16 17		16 36			16 54	17 20				18 02	18 20	18 20			
Montrose	d	15 38			16 08	16 31		16 52			17 08	17 33				18 16					
Laurencekirk §	d	15 49									17 19					18 27					
Stonehaven	d				16 30			17 15			17 33	17 55				18 41	18 54	18 53			
Portlethen	d																				
Aberdeen	a	16 19			16 50	17 11		17 37			17 52	18 15				19 00	19 13	19 13			
	240 d										17 56					19 07					
Dyce	240 ✈ a	*16 52*			*17 28*						18 04					19 16	*20 17*	*20 17*			
Inverurie	240 a										18 19					19 35					
Dunkeld & Birnam	d		15 11											17 37							
Pitlochry	d		15 24											17 50						18 33	
Blair Atholl	d		15 34											17 59							
Dalwhinnie	d		16 01																		
Newtonmore	d													18 32							
Kingussie	d		16 14											18 37						19 17	
Aviemore	d		16 27											18 48						19 29	
Carrbridge	d													18 54							
Inverness	a		17 05											19 34						20 08	

		SR	SR	SR	SR	SR	SR	SR	XC	XC	GR	GR	SR	SR	SR	SR	SR	SR	SR	XC
				SO	SX			SX	SO	SX	SX	SO								SX
		E	1◇ ⫪	1◇ ⫪	1◇ ⫪	1◇ ⫪		1	1◇ G ⫪	1◇ G ⫪	R 1 H ⊘ ⫪	R 1 H ☕ ⫪	1◇ ⫪	1	1	1◇ ⫪	1◇ ⫪	1◇ ⫪		1◇ G
Edinburgh 10	242 d	17 03	17j35	17c04	17c25	17 41	17c33	18 00	18 08	18 16	18 30	18 32	18c04	18 40	19 00	19 30	19c04	19 35	20 00	20 15
Haymarket	242 d	17 07	17k39	17c07	17c30	17u45	17c37	18 04	18 13	18 21	18 35	18 37	18c07	18k45	19 03	19 33	19c05	19 39	20 04	20 20
Inverkeithing	242 d	17 22						18 22	18 26	18 38	18 54	18 54		19 00	19 17			19 54	20 23	20 35
Kirkcaldy	242 d	17 39				18 16		18 40	18 42	19 00	19 11	19 11		19 18	19 33			20 10	20 45	20 51
Markinch	d	17 48				18 25		18 51	18 51	19 09				19 28	19 42			20 19	20 54	21 00
Ladybank	d	17 56				18 32		18 58	18 58	19 16				19 35	19 50			20 26	21 01	21 08
Springfield	d	18 01																		
Cupar	d	18 05	18 28					19 05	19 05	19 23					19 56	20 21			21 08	21 15
Leuchars 3	d	18 12	18 35					19 12	19 12	19 30	19 38	19 38			20 03	20 28			21 15	21 22
St Andrews Bus Station	🚌 a	18f30	18f50					19f29	19f29		19f59	19f59			20f29	20f59			21f38	21f38
Glasgow Queen Street 10	230 ⛴ d			17 41	17 40		18 11						18 41				19 41			
Larbert	230 d						18 30													
Stirling	230 d			18 07	18m15		18 41						19 07				20 07			
Dunblane	230 d			18 15	18 22		18 50						19 14							
Gleneagles	d			18 27	18 35		19 02						19 26							
Perth	a			18 43	18 52	18 58	19 19						19 42	20 02			20 36	20 53		
	d			18 44	18 53	18 59							19 43				20 36	20 54		
Invergowrie	d												20 01							
Dundee	a	18 34	18 47	19 06	19 15			19 27	19 24	19 44	19 52	19 52	20 07		20 20	20 40	20 59		21 30	21 45
	d	18 54	18 48	19 15	19 16				19 25	19 46	19 53	19 53	20 09			20 41	21 00			
Broughty Ferry	d	19 00																		
Carnoustie	d	19a17		19 27	19 28															
Arbroath	d		19 04	19 34	19 35				19 42	20 02	20 10	20 10	20 25			20 58	21 17			
Montrose	d		19 22	19 48	19 49				20 02	20 16	20 26	20 26	20 40			21 12				
Laurencekirk §	d																21 40			
Stonehaven	d		19 43	20 10	20 11				20 23	20 36	20 49	20 49				21 34	21 54			
Portlethen	d		19 52																	
Aberdeen	a		20 06	20 29	20 32				20 46	20 57	21 12	21 12	21 18			21 53	22 13			
	240 d															21 55				
Dyce	240 ✈ a				*21 05*				*21 05*							22 04	*22 59*			
Inverurie	240 a															22 16				
Dunkeld & Birnam	d					19 17												21 11		
Pitlochry	d					19 30												21 24		
Blair Atholl	d																	21 34		
Dalwhinnie	d																	22 00		
Newtonmore	d																	22 11		
Kingussie	d					20 12												22 21		
Aviemore	d					20 25												22 32		
Carrbridge	d																	22 41		
Inverness	a					21 03										00n05		23 14		

For general notes see front of timetable
For details of catering facilities see Directory of Train Operators

§ Will open during the currency of the timetable
A From London Kings Cross (Table 26). ⊘ and ⫪ Mondays to Fridays. ☕ and ⫪ Saturdays
B **The Northern Lights**
C **The Highland Chieftain.** From London Kings Cross (Table 26)
D Also stops at Falkirk Grahamston 1704
E Also stops at Balmossie 1903, Monifieth 1906, Barry Links 1910 and Golf Street 1913
G From Plymouth (Table 51)
H From London Kings Cross (Table 26)
b Change at Stirling. Saturdays dep. 1 minute earlier
c Change at Stirling
e By bus. Saturdays arr. 1530
f By bus
g By bus. Saturdays arr. 1730
h By bus. Saturdays arr. 1745
j Saturdays dep. 2 minutes later
k Saturdays dep. 1 minute earlier
m Arr. 1810
n Via Elgin (Table 240)

Edinburgh and Glasgow Queen Street → Perth, Inverness, Dundee, Aberdeen, Dyce and Inverurie

Network Diagram - see first page of Table 225

		XC SO 1 ◇ A	XC SO B 1 ◇ B	GR SX R 1 C ⊘ ♆	SR ◇	SR SX 1	SR SO 1	SR SO	SR SX	SR SO 1 ◇	SR	SR SX 1 ◇	SR SO 1 ◇	SR SX 1 ◇	SR D	SR	SR	SR	SR 1
Edinburgh 10	242 d	20 22	20 22	20 32	20b04	20 37	20 39	21 00	21 09	21 32	21 33	21 40	20c34	20c34	21 49	22 09	22 39	22e33	23 09
Haymarket	242 d	20 26	20 26	20 37	20b07	20 41	20 43	21 04	21 13	21 36	21 37	21 44	20c37	20c37	21 53	22 13	22 43	22c37	23 13
Inverkeithing	242 d	20 45	20 44	20 52		21 00	21 00	21 23	21 32						22 12	22 32	23 02		23 32
Kirkcaldy	242 d	21 00	21 01	21 09		21 17	21 17	21 45	21 54	22 04		22 12				22 54	23 24		23 54
Markinch	d	21 10	21 11			21 26	21 26	21 54	22 03						22 56	23 03	23 33		00 03
Ladybank	d	21 18	21 19			21 33	21 33	22 01	22 10						23 03	23 13	23 40		00 10
Springfield	d															23 18			
Cupar	d	21 25	21 28					22 08	22 17							23 22			00 17
Leuchars 3	d	21 32	21 36	21 33				22 15	22 24	22 28		22 34				23 29			00 24
St Andrews Bus Station	🚌 a	21f59	21f59	21f59				22f38		22f59		22f59				23f59			00f40
Glasgow Queen Street 10	230 ⛴ d				20 41								21 41	21 41				22 48	
Larbert	230 d										22 13							23 16	
Stirling	230 d				21 07						22 23		22 07	22 07				23g33	
Dunblane	230 d				21 14						22 34							23 42	
Gleneagles	d				21 26						22 47							23 55	
Perth	a				21 42	22 00	22 00				23 03		22 34	22 36	23 34		00 07	00 13	
	d				21 43								22 35	22 36					
Invergowrie	d				22 02														
Dundee	a	21 52	21 57	21 47	22 07			22 30	22 39	22 42		22 48	22 58	23 03		23 44			00 39
	d			21 48	22 08					22 43		22 49	22 58	23 03					
Broughty Ferry	d																		
Carnoustie	d												23 10	23 15					
Arbroath	d			22 05	22 25					23 00		23 05	23 17	23 22					
Montrose	d			22 22	22 39					23 14		23 24	23 33	23 40					
Laurencekirk §	d									23 25				23 51					
Stonehaven	d			22 45	23 01					23 39		23 45	23 55	00 05					
Portlethen	d											23 54	00 05						
Aberdeen	a			23 07	23 20					23 58		00 08	00 18	00 25					
	240 d																		
Dyce	240 ✈ a																		
Inverurie	240 a																		
Dunkeld & Birnam	d																		
Pitlochry	d																		
Blair Atholl	d																		
Dalwhinnie	d																		
Newtonmore	d																		
Kingussie	d																		
Aviemore	d																		
Carrbridge	d																		
Inverness	a																		

For general notes see front of timetable
For details of catering facilities see Directory of Train Operators

§ Will open during the currency of the timetable
A From 12 September. From Plymouth (Table 51)
B Until 5 September. From Newquay (Table 135)
C From London Kings Cross (Table 26)
D From Newcraighall (Table 242)
b Change at Stirling. Saturdays dep. 1 minute earlier
c Change at Stirling
e Change at Stirling. Saturdays dep. 2234
f By bus
g Arr. 2328

Table 229

Sundays

Edinburgh and Glasgow Queen Street → Perth, Inverness, Dundee, Aberdeen, Dyce and Inverurie

Network Diagram - see first page of Table 225

		XC	GR	SR	SR	SR	SR	SR	SR	SR	SR	SR	SR	SR	SR	SR	GR	SR
		[1]	[R] [1] 🍴 🛒		[1] ◇ 🛒	[1] ◇ 🛒	[1] ◇ 🛒		[1] ◇	[1] ◇ 🛒		[1] ◇ 🛒	[1] ◇ 🛒	[1] ◇ A 🛒		[1] ◇ 🛒	[R] [1] B C 🍴 🛒	[1] ◇
Edinburgh [10]	242 d	08 04	09 10	09 15		09 25	10 55	11 15	10b34	12 40	13 15	12b33	13 50	13b38	15 15	14b33	16 00	17 05
Haymarket	242 d	08 08	09 14	09 19		09 29	10 59	11 19	10b37	12 44	13 19	12b37	13 54	13b42	15 19	14b37	16 04	17 09
Inverkeithing	242 d	08 22	09 32	09 38		09 48	11 15	11 38		13 00	13 40		14 11		15 38		16 24	17 22
Kirkcaldy	242 d	08 37	09 49	10 03		10 10	11 31	12 03		13 16	14 05		14 28		16 03		16 41	17 38
Markinch	d			10 12				12 12			14 14				16 12			
Ladybank	d			10 18				12 18			14 20				16 18			
Springfield	d																	
Cupar	d	08 54		10 26				12 26			14 28				16 26			
Leuchars [3]	d		10 13	10 33			11 55	12 33		13 40	14 35				16 33		17 06	18 02
St Andrews Bus Station	🚌 a		10c51	10c51			12c13	12c59		13c59	14c59				16c59		17c29	18c29
Glasgow Queen Street [10]	230 🚆 d				09 38				11 45			13 45		14 40		15 45		
Larbert	230 d				10 01									15 00				
Stirling	230 d				10 12				12 12			14 12		15 09		16 12		
Dunblane	230 d				10 18				12 18			14 17		15 16		16 18		
Gleneagles	d				10 29				12 29			14 29		15 28		16 29		
Perth	a				10 46	10 51			12 46			14 46	15 12	15 45		16 45		
	d				10 47	10 52			12 47			14 48	15 13	15 46		16 47		
Invergowrie	d																	
Dundee	a	09 13	10 27	10 50	11 09		12 07	12 48	13 10	13 52	14 50	15 09			16 48	17 09	17 24	18 14
	d	09 14	10 28		11 11		12 08		13 11	13 53		15 11				17 11	17 24	18 15
Broughty Ferry	d																	
Carnoustie	d				11 23													
Arbroath	d	09 30	10 45		11 27		12 25		13 27	14 10		15 27				17 27	17 42	18 32
Montrose	d	09 44	11 01		11 42		12 37		13 42	14 24		15 42				17 42	18 00	18 46
Laurencekirk §	d				11 57							15 53						
Stonehaven	d	10 05	11 24		12 06		12 59		14 03	14 46		16 06				18 03	18 23	19 08
Portlethen	d						13 07											19 16
Aberdeen	a	10 28	11 47		12 30		13 23		14 23	15 05		16 26				18 23	18 46	19 30
	240 d																	
Dyce	240 ✈ a				*13 09*					*15 34*		*17 28*						
Inverurie	240 a																	
Dunkeld & Birnam	d					11 09							15 31					
Pitlochry	d					11 22							15 44	16 16				
Blair Atholl	d					11 33							15 54					
Dalwhinnie	d					12 00							16 19					
Newtonmore	d					12 10							16 29					
Kingussie	d					12 16							16 34	16 59				
Aviemore	d					12 28							16e48	17 12				
Carrbridge	d					12 37							17 03					
Inverness	a					13 09							17 38	17 50				

		GR	SR	SR	SR	XC	GR	SR	SR	SR	SR	SR	SR	SR
		[R] [1] C ⊘ 🛒		[1] ◇ 🛒	[1] ◇ A 🛒	[1] ◇ D 🛒	[R] [1] C 🍴 🛒		[1] ◇ 🛒	[1] ◇	[1] ◇ 🛒			[1]
Edinburgh [10]	242 d	17 12	17 15	17b12	17b34	18 10	18 42	19 15	18b33	21 00	20b33	22 25	22 36	22b36
Haymarket	242 d	17 16	17 19	17b16	17b37	18 15	18 47	19 19	18b37	21 05	20b37	22 29	22 40	22b40
Inverkeithing	242 d		17 38			18 29	19 02	19 38		21 18		22 48		
Kirkcaldy	242 d		18 00			18 44	19 19	20 00		21 34		23 10		
Markinch	d		18 09			18 53		20 09		21 43		23 19		
Ladybank	d		18 16			19 01		20 15		21 50		23 25		
Springfield	d													
Cupar	d		18 23			19 07		20 23		21 57		23 33		
Leuchars [3]	d		18 30			19 14	19 43	20 30		22 05		23 40		
St Andrews Bus Station	🚌 a		18c59			19c29	19c59	20c59		22c29				
Glasgow Queen Street [10]	230 🚆 d			17 45	18 10				19 45		21 45			23 35
Larbert	230 d				18 30								23 18	00 05
Stirling	230 d	17 52		18 12	18 39				20 12		22 11		23 27	00 14
Dunblane	230 d				18 46				20 17		22 17		23 37	00 23
Gleneagles	d	18 10			18 58				20 29		22 28		23 50	00 37
Perth	a	18 28		18 44	19 15				20 46		22 46		00 07	00 56
	d	18 29		18 45	19 16				20 47		22 46			
Invergowrie	d													
Dundee	a		18 46	19 08		19 28	19 57	20 45	21 10	22 17	23 09	23 56		
	d			19 09		19 30	19 58		21 11	22 18	23 09			
Broughty Ferry	d													
Carnoustie	d			19 21							23 21			
Arbroath	d			19 27		19 46	20 15		21 27	22 35	23 26			
Montrose	d			19 42		20 00	20 31		21 42	22 49	23 41			
Laurencekirk §	d			19 55										
Stonehaven	d			20 06		20 23	20 54		22 03	23 11	00 02			
Portlethen	d									23 20				
Aberdeen	a			20 29		20 47	21 17		22 24	23 33	00 25			
	240 d													
Dyce	240 ✈ a					*21 09*								
Inverurie	240 a													
Dunkeld & Birnam	d				19 34									
Pitlochry	d	19 00			19 47									
Blair Atholl	d				19 56									
Dalwhinnie	d				20 21									
Newtonmore	d				20 31									
Kingussie	d	19 52			20 36									
Aviemore	d	20 04			20 50									
Carrbridge	d				20 58									
Inverness	a	20 44			21 34									

For general notes see front of timetable
For details of catering facilities see Directory of Train Operators

§ Will open during the currency of the timetable

- **A** To Elgin (Table 240)
- **B** **The Northern Lights**
- **C** From London Kings Cross (Table 26)
- **D** From Plymouth (from 8 November from Birmingham New Street) (Table 51)
- **b** Change at Stirling
- **c** By bus
- **e** Arr. 1642

Inverurie, Dyce, Aberdeen, Dundee, Inverness and Perth → Glasgow Queen Street and Edinburgh

Network Diagram - see first page of Table 225

Miles	Miles	Miles	Miles	Miles	Station	SR SX	SR	SR SO A	SR		SR SX	SR SX	XC SX [1]◊ B 🛒	SR C		SR	SR [1]	SR SX	SR [1]◊ 🛒		SR SO 🛒	SR SX 🛒	SR SO	SR SX
—	—	0	0	0	**Inverness** d																			
—	—	28	28	28	Carrbridge d																			
—	—	34¾	34¾	34¾	Aviemore d																			
—	—	46½	46½	46½	Kingussie d																			
—	—	49¼	49¼	49¼	Newtonmore d																			
—	—	59½	59½	59½	Dalwhinnie d																			
—	—	82¾	82¾	82¾	Blair Atholl d																			
—	—	89½	89½	89½	Pitlochry d																			
—	—	102½	102½	102½	Dunkeld & Birnam d																			
0	0	—	—	—	**Inverurie** 240 d																			
10¾	10¾	—	—	—	**Dyce** 240 ✈ d																			
6¼	6¼	—	—	—	**Aberdeen** 240 a														05 33		05 56	05 56		
—	—	—	—	—	d														05 44					
14¼	14¼	—	—	—	Portlethen d														05 52		06 12	06 12		
22½	22½	—	—	—	Stonehaven d														06 06					
36¾	36¾	—	—	—	Laurencekirk § d														06 17		06 34	06 34		
46¾	46¾	—	—	—	Montrose d														06 31		06 48	06 48		
60½	60½	—	—	—	Arbroath d																06 55	06 55		
66¾	66¾	—	—	—	Carnoustie d									06 14										
73¼	73¼	—	—	—	Broughty Ferry d									06 29										
77½	77½	—	—	—	**Dundee** a									06 36					06 51		07 06	07 06		
—	—	—	—	—	d				06 05				06 32						06 52		07 08	07 08	07 20	07 20
81	—	—	—	—	Invergowrie d																			
98¼	—	118	118	118	**Perth** a														07 14					
—	—	—	—	—	d	05 10	05 16	05 35			06 09	06 14				06 39	06 55	07 03	07 15					
114	—	133¾	—	133¾	Gleneagles d		05 33				06 26					06 54		07 17	07 30					
121¼	—	146	—	146	Dunblane 230 d		05 46				06 40					07 08		07 29	07 44					
131¾	—	151½	—	151½	Stirling 230 d		05 53				06b52					07 16		07 38	07 53					
139¾	—	159½	—	159½	Larbert 230 d		06 01				06 59					07 25		07 47	08 02					
160¾	—	180½	—	—	**Glasgow Queen Street** [10] 230 🚇 a		06 34				07 34							08 20	08 34					
—	—	—	—	—	St Andrews Bus Station 🚌 d				05c48				06c18								06c55	06c55		07c10
—	85¾	—	—	—	Leuchars [3] d				06 16				06 46								07 20	07 20	07 32	07 32
—	92¼	—	—	—	Cupar d				06 24				06 54								07 28	07 28	07 39	07 39
—	94½	—	—	—	Springfield d																		07 44	07 44
—	97½	—	135¾	—	Ladybank d	05 36		05 58	06 32			06 37	07 03				07 17						07 49	07 49
—	103½	—	141	—	Markinch d	05 44		06 07	06 39			06 46	07 11				07 26						07 56	07 56
—	110¾	—	149	—	Kirkcaldy 242 d	05 53		06 16	06 49				07 21				07 38				07 49	07 48	08 06	08 06
—	123½	—	161¾	—	Inverkeithing 242 d	06 16		06 39	07 14			07 29	07 42				07 54						08 28	08 28
—	135½	—	173¾	186½	Haymarket 242 a	06 39	07e26	06 59	07 35			07 50	07 59			08f08	08f15	08g38	08g57		08 18	08 19	08 46	08 47
—	136¾	—	175	187¾	**Edinburgh** [10] 242 a	06 46	07g34	07 06	07 42			07 57	08 05			08 14	08 22	08g45	09g02		08 25	08 26	08 54	08 55

Station	XC [1]◊ B 🛒	SR SX [1]		SR SO [1]	SR [1]◊ 🛒	SR [1]	SR [1]◊ D 🛒		SR [1]◊ 🛒	SR [1]	SR [1]◊ D 🛒	GR SX [R] [1] E Ø 🛒		GR SO [R] [1] E 🍽 🛒	XC SO [1]◊ G 🛒	XC SX [1]◊ G 🛒	SR		GR SX [R] [1] E H Ø 🛒	GR SO [R] [1] E H 🍽 🛒	SR [1]	SR [1]◊ 🛒		SR [1]◊ 🛒
Inverness d							04h57		06 46	06 56									07 55	07 55				
Carrbridge d										07 28														
Aviemore d									07 22	07a38									08 29	08 29				
Kingussie d									07 33										08 42	08 42				
Newtonmore d																								
Dalwhinnie d																								
Blair Atholl d		07 12		07 12																				
Pitlochry d		07j26		07j26					08 16										09 23	09 23				
Dunkeld & Birnam d		07 39		07 39					08 27															
Inverurie 240 d							06 45				07 14													
Dyce 240 ✈ d							06 58				07 26											08 03		08 35
Aberdeen 240 a							07 10				07 37													
d					06 33		07 13				07 40	07 52		07 52	08 20	08 20						08 42		09 07
Portlethen d					06 43																			
Stonehaven d					06 52		07 29				07 56	08 09		08 09	08 38	08 38								
Laurencekirk § d							07 43																	09 35
Montrose d					07 13		07 54				08 18	08 32		08 32	08 59	08 59						09 18		09 46
Arbroath d					07 27		08 08				08 32	08 48		08 48	09 15	09 15						09 32		10 00
Carnoustie d					07 34		08 15				08 39											09 39		
Broughty Ferry d																								
Dundee a					07 50		08 26				08 53	09 05		09 05	09 31	09 31						09 52		10 15
d	07 35				07 52	08 18	08 27				08 53	09 06		09 06	09 33	09 33	09 42					09 52		10 17
Invergowrie d						08 23																		
Perth a		07 58		07 58	08 12	08 40			08 46		09 15								09 54	09 54		10 14		
d		07 59		07 59	08 12	08 41			08 47		09 15								09 55	09 55	09 51	10 14		
Gleneagles d					08 26	08 56													10 12	10 12				
Dunblane 230 d						09 06																		
Stirling 230 d					08 44	09 13					09 44								10 30	10 30		10 43		
Larbert 230 d																								
Glasgow Queen Street [10] 230 🚇 a					09 15	09 45					10 14											11 15		
St Andrews Bus Station 🚌 d	07c25						08c10					08c55		08c55	09c25	09c25								10c10
Leuchars [3] d	07 48						08 39					09 20		09 20	09 47	09 47	09 55							10 29
Cupar d	07 55						08 47								09 54	09 54	10 02							
Springfield d																								
Ladybank d	08 03	08 22		08 22											10 01	10 01	10 10				10 14			
Markinch d	08 11	08 31		08 31											10 09	10 09	10 17				10k33			
Kirkcaldy 242 d	08 20	08 41		08 41					09 24			09 44		09 44	10 17	10 17	10 27				10 42			
Inverkeithing 242 d	08 35	08 57		08 57								10 01		10 01	10 32	10 32	10 43				10 59			
Haymarket 242 a	08 53	09 16		09 13	09g55	10g26	09 33		09 52		10g56	10 19		10 21	10 51	10 52	11f00		11 08	11 09	11 17	11g56		11 20
Edinburgh [10] 242 a	08 58	09 24		09 25	10m02	10g31	09 40		10 01		11g02	10 25		10 27	10 58	11 01	11 09		11 15	11 15	11 26	12g01		11 29

For general notes see front of timetable
For details of catering facilities see Directory of Train Operators

- § Will open during the currency of the timetable
- A To Newcraighall (Table 242)
- B To Plymouth (Table 51)
- C Also stops at Golf Street 0616, Barry Links 0618, Monifieth 0623 and Balmossie 0625
- D 🛒 from Aberdeen
- E To London Kings Cross (Table 26)
- G To Penzance (Table 135)
- H **The Highland Chieftain.** Also stops at Falkirk Grahamston 1045
- b Arr. 0647
- c By bus
- e Change at Stirling. Saturdays arr. 0727
- f Saturdays arr. 1 minute earlier
- g Change at Stirling
- h Via Elgin (Table 240)
- j Arr. 5 minutes earlier
- k Arr. 1025
- m Change at Stirling. Saturdays arr. 1004

Inverurie, Dyce, Aberdeen, Dundee, Inverness and Perth → Glasgow Queen Street and Edinburgh

Network Diagram - see first page of Table 225

		SR	SR	SR	GR		SR	SR	SR	SR		SR	SR	SR	SR		SR	SR	SR	SR		SR	SR	SR	SR
														SX	SO										
			1	1◇	R 1			1◇	1	1◇		1◇	1	1◇	1◇		1◇	1◇	1	1		1◇	1◇		1◇
				A	B							A						A							
				🛒	Ø 🍴			🛒		🛒		🛒		🛒	🛒		🛒	🛒				🛒	🛒		🛒
Inverness	d							09 18						10 47	10 47										12 54
Carrbridge	d							09 49						11 21	11 21										
Aviemore	d							10 01						11 33	11 33										13 31
Kingussie	d							10 14						11 45	11 45										13 44
Newtonmore	d							10 18																	13 48
Dalwhinnie	d							10 30																	
Blair Atholl	d							10 51																	14 18
Pitlochry	d							11 01						12 27	12 27										14 28
Dunkeld & Birnam	d							11 16						12 40	12 40										14 40
Inverurie	240 d											10 38						11 35							
Dyce	240 ⇋ d			09 08	*09 27*							10 50					*11 15*	11 47							
Aberdeen	240 a			09 19								11 01						11 58							
	d			09 37	09 52					10 38		11 05					11 42	12 07				12 42	13 06		
Portlethen	d																	12 17							
Stonehaven	d			09 53	10 09							11 21						12 26				12 58	13 22		
Laurencekirk §	d											11 35													
Montrose	d			10 15	10 32					11 14		11 46					12 17					13 17	13 44		
Arbroath	d			10 29	10 49					11 28		12 00					12 31	13 00				13 31	13 58		
Carnoustie	d			10 36						11 35							12 38								
Broughty Ferry	d			10 43																					
Dundee	a			10 52	11 06					11 49		12 15					12 52	13 15				13 49	14 15		
	d	10 34		10 52	11 06		11 30			11 49		12 17	12 34				12 52	13 17	13 34			13 50	14 17	14 34	
Invergowrie	d																								
Perth	a			11 14				11 36		12 11				12 59	12 59		13 14					14 11			14 59
	d		10 57	11 14				11 37	11 59	12 11				13 01	13 01		13 14			13 58		14 11			15 00
Gleneagles	d							11 52																	
Dunblane	230 d							12 06																	
Stirling	230 d			11 43				12 13		12 42							13 43					14 40			
Larbert	230 d																								
Glasgow Queen Street 10	230 ⛴ a			12 15				12 46		13 14							14 15					15 15			
St Andrews Bus Station	🚌 d	*10b32*			*10b55*		*11b25*					*12b10*	*12b25*					*13b10*	*13b32*				*14b10*	*14b25*	
Leuchars 3	d	10 46			11 20		11 45					12 29	12 46					13 29	13 46				14 29	14 46	
Cupar	d	10 53					11 53						12 54						13 53					14 53	
Springfield	d																								
Ladybank	d	11 01	11 20				12 00		12 20				13 01						14 01	14 20				15 01	
Markinch	d	11 08	11 29				12 08		12 29				13 08	13 31	13 31				14 08	14 29				15 08	15 37
Kirkcaldy	242 d	11 18	11 39		11 44		12 17		12 39				13 18	13 41	13 41				14 18	14 39				15 18	15 47
Inverkeithing	242 d	11 34	11 55		12 01		12 33		12 55				13 34						14 34	14 55				15 34	
Haymarket	242 a	11 52	12 10	*12c56*	12 19		12 47	*13c26*	13 10	*13c56*		13 20	13 50	14 12	14 18		*14c56*	14 20	14 47	15 10		*15c56*	15 20	15 47	16 15
Edinburgh 10	242 a	12e01	12 17	*13c02*	12 25		12 55	*13c31*	13 19	*14c01*		13 27	13 57	14 19	14 25		*15c02*	14f27	14 55	15 19		*16c01*	15 27	15f55	16 23

		SR	SR		SR	SR	SR	GR		SR	SR	SR	SR		SR	SR	SR	SR		SR	SR	SR	SR		SR
								SX													SX				
		1◇	1◇			1	1◇	R 1		1◇	1◇		1		1◇		1	1◇		1◇	1		R 1		1◇
								C							A		D			A					
		🛒	🛒				🛒	Ø 🛒		🛒	🛒				🛒		🛒	🛒		🛒			🛒		🛒
Inverness	d									14 51													16 56		
Carrbridge	d																						17 27		
Aviemore	d									15 28													17 35		
Kingussie	d									15 40													17 48		
Newtonmore	d																						17 52		
Dalwhinnie	d									15 53															
Blair Atholl	d																						18 22		
Pitlochry	d									16 23													18g34		
Dunkeld & Birnam	d									16 35													18 46		
Inverurie	240 d														15 24					16 38					
Dyce	240 ⇋ d	*13 02*					*13 52*				*14 43*				15 38					16 54	17 05				*17 05*
Aberdeen	240 a														15 49					17 05	17 16				
	d	13 42	14 07				14 39	14 49			15 33				16 01			16 37		17 10	17 20				17 36
Portlethen	d																				17 31				
Stonehaven	d		14 23					15 06			15 49				16 18			16 53			17a41				17 52
Laurencekirk §	d		14 37												16 32					17 38					18 06
Montrose	d	14 17					15 12	15 29			16 11							17 13		17 49					18 17
Arbroath	d	14 31	15 00				15 26	15 45			16 25				16 55			17 29		18 03					18 31
Carnoustie	d	14 38					15 33								17 02										18 38
Broughty Ferry	d																								
Dundee	a	14 52	15 16				15 49	16 02			16 45				17 17			17 49		18 18					18 52
	d	14 52	15 17		15 35		15 49	16 03			16 46	16 50			17 17	17 26		17 51		18 19		18 46			18 52
Invergowrie	d										16 52														
Perth	a	15 14					16 11			16 54	17 10							18 11					19 08		19 14
	d	15 14				15 59	16 11			16 55	17 11		17 00				18 00	18 12					19 09		19 14
Gleneagles	d									17 11	17 26														
Dunblane	230 d									17 22	17 36							18 35							
Stirling	230 d	15 43					16 43			17 29	17 42							18 42							19 43
Larbert	230 d																								
Glasgow Queen Street 10	230 ⛴ a	16 15					17 17			18 09	18 15							19 14							20 15
St Andrews Bus Station	🚌 d		*15b10*		*15b25*			*15b55*				*16b40*			*17b10*	*17b17*				*18b10*		*18b25*			
Leuchars 3	d		15 29		15 47			16 17				17 02			17 29	17 39				18 31		18 56			
Cupar	d				15 53							17 09				17 47						19 04			
Springfield	d															17 51									
Ladybank	d				16 02	16 20						17 16	17 27			17 56	18 23					19 11			
Markinch	d				16 08	16 29						17 23	17 39			18 04	18 34					19 19	19 44		
Kirkcaldy	242 d				16 19	16 39		16 45				17 33	17 48			18 13	18 44					19 28	19 54		
Inverkeithing	242 d				16 35	16 55		17 01				17 55	18 04			18 29	19 00					19 46			
Haymarket	242 a	*16c56*	16 20		16 49	17 10	*17h55*	17 19		*18c26*	*18c56*	18 15	18 18		18 20	18 43	19 14	*19j55*		19 27		20 06	20 24		*20c55*
Edinburgh 10	242 a	*17k02*	16 27		16 56	17m18	*18c02*	17n27		*18c32*	*19q01*	18 22	18 25		18 32	18 50	19 21	*20c02*		19 34		20 13	20 29		*21c06*

For general notes see front of timetable
For details of catering facilities see Directory of Train Operators

- § Will open during the currency of the timetable
- **A** 🛒 from Aberdeen
- **B** **The Northern Lights.** To London Kings Cross (Table 26)
- **C** To London Kings Cross (Table 26)
- **D** To Newcraighall (Table 242)
- **b** By bus
- **c** Change at Stirling
- **e** Saturdays arr. 1 minute earlier
- **f** Saturdays arr. 1 minute later
- **g** Arr. 1831
- **h** Change at Stirling. Saturdays arr. 1756
- **j** Change at Stirling. Saturdays arr. 1956
- **k** Change at Stirling. Saturdays arr. 1704
- **m** Saturdays arr. 2 minutes later
- **n** Saturdays arr. 1725
- **q** Change at Stirling. Saturdays arr. 1902

Inverurie, Dyce, Aberdeen, Dundee, Inverness and Perth → Glasgow Queen Street and Edinburgh

Network Diagram - see first page of Table 225

		SR SO	GR SX	SR	SR		SR	SR	SR	SR		SR	SR	SR	XC SO		XC SX	SR	SR	SR FSX		SR FO			
		1 ◇	R 1	1	1 ◇		1 ◇		1 ◇	1 ◇			1 ◇	1 ◇	1 ◇		1 ◇	1 ◇	1	1		1			
							A					A													
		✕	⊡		✕		✕		✕	✕		✕													
Inverness	d								18 43									20 15							
Carrbridge	d								19 14																
Aviemore	d								19b29									21 00							
Kingussie	d								19 42									21 12							
Newtonmore	d								19 46									21 17							
Dalwhinnie	d								19 58									21 28							
Blair Atholl	d								20 19									21 50							
Pitlochry	d								20 29									22 02							
Dunkeld & Birnam	d								20 41									22 15							
Inverurie 240	d						18 43					19 40													
Dyce 240 ⇌	d	17 30	17 30		17 30		18 55			19 21		19 52	20 19							21 36		21 36			
Aberdeen 240	a						19 06					20 03													
	d	18 13	18 16		18 33		19 10			19 46		20 05	20 42	21 06	21 17		21 32			22 30		23 22			
Portlethen	d									19 56										22 40		23 32			
Stonehaven	d	18 29	18 33		18 49		19 26			20 05		20 21	20 58	21 22	21 35		21 49			22 49		23 41			
Laurencekirk §	d						19 40													23 03		23 55			
Montrose	d	18 51	18 56		19 10		19 51			20 23		20 43	21 20	21 44	21 55		22 10			23 13		00 05			
Arbroath	d	19 05	19 12		19 24		20 05			20 37		20 57	21 34	21 58	22 11		22 26			23 28		00 20			
Carnoustie	d				19 31							21 04								23 35		00 27			
Broughty Ferry	d																								
Dundee	a	19 20	19 29		19 46		20 20			20 56		21 15	21 52	22 15	22 27		22 42			23 50		00 42			
	d	19 22	19 30		19 46		20 21	20 42		20 56		21 16	21 52	22 15	22 29		22 43			23 51		00 43			
Invergowrie	d																			23 57		00 49			
Perth	a				20 07				21 00	21 17			22 14					22 29		00 15		01 07			
	d			19 57	20 11				21 02	21 17			22 14					22 30	22c38						
Gleneagles	d				20 25													22 47							
Dunblane 230	d																	22 58							
Stirling 230	d				20 40					21 45			22 43					23 05							
Larbert 230	d																								
Glasgow Queen Street 10 230 ⛴	a				21 14					22 19			23 15					23 38							
St Andrews Bus Station 🚌	d	19e10	19e25				20e15	20e35				21e00		22e00	22e15		22e30								
Leuchars 3	d	19 34	19 44				20 33	20 54				21 28		22 27	22 42		22 56								
Cupar	d							21 01				21 36		22 37	22 49		23 03								
Springfield	d																								
Ladybank	d			20 20				21 09				21 43		22 44	22 56		23 10		23 01						
Markinch	d			20 29				21 16	21 32			21 51		22 52	23 03		23 18		23 10						
Kirkcaldy 242	d	20 00	20 08	20 39				21 26	21 42			21 59		23 01	23 12		23 26								
Inverkeithing 242	d	20 16	20 24	20 55				21 49				22 22		23 24	23 36		23 42		23 52						
Haymarket 242	a	20 30	20s42	21 10	21f56		21 25	22 09	22 12	22f56		22 43		23 44	23 59		23 57	00f04	00 12						
Edinburgh 10 242	a	20 36	20 48	21 19	22f01		21g32	22 16	22 19	23f01		22 50		23 52	00 11		00 10	00f09	00 19						

For general notes see front of timetable
For details of catering facilities see Directory of Train Operators

§ Will open during the currency of the timetable

A ✕ from Aberdeen
b Arr. 1922
c Saturdays dep. 2 minutes later
e By bus
f Change at Stirling
g Saturdays arr. 1 minute earlier

Table 229

Sundays

Inverurie, Dyce, Aberdeen, Dundee, Inverness and Perth → Glasgow Queen Street and Edinburgh

Network Diagram - see first page of Table 225

		SR	SR	SR	SR	SR	GR	SR	GR	XC	SR	GR	SR	SR	SR	GR	SR	SR
			1			1 ◇	R 1 A		R 1 B C	1 ◇ D	1 ◇	R 1 E		1 ◇	1 ◇	R 1 E	1 ◇	
Inverness	d								09 38					12 30			13 25	
Carrbridge	d								10 08					13 08				
Aviemore	d								10 17					13 17			14 02	
Kingussie	d								10 30					13 30			14 15	
Newtonmore	d								10 35					13 35				
Dalwhinnie	d													13 46				
Blair Atholl	d								11 07					14 08				
Pitlochry	d								11b23					14 17			14 54	
Dunkeld & Birnam	d								11 36					14 30				
Inverurie	240 d																	
Dyce	240 ✈ d																	
Aberdeen	240 a														11 59			
	d					09 27	09 48			11 12	11 29	11 47			13 27	13 50		
Portlethen	d																	
Stonehaven	d					09 43	10 05			11 29	11 45	12 04			13 42	14 07		
Laurencekirk §	d					09 57									13 56			
Montrose	d					10 08	10 28			11 50	12 07	12 27			14 07	14 30		
Arbroath	d					10 22	10 44			12 06	12 21	12 43			14 21	14 46		
Carnoustie	d					10 29												
Broughty Ferry	d																	
Dundee	a					10 43	11 01			12 24	12 39	13 00			14 41	15 03		
	d	07 25	08 45		09 25	10 43	11 02	11 25		12 25	12 43	13 01	13 25		14 43	15 04		15 25
Invergowrie	d																	
Perth	a		09 03			11 05			11 56		13 03			14 49	15 03		15 23	
	d		09 03	09 27		11 05			11 56		13 05			14 50	15 05		15 25	
Gleneagles	d		09 20	09 42		11 20			12 13		13 20			15 05	15 20			
Dunblane	230 d		09 31	09 54		11 31			12 26		13 31			15 16	15 30			
Stirling	230 d		09 38	10 02		11 38			12 33		13 38			15 22	15 38			
Larbert	230 d		09 47	10 11										15 31				
Glasgow Queen Street 10	230 ⛴ a		10 15			12 11					14 11			15 56	16 12			
St Andrews Bus Station	🚌 d				09c15		11c00	11c15		12c15		12c45	13c15			15c00		15c15
Leuchars 3	d	07 37			09 37		11 16	11 37		12 38		13 15	13 37			15 18		15 37
Cupar	d	07 44			09 44			11 44		12 45			13 44					15 44
Springfield	d																	
Ladybank	d	07 52			09 52			11 52					13 52					15 52
Markinch	d	07 59			09 59			11 59					13 59					15 59
Kirkcaldy	242 d	08 08			10 08		11 40	12 08		13 03		13 39	14 08			15 42	16 03	16 08
Inverkeithing	242 d	08 30			10 30		11 56	12 30		13 18		13 55	14 30			15 58	16 19	16 30
Haymarket	242 a	08 52	10e51	10 51	10 58	12e56	12 17	12 58	13 12	13 36	14e56	14 18	14 58		16e56	16 19	16 35	16 54
Edinburgh 10	242 a	09 00	10e58	10 58	11 06	13e01	12 24	13 06	13 18	13 42	15e01	14 24	15 06		17e02	16 25	16 42	16 59

For general notes see front of timetable
For details of catering facilities see Directory of Train Operators

§ Will open during the currency of the timetable

A **The Northern Lights.** To London Kings Cross (Table 26)

B **The Highland Chieftain.** To London Kings Cross (Table 26)

C Also stops at Falkirk Grahamston 1249

D To Plymouth (from 8 November to Birmingham New Street) (Table 51)

E To London Kings Cross (Table 26)

b Arr. 1118

c By bus

e Change at Stirling

Table 229

Sundays

Inverurie, Dyce, Aberdeen, Dundee, Inverness and Perth → Glasgow Queen Street and Edinburgh

Network Diagram - see first page of Table 225

	SR 1◇ ⚒		SR 1◇ ⚒	SR		SR 1◇ ⚒	SR 1◇ ⚒		SR 1◇ ⚒	SR		SR 1◇ ⚒	SR 1◇ ⚒		SR 1◇ ⚒	SR 1◇ ⚒		XC 1◇	SR 1
Inverness d							16 15						18 30						
Carrbridge d							16 46						19 01						
Aviemore d							16 55						19 09						
Kingussie d							17 14						19 22						
Newtonmore d													19 26						
Dalwhinnie d													19 39						
Blair Atholl d							17 47						20 02						
Pitlochry d							17 56						20 11						
Dunkeld & Birnam d							18 09						20 24						
Inverurie 240 d																			
Dyce 240 ✈ d	*14 32*											*17 30*				*19 17*			
Aberdeen 240 a																			
d	15 10		15 30			17 10			17 47			19 10			19 35	20 10		21 28	22 29
Portlethen d	15 20															20 20			
Stonehaven d	15 26		15 46			17 26			18 03			19 26			19 51	20 26		21 45	22 48
Laurencekirk § d									18 17										
Montrose d	15 48		16 08			17 48			18 28			19 48			20 13	20 48		22 06	23 11
Arbroath d	16 02		16 22			18 02			18 42			20 02			20 27	21 02		22 22	23 25
Carnoustie d	16 09											20 09							23 32
Broughty Ferry d																			
Dundee a	16 23		16 41			18 17			19 00			20 18			20 42	21 19		22 38	23 46
d	16 25		16 43	17 25		18 19			19 02	19 27		20 20			20 43	21 21		22 39	23 47
Invergowrie d																			
Perth a			17 03				18 26		19 22				20 42		21 04				00 09
d			17 05				18 27		19 24				20 46		21 05				
Gleneagles d			17 20				18 44								21 20				
Dunblane 230 d			17 31				18 55								21 31				
Stirling 230 d			17 38				19 02		19 54						21 38				
Larbert 230 d							19 09								21 49				
Glasgow Queen Street 10 230 ⛴ a			18 12				19 36		20 31						22 15				
St Andrews Bus Station 🚌 d	*16b15*			*17b15*		*18b15*				*19b15*		*20b15*				*21b15*		*22b05*	
Leuchars 3 d	16 37			17 37		18 31				19 39		20 32				21 33		22 52	
Cupar d				17 44						19 46						21 39		22 59	
Springfield d																			
Ladybank d				17 52						19 54						21 48		23 06	
Markinch d				17 59						20 01						21 54		23 14	
Kirkcaldy 242 d	17 02			18 07		18 56				20 10		20 59	21 25			22 05		23 22	
Inverkeithing 242 d	17 18			18 29		19 12				20 31		21 15	21 41			22 21		23 38	
Haymarket 242 a	17 34		*18c56*	18 52		19 27	*20c01*		*20c56*	20 54		21 31	21 59		*22c56*	22 36		23 53	
Edinburgh 10 242 a	17 41		*19c01*	19 00		19 35	*20c06*		*21c01*	21 01		21 36	22 05		*23c01*	22 43		00 03	

For general notes see front of timetable
For details of catering facilities see Directory of Train Operators

§ Will open during the currency of the timetable

b By bus
c Change at Stirling

Table 230

Mondays to Fridays

Edinburgh, Glasgow Queen Street and Falkirk Grahamston → Stirling, Alloa and Dunblane
Edinburgh → Bathgate

Network Diagram - see first page of Table 225

Miles	Miles	Miles	Miles			SR	SR 1◇ A 🛒	SR	SR 1 B	SR 1 C 🛒	SR	SR 1 C 🛒	SR 1 B 🛒	SR	SR	SR 1 C 🛒	SR	SR 1 B 🛒		SR 1◇ D	SR 1 B 🛒	SR	SR	SR 1 C 🛒	SR
0	0	—	—	**Edinburgh** 10	d	05 18			05 55		06 03		06 30	06 33			06 36	06 45			07 00	07 04			07 06
1¼	—	—	—	Haymarket	d	05 22			05 59		06 06		06 33	06 36			06 40	06 49			07 03	07 07			07 10
3¾	—	—	—	Edinburgh Park	d	05 27					06 10			06 41			06 46					07 11			07 16
12½	—	—	—	Uphall	d						06 21						06 58								07 28
15½	—	—	—	Livingston North	d						06 25						07 02								07 32
18½	—	—	—	**Bathgate**	a						06 33						07 07								07 37
—	17½	—	—	Linlithgow	d	05 39			06 13				06 48	06 53				07a03				07 24			
—	22¼	—	—	Polmont 3	d	05 44			06a19				06a54	06 59							07a19	07 29			
—	—	0	0	**Glasgow Queen Street** 10 ⛴	d		05 55	06 13		06 30		06 45			06 48	07 00				07 06			07 18	07 30	
—	—	3¼	3¼	Bishopbriggs	d			06 20							06 53								07 23		
—	—	6¼	6¼	Lenzie 3	d			06 24		06a38					06 59	07a08							07 29		
—	—	11½	11½	Croy 3	d			06 32				06a56			07 05								07 35	07a41	
—	25½	—	—	**Falkirk Grahamston**	d	05 50								07 05								07 34			
—	27	—	—	Camelon	d	05 53								07 08								07 37			
—	28¼	21	21	Larbert	d	06 00	06 15	06 43						07 14	07 18							07 43	07 48		
—	36½	29	29	**Stirling**	d	06 09	06 24	06 51						07 23	07b38					07 33		07 53	08c05		
—	—	—	35¾	**Alloa**	a			07 05															08 17		
—	40	32½	—	Bridge of Allan	d	06 13								07 28	07 43							07 57			
—	42	34½	—	**Dunblane**	a	06 20	06 30							07 36	07 51					07 39		08 06			

		SR 1 B 🛒	SR 1◇ E 🛒	SR 1 B 🛒	SR	SR	SR 1 C 🛒	SR 1 B 🛒	SR	SR 1 B 🛒		SR	SR	SR 1 C 🛒	SR 1 B 🛒	SR 1◇ E 🛒	SR	SR	SR	SR 1 C 🛒	SR 1 B 🛒	SR	SR	SR	SR 1 C 🛒
Edinburgh 10	d	07 15		07 30	07 33			07 45	07 49	08 00		08 03			08 15		08 18	08 34			08 45	08 48	09 04		
Haymarket	d	07 18		07 33	07 36			07 48	07 51	08 03		08 06			08 18		08 21	08 37			08 48	08 51	09 07		
Edinburgh Park	d				07 41				07 55			08 11					08 25	08 41				08 55	09 11		
Uphall	d								08 09								08 37					09 07			
Livingston North	d								08 11								08 41					09 11			
Bathgate	a								08 19								08 49					09 18			
Linlithgow	d	07a33		07 48	07 53			08a03				08 23			08 33			08 53			09 03		09 23		
Polmont 3	d			07a54	07 58					08a19		08 28			08a39			08 58			09a09		09 28		
Glasgow Queen Street 10 ⛴	d		07 41			07 48	08 00						08 18	08 30		08 41			08 48	09 00				09 18	09 30
Bishopbriggs	d					07 53							08 23						08 53					09 23	
Lenzie 3	d					07 59							08 29						08 59					09 29	
Croy 3	d					08 05	08a11						08 35	08a41					09 05	09a11				09 35	09a41
Falkirk Grahamston	d				08 04							08 34						09 04					09 34		
Camelon	d				08 07							08 37						09 07					09 37		
Larbert	d				08 13	08 18						08 43	08 48					09 13	09 18				09 43	09 48	
Stirling	d		08 07		08 23	08 30						08 53	09 00			09a07		09 23	09 30				09 53	10 00	
Alloa	a												09 13											10 13	
Bridge of Allan	d				08 27	08 35						08 57						09 27	09 35				09 57		
Dunblane	a		08 14		08 36	08 43						09 06						09 36	09 43				10 06		

		SR 1 B 🛒		SR 1◇ E 🛒	SR	SR	SR	SR 1 C 🛒	SR 1 B 🛒	SR 1◇ D 🛒	SR	SR	SR	SR 1 C 🛒	SR 1 B 🛒	SR 1◇ E 🛒		SR	SR	SR	SR 1 C 🛒	SR 1 B 🛒	SR	SR	SR
Edinburgh 10	d	09 15			09 18	09 37			09 45		09 48	10 04			10 15			10 18	10 34			10 45	10 48	11 04	
Haymarket	d	09 18			09 21	09 40			09 48		09 51	10 07			10 18			10 21	10 37			10 48	10 51	11 07	
Edinburgh Park	d				09 25	09 45					09 55	10 12						10 25	10 41				10 55	11 11	
Uphall	d				09 37						10 07							10 37					11 07		
Livingston North	d				09 41						10 11							10 41					11 11		
Bathgate	a				09 50						10 19							10 48					11 18		
Linlithgow	d	09 33				09 53			10 03			10 24			10 33				10 53			11 03		11 23	
Polmont 3	d	09a39				09 58			10a09			10 28			10a39				10 58			11a09		11 28	
Glasgow Queen Street 10 ⛴	d			09 41			09 48	10 00		10 11			10 18	10 30		10 41				10 48	11 00				11 18
Bishopbriggs	d						09 53						10 23							10 53					11 23
Lenzie 3	d						09 59						10 29							10 59					11 29
Croy 3	d						10 05	10a11					10 35	10a41						11 05	11a11				11 35
Falkirk Grahamston	d					10 04						10 34							11 04					11 34	
Camelon	d					10 07						10 37							11 07					11 37	
Larbert	d					10 13	10 20					10 44	10 48						11 13	11 18				11 43	11 48
Stirling	d			10a07		10 23	10 32			10 42		10 54	11 00			11a07			11 23	11 30				11 53	12 00
Alloa	a												11 13												12 13
Bridge of Allan	d					10 27	10 37					10 57							11 27	11 35				11 57	
Dunblane	a					10 39	10 46			10 49		11 07							11 36	11 43				12 07	

For general notes see front of timetable
For details of catering facilities see Directory of Train Operators

A To Dyce (Table 229)
B To Glasgow Queen Street (Table 228)
C To Edinburgh (Table 228)
D To Inverness (Table 229)
E To Aberdeen (Table 229)
b Arr. 0728
c Arr. 0759

Edinburgh, Glasgow Queen Street and Falkirk Grahamston → Stirling, Alloa and Dunblane
Edinburgh → Bathgate

Network Diagram - see first page of Table 225

		SR 1 A	SR 1 B	SR 1 ◇ C	SR	SR	SR	SR 1 A		SR 1 B	SR	SR	SR	SR 1 A	SR 1 B	SR 1 ◇ C	SR	SR	SR	SR 1 A	SR 1 B	SR		SR	SR
Edinburgh 10	d		11 15		11 18	11 34				11 45	11 48	12 04			12 15		12 18	12 33			12 45	12 48		13 04	
Haymarket	d		11 18		11 21	11 37				11 48	11 51	12 07			12 18		12 21	12 36			12 48	12 51		13 07	
Edinburgh Park	d				11 25	11 41					11 55	12 11					12 25	12 41				12 55		13 11	
Uphall	d				11 37						12 07						12 37					13 07			
Livingston North	d				11 41						12 11						12 41					13 11			
Bathgate	a				11 49						12 18						12 48					13 18			
Linlithgow	d		11 33			11 53				12 03		12 23			12 33			12 53			13 03			13 23	
Polmont 3	d		11a39			11 58				12a09		12 28			12a39			12 58			13a09			13 28	
Glasgow Queen Street 10	d	11 30		11 41			11 48	12 00					12 18	12 30		12 41			12 48	13 00					13 18
Bishopbriggs	d						11 53						12 23						12 53						13 23
Lenzie 3	d						11 59						12 29						12 59						13 29
Croy 3	d	11a41					12 05	12a11					12 35	12a41					13 05	13a11					13 35
Falkirk Grahamston	d					12 04						12 34						13 04						13 34	
Camelon	d					12 07						12 37						13 07						13 37	
Larbert	d					12 13	12 18					12 43	12 48					13 13	13 18					13 43	13 48
Stirling	d			12a07		12 23	12 30					12 53	13 00			13a07		13 23	13 31					13 53	14 00
Alloa	a												13 13												14 13
Bridge of Allan	d					12 27	12 35					12 57						13 27	13 35					13 57	
Dunblane	a					12 36	12 43					13 06						13 36	13 43					14 06	

		SR 1 A	SR 1 B	SR 1 ◇ C	SR	SR	SR	SR 1 A	SR 1 B	SR	SR	SR	SR 1 A	SR 1 B		SR 1 ◇ C	SR	SR	SR	SR 1 A	SR 1 B	SR	SR	SR	SR 1 A
Edinburgh 10	d		13 15		13 18	13 34			13 45	13 48	14 04			14 15			14 18	14 34			14 45	14 48	15 04		
Haymarket	d		13 18		13 21	13 37			13 48	13 51	14 07			14 18			14 21	14 37			14 48	14 51	15 07		
Edinburgh Park	d				13 25	13 41				13 55	14 11						14 25	14 41				14 55	15 11		
Uphall	d				13 37					14 07							14 37					15 07			
Livingston North	d				13 41					14 11							14 41					15 11			
Bathgate	a				13 48					14 18							14 48					15 18			
Linlithgow	d		13 33			13 53			14 03		14 23			14 33				14 53			15 03		15 23		
Polmont 3	d		13a39			14 00			14a09		14 28			14a39				14 58			15a08		15 28		
Glasgow Queen Street 10	d	13 30		13 41			13 48	14 00				14 18	14 30			14 41			14 48	15 00				15 18	15 30
Bishopbriggs	d						13 53					14 23							14 53					15 23	
Lenzie 3	d						13 59					14 29							14 59					15 29	
Croy 3	d	13a41					14 05	14a11				14 35	14a41						15 05	15a11				15 35	15a41
Falkirk Grahamston	d					14 04					14 34							15 04					15 34		
Camelon	d					14 07					14 37							15 07					15 37		
Larbert	d					14 13	14 16				14 44	14 48						15 13	15 18				15 43	15 47	
Stirling	d			14a07		14 23	14 31				14 53	15 00				15a07		15 23	15 30				15 53	16 01	
Alloa	a											15 13												16 13	
Bridge of Allan	d					14 27	14 36				14 57							15 27	15 35				15 57		
Dunblane	a					14 36	14 43				15 06							15 36	15 43				16 06		

		SR 1 B	SR 1 ◇ C	SR	SR	SR		SR	SR 1 A	SR 1 B	SR 1 ◇ D	SR	SR	SR	SR 1 A	SR	SR 1 B	SR	GR R 1 E G ⌀	SR		SR	SR 1 A	SR	SR 1 B
Edinburgh 10	d	15 15		15 18	15 34					15 46		15 50	16 04				16 15	16 18	16 33	16 37					16 45
Haymarket	d	15 18		15 21	15 37					15 49		15 53	16 07				16 18	16 21	16 38	16 41					16 48
Edinburgh Park	d			15 25	15 41							15 57	16 11					16 25		16 46					
Uphall	d			15 37								16 08						16 37							
Livingston North	d			15 41								16 12						16 41							
Bathgate	a			15 49								16 20						16 48							
Linlithgow	d	15 33			15 53					16 04			16 23				16 33			16 58					17 03
Polmont 3	d	15a39			15 58					16a09			16 28				16a39			17 03					17a09
Glasgow Queen Street 10	d		15 41			15 48		15 51	16 00		16 11			16 19	16 30	16 33						16 48	17 00	17 03	
Bishopbriggs	d					15 53		15 56						16 24		16 39						16 53		17 08	
Lenzie 3	d					15 59		16 08						16 30		16a44						16 59		17 14	
Croy 3	d					16 05		16 15	16a11					16 36	16a41							17 05	17a11		
Falkirk Grahamston	d				16 04			16a33					16 34						17 04	17 08				17a33	
Camelon	d				16 07			16a27					16 37							17 11				17a30	
Larbert	d				16 15	16 18							16 43	16 49						17 18		17 23			
Stirling	d		16a07		16 23	16 30					16 37		16 53	17b08					17a19	17 27		17 35			
Alloa	a													17 20											
Bridge of Allan	d				16 27	16 35							16 57							17 31		17 40			
Dunblane	a				16 36	16 43					16 48		17 06							17 40		17 47			

For general notes see front of timetable
For details of catering facilities see Directory of Train Operators

- **A** To Edinburgh (Table 228)
- **B** To Glasgow Queen Street (Table 228)
- **C** To Aberdeen (Table 229)
- **D** To Inverness (Table 229)
- **E** From London Kings Cross (Table 26) to Inverness (Table 229)
- **G** **The Highland Chieftain**
- **b** Arr. 1700

Table 230

Mondays to Fridays

Edinburgh, Glasgow Queen Street and Falkirk Grahamston → Stirling, Alloa and Dunblane
Edinburgh → Bathgate

Network Diagram - see first page of Table 225

		SR	SR	SR	SR	SR 1	SR 1	SR	SR	SR	SR 1 ◇	SR		SR	SR 1	SR 1	SR	SR	SR	SR	SR 1	SR 1	SR 1 ◇	SR	SR
		A				B	C				D				B	C	A				B	C	D		
Edinburgh 10	d		16 48	17 04			17 15		17 18	17 25		17 33				17 45		17 48	18 04			18 15		18 18	
Haymarket	d		16 51	17 07			17 18		17 21	17 30		17 37				17 47		17 51	18 07			18 18		18 21	
Edinburgh Park	d		16 55	17 11					17 25			17 41						17 55	18 11					18 25	
Uphall	d		17 07						17 37									18 07						18 37	
Livingston North	d		17 11						17 41									18 11						18 41	
Bathgate	a		17 18						17 48									18 19						18 48	
Linlithgow	d			17 23			17 33					17 53				18 03			18 23			18 33			
Polmont 3	d			17 28			17a39					17 58				18a09			18 28			18a39			
Glasgow Queen Street 10	d	17 12			17 18	17 30		17 33			17 40			17 48	18 00		18 11			18 18	18 30		18 41		18 48
Bishopbriggs	d				17 23			17 38						17 53						18 23					18 53
Lenzie 3	d				17 29			17 43						17 59						18 29					18 59
Croy 3	d				17 35	17a41								18 05	18a11					18 35	18a41				19 05
Falkirk Grahamston	d			17 34				18a01				18 04							18 34						
Camelon	d			17 37				17a59				18 07							18 37						
Larbert	d	17 33		17 43	17 47					17 57		18 13		18 18			18 30		18 43	18 48					19 14
Stirling	d	17 45		17 53	17 59					18 06	18b15	18 23		18 33			18 41		18 53	19 00			19 07		19 31
Alloa	a				18 12															19 15					
Bridge of Allan	d	17 49		17 57						18 13		18 27		18 38			18 46		18 57						19 36
Dunblane	a	17 54		18 07						18 18	18 22	18 36		18 44			18 50		19 06				19 14		19 46

		SR 1	SR	SR 1		SR	SR	SR	SR 1	SR 1 ◇	SR	SR 1	SR	SR	SR 1	SR 1	SR	SR		SR ◇	SR	SR 1	SR	SR	SR 1
		B		C					C	D		C			B	C				D		C			B
Edinburgh 10	d		18 36	18 45		18 48	19 04		19 15		19 22	19 30	19 34			20 00	20 04				20 18	20 30	20 34		
Haymarket	d		18 38	18 48		18 51	19 05		19 18		19 23	19 33	19 37			20 03	20 07				20 21	20 33	20 37		
Edinburgh Park	d		18 43			18 55	19 11				19 27		19 41				20 11				20 25		20 41		
Uphall	d					19 07					19 39										20 37				
Livingston North	d					19 11					19 44										20 41				
Bathgate	a					19 18					19 52										20 48				
Linlithgow	d		18 55	19 03			19 23		19 33			19 48	19 53			20 18	20 23					20a48	20 53		
Polmont 3	d		19 00	19a09			19 28		19a39				19 58			20a24	20 29						20 58		
Glasgow Queen Street 10	d	19 00						19 18		19 41				19 48	20 00			20 18		20 41				20 48	21 00
Bishopbriggs	d							19 23						19 53				20 23						20 53	
Lenzie 3	d							19 29						19 59				20 29						20 59	
Croy 3	d	19a11						19 35				20a07		20 05	20a11			20 35						21 05	21a11
Falkirk Grahamston	d		19 05				19 34						20 04				20 34						21 04		
Camelon	d		19 08				19 37						20 07				20 37						21 07		
Larbert	d		19 15				19 43	19 48					20 14	20 18			20 43	20 48					21 13	21 18	
Stirling	d		19 25				19 53	20 00		20a07			20 23	20 30			20 53	21 00		21 07			21 23	21 30	
Alloa	a							20 13										21 13							
Bridge of Allan	d		19 28				19 57						20 27	20 35			20 57						21 27	21 35	
Dunblane	a		19 38				20 06						20 36	20 43			21 06			21 14			21 36	21 43	

		SR	SR 1	SR 1 ◇	SR	SR 1	SR	SR	SR 1	SR		SR 1	SR	SR 1	SR	SR	SR 1	SR	SR 1	SR 1	SR	SR 1	SR		
			C	D		C	A		B			C		C		A	B		C	B		C			
Edinburgh 10	d		21 00		21 18	21 30	21 33					22 00	22 18	22 30	22 33				23 00		23 18	23 30	23 33		
Haymarket	d		21 03		21 21	21 33	21 37					22 03	22 21	22 33	22 37				23 03		23 21	23 33	23 37		
Edinburgh Park	d				21 25		21 41						22 25		22 41						23 25		23 41		
Uphall	d				21 37								22 37								23 37				
Livingston North	d				21 41								22 41								23 41				
Bathgate	a				21 48								22 48								23 48				
Linlithgow	d		21 18			21a48	21 53					22 18		22a48	22 53				23 18			23 48	23 53		
Polmont 3	d		21a24				21 58					22a24			22 58				23a24			23a53	23 58		
Glasgow Queen Street 10	d	21 18		21 41				21 48	22 00	22 18						22 48	23 00	23 18		23 30					
Bishopbriggs	d	21 23						21 53		22 23						22 53		23 23							
Lenzie 3	d	21 29						21 59		22 29						22 59		23 29							
Croy 3	d	21 35						22 05	22a11	22 35						23 05	23a11	23 35		23a41					
Falkirk Grahamston	d						22 04								23 04								00 04		
Camelon	d						22 07								23 07								00 07		
Larbert	d	21 48					22 13	22 18		22 47					23 15	23 16		23 48					00 13		
Stirling	d	22 00		22a07			22 23	22 30		23c01					23 24	23e33		00a01					00 23		
Alloa	a	22 13								23 13															
Bridge of Allan	d						22 27	22 35							23 29	23 37							00 27		
Dunblane	a						22 34	22 43							23 37	23 42							00 35		

For general notes see front of timetable
For details of catering facilities see Directory of Train Operators

- **A** To Perth (Table 229)
- **B** To Edinburgh (Table 228)
- **C** To Glasgow Queen Street (Table 228)
- **D** To Aberdeen (Table 229)

- **b** Arr. 1810
- **c** Arr. 2256
- **e** Arr. 2328

Edinburgh, Glasgow Queen Street and Falkirk Grahamston → Stirling, Alloa and Dunblane
Edinburgh → Bathgate

Network Diagram - see first page of Table 225

		SR	SR 1◇ A	SR	SR 1 B	SR 1 C	SR	SR	SR 1 B		SR	SR	SR 1 C	SR 1◇ D	SR	SR 1 B	SR	SR		SR 1 C	SR	SR 1 B	SR 1◇ E	SR 1 B	SR
Edinburgh 10	d	05 18			05 55		06 03		06 30		06 33				06 36	07 00	07 04				07 07	07 15		07 30	07 33
Haymarket	d	05 22			05 59		06 06		06 33		06 36				06 40	07 03	07 07				07 12	07 18		07 33	07 36
Edinburgh Park	d	05 27					06 10				06 41				06 46		07 11				07 16				07 41
Uphall	d						06 21								06 58						07 28				
Livingston North	d						06 25								07 02						07 32				
Bathgate	a						06 33								07 07						07 37				
Linlithgow	d	05 39			06 13				06 48		06 53						07 23					07a33		07 47	07 53
Polmont 3	d	05 44			06a19				06a54		06 59					07a19	07 28							07a54	07 58
Glasgow Queen Street 10	d		05 55	06 13		06 30						06 48	07 00	07 06				07 18		07 30			07 41		
Bishopbriggs	d			06 20								06 53						07 23							
Lenzie 3	d			06 24		06 38						06 59	07a08					07 29							
Croy 3	d			06 32		06a44						07 05						07 35		07a41					
Falkirk Grahamston	d	05 50									07 05						07 34								08 04
Camelon	d	05 53									07 08						07 37								08 07
Larbert	d	06 00	06 15	06 43							07 14	07 18					07 43	07 48							08 13
Stirling	d	06 09	06 24	06 51				07 01			07 23	07b38		07 33			07 53	08c05					08 07		08 23
Alloa	a			07 05														08 17							
Bridge of Allan	d	06 13						07 05			07 28	07 43					07 57								08 27
Dunblane	a	06 20	06 30					07 12			07 36	07 51		07 39			08 06						08 14		08 36

		SR	SR 1 C	SR 1 B	SR		SR 1 B	SR	SR	SR 1 C	SR 1 B	SR 1◇ E	SR	SR 1 B		SR	SR	SR 1 C	SR 1 B	SR	SR	SR	SR 1 C		SR 1 B
Edinburgh 10	d			07 45	07 48		08 00	08 03			08 15		08 18	08 30		08 34			08 45	08 48	09 04				09 15
Haymarket	d			07 48	07 51		08 03	08 06			08 18		08 21	08 33		08 37			08 48	08 51	09 07				09 18
Edinburgh Park	d				07 55			08 11					08 26			08 41				08 55	09 11				
Uphall	d				08 07								08 37							09 07					
Livingston North	d				08 11								08 41							09 11					
Bathgate	a				08 19								08 49							09 18					
Linlithgow	d			08a03				08 23			08 33					08 53			09 03		09 23				09 33
Polmont 3	d						08a19	08 28			08a39					08 58			09a09		09 28				09a39
Glasgow Queen Street 10	d	07 48	08 00						08 18	08 30		08 41					08 48	09 00				09 18	09 30		
Bishopbriggs	d	07 53							08 23								08 53					09 23			
Lenzie 3	d	07 59							08 29								08 59					09 29			
Croy 3	d	08 05	08a11						08 35	08a41				09a03			09 05	09a11				09 35	09a41		
Falkirk Grahamston	d							08 34								09 04					09 34				
Camelon	d							08 37								09 07					09 37				
Larbert	d	08 18						08 43	08 48							09 13	09 18				09 43	09 48			
Stirling	d	08 30						08 53	09 00			09a07				09 23	09 30				09 53	10 00			
Alloa	a								09 13													10 13			
Bridge of Allan	d	08 35						08 57								09 27	09 35				09 57				
Dunblane	a	08 43						09 06								09 36	09 43				10 06				

		SR 1◇ E	SR	SR	SR	SR 1 C	SR 1 B	SR 1◇ D	SR		SR	SR	SR 1 C	SR 1 B	SR 1◇ E	SR	SR	SR		SR 1 C	SR 1 B	SR	SR	SR	SR 1 C
Edinburgh 10	d		09 18	09 33			09 45		09 48		10 04			10 15		10 18	10 33				10 45	10 48	11 04		
Haymarket	d		09 21	09 38			09 48		09 51		10 07			10 18		10 21	10 37				10 48	10 51	11 07		
Edinburgh Park	d		09 25	09 41					09 55		10 12					10 25	10 41					10 55	11 11		
Uphall	d		09 37						10 07							10 37						11 07			
Livingston North	d		09 41						10 11							10 41						11 11			
Bathgate	a		09 50						10 19							10 48						11 18			
Linlithgow	d			09 53			10 03				10 24			10 33			10 53				11 03		11 23		
Polmont 3	d			09 58			10a09				10 28			10a39			10 58				11a09		11 28		
Glasgow Queen Street 10	d	09 41			09 48	10 00		10 11				10 18	10 30		10 41			10 48		11 00				11 18	11 30
Bishopbriggs	d				09 53							10 23						10 53						11 23	
Lenzie 3	d				09 59							10 29						10 59						11 29	
Croy 3	d				10 05	10a11						10 35	10a41					11 05		11a11				11 35	11a41
Falkirk Grahamston	d			10 04							10 34						11 04						11 34		
Camelon	d			10 07							10 37						11 07						11 37		
Larbert	d			10 13	10 20						10 44	10 48					11 13	11 18					11 43	11 48	
Stirling	d	10a07		10 23	10 32			10 42			10 54	11 00			11a07		11 23	11 30					11 53	12 00	
Alloa	a											11 13												12 13	
Bridge of Allan	d			10 27	10 37						10 57						11 27	11 35					11 57		
Dunblane	a			10 39	10 46			10 49			11 07						11 36	11 43					12 07		

For general notes see front of timetable
For details of catering facilities see Directory of Train Operators

- **A** To Dyce (Table 229)
- **B** To Glasgow Queen Street (Table 228)
- **C** To Edinburgh (Table 228)
- **D** To Inverness (Table 229)
- **E** To Aberdeen (Table 229)
- **b** Arr. 0728
- **c** Arr. 0759

Table 230

Edinburgh, Glasgow Queen Street and Falkirk Grahamston → Stirling, Alloa and Dunblane
Edinburgh → Bathgate

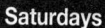

Network Diagram - see first page of Table 225

		SR 1 A	SR 1◇ B	SR	SR		SR	SR 1 C	SR 1 A	SR	SR	SR	SR 1 C	SR 1 A		SR 1◇ B	SR	SR	SR	SR 1 C	SR 1 A	SR	SR		SR
Edinburgh 10	d	11 15		11 18	11 34				11 45	11 48	12 04			12 15			12 18	12 33			12 45	12 48	13 03		
Haymarket	d	11 18		11 22	11 37				11 48	11 51	12 07			12 18			12 21	12 36			12 48	12 51	13 06		
Edinburgh Park	d			11 25	11 41					11 55	12 11						12 25	12 41				12 55	13 11		
Uphall	d			11 37						12 07							12 37					13 07			
Livingston North	d			11 41						12 11							12 41					13 11			
Bathgate	a			11 49						12 18							12 48					13 18			
Linlithgow	d	11 33			11 53				12 03		12 23			12 33				12 53			13 03		13 23		
Polmont 3	d	11a39			11 58				12a09		12 28			12a39				12 58			13a09		13 28		
Glasgow Queen Street 10	d		11 41				11 48	12 00				12 18	12 30			12 41			12 48	13 00					13 18
Bishopbriggs	d						11 53					12 23							12 53						13 23
Lenzie 3	d						11 59					12 29							12 59						13 29
Croy 3	d						12 05	12a11				12 35	12a41						13 05	13a11					13 35
Falkirk Grahamston	d				12 04						12 34							13 04					13 34		
Camelon	d				12 07						12 37							13 07					13 37		
Larbert	d				12 13		12 18				12 43	12 48						13 13	13 18				13 43		13 48
Stirling	d		12a07		12 23		12 30				12 53	13 00				13a07		13 23	13 31				13 53		14 00
Alloa	a											13 13													14 13
Bridge of Allan	d				12 27		12 35				12 57							13 27	13 35				13 57		
Dunblane	a				12 36		12 43				13 06							13 36	13 43				14 06		

		SR 1 C	SR 1 A	SR 1◇ B	SR	SR	SR	SR 1 C	SR 1 A		SR	SR	SR	SR 1 C	SR 1 A	SR 1◇ B	SR	SR		SR	SR 1 C	SR 1 A	SR	SR	SR
Edinburgh 10	d		13 15		13 18	13 34			13 45		13 48	14 04			14 15		14 18	14 33				14 45	14 48	15 04	
Haymarket	d		13 18		13 21	13 37			13 48		13 51	14 07			14 18		14 21	14 36				14 48	14 51	15 07	
Edinburgh Park	d				13 25	13 41					13 55	14 11					14 25	14 41					14 55	15 11	
Uphall	d				13 37						14 07						14 37						15 07		
Livingston North	d				13 41						14 11						14 41						15 11		
Bathgate	a				13 48						14 18						14 48						15 18		
Linlithgow	d		13 33			13 53			14 03			14 23			14 33			14 53				15 03		15 23	
Polmont 3	d		13a39			14 00			14a09			14 28			14a39			14 58				15a08		15 28	
Glasgow Queen Street 10	d	13 30		13 41			13 48	14 00					14 18	14 30		14 41				14 48	15 00				15 18
Bishopbriggs	d						13 53						14 23							14 53					15 23
Lenzie 3	d						13 59						14 29							14 59					15 29
Croy 3	d	13a41					14 05	14a11					14 35	14a41						15 05	15a11				15 35
Falkirk Grahamston	d					14 04						14 34						15 04						15 34	
Camelon	d					14 07						14 37						15 07						15 37	
Larbert	d					14 13	14 16					14 44	14 48					15 13		15 18				15 43	15 47
Stirling	d			14a07		14 23	14 31					14 53	15 00			15a07		15 23		15 30				15 53	16 01
Alloa	a												15 13												16 13
Bridge of Allan	d					14 27	14 36					14 57						15 27		15 35				15 57	
Dunblane	a					14 36	14 43					15 06						15 36		15 43				16 06	

		SR 1 C	SR 1 A	SR 1◇ B	SR		SR	SR	SR 1 C	SR 1 A	SR 1◇ D	SR	SR	SR		SR 1 C	SR 1 A	SR 1◇ B	SR	GR R 1 E G ⌀	SR	SR	SR 1 C		SR
Edinburgh 10	d		15 15		15 17		15 34			15 45		15 49	16 04				16 15		16 18	16 33	16 37				
Haymarket	d		15 18		15 21		15 37			15 48		15 51	16 07				16 18		16 21	16 38	16 41				
Edinburgh Park	d				15 27		15 41					15 55	16 11						16 25		16 46				
Uphall	d				15 37							16 07							16 37						
Livingston North	d				15 41							16 11							16 41						
Bathgate	a				15 49							16 19							16 48						
Linlithgow	d		15 33				15 53			16 03			16 23				16 33				16 58				
Polmont 3	d		15a39				15 58			16a09			16 28				16a39				17 03				
Glasgow Queen Street 10	d	15 30		15 41				15 48	16 00		16 11			16 19		16 30		16 41				16 48	17 00		17 03
Bishopbriggs	d							15 53						16 24								16 53			17 08
Lenzie 3	d							15 59						16 30								16 59			17 14
Croy 3	d	15a41						16 05	16a11					16 36		16a41						17 05	17a11		17 20
Falkirk Grahamston	d						16 04						16 34							17 04	17 08				
Camelon	d						16 07						16 37								17 11				
Larbert	d						16 15	16 18					16 43	16 49							17 18	17 23			17 33
Stirling	d			16a07			16 23	16 30			16 37		16 53	17b08				17a07		17a19	17 27	17 35			17 45
Alloa	a													17 20											
Bridge of Allan	d						16 27	16 35					16 57								17 31	17 40			17 49
Dunblane	a						16 36	16 43			16 48		17 06								17 40	17 47			17 55

For general notes see front of timetable
For details of catering facilities see Directory of Train Operators

- **A** To Glasgow Queen Street (Table 228)
- **B** To Aberdeen (Table 229)
- **C** To Edinburgh (Table 228)
- **D** To Inverness (Table 229)
- **E** From London Kings Cross (Table 26) to Inverness (Table 229)
- **G** **The Highland Chieftain**
- **b** Arr. 1700

Edinburgh, Glasgow Queen Street and Falkirk Grahamston → Stirling, Alloa and Dunblane
Edinburgh → Bathgate

Network Diagram - see first page of Table 225

Station		SR 1 A 🍴	SR	SR	SR	SR 1 B 🍴	SR 1 A 🍴	SR 1 ◇ C 🍴	SR		SR	SR	SR 1 B 🍴	SR 1 A 🍴	SR D	SR	SR	SR		SR 1 B 🍴	SR 1 A 🍴	SR 1 ◇ C 🍴	SR	SR	SR
Edinburgh 10	d	16 45	16 48	17 04			17 15		17 18		17 33			17 45		17 48	18 04				18 15		18 18	18 34	
Haymarket	d	16 48	16 51	17 07			17 18		17 21		17 37			17 47		17 51	18 07				18 18		18 21	18 37	
Edinburgh Park	d		16 55	17 11					17 25		17 41					17 55	18 11						18 25	18 41	
Uphall	d		17 07						17 37							18 07							18 37		
Livingston North	d		17 11						17 41							18 11							18 41		
Bathgate	a		17 18						17 48							18 19							18 48		
Linlithgow	d	17 03		17 23			17 33				17 53			18 03			18 23				18 33			18 53	
Polmont 3	d	17a09		17 28			17a39				17 58			18a09			18 28				18a39			18 59	
Glasgow Queen Street 10 ⛴	d				17 18	17 30		17 41				17 48	18 00		18 11			18 18		18 30		18 41			18 48
Bishopbriggs	d				17 23							17 53						18 23							18 53
Lenzie 3	d				17 29							17 59						18 29							18 59
Croy 3	d				17 35	17a41						18 05	18a11					18 35		18a41					19 05
Falkirk Grahamston	d			17 34							18 04						18 34							19 04	
Camelon	d			17 37							18 07						18 37							19 07	
Larbert	d			17 43	17 47						18 13	18 18			18 30		18 43	18 48						19 13	19 14
Stirling	d			17 53	17 59			18 07			18 23	18 33			18 41		18 53	19 00				19 07		19 23	19 31
Alloa	a				18 12													19 15							
Bridge of Allan	d			17 57							18 27	18 38			18 46		18 57							19 27	19 36
Dunblane	a			18 07				18 14			18 36	18 44			18 50		19 06					19 14		19 37	19 46

Station		SR 1 B 🍴	SR 1 A 🍴	SR	SR		SR	SR 1 A 🍴	SR 1 ◇ C 🍴	SR	SR 1 A 🍴	SR	SR	SR 1 B 🍴		SR 1 A 🍴	SR	SR	SR ◇ C	SR	SR 1 A 🍴	SR	SR		SR 1 B
Edinburgh 10	d		18 45	18 48	19 04			19 15		19 22	19 30	19 34				20 00	20 03			20 18	20 30	20 34			
Haymarket	d		18 48	18 51	19 05			19 18		19 23	19 33	19 37				20 03	20 06			20 21	20 33	20 37			
Edinburgh Park	d			18 55	19 11					19 27		19 41					20 11			20 25		20 41			
Uphall	d			19 07						19 39										20 37					
Livingston North	d			19 11						19 44										20 41					
Bathgate	a			19 18						19 52										20 48					
Linlithgow	d		19 03		19 23			19 33			19a48	19 53				20 18	20 23				20a48	20 53			
Polmont 3	d		19a09		19 28			19a39				19 58				20a24	20 29					20 58			
Glasgow Queen Street 10 ⛴	d	19 00					19 18		19 41				19 48	20 00				20 18	20 41				20 48		21 00
Bishopbriggs	d						19 23						19 53					20 23					20 53		
Lenzie 3	d						19 29						19 59					20 29					20 59		
Croy 3	d	19a11					19 35						20 05	20a11				20 35					21 05		21a11
Falkirk Grahamston	d				19 34							20 04					20 34					21 04			
Camelon	d				19 37							20 07					20 37					21 07			
Larbert	d				19 43		19 48					20 13	20 18				20 43	20 48				21 13	21 18		
Stirling	d				19 53		20 00		20a07			20 23	20 30				20 53	21 00	21 07			21 23	21 30		
Alloa	a						20 13											21 13							
Bridge of Allan	d				19 57							20 27	20 35				20 57					21 27	21 35		
Dunblane	a				20 06							20 36	20 43				21 06		21 14			21 36	21 43		

Station		SR	SR 1 A	SR 1 ◇ C	SR	SR 1 A	SR D	SR	SR 1 B		SR	SR 1 A	SR	SR 1 A	SR	SR D	SR 1 B	SR	SR 1 A	SR 1 B	SR	SR 1 A	SR		
Edinburgh 10	d		21 00		21 18	21 30	21 33					22 00	22 18	22 30	22 34				23 00		23 18	23 30	23 33		
Haymarket	d		21 03		21 21	21 33	21 37					22 03	22 21	22 33	22 37				23 03		23 21	23 33	23 37		
Edinburgh Park	d				21 25		21 41						22 25		22 41						23 25		23 41		
Uphall	d				21 37								22 37								23 37				
Livingston North	d				21 41								22 41								23 41				
Bathgate	a				21 48								22 48								23 48				
Linlithgow	d		21 18			21a48	21 53					22 18		22a48	22 53				23 18			23 48	23 53		
Polmont 3	d		21a24				21 58					22a24			22 58				23a24			23a53	23 58		
Glasgow Queen Street 10 ⛴	d	21 18		21 41				21 48	22 00		22 18					22 48	23 00	23 18		23 30					
Bishopbriggs	d	21 23						21 53			22 23					22 53		23 23							
Lenzie 3	d	21 29						21 59			22 29					22 59		23 29							
Croy 3	d	21 35						22 05	22a11		22 35					23 05	23a11	23 35		23a42					
Falkirk Grahamston	d						22 04								23 04								00 04		
Camelon	d						22 07								23 07								00 07		
Larbert	d	21 48					22 13	22 18			22 47				23 15	23 16		23 48					00 13		
Stirling	d	22 00		22a07			22 23	22 30			23b01				23 24	23c33		00a01					00 23		
Alloa	a	22 13									23 13														
Bridge of Allan	d						22 27	22 35							23 29	23 37							00 27		
Dunblane	a						22 34	22 43							23 37	23 42							00 35		

For general notes see front of timetable
For details of catering facilities see Directory of Train Operators

- **A** To Glasgow Queen Street (Table 228)
- **B** To Edinburgh (Table 228)
- **C** To Aberdeen (Table 229)
- **D** To Perth (Table 229)
- **b** Arr. 2256
- **c** Arr. 2328

Table 230

Sundays

Edinburgh, Glasgow Queen Street and Falkirk Grahamston → Stirling, Alloa and Dunblane
Edinburgh → Bathgate

Network Diagram - see first page of Table 225

			SR 1 A	SR B	SR 1 C ✠	SR 1 A ✠	SR B	SR B	SR 1 C	SR 1 A ✠	SR 1 ◇ D ✠	SR		SR B	SR	SR	SR 1 C ✠	SR 1 A ✠	SR B	SR	SR	SR	SR 1 C ✠		SR 1 A ✠	SR 1 ◇ D
Edinburgh 10	225, 242	d			08 00				09 00			09 03			09 34		10 00			10 18	10 34		11 00			
Haymarket	225, 242	d			08 03				09 03			09 07			09 37		10 03			10 21	10 37		11 03			
Edinburgh Park		d										09 11			09 41					10 25	10 41					
Uphall		d										09 29								10 37						
Livingston North		d										09 33								10 41						
Bathgate		a										09 38								10 54						
Linlithgow		d			08 18				09 18						10 00		10 18				10 53		11 18			
Polmont 3		d			08a24				09a24						10 05		10a24				10 58		11a24			
Glasgow Queen Street 10		d	07 50	08 15		08 30	08 48	09 12		09 30	09 38			09 47		10 15		10 30	10 47			11 15			11 30	11 45
Bishopbriggs		d		08 21			08 54	09 18						09 53		10 21			10 53			11 21				
Lenzie 3		d		08 27			09 00	09 24			09 47			09 59		10 27			10 59			11 27				
Croy 3		d	08a01	08a33		08a41	09a06	09a30		09a41				10a05		10 33		10a41	11a05			11 33			11a41	
Falkirk Grahamston		d													10 11						11 04					
Camelon		d													10 14						11 07					
Larbert		d									10 01				10 21	10 45					11 13	11 45				
Stirling		d									10 12				10 30	10 55					11 24	11 55				12 12
Alloa		a														11 07						12 07				
Bridge of Allan		d													10 34						11 27					
Dunblane		a									10 17				10 41						11 36					12 17

			SR B	SR	SR	SR	SR 1 C ✠	SR 1 A ✠	SR B	SR	SR 1 C ✠	SR		SR 1 A ✠	SR	SR 1 C ✠	SR 1 ◇ D ✠	SR B	SR	SR 1 C ✠	SR 1 A ✠	SR	SR		SR 1 C ✠	SR 1 ◇ E ✠
Edinburgh 10	225, 242	d		11 18	11 33		12 00			12 18	12 30	12 33				13 00			13 18	13 30		13 38			14 00	
Haymarket	225, 242	d		11 21	11 37		12 03			12 21	12 33	12 37				13 03			13 21	13 33		13 42			14 03	
Edinburgh Park		d		11 25	11 41					12 25		12 41							13 25			13 47				
Uphall		d		11 37						12 37									13 37							
Livingston North		d		11 41						12 41									13 41							
Bathgate		a		11 48						12 48									13 48							
Linlithgow		d			11 53		12 18				12a48	12 53				13 18				13a48		13 59			14 18	
Polmont 3		d			11 58		12a24					12 58				13a24						14 04			14a24	
Glasgow Queen Street 10		d	11 48			12 15		12 30	12 47					13 00	13 15		13 45	13 48			14 00		14 15			14 40
Bishopbriggs		d	11 54			12 21			12 53						13 21			13 54					14 21			
Lenzie 3		d	12 00			12 27			12 59						13 27			14 00					14 27			
Croy 3		d	12a06			12 33		12a41	13a05					13a11	13 33			14a06			14a11		14 33			
Falkirk Grahamston		d			12 04							13 04										14 10				
Camelon		d			12 07							13 07										14 13				
Larbert		d			12 13	12 45						13 14			13 45							14 20	14 45			15 00
Stirling		d			12 24	12 55						13 24			13 55		14 12					14 28	14 55			15 09
Alloa		a				13 07									14 07								15 07			
Bridge of Allan		d			12 27							13 27										14 33				
Dunblane		a			12 36							13 36					14 17					14 40				15 15

			SR B	SR	SR 1 C	SR	SR 1 A	SR	SR 1 C ✠	SR 1 ◇ D ✠	SR	SR 1 C ✠		SR B	SR	SR 1 A ✠	SR	SR 1 C ✠	SR B	SR	SR 1 C ✠	SR	SR 1 A ✠		SR 1 C ✠	GR R 1 G H ✠
Edinburgh 10	225, 242	d		14 18	14 30	14 33			15 00		15 18	15 30			15 34			16 00		16 18	16 30	16 34			17 00	17 12
Haymarket	225, 242	d		14 21	14 33	14 37			15 03		15 21	15 33			15 37			16 03		16 21	16 33	16 37			17 03	17 16
Edinburgh Park		d		14 25		14 41					15 25				15 41					16 25		16 41				
Uphall		d		14 37							15 37									16 37						
Livingston North		d		14 41							15 41									16 41						
Bathgate		a		14 48							15 48									16 48						
Linlithgow		d			14a48	14 54			15 18			15a46			15 53			16 18			16a48	16 53			17 18	
Polmont 3		d				14 58			15a24						15 58			16a24				16 58			17a24	
Glasgow Queen Street 10		d	14 47				15 00	15 15		15 45				15 48		16 00	16 15		16 47				17 00			
Bishopbriggs		d	14 53					15 21						15 54			16 21		16 53							
Lenzie 3		d	14 59					15 27						16 00			16 27		16 59							
Croy 3		d	15a05				15a11	15 33						16a06		16a11	16 33		17a05				17a11			
Falkirk Grahamston		d				15 04									16 04							17 04				17 37
Camelon		d				15 07									16 07							17 07				
Larbert		d				15 13		15 45							16 13		16 45					17 13				
Stirling		d				15 24		15 55		16 12					16 24		16 55					17 24				17a52
Alloa		a						16 07									17 07									
Bridge of Allan		d				15 27									16 27							17 27				
Dunblane		a				15 36				16 17					16 36							17 36				

For general notes see front of timetable
For details of catering facilities see Directory of Train Operators

A To Edinburgh (Table 228)
B 29 November and 6 December
C To Glasgow Queen Street (Table 228)
D To Aberdeen (Table 229)
E To Elgin (Table 240)
G From London Kings Cross (Table 26) to Inverness (Table 229)
H **The Highland Chieftain**

Table 230

Sundays

Edinburgh, Glasgow Queen Street and Falkirk Grahamston → Stirling, Alloa and Dunblane
Edinburgh → Bathgate

Network Diagram - see first page of Table 225

		SR	SR 1◊ A ✠	SR	SR B	SR 1 C	SR	SR 1 D ✠	SR 1◊ E ✠	SR	SR 1 C ✠	SR	SR 1 C ✠	SR	SR 1 D ✠	SR	SR 1 C ✠	SR 1◊ A ✠	SR	SR 1 C ✠	SR	SR 1 D ✠	SR
Edinburgh 10 225, 242	d			17 18		17 30	17 34				18 00	18 18	18 30	18 33			19 00		19 19	19 30	19 34		
Haymarket 225, 242	d			17 21		17 33	17 37				18 03	18 21	18 33	18 37			19 03		19 22	19 33	19 37		
Edinburgh Park	d			17 25			17 41					18 25		18 41					19 25		19 41		
Uphall	d			17 36								18 36							19 37				
Livingston North	d			17 40								18 40							19 41				
Bathgate	a			17 47								18 48							19 48				
Linlithgow	d					17a48	17 53				18 18		18a48	18 53			19 18			19a48	19 53		
Polmont 3	d						17 58				18a24			18 58			19a24				19 58		
Glasgow Queen Street 10	d	17 15	17 45		17 48			18 00	18 10	18 15					19 00	19 15		19 45				20 00	20 15
Bishopbriggs	d	17 21			17 54					18 21						19 21							20 21
Lenzie 3	d	17 27			18 00					18 27						19 27							20 27
Croy 3	d	17 33			18a06			18a11		18 33					19a11	19 33						20a11	20 33
Falkirk Grahamston	d						18 04							19 04							20 04		
Camelon	d						18 07							19 07							20 07		
Larbert	d	17 48					18 13		18 30	18 45				19 13		19 45					20 13		20 45
Stirling	d	17 57	18a12				18 24		18 39	18 55				19 25		19 55		20 12			20 24		20 55
Alloa	a	18 12								19 07						20 07							21 07
Bridge of Allan	d						18 27							19 30							20 27		
Dunblane	a						18 36		18 45					19 37				20 17			20 36		

		SR 1 C ✠	SR	SR 1 C ✠	SR	SR 1 D	SR	SR 1 C ✠	SR 1 D	SR 1◊ A ✠	SR	SR	SR	SR 1 C	SR 1 D	SR	SR G	SR 1 C	SR 1 D	SR 1 G	SR	SR 1 C
Edinburgh 10 225, 242	d	20 00	20 18	20 30	20 33			21 00			21 18	21 34		22 00		22 18	22 36	23 00			23 18	23 30
Haymarket 225, 242	d	20 03	20 21	20 33	20 37			21 03			21 21	21 37		22 02		22 20	22 40	23 02			23 21	23 33
Edinburgh Park	d		20 25		20 41						21 25	21 41				22 25	22 46				23 25	
Uphall	d		20 37								21 37					22 37					23 37	
Livingston North	d		20 41								21 41					22 41					23 41	
Bathgate	a		20 48								21 48					22 48					23 48	
Linlithgow	d	20 18		20a48	20 53			21 18				21 53		22 18			22 58	23 18				23 48
Polmont 3	d	20a24			20 58			21a23				21 58		22a24			23 03	23a24				23a54
Glasgow Queen Street 10	d					21 00	21 15		21 30	21 45			22 15		22 30				23 30	23 35		
Bishopbriggs	d						21 21						22 21							23 41		
Lenzie 3	d						21 27						22 27							23 47		
Croy 3	d					21a11	21 33		21a41				22 33		22a41				23a41	23 53		
Falkirk Grahamston	d				21 04							22 04					23 09					
Camelon	d				21 07							22 07					23 13					
Larbert	d				21 13		21 45					22 13	22 45				23 18			00 05		
Stirling	d				21 23		21 55			22 11		22 24	22 55				23 27			00 14		
Alloa	a						22 07						23 07									
Bridge of Allan	d				21 27							22 27					23 33			00 18		
Dunblane	a				21 36					22 17		22 36					23 37			00 22		

For general notes see front of timetable
For details of catering facilities see Directory of Train Operators

A To Aberdeen (Table 229)
B 29 November and 6 December
C To Glasgow Queen Street (Table 228)
D To Edinburgh (Table 228)
E To Elgin (Table 240)
G To Perth (Table 229)

Dunblane, Alloa and Stirling → Falkirk Grahamston, Glasgow Queen Street and Edinburgh
Bathgate → Edinburgh

Network Diagram - see first page of Table 225

Miles	Miles	Miles	Miles			SR MO [1] A	SR MX [1] A	SR	SR [1] B	SR C	SR	SR [1] A	SR [1] B 🛒	SR	SR	SR [1] B 🛒	SR	SR [1] B 🛒	SR [1] A 🛒	SR C	SR [1] B 🛒	SR [1] A 🛒	SR	SR C	SR
0	0	—	—	**Dunblane**	d			05 21		05 46					06 28					06 40				07 08	
2	2	—	—	Bridge of Allan	d			05 24		05 49					06 31					06 43				07 10	
—	—	—	0	**Alloa**	d									06 10											07 11
5½	5½	—	6¾	**Stirling**	d			05 30		05 53				06 21	06 36					06b52				07 16	07 22
13½	13½	—	14¾	Larbert	d			05 38		06 01				06 29	06 45					06 59				07 25	07 30
—	15	—	—	Camelon	d			05 44							06 49									07 30	
—	16½	—	—	**Falkirk Grahamston**	d			05 47							06 53									07 34	
24	—	—	25¼	Croy [3]	d	00 09	00 10			06 12		06 34		06 40					07 10	07 14		07 23			07 41
29¼	—	—	30½	Lenzie [3]	d		00 14			06 19				06 47						07 21			07 34		07 48
32¼	—	—	33½	Bishopbriggs	d					06 23				06 51						07 25			07 38		07 52
34½	—	—	35¾	**Glasgow Queen Street** [10] ⛴	a	00 25	00 27			06 34		06 49		07 01					07 25	07 34		07 39	07 47		08 05
—	19½	—	—	Polmont [3]	d			05 53	06 21				06 56		06 59			07 27			07 37			07 43	
—	24¼	—	—	Linlithgow	d			06 00	06 30				07 03		07 06	07 13		07 33			07 43			07 50	
—	—	0	—	**Bathgate**	d						06 39						07 13								
—	—	3	—	Livingston North	d						06 44						07 19								
—	—	6	—	Uphall	d						06 48						07 23								
—	38	14¾	—	Edinburgh Park	d			06 12			06 58				07 19		07 33							08 02	
—	40½	17¼	—	Haymarket	d			06 19	06s45		07 04		07s18		07 26	07s31	07 39	07s49			08s01			08 08	
—	41¾	18½	—	**Edinburgh** [10] 225, 242	a			06 24	06 50		07 10		07 24		07 34	07 37	07 43	07 55			08 07			08 14	

		SR	SR [1] B 🛒	SR	SR [1] B	SR [1] A 🛒	SR C	SR	SR [1] A 🛒	SR [1] B 🛒	SR	SR [1] ◇ D 🛒	SR [1] A 🛒	SR E	SR	SR [1] B 🛒	SR	SR [1] A 🛒		SR	SR	SR	SR [1] B 🛒	SR [1] ◇ D 🛒	SR [1] A 🛒
Dunblane	d	07 22					07 29					07 44			07 56					08 12		08 28			
Bridge of Allan	d	07 25					07 33					07 48			07 59					08 16		08 31			
Alloa	d																07 54								
Stirling	d	07 29					07 38	07 49				07 53			08 05		08 06			08 21		08 36		08 44	
Larbert	d	07 38					07 47	07 56				08 02			08 14		08 16			08 29		08 45			
Camelon	d							08 00						08 14	08 18							08 48			
Falkirk Grahamston	d							08 04						08 10	08 21							08 52			
Croy [3]	d					07 52	07 59		08 09								08 30	08 36		08 40					09 03
Lenzie [3]	d						08 06					08 17	08 25	08 30			08 35			08 47					
Bishopbriggs	d						08 10							08 35			08 39			08 51					
Glasgow Queen Street [10] ⛴	a					08 07	08 20		08 25			08 34	08 40	08 46			08 51	08 54		09 03				09 15	09 21
Polmont [3]	d				08 07			08 12		08 26					08 31							08 59	09 07		
Linlithgow	d		07 59		08 13			08 19							08 38	08 42						09 06	09 13		
Bathgate	d			07 57							08 25										08 54				
Livingston North	d			08 03							08 30										08 58				
Uphall	d			08 08							08 34										09 02				
Edinburgh Park	d			08 18				08 32			08 43				08 50						09 13	09 19			
Haymarket	d	08 13	08s16	08 23	08s32			08 39		08s45	08 53				08 58	09s00					09 19	09 27	09s31		
Edinburgh [10] 225, 242	a	08 19	08 22	08 28	08 37			08 45		08 50	08 59				09 02	09 05					09 25	09 32	09 36		

		SR	SR	SR	SR [1] B 🛒	SR [1] G	SR [1] A 🛒	SR	SR	SR	SR [1] B 🛒	SR [1] ◇ H 🛒	SR [1] A 🛒	SR	SR	SR	SR [1] B 🛒	SR [1] A 🛒	SR	GR [R] [1] J K Ø 🛒	SR [1] B 🛒	SR	SR	SR [1] B 🛒	SR [1] ◇ D 🛒
Dunblane	d			08 57		09 06		09 13		09 28						09 58			10 13				10 28		
Bridge of Allan	d			09 00				09 16		09 31						10 01			10 16				10 31		
Alloa	d		08 35											09 40											
Stirling	d		08c51	09 06		09 13		09 21		09 36		09 44		09 51		10 06			10 21	10 30			10 36		10 43
Larbert	d		08 59	09 15				09 29		09 45				09 59		10 15			10 29				10 45		
Camelon	d			09 18						09 48						10 18							10 48		
Falkirk Grahamston	d			09 22						09 52						10 22				10 45			10 52		
Croy [3]	d		09 12				09 33	09 40					10 03	10 10				10 33	10 40		10 41				
Lenzie [3]	d		09 19					09 47						10 17					10 47						
Bishopbriggs	d		09 23					09 51						10 21					10 51						
Glasgow Queen Street [10] ⛴	a		09 33			09 45	09 50	10 01				10 14	10 19	10 31				10 49	11 01						11 15
Polmont [3]	d			09 29	09 37					09 59	10 07					10 29	10 37						10 59	11 07	
Linlithgow	d			09 36	09 43					10 06	10 13					10 36	10 43						11 06	11 13	
Bathgate	d	09 24							09 54						10 24							10 54			
Livingston North	d	09 28							09 58						10 28							10 58			
Uphall	d	09 32							10 02						10 32							11 02			
Edinburgh Park	d	09 43		09 49					10 13	10 19					10 43	10 49						11 13	11 19		
Haymarket	d	09 49		09 55	10s01				10 21	10 26	10s30				10 53	10 56	11s00			11 09	11s13	11 20	11 26	11s30	
Edinburgh [10] 225, 242	a	09 54		10 02	10 06				10 25	10 31	10 35				10 59	11 02	11 05			11 15	11 19	11 25	11 31	11 35	

For general notes see front of timetable
For details of catering facilities see Directory of Train Operators

- **A** From Edinburgh (Table 228)
- **B** From Glasgow Queen Street (Table 228)
- **C** From Perth (Table 229)
- **D** From Aberdeen (Table 229)
- **E** From Ladybank
- **G** From Dundee (Table 229)
- **H** From Inverurie (Table 229)
- **J** From Inverness (Table 229) to London Kings Cross (Table 26)
- **K** **The Highland Chieftain**
- **b** Arr. 0647
- **c** Arr. 0845

Dunblane, Alloa and Stirling → Falkirk Grahamston, Glasgow Queen Street and Edinburgh Bathgate → Edinburgh

Network Diagram - see first page of Table 225

Station		SR 1 A	SR	SR	SR	SR 1 B	SR 1 A	SR	SR	SR		SR 1 B	SR 1◊ C	SR 1 A	SR	SR	SR	SR 1 B	SR 1◊ D	SR 1 A	SR	SR	SR	SR 1 B	SR 1◊ E
Dunblane	d				10 58			11 13		11 28							11 58		12 06		12 13		12 28		
Bridge of Allan	d				11 01			11 16		11 31							12 01				12 16		12 31		
Alloa	d		10 35												11 42										
Stirling	d		10b51		11 06			11 21		11 36			11 43		11 51		12 06		12 13		12 21		12 36		12 42
Larbert	d		10 59		11 15			11 29		11 45					11 59		12 15				12 29		12 45		
Camelon	d				11 18					11 48							12 18						12 48		
Falkirk Grahamston	d				11 22					11 52							12 22						12 52		
Croy 3	d	11 03	11 10				11 33	11 40						12 03	12 10					12 33	12 40				
Lenzie 3	d		11 17					11 47							12 17						12 47				
Bishopbriggs	d		11 22					11 51							12 21						12 51				
Glasgow Queen Street 10	a	11 19	11 34				11 49	12 02					12 15	12 19	12 35				12 46	12 49	13 01				13 14
Polmont 3	d				11 29	11 37				11 59		12 07					12 29	12 37					12 59	13 07	
Linlithgow	d				11 36	11 43				12 06		12 13					12 36	12 44					13 06	13 13	
Bathgate	d			11 24					11 54							12 24						12 54			
Livingston North	d			11 28					11 58							12 28						12 58			
Uphall	d			11 32					12 02							12 32						13 02			
Edinburgh Park	d			11 43	11 49				12 13	12 19						12 43	12 49					13 13	13 19		
Haymarket	d			11 50	11 56	12s00			12 19	12 26		12s29				12 54	12 56	13s01				13 20	13 26	13s30	
Edinburgh 10 225, 242	a			11 55	12 01	12 05			12 25	12 31		12 35				12 59	13 02	13 05				13 25	13 31	13 35	

Station		SR 1 A	SR	SR	SR	SR 1 B	SR 1 A	SR	SR	SR	SR 1 B	SR 1◊ E	SR 1 A	SR	SR	SR	SR 1 B	SR 1 A	SR	SR	SR	SR 1 B	SR 1◊ E	SR 1 A	SR
Dunblane	d				12 58			13 13		13 28						13 58			14 13		14 28				
Bridge of Allan	d				13 01			13 16		13 31						14 01			14 16		14 31				
Alloa	d		12 35											13 40											14 35
Stirling	d		12c51		13 06			13 21		13 36		13 43		13 51		14 06			14 21		14 36		14 40		14e51
Larbert	d		12 59		13 15			13 29		13 45				13 59		14 15			14 29		14 45				14 59
Camelon	d				13 18					13 48						14 18					14 48				
Falkirk Grahamston	d				13 22					13 52						14 22					14 52				
Croy 3	d	13 03	13 10				13 33	13 41					14 03	14 10				14 33	14 40					15 03	15 10
Lenzie 3	d		13 17					13 47						14 17					14 47						15 17
Bishopbriggs	d		13 21					13 51						14 21					14 51						15 21
Glasgow Queen Street 10	a	13 19	13 31				13 49	14 01				14 15	14 19	14 31				14 49	15 02				15 15	15 20	15 34
Polmont 3	d				13 29	13 37				13 59	14 07					14 29	14 37				14 59	15 07			
Linlithgow	d				13 36	13 43				14 06	14 13					14 36	14 43				15 06	15 13			
Bathgate	d			13 24					13 54						14 24					14 54					
Livingston North	d			13 28					13 58						14 28					14 58					
Uphall	d			13 32					14 02						14 32					15 02					
Edinburgh Park	d			13 43	13 49				14 13	14 19					14 43	14 49				15 13	15 19				
Haymarket	d			13 51	13 56	14s00			14 20	14 26	14s30				14 54	14 56	15s00			15 20	15 26	15s30			
Edinburgh 10 225, 242	a			13 55	14 01	14 05			14 25	14 31	14 35				14 59	15 02	15 05			15 25	15 32	15 35			

Station		SR		SR	SR 1 B	SR 1 A	SR	SR	SR	SR 1 B	SR 1◊ E	SR 1 A	SR	SR	SR	SR 1 B	SR 1 A	SR	SR	SR	SR 1 B	SR 1◊ E	SR 1 A	SR	SR 1 B
Dunblane	d			14 58			15 13		15 28						15 58			16 13		16 28					
Bridge of Allan	d			15 01			15 16		15 31						16 01			16 16		16 31					
Alloa	d												15 40											16 35	
Stirling	d			15 06			15 21		15 36		15 43		15 51		16 06			16 21		16 36		16 43		16f51	
Larbert	d			15 15			15 29		15 45				15 59		16 15			16 29		16 45				16 59	
Camelon	d			15 18					15 48						16 18					16 48					
Falkirk Grahamston	d			15 22					15 52						16 22					16 52					
Croy 3	d					15 33	15 40					16 03	16 10				16 33	16 41					17 03	17 10	
Lenzie 3	d						15 47						16 17					16 47						17 17	
Bishopbriggs	d						15 51						16 21					16 51						17 21	
Glasgow Queen Street 10	a					15 50	16 04				16 15	16 19	16 32				16 51	17 01				17 17	17 21	17 32	
Polmont 3	d			15 29	15 37				15 59	16 07					16 29	16 37				16 59	17 07				17 27
Linlithgow	d			15 36	15 43				16 06	16 13					16 36	16 43				17 06	17 13				
Bathgate	d	15 24						15 54						16 24					16 54						
Livingston North	d	15 28						15 58						16 28					16 58						
Uphall	d	15 32						16 02						16 32					17 02						
Edinburgh Park	d	15 43		15 49				16 13	16 19					16 43	16 49				17 13	17 19					
Haymarket	d	15 50		15 56	16s00			16 20	16 26	16s30				16 54	16 56	17s00			17 20	17 26	17s33				17s45
Edinburgh 10 225, 242	a	15 55		16 01	16 05			16 25	16 33	16 36				16 59	17 02	17 06			17 25	17 31	17 39				17 50

For general notes see front of timetable
For details of catering facilities see Directory of Train Operators

- A From Edinburgh (Table 228)
- B From Glasgow Queen Street (Table 228)
- C From Dyce (Table 229)
- D From Inverness (Table 229)
- E From Aberdeen (Table 229)

- b Arr. 1045
- c Arr. 1245
- e Arr. 1445
- f Arr. 1645

Dunblane, Alloa and Stirling → Falkirk Grahamston, Glasgow Queen Street and Edinburgh
Bathgate → Edinburgh

Network Diagram - see first page of Table 225

	SR	SR	SR	SR	SR	SR	SR	SR	SR	SR	SR	SR	SR	SR	SR		SR	SR	SR	SR	SR	SR	SR	SR
			1	1			1	1◇		1	1◇	1						1	1		1			1
			A	B			A	C		A	D	B						A	B		A			A
			⚲	⚲			⚲	⚲		⚲	⚲	⚲						⚲	⚲		⚲			⚲
Dunblane d		16 58						17 22	17 28		17 36						17 58			18 11			18 28	
Bridge of Allan d		17 01							17 31								18 01			18 14			18 31	
Alloa d														17 40										
Stirling d		17 06				17 21		17 29	17 36		17 42			17 51			18 06			18 19			18 36	
Larbert d		17 15				17 29			17 45					17 59			18 15			18 28			18 45	
Camelon d		17 18							17 48				18 00				18 18						18 48	
Falkirk Grahamston d		17 22							17 52				18 04				18 22						18 52	
Croy 3 d				17 33		17 40						18 03		18 10					18 33	18 39	18 41			
Lenzie 3 d						17 47						18 08		18 17						18 46				
Bishopbriggs d						17 51								18 21						18 50				
Glasgow Queen Street 10 ⛴ a				17 51		18 03		18 09			18 15	18 22		18 34					18 51	19 01				
Polmont 3 d		17 29					17 56		17 59	18 07			18 13				18 29	18 37					18 59	19 07
Linlithgow d		17 36	17 40				18 03		18 06	18 13			18a19				18 36	18 43					19 06	19 13
Bathgate d	17 28				17 53										18 24							18 54		
Livingston North d	17 32				17 58										18 28							18 58		
Uphall d	17 36				18 02										18 32							19 02		
Edinburgh Park d	17 47	17 49			18 12				18 19						18 43		18 49					19 13	19 19	
Haymarket d	17 53	17 55	18s00		18 18		18s21		18 26	18s31					18 53		18 56	19s00			19s12	19 20	19 26	19s30
Edinburgh 10 225, 242 a	17 58	18 02	18 06		18 23		18 26		18 32	18 37					18 59		19 01	19 05			19 18	19 24	19 32	19 36

	SR	SR	SR	SR	SR	SR	SR	SR	SR	SR	SR	SR	SR	SR	SR	SR	SR	SR	SR	SR	SR	SR	SR	SR
	1◇	1				1	1	1				1◇	1	1			1				1◇	1		1
	D	B				A	B	A				D	B	A			A				D	B		A
	⚲	⚲				⚲	⚲	⚲				⚲	⚲	⚲			⚲				⚲	⚲		
Dunblane d	18 35				18 58				19 14	19 28						20 02		20 13	20 28					
Bridge of Allan d					19 01				19 17	19 31						20 04		20 16	20 31					
Alloa d			18 35												19 42								20 40	
Stirling d	18 42				19 06				19 22	19 36		19 43			19 53	20 06		20 21	20 36		20 40		20 51	
Larbert d			18 59		19 15				19 30	19 45					20 01	20 15		20 29	20 45				20 59	
Camelon d					19 18					19 48						20 18			20 48					
Falkirk Grahamston d					19 22					19 52						20 22			20 52					
Croy 3 d		19 03	19 10				19 33		19 41				20 07		20 12			20 41				21 07	21 10	21 11
Lenzie 3 d			19 17						19 48						20 19			20 47					21 17	
Bishopbriggs d			19 21						19 52						20 23			20 51					21 21	
Glasgow Queen Street 10 ⛴ a	19 14	19 21	19 31				19 49		20 02			20 15	20 22		20 34			21 04			21 14	21 22	21 34	
Polmont 3 d					19 29	19 37		19 52		19 59						20 29	20 52		20 59					
Linlithgow d					19 36	19 43		19 58		20 06				20 28		20 36	20 58		21 06					21 28
Bathgate d				19 27							20 05									21 05				
Livingston North d				19 32							20 10									21 10				
Uphall d				19 36							20 14									21 14				
Edinburgh Park d				19 48	19 50					20 19	20 24					20 48			21 19	21 24				
Haymarket d				19 53	19 56	20s01		20s15		20 27	20 31			20s46		20 55	21s13		21 26	21 31				21s46
Edinburgh 10 225, 242 a				19 58	20 02	20 06		20 21		20 32	20 36			20 51		21 06	21 20		21 31	21 36				21 53

	SR	SR	SR	SR	SR	SR	SR	SR	SR	SR	SR	SR	SR	SR	SR	SR	SR	SR	SR	SR	SR	SR		
		1			1◇	1		1		1			1◇	1		1	1◇				1	1		
		A			D	B		A		A			D	B		A	C				B	A		
					⚲																			
Dunblane d	20 58			21 13					21 58			22 13					22 58	23 06						
Bridge of Allan d	21 01			21 16					22 01			22 16					23 02	23 09						
Alloa d							21 41								22 40				23 18					
Stirling d	21 06			21 21	21 45		21 52		22 06			22 21	22 43		22 51		23 05	23 14	23a28					
Larbert d	21 15			21 29			21 59		22 15			22 29			22 59			23 23						
Camelon d	21 18								22 18									23 29						
Falkirk Grahamston d	21 22								22 22									23 32						
Croy 3 d				21 40		22 07	22 10					22 40		23 07	23 10						23 39			
Lenzie 3 d				21 47			22 17					22 47		23 14	23 17						23 47			
Bishopbriggs d				21 51			22 21					22 51			23 21						23 51			
Glasgow Queen Street 10 ⛴ a				22 03	22 19	22 22	22 34					23 03	23 15	23 30	23 34		23 38				00 03			
Polmont 3 d	21 29	21 52							22 29	22 52						23 26		23 38				23 57		
Linlithgow d	21 36	21 58						22 28	22 36	22 58						23 33		23 45				00 04		
Bathgate d			22 03								23 03									23 52				
Livingston North d			22 08								23 08									23 57				
Uphall d			22 12								23 12									23 59				
Edinburgh Park d	21 49		22 22						22 49		23 22							23 57		00 11				
Haymarket d	21 56	22s18	22 28					22s45	22 56	23s15	23 29					23s49		00 04		00 17		00s19		
Edinburgh 10 225, 242 a	22 01	22 24	22 33					22 50	23 01	23 20	23 34					23 54		00 09		00 22		00 25		

For general notes see front of timetable
For details of catering facilities see Directory of Train Operators

A From Glasgow Queen Street (Table 228)
B From Edinburgh (Table 228)
C From Inverness (Table 229)
D From Aberdeen (Table 229)

Dunblane, Alloa and Stirling → Falkirk Grahamston, Glasgow Queen Street and Edinburgh
Bathgate → Edinburgh

Network Diagram - see first page of Table 225

	SR [1] A	SR	SR [1] B	SR C	SR	SR [1] A	SR	SR [1] B	SR	SR		SR [1] B 🍴	SR [1] A	SR	SR [1] B 🍴	SR C	SR	SR [1] B 🍴	SR	SR [1] B	SR [1] A 🍴		SR	SR [1] A 🍴
Dunblane d		05 21		05 46					06 28					06 45		07 08							07 29	
Bridge of Allan d		05 24		05 49					06 31					06 48		07 10							07 32	
Alloa d							06 10										07 11							
Stirling d		05 30		05 53			06 21		06 36					06 52		07 16	07 22						07 40	
Larbert d		05 38		06 01			06 29		06 45					06 59		07 25	07 30						07 46	
Camelon d		05 44							06 49							07 30								
Falkirk Grahamston d		05 47							06 53							07 34								
Croy [3] d	00 10			06 12		06 34	06 40						07 10	07 14			07 41				07 52		08 00	08 09
Lenzie [3] d	00 14			06 19			06 47							07 21			07 48						08 07	
Bishopbriggs d				06 23			06 51							07 25			07 52						08 11	
Glasgow Queen Street [10] ⛴ a	00 27			06 34		06 49	07 01						07 25	07 34			08 05				08 07		08 22	08 25
Polmont [3] d		05 53	06 21					06 59	06 59			07 27			07 37	07 43				08 07				
Linlithgow d		06 00	06 30					07 05	07 06			07 33			07 43	07 50		07 59		08 13				
Bathgate d					06 39					07 13									07 57					
Livingston North d					06 44					07 19									08 03					
Uphall d					06 48					07 23									08 08					
Edinburgh Park d		06 12			06 58				07 19	07 33						08 02			08 18					
Haymarket d		06 19	06s45		07 03			07s21	07 27	07 39		07s48			08s01	08 09		08s16	08 23	08s32				
Edinburgh [10] 225, 242 a		06 24	06 50		07 09			07 26	07 34	07 43		07 54			08 06	08 14		08 22	08 29	08 37				

	SR [1] B 🍴	SR	SR [1] ◇ D 🍴	SR	SR [1] A 🍴	SR [1] B 🍴	SR	SR [1] A 🍴	SR	SR		SR	SR [1] B 🍴	SR [1] ◇ D 🍴	SR [1] A 🍴	SR	SR	SR	SR [1] B 🍴	SR [1] E	SR [1] A 🍴		SR	SR
Dunblane d			07 44	07 56					08 12			08 28						08 57		09 06			09 13	
Bridge of Allan d			07 48	07 59					08 16			08 31						09 00					09 16	
Alloa d							07 54										08 35							
Stirling d			07 53	08 05			08 06		08 21			08 36		08 44			08b51	09 06		09 13			09 21	
Larbert d			08 02	08 14			08 16		08 29			08 45					08 59	09 15					09 29	
Camelon d				08 18								08 48						09 18						
Falkirk Grahamston d				08 21								08 52						09 22						
Croy [3] d							08 30	08 36	08 40						09 03		09 12				09 33		09 40	
Lenzie [3] d			08 17		08 25		08 35		08 47								09 19						09 47	
Bishopbriggs d					08 31		08 39		08 51								09 23						09 51	
Glasgow Queen Street [10] ⛴ a			08 34		08 40		08 51	08 54	09 03					09 15	09 21		09 33			09 45	09 51		10 01	
Polmont [3] d	08 26			08 31								08 59	09 07					09 29	09 37					
Linlithgow d				08 38		08 42						09 06	09 13					09 36	09 43					
Bathgate d		08 25								08 54						09 24								09 54
Livingston North d		08 30								08 58						09 28								09 58
Uphall d		08 34								09 02						09 32								10 02
Edinburgh Park d		08 43		08 50						09 13		09 19				09 43		09 49						10 13
Haymarket d	08s44	08 53		08 58		09s00				09 19		09 26	09s31			09 50		09 55	10s01					10 21
Edinburgh [10] 225, 242 a	08 50	08 59		09 02		09 08				09 25		09 32	09 37			09 56		10 04	10 07					10 25

	SR	SR [1] B	SR [1] ◇ G 🍴	SR [1] A 🍴	SR	SR	SR	SR [1] B 🍴	SR [1] A 🍴	SR		GR [R] [1] H J 🍽 🍴	SR	SR	SR [1] B 🍴	SR [1] ◇ D 🍴	SR [1] A 🍴	SR	SR	SR	SR [1] B 🍴		SR [1] A 🍴	SR
Dunblane d	09 28						09 58			10 13				10 28						10 58				11 13
Bridge of Allan d	09 31						10 01			10 16				10 31						11 01				11 16
Alloa d					09 40													10 35						
Stirling d	09 36		09 44		09 51		10 06			10 21		10 30		10 36		10 43		10c51		11 06				11 21
Larbert d	09 45				09 59		10 15			10 29				10 45				10 59		11 15				11 29
Camelon d	09 48						10 18							10 48						11 18				
Falkirk Grahamston d	09 52						10 22					10 45		10 52						11 22				
Croy [3] d				10 03	10 10				10 33	10 40							11 03	11 10					11 33	11 40
Lenzie [3] d					10 17					10 47								11 17						11 47
Bishopbriggs d					10 21					10 51								11 22						11 51
Glasgow Queen Street [10] ⛴ a			10 14	10 19	10 33				10 49	11 03						11 15	11 19	11 34					11 51	12 02
Polmont [3] d	09 59	10 07					10 29	10 37						10 59	11 07					11 29	11 37			
Linlithgow d	10 06	10 13					10 36	10 43						11 06	11 13					11 36	11 43			
Bathgate d						10 24							10 54						11 24					
Livingston North d						10 28							10 58						11 28					
Uphall d						10 32							11 02						11 32					
Edinburgh Park d	10 19					10 43	10 49						11 13	11 19					11 43	11 49				
Haymarket d	10 26	10s30				10 53	10 56	11s00				11 09	11 20	11 26	11s29				11 50	11 56	12s00			
Edinburgh [10] 225, 242 a	10 31	10 35				10 59	11 02	11 06				11 15	11 25	11 31	11 35				11 55	12 01	12 05			

For general notes see front of timetable
For details of catering facilities see Directory of Train Operators

- **A** From Edinburgh (Table 228)
- **B** From Glasgow Queen Street (Table 228)
- **C** From Perth (Table 229)
- **D** From Aberdeen (Table 229)
- **E** From Dundee (Table 229)
- **G** From Inverurie (Table 229)
- **H** From Inverness (Table 229) to London Kings Cross (Table 26)
- **J** **The Highland Chieftain**
- **b** Arr. 0845
- **c** Arr. 1045

Table 230

Saturdays

Dunblane, Alloa and Stirling → Falkirk Grahamston, Glasgow Queen Street and Edinburgh
Bathgate → Edinburgh

Network Diagram - see first page of Table 225

	SR	SR	SR	SR	SR	SR	SR	SR	SR	SR		SR	SR	SR	SR	SR	SR	SR	SR	SR	SR		SR	SR
			1 A ⊼	1 ◇ B ⊼	1 C ⊼				1 A ⊼	1 ◇ D ⊼		1 C ⊼				1 A ⊼	1 ◇ E ⊼	1 C ⊼					1 A ⊼	1 C ⊼
Dunblane d		11 28						11 58		12 06			12 13		12 28						12 58			
Bridge of Allan d		11 31						12 01					12 16		12 31						13 01			
Alloa d						11 42													12 35					
Stirling d		11 36		11 43		11 51		12 06		12 13			12 21		12 36		12 42		12b51		13 06			
Larbert d		11 45				11 59		12 15					12 29		12 45				12 59		13 15			
Camelon d		11 48						12 18							12 48						13 18			
Falkirk Grahamston d		11 52						12 22							12 52						13 22			
Croy 3 d					12 03	12 10						12 33	12 40					13 03	13 10					13 33
Lenzie 3 d						12 17							12 47						13 17					
Bishopbriggs d						12 21							12 51						13 21					
Glasgow Queen Street 10 ⛴ a				12 15	12 19	12 35				12 46		12 49	13 03				13 14	13 19	13 33					13 49
Polmont 3 d		11 59	12 07					12 29	12 37						12 59	13 07					13 29		13 37	
Linlithgow d		12 06	12 13					12 36	12 43						13 06	13 13					13 36		13 43	
Bathgate d	11 54						12 24							12 54						13 24				
Livingston North d	11 58						12 28							12 58						13 28				
Uphall d	12 02						12 32							13 02						13 32				
Edinburgh Park d	12 13	12 19					12 43	12 49						13 13	13 19					13 43	13 49			
Haymarket d	12 19	12 26	12s29				12 54	12 56	13s00					13 20	13 26	13s29				13 50	13 56		13s59	
Edinburgh 10 225, 242 a	12 25	12 31	12 35				12 59	13 02	13 05					13 25	13 31	13 35				13 55	14 01		14 05	

	SR	SR	SR	SR	SR	SR	SR	SR	SR	SR		SR	SR	SR	SR	SR	SR	SR	SR	SR	SR		SR	SR
				1 A ⊼	1 ◇ E ⊼	1 C ⊼				1 A ⊼		1 C ⊼				1 A ⊼	1 ◇ E ⊼	1 C ⊼					1 A ⊼	1 C ⊼
Dunblane d	13 13		13 28						13 58				14 13		14 28						14 58			
Bridge of Allan d	13 16		13 31						14 01				14 16		14 31						15 01			
Alloa d							13 40												14 35					
Stirling d	13 21		13 36		13 43		13 51		14 06				14 21		14 36		14 40		14c51		15 06			
Larbert d	13 29		13 45				13 59		14 15				14 29		14 45				14 59		15 15			
Camelon d			13 48						14 18						14 48						15 18			
Falkirk Grahamston d			13 52						14 22						14 52						15 22			
Croy 3 d	13 41					14 03	14 10					14 33	14 40					15 03	15 10					15 33
Lenzie 3 d	13 47						14 17						14 47						15 17					
Bishopbriggs d	13 51						14 21						14 51						15 21					
Glasgow Queen Street 10 ⛴ a	14 03				14 15	14 19	14 33					14 49	15 03				15 15	15 20	15 34					15 50
Polmont 3 d			13 59	14 07					14 29	14 37					14 59	15 07					15 29		15 37	
Linlithgow d			14 06	14 13					14 36	14 43					15 06	15 13					15 36		15 43	
Bathgate d		13 54						14 24						14 54						15 24				
Livingston North d		13 58						14 28						14 58						15 28				
Uphall d		14 02						14 32						15 02						15 32				
Edinburgh Park d		14 13	14 19					14 43	14 49					15 13	15 19					15 43	15 49			
Haymarket d		14 19	14 26	14s30				14 54	14 56	15s00				15 19	15 26	15s30				15 50	15 56		16s00	
Edinburgh 10 225, 242 a		14 25	14 31	14 37				14 59	15 02	15 06				15 24	15 34	15 37				15 54	16 01		16 05	

	SR	SR	SR	SR	SR	SR	SR	SR	SR	SR		SR	SR	SR	SR	SR	SR	SR	SR	SR	SR		SR	SR
				1 A ⊼	1 ◇ E ⊼	1 C ⊼				1 A ⊼		1 C ⊼				1 A	1 ◇ E ⊼	1 C ⊼		1 A ⊼				1 A ⊼
Dunblane d	15 13		15 28						15 58				16 13		16 28								16 58	
Bridge of Allan d	15 16		15 31						16 01				16 16		16 31								17 01	
Alloa d							15 40												16 35					
Stirling d	15 21		15 36		15 43		15 51		16 06				16 21		16 36		16 43		16e51				17 06	
Larbert d	15 29		15 45				15 59		16 15				16 29		16 45				16 59				17 15	
Camelon d			15 48						16 18						16 48								17 18	
Falkirk Grahamston d			15 52						16 22						16 52								17 22	
Croy 3 d	15 40					16 03	16 10					16 33	16 41					17 03	17 10					
Lenzie 3 d	15 47						16 17						16 47						17 17					
Bishopbriggs d	15 51						16 21						16 51						17 21					
Glasgow Queen Street 10 ⛴ a	16 04				16 15	16 19	16 32					16 51	17 01				17 17	17 21	17 32					
Polmont 3 d			15 59	16 07					16 29	16 37					16 59	17 07				17 27			17 29	
Linlithgow d			16 06	16 13					16 36	16 43					17 06	17 13							17 36	17 40
Bathgate d		15 54						16 24						16 54							17 28			
Livingston North d		15 58						16 28						16 58							17 32			
Uphall d		16 02						16 32						17 02							17 36			
Edinburgh Park d		16 13	16 19					16 43	16 49					17 13	17 19						17 47		17 49	
Haymarket d		16 20	16 25	16s33				16 54	16 56	17s00				17 20	17 26	17s34				17s47	17 53		17 56	18s01
Edinburgh 10 225, 242 a		16 25	16 33	16 39				16 59	17 04	17 07				17 25	17 31	17 39				17 52	17 58		18 02	18 06

For general notes see front of timetable
For details of catering facilities see Directory of Train Operators

- **A** From Glasgow Queen Street (Table 228)
- **B** From Dyce (Table 229)
- **C** From Edinburgh (Table 228)
- **D** From Inverness (Table 229)
- **E** From Aberdeen (Table 229)
- **b** Arr. 1245
- **c** Arr. 1445
- **e** Arr. 1645

Dunblane, Alloa and Stirling → Falkirk Grahamston, Glasgow Queen Street and Edinburgh
Bathgate → Edinburgh

Network Diagram - see first page of Table 225

		SR 1 A ⚒	SR	SR	SR 1 B ⚒	SR 1◊ C ⚒	SR	SR 1 B ⚒	SR 1◊ D ⚒	SR 1 A ⚒	SR		SR	SR	SR 1 B ⚒	SR 1 A ⚒	SR	SR	SR	SR 1 B ⚒	SR 1◊ D ⚒	SR 1 A ⚒		SR	SR
Dunblane	d			17 14		17 22	17 28		17 36					17 58			18 11		18 28		18 35				
Bridge of Allan	d			17 17			17 31							18 01			18 14		18 31						
Alloa	d										17 40													18 35	
Stirling	d			17 21		17 29	17 36		17 42		17 51			18 06			18 19		18 36		18 42			18 59	
Larbert	d			17 29			17 45				17 59			18 15			18 28		18 45						
Camelon	d						17 48							18 18					18 48						
Falkirk Grahamston	d						17 52							18 22					18 52						
Croy 3	d	17 33		17 40						18 03	18 10					18 33	18 39					19 03		19 10	
Lenzie 3	d			17 47						18 08	18 17						18 46							19 17	
Bishopbriggs	d			17 51							18 21						18 50							19 21	
Glasgow Queen Street 10 ⛴	a	17 51		18 03		18 09			18 15	18 22	18 34					18 50	19 01				19 14	19 21		19 31	
Polmont 3	d				17 56		17 59	18 07						18 29	18 37				18 59	19 07					
Linlithgow	d				18 02		18 06	18 13						18 36	18 43				19 06	19 13					
Bathgate	d		17 53										18 24					18 54							19 27
Livingston North	d		17 58										18 28					18 58							19 32
Uphall	d		18 02										18 32					19 02							19 36
Edinburgh Park	d		18 12				18 19						18 43	18 49				19 13	19 19						19 48
Haymarket	d		18 18		18s21		18 26	18s32					18 53	18 56	19s00			19 20	19 26	19s32					19 54
Edinburgh 10 225, 242	a		18 23		18 26		18 32	18 40					18 59	19 02	19 05			19 26	19 32	19 39					19 58

		SR	SR 1 B ⚒	SR 1 A ⚒	SR 1 B ⚒	SR	SR	SR	SR 1◊ D ⚒	SR 1 A ⚒	SR 1 B ⚒		SR	SR	SR 1 B ⚒	SR	SR	SR	SR 1◊ D ⚒	SR 1 A ⚒	SR	SR 1 B		SR	SR 1 B
Dunblane	d	18 58				19 14	19 28							20 02		20 13	20 28							20 58	
Bridge of Allan	d	19 01				19 17	19 31							20 04		20 16	20 31							21 01	
Alloa	d												19 42								20 40				
Stirling	d	19 06				19 22	19 36		19 43				19 53	20 06		20 21	20 36		20 40		20 51			21 06	
Larbert	d	19 15				19 30	19 45						20 01	20 15		20 29	20 45				20 59			21 15	
Camelon	d	19 18					19 48							20 18			20 48							21 18	
Falkirk Grahamston	d	19 22					19 52							20 22			20 52							21 22	
Croy 3	d			19 33		19 41				20 07			20 12			20 41				21 07	21 10				
Lenzie 3	d					19 48							20 19			20 47					21 17				
Bishopbriggs	d					19 52							20 23			20 51					21 21				
Glasgow Queen Street 10 ⛴	a			19 49		20 02			20 15	20 22			20 34			21 04			21 14	21 22	21 34				
Polmont 3	d	19 29	19 37		19 52		19 59							20 29	20 52		20 59							21 29	21 52
Linlithgow	d	19 36	19 43		19 58		20 06				20 28			20 36	20 58		21 06					21 28		21 36	21 58
Bathgate	d							20 05										21 05							
Livingston North	d							20 10										21 10							
Uphall	d							20 14										21 14							
Edinburgh Park	d	19 49					20 19	20 24						20 48			21 19	21 24						21 49	
Haymarket	d	19 56	20s01		20s15		20 26	20 31			20s45			20 55	21s13		21 26	21 30				21s46		21 56	22s18
Edinburgh 10 225, 242	a	20 02	20 09		20 20		20 32	20 35			20 50			21 06	21 20		21 31	21 35				21 53		22 01	22 23

		SR	SR	SR 1◊ D ⚒	SR 1 A	SR	SR 1 B	SR	SR 1 B ⚒	SR	SR		SR 1◊ D	SR 1 A	SR	SR 1 B	SR 1◊ C	SR	SR	SR	SR 1 A	SR 1 B			
Dunblane	d		21 13					21 58			22 13						22 58	23 06							
Bridge of Allan	d		21 16					22 01			22 16						23 02	23 09							
Alloa	d					21 41									22 40				23 18						
Stirling	d		21 21	21 45		21 52		22 06			22 21		22 43		22 51		23 05	23 14	23a28						
Larbert	d		21 29			21 59		22 15			22 29				22 59			23 23							
Camelon	d							22 18										23 29							
Falkirk Grahamston	d							22 22										23 32							
Croy 3	d		21 40		22 07	22 10					22 40			23 07	23 10						23 39				
Lenzie 3	d		21 47			22 17					22 47			23 14	23 17						23 47				
Bishopbriggs	d		21 51			22 21					22 51				23 21						23 51				
Glasgow Queen Street 10 ⛴	a		22 03	22 19	22 22	22 34					23 03		23 15	23 30	23 34		23 38				00 03				
Polmont 3	d							22 29	22 52							23 26		23 38				23 57			
Linlithgow	d						22 28	22 36	22 58							23 33		23 45				00 04			
Bathgate	d	22 03								23 03										23 52					
Livingston North	d	22 08								23 08										23 57					
Uphall	d	22 12								23 12										23 59					
Edinburgh Park	d	22 22						22 49		23 22								23 57		00 11					
Haymarket	d	22 28					22s44	22 56	23s15	23 29						23s49		00 05		00 17		00s20			
Edinburgh 10 225, 242	a	22 33					22 50	23 01	23 22	23 34						23 54		00 09		00 22		00 25			

For general notes see front of timetable
For details of catering facilities see Directory of Train Operators

A From Edinburgh (Table 228)
B From Glasgow Queen Street (Table 228)
C From Inverness (Table 229)
D From Aberdeen (Table 229)

Table 230

Dunblane, Alloa and Stirling → Falkirk Grahamston, Glasgow Queen Street and Edinburgh
Bathgate → Edinburgh

Network Diagram - see first page of Table 225

	SR 1 A	SR 1 B	SR 1 A trolley	SR 1 B trolley	SR C	SR C	SR	SR	SR 1 A		SR 1 B trolley	SR	SR 1 D	SR C	SR E	SR 1 A trolley	SR 1 B trolley	SR	SR		SR C	SR	SR 1 A trolley	SR 1 B trolley
Dunblane d													09 31		09 54							10 58		
Bridge of Allan d															09 58							11 01		
Alloa d												09 17							10 17					
Stirling d							09 05					09 28	09 38		10 02				10 28			11 06		
Larbert d							09 13					09 37	09 47		10 11				10 37			11 15		
Camelon d							09 19								10 16							11 18		
Falkirk Grahamston d							09 22								10 19							11 22		
Croy 3 d	00 10		08 39		08 49	09 15			09 39			09 48		10 15		10 39			10 45		11 15		11 39	
Lenzie 3 d	00 14				08 56	09 22						09 55	10 02	10 22					10 52		11 22			
Bishopbriggs d					09 00	09 26						09 59		10 26					10 56		11 26			
Glasgow Queen Street 10 a	00 28		08 59		09 10	09 35			10 00			10 08	10 15	10 35		11 00			11 08		11 35		11 56	
Polmont 3 d		08 16		08 56			09 28				09 56				10 25		10 56					11 29		11 56
Linlithgow d		08 22		09 02			09 35				10 02				10 32		11 02					11 36		12 02
Bathgate d								09 49										11 01						
Livingston North d								09 54										11 06						
Uphall d								09 58										11 10						
Edinburgh Park d							09 47	10 07							10 45			11 19				11 49		
Haymarket 225, 242 d		08s44		09s23			09 55	10 14			10s23				10 52		11s19	11 25				11 56		12s19
Edinburgh 10 225, 242 a		08 49		09 28			10 04	10 23			10 28				10 58		11 24	11 30				12 01		12 24

	SR	SR	SR 1 ◇ G trolley	SR C	SR	SR 1 A trolley	GR R 1 H J		SR 1 B trolley	SR	SR	SR 1 A trolley	SR 1 B trolley	SR C	SR	SR 1 B	SR		SR	SR 1 ◇ G trolley	SR 1 A trolley	SR 1 B trolley	SR C	SR
Dunblane d			11 31		11 58		12 26								12 58					13 31				13 58
Bridge of Allan d					12 01										13 01									14 01
Alloa d		11 13									12 13								13 13					
Stirling d		11 25	11 38		12 06		12 33				12 25				13 06				13 25	13 38				14 06
Larbert d		11 34			12 15						12 34				13 15				13 34					14 15
Camelon d					12 18										13 18									14 18
Falkirk Grahamston d					12 22		12 49								13 22									14 22
Croy 3 d		11 45		12 15		12 38					12 45	13 07		13 15					13 45		14 07		14 15	
Lenzie 3 d		11 52		12 22							12 52			13 22					13 52				14 22	
Bishopbriggs d		11 56		12 26							12 56			13 26					13 56				14 26	
Glasgow Queen Street 10 a		12 05	12 11	12 35		12 54					13 05	13 23		13 35					14 05	14 11	14 23		14 35	
Polmont 3 d					12 29				12 56						13 29	13 52								14 28
Linlithgow d					12 36				13 02				13 28		13 36	13 58						14 28		14 36
Bathgate d	12 01									13 02							13 58							
Livingston North d	12 06									13 06							14 03							
Uphall d	12 10									13 10							14 07							
Edinburgh Park d	12 19				12 49					13 19					13 49		14 17							14 49
Haymarket 225, 242 d	12 25				12 56		13 13		13s21	13 26			13s46		13 56	14s17	14 23					14s47		14 56
Edinburgh 10 225, 242 a	12 30				13 01		13 18		13 26	13 32			13 51		14 01	14 22	14 28					14 52		15 01

	SR 1 B trolley	SR	SR	SR 1 A	SR 1 B		SR C	SR	SR 1 B	SR 1 ◇ K trolley	SR	SR	SR 1 ◇ G trolley	SR 1 A trolley	SR 1 B trolley		SR C	SR	SR 1 B trolley	SR	SR	SR 1 A trolley	SR 1 B trolley	SR C
Dunblane d								14 58		15 16			15 30					15 58						
Bridge of Allan d								15 01										16 01						
Alloa d			14 13									15 15									16 13			
Stirling d			14 25					15 06		15 22		15 26	15 38					16 06			16 25			
Larbert d			14 34					15 15		15 31		15 34						16 15			16 34			
Camelon d								15 18										16 18						
Falkirk Grahamston d								15 22										16 22						
Croy 3 d			14 45	15 07			15 15					15 45		16 05			16 15				16 45	17 07		17 15
Lenzie 3 d			14 52				15 22					15 52					16 22				16 52			17 22
Bishopbriggs d			14 56				15 26					15 56					16 26				16 56			17 26
Glasgow Queen Street 10 a			15 05	15 22			15 35			15 56		16 09	16 12	16 22			16 35				17 05	17 22		17 35
Polmont 3 d	14 52							15 29	15 52									16 29	16 53					
Linlithgow d	14 58				15 28			15 36	15 58						16 28			16 36	16 58				17 28	
Bathgate d		14 58									15 59									16 59				
Livingston North d		15 03									16 03									17 03				
Uphall d		15 07									16 07									17 07				
Edinburgh Park d		15 17						15 49			16 17							16 49		17 17				
Haymarket 225, 242 d	15s16	15 23			15 46			15 56	16s17		16 23				16s48			16 56	17s16	17 23			17s47	
Edinburgh 10 225, 242 a	15 21	15 28			15 51			16 01	16 22		16 29				16 53			17 02	17 21	17 29			17 52	

For general notes see front of timetable
For details of catering facilities see Directory of Train Operators

A From Edinburgh (Table 228)
B From Glasgow Queen Street (Table 228)
C 29 November and 6 December
D From Dundee (Table 229)
E From Perth (Table 229)
G From Aberdeen (Table 229)
H From Inverness (Table 229) to London Kings Cross (Table 26)
J **The Highland Chieftain**
K From Inverness (Table 229)

Table 230

Sundays

Dunblane, Alloa and Stirling → Falkirk Grahamston, Glasgow Queen Street and Edinburgh
Bathgate → Edinburgh

Network Diagram - see first page of Table 225

		SR	SR 1 A 🛒	SR		SR	SR 1 ◇ B 🛒	SR 1 C	SR 1 A 🛒	SR D	SR	SR 1 A 🛒	SR	SR		SR 1 C 🛒	SR 1 A 🛒	SR D	SR 1 ◇ E 🛒	SR	SR 1 A 🛒	SR	SR	SR 1 C 🛒	SR 1 A 🛒
Dunblane	d	16 58					17 31				17 58								18 55	19 04					
Bridge of Allan	d	17 01									18 01									19 07					
Alloa	d					17 13								18 17									19 13		
Stirling	d	17 06				17 25	17 38				18 06			18 28					19 02	19 12			19 24		
Larbert	d	17 15				17 34					18 15			18 34					19 09	19 21			19 33		
Camelon	d	17 18									18 18									19 26					
Falkirk Grahamston	d	17 22									18 22									19 29					
Croy 3	d					17 45		18 07		18 15				18 45		19 07		19 13					19 44	20 07	
Lenzie 3	d					17 52				18 22				18 52				19 20					19 51		
Bishopbriggs	d					17 56				18 26				18 56				19 24					19 55		
Glasgow Queen Street 10	a					18 05	18 12	18 22		18 35				19 08		19 22		19 33	19 36				20 04	20 22	
Polmont 3	d	17 29	17 53								18 29	18 53								19 35	19 53				
Linlithgow	d	17 36	17 58						18 28		18 36	18 58					19 28			19 42	19 58				20 28
Bathgate	d			17 59									18 59									19 58			
Livingston North	d			18 03									19 03									20 03			
Uphall	d			18 07									19 07									20 07			
Edinburgh Park	d	17 50		18 17							18 50		19 17							19 54		20 17			
Haymarket 225, 242	d	17 57	18s17	18 22					18s50		18 57	19s16	19 23				19s47			20 01	20s16	20 22			20s46
Edinburgh 10 225, 242	a	18 01	18 22	18 30					18 55		19 01	19 21	19 29				19 52			20 06	20 21	20 29			20 51

		SR 1 ◇ B 🛒		SR	SR 1 A 🛒	SR	SR	SR 1 C 🛒	SR 1 A	SR	SR 1 C 🛒	SR 1 A		SR	SR	SR 1 ◇ B 🛒	SR	SR 1 C	SR 1 A	SR	SR 1 C	SR 1 A	SR		
Dunblane	d			19 58						20 58						21 31	21 58								
Bridge of Allan	d			20 01						21 01							22 01								
Alloa	d						20 13								21 13										
Stirling	d	19 54		20 06			20 25			21 06					21 25	21 38	22 06								
Larbert	d			20 15			20 34			21 15					21 34	21 49	22 15								
Camelon	d			20 18						21 18							22 18								
Falkirk Grahamston	d			20 22						21 22							22 22								
Croy 3	d						20 45	21 07			21 39				21 45			22 39			23 39				
Lenzie 3	d						20 52								21 52	22 02									
Bishopbriggs	d						20 56								21 56										
Glasgow Queen Street 10	a	20 31					21 05	21 22			21 55				22 05	22 15		22 55			23 55				
Polmont 3	d			20 29	20 53					21 29		21 56					22 29		22 56			23 56			
Linlithgow	d			20 36	20 58				21 28	21 36		22 02					22 36		23 02			00 02			
Bathgate	d					20 59								22 01						23 01			23 59		
Livingston North	d					21 03								22 06						23 06			00 04		
Uphall	d					21 07								22 10						23 10			00 08		
Edinburgh Park	d			20 50		21 17				21 49				22 19			22 49			23 20			00 19		
Haymarket 225, 242	d			20 57	21s17	21 23			21s45	21 56		22s19		22 26			22 56		23s19	23 26		00s19	00 26		
Edinburgh 10 225, 242	a			21 01	21 22	21 29			21 53	22 01		22 24		22 31			23 01		23 24	23 30		00 24	00 31		

For general notes see front of timetable
For details of catering facilities see Directory of Train Operators

A From Glasgow Queen Street (Table 228)
B From Aberdeen (Table 229)
C From Edinburgh (Table 228)
D 29 November and 6 December
E From Inverness (Table 229)

Mondays to Saturdays

Glasgow Queen Street — Maryhill and Annesland

Network Diagram - see first page of Table 220

Miles			SR A	SR B		SR	SR FO
0	**Glasgow Queen Street** [10]	⛴ d	06 26	06 56	and every 30 minutes until	23 26	23 54
2½	Ashfield	d	06 30	07 00		23 30	23 58
3	Possilpark & Parkhouse	d	06 33	07 03		23 33	00 01
3½	Gilshochill	d	06 35	07 05		23 35	00 03
4¼	Summerston	d	06 37	07 07		23 37	00 05
4¾	**Maryhill**	d	06 39	07 09		23 39	00 07
5½	Kelvindale	d	06 41	07 11		23 41	00 09
6¼	**Anniesland**	226 a	06 45	07 15		23 45	00 13

Sundays

from 29 November

		SR	SR	SR	SR	SR	SR	SR	SR	SR	SR
Glasgow Queen Street [10]	⛴ d	08 45	09 58	10 56	11 56	12 55	13 56	14 55	15 57	16 56	17 56
Ashfield	d	08 50	10 00	11 00	12 00	13 01	14 00	15 00	16 00	17 00	18 00
Possilpark & Parkhouse	d	08 53	10 03	11 03	12 03	13 03	14 03	15 03	16 03	17 03	18 03
Gilshochill	d	08 55	10 05	11 05	12 05	13 05	14 05	15 05	16 05	17 05	18 05
Summerston	d	08 57	10 07	11 07	12 07	13 08	14 07	15 07	16 07	17 07	18 07
Maryhill	d	08 59	10 09	11 09	12 09	13 09	14 09	15 09	16 09	17 09	18 09
Kelvindale	d	09 01	10 11	11 11	12 11	13 12	14 11	15 11	16 11	17 11	18 11
Anniesland	226 a	09 04	10 17	11 15	12 15	13 15	14 15	15 14	16 17	17 15	18 15

Mondays to Saturdays

Miles			SR	SR	SR	SR	SR SX C	SR	SR	SR		SR	SR	SR	SR	SR SO	SR SX
0	**Anniesland**	226 d	06 23	06 52	07 23	07 52		08 24	08 52	09 22	and every 30 minutes until	14 22	14 53	15 26	15 52	16 21	16 25
¾	Kelvindale	d	06 25	06 54	07 25	07 54		08 26	08 54	09 24		14 24	14 55	15 28	15 54	16 23	16 27
1½	**Maryhill**	d	06 27	06 56	07 27	07 56	08 16	08 28	08 56	09 26		14 26	14 57	15 30	15 56	16 25	16 29
2	Summerston	d	06 29	06 58	07 29	07 58		08 30	08 58	09 28		14 28	14 59	15 32	15 58	16 27	16 31
3	Gilshochill	d	06 31	07 00	07 31	08 00		08 32	09 00	09 30		14 30	15 01	15 34	16 00	16 29	16 33
3¼	Possilpark & Parkhouse	d	06 33	07 02	07 33	08 02	08 21	08 34	09 02	09 32		14 32	15 03	15 36	16 02	16 31	16 35
4	Ashfield	d	06 35	07 04	07 35	08 04		08 36	09 04	09 34		14 34	15 05	15 38	16 04	16 34	16 38
6¼	**Glasgow Queen Street** [10]	⛴ a	06 42	07 11	07 42	08 11	08 37	08 43	09 11	09 41		14 41	15 12	15 46	16 11	16 41	16 45

		SR	SR	SR	SR	SR	SR	SR	SR	SR	SR	SR	SR	SR	SR
Anniesland	226 d	16 54	17 24	17 53	18 22	18 52	19 22	19 52	20 22	20 52	21 23	21 52	22 22	22 52	23 22
Kelvindale	d	16 56	17 26	17 55	18 24	18 54	19 24	19 54	20 24	20 54	21 25	21 54	22 24	22 54	23 24
Maryhill	d	16 58	17 28	17 57	18 26	18 56	19 26	19 56	20 26	20 56	21 27	21 56	22 26	22 56	23 26
Summerston	d	17 00	17 30	17 59	18 28	18 58	19 28	19 58	20 28	20 58	21 29	21 58	22 28	22 58	23 28
Gilshochill	d	17 02	17 32	18 01	18 30	19 00	19 30	20 00	20 30	21 00	21 31	22 00	22 30	23 00	23 30
Possilpark & Parkhouse	d	17 04	17 34	18 03	18 32	19 02	19 32	20 02	20 32	21 02	21 33	22 02	22 32	23 02	23 32
Ashfield	d	17 06	17 36	18 05	18 34	19 04	19 34	20 04	20 34	21 04	21 35	22 04	22 34	23 04	23 34
Glasgow Queen Street [10]	⛴ a	17 14	17 44	18 12	18 41	19 11	19 41	20 11	20 41	21 11	21 42	22 11	22 41	23 11	23 41

Sundays

from 29 November

		SR	SR	SR	SR	SR	SR	SR	SR	SR	SR
Anniesland	226 d	09 22	10 22	11 22	12 22	13 22	14 22	15 22	16 22	17 22	18 22
Kelvindale	d	09 24	10 24	11 24	12 24	13 24	14 24	15 24	16 24	17 24	18 24
Maryhill	d	09 26	10 26	11 26	12 26	13 26	14 26	15 26	16 26	17 26	18 26
Summerston	d	09 28	10 28	11 28	12 28	13 28	14 28	15 28	16 28	17 28	18 28
Gilshochill	d	09 30	10 30	11 30	12 30	13 30	14 30	15 30	16 30	17 30	18 30
Possilpark & Parkhouse	d	09 32	10 32	11 32	12 32	13 32	14 32	15 32	16 32	17 32	18 32
Ashfield	d	09 34	10 34	11 34	12 34	13 35	14 34	15 35	16 34	17 34	18 34
Glasgow Queen Street [10]	⛴ a	09 41	10 41	11 41	12 41	13 41	14 41	15 41	16 41	17 41	18 41

For general notes see front of timetable
For details of catering facilities see Directory of Train Operators

A 0826 from Glasgow Queen Street dep. 0827, Anniesland arr. 0846.
1126 from Glasgow Queen Street arr. Anniesland 1146.
1226 from Glasgow Queen Street dep. 1227, Anniesland arr. 1246.
1826 from Glasgow Queen Street dep. 1827, Anniesland arr. 1846.
2126 from Glasgow Queen Street arr. Anniesland 2146

B 1556 from Glasgow Queen Street dep. 1557, Anniesland arr. 1616

C From Arrochar & Tarbet (Table 227)

Table 238

Mondays to Fridays

Haymarket and Edinburgh → North Berwick

Network Diagram - see first page of Table 225

Miles				SR	SR	SR A	SR	SR	SR	SR	SR	SR	SR	SR A	SR	SR	SR	SR	SR	SR	SR	SR
0	**Haymarket**	225, 230, 242	d	06 59	07 46	08 22	09 37	10 21	11 20	12 19	13 20	14 20	15 34	16 34	17 05	17 39	18 05	18 19	19 20	20 24	21 10	22 44
1¼	**Edinburgh** 10	225, 230, 242	a			08 35	09 39						15 38	16 39	17 09	17 43	18 08					
—			d	07 16	08 04	08 38	09 42	10 37	11 37	12 37	13 37	14 38	15 39	16 40	17 11	17 44	18 12	18 39	19 37	20 40	21 40	23 07
6½	Musselburgh		d	07 22	08 10	08 43	09 45	10 41	11 41	12 41	13 41	14 41	15 41	16 44	17 17	17 51	18 18	18 41	19 41	20 43	21 43	23 11
8¾	Wallyford		d	07 26		08 47	09 49	10 45	11 45	12 45	13 45	14 45	15 45	16 49	17 21	17 55	18 21	18 45	19 45	20 47	21 47	23 15
11	Prestonpans		d	07 29		08 50	09 52	10 48	11 48	12 48	13 48	14 48	15 48	16 51	17 25	17 58	18 25	18 48	19 48	20 50	21 50	23 18
14½	Longniddry		d	07 34		08 55	09 57	10 53	11 53	12 53	13 53	14 53	15 53	16 57	17 30	18 03	18 30	18 54	19 53	20 55	21 55	23 23
19	Drem		d	07 39		09 00	10 03	10 59	11 59	12 59	13 59	14 59	15 59	17 02	17 36	18 08	18 36	18 59	19 59	21 00	22 00	23 29
23½	**North Berwick**		a	07 49	08 28	09 11	10 15	11 10	12 12	13 10	14 10	15 11	16 13	17 15	17 47	18 20	18 48	19 12	20 10	21 13	22 13	23 50

Saturdays

			SR	SR A	SR	SR	SR	SR	SR	SR	SR	SR	SR	SR	SR
Haymarket	225, 230, 242	d	07 03	08 25	08 54	09 19	09 50	10 21	10 52	11 20	11 50	12 19	12 49	13 20	13 51
Edinburgh 10	225, 230, 242	a		08 33											
		d	07 37	08 38	09 08	09 37	10 08	10 38	11 08	11 37	12 08	12 38	13 08	13 37	14 08
Musselburgh		d	07 41	08 41	09 11	09 41	10 11	10 44	11 11	11 41	12 11	12 41	13 11	13 41	14 11
Wallyford		d	07 45	08 45	09 15	09 45	10 15	10 48	11 15	11 45	12 15	12 45	13 15	13 45	14 15
Prestonpans		d	07 48	08 48	09 18	09 48	10 18	10 51	11 18	11 48	12 18	12 48	13 18	13 48	14 18
Longniddry		d	07 53	08 53	09 23	09 53	10 23	10 56	11 23	11 53	12 23	12 53	13 23	13 53	14 23
Drem		d	07 58	08 59	09 29	09 59	10 29	11 01	11 29	11 59	12 29	12 59	13 29	14 00	14 29
North Berwick		a	08 10	09 11	09 41	10 10	10 41	11 11	11 41	12 10	12 41	13 12	13 41	14 13	14 41

			SR	SR	SR	SR	SR A	SR	SR	SR	SR	SR	SR	SR	SR
Haymarket	225, 230, 242	d	14 19	14 49	15 20	15 50	16 27	16 50	17 20	17 53	18 19	19 20	20 24	21 10	22 44
Edinburgh 10	225, 230, 242	a					16 35								
		d	14 37	15 08	15 38	16 08	16 41	17 08	17 37	18 08	18 37	19 37	20 40	21 40	23 07
Musselburgh		d	14 41	15 11	15 43	16 11	16 45	17 14	17 41	18 11	18 43	19 41	20 43	21 43	23 11
Wallyford		d	14 45	15 15	15 47	16 15	16 49	17 18	17 45	18 15	18 47	19 45	20 47	21 47	23 15
Prestonpans		d	14 48	15 18	15 50	16 18	16 52	17 21	17 48	18 18	18 50	19 48	20 50	21 50	23 18
Longniddry		d	14 53	15 23	15 55	16 23	16 57	17 26	17 53	18 23	18 55	19 53	20 55	21 55	23 23
Drem		d	14 59	15 29	16 02	16 29	17 02	17 31	17 59	18 29	19 02	19 59	21 00	22 00	23 29
North Berwick		a	15 10	15 43	16 11	16 41	17 14	17 41	18 09	18 41	19 10	20 10	21 13	22 13	23 50

Sundays

			SR	SR	SR	SR	SR	SR	SR	SR	SR	SR	SR	SR
Haymarket	225, 230, 242	d	10 14	10 58	11 56	13 13	13 56	14 58	15 56	16 56	17 57	18 57	20 01	20 57
Edinburgh 10	225, 230, 242	a												
		d	10 33	11 33	12 33	13 36	14 33	15 33	16 33	17 33	18 33	19 33	20 33	21 33
Musselburgh		d	10 39	11 39	12 39	13 39	14 39	15 39	16 39	17 39	18 39	19 39	20 39	21 39
Wallyford		d	10 43	11 43	12 43	13 43	14 43	15 43	16 43	17 43	18 43	19 43	20 43	21 43
Prestonpans		d	10 46	11 46	12 46	13 46	14 46	15 46	16 46	17 46	18 46	19 46	20 46	21 46
Longniddry		d	10 51	11 51	12 51	13 51	14 51	15 51	16 51	17 51	18 51	19 51	20 51	21 51
Drem		d	10 56	11 56	12 57	13 56	14 56	15 56	16 56	17 56	18 56	19 56	20 56	21 56
North Berwick		a	11 06	12 06	13 06	14 09	15 06	16 06	17 06	18 06	19 06	20 06	21 06	22 06

For general notes see front of timetable
For details of catering facilities see Directory of Train Operators

A From Glasgow Central (Table 225)

Table 238

Mondays to Fridays

North Berwick → Edinburgh and Haymarket

Network Diagram - see first page of Table 225

Miles			SR	SR	SR	SR A	SR	SR	SR
0	**North Berwick**	d	06 44	07 20		07 58	08 37	09 20	10 20
4½	Drem	d	06 51	07 27		08 06	08 44	09 27	10 27
9	Longniddry	d	06 57	07 33		08 12	08 50	09 33	10 33
12½	Prestonpans	d	07 03	07 38	08 08	08 16	08 55	09 38	10 38
14¾	Wallyford	d	07 06	07 41	08 11	08 19	08 58	09 41	10 41
17	Musselburgh	d	07 10	07 45	08 14	08 26	09 02	09 45	10 44
22¼	**Edinburgh** 10 225, 230, 242	a	07 18	07 55	08 22	08 34	09 10	09 53	10 53
—		d	07 21			08 38	09 11		
23½	**Haymarket** 225, 230, 242	a	07 24	*08 12*	*08 37*	08 41	09 14	*10 07*	*11 07*

Miles			SR	SR	SR	SR	SR	SR	SR	SR A	SR	SR	SR	SR	SR	SR
0	**North Berwick**	d	11 21	12 20	13 20	14 17	15 20	16 22	17 22	17 52	18 25	18 53	19 20	20 20	21 20	22 20
4½	Drem	d	11 27	12 27	13 27	14 24	15 27	16 27	17 27		18 32	18 57	19 27	20 27	21 27	22 27
9	Longniddry	d	11 33	12 33	13 33	14 30	15 33	16 33	17 33		18 38	19 03	19 33	20 33	21 33	22 33
12½	Prestonpans	d	11 38	12 38	13 38	14 35	15 38	16 38	17 38		18 43	19 08	19 38	20 38	21 38	22 38
14¾	Wallyford	d	11 41	12 41	13 41	14 38	15 41	16 41	17 41		18 46	19 11	19 41	20 41	21 41	22 41
17	Musselburgh	d	11 44	12 45	13 45	14 42	15 45	16 45	17 45	18 11	18 50	19 15	19 45	20 45	21 45	22 45
22¼	**Edinburgh** 10 225, 230, 242	a	11 54	12 53	13 53	14 50	15 53	16 55	17 55	18 21	18 58	19 26	19 56	20 53	21 53	22 53
—		d				15 07	15 54			18 26						
23½	**Haymarket** 225, 230, 242	a	*12 07*	*13 07*	*14 07*	15b10	15 58	*17 11*	*18 12*	18 27	*19 13*	*19 53*	*20 19*	*21 13*	*22 13*	*23 13*

Saturdays

		SR	SR A	SR	SR	SR	SR	SR	SR	SR	SR	SR	SR	SR
North Berwick	d	07 28	08 20	09 20	09 47	10 20	10 50	11 20	11 50	12 20	12 52	13 20	13 53	14 18
Drem	d	07 35	08 27	09 27	09 54	10 27	10 57	11 27	11 57	12 27	12 57	13 27	13 57	14 25
Longniddry	d	07 41	08 33	09 33	10 00	10 33	11 03	11 33	12 03	12 33	13 02	13 33	14 03	14 31
Prestonpans	d	07 46	08 38	09 38	10 05	10 38	11 08	11 38	12 08	12 38	13 07	13 38	14 08	14 36
Wallyford	d	07 49	08 41	09 41	10 08	10 41	11 11	11 41	12 11	12 41	13 10	13 41	14 11	14 39
Musselburgh	d	07 53	08 45	09 45	10 12	10 45	11 15	11 45	12 15	12 45	13 14	13 45	14 15	14 43
Edinburgh 10 225, 230, 242	a	08 01	08 52	09 53	10 20	10 53	11 23	11 53	12 23	12 53	13 25	13 53	14 26	14 51
	d		08 57											
Haymarket 225, 230, 242	a	*08 18*	08 59	*10 07*	*10 33*	*11 07*	*11 37*	*12 07*	*12 36*	*13 06*	*13 43*	*14 07*	*14 43*	*15 07*

		SR	SR A	SR	SR	SR	SR	SR	SR	SR	SR	SR	SR	SR
North Berwick	d	14 50	15 18	15 51	16 20	16 52	17 21	17 50	18 20	18 50	19 20	20 20	21 20	22 20
Drem	d	14 57	15 25	15 57	16 27	16 57	17 28	17 57	18 27	18 57	19 27	20 27	21 27	22 27
Longniddry	d	15 03	15 31	16 03	16 33	17 03	17 34	18 03	18 33	19 03	19 33	20 33	21 33	22 33
Prestonpans	d	15 08	15 36	16 08	16 38	17 08	17 39	18 08	18 38	19 08	19 38	20 38	21 38	22 38
Wallyford	d	15 11	15 39	16 11	16 41	17 11	17 42	18 11	18 41	19 11	19 41	20 41	21 41	22 41
Musselburgh	d	15 15	15 43	16 15	16 45	17 15	17 46	18 15	18 45	19 15	19 43	20 45	21 45	22 45
Edinburgh 10 225, 230, 242	a	15 23	15 51	16 27	16 56	17 28	17 56	18 24	18 53	19 23	19 53	20 53	21 53	22 53
	d		15 53											
Haymarket 225, 230, 242	a	*15 37*	15 57	*16 41*	*17 12*	*17 47*	*18 11*	*18 37*	*19 05*	*19 37*	*20 06*	*21 13*	*22 13*	*23 13*

Sundays

		SR	SR	SR	SR	SR	SR	SR	SR	SR	SR	SR	SR
North Berwick	d	11 20	12 20	13 24	14 23	15 20	16 20	17 20	18 20	19 20	20 20	21 20	22 20
Drem	d	11 27	12 27	13 28	14 27	15 27	16 27	17 27	18 27	19 27	20 27	21 27	22 27
Longniddry	d	11 33	12 33	13 34	14 33	15 33	16 33	17 33	18 33	19 33	20 33	21 33	22 33
Prestonpans	d	11 38	12 38	13 39	14 38	15 38	16 38	17 38	18 38	19 38	20 38	21 38	22 38
Wallyford	d	11 41	12 41	13 42	14 41	15 41	16 41	17 41	18 41	19 41	20 41	21 41	22 41
Musselburgh	d	11 45	12 45	13 46	14 45	15 45	16 45	17 45	18 45	19 45	20 45	21 45	22 45
Edinburgh 10 225, 230, 242	a	11 53	12 53	13 57	14 56	15 53	16 53	17 53	18 53	19 53	20 53	21 53	22 53
	d												
Haymarket 225, 230, 242	a	*12 07*	*13 19*	*14 19*	*15 17*	*16 19*	*17 09*	*18 13*	*19 19*	*20 15*	*21 15*	*22 20*	*23 21*

For general notes see front of timetable
For details of catering facilities see Directory of Train Operators

A To Glasgow Central (Table 225)
b By changing at Edinburgh, passengers may arrive at 1503

Inverness → Kyle of Lochalsh, Thurso and Wick

Network Diagram - see first page of Table 227

Miles	Miles																							
				SR	SR		SR	SR		SR	SR		SR	SR		SR	SR			SR	SR FSO			
				◇	◇		◇	◇			◇		◇				◇							
																	A							
							✠				✠		✠				✠							
—	—	Glasgow Queen Street [10] 229 ⛴	d					07 06		08b41			10 11			13b41				16c41				
—	—	Edinburgh [10] 229	d					06e33		08 33			09f37			13 35				16 33				
—	—	Aberdeen 240	d		06 20		07 14	08 23			10 14			11 59		13 40				18 20	20 07			
0	0	**Inverness**	d	07 06	09 00		10 38	11 03		12 16	13 31		13 56	14 39		17 15	17 52			20 53	23 20			
10	10	Beauly	d	07 20	09 14		10 52			12 30	13 45			14 53		17 29	18 06			21 07	23 34			
13	13	Muir of Ord	d	07 29	09 20		10 58	11 20		12 36	13 51		14g19	14 59		17 35	18 12			21 13	23 40			
18¾	18¾	Dingwall	d	07 43	09 31		11 07	11 31		12a47	14 01		14 28	15 11		17 46	18 26	18 29		21 24	23 51			
—	30½	Garve	d		09 53			11 53			14 26						18 49							
—	36	Lochluichart	d		10x02			12x01									18x57							
—	40¼	Achanalt	d		10x08			12x07									19x03							
—	46½	Achnasheen	d		10 19			12 18			14 52						19 17							
—	59¼	Achnashellach	d		10x36			12x36									19x35							
—	64½	Strathcarron	d		10 46			12 45			15 19						19 46							
—	67	Attadale	d		10x51			12x50									19x51							
—	72	Stromeferry	d		11 04			13 03									20 04							
—	75¾	Duncraig	d		11x12			13x11									20x12							
—	77	Plockton	d		11 16			13 15			15 47						20 15							
—	78½	Duirinish	d		11x19			13x18			15x50						20x18							
—	82¼	**Kyle of Lochalsh**	a		11 28			13 28			16 00						20 29							
28½	—	Alness	d	07 55			11 20						14 41	15 24		17 59		18 42		21 37	00x03			
31½	—	Invergordon	d	08 00			11 26						14 46	15a29		18 04		18 47		21 42	00 08			
40¾	—	Fearn	d	08 12			11 38						14 58			18 16		18 58		21x53	00x19			
44¾	—	Tain	d	08 18			11 45						15 04			18 22		19 05		21a59	00a25			
57¾	—	Ardgay	d	08 33			12 00						15 21			18a38		19 24						
61	—	Culrain	d	08 37			12 06											19 30						
61½	—	Invershin	d	08x38			12x07											19x31						
67	—	Lairg	d	08 52			12 19						15 44					19 44						
77	—	Rogart	d	09x05			12x32						15x58					19x57						
84½	—	Golspie	d	09 16			12 43						16 08					20 08						
87	—	Dunrobin Castle §	d	09h19			12j46											20j11						
90½	—	Brora	d	09 30			12 54						16 18					20 18						
101½	—	Helmsdale	d	09 46			13 09						16 33					20 33						
111	—	Kildonan	d	09x59			13x22											20x46						
118½	—	Kinbrace	d	10x08			13x31											20x55						
125¾	—	Forsinard	d	10 22			13 42						17 05					21 06						
134	—	Altnabreac	d	10x32			13x52											21x16						
143	—	Scotscalder	d	10x40			14x01											21x25						
147¼	—	Georgemas Junction	a	10 49			14 12						17 33					21 33						
—	—		d	10 52			14 14						17 35					21 35						
154	—	**Thurso**	a	11 01			14 24						17 45					21 45						
—	—		d	11 04			14 26						17 47					21 47						
160¾	—	Georgemas Junction	d	11 14			14 37						17 58					21 57						
175	—	**Wick**	a	11 32			14 55						18 15					22 14						

For general notes see front of timetable
For details of catering facilities see Directory of Train Operators

§ Summer Station only
A ✠ to Dingwall

b Change at Perth and Inverness
c Mondays to Fridays change at Perth and Inverness. Saturdays change at Stirling and Inverness
e Change at Stirling and Inverness
f Saturdays dep. 0935

g Arr. 1414
h Until 26 September only
j Until 26 September. Stops on request only

Table 239

Sundays

Inverness → Kyle of Lochalsh, Thurso and Wick

Network Diagram - see first page of Table 227

		SR	SR ◇	SR	SR	SR ◇ A 🍴		SR ◇ B 🍴	SR
Glasgow Queen Street 10	229 ⛴ d					13b45		14 40	
Edinburgh 10	229 d					13 50		13 50	
Aberdeen	240 d			10 00	13 00			15 25	17 18
Inverness	d	10 00	11 11	12 49	15 21	17 55		18 04	20 53
Beauly	d	10 14	11 25	13 03	15 35	18 09		18 18	21 07
Muir of Ord	d	10 20	11 31	13 09	15 43	18 15		18 24	21 13
Dingwall	d	10 32	11 44	13 22	15 54	18 29	18 29	18 35	21 24
Garve	d		12 05			18 52			
Lochluichart	d		12x14			19x00			
Achanalt	d		12x20			19x06			
Achnasheen	d		12 31			19 18			
Achnashellach	d		12x48			19x36			
Strathcarron	d		12 58			19 47			
Attadale	d		13x03			19x52			
Stromeferry	d		13 16			20 05			
Duncraig	d		13x24			20x13			
Plockton	d		13 28			20 16			
Duirinish	d		13x31			20x19			
Kyle of Lochalsh	a		13 40			20 29			
Alness	d	10 44		13x33	16x06		18 42	18 48	21 37
Invergordon	d	10 49		13 38	16a12		18 47	18 53	21 42
Fearn	d	11x00		13x49			18x58	19x04	21x53
Tain	d	11a05		13a55			19 05	19 10	21a59
Ardgay	d						19 24	19 24	
Culrain	d						19x30	19x30	
Invershin	d						19x31	19x31	
Lairg	d						19 44	19 44	
Rogart	d						19x57	19x57	
Golspie	d						20 08	20 07	
Dunrobin Castle §	d						20x11		
Brora	d						20 18	20 18	
Helmsdale	d						20 33	20 33	
Kildonan	d						20x46	20x45	
Kinbrace	d						20x55	20x55	
Forsinard	d						21 06	21 06	
Altnabreac	d						21x16	21x16	
Scotscalder	d						21x25	21x24	
Georgemas Junction	a						21 33	21 33	
	d						21 35	21 35	
Thurso	a						21 45	21 45	
	d						21 47	21 47	
Georgemas Junction	d						21 57	21 57	
Wick	a						22 14	22 14	

For general notes see front of timetable
For details of catering facilities see Directory of Train Operators

§ Summer Station only

A Until 27 September
B From 4 October
b Change at Perth and Inverness

Wick, Thurso and Kyle of Lochalsh → Inverness

Network Diagram - see first page of Table 227

Miles	Miles			SR ◇	SR	SR ◇	SR ◇ 🚲	SR ◇ 🚲	SR	SR ◇	SR	SR ◇ 🚲	SR ◇ 🚲	SR ◇ A	SR ◇ 🚲	SR	SR
0	—	**Wick**	d				06 20	08 12				12 36			16 00		
14¼	—	Georgemas Junction	d				06 37	08 29				12 53			16 17		
21	—	**Thurso**	a				06 46	08 38				13 02			16 26		
—	—		d				06 48	08 41				13 05			16 29		
27¾	—	Georgemas Junction	a				06 59					13 14			16 38		
—	—		d				07 00	08 53				13 17			16 41		
32	—	Scotscalder	d				07x06					13x23			16x47		
41	—	Altnabreac	d				07x15					13x32			16x56		
49¼	—	Forsinard	d				07 27	09 15				13 43			17 07		
56¾	—	Kinbrace	d				07x37					13x53			17x17		
64	—	Kildonan	d				07x48					14x03			17x25		
73½	—	Helmsdale	d				08 01	09 47				14 18			17 40		
84½	—	Brora	d				08 16	10 03				14 33			17 55		
88	—	Dunrobin Castle §	d				08b22					14b39			18b01		
90½	—	Golspie	d				08 26	10 11				14 42			18 04		
98	—	Rogart	d				08 35	10x19				14x51			18x13		
108	—	Lairg	d		06 34		08 53	10 38				15 08			18 30		
113½	—	Invershin	d		06 43		09x01					15x17			18x39		
114	—	Culrain	d		06 44		09 03					15 20			18 41		
117¼	—	Ardgay	d	06 25	06 51		09 11	10 51				15 25			18 49	19 26	
130¾	—	Tain	d	06 40	07 06		09 26	11 07				15 41			19 05	19 42	22 04
134¼	—	Fearn	d	06 45	07 12		09 31					15 47			19 11	19x47	22x09
143½	—	Invergordon	d	06 58	07 24		09 44	11 26			15 39	15 58			19 22	19 58	22 20
146½	—	Alness	d	07 02	07 28		09 48				15 44	16x03			19 27	20x03	22x25
—	0	**Kyle of Lochalsh**	d			06 21				12 03			14 37	17 15			
—	3¾	Duirinish	d			06x28				12x10			14x44	17x22			
—	5¼	Plockton	d			06 33				12 15			14 49	17 27			
—	6½	Duncraig	d			06x35				12x17				17x29			
—	10¼	Stromeferry	d			06 44				12 26				17 38			
—	15¼	Attadale	d			06x56				12x38				17x50			
—	17¾	Strathcarron	d			07 02				12c47			15 16	17 56			
—	23	Achnashellach	d			07x11				12x56				18x05			
—	35¾	Achnasheen	d			07 29				13 15			15 47	18 23			
—	42	Achanalt	d			07x39				13x25				18x33			
—	46¼	Lochluichart	d			07x45				13x32				18x40			
—	51¾	Garve	d			07 55				13 41			16 12	18 49			
156¼	63½	Dingwall	d	07 16	07 42	08 16	10 04	11 45	12 54	14 03	15 57	16 19	16 37	19 13	19 41	20 15	22 38
162	69¼	Muir of Ord	d	07 28	07 52	08 29	10 13	11 55	13 05	14 15	16 09	16 30	16 46	19 25	19 50	20 24	22 49
164¾	72¼	Beauly	d	07 33	07 57	08 35	10 19		13 11	14 20	16 14		16 52	19 30	19 56	20x28	22x53
175	82¼	**Inverness**	a	07 48	08 12	08 53	10 35	12 13	13 25	14 36	16 29	16 47	17 09	19 49	20 10	20 43	23 08
—	—	Aberdeen 240	a	11 26		11 26	13 13	14 54	16 41	17 41		19 32	20 30			23 39	
—	—	Edinburgh 10 229	a	13e19		13e19	14f19	16 23		18e25	20 29		22 19	00g09			
—	—	Glasgow Queen Street 10 229 ⛴	a	12 46		12 46	14e15	16e15		18 09	20e15		22e19	23 38			

For general notes see front of timetable
For details of catering facilities see Directory of Train Operators

§ Summer Station only

A To Elgin (Table 240)
b Until 26 September. Stops on request only
c Arr. 1243
e Change at Inverness and Perth
f Saturdays arr. 1425
g Change at Inverness and Stirling

Table 239

Sundays

Wick, Thurso and Kyle of Lochalsh → Inverness

Network Diagram - see first page of Table 227

		SR	SR ◇ A	SR	SR ◇	SR	SR ◇	SR
Wick	d				11 53			
Georgemas Junction	d				12 10			
Thurso	a				12 19			
	d				12 22			
Georgemas Junction	a				12 31			
	d				12 34			
Scotscalder	d				12x40			
Altnabreac	d				12x49			
Forsinard	d				13 00			
Kinbrace	d				13x10			
Kildonan	d				13x20			
Helmsdale	d				13 33			
Brora	d				13 48			
Dunrobin Castle §	d				13b54			
Golspie	d				13 58			
Rogart	d				14x07			
Lairg	d				14 24			
Invershin	d				14x33			
Culrain	d				14x34			
Ardgay	d				14 40			
Tain	d	11 10		14 00	14 55			22 04
Fearn	d	11x15		14x05	15x00			22x09
Invergordon	d	11 26		14 16	15 12	16 19		22 20
Alness	d	11x31		14x21	15x16	16x23		22x25
Kyle of Lochalsh	d		11ʃ21				15 22	
Duirinish	d		11x28				15x29	
Plockton	d		11ʃ33				15 34	
Duncraig	d		11x35				15x36	
Stromeferry	d		11ʃ44				15 45	
Attadale	d		11x56				15x57	
Strathcarron	d		12ʃ02				16 03	
Achnashellach	d		12x11				16x12	
Achnasheen	d		12ʃ29				16 30	
Achanalt	d		12x39				16x40	
Lochluichart	d		12x46				16x47	
Garve	d		12ʃ57				16 56	
Dingwall	d	11 43	13ʃ20	14 35	15 30	16 36	17 18	22 38
Muir of Ord	d	11 54	13ʃ34	14 46	15 42	16 47	17 29	22 49
Beauly	d	11 59	13ʃ39	14x51	15 47	16 52	17 34	22x53
Inverness	a	12 16	13ʃ54	15 06	16 02	17 07	17 49	23 08
Aberdeen 240	a	*14 43*		*17 41*	*19 28*			
Edinburgh 10 229	a	*16 42*			*20c06*		*22 05*	
Glasgow Queen Street 10 229	a	*15 56*			*19 36*		*22e15*	

For general notes see front of timetable
For details of catering facilities see Directory of Train Operators

§ Summer Station only

A Until 27 September

b Until 27 September. Stops on request only

c Change at Inverness and Stirling

e Change at Inverness and Perth

Scrabster — Stromness (Orkney Isles)

Operated by NorthLink Orkney & Shetland Ferries Ltd

		SO	SX	
Inverness	239 d	07 06	07 06	13 56
Thurso §	239 a	11b01	11b01	17b45
Scrabster	⛴ d	12 00	13 15	19 00
Stromness	⛴ a	13 30	14 45	20 30

Mondays to Saturdays

		SX	SO A	SO B	SX	SO A
Stromness	⛴ d	06 30	06 30	09 00	11 00	11 00
Scrabster	⛴ a	08c00	08c00	10c30	12c30	12c30
Thurso §	239 d	08 41	08 41	13 05	13 05	13 05
Inverness	239 a	12 13	12 13	16 47	16 47	16 47

Sundays

Stromness	⛴ d	09 00
Scrabster	⛴ a	10c30
Thurso §	239 d	12 22
Inverness	239 a	16 02

For general notes see front of timetable
For details of catering facilities see Directory of Train Operators

§ Stagecoach in the Highlands (01463 239 292) operate a connecting bus service between Thurso and Scrabster from whom details of bus times should be obtained

A 13 June to 15 August
B Until 6 June and from 22 August
b Stagecoach in the Highlands bus connection. Departs Thurso Railway Station
c Stagecoach in the Highlands bus connection. Arrives Thurso Railway Station

PASSENGER NOTICE: Please note NorthLink Ferries requires all passengers aged 16 and over to be in possession of photographic ID at check-in

until 24 October

Ullapool - Stornoway (Lewis), Uig (Skye), Tarbert (Harris) and Lochmaddy (North Uist)

Operated by Caledonian MacBrayne Ltd.

		TTh SX	TTh SO	WFO A	SX B	WFSX C	TThO	SO D	SO E	MFO	SO	WO	WFO A
Edinburgh 10	229 d			08 33	09b35	09b35	06b29	06b29	06b29	06b29	09b35	06b29	13 35
Glasgow Queen Street 10	229 d			08 41	10b11	10 11	07 06	07 06	07 06	07 06	10 11	07 06	13b41
Inverness §	229 a			11c54	13c27	13c27	10 29	10 29	10 29	10 29	13c27	10 29	17c05
Inverness	239 d	09 00	09 00				11 03	11 03	11 03	11 03		11 03	
Kyle of Lochalsh §	239 a	11e28	11e28				13f28	13f28	13f28	13f28		13f28	
Inverness ‡	bus d			13 30	15 00	15 00					15 40		19 50
Ullapool	bus a			14 50	16 20	16 20					17 00		21 10
Ullapool	ship d			15 50	17 35	17 35					18 15		22 00
Stornoway	ship a			18 35	20 20	20 20					21 00		00 45
Uig §	ship d	14 00	14 00				18 00	18 00	18 00	18 00		19 00	
Tarbert	ship a	15 40					19 40	19 40	19 40				
Lochmaddy	ship a		15 45					21 45		19 45		20 45	

Mondays to Saturdays

until 24 October

		MO G	MO H	WFO	WFO J	K	WFX L	TTh SO	TTh SO	TTh SX	WFO J	SX N	WFSX C	SO
Lochmaddy	ship d	05 30						07 30		11 50				
Tarbert	ship d	07 30	07 30	07 30					11 50					
Uig §	ship a	09g10	09g10	09g10				09g15	13h30	13h35				
Stornoway	ship d				06 15	07 00	07 00				12 40	13 50	13 50	14 30
Ullapool	ship a				09 00	09 45	09 45				15 25	16 35	16 35	17 15
Ullapool	bus d				09 05	09 50	09 50				15 30	16 40	16 40	17 20
Inverness ‡	bus a				10j25	11j10	11j10				16j50	18j00	18j00	18j40
Kyle of Lochalsh §	239 d	12 03	12 03	12 03				12 03	17 15	17 15				
Inverness	239 a	14 36	14 36	14 36				14 36	19 49	19 49				
Inverness	229 d	14 51	14 51	14 51	10 47	12 47	12 47	14 51	20 15	20 15	18 43	18 43	18 43	20 15
Glasgow Queen Street 10	229 a	18k09	18k09	18k09	14m15	16m15	16m15	18k09	23 38	23 38	22m19	22m19	22m19	23 38
Edinburgh 10	229 a	18m25	18m25	18m25	14 19	16 23	16 23	18m25	00k09	00k09	22 19	22 19	22 19	00k09

For general notes see front of timetable
For details of catering facilities see Directory of Train Operators

- § Connecting bus service between Uig-Kyle of Lochalsh operated by Scottish Citylink Coaches (08705 505050)from whom details of bus times should be obtained
- ‡ Bus Station. Connecting bus service between Inverness Bus Station-Ullapool operated by Scottish Citylink coaches (08705 505050)
- A 24 June to 28 August
- B Until 19 June and from 31 August
- C 22 June to 27 August
- D From 12 September
- E Until 5 September
- G From 14 September
- H Until 7 September
- J 24 June to 28 August
- K Until 20 June and from 31 August
- L 22 June to 29 August
- N Until 19 June and from 28 August
- b Change at Perth
- c Passengers make their own way between Bus Station and Rail Station
- e Bus connection dep. Kyle of Lochalsh 1215, Uig arr. 1350
- f Bus connection dep. Kyle of Lochalsh 1540, Uig arr. 1720
- g Bus connection dep. Uig 0930, Kyle of Lochalsh arr. 1114
- h Bus connection dep. Uig 1445, Kyle of Lochalsh arr. 1619
- j Passengers make their own way between Bus Station and Rail Station
- k Change at Stirling
- m Change at Perth

No Sunday Service

For details of sailings from 25 October 2009 telephone Caledonian MacBrayne on 08000 66 5000

For confirmation of Scottish Citylink Coach connections from 5 October please telephone 08705 50 50 50

Table 240

Mondays to Saturdays

Aberdeen and Elgin — Inverness

Network Diagram - please see first page of Table 225

Miles			SR 1◇	SR 1◇	SR 1◇ A	SR 1 B	SR 1◇	SR 1◇ C	SR 1◇ D	SR 1◇ 🛒
0	**Aberdeen**	d		06 20	07 14	07 50	08 23	08 50	10 00	10 14
6¼	Dyce ✈	d		06 30	07b31	08 03	08 36	09a01	10 09	10 23
17	**Inverurie**	a		06 43	07 44	08 17	08 48		10 22	10 35
—		d		06 46	07 49		08 48			10 35
27½	Insch	d		06 58	08 01		09 03			10 47
40¾	Huntly	d		07 19	08 17		09 19			11 03
53¼	Keith	d		07 33	08 31		09 33			11 18
71¼	**Elgin**	d	07 00	07 58	08 53		09 53			11 42
83½	Forres	d	07 14	08 12	09 07		10 11			11 56
93¼	Nairn	d	07 27	08 23	09f22		10 22			12 07
108¼	**Inverness**	a	07 48	08 41	09 40		10 40			12 25

		SR 1◇ D	SR 1◇ 🛒	SR 1	SR 1◇ 🛒	SR 1◇ D	SR 1◇ 🛒	SR 1◇ D	SR 1
Aberdeen	d	11 04	11 59	12 50	13 40	14 56	15 25	15 55	16 43
Dyce ✈	d	11 16	12 08	13 01	13 53	15 05	15 38	16 04	16a52
Inverurie	a	11 30	12 20	13 15	14 05	15 19	15 50	16 18	
	d		12 20		14 05		15 50		
Insch	d		12 33		14 17		16 02		
Huntly	d		12 49		14 33		16 18		
Keith	d		13 03		14 47		16 34		
Elgin	d		13 27		15 11		16 56		
Forres	d		13 41		15 25		17 10		
Nairn	d		13 52		15g41		17h29		
Inverness	a		14 10		15 59		17 47		

		SR 1◇ 🛒	SR 1◇ D	SR 1◇ 🛒	SR 1◇ D	SR 1◇ 🛒	SR 1	SR 1◇ D	SR 1
Aberdeen	d	17 18	17 56	18 20	19 07	20 07	20 56	21 55	22 50
Dyce ✈	d	17 29	18 05	18 29	19c22	20 20	21 05	22 05	22 59
Inverurie	a	17 40	18 19	18 41	19 35	20 32	21 19	22 16	23 13
	d	17 41		18 41		20 32		22 17	
Insch	d	17 53		18 53		20 44		22 29	
Huntly	d	18 09		19 09		21 00		22 46	
Keith	d	18 26		19 24		21 14		23 00	
Elgin	d	18e54		19 46		21 36		23 22	
Forres	d	19 08		20 00		21 55		23 36	
Nairn	d	19 19		20j15		22 06		23 47	
Inverness	a	19 38		20 33		22 24		00 05	

Sundays

		SR 1◇ 🛒	SR 1◇ 🛒	SR 1◇ 🛒	SR 1◇ 🛒	SR 1◇ 🛒
Aberdeen	d	10 00	13 00	15 25	17 18	21 00
Dyce ✈	d	10 09	13 09	15 34	17 29	21 09
Inverurie	a	10 21	13 21	15 46	17 41	21 21
	d	10 21	13 21	15 47	17 41	21 21
Insch	d	10 33	13 33	15 59	17 53	21 33
Huntly	d	10 49	13 51	16 15	18 09	21 49
Keith	d	11 05	14 04	16 35	18 24	22 09
Elgin	d	11 27	14 26	16 58	18 46	22 31
Forres	d	11 41	14 40	17 12	19 00	22 45
Nairn	d	11 52	14 51	17k32	19 11	22 56
Inverness	a	12 10	15 10	17 50	19 29	23 14

Mondays to Saturdays

Miles			SR 1◇ E	SR 1◇ G	SR 1◇ 🛒	SR 1	SR 1◇ G	SR 1◇	SR 1◇ E	SR 1◇ 🛒
0	**Inverness**	d	04 57		05 58			07 10		09 03
15	Nairn	d	05 14		06 15			07 28		09 21
24¾	Forres	d	05 25		06 26			07 39		09 37
37	**Elgin**	d	05 40		06 42			08m00		09 53
55	Keith	d	06 02		07 03			08 21		10 12
67½	Huntly	d	06 16		07 19			08 45		10 30
80¾	Insch	d	06 32		07 35			09 03		10 49
91¼	**Inverurie**	a	06 44		07 48			09 14		11 01
—		d	06 45	07 14	07 49	08 22		09 15	10 38	11 01
102	Dyce ✈	d	06 58	07 26	08 03	08 35	09 08	09 27	10 50	11 15
108¼	**Aberdeen**	a	07 10	07 37	08 14	08 46	09 19	09 38	11 01	11 26

		SR 1◇ E	SR 1◇ 🛒	SR 1	SR 1◇ 🛒	SR 1◇ E	SR 1◇ 🛒	SR 1◇ E	SR 1 H
Inverness	d		10 58		12 42		14 27		
Nairn	d		11 15		12 59		14 44		
Forres	d		11 26		13 10		14 55		
Elgin	d		11 42		13 26		15 11		
Keith	d		12 03		13 47		15 32		
Huntly	d		12 17		14 01		15 46		
Insch	d		12 35		14 19		16 04		
Inverurie	a		12 47		14 31		16 18		
	d	11 35	12 47	13 38	14 31	15 24	16 18	16 38	
Dyce ✈	d	11 47	13 02	13 52	14 43	15 38	16 31	16 54	17 05
Aberdeen	a	11 58	13 13	14 03	14 54	15 49	16 41	17 05	17 16

		SR 1◇	SR 1◇ E	SR 1◇ 🛒	SR E	SR 1◇	SR ◇ J	SR 1	SR 1◇
Inverness	d	15 21		17 11		18 10	19 57		21 20
Nairn	d	15 40		17 28		18 27	20 14		21 37
Forres	d	15 51		17 39		18 38	20 25		21 48
Elgin	d	16 07		17n58		18 55	20a41		22 06
Keith	d	16 28		18 19		19 16			22 27
Huntly	d	16 47		18 40		19 37			22q47
Insch	d	17 04		18 56		19 53			23 03
Inverurie	a	17 15		19 08		20 05			23 16
	d	17 16	18 43	19 09	19 40	20 05		21 24	23 16
Dyce ✈	d	17 30	18 55	19 21	19 52	20 19		21 36	23 28
Aberdeen	a	17 41	19 06	19 32	20 03	20 30		21 47	23 39

Sundays

		SR 1◇ 🛒	SR 1◇ 🛒	SR 1◇ 🛒	SR 1◇ 🛒	SR 1◇ K 🛒	SR 1◇ 🛒	SR 1◇ K 🛒
Inverness	d	09 55	12 30	15 27	17 12	18 00	21 00	21 42
Nairn	d	10 12	12 47	15 44	17 30	18 17	21 17	21 59
Forres	d	10 23	12 58	15 55	17 41	18 28	21 28	22 10
Elgin	d	10 38	13 13	16 10	17 56	18a44	21 44	22a26
Keith	d	10 59	13 35	16 32	18 18		22 05	
Huntly	d	11 18	13 52	16 46	18 37		22 19	
Insch	d	11 34	14 08	17 02	18 53		22 35	
Inverurie	a	11 47	14 20	17 14	19 05		22 47	
	d	11 47	14 20	17 14	19 05		22 47	
Dyce ✈	d	11 59	14 32	17 30	19 17		22 59	
Aberdeen	a	12 10	14 43	17 41	19 28		23 10	

For general notes see front of timetable
For details of catering facilities see
Directory of Train Operators

- **A** From Montrose (Table 229)
- **B** From Perth (Table 229)
- **C** From Glasgow Queen Street (Table 229)
- **D** From Edinburgh (Table 229)
- **E** To Edinburgh (Table 229)
- **G** To Glasgow Queen Street (Table 229)
- **H** Mondays to Fridays to Stonehaven (Table 229)
- **J** From Kyle of Lochalsh (Table 239)
- **K** From Glasgow Queen Street (Table 229)
- **b** Arr. 0724
- **c** Arr. 1916
- **e** Arr. 1847
- **f** Arr. 0917
- **g** Arr. 1536
- **h** Arr. 1721
- **j** Arr. 2010
- **k** Arr. 1724
- **m** Arr. 0754
- **n** Arr. 1753
- **q** Arr. 2241

Newcraighall and Edinburgh → Dunfermline, Kirkcaldy and Glenrothes with Thornton

Network Diagram - see first page of Table 225

Miles	Miles			SR 1◊ A	XC 1◊ B	SR	SR C	SR 1 B	SR D	SR	SR E	SR C	SR 1◊ G 🛒	SR 1 H	SR E	SR	SR 1 B	SR	SR J	SR 1◊ K 🛒	SR E	SR C	SR 1 B
0	—	**Newcraighall**	d				06 04			06 36		07 05				07 36			08 00			08 34	
¾	—	Brunstane	d				06 07			06 39		07 08				07 39			08 03			08 37	
4¾	0	**Edinburgh** 10	a				06 16			06 46		07 16				07 46			08 10			08 45	
—	—		d	05 30	05 33	06 09	06 18	06 29	06 32		07 10	07 18	07 30	07 35	07 38		08 00	08 08	08 12	08 33	08 38	08 46	08 59
6	1¼	Haymarket	d	05 33		06 13	06 22	06 33	06 37		07 13	07 22	07 33	07 39	07 42		08 03	08 12	08 14	08 37	08 42	08 50	09 03
9¼	4½	South Gyle	d			06 18	06 27		06 43		07 18	07 27			07 47			08 17	08 22		08 47	08 55	
14¼	9½	Dalmeny	d			06 24	06 33		06 50		07 25	07 34			07 54				08 28		08 53	09 01	
16	11¼	North Queensferry	d			06 28	06 37		06 54		07 28	07 37			07 57				08 32		08 57	09 05	
18	13¼	Inverkeithing	d	05 46	06a05	06 32	06 41	06 47	06 59		07 32	07 41		07 53	08 01		08 17	08 28	08 36		09 01	09 09	09 17
—	14¾	Rosyth	d				06 44					07 45							08 39			09 12	
—	17	**Dunfermline Town**	d				06 49					07 50							08 44			09 17	
—	18½	Dunfermline Queen Margaret	d				06 53					07 53							08 48			09 21	
—	22½	Cowdenbeath	d				06 59					08 00							08 54			09 27	
—	24¾	Lochgelly	d				07 05					08 05							09 00			09 33	
—	27	Cardenden	d				07 09					08 09							09 04			09 37	
19½	—	Dalgety Bay	d			06 35			07 03		07 35				08 04			08 31			09 04		
22¼	—	Aberdour	d			06 40			07 09		07 40				08 09			08 36			09 09		
25	—	Burntisland	d			06 44			07 14		07 44				08 13			08 40			09 13		
27½	—	Kinghorn	d			06 49			07 19		07 49				08 18			08 45			09 18		
30¾	—	Kirkcaldy	d	06a02		06a56		07a02	07 25		07 54		08a02	08a09	08 23		08a33	08a52		09a06	09 23		09a33
39¾	31¾	Glenrothes With Thornton	a				07 15		07 34		08 04	08 16			08 32				09 10		09 31	09 43	

		SR	SR	SR 1 H	SR E	SR C	SR 1 B	SR	SR	GR R 1 L 🛒	SR 1 H	SR E	SR C	SR 1 B	SR	SR	SR E	SR C	SR 1 B	SR	SR	SR 1 H
Newcraighall	d		09 06			09 33			10 05				10 37			11 07		11 35			12 07	
Brunstane	d		09 09			09 36			10 08				10 40			11 10		11 38			12 10	
Edinburgh 10	a		09 16			09 48			10 16				10 47			11 18		11 45			12 17	
	d	09 06	09 17	09 35	09 41	09 50	10 00	10 06	10 19	10 27	10 34	10 38	10 48	11 00	11 05	11 19	11 39	11 48	12 00	12 06	12 18	12 35
Haymarket	d	09 10	09 22	09 39	09 43	09 54	10 03	10 10	10 23	10 32	10 38	10 43	10 53	11 04	11 09	11 23	11 43	11 52	12 03	12 10	12 23	12 39
South Gyle	d	09 15	09 27		09 48	09 59		10 15	10 28			10 47	10 57		11 15	11 28	11 48	11 57		12 15	12 27	
Dalmeny	d	09 21	09 34		09 54	10 05		10 21	10 34			10 54	11 04		11 21	11 34	11 54	12 03		12 21	12 34	
North Queensferry	d	09 25	09 37		09 58	10 09		10 25	10 38			10 57	11 07		11 25	11 38	11 58	12 07		12 25	12 37	
Inverkeithing	d	09 29	09 41	09 53	10 02	10 13	10 18	10 29	10 42	10 47	10 53	11 01	11 11	11 17	11 29	11 42	12 02	12 11	12 17	12 29	12 41	12 53
Rosyth	d		09 45			10 16			10 45				11 15			11 45		12 14			12 45	
Dunfermline Town	d		09 50			10 21			10 50				11 20			11 50		12 19			12 50	
Dunfermline Queen Margaret	d		09 53			10 25			10 54				11 23			11 54		12 23			12 53	
Cowdenbeath	d		10a02			10 31			11a03				11 30			12a03		12 29			13a03	
Lochgelly	d					10 37							11 35					12 35				
Cardenden	d					10 41							11 39					12 39				
Dalgety Bay	d	09 32			10 05			10 32				11 04			11 32		12 05			12 32		
Aberdour	d	09 37			10 10			10 37				11 09			11 37		12 10			12 37		
Burntisland	d	09 41			10 14			10 41				11 13			11 41		12 14			12 41		
Kinghorn	d	09 46			10 19			10 46				11 18			11 46		12 19			12 46		
Kirkcaldy	d	09 51		10a08	10 24		10a33	10 51		11a04	11a10	11 23		11a33	11 51		12 24		12a34	12 51		13a08
Glenrothes With Thornton	a	10 03			10 32	10 47		11 03				11 32	11 46		12 02		12 32	12 46		13 02		

		SR E	SR C	SR 1 B	SR	SR	SR E	SR C	SR 1 B	SR	SR	SR 1 H	SR E	SR C	GR R 1 N Q 🛒	SR 1 B	SR	SR	SR 1 H	SR E	SR C	SR 1 B
Newcraighall	d		12 37			13 07		13 37			14 06			14 37				15 06			15 35	
Brunstane	d		12 40			13 10		13 40			14 09			14 40				15 09			15 38	
Edinburgh 10	a		12 47			13 17		13 47			14 17			14 47				15 17			15 46	
	d	12 39	12 49	13 00	13 06	13 18	13 39	13 49	14 00	14 05	14 18	14 35	14 39	14 49	15 00	15 03	15 08	15 19	15 35	15 39	15 49	16 00
Haymarket	d	12 43	12 53	13 03	13 10	13 23	13 43	13 53	14 04	14 09	14 23	14 38	14 43	14 53	15 04	15 09	15 13	15 23	15 39	15 43	15 53	16 04
South Gyle	d	12 48	12 58		13 15	13 27	13 48	13 58		14 14	14 28		14 48	14 58			15 18	15 28		15 48	15 58	
Dalmeny	d	12 54	13 04		13 21	13 34	13 54	14 04		14 20	14 34		14 54	15 05			15 24	15 34		15 54	16 04	
North Queensferry	d	12 58	13 08		13 25	13 37	13 58	14 08		14 24	14 38		14 58	15 08			15 28	15 38		15 58	16 08	
Inverkeithing	d	13 02	13 12	13 17	13 29	13 41	14 02	14 12	14 17	14 28	14 42	14 53	15 02	15 12	15 19	15 25	15 32	15 42	15 53	16 02	16 12	16 17
Rosyth	d		13 15			13 45		14 15			14 45			15 16				15 45			16 15	
Dunfermline Town	d		13 20			13 50		14 20			14 50			15 21				15 51			16 20	
Dunfermline Queen Margaret	d		13 24			13 53		14 24			14 54			15 24				15 53			16 24	
Cowdenbeath	d		13 30			14a02		14 30			15a04			15 31				16a04			16 30	
Lochgelly	d		13 36					14 36						15 36							16 36	
Cardenden	d		13 40					14 40						15 40							16 40	
Dalgety Bay	d	13 05			13 32		14 05			14 31			15 05				15 35			16 05		
Aberdour	d	13 10			13 37		14 10			14 36			15 10				15 40			16 10		
Burntisland	d	13 14			13 41		14 14			14 40			15 14				15 44			16 14		
Kinghorn	d	13 19			13 46		14 19			14 45			15 19				15 49			16 19		
Kirkcaldy	d	13 24		13a33	13 51		14 24		14a33	14 50		15a08	15 24		15a35	15a41	15 54		16a08	16 24		16a33
Glenrothes With Thornton	a	13 32	13 46		14 02		14 32	14 46		15 03			15 32	15 47			16 05			16 32	16 46	

For general notes see front of timetable
For details of catering facilities see Directory of Train Operators

- **A** To Aberdeen (Table 229)
- **B** To Dundee (Table 229)
- **C** To Edinburgh via Kirkcaldy
- **D** To Edinburgh via Cowdenbeath
- **E** To Newcraighall via Cowdenbeath
- **G** To Inverurie (Table 229)
- **H** To Perth (Table 229)
- **J** To Newcraighall via Kirkcaldy
- **K** To Inverness (Table 229)
- **L** From Leeds (Table 26) to Aberdeen (Table 229)
- **N** From London Kings Cross (Table 26) to Aberdeen (Table 229)
- **Q** **The Northern Lights**

Newcraighall and Edinburgh → Dunfermline, Kirkcaldy and Glenrothes with Thornton

Network Diagram - see first page of Table 225

		SR A	SR	SR 1 B	SR A	SR	SR C	SR D	SR E	SR	SR	SR 1◇ G 🍴
Newcraighall	d		16 03			16 30				16 59		
Brunstane	d		16 06			16 33				17 02		
Edinburgh 10	a		16 13			16 41				17 09		
	d	16 08	16 16	16 32	16 39	16 47	17 03		17 08	17 12	17 21	17 41
Haymarket	d	16 12	16 20	16 37	16 43	16 51	17 07		17 12	17 17	17 26	17u45
South Gyle	d	16 17	16 25		16 49	16 56			17 18	17 22	17 31	
Dalmeny	d	16 23	16 32		16 56	17 03		18 33		17 28	17 38	
North Queensferry	d	16 27	16 36		17 00	17 07				17 32	17 42	
Inverkeithing	d	16 31	16 40	16 51	17 05	17 11	17 22	18 42	17 28	17 36	17 47	
Rosyth	d		16 44			17 15			17 34		17 50	
Dunfermline Town	d		16 49			17 20			17 40		17 55	
Dunfermline Queen Margaret	d		16 52			17 23			17 45		17 59	
Cowdenbeath	d		17a02			17a32			17 53		18 05	
Lochgelly	d								17 59		18 11	
Cardenden	d								18 04		18a22	
Dalgety Bay	d	16 34			17 08			18 45		17 40		
Aberdour	d	16 39			17 13			18 50		17 45		
Burntisland	d	16 43			17 17			18 54		17 49		
Kinghorn	d	16 48			17 22			18 59		17 54		
Kirkcaldy	d	16 53		17a07	17 27		17a37	19a04		18a04		18a15
Glenrothes With Thornton	a	17 01			17 35				18 10			

		SR A	SR E	SR 1 H	SR A	XC 1◇ J 🍴	SR E	GR R 1 K ∅ 🍴	SR 1 B	SR	SR 1 H	SR
Newcraighall	d		17 37				18 07			18 35		
Brunstane	d		17 40				18 10			18 38		
Edinburgh 10	a		17 51				18 18			18 45		
	d	17 49	17 52	18 00	18 08	18 16	18 26	18 30	18 40	18 49	19 00	19 09
Haymarket	d	17 52	17 57	18 04	18 12	18 21	18 30	18 35	18 45	18 53	19 03	19 13
South Gyle	d	17 58	18 02		18 17		18 35			18 58		19 18
Dalmeny	d	18 05	18 08		18 23		18 41			19 04		19 24
North Queensferry	d	18 09	18 12		18 27		18 45			19 08		19 28
Inverkeithing	d	18 13	18 16	18 22	18 31	18 38	18 49	18 54	19 00	19 12	19 17	19 32
Rosyth	d		18 19				18 52			19 15		
Dunfermline Town	d		18 24				18 57			19 20		
Dunfermline Queen Margaret	d		18 28				19 01			19 24		
Cowdenbeath	d		18 34				19 07			19 30		
Lochgelly	d		18 40				19 13			19 36		
Cardenden	d		18 44				19 17			19 40		
Dalgety Bay	d	18 16			18 34							19 35
Aberdour	d	18 21			18 39							19 40
Burntisland	d	18 26			18 43							19 44
Kinghorn	d	18 31			18 48							19 49
Kirkcaldy	d	18 36		18a39	18 53	18a58		19a11	19a18		19a33	19a56
Glenrothes With Thornton	a	18 44	18 52		19 04		19 23			19 49		

		SR	SR 1◇ G 🍴	SR	SR H	XC 1◇ L	SR	GR R 1 K ∅ 🍴	SR 1 B	SR
Newcraighall	d	19 06		19 38			20 08			20 37
Brunstane	d	19 09		19 41			20 11			20 40
Edinburgh 10	a	19 16		19 48			20 19			20 47
	d	19 21	19 35	19 49	20 00	20 15	20 19	20 32	20 37	20 51
Haymarket	d	19 26	19 39	19 54	20 04	20 20	20a24	20 37	20 41	20 55
South Gyle	d	19 30		19 58	20 09					21 00
Dalmeny	d	19 37		20 05	20 15					21 06
North Queensferry	d	19 40		20 08	20 19					21 10
Inverkeithing	d	19 44	19 54	20 12	20 23	20 35		20 52	21 00	21 14
Rosyth	d	19 48		20 16						21 17
Dunfermline Town	d	19 53		20 21						21 22
Dunfermline Queen Margaret	d	19 56		20 24						21 26
Cowdenbeath	d	20 03		20 31						21 32
Lochgelly	d	20 08		20 36						21 38
Cardenden	d	20 12		20 40						21 42
Dalgety Bay	d				20 26					
Aberdour	d				20 31					
Burntisland	d				20 35					
Kinghorn	d				20 40					
Kirkcaldy	d		20a10		20a44	20a49		21a08	21a15	
Glenrothes With Thornton	a	20 22		20 50						21 52

		SR H	SR 1◇ N	SR B	SR H	SR B	SR	SR H	SR	SR
Newcraighall	d			21 37			22 37			23 37
Brunstane	d			21 40			22 40			23 40
Edinburgh 10	a			21 47			22 47			23 47
	d	21 09	21 40	21 49	22 09	22 39	22 50	23 09	23 19	23 49
Haymarket	d	21 13	21 44	21 53	22 13	22 43	22a54	23 13	23 23	23a53
South Gyle	d	21 18		21 58	22 18	22 48		23 18	23 28	
Dalmeny	d	21 24		22 04	22 24	22 54		23 24	23 34	
North Queensferry	d	21 28		22 08	22 28	22 58		23 28	23 38	
Inverkeithing	d	21 32		22 12	22 32	23 02		23 32	23 42	
Rosyth	d			22 15					23 45	
Dunfermline Town	d			22 20					23 50	
Dunfermline Queen Margaret	d			22 24					23 54	
Cowdenbeath	d			22 30					23 59	
Lochgelly	d			22 36					00 06	
Cardenden	d			22 40					00 10	
Dalgety Bay	d	21 35			22 35	23 05		23 35		
Aberdour	d	21 40			22 40	23 10		23 40		
Burntisland	d	21 44			22 44	23 14		23 44		
Kinghorn	d	21 49			22 49	23 19		23 49		
Kirkcaldy	d	21a53	22a12		22a53	23a23		23a53		
Glenrothes With Thornton	a			22 46					00 19	

Saturdays

		SR 1◇ N	XC 1◇ H	SR E	SR 1 H	SR A	SR	SR A	SR E	SR 1◇ Q 🍴	SR 1 B
Newcraighall	d			06 04			06 36		07 05		
Brunstane	d			06 07			06 39		07 08		
Edinburgh 10	a			06 16			06 46		07 16		
	d	05 30	05 33	06 18	06 29	06 39		07 10	07 18	07 30	07 35
Haymarket	d	05 33		06 22	06 33	06 43		07 13	07 22	07 33	07 39
South Gyle	d			06 27		06 48		07 18	07 27		
Dalmeny	d			06 33		06 54		07 25	07 34		
North Queensferry	d			06 37		06 58		07 28	07 37		
Inverkeithing	d	05 46	06a05	06 41	06 47	07 02		07 32	07 41		07 53
Rosyth	d			06 44					07 45		
Dunfermline Town	d			06 49					07 50		
Dunfermline Queen Margaret	d			06 53					07 53		
Cowdenbeath	d			06 59					08 00		
Lochgelly	d			07 05					08 05		
Cardenden	d			07 09					08 09		
Dalgety Bay	d					07 05		07 35			
Aberdour	d					07 10		07 40			
Burntisland	d					07 14		07 44			
Kinghorn	d					07 19		07 49			
Kirkcaldy	d	06a02			07a02	07 24		07 54		08a02	08a09
Glenrothes With Thornton	a			07 15		07 32		08 04	08 16		

		SR A	SR	SR 1 H	SR	SR U	SR 1◇ G 🍴	SR A	SR U	SR 1 H	SR
Newcraighall	d		07 36			07 56			08 34		
Brunstane	d		07 39			07 59			08 37		
Edinburgh 10	a		07 46			08 06			08 45		
	d	07 38		08 00	08 08	08 10	08 33	08 38	08 46	08 59	09 06
Haymarket	d	07 43		08 03	08 12	08 14	08 37	08 42	08 50	09 03	09 10
South Gyle	d	07 47			08 17	08 22		08 47	08 55		09 15
Dalmeny	d	07 54				08 28		08 53	09 01		09 21
North Queensferry	d	07 57				08 32		08 57	09 05		09 25
Inverkeithing	d	08 01		08 17	08 28	08 36		09 01	09 09	09 17	09 29
Rosyth	d					08 39			09 12		
Dunfermline Town	d					08 44			09 17		
Dunfermline Queen Margaret	d					08 48			09 21		
Cowdenbeath	d					08 54			09 27		
Lochgelly	d					09 00			09 33		
Cardenden	d					09 04			09 37		
Dalgety Bay	d	08 04			08 31			09 04			09 32
Aberdour	d	08 09			08 36			09 09			09 37
Burntisland	d	08 13			08 40			09 13			09 41
Kinghorn	d	08 18			08 45			09 18			09 46
Kirkcaldy	d	08 23		08a33	08a52		09a06	09 23		09a33	09 51
Glenrothes With Thornton	a	08 32				09 10		09 31	09 43		10 03

For general notes see front of timetable
For details of catering facilities see Directory of Train Operators

- **A** To Newcraighall via Cowdenbeath
- **B** To Perth (Table 229)
- **C** To Carnoustie (Table 229)
- **D** From Glasgow Queen Street (Table 230)
- **E** To Edinburgh via Kirkcaldy
- **G** To Inverness (Table 229)
- **H** To Dundee (Table 229)
- **J** From Plymouth (Table 51) to Aberdeen (Table 229)
- **K** From London Kings Cross (Table 26) to Aberdeen (Table 229)
- **L** From Plymouth (Table 51) to Dundee (Table 229)
- **N** To Aberdeen (Table 229)
- **Q** To Inverurie (Table 229)
- **U** To Newcraighall via Kirkcaldy

Table 242

Saturdays

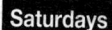

Newcraighall and Edinburgh → Dunfermline, Kirkcaldy and Glenrothes with Thornton

Network Diagram - see first page of Table 225

		SR	SR 1 A	SR B	SR C	SR 1 D	SR	SR	GR R 1 E	SR 1 A	SR B	SR C	SR 1 D	SR	SR	SR B	SR C	SR 1 D	SR	SR
Newcraighall	d	09 06			09 33			10 05				10 37			11 07		11 35			12 07
Brunstane	d	09 09			09 36			10 08				10 40			11 10		11 38			12 10
Edinburgh 10	a	09 16			09 48			10 16				10 47			11 18		11 45			12 17
	d	09 17	09 35	09 41	09 50	10 00	10 06	10 19	10 27	10 34	10 38	10 48	11 00	11 05	11 19	11 39	11 48	12 00	12 06	12 18
Haymarket	d	09 22	09 39	09 43	09 54	10 03	10 10	10 23	10 32	10 38	10 43	10 53	11 04	11 09	11 23	11 43	11 52	12 03	12 10	12 23
South Gyle	d	09 27		09 48	09 59		10 15	10 28			10 47	10 57		11 15	11 28	11 48	11 57		12 15	12 27
Dalmeny	d	09 34		09 54	10 05		10 21	10 34			10 54	11 04		11 21	11 34	11 54	12 03		12 21	12 34
North Queensferry	d	09 37		09 58	10 09		10 25	10 38			10 57	11 07		11 25	11 38	11 58	12 07		12 25	12 37
Inverkeithing	d	09 41	09 53	10 02	10 13	10 18	10 29	10 42	10 47	10 53	11 01	11 11	11 17	11 29	11 42	12 02	12 11	12 17	12 29	12 41
Rosyth	d	09 45			10 16			10 45				11 15			11 45		12 14			12 45
Dunfermline Town	d	09 50			10 21			10 50				11 20			11 50		12 19			12 50
Dunfermline Queen Margaret	d	09 53			10 25			10 54				11 23			11 54		12 23			12 53
Cowdenbeath	d	10a02			10 31			11a03				11 30			12a03		12 29			13a03
Lochgelly	d				10 37							11 35					12 35			
Cardenden	d				10 41							11 39					12 39			
Dalgety Bay	d			10 05			10 32				11 04			11 32		12 05			12 32	
Aberdour	d			10 10			10 37				11 09			11 37		12 10			12 37	
Burntisland	d			10 14			10 41				11 13			11 41		12 14			12 41	
Kinghorn	d			10 19			10 46				11 18			11 46		12 19			12 46	
Kirkcaldy	d		10a08	10 24		10a33	10 51		11a04	11a10	11 23		11a33	11 51		12 24		12a34	12 51	
Glenrothes With Thornton	a			10 32	10 47		11 03				11 32	11 46		12 02		12 32	12 46		13 02	

		SR 1 A	SR B	SR C	SR 1 D	SR	SR	SR B	SR C	SR 1 D	SR	SR	SR 1 A	SR B	SR C	GR R 1 G H	SR 1 D	SR	SR	SR 1 A	SR B
Newcraighall	d			12 37			13 07		13 37			14 06			14 37				15 06		
Brunstane	d			12 40			13 10		13 40			14 09			14 40				15 09		
Edinburgh 10	a			12 47			13 17		13 47			14 17			14 47				15 17		
	d	12 35	12 39	12 49	13 00	13 06	13 18	13 39	13 49	14 00	14 05	14 18	14 35	14 39	14 49	15 00	15 03	15 08	15 19	15 35	15 39
Haymarket	d	12 39	12 43	12 53	13 03	13 10	13 23	13 43	13 53	14 04	14 09	14 23	14 38	14 43	14 53	15 04	15 08	15 13	15 23	15 39	15 43
South Gyle	d		12 48	12 58		13 15	13 27	13 48	13 58		14 14	14 28		14 48	14 58			15 18	15 28		15 48
Dalmeny	d		12 54	13 04		13 21	13 34	13 54	14 04		14 20	14 34		14 54	15 05			15 24	15 34		15 54
North Queensferry	d		12 58	13 08		13 25	13 37	13 58	14 08		14 24	14 38		14 58	15 08			15 28	15 38		15 58
Inverkeithing	d	12 53	13 02	13 12	13 17	13 29	13 41	14 02	14 12	14 17	14 28	14 42	14 53	15 02	15 12	15 19	15 25	15 32	15 42	15 53	16 02
Rosyth	d			13 15			13 45		14 15			14 45			15 16				15 45		
Dunfermline Town	d			13 20			13 50		14 20			14 50			15 21				15 51		
Dunfermline Queen Margaret	d			13 24			13 53		14 24			14 54			15 24				15 53		
Cowdenbeath	d			13 30			14a02		14 30			15a04			15 31				16a04		
Lochgelly	d			13 36					14 36						15 36						
Cardenden	d			13 40					14 40						15 40						
Dalgety Bay	d		13 05			13 32		14 05			14 31			15 05				15 35			16 05
Aberdour	d		13 10			13 37		14 10			14 36			15 10				15 40			16 10
Burntisland	d		13 14			13 41		14 14			14 40			15 14				15 44			16 14
Kinghorn	d		13 19			13 46		14 19			14 45			15 19				15 49			16 19
Kirkcaldy	d	13a08	13 24		13a33	13 51		14 24		14a33	14 50		15a08	15 24		15a35	15a41	15 54		16a08	16 24
Glenrothes With Thornton	a		13 32	13 46		14 02		14 32	14 46		15 03			15 32	15 47			16 05			16 32

		SR C	SR 1 D	SR B	SR	SR 1 A	SR B	SR	SR J	SR C	SR	SR	SR 1 ◊ K	SR B	XC 1 ◊ L	SR B	SR C	GR R 1 G	SR 1 A	SR
Newcraighall	d	15 35			16 03			16 30			16 59			17 31			18 07			18 35
Brunstane	d	15 38			16 06			16 33			17 02			17 34			18 10			18 38
Edinburgh 10	a	15 46			16 13			16 41			17 09			17 43			18 18			18 45
	d	15 49	16 00	16 08	16 16	16 32	16 39	16 47	17 03	17 08	17 12	17 22	17 41	17 45	18 08	18 12	18 26	18 32	18 40	18 49
Haymarket	d	15 53	16 04	16 12	16 20	16 37	16 43	16 51	17 07	17 13	17 17	17 26	17u45	17 49	18 13	18 16	18 30	18 37	18 44	18 53
South Gyle	d	15 58		16 17	16 25		16 49	16 56		17 18	17 22	17 31		17 55		18 21	18 35			18 58
Dalmeny	d	16 04		16 23	16 32		16 56	17 03			17 28	17 38		18 01		18 27	18 41			19 04
North Queensferry	d	16 08		16 27	16 36		17 00	17 07			17 32	17 42		18 05		18 31	18 45			19 08
Inverkeithing	d	16 12	16 17	16 31	16 40	16 51	17 05	17 11	17 22	17 28	17 36	17 47		18 09	18 26	18 35	18 49	18 54	19 00	19 12
Rosyth	d	16 15			16 44			17 15		17 33		17 50					18 52			19 15
Dunfermline Town	d	16 20			16 49			17 20		17 38		17 55					18 57			19 20
Dunfermline Queen Margaret	d	16 24			16 52			17 23		17 42		17 59					19 01			19 24
Cowdenbeath	d	16 30			17a02			17a32		17 49		18 05					19 07			19 30
Lochgelly	d	16 36								17 55		18 11					19 13			19 36
Cardenden	d	16 40								17 59		18 15					19 17			19 40
Dalgety Bay	d			16 34			17 08				17 40			18 12		18 38				
Aberdour	d			16 39			17 13				17 45			18 17		18 43				
Burntisland	d			16 43			17 17				17 49			18 21		18 47				
Kinghorn	d			16 48			17 22				17 54			18 26		18 52				
Kirkcaldy	d		16a33	16 53		17a07	17 27		17a37		18a04		18a15	18 31	18a40	18 57		19a11	19a18	
Glenrothes With Thornton	a	16 46		17 01			17 35			18 05		18 24		18 39		19 04	19 23			19 49

For general notes see front of timetable
For details of catering facilities see Directory of Train Operators

- **A** To Perth (Table 229)
- **B** To Newcraighall via Cowdenbeath
- **C** To Edinburgh via Kirkcaldy
- **D** To Dundee (Table 229)
- **E** From Leeds (Table 26) to Aberdeen (Table 229)
- **G** From London Kings Cross (Table 26) to Aberdeen (Table 229)
- **H** **The Northern Lights**
- **J** To Carnoustie (Table 229)
- **K** To Inverness (Table 229)
- **L** From Plymouth (Table 51) to Aberdeen (Table 229)

Saturdays

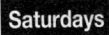

Newcraighall and Edinburgh → Dunfermline, Kirkcaldy and Glenrothes with Thornton

Network Diagram - see first page of Table 225

		SR [1] A	SR	SR	SR [1] ◇ B	SR	SR A	SR	XC [1] ◇ C	XC [1] ◇ D	SR [1] E	SR	SR A	SR [1] ◇ G	SR E	SR A	SR E	SR	SR A	SR	SR
Newcraighall	d			19 06		19 38		20 08				20 37			21 37			22 37			23 37
Brunstane	d			19 09		19 41		20 11				20 40			21 40			22 40			23 40
Edinburgh [10]	a			19 16		19 48		20 19				20 47			21 47			22 47			23 47
	d	19 00	19 09	19 21	19 35	19 49	20 00	20 19	20 22	20 22	20 39	20 51	21 00	21 32	21 49	22 09	22 39	22 50	23 09	23 19	23 49
Haymarket	d	19 03	19 13	19 26	19 39	19 54	20 04	20a24	20 26	20 26	20 43	20 55	21 04	21 36	21 53	22 13	22 43	22a54	23 13	23 23	23a53
South Gyle	d		19 18	19 30		19 58	20 09					21 00	21 09		21 58	22 18	22 48		23 18	23 28	
Dalmeny	d		19 24	19 37		20 05	20 15					21 06	21 15		22 04	22 24	22 54		23 24	23 34	
North Queensferry	d		19 28	19 40		20 08	20 19					21 10	21 19		22 08	22 28	22 58		23 28	23 38	
Inverkeithing	d	19 17	19 32	19 44	19 54	20 12	20 23		20 44	20 45	21 00	21 14	21 23		22 12	22 32	23 02		23 32	23 42	
Rosyth	d			19 48		20 16						21 17			22 15					23 45	
Dunfermline Town	d			19 53		20 21						21 22			22 20					23 50	
Dunfermline Queen Margaret	d			19 56		20 24						21 26			22 24					23 54	
Cowdenbeath	d			20 03		20 31						21 32			22 30					23 59	
Lochgelly	d			20 08		20 36						21 38			22 36					00 06	
Cardenden	d			20 12		20 40						21 42			22 40					00 10	
Dalgety Bay	d		19 35				20 26						21 26			22 35	23 05		23 35		
Aberdour	d		19 40				20 31						21 31			22 40	23 10		23 40		
Burntisland	d		19 44				20 35						21 35			22 44	23 14		23 44		
Kinghorn	d		19 49				20 40						21 40			22 49	23 19		23 49		
Kirkcaldy	d	19a33	19a56		20a10		20a44		21a00	20a59	21a15		21a44	22a04		22a53	23a23		23a53		
Glenrothes With Thornton	a			20 22		20 50						21 52			22 46					00 19	

Sundays

		XC [1] G	GR [R] [1] G	SR A	SR [1] ◇ B	SR [1] H	SR J	SR [1] ◇ G	SR A	SR H	SR J	SR [1] ◇ G	SR A	SR [1] ◇ B	SR H	SR J	SR A	SR H
Newcraighall	d																	
Brunstane	d																	
Edinburgh [10]	a																	
	d	08 04	09 10	09 15	09 25	09 55	10 15	10 55	11 15	11 55	12 15	12 40	13 15	13 50	14 00	14 15	15 15	15 55
Haymarket	d	08 08	09 14	09 19	09 29	09 59	10 19	10 59	11 19	11 59	12 19	12 44	13 19	13 54	14 04	14 19	15 19	15 59
South Gyle	d			09 24		10 04	10 24		11 24	12 04	12 24		13 24		14 08	14 24	15 24	16 04
Dalmeny	d			09 30		10 10	10 30		11 30	12 10	12 30		13 32		14 11	14 30	15 30	16 10
North Queensferry	d			09 34		10 14	10 34		11 34	12 14	12 34		13 36		14 15	14 34	15 34	16 14
Inverkeithing	d	08 22	09 32	09 38	09 48	10 18	10 38	11 15	11 38	12 18	12 38	13 00	13 40	14 11	14 22	14 41	15 38	16 18
Rosyth	d					10 23				12 23					14 27			16 21
Dunfermline Town	d					10 28				12 28					14 32			16 26
Dunfermline Queen Margaret	d					10 33				12 33					14 36			16 30
Cowdenbeath	d					10 38				12 38					14 42			16 36
Lochgelly	d					10 45				12 45					14 48			16 42
Cardenden	d					10 49				12 49					14 52			16 46
Dalgety Bay	d			09 44			10 44		11 44		12 44		13 46			14 44	15 44	
Aberdour	d			09 49			10 49		11 49		12 49		13 51			14 49	15 49	
Burntisland	d			09 53			10 53		11 53		12 53		13 55			14 53	15 53	
Kinghorn	d			09 58			10 58		11 58		12 58		14 00			14 58	15 58	
Kirkcaldy	d	08a36	09a48	10a03	10a10		11 03	11a31	12a02		13 03	13a16	14a04	14a27		15 03	16a02	
Glenrothes With Thornton	a					10 55	11 11			12 57	13 11				15 00	15 14		16 52

		GR [R] [1] K L	SR J	SR [1] ◇ G	SR A	SR [1] E	SR H	XC [1] ◇ Q	SR J	GR [R] [1] K	SR A	SR H	SR J	SR [1] ◇ G	SR	SR H	SR A	SR
Newcraighall	d																	
Brunstane	d																	
Edinburgh [10]	a																	
	d	16 00	16 15	17 05	17 15	17 50	17 55	18 10	18 15	18 42	19 15	19 55	20 15	21 00	21 15	21 55	22 25	23 36
Haymarket	d	16 04	16 19	17 09	17 19	17 54	17 59	18 15	18 19	18 47	19 19	19 59	20 19	21 05	21 19	21 59	22 29	23 40
South Gyle	d		16 24		17 24		18 04		18 24		19 24	20 04	20 24		21 24	22 04	22 34	23 45
Dalmeny	d		16 30		17 30		18 10		18 30		19 30	20 10	20 30		21 30	22 10	22 40	23 51
North Queensferry	d		16 34		17 34		18 14		18 34		19 34	20 14	20 34		21 34	22 14	22 44	23 55
Inverkeithing	d	16 24	16 38	17 22	17 38	18 07	18 18	18 29	18 38	19 02	19 38	20 18	20 38	21 18	21 38	22 18	22 48	23a58
Rosyth	d						18 21					20 21				22 21		
Dunfermline Town	d						18 26					20 26				22 26		
Dunfermline Queen Margaret	d						18 30					20 30				22 30		
Cowdenbeath	d						18 36					20 36				22 36		
Lochgelly	d						18 42					20 42				22 42		
Cardenden	d						18 46					20 46				22 46		
Dalgety Bay	d		16 41		17 41				18 41		19 41		20 41		21 41		22 51	
Aberdour	d		16 46		17 46				18 46		19 46		20 46		21 46		22 56	
Burntisland	d		16 50		17 50				18 50		19 50		20 50		21 50		23 00	
Kinghorn	d		16 55		17 55				18 55		19 55		20 55		21 55		23 05	
Kirkcaldy	d	16a41	17 00	17a38	17a59	18a23		18a43	19 00	19a18	19a59		21 00	21a34	22a02		23a09	
Glenrothes With Thornton	a		17 08				18 52		19 07			20 52	21 09			22 54		

For general notes see front of timetable
For details of catering facilities see Directory of Train Operators

A To Dundee (Table 229)
B To Inverness (Table 229)
C Until 5 September. From Newquay (Table 135) to Dundee (Table 229)
D From 12 September. From Plymouth (Table 51) to Dundee (Table 229)
E To Perth (Table 229)
G To Aberdeen (Table 229)
H To Edinburgh via Kirkcaldy
J To Edinburgh via Cowdenbeath
K From London Kings Cross (Table 26) to Aberdeen (Table 229)
L **The Northern Lights**
N To Perth
Q From Birmingham New Street (until 1 November from Plymouth) (Table 51) to Aberdeen (Table 229)

Table 242

Mondays to Fridays

Glenrothes with Thornton, Kirkcaldy and Dunfermline → Edinburgh and Newcraighall

Network Diagram - see first page of Table 225

Miles	Miles			SR	SR	SR A	SR B	SR	SR B		SR C	SR	SR A	SR D	XC [1]◇ E trolley	SR G		SR	SR [1] A	SR H trolley	SR	SR	SR J		SR C
0	0	Glenrothes With Thornton	d				06 02		06 30				06 52			07 15					07 28		07 35		
7¼	—	**Kirkcaldy**	d			05 53		06 27			06 49			07 14	07 21	07 27			07 38	07 48		07 54			08 06
10	—	Kinghorn	d			05 58		06 32			06 55			07 19		07 32						07 59			08 11
12¾	—	Burntisland	d			06 02		06 36			07 00			07 23		07 36						08 03			08 16
17½	—	Aberdour	d			06 07		06 41			07 05			07 28		07 41						08 08			08 20
20¼	—	Dalgety Bay	d			06 12		06 46			07 10			07 33		07 46						08 13			08 25
—	4¾	Cardenden	d				06 09		06 37				07 00								07 36		07 43		
—	7	Lochgelly	d				06 13		06 41				07 04								07 41		07 48		
—	9½	Cowdenbeath	d				06 19		06 47				07 10								07 50		07 58		
—	13½	Dunfermline Queen Margaret	d				06 24		06 52			07 08	07 16								07 57		08 04		
—	14¾	**Dunfermline Town**	d				06 28		06 56			07 11	07 19								08 01		08 08		
—	17	Rosyth	d				06 31		06 59			07 15	07 23								08 02		08 13		
21¾	18½	Inverkeithing	d			06 16	06 39	06 49	07 07		07 14	07 19	07 29	07 37	07 42	07 48			07 54		08 08	08 16	08 17		08 28
23¾	20½	North Queensferry	d			06 20	06 43	06 53	07 11			07 24	07 34			07 53							08 24		
25½	22¼	Dalmeny	d			06 23	06 46	06 57	07 14		07 21		07 38	07a42		07 57					08 16	08 23	06 50		
30½	27¼	South Gyle	d			06 29	06 53	07 03	07 21		07 28	07 32	07 44			08 03					08 22	08 29	08 32		08 40
33¾	30½	Haymarket	d	06 14	06 32	06 40	06 59	07 09	07 29		07 35	07 40	07 51		08 01	08 12			08 16	08 20	08 28	08 35	08 40		08 48
35	31¾	**Edinburgh** [10]	a	06 19	06 38	06 46	07 06	07 16	07 34		07 42	07 46	07 57		08 05	08 18			08 22	08 26	08 37	08 43	08 52		08 55
—	—		d	06 20	06 39		07 11		07 40									08 18				08 48			
39	—	Brunstane	d	06 28	06 46		07 18		07 47									08 25				08 54			
39¾	—	**Newcraighall**	a	06 31	06 51		07 23		07 53									08 29				08 59			

		XC [1]◇ E trolley	SR J	SR G	SR [1] K	SR J	SR		SR [1]◇ L trolley	SR G	GR [R] [1] N Ø trolley	SR J	SR G	XC [1]◇ Q trolley		SR C	SR	SR	SR [1] A	SR J	SR G		SR C	SR	SR
Glenrothes With Thornton	d		08 04	08 16		08 32				09 17		09 31	09 48					10 23		10 32	10 52				11 18
Kirkcaldy	d	08 20		08 28	08 41		09 12		09 24	09 30	09 44		10 00	10 17		10 27		10 32	10 42		11 03		11 18		11 27
Kinghorn	d			08 32			09 16			09 34			10 05					10 37			11 08				11 32
Burntisland	d			08 37			09 21			09 39			10 09					10 41			11 12				11 36
Aberdour	d			08 41			09 25			09 43			10 14					10 46			11 17				11 41
Dalgety Bay	d			08 46			09 30			09 48			10 18					10 51			11 21				11 46
Cardenden	d		08 11			08 39						09 39								10 40					
Lochgelly	d		08 15			08 43						09 43								10 44					
Cowdenbeath	d		08 24			08 52						09 52					10 21			10 53				11 23	
Dunfermline Queen Margaret	d		08 30			08 58						09 57					10 26			10 58				11 28	
Dunfermline Town	d		08 33			09 01						10 01					10 30			11 02				11 32	
Rosyth	d		08 37			09 05						10 04					10 33			11 05				11 35	
Inverkeithing	d	08 35	08 41	08 49	08 57	09 09	09 33			09 51	10 01	10 08	10 22	10 32		10 43	10 37	10 54	10 59	11 10	11 24		11 34	11 38	11 49
North Queensferry	d		08 45	08 53		09 13				09 55		10 12					10 41	10 58		11 14	11 29			11 42	
Dalmeny	d		08 49	08 57		09 17				09 59		10 16					10 45	11 02		11 18	11 32			11 46	
South Gyle	d		08 55	09 03		09 23				10 05		10 22	10 31				10 51	11 08		11 24	11 38			11 53	12 00
Haymarket	d	08 54	09 02	09 10	09 16	09 29	09 48		09 53	10 12	10 19	10 29	10 44	10 54		11 01	10 58	11 14	11 17	11 34	11 50		11 53	12 02	12 06
Edinburgh [10]	a	08 58	09 09	09 16	09 24	09 36	09 56		10 01	10 18	10 25	10 35	10 55	11 01		11 09	11 06	11 21	11 26	11 39	11 58		12 01	12 08	12 13
	d		09 10			09 37				10 21		10 41					11 11			11 45				12 11	
Brunstane	d		09 18			09 44				10 28		10 48					11 18			11 53				12 25	
Newcraighall	a		09 23			09 51				10 33		10 52					11 23			11 57				12 28	

		SR [1] A	GR [R] [1] N U Ø trolley	SR J	SR G	SR C		SR	SR	SR [1] A	SR J	SR G	SR [1] C		SR	SR	SR [1]◇ L trolley	SR J	SR G	SR [1] C		SR	SR	SR [1] A	SR J
Glenrothes With Thornton	d			11 32	11 48				12 18		12 32	12 48				13 18		13 32	13 48				14 18		14 32
Kirkcaldy	d	11 39	11 44		12 00	12 17			12 27	12 39		13 00	13 18			13 27	13 41		14 00	14 18			14 27	14 39	
Kinghorn	d				12 04				12 32			13 04				13 32			14 04				14 32		
Burntisland	d				12 09				12 36			13 09				13 36			14 09				14 36		
Aberdour	d				12 13				12 41			13 13				13 41			14 13				14 41		
Dalgety Bay	d				12 18				12 46			13 18				13 46			14 18				14 46		
Cardenden	d			11 40							12 40							13 40							14 40
Lochgelly	d			11 44							12 44							13 44							14 44
Cowdenbeath	d			11 53				12 22			12 53				13 23			13 53				14 22			14 53
Dunfermline Queen Margaret	d			11 58				12 27			12 58				13 28			13 58				14 27			14 58
Dunfermline Town	d			12 02				12 31			13 02				13 32			14 02				14 31			15 02
Rosyth	d			12 05				12 34			13 05				13 35			14 05				14 34			15 05
Inverkeithing	d	11 55	12 01	12 10	12 21	12 33		12 38	12 49	12 55	13 10	13 21	13 34		13 39	13 49		14 10	14 21	14 34		14 39	14 49	14 55	15 12
North Queensferry	d			12 13	12 25			12 42	12 53		13 14	13 25			13 43	13 53		14 14	14 25			14 43	14 53		15 16
Dalmeny	d			12 18	12 29			12 46	12 57		13 18	13 29			13 47	13 57		14 18	14 29			14 47	14 57		15 20
South Gyle	d			12 23	12 35			12 52	13 03		13 24	13 35			13 53	14 03		14 24	14 35			14 53	15 03		15 26
Haymarket	d	12 10	12 19	12 30	12 42	12 48		12 59	13 09	13 10	13 34	13 43	13 51		14 00	14 09	14 13	14 32	14 43	14 48		14 59	15 09	15 10	15 34
Edinburgh [10]	a	12 17	12 25	12 36	12 48	12 55		13 06	13 16	13 19	13 38	13 48	13 57		14 06	14 16	14 19	14 38	14 50	14 55		15 09	15 16	15 19	15 41
	d			12 41				13 11			13 41				14 11			14 41				15 10			15 45
Brunstane	d			12 48				13 18			13 48				14 18			14 54				15 18			15 53
Newcraighall	a			12 52				13 22			13 52				14 22			14 58				15 23			15 58

For general notes see front of timetable
For details of catering facilities see Directory of Train Operators

- **A** From Perth (Table 229)
- **B** From Markinch (Table 229)
- **C** From Dundee (Table 229)
- **D** From Ladybank to Glasgow Queen Street (Table 230)
- **E** From Dundee to Plymouth (Table 51)
- **G** From Newcraighall via Cowdenbeath
- **H** From Aberdeen (Table 229)
- **J** From Edinburgh via Kirkcaldy
- **K** From Blair Atholl (Table 229)
- **L** From Inverness (Table 229)
- **N** From Aberdeen (Table 229) to London Kings Cross (Table 26)
- **Q** From Aberdeen (Table 229) to Penzance (Table 135)
- **U** **The Northern Lights**

Table 242

Mondays to Fridays

Glenrothes with Thornton, Kirkcaldy and Dunfermline → Edinburgh and Newcraighall

Network Diagram - see first page of Table 225

		SR A	SR B	SR	SR		SR [1]◇ C ⊼	SR D	SR A	SR B	SR	SR		SR [1] E	GR [R] [1] G Ø ⊼	SR D	SR A	SR D	SR B		SR [1] E	SR D	SR B	SR [1] E ⊼	SR H
Glenrothes With Thornton	d	14 48			15 18			15 34	15 48		16 18					16 32	16 48	17 01				17 36			18 11
Kirkcaldy	d	15 00	15 18		15 27		15 47		16 00	16 19	16 27			16 39	16 45		17 00		17 33		17 48		18 13	18 44	18 22
Kinghorn	d	15 05			15 32				16 04		16 32						17 04		17 37						18 28
Burntisland	d	15 09			15 36				16 09		16 36						17 09		17 42						18 34
Aberdour	d	15 14			15 41				16 13		16 41						17 13		17 46						18 40
Dalgety Bay	d	15 18			15 46				16 18		16 46						17 18		17 51						18 46
Cardenden	d							15 42								16 40		17 09				17 43			
Lochgelly	d							15 46								16 47		17 13				17 47			
Cowdenbeath	d			15 22				15 55				16 24				16 53		17 22				17 56			
Dunfermline Queen Margaret	d			15 27				16 00				16 29				16 58		17 27				18 02			
Dunfermline Town	d			15 31				16 04				16 33				17 02		17 31				18 05			
Rosyth	d			15 34				16 07				16 36				17 05		17 34				18 09			
Inverkeithing	d	15 22	15 34	15 39	15 49			16 10	16 21	16 35	16 49	16 40		16 55	17 01	17 09	17 22	17 38	17 55		18 04	18 13	18 29	19 00	18 50
North Queensferry	d	15 26		15 43	15 53			16 14	16 25			16 44				17 13	17 27	17 42	17 59			18 17			
Dalmeny	d	15 30		15 47	15 57			16 18	16 29			16 48				17 17	17 31	17 46	18 03			18 21			18 54
South Gyle	d	15 36		15 53	16 03			16 24	16 35		17 00	16 54				17 23	17 37	17 52	18 09			18 27			19 12
Haymarket	d	15 42	15 48	15 59	16 09		16 15	16 32	16 43	16 50	17 08	17 01		17 10	17 20	17 31	17 44	18 01	18 15		18 19	18 34	18 43	19 14	19 22
Edinburgh 10	a	15 49	15 55	16 08	16 16		16 23	16 38	16 48	16 56	17 14	17 08		17 18	17 27	17 37	17 52	18 06	18 22		18 25	18 40	18 50	19 21	19 31
	d			16 13				16 43				17 15				17 40		18 19				18 46		19 22	
Brunstane	d			16 20				16 51				17 22				17 47		18 27				18 53		19 28	
Newcraighall	a			16 25				16 55				17 27				17 51		18 30				18 58		19 33	

		SR D	SR A	SR D		SR B	SR A	SR [R] [1] C ⊼	GR [R] [1] J ⊡	SR	SR		SR [1] E	SR	SR B	SR [1]◇ C ⊼	SR K ⊼	SR		SR [1]◇ J	XC [1]◇ J	SR [1] E			
Glenrothes With Thornton	d	18 44	18 52	19 04			19 23			20 02				21 02				22 02				23 15			
Kirkcaldy	d		19 04			19 28	19 36	19 54	20 08		20 27		20 39		21 26	21 42	21 59			23 01	23 26				
Kinghorn	d		19 08				19 40				20 32				21 31		22 04			23 06					
Burntisland	d		19 13				19 45				20 36				21 36		22 09			23 11					
Aberdour	d		19 17				19 49				20 41				21 40		22 13			23 15					
Dalgety Bay	d		19 22				19 54				20 46				21 45		22 18			23 20					
Cardenden	d	18 52		19 11						20 09				21 09				22 09				23 23			
Lochgelly	d	18 56		19 15						20 13				21 13				22 13				23 27			
Cowdenbeath	d	19 05		19 24						20 22				21 22				22 19				23 33			
Dunfermline Queen Margaret	d	19 10		19 30						20 27				21 27				22 24				23 38			
Dunfermline Town	d	19 14		19 33						20 31				21 31				22 28				23 42			
Rosyth	d	19 17		19 37						20 34				21 34				22 31				23 45			
Inverkeithing	d	19 21	19 25	19 41		19 46	19 57		20 24	20 39	20 49		20 55	21 39	21 49		22 22	22 39		23 24	23 42	23 52			
North Queensferry	d	19 25	19 29	19 45			20 01			20 43	20 53			21 43	21 53		22 26	22 43		23 28		23 56			
Dalmeny	d	19 29	19 33	19 49			20 05			20 47	20 57			21 47	21 57		22 30	22 47		23 32		23 59			
South Gyle	d	19 35	19 39	19 55			20 11			20 53	21 03			21 53	22 03		22 36	22 53		23 38		00 06			
Haymarket	d	19 42	19 46	20 03		20 06	20 19	20 24	20s42	21 00	21 09		21 10	22 00	22 09	22 13	22 44	23 00		23 45	23 58	00 13			
Edinburgh 10	a	19 48	19 55	20 08		20 13	20 26	20 29	20 48	21 06	21 16		21 19	22 06	22 16	22 19	22 50	23 06		23 52	00 10	00 19			
	d	19 49		20 11						21 12				22 11				23 11							
Brunstane	d	19 56		20 19						21 20				22 18				23 18							
Newcraighall	a	20 00		20 23						21 23				22 22				23 22							

Saturdays

		SR	SR	SR E	SR L	SR B	SR A	SR	SR [1] E	SR J ⊼	SR D	SR B	XC [1]◇ N ⊼	SR D	SR A	SR [1] Q	SR D	SR	SR [1]◇ C ⊼		SR A	GR [R] [1] G ⊡ ⊼	SR D	SR A	XC [1]◇ U ⊼
Glenrothes With Thornton	d				06 30		07 15				07 32			08 04	08 16		08 32				09 17		09 31	09 48	
Kirkcaldy	d			06 16		06 49	07 27		07 38	07 49		08 06	08 20		08 28	08 41		09 12	09 24		09 30	09 44		10 00	10 17
Kinghorn	d			06 21		06 55	07 32					08 11			08 32			09 16			09 34			10 05	
Burntisland	d			06 24		07 00	07 36					08 16			08 37			09 21			09 39			10 09	
Aberdour	d			06 29		07 05	07 41					08 20			08 41			09 25			09 43			10 14	
Dalgety Bay	d			06 35		07 10	07 46					08 25			08 46			09 30			09 48			10 18	
Cardenden	d				06 37						07 37			08 11			08 39						09 39		
Lochgelly	d				06 41						07 42			08 15			08 43						09 43		
Cowdenbeath	d				06 47						07 48			08 24			08 52						09 52		
Dunfermline Queen Margaret	d				06 52						07 55			08 30			08 58						09 57		
Dunfermline Town	d				06 56						07 59			08 33			09 01						10 01		
Rosyth	d				06 59						08 02			08 37			09 05						10 04		
Inverkeithing	d			06 39	07 07	07 14	07 48		07 54		08 08	08 28	08 35	08 41	08 49	08 57	09 09	09 33			09 51	10 01	10 08	10 22	10 32
North Queensferry	d			06 43	07 11		07 53				08 12			08 45	08 53		09 13				09 55		10 12		
Dalmeny	d			06 46	07 14	07 21	07 57				08 16			08 49	08 57		09 17				09 59		10 16		
South Gyle	d			06 53	07 21	07 28	08 03				08 22	08 39		08 55	09 03		09 23				10 05		10 22	10 31	
Haymarket	d	06 14	06 32	06 59	07 29	07 35	08 12		08 15	08 19	06 43	08 47	08 54	09 02	09 10	09 13	09 29	09 48	09 53		10 12	10 21	10 29	10 44	10 52
Edinburgh 10	a	06 19		07 06	07 37	07 42	08 18		08 22	08 25	08 35	08 54	08 58	09 09	09 16	09 25	09 36	09 56	09 59		10 18	10 27	10 35	10 55	10 58
	d	06 20		07 20	07 40			08 18			08 46			09 10			09 37				10 21		10 41		
Brunstane	d	06 28	06 46	07 27	07 47			08 25			08 53			09 18			09 44				10 28		10 48		
Newcraighall	a	06 31	06 51	07 31	07 53			08 29			08 58			09 23			09 51				10 33		10 52		

For general notes see front of timetable
For details of catering facilities see Directory of Train Operators

- **A** From Newcraighall via Cowdenbeath
- **B** From Dundee (Table 229)
- **C** From Inverness (Table 229)
- **D** From Edinburgh via Kirkcaldy
- **E** From Perth (Table 229)
- **G** From Aberdeen (Table 229) to London Kings Cross (Table 26)
- **H** From Edinburgh via Cowdenbeath
- **J** From Aberdeen (Table 229)
- **K** From Inverurie (Table 229)
- **L** From Markinch (Table 229)
- **N** From Dundee to Plymouth (Table 51)
- **Q** From Blair Atholl (Table 229)
- **U** From Aberdeen (Table 229) to Penzance (Table 135)

Glenrothes with Thornton, Kirkcaldy and Dunfermline → Edinburgh and Newcraighall

Network Diagram - see first page of Table 225

		SR A	SR	SR	SR [1] B	SR C	SR D	SR A	SR	SR	SR [1] B	GR [R] [1] E G 🍴 🛒	SR C	SR D	SR A	SR		SR	SR [1] B	SR C	SR D	SR [1] A	SR	SR	SR [1] ◇ H 🛒
Glenrothes With Thornton	d			10 23		10 32	10 52			11 18			11 32	11 48				12 18		12 32	12 48			13 18	
Kirkcaldy	d	10 27		10 32	10 42		11 03	11 18		11 27	11 39	11 44		12 00	12 17			12 27	12 39		13 00	13 18		13 27	13 41
Kinghorn	d			10 37			11 08			11 32				12 04				12 32			13 04			13 32	
Burntisland	d			10 41			11 12			11 36				12 09				12 36			13 09			13 36	
Aberdour	d			10 46			11 17			11 41				12 13				12 41			13 13			13 41	
Dalgety Bay	d			10 51			11 21			11 46				12 18				12 46			13 18			13 46	
Cardenden	d					10 40							11 40							12 40					
Lochgelly	d					10 44							11 44							12 44					
Cowdenbeath	d		10 21			10 53			11 23				11 53			12 22				12 53			13 23		
Dunfermline Queen Margaret	d		10 26			10 58			11 28				11 58			12 27				12 58			13 28		
Dunfermline Town	d		10 30			11 02			11 32				12 02			12 31				13 02			13 32		
Rosyth	d		10 33			11 05			11 35				12 05			12 34				13 05			13 35		
Inverkeithing	d	10 43	10 37	10 54	10 59	11 10	11 25	11 34	11 38	11 49	11 55	12 01	12 10	12 21	12 33	12 38		12 49	12 55	13 10	13 21	13 34	13 39	13 49	
North Queensferry	d		10 41	10 58		11 14	11 29		11 42				12 13	12 25		12 42		12 53		13 14	13 25		13 43	13 53	
Dalmeny	d		10 45	11 02		11 18	11 32		11 46				12 18	12 29		12 46		12 57		13 18	13 29		13 47	13 57	
South Gyle	d		10 51	11 08		11 24	11 38		11 53	12 00			12 23	12 35		12 52		13 03		13 24	13 35		13 53	14 03	
Haymarket	d	11 02	10 58	11 14	11 17	11 34	11 50	11 53	12 02	12 06	12 10	12 19	12 30	12 42	12 48	12 59		13 09	13 10	13 34	13 43	13 51	14 00	14 09	14 18
Edinburgh [10]	a	11 09	11 06	11 21	11 26	11 39	11 58	12 00	12 08	12 13	12 17	12 25	12 36	12 48	12 55	13 06		13 16	13 19	13 38	13 49	13 57	14 06	14 16	14 25
	d		11 11			11 45			12 11				12 41			13 11				13 41			14 11		
Brunstane	d		11 18			11 53			12 18				12 48			13 18				13 48			14 18		
Newcraighall	a		11 23			11 57			12 22				12 52			13 22				13 52			14 22		

		SR C	SR D	SR [1] A	SR	SR	SR [1] B	SR C	SR D	SR A	SR	SR	SR [1] ◇ H 🛒		SR C	SR D	SR A	SR	SR	SR [1] B	GR [R] [1] E ⊘ 🍴	SR C	SR D	SR C	SR A
Glenrothes With Thornton	d	13 32	13 48			14 18		14 32	14 48			15 18			15 34	15 48		16 18				16 32	16 48	17 01	
Kirkcaldy	d		14 00	14 18		14 27	14 39		15 00	15 18		15 27	15 47			16 00	16 19	16 27		16 39	16 45		17 00		17 33
Kinghorn	d		14 04			14 32			15 05			15 32				16 04		16 32					17 04		17 37
Burntisland	d		14 09			14 36			15 09			15 36				16 09		16 36					17 09		17 42
Aberdour	d		14 13			14 41			15 14			15 41				16 13		16 41					17 13		17 46
Dalgety Bay	d		14 18			14 46			15 18			15 46				16 18		16 46					17 18		17 51
Cardenden	d	13 40						14 40							15 42							16 40		17 09	
Lochgelly	d	13 44						14 44							15 46							16 47		17 13	
Cowdenbeath	d	13 53			14 22			14 53			15 22				15 55				16 24			16 53		17 22	
Dunfermline Queen Margaret	d	13 58			14 27			14 58			15 27				16 00				16 29			16 58		17 27	
Dunfermline Town	d	14 02			14 31			15 02			15 31				16 04				16 33			17 02		17 31	
Rosyth	d	14 05			14 34			15 05			15 34				16 07				16 36			17 05		17 34	
Inverkeithing	d	14 10	14 21	14 34	14 39	14 49	14 55	15 12	15 22	15 34	15 39	15 49			16 10	16 21	16 35	16 49	16 40	16 55	17 01	17 09	17 22	17 38	17 55
North Queensferry	d	14 14	14 25		14 43	14 53		15 16	15 26		15 43	15 53			16 14	16 25			16 44			17 13	17 25	17 42	17 59
Dalmeny	d	14 18	14 29		14 47	14 57		15 20	15 30		15 47	15 57			16 18	16 29			16 48			17 17	17 31	17 46	18 03
South Gyle	d	14 24	14 35		14 53	15 03		15 26	15 36		15 53	16 03			16 24	16 35		17 00	16 54			17 23	17 37	17 52	18 09
Haymarket	d	14 32	14 43	14 48	14 59	15 09	15 10	15 34	15 42	15 48	15 59	16 09	16 15		16 32	16 43	16 50	17 08	17 01	17 10	17 20	17 31	17 44	18 01	18 15
Edinburgh [10]	a	14 38	14 50	14 55	15 10	15 16	15 19	15 41	15 49	15 54	16 08	16 16	16 23		16 38	16 48	16 56	17 14	17 08	17 20	17 25	17 39	17 52	18 06	18 22
	d	14 41			15 10			15 45			16 13				16 43				17 15			17 44		18 12	
Brunstane	d	14 54			15 18			15 53			16 20				16 51				17 22			17 51		18 19	
Newcraighall	a	14 58			15 23			15 58			16 25				16 55				17 27			17 55		18 23	

		SR [1] B	SR C	SR A	SR J	SR [1] B 🛒	SR K	SR C	SR A	SR D	SR [R] [1] H 🛒	SR [1] ◇ L 🛒	SR	SR	SR [1] B	SR	SR A	SR [1] ◇ H 🛒	SR N 🛒	SR	SR [1] ◇ L	XC [1] ◇ L 🛒	SR [1] B		
Glenrothes With Thornton	d		17 36		18 10		18 39	19 04		19 23			20 02			21 02				22 02			23 15		
Kirkcaldy	d	17 48		18 13	18 23	18 44			19 28	19 36	19 54	20 00		20 27	20 39		21 26	21 42	21 59		23 01	23 12			
Kinghorn	d				18 28					19 40				20 32			21 31		22 04		23 06	23 17			
Burntisland	d				18 32					19 45				20 36			21 36		22 09		23 11	23 22			
Aberdour	d				18 37					19 49				20 41			21 40		22 13		23 15	23 26			
Dalgety Bay	d				18 42					19 54				20 46			21 45		22 18		23 20	23 31			
Cardenden	d		17 43				18 47	19 11					20 09			21 09				22 09			23 23		
Lochgelly	d		17 47				18 51	19 15					20 13			21 13				22 13			23 27		
Cowdenbeath	d		17 56				19 00	19 24					20 22			21 22				22 19			23 33		
Dunfermline Queen Margaret	d		18 02				19 05	19 30					20 27			21 27				22 24			23 38		
Dunfermline Town	d		18 05				19 09	19 33					20 31			21 31				22 28			23 42		
Rosyth	d		18 09				19 12	19 37					20 34			21 34				22 31			23 45		
Inverkeithing	d	18 04	18 13	18 29	18 45	19 00	19 16	19 41	19 46	19 57		20 16	20 39	20 49	20 55	21 39	21 49		22 22	22 39	23 24	23 36	23 52		
North Queensferry	d		18 17		18 49		19 20	19 45		20 01			20 43	20 53		21 43	21 53		22 26	22 43	23 28	23 40	23 56		
Dalmeny	d		18 21		18 53		19 24	19 49		20 05			20 47	20 57		21 47	21 57		22 30	22 47	23 32	23 44	23 59		
South Gyle	d		18 27		18 59		19 30	19 55		20 11			20 53	21 03		21 53	22 03		22 36	22 53	23 38	23 51	00 06		
Haymarket	d	18 19	18 34	18 43	19 05	19 14	19 37	20 03	20 06	20 19	20 24	20 30	21 00	21 09	21 10	22 00	22 09	22 13	22 44	23 00	23 45	00 01	00 13		
Edinburgh [10]	a	18 25	18 40	18 50	19 12	19 21	19 43	20 08	20 13	20 26	20 29	20 36	21 06	21 16	21 19	22 06	22 16	22 19	22 50	23 06	23 52	00 11	00 19		
	d		18 46			19 22	19 47	20 11					21 12			22 11				23 11					
Brunstane	d		18 53			19 29	19 55	20 19					21 20			22 18				23 18					
Newcraighall	a		18 58			19 33	19 58	20 23					21 23			22 22				23 22					

For general notes see front of timetable
For details of catering facilities see Directory of Train Operators

- **A** From Dundee (Table 229)
- **B** From Perth (Table 229)
- **C** From Edinburgh via Kirkcaldy
- **D** From Newcraighall via Cowdenbeath
- **E** From Aberdeen (Table 229) to London Kings Cross (Table 26)
- **G** **The Northern Lights**
- **H** From Inverness (Table 229)
- **J** From Edinburgh via Cowdenbeath
- **K** From Newcraighall via Kirkcaldy
- **L** From Aberdeen (Table 229)
- **N** From Inverurie (Table 229)

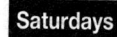

Table 242

Sundays

Glenrothes with Thornton, Kirkcaldy and Dunfermline → Edinburgh and Newcraighall

Network Diagram - see first page of Table 225

		SR	SR	SR	SR	GR	SR	XC	SR	SR	GR	SR	SR	SR	GR	SR	SR	SR
				1		R 1		1 ◇			R 1				R 1	1 ◇		1 ◇
		A	A	B	C	D E	A	G	B	C	D	A	B	C	D Ø	H	A	J
Glenrothes With Thornton	d			10 56	11 11				12 58	13 11			15 04	15 14				
Kirkcaldy	d	08 08	10 08	11 08		11 40	12 08	13 03	13 10		13 39	14 08	15 15		15 42	16 03	16 08	17 02
Kinghorn	d	08 13	10 13	11 13			12 13		13 15			14 13	15 20				16 13	
Burntisland	d	08 17	10 17	11 17			12 17		13 19			14 17	15 24				16 17	
Aberdour	d	08 22	10 22	11 22			12 22		13 24			14 22	15 29				16 22	
Dalgety Bay	d	08 27	10 27	11 27			12 27		13 28			14 27	15 33				16 27	
Cardenden	d				11 18					13 19				15 21				
Lochgelly	d				11 22					13 23				15 25				
Cowdenbeath	d				11 30					13 30				15 33				
Dunfermline Queen Margaret	d				11 36					13 36				15 39				
Dunfermline Town	d				11 39					13 39				15 42				
Rosyth	d				11 43					13 43				15 46				
Inverkeithing	d	08 30	10 30	11 30	11 47	11 56	12 30	13 18	13 31	13 47	13 55	14 30	15 37	15 50	15 58	16 19	16 30	17 18
North Queensferry	d	08 34	10 34	11 34	11 51		12 36		13 37	13 51		14 34	15 41	15 54			16 34	
Dalmeny	d	08 38	10 38	11 38	11 56		12 40		13 44	13 56		14 38	15 45	16 00			16 38	
South Gyle	d	08 44	10 44	11 44	12 02		12 46		13 50	14 02		14 44	15 51	16 06			16 44	
Haymarket	d	08 53	10 58	11 58	12 12	12 18	12 58	13 37	13 59	14 10	14 19	14 58	15 58	16 16	16 20	16 35	16 55	17 34
Edinburgh 10	a	09 00	11 06	12 06	12 19	12 24	13 06	13 42	14 08	14 18	14 24	15 06	16 07	16 21	16 25	16 42	16 59	17 41
	d																	
Brunstane	d																	
Newcraighall	a																	

		SR	SR	SR	SR	SR	SR	SR	SR	SR	SR	SR	SR	SR	SR	XC
					1 ◇				1 ◇		1 ◇		1 ◇			1 ◇
		B	C	A	J	B	C	A	J	B	H	C	J		K	
Glenrothes With Thornton	d	16 53	17 09			18 53	19 09			20 54		21 09			22 54	
Kirkcaldy	d	17 07		18 07	18 56	19 07		20 10	20 59	21 07	21 25		22 05	22 13	23 06	23 22
Kinghorn	d	17 12		18 12		19 12		20 15		21 11				22 17	23 10	
Burntisland	d	17 16		18 16		19 16		20 20		21 16				22 22	23 15	
Aberdour	d	17 21		18 21		19 21		20 24		21 20				22 26	23 19	
Dalgety Bay	d	17 25		18 26		19 25		20 29		21 25				22 31	23a24	
Cardenden	d		17 16				19 16					21 16				
Lochgelly	d		17 20				19 20					21 20				
Cowdenbeath	d		17 28				19 28					21 28				
Dunfermline Queen Margaret	d		17 34				19 34					21 34				
Dunfermline Town	d		17 37				19 38					21 37				
Rosyth	d		17 41				19 41					21 41				
Inverkeithing	d	17 29	17 45	18 29	19 12	19 29	19 45	20 31	21 15	21 28	21 41	21 45	22 21	22 34		23 38
North Queensferry	d	17 33	17 49	18 33		19 33	19 49	20 36		21 32		21 49		22 38		
Dalmeny	d	17 37	17 53	18 37		19 37	19 53	20 40		21 36		21 53		22 42		
South Gyle	d	17 43	18 00	18 43		19 43	20 00	20 46		21 40		22 00		22 48		
Haymarket	d	17 49	18 09	18 52	19 27	19 52	20 09	20 55	21 31	21 51	22 00	22 09	22 37	22 57		23 54
Edinburgh 10	a	17 56	18 14	19 00	19 35	19 56	20 15	21 01	21 36	21 55	22 05	22 13	22 43	23 01		00 03
	d															
Brunstane	d															
Newcraighall	a															

For general notes see front of timetable
For details of catering facilities see Directory of Train Operators

A From Dundee (Table 229)
B From Edinburgh via Cowdenbeath
C From Edinburgh via Kirkcaldy
D From Aberdeen (Table 229) to London Kings Cross (Table 26)
E **The Northern Lights**
G From Aberdeen to Plymouth (from 8 November to Birmingham New Street) (Table 51)
H From Inverness (Table 229)
J From Aberdeen (Table 229)
K From Edinburgh to Edinburgh

Sleeper Services

Sleepers enable you to make long distance journeys while having a relaxing night's sleep. You arrive early at your destination, saving a day's travel — or the early morning dash to the airport. Five Sleeper routes link London Euston direct with over 40 stations in Scotland including most principal business and holiday locations. Direct Sleeper services also link Southwest England with London. Customers joining at the starting point of the train may occupy cabins well before departure. At terminating stations customers may vacate cabins up to approximately 0800 on trains which arrive at an earlier time.

Full details of all Sleeper services are given in Tables 400–406 in this book.

Room Service

Sleepers have full air-conditioning and fingertip temperature control. Each cabin has wall-to-wall carpet, mirror, shaver sockets, drinking water — as well as hot water for the washbasin, and a comfortable bed.

Steward(ess) service is available at the touch of a button throughout the journey. **On First Great Western Sleepers,** additional benefits include a welcome toiletry pack, tea or coffee and biscuits, and a wake-up call. Showers and the First Class lounge are available on arrival at Paddington station, plus a free taxi transfer for Eurostar customers. The First Class package also includes complimentary orange juice, Croissant, preserve, tea and coffee and a morning newspaper (subject to availability).

On ScotRail's Caledonian Sleepers First Class customers receive a toiletry pack and will be woken with a light breakfast accompanied by tea or coffee and a complimentary newspaper. Standard Class customers are served a light morning snack with tea or coffee. Customer lounges are available at the following locations - London Euston, Inverness, Carlisle (Lakes Court Hotel) and Edinburgh Waverley. At Glasgow Central customers may use the on-train Lounge Car which is available prior to departure.

Full details of the Caledonian Sleeper on-train and station facilities can be found inside the Caledonian Sleeper Guide which is available from principal sleeper departure points.

Sleeper Supplements

Holders of First Class tickets enjoy a single berth cabin on payment of the First Class reservation supplement. Holders of Standard travel tickets travel in either a single or 2 berth cabin on payment of the relevant Standard supplement. The number of berths available to holders of discounted tickets may be restricted at any time.

On ScotRail's Caledonian Sleepers there are a number of berth inclusive fares available that include travel and accommodation at one all inclusive price. First Class travel is in single berth cabins while Standard Class is in twin berth cabins.

On First Great Western's Night Riviera there are a number of berth inclusive fares available that combine travel and accommodation on one ticket. First Class travel is available in single berth cabins, while Standard offers a choice of single berth or twin berth cabins.

Lounge Cars

The Lounge Car offers a pleasant relaxing atmosphere in which to unwind before a night's rest. **On First Great Western Sleepers,** a full range of drinks, snacks and meals are available. Hot and continental breakfasts are served in the morning. **On ScotRail's Caledonian Sleepers** customers can choose from a wide selection of food and drinks including sandwiches, baguettes, snacks and a well stocked bar. At busy times, use of the Lounge Car may be restricted to First Class ticket holders.

Sleeper Reservations

To book rail tickets and reserve Sleepers, simply visit any main rail station or rail appointed travel agent. Alternatively you can book by phone using most credit/debit cards.

ScotRail Telesales	08457 55 00 33
First Great Western Telesales	0845 700 0125

Enquiries by Telephone

For further information about rail tickets or services, call National Rail Enquiries on 08457 48 49 50 (calls may be recorded for training purposes).

Animals

Dogs and pets are not normally allowed in Sleeper cabins. There are special arrangements for guide dogs.

On First Great Western Sleepers, animals may be conveyed if properly labelled and muzzled, and in suitable containers, in the parcels accommodation on payment of the appropriate charge.

On ScotRail's Caledonian Sleepers accompanying dogs are only permitted in Sleeper Cabins providing the owner(s) has exclusive use of the cabin and pays the appropriate charge. There are special arrangements for guide dogs. Dogs and pets cannot be conveyed in the parcels accommodation.

ScotRail's Caledonian Sleepers

Please note that as a result of on-going engineering work some Sleeping Car services may be subject to diversion causing an extension in journey times between Scotland and London. For full details telephone National Rail Enquiries on 08457 48 49 50 (calls may be recorded for training purposes).

Sleeper Services

ScotRail Sleeper Services – The Caledonian Sleepers

Operated by ScotRail

Table 400 London and Edinburgh

		Mon–Thu R	Fri R	Sun A R	Sun B R
Cabins available from		*2300*	*2300*	*2245*	*2200*
London Euston	d	2350	2350	2327	2232
Watford Junction	d	0010*	0010*	2347	---
Carlisle ...	a	0511	0518	0504*	---
Carstairs ...	a	0620	0625	0624	---
Edinburgh ...	a	0720	0713	0720	0625*
Vacate cabins by		*0800*	*0800*	*0755*	*0755*

R Reservations Compulsory
* Following morning
Services in this table do not run on Saturday nights.
For details of overnight seated services, please refer to Table 65

		Mon–Thu R	Fri R	Sun A R	Sun B R
Cabins available from		*2300*	*2300*	*2230*	
Edinburgh	d	2340	2340	2315	2315
Carstairs ...	d	0016*	0016*	2347	---
Carlisle ...	d	0140	0140	0108*	---
Watford Junction	a	0614	0627	0623	---
London Euston...	a	0637	0650	0646	0705*
Vacate cabins by		*0800*	*0800*	*0800*	*0800*

A 17 May and from 12 July to 6 December 2009
B From 24 May to 5 July 2009

Table 401 London and Glasgow

		Mon–Thu R	Fri R	Sun A R	Sun B R
Cabins available from		*2300*	*2300*	*2245*	*2200*
London Euston...	d	2350	2350	2327	2232
Watford Junction	d	0010*	0010*	2347	---
Carlisle ...	a	0511	0518	0504*	---
Carstairs ...	a	0620	0625	0624	0713*
Motherwell	a	0701	0700	0701	0739
Glasgow Central	a	0718	0721	0718	0757
Vacate cabins by		*0800*	*0800*	*0800*	*0800*

R Reservations Compulsory
* Following morning
Services in this table do not run on Saturday nights.
For details of overnight seated services, please refer to Table 65

		Mon–Thu R	Fri R	Sun A R	Sun B R
Cabins available from		*2200*	*2200*	*2200*	*2100*
Glasgow Central...	d	2340	2340	2315	2140
Motherwell	d	2356	2356	2331	2201
Carstairs	d	0016*	0016*	2347	2222
Carlisle ...	d	0140	0140	0108*	---
Watford Junction...	a	0614	0627	0623	---
London Euston...	a	0637	0650	0646	0705*
Vacate cabins by		*0800*	*0800*	*0800*	*0800*

A 17 May and from 12 July to 6 December 2009
B From 24 May to 5 July 2009

Table 402 London and Aberdeen

		Mon–Thu R	Fri R	Sun A R	Sun B R
Cabins available from		*2030*	*2030*	*2015*	*1930*
London Euston	dep	2115	2115	2055	2007
Watford Junction	dep	2133	2133	2117	---
Crewe	dep	2354	2354	2342	---
Preston	dep	0052*	0052*	0030*	---
Inverkeithing•	arr	0458	0458	0458	0458*
Kirkcaldy•	arr	0517	0517	0517	0517
Leuchars for St Andrews•	arr	0546	0546	0546	0546
Dundee	arr	0608	0608	0608	0608
Carnoustie	arr	0622	0622	0622	0622
Arbroath	arr	0631	0631	0631	0631
Montrose	arr	0647	0647	0647	0647
Stonehaven	arr	0713	0713	0713	0713
Aberdeen	arr	0735	0735	0735	0735
Vacate cabins by		*0800*	*0800*	*0800*	*0800*

R Reservations Compulsory
* Following morning
• Customers may depart from London or Watford later, and vacate cabins later, by travelling on the London Euston to Edinburgh Sleeper; then by local connecting service from Edinburgh
Services in this table do not run on Saturday nights
For details of overnight seated services, please refer to Table 65

		Mon–Thu R	Fri R	Sun A R	Sun B R
Cabins available from		*2045*	*2045*	*2045*	*2045*
Aberdeen	dep	2140	2140	2142	2142
Stonehaven	dep	2200	2200	2200	2200
Montrose	dep	2225	2225	2225	2225
Arbroath	dep	2243	2243	2243	2243
Carnoustie	dep	2252	2252	2252	2252
Dundee	dep	2306	2306	2306	2306
Leuchars for St Andrews•	dep	2325	2325	2325	2325
Kirkcaldy•	dep	2353	2353	2353	2353
Inverkeithing•	dep	0012*	0012*	0012*	0012*
Preston	arr	0432	0432	0433	---
Crewe	arr	0532	0534	0537	---
London Euston	arr	0747	0748	0747	0921
Vacate cabins by		*0800*	*0800*	*0800*	*0930*

A 17 May and from 12 July to 6 December 2009
B From 24 May to 5 July 2009

Sleeper Services

ScotRail Sleeper Services – The Caledonian Sleepers

Operated by ScotRail

Table 403 London and Inverness

		Mon–Thu [R]	Fri [R]	Sun A [R]	Sun B [R]
Cabins available from		*2030*	*2030*	*2015*	*1930*
London Euston	dep	2115	2115	2055	2007
Watford Junction	dep	2133	2133	2117	---
Crewe	dep	2354	2354	2342	---
Preston	dep	0052*	0052*	0030*	---
Stirling•	arr	0456	0456	0456	0456*
Dunblane	arr	0505	0505	0505	0505
Gleneagles	arr	0520	0520	0520	0520
Perth•	arr	0539	0539	0539	0539
Dunkeld & Birnam	arr	0600	0600	0600	0600
Pitlochry	arr	0616	0616	0616	0616
Blair Atholl	arr	0628	0628	0628	0628
Dalwhinnie	arr	0659	0659	0659	0659
Newtonmore	arr	0711	0711	0711	0711
Kingussie	arr	0717	0717	0717	0717
Aviemore	arr	0741	0741	0741	0741
Inverness	arr	0830	0830	0830	0830
Vacate cabins by		*0830*	*0830*	*0830*	*0830*

[R] Reservations Compulsory
* Following morning
• Customers may depart from London or Watford later, and vacate cabins later, by travelling on the London Euston to Edinburgh Sleeper; then by local connecting service from Edinburgh.
Services in this table do not run on Saturday nights.
For details of overnight seated services, please refer to Table 65

		Mon–Thu [R]	Fri [R]	Sun A [R]	Sun B [R]
Cabins available from		*2000*	*2000*	*1945*	*1945*
Inverness	dep	2038	2038	2025	2025
Aviemore	dep	2128	2128	2108	2108
Kingussie	dep	2142	2142	2122	2122
Newtonmore	dep	2150	2150	2129	2129
Dalwhinnie	dep	2204	2204	2143	2143
Blair Atholl	dep	2230	2230	2209	2209
Pitlochry	dep	2243	2243	2222	2222
Dunkeld & Birnam	dep	2258	2258	2237	2237
Perth	dep	2321	2321	2300	2300
Gleneagles	dep	2339	2339	2318	2318
Dunblane	dep	2355	2355	2334	2334
Stirling•	dep	0006*	0006*	2345	2345
Falkirk Grahamston	dep	0023	0023	0002*	0002*
Preston	arr	0432	0432	0433	---
Crewe	arr	0532	0534	0537	---
London Euston	arr	0747	0748	0747	0921
Vacate cabins by		*0800*	*0800*	*0800*	*0930*

A 17 May and from 12 July to 6 December 2009
B From 24 May to 5 July 2009

Table 404 London and Fort William

		Mon–Thu [R]	Fri [R]	Sun A [R]	Sun B [R]
Cabins available from		*2030*	*2030*	*2015*	*1930*
London Euston	dep	2115	2115	2055	2007
Watford Junction	dep	2133	2133	2117	---
Crewe	dep	2354	2354	2342	---
Preston	dep	0052*	0052*	0030*	---
Westerton	arr	0555	0555	0555	0555*
Dalmuir	arr	0603	0603	0603	0603
Helensburgh Upper	arr	0626	0626	0626	0626
Garelochhead	arr	0640	0640	0640	0640
Arrochar & Tarbet	arr	0706	0706	0706	0706
Ardlui	arr	0721x	0721x	0721x	0721x
Crianlarich	arr	0742	0742	0742	0742
Upper Tyndrum	arr	0754	0754	0754	0754
Bridge of Orchy	arr	0812	0812	0812	0812
Rannoch	arr	0840	0840	0840	0840
Corrour	arr	0858x	0858x	0858x	0858x
Tulloch	arr	0917	0917	0917	0917
Roy Bridge	arr	0929x	0929x	0929x	0929x
Spean Bridge	arr	0936	0936	0936	0936
Fort William	arr	0954	0954	0954	0954
Vacate cabins by		*0956*	*0956*	*0956*	*0956*

[R] Reservations Compulsory
* Following morning
Services in this table do not run on Saturday nights.
For details of overnight seated services, please refer to Tables 65 and 227.

		Mon–Thu [R]	Fri [R]	Sun A [R]	Sun B [R]
Cabins available from		*1915*	*1915*	*1830*	*1830*
Fort William	dep	1950	1950	1900	1900
Spean Bridge	dep	2010	2010	1920	1920
Roy Bridge	dep	2017x	2017x	1927x	1927x
Tulloch	dep	2030	2030	1940	1940
Corrour	dep	2051x	2051x	2001x	2001x
Rannoch	dep	2106	2106	2015	2015
Bridge of Orchy	dep	2134	2134	2047	2047
Upper Tyndrum	dep	2152	2152	2105	2105
Crianlarich	dep	2205	2205	2118	2118
Ardlui	dep	2226x	2226x	2139x	2139x
Arrochar & Tarbet	dep	2244	2244	2157	2157
Garelochhead	dep	2310	2310	2223	2223
Helensburgh Upper	dep	2324	2324	2237	2237
Dalmuir	dep	2351	2351	2304	2304
Westerton	dep	2356	2356	2313	2313
Preston	arr	0432*	0432*	0433*	---
Crewe	arr	0532	0534	0537	---
London Euston	arr	0747	0748	0747	0921*
Vacate cabins by		*0800*	*0800*	*0800*	

A 17 May and from 12 July to 6 December 2009
B From 24 May to 5 July 2009

Sleeper Services

Table 406 London and Penzance

Operated by First Great Western

		Mon–Fri Until 4 Sep Ⓛ	Mon–Fri From 7 Sep Ⓛ	Sun Ⓛ
Occupy cabins at Paddington:		*2230*	*2230*	*2230*
London Paddington	dep	**2345**	**2345**	**2350**
Reading	dep	**0037***	**0037***	**0037***
Exeter St Davids	arr	**0414**	**0443**	**0405**
Newton Abbot	arr	**0437**	**0505**	**0455**
Plymouth	arr	**0518**	**0546**	**0535**
Liskeard	arr	**0614**	**0614**	**0706**
Bodmin Parkway	arr	**0628**	**0628**	**0721**
Lostwithiel	arr	**0635**	**0635**	**0728**
Par	arr	**0642**	**0642**	**0736**
St Austell	arr	**0650**	**0650**	**0744**
Truro	arr	**0709**	**0709**	**0803**
Redruth	arr	**0722**	**0722**	**0817**
Camborne	arr	**0730**	**0730**	**0825**
Hayle	arr	**0739**	**0739**	**0834**
St Erth	arr	**0743**	**0743**	**0840**
Penzance	arr	**0800**	**0800**	**0859**
Vacate cabins at Penzance by		*0800*	*0800*	*0900*

		Mon–Thur Until 3 Sep Ⓛ	Mon–Thur From 7 Sep Ⓛ	Fri Until 4 Sep Ⓛ	Fri From 11 Sep Ⓛ	Sun Ⓛ
Occupy cabins at Penzance:		*2105*	*2105*	*2105*	*2105*	*2045*
Penzance	dep	**2145**	**2145**	**2145**	**2145**	**2115**
St Erth	dep	**2155**	**2155**	**2155**	**2155**	**2125**
Camborne	dep	**2207**	**2207**	**2207**	**2207**	**2137**
Redruth	dep	**2214**	**2214**	**2214**	**2214**	**2144**
Truro	dep	**2227**	**2227**	**2227**	**2227**	**2159**
St Austell	dep	**2245**	**2245**	**2245**	**2245**	**2217**
Par	dep	**2253**	**2253**	**2253**	**2253**	**-**
Bodmin Parkway	dep	**2305**	**2305**	**2305**	**2305**	**2234**
Liskeard	dep	**2320**	**2320**	**2320**	**2320**	**2249**
Plymouth	dep	**2351**	**2351**	**2351**	**2351**	**2320**
Totnes	dep	**0019***	**0019***	**0019***	**0019***	**2348**
Newton Abbot	dep	**0032**	**0032**	**0032**	**0032**	**0001***
Exeter St Davids	dep	**0114**	**0102**	**0114**	**0102**	**0127**
Reading	arr	**0427**	**0427**	**0417**	**0417**	**0417**
London Paddington	arr	**0543**	**0543**	**0543**	**0543**	**0505**
Vacate cabins at Paddington by		*0715*	*0715*	*0715*	*0715*	*0715*

Ⓛ Sleeper Lounge Car

* Following morning

Services in this table do not run on Saturday nights.

For details of overnight seated services, please refer to Table 135.

Excursion Trains

A journey by train for leisure is a unique form of enjoyment which can be made all the more special and self indulgent if the train is tailored exclusively to your own needs or those of your party. Whether for business travel, leisure travel or as a promotional vehicle, the excursion train is in a class of it's own conveying you effortlessly to sporting event, leisure resorts and conferences or simply cruising through the landscape exploring lines not normally open to passenger trains or experiencing the thrill of haulage by a steam locomotive from a bygone age.

Excursion trains are operated by a number of train operating companies on behalf of independent excursion train promoters and passenger rolling stock owners. Covering the length and breadth of Britain's rail network and operating thoughout the year they provide a diverse, enjoyable and altogether more flexible alternative to scheduled services with an exciting range of on board catering options available to make your journey even more enjoyable and relaxing.

For the corporate client the flexibility of the excursion train can be further enhanced by the inclusion of exhibition vehicles or the provision of a complete exhibition train for that unique "product launch" opportunity.

Advertised Excursion Trains

A varied range of advertised excursion trains operate from many parts of the country catering for both individual and group bookings. Examples of such excursions regularly include scenic day trips, wine and dine land cruises, special rail enthusiast tours and steam hauled operations that recall the halcyon days of rail travel.

How to hire an Excursion Train

Excursion trains normally require between fourteen and ten weeks notice from the booking date through to the train running, although it is possible to arrange less complicated itineraries at shorter notice. Once a destination has been decided upon, please contact one of the independant rolling stock providers listed below for a price quotation. They will normally require the following information:

- Point of origin (and other calling points if required)
- Destination
- Your preferred point of origin departure time OR destination arrival time – whichever is most important
- Number of passengers and preferred type of rolling stock
- Type of catering required
- Number of days duration

You will be offered a quotation as quickly as possible but complex itineraries may take a little longer.

Alternatively some passenger train operating companies have trains available for private hire, subject to availability. Contact details for train operating companies are given in the blue pages at the front of the timetable.

Independent Excursion train rolling stock providers

Atlantic & North Western Ltd
1 Manor Gardens, St Erth, Hayle, Cornwall, TR27 6JH
Tel/Fax: 01736 756927 Mobile 07768 637229 Email: atlanticnwtrains@aol.com
Rolling stock available – Luxury vintage Pullman dining car train
Other services – A la Carte railway catering providers

Mid Hants Railway PLC
The Railway Station, Alresford, Hampshire SO24 9JG. Tel: 01962 733810. Fax: 01962 735448
Rolling stock available – First Class and Standard seating train with dining option.

Northern Belle
The Old Bookstall, Victoria Station, Station Approach, Todd Street, Manchester M3 1PB
Tel: 020 7805 5100. email: NorthernBelle@orient-express.com
Rolling stock available – Pullman style dining cars.

Alliance Charter Trains (EWS Railway Ltd and Riviera Trains Ltd)
116 Ladbroke Grove, London W10 5NE. Tel: 020 7727 4036. Fax: 020 7727 2083.
email: charles.paget@riviera-trains.co.uk
Rolling stock available – First Class Luxury dining Train, Premier Class and Standard seating train with dining option.

Excursion Trains

The Great Scottish & Western Railway Company Limited
Stationmaster's House, Windsor Central Station, Thames Street, Windsor SL4 1PJ. Tel: 0131 555 1021.
Rolling Stock available – Limited seating capacity Luxury vintage dining and Sleeper train.

The Scottish Highland Railway Company Limited
Bedford House, 62 London Road, Maidstone, Kent ME16 8QL. Tel: 01622 688899. Fax: 01622 688855.
email: control@resco.co.uk
Rolling Stock available – Limited seating capacity Luxury vintage dining train.

The Scottish Railway Preservation Society
SRPS Railtours, Marchwell, 7 Dalmahoy Road, Ratho, Midlothian EH28 8RE.
Tel: 0131 333 1281 (weekday evenings only). email: railtours@srps.org.uk
Rolling Stock available – First Class and Standard seating train with dining option.

Venice Simplon-Orient Express Limited
Sea Containers House, 20 Upper Ground, London DE1 9PF. Tel: 020 7805 5100.
Rolling Stock available – Luxury vintage Pullman dining train.

Vintage Trains Limited
Birmingham Railway Museum, 670 Warwick Road, Tyseley, Birmingham B11 2HL.
Tel: 0121 707 4696. Fax: 0121 764 4645. website: www.vintagetrains.co.uk. email: office@vintagetrains.co.uk

Wessex Trains Limited
P.O. Box 34067, Haslemere GU27 3WE. Tel: 01428 654072 Fax: 01428 654144 email: wessextrains@marleyhill.com
Rolling Stock available – Luxury Premier Class and Standard seating trains with high class meal service available.

West Coast Railway Company Limited
Jesson Way, Carnforth, Lancashire LA5 9UR. Tel: 01524 732100. Fax: 01524 735518.
Rolling Stock available – Pullman style dining train, First Class and Standard seating trains with dining option.

Heritage and Tourist Railways

Information has been provided by the Operators shown below and all enquiries should be made to the appropriate Operator.

Romney Hythe and Dymchurch Light Railway — Hythe, New Romney and Dungeness

Operated by Steam and Diesel Traction

This service is operated exclusively by the Romney, Hythe and Dymchurch Light Railway Company to whom all enquiries and communications should be addressed at New Romney, Kent TN28 8PL. Telephone: 01797 362353. www.rhdr.org.uk

Since it opened over 80 years ago, the Romney, Hythe and Dymchurch Railway has become one of the most popular family attractions in Southern England. The railway, which runs for nearly 14 miles across Kent's historic Romney Marsh, links the important holiday centres of Hythe, Dymchurch and New Romney to the fishermen's cottages and lighthouse at Dungeness. It is also the world's only 15" gauge 'MAIN LINE IN MINIATURE'.

The railway is probably best known for its superb fleet of one third full size steam locomotives, altogether there are 11, most of them based on the high-speed express locomotives of the 1920s, and with names like Green Goddess, Northern Chief, Hercules, Hurricane and Black Prince they all evoke nostalgia for the golden age of steam. Two diesel locomotives add a modern touch.

Nearest National Rail stations Folkestone Central (then by bus from Folkestone (Bouverie Square) to Hythe), Sandling (then by bus to Hythe) and Rye (then by bus to New Romney).

East Kent Railway — Shepherdswell, Dover, Kent

The East Kent Railway operates heritage trains between Sheperdswell and Eythorne. Services run on Sundays from Easter to 21 September, bank holidays and Saturdays in August. Special events are held throughout the year, including Halloween and Santa Trains.Further details on 01304 832042, www.eastkentrailway.com or write to East Kent Railway, Station Road, Shepherdswell, Kent CT15 7PD.

Kent and East Sussex Railway — Tenterden Town, Northiam and Bodiam

Operated by Steam and Diesel Traction

This service is operated exclusively by the Kent and East Sussex Railway Co. Ltd. to whom all enquiries should be addressed at Tenterden Town Station, Station Road, Tenterden, Kent TN30 6HE, www.kesr.org.uk. Seasonal service – please telephone for free colour leaflet – 01580 765155.

Savour the characteristic sights, sounds and smells of steam as you travel through 10½ miles of attractive countryside on this charming, rural railway. Locomotives and carriages dating from Victorian times to the 1960s have been restored as a living reminder of rail travel from more elegant times.

Bus connections to Tenterden are available from Ashford, Hastings, Headcorn, Maidstone, Rye and Tunbridge Wells (and Paddock Wood on Sundays).
Bus connections to Northiam are available from Hastings and Rye.

Sittingbourne & Kemsley Light Railway — Sittingbourne Viaduct — Milton Regis Halt — Kemsley Down

"A Truly Industrial Railway"

Operated by Steam & occasional Diesel Traction

This service is operated by the Sittingbourne & Kemsley Light Railway Limited to whom all enquiries should be addressed at PO Box 300, Sittingbourne, Kent ME10 2DZ. For Customer Information, Trains Times, Fares, Footplate Experience details and Special Event Information, call the 0871 222 1568. Information and advance bookings 0871 222 1569/01622 755313 (evenings only). Website: www.sklr.net. The railway opens from April (or Easter if earlier) - September including every Sunday, Bank Holidays and most Wednesdays during school holidays. Santa Specials run during December. Travel behind original locomotives, some of which have plied their trade along these tracks for 100 years! The Sittingbourne & Kemsley Light Railway is the preserved southern half of the former Edward Lloyd Paper Mill/Bowater's Industrial Railway, which, until 1969, was used to convey both raw materials and finished paper products between the mills at Sittingbourne and Kemsley, and the docks at Ridham. The railway was a 24-hour a day operation, and an integral part of the production process. Today things move at a more leisurely pace and the SKLR is the perfect place to unwind and relax - with or without the kids! Facilities include: Café, Museum, Souvenir Shop, Model Railways, Children's play area and Wildlife Gardens. Full timetable available at www.sklr.net or send an SAE to the address above for a copy of the printed timetable. Trains depart from Sittingbourne Viaduct Station - a ten minute walk from the National Rail Services nearest main-line station (Sittingbourne) see Table 212. Access to Kemsley Down is from "Saxon Shore Way" coastal footpath or by train only.

Heritage and Tourist Railways

Information has been provided by the Operators shown below and all enquiries should be made to the appropriate Operator.

Bluebell Railway — Sheffield Park, Horsted Keynes and Kingscote

Operated by 100% steam

Vintage steam trains run between Sheffield Park, Horsted Keynes and Kingscote. A connecting bus links East Grinstead station at weekends and during school holidays. Trains operate weekends throughout the year, daily March – October plus school holidays. Also "Santa Specials" in December and special events.

Pullman dining service Saturdays Evenings & Sunday lunchtimes. Address: Sheffield Park Station, near Uckfield, East Sussex TN22 3QL. Tel: 01825 720825 (24 hr talking timetable) 01825 720800 Customer Services 01825 720801 (Pullman reservations & charters)

Southern trains connect at East Grinstead with the Bluebell service 473 bus service weekends and school holidays to Kingscote. Through tickets available from all National Rail Stations all weekends (except Santa dates) and school holidays.

The Watercress Line — Alton and Alresford

Normally Operated by Steam Traction/Heritage Diesel

This service is operated exclusively by the Mid-Hants Railway Ltd, to whom all enquiries and communications should be addressed at The Railway Station, Alresford, Hants SO24 9JG. Telephone Alresford (01962) 733810. www.watercressline.co.uk.

The Watercress Line is the affectionate name given to the Mid-Hants Railway which reopened in 1977. It runs over 10 miles through unspoilt Hampshire countryside. At Alton the Watercress Line and National Rail share the station where simple interchange can be made. South West Trains services are half hourly to and from London Waterloo (see Table 158). Alternatively travel to Winchester (see Table 158) and take a bus to Alresford. At Ropley a variety of steam locomotives may be seen in various stages of restoration.

Stagecoach 64/X64, weekdays and 64A Sundays and Bank Holidays (Alton-Winchester) pass close to both the Ropley and Alresford stations, also stops at Alton station. At Winchester buses stop in City Road, approximately 5 minutes from the National Rail station.

Swanage Railway — Swanage — Corfe \Castle — Norden

Operated by Steam Traction

This service is operated exclusively by the Swanage Railway Company Limited to whom all enquiries and communications should be addressed at Station House, Swanage, Dorset BH19 1HB, telephone 01929 425800. www.swanagerailway.co.uk

The Swanage Railway now operates from Swanage to Norden via the historic village of Corfe Castle a distance of nearly six miles. Park and ride facilities are available at Norden. Coach parking at Norden.

Isle of Wight Steam Railway

Smallbrook Junction — Ashey — Havenstreet — Wootton

This service is operated by the Isle of Wight Railway Co Ltd., The Railway Station, Havenstreet, Ryde, Isle of Wight. Tel: (01983) 882204.

Primarily a tourist attraction, the Railway runs steam hauled trains of vintage rolling-stock over a five mile line and has direct interchange with 'Island Line' at Smallbrook Junction.

Bargain 'Island Liner' tickets, available at any Island station or on the train, allow a whole day's unlimited travel on the steam and electric lines. Available on all Steam Railway operating days (except Santa Specials and Day out with Thomas).

Trains run on selected days March to November and December (daily from late May until mid September).

Bodmin & Wenford Railway — Bodmin Parkway — Bodmin General — Boscarne Junction

This service is operated exclusively by the Bodmin and Wenford Railway plc to whom all enquiries and communications should be addressed to Bodmin General Station, Bodmin, Cornwall PL31 1AQ. Telephone: Bodmin (01208) 73666. www.bodminandwenfordrailway.co.uk.

Bodmin & Wenford trains run into a platform immediately adjacent to the main line platforms at Bodmin Parkway. For connecting National Rail services see tables 135 and 51.

Trains are usually steam-hauled (diesel on some Saturdays), and give an opportunity to sample steam train travel through the beautiful Cornish countryside. The line is 6½ miles long, and forms a convenient link from the National Rail station to Bodmin town centre, and on to Boscarne Junction (for the Camel Trail). Through tickets available from main line stations.

Heritage and Tourist Railways

Information has been provided by the Operators shown below and all enquiries should be made to the appropriate Operator.

Paignton and Dartmouth Steam Railway

This service is operated exclusively by the Dart Valley Railway PLC to whom all enquiries and communications should be addressed at Queens Park Station, Torbay Road, Paignton, Devon TQ4 6AF. Telephone: 01803 555872.

Paignton & Dartmouth Steam Railway from Paignton is the holiday line with steam trains running for seven miles in Great Western tradition along the spectacular Torbay coast to Churston and through the wooded slopes bordering the Dart estuary to Kingswear. The scenery is superb, with seascapes right across Lyme Bay to Portland Bill on clear days. Approaching Kingswear is the beautiful River Dart, with its fascinating craft, and on the far side, the olde worlde town of Dartmouth and the famous Britannia Royal Naval College, Butterwalk, Bayards Cove and Dartmouth Castle. Combined River Excursions available.

East Somerset Railway

This service is operated by the East Somerset Railway Company Ltd, Cranmore Railway Station, Shepton Mallet, Somerset BA4 4QP. Tel: 01749 880417, web: www.eastsomersetrailway.com, email: info@eastsomersetrailway.com. Located 3 miles east of Shepton Mallet on A361 between Shepton Mallet and Frome. Standard gauge steam railway recreating an ex-GWR branchline of the 1950's. Open when trains are running - Saturdays in March and November, Saturdays and Sundays April to October, plus some Wednesdays and Thursdays in Summer. Refer to brochure or to the ESR's website for details.

Station, Shop, Art Gallery, Small Museum, Engine Sheds and Workshops (except Christmas and Boxing Day). Childrens play area. Picnic sites. Restaurant open on Steam Days.

West Somerset Railway — Minehead and Bishops Lydeard with connecting bus service to Taunton

This service is operated exclusively by the West Somerset Railway plc to whom all enquiries and communications should be addressed at The Railway Station, Minehead, Somerset TA24 5BG, telephone 0643 704996 www.West-Somerset-Railway.co.uk

The West Somerset is Britain's longest heritage railway. From Minehead it runs along the coast to Dunster and Blue Anchor, inland to Washford, back to the coast at Watchet from where it turns inland to serve Williton, Stogumber, Crowcombe Heathfield before finishing at Bishops Lydeard.

Connections to Taunton mainline railway station and bus station are operated by First Group on a half hourly basis.

Severn Valley Railway — Bridgnorth and Kidderminster Town

This service is operated exclusively by the Severn Valley Railway Company Ltd. to whom all enquiries and communications should be addressed. The Railway Station, Bewdley, Worcestershire DY12 1BG. Tel. 01299 403816. www.svr.co.uk.

Severn Valley Railway is a standard gauge steam railway running from Kidderminster Town, SVR's splendid station immediately adjacent to the National Rail station, to Bridgnorth, a distance of 16 miles. The journey provides extremely fine views of the Severn Valley and visitors have the opportunity of alighting at any of the four intermediate stations before arriving at Bridgnorth, the main locomotive depot of the SVR. Refreshment facilities are available at most stations, and on most trains. Call the above number for dates of operation.

NATIONAL RAIL — SEVERN VALLEY LINK — Kidderminster Town Station is adjacent to National Rail Station (see Table 71). Through tickets available from any manned station on the national railway network – please ask for tickets "To Bridgnorth" (not "Severn Valley Railway"). All passengers are carried in accordance with the Company's terms and conditions.

Rheilffordd Llyn Tegid: Bala Lake Railway

This service is operated exclusively by the Bala Lake Railway, to whom all train service enquiries should be addressed at Llanuwchllyn, Gwynedd LL23 7DD. Telephone Llanuwchllyn (01678) 540666. www.bala-lake-railway.co.uk.

A delightful 4½ mile journey alongside Wales's largest natural lake through some of the most beautiful scenery in the Snowdonia National Park.

Aberystwyth — Devil's Bridge Vale of Rheidol Narrow Gauge Steam Railway

Narrow gauge line running through the magnificent scenery of the Rheidol Valley.

OPERATED BY STEAM TRACTION.

Vale of Rheidol Railway Locomotive Shed, Park Avenue, Aberystwyth, Ceredigion SY23 1PG.

For further details please telephone Aberystwyth (01970) 625819. Fax (01970) 623769. www.rheidolrailway.co.uk.

Brecon Mountain Railway: Merthyr Tydfil

Narrow gauge line running into the Brecon Beacons National Park.

This service is operated exclusively by Brecon Mountain Railway, Pant Station, Merthyr Tydfil CF48 2UP.

OPERATED BY STEAM TRACTION.

For further details please telephone Merthyr Tydfil (01685) 722988. Fax. (01685) 384854 or visit www.breconmountainrailway.co.uk.

Heritage and Tourist Railways

Information has been provided by the Operators shown below and all enquiries should be made to the appropriate Operator.

Dean Forest Railway

This service, operated largely by steam but with occasional diesel, runs between Lydney Junction (5 minutes walk from Lydney (NRT - table 57), Lydney Town, Norchard and Parkend. For train times etc. phone 01594 845840 (or 24 hour recorded information line 01594 843423), check web site: www.deanforestrailway.co.uk or write: Dean Forest Railway, Forest Road, Lydney GL15 4ET.

Talyllyn Railway — Tywyn, Abergynolwyn and Nant Gwernol

Operated by Steam Traction

This service is operated exclusively by the Talyllyn Railway Company to whom all enquiries and communications should be addressed at Wharf station, Tywyn, Gwynedd LL36 9EY. Telephone: Tywyn (01654) 710472. Fax (01654) 711755. www.talyllyn.co.uk For connecting National Rail services see Table 75.

Tywyn Wharf station is 300 yards from Tywyn station. Now with new cafe, shop and narrow gauge railway museum.

This, the World's First Preserved Railway, operates steam trains into The Snowdonia National Park to Dolgoch Falls and Nant Gwernol for splendid forest walks and waterfalls.

The Fairbourne Railway

Fairbourne — Penrhyn Point

This service is operated by the Fairbourne Railways Ltd to whom enquiries and communications should be addressed at Beach Road, Fairbourne, Gwynedd LL38 2EX. Tel (01341) 250362, Fax (01341) 250240, e-mail: fairbourne.rail@btconnect.com

Half-sized narrow gauge steam railway runs from Fairbourne to Barmouth Ferry Station where it meets the pedestrian ferry to Barmouth. Free Rowen Centre and model railway at Fairbourne Station.

Welsh Highland Railway — Porthmadog and Traeth Mawr

This service is operated by the Welsh Highland Railway Ltd (Porthmadog) to whom all train service enquiries and communications should be addressed - at Tremadog Road, Porthmadog, Gwynedd LL49 9DY. Telephone for general enquiries – (01766) 513402.

For connecting mainline service to nearest station (Porthmadog) see Table 75. The Welsh Highland station is immediately adjacent to the mainline station.

The narrow gauge Welsh Highland offers a short but nostalgic train journey, combined with a fascinating visit to The Engine Shed. Connections can be made to the main line WHR to Beddgelert and Caernarfon. The half mile extension to Traeth Mawr is now open, doubling the length of the railway. Please apply for full details to:- Tel. (01766) 513402 or email info@whr.co.uk, or visit www.whr.co.uk.

Snowdon Mountain Railway — Llanberis and Snowdon Summit

This service is operated by the Snowdon Mountain Railway. All train service enquiries should be addressed to Snowdon Mountain Railway, Llanberis Gwynedd LL55 4TY. Telephone: 0871 720 0033 Fax: 01286 872518 E-mail: info@snowdonrailway.co.uk. Website: www.snowdonrailway.co.uk. Trains run every day from Mid March to early November subject to weather conditions.

For National Rail service to nearest station (Bangor) see Table 83. There is a direct local bus service, Bangor – Llanberis and more frequent services Bangor – Caernarfon, and Caernarfon – Llanberis.

Opened 1896, Britain's only public rack and pinion railway climbs more than 3,000 feet in just five miles. On fine days spectacular views are unrivalled of the Isle of Man and the Wicklow Mountains in Ireland.

Avon Valley Railway

This service is operated exclusively by the Avon Valley Railway Company to whom all enquiries should be addressed at Bitton Station, Bath Road, Bitton, Bristol BS30 6HD. Telephone 0117 932 7296 (24 hour talking timetable), 0117 932 5538 (General enquiries).

The Avon Valley Railway is situated at Bitton Station, between Bristol and Bath on the A431 road, one mile from Keynsham (Tables 123 and 132). Trains run between Bitton, Oldland Common, and Avon Riverside Stations on most Sundays and Bank Holidays and some Saturdays between Easter and October, also Tuesdays, Wednesdays and Thursdays during school holidays. Santa Specials operate during December. Most trains are steam hauled.

Heritage and Tourist Railways

Information has been provided by the Operators shown below and all enquiries should be made to the appropriate Operator.

Llanberis to Penllyn Direct
Penllyn – Cei Llydan – Padarn Park – Llanberis } Llanberis Lake Railway / Rheilffordd Llyn Padarn

Operated by Steam Traction

This service is operated exclusively by Rheilffordd Llyn Padarn Cyf. to whom all train service enquiries and communications should be addressed at Llanberis, Gwynedd LL55 4TY. Tel. Llanberis (01286) 870549. www.lake-railway.co.uk.

The steam trains of the Lake Railway provide an enjoyable excursion away from the bustle of roads and traffic. Travelling from Llanberis Village to Penllyn along the length of Llyn Padarn, they pass rivers, woods and heathland. Across the lake are fine views of Llanberis and the mountains dominated by Snowdon. On the return journey the train stops at Cei Llydan, where there are lakeside and tree-shaded picnic sites, and at Padarn Park for the Welsh Slate Museum, Quarry Hospital, nature trails and craft workshops. Passengers may disembark here and return by a later train. For National Rail services to nearest station (Bangor) see Table 81. For bus connections from Bangor, Betws-y-Coed or Porthmadog stations visit www.gwynedd.gov.uk and follow transport links.

Llangollen Railway — Llangollen and Carrog

This service is operated exclusively by the Llangollen Railway plc to whom all enquiries and communications should be addressed at Llangollen Station, Abbey Road, Llangollen, Denbighshire LL20 8SN. Telephone 01978 860979. Email: llangollen.railway@btinternet.com. Ticket sales www.steamwales.co.uk.

Llangollen Railway has been opened to Carrog, in stages since 1981, along the route of the former Great Western Railway Ruabon to Barmouth line. Currently the railway extends nearly eight miles from near the centre of Llangollen along the amazingly beautiful Dee Valley, via Berwyn for The Horseshoe falls, and Glyndyfrdwy, to the picturesque village of Carrog.

Steam and heritage rail cars run at regular intervals daily from early April to early October, and most other weekends throughout the year.

The nearest national rail connection is Ruabon on the Chester/Wrexham/Shrewsbury line and there is a regular bus service from Ruabon station to Llangollen.

For further information on connecting bus and train services from Llangollen Tourist Information Centre on 01978 860828. A through ticket is available from most national rail ticket offices.

Ffestiniog Railway

The Ffestiniog Railway is the oldest independent railway company in the world, founded by Act of Parliament in 1832. It was the very first narrow gauge railway in the world to introduce steam engines - in 1863. We operate the unique Double Fairlie articulated locomotives, which were pioneered on the line. The railway climbs from sea level at Porthmadog, over 700 feet up into the mountains through spectacular scenery, to the slate mining town of Blaenau Ffestiniog. There are connections with the main network at Minffordd, for the Cambrian Coast, and at Blaenau Ffestiniog, for the Conwy Valley Line.
Timetable details available by phone – 01766 516000, by email – enquiries@festrail.co.uk or visit our website – www.festrail.co.uk
Ffestiniog Railway, Harbour Station, Porthmadog, Gwynedd, LL49 9NF.

Welsh Highland Railway (Caernarfon)

The Rheilffordd Eryri/Welsh Highland Railway is an exciting Millennium funded project, which is rebuilding the lost line back to Porthmadog, where it will join with the Ffestiniog Railway, so creating a 40 mile long narrow gauge railway. The main motive power comes from huge South African Garratts, the largest 2' gauge locomotives in the world. The railway starts close to the famous castle in Caernarfon and runs for nearly 13 miles into the heart of the Snowdonia National Park, revealing ever changing panoramas of the magnificent scenery on its way, to the village of Rhyd Ddu on the slopes of Snowdon.

Timetable details available by phone – 01766 516000, by email – enquiries@festrail.co.uk or visit our website – www.festrail.co.uk

Welsh Highland Railway, St Helens Road, Caernarfon, Gwynedd LL5S 2YD (see Ffestiniog Railway for postal address)

Heritage and Tourist Railways

Information has been provided by the Operators shown below and all enquiries should be made to the appropriate Operator.

East Lancashire Railway

Runs between Heywood – Bury – Ramsbottom – Rawtenstall

The service is operated by the East Lancashire Light Railway Company Limited. Bolton Street Station, Bolton Street, Bury, Lancashire BL9 0EY. Telephone number for information office 0161 764 7790. email: admin@east-lancs-rly.co.uk. website: www.east-lancs.rly.co.uk.

The East Lancashire Railway operates every weekend and bank holidays throughout the year (except Christmas Day). Passenger trains also operate from May to September on Wednesdays, Thursdays and Fridays. The Railway is 12 miles long (24 mile round trip) and passengers can enjoy the lovely scenic Irwell Valley, travelling across viaducts and through tunnels. We run steam footplate experiences throughout the year - please contact the information office.

Isle of Man Railways

These services are operated by the Isle of Man Dept. of Tourism and Leisure to whom all train service enquiries and communications should be addressed at Transport Headquarters, Banks Circus, Douglas, Isle of Man IM1 5PT. Telephone: (01624) 663366. website: www.iombusandrail.info.

Isle of Man Steam Railway – Douglas – Castletown – Port Erin

Built in 1874 to cater for the island's visiting tourists and to provide local transport to and from Douglas, this 3ft gauge steam worked line continues to fulfil that function today, still using the locomotives and rolling stock originally supplied. The trains pass through areas of outstanding scenic and varied beauty all the way along this 15 mile railway. Operates daily during the Summer months.

Manx Electric Railway – Douglas – Laxey – Ramsey

A unique example of Victorian technology, the 3ft. gauge 17¾ miles long M.E.R. continues to operate using much of its original rolling stock and equipment. Cars 1 & 2 of 1893 are the oldest electric vehicles in the world still in regular commercial service. The line passes through spectacular coastal and mountain scenery on its route to Ramsey.

Operates daily during the Summer months.

Snaefell Mountain Railway – Laxey and Snaefell Summit

The first Mountain Railway in Britain (opened 1895) and still the only one using electric traction, the 4¾ mile double track line of 3ft. 6in. gauge is adhesion worked on a gradient of 1 in 12. On fine days the view from the Summit encompasses five kingdoms.

Regular departures from LAXEY STATION between 1015 and 1545 (subject to weather).

Operates daily during the Summer months.

Great Central Railway — Loughborough, Quorn & Woodhouse, Rothley and Leicester North

Operated by Steam Traction

This service is operated exclusively by the Great Central Railway PLC to whom all communications and train service enquiries should be addressed at Great Central Station, Great Central Road, Loughborough, Leics LE11 1RW. Telephone (01509) 230726. www.gcrailway.co.uk

The Railway operates uniquely on a preserved stretch of former mainline. Running through beautiful countryside and across the picturesque Swithland reservoir. Passenger trains operate every weekend all year and summer midweek. Luxury dining services and drive a locomotive experience courses also feature all year round as well as many themed special events. Please see our website for up to date information.

Bo'ness and Kinneil Railway – Bo'ness and Birkhill

Operated by Steam and Diesel Traction

This service is operated by the Scottish Railway Preservation Society to whom all enquiries and communications should be addressed at Bo'ness Station, Union Street, Bo'ness, West Lothian, EH51 9AQ, telephone Bo'ness (01506) 825855, fax 01506 828766, website: www.srps.org.uk.

The Bo'ness and Kinneil Railway is a Registered Museum and is a standard gauge line running for 3½ miles from the station in the town centre beside the former dock in Bo'ness. The line runs along the foreshore of the Firth of Forth then climbs through woods with views across the Firth towards Fife, to the rural station at Birkhill. The Scottish Railway Exhibition, telling the story of Scotland's railways, is located at Bo'ness Station.

Services run at weekends from the end of April until the end of October and daily (except Mondays) in July and August. Special events throughout the year, Santa trains in December.

Nearest National Rail station is at Linlithgow (services operated by ScotRail), 4 miles from Bo'ness.

Heritage and Tourist Railways

Information has been provided by the Operators shown below and all enquiries should be made to the appropriate Operator.

Gloucestershire Warwickshire Railway

The all volunteer operated heritage railway offers a 20 mile round trip between Cheltenham Race Course Station and its operational base at Toddington.

The railway runs mainly on embankments, travelling through some of the most spectacular scenery the Cotswolds have to offer on both sides of the line.

It passes hamlets, villages, with splendid views over the Vale of Evesham to the distant Malverns, through the second longest tunnel in preservation to Winchombe Station, where we have a picnic area with lovely views, offers walks in the countryside.

Toddington is the present terminus where our Steam and Diesel fleet are maintained and restored. Souvenirs can be bought in the railway shop and refreshments from the Flag and Whistle Tea Room.

Voted Ian Allan Independent Railway of the Year and Heritage Railway Association's annual award for 2003.

Nearest mainline station is at Cheltenham Spa, then Stagecoach Bus to Race Course Park and Ride, then its a three quarters of a mile walk.

More information can be obtained from: GWR, The Railway Station, Toddington, Gloucestershire GL54 5DT. Telephone number: 01242-621405. Website: www.gwsr.com Email: enquiries@gwsr.com

Nene Valley Railway — Yarwell, Wansford, Ferry Meadows (Nene Park), Orton Mere and Peterborough (Nene Valley)

Operated by Steam and Diesel Traction

This service is operated exclusively by Nene Valley Railway to whom all train service enquiries and communications should be addressed at Wansford Station, Stibbington, Peterborough PE8 6LR. Telephone: Stamford (01780) 784444, Fax: 01780 784440 or Talking Timetable: Stamford (01780) 784404.

The Nene Valley Railway is a preserved steam and heritage diesel railway running on some $7^1/_2$ miles of track and features a unique collection of locomotives, carriages and wagons from Europe including Britain. Wansford Station Yard and Loco Sheds are open all year. Services operate on Sundays from January; weekends from Easter to end of October; Wednesdays from May; plus other mid-week services in Summer. Special events throughout the year.
Santa Specials in December.

Peterborough Nene Valley station, the eastern end of the Nene Valley Railway is approximately 20 minutes walk from the main line station (clearly signposted).

North Norfolk Poppy Line. Sheringham - Weybourne - Holt

Steam and heritage diesel services operated by the North Norfolk Railway plc to whom all communications should be addressed at Sheringham Station, Sheringham, Norfolk NR26 8RA. Telephone: Sheringham 01263 820 800. Fax: 01263 820 801. Website: www.nnr.co.uk.

The scenic Poppy Line runs on former M&GN Joint Railway tracks from Sheringham along the coast to Weybourne and up through heathland to Holt. Steam trains most days 1 April-end of October. 10% fare reduction on presentation of current mainline ticket to Sheringham.

For Railway connecting services see table 16.

The Poppy Line Sheringham station is adjacent to National Rail station.

Embsay & Bolton Abbey Steam Railway

This service is operated exclusively by the Yorkshire Dales Railway Museum Trust to whom all train service enquiries and communications should be addressed at Bolton Abbey Station, Bolton Abbey, Skipton, North Yorkshire BD23 6AF. Telephone Skipton (01756) 710614 or Talking Timetable, Skipton (01756) 795189. Website: embsayboltonabbeyrailway.org.uk. The Embsay & Bolton Abbey Steam Railway runs 4 miles between the new award winning station at Bolton Abbey and Embsay Station built in 1888. Services operate every Sunday throughout the year, weekends between Easter and the end of October and daily in the Summer season. The nearest railway network connection is at Skipton, 2 miles from Embsay or Ilkley, 3 miles from Bolton Abbey Station.

Strathspey Railway — Aviemore, Boat of Garten and Broomhill

Operated by Steam Traction

This service is operated exclusively by the Strathspey Railway Company Limited to whom all enquiries and communications should be addressed at Aviemore Station, Dalfaber Road, Aviemore, Inverness-shire PH22 1PY. Telephone: (01479) 810725. Steam trains operate from Aviemore Station and run for the 10 miles to Boat of Garten and Broomhill through scenery that has seen only minor changes since the line was built 140 years ago. Please send s.a.e. for timetable leaflet. Website: www.strathspeyrailway.co.uk, email address for enquiries – strathtrains@strathspeyrailway.co.uk.

Heritage and Tourist Railways

Information has been provided by the Operators shown below and all enquiries should be made to the appropriate Operator.

Chasewater Railway — Brownhills West and Chasetown

This service is operated by the Chasewater Light Railway & Museum Company, to whom all communications should be addressed at Chasewater Country Park, Pool Road, Nr. Brownhills, Staffs WS8 7NL, telephone 01543 452 623. Operating as "The Colliery Line", this standard gauge railway is located in Chasewater Country Park, off A5, Brownhills West, near Walsall, in the heart of the former Cannock Chase Coalfield.

Industrial steam and diesel services run every Sunday and Bank Holiday Monday throughout the year, together with Summer Saturdays, Tuesdays and Thursdays (for details visit our website www.chaserail.com). Santa Specials operate during December.

The Railway is a Charitable Trust, operated entirely by volunteers.

Peak Rail

Peak Rail operates a steam hauled heritage railway between Matlock Riverside, Darley Dale and Rowsley offering an 8 mile round trip through the Derwent Valley. The Railway also operates dedicated dining services on its Palatine Restaurant Car in addition to regular special events throughout the year.

The railway is served by good public transport services operated by East Midlands Trains and Trent Buses between Derby and Matlock for which tickets by either operator are valid on bus and train services between these designated points.

For further information about Peak Rail please write to us at Matlock Station, Matlock, Derbyshire DE4 3NA or telephone 01629 580381, fax 01629-760645, www.peakrail.co.uk or email peakrail@peakrail.co.uk.

Midland Railway – Butterley

Trains operate from Butterley Station along the 3.5 mile railway to Swanwick Junction where the visitor is encouraged to alight to see this unique attraction. A large railway museum with exhibits dating as far back as 1866 together with the Princess Royal Class Locomotive Trust Depot, a country park, a farm park, a narrow gauge railway, a miniature railway, a demonstration signal box, a Victorian railwaymans church, model railways and much more make the Midland Railway Butterley a day out to remember.

Trains run every Saturday and Sunday from mid January through to the end of December and daily during most school holidays.

Further information is available from the Midland Railway Butterley, Butterley Station, Ripley, Derbyshire DE5 3QZ or by telephoning 01773 570140. Website: www.midlandrailwaycentre.co.uk. Email mr_b2004@btconnect.com.

Spa Valley Railway — Tunbridge Wells West and Eridge

This service is operated by Tunbridge Wells and Eridge Railway Preservation Society to whom all enquiries should be addressed at West Station, Tunbridge Wells, Kent, TN2 5QY. Telephone 01892-537715.

This standard gauge railway reopened in 1996 and has its headquarters in the historic 1891 locomotive shed at Tunbridge Wells West. It runs from the spa town of Tunbridge Wells through pleasant countryside of the Weald to the village of Groombridge.

In Spring 2009 it is planned to re-open the line from Groombridge to Eridge where there will be interchange with National Rail services.

Please telephone for further details or visit our web site www.spavalleyrailway.co.uk.
Most services are operated by steam traction but sometimes diesel traction may be used.
Nearest National Rail station — Tunbridge Wells then 15 minute walk, or by frequent local bus, (also Eridge when services are extended).

South Devon Railway

The South Devon Railway traverses some of Devon's most glorious scenery. The River Dart is a fast flowing Salmon River, which has its origins high up on Dartmoor and becomes tidal just outside Totnes. Wildlife abounds in and around both the river and railway. Combine a nostalgic trip behind a steam locomotive, along a branch of the legendary Great Western Railway with a chance to view at leisure an almost inaccessible part of the countryside. Our station at Totnes is 464 yards from the mainline station and is within easy walking distance of the council car parks. Beside our station at Totnes is the Totnes Rare Breeds Centre, where there are many wild animals and birds to see. At Buckfastleigh there is ample free parking. As well as our preserved Great Western engines and coaches at Buckfastleigh, there is also a small museum, model railway, children's play area, shop, cafe and picnic area. Sharing our site at Buckfastleigh is the Buckfast Butterfly and Dartmoor Otter Sanctuary. Through tickets are available from any station in the country. On many days there is a free vintage bus service from our Buckfastleigh station to Buckfast, with it's famous Abbey and woollen mills and Buckfastleigh town, with the 'Valiant Soldier', a preserved pub. Whether you start at Totnes or Buckfastleigh enjoy a whole day out with us on the South Devon Railway. Check for dates and times of operation.

For further information contact South Devon Railway, The Station, Buckfastleigh, Devon TQ11 0DZ, tel: 0845-345-1466, www.southdevonrailway.org.

Heritage and Tourist Railways

Information has been provided by the Operators shown below and all enquiries should be made to the appropriate Operator.

Keighley & Worth Valley Railway — Keighley, Haworth and Oxenhope

This service is operated by the Keighley and Worth Valley Light Railway Ltd.; all enquiries to them at Haworth Station, Keighley, West Yorkshire BD22 8NJ. www.kwvr.co.uk. 24hr Talking Timetable 01535 647777. Other Enquiries 01535 645214. Fax 01535 647317.

Britain's last remaining complete branch line railway runs from Keighley to Oxenhope, along a rich seam of West Yorkshire's rail and cultural heritage. Travel via Ingrow, with its award winning Museum of Rail Travel and workshops, and Damems, the country's smallest complete station ("Ormston" in BBC TV's Born and Bred series), to Oakworth where the Railway Children was filmed. This is a superp example of an Edwardian Station, complete with authentic advertising signs, gas lighting and coal fires. From here, ride on to Haworth, home to another famous family - the Brontes. The line terminates 660 feet above sea level at Oxenhope, where a collection of historic locomotives and coaches can be inspected in the Exhibition Shed. There is a small buffet and a picnic site at the station, and why not take the Railway Children Walk which links Oakworth, Haworth and Oxenhope.

OPENING TIMES:

All year: weekends and public holidays; Tue-Thu mid June to early July, then daily until beginning of September.

North Yorkshire Moors Railway — Pickering — Levisham — Newton Dale Halt — Goathland — Grosmont — Whitby

Operated mainly by Steam Traction

This service is operated exclusively by the North Yorkshire Moors Railway to whom all enquiries and communications should be addressed at Customer Services, Pickering Station, Pickering, North Yorkshire, YO18 7AJ. Telephone 01751 472508. Fax 01751 476048. E-mail info@nymr.co.uk, website www.nymr.co.uk

For NYMR Whitby Endeavour Steam Services and National Rail Connection at Grosmont, see table 45, for Middlesbrough-Whitby (Esk Valley Line) through to Whitby on most days.

North Yorkshire Moors Railway is a standard Gauge steam railway running 18 miles from Pickering to Grosmont with services on many days now running a further 6 miles through to the quaint fishing port of Whitby. The journey takes the visitor through spectacular National Park scenery, moorland, forestry and scenic esk valley. Goathland station is better known as 'Aidensfield' in the YTV's 'Heartbeat' series. Dining and Special Events throughout the year.

A seasonal service of Heritage Trains (normally steam hauled) will run between Whitby, Grosmont and Goathland/Pickering.

All passengers carried in accordance with the company's terms and conditions.

Middleton Railway, Leeds

Operating in every year since 1758, the line runs from the station into Middleton Park at the edge of Yorkshire's biggest ancient woodland. Nature trails, playgrounds and picnic facilities.

A collection of 16 industrial steam and 8 diesel engines is on display. Many of the engines are over 100 years old.
The railway is proud to be:

1) The world's first railway to be enabled by an Act of Parliament - in 1758.

2) The place where the world's first commercially succesful steam engine operated. The first engine was called Salamanca and was built in 1812, 17 years before George Stephenson's Rocket.

3) The first preserved standard gauge railway in the UK in 1960.

Today the railway is run solely by volunteers and our new educational resource facility is supported by the heritage Lottery Fund.

Trains run on Saturdays (industrial diesel) from 1300; and Sundays and Bank Holiday Mondays (industrial steam) from 1100, Easter until end of November. Santa Specials in Christmas. Normal fare: Adults £4.50; children (3-15 years) £2.50; Family (2 Adults + 3 children) £12.00. Different prices apply at special events.

Location: Moor Road, Hunslet, Leeds LS10 2JQ. Adjacent M621 junction 5. Signposted also from A653 Dewsbury Road and A61 Hunslet Road. Ordinance Survey Grid Reference SE304310

Nearest mainline railway station Leeds City (2 miles) (Cross Country, East Midlands Trains, NXEC, Northern, WYPTE). Bus service from City Centre to Tunstall Road, off Dewsbury Road.

Address: The Station, Moor Road, Hunslet, Leeds LS10 2JQ **telephone** 0113 271 0320

Website: www.middletonrailway.org.uk **Email:** info@middletonrailway.org.uk

Heritage and Tourist Railways

Information has been provided by the Operators shown below and all enquiries should be made to the appropriate Operator.

Mid-Norfolk Railway

This service is operated by Mid-Norfolk Railway Preservation Trust to whom all enquiries should be addressed at The Railway Station, Station Road, Dereham, Norfolk NR19 1DF, www.mnr.org.uk, telephone 01362 690633. Seasonal service in operation – colour leaflet available on request.

The railway runs through 11 miles of attractive rural Norfolk, linking the ancient market towns of Dereham and Wymondham. It passes through river valleys and pretty villages and hamlets, providing both a great day out for visitors and a useful transport link for local people. Both Dereham and Wymondham are easily accessible by public transport.

Ravenglass and Eskdale Railway — Ravenglass and Dalegarth for Boot

This service is operated exclusively by the Ravenglass and Eskdale Railway Company Limited to whom all enquiries should be addressed at Ravenglass, Cumbria CA18 1SW Tel: 01229 717171 or email steam@ravenglass-railway.co.uk.

The Ravenglass and Eskdale is England's oldest narrow gauge railway and runs through seven miles of magnificent scenery totally within the Lake District National Park from coastal marshlands to the foot of England's highest mountains. Trains hauled by steam and diesel locomotives run daily from mid March until November with services varying from a minimum of seven return journeys a day to sixteen in high season. Restricted services do operate in the winter. Full timetable and other details can be found at www.ravenglass-railway.co.uk or by contacting the R&ER direct.

National Rail and R&ER stations adjoin at Ravenglass and money saving through tickets are available from main line stations and trains to Dalegarth for Boot. For connecting Northern services please see table 100.

Bure Valley Railway – Aylsham, Norfolk

Operated by Steam and Diesel Traction

This service is operated exclusively by the Bure Valley Railway Company to whom all enquiries and communications should be addressed at Aylsham Station, Norwich Road, Aylsham, Norwich, Norfolk NR11 6BW - www.bvrw.co.uk. Seasonal service – please telephone 01263 733858 or visit website for colour leaflet.

Opened in 1990, the BVR runs over the old Great Eastern Wroxham – Aylsham line and is paralleled throughout the entire 9 miles by the Bure Valley Walk and cycle path which offers excellent photographic opportunities.

Our steam and diesel trains pass through scenery which is as varied, interesting and beautiful as any to be found on a railway journey in England.

Combined train and boat tickets are available. These include a return train journey and a 1½ hours cruise on the Norfolk Broads. (Tickets must be booked in advance).

Trains run from March to October with services varying depending on the time of the year. Full timetable and other details can be found at www.bvrw.co.uk or by contacting the BVR direct.

National Rail and BVR stations adjoin at Wroxham and money saving through tickets are available from main line stations and trains to Wroxham.

For connecting services see table 16.

Passenger Representation

Passenger Focus

What is Passenger Focus?

Passenger Focus is the independent national rail consumer watchdog. Our mission is to get the best deal for Britain's rail passengers.

With a strong emphasis on evidence-based campaigning and research, we ensure that we know what is happening on the ground. We use our knowledge to influence decisions on behalf of rail passengers and we work with the rail industry, other passenger groups and government to secure journey improvements.

What can Passenger Focus do for me?

We're here to put the interests of rail passengers first. We do this by:

Campaigning for improvements

- we gather research and information, like the National Passenger Survey, where 50,000 passengers give us their views about their rail journeys, so we understand the issues that matter to you
- we work with Government and the rail industry to ensure that the passenger voice is heard when making decisions about the future of the railways
- we focus on a number of key issues:

- fares and tickets
- quality and level of services
- investment in the railway

Providing practical advice

- we provide passengers with advice on how to get the best from the national rail network, explain their rights and help them when things go wrong
- we work with other passenger groups to support them in their work

Resolving complaints

- if you make a complaint and you are unhappy with the response we can take up your complaint with the company involved

Making a complaint

If you have a complaint or comment about any aspect of your rail service, either on the train or at the station, please contact the railway company managing director concerned (contact details are shown on the TOC pages of this timetable).

What should you include in your complaint?

Depending on the nature of your complaint you should include:

- the reason for your complaint
- a description of the inconvenience caused
- which train and which day you travelled on, or which station you used and when
- how many people travelled with you
- your ticket(s) as evidence
- an explanation of the action you would like the company to take to rectify the problem

What next?

If you are not satisfied with the company's response you can contact Passenger Focus or, in the London area, London TravelWatch.

How to get in touch:

Telephone: 08453 022 022

8am - 8pm Monday - Friday
8am - 4pm at weekends

Address: Passenger Focus
FREEPOST
(RRRE-ETTC-LEET)
PO BOX 4257
MANCHESTER
M60 3AR

Fax: 0845 850 1392

E-mail: info@passengerfocus.org.uk

Website: www.passengerfocus.org.uk

London TravelWatch

London TravelWatch was set up under the Greater London Authority Act 1999 and represents the users of transport provided, procured or licensed by Transport for London and represents the users of rail services in and around London. London TravelWatch is independent of the transport industry and, like Passenger Focus, will consider representations from passengers who remain dissatisfied with the way that transport operators have dealt with their concerns.

If your journey began in London, please contact:

Telephone: 020 7505 9000

9.30am to 5pm Monday - Friday

Address: London TravelWatch
6 Middle Street
London
EC1A 7JA

Fax: 020 7505 9003

Website: www.londontravelwatch.org.uk

Compensation

Compensation may be payable under each rail company's Passenger's Charter scheme for poor performance (delays or cancellations). For daily tickets and weekly season tickets a fixed rate usually applies depending on the level of delay which you experience. Compensation is made in National Rail vouchers, as a rule, with a minimum of 20% of the fare for the affected journey leg.

Monthly or longer season tickets compensation can differ between companies. On some it is triggered if performance falls below agreed levels and is paid as discount on renewal. Others offer compensation on a journey-by journey basis like for daily tickets. Always check with the train company which issued your ticket or on which you travel for details of the relevant scheme.

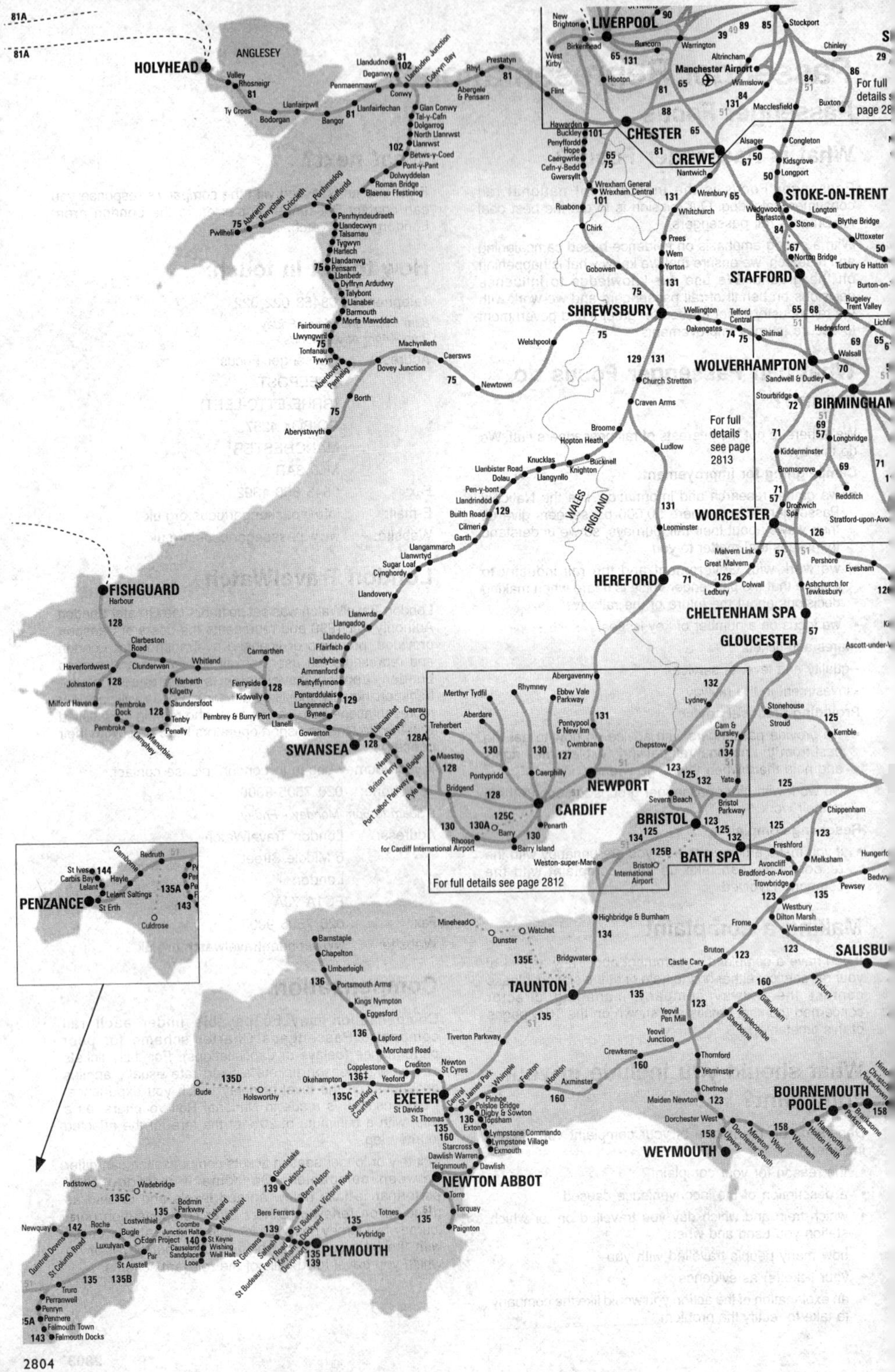

81A
HOLYHEAD
ANGLESEY
Valley
Rhosneigr
Ty Croes
Bodorgan
Llanfairpwll
Bangor
Llanfairfechan
Penmaenmawr
Llandudno
Deganwy
Llandudno Junction
Conwy
Colwyn Bay
Abergele & Pensarn
Rhyl
Prestatyn
Glan Conwy
Tal-y-Cafn
Dolgarrog
North Llanrwst
Llanrwst
Betws-y-Coed
Pont-y-Pant
Dolwyddelan
Roman Bridge
Blaenau Ffestiniog
Pwllheli
Abererch
Penychain
Criccieth
Porthmadog
Minffordd
Penrhyndeudraeth
Llandecwyn
Talsarnau
Tygwyn
Harlech
Llandanwg
Pensarn
Llanbedr
Dyffryn Ardudwy
Talybont
Llanaber
Barmouth
Morfa Mawddach
Fairbourne
Llwyngwril
Tonfanau
Tywyn
Aberdovey
Penhelig
Dovey Junction
Machynlleth
Caersws
Newtown
Borth
Aberystwyth
LIVERPOOL
New Brighton
Birkenhead
West Kirby
Runcorn
Warrington
Hooton
Flint
Manchester Airport
Altrincham
Wilmslow
Stockport
Chinley
Buxton
Macclesfield
For full details see page 28
CHESTER
Hawarden
Buckley
Penyffordd
Hope
Caergwrle
Cefn-y-Bedd
Gwersyllt
Wrexham General
Wrexham Central
Ruabon
Chirk
Gobowen
CREWE
Alsager
Congleton
Kidsgrove
Longport
Nantwich
Wrenbury
Whitchurch
Prees
Wem
Yorton
STOKE-ON-TRENT
Wedgwood
Barlaston
Stone
Longton
Blythe Bridge
Uttoxeter
Norton Bridge
Tutbury & Hatton
STAFFORD
Rugeley Trent Valley
SHREWSBURY
Wellington
Telford Central
Oakengates
Shifnal
Welshpool
Hednesford
Walsall
WOLVERHAMPTON
Sandwell & Dudley
Stourbridge
BIRMINGHAM
Church Stretton
Craven Arms
Broome
Hopton Heath
Bucknell
Knighton
Knucklas
Llangynllo
Llanbister Road
Dolau
Pen-y-bont
Llandrindod
Builth Road
Cilmeri
Garth
Llangammarch
Llanwrtyd
Sugar Loaf
Cynghordy
Llandovery
Llanwrda
Llangadog
Llandeilo
Ffairfach
Llandybie
Ammanford
Pantyffynnon
Pontarddulais
Llangennech
Bynea
Ludlow
Leominster
For full details see page 2813
Kidderminster
Longbridge
Bromsgrove
Droitwich Spa
Redditch
WORCESTER
Stratford-upon-Avon
WALES
ENGLAND
HEREFORD
Malvern Link
Great Malvern
Colwall
Ledbury
Pershore
Evesham
Ashchurch for Tewkesbury
CHELTENHAM SPA
GLOUCESTER
Ascott-under-Wychwood
FISHGUARD Harbour
Clarbeston Road
Haverfordwest
Clunderwen
Whitland
Carmarthen
Johnston
Milford Haven
Narberth
Kilgetty
Saundersfoot
Pembroke Dock
Pembroke
Lamphey
Manorbier
Penally
Tenby
Ferryside
Kidwelly
Pembrey & Burry Port
Llanelli
Gowerton
SWANSEA
Llansamlet
Skewen
Neath
Briton Ferry
Baglan
Port Talbot Parkway
Pyle
Caerau
Treherbert
Maesteg
Merthyr Tydfil
Aberdare
Rhymney
Ebbw Vale Parkway
Abergavenny
Pontypool & New Inn
Cwmbran
Pontypridd
Caerphilly
Bridgend
NEWPORT
CARDIFF
Barry
Penarth
Rhoose for Cardiff International Airport
Barry Island
Lydney
Chepstow
Stonehouse
Stroud
Kemble
Cam & Dursley
Yate
Severn Beach
Bristol Parkway
BRISTOL
BATH SPA
Weston-super-Mare
Bristol International Airport
For full details see page 2812
Chippenham
Freshford
Avoncliff
Bradford-on-Avon
Melksham
Trowbridge
Hungerford
Bedwyn
Pewsey
Westbury
Dilton Marsh
Warminster
Frome
SALISBURY
Highbridge & Burnham
Minehead
Dunster
Watchet
Bridgwater
TAUNTON
Bruton
Castle Cary
Tisbury
Gillingham
Templecombe
Sherborne
Yeovil Pen Mill
Yeovil Junction
Thornford
Yetminster
Chetnole
Maiden Newton
Dorchester West
Dorchester South
Upwey
WEYMOUTH
Moreton
Wool
Wareham
Holton Heath
Hamworthy
Parkstone
Branksome
BOURNEMOUTH
POOLE
Crewkerne
Axminster
Honiton
Feniton
Whimple
Pinhoe
Polsloe Bridge
Digby & Sowton
Topsham
Exton
Lympstone Commando
Lympstone Village
Exmouth
Barnstaple
Chapelton
Umberleigh
Portsmouth Arms
Kings Nympton
Eggesford
Lapford
Morchard Road
Copplestone
Yeoford
Crediton
Newton St Cyres
Tiverton Parkway
Okehampton
Sampford Courtenay
Bude
Holsworthy
EXETER
Central
St James Park
St Davids
St Thomas
Starcross
Dawlish Warren
Dawlish
Teignmouth
NEWTON ABBOT
Torre
Torquay
Paignton
Totnes
Ivybridge
PLYMOUTH
Gunnislake
Calstock
Bere Alston
Bere Ferrers
St Budeaux Victoria Road
St Budeaux Ferry Road
Keyham
Dockyard
Devonport
Saltash
St Germans
Padstow
Wadebridge
Bodmin Parkway
Liskeard
Menheniot
Coombe Junction Halt
St Keyne Wishing Well Halt
Causeland
Sandplace
Looe
Lostwithiel
Newquay
Quintrell Downs
St Columb Road
Roche
Bugle
Luxulyan
Eden Project
Par
St Austell
Truro
Perranwell
Penryn
Penmere
Falmouth Town
Falmouth Docks
PENZANCE
St Ives
Carbis Bay
Lelant
Lelant Saltings
St Erth
Hayle
Camborne
Redruth
Culdrose

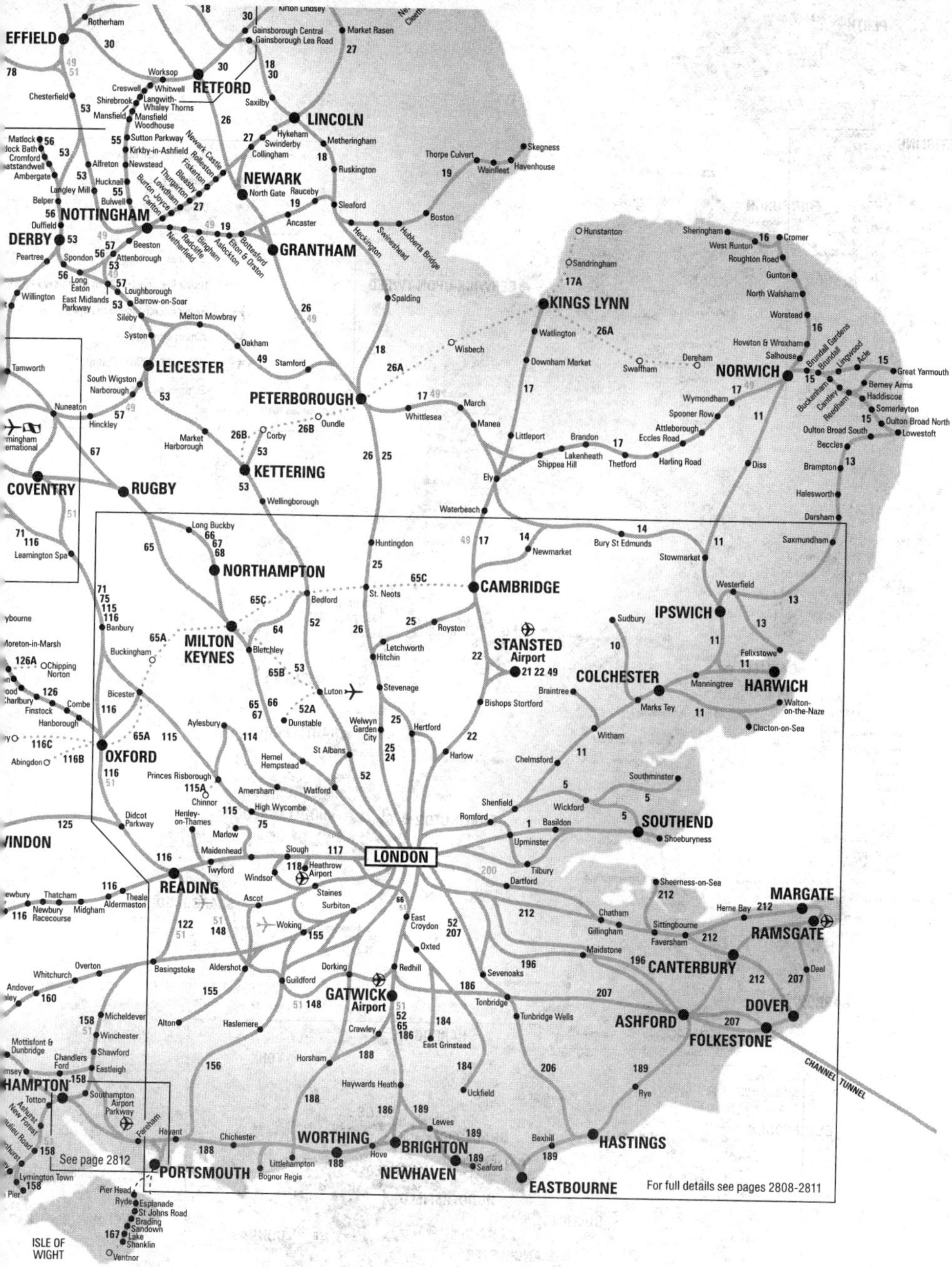

EFFIELD
Rotherham
Kirton Lindsey
Gainsborough Central
Gainsborough Lea Road
Market Rasen
Worksop
RETFORD
Creswell
Whitwell
Chesterfield
Shirebrook
Langwith-Whaley Thorns
Mansfield
Mansfield Woodhouse
Saxilby
LINCOLN
Hykeham
Swinderby
Collingham
Metheringham
Matlock
Cromford
Ambergate
Sutton Parkway
Kirkby-in-Ashfield
Newstead
Alfreton
Hucknall
Bulwell
Langley Mill
Belper
Duffield
Newark Castle
Rolleston
Fiskerton
Bleasby
Thurgarton
Lowdham
Burton Joyce
Carlton
NEWARK
North Gate
Rauceby
Ruskington
Sleaford
Thorpe Culvert
Wainfleet
Havenhouse
Skegness
Boston
NOTTINGHAM
DERBY
Peartree
Spondon
Beeston
Attenborough
Netherfield
Radcliffe
Bingham
Aslockton
Elton & Orston
Bottesford
Ancaster
GRANTHAM
Heckington
Swineshead
Hubberts Bridge
Long Eaton
East Midlands Parkway
Willington
Loughborough
Barrow-on-Soar
Sileby
Syston
Melton Mowbray
Oakham
Stamford
Spalding
Hunstanton
Sandringham
KINGS LYNN
Watlington
Downham Market
Wisbech
Swaffham
Dereham
Sheringham
West Runton
Cromer
Roughton Road
Gunton
North Walsham
Worstead
Hoveton & Wroxham
Salhouse
Brundall Gardens
Brundall
Lingwood
Acle
NORWICH
Great Yarmouth
Berney Arms
Haddiscoe
Somerleyton
Oulton Broad North
Lowestoft
Oulton Broad South
Beccles
Brampton
Halesworth
Darsham
Saxmundham
Buckenham
Cantley
Reedham
Tamworth
LEICESTER
South Wigston
Narborough
Nuneaton
Hinckley
PETERBOROUGH
Whittlesea
March
Manea
Littleport
Brandon
Lakenheath
Shippea Hill
Thetford
Harling Road
Eccles Road
Attleborough
Spooner Row
Wymondham
Diss
Ely
Oundle
Corby
Market Harborough
KETTERING
Wellingborough
COVENTRY
RUGBY
Leamington Spa
Long Buckby
NORTHAMPTON
Waterbeach
Huntingdon
Newmarket
Bury St Edmunds
Stowmarket
Westerfield
IPSWICH
Felixstowe
HARWICH
Manningtree
Walton-on-the-Naze
Clacton-on-Sea
Sudbury
COLCHESTER
Marks Tey
Braintree
Witham
Chelmsford
St. Neots
CAMBRIDGE
Bedford
Royston
Letchworth
Hitchin
Stevenage
STANSTED Airport
Bishops Stortford
Banbury
Buckingham
MILTON KEYNES
Bletchley
Luton
Dunstable
Welwyn Garden City
Hertford
Harlow
Moreton-in-Marsh
Chipping Norton
Charlbury
Combe
Finstock
Hanborough
Bicester
OXFORD
Abingdon
Aylesbury
Hemel Hempstead
St Albans
Watford
Princes Risborough
Chinnor
Amersham
High Wycombe
Didcot Parkway
Henley-on-Thames
Marlow
Maidenhead
Twyford
Slough
Heathrow Airport
Windsor
Staines
LONDON
Southminster
Shenfield
Wickford
Romford
Basildon
SOUTHEND
Shoeburyness
Upminster
Tilbury
Dartford
Sheerness-on-Sea
MARGATE
Herne Bay
RAMSGATE
Sittingbourne
Faversham
Chatham
Gillingham
Maidstone
CANTERBURY
Deal
DOVER
ASHFORD
FOLKESTONE
CHANNEL TUNNEL
VINDON
READING
Theale
Aldermaston
Thatcham
Newbury Racecourse
Midgham
Ascot
Surbiton
Woking
East Croydon
Oxted
Redhill
Sevenoaks
Tonbridge
Tunbridge Wells
Basingstoke
Aldershot
Guildford
Dorking
GATWICK Airport
Crawley
East Grinstead
Overton
Whitchurch
Andover
Micheldever
Winchester
Shawford
Eastleigh
Chandlers Ford
Mottisfont & Dunbridge
Alton
Haslemere
Horsham
Haywards Heath
Uckfield
Rye
HAMPTON
Totton
Southampton Airport Parkway
Ashurst New Forest
Beaulieu Road
Fareham
Havant
Chichester
WORTHING
BRIGHTON
Lewes
Bexhill
HASTINGS
See page 2812
PORTSMOUTH
Littlehampton
Bognor Regis
Hove
NEWHAVEN
Seaford
EASTBOURNE
For full details see pages 2808-2811
Lymington Town
Pier Head
Ryde
Esplanade
St Johns Road
Brading
Sandown
Lake
Shanklin
Ventnor
ISLE OF WIGHT

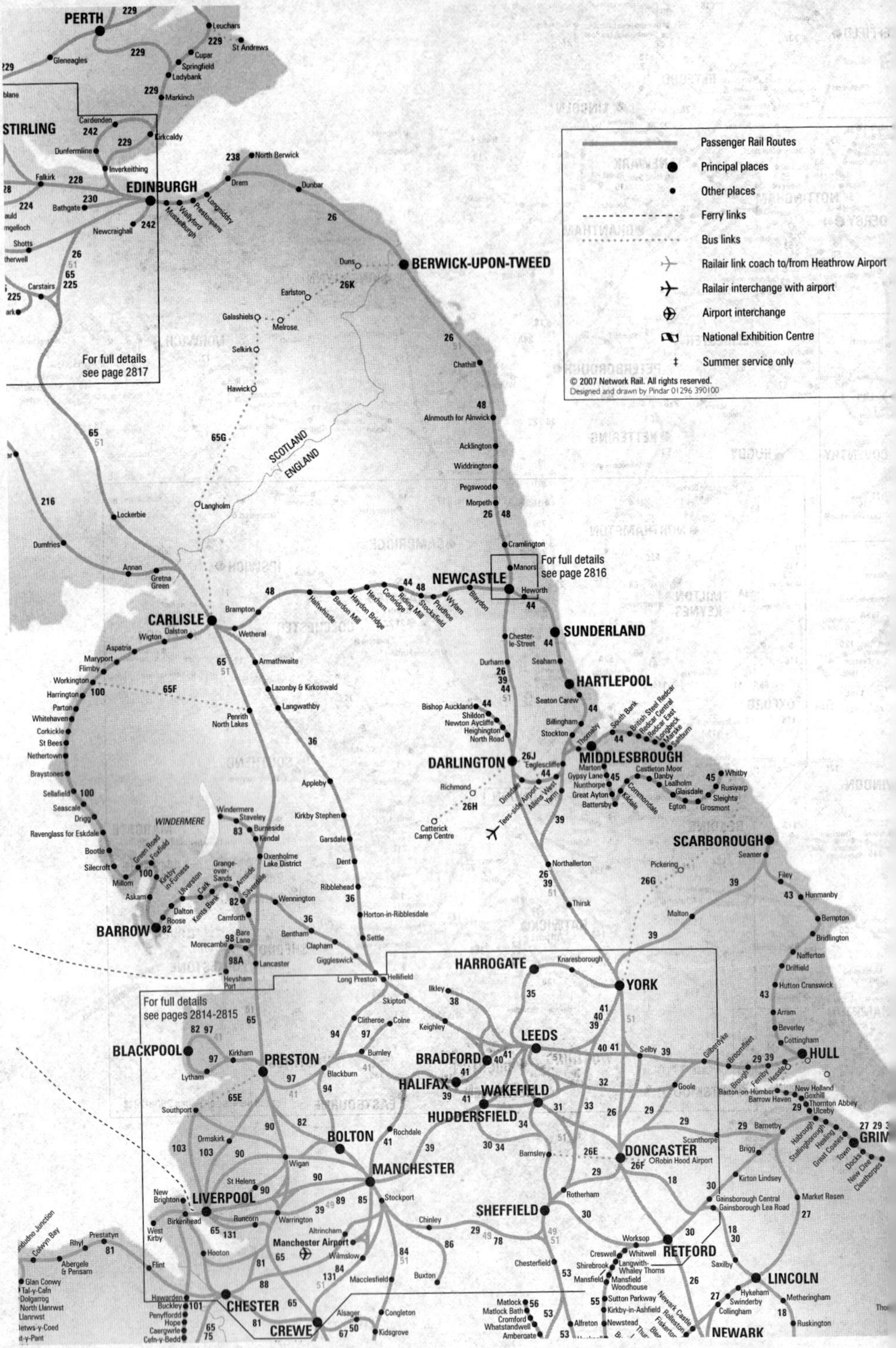
Passenger Rail Routes
Principal places
Other places
Ferry links
Bus links
Railair link coach to/from Heathrow Airport
Railair interchange with airport
Airport interchange
National Exhibition Centre
Summer service only
© 2007 Network Rail. All rights reserved.
Designed and drawn by Pindar 01296 390100
For full details see page 2817
For full details see page 2816
For full details see pages 2814-2815
SCOTLAND
ENGLAND
WINDERMERE
PERTH
Gleneagles
Leuchars
St Andrews
Cupar
Springfield
Ladybank
Markinch
Cardenden
Kirkcaldy
STIRLING
Dunfermline
Inverkeithing
Falkirk
EDINBURGH
Bathgate
Newcraighall
Shotts
Carstairs
North Berwick
Drem
Dunbar
Longniddry
Prestonpans
Wallyford
Musselburgh
BERWICK-UPON-TWEED
Duns
Earlston
Galashiels
Melrose
Selkirk
Hawick
Langholm
Lockerbie
Dumfries
Annan
Gretna Green
Chathill
Alnmouth for Alnwick
Acklington
Widdrington
Pegswood
Morpeth
Cramlington
Manors
NEWCASTLE
Heworth
Blaydon
Wylam
Prudhoe
Stocksfield
Riding Mill
Corbridge
Hexham
Haydon Bridge
Bardon Mill
Haltwhistle
Brampton
Wetheral
CARLISLE
Dalston
Wigton
Aspatria
Maryport
Flimby
Workington
Harrington
Parton
Whitehaven
Corkickle
St Bees
Nethertown
Braystones
Sellafield
Seascale
Drigg
Ravenglass for Eskdale
Bootle
Silecroft
Millom
Green Road
Foxfield
Kirkby-in-Furness
Askam
Ulverston
Cark
Kents Bank
Grange-over-Sands
Arnside
Silverdale
Dalton
Roose
BARROW
Carnforth
Morecambe
Bare Lane
Lancaster
Heysham Port
Windermere
Staveley
Burneside
Kendal
Oxenholme Lake District
Wennington
Bentham
Clapham
Giggleswick
Long Preston
Hellifield
Settle
Horton-in-Ribblesdale
Ribblehead
Dent
Garsdale
Kirkby Stephen
Appleby
Langwathby
Lazonby & Kirkoswald
Armathwaite
Penrith North Lakes
Chester-le-Street
SUNDERLAND
Seaham
Durham
HARTLEPOOL
Seaton Carew
Billingham
Stockton
Thornaby
South Bank
British Steel Redcar
Redcar Central
Redcar East
Longbeck
Marske
Saltburn
Bishop Auckland
Shildon
Newton Aycliffe
Heighington
North Road
DARLINGTON
Eaglescliffe
MIDDLESBROUGH
Marton
Gypsy Lane
Nunthorpe
Great Ayton
Battersby
Kildale
Commondale
Castleton Moor
Danby
Lealholm
Glaisdale
Egton
Grosmont
Sleights
Ruswarp
Whitby
Richmond
Catterick Camp Centre
Dinsdale
Tees-side Airport
Allens West
Yarm
Northallerton
Thirsk
SCARBOROUGH
Seamer
Pickering
Malton
Filey
Hunmanby
Bempton
Bridlington
Nafferton
Driffield
Hutton Cranswick
Arram
Beverley
Cottingham
HULL
Hessle
Ferriby
Brough
Broomfleet
Gilberdyke
HARROGATE
Knaresborough
YORK
Ilkley
Skipton
Keighley
LEEDS
BRADFORD
HALIFAX
WAKEFIELD
HUDDERSFIELD
Selby
Goole
Barton-on-Humber
Barrow Haven
New Holland
Goxhill
Thornton Abbey
Ulceby
Barnetby
Habrough
Stallingborough
Healing
Great Coates
Grimsby Town
Grimsby Docks
New Clee
Cleethorpes
Scunthorpe
Brigg
Kirton Lindsey
DONCASTER
Robin Hood Airport
Barnsley
Rotherham
SHEFFIELD
Chesterfield
Gainsborough Central
Gainsborough Lea Road
Market Rasen
Worksop
RETFORD
Creswell
Whitwell
Langwith-Whaley Thorns
Shirebrook
Mansfield Woodhouse
Mansfield
Sutton Parkway
Kirkby-in-Ashfield
Newstead
Alfreton
Saxilby
LINCOLN
Hykeham
Swinderby
Collingham
Metheringham
Ruskington
NEWARK
Newark Castle
Rolleston
Fiskerton
Matlock
Matlock Bath
Cromford
Whatstandwell
Ambergate
BLACKPOOL
Kirkham
Lytham
PRESTON
Clitheroe
Colne
Burnley
Blackburn
Southport
Ormskirk
BOLTON
Rochdale
Wigan
St Helens
MANCHESTER
Stockport
LIVERPOOL
New Brighton
Birkenhead
West Kirby
Runcorn
Warrington
Altrincham
Manchester Airport
Wilmslow
Chinley
Buxton
Macclesfield
Hooton
Flint
Hawarden
Buckley
Penyffordd
Hope
Caergwrle
Cefn-y-Bedd
CHESTER
CREWE
Alsager
Congleton
Kidsgrove
Llandudno Junction
Colwyn Bay
Rhyl
Prestatyn
Abergele & Pensarn
Glan Conwy
Tal-y-Cafn
Dolgarrog
North Llanrwst
Llanrwst
Betws-y-Coed
Pont-y-Pant

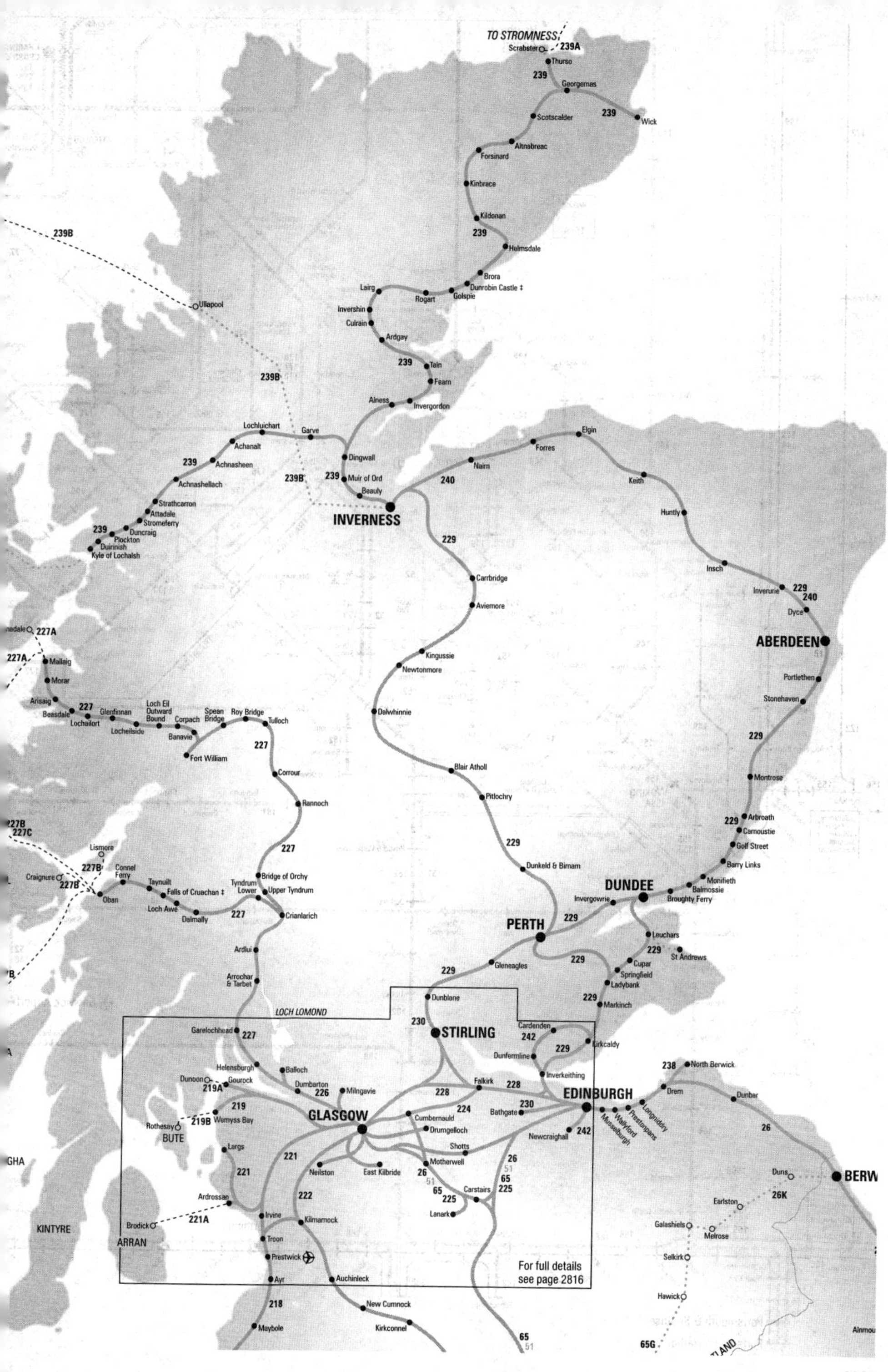
TO STROMNESS
Scrabster
239A
Thurso
239
Georgemas
239
Wick
Scotscalder
Altnabreac
Forsinard
Kinbrace
Kildonan
239
Helmsdale
Brora
Dunrobin Castle ‡
Golspie
Rogart
Lairg
Invershin
Culrain
Ardgay
239
Tain
Fearn
Alness
Invergordon
239B
Ullapool
239B
Lochluichart
Garve
Achanalt
239
Achnasheen
Achnashellach
Dingwall
239B
239
Muir of Ord
Beauly
INVERNESS
Strathcarron
Attadale
Stromeferry
239
Duncraig
Plockton
Duirinish
Kyle of Lochalsh
240
Nairn
Forres
Elgin
Keith
Huntly
Insch
Inverurie
229
240
Dyce
ABERDEEN
Portlethen
Stonehaven
229
Montrose
229
Arbroath
Carnoustie
Golf Street
Barry Links
Monifieth
Balmossie
Broughty Ferry
DUNDEE
Invergowrie
229
Carrbridge
Aviemore
Kingussie
Newtonmore
Dalwhinnie
Blair Atholl
Pitlochry
229
Dunkeld & Birnam
PERTH
229
Leuchars
229
St Andrews
Cupar
Springfield
Ladybank
229
Markinch
229
Gleneagles
Dunblane
230
STIRLING
Cardenden
242
229
Dunfermline
Kirkcaldy
Inverkeithing
227A
227A
Mallaig
Morar
Arisaig
227
Beasdale
Lochailort
Glenfinnan
Locheilside
Loch Eil Outward Bound
Corpach
Banavie
Spean Bridge
Roy Bridge
Tulloch
227
Fort William
Corrour
Rannoch
227
Bridge of Orchy
Tyndrum Lower
Upper Tyndrum
Crianlarich
227B
227C
Lismore
Craignure
227B
227B
Oban
Connel Ferry
Taynuilt
Falls of Cruachan ‡
Loch Awe
Dalmally
227
Ardlui
Arrochar & Tarbet
LOCH LOMOND
Garelochhead
227
Helensburgh
Balloch
Dunoon
219A
Gourock
Dumbarton
226
Milngavie
219
Rothesay
BUTE
219B
Wemyss Bay
GLASGOW
Largs
221
221
Neilston
East Kilbride
Ardrossan
Brodick
221A
ARRAN
KINTYRE
222
Irvine
Kilmarnock
Troon
Prestwick
Ayr
218
Maybole
Auchinleck
New Cumnock
Kirkconnel
228
Falkirk
228
224
Cumbernauld
Drumgelloch
230
Bathgate
Shotts
Motherwell
26
51
65
225
Carstairs
Lanark
26
51
65
225
Newcraighall
242
EDINBURGH
Musselburgh
Wallyford
Prestonpans
Longniddry
Drem
238
North Berwick
Dunbar
26
Duns
BERW
26K
Earlston
Galashiels
Melrose
Selkirk
Hawick
65G
65
51
For full details see page 2816

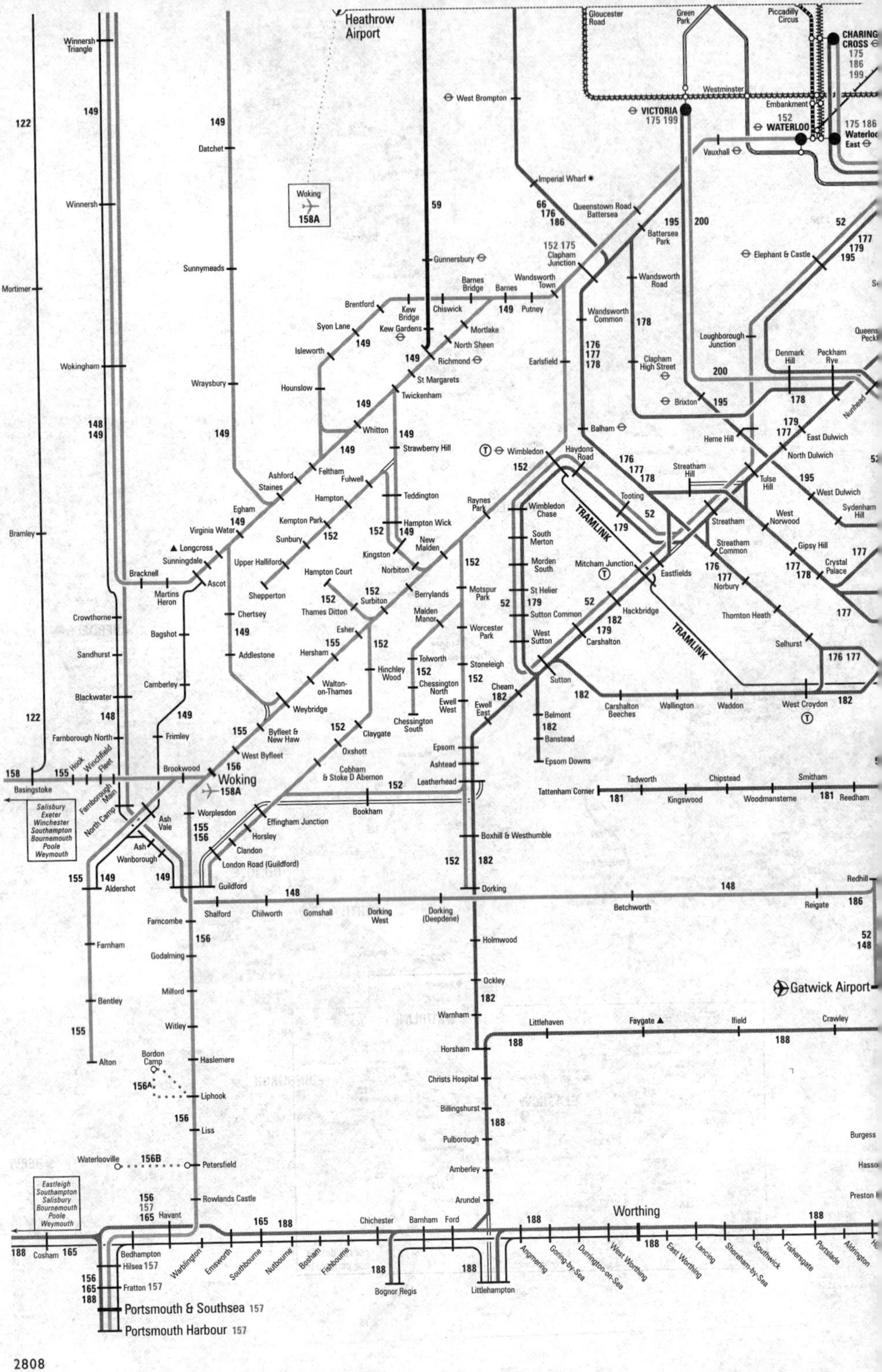
Heathrow Airport
Gloucester Road
Green Park
Piccadilly Circus
CHARING CROSS
175 186 199
West Brompton
Westminster
Embankment
VICTORIA
175 199
152
WATERLOO
175 186
Waterloo East
Vauxhall
Imperial Wharf
Queenstown Road Battersea
66 176 186
195
200
52
177 179 195
Battersea Park
152 175
Clapham Junction
Elephant & Castle
Wandsworth Road
Wandsworth Town
Gunnersbury
Barnes Bridge
Barnes
Putney
Brentford
Kew Bridge
Chiswick
Kew Gardens
Mortlake
North Sheen
Richmond
St Margarets
Twickenham
Syon Lane
Isleworth
Hounslow
Whitton
Strawberry Hill
Feltham
Fulwell
Teddington
Hampton
Hampton Wick
Kempton Park
Sunbury
Upper Halliford
Shepperton
Kingston
Norbiton
New Malden
Hampton Court
Thames Ditton
Surbiton
Berrylands
Malden Manor
Tolworth
Chessington North
Chessington South
Motspur Park
Worcester Park
Stoneleigh
Ewell West
Ewell East
Cheam
Epsom
Ashtead
Leatherhead
Boxhill & Westhumble
Dorking
Raynes Park
Wimbledon
Wimbledon Chase
South Merton
Morden South
St Helier
Sutton Common
West Sutton
Sutton
Belmont
Banstead
Epsom Downs
Haydons Road
Tooting
Earlsfield
Wandsworth Common
Balham
Clapham High Street
Brixton
Loughborough Junction
Denmark Hill
Peckham Rye
Nunhead
Herne Hill
East Dulwich
North Dulwich
West Dulwich
Sydenham Hill
Tulse Hill
Streatham Hill
Streatham
West Norwood
Gipsy Hill
Crystal Palace
Streatham Common
Norbury
Thornton Heath
Selhurst
Mitcham Junction
Eastfields
Hackbridge
Carshalton
TRAMLINK
Carshalton Beeches
Wallington
Waddon
West Croydon
Tattenham Corner
Tadworth
Kingswood
Chipstead
Woodmansterne
Smitham
Reedham
Redhill
Reigate
Betchworth
Gatwick Airport
Winnersh Triangle
Winnersh
Mortimer
Wokingham
Bramley
Crowthorne
Sandhurst
Blackwater
Farnborough North
Frimley
Camberley
Bagshot
Martins Heron
Bracknell
Ascot
Sunningdale
Longcross
Virginia Water
Egham
Staines
Ashford
Datchet
Sunnymeads
Wraysbury
Chertsey
Addlestone
Weybridge
Byfleet & New Haw
West Byfleet
Woking
158A
Brookwood
Basingstoke
Hook
Winchfield
Fleet
Farnborough Main
North Camp
Ash Vale
Ash
Wanborough
Aldershot
Farnham
Bentley
Alton
Salisbury
Exeter
Winchester
Southampton
Bournemouth
Poole
Weymouth
Worplesdon
Guildford
London Road (Guildford)
Clandon
Horsley
Effingham Junction
Bookham
Cobham & Stoke D Abernon
Oxshott
Claygate
Hinchley Wood
Esher
Hersham
Walton-on-Thames
Shalford
Chilworth
Gomshall
Dorking West
Dorking (Deepdene)
Farncombe
Godalming
Milford
Witley
Haslemere
Bordon Camp
156A
Liphook
Liss
Petersfield
Waterlooville
156B
Rowlands Castle
Havant
Holmwood
Ockley
Warnham
Horsham
Littlehaven
Faygate
Ifield
Crawley
Christs Hospital
Billingshurst
Pulborough
Amberley
Arundel
Burgess
Hasso
Preston
Worthing
Eastleigh
Southampton
Salisbury
Bournemouth
Poole
Weymouth
Cosham
Bedhampton
Hilsea
Fratton
Portsmouth & Southsea
Portsmouth Harbour
Warblington
Emsworth
Southbourne
Nutbourne
Bosham
Fishbourne
Chichester
Barnham
Ford
Bognor Regis
Littlehampton
Angmering
Goring-by-Sea
Durrington-on-Sea
West Worthing
East Worthing
Lancing
Shoreham-by-Sea
Southwick
Fishersgate
Portslade
Aldrington

Continued on pages 2810-2811

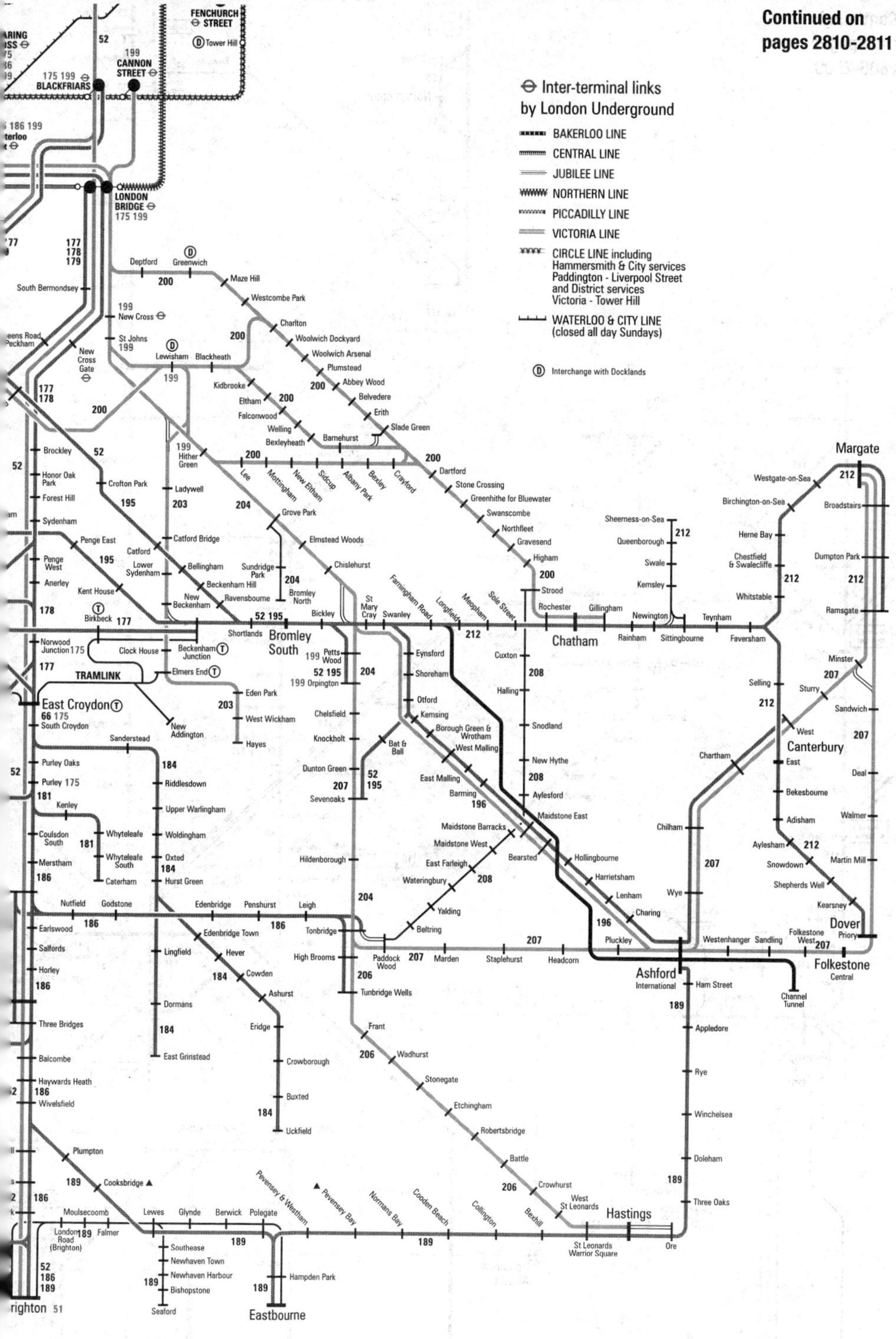

Continued
from pages
2808-2809

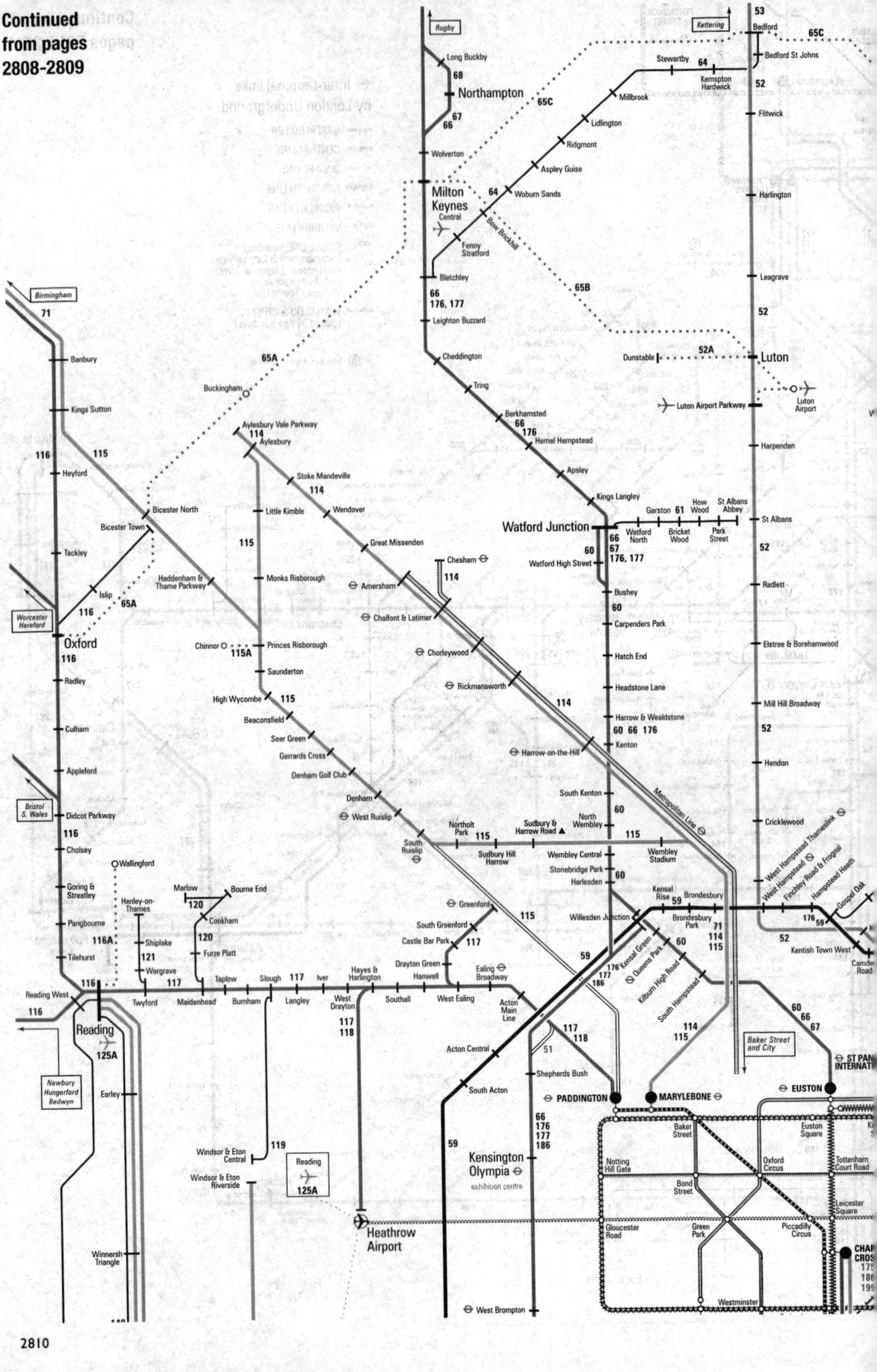

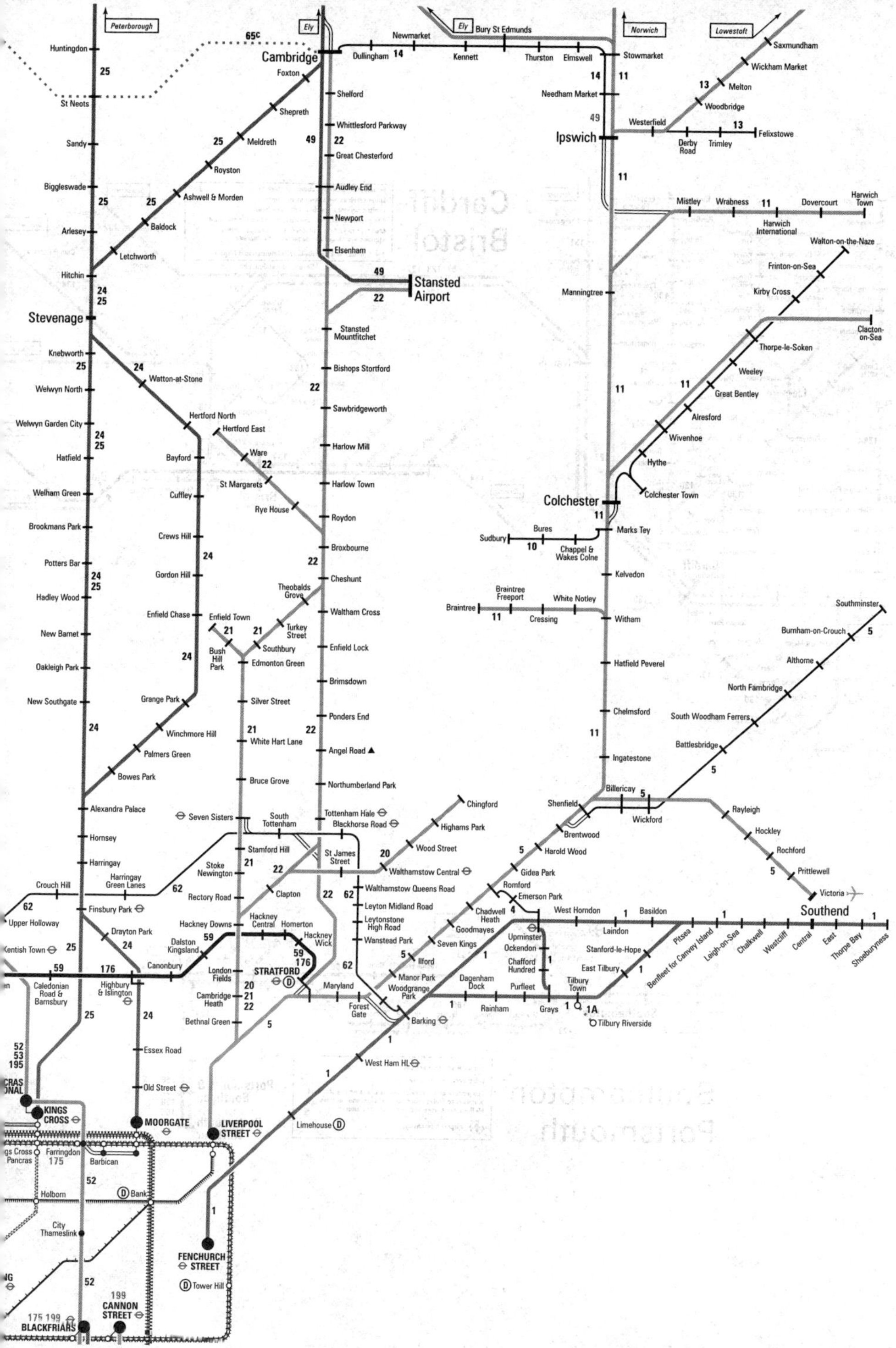

Peterborough
Ely
Ely
Norwich
Lowestoft
Huntingdon
65C
Cambridge
Newmarket
Bury St Edmunds
Dullingham
14
Kennett
Thurston
Elmswell
Stowmarket
Saxmundham
Wickham Market
Melton
Woodbridge
13
25
Foxton
St Neots
Shelford
14
11
Needham Market
Shepreth
49
Westerfield
Derby Road
Trimley
13
Felixstowe
Ipswich
Sandy
25
Meldreth
49
22
Whittlesford Parkway
Great Chesterford
Royston
Biggleswade
25
25
Ashwell & Morden
Audley End
11
Newport
Mistley
Wrabness
11
Dovercourt
Harwich Town
Harwich International
Arlesey
Baldock
Elsenham
Walton-on-the-Naze
Letchworth
Frinton-on-Sea
Hitchin
24
25
49
Stansted Airport
22
Kirby Cross
Manningtree
Stevenage
Clacton-on-Sea
Stansted Mountfitchet
Thorpe-le-Soken
Knebworth
25
24
Watton-at-Stone
Bishops Stortford
Weeley
Welwyn North
22
11
11
Great Bentley
Sawbridgeworth
Hertford North
Alresford
Welwyn Garden City
24
25
Hertford East
Wivenhoe
Hatfield
Bayford
Ware
22
Harlow Mill
Hythe
Welham Green
Cuffley
St Margarets
Harlow Town
Colchester Town
Colchester
Rye House
Roydon
11
Brookmans Park
Marks Tey
Bures
Sudbury
10
Chappel & Wakes Colne
Crews Hill
Broxbourne
24
Potters Bar
24
25
Gordon Hill
22
Cheshunt
Kelvedon
Theobalds Grove
Hadley Wood
Enfield Chase
Braintree Freeport
Braintree
11
White Notley
Cressing
Waltham Cross
Witham
Southminster
Enfield Town
21
21
Turkey Street
New Barnet
Burnham-on-Crouch
5
Southbury
Bush Hill Park
Edmonton Green
Enfield Lock
Oakleigh Park
24
Hatfield Peverel
Althorne
Brimsdown
North Fambridge
New Southgate
Grange Park
Silver Street
Ponders End
Chelmsford
South Woodham Ferrers
24
Winchmore Hill
21
22
White Hart Lane
11
Angel Road ▲
Battlesbridge
Palmers Green
Ingatestone
5
Bowes Park
Bruce Grove
Northumberland Park
Billericay
5
Shenfield
Alexandra Palace
Seven Sisters
South Tottenham
Tottenham Hale
Chingford
Wickford
Rayleigh
Blackhorse Road
Highams Park
Brentwood
Hornsey
Hockley
Stamford Hill
St James Street
Wood Street
5
Harold Wood
Rochford
Harringay
21
20
Stoke Newington
22
Walthamstow Central
Gidea Park
5
Prittlewell
Crouch Hill
Harringay Green Lanes
62
22
Walthamstow Queens Road
Romford
Victoria
62
Rectory Road
Clapton
22
62
Leyton Midland Road
Emerson Park
Southend
Finsbury Park
Chadwell Heath
4
West Horndon
1
Basildon
1
1
Upper Holloway
Hackney Downs
Hackney Central
Homerton
Leytonstone High Road
Goodmayes
Upminster
Laindon
Drayton Park
59
Hackney Wick
Wanstead Park
Seven Kings
1
Ockendon
Stanford-le-Hope
Pitsea
Benfleet for Canvey Island
Leigh-on-Sea
Chalkwell
Westcliff
Central
East
Thorpe Bay
Shoeburyness
Kentish Town
25
24
Dalston Kingsland
59
176
5
Ilford
Chafford Hundred
1
East Tilbury
1
59
176
Canonbury
London Fields
STRATFORD
62
Manor Park
Dagenham Dock
Purfleet
Tilbury Town
Caledonian Road & Barnsbury
Highbury & Islington
20
21
22
Maryland
Woodgrange Park
Cambridge Heath
Forest Gate
1
Rainham
Grays
1
1A
25
24
Bethnal Green
5
Barking
Tilbury Riverside
1
52
53
195
Essex Road
West Ham HL
1
Old Street
KINGS CROSS
MOORGATE
LIVERPOOL STREET
Limehouse
Farringdon
Barbican
175
52
Holborn
Bank
City Thameslink
1
FENCHURCH STREET
52
Tower Hill
199
CANNON STREET
175 199
BLACKFRIARS

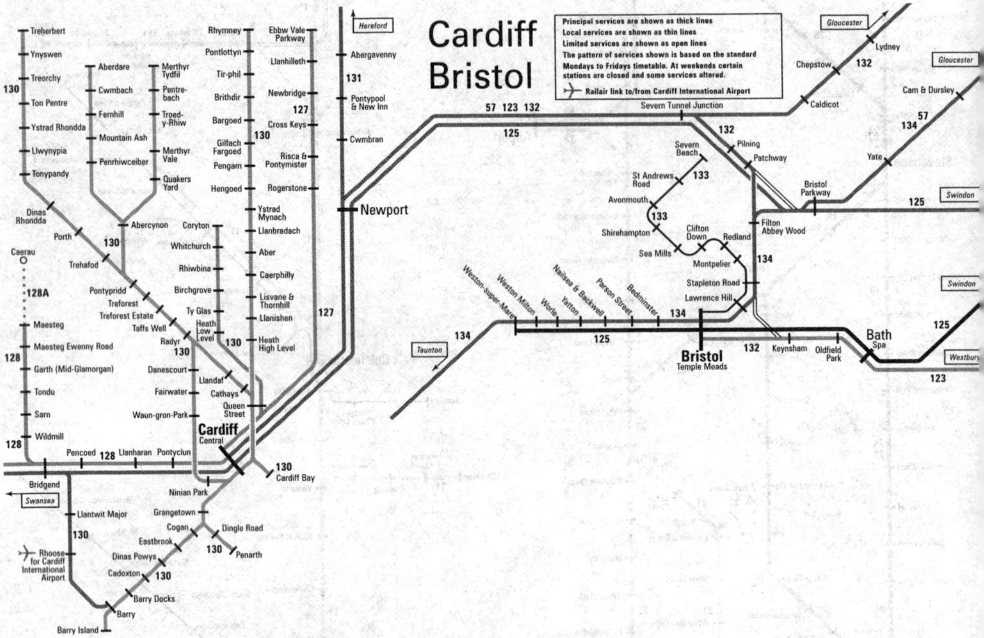
Cardiff
Bristol
Principal services are shown as thick lines
Local services are shown as thin lines
Limited services are shown as open lines
The pattern of services shown is based on the standard Mondays to Fridays timetable. At weekends certain stations are closed and some services altered.
Railair link to/from Cardiff International Airport
Treherbert
Ynyswen
Treorchy
Ton Pentre
Ystrad Rhondda
Llwynypia
Tonypandy
Dinas Rhondda
Porth
Trehafod
Aberdare
Cwmbach
Fernhill
Mountain Ash
Penrhiwceiber
Merthyr Tydfil
Pentre-bach
Troed-y-Rhiw
Merthyr Vale
Quakers Yard
Abercynon
Pontypridd
Treforest
Treforest Estate
Taffs Well
Radyr
Rhymney
Pontlottyn
Tir-phil
Brithdir
Bargoed
Gilfach Fargoed
Pengam
Hengoed
Ystrad Mynach
Llanbradach
Aber
Caerphilly
Lisvane & Thornhill
Llanishen
Heath High Level
Coryton
Whitchurch
Rhiwbina
Birchgrove
Ty Glas
Heath Low Level
Ebbw Vale Parkway
Llanhilleth
Newbridge
Cross Keys
Risca & Pontymister
Rogerstone
Hereford
Abergavenny
Pontypool & New Inn
Cwmbran
Newport
Caerau
128A
Maesteg
Maesteg Ewenny Road
Garth (Mid-Glamorgan)
Tondu
Sarn
Wildmill
Bridgend
Swansea
Pencoed
Llanharan
Pontyclun
Danescourt
Llandaf
Fairwater
Cathays
Queen Street
Waun-gron-Park
Cardiff Central
Cardiff Bay
Ninian Park
Grangetown
Dingle Road
Penarth
Cogan
Eastbrook
Dinas Powys
Cadoxton
Barry Docks
Barry
Barry Island
Llantwit Major
Rhoose for Cardiff International Airport
127
128
130
131
Severn Tunnel Junction
57 123 132
125
Gloucester
Lydney
Chepstow
Caldicot
Cam & Dursley
134 57
Yate
Bristol Parkway
Swindon
Severn Beach
St Andrews Road
Avonmouth
Shirehampton
Sea Mills
Clifton Down
Redland
Montpelier
Stapleton Road
Lawrence Hill
Pilning
Patchway
Filton Abbey Wood
133
134
Weston-super-Mare
Weston Milton
Worle
Yatton
Nailsea & Backwell
Parson Street
Bedminster
Taunton
Bristol Temple Meads
Keynsham
Oldfield Park
Bath Spa
Westbury
123
132

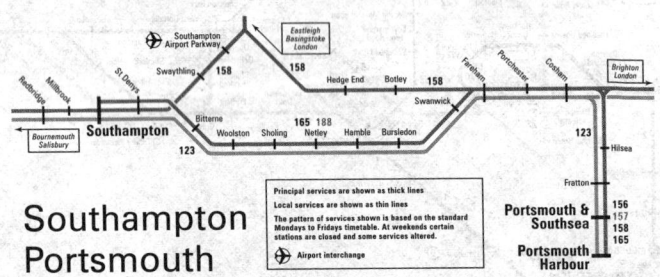

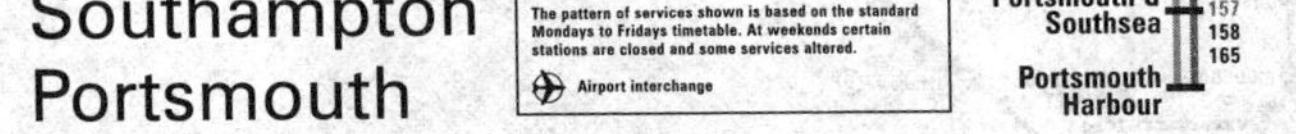
Southampton Airport Parkway
Eastleigh Basingstoke London
Swaythling
158
Hedge End
Botley
Redbridge
Millbrook
St Denys
Southampton
Bournemouth Salisbury
Bitterne
Woolston
Sholing
Netley
Hamble
Bursledon
165 188
123
Swanwick
Fareham
Portchester
Cosham
Brighton London
Hilsea
Fratton
Portsmouth & Southsea
156
157
158
165
Portsmouth Harbour
Southampton
Portsmouth
Principal services are shown as thick lines
Local services are shown as thin lines
The pattern of services shown is based on the standard Mondays to Fridays timetable. At weekends certain stations are closed and some services altered.
Airport interchange

Birmingham
West Midlands
Principal services are shown as thick lines
Local services are shown as thin lines
Limited services are shown as open lines
The pattern of services shown is based on the standard Mondays to Fridays timetable. At weekends certain stations are closed and some services altered.
Railair link to/from Birmingham Airport
Tram/Metro Interchange
Shrewsbury
Stafford
Derby
Leicester
Rugby
Banbury
Cheltenham Spa
Evesham
Wolverhampton
Birmingham
Coventry
Worcester
Penkridge
Cosford
Albrighton
Codsall
Bilbrook
Coseley
Tipton
Dudley Port
Sandwell & Dudley
Smethwick Galton Bridge
METRO
The Hawthorns
Jewellery Quarter
Snow Hill
Smethwick Rolfe Street
New Street
Moor Street
Bordesley
Rugeley Town
Hednesford
Cannock
Landywood
Bloxwich North
Bloxwich
Walsall
Bescot Stadium
Tame Bridge
Hamstead
Perry Barr
Witton
Aston
Duddeston
Lichfield Trent Valley
Lichfield City
Shenstone
Blake Street
Butlers Lane
Four Oaks
Sutton Coldfield
Wylde Green
Chester Road
Erdington
Gravelly Hill
Tamworth
Wilnecote
Polesworth
Atherstone
Water Orton
Coleshill Parkway
Nuneaton
Bedworth
Adderley Park
Stechford
Lea Hall
Marston Green
Birmingham International for National Exhibition Centre
Birmingham Airport
Hampton-in-Arden
Berkswell
Tile Hill
Canley
Small Heath
Tyseley
Acocks Green
Olton
Solihull
Widney Manor
Dorridge
Lapworth
Hatton
Warwick Parkway
Warwick
Leamington Spa
Claverdon
Bearley
Wilmcote
Stratford-upon-Avon
Spring Road
Hall Green
Yardley Wood
Shirley
Whitlocks End
Wythall
Earlswood
The Lakes
Wood End
Danzey
Henley-in-Arden
Wootton Wawen
Langley Green
Rowley Regis
Old Hill
Cradley Heath
Lye
Stourbridge Town
Stourbridge Junction
Hagley
Blakedown
Kidderminster
Hartlebury
Droitwich Spa
Five Ways
University
Selly Oak
Bournville
Kings Norton
Northfield
Longbridge
Barnt Green
Bromsgrove
Alvechurch
Redditch
Shrub Hill
66
67
68
69
70
71
72
74
75
57
58
115
115B
116
126

Liverpool Leeds Manchester Sheffield

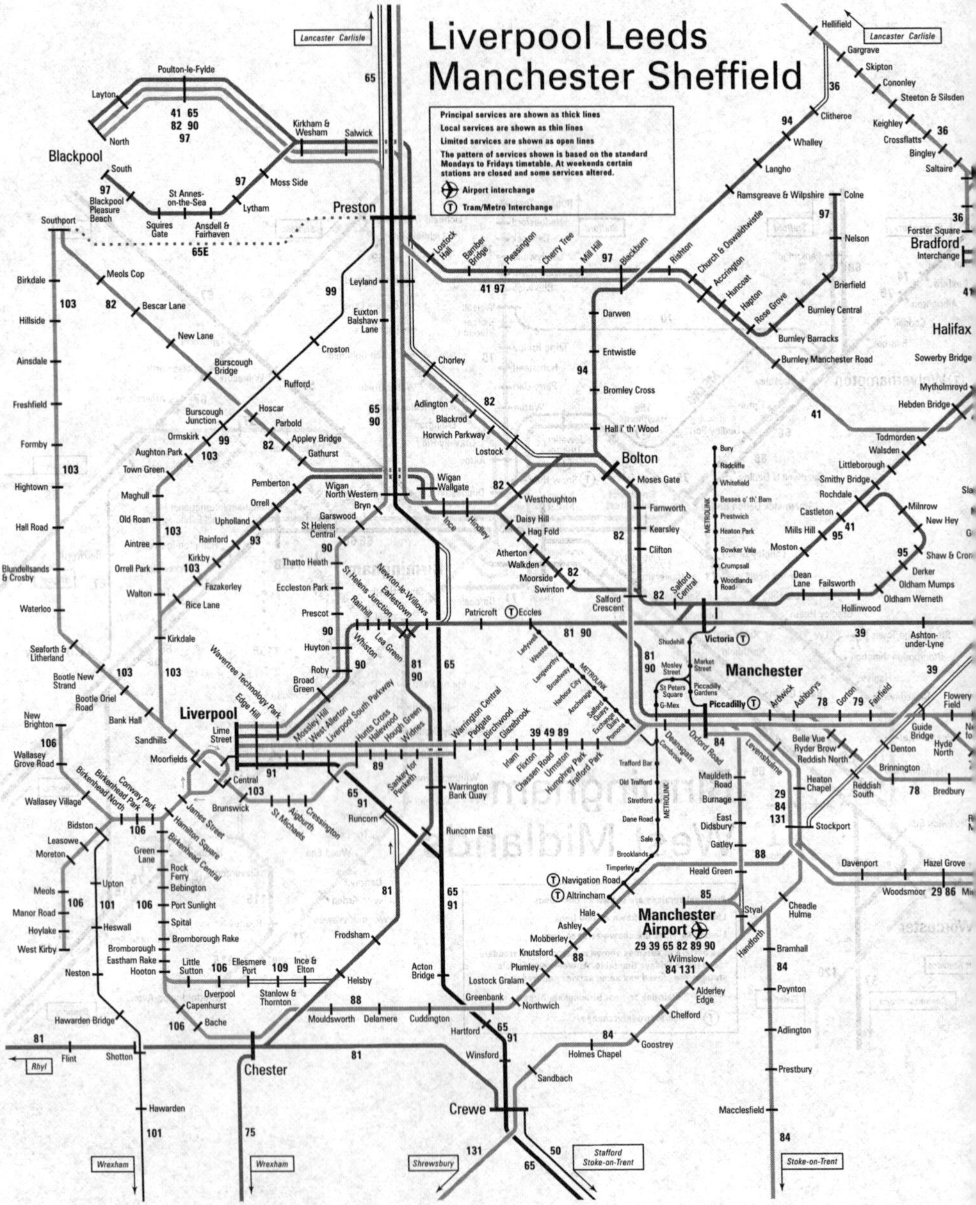

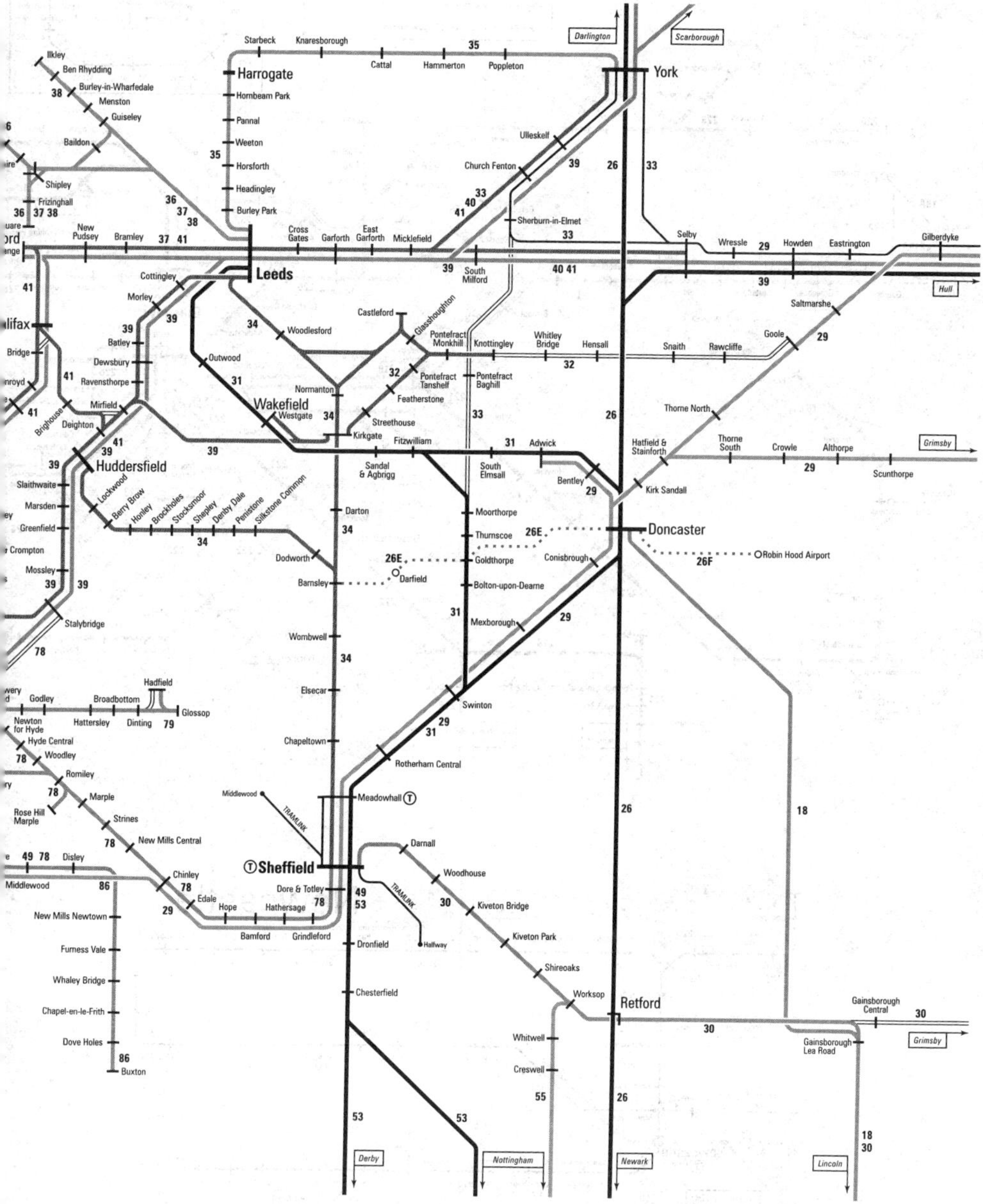
Darlington
Scarborough
York
Starbeck
Knaresborough
Cattal
Hammerton
Poppleton
35
Harrogate
Hornbeam Park
Pannal
Weeton
Horsforth
Headingley
Burley Park
Ilkley
Ben Rhydding
Burley-in-Wharfedale
Menston
Guiseley
Baildon
Shipley
Frizinghall
36 37 38
New Pudsey
Bramley
37 41
Cross Gates
Garforth
East Garforth
Micklefield
South Milford
Leeds
Ulleskelf
Church Fenton
Sherburn-in-Elmet
39
26
33
40 41
Selby
Wressle
29
Howden
Eastrington
Gilberdyke
Hull
Saltmarshe
Goole
Cottingley
Morley
Batley
Dewsbury
Ravensthorpe
Mirfield
Deighton
Brighouse
Halifax
Woodlesford
Outwood
Castleford
Glasshoughton
Pontefract Monkhill
Knottingley
Whitley Bridge
Hensall
Snaith
Rawcliffe
32
Pontefract Tanshelf
Pontefract Baghill
Featherstone
Normanton
Wakefield
Westgate
Kirkgate
Streethouse
Fitzwilliam
Adwick
31
Thorne North
Hatfield & Stainforth
Thorne South
Crowle
Althorpe
Scunthorpe
Grimsby
Huddersfield
Slaithwaite
Marsden
Greenfield
Crompton
Mossley
Stalybridge
Lockwood
Berry Brow
Honley
Brockholes
Stocksmoor
Shepley
Denby Dale
Penistone
Silkstone Common
Sandal & Agbrigg
South Elmsall
Bentley
Kirk Sandall
Darton
Moorthorpe
Thurnscoe
26E
Doncaster
Dodworth
Goldthorpe
Conisbrough
Robin Hood Airport
26F
Barnsley
Darfield
Bolton-upon-Dearne
Mexborough
Wombwell
Elsecar
Swinton
Chapeltown
Rotherham Central
Meadowhall
Middlewood
TRAMLINK
Sheffield
Hadfield
Godley
Broadbottom
Glossop
Newton for Hyde
Hattersley
Dinting
79
Hyde Central
Woodley
Romiley
Marple
Rose Hill Marple
Strines
New Mills Central
Disley
49 78
Chinley
Edale
Hope
Hathersage
Bamford
Grindleford
Dore & Totley
Middlewood
86
New Mills Newtown
Furness Vale
Whaley Bridge
Chapel-en-le-Frith
Dove Holes
Buxton
Darnall
Woodhouse
Kiveton Bridge
Kiveton Park
Shireoaks
Worksop
Halfway
Dronfield
Chesterfield
Retford
Gainsborough Central
Gainsborough Lea Road
18
30
Whitwell
Creswell
55
53
Derby
Nottingham
Newark
Lincoln

Glasgow Edinburgh

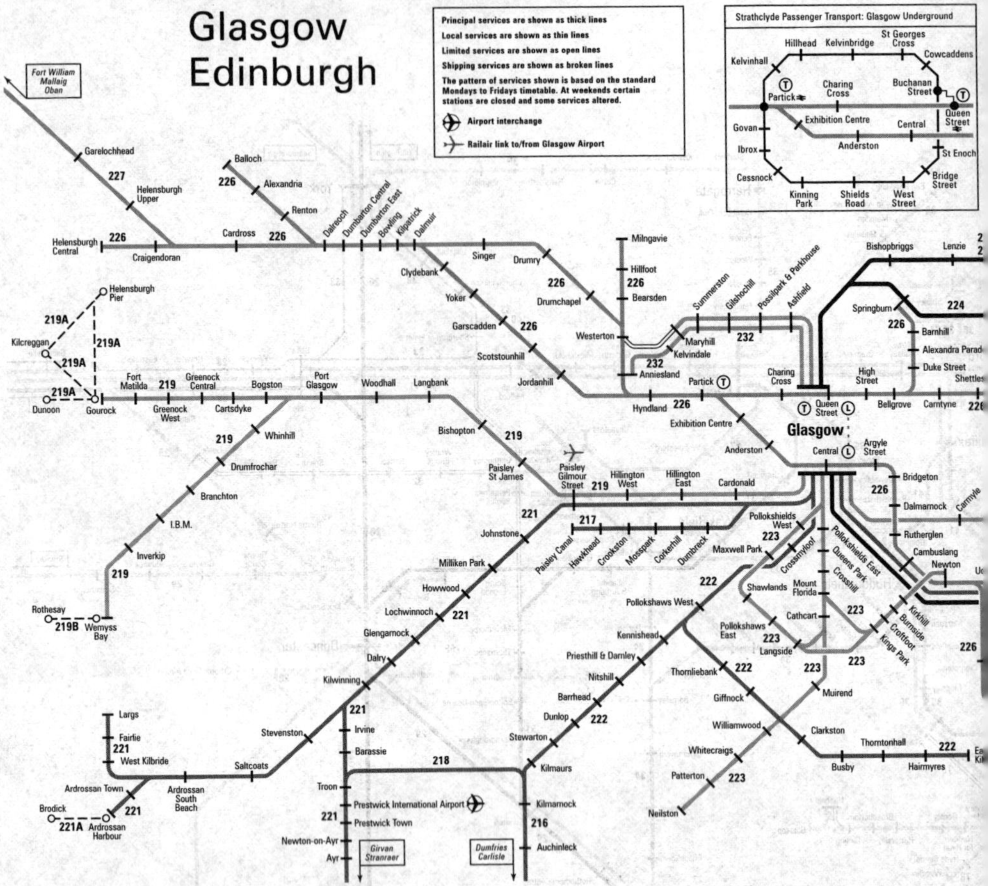

Newcastle

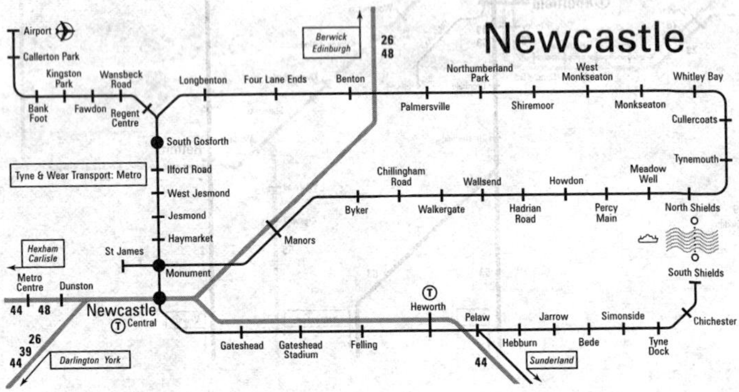

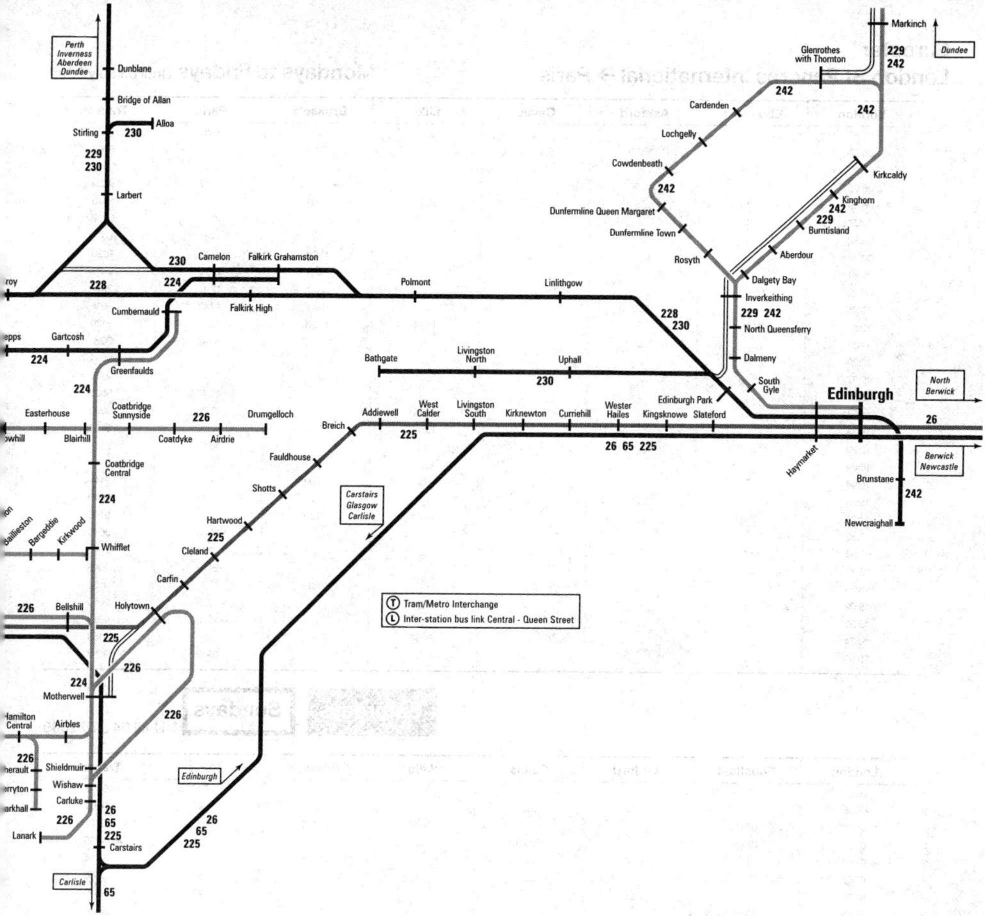

Perth Inverness Aberdeen Dundee
Dunblane
Bridge of Allan
Alloa
Stirling
230
229
230
Larbert
Camelon
Falkirk Grahamston
228
224
Falkirk High
Cumbernauld
Polmont
Linlithgow
228
230
Gartcosh
224
Greenfaulds
Bathgate
Livingston North
Uphall
Easterhouse
Blairhill
Coatbridge Sunnyside
Coatdyke
226
Airdrie
Drumgelloch
Coatbridge Central
Breich
Addiewell
West Calder
225
Livingston South
Kirknewton
Curriehill
Wester Hailes
Kingsknowe
Slateford
26 65 225
Fauldhouse
Shotts
Hartwood
Cleland
Carfin
Holytown
Bellshill
Whifflet
Carstairs Glasgow Carlisle
Tram/Metro Interchange
Inter-station bus link Central - Queen Street
Motherwell
Airbles
Shieldmuir
Wishaw
Carluke
Lanark
Carstairs
Carlisle
65
Edinburgh
26
65
225
Markinch
Dundee
Glenrothes with Thornton
Cardenden
Lochgelly
Cowdenbeath
242
Dunfermline Queen Margaret
Dunfermline Town
Rosyth
Kirkcaldy
Kinghorn
Burntisland
Aberdour
Dalgety Bay
Inverkeithing
229 242
North Queensferry
Dalmeny
South Gyle
Edinburgh Park
Edinburgh
North Berwick
Haymarket
Berwick Newcastle
Brunstane
Newcraighall

Eurostar™
London St Pancras International → Paris

Mondays to Fridays Until 03 July 2009

	London	Ebbsfleet	Ashford	Calais	Lille	Brussels	Paris	Train no
	05:25	05:42	.....	.....	.....	.....	08:50	9078
	05:57	.....	06:27	.....	.....	08:56	.....	9106
1	06:26	06:42	.....	.....	.....	.....	09:47	9002
	06:55	.....	07:25	.....	.....	.....	10:17	9004
	06:59	07:15	.....	.....	09:24	10:03	.....	9110
	07:27	07:45	.....	09:29	.....	.....	10:56	9006
	08:32	.....	.....	.....	.....	.....	11:47	9010
	08:34	.....	.....	.....	.....	11:29	.....	9120
	09:01	.....	.....	.....	11:21	.....	12:23	9012
	09:26	09:42	.....	.....	.....	.....	12:47	9014
	10:25	.....	10:55	.....	.....	.....	13:47	9018
	10:57	11:15	.....	.....	13:24	14:03	.....	9126
1	11:32	.....	.....	.....	.....	.....	14:47	9022
	12:29	12:45	.....	.....	.....	.....	15:50	9024
	12:57	13:15	.....	.....	15:24	16:03	.....	9132
	13:32	.....	.....	.....	.....	.....	16:47	9028
	14:04	.....	.....	.....	16:24	.....	17:26	9030
	14:34	.....	.....	.....	16:54	17:33	.....	9138
	15:29	15:45	.....	17:29	.....	.....	18:56	9036
1	16:04	.....	.....	.....	.....	18:59	.....	9144
2	16:04	.....	.....	.....	18:24	19:03	.....	9144
	16:25	.....	16:55	.....	.....	.....	19:47	9040
	17:27	17:45	.....	.....	19:54	20:33	.....	9150
	17:30	.....	.....	.....	.....	.....	20:47	9044
	17:56	18:12	.....	.....	.....	.....	21:17	9046
	18:32	.....	.....	.....	.....	.....	21:47	9048
	18:35	.....	.....	.....	.....	21:33	.....	9154
	19:02	.....	.....	.....	.....	.....	22:17	9050
1	19:32	.....	.....	.....	.....	.....	22:47	9052
	19:34	.....	.....	.....	21:54	22:33	.....	9158
	20:05	.....	.....	21:59	.....	.....	23:26	9054

Saturdays **Sundays** Until 04 July 2009

	London	Ebbsfleet	Ashford	Calais	Lille	Brussels	Paris	Train no
3	06:22	06:39	.....	.....	.....	.....	09:47	9002
3	06:55	.....	07:25	.....	.....	.....	10:17	9004
3	06:59	07:15	.....	.....	09:24	10:03	.....	9110
3	07:27	07:45	.....	09:29	.....	.....	10:56	9006
3	07:57	.....	08:28	.....	.....	10:56	.....	9114
4	07:52	08:09	.....	.....	.....	.....	11:17	9008
3	08:32	.....	.....	.....	.....	.....	11:47	9010
3	08:59	09:15	.....	.....	11:24	12:03	.....	9116
	09:26	09:42	.....	.....	.....	.....	12:47	9014
3--5	10:00	.....	.....	.....	.....	.....	13:17	9016
	10:25	.....	10:55	.....	.....	.....	13:47	9018
	10:57	11:15	.....	.....	13:24	14:03	.....	9126
	11:00	.....	.....	.....	.....	.....	14:17	9020
4	12:02	.....	.....	.....	.....	.....	15:17	9082
	12:29	12:45	.....	14:29	.....	.....	15:56	9024
	12:57	13:15	.....	.....	15:24	16:03	.....	9132
4	13:00	.....	.....	.....	.....	.....	16:17	9026
3	13:32	.....	.....	.....	.....	.....	16:47	9028
	14:04	.....	.....	.....	16:24	.....	17:26	9030
	14:34	.....	.....	.....	16:54	17:33	.....	9138
	15:29	15:45	.....	17:29	.....	.....	18:56	9036
4	16:04	.....	.....	17:59	.....	19:03	.....	9144
	16:25	.....	16:55	.....	.....	.....	19:47	9040
	16:57	17:15	.....	.....	19:24	20:03	.....	9148
	17:31	.....	.....	19:26	.....	.....	20:53	9044
4	17:56	18:12	.....	.....	.....	.....	21:17	9046
4	18:21	.....	18:55	.....	20:51	21:33	.....	9154
3	18:56	19:12	.....	.....	.....	.....	22:17	9050
4	19:02	.....	.....	.....	.....	.....	22:17	9050
	19:34	.....	.....	.....	21:54	22:33	.....	9158
	20:05	.....	.....	.....	.....	.....	23:20	9054
4	20:32	.....	.....	.....	.....	.....	23:47	9056

1 Friday only
2 Not Friday
3 Saturdays only
4 Sundays only
5 Runs from 18th April

Variations

Amended Eurostar services may run on and around Public Holidays. Eurostar timetables are correct at time of going to press. Times and services are subject to change. For up to date information, please refer to the Eurostar website - www.eurostar.com

Eurostar™

Paris → London St Pancras International

Mondays to Fridays Until 03 July 2009

	Paris	Brussels	Lille	Calais	Ashford	Ebbsfleet	London	Train no
	06:43	.....	.....	.....	.....	.....	07:58	9005
	.....	06:59	07:35	.....	.....	.....	07:55	9109
	07:13	.....	.....	.....	.....	.....	08:28	9007
	.....	08:05	.....	.....	.....	.....	08:56	9113
	07:43	.....	.....	.....	.....	.....	08:59	9009
	08:07	.....	.....	09:34	.....	09:18	09:34	9011
	09:13	.....	.....	.....	10:06	.....	10:36	9015
	.....	09:29	10:05	.....	.....	10:15	10:31	9119
	10:13	.....	.....	.....	.....	.....	11:28	9019
	11:13	.....	.....	.....	.....	.....	12:29	9023
	.....	11:29	12:05	.....	.....	.....	12:26	9181
	12:13	.....	.....	.....	.....	.....	13:28	9027
	13:01	.....	14:04	14:34	.....	14:18	14:34	9031
1	14:13	.....	.....	.....	.....	.....	15:29	9035
	.....	14:59	15:35	.....	.....	.....	15:56	9141
	15:13	.....	.....	.....	16:06	.....	16:36	9039
	.....	15:59	16:35	.....	.....	16:45	17:03	9145
	16:13	.....	.....	.....	.....	17:18	17:34	9043
	.....	16:59	17:35	.....	17:37	.....	18:07	9149
	17:13	.....	.....	.....	.....	18:18	18:34	9047
1	17:43	.....	.....	.....	.....	.....	18:59	9049
	.....	17:59	18:35	.....	.....	18:45	19:03	9153
	18:13	.....	.....	.....	.....	19:18	19:34	9051
	18:43	.....	.....	.....	19:36	.....	20:06	9053
	.....	18:59	19:35	.....	.....	.....	19:56	9157
	19:13	.....	.....	.....	.....	20:18	20:34	9055
	20:13	.....	.....	.....	.....	.....	21:29	9059
	.....	20:29	21:05	.....	.....	21:15	21:33	9163
	21:13	.....	.....	.....	.....	22:18	22:34	9063

Saturdays Sundays Until 04 July 2009

	Paris	Brussels	Lille	Calais	Ashford	Ebbsfleet	London	Train no
3	.....	06:59	07:35	.....	.....	.....	07:55	9109
3	07:13	.....	.....	.....	.....	.....	08:28	9007
3	.....	07:59	.....	09:02	.....	.....	08:56	9113
4	.....	07:59	08:35	.....	.....	.....	08:57	9113
	08:07	.....	.....	09:34	.....	09:18	09:34	9011
	09:13	.....	.....	.....	10:06	.....	10:36	9015
3	.....	09:29	10:05	.....	.....	10:15	10:31	9119
	10:13	.....	.....	.....	.....	.....	11:28	9019
	11:13	.....	.....	.....	.....	.....	12:29	9023
4	11:43	.....	.....	.....	.....	.....	12:59	9025
	.....	11:29	12:05	.....	.....	.....	12:26	9181
	12:13	.....	.....	.....	.....	.....	13:28	9027
	.....	12:59	13:35	.....	.....	13:45	14:03	9133
	13:01	.....	14:04	14:34	.....	14:18	14:34	9031
4	13:43	.....	.....	.....	.....	.....	14:59	9033
	14:13	.....	.....	.....	.....	.....	15:29	9035
	.....	14:29	15:05	.....	.....	.....	15:26	9139
	15:07	.....	.....	16:34	16:06	.....	16:36	9039
	16:13	.....	.....	.....	.....	17:18	17:34	9043
4	.....	16:59	17:35	.....	17:33	.....	18:03	9149
	17:13	.....	.....	.....	.....	18:18	18:34	9047
4	17:43	.....	.....	.....	.....	.....	18:59	9049
	.....	17:59	18:35	.....	.....	18:45	19:03	9153
	18:13	.....	.....	.....	.....	19:18	19:34	9051
4	.....	18:59	19:35	.....	.....	.....	19:56	9157
4	19:13	.....	.....	.....	.....	.....	20:29	9055
	20:13	.....	.....	.....	21:06	21:24	21:41	9059
4	20:43	.....	.....	.....	.....	.....	21:59	9061
4	.....	20:29	21:05	.....	.....	21:15	21:33	9163
	21:13	.....	.....	.....	.....	22:18	22:34	9063

1 Friday only
2 Not Friday
3 Saturdays only
4 Sundays only
5 Runs from 18th April

Variations

Amended Eurostar services may run on and around Public Holidays. Eurostar timetables are correct at time of going to press. Times and services are subject to change. For up to date information, please refer to the Eurostar website - www.eurostar.com

Eurostar™

London St Pancras International → Paris

Mondays to Fridays From 5 July to 31 August 2009

	London	Ebbsfleet	Ashford	Calais	Lille	Brussels	Paris	Train no
	05:25	05:42	.....	.....	.....	.....	08:50	9078
	05:57	.....	06:27	.....	.....	08:56	.....	9106
	06:26	06:42	.....	.....	.....	.....	09:47	9002
	06:55	.....	07:25	.....	.....	.....	10:17	9004
	06:59	07:15	.....	.....	09:24	10:03	.....	9110
	07:27	07:45	.....	09:29	.....	.....	10:56	9006
	08:32	.....	.....	.....	.....	.....	11:47	9010
	08:34	.....	.....	.....	.....	11:29	.....	9120
	09:01	.....	.....	.....	11:21	.....	12:23	9012
	09:26	09:42	.....	.....	.....	.....	12:47	9014
	10:25	.....	10:55	.....	.....	.....	13:47	9018
	10:57	11:15	.....	.....	13:24	14:03	.....	9126
	11:01	.....	.....	.....	.....	.....	14:17	9020
1	11:32	.....	.....	.....	.....	.....	14:47	9022
	12:29	12:45	.....	.....	.....	.....	15:50	9024
	12:57	13:15	.....	.....	15:24	16:03	.....	9132
	13:32	.....	.....	.....	.....	.....	16:47	9028
	14:04	.....	.....	.....	16:24	.....	17:26	9030
	14:34	.....	.....	.....	16:54	17:33	.....	9138
	15:29	15:45	.....	17:29	.....	.....	18:56	9036
1	16:04	.....	.....	.....	.....	18:59	.....	9144
2	16:04	.....	.....	.....	18:24	19:03	.....	9144
	16:25	.....	16:55	.....	.....	.....	19:47	9040
	17:27	17:45	.....	.....	19:54	20:33	.....	9150
	17:30	.....	.....	.....	.....	.....	20:47	9044
	17:56	18:12	.....	.....	.....	.....	21:17	9046
	18:32	.....	.....	.....	.....	.....	21:47	9048
1	18:34	.....	.....	.....	.....	21:33	.....	9154
	19:02	.....	.....	.....	.....	.....	22:17	9050
1	19:32	.....	.....	.....	.....	.....	22:47	9052
	19:34	.....	.....	.....	21:54	22:33	.....	9158
	20:05	.....	.....	21:59	.....	.....	23:26	9054

Saturdays Sundays From 5 July to 31 August 2009

	London	Ebbsfleet	Ashford	Calais	Lille	Brussels	Paris	Train no
3	05:25	05:42	.....	.....	.....	.....	08:50	9078
3	06:26	06:42	.....	.....	.....	.....	09:47	9002
3	06:55	.....	07:25	.....	.....	.....	10:17	9004
3	06:59	07:15	.....	.....	09:24	10:03	.....	9110
3	07:27	07:45	.....	09:29	.....	.....	10:56	9006
3	07:53	.....	08:28	.....	.....	10:56	.....	9114
4	07:52	08:09	.....	.....	.....	.....	11:17	9008
4	08:27	08:45	.....	.....	10:54	11:33	.....	9120
3	08:32	.....	.....	.....	.....	.....	11:47	9010
3	08:59	09:15	.....	.....	11:24	12:03	.....	9116
4	09:01	.....	.....	.....	11:21	.....	12:23	9012
	09:26	09:42	.....	.....	.....	.....	12:47	9014
3	10:00	.....	.....	.....	.....	.....	13:17	9016
	10:25	.....	10:55	.....	.....	.....	13:47	9018
	10:57	11:15	.....	.....	13:24	14:03	.....	9126
	11:01	.....	.....	.....	.....	.....	14:17	9020
3	11:32	.....	.....	.....	.....	.....	14:47	9022
	12:02	.....	.....	.....	.....	.....	15:17	9082
	12:29	12:45	.....	14:29	.....	.....	15:56	9024
	12:57	13:15	.....	.....	15:24	16:03	.....	9132
4	13:00	.....	.....	.....	.....	.....	16:17	9026
3	13:32	.....	.....	.....	.....	.....	16:47	9028
	14:04	.....	.....	.....	16:24	.....	17:26	9030
	14:34	.....	.....	.....	16:54	17:33	.....	9138
3	14:56	15:12	.....	.....	.....	.....	18:17	9034
	15:29	15:45	.....	17:29	.....	.....	18:56	9036
4	16:04	.....	.....	17:59	.....	19:03	.....	9144
	16:25	.....	16:55	.....	.....	.....	19:47	9040
	16:57	17:15	.....	.....	19:24	20:03	.....	9148
	17:31	.....	.....	19:26	.....	.....	20:53	9044
4	17:56	18:12	.....	.....	.....	.....	21:17	9046
4	18:21	.....	18:55	.....	20:51	21:33	.....	9154
3	18:56	19:12	.....	.....	.....	.....	22:17	9050
4	19:02	.....	.....	.....	.....	.....	22:17	9050
4	19:32	.....	.....	.....	.....	.....	22:47	9052
	19:34	.....	.....	.....	21:54	22:33	.....	9158
	20:05	.....	.....	.....	.....	.....	23:20	9054
4	20:32	.....	.....	.....	.....	.....	23:47	9056

Eurostar™

Paris → London St Pancras International

Mondays to Fridays From 5 July to 31 August 2009

	Paris	Brussels	Lille	Calais	Ashford	Ebbsfleet	London	Train no
	06:43	.....	.....	.....	.....	.....	07:58	9005
	.....	06:59	07:35	.....	.....	.....	07:55	9109
	07:13	.....	.....	.....	.....	.....	08:28	9007
5	.....	08:05	.....	.....	.....	.....	08:56	9113
	08:07	.....	.....	09:34	.....	09:18	09:34	9011
	09:13	.....	.....	.....	10:06	.....	10:36	9015
	.....	09:29	10:05	.....	.....	10:15	10:31	9119
	10:13	.....	.....	.....	.....	.....	11:28	9019
	11:13	.....	.....	.....	.....	.....	12:29	9023
1	11:43	.....	.....	.....	.....	.....	12:59	9025
	.....	11:29	12:05	.....	.....	.....	12:26	9181
	12:13	.....	.....	.....	.....	.....	13:28	9027
	13:01	.....	14:04	14:34	.....	14:18	14:34	9031
1	14:13	.....	.....	.....	.....	.....	15:29	9035
	14:43	.....	.....	.....	.....	.....	15:59	9037
	.....	14:59	15:35	.....	.....	.....	15:56	9141
	15:13	.....	.....	.....	16:06	.....	16:36	9039
	.....	15:59	16:35	.....	.....	16:45	17:03	9145
	16:13	.....	.....	.....	.....	17:18	17:34	9043
	.....	16:59	17:35	.....	17:37	.....	18:07	9149
	17:13	.....	.....	.....	.....	18:18	18:34	9047
1	17:43	.....	.....	.....	.....	.....	18:59	9049
	.....	17:59	18:35	.....	.....	18:45	19:03	9153
	18:13	.....	.....	.....	.....	19:18	19:34	9051
	18:43	.....	.....	.....	19:36	.....	20:06	9053
	.....	18:59	19:35	.....	.....	.....	19:56	9157
	19:13	.....	.....	.....	.....	20:18	20:34	9055
	20:13	.....	.....	.....	.....	.....	21:29	9059
	.....	20:29	21:05	.....	.....	21:15	21:33	9163
	21:13	.....	.....	.....	.....	22:18	22:34	9063

Saturdays Sundays

From 5 July to 31 August 2009

	Paris	Brussels	Lille	Calais	Ashford	Ebbsfleet	London	Train no
3	.....	06:59	07:35	.....	.....	.....	07:55	9109
3	07:13	.....	.....	.....	.....	.....	08:28	9007
3	.....	07:59	.....	09:02	.....	.....	08:56	9113
4	.....	07:59	08:35	.....	.....	.....	08:57	9113
	08:07	.....	.....	09:34	.....	09:18	09:34	9011
	09:13	.....	.....	.....	10:06	.....	10:36	9015
3	.....	09:29	10:05	.....	.....	10:15	10:31	9119
	10:13	.....	.....	.....	.....	.....	11:28	9019
	11:13	.....	.....	.....	.....	.....	12:29	9023
	11:43	.....	.....	.....	.....	.....	12:59	9025
	.....	11:29	12:05	.....	.....	.....	12:26	9181
	12:13	.....	.....	.....	.....	.....	13:28	9027
	.....	12:59	13:35	.....	.....	13:45	14:03	9133
	13:01	.....	14:04	14:34	.....	14:18	14:34	9031
4	13:43	.....	.....	.....	.....	.....	14:59	9033
	14:13	.....	.....	.....	.....	.....	15:29	9035
3	14:43	.....	.....	.....	.....	.....	15:59	9037
	.....	14:29	15:05	.....	.....	.....	15:26	9139
	15:07	.....	.....	16:34	16:06	.....	16:36	9039
	16:13	.....	.....	.....	.....	17:18	17:34	9043
4	16:43	.....	.....	.....	.....	.....	17:59	9045
4	.....	16:59	17:35	.....	17:33	.....	18:03	9149
	17:13	.....	.....	.....	.....	18:18	18:34	9047
4	17:43	.....	.....	.....	.....	.....	18:59	9049
	.....	17:59	18:35	.....	.....	18:45	19:03	9153
	18:13	.....	.....	.....	.....	19:18	19:34	9051
4	.....	18:59	19:35	.....	.....	.....	19:56	9157
	19:13	.....	.....	.....	.....	.....	20:29	9055
	20:13	.....	.....	.....	21:06	21:24	21:41	9059
4	20:43	.....	.....	.....	.....	.....	21:59	9061
	.....	20:29	21:05	.....	.....	21:15	21:33	9163
	21:13	.....	.....	.....	.....	22:18	22:34	9063

1 Friday only
2 Not Friday
3 Saturdays only
4 Sundays only
5 Mondays only

Variations

Amended Eurostar services may run on and around Public Holidays. Eurostar timetables are correct at time of going to press. Times and services are subject to change. For up to date information, please refer to the Eurostar website - www.eurostar.com

London St Pancras International → Disneyland® Resort Paris

Direct daily service

Until 12 December 2009

London	Ashford	Lille	Marne	Train no
09:53	10:28	12:24	13:31	9074

Marne	Lille	Ashford	London	Train no
19:37	20:38	20:37	21:12	9057

Station key

London	St Pancras International
Ebbsfleet	Ebsfleet International, Kent
Ashford	Ashford International, Kent
Calais	Calais Fréthun
Lille	Lille Europe
Brussels	Brussels-Mid/Zuid
Paris	Gare du Nord
Marne	Marne-la-Vallée

Notes

Notes

Notes

Notes

Notes

Notes

Notes

Notes

Notes

Notes